BECK

Baseball Card
ALPHABETICAL CHECKLIST

NUMBER
9

Edited by
DR. JAMES BECKETT
RICH KLEIN & GRANT SANDGROUND
with the Price Guide staff of
BECKETT BASEBALL CARD MONTHLY

Beckett Publications • Dallas, Texas

 Prices in this guide reflect current retail rates determined just prior to printing. They do not reflect for-sale prices by the author, publisher, distributors, advertisers, or any card dealers associated with this guide. Every effort has been made to eliminate errors. Readers are invited to write us noting any errors which may be researched and corrected in subsequent printings. The publisher will not be held responsible for losses which may occur in the sale or purchase of cards because of information contained herein.

BECKETT is a registered trademark of

BECKETT PUBLICATIONS
DALLAS, TEXAS

Manufactured in the United States of America
First Printing
ISBN 1-887432-77-9

Beckett Baseball Card Alphabetical

Table of Contents

Index to Advertisers

Player Listings

About the Author

Jim Beckett, the leading authority on sport card values in the United States, maintains a wide range of activities in the world of sports. He possesses one of the finest collections of sports cards and autographs in the world, has made numerous appearances on radio and television, and has been frequently cited in many national publications. He was awarded the first "Special Achievement Award" for Contributions to the Hobby by the National Sports Collectors Convention in 1980, the "Jock-Jaspersen Award" for Hobby Dedication in 1983, and the "Buck Barker, Spirit of the Hobby" Award in 1991.

Dr. Beckett is the author of *Beckett Baseball Card Price Guide, The Official Price Guide to Baseball Cards, Beckett Football Card Price Guide,Beckett Hockey Card Price Guide, Beckett Basketball Card Price Guide.* In addition, he is the founder, publisher, and editor of *Beckett Baseball Card Monthly, Beckett Basketball Card Monthly, Beckett Football Card Monthly, Beckett Hockey Collector, Beckett Sports Collectibles and Beckett Racing Motor Sports Marketplace.*

Jim Beckett received his Ph.D. in Statistics from Southern Methodist University in 1975. Prior to starting Beckett Publications in1984, Dr. Beckett served as an Associate Professor of Statistics at Bowling Green State University and as a vice president of a consulting firm in Dallas, Texas. He currently resides in Dallas.

About This Book

Isn't it great? Every year these books get bigger and better with all the new sets coming out. But even more exciting is that every year there are more collectors, more shows, more stores, and more interest in the cards we love so much. Many of the features contained in the other *Beckett Price Guides* have been incorporated into this premier edition since condition grading, terminology, and many other aspects of collecting are common to the card hobby in general. We hope you find the book both interesting and useful in your collecting pursuits.

This alphabetical checklist presents all the cards issued for any particular player (or person) included in the card sets listed in our annual Beckett Baseball Price Guide or Beckett Almanac of Baseball Cards and Collectibles. In some cases, it also includes cards that are checklisted but not yet priced in any of our books. It will prove to be an invaluable tool for seasoned and novice collectors alike. Although this book was carefully compiled and proofread, it is inevitable that errors, misspellings and inconsistencies may occur. Please keep a record of any errors that come to your attention and send them to the author, so that these corrections may be incorporated into future editions of the *Beckett* Football

Welcome to the world of baseball cards.

Jim Beckett

Introduction

Welcome to the exciting world of baseball card collecting, America's fastest-growing avocation. You have made a good choice in buying this book, since it will open up to you the entire panorama of this field in the simplest, most concise way.

The growth of *Beckett Baseball Card Monthly, Beckett Basketball Card Monthly, Beckett Football Card Monthly, Beckett Hockey collector, Beckett Sports collectibles and Beckett Racing Motor sports marketplace* is an indication of the unprecedented popularity of sports cards. Founded in 1984 by Dr. James Beckett, the author of this book, *Beckett Baseball Card Monthly* contains the most extensive and accepted monthly Price Guide, collectible glossy superstar covers, colorful feature articles, "Short Prints," Convention Calendar, tips for beginners, "Readers Write" letters to and responses from the editor, information on errors and varieties, autograph collecting tips and profiles of the sport's Hottest stars. Published every month, *BBCM* is the hobby's largest paid circulation periodical. The other five magazines were built on the success of *BBCM.*

So collecting baseball cards — while still pursued as a hobby with youthful exuberance by kids in the neighborhood — has also taken on the trappings of an industry, with thousands of full- and part-time card dealers, as well as vendors of supplies, clubs and conventions. In fact, each year since 1980 thousands of hobbyists have assembled for a National Sports Collectors Convention, at which hundreds of dealers have displayed their wares, seminars have been conducted, autographs penned by sports notables, and millions of cards changed hands. The Beckett Guide is the best annual guide available to the exciting world of football cards. Read it and use it. May your enjoyment and your card collection increase in the coming months and years.

How to Collect

Each collection is personal and reflects the individuality of its owner. There are no set rules on how to collect cards. Since card collecting is a hobby or leisure pastime, what you collect, how much you collect, and how much time and money you spend collecting are entirely up to you. The funds you have available for collecting and your own personal taste should determine how you collect. Information and ideas presented here are intended to help you get the most enjoyment from this hobby.

It is impossible to collect every card ever produced. Therefore, beginners as well as intermediate and advanced collectors usually specialize in some way. One of the reasons this hobby is popular is that individual collectors can define and tailor their collecting methods to match their own tastes. To give you some ideas of the various approaches to collecting, we will list some of the more popular areas of specialization.

Many collectors select complete sets from particular years. For example, they may concentrate on assembling complete sets from all the years since their birth or since they became avid sports fans. They may try to collect a card for every player during that specified period of time.

Many others wish to acquire only certain players. Usually such players are the superstars of the sport, but occasionally collectors will specialize in all the cards of players who attended a particular college or came from a certain town. Some collectors are only interested in the first cards or Rookie Cards of certain players. This is the guide for collectors interested in pursuing the hobby this way.

Obtaining Cards

Several avenues are open to card collectors. Cards still can be purchased in the traditional way: by the pack at the local candy, grocery, drug or major discount stores.

But there are also thousands of card shops across the country that specialize in selling cards individually or by the pack, box, or set. Another alternative is the thousands of card shows held each month around the country, which feature anywhere from eight to 800 tables of sports cards and memorabilia for sale.

For many years, it has been possible to purchase complete sets of baseball cards through mail-order advertisers found in traditional sports media publications, such as *The Sporting News, Baseball Digest, Street & Smith* yearbooks, and others. These sets also are advertised in the card collecting periodicals. Many collectors will begin by subscribing to at least one of the hobby periodicals, all with good up-to-date information. In fact, subscription offers can be found in the advertising section of this book.

Most serious card collectors obtain old (and new) cards from one or more of several main sources: (1) trading or buying from other collectors or dealers; (2) responding to sale or auction ads in the hobby publications; (3) buying at a local hobby store; and/or (4) attending sports collectibles shows or conventions.

We advise that you try all four methods since each has its own distinct advantages: (1) trading is a great way to make new friends; (2) hobby periodicals help you keep up with what's going on in the hobby (including when and where the conventions are happening); (3) stores provide the opportunity to enjoy personalized service and consider a great diversity of material in a relaxed sports-oriented atmosphere; and (4) shows allow you to choose from multiple dealers and thousands of cards under one roof in a competitive situation.

Preserving Your Cards

Cards are fragile. They must be handled properly in order to retain their value. Careless handling can easily result in creased or bent cards. It is, however, not recommended that tweezers or tongs be used to pick up your cards since such utensils might mar or indent card surfaces and thus reduce those cards' conditions and values.

In general, your cards should be handled directly as little as possible. This is sometimes easier to say than to do.

Although there are still many who use custom boxes, storage trays, or even shoe boxes, plastic sheets are the preferred method of many collectors for storing cards.

A collection stored in plastic pages in a three-ring album allows you to view your collection at any time without the need to touch the card itself. Cards can also be kept in single holders (of various types and thickness) designed for the enjoyment of each card individually.

For a large collection, some collectors may use a combination of the above methods. When purchasing plastic sheets for your cards, be sure that you find the pocket size that fits the cards snugly. Don't put your 1994 Extra Bases cards in a sheet designed to fit 1997 Fleer.

Most hobby and collectibles shops and virtually all collectors' conventions will have these plastic pages available in quantity for the various sizes offered, or you can purchase them directly from the advertisers in this book.

Also, remember that pocket size isn't the only factor to consider when looking for plastic sheets. Other factors such as safety, economy, appearance, availability, or personal preference also may indicate which types of sheets a collector may want to buy.

Damp, sunny and/or hot conditions — no, this is not a weather forecast — are three elements to avoid in extremes if you are interested in preserving your collection. Too much (or too little) humidity can cause the gradual deterioration of a card. Direct, bright sun (or fluorescent light) over time will bleach out the color of a card. Extreme heat accelerates the decomposition of the card. On the other hand, many cards have lasted more than 75 years without much scientific intervention. So be cautious, even if the above factors typically present a problem only when present in the extreme. It never hurts to be prudent.

Collecting vs. Investing

Collecting individual players and collecting complete sets are both popular vehicles for investment and speculation.

Most investors and speculators stock up on complete sets or on quantities of players they think have good investment potential.

There is obviously no guarantee in this book, or anywhere else for that matter, that cards will outperform the stock market or other investment alternatives in the future. After all, basketball cards do not pay quarterly dividends and cards cannot be sold at their "current values" as easily as stocks or bonds.

Nevertheless, investors have noticed a favorable long-term trend in the past performance of basketball and other sports collectibles, and certain cards and sets have outperformed just about any other investment in some years.

Many hobbyists maintain that the best investment is and always will be the building of a collection, which traditionally has held up better than outright speculation.

Some of the obvious questions are: Which cards? When to buy? When to sell? The best investment you can make is in your own education.

The more you know about your collection and the hobby, the more informed the decisions you will be able to make. We're not selling investment tips. We're selling information about the current value of baseball cards. It's up to you to use that information to your best advantage.

How to Use the Alphabetical Checklist

This alphabetical checklist has been designed to be user friendly.The set code abbreviations used throughout are easily identified and memorized. The format adopted for card identification is explained below. However, the large number of card sets contained in this volume require that the reader become familiar first with the abbreviations and format used in card identification. PLEASE READ THE FOLLOWING SECTION CAREFULLY BEFORE ATTEMPTING TO USE THE CHECKLIST.

The player cards are listed alphabetically by the player's current last name. Different players with identical first and last names are most often distinguished by middle initials or other additional information. The codes following the player's names are indented and give the set names and numbers of the cards on which the players appeared. When the year of issue extends beyond one calendar year (e.g., 1992-93), an abbreviated form of the earliest date is given for the year of issue (92 for 1992). The set code abbreviations are designed so that each code is distinctive for a particular card set.

Depending on the particular card set, the set code abbreviations consist of from three to four different elements: a) Year of issue (listed in ascending chronological order); b) Producer or sponsor; c) Set code suffixes (commonly used for insert cards); and d) Card number (always preceded by a dash). Here are a few examples of a typical listing:

Aaron, Hank
54Top-128
Year: 1954, Producer: Topps, Card Number: 128

Jr. Griffey, Ken
97PinCerMBlu-53
Year: 1997, Producer: Pinnacle, Set Code Suffix: Certified Mirror Blue, Card Number: 53

Clemente, Roberto
94TopArc1-251
Year: 1994, Producer: Topps, Set Code Suffix: Archives , Card Number: 251

When two different producers issued cards for a player in the same year, the cards are listed alphabetically according to the maker's name (e.g., 1991 Topps precedes 1991 Upper Deck). Note that mainly postal abbreviations have often been used to identify college sets (e.g., VA for Virginia).

The card number typically corresponds to the particular number on the card itself; in some instances, the card number also involves letter prefixes. In playing card sets (e.g., 1991 U.S. Playing Card All-Stars), the letter prefixes "C", "D", "H" and "S" have been added to the card numbers to denote the suits clubs, diamonds, hearts and spades, respectively. Cards in unnumbered sets are usually entered alphabetically according to the player's last name and assigned a number arbitrarily. In sets in which all the cards are numbered, a single unnumbered card is marked either "x(x)" or "NNO" for "no number".

Lastly, the user of this checklist will notice that the cards of players from sports other than baseball (as well as subjects not even from the world of sports) are contained in this checklist. This circumstance arose because of the decision to include multi-sport sets containing baseball cards in this checklist. (With most issues found in our Future Stars magazine, however, a decision was made to include only the baseball-related cards in the alphabetical checklist.) In the price guide, these multisport card sets are typically indicated by an asterisk (*), which is placed after the set code suffix in the alphabetical checklist.

Legend

SetAbbrev	SetName
'sA'sPos	A's Postcards
-97LinVen	Lineup Venezuela
00TopPre	Topps Pre-Production
199Fin	Finest
A's	A's
A's192T	A's 1929-31 TCMA
A'sCHP	A's CHP
A'sFirT20	A's Fireside T208
A'sGraG	A's Granny Goose
A'sGreT	A's Greats TCMA
A'sJacitB	A's Jack in the Box
A'sJayP	A's Jay Publishing
A'sMot	A's Mother's
A'sMotR	A's Mother's ROY's
A'sPinST	A's Pinnacle Season Ticket
A'sPos	A's Postcards
A'sRodM	A's Rodeo Meats
A'sRodMC	A's Rodeo Meat Commemorative
A'sSFE	A's S.F. Examiner
A'sSmoC	A's Smokey Colorgrams
A'sSmoM	A's Smokey McGwire
A'sTCM1P	A's 1910-14 TCMA Postcards
A'sTeal	A's Team Issue
A'sUno7P	A's Unocal 76 Pins
A'sVil	A's Villa
AccRegJ	Accel Reggie Jackson
ActPac	Action Packed
ActPac2G	Action Packed 24K Gold
ActPac2GD	Action Packed 24K Gold Diamond
ActPacA	Action Packed ASG
ActPacA2	Action Packed ASG 24K
ActPacAC	Action Packed ASG Coke/Amoco
ActPacAP	Action Packed ASG Prototypes
ActPacF	Action Packed
ActPacP	Action Packed Prototypes
ActPacSP	Action Packed Seaver Promos
ActPacT	Action Packed Test
AdeGiaF	Adelaide Giants Futura
AFUMus	AFUD Musial
AGFA	AGFA
AkrAer	Akron Aeros Best
AkrAerM	Akron Aeros Multi-Ad
AlaGol	Alaska Goldpanners
AlaGolAA60TI	Alaska Goldpanners All-Time AS '60s Team Issue
AlaGolAA70TI	Alaska Goldpanners All-Time AS '70s Team Issue
AlaGolTI	Alaska Goldpanners Team Issue
AlbA'sT	Albany A's TCMA
AlbA'sT	Albany-Colonie A's TCMA
AlbDecGB	Albany Yankees All Decade Best
AlbDukCa	Albuquerque Dukes Caruso
AlbDukCm	Albuquerque Dukes CMC
AlbDukCr	Albuquerque Dukes Cramer
AlbDukD	Albuquerque Dukes DARE

AlbDukF Albuquerque Dukes Fleer/ProCards
AlbDukG Albuquerque Dukes Grandstand
AlbDukGS Albuquerque Dukes Grandstand
AlbDukLD Albuquerque Dukes Line Drive
AlbDukP Albuquerque Dukes ProCards
AlbDukS Albuquerque Dukes SkyBox
AlbDukTc Albuquerque Dukes TCMA
AlbDukTI Albuquerque Dukes Team Issue
AlbDukTr Albuquerque Dukes Tribune
AlbDukUG Albuquerque Dukes Update Grandstand
AlbPolC Albany Polecats Classic
AlbPolCB Albany Polecats Classic/Best
AlbPolF Albany Polecats Fleer/ProCards
AlbYanB Albany Yankees Best
AlbYanCB Albany Yankees Classic/Best Kraft
AlbYanF Albany Yankees Fleer/ProCards
AlbYanLD Albany Yankees Line Drive
AlbYanP Albany Yankees ProCards
AlbYanSk Albany Yankees SkyBox
AlbYanSt Albany Yankees Star
AlbYanT Albany Yankees TCMA
AlbYanT Albany-Colonie Yankees TCMA
AlbYanTI Albany-Colonie Yankees Team Issue
AlDemDCR3 Al Demaree Die Cuts R304
AleDukT Alexandria Dukes TCMA
AllandGN Allen and Ginter N28 *
AllandGN Allen and Ginter N29 *
AllandGN Allen and Ginter N43 *
AllBasA All-Star Baseball Album
AllBasT All-American Baseball Team
AllGamPI All-Star Game Program Inserts
AllLadBC All-American Ladies Baseball Club
AllMysFR Topps All-Topps Mystery Finest Refractors
AllSpoPPaF All Sport PPF *
AllSpoPPaFR All Sport PPF Retro *
AllToo1 All-Star Toon-Ups I
AlrGri2TT Alrak Griffey 24 Taco Time
AlrGriAAS Alrak Griffey Ace Auto Supply
AlrGrifMVO Alrak Griffey Mt. Vernon Ohio
AlrGriG Alrak Griffey Gazette
AlrGriGM Alrak Griffey Golden Moments
AlrGriGMS Alrak Griffey Golden Moments Sheet
AlrGriM Alrak Griffey Metal
AlrGriMc Alrak Griffey McDonald's
AlrGriP Alrak Griffey Postcard
AlrGriT Alrak Griffey Two-sided
AlrGriTP Alrak Griffey Triple Play
AlrTacGJ Alrak Griffey Jr. Taco Time
AmaGolST Amarillo Gold Sox TCMA
AmeCarE106 American Caramel E106
AmeCarE122 American Caramel E122
AmeCarE126 American Caramel E126
AmeCarE90-1 American Caramel E90-1
AmeCarE91 American Caramel E91
AmeLeaPC American League Publishing Co. PC770
AmeNut&CCP American Nut and Chocolate Co. Pennant
AmeTraS American Tract Society
AmeYou Ameritech Yount
AncBucTI Anchorage Bucs Team Issue
AncGlaP Anchorage Glacier Pilots
AncGlaPC Anchorage Glacier Pilots Candaele
AncGlaPM Anchorage Glacier Pilots McGwire
AncGlaPTI Anchorage Glacier Pilots Team Issue
AndBraT Anderson Braves TCMA
AndRanT Anderson Rangers TCMA
AngAdoF Angels Adohr Farms
AngCHP Angels CHP
AngDexP Angels Dexter Press
AngFamF Angels Family Fun Centers
AngGreT Angels Greats TCMA
AngGriS Angels Grich Sheet
AngJacitB Angels Jack in the Box
AngJayP Angels Jay Publishing
AngLAT Angels L.A. Times
AngMatSA Angels Matchbook Santa Ana
AngMot Angels Mother's
AngPol Angels Police
AngSco Angels Score
AngScoP Angels Score Platinum
AngSmo Angels Smokey
AngStaCl Angels Stadium Club
AngStrH Angels Straw Hat
AngTeal Angels Team Issue
AppFoxBS Appleton Foxes Box Scores
AppFoxC Appleton Foxes Classic
AppFoxCB Appleton Foxes Classic/Best
AppFoxFl Appleton Foxes Fleer/ProCards
AppFoxFr Appleton Foxes Fritsch
AppFoxP Appleton Foxes ProCards
AppFoxT Appleton Foxes TCMA
AppLeaAB Appalachian League All-Stars Best
AppLeaTPB Appalachian League Top Prospects Best
AreHol Arena Holograms *
AreKidGCH Arena Kid Griffey Comic Holograms
AriBlaDB Lethbridge Black Diamonds Best
AriFalLS Arizona Fall League SplitSecond
AriLot Arizona Lottery
AriStaB Arizona State Boosters
AriStaBG Arizona State Baseball Greats
AriStaCC* Arizona State Collegiate Collection *
AriStaCCP* Arizona State Collegiate Collection Promos *
AriWilP Arizona Wildcats Police
ArkRaz Arkansas Razorbacks
ArkTra Arkansas Travelers Update Multi-Ad
ArkTraB Arkansas Travelers Best
ArkTraF Arkansas Travelers Fleer/ProCards
ArkTraGS Arkansas Travelers Grand Slam
ArkTraH Arkansas Travelers Highlights
ArkTraLD Arkansas Travelers Line Drive
ArkTraM Arkansas Travelers Multi-Ad
ArkTraP Arkansas Travelers ProCards
ArkTraS Arkansas Travelers SkyBox
ArkTraT Arkansas Travelers TCMA
ArkTraTI Arkansas Travelers Team Issue
ArmCoi Armour Coins
arSenW1 Harrisburg Senators WINK 104
ArtHaloFP Artvue Hall of Fame Postcards
ARuFalLS Arizona Fall League SplitSecond
ASABobF ASA Bob Feller
ASABroR ASA Brooks Robinson
ASADukS ASA Duke Snider
ASAFraR ASA Frank Robinson
ASAHanA ASA Hank Aaron
ASAJoeD ASA Joe DiMaggio
ASAJohM ASA Johnny Mize
ASAJuaM ASA Juan Marichal
ASAMicM ASA Mickey Mantle
ASAWilM1 ASA Willie Mays 12
ASAWS ASA Warren Spahn
ASAYogB ASA Yogi Berra
AshOil Ashland Oil
AshTou Asheville Tourists Best
AshTouB Asheville Tourists Best
AshTouC Asheville Tourists Classic
AshTouC Asheville Tourists Classic/Best
AshTouF Asheville Tourists Fleer/ProCards
AshTouM Asheville Tourists Multi-Ad
AshTouP Asheville Tourists ProCards
AshTouT Asheville Tourists TCMA
AshTouTI Asheville Tourists Team Issue

AshTouUTI	Asheville Tourists Update Team Issue
Ast	Astros
AstAstI	Astros Astrosports Inserts
AstBurK	Astros Burger King
AstCok	Astros Coke
AstCol4S	Astros Colt .45s Smokey
AstFouTIP	Astros Four-on-One Team Issue Posters
AstGreT	Astros Greats TCMA
AstHouP	Astros Houston Post
AstJayP	Astros Jay Publishing
AstLenH	Astros Lennox HSE
AstMilL	Astros Miller Lite
AstMot	Astros Mother's
AstPho	Astros Photo Album
AstPho	Astros Photos
AstPol	Astros Police
AstPos	Astros Postcards
AstPosD	Astros Post Dierker
AstSer1	Astros-Series One
AstShoSO	Astros Shooting Stars-Series One
AstShoSPO	Astros Shooting Stars Postcards-Series One
AstShoSPT	Astros Shooting Stars Postcards-Series Three
AstShoSPT	Astros Shooting Stars Postcards-Series Two
AstShoSTw	Astros Shooting Stars-Series Two
AstShowSTh	Astros Shooting Stars-Series Three
AstSmo	Astros Smokey
AstStaC	Astros Stadium Club
AstTeal	Astros Team Issue
AstTeal1	Astros Team Issue 12
AstTeal2	Astros Team Issue 25
AthJayP	A's Jay Publishing
AthMot	A's Mother's
AthStaC	Athletics Stadium Club
AtlBraBPPS	Braves Birthday Party Photo Stamps
AtlBraP	Braves Postcards
AtlBraS	Braves Stamps
AtlCon	Atlanta Convention *
AtlOil	Atlantic Oil *
AtlOilPBCC	Atlantic Oil Play Ball Contest Cards
AubAstB	Auburn Astros Best
AubAstC	Auburn Astros Classic
AubAstC	Auburn Astros Classic/Best
AubAstF	Auburn Astros Fleer/ProCards
AubAstP	Auburn Astros ProCards
AubAstT	Auburn Astros TCMA
AubAstTI	Auburn Astros Team Issue
AubDouB	Auburn Doubledays Best
AubDouTI	Auburn Doubledays Team Issue
AugBecN	August Beck N403
AugGre	Augusta Greenjackets Best
AugGreB	Augusta Greenjackets Best
AugGreC	Augusta Greenjackets Classic
AugGreF	Augusta GreenJackets Fleer/ProCards
AugGreM	Augusta Greenjackets Multi-Ad
AugPirC	Augusta Pirates Classic/Best
AugPirF	Augusta Pirates Fleer/ProCards
AugPirP	Augusta Pirates ProCards
AurComP	Pacific Aurora Complete Players
AurKinotML	Pacific Aurora Kings of the Major Leagues
AurOn DL	Pacific Aurora On Deck Laser-Cuts
AurPenF	Pacific Aurora Pennant Fever
AurPenF	Pacific Aurora Pennant Fever Copper
AurPenFB	Pacific Aurora Pennant Fever Blue
AurPenFS	Pacific Aurora Pennant Fever Silver
AurRec	Auravision Records
AurSpoMK	Aurora Sports Model Kits
AurSty	Pacific Aurora Styrotechs
AusFut	Australian Futera
AusFutGP	Australian Futera Gold Prospect
AusFutSFP	Australian Futera Strike Force-Fire Power
AutCol	Autographed Collection *
AutColA*	Autographed Collection Autographs *
AutColBRA*	Autographed Collection Blue Ribbon Autographs *
AutColSCU	Autographed Collection Sports City USA *
B18B	B18 Blankets
BabRCCE	Babe Ruth Candy Company E-Unc.
BabRutG	Baby Ruth Gum
BabRutS	Babe Ruth Story
BaeRutSP	Babe Ruth Story Premium
BakBlaB	Bakersfield Blaze Best
BakBlaTI	Bakersfield Blaze Team Issue
BakDodC	Bakersfield Dodgers Classic
BakDodCLC	Bakersfield Dodgers Cal League Cards
BakDodP	Bakersfield Dodgers ProCards
BalHOF1C	Bally's HOF 1936 Chips
BalIntR	Baltimore Orioles Ruth
BalOriDPCP	Orioles Dexter Press/Coca Cola Postcards
BalOriHMP	Orioles Health
BalOriP	Orioles Postcards
BalOriPC	Orioles Postcards Color
BalParF	Ball Park Franks
BalParF	Ball Park Franks Will Clark
BalSunRVC	Baltimore Sun Ripken Vending Card
BasAmeAAB	Baseball America AA All-Stars Best
BasAmeAPB	Baseball America AA Prospects Best
BasAmeTP	Baseball America's Top Prospects
BasAmeTPA	Baseball Americas Top Prospects Autographs
BasAmeTPBP	Baseball Americas Top Prospects Best Possibilities
BasAmeTPG	Baseball Americas Top Prospects Gold
BasAmeTPLM	Baseball Americas Top Prospects League MVP
BasAmeTPSC	Baseball Americas Top Prospects Scouts Choice
BasBatEU	Baseball Bats E-Unc.
BasBesAotM	Baseball's Best Aces of the Mound
BasBesHM	Baseball's Best Hit Men
BasBesHRK	Baseball's Best Home Run Kings
BasBesRB	Baseball's Best Record Breakers
BasCarN	Baseball Card News
BasCitRC	Baseball City Royals Classic/Best
BasCitRF	Baseball City Royals Fleer/ProCards
BasCitRP	Baseball City Royals ProCards
BasCitRS	Baseball City Royals Star
BasComT	Baseball Comics T203
BasGre	Baseball Greats
BasMagM	Baseball Magazine M118
BasPat	Baseball Patches
BasPen	Baseball Pens
BasPho	Baseball Photos
BasStaB	Baseball Star Buttons
BasTabP	Baseball Tabs
BasWit	Baseball Wit
BatCliC	Batavia Clippers Classic
BatCliCB	Batavia Clippers Classic/Best
BatCliF	Batavia Clippers Fleer/ProCards
BatCliP	Batavia Clippers ProCards
BatCliTI	Batavia Clippers Team Issue
BatMucTI	Batavia Muckdogs Team Issue
BatR31	Batter-Up R318
BatRouCT	Baton Rouge Cougars TCMA
BatTroT	Batavia Trojans TCMA
BatTroTI	Batavia Trojans Team Issue
Baz	Bazooka

BazA	Bazooka ATG
BazNumT	Bazooka Numbered Test
BazQua5A	Bazooka Quadracard '53 Archives
BazRedH	Bazooka Red Hot
BazTeaU	Bazooka Team USA
BazUnn	Bazooka Unnumbered
BBMJap	BBM Japan
BBMJapAS	BBM Japan All Stars
BBMJapN	BBM Japan Nippon
BBMJapSAG	BBM Japan Sanyo All-Star Game
BeaGolGP	Beaumont Golden Gators ProCards
BeaGolGT	Beaumont Golden Gators TCMA
BelBre2S	Beloit Brewers II Star
BelBreB	Beloit Brewers Best
BelBreC	Beloit Brewers Classic
BelBreCB	Beloit Brewers Classic/Best
BelBreFl	Beloit Brewers Fleer/ProCards
BelBreFr	Beloit Brewers Fritsch
BelBreGS	Beloit Brewers Grand Slam
BelBreIS	Beloit Brewers I Star
BelBreP	Beloit Brewers ProCards
BelBreS	Beloit Brewers Star
BelBreT	Beloit Brewers TCMA
BelBreTI	Beloit Snappers Team Issue
BelGiaTI	Bellingham Giants Team Issue
BelMarC	Bellingham Mariners Classic
BelMarCB	Bellingham Mariners Classic/Best
BelMarCr	Bellingham Mariners Cramer
BelMarF	Bellingham Mariners Fleer/ProCards
BelMarL	Bellingham Mariners Legoe
BelMarP	Bellingham Mariners ProCards
BelMarTI	Bellingham Mariners Team Issue
BelSnaB	Beloit Snappers Best
BelSnaM	Beloit Snappers Multi-Ad
BelSnaTI	Beloit Snappers Team Issue
BenBucCB	Bend Bucks Classic/Best
BenBucL	Bend Bucks Legoe
BenBucP	Bend Bucks ProCards
BenPhiC	Bend Phillies Cramer
BenRocC	Bend Rockies Classic
BenRocCB	Bend Rockies Classic/Best
BenRocF	Bend Rockies Fleer/ProCards
BerRos	Berk Ross
BerRos	Berk Ross *
Bes	Best
BesAll	Best All-Stars
BesAutAS	Best Autographs Autograph Series
BesAutP	Best Autographs Prospects
BesAutPOY	Best Autographs Player of the Year
BesAutS	Best Autograph Series
BesAutS1RP	Best Autograph Series 1st Round Picks
BesAutSA	Best Autograph Series Autographs
BesAutSBPP	Best Premium Preview
BesAutSC	Best Cornerstone
BesAutSS	Best Autographs Signature Series
BesBet	Best Bets
BesBetP	Best Bets Preview
BesCarCSP	Best Carolina Classic Show Promos
BesCasT	Best Case Topper
BesCon	Best Contenders
BesCor	Best Cornerstone
BesDiaB	Best Diamond Best
BesDiaBA	Best Diamond Best Autographs
BesFiv	Best Five
BesFra	Best Franchise
BesFulCA	Best Full Count Autographs
BesGun	Best Guns
BesIntB	Best International Best
BesLimA	Best Limited Autographs
BesLum	Best Lumber
BesNumOP	Best Number One Pick
BesPauK	Best Paul Konerko
BesPauKA	Best Paul Konerko Autographs
BesPlaotYAJ	Best Player of the Year Andruw Jones
BesPlaotYAJA	Best Player of the Year Andruw Jones Autographs
BesPlaotYP	Best Player of the Year Promos
BesPos	Best Possibilities
BesPreA	Best Premium Autographs
BesPro	Best Promos
BesWesR	Best Western Ryan
BesWhe	Best Wheels
BesYouG	Best Young Guns
BF2FP	BF2 Felt Pennants
BHCRSpoL	BHCR Sports Legends
BigEatEU	Big Eater E-Unc.
BigLeaC	Big League Chew
BigLeaC3	Big League Collectibles 30s
BigLeaCC	Big League Collectibles Clemente
BigLeaCOA	Big League Collectibles Original All-Stars
BigLeaIS	Big League Inc. Statues
BilMusF	Billings Mustangs Fleer/ProCards
BilMusP	Billings Mustangs ProCards
BilMusSP	Billings Mustangs Sports Pro
BilMusTI	Billings Mustangs Team Issue
BilZubR	Bill Zuber Restaurant
BimBreD	Bimbo Bread Discs
BinMetB	Binghamton Mets Best
BinMetF	Binghamton Mets Fleer/ProCards
BinMetQ	Binghamton Mets Q-Cards
BinMetS	Binghamton Mets SkyBox
BinMetTI	Binghamton Mets Team Issue
BirBarADB	Birmingham Barons All Decade Best
BirBarB	Birmingham Barons Best
BirBarC	Birmingham Barons Classic
BirBarF	Birmingham Barons Fleer/ProCards
BirBarG	Birmingham Barons Grandstand
BirBarLD	Birmingham Barons Line Drive
BirBarP	Birmingham Barons ProCards
BirBarS	Birmingham Barons SkyBox
BirBarT	Birmingham Barons TCMA
BirBarTI	Birmingham Barons Team Issue
BisCoaLE100	Bishop Coast League E100
BisCoaLE99	Bishop Coast League E99
BlaBacD	Blank Back Discs
BlaDis	Blankback Discs
BlaYNPRWL	Blanco Y Negro Puerto Rico Winter League
BlaYNPRWLU	Blanco Y Negro Puerto Rico Winter League Update
Ble	Bleachers
Ble23KGJ	Bleachers 23K Griffey Jr.
Ble23KJ	Bleachers 23K Justice
Ble23KR	Bleachers 23K Ryan
Ble23KT	Bleachers 23K Thomas
BlePro	Bleachers Promos
BleRya6	Bleachers Ryan 6
BluJay5	Blue Jays 5x7
BluJayAF	Blue Jays Ault Foods
BluJayB	Blue Jays Becker
BluJayB	Blue Jays Bookmarks
BluJayBY	Blue Jays Bubble Yum
BluJayCC	Blue Jays Cash Converters
BluJayCC	Blue Jays Coke Cups
BluJayCP1	Blue Jays Colla Postcards 15
BluJayCQI	Blue Jays Copi Quik Interleague
BluJayD	Blue Jays Dempster's
BluJayD4	Blue Jays Donruss 45
BluJayDM	Blue Jays Donruss McDonald's
BluJayDWS	Blue Jays Donruss World Series
BluJayFS	Blue Jays Fire Safety
BluJayGT	Blue Jays Greats TCMA

BluJayHS	Blue Jays Hostess Stickers
BluJayJR	Blue Jays Jackie Robinson
BluJayMH	Blue Jays Maxwell House
BluJayOH	Blue Jays Oh Henry!
BluJayP	Blue Jays Pins
BluJayP	Blue Jays Postcards
BluJayPLP	Blue Jays Pepsi/Frito Lay Pennants
BluJayS	Blue Jays Score
BluJayS	Blue Jays Scorebook
BluJayS	Blue Jays Sizzler
BluJayS	Blue Jays Sun
BluJayUSPC	Blue Jays U.S. Playing Cards
BluOriB	Bluefield Orioles Best
BluOriC	Bluefield Orioles Classic
BluOriC	Bluefield Orioles Classic/Best
BluOriF	Bluefield Orioles Fleer/ProCards
BluOriP	Bluefield Orioles ProCards
BluOriQ	Bluefield Orioles Q-Cards
BluOriS	Bluefield Orioles Star
BluTin	Blue Tint R346
BoaandB	Boardwalk and Baseball
BobCamRB	Richmond Braves Bob's Camera
BobParHoF	Bob Parker Hall of Fame
BobParMBC	Bob Parker More Baseball Cartoons
BobRic	Bobby Richardson
BoiHawB	Boise Hawks Best
BoiHawC	Boise Hawks Classic
BoiHawC	Boise Hawks Classic/Best
BoiHawF	Boise Hawks Fleer/ProCards
BoiHawG	Boise Hawks Grandstand
BoiHawP	Boise Hawks ProCards
BoiHawTI	Boise Hawks Team Issue
BonBreR	Bond Bread Robinson
BooProC	Book Promotional Cards
Bow	Bowman
Bow195E	Bowman 1952 Extension
Bow200RF	Bowman 2000 ROY Favorites
Bow98ROY	Bowman 1998 ROY Favorites
Bow99ROYF	Bowman 1999 ROY Favorites
BowAut	Bowman Autographs
BowBanD	Bowery Bank DiMaggio
BowBay	Bowie Baysox Best
BowBayB	Bowie Baysox Best
BowBayF	Bowie Baysox Fleer/ProCards
BowBayM	Bowie Baysox Multi-Ad
BowBayTI	Bowie Baysox Team Issue
BowBes	Bowman's Best
BowBesA	Bowman's Best Autographs
BowBesAAR	Bowman's Best Autographs Atomic Refractor
BowBesAAR	Bowman's Best Autographs Atomic Refractors
BowBesAR	Bowman's Best Atomic Refractors
BowBesAR	Bowman's Best Autographs Refractor
BowBesAR	Bowman's Best Autographs Refractors
BowBesBC	Bowman's Best Best Cuts
BowBesBCAR	Bowman's Best Best Cuts Atomic Refractor
BowBesBCR	Bowman's Best Best Cuts Refractor
BowBesC	Bowman's Best Cuts
BowBesCAR	Bowman's Best Cuts Atomic Refractors
BowBesCR	Bowman's Best Cuts Refractors
BowBesFBMI	Bowman's Best Franchise Best Mach I
BowBesFBMII	Bowman's Best Franchise Best Mach II
BowBesFBMIII	Bowman's Best Franchise Best Mach III
BowBesFF	Bowman's Best Franchise Favorites
BowBesFFA	Bowman's Best Franchise Favorites Autographs
BowBesFFMI	Bowman's Best Future Foundations Mach I
BowBesFFMI	Bowman's Best Future Foundations Mach III
BowBesFFMII	Bowman's Best Future Foundations Mach II
BowBesJ	Bowman's Best Jumbo
BowBesJAR	Bowman's Best Jumbo Atomic Refractor
BowBesJR	Bowman's Best Jumbo Refractor
BowBesJR	Bowman's Best Jumbo Refractors
BowBesMI	Bowman's Best Mirror Image
BowBesMIAR	Bowman's Best Mirror Image Atomic Refractor
BowBesMIAR	Bowman's Best Mirror Image Atomic Refractors
BowBesMIARI	Bowman's Best Mirror Image Atomic Refractor Inverted
BowBesMIF	Bowman's Best Mirror Image Fusion
BowBesMIFAR	Bowman's Best Mirror Image Fusion Atomic Refractors
BowBesMIFR	Bowman's Best Mirror Image Fusion Refractors
BowBesMII	Bowman's Best Mirror Image Inverted
BowBesMIR	Bowman's Best Mirror Image Refractor
BowBesMIR	Bowman's Best Mirror Image Refractors
BowBesMIRI	Bowman's Best Mirror Image Refractor Inverted
BowBesP	Bowman's Best Performers
BowBesP	Bowman's Best Previews
BowBesPAR	Bowman's Best Performers Atomic Refractors
BowBesPAR	Bowman's Best Preview Atomic Refractor
BowBesPAR	Bowman's Best Previews Atomic Refractors
BowBesPR	Bowman's Best Performers Refractors
BowBesPR	Bowman's Best Preview Refractor
BowBesPR	Bowman's Best Previews Refractors
BowBesR	Bowman's Best Refractors
BowBesRLRA	Bowman's Best Rookie Locker Room Autographs
BowBesRLRGUB	Bowman's Best Rookie Locker Room Game Used Bats
BowBesRLRGWJ	Bowman's Best Rookie Locker Room Game Worn Jerseys
BowBesROY	Bowman's Best Rookie of the Year
BowBW	Bowman B/W
BowC	Bowman Color
BowCerBlaIA	Bowman Certified Black Ink Autographs
BowCerBlueAU	Bowman Certified Blue Autographs
BowCerBluIA	Bowman Certified Blue Ink Autographs
BowCerGA	Bowman Certified Gold Autographs
BowCerGolIA	Bowman Certified Gold Ink Autographs
BowCerGreIJA	Bowman Certified Green Ink Jeter Autograph
BowCerSA	Bowman Certified Silver Autographs
BowChr	Bowman Chrome
BowChr1RFR	Bowman Chrome 1998 ROY Favorites Refractors
BowChr98RF	Bowman Chrome 1998 ROY Favorites
BowChrDA	Bowman Chrome Diamond Aces
BowChrDAR	Bowman Chrome Diamond Aces Refractors
BowChrG	Bowman Chrome Gold
BowChrGA	Bowman Chrome Golden Anniversary
BowChrGAR	Bowman Chrome Golden Anniversary Refractors
BowChrGR	Bowman Chrome Gold Refractors
BowChrI	Bowman Chrome International
BowChrIR	Bowman Chrome International Refractors
BowChrR	Bowman Chrome Refractors
BowChrR	Bowman Chrome Reprints
BowChrRR	Bowman Chrome Reprints Refractors

BowChrSC Bowman Chrome Scout's Choice
BowChrSCR Bowman Chrome Scout's Choice Refractors
BowChrSHR Bowman Chrome Scout's Honor Roll
BowChrSHRR Bowman Chrome Scout's Honor Roll Refractor
BowEarR Bowman Early Risers
BowFoi Bowman Foil
BowGol Bowman Gold
BowGolA Bowman Golden Anniversary
BowGolF Bowman Gold Foil
BowIns Bowman Inserts
BowInsL Bowman Insert Lithographs
BowInsT Bowman Inserts Tiffany
BowInsT Bowman Reprint Inserts Tiffany
BowInt Bowman International
BowIntB Bowman International Best
BowIntBAR Bowman International Best Atomic Refractor
BowIntBR Bowman International Best Refractor
BowLatB Bowman Late Bloomers
BowMinLM Bowman Minor League MVP's
BowMinLP Bowman Minor League POY
BowPCL Bowman PCL
BowPre Bowman Previews
BowPreProd Bowman Pre-Production
BowRepl Bowman Reprint Inserts
BowScoC Bowman Scout's Choice
BowScoHR Bowman Scout's Honor Roll
BowTif Bowman Tiffany
BoyScooAT Boy Scouts of America Treadway
Bra193NLA Bramac 1933 National League All-Stars
Bra195T Braves 1957 TCMA
Bra53F Braves 53 Fritsch
Bra8x1 Braves 8x10
BraAtlC Braves Atlanta Constitution
BraBilaBP Braves Bill and Bob Postcards PPC-741
BraBurKL Braves Burger King Lids
BraCok Braves Coke
BraDav Braves Davison's
BraDub Braves Dubuque
BraDubP Braves Dubuque Perforated
BraDubS Braves Dubuque Singles
BraFle Braves Fleer
BraFloA Braves Florida Agriculture
BraGolS Braves Golden Stamps
BraGreT Braves Greats TCMA
BraHos Braves Hostess
BraIrvD Braves Irvingdale Dairy
BraJayP Braves Jay Publishing
BraJohC Braves Johnston Cookies
BraKryPS Braves Krystal Postcard Sanders
BraLaktL Braves Lake to Lake
BraLykP Braves Lykes Perforated
BraLykS Braves Lykes Standard
BraMer Braves Merrell
BraPho Braves Photos
BraPhoC Braves Photo Cards
BraPol Braves Police
BraPos Braves Postcards
BraSco Braves Score
BraScoP Braves Score Platinum
BraScoPl Braves Score Platinum
BraScoPr Braves Score Premier
BraSmo Braves Smokey
BraSpiaS Braves Spic and Span
BraSpiaS3 Braves Spic and Span 3x5
BraSpiaS4 Braves Spic and Span 4x5
BraSpiaS7 Braves Spic and Span 7x10
BraSpiaSD Braves Spic and Span Die-Cut
BraSpiaSP Braves Spic and Span Postcards
BraStaC Braves Stadium Club
BraSubS Braves Dubuque Standard
BraTBSAT Braves TBS America's Team
BraTCC Braves TCC
BraTCM1 Braves 1914 TCMA
BraTeal Braves Team Issue
BraUSPC Braves U.S. Playing Cards
BreA&P Brewers A and P
BreBro Brewers Broadcasters
BreBtaTI Greenville Braves Team Issue
BreCarT Brewers Carlson Travel
BreCouMB Brevard County Manatees Best
BreCouMC Brevard County Manatees Classic
BreCouMF Brevard County Manatees Fleer/ProCards
BreE10 Breisch-Williams E107
BreGar Brewers Gardner's
BreGreT Brewers Greats TCMA
BreMcD Brewers McDonald's
BreMil Brewers Milk
BreMilB Brewers Miller Brewing
BrePlaM Brewers Placemats McDonalds
BrePlaPH Brewers Placemats Pizza Hut
BrePol Brewers Police
BreSen Brewers Sentry
BreSen5 Brewers Sentry 5x7
BreSenY Brewers Sentry Yount
BreTeal Brewers Team Issue
BreUSO Brewers U.S. Oil
BreYea Brewers Yearbook
Bri Briggs
BriBanF Brisbane Bandits Futura
BriBluM Bridgeport Bluefish Multi-Ad
BriE97 Briggs E97
BriRedST Bristol Red Sox TCMA
BriTigC Bristol Tigers Classic
BriTigC Bristol Tigers Classic/Best
BriTigF Bristol Tigers Fleer/ProCards
BriTigP Bristol Tigers ProCards
BriTigS Bristol Tigers Star
BriWhiSB Bristol White Sox Best
BriWhiSQ Bristol White Sox Q-Cards
BriYouC Brigham Young Cougars
Bro194F Browns '44 Fritsch
BroClu Dodgers 1890 Program TCMA
BroPenCB Browns Pencil Clip Buttons PPC-1
BroW75 Browns W753
BucDis Buchman Discs
BucN28 Buchner N284
BufBis Buffalo Bisons Best
BufBisB Buffalo Bisons Best
BufBisBS Buffalo Bisons Blue Shield
BufBisC Buffalo Bisons CMC
BufBisF Buffalo Bisons Fleer/ProCards
BufBisFJO Buffalo Bisons F.J. Offerman
BufBisG Buffalo Bisons Grandstand
BufBisJD Buffalo Bisons Jones Dairy
BufBisLD Buffalo Bisons Line Drive
BufBisP Buffalo Bisons ProCards
BufBisP Buffalo Bisons Pucko
BufBisS Buffalo Bisons SkyBox
BufBisT Buffalo Bisons TCMA
BufBisTI Buffalo Bisons Team Issue
BulDurM Bull Durham Movie
BulDurOS Bull Durham Orion Set
BurAstC Burlington Astros Classic/Best
BurAstF Burlington Astros Fleer/ProCards
BurAstP Burlington Astros ProCards
BurBeeB Burlington Bees Best
BurBeeC Burlington Bees Classic
BurBeeC Burlington Bees Classic/Best
BurBeeF Burlington Bees Fleer/ProCards

BurBeeM	Burlington Bees Multi-Ad
BurBeeT	Burlington Bees TCMA
BurBeeTI	Burlington Bees Team Issue
BurBraB	Burlington Braves Best
BurBraP	Burlington Braves ProCards
BurBraS	Burlington Braves Star
BurCheD	Burger Chef Discs
BurExpP	Burlington Expos ProCards
BurIndB	Burlington Indians Best
BurIndC	Burlington Indians Classic
BurIndC	Burlington Indians Classic/Best
BurIndF	Burlington Indians Fleer/ProCards
BurIndG	Burlington Indians Grandstand
BurIndP	Burlington Indians ProCards
BurIndS	Burlington Indians Star
BurKinA	Burger King All-Pro
BurKinPHR	Burger King Pitch/Hit/Run
BurKinR	Burger King Ripken
BurKinRG	Burger King Ripken Gold
BurRanF	Burlington Rangers Fritsch
BurRanT	Burlington Rangers TCMA
ButCanV	Butterfinger Canadian V94
ButCopKB	Butte Copper Kings Best
ButCopKG	Butte Copper Kings Grandstand
ButCopKK	Butte Copper Kings KBOW
ButCopKSP	Butte Copper Kings Sports Pro
ButCopKT	Butte Copper Kings TCMA
ButCopKtI	Butte Copper Kings Team Issue
ButCre	Butter Cream R306
ButPreR	Butterfinger Premiums R310
CadDis	Cadaco Discs
CadEllD	Cadaco Ellis Discs
Cal	Calbee
CalAngP	Angels Postcards
CalAngPPS	Angels Promotional Photo Sheet
CalCanB	Calgary Cannons Best
CalCanC	Calgary Cannons CMC
CalCanC	Calgary Cannons Cramer
CalCanF	Calgary Cannons Fleer/ProCards
CalCanLD	Calgary Cannons Line Drive
CalCanP	Calgary Cannons ProCards
CalCanS	Calgary Cannons SkyBox
CalHOFW	Callahan HOF W576
CalHok	Calbee Hokkaido
CalJap	Calbee Japanese
CalLeaA	California League All-Stars Cal League Cards
CalLeaACL	California League All-Stars Cal League Cards
CalLeaACLC	California League All-Stars Cal League Cards
CalLeaATI	California/Carolina League All-Stars Team Issue
CalLeaTP	California League Top Prospects Best
CalLeLA	California League All-Stars
CalLot	California Lottery
CamPepP	Cameo Pepsin Gum Pins
CanCarCC	Canseco Card Collectors Co.
CanIndB	Canton-Akron Indians Best
CanIndF	Canton-Akron Indians Fleer/ProCards
CanIndLD	Canton-Akron Indians Line Drive
CanIndP	Canton-Akron Indians ProCards
CanIndS	Canton-Akron Indians SkyBox
CanIndS	Canton-Akron Indians Star
CapCitB	Capital City Bombers Best
CapCitBC	Capital City Bombers Classic
CapCitBC	Capital City Bombers Classic/Best
CapCitBF	Capital City Bombers Fleer/ProCards
CapCitBF5	Capital City Bombers Fox 57
CapCitBM	Capital City Bombers Multi-Ad
CapCodPB	Cape Cod Prospects Ballpark
CapCodPPaLP	Cape Cod Prospects P and L Promotions
CapFeaCM	Cape Fear Crocs Multi-Ad
CapPub	Capital Publishing
Car	Cardinals
Car	Cardtoons
Car193T	Cardinals 1934 TCMA
Car194T	Cardinals 1942-1946 TCMA
Car5	Cardinals 5x7
Car5x7	Cardinals 5x7
CarCoi	Cardinals Coins
CarColBP	Cardinals Colonial Bread Porter
CarColJB	Card Collectors' Justice Boyhood
CarDis	Carousel Discs
CarGreT	Cardinals Greats TCMA
CarGuaPG	Card Guard Promo Griffey
CarHunW	Cardinals Hunter's Wieners
CarIGAS	Cardinals IGA Stores
CarJayP	Cardinals Jay Publishing
CarKASD	Cardinals KAS Discs
CarLeaA	Carolina League All-Stars
CarLeaA	Carolina League All-Time
CarLeaA1B	Carolina League All-Stars 1 Best
CarLeaA2B	Carolina League All-Stars 2 Best
CarLeaAC	Carolina League All-Stars Choice
CarLeaAF	Carolina League All-Stars Fleer/ProCards
CarLeaAGF	Carolina League All-Stars Fleer/ProCards
CarLeaAIB	Carolina League All-Stars Insert Best
CarLeaAP	Carolina League All-Stars ProCards
CarLeaAS	Carolina League All-Stars Star
CarLeaTP	Carolina League Top Prospects Best
CarLeaTPQ	Carolina League Top Prospects Q-Cards
CarMagG	Cardinals Magnets GM
CarMcD	Cardinals McDonald's/Pacific
CarMet	Cardinals Metropolitan
CarMudB	Carolina Mudcats Best
CarMudC	Carolina Mud Cats Best
CarMudF	Carolina Mudcats Fleer/ProCards
CarMudF	Reading Phillies TCMA
CarMudLD	Carolina Mudcats Line Drive
CarMudM	Carolina Mudcats Multi-Ad
CarMudP	Carolina Mudcats ProCards
CarMudS	Carolina Mudcats SkyBox
CarMudTI	Carolina Mudcats Team Issue
CarNewE	Carson Newman Eagles
CarPanP	Cardinals Pantera Placemats
CarPol	Cardinals Police
CarSchM	Cardinals Schnucks Milk
CarScoP	Cardinals Score Platinum
CarSmo	Cardinals Smokey
CarStaC	Cardinals Stadium Club
CarTeal	Cardinals Team Issue
CarW75	Cardinals W754
CedRapAT	Cedar Rapids Astros TCMA
CedRapCT	Cedar Rapids Cardinals TCMA
CedRapGT	Cedar Rapids Giants TCMA
CedRapK	Cedar Rapids Kernels Grandstand
CedRapKC	Cedar Rapids Kernels Classic
CedRapKC	Cedar Rapids Kernels Classic/Best
CedRapKF	Cedar Rapids Kernels Fleer/ProCards
CedRapKTI	Cedar Rapids Kernels Team Issue
CedRapRAB	Cedar Rapids Reds All-Decade Best
CedRapRB	Cedar Rapids Reds Best
CedRapRC	Cedar Rapids Reds Classic/Best
CedRapRDGB	Cedar Rapids Reds All Decade Best
CedRapRF	Cedar Rapids Reds Fleer/ProCards
CedRapRF	Cedar Rapids Reds Fritsch
CedRapRP	Cedar Rapids Reds ProCards
CedRapRS	Cedar Rapids Reds Star
CedRapRT	Cedar Rapids Reds TCMA
CenFlo	Centennial Flour
CenValRC	Central Valley Rockies Classic

CenValRC	Central Valley Rockies Classic/Best
CenValRF	Central Valley Rockies Fleer/ProCards
CerSup	Cereal Superstars
Cha	Charlotte Rangers Multi-Ad
ChaAllCM	Charleston Alley Cats Multi-Ad
ChaChaT	Charleston Charlies TCMA
ChaKni	Charlotte Knights Best
ChaKniB	Charlotte Knights Best
ChaKniF	Charlotte Knights Fleer/ProCards
ChaKniLD	Charlotte Knights Line Drive
ChaKniP	Charlotte Knights ProCards
ChaKniQ	Charlotte Knights Q-Cards
ChaKniS	Charlotte Knights SkyBox
ChaKniTI	Charlotte Knights Team Issue
ChaLoo	Chattanooga Lookouts Best
ChaLooB	Chattanooga Lookouts Best
ChaLooF	Chattanooga Lookouts Fleer/ProCards
ChaLooG	Chattanooga Lookouts Grandstand
ChaLooGS	Chattanooga Lookouts Grand Slam
ChaLooLD	Chattanooga Lookouts Line Drive
ChaLooLITI	Chattanooga Lookouts Legends II Team Issue
ChaLooLTI	Chattanooga Lookouts Legends Team Issue
ChaLooP	Chattanooga Lookouts ProCards
ChaLooS	Chattanooga Lookouts SkyBox
ChaLooT	Chattanooga Lookouts TCMA
ChaLooTI	Chattanooga Lookouts Team Issue
ChaO'sP	Charlotte O's Police
ChaO'sT	Charlotte O's TCMA
ChaO'sW	Charlotte O's W3TV
ChaO'sW	Charlotte O's WBTV
ChaOriW	Charlotte Orioles WBTV
ChaPatT	Charleston Patriots TCMA
ChaPirT	Charleston Pirates TCMA
ChaRaiB	Charleston Rainbows Best
ChaRaiC	Charleston Rainbows Classic/Best
ChaRaiF	Charleston Rainbows Fleer/ProCards
ChaRaiP	Charleston Rainbows ProCards
ChaRanC	Charlotte Rangers Classic/Best
ChaRanF	Charlotte Rangers Fleer/ProCards
ChaRanP	Charlotte Rangers ProCards
ChaRanS	Charlotte Rangers Star
ChaRivC	Charleston Riverdogs Classic
ChaRivDG	Charleston River Dogs Grandstand
ChaRivDG	Charleston RiverDogs Grandstand
ChaRivF	Charleston RiverDogs Fleer/ProCards
ChaRivTI	Charleston Riverdogs Team Issue
ChaRivUTIS	Charleston Riverdogs Update Team Issue
ChaRoyT	Charleston Royals TCMA
ChaSupJ	Charboneau Super Joe's
ChaTheY	Challenge The Yankees
ChaWheB	Charleston Wheelers Best
ChaWheC	Charleston Wheelers Classic
ChaWheC	Charleston Wheelers Classic/Best
ChaWheF	Charleston Wheelers Fleer/ProCards
ChaWheP	Charleston Wheelers ProCards
ChaWVWC	Charleston (WV) Wheelers Classic/Best
CheBoy	Chef Boyardee
ChePat	Chemstrand Patches
ChePri	Chevy Prints
ChiE	Chicago E90-3
ChiEveAP	Chicago Evening American Pins
ChiGre	Chicago Greats
ChiJonP	Chipper Jones Police
ChiWilD	Chilly Willie Discs
ChuHomS	Church's Hometown Stars
ChuHomSG	Church's Hometown Stars Gold
ChuShoS	Church's Show Stoppers
CinRedT	Reds 1939-40 TCMA
Cir	Circa
CirAcc	Circa Access
CirBos	Circa Boss
CirEmeA	Circa Emerald Autographs
CirEmeAR	Circa Emerald Autograph Redemptions
CirFasT	Circa Fast Track
CirIco	Circa Icons
CirK	Circle K
CirLimA	Circa Limited Access
CirRav	Circa Rave
CirRavR	Circa Rave Reviews
CirSupB	Circa Super Boss
CirThu	Circa Thunder
CirThuB	Circa Thunder Boss
CirThuFT	Circa Thunder Fast Track
CirThuLA	Circa Thunder Limited Access
CirThuQS	Circa Thunder Quick Strike
CirThuRav	Circa Thunder Rave
CirThuRR	Circa Thunder Rave Review
CirThuRS	Circa Thunder Rolen Sportsfest
CirThuSupRav	Circa Thunder Super Rave
CirThuTB	Circa Thunder Thunder Boomers
CitMetC	Citgo Metal Coins
CitPriC	City Pride Clemente
Cla	Classic
Cla#1DPMF	Classic #1 Draft Pick Mail-In
Cla/Bes	Classic/Best
Cla1	Classic I
Cla2	Classic II
Cla3	Classic III
Cla7/1PC	Classic 7/11 Phone Cards
ClaBlu	Classic Blue
ClaBluBF	Classic/Best Blue Bonus
ClaBonB	Classic Bonus Baby
ClaBreD3	Clark's Bread D-381-2
ClaBroR	Classic Brooks Robinson
ClaCar	Classic Cards
ClaCP	Classic C-3 Presidential
ClaCreotC	Classic Cream of the Crop
ClaDraP	Classic Draft Picks
ClaDraPFB	Classic Draft Picks Foil Bonus
ClaDraPP	Classic Draft Picks Previews
ClaDraPP	Classic Draft Picks Promos
ClaExp#PF	Classic/Best Expansion #1 Picks
ClaFanFPCP	Classic $10 Phone Cards Promos
ClaFisN	Classic/Best Fisher Nuts
ClaFS7	Classic/Best
ClaGam	Classic Game
ClaGolA	Classic/Best Gold Acetates
ClaGolB	Classic/Best Gold Bonus
ClaGolF	Classic/Best Gold
ClaGolLF	Classic/Best Gold LPs
ClaGolN1PLF	Classic/Best Gold #1 Pick LPs
ClaGolP	Classic/Best Gold Promos
ClaGolREF	Classic/Best Gold Rookie Express
ClaGolTP	Classic/Best Gold Tri-Star Promos
ClaInsC	Classic/Best Insert Cards
ClaLigB	Classic Light Blue
ClaMVPF	Classic/Best MVPs
ClaNolR1	Classic Nolan Ryan 10
ClaPhoC	Classic $10 Phone Cards
ClaPla&MotYF	Classic/Best Player and Manager of the Year
ClaPro	Classic/Best Promo
ClaPro	Classic/Best Promos
ClaRed	Classic Red
ClaRedB	Classic/Best Red Bonus
ClaTraO	Classic Travel Orange
ClaTraP	Classic Travel Purple
ClaTriF	Classic Tri-Cards
ClaUpd	Classic Update
ClaUpdCotC	Classic Update Cream of the Crop

ClaUpdY	Classic Update Yellow
ClaYel	Classic Yellow
ClaYouG	Classic/Best Young Guns
CleAaP	Clemens A and P
CleIndP	Indians Postcards
ClePhi	Clearwater Phillies Best
ClePhiC	Clearwater Phillies Classic
ClePhiC	Clearwater Phillies Classic/Best
ClePhiF	Clearwater Phillies Fleer/ProCards
ClePhiM	Clearwater Phillies Multi-Ad
ClePhiP	Clearwater Phillies ProCards
ClePhiS	Clearwater Phillies Star
ClePhiUM	Clearwater Phillies Update Multi-Ad
CleTheF	Clemens The Fan
CliDodT	Clinton Dodgers TCMA
CliGiaB	Clinton Giants Best
CliGiaC	Clinton Giants Classic/Best
CliGiaF	Clinton Giants Fleer/ProCards
CliGiaF	Clinton Giants Fritsch
CliGiaP	Clinton Giants ProCards
CliGiaT	Clinton Giants TCMA
CliGiaUTI	Clinton Giants Update Team Issue
CliLumC	Clinton Lumberkings Classic
CliLumF	Clinton LumberKings Fleer/ProCards
CliLumG	Clinton LumberKings Grandstand
CliLumKTI	Clinton Lumber Kings Team Issue
CliPilT	Clinton Pilots TCMA
CloFotW	Clopay Foto-Fun R329
CloHSS	Clovis HS Smokey
CMC	CMC
CMCBasG	CMC Baseball's Greatest
CMCCan	CMC Canseco
CMCMan	CMC Mantle
CMCMat	CMC Mattingly
CMCRut	CMC Ruth
CocAstT	Cocoa Astros TCMA
CokCapA	Coke Caps All-Stars
CokCapA	Coke Caps Astros
CokCapAAm	Coke Caps All-Stars AL
CokCapAs	Coke Caps Astros
CokCapAt	Coke Caps Athletics
CokCapB	Coke Caps Braves
CokCapBT	Coke Caps Baseball Tips
CokCapC	Coke Caps Cubs
CokCapD	Coke Caps Dodgers
CokCapDA	Coke Caps Dodgers/Angels
CokCapG	Coke Caps Giants
CokCapI	Coke Caps Indians
CokCapNLA	Coke Caps All-Stars NL
CokCapO	Coke Caps Orioles
CokCapPh	Coke Caps Phillies
CokCapPi	Coke Caps Pirates
CokCapR	Coke Caps Reds
CokCapRS	Coke Caps Red Sox
CokCapS	Coke Caps Senators
CokCapT	Coke Caps Tigers
CokCapTi	Coke Caps Tigers
CokCapTw	Coke Caps Twins
CokCapWS	Coke Caps White Sox
CokCapYM	Coke Caps Yankees and Mets
CokCasI	Coke Case Inserts
CokMat	Coke Mattingly
CokNL M	Coke/7-11 NL MVPs
CokTeaS	Coke Team Sets
CokTip	Coke Tips
Col	Collect-A-Books
Col.45B	Colt .45's Booklets
Col.45JP	Colt .45's Jay Publishing
Col45"P	Colt .45's Pepsi-Cola
Col45'HC	Colt .45's Houston Chronicle
Col45'JP	Colt .45's Jay Publishing
ColAllG	Colla All-Star Game
ColAllP	Colla All-Stars Promos
ColAstB	Columbus Astros Best
ColAstP	Columbus Astros ProCards
ColAstT	Columbus Astros TCMA
ColBag	Colla Bagwell
ColBon	Colla Bonds
ColC	Collector's Choice
ColCan	Colla Canseco
ColChiE	Colgan's Chips E254
ColCho	Collector's Choice
ColChoAC	Collector's Choice All-Star Connection
ColChoB5	Collector's Choice Blowups 5x7
ColChoBS	Collector's Choice Big Shots
ColChoBSGS	Collector's Choice Big Shots Gold Signatures
ColChoCG	Collector's Choice Cover Glory 5x7
ColChoCtA	Collector's Choice Crash the All-Star Game
ColChoCtAGR	Collector's Choice Crash the All-Star Game Redemption
ColChoCtG	Collector's Choice Crash the Game
ColChoCtGE	Collector's Choice Crash the Game Exchange
ColChoCtGExch	Collector's Choice Crash the Game Exchange
ColChoCtGG	Collector's Choice Crash the Game Gold
ColChoCtGGE	Collector's Choice Crash the Game Gold Exchange
ColChoCtGIW	Collector's Choice Crash the Game Instant Win
ColChoER	Collector's Choice Evolution Revolution
ColChoGACA	Collector's Choice Griffey A Cut Above
ColChoGJ5	Collector's Choice Golden Jubilee 5x7
ColChoGriCD	Collector's Choice Griffey Clearly Dominant
ColChoGS	Collector's Choice Gold Signature
ColChoHRA	Collector's Choice Home Run All-Stars
ColChoMBH	Collector's Choice Mini Bobbing Heads
ColChoNF	Collector's Choice New Frontier
ColChoNS	Collector's Choice Nomo Scrapbook
ColChoPCR	Collector's Choice Prime Choice Reserve
ColChoPP	Collector's Choice Premier Power
ColChoPPG	Collector's Choice Premier Power Gold
ColChoPPJ	Collector's Choice Premier Power Jumbos
ColChoRJ	Collector's Choice Retail Jumbos
ColChoS	Collector's Choice Stick'Ums
ColChoS'	Collector's Choice Stick 'Ums
ColChoSE	Collector's Choice SE
ColChoSEGS	Collector's Choice SE Gold Signature
ColChoSESS	Collector's Choice SE Silver Signature
ColChoSQ	Collector's Choice StarQuest
ColChoSQDouble	Collector's Choice StarQuest Double
ColChoSQHR	Collector's Choice StarQuest Home Run
ColChoSQSingle	Collector's Choice StarQuest Single
ColChoSQTriple	Collector's Choice StarQuest Triple
ColChoSR	Collector's Choice Stick'Ums Retail
ColChoSS	Collector's Choice Silver Signature
ColChoT	Collector's Choice Team vs. Team
ColChoT	Collector's Choice Teams
ColChoTBS	Collector's Choice The Big Show
ColChoTBSWH	Collector's Choice The Big Show World Headquarters
ColChoTotT	Collector's Choice Toast of the Town
ColChoU	Collector's Choice Update
ColChoYMtP	Collector's Choice You Make the Play
ColChoYMtPGS	Collector's Choice You Make the Play Gold Signature
ColCliB	Columbus Clippers Best
ColCliC	Columbus Clippers CMC

ColCliD	Columbus Clippers D.A.R.E.
ColCliF	Columbus Clippers Fleer/ProCards
ColCliLD	Columbus Clippers Line Drive
ColCliM	Columbus Clippers Multi-Ad
ColCliMCTI	Columbus Clippers Milk Caps Team Issue
ColCliP	Columbus Clippers Police
ColCliP	Columbus Clippers ProCards
ColCliS	Columbus Clippers SkyBox
ColCliT	Columbus Clippers TCMA
ColCliTI	Columbus Clippers Team Issue
ColE13	Collins-McCarthy E135
ColEdgDJ	Collector's Edge Dial Justice
ColGoo	Colla Gooden
ColGriJ	Colla Griffey Jr.
ColGwy	Colla Gwynn
ColIndC	Columbus Indians Classic/Best
ColIndP	Columbus Indians ProCards
ColJet	Columbus Jets
ColJoeC	Colla Joe Carter
ColJus	Colla Justice
ColMaa	Colla Maas
ColMat	Colla Mattingly
ColMcG	Colla McGwire
ColMeaPP	Colonial Meat Products Piersall
ColMetB	Columbia Mets Best
ColMetC	Columbia Mets Classic/Best
ColMetF	Columbia Mets Fleer/ProCards
ColMetGS	Columbia Mets Grand Slam
ColMetP	Columbia Mets ProCards
ColMetPI	Columbia Mets PLAY II
ColMetPIISPI	Columbia Mets Insert Set PLAY II
ColMetPPI	Columbia Mets Postcards Play II
ColMudB	Columbus Mudcats Best
ColMudP	Columbus Mudcats ProCards
ColMudS	Columbus Mudcats Star
ColPosD	Colla Postcards Dawson
ColPosG	Colla Postcards Grace
ColPosG	Colla Postcards Greenwell
ColPosM	Colla Postcards Mitchell
ColPosMc	Colla Postcards McGwire
ColPosOS	Colla Postcards Ozzie Smith
ColPosP	Colla Postcards Piazza
ColPosRJ	Colla Postcards Ripken Jr.
ColPosS	Colla Postcards Sandberg
ColPosWC	Colla Postcards Will Clark
ColPro	Colla Promos
ColRedB	Colgan's Red Border
ColRedC	Columbus Redstixx Classic
ColRedC	Columbus RedStixx Classic/Best
ColRedF	Columbus RedStixx Fleer/ProCards
ColRedSM	Columbus Red Stixx Multi-Ad
ColRobA	Colla Roberto Alomar
ColRya	Colla Ryan
ColSan	Colla Sandberg
ColSilB	Colorado Silver Bullets
ColSilB9	Colorado Silver Bullets Update
ColSilBC	Colorado Silver Bullets Coors
ColSprSATTI	Colorado Springs SkySox All-Time Team Team Issue
ColSprSS	Colorado Springs Sky Sox
ColSprSSC	Colorado Springs Sky Sox CMC
ColSprSSF	Colorado Springs Sky Sox Fleer/ProCards
ColSprSSLD	Colorado Springs Sky Sox Line Drive
ColSprSSP	Colorado Springs Sky Sox ProCards
ColSprSSS	Colorado Springs Sky Sox SkyBox
ColSprSSTI	Colorado Springs Sky Sox Team Issue
ColSprSTI	Colorado Springs SkySox Team Issue
ColStr	Colla Strawberry
ColtheSBM	Collect the Stars Baseball Magnetables
ColTho	Colla Thomas
ColTinT	Colgans Tin Tops
ColWilC	Colla Will Clark
ComIma	Comic Images
ComImaP	Comic Images Promo
ConAmeA	Conlon American All-Stars
ConHar	Conlon Hardee's/Coke
ConMar	Conlon Marketcom
ConMasB	Conlon Masters BW
ConMasC	Conlon Masters Color
ConNatA	Conlon National All-Stars
ConNegA	Conlon Negro All-Stars
ConSer1	Conlon Series 1
ConSer2	Conlon Series 2
ConSer3	Conlon Series 3
ConSer4	Conlon Series 4
ConSer5	Conlon Series 5
ConT20	Contentnea T209
ConTSN	Conlon TSN
ConTSN1N	Conlon TSN 13th National
ConTSNAP	Conlon TSN All-Star Program
ConTSNB	Conlon TSN Burgundy
ConTSNCI	Conlon TSN Color Inserts
ConTSNCMP	Conlon TSN Club Members Promos
ConTSNGI	Conlon TSN Gold Inserts
ConTSNGJ	Conlon TSN Griffey Jr.
ConTSNP	Conlon TSN Promos
ConTSNP	Conlon TSN Prototypes
CooPapB	Cool Papa Bell
CosBroPP	Costacos Bros. Puckett Promo
CouT21	Coupon T213
CouTimLBR	Country Time Legends Brooks Robinson
CraDis	Crane Discs
CraJac	Cracker Jack
CraJacE	Cracker Jack E145-1
CraJacE	Cracker Jack E145-2
CraJacP	Cracker Jack Pins
CroRoy	Crown Royale
CroRoyAS	Crown Royale All-Stars
CroRoyB	Crown Royale
CroRoyC2	Crown Royale Century 21
CroRoyCCDB	Crown Royale Cramer's Choice Dark Blue
CroRoyCCG	Crown Royale Cramer's Choice Gold
CroRoyCCG	Crown Royale Cramer's Choice Green
CroRoyCCLB	Crown Royale Cramer's Choice Light Blue
CroRoyCCP	Crown Royale Cramer's Choice Premiums
CroRoyCCP	Crown Royale Cramer's Choice Purple
CroRoyCCPA	Crown Royale Cramer's Choice Premiums Autographed
CroRoyCCPrem	Crown Royale Cramer's Choice Premiums
CroRoyCCR	Crown Royale Cramer's Choice Red
CroRoyDK	Crown Royale Diamond Knights
CroRoyFoB	Crown Royale Firestone on Baseball
CroRoyFoBA	Crown Royale Firestone on Baseball Autographed
CroRoyGCDCP	Crown Royale Gold Crown Die Cut Premiums
CroRoyHRF	Crown Royale Home Run Fever
CroRoyL	Crown Royale Limited
CroRoyLL	Crown Royale Living Legends
CroRoyMP	Crown Royale Master Performers
CroRoyOD	Crown Royale Opening Day
CroRoyPotG	Crown Royale Pillars of the Game
CroRoyPP	Crown Royale Pivotal Players
CroRoyPPN	Crown Royale Pivotal Players National
Cub190T	Cubs 1907 TCMA
CubA.CDPP	Cubs A.C. Dietsche Postcards PC765
CubAllT	Cubs All-Time TCMA

CubBriPC	Cubs Brickhouse Playing Cards
CubBumS	Cubs Bumper Stickers
CubCan	Cubs Canon
CubCerICP	Cubs Certified Ice Cream Pins
CubChi	Cubs Chi-Foursome
CubChiT	Cubs Chicago Tribune
CubDavB	Cubs David Berg
CubDunD	Cubs Dunkin Donuts
CubFle	Cubs Fleer
CubGat	Cubs Gatorade
CubGFGCP	Cubs G.F. Grignon Co. PC775
CubGreB	Cubs Greats Brace
CubGreT	Cubs Greats TCMA
CubJayP	Cubs Jay Publishing
CubJewT	Cubs Jewel Tea
CubLea	Cuban League
CubLioP	Cubs Lion Photo
CubMar	Cubs Marathon
CubOldS	Cubs Old Style
CubOldSBW	Cubs Old Style Billy Williams
CubPho	Cubs Photos
CubPos	Cubs Postcards
CubProPS	Cubs Pro's Pizza Supermarket
CubRedL	Cubs Red Lobster
CubRol	Cubs Rolaids
CubSev	Cubs Seven-Up
CubSosC	Cubs Sosa ComEd
CubStaC	Cubs Stadium Club
CubTeal	Cubs Team Issue
CubTealC	Cubs Team Issue Color
CubThoAV	Cubs Thorn Apple Valley
CubTri	Cubs Tribune
CubUno	Cubs Unocal
CubVanLS	Cubs Vance Law Smokey
CubVinL	Cubs Vine Line
CubWGN	Cubs WGN/Pepsi
CUIMCG	CUI Metal Cards Griffey
CUIMCR	CUI Metal Cards Ripken
D35RocB	A's Rochester/Williams Baking D359
DaiDolF	Daikyo Dolphins Futera
DaiIslD	Dairy Isle Discs
DaiQueKGJ	Dairy Queen Griffey Jr.
DaiQueS	Dairy Queen Statues
DalCon	Dallas Convention
DalNatCC	Dallas National Collectors Convention
DanBraB	Danville Braves Best
DanBraC	Danville Braves Classic
DanBraC	Danville Braves Classic/Best
DanBraF	Danville Braves Fleer/ProCards
DanBraQ	Danville Braves Q-Cards
DanBraTI	Danville Braves Team Issue
DanBurG	Daniels Burleigh Grimes
DanDee	Dan Dee
DanQ-C	Danville 97s Q-Cards
DanSunF	Danville Suns Fritsch
DarChoE	Darby Chocolates E271
DarFar	Darigold Farms
DavHaloFB	Davco Hall of Fame Boxes
DavLipB	David Lipscomb Bisons
DayBeaAP	Daytona Beach Admirals ProCards
DayBeaAT	Daytona Beach Astros TCMA
DayBealP	Daytona Beach Islanders ProCards
DayBealT	Daytona Beach Islanders TCMA
DayCubB	Daytona Cubs Best
DayCubC	Daytona Cubs Classic
DayCubC	Daytona Cubs Classic/Best
DayCubF	Daytona Cubs Fleer/ProCards
DayDaiNM	Dayton Daily News M137
DEL	Classic/Best Autographs
DelR33	Delong R333
DelRut	Delphi Ruth

DelSho	Delmarva Shorebirds Best
DelShoB	Delmarva Shorebirds Best
DelShoM	Delmarva Shorebirds Multi-Ad
DelShoUB	Delmarva Shorebirds Update Best
DenBal	Denver BallPark
DenHol	Denny's Holograms
DenHolGS	Denny's Holograms Grand Slam
DenHolGSAP	Denny's Holograms Grand Slam Artist's Proofs
DenZepC	Denver Zephrys CMC
DenZepC	Denver Zephyrs CMC
DenZepF	Denver Zephyrs Fleer/ProCards
DenZepLD	Denver Zephyrs Line Drive
DenZepP	Denver Zephyrs ProCards
DenZepS	Denver Zephyrs SkyBox
DeSCom	DeSa Commemorative
DesMoiHB	Des Moines Homestead Bruins
DetCaeD	Detroit Caesars Discs
DetTigP	Tigers Postcards
DevRayP	Devil Rays Pinnacle
DexHaloFP	Dexter Hall of Fame Postcards
DexPre	Dexter Press
Dia	Dimanche/Derniere Heure *
DiaBacP	Diamond Backs Pinnacle
DiaCla	Diamond Classics
DiaGre	Diamond Greats
DiaGumP	Diamond Gum Pins
DiaMar	Diamond Marks
DiaMarA	Diamond Marks Art
DiaMarP	Diamond Marks Prototypes
DiaMatCS2	Diamond Match Co. Series 2
DiaMatCS3T1	Diamond Match Co. Series 3 Type 1
DiaMatCS3T2	Diamond Match Co. Series 3 Type 2
DiaMatCS4	Diamond Match Co. Series 4
DiaMatCSB	Diamond Match Co. Silver Border
DiaMcD	Diamondbacks McDaddy
DiaStaCD	Diamond Stars Continuation Den's
DiaStaES	Diamond Stars Extension Set
DiaStaR	Diamond Stars R327
Dim2GT	Dimple II Glove Tags
DixLid	Dixie Lids
DixLid	Dixie Lids *
DixLidP	Dixie Premiums *
DixPre	Dixie Premiums
DixPre	Dixie Premiums *
DoctheV	Doc "The Video"
Dod	Dodgers
Dod	Dodgers Photos
Dod UNU7P	Dodgers UNOCAL 76 Pins
Dod194T	Dodgers 1941 TCMA
dod195T	Dodgers 1952 TCMA
Dod195T	Dodgers 1955 TCMA
DodBelB	Dodgers Bell Brand
DodBlu	Dodgers Blue
DodBoyoST	Dodgers Boys of Summer TCMA
DodCokP	Dodgers Coke Postcards
DodDaiN	Dodgers Daily News
DodDWPM	Dodgers DWP Magnets
DodFanA	Dodgers Fan Appreciation
DodFle	Dodgers Fleer
DodGolS	Dodgers Golden Stamps
DodGreT	Dodgers Greats TCMA
DodHea	Dodgers Heads-Up
DodJayP	Dodgers Jay Publishing
DodMor	Dodgers Morrell
DodMot	Dodgers Mother's
DodMot	Dodgers Mothers
DodPho	Dodgers Photos
DodPho	Twins Photos
DodPol	Dodgers Police
DodPos	Dodgers Postcards

DodRinP1	Dodgers Rini Postcards 1
DodRinP2	Dodgers Rini Postcards 2
DodRinP3	Dodgers Rini Postcards 3
DodRinP4	Dodgers Rini Postcards 4
DodROY	Dodgers ROYs
DodSco	Dodgers Score
DodScoP	Dodgers Score Platinum
DodScoPl	Dodgers Score Platinum
DodScoPr	Dodgers Score Premier
DodSmo	Dodgers Smokey
DodSmoA	Dodgers Smokey All-Stars
DodSmoG	Dodgers Smokey Greats
DodSt.V	Dodgers St. Vincent
DodStaC	Dodgers Stadium Club
DodStaSV	Dodgers Stamps St. Vincent
DodStaTA	Dodgers Stamps Trak Auto
DodTar	Dodgers Target
DodTCM4	Dodgers 1941 TCMA
DodTCMA	Dodgers All-Time TCMA
DodTeaI	Dodgers Team Issue
DodTic	Dodgers Ticketron
DodUniO	Dodgers Union Oil
DodUniOP	Dodgers Union Oil Photos
DodUniOV	Dodgers Union Oil Volpe
DodUno7P	Dodgers Unocal 76 Pins
DodVol	Dodgers Volpe
DodVolT	Dodgers Volpe Tumblers
DogBuiE	Dodgers Builders Emporium
DomDisP	Sweet Caporal "Domino" Discs
DomLeaS	Dominican League Stickers
Don	Donruss
DonActA	Donruss Action All-Stars
DonActAS	Donruss Action All-Stars
DonAll	Donruss All-Stars
DonAllB	Donruss All-Star Box
DonAnn8	Donruss Anniversary '84
DonArmaD	Donruss Armed and Dangerous
DonAwaWJ	Donruss Award Winner Jumbos
DonBasB	Donruss Baseball's Best
DonBesA	Donruss Best AL
DonBesN	Donruss Best NL
DonBomS	Donruss Bomb Squad
DonBonC	Donruss Bonus Cards
DOnBonM	Donruss Bonus MVP's
DonCha	Donruss Champions
DonCokR	Donruss Coke Ryan
DonCol	Donruss Collections Donruss
DonColE	Donruss Collections Elite
DonColL	Donruss Collections Leaf
DonColP	Donruss Collections Preferred
DonColS	Donruss Collections Samples
DonCraJ1	Donruss Cracker Jack I
DonCraJ2	Donruss Cracker Jack II
DonCruG	Donruss Crusade Green
DonCruP	Donruss Crusade Purple
DonCruR	Donruss Crusade Red
DonDay	Donruss Days
DonDiaK	Donruss Diamond Kings
DonDiaKC	Donruss Diamond Kings Canvas
DonDiaKJ	Donruss Diamond Kings Jumbo
DonDom	Donruss Dominators
DonDomJ	Donruss Dominators Jumbos
DonEli	Donruss Elite
DonEli	Donruss Elite Inserts
DonEliA	Donruss Elite Aspirations
DonEliBttF	Donruss Elite Back to the Future
DonEliBttFA	Donruss Elite Back to the Future Autographs
DonEliC	Donruss Elite Craftsmen
DonEliD	Donruss Elite Dominators
DonEliGS	Donruss Elite Gold Stars
DonEliI	Donruss Elite Inserts
DonEliLaL	Donruss Elite Leather and Lumber
DonEliMC	Donruss Elite Master Craftsmen
DonEliPN	Donruss Elite Prime Numbers
DonEliPNDC	Donruss Elite Prime Numbers Die Cuts
DonEliPNS	Donruss Elite Prime Numbers Samples
DonEliPtT	Donruss Elite Passing the Torch
DonEliPtTA	Donruss Elite Passing the Torch Autographs
DonEliS	Donruss Elite Status
DonEliS	Donruss Elite Supers
DonEliTotC	Donruss Elite Turn of the Century
DonEliTotCDC	Donruss Elite Turn of the Century Die Cuts
DonFANT	Donruss FANtasy Team
DonFANTDC	Donruss FANtasy Team Die Cuts
DonFraFea	Donruss Franchise Features
DonFreF	Donruss Freeze Frame
DonGolPP	Donruss Gold Press Proofs
DonGraS	Donruss Grand Slammers
DonHig	Donruss Highlights
DonHitL	Donruss Hit List
DonHOFH	Donruss HOF Heroes
DonHOFS	Donruss HOF Sluggers
DonLeaS	Donruss Learning Series
DonLim	Donruss Limited
DonLimE	Donruss Limited Exposure
DonLimENG	Donruss Limited Exposure Non-Glossy
DonLimESamp	Donruss Limited Exposure Samples
DonLimFotG	Donruss Limited Fabric of the Game
DonLonBL	Donruss Long Ball Leaders
DonLonL	Donruss Longball Leaders
DonMasotG	Donruss Masters of the Game
DonMat#	Mattingly's #23 Restaurant
DonMcD	Donruss McDonald's
DonMouM	Donruss Mound Marvels
DonMVP	Donruss MVPs
DonOpeD	Donruss Opening Day
DonP	Donruss Pop-Ups
DonPop	Donruss Pop-Ups
DonPowA	Donruss Power Alley
DonPowADC	Donruss Power Alley Die Cuts
DonPre	Donruss Preferred
DonPre	Donruss Previews
DonPreCttC	Donruss Preferred Cut to the Chase
DonPreGB	Donruss Preferred Green Boxes
DonPreGES	Donruss Preferred Great X-Pectations Samples
DonPreGoB	Donruss Preferred Gold Boxes
DonPreGX	Donruss Preferred Great X-Pectations
DonPreGXDC	Donruss Preferred Great X-Pectations Die Cuts
DonPreP	Donruss Press Proofs
DonPrePM	Donruss Preferred Precious Metals
DonPreS	Donruss Preferred Staremasters
DonPreSeat	Donruss Preferred Seating
DonPreSS	Donruss Preferred Staremasters Samples
DonPreTB	Donruss Preferred Tin Boxes
DonPreTBG	Donruss Preferred Tin Boxes Gold
DonPreTF	Donruss Preferred Tins Fanfest
DonPreTP	Donruss Preferred Tin Packs
DonPreTPD	Donruss Preferred Tin Packs Double-Wide
DonPreTPG	Donruss Preferred Tin Packs Gold
DonPreTPS	Donruss Preferred Tin Packs Silver
DonPreTW	Donruss Preferred Title Waves
DonPreXP	Donruss Preferred X-Ponential Power
DonPriCD	Donruss Prized Collections Donruss
DonPriCE	Donruss Prized Collections Elite
DonPriCL	Donruss Prized Collections Leaf

DonPriCP	Donruss Prized Collections Preferred
DonPro	Donruss Promos
DonProLO	Donruss Production Line On-Base
DonProLPI	Donruss Production Line Power Index
DonProLS	Donruss Production Line Slugging
DonPurP	Donruss Pure Power
DonRatR	Donruss Rated Rookies
DonRatRM	Donruss Rated Rookies Medalists
DonReaBY	Donruss Team Book Yankees
DonRipOWIK	Donruss Ripken The Only Way I Know
DonRocL	Donruss Rocket Launchers
DonRoo	Donruss Rookies
DonRooDK	Donruss Rookie Diamond Kings
DonRooDKC	Donruss Rookie Diamond Kings Canvas
DonRooP	Donruss Rookies Phenoms
DonRouT	Donruss Round Trippers
DonSam	Donruss Samples
DonSho	Donruss Showdown
DonSig	Donruss Signature
DonSigA	Donruss Signature Autographs
DonSigAC	Donruss Signature Autographs Century
DonSigAM	Donruss Signature Autographs Millenium
DonSigNN	Donruss Signature Notable Nicknames
DonSigP	Donruss Signature Proofs
DonSigPPP	Donruss Signature Platinum Press Proofs
DonSigSB	Donruss Signature Signing Bonus
DonSigSP	Donruss Signature Series Previews
DonSigSS	Donruss Signature Significant Signatures
DonSilPP	Donruss Silver Press Proofs
DonSonM9	Donruss MLB 99
DonSpeE	Donruss Special Edition
DonSpiotG	Donruss Spirit of the Game
DonSpiotGJ	Donruss Spirit of the Game Jumbos
DonSupD	Donruss Super DK's
DonTea	Donruss Team Sets
DonTeaBA	Donruss Team Book Athletics
DonTeaBC	Donruss Team Book Cubs
DonTeaBM	Donruss Team Book Mets
DonTeaBRS	Donruss Team Book Red Sox
DonTeaSMVP	Donruss Team Sets MVP's
DonTeaSPE	Donruss Team Sets Pennant Edition
DonTopotO	Donruss Top of the Order
DonTra	Donruss Traded
DonUpd	Donruss Update
DonUpdRIC	Donruss Update Ripken Info Card
DonVxP1	Donruss VxP 1.0
DonVxP1CD	Donruss VxP 1.0 CD Roms
DonWaxBC	Donruss Wax Box Cards
DonWin	Don Wingfield
Dor	Dormand
DorChe	Dorman's Cheese
DouAllB	Double-A All-Stars Best
DouDisP	Gum Inc "Doubleheader" Discs
DouPlaR	Double Play R330
Dra	Drake's
DubPacT	Dubuque Packers TCMA
DukCabN	Duke Cabinets N142
DukTotDZN	Duke Talk of the Diamond N135
DunBluJB	Dunedin Blue Jays Best
DunBluJC	Dunedin Blue Jays Classic
DunBluJC	Dunedin Blue Jays Classic/Best
DunBluJF	Dunedin Blue Jays Fleer/ProCards
DunBluJFFN	Dunedin Blue Jays Family Fun Night
DunBluJP	Dunedin Blue Jays ProCards
DunBluJS	Dunedin Blue Jays Star
DunBluJSB	Dunedin Blue Jays Stickers Team Issue
DunBluJT	Dunedin Blue Jays TCMA
DunBluJTI	Dunedin Blue Jays Team Issue
DunBluJUTI	Dunedin Blue Jays Update Team Issue
DunDonPPS	Pawtucket Red Sox Dunkin' Donuts
DurBulATI	Durham Bulls ATG Team Issue
DurBulBIB	Durham Bulls (Blue) Best
DurBulBrB	Durham Bulls (Brown) Best
DurBulC	Durham Bulls Classic
DurBulC	Durham Bulls Classic/Best
DurBulF	Durham Bulls Fleer/ProCards
DurBulIS	Durham Bulls I Star
DurBulIS	Durham Bulls II Star
DurBulP	Durham Bulls ProCards
DurBulS	Durham Bulls Star
DurBulT	Durham Bulls TCMA
DurBulTI	Durham Bulls Team Issue
DurBulUP	Durham Bulls Update ProCards
DurBulUTI	Durham Bulls Update Team Issue
DurPowP1	Duracell Power Players I
DurPowP2	Duracell Power Players II
DynRos	Dynasty Rose
E&SP	E and S Publishing
E-UOraBSC	E-Unc. Orange Bordered Strip Cards
E-X Cen	E-X Century
E-X CenECFut	E-X Century Essential Credentials Future
E-X CenECNow	E-X Century Essential Credentials Now
E-X CenEQ	E-X Century E-X Quisite
E-X2	E-X2000
E-X2	E-X2001
E-X2ACA	E-X2000 A Cut Above
E-X2ARodHawaii	E-X2001 Rodriguez Hawaii XIII Promo
E-X2Cheap	E-X2001 Cheap Seat Treats
E-X2Cred	E-X2000 Credentials
E-X2DesCoop	E-X2001 Destination Cooperstown
E-X2ECFut	E-X2001 Essential Credentials Future
E-X2ECNow	E-X2001 Essential Credentials Now
E-X2EmeAuto	E-X2000 Emerald Autographs
E-X2EmeAutoR	E-X2000 Emerald Autograph Redemptions
E-X2EssCre	E-X2000 Essential Credentials
E-X2Hall	E-X2000 Hall or Nothing
E-X2SD2000	E-X2000 Star Date 2000
E-X2SD2001	E-X2001 Star Date 2001
E-X2Sig2001	E-X2001 Signature 2001
E-XCenA	E-X Century Authen-Kicks
E-XCenFoF	E-X Century Favorites for Fenway '99
E-XCenMotC	E-X Century Milestones of the Century
E101	E101
E102	E102
E120	E120
E121So1	E121 Series of 120
E121So8	E121 Series of 80
E12AmeCDCE125	American Caramel Die Cuts E125
E94	E94
E98	E98
EagBalL	Eagle Ballpark Legends
EasLeaAP	Eastern League All-Stars ProCards
EasLeaDDP	Eastern League Diamond Diplomacy ProCards
EasLeaTPB	Eastern League Top Prospects Best
EasLeaTPM	Eastern League Top Prospects Multi-Ad
EdgR.WG	Edgerton R. Williams Game
EdmTraC	Edmonton Trappers CMC
EdmTraC	Edmonton Trappers Cramer
EdmTraF	Edmonton Trappers Fleer/ProCards
EdmTraLD	Edmonton Trappers Line Drive
EdmTraP	Edmonton Trappers ProCards
EdmTraRR	Edmonton Trappers Red Rooster
EdmTraS	Edmonton Trappers SkyBox
EdmTraT	Edmonton Trappers TCMA
EdmTraTI	Edmonton Trappers Team Issue
El PasDAGTI	El Paso Diablos All-Time Greats Team Issue

El PasDB	El Paso Diablos Best	EveGiaB	Everett Giants Best
El PasDF	El Paso Diablos Fleer/ProCards	EveGiaC	Everett Giants Classic
El PasDG	El Paso Diablos Grandstand	EveGiaC	Everett Giants Classic/Best
El RoyFM	El Roy Face Motel	EveGiaC	Everett Giants Cramer
EliSenL	Elite Senior League	EveGiaF	Everett Giants Fleer/ProCards
EliTwiC	Elizabethton Twins Classic	EveGiaIC	Everett Giants II Cramer
EliTwiC	Elizabethton Twins Classic/Best	EveGiaP	Everett Giants ProCards
EliTwiF	Elizabethton Twins Fleer/ProCards	EveGiaPC	Everett Giants Popcorn Cramer
EliTwiP	Elizabethton Twins ProCards	EveGiaS	Everett Giants Star
EliTwiS	Elizabethton Twins Star	Exc	Excel
ElmPio1C	Elmira Pioneers 100th Cain	ExcAll	Excel All-Stars
ElmPioBC	Elmira Pioneers (Black) Cain	ExcAllF	Excel All-Stars
ElmPioC	Elmira Pioneers Cain	ExcCli	Excel Climbing
ElmPioC	Elmira Pioneers Classic	ExcFirYP	Excel First Year Phenoms
ElmPioC	Elmira Pioneers Classic/Best	ExcFirYPF	Excel First Year Phenoms
ElmPioF	Elmira Pioneers Fleer/ProCards	ExcFS7	Excel
ElmPioP	Elmira Pioneers ProCards	ExcLeaL	Excel League Leaders
ElmPioP	Elmira Pioneers Pucko	ExcLeaLF	Excel League Leaders
ElmPioRC	Elmira Pioneers (Red) Cain	ExcSeaC	Excel Season Crowns
ElmPioRSP	Elmira Pioneer Red Sox ProCards	ExcTL	Excel Team Leaders
ElmPioRST	Elmira Pioneer Red Sox TCMA	Exh	Exhibits
ElmPioT	Elmira Pioneers TCMA	Exh	Exhibits Four-in-One
ElmPioTI	Elmira Pioneers Team Issue	ExhCan	Exhibits Canadian
ElmPioUTI	Elmira Pioneers Update Team Issue	ExhFou	Exhibits Four-in-One
ElPasDB	El Paso Diablos Best	ExhFou	Exhibits Four-in-One W463-4
ElPasDF	El Paso Diablos Fleer/ProCards	ExhFou	Exhibits Four-in-One W463-5
ElPasDGS	El Paso Diablos Grand Slam	ExhFou	Exhibits Four-in-One W463-6
ElPasDLD	El Paso Diablos Line Drive	ExhFou	Exhibits Four-in-One W463-7
ElPasDP	El Paso Diablos ProCards	ExhHoF	Exhibit Hall of Fame
ElPasDS	El Paso Diablos SkyBox	ExhPCL	Exhibits PCL
ElPasDT	El Paso Diablos TCMA	ExhSal	Exhibits Salutation
ElPasDTI	El Paso Diablos Team Issue	ExhStaB	Exhibit Stat Back
ElsHowS	Elston Howard Sausage	ExhTea	Exhibits Team
ElSidPog	El Sid Pogs	ExhWriH	Exhibits Wrigley HOF
Emo	Emotion	ExpBoo	Expos Bookmarks
EmoLegoB	Emotion-XL Legion of Boom	ExpColP7	Expos Postcards
EmoMas	Emotion Masters	ExpCup	Expos Cups
EmoN	Emotion N-Tense	ExpDis	Expos Discs
EmoN	Emotion-XL N-Tense	ExpDonD	Expos Donruss Durivage
EmoR	Emotion Ripken	ExpDonM	Expos Donruss McDonald's
EmoRarB	Emotion-XL Rare Breed	ExpFudP	Expos Fud's Photography
EmoRoo	Emotion Rookies	ExpGla	Expos Glasses
EmoXL	Emotion-XL	ExpGreT	Expos Greats TCMA
EmoXLD	Emotion-XL D-Fense	ExpHygM	Expos Hygrade Meats
EquSpoHoF	Equitable Sports Hall of Fame *	ExpLaPR	Expos La Pizza Royale
EriCarP	Erie Cardinals ProCards	ExpPin	Expos Pins
EriCarT	Erie Cardinals TCMA	ExpPos	Expos Postcards
EriOriS	Erie Orioles Star	ExpPosN	Expos Postcards Named
EriSaiC	Erie Sailors Classic/Best	ExpProPa	Expos Provigo Panels
EriSaiF	Erie Sailors Fleer/ProCards	ExpProPo	Expos Provigo Posters
EriSaiP	Erie Sailors ProCards	ExpPS	Expos Pro Stars
EriSaiS	Erie Sailors Star	ExpRed	Expos Redpath
EriSeaB	Erie Seawolves Best	ExpStu	Expos Stuart
EriSeaWB	Erie Sea Wolves Best	ExpWes	Expos Weston
EriSeaWM	Erie Sea Wolves Multi-Ad	ExpZel	Expos Zellers
EssCoi	Esso Coins	FanCar	FanFest Carlton
EugEme	Eugene Emeralds Grandstand	FanCle	FanFest Clemente
EugEmeB	Eugene Emeralds Best	FanCraAL	Fan Craze AL WG2
EugEmeC	Eugene Emeralds Classic	FanCraNL	Fan Craze NL WG3
EugEmeC	Eugene Emeralds Classic/Best	FanJacR	FanFest Jackie Robinson
EugEmeC	Eugene Emeralds Cramer	FanLouB	FanFest Brock
EugEmeF	Eugene Emeralds Fleer/ProCards	FanPin	FanFest Pins
EugEmeGS	Eugene Emeralds Grand Slam	FanRya	FanFest Ryan
EugEmeP	Eugene Emeralds Procards	FarRedHM	Fargo Red Hawks Multi-Ad
EugEmeTI	Eugene Emeralds Team Issue	FatPlaT	Fatima Players T222
EurSta	Eureka Stamps	FatT20	Fatima T200
EvaTriT	Evansville Triplets TCMA	FayGenB	Fayetteville Generals Best
EvaTriT	Evansville Tripletts TCMA	FayGenC	Fayetteville Generals Classic
EveAqaTI	Everett Aquasox Team Issue	FayGenC	Fayetteville Generals Classic/Best
EveAquB	Everett Aquasox Best	FayGenF	Fayetteville Generals Fleer/ProCards
EveAquG	Everett AquaSox Grandstand	FayGenP	Fayetteville Generals ProCards

FayGenTI	Fayetteville Generals Team Issue
FBIDis	FBI Discs
FegMurCG	Feg Murray's Cartoon Greats
FifNatC	Fifth National Convention
FifNatCT	Fifth National Convention Tickets
Fin	Finest
FinAarAwC	Finest Aaron Award Contenders
FinAarAwCR	Finest Aaron Award Contenders Refractors
FinBro	Finest Bronze
FinCen	Finest Centurions
FinCenR	Finest Centurions Refractors
FinCom	Finest Complements
FinComDualR	Finest Complements Dual Refractors
FinDouF	Finest Double Feature
FinDouFDualR	Finest Double Feature Dual Refractors
FinEmb	Finest Embossed
FinEmbR	Finest Embossed Refractors
FinFlaT	Finest Flame Throwers
FinFraR	Finest Franchise Records
FinFraRR	Finest Franchise Records Refractors
FinFutF	Finest Future's Finest
FinGolRef	Finest Gold Refractors
FinJum	Finest Jumbos
FinLan	Finest Landmark
FinLeaI	Finest Leading Indicators
FinMil	Finest Milestones
FinMysF1	Finest Mystery Finest 1
FinMysF2	Finest Mystery Finest 2
FinMysF2R	Finest Mystery Finest 2 Refractors
FinMysFO	Finest Mystery Finest Oversize
FinMysFOR	Finest Mystery Finest Oversize Refractors
FinMysFR	Finest Mystery Finest 1 Refractors
FinNo-	Finest No-Protectors
FinNo-R	Finest No-Protectors Refractors
FinOve	Finest Oversize
FinOveR	Finest Oversize Refractors
FinPeelHyp	Finest Peel and Reveal Hyperplaid
FinPeelSpark	Finest Peel and Reveal Sparkle
FinPeeSS	Finest Peel and Reveal Stadium Stars
FinPowK	Finest Power Kings
FinPowZ	Finest Power Zone
FinPre	Finest Pre-Production
FinPro	Finest Promos
FinProF	Finest Prominent Figures
FinProR	Finest Promo Refractors
FinRef	Finest Refractors
FinSplS	Finest Split Screen
FinSplSDR	Finest Split Screen Dual Refractors
FinStaS	Finest Stadium Stars
FinStaSJ	Finest Stadium Stars Jumbos
FinTeaFB	Finest Team Finest Blue
FinTeaFBR	Finest Team Finest Blue Refractors
FinTeaFG	Finest Team Finest Gold
FinTeaFGR	Finest Team Finest Gold Refractors
FinTeaFR	Finest Team Finest Red
FinTeaFRR	Finest Team Finest Red Refractors
FinTheM	Finest The Man
FinTheMR	Finest The Man Refractors
FisBakL	Fischer Baking Labels
Fla	Flair
FlaDiaC	Flair Diamond Cuts
FlaHotG	Flair Hot Gloves
FlaHotN	Flair Hot Numbers
FlaInfP	Flair Infield Power
FlaOutP	Flair Outfield Power
FlaPow	Flair Powerline
FlaPro	Flair Promos
FlaRip	Flair Ripken
FlaShoDC	Flair Showcase Diamond Cuts
FlaShoHG	Flair Showcase Hot Gloves
FlaShoLC	Flair Showcase Legacy Collection Row 2
FlaShoLeg	Flair Showcase Legacy Collection
FlaShoLeg0	Flair Showcase Legacy Collection Row 0
FlaShoLeg1	Flair Showcase Legacy Collection Row 1
FlaShoLeg2	Flair Showcase Legacy Collection Row 2
FlaShoLeg3	Flair Showcase Legacy Collection Row 3
FlaShoLegM	Flair Showcase Legacy Collection Masterpieces
FlaShoLegM1	Flair Showcase Legacy Masterpieces Row 1
FlaShoLegM2	Flair Showcase Legacy Masterpieces Row 2
FlaShoLegM3	Flair Showcase Legacy Masterpieces Row 3
FlaShoM	Flair Showcase Masterpieces
FlaShoMoG	Flair Showcase Measure of Greatness
FlaShoP1	Flair Showcase Perfect 10
FlaShoR0	Flair Showcase Row 0
FlaShoR1	Flair Showcase Row 1
FlaShoR2	Flair Showcase Row 2
FlaShoR3	Flair Showcase Row 3
FlaShoRSS	Flair Showcase Ripken Sample Strip
FlaShoSamp	Flair Showcase Samples
FlaShoWotF	Flair Showcase Wave of the Future
FlaTodS	Flair Today's Spotlight
FlaWavotF	Flair Wave of the Future
Fle	Fleer
Fle2PostMantle	Fleer Postcard Mantle Promo
FleAll	Fleer All-Stars
FleAllF	Fleer All-Fleer
FleAllR	Fleer All-Rookies
FleAllS	Fleer All-Stars
FleAndJA	Fleer Andruw Jones Autograph
FleASMG	Fleer AS Match Game
FleAtl	Fleer Atlantic
FleAutR	Fleer Autograph Redemption
FleAwaW	Fleer Award Winners
FleBasA	Fleer Baseball All-Stars
FleBasAC	Fleer Baseball All-Star Canadian
FleBasF	Fleer Baseball Firsts
FleBasM	Fleer Baseball MVP's
FleBasMC	Fleer Baseball MVP's Canadian
FleBleB	Fleer Bleacher Blasters
FleBreD	Fleischmann Bread D381
FleBri	Fleer Brilliants
FleBri2G	Fleer Brilliants 24-Karat Gold
FleBriBlu	Fleer Brilliants Blue
FleBriGol	Fleer Brilliants Gold
FleBriI	Fleer Brilliants Illuminators
FleBriSS	Fleer Brilliants Shining Stars
FleBriSSP	Fleer Brilliants Shining Stars Pulsar
FleCan	Fleer Canadian
FleChe	Fleer Checklists
FleCitTP	Fleer Citgo The Performer
FleCle	Fleer Clemens
FleCloS	Fleer Cloth Stickers
FleDatWD	Fleer Date With Destiny
FleDecERT	Fleer Decade of Excellence Rare Traditions
FleDecoE	Fleer Decade of Excellence
FleDecoERT	Fleer Decade of Excellence Rare Traditions
FleDiaM	Fleer Diamond Magic
FleDiamInk	Fleer Diamond Ink
FleDiaS	Fleer Diamond Standouts
FleDiaSCS	Fleer Diamond Skills Commemorative Sheet
FleDiaSkiSheet	Fleer Diamond Skills Commemorative Sheet
FleDiaT	Fleer Diamond Tribute
FleExcS	Fleer Exciting Stars

FleExtB	Fleer Extra Bases
FleExtBGB	Fleer Extra Bases Game Breakers
FleExtBMLH	Fleer Extra Bases Major League Hopefuls
FleExtBPD	Fleer Extra Bases Pitchers Duel
FleExtBRS	Fleer Extra Bases Rookie Standouts
FleExtBSYS	Fleer Extra Bases Second Year Stars
FleFamF	Fleer Famous Feats
FleFinE	Fleer Final Edition
FleFinEDT	Fleer Final Edition Diamond Tribute
FleFir	Fleer Firestone
FleForTR	Fleer For The Record
FleFruotL	Fleer Fruit of the Loom
FleFutHoF	Fleer Future Hall of Famers
FleGamW	Fleer Game Winners
FleGla	Fleer Glavine
FleGlo	Fleer Glossy
FleGoiYar	Fleer Going Yard
FleGolM	Fleer Golden Memories
FleGolM	Fleer Golden Moments
FleGolMJ	Fleer Golden Moments Jumbo
FleGouG	Fleer Goudey Greats
FleGouGF	Fleer Goudey Greats Foil
FleGwyCdA	Fleer Gwynn Casa de Amparo
FleHea	Fleer Headliners
FleHeroB	Fleer Heroes of Baseball
FleHotS	Fleer Hottest Stars
FleIn TC	Fleer In The Clutch
FleLeaL	Fleer League Leaders
FleLeaLC	Fleer League Leaders Canadian
FleLeaS	Fleer League Standouts
FleLimBC	Fleer Limited Box Cards
FleLimE	Fleer Limited Edition
FleLumC	Fleer Lumber Company
FleMajLP	Fleer Major League Prospects
FleManaS	Fleer Mantle and Sons
FleMicMMM	Fleer Mickey Mantle Monumental Moments
FleMicMMMG	Fleer Mickey Mantle Monumental Moments Gold
FleMilDM	Fleer Million Dollar Moments
FleMilDMR	Fleer Million Dollar Moments Redemption
FleMin	Fleer Mini
FleMys	Fleer Mystique
FleMysD	Fleer Mystique Destiny
FleMysE	Fleer Mystique Established
FleMysFI	Fleer Mystique Fresh Ink
FleMysFtG	Fleer Mystique Feel the Game
FleMysG	Fleer Mystique Gold
FleMysM	Fleer Mystique Masterpieces
FleMysP	Fleer Mystique Prophetic
FleNewH	Fleer New Horizons
FleNig&D	Fleer Night and Day
FlePio	Fleer Pioneers
FlePlaCS	Fleer/SkyBox Player's Choice Sheet
FlePosG	Fleer Postseason Glory
FlePowG	Fleer Power Game
FlePro	Fleer Pro-Visions
FlePro	Fleer Prospects
FleProF	Fleer Promising Forecast
FleRecS	Fleer Record Setters
FleRedS	Red Sox Fleer
FleRoaW	Fleer Road Warriors
FleRooFla	Fleer Rookie Flashback
FleRooS	Fleer Rookie Sensations
FleSal	Fleer Salmon
FleSlu	Fleer Sluggers/Pitchers
FleSluBC	Fleer Sluggers/Pitchers Box Cards
FleSmo'H	Fleer Smoke 'n Heat
FleSmo'nH	Fleer Smoke 'n Heat
FleSoaS	Fleer Soaring Stars
FleSoaSG	Fleer Soaring Stars Glowing
FleSta	Fleer Stamps
FleSta9	Fleer Starting 9
FleStaMMM	Fleer Stan Musial Monumental Moments
FleStaMMMA	Fleer Stan Musial Monumental Moments Autographs
FleStaS	Fleer Star Stickers
FleSti	Fleer Stickers
FleStiC	Fleer Sticker Cards
FleStiWBC	Fleer Stickers Wax Box Cards
FleSun	Fleer Sunoco
FleSup	Fleer Superstars
FleSupBC	Fleer Superstars Box Cards
FleTeaL	Fleer Team Leaders
FleTif	Fleer Tiffany
FleTomL	Fleer Tomorrow's Legends
FleUpd	Fleer Update
FleUpd	Fleer Update Diamond Tribute
FleUpdDT	Fleer Update Diamond Tribute
FleUpdG	Fleer Update Glossy
FleUpdH	Fleer Update Headliners
FleUpdNH	Fleer Update New Horizons
FleUpdRU	Fleer Update Rookie Update
FleUpdSL	Fleer Update Smooth Leather
FleUpdSS	Fleer Update Soaring Stars
FleUpdTC	Fleer Update Tiffany
FleVin'	Fleer Vintage '61
FleVin'	Fleer Vintage '63
FleVin'C	Fleer Vintage '63 Classic
FleWarT	Fleer Warning Track
FleWaxBC	Fleer Wax Box Cards
FleWil	Fleer Ted Williams
FleWilD	Fleer Wildest Days
FleWorS	Fleer World Series
FleZon	Fleer Zone
Flo	Flopps
FloStaLAF	Florida State League All-Stars Fleer/ProCards
FloStaLAP	Florida State League All-Stars ProCards
FloStaLAS	Florida State League All-Stars Star
FloStaLTPB	Florida State League Top Prospects Best
ForLauRSC	Fort Lauderdale Red Sox Classic/Best
ForLauRSFP	Fort Lauderdale Red Sox Fleer/ProCards
ForLauYC	Fort Lauderdale Yankees Classic/Best
ForLauYS	Fort Lauderdale Yankees Sussman
ForLauYS	Fort Lauderdale Yanks Sussman
ForLauYTI	Fort Lauderdale Yankees Team Issue
ForMyeM	Fort Myers Miracle Best
ForMyeMC	Fort Myers Miracle Classic
ForMyeMC	Fort Myers Miracle Classic/Best
ForMyeMF	Fort Myers Miracle Fleer/ProCards
ForMyeMTI	Fort Myers Miracle Team Issue
ForMyeRT	Fort Myers Royals TCMA
ForPosBS1	Forst Postcards Ballpark Series 1
ForPosBS2	Forst Postcards Ballpark Series 2
ForWayW	Fort Wayne Wizards Best
ForWayW!	Fort Wayne Wizards Q-Cards
ForWayWB	Fort Wayne Wizards Best
ForWayWC	Fort Wayne Wizards Classic
ForWayWC	Fort Wayne Wizards Classic/Best
ForWayWF	Fort Wayne Wizards Fleer/ProCards
ForWayWTI	Fort Wayne Wizards Team Issue
FouBal	Foul Ball
FouBasHN	Four Base Hits N-Unc.
FraBabR	Franchise Babe Ruth
FraBroR	Franchise Brooks Robinson
FraGloT	Franklin Glove Tag
FraGloT	Franklin Glove Tags
FraThoC	Frank Thomas Coin
Fre	French's
FreGiaSB	Fresno Giants Smokey Bear

FreGriG	Fresno Grizzlies Grandstand
FreKey	Frederick Keys Best
FreKeyB	Frederick Keys Best
FreKeyC	Frederick Keys Classic
FreKeyC	Frederick Keys Classic/Best
FreKeyF	Frederick Keys Fleer/ProCards
FreKeyM	Frederick Keys Multi-Ad
FreKeyP	Frederick Keys ProCards
FreKeyS	Frederick Keys Star
FreKeyTI	Frederick Keys Team Issue
FreStaBS	Fresno State Bulldogs Smokey
FreStaLBS	Fresno State Lady Bulldogs Smokey
FreStaS	Fresno State Smokey
FreSunCLC	Fresno Suns Cal League Cards
FreSunP	Fresno Suns ProCards
FRIAAG	Fritsch AAGPBL
FriBasCM	Fritsch Baseball Card Museum
FriOneYW	Fritsch One Year Winners
FroJoy	Fro Joy
FroRowAH	Front Row ATG Holograms
FroRowB	Front Row Brock
FroRowBa	Front Row Banks
FroRowBe	Front Row Berra
FroRowBL	Front Row Buck Leonard
FroRowBR	Front Row Brooks Robinson
FroRowC	Front Row Campanella
FroRowCGS	Front Row Campanella Gold Signature
FroRowCH	Front Row Campanella Hologram
FroRowD	Front Row Dandridge
FroRowDP	Front Row Draft Picks
FroRowDPG	Front Row Draft Picks Gold
FroRowDPP	Front Row Draft Picks Promos
FroRowDPPC	Front Row Draft Picks Promo Card
FroRowDPPS	Front Row Draft Picks Promo Sheet
FroRowDPS	Front Row Draft Picks Silver
FroRowF	Front Row Fingers
FroRowF	Front Row Ford
FroRowFR	Front Row Frankie Rodriguez
FroRowGCH	Front Row Griffey Club House
FroRowGG	Front Row Griffey Gold
FroRowGH	Front Row Griffey Holograms
FroRowGJGC	Front Row Griffey Jr. Gold Collection
FroRowGJOC	Front Row Griffey Jr. Oversized Card
FroRowI	Front Row Irvin
FroRowKGJ	Front Row Ken Griffey Jr.
FroRowN	Front Row Newhouser
FroRowP	Front Row Palmer
FroRowRF	Front Row Rick Ferrell
FroRowSe	Front Row Seaver
FroRowSt	Front Row Stargell
FroRowT	Front Row Thomas
FroRowTG	Front Row Thomas Gold
FroRowTG	Front Row Tyler Green
Ft.LauYC	Ft. Lauderdale Yankees Classic/Best
Ft.LauYF	Fort Lauderdale Yankees Fleer/ProCards
Ft.LauYP	Ft. Lauderdale Yankees ProCards
Ft.LauYS	Ft. Lauderdale Yankees Star
Ft.MyeMCB	Fort Myer Miracle Classic/Best
Ft.MyeMF	Fort Myers Miracle Fleer/ProCards
Ft.MyeRP	Ft. Myers Royals ProCards
Ft.MyeRT	Ft. Myers Royals TCMA
FtMyeMB	Fort Myers Miracle Best
FunBal	Fun Ball
FunFac	Funky Facts
FunFooP	Fun Foods Pins
FunPac	Fun Pack
FunPacA	Fun Pack All-Stars
FunPacM	Fun Pack Mascots
GadFunC	Gad Fun Cards *
GafGar	Gafline Garvey
GahWilMB	Gahan Wilson Monster Baseball
GalBasGHoF	Galasso Baseball's Great Hall of Fame
GalGloG	Galasso Glossy Greats
GalHaloFRL	Galasso Hall of Famers Ron Lewis
GalRegJ	Galasso Reggie Jackson
GandBCGCE	G and B Chewing Gum Co E223
GasAmeMBD	Gassler's American Maid Bread D381-1
GasRanB	Gastonia Rangers Best
GasRanC	Gastonia Rangers Classic/Best
GasRanF	Gastonia Rangers Fleer/ProCards
GasRanP	Gastonia Rangers ProCards
GasRanS	Gastonia Rangers Star
GasRanT	Gastonia Rangers TCMA
GatCitPP	Gate City Pioneers ProCards
GatCitPSP	Gate City Pioneers Sports Pro
GenCubC	Geneva Cubs Classic/Best
GenCubF	Geneva Cubs Fleer/ProCards
GenCubP	Geneva Cubs ProCards
GenCubS	Geneva Cubs Star
GenMilB	General Mills Booklets
GenMilS	General Mills Stickers
GeoBre3H	George Brett 3 000 Hit
GeoBreP	George Brett Promo
GeoBurP	George Burke PC744
GeoCMil	George C. Miller R300
GeoColC	Georgia College Colonials
GeoSteM	George Steinbrenner Menu
Gia	Giants
Gia195T	Giants 1951 TCMA
Gia196T	Giants 1962 TCMA
Gia25tATI	Giants 25th Anniversary Team Issue
GiaActIS	Giants Action Images Stand-Ups
GiaAllT	Giants All-Time TCMA
GiaAMC	Giants AMC
GiaArmT	Giants Armour Tabs
GiaATaTTP	Giants AT and T Team Postcards
GiaCheB	Giants Chevrolet Bonds
GiaCheHoFP	Giants Chevron Hall of Famer Pins
GiaEurFS	Giants Eureka Federal Savings
GiaFalBTP	Giants Falstaff Beer Team Photos
GiaFanFFB	Giants Fan Fair Fun Bucks
GiaGolS	Giants Golden Stamps
GiaGreT	Giants Greats TCMA
GiaJayP	Giants Jay Publishing
GiaKTV	Giants KTVU-TV
GiaMot	Giants Mother's
GiaPacGaE	Giants Pacific Gas and Electric
GiaPol	Giants Police
GiaPos	Giants Postcards
GiaSch	Giants Schedule
GiaSFC	Giants S.F. Chronicle
GiaSFCB	Giants S.F. Call-Bulletin
GiaSFE	Giants S.F. Examiner
GiaSmo	Giants Smokey
GiaStaC	Giants Stadium Club
GiaTarBC	Giants Target Bottle Caps
GiaTeal	Giants Team Issue
GiaTic	Giants Ticketron
GiaUllAFS	Giants Ullman's Art Frame Series
GiaUSPC	Giants U.S. Playing Cards
GilRazL	Gillette Razor Label
GleFalRC	Glens Falls Redbirds Classic/Best
GleFalRF	Glens Falls Redbirds Fleer/ProCards
GleFalTP	Glen Falls Tigers ProCards
GleFalTP	Glens Falls Tigers ProCards
GleFalWSBT	Glens Falls White Sox B/W TCMA
GleFalWSCT	Glens Falls White Sox Color TCMA
GleFalWST	Glen Falls White Sox TCMA
GleFalWST	Glens Falls White Sox TCMA
GofPos	Goff Postcards
Gol	Gold-Mine
GolCar	Gold Card

GolEntR Gold Entertainment Ruth
GolMedFR Gold Medal Flour R313A
GolPre Golden Press
GooHumICBLS Good Humor Ice Cream Big League Sticks
GooN16 Goodwin N162 *
Gou Goudey R319
Gou Goudey R320
Gou Goudey R324
GouBWR Goudey B/W R322
GouCanV Goudey Canadian V353
GouCanV Goudey Canadian V354
GouCarA Goudey Card Album
GouFliMR Goudey Flip Movies R326
GouHeaU Goudey Heads Up R323
GouKnoHR Goudey Knot Hole R325
GouPreR Goudey Premiums R309-1
GouPreR Goudey Premiums R309-2
GouPreR303A Goudey Premiums R303A
GouPreR303B Goudey Premiums R303B
GouPuzR Goudey Puzzle R321
GouThuMR Goudey Thum Movies R342
GouWidPPR Goudey Wide Pen Premiums R314
GreAmeSDFSB Great American San Diego First Savings Bank
GreBasS Grenada Baseball Stamps
GreBatB Greensboro Bats Best
GreBatC Greensboro Bats Classic
GreBatF Greensboro Bats Fleer/ProCards
GreBatM Greensboro Bats Multi-Ad
GreBatTI Greensboro Bats Team Issue
GreBraB Greenville Braves Best
GreBraC Greenville Braves Classic/Best
GreBraF Greenville Braves Fleer/ProCards
GreBraG Greenville Braves Grandstand
GreBraLD Greenville Braves Line Drive
GreBraP Greenville Braves ProCards
GreBraS Greenville Braves SkyBox
GreBraS Greenville Braves Star
GreBraT Greenwood Braves TCMA
GreBraTI Greenville Braves Team Issue
GreFalDB Great Falls Dodgers Best
GreFalDG Great Falls Dodgers Grandstand
GreFalDSP Great Falls Dodgers Sports Pro
GreFalDTI Great Falls Dodgers Sports Pro
GreFalDTI Great Falls Dodgers Team Issue
GreHeroBP Greyhound Heroes of Base Paths
GreHorB Greensboro Hornets Best
GreHorC Greensboro Hornets Classic/Best
GreHorF Greensboro Hornets Fleer/ProCards
GreHorP Greensboro Hornets ProCards
GreHorS Greensboro Hornets Star
GreHorT Greensboro Hornets TCMA
GrePlaG Great Plains Greats
GriCarCC Griffey Card Collectors Co.
GriNik Griffey Nike
GSGalAG GS Gallery All-Time Greats
GulCoaDF Gulf Coast Dodgers Fleer/ProCards
GulCoaMF Gulf Coast Mets Fleer/ProCards
GulCoaRSP Gulf Coast Rangers Sports Pro
GulCoaYF Gulf Coast Yankees Fleer/ProCards
GuyPotCP Guy's Potato Chip Pins
H-OInsOR H-O Instant Oatmeal Records
H80FouMH Four Mighty Heroes H801-6
HagSunB Hagerstown Suns Best
HagSunC Hagerstown Suns Classic
HagSunC Hagerstown Suns Classic/Best
HagSunDGB Hagerstown Suns All Decade Best
HagSunF Hagerstown Suns Fleer/ProCards
HagSunLD Hagerstown Suns Line Drive
HagSunM Hagerstown Suns Multi-Ad
HagSunP Hagerstown Suns ProCards
HagSunS Hagerstown Suns SkyBox
HagSunS Hagerstown Suns Star
HalHalR Halsey Hall Recalls
Halof FP Hall of Fame Postcards
HalofFB Hall of Fame Busts
HalofFPP Hall of Fame Picture Pack
HamHel Hamburger Helper
HamRedB Hamilton Redbirds Best
HamRedC Hamilton Redbirds Classic/Best
HamRedF Hamilton Redbirds Fleer/ProCards
HamRedP Hamilton Redbirds ProCards
HamRedS Hamilton Redbirds Star
HarCitRCB Hardware City Rock Cats Best
HarCitRCTI Hardware City Rock Cats Team Issue
HarHarW Reds Harry Hartman W711-2
HarSen Harrisburg Senators Best
HarSenB Harrisburg Senators Best
HarSenF Harrisburg Senators Fleer/ProCards
HarSenLD Harrisburg Senators Line Drive
HarSenM Harrisburg Senators Multi-Ad
HarSenP Harrisburg Senators ProCards
HarSenS Harrisburg Senators SkyBox
HarSenS Harrisburg Senators Star
HarSenTI Harrisburg Senators Team Issue
HarSta Hartland Statues
HarStaR Hartland Statue Ryan
HasTriFT Hassan Triple Folders T202
HawIsIC Hawaii Islanders Caruso
HawIsIC Hawaii Islanders Cramer
HawIsIP Hawaii Islanders ProCards
HawIsIT Hawaii Islanders TCMA
HawRai Hawaii Rainbows
HawWomS Hawaii-Hilo Women's Softball
HayComBP Hayes Company Bauer PC750
HelBreB Helena Brewers Best
HelBreF Helena Brewers Fleer/ProCards
HelBreM Helena Brewers Multi-Ad
HelBreSP Helena Brewers Sports Pro
HelBreTI Helena Brewers Team Issue
HelSta Helmar Stamps
HenHouW Henry House Wieners
HicCraB Hickory Crawdads Beige Best
HicCraB Hickory Crawdads Best
HicCraC Hickory Crawdads Classic
HicCraC Hickory Crawdads Classic/Best
HicCraF Hickory Crawdads Fleer/ProCards
HicCraM Hickory Crawdads Multi-Ad
HicCraRB Hickory Crawdads Red Best
HicCraUO Hickory Crawdads Update OSP
Hig5 High 5
Hig5S High 5 Superstars
HigDesMB High Desert Mavericks Best
HigDesMC High Desert Mavericks Classic
HigDesMC High Desert Mavericks Classic/Best
HigDesMF High Desert Mavericks Fleer/ProCards
HigDesMG High Desert Mavericks Grandstand
HigDesMP High Desert Mavericks Police
HigDesMP High Desert Mavericks ProCards
HigDesMUG High Desert Mavericks Update Grandstand
HigMinESC Highland Mint Elite Series Coins
HigMinM Highland Mint Mint-Coins
HigMinMCP Highland Mint Mint-Cards Pinnacle/UD
HigMinMCT Highland Mint Mint-Cards Topps
HigMinMM Highland Mint Mini Mint-Cards
HigMinMSM Highland Mint Magnum Series Medallions
HigSchPLS High School Prospects Little Sun
HilStaHWB Hilo Stars Hawaii Winter Ball
Hir Hires

HirTes	Hires Test
HitTheBB	Hit The Books Bookmarks
HOFStiB	HOF Sticker Book
HolBreD	Holsum Bread D327
HolInnD	Holiday Inn Discs
HolLeg	Hollywood Legends
HolMilT	Holyoke Millers TCMA
HomBon	Homogenized Bond *
HomCooC	Homers Cookies Classics
HomHer	Homerun Heroes
HomRunD	Home Run Derby
HomRunKE	Home Run Kisses E136-1
HonShaHWB	Honolulu Sharks Hawaii Winter Ball
Hos	Hostess
HosSti	Hostess Stickers
HosTwi	Hostess Twinkie
Hot50PS	Hottest 50 Players Stickers
Hot50RS	Hottest 50 Rookies Stickers
HouAstP	Astros Postcards
Houof J	House of Jazz
HouSho	Houston Show
HowPhoSP	Howard Photo Service PC751
HowUniR	Howard University Robinson
Hoy	Hoyle
HudValR	Hudson Valley Renegades OSP
HudValRB	Hudson Valley Renegades Best
HudValRC	Hudson Valley Renegades Classic
HudValRF	Hudson Valley Renegades Fleer/ProCards
HudValRTI	Hudson Valley Renegades Team Issue
HumDumC	Humpty Dumpty Canadian
HunCubC	Huntington Cubs Classic
HunCubC	Huntington Cubs Classic/Best
HunCubF	Huntington Cubs Fleer/ProCards
HunCubP	Huntington Cubs ProCards
HunStaB	Huntsville Stars Best
HunStaC	Huntsville Stars Classic/Best
HunStaDJ	Huntsville Stars Jennings
HunStaF	Huntsville Stars Fleer/ProCards
HunStaJ	Huntsville Stars Jennings
HunStaLD	Huntsville Stars Line Drive
HunStaP	Huntsville Stars ProCards
HunStaS	Huntsville Stars SkyBox
HunStaTI	Huntsville Stars Team Issue
HutPop	Hutchinson Popcorn
HygAllG	Hygrade All-Time Greats
HygMea	Hygrade Meats
IBAWorA	IBA World All-Stars
IdaFalAT	Idaho Falls Athletics TCMA
IdaFalATI	Idaho Falls A's Team Issue
IdaFalB	Idaho Falls Braves Team Issue
IdaFalBF	Idaho Falls Braves Fleer/ProCards
IdaFalBP	Idaho Falls Braves ProCards
IdaFalBSP	Idaho Falls Braves Sports Pro
IdaFalBTI	Idaho Falls Braves Team Issue
IdaFalGF	Idaho Falls Gems Fleer/ProCards
IdaFalGSP	Idaho Falls Gems Sports Pro
IllLot	Illinois Lottery
ImpProP	Imprinted Products Pin-Cards
ImpTobC	Imperial Tobacco C46
Ind	Indians
Ind192T	Indians 1920 TCMA
IndArtTC	Indians Arthur Treacher Cups
IndBurK	Indians Burger King
IndCarBL	Indians Carling Black Label
IndFanC	Indians Fan Club/McDonald's
IndFle	Indians Fleer
IndGat	Indians Gatorade
IndGolS	Indians Golden Stamps
IndGreT	Indians Greats TCMA
IndHag	Indians Hage's
IndInd	Indianapolis Indians Best
IndIndB	Indianapolis Indians Best
IndIndC	Indianapolis Indians CMC
IndIndF	Indianapolis Indians Fleer/ProCards
IndIndLD	Indianapolis Indians Line Drive
IndIndP	Indianapolis Indians ProCards
IndIndQ	Indianapolis Indians Q-Cards
IndIndS	Indianapolis Indians SkyBox
IndIndTI	Indianapolis Indians Team Issue
IndJayP	Indians Jay Publishing
IndJB R	Indians JB Robinson
IndNumN	Indians Num Num
IndOhH	Indians Oh Henry
IndPenCBP	Indians Pencil Clip Buttons PPC-2
IndPol	Indians Polaroid
IndPos	Indianapolis Postcards
IndPos	Indians Postcards
IndSco	Indians Score
IndScoP	Indians Score Platinum
IndScoPl	Indians Score Platinum
IndScoPr	Indians Score Premier
IndScoU	Indians Score Update
IndScoUTC	Indians Score Update Tribe Collection
IndSoh	Indians Sohio
IndSouPSoCP	Indians Souvenir Postcard Shop of Cleveland PC785
IndTeal	Indians Team Issue
IndUppD	Indians Upper Deck
IndVanPP	Indians Van Patrick PC-761
IndVisEl	Indians Vis Ed
IndVolC	Indians Volpe Tumblers
IndWhe	Indians Wheaties
IndWUA	Indians WUAB-TV
IntLeaASB	International League All Stars Broder
IntLeaAT	International League All-Stars TCMA
IowCub	Iowa Cubs Best
IowCubB	Iowa Cubs Best
IowCubC	Iowa Cubs CMC
IowCubF	Iowa Cubs Fleer/ProCards
IowCubLD	Iowa Cubs Line Drive
IowCubP	Iowa Cubs ProCards
IowCubQ	Iowa Cubs Q-Cards
IowCubS	Iowa Cubs SkyBox
IowCubT	Iowa Cubs TCMA
IowCubTI	Iowa Cubs Team Issue
IowOakP	Iowa Oaks Police
IowOakT	Iowa Oaks TCMA
IsaDis	Isaly Discs
ISCHooHA	ISCA Hoosier Hot-Stove All-Stars
JacExpB	Jacksonville Expos Best
JacExpP	Jacksonville Expos ProCards
JacExpT	Jacksonville Expos TCMA
JacGen	Jackson Generals Best
JacGenB	Jackson Generals Best
JacGenF	Jackson Generals Fleer/ProCards
JacGenLD	Jackson Generals Line Drive
JacGenM	Jackson Generals Multi-Ad
JacGenP	Jackson Generals ProCards
JacGenS	Jackson Generals SkyBox
JacGenS	Jackson Generals Smokey
JacGenTI	Jackson Generals Team Issue
JacMetF	Jackson Mets Feder
JacMetGS	Jackson Mets Grand Slam
JacMetT	Jackson Mets TCMA
JacSun	Jacksonville Suns Best
JacSunB	Jacksonville Suns Best
JacSunF	Jacksonville Suns Fleer/ProCards
JacSunLD	Jacksonville Suns Line Drive
JacSunM	Jacksonville Suns Multi-Ad
JacSunP	Jacksonville Suns ProCards
JacSunS	Jacksonville Suns SkyBox

JacSunT	Jacksonville Suns TCMA
JacSunTI	Jacksonville Suns Team Issue
JamExpC	Jamestown Expos Classic/Best
JamExpF	Jamestown Expos Fleer/ProCards
JamExpP	Jamestown Expos ProCards
JamExpP	Jamestown Expos Pucko
JamJamC	Jamestown Jammers Classic
JamJamF	Jamestown Jammers Fleer/ProCards
JapPlaB	Japan Play Ball
JayPubA	Jay Publishing All-Stars
JayPubAG	Jay Publishing All-Time Greats
JayPubS	Jay Publishing Sluggers
JefCarCC	Jefferies Card Collectors Co.
Jel	Jello
JerJonPC	Jerry Jonas Promotion Cards
JesHSA	Jesuit HS Alumni
JetPos	Jets Postcards
JHDABE	J.H. Dockman All-Star Baseball E-Unc.
JimDea	Jimmy Dean
JimDeaAG	Jimmy Dean All-Time Greats
JimDeaLL	Jimmy Dean Living Legends
JimDeaR	Jimmy Dean Rookies
JimDeaRS	Jimmy Dean Rookie Stars
JJKCopP	J.J.K. Copyart Photographers
JohCCTI	Johnson City Cardinals Team Issue
JohCitCC	Johnson City Cardinals Classic
JohCitCC	Johnson City Cardinals Classic/Best
JohCitCF	Johnson City Cardinals Fleer/ProCards
JohCitCP	Johnson City Cardinals ProCards
JohCitCS	Johnson City Cardinals Star
JohCitCTI	Johnson City Cardinals Team Issue
JohMiz	Johnny Mize
JonKeyaAC	Jones Keyser and Arras Cabinets
JosHalC	Joseph Hall Cabinets
JuJuDE	Ju Ju Drums E286
JupHamQ	Jupiter Hammerheads Q-Cards
JusSo	Just So
JustheS	Just the Start
JustheSAC	Just the Start Autograph Cards
JustheSAD	Just the Start Autographed Die-Cuts
JustheSJB	Just the Start Just Black
JustheSJD	Just the Start Just Due
JustheSJN	Just the Start Just News
JustheSJN	Just the Start Just Nine
JustheSJP	Just the Start Just Power
K-M	K-Mart
Kah	Kahn's
KahAtl	Kahn's Atlanta
KahComC	Kahn's Commemorative Coins
KahCoo	Kahn's Cooperstown
KalBatN	Kalamazoo Bats N690-1
KalTeaN	Kalamazoo Teams N690-2
KanCitRP	Royals Postcards
KanCouC	Kane County Cougars Team Issue
KanCouCC	Kane County Cougars Classic
KanCouCC	Kane County Cougars Classic/Best
KanCouCCP	Kane County Cougars Connie's Pizza
KanCouCF	Kane County Cougars Fleer/ProCards
KanCouCLTI	Kane County Cougars Legends Team Issue
KanCouCP	Kane County Cougars ProCards
KanCouCTI	Kane County Cougars Team Issue
KanCouCUTI	Kane County Cougars Update Team Issue
KASDis	KAS Discs
KayB	Kay-Bee
Kel	Kellogg's
Kel2D	Kellogg's 2D
Kel3D	Kellogg's 3D
KelAll	Kellogg's All-Stars
KelATG	Kellogg's ATG
KelCerB	Kellogg's Cereal Boxes
KelCle	Kellogg's Clemente
KelFroFBB	Kellogg's Frosted Flakes Box Back
KelLey	Kellogg's Leyendas
KelPep*	Kellogg's Pep *
KelPepS	Kellogg's Pep Stamps *
KelPin	Kelly's Potato Chips
KelRusSWC	Kelly Russell Studios Will Clark
KelStaU	Kellogg's Stand Ups
KenIndB	Kinston Indians Best
KenTwiB	Kenosha Twins Best
KenTwiC	Kenosha Twins Classic/Best
KenTwiF	Kenosha Twins Fleer/ProCards
KenTwiP	Kenosha Twins ProCards
KenTwiS	Kenosha Twins Star
KeyChal	Key Chain Inserts
KeyFooD	Key Food Discs
KimN18	Kimball's N184 *
Kin	King-B Discs
KinB	King-B Discs
KinBluJT	Kinston Blue Jays TCMA
KinBluJTI	Kinston Blue Jays Team Issue
KinDis	King-B Discs
KinEagP	Kinston Eagles ProCards
KinIndB	Kinston Indians Best
KinIndC	Kinston Indians Classic
KinIndC	Kinston Indians Classic/Best
KinIndF	Kinston Indians Fleer/ProCards
KinIndP	Kinston Indians ProCards
KinIndQ	Kinston Indians Q-Cards
KinIndS	Kinston Indians Star
KinIndTI	Kinston Indians Team Issue
KinMetB	Kingsport Mets Best
KinMetC	Kingsport Mets Classic
KinMetC	Kingsport Mets Classic/Best
KinMetF	Kingsport Mets Fleer/ProCards
KinMetP	Kingsport Mets ProCards
KinMetS	Kingsport Mets Star
KisCob	Kissimmee Cobras Best
KisCobB	Kissimmee Cobras Best
KisCobQ	Kissimmee Cobras Q-Cards
KisDodD	Kissimmee Dodgers Diamond
KisDodP	Kissimmee Dodgers ProCards
KitCloD	Kitty Clover Discs
KnoBluJB	Knoxville Blue Jays Best
KnoBluJF	Knoxville Blue Jays Fleer/ProCards
KnoBluJLD	Knoxville Blue Jays Line Drive
KnoBluJP	Knoxville Blue Jays ProCards
KnoBluJS	Knoxville Blue Jays SkyBox
KnoBluJS	Knoxville Blue Jays Star
KnoBluJT	Knoxville Blue Jays TCMA
KnoKnoST	Knoxville Knox Sox TCMA
KnoSG	Knoxville Smokies Grandstand
KnoSmo	Knoxville Smokies Best
KnoSmoB	Knoxville Smokies Best
KnoSmoF	Knoxville Smokies Fleer/ProCards
KoBreWSI	Koester's Bread World Series Issue D383
KodCelD	Kodak Celebration Denver
KolMotBPP	Kolbs Mothers' Bread Pins PB4
KonTraCOS	Kondritz Trading Cards Ozzie Smith
KonTraCVC	Kondritz Trading Cards Vince Coleman
Kra	Kraft
KraFoo	Kraft Foods
KylAbb	Kyle Abbott
L1L	L1 Leathers
LaBouMRD	La Bounty Moscow Red Devils
LafDriT	Lafayette Drillers TCMA
LaKdec	L and K Decals
LakElsSB	Lake Elsinore Storm Best
LakElsSC	Lake Elsinore Storm Classic

LakElsSF	Lake Elsinore Storm Fleer/ProCards
LakElsSG	Lake Elsinore Storm Grandstand
LakElsSTI	Lake Elsinore Storm Team Issue
LakTigB	Lakeland Tigers Best
LakTigC	Lakeland Tigers Classic
LakTigC	Lakeland Tigers Classic/Best
LakTigF	Lakeland Tigers Fleer/ProCards
LakTigM	Lakeland Tigers Multi-Ad
LakTigP	Lakeland Tigers ProCards
LakTigS	Lakeland Tigers Star
LanJet	Lancaster Jethawks Best
LanJetB	Lancaster Jethawks Best
LanJetG	Lancaster Jethawks Grandstand
LanLugB	Lansing Lugnuts Best
LanLugQ	Lansing Lugnuts Q-Cards
LanLugTS	Lansing Lugnuts Team Issue
LaPat	La Patrie
LaPre	La Presse
Las	Las Vegas Stars Multi-Ad
LasVegS1A	Las Vegas Stars 15th Anniversary Best
LasVegSB	Las Vegas Stars Best
LasVegSBHN	Las Vegas Stars Baseball Hobby News
LasVegSC	Las Vegas Stars CMC
LasVegSC	Las Vegas Stars Cramer
LasVegSF	Las Vegas Stars Fleer/ProCards
LasVegSLD	Las Vegas Stars Line Drive
LasVegSP	Las Vegas Stars ProCards
LasVegSS	Las Vegas Stars SkyBox
Lau300	Laughlin 300/400/500
LauAllG	Laughlin All-Star Games
LauBatB	Laughlin Batty Baseball
LauDiaJ	Laughlin Diamond Jubilee
LauEro	Laughlin Erorrs
LauFamF	Laughlin Famous Feats
LauGreF	Laughlin Great Feats
LauIndC	Laughlin Indianapolis Clowns
LauLonABS	Laughlin Long Ago Black Stars
LauOldTBS	Laughlin Old Time Black Stars
LauSpo	Laughlin Sportslang
LauWorS	Laughlin World Series
LavPro	Laval Provinciale
LawSemC	Lawrence Sermon Postcards
Lea	Leaf
Lea	Leaf/Donruss
Lea300C	Leaf 300 Club
LeaAllGMC	Leaf All-Star Game MVP Contenders
LeaAllGMCG	Leaf All-Star Game MVP Contenders Gold
LeaBanS	Leaf Banner Season
LeaBlaG	Leaf Black Gold
LeaChe	Leaf Checklists
LeaCleC	Leaf Clean-Up Crew
LeaCor	Leaf Cornerstones
LeaCruG	Leaf Crusade Green
LeaCruP	Leaf Crusade Purple
LeaCruR	Leaf Crusade Red
LeaDrefS	Leaf Dress for Success
LeaFas	Leaf Fasttrack
LeaFraDA	Leaf Fractal Diamond Axis
LeaFraF	Leaf Fractal Foundations
LeaFraM	Leaf Fractal Materials
LeaFraM	Leaf Fractal Matrix
LeaFraMDC	Leaf Fractal Materials Die Cuts
LeaFraMDC	Leaf Fractal Matrix Die Cuts
LeaFraMS	Leaf Fractal Materials Samples
LeaFraMZ2	Leaf Fractal Materials Z2 Axis
LeaGam	Leaf Gamers
LeaGet	Leaf Get-A-Grip
LeaGolA	Leaf Gold All-Stars
LeaGolP	Leaf Gold Previews
LeaGolR	Leaf Gold Rookies
LeaGolRJ	Leaf Gold Rookies Jumbo
LeaGolRNV	Leaf Gold Rookies Numbered Variations
LeaGolS	Leaf Gold Stars
LeaGreG	Leaf Great Gloves
LeaHatO	Leaf Hats Off
LeaHeaftH	Leaf Heading for the Hall
LeaHeaftHS	Leaf Heading for the Hall Samples
LeaJacRSNWG	Leaf Jackie Robinson Scratch 'N Win Game
LeaKnoG	Leaf Knot-Hole Gang
LeaL	Leaf Limited
LeaLeaotN	Leaf Leagues of the Nation
LeaLim	Leaf Limited
LeaLimG	Leaf Limited Gold
LeaLimGA	Leaf Limited Gold All-Stars
LeaLimIBP	Leaf Limited Bat Patrol
LeaLimL	Leaf Limited Lumberjacks
LeaLimLB	Leaf Limited Lumberjacks Black
LeaLimPC	Leaf Limited Pennant Craze
LeaLimR	Leaf Limited Rookies
LeaLimRG	Leaf Limited Rookies Gold
LeaLimRP	Leaf Limited Rookies Phenoms
LeaMVPC	Leaf MVP Contenders
LeaMVPCG	Leaf MVP Contenders Gold
LeaOpeD	Leaf Opening Day
LeaPicP	Leaf Picture Perfect
LeaPowB	Leaf Power Brokers
LeaPre	Leaf Preferred
LeaPre	Leaf Premiums
LeaPre	Leaf Previews
LeaPreP	Leaf Preferred Press Proofs
LeaPrePB	Leaf Press Proofs Bronze
LeaPrePG	Leaf Press Proofs Gold
LeaPrePS	Leaf Press Proofs Silver
LeaPreSG	Leaf Preferred Steel Gold
LeaPreSP	Leaf Preferred Steel Power
LeaPreSta	Leaf Preferred Staremaster
LeaPreSte	Leaf Preferred Steel
LeaPro	Leaf Promos
LeaRCMLHDSamp	Leaf Rookies and Stars Major League Hard Drives Samples
LeaRCrusUP	Leaf Rookies and Stars Crusade Update Purple
LeaRS	Leaf Rookies and Stars
LeaRSCross	Leaf Rookies and Stars Crosstraining
LeaRSCrusUG	Leaf Rookies and Stars Crusade Update Green
LeaRSCrusUR	Leaf Rookies and Stars Crusade Update Red
LeaRSExtM	Leaf Rookies and Stars Extreme Measures
LeaRSExtMDC	Leaf Rookies and Stars Extreme Measures Die Cuts
LeaRSFOSamp	Leaf Rookies and Stars Freshman Orientation Samples
LeaRSFresh	Leaf Rookies and Stars Freshman Orientation
LeaRSGAHSamp	Leaf Rookies and Stars Great American Heroes Samples
LeaRSGreAH	Leaf Rookies and Stars Great American Heroes
LeaRSGreHit	Leaf Rookies and Stars Greatest Hits
LeaRSHRDerby	Leaf Rookies and Stars Home Run Derby
LeaRSLHolo	Leaf Rookies and Stars Longevity Holographic
LeaRSLMVP	Leaf Rookies and Stars Leaf MVP's
LeaRSLMVPPE	Leaf Rookies and Stars Leaf MVP's Pennant Edition
LeaRSLong	Leaf Rookies and Stars Longevity
LeaRSMLHD	Leaf Rookies and Stars Major League Hard Drives

LeaRSSOSamp Leaf Rookies and Stars Standing Ovations Samples
LeaRSStaOva Leaf Rookies and Stars Standing Ovations
LeaRSTicMas Leaf Rookies and Stars Ticket Masters
LeaRSTicMasDC Leaf Rookies and Stars Ticket Masters Die Cuts
LeaRTrue Leaf Rookies and Stars True Blue
LeaSig Leaf Signature
LeaSigA Leaf Signature Autographs
LeaSigAG Leaf Signature Autographs Gold
LeaSigAS Leaf Signature Autographs Silver
LeaSigEA Leaf Signature Extended Autographs
LeaSigEACM Leaf Signature Extended Autographs Century Marks
LeaSigPPG Leaf Signature Press Proofs Gold
LeaSigPPP Leaf Signature Press Proofs Platinum
LeaSli Leaf Slideshow
LeaSpeO* Leaf Special Olympics *
LeaStaRep Leaf State Representatives
LeaStaS Leaf Statistical Standouts
LeaStaSDC Leaf Statistical Standouts Die Cuts
LeaTho Leaf Thomas
LeaThoA Leaf Thomas Akklaim
LeaThoC Leaf Thomas Collection
LeaThoGH Leaf Thomas Greatest Hits
LeaThoI Leaf Thomas Info
LeaThoJ Leaf Thomas Jumbos
LeaThoL Leaf Thomas Leukemia
LeaTotB Leaf Total Bases
LeaWarT Leaf Warning Track
Lec Lections
LegFoi Legendary Foils
LegFoiHI Legendary Foils Hawaii IX
LegFoiP Legendary Foils Promos
LegPosR Legends Postcard Ryan
LegSpoF Legends Sports Fingers
LeoDayCC Leon Day Commemorative Card
LetBlaDB Lethbridge Black Diamonds Best
LetBlaDG Lethbridge Black Diamonds Grandstand
LetMouF Lethbridge Mounties Fleer/ProCards
LetMouSP Lethbridge Mounties Sports Pro
LibSpo Liberty Sports
LimRocDP Lime Rock Dominican Promos
LimRocDWB Lime Rock Dominican Winter Baseball
LimRocGH Lime Rock Griffey Holograms
LinDri Line Drive
LinDriAA Line Drive AA
LinDriAAA Line Drive AAA
LinDriP Line Drive Previews
LinDriS Line Drive Sandberg
LinPor Linnett Portraits
LinSup Linnett Superstars
LinVen LineUp Venezuelan Baseball
LinVenB LineUp Venezuelan Baseball
LitFalMP Little Falls Mets ProCards
LitFalMP Little Falls Mets Pucko
LitFalMT Little Falls Mets TCMA
LitSunBS Little Sun Black Sox
LitSunMLL Little Sun Minor League Legends
LitSunW Little Sun Writers
LodDodT Lodi Dodgers TCMA
LonBeaPT Long Beach Press Telegram
LonJacN Lone Jack N370
LonTigF London Tigers Fleer/ProCards
LonTigLD London Tigers Line Drive
LonTigP London Tigers ProCards
LonTigS London Tigers SkyBox
LouRedB Louisville Redbirds Best
LouRedBC Louisville Red Birds CMC
LouRedBLBC Louisville Red Birds Louisville Baseball Club
LouRedBP Louisville Red Birds ProCards
LouRedBTI Louisville Red Birds Team Issue
LouRedE Louisville Redbirds Ehrlers
LouRedF Louisville Redbirds Fleer/ProCards
LouRedLD Louisville Redbirds Line Drive
LouRedP Louisville Redbirds ProCards
LouRedQ Louisville Redbirds Q-Cards
LouRedR Louisville Redbirds Riley's
LouRedS Louisville Redbirds SkyBox
LouRedTI Louisville Redbirds Team Issue
LouSlu Louisville Slugger
LowSpiB Lowell Spinners Best
LowSpiM Lowell Spinners Multi-Ad
LSUMcDM LSU Tigers Ben McDonald McDag
LSUTig LSU Tigers
LSUTigA LSU Tigers Anheuser-Busch
LSUTigGM LSU Tigers Greats McDag
LSUTigM LSU Tigers McDag
LSUTigMP LSU Tigers McDag Purple
LSUTigP LSU Tigers Police
LuxCigPP Luxello Cigar Pins
LynHil Lynchburg Hillcats Best
LynHilB Lynchburg Hillcats Best
LynHilQ Lynchburg Hillcats Q-Cards
LynHilTI Lynchburg Hillcats Team Issue
LynHilUB Lynchburg Hillcats Update Best
LynMetP Lynchburg Mets ProCards
LynMetT Lynchburg Mets TCMA
LynPirT Lynn Pirates TCMA
LynRanT Lynchburg Rangers TCMA
LynRedSC Lynchburg Red Sox Classic
LynRedSC Lynchburg Red Sox Classic/Best
LynRedSF Lynchburg Red Sox Fleer/ProCards
LynRedSP Lynchburg Red Sox ProCards
LynRedSS Lynchburg Red Sox Star
LynRedSTI Lynchburg Red Sox Team Issue
LynSaiT Lynn Sailors TCMA
M.Vpin M.V.P. Pins
MacBra Macon Braves Best
MacBraB Macon Braves Best
MacBraC Macon Braves Classic
MacBraC Macon Braves Classic/Best
MacBraF Macon Braves Fleer/ProCards
MacBraM Macon Braves Multi-Ad
MacBraP Macon Braves ProCards
MacBraTI Macon Braves Team Issue
MacBraUTI Macon Braves Update Team Issue
MacPirP Macon Pirates ProCards
MacSta MacGregor Staff
MadBlaW Madison Black Wolf
MadHatC Madison Hatters Classic
MadHatF Madison Hatters Fleer/ProCards
MadMusB Madison Muskies Best
MadMusC Madison Muskies Classic/Best
MadMusF Madison Muskies Fleer/ProCards
MadMusF Madison Muskies Fritsch
MadMusP Madison Muskies Police
MadMusP Madison Muskies ProCards
MadMusS Madison Muskies Star
MadMusT Madison Muskies TCMA
MaiGuiP Maine Guides ProCards
MaiGuiT Maine Guides TCMA
MaiPhiC Maine Phillies CMC
MaiPhiP Maine Phillies ProCards
MajLeaCP Major League Collector Pins
MajLeaM Major League Movie
Man191BSR Manning 1919 Black Sox Reprints
ManCarCC Mantle Card Collectors Co.
MandMSL M and M's Star Lineup
ManDonC Mantle Donor Card

ManVid	Mantle Video
MapCriV	Maple Crispette V117
MapLeaBH	Maple Leafs Bee Hive
MapLeaSF	Maple Leafs Shopsy's Frankfurters
MarCouH	Mariners Country Hearth
MarDaiQ	Mariners Dairy Queen
MarExh	Marchant Exhibits
MarExhH	Marchant Exhibits HOF
MarFloA	Marlins Florida Agriculture
MarGreT	Mariners Greats TCMA
MariStaClu	Mariners Stadium Club
MarlStaClu	Marlins Stadium Club
MarMcGLL	Mark McGwire Little League
MarMot	Mariners Mother's
MarMot	Mariners Mother's Cookies
MarNal	Mariners Nalley's
MarPac	Mariners Pacific
MarPac	Marlins Pacific
MarPacNB	Mariners Pacific Northwest Bell
MarPhiB	Martinsville Phillies Best
MarPhiC	Martinsville Phillies Classic
MarPhiC	Martinsville Phillies Classic/Best
MarPhiF	Martinsville Phillies Fleer/ProCards
MarPhiG	Martinsville Phillies Grandstand
MarPhiP	Martinsville Phillies ProCards
MarPhiS	Martinsville Phillies Star
MarPhiTI	Martinsville Phillies Team Issue
MarPol	Mariners Police
MarPos	Mariners Postcard
MarPos	Mariners Postcards
MarPub	Marlins Publix
MarRedAP	Mariners Red Apple Pin
MarSco	Mariners Score
MarScoP	Mariners Score Platinum
MarScoPl	Mariners Score Platinum
MarScoPr	Mariners Score Premier
MarTeal	Marlins Team Issue
MarUppD	Marlins Upper Deck
MarUSPC	Marlins U.S. Playing Cards
MasBreD	Master Bread Discs
MasMan	Mascot Mania
MatMin	Mattel Mini-Records
MauStiHWB	Maui Stingrays Hawaii Winter Ball
MaxPubP	Max Stein/United States Publishing House PC758
May	Mayo N300
McCCob	McCallum Cobb
McDCoi	McDonald's/TCI/Coca-Cola Coin
McGCarCC	McGwire Card Collectors Co.
McGCloT	McGregor Clothes Tags
McGDen	McGwire Dental
MCIAmb	MCI Ambassadors
MDAA	MDA All-Stars
MDAMVP	MDA MVP
MeaGolBB	Meadow Gold Blank Back
MeaGolM	Meadow Gold Milk
MeaGolSB	Meadow Gold Stat Back
MecDFT	Mecca Double Folders T201
MedA'sC	Medford A's Cramer
MedAthB	Medford Athletics Best
MedHatBJB	Medicine Hat Blue Jays Best
MedHatBJF	Medicine Hat Blue Jays Fleer/ProCards
MedHatBJP	Medicine Hat Blue Jays ProCards
MedHatBJSP	Medicine Hat Blue Jays Sports Pro
MedHatBJTI	Medicine Hat Blue Jays Team Issue
MegGriJWL	Megacards Griffey Jr. Wish List
MegRut	Megacards Ruth
MegRutP	Megacards Ruth Prototypes
MegRutS	Megacards Ruthian Shots
MelBusF	Melbourne Bushrangers Futura
MelMinE	Mello Mints E105
MemChiB	Memphis Chicks Best
MemChiBC	Memphis Chicks Britling Cafeterias
MemChiF	Memphis Chicks Fleer/ProCards
MemChiLD	Memphis Chicks Line Drive
MemChiP	Memphis Chicks ProCards
MemChiS	Memphis Chicks SkyBox
MemChiS	Memphis Chicks Star
MemChiSTOS	Memphis Chicks Silver Time Out Sports
MemChiT	Memphis Chicks TCMA
MemChiTI	Memphis Chicks Team Issue
MemChiTOS	Memphis Chicks Time Out Sports
MemRedG	Memphis Redbirds Grandstand
Met196C	Mets 1969 Calendar
Met196T	Mets 1969 TCMA
Met63 S	Mets '63 SSPC
Met69CCPP	Mets '69 Capital Cards Postcard Promos
Met69CS	Mets '69 Commemorative Sheet
Met69SP	Mets '69 Spectrum Promos
Met69T	Mets '69 Tribute
Met69Y	Mets '69 Year Book
MetAllEB	Mets All-Time Ed Broder
MetBak	Metz Baking
MetBoyS	Mets Boy Scouts
MetCit	Mets Citgo
MetCol8	Mets Colla 8x10
MetColP	Mets Colla Postcards
MetColP	Mets Color Postcards
MetComR	Mets Community Relations
MetDaiPA	Mets Dairylea Photo Album
MetFanC	Mets Fan Club
MetGal62	Mets Galasso '62
MetGreT	Mets Greats TCMA
MetHaloF	Mets Hall of Fame
MetIma	Metallic Images
MetImpG	Metallic Impressions Gehrig
MetImpG	Metallic Impressions Griffey
MetImpM	Metallic Impressions Mantle
MetImpR	Metallic Impressions Ruth
MetImpRi	Metallic Impressions Ripken
MetImpRy	Metallic Impressions Ryan
MetJapEB	Mets Japan Ed Broder
MetJayP	Mets Jay Publishing
MetKah	Mets Kahn's
MetMagM	Mets Magic Memory
MetMod	Mets Modell
MetMSAP	Mets MSA Placemats
MetMusoAB	Metropolitan Museum of Art Burdick
MetNewYDN	Mets New York Daily News
MetOriEB	Mets Original Ed Broder
MetPerPA	Mets Pergament Photo Album
MetPhoA	Mets Photo Album
MetPos	Mets Postcards
MetRinP69	Mets Rini Postcards 1969
MetShuST	Mets Shultz Chevrolet Spring Training
MetSSP	Mets SSPC
MetTCM	Mets TCMA
MetTeal	Mets Team Issue
MetTealA	Mets Team Issue Autographs
MetTealC	Mets Team Issue Color
MetTra	Mets Transogram Statues
MetTriS6S	Mets Tribute Sheet '69 Spectrum
MetTro	Mets Tropicana
MetUni	Metal Universe
MetUniAT	Metal Universe All-Galactic Team
MetUniBF	Metal Universe Blast Furnace
MetUniBWTW	Metal Universe Boyz With The Wood
MetUniDH	Metal Universe Diamond Heroes
MetUniDS	Metal Universe Diamond Soul
MetUniEA	Metal Universe Emerald Autographs
MetUniEAR	Metal Universe Emerald Autograph Redemptions

MetUniGM	Metal Universe Gem Masters
MetUniHM	Metal Universe Heavy Metal
MetUniL	Metal Universe Linchpins
MetUniMF	Metal Universe Magnetic Field
MetUniMfG	Metal Universe Mining for Gold
MetUniML	Metal Universe Mother Lode
MetUniN	Metal Universe Neophytes
MetUniP	Metal Universe Platinum
MetUniPM	Metal Universe Planet Metal
MetUniPMG	Metal Universe Precious Metal Gems
MetUniPP	Metal Universe Platinum Portraits
MetUniProS	Metal Universe Promo Sheet
MetUniSamp	Metal Universe Sample Sheet
MetUniT	Metal Universe Titanium
MetUniUL	Metal Universe Universal Language
MetVolC	Mets Volpe Tumblers
MetWIZ	Mets WIZ
MetWorSC	Mets World Series Champs
MexCitTT	Mexico City Tigers TCMA
MiaHur	Miami Hurricanes
MiaHurBB	Miami Hurricanes Bumble Bee
MiaMarP	Miami Marlins ProCards
MiaMarS	Miami Marlins Star
MiaMarT	Miami Marlins TCMA
MiaMirC	Miami Miracle Classic/Best
MiaMirIS	Miami Miracle I Star
MiaMirIS	Miami Miracle II Star
MiaMirP	Miami Miracle ProCards
MiaOriT	Miami Orioles TCMA
MicBatC	Michigan Battle Cats Best
MicBatCB	Michigan Battle Cats Best
MicBatCM	Michigan Battle Cats Multi-Ad
MicBatCTI	Michigan Battle Cats Team Issue
MicManHIP	Mantle Holiday Inn Postcard
MicManRL	Mickey Mantle Reserve Life
MidAng	Midland Angels Best
MidAngB	Midland Angels Best
MidAngF	Midland Angels Fleer/ProCards
MidAngG	Midland Angels Grandstand
MidAngGS	Midland Angels Grand Slam
MidAngLD	Midland Angels Line Drive
MidAngO	Midland Angels OHP
MidAngOHP	Midland Angels One Hour Photo
MidAngP	Midland Angels ProCards
MidAngS	Midland Angels SkyBox
MidAngT	Midland Angels TCMA
MidAngTI	Midland Angels Team Issue
MidBre	Middy Bread
MidCubT	Midland Cubs TCMA
MidLeaA	Midwest League All-Stars
MidLeaAB	Midwest League All-Stars Best
MidLeaAF	Midwest League All-Stars Fleer/ProCards
MidLeaAGF	Midwest League All-Stars Fleer/ProCards
MidLeaAGS	Midwest League All-Stars Grand Slam
MidLeaAP	Midwest League All-Stars ProCards
MidLeaASGS	Midwest League All-Stars Grand Slam
MidLeaATI	Midwest League All-Stars Team Issue
MidLeaPM	Midwest League Prospects Multi-Ad
MidLeaTP	Midwest League Top Prospects Best
MilBonSS	Milk Bone Super Stars
MilBra	Milton Bradley
MilDud	Milk Duds
MilLit	Miller Lite
MilSau	Milwaukee Sausage
Min	Minnesota
MinLeaTS1	Minor League Team Sets 1972-Present
MinTwiP	Twins Postcards
MisStaB	Mississippi State Bulldogs
MJBHolB	MJB Holographics Bagwell
MJBHolK	MJB Holographics Knoblauch
MJBHolP	MJB Holographics Prototypes
MLBBasB	MLBPA Baseball Buttons (Pins)
MLBKeyC	MLBPA Key Chains
MLBOffS	MLB Official Stamps
MLBPen	MLBPA Pencils
MLBPin	MLB Pins
MLBPin	MLBPA Pins
MobBayBB	Mobile Bay Bears Best
MobBayBTI	Mobile Bay Bears Team Issue
MobCooB	Mobil Coombs Booklets
ModA'sB	Modesto A's Best
ModA'sC	Modesto A's Chong
ModA'sC	Modesto A's Chong
ModA'sC	Modesto A's Classic
ModA'sC	Modesto A's Classic/Best
ModA'sCLC	Modesto A's Cal League Cards
ModA'sF	Modesto A's Fleer/ProCards
ModA'sG	Modesto A's Grandstand
ModA'sP	Modesto A's ProCards
ModA'sTI	Modesto A's Team Issue
MonExpP	Expos Postcards
MonNew	Montreal News *
MonRoyF	Montreal Royals FC53
MooGra	Moonlight Graham
MooSna	MooTown Snackers
MotBag	Mother's Bagwell
MotCan	Mother's Canseco
MotCoo	Mothers Cookies
MotGri	Mother's Griffeys
MotGriJ	Mother's Griffey Jr.
MotKno	Mother's Knoblauch
MotMatW	Mother's Matt Williams
MotMcG	Mother's McGwire
MotOldT	Motorola Old Timers
MotPia	Mother's Piazza
MotPia	Mother's Piazza/Salmon
MotRya	Mother's Ryan
MotRya7N	Mother's Ryan 7 No-Hitters
MotRyaA	Mother's Ryan Advertisement
MotRyaF	Mother's Ryan Farewell
MotSal	Mother's Salmon
MotWilC	Mother's Will Clark
MPR302-1	MP and Co. R302-1
MPR302-2	MP and Co. R302-2
Mr.TurS	Mr. Turkey Superstars
MrsShePP	Mrs. Sherlock's Bread Pins
MrsShePP	Mrs. Sherlock's Pins PB5-1
MrsShePP	Mrs. Sherlock's Pins PB5-2
MrsShePP	Mrs. Sherlock's Pins PB5-3
MrTurBG	Mr. Turkey Baseball Greats
MSABenSHD	MSA Ben's Super Hitters Discs
MSABenSPD	MSA Ben's Super Pitchers Discs
MSADis	MSA Discs
MSAFanSD	MSA Fantastic Sam's Discs
MSAHolD	MSA Holsum Discs
MSAHosD	MSA Hostess Discs
MSAIceTD	MSA Iced Tea Discs
MSAJayPCD	MSA Jay's Potato Chip Discs
MSAJifPD	MSA Jiffy Pop Discs
MSAMinD	MSA Mini Discs
MSASupS	MSA Super Stars
MTVRocnJ	MTV Rock n' Jock
MusTTC	Musial TTC
MVP	MVP Game
MVP2H	MVP 2 Highlights
MVPPin	MVP Pins
MyrBeaBJP	Myrtle Beach Blue Jays ProCards
MyrBeaHC	Myrtle Beach Hurricanes Classic/Best
MyrBeaHF	Myrtle Beach Hurricanes Fleer/ProCards
MyrBeaHP	Myrtle Beach Hurricanes ProCards
N526N7C	N526 No. 7 Cigars
Nab	Nabisco

NabAllA	Nabisco All-Star Autographs
NabTeaF	Nabisco Team Flakes
NadCarE	Nadja Caramel E92
NadE1	Nadja E104
NasAngT	Nashua Angels TCMA
NasHeaF	Nassau Health Ford
NaSouTI	Nashville Sounds Team Issue
NasPirP	Nashua Pirates ProCards
NasPirT	Nashua Pirates TCMA
NasSouB	Nashville Sounds Best
NasSouC	Nashville Sounds CMC
NasSouF	Nashville Sounds Fleer/ProCards
NasSouLD	Nashville Sounds Line Drive
NasSouP	Nashville Sounds ProCards
NasSouS	Nashville Sounds SkyBox
NasSouTI	Nashville Sounds Team Issue
NasSouTISS	Nashville Sounds Team Issue Stadium Set
NasXprF	Nashville Xpress Fleer/ProCards
NatCarE	National Caramel E220
NatChiFPR	National Chicle Fine Pen Premiums R313
NatChiMS	National Chicle Maranville Secrets R344
NatGamW	National Game WG5
NatLeaAC	National League All-Stars Commemorative
NatPac	National Packtime
NatPac2	National Packtime 2
NatTeaL	National Tea Labels
NebCor	Nebraska Cornhuskers
NegLeaBMKC	Negro League Baseball Museum Kansas City
NegLeaD	Negro League Duquesne
NegLeaF	Negro League Fritsch
NegLeaFS	Negro League Fritsch Samples
NegLeaK	Negro League Kraft
NegLeaL2	Negro League Legends II
NegLeaLI	Negro League Legends I
NegLeaPC	Negro League Playing Cards
NegLeaPD	Negro League Phil Dixon
NegLeaPL	Negro League Paul Lee
NegLeaRL	Negro League Ron Lewis
NegLeaRL2	Negro League Retort Legends II
NegLeaRLI	Negro League Retort Legends I
NegLeaRP	Negro League Rini Postcards
NegLeaS	Negro League Stars
Nei	Neilson's V61
Nes	Nestle
Nes792	Nestle 792
NesDreT	Nestle Dream Team
NesQuiB	Nestle Quik Bunnies
New	NewSport
NewBriRC	New Britain Rock Cats Best
NewBriRCM	New Britain Rock Cats Multi-Ad
NewBriRSB	New Britain Red Sox Best
NewBriRSF	New Britain Red Sox Fleer/ProCards
NewBriRSLD	New Britain Red Sox Line Drive
NewBriRSP	New Britain Red Sox ProCards
NewBriRSS	New Britain Red Sox SkyBox
NewBriRSS	New Britain Red Sox Star
NewCoPT	Newark Co-Pilots TCMA
NewEveWS	Newark Evening World Supplements
NewHavRB	New Haven Ravens Best
NewHavRF	New Haven Ravens Fleer/ProCards
NewHavRM	New Haven Ravens Multi-Ad
NewHavRMA	New Haven Ravens Maritime Aquarium
NewHavRTI	New Haven Ravens Team Issue
NewHavRUSTI	New Haven Raven Uncut Sheet Team Issue
NewJerCB	New Jersey Cardinals Best
NewJerCB	New Jersey Cardinals Strips
NewJerCC	New Jersey Cardinals Classic
NewJerCF	New Jersey Cardinals Fleer/ProCards
NewJerCM	New Jersey Cardinals Multi-Ad
NewJerCTI	New Jersey Cardinals Team Issue
NewN566	Newsboy N566
NewOriP	Newark Orioles ProCards
NewOriT	Newark Orioles TCMA
NewOrlZF	New Orleans Zephyrs Fleer/ProCards
NewOrlZM	New Orleans Zephyrs Multi-Ad
NewPin	New Pinnacle
NewPinAP	New Pinnacle Artist's Proofs
NewPinIE	New Pinnacle Interleague Encounter
NewPinKtP	New Pinnacle Keeping the Pace
NewPinMC	New Pinnacle Museum Collection
NewPinPP	New Pinnacle Press Plates
NewPinS	New Pinnacle Spellbound
NewWayCT	Newark Wayne Co-Pilots TCMA
NewYorJA	New York Journal American
NewYorL	New York Lottery
NewYorNTDiS	New York News This Day in Sports *
NewYorSNM	New York Sunday News M138
NiaFalRC	Niagara Falls Rapids Classic/Best
NiaFalRF	Niagara Falls Rapids Fleer/ProCards
NiaFalRP	Niagara Falls Rapids ProCards
NiaFalRP	Niagara Falls Rapids Pucko
NikMin	Nike Mini-Posters
NinGriJ	Nintendo Griffey Jr.
Nis	Nissen
NoiSatP	NoirTech Satchel Paige
NorBreL	Northland Bread Labels
NorNagUTI	Norwich Navigators Update Team Issue
NorNav	Norwich Navigators Best
NorNavB	Norwich Navigators Best
NorNavQ	Norwich Navigators Q-Cards
NorNavTI	Norwich Navigators Team Issue
NorTid	Norfolk Tides Team Issue
NorTidB	Norfolk Tides Best
NorTidF	Norfolk Tides Fleer/ProCards
NorTidP	Norfolk Tides Police/Fox33
NorTidQ	Norfolk Tides Q-Cards
NorTidTI	Norfolk Tides Team Issue
NotCov	Notebook Covers
nsBasASD	Inside Baseball/Douglas Allred San Diego
NuHi	Nu-Card Hi-Lites
NuSco	Nu-Card Scoops
NY NewFCP	NY News Frank Chance Pin
O'KAleMR	Montreal Royals O'Keefe Ale
O-PJumAF	O-Pee-Chee Jumbo All-Stars Foil
OakOak2A	Oakland Oaks 20th Anniversary
ObaPreT	Obak Premiums T4
ObaT21	Obak T212
Oco& SSBG	O'Connell and Son Baseball Greats
OCoandSI	O'Connell and Son Ink
OdgRapTI	Ogden Raptors Team Issue
OgdA'sT	Ogden A's TCMA
OgdRapF	Ogden Raptors Fleer/ProCards
OgdRapSP	Ogden Raptors Sports Pro
OgdRapTI	Ogden Raptors Team Issue
OhiHaloF	Ohio Hall of Fame
OhiLot	Ohio Lottery
OklCit8	Oklahoma City 89ers Best
OklCit8B	Oklahoma City 89ers Best
OklCit8C	Oklahoma City 89ers CMC
OklCit8F	Oklahoma City 89ers Fleer/ProCards
OklCit8LD	Oklahoma City 89ers Line Drive
OklCit8P	Oklahoma City 89ers ProCards
OklCit8S	Oklahoma City 89ers SkyBox
OklCit8T	Oklahoma City 89ers TCMA
OklCit8TI	Oklahoma City 89ers Team Issue
OklRedM	Oklahoma Redhawks Multi-Ad
OklSoo	Oklahoma Sooners
OklSta	Oklahoma State

OklStaC	Oklahoma State Cowboys
OklTodML	Oklahoma Today Major Leaguers
OldJudN	Old Judge N167
OldJudN	Old Judge N172
OldLonC	Old London Coins
OldMilT	Old Mill T210
OlmStu	Olmes Studios
OmaRoyB	Omaha Royals Best
OmaRoyC	Omaha Royals CMC
OmaRoyF	Omaha Royals Fleer/ProCards
OmaRoyLD	Omaha Royals Line Drive
OmaRoyM	Omaha Royals Multi-Ad
OmaRoyP	Omaha Royals Police
OmaRoyP	Omaha Royals ProCards
OmaRoyS	Omaha Royals Shurfine
OmaRoyS	Omaha Royals SkyBox
OmaRoyT	Omaha Royals TCMA
OmaRoyTI	Omaha Royals Team Issue
OmaRoyTT	Omaha Royals Top Trophies
OnDecD	On Deck Discs
OneYanC	Oneonta Yankees Classic
OneYanC	Oneonta Yankees Classic/Best
OneYanF	Oneonta Yankees Fleer/ProCards
OneYanG	Oneata Yankees Grandstand
OneYanP	Oneonta Yankees ProCards
OneYanT	Oneonta Yankees TCMA
OPC	O-Pee-Chee
OPCAllR	O-Pee-Chee All-Star Redemptions
OPCBatUV	O-Pee-Chee Batter Ups V300
OPCBoxB	O-Pee-Chee Box Bottoms
OPCBTC	O-Pee-Chee Blue Team Checklists
OPCDec	O-Pee-Chee Deckle
OPCDiaD	O-Pee-Chee Diamond Dynamos
OPCHotP	O-Pee-Chee Hot Prospects
OPCJumA	O-Pee-Chee Jumbo All-Stars
OPCPapI	O-Pee-Chee Paper Inserts
OPCPos	O-Pee-Chee Posters
OPCPre	O-Pee-Chee Premier
OPCPreSP	O-Pee-Chee Premier Star Performers
OPCPreSPF	O-Pee-Chee Premier Star Performers Foil
OPCPreTDP	O-Pee-Chee Premier Top Draft Picks
OPCTC	O-Pee-Chee Team Checklists
OPCWorC	O-Pee-Chee World Champions
OPCWorSH	O-Pee-Chee World Series Heroes
OrbDis	Orbakers Discs
OrbPinNP	Orbit Gum Pins "Numbered"
OrbPinUP	Orbit Gum Pins "Unnumbered"
OrcPhoAP	Orcajo Photo Art PC786
Ori	Orioles
Ori6F	Orioles 1966 Franchise
OriCha	Orioles Champions
OriCro	Orioles Crown
OriCroASU	Orioles Crown Action Stand Ups
OriDMV	Orioles DMV
OriEng	Orioles English's Discs
OriEngCL	Orioles English's Chicken Lids
OriEss	Orioles Esskay
OriFle	Orioles Fleer
OriFreB	Orioles French Bray
OriGreT	Orioles Greats TCMA
OriHea	Orioles Health
OriJayP	Orioles Jay Publishing
OriJohP	Orioles Johnny Pro
OriofB	Origins of Baseball
OriPos	Orioles Postcards
OriPro	Orioles Program
OriSco	Orioles Score
OriScoP	Orioles Score Platinum
OriScoPl	Orioles Score Platinum
OriScoPr	Orioles Score Premier
OriSun	Orioles Sun
OriTeal	Orioles Team Issue
OriUSPC	Orioles U.S. Playing Cards
OrlCubB	Orlando Cubs Best
OrlCubF	Orlando Cubs Fleer/ProCards
OrlRayB	Orlando Rays Best
OrlRayM	Orlando Rays Multi-Ad
OrlSunRB	Orlando Sun Rays Best
OrlSunRF	Orlando Sun Rays Fleer/ProCards
OrlSunRLD	Orlando Sun Rays Line Drive
OrlSunRP	Orlando Sun Rays ProCards
OrlSunRS	Orlando Sun Rays SkyBox
OrlSunRS	Orlando Sun Rays Star
OrlTwi8SCT	Orlando Twins 81 SL Champs TCMA
OrlTwiB	Orlando Twins Best
OrlTwiP	Orlando Twins ProCards
OrlTwiT	Orlando Twins TCMA
OrnOvaPP	Ornate Oval Pins
OscAstC	Osceola Astros Classic
OscAstC	Osceola Astros Classic/Best
OscAstF	Osceola Astros Fleer/ProCards
OscAstP	Osceola Astros ProCards
OscAstS	Osceola Astros Star
OscAstTI	Osceola Astros Team Issue
OscMayR	Oscar Mayer Round-Ups
OttLynF	Ottawa Lynx Fleer/ProCards
OurNatGPP	Our National Game Tabs
OurOwnTD	Our Own Tea Discs
OveCanR	Overland Candy R301
OxfConE	Oxford Confectionery E253
oySigST	Royals Signature Series Team
oyTeal	Royals Team Issue
Pac	Pacific
PacAll	Pacific All-Latino
PacAur	Pacific Aurora
PacAurCube	Pacific Aurora Cubes
PacAurHC	Pacific Aurora Hardball Cel-Fusions
PacAurKotML	Pacific Aurora Kings of the Major Leagues
PacAurOD	Pacific Aurora Opening Day
PacAurODLC	Pacific Aurora On Deck Laser Cuts
PacAurPF	Pacific Aurora Pennant Fever
PacAurPFC	Pacific Aurora Pennant Fever Copper
PacAurPFPB	Pacific Aurora Pennant Fever Platinum Blue
PacAurPFR	Pacific Aurora Pennant Fever Red
PacAurPFS	Pacific Aurora Pennant Fever Silver
PacBaeS	Pacific Baerga Softball
PacBeiA	Pacific Beisbol Amigos
PacBel	Packard Bell
PacCar	Pacific Card-Supials
PacCarM	Pacific Card-Supials Minis
PacCerCGT	Pinnacle Certified Certified Gold Team
PacChe	Pacific Checklists
PacCoaBD	Pacific Coast Biscuit D310
PacCoaBD	Pacific Coast Biscuit D311
PacCoaLAB	Pacific Coast League All-Stars Broder
PacCraC	Pacific Cramer's Choice
PacCraCh	Pacific Cramer's Choice
PacCraCho	Pacific Cramer's Choice
PacCroC	Pacific Crown Collection
PacCroC	Pacific Crown Collection Latinos of the Major Leagues
PacCroCITC	Pacific Crown Collection In The Cage
PacCroCPB	Pacific Crown Collection Platinum Blue
PacCroCPC	Pacific Crown Collection Pacific Cup
PacCroCTC	Pacific Crown Collection Team Checklists
PacCroCTM	Pacific Crown Collection Tape Measure
PacDynaD	Pacific Dynagon Diamond
PacDynaDT	Pacific Dynagon Diamond Titanium
PacEigMO	Pacific Eight Men Out
PacEstL	Pacific Estrellas Latinas

PacFirD	Pacific Fireworks Die Cuts
PacGolCD	Pacific Gold Crown Die Cuts
PacGolCDC	Pacific Gold Crown Die Cuts
PacGolP	Pacific Gold Prisms
PacGriCB	Pacific Griffey Candy Bar
PacGwyCB	Pacific Gwynn Candy Bar
PacHarR	Pacific Harvey Riebe
PacHom	Pacific Hometowns
PacHomRH	Pacific Home Run Heroes
PacHomRH	Pacific Home Run History
PacHomRH	Pacific Home Run Hitters
PacInCage	Pacific In The Cage
PacInv	Pacific Invincible
PacInvCCDB	Pacific Invincible Cramer's Choice Dark Blue
PacInvCCG	Pacific Invincible Cramer's Choice Gold
PacInvCCG	Pacific Invincible Cramer's Choice Green
PacInvCCLB	Pacific Invincible Cramer's Choice Light Blue
PacInvCCP	Pacific Invincible Cramer's Choice Purple
PacInvCCR	Pacific Invincible Cramer's Choice Red
PacInvDM	Pacific Invincible Diamond Magic
PacInvFP	Pacific Invincible Flash Point
PacInvGems	Pacific Invincible Gems of the Diamond
PacInvGotG	Pacific Invincible Giants of the Game
PacInvInt	Pacific Invincible Interleague Players
PacInvMiT	Pacific Invincible Moments in Time
PacInvOD	Pacific Invincible Opening Day
PacInvPB	Pacific Invincible Platinum Blue
PacInvPBlue	Pacific Invincible Platinum Blue
PacInvPhoto	Pacific Invincible Photoengravings
PacInvSF	Pacific Invincible Seismic Force
PacInvSFS	Pacific Invincible Seismic Force SportsFest
PacInvSH	Pacific Invincible Sandlot Heroes
PacInvSilv	Pacific Invincible Silver
PacInvTA	Pacific Invincible Thunder Alley
PacInvTeam	Pacific Invincible Team Checklists
PacJugC	Pacific Jugadores Calientes
PacLatD	Pacific Latinos Destacados
PacLatotML	Pacific Latinos of the Major Leagues
PacLeg	Pacific Legends
PacLegI	Pacific Legends I
PacLegI	Pacific Legends II
PacLigB	Pacific Light Blue
PacMil	Pacific Milestones
PacNes	Pacific Nestle
PacNolR	Pacific/Advil Nolan Ryan
PacOctM	Pacific October Moments
PacOme	Pacific Omega
PacOme	Pacific Omega Hit Machine 3000
PacOme5T	Pacific Omega 5-Tool Talents
PacOme5TT	Pacific Omega 5-Tool Talents Tiers
PacOmeC	Pacific Omega Copper
PacOmeDD	Pacific Omega Debut Duos
PacOmeDM	Pacific Omega Diamond Masters
PacOmeEP	Pacific Omega EO Portraits
PacOmeEP1o1	Pacific Omega EO Portraits 1 of 1
PacOmeEP1o1	Pacific Omega EO Portraits 1 of 1's
PacOmeFTF	Pacific Omega Face To Face
PacOmeG	Pacific Omega Gold
PacOmeH'	Pacific Omega HR 99
PacOmeOnIns	Pacific Omega Online Inserts
PacOmeP	Pacific Omega Prisms
PacOmePB	Pacific Omega Platinum Blue
PacOmeR	Pacific Omega Red
PacOmeRS	Pacific Omega Rising Stars
PacOmeRST1	Pacific Omega Rising Stars Tier 1
PacOmeRST2	Pacific Omega Rising Stars Tier 2
PacOmeRST3	Pacific Omega Rising Stars Tier 3
PacOmeRST4	Pacific Omega Rising Stars Tier 4
PacOmeRST5	Pacific Omega Rising Stars Tier 5
PacOnl	Pacific Online
PacOnlR	Pacific Online Red
PacOnlWC	Pacific Online Web Cards
PacPar	Pacific Paramount
PacParC	Pacific Paramount Copper
PacParCB	Pacific Paramount Cooperstown Bound
PacParCBPP	Pacific Paramount Cooperstown Bound Pacific Proofs
PacParFC	Pacific Paramount Fielder's Choice
PacParG	Pacific Paramount Gold
PacParHoloGold	Pacific Paramount Holo-Gold
PacParHS	Pacific Paramount Holographic Silver
PacParI	Pacific Paramount Inaugural
PacParOD	Pacific Paramount Opening Day
PacParPB	Pacific Paramount Personal Bests
PacParPB	Pacific Paramount Platinum Blue
PacParR	Pacific Paramount Red
PacParRed	Pacific Paramount Red
PacParSD	Pacific Paramount Special Delivery
PacParTC	Pacific Paramount Team Checklists
PacPlaB	Pacific Platinum Blue
PacPri	Pacific Prism
PacPri	Pacific Prisms
PacPriAotG	Pacific Prism Ahead of the Game
PacPriBL	Pacific Prism Ballpark Legends
PacPriC	Pacific Prisms Checklist
PacPriDG	Pacific Prism Diamond Glory
PacPriEP	Pacific Prism Epic Performers
PacPriFB	Pacific Prisms Fence Busters
PacPriFT	Pacific Prisms Flame Throwers
PacPriG	Pacific Prisms Gold
PacPriGA	Pacific Prisms Gate Attractions
PacPriGotD	Pacific Prisms Gems of the Diamond
PacPriHB	Pacific Prism Holographic Blue
PacPriHG	Pacific Prism Holographic Gold
PacPriHM	Pacific Prism Holographic Mirror
PacPriHP	Pacific Prism Holographic Purple
PacPriLB	Pacific Prisms Light Blue
PacPriP	Pacific Prisms Platinum
PacPriRed	Pacific Prism Red
PacPriRHS	Pacific Prisms Red Hot Stars
PacPriS	Pacific Private Stock
PacPriS206	Pacific Private Stock PS-206
PacPriS206R	Pacific Private Stock PS-206 Red
PacPriSE	Pacific Private Stock Exclusive
PacPriSH	Pacific Prisms Sluggers and Hurlers
PacPriSHRH	Pacific Private Stock Home Run History
PacPriSL	Pacific Prisms Sizzling Lumber
PacPriSP	Pacific Private Stock Platinum
PacPriSP	Pacific Private Stock Preferred
PacPriSV	Pacific Private Stock Vintage
PacPriTL	Pacific Prisms Team Logo
PacPro	Pacific Promos
PacPro	Pacific Prototype
PacRed	Pacific Red
PacRedT	Pacific Red Threatt
PacRya2S	Pacific Ryan 27th Season
PacRya7N	Pacific Ryan 7th No-Hitter
PacRyaFM	Pacific Ryan Farewell McCormick
PacRyaG	Pacific Ryan Gold
PacRyaI8	Pacific Ryan Inserts 8
PacRyaL	Pacific Ryan Limited
PacRyaM6	Pacific Ryan Magazine 6
PacRyaPI	Pacific Ryan Prism Inserts
PacRyaTEI	Pacific Ryan Texas Express I
PacRyaTEI	Pacific Ryan Texas Express II
PacSea	Pacific Seaver
PacSeaI6	Pacific Seaver Inserts 6
PacSenL	Pacific Senior League
PacSil	Pacific Silver

PacSilP Pacific Silver Prisms
PacSilPC Pacific Silver Prisms Circular
PacSpa Pacific Spanish
PacSpaGE Pacific Spanish Gold Estrellas
PacSpaPI Pacific Spanish Prism Inserts
PacTeaC Pacific Team Checklists
PacTim Pacific Timelines
PacTriCD Pacific Triple Crown Die Cuts
PadBohHB Padres Bohemian Hearth Bread
PadCarJ Padres Carl's Jr.
PadCHP Padres CHP
PadCok Padres Coke
PadDea Padres Dean's
PadFamF Padres Family Fun
PadFirPTB Padres Fire Prevention Tips Booklets
PadGreT Padres Greats TCMA
PadMag Padres Magazine
PadMag Padres Magazine/Rally's
PadMag Padres Magazine/Unocal
PadMcDD Padres McDonald Discs
PadMot Padres Mother's
PadPolD Padres Police DARE
PadPos Padres Postcards
PadSchC Padres Schedule Cards
PadShoK Padres Show Kay
PadSmo Padres Smokey
PadTeal Padres Team Issue
PadVol Padres Volpe
PalSprAC Palm Springs Angels Classic/Best
PalSprACLC Palm Springs Angels Cal League Cards
PalSprAF Palm Springs Angels Fleer/ProCards
PalSprAP Palm Springs Angels ProCards
PalSprAS Palm Springs Angels Smokey
PalSprP Palm Springs ProCards
PalStaP Pallos Stadium Postcards
PanAmTUBI Pan Am Team USA Blue INDEP
PanAmTURB Pan Am Team USA Red BDK
PanCanT1 Panini Canadian Top 15
PanFreS Panini French Stickers
PanSti Panini Stickers
PAORelT PAO Religious Tracts
PapGinD Papa Gino's Discs
Par Parkhurst
ParPatF Parramatta Patriots Futera
ParSpo Parade Sportive *
PatRut Pathe Ruth
PawRedS Pawtucket Red Sox Best
PawRedSC Pawtucket Red Sox CMC
PawRedSDD Pawtucket Red Sox Dunkin' Donuts
PawRedSF Pawtucket Red Sox Fleer/ProCards
PawRedSLD Pawtucket Red Sox Line Drive
PawRedSP Pawtucket Red Sox ProCards
PawRedSQ Pawtucket Red Sox Q-Cards
PawRedSS Pawtucket Red Sox SkyBox
PawRedST Pawtucket Red Sox TCMA
PawRedSTI Pawtucket Red Sox Dunkin' Donuts
PawRedSTI Pawtucket Red Sox Team Issue
PawRedTI Pawtucket Red Sox Team Issue
PC7AlbHoF Albertype Hall of Fame PC754-2
PC7HFGSS H.F. Gardner Sports Stars PC768 *
PC7HHB H.H. Bregstone PC743
PC7JM J.D. McCarthy PC753
PCLPin PCL Pins
PebBea Pebble Beach
PenOil Peninsula Oilers
PenOil Peninsula Oilers Team Issue
PenOilTI Peninsula Oilers Team Issue
PenPilBT Peninsula Pilots B/W TCMA
PenPilC Peninsula Pilots Classic/Best
PenPilCT Peninsula Pilots Color TCMA
PenPilF Peninsula Pilots Fleer/ProCards
PenPilP Peninsula Pilots ProCards
PenPilS Peninsula Pilots Star
PenWhiSP Peninsula White Sox ProCards
PeoChi Peoria Chiefs Best
PeoChiB Peoria Chiefs Best
PeoChiC Peoria Chiefs Classic
PeoChiC Peoria Chiefs Classic/Best
PeoChiCTI Peoria Chiefs Earl Cunningham Team Issue
PeoChiF Peoria Chiefs Fleer/ProCards
PeoChiM Peoria Chiefs Multi-Ad
PeoChiP Peoria Chiefs ProCards
PeoChiPW Peoria Chiefs Pizza World
PeoChiTI Peoria Chiefs Team Issue
PeoChiUTI Peoria Chiefs Update Team Issue
PeoSunF Peoria Suns Fritsch
PeoT21 People's T216
Pep Pepsi
PepCan Pepsi Canseco
PepDieM Pepsi Diet MSA
PepGloD Pepsi Glove Discs
PepGri Pepsi Griffeys
PepMcG Pepsi McGwire
PepRicH Pepsi Rickey Henderson
PepRicHD Pepsi Rickey Henderson Discs
PepSidF Pepsi Sid Fernandez
PepSup Pepsi Superstar
PerAll Perma-Graphic All-Stars
PerAllG Perma-Graphic All-Stars Gold
PerAllG Perma-Graphics All-Stars Gold
PerCelP Perez-Steele Celebration Postcards
PerCreC Perma-Graphic Credit Cards
PerCreCG Perma-Graphic Credit Cards Gold
PerGamC Perfect Game Canseco
PerGamGJ Perfect Game Griffey Jr.
PerGreM Perez-Steele Great Moments
PerHaloFP Perez-Steele Hall of Fame Postcards
PerHaloFPS Perez-Steele Hall of Fame Postcards Signed
PerHeaF Perth Heat Futera
PerMasW Perez-Steele Master Works
PetSta Petro-Canada Standups
Pew Sports Legends
PheGiaCr Phoenix Giants Cramer
Phi Phillies
Phi195T Phillies 1950 TCMA
PhiArcO Phillies Arco Oil
PhiBul Philadelphia Bulletin
PhiBul Philadelphia Bulletin *
PhiBurK Phillies Burger King
PhiCarE Philadelphia Caramel E95
PhiCarE Philadelphia Caramel E96
PhiCha Phillies Champion
PhiCIG Phillies CIGNA
PhiCopQ Phillies Copi Quik
PhiDaiN Philadelphia Daily News *
PhiFav Philadelphia Favorites
PhiGreT Phillies Greats TCMA
PhiJayP Phillies Jay Publishing
PhiJohP Phillies Johnny Pro
PhiKel Phillies Keller's
PhiLumPB Phillies Lummis Peanut Butter
PhiMed Phillies Medford
PhiMel Phillies Mellon
PhiPhiB Phillies Philadelphia Bulletin
PhiPhil Phillies Philadelphia Inquirer
PhiPhiP Phillies Postcards
PhiPol Phillies Police
PhiPos Phillies Postcards
PhiPosGM Phillies Postcards Great Moments
PhiPosGPaM Phillies Postcards Great Players and

	Managers
PhiProPS	Phillies Promotional Photo Sheet
PhiStaC	Phillies Stadium Club
PhiTas	Phillies Tastykake
PhiTeal	Phillies Team Issue
PhiTeaS	Phillies Team Set
PhiTopAS	Phillies Topps Ashburn Sheet
PhiUSPC	Phillies U.S. Playing Cards
PhoFilHoF	Photo File Hall of Fame
PhoFilR	Photo File Ryan
PhoFirB	Phoenix Firebirds Best
PhoFirC	Phoenix Firebirds CMC
PhoFirDTTI	Phoenix Firebirds/Giants Dream Team Team Issue
PhoFirF	Phoenix Firebirds Fleer/ProCards
PhoFirLD	Phoenix Firebirds Line Drive
PhoFirP	Phoenix Firebirds ProCards
PhoFirS	Phoenix Firebirds SkyBox
PhoFirTI	Phoenix Firebirds Team Issue
PhoGiaBHN	Phoenix Giants Baseball Hobby News
PhoGiaC	Phoenix Giants Caruso
PhoGiaC	Phoenix Giants Cramer
PhoGiaCa	Phoenix Giants Caruso
PhoGiaCC	Phoenix Giants Coca Cola
PhoGiaCC	Phoenix Giants Cramer Coke
PhoGiaCK	Phoenix Giants Circle K
PhoGiaCP	Phoenix Giants Coke Premium
PhoGiaVNB	Phoenix Giants Valley National Bank
PicCle	Pictureform Clemente
PieBolWB	Piedmont Boll Weevils Best
PieBolWM	Piedmont Boll Weevils Multi-Ad
PiePhiF	Piedmont Phillies Fleer/ProCards
PieStaT	Piedmont Stamps T330-2
Pil69G	Pilots 69 Galasso
PilPos	Pilots Post-Intelligencer
PilPosR	Pilots Post-Intelligencer Reprints
PilWhe	Pilots Wheeldon
Pin	Pinheads
Pin	Pinnacle
PinAfi	Pinnacle Aficionado
PinAfiAP	Pinnacle Aficionado Artist's Proofs
PinAfiFPP	Pinnacle Aficionado First Pitch Preview
PinAfiMN	Pinnacle Aficionado Magic Numbers
PinAfiP	Pinnacle Aficionado Promos
PinAfiR	Pinnacle Aficionado Rivals
PinAfiSP	Pinnacle Aficionado Slick Picks
PinAllFP	Pinnacle All-Star FanFest Promos
PinArtP	Pinnacle Artist's Proofs
PinArtP	Pinnacle Starburst Artist's Proofs
PinCar	Pinnacle Cardfrontations
PinCer	Pinnacle Certified
PinCerCMGT	Pinnacle Certified Certified Mirror Gold Team
PinCerCT	Pinnacle Certified Certified Team
PinCerLI	Pinnacle Certified Lasting Impressions
PinCerMBla	Pinnacle Certified Mirror Black
PinCerMBlu	Pinnacle Certified Mirror Blue
PinCerMG	Pinnacle Certified Mirror Gold
PinCerMR	Pinnacle Certified Mirror Red
PinCerR	Pinnacle Certified Red
PinChrBC	Pinnacle Christie Brinkley Collection
PinCoo	Pinnacle Cooperstown
PinCooD	Pinnacle Cooperstown Dufex
PinDiM	Pinnacle DiMaggio
PinDiMA	Pinnacle DiMaggio Autographs
PinEpixGE	Pinnacle Epix Game Emerald
PinEpixGO	Pinnacle Epix Game Orange
PinEpixGP	Pinnacle Epix Game Purple
PinEpixME	Pinnacle Epix Moment Emerald
PinEpixMO	Pinnacle Epix Moment Orange
PinEpixMP	Pinnacle Epix Moment Purple
PinEpixPE	Pinnacle Epix Play Emerald
PinEpixPO	Pinnacle Epix Play Orange
PinEpixPP	Pinnacle Epix Play Purple
PinEpixSE	Pinnacle Epix Season Emerald
PinEpixSO	Pinnacle Epix Season Orange
PinEpixSP	Pinnacle Epix Season Purple
PinEssotG	Pinnacle Essence of the Game
PinETA	Pinnacle ETA
PinExpOD	Pinnacle Expansion Opening Day
PinFan	Pinnacle FanFest
PinFirR	Pinnacle First Rate
PinFoil	Pinnacle Foil
PinGatA	Pinnacle Gate Attractions
PinHitIH	Pinnacle Hit It Here
PinHitiHS	Pinnacle Hit It Here Samples
PinHom	Pinnacle Home/Away
PinHomRC	Pinnacle Home Run Club
PinIns	Pinnacle Inside
PinInsBtN	Pinnacle Inside Behind the Numbers
PinInsC	Pinnacle Inside Cans
PinInsCE	Pinnacle Inside Club Edition
PinInsCG	Pinnacle Inside Cans Gold
PinInsDD	Pinnacle Inside Dueling Dugouts
PinInsDE	Pinnacle Inside Diamond Edition
PinInsFS	Pinnacle Inside 40 Something
PinInsSG	Pinnacle Inside Stand-Up Guys
PinInsSGS	Pinnacle Inside Stand-Up Guys Samples
PinMan	Pinnacle Mantle
PinMin	Pinnacle Mint
PinMinB	Pinnacle Mint Bronze
PinMinBM	Pinnacle Mint Benefactor Mail-Away
PinMinCB	Pinnacle Mint Coins Brass
PinMinCBAP	Pinnacle Mint Coins Brass Artist's Proofs
PinMinCBS	Pinnacle Mint Coins Brass Samples
PinMinCG	Pinnacle Mint Coins Gold-Plated
PinMinCGP	Pinnacle Mint Coins Gold Plated
PinMinCGPAP	Pinnacle Mint Coins Gold Plated Artist's Proofs
PinMinCGR	Pinnacle Mint Coins Gold Redemption
PinMinCN	Pinnacle Mint Coins Nickel
PinMinCNAP	Pinnacle Mint Coins Nickel Artist's Proofs
PinMinCSGR	Pinnacle Mint Coins Solid Gold Redemption
PinMinCSS	Pinnacle Mint Coins Solid Silver
PinMinDC	Pinnacle Mint
PinMinG	Pinnacle Mint Gold
PinMinMCSS	Pinnacle Mint Coins Solid Silver
PinMinMG	Pinnacle Mint Mint Gems
PinMinMGC	Pinnacle Mint Mint Gems Coins
PinMinS	Pinnacle Mint Samples
PinMinS	Pinnacle Mint Silver
PinMusC	Pinnacle Museum Collection
PinNewB	Pinnacle New Blood
PinNewG	Pinnacle New Generation
PinPasttM	Pinnacle Passport to the Majors
PinPer	Pinnacle Performers
PinPerBB	Pinnacle Performers Big Bang
PinPerBBSamp	Pinnacle Performers Big Bang Samples
PinPerBBSO	Pinnacle Performers Big Bang Seasonal Outburst
PinPerLP	Pinnacle Performers Launching Pad
PinPerPP	Pinnacle Performers Peak Performers
PinPerPT	Pinnacle Performers Power Trip
PinPerSftF	Pinnacle Performers Swing for the Fences
PinPerSftFPC	Pinnacle Performers Swing for the Fences Point Cards
PinPerSftFShop	Pinnacle Performers Swing for the Fences Shop Exchange
PinPin	Pinnacle Pins

PinPinR	Pinnacle Pin Redemption
PinPlu	Pinnacle Plus
PinPluAE	Pinnacle Plus All-Star Epix
PinPluAEE	Pinnacle Plus All-Star Epix Emerald
PinPluAEP	Pinnacle Plus All-Star Epix Purple
PinPluAP	Pinnacle Plus Artist's Proofs
PinPluGAP	Pinnacle Plus Gold Artist's Proofs
PinPluLM	Pinnacle Plus Lasting Memories
PinPluMAP	Pinnacle Plus Mirror Artist's Proofs
PinPluPieGame	Pinnacle Plus Piece of the Game
PinPluSamp	Pinnacle Plus Samples
PinPluTP	Pinnacle Plus Team Pinnacle
PinPluTPG	Pinnacle Plus Team Pinnacle Gold
PinPluTPM	Pinnacle Plus Team Pinnacle Mirror
PinPluY	Pinnacle Plus Yardwork
PinPow	Pinnacle Power
PinPowPJ	Pinnacle Power Pack Jumbos
PinPowPJS	Pinnacle Power Pack Jumbos Samples
PinPowS	Pinnacle Power Surge
PinPreP	Pinnacle Press Plates
PinPrePla	Pinnacle Press Plate Previews
PinProS	Pinnacle Project Stardom
PinRedH	Pinnacle Red Hot
PinRoo	Pinnacle Rookies
PinRooI	Pinnacle Rookie Idols
PinRooTP	Pinnacle Rookie Team Pinnacle
PinRunC	Pinnacle Run Creators
PinSam	Pinnacle Samples
PinSha	Pinnacle Shades
PinSky	Pinnacle Skylines
PinSlu	Pinnacle Slugfest
PinSna	Pinnacle Snapshots
PinSnaS	Pinnacle Snapshots Samples
PinSpe	Pinnacle Spellbound
PinSta	Pinnacle Starburst
PinT-5	Pinkerton T5
PinTea2	Pinnacle Team 2000
PinTea2	Pinnacle Team 2001
PinTeaP	Pinnacle Team Pinnacle
PinTeaS	Pinnacle Team Spirit
PinTeaT	Pinnacle Team Tomorrow
PinTheN	Pinnacle The Naturals
PinTotCPB	Pinnacle Totally Certified Platinum Blue
PinTotCPG	Pinnacle Totally Certified Platinum Gold
PinTotCPR	Pinnacle Totally Certified Platinum Red
PinTotCS	Pinnacle Totally Certified Samples
PinTri	Pinnacle Tribute
PinUnc	Pinnacle Uncut
PinUps	Pinnacle Upstarts
PinWhiH	Pinnacle White Hot
PinX-P	Pinnacle X-Press
PinX-PF&A	Pinnacle X-Press Far and Away
PinX-PMoS	Pinnacle X-Press Men of Summer
PinX-PMP	Pinnacle X-Press Melting Pot
PinX-PMW	Pinnacle X-Press Metal Works
PinX-PMWG	Pinnacle X-Press Metal Works Gold
PinX-PMWS	Pinnacle X-Press Metal Works Silver
PinX-PreMPS	Pinnacle X-Press Melting Pot Samples
PinX-PSfF	Pinnacle X-Press Swing for the Fences
PinX-PSfFU	Pinnacle X-Press Swing for the Fences Upgrade
Pir	Pirates
Pir196T	Pirates 1960 TCMA
PirActP	Pirates Action Photos
PirAmeCE	Pirates American Caramels E90-2
PirArc	Pirates Arco Oil
PirBloP	Pirates Blockbuster Pins
PirCocP	Pirates Coca-Cola Pogs
PirEasH	Pirates East Hills
PirFanT	Pirates FanFest Tokens
PirFil	Pirates Filmet
PirGre	Pirates Greiner
PirGreT	Pirates Greats TCMA
PirHerICP	Pirates Hermes Ice Cream Pins
PirHil	Pirates Hills
PirHomC	Pirates Homers Cookies
PirIDL	Pirates IDL
PirJacitB	Pirates Jack in the Box
PirJayP	Pirates Jay Publishing
PirKDK	Pirates KDKA
PirNatl	Pirates Nationwide Insurance
PirPos	Pirates Postcards
PirPosG	Pirates Post-Gazette
PirPosP	Pirates Post-Gazette Portraits
PirQui	Pirates Quintex
PirRigF	Pirates Riger Ford
PirTag	Pirates Tag-Ons
PirTCM1WC	Pirates 1960 World Champions TCMA
PirTeal	Pirates Team Issue
PirTipTD	Pirates Tip-Top D322
PirVerFJ	Pirates Very Fine Juice
PitCubP	Pittsfield Cubs ProCards
PitMet	Pittsfield Mets Best
PitMetB	Pittsfield Mets Best
PitMetC	Pittsfield Mets Classic
PitMetC	Pittsfield Mets Classic/Best
PitMetF	Pittsfield Mets Fleer/ProCards
PitMetM	Pittsfield Mets Multi-Ad
PitMetP	Pittsfield Mets ProCards
PitMetP	Pittsfield Mets Pucko
PitMetS	Pittsfield Mets Star
PitMetTI	Pittsfield Mets Team Issue
PitPirP	Pirates Postcards
PitPosH	Pitch Postcards HOF
PKKGriNP	PKK Griffey National Promo
PlaBal	Play Ball R334
PlaBal	Play Ball R335
PlaBal	Play Ball R336
PlaClu#D	Players Club #1 Die-Cuts *
PlaClu*	Players Club *
PlaCluPB	Players Club Play Backs *
PlaGriJ	Playball Griffey Jr.
PlaMat	Playball Mattingly
PlaMatG	Playball Mattingly Gold
PlaPri	PlayMakers Prints
PlaStr	Playball Strawberry
PlaWilC	Playball Will Clark
PloCanE	Plow's Candy E300
PM1StaP1	PM10 Stadium Pins 1 3/4'
PMGol	PM Gold
PMGolB	PM Gold Bench
PMGolCP	PM Gold Card Prototype
PMGolRP	PM Gold Ruth Prototype
PocGiaP	Pocatello Giants ProCards
PocGiaTB	Pocatello Giants The Bon
PocPioP	Pocatello Pioneers ProCards
PocPioSP	Pocatello Pioneers Sports Pro
PocPosF	Pocatello Posse Fleer/ProCards
PocPosSP	Pocatello Posse Sports Pro
PolAve	Police Avery
PolGroW	Polo Grounds WG4
PolMcG	Police McGwire
PolMet	Police Mets/Yankees
PomBlaBNLP	Pomegranate Black Ball Negro League Postcards
PomBlaBPB	Pomegranate Black Ball Postcard Book
PomNegLB	Pomegranate Negro League Bookmarks
PorandAR	Portraits and Action R315
PorandAR	Portraits and Action R316
PorBeaC	Portland Beavers CMC
PorBeaC	Portland Beavers Cramer
PorBeaF	Portland Beavers Fleer/ProCards

PorBeaLD	Portland Beavers Line Drive
PorBeaP	Portland Beavers Pins
PorBeaP	Portland Beavers ProCards
PorBeaS	Portland Beavers SkyBox
PorBeaT	Portland Beavers TCMA
PorChaRP	Port Charlotte Rangers ProCards
PorCitRB	Port City Roosters Best
PorCitRTI	Port City Roosters Team Issue
PorRocB	Portland Rockies Best
PorRocG	Portland Rockies Grandstand
PorSeaD	Portland Sea Dogs Best
PorSeaD5AQ	Portland Sea Dogs 5th Anniversary Q-Cards
PorSeaDB	Portland Sea Dogs Best
PorSeaDF	Portland Sea Dogs Fleer/ProCards
PorSeaDQ	Portland Sea Dogs Q-Cards
PorSeaDTI	Portland Sea Dogs Team Issue
Pos	Post
Pos	Post *
PosCan	Post Canadian
PosGarT	Post Garvey Tips
PreCon	Premier Concepts
PriDevR	Princeton Devil Rays Team Issue
PriPatD	Princeton Patriots Diamond
PriPirS	Princeton Pirates Star
PriRedC	Princeton Reds Classic
PriRedC	Princeton Reds Classic/Best
PriRedF	Princeton Reds Fleer/ProCards
PriRedP	Princeton Reds ProCards
PriWilC	Prince William Cannons Best
PriWilCASM	Prince William Cannons Anniversary Set Multi-Ad
PriWilCB	Prince William Cannons Best
PriWilCC	Prince William Cannons Classic
PriWilCC	Prince William Cannons Classic/Best
PriWilCF	Prince William Cannons Fleer/ProCards
PriWilCP	Prince William Cannons ProCards
PriWilCQ	Prince William Cannons Q-Cards
PriWilCS	Prince William Cannons Star
PriWilCTI	Prince William Cannons Team Issue
PriWilPP	Prince William Pirates ProCards
PriWilPT	Prince William Pirates TCMA
PriWilYP	Prince William Yankees ProCards
PriWilYS	Prince William Yankees Star
Pro	ProMint
Pro22KGB	ProMint 22K Gold Bonds
ProAaA	ProCards A and AA
ProAAAF	ProCards AAA
ProFS7	ProCards
ProMag	Pro Mags
ProMagA	Pro Mags All-Stars
ProMagDM	Pro Mags Die Cuts
ProMagP	Pro Mags Promo
ProPizC	Pro's Pizza Chicago
ProSta	Pro Stamps
ProStaP	Pro Stars Postcards
PubIntS	Publications International Stickers
PucSigN	Puckett Sight Night
PulBraB	Pulaski Braves Best
PulBraC	Pulaski Braves Classic/Best
PulBraF	Pulaski Braves Fleer/ProCards
PulBraP	Pulaski Braves ProCards
QuaBabRP	Quaker Babe Ruth Pin
QuaCitAB	Quad City Angels Best
QuaCitAC	Quad City Angels Classic/Best
QuaCitAGS	Quad City Angels Grand Slam
QuaCitAP	Quad City Angels ProCards
QuaCitAT	Quad City Angels TCMA
QuaCitCT	Quad City Cubs TCMA
QuaCitRB	Quad City River Bandits Best
QuaCitRBB	Quad City River Bandits Best
QuaCitRBC	Quad City River Bandits Classic
QuaCitRBC	Quad City River Bandits Classic/Best
QuaCitRBF	Quad City River Bandits Fleer/ProCards
QuaCitRBG	Quad City River Bandits Grandstand
QuaCitRBTI	Quad City River Bandits Team Issue
QuaGra	Quaker Granola
QuaOatR	Quaker Oats Ruth
R && NNTW	R and N Ted Williams Porcelain
R31PasP	R312 Pastel Photos
R31Pre	R311 Premiums
R33So2	R337 Series Of 24
R42SmaS	R423 Small Strip
RaiFooW	Rainbow Foods Winfield
RalPur	Ralston Purina
RamT20	Ramly T204
RanAffF	Rangers Affiliated Food
RanAllP	Rangers All-Stars Pins
RanBurK	Rangers Burger King
RanComS	Rangers Commemorative Sheet
RanCra	Rangers Crayola
RanCucQB	Rancho Cucamonga Quakes Best
RanCucQC	Rancho Cucamonga Quakes Classic
RanCucQC	Rancho Cucamonga Quakes Classic/Best
RanCucQF	Rancho Cucamonga Quakes Fleer/ProCards
RanCucQG	Rancho Cucamonga Quaker GTE
RanCucQG	Rancho Cucamonga Quakes Grandstand
RanCucQT	Rancho Cucamonga Quakes Team Issue
RanCucQUG	Rancho Cucamonga Quakes Update Grandstand
RanCup	Rangers Cups
RanDr P	Rangers Dr Pepper
RanDrP	Rangers Dr. Pepper
RanFle	Rangers Fleer
RanGreT	Rangers Greats TCMA
RanJarP	Rangers Jarvis Press
RanKee	Rangers Keebler
RanLit	Rangers Lite
RanMagM	Rangers Magic Marker
RanMinM	Rangers Minyard Magnets
RanMot	Rangers Mother's
RanPer	Rangers Performance
RanPinM	Rangers Pins MBNA
RanPos	Rangers Postcards
RanSco	Rangers Score
RanScoPl	Rangers Score Platinum
RanScoPr	Rangers Score Premier
RanSmo	Rangers Smokey
RanStaC	Rangers Stadium Club
RanTeal	Rangers Team Issue
raPho	Braves Photos
Rav1stIG	Rangers 1st Interleague Game
Raw	Rawlings
RawActT	Rawlings Activewear Tags
RawActTS	Rawlings Activewear Tags Seaver
RawGloT	Rawling's Glove Tags
RawGloT	Rawlings Glove Tags
RawMus	Rawlings Musial
RCColC	RC Cola Cans
ReaPhi	Reading Phillies Best
ReaPhiB	Reading Phillies Best
ReaPhiELC	Reading Phillies Eastern League Champions Team Issue
ReaPhiF	Reading Phillies Fleer/ProCards
ReaPhiLD	Reading Phillies Line Drive
ReaPhiM	Reading Phillies Multi-Ad
ReaPhiP	Reading Phillies ProCards
ReaPhiS	Reading Phillies SkyBox
ReaPhiS	Reading Phillies Star
ReaPhiT	Reading Phillies TCMA
ReaPhiTI	Reading Phillies Team Issue

ReaPhiUM	Reading Phillies Update Multi-Ad
ReaRem	Reading Remembers
Red196T	Reds 1961 TCMA
Red76K	Reds '76 Klosterman
RedBarD	Red Barn Discs
RedBor	Reds Borden's
RedBurB	Reds Burger Beer
RedBurBP	Reds Burger Beer Photos
RedCarP	Reds Cartoons Parker
RedCok	Reds Coke
RedCroT	Red Cross T215
RedEnq	Reds Enquirer
RedF	Red Foley
RedFol	Red Foley
RedFolMI	Red Foley's Magazine Inserts
RedFolS	Red Foley Stickers
RedFolSB	Red Foley Sticker Book
RedFreBC	Reds French Bauer Caps
RedGreT	Reds Greats TCMA
RedHeaF	Red Heart
RedIceL	Reds Icee Lids
RedJayP	Reds Jay Publishing
RedKah	Reds Kahn's
RedKro	Reds Kroger
RedMan	Red Man
RedOraW	Reds Orange/Gray W711-1
RedParC	Reds Parker Classic
RedPep	Reds Pepsi
RedPioT	Redwood Pioneers TCMA
RedShiBS	Reds Shillito's Boys Shop
RedSoh	Reds Sohio
RedSox	Red Sox
RedSox1T	Red Sox 1946 TCMA
RedSoxA	Red Sox Arco Oil
RedSoxAO	Red Sox Arco Oil
RedSoxBASP	Red Sox Boston American Series PC742-1
RedSoxBDASP	Red Sox Boston Daily American Souvenir PC742-2
RedSoxBG2S	Red Sox Boston Globe
RedSoxC	Red Sox Coke
RedSoxCL	Red Sox Clark Locksmith
RedSoxCPPC	Red Sox Color Photo Post Cards
RedSoxDD	Red Sox Dunkin' Donuts
RedSoxEF	Red Sox Early Favorites
RedSoxFNSMS	Red Sox First National Super Market Stores
RedSoxGT	Red Sox Greats TCMA
RedSoxJP	Red Sox Jay Publishing
RedSoxP	Red Sox Pepsi
RedSoxP	Red Sox Postcards
RedSoxS	Red Sox Score
RedSoxSAP	Red Sox Sports Action Postcards
RedSoxSM	Red Sox Star Market
RedSoxSP	Red Sox Score Platinum
RedSoxSPI	Red Sox Score Platinum
RedSoxSPr	Red Sox Score Premier
RedSoxTI	Red Sox Team Issue
RedSoxTI	Red Sox Team Issue Color
RedSoxUP	Red Sox Union Pins
RedSoxWHP	Red Sox Winter Haven Police
RedStoPaS	Red Stockings Peck and Snyder
RedSunT	Red Sun T211
RedTeaI	Reds Team Issue
RedTexG	Reds Texas Gold
RedVolC	Reds Volpe Tumblers
RedWinA	Red Wing Aces/Scarlets
RedWorCP	Reds World's Champions PCs
RedYea	Reds Yearbook
RegGloT	Regent Glove Tags
RelPam	Religious Pamphlet
RemBre	Remar Bread
RemUltK	Rembrandt Ultra-Pro Karros
RemUltP	Rembrandt Ultra-Pro Piazza
RemUltP	Rembrandt Ultra-Pro Promos
RemUltPP	Rembrandt Ultra Pro Piazza
RemUltPP	Rembrandt Ultra-Pro Piazza Promos
RenSilSCLC	Reno Silver Sox Cal League Cards
ReqKP	Yankee Requena K Postcards
ReuCysF	Reuss Cystic Fibrosis
Rev	Revolution
RevDiaL	Revolution Diamond Legacy
RevFouP	Revolution Foul Pole
RevLeg1	Revolutionary Legends 1
RevMLBIcon	Revolution MLB Icons
Revo	Revolution
RevoFP	Revolution Foul Pole
RevoMLI	Revolution Major League Icons
RevoPTP	Revolution Prime Time Performers
RevoRooHH	Revolution Rookies and Hardball Heroes
RevoRooHHG	Revolution Rookies and Hardball Heroes Gold
RevoShow	Revolution Showstoppers
RevoSS	Revolution Shadow Series
RevPremDate	Revolution Premiere Date
RevRet	Revolution Red
RevShaSS	Revolution Shadow Series
RevSup1	Revolutionary Superstars 1
RevThoitS	Revolution Thorn in the Side
RevTri	Revolution Tripleheader
RevTri	Revolution Tripleheader Tiers
RicBra	Richmond Braves Best
RicBra2ATI	Richmond Braves 25th Anniversary Team Issue
RicBraB	Richmond Braves Best
RicBraBB	Richmond Braves Bleacher Bums
RicBraBC	Richmond Braves Bob's Camera
RicBraC	Richmond Braves CMC
RicBraC	Richmond Braves Crown
RicBraF	Richmond Braves Fleer/ProCards
RicBraLD	Richmond Braves Line Drive
RicBraP	Richmond Braves Pepsi
RicBraP	Richmond Braves ProCards
RicBraQ	Richmond Braves Q-Cards
RicBraRC	Richmond Braves Richmond Camera
RicBraRC	Richmond Braves Richmond Comix
RicBraS	Richmond Braves SkyBox
RicBraT	Richmond Braves TCMA
RicBraTI	Richmond Braves Team Issue
RicBraUB	Richmond Braves Update Best
RinPosC	Rini Postcards Clemente
RinPosG	Rini Postcards Gehrig
RinPosM	Rini Postcards Mattingly 1
RinPosM	Rini Postcards Munson
RinPosM2	Rini Postcards Mattingly II
RinPosR1	Rini Postcards Ryan 1
RinPosR2	Rini Postcards Ryan 2
RitCE	Rittenhouse Candy E285
RivPilCLC	Riverside Pilots Cal League Cards
RivRedWB	Riverside Red Wave Best
RivRedWCLC	Riverside Red Wave Cal League Cards
RivRedWP	Riverside Red Wave ProCards
RobGouS	Robert Gould Statues
RobGouW	Robert Gould W605
RocAarP	Rockstad Aaron Poster
RocCok	Rockies Coke/7-11
RocCub	Rockford Cubs Best
RocCubM	Rockford Cubbies Multi-Ad
RocCubTI	Rockford Cubbies Team Issue
RocCubTI	Rockford Cubs Team Issue
RocExpC	Rockford Expos Classic/Best
RocExpF	Rockford Expos Fleer/ProCards

RocExpLC	Rockford Expos Litho Center
RocExpP	Rockford Expos ProCards
RocFle	Rockies Fleer
RocPE3	Rochester PE3
RocPol	Rockies Police
RocRedW	Rochester Red Wings Best
RocRedWB	Rochester Red Wings Best
RocRedWC	Rochester Red Wings CMC
RocRedWF	Rochester Red Wings Fleer/ProCards
RocRedWGC	Rochester Red Wings Governor's Cup
RocRedWGCP	Rochester Red Wings Governor's Cup Pucko
RocRedWLD	Rochester Red Wings Line Drive
RocRedWM	Rochester Red Wings McCurdy's
RocRedWP	Rochester Red Wings ProCards
RocRedWQ	Rochester Red Wings Q-Cards
RocRedWS	Rochester Red Wings SkyBox
RocRedWSP	Rochester Red Wings Schieble Press W745
RocRedWT	Rochester Red Wings TCMA
RocRedWTI	Rochester Red Wings Team Issue
RocRedWW	Rochester Red Wings WTF
RocRoyC	Rockford Royals Classic
RocRoyC	Rockford Royals Classic/Best
RocRoyF	Rockford Royals Fleer/ProCards
RocSco	Rockies Score
RocScoPl	Rockies Score Platinum
RocScoPr	Rockies Score Premier
RocStaC	Rockies Stadium Club
RocUSPC	Rockies U.S. Playing Cards
RosComP	Rose Company PC760
RotCP	Rotograph Co. PC782
RowExh	Rowe Exhibits
Roy	Royals
RoyAaP	Royals A and P
RoyDes	Royal Desserts
RoyGreT	Royals Greats TCMA
RoyKitCD	Royals Kitty Clover Discs
RoyMon	Royals Montreal
RoyNatP	Royals National Photo
RoyPol	Royals Police
RoyPos	Royals Postcards
RoyPre	Royal Premiums
RoyProPS	Royals Promotional Photo Sheet
RoySmo	Royals Smokey
RoySol	Royals Solon
RoySta2	Royals Star 25th
RoyStaC	Royals Stadium Club
RoyTasD	Royals Tastee Discs
RoyTeal	Royals Team Issue
RyaArlYP	Ryan Arlington Yellow Pages
RyaSSC	Ryan SSCA
S.FExaNLT	Negro League S.F. Examiner Tribute
S74Sil	S74 Silks
S81LarS	S81 Large Silks
SacSolC	Sacramento Solons Caruso
SafDis	Safelon Discs
SafSupLB	Safelon Superstar Lunch Bags
SagDis	Saga Discs
SaiSpiP	Sain Spinner Postcard
SalAngC	Salem Angels Cramer
SalAngP	Salem Angels ProCards
SalAva	Salem Avalanche Team Issue
SalAvaB	Salem Avalanche Best
SalAvaC	Salem Avalanche Choice
SalAvaTI	Salem Avalanche Team Issue
SalBucC	Salem Buccaneers Classic
SalBucC	Salem Buccaneers Classic/Best
SalBucF	Salem Buccaneers Fleer/ProCards
SalBucP	Salem Buccaneers ProCards
SalBucS	Salem Buccaneers Star
SalDodTI	Salem Dodgers Team Issue
SalLakB	Salt Lake Buzz Best
SalLakBF	Salt Lake Buzz Fleer/ProCards
SalLakBO	Salt Lake Buzz OSP
SalLakCAC	Salt Lake City Angels Caruso
SalLakCC	Salt Lake City Caruso
SalLakCGC	Salt Lake City Gulls Caruso
SalLakCGC	Salt Lake City Gulls Cramer
SalLakCGT	Salt Lake City Gulls TCMA
SalLakCTTI	Salt Lake City Trappers Team Issue
SalLakTP	Salt Lake Trappers ProCards
SalLakTSP	Salt Lake Trappers Sports Pro
SalLakTTI	Salt Lake Trappers Team Issue
SalLakTTT	Salt Lake Trappers Taco Time
SalMetC	Salada Metal Coins
SalPirT	Salem Pirates TCMA
SalPlaC	Salada Plastic Coins
SalRedBP	Salem Red Birds ProCards
SalSpuC	Salinas Spurs Classic/Best
SalSpuCLC	Salinas Spurs Cal League Cards
SalSpuF	Salinas Spurs Fleer/ProCards
SalSpuP	Salinas Spurs ProCards
SalSpuS	Salinas Spurs Smokey
SalVol	Salem-Keizer Volcanoes Grandstand
SalVolG	Salem-Keizer Volcanoes Grandstand
SanAntBT	San Antonio Brewers TCMA
SanAntBTI	San Antonio Brewers Team Issue
SanAntDTI	San Antonio Dodgers Team Issue
SanAntMB	San Antonio Missions Best
SanAntMF	San Antonio Missions Fleer/ProCards
SanAntMG	San Antonio Missions Grandstand
SanAntMGS	San Antonio Missions Grand Slam
SanAntMLD	San Antonio Missions Line Drive
SanAntMM	San Antonio Missions Multi-Ad
SanAntMP	San Antonio Missions ProCards
SanAntMS	San Antonio Missions SkyBox
SanAntMTI	San Antonio Missions Team Issue
SanBerC	San Bernardino Classic/Best
SanBerS	San Bernadino Stampede Best
SanBerS	San Bernardino Stampede Grandstand
SanBerSB	San Bernadino Spirit Best
SanBerSB	San Bernardino Spirit Best
SanBerSB	San Bernardino Stampede Best
SanBerSC	San Bernardino Spirit Classic
SanBerSC	San Bernardino Spirit Classic/Best
SanBerSCLC	San Bernadino Spirit Cal League Cards
SanBerSCLC	San Bernardino Spirit Cal League Cards
SanBerSF	San Bernardino Spirit Fleer/ProCards
SanBerSP	San Bernardino Spirit ProCards
SanBerSTI	San Bernardino Spirit Team Issue
SanBerSTIS	San Bernardino Stampede Team Issue Strips
SanCom	Sandberg Commemorative
SanDieS	San Diego State
SanDieSA3	San Diego State Aztecs 3D/Autograph Pro Image
SanDieSAAG	San Diego State Aztecs All-Time Greats
SanDieSAG	San Diego State All-Time Greats
SanDieSAS	San Diego State Aztecs Smokey
SanDieSC	San Diego Sports Collectors
SandSW	S and S WG8
SanFraGP	Giants Postcards
SanFraSTI	San Francisco Seals Team Issue
SanJosBC	San Jose Bees Colla
SanJosBP	San Jose Bees ProCards
SanJosG	San Jose Giants Best
SanJosGB	San Jose Giants Best
SanJosGC	San Jose Giants Classic
SanJosGC	San Jose Giants Classic/Best
SanJosGCLC	San Jose Giants Cal League Cards
SanJosGF	San Jose Giants Fleer/ProCards

SanJosGP	San Jose Giants ProCards
SanJosGQ	San Jose Giants Q-Cards
SanJosGS	San Jose Giants Star
SanJosMC	San Jose Missions Mr. Chef's
SanJosMJitB	San Jose Missions Jack in the Box
SanJosMMC	San Jose Missions Mr. Chef's
SarRedS	Sarasota Red Sox Best
SarRedSB	Sarasota Red Sox Best
SarRedSC	Sarasota Red Sox Classic
SarRedSF	Sarasota Red Sox Fleer/ProCards
SarWhiSC	Sarasota White Sox Classic/Best
SarWhiSCB	Sarasota White Sox Classic/Best
SarWhiSF	Sarasota White Sox Fleer/ProCards
SarWhiSP	Sarasota White Sox ProCards
SarWhiSS	Sarasota White Sox Star
SavBraT	Savannah Braves TCMA
SavCarC	Savannah Cardinals Classic
SavCarC	Savannah Cardinals Classic/Best
SavCarF	Savannah Cardinals Fleer/ProCards
SavCarP	Savannah Cardinals ProCards
SavCarT	Savannah Cardinals TCMA
SavSanB	Savannah Sandgnats Best
SavSanGM	Savannah Sand Gnats Multi-Ad
SCFOldT	SCFS Old Timers
SchDis	Schwebels Discs
SchR33	Schutter-Johnson R332
Sco	Score
Sco100RS	Score 100 Rising Stars
Sco100RS	Score Rising Stars
Sco100S	Score 100 Superstars
ScoAi	Score Airmail
ScoAll	Score All-Stars
ScoAllF	Score All-Star Fanfest
ScoAllST	Score All Score Team
ScoAllSTGJAU	Score All-Score Team Gold Jones Autograph
ScoAndJBPS	Score Andruw Jones Blister Pack Special
ScoAndJIC	Score Andruw Jones Icon Order Card
ScoArtPWB	Score Artist's Proofs White Border
ScoBigB	Score Big Bats
ScoBla	Score Blast Masters
ScoBoaAC	Autographed Collection *
ScoBoaACA	Autographed Collection Autographs *
ScoBoaACGB	Autographed Collection Game Breakers *
ScoBoaASP	All Sport PPF Revivals *
ScoBoaTS	Talk N' Sports *
ScoBoaTSE	Talk N' Sports Essentials *
ScoBoaTSPC$	Talk N' Sports Phone Cards $1 *
ScoBoaTSPC$	Talk N' Sports Phone Cards $10 *
ScoBoaTSPC$	Talk N' Sports Phone Cards $20 *
ScoBoxC	Score Box Cards
ScoBoyoS	Score Boys of Summer
ScoCar	Cardinals Score
ScoCokD	Score Coke/Hardees Discs
ScoComP	Score Complete Players
ScoComPG	Score Complete Players Gold
ScoConR	Score Contest Redemption
ScoCoo	Score Cooperstown
ScoCyc	Score Cycle
ScoDiaA	Score Diamond Aces
ScoDiM	Score DiMaggio
ScoDouGC	Score Double Gold Champs
ScoDraP	Score Draft Picks
ScoDreT	Score Dream Team
ScoDugC	Score Dugout Collection
ScoDugCAP	Score Dugout Collection Artist's Proofs
ScoDugCSamp	Score Dugout Collection Samples
ScoEpix	Score Epix
ScoFacI	Score Factory Inserts
ScoFirP	Score First Pitch
ScoFra	Score Franchise
ScoFraG	Score Franchise Glowing
ScoFutF	Score Future Franchise
ScoGlo	Score Glossy
ScoGolDT	Score Gold Dream Team
ScoGolR	Score Gold Rush
ScoGolS	Score Gold Stars
ScoHaloG	Score Hall of Gold
ScoHaloGYTE	Score Hall of Gold You Trade Em
ScoHeaotO	Score Heart of the Order
ScoHigZ	Score Highlight Zone
ScoHot1R	Score Hottest 100 Rookies
ScoHot1S	Score Hottest 100 Stars
ScoHotR	Score Hot Rookies
ScoImpP	Score Impact Players
ScoLoaL	Score Loaded Lineup
ScoMan	Score Mantle
ScoMan	Scoreboard Mantle
ScoManl	Scoreboard Mantle 7
Scomast	Scoremasters
ScoMcD	Score McDonald's
ScoNewS	Score New Season
ScoNumG	Score Numbers Game
ScoPitP	Score Pitcher Perfect
ScoPlaTS	Score Platinum Team Sets
ScoPowP	Score Power Pace
ScoPreS	Score Premium Stock
ScoPro	Score Promos
ScoProaG	Score Proctor and Gamble
ScoProP	Score/Pinnacle Promo Panels
ScoRef	Score Reflextions
ScoResC	Score Reserve Collection
ScoRoo	Score Rookie/Traded
ScoRoo	Score Rookies
ScoRooCP	Score Rookie/Traded Changing Places
ScoRooDT	Score Rookie Dream Team
ScoRooG	Score Rookie/Traded Glossy
ScoRooGR	Score Rookie/Traded Gold Rush
ScoRooS	Score Rookie/Traded Samples
ScoRooSR	Score Rookie/Traded Super Rookies
ScoRT	Score Rookie Traded
ScoRTASEpix	Score Rookie Traded All-Star Epix
ScoRTComPla	Score Rookie Traded Complete Players
ScoRTCPSamp	Score Rookie Traded Complete Players Samples
ScoRTSS	Score Rookie Traded Showcase Series
ScoRTSSAP	Score Rookie Traded Showcase Series Artist's Proofs
ScoRTSSAP1	Score Rookie Traded Showcase Series Artist's Proofs 1 of 1's
ScoRTStarGaz	Score Rookie Traded Star Gazing
ScoRul	Score Rules
ScoRulJ	Score Rules Jumbos
ScoRyaLaT	Score Ryan Life and Times
ScoSam	Score Samples
ScoShoS	Score Showcase Series
ScoShoSAP	Score Showcase Series Artist's Proofs
ScoSpoR	Score Sportflics Ryan
ScoSS	Score Showcase Series
ScoSSAP	Score Showcase Series Artist's Proofs
ScoStaaD	Score Stand and Deliver
ScoSteS	Score Stellar Season
ScoTitT	Score Titanic Taters
ScoYouS2	Score Young Superstars II
ScoYouSI	Score Young Superstars I
ScoYouTE	Score You Trade Em
ScrDC	Scrapps Die Cuts
ScrRedB	Scranton/Wilkes-Barre Red Barons Best
ScrRedB1ATI	Scranton/Wilkes-Barre Red Barons 10th Anniversary Team Issue
ScrRedBB	Scranton/Wilkes-Barre Red Barons Best
ScrRedBC	Scranton Red Barons CMC

ScrRedBF	Scranton/Wilkes-Barre Red Barons Fleer/ProCards
ScrRedBLD	Scranton Red Barons Line Drive
ScrRedBP	Scranton Red Barons ProCards
ScrRedBQ	Scranton/Wilkes-Barre Red Barons Q-Cards
ScrRedBS	Scranton/Wilkes-Barre Red Barons SkyBox
ScrRedBTI	Scranton/Wilkes-Barre Red Barons Team Issue
sDis	Customized Discs
SeaPop	Seattle Popcorn
SeaRaiC	Seattle Rainiers Cramer
SeaRaIT	Seattle Popcorn
SeaSLP	Sears-East St. Louis PC783
SeaTeal	Senators Team Issue
Sel	Select
SelAce	Select Aces
SelArtP	Select Artist's Proof
SelArtP	Select Artist's Proofs
SelBigS	Select Big Sticks
SelCanM	Select Can't Miss
SelCer	Select Certified
SelCerAP	Select Certified Artist's Proofs
SelCerC	Select Certified Checklists
SelCerCB	Select Certified Certified Blue
SelCerCR	Select Certified Certified Red
SelCerF	Select Certified Future
SelCerGT	Select Certified Gold Team
SelCerIP	Select Certified Interleague Preview
SelCerMB	Select Certified Mirror Blue
SelCerMG	Select Certified Mirror Gold
SelCerMR	Select Certified Mirror Red
SelCerPU	Select Certified Potential Unlimited 1975
SelCerPU9	Select Certified Potential Unlimited 903
SelCerS	Select Certified Samples
SelCerSF	Select Certified Select Few
SelChaR	Select Chase Rookies
SelChaS	Select Chase Stars
SelClaTF	Select Claim To Fame
SelCom	Select Company
SelCroC	Select Crown Contenders
SelDufIP	Select Dufex Insert Promos
SelEnF	Select En Fuego
SelRegG	Select Registered Gold
SelRoo	Select Rookie/Traded
SelRooA	Select Rookie Autographs
SelRooAR	Select Rookie/Traded All-Star Rookies
SelRooR	Select Rookie Revolution
SelRooS	Select Rookie Surge
SelSam	Select Samples
SelSelSamp	Select Selected Samples
SelSki	Select Skills
SelStaL	Select Stat Leaders
SelSurS	Select Sure Shots
SelTeaN	Select Team Nucleus
SelToootT	Select Tools of the Trade
SelToootTMB	Select Tools of the Trade Mirror Blue
SelTriC	Select Triple Crown
SenBarP	Senators Barr-Farnham Postcards
SenGunBP	Senators Gunther Beer PC
SenJayP	Senators Jay Publishing
SenNatPC	Senators National Photo Company
SenNewLP	Senators Newberrys Little Pro
SenOakT	Senators Oakland Tribune
SenPolP	Senators Police Pink
SenPolY	Senators Police Yellow
SenPos	Senators Postcards
SenTCM1	Senators 1924-25 TCMA
SenTeal	Senators Team Issue
SenTeal8	Senators Team Issue 8x10
SenTeal81/2	Senators Team Issue 8 1/2x 11
SenTealPW	Senators Team Issue Photos W-UNC
SenTealW	Senators Team Issue
SenTealW	Senators Team Issue W-UNC
SenUniMC	Senators Universal Match Corp.
SenWasT	Senators Washington Times
SenWri&D	Senators Wright and Ditson
SepAnoP	Sepia Anon PC796
SerSta	Sertoma Stars
Sev3DCN	Seven-Eleven 3-D Coins National
SevCoi	Seven-Eleven Coins
SevElev	Seven-Eleven
SevSluC	Seven-Eleven Slurpee Cups
SevTraC	Seven-Eleven Trading Cups
SFHaCN	S.F.Hess and Co. N338-1
SFHesCreN32	S.F. Hess and Co. Creole N321
ShaPiz	Shakey's Pizza
ShiPlaC	Shirriff Plastic Coins
ShrCap	Shreveport Captains Willis-Knighton SportsCare
ShrCapB	Shreveport Captains Best
ShrCapF	Shreveport Captains Fleer/ProCards
ShrCapFB	Shreveport Captains First Base
ShrCapLD	Shreveport Captains Line Drive
ShrCapM	Shreveport Captains Multi-Ad
ShrCapP	Shreveport Captains ProCards
ShrCapS	Shreveport Captains SkyBox
ShrCapS	Shreveport Captains Star
ShrCapT	Shreveport Captains TCMA
ShrCapWS	Shreveport Captains WK SportsCare
SigBatP	Signature Bats Promo
SigOil	Signal Oil
SigRoo	Signature Rookies
SigRooBS	Signature Rookies Bonus Signatures Draft Picks
SigRooCF	Signature Rookies Cliff Floyd
SigRooCFS	Signature Rookies Cliff Floyd Signatures
SigRooDDS	Signature Rookies Draft Day Stars
SigRooDDSS	Signature Rookies Draft Day Stars Signatures
SigRooDP	Signature Rookies Draft Picks
SigRooDPBSDP	Signature Rookies Draft Picks Bonus Signatures Draft Picks
SigRooDPS	Signature Rookies Signatures Draft Picks
SigRooFCD	Signature Rookies Flip Cards Draft Picks
SigRooFCS	Signature Rookies Flip Card Signatures Draft Picks
SigRooFD	Signature Rookies Future Dynasty
SigRooFDS	Signature Rookies Future Dynasty Signatures
SigRooG	Signature Rookies Griffey/Ryan
SigRooHP	Signature Rookies Hottest Prospects
SigRooHPMP	Signature Rookies Hottest Prospects Mail-In Promos
SigRooHPMPS	Signature Rookies Hottest Prospects Mail-In Promos Signatures
SigRooHPS	Signature Rookies Hottest Prospects Signatures
SigRooMOP	Signature Rookies Members Only Preview
SigRooMOPS	Signature Rookies Members Only Preview Signatures
SigRooMR	Signature Rookies Major Rookies
SigRooMRS	Signature Rookies Major Rookies Signatures
SigRooOHKG	Signature Rookies Old Judge Ken Griffey Jr.
SigRooOJ	Signature Rookies Old Judge
SigRooOJA	Signature Rookies Old Judge All-Stars
SigRooOJAS	Signature Rookies Old Judge All-Stars Signatures

SigRooOJHP	Signature Rookies Old Judge Hot Prospects
SigRooOJHPS	Signature Rookies Old Judge Hot Prospects Signatures
SigRooOJKGJA	Signature Rookies Old Judge Ken Griffey Jr. Signatures
SigRooOJMC	Signature Rookies Old Judge Marty Cordova
SigRooOJMR	Signature Rookies Old Judge Major Respect
SigRooOJP	Signature Rookies Old Judge Preview '95
SigRooOJPP	Signature Rookies Old Judge Peak Picks
SigRooOJPPS	Signature Rookies Old Judge Peak Picks Signatures
SigRooOJPS	Signature Rookies Old Judge Preview '95 Signatures
SigRooOJRS	Signature Rookies Old Judge Rising Stars
SigRooOJRSS	Signature Rookies Old Judge Rising Stars Signatures
SigRooOJS	Signature Rookies Old Judge Signatures
SigRooOJSS	Signature Rookies Old Judge Star Squad
SigRooOJSSS	Signature Rookies Old Judge Star Squad Signatures
SigRooOJTJD	Signature Rookies Old Judge Joe DiMaggio
SigRooOJTP	Signature Rookies Old Judge Top Prospect
SigRooOP	Signature Rookies Organizational Player of the Year
SigRooOPS	Signature Rookies Organizational Player of the Year Signatures
SigRooP	Signature Rookies Promos
SigRooP'P	Signature Rookies Preview '95 Promos
SigRooS	Signature Rookies Signatures
SigRooSig	Signature Rookies Signatures
SigRooTPD	Signature Rookies Top Prospects Draft Picks
SigRooTPS	Signature Rookies Top Prospects Signatures Draft Picks
SilHol	SilverStar Holograms
SimandSMLBL	Simon and Schuster More Little Big Leaguers
SkiBra	Skin Bracer
SkyAA F	SkyBox AA
SkyAAAF	SkyBox AAA
SkyDugA	SkyBox Dugout Axcess
SkyDugAAR	SkyBox Dugout Axcess Autograph Redemptions
SkyDugAD	SkyBox Dugout Axcess Dishwashers
SkyDugADH	SkyBox Dugout Axcess Double Header
SkyDugAFF	SkyBox Dugout Axcess Frequent Flyers
SkyDugAG	SkyBox Dugout Axcess Gronks
SkyDugAIA	SkyBox Dugout Axcess Inside Axcess
SkyDugAS	SkyBox Dugout Axcess SuperHeroes
SkyMolM	SkyBox Molten Metal
SkyMolMetAU	SkyBox Molten Metal Autograph Redemption
SkyMolMF	SkyBox Molten Metal Fusion
SkyMolMFS	SkyBox Molten Metal Fusion Sterling
SkyMolMFT	SkyBox Molten Metal Fusion Titanium
SkyMolMOA	SkyBox Molten Metal Oh Atlanta
SkyMolMX	SkyBox Molten Metal Xplosion
SkyOzzSC	SkyBox Ozzie Smith Coin
SkyPre	SkyBox Premium
SkyPreA	SkyBox Premium Autographics
SkyPreABlue	SkyBox Premium Autographics Blue Ink
SkyPreDD	SkyBox Premium Diamond Debuts
SkyPreIN	SkyBox Premium Intimidation Nation
SkyPreLB	SkyBox Premium Live Bats
SkyPreR	SkyBox Premium Rubies

SkyPreSB	SkyBox Premium Show Business
SkyPreSotG	SkyBox Premium Soul of the Game
SkyThu	SkyBox Thunder
SkyThuDial1	SkyBox Thunder Dial 1
SkyThuHip	SkyBox Thunder Hip-No-Tized
SkyThuInD	SkyBox Thunder In Depth
SkyThuRant	SkyBox Thunder Rant
SkyThuRave	SkyBox Thunder Rave
SkyThuTur	SkyBox Thunder Turbo-Charged
SkyThuUnl	SkyBox Thunder Unleashed
SkyThuwww	SkyBox Thunder www.batterz.com
SmiClo	Smith's Clothing
SmoAmeL	Smokey American League
SmoNatL	Smokey National League
SnaDeaC	Snapple Dean Chance
SocHer	Socko Hershiser
SolHug	Solons Hughes
SolSunP	Solon Sunbeam/Pureta PC759
SomandK	Sommer and Kaufman
SonGre	Sonic/Pepsi Greats
SotHalA	Sotheby's Halper Auction
Sou	Southeastern
SouAtlLAF	South Atlantic League All-Stars Fleer/ProCards
SouAtlLAGF	South Atlantic League All-Stars Fleer/ProCards
SouAtlLAGP	South Atlantic League All-Stars ProCards
SouAtlLAGS	South Atlantic League All-Stars Grand Slam
SouAtlLAGS	South Atlantic League All-Stars Grand Slam
SouAtlLAIPI	South Atlantic League All-Stars Inserts Play II
SouAtlLAPI	South Atlantic League All-Stars Play II
SouAtlLAS	South Atlantic League All-Stars Star
SouAtlLPM	South Atlantic League Prospects Multi-Ad
SouAtlTPB	South Atlantic Top Prospects Best
SouBenSH	South Bend Silver Hawks Best
SouBenSHC	South Bend Silver Hawks Classic
SouBenSHF	South Bend Silver Hawks Fleer/ProCards
SouBenSHM	South Bend Silver Hawks Multi-Ad
SouBenSHS	South Bend Silver Hawks Best
SouBenWSB	South Bend White Sox Best
SouBenWSC	South Bend White Sox Classic/Best
SouBenWSF	South Bend White Sox Fleer/ProCards
SouBenWSGS	South Bend White Sox Grand Slam
SouBenWSP	South Bend White Sox ProCards
SouCalS	Southern Cal Trojans Smokey
SouLeaAJ	Southern League All-Stars Jennings
SouLeaTP	Southern League Top Prospects Best
SouLeaTPG	Southern League Top Prospects Grandstand
SouOreAB	Southern Oregon A's Best
SouOreAC	Southern Oregon A's Classic/Best
SouOreAC	Southern Oregon Athletics Classic
SouOreAF	Southern Oregon A's Fleer/ProCards
SouOreAF	Southern Oregon Athletics Fleer/ProCards
SouOreAP	Southern Oregon A's ProCards
SouOreTB	Southern Oregon Timberjacks Best
SouOreTG	Southern Oregon Timberjacks Grandstand
SouOreTI	Southern Oregon Timberjacks Team Issue
SP	SP
SP Aut	SP Authentic
SP Aut	SP Authentic Sheer Dominance Gold
SP AutC	SP Authentic Chirography
SP AutCG	SP Authentic Chirography Gold
SP AutEF	SP Authentic Epic Figures

SP AutG3HR	SP Authentic Griffey 300th HR Redemption
SP AutHRC	SP Authentic Home Run Chronicles
SP AutR	SP Authentic Reflections
SP AutRC	SP Authentic Redemption Cards
SP AutSD	SP Authentic Sheer Dominance
SP AutSDT	SP Authentic Sheer Dominance Titanium
SP AutTrade	SP Authentic Trade Cards
SP MinDTSPE	SP Minors Destination The Show President's Edition
SP MinPE	SP Minors President's Edition
SP MinSTHPE	SP Minors Small Town Heroes President's Edition
SP SigAuto	SP Signature Autographs
SP SigAutoG	SP Signature Autographs Gold
SP SigLC	SP Signature Legendary Cuts
SP SPTSC	SP Minors Autographs
SP TopP	SP Top Prospects
SP TopPC	SP Top Prospects Chirography
SP TopPDtS	SP Top Prospects Destination the Show
SP TopPGF	SP Top Prospects Great Futures
SP TopPPE	SP Top Prospects President's Edition
SP TopPR	SP Top Prospects Retrospectives
SP TopPRAG	SP Top Prospects Retrospectives Autograph
SpaGloT	Spalding Glove Tags
SpaPhiB	Spartanburg Phillies Best
SpaPhiC	Spartanburg Phillies Classic/Best
SpaPhiF	Spartanburg Phillies Fleer/ProCards
SpaPhiP	Spartanburg Phillies ProCards
SpaPhiS	Spartanburg Phillies Star
SpaPhiT	Spartanburg Phillies TCMA
SparPhiC	Spartanburg Phillies Classic
SPAutGJ5x7	SP Authentic Game Jersey 5 x 7
SPAutHRCDC	SP Authentic Home Run Chronicles Die Cuts
SPBasH	SP Baseball Heroes
SPCha	SP Championship
SPChaCP	SP Championship Classic Performances
SPChaCPDC	SP Championship Classic Performances Die Cuts
SPChaDC	SP Championship Die Cuts
SPChaDFC	SP Championship Fall Classic
SPChaFCDC	SP Championship Fall Classic Die Cuts
SPDieC	SP Die Cuts
SpeGolSGJ	Spectrum Gold Signature Griffey Jr.
SpeGolSH	Spectrum Gold Signature Herman
SpeGolSS	Spectrum Gold Signature Seaver
SpeHOF2	Spectrum HOF II
SpeHOFI	Spectrum HOF I
SpeRya1	Spectrum Ryan 10
SpeRya2	Spectrum Ryan 23K
SpeRya5	Spectrum Ryan 5
SpeRyaTS	Spectrum Ryan Tribute Sheet
SPGamF	SP Game Film
SPGriH	SP Griffey Heroes
SPHol	SP Holoviews
SPHolDC	SP Holoviews Die Cuts
SPInsI	SP Inside Info
SPMarM	SP Marquee Matchups
SPMarMDC	SP Marquee Matchup Die Cuts
SPMin	SP Minors
SPMinDTS	SP Minors Destination The Show
SPMinSTH	SP Minors Small Town Heroes
SPML	SP Minors
SPMLA	SP Minors Autographs
SPMLDtS	SP Minors Destination the Show
SPMLMJC	SP Minors Michael Jordan Time Capsule
Spo	Sportflics
Spo	Sportflix
Spo	Sportscaster

Spo	Sportstix
SpoArtP	Sportflix Artist's Proofs
SpoBre	Spotbilt Brett
SpoCarfCOP	Sports Cards for Collectors Old-Timer Postcards
SpoComoA	Sport Company of America *
SpoCubG	Sports Cube Game *
SpoDeaP	Sportflics Dealer Panels
SpoDecG	Sportflics Decade Greats
SpoDecGS	Sportflics Decade Greats Samples
SpoDesJM	Sports Design J.D. McCarthy
SpoDesPW	Sports Design Products West
SpoDet	Sportflix Detonators
SpoDouT	Sportflix Double Take
SpoExcW	Sports Exchange W603
SpoFanA	Sportflics FanFest All-Stars
SpoGam	Sportflics Gamewinners
SpoHaloF	Sportrait Hall of Fame
SpoHamT	Sportflix Hammer Team
SpoHitP	Sportflix Hit Parade
SpoHobBG	Sports Hobbyist Baseball Greats
SpoHobFC	Sport Hobbyist Famous Cards
SpoIll	Sports Illustrated
SpoIllAC	Sports Illustrated Ad Cards*
SpoIllAM	Sports Illustrated Autographed Mini-Covers
SpoIllAuto	Sports Illustrated Autographs
SpoIllC	Sports Illustrated Covers
SpoIllCC	Sports Illustrated Cooperstown Collection
SpoIllDD	Sports Illustrated Diamond Dominators
SpoIllEC	Sports Illustrated Editor's Choice
SpoIllEE	Sports Illustrated Extra Edition
SpoIllF4	Sports Illustrated Fabulous 40's
SpoIllF4E	Sports Illustrated Fabulous 40's Extra
SpoIllFE	Sports Illustrated First Edition
SpoIllFK1	Sports Illustrated For Kids II *
SpoIllFKI	Sports Illustrated For Kids I *
SpoIllGotG	Sports Illustrated Greats of the Game
SpoIllGotGA	Sports Illustrated Greats of the Game Autographs
SpoIllGotGC	Sports Illustrated Greats of the Game Cover Collection
SpoIllGotGRB	Sports Illustrated Greats of the Game Record Breakers
SpoIllGotGRBG	Sports Illustrated Greats of the Game Record Breakers Gold
SpoIllGS	Sports Illustrated Great Shots
SpoIllH	Sports Illustrated Headliners
SpoIllODMP	Sports Illustrated Opening Day Mini Posters
SpoIllOTW	Sports Illustrated One's To Watch
SpoIllS	Sports Illustrated Stickers *
SpoIllTaN	Sports Illustrated Then and Now
SpoIllTaNA	Sports Illustrated Then and Now Autographs
SpoIllTaNAotG	Sports Illustrated Then and Now Art of the Game
SpoIllTaNAR	Sports Illustrated Then and Now Autograph Redemptions
SpoIllTaNC	Sports Illustrated Then and Now Covers
SpoIllTaNEE	Sports Illustrated Then and Now Extra Edition
SpoIllTaNGS	Sports Illustrated Then and Now Great Shots
SpoIllTaNRtC	Sports Illustrated Then and Now Road to Cooperstown
SpoIllWSF	Sports Illustrated World Series Fever
SpoIllWSFAE	Sports Illustrated World Series Fever Autumn Excellence
SpoIllWSFAEG	Sports Illustrated World Series Fever

	Autumn Excellence Gold
SpoIllWSFEE	Sports Illustrated World Series Fever Extra Edition
SpoIllWSFFE	Sports Illustrated World Series Fever First Edition
SpoIllWSFMC	Sports Illustrated World Series Fever MVP Collection
SpoIllWSFPP	Sports Illustrated World Series Fever Postcard Promo
SpoIllWSFRJP	Sports Illustrated World Series Fever Reggie Jackson's Picks
SpoIndB	Spokane Indians Best
SpoIndC	Spokane Indians Caruso
SpoIndC	Spokane Indians Classic
SpoIndC	Spokane Indians Classic/Best
SpoIndC	Spokane Indians Cramer
SpoIndF	Spokane Indians Fleer/ProCards
SpoIndG	Spokane Indians Grandstand
SpoIndGC	Spokane Indians Greats Cramer
SpoIndP	Spokane Indians ProCards
SpoIndSP	Spokane Indians Sports Pro
SpoIndT	Spokane Indians TCMA
SpoIndTI	Spokane Indians Team Issue
SpoKin	Sport Kings R338 *
SpoLifCW	Sporting Life Cabinets W600
SpoLifM	Sporting Life M116
SpoMagP	Sport Magazine Premiums *
SpoMemAG	Sports Memorabilia All-Time Greats
SpoMov	Sportflics Movers
SpoNewM	Sporting News M101-4
SpoNewM	Sporting News M101-5
SpoNewP	Sporting News PC757
SpoNewSM	Sporting News Supplements M101-2
SpoNewSM	Sporting News Supplements M101-7
SpoNSP	Sporting News Sports Page
SpoPowS	Sportflix Power Surge
SpoPro	Sportflics Prototypes
SpoPro	Sportflix ProMotion
SpoRea	Sports Reading
SpoRoo	Sportflics Rookie/Traded
SpoRoo	Sportflics Rookies
SpoRoo2	Sportflics Rookies II
SpoRooAP	Sportflics Rookie/Traded Artist's Proofs
SpoRooGGG	Sportflics Rookie/Traded Going Going Gone
SpoRooI	Sportflics Rookies I
SpoRooJ	Sportflix Rookie Jumbos
SpoRooP	Sportflics Rookie Packs
SpoRooRS	Sportflics Rookie/Traded Rookie Starflics
SpoRooS	Sportflics Rookie/Traded Samples
SpoSam	Sportflics Samples
SpoSam	Sportflix Samples
SpoScoHC	Sports Scoop HOF Candidates
SpoSha	Sportflics Shakers
SpoStaCC	Sports Stars Collector Coins
SpoSupD	Sportflics Superstar Discs
SpoTeaL	Sportflics Team Logo
SpoTeaP	Sportflics Team Preview
SpoTimM	Sporting Times M117
SPPlaP	SP Platinum Power
SPPre	SP Previews
SPPreF	SP Previews FanFest
SprCarB	Springfield Cardinals Best
SprCarC	Springfield Cardinals Classic/Best
SprCarDGB	Springfield Cardinals All Decade Best
SprCarF	Springfield Cardinals Fleer/ProCards
SprCarF	Springfield Cardinals Fritsch
SprCarP	Springfield Cardinals ProCards
SprCarT	Springfield Cardinals TCMA
SprRedWK	Springfield Redbirds Wiener King
SprSulC	Springfield Sultans Classic

SprSulF	Springfield Sultans Fleer/ProCards
SprSulTI	Springfield Sultans Team Issue
SPSig	SP Signature
SPSil	SP Silver
SPSpeF	SP Special FX
SPSpeFX	SP Special FX
SPSpeFXDC	SP Special FX Die Cuts
SPSpxF	SP SPx Force
SPSPxFA	SP SPx Force Autographs
SPVinAu	SP Vintage Autographs
SPx	SPx
SPxBoufG	SPx Bound for Glory
SPxBoufGSS	SPx Bound for Glory Supreme Signatures
SPxBro	SPx Bronze
SPxCorotG	SPx Cornerstones of the Game
SPxDom	SPx Dominance
SPxFin	SPx Finite
SPxFinHRH	SPx Finite Home Run Hysteria
SPxFinR	SPx Finite Radiance
SPxFinS	SPx Finite Sample
SPxFinS	SPx Finite Spectrum
SPxGol	SPx Gold
SPxGraF	SPx Grand Finale
SPxPowE	SPx Power Explosion
SPxPreS	SPx Premier Stars
SPxSil	SPx Silver
SPxStaF	SPx Star Focus
SPxSte	SPx Steel
SPxWinM	SPx Winning Materials
Squ	Squirt
SSP	SSPC
SSP18	SSPC 18
SSP188WS	SSPC 1887 World Series
SSP270	SSPC 270
SSP42	SSPC 42
SSPHOF	SSPC HOF
SSPPuzB	SSPC Puzzle Back
SSPSam	SSPC Samples
SSPYanOD	SSPC Yankees Old-Timers Day
St.CatBJC	St. Catharines Blue Jays Classic
St.CatBJC	St. Catharines Blue Jays Classic/Best
St.CatBJF	St. Catharines Blue Jays Fleer/ProCards
St.CatBJP	St. Catharines Blue Jays ProCards
St.CatSB	St. Catharines Stompers Best
St.CatSM	St. Catharines Stompers Multi-Ad
St.LouCP	Cardinals Postcards
St.LucM	St. Lucie Mets Best
St.LucMC	St. Lucie Mets Classic
St.LucMC	St. Lucie Mets Classic/Best
St.LucMCB	St. Lucie Mets Classic/Best
St.LucMF	St. Lucie Mets Fleer/ProCards
St.LucMM	St. Lucie Mets Multi-Ad
St.LucMP	St. Lucie Mets ProCards
St.LucMS	St. Lucie Mets Star
St.LuMF	St. Lucie Mets Fleer/ProCards
St.PauS	St. Paul Saints Team Issue
St.PauSTI	St. Paul Saints Team Issue
St.PetCC	St. Petersburg Cardinals Classic
St.PetCC	St. Petersburg Cardinals Classic/Best
St.PetCF	St. Petersburg Cardinals Fleer/ProCards
St.PetCP	St. Petersburg Cardinals ProCards
St.PetCS	St. Pete Cardinals Star
St.PetCS	St. Petersburg Cardinals Star
St.PetCT	St. Petersburg Cardinals TCMA
St.PetCTI	St. Petersburg Cardinals Team Issue
St.PetDR	St. Petersburg Devil Rays Best
St.PetDRM	St. Petersburg Devil Rays Multi-Ad
St.PetDRUB	St. Petersburg Devil Rays Update Best
St.VinHHS	St. Vincent HOF Heroes Stamps
Sta	Star

StaAbb	Star Abbott
StaAloB	Star Alomar Brothers
StaAve	Star Avery
StaAwaW	Star Award Winners
StaBag	Star Bagwell
StaBel	Star Bell
StaBel	Star Belle
StaBelRG	Star Belle Rookie Guild
StaBen	Star Benes
StaBis	Standard Biscuit
StaBlaM	Star Mattingly Blankback
StaBog	Star Boggs
StaBog	Star Boggs Hitman
StaBog/G	Star Boggs/Gwynn
StaBoJ	Star Bo Jackson
StaBre	Star Brett
StaCalL	Star Cal Large
StaCalS	Star Cal Small
StaCan	Star Canseco
StaCar	Star Carlton
StaCarE	Standard Caramel E93
StaCla	Star Clark/Grace
StaCla	Star Will Clark
StaCle	Star Clemens
StaCle	Star Clemens/Gooden
StaCle2	Star Clemens II
StaClu	Stadium Club
StaCluA	Stadium Club Autographs
StaCluB&B	Stadium Club Bash and Burn
StaCluBP	Stadium Club Bowman Previews
StaCluBPP	Stadium Club Bowman Prospect Previews
StaCluC	Stadium Club Chrome
StaCluC	Stadium Club Co-Signers
StaCluCB	Stadium Club Crystal Ball
StaCluCC	Stadium Club Clear Cut
StaCluCM	Stadium Club Charter Member *
StaCluCR	Stadium Club Chrome Refractors
StaCluCT	Stadium Club Crunch Time
StaCluD	Stadium Club Dome
StaCluDD	Stadium Club Dugout Dirt
StaCluDP	Stadium Club Draft Picks
StaCluDPFDI	Stadium Club Draft Picks First Day Issue
StaCluECN	Stadium Club East Coast National
StaCluEPB	Stadium Club Extreme Players Bronze
StaCluEPG	Stadium Club Extreme Players Gold
StaCluEPS	Stadium Club Extreme Players Silver
StaCluEWB	Stadium Club Extreme Winners Bronze
StaCluEWG	Stadium Club Extreme Winners Gold
StaCluEWS	Stadium Club Extreme Winners Silver
StaCluF	Stadium Club Finest
StaCluFDI	Stadium Club First Day Issue
StaCluFDP	Stadium Club First Draft Picks
StaCluFJ	Stadium Club Finest Jumbos
StaCluFR	Stadium Club Firebrand Redemption
StaCluFW	Stadium Club Firebrand Wood
StaCluGR	Stadium Club Golden Rainbow
StaClul	Stadium Club
StaClul	Stadium Club Inserts
StaClul	Stadium Club Instavision
StaCluITW	Stadium Club In The Wings
StaCluM	Stadium Club Millennium
StaCluM	Stadium Club Murphy
StaCluMa	Stadium Club Mantle
StaCluMat	Stadium Club Matrix
StaCluMeg	Stadium Club Megaheroes
StaCluMet	Stadium Club Metalists
StaCluMM	Stadium Club Midsummer Matchups
StaCluMMP	Stadium Club Murphy Master Photos
StaCluMO	Stadium Club Members Only
StaCluMO	Stadium Club Members Only *
StaCluMOF	Stadium Club Members Only Finest Bronze
StaCluMOP	Stadium Club Members Only Parallel
StaCluMP	Stadium Club Master Photos
StaCluNC	Stadium Club National Convention
StaCluNC	Stadium Club Never Compromise
StaCluOneK	Stadium Club One Of A Kind
StaCluOoaK	Stadium Club One of a Kind
StaCluP	Stadium Club Pre-Production
StaCluPC	Stadium Club Phone Cards
StaCluPC	Stadium Club Prime Cuts
StaCluPG	Stadium Club Pure Gold
StaCluPL	Stadium Club Patent Leather
StaCluPP	Stadium Club Power Packed
StaCluPP	Stadium Club Pre-Production
StaCluPP	Stadium Club Printing Plates
StaCluPS	Stadium Club Power Streak
StaCluPWP	Stadium Club Playing With Passion
StaCluPZ	Stadium Club Power Zone
StaCluRC	Stadium Club Royal Court
StaCluRL	Stadium Club Ring Leaders
StaCluSS	Stadium Club Super Skills
StaCluST	Stadium Club Super Teams
StaCluSTDW	Stadium Club Super Team Division Winners
StaCluSTMP	Stadium Club Super Team Master Photos
StaCluSTWS	Stadium Club Super Team World Series
StaCluT	Stadium Club Team
StaCluTA	Stadium Club TSC Awards
StaCluTF	Stadium Club Team Finest
StaCluTFDI	Stadium Club Team First Day Issue
StaCluTI	Stadium Club Triumvirate Illuminator
StaCluTIII	Stadium Club Triumvirate Illuminator
StaCluTL	Stadium Club Triumvirate Luminescent
StaCluTL	Stadium Club Triumvirate Luminous
StaCluTLme	Stadium Club Triumvirate Luminescent
StaCluTLmo	Stadium Club Triumvirate Luminous
StaCluU	Stadium Club Ultra-Pro
StaCluVE	Stadium Club Virtual Extremists
StaCluVR	Stadium Club Video Replay
StaCluVR	Stadium Club Virtual Reality
StaCluVRMO	Stadium Club Virtual Reality Members Only
StaCon	Star Cone
StaDav	Star Davis/McGwire
StaDaw	Star Dawson
StaEriD	Star Eric Davis
StaFie	Star Fielder
StaFS7	Star
StaFutS	Star Future Stars
StaGan	Star Gant
StaGar	Star Garvey
StaGarC	Star Gary Carter
StaGonRG	Star Gonzalez Rookie Guild
StaGoo	Star Gooden Orange
StaGooB	Star Gooden Blue
StaGor	Star Gordon
StaGre	Star Greenwell Red
StaGreP	Star Greenwell Purple
StaGri	Star Griffeys
StaGriJ	Star Griffey Jr.
StaGwy	Star Gwynn
StaHen	Star Henderson
StaHer	Star Hernandez
StaHer	Star Hershiser
StaHor	Star Horn
StaJef	Star Jefferies
StaJor	Star Jordan
StaJoyR	Star Joyner Red
StaJus	Star Justice

StaKarA	Star Karros Auto
StaKno	Star Knoblauch
StaLar	Star Larkin
StaLewRG	Star Lewis Rookie Guild
StaLinAl	Starting Lineup All-Stars
StaLinAn	Starting Lineup Angels
StaLinAs	Starting Lineup A's
StaLinAst	Starting Lineup Astros
StaLinBJ	Starting Lineup Blue Jays
StaLinBra	Starting Lineup Braves
StaLinBre	Starting Lineup Brewers
StaLinCa	Starting Lineup Cardinals
StaLinCu	Starting Lineup Cubs
StaLinD	Starting Lineup Dodgers
StaLinE	Starting Lineup Expos
StaLinG	Starting Lineup Giants
StaLinI	Starting Lineup Indians
StaLinMa	Starting Lineup Mariners
StaLinMe	Starting Lineup Mets
StaLinO	Starting Lineup Orioles
StaLinPa	Starting Lineup Padres
StaLinPh	Starting Lineup Phillies
StaLinPi	Starting Lineup Pirates
StaLinRa	Starting Lineup Rangers
StaLinRe	Starting Lineup Reds
StaLinRo	Starting Lineup Royals
StaLinRS	Starting Lineup Red Sox
StaLinTi	Starting Lineup Tigers
StaLinTw	Starting Lineup Twins
StaLinWS	Starting Lineup White Sox
StaLinY	Starting Lineup Yankees
StaLonJS	Starline Long John Silver
StaMaa	Star Maas
StaMat	Star Mattingly
StaMat	Star Sticker Mattingly
StaMat/S	Star Mattingly/Schmidt
StaMatW	Star Matt Williams
StaMcD	Star McDonald
StaMcG	Star McGwire
StaMcGG	Star McGwire Green
StaMcR	Star McReynolds
StaMey	Stahl Meyer
StaMit	Star Mitchell
StaMit	Star Mitchell/Yount
StaMit/C	Star Mitchell/Clark
StaMur	Star Murphy
StaNok	Star Nokes
StaoftFT	Stars of the Future TCMA
StaPal	Star Palmer
StaPinB	Starshots Pinback Badges
StaPinP2	PM10 Stadium Pins 2 1/8'
StaPla	Star Plantier
StaPlaCE	Star Player Candy E-Unc.
StaPro	Star Promos
StaPro	Starline Prototypes
StaPuc	Star Puckett
StaRai	Star Raines
StaRegJ	Star Reggie Jackson
StaRic	Star Rice
StaRip	Star Ripken
StaRya	Star Ryan
StaSab	Star Saberhagen/Davis
StaSan	Star Sandberg
StaSan	Star Santiago
StaSanA	Star Sandy Alomar
StaSch	Star Schmidt
StaSco	Star Scott
StaSea	Star Seaver
StaSei	Star Seitzer
StaSny	Star Snyder
StaStiC	Star Stickers Canseco
StaStiGB	Star Stickers George Bell
StaStiJ	Star Stickers Joyner Blue
StaStiS	Star Stickers Snyder
StaStiV	Star Sticker Valenzuela
StaStiW	Star Stickers Winfield
StaStr	Star Strawberry
StaTar	Star Tartabull
StaThoRG	Star Thomas Rookie Guild
StaTra	Star Trammell
StaVal	Star Valenzuela
StaVanP	Star Van Poppel
StaVen	Star Ventura
StaWal	Star Walton
StaWal/O	Star Walton/Olson
StaWilC	Star Will Clark
StaWin	Star Winfield
StaYou	Star Yount
StCatSB	St. Catharines Stompers Best
StCatSTI	St. Catherines Stompers Team Issue
SteDra	Sterling Dravecky
SteDugB	Stengel Dugan Brothers
StLucMTI	St. Lucie Mets Team Issue
StoPop	Stouffer Pop-ups
StoPor	Stockton Ports Best
StoPorB	Stockton Ports Best
StoPorC	Stockton Ports Classic
StoPorC	Stockton Ports Classic/Best
StoPorCLC	Stockton Ports Cal League Cards
StoPorF	Stockton Ports Fleer/ProCards
StoPorG	Stockton Ports Grandstand
StoPorP	Stockton Ports ProCards
StoPorS	Stockton Ports Star
StoPorUG	Stockton Ports Update Grandstand
StPetCB	St. Petersburg Cardinals Best
StrAll	Strat-O-Matic All-Stars
Stu	Studio
Stu8x10S	Studio 8 x 10 Samples
StuAut	Studio Autographs
StuAuto8X10	Studio Autographs 8 x 10
StuEdiC	Studio Editor's Choice
StuFF	Studio Freeze Frame
StuFFDC	Studio Freeze Frame Die Cuts
StuGolS	Studio Gold Series
StuGPP	Studio Gold Press Proofs
StuHarH	Studio Hard Hats
StuHer	Studio Heritage
StuHitP	Studio Hit Parade
StuHitPar	Studio Hit Parade
StuMas	Studio Masterstrokes
StuMasS	Studio Master Strokes
StuMasS8	Studio Master Strokes 8x10
StuMast	Studio Masterstrokes
StuPan	Stuart Panels
StuPlaS	Studio Platinum Series
StuPor8	Studio Portraits 8x10
StuPor8x10	Studio Portraits 8 x 10
StuPor8x10GP	Studio Portraits 8 x 10 Gold Proofs
StuPre	Studio Previews
StuPrePB	Studio Press Proofs Bronze
StuPrePG	Studio Press Proof Gold
StuPrePG	Studio Press Proofs Gold
StuPrePS	Studio Press Proof Silver
StuPrePS	Studio Press Proofs Silver
StuPro	Studio Promos
StuSerS	Studio Series Stars
StuSerSG	Studio Series Stars Gold
StuSil	Studio Silhouettes
StuSony99	Studio MLB 99
StuSPP	Studio Silver Press Proofs
StuStaGS	Studio Stained Glass Stars
StuSupoC	Studio Superstars on Canvas

StuTho	Studio Thomas
SubDis	Subway Discs
SucSav	Sucker Saver
Sum	Summit
Sum21C	Summit 21 Club
SumAbo&B	Summit Above and Beyond
SumArtP	Summit Artist's Proofs
SumBal	Summit Ballparks
SumBigB	Summit Big Bang
SumBigBM	Summit Big Bang Mirage
SumBraB	Sumter Braves Best
SumBraP	Sumter Braves ProCards
SumFlyC	Sumter Flyers Classic/Best
SumFlyP	Sumter Flyers ProCards
SumFoi	Summit Foil
SumHitI	Summit Hitters Inc.
SumNewA	Summit New Age
SumNthD	Summit Nth Degree
SumPos	Summit Positions
SumSam	Summit Samples
SunBre	Sunbeam Bread
SunBre	Sunbeam Bread Solons
SunPin	Sunoco Pins
SunPopK	Sun-Glo Pop Kaline
SunSee	Sunflower Seeds
SupActM	Superstar Action Marbles
SupMcDP	SuperSlam McDowell Promos
SweBasG	Swell Baseball Greats
SweCapPP	Sweet Caporal Tobacco Pins
SweSpoT	Swell Sport Thrills
SwiFra	Swifts Franks
SydWavF	Sydney Wave Futera
SyrChi	Syracuse Chiefs
SyrChi1A	Syracuse Chiefs 10th Anniversary
SyrChiC	Syracuse Chiefs CMC
SyrChiF	Syracuse Chiefs Fleer/ProCards
SyrChiK	Syracuse Chiefs Kraft
SyrChiLD	Syracuse Chiefs Line Drive
SyrChiMB	Syracuse Chiefs Merchants Bank
SyrChiP	Syracuse Chiefs ProCards
SyrChiS	Syracuse Chiefs SkyBox
SyrChiT	Syracuse Chiefs TCMA
SyrChiTI	Syracuse Chiefs Team Issue
SyrChiTT	Syracuse Chiefs Tallmadge Tire
SyrSkyCB	Syracuse Sky Chiefs Best
SyrSkyG	Syracuse Skychiefs Grandstand
T/MSenL	T/M Senior League
T/MUmp	T/M Umpires
T205	T205 Gold Border
T206	T206 White Border
T207	T207 Brown Background
T22SeroC	T227 Series of Champions
TacBan	Tacoma Bank
TacGia	Tacoma Giants
TacRai	Tacoma Rainiers Best
TacRaiB	Tacoma Rainiers Best
TacRaiQ	Tacoma Rainiers Q-Cards
TacRaiTI	Tacoma Rainers Team Issue
TacTigC	Tacoma Tigers CMC
TacTigC	Tacoma Tigers Cramer
TacTigF	Tacoma Tigers Fleer/ProCards
TacTigLD	Tacoma Tigers Line Drive
TacTigP	Tacoma Tigers ProCards
TacTigS	Tacoma Tigers SkyBox
TacTigT	Tacoma Tigers TCMA
TacTugT	Tacoma Tugs TCMA
TacTwiC	Tacoma Twins Caruso
TacTwiDQ	Tacoma Twins Dairy Queen
TacTwiK	Tacoma Twins KMMO
TacYanC	Tacoma Yankees Cramer
TamTarP	Tampa Tarpons ProCards
TamTarS	Tampa Tarpons Star
TamTarT	Tampa Tarpons TCMA
TamYan	Tampa Yankees Best
TamYanC	Tampa Yankees Classic
TamYanD	Tampa Yankees Diamond
TamYanF	Tampa Yankees Fleer/ProCards
TamYanM	Tampa Yankees Multi-Ad
TamYanY	Tampa Yankees Best
TamYanYI	Tampa Yankees Team Issue
TanBraE	Tango Brand Eggs
TarPla	Tara Plaques
TarThoBD	Tarzan Thoro Bread D382
TasDis	Tastee-Freez Discs
TatOrb	Tatoo Orbit R305
TatOrbSDR	Tatoo Orbit Self Develop R308
TayBow4	Taylor/Schmierer Bowman 47
TCM	TCMA
TCM195CI	Indians 1954 TCMA
TCM50	TCMA 50'S
TCM60I	TCMA 60'S I
TCM60I	TCMA 60's II
TCMAllG	TCMA All-Time Greats
TCMBruS	TCMA Bruce Stark Postcards
TCMGreH	TCMA Greatest Hitters
TCMGreP	TCMA Greatest Pitchers
TCMGreS	TCMA Greatest Sluggers
TCMGua	TCMA Guam
TCMHomRC	TCMA Home Run Champs
TCMHouoJ	TCMA House of Jazz
TCMJapPB	TCMA Japanese Pro Baseball
TCMLarFP	TCMA Larry French Postcards
TCMNic	TCMA Nicknames
TCMPhoC	TCMA Photo Classics
TCMPla1	TCMA Playball 1946
TCMPla1	TCMA Playball 1947
TCMPla1	TCMA Playball 1948
TCMPla1942	TCMA Playball 1942
TCMPla1943	TCMA Playball 1943
TCMPla1944	TCMA Playball 1944
TCMPla1945	TCMA Playball 1945
TCMPpl1	TCMA Playball 1949
TCMRut	TCMA Ruth
TCMStaot5	TCMA Stars of the 50's
TCMSupS	TCMA Superstars Simon
TCMthe1	TCMA the 1930's Panels
TCMthe3	TCMA's the 30's
TCMTheWY	TCMA The War Years
TCMUmp	TCMA Umpires
TeaBesR	Team Best Rookies
TeaBesR	Team Best Rookies Best Lumber
TeaBesRA	Team Best Rookies Autographs
TeaBesRBG	Team Best Rookies Best Guns
TeaBesRBW	Team Best Rookies Best Wheels
TeaBesRFS	Team Best Rookies Future Stars
TeaBesRG	Team Best Rookies Gold
TeaBesRS	Team Best Rookies Silver
TeaOut	Team Out
TedWil	Ted Williams
TedWil5C	Ted Williams 500 Club
TedWilBR	Ted Williams Brooks Robinson
TedWilDGC	Ted Williams Dan Gardiner Collection
TedWilLC	Ted Williams Locklear Collection
TedWilM	Ted Williams Memories
TedWilMS	Ted Williams Mike Schmidt
TedWilP	Ted Williams Promos
TedWilPC	Ted Williams POG Cards
TedWilRC	Ted Williams Roberto Clemente
TedWilRM	Ted Williams Roger Maris
TedWilTfB	Ted Williams Trade for Babe
TenKry	Tennessee Krystal
TenTec	Tennessee Tech

TenTecGE	Tennessee Tech Golden Eagles
TenVolW	Tennessee Volunteers Wendy's
TetTeaD	Tetley Tea Discs
Tex	Texas Longhorns
TexAllM	Texas/EL/SL All-Stars Multi-Ad
TexLeaAB	Texas League All-Stars Best
TexLeaAF	Texas League All-Stars Feder
TexLeaAGS	Texas League All-Stars Grand Slam
TexLeaTP	Texas League Top Prospects Best
TexLeaTPG	Texas League Top Prospects Grandstand
TexLon	Texas Longhorns
TexSupRS	Texas Supermarket Ryan Stickers
TexTomE	Texas Tommy E224
ThoMcAD	Thom McAn Discs
ThoMcAF	Thom McAn Feller
ThuSkySupR	SkyBox Thunder Super Rave
TidTidC	Tidewater Tides Candl
TidTidC	Tidewater Tides CMC
TidTidCa	Tidewater Tides Candl
TidTidCM	Tidewater Tides CMC
TidTidF	Tidewater Tides Fleer/ProCards
TidTidLD	Tidewater Tides Line Drive
TidTidP	Tidewater Tides ProCards
TidTidS	Tidewater Tides SkyBox
TidTidT	Tidewater Tides TCMA
TidTidTI	Tidewater Tides Team Issue
Tig	Tigers
TigACDPP	Tigers A.C. Dietsche Postcards PC765
TigAlKS	Tigers Al Kaline Story
TigBurK	Tigers Burger King
TigCaiD	Tigers Cain's Discs
TigCok	Tigers Coke
TigCok	Tigers Coke/Kroger
TigDeaCS	Tigers Dearborn Card Show
TigDetFPB	Tigers Detroit Free Press Bubblegumless
TigDetN	Tigers Detroit News
TigDexP	Tigers Dexter Press
TigDom	Tigers Domino's
TigFarJ	Tigers Farmer Jack
TigFliJ	Tigers Flint Journal
TigFreGWP	Tigers Fred G.Wright Postcards
TigFreP	Tigers Free Press
TigFreP	Tigers Free Press *
TigGat	Tigers Gatorade
TigGle	Tigers Glendale
TigGraASP	Tigers Graphic Arts Service PC749
TigGreT	Tigers Greats TCMA
TigHebN	Tigers Hebrew National
TigHMTP	Tigers H.M. Taylor PC773-2
TigJayP	Tigers Jay Publishing
TigJew	Tigers Jewel
TigKro	Tigers Kroger
TigLid	Tiger Lids
TigLitC	Tigers Little Caesars
TigMar	Tigers Marathon
TigMilH	Tigers Milk Henneman
TigMorBBBP	Tigers Morton's "Buster Brown" Bread Pins
TigMorPWBPP	Tigers Morton's "Pennant Winner" Bread Pins
TigOldTS	Tigers Old-Timers Troy Show
TigPep	Tigers Pepsi/Kroger
TigPepT	Tigers Pepsi Trammell
TigPol	Tigers Police
TigPos	Tigers Postcards
TigPosCF	Tiger Post Cards Ford
TigSecNP	Tigers Second National Plymouth
TigSpo	Tigers Sportservice
TigSpoD	Tigers Sports Design
TigTaCP	Tigers Topping and Company PC773-1
TigTCM1AC	Tigers TCMA 1934-35 AL Champions
TigTeaI	Tigers Team Issue
TigTeaIC	Tigers Team Issue Color
TigVolC	Tigers Volpe Tumblers
TigWavP	Tigers Wave Postcards
TigWen	Tigers Wendy's/Coke
TipTop	Tip Top
TobLit	Tobin Lithographs
TolMudHB	Toledo Mud Hens Best
TolMudHC	Toledo Mud Hens CMC
TolMudHF	Toledo Mud Hens Fleer/ProCards
TolMudHLD	Toledo Mud Hens Line Drive
TolMudHP	Toledo Mud Hens ProCards
TolMudHQ	Toledo Mud Hens Q-Cards
TolMudHS	Toledo Mud Hens SkyBox
TolMudHT	Toledo Mud Hens TCMA
TolMudHTI	Toledo Mud Hens Team Issue
TomBarW	Tom Barker WG6
TomPiz	Tombstone Pizza
Top	Topps
Top22kG	Topps 22k Gold
Top3-D	Topps 3-D
TopActF	Topps Action Flats
TopActFAU	Topps Action Flats Away Uniform
TopActFCU	Topps Action Flats Classic Uniform
TopActS	Topps Action Stickers
TopAll	Topps All-Matrix
TopAll	Topps All-Stars
TopAllMF	Topps All-Topps Mystery Finest
TopAme2C	Topps Ames 20/20 Club
TopAmeA	Topps Ames All-Stars
TopArc1	Topps Archives 1953
TopArc1	Topps Archives 1954
TopArc1G	Topps Archives 1954 Gold
TopArcBD	Topps Archives Brooklyn Dodgers
TopAut	Topps Autographs
TopAwaW	Topps Award Winners
TopAwel	Topps Awesome Impact
TopBabB	Topps Baby Boomers
TopBasT	Topps Baseball Talk/LJN
TopBatL	Topps Batting Leaders
TopBig	Topps Big
TopBigC	Topps Big Cards
TopBlaG	Topps Black Gold
TopBlaLC1	Topps Gold Label Class 1 Black
TopBlaLC2	Topps Gold Label Class 2 Black
TopBlaLC3	Topps Gold Label Class 3 Black
TopBluB	Topps Blue Backs
TopBluTC	Topps Blue Team Checklists
TopBoo	Topps Booklets
TopBowK	Topps Bowie Kuhn
TopBroLL	Topps Bronze League Leaders
TopBuc	Topps Bucks
TopCanL	Topps Candy Lid
TopCanL	Topps Candy Lids
TopCapC	Topps Cap'n Crunch
TopCas	Topps Cashen
TopCer	Topps Cereal
TopChr	Topps Chrome
TopChrA	Topps Chrome All-Etch
TopChrAR	Topps Chrome All-Etch Refractors
TopChrAS	Topps Chrome All-Stars
TopChrBB	Topps Chrome Baby Boomers
TopChrBBR	Topps Chrome Baby Boomers Refractors
TopChrC9	Topps Chrome Clout Nine
TopChrC9R	Topps Chrome Clout Nine Refractors
TopChrDD	Topps Chrome Diamond Duos
TopChrDDR	Topps Chrome Diamond Duos Refractors
TopChrERttH	Topps Chrome Early Road to the Hall
TopChrERttH	Topps Chrome Early Road to the Hall Refractors
TopChrF	Topps Chrome Flashback

TopChrF1 Topps Chrome Fortune 15
TopChrF1R Topps Chrome Fortune 15 Refractors
TopChrFR Topps Chrome Flashback Refractors
TopChrHB Topps Chrome HallBound
TopChrHBR Topps Chrome HallBound Refractors
TopChrJ Topps Chrome Jumbos
TopChrLotD Topps Chrome Lords of the Diamond
TopChrLotDR Topps Chrome Lords of the Diamond Refractors
TopChrM Topps Chrome Milestones
TopChrMotG Topps Chrome Masters of the Game
TopChrMotGR Topps Chrome Masters of the Game Refractors
TopChrMR Topps Chrome Milestones Refractors
TopChrNB Topps Chrome New Breed
TopChrNBR Topps Chrome New Breed Refractors
TopChrR Topps Chrome Refractors
TopChrRC Topps Chrome Rookie Class
TopChrRCRef Topps Chrome Rookie Class Refractors
TopChrRN Topps Chrome Record Numbers
TopChrRNR Topps Chrome Record Numbers Refractors
TopChrSAR Topps Chrome All-Stars Refractors
TopChrSB Topps Chrome Season's Best
TopChrSBR Topps Chrome Season's Best Refractors
TopChrWC Topps Chrome Wrecking Crew
TopChrWCR Topps Chrome Wrecking Crew Refractors
TopClaC Topps Classic Confrontations
TopCleF Topps Clemente Finest
TopCleFR Topps Clemente Finest Refractors
TopCleMMad Topps Clemente Memorabilia Madness
TopCleR Topps Clemente
TopCleS Topps Clemente Sealed
TopCleT Topps Clemente Tribute
TopCleTin Topps Clemente Tins
TopClo Topps Cloth
TopClo9 Topps Clout Nine
TopCloS Topps Cloth Stickers
TopCloT Topps Cloth Test
TopCoi Topps Coins
TopCoi Topps Coins Inserts
TopCom Topps Comics
TopComotH Topps Commanders of the Hill
TopConMA Topps Connie Mack All-Stars
TopCraJ2 Topps Cracker Jack II
TopCraJI Topps Cracker Jack I
TopCurA Topps Current All-Stars
TopCyb Topps Cyberstats
TopCybSiR Topps Cyber Season in Review
TopD3 Topps D3
TopD3Z Topps D3 Zone
TopDaiQTU Topps Dairy Queen Team USA
TopDeb89 Topps Debut '89
TopDeb90 Topps Debut '90
TopDeb91 Topps Debut '91
TopDec Topps Deckle Inserts
TopDecE Topps Deckle Edge
TopDecI Topps Decals Inserts
TopDesS Topps Desert Shield
TopDevR Topps Inaugural Devil Rays
TopDia Topps Inaugural Diamondbacks
TopDicG Topps Dice Game
TopDodRotY Topps Dodgers Rookies of the Year
TopDou Topps Doubleheaders
TopDouA Topps Doubleheaders All-Stars
TopDouH Topps Double Header
TopDouM Topps Doubleheaders Mets/Yankees Test
TopEasCN Topps East Coast National
TopEmb Topps Embossed
TopEmbGI Topps Embossed Golden Idols
TopEmbI Topps Embossed Inserts
TopEtc Topps Etch-A-Sketch
TopFinIns Topps Finest Inserts
TopFla Topps Flashback
TopFocP Topps Focal Points
TopFol Topps Foldouts
TopFou Topps Four-in-One
TopFruR Topps Fruit Roll-Ups
TopFulS Topps Full Shots
TopGal Topps Gallery
TopGalAG Topps Gallery Awards Gallery
TopGalAuc Topps Gallery Auction Points
TopGalAuto Topps Gallery Autographs
TopGalE Topps Gallery Exhibitions
TopGalE Topps Gallery Expressionists
TopGalGoH Topps Gallery Gallery of Heroes
TopGalGoHJ Topps Gallery Gallery of Heroes Jumbos
TopGalGP Topps Gallery Gallery Proofs
TopGalHer Topps Gallery Heritage
TopGalHerP Topps Gallery Heritage Proofs
TopGaloC Topps Gallery of Champions
TopGalOPP Topps Gallery Original Printing Plates
TopGalP Topps Gallery Previews
TopGalP Topps Gallery Promos
TopGalPG Topps Gallery Photo Gallery
TopGalPMS Topps Gallery Peter Max Serigraphs
TopGalPMSSS Topps Gallery Peter Max Signature Series Serigraphs
TopGalPP Topps Gallery Press Plates
TopGalPPI Topps Gallery Player's Private Issue
TopGalPPI Topps Gallery Players Private Issue
TopGalPPIA Topps Gallery Player's Private Issue Auction
TopGamI Topps Game Card Inserts
TopGar Topps Garagiola
TopGayP Topps Gaylord Perry
TopGia Topps Giants
TopGiaSU Topps Giant Stand Ups
TopGloA Topps Glossy All-Stars
TopGloS Topps Glossy Send-Ins
TopGol Topps Gold
TopGolL Topps Gold Label Class 3
TopGolLabC1 Topps Gold Label Class 1
TopGolLabC1B Topps Gold Label Class 1 Black
TopGolLabC1One Topps Gold Label Class 1 One to One
TopGolLabC1R Topps Gold Label Class 1 Red
TopGolLabC2 Topps Gold Label Class 2
TopGolLabC2B Topps Gold Label Class 2 Black
TopGolLabC2One Topps Gold Label Class 2 One to One
TopGolLabC2R Topps Gold Label Class 2 Red
TopGolLabC3 Topps Gold Label Class 3
TopGolLabC3B Topps Gold Label Class 3 Black
TopGolLabC3One Topps Gold Label Class 3 One to One
TopGolLabC3R Topps Gold Label Class 3 Red
TopGolLC1 Topps Gold Label Class 1
TopGolLC2 Topps Gold Label Class 2
TopGolLHRR Topps Gold Label Home Run Race
TopGolLHRRB Topps Gold Label Home Run Race Black
TopGolLHRRR Topps Gold Label Home Run Race Red
TopGolLOtO Topps Gold Label One to One
TopGolLP Topps Gold Label Pre-Production
TopGolLRtA Topps Gold Label Race to Aaron
TopGolLRtAB Topps Gold Label Race to Aaron Black
TopGolLRtAOtO Topps Gold Label Race to Aaron One to One
TopGolLRtAR Topps Gold Label Race to Aaron Red
TopGolPS Topps Gold Pre-Production Sheet
TopGolS Topps Golden Spikes
TopGolW Topps Gold Winners
TopGreM Topps Greatest Moments
TopHal Topps HallBound

TopHaloFC	Topps Hall of Fame Collection
TopHeaU	Topps Heads Up
TopHeaUT	Topps Heads Up Test
TopHilHM	Topps Hills Hit Men
TopHilTM	Topps Hills Team MVP's
TopHobM	Topps Hobby Masters
TopHocF	Topps Hocus Focus
TopInaM	Topps Inaugural Marlins
TopInaR	Topps Inaugural Rockies
TopIntF	Topps Inter-League Finest
TopIntFR	Topps Inter-League Finest Refractors
TopKid	Topps Kids
TopLas	Topps Laser
TopLasBS	Topps Laser Bright Spots
TopLasPC	Topps Laser Power Cuts
TopLasSS	Topps Laser Stadium Stars
TopLeaL	Topps League Leaders
TopLeaS	Topps Leader Sheet
TopLegot6M	Topps Legends of the '60s Medallions
TopLorotD	Topps Lords of the Diamond
TopMag	Topps Magazine
TopMagJRC	Topps Magazine Jumbo Rookie Cards
TopMagR	Topps Magic Rub-Offs
TopMan	Topps Mantle
TopManC	Topps Mantle Case
TopManC	Topps Mantle Ceramic
TopManF	Topps Mantle Finest
TopManFR	Topps Mantle Finest Refractors
TopManR	Topps Mantle Redemption
TopMasotG	Topps Masters of the Game
TopMatW	Topps Mattingly World
TopMay	Topps Mays
TopMayF	Topps Mays Finest
TopMayFR	Topps Mays Finest Refractors
TopMcD	Topps McDonald's
TopMem05	Topps Members Only 55
TopMic	Topps Micro
TopMil	Topps Milestones
TopMin	Topps Mini
TopMin	Topps/OPC Minis
TopMiniC	Topps Minted in Cooperstown
TopMinL	Topps Mini Leaders
TopMVPP	Topps MVP Promotion
TopMysF	Topps Mystery Finest
TopMysFB	Topps Mystery Finest Bordered
TopMysFB	Topps Mystery Finest Borderless
TopMysFBR	Topps Mystery Finest Bordered Refractors
TopMysFBR	Topps Mystery Finest Borderless Refractors
TopMysFR	Topps Mystery Finest Refractors
TopNewB	Topps New Breed
TopNikH	Topps Nikon House
TopOpeD	Topps Opening Day
TopOpeDO	Topps Opening Day Oversize
TopOver	Topps Oversize
TopPewB	Topps Pewter Bonuses
TopPho	Topps Photographers
TopPicP	Topps Picture Perfect
TopPin	Topps Pin-Ups
TopPin	Topps Pins
TopPirS	Topps Pirate Stickers
TopPla	Topps Plaks
TopPor	Topps Porcelain
TopPorP	Topps Porcelain Promo
TopPos	Topps Postcards
TopPos	Topps Posters
TopPos	Topps Posters Inserts
TopPowB	Topps Power Boosters
TopPowB	Topps Power Brokers
TopPowBR	Topps Power Brokers Refractors
TopPre	Topps Pre-Production
TopPreS	Topps Pre-Production Sheet
TopPreS	Topps Pre-Production Spectralite
TopPro	Topps Profiles
TopPuz	Topps Puzzles
TopRecN	Topps Record Numbers
TopRecNG	Topps Record Numbers Gold
TopRedB	Topps Red Backs
TopRedLC1	Topps Gold Label Class 1 Red
TopRedLC2	Topps Gold Label Class 2 Red
TopRedLC3	Topps Gold Label Class 3 Red
TopRedSS	Topps Red Sox Stickers
TopRep5	Topps Reprint 52
TopRetPC	Topps Retail Promotion Cards
TopRevLL	Topps Revco League Leaders
TopRitM	Topps Ritz Mattingly
TopRitTM	Topps Rite-Aid Team MVP's
TopRoaW	Topps Road Warriors
TopRoo	Topps Rookies
TopRooAB	Topps Rookie All-Star Banquet
TopRooCla	Topps Rookie Class
TopRos	Topps Rose
TopRubD	Topps Rub Downs
TopRubI	Topps Rub-Offs Inserts
TopRut	Topps Ruth
TopRyaAut	Topps Ryan Autographs
TopRyan	Topps Ryan
TopRyanF	Topps Ryan Finest
TopRyanFR	Topps Ryan Finest Refractors
TopScr	Topps Scratchoffs
TopScr	Topps Screenplays
TopScrPS	Topps Screenplays Premium Series
TopScrPST	Topps Screenplays Premium Series Tins
TopScrT	Topps Screenplays Tins
TopSeaB	Topps Season's Best
TopSenL	Topps Senior League
TopSpa	Topps Spanish
TopSpaFI	Topps Spanish Factory Inserts
TopSta	Topps Stamps
TopSta	Topps Stand-Ups
TopSta	Topps Stars
TopSta'S	Topps Stars 'N Steel
TopSta'SG	Topps Stars 'N Steel Gold
TopSta'SGDH	Topps Stars 'N Steel Gold Domed Holographic
TopSta'SGH	Topps Stars 'N Steel Gold Holographic
TopSta1Foil	Topps Stars One Star Foil
TopSta2Foil	Topps Stars Two Star Foil
TopSta3Foil	Topps Stars Three Star Foil
TopSta4Foil	Topps Stars Four Star Foil
TopSta97AS	Topps Stars '97 All-Stars
TopStaA	Topps Stamp Albums
TopStaAM	Topps Stars Always Mint
TopStaASM	Topps Stars All-Star Memories
TopStaB	Topps Stars Bronze
TopStaBF	Topps Stars Bright Futures
TopStaBFFoil	Topps Stars Bright Futures Foil
TopStaFAS	Topps Stars Future All-Stars
TopStaFoil	Topps Stars Foil
TopStaFS	Topps Stars Four Star
TopStaG	Topps Stars Galaxy
TopStaG	Topps Stars Galaxy Bronze
TopStaG	Topps Stars Gold
TopStaGFoil	Topps Stars Galaxy Foil
TopStaGG	Topps Stars Galaxy Gold
TopStaGGR	Topps Stars Galaxy Gold Rainbow
TopStaGR	Topps Stars Gold Rainbow
TopStaGS	Topps Stars Galaxy Silver
TopStaHRR	Topps Stars Rookie Reprints
TopStaI	Topps Stamps Inserts
TopStaLB	Topps Stars Luminaries Bronze

TopStaLG	Topps Stars Luminaries Gold
TopStaLGR	Topps Stars Luminaries Gold Rainbow
TopStaLS	Topps Stars Luminaries Silver
TopStaOS	Topps Stars One Star
TopStaP	Topps Stars Promos
TopStaPre	Topps Stars Pre-Production
TopStaRR	Topps Stars Rookie Reprints
TopStaRRA	Topps Stars Rookie Reprints Autographs
TopStaRRAU	Topps Stars Rookie Reprint Autographs
TopStaS	Topps Stars Silver
TopStaSB	Topps Stars Supernovas Bronze
TopStaSG	Topps Stars Supernovas Gold
TopStaSGR	Topps Stars Supernovas Gold Rainbow
TopStaSS	Topps Stars Supernovas Silver
TopStaSteG	Topps Stars 'N Steel Gold
TopStaTS	Topps Stars Three Star
TopStaTS	Topps Stars Two Star
TopStaU	Topps Stand Ups
TopSti	Topps Stickers
TopSti	Topps/O-Pee-Chee Stickers
TopStiB	Topps Sticker Backs
TopStiB	Topps Sticker Boxes
TopStiB	Topps/O-Pee-Chee Sticker Backs
TopStiI	Topps Stick-Ons Inserts
TopStiV	Topps Sticker Variations
TopSup	Topps Super
TopSup	Topps SuperChrome
TopSup	Topps SuperChrome Refractors
TopSupC	Topps SuperChrome
TopSupCR	Topps SuperChrome Refractors
TopSupHT	Topps Super Home Team
TopSupN	Topps Super National
TopSupS	Topps Superstar Samplers
TopSweS	Topps Sweet Strokes
TopTat	Topps Tattoos
TopTat	Topps/O-Pee-Chee Tattoos
TopTatI	Topps Tattoos Inserts
TopTea	Topps Teams
TopTeaC	Topps Team Checklists
TopTeaCS	Topps Team Checklist Sheet
TopTeaP	Topps Team Posters
TopTeaT	Topps Team Timber
TopTek	Topps Tek
TopTekD	Topps Tek Diffractors
TopTekFP	Topps Tek Fantastek Phenoms
TopTekG	Topps Tek Gold
TopTekP	Topps Tek Pre-Production
TopTekP	Topps Tek Preview
TopTekT	Topps Tek Teknicians
TopTes5	Topps Test 53
TopTesF	Topps Test Foil
TopTesS	Topps Test Stamps
TopTif	Topps Tiffany
TopTifT	Topps Traded Tiffany
TopTra	Topps Traded
TopTraBP	Topps Traded Bronze Premiums
TopTraFI	Topps Traded Finest Inserts
TopTraG	Topps Traded Gold
TopTraI	Topps Transfers Inserts
TopTraPB	Topps Traded Power Boosters
TopTraT	Topps Traded Tiffany
TopTriH	Topps Triple Headers
TopTVA	Topps TV All-Stars
TopTVCa	Topps TV Cardinals
TopTVCu	Topps TV Cubs
TopTVM	Topps TV Mets
TopTVRS	Topps TV Red Sox
TopTVY	Topps TV Yankees
TopUKM	Topps UK Minis
TopUKMT	Topps UK Minis Tiffany
TopVen	Topps Venezuelan
TopWaxBC	Topps Wax Box Cards
TopWreC	Topps Wrecking Crew
TopZes	Topps Zest
TowCluD	Towne Club Discs
Toy	Toys'R'Us
ToyMasP	Toys'R'Us Master Photos
ToyRoo	Toys'R'Us Rookies
TraSta	Transogram Statues
TreThuB	Trenton Thunder Best
TreThuF	Trenton Thunder Fleer/ProCards
TreThuM	Trenton Thunder Multi-Ad
TreThuTI	Trenton Thunder Team Issue
TriA AAC	Triple A All-Stars CMC
TriA AAGP	Triple A All-Stars ProCards
TriA AAS	Triple A All-Stars SkyBox
TriAAAC	Triple A All-Stars CMC
TriAAAGF	Triple A All-Stars Fleer/ProCards
TriAAAP	Triple A All-Stars ProCards
TriAAC	Triple A All-Stars CMC
TriAAF	Triple A All-Stars Fleer/ProCards
TriAllGP	Triple A All-Stars ProCards
TriPla	Triple Play
TriPlaA	Triple Play Action
TriPlaBS	Triple Play Bomb Squad
TriPlaG	Triple Play Gallery
TriPlaLL	Triple Play League Leaders
TriPlaM	Triple Play Medalists
TriPlaN	Triple Play Nicknames
TriPlaP	Triple Play Previews
TriPlaP	Triple Play Promos
TriTriC	Tri-Cities Triplets Cramer
TriTriT	Tri-Cities Triplets TCMA
TroAig	Trois-Rivieres Aigles
TruVal	True Value
TucTorB	Tucson Toros Best
TucTorC	Tucson Toros Caruso
TucTorC	Tucson Toros CMC
TucTorC	Tucson Toros Cramer
TucTorCa	Tucson Toros Caruso
TucTorF	Tucson Toros Fleer/ProCards
TucTorJP	Tucson Toros Jones Photo
TucTorLD	Tucson Toros Line Drive
TucTorP	Tucson Toros ProCards
TucTorS	Tucson Toros SkyBox
TucTorT	Tucson Toros TCMA
TucTorTI	Tucson Toros Team Issue
TucTotTI	Tucson Toros Team Issue
TulDriDGB	Tulsa Drillers All Decade Best
TulDriF	Tulsa Drillers Fleer/ProCards
TulDriGS	Tulsa Drillers Grand Slam
TulDriLD	Tulsa Drillers Line Drive
TulDriP	Tulsa Drillers ProCards
TulDriS	Tulsa Drillers SkyBox
TulDriT	Tulsa Drillers TCMA
TulDriTI	Tulsa Drillers Team Issue
TulOil	Tulsa Oilers
TulOil7	Tulsa Oilers 7-11
TulOilGP	Tulsa Oilers Goof's Pants
TurRedT	Turkey Red T3 *
TusSidM	Tucson Sidewinders Multi-Ad
TusTorB	Tucson Toros Best
TusTorCr	Tucson Toros Cramer
TVSpoM	TV Sports Mailbags
TVSpoMF5HRC	TV Sports Mailbag/Photo File 500 Home Run Club
Twi7	Twins 7-Eleven
TwiCloD	Twins Cloverleaf Dairy
TwiFaiG	Twins Fairway Grocery
TwiFri	Twins Frisz
TwiFriP	Twins Frisz Postcards
TwiGreT	Twins Greats TCMA

TwiJayP	Twins Jay Publishing
TwiMasBD	Twins Master Bread Discs
TwiPetM	Twins Peter's Meats
TwiPos	Twins Postcards
TwiSmoC	Twins Smokey Colorgrams
TwiSupV	Twins Super Valu
TwiTeal	Twins Team Issue
TwiTealC	Twins Team Issue Color
TwiUniMC	Twins Universal Match Corp.
TwiVol	Twins Volpe
UC3	UC3
UC3ArtP	UC3 Artist's Proofs
UC3CleS	UC3 Clear Shots
UC3CycS	UC3 Cyclone Squad
UC3InM	UC3 In Motion
UCLBruTI	UCLA Bruins Team Issue
UD Cho	UD Choice
UD ChoBU	UD Choice Blow Up
UD ChoBUCG	UD Choice Blow Up Cover Glory
UD ChoMBH	UD Choice Mini Bobbing Head
UD ChoP	UD Choice Preview
UD ChoPCR	UD Choice Prime Choice Reserve
UD ChoS	UD Choice StarQuest
UD ChoSD	UD Choice StarQuest Double
UD ChoSHR	UD Choice StarQuest Home Run
UD ChoST	UD Choice StarQuest Triple
UD ChoYW	UD Choice Yard Work
UD Ion	UD Ionix
UD IonC	UD Ionix Cyber
UD IonH	UD Ionix HoloGrFX
UD IonH	UD Ionix Hyper
UD IonN	UD Ionix Nitro
UD IonR	UD Ionix Reciprocal
UD IonWZ	UD Ionix Warp Zone
UD3	UD3
UD3DieCut	UD3 Die Cuts
UD3GenNex	UD3 Generation Next
UD3Marq	UD3 Marquee Attraction
UD3PCBlowup	UD3 Power Corps Blowups
UD3SupSign	UD3 Superb Signatures
UDAUnsBC	UDA Commemorative Cards
UDHolo	Upper Deck HoloGrFX
UDHoloAUsome	Upper Deck HoloGrFX AuSOME
UDHoloFF	Upper Deck HoloGrFX Future Fame
UDHoloFFG	Upper Deck HoloGrFX Future Fame Gold
UDHoloLau	Upper Deck HoloGrFX Launchers
UDHoloLauG	Upper Deck HoloGrFX Launchers Gold
UDHoloStar	Upper Deck HoloGrFX StarView
UDHoloStarG	Upper Deck HoloGrFX StarView Gold
UDHoloUDA	Upper Deck HoloGrFX UD Authentics
Ult	Ultra
UltAllR	Ultra All-Rookies
UltAllRGM	Ultra All-Rookies Gold Medallions
UltAllRJ	Ultra All-Rookies Jumbo
UltAllS	Ultra All-Stars
UltAllSGM	Ultra All-Stars Gold Medallion
UltArtT	Ultra Artistic Talents
UltAutE	Ultra Autographstix Emeralds
UltAwaW	Ultra Award Winners
UltAwaWGM	Ultra Award Winners Gold Medallion
UltBacttF	Ultra Back to the Future
UltBasC	Ultimate Baseball Card
UltBasR	Ultra Baseball Rules
UltBigS	Ultra Big Shots
UltCalttH	Ultra Call to the Hall
UltCalttHGM	Ultra Call to the Hall Gold Medallion
UltCarA	Ultra Career Achievement
UltChe	Ultra Checklists
UltCheGM	Ultra Checklists Gold Medallion
UltDamI	Ultra Damage Inc.
UltDiaI	Ultra Diamond Immortals
UltDiaP	Ultra Diamond Producers
UltDiaPGM	Ultra Diamond Producers Gold Medallion
UltDouT	Ultra Double Trouble
UltEck	Ultra Eckersley
UltFalC	Ultra Fall Classics
UltFamGam	Ultra Fame Game
UltFieC	Ultra Fielder's Choice
UltFir	Ultra Firemen
UltFreF	Ultra Fresh Foundations
UltFreFGM	Ultra Fresh Foundations Gold Medallions
UltGol	Ultra Gold
UltGolM	Ultra Gold Medallion
UltGolME	Ultra Gold Medallion
UltGolMR	Ultra Gold Medallion Rookies
UltGolP	Ultra Golden Prospects
UltGolP	Ultra Golden Prospects Hobby
UltGolPGM	Ultra Golden Prospects Gold Medallion
UltGolPHGM	Ultra Golden Prospects Hobby Gold Medallion
UltGwy	Ultra Gwynn
UltHitM	Ultra Hitting Machines
UltHitMGM	Ultra Hitting Machines Gold Medallion
UltHomRK	Ultra Home Run Kings
UltHomRKGM	Ultra Home Run Kings Gold Medallion
UltHomRKR	Ultra Home Run Kings Redemption
UltHomRKRGM	Ultra Home Run Kings Redemption Gold Medallion
UltHRK	Ultra Home Run Kings
UltIrabuComm	Ultra Irabu Commemorative
UltKidG	Ultra Kid Gloves
UltLeaL	Ultra League Leaders
UltLeaLGM	Ultra League Leaders Gold Medallion
UltLeaS	Ultra Leather Shop
UltMas	Ultra Masterpieces
UltMilM	Ultra Millennium Men
UltNot	Ultra Notables
UltOn-L	Ultra On-Base Leaders
UltOn-LGM	Ultra On-Base Leaders Gold Medallion
UltOnBL	Ultra On-Base Leaders
UltOnBLGM	Ultra On-Base Leaders Gold Medallion
UltPer	Ultra Performers
UltPhiF	Ultra Phillies Finest
UltPlaM	Ultra Platinum Medallion
UltPlaME	Ultra Platinum Medallion
UltPowP	Ultra Power Plus
UltPowPGM	Ultra Power Plus Gold Medallion
UltPriL	Ultra Prime Leather
UltPriLGM	Ultra Prime Leather Gold Medallion
UltPro	Ultra Promos
UltPromo	Ultra Promo Sheet
UltRaw	Ultra Rawhide
UltRawGM	Ultra Rawhide Gold Medallion
UltRBIK	Ultra RBI Kings
UltRBIKGM	Ultra RBI Kings Gold Medallion
UltRes	Ultra Respect
UltResGM	Ultra Respect Gold Medallion
UltRisS	Ultra Rising Stars
UltRisSGM	Ultra Rising Stars Gold Medallion
UltRoctS	Ultra Rocket to Stardom
UltRooR	Ultra Rookie Reflections
UltSeaC	Ultra Season Crowns
UltSeaCGM	Ultra Season Crowns Gold Medallion
UltSecYS	Ultra Second Year Standouts
UltSecYSGM	Ultra Second Year Standouts Gold Medallion
UltStaR	Ultra Starring Role
UltStrK	Ultra Strikeout Kings
UltStrKGM	Ultra Strikeout Kings Gold Medallion
UltTheBook	Ultra The Book On
UltThu	Ultra Thunderclap
UltThuGM	Ultra Thunderclap Gold Medallion

UltTicS Ultra Ticket Studs
UltTop3 Ultra Top 30
UltTop3GM Ultra Top 30 Gold Medallion
UltUpd Ultra Update
UltWinN Ultra Win Now
UltWorP Ultra World Premiere
UncJac Uncle Jack
Uniof HR Hawaii Rainbows
UniOil Union Oil
UniWayS United Way Sierra
UNLSmo UNLV Smokey
UPIS UPI Superstars
UppDec Upper Deck
UppDec10AP Upper Deck 10th Anniversary Preview
UppDec10ASwep Upper Deck 10th Anniversary Sweepstakes
UppDec10AT Upper Deck 10th Anniversary Team
UppDec10ATD Upper Deck 10th Anniversary Team Double
UppDec10ATHR Upper Deck 10th Anniversary Team Home Run
UppDec10ATT Upper Deck 10th Anniversary Team Triple
UppDec1APR Upper Deck 10th Anniversary Preview Retail
UppDec5x7 Upper Deck 5 x 7 Blow Ups
UppDecA Upper Deck All-Stars
UppDecA Upper Deck Autographs
UppDecAC Upper Deck All-Star Credentials
UppDecAG Upper Deck Amazing Greats
UppDecAGDC Upper Deck Amazing Greats Die Cuts
UppDecAH Upper Deck Aaron Heroes
UppDecAH Upper Deck All-Time Heroes
UppDecAH1 Upper Deck All-Time Heroes 125th
UppDecAH1A Upper Deck All-Time Heroes 1954 Archives
UppDecAHA Upper Deck All-Time Heroes Autographs
UppDecAHNIL Upper Deck All-Time Heroes Next In Line
UppDecAHP Upper Deck All-Time Heroes Preview
UppDecAJ Upper Deck All-Star Jumbos
UppDecAJG Upper Deck All-Star Jumbos Gold
UppDecAP Upper Deck A Piece of History 500 Club
UppDecAPA1 Upper Deck A Piece of the Action 1
UppDecAPA2 Upper Deck A Piece of the Action 2
UppDecAPA3 Upper Deck A Piece of the Action 3
UppDecAPH5AU Upper Deck A Piece of History 500 Club Autographs
UppDecAPoH Upper Deck A Piece of History
UppDecAWJ Upper Deck Award Winner Jumbos
UppDecBCP Upper Deck Blue Chip Prospects
UppDecBD Upper Deck Black Diamond
UppDecBDAPH Upper Deck Black Diamond A Piece of History
UppDecBDD Upper Deck Black Diamond Double
UppDecBDDom Upper Deck Black Diamond Dominance
UppDecBDDomE Upper Deck Black Diamond Dominance Emerald
UppDecBDMN Upper Deck Black Diamond Mystery Numbers
UppDecBDMNE Upper Deck Black Diamond Mystery Numbers Emerald
UppDecBDQ Upper Deck Black Diamond Quadruple
UppDecBDT Upper Deck Black Diamond Triple
UppDecBH Upper Deck Bench/Morgan Heroes
UppDecC Upper Deck Checklists
UppDecCB2 Upper Deck Comic Ball 2
UppDecCB3 Upper Deck Comic Ball 3
UppDecCBP Upper Deck Comic Ball Promos
UppDecCBR'RHoF Upper Deck Chris Berman Rock 'N Roll Hall of Fame
UppDecCD Upper Deck Clearly Dominant
UppDecCf7 Upper Deck Challengers for 70
UppDecCf7 Upper Deck Challengers for 70 Challengers Inserts
UppDecCf7Cf7P Upper Deck Challengers for 70 Challengers Inserts Parallel
UppDecCf7LL Upper Deck Challengers for 70 Longball Legends
UppDecCf7MoH Upper Deck Challengers for 70 Mark on History
UppDecCf7MoHP Upper Deck Challengers for 70 Mark on History Parallel
UppDecCf7SftF Upper Deck Challengers for 70 Swinging for the Fences
UppDecCG Upper Deck Crowning Glory
UppDecCGD Upper Deck Crowning Glory Double
UppDecCGHR Upper Deck Crowning Glory Home Run
UppDecCGT Upper Deck Crowning Glory Triple
UppDecCL Upper Deck Century Legends
UppDecCLA Upper Deck Century Legends Artifacts
UppDecCLCC Upper Deck Century Legends Century Collection
UppDecCLEM Upper Deck Century Legends Epic Milestones
UppDecCLES Upper Deck Century Legends Epic Signatures
UppDecCLESC Upper Deck Century Legends Epic Signatures Century
UppDecCLJotC Upper Deck Century Legends All-Century Team
UppDecCLJotC Upper Deck Century Legends Jerseys of the Century
UppDecCLLC Upper Deck Century Legends Legendary Cuts
UppDecCLM Upper Deck Century Legends MVPs
UppDecCLMS Upper Deck Century Legends Memorable Shots
UppDecCo7CE Upper Deck Challengers for 70 Challengers Edition
UppDecCo7SftFA Upper Deck Challengers for 70 Swinging for the Fences Autographed
UppDecCP Upper Deck Clutch Performers
UppDecCPH Upper Deck College POY Holograms
UppDecCRJ Upper Deck Clark Reggie Jackson
UppDecDC Upper Deck Diamond Collection
UppDecDD Upper Deck Diamond Destiny
UppDecDDG Upper Deck Diamond Destiny Gold
UppDecDDS Upper Deck Diamond Destiny Silver
UppDecDG Upper Deck Diamond Gallery
UppDecDS Upper Deck Destination Stardom
UppDecE Upper Deck Encore
UppDecE2C Upper Deck Encore 2K Countdown
UppDecEBPC Upper Deck Encore Batting Practice Caps
UppDecED Upper Deck Electric Diamond
UppDecEDF Upper Deck Encore Driving Forces
UppDecEDFFXG Upper Deck Encore Driving Forces FX Gold
UppDecEDG Upper Deck Electric Diamond Gold
UppDecEFXG Upper Deck Encore FX Gold
UppDecEL1 Upper Deck Exclusives Level 1
UppDecEL2 Upper Deck Exclusives Level 2
UppDecEM Upper Deck Encore McGwired
UppDecEMFXG Upper Deck Encore McGwired FX Gold
UppDecEPE Upper Deck Encore Pure Excitement
UppDecERE Upper Deck Encore Rookie Encore
UppDecEREFXG Upper Deck Encore Rookie Encore FX Gold
UppDecEUA Upper Deck Encore UD Authentics
UppDecEUR Upper Deck Encore Upper Realm
UppDecF Upper Deck FanFest
UppDecF Upper Deck Forte
UppDecFA Upper Deck Fifth Anniversary

UppDecFAJ	Upper Deck Fifth Anniversary Jumbo
UppDecFD	Upper Deck Forte Double
UppDecFE	Upper Deck Final Edition
UppDecFG	Upper Deck FanFest Gold
UppDecFH	Upper Deck Future Heroes
UppDecFQ	Upper Deck Forte Quadruple
UppDecFSP	Upper Deck Future Stock Prospects
UppDecFT	Upper Deck Forte Triple
UppDecG	Upper Deck Gameface
UppDecGHRC	Upper Deck Griffey Home Run Chronicles
UppDecGJ	Upper Deck Game Jersey
UppDecGJ	Upper Deck Game Jerseys
UppDecGJ	Upper Deck Griffey Jumbos
UppDecGMMHR	Upper Deck Griffey Most Memorable Home Runs
UppDecGold	Upper Deck Gold
UppDecHC	Upper Deck Hot Commodities
UppDecHH	Upper Deck Heroes Highlights
UppDecHoB	Upper Deck Heroes of Baseball
UppDecHoB5	Upper Deck Heroes of Baseball 5x7
UppDecHRH	Upper Deck Home Run Heroes
UppDecHTH	Upper Deck Home Team Heroes
UppDecIC	Upper Deck Iooss Collection
UppDecICJ	Upper Deck Iooss Collection Jumbo
UppDecIP	Upper Deck Immaculate Perception
UppDecIPD	Upper Deck Immaculate Perception Double
UppDecIPHR	Upper Deck Immaculate Perception Home Run
UppDecIPT	Upper Deck Immaculate Perception Triple
UppDecJH	Upper Deck Jackson Heroes
UppDecJHJ	Upper Deck Jackson Heroes Jumbo
UppDecKGJBB	Upper Deck Ken Griffey Jr. Box Blasters
UppDecKGJBBA	Upper Deck Ken Griffey Jr. Box Blasters Autographs
UppDecKGJHR	Upper Deck Ken Griffey Jr. Highlight Reels
UppDecLDC	Upper Deck Long Distance Connection
UppDecM	Upper Deck MVP
UppDecM	Upper Deck MVP Power Surge
UppDecMD	Upper Deck MVP Dynamics
UppDecMGS	Upper Deck MVP Gold Script
UppDecMGUS	Upper Deck MVP Game Used Souvenirs
UppDecMH	Upper Deck Mantle Heroes
UppDecMH	Upper Deck Mays Heroes
UppDecMHFS	Upper Deck MVP Super Script
UppDecMJ	Upper Deck McGwire Jumbo
UppDecML	Upper Deck Minors
UppDecMLFS	Upper Deck Minors Future Stock
UppDecMLMJJ	Upper Deck Minors Michael Jordan Season Highlights Jumbos
UppDecMLMJOoO	Upper Deck Michael Jordan One On One
UppDecMLMJS	Upper Deck Minors Michael Jordan's Scrapbook
UppDecMLMLA	Upper Deck Minor League Autographs
UppDecMLOP	Upper Deck Minors Organizational Profiles
UppDecMLPotY	Upper Deck Minors Player of the Year
UppDecMLPotYF	Upper Deck Minors Player of the Year
UppDecMLS	Upper Deck Mantle's Long Shots
UppDecMLSED	Upper Deck Mantle's Long Shots Electric Diamond
UppDecMLT1PF	Upper Deck Minors Top 10 Prospect
UppDecMLT1PJF	Upper Deck Minors Top 10 Prospect Jumbos
UppDecMLT1PMF	Upper Deck Minors Top 10 Prospect Mail-In
UppDecMLTPHF	Upper Deck Minors Top Prospect Holograms
UppDecMM	Upper Deck Memorable Moments
UppDecMMCf6	Upper Deck Mark McGwire's Chase for 62
UppDecMMI	Upper Deck Mantle Metallic Impressions
UppDecMP	Upper Deck Mariners Pepsi
UppDecMP	Upper Deck MVP Preview
UppDecMP	Upper Deck MVP ProSign
UppDecMPC	Upper Deck Mantle Phone Cards
UppDecMSC	Upper Deck MVP Scout's Choice
UppDecMSS	Upper Deck MVP Silver Script
UppDecMST	Upper Deck MVP Super Tools
UppDecMST	Upper Deck MVP Swing Time
UppDecMtSGR	Upper Deck Meet the Stars Griffey Redemption
UppDecNCJ	Upper Deck Nomo Collection Jumbos
UppDecNG	Upper Deck Next Generation
UppDecNGED	Upper Deck Next Generation Electric Diamond
UppDecNomH	Upper Deck Nomo Highlights
UppDecNP	Upper Deck National Pride
UppDecNRJ	Upper Deck Nomo ROY Japanese
UppDecO	Upper Deck Ovation
UppDecOAPoH	Upper Deck Ovation A Piece of History
UppDecOD	Upper Deck On Deck
UppDecOMP	Upper Deck Ovation Major Production
UppDecORM	Upper Deck Ovation ReMarkable Moments
UppDecOSO	Upper Deck Ovation Standing Ovation
UppDecOWP	Upper Deck Ovation Curtain Calls
UppDecP	Upper Deck Predictor
UppDecP	Upper Deck Promos
UppDecPAW	Upper Deck Predictor Award Winners
UppDecPAWE	Upper Deck Predictor Award Winner Exchange
UppDecPC	Upper Deck/GTS Phone Cards
UppDecPD	Upper Deck Power Driven
UppDecPE	Upper Deck Predictor Exchange
UppDecPHE	Upper Deck Predictor Hobby Exchange
UppDecPLL	Upper Deck Predictor League Leaders
UppDecPLLE	Upper Deck Predictor League Leaders Exchange
UppDecPN	Upper Deck Prime Nine
UppDecPP	Upper Deck Power Package
UppDecPPJ	Upper Deck Power Package Jumbo
UppDecPRE	Upper Deck Predictor Retail Exchange
UppDecPreH	Upper Deck Predictor Hobby
UppDecPreR	Upper Deck Predictor Retail
UppDecR	Upper Deck Retro
UppDecR	Upper Deck Retrospectives
UppDecRA	Upper Deck Richie Ashburn
UppDecRBBop	Upper Deck Retro Big Boppers
UppDecRCJ	Upper Deck Ripken Collection Jumbos
UppDecRDR	Upper Deck Retro Distant Replay
UppDecRDRL2	Upper Deck Retro Distant Replay Level 2
UppDecREP	Upper Deck Rookie Edition Preview
UppDecRG	Upper Deck Retro Gold
UppDecRGKoG	Upper Deck Retro Groovy Kind of Glove
UppDecRH	Upper Deck Ruth Heroes
UppDecRH	Upper Deck Ryan Heroes
UppDecRI	Upper Deck Retro Inkredible
UppDecRIL2	Upper Deck Retro Inkredible Level 2
UppDecRipC	Upper Deck Ripken Collection
UppDecRL	Upper Deck Retro Lunchboxes
UppDecRLC	Upper Deck Retro Legendary Cuts
UppDecRNF	Upper Deck Retro New Frontier
UppDecROSS	Upper Deck Retro Old School/New School
UppDecROSS	Upper Deck Retro Old School/New School Level 2
UppDecRP	Upper Deck Retro Platinum
UppDecRP	Upper Deck Run Producers

UppDecRQL	Upper Deck Retro Quantum Leap	UtiBluSC	Utica Blue Sox Classic
UppDecRSF	Upper Deck Rock Solid Foundation	UtiBluSC	Utica Blue Sox Classic/Best
UppDecRSotT	Upper Deck Retro Sign of the Times	UtiBluSF	Utica Blue Sox Fleer/ProCards
UppDecRTA	Upper Deck Retro Throwback Attack	UtiBluSP	Utica Blue Sox ProCards
UppDecRTAL2	Upper Deck Retro Throwback Attack Level 2	UtiBluSP	Utica Blue Sox Pucko
		UtiBluST	Utica Blue Sox TCMA
UppDecRTC	Upper Deck Retro Time Capsule	VanCanB	Vancouver Canadians Best
UppDecRunP	Upper Deck Run Producers	VanCanC	Vancouver Canadians CMC
UppDecS	Upper Deck Sheet	VanCanC	Vancouver Canadians Cramer
UppDecS	Upper Deck Sheets	VanCanF	Vancouver Canadians Fleer/ProCards
UppDecS	Upper Deck Shimano*	VanCanG	Vancouver Canadians Grandstand
UppDecSA	Upper Deck Star Attractions	VanCanLD	Vancouver Canadians Line Drive
UppDecSAG	Upper Deck Star Attractions Gold	VanCanP	Vancouver Canadians Postcards
UppDecSAT	Upper Deck Sister Assumpta Trivia	VanCanP	Vancouver Canadians ProCards
UppDecSDRJ	Upper Deck Sports Drink Jackson	VanCanS	Vancouver Canadians SkyBox
UppDecSE	Upper Deck Special Edition	VanCanT	Vancouver Canadians TCMA
UppDecSEG	Upper Deck Special Edition Gold	VanMouSO	Vancouver Mounties Standard Oil
UppDecSF	Upper Deck Special F/X	VasSwe	Vassar Sweaters
UppDecSFPD	Upper Deck Special F/X Power Zone	VenGulP	Ventura Gulls ProCards
UppDecSFPZOB	Upper Deck Special F/X Power Zone OctoberBest	VenLeaS	Venezuelan League Stickers
		VenLinU	LineUp Venezuelan Baseball
UppDecSFPZPD	Upper Deck Special F/X Power Zone Power Driven	VerBeaD	Vero Beach Dodgers Best
		VerBeaDB	Vero Beach Dodgers Best
UppDecSFPZSX	Upper Deck Special F/X Power Zone Superstar Xcitement	VerBeaDC	Vero Beach Dodgers Classic
		VerBeaDC	Vero Beach Dodgers Classic/Best
UppDecSH	Upper Deck Season Highlights	VerBeaDF	Vero Beach Dodgers Fleer/ProCards
UppDecSHoB	Upper Deck Sonic Heroes of Baseball	VerBeaDM	Vero Beach Dodgers Multi-Ad
UppDecSoaD	Upper Deck Steal of a Deal	VerBeaDP	Vero Beach Dodgers ProCards
UppDecSR	Upper Deck Scouting Report	VerBeaDS	Vero Beach Dodgers Star
UppDecSS	Upper Deck Silver Sluggers	VerBeaDT	Vero Beach Dodgers TCMA
UppDecT	Upper Deck Trade	VerBeaDTI	Vero Beach Dodgers Team Issue
UppDecTAE	Upper Deck: The American Epic	VerExpB	Vermont Expos Best
UppDecTAEGM	Upper Deck: The American Epic GM	VerExpC	Vermont Expos Classic
UppDecTAELD	Upper Deck: The American Epic Little Debbies	VerExpF	Vermont Expos Fleer/ProCards
		VerExpO	Vermont Expos OSP
UppDecTAN	Upper Deck Then And Now	VerMarP	Vermont Mariners ProCards
UppDecTE	Upper Deck Textbook Excellence	VerRedP	Vermont Reds ProCards
UppDecTED	Upper Deck Textbook Excellence Double	Vic	Victory
UppDecTEQ	Upper Deck Textbook Excellence Quadruple	VicPos	Victory Posters
		VicT21	Victory T214
UppDecTET	Upper Deck Textbook Excellence Triple	VirGenS	Virginia Generals Star
UppDecTMH	Upper Deck Team MVP Holograms	VisOakC	Visalia Oaks Classic/Best
UppDecTMT	Upper Deck Tape Measure Titans	VisOakCLC	Visalia Oaks Cal League Cards
UppDecTMTG	Upper Deck Tape Measure Titans Gold	VisOakF	Visalia Oaks Fleer/ProCards
UppDecTR	Upper Deck T202 Reprints	VisOakF	Visalia Oaks Fritsch
UppDecTriCro	Upper Deck Triple Crown	VisOakG	Visalia Oaks Grandstand
UppDecTTP	Upper Deck Top Ten Promo	VisOakP	Visalia Oaks ProCards
UppDecTTS	Upper Deck Ticket To Stardom	VisOakT	Visalia Oaks TCMA
UppDecU	Upper Deck Unparalleled	VisOakUP	Visalia Oaks Update ProCards
UppDecVJLS	Upper Deck V.J. Lovero Showcase	VisSig	Visions Signings *
UppDecVtaT	Upper Deck View to a Thrill	VisSigA	Visions Signings Artistry *
UppDecVtaTD	Upper Deck View to a Thrill Double	VisSigA	Visions Signings Autographs *
UppDecVtaTQ	Upper Deck View to a Thrill Quadruple	VisSigAA	Visions Signings Artistry Autographs *
UppDecVtaTT	Upper Deck View to a Thrill Triple	W/RMarG	W/R Mark Grace
UppDecWB	Upper Deck Williams Best	W501	W501
UppDecWH	Upper Deck Williams Heroes	W502	W502
UppDecWWB	Upper Deck Williams Wax Boxes	W503	W503
UppDecWY	Upper Deck Wonder Years	W512	W512 *
UppDecWYD	Upper Deck Wonder Years Double	W513	W513 *
UppDecWYHR	Upper Deck Wonder Years Home Run	W514	W514
UppDecWYT	Upper Deck Wonder Years Triple	W515	W515
UppDPDAG	Upper Deck Power Deck Audio Griffey	W516	W516-1
USCar*	U.S. Caramel R328 *	W517	W517
USDepoT	U.S. Department of Transportation	W52	W520
USGamSBL	U.S. Game Systems Baseball Legends	W551	W551
USPlaCA	U.S. Playing Card All-Stars	W554	W554
USPlaCA	U.S. Playing Cards Aces	W555	W555
USPlaCMLA	U.S. Playing Cards Aces	W56PlaC	W560 Playing Cards *
USPlaCR	U.S. Playing Cards Rookies	W572	W572
USPLegSC	USPS Legends Stamp Cards	W573	W573
UtiBluJT	Utica Blue Jays TCMA	W575	W575

W720HolS	Hollywood Stars
W725AngTI	W725 Angels Team Issue
W72HolS	Hollywood Stars
WalMaiW	Walter Mails WG7
WarBakSP	Ward's Sporties Bread Pins
WasVia	Washington Viacom
WatA'sT	Waterbury A's TCMA
WatBucTS	Waterloo Bucks Team Set
WatDiaB	Waterloo Diamonds Best
WatDiaC	Waterloo Diamonds Classic/Best
WatDiaF	Waterloo Diamonds Fleer/ProCards
WatDiaP	Waterloo Diamonds ProCards
WatDiaS	Waterloo Diamonds Star
WatDodT	Waterbury Dodgers TCMA
WatIndC	Watertown Indians Classic
WatIndC	Watertown Indians Classic/Best
WatIndF	Waterloo Indians Fritsch
WatIndF	Watertown Indians Fleer/ProCards
WatIndP	Waterbury Indians ProCards
WatIndP	Waterloo Indians ProCards
WatIndP	Watertown Indians ProCards
WatIndS	Watertown Indians Star
WatIndT	Waterbury Indians TCMA
WatIndT	Waterloo Indians TCMA
WatIndTI	Watertown Indians Team Issue
WatPirP	Watertown Pirates ProCards
WatPirP	Watertown Pirates Pucko
WatRedT	Waterbury Reds TCMA
WatRoyT	Waterloo Royals TCMA
WauMetT	Wausau Mets TCMA
WauTimB	Wausau Timbers Best
WauTimF	Wausau Timbers Fritsch
WauTimGS	Wausau Timbers Grand Slam
WauTimP	Wausau Timbers ProCards
WauTimS	Wausau Timbers Star
WauTimT	Wausau Timbers TCMA
WavRedF	Waverly Reds Futera
WeiMarD	Weis Market Discs
WelPirC	Welland Pirates Classic
WelPirC	Welland Pirates Classic/Best
WelPirF	Welland Pirates Fleer/ProCards
WelPirP	Welland Pirates ProCards
WelPirP	Welland Pirates Pucko
WenCle	Wendy's Clemente
WenDis	Wendy's Discs
WesHavAT	West Haven A's TCMA
WesHavWCT	West Haven White Caps TCMA
WesHavYT	West Haven Yankees TCMA
WesMicW	West Michigan Whitecaps Best
WesMicWB	West Michigan Whitecaps Best
WesMicWC	West Michigan Whitecaps Classic
WesMicWF	West Michigan Whitecaps Fleer/ProCards
WesMicWM	West Michigan Whitecaps Multi-Ad
WesMicWTI	West Michigan Whitecaps Team Issue
WesOahCHWB	West Oahu Canefires Hawaii Winter Ball
WesPalBEB	West Palm Beach Expos Best
WesPalBEC	West Palm Beach Expos Classic
WesPalBEC	West Palm Beach Expos Classic/Best
WesPalBEF	West Palm Beach Expos Fleer/ProCards
WesPalBEP	West Palm Beach Expos ProCards
WesPalBES	West Palm Beach Expos Star
WesPalBES	West Palm Beach Expos Sussman
WesTenDJM	West Tennessee Diamond Jaxx Multi-Ad
WesVirWC	West Virginia Wheelers Classic/Best
WesVirWF	West Virginia Wheelers Fleer/ProCards
WG1CarG	WG1 Card Game
WhaRya	Whataburger Ryan
Whe	Wheaties *
WheBB1	Wheaties BB1
WheBB10	Wheaties BB10
WheBB11	Wheaties BB11
WheBB12	Wheaties BB12
WheBB13	Wheaties BB13
WheBB14	Wheaties BB14
WheBB15	Wheaties BB15
WheBB3	Wheaties BB3
WheBB4	Wheaties BB4
WheBB5	Wheaties BB5
WheBB6	Wheaties BB6
WheBB7	Wheaties BB7
WheBB8	Wheaties BB8
WheBB9	Wheaties BB9
WheM4	Wheaties M4 *
WheM5	Wheaties M5 *
WheSta	Wheaties Stamps
WhiLegtL	Whitehall Legends to Life
WhiPro	Whitehall Prototypes
WhiSox	White Sox
WhiSox1T	White Sox 1919 TCMA
WhiSox1T	White Sox 1959 TCMA
WhiSoxC	White Sox Chi-Foursome
WhiSoxC	White Sox Coke
WhiSoxCM	White Sox Coke Magnet
WhiSoxDS	White Sox Durochrome Stickers
WhiSoxF	White Sox Fleer
WhiSoxGT	White Sox Greats TCMA
WhiSoxGWH	White Sox George W. Hull
WhiSoxHDP	White Sox Hawthorn-Mellody Dairy Pins
WhiSoxI	White Sox Iron-Ons
WhiSoxJP	White Sox Jay Publishing
WhiSoxJT	White Sox Jewel Tea
WhiSoxK	White Sox Kodak
WhiSoxL	White Sox Lotshaw's
WhiSoxROLC	White Sox Rainbow Orchard Laundry Cleaners
WhiSoxS	White Sox Score
WhiSoxSC	White Sox Stadium Club
WhiSoxSP	White Sox Score Platinum
WhiSoxSPI	White Sox Score Platinum
WhiSoxSPr	White Sox Score Premier
WhiSoxT	White Sox Tribune
WhiSoxTAG	White Sox TCMA All-Time Greats
WhiSoxTI	White Sox Team Issue
WhiSoxTI1	White Sox Team Issue
WhiSoxTS	White Sox Ticket Stubs
WhiSoxTV	White Sox True Value
WicAerDS	Wichita Aeros Dog'n Shake
WicAerJPKB	Wichita Aeros J.P. Kelly Bank
WicAerM	Wichita Aeros McDonald's
WicAerODF	Wichita Aeros One Day Film
WicAerRD	Wichita Aeros Rock's Dugout
WicAerT	Wichita Aeros TCMA
WicAerTI	Wichita Aeros Team Issue
WicBonR	Wichita Bonus Rock
WicChaR	Wichita Champions Rock
WicPilRD	Wichita Pilots Rock's Dugout
WicStaR	Wichita Stadium Rock
WicStaSGD	Wichita State Shockers Game Day
WicUpdR	Wichita Update Rock
WicWra	Wichita Wranglers Best
WicWraB	Wichita Wranglers Best
WicWraF	Wichita Wranglers Fleer/ProCards
WicWraLD	Wichita Wranglers Line Drive
WicWraM	Wichita Wranglers Multi-Ad
WicWraP	Wichita Wranglers ProCards
WicWraR	Wichita Wranglers Rock
WicWraRD	Wichita Wranglers Rock's Dugout
WicWraS	Wichita Wranglers SkyBox
WicWraTI	Wichita Wranglers Team Issue
WifBalD	Wiffle Ball Discs
Wil	Wilson

WilBilB	Williamsport Bills Best	Yan192G	Yankees 1927 Galasso
WilBilLD	Williamsport Bills Line Drive	Yan192T	Yankees 1927 TCMA
WilBilP	Williamsport Bills ProCards	Yan196	Yankees 1961
WilBilS	Williamsport Bills Star	Yan196T	Yankees 1961 TCMA
WilBluR	Wilmington Blue Rocks Team Issue	Yan61RL	Yankees 61 Ron Lewis
WilBluRB	Wilmington Blue Rocks Best	YanAllTT	Yankees All-Time Team TCMA
WilBluRC	Wilmington Blue Rocks Choice	YanArcO	Yankees Arco Oil
WilBluRC	Wilmington Blue Rocks Classic	YanASFY	Yankee A-S Fifty Years
WilBluRC	Wilmington Blue Rocks Classic/Best	YanBurK	Yankees Burger King
WilBluRF	Wilmington Blue Rocks Fleer/ProCards	YanCitAG	Yankee Citgo All-Time Greats
WilBluRTI	Wilmington Blue Rocks Team Issue	YanCliDP	Yankee Clinic Day Postcards
WilCarE	Williams Caramels E103	YanDyn1T	Yankee Dynasty 1936-39 TCMA
WilChoV	Willards Chocolates V100	YanFle	Yankees Fleer
WilCubB	Williamsport Cubs Best	YanGreT	Yankees Greats TCMA
WilCubC	Williamsport Cubs Classic	YanJayP	Yankees Jay Publishing
WilCubF	Williamsport Cubs Fleer/ProCards	YanKodW	Yankees Kodak Wells
WilCubJGTI	Williamsport Cubs Jeremi Gonzalez Team Issue	YanMal	Yankees Malanga
		YanMcDP	Yankees McDonald's Pins
WilCubKWPCTI	Williamsport Cubs Kerry Wood Phone Card Team Issue	YanMomPRP	Yankees Monument Park Rini Postcards
		YanNedC	Yankees Nedicks Cups
WilCubKWTI	Williamsport Cubs Kerry Wood Team Issue	YanPhoA	Yankees Photo Album
		YanPhoS	Yankees Photos SCFC
WilCubM	Williamsport Cubs Multi-Ad	YanPicA	Yankees Picture Album
WilGloT	Wilson Glove Tags	YanPin	Yankees Pins
WilJor	Wilson Jordan	YanRinP11	Yankees Rini Postcards 1961 1
WilMay	ASA Willie Mays 90	YanRinP12	Yankees Rini Postcards 1961 2
WilMulP	Willard Mullin Postcards	YanRinP13	Yankees Rini Postcards 1961 3
WilPatV	William Paterson V89	YanRoyRD	Yankees Roy Rogers Discs
WilSpoG	Wilson Sporting Goods	YanSch	Yankees Schedules
WilSpoGH828	Wilson Sporting Goods H828	YanSco	Yankees Score
WilSpoGH828-1	Wilson Sporting Goods H828-1	YanScoNW	Yankees Score Nat West
WilTomT	Williamsport Tomahawks TCMA	YanScoP	Yankees Score Platinum
WinDis	Windwalker Discs	YanScoPl	Yankees Score Platinum
WinHavRSC	Winter Haven Red Sox Classic/Best	YanScoPr	Yankees Score Premier
WinHavRSF	Winter Haven Red Sox Fleer/ProCards	YanSSP	Yankees SSPC
WinHavRSP	Winter Haven Red Sox ProCards	YanSSPD	Yankees SSPC Diary
WinHavRSS	Winter Haven Red Sox Star	YanSta	Yankees Stamps
WinSpiC	Winston-Salem Spirits Classic	YanStaC	Yankees Stadium Club
WinSpiC	Winston-Salem Spirits Classic/Best	YanTCM	Yankees TCMA
WinSpiF	Winston-Salem Spirits Fleer/ProCards	YanTCMP	Yankees TCMA Postcards
WinSpiP	Winston-Salem Spirits ProCards	YanTeal	Yankees Team Issue
WinSpiS	Winston-Salem Spirits Star	YanTeaT	Yankees Team Issue
WinSpiTI	Winston-Salem Spirits Team Issue	YanUppD	Yankees Upper Deck
WinWar	Winston-Salem Warthogs Q-Cards	YanUppDWSC	Yankees Upper Deck WS Commemorative
WisRapTF	Wisconsin Rapids Twins Fritsch		
WisRapTT	Wisconsin Rapids Twins TCMA	YanWIZ6	Yankees WIZ 60s
WisTimR	Wisconsin Timber Rattlers Best	YanWIZ7	Yankees WIZ 70s
WisTimRB	Wisconsin Timber Rattlers Best	YanWIZ8	Yankees WIZ 80s
WisTimRM	Wisconsin Timber Rattlers Multi-Ad	YanWIZA	Yankees WIZ All-Stars
WolNewDTPP	Tigers Wolverine News Postcards PC773-3	YanWIZH	Yankees WIZ HOF
		YanYealT	Yankee Yearbook Insert TCMA
WonBreS	Wonder Bread Stars	YelBasP	Yellow Basepath Pins
Woo	Woolworth's	Yoo	Yoo-Hoo
WorCig	Worch Cigar	YooMatBC	Yoo-Hoo Match Book Covers
WorCig(	Worch Cigar (Minors)	YorCarE	York Caramel E210
WorUniG	World University Games*	Yue	Yuenglings
WorWidGTP	World Wide Gum Trimmed Premiums V351B	ZCle	Z-Silk Clemente
		Zee	Zeenuts
WorWidGV	World Wide Gum V351A	Zee	Zeenuts (B and W)
WorWidGV	World Wide Gum V355	Zee	Zeenuts (Sepia)
WorWidGV	World Wide Gum V362	Zen	Zenith
WWSmiP	W.W. Smith Postcards	Zen Z-Z	Zenith Z-Team
WytCubP	Wytheville Cubs ProCards	Zen5 xx7	Zenith 5 x 7
WytCubS	Wytheville Cubs Star	Zen5x7GoldImp	Zenith 5 x 7 Gold Impulse
YakBeaC	Yakima Bears Classic	Zen5x7Imp	Zenith 5 x 7 Impulse
YakBeaC	Yakima Bears Classic/Best	Zen8x10	Zenith 8 x 10
YakBeaF	Yakima Bears Fleer/ProCards	Zen8x1D	Zenith 8x10 Dufex
YakBeaG	Yakima Bears Grandstand	ZenAllS	Zenith All-Star Salute
YakBeaP	Yakima Bears ProCards	ZenArtP	Zenith Artist's Proofs
YakBeaTI	Yakima Bears Team Issue	ZenDiaC	Zenith Diamond Club
Yan	Yankees	ZenDiaCP	Zenith Diamond Club Parallel

ZenEpi	Zenith Epix
ZenMoz	Zenith Mozaics
ZenRaitB	Zenith Raising the Bar
ZenRooRC	Zenith Rookie Roll Call
ZenRooT	Zenith Rookie Thrills
ZenSam	Zenith Samples
ZenSampL	Zenith Samples Large
ZenSamS	Zenith Samples Small
ZentheBP	Zenith the Big Picture
ZenV-2	Zenith V-2
ZenZ	Zenith Z-Team
ZenZ-G	Zenith Z-Gold
ZenZ-S	Zenith Z-Silver
ZenZ-T	Zenith Z-Team
ZenZ-T5x7	Zenith Z-Team 5 x 7
ZenZ-TG	Zenith Z-Team Gold
Zip	Ziploc
ZipDis	Zip'z Discs

Additional Reading

Each year Beckett Publications produces comprehensive annual price guides for each of the four major sports: *Beckett Baseball Card Price Guide, Beckett Football Card Price Guide, Beckett Basketball Card Price Guide,* and *Beckett Hockey Card Price Guide.* The aim of these annual guides is to provide information and accurate pricing on a wide array of sports cards, ranging from main issues by the major card manufacturers to various regional, promotional, and food issues. Also other alphabetical checklists, such as *The Beckett Baseball Card Alphabetical, The Beckett Football Card Alphabetical* and *The Beckett Hockey Card Price Guide and Alphabetical,* are published to assist the collector in identifying all the cards of any particular player. The seasoned collector will find these tools valuable sources of information that will enable him to pursue his hobby interests.

In addition, abridged editions of the Beckett Price Guides have been published for each of the four major sports as part of the House of Collectibles series: *The Official Price Guide to Baseball Cards, The Official Price Guide to Football Cards, The Official Price Guide to Basketball Cards,* and *The Official Price Guide to Hockey Cards.* Published in a convenient mass-market paperback format, these price guides provide information and accurate pricing on all the main issues by the major card manufacturers.

Advertising

Within this Book you will find advertisements for sports memorabilia material, mail order, and retail sports collectibles establishments. All advertisements were accepted in good faith based on the reputation of the advertiser; however, neither the author, the publisher, the distributors, nor the other advertisers in this Book accept any responsibility for any particular advertiser not complying with the terms of his or her ad.

Readers also should be aware that prices in advertisements are subject to change over the annual period before a new edition of this volume is issued each spring. When replying to an advertisement late in the baseball year, the reader should take this into account, and contact the dealer by phone or in writing for up-to-date price information. Should you come into contact with any of the advertisers in this guide as a result of their advertisement herein, please mention this source as your contact.

Acknowledgments

A great deal of diligence, hard work, and dedicated effort went into this year's volume. However, the high standards to which we hold ourselves could not have been met without the expert input and generous amount of time contributed by many people. Our sincere thanks are extended to each and every one of you.

A complete list of these invaluable contributors appears after the alphabetical section.

A's, Chatham
❑ 88CapCodPB-23
Aalbers, Brady
❑ 98BilMusTI-1
Aaron, Hank (Henry Louis)
❑ 47Exh-1
❑ 47PM1StaP1-1
❑ 53BraSpiaS3-28
❑ 54BraJohC-5
❑ 54BraMer-1
❑ 54BraSpiaSP-1
❑ 54Top-128
❑ 55Bow-179
❑ 55BraGolS-25
❑ 55BraJohC-44
❑ 55BraSpiaSD-1
❑ 55Top-47
❑ 55TopDouH-105
❑ 56BraBilaBP-1
❑ 56Top-31
❑ 56TopPin-16
❑ 56YelBasP-1
❑ 57BraSpiaS4-1
❑ 57SwiFra-13
❑ 57Top-20
❑ 58BraJayP-1
❑ 58HarSta-3
❑ 58Hir-44
❑ 58JayPubA-1
❑ 58JayPubS-1
❑ 58Top-30A
❑ 58Top-30B
❑ 58Top-351
❑ 58Top-418
❑ 58Top-488
❑ 59ArmCoi-1
❑ 59Baz-1
❑ 59HomRunD-1
❑ 59Top-212
❑ 59Top-380
❑ 59Top-467
❑ 59Top-561
❑ 60ArmCoi-1A
❑ 60ArmCoi-1B
❑ 60Baz-4
❑ 60BraDav-1
❑ 60BraJayP-1
❑ 60BraLaktL-1
❑ 60BraSpiaS-1
❑ 60KeyChal-1
❑ 60MacSta-1
❑ 60NuHi-62
❑ 60Top-300
❑ 60Top-566
❑ 60TopTat-1
❑ 61NuSco-462
❑ 61Pos-107A
❑ 61Pos-107B
❑ 61Top-43
❑ 61Top-415
❑ 61Top-484
❑ 61Top-577
❑ 61TopStaI-37
❑ 62Baz-29
❑ 62BraJayP-1
❑ 62ExhStaB-1
❑ 62Jel-149
❑ 62PC7HFGSS-1
❑ 62Pos-149
❑ 62PosCan-149
❑ 62SalPlaC-180
❑ 62ShiPlaC-180
❑ 62Top-320
❑ 62Top-394
❑ 62TopBuc-1
❑ 62TopStaI-143
❑ 63BasMagM-1
❑ 63Baz-9
❑ 63BraJayP-1
❑ 63ExhStaB-1
❑ 63Jel-152
❑ 63Pos-152
❑ 63SalMetC-24
❑ 63Top-1
❑ 63Top-3
❑ 63Top-242
❑ 63Top-390
❑ 63TopStiI-1
❑ 64Baz-9
❑ 64BraJayP-1
❑ 64ChatheY-26
❑ 64Top-7
❑ 64Top-9
❑ 64Top-11
❑ 64Top-300
❑ 64Top-423
❑ 64TopCoi-83
❑ 64TopCoi-149
❑ 64TopGia-49
❑ 64TopSta-84
❑ 64TopStaU-1
❑ 64TopTatI-21
❑ 64TopVen-7
❑ 64TopVen-9
❑ 64TopVen-11
❑ 64TopVen-300
❑ 64WheSta-1
❑ 65Baz-9
❑ 65ChaTheY-24
❑ 65Kah-1
❑ 65OldLonC-1
❑ 65OPC-2
❑ 65OPC-170
❑ 65Top-2
❑ 65Top-170
❑ 65TopEmbI-59
❑ 65TopTraI-37
❑ 66Baz-30
❑ 66BraPos-1
❑ 66Kah-1
❑ 66Top-215
❑ 66Top-500
❑ 66TopRubI-1
❑ 66TopVen-215
❑ 67Baz-30
❑ 67BraPho-1
❑ 67CokCapA-19
❑ 67CokCapB-3
❑ 67CokCapNLA-19
❑ 67DexPre-1
❑ 67Kah-1A
❑ 67Kah-1B
❑ 67OPCPapI-15
❑ 67Top-242
❑ 67Top-244
❑ 67Top-250
❑ 67TopGiaSU-20
❑ 67TopPos-15
❑ 67TopTesF-1
❑ 67TopVen-284
❑ 68AtlOilPBCC-1
❑ 68Baz-5
❑ 68BraPos-1
❑ 68CokCapB-3
❑ 68DexPre-1
❑ 68Kah-A1
❑ 68Kah-B1
❑ 68OPC-3
❑ 68OPC-5
❑ 68OPC-110
❑ 68Top-3
❑ 68Top-5
❑ 68Top-110
❑ 68Top-370
❑ 68TopActS-3A
❑ 68TopActS-10B
❑ 68TopActS-16A
❑ 68TopGamI-4
❑ 68TopPla-13
❑ 68TopPos-14
❑ 68TopVen-3
❑ 68TopVen-5
❑ 68TopVen-110
❑ 68TopVen-370
❑ 69AtlBraBPPS-1
❑ 69AtlBraBPPS-2
❑ 69CitMetC-16
❑ 69Kah-A1
❑ 69Kah-B1
❑ 69MilBra-1
❑ 69MLBOffS-109
❑ 69MLBPin-31
❑ 69NabTeaF-1
❑ 69OPC-100
❑ 69Top-100
❑ 69TopDecI-1
❑ 69TopSta-1
❑ 69TopSup-34
❑ 69TopTeaP-2
❑ 69TraSta-53
❑ 70AtlBraS-1
❑ 70DayDaiNM-7
❑ 70MilBra-1
❑ 70MLBOffS-1
❑ 70OPC-65
❑ 70OPC-462
❑ 70OPC-500
❑ 70Top-65
❑ 70Top-462
❑ 70Top-500
❑ 70TopCanL-1
❑ 70TopScr-1
❑ 70TopSup-24
❑ 70TraSta-4A
❑ 71AllBasA-1
❑ 71BazNumT-23
❑ 71BazUnn-32
❑ 71MatMin-1
❑ 71MatMin-2
❑ 71MilDud-33
❑ 71MLBOffS-1
❑ 71MLBOffS-553
❑ 71OPC-400
❑ 71Top-400
❑ 71TopCoi-137
❑ 71TopSup-44
❑ 71TopTat-71
❑ 71TopTat-72
❑ 72Dia-53
❑ 72MilBra-1
❑ 72OPC-87
❑ 72OPC-89
❑ 72OPC-299
❑ 72OPC-300
❑ 72ProStaP-13
❑ 72SevTraC-1
❑ 72Top-87
❑ 72Top-89
❑ 72Top-299
❑ 72Top-300
❑ 72TopCloT-1
❑ 72TopPos-9
❑ 73LinPor-1
❑ 73OPC-1
❑ 73OPC-100
❑ 73OPC-473
❑ 73SevTraC-1
❑ 73Top-1
❑ 73Top-100
❑ 73Top-473
❑ 73TopCanL-1
❑ 73TopCom-1
❑ 73TopPin-1
❑ 74BraPhoC-1
❑ 74LauAllG-72
❑ 74NewYorNTDiS-24
❑ 74OPC-1
❑ 74OPC-2
❑ 74OPC-3
❑ 74OPC-4
❑ 74OPC-5
❑ 74OPC-6
❑ 74OPC-7
❑ 74OPC-8
❑ 74OPC-9
❑ 74OPC-332
❑ 74Top-1
❑ 74Top-2
❑ 74Top-3
❑ 74Top-4
❑ 74Top-5
❑ 74Top-6
❑ 74Top-332
❑ 74TopDecE-57
❑ 74TopPuz-1
❑ 74TopSta-1
❑ 75BlaBacD-1
❑ 75Hos-130
❑ 75HosTwi-130
❑ 75OPC-1
❑ 75OPC-195
❑ 75OPC-660
❑ 75SSPPuzB-1
❑ 75SSPSam-1
❑ 75Top-1
❑ 75Top-195
❑ 75Top-660
❑ 75TopMin-1
❑ 75TopMin-195
❑ 75TopMin-660
❑ 76BlaDis-1
❑ 76BreA&P-1
❑ 76BucDis-1
❑ 76CarDis-1
❑ 76CraDis-1
❑ 76DailsID-1
❑ 76Hos-94
❑ 76IsaDis-1
❑ 76LauDiaJ-8
❑ 76LauIndC-34
❑ 76OPC-1
❑ 76OPC-550
❑ 76OrbDis-1
❑ 76RedBarD-1
❑ 76SafDis-1
❑ 76SafSupLB-1
❑ 76SafSupLB-2
❑ 76SafSupLB-3
❑ 76SafSupLB-4
❑ 76SafSupLB-5
❑ 76SSP-239
❑ 76Top-1
❑ 76Top-550
❑ 76TowCluD-1
❑ 77BobParMBC-1
❑ 77GalGloG-44
❑ 77GalGloG-231
❑ 77Spo-316
❑ 77Spo-1109
❑ 78AtlCon-1
❑ 78BraTCC-1
❑ 78TCM60I-290
❑ 79Pew-1
❑ 79Top-412
❑ 79Top-413
❑ 80Bra195T-32
❑ 80Lau300-16
❑ 80PacLeg-7
❑ 80PerHaloFP-177
❑ 80PerHaloFPS-42
❑ 80SSPHOF-177
❑ 81BraPol-44
❑ 81SanDieSC-2
❑ 81TCM60I-356
❑ 82BasCarN-6
❑ 82CraJac-9
❑ 82DavHaloFB-1
❑ 82DiaCla-82
❑ 82K-M-43
❑ 82TCMGreS-4
❑ 82TCMStaot5-6
❑ 83ASAHanA-1
❑ 83ASAHanA-2
❑ 83ASAHanA-3
❑ 83ASAHanA-4
❑ 83ASAHanA-5
❑ 83ASAHanA-6
❑ 83ASAHanA-7
❑ 83ASAHanA-8
❑ 83ASAHanA-9
❑ 83ASAHanA-10
❑ 83ASAHanA-11
❑ 83ASAHanA-12
❑ 83DonHOFH-34
❑ 83KelCerB-9
❑ 83MLBPin-19
❑ 83Oco& SSBG-1
❑ 83TopSti-1
❑ 83TopTraBP-7
❑ 84DonCha-8
❑ 84OCoandSI-36
❑ 84OCoandSI-99
❑ 84OCoandSI-144
❑ 84OCoandSI-160
❑ 84RocAarP-1
❑ 84WilMay-40
❑ 84WilMay-52
❑ 85CirK-1
❑ 85DonHOFS-7
❑ 85TCMHomRC-1
❑ 85Woo-1
❑ 86BigLeaC-1
❑ 86BraGreT-5
❑ 86Don-602
❑ 86DonAllB-PUZ
❑ 86DonSupD-NNO
❑ 86DonWaxBC-PUZ
❑ 86Lea-259
❑ 86SpoDecG-40
❑ 86SpoDesJM-9
❑ 86TCM-18
❑ 86TCMSupS-2
❑ 87Bra195T-1
❑ 87HygAllG-1
❑ 87K-M-1
❑ 87LeaSpeO*-H7
❑ 87NesDreT-29
❑ 87SpoRea-7
❑ 88GreBasS-38
❑ 88HouSho-2
❑ 88PacLegI-1
❑ 89HOFStiB-44
❑ 89PerCelP-1
❑ 89Top-663
❑ 89TopBasT-35
❑ 89TopBasT-41
❑ 89TopTif-663
❑ 90AGFA-6
❑ 90BasWit-6
❑ 90Col-22
❑ 90HOFStiB-81
❑ 90PacLeg-1
❑ 90PerGreM-9
❑ 90SweBasG-2
❑ 91Kel3D-2
❑ 91KelStaU-1
❑ 91SweBasG-102
❑ 91TopArc1-317
❑ 91TopEasCN-1
❑ 91UppDec-HH1
❑ 91UppDecAH-19
❑ 91UppDecAH-20
❑ 91UppDecAH-21
❑ 91UppDecAH-22
❑ 91UppDecAH-23
❑ 91UppDecAH-24
❑ 91UppDecAH-25
❑ 91UppDecAH-26
❑ 91UppDecAH-27
❑ 91UppDecAH-AU3
❑ 91USGamSBL-4C
❑ 91USGamSBL-4D
❑ 91USGamSBL-4H
❑ 91USGamSBL-4S
❑ 92BazQua5A-6
❑ 92FroRowAH-1
❑ 92MVP-10
❑ 92MVP2H-2
❑ 92TVSpoMF5HRC-1
❑ 92Zip-11
❑ 93Ble-1
❑ 93Ble-2
❑ 93Ble-3
❑ 93MetIma-1
❑ 93UppDecAH-1
❑ 93UppDecAH-149
❑ 93UppDecAH-150
❑ 94BreMilB-1
❑ 94BreSen-1
❑ 94TedWil5C-1
❑ 94Top-715
❑ 94TopArc1-128
❑ 94TopArc1-NNO
❑ 94TopArc1G-128
❑ 94TopArc1G-NNO
❑ 94TopGol-715
❑ 94TopSpa-715
❑ 94UppDecAH-5
❑ 94UppDecAH-75
❑ 94UppDecAH-121
❑ 94UppDecAH-144
❑ 94UppDecAH-164
❑ 94UppDecAH1-5
❑ 94UppDecAH1-75
❑ 94UppDecAH1-121
❑ 94UppDecAH1-144
❑ 94UppDecAH1-164
❑ 94UppDecAJ-47
❑ 94UppDecAJG-47
❑ 94UppDecS-3
❑ 94UppDecTAEGM-1
❑ 95NegLeaL2-1
❑ 95TopLegot6M-2
❑ 97MobBayBB-1
❑ 97MobBayBB-2
❑ 97NegLeaPC-13D
❑ 97SpoIllAM-6
❑ 97SpoIllCC-1
❑ 97St.VinHHS-1
❑ 97TopMan-24
❑ 97TopManF-24
❑ 97TopManFR-24
❑ 98DonEliBttF-5
❑ 98DonEliBttFA-5
❑ 99199Fin-300
❑ 99FinGolRef-300
❑ 99FinRef-300
❑ 99TopGalHer-TH1
❑ 99TopGalHerP-TH1
❑ 99TopOpeD-1
❑ 99TopOpeD-NNO
❑ 99UppDecCL-5
❑ 99UppDecCLA-1950
❑ 99UppDecCLCC-5
❑ 99UppDecCLEM-EM9
Aaron, Tommie Lee
❑ 62PC7HFGSS-1
❑ 63Top-46
❑ 64Top-454
❑ 65Top-567
❑ 68BraPos-2
❑ 68Top-394
❑ 69AtlBraBPPS-3
❑ 69OPC-128
❑ 69Top-128
❑ 69TopFou-3
❑ 70OPC-278
❑ 70Top-278
❑ 71MLBOffS-2
❑ 71OPC-717
❑ 71RicBraTI-1
❑ 71Top-717
❑ 72MilBra-2
❑ 78RicBraT-1
❑ 82BraPol-23
❑ 90RicBra2ATI-1
Aaron, Wil
❑ 75SanAntBT-1
❑ 76WilTomT-1
Aase, Don (Donald William)
❑ 76OPC-597
❑ 76Top-597
❑ 77Top-472
❑ 78AngFamF-1
❑ 78OPC-233
❑ 78Top-12
❑ 79Top-368
❑ 80OPC-126
❑ 80Top-239
❑ 81Don-411
❑ 81Fle-286
❑ 81LonBeaPT-15
❑ 81Top-601
❑ 82Don-267
❑ 82Fle-450
❑ 82FleSta-212
❑ 82OPC-199
❑ 82Top-199
❑ 83Don-38
❑ 83Fle-76
❑ 83Top-599
❑ 84AngSmo-1
❑ 85BalOriP-1
❑ 85Don-255
❑ 85Fle-293
❑ 85FleUpd-1
❑ 85OriHea-1
❑ 85Top-86
❑ 85TopTif-86
❑ 85TopTifT-1T
❑ 85TopTra-1T
❑ 86BalOriHMP-1
❑ 86Don-392
❑ 86DonHig-12
❑ 86Fle-268
❑ 86Top-288
❑ 86TopTif-288
❑ 87BalOriP-1
❑ 87ClaGam-99
❑ 87Don-231
❑ 87DonAll-47
❑ 87Fle-461
❑ 87Fle-627
❑ 87FleExcS-1
❑ 87FleGlo-461
❑ 87FleGlo-627
❑ 87FleMin-1
❑ 87FleStiC-1
❑ 87OPC-207
❑ 87SevCoi-M4
❑ 87Spo-165
❑ 87Spo-194
❑ 87SpoTeaP-21
❑ 87Top-766
❑ 87TopMinL-38
❑ 87TopSti-228
❑ 87TopTif-766
❑ 88Fle-553
❑ 88FleGlo-553
❑ 88OriFreB-41
❑ 88OriPos-1
❑ 88Sco-518
❑ 88ScoGlo-518
❑ 88Top-467
❑ 88TopTif-467
❑ 89FleUpd-100
❑ 89MetColP-20
❑ 89MetKah-1
❑ 89Sco-524
❑ 89TopTra-1T
❑ 89TopTraT-1T
❑ 89UppDec-450
❑ 90DodMot-27
❑ 90Fle-196
❑ 90FleCan-196
❑ 90OPC-301
❑ 90Sco-377
❑ 90ScoRoo-29T
❑ 90Top-301
❑ 90TopTif-301
❑ 90UppDec-131
❑ 91Fle-193
❑ 91MetWIZ-1
❑ 91OriCro-1

❑ 91Sco-289
Abad, Andy
❑ 94SarRedSC-2
❑ 94SarRedSF-1963
❑ 95TreThuTI-24
❑ 96SarRedSB-5
❑ 97TreThuB-5
❑ 98PawRedSQ-5
❑ 99Bow-132
❑ 99BowChr-132
❑ 99BowChrG-132
❑ 99BowChrGR-132
❑ 99BowChrI-132
❑ 99BowChrIR-132
❑ 99BowChrR-132
❑ 99BowGol-132
❑ 99BowInt-132
Abarbanel, Mickey
❑ 68Top-287
❑ 68TopVen-287
Abare, Bill
❑ 89St.CatBJP-2071
❑ 90MyrBeaBJP-2781
❑ 91DunBluJC-15
❑ 91DunBluJP-212
Abbaticchio, Ed
❑ 08RosComP-148
❑ 09ColChiE-1
❑ 09T206-1
❑ 09T206-2
❑ 10PirTipTD-14
❑ 10SweCapPP-65
❑ 11PinT-5-713
❑ 11PinT-5-866
❑ 11SpoLifM-243
❑ 11T205-1
❑ 12ColRedB-1
❑ 12ColTinT-1
❑ 67SpoHobFC-31
Abbatiello, Pat
❑ 87IdaFalBP-26
Abbe, Chris
❑ 92YakBeaF-3451
❑ 93ExcFS7-51
❑ 93SanAntMF-3007
❑ 94SanAntMF-2471
Abbey, Bert Wood
❑ 90DodTar-1
Abbey, Charlie (Charles S.)
❑ 95May-29
Abbott, Bud
❑ 93ActPacA-168
❑ 93ActPacA2-65G
Abbott, Chuck
❑ 96BoiHawB-4
❑ 97CedRapK-1
❑ 98MidAngG-1
❑ 98MidAngO-1
❑ 99Bow-191
❑ 99BowChr-191
❑ 99BowChrG-191
❑ 99BowChrGR-191
❑ 99BowChrI-191
❑ 99BowChrIR-191
❑ 99BowChrR-191
❑ 99BowGol-191
❑ 99BowInt-191
❑ 99SP TopP-11
❑ 99SP TopPPE-11
❑ 99Top-212
❑ 99TopChr-212
❑ 99TopChrR-212
Abbott, Fred (Frederick H.)
❑ 09ColChiE-2
❑ 09ObaT21-252
❑ 09T206-390
❑ 11PinT-5-1114
❑ 11Zee-1
❑ 12ColRedB-2
❑ 12ColTinT-2
❑ 12ObaPreT-1
Abbott, Glenn (W. Glenn)
❑ 74OPC-602
❑ 74Top-602
❑ 75OPC-591
❑ 75Top-591
❑ 75TopMin-591
❑ 76OPC-322
❑ 76SSP-485
❑ 76Top-322
❑ 77Hos-147
❑ 77OPC-219
❑ 77Top-207
❑ 78Hos-17
❑ 78OPC-92
❑ 78Top-31
❑ 79OPC-263
❑ 79Top-497
❑ 80MarPos-1
❑ 80OPC-92
❑ 80Top-166
❑ 81Don-47
❑ 81Fle-615
❑ 81MarPol-3
❑ 81MarPos-1
❑ 81OPC-174
❑ 81Top-699
❑ 82Don-302
❑ 82Fle-502
❑ 82MarPos-1
❑ 82Top-336
❑ 82Top-571
❑ 84Fle-74
❑ 84Nes792-356
❑ 84OPC-356
❑ 84TigTeal-3
❑ 84TigWavP-2
❑ 84Top-356
❑ 84TopTif-356
❑ 86JacMetT-25
❑ 86MarGreT-9
❑ 87JacMetF-20
❑ 88JacMetGS-5
❑ 89TidTidC-26
❑ 89TidTidP-1947
❑ 90HunStaB-25
❑ 91LinDriAAA-550
❑ 91TacTigLD-550
❑ 91TacTigP-2322
❑ 92TacTigF-2518
❑ 93HunStaF-2098
❑ 94HunStaF-1348
❑ 95HunStaTI-1
❑ 96HunStaTI-1
❑ 97VisOakG-1
❑ 98VisOakG-1
Abbott, Jeff
❑ 94SigRooDP-81
❑ 94SigRooDPS-81
❑ 95Bes-12
❑ 95Bow-243
❑ 95BowGolF-243
❑ 95PriWilCTI-1
❑ 95SPML-36
❑ 95Top-599
❑ 96Bow-210
❑ 96BowBes-125
❑ 96BowBesAR-125
❑ 96BowBesR-125
❑ 96BowFoi-210
❑ 96Exc-30
❑ 96ExcCli-1
❑ 96NasSouB-5
❑ 97Bow-128
❑ 97Bow98ROY-ROY1
❑ 97BowBes-190
❑ 97BowBesAR-190
❑ 97BowBesR-190
❑ 97BowCerBlaIA-CA1
❑ 97BowCerBluIA-CA1
❑ 97BowCerGolIA-CA1
❑ 97BowChr-140
❑ 97BowChr1RFR-ROY1
❑ 97BowChr98RF-ROY1
❑ 97BowChrI-140
❑ 97BowChrIR-140
❑ 97BowChrR-140
❑ 97BowInt-128
❑ 97ColCho-469
❑ 97DonSigA-1
❑ 97DonSigAC-1
❑ 97DonSigAM-1
❑ 97FlaShoLC-106
❑ 97FlaShoLeg0-106
❑ 97FlaShoLeg1-106
❑ 97FlaShoM-A106
❑ 97FlaShoM-B106
❑ 97FlaShoM-C106
❑ 97FlaShoR0-106
❑ 97FlaShoR1-106
❑ 97FlaShoR2-106
❑ 97FlaShoWotF-6
❑ 97Fle-668
❑ 97FleTif-668
❑ 97Sel-126
❑ 97SelArtP-126
❑ 97SelCom-126
❑ 97SelRegG-126
❑ 97Top-491
❑ 97Ult-500
❑ 97UltGolME-500
❑ 97UltPlaME-500
❑ 98Bow-147
❑ 98BowCerBlueAU-65
❑ 98BowCerGA-65
❑ 98BowCerSA-65
❑ 98BowChr-147
❑ 98BowChrGA-147
❑ 98BowChrGAR-147
❑ 98BowChrI-147
❑ 98BowChrIR-147
❑ 98BowChrR-147
❑ 98BowGolA-147
❑ 98BowInt-147
❑ 98ColCho-62
❑ 98Don-319
❑ 98DonColE-468
❑ 98DonColL-212
❑ 98DonColP-714
❑ 98DonEli-68
❑ 98DonEliA-68
❑ 98DonEliS-68
❑ 98DonGolPP-319
❑ 98DonPre-164
❑ 98DonPreSeat-164
❑ 98DonPriCE-468
❑ 98DonPriCL-212
❑ 98DonPriCP-714
❑ 98DonSilPP-319
❑ 98Fle-126
❑ 98Lea-12
❑ 98LeaFraDA-12
❑ 98LeaFraF-12
❑ 98LeaFraM-12
❑ 98LeaFraM-12
❑ 98LeaFraMDC-12
❑ 98LeaFraMDC-12
❑ 98LeaFraMZ2-12
❑ 98LeaRS-264
❑ 98LeaRSLHolo-264
❑ 98LeaRSLong-264
❑ 98LeaRTrue-264
❑ 98MetUni-2
❑ 98MetUniPMG-2
❑ 98PacInvGems-27
❑ 98PacOmeRS-14
❑ 98PacOmeRST4-14
❑ 98PacOnl-159
❑ 98PacOnlR-159
❑ 98PacOnlWC-159
❑ 98PinIns-123
❑ 98PinInsCE-123
❑ 98PinInsDE-123
❑ 98PinPer-96
❑ 98PinPerPP-96
❑ 98PinPlu-78
❑ 98PriWilCASM-10
❑ 98Ult-131
❑ 98UltGolM-131
❑ 98UltMas-131
❑ 98UltPlaM-131
❑ 98UppDec-264
❑ 98UppDecSF-144
❑ 98Zen-98
❑ 98Zen5 xx7-79
❑ 98Zen5x7GoldImp-79
❑ 98Zen5x7Imp-79
❑ 98ZenRooT-11
❑ 98ZenZ-G-98
❑ 98ZenZ-S-98
❑ 99Fle-298
❑ 99FleSta9-298
❑ 99FleWarT-298
❑ 99Pac-95
❑ 99PacPlaB-95
❑ 99PacRed-95
❑ 99SkyThu-13
❑ 99SkyThuRant-13
❑ 99SkyThuRave-13
❑ 99StaClu-303
❑ 99StaCluFDI-303
❑ 99StaCluOoaK-303
❑ 99StaCluPP-303
❑ 99ThuSkySupR-13
❑ 99Top-271
❑ 99TopChr-271
❑ 99TopChrR-271
❑ 99TopMVPP-271
❑ 99UppDec-343
❑ 99UppDecEL1-343
❑ 99UppDecEL2-343
Abbott, Jim
❑ 87PanAmTUBI-38
❑ 87PanAmTURB-25
❑ 88TopTra-1T
❑ 88TopTraT-1T
❑ 89Bow-39
❑ 89BowTif-39
❑ 89ClaTraP-151
❑ 89DonBasB-171
❑ 89DonRoo-16
❑ 89FleUpd-11
❑ 89ScoRoo-88T
❑ 89Top-573
❑ 89TopBig-322
❑ 89TopHeaUT-16
❑ 89TopTif-573
❑ 89TopTra-2T
❑ 89TopTraT-2T
❑ 89UppDec-755
❑ 89UppDecS-1
❑ 90AngSmo-1
❑ 90Baz-22
❑ 90Bow-288
❑ 90BowTif-288
❑ 90ClaBlu-40
❑ 90Col-27
❑ 90Don-108
❑ 90DonLeaS-44
❑ 90Fle-125
❑ 90FleCan-125
❑ 90FleSoaS-10
❑ 90GooHumICBLS-1
❑ 90Hot50RS-1
❑ 90KinDis-20
❑ 90Lea-31
❑ 90M.Vpin-13
❑ 90MLBBasB-95
❑ 90OPC-675
❑ 90PanSti-34
❑ 90Pos-13
❑ 90PubIntS-362
❑ 90Sco-330
❑ 90Sco100RS-5
❑ 90ScoYouSI-5
❑ 90Spo-99
❑ 90StaAbb-1
❑ 90StaAbb-2
❑ 90StaAbb-3
❑ 90StaAbb-4
❑ 90StaAbb-5
❑ 90StaAbb-6
❑ 90StaAbb-7
❑ 90StaAbb-8
❑ 90StaAbb-9
❑ 90StaAbb-10
❑ 90StaAbb-11
❑ 90SupActM-1
❑ 90Top-675
❑ 90TopBig-329
❑ 90TopDeb89-1
❑ 90TopDou-1
❑ 90TopGloS-50
❑ 90TopHeaU-16
❑ 90TopMag-19
❑ 90TopRoo-1
❑ 90TopSti-172
❑ 90TopSti-319
❑ 90TopTif-675
❑ 90ToyRoo-1
❑ 90UppDec-645
❑ 90WonBreS-3
❑ 91AngSmo-7
❑ 91Bow-200
❑ 91Cla3-T1
❑ 91ClaGam-5
❑ 91Don-78
❑ 91Fle-305
❑ 91Lea-162
❑ 91MajLeaCP-23
❑ 91OPC-285
❑ 91PanFreS-188
❑ 91PanSti-140
❑ 91Pos-20
❑ 91RedFolS-1
❑ 91Sco-105
❑ 91Sco100S-69
❑ 91SevCoi-SC1
❑ 91SimandSMLBL-1
❑ 91StaClu-124
❑ 91StaPinB-1
❑ 91Stu-22
❑ 91Top-285
❑ 91TopDesS-285
❑ 91TopMic-285
❑ 91TopSta-1
❑ 91TopTif-285
❑ 91Ult-43
❑ 91UppDec-554
❑ 92AngPol-1
❑ 92Bow-185
❑ 92Bow-572
❑ 92Cla1-T1
❑ 92Cla2-T1
❑ 92ClaGam-109
❑ 92Don-130
❑ 92DonCraJ1-3
❑ 92Fle-50
❑ 92FleSmo'nH-S12
❑ 92Hig5-11
❑ 92HitTheBB-1
❑ 92JimDea-1
❑ 92Lea-1
❑ 92LeaBlaG-1
❑ 92Mr.TurS-1
❑ 92MVPPin-15
❑ 92OPC-530
❑ 92OPCPre-140
❑ 92PanSti-12
❑ 92Pin-281
❑ 92Pin-539
❑ 92PinRool-2
❑ 92PinTea2-42
❑ 92PinTeaP-2
❑ 92RedFolS-1
❑ 92Sco-620
❑ 92Sco100S-19
❑ 92ScoImpP-14
❑ 92SevCoi-22
❑ 92SpollIFK1-50
❑ 92StaClu-210
❑ 92Stu-141
❑ 92StuPre-21
❑ 92SunSee-11
❑ 92Top-406
❑ 92Top-530
❑ 92TopDaiQTU-9
❑ 92TopGol-406
❑ 92TopGol-530
❑ 92TopGolW-406
❑ 92TopGolW-530
❑ 92TopKid-97
❑ 92TopMcD-20
❑ 92TopMic-406
❑ 92TopMic-530
❑ 92TriPla-204
❑ 92Ult-321
❑ 92UppDec-78
❑ 92UppDec-86
❑ 92UppDec-325
❑ 92UppDec-642
❑ 92UppDecS-13
❑ 92UppDecTMH-3
❑ 93Bow-131
❑ 93ClaGam-1
❑ 93Don-35
❑ 93DurPowP2-16
❑ 93Fin-46
❑ 93FinRef-46
❑ 93Fla-244
❑ 93Fle-187
❑ 93FleFinE-242
❑ 93FunPac-204
❑ 93FunPac-205
❑ 93HumDumC-13
❑ 93Kra-1
❑ 93Lea-253
❑ 93LeaGolA-R18
❑ 93MSABenSPD-18
❑ 93OPC-1
❑ 93OPCPre-130
❑ 93PacSpa-551
❑ 93Pin-11
❑ 93RedFolS-1
❑ 93Sco-646
❑ 93Sel-98
❑ 93SelRoo-30T
❑ 93SP-262
❑ 93StaClu-615
❑ 93StaCluFDI-615
❑ 93StaCluMO-1
❑ 93StaCluMOP-615
❑ 93Stu-29
❑ 93Top-780
❑ 93TopComotH-4
❑ 93TopGol-780
❑ 93TopInaM-780
❑ 93TopInaR-780
❑ 93TopMic-780
❑ 93TopTra-75T
❑ 93TriPla-258
❑ 93TriPlaG-GS7
❑ 93Ult-590
❑ 93UppDec-30
❑ 93UppDec-31
❑ 93UppDec-53
❑ 93UppDec-451
❑ 93UppDec-554
❑ 93UppDecFA-A4
❑ 93UppDecFAJ-A4
❑ 93UppDecGold-30
❑ 93UppDecGold-31
❑ 93UppDecGold-53
❑ 93UppDecGold-451
❑ 93UppDecGold-554
❑ 93UppDecOD-D1
❑ 93YanStaC-2
❑ 94Bow-193
❑ 94ColC-450
❑ 94ColChoGS-450
❑ 94ColChoSS-450
❑ 94DenHol-1
❑ 94Don-357
❑ 94DonSpeE-357
❑ 94Fin-149
❑ 94FinPre-149P
❑ 94FinRef-149
❑ 94Fla-318
❑ 94Fle-224
❑ 94FleExtB-127
❑ 94FleGolM-10
❑ 94FleGolMJ-10
❑ 94FUnPac-75
❑ 94Lea-38
❑ 94LeaL-53
❑ 94OPC-211
❑ 94OscMayR-1
❑ 94Pac-420
❑ 94PanSti-98
❑ 94Pin-110
❑ 94PinArtP-110
❑ 94PinMusC-110
❑ 94PinTri-TR2
❑ 94ProMag-86
❑ 94RedFolMI-17
❑ 94Sco-127
❑ 94Sco-626
❑ 94ScoGolR-127
❑ 94ScoGolR-626
❑ 94Sel-78
❑ 94SP-195
❑ 94SPDieC-195
❑ 94Spo-138
❑ 94StaClu-516
❑ 94StaCluFDI-516
❑ 94StaCluGR-516
❑ 94StaCluMOP-516
❑ 94StaCluT-184
❑ 94StaCluTFDI-184
❑ 94Stu-211
❑ 94SucSav-7
❑ 94TomPiz-16
❑ 94Top-350
❑ 94TopGol-350
❑ 94TopSpa-350
❑ 94TriPla-271
❑ 94Ult-397
❑ 94UppDec-310
❑ 94UppDecED-310
❑ 95AngTeal-1
❑ 95ColCho-525
❑ 95ColChoGS-525
❑ 95ColChoSE-241
❑ 95ColChoSEGS-241
❑ 95ColChoSESS-241
❑ 95ColChoSS-525
❑ 95Don-369
❑ 95DonPreP-369
❑ 95DonTopotO-30
❑ 95Emo-24
❑ 95Fin-190
❑ 95Fin-233
❑ 95FinRef-190
❑ 95FinRef-233
❑ 95Fla-240
❑ 95Fle-65
❑ 95FleUpd-32
❑ 95Lea-374
❑ 95Pac-292
❑ 95Pin-394
❑ 95PinArtP-394
❑ 95PinMusC-394
❑ 95Sco-452
❑ 95ScoGolR-452
❑ 95ScoPlaTS-452
❑ 95ScoYouTE-452T
❑ 95Sel-146
❑ 95SelArtP-146
❑ 95SP-142
❑ 95SPSil-142
❑ 95StaClu-7
❑ 95StaClu-569
❑ 95StaCluFDI-7

❑ 95StaCluMOP-7
❑ 95StaCluMOP-569
❑ 95StaCluSTWS-7
❑ 95StaCluSTWS-569
❑ 95StaCluVR-3
❑ 95StaCluVRMO-3
❑ 95Stu-137
❑ 95Top-60
❑ 95TopCyb-42
❑ 95TopTra-75T
❑ 95Ult-307
❑ 95UltGolM-307
❑ 95UppDec-207
❑ 95UppDec-438
❑ 95UppDec-451
❑ 95UppDecED-207
❑ 95UppDecED-438
❑ 95UppDecEDG-207
❑ 95UppDecEDG-438
❑ 95UppDecSE-155
❑ 95UppDecSEG-155
❑ 95WhiSoxK-1
❑ 96AngMot-5
❑ 96Cir-16
❑ 96CirRav-16
❑ 96ColCho-78
❑ 96ColChoGS-78
❑ 96ColChoSS-78
❑ 96Don-177
❑ 96DonPreP-177
❑ 96EmoXL-21
❑ 96Fin-S43
❑ 96FinRef-S43
❑ 96Fla-31
❑ 96Fle-40
❑ 96FleTif-40
❑ 96Kin-12
❑ 96Pac-268
❑ 96Pin-76
❑ 96Pin-228
❑ 96PinAfi-61
❑ 96PinAfiAP-61
❑ 96PinAfiFPP-61
❑ 96PinArtP-128
❑ 96PinFoil-228
❑ 96PinSta-128
❑ 96Sco-130
❑ 96ScoDugC-A81
❑ 96ScoDugCAP-A81
❑ 96Sel-107
❑ 96SelArtP-107
❑ 96SP-48
❑ 96StaClu-241
❑ 96StaCluMOP-241
❑ 96Sum-13
❑ 96SumAbo&B-13
❑ 96SumArtP-13
❑ 96SumFoi-13
❑ 96Top-372
❑ 96Ult-323
❑ 96UltGolM-323
❑ 96UppDec-292
❑ 96UppDecVJLS-VJ1
❑ 96VanCanB-4
❑ 97PacPriGotD-GD1
❑ 98HicCraUO-5
❑ 98WinWar-5
❑ 99Fle-314
❑ 99FleSta9-314
❑ 99FleWarT-314
❑ 99SkyPre-65
❑ 99SkyPreR-65
❑ 99UppDec-409
❑ 99UppDecEL1-409
❑ 99UppDecEL2-409
❑ 99Vic-213
Abbott, John
❑ 85ElmPioT-1
❑ 86GreHorP-1
❑ 88WinHavRSS-1
Abbott, Kurt
❑ 89MedAthB-27
❑ 90MadMusB-3
❑ 90MadMusP-2274
❑ 90MidLeaASGS-1
❑ 91HunStaTI-1
❑ 91ModA'sC-1
❑ 91ModA'sP-3092
❑ 92HunStaF-3954
❑ 92HunStaS-301
❑ 92SkyAA F-126
❑ 93TacTigF-3037
❑ 93TriAAAGF-50
❑ 94Bow-534
❑ 94ColC-31
❑ 94ColC-389
❑ 94ColChoGS-31
❑ 94ColChoGS-389
❑ 94ColChoSS-31
❑ 94ColChoSS-389
❑ 94Fin-431
❑ 94FinJum-431
❑ 94FinRef-431
❑ 94Fla-160
❑ 94FlaWavotF-A1
❑ 94FleAllR-M1
❑ 94FleExtB-256
❑ 94FleExtBRS-1
❑ 94FleMajLP-1
❑ 94FleUpd-132
❑ 94Lea-346
❑ 94LeaLimR-11
❑ 94Pin-226
❑ 94PinArtP-226
❑ 94PinMusC-226
❑ 94PinRooTP-5
❑ 94Sco-598
❑ 94ScoBoyoS-53
❑ 94ScoGolR-598
❑ 94ScoRoo-RT11
❑ 94ScoRooGR-RT11
❑ 94ScoRooSR-SU9
❑ 94Sel-187
❑ 94SelRooS-RS12
❑ 94Spo-153
❑ 94StaClu-588
❑ 94StaCluFDI-588
❑ 94StaCluGR-588
❑ 94StaCluMOP-588
❑ 94StaCluT-86
❑ 94StaCluTFDI-86
❑ 94Stu-105
❑ 94TopGol-773
❑ 94TopSpa-773
❑ 94Ult-104
❑ 94Ult-489
❑ 94UltAllR-1
❑ 94UltAllRJ-1
❑ 94UppDec-313
❑ 94UppDecED-313
❑ 95ColCho-303
❑ 95ColChoGS-303
❑ 95ColChoSS-303
❑ 95Don-70
❑ 95DonPreP-70
❑ 95DonTopotO-237
❑ 95Fin-2
❑ 95FinRef-2
❑ 95Fla-349
❑ 95Fle-323
❑ 95FleRooS-1
❑ 95Lea-191
❑ 95LeaLim-186
❑ 95Pac-164
❑ 95Pin-202
❑ 95PinArtP-202
❑ 95PinMusC-202
❑ 95Sco-358
❑ 95ScoGolR-358
❑ 95ScoPlaTS-358
❑ 95Sel-145
❑ 95SelArtP-145
❑ 95StaClu-327
❑ 95StaCluMOP-327
❑ 95StaCluSTWS-327
❑ 95StaCluVR-169
❑ 95StaCluVRMO-169
❑ 95Stu-81
❑ 95Top-460
❑ 95TopCyb-255
❑ 95Ult-160
❑ 95UltGolM-160
❑ 95UppDec-116
❑ 95UppDecED-116
❑ 95UppDecEDG-116
❑ 95UppDecSE-252
❑ 95UppDecSEG-252
❑ 96ColCho-154
❑ 96ColChoGS-154
❑ 96ColChoSS-154
❑ 96Don-428
❑ 96DonPreP-428
❑ 96EmoXL-181
❑ 96Fla-256
❑ 96Fle-380
❑ 96FleTif-380
❑ 96Lea-164
❑ 96LeaPrePB-164
❑ 96LeaPrePG-164
❑ 96LeaPrePS-164
❑ 96LeaSigA-1
❑ 96LeaSigAG-1
❑ 96LeaSigAS-1
❑ 96MetUni-161
❑ 96MetUniP-161
❑ 96Pac-74
❑ 96Pin-314
❑ 96PinFoil-314
❑ 96Sco-398
❑ 96StaClu-200
❑ 96StaClu-351
❑ 96StaCluEPB-351
❑ 96StaCluEPG-351
❑ 96StaCluEPS-351
❑ 96StaCluMOP-200
❑ 96StaCluMOP-351
❑ 96Top-118
❑ 96Ult-195
❑ 96UltGolM-195
❑ 96UppDec-334
❑ 97Fle-323
❑ 97FleTif-323
❑ 97MarPac-1
❑ 97Pac-294
❑ 97PacLigB-294
❑ 97PacSil-294
❑ 97Top-454
❑ 98A'sMot-14
❑ 98Pac-292
❑ 98PacOnl-523
❑ 98PacOnlR-523
❑ 98PacOnlWC-523
❑ 98PacPlaB-292
❑ 98PacRedT-292
❑ 98PacSil-292
❑ 98Top-98
❑ 98TopChr-98
❑ 98TopChrR-98
❑ 98TopDevR-98
❑ 98TopDia-98
❑ 98TopMiniC-98
Abbott, Kyle
❑ 89QuaCitAGS-13
❑ 90Bow-287
❑ 90BowTif-287
❑ 90MidAngGS-5
❑ 90OPC-444
❑ 90Sco-673
❑ 90Top-444
❑ 90TopTif-444
❑ 91Bow-187
❑ 91EdmTraLD-151
❑ 91EdmTraP-1507
❑ 91LinDriAAA-151
❑ 91UppDec-51
❑ 92Bow-310
❑ 92Cla1-T2
❑ 92Cla2-T57
❑ 92ClaGam-198
❑ 92Don-3
❑ 92DonRoo-1
❑ 92Fle-51
❑ 92Lea-495
❑ 92LeaBlaG-495
❑ 92OPC-763
❑ 92OPCPre-185
❑ 92PhiMed-1
❑ 92Pin-432
❑ 92PinTea2-75
❑ 92ProFS7-27
❑ 92Sco-849
❑ 92ScoRoo-2
❑ 92SpoStaCC-1
❑ 92StaClu-818
❑ 92Top-763
❑ 92TopDeb91-1
❑ 92TopGol-763
❑ 92TopGolW-763
❑ 92TopMic-763
❑ 92UppDec-8
❑ 92UppDec-754
❑ 93Bow-652
❑ 93Don-676
❑ 93Fle-483
❑ 93PhiMed-1
❑ 93PhiStaC-3
❑ 93Pin-378
❑ 93Sco-403
❑ 93ScrRedBF-2537
❑ 93ScrRedBTI-1
❑ 93Sel-332
❑ 93StaClu-201
❑ 93StaCluFDI-201
❑ 93StaCluMOP-201
❑ 93Top-317
❑ 93TopGol-317
❑ 93TopInaM-317
❑ 93TopInaR-317
❑ 93TopMic-317
❑ 93Ult-82
❑ 93UppDec-300
❑ 93UppDecGold-300
❑ 94Top-773
❑ 95Phi-1
❑ 95PhiMel-1
❑ 97KylAbb-1
Abbott, Ody Cleon
❑ 12Zee-22
❑ 13Zee-23
Abbott, Paul
❑ 86KenTwiP-1
❑ 87KenTwiP-24
❑ 88VisOakCLC-165
❑ 88VisOakP-92
❑ 89OrlTwiB-7
❑ 89OrlTwiP-1348
❑ 89SouLeaAJ-14
❑ 90CMC-553
❑ 90PorBeaC-1
❑ 90PorBeaP-168
❑ 90ProAAAF-238
❑ 91Bow-329
❑ 91Don-639
❑ 91LinDriAAA-401
❑ 91PorBeaLD-401
❑ 91PorBeaP-1558
❑ 91Sco-363
❑ 91TopDeb90-1
❑ 91UppDec-487
❑ 92Fle-667
❑ 92OPC-781
❑ 92Sco-697
❑ 92StaClu-567
❑ 92Top-781
❑ 92TopGol-781
❑ 92TopGolW-781
❑ 92TopMic-781
❑ 93CanIndF-2830
❑ 94OmaRoyF-1215
❑ 95IowCubTI-1
❑ 96LasVegSB-5
❑ 97TacRai-5
Abbott, Spencer
❑ 22KolMotBPP-1
❑ 31Zee-59
❑ 32Zee-70
Abbott, Terry
❑ 78GreBraT-1
❑ 89AugPirP-515
❑ 90CedRapRB-5
❑ 90CedRapRP-2338
❑ 90MidLeaASGS-53
❑ 92BilMusF-3374
❑ 92BilMusSP-29
❑ 93BilMusF-3963
❑ 93BilMusSP-28
❑ 94ChaLooF-1374
❑ 95ChaLooTI-26
❑ 98BilMusTI-2
Abbott, Todd
❑ 96WesMicWB-5
❑ 97VisOakG-2
❑ 98VisOakG-2
Abbs, Steve
❑ 94JohCitCC-1
❑ 94JohCitCF-3714
ABC's, Indianapolis
❑ 93NegLeaRL2-55
❑ 93TedWilPC-12
Abe, Keiji
❑ 90GatCitPP-3362
❑ 90GatCitPSP-23
Abe, Osamu
❑ 83SanJosBC-8
Abell, Antonio
❑ 96JohCitCTI-1
❑ 97NewJerCB-2
Abell, Scott
❑ 92EugEmeC-4
❑ 92EugEmeF-3031
Aber, Al (Albert Julius)
❑ 53Top-233
❑ 54Top-238
❑ 55Bow-24
❑ 56Top-317
❑ 57Top-141
❑ 59TigGraASP-1
❑ 91TopArc1-233
❑ 94TopArc1-238
❑ 94TopArc1G-238
Abercrombie, John
❑ 91HigDesMC-14
❑ 91HigDesMP-2397
❑ 92WatDiaC-19
❑ 92WatDiaF-2146
❑ 93WicWraF-2979
Abernathy, Brent
❑ 97HagSunB-13
❑ 98DunBluJSB-1
❑ 98DunBluJTI-2
Abernathy, Matt
❑ 95IdaFalBTI-18
❑ 96CliLumKTI-1
Abernathy, Ted
❑ 43A'STEAI-2
❑ 57Top-293
❑ 59Top-169
❑ 59TopVen-169
❑ 60Top-334
❑ 64Top-64
❑ 64TopVen-64
❑ 65Top-332
❑ 66BraPos-2
❑ 66CubTeal-1
❑ 66OPC-2
❑ 66Top-2
❑ 66TopVen-2
❑ 67Top-597
❑ 68Top-264
❑ 68TopVen-264
❑ 69CubJewT-1
❑ 69CubPho-1
❑ 69MilBra-2
❑ 69Top-483
❑ 69TopSta-21
❑ 70RoyTeal-1
❑ 70Top-562
❑ 71MLBOffS-409
❑ 71OPC-187
❑ 71oySigST-1
❑ 71Top-187
❑ 72MilBra-3
❑ 72OPC-519
❑ 72oyTeal-1
❑ 72Top-519
❑ 73OPC-22
❑ 73Top-22
❑ 84CubUno-9
❑ 89ChaLooLITI-1
Abernathy, Tom
❑ 36WorWidGV-122
Abernethy, Tom
❑ 89GenCubP-1858
Aberson, Cliff (Clifford A.)
❑ 48AngTeal-1
❑ 49AngTeal-1
❑ 49Lea-136A
❑ 49Lea-136B
❑ 49W725AngTI-1
❑ 74CapPub-75
Abeyta, Scott
❑ 98LetBlaDG-1
Ables, Harry Terrell
❑ 09ObaT21-269
❑ 11PacCoaBD-1
❑ 11Zee-20
❑ 12HomRunKE-18
❑ 12ObaPreT-18
❑ 12PCLPin-1
❑ 12Zee-23
❑ 13Zee-24
❑ 14Zee-26
❑ 15Zee-22
Abner, Ben
❑ 86MacPirP-1
❑ 87HarSenP-26
Abner, Mascot
❑ 98AubDouTI-1
Abner, Shawn
❑ 85LynMetT-25
❑ 85Top-282
❑ 85TopTif-282
❑ 86JacMetT-19
❑ 86MetTCM-35
❑ 87LasVegSP-2
❑ 88BlaYNPRWLU-14
❑ 88Don-33
❑ 88DonBasB-21
❑ 88DonRoo-5
❑ 88Fle-576
❑ 88FleGlo-576
❑ 88Lea-33
❑ 88PadSmo-1
❑ 88Sco-626
❑ 88ScoGlo-626
❑ 88Spo-223
❑ 88StaLinPa-1
❑ 89Don-323
❑ 89LasVegSC-22
❑ 89LasVegSP-21
❑ 89PadPos-1
❑ 89Sco-411
❑ 90ClaYel-T20
❑ 90OPC-122
❑ 90Sco-352
❑ 90Top-122
❑ 90TopTif-122
❑ 90UppDec-301
❑ 91Don-561
❑ 91Fle-522
❑ 91Lea-381
❑ 91OPC-697
❑ 91PadMag-8
❑ 91PadSmo-1
❑ 91Sco-261
❑ 91StaClu-291
❑ 91Top-697
❑ 91TopDesS-697
❑ 91TopMic-697
❑ 91TopTif-697
❑ 91Ult-300
❑ 91UppDec-795
❑ 92Don-736
❑ 92OPC-338
❑ 92Sco-616
❑ 92StaClu-197
❑ 92Top-338
❑ 92TopGol-338
❑ 92TopGolW-338
❑ 92TopMic-338
❑ 92UppDec-502
❑ 92VanCanS-626
❑ 92WhiSoxK-45
❑ 93Don-651
❑ 93Fle-579
❑ 93OmaRoyF-1689
❑ 93Sco-437
❑ 93StaClu-403
❑ 93StaCluFDI-403
❑ 93StaCluMOP-403
❑ 93Top-582
❑ 93TopGol-582
❑ 93TopInaM-582
❑ 93TopInaR-582
❑ 93TopMic-582
Abone, Joseph
❑ 80MemChiT-6
❑ 82WicAerTI-1
Abraham, Alan
❑ 81WesHavAT-18
Abraham, Brian
❑ 77SanJosMC-23
❑ 79OgdA'sT-10
❑ 80OgdA'sT-9
❑ 82WesHavAT-1
Abraham, Glenn
❑ 87EveGiaC-10
❑ 87PocGiaTB-31
Abraham, Timothy
❑ 96MauStiHWB-NNO
❑ 96PorSeaDB-3
❑ 96PorSeaDB-4
❑ 97PorSeaD-4
❑ 98PorSeaDQ-29
Abrams, Cal (Calvin Ross)
❑ 51Bow-152
❑ 52Bow-86
❑ 52Top-350
❑ 53BowC-160
❑ 53NorBreL-1
❑ 53Top-98
❑ 54Bow-91
❑ 54OriEss-1
❑ 54OriTeal-1
❑ 55Bow-55
❑ 55OriEss-1
❑ 74dod195T-2
❑ 83TopRep5-350
❑ 85TCMPpl1-4
❑ 88DodRinP1-10C
❑ 90DodTar-2
❑ 91OriCro-2
❑ 91TopArc1-98
❑ 95TopArcBD-34
❑ 97BalOriP-1
Abramvicius, Jason
❑ 93WelPirF-3346
❑ 94AugGreF-2999
❑ 94SalBucC-2
❑ 94SalBucF-2315
Abrego, Johnny
❑ 86Don-32
❑ 86IowCubP-1

❑ 86StaoftFT-13
Abrell, Thomas
❑ 86SumBraP-1
❑ 87ChaWheP-26
Abreu, Armand
❑ 77SpaPhiT-12
Abreu, Bob
❑ 92AshTouC-19
❑ 92ClaFS7-383
❑ 93ClaFS7-24
❑ 93ClaGolF-105
❑ 93LinVenB-194
❑ 93LinVenB-277
❑ 93OscAstC-2
❑ 93OscAstF-638
❑ 94ExcFS7-196
❑ 94JacGenF-227
❑ 94UppDecML-13
❑ 94VenLinU-51
❑ 95Bes-73
❑ 95Bow-4
❑ 95BowBes-B3
❑ 95BowBesR-B3
❑ 95Exc-199
❑ 95LinVen-11
❑ 95LinVen-311
❑ 95SigRooOJ-1
❑ 95SigRooOJP-1
❑ 95SigRooOJPS-1
❑ 95SigRooOJS-1
❑ 95SPML-64
❑ 95SPMLA-1
❑ 95Sum21C-TC1
❑ 95TucTotTI-1
❑ 95UppDecML-48
❑ 95UppDecMLFS-48
❑ 96-97LinVen-132
❑ 96Bow-199
❑ 96BowBes-155
❑ 96BowBesAR-155
❑ 96BowBesR-155
❑ 96BowFoi-199
❑ 96BowMinLP-3
❑ 96ColCho-450
❑ 96ColChoGS-450
❑ 96ColChoSS-450
❑ 96Exc-169
❑ 96Fla-271
❑ 96FlaWavotF-1
❑ 96FleUpd-U136
❑ 96FleUpdNH-1
❑ 96FleUpdTC-U136
❑ 96Pin-390
❑ 96PinAfi-153
❑ 96PinAfi-171
❑ 96PinAfiAP-153
❑ 96PinAfiAP-171
❑ 96PinFoil-390
❑ 96PinProS-8
❑ 96Sel-189
❑ 96SelArtP-189
❑ 96SelCer-104
❑ 96SelCerAP-104
❑ 96SelCerCB-104
❑ 96SelCerCR-104
❑ 96SelCerMB-104
❑ 96SelCerMG-104
❑ 96SelCerMR-104
❑ 96SP-18
❑ 96StaClu-256
❑ 96StaCluMOP-256
❑ 96Sum-166
❑ 96SumAbo&B-166
❑ 96SumArtP-166
❑ 96SumFoi-166
❑ 96Top-101
❑ 96TusTorB-1
❑ 96Ult-483
❑ 96UltGolM-483
❑ 96UltGolP-1
❑ 96UltGolPHGM-1
❑ 96UppDec-258
❑ 96UppDecPHE-H51
❑ 96UppDecPreH-H51
❑ 96Zen-105
❑ 96ZenArtP-105
❑ 97AstMot-19
❑ 97Bow-296
❑ 97BowBes-170
❑ 97BowBesAR-170
❑ 97BowBesBC-BC17
❑ 97BowBesBCAR-BC17
❑ 97BowBesBCR-BC17
❑ 97BowBesMI-MI10
❑ 97BowBesMIAR-MI10
❑ 97BowBesMIARI-MI10
❑ 97BowBesMII-MI10
❑ 97BowBesMIR-MI10
❑ 97BowBesMIRI-MI10
❑ 97BowBesR-170
❑ 97BowCerBlaIA-CA2
❑ 97BowCerBluIA-CA2
❑ 97BowCerGolIA-CA2
❑ 97BowChr-204
❑ 97BowChrI-204
❑ 97BowChrIR-204
❑ 97BowChrR-204
❑ 97BowChrSHR-SHR2
❑ 97BowChrSHRR-SHR2
❑ 97BowInt-296
❑ 97BowIntB-BBI16
❑ 97BowIntBAR-BBI16
❑ 97BowIntBR-BBI16
❑ 97BowScoHR-2
❑ 97Cir-246
❑ 97CirRav-246
❑ 97ColCho-120
❑ 97Don-353
❑ 97DonFraFea-15
❑ 97DonGolPP-353
❑ 97DonLim-15
❑ 97DonLim-144
❑ 97DonLimE-15
❑ 97DonLimE-144
❑ 97DonLimENG-15
❑ 97DonLimFotG-21
❑ 97DonPre-165
❑ 97DonPreCttC-165
❑ 97DonSigA-2
❑ 97DonSigAC-2
❑ 97DonSigAM-2
❑ 97DonSilPP-353
❑ 97E-X2-75
❑ 97E-X2Cred-75
❑ 97E-X2EssCre-75
❑ 97Fin-295
❑ 97FinEmb-295
❑ 97FinEmbR-295
❑ 97FinRef-295
❑ 97FlaShoLC-54
❑ 97FlaShoLeg0-54
❑ 97FlaShoLeg1-54
❑ 97FlaShoM-A54
❑ 97FlaShoM-B54
❑ 97FlaShoM-C54
❑ 97FlaShoR0-54
❑ 97FlaShoR1-54
❑ 97FlaShoR2-54
❑ 97FlaShoWotF-10
❑ 97Fle-338
❑ 97FleNewH-1
❑ 97FleRooS-12
❑ 97FleTif-338
❑ 97Lea-26
❑ 97LeaFraM-26
❑ 97LeaFraMDC-26
❑ 97MetUni-133
❑ 97MetUniMfG-1
❑ 97NewPin-173
❑ 97NewPinAP-173
❑ 97NewPinMC-173
❑ 97NewPinPP-173
❑ 97PacPriGotD-GD148
❑ 97Pin-48
❑ 97PinArtP-PP48
❑ 97PinCer-117
❑ 97PinCerMBla-117
❑ 97PinCerMBlu-117
❑ 97PinCerMG-117
❑ 97PinCerMR-117
❑ 97PinCerR-117
❑ 97PinMusC-48
❑ 97PinPrePla-48
❑ 97PinTotCPB-117
❑ 97PinTotCPG-117
❑ 97PinTotCPR-117
❑ 97PinX-P-122
❑ 97PinX-PMoS-122
❑ 97Sco-486
❑ 97ScoArtPWB-486
❑ 97ScoResC-486
❑ 97ScoShoS-486
❑ 97ScoShoSAP-486
❑ 97Sel-138
❑ 97SelArtP-138
❑ 97SelCom-138
❑ 97SelRegG-138
❑ 97SpoIll-1
❑ 97SpoIllEE-1
❑ 97StaClu-195
❑ 97StaClu-300
❑ 97StaCluM-M28
❑ 97StaCluMOP-195
❑ 97StaCluMOP-300
❑ 97StaCluMOP-M28
❑ 97Stu-161
❑ 97StuPrePG-161
❑ 97StuPrePS-161
❑ 97Top-416
❑ 97TopChr-148
❑ 97TopChrR-148
❑ 97TopGal-148
❑ 97TopGalPPI-148
❑ 97Ult-203
❑ 97UltGolME-203
❑ 97UltPlaME-203
❑ 97UppDec-363
❑ 97UppDecBCP-BC12
❑ 97UppDecTTS-TS11
❑ 98Bow-287
❑ 98BowChr-287
❑ 98BowChrGA-287
❑ 98BowChrGAR-287
❑ 98BowChrI-287
❑ 98BowChrIR-287
❑ 98BowChrR-287
❑ 98BowGolA-287
❑ 98BowInt-287
❑ 98CirThu-172
❑ 98CirThuRav-172
❑ 98CirThuSupRav-172
❑ 98ColCho-461
❑ 98CroRoy-104
❑ 98Don-318
❑ 98DonColE-469
❑ 98DonEli-69
❑ 98DonEliA-69
❑ 98DonEliS-69
❑ 98DonGolPP-318
❑ 98DonPriCE-469
❑ 98DonSilPP-318
❑ 98Fin-216
❑ 98FinNo--216
❑ 98FinNo-R-216
❑ 98FinRef-216
❑ 98Fle-360
❑ 98FleVin'-111
❑ 98FleVin'C-111
❑ 98LeaRS-265
❑ 98LeaRSLHolo-265
❑ 98LeaRSLong-265
❑ 98LeaRTrue-265
❑ 98Pac-310
❑ 98PacOnl-551
❑ 98PacOnlR-551
❑ 98PacOnlWC-551
❑ 98PacPlaB-310
❑ 98PacRedT-310
❑ 98PacSil-310
❑ 98PhiTeal-1
❑ 98PinIns-53
❑ 98PinInsCE-53
❑ 98PinInsDE-53
❑ 98PinPer-109
❑ 98PinPerP-109
❑ 98PinPlu-171
❑ 98ScoRT-132
❑ 98ScoRTSS-PP81
❑ 98ScoRTSSAP-PP81
❑ 98ScoRTSSAP1-PP81
❑ 98SPxFin-307
❑ 98SPxFinR-307
❑ 98SPxFinS-307
❑ 98StaCluFDI-394
❑ 98StaCluI-394
❑ 98StaCluOneK-394
❑ 98StaCluPP-394
❑ 98Stu-196
❑ 98StuGPP-196
❑ 98StuSPP-196
❑ 98Top-351
❑ 98TopChr-351
❑ 98TopChrR-351
❑ 98TopDevR-351
❑ 98TopDia-351
❑ 98TopMiniC-351
❑ 98Ult-306
❑ 98UltGolM-306
❑ 98UltMas-306
❑ 98UltPlaM-306
❑ 98UppDec-102
❑ 98UppDec-711
❑ 99199Fin-49
❑ 99FinGolRef-49
❑ 99FinRef-49
❑ 99FlaShoLeg1-88
❑ 99FlaShoLeg2-88
❑ 99FlaShoLeg3-88
❑ 99FlaShoLegM1-88
❑ 99FlaShoLegM2-88
❑ 99FlaShoLegM3-88
❑ 99FlaShoR1-88
❑ 99FlaShoR2-88
❑ 99FlaShoR3-88
❑ 99Fle-71
❑ 99FleBri-63
❑ 99FleBri2G-63
❑ 99FleBriBlu-63
❑ 99FleBriGol-63
❑ 99FleMys-8
❑ 99FleMysG-8
❑ 99FleMysM-8
❑ 99FleSta9-71
❑ 99FleWarT-71
❑ 99MetUni-172
❑ 99MetUniGM-172
❑ 99MetUniPMG-172
❑ 99Pac-320
❑ 99PacAur-140
❑ 99PacAurOD-140
❑ 99PacCroC-209
❑ 99PacCroCPB-209
❑ 99PacOme-177
❑ 99PacOmeC-177
❑ 99PacOmeG-177
❑ 99PacOmePB-177
❑ 99PacPar-176
❑ 99PacParC-176
❑ 99PacParG-176
❑ 99PacParHoloGold-176
❑ 99PacParHS-176
❑ 99PacParOD-176
❑ 99PacParPB-176
❑ 99PacParRed-176
❑ 99PacPlaB-320
❑ 99PacPri-107
❑ 99PacPriHB-107
❑ 99PacPriHG-107
❑ 99PacPriHM-107
❑ 99PacPriHP-107
❑ 99PacPriRed-107
❑ 99PacPriS-51
❑ 99PacPriS206-51
❑ 99PacPriS206R-51
❑ 99PacRed-320
❑ 99Rev-105
❑ 99RevPremDate-105
❑ 99RevRet-105
❑ 99RevShaSS-105
❑ 99SkyMolM-29
❑ 99SkyMolMX-29
❑ 99SkyPre-21
❑ 99SkyPreR-21
❑ 99SkyThu-232
❑ 99SkyThuRant-232
❑ 99SkyThuRave-232
❑ 99SP SigAuto-BA
❑ 99SPSig-155
❑ 99StaClu-39
❑ 99StaCluFDI-39
❑ 99StaCluOoaK-39
❑ 99StaCluPP-39
❑ 99ThuSkySupR-232
❑ 99Top-181
❑ 99TopChr-181
❑ 99TopChrR-181
❑ 99TopMVPP-181
❑ 99UD Cho-126
❑ 99UD ChoP-126
❑ 99UD ChoPCR-126
❑ 99Ult-110
❑ 99UltGolM-110
❑ 99UltMas-110
❑ 99UltPlaM-110
❑ 99UppDec-170
❑ 99UppDecE-66
❑ 99UppDecEFXG-66
❑ 99UppDecEL1-170
❑ 99UppDecEL2-170
❑ 99UppDecM-159
❑ 99UppDecMGS-159
❑ 99UppDecMHFS-159
❑ 99UppDecMP-159
❑ 99UppDecMSS-159
❑ 99UppDecR-66
❑ 99UppDecRG-66
❑ 99UppDecRP-66
❑ 99Vic-298
Abreu, Dennis
❑ 97MidLeaTP-22
❑ 97RocCub-7
Abreu, Francisco
❑ 87DayBeaAP-11
Abreu, Frank (Franklin)
❑ 87SavCarP-20
❑ 88SprCarB-21
❑ 89St.PetCS-1
❑ 90ArkTraGS-4
❑ 91ArkTraLD-26
❑ 91LinDriAA-26
❑ 92St.PetCC-8
❑ 92St.PetCF-2031
Abreu, Guillermo
❑ 94EliTwiC-1
❑ 94EliTwiF-3737
Abreu, Jose
❑ 95BurBeeTI-23
❑ 96BelGiaTI-31
Abreu, Juan
❑ 93LinVenB-221
❑ 95ButCopKtI-2
Abreu, Manny
❑ 72CedRapCT-13
❑ 80CarMudF-16
Abreu, Nelson
❑ 97RocCub-8
❑ 98RocCubM-1
❑ 98RocCubTI-1
Abreu, Oscar
❑ 97SouOreTB-18
❑ 98ModA'sG-1
Abreu, Winston
❑ 95DanBraTI-1
❑ 96BesAutS-1
❑ 96Exc-121
❑ 96MacBraB-1
❑ 98EugEme-1
Abril, Odie (Ernest)
❑ 85GreHorT-21
❑ 86FloStaLAP-1
❑ 86WinHavRSP-1
❑ 87WinHavRSP-15
❑ 88WinHavRSS-2
❑ 89WinHavRSS-1
❑ 90LynRedSTI-14
Abshier, Lanny
❑ 87SalAngP-27
Abstein, Bill (William H.)
❑ 09ColChiE-3A
❑ 09ColChiE-3B
❑ 09T206-3
❑ 10NadE1-1
❑ 10PirHerICP-1
❑ 11MecDFT-7
❑ 11PinT-5-106
❑ 11SpoLifCW-1
❑ 12ColRedB-3A
❑ 12ColRedB-3B
❑ 12ColTinT-3A
❑ 12ColTinT-3B
❑ 12ImpTobC-86
❑ 14Zee-1
❑ 15Zee-1
❑ 67SpoHobFC-37
❑ 72ClaCar-32
Acevedo, Carlos
❑ 98MarPhiG-1
Acevedo, Jesus
❑ 93EliTwiC-2
❑ 93EliTwiF-3418
❑ 93LinVenB-170
Acevedo, Jose
❑ 98ChaAllCM-1
Acevedo, Juan
❑ 93CenValRC-2
❑ 94NewHavRF-1540
❑ 95Bow-6
❑ 95BowBes-B19
❑ 95BowBesR-B19
❑ 95ColCho-42
❑ 95ColChoGS-42
❑ 95ColChoSS-42
❑ 95Exc-185
❑ 95ExcLeaL-1
❑ 95Sel-200
❑ 95SelArtP-200
❑ 95SelCer-130
❑ 95SelCerMG-130
❑ 95SigRooOP-OP1
❑ 95SigRooOPS-OP1
❑ 95SigRooP'P-P5
❑ 95SP-15
❑ 95SPSil-15
❑ 95StaClu-599
❑ 95StaCluMOP-599
❑ 95StaCluSTWS-599
❑ 95Sum-149
❑ 95SumNthD-149
❑ 95Top-316
❑ 95UppDec-265
❑ 95UppDecED-265
❑ 95UppDecEDG-265
❑ 95UppDecML-40
❑ 95UppDecMLFS-40
❑ 95UppDecMLOP-OP9
❑ 95Zen-129
❑ 96FleUpd-U154
❑ 96FleUpdTC-U154
❑ 96LeaSigA-2
❑ 96LeaSigAG-2
❑ 96LeaSigAS-2
❑ 96NorTidB-5
❑ 96Pin-324
❑ 96PinFoil-324
❑ 96Sel-148
❑ 96SelArtP-148
❑ 96SigRooOJTP-T1
❑ 96Ult-510
❑ 96UltGolM-510
❑ 97NorTid-5
❑ 97NorTidB-5
❑ 98Pac-360
❑ 98PacPlaB-360
❑ 98PacRedT-360
❑ 98PacSil-360
❑ 99Fle-337
❑ 99FleSta9-337
❑ 99FleWarT-337
❑ 99Pac-350
❑ 99PacPlaB-350
❑ 99PacRed-350
Acevedo, Milton
❑ 92LetMouSP-2
Aceves, Jonathan
❑ 98BriWhiSQ-7
Achilles, Matt
❑ 98DelShoM-6
Acker, Jim (James Austin)
❑ 84BluJayFS-1
❑ 84Don-146
❑ 84Fle-145
❑ 84Nes792-359
❑ 84OPC-359
❑ 84Top-359
❑ 84TopTif-359
❑ 85BluJayFS-1
❑ 85Fle-96
❑ 85OPC-101
❑ 85Top-101
❑ 85TopTif-101
❑ 86BluJayAF-1
❑ 86BluJayFS-1
❑ 86Don-363
❑ 86Fle-50
❑ 86OPC-46
❑ 86Top-569
❑ 86TopTif-569
❑ 87BraSmo-10
❑ 87Don-659
❑ 87Fle-509
❑ 87FleGlo-509
❑ 87Top-407
❑ 87TopTif-407
❑ 88Fle-531
❑ 88FleGlo-531
❑ 88OPC-293
❑ 88Sco-576
❑ 88ScoGlo-576
❑ 88StaLinBra-1
❑ 88Top-678
❑ 88TopSti-43
❑ 88TopTif-678
❑ 89BraDub-1
❑ 89Top-244
❑ 89TopTif-244
❑ 89UppDec-52
❑ 90BluJayFS-1
❑ 90Don-558
❑ 90OPC-728
❑ 90Top-728
❑ 90TopTif-728
❑ 91BluJayFS-1
❑ 91BluJayS-21
❑ 91Don-368
❑ 91Fle-167
❑ 91OPC-71
❑ 91Sco-122
❑ 91Top-71
❑ 91TopDesS-71
❑ 91TopMic-71
❑ 91TopTif-71
❑ 91UppDec-670
❑ 92Fle-322

❑ 92MarMot-23
❑ 92OPC-178
❑ 92Sco-63
❑ 92ScoProP-17
❑ 92TexLon-1
❑ 92Top-178
❑ 92TopGol-178
❑ 92TopGolW-178
❑ 92TopMic-178
Acker, Larry
❑ 85TucTorC-55
❑ 86TucTorP-1
❑ 87BirBarB-8
❑ 88MemChiB-7
Acker, Tom (Thomas James)
❑ 57Kah-1
❑ 57Top-219
❑ 58RedEnq-1
❑ 58Top-149
❑ 59RedEnq-1
❑ 59RedShiBS-1
❑ 59Top-201
❑ 60Top-274
Ackerman, John
❑ 84EveGiaC-27
Ackley, Fritz (Florian F.)
❑ 64Top-368
❑ 64TopVen-368
❑ 64WhiSoxI-1
❑ 64WhiSoxTS-1
❑ 65Top-477
❑ 78TCM60I-27A
Ackley, John
❑ 80ElmPioRST-12
Acosta, Bert
❑ 78NewWayCT-1
Acosta, Carlos
❑ 86TamTarP-1
Acosta, Cecilio
❑ 73OPC-379
❑ 73Top-379
❑ 74OPC-22
❑ 74Top-22
❑ 75OPC-634
❑ 75Top-634
❑ 75TopMin-634
Acosta, Clemente
❑ 90CMC-711
❑ 90PalSprACLC-226
❑ 90PalSprAP-2569
❑ 91LinDriAA-426
❑ 91MidAngLD-426
❑ 91MidAngP-426
❑ 92MidAngS-451
Acosta, Ed
❑ 71OPC-343
❑ 71Top-343
❑ 72OPC-123
❑ 72PadPos-1
❑ 72Top-123
❑ 73OPC-244
❑ 73Top-244
❑ 74HawIsIC-104
Acosta, Eddie
❑ 93HelBreF-4100
❑ 93HelBreSP-12
❑ 96DelShoB-4
❑ 96DelShoUB-4
Acosta, Jose
❑ 87WatPirP-17
❑ 88AugPirP-371
❑ 89AugPirP-492
Acosta, Oscar
❑ 89GasRanP-1025
❑ 91LinDriAA-600
❑ 91TulDriLD-600
❑ 91TulDriP-2789
❑ 91TulDriTI-1
❑ 92OklCit8F-1930
❑ 94DayCubC-28
❑ 94DayCubF-2370
❑ 96ColCliB-1
❑ 97ColCliB-3
❑ 98ColCliD-25
❑ 98ColCliM-3
Acre, Mark
❑ 92RenSilSCLC-36
❑ 93MadMusC-2
❑ 93MidLeaAGF-11
❑ 94A'sMot-22
❑ 94Bow-332
❑ 94BowBes-B44
❑ 94BowBesR-B44
❑ 94Cla-168
❑ 94ClaGolF-97
❑ 94ClaTriF-T58
❑ 94ExcFS7-116
❑ 94Fla-327
❑ 94FlaWavotF-B1
❑ 94FleExtB-143
❑ 94FleUpd-72
❑ 94LeaLimR-22
❑ 94ScoRoo-RT163
❑ 94ScoRooGR-RT163
❑ 94Sel-413
❑ 94TacTigF-3165
❑ 94TopTra-24T
❑ 94Ult-405
❑ 94UppDecML-68
❑ 95AthMot-26
❑ 95ColCho-18
❑ 95ColChoGS-18
❑ 95ColChoSS-18
❑ 95Don-76
❑ 95DonPreP-76
❑ 95Fla-291
❑ 95Fle-238
❑ 95Lea-329
❑ 95Pac-308
❑ 95Sco-501
❑ 95ScoGolR-501
❑ 95ScoPlaTS-501
❑ 95SigRoo-1
❑ 95SigRooSig-1
❑ 95StaClu-376
❑ 95StaCluMOP-376
❑ 95StaCluSTWS-376
❑ 95Top-224
❑ 95TopCyb-126
❑ 95Ult-89
❑ 95UltGolM-89
❑ 95UppDec-279
❑ 95UppDecED-279
❑ 95UppDecEDG-279
❑ 96ColCho-638
❑ 96ColChoGS-638
❑ 96ColChoSS-638
❑ 96Don-181
❑ 96DonPreP-181
❑ 96Fle-202
❑ 96FleTif-202
❑ 97A'sMot-21
❑ 97Fle-632
❑ 97FleTif-632
❑ 97PacPriGotD-GD77
Acro, Mascot
❑ 91PeoChiTI-29
Acta, Manny (Manuel)
❑ 88OscAstS-1
❑ 89ColMudB-2
❑ 89ColMudP-136
❑ 89ColMudS-1
❑ 90OscAstS-1
❑ 91BurAstC-12
❑ 91BurAstP-2806
❑ 92AshTouC-29
❑ 93AubAstC-28
❑ 93AubAstF-3460
❑ 94AubAstC-24
❑ 94AubAstF-3775
❑ 95AubAstTI-28
❑ 96AubDouB-24
❑ 97QuaCitRBB-1
❑ 98KisCobQ-2
Adachi, Tomo
❑ 94BriTigC-1
Adair, Bill
❑ 76ExpRed-1
❑ 76MonExpP-1
Adair, Derek
❑ 97BatCliTI-3
❑ 98ClePhiM-1
❑ 98ClePhiUM-1
❑ 98ClePhiUM-3
Adair, Jerry (Kenneth Jerry)
❑ 58BalOriP-1
❑ 59OklTodML-20
❑ 60Lea-28
❑ 61BalOriP-1
❑ 61Top-71
❑ 62BalOriP-1
❑ 62Top-449
❑ 62TopStal-2
❑ 63BalOriP-1
❑ 63Jel-61
❑ 63Pos-61
❑ 63Top-488
❑ 64BalOriP-1
❑ 64Top-22
❑ 64TopVen-22
❑ 65BalOriP-1
❑ 65OPC-231
❑ 65Top-231
❑ 66Top-533
❑ 66TopRubI-2
❑ 66WhiSoxTI-1
❑ 67CokCapWS-2
❑ 67Top-484
❑ 67TopVen-264
❑ 68CokCapRS-17
❑ 68DexPre-2
❑ 68Top-346
❑ 68TopVen-346
❑ 69MilBra-3
❑ 69MLBOffS-55
❑ 69OPC-159
❑ 69RoySol-1
❑ 69RoyTeal-1
❑ 69Top-159
❑ 69TopFou-1
❑ 69TopSta-181
❑ 69TopTeaP-7
❑ 70MLBOffS-217
❑ 70OPC-525
❑ 70RoyTeal-2
❑ 70Top-525
❑ 72MilBra-4
❑ 73OPC-179
❑ 73Top-179A
❑ 73Top-179B
❑ 75CalAngP-1
❑ 81RedSoxBG2S-68
❑ 83FraBroR-12
❑ 83FraBroR-18
❑ 91OriCro-3
Adair, Jimmy (James Aubrey)
❑ 67AstTeal2-1
❑ 87AstSer1-30
Adair, Rick
❑ 81WauTimT-14
❑ 82LynSaiT-1
❑ 83SalLakCGT-8
❑ 84ChaLooT-23
❑ 87WatIndP-29
❑ 89ColSprSSC-23
❑ 89ColSprSSP-247
❑ 90CMC-471
❑ 90ColSprSSC-19
❑ 90ColSprSSP-56
❑ 90ProAAAF-237
❑ 91ColSprSSLD-100
❑ 91ColSprSSP-2201
❑ 91LinDriAAA-100
❑ 92IndFanC-30
❑ 93IndWUA-33
❑ 94WicWraF-206
❑ 95TolMudHTI-3
Adair, Scott
❑ 96IdaFalB-1
Adam, David
❑ 92SanBerC-18
❑ 92SanBerSF-943
❑ 93RivPilCLC-3
❑ 94JacSunF-1403
❑ 95PorCitRTI-1
Adam, Justin
❑ 95SpoIndTI-2
❑ 96LanLugB-4
Adamczak, Jim
❑ 86JacMetT-1
Adames, Hernan
❑ 88TamTarS-1
Adames, Juan
❑ 88WytCubP-1997
❑ 89PeoChiTI-16
Adams, Ace Townsend
❑ 41DouPlaR-137
❑ 83TCMPla1943-43
❑ 88ConSer3-1
❑ 98VerExpO-2
Adams, Art
❑ 91BriTigC-29
❑ 91BriTigP-3594
❑ 92FayGenC-16
❑ 93FayGenF-119
Adams, Babe (Charles B.)
❑ 09ColChiE-4
❑ 09SpoNewSM-28
❑ 10E12AmeCDCE125-1
❑ 10NadE1-2
❑ 10PirAmeCE-1
❑ 10PirHerICP-2
❑ 10PirTipTD-9
❑ 11DiaGumP-1
❑ 11PinT-5-865
❑ 11PloCanE-1
❑ 11SpoLifCW-2
❑ 11SpoLifM-244
❑ 12ColRedB-4
❑ 12ColTinT-4
❑ 14B18B-74A
❑ 14B18B-74B
❑ 14CraJacE-63
❑ 15CraJacE-63
❑ 15SpoNewM-1
❑ 16FleBreD-1
❑ 16SpoNewM-1
❑ 19W514-54
❑ 20NatCarE-1
❑ 20W516-18
❑ 21E121So1-1
❑ 21Exh-1
❑ 21Nei-91
❑ 22E120-211
❑ 22W573-1
❑ 22W575-1
❑ 23W501-84
❑ 23W515-6
❑ 23WilChoV-1
❑ 26SpoComoA-1
❑ 61Fle-90
❑ 74CapPub-98
❑ 76ISCHooHA-23
❑ 80LauFamF-38
❑ 87ConSer2-7
❑ 92ConTSN-443
❑ 94ConTSN-1245
❑ 94ConTSNB-1245
Adams, Bert (John Bertram)
❑ 11HelSta-153
❑ 11PinT-5-625
❑ 12PhiCarE-1
❑ 12T207-1
❑ 21Zee-136
Adams, Bob
❑ 77EvaTriT-1
Adams, Bobby (Robert Henry)
❑ 49EurSta-76
❑ 49Lea-54
❑ 51Bow-288
❑ 52Bow-166
❑ 52Top-249
❑ 53BowC-108
❑ 53RedMan-NL2
❑ 53Top-152
❑ 54Bow-108
❑ 54Top-123
❑ 55Bow-118
❑ 55Top-178
❑ 56BalOriP-28
❑ 56Top-287
❑ 58Top-99
❑ 59SeaPop-14
❑ 59Top-249
❑ 83TopRep5-249
❑ 85TCMPpl1-17
❑ 91OriCro-4
❑ 91TopArc1-152
❑ 94TopArc1-123
❑ 94TopArc1G-123
Adams, Brian
❑ 90SpaPhiB-12
❑ 90SpaPhiP-2493
❑ 90SpaPhiS-1
Adams, Bud
❑ 87EugEmeP-2665
❑ 88BasCitRS-1
Adams, Buster (Elvin Clark)
❑ 43PhiTeal-1
❑ 46SeaSLP-1
❑ 83Car194T-25
Adams, Carl Ray
❑ 79NewCoPT-15
Adams, Craig
❑ 77WatIndT-1
❑ 81ChaLooT-20
❑ 82ChaLooT-22
Adams, Dan
❑ 75LafDriT-28
Adams, Daryl
❑ 80PenPilBT-2
❑ 80PenPilCT-2
Adams, Dave
❑ 90QuaCitAGS-12
❑ 90SpoIndSP-8
❑ 91ChaRaiC-14
❑ 91ChaRaiP-99
❑ 91QuaCitAC-1
❑ 91QuaCitAP-2618
❑ 92MidAngF-4018
❑ 92MidAngOHP-1
❑ 92MidAngS-452
❑ 92SkyAA F-191
❑ 92WatDiaC-24
❑ 92WatDiaF-2147
Adams, Derek
❑ 91BluOriC-12
❑ 91BluOriP-4132
❑ 92KanCouCC-21
❑ 92KanCouCF-96
❑ 92KanCouCTI-1
Adams, Dick (Richard Leroy)
❑ 47A'sTeal-2
❑ 84EdmTraC-104
Adams, Gary
❑ 90GatCitPP-3352
❑ 90GatCitPSP-1
❑ 91SumFlyC-22
❑ 91SumFlyP-2347
❑ 97UCLBruTI-27
Adams, Gerald
❑ 84NewOriT-20
❑ 85NewOriT-9
Adams, Glenn Charles
❑ 74PhoGiaC-85
❑ 76OPC-389
❑ 76SanFraGP-1
❑ 76SSP-108
❑ 76Top-389
❑ 78Top-497
❑ 78TwiFriP-1
❑ 79Top-193
❑ 79TwiFriP-1
❑ 80Top-604
❑ 80TwiPos-1
❑ 81Don-566A
❑ 81Don-566B
❑ 81Fle-562
❑ 81Top-18
❑ 81TwiPos-1
❑ 82Don-431
❑ 82Fle-545
❑ 82SyrChiT-19
❑ 82SyrChiTI-1
❑ 82Top-519
❑ 83OPC-374
❑ 83Top-574
❑ 87WatIndP-10
❑ 88CarLeaAS-21
❑ 95IowCubTI-2
❑ 96IowCubB-3
❑ 97IowCub-3
❑ 98IowCubQ-4
Adams, Herb (Herbert Loren)
❑ 85TCMPpl1-36
Adams, Jack
❑ 22Zee-115
Adams, Jason
❑ 90KinMetS-30
❑ 93KinMetC-2
❑ 93KinMetF-3807
❑ 94PitMetC-2
❑ 94PitMetF-3532
❑ 95AubAstTI-25
❑ 96QuaCitRB-6
❑ 97KisCob-1
❑ 98KisCobQ-6
Adams, Joe (Pres)
❑ 95OmaRoyTI-1
❑ 96OmaRoyB-6
❑ 97OmaRoyB-5
Adams, Joe PR
❑ 98OmaRoyM-25
Adams, John
❑ 20Zee-120
❑ 78BurBeeT-1
❑ 80HolMilT-16
❑ 83ArkTraT-10
❑ 84ArkTraT-12
❑ 98HigDesMG-1
Adams, Ken
❑ 86EugEmeC-46
❑ 88BasCitRS-2
❑ 89BasCitRS-1
Adams, Lionel
❑ 89IdaFalBP-2012
❑ 89SumBraP-1098
Adams, Mike
❑ 86VisOakP-1
❑ 87VisOakP-22
Adams, Mike (Robert Michael)
❑ 74OPC-573
❑ 74TacTwiC-22
❑ 74Top-573
Adams, Moose
❑ 91EveGiaC-20
❑ 91EveGiaP-3904
Adams, Morgan
❑ 90MedHatBJB-16
Adams, Pat
❑ 82AppFoxFr-27
❑ 83AppFoxFr-8
❑ 85PhoGiaC-186
❑ 87PhoFirP-21
❑ 88WesPalBES-1
Adams, Ralph
❑ 84LitFalMT-6
❑ 86LynMetP-1
Adams, Red (Charles Dwight)
❑ 47SigOil-21
❑ 48AngTeal-2
❑ 49BowPCL-24
❑ 53MotCoo-53
❑ 73OPC-569
❑ 73Top-569
❑ 74OPC-144
❑ 74Top-144
Adams, Ricky Lee
❑ 78DayBeaAT-1
❑ 80ElPasDT-21
❑ 81HolMilT-7
❑ 82HolMilT-13
❑ 84Don-85
❑ 84Nes792-487
❑ 84Top-487
❑ 84TopTif-487
❑ 85PhoGiaC-188
❑ 86PhoFirP-1
❑ 86Top-153
❑ 86TopTif-153
Adams, Rollo
❑ 81CliGiaT-26
Adams, Sparky (Earl John)
❑ 25Exh-17
❑ 26Exh-17
❑ 27Exh-9
❑ 29ExhFou-13
❑ 31CarMet-1
❑ 31Exh-15
❑ 33DouDisP-1
❑ 33ExhFou-8
❑ 33Gou-213
❑ 34DiaMatCSB-1
❑ 34DiaStaR-24
❑ 34TarThoBD-1
❑ 35GouPuzR-1H
❑ 35GouPuzR-3F
❑ 35GouPuzR-14F
❑ 35GouPuzR-15F
❑ 93ConTSN-695
Adams, Spencer (Spencer Dewey)
❑ 22Zee-116
❑ 24Zee-19
❑ 27MidBre-21
❑ 75SenTCM1-1
Adams, Steve
❑ 86WatPirP-1
❑ 87MacPirP-13
❑ 88SalBucS-1
❑ 89EasLeaDDP-DD27
❑ 89HarSenP-295
❑ 89HarSenS-1
❑ 90EasLeaAP-EL30
❑ 90HarSenP-1185
❑ 90HarSenS-1
❑ 91CarMudLD-101
❑ 91CarMudP-1078
❑ 91LinDriAA-101
Adams, Terry
❑ 76CedRapGT-1
Adams, Terry Wayne
❑ 91HunCubC-1
❑ 91HunCubP-3324
❑ 92ClaFS7-217
❑ 92PeoChiC-19
❑ 92PeoChiTI-1
❑ 92StaCluD-1
❑ 93DayCubC-2
❑ 93DayCubF-850
❑ 94DayCubC-2
❑ 94DayCubF-2343
❑ 95OrlCubF-1

❑ 96Bow-207
❑ 96BowFoi-207
❑ 96ColCho-491
❑ 96ColChoGS-491
❑ 96ColChoSS-491
❑ 96CubFle-1
❑ 96Fin-B212
❑ 96FinRef-B212
❑ 96FleUpd-U108
❑ 96FleUpdTC-U108
❑ 96LeaSigA-3
❑ 96LeaSigAG-3
❑ 96LeaSigAS-3
❑ 96Pin-389
❑ 96PinFoil-389
❑ 96Ult-447
❑ 96UltGolM-447
❑ 96UppDec-488U
❑ 97Cir-252
❑ 97CirRav-252
❑ 97ColCho-54
❑ 97Fle-272
❑ 97FleTif-272
❑ 97PacPriGotD-GD116
❑ 97StaClu-161
❑ 97StaCluMOP-161
❑ 97Top-191
❑ 97Ult-403
❑ 97UltGolME-403
❑ 97UltPlaME-403
❑ 98Fin-124
❑ 98FinNo--124
❑ 98FinNo-R-124
❑ 98FinRef-124
❑ 98PacOnl-134
❑ 98PacOnlR-134
❑ 98PacOnlWC-134
❑ 98StaCluFDI-129
❑ 98StaCluI-129
❑ 98StaCluOneK-129
❑ 98StaCluPP-129
❑ 98Top-78
❑ 98TopChr-78
❑ 98TopChrR-78
❑ 98TopDevR-78
❑ 98TopDia-78
❑ 98TopMiniC-78
❑ 98Ult-400
❑ 98UltGolM-400
❑ 98UltMas-400
❑ 98UltPlaM-400
❑ 98UppDec-324

Adams, Tim
❑ 89CarNewE-20
❑ 97ButCopKB-1
❑ 97ButCopKK-1

Adams, Tommy
❑ 89AriStaB-1
❑ 91BelMarCB-16
❑ 91BelMarP-3677
❑ 91Cla/Bes-430
❑ 91ClaDraP-49
❑ 92CalLeaACL-45
❑ 92ClaFS7-245
❑ 92SanBerC-1
❑ 92SanBerSF-969
❑ 92StaCluD-2
❑ 92UppDecML-247
❑ 92UppDecMLPotY-PY13
❑ 93Bow-683
❑ 93ClaFS7-178
❑ 93ClaGolF-141
❑ 94UppDecML-222
❑ 96SigRooOJ-1
❑ 96SigRooOJS-1

Adams, Willie Edward
❑ 92TopTra-1T
❑ 92TopTraG-1T
❑ 93StaCluM-183
❑ 94Bow-632
❑ 94ModA'sC-2
❑ 94ModA'sF-3055
❑ 94VerBeaDC-2
❑ 94VerBeaDF-85
❑ 95Bow-156
❑ 95HunStaTI-2
❑ 95Top-641
❑ 96Bow-133
❑ 96BowFoi-133
❑ 97A'sMot-23
❑ 97Bow-321
❑ 97BowCerBlaIA-CA3
❑ 97BowCerBluIA-CA3
❑ 97BowCerGolIA-CA3
❑ 97BowInt-321
❑ 97Cir-314
❑ 97CirRav-314
❑ 97ColCho-13
❑ 97Fin-12
❑ 97FinRef-12
❑ 97Fle-182
❑ 97FleTif-182
❑ 97StaClu-375
❑ 97StaCluMOP-375
❑ 97Top-337
❑ 97UppDec-243
❑ 98ColCho-194
❑ 98Top-227
❑ 98TopChr-227
❑ 98TopChrR-227
❑ 98TopDevR-227
❑ 98TopDia-227
❑ 98TopMiniC-227
❑ 98UppDec-466

Adamson, Joel
❑ 90PriPatD-1
❑ 92ClaFS7-74
❑ 92ClePhiC-14
❑ 92ClePhiF-2045
❑ 93HigDesMC-2
❑ 93HigDesMF-31
❑ 93Top-613
❑ 93TopGol-613
❑ 93TopInaM-613
❑ 93TopInaR-613
❑ 93TopMic-613
❑ 94PorSeaDF-669
❑ 94PorSeaDTI-7
❑ 95ChaKniTI-5
❑ 96ChaKniB-6
❑ 98DiaMcD-1
❑ 98PorSeaD5AQ-30

Adamson, Mike (John Michael)
❑ 67BalOriP-1
❑ 69OPC-66
❑ 69Top-66
❑ 71OPC-362
❑ 71Top-362
❑ 91OriCro-5

Adamson, Tony
❑ 91PerHeaF-18
❑ 93AusFut-70
❑ 93AusFut-121
❑ 95AusFut-85
❑ 95AusFut-104

Adamson, Wade
❑ 80OrlTwiT-1

Adcock, Joe (Joseph Wilbur)
❑ 47Exh-2A
❑ 47Exh-2B
❑ 51Bow-323
❑ 52Bow-69
❑ 52Top-347
❑ 53BowC-151
❑ 53BraJohC-17
❑ 53BraMer-1
❑ 53BraSpiaS3-1
❑ 53BraSpiaS7-1
❑ 54Bow-96
❑ 54BraJohC-9
❑ 54BraMer-2
❑ 54BraSpiaSP-2
❑ 55Bow-218
❑ 55BraGolS-16
❑ 55BraJohC-9
❑ 55BraSpiaSD-2
❑ 56BraBilaBP-2
❑ 56Top-320
❑ 56YelBasP-2
❑ 57Bra8x1-1
❑ 57BraSpiaS4-2
❑ 57Top-117
❑ 58BraJayP-2
❑ 58Top-325
❑ 58Top-351
❑ 59Top-315
❑ 60BraLaktL-2
❑ 60BraSpiaS-2
❑ 60NuHi-33
❑ 60Top-3
❑ 60TopVen-3
❑ 61NuSco-433
❑ 61Pos-104A
❑ 61Pos-104B
❑ 61Raw-1
❑ 61Top-245
❑ 61TopStal-38
❑ 62BraJayP-2
❑ 62Jel-145
❑ 62Pos-145A
❑ 62Pos-145B
❑ 62PosCan-145
❑ 62SalPlaC-125
❑ 62ShiPlaC-125
❑ 62Top-265
❑ 62TopBuc-2
❑ 62TopStal-144
❑ 63BasMagM-2
❑ 63Fle-46
❑ 63IndJayP-1
❑ 63Jel-148
❑ 63Pos-148
❑ 63Top-170
❑ 67Top-563
❑ 72LauGreF-42
❑ 78AtlCon-2
❑ 78BraTCC-2
❑ 78TCM60I-73
❑ 78TCM60I-108
❑ 80Bra195T-28
❑ 82GSGalAG-7
❑ 82TCMGreS-17
❑ 83Bra53F-9
❑ 83TopRep5-347
❑ 85TCMPhoC-12
❑ 86BraGreT-1
❑ 88PacLegI-31
❑ 89SweBasG-6
❑ 90HOFStiB-50
❑ 90LSUTigGM-12
❑ 91TopArc1-285
❑ 92BazQua5A-1
❑ 94TedWil-40
❑ 94TedWil-145

Adderly, Ken
❑ 87MiaMarP-18

Addis, Bob (Robert Gorden)
❑ 52Top-259
❑ 53BowC-94
❑ 53Top-157
❑ 79DiaGre-224
❑ 82Bow195E-260
❑ 83TopRep5-259
❑ 91TopArc1-157

Adduci, Jim (James David)
❑ 82ArkTraT-18
❑ 83LouRedR-19
❑ 84LouRedR-19
❑ 85VanCanC-206
❑ 86VanCanP-1
❑ 87DenZepP-16
❑ 87Don-495
❑ 88BrePol-14
❑ 88BreTeal-1
❑ 89Fle-176
❑ 89FleGlo-176
❑ 89PhiTas-37
❑ 89Sco-587
❑ 89Top-338
❑ 89TopTif-338
❑ 90CMC-238
❑ 90ProAAAF-306
❑ 90ScrRedBC-12
❑ 90ScrRedBP-604
❑ 94BreMilB-2

Aderholt, Morrie
❑ 90DodTar-888

Adge, Jason
❑ 95WatIndTI-1

Adkins, Adrian
❑ 89PriPirS-1

Adkins, Dewey (John Dewey)
❑ 48AngTeal-3

Adkins, Doc (Merle Theron)
❑ 09ColChiE-5
❑ 09T206-391
❑ 11T205-187
❑ 12ColRedB-5
❑ 12ColTinT-5
❑ 12ImpTobC-18

Adkins, Rob
❑ 92MyrBeaHC-4
❑ 92St.CatBJC-15
❑ 92St.CatBJF-3376
❑ 93ClaGolF-176
❑ 93MedHatBJF-3729
❑ 93MedHatBJSP-11

Adkins, Steve
❑ 87Ft.LauYP-22
❑ 87PriWilYP-20
❑ 88PriWilYS-1
❑ 89BasAmeAPB-AA3
❑ 89EasLeaAP-11
❑ 89Ft.LauYS-1
❑ 90AlbDecGB-28
❑ 90ClaUpd-T2
❑ 90CMC-201
❑ 90ColCliC-1
❑ 90ColCliP-17
❑ 90ColCliP-667
❑ 90ProAAAF-317
❑ 90TopTVY-35
❑ 91ColCliLD-101
❑ 91ColCliP-1
❑ 91ColCliP-588
❑ 91LinDriAAA-101
❑ 91Sco-716
❑ 91ScoRoo-16
❑ 91TopDeb90-2
❑ 92IowCubF-4044
❑ 92IowCubS-201
❑ 93SyrChiF-990
❑ 94BowBayF-2404
❑ 94RocRedWTI-1

Adkins, Terry
❑ 85PriWilPT-6

Adkins, Tim
❑ 92HigSchPLS-20
❑ 93ClaGolF-171
❑ 93St.CatBJC-2
❑ 93St.CatBJF-3965
❑ 94HagSunC-2
❑ 94HagSunF-2721
❑ 95DunBluJTI-1
❑ 96DunBluJB-1
❑ 96DunBluJTI-1
❑ 97DunBluJTI-1

Adler, Felix
❑ 40WheM4-13
❑ 41WheM5-14

Adler, Jimmy
❑ 90BriTigS-1

Adler, Marcus
❑ 88FayGenP-1085
❑ 89LakTigS-1

Adlesh, Dave (David George)
❑ 65AstJayP-1
❑ 67Ast-1
❑ 67OPC-51
❑ 67Top-51
❑ 68Top-576
❑ 69Top-341
❑ 87AstShowSTh-1
❑ 87AstShowSTh-27

Adolfo, Carlos
❑ 94VerExpC-1
❑ 94VerExpF-3919
❑ 96DelShoB-5
❑ 96DelShoUB-5
❑ 98JupHamQ-23

Adriana, Sharnol
❑ 91St.CatBJC-5
❑ 91St.CatBJP-3400
❑ 92DunBluJF-2004
❑ 93KnoSmoF-1255
❑ 94SyrChiF-975
❑ 94SyrChiTI-1
❑ 95KnoSmoF-45
❑ 96SyrChiTI-1
❑ 98DunBluJTI-3

Adriance, Dan
❑ 86TriTriC-190
❑ 87BelBreP-23
❑ 88BelBreGS-6
❑ 89SalSpuCLC-124
❑ 89SalSpuP-1818

Afenir, Tom
❑ 95WatIndTI-2
❑ 96WatIndTI-1

Afenir, Troy
❑ 85OscAstTI-13
❑ 86ColAstP-1
❑ 87ColAstP-4
❑ 88ColAstB-23
❑ 89HunStaB-3
❑ 90CMC-599
❑ 90ProAAAF-142
❑ 90TacTigC-22
❑ 90TacTigP-95
❑ 91Fle-1
❑ 91LinDriAAA-526
❑ 91Sco-745
❑ 91TacTigLD-526
❑ 91TacTigP-2308
❑ 92Bow-509
❑ 92DonRoo-2
❑ 92Fle-248
❑ 92Lea-525
❑ 92LeaBlaG-525
❑ 92NasSouS-276
❑ 92RedKah-38
❑ 92Sco-407
❑ 92StaClu-613
❑ 92StaCluECN-613
❑ 93IndIndF-1491

Affeldt, Jeremy
❑ 98LanLugQ-1

Agacinski, Kenny
❑ 93ForMyeMC-29
❑ 94ForMyeMC-30

Agado, David
❑ 89BatCliP-1926
❑ 90MarPhiP-3204

Agamennone, Brandon
❑ 98VerExpO-7

Agan, Tim
❑ 83TolMudHT-24
❑ 84TolMudHT-19

Agar, Jeff
❑ 86LakTigP-1
❑ 87GleFalTP-12

Agbayani, Benny
❑ 93PitMetC-2
❑ 93PitMetF-3722
❑ 94FloStaLAF-FSL37
❑ 94St.LucMC-2
❑ 94St.LucMF-1206
❑ 95StLucMTI-4
❑ 96BinMetB-1
❑ 96HilStaHWB-32
❑ 96NorTidB-6
❑ 97NorTid-6
❑ 97NorTidB-6
❑ 98NorTidP-1
❑ 98NorTidQ-1
❑ 99Bow-429
❑ 99BowGol-429
❑ 99BowInt-429

Agee, Tommie Lee
❑ 65OPC-166
❑ 65Top-166
❑ 66OPC-164
❑ 66Top-164
❑ 66TopVen-164
❑ 66WhiSoxTI-2
❑ 67Baz-2
❑ 67CokCapWS-18
❑ 67DexPre-2
❑ 67OPCPapI-4
❑ 67Top-455
❑ 67TopPos-4
❑ 67TopVen-224
❑ 68AtlOilPBCC-2
❑ 68Baz-6
❑ 68Baz-15
❑ 68Kah-B2
❑ 68Top-465
❑ 69MetBoyS-3
❑ 69MetCit-1
❑ 69MetNewYDN-1
❑ 69MetTeal-1
❑ 69MilBra-4
❑ 69MLBOffS-163
❑ 69Top-364
❑ 69TopSta-61
❑ 69TopTeaP-24
❑ 70DayDaiNM-84
❑ 70Kel-11
❑ 70MetTeal-1
❑ 70MetTra-23C
❑ 70MLBOffS-73
❑ 70OPC-50
❑ 70OPC-198
❑ 70OPC-307
❑ 70Top-50
❑ 70Top-198
❑ 70Top-307
❑ 70TopPos-13
❑ 70TopSup-42
❑ 71BazNumT-16
❑ 71BazUnn-1
❑ 71Kel-46
❑ 71MetTeal-1
❑ 71MetTealA-1
❑ 71MetTealC-1
❑ 71MLBOffS-145
❑ 71OPC-310
❑ 71Top-310
❑ 71TopCoi-91
❑ 71TopSup-36
❑ 71TopTat-73
❑ 72MetTeal-1
❑ 72MilBra-5
❑ 72OPC-245
❑ 72SevTraC-2
❑ 72Top-245
❑ 73OPC-420
❑ 73Top-420
❑ 74OPC-630
❑ 74Top-630
❑ 74TopTra-630T
❑ 81TCM60I-315
❑ 81TCM60I-322
❑ 86MetGreT-6
❑ 87AstShoSTw-26
❑ 89Met196C-1
❑ 89MetRinP69-3
❑ 90PacLeg-2
❑ 90SweBasG-19
❑ 91LinDri-30
❑ 91MetWIZ-2
❑ 91SweBasG-1
❑ 93UppDecAH-2
❑ 94Met69CCPP-7
❑ 94Met69CS-6
❑ 94Met69T-5
❑ 94TedWil-57
❑ 94UppDecAH-6
❑ 94UppDecAH-120
❑ 94UppDecAH-207
❑ 94UppDecAH1-6
❑ 94UppDecAH1-120
❑ 94UppDecAH1-207
❑ 99SpollIGotG-25
❑ 99SpollIGotGA-1

Agganis, Harry
❑ 55Top-152
❑ 81RedSoxBG2S-1
❑ 81RedSoxBG2S-12

Agler, Joe (Joseph Abram)
❑ 09ColChiE-6
❑ 12ColRedB-6
❑ 12ColTinT-6

Agnew, James
❑ 09ObaT21-77
❑ 09ObaT21-253
❑ 11PacCoaBD-2
❑ 11Zee-2
❑ 12ObaPreT-2

Agnew, Sam (Samuel Lester)
❑ 12HomRunKE-77
❑ 12Zee-136
❑ 14B18B-29A
❑ 14B18B-29B
❑ 15SpoNewM-2
❑ 16SpoNewM-2
❑ 17ColE13-1
❑ 20Zee-101
❑ 22Zee-94
❑ 23Zee-120
❑ 23Zee-121
❑ 24Zee-85
❑ 25Zee-104
❑ 26Zee-130
❑ 27Zee-107
❑ 28Zee-1

Agnoly, Earl
❑ 96KanCouCTI-1

Agostinelli, Peter
❑ 93BatCliCB-2
❑ 93BatCliF-3135
❑ 93SpaPhiC-2
❑ 93SpaPhiF-1046
❑ 94ClePhiC-2
❑ 94ClePhiF-2516
❑ 95ClePhiF-207

Agostinelli, Sal
❑ 84SavCarT-22
❑ 86St.PetCP-1
❑ 87ArkTraP-15
❑ 88LouRedBC-21
❑ 88LouRedBP-424
❑ 88LouRedBTI-5
❑ 89ReaPhiB-22
❑ 89ReaPhiP-654
❑ 89ReaPhiS-1
❑ 90CMC-237
❑ 90ReaPhiB-13
❑ 90ReaPhiP-1222
❑ 90ReaPhiS-1
❑ 90ScrRedBC-11
❑ 91LinDriAAA-476
❑ 91ScrRedBLD-476
❑ 91ScrRedBP-2540

Agosto, Juan Roberto
❑ 81EdmTraRR-5

❑ 82EdmTraT-12
❑ 84Don-208
❑ 84Fle-50
❑ 84Nes792-409
❑ 84Top-409
❑ 84TopTif-409
❑ 84WhiSoxTV-1
❑ 85Don-526
❑ 85Fle-506
❑ 85Top-351
❑ 85TopTif-351
❑ 85WhiSoxC-50
❑ 86Don-488
❑ 86Fle-197
❑ 86Top-657
❑ 86TopTif-657
❑ 86WhiSoxC-50
❑ 87Top-277
❑ 87TopTif-277
❑ 87TucTorP-1
❑ 88AstMot-24
❑ 88AstPol-1
❑ 88Fle-437
❑ 88FleGlo-437
❑ 88Sco-558
❑ 88ScoGlo-558
❑ 88StaLinAst-1
❑ 88TopTra-2T
❑ 88TopTraT-2T
❑ 89AstLenH-17
❑ 89AstMot-23
❑ 89AstSmo-1
❑ 89BlaYNPRWL-70
❑ 89Bow-321
❑ 89BowTif-321
❑ 89Don-354
❑ 89Fle-348
❑ 89FleGlo-348
❑ 89PanSti-81
❑ 89Sco-283
❑ 89Top-559
❑ 89TopTif-559
❑ 89UppDec-251
❑ 90AstLenH-1
❑ 90AstMot-26
❑ 90Don-477
❑ 90Fle-220
❑ 90FleCan-220
❑ 90OPC-181
❑ 90PubIntS-85
❑ 90Sco-284
❑ 90Top-181
❑ 90TopTif-181
❑ 90UppDec-450
❑ 91Bow-402
❑ 91CarPol-49
❑ 91Don-531
❑ 91Fle-497
❑ 91Lea-404
❑ 91OPC-703
❑ 91Sco-591
❑ 91StaClu-570
❑ 91Top-703
❑ 91TopDesS-703
❑ 91TopMic-703
❑ 91TopTif-703
❑ 91TopTra-1T
❑ 91TopTraT-1T
❑ 91UppDec-569
❑ 91UppDec-788
❑ 92CarPol-1
❑ 92Don-37
❑ 92Fle-574
❑ 92OPC-421
❑ 92Sco-329
❑ 92Top-421
❑ 92TopGol-421
❑ 92TopGolW-421
❑ 92TopMic-421
❑ 92Ult-562
❑ 92UppDec-693
❑ 93LasVegSF-935

Agosto, Stevenson
❑ 96CedRapKTI-1
❑ 97LakElsSG-1
❑ 98RanCucQG-1
❑ 98RanCucQG-1

Agramonte, Freddy
❑ 94GreFalDSP-1

Aguado, Victor
❑ 93UtiBluSC-2
❑ 93UtiBluSF-3538

Aguayo, Carmelo
❑ 82TulDriT-14

Aguayo, Luis
❑ 82Don-622
❑ 82Fle-238
❑ 82Top-449
❑ 83Don-546
❑ 83PhiTas-1
❑ 83PorBeaT-1
❑ 83Top-252
❑ 84PhiTas-28
❑ 85Don-503
❑ 85PhiTas-11
❑ 85PhiTas-28
❑ 85Top-663
❑ 85TopTif-663
❑ 86Don-503
❑ 86Fle-433
❑ 86PhiTas-16
❑ 86Top-69
❑ 86TopTif-69
❑ 87Fle-169
❑ 87FleGlo-169
❑ 87OPC-18
❑ 87PhiTas-16
❑ 87Top-755
❑ 87TopTif-755
❑ 88BlaYNPRWL-98
❑ 88Don-185
❑ 88Fle-297
❑ 88FleGlo-297
❑ 88PhiTas-1
❑ 88Sco-499
❑ 88ScoGlo-499
❑ 88StaLinPh-1
❑ 88Top-356
❑ 88TopBig-226
❑ 88TopTif-356
❑ 89BlaYNPRWL-103
❑ 89BlaYNPRWLU-44
❑ 89BlaYNPRWLU-57
❑ 89Bow-88
❑ 89BowTif-88
❑ 89Don-551
❑ 89Fle-249
❑ 89FleGlo-249
❑ 89IndTeal-1
❑ 89Sco-436
❑ 89Top-561
❑ 89TopTif-561
❑ 89UppDec-156
❑ 91LinDriAAA-351
❑ 91PawRedSDD-1
❑ 91PawRedSLD-351
❑ 91PawRedSP-43
❑ 92PawRedSS-351
❑ 92YanWIZ8-1
❑ 93PawRedSDD-1
❑ 93PawRedSF-2425
❑ 93PawRedSTI-25
❑ 94PawRedSDD-1
❑ 94PawRedSF-961
❑ 95PawRedSDD-1
❑ 95PawRedTI-16
❑ 97DunDonPPS-1

Aguiar, Douglas
❑ 95MarPhiTI-1
❑ 96-97LinVen-186
❑ 96MarPhiB-1
❑ 97BatCliTI-24

Aguilar, Alonso
❑ 96SpoIndB-3

Aguilar, Carlos
❑ 95LinVen-129
❑ 96-97LinVen-77

Aguilar, Jose
❑ 85MexCitTT-14

Aguilar, Mark
❑ 88StoPorCLC-191
❑ 88StoPorP-723
❑ 89MadMusS-1
❑ 96ColSilB-1

Aguilera, Rick
❑ 85TidTidT-11
❑ 86BasStaB-1
❑ 86Don-441
❑ 86Fle-74
❑ 86KayB-1
❑ 86Lea-216
❑ 86MetColP-14
❑ 86MetTCM-1
❑ 86MetWorSC-6
❑ 86Top-599
❑ 86TopTif-599
❑ 87ClaGam-79
❑ 87Don-620
❑ 87Fle-1
❑ 87FleExcS-2
❑ 87FleGlo-1
❑ 87Lea-89
❑ 87MetColP-22
❑ 87OPC-103
❑ 87Top-103
❑ 87TopTif-103
❑ 88Don-446
❑ 88DonTeaBM-446
❑ 88Fle-127
❑ 88FleGlo-127
❑ 88Lea-231
❑ 88MetColP-13
❑ 88MetKah-15
❑ 88Sco-521
❑ 88ScoGlo-521
❑ 88ScoYouS2-21
❑ 88Top-434
❑ 88TopClo-1
❑ 88TopTif-434
❑ 89Don-526
❑ 89DonBasB-265
❑ 89Fle-27
❑ 89FleGlo-27
❑ 89MetColP-21
❑ 89MetKah-2
❑ 89Sco-327
❑ 89Top-257
❑ 89TopTif-257
❑ 89UppDec-563
❑ 90Bow-405
❑ 90BowTif-405
❑ 90Don-391
❑ 90DonBesA-79
❑ 90Fle-365
❑ 90FleCan-365
❑ 90Lea-38
❑ 90OPC-711
❑ 90PubIntS-127
❑ 90Sco-519
❑ 90Top-711
❑ 90TopBig-284
❑ 90TopTif-711
❑ 90UppDec-11
❑ 91BasBesAotM-1
❑ 91Bow-334
❑ 91DodPho-8
❑ 91Don-172
❑ 91Fle-602
❑ 91Lea-471
❑ 91MetWIZ-3
❑ 91OPC-318
❑ 91PanFreS-308
❑ 91PanSti-243
❑ 91RedFolS-2
❑ 91Sco-170
❑ 91Sco100S-67
❑ 91StaClu-76
❑ 91Stu-81
❑ 91Top-318
❑ 91TopDesS-318
❑ 91TopMic-318
❑ 91TopTif-318
❑ 91Ult-185
❑ 91UppDec-542
❑ 91USPlaCA-7H
❑ 92Bow-89
❑ 92Don-95
❑ 92Fle-195
❑ 92Hig5-81
❑ 92Lea-34
❑ 92LeaBlaG-34
❑ 92OPC-44
❑ 92OPCPre-62
❑ 92Pin-211
❑ 92Sco-42
❑ 92Sco100S-4
❑ 92ScoProP-11
❑ 92StaClu-726
❑ 92StaCluD-3
❑ 92StaCluNC-726
❑ 92Stu-201
❑ 92Top-44
❑ 92TopGol-44
❑ 92TopGolW-44
❑ 92TopKid-114
❑ 92TopMic-44
❑ 92TriPla-65
❑ 92Ult-88
❑ 92UppDec-130
❑ 93Bow-453
❑ 93Don-19
❑ 93Fin-22
❑ 93FinRef-22
❑ 93Fla-233
❑ 93Fle-261
❑ 93Lea-32
❑ 93OPC-25
❑ 93PacSpa-168
❑ 93Pin-386
❑ 93PinTeaP-B11
❑ 93Sco-64
❑ 93Sel-206
❑ 93SelStaL-68
❑ 93SP-244
❑ 93StaClu-354
❑ 93StaCluFDI-354
❑ 93StaCluM-122
❑ 93StaCluMOP-354
❑ 93Top-625
❑ 93TopGol-625
❑ 93TopInaM-625
❑ 93TopInaR-625
❑ 93TopMic-625
❑ 93Ult-228
❑ 93UppDec-303
❑ 93UppDecGold-303
❑ 94Bow-132
❑ 94ColC-473
❑ 94ColChoGS-473
❑ 94ColChoSS-476
❑ 94Don-503
❑ 94Fin-280
❑ 94FinRef-280
❑ 94Fla-311
❑ 94Fle-198
❑ 94FleExtB-113
❑ 94FUnPac-73
❑ 94Lea-45
❑ 94OPC-92
❑ 94Pin-293
❑ 94PinArtP-293
❑ 94PinMusC-293
❑ 94RedFolMI-21
❑ 94Sco-129
❑ 94ScoGolR-129
❑ 94Sel-160
❑ 94SP-182
❑ 94SPDieC-182
❑ 94StaClu-275
❑ 94StaCluFDI-275
❑ 94StaCluGR-275
❑ 94StaCluMOP-275
❑ 94Top-280
❑ 94TopGol-280
❑ 94TopSpa-280
❑ 94TriPla-251
❑ 94Ult-384
❑ 94UppDec-141
❑ 94UppDecED-141
❑ 95Baz-50
❑ 95Bow-391
❑ 95ColCho-480
❑ 95ColChoGS-480
❑ 95ColChoSE-224
❑ 95ColChoSEGS-224
❑ 95ColChoSESS-224
❑ 95ColChoSS-480
❑ 95Don-53
❑ 95DonPreP-53
❑ 95DonTopotO-16
❑ 95Fin-154
❑ 95FinRef-154
❑ 95Fla-277
❑ 95Fle-196
❑ 95FleTeaL-9
❑ 95Lea-66
❑ 95Pac-244
❑ 95PacPri-78
❑ 95Pin-325
❑ 95PinArtP-325
❑ 95PinMusC-325
❑ 95RedFol-24
❑ 95Sco-122
❑ 95ScoGolR-122
❑ 95ScoPlaTS-122
❑ 95SP-169
❑ 95SPCha-128
❑ 95SPChaDC-128
❑ 95SPSil-169
❑ 95StaClu-177
❑ 95StaClu-404
❑ 95StaCluFDI-177
❑ 95StaCluMOP-177
❑ 95StaCluMOP-404
❑ 95StaCluSTWS-177
❑ 95StaCluSTWS-404
❑ 95Stu-60
❑ 95Top-65
❑ 95TopCyb-47
❑ 95TopEmb-62
❑ 95TopEmbGI-62
❑ 95Ult-71
❑ 95UltGolM-71
❑ 95UppDec-191
❑ 95UppDec-482
❑ 95UppDecED-191
❑ 95UppDecEDG-191
❑ 95UppDecSE-216
❑ 95UppDecSEG-216
❑ 96Baz-45
❑ 96ColCho-605
❑ 96ColChoGS-605
❑ 96ColChoSS-605
❑ 96Don-14
❑ 96DonPreP-14
❑ 96EmoXL-79
❑ 96Fla-110
❑ 96Fle-21
❑ 96FleTif-21
❑ 96FleUpd-U50
❑ 96FleUpdTC-U50
❑ 96Lea-133
❑ 96LeaPrePB-133
❑ 96LeaPrePG-133
❑ 96LeaPrePS-133
❑ 96Pac-256
❑ 96Pin-355
❑ 96PinFoil-355
❑ 96ProSta-130
❑ 96Sco-105
❑ 96ScoDugC-A74
❑ 96ScoDugCAP-A74
❑ 96SP-112
❑ 96StaClu-35
❑ 96StaClu-264
❑ 96StaCluEPB-35
❑ 96StaCluEPG-35
❑ 96StaCluEPS-35
❑ 96StaCluMOP-35
❑ 96StaCluMOP-264
❑ 96Top-305
❑ 96TopGal-65
❑ 96TopGalPPI-65
❑ 96TopLas-113
❑ 96Ult-12
❑ 96Ult-371
❑ 96UltGolM-12
❑ 96UltGolM-371
❑ 96UppDec-369
❑ 97Cir-202
❑ 97CirRav-202
❑ 97ColCho-156
❑ 97Don-113
❑ 97DonGolPP-113
❑ 97DonSilPP-113
❑ 97Fle-142
❑ 97FleTif-142
❑ 97Pac-132
❑ 97PacLigB-132
❑ 97PacSil-132
❑ 97Sco-125
❑ 97ScoArtPWB-125
❑ 97ScoPreS-125
❑ 97ScoShoS-125
❑ 97ScoShoSAP-125
❑ 97StaClu-310
❑ 97StaCluMOP-310
❑ 97Top-405
❑ 97Ult-85
❑ 97UltGolME-85
❑ 97UltPlaME-85
❑ 97UppDec-103
❑ 98ColCho-412
❑ 98Fin-269
❑ 98FinNo--269
❑ 98FinNo-R-269
❑ 98FinRef-269
❑ 98Fle-171
❑ 98Pac-128
❑ 98PacAur-50
❑ 98PacOme-139
❑ 98PacOmeR-139
❑ 98PacOnl-417
❑ 98PacOnlR-417
❑ 98PacOnlWC-417
❑ 98PacPar-60
❑ 98PacParC-60
❑ 98PacParG-60
❑ 98PacParHS-60
❑ 98PacParPB-60
❑ 98PacParR-60
❑ 98PacPlaB-128
❑ 98PacRedT-128
❑ 98PacSil-128
❑ 98SPxFin-298
❑ 98SPxFinR-298
❑ 98SPxFinS-298
❑ 98StaCluFDI-349
❑ 98StaClul-349
❑ 98StaCluOneK-349
❑ 98StaCluPP-349
❑ 98Top-95
❑ 98TopChr-95
❑ 98TopChrR-95
❑ 98TopDevR-95
❑ 98TopDia-95
❑ 98TopMiniC-95
❑ 98TopOpeD-47
❑ 98UppDec-132
❑ 98UppDecSF-79
❑ 99Fle-332
❑ 99FleSta9-332
❑ 99FleWarT-332
❑ 99MetUni-216
❑ 99MetUniGM-216
❑ 99MetUniPMG-216
❑ 99Pac-244
❑ 99PacCroC-157
❑ 99PacCroCPB-157
❑ 99PacPar-131
❑ 99PacParC-131
❑ 99PacParG-131
❑ 99PacParHoloGold-131
❑ 99PacParHS-131
❑ 99PacParOD-131
❑ 99PacParPB-131
❑ 99PacParRed-131
❑ 99PacPlaB-244
❑ 99PacRed-244
❑ 99SkyPre-162
❑ 99SkyPreR-162
❑ 99StaClu-276
❑ 99StaCluFDI-276
❑ 99StaCluOoaK-276
❑ 99StaCluPP-276
❑ 99Top-158
❑ 99TopChr-158
❑ 99TopChrR-158
❑ 99TopMVPP-158
❑ 99UppDec-412
❑ 99UppDecEL1-412
❑ 99UppDecEL2-412
❑ 99Vic-228

Aguirre, Hank (Henry John)
❑ 57Top-96
❑ 58Top-337
❑ 59TigGraASP-2
❑ 59Top-36
❑ 59TopVen-36
❑ 60Top-546
❑ 61Top-324
❑ 61TopStal-144
❑ 62TigPosCF-1
❑ 62Top-407
❑ 63Jel-54
❑ 63Pos-54
❑ 63SalMetC-32
❑ 63TigJayP-1
❑ 63Top-6
❑ 63Top-257
❑ 64TigJayP-1
❑ 64TigLid-1
❑ 64Top-39
❑ 64TopCoi-74
❑ 64TopSta-38
❑ 64TopStaU-2
❑ 64TopTatl-23
❑ 64TopVen-39
❑ 65TigJayP-1
❑ 65Top-522
❑ 66OPC-113
❑ 66TigVolC-1
❑ 66Top-113
❑ 66TopVen-113
❑ 67Top-263
❑ 67TopVen-252
❑ 68Top-553
❑ 69CubJewT-2
❑ 69OPC-94
❑ 69Top-94
❑ 70Top-699
❑ 73OPC-81
❑ 73Top-81A
❑ 73Top-81B
❑ 74OPC-354
❑ 74Top-354
❑ 75TucTorC-21
❑ 75TucTorTI-1
❑ 78TCM60I-225
❑ 81TigDetN-122
❑ 90DodTar-3

Aguirre, Jose
❑ 94CedRapKC-2
❑ 94CedRapKF-1101
❑ 95CedRapKTI-12

- 95LakElsSTI-1

Ah Yat, Paul
- 97AugGre-6
- 98Bow-417
- 98BowChr-417
- 98BowChrGA-417
- 98BowChrGAR-417
- 98BowChrI-417
- 98BowChrIR-417
- 98BowChrR-417
- 98BowGolA-417
- 98BowInt-417
- 98CarLeaTPQ-21
- 98LynHilQ-1
- 99BasAmeTP-1
- 99BasAmeTPG-1

Ahearne, Pat
- 92LakTigF-2271
- 93LakTigC-2
- 93LakTigF-1299
- 94TreThuF-2111
- 95BowBes-B30
- 95BowBesR-B30
- 95TolMudHTI-5
- 95TopTra-88T
- 97AlbDukGS-1

Ahern, Brian
- 88CapCodPPaLP-30
- 89EugEmeB-23
- 90AppFoxBS-2
- 90AppFoxP-2086
- 90CMC-875
- 92MemChiS-426
- 92OmaRoyF-2952
- 92SkyAA F-178
- 93OmaRoyF-1671

Ahern, Jeff
- 82DanSunF-3
- 83RedPioT-1

Ahlers, Steve
- 98ButCopKG-1

Ahr, Jeff
- 87NewOriP-20
- 88HagSunS-1

Ahrens, Kelly
- 90BenBucL-6
- 90CliGiaB-3
- 90CliGiaP-2551

Ahumada, Alejandro
- 97LowSpiB-4
- 98MicBatCM-5

Aiello, Talbot
- 81WisRapTT-20

Aikens, Willie Mays
- 75QuaCitAT-3
- 77SalLakCGC-22
- 78SalLakCGC-22
- 78SSP270-201
- 79RoyTeal-1
- 80OPC-191
- 80Top-368
- 81AllGamPI-1
- 81CokTeaS-73
- 81Don-220
- 81Fle-43
- 81OPC-23
- 81RoyPol-1
- 81RoyProPS-1
- 81Top-524
- 81TopScr-27
- 81TopSti-84
- 82Don-412
- 82Fle-404
- 82FleSta-206
- 82OPC-35
- 82Roy-1
- 82Top-35
- 82TopSti-196
- 82TopStiV-196
- 83AllGamPI-1
- 83Don-212
- 83Fle-104
- 83FleSta-1
- 83FleSti-101
- 83OPC-136
- 83RoyPol-1
- 83RoyPos-1
- 83Top-136
- 84BluJayFS-2
- 84Don-155
- 84Fle-341
- 84FleUpd-1
- 84Nes792-685
- 84OPC-137
- 84Top-685
- 84TopSti-276
- 84TopTif-685
- 84TopTra-1T
- 84TopTraT-1T
- 85BluJayFS-2
- 85Fle-97
- 85OPC-147
- 85Top-436
- 85TopTif-436
- 89PacSenL-147
- 89T/MSenL-2
- 89TopSenL-57
- 90EliSenL-107

Ainge, Danny (Daniel Rae)
- 77Spo-8608
- 78SyrChiT-1
- 79SyrChiTI-4
- 80SyrChiT-20
- 81Don-569
- 81Fle-418
- 81TopTra-727
- 82Don-638
- 82Fle-608
- 82OPC-125
- 82Top-125
- 84OCoandSI-223
- 92SyrChiTT-1

Ainsmith, Eddie (Edward W.)
- 10JuJuDE-1
- 12T207-2
- 14B18B-38
- 15SpoNewM-3
- 16SpoNewM-3
- 22E120-226
- 22W572-1
- 22W573-2
- 90DodTar-4

Ainsworth, Jeff
- 89MisStaB-45

Airoso, Kurt
- 98LakTigM-19

Aitcheson, Kevin
- 83KnoBluJT-15

Aitchison, Raleigh L.
- 90DodTar-889

Aker, Jack Delane
- 66Top-287
- 66TopVen-287
- 67CokCapAt-7
- 67DexPre-3
- 67OPC-110
- 67Top-110
- 68Top-224
- 68TopVen-224
- 69MLBOffS-91
- 69PilPos-9
- 69Top-612
- 69TopSta-221
- 69TopTeaP-9
- 69YanPhoS-54
- 70MLBOffS-241
- 70OPC-43
- 70Top-43
- 70YanPhoS-1
- 71MLBOffS-481
- 71OPC-593
- 71Top-593
- 71YanArcO-1
- 72Top-769
- 73OPC-262
- 73Top-262
- 74MetDaiPA-5
- 74OPC-562
- 74Top-562
- 77LynMetT-1
- 77PilPosR-9
- 78TCM60I-274
- 81TidTidT-21
- 82TidTidT-19
- 83BufBisT-25
- 83Pil69G-27
- 84BufBisT-18
- 85WatIndT-22
- 86IndOhH-NNO
- 86IndTeal-1
- 87IndGat-NNO
- 88BurBraP-29
- 91MetWIZ-4
- 92YanWIZ6-1
- 92YanWIZ7-1

Akerfelds, Darrel
- 84MadMusP-25
- 85HunStaJ-32
- 86TacTigP-1
- 87TacTigP-2
- 88ColSprSSC-1
- 88ColSprSSP-1537
- 88IndTeal-1
- 88Sco-632
- 88ScoGlo-632
- 88Top-82
- 88TopTif-82
- 89OklCit8C-1
- 89OklCit8P-1532
- 89RanSmo-1
- 90FleUpd-41
- 90Lea-526
- 90PhiTas-1
- 90TopTra-1T
- 90TopTraT-1T
- 91Bow-493
- 91Don-110
- 91Fle-386
- 91OPC-524
- 91PhiMed-1
- 91Sco-223
- 91StaClu-581
- 91Top-524
- 91TopDesS-524
- 91TopMic-524
- 91TopTif-524
- 91UppDec-619
- 92OklCit8S-313
- 93RanKee-45
- 93SyrChiF-991
- 95MidAngOHP-1
- 95MidAngTI-1
- 97CliLumG-1
- 98RanCucQG-2
- 98RanCucQG-2

Akers, Chad
- 93BilMusF-3950
- 93BilMusSP-16
- 94ChaWheC-3
- 94ChaWheF-2708
- 98FarRedHM-1
- 98FarRedHM-2

Akers, Howard
- 86KinEagP-1

Akimoto, Ratoo
- 87SanJosBP-14

Akin, Aaron
- 97Bow-432
- 97BowChr-292
- 97BowChrI-292
- 97BowChrIR-292
- 97BowChrR-292
- 97BowInt-432
- 97TopSta-114
- 97TopStaAM-114
- 98BesNumOP-1
- 98Bow-128
- 98BowChr-128
- 98BowChrGA-128
- 98BowChrGAR-128
- 98BowChrI-128
- 98BowChrIR-128
- 98BowChrR-128
- 98BowGolA-128
- 98BowInt-128
- 98KanCouC-1
- 98KanCouCCP-1
- 98MidLeaPM-11
- 98SP MinPE-59
- 98SPMin-59
- 98StaCluFDI-399
- 98StaCluI-399
- 98StaCluOneK-399
- 98StaCluPP-399
- 98Top-247
- 98TopChr-247
- 98TopChrR-247
- 98TopDevR-247
- 98TopDia-247
- 98TopMiniC-247

Akin, Jay
- 98StoPorG-1

Akin, Roy
- 09ObaT21-254
- 11PacCoaBD-3
- 11Zee-3
- 12ObaPreT-3

Akins, Carlos
- 96BluOriB-4
- 97CarLeaTP-18
- 97FreKey-4

Akins, Daron
- 86DavLipB-1

Akins, Sid
- 85BurRanT-12
- 85Top-390
- 85TopTif-390
- 87DurBulP-5
- 88BobCamRB-4
- 88RicBraC-7
- 88RicBraP-14
- 89GreBraP-1151

Akins, Tom
- 85IndIndTI-27
- 89IndIndP-1216

Ako, Gerry
- 80HolMilT-23
- 81ElPasDT-9
- 81VanCanT-22

Ala, Aurelio
- 52LavPro-106

Alamo, Efrain
- 97AshTou-1
- 97PorRocG-1
- 98AshTouM-1
- 99BasAmeTP-2
- 99BasAmeTPG-2

Alario, Dave
- 86BakDodP-1

Alayon, Elvis
- 96LowSpiB-4
- 97LowSpiB-5

Alazaus, Shawn
- 93OneYanC-2
- 93OneYanF-3494

Alba, Gibson
- 85DomLeaS-162
- 85SyrChiT-1
- 86SyrChiP-1
- 87BufBisP-14
- 88LouRedBC-6
- 88LouRedBP-442
- 88LouRedBTI-6
- 89LouRedBC-1
- 89LouRedBP-1252
- 89LouRedBTI-7
- 90CMC-102
- 90LouRedBC-2
- 90LouRedBLBC-5
- 90LouRedBP-393
- 90ProAAAF-507
- 90TopTVCa-37
- 91RicBraBC-5
- 91RicBraP-2559
- 91RicBraTI-7

Albaladejo, Randy
- 93AshTouC-2
- 93AshTouF-2278
- 94AubAstC-1
- 94AubAstF-3761
- 94QuaCitRBC-2
- 94QuaCitRBF-536

Albano, Tom
- 98OrlRayM-27
- 98OrlRayM-28

Albarado, Marc
- 94UtiBluSC-1
- 94UtiBluSF-3824

Albaral, Randy
- 96MedHatBJTI-1
- 97St.CatSB-5
- 98HagSunM-5

Alberro, Hector
- 87BelBreP-20
- 90JohCitCS-1

Alberro, Jose
- 91GulCoaRSP-2
- 92ChaRanF-2217
- 92GasRanC-6
- 93TulDriF-2725
- 93TulDriTI-1
- 94OklCit8F-1487
- 95FleUpd-80
- 95RanCra-2
- 96OklCit8B-4
- 96Sco-226
- 97OklCit8-5
- 98ColCliD-1
- 98ColCliM-4

Albert, Gus (August P.)
- 87OldJudN-1

Albert, Rashad
- 96BriWhiSB-8
- 97BriWhiSB-21
- 98HicCraUO-6

Albert, Rick (Richard)
- 75LynRanT-1
- 83AndBraT-2
- 85GreBraTI-1
- 86GreBraTI-1
- 87RicBraC-26
- 87RicBraT-26
- 88SumBraP-416
- 93DurBulC-27
- 93DurBulF-504
- 94DurBulC-29
- 94DurBulF-346
- 94DurBulTI-1
- 96EugEmeB-26
- 97DanBraB-4

Albert, Tim
- 92BelBreCB-15
- 92BelBreFI-416

Albert, William
- 29Zee-1

Alberts, Butch (Francis Burt)
- 77SalLakCGC-25
- 78SyrChiT-2
- 79SyrChiTI-14
- 80SyrChiT-10
- 80SyrChiTI-1

Albertson, John
- 88IdaFalBP-1839

Albertus, Meliano
- 98St.CatSM-2

Alborano, Pete
- 87EugEmeP-2660
- 88CarLeaAS-22
- 88VirGenS-1
- 89BasCitRS-2
- 89Sta-62
- 90MemChiB-3
- 90MemChiP-1020
- 90MemChiS-1
- 90StaFS7-82
- 91LinDriAA-401
- 91MemChiLD-401
- 91MemChiP-665
- 92ReaPhiF-585
- 92ReaPhiS-526

Albosta, Ed (Edward John)
- 47SigOil-1
- 78DodTCM4-6
- 90DodTar-5

Albrecht, Andy (Andrew)
- 88CapCodPPaLP-159
- 91OneYanP-4164
- 92PriWilCC-7
- 92PriWilCF-159
- 93SanJosGC-2
- 93SanJosGF-22

Albrecht, Jon
- 95SpoIndTI-3

Albright, Dave
- 81ChaRoyT-9

Albright, Eric
- 89NiaFalRP-2
- 90LakTigS-1
- 91Cla/Bes-39
- 91LakTigC-14
- 92LakTigC-3

Albright, Gilbert
- 80CliGiaT-25

Albro, Daryl
- 89MisStaB-1
- 90MisStaB-1
- 91MisStaB-1
- 92MisStaB-1
- 93MisStaB-1

Albury, Allan
- 91BriBanF-2

Albury, Vic (Victor)
- 72Top-778
- 73TacTwiC-1
- 74OPC-605
- 74Top-605
- 75OPC-368
- 75Top-368
- 75TopMin-368
- 75TwiPos-1
- 75TwiTeal-1
- 76OPC-336
- 76SSP-205
- 76Top-336
- 77Top-536
- 82WatIndF-3
- 82WatIndT-27
- 83ChaChaT-20
- 83WatIndF-27
- 84MaiGuiT-9

Alcala y porte, Bastidas
- 80VenLeaS-30

Alcala, Jesus
- 80VenLeaS-13
- 82OneYanT-12

Alcala, Juan
- 98EveAquG-1

Alcala, Julio
- 86FloStaLAP-2
- 86Ft.MyeRP-1
- 87MemChiB-5
- 87MemChiP-24
- 89MemChiB-6
- 89MemChiP-1183
- 89MemChiS-1

Alcala, Santo
- 76OPC-589
- 76Top-589
- 77ExpPos-1
- 77PepGloD-52
- 77Top-636
- 78OPC-36
- 78Top-321
- 81PorBeaT-3

Alcantara, Alvin
- 98JohCCTI-1

Alcantara, Francisco
- 90NiaFalRP-15
- 91RenSilSCLC-20

Alcantara, Israel
- 93BurBeeC-2
- 93BurBeeF-163
- 94WesPalBEC-1
- 94WesPalBEF-45
- 95HarSenTI-5
- 95SPML-94
- 96BesAutSA-1
- 96FleUpd-U146
- 96FleUpdTC-U146
- 96HarSenB-4
- 96Ult-500
- 96UltGolM-500
- 96UltGolP-2
- 96UltGolPHGM-2
- 97BesAutAS-1
- 97HarSen-2
- 98ReaPhiUM-2

Alcantara, Jose
- 75ForLauYS-24
- 76ForLauYS-4
- 77ForLauYS-4

Alcaraz, Luis (Angel Luis)
- 69Top-437
- 70RoyTeal-3
- 90DodTar-6

Alcazar, Jorge
- 86PenWhiSP-1
- 87BirBarB-27
- 88VanCanC-23
- 88VanCanP-772

Alcock, Scotty (John Forbes)
- 15Zee-23
- 18Zee-94
- 20Zee-135
- 21Zee-152

Alcott, Charles
- 87OldJudN-2

Alder, Jimmy
- 90BriTigP-3168
- 91FayGenC-17
- 91FayGenP-1176
- 92LakTigC-11
- 92LakTigF-2284
- 93LonTigF-2313

Alderman, Kurt
- 94VerExpC-2
- 94VerExpF-3911

Aldred, Scott
- 87FayGenP-11
- 88LakTigS-1
- 89LonTigP-1368
- 90Bow-344
- 90BowTif-344
- 90CMC-379
- 90ProAAAF-371
- 90TolMudHC-2
- 90TolMudHP-141
- 91Bow-147
- 91Don-422
- 91LinDriAAA-576
- 91OPC-658
- 91Sco-740
- 91ScoRoo-3
- 91StaClu-429
- 91TolMudHLD-576
- 91TolMudHP-1922
- 91Top-658

❑ 91TopDeb90-3
❑ 91TopDesS-658
❑ 91TopMic-658
❑ 91TopTif-658
❑ 91UppDec-7
❑ 92Cla1-T3
❑ 92Cla2-T75
❑ 92ClaGam-147
❑ 92Don-486
❑ 92Fle-127
❑ 92OPC-198
❑ 92Pin-354
❑ 92ProFS7-66
❑ 92Sco-729
❑ 92Sco100RS-41
❑ 92StaClu-762
❑ 92TigTeal-1
❑ 92Top-198
❑ 92TopGol-198
❑ 92TopGolW-198
❑ 92TopMic-198
❑ 93Don-733
❑ 93PacSpa-419
❑ 93RocStaC-7
❑ 93RocUSPC-4C
❑ 93RocUSPC-13H
❑ 93StaClu-573
❑ 93StaCluFDI-573
❑ 93StaCluMOP-573
❑ 93Top-463
❑ 93TopGol-463
❑ 93TopInaM-463
❑ 93TopInaR-463
❑ 93TopMic-463
❑ 93Ult-338
❑ 96LeaSigEA-1
❑ 98DurBulTI-1

Aldrete, Mike
❑ 86FleUpd-1
❑ 86GiaPos-1
❑ 86PhoFirP-2
❑ 86StaoftFT-38
❑ 87Don-450
❑ 87Fle-264
❑ 87FleGlo-264
❑ 87GiaMot-24
❑ 87GiaPos-1
❑ 87Top-71
❑ 87TopTif-71
❑ 88Don-362
❑ 88DonBasB-191
❑ 88Fle-76
❑ 88FleGlo-76
❑ 88GiaMot-5
❑ 88GiaPos-1
❑ 88OPC-351
❑ 88PanSti-426
❑ 88RedFolSB-1
❑ 88Sco-556
❑ 88ScoGlo-556
❑ 88ScoYouSI-35
❑ 88Spo-80
❑ 88StaLinG-1
❑ 88Top-602
❑ 88TopBig-119
❑ 88TopSti-89
❑ 88TopTif-602
❑ 89Bow-368
❑ 89BowTif-368
❑ 89Don-140
❑ 89DonTra-25
❑ 89ExpPos-1
❑ 89Fle-323
❑ 89FleGlo-323
❑ 89FleUpd-95
❑ 89OPC-9
❑ 89PanSti-219
❑ 89Sco-82
❑ 89ScoRoo-68T
❑ 89Top-158
❑ 89TopSti-80
❑ 89TopTif-158
❑ 89UppDec-239
❑ 89UppDec-738
❑ 90ExpPos-1
❑ 90OPC-589
❑ 90Sco-220A
❑ 90Sco-220B
❑ 90Top-589
❑ 90TopTif-589
❑ 90UppDec-415
❑ 91Fle-224
❑ 91OPC-483
❑ 91Sco-447
❑ 91Top-483
❑ 91TopDesS-483
❑ 91TopMic-483
❑ 91TopTif-483
❑ 92ColSprSSF-756
❑ 92ColSprSSS-76
❑ 92Don-621
❑ 92Fle-102
❑ 92OPC-256
❑ 92PanSti-45
❑ 92Sco-351
❑ 92StaClu-305
❑ 92Top-256
❑ 92TopGol-256
❑ 92TopGolW-256
❑ 92TopMic-256
❑ 93TacTigF-3042
❑ 94A'sMot-19
❑ 94Fle-252
❑ 94Sco-277
❑ 94ScoGolR-277
❑ 95AthMot-8
❑ 95Sco-192
❑ 95ScoGolR-192
❑ 95ScoPlaTS-192
❑ 96AngMot-22
❑ 96Bow-101
❑ 96BowFoi-101
❑ 96LeaSigEA-2
❑ 97ColSprSATTI-26

Aldrete, Richard
❑ 87EveGiaC-6
❑ 88CalLeaACLC-7
❑ 88SanJosGCLC-116
❑ 88SanJosGP-119
❑ 89ShrCapP-1847
❑ 90ShrCapP-1448
❑ 90ShrCapS-1
❑ 91LinDriAAA-376
❑ 91PhoFirLD-376
❑ 91PhoFirP-78
❑ 92ArkTraS-26

Aldrich, Jay
❑ 83BelBreFr-8
❑ 86ElPasDP-1
❑ 87DenZepP-4
❑ 88BlaYNPRWLU-30
❑ 88BrePol-33
❑ 88DenZepC-7
❑ 88DenZepP-1270
❑ 88Don-460
❑ 88Fle-155
❑ 88FleGlo-155
❑ 88Sco-578
❑ 88ScoGlo-578
❑ 88Top-616
❑ 88TopTif-616
❑ 89DenZepC-1
❑ 89DenZepP-42
❑ 90CMC-307
❑ 90ProAAAF-452
❑ 90RocRedWC-6
❑ 90RocRedWP-695
❑ 91OriCro-6
❑ 94BreMilB-3

Aldrich, Russell
❑ 80WatRedT-20
❑ 81WatRedT-18

Aldrich, Tom
❑ 88BriTigP-1881
❑ 89LonTigP-1386
❑ 90LonTigP-1272

Aldridge, Cory
❑ 98DanBraQ-1

Aldridge, Steve
❑ 93OneYanC-3
❑ 93OneYanF-3507
❑ 94GreBatF-477
❑ 97GreBatC-2

Aldridge, Vic
❑ 20Zee-1
❑ 21Nei-74
❑ 21Zee-1
❑ 22E120-151
❑ 22W572-2
❑ 22W573-3
❑ 28W56PlaC-C12A
❑ 94ConTSN-1114
❑ 94ConTSNB-1114

Alegre, Paul
❑ 90SalSpuCLC-133
❑ 90SalSpuP-2729

Alejo, Bob
❑ 96A'sMot-28
❑ 97A'sMot-28

Alejo, Nigel
❑ 94VenLinU-148
❑ 95LinVen-131
❑ 95MidLeaA-1
❑ 96-97LinVen-215
❑ 96BreCouMB-4
❑ 97BreCouMB-2

Aleno, Chuck (Charles)
❑ 45CenFlo-1

Aleshire, Troy
❑ 86AubAstP-1

Alesio, Chris
❑ 90HamRedB-22
❑ 90HamRedS-1

Alevras, Chad
❑ 97LowSpiB-6
❑ 98MicBatCM-6

Alexander, Bob (Robert S.)
❑ 52LaPat-1
❑ 52Par-63
❑ 53ExhCan-34
❑ 55OriEss-2
❑ 91OriCro-7
❑ 97BalOriP-2

Alexander, Chad
❑ 95AubAstTI-13
❑ 96Bow-330
❑ 96BowFoi-330
❑ 96QuaCitRB-7
❑ 97KisCob-2
❑ 98JacGenM-1

Alexander, Chuck (Charles)
❑ 88BurIndP-1785
❑ 89WatIndS-1

Alexander, Dale (David Dale)
❑ 29ExhFou-23
❑ 29PorandAR-2
❑ 31Exh-23
❑ 32OrbPinNP-27
❑ 32OrbPinUP-1
❑ 33DouDisP-2
❑ 33GeoCMil-1
❑ 33Gou-221
❑ 33TatOrb-1
❑ 33TatOrbSDR-181
❑ 33WorCig-2
❑ 61Fle-91
❑ 79RedSoxEF-8
❑ 81TigDetN-69
❑ 81TigSecNP-13
❑ 85BigLeaC3-57
❑ 88ConSer4-1
❑ 92ConTSN-616

Alexander, Dave
❑ 89AriStaB-2
❑ 89SalLakTTI-22
❑ 90MiaMirIS-1

Alexander, Don
❑ 90AubAstB-23
❑ 90AubAstP-3418
❑ 91AubAstC-25
❑ 91AubAstP-4290
❑ 93AshTouC-27
❑ 93AshTouF-2294
❑ 94AubAstC-25
❑ 94AubAstF-3776
❑ 95AubAstTI-26
❑ 95OdgRapTI-1
❑ 96QuaCitRB-3
❑ 97MobBayBB-6
❑ 98MobBayBTI-1

Alexander, Doyle L.
❑ 72OriPos-1
❑ 72Top-579
❑ 73BalOriP-1
❑ 73BalOriP-2
❑ 73OPC-109
❑ 73OriJohP-13
❑ 73OriTeal-1
❑ 73Top-109
❑ 74OPC-282
❑ 74Top-282
❑ 75BalOriP-1
❑ 75OPC-491
❑ 75Top-491
❑ 75TopMin-491
❑ 76BalOriP-1
❑ 76OPC-638
❑ 76SSP-374
❑ 76Top-638
❑ 77Hos-140
❑ 77Top-254
❑ 78OPC-52
❑ 78RanBurK-4
❑ 78RCColC-66
❑ 78SSP270-105
❑ 78Top-146
❑ 79OPC-230
❑ 79Top-442
❑ 80Top-67
❑ 81AllGamPI-163
❑ 81Don-448
❑ 81Fle-255
❑ 81GiaTeal-1
❑ 81Top-708
❑ 81TopTra-728
❑ 82Don-96
❑ 82Fle-383
❑ 82Top-364
❑ 82TopTra-1T
❑ 82YanPhoA-1
❑ 83Don-451
❑ 83Top-512
❑ 84BluJayFS-3
❑ 84Don-439
❑ 84Fle-146
❑ 84Nes792-677
❑ 84OPC-112
❑ 84Top-677
❑ 84TopTif-677
❑ 85AllGamPI-73
❑ 85BluJayFS-3
❑ 85Don-561
❑ 85Fle-98
❑ 85Lea-134
❑ 85OPC-218
❑ 85OPCPos-21
❑ 85SpoIndGC-1
❑ 85Top-218
❑ 85TopMin-218
❑ 85TopSti-365
❑ 85TopTif-218
❑ 86BluJayAF-2
❑ 86BluJayFS-2
❑ 86Don-390
❑ 86Fle-51
❑ 86FleLimE-1
❑ 86Lea-182
❑ 86OPC-196
❑ 86Spo-133
❑ 86Top-196
❑ 86TopMinL-34
❑ 86TopTif-196
❑ 87Don-657
❑ 87DonHig-52
❑ 87Fle-510
❑ 87FleGlo-510
❑ 87OPC-249
❑ 87Top-686
❑ 87TopTif-686
❑ 88Don-584
❑ 88DonBasB-13
❑ 88Fle-51
❑ 88FleGlo-51
❑ 88FleMin-21
❑ 88FleStiC-23
❑ 88OPC-316
❑ 88Sco-610
❑ 88ScoGlo-610
❑ 88StaLinTi-1
❑ 88TigPep-19
❑ 88TigPol-1
❑ 88Top-492
❑ 88TopBig-34
❑ 88TopTif-492
❑ 89Bow-94
❑ 89BowTif-94
❑ 89Don-178
❑ 89DonAll-12
❑ 89DonBasB-125
❑ 89Fle-128
❑ 89FleBasA-1
❑ 89FleGlo-128
❑ 89OPC-77
❑ 89RedFolSB-1
❑ 89Sco-129
❑ 89Spo-211
❑ 89TigMar-19
❑ 89TigPol-19
❑ 89Top-77
❑ 89TopBig-182
❑ 89TopSti-274
❑ 89TopTif-77
❑ 89UppDec-298
❑ 90DodTar-7
❑ 90Don-62
❑ 90Fle-599
❑ 90FleCan-599
❑ 90KayB-1
❑ 90OPC-748
❑ 90PublntS-467
❑ 90Sco-237
❑ 90Top-748
❑ 90TopTif-748
❑ 90UppDec-330
❑ 91OriCro-8
❑ 92YanWIZ7-2
❑ 92YanWIZ8-2
❑ 93RanKee-46

Alexander, Eric
❑ 89BluOriS-1
❑ 89Sta-113
❑ 91BluOriC-11
❑ 91BluOriP-4138
❑ 93GleFalRC-2
❑ 93GleFalRF-3992
❑ 94SavCarC-2
❑ 94SavCarF-495

Alexander, Gary
❑ 87AriWilP-1
❑ 88TexLeaAGS-4
❑ 88TulDriTI-12
❑ 89TexLeaAGS-31
❑ 89TulDriGS-5
❑ 89TulDriTI-1
❑ 90Bes-291
❑ 90EasLeaAP-EL19
❑ 90ReaPhiB-14
❑ 90ReaPhiP-1224
❑ 90ReaPhiS-2
❑ 90StaFS7-79
❑ 91LinDriAAA-477
❑ 91ScrRedBLD-477
❑ 91ScrRedBP-2542
❑ 92ScrRedBF-2451
❑ 92ScrRedBS-476

Alexander, Gary Wayne
❑ 75LafDriT-12
❑ 76PheGiaCr-25
❑ 76PhoGiaCa-11
❑ 76PhoGiaCC-1
❑ 76PhoGiaVNB-1
❑ 77GiaTeal-1
❑ 77PhoGiaCC-1
❑ 77PhoGiaCP-1
❑ 77Top-476
❑ 78OPC-72
❑ 78Top-624
❑ 79Hos-57
❑ 79OPC-168
❑ 79Top-332
❑ 80IndTeal-1
❑ 80OPC-78
❑ 80Top-141
❑ 81Don-200
❑ 81Fle-398
❑ 81Top-416
❑ 81TopTra-729
❑ 82Fle-475
❑ 82Top-11
❑ 89PacSenL-141

Alexander, Gerald
❑ 90ChaRanS-1
❑ 90OklCit8P-422
❑ 90ProAAAF-668
❑ 91Cla3-T11
❑ 91Don-419
❑ 91Fle-278
❑ 91LinDriAAA-301
❑ 91OklCit8LD-301
❑ 91OklCit8P-170
❑ 91RanMot-27
❑ 91Sco-733
❑ 91TopDeb90-4
❑ 91UppDecFE-72F
❑ 92Don-578
❑ 92Fle-297
❑ 92OklCit8F-1905
❑ 92OklCit8S-301
❑ 92Sco-163
❑ 92Sco100RS-99
❑ 92StaClu-185
❑ 93RanKee-47

Alexander, Grover C.
❑ 09SpoNewSM-74
❑ 11L1L-114
❑ 11S81LarS-89
❑ 13NatGamW-1
❑ 13TomBarW-1
❑ 14CraJacE-37
❑ 14FatPlaT-1
❑ 15CraJacE-37
❑ 15SpoNewM-4
❑ 16BF2FP-84
❑ 16FleBreD-2
❑ 16SpoNewM-4
❑ 17ColE13-2
❑ 17HolBreD-1
❑ 19W514-65
❑ 20NatCarE-2
❑ 20W516-9
❑ 21E121So1-2
❑ 21E121So8-1A
❑ 21E121So8-1B
❑ 21Exh-2
❑ 21Nei-69
❑ 21OxfConE-1
❑ 22AmeCarE122-1
❑ 22E120-152
❑ 22W572-3
❑ 22W573-4
❑ 22W575-2
❑ 22WilPatV-18
❑ 23W501-59
❑ 23W503-38
❑ 23W515-49
❑ 23WilChoV-2
❑ 24MrsShePP-1
❑ 25Exh-18
❑ 26SpoComoA-2
❑ 27AmeCarE126-13
❑ 27Exh-29
❑ 27MidBre-1
❑ 27YorCarE-44
❑ 28Exh-29
❑ 28W502-44
❑ 28W512-2
❑ 28Yue-44
❑ 29ExhFou-15
❑ 30SchR33-19
❑ 30SchR33-48
❑ 31W517-15
❑ 36Halof FP-1
❑ 39PC7AlbHoF-14
❑ 40PlaBal-119
❑ 48ExhHoF-1
❑ 48SweSpoT-11
❑ 49LeaPre-1
❑ 50CalHOFW-1
❑ 50CubGreB-1
❑ 51TopConMA-1
❑ 53ArtHalofFP-1
❑ 60ExhWriH-1
❑ 60Fle-5
❑ 61Fle-2
❑ 61GolPre-2
❑ 63BasMagM-3
❑ 63BazA-29
❑ 63HalofFB-21
❑ 67TopVen-171
❑ 68LauWorS-23
❑ 69Baz-2
❑ 69Baz-3
❑ 70FleWorS-23
❑ 71FleWorS-13
❑ 72FleFamF-13
❑ 72LauGreF-41
❑ 74CapPub-71
❑ 76GrePlaG-16
❑ 76JerJonPC-7
❑ 76MotOldT-10
❑ 76RowExh-6
❑ 76ShaPiz-14
❑ 77BobParHoF-1
❑ 77GalGloG-153
❑ 77PhiFav-23
❑ 77ShaPiz-5
❑ 78DexHaloFP-1
❑ 80Lau300-8
❑ 80LauFamF-40
❑ 80MarExhH-1
❑ 80PacLeg-124
❑ 80PerHaloFP-14
❑ 80SSPHOF-14
❑ 81ConTSN-10
❑ 82DavHaloFB-2
❑ 82DiaCla-94
❑ 82TCMGreP-18
❑ 83DonHOFH-23
❑ 83PhiPosGM-7
❑ 83PhiPosGPaM-2
❑ 84GalHaloFRL-14
❑ 84OCoandSI-137
❑ 85Woo-2
❑ 86ConSer1-3
❑ 86PhiGreT-5
❑ 87ConSer2-4
❑ 87HygAllG-2
❑ 88ConSer3-2
❑ 88GreBasS-9
❑ 89HOFStiB-72
❑ 90PerGreM-42

❑ 90SweBasG-30
❑ 91ConTSN-32
❑ 91SweBasG-128
❑ 92CarMcD-16
❑ 92ConTSN-534
❑ 92ConTSN-630
❑ 92ConTSNCI-15
❑ 92CubOldS-1
❑ 93ActPacA-92
❑ 93ActPacA2-26G
❑ 93ConTSN-932
❑ 93CraJac-7
❑ 93SpeHOF2-2
❑ 94ConTSN-1223
❑ 94ConTSNB-1223
❑ 94UppDecTAE-38
❑ 95ConTSN-1321
❑ 99UppDecCL-12
❑ 99UppDecCLCC-12

Alexander, Jon
❑ 88BasCitRS-3
❑ 89BasCitRS-3

Alexander, Jordy
❑ 97SpoIndG-1
❑ 98LanLugQ-2

Alexander, Manny
❑ 89BluOriS-2
❑ 89Sta-114
❑ 90Bes-241
❑ 90WauTimB-20
❑ 90WauTimP-2135
❑ 91CarLeaAP-CAR4
❑ 91Cla/Bes-97
❑ 91FreKeyC-15
❑ 91FreKeyP-2369
❑ 92Bow-41
❑ 92ClaFS7-119
❑ 92HagSunF-2560
❑ 92HagSunS-251
❑ 92OPC-551
❑ 92ProFS7-9
❑ 92SkyAA F-104
❑ 92Top-551
❑ 92TopGol-551
❑ 92TopGolW-551
❑ 92TopMic-551
❑ 93Bow-577
❑ 93Don-11
❑ 93FleMajLP-A4
❑ 93LimRocDWB-49
❑ 93LimRocDWB-145
❑ 93Pin-244
❑ 93PinRooTP-7
❑ 93RocRedWF-245
❑ 93Sco-234
❑ 93Sel-391
❑ 93Top-587
❑ 93TopGol-587
❑ 93TopInaM-587
❑ 93TopInaR-587
❑ 93TopMic-587
❑ 93UppDec-5
❑ 93UppDecGold-5
❑ 94Bow-215
❑ 94Cla-97
❑ 94OriPro-1
❑ 94OriUSPC-2S
❑ 94Pac-24
❑ 94Pin-35
❑ 94PinArtP-35
❑ 94PinMusC-35
❑ 94RocRedWF-1002
❑ 94RocRedWTI-2
❑ 94StaCluT-300
❑ 94StaCluTFDI-300
❑ 95BalOriP-1
❑ 95FleUpd-1
❑ 95TopTra-59T
❑ 95UltGolMR-M1
❑ 96BalOriP-1
❑ 96ColCho-53
❑ 96ColChoGS-53
❑ 96ColChoSS-53
❑ 96Don-210
❑ 96DonPreP-210
❑ 96Fle-1
❑ 96FleTif-1
❑ 96LeaSigA-4
❑ 96LeaSigAG-4
❑ 96LeaSigAS-4
❑ 96Pac-237
❑ 96PacPri-P73
❑ 96PacPriG-P73
❑ 96Sco-393
❑ 96Top-34
❑ 96Ult-1
❑ 96UltGolM-1
❑ 96UppDec-11
❑ 97Fle-695
❑ 97FleTif-695
❑ 97Pac-16
❑ 97PacLigB-16
❑ 97PacSil-16
❑ 98Pac-246
❑ 98PacOnl-135
❑ 98PacOnlR-135
❑ 98PacOnlWC-135
❑ 98PacPlaB-246
❑ 98PacRedT-246
❑ 98PacSil-246
❑ 98PinSna-CC2
❑ 98StaCluFDI-186
❑ 98StaClul-186
❑ 98StaCluOneK-186
❑ 98StaCluPP-186
❑ 98Top-424
❑ 98TopChr-424
❑ 98TopChrR-424
❑ 98TopDevR-424
❑ 98TopDia-424
❑ 98TopMiniC-424
❑ 98UppDec-327
❑ 99Fle-315
❑ 99FleSta9-315
❑ 99FleWarT-315
❑ 99Pac-79
❑ 99PacCroC-53
❑ 99PacCroCPB-53
❑ 99PacPlaB-79
❑ 99PacRed-79

Alexander, Matt
❑ 92DavLipB-1
❑ 93DavLipB-1

Alexander, Matt (Matthew)
❑ 73WicAerJPKB-1
❑ 76OPC-382
❑ 76SSP-501
❑ 76Top-382
❑ 77Top-644
❑ 78Top-102
❑ 81PorBeaT-4
❑ 81Top-68
❑ 82Top-528

Alexander, Pat
❑ 78CedRapGT-1
❑ 81ShrCapT-23

Alexander, Phil
❑ 91AdeGiaF-12

Alexander, Rob
❑ 88MadMusP-1
❑ 89ModA'sC-7
❑ 89ModA'sCLC-270

Alexander, Roberto
❑ 79CliDodT-4
❑ 82VerBeaDT-1
❑ 84AlbDukCr-166

Alexander, Roger
❑ 79RicBraT-12

Alexander, Tim
❑ 80AndBraT-6
❑ 83DurBulT-27
❑ 84DurBulT-10

Alexander, Tommy
❑ 85FreGiaSB-25
❑ 87WicPilRD-3
❑ 88JacExpB-9
❑ 88JacExpP-982

Alexander, Walt (Walter E.)
❑ 14Zee-27
❑ 16FleBreD-3
❑ 17ColE13-3

Alexis, Juan
❑ 91MarPhiC-28
❑ 91MarPhiP-3442

Aleys, Maximo
❑ 89EveGiaS-1
❑ 89Sta-187
❑ 90CliGiaB-22
❑ 90CliGiaP-2548
❑ 91Cla/Bes-87
❑ 91SanJosGC-13
❑ 91SanJosGP-1

Alfano, Donald
❑ 49AngTeal-2
❑ 49W725AngTI-2

Alfano, Jeff
❑ 96OgdRapTI-6
❑ 98StoPorG-2

Alfaro, Flavio
❑ 85DurBulT-18
❑ 85Top-391
❑ 85TopTif-391

Alfaro, Hermanos
❑ 80VenLeaS-134

Alfaro, Jesus
❑ 76VenLeaS-212
❑ 80VenLeaS-109
❑ 80VenLeaS-239
❑ 80WicAerT-14
❑ 84ChaO'sT-19
❑ 86ElPasDP-3
❑ 87ElPasDP-15
❑ 87TexLeaAF-30
❑ 88MidAngGS-19
❑ 89ElPasDGS-20
❑ 90El PasDAGTI-4
❑ 90ElPasDGS-3
❑ 90TexLeaAGS-10
❑ 93LinVenB-144
❑ 94VenLinU-55
❑ 95LinVen-18
❑ 96-97LinVen-163

Alfaro, Jose
❑ 74CedRapAT-14
❑ 75DubPacT-22
❑ 76VenLeaS-186
❑ 80VenLeaS-123
❑ 80VenLeaS-233

Alfonseca, Antonio
❑ 93JamExpC-2
❑ 94KanCouCC-2
❑ 94KanCouCF-152
❑ 94KanCouCTI-1
❑ 95PorSeaDTI-1
❑ 96BesAutS-2
❑ 96BowBes-107
❑ 96BowBesAR-107
❑ 96BowBesR-107
❑ 96ChaKniB-7
❑ 97ChaKni-7
❑ 98Fle-79
❑ 98Pac-293
❑ 98PacOmeRS-5
❑ 98PacOmeRST5-5
❑ 98PacOnl-288
❑ 98PacOnlR-288
❑ 98PacOnlWC-288
❑ 98PacPlaB-293
❑ 98PacRedT-293
❑ 98PacSil-293
❑ 98PorSeaD5AQ-22
❑ 98Ult-290
❑ 98UltGolM-290
❑ 98UltMas-290
❑ 98UltPlaM-290
❑ 99Pac-170
❑ 99PacCroC-111
❑ 99PacCroCPB-111
❑ 99PacPlaB-170
❑ 99PacRed-170

Alfonso, Carlos
❑ 75IowOakT-1
❑ 76IndIndTI-24
❑ 82AubAstT-18
❑ 86TucTorP-2
❑ 92GiaMot-28
❑ 92GiaPacGaE-1
❑ 93PhoFirF-1532
❑ 94PhoFirF-1535
❑ 96GiaMot-28
❑ 98GiaMot-28

Alfonso, Elieser
❑ 97JohCitCTI-1
❑ 98NewJerCM-2

Alfonso, Ossie
❑ 84VisOakT-6
❑ 85OrlTwiT-14

Alfonzo, Edgar (Edgardo)
❑ 86QuaCitAP-1
❑ 87PalSprP-20
❑ 88PalSprACLC-96
❑ 88QuaCitAGS-19
❑ 89PalSprACLC-44
❑ 89PalSprAP-464
❑ 91MidAngOHP-1
❑ 91PalSprAP-2021
❑ 92CalLeaACL-43
❑ 92PalSprAC-23
❑ 92PalSprAF-845
❑ 93BowBayF-2193
❑ 93ClaGolF-30
❑ 93LinVenB-151
❑ 94BowBayF-2417
❑ 95LinVen-7
❑ 95LinVen-307
❑ 95RocRedWTI-6
❑ 95SigRoo-2
❑ 95SigRooSig-2
❑ 96-97LinVen-136
❑ 96MidAngB-5
❑ 96MidAngOHP-1
❑ 98St.LucMM-29

Alfonzo, Edgardo Antonio
❑ 92PitMetC-10
❑ 92PitMetF-3301
❑ 93ClaFS7-92
❑ 93ClaGolF-210
❑ 93ExcFS7-68
❑ 93FloStaLAF-38
❑ 93LinVenB-129
❑ 93St.LucMC-1
❑ 93St.LuMF-2926
❑ 94BinMetF-708
❑ 94Bow-156
❑ 94BowBes-B13
❑ 94BowBesR-B13
❑ 94ClaGolF-166
❑ 94ExcFS7-232
❑ 94MetShuST-3
❑ 94UppDecML-241
❑ 94VenLinU-16
❑ 94VenLinU-52
❑ 95Bow-19
❑ 95BowBes-R81
❑ 95BowBesR-R81
❑ 95Emo-157
❑ 95EmoRoo-1
❑ 95Exc-230
❑ 95Fin-246
❑ 95FinRef-246
❑ 95Fla-380
❑ 95FleAllR-M1
❑ 95LinVen-76
❑ 95LinVen-316
❑ 95MetColP-6
❑ 95SelCer-128
❑ 95SelCerMG-128
❑ 95SP-22
❑ 95SPCha-11
❑ 95SPChaDC-11
❑ 95SPSil-22
❑ 95StaClu-563
❑ 95StaCluMOP-563
❑ 95StaCluSTWS-563
❑ 95Sum-135
❑ 95Sum21C-TC3
❑ 95SumNthD-135
❑ 95TopTra-54T
❑ 95UltGolMR-M2
❑ 95UppDec-255
❑ 95UppDecED-255
❑ 95UppDecEDG-255
❑ 95UppDecML-49
❑ 95UppDecMLFS-49
❑ 95UppDecSE-191
❑ 95UppDecSEG-191
❑ 95Zen-128
❑ 95ZenRooRC-14
❑ 96-97LinVen-11
❑ 96ColCho-218
❑ 96ColChoGS-218
❑ 96ColChoSS-218
❑ 96Don-195
❑ 96DonPreP-195
❑ 96Fla-315
❑ 96Fle-472
❑ 96FleTif-472
❑ 96Lea-116
❑ 96LeaPre-58
❑ 96LeaPreP-58
❑ 96LeaPrePB-116
❑ 96LeaPrePG-116
❑ 96LeaPrePS-116
❑ 96MetKah-1
❑ 96MetKah-1
❑ 96MetUni-197
❑ 96MetUniP-197
❑ 96Pac-140
❑ 96PacPri-P45
❑ 96PacPriG-P45
❑ 96PanSti-27
❑ 96Pin-239
❑ 96PinAfi-149
❑ 96PinAfiAP-149
❑ 96PinArtP-139
❑ 96PinFoil-239
❑ 96PinSta-139
❑ 96Sco-174
❑ 96ScoDugC-A98
❑ 96ScoDugCAP-A98
❑ 96Sel-85
❑ 96SelArtP-85
❑ 96SelCer-68
❑ 96SelCerAP-68
❑ 96SelCerCB-68
❑ 96SelCerCR-68
❑ 96SelCerMB-68
❑ 96SelCerMG-68
❑ 96SelCerMR-68
❑ 96StaClu-164
❑ 96StaCluMOP-164
❑ 96Sum-43
❑ 96SumAbo&B-43
❑ 96SumArtP-43
❑ 96SumFoi-43
❑ 96Top-99
❑ 96Ult-239
❑ 96UltGolM-239
❑ 96UppDec-142
❑ 96Zen-65
❑ 96ZenArtP-65
❑ 97Cir-58
❑ 97CirRav-58
❑ 97ColCho-397
❑ 97Don-57
❑ 97DonGolPP-57
❑ 97DonLim-72
❑ 97DonLimE-72
❑ 97DonLimENG-72
❑ 97DonSigA-3
❑ 97DonSigAC-3
❑ 97DonSigAM-3
❑ 97DonSilPP-57
❑ 97Fle-390
❑ 97FleTif-390
❑ 97Pac-357
❑ 97PacLigB-357
❑ 97PacSil-357
❑ 97Sco-372
❑ 97ScoArtPWB-372
❑ 97ScoResC-372
❑ 97ScoShoS-372
❑ 97ScoShoSAP-372
❑ 97StaClu-89
❑ 97StaCluMOP-89
❑ 97Top-212
❑ 97Ult-410
❑ 97UltGolME-410
❑ 97UltPlaME-410
❑ 98Bow-34
❑ 98BowChr-34
❑ 98BowChrGA-34
❑ 98BowChrGAR-34
❑ 98BowChrI-34
❑ 98BowChrIR-34
❑ 98BowChrR-34
❑ 98BowGolA-34
❑ 98BowInt-34
❑ 98CirThu-140
❑ 98CirThuRav-140
❑ 98CirThuSupRav-140
❑ 98ColCho-172
❑ 98Don-96
❑ 98DonCol-96
❑ 98DonColE-431
❑ 98DonColL-293
❑ 98DonColP-658
❑ 98DonColS-96
❑ 98DonCruG-86
❑ 98DonCruP-86
❑ 98DonCruR-86
❑ 98DonEli-31
❑ 98DonEliA-31
❑ 98DonEliS-31
❑ 98DonGolPP-96
❑ 98DonPre-108
❑ 98DonPreSeat-108
❑ 98DonPriCD-96
❑ 98DonPriCE-431
❑ 98DonPriCL-293
❑ 98DonPriCP-658
❑ 98DonSilPP-96
❑ 98Fin-101
❑ 98FinNo--101
❑ 98FinNo-R-101
❑ 98FinRef-101
❑ 98FlaShoLeg0-75
❑ 98FlaShoLeg1-75
❑ 98FlaShoLeg2-75
❑ 98FlaShoLeg3-75
❑ 98FlaShoLegM-75
❑ 98FlaShoR0-75
❑ 98FlaShoR1-75
❑ 98FlaShoR2-75
❑ 98FlaShoR3-75
❑ 98Fle-13
❑ 98Lea-94
❑ 98LeaFraDA-94
❑ 98LeaFraF-94
❑ 98LeaFraM-94
❑ 98LeaFraM-94
❑ 98LeaFraMDC-94
❑ 98LeaFraMDC-94
❑ 98LeaFraMS-94
❑ 98LeaFraMZ2-94
❑ 98LeaRS-101
❑ 98LeaRSLHolo-101
❑ 98LeaRSLong-101
❑ 98LeaRTrue-101
❑ 98MetUni-20
❑ 98MetUniPMG-20
❑ 98Pac-361
❑ 98PacAur-161
❑ 98PacInv-118
❑ 98PacInvPBlue-118
❑ 98PacInvSilv-118
❑ 98PacInvTeam-18
❑ 98PacLatotML-23
❑ 98PacOnl-469
❑ 98PacOnlR-469
❑ 98PacOnlWC-469
❑ 98PacPar-200
❑ 98PacParC-200
❑ 98PacParG-200
❑ 98PacParHS-200
❑ 98PacParPB-200
❑ 98PacParR-200
❑ 98PacPlaB-361
❑ 98PacRedT-361
❑ 98PacSil-361
❑ 98Pin-90
❑ 98PinIns-54
❑ 98PinInsCE-54
❑ 98PinInsDE-54
❑ 98PinPer-115
❑ 98PinPerPP-115
❑ 98PinPreP-90
❑ 98PinSna-NYM9
❑ 98Sco-39
❑ 98ScoRT-149
❑ 98ScoSS-PP13
❑ 98ScoSSAP-PP13
❑ 98SkyDugA-31
❑ 98SkyDugAIA-31
❑ 98SP Aut-136
❑ 98SpoIll-1
❑ 98SpoIllEE-1
❑ 98SpoIllFE-1
❑ 98SpoIllWSF-51
❑ 98SpoIllWSFEE-51
❑ 98SpoIllWSFFE-51
❑ 98SPxFin-102
❑ 98SPxFinR-102
❑ 98SPxFinS-102
❑ 98StaCluFDI-72
❑ 98StaClul-72
❑ 98StaCluOneK-72
❑ 98StaCluPP-72
❑ 98Stu-176
❑ 98StuGPP-176
❑ 98StuSPP-176
❑ 98Top-89
❑ 98TopChr-89
❑ 98TopChrR-89
❑ 98TopDevR-89
❑ 98TopDia-89
❑ 98TopGal-105
❑ 98TopGalGP-105
❑ 98TopGalOPP-105
❑ 98TopGalPPI-105
❑ 98TopGalPPIA-105
❑ 98TopMiniC-89
❑ 98TopOpeD-43
❑ 98TopSta-77
❑ 98TopStaB-77
❑ 98TopStaG-77
❑ 98TopStaGR-77
❑ 98TopStaS-77
❑ 98Ult-129
❑ 98UltGolM-129
❑ 98UltMas-129
❑ 98UltPlaM-129
❑ 98UppDec-163
❑ 98UppDecSF-87
❑ 99199Fin-232
❑ 99Bow-272
❑ 99BowGol-272
❑ 99BowInt-272
❑ 99FinGolRef-232
❑ 99FinRef-232
❑ 99FlaShoLeg1-119
❑ 99FlaShoLeg2-119

❑ 99FlaShoLeg3-119
❑ 99FlaShoLegM1-119
❑ 99FlaShoLegM2-119
❑ 99FlaShoLegM3-119
❑ 99FlaShoR1-119
❑ 99FlaShoR2-119
❑ 99FlaShoR3-119
❑ 99Fle-68
❑ 99FleSta9-68
❑ 99FleWarT-68
❑ 99Pac-274
❑ 99PacAur-117
❑ 99PacAurOD-117
❑ 99PacCroC-177
❑ 99PacCroCPB-177
❑ 99PacOme-150
❑ 99PacOmeC-150
❑ 99PacOmeG-150
❑ 99PacOmePB-150
❑ 99PacPar-148
❑ 99PacParC-148
❑ 99PacParG-148
❑ 99PacParHoloGold-148
❑ 99PacParHS-148
❑ 99PacParOD-148
❑ 99PacParPB-148
❑ 99PacParRed-148
❑ 99PacPlaB-274
❑ 99PacRed-274
❑ 99Rev-88
❑ 99RevPremDate-88
❑ 99RevRet-88
❑ 99RevShaSS-88
❑ 99SkyThu-20
❑ 99SkyThuRant-20
❑ 99SkyThuRave-20
❑ 99StaClu-138
❑ 99StaCluC-CS22
❑ 99StaCluC-CS28
❑ 99StaCluC-CS34
❑ 99StaCluC-CS40
❑ 99StaCluFDI-138
❑ 99StaCluOoaK-138
❑ 99StaCluPP-138
❑ 99ThuSkySupR-20
❑ 99Top-13
❑ 99TopChr-13
❑ 99TopChrR-13
❑ 99TopMVPP-13
❑ 99TopOpeD-9
❑ 99TopSta-113
❑ 99TopStaFoil-113
❑ 99UppDec-432
❑ 99UppDecEL1-432
❑ 99UppDecEL2-432
❑ 99UppDecR-54
❑ 99UppDecRG-54
❑ 99UppDecRP-54
❑ 99Vic-254

Alfonzo, Roberto
❑ 94KinMetC-1
❑ 94KinMetF-3828

Alford, Mike
❑ 89MisStaB-2
❑ 90MisStaB-2

Alfredson, Tom
❑ 86QuaCitAP-2
❑ 87PalSprP-19
❑ 88MidAngGS-15
❑ 89MidAngGS-4
❑ 90BirBarB-5
❑ 90BirBarP-1394

Alger, Kevin
❑ 92MarPhiC-24
❑ 92MarPhiF-3045
❑ 93SpaPhiC-3
❑ 93SpaPhiF-1047
❑ 94ClePhiC-3
❑ 94ClePhiF-2517

Alguacil, Jose
❑ 94CliLumC-2
❑ 94CliLumF-1985
❑ 96-97LinVen-47
❑ 96SanJosGB-2
❑ 97SanJosG-8

Alicano, Pedro
❑ 91PeoChiC-2
❑ 91PeoChiP-1333
❑ 91PeoChiTI-4
❑ 92WinSpiC-21
❑ 92WinSpiF-1198

Alicea, Edwin
❑ 88BlaYNPRWL-2
❑ 89BlaYNPRWL-170
❑ 89GreBraB-6
❑ 89GreBraP-1156
❑ 89GreBraS-1
❑ 90DurBulTI-13
❑ 91MiaMirC-26
❑ 91MiaMirP-419
❑ 92GreBraF-1163
❑ 92GreBraS-226
❑ 93ColSprSSF-3098
❑ 93GreBraF-355
❑ 93LinVenB-302
❑ 95NorTidTI-5

Alicea, Luis
❑ 85AncGlaPTI-1
❑ 86EriCarP-1
❑ 87ArkTraP-16
❑ 88BlaYNPRWLU-37
❑ 88CarSmo-24
❑ 88CarTeal-1
❑ 88DonRoo-52
❑ 88FleUpd-116
❑ 88FleUpdG-116
❑ 88LouRedBC-20
❑ 88LouRedBP-436
❑ 88LouRedBTI-7
❑ 88ScoRoo-98T
❑ 88ScoRooG-98T
❑ 88TopTra-3T
❑ 88TopTraT-3T
❑ 89Don-466
❑ 89Fle-443
❑ 89FleGlo-443
❑ 89LouRedBC-14
❑ 89LouRedBP-1263
❑ 89LouRedBTI-8
❑ 89PanSti-175
❑ 89RedFolSB-2
❑ 89Sco-231
❑ 89Top-261
❑ 89Top-588
❑ 89TopSti-37
❑ 89TopTif-261
❑ 89TopTif-588
❑ 89UppDec-281
❑ 90LouRedBLBC-6
❑ 91LinDriAAA-226
❑ 91LouRedLD-226
❑ 91LouRedP-2919
❑ 91LouRedTI-17
❑ 92Don-560
❑ 92Sco-607
❑ 92StaClu-103
❑ 93CarPol-1
❑ 93Don-416
❑ 93Fle-507
❑ 93PacBeiA-28
❑ 93PacBeiA-29
❑ 93PacBeiA-30
❑ 93PacSpa-293
❑ 93Sco-183
❑ 93StaClu-178
❑ 93StaCluFDI-178
❑ 93StaCluMOP-178
❑ 93Top-257
❑ 93TopGol-257
❑ 93TopInaM-257
❑ 93TopInaR-257
❑ 93TopMic-257
❑ 93UppDec-605
❑ 93UppDecGold-605
❑ 94CarPol-1
❑ 94ColC-32
❑ 94ColChoGS-32
❑ 94ColChoSS-32
❑ 94Don-534
❑ 94Fin-40
❑ 94FinRef-40
❑ 94Fle-627
❑ 94FleExtB-355
❑ 94Lea-203
❑ 94Pac-585
❑ 94Pin-319
❑ 94PinArtP-319
❑ 94PinMusC-319
❑ 94Sco-522
❑ 94ScoGolR-522
❑ 94StaClu-146
❑ 94StaCluFDI-146
❑ 94StaCluGR-146
❑ 94StaCluMOP-146
❑ 94StaCluT-309
❑ 94StaCluTFDI-309
❑ 94Top-416
❑ 94TopGol-416
❑ 94TopSpa-416
❑ 94Ult-562
❑ 94UppDec-239
❑ 94UppDecED-239
❑ 95Don-43
❑ 95DonPreP-43
❑ 95DonTopotO-17
❑ 95Fin-243
❑ 95FinRef-243
❑ 95Fle-493
❑ 95Lea-381
❑ 95Pac-404
❑ 95Sco-173
❑ 95ScoGolR-173
❑ 95ScoPlaTS-173
❑ 95Top-630
❑ 95TopCyb-396
❑ 95Ult-259
❑ 95UltGolM-259
❑ 96ColCho-59
❑ 96ColChoGS-59
❑ 96ColChoSS-59
❑ 96Don-221
❑ 96DonPreP-221
❑ 96Fle-22
❑ 96FleTif-22
❑ 96FleUpd-U181
❑ 96FleUpdTC-U181
❑ 96MetUni-11
❑ 96MetUniP-11
❑ 96Pac-259
❑ 96Sco-438
❑ 96StaClu-190
❑ 96StaClu-365
❑ 96StaCluMOP-190
❑ 96StaCluMOP-365
❑ 96Top-377
❑ 96Ult-13
❑ 96Ult-539
❑ 96UltGolM-13
❑ 96UltGolM-539
❑ 97AngMot-13
❑ 97Fle-657
❑ 97FleTif-657
❑ 97Pac-402
❑ 97PacLigB-402
❑ 97PacSil-402
❑ 97Ult-513
❑ 97UltGolME-513
❑ 97UltPlaME-513
❑ 98Pac-1
❑ 98PacOnl-726
❑ 98PacOnlR-726
❑ 98PacOnlWC-726
❑ 98PacPlaB-1
❑ 98PacRedT-1
❑ 98PacSil-1
❑ 98Top-209
❑ 98TopChr-209
❑ 98TopChrR-209
❑ 98TopDevR-209
❑ 98TopDia-209
❑ 98TopMiniC-209
❑ 99Fle-340
❑ 99FleSta9-340
❑ 99FleWarT-340
❑ 99PacCroC-280
❑ 99PacCroCPB-280

Alicea, Miguel
❑ 80PenPilBT-4
❑ 80PenPilCT-6
❑ 81ReaPhiT-6
❑ 85BelBreT-24
❑ 87ChaO'sW-16
❑ 88BlaYNPRWL-130
❑ 88EdmTraC-11
❑ 88EdmTraP-582
❑ 89BlaYNPRWL-3
❑ 89PalSprACLC-55

Alimena, Charles
❑ 92CliGiaC-19
❑ 93CliGiaC-2
❑ 93CliGiaF-2494
❑ 94CliLumC-3
❑ 94CliLumF-1986

Alkire, Jeff
❑ 91MiaHurBB-1
❑ 92TopTra-2T
❑ 92TopTraG-2T
❑ 93ClaFS7-93
❑ 93SavCarC-2
❑ 93SavCarF-677
❑ 93SouAtlLAGF-44
❑ 93StaCluM-163
❑ 93StaCluM-174
❑ 94ClaGolF-157
❑ 94ExcFS7-254
❑ 94UppDecML-238
❑ 96PorSeaDB-6

Allaire, Karl
❑ 85OscAstTI-16
❑ 86ColAstP-2
❑ 87ColAstP-14
❑ 88TucTorC-17
❑ 88TucTorJP-1
❑ 88TucTorP-167
❑ 90CMC-499
❑ 90EdmTraC-22
❑ 90EdmTraP-521
❑ 90ProAAAF-97
❑ 91LinDriAAA-577
❑ 91TolMudHLD-577
❑ 91TolMudHP-1937
❑ 92TolMudHF-1048
❑ 92TolMudHS-576

Allanson, Andy
❑ 84BufBisT-7
❑ 85WatIndT-24
❑ 86DonRoo-43
❑ 86FleUpd-2
❑ 86IndOhH-6
❑ 86IndTeal-2
❑ 86TopTra-1T
❑ 86TopTraT-1T
❑ 87BufBisP-3
❑ 87Don-95
❑ 87Fle-241
❑ 87FleGlo-241
❑ 87IndGat-6
❑ 87Lea-102
❑ 87Top-436
❑ 87TopRoo-1
❑ 87TopSti-311
❑ 87TopTif-436
❑ 87ToyRoo-1
❑ 88Don-465
❑ 88DonBasB-5
❑ 88FleUpd-21
❑ 88FleUpdG-21
❑ 88IndGat-6
❑ 88IndTeal-2
❑ 88Sco-586
❑ 88ScoGlo-586
❑ 88StaLinI-1
❑ 88Top-728
❑ 88TopBig-231
❑ 88TopClo-2
❑ 88TopTif-728
❑ 89Bow-83
❑ 89BowTif-83
❑ 89Don-138
❑ 89Fle-396
❑ 89FleGlo-396
❑ 89IndTeal-2
❑ 89OPC-283
❑ 89PanSti-323
❑ 89Sco-46
❑ 89Top-283
❑ 89TopBig-311
❑ 89TopSti-207
❑ 89TopTif-283
❑ 89UppDec-217
❑ 90Fle-483
❑ 90FleCan-483
❑ 90OPC-514
❑ 90PubIntS-551
❑ 90Sco-452
❑ 90TigTeal-1
❑ 90Top-514
❑ 90TopTif-514
❑ 90UppDec-590
❑ 91Lea-455
❑ 91TigCok-10
❑ 92BrePol-1
❑ 92DenZepF-2642
❑ 92Don-42
❑ 92Fle-128
❑ 92Lea-510
❑ 92LeaBlaG-510
❑ 92OPC-167
❑ 92Sco-537
❑ 92StaClu-238
❑ 92Top-167
❑ 92TopGol-167
❑ 92TopGolW-167
❑ 92TopMic-167
❑ 93PhoFirF-1517
❑ 94BreMilB-4
❑ 94SanBerSF-2761
❑ 95AngMot-23
❑ 95LakElsSTI-2

Allard, Brian M.
❑ 77AshTouT-1
❑ 79TucTorT-4
❑ 80ChaChaT-5
❑ 80Top-673
❑ 81MarPos-2
❑ 81SpoIndT-10
❑ 82MarPos-2
❑ 82Top-283
❑ 83SalLakCGT-6
❑ 84SalLakCGC-171
❑ 85IntLeaAT-43
❑ 85MaiGuiT-30
❑ 86WatIndP-1
❑ 87WilBilP-16
❑ 88EasLeaAP-50
❑ 88WilBilP-1311
❑ 89KenTwiP-1080
❑ 89KenTwiS-27
❑ 90CalLeaACLC-26
❑ 90VisOakCLC-80
❑ 90VisOakP-2171
❑ 91VisOakC-26
❑ 91VisOakP-1758
❑ 91VisOakP-1759
❑ 92VisOakC-25
❑ 92VisOakF-1030
❑ 93FayGenC-27
❑ 93FayGenF-145
❑ 93RanKee-48
❑ 94LakTigC-28
❑ 94LakTigF-3052
❑ 96TolMudHB-4

Allen, Bernie (Bernard Keith)
❑ 61TwiCloD-1
❑ 62Top-596
❑ 63Jel-2
❑ 63Pos-2
❑ 63Top-427
❑ 63TwiJayP-1
❑ 63TwiVol-1
❑ 64Top-455
❑ 64TopRooAB-11
❑ 65OPC-237
❑ 65Top-237
❑ 66Top-327
❑ 66TopVen-327
❑ 66TwiFaiG-1
❑ 67CokCapS-2
❑ 67DexPre-4
❑ 67OPC-118
❑ 67SenPos-1
❑ 67SenTeal-1
❑ 67Top-118
❑ 68Top-548
❑ 69MilBra-5
❑ 69MLBOffS-100
❑ 69OPC-27
❑ 69SenTeal8-1
❑ 69Top-27
❑ 69TopSta-231
❑ 69TopTeaP-23
❑ 70MLBOffS-277
❑ 70Top-577
❑ 71MLBOffS-529
❑ 71OPC-427
❑ 71SenTealW-1
❑ 71Top-427
❑ 72MilBra-6
❑ 72Top-644
❑ 73LinPor-126
❑ 73OPC-293
❑ 73Top-293
❑ 77SerSta-1
❑ 78TwiFri-26
❑ 92YanWIZ7-3

Allen, Bob
❑ 88CapCodPPaLP-157

Allen, Bob (Robert Gilman)
❑ 87OldJudN-5

Allen, Bob (Robert Gray)
❑ 61Top-452
❑ 62Top-543
❑ 63Top-266
❑ 64Top-209
❑ 64TopVen-209
❑ 66Top-538
❑ 67OPC-24
❑ 67Top-24
❑ 68OPC-176
❑ 68Top-176
❑ 68TopVen-176

Allen, Bob (Robert)
❑ 84AlbDukCr-156
❑ 86ElPasDP-2
❑ 87MidAngP-23

Allen, Brandon
❑ 96BatCliTI-18
❑ 97PieBolWB-5

Allen, Buck
❑ 98ClePhiM-2

Allen, Cedric
❑ 94PriRedC-2
❑ 94PriRedF-3253
❑ 95Exc-171
❑ 96Exc-144

Allen, Chad
❑ 89BurIndS-1
❑ 90WatIndS-1
❑ 91CarLeaAP-CAR11
❑ 91KinIndC-1
❑ 91KinIndP-313
❑ 92CanIndS-101
❑ 92KinIndF-2466
❑ 93CanIndF-2831
❑ 97ForMyeM-5
❑ 98EasLeaTPM-1
❑ 98NewBriRCM-5
❑ 99CroRoyB-80
❑ 99CroRoyL-80
❑ 99CroRoyOD-80
❑ 99FleBri-156
❑ 99FleBri2G-156
❑ 99FleBriBlu-156
❑ 99FleBriGol-156
❑ 99PacOme-141
❑ 99PacOmeC-141
❑ 99PacOmeG-141
❑ 99PacOmePB-141
❑ 99Rev-78
❑ 99RevPremDate-78
❑ 99RevRet-78
❑ 99RevShaSS-78
❑ 99SkyMolM-108
❑ 99SkyMolMF-8
❑ 99SkyMolMFS-8
❑ 99SkyMolMFT-8
❑ 99SkyMolMX-108
❑ 99SkyPre-237
❑ 99SkyPre-237
❑ 99SkyPreDD-11
❑ 99SkyPreR-237
❑ 99SkyPreR-237

Allen, Chris
❑ 96TreThuB-19

Allen, Clint
❑ 91MisStaB-2
❑ 92MisStaB-2

Allen, Craig
❑ 96GreFalDB-2
❑ 96GreFalDTI-1

Allen, Dave
❑ 85FreGiaSB-5
❑ 87UtiBluSP-32
❑ 88BatCliP-1684
❑ 90AubAstB-16
❑ 90AubAstP-3414
❑ 91BurAstP-2792

Allen, David
❑ 91BurAstC-1
❑ 91Cla/Bes-222

Allen, Dell
❑ 92MarPhiC-26
❑ 92MarPhiF-3062
❑ 93MarPhiC-2
❑ 93MarPhiF-3480

Allen, Dusty
❑ 96CliLumKTI-2
❑ 97MobBayBB-29
❑ 98MobBayBTI-2

Allen, Edward
❑ 83ButCopKT-23
❑ 83ChaRoyT-10

Allen, Ethan (Ethan Nathan)
❑ 29PorandAR-1
❑ 33Gou-46
❑ 33GouCanV-46
❑ 34BatR31-76
❑ 34DiaMatCSB-2
❑ 34DiaStaR-92
❑ 35DiaMatCS2-1
❑ 35DiaMatCS3T1-1
❑ 35GouPuzR-6C
❑ 36GouWidPPR-A1
❑ 79DiaGre-254
❑ 85BigLeaC3-14
❑ 92MegRut-150
❑ 93ConTSN-779
❑ 94ConTSN-1128
❑ 94ConTSNB-1128

Allen, Eugene
❑ 26Zee-39

Allen, Frank Leon

❑ 16FleBreD-4
❑ 90DodTar-9
Allen, Greg
❑ 78WisRapTT-1
Allen, Hank (Harold Andrew)
❑ 67SenPos-2
❑ 67Top-569
❑ 68Top-426
❑ 69MilBra-6
❑ 69SenTeal-1
❑ 69SenTeal8-2
❑ 69Top-623
❑ 70OPC-14
❑ 70Top-14
❑ 71MLBOffS-3
❑ 72MilBra-7
❑ 94BreMilB-95
Allen, Harold
❑ 88AshTouP-1060
❑ 89OscAstS-1
❑ 90Bes-161
❑ 90ColMudB-11
❑ 90ColMudP-1337
❑ 90ColMudS-1
❑ 91LinDriAAA-601
❑ 91TucTorLD-601
❑ 91TucTorP-2204
❑ 92JacGenF-3991
❑ 92JacGenS-326
Allen, Jamie (James Bradley)
❑ 80LynSaiT-18
❑ 81SpoIndT-31
❑ 82QuaCitCT-17
❑ 82SalLakCGT-2
❑ 84Don-267
❑ 84Fle-604
❑ 84Nes792-744
❑ 84SalLakCGC-182
❑ 84Top-744
❑ 84TopSti-350
❑ 84TopTif-744
Allen, Jeff
❑ 98SalVol-1
Allen, Jim
❑ 74AlbDukCa-79
❑ 75AlbDukCa-18
❑ 83QuaCitCT-18
❑ 89JohCitCS-1
Allen, John 90's
❑ 93LetMouF-4154
❑ 93LetMouSP-1
Allen, Johnny (John Thomas)
❑ 32OrbPinNP-103
❑ 34Gou-42
❑ 34GouCanV-96
❑ 35GouPuzR-8E
❑ 35GouPuzR-9E
❑ 35GouPuzR-11E
❑ 35GouPuzR-13C
❑ 35GouPuzR-15C
❑ 36R31PasP-1
❑ 37OPCBatUV-122
❑ 39WheBB12-2
❑ 41BroW75-1
❑ 42DodTeal-1
❑ 43DodTeal-1
❑ 73Dod194T-1
❑ 74CapPub-60
❑ 78DodTCM4-14
❑ 85BigLeaC3-33
❑ 90DodTar-10
❑ 92ConTSN-384
❑ 93ConTSN-722
Allen, Kim (Kim Bryant)
❑ 75QuaCitAT-31
❑ 78SalLakCGC-5
❑ 80SpoIndT-19
❑ 80VenLeaS-157
❑ 81Fle-612
❑ 81SpoIndT-27
❑ 89PacSenL-99
❑ 89TopSenL-53
❑ 91PacSenL-99
Allen, Larry
❑ 86PenWhiSP-2
❑ 87ChaWheP-11
❑ 88SouBenWSGS-2
Allen, Lee
❑ 90LitSunW-6
Allen, Lloyd Cecil
❑ 71OPC-152
❑ 71Top-152
❑ 72OPC-102
❑ 72Top-102
❑ 73OPC-267
❑ 73RanTeal-1
❑ 73Top-267
❑ 74OPC-539
❑ 74Top-539
❑ 76SSP-140
❑ 76TulOilGP-2
❑ 79IowOakP-2
❑ 93RanKee-49
Allen, Luke
❑ 97GreFalDTI-1
❑ 98Bow-323
❑ 98BowChr-323
❑ 98BowChrGA-323
❑ 98BowChrGAR-323
❑ 98BowChrI-323
❑ 98BowChrIR-323
❑ 98BowChrR-323
❑ 98BowGolA-323
❑ 98BowInt-323
❑ 98SanBerS-1
❑ 98SanBerSTIS-1
Allen, Marlon
❑ 94PriRedC-3
❑ 94PriRedF-3266
❑ 97Bow-359
❑ 97BowInt-359
❑ 97BurBeeB-2
❑ 98ChaLooG-1
Allen, Matt
❑ 91JamExpC-7
❑ 91JamExpP-3547
❑ 92AlbPolCB-5
❑ 92AlbPolF-2308
❑ 92JamExpC-16
❑ 92JamExpF-1504
❑ 93WesPalBEC-24
❑ 93WesPalBEF-1342
❑ 94WesPalBEC-2
❑ 94WesPalBEF-42
Allen, Mel
❑ 48YanTeal-1
❑ 49YanTeal-1
❑ 50YanTeal-1
❑ 92MegRut-146
❑ 92MegRut-147
Allen, Mike
❑ 80BufBisT-11
❑ 80WicAerT-13
Allen, Myron Smith
❑ 87OldJudN-4
Allen, Neil
❑ 77LynMetT-2A
❑ 77LynMetT-2B
❑ 78TidTidT-1
❑ 80Top-94
❑ 81AllGamPI-164
❑ 81CokTeaS-85
❑ 81Don-276
❑ 81Fle-322
❑ 81OPC-322
❑ 81Top-322
❑ 81TopSti-198
❑ 81TopSupHT-73
❑ 82Don-506
❑ 82Fle-520
❑ 82FleSta-84
❑ 82Kel-20
❑ 82MetPhoA-1
❑ 82OPC-205
❑ 82Top-205
❑ 82TopSti-66
❑ 83Don-98
❑ 83Fle-536
❑ 83FleSta-2
❑ 83FleSti-236
❑ 83Kel-34
❑ 83OPC-268
❑ 83Top-575
❑ 83TopSti-265
❑ 83TopTra-1T
❑ 84Car-1
❑ 84Car5x7-1
❑ 84Don-109
❑ 84Fle-318
❑ 84JacMetF-1
❑ 84Nes792-435
❑ 84OPC-183
❑ 84Top-435
❑ 84TopSti-147
❑ 84TopTif-435
❑ 85CarTeal-1
❑ 85Don-205
❑ 85Fle-219
❑ 85OPC-234
❑ 85Top-731
❑ 85TopMin-731
❑ 85TopSti-144
❑ 85TopTif-731
❑ 86Don-610
❑ 86Fle-98
❑ 86FleUpd-3
❑ 86Top-663
❑ 86TopTif-663
❑ 86TopTra-2T
❑ 86TopTraT-2T
❑ 86WhiSoxC-33
❑ 87Don-507
❑ 87Fle-484
❑ 87FleGlo-484
❑ 87OPC-113
❑ 87RedFolSB-93
❑ 87Top-113
❑ 87TopSti-292
❑ 87TopTif-113
❑ 87WhiSoxC-1
❑ 88Don-597
❑ 88Top-384
❑ 88TopTif-384
❑ 89ColSprSSC-6
❑ 89Don-196
❑ 89Fle-250A
❑ 89Fle-250B
❑ 89FleGlo-250
❑ 89Sco-375
❑ 89Top-61
❑ 89TopTif-61
❑ 89UppDec-567
❑ 90CMC-148
❑ 90NasSouC-23
❑ 90NasSouP-223
❑ 90ProAAAF-535
❑ 91MetWIZ-5
❑ 92YanWIZ8-3
❑ 96StCatSB-2
Allen, Newt (Newton)
❑ 78LauLonABS-3
❑ 86NegLeaF-104
❑ 90NegLeaS-30
❑ 94TedWil-100
Allen, Nick (Artemus)
❑ 20RedWorCP-1
❑ 86CarTeal-1
Allen, Paul
❑ 89WelPirP-32
Allen, Richie (Richard A.)
❑ 47StaPinP2-1
❑ 64PhiPhiB-1
❑ 64Top-243
❑ 64TopRooAB-19
❑ 64TopVen-243
❑ 65OldLonC-2
❑ 65Top-460
❑ 65TopEmbl-36
❑ 65TopTral-38
❑ 66Baz-4
❑ 66OPC-80
❑ 66PhiTeal-1
❑ 66Top-80
❑ 66TopRubl-3
❑ 66TopVen-80
❑ 67Baz-4
❑ 67CokCapA-1
❑ 67CokCapNLA-25
❑ 67CokCapPh-1
❑ 67DexPre-5
❑ 67PhiPol-1
❑ 67Top-242
❑ 67Top-244
❑ 67Top-309
❑ 67Top-450
❑ 67TopGiaSU-18
❑ 67TopVen-311
❑ 68Baz-14
❑ 68DexPre-3
❑ 68Top-225
❑ 68TopActS-12A
❑ 68TopGamI-23
❑ 68TopPla-14
❑ 68TopPos-15
❑ 68TopVen-225
❑ 69CitMetC-17
❑ 69MilBra-7
❑ 69MLBOffS-172
❑ 69MLBPin-33
❑ 69NabTeaF-2
❑ 69OPC-6
❑ 69OPCDec-1
❑ 69PhiTeal-1
❑ 69Top-6
❑ 69Top-350
❑ 69TopDec-26
❑ 69TopDecI-2
❑ 69TopSta-71
❑ 69TopSup-53
❑ 69TopTeaP-8
❑ 69TraSta-57
❑ 70CarTeal-1
❑ 70CarTeal-2
❑ 70DayDaiNM-80
❑ 70Kel-33
❑ 70MLBOffS-133
❑ 70OPC-40
❑ 70Top-40
❑ 70TopCanL-2
❑ 70TopScr-2
❑ 71BazNumT-44
❑ 71DodTic-1
❑ 71Kel-57
❑ 71MLBOffS-97
❑ 71OPC-650
❑ 71Top-650
❑ 71TopSup-40
❑ 71TopTat-53
❑ 72MilBra-8
❑ 72OPC-240
❑ 72SevTraC-3
❑ 72Top-240
❑ 72WhiSox-1
❑ 72WhiSoxDS-1
❑ 72WhiSoxTI1-1
❑ 73Kel2D-26
❑ 73LinPor-47
❑ 73OPC-62
❑ 73OPC-63
❑ 73OPC-310
❑ 73SevTraC-2
❑ 73Top-62
❑ 73Top-63
❑ 73Top-310
❑ 73TopCanL-2
❑ 73TopCom-2
❑ 73TopPin-2
❑ 74Kel-33
❑ 74OPC-70
❑ 74OPC-332
❑ 74Top-70
❑ 74Top-332
❑ 74TopDecE-39
❑ 74TopPuz-2
❑ 74TopSta-151
❑ 75Kel-42
❑ 75OPC-210
❑ 75OPC-307
❑ 75OPC-400
❑ 75PhiPhiP-1
❑ 75SSP42-4
❑ 75Top-210
❑ 75Top-307
❑ 75Top-400
❑ 75TopMin-210
❑ 75TopMin-307
❑ 75TopMin-400
❑ 76OPC-455
❑ 76PhiPhiP-1
❑ 76SSP-473
❑ 76Top-455
❑ 81TCM60I-415
❑ 82K-M-21
❑ 82TCMGreS-16
❑ 83PhiPosGPaM-7
❑ 84OCoandSI-203
❑ 85WhiSoxC-29
❑ 86PhiGreT-10
❑ 89WhiSoxK-1
❑ 90CedRapRB-8
❑ 90DodTar-8
❑ 92UppDecS-5
❑ 92UppDecS-24
❑ 93ActPacA-155
❑ 93UppDecS-15
❑ 94TedWil-71
Allen, Rick
❑ 88AlaGolTI-1
❑ 89BilMusP-2045
❑ 90CedRapRP-2331
❑ 91ChaLooLD-151
❑ 91ChaLooP-1964
❑ 91LinDriAA-151
❑ 92ChaLooS-176
❑ 92OrlSunRF-2851
❑ 93HolLeg-1
Allen, Robert Earl
❑ 82VerBeaDT-15
Allen, Rod (Roderick B.)
❑ 78AppFoxT-1
❑ 79KnoKnoST-24
❑ 81EdmTraRR-21
❑ 82SalLakCGT-3
❑ 83SalLakCGT-14
❑ 84TigTeal-4
❑ 85RocRedWT-10
❑ 87BufBisP-24
❑ 88ColSprSSC-19
❑ 88ColSprSSP-1545
❑ 88TriAAC-39
❑ 89Fle-397
❑ 89FleGlo-397
❑ 94KanCouCC-29
❑ 94KanCouCF-179
❑ 94KanCouCTI-2
❑ 95KanCouCTI-46
Allen, Rodney James
❑ 96EugEmeB-24
❑ 97EugEmeB-4
Allen, Ronnie
❑ 91BatCliCB-25
❑ 91BatCliP-3474
❑ 91Cla/Bes-417
❑ 91FroRowDP-13
❑ 91FroRowDPG-13
❑ 91FroRowDPS-13
❑ 92ClePhiC-23
❑ 92ClePhiF-2046
❑ 92StaCluD-4
❑ 93ReaPhiF-288
❑ 94LynRedSC-2
❑ 94LynRedSF-1883
Allen, Scott
❑ 88BurIndP-1784
Allen, Shane
❑ 81QuaCitCT-7
❑ 97GreFalDTI-2
❑ 98GreFalDG-1
Allen, Sterling
❑ 76BatRouCT-1
Allen, Steve
❑ 88ButCopKSP-26
❑ 89GasRanP-1022
❑ 89GasRanS-1
❑ 89Sta-133
❑ 90TexLeaAGS-36
❑ 90TulDriP-1148
❑ 90TulDriTI-1
❑ 91LinDriAA-526
❑ 91SanAntMLD-526
❑ 91SanAntMP-2965
❑ 92SanAntMF-3967
❑ 92SanAntMS-551
❑ 93AlbDukF-1451
❑ 93ColSprSSF-3080
❑ 94ColSprSSF-724
Allen, Tracy
❑ 90WinHavRSS-1
❑ 91WinHavRSC-1
❑ 91WinHavRSP-481
Allen, Troy
❑ 97DanBraB-8
❑ 98DanBraQ-5
Allenson, Gary M.
❑ 80Top-376
❑ 81Don-455
❑ 81Top-128
❑ 82Don-386
❑ 82Fle-287
❑ 82OPC-273
❑ 82RedSoxC-1
❑ 82Top-686
❑ 83Don-30
❑ 83Fle-177
❑ 83Top-472
❑ 84Don-335
❑ 84Fle-388
❑ 84Nes792-56
❑ 84OPC-56
❑ 84Top-56
❑ 84TopTif-56
❑ 85Fle-148
❑ 85SyrChiT-3
❑ 85Top-259
❑ 85TopTif-259
❑ 87OneYanP-24
❑ 88OneYanP-2064
❑ 89LynRedSS-23
❑ 89PacSenL-41
❑ 89T/MSenL-3
❑ 90EliSenL-92
❑ 90LynRedSTI-27
❑ 91LinDriAA-474
❑ 91NewBriRSLD-474
❑ 91NewBriRSP-367
❑ 91PacSenL-111
❑ 92RedSoxDD-1
❑ 93RedSoxP-1
❑ 96ChaRivTI-9601
❑ 97JacGen-1
❑ 97JacGenS-1
❑ 97TexAllM-32
❑ 98LouRedQ-31
Allensworth, Jermaine
❑ 93WelPirF-3371
❑ 94CarMudF-1590
❑ 94Cla-162
❑ 94ExcFirYPF-6
❑ 94ExcFS7-250
❑ 94Top-616
❑ 94TopGol-616
❑ 94TopSpa-616
❑ 94UppDec-541
❑ 94UppDecED-541
❑ 95CarMudF-169
❑ 95UppDecML-122
❑ 95UppDecMLFS-122
❑ 97Bow-247
❑ 97BowBes-27
❑ 97BowBesAR-27
❑ 97BowBesR-27
❑ 97BowInt-247
❑ 97Cir-290
❑ 97CirRav-290
❑ 97ColCho-6
❑ 97Don-155
❑ 97DonEli-93
❑ 97DonEliGS-93
❑ 97DonGolPP-155
❑ 97DonLim-103
❑ 97DonLimE-103
❑ 97DonLimENG-103
❑ 97DonSilPP-155
❑ 97E-X2-90
❑ 97E-X2Cred-90
❑ 97E-X2EssCre-90
❑ 97Fin-67
❑ 97FinRef-67
❑ 97Fle-423
❑ 97FleRooS-1
❑ 97FleTif-423
❑ 97Lea-23
❑ 97LeaFraM-23
❑ 97LeaFraMDC-23
❑ 97MetUni-236
❑ 97Pac-389
❑ 97PacLigB-389
❑ 97PacPri-132
❑ 97PacPriLB-132
❑ 97PacPriP-132
❑ 97PacSil-389
❑ 97PinIns-12
❑ 97PinInsCE-12
❑ 97PinInsDE-12
❑ 97PirPos-1
❑ 97Sco-313
❑ 97ScoArtPWB-313
❑ 97ScoPreS-313
❑ 97ScoShoS-313
❑ 97ScoShoSAP-313
❑ 97SpoIll-108
❑ 97SpoIllEE-108
❑ 97StaClu-97
❑ 97StaCluM-M14
❑ 97StaCluMOP-97
❑ 97StaCluMOP-M14
❑ 97Stu-65
❑ 97StuPrePG-65
❑ 97StuPrePS-65
❑ 97Top-341
❑ 97TopChr-115
❑ 97TopChrR-115
❑ 97TopGal-153
❑ 97TopGalPPI-153
❑ 97Ult-258
❑ 97UltGolME-258
❑ 97UltPlaME-258
❑ 97UppDec-226
❑ 98ColCho-466
❑ 98Fin-207
❑ 98FinNo--207
❑ 98FinNo-R-207
❑ 98FinRef-207
❑ 98Fle-424
❑ 98Pac-390
❑ 98PacOme-187
❑ 98PacOmeR-187
❑ 98PacOnl-578
❑ 98PacOnlR-578
❑ 98PacOnlWC-578

❑ 98PacPlaB-390
❑ 98PacRedT-390
❑ 98PacSil-390
❑ 98Sco-106
❑ 98ScoRT-128
❑ 98StaCluFDI-39
❑ 98StaCluI-39
❑ 98StaCluOneK-39
❑ 98StaCluPP-39
❑ 98Top-365
❑ 98TopChr-365
❑ 98TopChrR-365
❑ 98TopDevR-365
❑ 98TopDia-365
❑ 98TopMiniC-365
❑ 98Ult-412
❑ 98UltGolM-412
❑ 98UltMas-412
❑ 98UltPlaM-412
❑ 98UppDec-482
❑ 99Fle-320
❑ 99FleSta9-320
❑ 99FleWarT-320
Alley, Charles
❑ 97DelSho-2
Alley, Chipper
❑ 96AppLeaAB-1
❑ 96BluOriB-5
❑ 98FreKeyM-18
❑ 99BasAmeTP-3
❑ 99BasAmeTPG-3
Alley, Daniel
❑ 26Zee-107
Alley, Gene (Leonard Eugene)
❑ 64PirKDK-1
❑ 64Top-509
❑ 65OPC-121
❑ 65Top-121
❑ 66PirEasH-14
❑ 66Top-336
❑ 66TopVen-336
❑ 67CokCapPi-2
❑ 67DexPre-6
❑ 67Kah-2
❑ 67PirTeal-1
❑ 67Top-283
❑ 67TopPirS-1
❑ 67TopVen-322
❑ 68Kah-A2
❑ 68Kah-B3
❑ 68OPC-53
❑ 68PirKDK-22
❑ 68PirTeal-1
❑ 68Top-53
❑ 68Top-368
❑ 68TopGamI-25
❑ 68TopVen-53
❑ 68TopVen-368
❑ 69MilBra-8
❑ 69MLBOffS-181
❑ 69PirGre-1
❑ 69PirJacitB-1
❑ 69PirTeal-1
❑ 69Top-436
❑ 69TopSta-81
❑ 69TopTeaP-16
❑ 70DayDaiNM-152
❑ 70MLBOffS-97
❑ 70PirTeal-1
❑ 70Top-566
❑ 71MLBOffS-193
❑ 71OPC-416
❑ 71PirActP-1
❑ 71PirArc-1
❑ 71Top-416
❑ 72MilBra-9
❑ 72OPC-286
❑ 72Top-286
❑ 73OPC-635
❑ 73Top-635
❑ 94UppDecAH-138
❑ 94UppDecAH1-138
Alleyne, Isaac
❑ 87SalLakTTT-9
❑ 88JamExpP-1903
❑ 89RocExpLC-1
❑ 90ArkTraGS-5
Alleyne, Roberto
❑ 97QuaCitRBB-2
Allie, Gair R.
❑ 54Top-179
❑ 55Top-59
❑ 55TopDouH-71
❑ 58JetPos-1
❑ 94TopArc1-179
❑ 94TopArc1G-179
Allietta, Bob (Robert G.)
❑ 76OPC-623
❑ 76Top-623
❑ 79TacTugT-15
❑ 80TacTigT-11
Allinger, Bob
❑ 83MiaMarT-21
Allington, William
❑ 30Zee-164
Allison, Bob (William R.)
❑ 55DonWin-10
❑ 59HomRunD-2
❑ 59Top-116
❑ 59TopVen-116
❑ 60ArmCoi-2
❑ 60KeyChal-2
❑ 60NuHi-66
❑ 60SenJayP-1
❑ 60Top-320
❑ 60TopTat-2
❑ 61NuSco-466
❑ 61Pos-91A
❑ 61Pos-91B
❑ 61Top-355
❑ 61TopStal-176
❑ 61TwiJayP-1
❑ 61TwiUniMC-1
❑ 62AurRec-1
❑ 62Baz-1
❑ 62Jel-83
❑ 62Pos-83
❑ 62PosCan-83
❑ 62SalPlaC-22
❑ 62ShiPlaC-22
❑ 62Top-180
❑ 62TopStal-73
❑ 62TopVen-180
❑ 63BasMagM-4
❑ 63Jel-7
❑ 63Pos-7
❑ 63Top-75
❑ 63TwiJayP-2
❑ 63TwiVol-2
❑ 64Top-10
❑ 64Top-290
❑ 64TopCoi-19
❑ 64TopVen-10
❑ 64TopVen-290
❑ 64TwiJayP-1
❑ 64WheSta-2
❑ 65OldLonC-21
❑ 65OPC-180
❑ 65Top-180
❑ 65TopEmbl-38
❑ 65TopTral-1
❑ 65TwiPos-1
❑ 66Top-345
❑ 66TopVen-345
❑ 66TwiFaiG-2
❑ 67CokCapTw-2
❑ 67DexPre-7
❑ 67OPC-194
❑ 67Top-194
❑ 67Top-334
❑ 67TwiTeal-1
❑ 68DexPre-4
❑ 68Top-335
❑ 68TopVen-335
❑ 69MilBra-9
❑ 69MLBOffS-64
❑ 69OPC-30
❑ 69Top-30
❑ 69TopSta-191
❑ 69TopTeaP-15
❑ 69TwiTealC-1
❑ 70DayDaiNM-149
❑ 70MLBOffS-229
❑ 70Top-635
❑ 72MilBra-10
❑ 78TCM60I-26
❑ 78TwiFri-1
❑ 83MLBPin-1
❑ 86TwiGreT-5
❑ 89ChaLooLITI-2
❑ 89PacLegI-165
❑ 89SweBasG-27
❑ 93UppDecAH-3
Allison, Brad
❑ 96AriBlaDB-5
❑ 97SouBenSH-4
❑ 98SouBenSHM-2
Allison, Bubba
❑ 86BenPhiC-151
Allison, Chris
❑ 94UtiBluSC-2
❑ 94UtiBluSF-3825
❑ 95Bes-8
❑ 95MicBatCTI-1
❑ 95MidLeaA-2
❑ 96Exc-10
Allison, Cody
❑ 96BurIndB-17
❑ 97WatIndTI-1
❑ 98ColRedSM-13
Allison, Dana
❑ 89MedAthB-28
❑ 90ModA'sCLC-153
❑ 90ModA'sP-2203
❑ 91Bow-238
❑ 91ScoRoo-94T
❑ 91SouOreAAP-SOA19
❑ 91TacTigP-2295
❑ 91UppDec-771
❑ 92HunStaF-3940
❑ 92TacTigS-526
❑ 92TopDeb91-2
❑ 93HunStaF-2074
❑ 94TacTigF-3166
Allison, Fritz
❑ 94ElmPioC-1
❑ 94ElmPioF-3480
Allison, Jamie
❑ 88CalLeaACLC-21
❑ 88RenSilSCLC-279
❑ 89KinIndS-1
❑ 90KinIndTI-13
Allison, Jeff
❑ 87IdaFalBP-5
❑ 88MiaMarS-1
❑ 88SalLakCTTI-9
Allison, Jim
❑ 83TriTriT-12
❑ 85BurRanT-27
❑ 85UtiBluST-1
❑ 86DayBealP-1
Allison, Tom
❑ 90PitMetP-32
❑ 91ColMetPI-7
❑ 91ColMetPPI-5
❑ 92BinMetF-521
❑ 92BinMetS-51
❑ 93BinMetF-2339
❑ 94BinMetF-721
Allred, Beau
❑ 88CarLeaAS-23
❑ 88KinIndS-1
❑ 89BasAmeAPB-AA7
❑ 89BlaYNPRWL-56
❑ 89CanIndB-4
❑ 89CanIndP-1302
❑ 89CanIndS-1
❑ 89EasLeaAP-6
❑ 89Sta-154
❑ 89StaFutS-9
❑ 89StaFutS-10
❑ 90CMC-461
❑ 90ColSprSSC-9
❑ 90ColSprSSP-48
❑ 90Don-691
❑ 90FleUpd-88
❑ 90IndTeal-1
❑ 90OPC-419
❑ 90ProAAAF-229
❑ 90ScoRoo-70T
❑ 90Top-419
❑ 90TopDeb89-2
❑ 90TopTif-419
❑ 91Bow-80
❑ 91Fle-358
❑ 91IndFanC-1
❑ 91Lea-316
❑ 91Sco-338
❑ 91Sco100RS-56
❑ 91ScoRoo-22
❑ 91Ult-104
❑ 91UppDec-784
❑ 92ColSprSSF-762
❑ 92ColSprSSS-77
❑ 92SkyAAAF-34
❑ 93ChaKniF-554
❑ 94RicBraF-2857
Allred, Doug
❑ 87nsBasASD-1
Almada, Luis
❑ 29Zee-148
❑ 30Zee-165
❑ 32Zee-112
❑ 33Zee-12
❑ 33Zee-13
Almada, Mel (Baldomero M.)
❑ 34BatR31-147
❑ 35DiaMatCS3T1-2
❑ 36GouWidPPR-B1
❑ 36NatChiFPR-1
❑ 36OveCanR-1
❑ 39PlaBal-43
❑ 40PlaBal-71
❑ 40SolHug-1
❑ 90DodTar-11
❑ 91ConTSN-234
❑ 92ConTSN-550
Almante, Tom
❑ 86ArkTraP-1
Almanza, Armando
❑ 96PeoChiB-4
❑ 97CalLeaATI-50
❑ 97PriWilC-4
❑ 98ArkTraM-3
❑ 98PriWilCASM-2
❑ 98TexLeaTPG-1
Almanzar, Carlos
❑ 94MedHatBJF-3672
❑ 94MedHatBJSP-12
❑ 95KnoSmoF-31
❑ 96KnoSmoB-4
❑ 97KnoSmo-5
❑ 98PacOmeRS-3
❑ 98PacOmeRST2-3
❑ 98PacOnl-751
❑ 98PacOnlR-751
❑ 98PacOnlWC-751
❑ 98SyrSkyG-1
Almanzar, Richard
❑ 96BesAutS-3
❑ 96BesAutSA-2
❑ 96Bow-358
❑ 96BowFoi-358
❑ 96LakTigB-5
❑ 97BesAutAS-2
❑ 97BesAutP-R1
❑ 97BesLimA-1
❑ 97Bow-125
❑ 97BowInt-125
❑ 97JacSun-4
❑ 98BesPreA-1
❑ 98TolMudHQ-5
Almaraz, Joe
❑ 98LetBlaDG-2
Almaraz, Johnny
❑ 88BilMusP-1825
❑ 89GreHorP-431
Almeida, Rafael D.
❑ 12T207-3
Almon, Bill (William F.)
❑ 74HawIslC-106
❑ 75HawIslC-11
❑ 76HawIslC-10
❑ 77PadSchC-1A
❑ 77PadSchC-1B
❑ 77PadSchC-12
❑ 77Top-490
❑ 78PadFamF-1
❑ 78Top-392
❑ 79Kel-53
❑ 79PadFamF-10
❑ 79Top-616
❑ 80ExpPos-1
❑ 80OPC-225
❑ 80Top-436
❑ 81Fle-332
❑ 81Top-163
❑ 81TopTra-730
❑ 82Don-637
❑ 82Fle-335
❑ 82FleSta-185
❑ 82OPC-119
❑ 82Top-521
❑ 82TopSti-167
❑ 83Don-356
❑ 83Fle-228
❑ 83OPC-362
❑ 83Top-362
❑ 83TopTra-2T
❑ 84A'sMot-11
❑ 84Don-467
❑ 84Fle-436
❑ 84Nes792-241
❑ 84OPC-241
❑ 84Top-241
❑ 84TopSti-334
❑ 84TopTif-241
❑ 85Don-589
❑ 85Fle-414
❑ 85FleUpd-2
❑ 85Pir-1
❑ 85Top-273
❑ 85Top-607
❑ 85TopTif-273
❑ 85TopTif-607
❑ 85TopTifT-2T
❑ 85TopTra-2T
❑ 86Don-479
❑ 86Fle-602
❑ 86OPC-48
❑ 86Top-48
❑ 86TopSti-131
❑ 86TopTif-48
❑ 87Don-326
❑ 87Fle-601
❑ 87FleGlo-601
❑ 87OPC-159
❑ 87Top-447
❑ 87TopTif-447
❑ 87TopTra-1T
❑ 87TopTraT-1T
❑ 88Don-487
❑ 88PhiTas-2
❑ 88StaLinMe-1
❑ 88Top-787
❑ 88TopTif-787
❑ 91MetWIZ-6
Almond, Greg
❑ 93GleFalRC-3
❑ 93GleFalRF-4004
❑ 94MadHatC-1
❑ 94MadHatF-134
❑ 96PeoChiB-5
❑ 97PriWilC-5
❑ 98ArkTraM-4
Almonte, Daniel
❑ 97St.PauS-1
Almonte, Erick
❑ 98GreBatM-1
Almonte, Hector
❑ 98KanCouC-2
❑ 98KanCouCCP-2
❑ 99JustheS-1
❑ 99JustheSAC-1
❑ 99JustheSAD-1
❑ 99JustheSJB-1
Almonte, Wady
❑ 96FreKeyB-2
❑ 97BowBay-5
❑ 97FlaShoWotF-4
❑ 97Fle-613
❑ 97FleTif-613
❑ 97Ult-510
❑ 97UltGolME-510
❑ 97UltPlaME-510
Aloi, Dave
❑ 74CedRapAT-7
❑ 75DubPacT-24
Aloma, Luis
❑ 51Bow-231
❑ 52Top-308
❑ 54Bow-134
❑ 54Top-57
❑ 83TopRep5-308
❑ 94TopArc1-57
❑ 94TopArc1G-57
Alomar, Rafael
❑ 61TacBan-1
❑ 61UniOil-T30
Alomar, Roberto
❑ 87TexLeaAF-8
❑ 87WicPilRD-4
❑ 88BlaYNPRWL-34
❑ 88Don-34
❑ 88DonBasB-42
❑ 88DonRoo-35
❑ 88FleUpd-122
❑ 88FleUpdG-122
❑ 88LasVegSC-20
❑ 88LasVegSP-231
❑ 88Lea-34
❑ 88PadSmo-2
❑ 88ScoRoo-105T
❑ 88ScoRooG-105T
❑ 88TopTra-4T
❑ 88TopTraT-4T
❑ 89BimBreD-12
❑ 89BlaYNPRWL-104
❑ 89Bow-258
❑ 89Bow-458
❑ 89BowTif-258
❑ 89BowTif-458
❑ 89ClaTraO-127
❑ 89Don-246
❑ 89DonBasB-21
❑ 89Fle-299
❑ 89Fle-630
❑ 89FleGlo-299
❑ 89FleGlo-630
❑ 89FleSup-1
❑ 89OPC-206
❑ 89PadCok-1
❑ 89PadMag-9
❑ 89PadMag-14
❑ 89PadPos-2
❑ 89PanSti-191
❑ 89RedFolSB-3
❑ 89Sco-232
❑ 89ScoHot1R-72
❑ 89ScoYouSI-28
❑ 89Spo-20
❑ 89Top-206
❑ 89Top-231
❑ 89TopBig-102
❑ 89TopGloS-19
❑ 89TopRoo-1
❑ 89TopSti-104
❑ 89TopTif-206
❑ 89TopTif-231
❑ 89ToyRoo-1
❑ 89TVSpoM-47
❑ 89UppDec-471
❑ 90Bow-221
❑ 90BowTif-221
❑ 90ClaBlu-61
❑ 90Don-111
❑ 90DonBesN-35
❑ 90Fle-149
❑ 90FleCan-149
❑ 90FleLeaL-1
❑ 90FleLeaLC-1
❑ 90Lea-75
❑ 90OPC-517
❑ 90PadCok-1
❑ 90PadMag-10
❑ 90PanSti-349
❑ 90PubIntS-43
❑ 90PubIntS-607
❑ 90Sco-12
❑ 90Spo-93
❑ 90StaAloB-1
❑ 90StaAloB-3
❑ 90StaAloB-5
❑ 90StaAloB-7
❑ 90StaAloB-9
❑ 90StaAloB-11
❑ 90Top-517
❑ 90TopBig-9
❑ 90TopCoi-37
❑ 90TopGloS-27
❑ 90TopMag-85
❑ 90TopMinL-77
❑ 90TopSti-109
❑ 90TopStiB-4
❑ 90TopTif-517
❑ 90TopTVA-35
❑ 90UppDec-346
❑ 90UppDecS-3
❑ 90USPlaCA-4D
❑ 91BluJayFS-2
❑ 91BluJayFS-1
❑ 91BluJayS-13
❑ 91BluJayS-39
❑ 91Bow-9
❑ 91CadEIID-1
❑ 91Cla1-T94
❑ 91Cla2-T81
❑ 91ClaGam-113
❑ 91ColRobA-1
❑ 91ColRobA-2
❑ 91ColRobA-3
❑ 91ColRobA-4
❑ 91ColRobA-5
❑ 91ColRobA-6
❑ 91ColRobA-7
❑ 91ColRobA-8
❑ 91ColRobA-9
❑ 91ColRobA-10
❑ 91ColRobA-11
❑ 91ColRobA-12
❑ 91ColRobA-xx
❑ 91Don-12
❑ 91Don-682
❑ 91DonSupD-12
❑ 91Fle-523
❑ 91FleUpd-63
❑ 91Lea-267
❑ 91OPC-315
❑ 91OPCPre-1
❑ 91PanFreS-92
❑ 91PanSti-96

❑ 91RedFolS-3
❑ 91Sco-25
❑ 91Sco-887
❑ 91Sco100S-100
❑ 91ScoRoo-44T
❑ 91StaClu-304
❑ 91Stu-131
❑ 91SunSee-19
❑ 91Top-315
❑ 91TopDesS-315
❑ 91TopMic-315
❑ 91TopTif-315
❑ 91TopTra-2T
❑ 91TopTraT-2T
❑ 91TopTriH-A14
❑ 91Ult-358
❑ 91UppDec-80
❑ 91UppDec-335
❑ 91UppDec-763
❑ 91UppDecFE-83F
❑ 91USPlaCA-12H
❑ 92BluJayP-1
❑ 92Bow-20
❑ 92Cla1-T4
❑ 92ClaGam-121
❑ 92ColAllG-3
❑ 92ColAllP-3
❑ 92ColPro-1A
❑ 92ColPro-1B
❑ 92Don-28
❑ 92Don-58
❑ 92DonMcD-G1
❑ 92Fle-323
❑ 92Fle-698
❑ 92FleCitTP-24
❑ 92Fre-12
❑ 92Hig5-116
❑ 92Lea-233
❑ 92LeaBlaG-233
❑ 92MooSna-13
❑ 92Mr.TurS-2
❑ 92MSABenSHD-3
❑ 92New-1
❑ 92OPC-225
❑ 92OPCPre-130
❑ 92PanSti-26
❑ 92PanSti-273
❑ 92PepDieM-15
❑ 92Pin-45
❑ 92Pin-306
❑ 92Pin-586
❑ 92PinTea2-48
❑ 92PinTeaP-5
❑ 92PosCan-13
❑ 92RedFolS-2
❑ 92RedFolS-105
❑ 92RevSup1-13
❑ 92RevSup1-14
❑ 92RevSup1-15
❑ 92Sco-15
❑ 92Sco100S-82
❑ 92ScoCokD-1
❑ 92ScoImpP-10
❑ 92ScoProaG-3
❑ 92ScoProP-4
❑ 92SevCoi-5
❑ 92SpollIFK1-54
❑ 92SpollIFK1-497
❑ 92StaClu-159
❑ 92StaCluD-5
❑ 92StaPro-1
❑ 92Stu-251
❑ 92StuPre-13
❑ 92Top-225
❑ 92TopGol-225
❑ 92TopGolW-225
❑ 92TopKid-90
❑ 92TopMcD-4
❑ 92TopMic-225
❑ 92TriPla-84
❑ 92Ult-143
❑ 92UltAllS-2
❑ 92UltAwaW-20
❑ 92UppDec-81
❑ 92UppDec-355
❑ 92UppDecF-11
❑ 92UppDecFG-11
❑ 92UppDecTMH-4
❑ 92UppDecWB-T11
❑ 93BluJayCP1-1
❑ 93BluJayCP1-4
❑ 93BluJayD-2
❑ 93BluJayD4-2
❑ 93BluJayDM-12
❑ 93BluJayDM-18A
❑ 93BluJayDM-18B
❑ 93BluJayDM-28
❑ 93BluJayFS-1
❑ 93Bow-338
❑ 93ClaGam-2
❑ 93ColAllG-1
❑ 93DiaMar-1
❑ 93DiaMarA-1
❑ 93DiaMarP-1
❑ 93Don-132
❑ 93Don-425
❑ 93DonDiaK-DK20
❑ 93DonEli-26
❑ 93DonEliD-20
❑ 93DonEliS-8
❑ 93DonLonBL-LL8
❑ 93DonMasotG-10
❑ 93DonMVP-6
❑ 93DonPre-22
❑ 93DonSpiotG-SG3
❑ 93Fin-88
❑ 93FinJum-88
❑ 93FinPro-88
❑ 93FinProR-88
❑ 93FinRef-88
❑ 93Fla-287
❑ 93Fle-330
❑ 93Fle-357
❑ 93FleAll-AL2
❑ 93FleAtl-1
❑ 93FleFruotL-1
❑ 93FlePro-A1
❑ 93FleTeaL-AL9
❑ 93FunPac-10
❑ 93FunPac-22
❑ 93FunPac-54
❑ 93FunPac-55
❑ 93FunPacA-AS4
❑ 93Hos-14
❑ 93HumDumC-22
❑ 93Kra-2
❑ 93Lea-245
❑ 93LeaGolA-R13
❑ 93LeaGolA-U4
❑ 93OPC-4
❑ 93OPCPreSP-3
❑ 93OPCPreSPF-3
❑ 93OPCWorC-1
❑ 93PacBeiA-7
❑ 93PacSpa-319
❑ 93PacSpaPI-7
❑ 93PanSti-27
❑ 93Pin-30
❑ 93PinCoo-29
❑ 93PinCooD-29
❑ 93Pos-22
❑ 93PosCan-5
❑ 93RedFolS-2
❑ 93RedFolS-105
❑ 93Sco-14
❑ 93Sco-511
❑ 93Sco-542
❑ 93ScoFra-14
❑ 93ScoGolDT-11
❑ 93Sel-8
❑ 93SelChaS-14
❑ 93SelStaL-39
❑ 93SelStaL-51
❑ 93SP-1
❑ 93StaClu-142
❑ 93StaClu-596
❑ 93StaCluFDI-142
❑ 93StaCluFDI-596
❑ 93StaCluM-19
❑ 93StaCluM-191
❑ 93StaCluMOP-142
❑ 93StaCluMOP-596
❑ 93Stu-4
❑ 93Top-50
❑ 93TOPBLAG-23
❑ 93TopFulS-5
❑ 93TopGol-50
❑ 93TopInaM-50
❑ 93TopInaR-50
❑ 93TopMic-50
❑ 93TopMic-P50
❑ 93TopPreS-1
❑ 93Toy-13
❑ 93TriPla-2
❑ 93TriPla-200
❑ 93TriPlaA-13
❑ 93TriPlaP-2
❑ 93Ult-639
❑ 93UltAwaW-13
❑ 93UppDec-42
❑ 93UppDec-125
❑ 93UppDec-815
❑ 93UppDec-840
❑ 93UppDecCP-R1
❑ 93UppDecDG-4
❑ 93UppDecFA-A3
❑ 93UppDecFAJ-A3
❑ 93UppDecFH-55
❑ 93UppDecGold-42
❑ 93UppDecGold-125
❑ 93UppDecGold-815
❑ 93UppDecGold-840
❑ 93UppDecIC-WI4
❑ 93UppDecICJ-WI4
❑ 93UppDecOD-D2
❑ 93UppDecSH-HI1
❑ 93USPlaCA-2D
❑ 93USPlaCA-9H
❑ 94BluJayP-1
❑ 94BluJayUSPC-1D
❑ 94BluJayUSPC-7C
❑ 94BluJayUSPC-7S
❑ 94Bow-609
❑ 94BowBes-R7
❑ 94BowBesR-R7
❑ 94ChuHomS-11
❑ 94ChuHomSG-11
❑ 94ColC-33
❑ 94ColC-321
❑ 94ColC-331
❑ 94ColC-631
❑ 94ColChoGS-33
❑ 94ColChoGS-321
❑ 94ColChoGS-331
❑ 94ColChoGS-631
❑ 94ColChoSS-33
❑ 94ColChoSS-321
❑ 94ColChoSS-331
❑ 94ColChoSS-631
❑ 94ColChoT-1
❑ 94DenHol-2
❑ 94Don-6
❑ 94DonSpeE-6
❑ 94Fin-205
❑ 94FinJum-205
❑ 94FinRef-205
❑ 94Fla-115
❑ 94FlaHotN-1
❑ 94Fle-324
❑ 94FleAllS-1
❑ 94FleExtB-186
❑ 94FleSun-1
❑ 94FUnPac-12
❑ 94FUnPac-178
❑ 94FUnPac-201
❑ 94FUnPac-211
❑ 94FUnPac-217
❑ 94KinDis-20
❑ 94Lea-225
❑ 94LeaGolS-1
❑ 94LeaL-75
❑ 94LeaLimGA-3
❑ 94LeaPro-1
❑ 94LeaSli-5
❑ 94O-PJumAF-21
❑ 94OPC-96
❑ 94OPCAllR-21
❑ 94OPCJumA-21
❑ 94OPCWorC-6
❑ 94Pac-632
❑ 94PacAll-17
❑ 94PacSilP-5
❑ 94PacSilPC-5
❑ 94PanSti-134
❑ 94Pin-287
❑ 94PinArtP-287
❑ 94PinMusC-287
❑ 94PinRunC-RC6
❑ 94PinTheN-8
❑ 94PinTri-TR16
❑ 94Pos-18
❑ 94PosCan-3
❑ 94ProMag-136
❑ 94RedFolMI-1
❑ 94Sco-43
❑ 94ScoGolR-43
❑ 94ScoGolS-42
❑ 94Sel-229
❑ 94SP-39
❑ 94SPDieC-39
❑ 94SPHol-1
❑ 94SPHolDC-1
❑ 94Spo-31
❑ 94Spo-177
❑ 94SpoFanA-AS2
❑ 94SPPre-ER1
❑ 94StaClu-10
❑ 94StaClu-110
❑ 94StaCluFDI-10
❑ 94StaCluFDI-110
❑ 94StaCluGR-10
❑ 94StaCluGR-110
❑ 94StaCluMO-33
❑ 94StaCluMOP-10
❑ 94StaCluMOP-110
❑ 94StaCluT-153
❑ 94StaCluTF-1
❑ 94StaCluTFDI-153
❑ 94Stu-24
❑ 94Top-385
❑ 94Top-675
❑ 94TopBlaG-1
❑ 94TopGol-385
❑ 94TopGol-675
❑ 94TopSpa-385
❑ 94TopSpa-675
❑ 94TopSupS-1
❑ 94TriPla-31
❑ 94TriPlaM-5
❑ 94Ult-434
❑ 94UltAllS-3
❑ 94UltAwaW-3
❑ 94UltHitM-1
❑ 94UltOnBL-1
❑ 94UppDec-35
❑ 94UppDec-455
❑ 94UppDecAJ-16
❑ 94UppDecAJG-16
❑ 94UppDecDC-E1
❑ 94UppDecED-35
❑ 94UppDecED-455
❑ 94UppDecNG-1
❑ 94UppDecNGED-1
❑ 94USPlaCA-9D
❑ 94USPlaCA-12H
❑ 95Baz-81
❑ 95BazRedH-RH16
❑ 95BluJayB-1
❑ 95BluJayOH-1
❑ 95BluJayP-1
❑ 95BluJayUSPC-1H
❑ 95BluJayUSPC-5C
❑ 95Bow-368
❑ 95BowBes-R57
❑ 95BowBesR-R57
❑ 95ClaPhoC-57
❑ 95ColCho-140
❑ 95ColChoGS-140
❑ 95ColChoSE-51
❑ 95ColChoSEGS-51
❑ 95ColChoSESS-51
❑ 95ColChoSS-140
❑ 95DenHol-1
❑ 95Don-49
❑ 95DonAll-AL4
❑ 95DonDom-4
❑ 95DonPreP-49
❑ 95DonTopotO-171
❑ 95Emo-90
❑ 95Fin-137
❑ 95FinRef-137
❑ 95Fla-94
❑ 95FlaHotG-1
❑ 95Fle-87
❑ 95FleAllF-3
❑ 95FleAllS-3
❑ 95FleUpdSL-1
❑ 95KinDis-1
❑ 95Kra-1
❑ 95Lea-256
❑ 95LeaGreG-2
❑ 95LeaLim-4
❑ 95LeaLimG-14
❑ 95LeaLimIBP-17
❑ 95LinVen-320
❑ 95LinVen-325
❑ 95Pac-435
❑ 95PacGolCDC-19
❑ 95PacLatD-1
❑ 95PacPri-138
❑ 95PanSti-46
❑ 95Pin-222
❑ 95PinArtP-222
❑ 95PinFan-14
❑ 95PinMusC-222
❑ 95PinPin-8
❑ 95PinPinR-8
❑ 95PinRedH-RH23
❑ 95PinTeaP-TP4
❑ 95PinUps-US2
❑ 95PinWhiH-WH23
❑ 95Pos-5
❑ 95PosCan-2
❑ 95RedFol-36
❑ 95Sco-2
❑ 95Sco-553
❑ 95ScoDreT-DG2
❑ 95ScoGolR-2
❑ 95ScoGolR-553
❑ 95ScoHaloG-HG3
❑ 95ScoPlaTS-2
❑ 95ScoPlaTS-553
❑ 95ScoRul-SR8
❑ 95ScoRulJ-SR8
❑ 95ScoSam-2
❑ 95Sel-34
❑ 95SelArtP-34
❑ 95SelCer-75
❑ 95SelCerMG-75
❑ 95SelCerS-75
❑ 95SelSam-34
❑ 95SP-201
❑ 95SPCha-100
❑ 95SPCha-196
❑ 95SPChaCP-CP6
❑ 95SPChaCPDC-CP6
❑ 95SPChaDC-100
❑ 95SPChaDC-196
❑ 95Spo-128
❑ 95SpoArtP-128
❑ 95SpoDouT-3
❑ 95SpoSam-128
❑ 95SPSil-201
❑ 95SPSpeF-23
❑ 95StaClu-70
❑ 95StaCluFDI-70
❑ 95StaCluMOP-70
❑ 95StaCluMOP-SS1
❑ 95StaCluSS-SS1
❑ 95StaCluSTWS-70
❑ 95StaCluVR-43
❑ 95StaCluVRMO-43
❑ 95Stu-17
❑ 95StuGolS-17
❑ 95StuPlaS-17
❑ 95Sum-50
❑ 95SumNthD-50
❑ 95Top-438
❑ 95TopCyb-234
❑ 95TopD3-4
❑ 95TopEmb-91
❑ 95TopEmbGI-91
❑ 95UC3-78
❑ 95UC3ArtP-78
❑ 95Ult-116
❑ 95UltAwaW-3
❑ 95UltAwaWGM-3
❑ 95UltGolM-116
❑ 95UppDec-40
❑ 95UppDecED-40
❑ 95UppDecEDG-40
❑ 95UppDecPAW-H23
❑ 95UppDecPAWE-H23
❑ 95UppDecPC-MLB6
❑ 95UppDecSE-197
❑ 95UppDecSEG-197
❑ 95UppDecSoaD-SD6
❑ 95Zen-89
❑ 96BalOriP-2
❑ 96Baz-35
❑ 96Bow-45
❑ 96BowBes-65
❑ 96BowBesAR-65
❑ 96BowBesMI-2
❑ 96BowBesMIAR-2
❑ 96BowBesMIR-2
❑ 96BowBesR-65
❑ 96BowFoi-45
❑ 96Cir-1
❑ 96CirBos-1
❑ 96CirRav-1
❑ 96ColCho-339
❑ 96ColCho-463
❑ 96ColChoGS-339
❑ 96ColChoGS-463
❑ 96ColChoSS-339
❑ 96ColChoSS-463
❑ 96Don-103
❑ 96DonDiaK-6
❑ 96DonPreP-103
❑ 96EmoXL-1
❑ 96EmoXLD-1
❑ 96Fin-B228
❑ 96Fin-G197
❑ 96FinRef-B228
❑ 96FinRef-G197
❑ 96Fla-1
❑ 96FlaHotG-1
❑ 96Fle-267
❑ 96FleTif-267
❑ 96FleUpd-U1
❑ 96FleUpdH-1
❑ 96FleUpdSL-1
❑ 96FleUpdTC-U1
❑ 96Kin-20
❑ 96Lea-155
❑ 96LeaLim-50
❑ 96LeaLimG-50
❑ 96LeaPre-61
❑ 96LeaPreP-61
❑ 96LeaPrePB-155
❑ 96LeaPrePG-155
❑ 96LeaPrePS-155
❑ 96LeaPreSG-12
❑ 96LeaPreSte-12
❑ 96LeaSig-48
❑ 96LeaSigA-5
❑ 96LeaSigAG-5
❑ 96LeaSigAS-5
❑ 96LeaSigPPG-48
❑ 96LeaSigPPP-48
❑ 96MetUni-1
❑ 96MetUniP-1
❑ 96MLBPin-1
❑ 96OriFle-1
❑ 96Pac-450
❑ 96PacBaeS-5
❑ 96PacCraC-CC1
❑ 96PacEstL-EL1
❑ 96PacGolCD-DC1
❑ 96PacHom-HP10
❑ 96PacPri-P23
❑ 96PacPriG-P23
❑ 96PacPriRHS-RH1
❑ 96PanSti-159
❑ 96Pin-242
❑ 96PinAfi-97
❑ 96PinAfi-160
❑ 96PinAfiAP-97
❑ 96PinAfiAP-160
❑ 96PinAfiFPP-97
❑ 96PinArtP-142
❑ 96PinFoil-242
❑ 96PinSta-142
❑ 96RedF-12
❑ 96Sco-57
❑ 96Sco-365
❑ 96ScoDugC-A50
❑ 96ScoDugC-B90
❑ 96ScoDugCAP-A50
❑ 96ScoDugCAP-B90
❑ 96ScoRef-8
❑ 96Sel-122
❑ 96SelArtP-122
❑ 96SelCer-99
❑ 96SelCerAP-99
❑ 96SelCerCB-99
❑ 96SelCerCR-99
❑ 96SelCerMB-99
❑ 96SelCerMG-99
❑ 96SelCerMR-99
❑ 96SP-29
❑ 96Spo-73
❑ 96SpoArtP-73
❑ 96SpoDouT-2
❑ 96SPSpeFX-24
❑ 96SPSpeFXDC-24
❑ 96SPx-6
❑ 96SPxBoufG-7
❑ 96SPxGol-6
❑ 96StaClu-176
❑ 96StaCluEPB-176
❑ 96StaCluEPG-176
❑ 96StaCluEPS-176
❑ 96StaCluMOP-176
❑ 96Stu-29
❑ 96StuPrePB-29
❑ 96StuPrePG-29
❑ 96StuPrePS-29
❑ 96Sum-146
❑ 96SumAbo&B-146
❑ 96SumArtP-146
❑ 96SumFoi-146
❑ 96SumPos-2
❑ 96TeaOut-1
❑ 96TeaOut-C92
❑ 96Top-289
❑ 96TopChr-115
❑ 96TopChrR-115
❑ 96TopGal-78
❑ 96TopGalPPI-78
❑ 96TopLas-33
❑ 96TopPro-AL1
❑ 96Ult-142
❑ 96Ult-301
❑ 96Ult-573

❑ 96UltGolM-142
❑ 96UltGolM-301
❑ 96UltGolM-573
❑ 96UltPriL-3
❑ 96UltPriLGM-3
❑ 96UltRaw-1
❑ 96UltRawGM-1
❑ 96UppDec-275
❑ 96UppDec-370
❑ 96UppDecA-1
❑ 96UppDecDD-DD7
❑ 96UppDecDDG-DD7
❑ 96UppDecDDS-DD7
❑ 96UppDecHC-HC3
❑ 96UppDecPRE-R21
❑ 96UppDecPreR-R21
❑ 96Zen-18
❑ 96Zen-141
❑ 96ZenArtP-18
❑ 96ZenArtP-141
❑ 96ZenDiaC-11
❑ 96ZenDiaCP-11
❑ 96ZenMoz-8
❑ 96ZenZ-11
❑ 97BalOriP-1
❑ 97BluJayS-46
❑ 97BluJayS-48
❑ 97Bow-35
❑ 97BowBes-59
❑ 97BowBesAR-59
❑ 97BowBesR-59
❑ 97BowChr-30
❑ 97BowChrI-30
❑ 97BowChrIR-30
❑ 97BowChrR-30
❑ 97BowInt-35
❑ 97Cir-163
❑ 97CirRav-163
❑ 97ColCho-39
❑ 97ColCho-219
❑ 97ColChoAC-11
❑ 97ColChoT-BO4
❑ 97ColChoTBS-6
❑ 97ColChoTBSWH-6
❑ 97Don-37
❑ 97Don-414
❑ 97DonArmaD-14
❑ 97DonEli-20
❑ 97DonEliGS-20
❑ 97DonGolPP-37
❑ 97DonGolPP-414
❑ 97DonLim-21
❑ 97DonLim-62
❑ 97DonLim-145
❑ 97DonLimE-21
❑ 97DonLimE-62
❑ 97DonLimE-145
❑ 97DonLimENG-21
❑ 97DonLimFotG-64
❑ 97DonPre-106
❑ 97DonPreCttC-106
❑ 97DonPreXP-5A
❑ 97DonSig-9
❑ 97DonSigA-4
❑ 97DonSigAC-4
❑ 97DonSigAM-4
❑ 97DonSigPPP-9
❑ 97DonSilPP-37
❑ 97DonSilPP-414
❑ 97DonTea-32
❑ 97DonTeaSPE-32
❑ 97DonVxP1-6
❑ 97E-X2-4
❑ 97E-X2Cred-4
❑ 97E-X2EssCre-4
❑ 97E-X2Hall-19
❑ 97Fin-111
❑ 97Fin-205
❑ 97FinEmb-111
❑ 97FinEmbR-111
❑ 97FinRef-111
❑ 97FinRef-205
❑ 97FlaShoHG-1
❑ 97FlaShoLC-58
❑ 97FlaShoLeg0-58
❑ 97FlaShoLeg1-58
❑ 97FlaShoM-A58
❑ 97FlaShoM-B58
❑ 97FlaShoM-C58
❑ 97FlaShoR0-58
❑ 97FlaShoR1-58
❑ 97FlaShoR2-58
❑ 97Fle-1
❑ 97Fle-696
❑ 97FleTif-1
❑ 97FleTif-696

❑ 97HigMinM-0
❑ 97HigMinMCT-1
❑ 97HigMinMCT-2
❑ 97Lea-14
❑ 97Lea-393
❑ 97LeaFraM-14
❑ 97LeaFraM-393
❑ 97LeaFraMDC-14
❑ 97LeaFraMDC-393
❑ 97LeaGolS-33
❑ 97MetUni-1
❑ 97MetUniMF-1
❑ 97MetUniML-1
❑ 97NewPin-102
❑ 97NewPinAP-102
❑ 97NewPinMC-102
❑ 97NewPinPP-102
❑ 97OriSco-3
❑ 97OriScoPl-3
❑ 97OriScoPr-3
❑ 97OriSun-2
❑ 97OriSun-3
❑ 97OriSun-7
❑ 97Pac-17
❑ 97PacBaeS-6
❑ 97PacCar-1
❑ 97PacCarM-1
❑ 97PacCraC-1
❑ 97PacFirD-1
❑ 97PacGolCD-1
❑ 97PacLatotML-2
❑ 97PacLigB-17
❑ 97PacPri-7
❑ 97PacPriGA-GA1
❑ 97PacPriGotD-GD9
❑ 97PacPriLB-7
❑ 97PacPriP-7
❑ 97PacPriSL-SL1C
❑ 97PacSil-17
❑ 97PinCer-95
❑ 97PinCerLI-16
❑ 97PinCerMBla-95
❑ 97PinCerMBlu-95
❑ 97PinCerMG-95
❑ 97PinCerMR-95
❑ 97PinCerR-95
❑ 97PinIns-75
❑ 97PinInsCE-75
❑ 97PinInsDD-5
❑ 97PinInsDE-75
❑ 97PinPasttM-9
❑ 97PinTotCPB-95
❑ 97PinTotCPG-95
❑ 97PinTotCPR-95
❑ 97PinX-P-112
❑ 97PinX-PMoS-112
❑ 97PreCon-1
❑ 97Sco-67
❑ 97Sco-542
❑ 97ScoArtPWB-67
❑ 97ScoArtPWB-542
❑ 97ScoFra-9
❑ 97ScoFraG-9
❑ 97ScoHeaotO-11
❑ 97ScoPreS-67
❑ 97ScoResC-542
❑ 97ScoShoS-67
❑ 97ScoShoS-542
❑ 97ScoShoSAP-67
❑ 97ScoShoSAP-542
❑ 97ScoSteS-11
❑ 97Sel-59
❑ 97SelArtP-59
❑ 97SelCom-59
❑ 97SelRegG-59
❑ 97SP-29
❑ 97SpoIll-55
❑ 97SpoIllEE-55
❑ 97SpoIllGS-6
❑ 97SPSpeF-26
❑ 97SPSpxF-8
❑ 97SPSPxFA-8
❑ 97SPx-9
❑ 97SPxBro-9
❑ 97SPxGol-9
❑ 97SPxGraF-9
❑ 97SPxSil-9
❑ 97SPxSte-9
❑ 97StaClu-38
❑ 97StaClu-240
❑ 97StaCluMat-240
❑ 97StaCluMOP-38
❑ 97StaCluMOP-240
❑ 97StaCluMOP-PL12
❑ 97StaCluPL-PL12
❑ 97StrAll-1

❑ 97Stu-95
❑ 97StuPrePG-95
❑ 97StuPrePS-95
❑ 97Top-152
❑ 97TopChr-58
❑ 97TopChrR-58
❑ 97TopGal-47
❑ 97TopGalPPI-47
❑ 97TopSta-31
❑ 97TopSta97AS-AS12
❑ 97TopStaAM-31
❑ 97TopSweS-SS1
❑ 97UD3-33
❑ 97Ult-1
❑ 97UltDouT-1
❑ 97UltFamGam-15
❑ 97UltFieC-1
❑ 97UltGolME-1
❑ 97UltHitM-14
❑ 97UltLeaS-8
❑ 97UltPlaME-1
❑ 97UltTop3-19
❑ 97UltTop3GM-19
❑ 97UppDec-19
❑ 97UppDec-142
❑ 97UppDec-201
❑ 97UppDec-249
❑ 97UppDec-383
❑ 97UppDecAG-AG2
❑ 97Zen-5
❑ 98Bow-60
❑ 98BowBes-89
❑ 98BowBesAR-89
❑ 98BowBesR-89
❑ 98BowChr-60
❑ 98BowChrGA-60
❑ 98BowChrGAR-60
❑ 98BowChrI-60
❑ 98BowChrIR-60
❑ 98BowChrR-60
❑ 98BowGolA-60
❑ 98BowInt-60
❑ 98CirThu-77
❑ 98CirThuRav-77
❑ 98CirThuSupRav-77
❑ 98ColCho-310
❑ 98ColChoSQ-SQ51
❑ 98CroRoy-18
❑ 98CroRoyAS-1
❑ 98CroRoyPotG-7
❑ 98Don-63
❑ 98Don-354
❑ 98DonCol-63
❑ 98DonColE-434
❑ 98DonColL-358
❑ 98DonColP-579
❑ 98DonColS-63
❑ 98DonCruG-7
❑ 98DonCruP-7
❑ 98DonCruR-7
❑ 98DonEli-34
❑ 98DonEliA-34
❑ 98DonEliS-34
❑ 98DonGolPP-63
❑ 98DonGolPP-354
❑ 98DonPre-29
❑ 98DonPreSeat-29
❑ 98DonPriCD-63
❑ 98DonPriCE-434
❑ 98DonPriCL-358
❑ 98DonPriCP-579
❑ 98DonProLO-3
❑ 98DonSig-83
❑ 98DonSigA-1
❑ 98DonSigAC-1
❑ 98DonSigAM-1
❑ 98DonSigP-83
❑ 98DonSigSB-1
❑ 98DonSilPP-63
❑ 98DonSilPP-354
❑ 98E-X2-16
❑ 98E-X2ECFut-16
❑ 98E-X2ECNow-16
❑ 98Fin-60
❑ 98FinNo--60
❑ 98FinNo-R-60
❑ 98FinRef-60
❑ 98FlaShoLeg0-52
❑ 98FlaShoLeg1-52
❑ 98FlaShoLeg2-52
❑ 98FlaShoLeg3-52
❑ 98FlaShoLegM-52
❑ 98FlaShoR0-52
❑ 98FlaShoR1-52
❑ 98FlaShoR2-52
❑ 98FlaShoR3-52

❑ 98Fle-353
❑ 98FleDecERT-1
❑ 98FleDecoE-1
❑ 98FleVin'-76
❑ 98FleVin'C-76
❑ 98Lea-159
❑ 98LeaFraDA-159
❑ 98LeaFraF-159
❑ 98LeaFraM-159
❑ 98LeaFraM-159
❑ 98LeaFraMDC-159
❑ 98LeaFraMDC-159
❑ 98LeaFraMZ2-159
❑ 98LeaHeaftH-1
❑ 98LeaHeaftHS-1
❑ 98LeaRS-2
❑ 98LeaRSLHolo-2
❑ 98LeaRSLong-2
❑ 98LeaRSTicMas-3
❑ 98LeaRSTicMasDC-3
❑ 98LeaRTrue-2
❑ 98MetUni-146
❑ 98MetUniPMG-146
❑ 98OriSco-1
❑ 98OriScoP-1
❑ 98Pac-17
❑ 98PacAur-9
❑ 98PacAurPF-28
❑ 98PacAurPFC-28
❑ 98PacAurPFPB-28
❑ 98PacAurPFR-28
❑ 98PacAurPFS-28
❑ 98PacCraCh-2
❑ 98PacGolCDC-4
❑ 98PacInCage-2
❑ 98PacInv-6
❑ 98PacInvCCDB-2
❑ 98PacInvCCG-2
❑ 98PacInvCCG-2
❑ 98PacInvCCLB-2
❑ 98PacInvCCP-2
❑ 98PacInvCCR-2
❑ 98PacInvGems-8
❑ 98PacInvInt-1A
❑ 98PacInvPBlue-6
❑ 98PacInvSilv-6
❑ 98PacInvTeam-3
❑ 98PacLatotML-3
❑ 98PacNes-14
❑ 98PacOme-27
❑ 98PacOmeR-27
❑ 98PacOnl-79
❑ 98PacOnlR-79
❑ 98PacOnlWC-79
❑ 98PacPar-10
❑ 98PacParC-10
❑ 98PacParG-10
❑ 98PacParHS-10
❑ 98PacParI-41
❑ 98PacParPB-10
❑ 98PacParR-10
❑ 98PacPlaB-17
❑ 98PacRedT-17
❑ 98PacSil-17
❑ 98PacTeaC-2
❑ 98Pin-183
❑ 98PinArtP-PP86
❑ 98PinIns-12
❑ 98PinInsCE-12
❑ 98PinInsDE-12
❑ 98PinInsSG-14AB
❑ 98PinInsSG-14CD
❑ 98PinInsSG-15AB
❑ 98PinInsSG-15CD
❑ 98PinInsSGS-14AB
❑ 98PinInsSGS-14CD
❑ 98PinInsSGS-15AB
❑ 98PinInsSGS-15CD
❑ 98PinMusC-PP86
❑ 98PinPer-30
❑ 98PinPerPP-30
❑ 98PinPlu-1
❑ 98PinPluAP-PP1
❑ 98PinPluGAP-PP1
❑ 98PinPluMAP-PP1
❑ 98PinPluTP-3
❑ 98PinPluTPG-3
❑ 98PinPluTPM-3
❑ 98PinPowPJ-2
❑ 98PinPowPJS-2
❑ 98PinPreP-183
❑ 98PinSna-BO12
❑ 98PinSna-BO15
❑ 98PinUnc-183
❑ 98Revo-18
❑ 98RevoSS-18

❑ 98Sco-15
❑ 98ScoAllST-6
❑ 98ScoRT-34
❑ 98ScoRTSS-PP34
❑ 98ScoRTSSAP-PP34
❑ 98ScoRTSSAP1-PP34
❑ 98ScoSS-PP118
❑ 98ScoSSAP-PP118
❑ 98SkyDugA-54
❑ 98SkyDugAIA-54
❑ 98SP Aut-53
❑ 98SP Aut-SD34
❑ 98SP AutC-RA
❑ 98SP AutSD-SD34
❑ 98SP AutSDT-SD34
❑ 98SP AutTrade-1
❑ 98SpoIll-2
❑ 98SpoIllEE-2
❑ 98SpoIllFE-2
❑ 98SpoIllTaN-55
❑ 98SpoIllTaNEE-55
❑ 98SpoIllWSF-89
❑ 98SpoIllWSFEE-89
❑ 98SpoIllWSFFE-89
❑ 98SPxFin-61
❑ 98SPxFinR-61
❑ 98SPxFinS-61
❑ 98StaCluC-CS19
❑ 98StaCluC-CS22
❑ 98StaCluC-CS23
❑ 98StaCluFDI-24
❑ 98StaCluI-24
❑ 98StaCluOneK-24
❑ 98StaCluPP-24
❑ 98StaCluTIII-T12A
❑ 98StaCluTLme-T12A
❑ 98StaCluTLmo-T12A
❑ 98Stu-111
❑ 98StuFF-30
❑ 98StuFFDC-30
❑ 98StuGPP-111
❑ 98StuSPP-111
❑ 98Top-285
❑ 98TopChr-285
❑ 98TopChrR-285
❑ 98TopDevR-285
❑ 98TopDia-285
❑ 98TopGal-109
❑ 98TopGalGP-109
❑ 98TopGalOPP-109
❑ 98TopGalPPI-109
❑ 98TopGalPPIA-109
❑ 98TopGolLabC1-11
❑ 98TopGolLabC1B-11
❑ 98TopGolLabC1One-11
❑ 98TopGolLabC1R-11
❑ 98TopGolLabC2-11
❑ 98TopGolLabC2B-11
❑ 98TopGolLabC2One-11
❑ 98TopGolLabC2R-11
❑ 98TopGolLabC3-11
❑ 98TopGolLabC3B-11
❑ 98TopGolLabC3One-11
❑ 98TopGolLabC3R-11
❑ 98TopMiniC-285
❑ 98TopOpeD-112
❑ 98TopSta-121
❑ 98TopSta'S-1
❑ 98TopSta'SGH-1
❑ 98TopStaB-121
❑ 98TopStaG-121
❑ 98TopStaGR-121
❑ 98TopStaS-121
❑ 98TopStaSteG-1
❑ 98TopTek-67
❑ 98TopTekD-67
❑ 98UD3-81
❑ 98UD3-171
❑ 98UD3-261
❑ 98UD3DieCut-81
❑ 98UD3DieCut-171
❑ 98UD3DieCut-261
❑ 98Ult-156
❑ 98UltDouT-7
❑ 98UltGolM-156
❑ 98UltMas-156
❑ 98UltPlaM-156
❑ 98UltPriL-15
❑ 98UppDec-313
❑ 98UppDec10AP-26
❑ 98UppDec1APR-26
❑ 98UppDecAG-AG12
❑ 98UppDecAGDC-AG12
❑ 98UppDecAPA2-RA
❑ 98UppDecCD-CD12
❑ 98UppDecNP-NP28

❑ 98UppDecRGKoG-G1
❑ 98UppDecRQL-Q26
❑ 98UppDecSFPD-PZ14
❑ 98UppDecSFPZOB-PZ12
❑ 98Zen-26
❑ 98Zen5 xx7-64
❑ 98Zen5x7GoldImp-64
❑ 98Zen5x7Imp-64
❑ 98ZenZ-G-26
❑ 98ZenZ-S-26
❑ 99199Fin-180
❑ 99Bow-240
❑ 99BowBes-32
❑ 99BowBesAR-32
❑ 99BowBesR-32
❑ 99BowGol-240
❑ 99BowInt-240
❑ 99CroRoyB-41
❑ 99CroRoyL-41
❑ 99CroRoyOD-41
❑ 99E-X Cen-62
❑ 99E-X CenECFut-62
❑ 99E-X CenECNow-62
❑ 99FinGolRef-180
❑ 99FinRef-180
❑ 99FlaShoLeg1-78
❑ 99FlaShoLeg2-78
❑ 99FlaShoLeg3-78
❑ 99FlaShoLegM1-78
❑ 99FlaShoLegM2-78
❑ 99FlaShoLegM3-78
❑ 99FlaShoR1-78
❑ 99FlaShoR2-78
❑ 99FlaShoR3-78
❑ 99Fle-51
❑ 99FleBri-121
❑ 99FleBri2G-121
❑ 99FleBriBlu-121
❑ 99FleBriGol-121
❑ 99FleMys-69
❑ 99FleMysFI-1
❑ 99FleMysG-69
❑ 99FleMysM-69
❑ 99FleSta9-51
❑ 99FleWarT-51
❑ 99KinDis-6
❑ 99MetUni-11
❑ 99MetUniGM-11
❑ 99MetUniPMG-11
❑ 99Pac-45
❑ 99Pac-45A
❑ 99PacAur-50
❑ 99PacAurOD-50
❑ 99PacCroC-33
❑ 99PacCroC-1
❑ 99PacCroCPB-33
❑ 99PacInv-42
❑ 99PacInvOD-42
❑ 99PacInvPB-42
❑ 99PacOme-70
❑ 99PacOmeC-70
❑ 99PacOmeG-70
❑ 99PacOmePB-70
❑ 99PacPar-69
❑ 99PacParC-69
❑ 99PacParG-69
❑ 99PacParHoloGold-69
❑ 99PacParHS-69
❑ 99PacParOD-69
❑ 99PacParPB-12
❑ 99PacParPB-69
❑ 99PacParRed-69
❑ 99PacPlaB-45
❑ 99PacPlaB-45A
❑ 99PacPri-17
❑ 99PacPriHB-17
❑ 99PacPriHG-17
❑ 99PacPriHM-17
❑ 99PacPriHP-17
❑ 99PacPriRed-17
❑ 99PacPriS-21
❑ 99PacPriS206-21
❑ 99PacPriS206R-21
❑ 99PacPriSP-21
❑ 99PacPriSV-21
❑ 99PacRed-45
❑ 99PacRed-45A
❑ 99Rev-41
❑ 99RevPremDate-41
❑ 99RevRet-41
❑ 99RevShaSS-41
❑ 99SkyMolM-105
❑ 99SkyMolMF-5
❑ 99SkyMolMFS-5
❑ 99SkyMolMFT-5
❑ 99SkyMolMX-105

❑ 99SkyPre-6
❑ 99SkyPreA-1
❑ 99SkyPreABlue-1
❑ 99SkyPreR-6
❑ 99SkyThu-8
❑ 99SkyThuRant-8
❑ 99SkyThuRave-8
❑ 99SpoIll-22
❑ 99SpoIll-158
❑ 99SPxPreS-PS10
❑ 99StaClu-325
❑ 99StaCluFDI-325
❑ 99StaCluOoaK-325
❑ 99StaCluPP-325
❑ 99ThuSkySupR-8
❑ 99Top-248
❑ 99TopBlaLC1-47
❑ 99TopBlaLC2-47
❑ 99TopBlaLC3-47
❑ 99TopChr-248
❑ 99TopChrR-248
❑ 99TopGal-34
❑ 99TopGalPP-34
❑ 99TopGalPPI-34
❑ 99TopGolL-47
❑ 99TopGolLC1-47
❑ 99TopGolLC2-47
❑ 99TopGolLOtO-47
❑ 99TopMVPP-248
❑ 99TopOpeD-140
❑ 99TopRedLC1-47
❑ 99TopRedLC2-47
❑ 99TopRedLC3-47
❑ 99TopSta-71
❑ 99TopSta1Foil-71
❑ 99TopStaFoil-71
❑ 99TopStaOS-71
❑ 99TopTek-8A
❑ 99TopTek-8B
❑ 99TopTekG-8A
❑ 99TopTekG-8B
❑ 99Ult-177
❑ 99UltGolM-177
❑ 99UltMas-177
❑ 99UltPlaM-177
❑ 99UppDec-46
❑ 99UppDec-245
❑ 99UppDec-254
❑ 99UppDec-352
❑ 99UppDec10AT-X3
❑ 99UppDec10ATD-X3
❑ 99UppDec10ATHR-X3
❑ 99UppDec10ATT-X3
❑ 99UppDecCL-85
❑ 99UppDecCLCC-85
❑ 99UppDecCLM-C24
❑ 99UppDecE-29
❑ 99UppDecEFXG-29
❑ 99UppDecEL1-46
❑ 99UppDecEL1-245
❑ 99UppDecEL1-254
❑ 99UppDecEL1-352
❑ 99UppDecEL2-46
❑ 99UppDecEL2-245
❑ 99UppDecEL2-254
❑ 99UppDecEL2-352
❑ 99UppDecM-60
❑ 99UppDecMGS-60
❑ 99UppDecMHFS-60
❑ 99UppDecMSS-60
❑ 99UppDecTE-T7
❑ 99UppDecTED-T7
❑ 99UppDecTEQ-T7
❑ 99UppDecTET-T7
❑ 99Vic-121

Alomar, Sandy (Conde Santos) Sr.

❑ 65BraTeal-1
❑ 65OPC-82
❑ 65Top-82
❑ 66Top-428
❑ 67Top-561
❑ 68Top-541
❑ 69AngJacitB-1
❑ 69Top-283
❑ 69TopSta-151
❑ 69TopTeaP-11
❑ 69WhiSoxTI-1
❑ 70DayDaiNM-110
❑ 70MLBOffS-169
❑ 70OPC-29
❑ 70Top-29
❑ 71AngJacitB-1
❑ 71MLBOffS-337
❑ 71OPC-745
❑ 71Top-745
❑ 71TopCoi-28
❑ 72MilBra-11
❑ 72OPC-253
❑ 72Top-253
❑ 73OPC-123
❑ 73Top-123
❑ 74OPC-347
❑ 74Top-347
❑ 74TopSta-141
❑ 75OPC-266
❑ 75Top-266
❑ 75TopMin-266
❑ 75YanSSP-19
❑ 76OPC-629
❑ 76SSP-441
❑ 76Top-629
❑ 77Top-54
❑ 78RanBurK-15
❑ 78SSP270-86
❑ 78Top-533
❑ 79Top-144
❑ 86AngGreT-2
❑ 88PadSmo-3
❑ 89Bow-258
❑ 89BowTif-258
❑ 89PadMag-9
❑ 89PadPos-4
❑ 90PadMag-22
❑ 91MetWIZ-7
❑ 92Pin-586
❑ 92YanWIZ7-4
❑ 93RanKee-50

Alomar, Sandy (Santos) Jr.

❑ 86BeaGolGP-1
❑ 87TexLeaAF-10
❑ 87WicPilRD-5
❑ 88BlaYNPRWL-33
❑ 88LasVegSC-22
❑ 88LasVegSP-236
❑ 88TriAAAP-20
❑ 88TriAAC-31
❑ 89BlaYNPRWL-102
❑ 89BlaYNPRWL-105
❑ 89BlaYNPRWLU-45
❑ 89Bow-454
❑ 89BowTif-454
❑ 89ClaLigB-79
❑ 89Don-28
❑ 89DonRoo-21
❑ 89Fle-300
❑ 89Fle-630
❑ 89FleGlo-300
❑ 89FleGlo-630
❑ 89LasVegSC-11
❑ 89LasVegSP-8
❑ 89PadMag-2
❑ 89PadMag-9
❑ 89PadPos-3
❑ 89PanSti-192
❑ 89Sco-630
❑ 89ScoYouS2-1
❑ 89Spo-223
❑ 89SpoIllFKI-248
❑ 89Sta-125
❑ 89StaFutS-23
❑ 89StaFutS-24
❑ 89Top-648
❑ 89TopTif-648
❑ 89TriAAAP-AAA6
❑ 89UppDec-5
❑ 90Bow-337
❑ 90BowTif-337
❑ 90ClaUpd-T3
❑ 90ClaYel-T76
❑ 90Don-30
❑ 90DonBesA-97
❑ 90DonLeaS-40
❑ 90DonRoo-1
❑ 90Fle-150
❑ 90FleCan-150
❑ 90FleUpd-89
❑ 90Hot50RS-2
❑ 90IndTeal-2
❑ 90Lea-232
❑ 90OPC-353
❑ 90Sco-577
❑ 90ScoMcD-2
❑ 90ScoRoo-18T
❑ 90StaAloB-1
❑ 90StaAloB-2
❑ 90StaAloB-4
❑ 90StaAloB-6
❑ 90StaAloB-8
❑ 90StaAloB-10
❑ 90StaSanA-1
❑ 90StaSanA-2
❑ 90StaSanA-3
❑ 90StaSanA-4
❑ 90StaSanA-5
❑ 90StaSanA-6
❑ 90StaSanA-7
❑ 90StaSanA-8
❑ 90StaSanA-9
❑ 90StaSanA-10
❑ 90StaSanA-11
❑ 90Top-353
❑ 90TopBig-265
❑ 90TopMag-20
❑ 90TopTif-353
❑ 90TopTra-2T
❑ 90TopTraT-2T
❑ 90TriAAAC-31
❑ 90UppDec-655
❑ 90UppDec-756
❑ 90USPlaCA-2S
❑ 90WinDis-1
❑ 91Baz-20
❑ 91Bow-57
❑ 91Cla1-T39
❑ 91Cla2-T68
❑ 91ClaGam-194
❑ 91Don-13
❑ 91Don-51
❑ 91Don-489
❑ 91Don-693
❑ 91DonSupD-13
❑ 91Fle-359
❑ 91IndFanC-2
❑ 91JimDea-8
❑ 91KinDis-17
❑ 91Lea-189
❑ 91Lea-528
❑ 91LeaPre-17
❑ 91MajLeaCP-18
❑ 91MooSna-10
❑ 91OPC-165
❑ 91OPCPre-2
❑ 91PanCanT1-109
❑ 91PanFreS-166
❑ 91PanFreS-215
❑ 91PanSti-172
❑ 91PetSta-9
❑ 91Pos-6
❑ 91PosCan-23
❑ 91RedFolS-113
❑ 91Sco-400
❑ 91Sco-694
❑ 91Sco-793
❑ 91Sco-851
❑ 91Sco-879
❑ 91Sco100RS-1
❑ 91ScoHotR-6
❑ 91StaClu-61
❑ 91StaCluCM-1
❑ 91StaPinB-2
❑ 91Stu-41
❑ 91SunSee-21
❑ 91Top-165
❑ 91TopCraJI-5
❑ 91TopDesS-165
❑ 91TopGaloC-1
❑ 91TopGloA-9
❑ 91TopMic-165
❑ 91TopRoo-1
❑ 91TopSta-2
❑ 91TopTif-165
❑ 91TopTriH-A5
❑ 91ToyRoo-1
❑ 91Ult-105
❑ 91UppDec-46
❑ 91UppDec-144
❑ 91UppDecFE-81F
❑ 91USPlaCA-11D
❑ 91Woo-6
❑ 92Bow-140
❑ 92Cla2-T50
❑ 92ClaGam-46
❑ 92ColAllG-13
❑ 92ColAllP-13
❑ 92Don-29
❑ 92Don-203
❑ 92DonCraJ1-10
❑ 92DonMcD-11
❑ 92Fle-103
❑ 92Fle-698
❑ 92Fre-10
❑ 92Hig5-41
❑ 92HitTheBB-2
❑ 92IndFanC-1
❑ 92Lea-9
❑ 92LeaBlaG-9
❑ 92Mr.TurS-3
❑ 92MVPPin-12
❑ 92OPC-420
❑ 92OPCPre-164
❑ 92PanSti-44
❑ 92PanSti-271
❑ 92PepDieM-10
❑ 92Pin-436
❑ 92PinTea2-17
❑ 92PosCan-11
❑ 92RedFolS-3
❑ 92RedFolS-106
❑ 92RevSup1-13
❑ 92RevSup1-14
❑ 92RevSup1-15
❑ 92Sco-510
❑ 92Sco100S-49
❑ 92ScoCokD-2
❑ 92ScoImpP-40
❑ 92ScoProaG-1
❑ 92SevCoi-6
❑ 92SpoIllFK1-634
❑ 92StaClu-740
❑ 92StaCluD-6
❑ 92StaCluNC-740
❑ 92Stu-161
❑ 92Top-420
❑ 92TopGol-420
❑ 92TopGolW-420
❑ 92TopKid-71
❑ 92TopMic-420
❑ 92TriPla-227
❑ 92Ult-45
❑ 92UppDec-81
❑ 92UppDec-156
❑ 92UppDecF-12
❑ 92UppDecFG-12
❑ 93Bow-93
❑ 93DiaMar-2
❑ 93Don-39
❑ 93Fin-26
❑ 93FinRef-26
❑ 93Fle-212
❑ 93FunPac-106
❑ 93HumDumC-5
❑ 93IndWUA-1
❑ 93KinDis-18
❑ 93Kra-3
❑ 93Lea-83
❑ 93OPC-12
❑ 93PacBeiA-5
❑ 93PacBeiA-6
❑ 93PacBeiA-7
❑ 93PacSpa-91
❑ 93PacSpaGE-11
❑ 93PacSpaPI-8
❑ 93PanSti-47
❑ 93Pin-211
❑ 93RedFolS-3
❑ 93RedFolS-106
❑ 93Sco-116
❑ 93Sel-26
❑ 93SelSam-26
❑ 93SP-118
❑ 93StaClu-400
❑ 93StaCluFDI-400
❑ 93StaCluM-123
❑ 93StaCluMMP-1
❑ 93StaCluMOP-400
❑ 93Stu-13
❑ 93Top-85
❑ 93TopGol-85
❑ 93TopInaM-85
❑ 93TopInaR-85
❑ 93TopMic-85
❑ 93TriPla-251
❑ 93Ult-182
❑ 93UppDec-255
❑ 93UppDecGold-255
❑ 94Bow-139
❑ 94ColC-34
❑ 94ColChoGS-34
❑ 94ColChoSS-34
❑ 94Don-65
❑ 94Fin-251
❑ 94FinRef-251
❑ 94Fla-282
❑ 94Fle-98
❑ 94FleExtB-55
❑ 94FUnPac-93
❑ 94Lea-223
❑ 94OPC-201
❑ 94Pac-164
❑ 94PanSti-53
❑ 94Pin-44
❑ 94PinArtP-44
❑ 94PinMusC-44
❑ 94ProMag-36
❑ 94Sco-445
❑ 94ScoGolR-445
❑ 94Sel-366
❑ 94StaClu-144
❑ 94StaCluFDI-144
❑ 94StaCluGR-144
❑ 94StaCluMOP-144
❑ 94Stu-90
❑ 94Top-273
❑ 94TopGol-273
❑ 94TopSpa-273
❑ 94TriPla-111
❑ 94Ult-40
❑ 94UppDec-415
❑ 94UppDecED-415
❑ 95Baz-11
❑ 95ColCho-273
❑ 95ColChoGS-273
❑ 95ColChoSS-273
❑ 95Don-3
❑ 95DonPreP-3
❑ 95DonTopotO-56
❑ 95Fin-61
❑ 95FinRef-61
❑ 95Fla-249
❑ 95Fle-130
❑ 95Lea-121
❑ 95Pac-115
❑ 95PanSti-26
❑ 95Pin-39
❑ 95PinArtP-39
❑ 95PinMusC-39
❑ 95Sco-519
❑ 95ScoGolR-519
❑ 95ScoPlaTS-519
❑ 95StaClu-87
❑ 95StaClu-217
❑ 95StaCluFDI-87
❑ 95StaCluFDI-217
❑ 95StaCluMOP-87
❑ 95StaCluMOP-217
❑ 95StaCluSTWS-87
❑ 95StaCluSTWS-217
❑ 95StaCluVR-53
❑ 95StaCluVRMO-53
❑ 95Top-522
❑ 95TopCyb-308
❑ 95TopEmb-105
❑ 95TopEmbGI-105
❑ 95TopPre-PP4
❑ 95TopPreS-PP4
❑ 95Ult-35
❑ 95UltGolM-35
❑ 95UppDec-92
❑ 95UppDecED-92
❑ 95UppDecEDG-92
❑ 96Cir-31
❑ 96CirRav-31
❑ 96Don-41
❑ 96DonPreP-41
❑ 96EmoXL-44
❑ 96Fla-62
❑ 96Fle-80
❑ 96FleTif-80
❑ 96IndFle-1
❑ 96Lea-98
❑ 96LeaPrePB-98
❑ 96LeaPrePG-98
❑ 96LeaPrePS-98
❑ 96MetUni-42
❑ 96MetUniP-42
❑ 96Pac-295
❑ 96PinChrBC-13
❑ 96SchDis-19
❑ 96Sco-103
❑ 96StaClu-373
❑ 96StaCluEPB-373
❑ 96StaCluEPG-373
❑ 96StaCluEPS-373
❑ 96StaCluMOP-373
❑ 96Top-294
❑ 96Ult-340
❑ 96UltGolM-340
❑ 96UppDec-313
❑ 96UppDecA-2
❑ 97Bow-281
❑ 97BowChr-94
❑ 97BowChrI-94
❑ 97BowChrIR-94
❑ 97BowChrR-94
❑ 97BowInt-281
❑ 97Cir-257
❑ 97CirRav-257
❑ 97ColCho-93
❑ 97ColChoT-CI8
❑ 97Don-314
❑ 97DonGolPP-314
❑ 97DonLim-163
❑ 97DonLimE-163
❑ 97DonLimENG-163
❑ 97DonSig-63
❑ 97DonSigA-5
❑ 97DonSigAC-5
❑ 97DonSigAM-5
❑ 97DonSigPPP-63
❑ 97DonSilPP-314
❑ 97DonTea-87
❑ 97DonTeaSPE-87
❑ 97Fin-113
❑ 97FinEmb-113
❑ 97FinEmbR-113
❑ 97FinRef-113
❑ 97FlaShoLC-115
❑ 97FlaShoLeg0-115
❑ 97FlaShoLeg1-115
❑ 97FlaShoM-A115
❑ 97FlaShoM-B115
❑ 97FlaShoM-C115
❑ 97FlaShoR0-115
❑ 97FlaShoR1-115
❑ 97FlaShoR2-115
❑ 97Fle-74
❑ 97FleTif-74
❑ 97IndSco-9
❑ 97IndScoPl-9
❑ 97IndScoPr-9
❑ 97IndScoU-9
❑ 97IndScoUTC-9
❑ 97Lea-259
❑ 97LeaFraM-259
❑ 97LeaFraMDC-259
❑ 97NewPin-114
❑ 97NewPinAP-114
❑ 97NewPinMC-114
❑ 97NewPinPP-114
❑ 97Pac-66
❑ 97PacBaeS-4
❑ 97PacLigB-66
❑ 97PacPri-24
❑ 97PacPriLB-24
❑ 97PacPriP-24
❑ 97PacSil-66
❑ 97PinCer-12
❑ 97PinCerMBla-12
❑ 97PinCerMBlu-12
❑ 97PinCerMG-12
❑ 97PinCerMR-12
❑ 97PinCerR-12
❑ 97PinFan-FF21
❑ 97PinTotCPB-12
❑ 97PinTotCPG-12
❑ 97PinTotCPR-12
❑ 97PinX-PSfF-1
❑ 97PinX-PSfFU-1
❑ 97Sco-173
❑ 97ScoArtPWB-173
❑ 97ScoPreS-173
❑ 97ScoShoS-173
❑ 97ScoShoSAP-173
❑ 97SpoIll-34
❑ 97SpoIll-56
❑ 97SpoIllEE-34
❑ 97SpoIllEE-56
❑ 97StaClu-101
❑ 97StaCluMOP-101
❑ 97StrAll-2
❑ 97Top-245
❑ 97TopSta-72
❑ 97TopSta97AS-AS20
❑ 97TopStaAM-72
❑ 97TopStaASM-ASM10
❑ 97Ult-45
❑ 97UltGolME-45
❑ 97UltPlaME-45
❑ 97UppDec-343
❑ 98Bow-44
❑ 98BowBes-28
❑ 98BowBesAR-28
❑ 98BowBesR-28
❑ 98BowChr-44
❑ 98BowChrGA-44
❑ 98BowChrGAR-44
❑ 98BowChrI-44
❑ 98BowChrIR-44
❑ 98BowChrR-44
❑ 98BowChrR-15
❑ 98BowChrRR-15
❑ 98BowGolA-44
❑ 98BowInt-44
❑ 98CirThu-111

❑ 98CirThuRav-111
❑ 98CirThuSupRav-111
❑ 98ColCho-18
❑ 98ColCho-182
❑ 98ColCho-349
❑ 98CroRoy-42
❑ 98Don-24
❑ 98DonCol-24
❑ 98DonColE-454
❑ 98DonColL-286
❑ 98DonColP-630
❑ 98DonColS-24
❑ 98DonCruG-20
❑ 98DonCruP-20
❑ 98DonCruR-20
❑ 98DonEli-54
❑ 98DonEliA-54
❑ 98DonEliS-54
❑ 98DonGolPP-24
❑ 98DonPre-80
❑ 98DonPreSeat-80
❑ 98DonPriCD-24
❑ 98DonPriCE-454
❑ 98DonPriCL-286
❑ 98DonPriCP-630
❑ 98DonSig-61
❑ 98DonSigA-2
❑ 98DonSigAC-2
❑ 98DonSigAM-2
❑ 98DonSigP-61
❑ 98DonSigSB-2
❑ 98DonSigSP-1
❑ 98DonSilPP-24
❑ 98Fin-119
❑ 98FinNo--119
❑ 98FinNo-R-119
❑ 98FinRef-119
❑ 98Fle-129
❑ 98FleVin'-14
❑ 98FleVin'C-14
❑ 98IndSco-4
❑ 98IndScoP-4
❑ 98Lea-87
❑ 98LeaFraDA-87
❑ 98LeaFraF-87
❑ 98LeaFraM-87
❑ 98LeaFraM-87
❑ 98LeaFraMDC-87
❑ 98LeaFraMDC-87
❑ 98LeaFraMS-87
❑ 98LeaFraMZ2-87
❑ 98LeaRS-82
❑ 98LeaRSLHolo-82
❑ 98LeaRSLong-82
❑ 98LeaRTrue-82
❑ 98Pac-66
❑ 98PacAur-27
❑ 98PacAurPF-15
❑ 98PacAurPFC-15
❑ 98PacAurPFPB-15
❑ 98PacAurPFR-15
❑ 98PacAurPFS-15
❑ 98PacGolCDC-10
❑ 98PacInCage-6
❑ 98PacInv-22
❑ 98PacInvGems-37
❑ 98PacInvPBlue-22
❑ 98PacInvSilv-22
❑ 98PacInvTeam-8
❑ 98PacLatotML-9
❑ 98PacNes-13
❑ 98PacOme-69
❑ 98PacOmeFTF-3
❑ 98PacOmeOnIns-6
❑ 98PacOmeR-69
❑ 98PacOnl-210
❑ 98PacOnlR-210
❑ 98PacOnlWC-210
❑ 98PacPar-34
❑ 98PacParC-34
❑ 98PacParG-34
❑ 98PacParHS-34
❑ 98PacParPB-34
❑ 98PacParR-34
❑ 98PacPlaB-66
❑ 98PacRedT-66
❑ 98PacSil-66
❑ 98PacTeaC-5
❑ 98PinIns-15
❑ 98PinInsBtN-20
❑ 98PinInsCE-15
❑ 98PinInsDE-15
❑ 98PinInsSG-23AB
❑ 98PinInsSG-23CD
❑ 98PinInsSGS-23AB
❑ 98PinInsSGS-23CD
❑ 98PinPer-80
❑ 98PinPerPP-80
❑ 98PinPlu-2
❑ 98PinSna-CI9
❑ 98PinSna-CI12
❑ 98PreCon-13
❑ 98Revo-43
❑ 98RevoSS-43
❑ 98Sco-46
❑ 98ScoRT-106
❑ 98ScoRTSS-PP70
❑ 98ScoRTSSAP-PP70
❑ 98ScoRTSSAP1-PP70
❑ 98ScoSS-PP129
❑ 98ScoSSAP-PP129
❑ 98SkyDugA-62
❑ 98SkyDugAIA-62
❑ 98SP Aut-74
❑ 98SpoIll-3
❑ 98SpoIll-190
❑ 98SpoIllEE-3
❑ 98SpoIllEE-190
❑ 98SpoIllFE-3
❑ 98SpoIllFE-190
❑ 98SpoIllTaN-56
❑ 98SpoIllTaNEE-56
❑ 98SpoIllWSF-84
❑ 98SpoIllWSFEE-84
❑ 98SpoIllWSFFE-84
❑ 98SPxFin-268
❑ 98SPxFinR-268
❑ 98SPxFinS-268
❑ 98StaCluC-CS19
❑ 98StaCluC-CS20
❑ 98StaCluC-CS21
❑ 98StaCluFDI-22
❑ 98StaCluI-22
❑ 98StaCluOneK-22
❑ 98StaCluPP-22
❑ 98StaCluTIll-T10B
❑ 98StaCluTLme-T10B
❑ 98StaCluTLmo-T10B
❑ 98Stu-181
❑ 98StuGPP-181
❑ 98StuSPP-181
❑ 98Top-135
❑ 98Top-278
❑ 98TopChr-135
❑ 98TopChr-278
❑ 98TopChrR-135
❑ 98TopChrR-278
❑ 98TopDevR-135
❑ 98TopDevR-278
❑ 98TopDia-135
❑ 98TopDia-278
❑ 98TopGal-81
❑ 98TopGalGP-81
❑ 98TopGalOPP-81
❑ 98TopGalPPI-81
❑ 98TopGalPPIA-81
❑ 98TopGolLabC1-26
❑ 98TopGolLabC1B-26
❑ 98TopGolLabC1One-26
❑ 98TopGolLabC1R-26
❑ 98TopGolLabC2-26
❑ 98TopGolLabC2B-26
❑ 98TopGolLabC2One-26
❑ 98TopGolLabC2R-26
❑ 98TopGolLabC3-26
❑ 98TopGolLabC3B-26
❑ 98TopGolLabC3One-26
❑ 98TopGolLabC3R-26
❑ 98TopMiniC-135
❑ 98TopMiniC-278
❑ 98TopOpeD-68
❑ 98TopSta-26
❑ 98TopStaB-26
❑ 98TopStaG-26
❑ 98TopStaGR-26
❑ 98TopStaS-26
❑ 98TopTek-27
❑ 98TopTekD-27
❑ 98Ult-397
❑ 98UltGolM-397
❑ 98UltMas-397
❑ 98UltPlaM-397
❑ 98UppDec-76
❑ 98UppDec-427
❑ 98UppDec10AP-17
❑ 98UppDec1APR-17
❑ 98UppDecSF-47
❑ 98UppDecSFPD-PZ13
❑ 98UppDecSFPZOB-PZ11
❑ 98Zen-25
❑ 98Zen5 xx7-37
❑ 98Zen5x7GoldImp-37
❑ 98Zen5x7Imp-37
❑ 98ZenZ-G-25
❑ 98ZenZ-S-25
❑ 99199Fin-24
❑ 99BowBes-79
❑ 99BowBesAR-79
❑ 99BowBesR-79
❑ 99BowChr-4
❑ 99BowChrG-4
❑ 99BowChrGR-4
❑ 99BowChrI-4
❑ 99BowChrIR-4
❑ 99BowChrR-4
❑ 99FinGolRef-24
❑ 99FinRef-24
❑ 99FlaShoLeg1-140
❑ 99FlaShoLeg2-140
❑ 99FlaShoLeg3-140
❑ 99FlaShoLegM1-140
❑ 99FlaShoLegM2-140
❑ 99FlaShoLegM3-140
❑ 99FlaShoR1-140
❑ 99FlaShoR2-140
❑ 99FlaShoR3-140
❑ 99Fle-318
❑ 99FleSta9-318
❑ 99FleWarT-318
❑ 99Pac-123
❑ 99PacCroC-82
❑ 99PacCroC-6
❑ 99PacCroCPB-82
❑ 99PacInv-43
❑ 99PacInvOD-43
❑ 99PacInvPB-43
❑ 99PacOme-71
❑ 99PacOmeC-71
❑ 99PacOmeG-71
❑ 99PacOmePB-71
❑ 99PacPar-70
❑ 99PacParC-70
❑ 99PacParG-70
❑ 99PacParHoloGold-70
❑ 99PacParHS-70
❑ 99PacParOD-70
❑ 99PacParPB-70
❑ 99PacParRed-70
❑ 99PacPlaB-123
❑ 99PacPri-41
❑ 99PacPriHB-41
❑ 99PacPriHG-41
❑ 99PacPriHM-41
❑ 99PacPriHP-41
❑ 99PacPriRed-41
❑ 99PacRed-123
❑ 99SkyMolM-49
❑ 99SkyMolMX-49
❑ 99SP SigAuto-SA
❑ 99SPSig-138
❑ 99Top-245
❑ 99TopBlaLC1-58
❑ 99TopBlaLC2-58
❑ 99TopBlaLC3-58
❑ 99TopChr-245
❑ 99TopChrR-245
❑ 99TopGal-50
❑ 99TopGalPP-50
❑ 99TopGalPPI-50
❑ 99TopGolL-58
❑ 99TopGolLC1-58
❑ 99TopGolLC2-58
❑ 99TopGolLOtO-58
❑ 99TopMVPP-245
❑ 99TopOpeD-149
❑ 99TopSta-103
❑ 99TopStaFoil-103
❑ 99Ult-178
❑ 99UltGolM-178
❑ 99UltMas-178
❑ 99UltPlaM-178
❑ 99UppDec-77
❑ 99UppDec-244
❑ 99UppDec10AT-X23
❑ 99UppDec10ATD-X23
❑ 99UppDec10ATHR-X23
❑ 99UppDec10ATT-X23
❑ 99UppDecBD-27
❑ 99UppDecBDD-27
❑ 99UppDecBDQ-27
❑ 99UppDecBDT-27
❑ 99UppDecEL1-77
❑ 99UppDecEL1-244
❑ 99UppDecEL2-77
❑ 99UppDecEL2-244
❑ 99UppDecM-59
❑ 99UppDecMGS-59
❑ 99UppDecMHFS-59
❑ 99UppDecMP-59
❑ 99UppDecMSS-59
❑ 99Vic-120
❑ 99Bow-4
❑ 99BowGol-4
❑ 99BowInt-4
❑ 99CroRoyB-42
❑ 99CroRoyL-42
❑ 99CroRoyOD-42
❑ 99PacAur-51
❑ 99PacAurOD-51
❑ 99Rev-42
❑ 99RevPremDate-42
❑ 99RevRet-42
❑ 99RevShaSS-42
❑ 99SkyThu-37
❑ 99SkyThuRant-37
❑ 99SkyThuRave-37
❑ 99StaClu-172
❑ 99StaCluFDI-172
❑ 99StaCluOoaK-172
❑ 99StaCluPP-172
❑ 99ThuSkySupR-37
❑ 99TopRedLC1-58
❑ 99TopRedLC2-58
❑ 99TopRedLC3-58

❑

Alongi, Doug
❑ 93GenCubC-2
❑ 93GenCubF-3188

Alonso, Julio
❑ 77EvaTriT-2

Alonzo, Ray
❑ 83MadMusF-6

Alonzo, Steven
❑ 94BurBeeC-28
❑ 94BurBeeF-1098

Alou, Felipe Rojas
❑ 59Top-102
❑ 59TopVen-102
❑ 60Lea-6
❑ 60Top-287
❑ 61GiaJayP-1
❑ 61Top-565
❑ 62AmeTraS-52A
❑ 62AmeTraS-52B
❑ 62AmeTraS-52C
❑ 62AmeTraS-52D
❑ 62GiaJayP-1
❑ 62Jel-133
❑ 62Pos-133
❑ 62PosCan-133
❑ 62SalPlaC-130
❑ 62ShiPlaC-130
❑ 62Top-133
❑ 62TopStaI-193
❑ 62TopVen-133
❑ 63GiaJayP-1
❑ 63Jel-107
❑ 63Pos-107
❑ 63Top-270
❑ 64Top-65
❑ 64TopCoi-11
❑ 64TopSta-62
❑ 64TopVen-65
❑ 65Top-383
❑ 66BraPos-3
❑ 66Kah-2
❑ 66OPC-96
❑ 66Top-96
❑ 66TopVen-96
❑ 67BraPho-2
❑ 67CokCapB-12
❑ 67DexPre-8
❑ 67Kah-3
❑ 67OPCPapI-30
❑ 67Top-240
❑ 67Top-530
❑ 67TopPos-30
❑ 67TopVen-281
❑ 68AtlOilPBCC-3
❑ 68BraPos-3
❑ 68CokCapB-12
❑ 68DexPre-5
❑ 68Kah-B4
❑ 68OPC-55
❑ 68Top-55
❑ 68TopVen-55
❑ 69MilBra-10
❑ 69MLBOffS-110
❑ 69MLBPin-32
❑ 69OPC-2
❑ 69Top-2
❑ 69Top-300
❑ 69TopDec-17
❑ 69TopDecI-3
❑ 69TopSta-2
❑ 69TopSup-35
❑ 69TopTeaP-2
❑ 69TraSta-51
❑ 70DayDaiNM-65
❑ 70MLBOffS-253
❑ 70OPC-434
❑ 70Top-434
❑ 71Kel-7
❑ 71MLBOffS-505
❑ 71OPC-495
❑ 71Top-495
❑ 71TopCoi-8
❑ 71YanCliDP-9
❑ 72MilBra-12
❑ 72OPC-263
❑ 72Top-263
❑ 72YanSch-1
❑ 73LinPor-127
❑ 73OPC-650
❑ 73SyrChiTI-1
❑ 73Top-650
❑ 74OPC-485
❑ 74Top-485
❑ 74TopTra-485T
❑ 75SSP42-42
❑ 78AtlCon-3
❑ 78MemChiBC-1
❑ 78TCM60I-74
❑ 79ExpPos-1
❑ 80ExpPos-2
❑ 81Gia196T-9
❑ 82Don-650
❑ 82WicAerTI-2
❑ 83WicAerDS-2
❑ 84ExpPos-1
❑ 84ExpStu-6
❑ 84ExpStu-38
❑ 84GiaMot-19
❑ 85DomLeaS-145
❑ 85IndIndTI-2
❑ 86WesPalBEP-1
❑ 88FloStaLAS-2
❑ 88PacLegI-58
❑ 88WesPalBES-2
❑ 89WesPalBES-27
❑ 90FloStaLAS-23
❑ 90WesPalBES-29
❑ 91WesPalBEC-1
❑ 91WesPalBEP-1244
❑ 92ExpDonD-15B
❑ 92ExpPos-1
❑ 92TopTra-3T
❑ 92TopTraG-3T
❑ 92YanWIZ7-5
❑ 93Bow-701
❑ 93ExpDonM-31
❑ 93ExpDonM-AU0
❑ 93ExpPosN-1
❑ 93Top-508
❑ 93TopGol-508
❑ 93TopInaM-508
❑ 93TopInaR-508
❑ 93TopMic-508
❑ 94BreMilB-96
❑ 94TopSpa-L1
❑ 96ExpBoo-1
❑ 96ExpDis-1
❑ 97PhoFirDTTI-17

Alou, Jesus M.R.
❑ 64Top-47
❑ 64TopVen-47
❑ 65Top-545
❑ 66Top-242
❑ 66TopRubI-4
❑ 66TopVen-242
❑ 67CokCapG-18
❑ 67DexPre-9
❑ 67Top-332
❑ 67TopVen-330
❑ 68DexPre-6
❑ 68Top-452
❑ 69MilBra-11
❑ 69MLBOffS-136
❑ 69OPC-22
❑ 69Top-22
❑ 69TopSta-51
❑ 70AstPho-18
❑ 70DayDaiNM-141
❑ 70MLBOffS-37
❑ 70OPC-248
❑ 70Top-248
❑ 71AstCok-1
❑ 71MLBOffS-73
❑ 71OPC-337
❑ 71Top-337
❑ 72AstTeaI-1
❑ 72MilBra-13
❑ 72Top-716
❑ 73OPC-93
❑ 73Top-93
❑ 74OPC-654
❑ 74Top-654A
❑ 74Top-654B
❑ 75MetSSP-6
❑ 75OPC-253
❑ 75SSP42-42
❑ 75Top-253
❑ 75TopMin-253
❑ 76OPC-468
❑ 76SSP-538
❑ 76Top-468
❑ 78AstBurK-22
❑ 78AstPos-1
❑ 79AstPos-1
❑ 79Top-107
❑ 80Top-593
❑ 81TCM60I-406
❑ 85DomLeaS-143
❑ 87AstShoSPO-1
❑ 87AstShoSPO-31
❑ 87AstShoSTw-1
❑ 87AstShoSTw-26
❑ 91MetWIZ-8

Alou, Jose
❑ 87BurExpP-1076
❑ 88WesPalBES-3
❑ 89WesPalBES-1

Alou, Matty (Mateo Rojas)
❑ 60TacBan-1
❑ 61Top-327
❑ 62Top-413
❑ 63SalMetC-25
❑ 63Top-128
❑ 64Top-204
❑ 64TopVen-204
❑ 65Top-318
❑ 66OPC-94
❑ 66PirEasH-18
❑ 66Top-94
❑ 66TopVen-94
❑ 67Baz-47
❑ 67CokCapPi-17
❑ 67DexPre-10
❑ 67Kah-4A
❑ 67Kah-4B
❑ 67OPC-10
❑ 67OPCPapI-29
❑ 67PirTeal-2
❑ 67Top-10
❑ 67Top-240
❑ 67TopPirS-2
❑ 67TopPirS-28
❑ 67TopPos-29
❑ 67TopVen-298
❑ 68Baz-2
❑ 68Kah-B5
❑ 68OPC-1
❑ 68PirKDK-18
❑ 68PirTeal-2
❑ 68Top-1
❑ 68Top-270
❑ 68TopGamI-1
❑ 68TopVen-1
❑ 68TopVen-270
❑ 69Kah-B2
❑ 69MilBra-12
❑ 69MLBOffS-182
❑ 69OPC-2
❑ 69PirGre-2
❑ 69PirTeal-2
❑ 69Top-2
❑ 69Top-490
❑ 69TopDecI-4
❑ 69TopSta-82
❑ 69TopSup-56
❑ 69TopTeaP-16
❑ 69TraSta-58
❑ 70DayDaiNM-111
❑ 70Kel-28
❑ 70MLBOffS-98
❑ 70OPC-30
❑ 70OPC-460
❑ 70PirTeal-2
❑ 70Top-30
❑ 70Top-460
❑ 71CarTeal-1
❑ 71CarTeal-1
❑ 71Kel-53
❑ 71MLBOffS-265

❑ 71OPC-720
❑ 71Top-720
❑ 71TopCoi-47
❑ 72MilBra-14
❑ 72OPC-395
❑ 72Top-395
❑ 73LinPor-128
❑ 73NewYorSNM-19
❑ 73OPC-132
❑ 73SyrChiTI-2
❑ 73Top-132
❑ 74OPC-430
❑ 74PadDea-1
❑ 74PadMcDD-1
❑ 74Top-430
❑ 75SSP42-42
❑ 77PadSchC-2
❑ 78TCM60I-75
❑ 81Gia196T-15
❑ 85DomLeaS-144
❑ 86SpoDesJM-15
❑ 88PacLegI-37
❑ 91SweBasG-2
❑ 92YanWIZ7-6
❑ 93TedWil-74
❑ 93UppDecAH-4

Alou, Moises

❑ 86WatPirP-2
❑ 87WatPirP-27
❑ 88AugPirP-360
❑ 89SalBucS-1
❑ 89Sta-93
❑ 90Bow-178
❑ 90BowTif-178
❑ 90BufBisTI-1
❑ 90CMC-790
❑ 90Fle-650
❑ 90FleCan-650
❑ 90HarSenP-1204
❑ 90HarSenS-2
❑ 90ProAaA-29
❑ 90Sco-592
❑ 91Cla1-T60
❑ 91Don-38
❑ 91OPC-526
❑ 91OPCPre-3
❑ 91Sco-813
❑ 91StaClu-31
❑ 91Stu-191
❑ 91Top-526A
❑ 91Top-526B
❑ 91TopDeb90-5
❑ 91TopDesS-526
❑ 91TopMic-526
❑ 91TopTif-526
❑ 91UppDec-665
❑ 92Cla2-T36
❑ 92DonRooP-BC1
❑ 92ExpPos-2
❑ 92FleUpd-95
❑ 92JimDeaRS-9
❑ 92Lea-426
❑ 92LeaBlaG-426
❑ 92OPC-401
❑ 92Pin-572
❑ 92PinRoo-16
❑ 92Sco100RS-9
❑ 92SpoIllFK1-298
❑ 92SpoIllFK1-708
❑ 92StaClu-519
❑ 92TopTra-4T
❑ 92TopTraG-4T
❑ 92Ult-511
❑ 93Bow-452
❑ 93Bow-701
❑ 93ClaGam-3
❑ 93DiaMar-3
❑ 93Don-510
❑ 93ExpColP7-1
❑ 93ExpDonM-1
❑ 93ExpPosN-2
❑ 93Fin-189
❑ 93FinRef-189
❑ 93Fla-78
❑ 93Fle-70
❑ 93FleRooS-RSB1
❑ 93HumDumC-39
❑ 93Lea-147
❑ 93LimRocDWB-112
❑ 93LinVenB-303
❑ 93LinVenB-313
❑ 93LinVenB-321
❑ 93OPC-10
❑ 93PacBeiA-26
❑ 93PacJugC-19
❑ 93PacSpa-180
❑ 93PacSpaGE-1
❑ 93PanSti-232
❑ 93Pin-92
❑ 93Sco-187
❑ 93Sel-272
❑ 93SelChaR-2
❑ 93SP-100
❑ 93StaClu-239
❑ 93StaCluFDI-239
❑ 93StaCluMOP-239
❑ 93Stu-11
❑ 93Top-123
❑ 93TopGol-123
❑ 93TopInaM-123
❑ 93TopInaR-123
❑ 93TopMic-123
❑ 93Toy-96
❑ 93ToyMasP-1
❑ 93TriPla-244
❑ 93Ult-61
❑ 93UppDec-297
❑ 93UppDecGold-297
❑ 93USPlaCR-11S
❑ 94Bow-116
❑ 94BowBes-R52
❑ 94BowBesR-R52
❑ 94ColC-35
❑ 94ColChoGS-35
❑ 94ColChoSS-35
❑ 94Don-3
❑ 94DonDiaK-DK23
❑ 94DonDiaKJ-DK23
❑ 94DonMVP-8
❑ 94DonSpeE-3
❑ 94Fin-121
❑ 94FinPre-121P
❑ 94FinRef-121
❑ 94Fla-400
❑ 94Fle-531
❑ 94FleExtB-299
❑ 94Lea-252
❑ 94LeaL-123
❑ 94OPC-266
❑ 94Pac-372
❑ 94PanSti-206
❑ 94Pin-7
❑ 94PinArtP-7
❑ 94PinMusC-7
❑ 94PinSam-7
❑ 94PosCan-9
❑ 94ProMag-81
❑ 94Sco-90
❑ 94ScoGolR-90
❑ 94Sel-159
❑ 94SP-82
❑ 94SPDieC-82
❑ 94Spo-87
❑ 94StaClu-141
❑ 94StaCluFDI-141
❑ 94StaCluGR-141
❑ 94StaCluMOP-141
❑ 94Stu-74
❑ 94Top-50
❑ 94TopGol-50
❑ 94TopSpa-50
❑ 94TriPla-91
❑ 94Ult-222
❑ 94UppDec-351
❑ 94UppDecED-351
❑ 95Baz-70
❑ 95Bow-285
❑ 95BowBes-R4
❑ 95BowBesR-R4
❑ 95ColCho-250
❑ 95ColChoGS-250
❑ 95ColChoSE-104
❑ 95ColChoSEGS-104
❑ 95ColChoSESS-104
❑ 95ColChoSS-250
❑ 95DenHol-2
❑ 95Don-408
❑ 95DonDiaK-DK10
❑ 95DonDom-7
❑ 95DonPreP-408
❑ 95DonTopotO-276
❑ 95Emo-148
❑ 95Fin-128
❑ 95FinRef-128
❑ 95Fla-160
❑ 95Fle-344
❑ 95FleAllS-16
❑ 95FleTeaL-22
❑ 95FleUpdSS-1
❑ 95Kra-16
❑ 95Lea-288
❑ 95Lea300C-4
❑ 95LeaLim-158
❑ 95Pac-260
❑ 95PacLatD-2
❑ 95PacPri-84
❑ 95PanSti-78
❑ 95Pin-321
❑ 95PinArtP-321
❑ 95PinMusC-321
❑ 95PinUps-US23
❑ 95PosCan-5
❑ 95Sco-19
❑ 95Sco-572
❑ 95ScoGolR-19
❑ 95ScoGolR-572
❑ 95ScoHaloG-HG12
❑ 95ScoPlaTS-19
❑ 95ScoPlaTS-572
❑ 95Sel-78
❑ 95SelArtP-78
❑ 95SelCer-36
❑ 95SelCerMG-36
❑ 95SP-78
❑ 95SPCha-65
❑ 95SPChaDC-65
❑ 95Spo-115
❑ 95SpoArtP-115
❑ 95SPSil-78
❑ 95StaClu-295
❑ 95StaClu-503
❑ 95StaCluCC-CC21
❑ 95StaCluCT-16
❑ 95StaCluMO-1
❑ 95StaCluMOP-295
❑ 95StaCluMOP-503
❑ 95StaCluMOP-CC21
❑ 95StaCluSTWS-295
❑ 95StaCluSTWS-503
❑ 95StaCluVR-153
❑ 95StaCluVRMO-153
❑ 95Stu-35
❑ 95StuGolS-35
❑ 95Sum-37
❑ 95SumNthD-37
❑ 95TomPiz-19
❑ 95Top-584
❑ 95TopCyb-357
❑ 95TopD3-13
❑ 95TopEmb-24
❑ 95TopEmbGI-24
❑ 95TopFinIns-8
❑ 95TopLeaL-LL5
❑ 95UC3-36
❑ 95UC3ArtP-36
❑ 95Ult-186
❑ 95UltAllS-1
❑ 95UltAllSGM-1
❑ 95UltAwaW-25
❑ 95UltAwaWGM-25
❑ 95UltGolM-186
❑ 95UltRisS-1
❑ 95UltRisSGM-1
❑ 95UppDec-79
❑ 95UppDecED-79
❑ 95UppDecEDG-79
❑ 95UppDecPLL-R57
❑ 95UppDecPLLE-R57
❑ 95UppDecSE-138
❑ 95UppDecSEG-138
❑ 95USPlaCMLA-6D
❑ 95Zen-78
❑ 96Baz-52
❑ 96Bow-7
❑ 96BowBes-64
❑ 96BowBesAR-64
❑ 96BowBesR-64
❑ 96BowFoi-7
❑ 96Cir-147
❑ 96CirAcc-22
❑ 96CirBos-40
❑ 96CirRav-147
❑ 96ColCho-209
❑ 96ColCho-400
❑ 96ColChoGS-209
❑ 96ColChoGS-400
❑ 96ColChoSS-209
❑ 96ColChoSS-400
❑ 96DenHol-24
❑ 96Don-283
❑ 96DonPreP-283
❑ 96EmoXL-218
❑ 96ExpDis-2
❑ 96ExpDis-3
❑ 96Fin-B157
❑ 96Fin-B250
❑ 96FinRef-B157
❑ 96FinRef-B250
❑ 96Fla-301
❑ 96Fle-450
❑ 96FleTif-450
❑ 96Lea-182
❑ 96LeaPre-34
❑ 96LeaPreP-34
❑ 96LeaPrePB-182
❑ 96LeaPrePG-182
❑ 96LeaPrePS-182
❑ 96LeaPreSG-74
❑ 96LeaPreSte-74
❑ 96LeaSigA-6
❑ 96LeaSigAG-6
❑ 96LeaSigAS-6
❑ 96MetUni-188
❑ 96MetUniP-188
❑ 96Pac-133
❑ 96PacEstL-EL2
❑ 96PacPri-P40
❑ 96PacPriG-P40
❑ 96PanSti-17
❑ 96Pin-206
❑ 96PinAfi-87
❑ 96PinAfiAP-87
❑ 96PinAfiFPP-87
❑ 96PinArtP-106
❑ 96PinFan-26
❑ 96PinFoil-206
❑ 96PinSta-106
❑ 96RedF-1
❑ 96Sco-75
❑ 96ScoDugC-A61
❑ 96ScoDugCAP-A61
❑ 96Sel-49
❑ 96SelArtP-49
❑ 96SelCer-65
❑ 96SelCerAP-65
❑ 96SelCerCB-65
❑ 96SelCerCR-65
❑ 96SelCerMB-65
❑ 96SelCerMG-65
❑ 96SelCerMR-65
❑ 96SelTeaN-24
❑ 96SP-121
❑ 96Spo-67
❑ 96SpoArtP-67
❑ 96StaClu-138
❑ 96StaCluEPB-138
❑ 96StaCluEPG-138
❑ 96StaCluEPS-138
❑ 96StaCluMOP-138
❑ 96Stu-101
❑ 96StuPrePB-101
❑ 96StuPrePG-101
❑ 96StuPrePS-101
❑ 96Sum-73
❑ 96SumAbo&B-73
❑ 96SumArtP-73
❑ 96SumFoi-73
❑ 96Top-309
❑ 96TopChr-123
❑ 96TopChrR-123
❑ 96TopGal-6
❑ 96TopGalPPI-6
❑ 96TopLas-1
❑ 96Ult-228
❑ 96UltGolM-228
❑ 96UppDec-395
❑ 96Zen-79
❑ 96ZenArtP-79
❑ 96ZenMoz-17
❑ 97Bow-235
❑ 97BowBes-13
❑ 97BowBesAR-13
❑ 97BowBesR-13
❑ 97BowChr-62
❑ 97BowChrI-62
❑ 97BowChrIR-62
❑ 97BowChrR-62
❑ 97BowInt-235
❑ 97Cir-126
❑ 97CirRav-126
❑ 97ColCho-341
❑ 97ColChoT-FM12
❑ 97Don-66
❑ 97Don-279
❑ 97DonEli-62
❑ 97DonEliGS-62
❑ 97DonGolPP-66
❑ 97DonGolPP-279
❑ 97DonLim-3
❑ 97DonLim-162
❑ 97DonLimE-3
❑ 97DonLimE-162
❑ 97DonLimENG-162
❑ 97DonPre-113
❑ 97DonPreCttC-113
❑ 97DonSig-73
❑ 97DonSigA-6
❑ 97DonSigAC-6
❑ 97DonSigAM-6
❑ 97DonSigPPP-73
❑ 97DonSilPP-66
❑ 97DonSilPP-279
❑ 97E-X2-70
❑ 97E-X2Cred-70
❑ 97E-X2EssCre-70
❑ 97Fin-297
❑ 97FinEmb-297
❑ 97FinEmbR-297
❑ 97FinRef-297
❑ 97FlaShoLC-174
❑ 97FlaShoLeg0-174
❑ 97FlaShoLeg1-174
❑ 97FlaShoM-A174
❑ 97FlaShoM-B174
❑ 97FlaShoM-C174
❑ 97FlaShoR0-174
❑ 97FlaShoR1-174
❑ 97FlaShoR2-174
❑ 97Fle-374
❑ 97Fle-647
❑ 97FleTif-374
❑ 97FleTif-647
❑ 97Lea-219
❑ 97LeaFraM-219
❑ 97LeaFraMDC-219
❑ 97MarPac-2
❑ 97MetUni-152
❑ 97NewPin-149
❑ 97NewPinAP-149
❑ 97NewPinMC-149
❑ 97NewPinPP-149
❑ 97Pac-341
❑ 97PacBaeS-7
❑ 97PacLigB-341
❑ 97PacPri-117
❑ 97PacPriGotD-GD164
❑ 97PacPriLB-117
❑ 97PacPriP-117
❑ 97PacSil-341
❑ 97Pin-113
❑ 97PinArtP-PP113
❑ 97PinCer-71
❑ 97PinCerMBla-71
❑ 97PinCerMBlu-71
❑ 97PinCerMG-71
❑ 97PinCerMR-71
❑ 97PinCerR-71
❑ 97PinIns-6
❑ 97PinInsCE-6
❑ 97PinInsDE-6
❑ 97PinMusC-113
❑ 97PinPrePla-113
❑ 97PinTotCPB-71
❑ 97PinTotCPG-71
❑ 97PinTotCPR-71
❑ 97PinX-P-58
❑ 97PinX-PMoS-58
❑ 97PinX-PSfF-2
❑ 97PinX-PSfFU-2
❑ 97Sco-47
❑ 97Sco-358
❑ 97ScoArtPWB-47
❑ 97ScoArtPWB-358
❑ 97ScoPreS-47
❑ 97ScoResC-358
❑ 97ScoShoS-47
❑ 97ScoShoS-358
❑ 97ScoShoSAP-47
❑ 97ScoShoSAP-358
❑ 97Sel-152
❑ 97SelCom-152
❑ 97SP-76
❑ 97SpoIll-84
❑ 97SpoIllEE-84
❑ 97StaClu-80
❑ 97StaCluMOP-80
❑ 97StrAll-3
❑ 97Stu-116
❑ 97StuPrePG-116
❑ 97StuPrePS-116
❑ 97Top-460
❑ 97TopChr-161
❑ 97TopChrR-161
❑ 97TopGal-61
❑ 97TopGalPPI-61
❑ 97TopSta-14
❑ 97TopStaAM-14
❑ 97TopStaASM-ASM7
❑ 97Ult-225
❑ 97Ult-347
❑ 97UltDouT-16
❑ 97UltGolME-225
❑ 97UltGolME-347
❑ 97UltPlaME-225
❑ 97UltPlaME-347
❑ 97UppDec-534
❑ 98Bow-264
❑ 98BowBes-97
❑ 98BowBesAR-97
❑ 98BowBesR-97
❑ 98BowChr-264
❑ 98BowChrGA-264
❑ 98BowChrGAR-264
❑ 98BowChrI-264
❑ 98BowChrIR-264
❑ 98BowChrR-264
❑ 98BowGolA-264
❑ 98BowInt-264
❑ 98CirThu-124
❑ 98CirThuRav-124
❑ 98CirThuSupRav-124
❑ 98ColCho-385
❑ 98CroRoy-61
❑ 98CroRoyPotG-13
❑ 98Don-145
❑ 98Don-232
❑ 98DonCol-145
❑ 98DonColE-517
❑ 98DonColL-249
❑ 98DonColP-605
❑ 98DonColS-145
❑ 98DonCruG-73
❑ 98DonCruP-73
❑ 98DonCruR-73
❑ 98DonEli-117
❑ 98DonEliA-117
❑ 98DonEliS-117
❑ 98DonGolPP-145
❑ 98DonGolPP-232
❑ 98DonPre-55
❑ 98DonPreSeat-55
❑ 98DonPriCD-145
❑ 98DonPriCE-517
❑ 98DonPriCL-249
❑ 98DonPriCP-605
❑ 98DonSig-58
❑ 98DonSigA-3
❑ 98DonSigAC-3
❑ 98DonSigAM-3
❑ 98DonSigP-58
❑ 98DonSilPP-145
❑ 98DonSilPP-232
❑ 98E-X2-26
❑ 98E-X2ECFut-26
❑ 98E-X2ECNow-26
❑ 98Fin-185
❑ 98FinNo--185
❑ 98FinNo-R-185
❑ 98FinRef-185
❑ 98FlaShoLeg0-115
❑ 98FlaShoLeg1-115
❑ 98FlaShoLeg2-115
❑ 98FlaShoLeg3-115
❑ 98FlaShoLegM-115
❑ 98FlaShoR0-115
❑ 98FlaShoR1-115
❑ 98FlaShoR2-115
❑ 98FlaShoR3-115
❑ 98Fle-146
❑ 98Fle-367
❑ 98FlePlaCS-1
❑ 98FleVin'-24
❑ 98FleVin'-95
❑ 98FleVin'C-24
❑ 98FleVin'C-95
❑ 98Lea-50
❑ 98LeaCruG-73
❑ 98LeaCruP-73
❑ 98LeaCruR-73
❑ 98LeaFraDA-50
❑ 98LeaFraF-50
❑ 98LeaFraM-50
❑ 98LeaFraM-50
❑ 98LeaFraMDC-50
❑ 98LeaFraMDC-50
❑ 98LeaFraMZ2-50
❑ 98LeaRS-62
❑ 98LeaRSLHolo-62
❑ 98LeaRSLong-62
❑ 98LeaRTrue-62
❑ 98MetUni-21
❑ 98MetUniPMG-21
❑ 98Pac-294
❑ 98PacAur-135
❑ 98PacAurPF-36
❑ 98PacAurPFC-36

❑ 98PacAurPFPB-36
❑ 98PacAurPFR-36
❑ 98PacAurPFS-36
❑ 98PacGolCDC-15
❑ 98PacInv-95
❑ 98PacInvGems-150
❑ 98PacInvPBlue-95
❑ 98PacInvSilv-95
❑ 98PacLatotML-14
❑ 98PacOme-103
❑ 98PacOmeR-103
❑ 98PacOnl-309
❑ 98PacOnlR-309
❑ 98PacOnlWC-309
❑ 98PacPar-166
❑ 98PacParC-166
❑ 98PacParG-166
❑ 98PacParHS-166
❑ 98PacParPB-166
❑ 98PacParR-166
❑ 98PacPlaB-294
❑ 98PacRedT-294
❑ 98PacSil-294
❑ 98PacTeaC-19
❑ 98Pin-20
❑ 98PinArtP-PP20
❑ 98PinIns-85
❑ 98PinInsCE-85
❑ 98PinInsDE-85
❑ 98PinMusC-PP20
❑ 98PinPer-56
❑ 98PinPerPP-56
❑ 98PinPlu-42
❑ 98PinPreP-20
❑ 98Revo-64
❑ 98RevoFP-16
❑ 98RevoShow-29
❑ 98RevoSS-64
❑ 98ScoRT-148
❑ 98ScoRTSS-PP86
❑ 98ScoRTSSAP-PP86
❑ 98ScoRTSSAP1-PP86
❑ 98SkyDugA-21
❑ 98SkyDugAIA-21
❑ 98SP Aut-99
❑ 98SpoIll-4
❑ 98SpoIllEE-4
❑ 98SpoIllFE-4
❑ 98SpoIllWSF-92
❑ 98SpoIllWSFEE-92
❑ 98SpoIllWSFFE-92
❑ 98SPxFin-280
❑ 98SPxFin-341
❑ 98SPxFinR-280
❑ 98SPxFinR-341
❑ 98SPxFinS-280
❑ 98SPxFinS-341
❑ 98Stu-80
❑ 98StuGPP-80
❑ 98StuSPP-80
❑ 98Top-277
❑ 98Top-313
❑ 98TopChr-277
❑ 98TopChr-313
❑ 98TopChrR-277
❑ 98TopChrR-313
❑ 98TopDevR-277
❑ 98TopDevR-313
❑ 98TopDia-277
❑ 98TopDia-313
❑ 98TopGal-19
❑ 98TopGalGP-19
❑ 98TopGalOPP-19
❑ 98TopGalPPI-19
❑ 98TopGalPPIA-19
❑ 98TopGolLabC1-34
❑ 98TopGolLabC1B-34
❑ 98TopGolLabC1One-34
❑ 98TopGolLabC1R-34
❑ 98TopGolLabC2-34
❑ 98TopGolLabC2B-34
❑ 98TopGolLabC2One-34
❑ 98TopGolLabC2R-34
❑ 98TopGolLabC3-34
❑ 98TopGolLabC3B-34
❑ 98TopGolLabC3One-34
❑ 98TopGolLabC3R-34
❑ 98TopMiniC-277
❑ 98TopMiniC-313
❑ 98TopOpeD-139
❑ 98TopSta-22
❑ 98TopStaB-22
❑ 98TopStaG-22
❑ 98TopStaGR-22
❑ 98TopStaS-22
❑ 98TopTek-55
❑ 98TopTekD-55
❑ 98Ult-197
❑ 98Ult-387
❑ 98UltGolM-197
❑ 98UltGolM-387
❑ 98UltMas-197
❑ 98UltMas-387
❑ 98UltPlaM-197
❑ 98UltPlaM-387
❑ 98UppDec-96
❑ 98UppDec-426
❑ 98UppDec-685
❑ 98UppDecNP-NP12
❑ 98Zen-80
❑ 98ZenZ-G-80
❑ 98ZenZ-S-80
❑ 99199Fin-40
❑ 99Bow-8
❑ 99BowBes-77
❑ 99BowBesAR-77
❑ 99BowBesR-77
❑ 99BowChr-8
❑ 99BowChrG-8
❑ 99BowChrGR-8
❑ 99BowChrI-8
❑ 99BowChrIR-8
❑ 99BowChrR-8
❑ 99BowGol-8
❑ 99BowInt-8
❑ 99CroRoyB-62
❑ 99CroRoyL-62
❑ 99CroRoyOD-62
❑ 99E-X Cen-89
❑ 99E-X CenECFut-89
❑ 99E-X CenECNow-89
❑ 99FinGolRef-40
❑ 99FinRef-40
❑ 99FlaShoLeg1-55
❑ 99FlaShoLeg2-55
❑ 99FlaShoLeg3-55
❑ 99FlaShoLegM1-55
❑ 99FlaShoLegM2-55
❑ 99FlaShoLegM3-55
❑ 99FlaShoR1-55
❑ 99FlaShoR2-55
❑ 99FlaShoR3-55
❑ 99Fle-17
❑ 99FleBri-43
❑ 99FleBri2G-43
❑ 99FleBriBlu-43
❑ 99FleBriGol-43
❑ 99FleGoiYar-1
❑ 99FleSta9-17
❑ 99FleVin'-17
❑ 99FleWarT-17
❑ 99MetUni-173
❑ 99MetUniGM-173
❑ 99MetUniPMG-173
❑ 99Pac-184
❑ 99Pac-184A
❑ 99PacAur-78
❑ 99PacAurOD-78
❑ 99PacCroC-120
❑ 99PacCroC-30
❑ 99PacCroCITC-8
❑ 99PacCroCPB-120
❑ 99PacCroCTC-13
❑ 99PacCroCTM-8
❑ 99PacInv-64
❑ 99PacInvOD-64
❑ 99PacInvPB-64
❑ 99PacOme-102
❑ 99PacOmeC-102
❑ 99PacOmeG-102
❑ 99PacOmePB-102
❑ 99PacPar-100
❑ 99PacParC-100
❑ 99PacParG-100
❑ 99PacParHoloGold-100
❑ 99PacParHS-100
❑ 99PacParOD-100
❑ 99PacParPB-100
❑ 99PacParRed-100
❑ 99PacPlaB-184
❑ 99PacPlaB-184A
❑ 99PacPri-65
❑ 99PacPriHB-65
❑ 99PacPriHG-65
❑ 99PacPriHM-65
❑ 99PacPriHP-65
❑ 99PacPriRed-65
❑ 99PacPriS-22
❑ 99PacPriS206-22
❑ 99PacPriS206R-22
❑ 99PacPriSP-22
❑ 99PacPriSV-22
❑ 99PacRed-184
❑ 99PacRed-184A
❑ 99Pin-1
❑ 99SkyMolM-43
❑ 99SkyMolMX-43
❑ 99SkyPre-209
❑ 99SkyPreR-209
❑ 99SkyThu-291
❑ 99SkyThuRant-291
❑ 99SkyThuRave-291
❑ 99SP Aut-40
❑ 99SP AutHRC-HR23
❑ 99SPAutHRCDC-HR23
❑ 99SpoIll-140
❑ 99SPx-44
❑ 99SPxFinR-44
❑ 99SPxFinS-44
❑ 99SPxPowE-PE16
❑ 99SPxPreS-PS6
❑ 99StaClu-88
❑ 99StaCluC-CS25
❑ 99StaCluC-CS30
❑ 99StaCluC-CS37
❑ 99StaCluC-CS41
❑ 99StaCluFDI-88
❑ 99StaCluOoaK-88
❑ 99StaCluPP-88
❑ 99ThuSkySupR-291
❑ 99Top-400
❑ 99TopAut-A9
❑ 99TopBlaLC1-88
❑ 99TopBlaLC2-88
❑ 99TopBlaLC3-88
❑ 99TopChr-400
❑ 99TopChrR-400
❑ 99TopGal-85
❑ 99TopGalPP-85
❑ 99TopGalPPI-85
❑ 99TopGolL-88
❑ 99TopGolLC1-88
❑ 99TopGolLC2-88
❑ 99TopGolLOtO-88
❑ 99TopMVPP-400
❑ 99TopOpeD-108
❑ 99TopRedLC1-88
❑ 99TopRedLC2-88
❑ 99TopRedLC3-88
❑ 99TopSta-99
❑ 99TopSta'S-31
❑ 99TopSta'SG-31
❑ 99TopSta'SGDH-31
❑ 99TopSta1Foil-99
❑ 99TopStaFoil-99
❑ 99TopStaOS-99
❑ 99TopSupC-21
❑ 99TopSupCR-21
❑ 99TopTekP-PP2A
❑ 99UD Cho-91
❑ 99UD ChoPCR-91
❑ 99UD ChoYW-Y15
❑ 99UD Ion-32
❑ 99UD IonR-32
❑ 99Ult-158
❑ 99UltGolM-158
❑ 99UltMas-158
❑ 99UltPlaM-158
❑ 99UppDec-106
❑ 99UppDec-233
❑ 99UppDecBD-36
❑ 99UppDecBDD-36
❑ 99UppDecBDQ-36
❑ 99UppDecBDT-36
❑ 99UppDecCf7-20
❑ 99UppDecCf7-76
❑ 99UppDecCf7-C17
❑ 99UppDecCf7Cf7P-C17
❑ 99UppDecCf7LL-L26
❑ 99UppDecCL-74
❑ 99UppDecCLCC-74
❑ 99UppDecCLM-C42
❑ 99UppDecCo7CE-20
❑ 99UppDecCo7CE-76
❑ 99UppDecE-42
❑ 99UppDecEFXG-42
❑ 99UppDecEL1-106
❑ 99UppDecEL1-233
❑ 99UppDecEL2-106
❑ 99UppDecEL2-233
❑ 99UppDecM-91
❑ 99UppDecMGS-91
❑ 99UppDecMHFS-91
❑ 99UppDecMP-91
❑ 99UppDecMSS-91
❑ 99UppDecO-27
❑ 99UppDecOSO-27
❑ 99UppDecOWP-R15
❑ 99Vic-174

Alperman, Whitey (Charles A.)
❑ 08RosComP-94
❑ 09RamT20-1
❑ 09T206-4
❑ 11SpoLifCW-3
❑ 12ColRedB-7
❑ 12ColTinT-7
❑ 12ImpTobC-7
❑ 90DodTar-890

Alpert, George
❑ 81BatTroT-25
❑ 82WatIndF-27
❑ 82WatIndT-20

Alroso, Kurt
❑ 97LakTigB-4

Alstead, Jason
❑ 91FreKeyC-21
❑ 91FreKeyP-2375
❑ 92ClaFS7-106
❑ 92FreKeyC-9
❑ 92FreKeyF-1816
❑ 93FreKeyC-2
❑ 93FreKeyF-1038

Alston, Dell (Wendell)
❑ 78SSP270-4
❑ 78TacYanC-27
❑ 78Top-710
❑ 78YanSSPD-4
❑ 79TacTugT-19
❑ 79Top-54
❑ 80IndTeal-2
❑ 80TacTigT-24
❑ 80Top-198
❑ 81Don-322
❑ 92YanWIZ7-7

Alston, Garvin
❑ 92BenRocCB-5
❑ 92BenRocF-1465
❑ 92FroRowDP-54
❑ 92FroRowDPG-54
❑ 92FroRowDPS-54
❑ 93Bow-640
❑ 93CenValRC-3
❑ 93CenValRF-2883
❑ 93ClaFS7-163
❑ 93Top-661
❑ 93TopGol-661
❑ 93TopInaM-661
❑ 93TopInaR-661
❑ 93TopMic-661
❑ 94CenValRC-2
❑ 94CenValRF-3193
❑ 95NewHavRTI-16
❑ 96ColSprSSTI-1
❑ 97Fle-582
❑ 97FleTif-582
❑ 98ColSprSS-16

Alston, Tom (Thomas E.)
❑ 53MotCoo-24
❑ 54CarHunW-1
❑ 55Bow-257
❑ 55CarHunW-1

Alston, Walter E.
❑ 52Par-66
❑ 53ExhCan-61
❑ 55DodGolS-1
❑ 56Dod-1
❑ 56Top-8
❑ 58DodJayP-1
❑ 58DodTeal-1
❑ 58DodVol-1
❑ 58PacBel-1
❑ 58Top-314
❑ 59DodTeal-1
❑ 59DodVol-1
❑ 60DodBelB-18
❑ 60DodMor-1
❑ 60DodPos-1
❑ 60DodTeal-1
❑ 60DodUniO-1
❑ 60Top-212
❑ 61DodBelB-24
❑ 61DodJayP-1
❑ 61DodUniO-1
❑ 61Top-136
❑ 62DodBelB-24
❑ 62DodJayP-1
❑ 62Top-217
❑ 63DodJayP-1
❑ 63Top-154
❑ 64Top-101
❑ 64TopVen-101
❑ 65DodJayP-1
❑ 65DodTeal-1
❑ 65OPC-217
❑ 65Top-217
❑ 66OPC-116
❑ 66Top-116
❑ 66TopVen-116
❑ 67Top-294
❑ 68Top-472
❑ 69OPC-24
❑ 69Top-24
❑ 70OPC-242
❑ 70Top-242
❑ 71Dod-1
❑ 71DodTic-2
❑ 71OPC-567
❑ 71Top-567
❑ 72Top-749
❑ 73OPC-569
❑ 73Top-569
❑ 74OPC-144
❑ 74Top-144
❑ 75DodTCMA-1
❑ 75OPC-361
❑ 75Top-361
❑ 75TopMin-361
❑ 76DodPos-1
❑ 76OPC-46
❑ 76SSP-90
❑ 76Top-46
❑ 79DiaGre-95
❑ 79TCM50-187
❑ 80DodGreT-12
❑ 80PacLeg-14
❑ 80PerHaloFP-181
❑ 80PerHaloFPS-46
❑ 80SSPHOF-184
❑ 81TCM60I-306
❑ 82OhiHaloF-15
❑ 85UltBasC-14
❑ 86SpoDesJM-6
❑ 87Dod195T-1
❑ 87DodSmoA-1
❑ 88DodSmo-1
❑ 88WilMulP-16
❑ 89DodSmoG-1
❑ 90DodTar-12
❑ 91DodRinP4-12
❑ 92DodStaTA-6
❑ 92DodUno7P-5
❑ 95TopArcBD-109
❑ 95TopArcBD-141

Altaffer, Todd
❑ 91SouBenWSC-12
❑ 91SouBenWSP-2848
❑ 92WatDiaC-17
❑ 92WatDiaF-2132

Altamirano, Porfirio
❑ 80VenLeaS-251
❑ 81OklCit8T-1
❑ 83Fle-153
❑ 83PorBeaT-15
❑ 83Top-432
❑ 84IowCubT-23
❑ 84Nes792-101
❑ 84Top-101
❑ 84TopTif-101

Alten, Ernie (Ernest M.)
❑ 23Zee-122

Altenberger, Peter
❑ 88CapCodPPaLP-48

Altizer, Dave (David Tildon)
❑ 09ColChiE-8A
❑ 09ColChiE-8B
❑ 11PinT-5-422
❑ 12ColRedB-8A
❑ 12ColRedB-8B
❑ 12ColTinT-8A
❑ 12ColTinT-8B
❑ 72ClaCar-98

Altizer, Quentin
❑ 49AngTeal-3
❑ 49W725AngTI-3

Altman, Gene
❑ 98BurBeeM-2

Altman, George Lee
❑ 59Top-512
❑ 60CubJayP-1
❑ 60Top-259
❑ 61CubJayP-1
❑ 61Pos-195A
❑ 61Pos-195B
❑ 61Top-551
❑ 61TopStal-1
❑ 62CubJayP-1
❑ 62Jel-187
❑ 62Pos-187
❑ 62PosCan-187
❑ 62SalPlaC-128
❑ 62ShiPlaC-128
❑ 62Top-240
❑ 62TopBuc-3
❑ 62TopStal-103
❑ 63BasMagM-5
❑ 63Jel-171
❑ 63Pos-171
❑ 63SalMetC-31
❑ 63Top-357
❑ 64Baz-23
❑ 64MetTeal-1
❑ 64Top-95
❑ 64TopSta-69
❑ 64TopStaU-3
❑ 64TopVen-95
❑ 65CubJayP-1
❑ 65Top-528
❑ 66CubTeal-2
❑ 66OPC-146
❑ 66Top-146
❑ 66TopVen-146
❑ 67CokCapC-17
❑ 67DexPre-11
❑ 67OPC-87
❑ 67ProPizC-1
❑ 67Top-87
❑ 91MetWIZ-9

Altman, Heath
❑ 93EveGiaC-1
❑ 93EveGiaF-3756
❑ 94CliLumC-4
❑ 94CliLumF-1970
❑ 95BurBeeTI-24
❑ 96BreCouMB-5

Altman, John
❑ 77VisOakT-1

Altman, Joseph
❑ 12HomRunKE-60
❑ 12Zee-99

Altobelli, Joseph S.
❑ 57IndTeal-1
❑ 63RocRedWSP-1
❑ 75IntLeaAT-16
❑ 77Gia-1
❑ 77GiaTeal-2
❑ 77Top-211
❑ 78GiaTeal-1
❑ 78Top-256
❑ 79GiaPol-6
❑ 79Top-356
❑ 80ColCliP-16
❑ 80ColCliT-8
❑ 81YanPhoA-1
❑ 82YanPhoA-2
❑ 83OriPos-1
❑ 83TopTra-3T
❑ 84BalOriP-1
❑ 84Don-88
❑ 84Fle-643
❑ 84Fle-647
❑ 84FleSti-125
❑ 84Nes792-21
❑ 84Top-21
❑ 84TopTif-21
❑ 85Top-574
❑ 85TopGloA-12
❑ 85TopTif-574
❑ 86YanTCM-39
❑ 88CubDavB-NNO
❑ 89CubMar-NNO
❑ 90CubMar-28
❑ 90TopTVCu-2
❑ 91CubMar-NNO
❑ 91CubVinL-2
❑ 93RocRedWF-259

Alton, Allen
❑ 21Zee-22

Altrock, Nick (Nicholas)
❑ 04FanCraAL-1
❑ 07WhiSoxGWH-1
❑ 08RosComP-11
❑ 09ColChiE-9
❑ 11SpoLifCW-4
❑ 12ColRedB-9
❑ 12ColTinT-9
❑ 26SpoComoA-3
❑ 27YorCarE-40
❑ 31SenTealPW-1
❑ 36NatChiFPR-98
❑ 36R31PasP-40
❑ 46SpoExcW-1-8

❑ 60SenUniMC-1
❑ 61Fle-3
❑ 63GadFunC-45
❑ 74CapPub-93
❑ 75SenTCM1-2
❑ 77GalGloG-178
❑ 87ConSer2-8
❑ 88ConSer5-1
❑ 91ConTSN-226
❑ 94ConTSN-1119
❑ 94ConTSNB-1119

Alusik, George J.
❑ 62Top-261
❑ 63Top-51
❑ 64Top-431

Alva, John
❑ 86SumBraP-2
❑ 87DurBulP-25
❑ 88GreBraB-6
❑ 89GreBraB-7
❑ 89GreBraP-1154
❑ 89GreBraS-2
❑ 90CMC-299
❑ 90GreBraS-1
❑ 90ProAAAF-408
❑ 90RicBraC-23
❑ 90RicBraP-263
❑ 91LinDriAAA-426
❑ 91RicBraBC-19
❑ 91RicBraLD-426
❑ 91RicBraP-2574
❑ 91RicBraTI-13

Alvarado, Arnaldo
❑ 75DubPacT-5
❑ 76VenLeaS-58
❑ 80VenLeaS-66

Alvarado, Basilio
❑ 96DelShoB-6
❑ 96DelShoUB-3
❑ 96VerExpB-7

Alvarado, Carlos
❑ 97AugGre-7
❑ 98AugGreM-21

Alvarado, David
❑ 98EriSeaWM-1

Alvarado, Jose
❑ 85MexCitTT-15

Alvarado, Luis
❑ 94EliTwiC-2
❑ 94EliTwiF-3720
❑ 95ForWayWTI-1

Alvarado, Luis Cesar
❑ 70OPC-317
❑ 70RedSoxCPPC-1
❑ 70Top-317
❑ 71OPC-489
❑ 71Top-489
❑ 72Top-774
❑ 73OPC-627
❑ 73Top-627
❑ 74OPC-462
❑ 74Top-462
❑ 76TulOilGP-14
❑ 91MetWIZ-10

Alvarez, Alex
❑ 88CapCodPPaLP-7
❑ 93LinVenB-14
❑ 94VenLinU-65
❑ 95LinVen-240
❑ 96-97LinVen-254

Alvarez, Carlos
❑ 95LinVen-160
❑ 96-97LinVen-207
❑ 97WatIndTI-2

Alvarez, Carmelo
❑ 82VerBeaDT-16

Alvarez, Chris
❑ 86FloStaLAP-3
❑ 86Ft.LauYP-1
❑ 87AlbYanP-15
❑ 88ColCliC-24
❑ 88ColCliP-13
❑ 88ColCliP-323
❑ 89ColCliP-739
❑ 90LonTigP-1273

Alvarez, Clemente
❑ 88UtiBluSP-2
❑ 89SouBenWSGS-30
❑ 90SarWhiSS-1
❑ 91Cla/Bes-142
❑ 91SarWhiSC-12
❑ 91SarWhiSP-1115
❑ 92BirBarF-2585
❑ 92BirBarS-76
❑ 92ClaFS7-29
❑ 92SkyAA F-36
❑ 93BirBarF-1195
❑ 93Bow-188
❑ 93LinVenB-104
❑ 94NasSouF-1253
❑ 94VenLinU-21
❑ 95LinVen-86
❑ 96-97LinVen-17

Alvarez, Danny
❑ 97WatIndTI-3

Alvarez, David
❑ 89ElmPioP-1
❑ 90ElmPioP-2

Alvarez, Emenegilda
❑ 91MedHatBJP-4112
❑ 91MedHatBJSP-21

Alvarez, Gabe
❑ 95SPML-101
❑ 95SPMLA-2
❑ 96BesAutS-4
❑ 96Bow-309
❑ 96BowBes-140
❑ 96BowBesAR-140
❑ 96BowBesR-140
❑ 96BowFoi-309
❑ 96BowMinLP-12
❑ 96Exc-233
❑ 96ExcFirYP-1
❑ 96MemChiB-6
❑ 97Bow-397
❑ 97BowChrl-263
❑ 97BowChrIR-263
❑ 97BowChrR-263
❑ 97BowInt-397
❑ 97MobBayBB-10
❑ 97SouLeaTP-26
❑ 97Top-204
❑ 98ColCho-422
❑ 98ColChoPCR-422
❑ 98DonSigA-4
❑ 98DonSigAC-4
❑ 98DonSigAM-4
❑ 98FleUpd-U68
❑ 98LeaRS-269
❑ 98LeaRSLHolo-269
❑ 98LeaRSLong-269
❑ 98LeaRTrue-269
❑ 98SP Aut-11
❑ 98SPxFin-183
❑ 98SPxFinR-183
❑ 98SPxFinS-183
❑ 98Stu-21
❑ 98StuGPP-21
❑ 98StuSPP-21
❑ 98TolMudHQ-6
❑ 98UD3-23
❑ 98UD3-113
❑ 98UD3-203
❑ 98UD3DieCut-23
❑ 98UD3DieCut-113
❑ 98UD3DieCut-203
❑ 98UppDec-555
❑ 98UppDecDS-DS17
❑ 98UppDecR-112
❑ 98UppDecRNF-NF12
❑ 99E-X Cen-91
❑ 99E-X CenECFut-91
❑ 99E-X CenECNow-91
❑ 99Fle-59
❑ 99FleBri-34
❑ 99FleBri2G-34
❑ 99FleBriBlu-34
❑ 99FleBriGol-34
❑ 99FleSta9-59
❑ 99FleWarT-59
❑ 99MetUni-256
❑ 99MetUniGM-256
❑ 99MetUniN-14
❑ 99MetUniPMG-256
❑ 99PacCroC-102
❑ 99PacCroCPB-102
❑ 99Top-188
❑ 99TopChr-188
❑ 99TopChrR-188
❑ 99TopMVPP-188
❑ 99UD Cho-84
❑ 99UD ChoP-84
❑ 99UD ChoPCR-84
❑ 99Ult-226
❑ 99UltGolM-226
❑ 99UltMas-226
❑ 99UltPlaM-226
❑ 99UltWorP-1
❑ 99UppDec-99
❑ 99UppDecBD-101
❑ 99UppDecBDD-101
❑ 99UppDecBDQ-101
❑ 99UppDecBDT-101
❑ 99UppDecEL1-99
❑ 99UppDecEL2-99

Alvarez, German
❑ 98EugEme-2

Alvarez, Javier
❑ 89EugEmeB-15
❑ 90EugEmeGS-1

Alvarez, Joe
❑ 75ForLauYS-14
❑ 89VerBeaDS-27
❑ 90VerBeaDS-30

Alvarez, Jorge
❑ 89SalDodTI-5
❑ 90VerBeaDS-1
❑ 91LinDriAA-527
❑ 91SanAntMLD-527
❑ 92SanAntMF-3979
❑ 92SanAntMS-552
❑ 92SkyAA F-241
❑ 93LimRocDWB-73
❑ 93SanAntMF-3009
❑ 94PorSeaDF-683
❑ 94PorSeaDTI-8

Alvarez, Jose
❑ 76DubPacT-1
❑ 77MetDaiPA-1
❑ 92SalBucC-12
❑ 92SalBucF-54

Alvarez, Jose Lino
❑ 79SavBraT-12
❑ 81RicBraT-15
❑ 82RicBraT-1
❑ 83RicBraT-1
❑ 84TucTorC-51
❑ 86GreBraTI-2
❑ 88FleUpd-70
❑ 88FleUpdG-70
❑ 88RicBraC-8
❑ 88RicBraP-12
❑ 89BraDub-2
❑ 89Don-405
❑ 89Fle-585
❑ 89FleGlo-585
❑ 89PanSti-31
❑ 89Top-253
❑ 89TopTif-253
❑ 89UppDec-734
❑ 90Don-389
❑ 90Fle-574
❑ 90FleCan-574
❑ 90OPC-782
❑ 90PubIntS-106
❑ 90Sco-148
❑ 90Top-782
❑ 90TopTif-782
❑ 90UppDec-634

Alvarez, Juan
❑ 96CedRapKTI-2
❑ 97LakElsSG-2
❑ 98MidAngG-2
❑ 98MidAngO-2

Alvarez, Luis
❑ 80VenLeaS-186

Alvarez, Mike
❑ 81MiaOriT-11
❑ 82ForMyeRT-12
❑ 83OmaRoyT-1
❑ 84OmaRoyT-19
❑ 85Ft.MyeRT-27
❑ 86Ft.MyeRP-2
❑ 87AppFoxP-18
❑ 88SavCarP-353
❑ 90BasCitRS-29
❑ 91LinDriAA-425
❑ 91MemChiP-670
❑ 92MemChiF-2436
❑ 93OmaRoyF-1697
❑ 94OmaRoyF-1239
❑ 95OmaRoyTI-2
❑ 96OmaRoyB-3
❑ 97OmaRoyB-2
❑ 98GreBraG-1

Alvarez, Orlando
❑ 74AlbDukCa-66
❑ 74AlbDukTI-1
❑ 75AlbDukCa-1
❑ 75IntLeaASB-1
❑ 75PacCoaLAB-1
❑ 76SalLakCGC-11
❑ 77SalLakCGC-13
❑ 90DodTar-891

Alvarez, Ossie (Oswaldo G.)
❑ 58SeaTeal-1
❑ 59Top-504
❑ 60TacBan-2
❑ 85MexCitTT-4

Alvarez, Rafael
❑ 76VenLeaS-18
❑ 95ForWayWTI-21
❑ 96-97LinVen-242
❑ 96ForWayWB-2
❑ 96FtMyeMB-26
❑ 97SalLakB-8
❑ 98ForMyeMTI-1

Alvarez, Robbie
❑ 79WatIndT-27
❑ 81ChaLooT-3
❑ 82MiaMarT-12

Alvarez, Rogelio H.
❑ 58RedEnq-2
❑ 63Top-158

Alvarez, Shawn
❑ 95GreBatTI-1

Alvarez, Tavo
❑ 91Cla/Bes-48
❑ 91SumFlyC-1
❑ 91SumFlyP-2324
❑ 92Bow-165
❑ 92ClaFS7-439
❑ 92ProFS7-267
❑ 92UppDecML-262
❑ 92WesPalBEC-3
❑ 92WesPalBEF-2077
❑ 93Bow-16
❑ 93ClaFS7-121
❑ 93ClaGolF-46
❑ 93ExcFS7-55
❑ 93ExcLeaLF-12
❑ 93FleFinE-88
❑ 93OttLynF-2428
❑ 93Ult-410
❑ 93UppDec-501
❑ 93UppDecGold-501
❑ 94ColC-654
❑ 94ColChoGS-654
❑ 94ColChoSS-654
❑ 94UppDec-295
❑ 94UppDecED-295
❑ 94UppDecML-151
❑ 94UppDecML-170
❑ 96ColCho-612
❑ 96ColChoGS-612
❑ 96ColChoSS-612
❑ 96Don-516
❑ 96DonPreP-516
❑ 96Pac-122
❑ 96SelArtP-193
❑ 96Sum-168
❑ 96SumAbo&B-168
❑ 96SumArtP-168
❑ 96SumFoi-168
❑ 98NasSouTI-1
❑ 98NasSouTISS-1

Alvarez, Victor
❑ 97GreFalDTI-3

Alvarez, Wilson
❑ 88GasRanP-1017
❑ 89ChaRanS-1
❑ 89TulDriTI-2
❑ 90CMC-628
❑ 90ProAAAF-159
❑ 90TopDeb89-3
❑ 90UppDec-765
❑ 90VanCanC-1
❑ 90VanCanP-481
❑ 91BirBarLD-51
❑ 91BirBarP-1446
❑ 91Bow-354
❑ 91Cla/Bes-285
❑ 91LinDriAA-51
❑ 91OPC-378
❑ 91StaCluMO-1
❑ 91Top-378A
❑ 91Top-378B
❑ 91TopDesS-378
❑ 91TopMic-378
❑ 91TopTif-378
❑ 91UltUpd-13
❑ 91UppDecFE-42F
❑ 92Bow-69
❑ 92Cla1-T5
❑ 92ClaGam-114
❑ 92Don-495
❑ 92Don-630
❑ 92Fle-74
❑ 92Fle-684
❑ 92Lea-78
❑ 92LeaBlaG-78
❑ 92OPC-452
❑ 92OPCPre-122
❑ 92Pin-192
❑ 92ProFS7-41
❑ 92Sco-428
❑ 92Sco-760
❑ 92StaClu-761
❑ 92StaCluNC-761
❑ 92Top-452
❑ 92TopGol-452
❑ 92TopGolW-452
❑ 92TopMic-452
❑ 92Ult-32
❑ 92UppDec-573
❑ 92WhiSoxK-40
❑ 93Bow-387
❑ 93Don-37
❑ 93Fla-180
❑ 93Fle-199
❑ 93Lea-496
❑ 93LinVenB-6
❑ 93LinVenB-346
❑ 93PacSpa-66
❑ 93Pin-441
❑ 93RanKee-51
❑ 93Sco-609
❑ 93StaClu-181
❑ 93StaCluFDI-181
❑ 93StaCluMOP-181
❑ 93Top-737
❑ 93TopGol-737
❑ 93TopInaM-737
❑ 93TopInaR-737
❑ 93TopMic-737
❑ 93Ult-170
❑ 93UppDec-350
❑ 93UppDecGold-350
❑ 93WhiSoxK-1
❑ 93WhiSoxSC-10
❑ 94Bow-54
❑ 94BowBes-R26
❑ 94BowBesR-R26
❑ 94ColC-36
❑ 94ColChoGS-36
❑ 94ColChoSS-36
❑ 94Don-518
❑ 94Fin-139
❑ 94FinRef-139
❑ 94Fla-28
❑ 94Fle-73
❑ 94FleExtB-40
❑ 94FleExtBPD-5
❑ 94Lea-71
❑ 94LeaL-19
❑ 94Pac-118
❑ 94Pin-128
❑ 94PinArtP-128
❑ 94PinMusC-128
❑ 94Sco-220
❑ 94ScoGolR-220
❑ 94Sel-111
❑ 94SP-188
❑ 94SPDieC-188
❑ 94Spo-97
❑ 94StaClu-462
❑ 94StaCluFDI-462
❑ 94StaCluGR-462
❑ 94StaCluMO-12
❑ 94StaCluMOP-462
❑ 94StaCluT-132
❑ 94StaCluTFDI-132
❑ 94Stu-203
❑ 94Top-299
❑ 94TopGol-299
❑ 94TopSpa-299
❑ 94TriPla-261
❑ 94Ult-30
❑ 94UppDec-204
❑ 94UppDecED-204
❑ 94USPlaCA-8S
❑ 94VenLinU-201
❑ 94WhiSoxK-1
❑ 95Baz-35
❑ 95Bow-412
❑ 95ColCho-503
❑ 95ColChoGS-503
❑ 95ColChoSE-239
❑ 95ColChoSEGS-239
❑ 95ColChoSESS-239
❑ 95ColChoSS-503
❑ 95Don-57
❑ 95DonPreP-57
❑ 95Fin-144
❑ 95FinRef-144
❑ 95Fla-23
❑ 95Fle-109
❑ 95FleAllS-23
❑ 95Lea-27
❑ 95LinVen-40
❑ 95Pac-82
❑ 95PacLatD-3
❑ 95PacPri-27
❑ 95PanSti-11
❑ 95Pin-123
❑ 95PinArtP-123
❑ 95PinMusC-123
❑ 95RedFol-14
❑ 95Sco-90
❑ 95ScoGolR-90
❑ 95ScoPlaTS-90
❑ 95Sel-206
❑ 95SelArtP-206
❑ 95SP-143
❑ 95Spo-138
❑ 95SpoArtP-138
❑ 95SPSil-143
❑ 95StaClu-132
❑ 95StaClu-405
❑ 95StaCluFDI-132
❑ 95StaCluMOP-132
❑ 95StaCluMOP-405
❑ 95StaCluSTWS-132
❑ 95StaCluSTWS-405
❑ 95StaCluVR-68
❑ 95StaCluVRMO-68
❑ 95Stu-56
❑ 95Top-186
❑ 95TopCyb-106
❑ 95Ult-26
❑ 95UltGolM-26
❑ 95UppDec-197
❑ 95UppDecED-197
❑ 95UppDecEDG-197
❑ 95WhiSoxK-2
❑ 96-97LinVen-116
❑ 96Cir-24
❑ 96CirRav-24
❑ 96ColCho-89
❑ 96ColChoGS-89
❑ 96ColChoSS-89
❑ 96Don-174
❑ 96DonPreP-174
❑ 96Fin-B183
❑ 96FinRef-B183
❑ 96Fla-46
❑ 96Fle-61
❑ 96FleTif-61
❑ 96Lea-145
❑ 96LeaPrePB-145
❑ 96LeaPrePG-145
❑ 96LeaPrePS-145
❑ 96LeaSigA-7
❑ 96LeaSigAG-7
❑ 96LeaSigAS-7
❑ 96Pac-292
❑ 96PacPri-P87
❑ 96PacPriG-P87
❑ 96Sco-66
❑ 96StaClu-147
❑ 96StaClu-243
❑ 96StaCluMOP-147
❑ 96StaCluMOP-243
❑ 96Top-159
❑ 96Ult-35
❑ 96UltGolM-35
❑ 96UppDec-306
❑ 96WhiSoxF-1
❑ 97Cir-156
❑ 97CirRav-156
❑ 97ColCho-78
❑ 97ColChoT-CW2
❑ 97Don-75
❑ 97DonGolPP-75
❑ 97DonLim-98
❑ 97DonLimE-98
❑ 97DonLimENG-98
❑ 97DonSilPP-75
❑ 97DonTea-62
❑ 97DonTeaSPE-62
❑ 97Fin-74
❑ 97FinRef-74
❑ 97Fle-54
❑ 97FleTif-54
❑ 97Lea-68
❑ 97LeaFraM-68
❑ 97LeaFraMDC-68
❑ 97MetUni-52
❑ 97NewPin-73
❑ 97NewPinAP-73
❑ 97NewPinMC-73
❑ 97NewPinPP-73
❑ 97Pac-49
❑ 97PacLatotML-6

❑ 97PacLigB-49
❑ 97PacPri-18
❑ 97PacPriLB-18
❑ 97PacPriP-18
❑ 97PacPriSH-SH3B
❑ 97PacSil-49
❑ 97Sco-212
❑ 97ScoArtPWB-212
❑ 97ScoPreS-212
❑ 97ScoShoS-212
❑ 97ScoShoSAP-212
❑ 97StaClu-347
❑ 97StaCluMOP-347
❑ 97Stu-120
❑ 97StuPrePG-120
❑ 97StuPrePS-120
❑ 97Top-176
❑ 97TopGal-118
❑ 97TopGalPPI-118
❑ 97Ult-34
❑ 97UltGolME-34
❑ 97UltPlaME-34
❑ 97UppDec-36
❑ 97WhiSoxS-9
❑ 97WhiSoxSPl-9
❑ 97WhiSoxSPr-9
❑ 97WhiSoxTI-40
❑ 98CirThu-110
❑ 98CirThuRav-110
❑ 98CirThuSupRav-110
❑ 98ColCho-505
❑ 98DevRayP-1
❑ 98Don-239
❑ 98DonGolPP-239
❑ 98DonSigA-5
❑ 98DonSigAC-5
❑ 98DonSigAM-5
❑ 98DonSilPP-239
❑ 98E-X2-56
❑ 98E-X2ECFut-56
❑ 98E-X2ECNow-56
❑ 98Fin-196
❑ 98FinNo--196
❑ 98FinNo-R-196
❑ 98FinRef-196
❑ 98FlaShoLeg0-104
❑ 98FlaShoLeg1-104
❑ 98FlaShoLeg2-104
❑ 98FlaShoLeg3-104
❑ 98FlaShoLegM-104
❑ 98FlaShoR0-104
❑ 98FlaShoR1-104
❑ 98FlaShoR2-104
❑ 98FlaShoR3-104
❑ 98Fle-444
❑ 98MetUni-147
❑ 98MetUniPMG-147
❑ 98Pac-435
❑ 98PacOnl-702
❑ 98PacOnlR-702
❑ 98PacOnlWC-702
❑ 98PacPar-93
❑ 98PacParC-93
❑ 98PacParG-93
❑ 98PacParHS-93
❑ 98PacParPB-93
❑ 98PacParR-93
❑ 98PacPlaB-435
❑ 98PacRedT-435
❑ 98PacSil-435
❑ 98PinPlu-106
❑ 98PinSna-TBDR6
❑ 98Sco-219
❑ 98ScoSS-PP106
❑ 98ScoSSAP-PP106
❑ 98SkyDugA-84
❑ 98SkyDugAIA-84
❑ 98SP Aut-184
❑ 98SPxFin-323
❑ 98SPxFinR-323
❑ 98SPxFinS-323
❑ 98StaCluFDI-107
❑ 98StaCluFDI-316
❑ 98StaCluI-107
❑ 98StaCluI-316
❑ 98StaCluOneK-107
❑ 98StaCluOneK-316
❑ 98StaCluPP-107
❑ 98StaCluPP-316
❑ 98Stu-88
❑ 98StuGPP-88
❑ 98StuSPP-88
❑ 98Top-344
❑ 98TopChr-344
❑ 98TopChrR-344
❑ 98TopDevR-344
❑ 98TopDia-344
❑ 98TopGal-6
❑ 98TopGalGP-6
❑ 98TopGalOPP-6
❑ 98TopGalPPI-6
❑ 98TopGalPPIA-6
❑ 98TopMiniC-344
❑ 98Ult-73
❑ 98Ult-463
❑ 98UltGolM-73
❑ 98UltGolM-463
❑ 98UltMas-73
❑ 98UltMas-463
❑ 98UltPlaM-73
❑ 98UltPlaM-463
❑ 98UppDec-727
❑ 99Fle-339
❑ 99FleSta9-339
❑ 99FleWarT-339
❑ 99MetUni-84
❑ 99MetUniGM-84
❑ 99MetUniPMG-84
❑ 99Pac-406
❑ 99PacCroC-270
❑ 99PacCroCPB-270
❑ 99PacPlaB-406
❑ 99PacRed-406
❑ 99SkyPre-210
❑ 99SkyPreR-210
❑ 99Top-371
❑ 99TopChr-371
❑ 99TopChrR-371
❑ 99TopMVPP-371
❑ 99Ult-93
❑ 99UltGolM-93
❑ 99UltMas-93
❑ 99UltPlaM-93
❑ 99UppDec-209
❑ 99UppDecEL1-209
❑ 99UppDecEL2-209
❑ 99Vic-389

Alvis, Andy
❑ 80BatTroT-20

Alvis, Dave
❑ 86WatIndP-2
❑ 87WatIndP-7

Alvis, Max (Roy Maxwell)
❑ 47Exh-3
❑ 63Top-228
❑ 64IndJayP-1
❑ 64Kah-1
❑ 64Top-545
❑ 64TopCoi-48
❑ 64TopGia-46
❑ 64TopSta-7
❑ 64TopStaU-4
❑ 64TopTatI-22
❑ 65Kah-2
❑ 65OPC-185
❑ 65Top-185
❑ 65TopEmbl-3
❑ 65TopTral-2
❑ 66IndTeal-1
❑ 66IndVolC-1
❑ 66Kah-3
❑ 66Top-415
❑ 66TopRubl-5
❑ 67CokCapA-24
❑ 67CokCapAAm-34
❑ 67CokCapl-2
❑ 67DexPre-12
❑ 67Kah-5
❑ 67Top-520
❑ 67TopGiaSU-16
❑ 68AtlOilPBCC-4
❑ 68Baz-9
❑ 68Kah-A3
❑ 68Kah-B6
❑ 68Top-340
❑ 68TopActS-6A
❑ 68TopPla-1
❑ 68TopPos-2
❑ 68TopVen-340
❑ 69Kah-B3
❑ 69MilBra-13
❑ 69MLBOffS-37
❑ 69MLBPin-1
❑ 69OPC-145
❑ 69Top-145
❑ 69TopFou-5
❑ 69TopSta-161
❑ 69TopTeaP-13
❑ 70BreMcD-1
❑ 70BreTeal-1
❑ 70MLBOffS-193
❑ 70OPC-85
❑ 70Top-85
❑ 71BreTeal-1
❑ 72MilBra-15
❑ 78TCM60I-83
❑ 92TexLon-2
❑ 94BreMilB-97

Alviso, Jerome
❑ 97PorRocG-2
❑ 98AshTouM-2

Alvord, Aaron
❑ 97LakTigB-5

Alvord, Billy (William C.)
❑ 87OldJudN-6

Alyea, Brant
❑ 88GasRanP-1007
❑ 88SouAtlLAGS-16
❑ 89St.LucMS-1
❑ 90TulDriP-1165

Alyea, Brant (Garrabrant R.)
❑ 66OPC-11
❑ 66Top-11
❑ 66TopVen-11
❑ 69OPC-48
❑ 69Top-48
❑ 69TopTeaP-23
❑ 70OPC-303
❑ 70Top-303
❑ 70TwiSupV-1
❑ 70TwiTeal-1
❑ 71MLBOffS-457
❑ 71OPC-449
❑ 71Top-449
❑ 72MilBra-16
❑ 72OPC-383
❑ 72Top-383

Alzualde, Daniel
❑ 95BoiHawTI-1
❑ 95LinVen-161

Amado, Jose
❑ 94VenLinU-241
❑ 95EveAqaTI-1
❑ 95LinVen-204
❑ 96-97LinVen-173
❑ 96MidLeaAB-3
❑ 96WisTimRB-5
❑ 98Bow-212
❑ 98BowChr-212
❑ 98BowChrGA-212
❑ 98BowChrGAR-212
❑ 98BowChrI-212
❑ 98BowChrIR-212
❑ 98BowChrR-212
❑ 98BowGolA-212
❑ 98BowInt-212
❑ 98CarLeaTPQ-9
❑ 98WilBluRC-1

Amador, Bruce
❑ 82MadMusF-30

Amador, Manuel
❑ 93MarPhiC-3
❑ 93MarPhiF-3481
❑ 95ClePhiF-220
❑ 98ReaPhiM-14

Amalfitano, Joey (John J.)
❑ 55Bow-269
❑ 55GiaGolS-25
❑ 55Top-144
❑ 60Top-356
❑ 61Top-87
❑ 62Col.45B-1
❑ 62Col45'HC-1
❑ 62Col45'JP-1
❑ 62Jel-144
❑ 62Pos-144
❑ 62PosCan-144
❑ 62SalPlaC-193
❑ 62ShiPlaC-193
❑ 62Top-456
❑ 62TopStal-123
❑ 63Fle-36
❑ 63Top-199
❑ 64Top-451
❑ 65Top-402
❑ 67CubProPS-1
❑ 73OPC-252
❑ 73Top-252A
❑ 73Top-252B
❑ 74OPC-78
❑ 74Top-78
❑ 76SSP-629
❑ 77PadFamF-1
❑ 77PadSchC-3
❑ 78TCM60I-96
❑ 81Don-522
❑ 81Top-676
❑ 83DodPol-NNO
❑ 83PhiTas-2
❑ 84DodPol-NNO
❑ 85DodCokP-1
❑ 86DodCokP-1
❑ 87DodMot-27
❑ 87DodPol-29
❑ 88DodMot-28
❑ 89AstCol4S-15
❑ 89DodMot-27
❑ 89DodPol-1
❑ 90DodMot-28
❑ 90DodPol-NNO
❑ 91DodMot-28
❑ 91DodPol-NNO
❑ 91DodSt.V-7
❑ 92DodMot-28
❑ 92DodPol-NNO
❑ 93DodMot-28
❑ 93DodPol-30
❑ 94DodMot-28
❑ 94DodPol-30
❑ 95DodMot-28
❑ 95DodPol-30
❑ 96DodMot-28
❑ 96DodPol-8
❑ 97DodMot-27
❑ 97DodPol-30
❑ 98DodMot-28
❑ 98DodPol-30

Aman, Kevan
❑ 77WauMetT-1

Amante, Tom
❑ 87St.PetCP-10
❑ 90SprCarDGB-4

Amaral, Rich
❑ 86PitCubP-1
❑ 87PitCubP-22
❑ 88PitCubP-1362
❑ 89BirBarB-14
❑ 89BirBarP-91
❑ 90CMC-640
❑ 90ProAAAF-171
❑ 90VanCanC-13
❑ 90VanCanP-493
❑ 91CalCanLD-51
❑ 91CalCanP-520
❑ 91LinDriAAA-51
❑ 92Bow-386
❑ 92CalCanF-3737
❑ 92DonRoo-3
❑ 92Pin-581
❑ 92SkyAAAF-291
❑ 92StaClu-689
❑ 92StaCluECN-689
❑ 92TopDeb91-3
❑ 92Ult-430
❑ 93Fla-266
❑ 93FleFinE-263
❑ 93JimDeaR-1
❑ 93Lea-516
❑ 93MariStaClu-4
❑ 93MarMot-27
❑ 93OPCPre-114
❑ 93PacJugC-1
❑ 93PacSpa-617
❑ 93Sco-249
❑ 93SelRoo-145T
❑ 93SP-127
❑ 93StaClu-264
❑ 93StaCluFDI-264
❑ 93StaCluMOP-264
❑ 93Top-431
❑ 93TopGol-431
❑ 93TopInaM-431
❑ 93TopInaR-431
❑ 93TopMic-431
❑ 93Ult-265
❑ 93UppDec-551
❑ 93UppDecGold-551
❑ 94Bow-389
❑ 94ColC-37
❑ 94ColChoGS-37
❑ 94ColChoSS-37
❑ 94Don-66
❑ 94Fin-16
❑ 94FinJum-16
❑ 94FinRef-16
❑ 94Fle-278
❑ 94FleExtB-158
❑ 94Lea-104
❑ 94MarMot-11
❑ 94OPC-149
❑ 94Pac-561
❑ 94PanSti-120
❑ 94Pin-386
❑ 94PinArtP-386
❑ 94PinMusC-386
❑ 94Sco-210
❑ 94ScoGolR-210
❑ 94Sel-114
❑ 94StaClu-44
❑ 94StaCluFDI-44
❑ 94StaCluGR-44
❑ 94StaCluMOP-44
❑ 94Stu-98
❑ 94Top-233
❑ 94TopGol-233
❑ 94TopSpa-233
❑ 94TriPla-121
❑ 94Ult-116
❑ 94UppDec-211
❑ 94UppDecED-211
❑ 94USPlaCR-8H
❑ 94USPlaCR-11D
❑ 95ColCho-288
❑ 95ColChoGS-288
❑ 95ColChoSS-288
❑ 95Don-67
❑ 95DonPreP-67
❑ 95Fle-258
❑ 95Lea-177
❑ 95MarMot-13
❑ 95MarPac-18
❑ 95Pac-388
❑ 95Sco-539
❑ 95ScoGolR-539
❑ 95ScoPlaTS-539
❑ 95TopTra-142T
❑ 96ColCho-724
❑ 96ColChoGS-724
❑ 96ColChoSS-724
❑ 96Don-385
❑ 96DonPreP-385
❑ 96Fle-225
❑ 96FleTif-225
❑ 96LeaSigEA-3
❑ 96MarMot-6
❑ 96Pac-414
❑ 96Ult-121
❑ 96UltGolM-121
❑ 97DonTea-150
❑ 97DonTeaSPE-150
❑ 97Fle-201
❑ 97FleTif-201
❑ 97MarSco-12
❑ 97MarScoPl-12
❑ 97MarScoPr-12
❑ 97Pac-180
❑ 97PacLigB-180
❑ 97PacSil-180
❑ 97Sco-221
❑ 97ScoArtPWB-221
❑ 97ScoPreS-221
❑ 97ScoShoS-221
❑ 97ScoShoSAP-221
❑ 97UppDecMP-P9
❑ 98ColCho-497
❑ 98MarSco-14
❑ 98MarScoP-14
❑ 98Pac-178
❑ 98PacOnl-677
❑ 98PacOnlR-677
❑ 98PacOnlWC-677
❑ 98PacPlaB-178
❑ 98PacRedT-178
❑ 98PacSil-178
❑ 98PinSna-SM9
❑ 98Sco-197
❑ 98Top-229
❑ 98TopChr-229
❑ 98TopChrR-229
❑ 98TopDevR-229
❑ 98TopDia-229
❑ 98TopMiniC-229
❑ 98UppDec-512

Amaro, Ruben
❑ 59Top-178
❑ 59TopVen-178
❑ 60PhiJayP-1
❑ 61Top-103
❑ 62Jel-194
❑ 62Pos-194
❑ 62PosCan-194
❑ 62SalPlaC-163
❑ 62ShiPlaC-163
❑ 62Top-284
❑ 62TopStal-163
❑ 63Fle-50
❑ 63Top-455
❑ 64PhiJayP-1
❑ 64PhiPhiB-2
❑ 64Top-432
❑ 65PhiJayP-1
❑ 65Top-419
❑ 66OPC-186
❑ 66Top-186
❑ 66TopVen-186
❑ 67CokCapYM-V2
❑ 67Top-358
❑ 67YanPhoS-89
❑ 68OPC-138
❑ 68Top-138
❑ 68TopVen-138
❑ 68YanPhoS-59
❑ 69Top-598
❑ 69TopTeaP-17
❑ 76OklCit8TI-20
❑ 78TCM60I-28
❑ 83CubThoAV-NNO
❑ 83PhiPosGPaM-4
❑ 84CubChiT-1
❑ 84CubSev-NNO
❑ 85CubSev-NNO
❑ 86CubGat-NNO
❑ 89BriTigS-29
❑ 90BriTigP-3175
❑ 92YanWIZ6-2
❑ 93BriTigC-27
❑ 93BriTigF-3666
❑ 94TopSpa-L2
❑ 95LinVen-71
❑ 97RocCub-1
❑ 98RocCubM-2
❑ 98RocCubTI-2

Amaro, Ruben Jr.
❑ 87SalAngP-17
❑ 88CalLeaACLC-32
❑ 88PalSprACLC-97
❑ 88PalSprAP-1434
❑ 89QuaCitAB-30
❑ 89QuaCitAGS-18
❑ 90MidAngGS-4
❑ 91Bow-208
❑ 91Cla3-T19
❑ 91EdmTraLD-152
❑ 91EdmTraP-1526
❑ 91LinDriAAA-152
❑ 91TriA AAGP-AAA12
❑ 92Bow-184
❑ 92Don-733
❑ 92DonRoo-4
❑ 92Fle-52
❑ 92Lea-339
❑ 92LeaBlaG-339
❑ 92OPC-269
❑ 92OPCPre-16
❑ 92PhiMed-2
❑ 92Pin-570
❑ 92ProFS7-30
❑ 92ScoRoo-98T
❑ 92StaClu-870
❑ 92Top-269
❑ 92TopDeb91-4
❑ 92TopGol-269
❑ 92TopGolW-269
❑ 92TopMic-269
❑ 92TopTra-5T
❑ 92TopTraG-5T
❑ 92Ult-540
❑ 92UppDec-752
❑ 93Don-488
❑ 93Fle-97
❑ 93LinVenB-182
❑ 93OPC-18
❑ 93PacSpa-229
❑ 93PhiMed-2
❑ 93Sco-341
❑ 93ScrRedBTI-2
❑ 93StaClu-385
❑ 93StaCluFDI-385
❑ 93StaCluMOP-385
❑ 93Top-43
❑ 93TopGol-43
❑ 93TopInaM-43
❑ 93TopInaR-43
❑ 93TopMic-43
❑ 93Ult-83
❑ 93USPlaCR-9C
❑ 94ChaKniF-905
❑ 94Fle-581
❑ 94Pac-467
❑ 94Sco-265
❑ 94ScoGolR-265
❑ 95LinVen-67

❑ 95Pac-116
❑ 96-97LinVen-99
❑ 96-97LinVen-125
❑ 97PacPriGotD-GD180
❑ 97PhiCopQ-1
❑ 97PhiTeal-37
❑ 98PacOnl-552
❑ 98PacOnlR-552
❑ 98PacOnlWC-552
❑ 98PhiTeal-2
Amaya, Ben
❑ 86ChaLooP-1
Amaya, Frank
❑ 59SeaPop-1
Ambler, Wayne H.
❑ 39PlaBal-117
❑ 41Gou-7
Ambos, Willie
❑ 88SalLakCTTI-13
❑ 89SanBerSB-9
❑ 89SanBerSCLC-66
❑ 91SalLakTP-3202
❑ 91SalLakTSP-25
❑ 94OgdRapSP-24
❑ 95OdgRapTI-2
Ambres, Chip
❑ 99199Fin-293
❑ 99Bow-173
❑ 99BowBes-161
❑ 99BowBesAR-161
❑ 99BowBesR-161
❑ 99BowChr-173
❑ 99BowChrG-173
❑ 99BowChrGR-173
❑ 99BowChrI-173
❑ 99BowChrIR-173
❑ 99BowChrR-173
❑ 99BowGol-173
❑ 99BowInt-173
❑ 99FinGolRef-293
❑ 99FinRef-293
❑ 99StaClu-150
❑ 99StaCluFDI-150
❑ 99StaCluOoaK-150
❑ 99StaCluPP-150
❑ 99TeaBesR-1
❑ 99TeaBesRFS-10
❑ 99TeaBesRG-1
❑ 99TeaBesRS-1
❑ 99Top-443
❑ 99TopChr-443
❑ 99TopChrR-443
❑ 99TopMVPP-443
Ambrose, John
❑ 94SigRooDP-36
❑ 94SigRooDPS-36
❑ 95Bow-26
❑ 97CarLeaTP-27
❑ 98BirBarG-1
Ambrose, Mark
❑ 87ElPasDP-11
❑ 88ElPasDB-15
❑ 89StoPorB-10
❑ 89StoPorCLC-159
❑ 89StoPorP-377
Ambrosina, Pete
❑ 94JohCitCC-2
❑ 94JohCitCF-3707
Ambrosio, Ciro
❑ 90St.CatBJP-3467
❑ 91MyrBeaHC-15
❑ 91MyrBeaHP-2949
Amelung, Ed (Edward)
❑ 81VerBeaDT-1
❑ 83AlbDukTc-19
❑ 84AlbDukCr-163
❑ 85AlbDukCr-158
❑ 85DomLeaS-23
❑ 86AlbDukP-1
❑ 86StaoftFT-20
❑ 87EdmTraP-2071
❑ 88SanDieS-1
❑ 88SanDieSAAG-1
❑ 89SanDieSAG-2
❑ 90DodTar-13
American Giants, Chicago
❑ 92NegLeaRLI-87
❑ 92NegLeaRLI-88
❑ 93NegLeaRL2-49
❑ 93NegLeaRL2-73
Amerson, Archie
❑ 77OrlTwiT-1
❑ 78SanJosMMC-21
❑ 79TolMudHT-4
Amerson, Gordon
❑ 94SigRooDP-73
❑ 94SigRooDPS-73
❑ 95IdaFalBTI-28
❑ 96CliLumKTI-3
❑ 97CliLumG-2
Ames, Doug
❑ 86MadMusP-1
❑ 86MadMusP-1
Ames, Ken
❑ 80AndBraT-10
Ames, Red (Leon Kessling)
❑ 06FanCraNL-1
❑ 06GiaUllAFS-1
❑ 09ColChiE-10A
❑ 09ColChiE-10B
❑ 09T206-5
❑ 09T206-6
❑ 09T206-7
❑ 10CouT21-69
❑ 10CouT21-70
❑ 10CouT21-256
❑ 10DomDisP-1
❑ 10E12AmeCDCE125-2
❑ 10NadE1-3
❑ 10RedCroT-1
❑ 10RedCroT-89
❑ 10RedCroT-168
❑ 10StaCarE-1
❑ 10SweCapPP-106
❑ 10W555-1
❑ 11HelSta-120
❑ 11S74Sil-79
❑ 11SpoLifCW-5
❑ 11SpoLifM-204
❑ 11T205-2
❑ 11TurRedT-77
❑ 12ColRedB-10A
❑ 12ColRedB-10B
❑ 12ColTinT-10A
❑ 12ColTinT-10B
❑ 12HasTriFT-48A
❑ 12HasTriFT-74A
❑ 12PhiCarE-2
❑ 14PieStaT-1
❑ 15SpoNewM-5
❑ 16SpoNewM-5
❑ 17ColE13-4
❑ 72ClaCar-27
❑ 74CapPub-84
❑ 91ConTSN-153
❑ 92ConTSN-334
Ames, Rex
❑ 09ObaT21-152
Ametller, Jesus
❑ 97PriWilC-6
❑ 98PriWilCQ-15
Amezcua, Adan
❑ 98KisCobQ-7
Amezeua, Adan
❑ 94AubAstF-3762
❑ 96KisCobB-4
Aminoff, Matt
❑ 93EugEmeC-2
❑ 93EugEmeF-3844
❑ 94BelMarC-2
❑ 94BelMarF-3223
❑ 95SalAvaTI-8
Amman, Matt
❑ 94WelPirC-2
❑ 94WelPirF-3507
Ammons, Cary
❑ 98SpoIndG-1
Amoros, Sandy (Edmundo I.)
❑ 47PM1StaP1-2
❑ 53ExhCan-43
❑ 55DodGolS-19
❑ 55Top-75
❑ 55TopDouH-53
❑ 56Dod-2
❑ 56Top-42
❑ 56TopPin-49
❑ 57Top-201
❑ 58MonRoyF-1
❑ 58Top-93
❑ 59O'KAleMR-1
❑ 60Top-531
❑ 74dod195T-3
❑ 88DodRinP1-2A
❑ 90DodTar-14
❑ 95TopArcBD-97
❑ 95TopArcBD-143
Amos, Chad
❑ 93ForLauRSC-2
❑ 93ForLauRSFP-1587
❑ 94SarRedSF-1940
Amos, Chris
❑ 94OgdRapF-3739
❑ 94OgdRapSP-1
Amos, Perry
❑ 91HunCubC-2
❑ 91HunCubP-3325
Amrhein, Mark
❑ 97WilCubB-1
❑ 98RocCubM-3
❑ 98RocCubTI-3
Anaya, Mike
❑ 89Sta-22
❑ 90KinMetB-15
❑ 90KinMetS-1
❑ 91PitMetC-22
❑ 91PitMetP-3414
Anders, Scott
❑ 86PeoChiP-1
Andersen, Larry E.
❑ 75OklCit8TI-7
❑ 78Top-703
❑ 79TacTugT-4
❑ 80Top-665
❑ 82Don-428
❑ 82Top-52
❑ 83Don-181
❑ 83Fle-470
❑ 83PorBeaT-3
❑ 83Top-234
❑ 84PhiTas-14
❑ 85Don-570
❑ 85Fle-244
❑ 85PhiTas-9
❑ 85PhiTas-13
❑ 85Top-428
❑ 85TopTif-428
❑ 86Don-355
❑ 86Fle-434
❑ 86PhiTas-47
❑ 86Top-183
❑ 86TopTif-183
❑ 87AstMot-21
❑ 87AstPol-1
❑ 87Don-640
❑ 87Fle-49
❑ 87FleGlo-49
❑ 87Top-503
❑ 87TopTif-503
❑ 88AstMot-21
❑ 88AstPol-2
❑ 88Don-332
❑ 88Fle-438
❑ 88FleGlo-438
❑ 88Sco-133A
❑ 88Sco-133B
❑ 88ScoGlo-133A
❑ 88ScoGlo-133B
❑ 88StaLinAst-2
❑ 88Top-342
❑ 88TopTif-342
❑ 89AstLenH-18
❑ 89AstMot-20
❑ 89AstSmo-2
❑ 89Bow-325
❑ 89BowTif-325
❑ 89Don-359
❑ 89Fle-349
❑ 89FleGlo-349
❑ 89Sco-523
❑ 89Top-24
❑ 89TopTif-24
❑ 89UppDec-404
❑ 90AstLenH-2
❑ 90AstMot-20
❑ 90Bow-67
❑ 90BowTif-67
❑ 90Don-359
❑ 90Fle-221
❑ 90FleCan-221
❑ 90Lea-386
❑ 90PublntS-86
❑ 90Sco-282
❑ 90UppDec-407
❑ 91Bow-660
❑ 91Don-665
❑ 91Fle-83
❑ 91FleUpd-120
❑ 91Lea-407
❑ 91OPC-761
❑ 91PadMag-17
❑ 91PadSmo-2
❑ 91Sco-848
❑ 91ScoRoo-71T
❑ 91StaClu-390
❑ 91Stu-241
❑ 91Top-761
❑ 91TopDesS-761
❑ 91TopMic-761
❑ 91TopTif-761
❑ 91UppDec-41
❑ 91UppDec-793
❑ 92Don-687
❑ 92Fle-597
❑ 92OPC-616
❑ 92PadCarJ-1
❑ 92PadMot-21
❑ 92PadPolD-29
❑ 92PadSmo-1
❑ 92Pin-399
❑ 92Sco-263
❑ 92StaClu-91
❑ 92Top-616
❑ 92TopGol-616
❑ 92TopGolW-616
❑ 92TopMic-616
❑ 92UppDec-587
❑ 93Fle-518
❑ 93FleFinE-108
❑ 93Lea-491
❑ 93PacSpa-573
❑ 93PhiMed-3
❑ 93PhiStaC-2
❑ 93Sco-445
❑ 94Don-71
❑ 94Fle-582
❑ 94Pac-468
❑ 94PhiMed-1
❑ 94PhiMel-1
❑ 94Sco-237
❑ 94ScoGolR-237
❑ 94StaCluT-223
❑ 94StaCluTFDI-223
❑ 95Pac-324
❑ 95ReaPhiELC-2
❑ 95ReaPhiTI-33
❑ 96DouAllB-4
❑ 96ReaPhiB-27
❑ 97ScrRedB-25
Andersen, Mark
❑ 95BreCouMF-236
Andersh, Kevin
❑ 86MacPirP-2
❑ 89AugPirP-512
Anderson, Alf (Alfred W.)
❑ 77TCMTheWY-44
Anderson, Allan
❑ 83WisRapTF-3
❑ 84VisOakT-20
❑ 85TolMudHT-1
❑ 86DonRoo-3
❑ 86TolMudHP-1
❑ 87Don-368
❑ 87Fle-533
❑ 87FleGlo-533
❑ 87PorBeaP-4
❑ 87Top-336
❑ 87TopTif-336
❑ 88FleUpd-41
❑ 88FleUpdG-41
❑ 88PorBeaC-1
❑ 88PorBeaP-654
❑ 88Top-101
❑ 88TopTif-101
❑ 89Bow-149
❑ 89BowTif-149
❑ 89ClaTraP-178
❑ 89Don-419
❑ 89DonBasB-270
❑ 89Fle-102
❑ 89FleGlo-102
❑ 89FleLeaL-1
❑ 89OPC-20
❑ 89PanSti-381
❑ 89Sco-394
❑ 89ScoYouSI-34
❑ 89Spo-220
❑ 89Top-672
❑ 89TopMinL-60
❑ 89TopTif-672
❑ 89UppDec-85
❑ 90Bow-409
❑ 90BowTif-409
❑ 90Don-64
❑ 90DonBesA-52
❑ 90Fle-366
❑ 90FleCan-366
❑ 90Lea-5
❑ 90OPC-71
❑ 90PanSti-117
❑ 90PublntS-320
❑ 90PublntS-593
❑ 90RedFolSB-1
❑ 90Sco-292
❑ 90Spo-59
❑ 90Top-71
❑ 90TopSti-296
❑ 90TopTif-71
❑ 90UppDec-219
❑ 91Bow-327
❑ 91DodPho-10
❑ 91Don-527
❑ 91Fle-603
❑ 91Lea-259
❑ 91OPC-223
❑ 91Sco-135
❑ 91StaClu-188
❑ 91StaCluP-1
❑ 91Top-223
❑ 91TopDesS-223
❑ 91TopMic-223
❑ 91TopTif-223
❑ 91UppDec-503
❑ 92Fle-196
❑ 92OPC-417
❑ 92Sco-731
❑ 92StaClu-204
❑ 92StaClu-767
❑ 92Top-417
❑ 92TopGol-417
❑ 92TopGolW-417
❑ 92TopMic-417
❑ 92UppDec-506
❑ 93OklCit8F-1617
❑ 94ChaRivC-27
❑ 94ChaRivF-2690
Anderson, Andy
❑ 88ElPasDB-16
Anderson, Andy Holm
❑ 86NegLeaF-41
Anderson, Andy PCL
❑ 29Zee-149
Anderson, Bernie
❑ 86LakTigP-2
❑ 87LakTigP-10
❑ 88GleFalTP-928
❑ 89LonTigP-1364
Anderson, Bill
❑ 97RanCucQG-1
❑ 98MobBayBTI-3
Anderson, Bill (William)
❑ 91PomBlaBPB-2
Anderson, Blake
❑ 93MisStaB-2
❑ 96PorRocB-4
❑ 97AshTou-2
❑ 98SalAvaC-1
Anderson, Bob (Robert Carl)
❑ 55DesMoiHB-1
❑ 58Top-209
❑ 59Top-447
❑ 60CubJayP-2
❑ 60Top-412
❑ 61CubJayP-2
❑ 61Top-283
❑ 61TopStal-2
❑ 62CubJayP-2
❑ 62Top-557
❑ 63Top-379
Anderson, Brady
❑ 2000TopPre-PP1
❑ 85ElmPioT-2
❑ 86FloStaLAP-4
❑ 86WinHavRSP-2
❑ 87NewBriRSP-7
❑ 88DonRoo-14
❑ 88DonTeaBRS-NEW
❑ 88OriPos-2
❑ 88ScoRoo-70T
❑ 88ScoRooG-70T
❑ 88TopTra-5T
❑ 88TopTraT-5T
❑ 89BalOriP-1
❑ 89Bow-18
❑ 89BowTif-18
❑ 89Don-519
❑ 89Fle-606
❑ 89FleGlo-606
❑ 89OPC-161
❑ 89OriFreB-9
❑ 89Sco-563
❑ 89ScoYouSI-26
❑ 89Top-757
❑ 89TopRoo-2
❑ 89TopTif-757
❑ 89TopUKM-1
❑ 89ToyRoo-2
❑ 89TVSpoM-90
❑ 89UppDec-408
❑ 90Bow-258
❑ 90BowTif-258
❑ 90Don-638
❑ 90Fle-172
❑ 90FleCan-172
❑ 90MLBBasB-119
❑ 90OPC-598
❑ 90PublntS-572
❑ 90Sco-33
❑ 90Top-598
❑ 90TopMag-90
❑ 90TopTif-598
❑ 90UppDec-290
❑ 91BalOriP-1
❑ 91Bow-100
❑ 91Don-668
❑ 91Fle-466
❑ 91OPC-97
❑ 91OriCro-9
❑ 91Sco-249
❑ 91StaClu-410
❑ 91Top-97A
❑ 91Top-97B
❑ 91TopDesS-97
❑ 91TopMic-97
❑ 91TopTif-97
❑ 91UppDec-349
❑ 92BalOriP-1
❑ 92BalOriP-2
❑ 92Fle-1
❑ 92Lea-343
❑ 92LeaBlaG-343
❑ 92OPC-268
❑ 92Pin-452
❑ 92Sco-365
❑ 92SpollIFK1-386
❑ 92SpollIFK1-641
❑ 92StaClu-303
❑ 92Stu-121
❑ 92Top-268
❑ 92TopGol-268
❑ 92TopGolW-268
❑ 92TopMic-268
❑ 92Ult-301
❑ 92UppDec-185
❑ 93BalOriP-1
❑ 93Bow-409
❑ 93ClaGam-4
❑ 93DiaMar-4
❑ 93Don-89
❑ 93DonDiaK-DK23
❑ 93DonSpiotG-SG17
❑ 93Fin-71
❑ 93FinRef-71
❑ 93Fla-149
❑ 93Fle-163
❑ 93FleFruotL-2
❑ 93FleTeaL-AL7
❑ 93FunPac-131
❑ 93Lea-177
❑ 93MilBonSS-19
❑ 93OPC-16
❑ 93PacSpa-14
❑ 93PanSti-76
❑ 93Pin-70
❑ 93Sco-140
❑ 93Sel-56
❑ 93SelSam-56
❑ 93SelStaL-21
❑ 93SelStaL-57
❑ 93SP-154
❑ 93StaClu-507
❑ 93StaCluFDI-507
❑ 93StaCluM-169
❑ 93StaCluMOP-507
❑ 93Stu-17
❑ 93Top-355
❑ 93TOPBLAG-24
❑ 93TopGol-355
❑ 93TopInaM-355
❑ 93TopInaR-355
❑ 93TopMic-355
❑ 93Toy-52
❑ 93TriPla-166
❑ 93Ult-138
❑ 93UppDec-44
❑ 93UppDec-111
❑ 93UppDecGold-44
❑ 93UppDecGold-111
❑ 93USPlaCA-11H
❑ 94BalOriP-1
❑ 94Bow-233

❑ 94ColC-405
❑ 94ColChoGS-405
❑ 94ColChoSS-405
❑ 94Don-592
❑ 94Fin-131
❑ 94FinRef-131
❑ 94Fla-251
❑ 94Fle-1
❑ 94FleExtB-1
❑ 94FUnPac-149
❑ 94Lea-66
❑ 94OPC-3
❑ 94OriPro-2
❑ 94OriUSPC-8S
❑ 94OriUSPC-13D
❑ 94Pac-25
❑ 94PanSti-17
❑ 94Pin-165
❑ 94PinArtP-165
❑ 94PinMusC-165
❑ 94ProMag-6
❑ 94Sco-335
❑ 94ScoGolR-335
❑ 94Sel-55
❑ 94StaClu-53
❑ 94StaCluFDI-53
❑ 94StaCluGR-53
❑ 94StaCluMOP-53
❑ 94StaCluT-290
❑ 94StaCluTFDI-290
❑ 94Top-145
❑ 94TopGol-145
❑ 94TopSpa-145
❑ 94TriPla-151
❑ 94Ult-301
❑ 94UppDec-63
❑ 94UppDecED-63
❑ 95BalOriP-2
❑ 95Baz-84
❑ 95Bow-357
❑ 95ColCho-334
❑ 95ColChoGS-334
❑ 95ColChoSE-154
❑ 95ColChoSEGS-154
❑ 95ColChoSESS-154
❑ 95ColChoSS-334
❑ 95Don-201
❑ 95DonPreP-201
❑ 95DonTopotO-1
❑ 95Emo-1
❑ 95Fin-44
❑ 95FinRef-44
❑ 95Fla-1
❑ 95Fle-1
❑ 95Lea-100
❑ 95LeaLim-16
❑ 95Pac-17
❑ 95Pin-188
❑ 95PinArtP-188
❑ 95PinMusC-188
❑ 95Sco-421
❑ 95ScoGolR-421
❑ 95ScoPlaTS-421
❑ 95Sel-227
❑ 95SelArtP-227
❑ 95SP-118
❑ 95SPCha-116
❑ 95SPChaDC-116
❑ 95Spo-76
❑ 95SpoArtP-76
❑ 95SPSil-118
❑ 95StaClu-268
❑ 95StaCluFDI-268
❑ 95StaCluMOP-268
❑ 95StaCluSTWS-268
❑ 95StaCluVR-134
❑ 95StaCluVRMO-134
❑ 95Stu-187
❑ 95Top-613
❑ 95TopCyb-381
❑ 95TopEmb-44
❑ 95TopEmbGI-44
❑ 95TopLeaL-LL18
❑ 95Ult-1
❑ 95UltGolM-1
❑ 95UppDec-132
❑ 95UppDecED-132
❑ 95UppDecEDG-132
❑ 95USPlaCMLA-6H
❑ 96BalOriP-3
❑ 96Baz-32
❑ 96Bow-110
❑ 96BowBes-25
❑ 96BowBesAR-25
❑ 96BowBesR-25
❑ 96BowFoi-110
❑ 96Cir-2
❑ 96CirRav-2
❑ 96ColCho-462
❑ 96ColChoGS-462
❑ 96ColChoSS-462
❑ 96Don-538
❑ 96DonPreP-538
❑ 96EmoXL-2
❑ 96Fin-B45
❑ 96Fin-S346
❑ 96FinRef-B45
❑ 96FinRef-S346
❑ 96Fla-2
❑ 96Fle-2
❑ 96FleTif-2
❑ 96Lea-36
❑ 96LeaLim-64
❑ 96LeaLimG-64
❑ 96LeaPre-78
❑ 96LeaPreP-78
❑ 96LeaPrePB-36
❑ 96LeaPrePG-36
❑ 96LeaPrePS-36
❑ 96LeaSig-50
❑ 96LeaSigPPG-50
❑ 96LeaSigPPP-50
❑ 96MetUni-2
❑ 96MetUniP-2
❑ 96MLBPin-2
❑ 96OriFle-2
❑ 96Pac-236
❑ 96PanSti-134
❑ 96Pin-74
❑ 96ProMagA-1
❑ 96ProSta-78
❑ 96Sco-331
❑ 96ScoDugC-B56
❑ 96ScoDugCAP-B56
❑ 96Sel-119
❑ 96SelArtP-119
❑ 96SelCerIP-25
❑ 96SP-36
❑ 96StaClu-316
❑ 96StaCluEPB-316
❑ 96StaCluEPG-316
❑ 96StaCluEPS-316
❑ 96StaCluMOP-316
❑ 96Sum-118
❑ 96SumAbo&B-118
❑ 96SumArtP-118
❑ 96SumFoi-118
❑ 96TeaOut-2
❑ 96Top-258
❑ 96TopChr-102
❑ 96TopChrR-102
❑ 96TopGal-11
❑ 96TopGalPPI-11
❑ 96TopLas-97
❑ 96Ult-2
❑ 96UltGolM-2
❑ 96UppDec-278
❑ 96UppDecDD-DD9
❑ 96UppDecDDG-DD9
❑ 96UppDecDDS-DD9
❑ 96UppDecVJLS-VJ14
❑ 96Zen-92
❑ 96ZenArtP-92
❑ 97BalOriP-2
❑ 97Bow-268
❑ 97BowBes-91
❑ 97BowBesA-91
❑ 97BowBesAAR-91
❑ 97BowBesAR-91
❑ 97BowBesR-91
❑ 97BowChr-86
❑ 97BowChrI-86
❑ 97BowChrIR-86
❑ 97BowChrR-86
❑ 97BowInt-268
❑ 97Cir-352
❑ 97CirRav-352
❑ 97ColCho-275
❑ 97ColChoAC-6
❑ 97ColChoCtG-4A
❑ 97ColChoCtG-4B
❑ 97ColChoCtG-4C
❑ 97ColChoCtGE-CG4
❑ 97ColChoCtGIW-CG4
❑ 97ColChoPP-PP2
❑ 97ColChoPPG-PP2
❑ 97ColChoPPJ-PP2
❑ 97ColChoS-16
❑ 97ColChoSR-1
❑ 97ColChoT-BO12
❑ 97ColChoTotT-T6
❑ 97Don-16
❑ 97Don-416
❑ 97DonEli-36
❑ 97DonEliGS-36
❑ 97DonGolPP-16
❑ 97DonGolPP-416
❑ 97DonLim-129
❑ 97DonLim-130
❑ 97DonLim-166
❑ 97DonLim-184
❑ 97DonLimE-129
❑ 97DonLimE-130
❑ 97DonLimE-166
❑ 97DonLimE-184
❑ 97DonLimENG-129
❑ 97DonLimENG-166
❑ 97DonLimFotG-56
❑ 97DonLonL-4
❑ 97DonPre-95
❑ 97DonPre-193
❑ 97DonPreCttC-95
❑ 97DonPreCttC-193
❑ 97DonSig-69
❑ 97DonSigPPP-69
❑ 97DonSilPP-16
❑ 97DonSilPP-416
❑ 97DonTea-31
❑ 97DonTeaSPE-31
❑ 97DonVxP1-21
❑ 97E-X2-5
❑ 97E-X2Cred-5
❑ 97E-X2EssCre-5
❑ 97Fin-154
❑ 97Fin-312
❑ 97FinEmb-154
❑ 97FinEmb-312
❑ 97FinEmbR-154
❑ 97FinEmbR-312
❑ 97FinRef-154
❑ 97FinRef-312
❑ 97FlaShoLC-9
❑ 97FlaShoLeg0-9
❑ 97FlaShoLeg1-9
❑ 97FlaShoM-A9
❑ 97FlaShoM-B9
❑ 97FlaShoM-C9
❑ 97FlaShoR0-9
❑ 97FlaShoR1-9
❑ 97FlaShoR2-9
❑ 97Fle-2
❑ 97FleLumC-1
❑ 97FleTif-2
❑ 97KinB-1
❑ 97Lea-88
❑ 97Lea-377
❑ 97LeaFraM-88
❑ 97LeaFraM-377
❑ 97LeaFraMDC-88
❑ 97LeaFraMDC-377
❑ 97LeaWarT-13
❑ 97MetUni-2
❑ 97NewPin-78
❑ 97NewPin-183
❑ 97NewPin-196
❑ 97NewPinAP-78
❑ 97NewPinAP-183
❑ 97NewPinAP-196
❑ 97NewPinIE-2
❑ 97NewPinMC-78
❑ 97NewPinMC-183
❑ 97NewPinMC-196
❑ 97NewPinPP-78
❑ 97NewPinPP-183
❑ 97NewPinPP-196
❑ 97NewPinPP-I2B
❑ 97OriSco-5
❑ 97OriScoPl-5
❑ 97OriScoPr-5
❑ 97OriSun-4
❑ 97OriSun-7
❑ 97Pac-18
❑ 97PacCar-2
❑ 97PacCarM-2
❑ 97PacFirD-2
❑ 97PacGolCD-2
❑ 97PacLigB-18
❑ 97PacPri-8
❑ 97PacPriGA-GA2
❑ 97PacPriLB-8
❑ 97PacPriP-8
❑ 97PacSil-18
❑ 97PacTriCD-1
❑ 97Pin-98
❑ 97PinArtP-PP98
❑ 97PinCer-27
❑ 97PinCerLI-8
❑ 97PinCerMBla-27
❑ 97PinCerMBlu-27
❑ 97PinCerMG-27
❑ 97PinCerMR-27
❑ 97PinCerR-27
❑ 97PinIns-20
❑ 97PinInsCE-20
❑ 97PinInsDE-20
❑ 97PinInsFS-9
❑ 97PinMusC-98
❑ 97PinPrePla-98
❑ 97PinTotCPB-27
❑ 97PinTotCPG-27
❑ 97PinTotCPR-27
❑ 97PinX-P-38
❑ 97PinX-PF&A-16
❑ 97PinX-PMoS-38
❑ 97PinX-PSfF-3
❑ 97PinX-PSfFU-3
❑ 97Sco-96
❑ 97ScoArtPWB-96
❑ 97ScoHigZ-12
❑ 97ScoPreS-96
❑ 97ScoShoS-96
❑ 97ScoShoSAP-96
❑ 97ScoSteS-14
❑ 97ScoTitT-11
❑ 97Sel-55
❑ 97SelArtP-55
❑ 97SelCom-55
❑ 97SelRegG-55
❑ 97SP-32
❑ 97SpoIll-126
❑ 97SpoIllEE-126
❑ 97SPSpeF-23
❑ 97SPSpxF-2
❑ 97SPSPxFA-2
❑ 97SPx-11
❑ 97SPxBro-11
❑ 97SPxGol-11
❑ 97SPxGraF-11
❑ 97SPxSil-11
❑ 97SPxSte-11
❑ 97StaClu-253
❑ 97StaClu-388
❑ 97StaCluFR-F6
❑ 97StaCluFW-F6
❑ 97StaCluI-I7
❑ 97StaCluI-I20
❑ 97StaCluMat-253
❑ 97StaCluMOP-253
❑ 97StaCluMOP-388
❑ 97StaCluMOP-I7
❑ 97StaCluMOP-I20
❑ 97StaCluMOP-FB6
❑ 97StaCluMOP-PG1
❑ 97StaCluPG-PG1
❑ 97StrAll-4
❑ 97Stu-30
❑ 97StuHarH-17
❑ 97StuPrePG-30
❑ 97StuPrePS-30
❑ 97Top-6
❑ 97TopChr-3
❑ 97TopChrDD-DD7
❑ 97TopChrDDR-DD7
❑ 97TopChrR-3
❑ 97TopChrSB-7
❑ 97TopChrSBR-7
❑ 97TopGal-57
❑ 97TopGalPPI-57
❑ 97TopHobM-HM14
❑ 97TopMem05-1
❑ 97TopSeaB-SB7
❑ 97TopSta-44
❑ 97TopSta97AS-AS14
❑ 97TopStaAM-44
❑ 97TopTeaT-TT9
❑ 97UD3-2
❑ 97Ult-2
❑ 97UltGolME-2
❑ 97UltPlaME-2
❑ 97UltTop3-30
❑ 97UltTop3GM-30
❑ 97UppDec-23
❑ 97UppDec-215
❑ 97UppDecLDC-LD2
❑ 97UppDecP-6
❑ 97UppDecPE-6
❑ 97UppDecRP-RP7
❑ 97Zen-39
❑ 98Bow-272
❑ 98BowBes-50
❑ 98BowBesAR-50
❑ 98BowBesR-50
❑ 98BowChr-272
❑ 98BowChrGA-272
❑ 98BowChrGAR-272
❑ 98BowChrI-272
❑ 98BowChrIR-272
❑ 98BowChrR-272
❑ 98BowChrR-10
❑ 98BowChrRR-10
❑ 98BowGolA-272
❑ 98BowInt-272
❑ 98CirThu-214
❑ 98CirThuRav-214
❑ 98CirThuSupRav-214
❑ 98ColCho-316
❑ 98Don-19
❑ 98DonCol-19
❑ 98DonColE-456
❑ 98DonColP-622
❑ 98DonColS-19
❑ 98DonCruG-10
❑ 98DonCruP-10
❑ 98DonCruR-10
❑ 98DonEli-56
❑ 98DonEliA-56
❑ 98DonEliS-56
❑ 98DonGolPP-19
❑ 98DonPre-72
❑ 98DonPreSeat-72
❑ 98DonPriCD-19
❑ 98DonPriCE-456
❑ 98DonPriCP-622
❑ 98DonProLO-19
❑ 98DonProLPI-10
❑ 98DonSigAC-6
❑ 98DonSigAM-6
❑ 98DonSilPP-19
❑ 98E-X2-27
❑ 98E-X2ECFut-27
❑ 98E-X2ECNow-27
❑ 98Fin-233
❑ 98FinNo--233
❑ 98FinNo-R-233
❑ 98FinRef-233
❑ 98FlaShoLeg0-58
❑ 98FlaShoLeg1-58
❑ 98FlaShoLeg2-58
❑ 98FlaShoLeg3-58
❑ 98FlaShoLegM-58
❑ 98FlaShoR0-58
❑ 98FlaShoR1-58
❑ 98FlaShoR2-58
❑ 98FlaShoR3-58
❑ 98Fle-191
❑ 98KinDis-1
❑ 98LeaRS-61
❑ 98LeaRSLHolo-61
❑ 98LeaRSLong-61
❑ 98LeaRTrue-61
❑ 98MetUni-58
❑ 98MetUni-210
❑ 98MetUniPMG-58
❑ 98MetUniPMG-210
❑ 98OriSco-4
❑ 98OriScoP-4
❑ 98Pac-18
❑ 98PacAur-10
❑ 98PacAurPF-26
❑ 98PacAurPFC-26
❑ 98PacAurPFPB-26
❑ 98PacAurPFR-26
❑ 98PacAurPFS-26
❑ 98PacInv-7
❑ 98PacInvGems-9
❑ 98PacInvPBlue-7
❑ 98PacInvSilv-7
❑ 98PacInvTeam-3
❑ 98PacOme-28
❑ 98PacOmeR-28
❑ 98PacOnl-80
❑ 98PacOnlR-80
❑ 98PacOnlWC-80
❑ 98PacPar-11
❑ 98PacParC-11
❑ 98PacParG-11
❑ 98PacParHS-11
❑ 98PacParI-7
❑ 98PacParPB-11
❑ 98PacParR-11
❑ 98PacPlaB-18
❑ 98PacRedT-18
❑ 98PacSil-18
❑ 98Pin-191
❑ 98Pin-198
❑ 98PinArtP-PP94
❑ 98PinIns-82
❑ 98PinInsCE-82
❑ 98PinInsDE-82
❑ 98PinInsSG-15AB
❑ 98PinInsSG-15CD
❑ 98PinInsSG-20AB
❑ 98PinInsSG-20CD
❑ 98PinInsSGS-15AB
❑ 98PinInsSGS-15CD
❑ 98PinInsSGS-20AB
❑ 98PinInsSGS-20CD
❑ 98PinMusC-PP94
❑ 98PinPer-73
❑ 98PinPerPP-73
❑ 98PinPerSftF-1
❑ 98PinPlu-3
❑ 98PinPowPJ-10
❑ 98PinPowPJS-10
❑ 98PinPreP-191
❑ 98PinPreP-198
❑ 98PinSna-BO18
❑ 98PreCon-14
❑ 98Sco-81
❑ 98ScoRT-94
❑ 98ScoRTSS-PP67
❑ 98ScoRTSSAP-PP67
❑ 98ScoRTSSAP1-PP67
❑ 98ScoSS-PP34
❑ 98ScoSSAP-PP34
❑ 98SP Aut-56
❑ 98SpoIll-5
❑ 98SpoIllEE-5
❑ 98SpoIllFE-5
❑ 98SpoIllTaN-57
❑ 98SpoIllTaNEE-57
❑ 98SpoIllWSF-45
❑ 98SpoIllWSFEE-45
❑ 98SpoIllWSFFE-45
❑ 98SPxFin-251
❑ 98SPxFinR-251
❑ 98SPxFinS-251
❑ 98StaCluFDI-188
❑ 98StaCluI-188
❑ 98StaCluOneK-188
❑ 98StaCluPP-188
❑ 98StaCluTIII-T5A
❑ 98StaCluTLme-T5A
❑ 98StaCluTLmo-T5A
❑ 98Stu-153
❑ 98StuGPP-153
❑ 98StuSPP-153
❑ 98Top-91
❑ 98TopChr-91
❑ 98TopChrF-FB10
❑ 98TopChrFR-FB10
❑ 98TopChrR-91
❑ 98TopDevR-91
❑ 98TopDia-91
❑ 98TopFla-FB10
❑ 98TopGal-86
❑ 98TopGalGP-86
❑ 98TopGalOPP-86
❑ 98TopGalPPI-86
❑ 98TopGalPPIA-86
❑ 98TopMiniC-91
❑ 98TopOpeD-45
❑ 98TopSta-105
❑ 98TopStaB-105
❑ 98TopStaG-105
❑ 98TopStaGR-105
❑ 98TopStaS-105
❑ 98TopTek-16
❑ 98TopTekD-16
❑ 98UD3-77
❑ 98UD3-167
❑ 98UD3-257
❑ 98UD3DieCut-77
❑ 98UD3DieCut-167
❑ 98UD3DieCut-257
❑ 98Ult-152
❑ 98UltGolM-152
❑ 98UltMas-152
❑ 98UltPlaM-152
❑ 98UppDec-139
❑ 98UppDec-307
❑ 98UppDecR-16
❑ 98Zen-44
❑ 98Zen5 xx7-26
❑ 98Zen5x7GoldImp-26
❑ 98Zen5x7Imp-26
❑ 98ZenZ-G-44
❑ 98ZenZ-S-44
❑ 99Fle-84
❑ 99FleSta9-84
❑ 99FleWarT-84
❑ 99KinDis-1
❑ 99MetUni-135
❑ 99MetUniGM-135
❑ 99MetUniPMG-135

❑ 99Pac-46
❑ 99PacInv-18
❑ 99PacInvOD-18
❑ 99PacInvPB-18
❑ 99PacOme-29
❑ 99PacOmeC-29
❑ 99PacOmeG-29
❑ 99PacOmePB-29
❑ 99PacPar-30
❑ 99PacParC-30
❑ 99PacParG-30
❑ 99PacParHoloGold-30
❑ 99PacParHS-30
❑ 99PacParOD-30
❑ 99PacParPB-30
❑ 99PacParRed-30
❑ 99PacPlaB-46
❑ 99PacRed-46
❑ 99Rev-18
❑ 99RevPremDate-18
❑ 99RevRet-18
❑ 99RevShaSS-18
❑ 99SkyMolM-55
❑ 99SkyMolMX-55
❑ 99SkyPre-120
❑ 99SkyPreR-120
❑ 99SkyThu-78
❑ 99SkyThuRant-78
❑ 99SkyThuRave-78
❑ 99SP Aut-13
❑ 99SPxPowE-PE6
❑ 99StaClu-127
❑ 99StaCluFDI-127
❑ 99StaCluOoaK-127
❑ 99StaCluPP-127
❑ 99ThuSkySupR-78
❑ 99Top-41
❑ 99TopChr-41
❑ 99TopChrR-41
❑ 99TopMVPP-41
❑ 99TopOpeD-24
❑ 99TopSta-143
❑ 99TopStaFoil-143
❑ 99UD Cho-59
❑ 99UD ChoPCR-59
❑ 99Ult-16
❑ 99UltGolM-16
❑ 99UltMas-16
❑ 99UltPlaM-16
❑ 99UppDec-43
❑ 99UppDecBD-13
❑ 99UppDecBDD-13
❑ 99UppDecBDQ-13
❑ 99UppDecBDT-13
❑ 99UppDecEL1-43
❑ 99UppDecEL2-43
❑ 99UppDecM-26
❑ 99UppDecMGS-26
❑ 99UppDecMHFS-26
❑ 99UppDecMP-26
❑ 99UppDecMSS-26
❑ 99UppDecR-14
❑ 99UppDecRG-14
❑ 99UppDecRP-14
❑ 99Vic-52

Anderson, Brian

❑ 94AngMot-22
❑ 94Bow-39
❑ 94Bow-369
❑ 94ColC-21
❑ 94ColChoGS-21
❑ 94ColChoSS-21
❑ 94Fin-304
❑ 94FinRef-304
❑ 94Fla-19
❑ 94FleExtB-29
❑ 94FleExtBRS-2
❑ 94FleMajLP-2
❑ 94FleUpd-15
❑ 94LeaGolR-17
❑ 94LeaL-13
❑ 94Pin-432
❑ 94PinArtP-432
❑ 94PinMusC-432
❑ 94Sco-468
❑ 94ScoGolR-468
❑ 94ScoRoo-RT125
❑ 94ScoRooGR-RT125
❑ 94ScoRooSR-SU17
❑ 94Sel-383
❑ 94SP-21
❑ 94SPDieC-21
❑ 94SpoRoo-94
❑ 94SpoRooAP-94
❑ 94SpoRooRS-TR10
❑ 94StaClu-571
❑ 94StaCluFDI-571
❑ 94StaCluGR-571
❑ 94StaCluMOP-571
❑ 94TopTra-10T
❑ 94Ult-321
❑ 94UppDec-1
❑ 94UppDecED-1
❑ 95AngCHP-12
❑ 95AngMot-22
❑ 95Bow-317
❑ 95ColCho-104
❑ 95ColChoGS-104
❑ 95ColChoSE-33
❑ 95ColChoSEGS-33
❑ 95ColChoSESS-33
❑ 95ColChoSS-104
❑ 95Don-72
❑ 95DonPreP-72
❑ 95Fin-12
❑ 95FinRef-12
❑ 95Fle-218
❑ 95Lea-118
❑ 95Pac-50
❑ 95Pin-181
❑ 95PinArtP-181
❑ 95PinMusC-181
❑ 95PinUps-US30
❑ 95Sco-361
❑ 95ScoGolR-361
❑ 95ScoPlaTS-361
❑ 95Sel-70
❑ 95SelArtP-70
❑ 95StaClu-432
❑ 95StaCluMOP-432
❑ 95StaCluSTWS-432
❑ 95StaCluVR-227
❑ 95StaCluVRMO-227
❑ 95Stu-55
❑ 95Sum-103
❑ 95SumNthD-103
❑ 95Top-542
❑ 95TopCyb-323
❑ 95TopD3-20
❑ 95TopEmb-11
❑ 95TopEmbGI-11
❑ 95Ult-18
❑ 95UltGolM-18
❑ 95UppDec-18
❑ 95UppDecED-18
❑ 95UppDecEDG-18
❑ 96BufBisB-2
❑ 96ColCho-76
❑ 96ColChoGS-76
❑ 96ColChoSS-76
❑ 96Don-194
❑ 96DonPreP-194
❑ 96Fle-41
❑ 96FleTif-41
❑ 96ProSta-4
❑ 96Sco-204
❑ 96Ult-24
❑ 96UltGolM-24
❑ 96UppDec-29
❑ 97BufBis-4
❑ 97MidAngOHP-1
❑ 98CirThu-126
❑ 98CirThuRav-126
❑ 98CirThuSupRav-126
❑ 98ColCho-287
❑ 98DiaBacP-2
❑ 98DiaMcD-2
❑ 98Fle-450
❑ 98IndSco-3
❑ 98IndScoP-3
❑ 98PacOme-9
❑ 98PacOmeR-9
❑ 98PacOnl-27
❑ 98PacOnlR-27
❑ 98PacOnlWC-27
❑ 98PacPar-118
❑ 98PacParC-118
❑ 98PacParG-118
❑ 98PacParHS-118
❑ 98PacParPB-118
❑ 98PacParR-118
❑ 98PinPlu-144
❑ 98PinSna-AD16
❑ 98Sco-33
❑ 98ScoRT-221
❑ 98ScoRTSS-PP123
❑ 98ScoRTSSAP-PP123
❑ 98ScoRTSSAP1-PP123
❑ 98SP Aut-41
❑ 98SpoIll-197
❑ 98SpoIllEE-197
❑ 98SpoIllFE-197
❑ 98SPxFin-246
❑ 98SPxFinR-246
❑ 98SPxFinS-246
❑ 98Top-496
❑ 98TopChr-496
❑ 98TopChrR-496
❑ 98TopDevR-496
❑ 98TopDia-496
❑ 98TopMiniC-496
❑ 98Ult-457
❑ 98UltGolM-457
❑ 98UltMas-457
❑ 98UltPlaM-457
❑ 98UppDec-297
❑ 98UppDec-634
❑ 99Fle-58
❑ 99FleSta9-58
❑ 99FleWarT-58
❑ 99Pac-13
❑ 99PacPlaB-13
❑ 99PacRed-13
❑ 99SkyThu-212
❑ 99SkyThuRant-212
❑ 99SkyThuRave-212
❑ 99StaClu-278
❑ 99StaCluFDI-278
❑ 99StaCluOoaK-278
❑ 99StaCluPP-278
❑ 99ThuSkySupR-212
❑ 99Top-409
❑ 99TopChr-409
❑ 99TopChrR-409
❑ 99TopMVPP-409
❑ 99Ult-79
❑ 99UltGolM-79
❑ 99UltMas-79
❑ 99UltPlaM-79
❑ 99UppDec-26
❑ 99UppDecEL1-26
❑ 99UppDecEL2-26

Anderson, Bud (Karl Adam)

❑ 79SpoIndT-20
❑ 79Top-712
❑ 81ChaLooT-25
❑ 82ChaChaT-1
❑ 82Ind-1
❑ 83Fle-408
❑ 83IndPos-1
❑ 83IndWhe-1
❑ 83Top-367
❑ 84Don-590
❑ 84Fle-533
❑ 84MaiGuiT-8
❑ 84Nes792-497
❑ 84Top-497
❑ 84TopTif-497
❑ 91PacSenL-4

Anderson, Chad

❑ 90MarPhiP-3205
❑ 91MarPhiC-27
❑ 91MarPhiP-3443
❑ 92BatCliCB-3
❑ 92BatCliF-3254
❑ 93SpaPhiC-4
❑ 93SpaPhiF-1048

Anderson, Charlie (Charles)

❑ 90MisStaB-3
❑ 91MisStaB-3
❑ 92JohCitCC-7
❑ 92JohCitCF-3121
❑ 92MisStaB-3
❑ 93SavCarC-3
❑ 93SavCarF-690
❑ 94MadHatC-2
❑ 94MadHatF-137
❑ 95ArkTraTI-1

Anderson, Chris

❑ 91MiaHurBB-2
❑ 92BoiHawC-15
❑ 92BoiHawF-3634
❑ 93PalSprAC-2
❑ 93PalSprAF-74
❑ 96HudValRB-7
❑ 97ChaRivDG-1

Anderson, Clark

❑ 93EveGiaC-2
❑ 93EveGiaF-3757

Anderson, Cliff

❑ 92YakBeaC-14
❑ 92YakBeaF-3455
❑ 94VerBeaDC-3
❑ 94VerBeaDF-78
❑ 95VerBeaDTI-1
❑ 96SanBerSB-5
❑ 97SanBerS-19
❑ 98SanAntMG-1

Anderson, Craig (Norman C.)

❑ 62Top-593
❑ 63Top-59
❑ 81TCM60I-295
❑ 82MetGal62-15
❑ 91MetWIZ-11
❑ 92GulCoaRSP-14

Anderson, Dallas

❑ 96AriBlaDB-6
❑ 97LetBlaDB-18

Anderson, Dave

❑ 76CedRapGT-2
❑ 77CedRapGT-3

Anderson, Dave (David C.)

❑ 82AlbDukTc-14
❑ 84DodPol-10
❑ 84Don-642
❑ 84Nes792-376
❑ 84Top-376
❑ 84TopTif-376
❑ 85DodCokP-2
❑ 85Don-275
❑ 85Fle-366
❑ 85Top-654
❑ 85TopTif-654
❑ 86BasStaB-2
❑ 86DodCokP-2
❑ 86DodPol-10
❑ 86DodUniOP-1
❑ 86Fle-123
❑ 86OPC-29
❑ 86Top-758
❑ 86TopTif-758
❑ 87DodMot-17
❑ 87DodPho-1
❑ 87DodPol-4
❑ 87Fle-436
❑ 87FleGlo-436
❑ 87Top-73
❑ 87TopTif-73
❑ 88DodMot-17
❑ 88DodPol-10
❑ 88Don-475
❑ 88Fle-508
❑ 88FleGlo-508
❑ 88OPC-203
❑ 88PanSti-313
❑ 88Sco-166
❑ 88ScoGlo-166
❑ 88StaLinD-1
❑ 88Top-456
❑ 88TopTif-456
❑ 89DodMot-17
❑ 89DodPol-7
❑ 89DodStaSV-1
❑ 89Don-434
❑ 89Fle-53
❑ 89FleGlo-53
❑ 89OPC-117
❑ 89Sco-478
❑ 89Top-117
❑ 89TopTif-117
❑ 89UppDec-89
❑ 90DodTar-15
❑ 90Don-486
❑ 90FleUpd-59
❑ 90GiaMot-19
❑ 90OPC-248
❑ 90PubIntS-1
❑ 90Sco-238
❑ 90Top-248
❑ 90TopTif-248
❑ 90UppDec-510
❑ 91Fle-252
❑ 91GiaMot-19
❑ 91GiaPacGaE-18
❑ 91OPC-572
❑ 91Sco-641
❑ 91Stu-251
❑ 91Top-572
❑ 91TopDesS-572
❑ 91TopMic-572
❑ 91TopTif-572
❑ 91Ult-314
❑ 92AlbDukS-1
❑ 92Bow-394
❑ 92DodSmo-5392
❑ 92Don-759
❑ 92Fle-625
❑ 92Sco-167
❑ 92ScoRoo-45T
❑ 92UppDec-290
❑ 94JamJamC-27
❑ 94JamJamF-3984
❑ 96LakTigB-1
❑ 97JacSun-25
❑ 98JacSunM-25

Anderson, David

❑ 92Min-1

Anderson, Doug

❑ 91BelMarCB-19
❑ 91BelMarP-3654

Anderson, Dwain C.

❑ 72OPC-268
❑ 72Top-268
❑ 73IndTeal-1
❑ 73OPC-241
❑ 73Top-241

Anderson, Ed

❑ 77CocAstT-1
❑ 88SalLakCTTI-NNO

Anderson, Eddie

❑ 90NebCor-1

Anderson, Edward

❑ 76DubPacT-2

Anderson, Eric

❑ 82AubAstT-6
❑ 94EliTwiC-3
❑ 94EliTwiF-3721
❑ 95SprSulTI-1
❑ 96WilBluRB-15
❑ 97WilBluR-25

Anderson, Ferrell J.

❑ 46DodTeal-1
❑ 52Par-17
❑ 90DodTar-16

Anderson, Franklin

❑ 96SouBenSHS-4
❑ 98AugGreM-24
❑ 98EriSeaWM-2

Anderson, Fred (John Fred)

❑ 16FleBreD-5
❑ 17ColE13-5

Anderson, Garret

❑ 90HigSchPLS-19
❑ 91Cla/Bes-258
❑ 91QuaCitAC-22
❑ 91QuaCitAP-2641
❑ 92Bow-298
❑ 92CalLeaACL-46
❑ 92ClaFS7-209
❑ 92MidAngOHP-2
❑ 92PalSprAC-12
❑ 92PalSprAF-851
❑ 92ProFS7-34
❑ 92UppDecML-292
❑ 92UppDecMLPotY-PY1
❑ 93ExcFS7-139
❑ 93VanCanF-2608
❑ 94Bow-479
❑ 94Cla-105
❑ 94ExcAllF-7
❑ 94ExcFS7-23
❑ 94LeaLimR-62
❑ 94SigRoo-5
❑ 94SigRooS-5
❑ 94Top-84
❑ 94TopGol-84
❑ 94TopSpa-84
❑ 94TriAAF-AAA22
❑ 94Ult-322
❑ 94UppDecML-157
❑ 94UppDecML-183
❑ 94VanCanF-1873
❑ 95AngMot-17
❑ 95Bow-250
❑ 95BowBes-B46
❑ 95BowBesR-B46
❑ 95BowGolF-250
❑ 95ColCho-23
❑ 95ColChoGS-23
❑ 95ColChoSE-12
❑ 95ColChoSEGS-12
❑ 95ColChoSESS-12
❑ 95ColChoSS-23
❑ 95Don-281
❑ 95DonPreP-281
❑ 95Fin-30
❑ 95FinRef-30
❑ 95Fla-233
❑ 95FleMajLP-1
❑ 95FleUpd-64
❑ 95Lea-332
❑ 95LeaGolR-2
❑ 95LeaLim-167
❑ 95Pac-51
❑ 95Pin-133
❑ 95Pin-289
❑ 95PinArtP-133
❑ 95PinArtP-289
❑ 95PinMusC-133
❑ 95PinMusC-289
❑ 95PinNewB-NB4
❑ 95Sco-310
❑ 95ScoGolR-310
❑ 95ScoPlaTS-310
❑ 95ScoRooDT-RDT8
❑ 95Sel-113
❑ 95Sel-239
❑ 95SelArtP-113
❑ 95SelArtP-239
❑ 95SelCanM-CM9
❑ 95SelCer-135
❑ 95SelCerMG-135
❑ 95SelCerPU-9
❑ 95SelCerPU9-9
❑ 95SPCha-6
❑ 95Spo-151
❑ 95SpoArtP-151
❑ 95StaClu-384
❑ 95StaCluMOP-384
❑ 95StaCluSTWS-384
❑ 95Stu-84
❑ 95Sum-122
❑ 95SumNthD-122
❑ 95Ult-265
❑ 95UltGolM-265
❑ 95UppDec-216
❑ 95UppDecED-216
❑ 95UppDecEDG-216
❑ 95UppDecPAW-H35
❑ 95UppDecPAWE-H35
❑ 95UppDecSEG-128
❑ 95Zen-140
❑ 96AngMot-15
❑ 96Baz-31
❑ 96Bow-94
❑ 96BowBes-40
❑ 96BowBesAR-40
❑ 96BowBesR-40
❑ 96BowFoi-94
❑ 96Cir-17
❑ 96CirRav-17
❑ 96ColCho-69
❑ 96ColChoGS-69
❑ 96ColChoSS-69
❑ 96Don-73
❑ 96DonPreP-73
❑ 96EmoRarB-1
❑ 96EmoXL-22
❑ 96Fin-S73
❑ 96FinRef-S73
❑ 96Fla-32
❑ 96Fle-42
❑ 96FleRooS-1
❑ 96FleTif-42
❑ 96FleTomL-1
❑ 96Lea-114
❑ 96LeaLim-40
❑ 96LeaLimG-40
❑ 96LeaPre-55
❑ 96LeaPreP-55
❑ 96LeaPrePB-114
❑ 96LeaPrePG-114
❑ 96LeaPrePS-114
❑ 96LeaPreSG-21
❑ 96LeaPreSte-21
❑ 96LeaSig-125
❑ 96LeaSigA-8
❑ 96LeaSigAG-8
❑ 96LeaSigAS-8
❑ 96LeaSigPPG-125
❑ 96LeaSigPPP-125
❑ 96MetUni-23
❑ 96MetUniP-23
❑ 96MetUniPP-1
❑ 96Pac-274
❑ 96PacPri-P83
❑ 96PacPriG-P83
❑ 96PanSti-207
❑ 96PanSti-244
❑ 96Pin-5
❑ 96Pin-200
❑ 96Pin-282
❑ 96PinAfi-134
❑ 96PinAfiAP-134
❑ 96PinAfiSP-31
❑ 96PinArtP-5
❑ 96PinArtP-182
❑ 96PinFoil-282
❑ 96PinProS-12
❑ 96PinSam-5
❑ 96PinSta-5

❑ 96PinSta-182
❑ 96PinTeaT-7
❑ 96Sco-35
❑ 96Sco-375
❑ 96ScoDiaA-27
❑ 96ScoDugC-A34
❑ 96ScoDugC-B100
❑ 96ScoDugCAP-A34
❑ 96ScoDugCAP-B100
❑ 96ScoFutF-10
❑ 96ScoRef-7
❑ 96Sel-38
❑ 96SelArtP-38
❑ 96SelCer-95
❑ 96SelCerAP-95
❑ 96SelCerCB-95
❑ 96SelCerCR-95
❑ 96SelCerMB-95
❑ 96SelCerMG-95
❑ 96SelCerMR-95
❑ 96SelTeaN-23
❑ 96SigRooOJMR-M4
❑ 96SP-44
❑ 96Spo-63
❑ 96SpoArtP-63
❑ 96SpoPro-20
❑ 96StaClu-3
❑ 96StaClu-227
❑ 96StaCluEPB-3
❑ 96StaCluEPG-3
❑ 96StaCluEPS-3
❑ 96StaCluMO-49
❑ 96StaCluMOP-3
❑ 96StaCluMOP-227
❑ 96Stu-23
❑ 96StuPrePB-23
❑ 96StuPrePG-23
❑ 96StuPrePS-23
❑ 96Sum-94
❑ 96SumAbo&B-94
❑ 96SumArtP-94
❑ 96SumBigB-16
❑ 96SumBigBM-16
❑ 96SumFoi-94
❑ 96Top-132
❑ 96TopChr-36
❑ 96TopChrR-36
❑ 96TopGal-95
❑ 96TopGalPPI-95
❑ 96TopLas-17
❑ 96TopMysF-M6
❑ 96TopMysFR-M6
❑ 96Ult-25
❑ 96UltFreF-1
❑ 96UltFreFGM-1
❑ 96UltGolM-25
❑ 96UltRisS-1
❑ 96UltRisSGM-1
❑ 96UppDec-31
❑ 96UppDecBCP-BC19
❑ 96UppDecVJLS-VJ16
❑ 96Zen-69
❑ 96ZenArtP-69
❑ 96ZenMoz-7
❑ 97AngMot-8
❑ 97Cir-115
❑ 97CirRav-115
❑ 97ColCho-252
❑ 97Don-141
❑ 97DonEli-55
❑ 97DonEliGS-55
❑ 97DonGolPP-141
❑ 97DonLim-180
❑ 97DonLimE-180
❑ 97DonPre-5
❑ 97DonPreCttC-5
❑ 97DonSig-55
❑ 97DonSigA-7
❑ 97DonSigAC-7
❑ 97DonSigAM-7
❑ 97DonSigPPP-55
❑ 97DonSilPP-141
❑ 97DonTea-4
❑ 97DonTeaSPE-4
❑ 97Fin-21
❑ 97FinRef-21
❑ 97FlaShoLC-170
❑ 97FlaShoLeg0-170
❑ 97FlaShoLeg1-170
❑ 97FlaShoM-A170
❑ 97FlaShoM-B170
❑ 97FlaShoM-C170
❑ 97FlaShoR0-170
❑ 97FlaShoR1-170
❑ 97FlaShoR2-170
❑ 97Fle-34
❑ 97FleTif-34
❑ 97Lea-215
❑ 97LeaFraM-215
❑ 97LeaFraMDC-215
❑ 97MetUni-36
❑ 97NewPin-31
❑ 97NewPinAP-31
❑ 97NewPinMC-31
❑ 97NewPinPP-31
❑ 97Pac-1
❑ 97PacLigB-1
❑ 97PacSil-1
❑ 97Pin-2
❑ 97PinArtP-PP2
❑ 97PinIns-88
❑ 97PinInsCE-88
❑ 97PinInsDE-88
❑ 97PinMusC-2
❑ 97PinPrePla-2
❑ 97PinX-P-26
❑ 97PinX-PMoS-26
❑ 97Sco-30
❑ 97ScoArtPWB-30
❑ 97ScoPreS-30
❑ 97ScoShoS-30
❑ 97ScoShoSAP-30
❑ 97Sel-68
❑ 97SelArtP-68
❑ 97SelCom-68
❑ 97SelRegG-68
❑ 97SP-18
❑ 97StaClu-61
❑ 97StaCluMOP-61
❑ 97Stu-82
❑ 97StuPrePG-82
❑ 97StuPrePS-82
❑ 97Top-24
❑ 97TopChr-10
❑ 97TopChrR-10
❑ 97TopGal-157
❑ 97TopGalPPI-157
❑ 97Ult-22
❑ 97UltGolME-22
❑ 97UltPlaME-22
❑ 97UppDec-292
❑ 98AngSco-15
❑ 98AngScoP-15
❑ 98CirThu-149
❑ 98CirThuRav-149
❑ 98CirThuSupRav-149
❑ 98ColCho-28
❑ 98CroRoy-1
❑ 98Don-41
❑ 98DonCol-41
❑ 98DonColE-445
❑ 98DonColL-231
❑ 98DonColP-619
❑ 98DonColS-41
❑ 98DonCruG-2
❑ 98DonCruP-2
❑ 98DonCruR-2
❑ 98DonEli-45
❑ 98DonEliA-45
❑ 98DonEliS-45
❑ 98DonGolPP-41
❑ 98DonPre-69
❑ 98DonPreSeat-69
❑ 98DonPriCD-41
❑ 98DonPriCE-445
❑ 98DonPriCL-231
❑ 98DonPriCP-619
❑ 98DonSig-60
❑ 98DonSigP-60
❑ 98DonSilPP-41
❑ 98Fin-200
❑ 98FinNo--200
❑ 98FinNo-R-200
❑ 98FinRef-200
❑ 98FlaShoLeg0-83
❑ 98FlaShoLeg1-83
❑ 98FlaShoLeg2-83
❑ 98FlaShoLeg3-83
❑ 98FlaShoLegM-83
❑ 98FlaShoR0-83
❑ 98FlaShoR1-83
❑ 98FlaShoR2-83
❑ 98FlaShoR3-83
❑ 98Fle-174
❑ 98Lea-31
❑ 98LeaFraDA-31
❑ 98LeaFraF-31
❑ 98LeaFraM-31
❑ 98LeaFraM-31
❑ 98LeaFraMDC-31
❑ 98LeaFraMDC-31
❑ 98LeaFraMZ2-31
❑ 98LeaRS-68
❑ 98LeaRSLHolo-68
❑ 98LeaRSLong-68
❑ 98LeaRTrue-68
❑ 98MetUni-112
❑ 98MetUniPMG-112
❑ 98Pac-2
❑ 98PacAur-1
❑ 98PacInv-1
❑ 98PacInvPBlue-1
❑ 98PacInvSilv-1
❑ 98PacInvTeam-1
❑ 98PacOme-1
❑ 98PacOmeR-1
❑ 98PacOnl-1
❑ 98PacOnlR-1
❑ 98PacOnlWC-1
❑ 98PacPar-1
❑ 98PacParC-1
❑ 98PacParG-1
❑ 98PacParHS-1
❑ 98PacParPB-1
❑ 98PacParR-1
❑ 98PacPlaB-2
❑ 98PacRedT-2
❑ 98PacSil-2
❑ 98PinIns-68
❑ 98PinInsCE-68
❑ 98PinInsDE-68
❑ 98PinInsSG-16AB
❑ 98PinInsSG-16CD
❑ 98PinInsSGS-16AB
❑ 98PinInsSGS-16CD
❑ 98PinPer-70
❑ 98PinPerPP-70
❑ 98PinPlu-31
❑ 98PinSna-AA3
❑ 98PinSna-AA9
❑ 98Revo-1
❑ 98RevoSS-1
❑ 98Sco-218
❑ 98ScoRT-162
❑ 98ScoRTSS-PP92
❑ 98ScoRTSSAP-PP92
❑ 98ScoRTSSAP1-PP92
❑ 98ScoSS-PP105
❑ 98ScoSSAP-PP105
❑ 98SpoIll-6
❑ 98SpoIllEE-6
❑ 98SpoIllFE-6
❑ 98StaCluFDI-124
❑ 98StaCluI-124
❑ 98StaCluOneK-124
❑ 98StaCluPP-124
❑ 98Stu-81
❑ 98StuGPP-81
❑ 98StuSPP-81
❑ 98Top-31
❑ 98TopChr-31
❑ 98TopChrR-31
❑ 98TopDevR-31
❑ 98TopDia-31
❑ 98TopGal-21
❑ 98TopGalGP-21
❑ 98TopGalOPP-21
❑ 98TopGalPPI-21
❑ 98TopGalPPIA-21
❑ 98TopMiniC-31
❑ 98TopOpeD-20
❑ 98Ult-193
❑ 98UltGolM-193
❑ 98UltMas-193
❑ 98UltPlaM-193
❑ 98UppDec-25
❑ 98UppDecSF-15
❑ 99199Fin-193
❑ 99Bow-224
❑ 99BowGol-224
❑ 99BowInt-224
❑ 99FinGolRef-193
❑ 99FinRef-193
❑ 99Fle-66
❑ 99FleSta9-66
❑ 99FleWarT-66
❑ 99MetUni-154
❑ 99MetUniGM-154
❑ 99MetUniPMG-154
❑ 99Pac-1
❑ 99PacAur-1
❑ 99PacAurOD-1
❑ 99PacCroC-1
❑ 99PacCroCPB-1
❑ 99PacOme-1
❑ 99PacOmeC-1
❑ 99PacOmeDD-3
❑ 99PacOmeG-1
❑ 99PacOmePB-1
❑ 99PacPar-1
❑ 99PacParC-1
❑ 99PacParG-1
❑ 99PacParHoloGold-1
❑ 99PacParHS-1
❑ 99PacParOD-1
❑ 99PacParPB-1
❑ 99PacParRed-1
❑ 99PacPlaB-1
❑ 99PacPri-1
❑ 99PacPriHB-1
❑ 99PacPriHG-1
❑ 99PacPriHM-1
❑ 99PacPriHP-1
❑ 99PacPriRed-1
❑ 99PacPriS-52
❑ 99PacPriS206-52
❑ 99PacPriS206R-52
❑ 99PacRed-1
❑ 99SkyMolM-58
❑ 99SkyMolMX-58
❑ 99SkyThu-2
❑ 99SkyThuRant-2
❑ 99SkyThuRave-2
❑ 99StaClu-185
❑ 99StaCluFDI-185
❑ 99StaCluOoaK-185
❑ 99StaCluPP-185
❑ 99ThuSkySupR-2
❑ 99Top-58
❑ 99TopChr-58
❑ 99TopChrR-58
❑ 99TopMVPP-58
❑ 99TopOpeD-32
❑ 99TopSta-118
❑ 99TopStaFoil-118
❑ 99UD Cho-49
❑ 99UD ChoPCR-49
❑ 99Ult-140
❑ 99UltGolM-140
❑ 99UltMas-140
❑ 99UltPlaM-140
❑ 99UppDec-296
❑ 99UppDecEL1-296
❑ 99UppDecEL2-296
❑ 99Vic-9

Anderson, Glen
❑ 86BenPhiC-141

Anderson, Greg
❑ 76BurBeeT-1

Anderson, Harry W.
❑ 47PM1StaP1-3
❑ 57Top-404
❑ 58PhiJayP-1
❑ 58PhiTeal-1
❑ 58Top-171
❑ 59Top-85
❑ 59TopVen-85
❑ 60PhiJayP-2
❑ 60Top-285
❑ 61Top-76
❑ 80Red196T-21

Anderson, Jason A
❑ 97BoiHawG-1
❑ 97SouOreTB-14
❑ 98ButCopKG-2
❑ 98ModA'sG-2

Anderson, Jeff
❑ 86PenWhiSP-3

Anderson, Jesse
❑ 81AppFoxT-1
❑ 82AppFoxFr-10
❑ 83AlbA'sT-1

Anderson, Jim (James Lea)
❑ 78SalLakCGC-2
❑ 79Top-703
❑ 80MarPos-2
❑ 80Top-183
❑ 80VenLeaS-212
❑ 81Don-165
❑ 81Fle-598
❑ 81MarPol-4
❑ 81MarPos-3
❑ 81Top-613
❑ 82Don-181
❑ 82Don-352A
❑ 82Fle-503
❑ 82Top-497
❑ 83RanAffF-46
❑ 84Nes792-353
❑ 84RanJarP-14
❑ 84Top-353
❑ 84TopTif-353
❑ 85OklCit8T-6
❑ 87CliGiaP-5
❑ 88CliGiaP-703
❑ 89ShrCapP-1835
❑ 93RanKee-52

Anderson, Jimmy
❑ 96CarLeaA1B-4
❑ 96CarLeaA2B-4
❑ 96LynHilB-1
❑ 97Bow-181
❑ 97BowBes-139
❑ 97BowBesAR-139
❑ 97BowBesR-139
❑ 97BowInt-181
❑ 97CalCanB-5
❑ 97CarMudC-1
❑ 97SouLeaTP-4
❑ 97Top-492
❑ 98Bow-369
❑ 98BowChr-369
❑ 98BowChrGA-369
❑ 98BowChrGAR-369
❑ 98BowChrI-369
❑ 98BowChrIR-369
❑ 98BowChrR-369
❑ 98BowGolA-369
❑ 98BowInt-369
❑ 98NasSouTI-2
❑ 98NasSouTISS-2

Anderson, John
❑ 84ButCopKT-2
❑ 88MarPhiS-1
❑ 94AubAstC-2
❑ 94AubAstF-3750

Anderson, John C.
❑ 62Top-266
❑ 81TCM60I-301
❑ 91OriCro-10

Anderson, John Joseph
❑ 03BreE10-1
❑ 03BreE10-2
❑ 08RosComP-12
❑ 09RamT20-2
❑ 09T206-392
❑ 90DodTar-17

Anderson, Jon
❑ 91QuaCitAP-2629

Anderson, Kelly
❑ 79CedRapGT-24

Anderson, Ken
❑ 87SpoCubG-3

Anderson, Kent
❑ 86PalSprAP-1
❑ 88EdmTraC-17
❑ 88EdmTraP-574
❑ 89EdmTraC-17
❑ 89TopTra-3T
❑ 89TopTraT-3T
❑ 90Don-490
❑ 90Hot50RS-3
❑ 90OPC-16
❑ 90PubIntS-363
❑ 90Sco-412
❑ 90Sco100RS-86
❑ 90Top-16
❑ 90TopDeb89-4
❑ 90TopTif-16
❑ 90UppDec-691
❑ 91Bow-194
❑ 91Don-525
❑ 91EdmTraLD-153
❑ 91EdmTraP-1520
❑ 91Fle-306
❑ 91LinDriAAA-153
❑ 91OPC-667
❑ 91Sco-224A
❑ 91Sco-224B
❑ 91StaClu-241
❑ 91Top-667
❑ 91TopDesS-667
❑ 91TopMic-667
❑ 91TopTif-667
❑ 92CalCanF-3738
❑ 93IowCubF-2138

Anderson, Larry (Lawrence D.)
❑ 76OPC-593
❑ 76SSP-248
❑ 76SSP-249
❑ 76Top-593
❑ 77Top-487
❑ 80ChaO'sP-1
❑ 80ChaO'sW-1
❑ 80PorBeaT-23
❑ 81MarPos-4
❑ 82MarPos-3
❑ 94BreMilB-98

Anderson, Marlon
❑ 95BatCliTI-1
❑ 96BesAutS-5
❑ 96Bow-120
❑ 96BowFoi-120
❑ 96Exc-194
❑ 97Bes-84
❑ 97BesAutSBPP-43
❑ 97Bow-302
❑ 97BowBes-174
❑ 97BowBesAR-174
❑ 97BowBesR-174
❑ 97BowChr-210
❑ 97BowChrI-210
❑ 97BowChrIR-210
❑ 97BowChrR-210
❑ 97BowInt-302
❑ 97EasLeaTPB-25
❑ 97ReaPhi-5
❑ 98AriFalLTP-13
❑ 98Bow-436
❑ 98BowChr-436
❑ 98BowChrGA-436
❑ 98BowChrGAR-436
❑ 98BowChrI-436
❑ 98BowChrIR-436
❑ 98BowChrR-436
❑ 98BowGolA-436
❑ 98BowInt-436
❑ 98FleUpd-U41
❑ 98ScrRedBQ-1
❑ 98SP MinPE-95
❑ 98SP MinSTHPE-H22
❑ 98SPMin-95
❑ 98SPMinSTH-H22
❑ 98UppDec-572
❑ 99199Fin-136
❑ 99Bow-206
❑ 99BowBes-104
❑ 99BowBesAR-104
❑ 99BowBesR-104
❑ 99BowChr-206
❑ 99BowChrG-206
❑ 99BowChrGR-206
❑ 99BowChrI-206
❑ 99BowChrIR-206
❑ 99BowChrR-206
❑ 99BowChrSC-SC14
❑ 99BowChrSCR-SC14
❑ 99BowGol-206
❑ 99BowInt-206
❑ 99BowScoC-SC14
❑ 99CroRoyB-105
❑ 99CroRoyL-105
❑ 99CroRoyOD-105
❑ 99DumSet-145
❑ 99E-X Cen-118
❑ 99E-X CenECFut-118
❑ 99E-X CenECNow-118
❑ 99E-X CenEQ-12
❑ 99FinGolRef-136
❑ 99FinRef-136
❑ 99Fle-105
❑ 99FleBri-150
❑ 99FleBri2G-150
❑ 99FleBriBlu-150
❑ 99FleBriGol-150
❑ 99FleMys-145
❑ 99FleMysM-145
❑ 99FleSta9-105
❑ 99FleWarT-105
❑ 99PacCroC-210
❑ 99PacCroCPB-210
❑ 99PacInv-110
❑ 99PacInvOD-110
❑ 99PacInvPB-110
❑ 99PacOme-184
❑ 99PacOmeC-184
❑ 99PacOmeG-184
❑ 99PacOmePB-184
❑ 99SkyPre-266
❑ 99SkyPre-266
❑ 99SkyPreDD-5
❑ 99SkyPreR-266
❑ 99SkyPreR-266
❑ 99SkyThu-202
❑ 99SkyThuRant-202
❑ 99SkyThuRave-202
❑ 99SP SigAuto-MA
❑ 99SP SigAutoG-MA
❑ 99SpoIll-61
❑ 99SpoIllOTW-2
❑ 99SPSig-77
❑ 99StaClu-346
❑ 99StaCluFDI-346

❑ 99StaCluOoaK-346
❑ 99StaCluPP-346
❑ 99ThuSkySupR-202
❑ 99Top-427
❑ 99TopAll-AM22
❑ 99TopChr-427
❑ 99TopChrA-AE22
❑ 99TopChrAR-AE22
❑ 99TopChrR-427
❑ 99TopSta-97
❑ 99TopSta1Foil-97
❑ 99TopStaFoil-97
❑ 99TopStaOS-97
❑ 99UppDec-453
❑ 99UppDecE-69
❑ 99UppDecEFXG-69
❑ 99UppDecEL1-453
❑ 99UppDecEL2-453
❑ 99Vic-292

Anderson, Matt

❑ 98AriFalLTP-20
❑ 98Bes-51
❑ 98BesBet-1
❑ 98BesCor-1
❑ 98BesNumOP-2
❑ 98Bow-440
❑ 98BowBes-196
❑ 98BowBesAR-196
❑ 98BowBesR-196
❑ 98BowChr-440
❑ 98BowChrGA-440
❑ 98BowChrGAR-440
❑ 98BowChrI-440
❑ 98BowChrIR-440
❑ 98BowChrR-440
❑ 98BowGolA-440
❑ 98BowInt-440
❑ 98DonSig-98
❑ 98DonSigP-98
❑ 98FleUpd-U94
❑ 98LakTigM-26
❑ 98LeaRS-320
❑ 98LeaRSLHolo-320
❑ 98LeaRSLong-320
❑ 98LeaRTrue-320
❑ 98UppDecR-113
❑ 98UppDecRNF-NF13
❑ 99Fle-321
❑ 99FleBri-58
❑ 99FleBri2G-58
❑ 99FleBriBlu-58
❑ 99FleBriGol-58
❑ 99FleRooFla-1
❑ 99FleSta9-321
❑ 99FleWarT-321
❑ 99MetUni-254
❑ 99MetUniGM-254
❑ 99MetUniN-12
❑ 99MetUniPMG-254
❑ 99SkyPre-7
❑ 99SkyPreR-7
❑ 99SkyThu-297
❑ 99SkyThuRant-297
❑ 99SkyThuRave-297
❑ 99SP Aut-99
❑ 99SP AutC-MA
❑ 99SP AutCG-MA
❑ 99SPSig-128
❑ 99SPx-91
❑ 99SPxFinR-91
❑ 99SPxFinS-91
❑ 99StaClu-84
❑ 99StaCluFDI-84
❑ 99StaCluOoaK-84
❑ 99StaCluPP-84
❑ 99ThuSkySupR-297
❑ 99Top-21
❑ 99TopChr-21
❑ 99TopChrR-21
❑ 99TopMVPP-21
❑ 99UD Cho-3
❑ 99UD ChoPCR-3
❑ 99Ult-227
❑ 99UltGolM-227
❑ 99UltMas-227
❑ 99UltPlaM-227
❑ 99UltWorP-5
❑ 99UppDec-3
❑ 99UppDecBD-99
❑ 99UppDecBDD-99
❑ 99UppDecBDQ-99
❑ 99UppDecBDT-99
❑ 99UppDecE-93
❑ 99UppDecEFXG-93
❑ 99UppDecEL1-3
❑ 99UppDecEL2-3
❑ 99UppDecM-77
❑ 99UppDecMGS-77
❑ 99UppDecMHFS-77
❑ 99UppDecMP-77
❑ 99UppDecMP-MA
❑ 99UppDecMSS-77
❑ 99Vic-151

Anderson, Matthew

❑ 88OklSoo-9
❑ 89BluOriS-26
❑ 90CMC-872
❑ 90WauTimB-6
❑ 90WauTimP-2119
❑ 90WauTimS-1
❑ 91KanCouCC-3
❑ 91KanCouCP-2650
❑ 91KanCouCTI-1
❑ 92ClaFS7-107
❑ 92FreKeyC-19
❑ 92FreKeyF-1797
❑ 92ProFS7-11
❑ 92UppDecML-89
❑ 94AlbPolC-2
❑ 94AlbPolF-2227
❑ 94FreKeyC-2
❑ 94OriPro-3

Anderson, Mike

❑ 85LitFalMT-1
❑ 86LitFalMP-1
❑ 87ColMetP-20
❑ 87PalSprP-24
❑ 88PalSprACLC-98
❑ 88PalSprAP-1438
❑ 89GreHorP-428
❑ 89RenSilSCLC-239
❑ 90CedRapRB-20
❑ 90CedRapRP-2318
❑ 91ChaLooLD-152
❑ 91ChaLooP-1950
❑ 91LinDriAA-152
❑ 91OriCro-11
❑ 91WavRedF-4
❑ 92ChaLooF-3810
❑ 92ChaLooS-177
❑ 93ChaLooF-2352
❑ 93ChaRaiC-2
❑ 93ChaRaiF-1900
❑ 94ChaRanF-2489
❑ 94IowCubF-1269
❑ 95IowCubTI-3

Anderson, Mike (Michael A.)

❑ 72OPC-14
❑ 72Top-14
❑ 73OPC-147
❑ 73PhiTeal-1
❑ 73Top-147
❑ 74OPC-619
❑ 74PhiJohP-22
❑ 74Top-619
❑ 75OPC-118
❑ 75PhiPhiP-2
❑ 75Top-118
❑ 75TopMin-118
❑ 76OPC-527
❑ 76SSP-469
❑ 76St.LouCP-1
❑ 76Top-527
❑ 76TopTra-527T
❑ 77Car5-1
❑ 77CarTeal-1
❑ 77Top-72
❑ 78Top-714
❑ 79Top-102
❑ 80BurBeeT-18
❑ 80Top-317
❑ 81PorBeaT-5
❑ 82VanCanT-22
❑ 84VanCanC-46
❑ 85LouRedR-29
❑ 98TenKry-5

Anderson, Nub (Steve)

❑ 76LauIndC-14
❑ 76LauIndC-25

Anderson, Paul

❑ 91SprCarC-1
❑ 91SprCarP-731
❑ 92ArkTraF-1120
❑ 93ArkTraF-2803
❑ 94LouRedF-2970
❑ 95ArkTraTI-2
❑ 96HelBreTI-33
❑ 97StoPor-29
❑ 98StoPorG-3

Anderson, Rick (Richard A.)

❑ 79ColCliT-21
❑ 79JacMetT-16
❑ 81SpoIndT-28
❑ 81TidTidT-26
❑ 82TidTidT-12
❑ 84TidTidT-19
❑ 85IntLeaAT-19
❑ 85TidTidT-6
❑ 86MetWorSC-17
❑ 86TidTidP-1
❑ 87Fle-2
❑ 87FleGlo-2
❑ 87MetColP-23
❑ 87OmaRoyP-22
❑ 87Top-594
❑ 87TopTif-594
❑ 88OmaRoyC-1
❑ 88OmaRoyP-1512
❑ 88RoyTeal-1
❑ 89Sco-441
❑ 90KenTwiB-28
❑ 90KenTwiP-2311
❑ 90KenTwiS-26
❑ 91KenTwiC-20
❑ 91KenTwiP-2092
❑ 91MetWIZ-12
❑ 92KenTwiC-26
❑ 92KenTwiF-621
❑ 93NasXprF-418
❑ 94NasXprF-402
❑ 97SalLakB-4
❑ 98SalLakBO-2

Anderson, Rick (Richard Lee)

❑ 76ShrCapT-3
❑ 77WesHavYT-1
❑ 80SpoIndT-20
❑ 81Top-282
❑ 92YanWIZ7-8

Anderson, Roy

❑ 85MadMusP-1
❑ 85MadMusT-4
❑ 86ModA'sC-1
❑ 86ModA'sP-1A
❑ 86ModA'sP-1B
❑ 87HunStaTI-1

Anderson, Ryan

❑ 98Bes-1
❑ 98BesNumOP-3
❑ 98Bow-129
❑ 98BowBes-163
❑ 98BowBesAR-163
❑ 98BowBesMIF-MI9
❑ 98BowBesMIFAR-MI9
❑ 98BowBesMIFR-MI9
❑ 98BowBesR-163
❑ 98BowChr-129
❑ 98BowChrGA-129
❑ 98BowChrGAR-129
❑ 98BowChrI-129
❑ 98BowChrIR-129
❑ 98BowChrR-129
❑ 98BowGolA-129
❑ 98BowInt-129
❑ 98MidLeaPM-27
❑ 98StaCluBPP-BP3
❑ 98Top-491
❑ 98TopChr-491
❑ 98TopChrR-491
❑ 98TopDevR-491
❑ 98TopDia-491
❑ 98TopMiniC-491
❑ 98WisTimRM-1
❑ 99199Fin-143
❑ 99BasAmeTP-4
❑ 99BasAmeTPBP-1
❑ 99BasAmeTPG-4
❑ 99Bow-96
❑ 99Bow200RF-ROY1
❑ 99BowAut-BA12
❑ 99BowBes-109
❑ 99BowBesAR-109
❑ 99BowBesFFMI-FF6
❑ 99BowBesFFMI-FF6
❑ 99BowBesFFMII-FF6
❑ 99BowBesR-109
❑ 99BowChr-96
❑ 99BowChrDA-DA4
❑ 99BowChrDAR-DA4
❑ 99BowChrG-96
❑ 99BowChrGR-96
❑ 99BowChrI-96
❑ 99BowChrIR-96
❑ 99BowChrR-96
❑ 99BowChrSC-SC2
❑ 99BowChrSCR-SC2
❑ 99BowGol-96
❑ 99BowInt-96
❑ 99BowScoC-SC2
❑ 99FinFutF-FF4
❑ 99FinGolRef-143
❑ 99FinRef-143
❑ 99JustheS-3
❑ 99JustheSJB-3
❑ 99JustheSJP-1
❑ 99SP TopP-12
❑ 99SP TopPC-RA
❑ 99SP TopPDtS-D1
❑ 99SP TopPGF-GF1
❑ 99SP TopPPE-12
❑ 99StaClu-351
❑ 99StaCluFDI-351
❑ 99StaCluOoaK-351
❑ 99StaCluPP-351
❑ 99TeaBesRBG-1
❑ 99TeaBesRFS-23
❑ 99Top-210
❑ 99TopChr-210
❑ 99TopChrR-210
❑ 99TopGal-138
❑ 99TopGalPP-138
❑ 99TopGalPPI-138
❑ 99TopTekFP-F10

Anderson, Scott

❑ 82MadMusF-10
❑ 85TulDriTI-33
❑ 88OklCit8C-1
❑ 89IndIndC-6
❑ 89IndIndP-1234
❑ 90CMC-57
❑ 90IndIndC-7
❑ 90IndIndP-280
❑ 90ProAAAF-563
❑ 91Fle-225
❑ 91Sco-734
❑ 93EdmTraF-1129
❑ 93RanKee-53
❑ 94NewOrlZF-1460
❑ 95OmaRoyTI-3

Anderson, Sparky (George Lee)

❑ 59Top-338
❑ 60Lea-125
❑ 60MapLeaSF-1
❑ 60Top-34
❑ 60TopVen-34
❑ 61MapLeaBH-1
❑ 66St.PetCTI-1
❑ 70OPC-181
❑ 70Top-181
❑ 71OPC-688
❑ 71Top-688
❑ 72OPC-358
❑ 72Top-358
❑ 73OPC-296
❑ 73Top-296
❑ 74OPC-326
❑ 74Top-326
❑ 75OPC-531
❑ 75Top-531
❑ 75TopMin-531
❑ 76OPC-104
❑ 76RedParC-1
❑ 76SSP-22
❑ 76Top-104
❑ 77Top-287
❑ 78Pep-1
❑ 78SSP270-129
❑ 78Top-401
❑ 79Top-259
❑ 80Top-626
❑ 81Don-370
❑ 81Fle-460
❑ 81TCM60I-300
❑ 81TigDetN-18
❑ 81Top-666
❑ 82Don-29
❑ 83Don-533A
❑ 83Don-533B
❑ 83TigPos-1
❑ 83Top-666
❑ 84Fle-650
❑ 84Nes792-259
❑ 84TigWavP-1
❑ 84Top-259
❑ 84TopTif-259
❑ 85Fle-628
❑ 85FleStaS-125
❑ 85SevCoi-D2
❑ 85TigWen-1
❑ 85Top-307
❑ 85TopTif-307
❑ 86DonAll-58
❑ 86Top-411
❑ 86TopGloA-1
❑ 86TopTif-411
❑ 87Top-218
❑ 87TopTif-218
❑ 88PacLegI-46
❑ 88TigPep-11
❑ 88TigPol-2
❑ 88Top-14
❑ 88TopTif-14
❑ 89TigMar-11
❑ 89TigPol-NNO
❑ 89Top-193
❑ 89TopBasT-156
❑ 89TopTif-193
❑ 90OPC-609
❑ 90TigCok-1
❑ 90TigTeal-2
❑ 90Top-609
❑ 90TopTif-609
❑ 91OPC-519
❑ 91Stu-261
❑ 91TigCok-11
❑ 91TigPol-1
❑ 91Top-519
❑ 91TopDesS-519
❑ 91TopMic-519
❑ 91TopTif-519
❑ 92OPC-381
❑ 92TigKro-1
❑ 92TigTeal-2
❑ 92Top-381
❑ 92TopGol-381
❑ 92TopGolW-381
❑ 92TopMic-381
❑ 92UppDecS-30
❑ 93TigGat-1
❑ 93Top-506
❑ 93TopGol-506
❑ 93TopInaM-506
❑ 93TopInaR-506
❑ 93TopMic-506
❑ 96Red76K-1
❑ 96UppDec-480

Anderson, Spike

❑ 90WicStaSGD-2

Anderson, Steve

❑ 83BelBreFr-12
❑ 91OneYanP-4159
❑ 92GreHorC-18
❑ 92GreHorF-784
❑ 93SanBerSC-2
❑ 93SanBerSF-776

Anderson, Tim

❑ 87BakDodP-22

Anderson, Todd

❑ 91PocPioP-3794
❑ 91PocPioSP-16

Anderson, Tom

❑ 78WatIndT-1
❑ 79WatIndT-13
❑ 91AubAstC-8
❑ 92AshTouC-4
❑ 93FloStaLAF-34
❑ 93OscAstC-3
❑ 93OscAstF-618
❑ 94OscAstC-2
❑ 94OscAstF-1128

Anderson, Travis

❑ 98AshTouM-29

Anderson, Varney S.

❑ 87OldJudN-7

Anderson, Wes

❑ 99JustheS-2
❑ 99JustheSJB-2
❑ 99JustheSJP-2

Andino, Luis

❑ 94MarPhiC-2
❑ 94MarPhiF-3306
❑ 95MarPhiTI-2

Andoh, Manabu

❑ 98RanCucQG-3
❑ 98RanCucQG-3

Andra, Jeff

❑ 97SalVolG-1
❑ 98SanJosGQ-6

Andrade, Herberto

❑ 87GenCubP-8
❑ 88PeoChiTI-1
❑ 89ChaWheB-13
❑ 89ChaWheP-1759
❑ 93LinVenB-114
❑ 95LinVen-236
❑ 96-97LinVen-244

Andreopoulos, Alex

❑ 95BelBreTI-24
❑ 96StoPorB-17
❑ 97El PasDB-1
❑ 98El PasDG-1

Andres, Ernie (Ernest Henry)

❑ 46RedSoxTI-1

Andretta, Holly

❑ 89SalLakTI-10

Andrews, Clayton

❑ 96MedHatBJTI-2
❑ 97HagSunB-1
❑ 98HagSunM-6
❑ 98SouAtlLPM-1
❑ 99Bow-167
❑ 99BowBes-170
❑ 99BowBesAR-170
❑ 99BowBesR-170
❑ 99BowChr-167
❑ 99BowChrG-167
❑ 99BowChrGR-167
❑ 99BowChrI-167
❑ 99BowChrIR-167
❑ 99BowChrR-167
❑ 99BowGol-167
❑ 99BowInt-167
❑ 99JustheS-4
❑ 99JustheSJB-4
❑ 99StaClu-147
❑ 99StaCluFDI-147
❑ 99StaCluOoaK-147
❑ 99StaCluPP-147

Andrews, Daniel

❑ 90GreFalDSP-22
❑ 91GreFalDSP-19

Andrews, Ed

❑ 87TobLit-1

Andrews, Fred

❑ 76OklCit8TI-12
❑ 76VenLeaS-17
❑ 78TidTidT-2

Andrews, George E.

❑ 87BucN28-74A
❑ 87BucN28-74B
❑ 87OldJudN-8
❑ 87OldJudN-9
❑ 88GooN16-1
❑ 88WG1CarG-46
❑ 90KalBatN-1
❑ 94OriofB-43

Andrews, Ivy Paul

❑ 30Zee-70
❑ 31Zee-42
❑ 32OrbPinNP-1
❑ 32OrbPinUP-2
❑ 33GeoCMil-2
❑ 33TatOrb-2
❑ 33WorCig-3
❑ 34BatR31-106
❑ 34BatR31-115
❑ 36ExhFou-15
❑ 36NatChiFPR-2
❑ 75YanDyn1T-1
❑ 92ConTSN-420

Andrews, Jay III

❑ 91BasCitRC-23
❑ 91BasCitRP-1409

Andrews, Jeff

❑ 87PorChaRP-12
❑ 88TulDriTI-9
❑ 89TulDriGS-3
❑ 89TulDriTI-3
❑ 90TulDriP-1174
❑ 90TulDriTI-2
❑ 91LinDriAAA-303
❑ 91OklCit8LD-303
❑ 91OklCit8P-194
❑ 92JacSunS-375
❑ 94BilMusF-3672
❑ 94BilMusSP-1
❑ 94JacSunF-1427
❑ 95TacRaiTI-2
❑ 96TacRaiB-3
❑ 97SouBenSH-5
❑ 97TacRai-2
❑ 98SouBenSHM-14

Andrews, John

❑ 88SanDieSAAG-2
❑ 89SanDieSAG-1

Andrews, Kevin

❑ 94HudValRC-28

Andrews, Mike (Michael Jay)

❑ 67Top-314
❑ 67TopRedSS-7
❑ 68CokCapRS-13

❑ 68DexPre-7
❑ 68RedSoxTI-1
❑ 68Top-502
❑ 69MilBra-14
❑ 69MLBOffS-10
❑ 69OPC-52
❑ 69RedSoxAO-1
❑ 69RedSoxTI-1
❑ 69RedSoxTI-1
❑ 69Top-52
❑ 69TopSta-131
❑ 69TopTeaP-3
❑ 70MLBOffS-157
❑ 70OPC-406
❑ 70RedSoxCPPC-2
❑ 70Top-406
❑ 71OPC-191
❑ 71Top-191
❑ 72MilBra-17
❑ 72OPC-361
❑ 72Top-361
❑ 72WhiSoxC-1
❑ 72WhiSoxTI1-2
❑ 73OPC-42
❑ 73Top-42
❑ 81RedSoxBG2S-69
❑ 81TCM60I-417

Andrews, Nate (Nathan H.)
❑ 79DiaGre-259
❑ 93ConTSN-886

Andrews, Raymond
❑ 20Zee-2

Andrews, Rob (Robert P.)
❑ 75AstPos-1
❑ 75IntLeaAT-10
❑ 76OPC-568
❑ 76SSP-54
❑ 76Top-568
❑ 77GiaTeal-3
❑ 77Top-209
❑ 78GiaTeal-2
❑ 78Top-461
❑ 79GiaPol-21
❑ 79Top-34
❑ 80Top-279

Andrews, Scott
❑ 97MicBatC-5

Andrews, Shane
❑ 90ClaDraP-11
❑ 90ClaYel-T88
❑ 91Bow-452
❑ 91OPC-74
❑ 91Sco-674
❑ 91SumFlyC-10
❑ 91SumFlyP-2339
❑ 91Top-74
❑ 91TopCraJ2-13
❑ 91TopDesS-74
❑ 91TopMic-74
❑ 91TopTif-74
❑ 92AlbPolCB-1
❑ 92AlbPolF-2311
❑ 92ClaBluBF-BC3
❑ 92ClaFS7-8
❑ 92ClaRedB-BC3
❑ 92UppDecML-290
❑ 93Bow-378
❑ 93ClaFS7-122
❑ 93ClaGolF-71
❑ 93ExcFS7-56
❑ 93HarSenF-273
❑ 93SouAtlLAIPI-1
❑ 93SouAtlLAIPI-13
❑ 93SouAtlLAPI-1
❑ 94BowBes-B24
❑ 94BowBes-X93
❑ 94BowBesR-B24
❑ 94BowBesR-X93
❑ 94Cla-85
❑ 94ClaCreotC-C15
❑ 94ClaGolF-90
❑ 94ColC-651
❑ 94ColChoGS-651
❑ 94ColChoSS-651
❑ 94ExcFS7-222
❑ 94OttLynF-2902
❑ 94UppDec-2
❑ 94UppDecED-2
❑ 94UppDecML-153
❑ 94UppDecML-175
❑ 95Bow-60
❑ 95ColCho-548T
❑ 95Fin-271
❑ 95FinRef-271
❑ 95Fla-372
❑ 95FleUpd-103
❑ 95FleUpdRU-1
❑ 95Pin-410
❑ 95PinArtP-410
❑ 95PinMusC-410
❑ 95Sel-170
❑ 95SelArtP-170
❑ 95SelCer-108
❑ 95SelCerMG-108
❑ 95SP-73
❑ 95SPSil-73
❑ 95StaClu-609
❑ 95StaCluMOP-609
❑ 95StaCluSTWS-609
❑ 95Sum-116
❑ 95SumNthD-116
❑ 95Top-652
❑ 95UppDec-463
❑ 95UppDecML-136
❑ 95UppDecMLFS-136
❑ 95Zen-120
❑ 96ColCho-208
❑ 96ColChoGS-208
❑ 96ColChoSS-208
❑ 96Don-186
❑ 96DonPreP-186
❑ 96ExpBoo-2
❑ 96ExpDis-4
❑ 96Fla-302
❑ 96Fle-451
❑ 96FleTif-451
❑ 96Lea-178
❑ 96LeaPrePB-178
❑ 96LeaPrePG-178
❑ 96LeaPrePS-178
❑ 96LeaSigA-9
❑ 96LeaSigAG-9
❑ 96LeaSigAS-9
❑ 96Pin-293
❑ 96PinFoil-293
❑ 96StaClu-443
❑ 96StaCluMOP-443
❑ 96Ult-501
❑ 96UltGolM-501
❑ 96UppDec-394
❑ 97Cir-91
❑ 97CirRav-91
❑ 97ColCho-161
❑ 97Fle-375
❑ 97FleTif-375
❑ 97PacPriGotD-GD165
❑ 97Sco-422
❑ 97ScoArtPWB-422
❑ 97ScoResC-422
❑ 97ScoShoS-422
❑ 97ScoShoSAP-422
❑ 97Top-57
❑ 97Ult-366
❑ 97UltGolME-366
❑ 97UltPlaME-366
❑ 97UppDec-108
❑ 98Fle-529
❑ 98PacInvGems-175
❑ 98PacOme-147
❑ 98PacOmeR-147
❑ 98PacOnl-443
❑ 98PacOnlR-443
❑ 98PacOnlWC-443
❑ 98Ult-390
❑ 98UltGolM-390
❑ 98UltMas-390
❑ 98UltPlaM-390
❑ 99Fle-82
❑ 99FleSta9-82
❑ 99FleWarT-82
❑ 99Pac-259
❑ 99PacAur-109
❑ 99PacAurOD-109
❑ 99PacPlaB-259
❑ 99PacRed-259
❑ 99SkyThu-35
❑ 99SkyThuRant-35
❑ 99SkyThuRave-35
❑ 99ThuSkySupR-35
❑ 99UppDec-140
❑ 99UppDec-420
❑ 99UppDecEL1-140
❑ 99UppDecEL1-420
❑ 99UppDecEL2-140
❑ 99UppDecEL2-420

Andrews, Stan (Stanley J.)
❑ 41Gou-24
❑ 90DodTar-18

Andrews, Wally (William W.)
❑ 87OldJudN-10

Andrezejewski, Joe
❑ 89HelBreSP-1
❑ 90BelBreB-3
❑ 90BelBreS-1
❑ 90Bes-52
❑ 90MidLeaASGS-2
❑ 91EriSaiC-15
❑ 91EriSaiP-4059

Andujar, Hector
❑ 91WatIndC-16
❑ 91WatIndP-3371

Andujar, Joaquin
❑ 76HouAstP-1
❑ 77AstPho-1
❑ 77Top-67
❑ 78AstBurK-7
❑ 78AstPos-2
❑ 78Top-158
❑ 78TopZes-1
❑ 79AstPos-2
❑ 79OPC-246
❑ 79Top-471
❑ 80Kel-55
❑ 80OPC-324
❑ 80Top-617
❑ 81Don-381
❑ 81Fle-63
❑ 81FleStiC-48
❑ 81OPC-329
❑ 81Top-329
❑ 81TopTra-731
❑ 82Don-607
❑ 82Fle-110
❑ 82Top-533
❑ 83AllGamPI-163
❑ 83Car-1
❑ 83CarPanP-1
❑ 83Don-316
❑ 83DonActA-27
❑ 83Fle-1
❑ 83FleSta-3
❑ 83FleSti-7
❑ 83OPC-228
❑ 83Top-228
❑ 83Top-561
❑ 83TopSti-179
❑ 84AllGamPI-73
❑ 84Car-2
❑ 84Car5x7-2
❑ 84Don-181
❑ 84Fle-319
❑ 84FunFooP-90
❑ 84Nes792-785
❑ 84OPC-371
❑ 84Top-785
❑ 84TopTif-785
❑ 85AllGamPI-163
❑ 85CarTeal-2
❑ 85Don-13
❑ 85Don-449
❑ 85DonSupD-13
❑ 85Fle-220
❑ 85FleStaS-85
❑ 85Lea-13
❑ 85OPC-231
❑ 85SevCoi-C6
❑ 85Top-655
❑ 85TopGloS-12
❑ 85TopSti-136
❑ 85TopSup-38
❑ 85TopTif-655
❑ 86A'sMot-4
❑ 86AstMot-15
❑ 86CarKASD-11
❑ 86CarTeal-2
❑ 86Don-231
❑ 86Fle-26
❑ 86FleLimE-2
❑ 86FleUpd-4
❑ 86OPC-150
❑ 86Spo-101
❑ 86Spo-133
❑ 86Spo-185
❑ 86Top-150
❑ 86TopMinL-58
❑ 86TopSti-44
❑ 86TopTif-150
❑ 86TopTra-3T
❑ 86TopTraT-3T
❑ 87A'sSmoC-1
❑ 87AstShoSPO-2
❑ 87Don-548
❑ 87Fle-385
❑ 87FleGlo-385
❑ 87FleHotS-1
❑ 87FleMin-2
❑ 87Lea-162
❑ 87OPC-284
❑ 87RedFolSB-11
❑ 87Top-775
❑ 87TopSti-172
❑ 87TopTif-775
❑ 88AstMot-26
❑ 88AstPol-3
❑ 88Sco-193
❑ 88ScoGlo-193
❑ 88Top-47
❑ 88TopTif-47
❑ 89Sco-472
❑ 89TopSenL-93
❑ 89UppDec-79

Andujar, Juan
❑ 89JohCitCS-2
❑ 90Bes-13
❑ 90SprCarB-1
❑ 91Cla/Bes-80
❑ 91SprCarC-2
❑ 91SprCarP-746
❑ 92St.PetCC-6
❑ 92St.PetCF-2032
❑ 93CarLeaAGF-25
❑ 93KinIndC-2
❑ 93KinIndF-2252
❑ 93KinIndTI-1
❑ 94CarLeaAF-CAR33
❑ 94KinIndF-2649

Andujar, Luis
❑ 92SouBenWSC-4
❑ 92SouBenWSF-168
❑ 93SarWhiSC-2
❑ 93SarWhiSF-1360
❑ 94BirBarC-2
❑ 94BirBarF-614
❑ 94ExcFS7-33
❑ 96BirBarB-23
❑ 96Don-425
❑ 96DonPreP-425
❑ 96Fle-62
❑ 96FleTif-62
❑ 96NasSouB-6
❑ 96Pac-283
❑ 97BluJayOH-1
❑ 97SyrSkyCB-2
❑ 98PacInvGems-108
❑ 98SyrSkyG-2

Andux, Orlando
❑ 52LavPro-107

Anfinson, Edward
❑ 20Zee-102
❑ 21Zee-114
❑ 22Zee-95
❑ 23Zee-101
❑ 23Zee-123

Angel, Jason
❑ 92BilMusF-3346
❑ 92BilMusSP-4
❑ 92FroRowDP-10
❑ 92FroRowDPG-10
❑ 92FroRowDPS-10
❑ 93StaCluM-33
❑ 93WinSpiC-2
❑ 93WinSpiF-1562
❑ 94WinSpiC-2
❑ 94WinSpiF-262

Angeli, Doug
❑ 93BatCliCB-3
❑ 93BatCliF-3151
❑ 94SpaPhiF-1728
❑ 94SparPhiC-2
❑ 95ReaPhiELC-1
❑ 96ReaPhiB-15
❑ 97ReaPhi-6
❑ 98ReaPhiUM-3
❑ 98ScrRedBQ-2

Angelini, Norm (Norman S.)
❑ 73OPC-616
❑ 73Top-616
❑ 75OmaRoyTI-1

Angelo, Mark
❑ 83EriCarT-12
❑ 84SavCarT-11

Angels, California
❑ 64TopTatI-3
❑ 65Top-293
❑ 66OPC-131
❑ 66Top-131
❑ 66TopRubI-103
❑ 66TopVen-131
❑ 67Top-327
❑ 68Top-252
❑ 68TopVen-252
❑ 69FleCloS-4
❑ 69TopStaA-4
❑ 70OPC-522
❑ 70Top-522
❑ 71OPC-442
❑ 71Top-442
❑ 71TopTat-134
❑ 72OPC-71
❑ 72Top-71
❑ 73OPC-243
❑ 73OPCBTC-4
❑ 73Top-243
❑ 73TopBluTC-4
❑ 74OPC-114
❑ 74OPCTC-4
❑ 74Top-114
❑ 74TopStaA-4
❑ 74TopTeaC-4
❑ 78Top-214
❑ 83FleSta-228
❑ 83FleSti-NNO
❑ 83FleSti-NNO
❑ 87FleWaxBC-C13
❑ 87SpoTeaL-11
❑ 88PanSti-457
❑ 88RedFolSB-129
❑ 90PubIntS-638
❑ 90RedFolSB-120
❑ 91PanCanT1-132
❑ 94ImpProP-3
❑ 94Sco-319
❑ 94ScoGolR-319
❑ 95PacPriTL-3
❑ 95PanSti-150
❑ 96PanSti-211
❑ 99Vic-1

Angels, Los Angeles
❑ 61TopMagR-6
❑ 62GuyPotCP-10
❑ 62Top-132A
❑ 62Top-132B
❑ 62TopVen-132
❑ 63Top-39
❑ 64Top-213
❑ 64TopVen-213

Angels, Midland
❑ 87MidAngP-30

Angels, Quad City
❑ 86QuaCitAP-33

Angerhofer, Chad
❑ 96BilMusTI-1

Angero, Jose
❑ 87OmaRoyP-2

Anglen, Toby
❑ 95DanBraTI-2

Anglero, Jose
❑ 88BasCitRS-4
❑ 88BlaYNPRWLU-38
❑ 89BasCitRS-4
❑ 89BlaYNPRWL-137
❑ 90BasCitRS-1
❑ 91LakTigC-18
❑ 91LakTigP-271

Anglin, Russ
❑ 83AndBraT-25

Angotti, Donald
❑ 90OscAstS-2
❑ 91AubAstC-12
❑ 91AubAstP-4276
❑ 92TucTorF-504

Angulo, Ken
❑ 83RedPioT-2
❑ 85MidAngT-15

Angulo, Louis
❑ 98EugEme-3

Anicich, Mike
❑ 82JacMetT-14
❑ 82TidTidT-25
❑ 83MidCubT-20

Aniya, Sohachi
❑ 79TCMJapPB-88

Ankenman, Pat (Fred N.)
❑ 90DodTar-892

Ankiel, Rick
❑ 98Bes-52
❑ 98BesDiaB-11
❑ 98BesPro-1
❑ 98CarLeaTPQ-1
❑ 98MidLeaPM-17
❑ 98PeoChiM-1
❑ 98PriWilCQ-1
❑ 99BasAmeTP-5
❑ 99BasAmeTPA-1
❑ 99BasAmeTPBP-2
❑ 99BasAmeTPG-5
❑ 99BasAmeTPSC-1
❑ 99JustheS-5
❑ 99JustheSJB-5
❑ 99JustheSJN-1
❑ 99JustheSJN-1
❑ 99SP TopP-4
❑ 99SP TopP-13
❑ 99SP TopPC-RIA
❑ 99SP TopPDtS-D2
❑ 99SP TopPGF-GF2
❑ 99SP TopPPE-4
❑ 99SP TopPPE-13
❑ 99TeaBesRA-1
❑ 99TeaBesRBG-2
❑ 99TeaBesRFS-19

Ankrum, C.J.
❑ 97SalVolG-2

Annee, Tim
❑ 89MedAthB-23

Annis, Bill (William P.)
❑ 87OldJudN-11

Annunzio, Joe
❑ 37Zee-11

Ansley, Willie
❑ 89AshTouP-950
❑ 89Bow-332
❑ 89BowTif-332
❑ 89SouAtlLAGS-3
❑ 89Top-607
❑ 89TopTif-607
❑ 90Bes-3
❑ 90CMC-810
❑ 90ColMudB-1
❑ 90ColMudP-1356
❑ 90ColMudS-2
❑ 90ProAaA-57
❑ 90StaFS7-14
❑ 91Bow-549
❑ 91Cla/Bes-135
❑ 91JacGenLD-551
❑ 91JacGenP-935
❑ 91LinDriAA-551
❑ 92JacGenF-4010
❑ 93TucTorF-3071

Anson, Cap (Adrian C.)
❑ 36Halof FP-2
❑ 39PC7AlbHoF-17
❑ 50CalHOFW-2
❑ 50CubGreB-2
❑ 53ArtHaloFP-2
❑ 60ExhWriH-2
❑ 60Fle-44
❑ 61Fle-4
❑ 63BazA-39
❑ 63HalofFB-22
❑ 69Baz-9
❑ 74CapPub-21
❑ 75FlePio-1
❑ 76GrePlaG-30
❑ 76ShaPiz-21
❑ 77BobParHoF-2
❑ 77ShaPiz-12
❑ 80PerHaloFP-17
❑ 80SSPHOF-17
❑ 82TCMGreH-27
❑ 84CubBriPC-3H
❑ 84GalHaloFRL-21
❑ 87AllandGN-1
❑ 87BucN28-18A
❑ 87BucN28-18B
❑ 87OldJudN-12A
❑ 87OldJudN-12B
❑ 87TobLit-2
❑ 88AugBecN-1
❑ 88GandBCGCE-1
❑ 88GooN16-2
❑ 88SpoTimM-1
❑ 88WG1CarG-10
❑ 89EdgR.WG-1
❑ 89HOFStiB-5
❑ 90BasWit-66
❑ 90HOFStiB-9
❑ 90PerGreM-96
❑ 92CubOldS-2
❑ 94OriofB-46
❑ 94UppDecTAE-7
❑ 95May-1
❑ 98CamPepP-1

Anthony, Andy
❑ 86VerBeaDP-1

Anthony, Brian
❑ 96PorRocB-5

❑ 97AshTou-3
❑ 98SalAvaC-2

Anthony, Dane
❑ 79WatIndT-14
❑ 80WatIndT-2
❑ 82ChaLooT-8
❑ 83WatIndF-21

Anthony, Eric
❑ 89BasAmeAPB-AA11
❑ 89ColMudB-1
❑ 89ColMudP-134
❑ 89ColMudS-2
❑ 89SouLeaAJ-3
❑ 89Sta-1
❑ 89StaFutS-1
❑ 89StaFutS-2
❑ 89TucTorJP-1
❑ 90AstLenH-3
❑ 90AstMot-3
❑ 90Bow-81
❑ 90BowTif-81
❑ 90ClaBlu-70
❑ 90ColMudS-3
❑ 90Don-34
❑ 90DonBesN-28
❑ 90DonRoo-49
❑ 90Fle-222
❑ 90FleCan-222
❑ 90Hot50RS-4
❑ 90Lea-82
❑ 90LeaPre-7
❑ 90OPC-608
❑ 90PanSti-379
❑ 90Sco-584
❑ 90Sco100RS-45
❑ 90ScoRooDT-B10
❑ 90ScoYouSI-42
❑ 90Spo-179
❑ 90Top-608
❑ 90TopBig-197
❑ 90TopDeb89-5
❑ 90TopTif-608
❑ 90ToyRoo-2
❑ 90UppDec-28
❑ 91Bow-540
❑ 91Cla2-T34
❑ 91ClaGam-139
❑ 91Don-333
❑ 91Fle-498
❑ 91Lea-181
❑ 91LinDriAAA-602
❑ 91MajLeaCP-44
❑ 91OPC-331
❑ 91Sco-146
❑ 91Sco100RS-42
❑ 91StaClu-229
❑ 91Stu-171
❑ 91Top-331
❑ 91TopCraJ2-3
❑ 91TopDesS-331
❑ 91TopMic-331
❑ 91TopTif-331
❑ 91TucTorLD-602
❑ 91TucTorP-2223
❑ 91Ult-131
❑ 91UppDec-533
❑ 92AstMot-7
❑ 92Fle-424
❑ 92Pin-363
❑ 92PinTea2-28
❑ 92RedFolS-4
❑ 92Sco-315
❑ 92Sco100RS-8
❑ 92StaClu-575
❑ 92TriPla-18
❑ 93AstMot-8
❑ 93AstStaC-7
❑ 93Bow-152
❑ 93ClaGam-5
❑ 93DenHol-2
❑ 93Don-8
❑ 93Fin-179
❑ 93FinRef-179
❑ 93Fla-56
❑ 93Fle-45
❑ 93Lea-218
❑ 93LinVenB-219
❑ 93OPC-2
❑ 93PacSpa-474
❑ 93PanSti-176
❑ 93Pin-84
❑ 93PinHomRC-34
❑ 93Sco-173
❑ 93Sel-137
❑ 93StaClu-141
❑ 93StaCluFDI-141
❑ 93StaCluMOP-141
❑ 93Stu-3
❑ 93Top-89
❑ 93TopGol-89
❑ 93TopInaM-89
❑ 93TopInaR-89
❑ 93TopMic-89
❑ 93Toy-49
❑ 93ToyMasP-2
❑ 93TriPla-109
❑ 93Ult-389
❑ 93UppDec-183
❑ 93UppDecGold-183
❑ 93UppDecHRH-HR22
❑ 94Bow-445
❑ 94ColC-38
❑ 94ColC-411
❑ 94ColChoGS-38
❑ 94ColChoGS-411
❑ 94ColChoSS-38
❑ 94ColChoSS-411
❑ 94Don-480
❑ 94Fin-349
❑ 94FinRef-349
❑ 94Fla-98
❑ 94Fle-482
❑ 94FleExtB-159
❑ 94FleUpd-79
❑ 94Lea-229
❑ 94LeaL-64
❑ 94MarMot-3
❑ 94OPC-61
❑ 94Pac-256
❑ 94PanSti-188
❑ 94Pin-75
❑ 94PinArtP-75
❑ 94PinMusC-75
❑ 94ProMag-129
❑ 94Sco-400
❑ 94ScoGolR-400
❑ 94ScoRoo-RT27
❑ 94ScoRooGR-RT27
❑ 94Sel-286
❑ 94SP-102
❑ 94SPDieC-102
❑ 94SpoRoo-137
❑ 94SpoRooAP-137
❑ 94StaClu-548
❑ 94StaCluFDI-548
❑ 94StaCluGR-548
❑ 94StaCluMOP-548
❑ 94StaCluMOP-ST6
❑ 94StaCluST-ST6
❑ 94Stu-99
❑ 94Top-182
❑ 94TopGol-182
❑ 94TopSpa-182
❑ 94TopTra-27T
❑ 94TriPla-122
❑ 94Ult-202
❑ 94Ult-415
❑ 94UppDec-361
❑ 94UppDecED-361
❑ 95Don-31
❑ 95DonPreP-31
❑ 95Fle-259
❑ 95Pin-306
❑ 95PinArtP-306
❑ 95PinMusC-306
❑ 95RedKah-1
❑ 95Sco-506
❑ 95ScoGolR-506
❑ 95ScoPlaTS-506
❑ 95Top-565
❑ 95TopCyb-341
❑ 95Ult-98
❑ 95UltGolM-98
❑ 96FleUpd-U116
❑ 96FleUpdTC-U116
❑ 96Pin-287
❑ 96PinFoil-287
❑ 96Sco-415
❑ 98AlbDukG-1
❑ 98PacInvGems-166

Anthony, Greg Pepper
❑ 91ClaDraP-27
❑ 91FroRowDP-19
❑ 91FroRowDPG-19
❑ 91FroRowDPS-19
❑ 92ChaRaiF-111
❑ 92ClaFS7-51
❑ 92OPC-336
❑ 92StaCluD-7
❑ 92Top-336
❑ 92TopGol-336
❑ 92TopGolW-336
❑ 92TopMic-336
❑ 93WatDiaC-2
❑ 93WatDiaF-1758

Anthony, Lee
❑ 49BowPCL-1
❑ 50W720HolS-1

Anthony, Mark
❑ 90HigSchPLS-9
❑ 91SpoIndC-12
❑ 91SpoIndP-3959
❑ 92Bow-449
❑ 92ChaRaiC-3
❑ 92ChaRaiF-131
❑ 92UppDecML-125

Anthony, Omer
❑ 48AngTeal-4
❑ 49AngTeal-4

Anthony, Paul
❑ 77SalPirT-1

Antigua, Felix
❑ 89AugPirP-497
❑ 89PriPirS-2
❑ 89Sta-173
❑ 90AugPirP-2466
❑ 90SouAtlLAS-26

Antigua, Jose
❑ 93WhiSoxK-30

Antigua, Nilson
❑ 96EriSeaB-4
❑ 97LynHil-2

Antolick, Jeff
❑ 92OneYanC-26
❑ 93GreHorC-2
❑ 93GreHorF-876
❑ 93SouAtlLAGF-18
❑ 94TamYanC-2
❑ 94TamYanF-2372
❑ 95NorNavTI-40

Anton, Leroy
❑ 29Zee-60
❑ 30Zee-71
❑ 31Zee-43
❑ 32Zee-49
❑ 33Zee-19
❑ 33Zee-52
❑ 35PebBea-1

Antonelli, John L.
❑ 83BelBreFr-6

Antonelli, Johnny (John A.)
❑ 47Exh-4A
❑ 47Exh-4B
❑ 47PM1StaP1-4
❑ 47PM1StaP1-5
❑ 49EurSta-3
❑ 50Bow-74
❑ 50JJKCopP-1
❑ 51Bow-243
❑ 52Top-140
❑ 53BraJohC-2
❑ 53BraMer-2
❑ 53BraSpiaS3-2
❑ 53Top-106
❑ 54Bow-208
❑ 54NewYorJA-20
❑ 54RedMan-NL21
❑ 54Top-119
❑ 55ArmCoi-1
❑ 55BigLealS-1
❑ 55Bow-124
❑ 55DaiQueS-1
❑ 55GiaGolS-3
❑ 55RedMan-NL13
❑ 56GiaJayP-1
❑ 56Top-138
❑ 57GiaJayP-1
❑ 57Top-105
❑ 58GiaArmT-1
❑ 58GiaJayP-1
❑ 58GiaSFCB-1
❑ 58Hir-50
❑ 58HirTes-1
❑ 58PacBel-2
❑ 58Top-152
❑ 59ArmCoi-2
❑ 59Top-377
❑ 60Baz-35
❑ 60GiaJayP-1
❑ 60RawGloT-1
❑ 60Top-80
❑ 60Top-572
❑ 60TopTat-3
❑ 60TopVen-80
❑ 61Kah-1
❑ 61Pos-142A
❑ 61Pos-142B
❑ 61Top-115
❑ 61TopStal-132
❑ 70FleWorS-51
❑ 75TCMHouoJ-1
❑ 79DiaGre-316
❑ 80MarExh-1
❑ 83Bra53F-34
❑ 83TopRep5-140
❑ 84FifNatCT-10
❑ 84GiaMot-13
❑ 85TCMPhoC-11
❑ 85TCMPpl1-10
❑ 91TopArc1-106
❑ 92BazQua5A-22
❑ 94TopArc1-119
❑ 94TopArc1G-119

Antonello, Bill (William J.)
❑ 50W720HolS-2
❑ 53Top-272
❑ 70Houof J-1
❑ 72TopTes5-3
❑ 90DodTar-19
❑ 91TopArc1-272
❑ 95TopArcBD-57

Antonini, Adrian
❑ 92LSUTigM-2
❑ 93LSUTigM-9
❑ 94BatCliC-1
❑ 94BatCliF-3435
❑ 94LSUTig-5
❑ 94LSUTigMP-7
❑ 95BatCliTI-2

Antoon, Jeff
❑ 92EugEmeC-5
❑ 92EugEmeF-3034
❑ 93RocRoyC-2
❑ 93RocRoyF-721

Antrim, Patrick
❑ 97GreBatB-6

Antunez, Martin
❑ 82BelBreFr-23

Anyzeski, Fred
❑ 75AppFoxT-1

Apana, Matt
❑ 93BelMarCB-2
❑ 93BelMarF-3196
❑ 94RivPilCLC-1
❑ 95Bow-168
❑ 95TacRaiTI-4
❑ 96PorCitRB-5

Aparicio, Luis E.
❑ 47Exh-5A
❑ 47Exh-5B
❑ 56Top-292
❑ 56YelBasP-3
❑ 57Top-7
❑ 58HarSta-15
❑ 58JayPubA-2
❑ 58Top-85A
❑ 58Top-85B
❑ 58Top-483
❑ 58WhiSoxJP-1
❑ 59Top-310
❑ 59Top-408
❑ 59Top-560
❑ 59WilSpoG-1
❑ 60Baz-22
❑ 60KeyChal-3
❑ 60Lea-1
❑ 60Top-240
❑ 60Top-389
❑ 60Top-559
❑ 60WhiSoxJP-1
❑ 60WhiSoxTS-1
❑ 61Baz-35
❑ 61Pos-19A
❑ 61Pos-19B
❑ 61Top-440
❑ 61Top-574
❑ 61TopStal-120
❑ 61WhiSoxTS-1
❑ 62Baz-30
❑ 62ExhStaB-2
❑ 62Jel-49
❑ 62Pos-49
❑ 62PosCan-49
❑ 62SalPlaC-71
❑ 62ShiPlaC-71
❑ 62Top-325
❑ 62Top-469
❑ 62TopStal-22
❑ 62TopVen-200
❑ 62WhiSoxJP-1
❑ 62WhiSoxTS-1
❑ 63BalOriP-2
❑ 63BasMagM-6
❑ 63ExhStaB-2
❑ 63Jel-37
❑ 63Pos-37
❑ 63SalMetC-50
❑ 63Top-205
❑ 63TopStil-2
❑ 64BalOriP-2
❑ 64OriJayP-1
❑ 64Top-540
❑ 64TopCoi-31
❑ 64TopCoi-127
❑ 64TopGia-39
❑ 64TopRooAB-3
❑ 64WheSta-3
❑ 65BalOriP-2
❑ 65Top-410
❑ 65TopTral-3
❑ 66BalOriP-1
❑ 66OPC-90
❑ 66Top-90
❑ 66TopVen-90
❑ 67BalOriP-2
❑ 67CokCapO-2
❑ 67DexPre-13
❑ 67OPC-60
❑ 67Top-60
❑ 67TopVen-189
❑ 68CokCapO-2
❑ 68Top-310
❑ 68TopVen-310
❑ 69KelPin-1
❑ 69MilBra-15
❑ 69MLBOffS-28
❑ 69MLBPin-2
❑ 69OPC-75
❑ 69OPCDec-2
❑ 69Top-75
❑ 69TopDec-6
❑ 69TopDecl-5
❑ 69TopSta-152
❑ 69TopSup-10
❑ 69TopTeaP-11
❑ 69TraSta-24
❑ 69WhiSoxTI-2
❑ 70DayDaiNM-55
❑ 70Kel-22
❑ 70MLBOffS-181
❑ 70OPC-315
❑ 70Top-315
❑ 70TopCanL-3
❑ 70TopScr-3
❑ 70TopSup-3
❑ 70WhiSoxTI-1
❑ 71AllBasA-2
❑ 71BazNumT-8
❑ 71BazUnn-26
❑ 71Kel-19
❑ 71MilDud-1
❑ 71MLBOffS-313
❑ 71MLBOffS-554
❑ 71OPC-740
❑ 71RedSoxA-1
❑ 71RedSoxTI-1
❑ 71Top-740
❑ 71TopCoi-16
❑ 71TopGreM-51
❑ 71TopSup-23
❑ 71TopTat-44
❑ 72EssCoi-1
❑ 72MilBra-18
❑ 72OPC-313
❑ 72OPC-314
❑ 72Top-313
❑ 72Top-314
❑ 72TopCloT-2
❑ 73LinPor-14
❑ 73OPC-165
❑ 73Top-165
❑ 74OPC-61
❑ 74Top-61
❑ 74TopSta-131
❑ 76VenLeaS-181
❑ 77GalGloG-42
❑ 78TCM60I-250
❑ 80PerHaloFP-185
❑ 80PerHaloFPS-50
❑ 80SSPHOF-186
❑ 80VenLeaS-136
❑ 81Ori6F-3
❑ 81TCM60I-358
❑ 81WhiSox1T-3
❑ 82DiaCla-93
❑ 83FraBroR-12
❑ 83FraBroR-22
❑ 84OCoandSI-67
❑ 84SpoDesPW-2
❑ 84WhiSoxTV-2
❑ 85WhiSoxC-13
❑ 86OriGreT-9
❑ 86SpoDecG-37
❑ 87NesDreT-15
❑ 88GreBasS-28
❑ 88PacLegI-91
❑ 89HOFStiB-18
❑ 89PerCelP-2
❑ 89WhiSoxK-6
❑ 90AGFA-9
❑ 90BasWit-23
❑ 90PerGreM-43
❑ 91OriCro-12
❑ 92UppDecS-26
❑ 93ActPacA-122
❑ 93ActPacA2-56G
❑ 93LinVenB-11
❑ 93TedWil-25
❑ 94TopSpa-L3
❑ 94Yoo-1
❑ 95MCIAmb-14
❑ 97TopStaHRR-1
❑ 97TopStaRRAU-1
❑ 98SpollITaN-1
❑ 98SpollITaNEE-1
❑ 99SpollIGotG-11
❑ 99SpollIGotGA-2
❑ 99SpollIGotGC-8

Apicella, Jamie
❑ 94EveGiaC-1
❑ 94EveGiaF-3665

Apodaca, Bob (Robert John)
❑ 74MetDaiPA-7
❑ 74MetTeal-1
❑ 74OPC-608
❑ 74Top-608A
❑ 74Top-608B
❑ 75MetSSP-15
❑ 75OPC-659
❑ 75Top-659
❑ 75TopMin-659
❑ 76MetMSAP-3
❑ 76OPC-16
❑ 76SSP-548
❑ 76Top-16
❑ 77MetDaiPA-2
❑ 77Top-225
❑ 78MetDaiPA-27
❑ 78Top-592
❑ 79OPC-98
❑ 79Top-197
❑ 80Top-633
❑ 82JacMetT-23
❑ 86ColMetP-1
❑ 87ColMetP-2
❑ 89JacMetGS-21
❑ 90JacMetGS-4
❑ 91LinDriAAA-575
❑ 91MetWIZ-13
❑ 91TidTidP-2527
❑ 92TidTidF-913
❑ 93NorTidF-2586
❑ 94NorTidF-2937
❑ 95NorTidTI-2
❑ 96NorTidB-2

Apolinario, Oswaldo
❑ 90BurBraB-6
❑ 90BurBraP-2354
❑ 90BurBraS-1

Aponte, Edwin
❑ 80SanJosMJitB-2
❑ 81LynSaiT-15
❑ 83WatIndF-2
❑ 84BufBisT-19

Aponte, Juan
❑ 80VenLeaS-71

Aponte, Luis Eduardo
❑ 76VenLeaS-46
❑ 80VenLeaS-58
❑ 80VenLeaS-85
❑ 81PawRedST-8
❑ 83Don-109
❑ 83Fle-178
❑ 83Top-577
❑ 84Don-371
❑ 84Fle-389
❑ 84FleUpd-2
❑ 84Ind-1
❑ 84IndWhe-38
❑ 84Nes792-187
❑ 84Top-187
❑ 84TopTif-187
❑ 84TopTra-2T

❑ 84TopTraT-2T
❑ 85Fle-437
❑ 95LinVen-163
Aponte, Newlan
❑ 89WytCubS-1
Aponte, Rick (Ricardo)
❑ 78DayBeaAT-2
❑ 80ColAstT-16
❑ 87AubAstP-19
❑ 90AshTouC-27
❑ 90AshTouP-2765
❑ 91AshTouP-585
❑ 92BurAstC-27
❑ 92BurAstF-564
Appier, Kevin
❑ 87EugEmeP-2672
❑ 88BasCitRS-5
❑ 89FleUpd-35
❑ 89OmaRoyC-4
❑ 89OmaRoyP-1720
❑ 90Bow-367
❑ 90BowTif-367
❑ 90DonRoo-21
❑ 90Fle-100
❑ 90FleCan-100
❑ 90OPC-167
❑ 90RoyPos-1
❑ 90Sco-625
❑ 90Sco100RS-13
❑ 90Top-167
❑ 90TopDeb89-6
❑ 90TopTif-167
❑ 90UppDec-102
❑ 91Baz-21
❑ 91Bow-309
❑ 91Don-740
❑ 91Fle-549
❑ 91OPC-454
❑ 91PanCanT1-72
❑ 91PanCanT1-95
❑ 91RoyPol-1
❑ 91Sco-268
❑ 91Sco100RS-73
❑ 91StaClu-501
❑ 91Top-454A
❑ 91Top-454B
❑ 91TopDesS-454
❑ 91TopMic-454
❑ 91TopRoo-2
❑ 91TopTif-454
❑ 91ToyRoo-2
❑ 91Ult-143
❑ 91UppDec-566
❑ 92Bow-640
❑ 92Don-455
❑ 92Fle-150
❑ 92Lea-31
❑ 92LeaBlaG-31
❑ 92OPC-281
❑ 92Pin-434
❑ 92PinTea2-5
❑ 92RedFolS-5
❑ 92RoyPol-1
❑ 92Sco-542
❑ 92StaClu-523
❑ 92Top-281
❑ 92TopGol-281
❑ 92TopGolW-281
❑ 92TopMic-281
❑ 92TriPla-8
❑ 92Ult-66
❑ 92UppDec-159
❑ 92UppDecTMH-5
❑ 93Bow-41
❑ 93CadDis-1
❑ 93Don-43
❑ 93Fin-78
❑ 93FinRef-78
❑ 93Fla-212
❑ 93Fle-235
❑ 93FunPac-180
❑ 93Lea-101
❑ 93OPC-23
❑ 93PacSpa-131
❑ 93PanSti-101
❑ 93Pin-133
❑ 93RoyPol-2
❑ 93RoyStaC-5
❑ 93Sco-154
❑ 93Sel-102
❑ 93SelAce-9
❑ 93SelStaL-80
❑ 93SP-226
❑ 93StaClu-374
❑ 93StaCluFDI-374
❑ 93StaCluMOP-374
❑ 93Top-76
❑ 93TopComotH-8
❑ 93TopGol-76
❑ 93TopInaM-76
❑ 93TopInaR-76
❑ 93TopMic-76
❑ 93TriPla-234
❑ 93Ult-556
❑ 93UppDec-89
❑ 93UppDecGold-89
❑ 93USPlaCA-10S
❑ 94Bow-555
❑ 94ColC-351
❑ 94ColC-390
❑ 94ColChoGS-351
❑ 94ColChoGS-390
❑ 94ColChoSS-351
❑ 94ColChoSS-390
❑ 94DenHol-3
❑ 94Don-47
❑ 94DonSpeE-47
❑ 94Fin-174
❑ 94FinRef-174
❑ 94Fla-54
❑ 94Fle-147
❑ 94FleExtB-83
❑ 94FleLeaL-6
❑ 94FUnPac-55
❑ 94Lea-70
❑ 94OPC-225
❑ 94OscMayR-2
❑ 94Pac-279
❑ 94PanSti-71
❑ 94Pin-48
❑ 94PinArtP-48
❑ 94PinMusC-48
❑ 94Sco-359
❑ 94ScoGolR-359
❑ 94Sel-64
❑ 94SP-170
❑ 94SPDieC-170
❑ 94SPHol-2
❑ 94SPHolDC-2
❑ 94Spo-84
❑ 94StaClu-340
❑ 94StaCluFDI-340
❑ 94StaCluGR-340
❑ 94StaCluMO-14
❑ 94StaCluMOP-340
❑ 94Top-701
❑ 94TopGol-701
❑ 94TopSpa-701
❑ 94TriPla-231
❑ 94Ult-61
❑ 94UppDec-133
❑ 94UppDecAJ-13
❑ 94UppDecAJG-13
❑ 94UppDecED-133
❑ 94USPlaCA-12S
❑ 95Baz-110
❑ 95Bow-292
❑ 95BowBes-R6
❑ 95BowBesR-R6
❑ 95ClaPhoC-31
❑ 95ColCho-462
❑ 95ColChoGS-462
❑ 95ColChoSS-462
❑ 95Don-542
❑ 95DonPreP-542
❑ 95DonTopotO-82
❑ 95Emo-48
❑ 95Fin-108
❑ 95FinRef-108
❑ 95Fla-262
❑ 95Fle-152
❑ 95Lea-84
❑ 95LeaLim-24
❑ 95Pac-196
❑ 95Pin-70
❑ 95PinArtP-70
❑ 95PinFan-7
❑ 95PinMusC-70
❑ 95Sco-520
❑ 95ScoGolR-520
❑ 95ScoPlaTS-520
❑ 95Sel-23
❑ 95SelArtP-23
❑ 95SelCer-22
❑ 95SelCerMG-22
❑ 95SP-160
❑ 95SPCha-157
❑ 95SPCha-160
❑ 95SPChaDC-157
❑ 95SPChaDC-160
❑ 95Spo-62
❑ 95SpoArtP-62
❑ 95SPSil-160
❑ 95StaClu-445
❑ 95StaClu-516
❑ 95StaCluMOP-445
❑ 95StaCluMOP-516
❑ 95StaCluSTWS-445
❑ 95StaCluSTWS-516
❑ 95StaCluVR-236
❑ 95StaCluVRMO-236
❑ 95Sum-46
❑ 95SumNthD-46
❑ 95Top-325
❑ 95TopCyb-178
❑ 95TopEmb-43
❑ 95TopEmbGI-43
❑ 95TopLeaL-LL50
❑ 95UC3-21
❑ 95UC3ArtP-21
❑ 95Ult-53
❑ 95UltGolM-53
❑ 95UppDec-419
❑ 95UppDecED-419
❑ 95UppDecEDG-419
❑ 95Zen-63
❑ 96Baz-51
❑ 96Bow-68
❑ 96BowBes-45
❑ 96BowBesAR-45
❑ 96BowBesR-45
❑ 96BowFoi-68
❑ 96Cir-43
❑ 96CirRav-43
❑ 96ColCho-170
❑ 96ColChoGS-170
❑ 96ColChoSS-170
❑ 96ColChoYMtP-1
❑ 96ColChoYMtP-1A
❑ 96ColChoYMtPGS-1
❑ 96ColChoYMtPGS-1A
❑ 96DenHol-22
❑ 96Don-439
❑ 96DonPreP-439
❑ 96EmoXL-64
❑ 96Fin-B23
❑ 96FinRef-B23
❑ 96Fla-86
❑ 96Fle-123
❑ 96FleSmo'H-1
❑ 96FleTif-123
❑ 96Lea-108
❑ 96LeaPrePB-108
❑ 96LeaPrePG-108
❑ 96LeaPrePS-108
❑ 96LeaSig-135
❑ 96LeaSigPPG-135
❑ 96LeaSigPPP-135
❑ 96MetUni-62
❑ 96MetUniP-62
❑ 96Pac-329
❑ 96PacPri-P104
❑ 96PacPriG-P104
❑ 96PanSti-185
❑ 96Pin-101
❑ 96PinAfi-65
❑ 96PinAfiAP-65
❑ 96PinAfiFPP-65
❑ 96PinArtP-38
❑ 96PinSta-38
❑ 96ProSta-120
❑ 96RoyPol-1
❑ 96Sco-199
❑ 96Sco-284
❑ 96ScoDugC-B9
❑ 96ScoDugCAP-B9
❑ 96Sel-27
❑ 96SelArtP-27
❑ 96SelTeaN-17
❑ 96SP-96
❑ 96Spo-75
❑ 96SpoArtP-75
❑ 96StaClu-362
❑ 96StaCluEPB-362
❑ 96StaCluEPG-362
❑ 96StaCluEPS-362
❑ 96StaCluMOP-362
❑ 96Stu-111
❑ 96StuPrePB-111
❑ 96StuPrePG-111
❑ 96StuPrePS-111
❑ 96Sum-72
❑ 96SumAbo&B-72
❑ 96SumArtP-72
❑ 96SumFoi-72
❑ 96TeaOut-3
❑ 96Top-364
❑ 96TopChr-148
❑ 96TopChrR-148
❑ 96TopGal-64
❑ 96TopGalPPI-64
❑ 96TopLas-114
❑ 96Ult-67
❑ 96UltGolM-67
❑ 96UppDec-86
❑ 96UppDecPHE-H17
❑ 96UppDecPreH-H17
❑ 97Bow-26
❑ 97BowBes-49
❑ 97BowBesAR-49
❑ 97BowBesR-49
❑ 97BowChr-22
❑ 97BowChrI-22
❑ 97BowChrIR-22
❑ 97BowChrR-22
❑ 97BowInt-26
❑ 97Cir-158
❑ 97CirRav-158
❑ 97ColCho-130
❑ 97Don-206
❑ 97Don-434
❑ 97DonEli-106
❑ 97DonEliGS-106
❑ 97DonGolPP-206
❑ 97DonGolPP-434
❑ 97DonLim-147
❑ 97DonLim-172
❑ 97DonLimE-147
❑ 97DonLimE-172
❑ 97DonLimENG-147
❑ 97DonPre-66
❑ 97DonPreCttC-66
❑ 97DonSig-14
❑ 97DonSigPPP-14
❑ 97DonSilPP-206
❑ 97DonSilPP-434
❑ 97E-X2-23
❑ 97E-X2Cred-23
❑ 97E-X2EssCre-23
❑ 97Fin-85
❑ 97FinRef-85
❑ 97FlaShoLC-17
❑ 97FlaShoLeg0-17
❑ 97FlaShoLeg1-17
❑ 97FlaShoM-A17
❑ 97FlaShoM-B17
❑ 97FlaShoM-C17
❑ 97FlaShoR0-17
❑ 97FlaShoR1-17
❑ 97FlaShoR2-17
❑ 97Fle-109
❑ 97Fle-733
❑ 97FleTeaL-7
❑ 97FleTif-109
❑ 97FleTif-733
❑ 97Lea-34
❑ 97LeaFraM-34
❑ 97LeaFraMDC-34
❑ 97MetUni-90
❑ 97NewPin-59
❑ 97NewPinAP-59
❑ 97NewPinMC-59
❑ 97NewPinPP-59
❑ 97Pac-97
❑ 97PacLigB-97
❑ 97PacSil-97
❑ 97PinCar-4
❑ 97PinIns-59
❑ 97PinInsCE-59
❑ 97PinInsDE-59
❑ 97PinX-P-55
❑ 97PinX-PMoS-55
❑ 97RoyPol-1
❑ 97Sco-42
❑ 97ScoArtPWB-42
❑ 97ScoPreS-42
❑ 97ScoShoS-42
❑ 97ScoShoSAP-42
❑ 97SP-88
❑ 97SpoIll-156
❑ 97SpoIllEE-156
❑ 97StaClu-22
❑ 97StaCluMat-22
❑ 97StaCluMOP-22
❑ 97Stu-94
❑ 97StuPrePG-94
❑ 97StuPrePS-94
❑ 97Top-30
❑ 97TopChr-12
❑ 97TopChrR-12
❑ 97TopGal-71
❑ 97TopGalPPI-71
❑ 97TopSta-22
❑ 97TopStaAM-22
❑ 97Ult-65
❑ 97UltGolME-65
❑ 97UltPlaME-65
❑ 97UppDec-389
❑ 98CirThu-178
❑ 98CirThuRav-178
❑ 98CirThuSupRav-178
❑ 98ColCho-389
❑ 98Don-39
❑ 98DonCol-39
❑ 98DonColL-248
❑ 98DonColP-645
❑ 98DonColS-39
❑ 98DonCruG-27
❑ 98DonCruP-27
❑ 98DonCruR-27
❑ 98DonGolPP-39
❑ 98DonPre-95
❑ 98DonPreSeat-95
❑ 98DonPriCD-39
❑ 98DonPriCL-248
❑ 98DonPriCP-645
❑ 98DonSilPP-39
❑ 98Fin-37
❑ 98FinNo--37
❑ 98FinNo-R-37
❑ 98FinRef-37
❑ 98Fle-287
❑ 98Lea-49
❑ 98LeaFraDA-49
❑ 98LeaFraF-49
❑ 98LeaFraM-49
❑ 98LeaFraM-49
❑ 98LeaFraMDC-49
❑ 98LeaFraMDC-49
❑ 98LeaFraMZ2-49
❑ 98LeaRS-96
❑ 98LeaRS-165
❑ 98LeaRSLHolo-96
❑ 98LeaRSLHolo-165
❑ 98LeaRSLong-96
❑ 98LeaRSLong-165
❑ 98LeaRTrue-96
❑ 98LeaRTrue-165
❑ 98MetUni-28
❑ 98MetUniPMG-28
❑ 98Pac-98
❑ 98PacPar-52
❑ 98PacParC-52
❑ 98PacParG-52
❑ 98PacParHS-52
❑ 98PacParPB-52
❑ 98PacParR-52
❑ 98PacPlaB-98
❑ 98PacRedT-98
❑ 98PacSil-98
❑ 98Pin-42
❑ 98PinPer-84
❑ 98PinPerPP-84
❑ 98PinPlu-129
❑ 98PinPreP-42
❑ 98Sco-223
❑ 98ScoRT-231
❑ 98ScoSS-PP109
❑ 98ScoSSAP-PP109
❑ 98SkyDugA-68
❑ 98SkyDugAIA-68
❑ 98SpoIll-7
❑ 98SpoIllEE-7
❑ 98SpoIllFE-7
❑ 98SpoIllODMP-OD14
❑ 98SpoIllTaN-58
❑ 98SpoIllTaNEE-58
❑ 98SpoIllWSF-101
❑ 98SpoIllWSFEE-101
❑ 98SpoIllWSFFE-101
❑ 98StaCluFDI-169
❑ 98StaCluI-169
❑ 98StaCluOneK-169
❑ 98StaCluPP-169
❑ 98Stu-132
❑ 98StuGPP-132
❑ 98StuSPP-132
❑ 98Top-120
❑ 98TopChr-120
❑ 98TopChrR-120
❑ 98TopDevR-120
❑ 98TopDia-120
❑ 98TopGal-30
❑ 98TopGalGP-30
❑ 98TopGalOPP-30
❑ 98TopGalPPI-30
❑ 98TopGalPPIA-30
❑ 98TopMiniC-120
❑ 98TopOpeD-60
❑ 98Ult-76
❑ 98UltGolM-76
❑ 98UltMas-76
❑ 98UltPlaM-76
❑ 98UppDec-395
❑ 99Pac-199
❑ 99PacPlaB-199
❑ 99PacRed-199
❑ 99UppDec-392
❑ 99UppDecEL1-392
❑ 99UppDecEL2-392
❑ 99Vic-188
Applegate, Russ
❑ 84IdaFalATI-1
❑ 85MadMusP-2
❑ 85MadMusT-5
❑ 86ModA'sC-2
❑ 86ModA'sP-2
Appleton, Ed (Edward Sam)
❑ 17ColE13-6
❑ 90DodTar-893
Appleton, Pete (Peter W.)
❑ 39PlaBal-137
❑ 39WhiSoxTI-1
❑ 40PlaBal-128
❑ 40WhiSoxL-1
❑ 74CapPub-89
❑ 91ConTSN-76
Appling, Luke (Lucas B.)
❑ 31Exh-19
❑ 34BatR31-124
❑ 34DiaStaR-95
❑ 34ExhFou-10
❑ 34Gou-27
❑ 34GouCanV-84
❑ 35AlDemDCR3-18
❑ 35GouPuzR-1I
❑ 35GouPuzR-2F
❑ 35GouPuzR-16F
❑ 35GouPuzR-17F
❑ 36ExhFou-10
❑ 36GouWidPPR-B2
❑ 36GouWidPPR-C1
❑ 36OveCanR-2
❑ 36SandSW-1
❑ 36WheBB5-3
❑ 36WorWidGV-113
❑ 37ExhFou-10
❑ 37GouThuMR-7
❑ 37KelPepS-BB1
❑ 37OPCBatUV-115
❑ 37WheBB8-1
❑ 38BasTabP-1
❑ 38CloFotW-1
❑ 38ExhFou-10
❑ 38GouFliMR-7A
❑ 38GouFliMR-7B
❑ 39ExhSal-1A
❑ 39ExhSal-1B
❑ 39GouPreR303A-1
❑ 39GouPreR303B-1
❑ 39WhiSoxTI-2
❑ 39WorWidGTP-1
❑ 40WheM4-12
❑ 40WhiSoxL-2
❑ 41DouPlaR-69
❑ 47Exh-6
❑ 48BluTin-10
❑ 48WhiSoxTI-1
❑ 49Bow-175
❑ 49Lea-59
❑ 50Bow-37
❑ 50RoyDes-16
❑ 60Fle-27
❑ 60Top-461
❑ 63BalOriP-3
❑ 67TopVen-158
❑ 72TCMthe3-110
❑ 76ChiGre-1
❑ 76GalBasGHoF-1
❑ 76RowExh-1
❑ 76ShaPiz-95
❑ 76TayBow4-38
❑ 76WhiSoxTAG-1
❑ 77BobParHoF-3
❑ 77GalGloG-80
❑ 77TCMTheWY-12
❑ 80PacLeg-22
❑ 80PerHaloFP-95
❑ 80PerHaloFPS-10
❑ 80SSPHOF-95
❑ 80WhiSoxGT-4
❑ 82DiaCla-25

- ❑ 82TCMGreH-42
- ❑ 83ConMar-6
- ❑ 83DonHOFH-8
- ❑ 83TCMPla1942-16
- ❑ 84BraPol-55
- ❑ 84raPho-1
- ❑ 85WhiSoxC-1
- ❑ 87HygAllG-3
- ❑ 88ConAmeA-1
- ❑ 88PacLegI-4
- ❑ 89SweBasG-30
- ❑ 89WhiSoxK-6
- ❑ 90PacLeg-3
- ❑ 90SweBasG-18
- ❑ 91SweBasG-3
- ❑ 92ConTSN-475
- ❑ 92ConTSNGI-730
- ❑ 92PacSea-57
- ❑ 93ConTSN-730
- ❑ 93TedWil-26
- ❑ 94ConTSN-1008
- ❑ 94ConTSNB-1008
- ❑ 94UppDecAH-41
- ❑ 94UppDecAH1-41

Aquedo, Vasquez
- ❑ 87Ft.MyeRP-16

Aquino, Geronimo
- ❑ 93HicCraF-1290

Aquino, Julio
- ❑ 94GreFalDSP-2
- ❑ 95SanBerSTI-1
- ❑ 96HudValRB-22
- ❑ 97St.PetDR-7
- ❑ 97St.PetDRUB-6
- ❑ 98St.PetDRM-3

Aquino, Luis
- ❑ 86SyrChiP-2
- ❑ 87Don-655
- ❑ 87OPC-301
- ❑ 87SyrChiP-1937
- ❑ 87SyrChiT-1
- ❑ 87Top-301
- ❑ 87TopTif-301
- ❑ 88BlaYNPRWLU-22
- ❑ 88OmaRoyC-2
- ❑ 88OmaRoyP-1520
- ❑ 89BlaYNPRWL-71
- ❑ 89Don-534
- ❑ 89Fle-275
- ❑ 89FleGlo-275
- ❑ 89Top-266
- ❑ 89TopTif-266
- ❑ 90Don-179
- ❑ 90Fle-101
- ❑ 90FleCan-101
- ❑ 90OPC-707
- ❑ 90PubIntS-341
- ❑ 90RoyPos-2
- ❑ 90Sco-432
- ❑ 90Top-707
- ❑ 90TopTif-707
- ❑ 90UppDec-274
- ❑ 91Don-718
- ❑ 91Fle-550
- ❑ 91OPC-169
- ❑ 91RoyPol-2
- ❑ 91StaClu-451
- ❑ 91Top-169
- ❑ 91TopDesS-169
- ❑ 91TopMic-169
- ❑ 91TopTif-169
- ❑ 91UppDec-504
- ❑ 92Don-544
- ❑ 92Fle-151
- ❑ 92OPC-412
- ❑ 92Pin-454
- ❑ 92RoyPol-2
- ❑ 92Sco-369
- ❑ 92StaClu-365
- ❑ 92Top-412
- ❑ 92TopGol-412
- ❑ 92TopGolW-412
- ❑ 92TopMic-412
- ❑ 92UppDec-219
- ❑ 93Fle-615
- ❑ 93FleFinE-48
- ❑ 93Lea-509
- ❑ 93MarPub-1
- ❑ 93MarUppD-711
- ❑ 93PacSpa-130
- ❑ 93RoyPol-3
- ❑ 93Top-643
- ❑ 93TopGol-643
- ❑ 93TopInaM-643
- ❑ 93TopInaR-643
- ❑ 93TopMic-643
- ❑ 93TopTra-76T
- ❑ 93Ult-363
- ❑ 93UppDec-711
- ❑ 93UppDecGold-711
- ❑ 94ColC-39
- ❑ 94ColChoGS-39
- ❑ 94ColChoSS-39
- ❑ 94Don-67
- ❑ 94Fle-458
- ❑ 94Pac-233
- ❑ 94Pin-223
- ❑ 94PinArtP-223
- ❑ 94PinMusC-223
- ❑ 94Sco-255
- ❑ 94ScoGolR-255
- ❑ 94StaClu-160
- ❑ 94StaCluFDI-160
- ❑ 94StaCluGR-160
- ❑ 94StaCluMOP-160
- ❑ 94Top-76
- ❑ 94TopGol-76
- ❑ 94TopSpa-76
- ❑ 94Ult-191
- ❑ 95Fle-324
- ❑ 95Pac-165

Aquino, Pedro
- ❑ 87SpoIndP-20
- ❑ 88SpoIndP-1929

Arace, Pasquale
- ❑ 91AugPirC-19
- ❑ 91AugPirP-816
- ❑ 92SalBucC-8
- ❑ 92SalBucF-74

Aracena, Juan
- ❑ 96BurIndB-1
- ❑ 97BurIndG-1

Aracena, Luinis
- ❑ 92MadMusC-14
- ❑ 92MadMusF-1247
- ❑ 93MadMusC-3
- ❑ 93MadMusF-1833
- ❑ 93SouOreAC-2
- ❑ 93SouOreAF-4075

Aragon, Angelo
- ❑ 98CliLumG-1

Aragon, Joey
- ❑ 86VisOakP-2
- ❑ 87VisOakP-19
- ❑ 88OrlTwiB-11

Aragon, Reno
- ❑ 76DubPacT-3
- ❑ 77CocAstT-2

Aragon, Steve
- ❑ 82WisRapTF-23
- ❑ 83VisOakF-3
- ❑ 84VisOakT-24
- ❑ 85OrlTwiT-1
- ❑ 86OrlTwiP-1

Arai, Kiyoshi
- ❑ 92SalSpuC-1
- ❑ 92SalSpuF-3761

Araki, Daisuke
- ❑ 87JapPlaB-6

Aramboles, Ricardo
- ❑ 98Bow-300
- ❑ 98BowChr-300
- ❑ 98BowChrGA-300
- ❑ 98BowChrGAR-300
- ❑ 98BowChrI-300
- ❑ 98BowChrIR-300
- ❑ 98BowChrR-300
- ❑ 98BowGolA-300
- ❑ 98BowInt-300
- ❑ 99Bow-78
- ❑ 99BowChr-78
- ❑ 99BowChrG-78
- ❑ 99BowChrGR-78
- ❑ 99BowChrI-78
- ❑ 99BowChrIR-78
- ❑ 99BowChrR-78
- ❑ 99BowGol-78
- ❑ 99BowInt-78

Arango, Fernando
- ❑ 92OneYanC-29

Arangure, Maurillo
- ❑ 85MexCitTT-3

Arano, Eloy
- ❑ 94BriTigC-2
- ❑ 94BriTigF-3508

Aranzamendi, Alexis
- ❑ 92FroRowDP-72
- ❑ 92FroRowDPG-72
- ❑ 92FroRowDPS-72
- ❑ 94KanCouCC-3
- ❑ 94KanCouCF-167
- ❑ 94KanCouCTI-3

Aranzamendi, Jorge
- ❑ 77St.PetCT-12
- ❑ 78ArkTraT-1
- ❑ 79ArkTraT-12
- ❑ 80ArkTraT-3
- ❑ 81ArkTraT-8
- ❑ 82ArkTraT-24
- ❑ 83ArkTraT-24

Aranzullo, Mike
- ❑ 91SalLakTP-3215
- ❑ 91SalLakTSP-7

Arape, Ali
- ❑ 76VenLeaS-155

Araujo, Andy
- ❑ 85DomLeaS-28
- ❑ 86NewBriRSP-1
- ❑ 87PawRedSP-64
- ❑ 87PawRedST-1
- ❑ 88PawRedSC-5
- ❑ 88PawRedSP-446
- ❑ 89PawRedSC-8
- ❑ 89PawRedSP-679
- ❑ 89PawRedSTI-1
- ❑ 93LimRocDWB-114

Araujo, Danilo
- ❑ 97JohCitCTI-2
- ❑ 98NewJerCM-3

Araujo, Jesus
- ❑ 76VenLeaS-6

Araujo, Orlany
- ❑ 98GreFalDG-2

Arbogast, Charles
- ❑ 11PinT-5-1062
- ❑ 14Zee-28
- ❑ 15Zee-24

Arbuckle, Fatty (Roscoe)
- ❑ 19Zee-123

Archangel, Arsenio
- ❑ 98HelBreM-5

Archdeacon, Flash
- ❑ 94ConTSN-1307
- ❑ 94ConTSNB-1307

Archer, Carl
- ❑ 91PulBraC-4
- ❑ 91PulBraP-4010

Archer, Jim (James William)
- ❑ 56A'sPos-1
- ❑ 61AthJayP-1
- ❑ 61Top-552
- ❑ 62Jel-98
- ❑ 62Pos-98
- ❑ 62PosCan-98
- ❑ 62SalPlaC-75
- ❑ 62ShiPlaC-75
- ❑ 62Top-433
- ❑ 62TopBuc-4
- ❑ 62TopStal-52
- ❑ 63AthJayP-1

Archer, Jimmy (James Peter)
- ❑ 08AmeCarE91-34
- ❑ 08BufBisFJO-1
- ❑ 09ColChiE-11
- ❑ 09MaxPubP-20
- ❑ 09RamT20-3
- ❑ 09SpoNewSM-59
- ❑ 09TigMorBBBP-1
- ❑ 10ChiE-1
- ❑ 10DarChoE-1
- ❑ 10DomDisP-2
- ❑ 10OrnOvaPP-1
- ❑ 10SweCapPP-79A
- ❑ 10SweCapPP-79B
- ❑ 11HelSta-90
- ❑ 11PinT-5-210
- ❑ 11SpoLifM-165
- ❑ 11T205-3
- ❑ 12ColRedB-11
- ❑ 12ColTinT-11
- ❑ 12HasTriFT-13B
- ❑ 12HasTriFT-13C
- ❑ 12HasTriFT-13D
- ❑ 12HasTriFT-36A
- ❑ 12HasTriFT-36C
- ❑ 12HasTriFT-36D
- ❑ 14CraJacE-64
- ❑ 14FatPlaT-2
- ❑ 14PieStaT-2
- ❑ 14PolGroW-1
- ❑ 14TexTomE-1
- ❑ 15CraJacE-64
- ❑ 15SpoNewM-6
- ❑ 16BF2FP-65
- ❑ 16SpoNewM-6
- ❑ 17ColE13-7
- ❑ 90DodTar-20
- ❑ 93ConTSN-884

Archer, Kurt
- ❑ 90HelBreSP-15
- ❑ 90SanDieSA3-1
- ❑ 91Cla/Bes-223
- ❑ 91StoPorC-8
- ❑ 91StoPorP-3023
- ❑ 92StoPorC-22
- ❑ 92StoPorF-26
- ❑ 93El PasDF-2940
- ❑ 94ElPasDF-3137
- ❑ 94StoPorC-2

Archibald, Dan
- ❑ 88JamExpP-1920
- ❑ 89JamExpP-2142
- ❑ 90RocExpLC-1
- ❑ 90RocExpP-2684

Archibald, Jaime
- ❑ 86ColMetP-2
- ❑ 87LynMetP-9

Arcia, Jose R.
- ❑ 68Top-258
- ❑ 68TopVen-258
- ❑ 69MilBra-16
- ❑ 69Top-473A
- ❑ 69Top-473B
- ❑ 69TopSta-91
- ❑ 69TopTeaP-12
- ❑ 70Top-587
- ❑ 71MLBOffS-217
- ❑ 71OPC-134
- ❑ 71Top-134
- ❑ 72MilBra-19
- ❑ 73OPC-466
- ❑ 73Top-466

Ard, Johnny
- ❑ 89Bow-153
- ❑ 89BowTif-153
- ❑ 89CalLeaA-13
- ❑ 89VisOakCLC-96
- ❑ 89VisOakP-1427
- ❑ 90Bes-60
- ❑ 90Bow-406
- ❑ 90BowTif-406
- ❑ 90CMC-809
- ❑ 90OrlSunRB-23
- ❑ 90OrlSunRP-1075
- ❑ 90OrlSunRS-1
- ❑ 90ProAaA-39
- ❑ 91Bow-634
- ❑ 91LinDriAAA-385
- ❑ 91PhoFirLD-385
- ❑ 91PhoFirP-58
- ❑ 92PhoFirF-2814
- ❑ 92PhoFirS-376
- ❑ 92ProFS7-342
- ❑ 92SkyAAAF-173
- ❑ 93ClaFS7-41

Ardizola, Rinaldo
- ❑ 46RemBre-20

Ardner, Hoss (Joseph)
- ❑ 87OldJudN-13

Ardoin, Dan
- ❑ 96ModA'sB-3
- ❑ 97HunStaTI-1
- ❑ 98HunStaTI-20B

Arduini, Salvatore
- ❑ 52LavPro-84

Arellanes, Frank J.
- ❑ 09ObaT21-304
- ❑ 09RamT20-4
- ❑ 09T206-8
- ❑ 11BigEatEU-1
- ❑ 11PacCoaBD-4
- ❑ 11SpoLifCW-6
- ❑ 11SpoLifM-1
- ❑ 11Zee-62
- ❑ 12HomRunKE-46
- ❑ 12ObaPreT-53
- ❑ 12PhiCarE-3
- ❑ 12Zee-75
- ❑ 13Zee-75
- ❑ 14Zee-78
- ❑ 17Zee-100

Arellano, Carlos
- ❑ 94BurIndC-1
- ❑ 94BurIndF-3783

Arena, Rich
- ❑ 89OneYanP-2120
- ❑ 90GreHorB-29
- ❑ 90GreHorP-2681
- ❑ 90GreHorS-26
- ❑ 90TamYanD-28
- ❑ 92GulCoaYF-3707
- ❑ 93PriWilCC-27
- ❑ 93PriWilCF-673
- ❑ 96TamYanY-2

Arena, Sam
- ❑ 92ForLauYTI-1

Arendas, Dan
- ❑ 87Ft.LauYP-13
- ❑ 88Ft.LauYS-1

Arendas, David
- ❑ 88CapCodPPaLP-100

Arendt, Jim
- ❑ 91PriRedC-29

Arffa, Steve
- ❑ 94PitMetC-3
- ❑ 94PitMetF-3514
- ❑ 95StLucMTI-5
- ❑ 96StLucMTI-30

Arft, Hank (Henry Irven)
- ❑ 49Bow-139
- ❑ 51Bow-173
- ❑ 52Bow-229
- ❑ 52Top-284
- ❑ 53MotCoo-26
- ❑ 79DiaGre-192
- ❑ 83TopRep5-284

Argo, Billy
- ❑ 88BakDodCLC-244
- ❑ 89VerBeaDS-1

Arguelles, Fernando
- ❑ 89SalBucS-2
- ❑ 90SanBerSB-16
- ❑ 90SanBerSCLC-100
- ❑ 90SanBerSP-2636
- ❑ 91JacSunLD-326
- ❑ 91JacSunP-152
- ❑ 91LinDriAA-326

Arguto, Sam
- ❑ 93NiaFalRF-3377
- ❑ 94FayGenC-2
- ❑ 94FayGenF-2138

Arias, Alex
- ❑ 87WytCubP-27
- ❑ 88ChaWheB-9
- ❑ 88SouAtlLAGS-13
- ❑ 89PeoChiTI-17
- ❑ 90ChaKniTI-5
- ❑ 90TopTVCu-36
- ❑ 91ChaKniLD-126
- ❑ 91ChaKniP-1693
- ❑ 91Cla/Bes-10
- ❑ 91LinDriAA-126
- ❑ 92FleUpd-72
- ❑ 92IowCubF-4055
- ❑ 92IowCubS-202
- ❑ 92OPC-551
- ❑ 92ProFS7-202
- ❑ 92SkyAAAF-96
- ❑ 92Top-551
- ❑ 92TopGol-551
- ❑ 92TopGolW-551
- ❑ 92TopMic-551
- ❑ 93ClaGam-6
- ❑ 93Don-4
- ❑ 93Don-254
- ❑ 93Don-780
- ❑ 93Fla-45
- ❑ 93FleFinE-49
- ❑ 93FleMajLP-A16
- ❑ 93Lea-462
- ❑ 93LinVenB-311
- ❑ 93MarlStaClu-4
- ❑ 93MarPub-2
- ❑ 93MarUppD-631
- ❑ 93MarUSPC-1S
- ❑ 93MarUSPC-7H
- ❑ 93OPCPre-84
- ❑ 93PacSpa-452
- ❑ 93Pin-483
- ❑ 93Pin-612
- ❑ 93Sco-565
- ❑ 93StaClu-741
- ❑ 93StaCluFDI-741
- ❑ 93StaCluMOP-741
- ❑ 93Top-516
- ❑ 93TopGol-516
- ❑ 93TopInaM-516
- ❑ 93TopInaR-516
- ❑ 93TopMic-516
- ❑ 93Ult-364
- ❑ 93UppDec-631
- ❑ 93UppDecGold-631
- ❑ 94ColC-401
- ❑ 94ColChoGS-401
- ❑ 94ColChoSS-401
- ❑ 94Don-97
- ❑ 94Fle-459
- ❑ 94Pac-234
- ❑ 94Pin-390
- ❑ 94PinArtP-390
- ❑ 94PinMusC-390
- ❑ 94Sco-199
- ❑ 94ScoGolR-199
- ❑ 94Sel-137
- ❑ 94StaClu-230
- ❑ 94StaCluFDI-230
- ❑ 94StaCluGR-230
- ❑ 94StaCluMOP-230
- ❑ 94StaCluMOP-ST5
- ❑ 94StaCluST-ST5
- ❑ 94StaCluT-85
- ❑ 94StaCluTFDI-85
- ❑ 94Top-104
- ❑ 94TopGol-104
- ❑ 94TopSpa-104
- ❑ 94USPlaCR-2H
- ❑ 95Pac-166
- ❑ 95PacPri-53
- ❑ 95Sco-541
- ❑ 95ScoGolR-541
- ❑ 95ScoPlaTS-541
- ❑ 95StaClu-63
- ❑ 95StaCluFDI-63
- ❑ 95StaCluMOP-63
- ❑ 95StaCluSTWS-63
- ❑ 96ColCho-552
- ❑ 96ColChoGS-552
- ❑ 96ColChoSS-552
- ❑ 96Fle-381
- ❑ 96FleTif-381
- ❑ 96LeaSigEA-4
- ❑ 96Pac-71
- ❑ 96Sco-478
- ❑ 97Fle-324
- ❑ 97FleTif-324
- ❑ 97MarPac-3
- ❑ 97Pac-295
- ❑ 97PacLigB-295
- ❑ 97PacSil-295
- ❑ 98Pac-295
- ❑ 98PacOnl-553
- ❑ 98PacOnlR-553
- ❑ 98PacOnlWC-553
- ❑ 98PacPlaB-295
- ❑ 98PacRedT-295
- ❑ 98PacSil-295
- ❑ 98PhiTeal-3
- ❑ 99Pac-321
- ❑ 99PacCroC-211
- ❑ 99PacCroCPB-211
- ❑ 99PacPlaB-321
- ❑ 99PacRed-321

Arias, Alfredo
- ❑ 94St.CatBJC-2
- ❑ 94St.CatBJF-3631
- ❑ 95HagSunF-59

Arias, Amador
- ❑ 91CedRapRC-16
- ❑ 91CedRapRP-2724
- ❑ 91Cla/Bes-340
- ❑ 91EriSaiC-1
- ❑ 91EriSaiP-4074
- ❑ 92ChaWheF-13
- ❑ 92ChaWVWC-20
- ❑ 93LinVenB-120
- ❑ 93WinSpiC-3
- ❑ 93WinSpiF-1575
- ❑ 94WinSpiC-3
- ❑ 94WinSpiF-276
- ❑ 95ChaLooTI-1
- ❑ 95LinVen-85
- ❑ 96-97LinVen-76
- ❑ 96CarLeaA1B-17
- ❑ 96CarLeaA2B-17
- ❑ 98ChaAllCM-28

Arias, Francisco
- ❑ 87PocGiaTB-26
- ❑ 88PocGiaP-2078

Arias, George
- ❑ 94LakElsSC-2
- ❑ 94LakElsSF-1669
- ❑ 94Top-369
- ❑ 94TopGol-369
- ❑ 94TopSpa-369
- ❑ 95Bes-10
- ❑ 95BowBes-B66
- ❑ 95BowBesR-B66
- ❑ 95Exc-17
- ❑ 95MidAngOHP-2
- ❑ 95MidAngTI-2
- ❑ 95SPML-26
- ❑ 95SPMLA-3

❑ 95TopTra-122T
❑ 95UppDecML-139
❑ 95UppDecMLFS-139
❑ 96AngMot-12
❑ 96Bow-202
❑ 96BowBesMI-3
❑ 96BowBesMIAR-3
❑ 96BowBesMIR-3
❑ 96BowFoi-202
❑ 96ColCho-426
❑ 96ColChoGS-426
❑ 96ColChoSS-426
❑ 96EmoXL-23
❑ 96Exc-21
❑ 96ExcAll-4
❑ 96ExcTL-1
❑ 96Fin-G202
❑ 96FinRef-G202
❑ 96Fla-33
❑ 96FlaWavotF-2
❑ 96FleUpd-U19
❑ 96FleUpdNH-2
❑ 96FleUpdTC-U19
❑ 96LeaLimR-10
❑ 96LeaLimRG-10
❑ 96LeaPre-131
❑ 96LeaPreP-131
❑ 96LeaSig-111
❑ 96LeaSigPPG-111
❑ 96LeaSigPPP-111
❑ 96Pin-373
❑ 96PinAfi-161
❑ 96PinAfiAP-161
❑ 96PinFoil-373
❑ 96Sel-166
❑ 96SelArtP-166
❑ 96SelCer-115
❑ 96SelCerAP-115
❑ 96SelCerCB-115
❑ 96SelCerCR-115
❑ 96SelCerMB-115
❑ 96SelCerMG-115
❑ 96SelCerMR-115
❑ 96SP-2
❑ 96Stu-146
❑ 96StuPrePB-146
❑ 96StuPrePG-146
❑ 96StuPrePS-146
❑ 96Sum-170
❑ 96SumAbo&B-170
❑ 96SumArtP-170
❑ 96SumFoi-170
❑ 96Top-434
❑ 96Ult-324
❑ 96UltGolM-324
❑ 96UppDec-238
❑ 96UppDecFSP-FS1
❑ 96UppDecPHE-H21
❑ 96UppDecPreH-H21
❑ 96VanCanB-5
❑ 96Zen-107
❑ 96ZenArtP-107
❑ 97Bow-156
❑ 97BowInt-156
❑ 97Cir-195
❑ 97CirRav-195
❑ 97Don-127
❑ 97Don-393
❑ 97DonEli-72
❑ 97DonEliGS-72
❑ 97DonGolPP-127
❑ 97DonGolPP-393
❑ 97DonSilPP-127
❑ 97DonSilPP-393
❑ 97Fle-35
❑ 97FleTif-35
❑ 97Lea-4
❑ 97LeaFraM-4
❑ 97LeaFraMDC-4
❑ 97MetUni-37
❑ 97Pac-2
❑ 97PacLatotML-1
❑ 97PacLigB-2
❑ 97PacSil-2
❑ 97Pin-167
❑ 97PinArtP-PP167
❑ 97PinIns-135
❑ 97PinInsCE-135
❑ 97PinInsDE-135
❑ 97PinMusC-167
❑ 97PinPrePla-167
❑ 97Sco-128
❑ 97ScoArtPWB-128
❑ 97ScoPreS-128
❑ 97ScoShoS-128
❑ 97ScoShoSAP-128
❑ 97SelToootT-15
❑ 97SelToootTMB-15
❑ 97Stu-152
❑ 97StuPrePG-152
❑ 97StuPrePS-152
❑ 97Top-306
❑ 97Ult-23
❑ 97UltGolME-23
❑ 97UltPlaME-23
❑ 97UppDec-293
❑ 97VanCanB-5
❑ 98Las-5

Arias, German
❑ 90MarPhiP-3207

Arias, Jeison
❑ 97PriDevR-5

Arias, Jose
❑ 90HamRedS-2
❑ 90SavCarP-2058
❑ 91JohCitCC-27
❑ 96MarPhiB-2

Arias, Juan
❑ 78SalPirT-1
❑ 79BufBisT-11

Arias, Pedro
❑ 88BurIndP-1787

Arias, Rafael
❑ 98MicBatCM-7

Arias, Rogelio
❑ 95AshTouTI-18
❑ 96AshTouB-6
❑ 96PorRocB-6
❑ 97AshTou-4

Arias, Rudy (Rodolfo M.)
❑ 59Top-537
❑ 81WhiSox1T-35

Arias, Tony
❑ 85MadMusP-3
❑ 85MadMusT-6
❑ 86MadMusP-2
❑ 86MadMusP-2
❑ 88ModA'sTI-19

Arias, Wagner
❑ 93HelBreF-4084
❑ 93HelBreSP-6
❑ 94BelBreC-2
❑ 94BelBreFI-92
❑ 97StoPor-17

Arigoni, Scott
❑ 82ArkTraT-1
❑ 83SprCarF-9

Ariola, Anthony
❑ 88SouOreAP-1696
❑ 89MadMusS-2
❑ 89Sta-64
❑ 90CMC-581
❑ 90ProAAAF-131
❑ 90TacTigC-4
❑ 90TacTigP-84

Aristimuno, Jesus
❑ 76VenLeaS-159

Arita, Shuzo
❑ 91SalSpuC-27
❑ 91SalSpuP-2261

Arito, Michiyo
❑ 79TCMJapPB-63

Arkenburg, Levi
❑ 18Zee-54

Arland, Mark
❑ 90ChaWheB-20
❑ 90ChaWheP-2250
❑ 91ChaWheC-21
❑ 91ChaWheP-2898

Arlett, Alex
❑ 11Zee-21
❑ 13Zee-97
❑ 14Zee-99
❑ 17Zee-19
❑ 18Zee-17
❑ 19Zee-13
❑ 20Zee-17
❑ 21Zee-23

Arlett, Buzz (Russell Loris)
❑ 19Zee-14
❑ 20WalMaiW-1
❑ 20Zee-18
❑ 22Zee-21
❑ 23Zee-23
❑ 24Zee-20
❑ 25Zee-16
❑ 27Zee-42
❑ 28ExhPCL-1
❑ 30Zee-72
❑ 31Exh-11
❑ 33WorCig(-1
❑ 78HalHalR-15

Arlich, Don (Donald Louis)
❑ 77FriOneYW-90

Arlin, Steve (Stephen Ralph)
❑ 72OPC-78
❑ 72PadPos-2
❑ 72Top-78
❑ 73OPC-294
❑ 73Top-294
❑ 74OPC-406
❑ 74Top-406
❑ 75OPC-159
❑ 75Top-159
❑ 75TopMin-159
❑ 77PadSchC-4A
❑ 77PadSchC-4B

Arline, James
❑ 78RicBraT-2
❑ 79RicBraT-23

Armas, Familia
❑ 94VenLinU-141

Armas, Julio
❑ 93LinVenB-149
❑ 94VenLinU-163

Armas, Marcos
❑ 89MedAthB-24
❑ 90MadMusB-4
❑ 91HunStaC-1
❑ 91HunStaLD-276
❑ 91HunStaP-1807
❑ 91LinDriAA-276
❑ 91ModA'sP-3093
❑ 92ClaFS7-134
❑ 92HunStaF-3955
❑ 92HunStaS-302
❑ 92SkyAA F-127
❑ 93Bow-429
❑ 93ClaGolF-20
❑ 93FleFinE-253
❑ 93Lea-478
❑ 93LinVenB-175
❑ 93TacTigF-3043
❑ 93TopTra-100T
❑ 94Don-51
❑ 94Fle-253
❑ 94Pac-444
❑ 94Pin-398
❑ 94PinArtP-398
❑ 94PinMusC-398
❑ 94TacTigF-3180
❑ 94Top-311
❑ 94TopGol-311
❑ 94TopSpa-311
❑ 94VenLinU-123
❑ 94VenLinU-197
❑ 95LinVen-169
❑ 95LinVen-257
❑ 96-97LinVen-49

Armas, Tony (Antonio Rafael)
❑ 76VenLeaS-77
❑ 76VenLeaS-223
❑ 77Top-492
❑ 78Top-298
❑ 79Top-507
❑ 80Top-391
❑ 80VenLeaS-99
❑ 80VenLeaS-130
❑ 81A'sGraG-20
❑ 81AllGamPI-46
❑ 81Don-239
❑ 81Dra-30
❑ 81Fle-575
❑ 81FleStiC-5
❑ 81OPC-151
❑ 81Squ-24
❑ 81Top-629
❑ 81TopScr-6
❑ 81TopSti-116
❑ 82A'sGraG-1
❑ 82Don-365
❑ 82Dra-1
❑ 82Fle-85
❑ 82FleSta-128
❑ 82Kel-35
❑ 82OPC-60
❑ 82PerCreC-17
❑ 82PerCreCG-17
❑ 82Top-60
❑ 82Top-162
❑ 82TopSti-4
❑ 82TopSti-224
❑ 83AllGamPI-46
❑ 83Don-71
❑ 83Fle-513
❑ 83OPC-353
❑ 83Top-1
❑ 83Top-435
❑ 83TopSti-108
❑ 83TopSti-191
❑ 83TopSti-192
❑ 83TopTra-4T
❑ 84AllGamPI-136
❑ 84Don-294
❑ 84Fle-390
❑ 84FleSti-21
❑ 84FunFooP-24
❑ 84Nes792-105
❑ 84OPC-105
❑ 84Top-105
❑ 84TopGloS-20
❑ 84TopRubD-1
❑ 84TopSti-218
❑ 84TopTif-105
❑ 85AllGamPI-46
❑ 85Don-249
❑ 85Dra-1
❑ 85Fle-149
❑ 85FleStaS-12
❑ 85FleStaS-28
❑ 85Lea-112
❑ 85OPC-394
❑ 85Top-707
❑ 85Top-785
❑ 85TopGaloC-1
❑ 85TopGloS-18
❑ 85TopRubD-1
❑ 85TopSti-95
❑ 85TopSti-194
❑ 85TopSti-209
❑ 85TopSup-10
❑ 85TopTif-707
❑ 85TopTif-785
❑ 86Don-5
❑ 86Don-127
❑ 86DonSupD-5
❑ 86Fle-339
❑ 86Lea-5
❑ 86OPC-255
❑ 86Spo-61
❑ 86Spo-145
❑ 86Top-255
❑ 86TopSti-254
❑ 86TopTat-11
❑ 86TopTif-255
❑ 86Woo-1
❑ 87A'sMot-21
❑ 87BoaandB-15
❑ 87Don-498
❑ 87Fle-26
❑ 87FleGlo-26
❑ 87OPC-174
❑ 87Top-535
❑ 87TopTif-535
❑ 88AngSmo-5
❑ 88Fle-484
❑ 88FleGlo-484
❑ 88Sco-487
❑ 88ScoGlo-487
❑ 88Top-761
❑ 88TopClo-3
❑ 88TopTif-761
❑ 89Bow-51
❑ 89BowTif-51
❑ 89Don-580
❑ 89Fle-467
❑ 89FleGlo-467
❑ 89PanSti-295
❑ 89Sco-182
❑ 89Top-332
❑ 89TopBig-99
❑ 89TopTif-332
❑ 89UppDec-212
❑ 90Don-525
❑ 90Fle-126
❑ 90FleCan-126
❑ 90OPC-603
❑ 90PubIntS-364
❑ 90Sco-378
❑ 90Top-603
❑ 90TopTif-603
❑ 90UppDec-58
❑ 93LinVenB-281
❑ 93LinVenB-282
❑ 93LinVenB-283
❑ 93LinVenB-284
❑ 93LinVenB-285
❑ 93LinVenB-286
❑ 93LinVenB-287
❑ 95LinVen-162
❑ 95LinVen-257
❑ 96-97LinVen-213

Armas, Tony Jr.
❑ 95LinVen-133
❑ 97Bes-54
❑ 97GreBatB-7
❑ 98Bes-53
❑ 98BowBes-195
❑ 98BowBesAR-195
❑ 98BowBesR-195
❑ 98JupHamQ-5
❑ 99BasAmeTP-6
❑ 99BasAmeTPG-6
❑ 99Bow-192
❑ 99BowChr-192
❑ 99BowChrG-192
❑ 99BowChrGR-192
❑ 99BowChrI-192
❑ 99BowChrIR-192
❑ 99BowChrR-192
❑ 99BowGol-192
❑ 99BowInt-192

Armbrister, Ed (Edison R.)
❑ 72OPC-524
❑ 72Top-524
❑ 74OPC-601
❑ 74Top-601
❑ 75OPC-622
❑ 75Top-622
❑ 75TopMin-622
❑ 76OPC-652
❑ 76RedKro-1
❑ 76SSP-42
❑ 76Top-652
❑ 77Top-203
❑ 78IndIndTI-8
❑ 78SSP270-124
❑ 78Top-556

Armbruster, Charles
❑ 09ObaT21-114
❑ 11SpoLifCW-7

Armbruster, Harry (Herman)
❑ 09T206-393

Armendariz, Jesse
❑ 94WilCubC-1
❑ 94WilCubF-3753

Armer, Rick
❑ 77WauMetT-2

Armour, Bill
❑ 11SpoLifCW-8

Armstead, Al
❑ 79WatA'sT-10

Armstrong, Bill
❑ 79MemChiT-3
❑ 84EvaTriT-20

Armstrong, Eldridge
❑ 84IdaFalATI-2

Armstrong, Jack Fictional Character
❑ 35WheBB1-1
❑ 35WheBB1-2

Armstrong, Jack William
❑ 88NasSouC-1
❑ 88NasSouP-484
❑ 88NasSouTI-1
❑ 88RedKah-40
❑ 88ScoRoo-78T
❑ 88ScoRooG-78T
❑ 88TopTra-6T
❑ 88TopTraT-6T
❑ 89ClaLigB-97
❑ 89Don-493
❑ 89PanSti-63
❑ 89Sco-462
❑ 89ScoHot1R-99
❑ 89Top-317
❑ 89TopTif-317
❑ 89UppDec-257
❑ 90ClaYel-T74
❑ 90Don-544
❑ 90DonBesN-142
❑ 90Fle-412
❑ 90FleCan-412
❑ 90Lea-374
❑ 90OPC-642
❑ 90RedKah-1
❑ 90ScoYouS2-11
❑ 90Top-642
❑ 90TopBig-314
❑ 90TopTif-642
❑ 90TriAAAC-12
❑ 90UppDec-684
❑ 90USPlaCA-JKO
❑ 91BasBesAotM-2
❑ 91Bow-679
❑ 91ClaGam-6
❑ 91Don-439
❑ 91Don-571
❑ 91Fle-55
❑ 91Lea-459
❑ 91OPC-175
❑ 91PanFreS-165
❑ 91PanSti-126
❑ 91RedFolS-114
❑ 91RedKah-40
❑ 91RedPep-1
❑ 91Sco-231
❑ 91Sco100S-83
❑ 91StaClu-510
❑ 91Top-175
❑ 91TopDesS-175
❑ 91TopGloA-21
❑ 91TopMic-175
❑ 91TopTif-175
❑ 91UppDec-373
❑ 92Bow-252
❑ 92Don-762
❑ 92Fle-398
❑ 92IndFanC-2
❑ 92Lea-247
❑ 92LeaBlaG-247
❑ 92OPC-77
❑ 92OPCPre-192
❑ 92RedFolS-6
❑ 92Sco-488
❑ 92ScoRoo-58T
❑ 92StaClu-791
❑ 92StaCluNC-791
❑ 92Stu-162
❑ 92Top-77
❑ 92TopGol-77
❑ 92TopGolW-77
❑ 92TopMic-77
❑ 92TopTra-6T
❑ 92TopTraG-6T
❑ 92Ult-344
❑ 92UppDec-296
❑ 92UppDec-789
❑ 93Don-69
❑ 93Don-777
❑ 93Fla-46
❑ 93Fle-417
❑ 93FleFinE-50
❑ 93Lea-235
❑ 93MarlStaClu-9
❑ 93MarPub-3
❑ 93MarUppD-758
❑ 93MarUSPC-2D
❑ 93MarUSPC-11S
❑ 93PacSpa-453
❑ 93Pin-513
❑ 93Sco-655
❑ 93StaClu-567
❑ 93StaCluFDI-567
❑ 93StaCluMOP-567
❑ 93Top-434
❑ 93TopGol-434
❑ 93TopInaM-434
❑ 93TopInaR-434
❑ 93TopMic-434
❑ 93TopTra-80T
❑ 93Ult-365
❑ 93UppDec-758
❑ 93UppDecGold-758
❑ 94ColC-40
❑ 94ColC-418
❑ 94ColChoGS-40
❑ 94ColChoGS-418
❑ 94ColChoSS-40
❑ 94ColChoSS-418
❑ 94Don-466
❑ 94Fla-107
❑ 94Fle-460
❑ 94Lea-226
❑ 94Pac-235
❑ 94Pin-166
❑ 94PinArtP-166
❑ 94PinMusC-166
❑ 94RanMagM-1
❑ 94Sco-410
❑ 94ScoGolR-410
❑ 94ScoRoo-RT45
❑ 94ScoRooGR-RT45
❑ 94StaClu-594
❑ 94StaCluFDI-594
❑ 94StaCluGR-594
❑ 94StaCluMOP-594
❑ 94StaCluT-256

❑ 94StaCluTFDI-256
❑ 94Top-551
❑ 94TopGol-551
❑ 94TopSpa-551
❑ 94UppDec-469
❑ 94UppDecED-469
❑ 95Top-222

Armstrong, Jim
❑ 91IdaFalBP-4319
❑ 91IdaFalBSP-10

Armstrong, Kevin
❑ 85LitFalMT-2
❑ 86ColMetP-3
❑ 87WicPilRD-2
❑ 88RivRedWCLC-206
❑ 89SanAntMB-6

Armstrong, Mike (Michael D.)
❑ 79NaSouTI-3
❑ 80HawIslT-16
❑ 80VenLeaS-208
❑ 81Fle-503
❑ 81HawIslT-11
❑ 82OmaRoyT-1
❑ 82Roy-2
❑ 82Top-731
❑ 83Fle-105
❑ 83RoyPos-2
❑ 83Top-219
❑ 84Don-217
❑ 84Fle-342
❑ 84Nes792-417
❑ 84Top-417
❑ 84TopTif-417
❑ 84TopTra-3T
❑ 84TopTraT-3T
❑ 85Don-602
❑ 85Fle-120
❑ 85Top-612
❑ 85TopTif-612
❑ 85YanTCMP-7
❑ 86ColCliP-1
❑ 86ColCliP-1
❑ 86YanTCM-4
❑ 87ColCliP-1
❑ 87ColCliP-21
❑ 92YanWIZ8-4

Armstrong, William
❑ 83EvaTriT-23

Arndt, Harry J.
❑ 09T206-394
❑ 11SpoLifCW-9

Arndt, Larry
❑ 86MadMusP-3
❑ 86MadMusP-3
❑ 87HunStaTI-2
❑ 89TacTigC-22
❑ 89TacTigP-1557
❑ 90CMC-600
❑ 90ProAAAF-144
❑ 90TacTigC-23
❑ 90TacTigP-97
❑ 90TopDeb89-7
❑ 91SouOreAAP-SOA10

Arner, Michael
❑ 90Bes-200
❑ 90CMC-479
❑ 90GasRanB-19
❑ 90GasRanP-2511
❑ 90GasRanS-1
❑ 90ProAaA-80
❑ 90SouAtlLAS-1
❑ 90StaFS7-96
❑ 91ChaRanC-1
❑ 91ChaRanP-1305
❑ 92ChaRanC-24
❑ 93TulDriF-2726
❑ 93TulDriTI-2

Arnerich, Ken
❑ 82QuaCitCT-18

Arnett, Curt
❑ 74GasRanT-1
❑ 75LynRanT-2

Arnett, Jon
❑ 58HarSta-21

Arnette, Steve
❑ 89TenTecGE-1

Arney, Jeff
❑ 82WisRapTF-25
❑ 83VisOakF-2
❑ 85WatIndT-14
❑ 86WatIndP-1

Arnold, Bryan
❑ 88WatPirP-14

Arnold, Chris
❑ 72OPC-232
❑ 72Top-232
❑ 73OPC-584
❑ 73Top-584
❑ 74OPC-432
❑ 74Top-432
❑ 76SanFraGP-2
❑ 76SSP-99
❑ 77PhoGiaCC-2
❑ 77PhoGiaCP-2
❑ 77PhoGiaVNB-1
❑ 77Top-591
❑ 79TCMJapPB-43

Arnold, Gary
❑ 87NewOriP-6
❑ 88GenCubP-1636
❑ 89GenCubP-1858

Arnold, Greg
❑ 89PulBraP-1912

Arnold, James
❑ 47SmiClo-10

Arnold, Jamie
❑ 92ClaBluBF-BC25
❑ 92ClaDraP-16
❑ 92ClaDraPFB-BC15
❑ 92ClaFS7-407
❑ 92UppDecML-12
❑ 93ClaFS7-42
❑ 93ClaGolF-110
❑ 93MacBraC-2
❑ 93MacBraF-1391
❑ 93Pin-455
❑ 93Sco-487
❑ 93Sel-303
❑ 93StaCluM-65
❑ 93Top-559
❑ 93TopGol-559
❑ 93TopInaM-559
❑ 93TopInaR-559
❑ 93TopMic-559
❑ 94CarLeaAF-CAR27
❑ 94Cla-135
❑ 94ClaGolF-113
❑ 94ClaTriF-T1
❑ 94DurBulC-2
❑ 94DurBulF-319
❑ 94DurBulTI-2
❑ 94ExcFS7-151
❑ 94UppDecML-36
❑ 95BreBtaTI-34
❑ 95DurBulTI-1
❑ 95UppDecML-159
❑ 95UppDecMLFS-159
❑ 96GreBraB-5
❑ 96GreBraTI-46
❑ 98RicBraQ-2

Arnold, Jay
❑ 96OgdRapTI-37

Arnold, Jeff
❑ 84NewOriT-25

Arnold, Joe
❑ 98OneYanG-1

Arnold, John
❑ 77WatIndT-2

Arnold, John A.
❑ 96EugEmeB-21
❑ 97EugEmeB-17

Arnold, Ken
❑ 91HunCubC-3
❑ 91HunCubP-3339
❑ 92PeoChiC-27
❑ 92PeoChiTI-2
❑ 92ProFS7-212
❑ 94BowBayF-2418
❑ 96TulDriTI-1

Arnold, Neal
❑ 97NewJerCB-3
❑ 98PeoChiM-2

Arnold, Ron
❑ 84AlbA'sT-2
❑ 84TacTigC-75

Arnold, Scott
❑ 86FloStaLAP-5
❑ 86St.PetCP-2
❑ 87ArkTraP-13
❑ 87TexLeaAF-21
❑ 88LouRedBTI-8
❑ 88TexLeaAGS-20
❑ 89LouRedBC-2
❑ 89LouRedBP-1248
❑ 89LouRedBTI-9
❑ 90CMC-101
❑ 90LouRedBC-1
❑ 90LouRedBLBC-7
❑ 90LouRedBP-394
❑ 90ProAAAF-508
❑ 90SprCarDGB-18
❑ 90TopTVCa-38

Arnold, Sheila
❑ 88GenCubP-1660

Arnold, Tim
❑ 86FloStaLAP-6
❑ 86WesPalBEP-2
❑ 87JacExpP-430
❑ 88VisOakCLC-149
❑ 88VisOakP-97
❑ 89OrlTwiB-8
❑ 89OrlTwiP-1353

Arnold, Tony
❑ 84ChaO'sT-26
❑ 85ChaO'sT-8
❑ 86RocRedWP-1
❑ 87BalOriP-2
❑ 87OriFreB-57
❑ 88AlbDukCm-5
❑ 88AlbDukP-261
❑ 89SanAntMB-5
❑ 90YakBeaTI-19
❑ 91OriCro-13
❑ 91YakBeaP-4265
❑ 92TexLon-3
❑ 92YakBeaC-26
❑ 93WatIndC-30
❑ 94WatIndC-29
❑ 95KinIndTI-1
❑ 96CanIndB-2
❑ 97AkrAer-2
❑ 98AkrAerM-2

Arnovich, Morrie (Morris)
❑ 38CloFotW-2
❑ 38ExhFou-6
❑ 39PlaBal-46
❑ 39WorWidGV-1
❑ 40PhiTeal-1
❑ 40PlaBal-97
❑ 40WheM4-4
❑ 41DouPlaR-139
❑ 41Gou-25
❑ 41HarHarW-1
❑ 41PhiTeal-1
❑ 41PlaBal-57
❑ 77CinRedT-26
❑ 92ConTSN-500

Arnsberg, Brad
❑ 84GreHorT-10
❑ 85AlbYanT-1
❑ 86ColCliP-2
❑ 86ColCliP-2
❑ 86YanTCM-2
❑ 87ColCliP-2
❑ 87ColCliP-24
❑ 87ColCliT-1
❑ 87IntLeaAT-3
❑ 88Fle-202
❑ 88FleGlo-202
❑ 88Top-159
❑ 88TopTif-159
❑ 89RanMot-15
❑ 89RanSmo-2
❑ 90AlbDecGB-27
❑ 90CMC-157
❑ 90Lea-495
❑ 90OklCit8C-7
❑ 90OklCit8P-423
❑ 90ProAAAF-669
❑ 90Sco100RS-72
❑ 90TopTra-3T
❑ 90TopTraT-3T
❑ 91Bow-279
❑ 91Don-633
❑ 91Fle-279
❑ 91OPC-706
❑ 91PacRyaTEI-68
❑ 91RanMot-25
❑ 91Sco-510
❑ 91StaClu-540
❑ 91Top-706A
❑ 91Top-706B
❑ 91TopDesS-706
❑ 91TopMic-706
❑ 91TopTif-706
❑ 91Ult-346
❑ 91UppDec-608
❑ 92ColSprSSF-742
❑ 92Fle-298
❑ 92IndFanC-3
❑ 92IowCubF-4045
❑ 92StaClu-668
❑ 92StaCluECN-668
❑ 92YanWIZ8-5
❑ 93PacSpa-92
❑ 93RanKee-54
❑ 93TacTigF-3024
❑ 95ChaRivTI-28
❑ 96ChaRivTI-9603
❑ 97TulDriTI-1
❑ 98TexLeaC-1
❑ 98TulDriTI-24

Arnsberg, Tim
❑ 86AshTouP-1
❑ 87OscAstP-26

Arntzen, Brian
❑ 90NebCor-2
❑ 92WatIndC-15
❑ 92WatIndF-3237
❑ 93ColRedC-2
❑ 93ColRedF-600

Arntzen, Orie Edgar
❑ 43A'STEAI-3

Arocha, Rene
❑ 92LouRedF-1879
❑ 92LouRedS-251
❑ 92SkyAAAF-122
❑ 92TriA AAS-251
❑ 92UppDecML-136
❑ 93Bow-276
❑ 93CarPol-2
❑ 93CarStaC-2
❑ 93Don-572
❑ 93ExcFS7-95
❑ 93Fla-119
❑ 93FleFinE-123
❑ 93LeaGolR-R15
❑ 93LeaGolRJ-R15
❑ 93OPCPre-6
❑ 93PacBeiA-29
❑ 93PacSpa-628
❑ 93Pin-599
❑ 93SelRoo-62T
❑ 93SelRooAR-9
❑ 93SP-73
❑ 93StaClu-712
❑ 93StaCluFDI-712
❑ 93StaCluMOP-712
❑ 93Top-742
❑ 93TopGol-742
❑ 93TopInaM-742
❑ 93TopInaR-742
❑ 93TopMic-742
❑ 93TopTra-77T
❑ 93Toy-78
❑ 93Ult-460
❑ 93UltAllR-1
❑ 93UppDec-3
❑ 93UppDecGold-3
❑ 94Bow-208
❑ 94CarMagG-5
❑ 94CarPol-2
❑ 94ColC-41
❑ 94ColChoGS-41
❑ 94ColChoSS-41
❑ 94Don-60
❑ 94Fin-5
❑ 94FinJum-5
❑ 94FinRef-5
❑ 94Fla-223
❑ 94Fle-628
❑ 94FleExtB-356
❑ 94FleRooS-1
❑ 94Lea-228
❑ 94OPC-234
❑ 94Pac-586
❑ 94Pin-107
❑ 94PinArtP-107
❑ 94PinMusC-107
❑ 94Sco-164
❑ 94ScoBoyoS-25
❑ 94ScoGolR-164
❑ 94Sel-300
❑ 94StaClu-306
❑ 94StaCluFDI-306
❑ 94StaCluGR-306
❑ 94StaCluMOP-306
❑ 94StaCluT-315
❑ 94StaCluTFDI-315
❑ 94Top-348
❑ 94TopGol-348
❑ 94TopSpa-348
❑ 94Ult-264
❑ 94UppDec-191
❑ 94UppDecED-191
❑ 94USPlaCR-10S
❑ 95ColCho-197
❑ 95ColChoGS-197
❑ 95ColChoSS-197
❑ 95Don-2
❑ 95DonPreP-2
❑ 95Fin-46
❑ 95FinRef-46
❑ 95Fla-191
❑ 95Fle-494
❑ 95Lea-166
❑ 95Pac-405
❑ 95PacPri-130
❑ 95Sco-374
❑ 95ScoGolR-374
❑ 95ScoPlaTS-374
❑ 95StaClu-16
❑ 95StaCluFDI-16
❑ 95StaCluMOP-16
❑ 95StaCluSTWS-16
❑ 95StaCluVR-10
❑ 95StaCluVRMO-10
❑ 95Top-24
❑ 95TopCyb-20
❑ 95Ult-221
❑ 95UltGolM-221
❑ 95UppDecSE-94
❑ 95UppDecSEG-94
❑ 97PhoFirTI-1
❑ 98NewOrlZM-1

Arola, Bruce
❑ 88MadMusP-2
❑ 89BoiHawP-1996
❑ 91SalSpuC-22
❑ 91SalSpuP-2234
❑ 92SalSpuF-3748

Aronetz, Cam
❑ 91GreFalDSP-22
❑ 92BakDodCLC-2
❑ 93BelBreCB-1
❑ 93BelBreFI-1700

Aronson, Chris
❑ 98ButCopKG-3

Arp, Ron
❑ 76BatTroTI-1

Arrandale, Matt
❑ 93GleFalRC-4
❑ 93GleFalRF-3993
❑ 94SavCarC-3
❑ 94SavCarF-496
❑ 94SouAtlLAF-SAL46
❑ 95ArkTraTI-3
❑ 95Exc-260
❑ 95Top-316
❑ 95UppDecML-44
❑ 95UppDecMLFS-44
❑ 96LouRedB-6
❑ 97LouRedB-6
❑ 98MemRedG-1

Arredondo, Hernando
❑ 96ButCopKB-9
❑ 97ChaRivDG-2
❑ 97HudValRB-20

Arredondo, Joe
❑ 90PitMetP-6
❑ 91PitMetC-13
❑ 91PitMetP-3427

Arredondo, Roberto
❑ 90ChaRaiB-9
❑ 90ChaRaiP-2045
❑ 91MidLeaAP-MWL29
❑ 91WatDiaC-14
❑ 91WatDiaP-1261
❑ 92ClaFS7-10
❑ 92HigDesMC-6
❑ 92ProFS7-338

Arrevalos, Ryan
❑ 95HelBreTI-4

Arriete, Nelson
❑ 88MisStaB-1
❑ 89MisStaB-3

Arrigo, Jerry (Gerald W.)
❑ 64Top-516
❑ 65OPC-39
❑ 65RedEnq-1
❑ 65Top-39
❑ 66Top-357
❑ 66TopVen-357
❑ 67Top-488
❑ 68Kah-B7
❑ 68Top-302
❑ 68TopVen-302
❑ 69Kah-B4
❑ 69OPC-213
❑ 69Top-213
❑ 69TopFou-14
❑ 69TopSta-22
❑ 69TopTeaP-20
❑ 70OPC-274
❑ 70Top-274
❑ 72MilBra-20
❑ 78TCM60I-64
❑ 78TCM60I-86
❑ 91MetWIZ-14

Arrington, Dave
❑ 74WicAerODF-122

Arrington, Mike
❑ 76AshTouT-13

Arrington, Sam
❑ 80WisRapTT-1
❑ 82OrlTwiT-23
❑ 83VisOakF-4

Arrington, Tom
❑ 86BurExpP-1

Arrington, Warren
❑ 87WytCubP-26
❑ 88PeoChiTI-2
❑ 89PeoChiTI-23

Arrojo, Rolando
❑ 97Bes-23
❑ 97BesAutSBPP-9
❑ 97BesBetP-10
❑ 97BesGun-2
❑ 97St.PetDRUB-1
❑ 98CirThu-198
❑ 98CirThuRav-198
❑ 98CirThuSupRav-198
❑ 98CroRoy-130
❑ 98DevRayP-2
❑ 98Don-221
❑ 98DonGolPP-221
❑ 98DonSig-105
❑ 98DonSigP-105
❑ 98DonSilPP-221
❑ 98Fle-499
❑ 98FlePlaCS-1
❑ 98FleProF-PF1
❑ 98LeaRS-222
❑ 98LeaRSLHolo-222
❑ 98LeaRSLong-222
❑ 98LeaRTrue-222
❑ 98PacAur-78
❑ 98PacOme-228
❑ 98PacOmeR-228
❑ 98PacOmeRS-22
❑ 98PacOmeRST3-22
❑ 98PacOnl-703
❑ 98PacOnlR-703
❑ 98PacOnlWC-703
❑ 98Revo-137
❑ 98RevoRooHH-19
❑ 98RevoRooHHG-19
❑ 98RevoSS-137
❑ 98SkyDugA-96
❑ 98SkyDugAIA-96
❑ 98SP Aut-9
❑ 98SP MinDTSPE-DS8
❑ 98SP MinPE-117
❑ 98SPMin-117
❑ 98SPMinDTS-DS8
❑ 98SPxFin-192
❑ 98SPxFinR-192
❑ 98SPxFinS-192
❑ 98St.PetDRM-2
❑ 98UD3-13
❑ 98UD3-103
❑ 98UD3-193
❑ 98UD3DieCut-13
❑ 98UD3DieCut-103
❑ 98UD3DieCut-193
❑ 98Ult-466
❑ 98UltGolM-466
❑ 98UltMas-466
❑ 98UltPlaM-466
❑ 98UppDec-592
❑ 98UppDecDS-DS59
❑ 98UppDecR-130
❑ 98UppDecRNF-NF30
❑ 99CroRoyB-132
❑ 99CroRoyL-132
❑ 99CroRoyOD-132
❑ 99E-X Cen-52
❑ 99E-X CenECFut-52
❑ 99E-X CenECNow-52
❑ 99FlaShoLeg1-103
❑ 99FlaShoLeg2-103
❑ 99FlaShoLeg3-103
❑ 99FlaShoLegM1-103
❑ 99FlaShoLegM2-103
❑ 99FlaShoLegM3-103
❑ 99FlaShoR1-103
❑ 99FlaShoR2-103
❑ 99FlaShoR3-103
❑ 99Fle-77
❑ 99FleBri-45
❑ 99FleBri2G-45
❑ 99FleBriBlu-45
❑ 99FleBriGol-45

❑ 99FleMys-40
❑ 99FleMysG-40
❑ 99FleMysM-40
❑ 99FleRooFla-2
❑ 99FleSta9-77
❑ 99FleWarT-77
❑ 99MetUni-142
❑ 99MetUniGM-142
❑ 99MetUniPMG-142
❑ 99Pac-407
❑ 99PacAur-182
❑ 99PacAurOD-182
❑ 99PacCroC-271
❑ 99PacCroC-19
❑ 99PacCroCPB-271
❑ 99PacInv-138
❑ 99PacInvOD-138
❑ 99PacInvPB-138
❑ 99PacOme-226
❑ 99PacOmeC-226
❑ 99PacOmeG-226
❑ 99PacOmePB-226
❑ 99PacPar-223
❑ 99PacParC-223
❑ 99PacParG-223
❑ 99PacParHoloGold-223
❑ 99PacParHS-223
❑ 99PacParOD-223
❑ 99PacParPB-223
❑ 99PacParRed-223
❑ 99PacPlaB-407
❑ 99PacPri-137
❑ 99PacPriHB-137
❑ 99PacPriHG-137
❑ 99PacPriHM-137
❑ 99PacPriHP-137
❑ 99PacPriRed-137
❑ 99PacPriS-53
❑ 99PacPriS206-53
❑ 99PacPriS206R-53
❑ 99PacRed-407
❑ 99SkyPre-5
❑ 99SkyPreR-5
❑ 99SkyThu-100
❑ 99SkyThuRant-100
❑ 99SkyThuRave-100
❑ 99SP Aut-82
❑ 99SpoIll-137
❑ 99SPSig-115
❑ 99ThuSkySupR-100
❑ 99UD Cho-146
❑ 99UD ChoP-146
❑ 99UD ChoPCR-146
❑ 99UD Ion-56
❑ 99UD IonR-56
❑ 99Ult-109
❑ 99UltGolM-109
❑ 99UltMas-109
❑ 99UltPlaM-109
❑ 99UppDec-229
❑ 99UppDec-250
❑ 99UppDec-500
❑ 99UppDecBD-119
❑ 99UppDecBDD-119
❑ 99UppDecBDDom-D9
❑ 99UppDecBDDomE-D9
❑ 99UppDecBDQ-119
❑ 99UppDecBDT-119
❑ 99UppDecCLM-C91
❑ 99UppDecEL1-229
❑ 99UppDecEL1-250
❑ 99UppDecEL1-500
❑ 99UppDecEL2-229
❑ 99UppDecEL2-250
❑ 99UppDecEL2-500
❑ 99UppDecM-198
❑ 99UppDecMGS-198
❑ 99UppDecMHFS-198
❑ 99UppDecMSS-198
❑ 99Vic-387

Arrollado, Courtney
❑ 95ButCopKtl-3
❑ 96SpoIndB-4

Arroyd, Freddie
❑ 86SanJosBP-1

Arroyo, Bronson
❑ 95TopTra-47T
❑ 96AugGreB-4
❑ 97CalLeaATI-48
❑ 97CarLeaTP-4
❑ 97LynHil-3
❑ 98Bow-145
❑ 98BowChr-145
❑ 98BowChrGA-145
❑ 98BowChrGAR-145
❑ 98BowChrI-145
❑ 98BowChrIR-145
❑ 98BowChrR-145
❑ 98BowGolA-145
❑ 98BowInt-145
❑ 98CarMudM-1
❑ 98SouLeaTPG-25
❑ 99BasAmeTP-7
❑ 99BasAmeTPG-7

Arroyo, Carlos R.
❑ 81OklCit8T-2
❑ 86ClePhiP-1
❑ 87ClePhiP-15
❑ 88ReaPhiP-888
❑ 89BlaYNPRWL-197
❑ 90BatCliP-3084
❑ 91BatCliCB-18
❑ 91BatCliP-3501
❑ 92ReaPhiF-592
❑ 92ReaPhiS-550
❑ 93ReaPhiF-311
❑ 94ReaPhiF-2079

Arroyo, Felipe
❑ 80AndBraT-11

Arroyo, Fernando
❑ 75DetTigP-1
❑ 76OPC-614
❑ 76SSP-357
❑ 76Top-614
❑ 78TigTeal-1
❑ 78Top-607
❑ 81Top-408
❑ 81TwiPos-2
❑ 82Don-177
❑ 82Fle-546
❑ 82Top-18
❑ 82Top-396
❑ 82TwiPos-1
❑ 91LakTigC-17
❑ 91LakTigP-283
❑ 93EdmTraF-1153

Arroyo, Hector
❑ 81ChaRoyT-2

Arroyo, Luis
❑ 93WatDiaC-3
❑ 94MidLeaAF-MDW55
❑ 94SprSulC-2
❑ 94SprSulF-2028
❑ 95RanCucQT-21
❑ 96StLucMTI-6
❑ 97St.LucM-1
❑ 98BinMetQ-5
❑ 98NorTidQ-2

Arroyo, Luis Enrique
❑ 47StaPinP2-2
❑ 56PirTeal-1
❑ 56Top-64
❑ 56TopPin-45
❑ 57Top-394
❑ 58JetPos-2
❑ 61Top-142
❑ 61TopStal-188
❑ 61Yan61RL-17
❑ 62Jel-12
❑ 62Pos-12
❑ 62PosCan-12
❑ 62Top-455
❑ 62YanJayP-1
❑ 63Top-569
❑ 78TCM60I-258
❑ 83Yan196-17
❑ 83YanASFY-2
❑ 89BlaYNPRWL-64
❑ 91YanRinP11-6
❑ 92YanWIZ6-3
❑ 92YanWIZA-1

Arroyo, Rolando
❑ 97BesIntB-IB4

Arsenault, Ed
❑ 75SanAntBT-2
❑ 76WilTomT-2

Arsenault, Pierre
❑ 92ExpPos-3

Arst, Matt
❑ 90WicStaSGD-3

Arteaga, Edito
❑ 76VenLeaS-171

Arteaga, Ivan
❑ 93BurBeeC-3
❑ 93BurBeeF-148
❑ 93LinVenB-5
❑ 94NewHavRF-1541
❑ 94VenLinU-2
❑ 95Bow-97
❑ 95LinVen-96
❑ 95NewHavRTI-22
❑ 95SigRoo-3
❑ 95SigRooSig-3
❑ 96-97LinVen-27
❑ 98BinMetQ-6

Arteaga, J.D.
❑ 97PitMet-5
❑ 98BinMetQ-7
❑ 98St.LucMM-24

Arthurs, Shane
❑ 98BesNumOP-4
❑ 98VerExpO-8

Artiaga, Sal
❑ 90CalLeaACLC-28

Arundel, Tug (John Thomas)
❑ 87BucN28-36
❑ 87OldJudN-14

Arvelo, Thomas
❑ 92GulCoaMF-3486
❑ 94KinMetC-2
❑ 94KinMetF-3829
❑ 95PitMetTI-21

Arvesen, Scott
❑ 89WelPirP-2
❑ 90AugPirP-2455
❑ 91AugPirC-2
❑ 91AugPirP-795

Arzola, Richard
❑ 86St.PetCP-3

Asadoor, Randy
❑ 84TulDriTI-18
❑ 85LasVegSC-116
❑ 86LasVegSP-1
❑ 87Don-574
❑ 87Fle-650
❑ 87FleGlo-650
❑ 87LasVegSP-7
❑ 87Spo-158
❑ 87SpoTeaP-16

Asai, Itsuki
❑ 90GatCitPP-3345
❑ 90GatCitPSP-2

Asano, Keishi
❑ 92SalSpuC-29
❑ 92SalSpuF-3774

Asbe, Daryl
❑ 86BurExpP-2

Asbell, Frank
❑ 40SolHug-2

Asbell, John
❑ 79WatIndT-12
❑ 80WatIndT-10
❑ 81WatIndT-5

Asbill, Darin
❑ 88MisStaB-2
❑ 89MisStaB-4

Asbjornson, Asby (Robert A.)
❑ 94ConTSN-1315
❑ 94ConTSNB-1315

Ascencio, Juan
❑ 86BenPhiC-152

Asche, Mike
❑ 94WelPirC-3
❑ 94WelPirF-3501
❑ 96HonShaHWB-7
❑ 96LynHilB-2
❑ 97CarMudC-14
❑ 98CarMudM-19

Asche, Scott
❑ 91MiaMirC-5
❑ 91MiaMirP-399

Aschoff, Jerry
❑ 92BelMarCB-4
❑ 92BelMarF-1432
❑ 93AppFoxCB-2
❑ 93AppFoxFl-2451

Asencio, Alex
❑ 94GreFalDSP-7
❑ 96VerBeaDB-5

Asermely, Bill
❑ 93BluOriC-2
❑ 93BluOriF-4136

Asgewan, Cecil
❑ 94ButCopKSP-14

Ash, Ken (Kenneth Lowther)
❑ 92ConTSN-601

Ashburn, Richie (Don Richard)
❑ 47Exh-7A
❑ 47Exh-7B
❑ 47Exh-7C
❑ 47PM1StaP1-6
❑ 49Bow-214
❑ 49EurSta-127
❑ 49PhiBul-1
❑ 49PhiLumPB-1
❑ 50Bow-84
❑ 50PhiPhil-1
❑ 51BerRos-A9
❑ 51Bow-186
❑ 51R42SmaS-1
❑ 51TopBluB-3
❑ 52BasPho-1
❑ 52BerRos-1
❑ 52Bow-53
❑ 52DixLid-1
❑ 52DixPre-1
❑ 52RedMan-NL2
❑ 52StaCalL-77A
❑ 52StaCalS-89C
❑ 52Top-216
❑ 53BowC-10
❑ 53DixLid-1
❑ 53DixPre-1
❑ 53NorBreL-2
❑ 53RedMan-NL3
❑ 54Bow-15
❑ 54DixLid-1
❑ 54RedHeaF-1
❑ 54RedMan-NL1
❑ 54Top-45
❑ 55Bow-130
❑ 55RedMan-NL1
❑ 55RobGouS-22
❑ 55RobGouW-22
❑ 56PhiPos-1
❑ 56Top-120
❑ 56YelBasP-4
❑ 57SwiFra-17
❑ 57Top-70
❑ 58Hir-10
❑ 58PhiJayP-2
❑ 58PhiTeal-2
❑ 58Top-230
❑ 59ArmCoi-3
❑ 59Baz-2
❑ 59Top-300
❑ 59Top-317
❑ 60Baz-24
❑ 60CubJayP-3
❑ 60KeyChal-4
❑ 60MacSta-2
❑ 60RawGloT-2
❑ 60Top-305
❑ 60TopTat-4
❑ 60TopTat-87
❑ 61CubJayP-3
❑ 61Pos-192A
❑ 61Pos-192B
❑ 61Top-88
❑ 61TopStal-3
❑ 62Jel-186
❑ 62Pos-186
❑ 62PosCan-186
❑ 62SalPlaC-171
❑ 62ShiPlaC-171
❑ 62Top-213
❑ 62TopBuc-5
❑ 63BasMagM-7
❑ 63Jel-197
❑ 63Pos-197
❑ 63SalMetC-27
❑ 63Top-135
❑ 63TopStil-3
❑ 70Houof J-2
❑ 74MetOriEB-1
❑ 75Phi195T-1
❑ 75TCMHouoJ-2
❑ 77GalGloG-14
❑ 77PhiFav-19
❑ 79DiaGre-318
❑ 79PhiTeal-1
❑ 79TCM50-17
❑ 80MarExh-2
❑ 80PacLeg-94
❑ 80PerHaloFP-220
❑ 80PerHaloFPS-79
❑ 80Phi195T-1
❑ 82DiaCla-42
❑ 82GSGalAG-23
❑ 82MetGal62-2
❑ 82TCMGreH-9
❑ 83PhiPosGM-1
❑ 83TopRep5-216
❑ 84OCoandSI-59
❑ 84OCoandSI-220
❑ 84PhiTas-7
❑ 84SpoDesPW-38
❑ 86PhiGreT-2
❑ 87Phi195T-7
❑ 88PacLegI-8
❑ 88PhiTas-39
❑ 88PhiTopAS-1
❑ 88PhiTopAS-2
❑ 88PhiTopAS-3
❑ 88PhiTopAS-4
❑ 88PhiTopAS-5
❑ 88PhiTopAS-6
❑ 88PhiTopAS-7
❑ 88PhiTopAS-8
❑ 88PhiTopAS-9
❑ 88PhiTopAS-10
❑ 88PhiTopAS-11
❑ 88PhiTopAS-12
❑ 88PhiTopAS-13
❑ 89BowInsT-1
❑ 89BowRepI-1
❑ 89BowTif-R1
❑ 89SweBasG-85
❑ 90PacLeg-70
❑ 90PerGreM-98
❑ 90PhiTas-29
❑ 90PhiTas-35
❑ 91MetWIZ-15
❑ 91SweBasG-4
❑ 91TopArc1-311
❑ 92ActPacA-24
❑ 92BazQua5A-5
❑ 93TedWil-70
❑ 94TopArc1-45
❑ 94TopArc1G-45
❑ 95Phi-2
❑ 97TopStaHRR-2
❑ 98SpoIllTaN-2
❑ 98SpoIllTaNEE-2
❑ 98UppDecRA-1

Ashby, Alan Dean
❑ 75CleIndP-1
❑ 76OPC-209
❑ 76SSP-514
❑ 76Top-209
❑ 77Hos-124
❑ 77OPC-148
❑ 77Top-564
❑ 77TopCloS-1
❑ 78BluJayP-1
❑ 78OPC-76
❑ 78Top-319
❑ 79AstPos-3
❑ 79AstTeal-2
❑ 79Hos-142
❑ 79OPC-14
❑ 79Top-36
❑ 80OPC-105
❑ 80Top-187
❑ 81AllGamPI-127
❑ 81AstPos-1
❑ 81CokTeaS-61
❑ 81Don-259
❑ 81Fle-64
❑ 81OPC-146
❑ 81Top-696
❑ 82AstAstI-6
❑ 82AstPos-1
❑ 82Don-317
❑ 82Fle-212
❑ 82OPC-184
❑ 82Top-433
❑ 82TopSti-48
❑ 83AllGamPI-127
❑ 83AstPos-1
❑ 83Don-144
❑ 83Fle-445
❑ 83FleSta-4
❑ 83FleSti-141
❑ 83FleSti-212
❑ 83OPC-84
❑ 83Top-774
❑ 83TopSti-241
❑ 84AllGamPI-37
❑ 84AstMot-3
❑ 84AstPos-1
❑ 84Don-539
❑ 84Fle-220
❑ 84Nes792-217
❑ 84OPC-217
❑ 84Top-217
❑ 84TopSti-72
❑ 84TopTif-217
❑ 85AstHouP-5
❑ 85AstMot-13
❑ 85Don-283
❑ 85Fle-343
❑ 85OPC-29
❑ 85Top-564
❑ 85TopTif-564
❑ 86AstMilL-1
❑ 86AstPol-8
❑ 86AstTeal-1
❑ 86BasStaB-3
❑ 86Don-405
❑ 86Fle-292
❑ 86OPC-331
❑ 86Top-331
❑ 86TopTif-331
❑ 87AstMot-11
❑ 87AstPol-21
❑ 87AstShoSPT-1
❑ 87Don-332
❑ 87DonOpeD-17
❑ 87Fle-50
❑ 87FleGlo-50
❑ 87Top-112
❑ 87TopTif-112
❑ 88AstMot-11
❑ 88AstPol-4
❑ 88Don-163
❑ 88DonBasB-8
❑ 88Fle-439
❑ 88FleGlo-439
❑ 88OPC-48
❑ 88PanSti-291
❑ 88RedFolSB-2
❑ 88Sco-73
❑ 88ScoGlo-73
❑ 88Spo-219
❑ 88StaLinAst-3
❑ 88Top-48
❑ 88TopSti-32
❑ 88TopTif-48
❑ 89AstMot-10
❑ 89AstSmo-3
❑ 89Bow-327
❑ 89BowTif-327
❑ 89Don-88
❑ 89Fle-350A
❑ 89Fle-350B
❑ 89FleGlo-350
❑ 89OPC-359
❑ 89RedFolSB-4
❑ 89Sco-366
❑ 89Top-492
❑ 89TopDouA-20
❑ 89TopTif-492
❑ 89UppDec-305
❑ 90EliSenL-63
❑ 90MLBBasB-39
❑ 93UppDecS-1
❑ 96KisCobB-1
❑ 97AstMot-28

Ashby, Andy (Andrew)
❑ 86BenPhiC-139
❑ 87SpaPhiP-13
❑ 87UtiBluSP-25
❑ 90Bes-46
❑ 90CMC-784
❑ 90ProAaA-22
❑ 90ReaPhiB-7
❑ 90ReaPhiP-1211
❑ 90ReaPhiS-3
❑ 91Bow-485
❑ 91FleUpd-105
❑ 91LinDriAAA-478
❑ 91PhiMed-2
❑ 91ScrRedBLD-478
❑ 91ScrRedBP-2530
❑ 91StaCluMO-2
❑ 91UppDecFE-64F
❑ 92Bow-286
❑ 92Cla1-T6
❑ 92ClaGam-200
❑ 92Don-11
❑ 92Fle-521
❑ 92Lea-405
❑ 92LeaBlaG-405
❑ 92OPC-497
❑ 92PhiMed-3
❑ 92Pin-265
❑ 92ProFS7-294
❑ 92Sco-396
❑ 92ScoRoo-18
❑ 92StaClu-717
❑ 92StaCluECN-717
❑ 92Top-497
❑ 92TopDeb91-5
❑ 92TopGol-497
❑ 92TopGolW-497
❑ 92TopMic-497
❑ 92TriPla-128
❑ 92Ult-541
❑ 92UppDec-19
❑ 92UppDecSR-SR1
❑ 93Don-743

❑ 93Fle-401
❑ 93FleFinE-21
❑ 93PacSpa-420
❑ 93Pin-572
❑ 93RocStaC-18
❑ 93RocUSPC-3H
❑ 93RocUSPC-10C
❑ 93StaClu-700
❑ 93StaCluFDI-700
❑ 93StaCluMOP-700
❑ 93Top-794
❑ 93TopGol-794
❑ 93TopInaM-794
❑ 93TopInaR-794
❑ 93TopMic-794
❑ 93Ult-339
❑ 93UppDec-763
❑ 93UppDecGold-763
❑ 94Don-70
❑ 94Fin-255
❑ 94FinRef-255
❑ 94Fla-433
❑ 94Fle-652
❑ 94FleExtB-367
❑ 94Lea-32
❑ 94PadMot-21
❑ 94StaClu-524
❑ 94StaCluFDI-524
❑ 94StaCluGR-524
❑ 94StaCluMOP-524
❑ 94Top-648
❑ 94TopGol-648
❑ 94TopSpa-648
❑ 94Ult-275
❑ 95ColCho-358
❑ 95ColChoGS-358
❑ 95ColChoSS-358
❑ 95Don-86
❑ 95DonPreP-86
❑ 95DonTopotO-336
❑ 95Fla-198
❑ 95Fle-553
❑ 95Lea-68
❑ 95Pac-356
❑ 95PadCHP-3
❑ 95PadMot-23
❑ 95Pin-425
❑ 95PinArtP-425
❑ 95PinMusC-425
❑ 95Sco-175
❑ 95ScoGolR-175
❑ 95ScoPlaTS-175
❑ 95StaClu-228
❑ 95StaCluFDI-228
❑ 95StaCluMOP-228
❑ 95StaCluSTWS-228
❑ 95Top-85
❑ 95TopCyb-60
❑ 95Ult-435
❑ 95UltGolM-435
❑ 96Cir-183
❑ 96CirRav-183
❑ 96ColCho-698
❑ 96ColChoGS-698
❑ 96ColChoSS-698
❑ 96Don-450
❑ 96DonPreP-450
❑ 96EmoXL-273
❑ 96Fla-369
❑ 96Fle-559
❑ 96FleTif-559
❑ 96Lea-62
❑ 96LeaPrePB-62
❑ 96LeaPrePG-62
❑ 96LeaPrePS-62
❑ 96LeaSigA-10
❑ 96LeaSigAG-10
❑ 96LeaSigAS-10
❑ 96MetUni-231
❑ 96MetUniP-231
❑ 96Pac-185
❑ 96PadMot-21
❑ 96PanSti-102
❑ 96ProSta-84
❑ 96Sco-216
❑ 96SP-162
❑ 96StaClu-134
❑ 96StaClu-246
❑ 96StaCluMOP-134
❑ 96StaCluMOP-246
❑ 96Top-82
❑ 96TopGal-61
❑ 96TopGalPPI-61
❑ 96TopLas-49
❑ 96Ult-280
❑ 96UltGolM-280
❑ 96UppDec-187
❑ 97Cir-188
❑ 97CirRav-188
❑ 97ColCho-449
❑ 97Don-313
❑ 97DonGolPP-313
❑ 97DonLim-67
❑ 97DonLimE-67
❑ 97DonLimENG-67
❑ 97DonPre-25
❑ 97DonPreCttC-25
❑ 97DonSigA-8
❑ 97DonSigAC-8
❑ 97DonSigAM-8
❑ 97DonSilPP-313
❑ 97Fin-192
❑ 97FinRef-192
❑ 97Fle-456
❑ 97FleTif-456
❑ 97Lea-307
❑ 97LeaFraM-307
❑ 97LeaFraMDC-307
❑ 97MetUni-216
❑ 97Pac-419
❑ 97PacLigB-419
❑ 97PacSil-419
❑ 97PadMot-21
❑ 97PinX-P-91
❑ 97PinX-PMoS-91
❑ 97Sco-138
❑ 97ScoArtPWB-138
❑ 97ScoPreS-138
❑ 97ScoShoS-138
❑ 97ScoShoSAP-138
❑ 97SpoIll-37
❑ 97SpoIllEE-37
❑ 97SpoIllGS-19
❑ 97StaClu-294
❑ 97StaCluMOP-294
❑ 97Stu-137
❑ 97StuPrePG-137
❑ 97StuPrePS-137
❑ 97Top-15
❑ 97Ult-279
❑ 97UltGolME-279
❑ 97UltPlaME-279
❑ 97UppDec-164
❑ 98CirThu-131
❑ 98CirThuRav-131
❑ 98CirThuSupRav-131
❑ 98ColCho-481
❑ 98Fle-41
❑ 98Pac-420
❑ 98PacOnl-630
❑ 98PacOnlR-630
❑ 98PacOnlWC-630
❑ 98PacPlaB-420
❑ 98PacRedT-420
❑ 98PacSil-420
❑ 98PadMot-14
❑ 98ScoRT-150
❑ 98ScrRedB1ATI-1
❑ 98ScrRedB1ATI-2
❑ 98StaCluFDI-61
❑ 98StaCluI-61
❑ 98StaCluOneK-61
❑ 98StaCluPP-61
❑ 98Top-434
❑ 98TopChr-434
❑ 98TopChrR-434
❑ 98TopDevR-434
❑ 98TopDia-434
❑ 98TopMiniC-434
❑ 98Ult-20
❑ 98UltGolM-20
❑ 98UltMas-20
❑ 98UltPlaM-20
❑ 98UppDec-207
❑ 98UppDecSF-112
❑ 99199Fin-91
❑ 99Bow-232
❑ 99BowGol-232
❑ 99BowInt-232
❑ 99FinGolRef-91
❑ 99FinRef-91
❑ 99Fle-72
❑ 99FleBri-67
❑ 99FleBri2G-67
❑ 99FleBriBlu-67
❑ 99FleBriGol-67
❑ 99FleSta9-72
❑ 99FleWarT-72
❑ 99MetUni-180
❑ 99MetUniGM-180
❑ 99MetUniPMG-180
❑ 99Pac-363
❑ 99PacAur-159
❑ 99PacAurOD-159
❑ 99PacCroC-237
❑ 99PacCroCPB-237
❑ 99PacOme-200
❑ 99PacOmeC-200
❑ 99PacOmeG-200
❑ 99PacOmePB-200
❑ 99PacPar-197
❑ 99PacParC-197
❑ 99PacParG-197
❑ 99PacParHoloGold-197
❑ 99PacParHS-197
❑ 99PacParOD-197
❑ 99PacParPB-197
❑ 99PacParRed-197
❑ 99PacPlaB-363
❑ 99PacRed-363
❑ 99SkyPre-105
❑ 99SkyPreR-105
❑ 99SkyThu-5
❑ 99SkyThuRant-5
❑ 99SkyThuRave-5
❑ 99StaClu-133
❑ 99StaCluFDI-133
❑ 99StaCluOoaK-133
❑ 99StaCluPP-133
❑ 99ThuSkySupR-5
❑ 99Top-332
❑ 99TopChr-332
❑ 99TopChrR-332
❑ 99TopMVPP-332
❑ 99TopOpeD-132
❑ 99TopSta-112
❑ 99TopStaFoil-112
❑ 99UppDec-189
❑ 99UppDecEL1-189
❑ 99UppDecEL2-189
❑ 99Vic-345

Ashby, Christopher
❑ 95GreBatTI-2
❑ 96TamYanY-3
❑ 97NorNav-6
❑ 97NorNavTI-1
❑ 98NorNavQ-2

Ashby, Gary
❑ 81HawIsIT-3

Ashford, Emmett
❑ 77Spo-7315

Ashford, Tucker (Thomas S.)
❑ 78PadFamF-2
❑ 78Top-116
❑ 79HawIsIC-8
❑ 79Top-247
❑ 80ChaChaT-16
❑ 81ColCliP-12
❑ 81ColCliT-2
❑ 82ColCliP-12
❑ 82ColCliT-2
❑ 83TidTidT-26
❑ 84Nes792-492
❑ 84Top-492
❑ 84TopTif-492
❑ 87JacMetF-4
❑ 88JacMetGS-4
❑ 91MetWIZ-16
❑ 92YanWIZ8-6
❑ 93RanKee-55

Ashkinazy, Alan
❑ 85GreHorT-2
❑ 86GreHorP-2

Ashley, Billy
❑ 90BakDodCLC-260
❑ 91Cla/Bes-210
❑ 91VerBeaDC-24
❑ 91VerBeaDP-785
❑ 92AlbDukF-731
❑ 92Bow-168
❑ 92ClaFS7-243
❑ 92DonRoo-5
❑ 92SanAntMS-553
❑ 92SkyAA F-242
❑ 93AlbDukF-1473
❑ 93Bow-210
❑ 93ClaFS7-123
❑ 93DodStaC-22
❑ 93Don-56
❑ 93FleMajLP-A9
❑ 93Lea-100
❑ 93Pin-281
❑ 93PinTea2-16
❑ 93Sco-267
❑ 93ScoBoyoS-1
❑ 93StaClu-342
❑ 93StaCluFDI-342
❑ 93StaCluMOP-342
❑ 93Top-815
❑ 93TopGol-815
❑ 93TopInaM-815
❑ 93TopInaR-815
❑ 93TopMic-815
❑ 93Toy-86
❑ 93TriAAAGF-13
❑ 93UppDec-22
❑ 93UppDecGold-22
❑ 94BowBes-B32
❑ 94BowBesR-B32
❑ 94Cla-27
❑ 94DodPol-1
❑ 94Don-420
❑ 94Fle-504
❑ 94Lea-111
❑ 94LeaLimR-53
❑ 94Pin-324
❑ 94PinArtP-324
❑ 94PinMusC-324
❑ 94PinNewG-NG21
❑ 94SpoRoo-111
❑ 94SpoRooAP-111
❑ 94Top-53
❑ 94TopGol-53
❑ 94TopSpa-53
❑ 94TriAAF-AAA24
❑ 94TriPla-287
❑ 94Ult-513
❑ 95ActPac2G-8G
❑ 95ActPacF-18
❑ 95ActPacF-69
❑ 95Baz-127
❑ 95Bow-223
❑ 95BowGolF-223
❑ 95ColCho-225
❑ 95ColChoGS-225
❑ 95ColChoSS-225
❑ 95DodMot-14
❑ 95DodPol-1
❑ 95Don-180
❑ 95DonPreP-180
❑ 95DonTopotO-262
❑ 95Fin-278
❑ 95FinRef-278
❑ 95Fla-150
❑ 95Fle-532
❑ 95Lea-196
❑ 95LeaLim-9
❑ 95Pin-31
❑ 95Pin-290
❑ 95PinArtP-31
❑ 95PinArtP-290
❑ 95PinMusC-31
❑ 95PinMusC-290
❑ 95PinNewB-NB8
❑ 95PinUps-US29
❑ 95ScoAi-AM8
❑ 95Sel-71
❑ 95Sel-233
❑ 95SelArtP-71
❑ 95SelArtP-233
❑ 95SelCanM-CM6
❑ 95SelCer-82
❑ 95SelCerMG-82
❑ 95SelCerPU-5
❑ 95SelCerPU9-5
❑ 95SigRooFD-FD1
❑ 95SigRooFDS-FD1
❑ 95SigRooOJHP-HP1
❑ 95SigRooOJHPS-HP1
❑ 95SigRooOJSS-5
❑ 95SigRooOJSSS-5
❑ 95SP-71
❑ 95SPCha-62
❑ 95SPChaDC-62
❑ 95Spo-39
❑ 95SpoArtP-39
❑ 95SPSil-71
❑ 95SPSpeF-41
❑ 95StaClu-469
❑ 95StaCluCB-CB5
❑ 95StaCluMOP-469
❑ 95StaCluMOP-CB5
❑ 95StaCluSTWS-469
❑ 95Stu-127
❑ 95Sum-12
❑ 95SumNewA-NA5
❑ 95SumNthD-12
❑ 95Top-489
❑ 95TopCyb-280
❑ 95UC3-89
❑ 95UC3ArtP-89
❑ 95UC3CleS-CS6
❑ 95Ult-392
❑ 95UltGolM-392
❑ 95UppDec-75
❑ 95UppDecED-75
❑ 95UppDecEDG-75
❑ 95UppDecSE-169
❑ 95UppDecSEG-169
❑ 95Zen-8
❑ 96ColCho-178
❑ 96ColChoGS-178
❑ 96ColChoSS-178
❑ 96DodMot-13
❑ 96DodPol-1
❑ 96Don-7
❑ 96DonPreP-7
❑ 96Fle-425
❑ 96FleTif-425
❑ 96Lea-117
❑ 96LeaPrePB-117
❑ 96LeaPrePG-117
❑ 96LeaPrePS-117
❑ 96Sco-170
❑ 96ScoDugC-A96
❑ 96ScoDugCAP-A96
❑ 96SelCer-79
❑ 96SelCerAP-79
❑ 96SelCerCB-79
❑ 96SelCerCR-79
❑ 96SelCerMB-79
❑ 96SelCerMG-79
❑ 96SelCerMR-79
❑ 96Ult-216
❑ 96UltGolM-216
❑ 97DodMot-14
❑ 97DodPol-1
❑ 97PacPriGotD-GD155
❑ 97Sco-409
❑ 97ScoArtPWB-409
❑ 97ScoResC-409
❑ 97ScoShoS-409
❑ 97ScoShoSAP-409
❑ 98DodSco-15
❑ 98DodScoP-15
❑ 98PawRedSQ-6
❑ 98Sco-210

Ashley, Duane
❑ 91JamExpC-16
❑ 91JamExpP-3534

Ashley, Shon
❑ 86BelBreP-1
❑ 87BelBreP-4
❑ 88CalLeaACLC-14
❑ 88StoPorCLC-194
❑ 88StoPorP-724
❑ 89ElPasDGS-25
❑ 89TexLeaAGS-14
❑ 90ElPasDGS-4
❑ 91ElPasDLD-176
❑ 91ElPasDP-2758
❑ 91LinDriAA-176
❑ 92IndIndF-1871
❑ 92IndIndS-176
❑ 92ProFS7-85
❑ 92SkyAAAF-84

Ashley, Steve
❑ 97DanBraB-9
❑ 97EugEmeB-18

Ashman, Mike
❑ 82MadMusF-23
❑ 83AlbA'sT-11
❑ 84AlbA'sT-21
❑ 85TacTigC-136
❑ 86NasPirP-1
❑ 90AlbDecGB-2

Ashmore, Mitch
❑ 82ChaRoyT-7
❑ 82OmaRoyT-13
❑ 84MemChiT-8

Ashton, Jeff
❑ 92PriRedC-3
❑ 92PriRedF-3092
❑ 93BilMusF-3951

Ashworth, Kym
❑ 93GreFalDSP-4
❑ 94BakDodC-1
❑ 94Bow-157
❑ 94BowBes-B74
❑ 94BowBesR-B74
❑ 94Cla-194
❑ 94ClaTriF-T40
❑ 95AusFut-22
❑ 95AusFutGP-2
❑ 95Bow-148
❑ 95SigRooOJ-2
❑ 95SigRooOJP-2
❑ 95SigRooOJPS-2
❑ 95SigRooOJS-2
❑ 95VerBeaDTI-2
❑ 96BesAutS-6
❑ 97SanBerS-4
❑ 98LakTigM-1

Ashworth, Mike
❑ 88BurIndP-1793
❑ 89SalLakTTI-28

Asinof, Eliot
❑ 73BooProC-23

Asp, Bryan
❑ 89EliTwiS-1

Aspray, Mike
❑ 87GenCubP-1
❑ 88PeoChiTI-3
❑ 89WinSpiS-NNO
❑ 90VisOakCLC-59
❑ 90VisOakP-2151

Aspromonte, Bob (Robert T.)
❑ 47Exh-8
❑ 58MonRoyF-2
❑ 59O'KAleMR-2
❑ 60Top-547
❑ 61Top-396
❑ 62Baz-9
❑ 62Col.45B-2
❑ 62Col45'HC-2
❑ 62Col45'JP-2
❑ 62Top-248
❑ 62TopStal-124
❑ 63Col45"P-1
❑ 63Col45'JP-1
❑ 63ExhStaB-3
❑ 63Fle-37
❑ 63Jel-187
❑ 63Pos-187
❑ 63Top-45
❑ 63TopStil-4
❑ 64Col.45JP-1
❑ 64Top-467
❑ 64TopCoi-84
❑ 64TopCoi-163
❑ 64TopSta-16
❑ 64TopStaU-5
❑ 65AstJayP-2
❑ 65Baz-19
❑ 65OPC-175
❑ 65Top-175
❑ 65TopEmbl-61
❑ 66Baz-24
❑ 66Top-273
❑ 66Top-352
❑ 66TopRubl-6
❑ 66TopVen-273
❑ 66TopVen-352
❑ 67Ast-2
❑ 67AstTeal1-1
❑ 67AstTeal2-2
❑ 67Baz-24
❑ 67CokCapAs-2
❑ 67DexPre-14
❑ 67Top-274
❑ 67TopVen-269
❑ 68AtlOilPBCC-5
❑ 68CokCapA-2
❑ 68DexPre-8
❑ 68OPC-95
❑ 68Top-95
❑ 68TopActS-4C
❑ 68TopActS-15C
❑ 68TopVen-95
❑ 69MilBra-17
❑ 69MLBOffS-111
❑ 69Top-542
❑ 69TopSta-31
❑ 70MLBOffS-2
❑ 70OPC-529
❑ 70Top-529
❑ 71MetTealC-2
❑ 71MLBOffS-146
❑ 71OPC-469
❑ 71Top-469
❑ 72MilBra-21
❑ 72Top-659
❑ 87AstSer1-1
❑ 87AstSer1-29
❑ 89AstCol4S-16
❑ 90DodTar-21
❑ 91MetWIZ-17

Aspromonte, Ken
❑ 58SeaTeal-2
❑ 58Top-405
❑ 59SenTealW-1
❑ 59Top-424
❑ 60Top-114
❑ 60TopVen-114

❑ 61AngJayP-1
❑ 61Pos-65A
❑ 61Pos-65B
❑ 61Top-176
❑ 61TopStal-133
❑ 62Jel-19
❑ 62SalPlaC-7A
❑ 62SalPlaC-7B
❑ 62ShiPlaC-7
❑ 62Top-563
❑ 63Top-464
❑ 64Top-252
❑ 64TopVen-252
❑ 65TopTral-39
❑ 70WicAerM-1
❑ 72Top-784
❑ 73IndTeal-2
❑ 73OPC-449
❑ 73Top-449A
❑ 73Top-449B
❑ 74OPC-521
❑ 74Top-521
❑ 81RedSoxBG2S-2

Asselstine, Brian H.
❑ 77Top-479
❑ 78Top-372
❑ 79Top-529
❑ 81BraPol-30
❑ 81Don-186
❑ 81Fle-256
❑ 81Top-64
❑ 82Don-184
❑ 82Fle-428
❑ 82Top-214
❑ 83PhoGiaBHN-4

Assenmacher, Paul
❑ 84DurBulT-20
❑ 85DurBulT-1
❑ 86BraPol-30
❑ 86DonRoo-28
❑ 86FleUpd-5
❑ 86SpoRoo-24
❑ 86TopTra-4T
❑ 86TopTraT-4T
❑ 87BraSmo-8
❑ 87Don-290
❑ 87Fle-511
❑ 87FleGlo-511
❑ 87Lea-164
❑ 87SpoTeaP-24
❑ 87Top-132
❑ 87TopSti-37
❑ 87TopTif-132
❑ 87ToyRoo-2
❑ 88Fle-532
❑ 88FleGlo-532
❑ 88StaLinBra-2
❑ 88Top-266
❑ 88TopTif-266
❑ 89Bow-265
❑ 89BowTif-265
❑ 89BraDub-3
❑ 89Don-357
❑ 89Fle-586
❑ 89FleGlo-586
❑ 89PanSti-33
❑ 89Sco-373
❑ 89Top-454
❑ 89TopTif-454
❑ 89UppDec-566
❑ 90CubMar-1
❑ 90Don-459
❑ 90Fle-25
❑ 90FleCan-25
❑ 90Lea-493
❑ 90OPC-644
❑ 90PublntS-107
❑ 90Top-644
❑ 90TopTif-644
❑ 90TopTVCu-7
❑ 90UppDec-660
❑ 91Bow-431
❑ 91CubMar-45
❑ 91CubVinL-1
❑ 91Don-144
❑ 91Fle-413
❑ 91Lea-53
❑ 91OPC-12
❑ 91Sco-147
❑ 91StaClu-586
❑ 91Top-12
❑ 91TopDesS-12
❑ 91TopMic-12
❑ 91TopTif-12
❑ 91UppDec-491
❑ 92CubMar-45
❑ 92Don-159
❑ 92Fle-375
❑ 92Lea-117
❑ 92LeaBlaG-117
❑ 92OPC-753
❑ 92Pin-466
❑ 92Sco-360
❑ 92StaClu-731
❑ 92StaCluNC-731
❑ 92Top-753
❑ 92TopGol-753
❑ 92TopGolW-753
❑ 92TopMic-753
❑ 92Ult-172
❑ 92UppDec-590
❑ 93CubMar-1
❑ 93CubStaC-13
❑ 93Don-54
❑ 93Fle-17
❑ 93PacSpa-375
❑ 93StaClu-332
❑ 93StaCluFDI-332
❑ 93StaCluMOP-332
❑ 93Top-319
❑ 93TopGol-319
❑ 93TopInaM-319
❑ 93TopInaR-319
❑ 93TopMic-319
❑ 93Ult-14
❑ 93UppDec-320
❑ 93UppDecGold-320
❑ 94Don-57
❑ 94Fle-225
❑ 94Sco-224
❑ 94ScoGolR-224
❑ 94StaClu-133
❑ 94StaClu-646
❑ 94StaCluFDI-133
❑ 94StaCluFDI-646
❑ 94StaCluGR-133
❑ 94StaCluGR-646
❑ 94StaCluMOP-133
❑ 94StaCluMOP-646
❑ 94StaCluT-195
❑ 94StaCluTFDI-195
❑ 94Top-239
❑ 94TopGol-239
❑ 94TopSpa-239
❑ 94WhiSoxK-2
❑ 95Fle-110
❑ 95FleUpd-39
❑ 96ColCho-523
❑ 96ColChoGS-523
❑ 96ColChoSS-523
❑ 96Fle-81
❑ 96FleTif-81
❑ 96IndFle-2
❑ 96LeaSigEA-5
❑ 96Sco-400
❑ 97IndScoU-13
❑ 97IndScoUTC-13
❑ 98Pac-67
❑ 98PacOnl-211
❑ 98PacOnlR-211
❑ 98PacOnlWC-211
❑ 98PacPlaB-67
❑ 98PacRedT-67
❑ 98PacSil-67
❑ 98UppDec-672

Assumpta, Sister Mary
❑ 97UppDecSAT-1

Astacio, Pedro
❑ 90VerBeaDS-2
❑ 90YakBeaTI-12
❑ 91Cla/Bes-280
❑ 91SanAntMP-2966
❑ 91VerBeaDC-1
❑ 91VerBeaDP-762
❑ 92AlbDukF-710
❑ 92AlbDukS-2
❑ 92Bow-689
❑ 92DonRoo-6
❑ 92Pin-551
❑ 92SkyAAAF-1
❑ 93Bow-238
❑ 93ClaGam-7
❑ 93DodMot-26
❑ 93DodPol-1
❑ 93DodStaC-12
❑ 93Don-407
❑ 93Fle-57
❑ 93FleRooS-RSB2
❑ 93Lea-71
❑ 93LimRocDWB-60
❑ 93OPC-9
❑ 93PacSpa-496
❑ 93Pin-396
❑ 93Sco-231
❑ 93Sel-325
❑ 93SelChaR-13
❑ 93StaClu-511
❑ 93StaCluFDI-511
❑ 93StaCluMOP-511
❑ 93Top-93
❑ 93TopGol-93
❑ 93TopInaM-93
❑ 93TopInaR-93
❑ 93TopMic-93
❑ 93Toy-44
❑ 93TriPla-29
❑ 93Ult-49
❑ 93UppDec-367
❑ 93UppDecGold-367
❑ 93USPlaCR-4S
❑ 94Bow-294
❑ 94ColC-496
❑ 94ColChoGS-496
❑ 94ColChoSS-496
❑ 94DodDaiN-11
❑ 94DodMot-16
❑ 94DodPol-2
❑ 94Don-62
❑ 94Fin-343
❑ 94FinRef-343
❑ 94Fla-177
❑ 94Fle-505
❑ 94FleExtB-283
❑ 94Lea-237
❑ 94Pac-302
❑ 94Pin-454
❑ 94PinArtP-454
❑ 94PinMusC-454
❑ 94Sel-82
❑ 94StaClu-343
❑ 94StaCluFDI-343
❑ 94StaCluGR-343
❑ 94StaCluMOP-343
❑ 94Top-431
❑ 94TopGol-431
❑ 94TopSpa-431
❑ 94TriPla-81
❑ 94Ult-212
❑ 94UppDec-158
❑ 94UppDecED-158
❑ 95ColCho-228
❑ 95ColChoGS-228
❑ 95ColChoSS-228
❑ 95DodMot-11
❑ 95DodPol-2
❑ 95Don-337
❑ 95DonPreP-337
❑ 95Fla-151
❑ 95Fle-533
❑ 95Lea-137
❑ 95Pac-212
❑ 95Pin-56
❑ 95PinArtP-56
❑ 95PinMusC-56
❑ 95Sco-460
❑ 95ScoGolR-460
❑ 95ScoPlaTS-460
❑ 95StaClu-358
❑ 95StaCluMOP-358
❑ 95StaCluSTWS-358
❑ 95StaCluVR-188
❑ 95StaCluVRMO-188
❑ 95Top-589
❑ 95TopCyb-361
❑ 95Ult-393
❑ 95UltGolM-393
❑ 95UppDec-318
❑ 95UppDecED-318
❑ 95UppDecEDG-318
❑ 96ColCho-582
❑ 96ColChoGS-582
❑ 96ColChoSS-582
❑ 96DodMot-12
❑ 96DodPol-2
❑ 96LeaSigA-11
❑ 96LeaSigAG-11
❑ 96LeaSigAS-11
❑ 96Pac-105
❑ 97Cir-168
❑ 97CirRav-168
❑ 97ColCho-363
❑ 97DodMot-22
❑ 97DodPol-2
❑ 97Fle-667
❑ 97FleTif-667
❑ 97Pac-325
❑ 97PacLigB-325
❑ 97PacSil-325
❑ 97StaClu-74
❑ 97StaCluMOP-74
❑ 97Top-51
❑ 97Ult-442
❑ 97UltGolME-442
❑ 97UltPlaME-442
❑ 98CirThu-161
❑ 98CirThuRav-161
❑ 98CirThuSupRav-161
❑ 98ColCho-359
❑ 98Fin-137
❑ 98FinNo--137
❑ 98FinNo-R-137
❑ 98FinRef-137
❑ 98Fle-443
❑ 98PacOnl-237
❑ 98PacOnlR-237
❑ 98PacOnlWC-237
❑ 98PacPar-150
❑ 98PacParC-150
❑ 98PacParG-150
❑ 98PacParHS-150
❑ 98PacParPB-150
❑ 98PacParR-150
❑ 98PinPlu-164
❑ 98PinSna-CR2
❑ 98SPxFin-271
❑ 98SPxFinR-271
❑ 98SPxFinS-271
❑ 98StaCluFDI-102
❑ 98StaClul-102
❑ 98StaCluOneK-102
❑ 98StaCluPP-102
❑ 98TopGal-23
❑ 98TopGalGP-23
❑ 98TopGalOPP-23
❑ 98TopGalPPI-23
❑ 98TopGalPPIA-23
❑ 98Ult-258
❑ 98UltGolM-258
❑ 98UltMas-258
❑ 98UltPlaM-258
❑ 98UppDec-357
❑ 99Fle-319
❑ 99FleSta9-319
❑ 99FleWarT-319
❑ 99Pac-139
❑ 99PacCroC-92
❑ 99PacCroCPB-92
❑ 99PacPlaB-139
❑ 99PacRed-139
❑ 99Top-317
❑ 99TopChr-317
❑ 99TopChrR-317
❑ 99TopMVPP-317
❑ 99UppDec-86
❑ 99UppDecEL1-86
❑ 99UppDecEL2-86
❑ 99Vic-136

Astacio, Rafael
❑ 91EriSaiC-2
❑ 91EriSaiP-4075

Astros, Auburn
❑ 92AubAstC-30
❑ 92AubAstF-1373

Astros, Cedar Rapids
❑ 73CedRapAT-26

Astros, Houston
❑ 64TopTatl-9
❑ 66TopRubl-109
❑ 69FleCloS-10
❑ 69FleCloS-26
❑ 69TopStaA-10
❑ 70OPC-448
❑ 70Top-448
❑ 71OPC-722
❑ 71Top-722
❑ 71TopTat-102
❑ 72OPC-282
❑ 72Top-282
❑ 73OPC-158
❑ 73OPCBTC-10
❑ 73Top-158
❑ 73TopBluTC-10
❑ 74OPC-154
❑ 74OPCTC-10
❑ 74Top-154
❑ 74TopStaA-10
❑ 74TopTeaC-10
❑ 78Top-112
❑ 83FleSta-234
❑ 83FleSti-NNO
❑ 87AstSer1-31
❑ 87AstShoSO-30
❑ 87AstShoSO-31
❑ 87AstShoSO-32
❑ 87AstShoSPT-25
❑ 87AstShoSPT-26
❑ 87AstShoSPT-27
❑ 87AstShoSPT-28
❑ 87AstShoSPT-29
❑ 87AstShoSPT-30
❑ 87AstShoSPT-31
❑ 87AstShoSPT-32
❑ 87AstShoSTw-30
❑ 87AstShoSTw-31
❑ 87AstShoSTw-32
❑ 87AstShowSTh-30
❑ 87AstShowSTh-31
❑ 87AstShowSTh-32
❑ 87FleWaxBC-C9
❑ 87SpoTeaL-8
❑ 88PanSti-472
❑ 88RedFolSB-113
❑ 89FleWaxBC-C24
❑ 90PublntS-627
❑ 90RedFolSB-117
❑ 94ImpProP-20
❑ 94Sco-652
❑ 94ScoGolR-652
❑ 95PacPriTL-20
❑ 95PanSti-140
❑ 96PanSti-61
❑ 99Vic-166

Astroth, Joe (Joseph Henry)
❑ 49A'sTeal-4
❑ 49PhiBul-2
❑ 50A'sTeal-1
❑ 51A'sTeal-2
❑ 51Bow-298
❑ 52A'sTeal-3
❑ 52Bow-170
❑ 52Top-290
❑ 53A'sTeal-2
❑ 53BowC-82
❑ 53Top-103
❑ 54A'STEAl-2
❑ 54Bow-131
❑ 55A'sRodM-1
❑ 55A'sTeal-1
❑ 55Bow-119
❑ 56A'sRodM-1
❑ 56Top-106
❑ 76A'sRodMC-3
❑ 79DiaGre-345
❑ 83TopRep5-290
❑ 91TopArc1-103

Astroth, Jon
❑ 74GasRanT-2
❑ 75SpoIndC-13

Atchley, Justin
❑ 95BilMusTI-2
❑ 96Exc-145
❑ 97ChaLoo-6
❑ 98ChaLooG-2

Atencio, Enrique
❑ 93AppFoxCB-3
❑ 93AppFoxFl-2465

Atha, Jeff
❑ 88JamExpP-1901

Atherton, Keith Rowe
❑ 79WatA'sT-6
❑ 80WesHavWCT-16
❑ 81WesHavAT-2
❑ 82TacTigT-23
❑ 83TacTigT-1
❑ 84A'sMot-26
❑ 84Don-497
❑ 84Fle-437
❑ 84Nes792-529
❑ 84Top-529
❑ 84TopTif-529
❑ 85A'sMot-17
❑ 85Don-340
❑ 85Fle-415
❑ 85Top-166
❑ 85TopTif-166
❑ 86A'sMot-17
❑ 86Fle-410
❑ 86Top-353
❑ 86TopTif-353
❑ 87Don-272
❑ 87Fle-534
❑ 87FleGlo-534
❑ 87Top-52
❑ 87TopTif-52
❑ 87TwiPos-1
❑ 87TwiTeal-14
❑ 88Don-318
❑ 88DonBasB-270
❑ 88Fle-1
❑ 88FleGlo-1
❑ 88Sco-613
❑ 88ScoGlo-613
❑ 88Top-451
❑ 88TopClo-4
❑ 88TopTif-451
❑ 89Don-273
❑ 89Fle-103
❑ 89FleGlo-103
❑ 89FleUpd-24
❑ 89IndTeal-3
❑ 89Sco-381
❑ 89Top-698
❑ 89TopTif-698
❑ 89TopTra-4T
❑ 89TopTraT-4T
❑ 89UppDec-599
❑ 90PublntS-552

Athletics, 19th C (Philadelphia)
❑ 90KalTeaN-1

Athletics, Kansas City
❑ 56Top-236
❑ 57Top-204
❑ 58Top-174
❑ 59Top-172
❑ 59TopVen-172
❑ 60Top-413
❑ 60TopTat-69
❑ 61Top-297
❑ 61TopMagR-7
❑ 62GuyPotCP-9
❑ 62Top-384
❑ 63Top-397
❑ 64Top-151
❑ 64TopTatl-10
❑ 64TopVen-151
❑ 65OPC-151
❑ 65Top-151
❑ 66Top-492
❑ 66TopRubl-110
❑ 67Top-262
❑ 90FleWaxBC-C9

Athletics, Oakland
❑ 68Top-554
❑ 69FleCloS-17
❑ 69FleCloS-35
❑ 69TopStaA-17
❑ 70Top-631
❑ 71OPC-624
❑ 71Top-624
❑ 71TopTat-34
❑ 72OPC-454
❑ 72Top-454
❑ 73OPC-500
❑ 73OPCBTC-18
❑ 73Top-500
❑ 73TopBluTC-18
❑ 74OPC-246
❑ 74OPCTC-18
❑ 74Top-246
❑ 74TopStaA-18
❑ 74TopTeaC-18
❑ 76OPC-421
❑ 76Top-421
❑ 78Top-577
❑ 83FleSta-242
❑ 83FleSti-NNO
❑ 87SpoTeaL-23
❑ 87Top-456
❑ 87TopTif-456
❑ 88PanSti-465
❑ 88RedFolSB-120
❑ 89FleWaxBC-C5
❑ 90FleWorS-12
❑ 90PublntS-635
❑ 90RedFolSB-127
❑ 91PanCanT1-134
❑ 91PanCanT1-135
❑ 93TedWilPC-18
❑ 94ImpProP-11
❑ 94Sco-327
❑ 94ScoGolR-327
❑ 95PacPriTL-11
❑ 95PanSti-154
❑ 96PanSti-219
❑ 99Vic-277

Athletics, Philadelphia
❑ 09SpoNewSM-52
❑ 13FatT20-6
❑ 38BasTabP-28
❑ 42A'sTeal-38
❑ 43A'STEAl-1
❑ 45A'sTeal-1

❑ 46A'sTeal-1
❑ 47A'sTeal-1
❑ 48A'sTeal-1
❑ 49A'sTeal-1
❑ 49A'sTeal-2
❑ 51A'sTeal-1
❑ 51TopTea-6
❑ 52A'sTeal-1
❑ 53A'sTeal-1
❑ 54A'STEAI-1
❑ 68LauWorS-7
❑ 68LauWorS-10
❑ 68LauWorS-11
❑ 68LauWorS-26
❑ 68LauWorS-27
❑ 70FleWorS-10
❑ 70FleWorS-11
❑ 70FleWorS-26
❑ 70FleWorS-27
❑ 71FleWorS-12
❑ 71FleWorS-27
❑ 74A's192T-29
Atilano, Luis
❑ 75CliPilT-21
Atkins, Ross
❑ 95WatIndTI-3
❑ 97KinIndB-1
❑ 98AkrAerM-5
Atkins, Tommy (Francis M.)
❑ 11PinT-5-521
❑ 11SpoLifM-85
❑ 12ColRedB-12A
❑ 12ColRedB-12B
❑ 12ColTinT-12A
❑ 12ColTinT-12B
Atkinson, Bill (William C.)
❑ 72Dia-1
❑ 77ExpPos-2
❑ 77ExpPos-3
❑ 78OPC-144
❑ 78Top-43
❑ 80OPC-133
❑ 80Top-415
❑ 81EdmTraRR-12
❑ 83AppFoxFr-19
Atkinson, Neil
❑ 93EugEmeC-3
❑ 93EugEmeF-3845
❑ 94RocRoyC-2
❑ 94RocRoyF-554
❑ 95WicWraTI-31
Atlantics, Brooklyn
❑ 94OriofB-16
Attardi, Jay
❑ 76AppFoxT-1
Attebery, Russ
❑ 76SeaRaiC-1
Attell, Abe
❑ 88LitSunBS-13
❑ 88PacEigMO-28
Attreau, Dick (Richard G.)
❑ 94ConTSN-1289
❑ 94ConTSNB-1289
Atwater, Buck
❑ 90GatCitPP-3353
❑ 91PocPioP-3787
Atwater, Joe
❑ 94PitMetC-4
❑ 94PitMetF-3515
❑ 96StLucMTI-12
Atwater, Tyrone
❑ 90GatCitPSP-3
❑ 91PocPioSP-23
Atwell, Gary
❑ 75LafDriT-7
Atwell, Toby (Maurice D.)
❑ 47Exh-9
❑ 50WorWidGV-34
❑ 52Top-356
❑ 53BowC-112
❑ 53Top-23
❑ 54Bow-123
❑ 55Bow-164
❑ 56Top-232
❑ 83TopRep5-356
❑ 91TopArc1-23
Atwood, Bill (William F.)
❑ 40PhiTeal-2
❑ 40PlaBal-240
❑ 41PhiTeal-2
❑ 93ConTSN-750
Atwood, Derek
❑ 91PocPioP-3773
❑ 91PocPioSP-13
Atwood, Jason
❑ 93PocPosF-4199
Atz, Jacob Henry
❑ 09ColChiE-13
❑ 09T206-9
❑ 12ColRedB-13
❑ 12ColTinT-13
Aube, Paul
❑ 76DalCon-1
Aube, Richard
❑ 83ChaRoyT-14
Aubel, Larry
❑ 72CedRapCT-25
Aubel, Mike
❑ 92AubAstC-8
❑ 92AubAstF-1365
Aubin, Kevin
❑ 91PriRedC-1
❑ 91PriRedP-3516
Aubin, Yves
❑ 52LavPro-101
Aubrey, Harvey H.
❑ 11SpoLifCW-10
Auchard, Dan
❑ 89KinMetS-1
Aucoin, Derek
❑ 90JamExpP-13
❑ 91SumFlyC-2
❑ 91SumFlyP-2325
❑ 92RocExpC-7
❑ 92RocExpF-2106
❑ 93WesPalBEC-2
❑ 93WesPalBEF-1330
❑ 96Bow-356
❑ 96BowFoi-356
❑ 96ExpDis-5
❑ 97PacPriGotD-GD166
❑ 97Ult-226
❑ 97UltGolME-226
❑ 97UltPlaME-226
Aucutt, Mark
❑ 97SalAva-37
Audain, Miguel
❑ 87PenWhiSP-13
Aude, Rich
❑ 90AugPirP-2469
❑ 90CMC-851
❑ 91SalBucC-3
❑ 91SalBucP-957
❑ 92SalBucC-3
❑ 92SalBucF-68
❑ 93CarMudF-2059
❑ 93CarMudTI-3
❑ 94Bow-462
❑ 94BufBisF-1842
❑ 94ColC-42
❑ 94ColChoGS-42
❑ 94ColChoSS-42
❑ 94FleMajLP-3
❑ 94Top-787
❑ 94TopGol-787
❑ 94TopSpa-787
❑ 94TriAAF-AAA26
❑ 95Bow-117
❑ 95FleUpd-145
❑ 95Pin-444
❑ 95PinArtP-444
❑ 95PinMusC-444
❑ 95PirFil-1
❑ 95Sel-207
❑ 95SelArtP-207
❑ 95SigRoo-4
❑ 95SigRooSig-4
❑ 95Sum-137
❑ 95SumNthD-137
❑ 96Don-389
❑ 96DonPreP-389
❑ 96Pac-167
❑ 97SyrSkyCB-1
Audley, Jim
❑ 90WicStaSGD-4
❑ 91KanCouCTI-2
❑ 92FreKeyC-2
❑ 92FreKeyF-1817
Auer, Otto
❑ 12HomRunKE-61
❑ 12Zee-100
Auerbach, Rick (Frederick)
❑ 72OPC-153
❑ 72Top-153
❑ 73OPC-427
❑ 73Top-427
❑ 74OPC-289
❑ 74Top-289
❑ 75OPC-588
❑ 75Top-588
❑ 75TopMin-588
❑ 76OPC-622
❑ 76SSP-74
❑ 76Top-622
❑ 78Pep-2
❑ 78SSP270-126
❑ 78Top-646
❑ 79Top-174
❑ 80RedEnq-23
❑ 80Top-354
❑ 81MarPos-5
❑ 82Top-72
❑ 90DodTar-22
❑ 94BreMilB-99
Aufdermauer, Bud
❑ 85AncGlaPTI-44
August, Brian
❑ 98OneYanG-2
❑ 99BasAmeTPLM-1
August, Don
❑ 85Top-392
❑ 85TopTif-392
❑ 86TucTorP-3
❑ 87DenZepP-17
❑ 88BreTeal-2
❑ 88DenZepC-8
❑ 88DenZepP-1259
❑ 88Don-602
❑ 88FleUpd-37
❑ 88FleUpdG-37
❑ 88ScoRoo-104T
❑ 88ScoRooG-104T
❑ 88TopTra-7T
❑ 88TopTraT-7T
❑ 89Bow-130
❑ 89BowTif-130
❑ 89BreGar-15
❑ 89BrePol-38
❑ 89BreYea-38
❑ 89Don-410
❑ 89Fle-177
❑ 89FleGlo-177
❑ 89PanSti-365
❑ 89Sco-419
❑ 89ScoHot1R-83
❑ 89ScoYouS2-28
❑ 89Spo-131
❑ 89Top-696
❑ 89TopBig-33
❑ 89TopTif-696
❑ 89UppDec-325
❑ 90BrePol-38
❑ 90ClaBlu-124
❑ 90CMC-45
❑ 90DenZepC-20
❑ 90DenZepP-616
❑ 90Don-617
❑ 90OPC-192
❑ 90ProAAAF-641
❑ 90PubIntS-488
❑ 90Sco-144
❑ 90Top-192
❑ 90TopTif-192
❑ 90UppDec-295
❑ 91BreMilB-1
❑ 91BrePol-1
❑ 92Don-140
❑ 92LonTigF-623
❑ 92Sco-533
❑ 92Ult-78
❑ 94BreMilB-100
August, Sam
❑ 87AshTouP-20
❑ 88OscAstS-2
❑ 89ColMudP-140
❑ 91Cla/Bes-298
❑ 91JacGenLD-552
❑ 91JacGenP-916
❑ 91LinDriAA-552
❑ 92JacGenS-327
❑ 92SkyAA F-139
❑ 94RivPilCLC-28
Augustine, Andy
❑ 94BelMarC-3
❑ 94BelMarF-3238
❑ 96LanJetB-5
Augustine, Dave (David R.)
❑ 74OPC-598
❑ 74Top-598
❑ 75OPC-616
❑ 75Top-616
❑ 75TopMin-616
❑ 77ColCliT-1
❑ 78ChaChaT-1
❑ 79ChaChaT-12
❑ 80OmaRoyP-1
❑ 81PorBeaT-6
❑ 82PorBeaT-18
Augustine, Jerry (Gerald Lee)
❑ 77BurCheD-82
❑ 77Top-577
❑ 78Top-133
❑ 79Top-357
❑ 80BreTeal-1
❑ 80Top-243
❑ 81Don-445
❑ 81Top-596
❑ 82BrePol-46
❑ 82Don-332
❑ 82Fle-133
❑ 82Top-46
❑ 83BrePol-46
❑ 83Fle-26
❑ 83Top-424
❑ 84BrePol-46
❑ 84Fle-194
❑ 84Nes792-658
❑ 84Top-658
❑ 84TopTif-658
❑ 85RocRedWT-14
❑ 92BreCarT-1
❑ 93UppDecS-9
❑ 94BreMilB-189
Augustine, Rob
❑ 92BurIndC-15
❑ 92BurIndF-1644
❑ 93WatIndC-2
❑ 93WatIndF-3551
❑ 94HigDesMC-2
❑ 94HigDesMF-2778
Auker, Eldon Leroy
❑ 34BatR31-120
❑ 34DiaMatCSB-3
❑ 34TigTeal-1
❑ 35DiaMatCS3T1-3
❑ 35GouPreR-4
❑ 36NatChiFPR-3
❑ 38CloFotW-3
❑ 39PlaBal-4
❑ 40PlaBal-139
❑ 41BroW75-2
❑ 41PlaBal-45
❑ 72TCMthe3-118
❑ 74TigTCM1AC-1
❑ 74TigTCM1AC-35
❑ 76TigOldTS-1
❑ 79DiaGre-379
❑ 81TigDetN-91
❑ 88ConSer3-3
Aulenback, Jim
❑ 83AleDukT-13
❑ 84PriWilPT-14
Ault, Doug (Douglas Reagan)
❑ 75SpoIndC-10
❑ 76SacSolC-9
❑ 77OPC-202
❑ 77Top-477
❑ 78BluJayP-2
❑ 78OPC-202
❑ 78Top-267
❑ 79OPC-205
❑ 79SyrChiT-15
❑ 79SyrChiTI-17
❑ 79Top-392
❑ 80SyrChiT-2
❑ 80SyrChiTI-2
❑ 81Fle-424
❑ 82SyrChiT-24
❑ 82SyrChiTI-2
❑ 83KnoBluJT-20
❑ 85SyrChiT-21
❑ 86SyrChiP-3
❑ 87SyrChiP-1934
❑ 87SyrChiT-23
❑ 88DunBluJS-25
❑ 89DunBluJS-26
❑ 90St.CatBJP-3482
❑ 91St.CatBJC-26
❑ 91St.CatBJP-3411
❑ 92MyrBeaHC-27
❑ 92MyrBeaHF-2213
❑ 92Nab-30
❑ 93DunBluJFFN-1
❑ 93RanKee-56
Aurila, Brad
❑ 92JamExpC-15
❑ 92JamExpF-1506
Aurilia, Rich
❑ 92ButCopKSP-6
❑ 93ChaRanC-2
❑ 93ChaRanF-1946
❑ 93FloStaLAF-1
❑ 94Cla-148
❑ 94ClaGolF-32
❑ 94ExcFS7-130
❑ 94TulDriF-248
❑ 94TulDriTI-1
❑ 96Bow-350
❑ 96BowFoi-350
❑ 96ColCho-719
❑ 96ColChoGS-719
❑ 96ColChoSS-719
❑ 96Fin-B351
❑ 96FinRef-B351
❑ 96FleUpd-U202
❑ 96FleUpdTC-U202
❑ 96PhoFirB-6
❑ 97ColCho-226
❑ 97Fle-474
❑ 97FleTif-474
❑ 97Pac-435
❑ 97PacLigB-435
❑ 97PacSil-435
❑ 97StaClu-325
❑ 97StaCluMOP-325
❑ 97Top-396
❑ 97UppDec-173
❑ 98CroRoy-120
❑ 98GiaMot-11
❑ 98PacInvGems-215
❑ 98PacOnl-653
❑ 98PacOnlR-653
❑ 98PacOnlWC-653
❑ 98UppDec-509
❑ 99Fle-330
❑ 99FleSta9-330
❑ 99FleWarT-330
❑ 99Pac-377
❑ 99PacAur-167
❑ 99PacAurOD-167
❑ 99PacCroC-249
❑ 99PacCroCPB-249
❑ 99PacOme-208
❑ 99PacOmeC-208
❑ 99PacOmeG-208
❑ 99PacOmePB-208
❑ 99PacPar-206
❑ 99PacParC-206
❑ 99PacParG-206
❑ 99PacParHoloGold-206
❑ 99PacParHS-206
❑ 99PacParOD-206
❑ 99PacParPB-206
❑ 99PacParRed-206
❑ 99PacPlaB-377
❑ 99PacRed-377
Ausanio, Joe
❑ 88WatPirP-2
❑ 89SalBucS-3
❑ 90HarSenP-1186
❑ 90ProAaA-12
❑ 91Bow-528
❑ 91Cla/Bes-186
❑ 92BufBisBS-1
❑ 92BufBisF-315
❑ 92BufBisS-26
❑ 92SkyAAAF-12
❑ 94ColCliF-2940
❑ 94ColCliP-1
❑ 94LeaLimR-15
❑ 95ColCliP-1
❑ 95ColCliTI-1
❑ 95Don-501
❑ 95DonPreP-501
❑ 95Fle-66
❑ 95Sco-574
❑ 95ScoGolR-574
❑ 95ScoPlaTS-574
❑ 95SigRoo-5
❑ 95SigRooSig-5
❑ 95StaClu-301
❑ 95StaCluMOP-301
❑ 95StaCluSTWS-301
❑ 96NorTidB-7
Ausman, Paul
❑ 76TacTwiDQ-1
❑ 77OrlTwiT-2
Ausmus, Brad
❑ 89OneYanP-2110
❑ 90PriWilCTI-5
❑ 91Cla/Bes-17
❑ 91PriWilCC-13
❑ 91PriWilCP-1429
❑ 92ClaFS7-3
❑ 92ColCliF-355
❑ 92OPC-58
❑ 92ProFS7-120
❑ 92Top-58
❑ 92TopGol-58
❑ 92TopGolW-58
❑ 92TopMic-58
❑ 93ClaFS7-153
❑ 93ColSprSSF-3088
❑ 93Don-773
❑ 93RocStaC-30
❑ 93SelRoo-83T
❑ 93StaClu-367
❑ 93StaCluFDI-367
❑ 93StaCluMOP-367
❑ 94Bow-504
❑ 94ColC-43
❑ 94ColChoGS-43
❑ 94ColChoSS-43
❑ 94Don-100
❑ 94Fin-29
❑ 94FinRef-29
❑ 94Fle-653
❑ 94FleExtB-368
❑ 94Lea-239
❑ 94PadMot-22
❑ 94PanSti-251
❑ 94Pin-391
❑ 94PinArtP-391
❑ 94PinMusC-391
❑ 94Sco-579
❑ 94ScoBoyoS-43
❑ 94ScoGolR-579
❑ 94Sel-106
❑ 94StaClu-412
❑ 94StaCluFDI-412
❑ 94StaCluGR-412
❑ 94StaCluMOP-412
❑ 94Stu-129
❑ 94Top-127
❑ 94TopGol-127
❑ 94TopSpa-127
❑ 94TriPla-161
❑ 94Ult-276
❑ 94UppDec-232
❑ 94UppDecED-232
❑ 95ColCho-357
❑ 95ColChoGS-357
❑ 95ColChoSS-357
❑ 95Don-178
❑ 95DonPreP-178
❑ 95DonTopotO-337
❑ 95Fle-554
❑ 95Lea-150
❑ 95PadCHP-2
❑ 95PadMot-19
❑ 95Sco-465
❑ 95ScoGolR-465
❑ 95ScoPlaTS-465
❑ 95StaClu-77
❑ 95StaCluFDI-77
❑ 95StaCluMOP-77
❑ 95StaCluSTWS-77
❑ 95Top-595
❑ 95TopCyb-367
❑ 95Ult-230
❑ 95UltGolM-230
❑ 96ColCho-291
❑ 96ColChoGS-291
❑ 96ColChoSS-291
❑ 96Don-34
❑ 96DonPreP-34
❑ 96EmoXL-274
❑ 96Fla-370
❑ 96Fle-560
❑ 96FleTif-560
❑ 96Lea-9
❑ 96LeaPrePB-9
❑ 96LeaPrePG-9
❑ 96LeaPrePS-9
❑ 96LeaSigA-12
❑ 96LeaSigAG-12
❑ 96LeaSigAS-12
❑ 96MetUni-232
❑ 96MetUniP-232
❑ 96Pac-188
❑ 96PadMot-25
❑ 96PanSti-98
❑ 96Sco-479
❑ 96StaClu-142
❑ 96StaCluMOP-142
❑ 96TigHebN-24
❑ 96Top-208

❑ 96Ult-281
❑ 96UltGolM-281
❑ 96UppDec-191
❑ 97AstMot-17
❑ 97ColCho-347
❑ 97Don-320
❑ 97DonGolPP-320
❑ 97DonSilPP-320
❑ 97Fle-93
❑ 97Fle-552
❑ 97FleTif-93
❑ 97FleTif-552
❑ 97Lea-289
❑ 97LeaFraM-289
❑ 97LeaFraMDC-289
❑ 97Pac-83
❑ 97PacLigB-83
❑ 97PacSil-83
❑ 97Sco-370
❑ 97ScoArtPWB-370
❑ 97ScoResC-370
❑ 97ScoShoS-370
❑ 97ScoShoSAP-370
❑ 97Top-402
❑ 97Ult-348
❑ 97UltGolME-348
❑ 97UltPlaME-348
❑ 98ColCho-131
❑ 98ColCho-188
❑ 98Fle-260
❑ 98Pac-311
❑ 98PacOnl-310
❑ 98PacOnlR-310
❑ 98PacOnlWC-310
❑ 98PacPlaB-311
❑ 98PacRedT-311
❑ 98PacSil-311
❑ 98Sco-217
❑ 98ScoRT-101
❑ 98StaCluFDI-257
❑ 98StaClul-257
❑ 98StaCluOneK-257
❑ 98StaCluPP-257
❑ 98Top-43
❑ 98TopChr-43
❑ 98TopChrR-43
❑ 98TopDevR-43
❑ 98TopDia-43
❑ 98TopMiniC-43
❑ 98Ult-437
❑ 98UltGolM-437
❑ 98UltMas-437
❑ 98UltPlaM-437
❑ 98UppDec-105
❑ 98UppDecSF-64
❑ 99Fle-324
❑ 99FleSta9-324
❑ 99FleWarT-324
❑ 99Pac-185
❑ 99PacPlaB-185
❑ 99PacRed-185
❑ 99Top-304
❑ 99TopChr-304
❑ 99TopChrR-304
❑ 99TopMVPP-304
❑ 99UppDec-369
❑ 99UppDecEL1-369
❑ 99UppDecEL2-369
Aust, Dennis Kay
❑ 65CarTeal-1
❑ 66OPC-179
❑ 66Top-179
❑ 66TopVen-179
Austelle, Al
❑ 86DavLipB-2
❑ 92DavLipB-2
Austerman, Carl
❑ 75SacSolC-16
Austin, Corey
❑ 92SouBenWSC-8
❑ 92SouBenWSF-188
Austin, Dero
❑ 76LauIndC-2
❑ 76LauIndC-13
❑ 76LauIndC-28
Austin, Frank
❑ 52MotCoo-18
❑ 86NegLeaF-74
Austin, Jacob
❑ 92WelPirC-1
Austin, Jake
❑ 93AugPirC-2
❑ 93AugPirF-1549
❑ 94SalBucC-3
❑ 94SalBucF-2335
❑ 95CarMudF-170
❑ 95Exc-249
Austin, James Taylor
❑ 86SpoIndC-178
❑ 88RivRedWCLC-207
❑ 89ElPasDGS-3
❑ 90El PasDAGTI-22
❑ 90ElPasDGS-5
❑ 91BreMilB-2
❑ 91DenZepLD-127
❑ 91DenZepP-114
❑ 91LinDriAAA-127
❑ 92BrePol-2
❑ 92DonRoo-7
❑ 92FleUpd-33
❑ 92Sco-747
❑ 92ScoRoo-107T
❑ 92StaClu-411
❑ 92StaCluD-8
❑ 92TopDeb91-6
❑ 92WesPalBEC-5
❑ 93BrePol-1
❑ 93Don-659
❑ 93FleRooS-RSB3
❑ 93Lea-12
❑ 93OPC-6
❑ 93PacSpa-507
❑ 93Sco-331
❑ 93Sel-322
❑ 93StaClu-587
❑ 93StaCluFDI-587
❑ 93StaCluMOP-587
❑ 93Top-449
❑ 93TopGol-449
❑ 93TopInaM-449
❑ 93TopInaR-449
❑ 93TopMic-449
❑ 93Ult-217
❑ 93UppDec-787
❑ 93UppDecGold-787
❑ 94BreMilB-190
❑ 94StaCluT-202
❑ 94StaCluTFDI-202
Austin, Jim (James Parker)
❑ 87ChaRaiP-7
❑ 88WicPilRD-25
❑ 89AriStaB-3
❑ 91JamExpC-5
❑ 91JamExpP-3557
❑ 92ClaFS7-301
❑ 92ProFS7-274
❑ 92WesPalBEF-2098
❑ 93WesPalBEC-3
❑ 93WesPalBEF-1352
Austin, Jimmy (James Phillip)
❑ 09BriE97-1
❑ 09ColChiE-14A
❑ 09ColChiE-14B
❑ 10DomDisP-3
❑ 10JuJuDE-2
❑ 10SweCapPP-51A
❑ 10SweCapPP-51B
❑ 10W555-2
❑ 11E94-1
❑ 11HelSta-60
❑ 11PinT-5-806
❑ 11SpoLifCW-11
❑ 11SpoLifM-74
❑ 11T205-4
❑ 12ColRedB-14A
❑ 12ColRedB-14B
❑ 12ColTinT-14A
❑ 12ColTinT-14B
❑ 12HasTriFT-9
❑ 12HasTriFT-65
❑ 12HasTriFT-75C
❑ 12T207-4
❑ 12T207-5
❑ 14B18B-30A
❑ 14B18B-30B
❑ 14CraJacE-40
❑ 14FatPlaT-3
❑ 14PieStaT-3
❑ 14TexTomE-2
❑ 15CraJacE-40
❑ 15SpoNewM-7
❑ 16SpoNewM-7
❑ 17ColE13-8
❑ 17HolBreD-2
❑ 20NatCarE-3
❑ 23WilChoV-3
❑ 74CapPub-79
❑ 91ConTSN-236
Austin, Pat
❑ 87LakTigP-18
❑ 88GleFalTP-914
❑ 89TolMudHC-18
❑ 89TolMudHP-766
❑ 90CMC-123
❑ 90HagSunP-1418
❑ 90HagSunS-1
❑ 90LouRedBC-23
❑ 90LouRedBP-406
❑ 90ProAAAF-520
❑ 90Sco-626
Austin, Paul
❑ 89SanDieSAS-1
Austin, Peter
❑ 97EriSeaWB-1
Austin, Rick
❑ 80WisRapTT-13
❑ 82OrlTwiT-14
❑ 83TolMudHT-11
Austin, Rick Gerald
❑ 71MLBOffS-361
❑ 71OPC-41
❑ 71Top-41
❑ 75SacSolC-14
❑ 76OPC-269
❑ 76SpoIndC-21
❑ 76SSP-248
❑ 76SSP-249
❑ 76Top-269
❑ 94BreMilB-191
Austin, Shawn
❑ 97SalVolG-3
Austin, Terry
❑ 81QuaCitCT-12
Austin, Tracy
❑ 82MonNew-1
Auten, Jim
❑ 83MemChiT-16
❑ 84MidCubT-19
Auterson, Jeff
❑ 96GreFalDB-3
❑ 96GreFalDTI-27
❑ 97GreFalDTI-4
❑ 98SanBerS-2
❑ 98SanBerSTIS-2
❑ 98YakBeaG-1
Auth, Bob
❑ 86QuaCitAP-3
Autry, Al (Albert)
❑ 75OmaRoyTI-2
❑ 78SprRedWK-15
Autry, Bucky
❑ 84LitFalMT-18
Autry, Chick (William Askew)
❑ 16Zee-96
❑ 30WhiSoxTI-1
Autry, Gene
❑ 61NuSco-414
❑ 75CalAngP-2
❑ 85AngStrH-1
❑ 87CalAngPPS-1
❑ 92AngPol-2
❑ 93AngPol-1
❑ 93PacRya2S-246
Autry, Martin Gordon
❑ 29ExhFou-20
Avalos, Gilbert
❑ 94PeoChiC-2
❑ 94PeoChiF-2271
❑ 95RocCubTI-2
❑ 96DayCubB-2
Aven, Bruce
❑ 94WatIndC-1
❑ 94WatIndF-3948
❑ 95KinIndTI-2
❑ 96Bow-354
❑ 96BowFoi-354
❑ 96CanIndB-4
❑ 96Exc-39
❑ 97Bow-316
❑ 97BowChr-218
❑ 97BowChrI-218
❑ 97BowChrIR-218
❑ 97BowChrR-218
❑ 97BowInt-316
❑ 97BufBis-5
❑ 98BufBisG-1
❑ 98Fle-39
❑ 98Ult-401
❑ 98UltGolM-401
❑ 98UltMas-401
❑ 98UltPlaM-401
❑ 98UppDec-349
❑ 99PacOme-95
❑ 99PacOmeC-95
❑ 99PacOmeG-95
❑ 99PacOmePB-95
Avent, Stephen
❑ 90BenBucL-18
❑ 91SpaPhiC-13
❑ 91SpaPhiP-898
Averette, Robert
❑ 98ChaAllCM-2
Averill, Earl (Howard Earl)
❑ 26Zee-131
❑ 27Zee-108
❑ 28ExhPCL-2
❑ 28PorandAR-A1
❑ 28PorandAR-B1
❑ 28Zee-125
❑ 29ExhFou-22
❑ 30UncJac-1
❑ 31Exh-22
❑ 31W517-51
❑ 32OrbPinNP-12
❑ 32OrbPinUP-3
❑ 33ButCanV-1
❑ 33ButCre-1
❑ 33DouDisP-3
❑ 33ExhFou-11
❑ 33GeoCMil-3
❑ 33Gou-194
❑ 33TatOrb-3
❑ 33TatOrbSDR-160
❑ 33WorCig-4
❑ 33WorCig-5
❑ 34BabRutG-1
❑ 34BatR31-24
❑ 34BatR31-113
❑ 34ButPreR-1
❑ 34DiaStaR-35
❑ 34DiaStaR-100
❑ 34ExhFou-11
❑ 35ExhFou-11
❑ 35GouPuzR-1L
❑ 35GouPuzR-2E
❑ 35GouPuzR-16E
❑ 35GouPuzR-17E
❑ 36ExhFou-11
❑ 36GouWidPPR-A2
❑ 36GouWidPPR-C2
❑ 36NatChiFPR-4
❑ 36OveCanR-3
❑ 36R31Pre-G1
❑ 36SandSW-2
❑ 36WheBB3-1
❑ 36WheBB5-12
❑ 37ExhFou-11
❑ 37OPCBatUV-103
❑ 37WheBB8-2
❑ 38BasTabP-2
❑ 38ExhFou-11
❑ 39ExhSal-2
❑ 39GouPreR303A-2
❑ 39PlaBal-143
❑ 39TigSpo-1
❑ 39WorWidGTP-2
❑ 40PlaBal-46
❑ 60Fle-71
❑ 61Fle-5
❑ 73SpoScoHC-1
❑ 73SpoScoHC-2
❑ 73SpoScoHC-3
❑ 75ShaPiz-4
❑ 75TCMAllG-1
❑ 76RowExh-5
❑ 76ShaPiz-147
❑ 76ShaPiz-A
❑ 76SSPYanOD-1
❑ 77GalGloG-79
❑ 77GalGloG-202
❑ 77ShaPiz-A
❑ 79DiaGre-280
❑ 80MarExh-3
❑ 80PacLeg-4
❑ 80PerHaloFP-147
❑ 80SSPHOF-147
❑ 81ConTSN-20
❑ 82DiaCla-17
❑ 82OhiHaloF-23
❑ 82TCMGreS-45
❑ 83BigLeaCOA-6
❑ 83ConMar-16
❑ 83TCMRut-1
❑ 85BigLeaC3-35
❑ 86SpoDecG-15
❑ 87SpoCubG-3
❑ 88ConAmeA-2
❑ 89PacLegI-203
❑ 91ConTSN-31
❑ 92ConTSN-597
❑ 93ConTSN-668
❑ 94ConTSN-1089
❑ 94ConTSNB-1089
❑ 95ConTSN-1377
Averill, Earl (James)
❑ 86EveGiaPC-1
Averill, Earl D. Jr.
❑ 59Top-301
❑ 60Lea-110
❑ 60Top-39
❑ 60TopVen-39
❑ 61Top-358
❑ 62AngJayP-1
❑ 62Jel-80
❑ 62Pos-80
❑ 62PosCan-80
❑ 62SalPlaC-24A
❑ 62SalPlaC-24B
❑ 62ShiPlaC-24
❑ 62Top-452
❑ 63Top-139
❑ 64SeaPop-1
❑ 65SeaPop-1
Aversa, Joe
❑ 90JohCitCS-2
❑ 91SprCarC-3
❑ 91SprCarP-747
❑ 92St.PetCC-14
❑ 93ArkTraF-2816
❑ 94St.PetCC-2
❑ 94St.PetCF-2589
❑ 95LouRedF-279
Avery, John
❑ 92PulBraC-2
❑ 92PulBraF-3169
Avery, Larry
❑ 81BurBeeT-29
❑ 82BurRanF-2
❑ 82BurRanT-27
Avery, Mark
❑ 96PriWilCB-4
Avery, Paul
❑ 98YakBeaG-2
Avery, Steve
❑ 89BasAmeAPB-AA13
❑ 89Bow-268
❑ 89BowTif-268
❑ 89DurBullS-1
❑ 89DurBullS-1
❑ 89DurBulTI-1
❑ 89GreBraB-28
❑ 89Sta-67
❑ 89Top-784
❑ 89TopTif-784
❑ 90Bow-9
❑ 90BowTif-9
❑ 90BraDubS-1
❑ 90ClaUpd-T4
❑ 90CMC-277
❑ 90Don-39
❑ 90DonRoo-42
❑ 90FleUpd-1
❑ 90Lea-481
❑ 90ProAAAF-397
❑ 90RicBraBC-7
❑ 90RicBraC-1
❑ 90RicBraP-252
❑ 90RicBraTI-1
❑ 90ScoRoo-109T
❑ 90TopMag-29
❑ 90TopTra-4T
❑ 90TopTraT-4T
❑ 90UppDec-65
❑ 91Bow-566
❑ 91BraDubP-1
❑ 91BraSubS-1
❑ 91Cla2-T26
❑ 91ClaGam-138
❑ 91Don-187
❑ 91Fle-681
❑ 91Lea-510
❑ 91OPC-227
❑ 91RedFolS-105
❑ 91Sco-80
❑ 91Sco100RS-5
❑ 91StaClu-48
❑ 91Stu-141
❑ 91Top-227
❑ 91TopDeb90-6
❑ 91TopDesS-227
❑ 91TopMic-227
❑ 91TopRoo-3
❑ 91TopTif-227
❑ 91ToyRoo-3
❑ 91Ult-1
❑ 91UppDec-365
❑ 92Bow-180
❑ 92BraLykP-1
❑ 92BraLykS-1
❑ 92Cla1-T7
❑ 92Cla1-NNO
❑ 92Cla2-T12
❑ 92ClaGam-188
❑ 92Don-81
❑ 92DonCraJ1-4
❑ 92Fle-349
❑ 92FleSmo'nH-S10
❑ 92Fre-18
❑ 92Hig5-21
❑ 92Hig5S-1
❑ 92JimDea-5
❑ 92KinDis-11
❑ 92Lea-59
❑ 92LeaBlaG-59
❑ 92LeaGolP-1
❑ 92LeaPre-1
❑ 92MVPPin-30
❑ 92OPC-574
❑ 92OPCPre-170
❑ 92PanSti-169
❑ 92Pin-231
❑ 92Pin-585
❑ 92Pin-612
❑ 92PinTea2-66
❑ 92PinTeaP-2
❑ 92PolAve-1
❑ 92RedFolS-7
❑ 92Sco-241
❑ 92Sco-797
❑ 92Sco100S-34
❑ 92ScoImpP-12
❑ 92ScoSam-4
❑ 92StaAve-1
❑ 92StaAve-2
❑ 92StaAve-3
❑ 92StaAve-4
❑ 92StaAve-5
❑ 92StaAve-6
❑ 92StaAve-7
❑ 92StaAve-8
❑ 92StaAve-9
❑ 92StaAve-10
❑ 92StaAve-11
❑ 92StaClu-60
❑ 92StaClu-594
❑ 92StaCluD-9
❑ 92StaPro-2
❑ 92Stu-1
❑ 92Top-574
❑ 92TopGol-574
❑ 92TopGolW-574
❑ 92TopKid-36
❑ 92TopMcD-16
❑ 92TopMic-574
❑ 92TriPla-85
❑ 92Ult-157
❑ 92UppDec-41
❑ 92UppDec-475
❑ 92UppDecF-1
❑ 92UppDecFG-1
❑ 92UppDecTMH-6
❑ 93Bow-198
❑ 93BraFloA-2
❑ 93BraLykP-1
❑ 93BraLykS-1
❑ 93BraStaC-10
❑ 93ClaGam-8
❑ 93DiaMar-5
❑ 93Don-26
❑ 93Fin-160
❑ 93FinRef-160
❑ 93Fla-1
❑ 93Fle-1
❑ 93FunPac-62
❑ 93HumDumC-26
❑ 93KinDis-5
❑ 93Lea-121
❑ 93LeaFas-13
❑ 93OPC-5
❑ 93PacSpa-331
❑ 93Pin-315
❑ 93RedFolS-4
❑ 93Sco-169
❑ 93Sel-109
❑ 93SP-55
❑ 93StaClu-626
❑ 93StaCluFDI-626
❑ 93StaCluMOP-626
❑ 93Stu-5
❑ 93Top-615
❑ 93TopGol-615
❑ 93TopInaM-615

❑ 93TopInaR-615
❑ 93TopMic-615
❑ 93Toy-95
❑ 93TriPla-30
❑ 93Ult-1
❑ 93UppDec-246
❑ 93UppDec-472
❑ 93UppDec-816
❑ 93UppDecGold-246
❑ 93UppDecGold-472
❑ 93UppDecGold-816
❑ 93UppDecIC-WI5
❑ 93UppDecICJ-WI5
❑ 93UppDecSH-HI2
❑ 94Bow-189
❑ 94BowBes-R20
❑ 94BowBes-X109
❑ 94BowBesR-R20
❑ 94BowBesR-X109
❑ 94BraLykP-1
❑ 94BraLykS-1
❑ 94BraUSPC-6C
❑ 94BraUSPC-12H
❑ 94CarLeaA-DJ16
❑ 94ColC-44
❑ 94ColChoGS-44
❑ 94ColChoSS-44
❑ 94Don-41
❑ 94DonDiaK-DK3
❑ 94DonDiaKJ-DK3
❑ 94DonSpeE-41
❑ 94Fin-359
❑ 94FinRef-359
❑ 94Fla-352
❑ 94Fle-350
❑ 94FleAllS-26
❑ 94FleExtB-199
❑ 94FleExtBPD-6
❑ 94FUnPac-33
❑ 94Lea-138
❑ 94LeaL-81
❑ 94OPC-196
❑ 94Pac-1
❑ 94Pin-8
❑ 94PinArtP-8
❑ 94PinMusC-8
❑ 94PinSam-8
❑ 94Sco-166
❑ 94ScoGolR-166
❑ 94Sel-87
❑ 94SP-47
❑ 94SPDieC-47
❑ 94Spo-60
❑ 94StaClu-254
❑ 94StaCluFDI-254
❑ 94StaCluGR-254
❑ 94StaCluMOP-254
❑ 94StaCluT-32
❑ 94StaCluTFDI-32
❑ 94Stu-33
❑ 94Top-137
❑ 94TopGol-137
❑ 94TopSpa-137
❑ 94TriPla-41
❑ 94Ult-147
❑ 94UppDec-41
❑ 94UppDec-420
❑ 94UppDecAJ-18
❑ 94UppDecAJG-18
❑ 94UppDecED-41
❑ 94UppDecED-420
❑ 94USPlaCA-9S
❑ 95Baz-99
❑ 95Bow-377
❑ 95BraAtlC-1
❑ 95ColCho-161
❑ 95ColChoGS-161
❑ 95ColChoSE-66
❑ 95ColChoSEGS-66
❑ 95ColChoSESS-66
❑ 95ColChoSS-161
❑ 95Don-87
❑ 95DonPreP-87
❑ 95DonTopotO-181
❑ 95Emo-99
❑ 95Fin-72
❑ 95FinRef-72
❑ 95Fla-320
❑ 95Fle-299
❑ 95Lea-209
❑ 95LeaLim-5
❑ 95Pac-1
❑ 95Pin-185
❑ 95PinArtP-185
❑ 95PinMusC-185
❑ 95Sco-185
❑ 95ScoGolR-185
❑ 95ScoHaloG-HG92
❑ 95ScoPlaTS-185
❑ 95Sel-7
❑ 95SelArtP-7
❑ 95SP-33
❑ 95SPSil-33
❑ 95StaClu-151
❑ 95StaCluFDI-151
❑ 95StaCluMOP-151
❑ 95StaCluSTDW-B151
❑ 95StaCluSTMP-1
❑ 95StaCluSTWS-151
❑ 95Stu-51
❑ 95Top-430
❑ 95TopCyb-227
❑ 95Ult-345
❑ 95UltGolM-345
❑ 95UppDec-292
❑ 95UppDecED-292
❑ 95UppDecEDG-292
❑ 95UppDecSE-12
❑ 95UppDecSEG-12
❑ 96BraFle-1
❑ 96ColCho-453
❑ 96ColChoGS-453
❑ 96ColChoSS-453
❑ 96Don-33
❑ 96DonPreP-33
❑ 96EmoXL-138
❑ 96Fin-B57
❑ 96FinRef-B57
❑ 96Fla-194
❑ 96Fle-285
❑ 96FleTif-285
❑ 96Lea-137
❑ 96LeaPrePB-137
❑ 96LeaPrePG-137
❑ 96LeaPrePS-137
❑ 96MetUni-126
❑ 96MetUniP-126
❑ 96Pac-1
❑ 96Pin-82
❑ 96Sco-101
❑ 96ScoDugC-A73
❑ 96ScoDugCAP-A73
❑ 96StaClu-275
❑ 96StaCluEPB-275
❑ 96StaCluEPG-275
❑ 96StaCluEPS-275
❑ 96StaCluMOP-275
❑ 96Top-165
❑ 96TopChr-47
❑ 96TopChrR-47
❑ 96Ult-437
❑ 96UltGolM-437
❑ 96UppDec-269
❑ 97Cir-87
❑ 97CirRav-87
❑ 97Don-204
❑ 97Don-295
❑ 97DonGolPP-204
❑ 97DonGolPP-295
❑ 97DonSilPP-204
❑ 97DonSilPP-295
❑ 97DonTea-55
❑ 97DonTeaSPE-55
❑ 97DurBulATI-3
❑ 97E-X2-9
❑ 97E-X2Cred-9
❑ 97E-X2EssCre-9
❑ 97FlaShoLC-113
❑ 97FlaShoLeg0-113
❑ 97FlaShoLeg1-113
❑ 97FlaShoM-A113
❑ 97FlaShoM-B113
❑ 97FlaShoM-C113
❑ 97FlaShoR0-113
❑ 97FlaShoR1-113
❑ 97FlaShoR2-113
❑ 97Fle-251
❑ 97Fle-637
❑ 97FleTif-251
❑ 97FleTif-637
❑ 97PacPriGotD-GD108
❑ 97Sco-450
❑ 97ScoArtPWB-450
❑ 97ScoResC-450
❑ 97ScoShoS-450
❑ 97ScoShoSAP-450
❑ 97SP-36
❑ 97StaClu-72
❑ 97StaCluMOP-72
❑ 97Top-11
❑ 97Ult-390
❑ 97UltGolME-390
❑ 97UltPlaME-390
❑ 98ColCho-48
❑ 98Pac-35
❑ 98PacAur-16
❑ 98PacInv-13
❑ 98PacInvPBlue-13
❑ 98PacInvSilv-13
❑ 98PacInvTeam-4
❑ 98PacOnl-106
❑ 98PacOnlR-106
❑ 98PacOnlWC-106
❑ 98PacPar-19
❑ 98PacParC-19
❑ 98PacParG-19
❑ 98PacParHS-19
❑ 98PacParPB-19
❑ 98PacParR-19
❑ 98PacPlaB-35
❑ 98PacRedT-35
❑ 98PacSil-35
❑ 98PinSna-BRS15
❑ 98RedSoxS-1
❑ 98RedSoxSP-1
❑ 98Sco-11
❑ 98Top-114
❑ 98TopChr-114
❑ 98TopChrR-114
❑ 98TopDevR-114
❑ 98TopDia-114
❑ 98TopMiniC-114
❑ 98UppDec-318
❑ 99Pac-62
❑ 99PacPlaB-62
❑ 99PacRed-62
❑ 99SkyMolMOA-15
❑ 99SkyPre-142
❑ 99SkyPreR-142
❑ 99UppDec-344
❑ 99UppDecEL1-344
❑ 99UppDecEL2-344

Avila, Bobby (Roberto G.)
❑ 49IndTeal-1
❑ 50IndNumN-1
❑ 50IndTeal-1
❑ 51Bow-188
❑ 52Bow-167
❑ 52IndNumN-14
❑ 52RedMan-AL2
❑ 52Top-257
❑ 53BowC-29
❑ 53IndPenCBP-1
❑ 53RedMan-AL26
❑ 54Bow-68
❑ 54DanDee-1
❑ 54RedMan-AL1
❑ 55BigLeaIS-2
❑ 55Bow-19
❑ 55DaiQueS-2
❑ 55IndGolS-12
❑ 55RedMan-AL15
❑ 56Top-132
❑ 57IndSoh-1
❑ 57IndTeal-2
❑ 57Top-195
❑ 58Hir-33
❑ 58IndTeal-1
❑ 58Top-276
❑ 59Top-363
❑ 60Lea-59
❑ 60Top-90
❑ 60TopVen-90
❑ 67TopVen-185
❑ 75TCM195CI-1
❑ 81RedSoxBG2S-3
❑ 83TopRep5-257
❑ 85TCMPhoC-25
❑ 91OriCro-14

Avila, Carlos
❑ 76VenLeaS-31

Avila, Edwin
❑ 95BoiHawTI-2

Avila, Jesus
❑ 76VenLeaS-3
❑ 80VenLeaS-3
❑ 96-97LinVen-92

Avila, Jose
❑ 96EriSeaB-5

Avila, Ralph
❑ 95DodPol-30

Avila, Rolando
❑ 94BluOriC-1
❑ 94BluOriF-3573
❑ 96HigDesMB-5
❑ 97CalLeaTP-19
❑ 97SanBerS-26

Aviles, Brian Keith
❑ 84DurBulT-25
❑ 85GreBraTI-2
❑ 87GreBraB-15

Aviles, Ramon Antonio
❑ 78SSP270-163
❑ 80Top-682
❑ 81Fle-23
❑ 81Top-644
❑ 82Fle-239
❑ 82OklCit8T-4
❑ 82Top-152
❑ 83PorBeaT-10
❑ 86ReaPhiP-1
❑ 87SpaPhiP-11
❑ 88MaiPhiC-24
❑ 88MaiPhiP-302
❑ 89BlaYNPRWL-36
❑ 89BlaYNPRWLU-43
❑ 89ReaPhiB-25
❑ 89ReaPhiP-671
❑ 89ReaPhiS-26b
❑ 90ReaPhiB-6
❑ 90ReaPhiP-1236
❑ 90ReaPhiS-27
❑ 91BatCliCB-27
❑ 91BatCliP-3500
❑ 92BatCliCB-29
❑ 92BatCliF-3282

Aviles, Willie
❑ 98WatIndTI-1

Avram, Brian
❑ 91JohCitCC-23
❑ 91JohCitCP-3968

Avrard, Corey
❑ 95Bow-178
❑ 96PeoChiB-6
❑ 97PeoChi-2
❑ 98PriWilCQ-2

Awkard, H.B.
❑ 91GulCoaRSP-29

Awkard, Russell
❑ 95NegLeaL2-23

Ayala, Adan
❑ 91ChaRaiC-12
❑ 91ChaRaiP-97
❑ 92ChaRaiC-2
❑ 92ChaRaiF-121

Ayala, Benny (Benigno Felix)
❑ 74MetTeal-2
❑ 75OPC-619
❑ 75TidTidTI-1
❑ 75Top-619
❑ 75TopMin-619
❑ 78SprRedWK-8
❑ 79BalOriP-1
❑ 80BalOriP-1
❑ 80Top-262
❑ 81BalOriP-1
❑ 81Don-236
❑ 81Fle-185
❑ 81Top-101
❑ 82Don-581
❑ 82Fle-157
❑ 82Top-331
❑ 83Don-331
❑ 83Fle-52
❑ 83OriPos-2
❑ 83Top-59
❑ 84BalOriP-2
❑ 84Don-270
❑ 84Nes792-443
❑ 84Top-443
❑ 84TopSti-22
❑ 84TopTif-443
❑ 85IndPol-12
❑ 85SubDis-1
❑ 85ThoMcAD-1
❑ 85Top-624
❑ 85TopTif-624
❑ 85TopTifT-3T
❑ 85TopTra-3T
❑ 91MetWIZ-18
❑ 91OriCro-15

Ayala, Bobby
❑ 90CedRapRB-15
❑ 90CedRapRP-2314
❑ 91ChaLooLD-153
❑ 91ChaLooP-1951
❑ 91LinDriAA-153
❑ 92ChaLooF-3811
❑ 92ChaLooS-178
❑ 92SkyAA F-79
❑ 93Bow-498
❑ 93Don-30
❑ 93Fle-29
❑ 93PacSpa-397
❑ 93RedKah-1
❑ 93ScoBoyoS-19
❑ 94Bow-501
❑ 94ColC-572
❑ 94ColChoGS-572
❑ 94ColChoSS-572
❑ 94Don-75
❑ 94Fin-409
❑ 94FinRef-409
❑ 94Fla-335
❑ 94Fle-404
❑ 94FleExtB-160
❑ 94FleExtBSYS-1
❑ 94FleUpd-80
❑ 94Lea-253
❑ 94MarMot-14
❑ 94Pin-482
❑ 94PinArtP-482
❑ 94PinMusC-482
❑ 94ScoRoo-RT61
❑ 94ScoRooGR-RT61
❑ 94StaClu-713
❑ 94StaCluFDI-713
❑ 94StaCluGR-713
❑ 94StaCluMOP-713
❑ 94Top-673
❑ 94TopGol-673
❑ 94TopSpa-673
❑ 94TopTra-75T
❑ 94Ult-416
❑ 94UppDec-506
❑ 94UppDecED-506
❑ 95ColCho-292
❑ 95ColChoGS-292
❑ 95ColChoSS-292
❑ 95Don-157
❑ 95DonPreP-157
❑ 95DonTopotO-144
❑ 95Fin-67
❑ 95FinRef-67
❑ 95Fla-78
❑ 95Fle-260
❑ 95Lea-111
❑ 95MarMot-14
❑ 95MarPac-19
❑ 95Pac-389
❑ 95Pin-431
❑ 95PinArtP-431
❑ 95PinMusC-431
❑ 95Sco-442
❑ 95ScoGolR-442
❑ 95ScoPlaTS-442
❑ 95StaClu-13
❑ 95StaCluFDI-13
❑ 95StaCluMOP-13
❑ 95StaCluSTWS-13
❑ 95StaCluVR-8
❑ 95StaCluVRMO-8
❑ 95Top-193
❑ 95TopCyb-110
❑ 95Ult-324
❑ 95UltGolM-324
❑ 95UppDec-346
❑ 95UppDecED-346
❑ 95UppDecEDG-346
❑ 95UppDecSE-117
❑ 95UppDecSEG-117
❑ 96ColCho-311
❑ 96ColChoGS-311
❑ 96ColChoSS-311
❑ 96Don-199
❑ 96DonPreP-199
❑ 96Fla-155
❑ 96Fle-226
❑ 96FleTif-226
❑ 96LeaSigA-13
❑ 96LeaSigAG-13
❑ 96LeaSigAS-13
❑ 96MarMot-20
❑ 96Ult-122
❑ 96UltGolM-122
❑ 97Fle-616
❑ 97FleTif-616
❑ 97Pac-181
❑ 97PacLigB-181
❑ 97PacSil-181
❑ 97UppDecMP-P17
❑ 98Fle-436
❑ 98MarSco-5
❑ 98MarScoP-5
❑ 98Pac-179
❑ 98PacOnl-678
❑ 98PacOnlR-678
❑ 98PacOnlWC-678
❑ 98PacPlaB-179
❑ 98PacRedT-179
❑ 98PacSil-179
❑ 98Sco-45
❑ 98Top-241
❑ 98TopChr-241
❑ 98TopChrR-241
❑ 98TopDevR-241
❑ 98TopDia-241
❑ 98TopMiniC-241

Ayala, Eric
❑ 80AndBraT-20

Ayala, Fernando
❑ 94GreFalDSP-3

Ayala, Jason
❑ 91ButCopKSP-2

Ayala, Julio
❑ 96EveAquB-2
❑ 97WisTimR-4
❑ 98LanJetG-1

Ayala, Moises
❑ 92BriTigC-15
❑ 92BriTigF-1413
❑ 93BriTigC-2

Aybar, Manny
❑ 96ArkTraB-5
❑ 97Bes-49
❑ 97LouRedB-7
❑ 98Don-263
❑ 98DonGolPP-263
❑ 98DonSilPP-263
❑ 98Fle-95
❑ 98LeaRS-224
❑ 98LeaRSLHolo-224
❑ 98LeaRSLong-224
❑ 98LeaRTrue-224
❑ 98MemRedG-2
❑ 98PacInvGems-198
❑ 98PacOnl-603
❑ 98PacOnlR-603
❑ 98PacOnlWC-603
❑ 98UppDec-561
❑ 99Bow-83
❑ 99BowChr-83
❑ 99BowChrG-83
❑ 99BowChrGR-83
❑ 99BowChrI-83
❑ 99BowChrIR-83
❑ 99BowChrR-83
❑ 99BowGol-83
❑ 99BowInt-83
❑ 99UppDec-469
❑ 99UppDecEL1-469
❑ 99UppDecEL2-469

Aydelott, Jake (Jacob S.)
❑ 25Zee-103

Ayer, Jack
❑ 82ArkTraT-20
❑ 84LouRedR-21
❑ 85LouRedR-21
❑ 86LouRedTI-4
❑ 87LouRedTI-3

Ayers, Bill (William Oscar)
❑ 47TipTop-120

Ayers, Brooks
❑ 89MisStaB-45

Ayers, Doc (Yancy Wyatt)
❑ 22MrsShePP-5

Ayers, Jason
❑ 93MisStaB-48

Ayers, Jim
❑ 75CedRapGT-23

Ayers, Kevin
❑ 86VerBeaDP-2

Ayers, Lenny
❑ 91EveGiaC-22

Ayers, Mike
❑ 97LynHil-4
❑ 98LynHilQ-2

Ayers, Scott
❑ 86WesPalBEP-3
❑ 87JamExpP-2556

Aylmer, Bobby
❑ 90St.CatBJP-3465
❑ 91MyrBeaHC-1
❑ 91MyrBeaHP-2935

Aylor, Brian
❑ 97GreBatB-8

Aylward, Dick (Richard John)
❑ 57HygMea-1
❑ 57SeaPop-1

Aylward, Jim
❑ 88QuaCitAGS-22
❑ 88RenSilSCLC-280
❑ 89QuaCitAB-8
❑ 89QuaCitAGS-27
❑ 90MidAngGS-14
Ayoub, Sam
❑ 71RicBraTI-2
❑ 81RicBraT-25
❑ 82RicBraT-30
❑ 83RicBraT-7
❑ 84RicBraT-22
❑ 85RicBraT-24
❑ 86RicBraP-1
❑ 87RicBraC-NNO
❑ 87RicBraT-29
❑ 88RicBraP-6
❑ 89RicBraC-14
❑ 89RicBraP-820
❑ 90CMC-294
❑ 90RicBra2ATI-2
❑ 90RicBraC-18
❑ 90RicBraTI-2
Ayrault, Bob
❑ 89RenSilSCLC-240
❑ 90Bes-303
❑ 90CMC-800
❑ 90EasLeaAP-EL31
❑ 90ProAaA-23
❑ 90ReaPhiB-2
❑ 90ReaPhiP-1212
❑ 90ReaPhiS-4
❑ 90StaFS7-80
❑ 91LinDriAAA-479
❑ 91ScrRedBLD-479
❑ 91ScrRedBP-2531
❑ 92DonRoo-8
❑ 92PhiMed-37
❑ 92ScrRedBS-477
❑ 92SkyAAAF-216
❑ 93Don-16
❑ 93Fle-484
❑ 93PacSpa-574
❑ 93PhiMed-4
❑ 93PhiStaC-9
❑ 93Pin-229
❑ 93Sco-289
❑ 93StaClu-4
❑ 93StaCluFDI-4
❑ 93StaCluMOP-4
❑ 93Top-126
❑ 93TopGol-126
❑ 93TopInaM-126
❑ 93TopInaR-126
❑ 93TopMic-126
❑ 94ColC-45
❑ 94ColChoGS-45
❑ 94ColChoSS-45
Ayrault, Joe
❑ 91PulBraC-1
❑ 91PulBraP-4007
❑ 92MacBraC-9
❑ 92MacBraF-270
❑ 93CarLeaAGF-35
❑ 93DurBulC-2
❑ 93DurBulF-488
❑ 93DurBulTI-33
❑ 93SouAtlLAPI-2
❑ 94GreBraF-416
❑ 94GreBraTI-5
❑ 95BreBtaTI-42
❑ 96RicBraB-5
❑ 96RicBraRC-14
❑ 96RicBraUB-2
Ayres, Lenny
❑ 90EveGiaB-24
❑ 90EveGiaP-3117
❑ 91EveGiaP-3905
❑ 92CliGiaC-8
❑ 92CliGiaF-3588
Azar, Todd
❑ 88WauTimGS-15
Azcue, Joe (Jose Joaquin)
❑ 62Top-417
❑ 63Top-501
❑ 64IndJayP-2
❑ 64Top-199
❑ 64TopCoi-110
❑ 64TopVen-199
❑ 65Kah-3
❑ 65Top-514
❑ 66IndTeal-2
❑ 66IndVolC-2
❑ 66Top-452
❑ 67CokCapI-9
❑ 67DexPre-15
❑ 67Top-336
❑ 68Baz-4
❑ 68Top-443
❑ 69AngJacitB-2
❑ 69MilBra-18
❑ 69MLBOffS-38
❑ 69OPC-176
❑ 69Top-176
❑ 69TopFou-21
❑ 69TopSta-162
❑ 69TopTeaP-13
❑ 69TraSta-1
❑ 70DayDaiNM-101
❑ 70MLBOffS-170
❑ 70OPC-294
❑ 70Top-294
❑ 71MLBOffS-338
❑ 71OPC-657
❑ 71Top-657
❑ 72MilBra-22
❑ 78TCM60I-36
❑ 94BreMilB-283
Azocar, Oscar
❑ 88AlbYanP-1347
❑ 89AlbYanB-19
❑ 89AlbYanP-332
❑ 89AlbYanSt-1
❑ 90CMC-213
❑ 90ColCliC-13
❑ 90ColCliP-12
❑ 90ColCliP-688
❑ 90FleUpd-111
❑ 90ProAAAF-338
❑ 90ScoRoo-71T
❑ 90TopTVY-36
❑ 91Bow-652
❑ 91Cla1-T62
❑ 91Don-331
❑ 91Fle-655
❑ 91LasVegSLD-276
❑ 91LasVegSP-247
❑ 91LinDriAAA-276
❑ 91OPC-659
❑ 91PanFreS-329
❑ 91PanSti-270
❑ 91Sco-72
❑ 91Sco100RS-46
❑ 91StaClu-450
❑ 91Top-659
❑ 91TopDeb90-7
❑ 91TopDesS-659
❑ 91TopMic-659
❑ 91TopTif-659
❑ 91UppDec-464
❑ 92Fle-598
❑ 92OPC-112
❑ 92PadCarJ-2
❑ 92PadMot-12
❑ 92PadPolD-1
❑ 92PadSmo-2
❑ 92Sco-692
❑ 92StaClu-552
❑ 92Top-112
❑ 92TopGol-112
❑ 92TopGolW-112
❑ 92TopMic-112
❑ 93LinVenB-50
❑ 93PanSti-263
❑ 93StaClu-257
❑ 93StaCluFDI-257
❑ 93StaCluMOP-257
❑ 94VenLinU-12
❑ 95LinVen-73
❑ 96-97LinVen-61
Azuaje, Jesus
❑ 93BurIndC-2
❑ 93BurIndF-3303
❑ 94ColRedC-2
❑ 94ColRedF-447
❑ 94VenLinU-107
❑ 95StLucMTI-6
❑ 96-97LinVen-48
❑ 96BinMetB-2
❑ 97BinMetB-5
❑ 98BinMetQ-8
B.C., Mascot
❑ 96FayGenB-30
Baar, Bryan
❑ 89GreFalDSP-19
❑ 90BakDodCLC-256
❑ 91Cla/Bes-292
❑ 91LinDriAA-528
❑ 91SanAntMLD-528
❑ 91SanAntMP-2978
❑ 92AlbDukS-3
❑ 92SkyAAAF-2
Baase, Michael
❑ 92StoPorC-5
Babb, Charlie (Charles Amos)
❑ 09ColChiE-15A
❑ 09ColChiE-15B
❑ 11SpoLifCW-12
❑ 12ColRedB-15A
❑ 12ColRedB-15B
❑ 12ColTinT-15A
❑ 12ColTinT-15B
❑ 90DodTar-23
Babbitt, Gene
❑ 47SunBre-1
Babbitt, Troy
❑ 91EugEmeC-5
❑ 91EugEmeP-3730
❑ 92AppFoxFI-989
Babcock, Bill
❑ 82AppFoxFr-19
Babcock, Bob (Robert E.)
❑ 77TucTorC-20
❑ 78TucTorC-20
❑ 80ChaChaT-17
❑ 81Top-41
❑ 82Don-565
❑ 82Top-567
❑ 83SalLakCGT-3
❑ 93RanKee-57
Babcock, Tom
❑ 74WicAerODF-103B
Babcock, Walter
❑ 74WicAerODF-103A
Babe, Loren Rolland
❑ 53A'sTeal-3
❑ 66TolMudHTI-1
❑ 66TolMudHTI-22
Baber, Larue
❑ 90HelBreSP-13
❑ 91HelBreSP-9
❑ 92BelBreCB-21
❑ 92BelBreFI-417
❑ 92ClaFS7-363
❑ 93WatDiaC-4
❑ 93WatDiaF-1779
❑ 94RanCucQC-2
❑ 94RanCucQF-1648
Babich, Johnny (John Charles)
❑ 32Zee-94
❑ 33Zee-14
❑ 34BatR31-167
❑ 34DiaStaR-82A
❑ 34DiaStaR-82B
❑ 35GouPreR-5
❑ 36NatChiFPR-86
❑ 40PlaBal-191
❑ 41DouPlaR-127
❑ 41PlaBal-40
❑ 42A'sTeal-1
❑ 43CenFlo-1
❑ 44CenFlo-1
❑ 48SigOil-1
❑ 48SmiClo-22
❑ 90DodTar-24
Babik, Bill
❑ 52LavPro-72
Babin, Brady
❑ 95BreCouMF-251
Babineaux, Darrin
❑ 95YakBeaTI-1
❑ 97VerBeaD-4
❑ 98SanAntMG-2
Babington, Charlie (Charles P.)
❑ 22KolMotBPP-2
Babitt, Shooty (Mack Neal) II
❑ 79WatA'sT-11
❑ 80OgdA'sT-21
❑ 80WesHavWCT-17
❑ 82Don-556
❑ 82Fle-86
❑ 82TacTigT-28
❑ 82Top-578
❑ 83MemChiT-1
❑ 83WicAerDS-3
❑ 84IndIndTI-14
Babki, Blake
❑ 91JamExpC-2
❑ 91JamExpP-3558
❑ 92LetMouSP-12
Baby, Jim
❑ 75WesPalBES-3
Baca, Mark A.
❑ 88PalSprACLC-99
❑ 88PalSprAP-1456
Bacci, Tony
❑ 97EriSeaWB-2
❑ 98AugGreM-12
Bacciocu, Jack
❑ 49SomandK-19
Bach, Jan
❑ 78CliDodT-1
Bach, Rich
❑ 78CliDodT-1
❑ 80BurBeeT-16
Bachman, Kent
❑ 86WesPalBEP-4
Backe, Brandon
❑ 98HudValR-1
Backer, Leonard
❑ 27Zee-85
❑ 28Zee-103
❑ 29Zee-103
❑ 30Zee-114
❑ 31Zee-79
❑ 32Zee-78
❑ 33Zee-98
Backlund, Brett
❑ 93Bow-134
❑ 93BufBisF-508
❑ 93StaCluM-61
❑ 94CarMudF-1569
❑ 94UppDecML-112
❑ 97HigDesMUG-4
Backman, Les (Lester John)
❑ 11SpoLifM-262
Backman, Wally (Walter W.)
❑ 79JacMetT-2
❑ 80TidTidT-4
❑ 81Fle-336
❑ 81TidTidT-8
❑ 82MetPhoA-2
❑ 83Don-618
❑ 83Fle-537
❑ 83TidTidT-3
❑ 83Top-444
❑ 84JacMetF-2
❑ 85Don-319
❑ 85Fle-72
❑ 85Lea-79
❑ 85MetColP-18
❑ 85MetFanC-1
❑ 85MetTCM-21
❑ 85OPC-162
❑ 85Top-677
❑ 85TopSti-106
❑ 85TopTif-677
❑ 86BasStaB-4
❑ 86Don-238
❑ 86Fle-75
❑ 86MetColP-16
❑ 86MetFanC-1
❑ 86MetTCM-16
❑ 86MetWorSC-3
❑ 86OPC-191
❑ 86Top-191
❑ 86TopSti-97
❑ 86TopTif-191
❑ 87Don-316
❑ 87Fle-3
❑ 87FleGlo-3
❑ 87Lea-59
❑ 87MetColP-10
❑ 87OPC-48
❑ 87Spo-124
❑ 87SpoTeaP-2
❑ 87Top-48
❑ 87TopSti-100
❑ 87TopTif-48
❑ 88Don-241
❑ 88DonTeaBM-241
❑ 88Fle-128
❑ 88FleGlo-128
❑ 88Lea-202
❑ 88MetColP-14
❑ 88MetKah-6
❑ 88OPC-333
❑ 88PanSti-340
❑ 88Sco-303
❑ 88ScoGlo-303
❑ 88StaLinMe-2
❑ 88Top-333
❑ 88TopTif-333
❑ 89Bow-159
❑ 89BowTif-159
❑ 89Don-383
❑ 89DonBasB-186
❑ 89DonTra-10
❑ 89Fle-28
❑ 89FleGlo-28
❑ 89FleUpd-43
❑ 89OPC-72
❑ 89Sco-315
❑ 89ScoRoo-34T
❑ 89Top-508
❑ 89TopBig-300
❑ 89TopTif-508
❑ 89TopTra-5T
❑ 89TopTraT-5T
❑ 89UppDec-188
❑ 89UppDec-732
❑ 90Bow-177
❑ 90BowTif-177
❑ 90Don-155
❑ 90DonBesN-130
❑ 90Fle-367
❑ 90FleCan-367
❑ 90FleUpd-47
❑ 90Lea-341
❑ 90OPC-218
❑ 90PirHomC-1
❑ 90PubIntS-321
❑ 90Sco-281
❑ 90ScoRoo-37T
❑ 90Top-218
❑ 90TopBig-233
❑ 90TopTif-218
❑ 90TopTra-5T
❑ 90TopTraT-5T
❑ 90UppDec-158
❑ 91Bow-490
❑ 91Don-177
❑ 91Fle-29
❑ 91FleUpd-106
❑ 91Lea-482
❑ 91MetWIZ-19
❑ 91OPC-722
❑ 91PhiMed-3
❑ 91RedFolS-5
❑ 91Sco-16
❑ 91ScoRoo-8T
❑ 91StaClu-368
❑ 91Top-722
❑ 91TopDesS-722
❑ 91TopMic-722
❑ 91TopTif-722
❑ 91TopTra-3T
❑ 91TopTraT-3T
❑ 91UltUpd-98
❑ 91UppDec-185
❑ 91UppDec-790
❑ 92Don-478
❑ 92OPC-434
❑ 92PhiMed-4
❑ 92Sco-177
❑ 92StaClu-4
❑ 92Top-434
❑ 92TopGol-434
❑ 92TopGolW-434
❑ 92TopMic-434
❑ 92UppDec-350
Backowski, Lance
❑ 95YakBeaTI-2
❑ 96SavSanB-6
❑ 97YakBeaG-1
Backs, Jason
❑ 89SpaPhiP-1038
❑ 89SpaPhiS-1
❑ 91LinDriAA-501
❑ 91ReaPhiLD-501
❑ 91ReaPhiP-1362
Backus, Jerry
❑ 88BoiHawP-1618
Bacon, Rick
❑ 93EugEmeC-4
❑ 93EugEmeF-3846
Bacosa, Al
❑ 88IdaFalBP-1848
Bacsik, Mike (Michael James)
❑ 74GasRanT-3
❑ 75RanPos-1
❑ 75SpoIndC-18
❑ 76SacSolC-6
❑ 76VenLeaS-82
❑ 77Top-103
❑ 77TucTorC-52
❑ 78TucTorC-45
❑ 80Top-453
❑ 93RanKee-58
❑ 96BurIndB-2
❑ 98CarLeaAC-18
❑ 98KinIndQ-1
❑ 99BasAmeTP-8
❑ 99BasAmeTPG-8
Baczewski, Fred
❑ 54Bow-60
❑ 55Bow-190
❑ 56SeaPop-1
Badacour, Bob
❑ 89CarNewE-18
❑ 90MarPhiP-3189
Badcock, Tom
❑ 73WicAerJPKB-2
❑ 75WatDodT-1
Badeaux, Brooks
❑ 98HudValR-2
Baderdeen, Kevin
❑ 98ChaAllCM-16
Badgro, Red (Morris Hiram)
❑ 81ConTSN-30
❑ 88ConSer4-2
Badke, David
❑ 93AusFut-44
Badorek, Mike
❑ 91HamRedC-5
❑ 91HamRedP-4026
❑ 92MidLeaATI-1
❑ 92SprCarC-9
❑ 92SprCarF-859
❑ 93St.PetCC-2
❑ 93St.PetCF-2617
❑ 94ArkTraF-3081
❑ 94ExcFS7-255
❑ 95ArkTraTI-4
❑ 96LouRedB-7
❑ 98MadBlaW-2
Badowski, Andrew
❑ 97HicCraRB-5
Bady, Ed
❑ 94VerExpC-3
❑ 94VerExpF-3920
❑ 96WesPalBEB-28
❑ 97HarSen-3
❑ 98arSenW1-1
❑ 98HarSenM-1
Baecht, Ed (Edward Joseph)
❑ 30Zee-21
❑ 31CubTeal-1
❑ 93ConTSN-971
Baehr, Dave
❑ 82IdaFalAT-1
❑ 83WisRapTF-25
Baerga, Carlos
❑ 83KelCerB-4
❑ 86ChaRaiP-1
❑ 87ChaRaiP-2
❑ 88BlaYNPRWL-131
❑ 88TexLeaAGS-32
❑ 88WicPilRD-15
❑ 89BlaYNPRWL-4
❑ 89BlaYNPRWLU-40
❑ 89BlaYNPRWLU-47
❑ 89BlaYNPRWLU-57
❑ 89BlaYNPRWLU-60
❑ 89LasVegSC-18
❑ 89LasVegSP-9
❑ 90Bow-339
❑ 90BowTif-339
❑ 90ClaYel-T35
❑ 90DonRoo-19
❑ 90FleUpd-90
❑ 90IndTeal-3
❑ 90Lea-443
❑ 90ScoRoo-74T
❑ 90ScoYouS2-32
❑ 90TopBig-229
❑ 90TopMag-97
❑ 90TopTra-6T
❑ 90TopTraT-6T
❑ 90UppDec-737
❑ 91Bow-69
❑ 91Cla3-T22
❑ 91Don-274
❑ 91Fle-360
❑ 91IndFanC-3
❑ 91Lea-225
❑ 91OPC-147
❑ 91PanFreS-218
❑ 91PanSti-180
❑ 91Sco-74
❑ 91Sco100RS-30
❑ 91StaClu-115
❑ 91Top-147
❑ 91TopDeb90-8
❑ 91TopDesS-147

❑ 91TopMic-147
❑ 91TopRoo-4
❑ 91TopTif-147
❑ 91ToyRoo-4
❑ 91Ult-106
❑ 91UppDec-125
❑ 92Bow-531
❑ 92Cla2-T48
❑ 92Don-120
❑ 92Fle-104
❑ 92Hig5-42
❑ 92IndFanC-4
❑ 92Lea-202
❑ 92LeaBlaG-202
❑ 92OPC-33
❑ 92PanSti-47
❑ 92Pin-3
❑ 92PinTea2-56
❑ 92RedFolS-8
❑ 92Sco-128
❑ 92SpoIllFK1-244
❑ 92StaClu-143
❑ 92StaCluMO-1
❑ 92Stu-163
❑ 92Top-33
❑ 92TopGol-33
❑ 92TopGolW-33
❑ 92TopMic-33
❑ 92TriPla-235
❑ 92Ult-46
❑ 92UppDec-231
❑ 93Bow-585
❑ 93CadDis-2
❑ 93ClaGam-9
❑ 93DiaMar-6
❑ 93Don-405
❑ 93DonDiaK-DK13
❑ 93DonMVP-16
❑ 93DonSpiotG-SG15
❑ 93DurPowP1-15
❑ 93Fin-57
❑ 93FinRef-57
❑ 93Fla-191
❑ 93Fle-213
❑ 93Fle-357
❑ 93FleTeaL-AL6
❑ 93FunPac-105
❑ 93FunPac-107
❑ 93Hos-15
❑ 93IndWUA-2
❑ 93Lea-233
❑ 93LeaFas-11
❑ 93LeaGolA-R4
❑ 93OPC-39
❑ 93OPCPre-51
❑ 93PacBeiA-5
❑ 93PacBeiA-6
❑ 93PacSpa-93
❑ 93PacSpaGE-12
❑ 93PacSpaPI-9
❑ 93PanSti-51
❑ 93Pin-6
❑ 93PinHomRC-39
❑ 93PinSlu-29
❑ 93PinTea2-7
❑ 93PinTeaP-5
❑ 93Sco-9
❑ 93ScoFra-5
❑ 93Sel-122
❑ 93SelStaL-8
❑ 93SP-119
❑ 93StaClu-61
❑ 93StaClu-593
❑ 93StaCluFDI-61
❑ 93StaCluFDI-593
❑ 93StaCluM-189
❑ 93StaCluMOP-61
❑ 93StaCluMOP-593
❑ 93StaCluMP-1
❑ 93Stu-50
❑ 93StuHer-9
❑ 93Top-221
❑ 93Top-402
❑ 93TOPBLAG-25
❑ 93TopFulS-14
❑ 93TopGol-221
❑ 93TopGol-402
❑ 93TopInaM-221
❑ 93TopInaM-402
❑ 93TopInaR-221
❑ 93TopInaR-402
❑ 93TopMic-221
❑ 93TopMic-402
❑ 93Toy-51
❑ 93ToyMasP-3
❑ 93TriPla-80
❑ 93TriPlaA-18
❑ 93Ult-183
❑ 93UltAllS-13
❑ 93UppDec-45
❑ 93UppDec-174
❑ 93UppDecDG-12
❑ 93UppDecFA-A8
❑ 93UppDecFAJ-A8
❑ 93UppDecGold-45
❑ 93UppDecGold-174
❑ 93UppDecOD-D3
❑ 93USPlaCA-4D
❑ 94Bow-307
❑ 94BowBes-R35
❑ 94BowBes-X103
❑ 94BowBesR-R35
❑ 94BowBesR-X103
❑ 94ChuHomS-19
❑ 94ChuHomSG-19
❑ 94ColC-444
❑ 94ColChoGS-444
❑ 94ColChoSS-444
❑ 94Don-14
❑ 94DonSpeE-14
❑ 94Fin-231
❑ 94FinJum-231
❑ 94FinRef-231
❑ 94Fla-37
❑ 94FlaHotN-2
❑ 94Fle-99
❑ 94FleAllS-2
❑ 94FleExtB-56
❑ 94FleGolM-2
❑ 94FleGolMJ-2
❑ 94FlePro-4
❑ 94FleSun-2
❑ 94FleTeaL-5
❑ 94FUnPac-109
❑ 94FUnPac-201
❑ 94Kra-1
❑ 94Lea-247
❑ 94LeaGolS-9
❑ 94LeaL-26
❑ 94LeaMVPC-A1
❑ 94LeaMVPCG-A1
❑ 94O-PJumAF-6
❑ 94OPC-106
❑ 94OPCAllR-6
❑ 94OPCJumA-6
❑ 94Pac-166
❑ 94PacPro-P1
❑ 94PacSilP-16
❑ 94PacSilPC-16
❑ 94PanSti-54
❑ 94Pin-2
❑ 94PinArtP-2
❑ 94PinMusC-2
❑ 94PinPowS-PS12
❑ 94PinPowS-PS12P
❑ 94PinRunC-RC15
❑ 94PinSam-2
❑ 94PinTeaP-2
❑ 94PinTheN-22
❑ 94ProMag-37
❑ 94RedFolMI-4
❑ 94Sco-53
❑ 94ScoCyc-TC4
❑ 94ScoDreT-4
❑ 94ScoGolR-53
❑ 94ScoGolS-38
❑ 94Sel-279
❑ 94SP-96
❑ 94SPDieC-96
❑ 94Spo-71
❑ 94SpoMov-MM11
❑ 94StaClu-169
❑ 94StaCluFDI-169
❑ 94StaCluGR-169
❑ 94StaCluMO-45
❑ 94StaCluMOP-169
❑ 94StaCluMOP-ST19
❑ 94StaCluST-ST19
❑ 94Stu-91
❑ 94Top-450
❑ 94TopBlaG-2
❑ 94TopGol-450
❑ 94TopSpa-450
❑ 94TopSupS-2
❑ 94TriPla-112
❑ 94TriPlaM-5
❑ 94Ult-343
❑ 94UltHitM-2
❑ 94UltRBIK-6
❑ 94UltRisS-1
❑ 94UppDec-49
❑ 94UppDec-115
❑ 94UppDecED-49
❑ 94UppDecED-115
❑ 94USPlaCA-6D
❑ 95Baz-103
❑ 95BazRedH-RH20
❑ 95Bow-336
❑ 95BowBes-R37
❑ 95BowBesR-R37
❑ 95ClaPhoC-20
❑ 95ColCho-56
❑ 95ColCho-270
❑ 95ColChoGS-56
❑ 95ColChoGS-270
❑ 95ColChoSE-118
❑ 95ColChoSEGS-118
❑ 95ColChoSESS-118
❑ 95ColChoSS-56
❑ 95ColChoSS-270
❑ 95Don-326
❑ 95DonDom-4
❑ 95DonPreP-326
❑ 95DonTopotO-57
❑ 95Emo-31
❑ 95Fin-199
❑ 95FinRef-199
❑ 95Fla-29
❑ 95Fle-131
❑ 95Lea-158
❑ 95Lea300C-9
❑ 95LeaLim-123
❑ 95LeaLimIBP-13
❑ 95LinVen-317
❑ 95LinVen-325
❑ 95Pac-117
❑ 95PacLatD-4
❑ 95PacPri-37
❑ 95PanSti-49
❑ 95Pin-200
❑ 95Pin-280
❑ 95PinArtP-200
❑ 95PinArtP-280
❑ 95PinMusC-200
❑ 95PinMusC-280
❑ 95PinRedH-RH25
❑ 95PinWhiH-WH25
❑ 95RedFol-16
❑ 95Sco-51
❑ 95Sco-565
❑ 95ScoGolR-51
❑ 95ScoGolR-565
❑ 95ScoHaloG-HG23
❑ 95ScoPlaTS-51
❑ 95ScoPlaTS-565
❑ 95Sel-124
❑ 95SelArtP-124
❑ 95SelCer-43
❑ 95SelCerMG-43
❑ 95SP-144
❑ 95SPCha-143
❑ 95SPChaDC-143
❑ 95Spo-64
❑ 95SpoArtP-64
❑ 95SPSil-144
❑ 95SPSpeF-8
❑ 95StaClu-36
❑ 95StaClu-48
❑ 95StaClu-403
❑ 95StaCluCT-12
❑ 95StaCluFDI-36
❑ 95StaCluFDI-48
❑ 95StaCluMOP-36
❑ 95StaCluMOP-48
❑ 95StaCluMOP-403
❑ 95StaCluSTDW-I19T
❑ 95StaCluSTDW-I36
❑ 95StaCluSTMP-11
❑ 95StaCluSTWS-36
❑ 95StaCluSTWS-48
❑ 95StaCluSTWS-403
❑ 95StaCluVR-25
❑ 95StaCluVRMO-25
❑ 95Stu-36
❑ 95StuGolS-36
❑ 95Sum-100
❑ 95SumNthD-100
❑ 95Top-385
❑ 95Top-596
❑ 95TopCyb-368
❑ 95TopCybSiR-5
❑ 95TopEmb-95
❑ 95TopEmbGI-95
❑ 95TopTra-157T
❑ 95UC3-43
❑ 95UC3-140
❑ 95UC3ArtP-43
❑ 95UC3ArtP-140
❑ 95Ult-278
❑ 95UltGolM-278
❑ 95UppDec-109
❑ 95UppDec-339
❑ 95UppDecED-109
❑ 95UppDecED-339
❑ 95UppDecEDG-109
❑ 95UppDecEDG-339
❑ 95UppDecSE-27
❑ 95UppDecSEG-27
❑ 95UppDecSoaD-SD11
❑ 95Zen-13
❑ 95ZenAllS-14
❑ 95ZenZ-18
❑ 96Baz-33
❑ 96Bow-46
❑ 96BowBes-86
❑ 96BowBesAR-86
❑ 96BowBesP-BBP22
❑ 96BowBesPAR-BBP22
❑ 96BowBesPR-BBP22
❑ 96BowBesR-86
❑ 96BowFoi-46
❑ 96Cir-154
❑ 96CirRav-154
❑ 96ColCho-119
❑ 96ColCho-337
❑ 96ColChoGS-119
❑ 96ColChoGS-337
❑ 96ColChoSS-119
❑ 96ColChoSS-337
❑ 96ColChoYMtP-2
❑ 96ColChoYMtP-2A
❑ 96ColChoYMtPGS-2
❑ 96ColChoYMtPGS-2A
❑ 96Don-435
❑ 96DonHitL-5
❑ 96DonPreP-435
❑ 96EmoXL-45
❑ 96Fin-B282
❑ 96Fin-S69
❑ 96FinRef-B282
❑ 96FinRef-S69
❑ 96Fla-63
❑ 96Fle-82
❑ 96FleTif-82
❑ 96IndFle-3
❑ 96Lea-157
❑ 96LeaLim-32
❑ 96LeaLimG-32
❑ 96LeaPre-32
❑ 96LeaPreP-32
❑ 96LeaPrePB-157
❑ 96LeaPrePG-157
❑ 96LeaPrePS-157
❑ 96LeaPreSG-24
❑ 96LeaPreSte-24
❑ 96LeaSig-146
❑ 96LeaSigA-14
❑ 96LeaSigAG-14
❑ 96LeaSigAS-14
❑ 96LeaSigPPG-146
❑ 96LeaSigPPP-146
❑ 96LeaTotB-10
❑ 96MetUni-43
❑ 96MetUniP-43
❑ 96Pac-300
❑ 96PacBaeS-1
❑ 96PacEstL-EL3
❑ 96PacGolCD-DC22
❑ 96PacHom-HP4
❑ 96PacOctM-OM1
❑ 96PacPri-P93
❑ 96PacPriG-P93
❑ 96PanSti-181
❑ 96Pin-218
❑ 96Pin-304
❑ 96PinAfi-72
❑ 96PinAfiAP-72
❑ 96PinAfiFPP-72
❑ 96PinArtP-118
❑ 96PinArtP-188
❑ 96PinChrBC-12
❑ 96PinFoil-218
❑ 96PinFoil-304
❑ 96PinSta-118
❑ 96PinSta-188
❑ 96RedF-24
❑ 96SchDis-17
❑ 96Sco-15
❑ 96Sco-372
❑ 96ScoBigB-12
❑ 96ScoDiaA-25
❑ 96ScoDreT-3
❑ 96ScoDugC-A14
❑ 96ScoDugC-B97
❑ 96ScoDugCAP-A14
❑ 96ScoDugCAP-B97
❑ 96ScoGolS-28
❑ 96ScoRef-8
❑ 96Sel-21
❑ 96SelArtP-21
❑ 96SelCer-58
❑ 96SelCerAP-58
❑ 96SelCerCB-58
❑ 96SelCerCR-58
❑ 96SelCerMB-58
❑ 96SelCerMG-58
❑ 96SelCerMR-58
❑ 96SelTeaN-1
❑ 96SP-67
❑ 96Spo-70
❑ 96SpoArtP-70
❑ 96StaClu-188
❑ 96StaClu-331
❑ 96StaCluEPB-331
❑ 96StaCluEPG-331
❑ 96StaCluEPS-331
❑ 96StaCluMM-MM4
❑ 96StaCluMO-1
❑ 96StaCluMOP-188
❑ 96StaCluMOP-331
❑ 96StaCluMOP-MM4
❑ 96Stu-88
❑ 96StuPrePB-88
❑ 96StuPrePG-88
❑ 96StuPrePS-88
❑ 96Sum-98
❑ 96SumAbo&B-98
❑ 96SumArtP-98
❑ 96SumFoi-98
❑ 96TeaOut-4
❑ 96Top-75
❑ 96Top-226
❑ 96TopChr-26
❑ 96TopChr-86
❑ 96TopChrR-26
❑ 96TopChrR-86
❑ 96TopGal-2
❑ 96TopGalE-5
❑ 96TopGalPPI-2
❑ 96TopLas-98
❑ 96TopLasSS-1
❑ 96TopPro-AL2
❑ 96Ult-45
❑ 96UltGolM-45
❑ 96UppDec-53
❑ 96UppDecPRE-R22
❑ 96UppDecPreR-R22
❑ 96Zen-82
❑ 96ZenArtP-82
❑ 96ZenMoz-18
❑ 97BowBes-99
❑ 97BowBesAR-99
❑ 97BowBesR-99
❑ 97Cir-155
❑ 97CirRav-155
❑ 97ColCho-169
❑ 97Don-135
❑ 97DonEli-114
❑ 97DonEliGS-114
❑ 97DonGolPP-135
❑ 97DonLim-39
❑ 97DonLim-188
❑ 97DonLimE-39
❑ 97DonLimE-188
❑ 97DonLimENG-39
❑ 97DonSilPP-135
❑ 97Fin-230
❑ 97FinRef-230
❑ 97Fle-391
❑ 97FleTif-391
❑ 97Lea-255
❑ 97LeaFraM-255
❑ 97LeaFraMDC-255
❑ 97NewPin-54
❑ 97NewPinAP-54
❑ 97NewPinMC-54
❑ 97NewPinPP-54
❑ 97Pac-358
❑ 97PacBaeS-1
❑ 97PacLatotML-33
❑ 97PacLigB-358
❑ 97PacPri-122
❑ 97PacPriLB-122
❑ 97PacPriP-122
❑ 97PacSil-358
❑ 97PinPasttM-14
❑ 97Sco-135
❑ 97ScoArtPWB-135
❑ 97ScoPreS-135
❑ 97ScoShoS-135
❑ 97ScoShoSAP-135
❑ 97SP-117
❑ 97StaClu-218
❑ 97StaCluMat-218
❑ 97StaCluMOP-218
❑ 97Top-381
❑ 97TopChr-131
❑ 97TopChrR-131
❑ 97TopGal-113
❑ 97TopGalPPI-113
❑ 97TopMemO5-2
❑ 97TopSta-12
❑ 97TopStaAM-12
❑ 97Ult-236
❑ 97UltGolME-236
❑ 97UltPlaME-236
❑ 97UppDec-436
❑ 98CirThu-275
❑ 98CirThuRav-275
❑ 98CirThuSupRav-275
❑ 98ColCho-174
❑ 98CroRoy-86
❑ 98Don-247
❑ 98DonGolPP-247
❑ 98DonSilPP-247
❑ 98Fin-186
❑ 98FinNo--186
❑ 98FinNo-R-186
❑ 98FinRef-186
❑ 98Fle-492
❑ 98MetUni-12
❑ 98MetUniPMG-12
❑ 98Pac-362
❑ 98PacAur-162
❑ 98PacInv-119
❑ 98PacInvPBlue-119
❑ 98PacInvSilv-119
❑ 98PacInvTeam-18
❑ 98PacLatotML-24
❑ 98PacNes-7
❑ 98PacOme-154
❑ 98PacOmeR-154
❑ 98PacOnl-470
❑ 98PacOnlR-470
❑ 98PacOnlWC-470
❑ 98PacPar-201
❑ 98PacParC-201
❑ 98PacParG-201
❑ 98PacParHS-201
❑ 98PacParPB-201
❑ 98PacParR-201
❑ 98PacPlaB-362
❑ 98PacRedT-362
❑ 98PacSil-362
❑ 98PacTeaC-23
❑ 98Pin-91
❑ 98PinPreP-91
❑ 98PinSna-NYM8
❑ 98ScoRT-194
❑ 98StaCluFDI-181
❑ 98StaCluI-181
❑ 98StaCluOneK-181
❑ 98StaCluPP-181
❑ 98Top-13
❑ 98TopChr-13
❑ 98TopChrR-13
❑ 98TopDevR-13
❑ 98TopDia-13
❑ 98TopMiniC-13
❑ 98TopOpeD-11
❑ 98TopPre-PP1
❑ 98Ult-183
❑ 98UltGolM-183
❑ 98UltMas-183
❑ 98UltPlaM-183
❑ 98UppDec10AP-31
❑ 98UppDec1APR-31
❑ 99Fle-360
❑ 99FleSta9-360
❑ 99FleWarT-360
❑ 99Pac-275
❑ 99PacCroC-178
❑ 99PacCroC-35
❑ 99PacCroCPB-178
❑ 99PacPlaB-275
❑ 99PacPri-91
❑ 99PacPriHB-91
❑ 99PacPriHG-91
❑ 99PacPriHM-91
❑ 99PacPriHP-91
❑ 99PacPriRed-91
❑ 99PacRed-275
❑ 99Ult-116
❑ 99UltGolM-116
❑ 99UltMas-116
❑ 99UltPlaM-116

❑ 99UppDecBD-54
❑ 99UppDecBDD-54
❑ 99UppDecBDQ-54
❑ 99UppDecBDT-54
Baerns, Scott
❑ 89TenTecGE-3
Baerwald, Rudolph
❑ 09ColChiE-16
❑ 12ColRedB-16
❑ 12ColTinT-16
❑ 15Zee-94
Baez, Angel
❑ 81BufBisT-17
Baez, Benito
❑ 96WesMicWB-6
❑ 97VisOakG-3
❑ 98HunStaTI-16
Baez, Diogenes
❑ 92WinHavRSC-6
❑ 92WinHavRSF-1790
❑ 93LynRedSC-1
❑ 93LynRedSF-2528
❑ 93UtiBluSC-3
❑ 93UtiBluSF-3544
❑ 94UtiBluSC-3
Baez, Eddie
❑ 76VenLeaS-69
Baez, Francisco
❑ 90AppFoxBS-3
❑ 90AppFoxP-2087
❑ 90EugEmeGS-2
❑ 91AppFoxCB-1
❑ 91AppFoxP-1707
❑ 92AppFoxCB-11
❑ 92AppFoxFl-974
❑ 93WilBluRC-2
❑ 93WilBluRF-1987
Baez, Homer
❑ 96-97LinVen-255
Baez, Igor
❑ 89GreHorP-408
Baez, Jesse
❑ 79LodDodT-9
❑ 81WauTimT-13
❑ 83WauTimF-17
Baez, Jose Antonio
❑ 75WatDodT-2
❑ 77MarPos-1
❑ 78Top-311
❑ 95ForWayWTI-28
❑ 96ForWayWB-29
❑ 97NewBriRC-29
Baez, Juan
❑ 98HelBreM-6
Baez, Kevin
❑ 88LitFalMP-2
❑ 89ColMetB-12
❑ 89ColMetGS-6
❑ 89SouAtlLAGS-19
❑ 90JacMetGS-16
❑ 91LinDriAAA-551
❑ 91MetColP-22
❑ 91MetWIZ-20
❑ 91TidTidLD-551
❑ 91TidTidP-2515
❑ 91TopDeb90-9
❑ 92DonRoo-9
❑ 92SkyAAAF-247
❑ 92StaClu-543
❑ 92TidTidF-902
❑ 92TidTidS-551
❑ 93Don-361
❑ 93FleFinE-98
❑ 93NorTidF-2574
❑ 94Don-68
❑ 94RocRedWF-1003
❑ 94RocRedWTI-3
❑ 94StaClu-247
❑ 94StaCluFDI-247
❑ 94StaCluGR-247
❑ 94StaCluMOP-247
❑ 95TolMudHTI-6
❑ 96TolMudHB-5
❑ 97SalLakB-9
Baez, Miguel
❑ 97BurIndG-2
Baez, Pedro
❑ 88MadMusP-3
❑ 89ModA'sC-8
❑ 89ModA'sCLC-267
Baez, Raul
❑ 94UtiBluSF-3831
Baeza, Art
❑ 97BakBlaB-16
❑ 97BakBlaTI-16
❑ 97SalVolG-4

Bafia, Bob
❑ 86WinSpiP-2
❑ 87WinSpiP-8
❑ 88PitCubP-1363
❑ 89ChaKniTI-22
❑ 90CMC-86
❑ 90IowCubC-11
❑ 90IowCubP-323
❑ 90ProAAAF-630
❑ 90TopTVCu-37
❑ 91HunStaC-2
❑ 91HunStaLD-277
❑ 91HunStaP-1800
❑ 91LinDriAA-277
Bagby, James C.J. Jr.
❑ 39PlaBal-40
❑ 40PlaBal-32
❑ 46RedSoxTI-2
❑ 75RedSox1T-1
❑ 79DiaGre-233
❑ 83TCMPla1942-12
❑ 93ConTSN-936
Bagby, James C.J. Sr.
❑ 17ColE13-9
❑ 17HolBreD-4
❑ 20NatCarE-4
❑ 20WalMaiW-2
❑ 21E121So1-3
❑ 21E121So8-2
❑ 21Exh-3
❑ 22AmeCarE122-2
❑ 22E120-31
❑ 22W575-3
❑ 23W501-20
❑ 23WilChoV-4
❑ 25Zee-128
❑ 38CloFotW-4
❑ 61Fle-92
❑ 74CapPub-96
❑ 77Ind192T-1
❑ 92ConTSN-487
❑ 95ConTSN-1364
Baggott, Dave
❑ 88SalLakCTTI-4
❑ 89SalLakTTI-4
❑ 94OgdRapSP-29
Bagialemani, Panther
❑ 90IBAWorA-15
Bagiotti, Aldo
❑ 81RedPioT-10
Bagley, Lorenzo
❑ 96MedHatBJTI-3
❑ 97St.CatSB-6
❑ 98HagSunM-7
Bagley, Sean
❑ 97VerExpB-7
Bagnall, Jim
❑ 83ButCopKT-16
❑ 83ChaRoyT-4
Bagshaw, Lance
❑ 87SalLakTTT-7
Bagshaw, Ryan
❑ 88SalLakCTTI-6
Bagwell, Bill (William M.)
❑ 26Zee-89
❑ 27Zee-65
❑ 94ConTSN-1310
❑ 94ConTSNB-1310
Bagwell, Jeff
❑ 88CapCodPB-4
❑ 88CapCodPPaLP-57
❑ 90Bes-132
❑ 90CMC-739
❑ 90EasLeaAP-EL40
❑ 90NewBriRSB-7
❑ 90NewBriRSP-1324
❑ 90NewBriRSS-1
❑ 90ProAaA-26
❑ 90StaFS7-30
❑ 90TopMag-61
❑ 91AstMot-8
❑ 91Bow-183
❑ 91Cla2-T84
❑ 91ClaGam-90
❑ 91DonRoo-30
❑ 91FleUpd-87
❑ 91LeaGolR-BC14
❑ 91ScoRoo-96T
❑ 91StaClu-388
❑ 91StaCluMO-11
❑ 91Stu-172
❑ 91TopTra-4T
❑ 91TopTraT-4T
❑ 91TopTriH-N4
❑ 91UltUpd-79

❑ 91UppDec-702
❑ 91UppDec-755
❑ 92AstMot-8
❑ 92Bow-200
❑ 92Cla1-T8
❑ 92Cla2-T2
❑ 92ClaGam-187
❑ 92ColBag-1
❑ 92ColBag-2
❑ 92ColBag-3
❑ 92ColBag-4
❑ 92ColBag-5
❑ 92ColBag-6
❑ 92ColBag-7
❑ 92ColBag-8
❑ 92ColBag-9
❑ 92ColBag-10
❑ 92ColBag-11
❑ 92ColBag-12
❑ 92ColBag-AU
❑ 92ColPro-2
❑ 92Don-358
❑ 92DonBonC-BC6
❑ 92DonCraJ1-2
❑ 92DonDiaK-DK11
❑ 92DonMcD-24
❑ 92DonSupD-DK11
❑ 92Fle-425
❑ 92FleCitTP-19
❑ 92FleRooS-4
❑ 92Fre-1
❑ 92Hig5-36
❑ 92Hig5S-2
❑ 92JimDea-3
❑ 92Lea-28
❑ 92LeaBlaG-28
❑ 92LeaGolP-4
❑ 92LeaPre-4
❑ 92MJBHolB-1
❑ 92MJBHolB-2
❑ 92MJBHolB-3
❑ 92MJBHolB-4
❑ 92MJBHolB-AU
❑ 92MJBHolP-R1
❑ 92MooSna-2
❑ 92MotBag-1
❑ 92MotBag-2
❑ 92MotBag-3
❑ 92MotBag-4
❑ 92MVPPin-28
❑ 92OPC-520
❑ 92OPCPre-107
❑ 92PanSti-152
❑ 92Pin-70
❑ 92PinSlu-15
❑ 92PinTea2-10
❑ 92Pos-1
❑ 92Sco-576
❑ 92Sco-793
❑ 92Sco100RS-35
❑ 92ScoCokD-3
❑ 92ScoImpP-2
❑ 92ScoProP-19
❑ 92SpoIllFK1-278
❑ 92SpoIllFK1-652
❑ 92StaBag-1
❑ 92StaBag-2
❑ 92StaBag-3
❑ 92StaBag-4
❑ 92StaBag-5
❑ 92StaBag-6
❑ 92StaBag-7
❑ 92StaBag-8
❑ 92StaBag-9
❑ 92StaBag-10
❑ 92StaBag-11
❑ 92StaClu-330
❑ 92StaClu-606
❑ 92StaCluECN-606
❑ 92StaPro-3
❑ 92Stu-31
❑ 92StuHer-BC12
❑ 92StuPre-16
❑ 92Top-520
❑ 92TopDeb91-7
❑ 92TopGol-520
❑ 92TopGolW-520
❑ 92TopKid-44
❑ 92TopMcD-34
❑ 92TopMic-520
❑ 92TriPla-200
❑ 92TriPlaG-GS7
❑ 92Ult-198
❑ 92UltAwaW-3
❑ 92UppDec-276
❑ 92UppDecF-3

❑ 92UppDecFG-3
❑ 92UppDecHRH-HR25
❑ 92UppDecTMH-7
❑ 92UppDecWB-T12
❑ 93AstMot-7
❑ 93AstStaC-8
❑ 93Bow-420
❑ 93ClaGam-10
❑ 93DiaMar-7
❑ 93Don-428
❑ 93DonLonBL-LL17
❑ 93DonMVP-24
❑ 93DonPre-4
❑ 93Fin-11
❑ 93FinRef-11
❑ 93Fla-57
❑ 93Fle-46
❑ 93FleFruotL-3
❑ 93FleTeaL-NL9
❑ 93FunPac-42
❑ 93FunPac-43
❑ 93Hos-19
❑ 93HumDumC-32
❑ 93Lea-125
❑ 93LeaFas-17
❑ 93LeaGolA-R3
❑ 93OPC-29
❑ 93PacJugC-20
❑ 93PacSpa-117
❑ 93PanSti-170
❑ 93Pin-10
❑ 93Pin-297
❑ 93PinHomRC-28
❑ 93PinSlu-14
❑ 93PinTea2-9
❑ 93RedFolS-5
❑ 93Sco-89
❑ 93ScoFra-18
❑ 93Sel-113
❑ 93SP-28
❑ 93StaClu-384
❑ 93StaCluFDI-384
❑ 93StaCluMOP-384
❑ 93Stu-34
❑ 93StuSil-3
❑ 93TedWil-156
❑ 93TedWil-157
❑ 93TedWil-158
❑ 93TedWil-159
❑ 93Top-227
❑ 93TopFulS-8
❑ 93TopGol-227
❑ 93TopInaM-227
❑ 93TopInaR-227
❑ 93TopMic-227
❑ 93Toy-56
❑ 93TriPla-43
❑ 93TriPlaA-12
❑ 93Ult-390
❑ 93UppDec-256
❑ 93UppDec-452
❑ 93UppDec-475
❑ 93UppDec-813
❑ 93UppDecDG-2
❑ 93UppDecGold-256
❑ 93UppDecGold-452
❑ 93UppDecGold-475
❑ 93UppDecGold-813
❑ 93UppDecIC-WI2
❑ 93UppDecICJ-WI2
❑ 94AstMot-3
❑ 94Bow-118
❑ 94BowBes-R53
❑ 94BowBesR-R53
❑ 94ChuHomS-6
❑ 94ChuHomSG-6
❑ 94ColC-329
❑ 94ColC-590
❑ 94ColChoGS-329
❑ 94ColChoGS-590
❑ 94ColChoSS-329
❑ 94ColChoSS-590
❑ 94ColChoT-8
❑ 94DenHol-4
❑ 94Don-365
❑ 94DonDiaK-DK27
❑ 94DonDiaKJ-DK27
❑ 94DonMVP-6
❑ 94DonSpeE-365
❑ 94Fin-212
❑ 94FinJum-212
❑ 94FinRef-212
❑ 94Fla-385
❑ 94FlaInfP-1
❑ 94Fle-483
❑ 94FleExtB-268

❑ 94FleExtBGB-1
❑ 94FleSun-3
❑ 94FleTeaL-20
❑ 94FUnPac-152
❑ 94Kra-16
❑ 94Lea-221
❑ 94LeaL-110
❑ 94LeaMVPC-N1
❑ 94LeaMVPCG-N1
❑ 94O-PJumAF-5
❑ 94OPC-212
❑ 94OPCAllR-5
❑ 94OPCJumA-5
❑ 94OscMayR-16
❑ 94Pac-257
❑ 94PacSilP-24
❑ 94PacSilPC-24
❑ 94PanSti-189
❑ 94Pin-290
❑ 94PinArtP-290
❑ 94PinMusC-290
❑ 94PinPowS-PS16
❑ 94PinRunC-RC36
❑ 94PinTeaP-1
❑ 94Pos-29
❑ 94ProMag-56
❑ 94RedFolMI-2
❑ 94Sco-4
❑ 94ScoGolR-4
❑ 94ScoGolS-8
❑ 94ScoSam-4
❑ 94ScoSam-4GR
❑ 94Sel-234
❑ 94SP-27
❑ 94SPDieC-27
❑ 94SPHol-3
❑ 94SPHolDC-3
❑ 94Spo-7
❑ 94SpoSha-SH3
❑ 94SPPre-CR1
❑ 94StaClu-108
❑ 94StaCluF-F1
❑ 94StaCluFDI-108
❑ 94StaCluFJ-F1
❑ 94StaCluGR-108
❑ 94StaCluMOP-108
❑ 94StaCluMOP-F1
❑ 94Stu-16
❑ 94SucSav-16
❑ 94TomPiz-1
❑ 94Top-40
❑ 94TopBlaG-23
❑ 94TopGol-40
❑ 94TopSpa-40
❑ 94TopSupS-3
❑ 94TriPla-21
❑ 94TriPlaM-4
❑ 94Ult-203
❑ 94UltRisS-2
❑ 94UppDec-272
❑ 94UppDec-480
❑ 94UppDecAJ-36
❑ 94UppDecAJG-36
❑ 94UppDecDC-C1
❑ 94UppDecED-272
❑ 94UppDecED-480
❑ 94UppDecMLS-MM1
❑ 94UppDecMLSED-MM1
❑ 94USPlaCA-5D
❑ 95AstMot-2
❑ 95Baz-61
❑ 95BazRedH-RH13
❑ 95Bow-279
❑ 95BowBes-R16
❑ 95BowBes-X15
❑ 95BowBesR-R16
❑ 95BowBesR-X15
❑ 95ClaPhoC-30
❑ 95ColCho-76
❑ 95ColCho-528
❑ 95ColChoCtG-CG1
❑ 95ColChoCtG-CG1B
❑ 95ColChoCtG-CG1C
❑ 95ColChoCtGE-1
❑ 95ColChoCtGG-CG1
❑ 95ColChoCtGG-CG1B
❑ 95ColChoCtGG-CG1C
❑ 95ColChoCtGGE-1
❑ 95ColChoGS-76
❑ 95ColChoGS-528
❑ 95ColChoSE-40
❑ 95ColChoSE-138
❑ 95ColChoSE-254
❑ 95ColChoSEGS-40
❑ 95ColChoSEGS-138
❑ 95ColChoSEGS-254

❑ 95ColChoSESS-40
❑ 95ColChoSESS-138
❑ 95ColChoSESS-254
❑ 95ColChoSS-76
❑ 95ColChoSS-528
❑ 95DenHol-3
❑ 95Don-20
❑ 95DonBomS-2
❑ 95DonDiaK-DK2
❑ 95DonDom-3
❑ 95DonEli-49
❑ 95DonLonBL-8
❑ 95DonPreP-20
❑ 95DonTopotO-249
❑ 95Emo-134
❑ 95EmoN-1
❑ 95Fin-117
❑ 95FinPowK-PK7
❑ 95FinRef-117
❑ 95Fla-143
❑ 95FlaHotN-1
❑ 95FlaInfP-1
❑ 95FlaTodS-1
❑ 95Fle-451
❑ 95FleAllS-13
❑ 95FleAwaW-2
❑ 95FleLeaL-8
❑ 95FleLumC-1
❑ 95FlePro-3
❑ 95FleTeaL-20
❑ 95FleUpdDT-1
❑ 95FleUpdH-1
❑ 95KinDis-2
❑ 95Kra-17
❑ 95Lea-119
❑ 95Lea300C-12
❑ 95LeaChe-8
❑ 95LeaCor-4
❑ 95LeaGolS-1
❑ 95LeaGreG-1
❑ 95LeaHeaftH-3
❑ 95LeaLim-132
❑ 95LeaLimG-2
❑ 95LeaLimIBP-6
❑ 95LeaLimL-10
❑ 95LeaOpeD-2
❑ 95LeaSli-5A
❑ 95LeaSli-5B
❑ 95NatPac-18
❑ 95Pac-180
❑ 95PacGolCDC-10
❑ 95PacGolP-16
❑ 95PacPri-58
❑ 95PanSti-31
❑ 95PanSti-110
❑ 95PanSti-117
❑ 95Pin-1
❑ 95Pin-301
❑ 95Pin-449
❑ 95Pin-450
❑ 95PinArtP-1
❑ 95PinArtP-301
❑ 95PinArtP-449
❑ 95PinArtP-450
❑ 95PinFan-25
❑ 95PinGatA-GA4
❑ 95PinMusC-1
❑ 95PinMusC-301
❑ 95PinMusC-449
❑ 95PinMusC-450
❑ 95PinPin-5
❑ 95PinPinR-5
❑ 95PinRedH-RH4
❑ 95PinTeaP-TP3
❑ 95PinWhiH-WH4
❑ 95Pos-2
❑ 95PosCan-16
❑ 95RedFol-20
❑ 95Sco-221
❑ 95Sco-554
❑ 95ScoDouGC-GC9
❑ 95ScoGolR-221
❑ 95ScoGolR-554
❑ 95ScoHaloG-HG4
❑ 95ScoPlaTS-221
❑ 95ScoPlaTS-554
❑ 95ScoRul-SR4
❑ 95ScoRulJ-SR4
❑ 95ScoSam-221
❑ 95Sel-37
❑ 95Sel-249
❑ 95Sel-250
❑ 95SelArtP-37
❑ 95SelArtP-249
❑ 95SelArtP-250
❑ 95SelBigS-BS8

❑ 95SelCer-54
❑ 95SelCerC-4
❑ 95SelCerGT-4
❑ 95SelCerMG-54
❑ 95SelSam-37
❑ 95SP-60
❑ 95SPCha-50
❑ 95SPCha-55
❑ 95SPChaDC-50
❑ 95SPChaDC-55
❑ 95Spo-48
❑ 95Spo-166
❑ 95SpoArtP-48
❑ 95SpoArtP-166
❑ 95SpoDet-DE1
❑ 95SpoDouT-1
❑ 95SpoHamT-HT3
❑ 95SpoPro-PM4
❑ 95SPPlaP-PP1
❑ 95SPSil-60
❑ 95SPSpeF-38
❑ 95StaClu-240
❑ 95StaClu-375
❑ 95StaClu-501
❑ 95StaCluCC-CC15
❑ 95StaCluCT-1
❑ 95StaCluFDI-240
❑ 95StaCluMO-2
❑ 95StaCluMOP-240
❑ 95StaCluMOP-375
❑ 95StaCluMOP-501
❑ 95StaCluMOP-CC15
❑ 95StaCluMOP-PZ1
❑ 95StaCluMOP-RL1
❑ 95StaCluMOP-VRE3
❑ 95StaCluPZ-PZ1
❑ 95StaCluRL-RL1
❑ 95StaCluSTWS-240
❑ 95StaCluSTWS-375
❑ 95StaCluSTWS-501
❑ 95StaCluVE-VRE3
❑ 95StaCluVR-198
❑ 95StaCluVRMO-198
❑ 95Stu-2
❑ 95StuGolS-2
❑ 95StuPlaS-2
❑ 95Sum-96
❑ 95Sum-177
❑ 95Sum-197
❑ 95SumBigB-BB4
❑ 95SumNthD-96
❑ 95SumNthD-177
❑ 95SumNthD-197
❑ 95TomPiz-4
❑ 95Top-384
❑ 95Top-405
❑ 95TopCyb-206
❑ 95TopD3Z-3
❑ 95TopEmb-118
❑ 95TopEmbGI-118
❑ 95TopFinIns-1
❑ 95TopLeaL-LL11
❑ 95TopLeaL-LL27
❑ 95TopLeaL-LL32
❑ 95TopTra-8T
❑ 95TopTraPB-8
❑ 95UC3-55
❑ 95UC3-144
❑ 95UC3ArtP-55
❑ 95UC3ArtP-144
❑ 95UC3CycS-CS3
❑ 95Ult-169
❑ 95UltAwaW-11
❑ 95UltAwaW-20
❑ 95UltAwaWGM-11
❑ 95UltAwaWGM-20
❑ 95UltGolM-169
❑ 95UltHitM-1
❑ 95UltHitMGM-1
❑ 95UltHomRK-7
❑ 95UltHomRKGM-7
❑ 95UltOnBL-1
❑ 95UltOnBLGM-1
❑ 95UltPowP-4
❑ 95UltPowPGM-4
❑ 95UltRBIK-6
❑ 95UltRBIKGM-6
❑ 95UltRisS-2
❑ 95UltRisSGM-2
❑ 95UppDec-275
❑ 95UppDecED-275
❑ 95UppDecEDG-275
❑ 95UppDecPAW-H6
❑ 95UppDecPAWE-H6
❑ 95UppDecPC-MLB7
❑ 95UppDecPLL-R6
❑ 95UppDecPLL-R16
❑ 95UppDecPLL-R26
❑ 95UppDecPLLE-R6
❑ 95UppDecPLLE-R16
❑ 95UppDecPLLE-R26
❑ 95UppDecSE-45
❑ 95UppDecSEG-45
❑ 95UppDecSoaD-SD5
❑ 95USPlaCMLA-12C
❑ 95USPlaCMLA-13D
❑ 95Zen-47
❑ 95ZenZ-9
❑ 96AstMot-2
❑ 96Baz-40
❑ 96Bow-77
❑ 96BowBes-20
❑ 96BowBesAR-20
❑ 96BowBesMI-1
❑ 96BowBesMIAR-1
❑ 96BowBesMIR-1
❑ 96BowBesP-BBP16
❑ 96BowBesPAR-BBP16
❑ 96BowBesPR-BBP16
❑ 96BowBesR-20
❑ 96BowFoi-77
❑ 96Cir-133
❑ 96CirAcc-19
❑ 96CirBos-37
❑ 96CirRav-133
❑ 96ColCho-160
❑ 96ColCho-402
❑ 96ColChoCtG-CG19
❑ 96ColChoCtG-CG19B
❑ 96ColChoCtG-CG19C
❑ 96ColChoCtGE-CR19
❑ 96ColChoCtGG-CG19
❑ 96ColChoCtGG-CG19B
❑ 96ColChoCtGG-CG19C
❑ 96ColChoCtGGE-CR19
❑ 96ColChoGS-160
❑ 96ColChoGS-402
❑ 96ColChoSS-160
❑ 96ColChoSS-402
❑ 96ColChoYMtP-3
❑ 96ColChoYMtP-3A
❑ 96ColChoYMtPGS-3
❑ 96ColChoYMtPGS-3A
❑ 96DenHol-6
❑ 96DenHolGS-7
❑ 96DenHolGSAP-7
❑ 96Don-81
❑ 96DonHitL-11
❑ 96DonPreP-81
❑ 96DonRouT-3
❑ 96EmoXL-193
❑ 96Fin-B299
❑ 96Fin-G42
❑ 96Fin-S161
❑ 96FinBro-3
❑ 96FinRef-B299
❑ 96FinRef-G42
❑ 96FinRef-S161
❑ 96Fla-272
❑ 96FlaDiaC-1
❑ 96Fle-400
❑ 96FleTeaL-20
❑ 96FleTif-400
❑ 96FleUpd-U211
❑ 96FleUpdH-2
❑ 96FleUpdSS-1
❑ 96FleUpdTC-U211
❑ 96Kin-4
❑ 96Lea-199
❑ 96LeaAllGMC-5
❑ 96LeaAllGMCG-5
❑ 96LeaLim-9
❑ 96LeaLimG-9
❑ 96LeaLimL-9
❑ 96LeaLimLB-9
❑ 96LeaPicP-9
❑ 96LeaPre-8
❑ 96LeaPre-148
❑ 96LeaPreP-8
❑ 96LeaPreP-148
❑ 96LeaPrePB-199
❑ 96LeaPrePG-199
❑ 96LeaPrePS-199
❑ 96LeaPreSG-39
❑ 96LeaPreSP-7
❑ 96LeaPreSta-11
❑ 96LeaPreSte-39
❑ 96LeaSig-22
❑ 96LeaSigPPG-22
❑ 96LeaSigPPP-22
❑ 96MetUni-172
❑ 96MetUniP-172
❑ 96Pac-89
❑ 96PacGolCD-DC10
❑ 96PacPri-P29
❑ 96PacPriG-P29
❑ 96PacPriRHS-RH6
❑ 96PanSti-59
❑ 96Pin-10
❑ 96Pin-151
❑ 96Pin-197
❑ 96Pin-259
❑ 96Pin-305B
❑ 96PinAfi-73
❑ 96PinAfiAP-73
❑ 96PinAfiFPP-73
❑ 96PinAfiMN-5
❑ 96PinAfiR-13
❑ 96PinAfiR-14
❑ 96PinAfiR-15
❑ 96PinAfiR-18
❑ 96PinAfiR-20
❑ 96PinAfiR-22
❑ 96PinAfiSP-9
❑ 96PinArtP-7
❑ 96PinArtP-78
❑ 96PinArtP-159
❑ 96PinArtP-190
❑ 96PinEssotG-11
❑ 96PinFan-5
❑ 96PinFoil-259
❑ 96PinFoil-305B
❑ 96PinPow-11
❑ 96PinSky-16
❑ 96PinSlu-3
❑ 96PinSta-7
❑ 96PinSta-78
❑ 96PinSta-159
❑ 96PinSta-190
❑ 96PinTeaP-1
❑ 96PinTeaS-7
❑ 96Pro-1
❑ 96ProMagA-13
❑ 96ProSta-13
❑ 96Sco-269
❑ 96Sco-304
❑ 96ScoAll-14
❑ 96ScoBigB-4
❑ 96ScoDiaA-24
❑ 96ScoDugC-B29
❑ 96ScoDugCAP-B29
❑ 96ScoGolS-16
❑ 96ScoNumG-7
❑ 96ScoRef-15
❑ 96ScoTitT-9
❑ 96Sel-12
❑ 96Sel-160
❑ 96SelArtP-12
❑ 96SelArtP-160
❑ 96SelCer-54
❑ 96SelCerAP-54
❑ 96SelCerCB-54
❑ 96SelCerCR-54
❑ 96SelCerIP-12
❑ 96SelCerMB-54
❑ 96SelCerMG-54
❑ 96SelCerMR-54
❑ 96SelClaTF-7
❑ 96SelEnF-5
❑ 96SelTeaN-26
❑ 96SP-95
❑ 96SPMarM-MM13
❑ 96SPMarMDC-13
❑ 96Spo-21
❑ 96Spo-115
❑ 96SpoArtP-21
❑ 96SpoArtP-115
❑ 96SpoDouT-12
❑ 96SpoHitP-7
❑ 96SpoPowS-19
❑ 96SpoPro-8
❑ 96SPSpeFX-44
❑ 96SPSpeFXDC-44
❑ 96SPx-29
❑ 96SPxGol-29
❑ 96StaClu-183
❑ 96StaClu-429
❑ 96StaCluEPB-429
❑ 96StaCluEPG-429
❑ 96StaCluEPS-429
❑ 96StaCluMet-M1
❑ 96StaCluMOP-183
❑ 96StaCluMOP-429
❑ 96StaCluMOP-M1
❑ 96Stu-49
❑ 96StuHitP-4
❑ 96StuMas-3
❑ 96StuPrePB-49
❑ 96StuPrePG-49
❑ 96StuPrePS-49
❑ 96StuStaGS-8
❑ 96Sum-7
❑ 96SumAbo&B-7
❑ 96SumArtP-7
❑ 96SumBal-14
❑ 96SumBigB-7
❑ 96SumBigBM-7
❑ 96SumFoi-7
❑ 96SumPos-1
❑ 96TeaOut-5
❑ 96Top-4
❑ 96Top-380
❑ 96TopChr-4
❑ 96TopChr-153
❑ 96TopChrR-4
❑ 96TopChrR-153
❑ 96TopChrWC-WC1
❑ 96TopChrWCR-WC1
❑ 96TopGal-164
❑ 96TopGalPPI-164
❑ 96TopLas-34
❑ 96TopLasPC-9
❑ 96TopMysF-M20
❑ 96TopMysFR-M20
❑ 96TopPowB-4
❑ 96TopPro-NL1
❑ 96TopWreC-WC1
❑ 96Ult-205
❑ 96Ult-574
❑ 96UltChe-A1
❑ 96UltCheGM-A1
❑ 96UltGolM-205
❑ 96UltGolM-574
❑ 96UltPowP-1
❑ 96UltPowPGM-1
❑ 96UppDec-80
❑ 96UppDecA-3
❑ 96UppDecDD-DD21
❑ 96UppDecDDG-DD21
❑ 96UppDecDDS-DD21
❑ 96UppDecPHE-H31
❑ 96UppDecPRE-R41
❑ 96UppDecPRE-R51
❑ 96UppDecPreH-H31
❑ 96UppDecPreR-R41
❑ 96UppDecPreR-R51
❑ 96Zen-24
❑ 96ZenArtP-24
❑ 96ZenDiaC-7
❑ 96ZenDiaCP-7
❑ 96ZenMoz-25
❑ 97AstMot-2
❑ 97Bow-243
❑ 97BowBes-58
❑ 97BowBesAR-58
❑ 97BowBesBC-BC7
❑ 97BowBesBCAR-BC7
❑ 97BowBesBCR-BC7
❑ 97BowBesMI-MI2
❑ 97BowBesMIAR-MI2
❑ 97BowBesMIARI-MI2
❑ 97BowBesMII-MI2
❑ 97BowBesMIR-MI2
❑ 97BowBesMIRI-MI2
❑ 97BowBesP-10
❑ 97BowBesPAR-10
❑ 97BowBesPR-10
❑ 97BowBesR-58
❑ 97BowChr-68
❑ 97BowChrI-68
❑ 97BowChrIR-68
❑ 97BowChrR-68
❑ 97BowInt-243
❑ 97Cir-102
❑ 97CirBos-1
❑ 97CirLimA-1
❑ 97CirRav-102
❑ 97CirSupB-1
❑ 97ColCho-125
❑ 97ColChoAC-19
❑ 97ColChoCtG-18A
❑ 97ColChoCtG-18B
❑ 97ColChoCtG-18C
❑ 97ColChoCtGE-CG18
❑ 97ColChoCtGIW-CG18
❑ 97ColChoNF-NF26
❑ 97ColChoS-5
❑ 97ColChoSR-2
❑ 97ColChoTBS-24
❑ 97ColChoTBSWH-24
❑ 97ColChoTotT-T14
❑ 97CraJac-1
❑ 97DenHol-19
❑ 97Don-146
❑ 97Don-409
❑ 97DonDiaK-5
❑ 97DonDiaKC-5
❑ 97DonEli-17
❑ 97DonEli-8
❑ 97DonEliGS-17
❑ 97DonGolPP-146
❑ 97DonGolPP-409
❑ 97DonLim-11
❑ 97DonLim-27
❑ 97DonLim-70
❑ 97DonLimE-11
❑ 97DonLimE-27
❑ 97DonLimE-70
❑ 97DonLimENG-11
❑ 97DonLimFotG-52
❑ 97DonLimFotG-65
❑ 97DonLonL-10
❑ 97DonPowA-4
❑ 97DonPowADC-4
❑ 97DonPre-69
❑ 97DonPre-177
❑ 97DonPreCttC-69
❑ 97DonPreCttC-177
❑ 97DonPrePM-13
❑ 97DonPreS-8
❑ 97DonPreSS-8
❑ 97DonPreTB-1
❑ 97DonPreTBG-1
❑ 97DonPreTF-1
❑ 97DonPreTP-1
❑ 97DonPreTPG-1
❑ 97DonRocL-8
❑ 97DonSig-19
❑ 97DonSigAC-9
❑ 97DonSigAM-9
❑ 97DonSigPPP-19
❑ 97DonSilPP-146
❑ 97DonSilPP-409
❑ 97DonTeaSMVP-4
❑ 97DonVxP1-29
❑ 97E-X2-76
❑ 97E-X2Cred-76
❑ 97E-X2EssCre-76
❑ 97E-X2Hall-16
❑ 97Fin-10
❑ 97Fin-159
❑ 97Fin-318
❑ 97FinEmb-159
❑ 97FinEmb-318
❑ 97FinEmbR-159
❑ 97FinEmbR-318
❑ 97FinPro-159
❑ 97FinRef-10
❑ 97FinRef-159
❑ 97FinRef-318
❑ 97FlaShoDC-1
❑ 97FlaShoLC-5
❑ 97FlaShoLeg0-5
❑ 97FlaShoLeg1-5
❑ 97FlaShoM-A5
❑ 97FlaShoM-B5
❑ 97FlaShoM-C5
❑ 97FlaShoR0-5
❑ 97FlaShoR1-5
❑ 97FlaShoR2-5
❑ 97Fle-339
❑ 97Fle-697
❑ 97Fle-732
❑ 97FleHea-1
❑ 97FleLumC-2
❑ 97FleMilDM-50
❑ 97FleMilDMR-50
❑ 97FleTeaL-20
❑ 97FleTif-339
❑ 97FleTif-697
❑ 97FleTif-732
❑ 97FleZon-1
❑ 97HigMinM-1
❑ 97HigMinM-2
❑ 97HigMinMCP-1
❑ 97HigMinMCP-2
❑ 97KinB-7
❑ 97Lea-54
❑ 97Lea-352
❑ 97LeaBanS-1
❑ 97LeaDrefS-7
❑ 97LeaFraM-54
❑ 97LeaFraM-352
❑ 97LeaFraMDC-54
❑ 97LeaFraMDC-352
❑ 97LeaGet-6
❑ 97LeaGolS-6
❑ 97LeaKnoG-6
❑ 97LeaLeaotN-10
❑ 97MetUni-134
❑ 97MetUniBF-1
❑ 97MetUniMF-2
❑ 97MetUniML-2
❑ 97MetUniT-1
❑ 97NewPin-57
❑ 97NewPinAP-57
❑ 97NewPinIE-10
❑ 97NewPinMC-57
❑ 97NewPinPP-57
❑ 97NewPinPP-I10B
❑ 97Pac-311
❑ 97PacCar-28
❑ 97PacCarM-28
❑ 97PacCerCGT-2
❑ 97PacGolCD-28
❑ 97PacLigB-311
❑ 97PacPri-105
❑ 97PacPriGA-GA23
❑ 97PacPriLB-105
❑ 97PacPriP-105
❑ 97PacPriSH-SH10A
❑ 97PacPriSL-SL10A
❑ 97PacSil-311
❑ 97PacTriCD-17
❑ 97Pin-76
❑ 97PinArtP-PP76
❑ 97PinCar-18
❑ 97PinCer-5
❑ 97PinCer-145
❑ 97PinCerCMGT-2
❑ 97PinCerCT-2
❑ 97PinCerMBla-5
❑ 97PinCerMBla-145
❑ 97PinCerMBlu-5
❑ 97PinCerMBlu-145
❑ 97PinCerMG-5
❑ 97PinCerMG-145
❑ 97PinCerMR-5
❑ 97PinCerMR-145
❑ 97PinCerR-5
❑ 97PinCerR-145
❑ 97PinEpixGO-E3
❑ 97PinEpixPE-E3
❑ 97PinFan-FF2
❑ 97PinHom-9
❑ 97PinHom-10
❑ 97PinIns-63
❑ 97PinInsC-13
❑ 97PinInsCE-63
❑ 97PinInsDD-2
❑ 97PinInsDE-63
❑ 97PinMin-13
❑ 97PinMinB-13
❑ 97PinMinCB-13
❑ 97PinMinCG-13
❑ 97PinMinCGR-13
❑ 97PinMinCN-13
❑ 97PinMinCSS-13
❑ 97PinMinG-13
❑ 97PinMinS-13
❑ 97PinMusC-76
❑ 97PinPrePla-76
❑ 97PinTeaP-1
❑ 97PinTeaP-10
❑ 97PinTotCPB-5
❑ 97PinTotCPB-145
❑ 97PinTotCPG-5
❑ 97PinTotCPG-145
❑ 97PinTotCPR-5
❑ 97PinTotCPR-145
❑ 97PinX-P-78
❑ 97PinX-PF&A-5
❑ 97PinX-PMoS-78
❑ 97PinX-PMW-12
❑ 97PinX-PMWG-12
❑ 97PinX-PMWS-12
❑ 97PinX-PSfF-4
❑ 97PinX-PSfFU-4
❑ 97PreCon-8
❑ 97Sco-1
❑ 97Sco-502
❑ 97ScoAllF-2
❑ 97ScoArtPWB-1
❑ 97ScoArtPWB-502
❑ 97ScoBla-10
❑ 97ScoHigZ-9
❑ 97ScoPreS-1
❑ 97ScoResC-502
❑ 97ScoShoS-1
❑ 97ScoShoS-502
❑ 97ScoShoSAP-1
❑ 97ScoShoSAP-502
❑ 97ScoStaaD-22
❑ 97ScoSteS-3
❑ 97ScoTitT-8
❑ 97Sel-51

❑ 97SelArtP-51
❑ 97SelCom-51
❑ 97SelRegG-51
❑ 97SelToootT-10
❑ 97SelToootTMB-10
❑ 97SP-85
❑ 97SPInsI-9
❑ 97SPMarM-MM12
❑ 97SpollI-101
❑ 97SpollIEE-101
❑ 97SPSpeF-9
❑ 97SPSpxF-3
❑ 97SPSPxFA-3
❑ 97SPVinAu-1
❑ 97SPVinAu-2
❑ 97SPVinAu-3
❑ 97SPVinAu-4
❑ 97SPx-27
❑ 97SPxBoufG-11
❑ 97SPxBoufGSS-1
❑ 97SPxBro-27
❑ 97SPxCorotG-6
❑ 97SPxGol-27
❑ 97SPxGraF-27
❑ 97SPxSil-27
❑ 97SPxSte-27
❑ 97StaClu-13
❑ 97StaClu-382
❑ 97StaCluFR-F1
❑ 97StaCluFW-F1
❑ 97StaCluMat-13
❑ 97StaCluMOP-13
❑ 97StaCluMOP-382
❑ 97StaCluMOP-FB1
❑ 97StaCluMOP-PG14
❑ 97StaCluPG-PG14
❑ 97StrAll-5
❑ 97Stu-102
❑ 97StuMasS-2
❑ 97StuMasS8-2
❑ 97StuPor8-15
❑ 97StuPrePG-102
❑ 97StuPrePS-102
❑ 97Top-295
❑ 97TopChr-100
❑ 97TopChrDD-DD5
❑ 97TopChrDDR-DD5
❑ 97TopChrR-100
❑ 97TopGal-126
❑ 97TopGalGoH-GH8
❑ 97TopGalPPI-126
❑ 97TopHobM-HM6
❑ 97TopIntF-ILM9
❑ 97TopIntFR-ILM9
❑ 97TopMem05-3
❑ 97TopScr-1
❑ 97TopScrT-1
❑ 97TopSta-8
❑ 97TopSta97AS-AS4
❑ 97TopStaAM-8
❑ 97TopSweS-SS2
❑ 97TopTeaT-TT4
❑ 97UD3-38
❑ 97Ult-204
❑ 97UltDiaP-1
❑ 97UltDouT-14
❑ 97UltFamGam-8
❑ 97UltFieC-2
❑ 97UltGolME-204
❑ 97UltHitM-10
❑ 97UltLeaS-7
❑ 97UltPlaME-204
❑ 97UltPowP-A1
❑ 97UltPowP-B9
❑ 97UltRBIK-1
❑ 97UltThu-4
❑ 97UltTop3-13
❑ 97UltTop3GM-13
❑ 97UppDec-83
❑ 97UppDec-370
❑ 97UppDecAG-AG14
❑ 97UppDecPP-PP7
❑ 97UppDecPPJ-PP7
❑ 97UppDecRP-RP23
❑ 97UppDecSA-3
❑ 97UppDecSAG-3
❑ 97Zen-3
❑ 97Zen8x10-3
❑ 97Zen8x1D-3
❑ 98Bow-15
❑ 98BowBes-33
❑ 98BowBesAR-33
❑ 98BowBesMIF-MI11
❑ 98BowBesMIFAR-MI11
❑ 98BowBesMIFR-MI11
❑ 98BowBesR-33
❑ 98BowChr-15
❑ 98BowChrGA-15
❑ 98BowChrGAR-15
❑ 98BowChrI-15
❑ 98BowChrIR-15
❑ 98BowChrR-15
❑ 98BowChrR-25
❑ 98BowChrRR-25
❑ 98BowGolA-15
❑ 98BowInt-15
❑ 98BowMinLM-MVP1
❑ 98CirThu-150
❑ 98CirThuB-1
❑ 98CirThuLA-1
❑ 98CirThuQS-1
❑ 98CirThuRav-150
❑ 98CirThuRR-1
❑ 98CirThuSupRav-150
❑ 98CirThuTB-1
❑ 98ColCho-380
❑ 98ColChoCtG-CG22A
❑ 98ColChoCtG-CG22B
❑ 98ColChoCtG-CG22C
❑ 98ColChoCtGExch-CG22
❑ 98ColChoCtGIW-CG22
❑ 98ColChoER-ER12
❑ 98ColChoMBH-16
❑ 98ColChoRJ-SQ75
❑ 98ColChoS'-14
❑ 98ColChoSQ-SQ37
❑ 98ColChoSQ-SQ75
❑ 98ColChoSQDouble-17
❑ 98ColChoSQHR-17
❑ 98ColChoSQSingle-17
❑ 98ColChoSQTriple-17
❑ 98CroRoy-62
❑ 98CroRoyDK-10
❑ 98Don-26
❑ 98Don-373
❑ 98Don-411
❑ 98DonCol-26
❑ 98DonColE-412
❑ 98DonColE-529
❑ 98DonColL-348
❑ 98DonColP-560
❑ 98DonColP-727
❑ 98DonColS-26
❑ 98DonCruG-77
❑ 98DonCruP-77
❑ 98DonCruR-77
❑ 98DonDay-9
❑ 98DonDom-4
❑ 98DonEli-12
❑ 98DonEli-129
❑ 98DonEliA-12
❑ 98DonEliA-129
❑ 98DonEliBttF-2
❑ 98DonEliBttFA-2
❑ 98DonEliC-18
❑ 98DonEliI-1
❑ 98DonEliMC-18
❑ 98DonEliPN-9A
❑ 98DonEliPN-9B
❑ 98DonEliPN-9C
❑ 98DonEliPNDC-9A
❑ 98DonEliPNDC-9B
❑ 98DonEliPNDC-9C
❑ 98DonEliPNS-9A
❑ 98DonEliPNS-9B
❑ 98DonEliPNS-9C
❑ 98DonEliS-12
❑ 98DonEliS-129
❑ 98DonFANT-20
❑ 98DonFANTDC-20
❑ 98DonGolPP-26
❑ 98DonGolPP-373
❑ 98DonGolPP-411
❑ 98DonLonL-14
❑ 98DonPre-10
❑ 98DonPre-177
❑ 98DonPreGB-10
❑ 98DonPreGES-1
❑ 98DonPreGoB-10
❑ 98DonPreGX-1
❑ 98DonPreGXDC-1
❑ 98DonPrePM-10
❑ 98DonPreSeat-10
❑ 98DonPreSeat-177
❑ 98DonPreTP-10
❑ 98DonPreTPD-5
❑ 98DonPreTPG-10
❑ 98DonPreTPS-10
❑ 98DonPreTW-5
❑ 98DonPriCD-26
❑ 98DonPriCE-412
❑ 98DonPriCE-529
❑ 98DonPriCL-348
❑ 98DonPriCP-560
❑ 98DonPriCP-727
❑ 98DonProL0-8
❑ 98DonProLPI-4
❑ 98DonProLS-7
❑ 98DonSig-5
❑ 98DonSigP-5
❑ 98DonSilPP-26
❑ 98DonSilPP-373
❑ 98DonSilPP-411
❑ 98DonSonM9-11
❑ 98E-X2-17
❑ 98E-X2Cheap-8
❑ 98E-X2DesCoop-11
❑ 98E-X2ECFut-17
❑ 98E-X2ECNow-17
❑ 98Fin-209
❑ 98FinCen-C10
❑ 98FinCenR-C10
❑ 98FinMysF1-M42
❑ 98FinMysF1-M45
❑ 98FinMysF1-M48
❑ 98FinMysF1-M49
❑ 98FinMysF2-M19
❑ 98FinMysF2-M22
❑ 98FinMysF2-M23
❑ 98FinMysF2R-M19
❑ 98FinMysF2R-M22
❑ 98FinMysF2R-M23
❑ 98FinMysFO-3
❑ 98FinMysFOR-3
❑ 98FinMysFR-M42
❑ 98FinMysFR-M45
❑ 98FinMysFR-M48
❑ 98FinMysFR-M49
❑ 98FinNo--209
❑ 98FinNo-R-209
❑ 98FinOve-B8
❑ 98FinOveR-B8
❑ 98FinPowZ-P2
❑ 98FinRef-209
❑ 98FinStaS-SS13
❑ 98FinTheM-TM13
❑ 98FinTheMR-TM13
❑ 98FlaShoLeg0-38
❑ 98FlaShoLeg1-38
❑ 98FlaShoLeg2-38
❑ 98FlaShoLeg3-38
❑ 98FlaShoLegM-38
❑ 98FlaShoR0-38
❑ 98FlaShoR1-38
❑ 98FlaShoR2-38
❑ 98FlaShoR3-38
❑ 98Fle-50
❑ 98Fle-321
❑ 98Fle-576
❑ 98FleDiaS-1
❑ 98FleDiaSCS-NNO
❑ 98FleDiaT-DT1
❑ 98FleIn TC-IC1
❑ 98FleLumC-1
❑ 98FlePowG-1
❑ 98FleVin'-29
❑ 98FleVin'C-29
❑ 98FleZon-1
❑ 98KinDis-7
❑ 98Lea-149
❑ 98LeaFraDA-149
❑ 98LeaFraF-149
❑ 98LeaFraM-149
❑ 98LeaFraM-149
❑ 98LeaFraMDC-149
❑ 98LeaFraMDC-149
❑ 98LeaFraMZ2-149
❑ 98LeaHeaftH-2
❑ 98LeaHeaftHS-2
❑ 98LeaRCMLHDSamp-1
❑ 98LeaRS-35
❑ 98LeaRS-153
❑ 98LeaRSCross-8
❑ 98LeaRSExtM-9
❑ 98LeaRSExtMDC-9
❑ 98LeaRSGAHSamp-9
❑ 98LeaRSGreAH-9
❑ 98LeaRSGreHit-10
❑ 98LeaRSHRDerby-15
❑ 98LeaRSLHolo-35
❑ 98LeaRSLHolo-153
❑ 98LeaRSLMVP-11
❑ 98LeaRSLMVPPE-11
❑ 98LeaRSLong-35
❑ 98LeaRSLong-153
❑ 98LeaRSMLHD-1
❑ 98LeaRSTicMas-7
❑ 98LeaRSTicMasDC-7
❑ 98LeaRTrue-35
❑ 98LeaRTrue-153
❑ 98LeaStaRep-20
❑ 98LeaStaS-9
❑ 98LeaStaSDC-9
❑ 98MetUni-80
❑ 98MetUniAT-6
❑ 98MetUniPMG-80
❑ 98MetUniUL-6
❑ 98Pac-312
❑ 98PacAur-136
❑ 98PacAurHC-8
❑ 98PacAurPF-6
❑ 98PacAurPFC-6
❑ 98PacAurPFPB-6
❑ 98PacAurPFR-6
❑ 98PacAurPFS-6
❑ 98PacGolCDC-18
❑ 98PacHomRH-12
❑ 98PacInv-102
❑ 98PacInvGems-160
❑ 98PacInvPBlue-102
❑ 98PacInvSilv-102
❑ 98PacInvTeam-12
❑ 98PacOme-104
❑ 98PacOmeEP-16
❑ 98PacOmeEP1o1-16
❑ 98PacOmeOnIns-30
❑ 98PacOmeR-104
❑ 98PacOnl-311A
❑ 98PacOnl-311B
❑ 98PacOnl-334
❑ 98PacOnlR-311A
❑ 98PacOnlR-311B
❑ 98PacOnlR-334
❑ 98PacOnlWC-311A
❑ 98PacOnlWC-311B
❑ 98PacOnlWC-334
❑ 98PacPar-167
❑ 98PacParC-167
❑ 98PacParFC-8
❑ 98PacParG-167
❑ 98PacParHS-167
❑ 98PacParI-22
❑ 98PacParPB-167
❑ 98PacParR-167
❑ 98PacParSD-9
❑ 98PacParTC-21
❑ 98PacPlaB-312
❑ 98PacRedT-312
❑ 98PacSil-312
❑ 98PacTeaC-20
❑ 98Pin-28
❑ 98Pin-192
❑ 98Pin-198
❑ 98PinArtP-PP28
❑ 98PinArtP-PP95
❑ 98PinEpixGE-E3
❑ 98PinEpixGP-E3
❑ 98PinEpixPO-E3
❑ 98PinEpixPP-E3
❑ 98PinEpixSE-E3
❑ 98PinEpixSO-E3
❑ 98PinEpixSP-E3
❑ 98PinHitIH-10
❑ 98PinHitiHS-10
❑ 98PinIns-26
❑ 98PinIns-137
❑ 98PinInsBtN-17
❑ 98PinInsCE-26
❑ 98PinInsCE-137
❑ 98PinInsDE-26
❑ 98PinInsDE-137
❑ 98PinInsSG-5AB
❑ 98PinInsSG-5CD
❑ 98PinInsSG-22AB
❑ 98PinInsSG-22CD
❑ 98PinInsSG-24AB
❑ 98PinInsSG-24CD
❑ 98PinInsSGS-5AB
❑ 98PinInsSGS-5CD
❑ 98PinInsSGS-22AB
❑ 98PinInsSGS-22CD
❑ 98PinInsSGS-24AB
❑ 98PinInsSGS-24CD
❑ 98PinMinB-1
❑ 98PinMinCB-1
❑ 98PinMinCBAP-1
❑ 98PinMinCGP-1
❑ 98PinMinCGPAP-1
❑ 98PinMinCN-1
❑ 98PinMinCNAP-1
❑ 98PinMinCSGR-1
❑ 98PinMinDC-1
❑ 98PinMinG-1
❑ 98PinMinMCSS-1
❑ 98PinMinS-1
❑ 98PinMusC-PP28
❑ 98PinMusC-PP95
❑ 98PinPer-10
❑ 98PinPer-147
❑ 98PinPerBB-7
❑ 98PinPerBBSamp-7
❑ 98PinPerBBSO-7
❑ 98PinPerPP-10
❑ 98PinPerPP-147
❑ 98PinPerPT-4
❑ 98PinPerSftF-27
❑ 98PinPerSftFShop-1
❑ 98PinPlu-59
❑ 98PinPluAE-3
❑ 98PinPluAEE-3
❑ 98PinPluAEP-3
❑ 98PinPluAP-PP26
❑ 98PinPluGAP-PP26
❑ 98PinPluLM-17
❑ 98PinPluMAP-PP26
❑ 98PinPluTP-10
❑ 98PinPluTPG-10
❑ 98PinPluTPM-10
❑ 98PinPluY-11
❑ 98PinPowPJ-11
❑ 98PinPowPJ-22
❑ 98PinPowPJS-11
❑ 98PinPowPJS-22
❑ 98PinPreP-28
❑ 98PinPreP-192
❑ 98PinPreP-198
❑ 98PinPreP-E3
❑ 98PinPreP-H10
❑ 98PreCon-1
❑ 98Revo-65
❑ 98RevoPTP-17
❑ 98RevoSS-65
❑ 98Sco-38
❑ 98ScoEpix-E3
❑ 98ScoFirP-12
❑ 98ScoRT-20
❑ 98ScoRT-257
❑ 98ScoRTASEpix-3
❑ 98ScoRTComPla-5A
❑ 98ScoRTComPla-5B
❑ 98ScoRTComPla-5C
❑ 98ScoRTCPSamp-5A
❑ 98ScoRTCPSamp-5B
❑ 98ScoRTCPSamp-5C
❑ 98ScoRTSS-PP20
❑ 98ScoRTSS-PP150
❑ 98ScoRTSSAP-PP20
❑ 98ScoRTSSAP-PP150
❑ 98ScoRTSSAP1-PP20
❑ 98ScoRTSSAP1-PP150
❑ 98ScoSS-PP125
❑ 98ScoSSAP-PP125
❑ 98SkyDugA-19
❑ 98SkyDugA-130
❑ 98SkyDugADH-DH1
❑ 98SkyDugAG-G1
❑ 98SkyDugAIA-19
❑ 98SkyDugAIA-130
❑ 98SP Aut-100
❑ 98SP Aut-SD38
❑ 98SP AutSD-SD38
❑ 98SP AutSDT-SD38
❑ 98SpollI-8
❑ 98SpollI-183
❑ 98SpollIEC-EC9
❑ 98SpollIEE-8
❑ 98SpollIEE-183
❑ 98SpollIFE-8
❑ 98SpollIFE-183
❑ 98SpollIODMP-OD13
❑ 98SpollITaN-43
❑ 98SpollITaN-59
❑ 98SpollITaNEE-43
❑ 98SpollITaNEE-59
❑ 98SpollITaNGS-10
❑ 98SpollIWSF-103
❑ 98SpollIWSFEE-103
❑ 98SpollIWSFFE-103
❑ 98SpollIWSFRJP-14
❑ 98SPxFin-36
❑ 98SPxFin-87
❑ 98SPxFin-155
❑ 98SPxFin-174
❑ 98SPxFin-234
❑ 98SPxFinR-36
❑ 98SPxFinR-87
❑ 98SPxFinR-155
❑ 98SPxFinR-174
❑ 98SPxFinR-234
❑ 98SPxFinS-36
❑ 98SPxFinS-87
❑ 98SPxFinS-155
❑ 98SPxFinS-174
❑ 98SPxFinS-234
❑ 98StaCluFDI-56
❑ 98StaCluI-56
❑ 98StaCluNC-NC14
❑ 98StaCluOneK-56
❑ 98StaCluPP-56
❑ 98StaCluRC-RC7
❑ 98Stu-13
❑ 98Stu-CL1
❑ 98StuFF-11
❑ 98StuFFDC-11
❑ 98StuGPP-13
❑ 98StuGPP-CL1
❑ 98StuHitPar-10
❑ 98StuMast-11
❑ 98StuPor8x10-5
❑ 98StuPor8x10GP-5
❑ 98StuSony99-11
❑ 98StuSPP-13
❑ 98StuSPP-CL1
❑ 98Top-35
❑ 98Top-480
❑ 98TopChr-35
❑ 98TopChr-480
❑ 98TopChrR-35
❑ 98TopChrR-480
❑ 98TopDevR-35
❑ 98TopDevR-480
❑ 98TopDia-35
❑ 98TopDia-480
❑ 98TopGal-135
❑ 98TopGalGoH-GH11
❑ 98TopGalGoHJ-GH11
❑ 98TopGalGP-135
❑ 98TopGalOPP-135
❑ 98TopGalPG-PG9
❑ 98TopGalPPI-135
❑ 98TopGalPPIA-135
❑ 98TopGolLabC1-20
❑ 98TopGolLabC1B-20
❑ 98TopGolLabC1One-20
❑ 98TopGolLabC1R-20
❑ 98TopGolLabC2-20
❑ 98TopGolLabC2B-20
❑ 98TopGolLabC2One-20
❑ 98TopGolLabC2R-20
❑ 98TopGolLabC3-20
❑ 98TopGolLabC3B-20
❑ 98TopGolLabC3One-20
❑ 98TopGolLabC3R-20
❑ 98TopMiniC-35
❑ 98TopMiniC-480
❑ 98TopMysFB-M17
❑ 98TopMysFB-M17
❑ 98TopMysFBR-M17
❑ 98TopMysFBR-M17
❑ 98TopOpeD-24
❑ 98TopPre-PP2
❑ 98TopSta-140
❑ 98TopSta'S-2
❑ 98TopSta'SGH-2
❑ 98TopStaB-140
❑ 98TopStaG-G2
❑ 98TopStaG-140
❑ 98TopStaGG-G2
❑ 98TopStaGGR-G2
❑ 98TopStaGR-140
❑ 98TopStaGS-G2
❑ 98TopStaS-140
❑ 98TopStaSteG-2
❑ 98TopSup-9
❑ 98TopSup-9
❑ 98TopTek-74
❑ 98TopTekD-74
❑ 98UD3-53
❑ 98UD3-143
❑ 98UD3-233
❑ 98UD3DieCut-53
❑ 98UD3DieCut-143
❑ 98UD3DieCut-233
❑ 98Ult-31
❑ 98Ult-211
❑ 98Ult-495
❑ 98UltArtT-13
❑ 98UltBigS-6
❑ 98UltDiaP-11
❑ 98UltDouT-11
❑ 98UltFalC-12
❑ 98UltGolM-31
❑ 98UltGolM-211
❑ 98UltGolM-495
❑ 98UltMas-31
❑ 98UltMas-211

❑ 98UltMas-495
❑ 98UltNot-6
❑ 98UltPlaM-31
❑ 98UltPlaM-211
❑ 98UltPlaM-495
❑ 98UltPowP-8
❑ 98UltPriL-13
❑ 98UltTop3-6
❑ 98UltWinN-10
❑ 98UppDec-385
❑ 98UppDec-611
❑ 98UppDec10AP-25
❑ 98UppDec1APR-25
❑ 98UppDec5x7-385
❑ 98UppDec5x7-611
❑ 98UppDecAC-AS13
❑ 98UppDecAG-AG5
❑ 98UppDecAGDC-AG5
❑ 98UppDecCD-CD5
❑ 98UppDecR-39
❑ 98UppDecR-25
❑ 98UppDecRBBop-BB26
❑ 98UppDecRQL-Q16
❑ 98UppDecRTC-TC39
❑ 98UppDecSFPD-PZ18
❑ 98UppDecSFPZOB-PZ5
❑ 98UppDecSFPZPD-PZ6
❑ 98UppDecTMT-3
❑ 98UppDecTMTG-3
❑ 98UppDecU-11
❑ 98Zen-29
❑ 98Zen5 xx7-8
❑ 98Zen5x7GoldImp-8
❑ 98Zen5x7Imp-8
❑ 98ZenEpi-E3
❑ 98ZenRaitB-13
❑ 98ZenZ-G-29
❑ 98ZenZ-S-29
❑ 99199Fin-108
❑ 99199Fin-230
❑ 99AllMysFR-M1
❑ 99AurOn DL-9
❑ 99AurPenF-10
❑ 99AurPenF-10
❑ 99AurPenFB-10
❑ 99AurPenFS-10
❑ 99AurSty-10
❑ 99Bow-268
❑ 99BowBes-82
❑ 99BowBesAR-82
❑ 99BowBesR-82
❑ 99BowEarR-ER3
❑ 99BowGol-268
❑ 99BowInt-268
❑ 99CroRoyB-63
❑ 99CroRoyL-63
❑ 99CroRoyOD-63
❑ 99CroRoyPotG-10
❑ 99DumSet-ER3
❑ 99E-X Cen-15
❑ 99E-X CenECFut-15
❑ 99E-X CenECNow-15
❑ 99FinDouF-DF4
❑ 99FinDouFDualR-DF4
❑ 99FinGolRef-108
❑ 99FinGolRef-230
❑ 99FinLeaI-L10
❑ 99FinMil-M21
❑ 99FinPeelHyp-14
❑ 99FinPeelSpark-14
❑ 99FinPeeSS-14
❑ 99FinProF-PF9
❑ 99FinProF-PF19
❑ 99FinProF-PF36
❑ 99FinProF-PF45
❑ 99FinRef-108
❑ 99FinRef-230
❑ 99FinTeaFB-TF14
❑ 99FinTeaFBR-TF14
❑ 99FinTeaFG-TF14
❑ 99FinTeaFGR-TF14
❑ 99FinTeaFR-TF14
❑ 99FinTeaFRR-TF14
❑ 99FlaShoLeg1-7
❑ 99FlaShoLeg2-7
❑ 99FlaShoLeg3-7
❑ 99FlaShoLegM1-7
❑ 99FlaShoLegM2-7
❑ 99FlaShoLegM3-7
❑ 99FlaShoR1-7
❑ 99FlaShoR2-7
❑ 99FlaShoR3-7
❑ 99Fle-39
❑ 99FleBri-5
❑ 99FleBri2G-5
❑ 99FleBriBlu-5
❑ 99FleBriGol-5
❑ 99FleMys-12
❑ 99FleMysG-12
❑ 99FleMysM-12
❑ 99FleSta9-39
❑ 99FleVin'-39
❑ 99FleWarT-39
❑ 99KinDis-5
❑ 99MetUni-5
❑ 99MetUni-279
❑ 99MetUniBWTW-3
❑ 99MetUniGM-5
❑ 99MetUniGM-279
❑ 99MetUniPM-15
❑ 99MetUniPMG-5
❑ 99MetUniPMG-279
❑ 99Pac-186
❑ 99Pac-186A
❑ 99PacAur-79
❑ 99PacAurOD-79
❑ 99PacCroC-121
❑ 99PacCroCPB-121
❑ 99PacCroCTM-9
❑ 99PacDynaD-14
❑ 99PacDynaDT-14
❑ 99PacGolCDC-27
❑ 99PacInv-65
❑ 99PacInvOD-65
❑ 99PacInvPB-65
❑ 99PacOme-103
❑ 99PacOme5T-21
❑ 99PacOme5TT-21
❑ 99PacOmeC-103
❑ 99PacOmeDM-16
❑ 99PacOmeEP-9
❑ 99PacOmeEP1o1-9
❑ 99PacOmeG-103
❑ 99PacOmeH'-9
❑ 99PacOmePB-103
❑ 99PacPar-101
❑ 99PacParC-101
❑ 99PacParFC-10
❑ 99PacParG-101
❑ 99PacParHoloGold-101
❑ 99PacParHS-101
❑ 99PacParOD-101
❑ 99PacParPB-16
❑ 99PacParPB-101
❑ 99PacParRed-101
❑ 99PacParTC-13
❑ 99PacPlaB-186
❑ 99PacPlaB-186A
❑ 99PacPri-66
❑ 99PacPriAotG-11
❑ 99PacPriDG-11
❑ 99PacPriHB-66
❑ 99PacPriHG-66
❑ 99PacPriHM-66
❑ 99PacPriHP-66
❑ 99PacPriRed-66
❑ 99PacPriS-1
❑ 99PacPriS206-1
❑ 99PacPriS206R-1
❑ 99PacPriSE-1
❑ 99PacPriSP-1
❑ 99PacPriSP-1
❑ 99PacPriSV-1
❑ 99PacRed-186
❑ 99PacRed-186A
❑ 99PacTeaC-21
❑ 99Pin-2
❑ 99Rev-61
❑ 99RevDiaL-16
❑ 99RevFouP-8
❑ 99RevPremDate-61
❑ 99RevRet-61
❑ 99RevShaSS-61
❑ 99RevThoitS-9
❑ 99RevTri-15
❑ 99RevTri-15
❑ 99SkyMolM-148
❑ 99SkyMolMF-48
❑ 99SkyMolMFS-48
❑ 99SkyMolMFT-48
❑ 99SkyMolMX-148
❑ 99SkyPre-96
❑ 99SkyPre-275
❑ 99SkyPreLB-3
❑ 99SkyPreR-96
❑ 99SkyPreR-275
❑ 99SkyPreSotG-10
❑ 99SkyThu-281
❑ 99SkyThuRant-281
❑ 99SkyThuRave-281
❑ 99SP Aut-39
❑ 99SP AutEF-E15
❑ 99SP AutHRC-HR26
❑ 99SP AutR-R15
❑ 99SPAutHRCDC-HR26
❑ 99SpoIll-161
❑ 99SpoIllH-5
❑ 99SPx-42
❑ 99SPxDom-FB10
❑ 99SPxFinR-42
❑ 99SPxFinS-42
❑ 99SPxPowE-PE15
❑ 99SPxPreS-PS8
❑ 99SPxStaF-SF13
❑ 99StaClu-285
❑ 99StaCluC-SCC3
❑ 99StaCluCR-SCC3
❑ 99StaCluFDI-285
❑ 99StaCluNC-NC16
❑ 99StaCluOoaK-285
❑ 99StaCluPP-285
❑ 99StaCluTI-T6A
❑ 99StaCluTI-T16C
❑ 99StaCluTL-T6A
❑ 99StaCluTL-T16C
❑ 99StaCluTL-T6A
❑ 99StaCluTL-T16C
❑ 99ThuSkySupR-281
❑ 99Top-150
❑ 99Top-450
❑ 99TopAllMF-M1
❑ 99TopBlaLC1-80
❑ 99TopBlaLC2-80
❑ 99TopBlaLC3-80
❑ 99TopChr-150
❑ 99TopChr-450
❑ 99TopChrERttH-ER8
❑ 99TopChrERttH-ER8
❑ 99TopChrLotD-LD6
❑ 99TopChrLotDR-LD6
❑ 99TopChrR-150
❑ 99TopChrR-450
❑ 99TopGal-10
❑ 99TopGalE-E11
❑ 99TopGalPP-10
❑ 99TopGalPPI-10
❑ 99TopGolL-80
❑ 99TopGolLC1-80
❑ 99TopGolLC2-80
❑ 99TopGolLOtO-80
❑ 99TopLorotD-LD6
❑ 99TopMVPP-150
❑ 99TopMVPP-450
❑ 99TopOpeD-86
❑ 99TopPicP-P9
❑ 99TopPowB-PB8
❑ 99TopPowBR-PB8
❑ 99TopRedLC1-80
❑ 99TopRedLC2-80
❑ 99TopRedLC3-80
❑ 99TopSta-22
❑ 99TopSta-167
❑ 99TopSta'S-43
❑ 99TopSta'SG-43
❑ 99TopSta'SGDH-43
❑ 99TopSta1Foil-22
❑ 99TopSta2Foil-22
❑ 99TopStaFoil-22
❑ 99TopStaFoil-167
❑ 99TopStaOS-22
❑ 99TopStaTS-22
❑ 99TopTek-31A
❑ 99TopTek-31B
❑ 99TopTekG-31A
❑ 99TopTekG-31B
❑ 99UD Cho-90
❑ 99UD ChoP-90
❑ 99UD ChoPCR-90
❑ 99UD ChoS-23
❑ 99UD ChoSD-23
❑ 99UD ChoSHR-23
❑ 99UD ChoST-23
❑ 99UD ChoYW-Y14
❑ 99UD Ion-31
❑ 99UD Ion-75
❑ 99UD IonC-C19
❑ 99UD IonH-H19
❑ 99UD IonR-31
❑ 99UD IonR-75
❑ 99UDHolo-25
❑ 99UDHoloAUsome-25
❑ 99UDHoloLau-L15
❑ 99UDHoloLauG-L15
❑ 99Ult-207
❑ 99UltGolM-207
❑ 99UltMas-207
❑ 99UltPlaM-207
❑ 99UltRBIK-6
❑ 99UltTheBook-6
❑ 99UltThu-8
❑ 99UppDec-383
❑ 99UppDec10AT-X24
❑ 99UppDec10ATD-X24
❑ 99UppDec10ATHR-X24
❑ 99UppDec10ATT-X24
❑ 99UppDecBD-37
❑ 99UppDecBDD-37
❑ 99UppDecBDDom-D5
❑ 99UppDecBDDomE-D5
❑ 99UppDecBDMN-M22
❑ 99UppDecBDMNE-M22
❑ 99UppDecBDQ-37
❑ 99UppDecBDT-37
❑ 99UppDecCf7-19
❑ 99UppDecCf7-75
❑ 99UppDecCf7-C16
❑ 99UppDecCf7Cf7P-C16
❑ 99UppDecCf7LL-L11
❑ 99UppDecCL-82
❑ 99UppDecCLCC-82
❑ 99UppDecCLM-C41
❑ 99UppDecCo7CE-19
❑ 99UppDecCo7CE-75
❑ 99UppDecE-45
❑ 99UppDecE-150
❑ 99UppDecEDF-D8
❑ 99UppDecEDFFXG-D8
❑ 99UppDecEFXG-45
❑ 99UppDecEFXG-150
❑ 99UppDecEL1-383
❑ 99UppDecEL2-383
❑ 99UppDecEPE-P14
❑ 99UppDecF-F14
❑ 99UppDecFD-F14
❑ 99UppDecFQ-F14
❑ 99UppDecFT-F14
❑ 99UppDecIP-I1
❑ 99UppDecIPD-I1
❑ 99UppDecIPHR-I1
❑ 99UppDecIPT-I1
❑ 99UppDecM-90
❑ 99UppDecM-P12
❑ 99UppDecMD-D12
❑ 99UppDecMGS-90
❑ 99UppDecMGUS-GUJB
❑ 99UppDecMHFS-90
❑ 99UppDecMP-90
❑ 99UppDecMSS-90
❑ 99UppDecO-35
❑ 99UppDecOMP-S15
❑ 99UppDecOSO-35
❑ 99UppDecR-38
❑ 99UppDecRG-38
❑ 99UppDecROSS-S8
❑ 99UppDecROSS-S8
❑ 99UppDecRP-38
❑ 99UppDecTE-T12
❑ 99UppDecTED-T12
❑ 99UppDecTEQ-T12
❑ 99UppDecTET-T12
❑ 99UppDecVtaT-V14
❑ 99UppDecVtaTD-V14
❑ 99UppDecVtaTQ-V14
❑ 99UppDecVtaTT-V14
❑ 99UppDecWY-W3
❑ 99UppDecWYD-W3
❑ 99UppDecWYHR-W3
❑ 99UppDecWYT-W3
❑ 99Vic-169
❑ 99Vic-170
❑ 99Vic-457

Baham, Leon
❑ 82IdaFalAT-16
❑ 87SanBerSP-14
❑ 88TamTarS-2

Bahnert, Barrie
❑ 93AusFut-12
❑ 95AusFut-13
❑ 95AusFut-88
❑ 95AusFut-106

Bahns, Ed
❑ 78AppFoxT-2
❑ 79AppFoxT-4

Bahnsen, Stan (Stanley R.)
❑ 66TolMudHTI-2
❑ 67OPC-93
❑ 67Top-93
❑ 68Top-214
❑ 68TopVen-214
❑ 68YanPhoS-60
❑ 69CitMetC-9
❑ 69Top-380
❑ 69TopSta-201
❑ 69TopTeaP-19
❑ 70Top-568
❑ 70YanCliDP-8
❑ 70YanPhoS-2
❑ 71MilDud-2
❑ 71MLBOffS-482
❑ 71OPC-184
❑ 71Top-184
❑ 71YanArcO-2
❑ 71YanCliDP-1
❑ 72Top-662
❑ 72WhiSox-2
❑ 72WhiSoxTI1-3
❑ 73OPC-20
❑ 73Top-20
❑ 74OPC-254
❑ 74Top-254
❑ 74TopSta-152
❑ 75OPC-161
❑ 75SSP18-15
❑ 75Top-161
❑ 75TopMin-161
❑ 76OPC-534
❑ 76SSP-486
❑ 76Top-534
❑ 77BurCheD-112
❑ 77ExpPos-4
❑ 77Top-383
❑ 78ExpPos-1
❑ 78OPC-54
❑ 78Top-97
❑ 79ExpPos-2
❑ 79OPC-244
❑ 79Top-468
❑ 80ExpPos-3
❑ 80OPC-345
❑ 80Top-653
❑ 81Don-452
❑ 81Fle-156
❑ 81OPC-267
❑ 81TCM60I-369
❑ 81Top-267
❑ 82Don-392
❑ 82Fle-183
❑ 82OPC-131
❑ 82Top-131
❑ 83PorBeaT-23
❑ 89PacSenL-78
❑ 89SweBasG-39
❑ 89T/MSenL-4
❑ 89TopSenL-62
❑ 92YanWIZ6-4
❑ 92YanWIZ7-9

Bahr, Chris
❑ 25Zee-85

Bahr, Ed (Edson Garfield)
❑ 84TCMPla1-40

Bahrens, Scott
❑ 92IdaFalGSP-14

Baier, Marty
❑ 82CliGiaF-15
❑ 83CliGiaF-7

Bailes, Scott
❑ 83AleDukT-10
❑ 85NasPirT-1
❑ 86DonRoo-25
❑ 86FleUpd-6
❑ 86IndOhH-43
❑ 86IndTeal-3
❑ 86SpoRoo-9
❑ 86TopTra-5T
❑ 86TopTraT-5T
❑ 87Don-227
❑ 87Fle-242
❑ 87FleGlo-242
❑ 87IndGat-43
❑ 87OPC-134
❑ 87Top-585
❑ 87TopTif-585
❑ 87ToyRoo-3
❑ 88Don-104
❑ 88DonBasB-285
❑ 88Fle-600
❑ 88FleGlo-600
❑ 88IndGat-43
❑ 88IndTeal-3
❑ 88OPC-107
❑ 88PanSti-68
❑ 88StaLinI-2
❑ 88Top-107
❑ 88TopSti-206
❑ 88TopTif-107
❑ 89Don-202
❑ 89Fle-398
❑ 89FleGlo-398
❑ 89IndTeal-4
❑ 89Sco-424
❑ 89Top-339
❑ 89TopSti-217
❑ 89TopTif-339
❑ 89UppDec-209
❑ 90AngSmo-19
❑ 90Don-468
❑ 90Fle-484
❑ 90FleCan-484
❑ 90Lea-380
❑ 90OPC-784
❑ 90PubIntS-553
❑ 90RedFolSB-2
❑ 90Sco-218
❑ 90ScoRoo-64T
❑ 90Top-784
❑ 90TopTif-784
❑ 91Bow-205
❑ 91Sco-535
❑ 91UppDec-190
❑ 92Don-357
❑ 92Fle-53
❑ 92OPC-95
❑ 92Sco-331
❑ 92StaClu-167
❑ 92Top-95
❑ 92TopGol-95
❑ 92TopGolW-95
❑ 92TopMic-95
❑ 93PacSpa-40
❑ 97OklCit8-6
❑ 98Pac-197
❑ 98PacOnl-727
❑ 98PacOnlR-727
❑ 98PacOnlWC-727
❑ 98PacPlaB-197
❑ 98PacRedT-197
❑ 98PacSil-197

Bailey, Ben
❑ 95BilMusTI-8
❑ 97LakTigB-6

Bailey, Bill (William F.)
❑ 09AmeCarE90-1-1
❑ 09ColChiE-17
❑ 09PC7HHB-1
❑ 10NadCarE-1
❑ 11PinT-5-113
❑ 11SpoLifM-106
❑ 11T205-5
❑ 12ColRedB-17
❑ 12ColTinT-17

Bailey, Bob (Robert S.)
❑ 63Kah-1
❑ 63PirIDL-1
❑ 63PirJayP-1
❑ 63Top-228
❑ 64Kah-2
❑ 64PirKDK-2
❑ 64Top-91
❑ 64TopGia-4
❑ 64TopVen-91
❑ 65Kah-4
❑ 65Top-412
❑ 66Kah-4
❑ 66PirEasH-7
❑ 66Top-485
❑ 67CokCapD-2
❑ 67CokCapDA-2
❑ 67DexPre-16
❑ 67OPC-32
❑ 67Top-32
❑ 68Top-580
❑ 69ExpFudP-1
❑ 69MLBOffS-154
❑ 69Top-399
❑ 69TopSta-52
❑ 69TopTeaP-10
❑ 70ExpPin-2
❑ 70ExpPos-6
❑ 70MLBOffS-62
❑ 70OPC-293
❑ 70Top-293
❑ 71ExpLaPR-1
❑ 71ExpPS-1
❑ 71MLBOffS-121
❑ 71OPC-157
❑ 71Top-157
❑ 71TopCoi-59
❑ 72MilBra-23
❑ 72OPC-493
❑ 72ProStaP-1
❑ 72Top-493
❑ 72Top-526

❑ 73OPC-505
❑ 73Top-505
❑ 74ExpWes-1
❑ 74OPC-97
❑ 74Top-97
❑ 74TopSta-51
❑ 75ExpPos-1
❑ 75Hos-55
❑ 75OPC-365
❑ 75Top-365
❑ 75TopMin-365
❑ 76OPC-338
❑ 76RedKro-2
❑ 76SSP-333
❑ 76Top-338
❑ 76TopTra-338T
❑ 77Top-221
❑ 78PapGinD-20
❑ 78SSP270-173
❑ 78Top-457
❑ 79OPC-282
❑ 79Top-549
❑ 81TCM60I-310
❑ 86ExpGreT-4
❑ 86PenWhiSP-4
❑ 87HawIsIP-26
❑ 90DodTar-25
❑ 92Nab-11

Bailey, Brandon
❑ 86ColMetP-4
❑ 87ColMetP-3
❑ 88St.LucMS-1

Bailey, Buddy
❑ 80AndBraT-17
❑ 82DurBulT-23
❑ 86DurBulP-1
❑ 87SumBraP-10
❑ 88BasAmeAAB-30
❑ 88DurBulS-4B
❑ 89GreBraB-20
❑ 89GreBraP-1178
❑ 89GreBraS-25
❑ 89SouLeaAJ-23
❑ 90GreBraP-1143
❑ 90GreBraS-24
❑ 91CarLeaAP-CAR21
❑ 91LynRedSC-25
❑ 91LynRedSP-1215
❑ 92LynRedSC-26
❑ 93PawRedSDD-2
❑ 93PawRedSF-2424
❑ 93PawRedSTI-1
❑ 94PawRedSDD-2
❑ 94PawRedSF-960
❑ 95PawRedSDD-2
❑ 95PawRedTI-26
❑ 96PawRedSDD-1

Bailey, Cory
❑ 91ElmPioC-16
❑ 91ElmPioP-3261
❑ 92LynRedSC-5
❑ 92LynRedSF-2898
❑ 92ProFS7-25
❑ 93ExcFS7-129
❑ 93PawRedSDD-3
❑ 93PawRedSF-2399
❑ 93PawRedSTI-2
❑ 94Bow-447
❑ 94FleMajLP-4
❑ 94LeaLimR-55
❑ 94PawRedSDD-3
❑ 94PawRedSF-939
❑ 94Pin-420
❑ 94PinArtP-420
❑ 94PinMusC-420
❑ 94SpoRoo-30
❑ 94SpoRooAP-30
❑ 94Top-764
❑ 94TopGol-764
❑ 94TopSpa-764
❑ 95Don-344
❑ 95DonPreP-344
❑ 95LeaGolR-14
❑ 95LouRedF-266
❑ 95Sco-596
❑ 95ScoGolR-596
❑ 95ScoPlaTS-596
❑ 95Top-632
❑ 96FleUpd-U182
❑ 96FleUpdTC-U182
❑ 97OklCit8-7
❑ 98FreGriG-1

Bailey, Darryl
❑ 77BurBeeT-1
❑ 78BurBeeT-2
❑ 79HolMilT-22

Bailey, Ed (Lonas Edgar)
❑ 47Exh-10A
❑ 47Exh-10B
❑ 53Top-206
❑ 54Top-184
❑ 55Top-69
❑ 55TopDouH-29
❑ 56Kah-1
❑ 56RedBurB-1
❑ 57Kah-2
❑ 57RedSoh-1
❑ 57SwiFra-5
❑ 57Top-128
❑ 58Kah-1
❑ 58RedEnq-3
❑ 58RedJayP-1
❑ 58Top-330
❑ 58Top-386
❑ 58Top-490
❑ 59Kah-1
❑ 59RedBurBP-1
❑ 59RedEnq-2
❑ 59RedShiBS-2
❑ 59Top-210
❑ 60Kah-1
❑ 60Top-411
❑ 61Baz-21
❑ 61Kah-2
❑ 61Pos-188A
❑ 61Pos-188B
❑ 61Raw-2
❑ 61RedJayP-1
❑ 61Top-418
❑ 61TopStaI-13
❑ 62GiaJayP-2
❑ 62Jel-137
❑ 62Pos-137
❑ 62PosCan-137
❑ 62SalPlaC-113A
❑ 62SalPlaC-113B
❑ 62ShiPlaC-113
❑ 62Top-459
❑ 62TopStaI-194
❑ 63Top-368
❑ 64Top-437
❑ 64WheSta-4
❑ 65Top-559
❑ 66Top-246
❑ 66TopVen-246
❑ 78TCM60I-37
❑ 78TCM60I-173
❑ 79TCM50-11
❑ 80Red196T-26
❑ 81Gia196T-5
❑ 84GiaMot-17
❑ 91TopArc1-206
❑ 91UppDecS-9
❑ 94TopArc1-184
❑ 94TopArc1G-184

Bailey, Greg
❑ 83TriTriT-21
❑ 86TulDriTI-18

Bailey, Howard Lee
❑ 82EvaTriT-1
❑ 82Top-261
❑ 83TigPos-3
❑ 84Don-212
❑ 84EvaTriT-2
❑ 84Fle-75
❑ 84Nes792-284
❑ 84Top-284
❑ 84TopTif-284

Bailey, Jay
❑ 93MisStaB-48

Bailey, Jim
❑ 82IdaFalAT-2
❑ 86DavLipB-3

Bailey, Lash
❑ 89BelMarL-17
❑ 90PenPilS-1

Bailey, Mark (John Mark)
❑ 84AstPos-2
❑ 84FleUpd-3
❑ 85AstHouP-17
❑ 85AstMot-17
❑ 85Don-450
❑ 85Fle-344
❑ 85OPC-64
❑ 85Top-64
❑ 85TopTif-64
❑ 86AstMilL-2
❑ 86AstPol-14
❑ 86Don-354
❑ 86Fle-293
❑ 86Top-432
❑ 86TopSti-30
❑ 86TopTif-432
❑ 87AstMot-15
❑ 87AstPol-2
❑ 87Don-235
❑ 87Top-197
❑ 87TopTif-197
❑ 88AstMot-15
❑ 88AstPol-5
❑ 88TopBig-248
❑ 89TidTidC-29
❑ 89TidTidP-1949
❑ 90CMC-540
❑ 90PhoFirC-13
❑ 90PhoFirP-13
❑ 90ProAAAF-39
❑ 91LinDriAAA-377
❑ 91PhoFirLD-377
❑ 91PhoFirP-69
❑ 92PhoFirF-2823
❑ 92PhoFirS-377
❑ 98KisCobQ-3

Bailey, Mel
❑ 56RedBurB-2

Bailey, Mike
❑ 91EugEmeC-25
❑ 91EugEmeP-3714
❑ 94SouBenSHC-2
❑ 94SouBenSHF-585

Bailey, Otha
❑ 92NegLeaRLI-1

Bailey, Pat
❑ 86EugEmeC-31
❑ 87AppFoxP-19

Bailey, Phillip
❑ 95BelGiaTI-41
❑ 96SanJosGB-22
❑ 97SanJosG-6
❑ 98MadBlaW-3

Bailey, Robert
❑ 89WelPirP-3
❑ 90SalBucS-1
❑ 91SalBucC-4
❑ 91SalBucP-958
❑ 92SalBucC-18
❑ 92SalBucF-75

Bailey, Roger
❑ 92BenRocCB-2
❑ 92BenRocF-1466
❑ 92ClaDraP-71
❑ 92FroRowDP-96
❑ 92FroRowDPG-96
❑ 92FroRowDPS-96
❑ 92UppDecML-23
❑ 93Bow-120
❑ 93CenValRC-4
❑ 93CenValRF-2884
❑ 93ClaFS7-94
❑ 93ExcFS7-31
❑ 93RocStaC-29
❑ 93StaCluM-120
❑ 93Top-433
❑ 93TopGol-433
❑ 93TopInaM-433
❑ 93TopInaR-433
❑ 93TopMic-433
❑ 94NewHavRF-1542
❑ 95Fla-342
❑ 95FleUpd-164
❑ 95TopTra-76T
❑ 95UppDecML-91
❑ 95UppDecMLFS-91
❑ 96ColSprSSTI-2
❑ 96Fle-358
❑ 96FleTif-358
❑ 96LeaSigEA-6
❑ 96RocPol-1
❑ 96StaClu-340
❑ 96StaCluMOP-340
❑ 97DonTea-102
❑ 97DonTeaSPE-102
❑ 97PacPriGotD-GD132
❑ 98Pac-277
❑ 98PacPlaB-277
❑ 98PacRedT-277
❑ 98PacSil-277
❑ 98Pin-141
❑ 98PinPreP-141
❑ 98PinSna-CR14
❑ 98Sco-158
❑ 98Top-63
❑ 98TopChr-63
❑ 98TopChrR-63
❑ 98TopDevR-63
❑ 98TopDia-63
❑ 98TopMiniC-63

Bailey, Roy
❑ 90HamRedB-2
❑ 90HamRedS-3
❑ 91SavCarC-1
❑ 91SavCarP-1642
❑ 92St.PetCC-4
❑ 92St.PetCF-2017
❑ 93St.PetCC-3
❑ 93St.PetCF-2618

Bailey, Seymour
❑ 28LaPre-4

Bailey, Troy
❑ 88WytCubP-2003
❑ 89WytCubS-2

Bailey, Vince
❑ 79BurBeeT-18

Bailie, Matt
❑ 98MarPhiG-2

Bailor, Bob (Robert M.)
❑ 76BalOriP-2
❑ 76SSP-386
❑ 77OPC-48
❑ 77Top-474
❑ 78Hos-148
❑ 78Kel-39
❑ 78OPC-148
❑ 78SagDis-26
❑ 78TasDis-26
❑ 78Top-196
❑ 79BluJayBY-1
❑ 79Hos-105A
❑ 79Hos-105B
❑ 79OPC-259
❑ 79Top-492
❑ 80Kel-16
❑ 80OPC-304
❑ 80Top-581
❑ 81Don-389
❑ 81Fle-409
❑ 81OPC-297
❑ 81Top-297
❑ 81TopTra-732
❑ 82Don-308
❑ 82Fle-521
❑ 82MetPhoA-3
❑ 82Top-79
❑ 83Don-506
❑ 83Fle-538
❑ 83FleSta-5
❑ 83FleSti-230
❑ 83Top-343
❑ 83TopSti-260
❑ 84DodPol-21
❑ 84Don-595
❑ 84Fle-580
❑ 84FleUpd-4
❑ 84Nes792-654
❑ 84Top-654
❑ 84TopSti-109
❑ 84TopTif-654
❑ 84TopTra-4T
❑ 84TopTraT-4T
❑ 85DodCokP-3
❑ 85Don-397
❑ 85Fle-367
❑ 85Top-728
❑ 85TopTif-728
❑ 86BluJayGT-2
❑ 86Fle-124
❑ 86Top-522
❑ 86TopTif-522
❑ 87DunBluJP-928
❑ 88SyrChiC-24
❑ 88SyrChiP-817
❑ 89SyrChiC-25
❑ 89SyrChiMB-25
❑ 89SyrChiP-796
❑ 90CMC-674
❑ 90DodTar-26
❑ 90ProAAAF-368
❑ 90SyrChiC-26
❑ 90SyrChiMB-1
❑ 90SyrChiP-588
❑ 90TriAllGP-AAA11
❑ 91BluJayFS-2
❑ 91LinDriAAA-524
❑ 91MetWIZ-21
❑ 91OriCro-16
❑ 91SyrChiLD-524
❑ 91SyrChiMB-1
❑ 91SyrChiP-2496
❑ 92Nab-36
❑ 92UppDecS-3
❑ 93BluJayFS-2
❑ 93UppDecS-1
❑ 95BluJayOH-2

Bain, Paul
❑ 77CliDodT-1
❑ 78LodDodT-1
❑ 79LodDodT-3

Bain, Tyler
❑ 96ButCopKB-10
❑ 97ChaRivDG-3

Baine, David
❑ 92EveGiaC-24
❑ 92EveGiaF-1676
❑ 93CliGiaC-3
❑ 93EveGiaF-3758

Baine, Tom (John T.)
❑ 86EriCarP-2
❑ 87SprCarB-8
❑ 88TexLeaAGS-16
❑ 89LouRedBC-20
❑ 89LouRedBP-1265
❑ 89LouRedBTI-10
❑ 90SprCarDGB-23

Baines, Harold D.
❑ 78KnoKnoST-1
❑ 79IowOakP-3
❑ 81Fle-346
❑ 81OPC-347
❑ 81Top-347
❑ 82Don-568
❑ 82Fle-336
❑ 82FleSta-184
❑ 82OPC-56
❑ 82Top-684
❑ 83AllGamPI-47
❑ 83Don-143
❑ 83Fle-229
❑ 83FleSta-6
❑ 83FleSti-155
❑ 83Kel-16
❑ 83OPC-177
❑ 83Top-177
❑ 83TopSti-52
❑ 83WhiSoxTV-3
❑ 84AllGamPI-137
❑ 84Don-58
❑ 84DonActAS-11
❑ 84Fle-51
❑ 84FleSti-4
❑ 84FunFooP-110
❑ 84Nes792-434
❑ 84OPC-197
❑ 84Top-434
❑ 84TopRubD-1
❑ 84TopSti-242
❑ 84TopTif-434
❑ 84WhiSoxTV-3
❑ 85AllGamPI-47
❑ 85Don-58
❑ 85DonActA-58
❑ 85Dra-2
❑ 85Fle-507
❑ 85FleStaS-21
❑ 85Lea-231
❑ 85OPC-249
❑ 85SevCoi-G6
❑ 85Top-249
❑ 85Top-275
❑ 85TopGloS-34
❑ 85TopRubD-1
❑ 85TopSti-234
❑ 85TopSup-51
❑ 85TopTif-249
❑ 85TopTif-275
❑ 85WhiSoxC-3
❑ 86Don-13
❑ 86Don-180
❑ 86DonAll-49
❑ 86DonSupD-13
❑ 86Dra-24
❑ 86Fle-198
❑ 86FleLimE-3
❑ 86FleMin-42
❑ 86FleSluBC-M1
❑ 86FleStiC-1
❑ 86GenMilB-2A
❑ 86Lea-13
❑ 86MSAJayPCD-1
❑ 86OPC-65
❑ 86SevCoi-C4
❑ 86SevCoi-E4
❑ 86SevCoi-S4
❑ 86SevCoi-W4
❑ 86Spo-7
❑ 86Spo-52
❑ 86Top-755
❑ 86TopMinL-8
❑ 86TopSti-288
❑ 86TopSup-9
❑ 86TopTat-4
❑ 86TopTif-755
❑ 86WhiSoxC-3
❑ 87BoaandB-16
❑ 87ClaGam-42
❑ 87Don-429
❑ 87DonAll-25
❑ 87DonOpeD-236
❑ 87Dra-22
❑ 87Fle-485
❑ 87Fle-643
❑ 87FleBasA-1
❑ 87FleGamW-1
❑ 87FleGlo-485
❑ 87FleGlo-643
❑ 87FleHotS-2
❑ 87FleMin-3
❑ 87FleStiC-2
❑ 87HosSti-21
❑ 87KayB-1
❑ 87KraFoo-13
❑ 87Lea-52
❑ 87MandMSL-8
❑ 87OPC-309
❑ 87RedFolSB-119
❑ 87SevCoi-C1
❑ 87SmoAmeL-4
❑ 87Spo-153
❑ 87Spo-171
❑ 87SpoTeaP-26
❑ 87StuPan-17
❑ 87Top-772
❑ 87TopCoi-1
❑ 87TopGloS-14
❑ 87TopSti-284
❑ 87TopTif-772
❑ 87WhiSoxC-2
❑ 88Don-211
❑ 88DonAll-12
❑ 88DonBasB-11
❑ 88Fle-391
❑ 88FleExcS-1
❑ 88FleGlo-391
❑ 88GreBasS-4
❑ 88Lea-157
❑ 88OPC-35
❑ 88PanSti-62
❑ 88RedFolSB-3
❑ 88Sco-590
❑ 88ScoGlo-590
❑ 88Spo-33
❑ 88StaLinWS-1
❑ 88TarPla-1
❑ 88Top-35
❑ 88Top-321
❑ 88TopBig-224
❑ 88TopCoi-5
❑ 88TopRitTM-16
❑ 88TopSti-293
❑ 88TopTif-35
❑ 88TopTif-321
❑ 88TopUKM-1
❑ 88TopUKMT-1
❑ 88WhiSoxC-1
❑ 88WhiSoxK-5
❑ 89Bow-72
❑ 89BowTif-72
❑ 89CadEllD-1
❑ 89Don-148
❑ 89DonBasB-81
❑ 89Fle-491
❑ 89FleExcS-1
❑ 89FleGlo-491
❑ 89FleSup-2
❑ 89K-M-22
❑ 89OPC-152
❑ 89PanSti-310
❑ 89Sco-128
❑ 89ScoRoo-62T
❑ 89Spo-157
❑ 89Top-585
❑ 89TopBasT-88
❑ 89TopBig-266
❑ 89TopCoi-33
❑ 89TopHilTM-1
❑ 89TopSti-304
❑ 89TopTif-585
❑ 89TopUKM-2
❑ 89TVSpoM-113
❑ 89UppDec-211
❑ 89UppDec-692
❑ 89UppDecS-1
❑ 89WhiSoxC-5
❑ 89WhiSoxK-4

❑ 90Bow-501
❑ 90BowTif-501
❑ 90ClaBlu-69
❑ 90Don-402
❑ 90Don-660A
❑ 90Don-660B
❑ 90Don-660C
❑ 90Don-660D
❑ 90DonBesA-69
❑ 90Fle-290
❑ 90FleAll-1
❑ 90FleCan-290
❑ 90Lea-126
❑ 90M.Vpin-101
❑ 90OPC-345
❑ 90PanSti-167
❑ 90PanSti-200
❑ 90PubIntS-275
❑ 90PubIntS-383
❑ 90RanMot-6
❑ 90Sco-470
❑ 90Spo-125
❑ 90Top-345
❑ 90TopBig-157
❑ 90TopHilHM-30
❑ 90TopSti-158
❑ 90TopSti-245
❑ 90TopTif-345
❑ 90UppDec-353
❑ 91A'sMot-14
❑ 91A'sSFE-1
❑ 91Bow-231
❑ 91CadEllD-2
❑ 91ClaGam-13
❑ 91Don-748
❑ 91Fle-2
❑ 91Lea-196
❑ 91OPC-166
❑ 91RedFolS-6
❑ 91Sco-291
❑ 91StaClu-303
❑ 91StuPre-8
❑ 91Top-166
❑ 91TopDesS-166
❑ 91TopMic-166
❑ 91TopTif-166
❑ 91UltUpd-45
❑ 91UppDec-562
❑ 91USPlaCA-9D
❑ 92A'sUno7P-5
❑ 92AthMot-14
❑ 92Bow-171
❑ 92ClaGam-6
❑ 92Don-68
❑ 92DonDiaK-DK14
❑ 92DonSupD-DK14
❑ 92Fle-249
❑ 92Fle-707
❑ 92Hig5-101
❑ 92KinDis-22
❑ 92Lea-126
❑ 92LeaBlaG-126
❑ 92OPC-635
❑ 92Pin-41
❑ 92Sco-137
❑ 92ScoProP-13
❑ 92StaClu-536
❑ 92StaCluD-10
❑ 92Stu-221
❑ 92Top-635
❑ 92TopGol-635
❑ 92TopGolW-635
❑ 92TopKid-120
❑ 92TopMic-635
❑ 92TriPla-34
❑ 92Ult-109
❑ 92UppDec-158
❑ 93BalOriP-2
❑ 93Bow-281
❑ 93CadDis-3
❑ 93Don-725
❑ 93Fin-153
❑ 93FinRef-153
❑ 93Fle-659
❑ 93FleFinE-156
❑ 93Lea-249
❑ 93OPC-3
❑ 93OPCPre-68
❑ 93PacSpa-216
❑ 93Pin-111
❑ 93Pin-488
❑ 93RanKee-59
❑ 93RedFolS-6
❑ 93Sco-585
❑ 93Sel-257
❑ 93SelRoo-8T
❑ 93StaClu-666
❑ 93StaCluFDI-666
❑ 93StaCluM-187
❑ 93StaCluMOP-666
❑ 93Stu-190
❑ 93Top-345
❑ 93TopGol-345
❑ 93TopInaM-345
❑ 93TopInaR-345
❑ 93TopMic-345
❑ 93Ult-492
❑ 93UppDec-81
❑ 93UppDec-765
❑ 93UppDecGold-81
❑ 93UppDecGold-765
❑ 93UppDecSH-HI3
❑ 94BalOriP-2
❑ 94Bow-19
❑ 94ColC-478
❑ 94ColChoGS-478
❑ 94ColChoSS-478
❑ 94Don-486
❑ 94Fin-254
❑ 94FinRef-254
❑ 94Fla-1
❑ 94Fle-2
❑ 94FleExtB-2
❑ 94Lea-84
❑ 94LeaCleC-12
❑ 94OPC-221
❑ 94OriPro-4
❑ 94OriUSPC-2H
❑ 94OriUSPC-7H
❑ 94OriUSPC-13S
❑ 94Pac-26
❑ 94PanSti-18
❑ 94Pin-408
❑ 94PinArtP-408
❑ 94PinMusC-408
❑ 94Sco-469
❑ 94ScoGolR-469
❑ 94Sel-31
❑ 94StaClu-16
❑ 94StaCluFDI-16
❑ 94StaCluGR-16
❑ 94StaCluMOP-16
❑ 94StaCluT-278
❑ 94StaCluTFDI-278
❑ 94Stu-121
❑ 94Top-420
❑ 94TopGol-420
❑ 94TopSpa-420
❑ 94TriPla-152
❑ 94TriPlaM-15
❑ 94Ult-302
❑ 94UppDec-188
❑ 94UppDecED-188
❑ 95BalOriP-3
❑ 95ColCho-338
❑ 95ColChoGS-338
❑ 95ColChoSS-338
❑ 95Don-538
❑ 95DonPreP-538
❑ 95DonTopotO-2
❑ 95Fla-2
❑ 95Fle-2
❑ 95Lea-309
❑ 95LeaLim-154
❑ 95Pac-18
❑ 95PanSti-93
❑ 95Pin-422
❑ 95PinArtP-422
❑ 95PinMusC-422
❑ 95Sco-57
❑ 95ScoGolR-57
❑ 95ScoPlaTS-57
❑ 95Sel-156
❑ 95SelArtP-156
❑ 95SP-122
❑ 95SPSil-122
❑ 95StaClu-444
❑ 95StaCluMOP-444
❑ 95StaCluSTWS-444
❑ 95StaCluVR-235
❑ 95StaCluVRMO-235
❑ 95Stu-197
❑ 95Top-232
❑ 95TopCyb-130
❑ 95Ult-251
❑ 95UltGolM-251
❑ 95UppDec-128
❑ 95UppDecED-128
❑ 95UppDecEDG-128
❑ 95UppDecSE-183
❑ 95UppDecSEG-183
❑ 96Cir-25
❑ 96CirRav-25
❑ 96ColCho-55
❑ 96ColCho-510
❑ 96ColChoGS-55
❑ 96ColChoGS-510
❑ 96ColChoSS-55
❑ 96ColChoSS-510
❑ 96Don-208
❑ 96DonPreP-208
❑ 96EmoXL-33
❑ 96Fin-B205
❑ 96FinRef-B205
❑ 96Fla-47
❑ 96Fle-3
❑ 96FleTif-3
❑ 96FleUpd-U23
❑ 96FleUpdTC-U23
❑ 96LeaSigA-15
❑ 96LeaSigAG-15
❑ 96LeaSigAS-15
❑ 96Pac-232
❑ 96Pin-80
❑ 96Pin-241
❑ 96PinArtP-141
❑ 96PinFoil-241
❑ 96PinSta-141
❑ 96Sco-408
❑ 96SP-56
❑ 96Top-357
❑ 96Ult-330
❑ 96UltGolM-330
❑ 96UppDec-112
❑ 96UppDec-490U
❑ 96WhiSoxF-2
❑ 97Bow-38
❑ 97BowBes-96
❑ 97BowBesAR-96
❑ 97BowBesR-96
❑ 97BowChr-33
❑ 97BowChrI-33
❑ 97BowChrIR-33
❑ 97BowChrR-33
❑ 97BowInt-38
❑ 97Cir-343
❑ 97CirRav-343
❑ 97ColCho-75
❑ 97ColChoT-CW6
❑ 97Don-199
❑ 97DonGolPP-199
❑ 97DonSilPP-199
❑ 97DonTea-67
❑ 97DonTeaSPE-67
❑ 97Fin-126
❑ 97FinEmb-126
❑ 97FinEmbR-126
❑ 97FinRef-126
❑ 97Fle-55
❑ 97FleTif-55
❑ 97MetUni-53
❑ 97Pac-50
❑ 97PacLigB-50
❑ 97PacPri-19
❑ 97PacPriLB-19
❑ 97PacPriP-19
❑ 97PacPriSL-SL2C
❑ 97PacSil-50
❑ 97Pin-87
❑ 97PinArtP-PP87
❑ 97PinMusC-87
❑ 97PinPrePla-87
❑ 97Sco-104
❑ 97ScoArtPWB-104
❑ 97ScoPreS-104
❑ 97ScoShoS-104
❑ 97ScoShoSAP-104
❑ 97SP-49
❑ 97StaClu-70
❑ 97StaCluMOP-70
❑ 97Top-46
❑ 97TopChr-17
❑ 97TopChrR-17
❑ 97TopGal-10
❑ 97TopGalPPI-10
❑ 97TopSta-30
❑ 97TopStaAM-30
❑ 97Ult-35
❑ 97UltDouT-4
❑ 97UltGolME-35
❑ 97UltPlaME-35
❑ 97UppDec-37
❑ 97WhiSoxS-5
❑ 97WhiSoxSPI-5
❑ 97WhiSoxSPr-5
❑ 97WhiSoxTI-3
❑ 98ColCho-39
❑ 98CroRoy-19
❑ 98DonColL-220
❑ 98DonPriCL-220
❑ 98Fin-202
❑ 98FinNo--202
❑ 98FinNo-R-202
❑ 98FinRef-202
❑ 98Fle-138
❑ 98Lea-20
❑ 98LeaFraDA-20
❑ 98LeaFraF-20
❑ 98LeaFraM-20
❑ 98LeaFraM-20
❑ 98LeaFraMDC-20
❑ 98LeaFraMDC-20
❑ 98LeaFraMZ2-20
❑ 98Pac-19
❑ 98PacOnl-81
❑ 98PacOnlR-81
❑ 98PacOnlWC-81
❑ 98PacPlaB-19
❑ 98PacRedT-19
❑ 98PacSil-19
❑ 98StaCluFDI-144
❑ 98StaCluI-144
❑ 98StaCluOneK-144
❑ 98StaCluPP-144
❑ 98Top-399
❑ 98TopChr-399
❑ 98TopChrR-399
❑ 98TopDevR-399
❑ 98TopDia-399
❑ 98TopMiniC-399
❑ 98Ult-310
❑ 98UltGolM-310
❑ 98UltMas-310
❑ 98UltPlaM-310
❑ 98UppDec-36
❑ 98UppDecR-3
❑ 99Fle-316
❑ 99FleSta9-316
❑ 99FleWarT-316
❑ 99Pac-47
❑ 99PacOme-30
❑ 99PacOmeC-30
❑ 99PacOmeG-30
❑ 99PacOmePB-30
❑ 99PacPlaB-47
❑ 99PacRed-47
❑ 99UppDec-44
❑ 99UppDecEL1-44
❑ 99UppDecEL2-44
❑ 99Vic-54

Bair, Dennis
❑ 96DayCubB-3

Bair, Doug (Charles Douglas)
❑ 78OPC-229
❑ 78Pep-3
❑ 78SSP270-114
❑ 78Top-353
❑ 79Hos-3
❑ 79OPC-58
❑ 79Top-126
❑ 80OPC-234
❑ 80RedEnq-40
❑ 80Top-449
❑ 81Don-64
❑ 81Fle-213
❑ 81OPC-73
❑ 81Top-73
❑ 82Top-262
❑ 83Car-2
❑ 83Don-372
❑ 83Fle-2
❑ 83Top-627
❑ 83TopTra-5T
❑ 84Don-369
❑ 84Fle-76
❑ 84Nes792-536
❑ 84TigTeal-5
❑ 84TigWavP-3
❑ 84Top-536
❑ 84TopTif-536
❑ 85Don-369
❑ 85Fle-1
❑ 85TigCaiD-1
❑ 85TigWen-2
❑ 85Top-744
❑ 85TopTif-744
❑ 87Fle-386
❑ 87FleGlo-386
❑ 87MaiGuiP-2
❑ 87PhiTas-58
❑ 88SyrChiC-9
❑ 88SyrChiP-816
❑ 89SyrChiC-1
❑ 89SyrChiMB-1
❑ 89SyrChiP-807
❑ 90PirHomC-2
❑ 90Sco-517

Bair, Rich
❑ 84NewOriT-9

Bair, Rod
❑ 96PorRocB-7
❑ 97SalAva-6
❑ 98SalAvaC-3

Baird, Allard
❑ 89AppFoxP-870

Baird, Brandon
❑ 97LanLugTS-1
❑ 98WilBluRC-2

Baird, Chris
❑ 85DurBulT-19

Baird, Doug (Howard D.)
❑ 16SpoNewM-8
❑ 17ColE13-10
❑ 90DodTar-894

Baird, Hal
❑ 75OmaRoyTI-3
❑ 76OmaRoyTT-2

Baisley, Brad
❑ 99JustheS-6
❑ 99JustheSAC-2
❑ 99JustheSAD-2
❑ 99JustheSJB-6

Bajda, Mike
❑ 94JamJamC-2
❑ 94JamJamF-3956

Bajus, Mark
❑ 80BatTroT-3
❑ 81BatTroT-1
❑ 81WatIndT-6

Bakely, Jersey (Edward Enoch)
❑ 88SpoTimM-2

Bakenhaster, Dave (David L.)
❑ 64Top-479
❑ 66St.PetCTI-2

Baker, Al (Albert Jones)
❑ 75CliPilT-23

Baker, Andy
❑ 89BurIndS-2
❑ 91CollndC-8
❑ 91CollndP-1475
❑ 92ColRedC-20
❑ 92ColRedF-2378

Baker, Bill (William)
❑ 37Zee-30
❑ 41HarHarW-2
❑ 49EurSta-177
❑ 77CinRedT-10

Baker, Chuck (Charles Joseph)
❑ 78PadFamF-3
❑ 79HawIslC-11
❑ 79HawIslT-16
❑ 79Top-456
❑ 80HawIslT-1
❑ 81Fle-500
❑ 81TwiPos-3
❑ 82Fle-561
❑ 82Top-253

Baker, Curt
❑ 78WauMetT-1

Baker, Darnell
❑ 78CedRapGT-2

Baker, Dave (David Glen)
❑ 79SyrChiT-11
❑ 79SyrChiTI-5
❑ 80SyrChiT-17
❑ 80SyrChiTI-3
❑ 81SyrChiT-11
❑ 81SyrChiTI-1
❑ 82SyrChiT-14
❑ 82SyrChiTI-3
❑ 83TolMudHT-13
❑ 84TolMudHT-20

Baker, Del (Delmar David)
❑ 14B18B-10A
❑ 14B18B-10B
❑ 14B18B-10C
❑ 17Zee-80
❑ 17Zee-81
❑ 19Zee-32
❑ 20Zee-41
❑ 21Zee-42
❑ 23Zee-24
❑ 24Zee-21
❑ 25Zee-17
❑ 26Zee-65
❑ 27Zee-43
❑ 28Zee-64
❑ 34DiaMatCSB-4
❑ 34TigTeal-2
❑ 36WorWidGV-31
❑ 49SolSunP-1
❑ 54Top-133
❑ 60Top-456
❑ 74TigTCM1AC-2
❑ 81TigDetN-58
❑ 88ConSer5-2
❑ 94ConTSN-1215
❑ 94ConTSNB-1215
❑ 94TopArc1-133
❑ 94TopArc1G-133

Baker, Derek
❑ 92GulCoaMF-3470
❑ 93KinMetC-3
❑ 93KinMetF-3787
❑ 94PitMetC-5
❑ 94PitMetF-3516

Baker, Derrell
❑ 86IndIndTI-13
❑ 87WesPalBEP-658
❑ 88JacExpB-14
❑ 88JacExpP-968
❑ 89RocExpLC-2

Baker, Doug (Douglas)
❑ 83BirBarT-8
❑ 84EvaTriT-13
❑ 84TigWavP-4
❑ 85NasSouTI-1
❑ 85Top-269
❑ 85TopTif-269
❑ 86NasSouTI-1
❑ 87TolMudHP-17
❑ 87TolMudHT-20
❑ 88PorBeaC-13
❑ 88PorBeaP-647
❑ 89BirBarADB-4
❑ 89PorBeaC-14
❑ 89PorBeaP-230
❑ 90BirBarADB-4
❑ 90CMC-570
❑ 90Fle-368
❑ 90FleCan-368
❑ 90PorBeaC-18
❑ 90PorBeaP-182
❑ 90ProAAAF-252
❑ 90PubIntS-322
❑ 91LinDriAAA-603
❑ 91TucTorLD-603
❑ 91TucTorP-2217
❑ 92DurBulF-1116
❑ 92PulBraC-28
❑ 92PulBraF-3196
❑ 93CedRapKC-29
❑ 94CedRapKC-26
❑ 98MidAngG-3

Baker, Dusty (Johnny B.)
❑ 71OPC-709
❑ 71RicBraTI-3
❑ 71Top-709
❑ 72Top-764
❑ 73OPC-215
❑ 73SevTraC-3
❑ 73Top-215
❑ 73TopCanL-3
❑ 74BraPhoC-2
❑ 74OPC-320
❑ 74Top-320
❑ 74TopSta-2
❑ 75AtlBraP-1
❑ 75Hos-117
❑ 75OPC-33
❑ 75Top-33
❑ 75TopMin-33
❑ 76DodPos-2
❑ 76OPC-28
❑ 76SSP-16
❑ 76Top-28
❑ 76TopTra-28T
❑ 77Top-146
❑ 78Hos-56
❑ 78RCColC-67
❑ 78SSP270-57
❑ 78Top-668
❑ 79DodBlu-1
❑ 79OPC-290
❑ 79Top-562
❑ 80DodPol-12

❑ 80OPC-135
❑ 80Top-255
❑ 81AllGamPI-136
❑ 81Dod-1
❑ 81Dod-1
❑ 81DodPol-12
❑ 81DodPos-1
❑ 81Don-179
❑ 81Fle-115
❑ 81FleStiC-62
❑ 81LonBeaPT-5
❑ 81PerCreC-27
❑ 81Squ-17
❑ 81Top-495
❑ 81TopScr-71
❑ 81TopSti-182
❑ 81TopSupHT-43
❑ 82DodPol-12
❑ 82DodUniOV-1
❑ 82DogBuiE-1
❑ 82Don-336
❑ 82Fle-1
❑ 82FleSta-4
❑ 82Kel-50
❑ 82OPC-375
❑ 82SevSluC-1
❑ 82Top-311
❑ 82Top-375
❑ 82TopSti-52
❑ 83AllGamPI-136
❑ 83DodPol-12
❑ 83DodPos-1
❑ 83Don-462
❑ 83Fle-201
❑ 83FleSta-7
❑ 83FleSti-121
❑ 83FleSti-140
❑ 83OPC-220
❑ 83SevCoi-6
❑ 83Top-220
❑ 83TopGloS-22
❑ 83TopSti-245
❑ 84DodUniO-8
❑ 84Don-226
❑ 84DonActAS-47
❑ 84Fle-96
❑ 84FleUpd-5
❑ 84GiaPos-1
❑ 84Nes792-40
❑ 84OPC-40
❑ 84SevCoi-W18
❑ 84Top-40
❑ 84TopSti-80
❑ 84TopTif-40
❑ 84TopTra-5T
❑ 84TopTraT-5T
❑ 85A'sMot-15
❑ 85Don-445
❑ 85Fle-602
❑ 85FleUpd-3
❑ 85OPC-165
❑ 85Top-165
❑ 85TopMin-165
❑ 85TopTif-165
❑ 85TopTifT-4T
❑ 85TopTra-4T
❑ 86A'sMot-3
❑ 86Don-467
❑ 86Fle-411
❑ 86Lea-231
❑ 86OPC-31
❑ 86Top-645
❑ 86TopTif-645
❑ 87DodSmoA-2
❑ 87Fle-387
❑ 87FleGlo-387
❑ 87Top-565
❑ 87TopTif-565
❑ 88DodSmo-21
❑ 88DodSmo-22
❑ 88GiaMot-27
❑ 88GiaPos-2
❑ 89DodSmoG-93
❑ 89GiaMot-28
❑ 90DodTar-27
❑ 90GiaMot-21
❑ 90GiaSmo-1
❑ 90PacLeg-71
❑ 90RicBra2ATI-3
❑ 91DodUno7P-5
❑ 91GiaMot-27
❑ 92DodStaTA-21
❑ 92GiaFanFFB-1
❑ 92GiaMot-28
❑ 92GiaPacGaE-2
❑ 93GiaMot-1
❑ 93GiaPos-1
❑ 93Top-514
❑ 93TopGol-514
❑ 93TopInaM-514
❑ 93TopInaR-514
❑ 93TopMic-514
❑ 94GiaAMC-1
❑ 94GiaKTV-1
❑ 94GiaMot-1
❑ 94GiaSFC-1
❑ 94GiaTarBC-1
❑ 94GiaTeal-1
❑ 94GiaTeal-2
❑ 95GiaMot-1
❑ 96GiaMot-1
❑ 98GiaMot-1

Baker, Ernie
❑ 89JohCitCS-7
❑ 89Sta-162
❑ 90SavCarP-2059
❑ 91St.PetCC-1
❑ 91St.PetCP-2265
❑ 92St.PetCC-23
❑ 92St.PetCF-2018

Baker, Floyd Wilson
❑ 47TipTop-16
❑ 48WhiSoxTI-2
❑ 49Bow-119
❑ 49Lea-153
❑ 50Bow-146
❑ 51Bow-87
❑ 52Top-292
❑ 53BowBW-49
❑ 53BowC-159
❑ 75RedSox1T-2
❑ 75RedSox1T-39
❑ 83TopRep5-292
❑ 85TCMPla1-12
❑ 96Bro194F-29

Baker, Frank
❑ 70Top-704
❑ 70WicAerM-2
❑ 71OPC-689
❑ 71Top-689

Baker, Frank Watts
❑ 70YanPhoS-3
❑ 71OPC-213
❑ 71Top-213
❑ 71YanArcO-3
❑ 71YanCliDP-8
❑ 72OPC-409
❑ 72Top-409
❑ 73BalOriP-3
❑ 73OriJohP-15
❑ 73OriTeal-2
❑ 74OPC-411
❑ 74Top-411
❑ 91OriCro-17
❑ 92YanWIZ7-10

Baker, Gene (Eugene Walter)
❑ 47Exh-11
❑ 52MotCoo-45
❑ 55Bow-7
❑ 56Top-142
❑ 56YelBasP-5
❑ 57Top-176A
❑ 57Top-176B
❑ 58Hir-65
❑ 58Kah-2
❑ 58Top-358
❑ 59Top-238
❑ 60Top-539
❑ 61Top-339
❑ 77PirTCM1WC-15
❑ 79DiaGre-121
❑ 79TCM50-48
❑ 87NegLeaPD-32

Baker, George F.
❑ 92SalLakTSP-25

Baker, Gerald
❑ 86QuaCitAP-4

Baker, Greg
❑ 81ShrCapT-16

Baker, Home Run (Frank)
❑ 08AmeCarE91-35
❑ 09AmeCarE90-1-2
❑ 09ColChiE-18
❑ 09SpoNewSM-42
❑ 09T206-10
❑ 10CouT21-71
❑ 10CouT21-72
❑ 10CouT21-73
❑ 10CouT21-257
❑ 10DomDisP-4
❑ 10E12AmeCDCE125-3
❑ 10LuxCigPP-1
❑ 10NadE1-4
❑ 10RedCroT-2
❑ 10RedCroT-169
❑ 10SweCapPP-40
❑ 11A'sFirT20-1
❑ 11BasBatEU-1
❑ 11D35RocB-1
❑ 11DiaGumP-2
❑ 11HelSta-52
❑ 11L1L-120
❑ 11MecDFT-1
❑ 11MecDFT-17
❑ 11PinT-5-512
❑ 11PloCanE-2
❑ 11S74Sil-26
❑ 11S81LarS-95
❑ 11SpoLifCW-13
❑ 11SpoLifM-86
❑ 11T205-6
❑ 11TurRedT-78
❑ 12ColRedB-18
❑ 12ColTinT-18
❑ 12HasTriFT-6
❑ 12HasTriFT-18
❑ 12HasTriFT-25B
❑ 12HasTriFT-70A
❑ 12PhiCarE-4
❑ 12T22SeroC-1
❑ 13NatGamW-2
❑ 14CraJacE-2
❑ 14PieStaT-4
❑ 14PolGroW-2
❑ 14TexTomE-3
❑ 15CraJacE-2
❑ 15SpoNewM-8
❑ 16BF2FP-34
❑ 16SpoNewM-9
❑ 17ColE13-11
❑ 17HolBreD-3
❑ 19W514-75
❑ 20NatCarE-5
❑ 21E121So8-3A
❑ 21E121So8-3B
❑ 21Exh-4
❑ 21KoBreWSI-27
❑ 22AmeCarE122-3
❑ 22E120-61
❑ 22W573-5
❑ 22W575-4
❑ 23W515-15
❑ 23W551-1
❑ 23WilChoV-5
❑ 40PlaBal-177
❑ 50CalHOFW-3
❑ 53ArtHaloFP-3
❑ 60ExhWriH-3
❑ 60Fle-41
❑ 61Fle-1
❑ 61Fle-6
❑ 61GolPre-21
❑ 68SCFOldT-24
❑ 71FleWorS-9
❑ 72ClaCar-23
❑ 74A'sTCM1P-1
❑ 74CapPub-25
❑ 75FlePio-16
❑ 76ShaPiz-78
❑ 77BobParHoF-78
❑ 77GalGloG-155
❑ 77GalGloG-180
❑ 77PhiFav-7
❑ 77SerSta-2
❑ 80PacLeg-41
❑ 80PerHaloFP-74
❑ 80SSPHOF-74
❑ 81SpoHaloF-11
❑ 82DiaCla-19
❑ 82TCMGreS-35
❑ 83A'sGreT-3
❑ 85UltBasC-5
❑ 89PacLegI-146
❑ 90PerGreM-76
❑ 92ConTSN-565
❑ 92YanWIZH-1
❑ 93ConMasC-6
❑ 94ConTSNCI-39
❑ 96PitPosH-1

Baker, Jack Edward
❑ 11BasBatEU-2

Baker, Jared
❑ 92ClaDraP-63
❑ 92FroRowDP-12
❑ 92FroRowDPG-12
❑ 92FroRowDPS-12
❑ 92SpoIndC-1
❑ 92SpoIndF-1284
❑ 92UppDecML-22
❑ 93RanCucQC-2
❑ 93RanCucQF-818
❑ 94RanCucQC-3
❑ 94RanCucQF-1626
❑ 95RanCucQT-36
❑ 95SigRooOJ-3
❑ 95SigRooOJP-3
❑ 95SigRooOJPS-3
❑ 95SigRooOJS-3

Baker, Jason
❑ 92EliTwiC-20
❑ 92EliTwiF-3690
❑ 93BilMusF-3957
❑ 93BilMusSP-21
❑ 93EliTwiC-3
❑ 93EliTwiF-3425
❑ 94ForWayWC-2
❑ 94ForWayWF-2020
❑ 94MidLeaAF-MDW11
❑ 94VerExpC-4
❑ 94VerExpF-3898
❑ 95ForMyeMTI-1
❑ 95GreFalDTI-21
❑ 96DelShoB-7
❑ 96DelShoUB-2
❑ 97Bow-366
❑ 97BowInt-366
❑ 97FloStaLTPB-28
❑ 98arSenW1-2
❑ 98HarSenM-2

Baker, Jay
❑ 88GasRanP-999

Baker, Jesse Ormond
❑ 09ObaT21-205
❑ 12Zee-101
❑ 12Zee-102
❑ 13Zee-98

Baker, Jim
❑ 80UtiBluJT-4
❑ 83SyrChiT-4
❑ 84SyrChiT-29

Baker, John
❑ 83AndBraT-7

Baker, Ken
❑ 89FreStaBS-1

Baker, Kenny
❑ 79WesHavYT-12
❑ 80NasSouTI-1
❑ 82BirBarT-10
❑ 83EvaTriT-17
❑ 85OmaRoyT-27
❑ 89BirBarADB-6
❑ 90BirBarADB-6

Baker, Kerry
❑ 84PriWilPT-32
❑ 85NasPirT-2
❑ 86NasPirP-2

Baker, Loris
❑ 27Zee-109
❑ 29Zee-124
❑ 30Zee-136
❑ 31Zee-11
❑ 32Zee-19

Baker, Mark
❑ 83QuaCitCT-6
❑ 85OscAstTI-3
❑ 86ColAstP-3
❑ 87ColAstP-13
❑ 95WatIndTI-4
❑ 96WatIndTI-2
❑ 97WatIndTI-4
❑ 98WatIndTI-2

Baker, Mike
❑ 86ElmPioRSP-1
❑ 87GreHorP-21
❑ 88WinHavRSS-3
❑ 89LynRedSS-1

Baker, R.L.
❑ 40WheM4-4
❑ 41WheM5-18

Baker, Ricky (Rick)
❑ 80WatIndT-26
❑ 81ChaLooT-15
❑ 82ChaLooT-7
❑ 83MidCubT-25
❑ 84MidCubT-18

Baker, Sam
❑ 90BurIndP-3001
❑ 91ColIndC-9
❑ 91ColIndP-1476
❑ 91WatIndC-1
❑ 91WatIndP-3356
❑ 92ColRedF-2379

Baker, Scott
❑ 90JohCitCS-3
❑ 91SavCarP-1643
❑ 92St.PetCC-10
❑ 92St.PetCF-2019
❑ 93AthStaC-25
❑ 93HunStaF-2075
❑ 94HunStaF-1323
❑ 95EdmTraTI-1

Baker, Steve (Steven Byrne)
❑ 78TigTeal-2
❑ 80EvaTriT-12
❑ 81SyrChiT-1
❑ 81SyrChiTI-2
❑ 83TopTra-6T
❑ 84LouRedR-25
❑ 85IndIndTI-6

Baker, Tom (Thomas Calvin)
❑ 90DodTar-28
❑ 93ConTSN-739

Bakkum, Scott
❑ 92Min-2
❑ 93LynRedSC-2
❑ 93LynRedSF-2508
❑ 94SarRedSC-3
❑ 94SarRedSF-1941
❑ 95TreThuTI-6

Bakley, Jersey (Edward)
❑ 87OldJudN-15

Bakner, Brett
❑ 94LetMouF-3889
❑ 94LetMouSP-1

Bako, Paul
❑ 93BilMusF-3948
❑ 93BilMusSP-13
❑ 94Bow-158
❑ 94Cla-192
❑ 94ClaTriF-T19
❑ 94Top-686
❑ 94TopGol-686
❑ 94TopSpa-686
❑ 94WinSpiC-4
❑ 94WinSpiF-273
❑ 95SigRooOJ-4
❑ 95SigRooOJP-4
❑ 95SigRooOJPS-4
❑ 95SigRooOJS-4
❑ 96ChaLooB-6
❑ 96DouAllB-39
❑ 97IndInd-4
❑ 98FleUpd-U76
❑ 98TolMudHQ-7
❑ 99Fle-92
❑ 99FleSta9-92
❑ 99FleWarT-92
❑ 99MetUni-193
❑ 99MetUniGM-193
❑ 99MetUniPMG-193
❑ 99SkyPreA-2
❑ 99SkyPreABlue-2

Balabon, Anthony
❑ 86Ft.LauYP-2

Balabon, Rick
❑ 87PriWilYP-9
❑ 89SanBerSB-4
❑ 89SanBerSCLC-74
❑ 90CarLeaA-45
❑ 90PenPilS-2
❑ 91CalCanLD-52
❑ 91CalCanP-508
❑ 91LinDriAAA-52

Balance, Dale
❑ 92LetMouSP-6
❑ 93LetMouF-4142
❑ 93LetMouSP-17
❑ 94LetMouF-3868
❑ 94LetMouSP-6

Balaz, John Lawrence
❑ 75CalAngP-3
❑ 75SalLakCC-3
❑ 76OPC-539
❑ 76Top-539

Balboni, Steve (Stephen C.)
❑ 80NasSouTI-2
❑ 81ColCliP-37
❑ 81ColCliT-11
❑ 82ColCliP-35
❑ 82ColCliT-4
❑ 82Top-83
❑ 83ColCliT-15
❑ 83Don-73
❑ 83OPC-8
❑ 83Top-8
❑ 83YanPhoA-1
❑ 84FleUpd-6
❑ 84Nes792-782
❑ 84RoyPos-1
❑ 84Top-782
❑ 84TopTif-782
❑ 84TopTra-6T
❑ 84TopTraT-6T
❑ 85Don-419
❑ 85Fle-196
❑ 85Lea-95
❑ 85OPC-152
❑ 85RoyTeal-1
❑ 85Top-486
❑ 85TopSti-271
❑ 85TopTif-486
❑ 86BasStaB-5
❑ 86Don-222
❑ 86Dra-20
❑ 86Fle-1
❑ 86Lea-98
❑ 86OPC-164
❑ 86RoyKitCD-17
❑ 86RoyNatP-45
❑ 86RoyTeal-1
❑ 86Spo-186
❑ 86Top-164
❑ 86TopGloS-6
❑ 86TopMinL-17
❑ 86TopSti-265
❑ 86TopTat-21
❑ 86TopTif-164
❑ 87Don-102
❑ 87DonOpeD-199
❑ 87Fle-362
❑ 87FleGlo-362
❑ 87Lea-262
❑ 87OPC-240
❑ 87RedFolSB-85
❑ 87Top-240
❑ 87TopSti-263
❑ 87TopTif-240
❑ 88Don-424
❑ 88Fle-251
❑ 88FleGlo-251
❑ 88RoyTeal-2
❑ 88Sco-273
❑ 88ScoGlo-273
❑ 88ScoRoo-46T
❑ 88ScoRooG-46T
❑ 88StaLinRo-1
❑ 88Top-638
❑ 88TopClo-5
❑ 88TopTif-638
❑ 89Don-143
❑ 89DonBasB-188
❑ 89DonTra-48
❑ 89Fle-538
❑ 89FleGlo-538
❑ 89FleUpd-45
❑ 89OPC-336
❑ 89Sco-353
❑ 89ScoRoo-27T
❑ 89Top-336
❑ 89TopSti-222
❑ 89TopTif-336
❑ 89TopTra-6T
❑ 89TopTraT-6T
❑ 89UppDec-111
❑ 89YanScoNW-17
❑ 90Bow-436
❑ 90BowTif-436
❑ 90Don-315
❑ 90Fle-436
❑ 90FleCan-436
❑ 90Lea-373
❑ 90MLBBasB-66
❑ 90OPC-716
❑ 90PubIntS-424
❑ 90Sco-327
❑ 90Top-716
❑ 90TopBig-160
❑ 90TopTif-716
❑ 90TopTVY-22
❑ 90UppDec-497
❑ 90YanScoNW-25
❑ 91Don-650
❑ 91Fle-656
❑ 91OPC-511
❑ 91Sco-159
❑ 91StaClu-134
❑ 91StaCluP-2
❑ 91Top-511
❑ 91TopDesS-511
❑ 91TopMic-511

❑ 91TopTif-511
❑ 92OklCit8F-1918
❑ 92OklCit8S-302
❑ 92YanWIZ8-7
❑ 93OklCit8F-1630
❑ 93RanKee-394
❑ 98SpoIndG-2
Balbuena, Mike
❑ 97GreFalDTI-5
❑ 98YakBeaG-3
Balcena, Bobby (Robert R.)
❑ 52Par-20
❑ 55SeaPop-1
❑ 56SeaPop-2
❑ 57HygMea-2
❑ 57SeaPop-2
❑ 58SeaRaIT-1
Baldrick, Bob
❑ 83WauTimF-22
❑ 86ChaLooP-2
Baldschun, Jack
❑ 62Top-46
❑ 62TopStaI-164
❑ 62TopVen-46
❑ 63Top-341
❑ 64PhiJayP-2
❑ 64PhiPhiB-3
❑ 64Top-520
❑ 64TopCoi-69
❑ 64TopSta-90
❑ 64TopStaU-6
❑ 65PhiJayP-2
❑ 65Top-555
❑ 65TopEmbI-34
❑ 66Top-272
❑ 66TopVen-272
❑ 67OPC-114
❑ 67Top-114
❑ 70OPC-284
❑ 70Top-284
❑ 78TCM60I-104
Baldwin, Billy (Robert H.)
❑ 75DetTigP-2
❑ 76SSP-370
❑ 77MetDaiPA-3
❑ 91MetWIZ-23
Baldwin, Brian
❑ 87BelMarTI-19
❑ 88WauTimGS-21
❑ 89SanBerSB-8
❑ 89SanBerSCLC-73
Baldwin, Dave
❑ 67SenPos-3
❑ 68Top-231
❑ 68TopVen-231
❑ 69OPC-132
❑ 69SenTeal8-3
❑ 69Top-132
❑ 69TopFou-17
❑ 70Top-613
❑ 71MLBOffS-433
❑ 71OPC-48
❑ 71Top-48
❑ 81TCM60I-309
❑ 94BreMilB-5
Baldwin, Earl
❑ 17Zee-42
❑ 19Zee-81
❑ 20Zee-121
❑ 21Zee-2
❑ 22Zee-1
❑ 23Zee-1
❑ 24Zee-113
❑ 25Zee-129
❑ 28Zee-44
❑ 29Zee-37
❑ 30Zee-44
❑ 31Zee-98
Baldwin, James
❑ 92MidLeaATI-2
❑ 92SouBenWSF-169
❑ 92UppDecML-319
❑ 93BirBarF-1185
❑ 93Bow-611
❑ 93ClaFS7-61
❑ 93ClaGolF-204
❑ 93ExcFS7-149
❑ 94ActPac-31
❑ 94ActPac-63
❑ 94ActPac2G-9G
❑ 94ActPac2GD-9G
❑ 94Bow-155
❑ 94Bow-370
❑ 94BowBes-B4
❑ 94BowBesR-B4
❑ 94Cla-123
❑ 94ClaCreotC-C14
❑ 94ColC-652
❑ 94ColChoGS-652
❑ 94ColChoSS-652
❑ 94ExcFS7-34
❑ 94ExcLeaLF-1
❑ 94FleExtB-41
❑ 94FleExtBMLH-1
❑ 94NasSouF-1242
❑ 94OPC-210
❑ 94StaCluT-145
❑ 94StaCluTFDI-145
❑ 94Top-766
❑ 94TopGol-766
❑ 94TopSpa-766
❑ 94Ult-333
❑ 94UppDec-3
❑ 94UppDecED-3
❑ 94UppDecML-146
❑ 94UppDecML-245
❑ 94UppDecMLPotYF-PY27
❑ 95ActPacF-19
❑ 95Bow-196
❑ 95BowBes-B77
❑ 95BowBesR-B77
❑ 95Exc-25
❑ 95ExcLeaL-2
❑ 95Fla-241
❑ 95FleMajLP-2
❑ 95FleUpd-33
❑ 95NasSouTI-1
❑ 95Pin-413
❑ 95PinArtP-413
❑ 95PinMusC-413
❑ 95SelCer-97
❑ 95SelCerMG-97
❑ 95Sum-146
❑ 95SumNthD-146
❑ 95Top-49
❑ 95UltGolP-1
❑ 95UltGolPGM-1
❑ 95UppDecML-43
❑ 95UppDecMLFS-43
❑ 95UppDecMLT1PF-2
❑ 95Zen-123
❑ 96ColCho-91
❑ 96ColChoGS-91
❑ 96ColChoSS-91
❑ 96NasSouB-7
❑ 96Sco-245
❑ 97Cir-73
❑ 97CirRav-73
❑ 97ColCho-299
❑ 97ColChoT-CW5
❑ 97Don-176
❑ 97DonEli-111
❑ 97DonEliGS-111
❑ 97DonGolPP-176
❑ 97DonPre-82
❑ 97DonPreCttC-82
❑ 97DonSilPP-176
❑ 97DonTea-66
❑ 97DonTeaSPE-66
❑ 97Fin-54
❑ 97FinRef-54
❑ 97Fle-56
❑ 97FleRooS-2
❑ 97FleTif-56
❑ 97Lea-138
❑ 97LeaFraM-138
❑ 97LeaFraMDC-138
❑ 97MetUni-54
❑ 97MetUniPP-1
❑ 97PacPriGotD-GD26
❑ 97Pin-85
❑ 97PinArtP-PP85
❑ 97PinIns-77
❑ 97PinInsCE-77
❑ 97PinInsDE-77
❑ 97PinMusC-85
❑ 97PinPrePla-85
❑ 97Sco-54
❑ 97ScoArtPWB-54
❑ 97ScoPreS-54
❑ 97ScoShoS-54
❑ 97ScoShoSAP-54
❑ 97StaClu-317
❑ 97StaCluMOP-317
❑ 97Stu-54
❑ 97StuPrePG-54
❑ 97StuPrePS-54
❑ 97Top-310
❑ 97TopChr-104
❑ 97TopChrR-104
❑ 97TopGal-164
❑ 97TopGalPPI-164
❑ 97Ult-36
❑ 97UltGolME-36
❑ 97UltPlaME-36
❑ 97UltRooR-1
❑ 97UppDec-39
❑ 97WhiSoxS-2
❑ 97WhiSoxSPl-2
❑ 97WhiSoxSPr-2
❑ 97WhiSoxTI-37
❑ 98CirThu-151
❑ 98CirThuRav-151
❑ 98CirThuSupRav-151
❑ 98ColCho-338
❑ 98Fin-74
❑ 98FinNo--74
❑ 98FinNo-R-74
❑ 98FinRef-74
❑ 98Fle-208
❑ 98Pac-51
❑ 98PacOnl-160
❑ 98PacOnlR-160
❑ 98PacOnlWC-160
❑ 98PacPar-26
❑ 98PacParC-26
❑ 98PacParG-26
❑ 98PacParHS-26
❑ 98PacParPB-26
❑ 98PacParR-26
❑ 98PacPlaB-51
❑ 98PacRedT-51
❑ 98PacSil-51
❑ 98Sco-193
❑ 98StaCluFDI-167
❑ 98StaCluI-167
❑ 98StaCluOneK-167
❑ 98StaCluPP-167
❑ 98Top-88
❑ 98TopChr-88
❑ 98TopChrR-88
❑ 98TopDevR-88
❑ 98TopDia-88
❑ 98TopMiniC-88
❑ 98Ult-273
❑ 98UltGolM-273
❑ 98UltMas-273
❑ 98UltPlaM-273
❑ 98UppDec-334
❑ 98WhiSoxS-14
❑ 98WhiSoxSP-14
❑ 99Fle-349
❑ 99FleSta9-349
❑ 99FleWarT-349
❑ 99Pac-96
❑ 99PacAur-38
❑ 99PacAurOD-38
❑ 99PacCroC-63
❑ 99PacCroCPB-63
❑ 99PacPlaB-96
❑ 99PacRed-96
Baldwin, Jeff
❑ 86AshTouP-2
❑ 87OscAstP-10
❑ 88OscAstS-3
❑ 89ColMudB-13
❑ 89ColMudP-135
❑ 89ColMudS-3
❑ 90CMC-753
❑ 90ColMudB-9
❑ 90ColMudP-1357
❑ 90ColMudS-4
❑ 91JacGenLD-553
❑ 91JacGenP-930
❑ 91LinDriAA-553
❑ 91TopDeb90-10
❑ 92JacGenF-4011
❑ 92JacGenS-328
Baldwin, Johnny
❑ 83GreHorT-1
❑ 84NasSouTI-1
Baldwin, Kid (Clarence G.)
❑ 87OldJudN-16
Baldwin, Kirk
❑ 89EugEmeB-3
❑ 90AppFoxBS-4
❑ 90AppFoxP-2088
Baldwin, Lady (Charles)
❑ 87OldJudN-18
❑ 88AugBecN-2
❑ 88GandBCGCE-2
❑ 90DodTar-895
Baldwin, Mark (Marcus E.)
❑ 87OldJudN-17
❑ 94OriofB-65
Baldwin, Reggie (Reginald C.)
❑ 79ChaChaT-4
❑ 80TidTidT-13
❑ 80Top-678
❑ 87AstShoSPT-2
Baldwin, Rick (Rickey Alan)
❑ 75MetSSP-22
❑ 76OPC-372
❑ 76SSP-552
❑ 76Top-372
❑ 77Top-587
❑ 78SanJosMMC-11
❑ 91MetWIZ-22
Baldwin, Scott
❑ 93SouOreAC-3
❑ 93SouOreAF-4054
❑ 94MidLeaAF-MDW30
❑ 94WesMicWC-2
❑ 94WesMicWF-2287
Baldwin, Ted
❑ 24Zee-114
❑ 26Zee-158
Baldwin, Tony
❑ 88SumBraP-391
❑ 89BurBraP-1608
❑ 89BurBraS-1
❑ 90BurBraB-19
❑ 90BurBraP-2361
❑ 90BurBraS-2
Bale, John
❑ 96StCatSB-4
❑ 97HagSunB-2
❑ 97SouAtlTPB-19
❑ 98BesAutSS-1
❑ 98DunBluJTI-4
Balelo, Nesi
❑ 87ChaLooB-19
❑ 88VerMarP-949
Balentine, Bryant
❑ 91PriRedC-24
❑ 91PriRedP-3504
Bales, Daniel
❑ 95IdaFalBTI-23
Bales, Joe
❑ 96BriWhiSB-9
❑ 97HicCraRB-6
Bales, Lee (Wesley Owen)
❑ 67OPC-51
❑ 67Top-51
❑ 81TCM60I-370
Bales, Tom
❑ 88LitFalMP-3
Balfanz, John
❑ 88St.PetCS-1
❑ 89CalLeaA-37
❑ 89RenSilSCLC-261
Balfe, Ryan
❑ 94BriTigC-3
❑ 94BriTigF-3509
❑ 95FayGenTI-1
❑ 96LakTigB-6
❑ 97LakTigB-7
❑ 98MobBayBTI-4
Balint, Rob
❑ 94BriTigC-4
❑ 94BriTigF-3505
❑ 95FayGenTI-2
Ball, Harry (Harrison)
❑ 88CapCodPB-19
❑ 88CapCodPPaLP-27
❑ 90JohCitCS-4
Ball, Jeff D.
❑ 90AubAstB-9
❑ 90AubAstP-3408
❑ 91OscAstC-16
❑ 91OscAstP-690
❑ 92JacGenF-4002
❑ 92JacGenS-329
❑ 93MidLeaAGF-45
❑ 93QuaCitRBC-2
❑ 93QuaCitRBF-105
❑ 94JacGenF-221
❑ 95TucTotTI-2
❑ 96TusTorB-2
❑ 97PhoFirTI-2
❑ 98FreGriG-2
Ball, Jeff G.
❑ 87HawRai-17
❑ 90BoiHawP-3310
Ball, Jim
❑ 77QuaCitAT-1
Ball, Jim (James Chandler)
❑ 09RamT20-5
Ball, Neal (Cornelius)
❑ 09RamT20-6
❑ 09T206-11
❑ 09T206-12
❑ 10DomDisP-5
❑ 10RedCroT-3
❑ 10RedCroT-170
❑ 10SweCapPP-16
❑ 11HelSta-21
❑ 11PinT-5-621
❑ 11T205-7
❑ 12HasTriFT-21
❑ 12T207-6
❑ 67SpoHobFC-36
❑ 72ClaCar-21
❑ 91ConTSN-203
Ball, Robert
❑ 80AshTouT-10
❑ 81TulDriT-26
❑ 82TulDriT-21
Ball, Thomas
❑ 93GenCubC-3
❑ 93GenCubF-3165
Balla, Gary
❑ 77QuaCitAT-2
❑ 78QuaCitAT-1
Ballanfant, Lee
❑ 55Bow-295
Ballanger, Mark
❑ 77JacSunT-1
Ballara, Juan
❑ 92JohCitCC-6
❑ 92JohCitCF-3118
❑ 94St.PetCC-3
❑ 94St.PetCF-2587
❑ 95PeoChiTI-15
Ballard, Butch (Glenn)
❑ 77SpaPhiT-14
❑ 80OrlTwiT-14
❑ 80WisRapTT-14
Ballard, Jeff
❑ 86HagSunP-1
❑ 87BalOriP-3
❑ 87IntLeaAT-28
❑ 87RocRedWP-25
❑ 87RocRedWT-1
❑ 88Don-520
❑ 88Fle-554
❑ 88FleGlo-554
❑ 88OriFreB-34
❑ 88OriPos-3
❑ 88RocRedWC-1
❑ 88RocRedWP-199
❑ 88RocRedWTI-1
❑ 88Top-782
❑ 88TopTif-782
❑ 89BalOriP-2
❑ 89Bow-7
❑ 89BowTif-7
❑ 89Don-495
❑ 89DonBasB-30
❑ 89Fle-607
❑ 89FleGlo-607
❑ 89OriFreB-29
❑ 89PanSti-253
❑ 89Sco-551
❑ 89Top-69
❑ 89TopSti-230
❑ 89TopTif-69
❑ 89UppDec-595
❑ 90BalOriP-1
❑ 90Bow-244
❑ 90BowTif-244
❑ 90ClaBlu-89
❑ 90Don-51
❑ 90DonBesA-29
❑ 90Fle-173
❑ 90FleAwaW-1
❑ 90FleCan-173
❑ 90HagSunDGB-1
❑ 90Hot50RS-5
❑ 90K-M-27
❑ 90Lea-118
❑ 90MLBBasB-110
❑ 90OPC-296
❑ 90OPC-394
❑ 90PanSti-13
❑ 90PubIntS-573
❑ 90RedFolSB-3
❑ 90Sco-349
❑ 90ScoYouSI-25
❑ 90Spo-123
❑ 90Top-296
❑ 90Top-394
❑ 90TopBig-278
❑ 90TopDou-2
❑ 90TopGloS-17
❑ 90TopMinL-1
❑ 90TopSti-232
❑ 90TopStiB-61
❑ 90TopTif-296
❑ 90TopTif-394
❑ 90TopTVA-27
❑ 90UppDec-259
❑ 91BalOriP-2
❑ 91Bow-98
❑ 91Don-279
❑ 91Fle-467
❑ 91Lea-522
❑ 91OPC-546
❑ 91OriCro-18
❑ 91Sco-243
❑ 91StaClu-283
❑ 91StaCluP-3
❑ 91Top-546
❑ 91TopDesS-546
❑ 91TopMic-546
❑ 91TopTif-546
❑ 91UppDec-260
❑ 92Don-74
❑ 92LouRedF-1880
❑ 92LouRedS-252
❑ 92OPC-104
❑ 92Sco-129
❑ 92StaClu-771
❑ 92StaCluECN-771
❑ 92Top-104
❑ 92TopGol-104
❑ 92TopGolW-104
❑ 92TopMic-104
❑ 94Pac-491
Ballard, Matt
❑ 89TenTecGE-2
Ballard, Tim
❑ 78GreBraT-2
❑ 82ChaRoyT-13
Ballenger, Pelham A.
❑ 27Zee-129
Baller, Jay (Jay Scott)
❑ 82ReaPhiT-1
❑ 83ChaChaT-1
❑ 83IndPos-2
❑ 83IndWhe-2
❑ 84BufBisT-9
❑ 85IowCubT-12
❑ 86CubGat-48
❑ 86CubUno-1
❑ 86Don-613
❑ 86FleUpd-7
❑ 87IowCubTI-5
❑ 88CalCanC-5
❑ 88CalCanP-792
❑ 88Top-717
❑ 88TopTif-717
❑ 89IndIndC-7
❑ 89IndIndP-1231
❑ 90CMC-176
❑ 90OmaRoyC-1
❑ 92ScrRedBF-2439
❑ 92ScrRedBS-478
❑ 93Don-356
❑ 93LinVenB-16
❑ 93LinVenB-277
❑ 98ScrRedB1ATI-3
Ballinger, Mark A.
❑ 76OmaRoyTT-3
Ballou, Bill
❑ 30Zee-22
❑ 89UtiBluSP-29
❑ 90UtiBluSP-26
❑ 91UtiBluSC-22
❑ 91UtiBluSP-3258
❑ 96AubDouB-25
❑ 97AubDouTI-12
❑ 98QuaCitRBG-1
Ballou, Noble
❑ 32Zee-20
❑ 33Zee-100
❑ 37Zee-64
Ballou, Win
❑ 27MidBre-22
❑ 33Zee-99
❑ 90DodTar-896
Ballwinkle, Mascot
❑ 95BinMetTI-NNO
❑ 96BinMetB-3
❑ 97BinMetB-32
Balmer, Steve

- 83QuaCitCT-7

Balsley, Darren
- 84IdaFalATI-3
- 86ModA'sC-3
- 86ModA'sP-3
- 87DunBluJP-931
- 88KnoBluJB-10
- 89KnoBluJB-3
- 89KnoBluJP-1137
- 89KnoBluJS-5
- 90St.CatBJP-3484
- 91MyrBeaHC-28
- 91MyrBeaHP-2962
- 92MyrBeaHC-29
- 92MyrBeaHF-2214
- 93HagSunC-27
- 93HagSunF-1896
- 94MedHatBJF-3697
- 94MedHatBJSP-26
- 96HagSunB-28
- 97DunBluJTI-2

Baltes, Nick
- 89BoiHawP-1978

Balthazar, Doyle
- 87ChaWheP-28
- 87LakTigP-8
- 88LakTigS-2
- 89LonTigP-1384
- 90FloStaLAS-25
- 90LakTigS-2
- 91LinDriAA-376
- 91LonTigLD-376
- 91LonTigP-1880
- 92SanBerC-14
- 92SanBerSF-956

Baltz, Nick
- 76BatRouCT-2

Baltzell, Beau
- 96AriBlaDB-7

Bamberger, George I.
- 50RemBre-1
- 53MotCoo-38
- 59Top-529
- 67BalOriP-3
- 67BalOriP-4
- 70BalOriP-1
- 71BalOriP-1
- 72OriPos-2
- 73BalOriP-4
- 73OPC-136
- 73OriTeal-3
- 73Top-136A
- 73Top-136B
- 74OPC-306
- 74Top-306
- 75BalOriP-2
- 75Gia195T-1
- 76BalOriP-3
- 79Top-577
- 80Top-659
- 81TCM60I-307
- 82MetPhoA-4
- 83Top-246
- 85BreGar-1
- 85BrePol-31
- 85TopTifT-5T
- 85TopTra-5T
- 86BrePol-31
- 86Top-21
- 86TopTif-21
- 87Top-468
- 87TopTif-468
- 90PacLeg-11
- 90SweBasG-23
- 91OriCro-19

Ban, George
- 75LynRanT-3

Ban, Mark
- 86QuaCitAP-5

Ban, Yoshitiro
- 92NiaFalRC-10
- 92NiaFalRF-3314

Banach, Joe
- 81CliGiaT-1

Bananas, Willie P.
- 89WesPalBES-26
- 93WesPalBEC-30

Banasiak, Edward
- 87ElmPioBC-24
- 87ElmPioRC-24
- 88WinHavRSS-4

Bancells, Richard
- 81RocRedWT-20
- 83RocRedWT-24

Bancroft, Dave (David James)
- 09RamT20-7
- 12HomRunKE-32
- 12Zee-50
- 14Zee-51
- 15SpoNewM-9
- 16BF2FP-85
- 16FleBreD-6
- 16SpoNewM-10
- 17ColE13-12
- 19W514-40
- 20NatCarE-6
- 20W516-30
- 20W52-1
- 20WalMaiW-3
- 21E121So1-4
- 21E121So8-4A
- 21E121So8-4B
- 21Exh-5
- 21KoBreWSI-1
- 21Nei-73
- 21OxfConE-2
- 22AmeCarE122-4
- 22E120-181
- 22W572-4
- 22W573-6
- 22W575-5
- 22WilPatV-38
- 23W501-64
- 23W503-25
- 23W515-4
- 23W551-2
- 23WilChoV-6
- 25Exh-1
- 26Exh-4
- 26SpoComoA-4
- 27AmeCarE126-52
- 27Exh-1
- 27YorCarE-19
- 28Exh-5
- 28StaPlaCE-1
- 28W502-19
- 28W512-1
- 28Yue-19
- 29ExhFou-4
- 33WorCig(-2
- 33WorCig(-3
- 61Fle-7
- 70SpoCarfCOP-21
- 76GrePlaG-13
- 76RowExh-12
- 76ShaPiz-119
- 77GalGloG-122
- 80PerHaloFP-119
- 80SSPHOF-119
- 83PhiPosGPaM-4
- 89DodSmoG-2
- 89HOFStiB-20
- 90DodTar-29
- 91ConTSN-17
- 92ConTSN-598
- 94ConTSN-1065
- 94ConTSNB-1065

Bando, Chris (Christopher M.)
- 81ChaChaT-8
- 81Top-451
- 82Don-551
- 82Ind-2
- 82IndWhe-11
- 82Top-141
- 83Don-33
- 83Fle-400
- 83IndPos-3
- 83IndWhe-3
- 83Top-227
- 84Don-224
- 84Fle-534
- 84Ind-2
- 84IndWhe-23
- 84Nes792-431
- 84Top-431
- 84TopTif-431
- 85Don-520
- 85Fle-438
- 85Ind-1
- 85IndPol-23
- 85Lea-39
- 85OPC-14
- 85Top-14
- 85TopTif-14
- 86Don-373
- 86Fle-579
- 86IndOhH-23
- 86IndTeal-4
- 86OPC-211
- 86Top-594
- 86TopTif-594
- 87Don-501
- 87DonOpeD-105
- 87Fle-243
- 87FleGlo-243
- 87IndGat-23
- 87Top-322
- 87TopTif-322
- 88ChaLooLTI-1
- 88Don-95
- 88Fle-601
- 88FleGlo-601
- 88IndGat-23
- 88IndTeal-4
- 88OPC-51
- 88PanSti-71
- 88Sco-172
- 88ScoGlo-172
- 88StaLinI-3
- 88Top-604
- 88TopSti-209
- 88TopTif-604
- 90CalLeaACLC-29
- 90StoPorB-27
- 90StoPorCLC-200
- 90StoPorP-2200
- 91StoPorC-24
- 91StoPorP-3047
- 92ElPasDF-3937
- 92ElPasDS-224
- 93NewOrlZF-986
- 94NewOrlZF-1483
- 97AriStaBG-1
- 97BrePol-1

Bando, Sal (Salvatore L.)
- 67OPC-33
- 67Top-33
- 67VanMouSO-1
- 68OPC-146
- 68Top-146
- 68TopVen-146
- 69A'sJacitB-1
- 69MLBOffS-82
- 69Top-371
- 69Top-556
- 69TopSta-211
- 69TopTeaP-21
- 70Kel-51
- 70MLBOffS-254
- 70OPC-120
- 70Top-120
- 70TopScr-4
- 70TopSup-2
- 71MLBOffS-506
- 71OPC-285
- 71Top-285
- 71TopCoi-132
- 71TopGreM-5
- 71TopSup-57
- 71TopTat-1
- 72'sA'sPos-15
- 72Kel-52A
- 72Kel-52B
- 72MilBra-24
- 72OPC-348
- 72SevTraC-4
- 72Top-348
- 72Top-650
- 73A'sPos-40
- 73LinPor-137
- 73OPC-155
- 73Top-155
- 73TopCanL-4
- 74A'sPos-51
- 74Kel-51
- 74OPC-103
- 74Top-103
- 74TopSta-221
- 75Hos-4
- 75HosTwi-4
- 75OPC-380
- 75SSP42-13
- 75Top-380
- 75TopMin-380
- 76A'sPos-70
- 76OPC-90
- 76SSP-497
- 76Top-90
- 77BurCheD-87
- 77ChiWilD-1
- 77DailsID-1
- 77DetCaeD-1
- 77HolInnD-1
- 77Hos-126
- 77MSADis-1
- 77OPC-145
- 77RCColC-1
- 77SagDis-1
- 77sDis-1
- 77Spo-1409
- 77Top-498
- 77WenDis-1
- 77ZipDis-1
- 78Hos-94
- 78OPC-174
- 78RCColC-41
- 78Top-265
- 78WifBalD-1
- 79Hos-119
- 79OPC-283
- 79Top-550
- 80BreTeal-2
- 80OPC-363
- 80Top-715
- 81Don-84
- 81Fle-510
- 81OPC-276
- 81Top-623
- 82Don-592
- 82Fle-134
- 86A'sGreT-4
- 87A'sMot-4
- 88PacLegI-99
- 89SweBasG-63
- 90PacLeg-4
- 90SweBasG-7
- 92ActPacA-40
- 93TedWil-42
- 93UppDecAH-5
- 94BreMilB-6
- 94UppDecAH-88
- 94UppDecAH1-88
- 97AriStaBG-2

Bando, Sal Jr.
- 93GleFalRC-5
- 93GleFalRF-4007
- 94NewJerCC-1
- 94NewJerCF-3422

Bandy, Ken
- 87QuaCitAP-28

Bane, Craig
- 90MisStaB-4
- 91MisStaB-4
- 92MisStaB-4
- 93MisStaB-3

Bane, Ed (Edward Lee)
- 74OPC-592
- 74TacTwiC-5
- 74Top-592
- 75IntLeaASB-2
- 75PacCoaLAB-2
- 75TacTwiK-13
- 76SSP-212
- 77TacTwiDQ-11
- 77Top-486
- 97AriStaBG-3

Bane, Jaymie
- 97ButCopKB-2
- 97ButCopKK-2
- 98LakElsSG-1

Banes, Dave
- 82NasSouTI-1

Baney, Dick (Richard Lee)
- 69PilPos-39
- 70OPC-88
- 70Top-88
- 74OPC-608
- 74Top-608A
- 74Top-608B
- 77PilPosR-39
- 83Pil69G-5

Banez, Marco
- 98JohCCTI-2

Bangert, Greg
- 81CliGiaT-10

Bangston, Pat
- 88KenTwiP-1406
- 88MidLeaAGS-34
- 89OrlTwiB-9
- 89OrlTwiP-1338
- 90CMC-554
- 90PorBeaC-2
- 90PorBeaP-169
- 90ProAAAF-239
- 91LinDriAA-476
- 91OrlSunRLD-476
- 91OrlSunRP-1842

Banister, Jeff
- 86WatPirP-3
- 87MacPirP-4
- 88HarSenP-855
- 89EasLeaAP-23
- 89EasLeaDDP-DD28
- 89HarSenP-306
- 89HarSenS-2
- 90HarSenP-1195
- 90HarSenS-3
- 91BufBisLD-26
- 91BufBisP-544
- 91LinDriAAA-26
- 92TopDeb91-8
- 93CarMudF-2056
- 94WelPirC-29
- 94WelPirF-3511
- 96HonShaHWB-28
- 96LynHilB-27
- 97LynHil-27
- 98CarMudM-24

Bankhead, Dan (Daniel R.)
- 51Bow-225
- 52Par-64
- 79TCM50-159
- 86NegLeaF-102
- 90DodTar-30
- 91DodRinP3-6

Bankhead, Fred
- 97NegLeaPC-4C

Bankhead, Sam
- 78LauLonABS-31
- 86NegLeaF-97

Bankhead, Scott
- 85Top-393
- 85TopTif-393
- 86DonRoo-36
- 86FleUpd-8
- 86OmaRoyP-1
- 86OmaRoyT-25
- 86RoyTeal-2
- 86SpoRoo-39
- 87Fle-363
- 87FleGlo-363
- 87FleUpd-1
- 87FleUpdG-1
- 87MarMot-13
- 87SpoTeaP-25
- 87Top-508
- 87TopTif-508
- 87TopTra-2T
- 87TopTraT-2T
- 88Don-70
- 88Fle-368
- 88FleGlo-368
- 88MarMot-13
- 88OPC-246
- 88PanSti-180
- 88Sco-238
- 88ScoGlo-238
- 88ScoYouS2-37
- 88Top-738
- 88TopTif-738
- 89Bow-203
- 89BowTif-203
- 89Don-463
- 89DonBasB-219
- 89Fle-539
- 89FleGlo-539
- 89MarMot-13
- 89OPC-79
- 89PanSti-429
- 89Sco-341
- 89ScoYouSI-42
- 89Top-79
- 89TopTif-79
- 89UppDec-316
- 90Bow-466
- 90BowTif-466
- 90Don-261
- 90DonBesA-40
- 90Fle-505
- 90FleCan-505
- 90Lea-127
- 90MarMot-24
- 90OPC-213
- 90PanSti-147
- 90PublntS-426
- 90Sco-555
- 90Spo-41
- 90Top-213
- 90TopSti-222
- 90TopTif-213
- 90UppDec-561
- 91Bow-254
- 91Don-189
- 91Fle-442
- 91Lea-345
- 91MarCouH-11
- 91OPC-436
- 91Sco-817
- 91StaClu-597
- 91Top-436
- 91TopDesS-436
- 91TopMic-436
- 91TopTif-436
- 91UppDec-294
- 92Don-304
- 92FleUpd-78
- 92Lea-485
- 92LeaBlaG-485
- 92OPC-155
- 92OPCPre-18
- 92Pin-580
- 92RedFolS-9
- 92RedKah-25
- 92Sco-594
- 92ScoRoo-47T
- 92StaClu-375
- 92StaClu-701
- 92StaCluNC-701
- 92Top-155
- 92TopDaiQTU-6
- 92TopGol-155
- 92TopGolW-155
- 92TopMic-155
- 92TopTra-7T
- 92TopTraG-7T
- 92Ult-478
- 93Don-690
- 93Fle-386
- 93FleFinE-169
- 93OPC-21
- 93OPCPre-94
- 93PacSpa-353
- 93RedSoxP-2
- 93RedSoxWHP-2
- 93Sco-584
- 93Sel-265
- 93SelRoo-122T
- 93StaClu-145
- 93StaCluFDI-145
- 93StaCluMOP-145
- 93Top-361
- 93TopGol-361
- 93ToplnaM-361
- 93ToplnaR-361
- 93TopMic-361
- 93Ult-505
- 93UppDec-329
- 93UppDec-760
- 93UppDecGold-329
- 93UppDecGold-760
- 94Don-429
- 94Fla-10
- 94Fle-25
- 94Pac-48
- 94Sco-139
- 94ScoGolR-139
- 94Top-633
- 94TopGol-633
- 94TopSpa-633

Banko, Joe
- 89AncGlaP-1

Bankowski, Chris
- 81RedPioT-27
- 83RedPioT-3

Banks, Brian
- 93HelBreF-4107
- 94BelBreC-3
- 94BelBreFI-113
- 94ExcFS7-77
- 94MidLeaAF-MDW6
- 95ElPasDTI-1
- 95SPML-83
- 96BesAutSA-3
- 96Bow-287
- 96BowFoi-287
- 96Exc-68
- 96Top-435
- 97Bow-352
- 97BowCerBlaIA-CA4
- 97BowCerBluIA-CA4
- 97BowCerGolIA-CA4
- 97BowChr-237
- 97BowChrI-237
- 97BowChrIR-237
- 97BowChrR-237
- 97BowInt-352
- 97Cir-106
- 97CirRav-106
- 97Fle-508
- 97FleTif-508

❑ 97Sel-170
❑ 97SelCom-170
❑ 97TucTorB-22
❑ 97Ult-540
❑ 97UltGolME-540
❑ 97UltPlaME-540
❑ 97UppDec-481
❑ 98LouRedQ-12

Banks, Darryl
❑ 82QuaCitCT-1
❑ 83MidCubT-12
❑ 84MidCubT-8

Banks, Dave
❑ 86AubAstP-2

Banks, Dean
❑ 91PocPioP-3788
❑ 91PocPioSP-10

Banks, Ernie (Ernest)
❑ 47Exh-12A
❑ 47Exh-12B
❑ 47Exh-12C
❑ 54Top-94
❑ 55Bow-242
❑ 55DonWin-11
❑ 55RobGouS-26
❑ 55RobGouW-26
❑ 55Top-28
❑ 55TopDouH-31
❑ 56Top-15
❑ 56TopPin-5
❑ 56YelBasP-6
❑ 57Top-55
❑ 58HarSta-11
❑ 58Top-310
❑ 58Top-482
❑ 59ArmCoi-4
❑ 59Baz-3
❑ 59HomRunD-3
❑ 59Top-147
❑ 59Top-350
❑ 59Top-469
❑ 59Top-559
❑ 59TopVen-147
❑ 59WilSpoG-2
❑ 60ArmCoi-3
❑ 60Baz-1
❑ 60CubJayP-4
❑ 60KeyChal-5
❑ 60NuHi-20
❑ 60RawGloT-3
❑ 60Top-10
❑ 60Top-560
❑ 60TopTat-5
❑ 60TopVen-10
❑ 61Baz-19
❑ 61ChePat-1
❑ 61CubJayP-4
❑ 61NuSco-420
❑ 61Pos-191A
❑ 61Pos-191B
❑ 61SevElev-23
❑ 61Top-43
❑ 61Top-350
❑ 61Top-485
❑ 61Top-575
❑ 61TopMagR-21
❑ 61TopStal-4
❑ 62AurRec-2
❑ 62Baz-32
❑ 62CubJayP-3
❑ 62ExhStaB-3
❑ 62Jel-188
❑ 62Pos-188
❑ 62PosCan-188
❑ 62SalPlaC-177A
❑ 62SalPlaC-177B
❑ 62ShiPlaC-177
❑ 62Top-25
❑ 62TopBuc-6
❑ 62TopStal-104
❑ 62TopVen-25
❑ 63BasMagM-8
❑ 63Baz-3
❑ 63CubJayP-1
❑ 63ExhStaB-4
❑ 63Jel-169
❑ 63Pos-169
❑ 63SalMetC-17
❑ 63Top-3
❑ 63Top-242
❑ 63Top-380
❑ 63TopStil-5
❑ 64CubJayP-1
❑ 64Top-55
❑ 64TopCoi-42
❑ 64TopSta-25
❑ 64TopStaU-7
❑ 64TopTatI-24
❑ 64TopVen-55
❑ 65CubJayP-2
❑ 65OldLonC-3
❑ 65Top-510
❑ 65TopEmbI-58
❑ 66CubTeal-3
❑ 66OPC-110
❑ 66Top-110
❑ 66TopRubI-7
❑ 66TopVen-110
❑ 67CokCapA-21
❑ 67CokCapC-2
❑ 67CokCapNLA-27
❑ 67CubProPS-2
❑ 67DexPre-17
❑ 67ProPizC-2
❑ 67Top-215
❑ 67TopVen-275
❑ 68AtlOilPBCC-6
❑ 68Top-355
❑ 68TopActS-6C
❑ 68TopVen-355
❑ 69CubBumS-1
❑ 69CubJewT-3
❑ 69CubPho-2
❑ 69CubTealC-1
❑ 69EquSpoHoF-BB1
❑ 69KelPin-2
❑ 69MilBra-19
❑ 69MLBOffS-118
❑ 69MLBPin-34
❑ 69OPC-6
❑ 69OPC-20
❑ 69Top-6
❑ 69Top-20
❑ 69TopSta-11
❑ 69TopTeaP-4
❑ 69TraSta-40
❑ 70CubDunD-1
❑ 70DayDaiNM-18
❑ 70Houof J-3
❑ 70Kel-40
❑ 70MilBra-3
❑ 70MLBOffS-13
❑ 70SunPin-1
❑ 70Top-630
❑ 70TopBoo-14
❑ 70TraSta-3C
❑ 71AllBasA-3
❑ 71Kel-50
❑ 71MatMin-3
❑ 71MatMin-4
❑ 71MilDud-34
❑ 71MLBOffS-25
❑ 71MLBOffS-555
❑ 71OPC-525
❑ 71Top-525
❑ 71TopGreM-36
❑ 72CubChi-1
❑ 72CubTeal-1
❑ 72MilBra-25
❑ 73OPC-81
❑ 73Top-81A
❑ 73Top-81B
❑ 75OPC-196
❑ 75OPC-197
❑ 75TCMHouoJ-3
❑ 75Top-196
❑ 75Top-197
❑ 75TopMin-196
❑ 75TopMin-197
❑ 76ChiGre-2
❑ 76GalBasGHoF-2
❑ 76LauDiaJ-2
❑ 77BobParHoF-4
❑ 77BobParMBC-2
❑ 77CubAllT-1
❑ 77GalGloG-29
❑ 77GalGloG-254
❑ 77Spo-1207
❑ 78TCM60I-255
❑ 79BasGre-69
❑ 79TCM50-5
❑ 80CubGreT-12
❑ 80Lau300-27
❑ 80MarExh-4
❑ 80PacLeg-33
❑ 80PerHaloFP-158
❑ 80PerHaloFPS-33
❑ 80SSPHOF-158
❑ 82BasCarN-11
❑ 82CraJac-10
❑ 82DiaCla-56
❑ 82TCMGreS-8
❑ 83KelCerB-11
❑ 84CubBriPC-12D
❑ 84CubUno-2
❑ 84CubUno-3
❑ 84CubUno-4
❑ 84CubUno-7
❑ 84OCoandSI-46
❑ 84SpoDesPW-21
❑ 84WilMay-32
❑ 85CirK-10
❑ 85Woo-3
❑ 86BigLeaC-9
❑ 86SpoDecG-29
❑ 86SpoDesJM-7
❑ 86SpoDesJM-19
❑ 86TCMSupS-46
❑ 87HygAllG-4
❑ 87NesDreT-26
❑ 88GreBasS-64
❑ 88HouSho-6
❑ 88PacLegI-36
❑ 89HOFStiB-6
❑ 89PerCelP-3
❑ 89TopBasT-17
❑ 90BasWit-19
❑ 90Col-11
❑ 90PacLeg-5
❑ 90PerGreM-21
❑ 90SweBasG-95
❑ 91Kel3D-4
❑ 91KelStaU-2
❑ 91LinDri-18
❑ 91SweBasG-5
❑ 92CubOldS-3
❑ 92FroRowBa-1
❑ 92FroRowBa-1AU
❑ 92FroRowBa-2
❑ 92FroRowBa-3
❑ 92FroRowBa-4
❑ 92FroRowBa-5
❑ 92MVP-11
❑ 92MVP2H-5
❑ 92TVSpoMF5HRC-2
❑ 92UppDecS-28
❑ 93NabAllA-1
❑ 93UppDecS-6
❑ 94CubWGN-8
❑ 94TopArc1-94
❑ 94TopArc1G-94
❑ 95NegLeaL2-1
❑ 96AriLot-1
❑ 96IllLot-1
❑ 97DonSigNN-1
❑ 97DonSigSS-1
❑ 97HigMinMCT-3
❑ 97HigMinMCT-4
❑ 97NegLeaPC-13H
❑ 97St.VinHHS-2
❑ 98DonSigSB-3
❑ 98DonSigSS-1
❑ 98SpoIllTaN-3
❑ 98SpoIllTaNEE-3
❑ 98UppDecR-16
❑ 98UppDecRSotT-EB
❑ 99SpoIllGotG-14
❑ 99SpoIllGotGA-3
❑ 99TopHaloFC-HOF7
❑ 99TopStaRR-2
❑ 99TopStaRRA-2
❑ 99UppDecAP-EB
❑ 99UppDecAPH5AU-EBAU
❑ 99UppDecCL-38
❑ 99UppDecCLA-1960
❑ 99UppDecCLCC-38
❑ 99UppDecCLES-EB
❑ 99UppDecCLESC-EB
❑ 99UppDecCLJotC-AC7
❑ 99UppDecR-108
❑ 99UppDecRG-108
❑ 99UppDecRP-108

Banks, George Edward
❑ 61TwiCloD-2
❑ 63Top-564
❑ 63TwiVol-3
❑ 64Top-223
❑ 64TopVen-223
❑ 65Top-348
❑ 66Top-488
❑ 67SeaPop-1

Banks, James
❑ 92SouOreAC-20
❑ 92SouOreAF-3404
❑ 93MadMusC-4
❑ 93MadMusF-1814
❑ 94ModA'sC-3
❑ 94ModA'sF-3056
❑ 95Exc-106
❑ 95HunStaTI-3

Banks, Lance
❑ 90ChaRaiB-2
❑ 90ChaRaiP-2032
❑ 91WatDiaC-1
❑ 91WatDiaP-1248

Banks, Tony
❑ 93SouOreAC-4
❑ 93SouOreAF-4076
❑ 94WesMicWC-3
❑ 94WesMicWF-2307
❑ 95ModA'sTI-1

Banks, Willie
❑ 88KenTwiP-1380
❑ 89CalLeaA-4
❑ 89VisOakCLC-101
❑ 89VisOakP-1426
❑ 90Bes-11
❑ 90Bow-411
❑ 90BowTif-411
❑ 90ClaYel-T31
❑ 90CMC-808
❑ 90OrlSunRB-1
❑ 90OrlSunRP-1076
❑ 90OrlSunRS-2
❑ 90ProAaA-40
❑ 90StaFS7-45
❑ 91Bow-341
❑ 91Cla2-T57
❑ 91LeaGolR-BC5
❑ 91LeaGolRNV-269
❑ 91LinDriAAA-402
❑ 91PorBeaLD-402
❑ 91PorBeaP-1559
❑ 91Ult-373
❑ 91UppDec-74
❑ 92Bow-553
❑ 92ClaGam-160
❑ 92Don-760
❑ 92Fle-657
❑ 92OPC-747
❑ 92Pin-575
❑ 92PinRool-6
❑ 92PorBeaF-2659
❑ 92PorBeaS-401
❑ 92ScoRoo-39
❑ 92SkyAAAF-182
❑ 92StaClu-321
❑ 92Top-747
❑ 92TopDeb91-9
❑ 92TopGol-747
❑ 92TopGolW-747
❑ 92TopMic-747
❑ 92Ult-393
❑ 92UppDec-14
❑ 92UppDecSR-SR2
❑ 93Bow-76
❑ 93Don-79
❑ 93Fle-637
❑ 93Lea-351
❑ 93PacSpa-518
❑ 93PanSti-127
❑ 93Sco-235
❑ 93Sel-314
❑ 93StaClu-170
❑ 93StaCluFDI-170
❑ 93StaCluMOP-170
❑ 93Top-226
❑ 93TopGol-226
❑ 93TopInaM-226
❑ 93TopInaR-226
❑ 93TopMic-226
❑ 93Toy-54
❑ 93Ult-579
❑ 93UppDec-686
❑ 93UppDecGold-686
❑ 94ColC-46
❑ 94ColC-522
❑ 94ColChoGS-46
❑ 94ColChoGS-522
❑ 94ColChoSS-46
❑ 94ColChoSS-522
❑ 94Don-79
❑ 94Fin-286
❑ 94FinRef-286
❑ 94Fla-134
❑ 94Fle-199
❑ 94FleExtB-215
❑ 94FleUpd-106
❑ 94Lea-245
❑ 94Pac-349
❑ 94PanSti-89
❑ 94Pin-177
❑ 94PinArtP-177
❑ 94PinMusC-177
❑ 94Sco-185
❑ 94ScoGolR-185
❑ 94ScoRoo-RT41
❑ 94ScoRooGR-RT41
❑ 94SpoRoo-84
❑ 94SpoRooAP-84
❑ 94StaClu-692
❑ 94StaCluFDI-692
❑ 94StaCluGR-692
❑ 94StaCluMOP-692
❑ 94StaCluT-334
❑ 94StaCluTFDI-334
❑ 94Top-14
❑ 94TopGol-14
❑ 94TopSpa-14
❑ 94TopTra-15T
❑ 94Ult-83
❑ 94Ult-453
❑ 94UppDec-434
❑ 94UppDecED-434
❑ 95ColCho-213
❑ 95ColChoGS-213
❑ 95ColChoSS-213
❑ 95Don-515
❑ 95DonPreP-515
❑ 95Fle-408
❑ 95Lea-201
❑ 95Pac-66
❑ 95Pin-337
❑ 95PinArtP-337
❑ 95PinMusC-337
❑ 95Sco-191
❑ 95ScoGolR-191
❑ 95ScoPlaTS-191
❑ 95StaClu-127
❑ 95StaCluFDI-127
❑ 95StaCluMOP-127
❑ 95StaCluSTWS-127
❑ 95Top-470
❑ 95TopCyb-264
❑ 95Ult-134
❑ 95UltGolM-134
❑ 95UppDec-64
❑ 95UppDecED-64
❑ 95UppDecEDG-64
❑ 97ColCliB-4
❑ 97ColCliD-1
❑ 98PacOnl-495
❑ 98PacOnlR-495
❑ 98PacOnlWC-495

Banning, Doug
❑ 86MidAngP-1
❑ 87EdmTraP-2067
❑ 87MidAngP-6
❑ 90ChaLooGS-4

Banning, Jim (James M.)
❑ 87OldJudN-19

Bannister, Alan
❑ 75PhiPhiP-3
❑ 77Top-559
❑ 77WhiSoxJT-1
❑ 78Kel-38
❑ 78SSP270-151
❑ 78Top-213
❑ 79Top-134
❑ 80OPC-317
❑ 80Top-608
❑ 81Top-632
❑ 82Don-159
❑ 82Fle-359
❑ 82Ind-3
❑ 82IndWhe-21
❑ 82Top-287
❑ 83Don-285
❑ 83Fle-401
❑ 83IndPos-4
❑ 83IndWhe-4
❑ 83OPC-348
❑ 83Top-348
❑ 84AstMot-21
❑ 84Don-154
❑ 84Fle-535
❑ 84FleUpd-7
❑ 84Nes792-478
❑ 84RanJarP-2
❑ 84Top-478
❑ 84TopSti-257
❑ 84TopTif-478
❑ 84TopTra-7T
❑ 84TopTraT-7T
❑ 85Fle-555
❑ 85RanPer-5
❑ 85Top-76
❑ 85TopTif-76
❑ 86Don-525
❑ 86Fle-556
❑ 86Top-784
❑ 86TopTif-784
❑ 88RocExpLC-1
❑ 89JacExpB-2
❑ 89JacExpP-151
❑ 89PacSenL-14
❑ 89T/MSenL-5
❑ 89TopSenL-30
❑ 91LinDriAAA-400
❑ 91PhoFirLD-400
❑ 91PhoFirP-84
❑ 93RanKee-60
❑ 97AriStaBG-4

Bannister, Floyd F.
❑ 77AstPho-2
❑ 77WhiSoxT-1
❑ 78AstBurK-6
❑ 78AstPos-3
❑ 78Top-39
❑ 79OPC-154
❑ 79Top-306
❑ 80MarPos-3
❑ 80OPC-352
❑ 80Top-699
❑ 81AllGamPI-73
❑ 81Don-286
❑ 81Fle-599
❑ 81MarPol-2
❑ 81MarPos-6
❑ 81OPC-166
❑ 81Top-166
❑ 81TopSti-128
❑ 82Don-100
❑ 82Fle-504
❑ 82MarPos-4
❑ 82Top-468
❑ 82TopSti-234
❑ 83Don-21
❑ 83Don-50
❑ 83Fle-471
❑ 83FleSta-8
❑ 83FleSti-182
❑ 83Kel-41
❑ 83OPC-203
❑ 83Top-545
❑ 83Top-706
❑ 83TopSti-18
❑ 83TopSti-113
❑ 83TopTra-7T
❑ 83WhiSoxTV-24
❑ 84Don-366
❑ 84Fle-52
❑ 84FleSti-84
❑ 84Nes792-280
❑ 84OPC-280
❑ 84Top-280
❑ 84TopSti-247
❑ 84TopTif-280
❑ 84WhiSoxTV-4
❑ 85Don-379
❑ 85Don-424A
❑ 85Fle-508
❑ 85OPC-354
❑ 85Top-274
❑ 85Top-725
❑ 85TopMin-725
❑ 85TopTif-274
❑ 85TopTif-725
❑ 85WhiSoxC-24
❑ 86Don-244
❑ 86Fle-199
❑ 86Lea-118
❑ 86OPC-64
❑ 86Top-64
❑ 86TopMinL-9
❑ 86TopTif-64
❑ 86WhiSoxC-19
❑ 87AstShoSPT-1
❑ 87Don-211
❑ 87Fle-486
❑ 87FleGlo-486
❑ 87FleLimE-1
❑ 87FleStiC-3
❑ 87OPC-356
❑ 87Top-737
❑ 87TopSti-286
❑ 87TopTif-737
❑ 87WhiSoxC-3
❑ 88AlaGolAA70TI-18
❑ 88Don-383
❑ 88DonBasB-7
❑ 88Fle-392
❑ 88FleGlo-392
❑ 88OPC-357

❑ 88PanSti-52
❑ 88RedFolSB-4
❑ 88RoySmo-8
❑ 88RoyTeal-3
❑ 88Sco-622
❑ 88ScoGlo-622
❑ 88ScoRoo-63T
❑ 88ScoRooG-63T
❑ 88StaLinWS-2
❑ 88Top-357
❑ 88TopBig-174
❑ 88TopTif-357
❑ 88TopTra-8T
❑ 88TopTraT-8T
❑ 89Bow-112
❑ 89BowTif-112
❑ 89Don-262
❑ 89Fle-276
❑ 89FleGlo-276
❑ 89OPC-194
❑ 89RedFolSB-5
❑ 89Sco-249
❑ 89Spo-154
❑ 89Top-638
❑ 89TopSti-269
❑ 89TopTif-638
❑ 89UppDec-549
❑ 90OPC-116
❑ 90PubIntS-342
❑ 90Top-116
❑ 90TopTif-116
❑ 90UppDec-695
❑ 91Bow-190
❑ 91FleUpd-8
❑ 91Lea-439
❑ 92RanMot-13
❑ 92RanTeal-1
❑ 92StaClu-743
❑ 92Ult-437
❑ 93RanKee-61
❑ 93UppDecS-14
❑ 97AriStaBG-5

Bannister, Tim
❑ 77BurBeeT-2
❑ 78BurBeeT-3

Bannon, Jimmy (James Henry)
❑ 95May-2
❑ 98CamPepP-2

Banta, Jack (John Kay)
❑ 43ParSpo-73
❑ 49EurSta-28
❑ 50Bow-224
❑ 79TCM50-203
❑ 90DodTar-31
❑ 91DodRinP3-2

Banton, Scott
❑ 89HamRedS-1
❑ 90SavCarP-2079
❑ 91SprCarC-4
❑ 91SprCarP-753

Baptist, Travis
❑ 91MedHatBJP-4089
❑ 91MedHatBJSP-10
❑ 92MyrBeaHF-2188
❑ 93ClaFS7-62
❑ 93ExcFS7-237
❑ 93ExcLeaLF-1
❑ 93KnoSmoF-1240
❑ 94SyrChiF-964
❑ 94SyrChiTI-2
❑ 94UppDecML-71
❑ 95SyrChiTI-1
❑ 96SigRooOJ-2
❑ 96SigRooOJS-2
❑ 96SyrChiTI-2
❑ 97NewBriRC-2
❑ 98SalLakBO-8

Barajas, Greg
❑ 98HelBreM-4

Barajas, Rod
❑ 96AriBlaDB-8
❑ 97HigDesMUG-6
❑ 97Top-469
❑ 98Bow-429
❑ 98BowChr-429
❑ 98BowChrGA-429
❑ 98BowChrGAR-429
❑ 98BowChrI-429
❑ 98BowChrIR-429
❑ 98BowChrR-429
❑ 98BowGolA-429
❑ 98BowInt-429
❑ 98HigDesMG-2
❑ 99Bow-86
❑ 99BowChr-86
❑ 99BowChrG-86
❑ 99BowChrGR-86
❑ 99BowChrI-86
❑ 99BowChrIR-86
❑ 99BowChrR-86
❑ 99BowGol-86
❑ 99BowInt-86

Baranoski, Jim
❑ 89IdaFalBP-2025

Barath, Steve
❑ 33Zee-101

Barba, Doug
❑ 84CedRapRT-4

Barba, Michael
❑ 82HolMilT-1
❑ 83ArkTraT-6

Barbao, Joe
❑ 94BatCliC-2
❑ 94BatCliF-3436
❑ 95PiePhiF-178
❑ 96PieBolWB-4
❑ 97ReaPhi-7
❑ 98ReaPhiM-27

Barbara, Dan (Daniel)
❑ 89SanBerSB-7
❑ 89SanBerSCLC-76
❑ 90PenPilS-3
❑ 90StaFS7-77

Barbara, Don
❑ 91MidAngOHP-2
❑ 91MidLeaAP-MWL24
❑ 91QuaCitAC-15
❑ 91QuaCitAP-2633
❑ 92EdmTraF-3543
❑ 92EdmTraS-151
❑ 92SkyAAAF-73
❑ 94AlbDukF-846
❑ 95PawRedSDD-3
❑ 95PawRedTI-37

Barbare, Walter L.
❑ 21Exh-6
❑ 22E120-121

Barbary, Travis
❑ 94GreFalDSP-12

Barbe, Yogi (Jim)
❑ 78AshTouT-1
❑ 79TulDriT-17

Barbeau, Jap (William J.)
❑ 08AmeCarE91-67
❑ 09T206-13
❑ 11PinT-5-1003
❑ 11SpoLifCW-14
❑ 16Zee-19
❑ 67SpoHobFC-32

Barbee, Dave (David Monroe)
❑ 29Zee-150
❑ 30Zee-166
❑ 31Zee-1

Barbein, Joe
❑ 92YakBeaC-23
❑ 92YakBeaF-3438

Barber, Andrew
❑ 97PorRocG-3

Barber, Brian
❑ 91Cla/Bes-443
❑ 91ClaDraP-18
❑ 91FroRowDP-21
❑ 91FroRowDPG-21
❑ 91FroRowDPS-21
❑ 91JohCitCC-18
❑ 91JohCitCP-3969
❑ 92Bow-29
❑ 92ClaFS7-268
❑ 92OPC-594
❑ 92Pin-298
❑ 92ProFS7-324
❑ 92Sco-803
❑ 92SprCarC-4
❑ 92SprCarF-860
❑ 92St.PetCF-2020
❑ 92StaCluD-11
❑ 92Top-594
❑ 92TopGol-594
❑ 92TopGolW-594
❑ 92TopMic-594
❑ 92UppDecML-178
❑ 93ArkTraF-2804
❑ 93Bow-136
❑ 93CarStaC-29
❑ 93ClaFS7-124
❑ 93ExcFS7-96
❑ 93Ult-461
❑ 94ActPac-21
❑ 94Bow-180
❑ 94Bow-364
❑ 94BowBes-B10
❑ 94BowBesR-B10
❑ 94Cla-82
❑ 94ClaGolF-13
❑ 94ExcFS7-256
❑ 94LouRedF-2971
❑ 94SigRoo-24
❑ 94SigRooS-24
❑ 94Top-788
❑ 94TopGol-788
❑ 94TopSpa-788
❑ 94Ult-563
❑ 94UppDecML-236
❑ 95Bow-31
❑ 95BowBes-B8
❑ 95BowBesR-B8
❑ 95LouRedF-267
❑ 95Sel-168
❑ 95SelArtP-168
❑ 96ColCho-24
❑ 96ColChoGS-24
❑ 96ColChoSS-24
❑ 96Don-547
❑ 96DonPreP-547
❑ 96LouRedB-8
❑ 96Pin-167
❑ 96Sco-237
❑ 96StaClu-409
❑ 96StaCluMOP-409
❑ 96Top-433
❑ 96Ult-270
❑ 96UltGolM-270
❑ 96UppDecFSP-FS2
❑ 97LouRedB-8
❑ 97PacPriGotD-GD196
❑ 98OmaRoyM-4

Barber, David
❑ 83QuaCitCT-5

Barber, Greg
❑ 96SouBenSHS-3
❑ 98HigDesMG-3

Barber, Red
❑ 88DodRinP1-4C
❑ 88DodRinP1-5C

Barber, Steve (Stephen David)
❑ 47Exh-13
❑ 58BalOriP-2
❑ 60Top-514
❑ 61Pos-74A
❑ 61Pos-74B
❑ 61Top-125
❑ 61TopStal-97
❑ 62BalOriP-2
❑ 62BalOriP-3
❑ 62SalPlaC-11
❑ 62ShiPlaC-11
❑ 62Top-57
❑ 62Top-355
❑ 62TopVen-57
❑ 63BalOriP-4
❑ 63BasMagM-9
❑ 63ExhStaB-5
❑ 63Fle-1
❑ 63Jel-64
❑ 63Pos-64
❑ 63ReqKP-1
❑ 63Top-12
❑ 64BalOriP-3
❑ 64BalOriP-4
❑ 64Baz-3
❑ 64OriJayP-2
❑ 64Top-450
❑ 64TopCoi-8
❑ 64TopSta-54
❑ 64TopStaU-8
❑ 64TopTatl-25
❑ 64WheSta-5
❑ 65BalOriP-3
❑ 65OPC-113
❑ 65Top-113
❑ 66BalOriP-2
❑ 66Top-477
❑ 67BalOriP-5
❑ 67OPC-82
❑ 67Top-82
❑ 67YanPhoS-90
❑ 68Top-316
❑ 68TopVen-316
❑ 68YanPhoS-61
❑ 69MilBra-20
❑ 69MLBOffS-92
❑ 69PilPos-12
❑ 69Top-233
❑ 69TopSta-222
❑ 69TopTeaP-9
❑ 70MLBOffS-265
❑ 70OPC-224
❑ 70Top-224
❑ 70TwiTeal-2
❑ 72MilBra-26
❑ 72OPC-333
❑ 72Top-333
❑ 73OPC-36
❑ 73Top-36
❑ 74OPC-631
❑ 74Top-631
❑ 77PilPosR-12
❑ 78TCM60I-57
❑ 81Ori6F-4
❑ 83Pil69G-26
❑ 91OriCro-20
❑ 92YanWIZ6-5

Barber, Turner (Tyrus Turner)
❑ 20NatCarE-7
❑ 21E121So1-5
❑ 21Exh-7
❑ 22E120-153
❑ 22W573-7
❑ 23W501-60
❑ 23WilChoV-7

Barberich, Frank F.
❑ 12ImpTobC-16

Barberie, Bret
❑ 88TopTra-9T
❑ 88TopTraT-9T
❑ 89Sta-32
❑ 89TopBig-19
❑ 89WesPalBES-2
❑ 90JacExpB-3
❑ 90JacExpP-1379
❑ 91IndIndLD-176
❑ 91IndIndP-465
❑ 91LinDriAAA-176
❑ 91UltUpd-90
❑ 91UppDecFE-67F
❑ 92Bow-467
❑ 92Cla1-T9
❑ 92Don-449
❑ 92ExpDonD-1
❑ 92ExpPos-4
❑ 92Fle-472
❑ 92Lea-288
❑ 92LeaBlaG-288
❑ 92LeaGolP-6
❑ 92LeaPre-6
❑ 92OPC-224
❑ 92OPCPre-36
❑ 92Pin-93
❑ 92PinTea2-50
❑ 92ProFS7-256
❑ 92Sco-419
❑ 92Sco100RS-14
❑ 92StaClu-427
❑ 92Stu-51
❑ 92Top-224
❑ 92TopDaiQTU-16
❑ 92TopDeb91-10
❑ 92TopGol-224
❑ 92TopGolW-224
❑ 92TopMic-224
❑ 92TriPla-134
❑ 92Ult-512
❑ 92UppDec-363
❑ 93Bow-446
❑ 93Don-12
❑ 93Don-759
❑ 93Fla-47
❑ 93Fle-418
❑ 93FleFinE-51
❑ 93FunPac-118
❑ 93Lea-256
❑ 93MarFloA-6
❑ 93MarlStaClu-18
❑ 93MarPub-4
❑ 93MarUppD-552
❑ 93MarUSPC-6S
❑ 93MarUSPC-11D
❑ 93PacSpa-454
❑ 93Pin-553
❑ 93PinExpOD-4
❑ 93RedFolS-7
❑ 93Sco-617
❑ 93SP-136
❑ 93StaClu-481
❑ 93StaCluFDI-481
❑ 93StaCluMOP-481
❑ 93TriPla-195
❑ 93Ult-366
❑ 93UppDec-479
❑ 93UppDec-552
❑ 93UppDecGold-479
❑ 93UppDecGold-552
❑ 94Bow-674
❑ 94ColC-47
❑ 94ColChoGS-47
❑ 94ColChoSS-47
❑ 94Don-127
❑ 94Fin-187
❑ 94FinRef-187
❑ 94Fla-378
❑ 94Fle-461
❑ 94FleExtB-257
❑ 94FUnPac-61
❑ 94Lea-62
❑ 94MarTeal-1
❑ 94PanSti-179
❑ 94Pin-136
❑ 94PinArtP-136
❑ 94PinMusC-136
❑ 94Sco-434
❑ 94ScoGolR-434
❑ 94Sel-133
❑ 94StaClu-415
❑ 94StaCluFDI-415
❑ 94StaCluGR-415
❑ 94StaCluMOP-415
❑ 94StaCluT-62
❑ 94StaCluTFDI-62
❑ 94Stu-106
❑ 94Top-132
❑ 94TopGol-132
❑ 94TopSpa-132
❑ 94TriPla-131
❑ 94Ult-192
❑ 94UppDec-151
❑ 94UppDecED-151
❑ 95BalOriP-4
❑ 95ColCho-341
❑ 95ColChoGS-341
❑ 95ColChoSE-132
❑ 95ColChoSEGS-132
❑ 95ColChoSESS-132
❑ 95ColChoSS-341
❑ 95Don-85
❑ 95DonPreP-85
❑ 95DonTopotO-3
❑ 95Fla-217
❑ 95Fle-325
❑ 95FleUpd-2
❑ 95Lea-382
❑ 95Pac-167
❑ 95PacPri-54
❑ 95Pin-80
❑ 95PinArtP-80
❑ 95PinMusC-80
❑ 95Sco-395
❑ 95ScoGolR-395
❑ 95ScoPlaTS-395
❑ 95StaClu-265
❑ 95StaCluFDI-265
❑ 95StaCluMOP-265
❑ 95StaCluSTWS-265
❑ 95StaCluVR-133
❑ 95StaCluVRMO-133
❑ 95Top-44
❑ 95TopCyb-33
❑ 95TopTra-136T
❑ 95Ult-252
❑ 95UltGolM-252
❑ 95UppDec-126
❑ 95UppDecED-126
❑ 95UppDecEDG-126
❑ 96IowCubB-6
❑ 98OklRedM-4

Barbieri, Jim (James P.)
❑ 67OPC-76
❑ 67Top-76
❑ 90DodTar-32

Barbisan, Vince
❑ 76SeaRaiC-2

Barbone, Tony
❑ 98VerExpO-1

Barbosa, Rafael
❑ 84DurBulT-11

Barbour, Louis
❑ 15Zee-73

Barboza, Carlos
❑ 98PorRocG-1

Barboza, Domingo
❑ 76VenLeaS-183
❑ 80VenLeaS-228

Barboza, James
❑ 85CloHSS-2

Barcelo, Lorenzo
❑ 95BelGiaTI-14
❑ 96BurBeeTI-1
❑ 96MidLeaAB-12
❑ 97SanJosG-7
❑ 98Bes-2

Barcelo, Marc
❑ 94ClaGolF-183
❑ 94NasXprF-377
❑ 94Top-747
❑ 94TopGol-747
❑ 94TopSpa-747
❑ 95Bow-155
❑ 95Exc-78
❑ 95SigRoo-6
❑ 95SigRooSig-6
❑ 95Top-639
❑ 95UppDecML-51
❑ 95UppDecMLFS-51
❑ 96BesAutS-7
❑ 96BesAutSA-4
❑ 96PinAfi-189
❑ 96PinAfiAP-189
❑ 96Sel-176
❑ 97BesAutAS-3
❑ 97NewBriRC-3

Barclay, Curt (Curtis C.)
❑ 57Top-361
❑ 58GiaArmT-2
❑ 58GiaJayP-2
❑ 58GiaSFCB-2
❑ 58Hir-70
❑ 58Top-21
❑ 59Top-307

Barczi, Scott
❑ 87WatPirP-7
❑ 88AugPirP-368
❑ 89SalBucS-4
❑ 90HarSenP-1196
❑ 90HarSenS-4

Bard, Michael
❑ 91BenBucCB-26
❑ 91BenBucP-3699

Bard, Paul Z.
❑ 81VerBeaDT-2
❑ 82VerBeaDT-12
❑ 84ChaO'sT-21

Barden, Geoff
❑ 91BriBanF-8

Barden, Steve
❑ 89RicBraP-819

Bardot, Gene
❑ 76WauMetT-1
❑ 77LynMetT-3

Bare, Ray (Raymond Douglas)
❑ 75DetTigP-3
❑ 76DetTigP-1
❑ 76OPC-507
❑ 76SSP-613
❑ 76Top-507
❑ 77Top-43
❑ 78RocRedWT-1

Barefoot, Mike
❑ 89MiaMirIS-1

Barfield, Brian
❑ 96JohCitCTI-2

Barfield, Jesse Lee
❑ 78DunBluJT-1
❑ 80KnoBluJT-13
❑ 82BluJayS-1
❑ 82OPC-203
❑ 82Top-203
❑ 82TopTra-2T
❑ 83Don-595
❑ 83Fle-424
❑ 83OPC-257
❑ 83Top-257
❑ 83TopSti-307
❑ 84AllGamPI-139
❑ 84BluJayFS-4
❑ 84Don-193
❑ 84Fle-147
❑ 84Nes792-488
❑ 84OPC-316
❑ 84Top-488
❑ 84TopSti-372
❑ 84TopTif-488
❑ 85AllGamPI-48
❑ 85BluJayCC-1
❑ 85BluJayFS-4
❑ 85BluJayPLP-1
❑ 85Don-195
❑ 85Fle-99
❑ 85Lea-209

❑ 85OPC-24
❑ 85OPCPos-20
❑ 85Top-24
❑ 85TopSti-362
❑ 85TopTif-24
❑ 86BluJayAF-3
❑ 86BluJayFS-3
❑ 86Don-193
❑ 86Fle-52
❑ 86FleMin-12
❑ 86FleStiC-2
❑ 86GenMilB-3A
❑ 86Lea-254
❑ 86OPC-234
❑ 86SevCoi-E16
❑ 86Spo-76
❑ 86Top-593
❑ 86TopSti-192
❑ 86TopTat-2
❑ 86TopTif-593
❑ 87BluJayFS-1
❑ 87ClaGam-58
❑ 87Don-121
❑ 87DonAll-23
❑ 87DonOpeD-34
❑ 87Fle-219
❑ 87Fle-643
❑ 87FleBasA-2
❑ 87FleExcS-3
❑ 87FleGlo-219
❑ 87FleGlo-643
❑ 87FleLeaL-1
❑ 87FleMin-4
❑ 87FleSlu-2
❑ 87FleStiC-4
❑ 87FleWaxBC-C2
❑ 87GenMilB-1A
❑ 87HosSti-1
❑ 87KayB-2
❑ 87KraFoo-41
❑ 87Lea-127
❑ 87OPC-24
❑ 87RedFolSB-3
❑ 87Spo-14
❑ 87Spo-153
❑ 87SpoTeaP-5
❑ 87StuPan-27
❑ 87Top-106
❑ 87Top-655
❑ 87TopCoi-2
❑ 87TopGaloC-1
❑ 87TopGloS-35
❑ 87TopMinL-73
❑ 87TopSti-184
❑ 87TopTif-106
❑ 87TopTif-655
❑ 87Woo-9
❑ 88BluJay5-1
❑ 88BluJayFS-1
❑ 88Don-442
❑ 88DonBasB-216
❑ 88Fle-102
❑ 88FleGlo-102
❑ 88FleRecS-1
❑ 88FleStiC-70
❑ 88Lea-225
❑ 88MSAHosD-19
❑ 88OPC-140
❑ 88PanSti-223
❑ 88Sco-8
❑ 88ScoGlo-8
❑ 88Spo-13
❑ 88StaLinBJ-1
❑ 88Top-140
❑ 88TopBig-92
❑ 88TopGloS-2
❑ 88TopSti-192
❑ 88TopStiB-46
❑ 88TopTif-140
❑ 89BluJayFS-1
❑ 89Bow-257
❑ 89BowTif-257
❑ 89ClaLigB-66
❑ 89Don-425
❑ 89DonBasB-132
❑ 89DonGraS-11
❑ 89Fle-225
❑ 89FleGlo-225
❑ 89FleUpd-46
❑ 89OPC-325
❑ 89PanSti-471
❑ 89RedFolSB-6
❑ 89Sco-160
❑ 89ScoRoo-22T
❑ 89Spo-9
❑ 89Top-325
❑ 89TopAme2C-1
❑ 89TopTif-325
❑ 89TopTra-7T
❑ 89TopTraT-7T
❑ 89UppDec-149
❑ 89UppDec-702
❑ 89YanScoNW-5
❑ 90BluJayHS-2
❑ 90BluJayHS-5
❑ 90Bow-433
❑ 90BowTif-433
❑ 90ClaBlu-99
❑ 90Don-74
❑ 90DonBesA-109
❑ 90Fle-437
❑ 90FleCan-437
❑ 90Lea-201
❑ 90MLBBasB-61
❑ 90OPC-740
❑ 90PacLeg-110
❑ 90PanSti-120
❑ 90PubIntS-530
❑ 90RedFolSB-4
❑ 90Sco-222
❑ 90Spo-10
❑ 90Top-740
❑ 90TopBig-188
❑ 90TopHilHM-24
❑ 90TopSti-314
❑ 90TopTif-740
❑ 90TopTVY-29
❑ 90UppDec-476
❑ 90YanScoNW-5
❑ 91BasBesHRK-1
❑ 91Bow-169
❑ 91ClaGam-61
❑ 91Don-498
❑ 91Fle-657
❑ 91Lea-308
❑ 91OPC-85
❑ 91PanFreS-330
❑ 91Sco-148
❑ 91Sco-414
❑ 91SimandSMLBL-2
❑ 91StaClu-103
❑ 91StaCluP-4
❑ 91Stu-91
❑ 91Top-85
❑ 91TopDesS-85
❑ 91TopMic-85
❑ 91TopTif-85
❑ 91Ult-228
❑ 91UppDec-485
❑ 92Bow-295
❑ 92Don-316
❑ 92Fle-221
❑ 92OPC-650
❑ 92PanSti-139
❑ 92Pin-425
❑ 92Sco-565
❑ 92StaClu-214
❑ 92Top-650
❑ 92TopGol-650
❑ 92TopGolW-650
❑ 92TopMic-650
❑ 92Ult-99
❑ 92UppDec-139
❑ 92UppDec-644
❑ 92YanWIZ8-8
❑ 93BluJayDM-2
❑ 95AstMot-28
❑ 96BluJayB-2
❑ 97BluJayS-34
❑ 99SpoIllGotG-63
❑ 99SpoIllGotGA-4

Barfield, John D.
❑ 87PorChaRP-5
❑ 88TexLeaAGS-17
❑ 88TulDriTI-14
❑ 89BlaYNPRWLU-12
❑ 89OklCit8C-2
❑ 89OklCit8P-1518
❑ 90CMC-159
❑ 90OklCit8C-9
❑ 90OklCit8P-424
❑ 90ProAAAF-670
❑ 90TopDeb89-8
❑ 91Don-688
❑ 91FleUpd-58
❑ 91OPC-428
❑ 91RanMot-13
❑ 91Sco-573
❑ 91Top-428
❑ 91TopDesS-428
❑ 91TopMic-428
❑ 91TopTif-428
❑ 91UppDec-629
❑ 92Don-168
❑ 92OklCit8F-1906
❑ 92Sco-683
❑ 92StaClu-364
❑ 92UppDec-691
❑ 93RanKee-62
❑ 94SanAntMF-2458
❑ 94VenLinU-153

Barfoot, Clyde R.
❑ 25Zee-147
❑ 28Zee-24
❑ 29Zee-13
❑ 30Zee-23

Bargar, Greg (Gregory R.)
❑ 80MemChiT-5
❑ 83MemChiT-20
❑ 83WicAerDS-4
❑ 84IndIndTI-13
❑ 84IndIndTI-18
❑ 84Nes792-474
❑ 84OPC-292
❑ 84Top-474
❑ 84TopTif-474
❑ 85IndIndTI-13
❑ 86CarTeal-3
❑ 87LouRedTI-4
❑ 88LouRedBTI-9

Bargas, Rob
❑ 91WesPalBEC-18
❑ 91WesPalBEP-1234

Barger, Bob
❑ 76WauMetT-2

Barger, Cy (Eros Bolivar)
❑ 09T206-395
❑ 10CouT21-74
❑ 10DomDisP-6
❑ 10SweCapPP-69
❑ 11HelSta-82
❑ 11PinT-5-463
❑ 11PloCanE-3
❑ 11S74Sil-48
❑ 11SpoLifCW-15
❑ 11SpoLifM-148
❑ 11T205-8A
❑ 11T205-8B
❑ 12HasTriFT-3A
❑ 12HasTriFT-61A
❑ 12T207-7
❑ 14CraJacE-141
❑ 14PieStaT-5
❑ 15CraJacE-141
❑ 72ClaCar-76

Barger, David W.
❑ 89CarNewE-26

Barger, Mike
❑ 93BelMarCB-3
❑ 93BelMarF-3221
❑ 94AppFoxC-2
❑ 94AppFoxFl-1065
❑ 96PorCitRB-6

Barger, Vince
❑ 85DurBulT-2

Bargerhuff, Brian
❑ 83CliGiaF-17
❑ 86ChaLooP-3

Bargfeldt, John
❑ 79QuaCitCT-19

Barham, Wayne
❑ 14Zee-100

Barillari, Al
❑ 52LavPro-50

Bark, Brian
❑ 88CapCodPPaLP-114
❑ 90PulBraB-1
❑ 90PulBraP-3101
❑ 91DurBulC-2
❑ 91DurBulP-1535
❑ 92GreBraF-1147
❑ 92GreBraS-227
❑ 92SkyAA F-97
❑ 93RicBraBB-10
❑ 93RicBraF-176
❑ 93RicBraP-3
❑ 93RicBraRC-12
❑ 93RicBraRC-5
❑ 94RicBraF-2837
❑ 95RicBraRC-1
❑ 96NorTidB-8

Barker, Bob
❑ 87AlbYanP-3

Barker, Glen
❑ 93NiaFalRF-3400
❑ 94FayGenC-3
❑ 94FayGenF-2159
❑ 95JacSunTI-1
❑ 96JacSunB-5
❑ 97TolMudHB-5
❑ 98JacSunM-2
❑ 99DumSet-103
❑ 99FleMys-103
❑ 99FleMysM-103
❑ 99SkyPre-234
❑ 99SkyPre-234
❑ 99SkyPreR-234
❑ 99SkyPreR-234

Barker, Jeff
❑ 94JamJamC-3
❑ 94JamJamF-3957

Barker, Jeff 70's
❑ 78HolMilT-1

Barker, Kevin
❑ 96OgdRapTI-4
❑ 97CalLeaTP-25
❑ 97StoPor-5
❑ 98BesAutSS-2
❑ 98Bow-418
❑ 98BowChr-418
❑ 98BowChrGA-418
❑ 98BowChrGAR-418
❑ 98BowChrI-418
❑ 98BowChrIR-418
❑ 98BowChrR-418
❑ 98BowGolA-418
❑ 98BowInt-418
❑ 98El PasDG-2
❑ 98LouRedQ-28
❑ 98SP MinPE-74
❑ 98SPMin-74
❑ 98TexLeaTPG-2
❑ 99BasAmeTP-9
❑ 99BasAmeTPG-9
❑ 99Bow-97
❑ 99BowChr-97
❑ 99BowChrG-97
❑ 99BowChrGR-97
❑ 99BowChrI-97
❑ 99BowChrIR-97
❑ 99BowChrR-97
❑ 99BowGol-97
❑ 99BowInt-97
❑ 99JustheS-7
❑ 99JustheSJB-7
❑ 99SP SigAuto-KB
❑ 99SP SigAutoG-KB
❑ 99SPSig-79
❑ 99UppDec-406
❑ 99UppDecEL1-406
❑ 99UppDecEL2-406

Barker, Len (Leonard H.)
❑ 74GasRanT-4
❑ 76SacSolC-20
❑ 76VenLeaS-93
❑ 77Top-489
❑ 77TucTorC-40
❑ 78RanBurK-9
❑ 78SSP270-91
❑ 78Top-634
❑ 79OPC-40
❑ 79Top-94
❑ 80IndTeal-3
❑ 80Top-227
❑ 81AllGamPI-74
❑ 81Don-320
❑ 81Fle-408
❑ 81OPC-3
❑ 81Top-6
❑ 81Top-432
❑ 81TopSti-5
❑ 81TopSti-72
❑ 82Don-6
❑ 82Don-137
❑ 82Fle-360
❑ 82Fle-639
❑ 82FleSta-200
❑ 82Ind-4
❑ 82IndWhe-12
❑ 82Kel-37
❑ 82OPC-360
❑ 82Top-166
❑ 82Top-360
❑ 82TopSti-12
❑ 82TopSti-113
❑ 82TopSti-178
❑ 83Don-111
❑ 83Fle-402
❑ 83Fle-642
❑ 83FleSta-9
❑ 83FleSti-245
❑ 83IndPos-5
❑ 83IndWhe-5
❑ 83Kel-33
❑ 83OPC-120
❑ 83Top-120
❑ 83TopSti-57
❑ 84BraPol-39
❑ 84Don-443
❑ 84Fle-170
❑ 84Nes792-614
❑ 84OPC-309
❑ 84raPho-2
❑ 84Top-614
❑ 84TopTif-614
❑ 85BraHos-2
❑ 85BraPol-39
❑ 85Don-165
❑ 85Fle-318
❑ 85Top-557
❑ 85TopTif-557
❑ 86Don-409
❑ 86Fle-507
❑ 86IndIndTI-20
❑ 86Top-24
❑ 86TopTif-24
❑ 91PacSenL-153
❑ 93RanKee-63
❑ 94BreMilB-7

Barker, Marvin
❑ 91PomBlaBPB-2

Barker, Ray (Raymond H.)
❑ 61Top-428
❑ 65Top-546
❑ 66Top-323
❑ 66TopVen-323
❑ 67Top-583
❑ 81TCM60I-314
❑ 91OriCro-21
❑ 92YanWIZ6-6

Barker, Richard
❑ 94HunCubC-2
❑ 94HunCubF-3542
❑ 95RocCubTI-27
❑ 96DayCubB-4
❑ 98WesTenDJM-2

Barker, Tim (Timothy C.)
❑ 86TamTarP-2
❑ 87BelBreP-17
❑ 88ChaRaiP-1221
❑ 89GreFalDSP-14
❑ 90BakDodCLC-255
❑ 90CalLeaACLC-8
❑ 91LinDriAA-529
❑ 91SanAntMLD-529
❑ 92SanAntMF-3980
❑ 92SanAntMS-554
❑ 92SkyAA F-243
❑ 93OttLynF-2440
❑ 94NewOrlZF-1473
❑ 96ColCliB-2
❑ 97ColCliB-5
❑ 97ColCliD-2
❑ 98ColSprSS-23

Barker, Timothy N..
❑ 91SanAntMP-2980

Barkett, Andy
❑ 93BazTeaU-3
❑ 93TopTra-93T
❑ 95ButCopKtl-30
❑ 97TulDriTI-2

Barkley, Brian
❑ 96BesAutS-8
❑ 96Bow-240
❑ 96BowFoi-240
❑ 96TreThuB-5
❑ 97TreThuB-6
❑ 98PawRedSQ-7
❑ 99SpoIll-65

Barkley, Charles
❑ 91UppDecS-2

Barkley, Jeff
❑ 83WatIndF-20
❑ 84MaiGuiT-15
❑ 85IndPol-49
❑ 85MaiGuiT-1
❑ 86Top-567
❑ 86TopTif-567

Barkley, Red
❑ 90DodTar-33

Barkley, Sam (Samuel E.)
❑ 87BucN28-84
❑ 87BucN28-93
❑ 87OldJudN-20

Barksdale, Joey
❑ 95MicBatCTI-2
❑ 96SarRedSB-6

Barksdale, Shane
❑ 97AubDouTI-28
❑ 97KisCob-3

Barley, Ned
❑ 90MedHatBJB-12

Barlick, Al
❑ 55Bow-265
❑ 80PerHaloFP-201
❑ 80PerHaloFPS-64
❑ 90PerGreM-86
❑ 90T/MUmp-71

Barling, Glenn
❑ 82CliGiaF-6

Barlok, Todd
❑ 95GreFalDTI-29
❑ 96VerBeaDB-6
❑ 97SanBerS-20

Barlow, Andy
❑ 90JamExpP-31

Barlow, Clem
❑ 91BelMarCB-1
❑ 91BelMarP-3678

Barlow, Ethan
❑ 96VerExpB-8

Barlow, Mike
❑ 76HouAstP-2
❑ 76SSP-298
❑ 77SalLakCGC-21
❑ 78AngFamF-2
❑ 78SalLakCGC-21
❑ 78Top-429
❑ 80SyrChiT-13
❑ 80SyrChiTI-4
❑ 80Top-312
❑ 81OPC-77
❑ 81Top-77
❑ 82SyrChiT-1
❑ 82SyrChiTI-4

Barlow, Ricky
❑ 86GleFalTP-1
❑ 87TolMudHP-9
❑ 87TolMudHT-19

Barlow, Stuart
❑ 91SydWavF-16

Barna, Babe (Herbert Paul)
❑ 78HalHalR-7

Barnard, Alan
❑ 90LSUTigA-8

Barnard, Jeff
❑ 81AppFoxT-2

Barnard, Steve
❑ 85PriWilPT-11

Barnard, Tom
❑ 88WatPirP-32
❑ 92WelPirC-30
❑ 92WelPirF-1341
❑ 98EriSeaWM-29

Barnden, Miles
❑ 93AlbPolCB-2
❑ 93AusFut-95
❑ 93BluOriC-3
❑ 93BluOriF-4130
❑ 94AlbPolC-3
❑ 94AlbPolF-2241
❑ 94OriPro-5

Barndollar, Jeff
❑ 98LetBlaDG-3

Barner, Doug
❑ 97ChaRivDG-4

Barnes, Alan
❑ 80ElmPioRST-1

Barnes, Brian
❑ 88CapCodPPaLP-130
❑ 90Bes-261
❑ 90CMC-660
❑ 90JacExpB-14
❑ 90JacExpP-1365
❑ 90ProAaA-36
❑ 91Bow-438
❑ 91ClaGam-8
❑ 91Don-415
❑ 91ExpPos-1
❑ 91OPC-211
❑ 91OPCPre-4
❑ 91Sco-708
❑ 91ScoRoo-10
❑ 91StaClu-114
❑ 91Stu-192
❑ 91Top-211
❑ 91TopDeb90-11
❑ 91TopDesS-211
❑ 91TopMic-211

❑ 91TopTif-211
❑ 91UppDec-12
❑ 92Bow-501
❑ 92Don-117
❑ 92ExpDonD-2B
❑ 92Fle-473
❑ 92IndIndS-177
❑ 92OPC-73
❑ 92OPCPre-52
❑ 92Sco-715
❑ 92Sco100RS-78
❑ 92SkyAAAF-85
❑ 92StaClu-549
❑ 92Top-73
❑ 92TopGol-73
❑ 92TopGolW-73
❑ 92TopMic-73
❑ 92UppDec-361
❑ 93Don-88
❑ 93ExpPosN-3
❑ 93Fle-457
❑ 93OPC-249
❑ 93PacSpa-181
❑ 93StaClu-500
❑ 93StaCluFDI-500
❑ 93StaCluMOP-500
❑ 93Top-112
❑ 93TopGol-112
❑ 93TopInaM-112
❑ 93TopInaR-112
❑ 93TopMic-112
❑ 93UppDec-214
❑ 93UppDecGold-214
❑ 94Fle-532
❑ 94Pac-373
❑ 94Sco-289
❑ 94ScoGolR-289
❑ 94Top-694
❑ 94TopGol-694
❑ 94TopSpa-694
❑ 97TolMudHB-6
❑ 98MemRedG-3

Barnes, Chris
❑ 88CapCodPPaLP-115

Barnes, Colin
❑ 91SydWavF-8

Barnes, Craig
❑ 75LafDriT-9

Barnes, Donald L.
❑ 41BroW75-3

Barnes, Frank
❑ 60Top-538
❑ 93NegLeaRL2-1

Barnes, Harry
❑ 92NegLeaRLI-2

Barnes, Jeff
❑ 91MidAngOHP-3
❑ 92ModA'sC-12

Barnes, Jesse L.
❑ 19W514-120
❑ 20W516-12
❑ 20W52-4
❑ 21KoBreWSI-2
❑ 22E120-182
❑ 22W572-5
❑ 22W573-8
❑ 22W575-6
❑ 23MapCriV-1
❑ 23W503-22
❑ 23W515-31
❑ 23W551-3
❑ 23WilChoV-8
❑ 25Exh-2
❑ 26SpoComoA-5
❑ 90DodTar-34
❑ 92ConTSN-355

Barnes, John S.
❑ 91HigSchPLS-10
❑ 91HigSchPLS-18
❑ 92ChaRaiC-18
❑ 97Bes-55
❑ 97Bow-422
❑ 97BowChr-282
❑ 97BowChrI-282
❑ 97BowChrIR-282
❑ 97BowChrR-282
❑ 97BowInt-422
❑ 97HarSen-27
❑ 97MicBatC-6
❑ 98Bes-54
❑ 98Bow-363
❑ 98BowChr-363
❑ 98BowChrGA-363
❑ 98BowChrGAR-363
❑ 98BowChrI-363
❑ 98BowChrIR-363
❑ 98BowChrR-363
❑ 98BowGolA-363
❑ 98BowInt-363
❑ 98Top-263
❑ 98TopChr-263
❑ 98TopChrR-263
❑ 98TopDevR-263
❑ 98TopDia-263
❑ 98TopMiniC-263
❑ 98TreThuM-6

Barnes, JoJo
❑ 75OakOak2A-2

Barnes, Jon
❑ 91ClaDraP-47
❑ 91FroRowDP-20
❑ 91FroRowDPG-20
❑ 91FroRowDPS-20
❑ 92ChaRaiF-112
❑ 92StaCluD-12
❑ 93WatDiaC-5
❑ 93WatDiaF-1759
❑ 94RanCucQC-4
❑ 94RanCucQF-1627

Barnes, Keith
❑ 94AshTouC-2
❑ 94AshTouF-1771
❑ 95AshTouUTI-31
❑ 95SalAvaTI-4
❑ 96SalAvaB-2

Barnes, Kelvin
❑ 96RocCubTI-1

Barnes, Larry
❑ 94SigRooDP-57
❑ 94SigRooDPS-57
❑ 94StaCluDP-40
❑ 94StaCluDPFDI-40
❑ 94TopTra-38T
❑ 96OgdRapTI-43
❑ 97BelSnaB-8

Barnes, Larry Richard
❑ 96CedRapKTI-4
❑ 96MidLeaAB-15
❑ 97Bow-322
❑ 97BowChr-221
❑ 97BowChrI-221
❑ 97BowChrIR-221
❑ 97BowChrR-221
❑ 97BowInt-322
❑ 97CalLeaTP-7
❑ 97LakElsSG-3
❑ 98LakElsSG-2
❑ 98SP MinPE-13
❑ 98SPMin-13

Barnes, Lute (Luther Owen)
❑ 91MetWIZ-24

Barnes, Mike
❑ 80BufBisT-1

Barnes, Red (Emile Deering)
❑ 28StaPlaCE-2
❑ 30WhiSoxTI-2
❑ 93ConTSN-984

Barnes, Richard
❑ 78KnoKnoST-2
❑ 79KnoKnoST-5
❑ 80IowOakP-1
❑ 81EdmTraRR-10
❑ 82EdmTraT-19
❑ 84Don-608
❑ 84MaiGuiT-6

Barnes, Skeeter (William Henry)
❑ 79NaSouTI-4
❑ 80WatRedT-15
❑ 81IndIndTI-29
❑ 82WatRedT-13
❑ 83IndIndTI-31
❑ 84WicAerRD-16
❑ 85Don-530
❑ 85ExpPos-1
❑ 86IndIndTI-16
❑ 88BufBisC-23
❑ 88BufBisP-1487
❑ 88NasSouTI-2
❑ 89NasSouC-13
❑ 89NasSouP-1289
❑ 89NasSouTI-1
❑ 89TriAAAP-AAA15
❑ 90CMC-138
❑ 90NasSouC-13
❑ 90NasSouP-244
❑ 90ProAAAF-556
❑ 90TriAAAC-6
❑ 91LinDriAAA-578
❑ 91TolMudHLD-578
❑ 91TolMudHP-1942
❑ 91TopTra-5T
❑ 91TopTraT-5T
❑ 92Don-749
❑ 92OPC-221
❑ 92Pin-218
❑ 92Sco-569
❑ 92StaClu-585
❑ 92TigKro-2
❑ 92Top-221
❑ 92TopGol-221
❑ 92TopGolW-221
❑ 92TopMic-221
❑ 92Ult-358
❑ 92UppDec-470
❑ 93Don-437
❑ 93Fle-603
❑ 93PacSpa-441
❑ 93PanSti-121
❑ 93StaClu-389
❑ 93StaCluFDI-389
❑ 93StaCluMOP-389
❑ 93TigGat-2
❑ 93Top-26
❑ 93TopGol-26
❑ 93TopInaM-26
❑ 93TopInaR-26
❑ 93TopMic-26
❑ 94Fle-124
❑ 94Pac-210
❑ 94Sco-232
❑ 94ScoGolR-232
❑ 94StaClu-50
❑ 94StaCluFDI-50
❑ 94StaCluGR-50
❑ 94StaCluMOP-50
❑ 94TolMudHF-1036
❑ 94Top-561
❑ 94TopGol-561
❑ 94TopSpa-561
❑ 95Pac-148
❑ 95TolMudHTI-2
❑ 96TolMudHB-3
❑ 97WesMicW-2
❑ 98WesMicWM-3

Barnes, Tom
❑ 52LavPro-90

Barnes, Virgil
❑ 23W515-31
❑ 28Exh-17

Barnett, Brian
❑ 97St.CatSB-7
❑ 98St.CatSM-3

Barnett, Larry
❑ 76TCMUmp-1
❑ 88T/MUmp-7
❑ 89T/MUmp-5
❑ 89T/MUmp-60
❑ 90T/MUmp-5

Barnett, Marty
❑ 95BatCliTI-3
❑ 96HicCraB-28
❑ 98ReaPhiM-12
❑ 98ReaPhiUM-4

Barnett, Mike
❑ 90SouBenWSB-26
❑ 90SouBenWSGS-30
❑ 91SarWhiSC-28
❑ 91SarWhiSP-1130
❑ 92SarWhiSCB-29
❑ 92SarWhiSF-225
❑ 93BirBarF-1208
❑ 94BirBarC-28
❑ 94BirBarF-638
❑ 98TusSidM-3

Barnett, Rick
❑ 93BluOriF-4115

Barnette, Lynn
❑ 98OrlRayM-27

Barney, Ed (Edmund J.)
❑ 22Zee-117
❑ 23Zee-156

Barney, Rex
❑ 47HomBon-1
❑ 48Bow-41
❑ 48DodTeal-1
❑ 49Bow-61
❑ 49EurSta-29
❑ 50Bow-76
❑ 51Bow-153
❑ 90BalOriP-2
❑ 90DodTar-35
❑ 91DodRinP4-8
❑ 95BalOriP-5

Barnhart, Clyde Lee
❑ 21Exh-8
❑ 21Nei-108
❑ 22E120-212
❑ 27AmeCarE126-2
❑ 79DiaGre-353

Barnhart, Rick
❑ 79WatIndT-11
❑ 79WauTimT-13
❑ 80WatIndT-13

Barnhill, Dave
❑ 78HalHalR-18
❑ 86NegLeaF-101

Barnhouse, Scott
❑ 83WauTimF-18

Barniak, Jim
❑ 90PhiTas-36

Barnicle, George B.
❑ 77TCMTheWY-63

Barnicle, Ted
❑ 76CedRapGT-3
❑ 79KnoKnoST-21
❑ 80GleFalWSBT-11
❑ 80GleFalWSCT-19

Barnie, Billy (William H.)
❑ 87OldJudN-21
❑ 90DodTar-36

Barnowski, Ed (Edward A.)
❑ 66Top-442
❑ 67Top-507
❑ 91OriCro-22

Barns, Jeff
❑ 88PalSprACLC-100
❑ 88PalSprAP-1451
❑ 89MidAngGS-5
❑ 90MidAngGS-9
❑ 90TexLeaAGS-11
❑ 91LinDriAA-427
❑ 91MidAngLD-427
❑ 91MidAngP-438
❑ 92ModA'sF-3904
❑ 93ModA'sC-2
❑ 93ModA'sF-804
❑ 94MidAngF-2454
❑ 94MidAngOHP-1
❑ 95MidAngOHP-3
❑ 95MidAngTI-3
❑ 96MidAngB-3
❑ 96MidAngOHP-2
❑ 97WicWra-27

Barnsby, Scott
❑ 98YakBeaG-4

Barnwell, Rich (Richard)
❑ 90Ft.LauYS-1
❑ 91Ft.LauYC-24
❑ 91Ft.LauYP-2438
❑ 92AlbYanF-2236
❑ 92AlbYanSk-2
❑ 93AlbYanF-2173
❑ 94ColCliF-2962

Barnwell, Rob
❑ 87WatPirP-21

Barojas, Salome
❑ 83Don-67
❑ 83Fle-230
❑ 83FleSti-154
❑ 83WhiSoxTV-30
❑ 84Don-570
❑ 84Fle-53
❑ 84WhiSoxTV-5
❑ 85Don-605
❑ 85Fle-482
❑ 85MarMot-19

Baron, Jimmy
❑ 93StaCluM-134
❑ 93Top-538
❑ 93TopGol-538
❑ 93TopInaM-538
❑ 93TopInaR-538
❑ 93TopMic-538
❑ 94SprSulC-3
❑ 94SprSulF-2029
❑ 95IdaFalBTI-20
❑ 96HilStaHWB-22
❑ 96RanCucQB-6
❑ 97RanCucQG-2
❑ 98NorNavQ-3

Baron, Sean
❑ 88BurIndP-1778

Barone, Dick (Richard A.)
❑ 57JetPos-1
❑ 61UniOil-SD1
❑ 77PirTCM1WC-38

Barons, Bismarck
❑ 93NegLeaRL2-58

Barr, Bob
❑ 76WatRoyT-1

Barr, Bob (Robert A.)
❑ 90DodTar-897

Barr, Jim (James Leland)
❑ 72OPC-232
❑ 72Top-232
❑ 73OPC-387
❑ 73Top-387
❑ 74OPC-233
❑ 74Top-233
❑ 75GiaTeal-1
❑ 75Hos-13
❑ 75HosTwi-13
❑ 75OPC-107
❑ 75Top-107
❑ 75TopMin-107
❑ 76OPC-308
❑ 76SanFraGP-3
❑ 76SSP-92
❑ 76Top-308
❑ 77BurCheD-103
❑ 77Gia-2
❑ 77GiaTeal-4
❑ 77Hos-83
❑ 77OPC-119
❑ 77Top-609
❑ 78GiaTeal-3
❑ 78OPC-19
❑ 78Top-62
❑ 79Top-461
❑ 80OPC-275
❑ 80Top-529
❑ 81Don-412
❑ 81Fle-287
❑ 81Top-717
❑ 82Gia25tATI-1
❑ 83Don-398
❑ 83Fle-252
❑ 83GiaPos-1
❑ 83Top-133
❑ 84Don-79
❑ 84Fle-365
❑ 84Nes792-282
❑ 84Top-282
❑ 84TopTif-282
❑ 88AlaGolAA60TI-9

Barr, Steve (Steven Charles)
❑ 76OPC-595
❑ 76Top-595
❑ 76VenLeaS-80
❑ 93RanKee-64

Barr, Tim
❑ 78GreBraT-3
❑ 80OrlTwiT-2

Barr, Tucker
❑ 97QuaCitRBB-3
❑ 98KisCobQ-8

Barragan, Cuno (Facundo A.)
❑ 59DarFar-1
❑ 62Top-66
❑ 62TopVen-66
❑ 63Top-557

Barragan, Gerry
❑ 87MadMusP-1
❑ 87MadMusP-12
❑ 88ModA'sCLC-73

Barragan, Jimmy (Jaime)
❑ 87UtiBluSP-27
❑ 88SpaPhiP-1036
❑ 88SpaPhiS-17
❑ 89ClePhiS-1
❑ 90ClePhiS-1

Barranca, German
❑ 75WatRoyT-1A
❑ 75WatRoyT-1B
❑ 76WatRoyT-2
❑ 77JacSunT-2
❑ 80OmaRoyP-2
❑ 81IndIndTI-25
❑ 83EvaTriT-25
❑ 84OklCit8T-24
❑ 85WatIndT-17

Barranco, Vince
❑ 88BurIndP-1777

Barreiro, Efrain
❑ 90AshTouC-1
❑ 90AubAstB-5
❑ 90AubAstP-3413
❑ 91AshTouP-559

Barreiro, Fernando
❑ 91SprCarC-5
❑ 91SprCarP-732

Barrenkamp, William
❑ 14Zee-29

Barrera, Nelson
❑ 85BufBisT-7

Barrera, Ruben
❑ 95GreFalDTI-34

Barreto, Miguel
❑ 76VenLeaS-160
❑ 80VenLeaS-147

Barreto, Saul
❑ 87GasRanP-6
❑ 88BlaYNPRWL-3

Barreto, Simon
❑ 76VenLeaS-22

Barrett, Bessie
❑ 08AllLadBC-1

Barrett, Bill (William J.)
❑ 93ConTSN-977

Barrett, Bob (Robert S.)
❑ 90DodTar-37

Barrett, Charles
❑ 77LodDodT-1

Barrett, Dick
❑ 43CubTeal-1
❑ 47CenFlo-1
❑ 50W720HolS-3

Barrett, Jimmy (James E.)
❑ 03BreE10-3
❑ 04FanCraAL-2
❑ 11MecDFT-32
❑ 11SpoLifCW-16
❑ 74CapPub-70

Barrett, Johnny (John Joseph)
❑ 47PadTeal-1
❑ 77TCMTheWY-37
❑ 83TCMPla1944-26

Barrett, Keith
❑ 87BelMarL-20

Barrett, Kewpie
❑ 47SigOil-74

Barrett, Mark
❑ 94SpoIndC-2
❑ 94SpoIndF-3313

Barrett, Marty (Martin Glen)
❑ 81PawRedST-14
❑ 83PawRedST-14
❑ 84FleUpd-8
❑ 84Nes792-683
❑ 84Top-683
❑ 84TopTif-683
❑ 85AllGamPI-10
❑ 85Don-127
❑ 85Fle-150
❑ 85Lea-229
❑ 85Top-298
❑ 85TopSti-219
❑ 85TopTif-298
❑ 86Don-294
❑ 86Fle-340
❑ 86Lea-169
❑ 86OPC-314
❑ 86Top-734
❑ 86TopSti-250
❑ 86TopTif-734
❑ 87ClaGam-61
❑ 87Don-523
❑ 87DonOpeD-188
❑ 87Fle-27
❑ 87FleAwaW-1
❑ 87FleGlo-27
❑ 87FleGlo-WS6
❑ 87FleLimE-2
❑ 87FleStiC-5
❑ 87FleWorS-6
❑ 87Lea-165
❑ 87OPC-39
❑ 87RedSoxP-1
❑ 87RedSoxSAP-1
❑ 87SevCoi-M2
❑ 87Spo-112
❑ 87Spo-182
❑ 87SpoTeaP-9
❑ 87Top-39
❑ 87TopSti-18
❑ 87TopTif-39
❑ 87Woo-17
❑ 88Don-276
❑ 88DonBasB-9

❑ 88DonTeaBRS-276
❑ 88Fle-343
❑ 88FleGlo-343
❑ 88Lea-141
❑ 88OPC-338
❑ 88PanSti-28
❑ 88Sco-155
❑ 88ScoGlo-155
❑ 88Spo-157
❑ 88StaLinRS-1
❑ 88Top-525
❑ 88TopBig-54
❑ 88TopSti-248
❑ 88TopTif-525
❑ 89Bow-28
❑ 89BowTif-28
❑ 89Don-184
❑ 89DonBasB-252
❑ 89Fle-78
❑ 89FleGlo-78
❑ 89OPC-155
❑ 89PanSti-276
❑ 89Sco-63
❑ 89Spo-198
❑ 89Top-155
❑ 89TopBig-278
❑ 89TopSti-257
❑ 89TopTif-155
❑ 89TVSpoM-66
❑ 89UppDec-173
❑ 90Bow-282
❑ 90BowTif-282
❑ 90Don-240
❑ 90Fle-266
❑ 90FleCan-266
❑ 90OPC-355
❑ 90PanSti-15
❑ 90PubIntS-446
❑ 90RedSoxP-1
❑ 90RedSoxP-20
❑ 90Sco-15
❑ 90Top-355
❑ 90TopBig-44
❑ 90TopSti-256
❑ 90TopTif-355
❑ 90TopTVRS-21
❑ 90UppDec-133
❑ 91Bow-648
❑ 91Fle-84
❑ 91Lea-474
❑ 91OPC-496
❑ 91PadMag-10
❑ 91Sco-228
❑ 91Top-496
❑ 91TopDesS-496
❑ 91TopMic-496
❑ 91TopTif-496
❑ 91UppDec-90
❑ 93LasVegSF-961
❑ 94LasVegSF-884
❑ 95RanCucQT-17

Barrett, Michael
❑ 95Bes-124
❑ 95BowBes-X7
❑ 95BowBesR-X7
❑ 95TopTra-25T
❑ 96Bow-249
❑ 96BowFoi-249
❑ 96DelShoB-8
❑ 96HonShaHWB-15
❑ 96Top-15
❑ 96TopPowB-15
❑ 97Bow-122
❑ 97BowChr-136
❑ 97BowChrI-136
❑ 97BowChrIR-136
❑ 97BowChrR-136
❑ 97BowInt-122
❑ 97FloStaLTPB-29
❑ 98AriFalLTP-11
❑ 98arSenW1-3
❑ 98BesDiaB-12
❑ 98BesNumOP-5
❑ 98Bow-79
❑ 98BowChr-79
❑ 98BowChrGA-79
❑ 98BowChrGAR-79
❑ 98BowChrI-79
❑ 98BowChrIR-79
❑ 98BowChrR-79
❑ 98BowGolA-79
❑ 98BowInt-79
❑ 98DonSig-137
❑ 98DonSigP-137
❑ 98EasLeaTPM-2
❑ 98FleUpd-U36
❑ 98HarSenM-3
❑ 98LeaRS-330
❑ 98LeaRSLHolo-330
❑ 98LeaRSLong-330
❑ 98LeaRTrue-330
❑ 99199Fin-148
❑ 99BasAmeTPA-2
❑ 99Bow-123
❑ 99BowAut-BA35
❑ 99BowBes-110
❑ 99BowBesAR-110
❑ 99BowBesR-110
❑ 99BowBesRLRA-RA2
❑ 99BowBesRLRGUB-RB2
❑ 99BowBesRLRGWJ-RJ2
❑ 99BowChr-123
❑ 99BowChrG-123
❑ 99BowChrGR-123
❑ 99BowChrI-123
❑ 99BowChrIR-123
❑ 99BowChrR-123
❑ 99BowChrSC-SC21
❑ 99BowChrSCR-SC21
❑ 99BowGol-123
❑ 99BowInt-123
❑ 99BowScoC-SC21
❑ 99CroRoyB-85
❑ 99CroRoyL-85
❑ 99CroRoyOD-85
❑ 99DumSet-140
❑ 99FinFutF-FF8
❑ 99FinGolRef-148
❑ 99FinRef-148
❑ 99FlaShoLeg1-43
❑ 99FlaShoLeg2-43
❑ 99FlaShoLeg3-43
❑ 99FlaShoLegM1-43
❑ 99FlaShoLegM2-43
❑ 99FlaShoLegM3-43
❑ 99FlaShoR1-43
❑ 99FlaShoR2-43
❑ 99FlaShoR3-43
❑ 99Fle-331
❑ 99FleBri-168
❑ 99FleBri2G-168
❑ 99FleBriBlu-168
❑ 99FleBriGol-168
❑ 99FleMys-140
❑ 99FleMysFI-2
❑ 99FleMysM-140
❑ 99FleSta9-331
❑ 99FleWarT-331
❑ 99JustheS-8
❑ 99JustheSAC-3
❑ 99JustheSAD-3
❑ 99JustheSJB-8
❑ 99JustheSJD-1
❑ 99JustheSJN-2
❑ 99PacInv-89
❑ 99PacInvOD-89
❑ 99PacInvPB-89
❑ 99PacOme-143
❑ 99PacOmeC-143
❑ 99PacOmeG-143
❑ 99PacOmePB-143
❑ 99Rev-83
❑ 99RevPremDate-83
❑ 99RevRet-83
❑ 99RevShaSS-83
❑ 99SkyMolM-119
❑ 99SkyMolMF-19
❑ 99SkyMolMFS-19
❑ 99SkyMolMFT-19
❑ 99SkyMolMX-119
❑ 99SkyPre-263
❑ 99SkyPre-263
❑ 99SkyPreA-3
❑ 99SkyPreABlue-3
❑ 99SkyPreDD-12
❑ 99SkyPreR-263
❑ 99SkyPreR-263
❑ 99SP Aut-109
❑ 99SP SigAuto-MB
❑ 99SP SigAutoG-MB
❑ 99SP TopP-14
❑ 99SP TopPPE-14
❑ 99SPSig-57
❑ 99SPx-106
❑ 99SPxFinR-106
❑ 99SPxFinS-106
❑ 99StaClu-349
❑ 99StaCluFDI-349
❑ 99StaCluOoaK-349
❑ 99StaCluPP-349
❑ 99TeaBesR-1
❑ 99TeaBesRA-2
❑ 99Top-208
❑ 99TopChr-208
❑ 99TopChrR-208
❑ 99TopGal-142
❑ 99TopGalPP-142
❑ 99TopGalPPI-142
❑ 99TopSta-25
❑ 99TopSta1Foil-25
❑ 99TopSta2Foil-25
❑ 99TopStaBF-BF4
❑ 99TopStaBFFoil-BF4
❑ 99TopStaFoil-25
❑ 99TopStaOS-25
❑ 99TopStaTS-25
❑ 99UD Cho-8
❑ 99UD ChoPCR-8
❑ 99UppDec-273
❑ 99UppDecCf7-45
❑ 99UppDecCf7-87
❑ 99UppDecCo7CE-45
❑ 99UppDecCo7CE-87
❑ 99UppDecE-116
❑ 99UppDecEFXG-116
❑ 99UppDecEL1-273
❑ 99UppDecEL2-273
❑ 99UppDecERE-R9
❑ 99UppDecEREFXG-R9
❑ 99UppDecEUA-MB
❑ 99UppDecM-128
❑ 99UppDecMGS-128
❑ 99UppDecMHFS-128
❑ 99UppDecMSS-128
❑ 99UppDecO-79
❑ 99UppDecOSO-79
❑ 99UppDecR-51
❑ 99UppDecRG-51
❑ 99UppDecROSS-S23
❑ 99UppDecROSS-S23
❑ 99UppDecRP-51
❑ 99Vic-236

Barrett, Red (Charles H.)
❑ 38CloFotW-5
❑ 39ExhSal-3
❑ 46SeaSLP-2
❑ 47TipTop-76
❑ 49Bow-213
❑ 49EurSta-4
❑ 52Par-14
❑ 77TCMTheWY-23
❑ 79DiaGre-213
❑ 83Car194T-58
❑ 83TCMPla1945-28
❑ 95ConTSN-1403

Barrett, Scott
❑ 93EveGiaC-3
❑ 93EveGiaF-3770
❑ 98AubDouTI-2
❑ 99TeaBesR-2
❑ 99TeaBesRG-2
❑ 99TeaBesRS-2

Barrett, Tim
❑ 86IndIndTI-34
❑ 87IndIndTI-9
❑ 88IndIndC-5
❑ 88IndIndP-502
❑ 89IndIndC-1
❑ 89IndIndP-1229

Barrett, Tom
❑ 84NasSouTI-2
❑ 85ColCliP-1
❑ 85ColCliT-13
❑ 86AlbYanT-5
❑ 87ReaPhiP-7
❑ 88BlaYNPRWL-145
❑ 88MaiPhiC-16
❑ 88MaiPhiP-284
❑ 88PhiTas-27
❑ 88TriAAC-18
❑ 89BlaYNPRWL-57
❑ 89ScrRedBC-11
❑ 89ScrRedBP-725
❑ 89Top-653
❑ 89TopBig-177
❑ 89TopTif-653
❑ 90AlbDecGB-15
❑ 90Sco-633A
❑ 90Sco-633B
❑ 91LinDriAAA-352
❑ 91PawRedSDD-2
❑ 91PawRedSLD-352
❑ 91PawRedSP-44
❑ 92PawRedSF-928
❑ 92PawRedSS-352
❑ 93TucTorF-3063
❑ 94NewBriRSF-666
❑ 96MicBatCB-1
❑ 97DunDonPPS-2

Barretto, Saul M.
❑ 88GasRanP-1022

Barrick, Andy
❑ 88BatCliP-1687

Barrick, Troy
❑ 94NewJerCC-2
❑ 94NewJerCF-3404
❑ 94SavCarC-4
❑ 94SavCarF-497

Barrilleaux, John
❑ 89OneYanP-2099

Barringer, Reggie
❑ 85PriWilPT-20
❑ 86PriWilPP-1
❑ 87SalBucP-23

Barrios, Eugene
❑ 85GreHorT-24

Barrios, Francisco
❑ 77Top-222
❑ 77WhiSoxJT-2
❑ 77WhiSoxT-2
❑ 78SSP270-144
❑ 78Top-552
❑ 79Hos-21
❑ 79Top-386
❑ 80OPC-58
❑ 80Top-107
❑ 81Fle-352

Barrios, Gregg
❑ 86WinHavRSP-3

Barrios, Jose Manuel
❑ 76CedRapGT-4
❑ 80PhoGiaVNB-17
❑ 80VenLeaS-26
❑ 81PhoGiaVNB-12
❑ 82PhoGiaVNB-24

Barrios, Manuel
❑ 94QuaCitRBC-3
❑ 94QuaCitRBF-525
❑ 95QuaCitRBTI-1
❑ 96JacGenB-4
❑ 96TexLeaAB-1
❑ 98ChaKniQ-6
❑ 98Don-331
❑ 98DonGolPP-331
❑ 98DonSilPP-331
❑ 98LeaRS-243
❑ 98LeaRSLHolo-243
❑ 98LeaRSLong-243
❑ 98LeaRTrue-243

Barron, Jose
❑ 95AubAstTI-9
❑ 96AubDouB-28

Barron, Tony (Anthony)
❑ 89Sta-26
❑ 89VerBeaDS-2
❑ 90StaFS7-18
❑ 90VerBeaDS-3
❑ 91LinDriAA-530
❑ 91SanAntMLD-530
❑ 91SanAntMP-2986
❑ 92AlbDukF-732
❑ 92SanAntMS-555
❑ 93AlbDukF-1474
❑ 94JacSunF-1423
❑ 96HarSenB-5
❑ 97ScrRedB-19
❑ 98ColCho-202
❑ 98ScrRedB1ATI-4
❑ 98ScrRedBQ-3

Barros, Ellie
❑ 82DanSunF-17

Barrow, Edward G.
❑ 50CalHOFW-4
❑ 53ArtHaloFP-4
❑ 60Fle-23
❑ 76ShaPiz-65
❑ 77GalGloG-174
❑ 79Yan192T-1
❑ 80PerHaloFP-63
❑ 80SSPHOF-63
❑ 81TigDetN-77
❑ 84Yan192G-4
❑ 89HOFStiB-94
❑ 92YanWIZH-2
❑ 95ConTSN-1394

Barrow, Mel
❑ 75LynRanT-4
❑ 76SanAntBTI-1
❑ 79TucTorT-22
❑ 79TulDriT-21
❑ 80TulDriT-11
❑ 81TulDriT-6
❑ 90TulDriDGB-26

Barrs, Stan
❑ 88SavCarP-349

Barry, Dan
❑ 90GeoColC-35

Barry, Eric
❑ 84ModA'sC-1

Barry, Jack (John Joseph)
❑ 08AmeCarE91-36
❑ 09AmeCarE90-1-3
❑ 09ColChiE-19
❑ 09SpoNewSM-65
❑ 09T206-14
❑ 10DomDisP-7
❑ 10E101-1
❑ 10E12AmeCDCE125-4
❑ 10LuxCigPP-2
❑ 10MelMinE-1
❑ 10NadCarE-2
❑ 10NadE1-5
❑ 10PeoT21-1A
❑ 10PeoT21-1B
❑ 10SweCapPP-41
❑ 11A'sFirT20-2
❑ 11D35RocB-2
❑ 11HelSta-53
❑ 11MecDFT-2
❑ 11PinT-5-515
❑ 11PloCanE-4
❑ 11S74Sil-27
❑ 11SpoLifCW-18
❑ 11SpoLifM-87
❑ 11T205-9
❑ 11TurRedT-78
❑ 12ColRedB-19
❑ 12ColTinT-19
❑ 12HasTriFT-18
❑ 12HasTriFT-70A
❑ 12T207-8
❑ 14CraJacE-28
❑ 14FatPlaT-4
❑ 14PieStaT-6
❑ 15AmeCarE106-1
❑ 15CraJacE-28
❑ 15SpoNewM-10
❑ 16BF2FP-1
❑ 16FleBreD-7
❑ 16SpoNewM-11
❑ 17ColE13-13
❑ 67SpoHobFC-5
❑ 68SCFOldT-17
❑ 74A'sTCM1P-2
❑ 74CapPub-68
❑ 77GalGloG-180
❑ 83A'sGreT-4
❑ 84OCoandSI-180
❑ 88ConSer3-4
❑ 91ConTSN-139

Barry, Jeff
❑ 89AncGlaP-2
❑ 89SanDieSAS-2
❑ 90JamExpP-7
❑ 90SanDieSA3-2
❑ 91Cla/Bes-365
❑ 91WesPalBEC-24
❑ 91WesPalBEP-1239
❑ 92St.LucMF-1759
❑ 93ClaFS7-95
❑ 93St.LucMC-2
❑ 93St.LuMF-2931
❑ 94BinMetF-714
❑ 95BinMetTI-27
❑ 95TopTra-22T
❑ 96MemChiB-7
❑ 96MetKah-2
❑ 97NewHavRB-5
❑ 98ColSprSS-24

Barry, Joe
❑ 85RedWinA-23
❑ 86RedWinA-14

Barry, John
❑ 86CliGiaP-1
❑ 88FreSunCLC-10
❑ 88FreSunP-1227

Barry, Malcomb
❑ 16Zee-20

Barry, Mike
❑ 85RedWinA-2
❑ 86RedWinA-8

Barry, Shad (John C.)
❑ 08RosComP-160
❑ 09ObaT21-288
❑ 09PC7HHB-2
❑ 09T206-396
❑ 11SpoLifCW-17
❑ 11Zee-44
❑ 12ObaPreT-37

Barry, Shawn
❑ 97PitMet-6
❑ 98CapCitBF5-2
❑ 98CapCitBM-2

Barstad, Scott
❑ 93MarPhiC-4
❑ 93MarPhiF-3463

Bartee, Kimera
❑ 93BluOriC-4
❑ 93BluOriF-4137
❑ 94CarLeaAF-CAR1
❑ 94FreKeyC-1
❑ 94FreKeyF-2625
❑ 94OriPro-6
❑ 95AusFut-37
❑ 95Bes-30
❑ 95Bow-124
❑ 95BowBayTI-18
❑ 95Exc-1
❑ 95RocRedWTI-7
❑ 95SPML-88
❑ 95UppDecML-42
❑ 95UppDecMLFS-42
❑ 96BesAutSA-5
❑ 96Exc-1
❑ 96Fin-S223
❑ 96FinRef-S223
❑ 96FleUpdTC-U33
❑ 96LeaSig-124
❑ 96LeaSigPPG-124
❑ 96LeaSigPPP-124
❑ 96TigHebN-1
❑ 96Ult-345
❑ 96UltGolM-345
❑ 97DonEli-126
❑ 97DonEliGS-126
❑ 97DonRatR-5
❑ 97Fle-94
❑ 97FleTif-94
❑ 97Lea-29
❑ 97LeaFraM-29
❑ 97LeaFraMDC-29
❑ 97Pac-84
❑ 97PacLigB-84
❑ 97PacSil-84
❑ 97Pin-63
❑ 97PinArtP-PP63
❑ 97PinIns-9
❑ 97PinInsCE-9
❑ 97PinInsDE-9
❑ 97PinMusC-63
❑ 97PinPrePla-63
❑ 97Sco-166
❑ 97ScoArtPWB-166
❑ 97ScoPreS-166
❑ 97ScoShoS-166
❑ 97ScoShoSAP-166
❑ 97TolMudHB-7
❑ 97Top-309
❑ 97UppDec-74
❑ 98PacInvGems-45
❑ 98PacOnl-263
❑ 98PacOnlR-263
❑ 98PacOnlWC-263
❑ 98TolMudHQ-8
❑ 99Pac-156
❑ 99PacCroC-103
❑ 99PacCroCPB-103
❑ 99PacPlaB-156
❑ 99PacRed-156

Bartell, Dick (Richard)
❑ 29ExhFou-13
❑ 31Exh-12
❑ 32OrbPinNP-15
❑ 32OrbPinUP-4
❑ 32R33So2-424
❑ 33DouDisP-4
❑ 33ExhFou-6
❑ 33GeoCMil-4
❑ 33Gou-28
❑ 33GouCanV-28
❑ 33NatLeaAC-3
❑ 33RitCE-4S
❑ 33TatOrb-4
❑ 33TatOrbSDR-158
❑ 33WorCig-6
❑ 34BabRutG-2
❑ 34BatR31-4
❑ 34ButPreR-2
❑ 34DiaMatCSB-5
❑ 34DiaStaR-15A
❑ 34DiaStaR-15B
❑ 34DiaStaR-101
❑ 34ExhFou-6

❑ 35DiaMatCS3T1-4
❑ 35GouPreR-6
❑ 35GouPuzR-4A
❑ 35GouPuzR-7A
❑ 35GouPuzR-12A
❑ 36GouWidPPR-A3
❑ 36GouWidPPR-A4
❑ 36WorWidGV-37
❑ 38GouHeaU-248
❑ 38GouHeaU-272
❑ 39CubTeal-1
❑ 41DouPlaR-55
❑ 47PM1StaP1-7
❑ 55Bow-234
❑ 74Bra193NLA-3
❑ 77GalGloG-212
❑ 83BigLeaCOA-33
❑ 88ConSer4-3
❑ 92ConTSN-452
❑ 93ConTSN-684
❑ 94ConTSN-1243
❑ 94ConTSNB-1243
Bartell, Mike
❑ 75CliPilT-26
Bartels, Bill
❑ 85AncGlaPTI-2
❑ 87VerBeaDP-26
❑ 88LynRedSS-1
Bartels, Todd
❑ 96ForWayWB-3
Barthelson, Bob (Robert E.)
❑ 47SunBre-2
Barthol, Blake
❑ 96SalAvaB-3
❑ 97EasLeaTPB-16
❑ 97NewHavRB-4
❑ 98CarLeaTPQ-13
❑ 98SalAvaC-4
Bartholow, Bud
❑ 83ReaPhiT-1
Bartilinski, Al
❑ 75WatRoyT-2
Bartirome, Tony (Anthony J.)
❑ 52Top-332
❑ 53Top-71
❑ 58JetPos-3
❑ 83TopRep5-332
❑ 91TopArc1-71
Bartlett, Bob
❑ 40WheM4-9
❑ 75TidTidTI-2
Bartley, Bill (William J.)
❑ 09ColChiE-20
❑ 12ColRedB-20
❑ 12ColTinT-20
Bartley, Boyd Owen
❑ 90DodTar-898
Bartley, Greg
❑ 84ChaLooT-29
❑ 86CalCanP-1
❑ 87ChaLooB-3
Bartolomucci, Tony
❑ 86AppFoxP-1
Barton, Bob (Robert Wilbur)
❑ 66Top-511
❑ 67CokCapG-10
❑ 67Top-462
❑ 68Top-351
❑ 68TopVen-351
❑ 69OPC-41
❑ 69Top-41
❑ 70OPC-352
❑ 70Top-352
❑ 71MLBOffS-218
❑ 71OPC-589
❑ 71Top-589
❑ 72MilBra-27
❑ 72OPC-39
❑ 72OPC-40
❑ 72PadPos-3
❑ 72Top-39
❑ 72Top-40
❑ 73OPC-626
❑ 73Top-626
❑ 74PadDea-2
❑ 74PadTeal-1
❑ 77PadSchC-5
Barton, Carroll
❑ 14Zee-2
Barton, Chris
❑ 98HelBreM-7
Barton, Harry Lamb
❑ 11SpoLifCW-19
Barton, Jeff
❑ 89SpoIndSP-21
❑ 90ChaRaiB-3
❑ 90ChaRaiP-2051
Barton, Ken
❑ 76CedRapGT-5
❑ 77CedRapGT-10
❑ 81ChaChaT-10
Barton, Larry
❑ 40SolHug-3
❑ 47SigOil-22
Barton, Paul
❑ 91St.CatBJC-18
❑ 91St.CatBJP-3386
Barton, Scott
❑ 92HunCubC-11
❑ 92HunCubF-3150
Barton, Shawn
❑ 86ReaPhiP-2
❑ 86SanJosBP-2
❑ 87MaiGuiP-6
❑ 87MaiGuiT-1
❑ 87PhiTas-xx
❑ 87SanJosBP-29
❑ 88JacMetGS-19
❑ 89CalLeaA-42
❑ 89RenSilSCLC-260
❑ 89TidTidC-8
❑ 89TidTidP-1969
❑ 90CMC-352
❑ 90ProAAAF-265
❑ 90RenSilSCLC-272
❑ 90TidTidC-1
❑ 90TidTidP-534
❑ 90TopTVM-35
❑ 91JacSunLD-327
❑ 91JacSunP-141
❑ 91LinDriAA-327
❑ 92CalCanS-53
❑ 93CalCanF-1156
❑ 93Don-53
❑ 93Pin-250
❑ 93Top-569
❑ 93TopGol-569
❑ 93TopInaM-569
❑ 93TopInaR-569
❑ 93TopMic-569
❑ 95PhoFirTI-18
❑ 96Pac-199
❑ 96PhoFirB-7
❑ 97SalVolG-5
Barton, Vince (Vincent David)
❑ 31Zee-12
Bartorillo, John
❑ 91BriBanF-1
Barun, Barton
❑ 82RedPioT-24
Barwick, Lyall
❑ 92BoiHawC-9
❑ 92BoiHawF-3641
❑ 93BoiHawC-2
❑ 93BoiHawF-3926
❑ 94CedRapKC-3
❑ 94CedRapKF-1111
Barylak, Alex
❑ 94WilCubC-2
❑ 94WilCubF-3754
Basabe, Jesus
❑ 98SouOreTG-1
Baseball, Seymore
❑ 78RicBraT-20
❑ 79RicBraT-8
Basey, Marsalis
❑ 93AubAstC-2
❑ 93AubAstF-3449
Basgall, Matt
❑ 85CloHSS-3
Basgall, Monty (Romanus)
❑ 49EurSta-152
❑ 52Top-12
❑ 55SeaPop-2
❑ 73OPC-569
❑ 73Top-569
❑ 74OPC-144
❑ 74Top-144
❑ 81Dod-2
❑ 81DodPol-NNO
❑ 83DodPol-NNO
❑ 83TopRep5-12
❑ 84DodPol-NNO
❑ 85DodCokP-4
❑ 86DodCokP-3
❑ 86DodPol-NNO
Basham, Gene
❑ 96HudValRB-27
Basinski, Eddie (Edward F.)
❑ 47TipTop-136
❑ 52MotCoo-6
❑ 53MotCoo-32
❑ 57SeaPop-3
❑ 58SeaRalT-2
❑ 83TCMPla1945-29
❑ 90DodTar-899
Bass, Aaron
❑ 97HudValRB-16
❑ 98ChaRivDG-1
Bass, Barry
❑ 83BurRanF-9
❑ 83BurRanT-1
❑ 84TulDriTI-22
❑ 85TulDriTI-26
❑ 87ElPasDP-27
❑ 88ElPasDB-17
Bass, Bart
❑ 77CedRapGT-16
Bass, Earl
❑ 76TulOilGP-25
❑ 76VenLeaS-126
❑ 78ArkTraT-2
Bass, Ed
❑ 85Ft.MyeRT-1
Bass, Jayson
❑ 93BriTigC-3
❑ 93BriTigF-3658
❑ 94JamJamC-4
❑ 94JamJamF-3977
❑ 95DanBraTI-3
❑ 95FayGenTI-3
❑ 96DanBraB-4
❑ 96FayGenB-5
❑ 97DurBulTI-29
❑ 97FloStaLTPB-15
❑ 98DanQ-C-27
❑ 98GreBraG-2
❑ 98LanJetG-2
Bass, Jerry
❑ 78CliDodT-2
❑ 79LodDodT-16
❑ 82BirBarT-18
Bass, John E.
❑ 75WatRoyT-3
Bass, Kevin
❑ 77NewCoPT-1
❑ 78BurBeeT-4
❑ 79HolMilT-5
❑ 79Top-708
❑ 80HolMilT-13
❑ 81VanCanT-24
❑ 82BrePol-26
❑ 82VanCanT-4
❑ 83AstPos-2
❑ 84AstPos-3
❑ 84Don-450
❑ 84Fle-221
❑ 84Nes792-538
❑ 84Top-538
❑ 84TopTif-538
❑ 85AstHouP-12
❑ 85AstMot-22
❑ 85Don-136
❑ 85Fle-345
❑ 85FleStaS-52
❑ 85Top-326
❑ 85TopTif-326
❑ 86AstMilL-3
❑ 86AstPol-4
❑ 86AstTeal-2
❑ 86Don-548
❑ 86DonHig-21
❑ 86Fle-294
❑ 86OPC-52
❑ 86Top-458
❑ 86TopSti-28
❑ 86TopTif-458
❑ 87AstMot-9
❑ 87AstPol-22
❑ 87ClaGam-17
❑ 87Don-410
❑ 87DonAll-40
❑ 87DonOpeD-14
❑ 87Dra-17
❑ 87Fle-51
❑ 87FleGlo-51
❑ 87FleHotS-3
❑ 87FleMin-5
❑ 87FleSlu-1
❑ 87FleStiC-6
❑ 87GenMilB-6A
❑ 87Lea-211
❑ 87OPC-85
❑ 87Spo-117
❑ 87Spo-175
❑ 87SpoTeaP-8
❑ 87Top-85
❑ 87TopGloS-34
❑ 87TopMinL-7
❑ 87TopSti-34
❑ 87TopTif-85
❑ 88AstMot-9
❑ 88AstPol-6
❑ 88Don-286
❑ 88DonBasB-38
❑ 88Fle-440
❑ 88FleExcS-2
❑ 88FleGlo-440
❑ 88FleMin-77
❑ 88FleStiC-85
❑ 88Lea-137
❑ 88OPC-175
❑ 88PanSti-298
❑ 88Sco-33
❑ 88ScoGlo-33
❑ 88Spo-55
❑ 88StaLinAst-4
❑ 88Top-175
❑ 88Top-291
❑ 88TopBig-77
❑ 88TopSti-29
❑ 88TopTif-175
❑ 88TopTif-291
❑ 89AstLenH-5
❑ 89AstMot-8
❑ 89AstSmo-4
❑ 89Don-325
❑ 89Fle-351
❑ 89FleGlo-351
❑ 89OPC-102
❑ 89PanSti-91
❑ 89Sco-226
❑ 89Spo-11
❑ 89Top-646
❑ 89TopAme2C-2
❑ 89TopBasT-98
❑ 89TopBig-187
❑ 89TopSti-14
❑ 89TopTif-646
❑ 89UppDec-425
❑ 90Bow-240
❑ 90BowTif-240
❑ 90Don-589
❑ 90DonBesN-36
❑ 90DonGraS-10
❑ 90Fle-223
❑ 90FleCan-223
❑ 90FleUpd-60
❑ 90GiaMot-24
❑ 90Lea-305
❑ 90MLBBasB-45
❑ 90OPC-281
❑ 90PanSti-261
❑ 90PubIntS-87
❑ 90Sco-279
❑ 90Sco100S-100
❑ 90ScoRoo-2T
❑ 90Spo-198
❑ 90Top-281
❑ 90TopBig-236
❑ 90TopSti-17
❑ 90TopTif-281
❑ 90TopTra-7T
❑ 90TopTraT-7T
❑ 90UppDec-302
❑ 90UppDec-793
❑ 91Bow-625
❑ 91Don-630
❑ 91Fle-253
❑ 91GiaMot-24
❑ 91GiaPacGaE-10
❑ 91GiaSFE-1
❑ 91Lea-365
❑ 91OPC-752
❑ 91Sco-616
❑ 91SimandSMLBL-3
❑ 91StaClu-29
❑ 91Top-752
❑ 91TopDesS-752
❑ 91TopMic-752
❑ 91TopTif-752
❑ 91Ult-315
❑ 91UppDec-287
❑ 92Don-373
❑ 92Fle-626
❑ 92GiaMot-24
❑ 92GiaPacGaE-3
❑ 92Lea-76
❑ 92LeaBlaG-76
❑ 92OPC-513
❑ 92PanSti-216
❑ 92Pin-53
❑ 92Sco-139
❑ 92ScoRoo-76T
❑ 92StaClu-6
❑ 92Stu-111
❑ 92Top-513
❑ 92TopGol-513
❑ 92TopGolW-513
❑ 92TopMic-513
❑ 92Ult-284
❑ 92UppDec-107
❑ 93AstMot-16
❑ 93AstStaC-18
❑ 93Don-745
❑ 93Fle-466
❑ 93FleFinE-76
❑ 93Sco-578
❑ 93Top-672
❑ 93TopGol-672
❑ 93TopInaM-672
❑ 93TopInaR-672
❑ 93TopMic-672
❑ 93UppDec-679
❑ 93UppDecGold-679
❑ 94AstMot-21
❑ 94BreMilB-8
❑ 94ColC-521
❑ 94ColChoGS-521
❑ 94ColChoSS-521
❑ 94Fle-484
❑ 94Pac-258
❑ 94Sco-128
❑ 94ScoGolR-128
❑ 94StaClu-590
❑ 94StaCluFDI-590
❑ 94StaCluGR-590
❑ 94StaCluMOP-590
❑ 94Top-362
❑ 94TopGol-362
❑ 94TopSpa-362
❑ 95BalOriP-6
❑ 95Don-411
❑ 95DonPreP-411
❑ 95Fle-452
❑ 95Pac-181
❑ 95Sco-372
❑ 95ScoGolR-372
❑ 95ScoPlaTS-372
Bass, Malik
❑ 97LakTigB-8
Bass, Norm
❑ 61AthJayP-2
❑ 62Top-122
❑ 62TopVen-122
❑ 63AthJayP-2
❑ 63Top-461
Bass, Randy William
❑ 75TacTwiK-7
❑ 76TacTwiDQ-2
❑ 77TacTwiDQ-23
❑ 79Top-707
❑ 81PadFamF-1
❑ 82Don-439
❑ 82Fle-566
❑ 82Top-307
❑ 87JapPlaB-7
❑ 89TopSenL-50
❑ 90EliSenL-49
❑ 93RanKee-65
Bass, Regan
❑ 86DayBealP-2
Basse, Mike
❑ 91HelBreSP-25
❑ 92CalLeaACL-18
❑ 92StoPorF-46
❑ 93El PasDF-2961
❑ 94NewOrlZF-1479
Bassett, Charley (Charles E.)
❑ 87BucN28-37
❑ 87OldJudN-22
❑ 88WG1CarG-28
Bassett, Matt
❑ 84OmaRoyT-29
❑ 85OmaRoyT-2
Bassett, Pepper
❑ 86NegLeaF-103
Bassler, Johnny (John Landis)
❑ 14B18B-1A
❑ 14B18B-1B
❑ 16Zee-1
❑ 17Zee-1
❑ 20WalMaiW-4
❑ 20Zee-3
❑ 21Exh-9
❑ 22E120-46
❑ 22W572-6
❑ 22W573-9
❑ 22W575-7
❑ 23MapCriV-10
❑ 23WilChoV-9
❑ 25Exh-89
❑ 26Exh-89
❑ 27AmeCarE126-55
❑ 27Exh-45
❑ 28Zee-2
❑ 29Zee-2
❑ 30Zee-1
❑ 31Zee-2
❑ 32Zee-1
❑ 33Zee-1
❑ 92ConTSN-414
❑ 93ConTSN-878
Basso, Mike (Michael A.)
❑ 86SpoIndC-167
❑ 87ChaRaiP-20
❑ 88BlaYNPRWL-179
❑ 88TexLeaAGS-23
❑ 88WicPilRD-16
❑ 89WicChaR-10
❑ 89WicStaR-9
❑ 89WicWraR-16
❑ 90CMC-514
❑ 90LasVegSC-11
❑ 90LasVegSP-126
❑ 90ProAAAF-14
❑ 91LinDriAA-601
❑ 91WicWraLD-601
❑ 91WicWraP-2601
❑ 91WicWraRD-11
❑ 92LasVegSF-2798
❑ 93LasVegSF-947
❑ 94RanCucQC-5
❑ 94RanCucQF-1652
❑ 95IdaFalBTI-35
❑ 96RanCucQB-2
❑ 97RanCucQG-3
❑ 98RanCucQG-4
❑ 98RanCucQG-4
Bast, Ryan
❑ 98ButCopKG-4
Bast, Steve (Steven)
❑ 86ElmPioRSP-2
❑ 87NewBriRSP-11
❑ 89NewBriRSP-608
❑ 89PawRedSTI-2
❑ 90CMC-260
❑ 90PawRedSC-9
❑ 90PawRedSDD-1
❑ 90PawRedSP-452
❑ 90ProAAAF-424
❑ 90TopTVRS-36
Bastable, John M.
❑ 76OklCit8TI-24
❑ 76VenLeaS-84
Bastian, Charlie (Charles J.)
❑ 87BucN28-75
❑ 87OldJudN-23
❑ 87OldJudN-24
❑ 88WG1CarG-47
❑ 90KalBatN-2
Bastian, Jack (John K.)
❑ 09T206-476
Bastian, Jose
❑ 75WesPalBES-6
❑ 79RocRedWT-17
❑ 81TolMudHT-3
Bastian, Robert
❑ 81RedPioT-1
❑ 83NasAngT-1
❑ 85EdmTraC-21
❑ 86EdmTraP-1
Baston, Stanley
❑ 96MedHatBJTI-4
❑ 97St.CatSB-8
❑ 98BilMusTI-3
Bastrire, Frank
❑ 67VanMouSO-2
Batch, Emil Henry
❑ 09T206-397
❑ 11SpoLifCW-20
❑ 11T205-198
❑ 12ImpTobC-48
Batchelor, Rich

(Richard Anthony)
❑ 91Cla/Bes-54
❑ 91FloStaLAP-FSL11
❑ 91Ft.LauYC-1
❑ 91Ft.LauYP-2416
❑ 92AlbYanF-2217
❑ 92AlbYanSk-3
❑ 92ProFS7-119
❑ 92SkyAA F-1
❑ 93AlbYanF-2153
❑ 94CarPol-3
❑ 94Don-649
❑ 94Fin-269
❑ 94FinRef-269
❑ 94LouRedF-2972
❑ 94StaClu-344
❑ 94StaCluFDI-344
❑ 94StaCluGR-344
❑ 94StaCluMOP-344
❑ 94StaCluT-327
❑ 94StaCluTFDI-327
❑ 94Top-788
❑ 94TopGol-788
❑ 94TopSpa-788
❑ 94Ult-265
❑ 95LouRedF-268
❑ 96LouRedB-9
❑ 98BufBisG-2

Bateman, John Alvin
❑ 63Col45"P-2
❑ 63Top-386
❑ 64Top-142
❑ 64TopCoi-107
❑ 64TopVen-142
❑ 65AstJayP-3
❑ 65Top-433
❑ 66OPC-86
❑ 66Top-86
❑ 66TopVen-86
❑ 67Ast-3
❑ 67AstTeal1-2
❑ 67AstTeal2-3
❑ 67CokCapAs-9
❑ 67DexPre-18
❑ 67Top-231
❑ 68CokCapA-9
❑ 68DexPre-9
❑ 68Top-592
❑ 69ExpFudP-2
❑ 69ExpPin-1
❑ 69MilBra-21
❑ 69MLBOffS-155
❑ 69OPC-138
❑ 69Top-138
❑ 69TopFou-23
❑ 69TopSta-53
❑ 69TopTeaP-10
❑ 70ExpPin-3
❑ 70ExpPos-14
❑ 70MLBOffS-61
❑ 70OPC-417
❑ 70Top-417
❑ 71ExpPS-2
❑ 71MLBOffS-122
❑ 71OPC-31
❑ 71OPC-628
❑ 71Top-628
❑ 71TopCoi-19
❑ 72MilBra-28
❑ 72OPC-5
❑ 72Top-5
❑ 86ExpGreT-8
❑ 87AstSer1-2
❑ 87AstShowSTh-2
❑ 87AstShowSTh-27

Bates, Benny
❑ 36WorWidGV-126

Bates, Billy
❑ 86ElPasDP-4
❑ 87DenZepP-7
❑ 88DenZepC-17
❑ 88DenZepP-1271
❑ 89BlaYNPRWL-89
❑ 89DenZepC-15
❑ 89DenZepP-38
❑ 89TriAAAP-AAA41
❑ 90BrePol-34
❑ 90El PasDAGTI-1
❑ 90IdaFalBP-3267
❑ 90Sco-608A
❑ 90Sco-608B
❑ 90Sco100RS-80
❑ 90TopDeb89-9
❑ 91LinDriAAA-251
❑ 91NasSouLD-251
❑ 92IowCubF-4056
❑ 92TexLon-4
❑ 94BreMilB-101

Bates, Buddy (Hubert Edgar)
❑ 36GouWidPPR-D1

Bates, Casey
❑ 98NewJerCM-4

Bates, Charles W.
❑ 29Zee-83
❑ 30Zee-100

Bates, Delbert O.
❑ 66SeaPop-1

Bates, Dick (Richard)
❑ 69PilPos-22
❑ 77PilPosR-22
❑ 83Pil69G-12

Bates, Eric
❑ 89BilMusP-2061

Bates, Fletcher
❑ 95PitMetTI-39
❑ 96Bow-359
❑ 96BowFoi-359
❑ 97CapCitB-23
❑ 97St.LucM-2
❑ 98PorSeaDQ-22
❑ 98SP MinPE-83
❑ 98SPMin-83
❑ 99BasAmeTP-10
❑ 99BasAmeTPG-10

Bates, Jason
❑ 92AriWilP-1
❑ 92BenRocCB-6
❑ 92BenRocF-1478
❑ 93Bow-176
❑ 93ClaFS7-168
❑ 93ColSprSSF-3090
❑ 93ExcFS7-32
❑ 93Top-579
❑ 93TopGol-579
❑ 93TopInaM-579
❑ 93TopInaR-579
❑ 93TopMic-579
❑ 94ColSprSSF-738
❑ 94ExcFS7-183
❑ 94Top-780
❑ 94TopGol-780
❑ 94TopSpa-780
❑ 94UppDecML-181
❑ 95Bow-76
❑ 95BowBes-R78
❑ 95BowBesR-R78
❑ 95ColCho-578T
❑ 95DonTopotO-224
❑ 95Emo-122
❑ 95EmoRoo-2
❑ 95Fin-288
❑ 95FinRef-288
❑ 95Fla-343
❑ 95FlaWavotF-1
❑ 95FleAllR-M2
❑ 95RocPol-1
❑ 95SigRooOJ-5
❑ 95SigRooOJP-5
❑ 95SigRooOJPS-5
❑ 95SigRooOJS-5
❑ 95SP-47
❑ 95SPCha-18
❑ 95SPChaDC-18
❑ 95SPSil-47
❑ 95StaClu-529
❑ 95StaCluCB-CB7
❑ 95StaCluMOP-529
❑ 95StaCluMOP-CB7
❑ 95StaCluSTWS-529
❑ 95TopTra-67T
❑ 95TopTra-100T
❑ 95UltGolMR-M3
❑ 95UppDec-240
❑ 95UppDecED-240
❑ 95UppDecEDG-240
❑ 95UppDecSE-239
❑ 95UppDecSEG-239
❑ 95Zen-127
❑ 96ColCho-129
❑ 96ColChoGS-129
❑ 96ColChoSS-129
❑ 96Don-2
❑ 96DonPreP-2
❑ 96EmoXL-171
❑ 96Fla-242
❑ 96Fle-359
❑ 96FleTif-359
❑ 96LeaSigA-16
❑ 96LeaSigAG-16
❑ 96LeaSigAS-16
❑ 96Pac-59
❑ 96Pin-16
❑ 96RocFle-1
❑ 96RocPol-2
❑ 96Sco-422
❑ 96Top-336
❑ 96Ult-185
❑ 96UltGolM-185
❑ 96UppDec-326
❑ 97Pac-278
❑ 97PacLigB-278
❑ 97PacSil-278
❑ 97Sco-427
❑ 97ScoArtPWB-427
❑ 97ScoResC-427
❑ 97ScoShoS-427
❑ 97ScoShoSAP-427
❑ 98PacInvGems-142
❑ 98PacOnl-238
❑ 98PacOnlR-238
❑ 98PacOnlWC-238
❑ 99Pac-140
❑ 99PacPlaB-140
❑ 99PacRed-140

Bates, Johnny (John William)
❑ 09ColChiE-21A
❑ 09ColChiE-21B
❑ 09RamT20-8
❑ 09T206-15
❑ 10DomDisP-8
❑ 10LuxCigPP-3
❑ 10NadE1-6
❑ 10SweCapPP-94
❑ 10W555-3
❑ 11E94-2
❑ 11HelSta-109
❑ 11PinT-5-403
❑ 11PloCanE-5
❑ 11S74Sil-97
❑ 11SpoLifCW-21
❑ 11SpoLifM-224
❑ 11T205-10
❑ 12ColRedB-21A
❑ 12ColRedB-21B
❑ 12ColTinT-21A
❑ 12ColTinT-21B
❑ 12HasTriFT-56
❑ 14PieStaT-7

Bates, Kevin
❑ 84ShrCapFB-1

Bates, Ray (Raymond)
❑ 15Zee-54
❑ 16Zee-124
❑ 21Zee-137

Bates, Steve
❑ 86AncGlaPTI-1
❑ 88ClePhiS-1

Bates, Tommy
❑ 91WatIndC-17
❑ 91WatIndP-3372
❑ 92KinIndC-7
❑ 92KinIndF-2480

Batesole, Michael
❑ 86BakDodP-2
❑ 87VerBeaDP-15
❑ 88VerBeaDS-1

Bathe, Bill
❑ 82WesHavAT-10
❑ 83TacTigT-10
❑ 84TacTigC-80
❑ 85TacTigC-148
❑ 86A'sMot-23
❑ 86DonRoo-41
❑ 86FleUpd-9
❑ 87Don-281
❑ 88IowCubC-23
❑ 88IowCubP-527
❑ 88TriAAAP-16
❑ 88TriAAC-1
❑ 89PhoFirC-11
❑ 89PhoFirP-1495
❑ 90Bow-234
❑ 90BowTif-234
❑ 90Don-680
❑ 90GiaMot-22
❑ 90UppDec-478A
❑ 91OPC-679
❑ 91Top-679
❑ 91TopDesS-679
❑ 91TopMic-679
❑ 91TopTif-679

Bathe, Bob
❑ 84AlbA'sT-23
❑ 85TacTigC-143
❑ 86IowCubP-2

Batina, John
❑ 87BriYouC-11

Batista, Dario
❑ 94BelMarC-4
❑ 94BelMarF-3248

Batista, Decartes (Miguel Jerez)
❑ 93Bow-564

Batista, Francisco
❑ 82SprCarF-24
❑ 83ArkTraT-20
❑ 83St.PetCT-20
❑ 90SprCarDGB-5

Batista, Juan
❑ 93JamExpC-3
❑ 93JamExpF-3332
❑ 94BurBeeC-2
❑ 94BurBeeF-1086

Batista, Miguel
❑ 86ChaRaiP-2A
❑ 86ChaRaiP-2B
❑ 88BenBucL-17
❑ 92WesPalBEC-9
❑ 92WesPalBEF-2078
❑ 93HarSenF-260
❑ 93LimRocDWB-8
❑ 93LimRocDWB-140
❑ 94HarSenF-2082
❑ 95ChaKniTI-6
❑ 96ChaKniB-8
❑ 97IowCub-5
❑ 97Pac-296
❑ 97PacLigB-296
❑ 97PacSil-296
❑ 98Pac-247
❑ 98PacInv-81
❑ 98PacInvPBlue-81
❑ 98PacInvSilv-81
❑ 98PacOnl-444
❑ 98PacOnlR-444
❑ 98PacOnlWC-444
❑ 98PacPlaB-247
❑ 98PacRedT-247
❑ 98PacSil-247
❑ 99PacCroC-167
❑ 99PacCroCPB-167

Batista, Rafael
❑ 75AstPos-2

Batista, Tony
❑ 94ModA'sC-4
❑ 94ModA'sF-3067
❑ 95Exc-107
❑ 95HunStaTI-4
❑ 96Fla-141
❑ 96FlaWavotF-3
❑ 96FleUpd-U70
❑ 96FleUpdNH-3
❑ 96FleUpdTC-U70
❑ 96Ult-396
❑ 96UltGolM-396
❑ 96UltGolP-3
❑ 96UltGolPHGM-3
❑ 97A'sMot-11
❑ 97BowBes-136
❑ 97BowBesAR-136
❑ 97BowBesR-136
❑ 97Cir-95
❑ 97CirRav-95
❑ 97ColCho-411
❑ 97Fle-183
❑ 97FleTif-183
❑ 97MetUni-126
❑ 97Pac-164
❑ 97PacLigB-164
❑ 97PacPri-56
❑ 97PacPriLB-56
❑ 97PacPriP-56
❑ 97PacSil-164
❑ 97StaClu-344
❑ 97StaCluMOP-344
❑ 97Top-344
❑ 97Ult-108
❑ 97UltGolME-108
❑ 97UltPlaME-108
❑ 97UppDec-447
❑ 98ColCho-293
❑ 98DiaBacP-15
❑ 98DiaMcD-3
❑ 98Fle-502
❑ 98PacInvGems-82
❑ 98PacOnl-28
❑ 98PacOnlR-28
❑ 98PacOnlWC-28
❑ 98PinPlu-109
❑ 98PinSna-AD6
❑ 98UppDec-638
❑ 99Fle-81
❑ 99FleSta9-81
❑ 99FleWarT-81
❑ 99Pac-14
❑ 99PacCroC-11
❑ 99PacCroCPB-11
❑ 99PacPar-10
❑ 99PacParC-10
❑ 99PacParG-10
❑ 99PacParHoloGold-10
❑ 99PacParHS-10
❑ 99PacParOD-10
❑ 99PacParPB-10
❑ 99PacParRed-10
❑ 99PacPlaB-14
❑ 99PacPriS-54
❑ 99PacPriS206-54
❑ 99PacPriS206R-54
❑ 99PacRed-14
❑ 99SkyThu-182
❑ 99SkyThuRant-182
❑ 99SkyThuRave-182
❑ 99ThuSkySupR-182
❑ 99Top-272
❑ 99TopChr-272
❑ 99TopChrR-272
❑ 99TopMVPP-272
❑ 99UppDec-306
❑ 99UppDecEL1-306
❑ 99UppDecEL2-306
❑ 99Vic-23

Batiste, Chris
❑ 89BluOriS-3

Batiste, Darnell
❑ 93BurIndC-3
❑ 93BurIndF-3304
❑ 94BurIndC-2
❑ 94BurIndF-3800

Batiste, Kevin
❑ 87DunBluJP-941
❑ 88KnoBluJB-7
❑ 89KnoBluJB-2
❑ 89KnoBluJP-1124
❑ 89KnoBluJS-7
❑ 90GreBraB-18
❑ 90GreBraP-1140
❑ 90GreBraS-2
❑ 90TopDeb89-10
❑ 90UppDec-115

Batiste, Kim
❑ 87UtiBluSP-4
❑ 88SpaPhiP-1035
❑ 88SpaPhiS-18
❑ 89ClePhiS-2
❑ 90Bes-227
❑ 90CMC-803
❑ 90EasLeaAP-EL20
❑ 90ReaPhiB-15
❑ 90ReaPhiP-1225
❑ 90ReaPhiS-5
❑ 90StaFS7-81
❑ 91Bow-488
❑ 91LinDriAAA-480
❑ 91ScrRedBLD-480
❑ 91ScrRedBP-2543
❑ 92Bow-44
❑ 92Cla1-T10
❑ 92ClaGam-191
❑ 92Don-402
❑ 92Fle-522
❑ 92Lea-421
❑ 92LeaBlaG-421
❑ 92OPC-514
❑ 92PhiMed-5
❑ 92Pin-266
❑ 92PinRoo-18
❑ 92PinRool-9
❑ 92PinTea2-69
❑ 92ProFS7-293
❑ 92Sco-833
❑ 92ScoImpP-86
❑ 92ScoRoo-37
❑ 92StaClu-788
❑ 92StaCluECN-788
❑ 92Stu-71
❑ 92Top-514
❑ 92TopDeb91-11
❑ 92TopGol-514
❑ 92TopGolW-514
❑ 92TopMic-514
❑ 92Ult-542
❑ 92UppDec-422
❑ 92UppDecSR-SR3
❑ 93Don-148
❑ 93Fle-485
❑ 93PacSpa-230
❑ 93PhiMed-5
❑ 93Pin-390
❑ 93Sco-191
❑ 93Top-679
❑ 93TopGol-679
❑ 93TopInaM-679
❑ 93TopInaR-679
❑ 93TopMic-679
❑ 93Ult-436
❑ 93UppDec-516
❑ 93UppDecGold-516
❑ 94ColC-48
❑ 94ColChoGS-48
❑ 94ColChoSS-48
❑ 94Don-470
❑ 94Fle-583
❑ 94Pac-469
❑ 94PhiMed-2
❑ 94PhiMel-2
❑ 94PhiUSPC-3H
❑ 94PhiUSPC-11S
❑ 94Pin-207
❑ 94PinArtP-207
❑ 94PinMusC-207
❑ 94Sco-540
❑ 94ScoGolR-540
❑ 94StaClu-303
❑ 94StaCluFDI-303
❑ 94StaCluGR-303
❑ 94StaCluMOP-303
❑ 94StaCluT-212
❑ 94StaCluTFDI-212
❑ 94Top-238
❑ 94TopGol-238
❑ 94TopSpa-238
❑ 94Ult-242
❑ 95BowBayTI-13
❑ 95Pac-325
❑ 95Sco-183
❑ 95ScoGolR-183
❑ 95ScoPlaTS-183
❑ 95Top-173
❑ 96GiaMot-26
❑ 97Pac-436
❑ 97PacLigB-436
❑ 97PacSil-436

Batiste, Terrance
❑ 88NebCor-10

Battell, Mark
❑ 88HamRedP-1725
❑ 89HamRedS-2

Batten, Mark
❑ 80SanJosMJitB-3
❑ 81WauTimT-8

Battey, Earl Jesse
❑ 47Exh-14
❑ 55DonWin-12
❑ 57Top-401
❑ 58Top-364
❑ 59Top-114
❑ 59TopVen-114
❑ 60Lea-66
❑ 60Top-328
❑ 60WhiSoxTS-2
❑ 61Baz-28
❑ 61Pos-97A
❑ 61Pos-97B
❑ 61Top-315
❑ 61Top-582
❑ 61TopDicG-1
❑ 61TopStal-177
❑ 61TwiCloD-3
❑ 61TwiJayP-2
❑ 61TwiPetM-22
❑ 61TwiUniMC-2
❑ 62Baz-4
❑ 62Jel-90
❑ 62Pos-90
❑ 62PosCan-90
❑ 62SalPlaC-19
❑ 62ShiPlaC-19
❑ 62Top-371
❑ 62TopBuc-7
❑ 62TopStal-74
❑ 63BasMagM-10
❑ 63ExhStaB-6
❑ 63Jel-8
❑ 63Pos-8
❑ 63SalMetC-44
❑ 63Top-306
❑ 63Top-410
❑ 63TwiJayP-3
❑ 63TwiVol-4
❑ 64Top-90
❑ 64TopCoi-101
❑ 64TopCoi-136
❑ 64TopSta-71

- ❑ 64TopStaU-9
- ❑ 64TopVen-90
- ❑ 64TwiJayP-2
- ❑ 64WheSta-6
- ❑ 65Top-490
- ❑ 65TopEmbl-70
- ❑ 65TwiPos-2
- ❑ 66Top-240
- ❑ 66TopRubl-8
- ❑ 66TopVen-240
- ❑ 66TwiFaiG-3
- ❑ 67CokCapTw-3
- ❑ 67DexPre-19
- ❑ 67OPC-15
- ❑ 67Top-15
- ❑ 67TopVen-222
- ❑ 67TwiTeal-2
- ❑ 78TCM60I-113
- ❑ 78TwiFri-2
- ❑ 81WhiSox1T-18
- ❑ 86TwiGreT-8
- ❑ 88PacLegI-35
- ❑ 94TedWil-46

Battle, Allen
- ❑ 92ClaFS7-269
- ❑ 92MidLeaATI-3
- ❑ 92SprCarC-6
- ❑ 92SprCarF-880
- ❑ 93ArkTraF-2822
- ❑ 93ClaGolF-182
- ❑ 94LouRedF-2992
- ❑ 94TriAAF-AAA35
- ❑ 95ActPacF-50
- ❑ 95Bow-45
- ❑ 95Exc-261
- ❑ 95ExcLeaL-3
- ❑ 95FleUpd-153
- ❑ 95LouRedF-286
- ❑ 95SigRoo-7
- ❑ 95SigRooSig-7
- ❑ 95Sum-156
- ❑ 95SumNthD-156
- ❑ 95UppDec-304
- ❑ 95UppDecED-304
- ❑ 95UppDecEDG-304
- ❑ 95UppDecML-123
- ❑ 95UppDecMLFS-123
- ❑ 96ColCho-283
- ❑ 96ColChoGS-283
- ❑ 96ColChoSS-283
- ❑ 96Don-22
- ❑ 96DonPreP-22
- ❑ 96EmoXL-100
- ❑ 96Fla-142
- ❑ 96Fle-537
- ❑ 96FleTif-537
- ❑ 96FleUpd-U71
- ❑ 96FleUpdTC-U71
- ❑ 96LeaSigA-17
- ❑ 96LeaSigAG-17
- ❑ 96LeaSigAS-17
- ❑ 96Sco-443
- ❑ 96Ult-397
- ❑ 96UltGolM-397
- ❑ 97PacPriGotD-GD78

Battle, Howard
- ❑ 90MedHatBJB-26
- ❑ 91Cla/Bes-29
- ❑ 91MyrBeaHC-16
- ❑ 91MyrBeaHP-2950
- ❑ 91SouAtlLAGP-SAL36
- ❑ 92Bow-183
- ❑ 92ClaFS7-88
- ❑ 92DunBluJC-5
- ❑ 92DunBluJF-2005
- ❑ 92ProFS7-172
- ❑ 92UppDecML-27
- ❑ 92UppDecML-280
- ❑ 93Bow-195
- ❑ 93ClaFS7-43
- ❑ 93ClaGolF-85
- ❑ 93ExcFS7-238
- ❑ 93KnoSmoF-1256
- ❑ 93LinVenB-119
- ❑ 94Cla-107
- ❑ 94ClaCreotC-C6
- ❑ 94ClaGolF-108
- ❑ 94ExcFS7-138
- ❑ 94SyrChiF-976
- ❑ 94SyrChiTI-3
- ❑ 94TedWil-118
- ❑ 94TedWilDGC-DG5
- ❑ 94UppDecML-144
- ❑ 94VenLinU-105
- ❑ 95BluJayOH-3
- ❑ 95Exc-133
- ❑ 95LinVen-170
- ❑ 95SyrChiTI-2
- ❑ 95UppDecML-124
- ❑ 95UppDecMLFS-124
- ❑ 96Fle-491
- ❑ 96FleTif-491
- ❑ 96PhiTeal-1
- ❑ 96Pin-181
- ❑ 96Sco-510
- ❑ 96ScrRedBB-5
- ❑ 96Spo-135
- ❑ 96SpoArtP-135
- ❑ 96SpoRooJ-7
- ❑ 97AlbDukGS-2
- ❑ 98BirBarG-2

Battles, Jeff
- ❑ 93JohCitCC-2
- ❑ 93JohCitCF-3668
- ❑ 94SavCarC-5
- ❑ 94SavCarF-498

Batton, Chris
- ❑ 76TusTorCr-10
- ❑ 76VenLeaS-156
- ❑ 77ColCliT-2
- ❑ 77Top-475

Batts, Matt (Matthew Daniel)
- ❑ 47Exh-15
- ❑ 48RedSoxTI-1
- ❑ 49Lea-108
- ❑ 49RedSoxTI-1
- ❑ 50RedSoxTI-1
- ❑ 51Bow-129
- ❑ 52Bow-216
- ❑ 52Top-230
- ❑ 53BowBW-22
- ❑ 53TigGle-1
- ❑ 54Bow-183
- ❑ 54Top-88
- ❑ 55Bow-161
- ❑ 76BatRouCT-3
- ❑ 79DiaGre-243
- ❑ 83TopRep5-230
- ❑ 94TopArc1-88
- ❑ 94TopArc1G-88

Batts, Rodney
- ❑ 96BatCliTI-17
- ❑ 97BatCliTI-23

Bauder, Mike
- ❑ 97ForWayW-5
- ❑ 98ForMyeMTI-2

Bauer, Alice
- ❑ 52Whe-1A
- ❑ 52Whe-1B

Bauer, Charles
- ❑ 95HudValRTI-17

Bauer, Chuck
- ❑ 96ChaRivTI-9606

Bauer, Dave
- ❑ 89PenPilS-1

Bauer, Eric
- ❑ 85SpoIndC-1
- ❑ 87WicPilRD-22
- ❑ 88WicPilRD-33

Bauer, Hank (Henry Albert)
- ❑ 47Exh-16A
- ❑ 47Exh-16B
- ❑ 47StaPinP2-3
- ❑ 50Bow-219
- ❑ 50YanTeal-2
- ❑ 51BerRos-A4
- ❑ 51Bow-183
- ❑ 51TopRedB-24
- ❑ 52BerRos-2
- ❑ 52Bow-65
- ❑ 52CokTip-1
- ❑ 52TipTop-1
- ❑ 52Top-215
- ❑ 53BowC-44
- ❑ 53BowC-84
- ❑ 53Bri-29
- ❑ 53Dor-104
- ❑ 53RedMan-AL2
- ❑ 53StaMey-1
- ❑ 54Bow-129
- ❑ 54DanDee-2
- ❑ 54NewYorJA-40
- ❑ 54RedMan-AL23
- ❑ 54StaMey-1
- ❑ 54Top-130
- ❑ 55Bow-246
- ❑ 55RedMan-AL22
- ❑ 55StaMey-1
- ❑ 55Top-166
- ❑ 56Top-177
- ❑ 56YanJayP-1
- ❑ 56YanTeal-1
- ❑ 57Top-240
- ❑ 57YanJayP-1
- ❑ 58Top-9
- ❑ 58YanJayP-1
- ❑ 59HayComBP-1
- ❑ 59Top-240
- ❑ 60A's-1
- ❑ 60A'sJayP-1
- ❑ 60A'sTeal-1
- ❑ 60RawGloT-4
- ❑ 60Top-262
- ❑ 61AthJayP-3
- ❑ 61Pos-90A
- ❑ 61Pos-90B
- ❑ 61Top-119
- ❑ 61Top-398
- ❑ 61TopStaI-156
- ❑ 62Top-127
- ❑ 62Top-463
- ❑ 62TopVen-127
- ❑ 63BalOriP-5
- ❑ 64BalOriP-5
- ❑ 64OriJayP-3
- ❑ 64Top-178
- ❑ 64TopVen-178
- ❑ 65BalOriP-4
- ❑ 65Top-323
- ❑ 66Top-229
- ❑ 66TopVen-229
- ❑ 67BalOriP-6
- ❑ 67OPC-1
- ❑ 67Top-1
- ❑ 67Top-534
- ❑ 68LauWorS-55
- ❑ 68Top-513
- ❑ 69A'sJacitB-2
- ❑ 69OPC-124
- ❑ 69Top-124
- ❑ 69TopFou-13
- ❑ 70Houof J-4
- ❑ 71FleWorS-56
- ❑ 75TCMHouoJ-4
- ❑ 79TCM50-22
- ❑ 81Ori6F-5
- ❑ 83FraBroR-21
- ❑ 83FraBroR-24
- ❑ 83TopRep5-215
- ❑ 83YanASFY-3
- ❑ 84FifNatCT-1
- ❑ 85TCMPpl1-30
- ❑ 86OriGreT-2
- ❑ 89PacLegI-144
- ❑ 89SweBasG-82
- ❑ 91TopArc1-290
- ❑ 92UppDecS-16
- ❑ 92YanWIZA-2
- ❑ 93UppDecAH-6
- ❑ 94TopArc1-130
- ❑ 94TopArc1G-130
- ❑ 94UppDecAH-93
- ❑ 94UppDecAH1-93
- ❑ 97TopMan-21
- ❑ 97TopManF-21
- ❑ 97TopManFR-21
- ❑ 99SpoIllGotG-74
- ❑ 99SpoIllGotGA-5

Bauer, Mark
- ❑ 84ModA'sC-2
- ❑ 85HunStaJ-26
- ❑ 85ModA'sC-19

Bauer, Marlene
- ❑ 52Whe-2A
- ❑ 52Whe-2B

Bauer, Matt
- ❑ 91BriTigC-21
- ❑ 91BriTigP-3595
- ❑ 92LakTigC-15
- ❑ 92NiaFalRF-3315
- ❑ 93FayGenC-2
- ❑ 93FayGenF-120
- ❑ 94TreThuF-2112

Bauer, Pete (Peter)
- ❑ 86LitFalMP-2
- ❑ 87LynMetP-14
- ❑ 88ColMetGS-2
- ❑ 89JacMetGS-23
- ❑ 90OscAstS-3
- ❑ 91JacGenLD-554
- ❑ 91JacGenP-917
- ❑ 91LinDriAA-554

Bauer, Phil
- ❑ 76CliPilT-1
- ❑ 78AppFoxT-3
- ❑ 79AppFoxT-14

Bauer, Rick
- ❑ 98DelShoM-7

Bauers, Russell
- ❑ 40PlaBal-219
- ❑ 48AngTeal-5
- ❑ 52Par-4

Baugh, Darren
- ❑ 96HicCraB-2

Baugh, Gavin
- ❑ 93LetMouF-4155
- ❑ 93LetMouSP-7
- ❑ 93Top-641
- ❑ 93TopGol-641
- ❑ 93TopInaM-641
- ❑ 93TopInaR-641
- ❑ 93TopMic-641
- ❑ 94KanCouCC-4
- ❑ 94KanCouCF-168
- ❑ 94KanCouCTI-4
- ❑ 95BreCouMF-252

Baughman, Justin
- ❑ 95BoiHawTI-3
- ❑ 96CedRapKTI-3
- ❑ 97LakElsSG-4
- ❑ 98Bow-304
- ❑ 98BowChr-304
- ❑ 98BowChrGA-304
- ❑ 98BowChrGAR-304
- ❑ 98BowChrI-304
- ❑ 98BowChrIR-304
- ❑ 98BowChrR-304
- ❑ 98BowGolA-304
- ❑ 98BowInt-304
- ❑ 98FleUpd-U33
- ❑ 98LeaRS-303
- ❑ 98LeaRSLHolo-303
- ❑ 98LeaRSLong-303
- ❑ 98LeaRTrue-303
- ❑ 98RevoRooHH-1
- ❑ 98RevoRooHHG-1
- ❑ 98UppDecR-101
- ❑ 98UppDecRNF-NF1
- ❑ 98VanCanG-1
- ❑ 99Fle-310
- ❑ 99FleSta9-310
- ❑ 99FleWarT-310
- ❑ 99Top-414
- ❑ 99TopChr-414
- ❑ 99TopChrR-414
- ❑ 99TopMVPP-414
- ❑ 99UppDec-13
- ❑ 99UppDecEL1-13
- ❑ 99UppDecEL2-13

Bauldree, Joe
- ❑ 96DanBraB-5
- ❑ 97MacBra-23

Baum, Charles
- ❑ 09ObaT21-34
- ❑ 09ObaT21-133
- ❑ 09ObaT21-305
- ❑ 11BigEatEU-2
- ❑ 11PacCoaBD-5
- ❑ 11Zee-63
- ❑ 12ObaPreT-54
- ❑ 12Zee-76
- ❑ 13Zee-130
- ❑ 14Zee-101
- ❑ 15Zee-95
- ❑ 16Zee-97
- ❑ 17Zee-82
- ❑ 18Zee-75
- ❑ 19Zee-82
- ❑ 20Zee-77

Baum, Jeff
- ❑ 88AppFoxP-158

Bauman, Brad
- ❑ 81ShrCapT-10

Baumann, David
- ❑ 90GreFalDSP-13
- ❑ 91VerBeaDC-2
- ❑ 91VerBeaDP-763
- ❑ 91YakBeaC-21

Baumann, Frank
- ❑ 58Top-167
- ❑ 59Top-161
- ❑ 59TopVen-161
- ❑ 60Top-306
- ❑ 60WhiSoxTS-3
- ❑ 61Pos-34
- ❑ 61Top-46
- ❑ 61Top-550
- ❑ 61WhiSoxTS-2
- ❑ 62Top-161
- ❑ 62TopVen-161
- ❑ 62WhiSoxJP-2
- ❑ 62WhiSoxTS-2
- ❑ 63Top-381
- ❑ 63WhiSoxTS-1
- ❑ 64Top-453
- ❑ 64WhiSoxI-2
- ❑ 64WhiSoxTS-2
- ❑ 65OPC-161
- ❑ 65Top-161
- ❑ 81RedSoxBG2S-4

Baumann, Matt
- ❑ 93EveGiaC-4
- ❑ 93EveGiaF-3759

Baumann, Paddy (Charles John)
- ❑ 12T207-9
- ❑ 14B18B-11A
- ❑ 14B18B-11B
- ❑ 14B18B-11C

Baumer, Jim (James Sloan)
- ❑ 58JetPos-4
- ❑ 61RedJayP-2
- ❑ 61Top-292
- ❑ 80Red196T-17

Baumgardner, George
- ❑ 14CraJacE-131
- ❑ 14FatPlaT-5
- ❑ 15CraJacE-131

Baumgarner, Jeff
- ❑ 91HagSunLD-226
- ❑ 92HagSunF-2549

Baumgarten, Ross
- ❑ 78AppFoxT-4
- ❑ 79Top-704
- ❑ 80Top-138
- ❑ 81Don-41
- ❑ 81OPC-328
- ❑ 81Top-398
- ❑ 82Don-104
- ❑ 82Fle-337
- ❑ 82OPC-322
- ❑ 82Top-563
- ❑ 82TopTra-3T
- ❑ 83Fle-302
- ❑ 83Top-97

Baumgartner, Stan
- ❑ 27Zee-66
- ❑ 81ConTSN-8
- ❑ 94ConTSN-1317
- ❑ 94ConTSNB-1317

Baumholtz, Frank C.
- ❑ 47Exh-17
- ❑ 49Bow-21
- ❑ 51R42SmaS-3
- ❑ 52Bow-195
- ❑ 52Top-225
- ❑ 54Bow-221
- ❑ 54RedHeaF-2
- ❑ 54Top-60
- ❑ 55Bow-227
- ❑ 55Top-172
- ❑ 56Top-274
- ❑ 73BooProC-2
- ❑ 83TopRep5-225
- ❑ 85TCMPla1-15
- ❑ 94TopArc1-60
- ❑ 94TopArc1G-60

Baur, Al
- ❑ 89MarPhiS-1
- ❑ 90BatCliP-3056

Bausher, Andrew
- ❑ 97EriSeaWB-3
- ❑ 98AugGreM-8

Bauta, Ed
- ❑ 61UniOil-P1
- ❑ 62Top-344
- ❑ 63Top-336
- ❑ 76Met63 S-1
- ❑ 91MetWIZ-25

Bautista, Antonio
- ❑ 76ForLauYS-12
- ❑ 77WesHavYT-2

Bautista, Benny
- ❑ 85NewOriT-12
- ❑ 87HagSunP-6

Bautista, Danny (Daniel)
- ❑ 90BriTigP-3154
- ❑ 91FayGenC-23
- ❑ 91FayGenP-1182
- ❑ 92FayGenC-13
- ❑ 92FayGenF-2179
- ❑ 93Bow-95
- ❑ 93ClaFS7-167
- ❑ 93LimRocDWB-6
- ❑ 93LonTigF-2319
- ❑ 94Bow-97
- ❑ 94BowBes-B16
- ❑ 94BowBesR-B16
- ❑ 94ColC-557
- ❑ 94ColChoGS-557
- ❑ 94ColChoSS-557
- ❑ 94Don-442
- ❑ 94Fin-435
- ❑ 94FinJum-435
- ❑ 94FinRef-435
- ❑ 94Fla-291
- ❑ 94FleMajLP-5
- ❑ 94FleUpd-39
- ❑ 94LeaGolR-7
- ❑ 94LeaLimR-12
- ❑ 94Pac-211
- ❑ 94Pin-234
- ❑ 94PinArtP-234
- ❑ 94PinMusC-234
- ❑ 94PinNewG-NG24
- ❑ 94Sco-559
- ❑ 94ScoBoyoS-51
- ❑ 94ScoGolR-559
- ❑ 94ScoRoo-RT84
- ❑ 94ScoRooGR-RT84
- ❑ 94Sel-186
- ❑ 94SpoRoo-124
- ❑ 94SpoRooAP-124
- ❑ 94StaClu-155
- ❑ 94StaCluFDI-155
- ❑ 94StaCluGR-155
- ❑ 94StaCluMOP-155
- ❑ 94Top-768
- ❑ 94TopGol-768
- ❑ 94TopSpa-768
- ❑ 95ColCho-466
- ❑ 95ColChoGS-466
- ❑ 95ColChoSS-466
- ❑ 95Don-249
- ❑ 95DonPreP-249
- ❑ 95DonTopotO-70
- ❑ 95Fle-44
- ❑ 95Lea-248
- ❑ 95PacPri-47
- ❑ 95Pin-15
- ❑ 95PinArtP-15
- ❑ 95PinMusC-15
- ❑ 95Sco-496
- ❑ 95ScoGolR-496
- ❑ 95ScoPlaTS-496
- ❑ 95Sel-31
- ❑ 95SelArtP-31
- ❑ 95StaClu-78
- ❑ 95StaCluFDI-78
- ❑ 95StaCluMOP-78
- ❑ 95StaCluSTWS-78
- ❑ 95StaCluVR-48
- ❑ 95StaCluVRMO-48
- ❑ 95Top-557
- ❑ 95TopCyb-242
- ❑ 95Ult-44
- ❑ 95UltGolM-44
- ❑ 96Don-465
- ❑ 96DonPreP-465
- ❑ 96Fle-105
- ❑ 96FleTif-105
- ❑ 96Pac-308
- ❑ 96Sco-390
- ❑ 97RicBra-5
- ❑ 98PacInvGems-117
- ❑ 98PacOnl-53
- ❑ 98PacOnlR-53
- ❑ 98PacOnlWC-53

Bautista, Ed
- ❑ 93SanJosGC-30

Bautista, Francisco
- ❑ 97SpoIndG-2
- ❑ 98SpoIndG-3

Bautista, German
- ❑ 86MiaMarP-1

Bautista, Hector
- ❑ 90WauTimB-25
- ❑ 90WauTimP-2139
- ❑ 90WauTimS-2

Bautista, J.J.
- ❑ 90CMC-321
- ❑ 90RocRedWC-20

Bautista, John
- ❑ 98BirBarG-3

Bautista, Jorge
- ❑ 98KanCouC-3
- ❑ 98KanCouCCP-3

Bautista, Jose
- ❑ 85LynMetT-9
- ❑ 87JacMetF-3
- ❑ 87MetColP-24
- ❑ 88DonRoo-41

- 88FleUpd-1
- 88FleUpdG-1
- 88OriFreB-48
- 88OriPos-4
- 88TopTra-10T
- 88TopTraT-10T
- 89BalOriP-3
- 89Bow-3
- 89BowTif-3
- 89Don-451
- 89Fle-608
- 89FleGlo-608
- 89OriFreB-48
- 89Sco-573
- 89Top-469
- 89TopSti-229
- 89TopTif-469
- 89UppDec-574
- 90ProAAAF-453
- 90PubIntS-574
- 90RocRedWGC-28
- 90RocRedWP-696
- 90UppDec-8
- 91OriCro-23
- 92Fle-2
- 92OmaRoyF-2953
- 92OmaRoyS-326
- 93CubMar-2
- 93CubStaC-30
- 93FleFinE-6
- 93LimRocDWB-99
- 93PacSpa-376
- 94ColC-623
- 94ColChoGS-623
- 94ColChoSS-623
- 94Don-458
- 94Fin-175
- 94FinRef-175
- 94Fle-379
- 94Lea-88
- 94Pac-94
- 94Pin-445
- 94PinArtP-445
- 94PinMusC-445
- 94Sco-249
- 94ScoGolR-249
- 94StaClu-421
- 94StaCluFDI-421
- 94StaCluGR-421
- 94StaCluMOP-421
- 94StaCluT-340
- 94StaCluTFDI-340
- 94Top-92
- 94TopGol-92
- 94TopSpa-92
- 94Ult-159
- 94UppDec-108
- 94UppDecED-108
- 95Don-243
- 95DonPreP-243
- 95Fle-409
- 95GiaMot-26
- 95Pac-67
- 95Top-42
- 96Pac-204
- 96PhoFirB-8
- 97Pac-437
- 97PacLigB-437
- 97PacSil-437
- 98PacInvGems-199

Bautista, Juan
- 93AlbPolCB-3
- 93AlbPolF-2030
- 93JohCitCC-3
- 93JohCitCF-3693
- 94JohCitCC-3
- 94JohCitCF-3715
- 94OriPro-7
- 95PeoChiTI-28
- 96BowBayB-5
- 97BowBay-6
- 98SouBenSHM-4

Bautista, Martin
- 98ColRedSM-2

Bautista, Ramon
- 80CliGiaT-4
- 82CliGiaF-13
- 83CliGiaF-8
- 88WatIndP-676
- 89KinIndS-2
- 90KinIndTI-16
- 91CanIndLD-76
- 91CanIndP-983
- 91LinDriAA-76

Bavasi, Buzzie
- 77PadSchC-6

Baxes, Jim
- 49W72HolS-1
- 59Top-547
- 60Top-318
- 90DodTar-38

Baxes, Mike (Michael)
- 56A'sPos-2
- 58Top-302
- 59Top-381

Baxter, Bob
- 90JamExpP-14
- 91RocExpC-1
- 91RocExpP-2037
- 92WesPalBEC-16
- 92WesPalBEF-2079
- 94HarSenF-2083

Baxter, Duke
- 98MadBlaW-4

Baxter, Herb
- 93YakBeaC-2
- 93YakBeaF-3873
- 94VerBeaDC-4
- 94VerBeaDF-61
- 95ModA'sTI-2

Baxter, Jim
- 88WatIndP-671
- 89LakTigS-2
- 91LinDriAA-402
- 91MemChiLD-402
- 91MemChiP-657

Baxter, William
- 12ImpTobC-80

Bay, Harry Elbert
- 03BreE10-10
- 04FanCraAL-3
- 05IndSouPSoCP-1
- 08AmeLeaPC-1
- 09T206-477
- 10CouT21-1
- 11SpoLifCW-22

Bayas, Subby (Richard Thomas)
- 87NegLeaPD-16

Bayer, Chris
- 86ColMetP-5
- 88St.LucMS-2

Bayless, Dick (Harry Owen)
- 09ColChiE-22
- 12ColRedB-22
- 12ColTinT-22
- 12HomRunKE-78
- 12Zee-137
- 13Zee-131
- 14Zee-126
- 15Zee-121
- 16Zee-73

Baylor, Don Edward
- 71OPC-709
- 71Top-709
- 72OPC-474
- 72OriPos-3
- 72Top-474
- 73BalOriP-5
- 73OPC-384
- 73OriJohP-25
- 73OriTeal-4
- 73Top-384
- 74OPC-187
- 74Top-187
- 74TopSta-121
- 75BalOriP-3
- 75OPC-382
- 75Top-382
- 75TopMin-382
- 76Hos-118
- 76OPC-125
- 76SSP-394
- 76Top-125
- 77A'sPos-81
- 77Hos-129
- 77OPC-133
- 77Top-462
- 78AngFamF-3
- 78OPC-173
- 78SSP270-208
- 78Top-48
- 79Hos-63
- 79OPC-335
- 79Top-635
- 80BurKinPHR-12
- 80Kel-56
- 80OPC-150
- 80Top-203
- 80Top-285
- 80TopSup-9
- 81AllGamPI-47
- 81Don-413
- 81Fle-271
- 81FleStiC-122
- 81Kel-15
- 81LonBeaPT-5
- 81OPC-309
- 81Top-580
- 81TopSti-51
- 81TopSupHT-55
- 82Don-493
- 82Fle-451
- 82FleSta-220
- 82K-M-35
- 82OPC-234
- 82Top-415
- 82TopSti-158
- 83Don-493
- 83Dra-1
- 83Fle-77
- 83FleSta-10
- 83FleSti-33
- 83Kel-29
- 83OPC-105
- 83Top-105
- 83TopFol-5
- 83TopSti-40
- 83TopTra-8T
- 83YanPhoA-2
- 84AllGamPI-138
- 84Don-152
- 84Dra-1
- 84Fle-119
- 84FleSti-45
- 84FunFooP-39
- 84Nes792-335
- 84Nes792-486
- 84OPC-335
- 84Top-335
- 84Top-486
- 84TopRubD-2
- 84TopSti-320
- 84TopTif-335
- 84TopTif-486
- 85AllGamPI-49
- 85AngStrH-2
- 85Don-173
- 85DonHig-35
- 85Dra-3
- 85Fle-121
- 85FleStaS-49
- 85Lea-146
- 85OPC-70
- 85Top-70
- 85TopRubD-2
- 85TopSti-311
- 85TopTif-70
- 85YanTCMP-33
- 86BasStaB-6
- 86Don-347
- 86Fle-99
- 86Fle-631
- 86FleStiC-3
- 86FleUpd-10
- 86OPC-184
- 86Spo-57
- 86Top-765
- 86TopSti-300
- 86TopTif-765
- 86TopTra-6T
- 86TopTraT-6T
- 86Woo-2
- 87BoaandB-17
- 87ClaGam-14
- 87Don-339
- 87DonOpeD-186
- 87Fle-28
- 87FleGamW-2
- 87FleGlo-28
- 87FleHotS-4
- 87FleMin-6
- 87FleStiC-7
- 87KayB-3
- 87Lea-232
- 87OPC-230
- 87OPCBoxB-A
- 87RedSoxP-2
- 87RedSoxSAP-2
- 87SevCoi-E2
- 87Spo-163
- 87SpoTeaP-9
- 87StuPan-15
- 87Top-230
- 87TopGloS-27
- 87TopSti-252
- 87TopTif-230
- 87TopWaxBC-A
- 87TwiTeal-12
- 88A'sMot-8
- 88DonTeaBA-NEW
- 88Fle-2
- 88FleGlo-2
- 88FleGlo-WS11
- 88FleStiWBC-S6
- 88FleWorS-11
- 88OPCBoxB-A
- 88Sco-250
- 88ScoGlo-250
- 88ScoRoo-55T
- 88ScoRooG-55T
- 88StaLinTw-1
- 88Top-545
- 88TopBig-162
- 88TopSti-10
- 88TopTif-545
- 88TopTra-11T
- 88TopTraT-11T
- 88TopWaxBC-A
- 88Woo-1
- 88Woo-29
- 89AngSmo-13
- 89Fle-1
- 89FleGlo-1
- 89Sco-205
- 89Top-673
- 89TopAme2C-3
- 89TopTif-673
- 89UppDec-601
- 90BasWit-5
- 90BreMilB-32
- 90BrePol-NNO
- 90PacLeg-6
- 91BreMilB-32
- 91BrePol-NNO
- 91Kel3D-14
- 91LinDri-14
- 91OriCro-24
- 91SweBasG-6
- 92MDAMVP-13
- 92MVP-1
- 92MVP2H-15
- 92YanWIZ8-9
- 93TedWil-59
- 93Top-504
- 93TopGol-504
- 93TopInaM-504
- 93TopInaR-504
- 93TopMic-504
- 93UppDecAH-7
- 94RocPol-1
- 94UppDecAH-179
- 94UppDecAH1-179
- 95RocPol-2
- 96RocPol-3
- 97RocPol-1

Bayne, William
- 22E120-91

Bazan, Pete
- 80QuaCitCT-14

Bazydlo, Edward
- 52LavPro-17

Bazzani, Matt
- 96SarRedSB-7
- 97SarRedS-2

Beach, Randy
- 75TacTwiK-6

Beach, William
- 88KimN18-1

Beacom, Chris
- 89St.CatBJP-2085
- 90DunBluJS-1

Beahan, Scott
- 83GreHorT-2

Beal, Sally
- 78NewWayCT-2

Beal, Tony
- 86NewBriRSP-2

Beale, Charles
- 96LowSpiB-5
- 97MicBatC-7
- 98TreThuM-7

Beall, Bob (Robert Brooks)
- 75AtlBraP-3
- 76SSP-21
- 79Top-222
- 80RicBraT-19
- 81PorBeaT-7

Beall, Johnny (John Woolf)
- 09ObaT21-1

Beall, Mike
- 89AppFoxP-864
- 90BasCitRS-2

Beall, Walter
- 75Yan192T-1
- 79Yan192T-2
- 84Yan192G-14
- 94ConTSN-1288
- 94ConTSNB-1288

Beals, Bryan
- 88GreFalDTI-19
- 89BakDodCLC-197
- 90BakDodCLC-257

Beals, Greg
- 91PitMetC-2
- 91PitMetP-3425
- 92ColMetC-7
- 92ColMetF-298
- 92ColMetPI-8
- 93St.LucMC-3
- 93St.LuMF-2923

Beamesderfer, Kurt
- 86ChaOriW-1
- 87ChaO'sW-19

Beamon, Charlie (Charles Alon.)
- 56BalOriP-1
- 59Top-192
- 59TopVen-192
- 60HenHouW-30
- 60SeaPop-1
- 75OakOak2A-3
- 75WatRoyT-4
- 77SanJosMC-9
- 78SanJosMMC-12
- 79SpoIndT-6
- 80SpoIndT-24
- 80Top-672
- 81SyrChiT-12
- 81SyrChiTI-3
- 82SyrChiT-15
- 82SyrChiTI-5
- 91OriCro-25

Beamon, Pepper (Nick)
- 80WesHavWCT-18A

Beamon, Trey
- 92ClaDraP-44
- 92ClaFS7-431
- 93AugPirC-3
- 93AugPirF-1557
- 93Bow-302
- 93ClaFS7-125
- 93StaCluM-143
- 94Bow-518
- 94BowBes-B64
- 94BowBesR-B64
- 94CarMudF-1591
- 94Cla-11
- 94ClaGolF-10
- 94UppDecML-198
- 95Bes-47
- 95Bow-272
- 95BowBes-B75
- 95BowBesR-B75
- 95BowGolF-272
- 95ColCho-36
- 95ColChoGS-36
- 95ColChoSS-36
- 95Exc-250
- 95ExcAll-6
- 95PinETA-5
- 95SigRooOJA-AS1
- 95SigRooOJAS-AS1
- 95SPML-6
- 95SPML-135
- 95SPMLA-4
- 95SPMLDtS-DS14
- 95Top-288
- 95UppDecML-41
- 95UppDecMLFS-41
- 95UppDecMLOP-OP22
- 96Bow-197
- 96BowBes-147
- 96BowBesAR-147
- 96BowBesR-147
- 96BowFoi-197
- 96ColCho-435
- 96ColChoGS-435
- 96ColChoSS-435
- 96LeaSig-140
- 96LeaSigPPG-140
- 96LeaSigPPP-140
- 96Top-439
- 96UppDec-235
- 96UppDecFSP-FS3
- 96UppDecPHE-H52
- 96UppDecPreH-H52
- 97Cir-88
- 97CirRav-88
- 97Don-376
- 97DonEli-102
- 97DonEliGS-102
- 97DonEliTotC-6
- 97DonEliTotCDC-6
- 97DonGolPP-376
- 97DonLim-113
- 97DonLimE-113
- 97DonLimENG-113
- 97DonRatR-4
- 97DonSigA-9
- 97DonSigAC-10
- 97DonSigAM-10
- 97DonSilPP-376
- 97Fle-424
- 97FleTif-424
- 97LasVegS1A-5
- 97Lea-172
- 97LeaFraM-172
- 97LeaFraMDC-172
- 97PacPriGotD-GD188
- 97Pin-200
- 97PinArtP-PP200
- 97PinIns-43
- 97PinInsCE-43
- 97PinInsDE-43
- 97PinMusC-200
- 97PinPrePla-200
- 97Sco-317
- 97ScoArtPWB-317
- 97ScoPreS-317
- 97ScoShoS-317
- 97ScoShoSAP-317
- 97Sel-73
- 97SelArtP-73
- 97SelCom-73
- 97SelRegG-73
- 97SelRooR-19
- 97Stu-159
- 97StuPrePG-159
- 97StuPrePS-159
- 97Top-476
- 97Ult-259
- 97UltGolME-259
- 97UltPlaME-259
- 97UppDec-457
- 98ScoRT-230
- 98TolMudHQ-9

Beams, Michael
- 88AshTouP-1054
- 88AubAstP-1962
- 89AshTouP-968
- 90OscAstS-4
- 91LinDriAA-451
- 91NewBriRSLD-451
- 91NewBriRSP-362
- 92NewBriRSF-444
- 92NewBriRSS-476
- 93NewBriRSF-1232
- 93PawRedSTI-3

Bean, Belve
- 93ConTSN-974

Bean, Billy
- 87TolMudHP-26
- 88TolMudHC-12
- 88TolMudHP-595
- 88Top-267
- 88TopClo-6
- 88TopTif-267
- 89ClaLigB-33
- 89DodStaSV-7
- 89ScoHot1R-19
- 89TolMudHP-772
- 90AlbDukCm-25
- 90AlbDukP-356
- 90AlbDukTr-1
- 90CMC-427
- 90DodTar-39
- 90ProAAAF-77
- 91AlbDukLD-1
- 91AlbDukP-1152
- 91LinDriAAA-1
- 91Top-279A
- 93LasVegSF-949
- 94Fle-654
- 94Pac-515
- 94PadMot-13
- 94StaClu-669
- 94StaCluFDI-669
- 94StaCluGR-669
- 94StaCluMOP-669

Bean, Kenneth
- 88MarPhiS-2

❑ 89MarPhiS-2
Beanblossom, Brad
❑ 88CapCodPPaLP-147
❑ 91St.PetCC-17
❑ 91St.PetCP-2280
❑ 92ArkTraF-1134
❑ 92ArkTraS-27
Beane, Billy (William Lamar)
❑ 82JacMetT-19
❑ 84JacMetT-17
❑ 85IntLeaAT-7
❑ 85MetTCM-30
❑ 85TidTidT-14
❑ 86Don-647
❑ 86FleUpd-11
❑ 86TwiTeal-15
❑ 87Fle-535
❑ 87FleGlo-535
❑ 87PorBeaP-5
❑ 87Top-114
❑ 87TopTif-114
❑ 91MetWIZ-26
Bear, Bay B. (Mascot)
❑ 97MobBayBB-4
Bear, Cubbie
❑ 88IowCubP-554
Bear, Smokey
❑ 84AngSmo-28
❑ 84DodSmo-1
❑ 84DodSmo-2
❑ 84DodSmo-3
❑ 84DodSmo-4
❑ 84PadSmo-23
❑ 85CloHSS-39
❑ 86FreGiaSB-29
❑ 86FreGiaSB-30
❑ 86FreGiaSB-31
❑ 87BraSmo-NNO
❑ 87SalSpuS-31
❑ 87SmoNatL-13
❑ 88CubVanLS-4
❑ 88DodSmo-NNO
❑ 88RoySmo-27
Beard, Dave
❑ 79WatA'sT-24
❑ 80OgdA'sT-15
❑ 81TacTigT-24
❑ 81Top-96
❑ 82Fle-87
❑ 83A'sGraG-33
❑ 83Don-113
❑ 83Fle-514
❑ 83FleSta-11
❑ 83FleSti-187
❑ 83Top-102
❑ 84AllGamPI-163
❑ 84Don-218
❑ 84Fle-438
❑ 84FleUpd-9
❑ 84MarMot-11
❑ 84Nes792-513
❑ 84OPC-149
❑ 84Top-513
❑ 84TopSti-336
❑ 84TopTif-513
❑ 84TopTra-8T
❑ 84TopTraT-8T
❑ 85Fle-483
❑ 85MaiGuiT-2
❑ 85Top-232
❑ 85TopTif-232
❑ 86RicBraP-2
❑ 88TolMudHC-1
❑ 88TolMudHP-586
❑ 89TolMudHC-10
❑ 89TolMudHP-777
Beard, Garrett
❑ 89SalDodTI-6
❑ 90YakBeaTI-1
❑ 91BakDodCLC-23
❑ 92ModA'sC-7
❑ 92ModA'sF-3901
❑ 93ModA'sC-3
❑ 93ModA'sF-805
❑ 93TacTigF-3038
❑ 94HunStaF-1334
❑ 95HunStaTI-5
Beard, Mike
❑ 75AtlBraP-4
❑ 76AtlBraP-1
❑ 76OPC-53
❑ 76Top-53
Beard, Ralph
❑ 55Bow-206
Beard, Ted
❑ 81TCM60I-302
Beard, Ted (Cramer T.)
❑ 50PirTeal-1
❑ 51Bow-308
❑ 52Top-150
❑ 77SerSta-3
❑ 83TopRep5-150
❑ 85TCMPla1-19
Bearden, Brent
❑ 94St.CatBJC-3
❑ 94St.CatBJF-3632
Bearden, Doug
❑ 96BriWhiSB-10
❑ 97BelSnaB-9
❑ 98StoPorG-4
Bearden, Gene
❑ 46RemBre-17
❑ 46SpoExcW-1-12
❑ 47Exh-18
❑ 48IndTeal-1
❑ 49Bow-57
❑ 49IndTeal-3
❑ 49IndVisEI-1
❑ 50Bow-93
❑ 50IndNumN-2
❑ 50IndTeal-2
❑ 51Bow-284
❑ 52Bow-173
❑ 52NatTeaL-1
❑ 52Top-229
❑ 53ExhCan-3
❑ 53IndPenCBP-2
❑ 54SeaPop-1
❑ 79TCM50-222
❑ 83TopRep5-229
❑ 85TCMPla1-38
Beardman, Larry
❑ 84MadMusP-24
Beardsley, Chris
❑ 89PalSprACLC-58
Beardsley, Marve
❑ 88KimN18-2
Beare, Gary Ray
❑ 76SpoIndC-14
❑ 76VenLeaS-79
❑ 78SpoIndC-27
❑ 78Top-516
❑ 94BreMilB-102
Bearer, Sean
❑ 98arSenW1-27
❑ 98HarSenM-27
Bearnarth, Larry
❑ 63Top-386
❑ 64MetJayP-1
❑ 64MetTeal-2
❑ 64Top-527
❑ 65MetJayP-1
❑ 65OPC-258
❑ 65Top-258
❑ 66MetVolC-1
❑ 66Top-464
❑ 76ExpRed-2
❑ 76MonExpP-2
❑ 78TCM60I-61
❑ 80MemChiT-8
❑ 85ExpPos-2
❑ 86ExpProPa-14
❑ 87ExpPos-1
❑ 88ExpPos-1
❑ 89ExpPos-2
❑ 90ExpPos-2
❑ 91MetWIZ-27
❑ 94BreMilB-103
❑ 94RocPol-27
Bears, Yakima
❑ 90YakBeaTI-NNO
Bearse, Kevin
❑ 88CarLeaAS-24
❑ 88KinIndS-2
❑ 89CanIndB-1
❑ 89CanIndP-1306
❑ 90Bow-330
❑ 90BowTif-330
❑ 90FleUpd-91
❑ 90IndTeal-4
❑ 90UppDec-715
❑ 91Fle-361
❑ 91IndIndLD-177
❑ 91IndIndP-453
❑ 91LinDriAAA-177
❑ 91TopDeb90-12
Beasley, Andy
❑ 90HamRedS-4
❑ 91SprCarC-6
❑ 91SprCarP-743
❑ 92ClaFS7-277
❑ 92St.PetCC-3
❑ 92St.PetCF-2029
❑ 93St.PetCC-4
❑ 93St.PetCF-2628
Beasley, Bud
❑ 46SunBre-1
❑ 47SigOil-58
❑ 47SunBre-3
Beasley, Chris
❑ 86WatIndP-2
❑ 87WilBilP-22
❑ 89PalSprAP-488
❑ 90CMC-501
❑ 90EdmTraC-4
❑ 90EdmTraP-509
❑ 90ProAAAF-85
❑ 91EdmTraP-1508
❑ 92EdmTraF-3533
❑ 92EdmTraS-152
❑ 92Fle-54
❑ 92SkyAAAF-74
❑ 92StaClu-492
❑ 92TopDeb91-12
❑ 92UppDec-614
Beasley, Lew (Lewis Paige)
❑ 76SacSolC-18
❑ 77TucTorC-4
❑ 93RanKee-66
Beasley, Ray
❑ 96DanBraB-6
❑ 97MacBra-17
❑ 98DanQ-C-24
Beasley, Tony
❑ 89EriOriS-1
❑ 90FreKeyTI-4
❑ 91CarLeaAP-CAR5
❑ 91FreKeyC-16
❑ 91FreKeyP-2370
❑ 92SalBucC-25
❑ 92SalBucF-69
❑ 93CarMudF-2060
❑ 93CarMudTI-4
❑ 95CarMudF-162
❑ 96CarMudB-16
❑ 97CalCanB-6
❑ 98CarMudM-27
Beason-Samuels, Cody
❑ 92GulCoaYF-3795
Beatin, Ebenezer
❑ 87OldJudN-25
Beatriz, Ramy
❑ 97HelBreB-4
❑ 98BelSnaM-7
Beattie, Andrew
❑ 98BilMusTI-4
Beattie, Burt
❑ 87KenTwiP-8
Beattie, Jim
❑ 77Spo-8824
❑ 77WesHavYT-3
❑ 78YanPhoA-1
❑ 79ColCliT-8
❑ 79OPC-86
❑ 79Top-179
❑ 79YanBurK-7
❑ 79YanPicA-1
❑ 80MarPos-4
❑ 80Top-334
❑ 81Don-166
❑ 81SpoIndT-29
❑ 81Top-443
❑ 82Don-478
❑ 82MarPos-5
❑ 82Top-22
❑ 83Don-176
❑ 83Fle-472
❑ 83FleSta-12
❑ 83OPC-191
❑ 83Top-675
❑ 83Top-711
❑ 84Don-191
❑ 84Fle-605
❑ 84MarMot-12
❑ 84Nes792-288
❑ 84OPC-288
❑ 84Top-288
❑ 84TopSti-346
❑ 84TopTif-288
❑ 85Don-313
❑ 85Fle-484
❑ 85Lea-85
❑ 85MarMot-15
❑ 85OPC-303
❑ 85Top-505
❑ 85TopSti-334
❑ 85TopTif-505
❑ 86Don-196
❑ 86Fle-458
❑ 86MarMot-27
❑ 86MarPacNB-1
❑ 86Top-729
❑ 86TopTif-729
❑ 87Top-117
❑ 87TopTif-117
❑ 92YanWIZ7-11
Beatty, Blaine
❑ 87HagSunP-12
❑ 88JacMetGS-15
❑ 88TexLeaAGS-18
❑ 89MetColP-22
❑ 89TidTidC-9
❑ 89TidTidP-1964
❑ 90Bow-130
❑ 90BowTif-130
❑ 90Fle-197
❑ 90FleCan-197
❑ 90HagSunDGB-2
❑ 90MetColP-25
❑ 90Sco-632
❑ 90TopDeb89-11
❑ 90TopTVM-7
❑ 90UppDec-23
❑ 91LinDriAAA-552
❑ 91MetColP-23
❑ 91MetWIZ-28
❑ 91TidTidLD-552
❑ 91TidTidP-2500
❑ 92IndIndF-1852
❑ 92IndIndS-183
❑ 92Sco-843
❑ 92SkyAAAF-86
❑ 93CarMudF-2044
❑ 93CarMudTI-12
❑ 94ChaLooF-1350
❑ 95IndIndF-88
❑ 96CarMudB-1
❑ 97CalCanB-7
❑ 98EriSeaWM-28
Beatty, Gary
❑ 91BatCliCB-30
❑ 92SpaPhiC-25
Beatty, Justin
❑ 15Zee-2
Beauchamp, Jim (James E.)
❑ 62KahAtl-1
❑ 64Top-492
❑ 65Top-409
❑ 66OPC-84
❑ 66Top-84
❑ 66TopVen-84
❑ 67Top-307
❑ 69Top-613
❑ 70CarTeal-3
❑ 71CarTeal-2
❑ 71MLBOffS-266
❑ 71OPC-322
❑ 71Top-322
❑ 72Top-594
❑ 73OPC-137
❑ 73Top-137
❑ 74OPC-424
❑ 74Top-424
❑ 78ChaChaT-2
❑ 79ChaChaT-2
❑ 80IndIndTI-2
❑ 81IndIndTI-2
❑ 82SyrChiT-26
❑ 82SyrChiTI-6
❑ 83SyrChiT-1
❑ 84SyrChiT-1
❑ 85GreBraTI-3
❑ 86GreBraTI-3
❑ 87AstSer1-3
❑ 87GreBraB-1
❑ 87SouLeaAJ-22
❑ 88RicBraC-23
❑ 88RicBraP-15
❑ 89RicBraBC-1
❑ 89RicBraC-25
❑ 89RicBraP-822
❑ 89RicBraTI-1
❑ 89TriAAAP-AAA53
❑ 90CMC-283
❑ 90ProAAAF-419
❑ 90RicBra2ATI-4
❑ 90RicBraC-7
❑ 90RicBraP-274
❑ 90RicBraTI-3
❑ 91BraSubS-2
❑ 91MetWIZ-29
❑ 92BraLykS-2
❑ 93BraLykS-2
❑ 93ColRedC-3
❑ 93ColRedF-588
❑ 94BraLykP-2
❑ 94BraLykS-2
Beauchamp, Kash
❑ 86KnoBluJP-1
❑ 87SyrChiT-29
❑ 88KnoBluJB-9
❑ 89RicBraBC-2
❑ 89RicBraC-23
❑ 89RicBraP-836
❑ 89RicBraTI-2
❑ 90CMC-544
❑ 90PhoFirC-17
❑ 90PhoFirP-21
❑ 90ProAAAF-47
❑ 94AlbDukF-853
❑ 94SanAntMF-2480
❑ 96WesPalBEB-4
Beaulac, Joe
❑ 89SalLakTTI-24
❑ 90MiaMirIS-2
Beaumont, Ginger (Clarence H.)
❑ 03BreE10-4
❑ 06FanCraNL-2
❑ 08RosComP-88
❑ 09ColChiE-23A
❑ 09ColChiE-23B
❑ 09ColChiE-23C
❑ 09T206-16
❑ 11PinT-5-220
❑ 11SpoLifCW-23
❑ 11SpoLifM-166
❑ 12ColRedB-23A
❑ 12ColRedB-23B
❑ 12ColRedB-23C
❑ 12ColTinT-23A
❑ 12ColTinT-23B
❑ 12ColTinT-23C
Beaumont, Matt
❑ 93BazTeaU-18
❑ 93TopTra-30T
❑ 94SigRooDPBSDP-1
❑ 94StaCluDP-48
❑ 94StaCluDPFDI-48
❑ 95Bes-11
❑ 95LakElsSTI-3
❑ 95SigRooDDS-DD1
❑ 95SigRooDDSS-DD1
❑ 95SigRooMOP-P10
❑ 95SigRooMOPS-P10
❑ 95SPML-27
❑ 96Bow-331
❑ 96BowFoi-331
❑ 96Exc-22
❑ 96ExcSeaC-1
❑ 96HilStaHWB-33
❑ 96MidAngB-6
❑ 96MidAngOHP-3
❑ 96TexLeaAB-19
❑ 97LakElsSG-5
❑ 97MidAng-5
❑ 98MidAngG-4
❑ 98MidAngO-3
Beaurivage, Ron
❑ 77ModA'sC-19
Beaver, Greg
❑ 98EveAquG-2
Beavers, Alan
❑ 92HamRedC-14
❑ 92HamRedF-1579
Beavers, Mark
❑ 85AncGlaPTI-3
❑ 86MedA'sC-55
❑ 86ModA'sC-23
❑ 87MadMusP-2
❑ 87MadMusP-20
❑ 88ModA'sCLC-61
❑ 89RivRedWB-2
❑ 89RivRedWCLC-23
❑ 89RivRedWP-1390
Beazley, Johnny
❑ 46SeaSLP-3
❑ 79DiaGre-220
❑ 83Car194T-41
❑ 84TCMPla1-26
BeBop, Spec
❑ 76LauIndC-20
Beck, Boom Boom (Walter)
❑ 27MidBre-23
❑ 33Zee-17
❑ 34DiaMatCSB-6
❑ 34Gou-50
❑ 37Zee-12
❑ 40PhiTeal-3
❑ 40PlaBal-217
❑ 41PhiTeal-3
❑ 43PhiTeal-2
❑ 55Bow-281
❑ 58SeaTeal-3
❑ 77TCMTheWY-28
❑ 79DiaGre-310
❑ 90DodTar-40
❑ 93ConTSN-734
Beck, Brian
❑ 90ChaRaiB-4
❑ 90ChaRaiP-2050
❑ 91ChaRaiC-20
❑ 91ChaRaiP-106
❑ 92AugPirC-21
❑ 92AugPirF-249
❑ 93WelPirC-2
❑ 93WelPirF-3347
Beck, Chris
❑ 94BelMarC-5
❑ 94BelMarF-3224
❑ 96LanJetB-6
❑ 97LanJet-5
Beck, Clyde Eugene
❑ 24Zee-1
❑ 25Zee-1
❑ 29ExhFou-5
❑ 30CubTeal-1
❑ 33WorCig(-4
❑ 33Zee-15
❑ 33Zee-16
❑ 37Zee-31
Beck, Dion
❑ 85BenPhiC-1
❑ 87ReaPhiP-8
❑ 91RenSilSCLC-23
Beck, Erve (Ervin Thomas)
❑ 03BreE10-5
❑ 90DodTar-900
Beck, Fred (Frederick T.)
❑ 09T206-17
❑ 11PinT-5-703
❑ 11S74Sil-42
❑ 11SpoLifCW-24
❑ 11SpoLifM-135
❑ 11T205-11
Beck, Greg
❑ 94HelBreF-3604
❑ 94HelBreSP-22
❑ 95BelBreTI-10
❑ 96StoPorB-12
❑ 97StoPor-19
❑ 98El PasDG-3
Beck, Johnny
❑ 30Zee-101
❑ 94MarPhiC-3
❑ 94MarPhiF-3282
Beck, Rich
❑ 66Top-234
❑ 66TopVen-234
❑ 81TCM60I-476
❑ 92YanWIZ6-7
Beck, Rod
❑ 88CliGiaP-695
❑ 88MidLeaAGS-5
❑ 89SanJosGB-2
❑ 89SanJosGCLC-209
❑ 89SanJosGP-459
❑ 89SanJosGS-1
❑ 89Sta-82
❑ 90ShrCapP-1435
❑ 90ShrCapS-2
❑ 91LinDriAAA-378
❑ 91PhoFirLD-378
❑ 91PhoFirP-59
❑ 92Don-461
❑ 92Fle-627
❑ 92GiaMot-14
❑ 92GiaPacGaE-4
❑ 92OPCPre-197
❑ 92Pin-613
❑ 92Sco-746
❑ 92TopDeb91-13
❑ 92TopGol-264
❑ 92TopGolW-264
❑ 92Ult-586
❑ 93Bow-308
❑ 93Don-420
❑ 93Fla-137

- 93Fle-150
- 93GiaMot-12
- 93GiaPos-2
- 93GiaStaC-12
- 93Lea-232
- 93OPC-11
- 93Pin-398
- 93Sco-391
- 93SP-109
- 93StaClu-81
- 93StaCluFDI-81
- 93StaCluMOP-81
- 93Top-604
- 93TopGol-604
- 93TopInaM-604
- 93TopInaR-604
- 93TopMic-604
- 93Ult-126
- 93UppDec-73
- 93UppDecGold-73
- 94Bow-191
- 94BowBes-R14
- 94BowBesR-R14
- 94ColC-49
- 94ColChoGS-49
- 94ColChoSS-49
- 94Don-604
- 94Fin-169
- 94FinPre-169P
- 94FinRef-169
- 94Fla-442
- 94Fle-680
- 94FleAllS-27
- 94FleExtB-381
- 94FleExtBGB-2
- 94FUnPac-95
- 94GiaAMC-2
- 94GiaKTV-2
- 94GiaMot-8
- 94GiaTarBC-2
- 94GiaUSPC-6H
- 94GiaUSPC-13S
- 94Lea-224
- 94LeaL-155
- 94OPC-182
- 94Pac-538
- 94PanSti-260
- 94Pin-118
- 94PinArtP-118
- 94PinMusC-118
- 94Sco-508
- 94ScoGolR-508
- 94Sel-328
- 94SP-89
- 94SPDieC-89
- 94Spo-129
- 94StaClu-436
- 94StaCluFDI-436
- 94StaCluGR-436
- 94StaCluMO-44
- 94StaCluMOP-436
- 94StaCluT-30
- 94StaCluTFDI-30
- 94Stu-82
- 94Top-146
- 94TopGol-146
- 94TopSpa-146
- 94TriPla-101
- 94Ult-285
- 94UltFir-7
- 94UppDec-46
- 94UppDec-142
- 94UppDecED-46
- 94UppDecED-142
- 95Baz-73
- 95Bow-319
- 95ColCho-251
- 95ColChoGS-251
- 95ColChoSE-112
- 95ColChoSEGS-112
- 95ColChoSESS-112
- 95ColChoSS-251
- 95Don-113
- 95DonPreP-113
- 95DonTopotO-347
- 95Emo-191
- 95Fin-34
- 95FinRef-34
- 95Fla-206
- 95Fle-572
- 95FleAllS-23
- 95FleTeaL-28
- 95GiaMot-10
- 95Lea-328
- 95PacPri-119
- 95PanSti-3
- 95Pin-326
- 95PinArtP-326
- 95PinMusC-326
- 95RedFol-33
- 95Sco-165
- 95ScoGolR-165
- 95ScoHaloG-HG53
- 95ScoPlaTS-165
- 95SP-112
- 95SPCha-97
- 95SPChaDC-97
- 95SPSil-112
- 95StaClu-59
- 95StaCluFDI-59
- 95StaCluMOP-59
- 95StaCluSTWS-59
- 95StaCluVR-36
- 95StaCluVRMO-36
- 95Stu-146
- 95Top-417
- 95TopCyb-217
- 95TopEmb-138
- 95TopEmbGI-138
- 95Ult-239
- 95UltGolM-239
- 95UppDec-86
- 95UppDecED-86
- 95UppDecEDG-86
- 95UppDecSE-202
- 95UppDecSEG-202
- 96Baz-56
- 96Cir-191
- 96CirRav-191
- 96ColCho-715
- 96ColChoGS-715
- 96ColChoSS-715
- 96Don-165
- 96DonPreP-165
- 96EmoXL-285
- 96Fin-B111
- 96FinRef-B111
- 96Fla-383
- 96Fle-581
- 96FleTif-581
- 96GiaMot-3
- 96Lea-204
- 96LeaPrePB-204
- 96LeaPrePG-204
- 96LeaPrePS-204
- 96MetUni-240
- 96MetUniP-240
- 96Pac-209
- 96PanSti-106
- 96Pin-292
- 96PinFoil-292
- 96Sco-428
- 96SelTeaN-18
- 96SP-168
- 96StaClu-59
- 96StaClu-270
- 96StaCluEPB-59
- 96StaCluEPG-59
- 96StaCluEPS-59
- 96StaCluMOP-59
- 96StaCluMOP-270
- 96Top-201
- 96TopChr-68
- 96TopChrR-68
- 96TopGal-27
- 96TopGalPPI-27
- 96Ult-564
- 96UltGolM-564
- 96UppDec-453
- 97Cir-260
- 97CirRav-260
- 97ColCho-453
- 97Don-329
- 97DonGolPP-329
- 97DonLim-92
- 97DonLimE-92
- 97DonLimENG-92
- 97DonSilPP-329
- 97Fin-263
- 97FinRef-263
- 97Fle-475
- 97FleTif-475
- 97MetUni-241
- 97Pac-438
- 97PacLigB-438
- 97PacSil-438
- 97SpoIll-123
- 97SpoIllEE-123
- 97StaClu-140
- 97StaCluMOP-140
- 97StrAll-6
- 97Top-429
- 97TopChr-152
- 97TopChrR-152
- 97TopSta-79
- 97TopStaAM-79
- 97Ult-301
- 97UltGolME-301
- 97UltPlaME-301
- 97UppDec-496
- 98Bow-236
- 98BowChr-236
- 98BowChrGA-236
- 98BowChrGAR-236
- 98BowChrI-236
- 98BowChrIR-236
- 98BowChrR-236
- 98BowGolA-236
- 98BowInt-236
- 98ColCho-328
- 98Fle-160
- 98Fle-439
- 98MetUni-62
- 98MetUniPMG-62
- 98Pac-436
- 98PacAur-110
- 98PacInvTeam-25
- 98PacOnl-136
- 98PacOnlR-136
- 98PacOnlWC-136
- 98PacPar-136
- 98PacParC-136
- 98PacParG-136
- 98PacParHS-136
- 98PacParPB-136
- 98PacParR-136
- 98PacPlaB-436
- 98PacRedT-436
- 98PacSil-436
- 98Pin-12
- 98PinArtP-PP12
- 98PinMusC-PP12
- 98PinPreP-12
- 98StaCluFDI-374
- 98StaCluI-374
- 98StaCluOneK-374
- 98StaCluPP-374
- 98Top-437
- 98TopChr-437
- 98TopChrR-437
- 98TopDevR-437
- 98TopDia-437
- 98TopMiniC-437
- 98TopSta-3
- 98TopStaB-3
- 98TopStaG-3
- 98TopStaGR-3
- 98TopStaS-3
- 98Ult-56
- 98Ult-435
- 98UltGolM-56
- 98UltGolM-435
- 98UltMas-56
- 98UltMas-435
- 98UltPlaM-56
- 98UltPlaM-435
- 98UppDec-658
- 99199Fin-93
- 99FinGolRef-93
- 99FinRef-93
- 99Fle-61
- 99FleSta9-61
- 99FleWarT-61
- 99MetUni-85
- 99MetUniGM-85
- 99MetUniPMG-85
- 99Pac-80
- 99PacAur-32
- 99PacAurOD-32
- 99PacCroC-54
- 99PacCroCPB-54
- 99PacPar-46
- 99PacParC-46
- 99PacParG-46
- 99PacParHoloGold-46
- 99PacParHS-46
- 99PacParOD-46
- 99PacParPB-46
- 99PacParRed-46
- 99PacPlaB-80
- 99PacPri-27
- 99PacPriHB-27
- 99PacPriHG-27
- 99PacPriHM-27
- 99PacPriHP-27
- 99PacPriRed-27
- 99PacPriS-55
- 99PacPriS206-55
- 99PacPriS206R-55
- 99PacRed-80
- 99SkyPre-81
- 99SkyPreR-81
- 99SkyThu-217
- 99SkyThuRant-217
- 99SkyThuRave-217
- 99StaClu-54
- 99StaCluFDI-54
- 99StaCluOoaK-54
- 99StaCluPP-54
- 99ThuSkySupR-217
- 99Top-56
- 99TopChr-56
- 99TopChrR-56
- 99TopGal-89
- 99TopGalPP-89
- 99TopGalPPI-89
- 99TopMVPP-56
- 99TopOpeD-31
- 99Ult-41
- 99UltGolM-41
- 99UltMas-41
- 99UltPlaM-41
- 99UppDec-57
- 99UppDecEL1-57
- 99UppDecEL2-57
- 99UppDecM-42
- 99UppDecMGS-42
- 99UppDecMHFS-42
- 99UppDecMP-42
- 99UppDecMSS-42
- 99Vic-87

Beck, Wynn

- 90MadMusB-28
- 90MadMusP-2271

Beck, Zinn Bertram

- 11HelSta-140
- 15SpoNewM-11
- 16SpoNewM-12
- 19Zee-124
- 67SpoHobFC-41

Beckendorf, Heinie (Henry W.)

- 07TigACDPP-16
- 09TigMorBBBP-2
- 09TigTaCP-1
- 10JHDABE-1
- 11SpoLifCW-25
- 11SpoLifM-53

Becker, Beals

- 09ColChiE-24
- 09T206-18
- 10CouT21-2
- 10DomDisP-9
- 10SweCapPP-107
- 11HelSta-121
- 11PinT-5-266
- 11S74Sil-80
- 11T205-12
- 12ColRedB-24
- 12ColTinT-24
- 12HasTriFT-48D
- 12T207-10
- 14CraJacE-96
- 14PieStaT-8
- 15CraJacE-96
- 16FleBreD-8
- 25Zee-148
- 74CapPub-80

Becker, Brian

- 97ChaRivDG-5
- 98St.PetDRM-18

Becker, David

- 92ClaDraP-106
- 94MedHatBJF-3686
- 94MedHatBJSP-10

Becker, Gregory

- 87St.PetCP-23
- 88MidLeaAGS-27
- 88SprCarB-5
- 89St.PetCS-2
- 89Sta-47

Becker, Heinz R.

- 43CubTeal-2
- 44CubTeal-1
- 58DodTeal-2

Becker, Jesse

- 13Zee-25

Becker, Joe (Joseph Edward)

- 33Zee-102
- 52Par-1
- 55DodGolS-29
- 56Dod-3
- 60DodUniO-23
- 60Top-463
- 65CarTeal-2
- 72TCMthe3-107
- 79TCM50-187

Becker, July

- 52LavPro-105

Becker, Kevin

- 94UtiBluSC-4
- 94UtiBluSF-3810

Becker, Rich

- 90EliTwiS-1
- 91Cla/Bes-345
- 91KenTwiC-25
- 91KenTwiP-2086
- 92Bow-330
- 92CalLeaACL-37
- 92ClaFS7-293
- 92UppDecML-245
- 92VisOakC-2
- 92VisOakF-1025
- 93Bow-593
- 93ClaFS7-151
- 93ClaGolF-41
- 93ExcFS7-197
- 93ExcLeaLF-9
- 93NasXprF-413
- 93Top-658
- 93TopGol-658
- 93TopInaM-658
- 93TopInaR-658
- 93TopMic-658
- 93UppDec-447
- 93UppDecGold-447
- 94Bow-216
- 94Bow-375
- 94ColC-1
- 94ColChoGS-1
- 94ColChoSS-1
- 94Fla-72
- 94FleAllR-M2
- 94FleExtB-114
- 94FleUpd-59
- 94FUnPac-9
- 94LeaGolR-16
- 94LeaLimR-4
- 94Pin-529
- 94PinArtP-529
- 94PinMusC-529
- 94ScoRoo-RT94
- 94ScoRooGR-RT94
- 94ScoRooSR-SU12
- 94Sel-390
- 94SelRooS-RS14
- 94SP-183
- 94SPDieC-183
- 94SpoRoo-102
- 94SpoRooAP-102
- 94SpoRooRS-TR17
- 94SpoRooS-102
- 94Top-71
- 94TopGol-71
- 94TopSpa-71
- 94Ult-385
- 94UppDec-4
- 94UppDecED-4
- 95Bow-421
- 95ColCho-491
- 95ColChoGS-491
- 95ColChoSS-491
- 95Don-88
- 95DonPreP-88
- 95Fin-310
- 95FinRef-310
- 95Fle-197
- 95Pac-245
- 95Pin-211
- 95PinArtP-211
- 95PinMusC-211
- 95Sco-296
- 95ScoGolR-296
- 95ScoPlaTS-296
- 95Sel-150
- 95SelArtP-150
- 95SP-174
- 95SPSil-174
- 95Stu-126
- 95Ult-72
- 95UltGolM-72
- 95UppDecSE-82
- 95UppDecSEG-82
- 95Zen-118
- 96ColCho-608
- 96ColChoGS-608
- 96ColChoSS-608
- 96Don-436
- 96DonPreP-436
- 96Fla-111
- 96Fle-163
- 96FleTif-163
- 96LeaSigA-18
- 96LeaSigAG-18
- 96LeaSigAS-18
- 96Pac-364
- 96Sco-2
- 96ScoDugC-A2
- 96ScoDugCAP-A2
- 96Top-28
- 96Ult-372
- 96UltGolM-372
- 97Cir-54
- 97CirRav-54
- 97ColCho-152
- 97Don-230
- 97DonGolPP-230
- 97DonLim-66
- 97DonLimE-66
- 97DonLimENG-66
- 97DonSilPP-230
- 97Fle-143
- 97FleTif-143
- 97Lea-117
- 97LeaFraM-117
- 97LeaFraMDC-117
- 97MetUni-208
- 97Pac-133
- 97PacLigB-133
- 97PacSil-133
- 97Sco-417
- 97ScoArtPWB-417
- 97ScoResC-417
- 97ScoShoS-417
- 97ScoShoSAP-417
- 97SP-106
- 97StaClu-282
- 97StaCluMOP-282
- 97Top-148
- 97Ult-409
- 97UltGolME-409
- 97UltPlaME-409
- 97UppDec-409
- 98ColCho-439
- 98Fle-111
- 98Pac-129
- 98PacOnl-471
- 98PacOnlR-471
- 98PacOnlWC-471
- 98PacPlaB-129
- 98PacRedT-129
- 98PacSil-129
- 98PinPlu-97
- 98PinSna-NYM4
- 98StaCluFDI-221
- 98StaCluI-221
- 98StaCluOneK-221
- 98StaCluPP-221
- 98Top-82
- 98TopChr-82
- 98TopChrR-82
- 98TopDevR-82
- 98TopDia-82
- 98TopMiniC-82
- 98Ult-404
- 98UltGolM-404
- 98UltMas-404
- 98UltPlaM-404
- 98UppDec-701

Becker, Tim

- 87Ft.LauYP-1
- 88AlbYanP-1341
- 89AlbYanB-20
- 89AlbYanP-315
- 89AlbYanSt-2

Becker, Tom

- 88LitFalMP-4
- 96GreBatB-5
- 97TamYan-5

Beckerman, Andy

- 92PitMetC-5
- 92PitMetF-3286
- 93CapCitBC-2
- 93CapCitBF-451
- 93SouAtlLAGF-34
- 94BinMetF-696

Beckert, Glenn Alfred

- 65Top-549
- 66CubTeal-4
- 66Top-232
- 66TopVen-232
- 67CokCapC-3
- 67CubProPS-3
- 67DexPre-20
- 67ProPizC-3

❑ 67Top-296
❑ 68OPC-101
❑ 68Top-101
❑ 68TopVen-101
❑ 69CubBumS-2
❑ 69CubJewT-4
❑ 69CubPho-3
❑ 69CubTealC-2
❑ 69KelPin-3
❑ 69MilBra-22
❑ 69MLBOffS-119
❑ 69OPC-171
❑ 69Top-171
❑ 69TopFou-5
❑ 69TopSta-12
❑ 69TopTeaP-4
❑ 70CubDunD-2
❑ 70DayDaiNM-102b
❑ 70Kel-43
❑ 70MLBOffS-14
❑ 70OPC-480
❑ 70SunPin-2
❑ 70Top-480
❑ 70TopScr-5
❑ 71Kel-71
❑ 71MilDud-35
❑ 71MLBOffS-26
❑ 71OPC-390
❑ 71Top-390
❑ 71TopCoi-143
❑ 71TopSup-50
❑ 71TopTat-10
❑ 72CubChi-2
❑ 72CubTeal-2
❑ 72Kel-24
❑ 72MilBra-29
❑ 72OPC-45
❑ 72OPC-46
❑ 72OPC-85
❑ 72Top-45A
❑ 72Top-45B
❑ 72Top-46
❑ 72Top-85
❑ 73OPC-440
❑ 73Top-440
❑ 74OPC-241
❑ 74PadDea-3
❑ 74PadMcDD-2
❑ 74PadTeal-2
❑ 74Top-241A
❑ 74Top-241B
❑ 74TopSta-11
❑ 75Hos-103
❑ 75HosTwi-103
❑ 75OPC-484
❑ 75Top-484
❑ 75TopMin-484
❑ 77PadSchC-7
❑ 81TCM60I-367
❑ 84CubUno-2
❑ 84CubUno-7
❑ 89PacLegI-142
❑ 89SweBasG-116
❑ 93UppDecAH-8

Beckett, Dr. (Jim)
❑ 85DalNatCC-12

Beckett, Robbie
❑ 90ClaDraP-25
❑ 91Bow-655
❑ 91ChaRaiC-1
❑ 91ChaRaiP-87
❑ 91Cla/Bes-162
❑ 91Sco-673
❑ 92Bow-508
❑ 92WatDiaC-14
❑ 92WatDiaF-2133
❑ 93Bow-406
❑ 93ClaFS7-154
❑ 93RanCucQC-3
❑ 93RanCucQF-819
❑ 94BowBes-B27
❑ 94BowBesR-B27
❑ 94Cla-93
❑ 94SigRoo-23
❑ 94SigRooS-23
❑ 94WicWraF-182
❑ 95MemChiTI-11
❑ 96NewHavRB-5
❑ 96PorSeaDB-7
❑ 97ColSprSTI-1
❑ 98ColSprSS-41

Beckley, Jake (Jacob Peter)
❑ 03BreE10-6
❑ 06FanCraNL-3
❑ 09T206-398
❑ 76GrePlaG-7
❑ 76ShaPiz-120
❑ 80PerHaloFP-120
❑ 80SSPHOF-120
❑ 87OldJudN-26
❑ 94OriofB-69

Beckman, Bernie
❑ 74AlbDukTI-2
❑ 83SyrChiT-2

Beckman, Bill
❑ 42A'sTeal-2
❑ 92ConTSN-623

Becks, Ryan
❑ 97VerExpB-8
❑ 98CapFeaCM-1

Beckwith, Joe
❑ 79AlbDukTc-20
❑ 80AlbDukTc-2
❑ 80DodPol-27
❑ 80Top-679
❑ 81Dod-3
❑ 81DodPol-27
❑ 81Top-231
❑ 82AlbDukTc-1
❑ 83DodPol-27
❑ 83Fle-202
❑ 84Don-337
❑ 84Fle-97
❑ 84FleUpd-10
❑ 84Nes792-454
❑ 84RoyPos-3
❑ 84Top-454
❑ 84TopTif-454
❑ 84TopTra-9T
❑ 84TopTraT-9T
❑ 85Don-541
❑ 85Fle-197
❑ 85RoyTeal-2
❑ 85Top-77
❑ 85TopTif-77
❑ 86Fle-2
❑ 86SyrChiP-4
❑ 86Top-562
❑ 86TopTif-562
❑ 90DodTar-41

Beckwith, John
❑ 74LauOldTBS-6
❑ 86NegLeaF-67
❑ 90NegLeaS-22

Becquer, Julio V.
❑ 58SeaTeal-4
❑ 58Top-458
❑ 59SenTealW-2
❑ 59Top-93
❑ 59TopVen-93
❑ 60Lea-43
❑ 60SenJayP-2
❑ 60Top-271
❑ 61AngJayP-2
❑ 61Top-329

Bedard, Roger
❑ 52LavPro-49

Bedell, Howard W.
❑ 61Top-353
❑ 62SalPlaC-217
❑ 62ShiPlaC-217
❑ 62Top-76
❑ 62TopVen-76
❑ 84RoyPos-2
❑ 93BenRocCB-27
❑ 93BenRocF-3283

Bedell, Jeff
❑ 86Ft.MyeRP-3

Bedinger, Doug
❑ 95ForWayWTI-2

Bedrosian, Dave
❑ 76WauMetT-3

Bedrosian, Steve
❑ 79SavBraT-14
❑ 81RicBraT-12
❑ 82BraBurKL-2
❑ 82BraPol-32
❑ 82Don-401
❑ 82Top-502
❑ 82TopTra-4T
❑ 83BraPol-32
❑ 83Don-173
❑ 83Fle-129
❑ 83FleSti-89
❑ 83OPC-157
❑ 83Top-157
❑ 84AllGamPI-74
❑ 84BraPol-32
❑ 84Don-565
❑ 84Fle-171
❑ 84Nes792-365
❑ 84OPC-365
❑ 84raPho-3
❑ 84Top-365
❑ 84TopSti-38
❑ 84TopTif-365
❑ 85AllGamPI-164
❑ 85BraHos-3
❑ 85BraPol-32
❑ 85Don-628
❑ 85Fle-319
❑ 85Lea-51
❑ 85OPC-25
❑ 85SevCoi-S6
❑ 85Top-25
❑ 85TopMin-25
❑ 85TopSti-23
❑ 85TopTif-25
❑ 86Don-199
❑ 86Fle-508
❑ 86FleUpd-12
❑ 86OPC-181
❑ 86PhiCIG-11
❑ 86PhiTas-40
❑ 86Top-648
❑ 86TopSti-40
❑ 86TopTif-648
❑ 86TopTra-7T
❑ 86TopTraT-7T
❑ 87Don-185
❑ 87DonHig-9
❑ 87Fle-170
❑ 87FleGlo-170
❑ 87FleLimE-3
❑ 87FleSluBC-M1
❑ 87FleStiC-8
❑ 87OPC-233
❑ 87PhiTas-40
❑ 87RedFolSB-98
❑ 87SmoNatL-7
❑ 87Spo-110
❑ 87SpoTeaP-6
❑ 87Top-736
❑ 87TopMinL-27
❑ 87TopSti-124
❑ 87TopTif-736
❑ 88ClaBlu-222
❑ 88Don-62
❑ 88DonAll-61
❑ 88DonBasB-16
❑ 88Fle-298
❑ 88Fle-627
❑ 88FleAwaW-1
❑ 88FleGlo-298
❑ 88FleGlo-627
❑ 88FleMin-98
❑ 88FleStiC-107
❑ 88FleSup-1
❑ 88KeyFooD-18
❑ 88Lea-82
❑ 88MSAIceTD-19
❑ 88Nes-25
❑ 88OPC-344
❑ 88OPCBoxB-B
❑ 88OurOwnTD-18
❑ 88PanSti-351
❑ 88PanSti-440
❑ 88PhiTas-3
❑ 88Sco-161
❑ 88Sco-656
❑ 88ScoGlo-161
❑ 88ScoGlo-656
❑ 88Spo-70
❑ 88Spo-222
❑ 88StaLinPh-2
❑ 88TarPla-2
❑ 88TetTeaD-18
❑ 88Top-407
❑ 88Top-440
❑ 88TopBig-23
❑ 88TopClo-7
❑ 88TopCoi-34
❑ 88TopGaloC-1
❑ 88TopGloS-28
❑ 88TopMinL-64
❑ 88TopRevLL-11
❑ 88TopSti-6
❑ 88TopSti-116
❑ 88TopStiB-31
❑ 88TopTif-407
❑ 88TopTif-440
❑ 88TopUKM-2
❑ 88TopUKMT-2
❑ 88TopWaxBC-B
❑ 88WeiMarD-18
❑ 88Woo-10
❑ 89Bow-395
❑ 89BowTif-395
❑ 89ClaLigB-34
❑ 89Don-24
❑ 89Don-75
❑ 89DonBasB-303
❑ 89DonSupD-24
❑ 89Fle-562
❑ 89FleBasM-1
❑ 89FleGlo-562
❑ 89KeyFooD-15
❑ 89MSAIceTD-15
❑ 89OurOwnTD-15
❑ 89PanSti-145
❑ 89PhiTas-1
❑ 89Sco-260
❑ 89ScoHot1S-29
❑ 89ScoRoo-49T
❑ 89Spo-63
❑ 89TetTeaD-15
❑ 89Top-20
❑ 89TopBasT-147
❑ 89TopBig-137
❑ 89TopSti-112
❑ 89TopTif-20
❑ 89TopTra-8T
❑ 89TopTraT-8T
❑ 89UppDec-511
❑ 89WeiMarD-15
❑ 90Bow-226
❑ 90BowTif-226
❑ 90ClaBlu-62
❑ 90Don-295
❑ 90DonBesN-99
❑ 90Fle-50
❑ 90FleCan-50
❑ 90GiaMot-6
❑ 90GiaSmo-2
❑ 90Lea-3
❑ 90OPC-310
❑ 90PanSti-364
❑ 90PubIntS-232
❑ 90Sco-379
❑ 90Sco100S-31
❑ 90Spo-104
❑ 90Top-310
❑ 90TopBig-275
❑ 90TopSti-86
❑ 90TopTif-310
❑ 90UppDec-618
❑ 91Bow-317
❑ 91DodPho-9
❑ 91Don-207
❑ 91Fle-254
❑ 91Lea-505
❑ 91OPC-125
❑ 91OPCPre-5
❑ 91RedFolS-7
❑ 91Sco-459
❑ 91ScoRoo-14T
❑ 91StaClu-531
❑ 91Stu-82
❑ 91Top-125
❑ 91TopDesS-125
❑ 91TopMic-125
❑ 91TopTif-125
❑ 91TopTra-6T
❑ 91TopTraT-6T
❑ 91UppDec-422
❑ 91UppDec-738
❑ 92Don-184
❑ 92Fle-197
❑ 92OPC-267
❑ 92Sco-17
❑ 92Top-267
❑ 92TopGol-267
❑ 92TopGolW-267
❑ 92TopMic-267
❑ 92UppDec-622
❑ 93BraLykP-2
❑ 93BraLykS-3
❑ 93FleFinE-1
❑ 93StaClu-708
❑ 93StaCluFDI-708
❑ 93StaCluMOP-708
❑ 93Ult-301
❑ 93UppDec-701
❑ 93UppDecGold-701
❑ 94BraLykP-3
❑ 94BraLykS-3
❑ 94BraUSPC-6S
❑ 94BraUSPC-10D
❑ 94Don-479
❑ 94Fle-351
❑ 94Pac-2
❑ 94Sco-247
❑ 94ScoGolR-247
❑ 94StaClu-64
❑ 94StaCluFDI-64
❑ 94StaCluGR-64
❑ 94StaCluMOP-64
❑ 94StaCluT-43
❑ 94StaCluTFDI-43
❑ 94Top-617
❑ 94TopGol-617
❑ 94TopSpa-617
❑ 94Ult-148
❑ 95Fle-300
❑ 95Top-523
❑ 95TopCyb-345
❑ 96DanBraB-2

Bee, Buddy the
❑ 95BinMetTI-NNO
❑ 96BinMetB-3
❑ 97BinMetB-32

Beebe, Fred
❑ 08RosComP-161
❑ 09ColChiE-25
❑ 09PC7HHB-3
❑ 09RamT20-9
❑ 10SweCapPP-95
❑ 11PinT-5-409
❑ 11SpoLifCW-26
❑ 11SpoLifM-186
❑ 12ColRedB-25
❑ 12ColTinT-25
❑ 12ImpTobC-54

Beebe, Hans
❑ 96PitMetB-5
❑ 97PitMet-7

Beech, Matt
❑ 94BatCliC-3
❑ 94BatCliF-3437
❑ 95ClePhiF-208
❑ 95ReaPhiELC-3
❑ 96Bow-346
❑ 96BowFoi-346
❑ 96DouAllB-10
❑ 96ReaPhiB-1
❑ 97ColCho-16
❑ 97Fle-406
❑ 97FleTif-406
❑ 97PhiCopQ-2
❑ 97ScrRedB-29
❑ 97UppDec-237
❑ 98PacOnl-554
❑ 98PacOnlR-554
❑ 98PacOnlWC-554
❑ 98PhiTeal-4
❑ 98StaCluFDI-238
❑ 98StaCluI-238
❑ 98StaCluOneK-238
❑ 98StaCluPP-238
❑ 98UppDec-478
❑ 99Fle-335
❑ 99FleSta9-335
❑ 99FleWarT-335

Beecher, Ed (Edward H.)
❑ 87BucN28-85

Beecroft, Mike
❑ 81BirBarT-25
❑ 82BirBarT-6

Beeler, Jodie (Joseph Sam)
❑ 76DalCon-2

Beeler, Pete
❑ 87TamTarP-27
❑ 88CedRapRP-1147
❑ 88MidLeaAGS-8
❑ 89CedRapRS-25
❑ 89ChaLooB-11
❑ 89ChaLooGS-4
❑ 91ChaLooLD-154
❑ 91LinDriAA-154
❑ 91NasSouP-2158
❑ 91WavRedF-3
❑ 92BufBisF-325
❑ 92BufBisS-27

Beene, Andy
❑ 82ElPasDT-14
❑ 84VanCanC-26
❑ 94BreMilB-104

Beene, Fred
❑ 67BalOriP-7
❑ 70OPC-121
❑ 70Top-121
❑ 71MLBOffS-219
❑ 73IndTeal-3
❑ 73OPC-573
❑ 73Top-573
❑ 74OPC-274
❑ 74Top-274
❑ 75CleIndP-2
❑ 75OPC-181
❑ 75Top-181
❑ 75TopMin-181
❑ 76SSP-504
❑ 80TidTidT-14
❑ 91OriCro-26
❑ 92YanWIZ7-12

Beene, Steve
❑ 76WatRoyT-3
❑ 77DayBealT-1

Beeney, Ryan
❑ 94OneYanC-2
❑ 94OneYanF-3797
❑ 94StaCluDP-67
❑ 94StaCluDPFDI-67
❑ 96TamYanY-4

Beer, Darrin
❑ 89GenCubP-1863

Beer, Sam
❑ 15Zee-25
❑ 16Zee-21
❑ 17Zee-20

Beerbrower, Dan
❑ 76QuaCitAT-1

Bees, Burlington
❑ 96BurBeeTI-31
❑ 98BurBeeM-30

Beesley, Mascot
❑ 96BurBeeTI-30

Beeston, Paul
❑ 93BluJayDM-24

Befort, Curt
❑ 87ClePhiP-3

Befort, Jay
❑ 85RedWinA-22

BeFort, Lyle
❑ 86AncGlaPTI-2

Beggs, Joe
❑ 41HarHarW-3
❑ 47Exh-19
❑ 75YanDyn1T-2
❑ 77CinRedT-20
❑ 79DiaGre-20

Begnaud, Gary
❑ 77ReaPhiT-1

Begue, Roger
❑ 82LynMetT-18

Behel, Steven A.D.
❑ 87OldJudN-27

Behenna, Rick
❑ 81DurBulT-15
❑ 83BraPol-49
❑ 84Don-346
❑ 84Ind-3
❑ 85Ind-2
❑ 85IndPol-32

Behm, Bill
❑ 84TigWavP-5

Behn, Brendan
❑ 98PitMetM-5

Behney, Mel
❑ 72OPC-524
❑ 72Top-524
❑ 73OPC-602
❑ 73Top-602

Behnsch, Bobby
❑ 87ClePhiP-7

Behny, Mark
❑ 86EriCarP-3
❑ 87SavCarP-24
❑ 88SavCarP-339

Behr, George
❑ 92HelBreF-1719
❑ 92HelBreSP-8
❑ 92Min-3

Behrend, Mike
❑ 83EriCarT-11
❑ 84SavCarT-26

Behrens, Scott
❑ 91IdaFalBP-4320
❑ 91PulBraC-16
❑ 91PulBraP-3995
❑ 92IdaFalGF-3501

Behrman, Hank (Henry)
❑ 46DodTeal-2
❑ 49EurSta-101
❑ 49GiaTeal-1
❑ 50RemBre-2
❑ 90DodTar-42
❑ 91DodRinP3-7

Beimel, Joe
❑ 98EriSeaWM-3

Beiras, Mike
❑ 87BelMarL-26

Beirman, Jim
❑ 75ForLauYS-16
Beirne, Kevin
❑ 96SouBenSHS-5
❑ 98BirBarG-4
❑ 99Bow-430
❑ 99BowGol-430
❑ 99BowInt-430
Beitey, Dan
❑ 75CedRapGT-10
Beja, Aaron
❑ 91FayGenC-25
Bejma, Ollie (Aloysius Frank)
❑ 34BatR31-55
❑ 34BatR31-93
❑ 35DiaMatCS3T1-5
❑ 35DiaMatCS3T1-6
❑ 36R31PasP-26
❑ 79DiaGre-138
Bekkedal, Matt
❑ 96BriWhiSB-4
❑ 97BriWhiSB-29
❑ 98WinWar-4
Belan, Lance
❑ 86PriWilPP-2
Belanger, Lee
❑ 82OrlTwiT-2
❑ 83VisOakF-1
Belanger, Mark Henry
❑ 67BalOriP-8
❑ 67BalOriP-9
❑ 67BalOriP-10
❑ 67Top-558
❑ 68BalOriDPCP-1
❑ 68CokCapO-14
❑ 68DexPre-10
❑ 68OPC-118
❑ 68Top-118
❑ 68TopVen-118
❑ 69Top-299
❑ 69TopSta-121
❑ 69TopTeaP-5
❑ 70BalOriP-2
❑ 70DayDaiNM-159
❑ 70MLBOffS-145
❑ 70Ori-1
❑ 70Top-615
❑ 71BalOriP-2
❑ 71MLBOffS-289
❑ 71OPC-99
❑ 71OriCha-1
❑ 71Top-99
❑ 72OPC-224
❑ 72OPC-456
❑ 72OriDMV-1
❑ 72OriPos-4
❑ 72Top-224
❑ 72Top-456
❑ 73BalOriP-6
❑ 73LinPor-7
❑ 73OPC-253
❑ 73OriJohP-7
❑ 73OriTeal-5
❑ 73Top-253
❑ 74OPC-329
❑ 74Top-329
❑ 74TopSta-122
❑ 75BalOriP-4
❑ 75OPC-74
❑ 75Top-74
❑ 75TopMin-74
❑ 76BalOriP-4
❑ 76OPC-505
❑ 76Top-505
❑ 77BalOriP-1
❑ 77BurCheD-38
❑ 77Hos-71
❑ 77OPC-154
❑ 77RCColC-2
❑ 77Top-135
❑ 78BalOriP-1
❑ 78OPC-125
❑ 78RCColC-8
❑ 78Top-315
❑ 79OPC-27
❑ 79Top-65
❑ 80BalOriP-2
❑ 80OPC-217
❑ 80Top-425
❑ 81AllGamPI-19
❑ 81Don-472
❑ 81Fle-175
❑ 81FleStiC-39
❑ 81Top-641
❑ 82DodPol-8
❑ 82DodUniOV-2
❑ 82Fle-158
❑ 82FleSta-148
❑ 82OPC-42
❑ 82Top-776
❑ 82TopTra-5T
❑ 83Don-514
❑ 83FraBroR-26
❑ 83Top-273
❑ 90DodTar-43
❑ 91OriCro-27
❑ 96UppDecRCJ-21
Belardi, Wayne (Carroll W.)
❑ 55Bow-36
❑ 79TCM50-110
❑ 90DodTar-44
Belbru, Juan
❑ 88BlaYNPRWLU-23
❑ 89BlaYNPRWL-138
❑ 89SavCarP-356
❑ 90HamRedS-5
Belcher, Glenn
❑ 87FayGenP-27
❑ 88FayGenP-1080
❑ 89FayGenP-1568
Belcher, Kevin
❑ 88GasRanP-1010
❑ 89GasRanP-1004
❑ 89GasRanS-2
❑ 89SouAtlLAGS-30
❑ 89Sta-134
❑ 90CMC-744
❑ 90ProAaA-67
❑ 90TexLeaAGS-26
❑ 90TulDriP-1166
❑ 90TulDriT-3
❑ 91Don-46
❑ 91Fle-280
❑ 91LinDriAAA-302
❑ 91OklCit8LD-302
❑ 91OklCit8P-189
❑ 91Sco-714
❑ 91ScoRoo-15
❑ 91Stu-121
❑ 91TopDeb90-13
❑ 91UppDec-26
❑ 92TulDriF-2706
❑ 92TulDriS-602
❑ 93BirBarF-1203
❑ 93RanKee-67
Belcher, Tim
❑ 84MadMusP-9
❑ 85HunStaJ-31
❑ 85Top-281
❑ 85TopTif-281
❑ 86HunStaDJ-31
❑ 87TacTigP-21
❑ 88DodMot-23
❑ 88DodPol-49
❑ 88Don-587
❑ 88DonBasB-10
❑ 88DonRoo-28
❑ 88Fle-509
❑ 88FleGlo-509
❑ 88ScoRoo-101T
❑ 88ScoRooG-101T
❑ 88TopTra-12T
❑ 88TopTraT-12T
❑ 89Baz-1
❑ 89Bow-336
❑ 89BowTif-336
❑ 89ClaLigB-57
❑ 89DodMot-23
❑ 89DodPol-25
❑ 89DodStaSV-2
❑ 89Don-203
❑ 89DonBasB-234
❑ 89Fle-54
❑ 89FleGlo-54
❑ 89FleGlo-WS2
❑ 89FleSup-3
❑ 89FleWorS-2
❑ 89K-M-9
❑ 89OPC-177
❑ 89PanSti-21
❑ 89PanSti-95
❑ 89Sco-418
❑ 89ScoHot1R-94
❑ 89ScoYouSI-36
❑ 89Spo-121
❑ 89Top-456
❑ 89TopBig-145
❑ 89TopGloS-30
❑ 89TopRoo-3
❑ 89TopSti-317
❑ 89TopTif-456
❑ 89ToyRoo-3
❑ 89UppDec-648
❑ 89Woo-19
❑ 89Woo-29
❑ 90Bow-85
❑ 90BowTif-85
❑ 90DodMot-9
❑ 90DodPol-49
❑ 90DodTar-45
❑ 90Don-79
❑ 90DonBesN-17
❑ 90Fle-389
❑ 90FleAwaW-2
❑ 90FleCan-389
❑ 90FleLeaL-2
❑ 90FleLeaLC-2
❑ 90FleWaxBC-C2
❑ 90Lea-200
❑ 90OPC-173
❑ 90PanSti-281
❑ 90PubIntS-2
❑ 90PubIntS-608
❑ 90Sco-126
❑ 90Top-173
❑ 90TopBig-246
❑ 90TopCoi-38
❑ 90TopMinL-57
❑ 90TopTif-173
❑ 90UppDec-547
❑ 91BasBesAotM-3
❑ 91Bow-605
❑ 91DodMot-9
❑ 91DodPho-7
❑ 91DodPol-49
❑ 91DodSt.V-15
❑ 91Don-70
❑ 91Fle-194
❑ 91Lea-508
❑ 91OPC-25
❑ 91Sco-187
❑ 91StaClu-152
❑ 91Top-25
❑ 91TopDesS-25
❑ 91TopMic-25
❑ 91TopTif-25
❑ 91Ult-159
❑ 91UppDec-576
❑ 92Bow-319
❑ 92Bow-664
❑ 92Cla2-T78
❑ 92Don-78
❑ 92Fle-447
❑ 92FleUpd-79
❑ 92Lea-417
❑ 92LeaBlaG-417
❑ 92OPC-688
❑ 92OPCPre-113
❑ 92Pin-384
❑ 92RedKah-31
❑ 92Sco-368
❑ 92ScoRoo-65T
❑ 92StaClu-842
❑ 92StaCluNC-842
❑ 92Top-688
❑ 92TopGol-688
❑ 92TopGolW-688
❑ 92TopMic-688
❑ 92TopTra-8T
❑ 92TopTraG-8T
❑ 92Ult-479
❑ 92UppDec-668
❑ 92UppDec-761
❑ 93Bow-118
❑ 93Don-82
❑ 93Fla-24
❑ 93Fle-30
❑ 93Lea-243
❑ 93OPC-48
❑ 93PacSpa-398
❑ 93Pin-357
❑ 93RedKah-2
❑ 93Sco-423
❑ 93Sel-191
❑ 93SelRoo-3T
❑ 93StaClu-9
❑ 93StaCluFDI-9
❑ 93StaCluMOP-9
❑ 93Top-382
❑ 93TopGol-382
❑ 93TopInaM-382
❑ 93TopInaR-382
❑ 93TopMic-382
❑ 93TriPla-163
❑ 93Ult-26
❑ 93UppDec-368
❑ 93UppDecGold-368
❑ 94Bow-677
❑ 94ColC-561
❑ 94ColChoGS-561
❑ 94ColChoSS-561
❑ 94Don-56
❑ 94Fin-301
❑ 94FinRef-301
❑ 94Fle-74
❑ 94FleUpd-40
❑ 94Lea-232
❑ 94OPC-70
❑ 94Pac-119
❑ 94Pin-491
❑ 94PinArtP-491
❑ 94PinMusC-491
❑ 94Sco-470
❑ 94ScoGolR-470
❑ 94Sel-248
❑ 94StaClu-255
❑ 94StaClu-582
❑ 94StaCluFDI-255
❑ 94StaCluFDI-582
❑ 94StaCluGR-255
❑ 94StaCluGR-582
❑ 94StaCluMOP-255
❑ 94StaCluMOP-582
❑ 94Top-62
❑ 94TopGol-62
❑ 94TopSpa-62
❑ 94TopTra-32T
❑ 94Ult-353
❑ 94UppDec-364
❑ 94UppDecED-364
❑ 95Don-339
❑ 95DonPreP-339
❑ 95IndIndF-89
❑ 95MarMot-21
❑ 95MarPac-20
❑ 95Pac-149
❑ 95Sco-484
❑ 95ScoGolR-484
❑ 95ScoPlaTS-484
❑ 95Top-209
❑ 95TopCyb-123
❑ 96Fle-227
❑ 96FleTif-227
❑ 96FleUpd-U33
❑ 96FleUpd-U38
❑ 96FleUpdTC-U38
❑ 96RoyPol-2
❑ 96StaClu-322
❑ 96StaCluMOP-322
❑ 96Top-38
❑ 97ColCho-129
❑ 97Don-223
❑ 97DonGolPP-223
❑ 97DonSilPP-223
❑ 97Fle-110
❑ 97FleTif-110
❑ 97Pac-98
❑ 97PacLigB-98
❑ 97PacSil-98
❑ 97Pin-146
❑ 97PinArtP-PP146
❑ 97PinMusC-146
❑ 97PinPrePla-146
❑ 97RoyPol-2
❑ 97Sco-390
❑ 97ScoArtPWB-390
❑ 97ScoResC-390
❑ 97ScoShoS-390
❑ 97ScoShoSAP-390
❑ 97StaClu-266
❑ 97StaCluMOP-266
❑ 97Top-422
❑ 97Ult-505
❑ 97UltGolME-505
❑ 97UltPlaME-505
❑ 97UppDec-87
❑ 98ColCho-142
❑ 98Fin-163
❑ 98FinNo--163
❑ 98FinNo-R-163
❑ 98FinRef-163
❑ 98PacOme-111
❑ 98PacOmeR-111
❑ 98PacOnl-335
❑ 98PacOnlR-335
❑ 98PacOnlWC-335
❑ 98Pin-156
❑ 98PinPreP-156
❑ 98SP Aut-104
❑ 98SPxFin-286
❑ 98SPxFinR-286
❑ 98SPxFinS-286
❑ 98StaCluFDI-190
❑ 98StaCluI-190
❑ 98StaCluOneK-190
❑ 98StaCluPP-190
❑ 98Top-244
❑ 98TopChr-244
❑ 98TopChrR-244
❑ 98TopDevR-244
❑ 98TopDia-244
❑ 98TopMiniC-244
❑ 98UppDec-107
❑ 98UppDecSF-66
❑ 99199Fin-213
❑ 99FinGolRef-213
❑ 99FinRef-213
❑ 99Pac-200
❑ 99PacPlaB-200
❑ 99PacRed-200
❑ 99StaClu-124
❑ 99StaCluFDI-124
❑ 99StaCluOoaK-124
❑ 99StaCluPP-124
❑ 99UppDecM-2
❑ 99UppDecMGS-2
❑ 99UppDecMHFS-2
❑ 99UppDecMSS-2
Belcik, Keith
❑ 84LitFalMT-2
Belen, Lance
❑ 85PriWilPT-14
❑ 87HarSenP-11
❑ 88HarSenP-844
Belen, Mattie
❑ 89BluOriS-4
Belford, John
❑ 89WelPirP-35
❑ 95StCatSTI-30
Belinda, Stan
❑ 87MacPirP-17
❑ 88CarLeaAS-3
❑ 88SalBucS-2
❑ 89HarSenP-305
❑ 89HarSenS-3
❑ 90BufBisC-1
❑ 90BufBisP-365
❑ 90CMC-1
❑ 90FleUpd-48
❑ 90Lea-486
❑ 90OPC-354
❑ 90ProAAAF-480
❑ 90Sco-634
❑ 90Top-354
❑ 90TopDeb89-12
❑ 90TopTif-354
❑ 90TriAAAC-13
❑ 90UppDec-759
❑ 91Don-699
❑ 91Fle-30
❑ 91OPC-522
❑ 91Sco-296
❑ 91Sco100RS-8
❑ 91StaClu-453
❑ 91Top-522
❑ 91TopDesS-522
❑ 91TopMic-522
❑ 91TopTif-522
❑ 91Ult-273
❑ 91UppDec-161
❑ 92Bow-455
❑ 92Don-501
❑ 92Fle-548
❑ 92Lea-287
❑ 92LeaBlaG-287
❑ 92OPC-466
❑ 92Pin-370
❑ 92PirNatI-1
❑ 92Sco-325
❑ 92StaClu-75
❑ 92Top-466
❑ 92TopGol-466
❑ 92TopGolW-466
❑ 92TopMic-466
❑ 92Ult-550
❑ 92UppDec-202
❑ 93Bow-22
❑ 93Don-490
❑ 93Fla-109
❑ 93Fle-110
❑ 93Lea-339
❑ 93PacSpa-242
❑ 93PanSti-282
❑ 93Pin-142
❑ 93PirHil-1
❑ 93PirNatI-1
❑ 93Sco-369
❑ 93SP-181
❑ 93StaClu-268
❑ 93StaCluFDI-268
❑ 93StaCluMOP-268
❑ 93Top-748
❑ 93TopGol-748
❑ 93TopInaM-748
❑ 93TopInaR-748
❑ 93TopMic-748
❑ 93Ult-95
❑ 93UppDec-359
❑ 93UppDecGold-359
❑ 94ColC-377
❑ 94ColChoGS-377
❑ 94ColChoSS-377
❑ 94Don-77
❑ 94Fla-55
❑ 94Fle-148
❑ 94Sco-160
❑ 94ScoGolR-160
❑ 94StaClu-8
❑ 94StaCluFDI-8
❑ 94StaCluGR-8
❑ 94StaCluMOP-8
❑ 94Top-247
❑ 94TopGol-247
❑ 94TopSpa-247
❑ 94Ult-360
❑ 95FleUpd-8
❑ 95Pac-197
❑ 95StaClu-222
❑ 95StaCluFDI-222
❑ 95StaCluMOP-222
❑ 95StaCluSTWS-222
❑ 95TopTra-153T
❑ 96ColCho-477
❑ 96ColChoGS-477
❑ 96ColChoSS-477
❑ 96Don-427
❑ 96DonPreP-427
❑ 96Fle-23
❑ 96FleRedS-1
❑ 96FleTif-23
❑ 96Sco-203
❑ 96Ult-14
❑ 96UltGolM-14
❑ 96UppDec-24
❑ 98PacOnl-185
❑ 98PacOnlR-185
❑ 98PacOnlWC-185
Belinskas, Dan
❑ 86CedRapRT-1
Belinsky, Bo
❑ 62Top-592
❑ 63AngJayP-1
❑ 63Top-33
❑ 64Top-315
❑ 64TopVen-315
❑ 65OPC-225
❑ 65Top-225
❑ 66Top-506
❑ 67Top-447A
❑ 67Top-447B
❑ 69Top-366
❑ 73BooProC-1
❑ 81TCM60I-447
❑ 85AngStrH-3
❑ 87AstShoSTw-28
❑ 87AstShoSTw-29
❑ 87AstShowSTh-3
❑ 89PacLegI-130
❑ 89SweBasG-16
❑ 99SpoIllGotG-29
❑ 99SpoIllGotGA-6
Belisle, Matt
❑ 99199Fin-297
❑ 99Bow-92
❑ 99BowBes-153
❑ 99BowBesAR-153
❑ 99BowBesR-153
❑ 99BowChr-92
❑ 99BowChrG-92
❑ 99BowChrGR-92
❑ 99BowChrI-92
❑ 99BowChrIR-92
❑ 99BowChrR-92
❑ 99BowGol-92
❑ 99BowInt-92
❑ 99FinGolRef-297
❑ 99FinRef-297
❑ 99StaClu-339
❑ 99StaCluFDI-339
❑ 99StaCluOoaK-339
❑ 99StaCluPP-339
❑ 99Top-438
❑ 99TopBlaLC1-93
❑ 99TopBlaLC2-93

❑ 99TopBlaLC3-93
❑ 99TopChr-438
❑ 99TopChrR-438
❑ 99TopGal-130
❑ 99TopGalPP-130
❑ 99TopGalPPI-130
❑ 99TopGolL-93
❑ 99TopGolLC1-93
❑ 99TopGolLC2-93
❑ 99TopGolLOtO-93
❑ 99TopMVPP-438
❑ 99TopRedLC1-93
❑ 99TopRedLC2-93
❑ 99TopRedLC3-93
❑ 99TopSta-50
❑ 99TopSta1Foil-50
❑ 99TopSta2Foil-50
❑ 99TopStaFoil-50
❑ 99TopStaOS-50
❑ 99TopStaTS-50

Belitz, Todd
❑ 97HudValRB-9
❑ 98BesAutSS-3
❑ 98Bow-431
❑ 98BowChr-431
❑ 98BowChrGA-431
❑ 98BowChrGAR-431
❑ 98BowChrI-431
❑ 98BowChrIR-431
❑ 98BowChrR-431
❑ 98BowGolA-431
❑ 98BowInt-431
❑ 98ChaRivDG-2

Belk, Chuck
❑ 79WisRapTT-20

Belk, Tim
❑ 92BilMusF-3360
❑ 92BilMusSP-24
❑ 93CarLeaAGF-40
❑ 93ClaFS7-271
❑ 93ExcFS7-16
❑ 93WinSpiC-4
❑ 93WinSpiF-1576
❑ 94Bow-588
❑ 94BowBes-B57
❑ 94BowBesR-B57
❑ 94ChaLooF-1362
❑ 94Cla-38
❑ 94ExcFS7-172
❑ 95Bow-119
❑ 95BowBes-B36
❑ 95BowBesR-B36
❑ 95IndIndF-99
❑ 95Sel-158
❑ 95SelArtP-158
❑ 95SigRooOJA-AS2
❑ 95SigRooOJAS-AS2
❑ 95Sum-167
❑ 95SumNthD-167
❑ 95Top-647
❑ 96Bow-366
❑ 96BowFoi-366
❑ 96IndIndB-6
❑ 97BesAutAS-4
❑ 97BesAutP-R2
❑ 97Don-257
❑ 97DonGolPP-257
❑ 97DonSilPP-257
❑ 97IndInd-5
❑ 97Ult-173
❑ 97UltGolME-173
❑ 97UltPlaME-173
❑ 98TolMudHQ-10

Bell, Beau (Roy Chester)
❑ 35DiaMatCS3T1-7
❑ 36R31PasP-41
❑ 37OPCBatUV-105
❑ 38CloFotW-6
❑ 38ExhFou-15
❑ 38WheBB10-7
❑ 39PlaBal-136
❑ 39TigSpo-2
❑ 40PlaBal-138
❑ 72TCMthe3-1
❑ 93ConTSN-781

Bell, Bobby
❑ 86PalSprAP-2
❑ 86PalSprAS-5
❑ 87PalSprP-25
❑ 88PalSprAP-1459

Bell, Brent
❑ 91MarPhiC-14
❑ 91MarPhiP-3457
❑ 92MarPhiC-18
❑ 92MarPhiF-3063
❑ 93BatCliCB-4
❑ 93BatCliF-3156

Bell, Buddy (David Gus)
❑ 54RedHeaF-3
❑ 54RedMan-NL19B
❑ 55RedMan-NL23
❑ 55RobGouS-16
❑ 55RobGouW-16
❑ 57RedSoh-2
❑ 60MacSta-3
❑ 61Pos-186A
❑ 62Pos-120
❑ 73IndArtTC-1
❑ 73IndTeal-4
❑ 73LinPor-60
❑ 73OPC-31
❑ 73Top-31
❑ 74Kel-10
❑ 74OPC-257
❑ 74Top-257
❑ 74TopDecE-37
❑ 74TopSta-161
❑ 75CleIndP-3
❑ 75Hos-30
❑ 75HosTwi-30
❑ 75IndJB R-1
❑ 75OPC-38
❑ 75Top-38
❑ 75TopMin-38
❑ 76Hos-95
❑ 76OPC-66
❑ 76OPC-358
❑ 76Spo-7
❑ 76SSP-517
❑ 76Top-66
❑ 76Top-358
❑ 77BurCheD-57
❑ 77ChiWilD-2
❑ 77DailsID-2
❑ 77DetCaeD-2
❑ 77HolInnD-2
❑ 77Hos-69
❑ 77MSADis-2
❑ 77OPC-86
❑ 77PepGloD-11
❑ 77SagDis-2
❑ 77sDis-2
❑ 77Top-590
❑ 77TopCloS-2
❑ 77WenDis-2
❑ 77ZipDis-2
❑ 78Hos-15
❑ 78IndTeal-1
❑ 78OPC-234
❑ 78PapGinD-34
❑ 78Pep-26
❑ 78SagDis-1
❑ 78TasDis-1
❑ 78Top-280
❑ 78WifBalD-2
❑ 79BasPat-1
❑ 79Hos-147
❑ 79Kel-14A
❑ 79Kel-14B
❑ 79OPC-367
❑ 79Top-690
❑ 80Kel-53
❑ 80OPC-107
❑ 80Top-190
❑ 80TopSup-47
❑ 80WilGloT-1
❑ 81AllGamPI-28
❑ 81Don-145
❑ 81Fle-625
❑ 81FleStiC-11
❑ 81Kel-64
❑ 81MSAMinD-1
❑ 81OPC-66
❑ 81Top-475
❑ 81TopScr-21
❑ 81TopSti-130
❑ 81TopSupHT-91
❑ 81TopSupN-1
❑ 82Don-23
❑ 82Don-368
❑ 82Dra-2
❑ 82Fle-313
❑ 82FleSta-172
❑ 82FleSta-239
❑ 82Kel-33
❑ 82OnDecD-1
❑ 82OPC-50
❑ 82SevSluC-2
❑ 82Top-50
❑ 82TopSti-238
❑ 82WilSpoG-1
❑ 83AllGamPI-28
❑ 83Don-215
❑ 83DonActA-40
❑ 83Fle-562
❑ 83Fle-632
❑ 83FleSta-13
❑ 83FleSti-148
❑ 83FleSti-164
❑ 83Kel-12
❑ 83OPC-330
❑ 83RanAffF-25
❑ 83Top-330
❑ 83Top-412
❑ 83TopGloS-9
❑ 83TopSti-119
❑ 84AllGamPI-118
❑ 84Don-56
❑ 84DonActAS-12
❑ 84Fle-413
❑ 84FunFooP-76
❑ 84Nes792-37
❑ 84Nes792-665
❑ 84OPC-347
❑ 84RanJarP-25
❑ 84SevCoi-W11
❑ 84Top-37
❑ 84Top-665
❑ 84TopRubD-3
❑ 84TopSti-351
❑ 84TopTif-37
❑ 84TopTif-665
❑ 85AllGamPI-28
❑ 85Don-56
❑ 85DonActA-11
❑ 85Fle-556
❑ 85FleLimE-1
❑ 85FleStaS-7
❑ 85GenMilS-13
❑ 85Lea-174
❑ 85OPC-176
❑ 85RanPer-25
❑ 85SubDis-2
❑ 85ThoMcAD-2
❑ 85Top-131
❑ 85Top-745
❑ 85TopRubD-3
❑ 85TopSti-347
❑ 85TopSup-53
❑ 85TopTif-131
❑ 85TopTif-745
❑ 86BasStaB-7
❑ 86Don-447
❑ 86Fle-172
❑ 86FleMin-37
❑ 86OPC-285
❑ 86RedTexG-25
❑ 86SevCoi-S10
❑ 86Spo-151
❑ 86Top-285
❑ 86TopSti-139
❑ 86TopTat-15
❑ 86TopTif-285
❑ 86TruVal-20
❑ 87BoaandB-21
❑ 87Don-556
❑ 87DonOpeD-196
❑ 87Fle-193
❑ 87FleGlo-193
❑ 87Lea-169
❑ 87OPC-104
❑ 87RedFolSB-38
❑ 87RedKah-25
❑ 87Spo-141
❑ 87SpoTeaP-4
❑ 87StuPan-4
❑ 87Top-545
❑ 87TopSti-143
❑ 87TopTif-545
❑ 88Don-206
❑ 88Fle-227
❑ 88FleGlo-227
❑ 88Lea-192
❑ 88MSAJifPD-1
❑ 88Nes-30
❑ 88OPC-130
❑ 88PacLegI-65
❑ 88PanSti-279
❑ 88RedFolSB-5
❑ 88Sco-99
❑ 88ScoGlo-99
❑ 88Spo-147
❑ 88StaLinAl-1
❑ 88StaLinRe-1
❑ 88Top-130
❑ 88TopSti-138
❑ 88TopTif-130
❑ 88TopTra-13T
❑ 88TopTraT-13T
❑ 89Bow-229
❑ 89BowTif-229
❑ 89Fle-352
❑ 89FleGlo-352
❑ 89OPC-92
❑ 89RanMot-9
❑ 89RanSmo-3
❑ 89Sco-610
❑ 89Top-461
❑ 89TopBig-270
❑ 89TopSti-18
❑ 89TopTif-461
❑ 89UppDec-112
❑ 90ColSprSSP-55
❑ 90PacLeg-74
❑ 90ProAAAF-236
❑ 90PubIntS-404
❑ 91MetWIZ-30
❑ 91SweBasG-7
❑ 91TopArc1-118
❑ 92BazQua5A-14
❑ 93RanKee-68
❑ 93TedWil-31
❑ 94RanAllP-8
❑ 94RanAllP-9
❑ 94RanAllP-10
❑ 94RanAllP-12
❑ 94UppDecAH-183
❑ 94UppDecAH1-183
❑ 96TigHebN-26

Bell, Cliff
❑ 86NegLeaF-100

Bell, Cool Papa (James)
❑ 74LauOldTBS-24
❑ 76CooPapB-1
❑ 76CooPapB-2
❑ 76CooPapB-3
❑ 76CooPapB-4
❑ 76CooPapB-5
❑ 76CooPapB-6
❑ 76CooPapB-7
❑ 76CooPapB-8
❑ 76CooPapB-9
❑ 76CooPapB-10
❑ 76CooPapB-11
❑ 76CooPapB-12
❑ 76CooPapB-13
❑ 76GrePlaG-21
❑ 76ShaPiz-141
❑ 80PerHaloFP-141
❑ 80PerHaloFPS-23
❑ 80SSPHOF-141
❑ 83ConMar-49
❑ 83DonHOFH-25
❑ 86NegLeaF-3
❑ 86NegLeaF-90
❑ 87LeaSpeO*-H12
❑ 87NegLeaPD-24
❑ 88ConHar-1
❑ 88ConNegA-1
❑ 88NegLeaD-14
❑ 89KahCoo-1
❑ 89NegLeaRP-7
❑ 89PerCelP-4
❑ 90NegLeaS-28
❑ 90PerGreM-51
❑ 90PomBlaBNLP-2543
❑ 91PomBlaBPB-1
❑ 91PomBlaBPB-16
❑ 93DiaStaES-N1
❑ 93TedWil-97
❑ 94PomNegLB-8
❑ 94UppDecTAE-49
❑ 95S.FExaNLT-2
❑ 97NegLeaPC-1H

Bell, Curt
❑ 92NiaFalRC-24
❑ 92NiaFalRF-3326
❑ 93FayGenC-3
❑ 93FayGenF-131

Bell, David
❑ 90SprCarB-3
❑ 91Cla/Bes-104
❑ 91CollndC-22
❑ 91CollndP-1489
❑ 92KinIndC-18
❑ 92KinIndF-2481
❑ 92UppDecML-80
❑ 93CanIndF-2844
❑ 94ChaKniF-899
❑ 94Top-369
❑ 94TopGol-369
❑ 94TopSpa-369
❑ 94UppDecML-105
❑ 95ARuFalLS-1
❑ 95Bow-179
❑ 95Exc-35
❑ 95SelCer-119
❑ 95SelCerMG-119
❑ 95Sum-126
❑ 95SumNthD-126
❑ 95Top-581
❑ 95UppDec-241
❑ 95UppDecED-241
❑ 95UppDecEDG-241
❑ 95UppDecML-16
❑ 95UppDecMLFS-16
❑ 96ColCho-656
❑ 96ColCho-687
❑ 96ColChoGS-656
❑ 96ColChoGS-687
❑ 96ColChoSS-656
❑ 96ColChoSS-687
❑ 96Don-92
❑ 96DonPreP-92
❑ 96Fle-538
❑ 96FleTif-538
❑ 96Lea-70
❑ 96LeaPrePB-70
❑ 96LeaPrePG-70
❑ 96LeaPrePS-70
❑ 96LeaSigA-19
❑ 96LeaSigAG-19
❑ 96LeaSigAS-19
❑ 96Pin-193
❑ 96StaClu-125
❑ 96StaCluMOP-125
❑ 96Top-388
❑ 96Ult-540
❑ 96UltGolM-540
❑ 97PacPriGotD-GD197
❑ 98PacInvGems-200
❑ 98Top-213
❑ 98TopChr-213
❑ 98TopChrR-213
❑ 98TopDevR-213
❑ 98TopDia-213
❑ 98TopMiniC-213
❑ 99Fle-336
❑ 99FleSta9-336
❑ 99FleWarT-336
❑ 99Pac-391
❑ 99PacOme-217
❑ 99PacOmeC-217
❑ 99PacOmeG-217
❑ 99PacOmePB-217
❑ 99PacPlaB-391
❑ 99PacRed-391
❑ 99Vic-377

Bell, Derek
❑ 88MyrBeaBJP-1171
❑ 88OPC-311
❑ 88SouAtlLAGS-20
❑ 89KnoBluJB-1
❑ 89KnoBluJP-1149
❑ 89KnoBluJS-1
❑ 90CMC-340
❑ 90ProAAAF-362
❑ 90ScoRoo-81T
❑ 90SyrChiC-14
❑ 90SyrChiMB-2
❑ 90SyrChiP-582
❑ 91BluJayFS-3
❑ 91BluJayS-20
❑ 91Cla3-T28
❑ 91Don-32
❑ 91Fle-168
❑ 91LinDriAAA-501
❑ 91Sco100RS-32
❑ 91SyrChiK-1
❑ 91SyrChiLD-501
❑ 91SyrChiMB-2
❑ 91SyrChiP-2491
❑ 91TopTra-7T
❑ 91TopTraT-7T
❑ 91TriA AAGP-AAA42
❑ 91UppDecFE-26F
❑ 92Bow-237
❑ 92Bow-559
❑ 92Cla1-T11
❑ 92ClaGam-74
❑ 92Don-581
❑ 92Fle-324
❑ 92Lea-243
❑ 92LeaBlaG-243
❑ 92OPC-121
❑ 92OPCPre-189
❑ 92Pin-250
❑ 92PinRoo-7
❑ 92PinRooI-18
❑ 92ProFS7-158
❑ 92Sco-402
❑ 92Sco100RS-64
❑ 92ScoHotR-9
❑ 92ScoImpP-23
❑ 92ScoRoo-3
❑ 92SkyAAAF-290
❑ 92SkyAAAF-292
❑ 92StaClu-555
❑ 92Stu-252
❑ 92SyrChiTT-2
❑ 92Top-121
❑ 92TopDeb91-14
❑ 92TopGol-121
❑ 92TopGolW-121
❑ 92TopMcD-36
❑ 92TopMic-121
❑ 92Ult-448
❑ 92UppDec-26
❑ 92UppDecSR-SR4
❑ 93BluJayD4-3
❑ 93BluJayDWS-3
❑ 93BluJayDWS-7
❑ 93CadDis-4
❑ 93DiaMar-8
❑ 93Don-557
❑ 93Fla-131
❑ 93Fle-331
❑ 93FleFinE-134
❑ 93Lea-179
❑ 93OPC-31
❑ 93PacSpa-320
❑ 93PadMot-12
❑ 93PanSti-32
❑ 93Pin-171
❑ 93PinHomRC-37
❑ 93RedFolS-8
❑ 93Sco-122
❑ 93Sel-286
❑ 93SelRoo-132T
❑ 93SP-163
❑ 93StaClu-504
❑ 93StaCluFDI-504
❑ 93StaCluMOP-504
❑ 93Stu-18
❑ 93Top-268
❑ 93TopGol-268
❑ 93TopInaM-268
❑ 93TopInaR-268
❑ 93TopMic-268
❑ 93TopTra-55T
❑ 93Toy-93
❑ 93TriPla-255
❑ 93Ult-286
❑ 93Ult-469
❑ 93UppDec-158
❑ 93UppDec-696
❑ 93UppDecGold-158
❑ 93UppDecGold-696
❑ 93USPlaCR-5S
❑ 94Bow-288
❑ 94ColC-490
❑ 94ColChoGS-490
❑ 94ColChoSS-490
❑ 94Don-591
❑ 94Fin-114
❑ 94FinRef-114
❑ 94Fla-231
❑ 94Fle-655
❑ 94FleExtB-369
❑ 94FUnPac-156
❑ 94Lea-113
❑ 94LeaL-150
❑ 94OPC-64
❑ 94Pac-517
❑ 94PadMot-8
❑ 94PanSti-252
❑ 94Pin-22
❑ 94PinArtP-22
❑ 94PinMusC-22
❑ 94PinPowS-PS22
❑ 94ProMag-116
❑ 94Sco-338
❑ 94ScoGolR-338
❑ 94Sel-146
❑ 94SP-128
❑ 94SPDieC-128
❑ 94StaClu-286
❑ 94StaCluFDI-286
❑ 94StaCluGR-286
❑ 94StaCluMOP-286
❑ 94Stu-130
❑ 94Top-364
❑ 94TopGol-364

❑ 94TopSpa-364
❑ 94TriPla-162
❑ 94Ult-572
❑ 94UppDec-495
❑ 94UppDecED-495
❑ 94VenLinU-101
❑ 95AstMot-5
❑ 95ColCho-115
❑ 95ColChoGS-115
❑ 95ColChoSE-165
❑ 95ColChoSEGS-165
❑ 95ColChoSESS-165
❑ 95ColChoSS-115
❑ 95Don-364
❑ 95DonPreP-364
❑ 95DonTopotO-250
❑ 95Emo-135
❑ 95Fin-290
❑ 95FinRef-290
❑ 95Fla-357
❑ 95Fle-555
❑ 95FleUpd-138
❑ 95Lea-268
❑ 95LeaLim-58
❑ 95Pac-357
❑ 95PacPri-115
❑ 95Pin-362
❑ 95PinArtP-362
❑ 95PinMusC-362
❑ 95Sco-426
❑ 95ScoGolR-426
❑ 95ScoPlaTS-426
❑ 95SelCer-49
❑ 95SelCerMG-49
❑ 95SP-64
❑ 95SPCha-56
❑ 95SPChaDC-56
❑ 95Spo-136
❑ 95SpoArtP-136
❑ 95SPSil-64
❑ 95StaClu-143
❑ 95StaClu-619
❑ 95StaCluFDI-143
❑ 95StaCluMOP-143
❑ 95StaCluMOP-619
❑ 95StaCluSTWS-143
❑ 95StaCluSTWS-619
❑ 95StaCluVR-73
❑ 95StaCluVRMO-73
❑ 95Stu-128
❑ 95Sum-33
❑ 95SumNthD-33
❑ 95Top-616
❑ 95TopCyb-384
❑ 95TopTra-27T
❑ 95Ult-231
❑ 95UltGolM-231
❑ 95UppDec-274
❑ 95UppDecED-274
❑ 95UppDecEDG-274
❑ 95UppDecSE-179
❑ 95UppDecSEG-179
❑ 95Zen-28
❑ 96AstMot-4
❑ 96Baz-88
❑ 96Bow-103
❑ 96BowBes-80
❑ 96BowBesAR-80
❑ 96BowBesR-80
❑ 96BowFoi-103
❑ 96Cir-134
❑ 96CirRav-134
❑ 96ColCho-165
❑ 96ColCho-358
❑ 96ColChoGS-165
❑ 96ColChoGS-358
❑ 96ColChoSS-165
❑ 96ColChoSS-358
❑ 96Don-126
❑ 96DonDiaK-23
❑ 96DonPreP-126
❑ 96EmoXL-194
❑ 96Fin-B133
❑ 96Fin-S328
❑ 96FinRef-B133
❑ 96FinRef-S328
❑ 96Fla-273
❑ 96Fle-401
❑ 96FleRoaW-1
❑ 96FleTif-401
❑ 96FleUpd-U212
❑ 96FleUpdTC-U212
❑ 96Lea-195
❑ 96LeaLim-88
❑ 96LeaLimG-88
❑ 96LeaPre-104
❑ 96LeaPreP-104
❑ 96LeaPrePB-195
❑ 96LeaPrePG-195
❑ 96LeaPrePS-195
❑ 96LeaPreSG-18
❑ 96LeaPreSte-18
❑ 96LeaSig-62
❑ 96LeaSigPPG-62
❑ 96LeaSigPPP-62
❑ 96MetUni-173
❑ 96MetUniP-173
❑ 96Pac-87
❑ 96PacPri-P30
❑ 96PacPriG-P30
❑ 96PanSti-62
❑ 96Pin-244
❑ 96PinAfi-148
❑ 96PinAfiAP-148
❑ 96PinArtP-144
❑ 96PinFoil-244
❑ 96PinSta-144
❑ 96ProSta-11
❑ 96Sco-110
❑ 96ScoBigB-14
❑ 96ScoDiaA-19
❑ 96ScoDugC-A75
❑ 96ScoDugCAP-A75
❑ 96ScoNumG-8
❑ 96ScoSam-110
❑ 96Sel-96
❑ 96SelArtP-96
❑ 96SelTeaN-26
❑ 96SP-91
❑ 96Spo-65
❑ 96SpoArtP-65
❑ 96SPx-30
❑ 96SPxGol-30
❑ 96StaClu-14
❑ 96StaCluEPB-14
❑ 96StaCluEPG-14
❑ 96StaCluEPS-14
❑ 96StaCluMO-2
❑ 96StaCluMOP-14
❑ 96Stu-107
❑ 96StuPrePB-107
❑ 96StuPrePG-107
❑ 96StuPrePS-107
❑ 96Sum-109
❑ 96SumAbo&B-109
❑ 96SumArtP-109
❑ 96SumFoi-109
❑ 96Top-160
❑ 96TopChr-45
❑ 96TopChrR-45
❑ 96TopGal-39
❑ 96TopGalPPI-39
❑ 96TopLas-2
❑ 96TopPro-NL2
❑ 96TopRoaW-RW1
❑ 96Ult-206
❑ 96UltGolM-206
❑ 96UltRBIK-1
❑ 96UltRBIKGM-1
❑ 96UppDec-85
❑ 96UppDec-420
❑ 96UppDecPRE-R52
❑ 96UppDecPreR-R52
❑ 96Zen-89
❑ 96ZenArtP-89
❑ 96ZenMoz-25
❑ 97AstMot-13
❑ 97BluJayS-34
❑ 97Bow-264
❑ 97BowBes-92
❑ 97BowBesAR-92
❑ 97BowBesR-92
❑ 97BowInt-264
❑ 97Cir-298
❑ 97CirRav-298
❑ 97ColCho-119
❑ 97Don-38
❑ 97DonEli-146
❑ 97DonEliGS-146
❑ 97DonGolPP-38
❑ 97DonSilPP-38
❑ 97Fin-198
❑ 97FinRef-198
❑ 97FlaShoLC-129
❑ 97FlaShoLeg0-129
❑ 97FlaShoLeg1-129
❑ 97FlaShoM-A129
❑ 97FlaShoM-B129
❑ 97FlaShoM-C129
❑ 97FlaShoR0-129
❑ 97FlaShoR1-129
❑ 97FlaShoR2-129
❑ 97Fle-340
❑ 97FleTif-340
❑ 97Lea-235
❑ 97LeaFraM-235
❑ 97LeaFraMDC-235
❑ 97MetUni-135
❑ 97NewPin-109
❑ 97NewPinAP-109
❑ 97NewPinMC-109
❑ 97NewPinPP-109
❑ 97Pac-312
❑ 97PacLigB-312
❑ 97PacPri-106
❑ 97PacPriLB-106
❑ 97PacPriP-106
❑ 97PacPriSL-SL10C
❑ 97PacSil-312
❑ 97PinIns-124
❑ 97PinInsCE-124
❑ 97PinInsDE-124
❑ 97PinX-PSfF-5
❑ 97PinX-PSfFU-5
❑ 97Sco-271
❑ 97ScoArtPWB-271
❑ 97ScoPreS-271
❑ 97ScoShoS-271
❑ 97ScoShoSAP-271
❑ 97Sel-96
❑ 97SelArtP-96
❑ 97SelCom-96
❑ 97SelRegG-96
❑ 97SP-82
❑ 97SpoIll-102
❑ 97SpoIllEE-102
❑ 97StaClu-208
❑ 97StaCluMat-208
❑ 97StaCluMOP-208
❑ 97Stu-84
❑ 97StuPrePG-84
❑ 97StuPrePS-84
❑ 97Top-93
❑ 97TopChr-37
❑ 97TopChrR-37
❑ 97TopGal-125
❑ 97TopGalPPI-125
❑ 97Ult-205
❑ 97UltDouT-14
❑ 97UltGolME-205
❑ 97UltPlaME-205
❑ 97UppDec-365
❑ 98Bow-246
❑ 98BowChr-246
❑ 98BowChrGA-246
❑ 98BowChrGAR-246
❑ 98BowChrI-246
❑ 98BowChrIR-246
❑ 98BowChrR-246
❑ 98BowGolA-246
❑ 98BowInt-246
❑ 98CirThu-283
❑ 98CirThuRav-283
❑ 98CirThuSupRav-283
❑ 98ColCho-384
❑ 98CroRoy-63
❑ 98Don-180
❑ 98DonGolPP-180
❑ 98DonSilPP-180
❑ 98Fin-143
❑ 98FinNo--143
❑ 98FinNo-R-143
❑ 98FinRef-143
❑ 98Fle-240
❑ 98LeaRS-129
❑ 98LeaRSLHolo-129
❑ 98LeaRSLong-129
❑ 98LeaRTrue-129
❑ 98MetUni-6
❑ 98MetUniPMG-6
❑ 98Pac-313
❑ 98PacAur-137
❑ 98PacOme-105
❑ 98PacOmeR-105
❑ 98PacOnl-312
❑ 98PacOnlR-312
❑ 98PacOnlWC-312
❑ 98PacPar-168
❑ 98PacParC-168
❑ 98PacParG-168
❑ 98PacParHS-168
❑ 98PacParPB-168
❑ 98PacParR-168
❑ 98PacPlaB-313
❑ 98PacRedT-313
❑ 98PacSil-313
❑ 98Pin-83
❑ 98PinPreP-83
❑ 98Revo-66
❑ 98RevoSS-66
❑ 98ScoRT-81
❑ 98SPxFin-89
❑ 98SPxFinR-89
❑ 98SPxFinS-89
❑ 98StaCluFDI-210
❑ 98StaCluI-210
❑ 98StaCluOneK-210
❑ 98StaCluPP-210
❑ 98Top-299
❑ 98TopChr-299
❑ 98TopChrR-299
❑ 98TopDevR-299
❑ 98TopDia-299
❑ 98TopGal-28
❑ 98TopGalGP-28
❑ 98TopGalOPP-28
❑ 98TopGalPPI-28
❑ 98TopGalPPIA-28
❑ 98TopGolLabC1-31
❑ 98TopGolLabC1B-31
❑ 98TopGolLabC1One-31
❑ 98TopGolLabC1R-31
❑ 98TopGolLabC2-31
❑ 98TopGolLabC2B-31
❑ 98TopGolLabC2One-31
❑ 98TopGolLabC2R-31
❑ 98TopGolLabC3-31
❑ 98TopGolLabC3B-31
❑ 98TopGolLabC3One-31
❑ 98TopGolLabC3R-31
❑ 98TopMiniC-299
❑ 98TopOpeD-126
❑ 98TopSta-68
❑ 98TopStaB-68
❑ 98TopStaG-68
❑ 98TopStaGR-68
❑ 98TopStaS-68
❑ 98TopTek-42
❑ 98TopTekD-42
❑ 98Ult-184
❑ 98UltGolM-184
❑ 98UltMas-184
❑ 98UltPlaM-184
❑ 98UppDec-386
❑ 99199Fin-242
❑ 99Bow-56
❑ 99BowChr-56
❑ 99BowChrG-56
❑ 99BowChrGR-56
❑ 99BowChrI-56
❑ 99BowChrIR-56
❑ 99BowChrR-56
❑ 99BowGol-56
❑ 99BowInt-56
❑ 99CroRoyB-64
❑ 99CroRoyL-64
❑ 99CroRoyOD-64
❑ 99FinGolRef-242
❑ 99FinRef-242
❑ 99FlaShoLeg1-104
❑ 99FlaShoLeg2-104
❑ 99FlaShoLeg3-104
❑ 99FlaShoLegM1-104
❑ 99FlaShoLegM2-104
❑ 99FlaShoLegM3-104
❑ 99FlaShoR1-104
❑ 99FlaShoR2-104
❑ 99FlaShoR3-104
❑ 99Fle-62
❑ 99FleMys-61
❑ 99FleMysG-61
❑ 99FleMysM-61
❑ 99FleSta9-62
❑ 99FleWarT-62
❑ 99Pac-187
❑ 99PacAur-80
❑ 99PacAurOD-80
❑ 99PacCroC-122
❑ 99PacCroCPB-122
❑ 99PacOme-105
❑ 99PacOmeC-105
❑ 99PacOmeG-105
❑ 99PacOmePB-105
❑ 99PacPar-102
❑ 99PacParC-102
❑ 99PacParG-102
❑ 99PacParHoloGold-102
❑ 99PacParHS-102
❑ 99PacParOD-102
❑ 99PacParPB-102
❑ 99PacParRed-102
❑ 99PacPlaB-187
❑ 99PacPri-67
❑ 99PacPriHB-67
❑ 99PacPriHG-67
❑ 99PacPriHM-67
❑ 99PacPriHP-67
❑ 99PacPriRed-67
❑ 99PacPriS-56
❑ 99PacPriS206-56
❑ 99PacPriS206R-56
❑ 99PacRed-187
❑ 99Rev-62
❑ 99RevPremDate-62
❑ 99RevRet-62
❑ 99RevShaSS-62
❑ 99SkyPre-82
❑ 99SkyPreR-82
❑ 99SkyThu-77
❑ 99SkyThuRant-77
❑ 99SkyThuRave-77
❑ 99SpoIll-130
❑ 99StaClu-42
❑ 99StaCluFDI-42
❑ 99StaCluOoaK-42
❑ 99StaCluPP-42
❑ 99ThuSkySupR-77
❑ 99Top-99
❑ 99TopBlaLC1-14
❑ 99TopBlaLC2-14
❑ 99TopBlaLC3-14
❑ 99TopChr-99
❑ 99TopChrR-99
❑ 99TopGal-55
❑ 99TopGalP-55
❑ 99TopGalPPI-55
❑ 99TopGolL-14
❑ 99TopGolLC1-14
❑ 99TopGolLC2-14
❑ 99TopGolLOtO-14
❑ 99TopMVPP-99
❑ 99TopOpeD-57
❑ 99TopRedLC1-14
❑ 99TopRedLC2-14
❑ 99TopRedLC3-14
❑ 99UppDec-384
❑ 99UppDecEL1-384
❑ 99UppDecEL2-384
❑ 99UppDecM-95
❑ 99UppDecMGS-95
❑ 99UppDecMHFS-95
❑ 99UppDecMP-95
❑ 99UppDecMSS-95
❑ 99Vic-173

Bell, Eric

❑ 84NewOriT-2
❑ 86ChaOriW-2
❑ 87BalOriP-4
❑ 87Don-39
❑ 87DonRoo-2
❑ 87FleUpd-2
❑ 87FleUpdG-2
❑ 87Lea-39
❑ 87OriFreB-45
❑ 87SpoRool-1
❑ 87SpoTeaP-21
❑ 87TopTra-3T
❑ 87TopTraT-3T
❑ 88ClaRed-193
❑ 88Don-125
❑ 88Fle-555
❑ 88FleGlo-555
❑ 88OPC-383
❑ 88OriPos-5
❑ 88PanSti-3
❑ 88RocRedWC-2
❑ 88RocRedWP-194
❑ 88RocRedWTI-2
❑ 88Sco-101
❑ 88ScoGlo-101
❑ 88ScoYouS2-38
❑ 88StaLinO-1
❑ 88Top-383
❑ 88TopSti-224
❑ 88TopTif-383
❑ 90HagSunDGB-3
❑ 90ProAAAF-454
❑ 90RocRedWGC-16
❑ 90RocRedWP-697
❑ 91CanIndLD-77
❑ 91CanIndP-971
❑ 91LinDriAA-77
❑ 91OriCro-28
❑ 92ColSprSSF-743
❑ 92IndFanC-5
❑ 92Lea-379
❑ 92LeaBlaG-379
❑ 93AstMot-25
❑ 93TucTorF-3051
❑ 94TucTorF-752
❑ 96TusTorB-3
❑ 97ColSprSATTI-27

Bell, Gary

❑ 58IndTeal-25
❑ 59Kah-2
❑ 59Top-327
❑ 60Kah-2
❑ 60Top-441
❑ 61Kah-3
❑ 61Pos-58A
❑ 61Pos-58B
❑ 61Top-274
❑ 62IndJayP-1
❑ 62Kah-1A
❑ 62Kah-1B
❑ 62SalPlaC-213
❑ 62ShiPlaC-213
❑ 62Top-273
❑ 63IndJayP-2
❑ 63Top-129
❑ 64Top-234
❑ 64TopVen-234
❑ 65Top-424
❑ 66Top-525
❑ 67CokCapI-7
❑ 67DexPre-21
❑ 67Top-479
❑ 68CokCapRS-3
❑ 68DexPre-11
❑ 68OPC-43
❑ 68Top-43
❑ 68TopVen-43
❑ 69MilBra-23
❑ 69MLBOffS-93
❑ 69PilPos-7
❑ 69Top-377
❑ 69TopSta-223
❑ 69TopTeaP-9
❑ 77PilPosR-7
❑ 81RedSoxBG2S-70
❑ 83Pil69G-34
❑ 89PacLegI-213

Bell, George (Jorge Antonio)

❑ 80CarMudF-13
❑ 82Don-54
❑ 82Fle-609
❑ 82OPC-254
❑ 82SyrChiT-20
❑ 82SyrChiTI-7
❑ 82Top-254
❑ 83SyrChiT-21
❑ 84BluJayFS-5
❑ 84Don-73
❑ 84Fle-148
❑ 84FunFooP-113
❑ 84Nes792-278
❑ 84OPC-278
❑ 84Top-278
❑ 84TopTif-278
❑ 85AllGamPI-50
❑ 85BluJayFS-5
❑ 85DomLeaS-19
❑ 85Don-146
❑ 85Fle-100
❑ 85FleStaS-39
❑ 85Lea-248
❑ 85OPC-59
❑ 85OPCPos-18
❑ 85Top-698
❑ 85TopSti-360
❑ 85TopTif-698
❑ 86BasStaB-8
❑ 86BluJayAF-4
❑ 86BluJayFS-4
❑ 86Don-4
❑ 86Don-71
❑ 86DonSupD-4
❑ 86Fle-53
❑ 86FleMin-13
❑ 86GenMilB-3B
❑ 86Lea-4
❑ 86OPC-338
❑ 86OPCBoxB-A
❑ 86SevCoi-E11
❑ 86Spo-102
❑ 86Top-338
❑ 86Top-718
❑ 86TopGloS-47
❑ 86TopSti-187
❑ 86TopSup-10
❑ 86TopTat-3
❑ 86TopTif-338
❑ 86TopTif-718
❑ 86TopWaxBC-A
❑ 87BluJayFS-2

❑ 87ClaGam-56
❑ 87Don-271
❑ 87DonOpeD-39
❑ 87Fle-220
❑ 87FleAll-9
❑ 87FleAwaW-2
❑ 87FleGamW-3
❑ 87FleGlo-220
❑ 87FleLimE-4
❑ 87FleMin-7
❑ 87FleSlu-3
❑ 87FleStiC-9
❑ 87GenMilB-1B
❑ 87HosSti-3
❑ 87KraFoo-43
❑ 87Lea-184
❑ 87OPC-12
❑ 87Spo-51
❑ 87Spo-80
❑ 87StuPan-27
❑ 87SyrChi1A-10
❑ 87Top-106
❑ 87Top-612
❑ 87Top-681
❑ 87TopCoi-3
❑ 87TopGloS-45
❑ 87TopMinL-74
❑ 87TopSti-193
❑ 87TopTif-106
❑ 87TopTif-612
❑ 87TopTif-681
❑ 88Baz-1
❑ 88BluJay5-2
❑ 88BluJayFS-2
❑ 88CheBoy-4
❑ 88ClaBlu-242
❑ 88Don-656
❑ 88DonAll-6
❑ 88DonBasB-31
❑ 88DonBonM-BC19
❑ 88DonPop-6
❑ 88Dra-22
❑ 88Fle-103
❑ 88Fle-623
❑ 88FleAll-5
❑ 88FleAwaW-2
❑ 88FleBasA-1
❑ 88FleBasM-1
❑ 88FleExcS-3
❑ 88FleGlo-103
❑ 88FleGlo-623
❑ 88FleHotS-1
❑ 88FleLeaL-1
❑ 88FleMin-59
❑ 88FleRecS-2
❑ 88FleSlu-1
❑ 88FleStiC-71
❑ 88FleSup-2
❑ 88FleTeaL-1
❑ 88GreBasS-76
❑ 88K-M-1
❑ 88KayB-1
❑ 88Lea-213
❑ 88Lea-214
❑ 88Lea-254
❑ 88MSAFanSD-7
❑ 88MSAHosD-22
❑ 88Nes-34
❑ 88OPC-173
❑ 88PanSti-224
❑ 88PanSti-230
❑ 88RedFolSB-6
❑ 88Sco-540
❑ 88ScoBoxC-6
❑ 88ScoGlo-540
❑ 88Spo-4
❑ 88StaBel-1
❑ 88StaBel-2
❑ 88StaBel-3
❑ 88StaBel-4
❑ 88StaBel-5
❑ 88StaBel-6
❑ 88StaBel-7
❑ 88StaBel-8
❑ 88StaBel-9
❑ 88StaBel-10
❑ 88StaBel-11
❑ 88StaLinAl-2
❑ 88StaLinBJ-2
❑ 88StaStiGB-1
❑ 88StaStiGB-2
❑ 88StaStiGB-3
❑ 88StaStiGB-4
❑ 88StaStiGB-5
❑ 88StaStiGB-6
❑ 88StaStiGB-7
❑ 88StaStiGB-8
❑ 88StaStiGB-9
❑ 88StaStiGB-10
❑ 88TarPla-3
❑ 88Top-390
❑ 88Top-590
❑ 88Top-729
❑ 88TopBig-15
❑ 88TopClo-8
❑ 88TopCoi-1
❑ 88TopGaloC-2
❑ 88TopGloA-6
❑ 88TopGloS-31
❑ 88TopMinL-37
❑ 88TopRevLL-18
❑ 88TopRitTM-26
❑ 88TopSti-158
❑ 88TopSti-188
❑ 88TopStiB-47
❑ 88TopTif-390
❑ 88TopTif-590
❑ 88TopTif-729
❑ 88TopUKM-3
❑ 88TopUKMT-3
❑ 88Woo-9
❑ 89BluJayFS-2
❑ 89Bow-256
❑ 89BowTif-256
❑ 89ClaLigB-43
❑ 89Don-149
❑ 89DonBasB-272
❑ 89Fle-226
❑ 89FleBasA-2
❑ 89FleBasM-2
❑ 89FleGlo-226
❑ 89FleHeroB-1
❑ 89K-M-17
❑ 89OPC-50
❑ 89PanSti-472
❑ 89RedFolSB-7
❑ 89Sco-347
❑ 89ScoHot1S-91
❑ 89Spo-25
❑ 89Top-1
❑ 89Top-50
❑ 89TopAme2C-4
❑ 89TopBasT-53
❑ 89TopBig-318
❑ 89TopGloS-27
❑ 89TopMinL-75
❑ 89TopSti-1
❑ 89TopSti-193
❑ 89TopTif-1
❑ 89TopTif-50
❑ 89TopUKM-3
❑ 89TVSpoM-79
❑ 89UppDec-255
❑ 89Woo-7
❑ 90BluJayFS-2
❑ 90BluJayHS-1
❑ 90BluJayHS-2
❑ 90BluJayHS-5
❑ 90Bow-515
❑ 90BowTif-515
❑ 90ClaBlu-84
❑ 90Don-206
❑ 90DonBesA-139
❑ 90DOnBonM-BC13
❑ 90DonLeaS-25
❑ 90Fle-76
❑ 90Fle-628
❑ 90FleBasM-1
❑ 90FleBasMC-1
❑ 90FleCan-76
❑ 90FleCan-628
❑ 90FleLeaL-3
❑ 90FleLeaLC-3
❑ 90GooHumICBLS-2
❑ 90Hot50PS-1
❑ 90Lea-185
❑ 90M.Vpin-105
❑ 90MLBBasB-67
❑ 90MSAHolD-1
❑ 90MSAIceTD-9
❑ 90OPC-170
❑ 90PanSti-180
❑ 90PublntS-276
❑ 90PublntS-509
❑ 90Sco-286
❑ 90Sco100S-27
❑ 90ScoMcD-20
❑ 90ScoYouSI-19
❑ 90Spo-17
❑ 90Top-170
❑ 90TopAmeA-22
❑ 90TopBig-153
❑ 90TopCoi-5
❑ 90TopDou-3
❑ 90TopGloS-24
❑ 90TopHilHM-12
❑ 90TopMinL-41
❑ 90TopSti-192
❑ 90TopStiB-46
❑ 90TopTif-170
❑ 90TopTVA-21
❑ 90UppDec-95
❑ 90UppDec-127
❑ 90USPlaCA-12C
❑ 90VicPos-1
❑ 90WinDis-6
❑ 91BasBesHM-1
❑ 91Bow-418
❑ 91Cla2-T30
❑ 91ClaGam-104
❑ 91CubMar-11
❑ 91CubVinL-3
❑ 91CubVinL-36
❑ 91Don-642
❑ 91Fle-169
❑ 91FleUpd-77
❑ 91Lea-389
❑ 91OPC-440
❑ 91OPCPre-6
❑ 91PanFreS-340
❑ 91PanSti-158
❑ 91Sco-195
❑ 91Sco100S-40
❑ 91ScoRoo-13T
❑ 91StaClu-504
❑ 91StaPro-1
❑ 91Stu-151
❑ 91Top-440
❑ 91TopDesS-440
❑ 91TopMic-440
❑ 91TopTif-440
❑ 91TopTra-8T
❑ 91TopTraT-8T
❑ 91TopTriH-N2
❑ 91Ult-55
❑ 91UppDec-532
❑ 91UppDec-725
❑ 91UppDec-742
❑ 91USPlaCA-6S
❑ 92Cla2-T86
❑ 92ClaGam-26
❑ 92Don-127
❑ 92DonCraJ2-6
❑ 92DonDiaK-DK7
❑ 92DonSupD-DK7
❑ 92DonUpd-U12
❑ 92Fle-376
❑ 92FleUpd-12
❑ 92Hig5-26
❑ 92Lea-462
❑ 92LeaBlaG-462
❑ 92OPC-320
❑ 92OPCPre-182
❑ 92PanSti-188
❑ 92Pin-37
❑ 92RedFolS-10
❑ 92Sco-45
❑ 92Sco100S-88
❑ 92ScoProP-7
❑ 92ScoProP-14
❑ 92ScoRoo-24T
❑ 92StaClu-525
❑ 92StaClu-840
❑ 92StaCluD-13
❑ 92StaCluECN-840
❑ 92Stu-151
❑ 92Top-320
❑ 92TopGol-320
❑ 92TopGolW-320
❑ 92TopKid-3
❑ 92TopMic-320
❑ 92TopTra-9T
❑ 92TopTraG-9T
❑ 92TriPla-42
❑ 92Ult-173
❑ 92Ult-332
❑ 92UppDec-236
❑ 92UppDec-724
❑ 92WhiSoxK-21
❑ 93BluJayDM-4
❑ 93Bow-639
❑ 93CadDis-5
❑ 93ClaGam-11
❑ 93Don-95
❑ 93DonSpiotG-SG6
❑ 93Fin-175
❑ 93FinRef-175
❑ 93Fle-200
❑ 93FunPac-198
❑ 93Lea-217
❑ 93OPC-26
❑ 93PacBeiA-3
❑ 93PacSpa-67
❑ 93PacSpaPl-10
❑ 93PanSti-143
❑ 93Pin-387
❑ 93PinSlu-25
❑ 93Sco-387
❑ 93Sel-100
❑ 93StaClu-330
❑ 93StaCluFDI-330
❑ 93StaCluMOP-330
❑ 93Stu-28
❑ 93Top-790
❑ 93TopGol-790
❑ 93TopInaM-790
❑ 93TopInaR-790
❑ 93TopMic-790
❑ 93TriPla-247
❑ 93Ult-171
❑ 93UppDec-345
❑ 93UppDecGold-345
❑ 93UppDecHRH-HR12
❑ 93WhiSoxK-2
❑ 93WhiSoxSC-22
❑ 94Fle-75
❑ 94PanSti-44
❑ 94Sco-541
❑ 94ScoGolR-541
❑ 94Top-214
❑ 94TopGol-214
❑ 94TopSpa-214
❑ 96BluJayB-3
❑ 96BluJayOH-1
❑ 97BluJayS-34

Bell, George G.

❑ 09AmeCarE90-1-4
❑ 09ColChiE-26
❑ 09RamT20-10
❑ 09SpoNewSM-20
❑ 09T206-19
❑ 09T206-20
❑ 10DomDisP-10
❑ 10SweCapPP-70A
❑ 10SweCapPP-70B
❑ 11HelSta-83
❑ 11PinT-5-459
❑ 11S74Sil-49
❑ 11SpoLifCW-27
❑ 11SpoLifM-149
❑ 11T205-13
❑ 11TurRedT-79
❑ 12ColRedB-26
❑ 12ColTinT-26
❑ 67SpoHobFC-47
❑ 90DodTar-46

Bell, Greg

❑ 86WinSpiP-1
❑ 87PitCubP-2

Bell, Gus (David Russell)

❑ 47PM1StaP1-8
❑ 50PirTeal-2
❑ 51Bow-40
❑ 51TopRedB-17
❑ 52Top-170
❑ 53BowBW-1
❑ 53NorBreL-3
❑ 53Top-118
❑ 54Bow-124
❑ 55Bow-243
❑ 55Kah-1
❑ 56Kah-2
❑ 56Top-162
❑ 57Kah-3
❑ 57Top-180
❑ 58Kah-3
❑ 58RedEnq-4
❑ 58RedJayP-2
❑ 58Top-75
❑ 59Kah-3
❑ 59RedBurBP-2
❑ 59RedShiBS-3
❑ 59Top-365
❑ 60Kah-3
❑ 60KeyChal-6
❑ 60RedJayP-1
❑ 60Top-235
❑ 60Top-352
❑ 61Kah-4
❑ 61Pos-186B
❑ 61RedJayP-3
❑ 61Top-25
❑ 61Top-215
❑ 61TopStal-14
❑ 62Jel-120
❑ 62MetJayP-1
❑ 62PosCan-120
❑ 62SalPlaC-158A
❑ 62SalPlaC-158B
❑ 62ShiPlaC-158
❑ 62Top-408
❑ 62TopBuc-8
❑ 62TopStal-153
❑ 63Top-547
❑ 64Top-534
❑ 74MetOriEB-2
❑ 76OPC-66
❑ 76Top-66
❑ 79TCM50-89
❑ 80Red196T-13
❑ 82OhiHaloF-35
❑ 83TopRep5-170
❑ 85Top-131
❑ 85TopTif-131

Bell, Hi (Herman)

❑ 27MidBre-2
❑ 34DiaMatCSB-7
❑ 34Gou-52
❑ 92ConTSN-632

Bell, Jason

❑ 96Bow-253
❑ 96BowFoi-253
❑ 96FtMyeMB-4
❑ 96HarCitRCB-7
❑ 97NewBriRC-4
❑ 98NewBriRCM-6

Bell, Jay

❑ 85VisOakT-8
❑ 86IndTeal-5
❑ 86WatIndP-4
❑ 87BufBisP-4
❑ 88Don-637
❑ 88DonBasB-61
❑ 88Fle-602
❑ 88FleGlo-602
❑ 88IndGat-16
❑ 88IndTeal-5
❑ 88StaLinI-4
❑ 88Top-637
❑ 88TopTif-637
❑ 89BufBisC-4
❑ 89BufBisP-1679
❑ 89Don-350
❑ 89PirVerFJ-3
❑ 89Sco-352
❑ 89Top-144
❑ 89TopTif-144
❑ 89TriAAAP-AAA7
❑ 89UppDec-489
❑ 90Bow-174
❑ 90BowTif-174
❑ 90Don-488
❑ 90DonBesN-136
❑ 90Fle-459
❑ 90FleCan-459
❑ 90Lea-248
❑ 90OPC-523
❑ 90PanSti-321
❑ 90PirHomC-4
❑ 90Sco-563
❑ 90ScoYouS2-12
❑ 90Top-523
❑ 90TopTif-523
❑ 90UppDec-517
❑ 91Bow-522
❑ 91Don-289
❑ 91Fle-31
❑ 91Lea-130
❑ 91OPC-293
❑ 91PanFreS-118
❑ 91PanSti-110
❑ 91Sco-323
❑ 91StaClu-84
❑ 91Stu-221
❑ 91Top-293
❑ 91TopDesS-293
❑ 91TopMic-293
❑ 91TopTif-293
❑ 91Ult-274
❑ 91UppDec-183
❑ 92Bow-519
❑ 92Cla1-T12
❑ 92Don-100
❑ 92DonDiaK-DK17
❑ 92DonSupD-DK17
❑ 92Fle-549
❑ 92HitTheBB-3
❑ 92Lea-143
❑ 92LeaBlaG-143
❑ 92OPC-779
❑ 92PanSti-255
❑ 92Pin-34
❑ 92PirNatl-2
❑ 92Sco-180
❑ 92StaClu-507
❑ 92Stu-81
❑ 92Top-779
❑ 92TopGol-779
❑ 92TopGolW-779
❑ 92TopMic-779
❑ 92TriPla-181
❑ 92Ult-250
❑ 92UppDec-115
❑ 93Bow-330
❑ 93CadDis-6
❑ 93DiaMar-9
❑ 93Don-18
❑ 93Fin-194
❑ 93FinRef-194
❑ 93Fla-110
❑ 93Fle-111
❑ 93FunPac-149
❑ 93Lea-116
❑ 93OPC-19
❑ 93PacSpa-243
❑ 93PanSti-283
❑ 93Pin-48
❑ 93PirNatl-2
❑ 93RedFolS-9
❑ 93Sco-32
❑ 93Sel-81
❑ 93SP-182
❑ 93StaClu-138
❑ 93StaCluFDI-138
❑ 93StaCluMOP-138
❑ 93Stu-20
❑ 93Top-354
❑ 93TopGol-354
❑ 93TopInaM-354
❑ 93TopInaR-354
❑ 93TopMic-354
❑ 93TriPla-140
❑ 93TriPla-261
❑ 93Ult-96
❑ 93UppDec-103
❑ 93UppDec-480
❑ 93UppDec-830
❑ 93UppDecGold-103
❑ 93UppDecGold-480
❑ 93UppDecGold-830
❑ 94Bow-106
❑ 94ChuHomS-20
❑ 94ChuHomSG-20
❑ 94ColC-497
❑ 94ColChoGS-497
❑ 94ColChoSS-497
❑ 94Don-21
❑ 94DonSpeE-21
❑ 94Fin-411
❑ 94FinRef-411
❑ 94Fla-214
❑ 94Fle-605
❑ 94FleAllS-28
❑ 94FleExtB-343
❑ 94FleSun-4
❑ 94FleTeaL-25
❑ 94FUnPac-161
❑ 94Lea-12
❑ 94LeaL-139
❑ 94OPC-222
❑ 94Pac-492
❑ 94PanSti-233
❑ 94[illegible]-151
❑ 94PinArtP-151
❑ 94PinMusC-151
❑ 94PinRunC-RC37
❑ 94PinTeaP-4
❑ 94PirBloP-1
❑ 94PirQui-1
❑ 94ProMag-107
❑ 94RedFolMI-3
❑ 94Sco-32
❑ 94ScoCyc-TC15
❑ 94ScoGolR-32
❑ 94ScoGolS-12
❑ 94Sel-5
❑ 94SP-140
❑ 94SPDieC-140
❑ 94Spo-95
❑ 94Spo-188
❑ 94StaClu-18
❑ 94StaCluFDI-18
❑ 94StaCluGR-18
❑ 94StaCluMOP-18
❑ 94StaCluMOP-ST11

- 94StaCluST-ST11
- 94Stu-144
- 94TomPiz-2
- 94Top-15
- 94TopBlaG-24
- 94TopGol-15
- 94TopSpa-15
- 94TriPla-181
- 94TriPlaM-8
- 94Ult-254
- 94UltAllS-14
- 94UltAwaW-14
- 94UppDec-177
- 94UppDec-277
- 94UppDecAJ-37
- 94UppDecAJG-37
- 94UppDecED-177
- 94UppDecED-277
- 95Baz-96
- 95Bow-363
- 95ColCho-380
- 95ColChoGS-380
- 95ColChoSE-175
- 95ColChoSEGS-175
- 95ColChoSESS-175
- 95ColChoSS-380
- 95Don-206
- 95DonPreP-206
- 95DonTopotO-312
- 95Emo-172
- 95Fin-122
- 95FinRef-122
- 95Fla-184
- 95Fle-472
- 95FleTeaL-25
- 95Lea-179
- 95LeaLim-19
- 95Pac-340
- 95PacPri-111
- 95PanSti-61
- 95Pin-86
- 95PinArtP-86
- 95PinMusC-86
- 95PirFil-2
- 95Sco-438
- 95ScoGolR-438
- 95ScoHaloG-HG81
- 95ScoPlaTS-438
- 95Sel-24
- 95SelArtP-24
- 95SelCer-73
- 95SelCerMG-73
- 95SP-95
- 95SPCha-79
- 95SPCha-82
- 95SPChaDC-79
- 95SPChaDC-82
- 95Spo-43
- 95SpoArtP-43
- 95SPSil-95
- 95StaClu-125
- 95StaCluCC-CC11
- 95StaCluFDI-125
- 95StaCluMOP-125
- 95StaCluMOP-CC11
- 95StaCluSTWS-125
- 95StaCluVR-64
- 95StaCluVRMO-64
- 95Stu-119
- 95Sum-95
- 95SumNthD-95
- 95Top-230
- 95TopCyb-129
- 95TopEmb-15
- 95TopEmbGI-15
- 95UC3-76
- 95UC3ArtP-76
- 95Ult-423
- 95UltGolM-423
- 95UppDec-150
- 95UppDecED-150
- 95UppDecEDG-150
- 95UppDecSE-220
- 95UppDecSEG-220
- 95Zen-45
- 96Baz-41
- 96Bow-52
- 96BowFoi-52
- 96Cir-170
- 96CirAcc-25
- 96CirBos-44
- 96CirRav-170
- 96ColCho-405
- 96ColCho-675
- 96ColChoGS-405
- 96ColChoGS-675
- 96ColChoSS-405
- 96ColChoSS-675
- 96ColChoYMtP-4
- 96ColChoYMtP-4A
- 96ColChoYMtPGS-4
- 96ColChoYMtPGS-4A
- 96DenHol-28
- 96Don-21
- 96DonPreP-21
- 96EmoXL-252
- 96Fin-B106
- 96FinRef-B106
- 96Fla-343
- 96Fle-514
- 96FleTif-514
- 96Lea-152
- 96LeaPre-11
- 96LeaPreP-11
- 96LeaPrePB-152
- 96LeaPrePG-152
- 96LeaPrePS-152
- 96LeaSig-34
- 96LeaSigPPG-34
- 96LeaSigPPP-34
- 96MetUni-214
- 96MetUniP-214
- 96Pac-173
- 96PacPri-P55
- 96PacPriG-P55
- 96PanSti-65
- 96Pin-64
- 96PinAfi-2
- 96PinAfiAP-2
- 96PinAfiFPP-2
- 96PinArtP-56
- 96PinFan-20
- 96PinSta-56
- 96ProSta-93
- 96RedF-6
- 96Sco-300
- 96ScoDugC-B25
- 96ScoDugCAP-B25
- 96Sel-16
- 96SelArtP-16
- 96SelCer-9
- 96SelCerAP-9
- 96SelCerCB-9
- 96SelCerCR-9
- 96SelCerMB-9
- 96SelCerMG-9
- 96SelCerMR-9
- 96SelTeaN-3
- 96SP-150
- 96Spo-92
- 96SpoArtP-92
- 96StaClu-172
- 96StaCluEPB-172
- 96StaCluEPG-172
- 96StaCluEPS-172
- 96StaCluMOP-172
- 96Stu-83
- 96StuPrePB-83
- 96StuPrePG-83
- 96StuPrePS-83
- 96Sum-25
- 96SumAbo&B-25
- 96SumArtP-25
- 96SumFoi-25
- 96Top-156
- 96TopLas-18
- 96Ult-260
- 96UltGolM-260
- 96UppDec-435
- 96Zen-27
- 96ZenArtP-27
- 96ZenMoz-23
- 97Bow-249
- 97BowChr-73
- 97BowChrI-73
- 97BowChrIR-73
- 97BowChrR-73
- 97BowInt-249
- 97Cir-79
- 97CirRav-79
- 97ColChoU-U15
- 97Don-124
- 97DonGolPP-124
- 97DonSilPP-124
- 97Fin-178
- 97FinRef-178
- 97FlaShoLC-145
- 97FlaShoLeg0-145
- 97FlaShoLeg1-145
- 97FlaShoM-A145
- 97FlaShoM-B145
- 97FlaShoM-C145
- 97FlaShoR0-145
- 97FlaShoR1-145
- 97FlaShoR2-145
- 97Fle-425
- 97Fle-541
- 97FleTif-425
- 97FleTif-541
- 97Lea-150
- 97LeaFraM-150
- 97LeaFraMDC-150
- 97NewPin-60
- 97NewPinAP-60
- 97NewPinMC-60
- 97NewPinPP-60
- 97Pac-390
- 97PacLigB-390
- 97PacSil-390
- 97PinX-PSfF-6
- 97PinX-PSfFU-6
- 97RoyPol-3
- 97Sco-77
- 97Sco-433
- 97ScoArtPWB-77
- 97ScoArtPWB-433
- 97ScoPreS-77
- 97ScoResC-433
- 97ScoShoS-77
- 97ScoShoS-433
- 97ScoShoSAP-77
- 97ScoShoSAP-433
- 97SP-89
- 97SpoIll-154
- 97SpoIllEE-154
- 97StaClu-261
- 97StaCluMOP-261
- 97Top-259
- 97Ult-302
- 97UltGolME-302
- 97UltPlaME-302
- 97UppDec-537
- 98Bow-283
- 98BowBes-24
- 98BowBesAR-24
- 98BowBesR-24
- 98BowChr-283
- 98BowChrGA-283
- 98BowChrGAR-283
- 98BowChrI-283
- 98BowChrIR-283
- 98BowChrR-283
- 98BowGolA-283
- 98BowInt-283
- 98CirThu-222
- 98CirThuRav-222
- 98CirThuSupRav-222
- 98ColCho-288
- 98DiaBacP-16
- 98DiaMcD-4
- 98Don-186
- 98DonColL-261
- 98DonGolPP-186
- 98DonPriCL-261
- 98DonSigA-6
- 98DonSigAC-7
- 98DonSigAM-7
- 98DonSilPP-186
- 98Fin-168
- 98FinNo--168
- 98FinNo-R-168
- 98FinRef-168
- 98Fle-121
- 98Fle-390
- 98FleVin'-65
- 98FleVin'C-65
- 98Lea-62
- 98LeaFraDA-62
- 98LeaFraF-62
- 98LeaFraM-62
- 98LeaFraM-62
- 98LeaFraMDC-62
- 98LeaFraMDC-62
- 98LeaFraMZ2-62
- 98LeaRS-123
- 98LeaRSLHolo-123
- 98LeaRSLong-123
- 98LeaRTrue-123
- 98MetUni-126
- 98MetUniPMG-126
- 98Pac-99
- 98PacAur-96
- 98PacInvTeam-29
- 98PacOme-10
- 98PacOmeR-10
- 98PacOnl-29
- 98PacOnlR-29
- 98PacOnlWC-29
- 98PacPar-119
- 98PacParC-119
- 98PacParG-119
- 98PacParHS-119
- 98PacParPB-119
- 98PacParR-119
- 98PacPlaB-99
- 98PacRedT-99
- 98PacSil-99
- 98PacTeaC-29
- 98Pin-122
- 98PinPlu-138
- 98PinPreP-122
- 98PinSna-AD3
- 98PinSna-AD7
- 98Revo-6
- 98RevoSS-6
- 98Sco-63
- 98ScoRT-213
- 98ScoSS-PP26
- 98ScoSSAP-PP26
- 98SP Aut-39
- 98SpoIll-9
- 98SpoIllEE-9
- 98SpoIllFE-9
- 98SPxFin-243
- 98SPxFinR-243
- 98SPxFinS-243
- 98StaCluFDI-308
- 98StaCluI-308
- 98StaCluOneK-308
- 98StaCluPP-308
- 98Stu-8
- 98StuGPP-8
- 98StuSPP-8
- 98Top-140
- 98Top-455
- 98TopChr-140
- 98TopChr-455
- 98TopChrR-140
- 98TopChrR-455
- 98TopDevR-140
- 98TopDevR-455
- 98TopDia-140
- 98TopDia-455
- 98TopGal-8
- 98TopGalGP-8
- 98TopGalOPP-8
- 98TopGalPPI-8
- 98TopGalPPIA-8
- 98TopGolLabC1-9
- 98TopGolLabC1B-9
- 98TopGolLabC1One-9
- 98TopGolLabC1R-9
- 98TopGolLabC2-9
- 98TopGolLabC2B-9
- 98TopGolLabC2One-9
- 98TopGolLabC2R-9
- 98TopGolLabC3-9
- 98TopGolLabC3B-9
- 98TopGolLabC3One-9
- 98TopGolLabC3R-9
- 98TopMiniC-140
- 98TopMiniC-455
- 98TopOpeD-71
- 98TopSta-127
- 98TopStaB-127
- 98TopStaG-127
- 98TopStaGR-127
- 98TopStaS-127
- 98Ult-111
- 98Ult-458
- 98UltGolM-111
- 98UltGolM-458
- 98UltMas-111
- 98UltMas-458
- 98UltPlaM-111
- 98UltPlaM-458
- 98UppDec-112
- 98UppDec-635
- 98UppDecR-4
- 99199Fin-83
- 99Bow-281
- 99BowGol-281
- 99BowInt-281
- 99CroRoyB-6
- 99CroRoyL-6
- 99CroRoyOD-6
- 99FinGolRef-83
- 99FinRef-83
- 99Fle-114
- 99FleSta9-114
- 99FleWarT-114
- 99MetUni-102
- 99MetUniGM-102
- 99MetUniPMG-102
- 99Pac-15
- 99PacAur-7
- 99PacAurOD-7
- 99PacCroC-12
- 99PacCroCPB-12
- 99PacOme-10
- 99PacOmeC-10
- 99PacOmeG-10
- 99PacOmePB-10
- 99PacPar-11
- 99PacParC-11
- 99PacParG-11
- 99PacParHoloGold-11
- 99PacParHS-11
- 99PacParOD-11
- 99PacParPB-11
- 99PacParRed-11
- 99PacPlaB-15
- 99PacPri-6
- 99PacPriHB-6
- 99PacPriHG-6
- 99PacPriHM-6
- 99PacPriHP-6
- 99PacPriRed-6
- 99PacRed-15
- 99SkyPre-130
- 99SkyPreR-130
- 99SkyThu-154
- 99SkyThuRant-154
- 99SkyThuRave-154
- 99StaClu-13
- 99StaCluFDI-13
- 99StaCluOoaK-13
- 99StaCluPP-13
- 99ThuSkySupR-154
- 99Top-78
- 99TopChr-78
- 99TopChrR-78
- 99TopMVPP-78
- 99TopOpeD-44
- 99UD Cho-51
- 99UD ChoPCR-51
- 99Ult-126
- 99UltGolM-126
- 99UltMas-126
- 99UltPlaM-126
- 99UppDec-27
- 99UppDecBD-6
- 99UppDecBDD-6
- 99UppDecBDQ-6
- 99UppDecBDT-6
- 99UppDecEL1-27
- 99UppDecEL2-27
- 99UppDecM-13
- 99UppDecMGS-13
- 99UppDecMHFS-13
- 99UppDecMP-13
- 99UppDecMSS-13
- 99Vic-19

Bell, Jeremiah
- 97JohCitCTI-3

Bell, Jerry
- 72OPC-162
- 72Top-162
- 73OPC-92
- 73Top-92
- 74OPC-261
- 74SalLakCAC-98
- 74Top-261
- 74TopSta-191
- 75SanAntBT-3
- 94BreMilB-105

Bell, Juan
- 87BakDodP-7
- 88BasAmeAAB-23
- 88SanAntMB-24
- 88TriAAC-44
- 89Bow-11
- 89BowTif-11
- 89ClaTraP-170
- 89RocRedWC-21
- 89RocRedWP-1658
- 89UppDec-20
- 89UppDec-747
- 90CMC-312
- 90OPC-724
- 90ProAAAF-464
- 90RocRedWC-13
- 90RocRedWGC-9
- 90RocRedWP-707
- 90Sco-603
- 90Top-724
- 90TopDeb89-13
- 90TopTif-724
- 91BalOriP-3
- 91Bow-96
- 91Fle-468
- 91Lea-262
- 91OPCPre-7
- 91OriCro-29
- 91Sco100RS-59
- 91StuPre-1
- 91UppDecFE-59F
- 92Don-479
- 92Fle-3
- 92FleUpd-108
- 92OPC-52
- 92RocRedWS-451
- 92Sco-646
- 92StaClu-835
- 92StaCluNC-835
- 92Top-52
- 92TopGol-52
- 92TopGolW-52
- 92TopMic-52
- 93Bow-48
- 93Don-200
- 93Fle-98
- 93FleFinE-222
- 93Lea-205
- 93PacSpa-231
- 93PhiMed-6
- 93Pin-566
- 93Sco-588
- 93StaClu-157
- 93StaCluFDI-157
- 93StaCluMOP-157
- 93TriPla-98
- 93Ult-84
- 93UppDec-580
- 93UppDecGold-580
- 94BreMilB-106
- 94Fle-173
- 94Pac-325
- 94Sco-282
- 94ScoGolR-282
- 94StaClu-236
- 94StaCluFDI-236
- 94StaCluGR-236
- 94StaCluMOP-236
- 94Top-651
- 94TopGol-651
- 94TopSpa-651
- 94Ult-72
- 94WesPalBEC-3
- 94WesPalBEF-46
- 95Pac-261
- 95PawRedSDD-4
- 95PawRedTI-23
- 95Sco-412
- 95ScoGolR-412
- 95ScoPlaTS-412

Bell, Kevin Robert
- 75AppFoxT-2
- 77Top-83
- 77WhiSoxT-3
- 78SSP270-150
- 78Top-463
- 79IowOakP-4
- 79Top-662
- 80OPC-197
- 80Top-379
- 81Don-39
- 81Fle-343
- 81TacTigT-25
- 82TacTigT-13

Bell, L. T.
- 22Zee-118

Bell, Lenny
- 88PeoChiTI-4
- 89WinSpiS-1

Bell, Les (Lester Rowland)
- 25Exh-57
- 26Exh-57
- 27MidBre-3
- 27YorCarE-58B
- 28W502-58
- 28W56PlaC-JOK
- 28Yue-58
- 30ChiEveAP-1
- 30CubTeal-2
- 31CubTeal-2
- 35GouPreR-7
- 79DiaGre-151
- 92ConTSN-651

Bell, Matt
- 97SouBenSH-7

Bell, Matty (Madison)
- 40WheM4-5

Bell, Michael Allen
- 87SumBraP-16

❑ 88CarLeaAS-25
❑ 88DurBulS-1
❑ 89GreBraB-4
❑ 89GreBraP-1173
❑ 89GreBraS-3
❑ 89Sta-34
❑ 90GreBraP-1134
❑ 90GreBraS-3
❑ 90ProAaA-64
❑ 90StaFS7-94
❑ 91BraSubS-3
❑ 91Fle-682
❑ 91LinDriAAA-427
❑ 91RicBraBC-20
❑ 91RicBraLD-427
❑ 91RicBraP-2575
❑ 91RicBraTI-8
❑ 91Sco-375
❑ 91TopDeb90-14
❑ 91UppDec-644
❑ 92Fle-350
❑ 92GreBraF-1158
❑ 92GreBraS-228
❑ 92Sco-249
❑ 93BufBisF-522
Bell, Michael J.
❑ 96DelShoUB-6
Bell, Mike
❑ 94Bow-350
❑ 94ChaRivC-1
❑ 94ChaRivF-2679
❑ 94Cla-171
❑ 94ClaGolF-78
❑ 94ClaTriF-T79
❑ 94SouAtlLAF-SAL3
❑ 94SP-1
❑ 94SPDieC-1
❑ 94Top-201
❑ 94TopGol-201
❑ 94TopSpa-201
❑ 94UppDec-542
❑ 94UppDecAHNIL-1
❑ 94UppDecED-542
❑ 94UppDecML-218
❑ 95Bow-192
❑ 95Exc-124
❑ 95SPML-158
❑ 95UppDecML-26
❑ 95UppDecMLFS-26
❑ 95UppDecMLMLA-1
❑ 96BesAutS-9
❑ 96Bow-188
❑ 96BowFoi-188
❑ 96DelShoB-9
❑ 96TulDriTI-2
❑ 97OklCit8-8
❑ 98BinMetQ-9
❑ 98FreKeyM-7
❑ 98NorTidP-2
Bell, Randy
❑ 92DavLipB-3
Bell, Ricky
❑ 97YakBeaG-2
❑ 98SanBerS-3
❑ 98SanBerSTIS-3
Bell, Rob A.
❑ 98DanQ-C-1
❑ 99BasAmeTP-11
❑ 99BasAmeTPG-11
❑ 99SP SigAuto-ROB
❑ 99SP SigAutoG-ROB
❑ 99SPSig-89
Bell, Robbie
❑ 95TopTra-88T
❑ 96EugEmeB-2
❑ 97Bow-353
❑ 97BowChr-238
❑ 97BowChrI-238
❑ 97BowChrIR-238
❑ 97BowChrR-238
❑ 97BowInt-353
❑ 97MacBra-2
❑ 97SouAtlTPB-24
❑ 98Bes-55
❑ 98Bow-176
❑ 98BowChr-176
❑ 98BowChrGA-176
❑ 98BowChrGAR-176
❑ 98BowChrI-176
❑ 98BowChrIR-176
❑ 98BowChrR-176
❑ 98BowGolA-176
❑ 98BowInt-176
❑ 98CarLeaTPQ-5
❑ 98SP MinPE-23
❑ 98SPMin-23
❑ 99Bow-354
❑ 99BowGol-354
❑ 99BowInt-354
Bell, Robert
❑ 86EugEmeC-34
❑ 99BowBes-119
❑ 99BowBesAR-119
❑ 99BowBesR-119
Bell, Ron
❑ 77SanJosMC-20
Bell, Sam
❑ 39WorWidGV-2
Bell, Scott
❑ 98YakBeaG-5
Bell, Stewart
❑ 91ParPatF-15
Bell, Terry
❑ 86ChaLooP-4
❑ 86MemChiSTOS-1
❑ 86MemChiTOS-1
❑ 87MemChiB-23
❑ 87MemChiP-17
❑ 88GreBraB-2
❑ 89GreBraB-19
❑ 89GreBraP-1162
❑ 89GreBraS-4
Bell, Tito
❑ 93LimRocDWB-58
Bell, Tom
❑ 88FreSunCLC-27
❑ 88FreSunP-1248
Bell, William
❑ 86NegLeaF-99
Bella, Zeke (John)
❑ 56A'sPos-3
❑ 59Top-254
❑ 60A'sTeal-2
Bellacetin, Juan
❑ 85MexCitTT-27
Bellaman, Mike
❑ 86WatIndP-3
❑ 87WilBilP-10
Belle, Albert (Joey)
❑ 87LSUTigP-1
❑ 88KinIndS-3
❑ 89CanIndS-25
❑ 89FleUpd-25
❑ 89ScoRoo-106T
❑ 89Sta-199
❑ 90Bow-333
❑ 90BowTif-333
❑ 90ClaBlu-100
❑ 90Don-390
❑ 90Fle-485
❑ 90FleCan-485
❑ 90Hot50RS-6
❑ 90IndTeal-5
❑ 90Lea-180
❑ 90OPC-283
❑ 90Sco-508
❑ 90Sco100RS-9
❑ 90ScoYouSI-3
❑ 90Spo-159
❑ 90Top-283
❑ 90TopDeb89-14
❑ 90TopRoo-2
❑ 90TopSti-212
❑ 90TopTif-283
❑ 90ToyRoo-3
❑ 90UppDec-446
❑ 91Bow-81
❑ 91Cla3-T37
❑ 91FleUpd-16
❑ 91IndFanC-4
❑ 91Lea-239
❑ 91OPCPre-8
❑ 91StaBelRG-1
❑ 91StaBelRG-2
❑ 91StaBelRG-3
❑ 91StaBelRG-4
❑ 91StaBelRG-5
❑ 91StaBelRG-6
❑ 91StaBelRG-7
❑ 91StaBelRG-8
❑ 91StaBelRG-9
❑ 91StaBelRG-10
❑ 91StaBelRG-11
❑ 91StaClu-465
❑ 91Ult-107
❑ 91UppDec-764
❑ 92Bow-329
❑ 92Cla1-T13
❑ 92ClaGam-140
❑ 92DenHol-6
❑ 92Don-500
❑ 92Fle-105
❑ 92Hig5-43
❑ 92IndFanC-6
❑ 92Lea-350
❑ 92LeaBlaG-350
❑ 92MooSna-1
❑ 92OPC-785
❑ 92OPCPre-100
❑ 92PanSti-51
❑ 92Pin-31
❑ 92PinTea2-18
❑ 92RedFolS-11
❑ 92Sco-31
❑ 92Sco100S-39
❑ 92ScoProP-10
❑ 92SpollIFK1-187
❑ 92SpollIFK1-416
❑ 92SpoStaCC-2
❑ 92StaBel-1
❑ 92StaBel-2
❑ 92StaBel-3
❑ 92StaBel-4
❑ 92StaBel-5
❑ 92StaBel-6
❑ 92StaBel-7
❑ 92StaBel-8
❑ 92StaBel-9
❑ 92StaBel-10
❑ 92StaBel-11
❑ 92StaClu-220
❑ 92Stu-164
❑ 92Top-785
❑ 92TopGol-785
❑ 92TopGolW-785
❑ 92TopKid-73
❑ 92TopMic-785
❑ 92TriPla-103
❑ 92Ult-47
❑ 92UppDec-137
❑ 92UppDecHRH-HR13
❑ 92UppDecTMH-8
❑ 92UppDecWB-T13
❑ 93Bow-445
❑ 93ClaGam-12
❑ 93DenHol-12
❑ 93DiaMar-10
❑ 93Don-435
❑ 93DonEliD-17
❑ 93DonLonBL-LL3
❑ 93Fin-16
❑ 93FinRef-16
❑ 93Fla-192
❑ 93Fle-590
❑ 93Fle-712
❑ 93FleFruotL-4
❑ 93FunPac-108
❑ 93IndWUA-3
❑ 93Lea-18
❑ 93OPC-66
❑ 93PacSpa-94
❑ 93PanSti-52
❑ 93Pin-93
❑ 93PinHomRC-5
❑ 93PinSlu-11
❑ 93RedFolS-10
❑ 93Sco-84
❑ 93Sel-50
❑ 93SP-120
❑ 93SPPlaP-PP1
❑ 93StaClu-102
❑ 93StaCluFDI-102
❑ 93StaCluMOP-102
❑ 93Stu-95
❑ 93Top-635
❑ 93TopGol-635
❑ 93TopInaM-635
❑ 93TopInaR-635
❑ 93TopMic-635
❑ 93TriPla-94
❑ 93Ult-538
❑ 93UltHomRK-5
❑ 93UppDec-45
❑ 93UppDec-586
❑ 93UppDec-823
❑ 93UppDecGold-45
❑ 93UppDecGold-586
❑ 93UppDecGold-823
❑ 93UppDecHRH-HR5
❑ 93UppDecIC-WI12
❑ 93UppDecICJ-WI12
❑ 93UppDecOD-D4
❑ 93USPlaCA-9C
❑ 94Bow-411
❑ 94BowBes-R41
❑ 94BowBes-X98
❑ 94BowBesR-R41
❑ 94BowBesR-X98
❑ 94BowPre-3
❑ 94ChuShoS-7
❑ 94ColC-314
❑ 94ColC-339
❑ 94ColC-620
❑ 94ColChoGS-314
❑ 94ColChoGS-339
❑ 94ColChoGS-620
❑ 94ColChoHRA-HA6
❑ 94ColChoSS-314
❑ 94ColChoSS-339
❑ 94ColChoSS-620
❑ 94ColChoT-9
❑ 94DenHol-5
❑ 94Don-351
❑ 94DonDiaK-DK8
❑ 94DonDiaKJ-DK8
❑ 94DonEli-40
❑ 94DonMVP-19
❑ 94DonSpeE-351
❑ 94Fin-208
❑ 94FinJum-208
❑ 94FinRef-208
❑ 94Fla-38
❑ 94FlaOutP-1
❑ 94Fle-100
❑ 94FleAllS-3
❑ 94FleExtB-57
❑ 94FleExtBGB-3
❑ 94FleLeaL-2
❑ 94FleLumC-1
❑ 94FUnPac-130
❑ 94FUnPac-183
❑ 94FUnPac-204
❑ 94KinDis-9
❑ 94Lea-251
❑ 94LeaCleC-11
❑ 94LeaL-27
❑ 94LeaMVPC-A2
❑ 94LeaMVPCG-A2
❑ 94LeaPowB-10
❑ 94O-PJumAF-12
❑ 94OPC-43
❑ 94OPCAllR-12
❑ 94OPCJumA-12
❑ 94Pac-165
❑ 94PacGolP-4
❑ 94PanSti-7
❑ 94PanSti-55
❑ 94Pin-15
❑ 94PinArtP-15
❑ 94PinMusC-15
❑ 94PinPowS-PS11
❑ 94PinRunC-RC8
❑ 94PinTheN-6
❑ 94Pos-27
❑ 94ProMag-38
❑ 94RedFolMI-4
❑ 94Sco-7
❑ 94ScoCyc-TC20
❑ 94ScoGolR-7
❑ 94ScoGolS-46
❑ 94ScoSam-7
❑ 94ScoSam-7GR
❑ 94Sel-235
❑ 94SP-97
❑ 94SPDieC-97
❑ 94Spo-10
❑ 94SpoRooGGG-GG11
❑ 94StaClu-219
❑ 94StaClu-258
❑ 94StaCluF-F2
❑ 94StaCluFDI-219
❑ 94StaCluFDI-258
❑ 94StaCluFJ-F2
❑ 94StaCluGR-219
❑ 94StaCluGR-258
❑ 94StaCluMO-18
❑ 94StaCluMOP-219
❑ 94StaCluMOP-258
❑ 94StaCluMOP-F2
❑ 94StaCluMOP-ST19
❑ 94StaCluST-ST19
❑ 94Stu-92
❑ 94TomPiz-17
❑ 94Top-390
❑ 94Top-480
❑ 94TopBlaG-3
❑ 94TopGol-390
❑ 94TopGol-480
❑ 94TopSpa-390
❑ 94TopSpa-480
❑ 94TopSupS-4
❑ 94TriPla-113
❑ 94TriPlaBS-9
❑ 94TriPlaM-11
❑ 94Ult-41
❑ 94UltAllS-6
❑ 94UltHomRK-4
❑ 94UltRBIK-1
❑ 94UltRisS-3
❑ 94UppDec-40
❑ 94UppDec-131
❑ 94UppDec-285
❑ 94UppDecAJ-29
❑ 94UppDecAJG-29
❑ 94UppDecED-40
❑ 94UppDecED-131
❑ 94UppDecED-285
❑ 94UppDecMLS-MM2
❑ 94UppDecMLSED-MM2
❑ 94USPlaCA-9C
❑ 95Baz-116
❑ 95BazRedH-RH21
❑ 95Bow-276
❑ 95BowBes-R50
❑ 95BowBesJR-1
❑ 95BowBesR-R50
❑ 95ClaPhoC-19
❑ 95ColCho-83
❑ 95ColChoCtA-1
❑ 95ColChoCtAGR-1
❑ 95ColChoCtG-CG2
❑ 95ColChoCtG-CG2B
❑ 95ColChoCtG-CG2C
❑ 95ColChoCtGE-2
❑ 95ColChoCtGG-CG2
❑ 95ColChoCtGG-CG2B
❑ 95ColChoCtGG-CG2C
❑ 95ColChoCtGGE-2
❑ 95ColChoGS-83
❑ 95ColChoSE-120
❑ 95ColChoSEGS-120
❑ 95ColChoSESS-120
❑ 95ColChoSS-83
❑ 95DenHol-4
❑ 95Don-264
❑ 95DonBomS-3
❑ 95DonDom-7
❑ 95DonEli-60
❑ 95DonPreP-264
❑ 95DonTopotO-58
❑ 95Emo-32
❑ 95EmoN-2
❑ 95Fin-82
❑ 95FinPowK-PK11
❑ 95FinRef-82
❑ 95Fla-30
❑ 95FlaHotN-2
❑ 95FlaOutP-1
❑ 95Fle-132
❑ 95FleAllS-17
❑ 95FleLumC-2
❑ 95FleTeaL-5
❑ 95FleUpdDT-2
❑ 95FleUpdH-2
❑ 95Lea-284
❑ 95LeaGolS-2
❑ 95LeaLim-147
❑ 95LeaLimG-5
❑ 95LeaLimIBP-23
❑ 95LeaLimL-1
❑ 95NatPac2-1
❑ 95Pac-118
❑ 95PacGolCDC-7
❑ 95PacGolP-14
❑ 95PacPri-38
❑ 95PanSti-90
❑ 95Pin-233
❑ 95Pin-298
❑ 95PinArtP-233
❑ 95PinArtP-298
❑ 95PinFan-4
❑ 95PinGatA-GA8
❑ 95PinMusC-233
❑ 95PinMusC-298
❑ 95PinPer-PP2
❑ 95PinPin-16
❑ 95PinPinR-16
❑ 95PinRedH-RH7
❑ 95PinTeaP-TP8
❑ 95PinUps-US5
❑ 95PinWhiH-WH7
❑ 95Pos-13
❑ 95RedFol-16
❑ 95Sco-223
❑ 95Sco-557
❑ 95ScoDreT-DG6
❑ 95ScoGolR-223
❑ 95ScoGolR-557
❑ 95ScoHaloG-HG9
❑ 95ScoPlaTS-223
❑ 95ScoPlaTS-557
❑ 95ScoRul-SR6
❑ 95ScoRulJ-SR6
❑ 95ScoSam-223
❑ 95Sel-60
❑ 95Sel-244
❑ 95SelArtP-60
❑ 95SelArtP-244
❑ 95SelBigS-BS12
❑ 95SelCer-56
❑ 95SelCerMG-56
❑ 95SP-145
❑ 95SPCha-145
❑ 95SPChaDC-145
❑ 95SPChaDFC-3
❑ 95SPChaFCDC-3
❑ 95Spo-14
❑ 95SpoArtP-14
❑ 95SpoDet-DE7
❑ 95SpoDouT-10
❑ 95SpoHamT-HT6
❑ 95SpoPro-PM7
❑ 95SPPlaP-PP9
❑ 95SPSil-145
❑ 95SPSpeF-9
❑ 95StaClu-489
❑ 95StaClu-514
❑ 95StaCluCC-CC16
❑ 95StaCluCT-4
❑ 95StaCluMO-3
❑ 95StaCluMOP-489
❑ 95StaCluMOP-514
❑ 95StaCluMOP-CC16
❑ 95StaCluMOP-PZ2
❑ 95StaCluMOP-RL22
❑ 95StaCluMOP-VRE4
❑ 95StaCluPZ-PZ2
❑ 95StaCluRL-RL22
❑ 95StaCluSTDW-I19T
❑ 95StaCluSTDW-I489
❑ 95StaCluSTMP-12
❑ 95StaCluSTWS-489
❑ 95StaCluSTWS-514
❑ 95StaCluVE-VRE4
❑ 95StaCluVR-269
❑ 95StaCluVRMO-269
❑ 95Stu-15
❑ 95StuGolS-15
❑ 95StuPlaS-15
❑ 95Sum-11
❑ 95Sum-187
❑ 95SumBigB-BB14
❑ 95SumNthD-11
❑ 95SumNthD-187
❑ 95SumSam-11
❑ 95Top-389
❑ 95Top-503
❑ 95TopCyb-293
❑ 95TopD3-7
❑ 95TopEmb-125
❑ 95TopEmbGI-125
❑ 95TopFinIns-2
❑ 95TopLeaL-LL1
❑ 95TopLeaL-LL14
❑ 95TopLeaL-LL33
❑ 95TopTra-4T
❑ 95TopTra-161T
❑ 95TopTraPB-4
❑ 95UC3-58
❑ 95UC3-131
❑ 95UC3ArtP-58
❑ 95UC3ArtP-131
❑ 95UC3CycS-CS12
❑ 95Ult-36
❑ 95UltAllS-2
❑ 95UltAllSGM-2
❑ 95UltGolM-36
❑ 95UltHitM-2
❑ 95UltHitMGM-2
❑ 95UltHomRK-3
❑ 95UltHomRKGM-3
❑ 95UltOnBL-2
❑ 95UltOnBLGM-2
❑ 95UltPowP-1
❑ 95UltPowPGM-1
❑ 95UltRBIK-3
❑ 95UltRBIKGM-3
❑ 95UltRisS-3
❑ 95UltRisSGM-3
❑ 95UppDec-340
❑ 95UppDecED-340
❑ 95UppDecEDG-340
❑ 95UppDecPAW-H1
❑ 95UppDecPAWE-H1
❑ 95UppDecPLL-R1
❑ 95UppDecPLL-R11

- ❑ 95UppDecPLL-R59
- ❑ 95UppDecPLLE-R1
- ❑ 95UppDecPLLE-R11
- ❑ 95UppDecPLLE-R59
- ❑ 95UppDecSE-25
- ❑ 95UppDecSEG-25
- ❑ 95USPlaCMLA-9C
- ❑ 95USPlaCMLA-11D
- ❑ 95Zen-1
- ❑ 95ZenAllS-11
- ❑ 95ZenZ-14
- ❑ 96Baz-59
- ❑ 96Bow-92
- ❑ 96BowBes-6
- ❑ 96BowBesAR-6
- ❑ 96BowBesMI-5
- ❑ 96BowBesMIAR-5
- ❑ 96BowBesMIR-5
- ❑ 96BowBesR-6
- ❑ 96BowFoi-92
- ❑ 96Cir-32
- ❑ 96CirAcc-5
- ❑ 96CirBos-8
- ❑ 96CirRav-32
- ❑ 96ColCho-3
- ❑ 96ColCho-4
- ❑ 96ColCho-279
- ❑ 96ColCho-364
- ❑ 96ColCho-530
- ❑ 96ColChoCtG-CG11
- ❑ 96ColChoCtG-CG11B
- ❑ 96ColChoCtG-CG11C
- ❑ 96ColChoCtGE-CR11
- ❑ 96ColChoCtGG-CG11
- ❑ 96ColChoCtGG-CG11B
- ❑ 96ColChoCtGG-CG11C
- ❑ 96ColChoCtGGE-CR11
- ❑ 96ColChoGS-3
- ❑ 96ColChoGS-4
- ❑ 96ColChoGS-279
- ❑ 96ColChoGS-364
- ❑ 96ColChoGS-530
- ❑ 96ColChoSS-3
- ❑ 96ColChoSS-4
- ❑ 96ColChoSS-279
- ❑ 96ColChoSS-364
- ❑ 96ColChoSS-530
- ❑ 96ColChoYMtP-5
- ❑ 96ColChoYMtP-5A
- ❑ 96ColChoYMtPGS-5
- ❑ 96ColChoYMtPGS-5A
- ❑ 96DenHol-4
- ❑ 96DenHolGS-8
- ❑ 96DenHolGSAP-8
- ❑ 96Don-222
- ❑ 96DonFreF-6
- ❑ 96DonPowA-4
- ❑ 96DonPowADC-4
- ❑ 96DonPreP-222
- ❑ 96DonPurP-3
- ❑ 96DonRouT-1
- ❑ 96EmoLegoB-1
- ❑ 96EmoN-1
- ❑ 96EmoXL-46
- ❑ 96Fin-B214
- ❑ 96Fin-G9
- ❑ 96Fin-S188
- ❑ 96FinLan-2
- ❑ 96FinRef-B214
- ❑ 96FinRef-G9
- ❑ 96FinRef-S188
- ❑ 96Fla-64
- ❑ 96FlaDiaC-2
- ❑ 96FlaPow-1
- ❑ 96Fle-83
- ❑ 96FleGolM-1
- ❑ 96FleLumC-1
- ❑ 96FleTif-83
- ❑ 96FleUpd-U213
- ❑ 96FleUpdH-3
- ❑ 96FleUpdTC-U213
- ❑ 96FleZon-1
- ❑ 96IndFle-4
- ❑ 96Kin-9
- ❑ 96Lea-94
- ❑ 96LeaAllGMC-17
- ❑ 96LeaAllGMCG-17
- ❑ 96LeaGolS-10
- ❑ 96LeaHatO-7
- ❑ 96LeaLim-41
- ❑ 96LeaLimG-41
- ❑ 96LeaLimPC-5
- ❑ 96LeaPicP-8
- ❑ 96LeaPre-46
- ❑ 96LeaPreP-46
- ❑ 96LeaPrePB-94
- ❑ 96LeaPrePG-94
- ❑ 96LeaPrePS-94
- ❑ 96LeaPreSG-68
- ❑ 96LeaPreSP-1
- ❑ 96LeaPreSta-9
- ❑ 96LeaPreSte-68
- ❑ 96LeaSig-59
- ❑ 96LeaSigPPG-59
- ❑ 96LeaSigPPP-59
- ❑ 96LeaStaS-7
- ❑ 96LeaTotB-2
- ❑ 96LibSpo-14
- ❑ 96MetUni-44
- ❑ 96MetUniHM-1
- ❑ 96MetUniP-44
- ❑ 96MetUniT-1
- ❑ 96Pac-307
- ❑ 96PacGolCD-DC26
- ❑ 96PacMil-M1
- ❑ 96PacOctM-OM2
- ❑ 96PacPri-P94
- ❑ 96PacPriFB-FB1
- ❑ 96PacPriG-P94
- ❑ 96PacPriRHS-RH11
- ❑ 96PanSti-121
- ❑ 96PanSti-175
- ❑ 96Pin-137
- ❑ 96Pin-207
- ❑ 96Pin-262
- ❑ 96PinAfi-77
- ❑ 96PinAfi-197
- ❑ 96PinAfiAP-77
- ❑ 96PinAfiAP-197
- ❑ 96PinAfiFPP-77
- ❑ 96PinAfiMN-7
- ❑ 96PinAfiP-MN7
- ❑ 96PinAfiSP-8
- ❑ 96PinArtP-64
- ❑ 96PinArtP-107
- ❑ 96PinArtP-162
- ❑ 96PinChrBC-10
- ❑ 96PinEssotG-13
- ❑ 96PinFan-8
- ❑ 96PinFoil-207
- ❑ 96PinFoil-262
- ❑ 96PinPow-13
- ❑ 96PinSky-5
- ❑ 96PinSlu-6
- ❑ 96PinSta-64
- ❑ 96PinSta-107
- ❑ 96PinSta-162
- ❑ 96PinTeaP-7
- ❑ 96PinTeaS-9
- ❑ 96Pro-2
- ❑ 96ProMagA-9
- ❑ 96ProMagDM-10
- ❑ 96ProSta-57
- ❑ 96SchDis-9
- ❑ 96Sco-72
- ❑ 96Sco-275
- ❑ 96Sco-379
- ❑ 96ScoAll-2
- ❑ 96ScoBigB-10
- ❑ 96ScoDiaA-21
- ❑ 96ScoDugC-A59
- ❑ 96ScoDugC-B104
- ❑ 96ScoDugCAP-A59
- ❑ 96ScoDugCAP-B104
- ❑ 96ScoGolS-11
- ❑ 96ScoNumG-13
- ❑ 96ScoPowP-2
- ❑ 96ScoRef-12
- ❑ 96ScoTitT-1
- ❑ 96Sel-36
- ❑ 96Sel-154
- ❑ 96SelArtP-36
- ❑ 96SelArtP-154
- ❑ 96SelCer-22
- ❑ 96SelCer-140
- ❑ 96SelCerAP-22
- ❑ 96SelCerAP-140
- ❑ 96SelCerCB-22
- ❑ 96SelCerCB-140
- ❑ 96SelCerCR-22
- ❑ 96SelCerCR-140
- ❑ 96SelCerIP-24
- ❑ 96SelCerMB-22
- ❑ 96SelCerMB-140
- ❑ 96SelCerMG-22
- ❑ 96SelCerMG-140
- ❑ 96SelCerMR-22
- ❑ 96SelCerMR-140
- ❑ 96SelCerSF-4
- ❑ 96SelClaTF-6
- ❑ 96SelEnF-8
- ❑ 96SelTeaN-1
- ❑ 96SP-70
- ❑ 96SPBasH-83
- ❑ 96SPMarM-MM12
- ❑ 96SPMarMDC-12
- ❑ 96Spo-7
- ❑ 96Spo-101
- ❑ 96SpoArtP-7
- ❑ 96SpoArtP-101
- ❑ 96SpoDouT-8
- ❑ 96SpoHitP-6
- ❑ 96SpoPowS-5
- ❑ 96SpoPro-4
- ❑ 96SPPreF-3
- ❑ 96SPSpeFX-30
- ❑ 96SPSpeFXDC-30
- ❑ 96SPx-19
- ❑ 96SPxGol-19
- ❑ 96StaClu-201
- ❑ 96StaClu-297
- ❑ 96StaCluEPB-297
- ❑ 96StaCluEPG-297
- ❑ 96StaCluEPS-297
- ❑ 96StaCluMM-MM7
- ❑ 96StaCluMO-3
- ❑ 96StaCluMOP-201
- ❑ 96StaCluMOP-297
- ❑ 96StaCluMOP-MM7
- ❑ 96StaCluMOP-PC1
- ❑ 96StaCluMOP-PP1
- ❑ 96StaCluMOP-PS3
- ❑ 96StaCluMOP-TSCA2
- ❑ 96StaCluPC-PC1
- ❑ 96StaCluPP-PP1
- ❑ 96StaCluPS-PS3
- ❑ 96StaCluTA-2
- ❑ 96Stu-143
- ❑ 96StuHitP-8
- ❑ 96StuPrePB-143
- ❑ 96StuPrePG-143
- ❑ 96StuPrePS-143
- ❑ 96StuStaGS-7
- ❑ 96Sum-82
- ❑ 96SumAbo&B-82
- ❑ 96SumArtP-82
- ❑ 96SumBal-2
- ❑ 96SumBigB-3
- ❑ 96SumBigBM-3
- ❑ 96SumFoi-82
- ❑ 96SumHitI-8
- ❑ 96SumPos-7
- ❑ 96TeaOut-6
- ❑ 96TeaOut-C93
- ❑ 96Top-45
- ❑ 96Top-223
- ❑ 96TopBigC-1
- ❑ 96TopChr-17
- ❑ 96TopChr-83
- ❑ 96TopChrR-17
- ❑ 96TopChrR-83
- ❑ 96TopChrWC-WC2
- ❑ 96TopChrWCR-WC2
- ❑ 96TopGal-157
- ❑ 96TopGalE-19
- ❑ 96TopGalPG-PG9
- ❑ 96TopGalPPI-157
- ❑ 96TopLas-99
- ❑ 96TopLasPC-1
- ❑ 96TopMysF-M17
- ❑ 96TopMysFR-M17
- ❑ 96TopPro-AL3
- ❑ 96TopRoaW-RW2
- ❑ 96TopWreC-WC2
- ❑ 96Ult-46
- ❑ 96Ult-575
- ❑ 96UltChe-B1
- ❑ 96UltCheGM-B1
- ❑ 96UltDiaP-1
- ❑ 96UltDiaPGM-1
- ❑ 96UltGolM-46
- ❑ 96UltGolM-575
- ❑ 96UltHitM-1
- ❑ 96UltHitMGM-1
- ❑ 96UltHomRK-1
- ❑ 96UltHomRKGM-1
- ❑ 96UltHomRKR-1
- ❑ 96UltHomRKRGM-1
- ❑ 96UltRBIK-2
- ❑ 96UltRBIKGM-2
- ❑ 96UltThu-1
- ❑ 96UltThuGM-1
- ❑ 96UppDec-315
- ❑ 96UppDec-371
- ❑ 96UppDecA-4
- ❑ 96UppDecDD-DD16
- ❑ 96UppDecDDG-DD16
- ❑ 96UppDecDDS-DD16
- ❑ 96UppDecG-GF4
- ❑ 96UppDecHC-HC5
- ❑ 96UppDecPD-PD1
- ❑ 96UppDecPHE-H1
- ❑ 96UppDecPRE-R1
- ❑ 96UppDecPRE-R11
- ❑ 96UppDecPreH-H1
- ❑ 96UppDecPreR-R1
- ❑ 96UppDecPreR-R11
- ❑ 96UppDecRunP-RP1
- ❑ 96Zen-95
- ❑ 96Zen-131
- ❑ 96ZenArtP-95
- ❑ 96ZenArtP-131
- ❑ 96ZenDiaC-1
- ❑ 96ZenDiaCP-1
- ❑ 96ZenMoz-18
- ❑ 96ZenZ-2
- ❑ 97Bow-67
- ❑ 97BowBes-3
- ❑ 97BowBesAR-3
- ❑ 97BowBesBC-BC10
- ❑ 97BowBesBCAR-BC10
- ❑ 97BowBesBCR-BC10
- ❑ 97BowBesMI-MI10
- ❑ 97BowBesMIAR-MI10
- ❑ 97BowBesMIARI-MI10
- ❑ 97BowBesMII-MI10
- ❑ 97BowBesMIR-MI10
- ❑ 97BowBesMIRI-MI10
- ❑ 97BowBesR-3
- ❑ 97BowChr-48
- ❑ 97BowChrI-48
- ❑ 97BowChrIR-48
- ❑ 97BowChrR-48
- ❑ 97BowInt-67
- ❑ 97Cir-250
- ❑ 97CirBos-2
- ❑ 97CirLimA-2
- ❑ 97CirRav-250
- ❑ 97CirRavR-1
- ❑ 97CirSupB-2
- ❑ 97ColCho-58
- ❑ 97ColCho-76
- ❑ 97ColCho-329
- ❑ 97ColChoAC-7
- ❑ 97ColChoCtG-9A
- ❑ 97ColChoCtG-9B
- ❑ 97ColChoCtG-9C
- ❑ 97ColChoCtGE-CG9
- ❑ 97ColChoCtGIW-CG9
- ❑ 97ColChoNF-NF25
- ❑ 97ColChoPP-PP4
- ❑ 97ColChoPPG-PP4
- ❑ 97ColChoPPJ-PP4
- ❑ 97ColChoS-8
- ❑ 97ColChoSR-3
- ❑ 97ColChoT-CW7
- ❑ 97ColChoTBS-15
- ❑ 97ColChoTBSWH-15
- ❑ 97ColChoTotT-T10
- ❑ 97ColSprSATTI-1
- ❑ 97CraJac-18
- ❑ 97Don-160
- ❑ 97Don-289
- ❑ 97Don-442
- ❑ 97DonDom-6
- ❑ 97DonEli-9
- ❑ 97DonEliGS-9
- ❑ 97DonGolPP-160
- ❑ 97DonGolPP-289
- ❑ 97DonGolPP-442
- ❑ 97DonLim-51
- ❑ 97DonLim-63
- ❑ 97DonLim-111
- ❑ 97DonLimE-51
- ❑ 97DonLimE-63
- ❑ 97DonLimE-111
- ❑ 97DonLimENG-51
- ❑ 97DonLimFotG-13
- ❑ 97DonLimFotG-62
- ❑ 97DonLonL-2
- ❑ 97DonPowA-8
- ❑ 97DonPowADC-8
- ❑ 97DonPre-13
- ❑ 97DonPre-187
- ❑ 97DonPreCttC-13
- ❑ 97DonPreCttC-187
- ❑ 97DonPrePM-4
- ❑ 97DonPreS-12
- ❑ 97DonPreSS-12
- ❑ 97DonPreTB-2
- ❑ 97DonPreTBG-2
- ❑ 97DonPreTF-2
- ❑ 97DonPreTP-2
- ❑ 97DonPreTPG-2
- ❑ 97DonPreXP-4A
- ❑ 97DonRocL-2
- ❑ 97DonSig-54
- ❑ 97DonSigAC-11
- ❑ 97DonSigAM-11
- ❑ 97DonSigPPP-54
- ❑ 97DonSilPP-160
- ❑ 97DonSilPP-289
- ❑ 97DonSilPP-442
- ❑ 97DonTea-70
- ❑ 97DonTeaSMVP-11
- ❑ 97DonTeaSPE-70
- ❑ 97DonVxP1-41
- ❑ 97E-X2-12
- ❑ 97E-X2ACA-4
- ❑ 97E-X2Cred-12
- ❑ 97E-X2EssCre-12
- ❑ 97E-X2Hall-14
- ❑ 97Fin-240
- ❑ 97Fin-319
- ❑ 97Fin-347
- ❑ 97FinEmb-319
- ❑ 97FinEmb-347
- ❑ 97FinEmbR-319
- ❑ 97FinEmbR-347
- ❑ 97FinRef-240
- ❑ 97FinRef-319
- ❑ 97FinRef-347
- ❑ 97FlaShoDC-2
- ❑ 97FlaShoLC-48
- ❑ 97FlaShoLeg0-48
- ❑ 97FlaShoLeg1-48
- ❑ 97FlaShoM-A48
- ❑ 97FlaShoM-B48
- ❑ 97FlaShoM-C48
- ❑ 97FlaShoR0-48
- ❑ 97FlaShoR1-48
- ❑ 97FlaShoR2-48
- ❑ 97Fle-75
- ❑ 97Fle-491
- ❑ 97Fle-600
- ❑ 97FleBleB-1
- ❑ 97FleDiaT-1
- ❑ 97FleHea-2
- ❑ 97FleLumC-3
- ❑ 97FleMilDM-36
- ❑ 97FleMilDMR-36
- ❑ 97FleSoaS-1
- ❑ 97FleSoaSG-1
- ❑ 97FleTeaL-5
- ❑ 97FleTif-75
- ❑ 97FleTif-491
- ❑ 97FleTif-600
- ❑ 97FleZon-2
- ❑ 97HigMinM-5
- ❑ 97IndSco-1
- ❑ 97IndScoPl-1
- ❑ 97IndScoPr-1
- ❑ 97Lea-190
- ❑ 97Lea-202
- ❑ 97Lea-375
- ❑ 97LeaDrefS-3
- ❑ 97LeaFraM-190
- ❑ 97LeaFraM-202
- ❑ 97LeaFraM-375
- ❑ 97LeaFraMDC-190
- ❑ 97LeaFraMDC-202
- ❑ 97LeaFraMDC-375
- ❑ 97LeaGet-9
- ❑ 97LeaGolS-20
- ❑ 97LeaLeaotN-9
- ❑ 97LeaStaS-1
- ❑ 97LeaWarT-2
- ❑ 97MetUni-55
- ❑ 97MetUniBF-2
- ❑ 97MetUniT-2
- ❑ 97NewPin-12
- ❑ 97NewPin-193
- ❑ 97NewPinAP-12
- ❑ 97NewPinAP-193
- ❑ 97NewPinIE-1
- ❑ 97NewPinMC-12
- ❑ 97NewPinMC-193
- ❑ 97NewPinPP-12
- ❑ 97NewPinPP-193
- ❑ 97NewPinPP-I1A
- ❑ 97NewPinPP-AB1
- ❑ 97NewPinPP-AB2
- ❑ 97NewPinPP-AB3
- ❑ 97NewPinPP-AB4
- ❑ 97NewPinPP-AB5
- ❑ 97NewPinS-AB1
- ❑ 97NewPinS-AB2
- ❑ 97NewPinS-AB3
- ❑ 97NewPinS-AB4
- ❑ 97NewPinS-AB5
- ❑ 97Pac-67
- ❑ 97PacCar-8
- ❑ 97PacCarM-8
- ❑ 97PacCerCGT-15
- ❑ 97PacCraC-3
- ❑ 97PacFirD-6
- ❑ 97PacGolCD-8
- ❑ 97PacLigB-67
- ❑ 97PacPri-25
- ❑ 97PacPriGotD-GD33
- ❑ 97PacPriLB-25
- ❑ 97PacPriP-25
- ❑ 97PacPriSL-SL3A
- ❑ 97PacSil-67
- ❑ 97PacTriCD-5
- ❑ 97Pin-100
- ❑ 97PinArtP-PP100
- ❑ 97PinCar-6
- ❑ 97PinCer-17
- ❑ 97PinCer-140
- ❑ 97PinCerCMGT-15
- ❑ 97PinCerCT-15
- ❑ 97PinCerMBla-17
- ❑ 97PinCerMBla-140
- ❑ 97PinCerMBlu-17
- ❑ 97PinCerMBlu-140
- ❑ 97PinCerMG-17
- ❑ 97PinCerMG-140
- ❑ 97PinCerMR-17
- ❑ 97PinCerMR-140
- ❑ 97PinCerR-17
- ❑ 97PinCerR-140
- ❑ 97PinEpixGO-E10
- ❑ 97PinHom-23
- ❑ 97PinHom-24
- ❑ 97PinIns-35
- ❑ 97PinInsC-9
- ❑ 97PinInsCE-35
- ❑ 97PinInsDD-3
- ❑ 97PinInsDE-35
- ❑ 97PinInsFS-6
- ❑ 97PinMin-8
- ❑ 97PinMinB-8
- ❑ 97PinMinCB-8
- ❑ 97PinMinCG-8
- ❑ 97PinMinCGR-8
- ❑ 97PinMinCN-8
- ❑ 97PinMinCSS-8
- ❑ 97PinMinG-8
- ❑ 97PinMinS-8
- ❑ 97PinMusC-100
- ❑ 97PinPrePla-100
- ❑ 97PinTeaP-6
- ❑ 97PinTeaP-10
- ❑ 97PinTotCPB-17
- ❑ 97PinTotCPB-140
- ❑ 97PinTotCPG-17
- ❑ 97PinTotCPG-140
- ❑ 97PinTotCPR-17
- ❑ 97PinTotCPR-140
- ❑ 97PinX-P-47
- ❑ 97PinX-PF&A-1
- ❑ 97PinX-PMoS-47
- ❑ 97PinX-PMW-13
- ❑ 97PinX-PMWG-13
- ❑ 97PinX-PMWS-13
- ❑ 97PinX-PSfF-7
- ❑ 97PinX-PSfFU-7
- ❑ 97PreCon-9
- ❑ 97Sco-12
- ❑ 97Sco-428
- ❑ 97Sco-495
- ❑ 97ScoAllF-9
- ❑ 97ScoArtPWB-12
- ❑ 97ScoArtPWB-428
- ❑ 97ScoArtPWB-495
- ❑ 97ScoBla-4
- ❑ 97ScoFra-6
- ❑ 97ScoFraG-6
- ❑ 97ScoHeaotO-5
- ❑ 97ScoHigZ-4
- ❑ 97ScoPreS-12
- ❑ 97ScoResC-428
- ❑ 97ScoResC-495
- ❑ 97ScoShoS-12
- ❑ 97ScoShoS-428
- ❑ 97ScoShoS-495
- ❑ 97ScoShoSAP-12
- ❑ 97ScoShoSAP-428
- ❑ 97ScoShoSAP-495
- ❑ 97ScoSteS-10
- ❑ 97ScoTitT-6
- ❑ 97Sel-17
- ❑ 97SelArtP-17
- ❑ 97SelCom-17
- ❑ 97SelRegG-17

❑ 97SelToootT-5
❑ 97SelToootTMB-5
❑ 97SP-45
❑ 97SPInsI-15
❑ 97SpoIll-149
❑ 97SpoIllEE-149
❑ 97SpoIllGS-9
❑ 97SPSpeF-4
❑ 97SPSpxF-2
❑ 97SPSPxFA-2
❑ 97SPx-18
❑ 97SPxBoufG-8
❑ 97SPxBro-18
❑ 97SPxCorotG-2
❑ 97SPxGol-18
❑ 97SPxGraF-18
❑ 97SPxSil-18
❑ 97SPxSte-18
❑ 97StaClu-227
❑ 97StaClu-379
❑ 97StaCluFR-F2
❑ 97StaCluFW-F2
❑ 97StaCluI-I14
❑ 97StaCluMat-227
❑ 97StaCluMOP-227
❑ 97StaCluMOP-379
❑ 97StaCluMOP-I14
❑ 97StaCluMOP-FB2
❑ 97StaCluMOP-PG2
❑ 97StaCluPG-PG2
❑ 97StrAll-7
❑ 97Stu-98
❑ 97StuHarH-2
❑ 97StuMasS-16
❑ 97StuMasS8-16
❑ 97StuPor8-9
❑ 97StuPrePG-98
❑ 97StuPrePS-98
❑ 97Top-69
❑ 97TopAll-AS11
❑ 97TopChr-24
❑ 97TopChrAS-AS11
❑ 97TopChrDD-DD10
❑ 97TopChrDDR-DD10
❑ 97TopChrR-24
❑ 97TopChrSAR-AS11
❑ 97TopChrSB-9
❑ 97TopChrSB-12
❑ 97TopChrSBR-9
❑ 97TopChrSBR-12
❑ 97TopGal-82
❑ 97TopGalPMS-2
❑ 97TopGalPMSSS-2
❑ 97TopGalPPI-82
❑ 97TopHobM-HM4
❑ 97TopIntF-ILM6
❑ 97TopIntFR-ILM6
❑ 97TopMem05-4
❑ 97TopScr-2
❑ 97TopScrT-2
❑ 97TopSeaB-SB9
❑ 97TopSeaB-SB12
❑ 97TopSta-39
❑ 97TopStaAM-39
❑ 97TopSweS-SS3
❑ 97TopTeaT-TT14
❑ 97UD3-4
❑ 97UD3Marq-MA6
❑ 97Ult-46
❑ 97Ult-411
❑ 97UltDouT-5
❑ 97UltFamGam-10
❑ 97UltGolME-46
❑ 97UltGolME-411
❑ 97UltHitM-8
❑ 97UltHRK-1
❑ 97UltPlaME-46
❑ 97UltPlaME-411
❑ 97UltPowP-B7
❑ 97UltRBIK-2
❑ 97UltSeaC-1
❑ 97UltStaR-11
❑ 97UltTop3-11
❑ 97UltTop3GM-11
❑ 97UppDec-50
❑ 97UppDec-333
❑ 97UppDec-419
❑ 97UppDecAG-AG8
❑ 97UppDecAWJ-5
❑ 97UppDecHC-HC12
❑ 97UppDecHTH-HT10
❑ 97UppDecLDC-LD4
❑ 97UppDecMM-B2
❑ 97UppDecP-10
❑ 97UppDecPE-10
❑ 97UppDecPP-PP8
❑ 97UppDecPPJ-PP8
❑ 97UppDecRP-RP3
❑ 97UppDecSA-9
❑ 97UppDecSAG-9
❑ 97WhiSoxTI-8
❑ 97Zen-7
❑ 97Zen8x10-8
❑ 97Zen8x1D-8
❑ 98Bow-42
❑ 98BowBes-20
❑ 98BowBesA-20
❑ 98BowBesAAR-20
❑ 98BowBesAR-20
❑ 98BowBesAR-20
❑ 98BowBesR-20
❑ 98BowChr-42
❑ 98BowChrGA-42
❑ 98BowChrGAR-42
❑ 98BowChrI-42
❑ 98BowChrIR-42
❑ 98BowChrR-42
❑ 98BowGolA-42
❑ 98BowInt-42
❑ 98CirThu-286
❑ 98CirThuRav-286
❑ 98CirThuSupRav-286
❑ 98ColChoCtG-CG11A
❑ 98ColChoCtG-CG11B
❑ 98ColChoCtG-CG11C
❑ 98ColChoCtGExch-CG11
❑ 98ColChoCtGIW-CG11
❑ 98ColChoRJ-SQ70
❑ 98ColChoS'-9
❑ 98ColChoSQ-SQ70
❑ 98CroRoy-33
❑ 98CroRoyHRF-3
❑ 98Don-36
❑ 98Don-349
❑ 98DonCol-36
❑ 98DonColE-415
❑ 98DonColE-532
❑ 98DonColL-359
❑ 98DonColP-571
❑ 98DonColP-746
❑ 98DonColS-36
❑ 98DonCruG-15
❑ 98DonCruP-15
❑ 98DonCruR-15
❑ 98DonDom-26
❑ 98DonEli-15
❑ 98DonEli-132
❑ 98DonEliA-15
❑ 98DonEliA-132
❑ 98DonEliC-22
❑ 98DonEliMC-22
❑ 98DonEliS-15
❑ 98DonEliS-132
❑ 98DonGolPP-36
❑ 98DonGolPP-349
❑ 98DonLonL-6
❑ 98DonPre-21
❑ 98DonPre-196
❑ 98DonPreGES-9
❑ 98DonPreGX-9
❑ 98DonPreGXDC-9
❑ 98DonPreSeat-21
❑ 98DonPreSeat-196
❑ 98DonPreTW-26
❑ 98DonPriCD-36
❑ 98DonPriCE-415
❑ 98DonPriCE-532
❑ 98DonPriCL-359
❑ 98DonPriCP-571
❑ 98DonPriCP-746
❑ 98DonProLPI-12
❑ 98DonSig-8
❑ 98DonSigAC-8
❑ 98DonSigAM-8
❑ 98DonSigP-8
❑ 98DonSilPP-36
❑ 98DonSilPP-349
❑ 98E-X2-19
❑ 98E-X2Cheap-10
❑ 98E-X2ECFut-19
❑ 98E-X2ECNow-19
❑ 98Fin-120
❑ 98FinMysF2-M2
❑ 98FinMysF2-M4
❑ 98FinMysF2-M6
❑ 98FinMysF2-M31
❑ 98FinMysF2R-M2
❑ 98FinMysF2R-M4
❑ 98FinMysF2R-M6
❑ 98FinMysF2R-M31
❑ 98FinNo--120
❑ 98FinNo-R-120
❑ 98FinPowZ-P17
❑ 98FinRef-120
❑ 98FinStaS-SS6
❑ 98FlaShoLeg0-23
❑ 98FlaShoLeg1-23
❑ 98FlaShoLeg2-23
❑ 98FlaShoLeg3-23
❑ 98FlaShoLegM-23
❑ 98FlaShoR0-23
❑ 98FlaShoR1-23
❑ 98FlaShoR2-23
❑ 98FlaShoR3-23
❑ 98Fle-322
❑ 98Fle-355
❑ 98FlePowG-2
❑ 98FleVin'-85
❑ 98FleVin'C-85
❑ 98Lea-160
❑ 98LeaCruG-15
❑ 98LeaCruP-15
❑ 98LeaCruR-15
❑ 98LeaFraDA-160
❑ 98LeaFraF-160
❑ 98LeaFraM-160
❑ 98LeaFraM-160
❑ 98LeaFraMDC-160
❑ 98LeaFraMDC-160
❑ 98LeaFraMS-160
❑ 98LeaFraMZ2-160
❑ 98LeaHeaftH-3
❑ 98LeaHeaftHS-3
❑ 98LeaRS-46
❑ 98LeaRS-148
❑ 98LeaRSHRDerby-20
❑ 98LeaRSLHolo-46
❑ 98LeaRSLHolo-148
❑ 98LeaRSLMVP-6
❑ 98LeaRSLMVPPE-6
❑ 98LeaRSLong-46
❑ 98LeaRSLong-148
❑ 98LeaRSTicMas-2
❑ 98LeaRSTicMasDC-2
❑ 98LeaRTrue-46
❑ 98LeaRTrue-148
❑ 98MetUni-127
❑ 98MetUniAT-4
❑ 98MetUniPMG-127
❑ 98MetUniUL-4
❑ 98Pac-52
❑ 98PacAur-22
❑ 98PacAurPF-20
❑ 98PacAurPFC-20
❑ 98PacAurPFPB-20
❑ 98PacAurPFR-20
❑ 98PacAurPFS-20
❑ 98PacHomRH-5
❑ 98PacHomRH-4
❑ 98PacInv-17
❑ 98PacInvGems-28
❑ 98PacInvInt-6A
❑ 98PacInvPBlue-17
❑ 98PacInvSilv-17
❑ 98PacInvTeam-6
❑ 98PacOme-53
❑ 98PacOmeR-53
❑ 98PacOnl-161
❑ 98PacOnlR-161
❑ 98PacOnlWC-161
❑ 98PacPar-27
❑ 98PacParC-27
❑ 98PacParG-27
❑ 98PacParHS-27
❑ 98PacParI-1
❑ 98PacParPB-27
❑ 98PacParR-27
❑ 98PacPlaB-52
❑ 98PacRedT-52
❑ 98PacSil-52
❑ 98PacTeaC-4
❑ 98PinEpixGE-E10
❑ 98PinEpixGP-E10
❑ 98PinEpixME-E10
❑ 98PinEpixMO-E10
❑ 98PinEpixMP-E10
❑ 98PinEpixSE-E10
❑ 98PinEpixSO-E10
❑ 98PinEpixSP-E10
❑ 98PinHitIH-6
❑ 98PinHitIHS-6
❑ 98PinIns-16
❑ 98PinIns-143
❑ 98PinInsCE-16
❑ 98PinInsCE-143
❑ 98PinInsDE-16
❑ 98PinInsDE-143
❑ 98PinInsSG-24AB
❑ 98PinInsSG-24CD
❑ 98PinInsSGS-24AB
❑ 98PinInsSGS-24CD
❑ 98PinMinB-2
❑ 98PinMinCB-2
❑ 98PinMinCBAP-2
❑ 98PinMinCGP-2
❑ 98PinMinCGPAP-2
❑ 98PinMinCN-2
❑ 98PinMinCNAP-2
❑ 98PinMinCSGR-2
❑ 98PinMinDC-2
❑ 98PinMinG-2
❑ 98PinMinMCSS-2
❑ 98PinMinS-2
❑ 98PinPer-21
❑ 98PinPerBB-9
❑ 98PinPerBBSamp-9
❑ 98PinPerBBSO-9
❑ 98PinPerPP-21
❑ 98PinPerSftF-2
❑ 98PinPlu-4
❑ 98PinPluAE-10
❑ 98PinPluAEE-10
❑ 98PinPluAEP-10
❑ 98PinPluAP-PP2
❑ 98PinPluGAP-PP2
❑ 98PinPluLM-25
❑ 98PinPluMAP-PP2
❑ 98PinPluTP-8
❑ 98PinPluTPG-8
❑ 98PinPluTPM-8
❑ 98PinPluY-3
❑ 98PinPreP-E10
❑ 98PinPreP-H6
❑ 98Revo-34
❑ 98RevoSS-34
❑ 98Sco-7
❑ 98ScoEpix-E10
❑ 98ScoFirP-18
❑ 98ScoRT-36
❑ 98ScoRTASEpix-10
❑ 98ScoRTSS-PP36
❑ 98ScoRTSSAP-PP36
❑ 98ScoRTSSAP1-PP36
❑ 98ScoSS-PP114
❑ 98ScoSSAP-PP114
❑ 98SkyDugA-58
❑ 98SkyDugADH-DH2
❑ 98SkyDugAG-G2
❑ 98SkyDugAIA-58
❑ 98SP Aut-66
❑ 98SP Aut-SD26
❑ 98SP AutSD-SD26
❑ 98SP AutSDT-SD26
❑ 98SP AutTrade-2
❑ 98SpoIll-10
❑ 98SpoIllEE-10
❑ 98SpoIllFE-10
❑ 98SpoIllTaN-41
❑ 98SpoIllTaN-60
❑ 98SpoIllTaNEE-41
❑ 98SpoIllTaNEE-60
❑ 98SpoIllWSF-31
❑ 98SpoIllWSFEE-31
❑ 98SpoIllWSFFE-31
❑ 98SPxFin-39
❑ 98SPxFin-71
❑ 98SPxFin-149
❑ 98SPxFin-223
❑ 98SPxFinHRH-HR4
❑ 98SPxFinR-39
❑ 98SPxFinR-71
❑ 98SPxFinR-149
❑ 98SPxFinR-223
❑ 98SPxFinS-39
❑ 98SPxFinS-71
❑ 98SPxFinS-149
❑ 98SPxFinS-223
❑ 98StaCluFDI-77
❑ 98StaCluI-77
❑ 98StaCluOneK-77
❑ 98StaCluPP-77
❑ 98StaCluTIll-T4A
❑ 98StaCluTIll-T15C
❑ 98StaCluTLme-T4A
❑ 98StaCluTLme-T15C
❑ 98StaCluTLmo-T4A
❑ 98StaCluTLmo-T15C
❑ 98Stu-59
❑ 98StuGPP-59
❑ 98StuHitPar-9
❑ 98StuSPP-59
❑ 98Top-331
❑ 98TopChr-331
❑ 98TopChrR-331
❑ 98TopDevR-331
❑ 98TopDia-331
❑ 98TopEtc-ES1
❑ 98TopGal-25
❑ 98TopGalGP-25
❑ 98TopGalOPP-25
❑ 98TopGalPPI-25
❑ 98TopGalPPIA-25
❑ 98TopGolLabC1-3
❑ 98TopGolLabC1B-3
❑ 98TopGolLabC1One-3
❑ 98TopGolLabC1R-3
❑ 98TopGolLabC2-3
❑ 98TopGolLabC2B-3
❑ 98TopGolLabC2One-3
❑ 98TopGolLabC2R-3
❑ 98TopGolLabC3-3
❑ 98TopGolLabC3B-3
❑ 98TopGolLabC3One-3
❑ 98TopGolLabC3R-3
❑ 98TopMiniC-331
❑ 98TopMysF-ILM20
❑ 98TopMysFB-M4
❑ 98TopMysFB-M4
❑ 98TopMysFBR-M4
❑ 98TopMysFBR-M4
❑ 98TopMysFR-ILM20
❑ 98TopOpeD-158
❑ 98TopSta-133
❑ 98TopSta'S-3
❑ 98TopSta'SGH-3
❑ 98TopStaB-133
❑ 98TopStaG-133
❑ 98TopStaGR-133
❑ 98TopStaS-133
❑ 98TopStaSteG-3
❑ 98TopSup-32
❑ 98TopSup-32
❑ 98TopTek-47
❑ 98TopTekD-47
❑ 98UD3-49
❑ 98UD3-139
❑ 98UD3-229
❑ 98UD3DieCut-49
❑ 98UD3DieCut-139
❑ 98UD3DieCut-229
❑ 98Ult-28
❑ 98Ult-497
❑ 98UltArtT-10
❑ 98UltBigS-4
❑ 98UltDouT-6
❑ 98UltFalC-10
❑ 98UltGolM-28
❑ 98UltGolM-497
❑ 98UltMas-28
❑ 98UltMas-497
❑ 98UltNot-4
❑ 98UltPlaM-28
❑ 98UltPlaM-497
❑ 98UltPowP-6
❑ 98UltPriL-10
❑ 98UltTop3-4
❑ 98UppDec-60
❑ 98UppDec10AP-45
❑ 98UppDec1APR-45
❑ 98UppDec5x7-60
❑ 98UppDecAG-AG30
❑ 98UppDecAGDC-AG30
❑ 98UppDecCD-CD9
❑ 98UppDecR-20
❑ 98UppDecR-19
❑ 98UppDecRBBop-BB7
❑ 98UppDecRQL-Q30
❑ 98UppDecRTC-TC7
❑ 98UppDecSF-35
❑ 98UppDecTMT-9
❑ 98UppDecTMTG-9
❑ 98WhiSoxS-1
❑ 98WhiSoxSP-1
❑ 98Zen-23
❑ 98Zen5 xx7-17
❑ 98Zen5x7GoldImp-17
❑ 98Zen5x7Imp-17
❑ 98ZenEpi-E10
❑ 98ZenZ-G-23
❑ 98ZenZ-S-23
❑ 99199Fin-240
❑ 99199Fin-259
❑ 99Bow-233
❑ 99BowBes-65
❑ 99BowBesAR-65
❑ 99BowBesR-65
❑ 99BowGol-233
❑ 99BowInt-233
❑ 99CroRoyB-18
❑ 99CroRoyL-18
❑ 99CroRoyOD-18
❑ 99CroRoyPotG-4
❑ 99CroRoyPP-4
❑ 99CroRoyPPN-4
❑ 99E-X Cen-27
❑ 99E-X CenECFut-27
❑ 99E-X CenECNow-27
❑ 99FinAarAwC-HA4
❑ 99FinAarAwCR-HA4
❑ 99FinDouF-DF6
❑ 99FinDouFDualR-DF6
❑ 99FinGolRef-240
❑ 99FinGolRef-259
❑ 99FinLeaI-L5
❑ 99FinMil-M17
❑ 99FinMil-M24
❑ 99FinMil-M32
❑ 99FinProF-PF20
❑ 99FinProF-PF34
❑ 99FinProF-PF43
❑ 99FinRef-240
❑ 99FinRef-259
❑ 99FinSplS-SS4
❑ 99FinSplSDR-SS4
❑ 99FlaShoLeg1-41
❑ 99FlaShoLeg2-41
❑ 99FlaShoLeg3-41
❑ 99FlaShoLegM1-41
❑ 99FlaShoLegM2-41
❑ 99FlaShoLegM3-41
❑ 99FlaShoR1-41
❑ 99FlaShoR2-41
❑ 99FlaShoR3-41
❑ 99Fle-13
❑ 99FleBri-107
❑ 99FleBri2G-107
❑ 99FleBriBlu-107
❑ 99FleBriGol-107
❑ 99FleGoiYar-2
❑ 99FleGolM-1
❑ 99FleMys-82
❑ 99FleMysG-82
❑ 99FleMysM-82
❑ 99FleSta9-13
❑ 99FleVin'-13
❑ 99FleWarT-13
❑ 99MetUni-27
❑ 99MetUni-285
❑ 99MetUniGM-27
❑ 99MetUniGM-285
❑ 99MetUniPMG-27
❑ 99MetUniPMG-285
❑ 99MetUniSamp-NNOA
❑ 99MetUniSamp-NNO
❑ 99Pac-97
❑ 99PacAur-21
❑ 99PacAurOD-21
❑ 99PacCroC-64
❑ 99PacCroCPB-64
❑ 99PacInv-19
❑ 99PacInvOD-19
❑ 99PacInvPB-19
❑ 99PacOme-31
❑ 99PacOmeC-31
❑ 99PacOmeG-31
❑ 99PacOmeH'-4
❑ 99PacOmePB-31
❑ 99PacPar-31
❑ 99PacParC-31
❑ 99PacParG-31
❑ 99PacParHoloGold-31
❑ 99PacParHS-31
❑ 99PacParOD-31
❑ 99PacParPB-6
❑ 99PacParPB-31
❑ 99PacParRed-31
❑ 99PacPlaB-97
❑ 99PacPri-32
❑ 99PacPriHB-32
❑ 99PacPriHG-32
❑ 99PacPriHM-32
❑ 99PacPriHP-32
❑ 99PacPriRed-32
❑ 99PacPriS-23
❑ 99PacPriS206-23
❑ 99PacPriS206R-23
❑ 99PacPriSP-23
❑ 99PacPriSV-23
❑ 99PacRed-97
❑ 99Rev-19
❑ 99RevDiaL-7
❑ 99RevPremDate-19
❑ 99RevRet-19
❑ 99RevShaSS-19
❑ 99SkyMolM-107
❑ 99SkyMolMF-7

❑ 99SkyMolMFS-7
❑ 99SkyMolMFT-7
❑ 99SkyMolMX-107
❑ 99SkyPre-107
❑ 99SkyPre-282
❑ 99SkyPreR-107
❑ 99SkyPreR-282
❑ 99SkyThu-284
❑ 99SkyThuInD-ID1
❑ 99SkyThuRant-284
❑ 99SkyThuRave-284
❑ 99SP Aut-14
❑ 99SP AutHRC-HR6
❑ 99SP SigAuto-AB
❑ 99SP SigAutoG-AB
❑ 99SPAutHRCDC-HR6
❑ 99SpoIll-28
❑ 99SpoIll-114
❑ 99SpoIllF4-5
❑ 99SpoIllF4E-5
❑ 99SPSig-51
❑ 99SPx-21
❑ 99SPxDom-FB7
❑ 99SPxFinR-21
❑ 99SPxFinS-21
❑ 99SPxPowE-PE7
❑ 99SPxPreS-PS20
❑ 99SPxStaF-SF7
❑ 99StaClu-315
❑ 99StaCluA-SCA8
❑ 99StaCluC-SCC5
❑ 99StaCluCR-SCC5
❑ 99StaCluFDI-315
❑ 99StaCluOoaK-315
❑ 99StaCluPP-315
❑ 99ThuSkySupR-284
❑ 99Top-93
❑ 99TopAll-AM5
❑ 99TopBlaLC1-17
❑ 99TopBlaLC2-17
❑ 99TopBlaLC3-17
❑ 99TopChr-93
❑ 99TopChrA-AE5
❑ 99TopChrAR-AE5
❑ 99TopChrR-93
❑ 99TopGal-44
❑ 99TopGalPP-44
❑ 99TopGalPPI-44
❑ 99TopGolL-17
❑ 99TopGolLC1-17
❑ 99TopGolLC2-17
❑ 99TopGolLOtO-17
❑ 99TopGolLRtA-RA5
❑ 99TopGolLRtAB-RA5
❑ 99TopGolLRtAOtO-RA5
❑ 99TopGolLRtAR-RA5
❑ 99TopMVPP-93
❑ 99TopOpeD-52
❑ 99TopRedLC1-17
❑ 99TopRedLC2-17
❑ 99TopRedLC3-17
❑ 99TopSta-16
❑ 99TopSta-155
❑ 99TopSta'S-18
❑ 99TopSta'SG-18
❑ 99TopSta'SGDH-18
❑ 99TopSta1Foil-16
❑ 99TopSta2Foil-16
❑ 99TopSta3Foil-16
❑ 99TopStaFoil-16
❑ 99TopStaFoil-155
❑ 99TopStaOS-16
❑ 99TopStaTS-16
❑ 99TopStaTS-16
❑ 99TopSupC-15
❑ 99TopSupCR-15
❑ 99TopTek-14A
❑ 99TopTek-14B
❑ 99TopTekG-14A
❑ 99TopTekG-14B
❑ 99UD Cho-70
❑ 99UD ChoP-70
❑ 99UD ChoPCR-70
❑ 99UD ChoYW-Y8
❑ 99UD Ion-17
❑ 99UD IonR-17
❑ 99UDHolo-11
❑ 99UDHoloAUsome-11
❑ 99UDHoloLau-L12
❑ 99UDHoloLauG-L12
❑ 99Ult-78
❑ 99UltGolM-78
❑ 99UltMas-78
❑ 99UltPlaM-78
❑ 99UltRBIK-5
❑ 99UltTheBook-4
❑ 99UppDec-315
❑ 99UppDec10AT-X17
❑ 99UppDec10ATD-X17
❑ 99UppDec10ATHR-X17
❑ 99UppDec10ATT-X17
❑ 99UppDecBD-22
❑ 99UppDecBDD-22
❑ 99UppDecBDQ-22
❑ 99UppDecBDT-22
❑ 99UppDecCf7-5
❑ 99UppDecCf7-49
❑ 99UppDecCf7-C5
❑ 99UppDecCf7Cf7P-C5
❑ 99UppDecCf7LL-L13
❑ 99UppDecCL-64
❑ 99UppDecCLCC-64
❑ 99UppDecCLM-C12
❑ 99UppDecCo7CE-5
❑ 99UppDecCo7CE-49
❑ 99UppDecE-13
❑ 99UppDecE-139
❑ 99UppDecEDF-D4
❑ 99UppDecEDFFXG-D4
❑ 99UppDecEFXG-13
❑ 99UppDecEFXG-139
❑ 99UppDecEL1-315
❑ 99UppDecEL2-315
❑ 99UppDecF-F8
❑ 99UppDecFD-F8
❑ 99UppDecFQ-F8
❑ 99UppDecFT-F8
❑ 99UppDecM-25
❑ 99UppDecM-P9
❑ 99UppDecMGS-25
❑ 99UppDecMHFS-25
❑ 99UppDecMSS-25
❑ 99UppDecO-16
❑ 99UppDecOMP-S12
❑ 99UppDecOSO-16
❑ 99UppDecOWP-R17
❑ 99UppDecR-12
❑ 99UppDecRG-12
❑ 99UppDecRP-12
❑ 99UppDecTE-T6
❑ 99UppDecTED-T6
❑ 99UppDecTEQ-T6
❑ 99UppDecTET-T6
❑ 99Vic-48

Bellenger, Butch
❑ 96EriSeaB-6

Bellhorn, Mark
❑ 96Bow-221
❑ 96BowBesMI-4
❑ 96BowBesMIAR-4
❑ 96BowBesMIR-4
❑ 96BowFoi-221
❑ 96HunStaTI-3
❑ 96Top-22
❑ 96TopPowB-22
❑ 97Bow-167
❑ 97BowChr-163
❑ 97BowChrI-163
❑ 97BowChrIR-163
❑ 97BowChrR-163
❑ 97BowInt-167
❑ 97Top-487
❑ 98ColCho-198
❑ 98DonColL-280
❑ 98DonPriCL-280
❑ 98Fle-251
❑ 98Lea-81
❑ 98LeaFraDA-81
❑ 98LeaFraF-81
❑ 98LeaFraM-81
❑ 98LeaFraM-81
❑ 98LeaFraMDC-81
❑ 98LeaFraMDC-81
❑ 98LeaFraMS-81
❑ 98LeaFraMZ2-81
❑ 98MetUni-51
❑ 98MetUniPMG-51
❑ 98PacInvGems-83
❑ 98PacPar-76
❑ 98PacParC-76
❑ 98PacParG-76
❑ 98PacParHS-76
❑ 98PacParPB-76
❑ 98PacParR-76
❑ 98ScoRT-184
❑ 98StaCluFDI-103
❑ 98StaCluI-103
❑ 98StaCluOneK-103
❑ 98StaCluPP-103
❑ 98Top-347
❑ 98TopChr-347
❑ 98TopChrR-347
❑ 98TopDevR-347
❑ 98TopDia-347
❑ 98TopMiniC-347
❑ 98Ult-65
❑ 98UltGolM-65
❑ 98UltMas-65
❑ 98UltPlaM-65
❑ 98UppDec-177

Bellhorn, Todd
❑ 98PitMetM-6
❑ 99TeaBesR-3
❑ 99TeaBesRG-3
❑ 99TeaBesRS-3

Belliard, Carlos
❑ 93MadMusC-5
❑ 93MadMusF-1815
❑ 94ModA'sC-5

Belliard, Rafael
❑ 83LynPirT-14
❑ 84Pir-1
❑ 85DomLeaS-132
❑ 85Pir-2
❑ 87Don-538
❑ 87DonOpeD-165
❑ 87Fle-602
❑ 87FleGlo-602
❑ 87Top-541
❑ 87TopTif-541
❑ 88Fle-321
❑ 88FleGlo-321
❑ 88PirTeal-1
❑ 88Sco-453
❑ 88ScoGlo-453
❑ 88StaLinPi-1
❑ 88Top-221
❑ 88TopBig-175
❑ 88TopTif-221
❑ 89Fle-201
❑ 89FleGlo-201
❑ 89OPC-119
❑ 89PirVerFJ-6
❑ 89Sco-379
❑ 89Top-723
❑ 89TopBig-196
❑ 89TopSti-133
❑ 89TopTif-723
❑ 89UppDec-90
❑ 90Don-252
❑ 90Fle-460
❑ 90FleCan-460
❑ 90OPC-143
❑ 90PirHomC-3
❑ 90PubIntS-148
❑ 90Sco-520
❑ 90Top-143
❑ 90TopTif-143
❑ 90UppDec-208
❑ 91Bow-578
❑ 91BraDubP-2
❑ 91BraSubS-4
❑ 91Fle-32
❑ 91FleUpd-70
❑ 91Lea-453
❑ 91OPC-487
❑ 91ScoRoo-76T
❑ 91StaClu-404
❑ 91Top-487
❑ 91TopDesS-487
❑ 91TopMic-487
❑ 91TopTif-487
❑ 91TopTra-9T
❑ 91TopTraT-9T
❑ 91UltUpd-65
❑ 91UppDec-706
❑ 92Bow-75
❑ 92BraLykP-2
❑ 92BraLykS-3
❑ 92Don-107
❑ 92Fle-351
❑ 92Lea-310
❑ 92LeaBlaG-310
❑ 92OPC-367
❑ 92PanSti-165
❑ 92Pin-357
❑ 92Sco-116
❑ 92StaClu-105
❑ 92Top-367
❑ 92TopGol-367
❑ 92TopGolW-367
❑ 92TopMic-367
❑ 92Ult-158
❑ 92UppDec-510
❑ 93BraLykP-3
❑ 93BraLykS-4
❑ 93BraStaC-20
❑ 93Don-398
❑ 93Fle-361
❑ 93PacSpa-1
❑ 93Pin-494
❑ 93Sco-478
❑ 93Sel-267
❑ 93StaClu-58
❑ 93StaCluFDI-58
❑ 93StaCluMOP-58
❑ 93Top-62
❑ 93TopGol-62
❑ 93TopInaM-62
❑ 93TopInaR-62
❑ 93TopMic-62
❑ 93TriPla-15
❑ 93Ult-2
❑ 93UppDec-91
❑ 93UppDecGold-91
❑ 94BraLykP-4
❑ 94BraLykS-4
❑ 94BraUSPC-4H
❑ 94BraUSPC-10C
❑ 94Fle-352
❑ 94Sco-303
❑ 94ScoGolR-303
❑ 94StaClu-426
❑ 94StaCluFDI-426
❑ 94StaCluGR-426
❑ 94StaCluMOP-426
❑ 94StaCluT-59
❑ 94StaCluTFDI-59
❑ 94Top-261
❑ 94TopGol-261
❑ 94TopSpa-261
❑ 95Fle-301
❑ 95Pac-2
❑ 95Sco-10
❑ 95ScoGolR-10
❑ 95ScoPlaTS-10
❑ 95StaClu-234
❑ 95StaCluFDI-234
❑ 95StaCluMOP-234
❑ 95StaCluSTWS-234
❑ 95Top-117
❑ 96ColCho-457
❑ 96ColChoGS-457
❑ 96ColChoSS-457
❑ 96Fle-286
❑ 96FleTif-286
❑ 96LeaSigA-20
❑ 96LeaSigAG-20
❑ 96LeaSigAS-20
❑ 96Pac-11
❑ 97Pac-230
❑ 97PacLigB-230
❑ 97PacSil-230
❑ 98Pac-229
❑ 98PacOnl-54
❑ 98PacOnlR-54
❑ 98PacOnlWC-54
❑ 98PacPlaB-229
❑ 98PacRedT-229
❑ 98PacSil-229

Belliard, Ron
❑ 95BelBreTI-25
❑ 96El PasDB-6
❑ 96TexLeaAB-20
❑ 97Bow-372
❑ 97BowChr-248
❑ 97BowChrI-248
❑ 97BowChrIR-248
❑ 97BowChrR-248
❑ 97BowInt-372
❑ 97Sel-139
❑ 97SelArtP-139
❑ 97SelCom-139
❑ 97SelRegG-139
❑ 97TucTorB-15
❑ 98FleUpd-U26
❑ 98LouRedQ-4
❑ 99BasAmeTP-12
❑ 99BasAmeTPG-12
❑ 99Bow-159
❑ 99BowBes-105
❑ 99BowBesAR-105
❑ 99BowBesR-105
❑ 99BowChr-159
❑ 99BowChrG-159
❑ 99BowChrGR-159
❑ 99BowChrI-159
❑ 99BowChrIR-159
❑ 99BowChrR-159
❑ 99BowGol-159
❑ 99BowInt-159
❑ 99Fle-161
❑ 99FleSta9-161
❑ 99FleWarT-161
❑ 99PacOme-128
❑ 99PacOmeC-128
❑ 99PacOmeG-128
❑ 99PacOmePB-128
❑ 99SkyThu-226
❑ 99SkyThuRant-226
❑ 99SkyThuRave-226
❑ 99SP SigAuto-RBE
❑ 99SP SigAutoG-RBE
❑ 99SpoIll-47
❑ 99SPSig-80
❑ 99SPx-103
❑ 99SPxFinR-103
❑ 99SPxFinS-103
❑ 99StaClu-347
❑ 99StaCluFDI-347
❑ 99StaCluOoaK-347
❑ 99StaCluPP-347
❑ 99ThuSkySupR-226
❑ 99Top-427
❑ 99TopAll-AM21
❑ 99TopChr-427
❑ 99TopChrA-AE21
❑ 99TopChrAR-AE21
❑ 99TopChrR-427
❑ 99TopMVPP-427
❑ 99UppDec-288
❑ 99UppDecE-131
❑ 99UppDecEFXG-131
❑ 99UppDecEL1-288
❑ 99UppDecEL2-288
❑ 99Vic-208

Bellinger, Clay
❑ 90Bes-33
❑ 90CliGiaB-1
❑ 90CliGiaP-2558
❑ 90CMC-844
❑ 91CalLeLA-41
❑ 91SanJosGC-4
❑ 91SanJosGP-15
❑ 92ShrCapF-3877
❑ 92ShrCapS-576
❑ 92SkyAA F-253
❑ 93PhoFirF-1519
❑ 94PhoFirF-1524
❑ 95PhoFirTI-20
❑ 96RocRedWB-5
❑ 97ColCliB-6
❑ 97ColCliD-3
❑ 98ColCliD-2
❑ 98ColCliM-5
❑ 99DumSet-104
❑ 99FleMys-104
❑ 99FleMysM-104
❑ 99SkyPre-242
❑ 99SkyPre-242
❑ 99SkyPreR-242
❑ 99SkyPreR-242

Bellino, Frank
❑ 85NewOriT-25
❑ 86HagSunP-2
❑ 87HagSunP-21
❑ 88FreSunCLC-8
❑ 89EasLeaDDP-DD39
❑ 89ReaPhiB-18
❑ 89ReaPhiP-659
❑ 89ReaPhiS-2
❑ 90Bes-266
❑ 90ReaPhiB-20
❑ 90ReaPhiP-1230
❑ 90ReaPhiS-6

Bellino, Ray
❑ 55DesMoiHB-2

Bellman, Bill
❑ 92KinMetF-1520

Bello, Duben
❑ 88FayGenP-1091

Bello, Emerson
❑ 97EveAquG-1
❑ 98WisTimRM-2

Bello, Gilberto
❑ 98BluOriQ-13

Belloir, Bob (Robert E.)
❑ 77Top-312
❑ 78Top-681

Bellomo, Bill
❑ 79CedRapGT-12

Bellomo, Kevin
❑ 91EveGiaC-28
❑ 91EveGiaP-3926
❑ 92ClaFS7-236
❑ 93SanJosGC-3
❑ 93SanJosGF-23

Bellum, Donnie
❑ 92HamRedC-6
❑ 92HamRedF-1604

Bellver, Juan
❑ 86MiaMarP-2

Belmonte, Nick
❑ 91SalLakTP-3227
❑ 91SalLakTSP-28
❑ 92SalLakTSP-30

Belmonte, Pedro
❑ 92KinMetC-19
❑ 92KinMetF-1521
❑ 93LinVenB-13
❑ 95LinVen-24
❑ 96-97LinVen-154

Belmonte, Phil
❑ 80QuaCitCT-25

Belru, Juan
❑ 90HamRedB-26

Beltran, Alonso
❑ 92MedHatBJF-3201
❑ 92MedHatBJSP-7
❑ 93St.CatBJC-3
❑ 93St.CatBJF-3966
❑ 94DunBluJC-2
❑ 94DunBluJF-2546
❑ 95KnoSmoF-32

Beltran, Angel
❑ 89WelPirP-4

Beltran, Carlos
❑ 95SPML-111
❑ 95TopTra-18T
❑ 96BesAutS-10
❑ 96LanLugB-5
❑ 96SpoIndB-5
❑ 97Bow-377
❑ 97BowBes-176
❑ 97BowBesAR-176
❑ 97BowBesR-176
❑ 97BowInt-377
❑ 97CarLeaTP-13
❑ 97WilBluR-10
❑ 98CarLeaAC-9
❑ 98CarLeaTPQ-10
❑ 98FleUpd-U37
❑ 98LeaRS-323
❑ 98LeaRSLHolo-323
❑ 98LeaRSLong-323
❑ 98LeaRTrue-323
❑ 98WilBluRC-3
❑ 99199Fin-281
❑ 99Bow-329
❑ 99BowBes-107
❑ 99BowBesAR-107
❑ 99BowBesMI-M7
❑ 99BowBesMIAR-M7
❑ 99BowBesMIR-M7
❑ 99BowBesR-107
❑ 99BowChrDA-DA6
❑ 99BowChrDAR-DA6
❑ 99BowChrSC-SC8
❑ 99BowChrSCR-SC8
❑ 99BowGol-329
❑ 99BowInt-329
❑ 99BowScoC-SC8
❑ 99CroRoyB-67
❑ 99CroRoyL-67
❑ 99CroRoyOD-67
❑ 99DumSet-149
❑ 99E-X Cen-108
❑ 99E-X CenECFut-108
❑ 99E-X CenECNow-108
❑ 99FinGolRef-281
❑ 99FinRef-281
❑ 99FlaShoLeg1-84
❑ 99FlaShoLeg2-84
❑ 99FlaShoLeg3-84
❑ 99FlaShoLegM1-84
❑ 99FlaShoLegM2-84
❑ 99FlaShoLegM3-84
❑ 99FlaShoR1-84
❑ 99FlaShoR2-84
❑ 99FlaShoR3-84
❑ 99Fle-245
❑ 99FleBri-146
❑ 99FleBri2G-146
❑ 99FleBriBlu-146
❑ 99FleBriGol-146
❑ 99FleMys-149
❑ 99FleMysM-149
❑ 99FleSta9-245
❑ 99FleWarT-245
❑ 99PacInv-70
❑ 99PacInvOD-70
❑ 99PacInvPB-70
❑ 99PacOme-111
❑ 99PacOme5T-8
❑ 99PacOme5TT-8

❑ 99PacOmeC-111
❑ 99PacOmeG-111
❑ 99PacOmePB-111
❑ 99Rev-65
❑ 99RevPremDate-65
❑ 99RevRet-65
❑ 99RevShaSS-65
❑ 99SkyMolM-67
❑ 99SkyMolMX-67
❑ 99SkyPre-267
❑ 99SkyPre-267
❑ 99SkyPreR-267
❑ 99SkyPreR-267
❑ 99SkyThu-268
❑ 99SkyThuRant-268
❑ 99SkyThuRave-268
❑ 99SkyThuUnl-U1
❑ 99SP Aut-102
❑ 99SP AutC-CB
❑ 99SP AutCG-CB
❑ 99SP SigAuto-CBE
❑ 99SP SigAutoG-CBE
❑ 99SP TopP-15
❑ 99SP TopPPE-15
❑ 99SPSig-23
❑ 99SPx-96
❑ 99SPxFinR-96
❑ 99SPxFinS-96
❑ 99ThuSkySupR-268
❑ 99TopGal-136
❑ 99TopGalPP-136
❑ 99TopGalPPI-136
❑ 99TopSta-92
❑ 99TopSta1Foil-92
❑ 99TopStaFoil-92
❑ 99TopStaOS-92
❑ 99TopTekFP-F7
❑ 99UD Cho-9
❑ 99UD ChoPCR-9
❑ 99UDHolo-28
❑ 99UDHoloAUsome-28
❑ 99UDHoloUDA-CB
❑ 99UppDec-287
❑ 99UppDecCL-108
❑ 99UppDecCLCC-108
❑ 99UppDecCLM-C44
❑ 99UppDecE-130
❑ 99UppDecEBPC-C-CB
❑ 99UppDecEFXG-130
❑ 99UppDecEL1-287
❑ 99UppDecEL2-287
❑ 99UppDecERE-R5
❑ 99UppDecEREFXG-R5
❑ 99UppDecM-98
❑ 99UppDecMGS-98
❑ 99UppDecMHFS-98
❑ 99UppDecMP-98
❑ 99UppDecMP-CB
❑ 99UppDecMSC-SC5
❑ 99UppDecMSS-98
❑ 99UppDecO-64
❑ 99UppDecOSO-64
❑ 99UppDecR-41
❑ 99UppDecRG-41
❑ 99UppDecRI-CBE
❑ 99UppDecRIL2-CBE
❑ 99UppDecROSS-S24
❑ 99UppDecROSS-S24
❑ 99UppDecRP-41
❑ 99Vic-181
Beltran, Julio
❑ 78DayBeaAT-3
❑ 82MiaMarT-13
Beltran, Rigo
❑ 91HamRedC-6
❑ 91HamRedP-4027
❑ 92ClaFS7-367
❑ 92SavCarC-17
❑ 92SavCarF-652
❑ 93ArkTraF-2805
❑ 94ArkTraF-3082
❑ 94LouRedF-2973
❑ 95LouRedF-269
❑ 95SigRoo-8
❑ 95SigRooSig-8
❑ 96LouRedB-10
❑ 97LouRedB-9
❑ 98Don-321
❑ 98DonGolPP-321
❑ 98DonSilPP-321
❑ 98Fle-295
❑ 98NorTidP-3
❑ 98NorTidQ-3
❑ 98PacInvGems-201
Beltre, Adrian
❑ 96SavSanB-2
❑ 96SavSanB-30
❑ 97Bes-21
❑ 97Bes-96
❑ 97BesAll-14
❑ 97BesAutSBPP-4
❑ 97BesAutSC-2
❑ 97BesBetP-2
❑ 97BesIntB-IB3
❑ 97BesLum-1
❑ 97Bow-194
❑ 97BowBes-117
❑ 97BowBesAR-117
❑ 97BowBesMI-MI9
❑ 97BowBesMIAR-MI9
❑ 97BowBesMIARI-MI9
❑ 97BowBesMII-MI9
❑ 97BowBesMIR-MI9
❑ 97BowBesMIRI-MI9
❑ 97BowBesR-117
❑ 97BowChr-182
❑ 97BowChrI-182
❑ 97BowChrIR-182
❑ 97BowChrR-182
❑ 97BowInt-194
❑ 97FloStaLTPB-25
❑ 97VerBeaD-5
❑ 98BesDiaB-2
❑ 98Bow-123
❑ 98Bow99ROYF-ROY1
❑ 98BowBes-120
❑ 98BowBesA-120
❑ 98BowBesAAR-120
❑ 98BowBesAR-120
❑ 98BowBesAR-120
❑ 98BowBesMIF-MI15
❑ 98BowBesMIFAR-MI15
❑ 98BowBesMIFR-MI15
❑ 98BowBesP-BP7
❑ 98BowBesPAR-BP7
❑ 98BowBesPR-BP7
❑ 98BowBesR-120
❑ 98BowCerBlueAU-1
❑ 98BowCerGA-1
❑ 98BowCerSA-1
❑ 98BowChr-123
❑ 98BowChrGA-123
❑ 98BowChrGAR-123
❑ 98BowChrI-123
❑ 98BowChrIR-123
❑ 98BowChrR-123
❑ 98BowGolA-123
❑ 98BowInt-123
❑ 98BowScoC-SC10
❑ 98DonSig-127
❑ 98DonSigA-7
❑ 98DonSigAC-9
❑ 98DonSigAM-9
❑ 98DonSigP-127
❑ 98FleUpd-U70
❑ 98LeaRS-319
❑ 98LeaRSLHolo-319
❑ 98LeaRSLong-319
❑ 98LeaRTrue-319
❑ 98SanAntMG-3
❑ 98SP MinDTSPE-DS10
❑ 98SP MinPE-68
❑ 98SP MinSTHPE-H4
❑ 98SP SPTSC-AB
❑ 98SPMin-68
❑ 98SPMinDTS-DS10
❑ 98SPMinSTH-H4
❑ 98StaCluFDI-361
❑ 98StaCluI-361
❑ 98StaCluOneK-361
❑ 98StaCluPP-361
❑ 98TexLeaTPG-3
❑ 98Top-254
❑ 98TopChr-254
❑ 98TopChrR-254
❑ 98TopDevR-254
❑ 98TopDia-254
❑ 98TopMiniC-254
❑ 98TopStaSB-S4
❑ 98TopStaSG-S4
❑ 98TopStaSGR-S4
❑ 98TopStaSS-S4
❑ 98TopTek-49
❑ 98TopTekD-49
❑ 98UppDecR-118
❑ 98UppDecRNF-NF18
❑ 99199Fin-126
❑ 99199Fin-182
❑ 99Bow-219
❑ 99BowAut-BA37
❑ 99BowBes-142
❑ 99BowBesAR-142
❑ 99BowBesFFMI-FF5
❑ 99BowBesFFMI-FF5
❑ 99BowBesFFMII-FF5
❑ 99BowBesR-142
❑ 99BowChr-219
❑ 99BowChrDA-DA7
❑ 99BowChrDAR-DA7
❑ 99BowChrG-219
❑ 99BowChrGR-219
❑ 99BowChrI-219
❑ 99BowChrIR-219
❑ 99BowChrR-219
❑ 99BowChrSC-SC6
❑ 99BowChrSCR-SC6
❑ 99BowGol-219
❑ 99BowInt-219
❑ 99BowScoC-SC6
❑ 99DodPol-1
❑ 99E-X Cen-93
❑ 99E-X CenECFut-93
❑ 99E-X CenECNow-93
❑ 99E-X CenEQ-9
❑ 99FinFutF-FF9
❑ 99FinGolRef-126
❑ 99FinGolRef-182
❑ 99FinRef-126
❑ 99FinRef-182
❑ 99Fle-65
❑ 99Fle-576
❑ 99FleBri-92
❑ 99FleBri2G-92
❑ 99FleBriBlu-92
❑ 99FleBriGol-92
❑ 99FleMys-28
❑ 99FleMysFtG-1
❑ 99FleMysG-28
❑ 99FleMysM-28
❑ 99FleRooFla-3
❑ 99FleSta9-65
❑ 99FleSta9-576
❑ 99FleWarT-65
❑ 99FleWarT-576
❑ 99MetUni-262
❑ 99MetUniGM-262
❑ 99MetUniN-15
❑ 99MetUniPMG-262
❑ 99SkyMolM-116
❑ 99SkyMolMF-16
❑ 99SkyMolMFS-16
❑ 99SkyMolMFT-16
❑ 99SkyMolMX-116
❑ 99SkyPre-205
❑ 99SkyPreR-205
❑ 99SkyThu-298
❑ 99SkyThuRant-298
❑ 99SkyThuRave-298
❑ 99SkyThuUnl-U2
❑ 99SP SigAuto-ABE
❑ 99SP SigAutoG-ABE
❑ 99SPSig-70
❑ 99SPx-99
❑ 99SPxFinR-99
❑ 99SPxFinS-99
❑ 99StaClu-162
❑ 99StaCluC-SCC32
❑ 99StaCluCR-SCC32
❑ 99StaCluFDI-162
❑ 99StaCluOoaK-162
❑ 99StaCluPP-162
❑ 99ThuSkySupR-298
❑ 99Top-369
❑ 99TopBlaLC1-94
❑ 99TopBlaLC2-94
❑ 99TopBlaLC3-94
❑ 99TopChr-369
❑ 99TopChrNB-NB15
❑ 99TopChrNBR-NB15
❑ 99TopChrR-369
❑ 99TopGal-134
❑ 99TopGalAuto-GA2
❑ 99TopGalPP-134
❑ 99TopGalPPI-134
❑ 99TopGolL-94
❑ 99TopGolLC1-94
❑ 99TopGolLC2-94
❑ 99TopGolLOtO-94
❑ 99TopMVPP-369
❑ 99TopNewB-NB15
❑ 99TopRedLC1-94
❑ 99TopRedLC2-94
❑ 99TopRedLC3-94
❑ 99TopSta-40
❑ 99TopSta1Foil-40
❑ 99TopSta2Foil-40
❑ 99TopStaBF-BF3
❑ 99TopStaBFFoil-BF3
❑ 99TopStaFoil-40
❑ 99TopStaOS-40
❑ 99TopStaTS-40
❑ 99TopTek-18A
❑ 99TopTek-18B
❑ 99TopTekFP-F8
❑ 99TopTekG-18A
❑ 99TopTekG-18B
❑ 99UD Cho-24
❑ 99UD ChoMBH-B14
❑ 99UD ChoPCR-24
❑ 99UD ChoS-27
❑ 99UD ChoSD-27
❑ 99UD ChoSHR-27
❑ 99UD ChoST-27
❑ 99UD Ion-34
❑ 99UD IonR-34
❑ 99Ult-228
❑ 99UltGolM-228
❑ 99UltMas-228
❑ 99UltPlaM-228
❑ 99UltWorP-7
❑ 99UppDec-2
❑ 99UppDecBD-105
❑ 99UppDecBDD-105
❑ 99UppDecBDQ-105
❑ 99UppDecBDT-105
❑ 99UppDecE-92
❑ 99UppDecEFXG-92
❑ 99UppDecEL1-2
❑ 99UppDecEL2-2
❑ 99UppDecERE-R8
❑ 99UppDecEREFXG-R8
❑ 99UppDecGJ-AB
❑ 99UppDecM-107
❑ 99UppDecMGS-107
❑ 99UppDecMHFS-107
❑ 99UppDecMSS-107
❑ 99UppDecO-63
❑ 99UppDecOSO-63
❑ 99UppDecR-44
❑ 99UppDecRG-44
❑ 99UppDecRP-44
❑ 99Vic-201
Beltre, Eddy
❑ 92KinMetC-17
❑ 92KinMetF-1536
❑ 94HicCraC-2
❑ 94HicCraF-2182
Beltre, Esteban
❑ 85UtiBluST-12
❑ 86WesPalBEP-5
❑ 87JacExpP-439
❑ 88JacExpB-17
❑ 88JacExpP-991
❑ 89RocExpLC-3
❑ 90CMC-74
❑ 90IndIndC-24
❑ 90IndIndP-281
❑ 90ProAAAF-564
❑ 91DenZepLD-128
❑ 91DenZepP-127
❑ 91LinDriAAA-128
❑ 92Bow-458
❑ 92Cla2-T84
❑ 92DonRoo-10
❑ 92Fle-75
❑ 92Pin-535
❑ 92Sco-766
❑ 92ScoRoo-24
❑ 92StaClu-611
❑ 92StaCluECN-611
❑ 92TopDeb91-15
❑ 92Ult-333
❑ 93Don-595
❑ 93LimRocDWB-106
❑ 93NasSouF-573
❑ 93StaClu-375
❑ 93StaCluFDI-375
❑ 93StaCluMOP-375
❑ 93Top-13
❑ 93TopGol-13
❑ 93TopInaM-13
❑ 93TopInaR-13
❑ 93TopMic-13
❑ 94RanMagM-2
❑ 94StaCluT-146
❑ 94StaCluTFDI-146
❑ 95Don-153
❑ 95DonPreP-153
❑ 95Pac-420
❑ 95RanCra-3
❑ 95Sco-6
❑ 95ScoGolR-6
❑ 95ScoPlaTS-6
❑ 96Pac-433
❑ 97Pac-32
❑ 97PacLigB-32
❑ 97PacSil-32
❑ 98SalLakBO-9
Beltre, Sergio
❑ 79JacMetT-9
❑ 81TidTidT-10
Belyeu, Randy
❑ 91HunCubC-4
❑ 91HunCubP-3336
Bemis, Gregg
❑ 77TacTwiDQ-14
Bemis, Harry Parker
❑ 03BreE10-7
❑ 05IndSouPSoCP-2
❑ 08RosComP-21
❑ 09AmeCarE90-1-5
❑ 09ColChiE-27A
❑ 09ColChiE-27B
❑ 10E101-2
❑ 10MelMinE-2
❑ 10NadCarE-3
❑ 10PeoT21-2
❑ 11PinT-5-606
❑ 11SpoLifCW-28
❑ 11SpoLifM-37
❑ 12ColRedB-27A
❑ 12ColRedB-27B
❑ 12ColTinT-27A
❑ 12ColTinT-27B
Ben, Elijah
❑ 83BurRanF-8
❑ 83BurRanT-12
Benard, Marvin
❑ 92EveGiaC-4
❑ 92EveGiaF-1702
❑ 93CliGiaC-4
❑ 93CliGiaF-2499
❑ 94ShrCapF-1617
❑ 95PhoFirTI-4
❑ 96-97LinVen-288
❑ 96ColCho-717
❑ 96ColChoGS-717
❑ 96ColChoSS-717
❑ 96Don-459
❑ 96DonPreP-459
❑ 96Fin-B326
❑ 96FinRef-B326
❑ 96Fle-582
❑ 96FleTif-582
❑ 96PhoFirB-9
❑ 96Sco-502
❑ 96Sel-193
❑ 96UppDecPHE-H56
❑ 96UppDecPreH-H56
❑ 97ColCho-217
❑ 97Don-183
❑ 97Don-387
❑ 97DonGolPP-183
❑ 97DonGolPP-387
❑ 97DonSilPP-183
❑ 97DonSilPP-387
❑ 97Fle-476
❑ 97FleTif-476
❑ 97Lea-181
❑ 97Lea-336
❑ 97LeaFraM-181
❑ 97LeaFraM-336
❑ 97LeaFraMDC-181
❑ 97LeaFraMDC-336
❑ 97Pac-439
❑ 97PacLigB-439
❑ 97PacSil-439
❑ 97Pin-174
❑ 97PinArtP-PP174
❑ 97PinMusC-174
❑ 97PinPrePla-174
❑ 97Sco-325
❑ 97ScoArtPWB-325
❑ 97ScoPreS-325
❑ 97ScoShoS-325
❑ 97ScoShoSAP-325
❑ 97StaClu-151
❑ 97StaCluMOP-151
❑ 97Top-114
❑ 97UppDec-172
❑ 98GiaMot-23
❑ 98PacOnl-654
❑ 98PacOnlR-654
❑ 98PacOnlWC-654
❑ 98UppDecNP-NP25
❑ 99Fle-366
❑ 99FleSta9-366
❑ 99FleWarT-366
❑ 99PacAur-168
❑ 99PacAurOD-168
❑ 99PacOme-209
❑ 99PacOmeC-209
❑ 99PacOmeG-209
❑ 99PacOmePB-209
❑ 99PacPar-207
❑ 99PacParC-207
❑ 99PacParG-207
❑ 99PacParHoloGold-207
❑ 99PacParHS-207
❑ 99PacParOD-207
❑ 99PacParPB-207
❑ 99PacParRed-207
❑ 99PacPriS-57
❑ 99PacPriS206-57
❑ 99PacPriS206R-57
❑ 99UppDec-482
❑ 99UppDecEL1-482
❑ 99UppDecEL2-482
❑ 99Vic-361
Benavente, Ronny
❑ 94VenLinU-86
Benavides, Al
❑ 92ClaFS7-235
❑ 92SanJosGC-25
❑ 93FreKeyC-3
❑ 93FreKeyF-1016
Benavides, Freddie (Alfredo)
❑ 88CedRapRP-1142
❑ 89ChaLooB-12
❑ 89ChaLooGS-5
❑ 89NasSouTI-2
❑ 90ChaLooGS-5
❑ 91Bow-672
❑ 91FleUpd-84
❑ 91LinDriAAA-252
❑ 91NasSouLD-252
❑ 91NasSouP-2161
❑ 91RedKah-57
❑ 91ScoRoo-98T
❑ 91UppDecFE-32F
❑ 92Don-573
❑ 92Fle-399
❑ 92Pin-278
❑ 92RedKah-12
❑ 92Sco-813
❑ 92Sco100RS-53
❑ 92StaClu-394
❑ 92TopDeb91-16
❑ 92TopTra-10T
❑ 92TopTraG-10T
❑ 92Ult-480
❑ 93Bow-472
❑ 93Don-746
❑ 93Fle-402
❑ 93Lea-244
❑ 93PacBeiA-22
❑ 93PacSpa-421
❑ 93Pin-548
❑ 93PinExpOD-6
❑ 93RocStaC-21
❑ 93RocUSPC-4S
❑ 93RocUSPC-13D
❑ 93Sco-627
❑ 93StaClu-456
❑ 93StaCluFDI-456
❑ 93StaCluMOP-456
❑ 93Top-356
❑ 93TopGol-356
❑ 93TopInaM-356
❑ 93TopInaR-356
❑ 93TopMic-356
❑ 93TopTra-7T
❑ 93Ult-340
❑ 93UppDec-732
❑ 93UppDecGold-732
❑ 94Don-76
❑ 94Fle-432
❑ 94Pac-187
❑ 94PanSti-170
❑ 94Sco-229
❑ 94ScoGolR-229
❑ 94StaClu-132
❑ 94StaCluFDI-132
❑ 94StaCluGR-132
❑ 94StaCluMOP-132
❑ 94Top-553
❑ 94TopGol-553
❑ 94TopSpa-553
❑ 94Ult-180
❑ 95IowCubTI-4
❑ 95Pac-262
❑ 95Top-164
Benavidez, Eric
❑ 97PriDevR-13
Benbow, Lou

❑ 91St.CatBJC-3
❑ 91St.CatBJP-3401
❑ 92St.CatBJC-12
❑ 92St.CatBJF-3391
❑ 93HagSunC-2
❑ 93HagSunF-1884
❑ 94DunBluJC-3
❑ 94DunBluJF-2562
❑ 94St.LucMC-3
❑ 95DurBulTI-2
❑ 95StLucMTI-7
❑ 96RicBraB-6
❑ 96RicBraRC-25
❑ 96RicBraUB-3
❑ 97GreBraG-1

Bench, Johnny Lee

❑ 68Kah-B8
❑ 68Top-247
❑ 68TopVen-247
❑ 69MilBra-24
❑ 69MLBOffS-127
❑ 69MLBPin-35
❑ 69OPC-95
❑ 69Top-95
❑ 69Top-430
❑ 69TopSta-23
❑ 69TopTeaP-20
❑ 70DayDaiNM-2
❑ 70Kel-58
❑ 70MLBOffS-25
❑ 70OPC-464
❑ 70Top-464
❑ 70Top-660
❑ 70TopCanL-4
❑ 70TopPos-11
❑ 70TopSup-8
❑ 71AllBasA-4
❑ 71BazNumT-29
❑ 71BazUnn-8
❑ 71MilDud-36
❑ 71MLBOffS-49
❑ 71MLBOffS-556
❑ 71OPC-64
❑ 71OPC-66
❑ 71OPC-250
❑ 71Top-64
❑ 71Top-66
❑ 71Top-250
❑ 71TopCoi-149
❑ 71TopGreM-13
❑ 71TopSup-32
❑ 71TopTat-87
❑ 71TopTat-88
❑ 72Dia-54
❑ 72MilBra-30
❑ 72OPC-433
❑ 72OPC-434
❑ 72ProStaP-14
❑ 72SevTraC-5
❑ 72Top-433
❑ 72Top-434
❑ 73LinPor-54
❑ 73OPC-62
❑ 73OPC-63
❑ 73OPC-208
❑ 73OPC-380
❑ 73SevTraC-4
❑ 73Top-62
❑ 73Top-63
❑ 73Top-208
❑ 73Top-380
❑ 73TopCanL-5
❑ 73TopCom-3
❑ 73TopPin-3
❑ 74Kel-28
❑ 74NewYorNTDiS-1
❑ 74OPC-10
❑ 74OPC-331
❑ 74Top-10
❑ 74Top-331
❑ 74TopDecE-71
❑ 74TopPuz-3
❑ 74TopSta-21
❑ 75BlaBacD-2
❑ 75Hos-83
❑ 75Kel-7
❑ 75OPC-208
❑ 75OPC-210
❑ 75OPC-260
❑ 75OPC-308
❑ 75SSP42-29
❑ 75SSPPuzB-2
❑ 75Top-208
❑ 75Top-210
❑ 75Top-260
❑ 75Top-308
❑ 75TopMin-208
❑ 75TopMin-210
❑ 75TopMin-260
❑ 75TopMin-308
❑ 76BlaDis-2
❑ 76BucDis-2
❑ 76CarDis-2
❑ 76CraDis-2
❑ 76DailsID-2
❑ 76Hos-22
❑ 76HosTwi-22
❑ 76IsaDis-2
❑ 76Kel-36
❑ 76LinSup-91
❑ 76OPC-195
❑ 76OPC-300
❑ 76OrbDis-2
❑ 76RedBarD-2
❑ 76RedIceL-1
❑ 76RedKro-3
❑ 76SafDis-2
❑ 76SafSupLB-1
❑ 76SafSupLB-6
❑ 76SafSupLB-7
❑ 76SafSupLB-8
❑ 76SafSupLB-9
❑ 76SSP-31
❑ 76Top-195
❑ 76Top-300
❑ 76TowCluD-2
❑ 77BurCheD-205
❑ 77ChiWilD-3
❑ 77DailsID-3
❑ 77DetCaeD-3
❑ 77HolInnD-3
❑ 77Hos-6
❑ 77MSADis-3
❑ 77OPC-100
❑ 77PepGloD-44
❑ 77RCColC-3
❑ 77RedCarP-2
❑ 77SagDis-3
❑ 77sDis-3
❑ 77Spo-422
❑ 77Spo-1509
❑ 77Spo-3515
❑ 77Top-70
❑ 77Top-411
❑ 77Top-412
❑ 77TopCloS-3
❑ 77WenDis-3
❑ 77ZipDis-3
❑ 78Hos-44
❑ 78OPC-50
❑ 78Pep-4
❑ 78RCColC-65
❑ 78SSP270-128
❑ 78Top-700
❑ 78WifBalD-3
❑ 79BasPat-2
❑ 79Hos-128
❑ 79OPC-101
❑ 79Top-200
❑ 79TopCom-21
❑ 80Kel-52
❑ 80OPC-55
❑ 80PerHaloFP-202
❑ 80PerHaloFPS-65
❑ 80RedEnq-5
❑ 80Top-100
❑ 80TopSup-3
❑ 81AllGamPI-128
❑ 81CokTeaS-37
❑ 81Don-62
❑ 81Don-182
❑ 81Fle-196
❑ 81FleStiC-37
❑ 81Kel-65
❑ 81MSAMinD-2
❑ 81OPC-286
❑ 81PerCreC-1
❑ 81Squ-20
❑ 81Top-201
❑ 81Top-600
❑ 81TopScr-64
❑ 81TopSti-160
❑ 81TopSupHT-31
❑ 81TopSupN-2
❑ 82Don-400
❑ 82Don-628
❑ 82Dra-3
❑ 82Fle-57
❑ 82Fle-634
❑ 82FleSta-17
❑ 82K-M-18
❑ 82K-M-22
❑ 82Kel-30
❑ 82OnDecD-2
❑ 82OPC-18
❑ 82OPC-304
❑ 82PerCreC-1
❑ 82PerCreCG-1
❑ 82RedCok-1
❑ 82Top-400
❑ 82Top-401
❑ 82TopSti-35
❑ 83Don-22
❑ 83Don-500
❑ 83DonActA-14
❑ 83Fle-584
❑ 83FleSta-14
❑ 83FleSti-214
❑ 83Oco& SSBG-2
❑ 83OPC-60
❑ 83OPC-61
❑ 83RedYea-5
❑ 83Top-60
❑ 83Top-61
❑ 83TopFol-2
❑ 83TopSti-7
❑ 83TopSti-229
❑ 84Don-B
❑ 84DonCha-51
❑ 84Fle-462
❑ 84Fle-640
❑ 84FleSti-96
❑ 84Nes792-6
❑ 84OCoandSI-24
❑ 84OCoandSI-85
❑ 84OCoandSI-161
❑ 84OCoandSI-230
❑ 84Top-6
❑ 84TopGloA-22
❑ 84TopTif-6
❑ 85CirK-22
❑ 86RedGreT-12
❑ 87K-M-12
❑ 87NesDreT-30
❑ 88GreBasS-1
❑ 88PacLegI-110
❑ 89KahComC-1
❑ 89KahCoo-2
❑ 89PerCelP-5
❑ 89TopBasT-14
❑ 90BasWit-54
❑ 90OPC-664
❑ 90PerGreM-49
❑ 90Top-664
❑ 90TopTif-664
❑ 92UppDecBH-37
❑ 92UppDecBH-38
❑ 92UppDecBH-39
❑ 92UppDecBH-42
❑ 92UppDecBH-43
❑ 92UppDecBH-44
❑ 92UppDecBH-AU5
❑ 93PMGolB-1
❑ 93TedWil-28
❑ 93TedWilM-16
❑ 93Yoo-1
❑ 94CarLeaA-DJ33
❑ 95TomPiz-AU1
❑ 96Red76K-2
❑ 96Red76K-3
❑ 97DonSigSS-2
❑ 97HigMinMCT-5
❑ 97HigMinMCT-6
❑ 98TopStaRR-1
❑ 98TopStaRRA-1
❑ 99UppDecCL-16
❑ 99UppDecCL-134
❑ 99UppDecCLA-1960
❑ 99UppDecCLCC-16
❑ 99UppDecCLCC-134
❑ 99UppDecCLES-JB
❑ 99UppDecCLESC-JB
❑ 99UppDecCLJotC-AC8

Bencomo, Omar

❑ 85KinBluJT-2
❑ 87KnoBluJP-1507
❑ 88KnoBluJB-17
❑ 93LinVenB-124
❑ 94VenLinU-203
❑ 95LinVen-63
❑ 96-97LinVen-115

Bender, Chief (Charles A.)

❑ 03BreE10-8
❑ 03WilCarE-1
❑ 04FanCraAL-4
❑ 08AmeCarE91-1
❑ 08AmeCarE91-37
❑ 08RosComP-55
❑ 09AmeCarE90-1-6
❑ 09PhiCarE-1
❑ 09RamT20-11
❑ 09SpoNewSM-54
❑ 09T206-21
❑ 09T206-22
❑ 09T206-23
❑ 10CouT21-3
❑ 10CouT21-75
❑ 10CouT21-76
❑ 10CouT21-77
❑ 10CouT21-78
❑ 10CouT21-79
❑ 10CouT21-80
❑ 10CouT21-258
❑ 10CouT21-259
❑ 10DarChoE-2
❑ 10DomDisP-11
❑ 10E101-3A
❑ 10E101-3B
❑ 10E102-1
❑ 10E12AmeCDCE125-5
❑ 10E98-1
❑ 10JuJuDE-3
❑ 10MelMinE-3A
❑ 10MelMinE-3B
❑ 10NadCarE-4A
❑ 10NadCarE-4B
❑ 10NadE1-7
❑ 10PeoT21-3A
❑ 10PeoT21-3B
❑ 10PeoT21-3C
❑ 10PeoT21-3D
❑ 10RedCroT-4
❑ 10RedCroT-5
❑ 10RedCroT-90
❑ 10RedCroT-91
❑ 10RedCroT-171
❑ 10StaCarE-2
❑ 10SweCapPP-42A
❑ 10SweCapPP-42B
❑ 10W555-4
❑ 11A'sFirT20-3
❑ 11BasBatEU-3
❑ 11D35RocB-3
❑ 11DiaGumP-3
❑ 11HelSta-54
❑ 11L1L-119
❑ 11MecDFT-38
❑ 11PinT-5-501
❑ 11PloCanE-6
❑ 11S74Sil-28
❑ 11S81LarS-94
❑ 11SpoLifCW-29
❑ 11SpoLifM-88
❑ 11T205-14
❑ 11TurRedT-80
❑ 12HasTriFT-19
❑ 12T207-11
❑ 12T22SeroC-2
❑ 13NatGamW-3
❑ 13TomBarW-2
❑ 14CraJacE-19
❑ 14PieStaT-9
❑ 14TexTomE-4
❑ 15AmeCarE106-2A
❑ 15AmeCarE106-2B
❑ 15CraJacE-19
❑ 15VicT21-1
❑ 16BF2FP-86
❑ 16SpoNewM-13
❑ 22KolMotBPP-5
❑ 40PlaBal-172
❑ 50CalHOFW-5
❑ 51A'sTeal-3
❑ 53A'sTeal-4
❑ 53ArtHaloFP-5
❑ 60Fle-7
❑ 61Fle-8
❑ 61GolPre-18
❑ 63BazA-11
❑ 67SpoHobFC-15
❑ 67SpoHobFC-49
❑ 68SCFOldT-36
❑ 69Baz-3
❑ 70FleWorS-7
❑ 71FleWorS-3
❑ 72ClaCar-100
❑ 74A'sTCM1P-3
❑ 74CapPub-55
❑ 76GrePlaG-10
❑ 76ShaPiz-66
❑ 77BobParHoF-5
❑ 77DanBurG-12
❑ 77GalGloG-142
❑ 80PacLeg-93
❑ 80PerHaloFP-64
❑ 80SSPHOF-64
❑ 82DiaCla-105
❑ 82TCMGreP-45
❑ 83A'sGreT-9
❑ 86ConSer1-39
❑ 90PerGreM-90
❑ 91ConTSN-20
❑ 92ConTSN-335
❑ 93ConTSN-774

Bender, Gary

❑ 75BreBro-2

Bender, Heath

❑ 97WatIndTI-5

Bendix, William

❑ 48BabRutS-1
❑ 48BabRutS-4
❑ 48BabRutS-9
❑ 48BabRutS-11
❑ 48BabRutS-12
❑ 48BabRutS-22
❑ 48BabRutS-23
❑ 48BabRutS-24
❑ 48BabRutS-25
❑ 48BabRutS-26
❑ 48BabRutS-28
❑ 85TCMPhoC-36

Bendorf, Jerry

❑ 82VerBeaDT-17

Bene, Bill

❑ 88GreFalDTI-1
❑ 89BakDodCLC-184
❑ 89Bow-340
❑ 89BowTif-340
❑ 89SalDodTI-7
❑ 89Top-84
❑ 89TopTif-84
❑ 90VerBeaDS-4
❑ 91VerBeaDC-3
❑ 91VerBeaDP-764
❑ 92SanAntMS-556
❑ 92SkyAA F-244
❑ 93SanAntMF-2996
❑ 94AlbDukF-835
❑ 97VanCanB-6

Benedetti, Don

❑ 75CedRapGT-26

Benedict, Bruce Edwin

❑ 78RicBraT-3
❑ 79Top-715
❑ 80Top-675
❑ 81BraPol-20
❑ 81Don-208
❑ 81Fle-248
❑ 81Top-108
❑ 82BraBurKL-1
❑ 82BraPol-20
❑ 82Don-375
❑ 82Fle-429
❑ 82OPC-168
❑ 82Top-424
❑ 82TopSti-21
❑ 82TopStiV-21
❑ 83AllGamPI-128
❑ 83BraPol-20
❑ 83Don-299
❑ 83Fle-130
❑ 83OPC-204
❑ 83Top-521
❑ 83TopSti-151
❑ 83TopSti-152
❑ 83TopSti-154
❑ 83TopSti-217
❑ 84AllGamPI-38
❑ 84BraPol-20
❑ 84Don-409
❑ 84Fle-172
❑ 84Nes792-255
❑ 84OPC-255
❑ 84raPho-4
❑ 84Top-255
❑ 84TopRubD-4
❑ 84TopSti-34
❑ 84TopTif-255
❑ 85BraHos-4
❑ 85BraPol-20
❑ 85Don-263
❑ 85Fle-320
❑ 85Lea-196
❑ 85OPC-335
❑ 85Top-335
❑ 85TopRubD-4
❑ 85TopSti-31
❑ 85TopTif-335
❑ 86BraPol-20
❑ 86Don-554
❑ 86Fle-509
❑ 86OPC-78
❑ 86Top-78
❑ 86TopTif-78
❑ 87BraSmo-11
❑ 87Don-448
❑ 87Fle-512
❑ 87FleGlo-512
❑ 87StuPan-2
❑ 87Top-186
❑ 87TopTif-186
❑ 88Sco-423
❑ 88ScoGlo-423
❑ 88Top-652
❑ 88TopClo-9
❑ 88TopTif-652
❑ 89Bow-271
❑ 89BowTif-271
❑ 89BraDub-4
❑ 89Don-475
❑ 89Fle-587
❑ 89FleGlo-587
❑ 89OPC-353
❑ 89Sco-502
❑ 89Top-778
❑ 89TopBig-83
❑ 89TopTif-778
❑ 89UppDec-121
❑ 90OPC-583
❑ 90PubIntS-108
❑ 90Top-583
❑ 90TopTif-583
❑ 92UppDecS-4
❑ 93DanBraC-30
❑ 93DanBraF-3637
❑ 94GreBraF-428
❑ 94GreBraTI-1
❑ 95BreBtaTI-20
❑ 96NorTidB-3

Benedict, Jim

❑ 91ButCopKSP-29
❑ 93EriSaiC-29
❑ 93EriSaiF-3132

Benedict, Tom

❑ 91PacSenL-94

Benefield, Brian

❑ 97WatIndTI-6
❑ 98KinIndQ-2
❑ 99SP TopP-81
❑ 99SP TopPPE-81

Benes, Adam

❑ 95NewJerCTI-1
❑ 95SPML-103
❑ 96PeoChiB-7
❑ 97PriWilC-7
❑ 98PriWilCQ-3

Benes, Alan

❑ 94Bow-12
❑ 94BowBes-B61
❑ 94BowBesR-B61
❑ 94Cla-172
❑ 94ClaGolF-25
❑ 94ClaGolN1PLF-LP1
❑ 94ClaGolREF-RE1
❑ 94ColC-641
❑ 94ColChoGS-641
❑ 94ColChoSS-641
❑ 94ExcFS7-257
❑ 94FloStaLAF-FSL41
❑ 94SavCarC-1
❑ 94SavCarF-499
❑ 94SigRoo-22
❑ 94SigRooS-22
❑ 94SigRooTPD-T5
❑ 94SigRooTPS-T5
❑ 94St.PetCC-1
❑ 94Top-202
❑ 94TopGol-202
❑ 94TopSpa-202
❑ 94UppDec-529
❑ 94UppDecAHNIL-2
❑ 94UppDecED-529
❑ 94UppDecML-90
❑ 95ActPac2G-11G
❑ 95ActPacF-43
❑ 95ActPacF-72
❑ 95ARuFalLS-2
❑ 95Bow-273
❑ 95BowBes-B55
❑ 95BowBesR-B55
❑ 95BowGolF-273
❑ 95ColChoSE-11
❑ 95ColChoSEGS-11
❑ 95ColChoSESS-11
❑ 95Exc-262

❑ 95ExcAll-10
❑ 95FleMajLP-3
❑ 95LouRedF-270
❑ 95Top-233
❑ 95UltGolP-2
❑ 95UltGolPGM-2
❑ 95UppDec-217
❑ 95UppDecED-217
❑ 95UppDecEDG-217
❑ 95UppDecML-11
❑ 95UppDecML-161
❑ 95UppDecMLFS-11
❑ 95UppDecMLFS-161
❑ 95UppDecMLMLA-2
❑ 95UppDecMLOP-OP23
❑ 95UppDecMLT1PF-8
❑ 95UppDecPAW-H16
❑ 95UppDecPAWE-H16
❑ 95UppDecSE-92
❑ 95UppDecSEG-92
❑ 96Bow-75
❑ 96BowBes-51
❑ 96BowBesAR-51
❑ 96BowBesP-BBP2
❑ 96BowBesPAR-BBP2
❑ 96BowBesPR-BBP2
❑ 96BowBesR-51
❑ 96BowFoi-75
❑ 96CarPol-1
❑ 96Cir-175
❑ 96CirRav-175
❑ 96ColCho-654
❑ 96ColCho-695
❑ 96ColChoGS-654
❑ 96ColChoGS-695
❑ 96ColChoSS-654
❑ 96ColChoSS-695
❑ 96EmoXL-261
❑ 96Fin-B76
❑ 96FinRef-B76
❑ 96Fla-354
❑ 96FlaWavotF-4
❑ 96Fle-539
❑ 96FleTif-539
❑ 96Lea-212
❑ 96LeaPre-128
❑ 96LeaPreP-128
❑ 96LeaPrePB-212
❑ 96LeaPrePG-212
❑ 96LeaPrePS-212
❑ 96LeaPreSG-67
❑ 96LeaPreSte-67
❑ 96LeaSig-78
❑ 96LeaSigPPG-78
❑ 96LeaSigPPP-78
❑ 96MLBPin-3
❑ 96Pin-379
❑ 96PinAfi-179
❑ 96PinAfiAP-179
❑ 96PinFoil-379
❑ 96PinProS-9
❑ 96Sel-172
❑ 96SelArtP-172
❑ 96SelCer-101
❑ 96SelCerAP-101
❑ 96SelCerCB-101
❑ 96SelCerCR-101
❑ 96SelCerMB-101
❑ 96SelCerMG-101
❑ 96SelCerMR-101
❑ 96SelCerSF-13
❑ 96SigRooOJRS-R5
❑ 96SigRooOJRSS-R5
❑ 96SP-10
❑ 96SP-152
❑ 96StaClu-433
❑ 96StaCluMOP-433
❑ 96StPetCB-4
❑ 96Stu-121
❑ 96StuPrePB-121
❑ 96StuPrePG-121
❑ 96StuPrePS-121
❑ 96Sum-155
❑ 96Sum-173
❑ 96SumAbo&B-155
❑ 96SumAbo&B-173
❑ 96SumArtP-155
❑ 96SumArtP-173
❑ 96SumFoi-155
❑ 96SumFoi-173
❑ 96Top-216
❑ 96TopChr-78
❑ 96TopChrR-78
❑ 96TopLas-50
❑ 96TopLasBS-9
❑ 96Ult-541
❑ 96UltGolM-541
❑ 96UppDec-444
❑ 96UppDecBCP-BC13
❑ 96Zen-102
❑ 96ZenArtP-102
❑ 97Bow-229
❑ 97BowInt-229
❑ 97CarPol-1
❑ 97Cir-383
❑ 97CirRav-383
❑ 97ColCho-204
❑ 97Don-184
❑ 97DonEli-117
❑ 97DonEliGS-117
❑ 97DonGolPP-184
❑ 97DonLim-124
❑ 97DonLimE-124
❑ 97DonLimENG-124
❑ 97DonSig-27
❑ 97DonSigA-10
❑ 97DonSigAC-12
❑ 97DonSigAM-12
❑ 97DonSigPPP-27
❑ 97DonSilPP-184
❑ 97DonTea-157
❑ 97DonTeaSPE-157
❑ 97Fin-208
❑ 97FinRef-208
❑ 97FlaShoLC-128
❑ 97FlaShoLeg0-128
❑ 97FlaShoLeg1-128
❑ 97FlaShoM-A128
❑ 97FlaShoM-B128
❑ 97FlaShoM-C128
❑ 97FlaShoR0-128
❑ 97FlaShoR1-128
❑ 97FlaShoR2-128
❑ 97Fle-438
❑ 97FleRooS-3
❑ 97FleTif-438
❑ 97Lea-104
❑ 97LeaFraM-104
❑ 97LeaFraMDC-104
❑ 97LeaGet-13
❑ 97MetUni-227
❑ 97NewPin-88
❑ 97NewPinAP-88
❑ 97NewPinMC-88
❑ 97NewPinPP-88
❑ 97Pac-403
❑ 97PacLigB-403
❑ 97PacSil-403
❑ 97Pin-11
❑ 97PinArtP-PP11
❑ 97PinCer-6
❑ 97PinCerMBla-6
❑ 97PinCerMBlu-6
❑ 97PinCerMG-6
❑ 97PinCerMR-6
❑ 97PinCerR-6
❑ 97PinIns-106
❑ 97PinInsCE-106
❑ 97PinInsDE-106
❑ 97PinMusC-11
❑ 97PinPrePla-11
❑ 97PinTotCPB-6
❑ 97PinTotCPG-6
❑ 97PinTotCPR-6
❑ 97Sco-84
❑ 97ScoArtPWB-84
❑ 97ScoPreS-84
❑ 97ScoShoS-84
❑ 97ScoShoSAP-84
❑ 97Sel-98
❑ 97SelArtP-98
❑ 97SelCom-98
❑ 97SelRegG-98
❑ 97SP-148
❑ 97StaClu-86
❑ 97StaCluC-CO6
❑ 97StaCluM-M11
❑ 97StaCluMOP-86
❑ 97StaCluMOP-M11
❑ 97Stu-18
❑ 97StuPrePG-18
❑ 97StuPrePS-18
❑ 97Top-351
❑ 97TopChr-118
❑ 97TopChrR-118
❑ 97TopGal-176
❑ 97TopGalPPI-176
❑ 97Ult-268
❑ 97UltGolME-268
❑ 97UltPlaME-268
❑ 97UppDec-466
❑ 97UppDecRSF-RS19
❑ 98CarScoP-11
❑ 98CirThu-92
❑ 98CirThuRav-92
❑ 98CirThuSupRav-92
❑ 98ColCho-218
❑ 98Don-53
❑ 98DonCol-53
❑ 98DonColE-467
❑ 98DonColL-294
❑ 98DonColP-659
❑ 98DonColS-53
❑ 98DonCruG-95
❑ 98DonCruP-95
❑ 98DonCruR-95
❑ 98DonEli-67
❑ 98DonEliA-67
❑ 98DonEliS-67
❑ 98DonGolPP-53
❑ 98DonPre-109
❑ 98DonPreSeat-109
❑ 98DonPriCD-53
❑ 98DonPriCE-467
❑ 98DonPriCL-294
❑ 98DonPriCP-659
❑ 98DonSilPP-53
❑ 98Fin-105
❑ 98FinNo--105
❑ 98FinNo-R-105
❑ 98FinRef-105
❑ 98FlaShoLeg0-112
❑ 98FlaShoLeg1-112
❑ 98FlaShoLeg2-112
❑ 98FlaShoLeg3-112
❑ 98FlaShoLegM-112
❑ 98FlaShoR0-112
❑ 98FlaShoR1-112
❑ 98FlaShoR2-112
❑ 98FlaShoR3-112
❑ 98Fle-141
❑ 98Lea-95
❑ 98LeaCruG-95
❑ 98LeaCruP-95
❑ 98LeaCruR-95
❑ 98LeaFraDA-95
❑ 98LeaFraF-95
❑ 98LeaFraM-95
❑ 98LeaFraM-95
❑ 98LeaFraMDC-95
❑ 98LeaFraMDC-95
❑ 98LeaFraMS-95
❑ 98LeaFraMZ2-95
❑ 98LeaRS-102
❑ 98LeaRSLHolo-102
❑ 98LeaRSLong-102
❑ 98LeaRTrue-102
❑ 98MetUni-182
❑ 98MetUniPMG-182
❑ 98PacPar-226
❑ 98PacParC-226
❑ 98PacParG-226
❑ 98PacParHS-226
❑ 98PacParPB-226
❑ 98PacParR-226
❑ 98Pin-93
❑ 98PinIns-66
❑ 98PinInsCE-66
❑ 98PinInsDE-66
❑ 98PinPer-91
❑ 98PinPerPP-91
❑ 98PinPlu-87
❑ 98PinPreP-93
❑ 98PinSna-SLC1
❑ 98Sco-155
❑ 98ScoCar-11
❑ 98ScoRT-51
❑ 98ScoRTSS-PP51
❑ 98ScoRTSSAP-PP51
❑ 98ScoRTSSAP1-PP51
❑ 98StaCluFDI-114
❑ 98StaCluI-114
❑ 98StaCluOneK-114
❑ 98StaCluPP-114
❑ 98Stu-134
❑ 98StuGPP-134
❑ 98StuSPP-134
❑ 98Top-387
❑ 98TopBabB-BB15
❑ 98TopChr-387
❑ 98TopChrBB-BB15
❑ 98TopChrBBR-BB15
❑ 98TopChrR-387
❑ 98TopDevR-387
❑ 98TopDia-387
❑ 98TopGal-26
❑ 98TopGalGP-26
❑ 98TopGalOPP-26
❑ 98TopGalPPI-26
❑ 98TopGalPPIA-26
❑ 98TopMiniC-387
❑ 98Ult-113
❑ 98UltGolM-113
❑ 98UltMas-113
❑ 98UltPlaM-113
❑ 98UppDec-201
❑ 98UppDecSF-108
❑ 99Fle-371
❑ 99FleSta9-371
❑ 99FleWarT-371
❑ 99Top-359
❑ 99TopChr-359
❑ 99TopChrR-359
❑ 99TopMVPP-359

Benes, Andy

❑ 88TopTra-14T
❑ 88TopTraT-14T
❑ 89BasAmeAPB-AA24
❑ 89Bow-448
❑ 89BowTif-448
❑ 89Sta-111
❑ 89StaFutS-17
❑ 89StaFutS-18
❑ 89TexLeaAGS-10
❑ 89Top-437
❑ 89TopBig-114
❑ 89TopTif-437
❑ 89WicChaR-19
❑ 89WicStaR-8
❑ 89WicUpdR-5
❑ 89WicUpdR-19
❑ 89WicWraR-30
❑ 90Bow-207
❑ 90BowTif-207
❑ 90ClaBlu-120
❑ 90Don-41
❑ 90DonBesN-47
❑ 90Fle-151
❑ 90FleCan-151
❑ 90Hot50RS-7
❑ 90Lea-56
❑ 90OPC-193
❑ 90PacCok-2
❑ 90PadMag-9
❑ 90PanSti-382
❑ 90Sco-578
❑ 90Sco100RS-69
❑ 90ScoYouS2-13
❑ 90Spo-90
❑ 90StaBen-1
❑ 90StaBen-2
❑ 90StaBen-3
❑ 90StaBen-4
❑ 90StaBen-5
❑ 90StaBen-6
❑ 90StaBen-7
❑ 90StaBen-8
❑ 90StaBen-9
❑ 90StaBen-10
❑ 90StaBen-11
❑ 90Top-193
❑ 90TopBig-260
❑ 90TopDeb89-15
❑ 90TopRoo-3
❑ 90TopTif-193
❑ 90ToyRoo-4
❑ 90TriAAAC-43
❑ 90UppDec-55
❑ 91Bow-665
❑ 91Cla3-T7
❑ 91ClaGam-85
❑ 91Don-627
❑ 91Fle-524
❑ 91Lea-275
❑ 91OPC-307
❑ 91PadMag-18
❑ 91PadSmo-3
❑ 91PanFreS-99
❑ 91PanSti-92
❑ 91Sco-538
❑ 91StaClu-51
❑ 91StaCluP-5
❑ 91Stu-242
❑ 91Top-307
❑ 91TopDesS-307
❑ 91TopMic-307
❑ 91TopTif-307
❑ 91Ult-301
❑ 91UppDec-275
❑ 92Bow-249
❑ 92Bow-599
❑ 92Cla1-T14
❑ 92ClaGam-150
❑ 92Don-524
❑ 92Fle-599
❑ 92FleSmo'nH-S9
❑ 92Lea-74
❑ 92LeaBlaG-74
❑ 92LeaGolP-29
❑ 92OPC-682
❑ 92PadCarJ-3
❑ 92PadMot-16
❑ 92PadPolD-3
❑ 92PadSmo-3
❑ 92Pin-74
❑ 92PinTea2-12
❑ 92RedFolS-12
❑ 92Sco-133
❑ 92ScoImpP-88
❑ 92StaClu-423
❑ 92Stu-101
❑ 92Top-682
❑ 92TopDaiQTU-13
❑ 92TopGol-682
❑ 92TopGolW-682
❑ 92TopMic-682
❑ 92TriPla-33
❑ 92Ult-274
❑ 92UppDec-323
❑ 92UppDecTMH-9
❑ 93Bow-518
❑ 93Don-22
❑ 93Fin-19
❑ 93FinRef-19
❑ 93Fla-132
❑ 93Fle-519
❑ 93FunPac-137
❑ 93Lea-192
❑ 93OPC-17
❑ 93PacSpa-255
❑ 93PadMot-14
❑ 93PanSti-265
❑ 93Pin-42
❑ 93RedFolS-11
❑ 93Sco-91
❑ 93Sel-117
❑ 93SP-164
❑ 93StaClu-581
❑ 93StaCluFDI-581
❑ 93StaCluMOP-581
❑ 93Stu-53
❑ 93Top-568
❑ 93TopComotH-28
❑ 93TopGol-568
❑ 93TopInaM-568
❑ 93TopInaR-568
❑ 93TopMic-568
❑ 93TriPla-201
❑ 93Ult-116
❑ 93UppDec-261
❑ 93UppDecGold-261
❑ 94Bow-392
❑ 94ColC-570
❑ 94ColChoGS-570
❑ 94ColChoSS-570
❑ 94Don-332
❑ 94DonSpeE-332
❑ 94Fin-328
❑ 94FinRef-328
❑ 94Fla-434
❑ 94Fle-656
❑ 94FleAllS-29
❑ 94FleExtB-370
❑ 94FUnPac-40
❑ 94Lea-143
❑ 94LeaL-151
❑ 94OPC-83
❑ 94Pac-516
❑ 94PadMot-3
❑ 94PanSti-253
❑ 94Pin-51
❑ 94PinArtP-51
❑ 94PinMusC-51
❑ 94ProMag-117
❑ 94RedFolMI-5
❑ 94Sco-44
❑ 94ScoGolR-44
❑ 94Sel-363
❑ 94SP-129
❑ 94SPDieC-129
❑ 94Spo-52
❑ 94StaClu-102
❑ 94StaCluFDI-102
❑ 94StaCluGR-102
❑ 94StaCluMOP-102
❑ 94Stu-131
❑ 94Top-70
❑ 94TopGol-70
❑ 94TopSpa-70
❑ 94TriPla-163
❑ 94Ult-573
❑ 94UppDec-388
❑ 94UppDecED-388
❑ 95Baz-111
❑ 95Bow-399
❑ 95BowBes-R48
❑ 95BowBesR-R48
❑ 95ColCho-350
❑ 95ColChoGS-350
❑ 95ColChoSE-162
❑ 95ColChoSEGS-162
❑ 95ColChoSESS-162
❑ 95ColChoSS-350
❑ 95Don-336
❑ 95DonPreP-336
❑ 95DonTopotO-145
❑ 95Emo-184
❑ 95Fin-111
❑ 95FinRef-111
❑ 95Fla-414
❑ 95Fle-556
❑ 95FleLeaL-10
❑ 95FleTeaL-27
❑ 95Lea-227
❑ 95LeaLim-185
❑ 95MarPac-21
❑ 95Pac-358
❑ 95PadMot-6
❑ 95PanSti-10
❑ 95PanSti-119
❑ 95Pin-328
❑ 95PinArtP-328
❑ 95PinMusC-328
❑ 95RedFol-32
❑ 95Sco-411
❑ 95ScoGolR-411
❑ 95ScoHaloG-HG98
❑ 95ScoPlaTS-411
❑ 95Sel-75
❑ 95SelArtP-75
❑ 95SelCer-25
❑ 95SelCerMG-25
❑ 95SP-106
❑ 95Spo-37
❑ 95SpoArtP-37
❑ 95SPSil-106
❑ 95StaClu-26
❑ 95StaCluFDI-26
❑ 95StaCluMO-4
❑ 95StaCluMOP-26
❑ 95StaCluSTWS-26
❑ 95StaCluVR-18
❑ 95StaCluVRMO-18
❑ 95Stu-189
❑ 95Sum-14
❑ 95SumNthD-14
❑ 95Top-449
❑ 95TopCyb-245
❑ 95TopD3-12
❑ 95TopEmb-40
❑ 95TopEmbGI-40
❑ 95TopLeaL-LL22
❑ 95UC3-24
❑ 95UC3ArtP-24
❑ 95Ult-232
❑ 95UltGolM-232
❑ 95UltLeaL-9
❑ 95UltLeaLGM-9
❑ 95UltStrK-1
❑ 95UltStrKGM-1
❑ 95UppDec-134
❑ 95UppDec-468
❑ 95UppDecED-134
❑ 95UppDecEDG-134
❑ 95UppDecSE-133
❑ 95UppDecSEG-133
❑ 95Zen-3
❑ 96CarPol-2
❑ 96ColCho-317
❑ 96ColCho-786
❑ 96ColChoGS-317
❑ 96ColChoSS-317
❑ 96Don-166
❑ 96DonPreP-166
❑ 96EmoXL-262
❑ 96Fin-B273
❑ 96FinRef-B273
❑ 96Fla-355
❑ 96Fle-228
❑ 96FleTif-228
❑ 96FleUpd-U183
❑ 96FleUpdTC-U183
❑ 96LeaSigA-21
❑ 96LeaSigAG-21
❑ 96LeaSigAS-21
❑ 96MetUni-221

❑ 96MetUniP-221
❑ 96MLBPin-4
❑ 96Pac-406
❑ 96Pin-7
❑ 96Pin-344
❑ 96PinAfi-95
❑ 96PinAfiAP-95
❑ 96PinAfiFPP-95
❑ 96PinFoil-344
❑ 96Sco-198
❑ 96Sco-314
❑ 96ScoDugC-B39
❑ 96ScoDugCAP-B39
❑ 96Sel-132
❑ 96SelArtP-132
❑ 96SelCerIP-15
❑ 96SP-152
❑ 96StaClu-116
❑ 96StaCluEPB-116
❑ 96StaCluEPG-116
❑ 96StaCluEPS-116
❑ 96StaCluMOP-116
❑ 96Sum-64
❑ 96Sum-155
❑ 96SumAbo&B-64
❑ 96SumAbo&B-155
❑ 96SumArtP-64
❑ 96SumArtP-155
❑ 96SumFoi-64
❑ 96SumFoi-155
❑ 96Top-314
❑ 96TopLas-51
❑ 96Ult-542
❑ 96UltGolM-542
❑ 96UppDec-204
❑ 96UppDec-508U
❑ 97Bow-13
❑ 97BowChr-9
❑ 97BowChrI-9
❑ 97BowChrIR-9
❑ 97BowChrR-9
❑ 97BowInt-13
❑ 97CarPol-2
❑ 97Cir-147
❑ 97CirRav-147
❑ 97ColCho-437
❑ 97Don-40
❑ 97DonGolPP-40
❑ 97DonLim-109
❑ 97DonLimE-109
❑ 97DonLimENG-109
❑ 97DonPre-88
❑ 97DonPreCttC-88
❑ 97DonSilPP-40
❑ 97DonTea-152
❑ 97DonTeaSPE-152
❑ 97Fin-34
❑ 97FinRef-34
❑ 97FlaShoLC-140
❑ 97FlaShoLeg0-140
❑ 97FlaShoLeg1-140
❑ 97FlaShoM-A140
❑ 97FlaShoM-B140
❑ 97FlaShoM-C140
❑ 97FlaShoR0-140
❑ 97FlaShoR1-140
❑ 97FlaShoR2-140
❑ 97Fle-439
❑ 97FleTif-439
❑ 97Lea-90
❑ 97LeaFraM-90
❑ 97LeaFraMDC-90
❑ 97MetUni-228
❑ 97NewPin-77
❑ 97NewPinAP-77
❑ 97NewPinMC-77
❑ 97NewPinPP-77
❑ 97Pac-404
❑ 97PacLigB-404
❑ 97PacSil-404
❑ 97PinCar-12
❑ 97PinCer-16
❑ 97PinCerMBla-16
❑ 97PinCerMBlu-16
❑ 97PinCerMG-16
❑ 97PinCerMR-16
❑ 97PinCerR-16
❑ 97PinTotCPB-16
❑ 97PinTotCPG-16
❑ 97PinTotCPR-16
❑ 97PinX-P-103
❑ 97PinX-PMoS-103
❑ 97Sco-174
❑ 97ScoArtPWB-174
❑ 97ScoPreS-174
❑ 97ScoShoS-174
❑ 97ScoShoSAP-174
❑ 97SP-147
❑ 97StaClu-120
❑ 97StaCluMOP-120
❑ 97Top-190
❑ 97TopChr-74
❑ 97TopChrR-74
❑ 97TopChrSB-20
❑ 97TopChrSBR-20
❑ 97TopGal-85
❑ 97TopGalPPI-85
❑ 97TopSeaB-SB20
❑ 97Ult-342
❑ 97UltGolME-342
❑ 97UltPlaME-342
❑ 97UppDec-372
❑ 97UppDec-465
❑ 98BowBes-37
❑ 98BowBesAR-37
❑ 98BowBesR-37
❑ 98CarScoP-1
❑ 98CirThu-114
❑ 98CirThuRav-114
❑ 98CirThuSupRav-114
❑ 98ColCho-295
❑ 98DiaBacP-3
❑ 98DiaMcD-5
❑ 98Don-99
❑ 98Don-192
❑ 98DonCol-99
❑ 98DonColL-322
❑ 98DonColS-99
❑ 98DonGolPP-99
❑ 98DonGolPP-192
❑ 98DonPriCD-99
❑ 98DonPriCL-322
❑ 98DonSigA-8
❑ 98DonSigAC-10
❑ 98DonSigAM-10
❑ 98DonSigSP-2
❑ 98DonSilPP-99
❑ 98DonSilPP-192
❑ 98Fin-201
❑ 98FinNo--201
❑ 98FinNo-R-201
❑ 98FinRef-201
❑ 98Fle-564
❑ 98FleVin'-66
❑ 98FleVin'C-66
❑ 98Lea-123
❑ 98LeaFraDA-123
❑ 98LeaFraF-123
❑ 98LeaFraM-123
❑ 98LeaFraM-123
❑ 98LeaFraMDC-123
❑ 98LeaFraMDC-123
❑ 98LeaFraMZ2-123
❑ 98Pac-405
❑ 98PacAur-97
❑ 98PacOme-11
❑ 98PacOmeR-11
❑ 98PacOnl-30
❑ 98PacOnlR-30
❑ 98PacOnlWC-30
❑ 98PacPar-120
❑ 98PacParC-120
❑ 98PacParG-120
❑ 98PacParHS-120
❑ 98PacParPB-120
❑ 98PacParR-120
❑ 98PacPlaB-405
❑ 98PacRedT-405
❑ 98PacSil-405
❑ 98PinSna-AD5
❑ 98Sco-23
❑ 98ScoCar-1
❑ 98ScoRT-95
❑ 98ScoSS-PP8
❑ 98ScoSS-PP64
❑ 98ScoSSAP-PP8
❑ 98ScoSSAP-PP64
❑ 98SkyDugA-3
❑ 98SkyDugAIA-3
❑ 98SP Aut-38
❑ 98SpoIllWSF-55
❑ 98SpoIllWSFEE-55
❑ 98SpoIllWSFFE-55
❑ 98SPxFin-244
❑ 98SPxFinR-244
❑ 98SPxFinS-244
❑ 98StaCluFDI-95
❑ 98StaCluFDI-310
❑ 98StaCluI-95
❑ 98StaCluI-310
❑ 98StaCluOneK-95
❑ 98StaCluOneK-310
❑ 98StaCluPP-95
❑ 98StaCluPP-310
❑ 98Stu-68
❑ 98StuGPP-68
❑ 98StuSPP-68
❑ 98Top-354
❑ 98TopChr-354
❑ 98TopChrR-354
❑ 98TopDevR-354
❑ 98TopDia-354
❑ 98TopMiniC-354
❑ 98TopSta-11
❑ 98TopStaB-11
❑ 98TopStaG-11
❑ 98TopStaGR-11
❑ 98TopStaS-11
❑ 98Ult-455
❑ 98UltGolM-455
❑ 98UltMas-455
❑ 98UltPlaM-455
❑ 98UppDec-645
❑ 99199Fin-216
❑ 99Bow-68
❑ 99BowChr-68
❑ 99BowChrG-68
❑ 99BowChrGR-68
❑ 99BowChrI-68
❑ 99BowChrIR-68
❑ 99BowChrR-68
❑ 99BowGol-68
❑ 99BowInt-68
❑ 99FinGolRef-216
❑ 99FinRef-216
❑ 99FlaShoLeg1-143
❑ 99FlaShoLeg2-143
❑ 99FlaShoLeg3-143
❑ 99FlaShoLegM1-143
❑ 99FlaShoLegM2-143
❑ 99FlaShoLegM3-143
❑ 99FlaShoR1-143
❑ 99FlaShoR2-143
❑ 99FlaShoR3-143
❑ 99Fle-145
❑ 99FleSta9-145
❑ 99FleWarT-145
❑ 99KinDis-16
❑ 99MetUni-116
❑ 99MetUniGM-116
❑ 99MetUniPMG-116
❑ 99Pac-16
❑ 99PacPar-12
❑ 99PacParC-12
❑ 99PacParG-12
❑ 99PacParHoloGold-12
❑ 99PacParHS-12
❑ 99PacParOD-12
❑ 99PacParPB-12
❑ 99PacParRed-12
❑ 99PacPlaB-16
❑ 99PacRed-16
❑ 99SkyPre-108
❑ 99SkyPreR-108
❑ 99SkyThu-123
❑ 99SkyThuRant-123
❑ 99SkyThuRave-123
❑ 99StaClu-132
❑ 99StaCluFDI-132
❑ 99StaCluOoaK-132
❑ 99StaCluPP-132
❑ 99ThuSkySupR-123
❑ 99Top-244
❑ 99TopChr-244
❑ 99TopChrR-244
❑ 99TopMVPP-244
❑ 99TopOpeD-117
❑ 99Ult-133
❑ 99UltGolM-133
❑ 99UltMas-133
❑ 99UltPlaM-133
❑ 99UppDec-28
❑ 99UppDecEL1-28
❑ 99UppDecEL2-28

Benes, Joe (Joseph Anthony)
❑ 82WauTimF-7

Benesh, Ed
❑ 97ChaRivDG-6
❑ 98St.PetDRM-4

Benge, Brett
❑ 91BluOriC-22
❑ 91BluOriP-4119

Benge, Ray
❑ 29ExhFou-12
❑ 33ExhFou-6
❑ 33Gou-141
❑ 34BatR31-11
❑ 34BatR31-99
❑ 34DiaMatCSB-8
❑ 34Gou-24
❑ 34GouCanV-13
❑ 34GouCanV-49
❑ 35GouPuzR-8A
❑ 35GouPuzR-8M
❑ 72TCMthe3-105
❑ 74TCMNic-5
❑ 79DiaGre-93
❑ 90DodTar-47

Bengoechea, Brandy
❑ 93SouOreAC-5
❑ 94SouOreAC-1
❑ 94SouOreAF-3628
❑ 95ModA'sTI-3

Bengough, Benny (Bernard O.)
❑ 28PorandAR-A2
❑ 28PorandAR-B2
❑ 29ExhFou-25
❑ 31Exh-11
❑ 33Gou-1
❑ 33GouCanV-1
❑ 49EurSta-128
❑ 49PhiBul-3
❑ 75Phi195T-2
❑ 75Yan192T-2
❑ 79Yan192T-3
❑ 80Phi195T-2
❑ 84Yan192G-24
❑ 91ConTSN-103
❑ 93ConTSN-860
❑ 94ConTSNCI-32

Benham, Arthur
❑ 15Zee-96

Benham, David
❑ 98LowSpiM-4

Benham, Jason
❑ 98BluOriQ-25

Benhardt, Chris
❑ 91SpoIndC-24
❑ 91SpoIndP-3937
❑ 92WatDiaF-2134

Beniquez, Juan Jose
❑ 72RedSoxTI-1
❑ 74OPC-647
❑ 74Top-647
❑ 75OPC-601
❑ 75Top-601
❑ 75TopMin-601
❑ 76OPC-496
❑ 76SSP-406
❑ 76Top-496
❑ 77BurCheD-27
❑ 77Top-81
❑ 78RanBurK-18
❑ 78SSP270-103
❑ 78Top-238
❑ 79Top-478
❑ 79YanBurK-22
❑ 79YanPicA-2
❑ 80MarPos-5
❑ 80Top-114
❑ 81Don-518
❑ 81Fle-596
❑ 81LonBeaPT-17
❑ 81LonBeaPT-22
❑ 81Top-306
❑ 81TopTra-733
❑ 82Don-587
❑ 82Fle-452
❑ 82Top-572
❑ 83Don-640
❑ 83Fle-78
❑ 83Top-678
❑ 84AngSmo-2
❑ 84Don-207
❑ 84Fle-508
❑ 84Nes792-53
❑ 84Top-53
❑ 84TopTif-53
❑ 85AngSmo-14
❑ 85Don-573
❑ 85Fle-294
❑ 85SubDis-3
❑ 85ThoMcAD-3
❑ 85Top-226
❑ 85TopTif-226
❑ 86BalOriP-1
❑ 86Don-352
❑ 86Fle-148
❑ 86FleStiC-4
❑ 86FleUpd-13
❑ 86Lea-156
❑ 86OPC-325
❑ 86Top-325
❑ 86TopSti-185
❑ 86TopTif-325
❑ 86TopTra-8T
❑ 86TopTraT-8T
❑ 87Don-371
❑ 87Fle-462
❑ 87FleGlo-462
❑ 87FleUpd-3
❑ 87FleUpdG-3
❑ 87OPC-173
❑ 87Top-688
❑ 87TopTif-688
❑ 87TopTra-4T
❑ 87TopTraT-4T
❑ 88BlaYNPRWL-162
❑ 88BluJayFS-3
❑ 88Fle-104
❑ 88FleGlo-104
❑ 88OPC-77
❑ 88OPCBoxB-C
❑ 88StaLinBJ-3
❑ 88Top-541
❑ 88TopSti-12
❑ 88TopTif-541
❑ 88TopWaxBC-C
❑ 89BimBreD-8
❑ 89PacSenL-119
❑ 89T/MSenL-6
❑ 89TopSenL-131
❑ 90EliSenL-108
❑ 91OriCro-30
❑ 92YanWIZ7-13
❑ 93RanKee-69

Benitez, Armando
❑ 92BluOriC-21
❑ 92BluOriF-2352
❑ 93AlbPolCB-4
❑ 93AlbPolF-2017
❑ 93LimRocDWB-40
❑ 94BowBayF-2405
❑ 94Cla-52
❑ 94ExcFS7-1
❑ 94LeaLimR-74
❑ 94OriPro-8
❑ 95ActPacF-42
❑ 95BalOriP-7
❑ 95Bow-429
❑ 95BowBes-B65
❑ 95BowBesR-B65
❑ 95ColCho-4
❑ 95ColChoGS-4
❑ 95ColChoSE-13
❑ 95ColChoSEGS-13
❑ 95ColChoSESS-13
❑ 95ColChoSS-4
❑ 95Don-216
❑ 95DonPreP-216
❑ 95DonTopotO-4
❑ 95Fin-20
❑ 95FinRef-20
❑ 95Fla-218
❑ 95FlaWavotF-2
❑ 95FleMajLP-4
❑ 95FleUpd-3
❑ 95Lea-342
❑ 95LeaGolR-4
❑ 95Pac-19
❑ 95Pin-134
❑ 95PinArtP-134
❑ 95PinMusC-134
❑ 95Sco-299
❑ 95ScoGolR-299
❑ 95ScoPlaTS-299
❑ 95ScoRooDT-RDT11
❑ 95Sel-208
❑ 95SelArtP-208
❑ 95SelCer-100
❑ 95SelCerMG-100
❑ 95Spo-148
❑ 95SpoArtP-148
❑ 95StaClu-254
❑ 95StaCluFDI-254
❑ 95StaCluMOP-254
❑ 95StaCluSTWS-254
❑ 95Stu-66
❑ 95Sum-136
❑ 95SumNthD-136
❑ 95Top-346
❑ 95UC3-102
❑ 95UC3ArtP-102
❑ 95Ult-253
❑ 95UltGolM-253
❑ 95UltGolP-3
❑ 95UltGolPGM-3
❑ 95UppDec-218
❑ 95UppDecED-218
❑ 95UppDecEDG-218
❑ 95UppDecPAW-H11
❑ 95UppDecPAWE-H11
❑ 95UppDecSE-48
❑ 95UppDecSEG-48
❑ 95Zen-112
❑ 96BalOriP-4
❑ 96ColCho-52
❑ 96ColChoGS-52
❑ 96ColChoSS-52
❑ 96Don-513
❑ 96DonPreP-513
❑ 96Fle-4
❑ 96FleTif-4
❑ 96LeaSigA-22
❑ 96LeaSigAG-22
❑ 96LeaSigAS-22
❑ 96OriFle-3
❑ 96Pac-245
❑ 96Sco-152
❑ 96StaClu-366
❑ 96StaCluMOP-366
❑ 96Ult-302
❑ 96UltGolM-302
❑ 97BalOriP-3
❑ 97Cir-77
❑ 97CirRav-77
❑ 97DonTea-40
❑ 97DonTeaSPE-40
❑ 97Fle-558
❑ 97FleTif-558
❑ 97Pac-19
❑ 97PacLigB-19
❑ 97PacSil-19
❑ 97Sco-386
❑ 97ScoArtPWB-386
❑ 97ScoResC-386
❑ 97ScoShoS-386
❑ 97ScoShoSAP-386
❑ 97Top-484
❑ 97Ult-349
❑ 97UltGolME-349
❑ 97UltPlaME-349
❑ 98CirThu-136
❑ 98CirThuRav-136
❑ 98CirThuSupRav-136
❑ 98ColCho-43
❑ 98Fin-267
❑ 98FinNo--267
❑ 98FinNo-R-267
❑ 98FinRef-267
❑ 98Fle-406
❑ 98OriSco-12
❑ 98OriScoP-12
❑ 98Pac-20
❑ 98PacOnl-82
❑ 98PacOnlR-82
❑ 98PacOnlWC-82
❑ 98PacPlaB-20
❑ 98PacRedT-20
❑ 98PacSil-20
❑ 98PinSna-BO11
❑ 98Sco-170
❑ 98ScoSS-PP73
❑ 98ScoSSAP-PP73
❑ 98StaCluFDI-173
❑ 98StaCluI-173
❑ 98StaCluOneK-173
❑ 98StaCluPP-173
❑ 98Top-203
❑ 98TopChr-203
❑ 98TopChrR-203
❑ 98TopDevR-203
❑ 98TopDia-203
❑ 98TopMiniC-203
❑ 98TopOpeD-101
❑ 98UppDec-312
❑ 99Fle-67
❑ 99FleSta9-67
❑ 99FleWarT-67
❑ 99MetUni-128
❑ 99MetUniGM-128
❑ 99MetUniPMG-128
❑ 99PacCroC-34
❑ 99PacCroCPB-34
❑ 99SkyPre-36
❑ 99SkyPreR-36
❑ 99SkyThu-221
❑ 99SkyThuRant-221
❑ 99SkyThuRave-221
❑ 99ThuSkySupR-221
❑ 99Top-46
❑ 99TopChr-46
❑ 99TopChrR-46
❑ 99TopMVPP-46

❑ 99Ult-123
❑ 99UltGolM-123
❑ 99UltMas-123
❑ 99UltPlaM-123
Benitez, Christian
❑ 89BluOriS-5
❑ 90WauTimB-22
❑ 90WauTimP-2136
❑ 90WauTimS-3
Benitez, Eduardo
❑ 76VenLeaS-48
Benitez, Fernando
❑ 93DanBraC-2
❑ 93DanBraF-3620
Benitez, Luis
❑ 80VenLeaS-174
❑ 89ChaWheB-12
❑ 89ChaWheP-1749
❑ 89GenCubP-1870
❑ 90GenCubP-3050
❑ 90GenCubS-1
Benitez, Manuel
❑ 86BakDodP-3
❑ 87VerBeaDP-12
Benitez, Yamil
❑ 92AlbPolCB-17
❑ 92JamExpC-19
❑ 92JamExpF-1511
❑ 93BurBeeC-1
❑ 93BurBeeF-169
❑ 93ExcFS7-57
❑ 94HarSenF-2103
❑ 95Bow-217
❑ 95Emo-149
❑ 95Exc-219
❑ 95SigRooOJ-6
❑ 95SigRooOJP-6
❑ 95SigRooOJPS-6
❑ 95SigRooOJS-6
❑ 95UppDecML-147
❑ 95UppDecMLFS-147
❑ 96Bow-364
❑ 96BowFoi-364
❑ 96Cir-148
❑ 96CirRav-148
❑ 96ColCho-613
❑ 96ColChoGS-613
❑ 96ColChoSS-613
❑ 96Don-486
❑ 96DonPreP-486
❑ 96EmoXL-219
❑ 96Fla-303
❑ 96FlaWavotF-5
❑ 96Fle-452
❑ 96FlePro-1
❑ 96FleTif-452
❑ 96Lea-186
❑ 96LeaPrePB-186
❑ 96LeaPrePG-186
❑ 96LeaPrePS-186
❑ 96MetUni-189
❑ 96MetUniMFG-1
❑ 96MetUniP-189
❑ 96Pac-129
❑ 96SelArtP-176
❑ 96Spo-131
❑ 96SpoArtP-131
❑ 96Top-439
❑ 96Ult-502
❑ 96UltGolM-502
❑ 96UltGolP-1
❑ 96UltGolPGM-1
❑ 96UppDecFSP-FS4
❑ 96UppDecPHE-H53
❑ 96UppDecPreH-H53
❑ 97Don-193
❑ 97DonGolPP-193
❑ 97DonSilPP-193
❑ 97FlaShoLC-155
❑ 97FlaShoLeg0-155
❑ 97FlaShoLeg1-155
❑ 97FlaShoM-A155
❑ 97FlaShoM-B155
❑ 97FlaShoM-C155
❑ 97FlaShoR0-155
❑ 97FlaShoR1-155
❑ 97FlaShoR2-155
❑ 97Fle-376
❑ 97FleTif-376
❑ 97OmaRoyB-21
❑ 97Sco-303
❑ 97ScoArtPWB-303
❑ 97ScoPreS-303
❑ 97ScoShoS-303
❑ 97ScoShoSAP-303
❑ 97Ult-227
❑ 97UltGolME-227
❑ 97UltPlaME-227
❑ 98ColCho-137
❑ 98ColCho-291
❑ 98DiaBacP-20
❑ 98DiaMcD-6
❑ 98Fle-433
❑ 98Pac-100
❑ 98PacInv-35
❑ 98PacInvPBlue-35
❑ 98PacInvSilv-35
❑ 98PacInvTeam-29
❑ 98PacOme-12
❑ 98PacOmeR-12
❑ 98PacOnl-31
❑ 98PacOnlR-31
❑ 98PacOnlWC-31
❑ 98PacPar-121
❑ 98PacParC-121
❑ 98PacParG-121
❑ 98PacParHS-121
❑ 98PacParPB-121
❑ 98PacParR-121
❑ 98PacPlaB-100
❑ 98PacRedT-100
❑ 98PacSil-100
❑ 98Pin-142
❑ 98PinPlu-176
❑ 98PinPreP-142
❑ 98PinSna-AD12
❑ 98Top-467
❑ 98TopChr-467
❑ 98TopChrR-467
❑ 98TopDevR-467
❑ 98TopDia-467
❑ 98TopMiniC-467
❑ 98UppDec-648
❑ 99Pac-17
❑ 99PacCroC-13
❑ 99PacCroCPB-13
❑ 99PacPlaB-17
❑ 99PacRed-17
Benjamin, Bobby
❑ 88NebCor-11
❑ 90NebCor-3
❑ 91BelBreCB-17
❑ 91BelBreP-2114
❑ 92SalLakTSP-24
❑ 92StoPorC-3
Benjamin, Jerry
❑ 86NegLeaF-82
Benjamin, Kyle
❑ 83QuaCitCT-5
Benjamin, Mike
❑ 88ShrCapP-1283
❑ 88TexLeaAGS-11
❑ 89PhoFirC-16
❑ 89PhoFirP-1500
❑ 90CMC-549
❑ 90Fle-51
❑ 90FleCan-51
❑ 90PhoFirC-22
❑ 90PhoFirP-15
❑ 90ProAAAF-41
❑ 90TopDeb89-16
❑ 90UppDec-750
❑ 91Cla1-T6
❑ 91Don-432
❑ 91GiaPacGaE-20
❑ 91GiaSFE-2
❑ 91OPC-791
❑ 91Sco-345
❑ 91ScoRoo-25
❑ 91StaClu-143
❑ 91Stu-252
❑ 91Top-791
❑ 91TopDesS-791
❑ 91TopMic-791
❑ 91TopTif-791
❑ 91UppDec-651
❑ 92GiaPacGaE-5
❑ 92PhoFirF-2825
❑ 92Sco-649
❑ 92Sco100RS-7
❑ 92StaClu-314
❑ 92UppDec-268
❑ 93Don-472
❑ 93Fle-526
❑ 93GiaMot-19
❑ 93GiaPos-3
❑ 93OPC-377
❑ 93PacSpa-606
❑ 93Sco-603
❑ 93StaClu-405
❑ 93StaCluFDI-405
❑ 93StaCluMOP-405
❑ 93Top-384
❑ 93TopGol-384
❑ 93TopInaM-384
❑ 93TopInaR-384
❑ 93TopMic-384
❑ 93Ult-127
❑ 94Fin-197
❑ 94FinRef-197
❑ 94Fle-681
❑ 94GiaAMC-3
❑ 94GiaMot-22
❑ 94GiaTarBC-3
❑ 94GiaUSPC-3D
❑ 94GiaUSPC-10C
❑ 94Sco-273
❑ 94ScoGolR-273
❑ 94StaClu-318
❑ 94StaCluFDI-318
❑ 94StaCluGR-318
❑ 94StaCluMOP-318
❑ 94StaCluT-12
❑ 94StaCluTFDI-12
❑ 94Top-487
❑ 94TopGol-487
❑ 94TopSpa-487
❑ 95Don-546
❑ 95DonPreP-546
❑ 95DonTopotO-348
❑ 95Fin-325
❑ 95FinRef-325
❑ 95Fle-573
❑ 95GiaMot-23
❑ 96PhiTeal-2
❑ 97PawRedS-6
❑ 98PacInvGems-19
❑ 98PacOnl-107
❑ 98PacOnlR-107
❑ 98PacOnlWC-107
Benjamin, Stan (Alfred S.)
❑ 40PhiTeal-4
❑ 41PhiTeal-4
Benner, Brian
❑ 95ButCopKtl-4
Bennese, Larry
❑ 91KinMetC-25
❑ 92PitMetC-21
❑ 93St.LucMC-28
❑ 94St.LucMC-26
❑ 95StLucMTl-3
Bennett, Albert
❑ 88MarPhiS-3
❑ 89BatCliP-1920
❑ 91SpaPhiC-21
❑ 91SpaPhiP-906
❑ 92SpaPhiC-12
❑ 92SpaPhiF-1273
Bennett, Bob
❑ 89FreStaBS-2
❑ 89FreStaBS-3
❑ 90FreStaS-1
❑ 91FreStaBS-1
❑ 92FroRowDP-90
❑ 92FroRowDPG-90
❑ 92FroRowDPS-90
❑ 92SouOreAC-2
❑ 92SouOreAF-3405
❑ 94ModA'sF-3057
❑ 94WesMicWC-1
❑ 94WesMicWF-2288
❑ 95HunStaTl-6
❑ 96HunStaTl-2
❑ 97HunStaTl-2
Bennett, Brad
❑ 82SprCarF-23
Bennett, Brian
❑ 89AshTouP-954
Bennett, Charlie (Charles W.)
❑ 76SSP188WS-16
❑ 81TigDetN-2
❑ 87AllandGN-2
❑ 87BucN28-27
❑ 87OldJudN-28
❑ 87ScrDC-10
❑ 88WG1CarG-19
❑ 89N526N7C-1
Bennett, Chris
❑ 89WesPalBES-3
❑ 90Bes-213
❑ 90JacExpB-15
❑ 90JacExpP-1366
❑ 91IndIndP-454
Bennett, Dave
❑ 64Top-561
❑ 65Top-521
Bennett, Dennis
❑ 63Top-56
❑ 64PhiPhiB-4
❑ 64Top-396
❑ 65OPC-147
❑ 65RedSoxTl-1
❑ 65Top-147
❑ 66RedSoxTl-1
❑ 66Top-491
❑ 67CokCapRS-14
❑ 67Top-206
❑ 67TopRedSS-1
❑ 78TCM60I-93
❑ 81RedSoxBG2S-71
❑ 91MetWIZ-31
Bennett, Doug
❑ 90ArkRaz-1
❑ 91YakBeaC-22
❑ 91YakBeaP-4237
❑ 92StaCluD-14
❑ 92YakBeaC-1
❑ 92YakBeaF-3439
Bennett, Eddie
❑ 79Yan192T-4
❑ 88SFHesCreN32-1
Bennett, Erik
❑ 88CapCodPPaLP-153
❑ 89BenBucL-1
❑ 90QuaCitAGS-14
❑ 92QuaCitRBF-800
❑ 93MidAngF-314
❑ 94VanCanF-1856
❑ 96LeaSigEA-7
Bennett, Gary
❑ 90MarPhiP-3190
❑ 91MarPhiC-16
❑ 91MarPhiP-3454
❑ 92BatCliCB-4
❑ 92BatCliF-3267
❑ 93SpaPhiC-5
❑ 93SpaPhiF-1057
❑ 94ClePhiC-4
❑ 94ClePhiF-2529
❑ 95ReaPhiELC-4
❑ 95ReaPhiTl-17
❑ 96ScrRedBB-6
❑ 97PawRedS-7
❑ 98ScrRedBQ-4
❑ 99FleBri-159
❑ 99FleBri2G-159
❑ 99FleBriBlu-159
❑ 99FleBriGol-159
❑ 99Pac-322
❑ 99Pac-322A
❑ 99PacAur-141
❑ 99PacAurOD-141
❑ 99PacPlaB-322
❑ 99PacPlaB-322A
❑ 99PacRed-322
❑ 99PacRed-322A
❑ 99SkyPre-254
❑ 99SkyPre-254
❑ 99SkyPreR-254
❑ 99SkyPreR-254
❑ 99SpoIll-61
Bennett, Herschel E.
❑ 27MidBre-24
❑ 93ConTSN-986
Bennett, Jason
❑ 95WatIndTl-5
Bennett, Jim
❑ 82WesHavAT-20
❑ 83TacTigT-14
❑ 84AlbA'sT-1
❑ 87MemChiB-7
❑ 87MemChiP-25
❑ 89WauTimGS-17
❑ 90SanBerSB-4
❑ 90SanBerSCLC-91
❑ 90SanBerSP-2625
❑ 92LetMouSP-11
❑ 95BoiHawTl-4
❑ 96BoiHawB-3
❑ 97LakElsSG-6
Bennett, Joel
❑ 92WinHavRSC-15
❑ 92WinHavRSF-1767
❑ 93CarLeaAGF-5
❑ 93LynRedSC-3
❑ 93LynRedSF-2509
❑ 94Bow-287
❑ 94ExcFS7-18
❑ 94ExcLeaLF-2
❑ 94NewBriRSF-642
❑ 95PawRedSDD-5
❑ 95PawRedTl-18
❑ 97BowBay-7
❑ 98RocRedWQ-6
Bennett, Jose
❑ 86BelMarCr-104
❑ 87WauTimP-11
Bennett, Keith
❑ 86WatIndP-3
❑ 87EriCarP-13
❑ 87WilBilP-2
❑ 88ColSprSSP-1535
❑ 88WatIndP-684
Bennett, Marshall
❑ 98BriBluM-5
Bennett, Matt
❑ 95NewJerCTl-2
Bennett, Pug (Justin Titus)
❑ 09ObaT21-405
❑ 11SpoLifCW-30
❑ 12ObaPreT-154
Bennett, Rick
❑ 90OklSoo-19
❑ 93HicCraC-2
❑ 93HicCraF-1269
❑ 94SouBenSHC-3
❑ 94SouBenSHF-586
Bennett, Ryan
❑ 96PitMetB-6
❑ 98CapCitBF5-16
❑ 98CapCitBM-16
Bennett, Shayne
❑ 94Bow-587
❑ 95AusFut-68
❑ 96BesAutS-11
❑ 96Bow-381
❑ 96BowFoi-381
❑ 96HarSenB-6
❑ 97HarSen-4
❑ 98Fle-510
❑ 98PacInvGems-176
❑ 98PacOmeRS-6
❑ 98PacOmeRST4-6
❑ 98PacOnl-445
❑ 98PacOnlR-445
❑ 98PacOnlWC-445
❑ 99Fle-357
❑ 99FleSta9-357
❑ 99FleWarT-357
❑ 99Pac-260
❑ 99PacPlaB-260
❑ 99PacRed-260
Bennett, Tom
❑ 97CalLeaTP-13
❑ 97ModA'sG-1
❑ 98Bow-383
❑ 98BowChr-383
❑ 98BowChrGA-383
❑ 98BowChrGAR-383
❑ 98BowChrI-383
❑ 98BowChrIR-383
❑ 98BowChrR-383
❑ 98BowGolA-383
❑ 98BowInt-383
❑ 98HunStaTl-1
Bennington, Jeff
❑ 91BurAstC-23
❑ 91BurAstP-2803
Benny, Peter
❑ 95HelBreTl-26
❑ 96BelSnaTl-1
❑ 96MidLeaAB-9
Benoit, Dickens
❑ 87EveGiaC-28
❑ 89SalSpuCLC-137
❑ 89SalSpuP-1827
Benoit, Joaquin
❑ 98SavSanGM-3
Bensch, Bob
❑ 87PanAmTUBI-NNO
Bensching, Bruce
❑ 90SpoIndSP-22
❑ 91WatDiaC-2
❑ 91WatDiaP-1249
❑ 92WatDiaC-6
❑ 92WatDiaF-2135
Benson, Coach
❑ 80WesHavWCT-23A
Benson, Gene
❑ 91NegLeaRL-27
❑ 91PomBlaBPB-2
❑ 92NegLeaRLI-3
❑ 93TedWil-99
❑ 95NegLeaLl-27
❑ 97NegLeaPC-7S
Benson, George
❑ 76SeaRaiC-3
❑ 77ReaPhiT-2
Benson, Jeremy
❑ 94OneYanC-3
❑ 94OneYanF-3779
Benson, Kris
❑ 97Bes-5
❑ 97BesAll-12
❑ 97BesAutSC-12
❑ 97BesBetP-4
❑ 97BesDiaB-6
❑ 97BesFiv-1
❑ 97BesGun-8
❑ 97BesLimA-2
❑ 97Bow-175
❑ 97BowBes-116
❑ 97BowBesAR-116
❑ 97BowBesMI-MI3
❑ 97BowBesMIAR-MI3
❑ 97BowBesMIARI-MI3
❑ 97BowBesMII-MI3
❑ 97BowBesMIR-MI3
❑ 97BowBesMIRI-MI3
❑ 97BowBesR-116
❑ 97BowCerBlaIA-CA5
❑ 97BowCerBluIA-CA5
❑ 97BowCerGolIA-CA5
❑ 97BowChr-167
❑ 97BowChrI-167
❑ 97BowChrIR-167
❑ 97BowChrR-167
❑ 97BowInt-175
❑ 97CalLeaATl-27
❑ 97CarLeaTP-1
❑ 97LynHil-1
❑ 97Top-481
❑ 97TopSta-103
❑ 97TopStaAM-103
❑ 98Bes-56
❑ 98BesAutPOY-1
❑ 98BesCasT-1
❑ 98BesDiaBA-1
❑ 98BesFulCA-1
❑ 98BesNumOP-6
❑ 98BesPos-1
❑ 98BesPreA-2
❑ 98Bow-296
❑ 98Bow99ROYF-ROY6
❑ 98BowBes-148
❑ 98BowBesAR-148
❑ 98BowBesR-148
❑ 98BowCerBlueAU-49
❑ 98BowCerGA-49
❑ 98BowCerSA-49
❑ 98BowChr-296
❑ 98BowChrGA-296
❑ 98BowChrGAR-296
❑ 98BowChrI-296
❑ 98BowChrIR-296
❑ 98BowChrR-296
❑ 98BowGolA-296
❑ 98BowInt-296
❑ 98BowScoC-SC19
❑ 98NasSouTl-3
❑ 98NasSouTlSS-3
❑ 98SP MinDTSPE-DS25
❑ 98SP MinPE-99
❑ 98SP MinSTHPE-H8
❑ 98SP SPTSC-KB
❑ 98SPMin-99
❑ 98SPMinDTS-DS25
❑ 98SPMinSTH-H8
❑ 98StaCluFDI-371
❑ 98StaCluI-371
❑ 98StaCluOneK-371
❑ 98StaCluPP-371
❑ 98Top-259
❑ 98TopChr-259
❑ 98TopChrR-259
❑ 98TopDevR-259
❑ 98TopDia-259
❑ 98TopMiniC-259
❑ 99Bow-339
❑ 99BowGol-339
❑ 99BowInt-339
❑ 99DumSet-136
❑ 99FlaShoLeg1-34
❑ 99FlaShoLeg2-34
❑ 99FlaShoLeg3-34
❑ 99FlaShoLegM1-34
❑ 99FlaShoLegM2-34
❑ 99FlaShoLegM3-34
❑ 99FlaShoR1-34
❑ 99FlaShoR2-34
❑ 99FlaShoR3-34
❑ 99FleBri-173
❑ 99FleBri2G-173

❑ 99FleBriBlu-173
❑ 99FleBriGol-173
❑ 99FleMys-136
❑ 99FleMysFI-3
❑ 99FleMysM-136
❑ 99JustheS-9
❑ 99JustheSAC-4
❑ 99JustheSAD-4
❑ 99JustheSJB-9
❑ 99JustheSJD-2
❑ 99PacInv-117
❑ 99PacInvOD-117
❑ 99PacInvPB-117
❑ 99PacOme-191
❑ 99PacOmeC-191
❑ 99PacOmeG-191
❑ 99PacOmePB-191
❑ 99SkyPre-241
❑ 99SkyPre-241
❑ 99SkyPreA-4
❑ 99SkyPreABlue-4
❑ 99SkyPreR-241
❑ 99SkyPreR-241
❑ 99SP TopP-17
❑ 99SP TopPPE-17
❑ 99UppDec-291
❑ 99UppDecE-134
❑ 99UppDecEFXG-134
❑ 99UppDecEL1-291
❑ 99UppDecEL2-291
❑ 99Vic-305

Benson, Mark
❑ 79CedRapGT-3

Benson, Matt
❑ 91HelBreSP-3

Benson, Nate
❑ 90KinMetB-18
❑ 90KinMetS-2

Benson, Neal
❑ 86DavLipB-4

Benson, Randy
❑ 76BatRouCT-4
❑ 80SyrChiT-18
❑ 80SyrChiTI-5
❑ 80VenLeaS-52

Benson, Steve
❑ 80OrlTwiT-11
❑ 83ColAstT-8

Benson, Tom
❑ 89EliTwiS-2
❑ 90EliTwiS-2

Benson, Vern (Vernon A.)
❑ 53Top-205
❑ 61UniOil-P2
❑ 70CarTeal-5
❑ 71CarTeal-3
❑ 71CarTeal-2
❑ 73OPC-497
❑ 73Top-497A
❑ 73Top-497B
❑ 74OPC-236
❑ 74Top-236
❑ 76AtlBraP-2
❑ 78SyrChiT-3
❑ 79SyrChiT-2
❑ 79SyrChiTI-8
❑ 80GiaPol-8
❑ 80VenLeaS-46
❑ 91TopArc1-205

Bentley, Blake
❑ 91PriRedC-20
❑ 91PriRedP-3525

Bentley, Jack (John N.)
❑ 20WalMaiW-5
❑ 22WilPatV-26
❑ 23W515-12
❑ 26Exh-41
❑ 27Exh-17
❑ 93ConTSN-919
❑ 95ConTSN-1326

Benton, Al (John Alton)
❑ 46SpoExcW-1-2
❑ 49IndTeal-2
❑ 50IndNumN-3
❑ 50IndTeal-3
❑ 52Top-374
❑ 53IndPenCBP-3
❑ 53MotCoo-27
❑ 81TigDetN-57
❑ 81TigSecNP-28
❑ 83TopRep5-374

Benton, Butch (Alfred Lee)
❑ 76WauMetT-4
❑ 77LynMetT-4A
❑ 77LynMetT-4B
❑ 79TidTidT-8
❑ 80TidTidT-8
❑ 82IowCubT-1
❑ 83WicAerDS-5
❑ 85Ind-3
❑ 89PacSenL-24
❑ 89TopSenL-66
❑ 91MetWIZ-32
❑ 91PacSenL-145

Benton, Larry (Lawrence)
❑ 25Exh-3
❑ 26Exh-1
❑ 28PorandAR-A3
❑ 28PorandAR-B3
❑ 28W56PlaC-D9
❑ 29ExhFou-9
❑ 29PorandAR-3
❑ 33ButCanV-2
❑ 33Gou-45
❑ 33GouCanV-45
❑ 34BabRutG-3
❑ 34ButPreR-3
❑ 34DiaMatCSB-9
❑ 35GouPuzR-8L
❑ 35GouPuzR-9L
❑ 91ConTSN-182

Benton, Rube (John C.)
❑ 11L1L-113
❑ 11S81LarS-88
❑ 14CraJacE-97
❑ 14FatPlaT-6
❑ 15CraJacE-97
❑ 20WalMaiW-6
❑ 28W513-69
❑ 33WorCig(-5
❑ 33WorCig(-6
❑ 74CapPub-101
❑ 78HalHalR-17

Benton, Stan (Stanley)
❑ 24Zee-38

Benz, Jake
❑ 94VerExpC-5
❑ 94VerExpF-3899
❑ 96Exc-184
❑ 96HarSenB-7
❑ 98arSenW1-4
❑ 98HarSenM-4

Benz, Joseph Louis
❑ 11PloCanE-7
❑ 12T207-12
❑ 14E&SP-1
❑ 15CraJacE-175
❑ 15SpoNewM-13
❑ 16BF2FP-8
❑ 16SpoNewM-14
❑ 17ColE13-14
❑ 18WhiSoxTI-2
❑ 75WhiSox1T-1
❑ 92Man191BSR-1

Benza, Brett
❑ 82TulDriT-26
❑ 83SprCarF-10

Benzing, Skipp
❑ 97LowSpiB-17

Benzinger, Todd
❑ 86PawRedSP-2
❑ 87DonRoo-30
❑ 87IntLeaAT-20
❑ 87PawRedSP-57
❑ 87PawRedST-13
❑ 87SpoRoo2-47
❑ 88ClaBlu-245
❑ 88Don-297
❑ 88DonBasB-289
❑ 88DonTeaBRS-297
❑ 88Fle-344
❑ 88Fle-630
❑ 88FleGlo-344
❑ 88FleGlo-630
❑ 88Lea-111
❑ 88OPC-96
❑ 88Sco-546
❑ 88ScoGlo-546
❑ 88ScoYouSI-31
❑ 88StaLinRS-2
❑ 88Top-96
❑ 88TopTif-96
❑ 88ToyRoo-1
❑ 89Bow-312
❑ 89BowTif-312
❑ 89Don-358
❑ 89DonBasB-174
❑ 89DonTra-47
❑ 89Fle-79
❑ 89FleGlo-79
❑ 89FleUpd-83
❑ 89OPC-188
❑ 89PanSti-275
❑ 89RedKah-25
❑ 89Sco-371
❑ 89ScoRoo-15T
❑ 89Top-493
❑ 89TopTif-493
❑ 89TopTra-9T
❑ 89TopTraT-9T
❑ 89UppDec-184
❑ 89UppDec-785
❑ 89UppDecS-2
❑ 90Bow-55
❑ 90BowTif-55
❑ 90Don-257
❑ 90DonBesN-101
❑ 90DonGraS-8
❑ 90Fle-413
❑ 90FleCan-413
❑ 90Lea-15
❑ 90OPC-712
❑ 90PanSti-250
❑ 90PubIntS-22
❑ 90RedKah-2
❑ 90Sco-65
❑ 90Spo-56
❑ 90Top-712
❑ 90TopBig-14
❑ 90TopSti-138
❑ 90TopTif-712
❑ 90UppDec-186
❑ 91Don-640
❑ 91Fle-56
❑ 91OPC-334
❑ 91PanFreS-127
❑ 91RedKah-25
❑ 91RedPep-2
❑ 91Sco-90
❑ 91StaClu-113
❑ 91Top-334
❑ 91TopDesS-334
❑ 91TopMic-334
❑ 91TopTif-334
❑ 91Ult-87
❑ 91UltUpd-25
❑ 91UppDec-280
❑ 91UppDecFE-41F
❑ 92Bow-141
❑ 92DodMot-11
❑ 92DodPol-36
❑ 92DodSmo-5492
❑ 92Don-536
❑ 92Fle-152
❑ 92Lea-257
❑ 92LeaBlaG-257
❑ 92OPC-506
❑ 92PanSti-94
❑ 92Pin-438
❑ 92Sco-563
❑ 92StaClu-764
❑ 92Top-506
❑ 92TopGol-506
❑ 92TopGolW-506
❑ 92TopMic-506
❑ 92TopTra-11T
❑ 92TopTraG-11T
❑ 92Ult-499
❑ 92UppDec-518
❑ 93Don-562
❑ 93Fle-58
❑ 93FleFinE-149
❑ 93GiaMot-11
❑ 93GiaPos-4
❑ 93Top-620
❑ 93TopGol-620
❑ 93TopInaM-620
❑ 93TopInaR-620
❑ 93TopMic-620
❑ 93Ult-481
❑ 93UppDec-790
❑ 93UppDecGold-790
❑ 94ColC-551
❑ 94ColChoGS-551
❑ 94ColChoSS-551
❑ 94Fla-238
❑ 94Fle-682
❑ 94FleExtB-382
❑ 94GiaAMC-4
❑ 94GiaMot-20
❑ 94GiaTarBC-4
❑ 94GiaUSPC-4S
❑ 94GiaUSPC-10D
❑ 94Lea-85
❑ 94Pac-539
❑ 94Pin-39
❑ 94PinArtP-39
❑ 94PinMusC-39
❑ 94Sco-301
❑ 94ScoGolR-301
❑ 94Sel-365
❑ 94StaClu-61
❑ 94StaCluFDI-61
❑ 94StaCluGR-61
❑ 94StaCluMOP-61
❑ 94StaCluT-29
❑ 94StaCluTFDI-29
❑ 94Top-398
❑ 94TopGol-398
❑ 94TopSpa-398
❑ 94Ult-586
❑ 94UppDec-163
❑ 94UppDecED-163
❑ 95ColCho-262
❑ 95ColChoGS-262
❑ 95ColChoSS-262
❑ 95Pac-372
❑ 95Pin-307
❑ 95PinArtP-307
❑ 95PinMusC-307
❑ 95Sco-260
❑ 95ScoGolR-260
❑ 95ScoPlaTS-260
❑ 95Top-124

Berardi, Scott
❑ 94LSUTig-12

Berardino, Dick
❑ 79ElmPioRST-21
❑ 80ElmPioRST-29
❑ 86PawRedSP-1
❑ 87GreHorP-3
❑ 90TopTVRS-2
❑ 97LowSpiB-1
❑ 98LowSpiM-1

Berardino, Johnny (John)
❑ 41BroW75-4
❑ 46SeaSLP-4
❑ 47TipTop-61
❑ 48IndTeal-2
❑ 49IndTeal-4
❑ 51Bow-245
❑ 52Top-253
❑ 83TopRep5-253
❑ 84TCMPla1-18

Berberet, Lou (Louis J.)
❑ 56Top-329
❑ 57Top-315
❑ 58Top-188
❑ 58Top-383
❑ 59Top-96
❑ 59TopVen-96
❑ 60Lea-24
❑ 60MacSta-4
❑ 60TigJayP-1
❑ 60Top-6
❑ 60TopVen-6
❑ 61Pos-43A
❑ 61Pos-43B
❑ 81RedSoxBG2S-5

Berblinger, Jeff
❑ 93GleFalRC-6
❑ 93GleFalRF-4008
❑ 94ExcFirYPF-3
❑ 94ExcFS7-258
❑ 94SavCarC-6
❑ 94SavCarF-512
❑ 94SouAtlLAF-SAL47
❑ 95ArkTraTI-5
❑ 95Exc-263
❑ 96ArkTraB-6
❑ 96TexLeaAB-2
❑ 97LouRedB-10
❑ 98TacRaiQ-5

Bere, Jason
❑ 91SouBenWSC-13
❑ 91SouBenWSP-2849
❑ 92Bow-358
❑ 92ClaFS7-253
❑ 92SarWhiSCB-6
❑ 92SarWhiSF-198
❑ 93Bow-91
❑ 93Bow-364
❑ 93ClaFS7-157
❑ 93ClaGolF-203
❑ 93FlaWavotF-1
❑ 93FleFinE-192
❑ 93Lea-524
❑ 93NasSouF-563
❑ 93SelRoo-81T
❑ 93SP-271
❑ 93TopTra-26T
❑ 93Ult-527
❑ 93UppDec-453
❑ 93UppDecGold-453
❑ 93WhiSoxK-3
❑ 93WhiSoxSC-25
❑ 94Bow-381
❑ 94Bow-567
❑ 94ColC-50
❑ 94ColChoGS-50
❑ 94ColChoSS-50
❑ 94Don-86
❑ 94Fin-12
❑ 94FinJum-12
❑ 94FinRef-12
❑ 94Fla-29
❑ 94Fle-76
❑ 94FleExtB-42
❑ 94FleExtBSYS-2
❑ 94FleRooS-2
❑ 94FUnPac-50
❑ 94Lea-241
❑ 94LeaL-20
❑ 94OPC-206
❑ 94OPCDiaD-13
❑ 94Pac-120
❑ 94Pin-347
❑ 94PinArtP-347
❑ 94PinMusC-347
❑ 94PinNewG-NG3
❑ 94Sco-563
❑ 94ScoBoyoS-18
❑ 94ScoGolR-563
❑ 94Sel-259
❑ 94SP-189
❑ 94SPDieC-189
❑ 94Spo-68
❑ 94SpoSha-SH4
❑ 94StaClu-212
❑ 94StaClu-702
❑ 94StaCluFDI-212
❑ 94StaCluFDI-702
❑ 94StaCluGR-212
❑ 94StaCluGR-702
❑ 94StaCluMOP-212
❑ 94StaCluMOP-702
❑ 94StaCluT-144
❑ 94StaCluTFDI-144
❑ 94Top-118
❑ 94TopGol-118
❑ 94TopSpa-118
❑ 94TriPla-262
❑ 94Ult-31
❑ 94UltSecYS-1
❑ 94UppDec-42
❑ 94UppDec-146
❑ 94UppDecED-42
❑ 94UppDecED-146
❑ 94USPlaCR-13S
❑ 94WhiSoxK-3
❑ 95Baz-5
❑ 95Bow-388
❑ 95ColCho-504
❑ 95ColChoGS-504
❑ 95ColChoSE-233
❑ 95ColChoSEGS-233
❑ 95ColChoSESS-233
❑ 95ColChoSS-504
❑ 95DenHol-5
❑ 95Don-332
❑ 95DonMouM-8
❑ 95DonPreP-332
❑ 95DonTopotO-45
❑ 95Emo-25
❑ 95Fin-101
❑ 95FinFlaT-FT1
❑ 95FinRef-101
❑ 95Fla-24
❑ 95FlaTodS-2
❑ 95Fle-111
❑ 95FleAllS-25
❑ 95FleUpdSS-2
❑ 95Lea-235
❑ 95LeaLim-27
❑ 95Pac-83
❑ 95PanSti-19
❑ 95Pin-334
❑ 95PinArtP-334
❑ 95PinMusC-334
❑ 95PinPer-PP18
❑ 95PinUps-US19
❑ 95Sco-394
❑ 95ScoGolR-394
❑ 95ScoHaloG-HG59
❑ 95ScoPlaTS-394
❑ 95ScoRul-SR22
❑ 95ScoRulJ-SR22
❑ 95Sel-68
❑ 95SelArtP-68
❑ 95SelCer-85
❑ 95SelCerMG-85
❑ 95SP-137
❑ 95SPCha-137
❑ 95SPChaDC-137
❑ 95SPSil-137
❑ 95SPSpeF-7
❑ 95StaClu-457
❑ 95StaCluMOP-457
❑ 95StaCluSTWS-457
❑ 95StaCluVR-247
❑ 95StaCluVRMO-247
❑ 95Stu-91
❑ 95Sum-84
❑ 95SumNthD-84
❑ 95Top-444
❑ 95TopCyb-240
❑ 95TopEmb-8
❑ 95TopEmbGI-8
❑ 95UC3-92
❑ 95UC3ArtP-92
❑ 95Ult-273
❑ 95UltGolM-273
❑ 95UppDec-202
❑ 95UppDecED-202
❑ 95UppDecEDG-202
❑ 95WhiSoxK-3
❑ 96ColCho-506
❑ 96ColChoGS-506
❑ 96ColChoSS-506
❑ 96Don-37
❑ 96DonPreP-37
❑ 96EmoXL-34
❑ 96Fla-48
❑ 96Fle-63
❑ 96FleTif-63
❑ 96Lea-187
❑ 96LeaPrePB-187
❑ 96LeaPrePG-187
❑ 96LeaPrePS-187
❑ 96LeaSigA-23
❑ 96LeaSigAG-23
❑ 96LeaSigAS-23
❑ 96Pin-133
❑ 96Sco-409
❑ 96Ult-331
❑ 96UltGolM-331
❑ 96UppDec-301
❑ 96WhiSoxF-3
❑ 97Fle-57
❑ 97FleTif-57
❑ 97Top-378
❑ 98PacOnl-162
❑ 98PacOnlR-162
❑ 98PacOnlWC-162

Berenger, Tom
❑ 89MajLeaM-1
❑ 89MajLeaM-10

Berenguer, Juan
❑ 76VenLeaS-143
❑ 78TidTidT-3
❑ 79TacTugT-6
❑ 79Top-721
❑ 80TidTidT-3
❑ 80VenLeaS-206
❑ 81RoyProPS-3
❑ 81Top-259
❑ 82Don-580
❑ 82EvaTriT-2
❑ 82OPC-107
❑ 82OPCPos-12
❑ 82Top-437
❑ 83TigPos-4
❑ 84Don-125
❑ 84Fle-77
❑ 84Nes792-174
❑ 84TigTeal-6
❑ 84TigWavP-6
❑ 84Top-174
❑ 84TopTif-174
❑ 85Don-272
❑ 85Fle-2
❑ 85TigCaiD-2
❑ 85TigWen-3
❑ 85Top-672
❑ 85TopTif-672
❑ 86Fle-221
❑ 86GiaMot-27
❑ 86GiaPos-2

❑ 86Top-47
❑ 86TopTif-47
❑ 86TopTra-9T
❑ 86TopTraT-9T
❑ 87Don-616
❑ 87Fle-265
❑ 87FleGlo-265
❑ 87FleUpd-4
❑ 87FleUpdG-4
❑ 87Top-303
❑ 87TopTif-303
❑ 87TopTra-5T
❑ 87TopTraT-5T
❑ 87TwiPos-2
❑ 87TwiTeal-25
❑ 88Don-395
❑ 88DonBasB-298
❑ 88Fle-3
❑ 88FleGlo-3
❑ 88StaLinTw-2
❑ 88Top-526
❑ 88TopBig-222
❑ 88TopTif-526
❑ 88TwiMasBD-3
❑ 89Bow-152
❑ 89BowTif-152
❑ 89Don-81
❑ 89DonBasB-46
❑ 89Fle-104
❑ 89FleGlo-104
❑ 89OPC-294
❑ 89Sco-414
❑ 89Top-294
❑ 89TopBig-117
❑ 89TopSti-291
❑ 89TopTif-294
❑ 89UppDec-232
❑ 90Bow-410
❑ 90BowTif-410
❑ 90Don-301
❑ 90Fle-369
❑ 90FleCan-369
❑ 90Lea-169
❑ 90OPC-709
❑ 90PubIntS-323
❑ 90Sco-223
❑ 90Top-709
❑ 90TopTif-709
❑ 90UppDec-440
❑ 91Bow-572
❑ 91BraDubP-3
❑ 91BraSubS-5
❑ 91Don-340
❑ 91Fle-604
❑ 91FleUpd-71
❑ 91Lea-526
❑ 91MetWIZ-33
❑ 91OPC-449
❑ 91Sco-111
❑ 91ScoPro-111
❑ 91ScoRoo-73T
❑ 91StaClu-460
❑ 91Top-449
❑ 91TopDesS-449
❑ 91TopMic-449
❑ 91TopTif-449
❑ 91UltUpd-66
❑ 91UppDec-411
❑ 92BraLykP-3
❑ 92BraLykS-4
❑ 92Don-205
❑ 92Fle-352
❑ 92OPC-172
❑ 92Pin-515
❑ 92Sco-216
❑ 92StaClu-44
❑ 92Top-172
❑ 92TopGol-172
❑ 92TopGolW-172
❑ 92TopMic-172
❑ 92Ult-455
❑ 92UppDec-493

Berenyi, Bruce
❑ 79IndIndTI-14
❑ 80IndIndTI-9
❑ 81Top-606
❑ 82Fle-58
❑ 82RedCok-2
❑ 82Top-459
❑ 83Don-103
❑ 83Fle-585
❑ 83OPC-139
❑ 83RedYea-38
❑ 83Top-139
❑ 84Don-487
❑ 84Fle-463
❑ 84Nes792-297
❑ 84OPC-297
❑ 84RedEnq-20
❑ 84Top-297
❑ 84TopTif-297
❑ 84TopTra-10T
❑ 84TopTraT-10T
❑ 85Don-625
❑ 85Fle-73
❑ 85IndIndTI-32
❑ 85MetColP-7
❑ 85MetFanC-2
❑ 85MetTCM-6
❑ 85OPC-27
❑ 85Top-27
❑ 85TopTif-27
❑ 86MetColP-19
❑ 86MetTCM-2
❑ 86MetWorSC-10
❑ 86Top-339
❑ 86TopTif-339
❑ 87Top-582
❑ 87TopTif-582
❑ 91MetWIZ-34

Berg, Chris
❑ 91WasVia-1
❑ 92KinMetF-1522

Berg, Dave
❑ 93ElmPioC-2
❑ 93ElmPioF-3829
❑ 94KanCouCC-5
❑ 94KanCouCF-169
❑ 94KanCouCTI-5
❑ 95BreCouMF-253
❑ 96PorSeaDB-8
❑ 97ChaKni-8
❑ 98PacOmeRS-16
❑ 98PacOmeRST1-16
❑ 98PacOnl-289
❑ 98PacOnlR-289
❑ 98PacOnlWC-289
❑ 98PorSeaD5AQ-12
❑ 99Fle-354
❑ 99FleSta9-354
❑ 99FleWarT-354
❑ 99Pac-171
❑ 99PacPlaB-171
❑ 99PacPriS-58
❑ 99PacPriS206-58
❑ 99PacPriS206R-58
❑ 99PacRed-171

Berg, Joseph
❑ 16Zee-22

Berg, Moe (Morris)
❑ 29PorandAR-4
❑ 30ChiEveAP-11
❑ 30WhiSoxTI-3
❑ 33Gou-158
❑ 33GouCanV-84
❑ 34BatR31-149
❑ 36NatChiFPR-6
❑ 39PlaBal-103
❑ 40PlaBal-30
❑ 74CapPub-76
❑ 85BigLeaC3-21
❑ 88ConSer5-3
❑ 90DodTar-48
❑ 91ConTSN-184
❑ 93DiaStaES-121
❑ 95ConTSN-1350
❑ 95ConTSN-1400

Berg, Patty
❑ 52Whe-3A
❑ 52Whe-3B

Berg, Rich
❑ 88ModA'sTI-4
❑ 89MadMusS-3
❑ 90HunStaB-2
❑ 91StoPorC-7
❑ 91StoPorP-3024

Berg, Rick
❑ 88BurBraP-22
❑ 90ProAAAF-423
❑ 90RicBraBC-22
❑ 90RicBraP-278
❑ 90RicBraTI-4
❑ 91RicBraBC-42
❑ 91RicBraP-2584

Bergamo, Augie (August S.)
❑ 83Car194T-27

Bergan, Tom
❑ 97HudValRB-23

Berge, Jordan
❑ 84CedRapRT-10
❑ 86VerRedP-1

Berge, Lou
❑ 86LitFalMP-3

Bergen, Bill (William A.)
❑ 06FanCraNL-4
❑ 09T206-24
❑ 09T206-25
❑ 10DomDisP-12
❑ 10E-UOraBSC-3
❑ 10E101-4
❑ 10MelMinE-4
❑ 10NadCarE-5
❑ 10PeoT21-4
❑ 10SweCapPP-71
❑ 11MecDFT-3
❑ 11PinT-5-465
❑ 11PloCanE-8
❑ 11S74Sil-50
❑ 11SpoLifCW-31
❑ 11SpoLifM-150
❑ 11T205-15
❑ 11TurRedT-2
❑ 12HasTriFT-3A
❑ 12HasTriFT-3B
❑ 12HasTriFT-61A
❑ 67SpoHobFC-48
❑ 72ClaCar-89
❑ 90DodTar-49

Bergen, Marty (Martin)
❑ 98CamPepP-3

Bergendahl, Wray
❑ 83WauTimF-28
❑ 85LynMetT-7
❑ 86JacMetT-3

Berger, Boze (Louis William)
❑ 34BatR31-84
❑ 34DiaMatCSB-10
❑ 35DiaMatCS3T1-8
❑ 72TCMthe1-172
❑ 95ConTSN-1342

Berger, Brandon
❑ 96SpoIndB-6
❑ 97LanLugTS-2
❑ 98WilBluRC-4

Berger, Carl
❑ 28ExhPCL-3

Berger, Craig
❑ 98PitMetM-7

Berger, Fred
❑ 31Zee-25
❑ 31Zee-60
❑ 32Zee-71

Berger, Heinie (Charles)
❑ 08AmeLeaPC-2
❑ 09ColChiE-28A
❑ 09ColChiE-28B
❑ 09T206-26
❑ 11SpoLifCW-32
❑ 11SpoLifM-38
❑ 12ColRedB-28A
❑ 12ColRedB-28B
❑ 12ColTinT-28A
❑ 12ColTinT-28B

Berger, Joe (Joseph August)
❑ 12Zee-1
❑ 15Zee-122
❑ 16Zee-23

Berger, Ken
❑ 77SpaPhiT-24

Berger, Matt
❑ 97BriWhiSB-15
❑ 98HicCraM-6
❑ 98HicCraUO-7

Berger, Mike
❑ 84PriWilPT-7
❑ 85NasPirT-3
❑ 86NasPirP-3
❑ 87JacExpP-434
❑ 88IndIndC-20
❑ 88IndIndP-519
❑ 89OklCit8C-11
❑ 89OklCit8P-1515
❑ 90CMC-160
❑ 90OklCit8C-10
❑ 90OklCit8P-434
❑ 90ProAAAF-680
❑ 91OklCit8P-181
❑ 92OklCit8F-1931
❑ 92OklCit8S-325
❑ 93OklCit8F-1640
❑ 94OklCit8F-1509
❑ 95ChaRivTI-29

Berger, Sy
❑ 64TopRooAB-6

Berger, Wally (Walter Anton)
❑ 28Zee-25
❑ 29Zee-14
❑ 30SchR33-12
❑ 31Exh-2
❑ 32OrbPinNP-51
❑ 32OrbPinUP-5
❑ 32USCar*-19
❑ 33DouDisP-5
❑ 33ExhFou-1
❑ 33GeoCMil-5
❑ 33Gou-98
❑ 33NatLeaAC-9
❑ 33RitCE-7C
❑ 33TatOrb-5
❑ 33WorCig-7
❑ 33WorCig-8
❑ 34BabRutG-4
❑ 34BatR31-1
❑ 34BatR31-172
❑ 34ButPreR-4
❑ 34DiaMatCSB-11
❑ 34DiaStaR-25
❑ 34DiaStaR-108
❑ 34ExhFou-1
❑ 35AlDemDCR3-137
❑ 35DiaMatCS2-2
❑ 35DiaMatCS3T1-9
❑ 35ExhFou-1
❑ 35GouPreR-8
❑ 35WheBB1-3
❑ 36ExhFou-1
❑ 36GouBWR-1
❑ 36GouWidPPR-A5
❑ 36NatChiFPR-7
❑ 36OveCanR-4
❑ 36WorWidGV-35
❑ 37ExhFou-1
❑ 37GouThuMR-13
❑ 38CloFotW-7
❑ 38GouFliMR-13A
❑ 38GouFliMR-13B
❑ 38OurNatGPP-1
❑ 38RedOraW-1
❑ 39GouPreR303A-3
❑ 39OrcPhoAP-1
❑ 39PlaBal-99
❑ 39RedTeal-1
❑ 39WorWidGTP-3
❑ 40PlaBal-81
❑ 74Bra193NLA-9
❑ 76RedParC-2
❑ 77CinRedT-2
❑ 77GalGloG-220
❑ 79DiaGre-201
❑ 82DiaCla-10
❑ 83BigLeaCOA-37
❑ 83ConMar-33
❑ 86BraGreT-6
❑ 88ConNatA-1
❑ 88ConSer3-5
❑ 91ConTSN-229
❑ 93ConTSN-686
❑ 94ConTSN-1098
❑ 94ConTSNB-1098

Bergeron, Gilles
❑ 87JamExpP-2559

Bergeron, Peter
❑ 96YakBeaTI-25
❑ 97SouAtlTPB-29
❑ 98SanAntMG-4
❑ 99BasAmeTP-13
❑ 99BasAmeTPG-13
❑ 99Bow-322
❑ 99BowAut-BA38
❑ 99BowBes-150
❑ 99BowBesAR-150
❑ 99BowBesR-150
❑ 99BowGol-322
❑ 99BowInt-322
❑ 99JustheS-10
❑ 99JustheSJB-10
❑ 99JustheSJD-3
❑ 99Top-207
❑ 99TopChr-207
❑ 99TopChrR-207

Bergert, Ned
❑ 76QuaCitAT-2
❑ 77QuaCitAT-3
❑ 78QuaCitAT-2

Bergey, Bill
❑ 80PhiBul-5

Bergman, Dave (David Bruce)
❑ 76SSP-454
❑ 78AstBurK-21
❑ 78AstPos-4
❑ 78Top-705
❑ 79ChaChaT-8
❑ 79Top-697
❑ 81Don-139
❑ 81Fle-76
❑ 81GiaTeal-2
❑ 81Top-253
❑ 81TopTra-734
❑ 82Don-146
❑ 82Gia25tATI-2
❑ 82Top-498
❑ 83Don-550
❑ 83Fle-253
❑ 83GiaMot-18
❑ 83GiaPos-2
❑ 83Top-32
❑ 84Don-624
❑ 84Fle-366
❑ 84FleUpd-11
❑ 84Nes792-522
❑ 84TigFarJ-1
❑ 84TigTeal-7
❑ 84TigWavP-7
❑ 84Top-522
❑ 84TopTif-522
❑ 84TopTra-11T
❑ 84TopTraT-11T
❑ 85Don-537
❑ 85Fle-3
❑ 85OPC-368
❑ 85TigCaiD-3
❑ 85TigWen-4
❑ 85Top-368
❑ 85TopTif-368
❑ 86BasStaB-9
❑ 86Don-471
❑ 86Fle-222
❑ 86TigCaiD-1
❑ 86Top-101
❑ 86TopTif-101
❑ 87AstShoSPO-3
❑ 87Don-420
❑ 87Fle-144
❑ 87FleGlo-144
❑ 87OPC-256
❑ 87TigCaiD-4
❑ 87TigCok-9
❑ 87Top-700
❑ 87TopTif-700
❑ 88Don-373
❑ 88Fle-52
❑ 88FleGlo-52
❑ 88Sco-217
❑ 88ScoGlo-217
❑ 88StaLinTi-2
❑ 88TigPep-14
❑ 88TigPol-3
❑ 88Top-289
❑ 88TopClo-10
❑ 88TopTif-289
❑ 89Don-389
❑ 89Fle-129
❑ 89FleGlo-129
❑ 89Sco-469
❑ 89TigMar-14
❑ 89TigPol-14
❑ 89Top-631
❑ 89TopTif-631
❑ 89UppDec-266
❑ 90Bow-355
❑ 90BowTif-355
❑ 90Don-445
❑ 90Fle-600
❑ 90FleCan-600
❑ 90Lea-244
❑ 90OPC-77
❑ 90PanSti-67
❑ 90PubIntS-468
❑ 90Sco-254
❑ 90TigCok-2
❑ 90TigTeal-3
❑ 90Top-77
❑ 90TopSti-285
❑ 90TopTif-77
❑ 90UppDec-381
❑ 91Don-342
❑ 91Fle-331
❑ 91Lea-92
❑ 91OPC-412
❑ 91PanSti-241
❑ 91Sco-562
❑ 91StaClu-386
❑ 91TigCok-14
❑ 91TigPol-2
❑ 91Top-412
❑ 91TopDesS-412
❑ 91TopMic-412
❑ 91TopTif-412
❑ 91Ult-120
❑ 91UppDec-599
❑ 92OPC-354
❑ 92Sco-543
❑ 92StaClu-171
❑ 92TigKro-3
❑ 92TigTeal-4
❑ 92Top-354
❑ 92TopGol-354
❑ 92TopGolW-354
❑ 92TopMic-354
❑ 92Ult-56
❑ 92YanWIZ7-14

Bergman, Sean
❑ 91NiaFalRC-24
❑ 91NiaFalRP-3624
❑ 92LakTigC-19
❑ 92StaCluD-15
❑ 93Bow-531
❑ 93ClaFS7-164
❑ 93TolMudHF-1643
❑ 94Bow-41
❑ 94TolMudHF-1017
❑ 94Top-768
❑ 94TopGol-768
❑ 94TopSpa-768
❑ 94TriAAF-AAA21
❑ 95ColCho-467
❑ 95ColChoGS-467
❑ 95ColChoSS-467
❑ 95Fin-306
❑ 95FinRef-306
❑ 95FleUpd-17
❑ 95Lea-254
❑ 95Top-636
❑ 95UppDec-189
❑ 95UppDecED-189
❑ 95UppDecEDG-189
❑ 96Don-9
❑ 96DonPreP-9
❑ 96FleUpd-U195
❑ 96FleUpdTC-U195
❑ 96LeaSigEA-8
❑ 96PadMot-13
❑ 96PanSti-150
❑ 96Sco-120
❑ 96StaClu-84
❑ 96StaCluMOP-84
❑ 96Top-42
❑ 96Ult-554
❑ 96UltGolM-554
❑ 97PadMot-13
❑ 98PacOnl-313
❑ 98PacOnlR-313
❑ 98PacOnlWC-313
❑ 99Fle-355
❑ 99FleSta9-355
❑ 99FleWarT-355
❑ 99StaClu-186
❑ 99StaCluFDI-186
❑ 99StaCluOoaK-186
❑ 99StaCluPP-186
❑ 99Top-38
❑ 99TopChr-38
❑ 99TopChrR-38
❑ 99TopMVPP-38

Bergoechea, Brandy
❑ 93SouOreAF-4068

Beringer, Carroll
❑ 73OPC-486
❑ 73PhiTeal-27
❑ 73Top-486A
❑ 73Top-486B
❑ 74OPC-119
❑ 74Top-119
❑ 75PhiPhiP-4
❑ 76PhiPhiP-2
❑ 78SSP270-34

Beringhele, Vince
❑ 85VerBeaDT-17
❑ 97UCLBruTI-28

Berkman, Lance
❑ 97Bow-438
❑ 97BowChr-298
❑ 97BowChrI-298
❑ 97BowChrIR-298
❑ 97BowChrR-298
❑ 97BowInt-438
❑ 97TopSta-125
❑ 97TopStaAM-125

❑ 98Bes-57
❑ 98BesBet-2
❑ 98BesCor-2
❑ 98BesNumOP-7
❑ 98Bow-194
❑ 98BowBes-102
❑ 98BowBesAR-102
❑ 98BowBesR-102
❑ 98BowChr-194
❑ 98BowChrGA-194
❑ 98BowChrGAR-194
❑ 98BowChrI-194
❑ 98BowChrIR-194
❑ 98BowChrR-194
❑ 98BowGolA-194
❑ 98BowInt-194
❑ 98JacGenM-2
❑ 98TexLeaTPG-4
❑ 98Top-246
❑ 98TopChr-246
❑ 98TopChrR-246
❑ 98TopDevR-246
❑ 98TopDia-246
❑ 98TopMiniC-246
❑ 99199Fin-147
❑ 99BasAmeTP-14
❑ 99BasAmeTPA-3
❑ 99BasAmeTPBP-4
❑ 99BasAmeTPG-14
❑ 99BasAmeTPSC-2
❑ 99Bow-295
❑ 99BowAut-BA70
❑ 99BowBes-140
❑ 99BowBesAR-140
❑ 99BowBesR-140
❑ 99BowGol-295
❑ 99BowInt-295
❑ 99FinGolRef-147
❑ 99FinRef-147
❑ 99JustheS-11
❑ 99JustheSJB-11
❑ 99JustheSJD-4
❑ 99JustheSJN-3
❑ 99JustheSJP-3
❑ 99SP TopP-7
❑ 99SP TopP-18
❑ 99SP TopPC-LB
❑ 99SP TopPDtS-D3
❑ 99SP TopPGF-GF3
❑ 99SP TopPPE-7
❑ 99SP TopPPE-18
❑ 99TeaBesR-2
❑ 99TeaBesRA-3
❑ 99Top-205
❑ 99TopChr-205
❑ 99TopChrR-205
Berley, John
❑ 36WorWidGV-118
Berlin, Mike
❑ 92BriTigC-1
❑ 92BriTigF-1399
❑ 93FayGenC-4
❑ 93FayGenF-121
❑ 94LakTigC-2
Berlin, Randy
❑ 89HamRedS-12
❑ 89Sta-104
❑ 90SprCarB-4
❑ 91FreKeyC-17
❑ 91FreKeyP-2371
Berman, Chris
❑ 97UppDecCBR'RHoF-1
Berman, Gary
❑ 86BenPhiC-150
❑ 87ClePhiP-18
❑ 88ReaPhiP-873
Bermudez, Manuel
❑ 95BelGiaTI-39
❑ 96BurBeeTI-2
❑ 97BakBlaB-21
❑ 97BakBlaTI-21
❑ 97SanJosG-12
❑ 98SanJosGQ-21
Bernabe, Sam
❑ 84lowCubT-13
❑ 85lowCubT-18
Bernal, Manuel
❑ 96LanLugB-6
❑ 97WilBluR-15
Bernal, Vic
❑ 77PadSchC-8
❑ 79HawIslC-10
❑ 79HawIslT-8
Bernard, Andrew
❑ 24Zee-121
Bernard, Claude
❑ 09ObaT21-63
❑ 09ObaT21-78
Bernard, Curt (Curtis Henry)
❑ 09ObaT21-255
❑ 11PacCoaBD-6
❑ 11Zee-4
❑ 12ObaPreT-4
Bernard, Dwight
❑ 75TidTidTI-3
❑ 78TidTidT-4
❑ 79TidTidT-6
❑ 79Top-721
❑ 81VanCanT-4
❑ 82BrePol-47
❑ 83BreGar-2
❑ 83Don-28
❑ 83Fle-27
❑ 83Top-244
❑ 84TucTorC-55
❑ 86MacPirP-4
❑ 87KenTwiP-16
❑ 88KenTwiP-1381
❑ 89OrlTwiB-4
❑ 89OrlTwiP-1342
❑ 91MetWIZ-35
❑ 92BreCarT-2
❑ 94BreMilB-107
❑ 94EliTwiF-3747
❑ 98El PasDG-4
Bernard, Erik
❑ 84AlbA'sT-16
❑ 85AlbYanT-29
❑ 86AlbYanT-12
Bernardo, Rick
❑ 87PorChaRP-18
❑ 88ChaRanS-1
❑ 89ChaRanS-2
❑ 89MiaMirlS-1
Bernardo, Robert
❑ 86WauTimP-1
❑ 87SalSpuS-13
Bernazard, Tony (Antonio)
❑ 75WesPalBES-29A
❑ 75WesPalBES-30
❑ 79ExpPos-3
❑ 80ExpPos-4
❑ 80OPC-351
❑ 80Top-680
❑ 81Don-449
❑ 81Fle-168
❑ 81OPC-194
❑ 81Top-413
❑ 81TopTra-735
❑ 82Don-143
❑ 82Fle-338
❑ 82Top-206
❑ 82TopSti-171
❑ 82TopStiV-171
❑ 83Don-482
❑ 83Fle-231
❑ 83OPC-369
❑ 83Top-698
❑ 83TopSti-49
❑ 83TopTra-9T
❑ 83WhiSoxTV-14
❑ 84Don-240
❑ 84Fle-606
❑ 84FleUpd-12
❑ 84Ind-4
❑ 84IndWhe-4
❑ 84Nes792-41
❑ 84OPC-41
❑ 84Top-41
❑ 84TopSti-340
❑ 84TopTif-41
❑ 84TopTra-12T
❑ 84TopTraT-12T
❑ 85Don-102
❑ 85Fle-439
❑ 85Ind-4
❑ 85IndPol-4
❑ 85OPC-171
❑ 85SubDis-4
❑ 85ThoMcAD-4
❑ 85Top-533
❑ 85TopSti-252
❑ 85TopTif-533
❑ 86Don-520
❑ 86Fle-580
❑ 86IndOhH-4
❑ 86IndTeal-6
❑ 86Lea-249
❑ 86OPC-354
❑ 86Top-354
❑ 86TopSti-210
❑ 86TopTat-14
❑ 86TopTif-354
❑ 87Don-377
❑ 87DonOpeD-110
❑ 87Fle-244
❑ 87FleGamW-4
❑ 87FleGlo-244
❑ 87FleMin-8
❑ 87IndGat-4
❑ 87OPC-394
❑ 87RedFolSB-105
❑ 87Spo-60
❑ 87Spo-112
❑ 87SpoTeaP-3
❑ 87Top-607
❑ 87Top-758
❑ 87TopGloS-43
❑ 87TopSti-207
❑ 87TopTif-607
❑ 87TopTif-758
❑ 88Don-344
❑ 88Fle-275
❑ 88FleGlo-275
❑ 88OPC-122
❑ 88Sco-604
❑ 88ScoGlo-604
❑ 88StaLinAs-1
❑ 88Top-122
❑ 88TopTif-122
❑ 91Bow-143
Bernhard, Bill (William H.)
❑ 03BreE10-9
❑ 04FanCraAL-5
❑ 05IndSouPSoCP-3
❑ 09T206-478
❑ 10CouT21-4
❑ 11SpoLifCW-33
❑ 17Zee-59
Bernhard, David
❑ 96AubDouB-11
Bernhard, Cesar
❑ 88SouBenWSGS-1
❑ 89SouBenWSGS-24
❑ 90Bes-80
❑ 90BirBarB-6
❑ 90BirBarP-1114
❑ 90CMC-821
❑ 91Bow-360
❑ 91LinDriAAA-626
❑ 91VanCanLD-626
❑ 91VanCanP-1599
❑ 92BirBarS-77
❑ 92OPC-179
❑ 92SkyAA F-37
❑ 92Top-179
❑ 92TopGol-179
❑ 92TopGolW-179
❑ 93LimRocDWB-51
Bernhardt, Jossephang
❑ 98St.CatSM-1
Bernhardt, Juan Ramon
❑ 77Top-494
❑ 78SanJosMMC-13
❑ 78Top-698
❑ 79OPC-189
❑ 79Top-366
❑ 92YanWIZ7-15
Bernhardt, Moncho
❑ 79SpoIndT-24
Bernhardt, Steven
❑ 93BenRocCB-2
❑ 93BenRocF-3274
❑ 94CenValRC-3
❑ 94CenValRF-3209
❑ 95SalAvaTI-17
❑ 96SalAvaB-4
❑ 97NewHavRB-6
Berni, Denny
❑ 91LynRedSC-11
❑ 91LynRedSP-1201
❑ 92LynRedSC-8
❑ 92LynRedSF-2909
Bernier, Carlos R.
❑ 53Top-243
❑ 54Bow-171
❑ 91TopArc1-243
Berninger, Darren
❑ 95HelBreTI-8
❑ 96BelSnaTI-2
❑ 97StoPor-20
Berns, Robert
❑ 97PriDevR-14
❑ 98ChaRivDG-3
Bernsen, Corbin
❑ 89MajLeaM-2
Bernstine, Pookie
❑ 83WatIndF-16
❑ 84BufBisT-23
❑ 86lowCubP-3
❑ 86StaoftFT-12
❑ 87lowCubTI-16
❑ 88PeoChiTI-5
❑ 89GenCubP-1886
❑ 89PeoChiTI-29
❑ 96MicBatCB-2
Berra, Dale Anthony
❑ 77ColCliT-3
❑ 78ColCliT-1
❑ 79Top-723
❑ 80Top-292
❑ 81Don-253
❑ 81Fle-369
❑ 81OPC-147
❑ 81Top-147
❑ 82Don-250
❑ 82Fle-476
❑ 82Top-588
❑ 83Don-185
❑ 83Fle-303
❑ 83FleSta-15
❑ 83FleSti-77
❑ 83OPC-271
❑ 83Top-433
❑ 83TopSti-279
❑ 84AllGamPI-19
❑ 84Don-430
❑ 84Fle-245
❑ 84Nes792-18
❑ 84OPC-18
❑ 84Pir-2
❑ 84Top-18
❑ 84TopSti-136
❑ 84TopTif-18
❑ 85Don-444
❑ 85Fle-461
❑ 85FleUpd-4
❑ 85OPC-305
❑ 85Top-132
❑ 85Top-305
❑ 85TopSti-133
❑ 85TopTif-132
❑ 85TopTif-305
❑ 85TopTifT-6T
❑ 85TopTra-6T
❑ 85YanTCMP-24
❑ 86Don-295
❑ 86Fle-100
❑ 86OPC-366
❑ 86Top-692
❑ 86TopTif-692
❑ 86YanTCM-21
❑ 87TucTorP-8
❑ 88RocRedWC-12
❑ 88RocRedWGCP-3
❑ 88RocRedWP-193
❑ 88RocRedWTI-3
❑ 92YanWIZ8-10
Berra, Yogi (Lawrence Peter)
❑ 46SpoExcW-5-11
❑ 47Exh-20A
❑ 47Exh-20B
❑ 47HomBon-2
❑ 47PM1StaP1-9
❑ 47PM1StaP1-10
❑ 47PM1StaP1-11
❑ 47StaPinP2-4
❑ 47TipTop-46
❑ 47YanTeaT-1
❑ 48Bow-6
❑ 48YanTeal-2
❑ 49Bow-60
❑ 49MPR302-2-117
❑ 49YanTeal-2
❑ 50Bow-46
❑ 50Dra-24
❑ 50YanTeal-3
❑ 51BerRos-B4
❑ 51Bow-2
❑ 51R42SmaS-5
❑ 51TopCurA-1
❑ 51TopRedB-1
❑ 52BerRos-3
❑ 52Bow-1
❑ 52NatTeaL-2
❑ 52RedMan-AL3
❑ 52StaCalL-70C
❑ 52StaCalS-84B
❑ 52TipTop-2
❑ 52Top-191
❑ 52Whe-4A
❑ 52Whe-4B
❑ 53BowC-44
❑ 53BowC-121
❑ 53Dor-102
❑ 53RedMan-AL3
❑ 53Top-104
❑ 54Bow-161
❑ 54NewYorJA-41
❑ 54RedMan-AL20
❑ 54Top-50
❑ 55ArmCoi-2
❑ 55BigLealS-3
❑ 55Bow-168
❑ 55DaiQueS-3
❑ 55RedMan-AL16
❑ 55Top-198
❑ 56Top-110
❑ 56TopPin-27
❑ 56YanJayP-2
❑ 56YanTeal-2
❑ 56YelBasP-7
❑ 57Top-2
❑ 57Top-407
❑ 57YanJayP-2
❑ 58HarSta-8
❑ 58JayPubS-2
❑ 58Top-370
❑ 58YanJayP-2
❑ 58YooMatBC-1
❑ 59Top-180
❑ 59TopVen-180
❑ 59Yoo-1
❑ 60Baz-8
❑ 60KeyChal-7
❑ 60NuHi-28
❑ 60Top-480
❑ 60TopTat-6
❑ 60YanJayP-1
❑ 61ChePat-2
❑ 61NuSco-453
❑ 61Pos-1A
❑ 61Pos-1B
❑ 61SevElev-22
❑ 61Top-425
❑ 61Top-472
❑ 61TopMagR-23
❑ 61TopStal-189
❑ 61Yan61RL-8
❑ 61YanJayP-1
❑ 62ExhStaB-4
❑ 62Jel-7
❑ 62Pos-7
❑ 62PosCan-7
❑ 62SalPlaC-33
❑ 62ShiPlaC-33
❑ 62Top-88
❑ 62Top-360
❑ 62TopBuc-9
❑ 62TopStal-83
❑ 62TopVen-88
❑ 62YanJayP-2
❑ 63BasMagM-11
❑ 63ExhStaB-7
❑ 63Jel-17
❑ 63Pos-17
❑ 63ReqKP-2A
❑ 63ReqKP-2B
❑ 63SalMetC-62
❑ 63Top-340
❑ 63YanJayP-1
❑ 64ChatheY-1
❑ 64Top-21
❑ 64TopVen-21
❑ 64YanJayP-1
❑ 65MetJayP-2
❑ 65MetPos-1
❑ 65Top-470
❑ 66MetTeal-1
❑ 66MetVolC-2
❑ 67MetTeal-1
❑ 67TopVen-179
❑ 69MetTeal-2
❑ 71MetTeal-2
❑ 73HalofFPP-1
❑ 73MetAllEB-1
❑ 73NewYorSNM-1
❑ 73OPC-257
❑ 73SevTraC-5
❑ 73Top-257A
❑ 73Top-257B
❑ 74MetDaiPA-13
❑ 74MetJapEB-1
❑ 74NewYorNTDiS-1
❑ 74NewYorNTDiS-11
❑ 74NewYorNTDiS-28
❑ 74OPC-179
❑ 74Top-179
❑ 75MetSSP-19
❑ 75OPC-189
❑ 75OPC-192
❑ 75OPC-193
❑ 75OPC-421
❑ 75SSP18-5
❑ 75SSP42-40
❑ 75Top-189
❑ 75Top-192
❑ 75Top-193
❑ 75Top-421
❑ 75TopMin-189
❑ 75TopMin-192
❑ 75TopMin-193
❑ 75TopMin-421
❑ 76GalBasGHoF-3
❑ 76GrePlaG-22
❑ 76ShaPiz-127
❑ 76TayBow4-10
❑ 77BobParHoF-79
❑ 78YanPhoA-2
❑ 79BasGre-71
❑ 79TCM50-2
❑ 79YanPicA-3
❑ 80PacLeg-67
❑ 80PerHaloFP-127
❑ 80PerHaloFPS-16
❑ 80SSPHOF-127
❑ 80YanPhoA-1
❑ 81Don-351
❑ 81TCM60I-382
❑ 81TCM60I-407
❑ 81TCM60I-474
❑ 81YanPhoA-1
❑ 82ASAMicM-19
❑ 82ASAMicM-42
❑ 82BasCarN-4
❑ 82Don-387
❑ 82TCMGreS-15
❑ 82TCMStaot5-18
❑ 82YanPhoA-2
❑ 83ASAJohM-11
❑ 83ASAYogB-1
❑ 83ASAYogB-2
❑ 83ASAYogB-3
❑ 83ASAYogB-4
❑ 83ASAYogB-5
❑ 83ASAYogB-6
❑ 83ASAYogB-7
❑ 83ASAYogB-8
❑ 83ASAYogB-9
❑ 83ASAYogB-10
❑ 83ASAYogB-11
❑ 83ASAYogB-12
❑ 83DonHOFH-24
❑ 83FraBroR-9
❑ 83KelCerB-8
❑ 83MLBPin-2
❑ 83Oco& SSBG-3
❑ 83TopRep5-191
❑ 83Yan196-8
❑ 83YanASFY-4
❑ 83YanPhoA-3
❑ 83YanYealT-8
❑ 84FifNatCT-2
❑ 84OCoandSI-39
❑ 84OCoandSI-136
❑ 84SpoDesPW-31
❑ 84TopTra-13T
❑ 84TopTraT-13T
❑ 85CirK-33
❑ 85GeoSteM-1
❑ 85TCMPla1-29
❑ 85Top-132
❑ 85Top-155
❑ 85TopTif-132
❑ 85TopTif-155
❑ 85Woo-4
❑ 85YanTCMP-2
❑ 86AstPol-26
❑ 86SpoDecG-31
❑ 86TCM-11
❑ 86TCMSupS-9
❑ 86TCMSupS-39
❑ 87AstMot-27
❑ 87AstPol-26
❑ 87HygAllG-5
❑ 87LeaSpeO*-H2
❑ 87NesDreT-19
❑ 87Top-531
❑ 87TopTif-531
❑ 87Yan196T-6

❑ 88AstMot-27
❑ 88HouSho-11
❑ 88PacLegI-53
❑ 89AstLenH-14
❑ 89AstMot-27
❑ 89AstSmo-5
❑ 89BowInsT-2
❑ 89BowRepI-2
❑ 89BowTif-R2
❑ 89CMCMan-10
❑ 89MetRinP69-35
❑ 89PerCelP-6
❑ 90AGFA-22
❑ 90BasWit-24
❑ 90PacLeg-7
❑ 90PerGreM-53
❑ 90PerMasW-26
❑ 90PerMasW-27
❑ 90PerMasW-28
❑ 90PerMasW-29
❑ 90PerMasW-30
❑ 90SweBasG-105
❑ 91Col-35
❑ 91Kel3D-11
❑ 91KelStaU-3
❑ 91LinDri-7
❑ 91MDAA-11
❑ 91MetWIZ-36
❑ 91SweBasG-8
❑ 91TopArc1-104
❑ 91UppDecS-8
❑ 91YanRinP11-1
❑ 92ActPacA-1
❑ 92ActPacA2-1G
❑ 92ActPacAP-1
❑ 92BazQua5A-4
❑ 92FroRowBe-1
❑ 92FroRowBe-1AU
❑ 92FroRowBe-2
❑ 92FroRowBe-3
❑ 92FroRowBe-4
❑ 92FroRowBe-5
❑ 92MDAMVP-1
❑ 92MVP-2
❑ 92MVP2H-4
❑ 92PinMan-25
❑ 92RevLeg1-10
❑ 92RevLeg1-11
❑ 92RevLeg1-12
❑ 92SpoIllFK1-212
❑ 92YanWIZ6-8
❑ 92YanWIZA-3
❑ 92YanWIZH-3
❑ 92Zip-10
❑ 93ActPacAC-1
❑ 93MetIma-3
❑ 93TedWil-58
❑ 93TedWilLC-1
❑ 93TedWilPC-21
❑ 93UppDecAH-9
❑ 93Yoo-2
❑ 94Met69CCPP-4
❑ 94Met69CS-3
❑ 94Met69T-30
❑ 94TedWilM-M25
❑ 94TopArc1-50
❑ 94TopArc1G-50
❑ 94UppDecAH-114
❑ 94UppDecAH-145
❑ 94UppDecAH-158
❑ 94UppDecAH1-114
❑ 94UppDecAH1-145
❑ 94UppDecAH1-158
❑ 94UppDecTAE-62
❑ 95BalParF-1
❑ 95StoPop-1
❑ 97DonSigSS-3
❑ 97JimDea-1
❑ 97NewYorL-1
❑ 97SpoIllCC-2
❑ 97TopMan-21
❑ 97TopMan-23
❑ 97TopManF-21
❑ 97TopManF-23
❑ 97TopManFR-21
❑ 97TopManFR-23
❑ 98BowChrR-1
❑ 98BowChrRR-1
❑ 98DonSigSS-2
❑ 98SpoIllTaN-4
❑ 98SpoIllTaNEE-4
❑ 98SpoIllTaNGS-23
❑ 98SpoIllWSFAE-8
❑ 98SpoIllWSFAEG-8
❑ 98UppDecR-66
❑ 98UppDecRSotT-YB
❑ 99TopHaloFC-HOF10
❑ 99TopStaRR-3
❑ 99TopStaRRA-3
❑ 99UppDecCL-40
❑ 99UppDecCLCC-40
❑ 99UppDecCLES-YB
❑ 99UppDecCLESC-YB

Berres, Ray (Raymond F.)
❑ 34DiaMatCSB-12
❑ 39PlaBal-156
❑ 40PlaBal-164
❑ 60Top-458
❑ 79DiaGre-216
❑ 81WhiSox1T-43
❑ 90DodTar-50

Berringer, John
❑ 87PeoChiP-10
❑ 88WinSpiS-1

Berrios, Harry
❑ 92LSUTigM-4
❑ 93LSUTigM-10
❑ 94AlbPolC-4
❑ 94FreKeyC-3
❑ 94LSUTigMP-8
❑ 95Bow-58
❑ 95Exc-2
❑ 95ExcLeaL-4
❑ 96BowBayB-6

Berrios, Hector
❑ 87FayGenP-1
❑ 88BlaYNPRWL-132
❑ 88GleFalTP-935
❑ 89BlaYNPRWL-5
❑ 90LakTigS-3
❑ 91MidAngOHP-4
❑ 91PalSprAP-2007
❑ 92AlbDukS-4
❑ 92IowCubF-4046
❑ 98HagSunM-2

Berrios, Juan
❑ 87EugEmeP-2669

Berroa, Ed
❑ 79ElmPioRST-22

Berroa, Geronimo
❑ 85KinBluJT-21
❑ 86VenGulP-1
❑ 87KnoBluJP-1508
❑ 87SouLeaAJ-3
❑ 88Don-659
❑ 88SyrChiC-13
❑ 88SyrChiP-808
❑ 88TriAAAP-36
❑ 89Bow-279
❑ 89BowTif-279
❑ 89DonRoo-19
❑ 89FleUpd-72
❑ 89Sco-632
❑ 89ScoHot1R-30
❑ 89ScoYouS2-17
❑ 89Spo-225
❑ 89TopBig-297
❑ 89TopTra-10T
❑ 89TopTraT-10T
❑ 90ClaBlu-83
❑ 90CMC-292
❑ 90Don-104
❑ 90Fle-575
❑ 90FleCan-575
❑ 90OPC-617
❑ 90ProAAAF-414
❑ 90RicBraBC-15
❑ 90RicBraC-16
❑ 90RicBraP-269
❑ 90RicBraTI-5
❑ 90Sco-151
❑ 90Sco100RS-36
❑ 90Top-617
❑ 90TopDeb89-17
❑ 90TopTif-617
❑ 90UppDec-531
❑ 91ColSprSSP-2195
❑ 92NasSouF-1843
❑ 92NasSouS-284
❑ 92TriA AAS-284
❑ 93Don-214
❑ 93EdmTraF-1147
❑ 93FleFinE-52
❑ 93LimRocDWB-29
❑ 93MarlStaClu-23
❑ 93TopTra-117T
❑ 94A'sMot-13
❑ 94Fin-245
❑ 94FinRef-245
❑ 94Fla-328
❑ 94FleExtB-144
❑ 94FleUpd-73
❑ 94Pin-387
❑ 94PinArtP-387
❑ 94PinMusC-387
❑ 94Sel-374
❑ 94SpoRoo-12
❑ 94SpoRooAP-12
❑ 94StaClu-591
❑ 94StaCluFDI-591
❑ 94StaCluGR-591
❑ 94StaCluMOP-591
❑ 94TopTra-86T
❑ 95A'sCHP-3
❑ 95AthMot-12
❑ 95ColCho-131
❑ 95ColChoGS-131
❑ 95ColChoSS-131
❑ 95Don-84
❑ 95DonPreP-84
❑ 95DonTopotO-132
❑ 95Emo-69
❑ 95Fin-286
❑ 95FinRef-286
❑ 95Fla-292
❑ 95Fle-239
❑ 95Lea-56
❑ 95LeaLim-2
❑ 95Pac-309
❑ 95PacLatD-5
❑ 95PacPri-101
❑ 95Pin-210
❑ 95PinArtP-210
❑ 95PinMusC-210
❑ 95Sco-502
❑ 95ScoGolR-502
❑ 95ScoPlaTS-502
❑ 95StaClu-296
❑ 95StaCluMOP-296
❑ 95StaCluSTWS-296
❑ 95StaCluVR-154
❑ 95StaCluVRMO-154
❑ 95Stu-198
❑ 95Top-187
❑ 95TopCyb-107
❑ 95Ult-90
❑ 95UltGolM-90
❑ 95UppDec-29
❑ 95UppDecED-29
❑ 95UppDecEDG-29
❑ 95UppDecSE-246
❑ 95UppDecSEG-246
❑ 96A'sMot-14
❑ 96Cir-71
❑ 96CirRav-71
❑ 96ColCho-238
❑ 96ColChoGS-238
❑ 96ColChoSS-238
❑ 96Don-391
❑ 96DonPreP-391
❑ 96EmoXL-101
❑ 96Fla-143
❑ 96Fle-203
❑ 96FleTif-203
❑ 96Lea-158
❑ 96LeaPrePB-158
❑ 96LeaPrePG-158
❑ 96LeaPrePS-158
❑ 96LeaSigA-24
❑ 96LeaSigAG-24
❑ 96LeaSigAS-24
❑ 96MetUni-98
❑ 96MetUniP-98
❑ 96Pac-397
❑ 96PacEstL-EL4
❑ 96PacPri-P124
❑ 96PacPriG-P124
❑ 96PanSti-217
❑ 96ProSta-10
❑ 96Sco-470
❑ 96StaClu-225
❑ 96StaClu-358
❑ 96StaCluEPB-358
❑ 96StaCluEPG-358
❑ 96StaCluEPS-358
❑ 96StaCluMOP-225
❑ 96StaCluMOP-358
❑ 96Stu-35
❑ 96StuPrePB-35
❑ 96StuPrePG-35
❑ 96StuPrePS-35
❑ 96Top-154
❑ 96TopGal-57
❑ 96TopGalPPI-57
❑ 96Ult-110
❑ 96UltGolM-110
❑ 96UppDec-160
❑ 97A'sMot-5
❑ 97Bow-41
❑ 97BowInt-41
❑ 97Cir-178
❑ 97CirRav-178
❑ 97ColCho-185
❑ 97Don-95
❑ 97Don-302
❑ 97DonGolPP-95
❑ 97DonGolPP-302
❑ 97DonLim-170
❑ 97DonLimE-170
❑ 97DonLimENG-170
❑ 97DonSigA-11
❑ 97DonSigAC-13
❑ 97DonSigAM-13
❑ 97DonSilPP-95
❑ 97DonSilPP-302
❑ 97Fin-189
❑ 97FinRef-189
❑ 97FlaShoLC-92
❑ 97FlaShoLeg0-92
❑ 97FlaShoLeg1-92
❑ 97FlaShoM-A92
❑ 97FlaShoM-B92
❑ 97FlaShoM-C92
❑ 97FlaShoR0-92
❑ 97FlaShoR1-92
❑ 97FlaShoR2-92
❑ 97Fle-184
❑ 97FleTif-184
❑ 97Lea-141
❑ 97LeaFraM-141
❑ 97LeaFraMDC-141
❑ 97MetUni-127
❑ 97Pac-165
❑ 97PacLatotML-17
❑ 97PacLigB-165
❑ 97PacPri-57
❑ 97PacPriGA-GA12
❑ 97PacPriLB-57
❑ 97PacPriP-57
❑ 97PacPriSL-SL5C
❑ 97PacSil-165
❑ 97PinX-PSfF-8
❑ 97PinX-PSfFU-8
❑ 97Sco-37
❑ 97ScoArtPWB-37
❑ 97ScoPreS-37
❑ 97ScoShoS-37
❑ 97ScoShoSAP-37
❑ 97Sel-180
❑ 97SelCom-180
❑ 97SP-132
❑ 97StaClu-243
❑ 97StaCluMat-243
❑ 97StaCluMOP-243
❑ 97Top-169
❑ 97TopChr-68
❑ 97TopChrR-68
❑ 97TopGal-67
❑ 97TopGalPPI-67
❑ 97Ult-109
❑ 97UltGolME-109
❑ 97UltPlaME-109
❑ 97UppDec-130
❑ 98ColCho-351
❑ 98Don-240
❑ 98DonColL-246
❑ 98DonGolPP-240
❑ 98DonPriCL-246
❑ 98DonSilPP-240
❑ 98Fin-4
❑ 98FinNo--4
❑ 98FinNo-R-4
❑ 98FinRef-4
❑ 98Fle-456
❑ 98Lea-47
❑ 98LeaFraDA-47
❑ 98LeaFraF-47
❑ 98LeaFraM-47
❑ 98LeaFraM-47
❑ 98LeaFraMDC-47
❑ 98LeaFraMDC-47
❑ 98LeaFraMZ2-47
❑ 98OriSco-5
❑ 98OriScoP-5
❑ 98Pac-21
❑ 98PacInv-8
❑ 98PacInvPBlue-8
❑ 98PacInvSilv-8
❑ 98PacLatotML-4
❑ 98PacOnl-212
❑ 98PacOnlR-212
❑ 98PacOnlWC-212
❑ 98PacPar-35
❑ 98PacParC-35
❑ 98PacParG-35
❑ 98PacParHS-35
❑ 98PacParPB-35
❑ 98PacParR-35
❑ 98PacPlaB-21
❑ 98PacRedT-21
❑ 98PacSil-21
❑ 98Pin-78
❑ 98PinPlu-61
❑ 98PinPreP-78
❑ 98PinSna-CI14
❑ 98Sco-84
❑ 98ScoRT-199
❑ 98ScoSS-PP38
❑ 98ScoSSAP-PP38
❑ 98Top-363
❑ 98TopChr-363
❑ 98TopChrR-363
❑ 98TopDevR-363
❑ 98TopDia-363
❑ 98TopMiniC-363
❑ 98Ult-316
❑ 98UltGolM-316
❑ 98UltMas-316
❑ 98UltPlaM-316
❑ 98UppDec-311
❑ 98UppDec-667
❑ 99Pac-157
❑ 99PacPlaB-157
❑ 99PacRed-157

Berry, Al
❑ 91HigSchPLS-34

Berry, Charlie (Charles F.)
❑ 26Zee-90
❑ 31Exh-17
❑ 33CraJacP-1
❑ 33ExhFou-9
❑ 33ExhFou-10
❑ 33Gou-184
❑ 34DiaMatCSB-13
❑ 35GouPuzR-4C
❑ 35GouPuzR-7C
❑ 35GouPuzR-12C
❑ 36ExhFou-14
❑ 36NatChiFPR-8
❑ 40PlaBal-190
❑ 45A'sTeal-2
❑ 92ConTSN-398
❑ 94ConTSN-1044
❑ 94ConTSNB-1044

Berry, Claude Elzy
❑ 09ObaT21-47
❑ 09ObaT21-153
❑ 09ObaT21-321
❑ 11PacCoaBD-7
❑ 11Zee-82
❑ 12HomRunKE-62
❑ 12ObaPreT-70
❑ 12Zee-103
❑ 13Zee-51

Berry, Jason
❑ 94OneYanC-4
❑ 94OneYanF-3780
❑ 96HudValRB-18
❑ 96WesOahCHWB-34
❑ 97St.PetDR-8

Berry, Jeff
❑ 94SarRedSC-4
❑ 94SarRedSF-1953
❑ 94UtiBluSC-5
❑ 94UtiBluSF-3821

Berry, Joe (Joseph H.)
❑ 21KoBreWSI-3
❑ 22W575-8

Berry, Ken (Allen Kent)
❑ 65Top-368
❑ 66OPC-127
❑ 66Top-127
❑ 66TopVen-127
❑ 66WhiSoxTI-3
❑ 67CokCapWS-17
❑ 67DexPre-22
❑ 67OPC-67
❑ 67Top-67
❑ 67TopVen-250
❑ 68Top-485
❑ 69MilBra-25
❑ 69MLBOffS-29
❑ 69Top-494
❑ 69TopSta-153
❑ 69TopTeaP-11
❑ 69WhiSoxTI-3
❑ 70MLBOffS-182
❑ 70OPC-239
❑ 70Top-239
❑ 70WhiSoxTI-2
❑ 71AngJacitB-2
❑ 71MLBOffS-339
❑ 71OPC-466
❑ 71Top-466
❑ 72MilBra-31
❑ 72OPC-379
❑ 72Top-379
❑ 73OPC-445
❑ 73Top-445
❑ 74OPC-163
❑ 74Top-163
❑ 75CleIndP-4
❑ 75OPC-432
❑ 75Top-432
❑ 75TopMin-432
❑ 78TCM60I-53
❑ 82OneYanT-4
❑ 87AppFoxP-24
❑ 89BirBarADB-3
❑ 89BirBarB-20
❑ 89BirBarP-89
❑ 90BirBarADB-3
❑ 90BirBarB-28
❑ 90BirBarP-1397
❑ 94BreMilB-9
❑ 98BinMetQ-2

Berry, Kevin
❑ 90BilMusP-3211
❑ 91CedRapRC-1
❑ 91CedRapRP-2709

Berry, Kirk
❑ 86MacPirP-3

Berry, Mark
❑ 85CedRapRT-14
❑ 86FloStaLAP-7
❑ 86TamTarP-3
❑ 87NasSouTI-1
❑ 87VerRedP-24
❑ 88GreHorP-1575
❑ 89GreHorP-405
❑ 90ChaWheP-2256
❑ 91CedRapRC-27
❑ 91CedRapRP-2736
❑ 92CedRapRC-28
❑ 92CedRapRF-1089
❑ 93WinSpiC-25
❑ 93WinSpiF-1584
❑ 94CarLeaAF-CAR44
❑ 94WinSpiC-26
❑ 94WinSpiF-287
❑ 96ChaLooB-1
❑ 97ChaLoo-1
❑ 98ChaLooG-3

Berry, Mary
❑ 90ChaWheB-25

Berry, Mike
❑ 96HigDesMB-6
❑ 97BowBay-8
❑ 98ColCliM-6
❑ 98NorNavQ-4

Berry, Neil (Cornelius John)
❑ 49Bow-180
❑ 50Bow-241
❑ 51Bow-213
❑ 52Bow-219
❑ 54OriEss-2
❑ 85TCMPpl1-27
❑ 91OriCro-31

Berry, Perry
❑ 91OscAstC-17
❑ 91OscAstP-691
❑ 92BurAstC-20
❑ 92BurAstF-552
❑ 93OscAstC-4
❑ 93OscAstF-633

Berry, Rich
❑ 21Zee-87

Berry, Sean
❑ 86EugEmeC-38
❑ 87Ft.MyeRP-7
❑ 88BasCitRS-6
❑ 89BasCitRS-5
❑ 90Bes-86
❑ 90MemChiB-6
❑ 90MemChiP-1016
❑ 90MemChiS-2
❑ 90ProAaA-49
❑ 91LinDriAAA-326
❑ 91OmaRoyLD-326
❑ 91OmaRoyP-1039
❑ 91Sco-764
❑ 91TopDeb90-15

❑ 91UppDec-10
❑ 92Cla1-T15
❑ 92Don-651
❑ 92Fle-680
❑ 92OmaRoyF-2966
❑ 92OmaRoyS-327
❑ 92Pin-271
❑ 92Sco-678
❑ 92SkyAAAF-149
❑ 92StaClu-114
❑ 93Don-275
❑ 93ExpPosN-4
❑ 93Fle-458
❑ 93Lea-336
❑ 93OPC-37
❑ 93OPCPre-97
❑ 93PacSpa-529
❑ 93Pin-212
❑ 93Sco-543
❑ 93ScoBoyoS-16
❑ 93SelRoo-146T
❑ 93StaClu-184
❑ 93StaCluFDI-184
❑ 93StaCluMOP-184
❑ 93Top-758
❑ 93TopGol-758
❑ 93TopInaM-758
❑ 93TopInaR-758
❑ 93TopMic-758
❑ 93Ult-411
❑ 93UppDec-644
❑ 93UppDecGold-644
❑ 94ColC-51
❑ 94ColChoGS-51
❑ 94ColChoSS-51
❑ 94Don-461
❑ 94Fin-342
❑ 94FinRef-342
❑ 94Fla-186
❑ 94Fle-533
❑ 94FleExtB-300
❑ 94Lea-42
❑ 94Pac-374
❑ 94PanSti-207
❑ 94Pin-456
❑ 94PinArtP-456
❑ 94PinMusC-456
❑ 94Sel-373
❑ 94StaClu-67
❑ 94StaClu-649
❑ 94StaCluFDI-67
❑ 94StaCluFDI-649
❑ 94StaCluGR-67
❑ 94StaCluGR-649
❑ 94StaCluMOP-67
❑ 94StaCluMOP-649
❑ 94Stu-75
❑ 94Top-344
❑ 94TopGol-344
❑ 94TopSpa-344
❑ 94Ult-223
❑ 94UppDec-427
❑ 94UppDecED-427
❑ 95ColCho-234
❑ 95ColChoGS-234
❑ 95ColChoSS-234
❑ 95Don-293
❑ 95DonPreP-293
❑ 95DonTopotO-277
❑ 95Fle-345
❑ 95Lea-291
❑ 95Pac-263
❑ 95Sco-514
❑ 95ScoGolR-514
❑ 95ScoPlaTS-514
❑ 95StaClu-391
❑ 95StaCluMOP-391
❑ 95StaCluSTWS-391
❑ 95StaCluVR-205
❑ 95StaCluVRMO-205
❑ 95Top-530
❑ 95TopCyb-315
❑ 95Ult-187
❑ 95UltGolM-187
❑ 95UppDec-76
❑ 95UppDecED-76
❑ 95UppDecEDG-76
❑ 96AstMot-6
❑ 96ColCho-773
❑ 96Don-368
❑ 96DonPreP-368
❑ 96EmoXL-195
❑ 96Fin-S274
❑ 96FinRef-S274
❑ 96Fla-274
❑ 96Fle-453
❑ 96FleTif-453
❑ 96FleUpd-U137
❑ 96FleUpdTC-U137
❑ 96MetUni-174
❑ 96MetUniP-174
❑ 96Pac-120
❑ 96Pin-337
❑ 96PinFoil-337
❑ 96Sco-435
❑ 96StaClu-67
❑ 96StaCluMOP-67
❑ 96Top-113
❑ 96Ult-484
❑ 96UltGolM-484
❑ 96UppDec-134
❑ 96UppDec-497U
❑ 97AstMot-8
❑ 97Cir-17
❑ 97CirRav-17
❑ 97ColCho-348
❑ 97Fle-341
❑ 97FleTif-341
❑ 97Pac-313
❑ 97PacLigB-313
❑ 97PacPri-107
❑ 97PacPriLB-107
❑ 97PacPriP-107
❑ 97PacSil-313
❑ 97Sco-41
❑ 97ScoArtPWB-41
❑ 97ScoPreS-41
❑ 97ScoShoS-41
❑ 97ScoShoSAP-41
❑ 97StaClu-259
❑ 97StaCluMOP-259
❑ 97Top-248
❑ 97Ult-206
❑ 97UltGolME-206
❑ 97UltPlaME-206
❑ 97UppDec-366
❑ 98Fle-427
❑ 98Pac-314
❑ 98PacOme-106
❑ 98PacOmeR-106
❑ 98PacOnl-314
❑ 98PacOnlR-314
❑ 98PacOnlWC-314
❑ 98PacPlaB-314
❑ 98PacRedT-314
❑ 98PacSil-314
❑ 98Pin-135
❑ 98PinPreP-135
❑ 98StaCluFDI-284
❑ 98StaCluI-284
❑ 98StaCluOneK-284
❑ 98StaCluPP-284
❑ 98Top-137
❑ 98TopChr-137
❑ 98TopChrR-137
❑ 98TopDevR-137
❑ 98TopDia-137
❑ 98TopMiniC-137
❑ 98UppDec-682
❑ 99Fle-380
❑ 99FleSta9-380
❑ 99FleWarT-380
❑ 99Pac-188
❑ 99PacPlaB-188
❑ 99PacRed-188
❑ 99SPSig-158
❑ 99UppDec-107
❑ 99UppDec-405
❑ 99UppDecCLM-C51
❑ 99UppDecEL1-107
❑ 99UppDecEL1-405
❑ 99UppDecEL2-107
❑ 99UppDecEL2-405
❑ 99UppDecM-110
❑ 99UppDecMGS-110
❑ 99UppDecMHFS-110
❑ 99UppDecMSS-110
❑ 99Vic-214

Berry, Tony
❑ 89GasRanP-1009
❑ 89GasRanS-3

Berryhill, Damon
❑ 86PitCubP-2
❑ 87IowCubTI-15
❑ 88CubDavB-9
❑ 88Don-639
❑ 88DonBasB-261
❑ 88DonRoo-31
❑ 88DonTeaBC-639
❑ 88Fle-642
❑ 88FleGlo-642
❑ 88FleUpd-75
❑ 88FleUpdG-75
❑ 88IowCubC-12
❑ 88IowCubP-537
❑ 88ScoRoo-82T
❑ 88ScoRooG-82T
❑ 88TopTra-15T
❑ 88TopTraT-15T
❑ 89Baz-2
❑ 89Bow-288
❑ 89BowTif-288
❑ 89CubMar-9
❑ 89Don-275
❑ 89Don-491
❑ 89DonBasB-116
❑ 89Fle-418
❑ 89FleGlo-418
❑ 89K-M-8
❑ 89OPC-6
❑ 89PanSti-52
❑ 89Sco-336
❑ 89ScoHot1R-77
❑ 89ScoYouSI-24
❑ 89Spo-216
❑ 89Top-543
❑ 89TopBig-60
❑ 89TopGloS-39
❑ 89TopRoo-4
❑ 89TopSti-51
❑ 89TopSti-318
❑ 89TopTif-543
❑ 89ToyRoo-4
❑ 89TVSpoM-22
❑ 89UppDec-455
❑ 90Bow-33
❑ 90BowTif-33
❑ 90Don-167
❑ 90Fle-26
❑ 90FleCan-26
❑ 90MLBBasB-52
❑ 90OPC-362
❑ 90PanSti-234
❑ 90PeoChiUTI-U3
❑ 90PubIntS-190
❑ 90Sco-163
❑ 90Spo-164
❑ 90Top-362
❑ 90TopSti-49
❑ 90TopTif-362
❑ 90TopTVCu-19
❑ 90UppDec-322
❑ 91CubMar-9
❑ 91CubVinL-4
❑ 91Don-631
❑ 91Fle-414
❑ 91Lea-156
❑ 91OPC-188
❑ 91Sco-881
❑ 91StaClu-28
❑ 91Top-188
❑ 91TopDesS-188
❑ 91TopMic-188
❑ 91TopTif-188
❑ 91Ult-56
❑ 91UppDec-319
❑ 92BraLykP-4
❑ 92BraLykS-5
❑ 92Don-771
❑ 92Lea-423
❑ 92LeaBlaG-423
❑ 92OPC-49
❑ 92Pin-390
❑ 92StaClu-856
❑ 92StaCluNC-856
❑ 92Top-49
❑ 92TopGol-49
❑ 92TopGolW-49
❑ 92TopMic-49
❑ 92Ult-456
❑ 92UppDec-706
❑ 93BluJayDM-19
❑ 93BraLykP-4
❑ 93BraLykS-5
❑ 93BraStaC-14
❑ 93Don-78
❑ 93Don-254
❑ 93Fle-362
❑ 93Lea-196
❑ 93OPC-32
❑ 93PacSpa-332
❑ 93Pin-392
❑ 93Sco-373
❑ 93StaClu-261
❑ 93StaCluFDI-261
❑ 93StaCluM-62
❑ 93StaCluMOP-261
❑ 93Top-306
❑ 93TopGol-306
❑ 93TopInaM-306
❑ 93TopInaR-306
❑ 93TopMic-306
❑ 93TriPla-113
❑ 93Ult-3
❑ 93UppDec-606
❑ 93UppDecGold-606
❑ 93UppDecSH-HI4
❑ 94ColC-602
❑ 94ColChoGS-602
❑ 94ColChoSS-602
❑ 94Don-58
❑ 94Fla-259
❑ 94Fle-353
❑ 94FleUpd-9
❑ 94Pac-3
❑ 94Sco-275
❑ 94ScoGolR-275
❑ 94Top-289
❑ 94TopGol-289
❑ 94TopSpa-289
❑ 94TopTra-11T
❑ 94Ult-149
❑ 95Fle-23
❑ 95RedKah-2
❑ 95Sco-251
❑ 95ScoGolR-251
❑ 95ScoPlaTS-251
❑ 97Ult-454
❑ 97UltGolME-454
❑ 97UltPlaME-454
❑ 98PacInvGems-216

Berryman, Chad
❑ 98ButCopKG-5

Berryman, Robb
❑ 93UtiBluSC-4
❑ 93UtiBluSF-3525

Bertaina, Frank
❑ 64BalOriP-6
❑ 65Top-396
❑ 66BalOriP-3
❑ 66Top-579
❑ 67BalOriP-11
❑ 67BalOriP-12
❑ 67SenPos-4
❑ 68OPC-131
❑ 68SenTeal-1
❑ 68Top-131
❑ 68TopVen-131
❑ 69MilBra-26
❑ 69Top-554
❑ 70Top-638
❑ 71MLBOffS-267
❑ 71OPC-422
❑ 71Top-422
❑ 72MilBra-32
❑ 81TCM60I-446
❑ 91OriCro-32

Bertell, Dick (Richard G.)
❑ 61Top-441
❑ 62TopStal-105
❑ 63CubJayP-2
❑ 63Jel-176
❑ 63Pos-176
❑ 63Top-287
❑ 64CubJayP-2
❑ 64Top-424
❑ 65CubJayP-3
❑ 65OPC-27
❑ 65Top-27
❑ 66Top-587

Berteotti, Jerry
❑ 94YakBeaC-1
❑ 94YakBeaF-3853

Berthau, Terrell
❑ 91ButCopKSP-4

Berthel, Dan
❑ 89EriOriS-2
❑ 90CarLeaA-6
❑ 90FreKeyTI-19
❑ 91FreKeyC-22
❑ 91FreKeyP-2376

Berthelot, Eric
❑ 94LSUTig-15
❑ 98PitMetM-8

Berti, Don
❑ 83DayBeaAT-14

Bertman, Skip
❑ 90LSUTigGM-1
❑ 90LSUTigP-1
❑ 91LSUTigP-3
❑ 92LSUTigM-1
❑ 93LSUTigM-2
❑ 94LSUTig-1

Bertoia, Reno Peter
❑ 54Top-131
❑ 55Top-94
❑ 57Top-390
❑ 58Top-232
❑ 59SenTealW-3
❑ 59TigGraASP-3
❑ 59Top-84
❑ 59TopVen-84
❑ 60Top-297
❑ 61Pos-95A
❑ 61Pos-95B
❑ 61Top-392
❑ 61TopStal-178
❑ 61TwiPetM-20
❑ 61TwiUniMC-3
❑ 94TopArc1-131
❑ 94TopArc1G-131

Bertolani, Jerry
❑ 86PenWhiSP-5
❑ 87DayBeaAP-22
❑ 88BirBarB-23
❑ 88SouLeaAJ-8
❑ 89BirBarB-12
❑ 89BirBarP-100

Bertolotti, Fulvio
❑ 78St.PetCT-1
❑ 79ArkTraT-15

Bertoni, Jeff
❑ 78QuaCitAT-3
❑ 80SalLakCGT-9
❑ 80VenLeaS-112
❑ 81SalLakCGT-16
❑ 82SpoIndT-13
❑ 83EvaTriT-13

Bertotti, Mike
❑ 91UtiBluSC-4
❑ 91UtiBluSP-3232
❑ 92SouBenWSC-11
❑ 92SouBenWSF-170
❑ 92UtiBluSC-25
❑ 93HicCraC-3
❑ 93HicCraF-1270
❑ 94BirBarC-3
❑ 94PriWilCC-2
❑ 94PriWilCF-1912
❑ 95Exc-26
❑ 96NasSouB-8

Bertrand, Ben
❑ 98SalVol-2

Bertucio, Charlie
❑ 83SanJosBC-3

Berube, Joe Henry
❑ 93BelMarCB-4
❑ 93BelMarF-3211

Berube, Luc (George)
❑ 87Ft.LauYP-11
❑ 87OneYanP-31
❑ 88Ft.LauYS-2

Berumen, Andres
❑ 91BasCitRC-1
❑ 91BasCitRP-1388
❑ 91Cla/Bes-65
❑ 92AppFoxCB-2
❑ 92AppFoxFl-975
❑ 93HigDesMC-3
❑ 93HigDesMF-32
❑ 93Top-627
❑ 93TopGol-627
❑ 93TopInaM-627
❑ 93TopInaR-627
❑ 93TopMic-627
❑ 94Bow-92
❑ 94Cla-57
❑ 94LasVegSF-862
❑ 94UppDecML-61
❑ 95Fla-415
❑ 95FleUpd-180
❑ 95PadMot-25
❑ 95Top-657
❑ 95UltGolMR-M4
❑ 96ColCho-293
❑ 96ColChoGS-293
❑ 96ColChoSS-293
❑ 96LasVegSB-6
❑ 97LasVegS1A-6
❑ 97PacPriGotD-GD204
❑ 98TacRaiQ-6

Besana, Fred
❑ 75OakOak2A-4
❑ 91OriCro-33

Bescher, Bob (Robert Henry)
❑ 09AmeCarE90-1-7
❑ 09ColChiE-29
❑ 09SpoNewSM-64
❑ 09T206-27
❑ 09T206-28
❑ 10DarChoE-3
❑ 10DomDisP-13
❑ 10E101-5
❑ 10E102-2
❑ 10MelMinE-5
❑ 10NadCarE-6
❑ 10PeoT21-5A
❑ 10PeoT21-5B
❑ 10SweCapPP-96
❑ 10W555-5
❑ 11E94-3
❑ 11HelSta-110
❑ 11S74Sil-72
❑ 11SpoLifCW-34
❑ 11SpoLifM-187
❑ 11T205-16
❑ 11TurRedT-81
❑ 12ColRedB-29
❑ 12ColTinT-29
❑ 12HasTriFT-56
❑ 12T207-13
❑ 13NatGamW-4
❑ 13TomBarW-3
❑ 14CraJacE-110
❑ 14PieStaT-10
❑ 14TexTomE-5
❑ 15AmeCarE106-3
❑ 15CraJacE-110
❑ 15SpoNewM-14
❑ 16SpoNewM-15
❑ 16TanBraE-1

Besh, Jeff
❑ 89GeoColC-1

Bess, Johnny
❑ 92PriRedC-10
❑ 92PriRedF-3089
❑ 93WesVirWC-2
❑ 93WesVirWF-2868
❑ 94WinSpiC-5
❑ 94WinSpiF-274
❑ 97SanJosG-5

Bessard, Lloyd
❑ 79ElmPioRST-1

Besse, Herman
❑ 43A'STEAI-4
❑ 47SigOil-75
❑ 49BowPCL-29
❑ 77TCMTheWY-34

Bessent, Don
❑ 56Dod-4
❑ 56Top-184
❑ 57Top-178
❑ 58DodTeal-3
❑ 58Top-401
❑ 59DodTeal-2
❑ 59Top-71
❑ 59TopVen-71
❑ 90DodTar-51
❑ 95TopArcBD-154

Bessie, Herman
❑ 42A'sTeal-3

Best, Bill
❑ 81ChaRoyT-21
❑ 82ForMyeRT-18
❑ 84MemChiT-5

Best, Jayson
❑ 89EliTwiS-3
❑ 90Bes-225
❑ 90KenTwiB-17
❑ 90KenTwiP-2286
❑ 90KenTwiS-1
❑ 90MidLeaASGS-3
❑ 91VisOakC-1
❑ 91VisOakP-1735
❑ 92ClaFS7-334
❑ 92Ft.MyeMCB-1
❑ 92Ft.MyeMF-2737
❑ 93NasXprF-394

Best, Jim
❑ 83AppFoxFr-6

Best, Karl
❑ 80LynSaiT-11
❑ 81LynSaiT-1
❑ 82LynSaiT-2
❑ 83SalLakCGT-5
❑ 84SalLakCGC-189
❑ 85CalCanC-76
❑ 85FleUpd-5
❑ 86Don-511
❑ 86Fle-459
❑ 86MarMot-19
❑ 86MarPacNB-2
❑ 86SevCoi-W16
❑ 86Top-61

❑ 86TopTif-61
❑ 87CalCanP-2318
❑ 87Don-198
❑ 87Fle-579
❑ 87FleGlo-579
❑ 87Top-439
❑ 87TopTif-439
❑ 88PorBeaC-2
❑ 88PorBeaP-646
❑ 88TriAAC-43
Beswick, Jim (James W.)
❑ 79HawIslC-21
❑ 79HawIslT-10
❑ 79Top-725
❑ 80HawIslT-8
❑ 81HawIslT-7
❑ 83NasAngT-17
Betances, Junior
❑ 94HelBreF-3619
❑ 94HelBreSP-4
❑ 95BelBreTI-19
❑ 96StoPorB-25
❑ 97KinIndB-2
❑ 98AkrAerM-20
Betances, Marcos
❑ 88BriTigP-1882
❑ 89FayGenP-1574
❑ 89NiaFalRP-3
❑ 90HamRedB-3
❑ 90HamRedS-6
❑ 90SavCarP-2060
Betancourt, Damaso
❑ 93LinVenB-20
❑ 95LinVen-34
❑ 96-97LinVen-158
Betancourt, Jose
❑ 93LinVenB-133
Betancourt, Oscar
❑ 97BoiHawG-2
❑ 98CedRapKTI-1
❑ 98CedRapKTI-2
Betancourt, Rafael
❑ 95LinVen-158
❑ 96MicBatCB-5
Betemit, Manuel
❑ 77NewCoPT-2
❑ 78BurBeeT-5
Bethancourt, Jose
❑ 90EliTwiS-3
Bethea, Bill (William Lamar)
❑ 60DarFar-4
❑ 66TolMudHTI-3
❑ 77FriOneYW-31
❑ 92TexLon-5
Bethea, Larry
❑ 95GreFalDTI-25
Bethea, Scott
❑ 90LSUTigP-10
❑ 91LynRedSC-14
❑ 91LynRedSP-1204
❑ 92NewBriRSF-438
❑ 92NewBriRSS-477
❑ 93NewBriRSF-1226
❑ 94HigDesMC-3
❑ 94HigDesMF-2794
Bethea, Steve
❑ 89SpoIndSP-25
❑ 90RivRedWB-2
❑ 90RivRedWCLC-7
❑ 90RivRedWP-2612
❑ 91Cla/Bes-148
❑ 91HigDesMC-18
❑ 91HigDesMP-2401
❑ 92WicWraF-3660
❑ 92WicWraS-626
❑ 93LasVegSF-950
Bethke, James
❑ 65Top-533
❑ 81TCM60I-413
❑ 91MetWIZ-37
Bethke, Jamie
❑ 91GulCoaRSP-7
❑ 92ButCopKSP-5
❑ 93ChaRaiC-3
❑ 93ChaRaiF-1913
❑ 94HigDesMC-4
❑ 94HigDesMF-2791
Bethune, Ian
❑ 96NewHavRB-31
❑ 97NewHavRB-30
Betten, Randy
❑ 95BoiHawTI-5
❑ 96LakElsSB-14
❑ 98MidAngO-4
Bettencourt, Justin
❑ 94BriTigC-5
❑ 94BriTigF-3492
❑ 96FayGenB-6
❑ 97LakTigB-9
❑ 98LakTigM-2
Bettendorf, Dave
❑ 86AncGlaPTI-3
❑ 88HagSunS-2
❑ 89HagSunB-9
❑ 89HagSunP-273
❑ 89HagSunS-1
❑ 89Sta-132
❑ 90HagSunDGB-4
❑ 90HagSunP-1419
Bettendorf, Jeff
❑ 83LynMetT-4
❑ 84A'sMot-25
❑ 84JacMetT-9
❑ 85MetTCM-7
❑ 85TidTidT-4
❑ 86ColAstP-4
❑ 87BirBarB-9
❑ 87SouLeaAJ-21
❑ 93HolLeg-2
Betti, Richard
❑ 96SarRedSB-8
❑ 96TreThuB-6
❑ 97TreThuB-7
Betto, Kaoru
❑ 79TCMJapPB-50
Betts, Darrell
❑ 95NewJerCTI-3
❑ 96NewJerCB-2
Betts, Huck (Walter)
❑ 22E120-196
❑ 33WorCig-9
❑ 34DiaMatCSB-14
❑ 34Gou-36
❑ 34GouCanV-83
❑ 34TarThoBD-2
❑ 79DiaGre-212
Betts, Todd
❑ 93BurIndC-4
❑ 93BurIndF-3305
❑ 94WatIndC-2
❑ 94WatIndF-3942
❑ 95Exc-36
❑ 95KinIndTI-3
❑ 96CanIndB-5
❑ 97AkrAer-4
❑ 98AkrAerM-21
Betz, Robert
❑ 52Par-80
Betzel, Bruno (Christian)
❑ 15SpoNewM-15
❑ 16SpoNewM-16
❑ 17ColE13-15
Betzsold, Jim
❑ 94WatIndC-3
❑ 94WatIndF-3949
❑ 95Exc-37
❑ 95KinIndTI-4
❑ 96CanIndB-6
❑ 96WesOahCHWB-21
❑ 97AkrAer-5
❑ 97TexAllM-5
❑ 98BufBisG-3
Beuder, John
❑ 87SalLakTTT-4
❑ 88BakDodCLC-246
Beuder, Mike
❑ 83VerBeaDT-1
Beuerlein, Ed
❑ 90AshTouP-2751
❑ 91OscAstC-14
❑ 91OscAstP-867
❑ 92AshTouC-5
Beuerlein, John
❑ 86StoPorP-1
❑ 87DenZepP-14
Beumiller, Albert
❑ 15Zee-3
Bevacqua, Kurt A.
❑ 72OPC-193
❑ 72Top-193
❑ 74OPC-454
❑ 74RoyPos-1
❑ 74Top-454
❑ 74TopTra-454T
❑ 76OPC-427
❑ 76OPC-564
❑ 76SpoIndC-15
❑ 76SSP-233
❑ 76Top-427
❑ 76Top-564
❑ 77Top-317
❑ 77TucTorC-33
❑ 78RanBurK-16
❑ 78SSP270-93
❑ 78Top-725
❑ 79Top-44
❑ 80Top-584
❑ 81Fle-382A
❑ 81Fle-382B
❑ 81PadFamF-2
❑ 81Top-118
❑ 82Fle-477
❑ 82Top-267
❑ 82TopTra-6T
❑ 83Fle-352
❑ 83PadTeal-1
❑ 83Top-674
❑ 84Don-80
❑ 84Fle-294
❑ 84FleSti-43
❑ 84Nes792-346
❑ 84PadMot-6
❑ 84PadSmo-1
❑ 84Top-346
❑ 84TopTif-346
❑ 85Don-647
❑ 85Fle-26
❑ 85PadMot-14
❑ 85Top-478
❑ 85TopSti-16
❑ 85TopTif-478
❑ 86Don-528
❑ 86Fle-315
❑ 86Top-789
❑ 86TopTif-789
❑ 93RanKee-70
❑ 94BreMilB-192
Bevan, Hal (Harold Joseph)
❑ 52A'sTeal-4
❑ 53BowBW-43
❑ 55A'sRodM-2
❑ 55JetPos-1
❑ 57SeaPop-4
❑ 58SeaRaIT-3
❑ 59SeaPop-2
❑ 60HenHouW-10
❑ 60SeaPop-2
❑ 60UniOil-22
❑ 61Top-456
❑ 80Red196T-36
Bevel, Bobby
❑ 96AshTouB-7
❑ 97SalAva-7
❑ 98SalAvaC-5
Bevenour, Keith
❑ 89WatIndS-2
Bevens, Bill (Floyd)
❑ 46SpoExcW-1-7
❑ 47TipTop-47
❑ 47YanTeaT-2
❑ 48Bow-22
❑ 60NuHi-3
❑ 83TCMPla1945-11
Beverlin, Jason
❑ 94SigRooDP-72
❑ 94SigRooDPS-72
❑ 95WesMicWTI-15
❑ 97NorNav-7
❑ 97NorNavTI-2
❑ 98NorNavQ-5
Beverly, Bill
❑ 92NegLeaRLI-4
Beverly, Demetrius
❑ 98BatMucTI-1
Bevil, Brian
❑ 92AppFoxCB-9
❑ 92AppFoxFI-976
❑ 92MidLeaATI-4
❑ 93Bow-125
❑ 93ClaGolF-103
❑ 93ExcFS7-172
❑ 93WilBluRC-3
❑ 93WilBluRF-1988
❑ 94ExcFS7-64
❑ 94MemChiF-349
❑ 94SigRoo-4
❑ 94SigRooS-4
❑ 94UppDecML-46
❑ 96TexLeaAB-21
❑ 96WicWraB-17
❑ 97Fle-677
❑ 97FleTif-677
❑ 97UppDec-286
❑ 98PacOme-112
❑ 98PacOmeR-112
❑ 98PacOmeRS-7
❑ 98PacOmeRST3-7
❑ 98PacOnl-336
❑ 98PacOnlR-336
❑ 98PacOnlWC-336
Beville, Monte (Henry Monte)
❑ 11SpoLifCW-35
Bevington, Terry
❑ 78BurBeeT-6
❑ 79HolMilT-2
❑ 80VanCanT-6
❑ 81BurBeeT-30
❑ 82BelBreFr-24
❑ 84ElPasDT-12
❑ 86VanCanP-2
❑ 87DenZepP-13
❑ 88VanCanP-778
❑ 90WhiSoxC-30
❑ 91WhiSoxK-NNO
❑ 92WhiSoxK-NNO
❑ 93WhiSoxK-30
❑ 94WhiSoxK-30
❑ 95WhiSoxK-4
❑ 95WhiSoxK-31
❑ 97WhiSoxTI-18
❑ 98SyrSkyG-3
Bevins, Andy
❑ 97NewJerCB-4
❑ 98PeoChiM-3
Beyeler, Arnie
❑ 87FayGenP-19
❑ 88LakTigS-3
❑ 89LonTigP-1371
❑ 90EasLeaAP-EL7
❑ 90LonTigP-1274
❑ 91LinDriAAA-579
❑ 91TolMudHLD-579
❑ 91TolMudHP-1938
❑ 98NorNavQ-28
Beyers, Tom
❑ 87VerBeaDP-22
❑ 89SalDodTI-1
❑ 90BakDodCLC-244
❑ 91CalLeLA-23
❑ 92BakDodCLC-30
❑ 93AlbDukF-1479
❑ 94SanAntMF-2486
Beyna, Terry
❑ 94AubAstC-3
❑ 94AubAstF-3764
Bezdek, Hugo
❑ 19W514-83
❑ 92ConTSN-396
Bhagwat, Tom
❑ 80ElPasDT-13
Biagini, Greg
❑ 86ChaOriW-3
❑ 87ChaO'sW-24
❑ 87SouLeaAJ-24
❑ 88ChaKniTI-23
❑ 89RocRedWC-25
❑ 89RocRedWP-1660
❑ 90CMC-326
❑ 90ProAAAF-477
❑ 90RocRedWC-25
❑ 90RocRedWGC-34
❑ 90RocRedWP-720
❑ 91LinDriAAA-474
❑ 91LinDriAAA-475
❑ 91RocRedWLD-474
❑ 91RocRedWP-1918
❑ 91TriA AAGP-AAA39
❑ 92BalOriP-3
❑ 93BalOriP-3
❑ 94BalOriP-3
❑ 96OklCit8B-1
❑ 97OklCit8-1
❑ 98OklRedM-1
Bialas, Dave
❑ 78SprRedWK-7
❑ 82SprCarF-2
❑ 83SprCarF-22
❑ 84ArkTraT-14
❑ 86FloStaLAP-8
❑ 86St.PetCP-4
❑ 87St.PetCP-18
❑ 89St.PetCS-27
❑ 90ArkTraGS-1
❑ 90SprCarDGB-22
❑ 91St.PetCC-9
❑ 91St.PetCP-2292
❑ 92St.PetCC-27
❑ 92St.PetCF-2041
❑ 93PadMot-28
❑ 94PadMot-28
Biancalana, Buddy (Roland A.)
❑ 82OmaRoyT-14
❑ 83OmaRoyT-13
❑ 84RoyPos-4
❑ 85RoyTeal-3
❑ 85Top-387
❑ 85TopTif-387
❑ 86BasStaB-10
❑ 86Don-605
❑ 86Fle-3
❑ 86RoyKitCD-2
❑ 86RoyNatP-1
❑ 86RoyTeal-3
❑ 86Spo-200
❑ 86Top-99
❑ 86TopSti-21
❑ 86TopTif-99
❑ 87Don-527
❑ 87DonOpeD-202
❑ 87Fle-364
❑ 87FleGlo-364
❑ 87SmoAmeL-7
❑ 87Top-554
❑ 87TopTif-554
❑ 88OmaRoyC-20
❑ 88OmaRoyP-1502
❑ 88Sco-383
❑ 88ScoGlo-383
❑ 93UppDecAH-10
Biancamano, John
❑ 91SpoIndC-22
❑ 91SpoIndP-3953
Bianchi, Ben
❑ 86VisOakP-3
❑ 87PorBeaP-16
❑ 89OrlTwiB-10
❑ 89OrlTwiP-1329
Bianchi, Steve
❑ 77AshTouT-2
❑ 79TucTorT-9
Bianchi, Whitey
❑ 90IBAWorA-33
Bianco, Robert
❑ 75AppFoxT-3
Bianco, Ron
❑ 86SumBraP-3
Bianco, Toby
❑ 75SacSolC-5
❑ 76SpoIndC-20
Bianco, Tommy (Thomas A.)
❑ 74SacSolC-50
❑ 76SSP-250
❑ 77EvaTriT-3
❑ 78RocRedWT-2
❑ 79RocRedWT-11
❑ 94BreMilB-193
Biasatti, Hank (Henry A.)
❑ 49A'sTeal-5
❑ 49PhiBul-4
❑ 50WorWidGV-44
Biasucci, Joe
❑ 91WinSpiC-16
❑ 91WinSpiP-2833
❑ 92PeoChiTI-3
❑ 92WinSpiC-19
❑ 93MidLeaAGF-48
❑ 93SprCarC-2
❑ 93SprCarF-1855
❑ 94ArkTraF-3093
❑ 94Bow-346
❑ 94ExcFS7-259
Bibb, Mitch
❑ 90WauTimS-29
❑ 91FreKeyC-30
❑ 95BowBayTI-NNO
❑ 96BowBayB-4
❑ 97BowBay-4
❑ 98BowBayM-4
Bibby, Jim
❑ 72OPC-316
❑ 72Top-316
❑ 73LinPor-172
❑ 73RanTeal-2
❑ 74OPC-11
❑ 74Top-11
❑ 74TopSta-231
❑ 75OPC-155
❑ 75RanPos-2
❑ 75SSP18-2
❑ 75Top-155
❑ 75TopMin-155
❑ 76OPC-324
❑ 76Top-324
❑ 77IndTeal-1
❑ 77Top-501
❑ 78OPC-61
❑ 78Top-636
❑ 79OPC-39
❑ 79Top-92
❑ 80Top-229
❑ 81AllGamPI-165
❑ 81CokTeaS-109
❑ 81Don-134
❑ 81Fle-370
❑ 81FleStiC-65
❑ 81OPC-93
❑ 81Top-430
❑ 81TopScr-105
❑ 81TopSti-216
❑ 81TopSti-260
❑ 82Don-171
❑ 82Fle-478
❑ 82FleSta-78
❑ 82FleSta-106
❑ 82OPC-170
❑ 82Top-170
❑ 82TopSti-86
❑ 83Top-355
❑ 84Fle-246
❑ 84Nes792-566
❑ 84Top-566
❑ 84TopTif-566
❑ 85LynMetT-2
❑ 86LynMetP-2
❑ 87LynMetP-20
❑ 89LynRedSS-24
❑ 89PacSenL-52
❑ 89T/MSenL-7
❑ 89TopSenL-128
❑ 90LynRedSTI-26
❑ 91LynRedSC-26
❑ 91LynRedSP-1216
❑ 93LynRedSC-27
❑ 93LynRedSF-2534
❑ 93RanKee-71
❑ 94LynRedSC-27
❑ 94LynRedSF-1909
❑ 95LynHilTI-1
❑ 96LynHilB-28
❑ 96RanCup-1
❑ 97LynHil-28
❑ 98LynHilQ-25
Biberdorf, Cam
❑ 88GreFalDTI-24
❑ 89BakDodCLC-190
❑ 90FloStaLAS-1
❑ 90VerBeaDS-5
❑ 91LinDriAA-531
❑ 91SanAntMLD-531
Bible, Mike
❑ 89SalLakTTI-21
Bice, Justin
❑ 96AriBlaDB-9
❑ 97HigDesMG-1
Bichette, Dante
❑ 86PalSprAP-3
❑ 88EdmTraC-23
❑ 88EdmTraP-576
❑ 89ClaTraP-199
❑ 89Don-634
❑ 89DonRoo-29
❑ 89Fle-468
❑ 89FleGlo-468
❑ 89PanSti-283
❑ 89Top-761
❑ 89TopTif-761
❑ 89UppDec-24
❑ 90ClaYel-T11
❑ 90Fle-127
❑ 90FleCan-127
❑ 90Lea-340
❑ 90OPC-43
❑ 90PubIntS-365
❑ 90ScoYouS2-10
❑ 90Top-43
❑ 90TopTif-43
❑ 90UppDec-688
❑ 91Bow-31
❑ 91BreMilB-3
❑ 91BrePol-2
❑ 91Don-303
❑ 91Fle-307
❑ 91FleUpd-29
❑ 91Lea-242
❑ 91OPC-564
❑ 91PanFreS-186
❑ 91PanSti-139
❑ 91Sco-463

❑ 91ScoRoo-37T
❑ 91StaClu-211
❑ 91Top-564
❑ 91TopDesS-564
❑ 91TopMic-564
❑ 91TopTif-564
❑ 91TopTra-10T
❑ 91TopTraT-10T
❑ 91UppDec-317
❑ 91UppDec-712
❑ 92Bow-264
❑ 92BrePol-3
❑ 92Don-347
❑ 92Fle-173
❑ 92Lea-134
❑ 92LeaBlaG-134
❑ 92OPC-371
❑ 92PanSti-39
❑ 92Pin-514
❑ 92Sco-316
❑ 92SpoIllFK1-712
❑ 92StaClu-7
❑ 92Stu-191
❑ 92Top-371
❑ 92TopGol-371
❑ 92TopGolW-371
❑ 92TopMic-371
❑ 92Ult-79
❑ 92UppDec-378
❑ 93Bow-92
❑ 93DenHol-23
❑ 93DiaMar-11
❑ 93Don-45
❑ 93Don-783
❑ 93Fla-35
❑ 93Fle-403
❑ 93FleFinE-22
❑ 93FunPac-174
❑ 93Lea-258
❑ 93MetBak-21
❑ 93PacSpa-422
❑ 93Pin-232
❑ 93PinExpOD-9
❑ 93RocStaC-5
❑ 93RocUSPC-3D
❑ 93RocUSPC-11H
❑ 93Sco-428
❑ 93Sel-114
❑ 93SP-217
❑ 93StaClu-616
❑ 93StaCluFDI-616
❑ 93StaCluMOP-616
❑ 93Stu-24
❑ 93Top-644
❑ 93TopGol-644
❑ 93TopInaM-644
❑ 93TopInaR-644
❑ 93TopMic-644
❑ 93TriPla-154
❑ 93Ult-341
❑ 93UppDec-478
❑ 93UppDec-683
❑ 93UppDecGold-478
❑ 93UppDecGold-683
❑ 94Bow-666
❑ 94BowBes-R17
❑ 94BowBesR-R17
❑ 94BreMilB-194
❑ 94ChuHomS-28
❑ 94ChuHomSG-28
❑ 94ColC-52
❑ 94ColChoGS-52
❑ 94ColChoSS-52
❑ 94Don-418
❑ 94Fin-59
❑ 94FinPre-59P
❑ 94FinRef-59
❑ 94Fla-151
❑ 94Fle-433
❑ 94FleExtB-242
❑ 94FUnPac-68
❑ 94Lea-81
❑ 94LeaL-100
❑ 94LeaMVPC-N2
❑ 94LeaMVPCG-N2
❑ 94OPC-30
❑ 94Pac-188
❑ 94PanSti-171
❑ 94Pin-346
❑ 94PinArtP-346
❑ 94PinMusC-346
❑ 94PinRunC-RC41
❑ 94ProMag-41
❑ 94RocPol-2
❑ 94Sco-110
❑ 94ScoCyc-TC9
❑ 94ScoGolR-110
❑ 94ScoGolS-22
❑ 94Sel-147
❑ 94SP-164
❑ 94SPDieC-164
❑ 94Spo-22
❑ 94StaClu-366
❑ 94StaCluFDI-366
❑ 94StaCluGR-366
❑ 94StaCluMOP-366
❑ 94StaCluT-105
❑ 94StaCluTFDI-105
❑ 94Stu-175
❑ 94Top-468
❑ 94TopGol-468
❑ 94TopSpa-468
❑ 94TriPla-221
❑ 94Ult-181
❑ 94UppDec-454
❑ 94UppDecED-454
❑ 95Baz-114
❑ 95Bow-384
❑ 95BowBes-R24
❑ 95BowBesR-R24
❑ 95ClaPhoC-24
❑ 95ColCho-450
❑ 95ColChoGS-450
❑ 95ColChoSE-209
❑ 95ColChoSE-260
❑ 95ColChoSEGS-209
❑ 95ColChoSEGS-260
❑ 95ColChoSESS-209
❑ 95ColChoSESS-260
❑ 95ColChoSS-450
❑ 95Don-302
❑ 95DonDiaK-DK4
❑ 95DonPreP-302
❑ 95DonTopotO-225
❑ 95Emo-123
❑ 95Fin-68
❑ 95FinPowK-PK13
❑ 95FinRef-68
❑ 95Fla-344
❑ 95FlaOutP-2
❑ 95Fle-514
❑ 95FleAllS-18
❑ 95FleTeaL-18
❑ 95Lea-135
❑ 95LeaLim-23
❑ 95LeaLimIBP-24
❑ 95Pac-132
❑ 95PacPri-43
❑ 95PanSti-71
❑ 95Pin-336
❑ 95PinArtP-336
❑ 95PinMusC-336
❑ 95RedFol-17
❑ 95RocPol-3
❑ 95Sco-15
❑ 95ScoGolR-15
❑ 95ScoHaloG-HG19
❑ 95ScoPlaTS-15
❑ 95Sel-10
❑ 95SelArtP-10
❑ 95SelCer-68
❑ 95SelCerMG-68
❑ 95SP-52
❑ 95SPCha-44
❑ 95SPChaDC-44
❑ 95Spo-125
❑ 95SpoArtP-125
❑ 95SPSil-52
❑ 95SPSpeF-34
❑ 95StaClu-326
❑ 95StaCluCT-11
❑ 95StaCluMO-5
❑ 95StaCluMOP-326
❑ 95StaCluSTWS-326
❑ 95StaCluVR-168
❑ 95StaCluVRMO-168
❑ 95Stu-71
❑ 95Sum-105
❑ 95SumNthD-105
❑ 95Top-140
❑ 95Top-390
❑ 95TopCyb-85
❑ 95TopEmb-83
❑ 95TopEmbGI-83
❑ 95TopFinIns-6
❑ 95TopLeaL-LL38
❑ 95UC3-71
❑ 95UC3ArtP-71
❑ 95Ult-151
❑ 95UltGolM-151
❑ 95UltHitM-3
❑ 95UltHitMGM-3
❑ 95UltRBIK-8
❑ 95UltRBIKGM-8
❑ 95UppDec-175
❑ 95UppDecED-175
❑ 95UppDecEDG-175
❑ 95UppDecPLL-R49
❑ 95UppDecPLLE-R49
❑ 95UppDecSE-242
❑ 95UppDecSEG-242
❑ 95USPlaCMLA-3C
❑ 95Zen-20
❑ 95ZenSam-20
❑ 96Baz-38
❑ 96Bow-25
❑ 96BowBes-14
❑ 96BowBesAR-14
❑ 96BowBesR-14
❑ 96BowFoi-25
❑ 96Cir-120
❑ 96CirBos-33
❑ 96CirRav-120
❑ 96ColCho-3
❑ 96ColCho-4
❑ 96ColCho-135
❑ 96ColCho-278
❑ 96ColCho-407
❑ 96ColCho-753
❑ 96ColChoCtG-CG14
❑ 96ColChoCtG-CG14B
❑ 96ColChoCtG-CG14C
❑ 96ColChoCtGE-CR14
❑ 96ColChoCtGG-CG14
❑ 96ColChoCtGG-CG14B
❑ 96ColChoCtGG-CG14C
❑ 96ColChoCtGGE-CR14
❑ 96ColChoGS-3
❑ 96ColChoGS-4
❑ 96ColChoGS-135
❑ 96ColChoGS-278
❑ 96ColChoGS-407
❑ 96ColChoGS-753
❑ 96ColChoSS-3
❑ 96ColChoSS-4
❑ 96ColChoSS-135
❑ 96ColChoSS-278
❑ 96ColChoSS-407
❑ 96ColChoSS-753
❑ 96DenHol-19
❑ 96Don-224
❑ 96DonEli-71
❑ 96DonPowA-6
❑ 96DonPowADC-6
❑ 96DonPreP-224
❑ 96DonPurP-6
❑ 96DonRouT-10
❑ 96EmoXL-172
❑ 96Fin-B126
❑ 96Fin-G66
❑ 96Fin-S289
❑ 96FinRef-B126
❑ 96FinRef-G66
❑ 96FinRef-S289
❑ 96Fla-243
❑ 96Fle-360
❑ 96FleLumC-2
❑ 96FleTeaL-18
❑ 96FleTif-360
❑ 96Kin-3
❑ 96Lea-101
❑ 96LeaAllGMC-9
❑ 96LeaAllGMCG-9
❑ 96LeaGolS-2
❑ 96LeaLim-48
❑ 96LeaLimG-48
❑ 96LeaPre-59
❑ 96LeaPreP-59
❑ 96LeaPrePB-101
❑ 96LeaPrePG-101
❑ 96LeaPrePS-101
❑ 96LeaPreSG-71
❑ 96LeaPreSte-71
❑ 96LeaSig-47
❑ 96LeaSigPPG-47
❑ 96LeaSigPPP-47
❑ 96MetUni-154
❑ 96MetUniP-154
❑ 96Pac-53
❑ 96PacGolCD-DC29
❑ 96PacOctM-OM3
❑ 96PacPri-P19
❑ 96PacPriFB-FB2
❑ 96PacPriG-P19
❑ 96PanSti-81
❑ 96PanSti-114
❑ 96PanSti-115
❑ 96Pin-3
❑ 96Pin-139
❑ 96Pin-272
❑ 96PinAfi-31
❑ 96PinAfiAP-31
❑ 96PinAfiFPP-31
❑ 96PinAfiSP-10
❑ 96PinArtP-3
❑ 96PinArtP-66
❑ 96PinArtP-172
❑ 96PinFan-11
❑ 96PinFoil-272
❑ 96PinPow-9
❑ 96PinSam-3
❑ 96PinSlu-9
❑ 96PinSta-3
❑ 96PinSta-66
❑ 96PinSta-172
❑ 96ProMagA-18
❑ 96ProMagDM-12
❑ 96ProSta-111
❑ 96RocFle-2
❑ 96RocPol-4
❑ 96Sco-271
❑ 96Sco-298
❑ 96ScoAll-8
❑ 96ScoDugC-B23
❑ 96ScoDugCAP-B23
❑ 96ScoGolS-23
❑ 96ScoPowP-11
❑ 96ScoTitT-7
❑ 96Sel-62
❑ 96SelArtP-62
❑ 96SelCer-71
❑ 96SelCerAP-71
❑ 96SelCerCB-71
❑ 96SelCerCR-71
❑ 96SelCerMB-71
❑ 96SelCerMG-71
❑ 96SelCerMR-71
❑ 96SelClaTF-16
❑ 96SelEnF-18
❑ 96SelTeaN-4
❑ 96SP-75
❑ 96Spo-4
❑ 96Spo-103
❑ 96SpoArtP-4
❑ 96SpoArtP-103
❑ 96SpoHitP-11
❑ 96SpoPowS-7
❑ 96SpoPro-13
❑ 96SPSpeFX-26
❑ 96SPSpeFXDC-26
❑ 96SPx-22
❑ 96SPxGol-22
❑ 96StaClu-204
❑ 96StaClu-336
❑ 96StaCluEPB-336
❑ 96StaCluEPG-336
❑ 96StaCluEPS-336
❑ 96StaCluMO-4
❑ 96StaCluMOP-204
❑ 96StaCluMOP-336
❑ 96StaCluMOP-PP15
❑ 96StaCluMOP-PS4
❑ 96StaCluPP-PP15
❑ 96StaCluPS-PS4
❑ 96Stu-137
❑ 96StuPrePB-137
❑ 96StuPrePG-137
❑ 96StuPrePS-137
❑ 96Sum-11
❑ 96SumAbo&B-11
❑ 96SumArtP-11
❑ 96SumBal-3
❑ 96SumBigB-12
❑ 96SumBigBM-12
❑ 96SumFoi-11
❑ 96SumHitI-12
❑ 96TeaOut-7
❑ 96Top-195
❑ 96TopChr-63
❑ 96TopChrR-63
❑ 96TopGal-3
❑ 96TopGalPG-PG14
❑ 96TopGalPPI-3
❑ 96TopLas-35
❑ 96TopMysF-M18
❑ 96TopMysFR-M18
❑ 96TopPro-NL11
❑ 96Ult-186
❑ 96UltGolM-186
❑ 96UltHomRK-2
❑ 96UltHomRKGM-2
❑ 96UltHomRKR-2
❑ 96UltHomRKRGM-2
❑ 96UltRBIK-3
❑ 96UltRBIKGM-3
❑ 96UppDec-320
❑ 96UppDecA-5
❑ 96UppDecDD-DD19
❑ 96UppDecDDG-DD19
❑ 96UppDecDDS-DD19
❑ 96UppDecPHE-H32
❑ 96UppDecPRE-R31
❑ 96UppDecPRE-R42
❑ 96UppDecPRE-R53
❑ 96UppDecPreH-H32
❑ 96UppDecPreR-R31
❑ 96UppDecPreR-R42
❑ 96UppDecPreR-R53
❑ 96UppDecRunP-RP2
❑ 96UppDecVJLS-VJ18
❑ 96Zen-13
❑ 96ZenArtP-13
❑ 96ZenMoz-12
❑ 97Bow-241
❑ 97BowBes-100
❑ 97BowBesAR-100
❑ 97BowBesR-100
❑ 97BowChr-67
❑ 97BowChrI-67
❑ 97BowChrIR-67
❑ 97BowChrR-67
❑ 97BowInt-241
❑ 97Cir-172
❑ 97CirRav-172
❑ 97ColCho-100
❑ 97ColChoCtG-14A
❑ 97ColChoCtG-14B
❑ 97ColChoCtG-14C
❑ 97ColChoCtGE-CG14
❑ 97ColChoCtGIW-CG14
❑ 97ColChoNF-NF14
❑ 97ColChoS-12
❑ 97ColChoSR-4
❑ 97ColChoT-CR1
❑ 97ColChoTBS-21
❑ 97ColChoTBSWH-21
❑ 97DenHol-18
❑ 97Don-80
❑ 97Don-418
❑ 97DonEli-60
❑ 97DonEliGS-60
❑ 97DonGolPP-80
❑ 97DonGolPP-418
❑ 97DonLim-140
❑ 97DonLim-178
❑ 97DonLimE-140
❑ 97DonLimE-178
❑ 97DonLimENG-178
❑ 97DonPre-48
❑ 97DonPreCttC-48
❑ 97DonSig-65
❑ 97DonSigPPP-65
❑ 97DonSilPP-80
❑ 97DonSilPP-418
❑ 97DonTea-94
❑ 97DonTeaSPE-94
❑ 97E-X2-67
❑ 97E-X2Cred-67
❑ 97E-X2EssCre-67
❑ 97Fin-5
❑ 97Fin-103
❑ 97Fin-346
❑ 97FinEmb-103
❑ 97FinEmb-346
❑ 97FinEmbR-103
❑ 97FinEmbR-346
❑ 97FinRef-5
❑ 97FinRef-103
❑ 97FinRef-346
❑ 97FlaShoLC-110
❑ 97FlaShoLeg0-110
❑ 97FlaShoLeg1-110
❑ 97FlaShoM-A110
❑ 97FlaShoM-B110
❑ 97FlaShoM-C110
❑ 97FlaShoR0-110
❑ 97FlaShoR1-110
❑ 97FlaShoR2-110
❑ 97Fle-307
❑ 97FleTif-307
❑ 97KinB-23
❑ 97Lea-135
❑ 97LeaDrefS-5
❑ 97LeaFraM-135
❑ 97LeaFraMDC-135
❑ 97MetUni-71
❑ 97NewPin-130
❑ 97NewPinAP-130
❑ 97NewPinMC-130
❑ 97NewPinPP-130
❑ 97Pac-279
❑ 97PacLigB-279
❑ 97PacPri-96
❑ 97PacPriLB-96
❑ 97PacPriP-96
❑ 97PacPriSL-SL9A
❑ 97PacSil-279
❑ 97PacTriCD-14
❑ 97Pin-44
❑ 97PinArtP-PP44
❑ 97PinCer-36
❑ 97PinCerMBla-36
❑ 97PinCerMBlu-36
❑ 97PinCerMG-36
❑ 97PinCerMR-36
❑ 97PinCerR-36
❑ 97PinIns-125
❑ 97PinInsCE-125
❑ 97PinInsDE-125
❑ 97PinMin-20
❑ 97PinMinB-20
❑ 97PinMinCB-20
❑ 97PinMinCG-20
❑ 97PinMinCGR-20
❑ 97PinMinCN-20
❑ 97PinMinCSS-20
❑ 97PinMinG-20
❑ 97PinMinS-20
❑ 97PinMusC-44
❑ 97PinPrePla-44
❑ 97PinTotCPB-36
❑ 97PinTotCPG-36
❑ 97PinTotCPR-36
❑ 97PinX-P-28
❑ 97PinX-PMoS-28
❑ 97PinX-PSfF-9
❑ 97PinX-PSfFU-9
❑ 97RocCok-1
❑ 97RocCok-2
❑ 97RocPol-2
❑ 97RocSco-1
❑ 97RocScoPl-1
❑ 97RocScoPr-1
❑ 97Sco-25
❑ 97ScoArtPWB-25
❑ 97ScoBla-11
❑ 97ScoPreS-25
❑ 97ScoShoS-25
❑ 97ScoShoSAP-25
❑ 97Sel-86
❑ 97SelArtP-86
❑ 97SelCom-86
❑ 97SelRegG-86
❑ 97SP-64
❑ 97SpoIll-110
❑ 97SpoIllEE-110
❑ 97SPSpxF-1
❑ 97SPSPxFA-1
❑ 97SPx-23
❑ 97SPxBro-23
❑ 97SPxGol-23
❑ 97SPxGraF-23
❑ 97SPxSil-23
❑ 97SPxSte-23
❑ 97StaClu-30
❑ 97StaCluMat-30
❑ 97StaCluMOP-30
❑ 97StaCluMOP-PG3
❑ 97StaCluPG-PG3
❑ 97Stu-34
❑ 97StuPrePG-34
❑ 97StuPrePS-34
❑ 97Top-380
❑ 97TopChr-130
❑ 97TopChrDD-DD9
❑ 97TopChrDDR-DD9
❑ 97TopChrR-130
❑ 97TopGal-58
❑ 97TopGalPPI-58
❑ 97TopIntF-ILM3
❑ 97TopIntFR-ILM3
❑ 97TopMemO5-5
❑ 97TopSta-62
❑ 97TopStaAM-62
❑ 97Ult-183
❑ 97UltChe-A1
❑ 97UltDouT-13
❑ 97UltGolME-183
❑ 97UltPlaME-183
❑ 97UltRBIK-3
❑ 97UltSeaC-2
❑ 97UppDec-60
❑ 97UppDecP-14
❑ 97UppDecPE-14
❑ 97UppDecRP-RP14
❑ 98Bow-233

❑ 98BowBes-4
❑ 98BowBesAR-4
❑ 98BowBesR-4
❑ 98BowChr-233
❑ 98BowChrGA-233
❑ 98BowChrGAR-233
❑ 98BowChrI-233
❑ 98BowChrIR-233
❑ 98BowChrR-233
❑ 98BowGolA-233
❑ 98BowInt-233
❑ 98CirThu-93
❑ 98CirThuRav-93
❑ 98CirThuSupRav-93
❑ 98ColCho-363
❑ 98CroRoy-49
❑ 98Don-149
❑ 98DonCol-149
❑ 98DonColL-275
❑ 98DonColP-606
❑ 98DonColS-149
❑ 98DonCruG-68
❑ 98DonCruP-68
❑ 98DonCruR-68
❑ 98DonGolPP-149
❑ 98DonPre-56
❑ 98DonPreSeat-56
❑ 98DonPriCD-149
❑ 98DonPriCL-275
❑ 98DonPriCP-606
❑ 98DonSig-6
❑ 98DonSigP-6
❑ 98DonSilPP-149
❑ 98Fin-176
❑ 98FinNo--176
❑ 98FinNo-R-176
❑ 98FinRef-176
❑ 98FlaShoLeg0-66
❑ 98FlaShoLeg1-66
❑ 98FlaShoLeg2-66
❑ 98FlaShoLeg3-66
❑ 98FlaShoLegM-66
❑ 98FlaShoR0-66
❑ 98FlaShoR1-66
❑ 98FlaShoR2-66
❑ 98FlaShoR3-66
❑ 98Fle-561
❑ 98KinDis-17
❑ 98Lea-76
❑ 98LeaFraDA-76
❑ 98LeaFraF-76
❑ 98LeaFraM-76
❑ 98LeaFraM-76
❑ 98LeaFraMDC-76
❑ 98LeaFraMDC-76
❑ 98LeaFraMS-76
❑ 98LeaFraMZ2-76
❑ 98LeaRS-73
❑ 98LeaRSLHolo-73
❑ 98LeaRSLong-73
❑ 98LeaRTrue-73
❑ 98MetUni-196
❑ 98MetUniPMG-196
❑ 98Pac-278
❑ 98PacAur-123
❑ 98PacInv-90
❑ 98PacInvPBlue-90
❑ 98PacInvSilv-90
❑ 98PacInvTeam-9
❑ 98PacOme-79
❑ 98PacOmeR-79
❑ 98PacOnl-239
❑ 98PacOnlR-239
❑ 98PacOnlWC-239
❑ 98PacPar-151
❑ 98PacParC-151
❑ 98PacParG-151
❑ 98PacParHS-151
❑ 98PacParI-11
❑ 98PacParPB-151
❑ 98PacParR-151
❑ 98PacPlaB-278
❑ 98PacRedT-278
❑ 98PacSil-278
❑ 98Pin-111
❑ 98PinArtP-PP64
❑ 98PinIns-96
❑ 98PinInsCE-96
❑ 98PinInsDE-96
❑ 98PinInsSG-10AB
❑ 98PinInsSG-10CD
❑ 98PinInsSG-24AB
❑ 98PinInsSG-24CD
❑ 98PinInsSGS-10AB
❑ 98PinInsSGS-10CD
❑ 98PinInsSGS-24AB
❑ 98PinInsSGS-24CD
❑ 98PinMusC-PP64
❑ 98PinPer-57
❑ 98PinPerPP-57
❑ 98PinPerSftF-28
❑ 98PinPlu-110
❑ 98PinPreP-111
❑ 98PinSna-CR9
❑ 98PinSna-CR16
❑ 98Revo-50
❑ 98RevoSS-50
❑ 98ScoRT-130
❑ 98ScoRTSS-PP79
❑ 98ScoRTSSAP-PP79
❑ 98ScoRTSSAP1-PP79
❑ 98SP Aut-86
❑ 98SpoIII-11
❑ 98SpoIIIEE-11
❑ 98SpoIIIFE-11
❑ 98SpoIIITaN-61
❑ 98SpoIIITaNEE-61
❑ 98SpoIIIWSF-48
❑ 98SpoIIIWSFEE-48
❑ 98SpoIIIWSFFE-48
❑ 98SPxFin-79
❑ 98SPxFinR-79
❑ 98SPxFinS-79
❑ 98StaCluFDI-192
❑ 98StaCluI-192
❑ 98StaCluOneK-192
❑ 98StaCluPP-192
❑ 98Stu-83
❑ 98StuGPP-83
❑ 98StuSPP-83
❑ 98Top-155
❑ 98TopChr-155
❑ 98TopChrR-155
❑ 98TopDevR-155
❑ 98TopDia-155
❑ 98TopGal-106
❑ 98TopGalGP-106
❑ 98TopGalOPP-106
❑ 98TopGalPPI-106
❑ 98TopGalPPIA-106
❑ 98TopGolLabC1-77
❑ 98TopGolLabC1B-77
❑ 98TopGolLabC1One-77
❑ 98TopGolLabC1R-77
❑ 98TopGolLabC2-77
❑ 98TopGolLabC2B-77
❑ 98TopGolLabC2One-77
❑ 98TopGolLabC2R-77
❑ 98TopGolLabC3-77
❑ 98TopGolLabC3B-77
❑ 98TopGolLabC3One-77
❑ 98TopGolLabC3R-77
❑ 98TopMiniC-155
❑ 98TopOpeD-82
❑ 98TopSta-143
❑ 98TopSta'S-4
❑ 98TopSta'SGH-4
❑ 98TopStaB-143
❑ 98TopStaG-143
❑ 98TopStaGR-143
❑ 98TopStaS-143
❑ 98TopStaSteG-4
❑ 98TopTek-8
❑ 98TopTekD-8
❑ 98UD3-76
❑ 98UD3-166
❑ 98UD3-256
❑ 98UD3DieCut-76
❑ 98UD3DieCut-166
❑ 98UD3DieCut-256
❑ 98Ult-145
❑ 98UltGolM-145
❑ 98UltMas-145
❑ 98UltPlaM-145
❑ 98UppDec-78
❑ 98UppDecR-33
❑ 98UppDecRTC-TC36
❑ 98UppDecSF-49
❑ 98Zen-49
❑ 98ZenZ-G-49
❑ 98ZenZ-S-49
❑ 99199Fin-78
❑ 99Bow-262
❑ 99BowBes-14
❑ 99BowBesAR-14
❑ 99BowBesR-14
❑ 99BowGol-262
❑ 99BowInt-262
❑ 99CroRoyB-47
❑ 99CroRoyL-47
❑ 99CroRoyOD-47
❑ 99E-X Cen-43
❑ 99E-X CenECFut-43
❑ 99E-X CenECNow-43
❑ 99FinGolRef-78
❑ 99FinRef-78
❑ 99FlaShoLeg1-114
❑ 99FlaShoLeg2-114
❑ 99FlaShoLeg3-114
❑ 99FlaShoLegM1-114
❑ 99FlaShoLegM2-114
❑ 99FlaShoLegM3-114
❑ 99FlaShoR1-114
❑ 99FlaShoR2-114
❑ 99FlaShoR3-114
❑ 99Fle-15
❑ 99FleBri-32
❑ 99FleBri2G-32
❑ 99FleBriBlu-32
❑ 99FleBriGol-32
❑ 99FleMys-93
❑ 99FleMysG-93
❑ 99FleMysM-93
❑ 99FleSta9-15
❑ 99FleVin'-15
❑ 99FleWarT-15
❑ 99KinDis-13
❑ 99MetUni-218
❑ 99MetUniGM-218
❑ 99MetUniPMG-218
❑ 99Pac-141
❑ 99Pac-141A
❑ 99PacAur-58
❑ 99PacAurOD-58
❑ 99PacCroC-93
❑ 99PacCroCPB-93
❑ 99PacInv-48
❑ 99PacInvOD-48
❑ 99PacInvPB-48
❑ 99PacOme-80
❑ 99PacOmeC-80
❑ 99PacOmeG-80
❑ 99PacOmePB-80
❑ 99PacPar-79
❑ 99PacParC-79
❑ 99PacParG-79
❑ 99PacParHoloGold-79
❑ 99PacParHS-79
❑ 99PacParOD-79
❑ 99PacParPB-79
❑ 99PacParRed-79
❑ 99PacPlaB-141
❑ 99PacPlaB-141A
❑ 99PacPri-49
❑ 99PacPriHB-49
❑ 99PacPriHG-49
❑ 99PacPriHM-49
❑ 99PacPriHP-49
❑ 99PacPriRed-49
❑ 99PacPriS-59
❑ 99PacPriS206-59
❑ 99PacPriS206R-59
❑ 99PacRed-141
❑ 99PacRed-141A
❑ 99Rev-48
❑ 99RevPremDate-48
❑ 99RevRet-48
❑ 99RevShaSS-48
❑ 99SkyMolM-6
❑ 99SkyMolMX-6
❑ 99SkyPre-66
❑ 99SkyPreR-66
❑ 99SkyThu-220
❑ 99SkyThuRant-220
❑ 99SkyThuRave-220
❑ 99SpoIII-138
❑ 99StaClu-105
❑ 99StaCluFDI-105
❑ 99StaCluOoaK-105
❑ 99StaCluPP-105
❑ 99ThuSkySupR-220
❑ 99Top-227
❑ 99Top-415
❑ 99TopBlaLC1-19
❑ 99TopBlaLC2-19
❑ 99TopBlaLC3-19
❑ 99TopChr-227
❑ 99TopChr-415
❑ 99TopChrR-227
❑ 99TopChrR-415
❑ 99TopGal-84
❑ 99TopGalPP-84
❑ 99TopGalPPI-84
❑ 99TopGolL-19
❑ 99TopGolLC1-19
❑ 99TopGolLC2-19
❑ 99TopGolLOtO-19
❑ 99TopMVPP-415
❑ 99TopOpeD-159
❑ 99TopRedLC1-19
❑ 99TopRedLC2-19
❑ 99TopRedLC3-19
❑ 99TopSta-90
❑ 99TopSta'S-42
❑ 99TopSta'SGDH-42
❑ 99TopSta1Foil-90
❑ 99TopStaFoil-90
❑ 99TopStaOS-90
❑ 99Ult-61
❑ 99UltGolM-61
❑ 99UltMas-61
❑ 99UltPlaM-61
❑ 99UppDec-361
❑ 99UppDecCLM-C31
❑ 99UppDecE-34
❑ 99UppDecEFXG-34
❑ 99UppDecEL1-361
❑ 99UppDecEL2-361
❑ 99UppDecM-72
❑ 99UppDecMGS-72
❑ 99UppDecMHFS-72
❑ 99UppDecMP-72
❑ 99UppDecMSS-72
❑ 99Vic-131

Bickford, Charles
❑ 48BabRutS-5

Bickford, Vern
❑ 49Bow-1
❑ 50Bow-57
❑ 51Bow-42
❑ 51FisBakL-1
❑ 52Bow-48
❑ 52Top-252
❑ 53BraJohC-3
❑ 53BraSpiaS3-3
❑ 53Top-161
❑ 54Bow-176
❑ 79TCM50-114
❑ 83ASAWS-4
❑ 83TopRep5-252
❑ 85TCMPla1-10
❑ 91OriCro-34
❑ 91TopArc1-161

Bickhardt, Eric
❑ 89ButCopKSP-5
❑ 90GasRanB-14
❑ 90GasRanP-2512
❑ 90GasRanS-2
❑ 91ChaRanC-2
❑ 91ChaRanP-1306

Bicknell, Charlie
❑ 49EurSta-129
❑ 49PhiBul-5

Bicknell, Greg
❑ 89St.CatBJP-2090
❑ 90MyrBeaBJP-2767
❑ 91MyrBeaHC-2
❑ 91MyrBeaHP-2936
❑ 92PenPilC-20
❑ 92PenPilF-2924
❑ 93JacSunF-2703
❑ 94ElPasDF-3138
❑ 94SanBerSF-2750

Biddle, Rocky
❑ 97HicCraB-5
❑ 98BesNumOP-8
❑ 98WinWar-6

Bido, Jose
❑ 98LetBlaDG-4

Biebel, Don
❑ 55DesMoiHB-3

Bieger, Philip
❑ 87AncGlaP-1
❑ 89AncGlaP-3

Biehl, Rod
❑ 91AubAstC-4
❑ 91AubAstP-4267
❑ 92BurAstC-12
❑ 92BurAstF-536

Bieksha, Steve
❑ 87BelMarTI-29
❑ 88WauTimGS-18

Bielanin, Ray
❑ 89GreFalDSP-11

Bielecki, Mike
❑ 82BufBisT-16
❑ 83LynPirT-1
❑ 84HawIsIC-131
❑ 85Don-28
❑ 85Fle-650
❑ 85Pir-3
❑ 86Fle-603
❑ 86TopTra-10T
❑ 86TopTraT-10T
❑ 87Don-415
❑ 87Fle-603
❑ 87FleGlo-603
❑ 87Top-394
❑ 87TopTif-394
❑ 87VanCanP-1598
❑ 88Don-484
❑ 88DonTeaBC-NEW
❑ 88Sco-611
❑ 88ScoGlo-611
❑ 88Top-436
❑ 88TopClo-11
❑ 88TopTif-436
❑ 88TriAAAP-18
❑ 89CubMar-36
❑ 89Don-512
❑ 89DonBasB-194
❑ 89Fle-419
❑ 89FleGlo-419
❑ 89Top-668
❑ 89TopTif-668
❑ 89UppDec-321A
❑ 90Bow-22
❑ 90BowTif-22
❑ 90CubMar-2
❑ 90Don-9
❑ 90Don-373
❑ 90DonBesN-3
❑ 90DonSupD-9
❑ 90Fle-27
❑ 90FleCan-27
❑ 90Lea-45
❑ 90OPC-114
❑ 90PanSti-242
❑ 90PubIntS-191
❑ 90Sco-484
❑ 90Top-114
❑ 90TopBig-129
❑ 90TopMinL-48
❑ 90TopSti-54
❑ 90TopTif-114
❑ 90TopTVCu-8
❑ 90UppDec-359
❑ 91Bow-422
❑ 91CubMar-36
❑ 91CubVinL-5
❑ 91Don-87
❑ 91Fle-415
❑ 91OPC-501
❑ 91Sco-453
❑ 91StaClu-109
❑ 91Top-501
❑ 91TopDesS-501
❑ 91TopMic-501
❑ 91TopTif-501
❑ 91Ult-57
❑ 91UppDec-597
❑ 92BraLykP-5
❑ 92BraLykS-6
❑ 92Don-776
❑ 92Lea-505
❑ 92LeaBlaG-505
❑ 92OPC-26
❑ 92Pin-566
❑ 92StaClu-656
❑ 92Top-26
❑ 92TopGol-26
❑ 92TopGolW-26
❑ 92TopMic-26
❑ 92Ult-457
❑ 92UppDec-730
❑ 93Fle-363
❑ 93IndWUA-4
❑ 93Lea-270
❑ 93OPCPre-112
❑ 93Sco-457
❑ 93StaClu-721
❑ 93StaCluFDI-721
❑ 93StaCluMOP-721
❑ 93Top-251
❑ 93TopGol-251
❑ 93TopInaM-251
❑ 93TopInaR-251
❑ 93TopMic-251
❑ 93Ult-539
❑ 93UppDec-659
❑ 93UppDecGold-659
❑ 94BraLykP-5
❑ 94BraLykS-5
❑ 95AngMot-18
❑ 97PacPriGotD-GD109
❑ 97Ult-526
❑ 97UltGolME-526
❑ 97UltPlaME-526

Bielenberg, Bruce
❑ 84IowCubT-19
❑ 85IowCubT-33
❑ 89MiaMirIS-21
❑ 90MiaMirIS-30

Bienek, Vince
❑ 79AppFoxT-18
❑ 80GleFalWSBT-20
❑ 80GleFalWSCT-11
❑ 81GleFalWST-17
❑ 82GleFalWST-1

Bieniasz, Derek
❑ 97EveAquG-2

Bieniek, Carrie
❑ 96BelSnaTI-3

Bierbauer, Lou (Louis W.)
❑ 87OldJudN-29
❑ 87OldJudN-30
❑ 90KalBatN-3
❑ 90KalBatN-4
❑ 98CamPepP-4

Bierbrodt, Nick
❑ 96BesAutS1RP-FR16
❑ 97MidLeaTP-24
❑ 97SouBenSH-2
❑ 97Top-249
❑ 98Bow-74
❑ 98BowChr-74
❑ 98BowChrGA-74
❑ 98BowChrGAR-74
❑ 98BowChrI-74
❑ 98BowChrIR-74
❑ 98BowChrR-74
❑ 98BowGolA-74
❑ 98BowInt-74
❑ 98HigDesMG-4
❑ 98SP MinPE-17
❑ 98SPMin-17
❑ 98Top-499
❑ 98TopChr-499
❑ 98TopChrR-499
❑ 98TopDevR-499
❑ 98TopDia-499
❑ 98TopMiniC-499
❑ 99BasAmeTP-15
❑ 99BasAmeTPG-15
❑ 99Bow-390
❑ 99BowGol-390
❑ 99BowInt-390

Biercevicz, Greg
❑ 78SanJosMMC-3
❑ 79SpoIndT-21
❑ 79Top-712
❑ 80SpoIndT-3
❑ 81SpoIndT-8
❑ 81Top-282
❑ 82TidTidT-17
❑ 83TidTidT-15
❑ 85RocRedWT-30

Bierek, Kurt
❑ 93OneYanC-4
❑ 93OneYanF-3508
❑ 94GreBatF-481
❑ 95TamYanYI-1
❑ 96TamYanY-14
❑ 97GreBatC-3
❑ 97NorNav-8
❑ 97NorNavTI-3
❑ 98NorNavQ-6

Bierley, Brad
❑ 85VisOakT-7
❑ 86OrlTwiP-2
❑ 87OrlTwiP-14
❑ 88PorBeaC-16
❑ 88PorBeaP-639
❑ 89PorBeaC-18
❑ 89PorBeaP-231
❑ 90CMC-97
❑ 90IowCubC-22
❑ 90IowCubP-329
❑ 90ProAAAF-636
❑ 90TopTVCu-38
❑ 91IowCubLD-201
❑ 91IowCubP-1073
❑ 91LinDriAAA-201
❑ 92GenCubC-28
❑ 92GenCubF-1576

Bierman, Bernie
❑ 40WheM4-3
❑ 41WheM5-15

Bierman, Steve
❑ 93JohCitCC-4
❑ 93JohCitCF-3684
❑ 94SavCarC-7
❑ 94SavCarF-513
❑ 95PeoChiTI-1

❑ 96StPetCB-5
Biernat, Joe
❑ 93GenCubC-4
❑ 93GenCubF-3179
❑ 94PeoChiC-3
❑ 94PeoChiF-2272
Bierscheid, Gene
❑ 87SpaPhiP-3
Bieser, Steve
❑ 89BatCliP-1934
❑ 90BatCliP-3078
❑ 91SpaPhiC-22
❑ 91SpaPhiP-907
❑ 92ClePhiC-5
❑ 92ClePhiF-2058
❑ 93ReaPhiF-305
❑ 93ScrRedBF-2554
❑ 94ScrRedBF-930
❑ 95ScrRedBTI-1
❑ 97ColChoU-U18
❑ 98NasSouTI-4
❑ 98NasSouTISS-4
Bifone, Pete
❑ 94SpoIndC-3
❑ 94SpoIndF-3327
Bigbee, Carson Lee
❑ 21E121So1-6A
❑ 21E121So1-6B
❑ 21E121So1-6C
❑ 21E121So1-6D
❑ 21Exh-10
❑ 21Nei-56
❑ 22E120-213
❑ 22W573-10
❑ 22W575-9
❑ 23W501-85
❑ 23W503-52
❑ 25Exh-49
❑ 26Exh-49
❑ 27Zee-130
❑ 28Zee-26
❑ 28Zee-88
Bigbee, Lyle Randolph
❑ 19Zee-107
❑ 24Zee-2
Bigelow, Elliott A.
❑ 94ConTSN-1285
❑ 94ConTSNB-1285
Biggers, Allan
❑ 89HamRedS-3
❑ 89SavCarP-362
Biggers, Brian
❑ 91SalLakTP-3216
❑ 91SalLakTSP-8
Biggerstaff, Kent
❑ 75TidTidTI-4
❑ 78HolMilT-2
❑ 79VanCanT-22A
❑ 80VanCanT-12
❑ 81PorBeaT-27
Biggins, Kym
❑ 93AusFut-3
Biggio, Craig
❑ 88FleUpd-89
❑ 88FleUpdG-89
❑ 88ScoRoo-103T
❑ 88ScoRooG-103T
❑ 88TucTorC-15
❑ 88TucTorJP-2
❑ 88TucTorP-166
❑ 89AstLenH-24
❑ 89AstMot-14
❑ 89AstSmo-6
❑ 89ClaLigB-51
❑ 89Don-561
❑ 89DonBasB-176
❑ 89Fle-353
❑ 89FleGlo-353
❑ 89PanSti-79
❑ 89Sco-237
❑ 89ScoHot1R-98
❑ 89ScoYouS2-33
❑ 89Top-49
❑ 89TopTif-49
❑ 89UppDec-273
❑ 90AstLenH-4
❑ 90AstMot-5
❑ 90Bow-78
❑ 90BowTif-78
❑ 90ClaBlu-57
❑ 90Don-306
❑ 90DonBesN-89
❑ 90Fle-224
❑ 90FleCan-224
❑ 90K-M-8
❑ 90Lea-37
❑ 90M.Vpin-39
❑ 90OPC-157
❑ 90OPC-404
❑ 90PanSti-259
❑ 90PubIntS-88
❑ 90Sco-275
❑ 90Spo-22
❑ 90SupActM-13
❑ 90Top-157
❑ 90Top-404
❑ 90TopBig-111
❑ 90TopCoi-39
❑ 90TopGloS-54
❑ 90TopHeaU-6
❑ 90TopSti-23
❑ 90TopStiB-22
❑ 90TopTif-157
❑ 90TopTif-404
❑ 90TopTVA-41
❑ 90UppDec-104
❑ 91AstMot-5
❑ 91Bow-556
❑ 91CadElD-3
❑ 91Cla3-T2
❑ 91ClaGam-7
❑ 91DenHol-24
❑ 91Don-2
❑ 91Don-595
❑ 91DonSupD-2
❑ 91Fle-499
❑ 91JimDea-16
❑ 91KinDis-13
❑ 91Lea-12
❑ 91LeaPre-4
❑ 91MooSna-22
❑ 91OPC-565
❑ 91PanFreS-6
❑ 91PanSti-10
❑ 91RedFolS-8
❑ 91Sco-161
❑ 91Sco-872
❑ 91Sco100S-55
❑ 91SevCoi-T1
❑ 91SimandSMLBL-4
❑ 91StaClu-176
❑ 91Stu-173
❑ 91Top-565
❑ 91TopDesS-565
❑ 91TopMic-565
❑ 91TopTif-565
❑ 91TopTriH-N4
❑ 91Ult-132
❑ 91UppDec-158
❑ 91USPlaCA-9C
❑ 92AstMot-5
❑ 92Bow-484
❑ 92ClaGam-2
❑ 92Don-75
❑ 92DonCraJ2-1
❑ 92Fle-426
❑ 92Hig5-37
❑ 92HitTheBB-4
❑ 92KinDis-21
❑ 92Lea-315
❑ 92LeaBlaG-315
❑ 92Mr.TurS-4
❑ 92OPC-715
❑ 92OPCPre-135
❑ 92PanSti-151
❑ 92Pin-140
❑ 92RedFolS-13
❑ 92Sco-460
❑ 92Sco-888
❑ 92Sco100S-52
❑ 92ScoImpP-22
❑ 92SevCoi-12
❑ 92SpoIllFK1-478
❑ 92StaClu-200
❑ 92StaCluD-16
❑ 92Stu-32
❑ 92Top-393
❑ 92Top-715
❑ 92TopGol-393
❑ 92TopGol-715
❑ 92TopGolW-393
❑ 92TopGolW-715
❑ 92TopKid-43
❑ 92TopMic-393
❑ 92TopMic-715
❑ 92TriPla-150
❑ 92Ult-199
❑ 92UppDec-31
❑ 92UppDec-162
❑ 93AstMot-4
❑ 93AstStaC-14
❑ 93Bow-560
❑ 93ClaGam-13
❑ 93DiaMar-12
❑ 93Don-84
❑ 93DonDiaK-DK24
❑ 93DurPowP1-7
❑ 93Fin-119
❑ 93FinRef-119
❑ 93Fla-58
❑ 93Fle-47
❑ 93FleFruotL-5
❑ 93FunPac-44
❑ 93Lea-223
❑ 93LeaGolA-R13
❑ 93MilBonSS-20
❑ 93OPC-56
❑ 93PacSpa-118
❑ 93PanSti-171
❑ 93Pin-50
❑ 93RedFolS-12
❑ 93Sco-18
❑ 93Sel-25
❑ 93SP-29
❑ 93StaClu-183
❑ 93StaCluFDI-183
❑ 93StaCluM-115
❑ 93StaCluMOP-183
❑ 93Stu-86
❑ 93Top-680
❑ 93TopGol-680
❑ 93TopInaM-680
❑ 93TopInaR-680
❑ 93TopMic-680
❑ 93TriPla-100
❑ 93Ult-37
❑ 93UppDec-114
❑ 93UppDec-475
❑ 93UppDecGold-114
❑ 93UppDecGold-475
❑ 94AstMot-5
❑ 94Bow-390
❑ 94ColC-456
❑ 94ColChoGS-456
❑ 94ColChoSS-456
❑ 94Don-12
❑ 94DonSpeE-12
❑ 94Fin-382
❑ 94FinRef-382
❑ 94Fla-386
❑ 94Fle-485
❑ 94FleExtB-269
❑ 94FUnPac-158
❑ 94FUnPac-218
❑ 94Lea-236
❑ 94LeaL-111
❑ 94OPC-230
❑ 94Pac-259
❑ 94PanSti-190
❑ 94Pin-20
❑ 94PinArtP-20
❑ 94PinMusC-20
❑ 94PinRunC-RC33
❑ 94ProMag-59
❑ 94Sco-48
❑ 94ScoGolR-48
❑ 94Sel-296
❑ 94SP-28
❑ 94SPDieC-28
❑ 94StaClu-374
❑ 94StaCluFDI-374
❑ 94StaCluGR-374
❑ 94StaCluMOP-374
❑ 94Stu-17
❑ 94Top-305
❑ 94TopBlaG-25
❑ 94TopGol-305
❑ 94TopSpa-305
❑ 94TriPla-22
❑ 94TriPlaM-6
❑ 94Ult-499
❑ 94UppDec-312
❑ 94UppDecAJ-36
❑ 94UppDecAJG-36
❑ 94UppDecED-312
❑ 95AstMot-7
❑ 95Baz-33
❑ 95Bow-369
❑ 95BowBes-R32
❑ 95BowBes-X6
❑ 95BowBesR-R32
❑ 95BowBesR-X6
❑ 95ClaPhoC-29
❑ 95ColCho-109
❑ 95ColChoGS-109
❑ 95ColChoSE-38
❑ 95ColChoSE-255
❑ 95ColChoSEGS-38
❑ 95ColChoSEGS-255
❑ 95ColChoSESS-38
❑ 95ColChoSESS-255
❑ 95ColChoSS-109
❑ 95Don-456
❑ 95DonDom-4
❑ 95DonPreP-456
❑ 95DonTopotO-251
❑ 95Emo-136
❑ 95Fin-129
❑ 95FinRef-129
❑ 95Fla-144
❑ 95Fle-453
❑ 95FleAllS-14
❑ 95Lea-126
❑ 95LeaLim-68
❑ 95Pac-182
❑ 95PacPri-59
❑ 95PanSti-45
❑ 95PanSti-118
❑ 95Pin-266
❑ 95PinArtP-266
❑ 95PinMusC-266
❑ 95PinPin-7
❑ 95PinPinR-7
❑ 95PinTeaP-TP4
❑ 95RedFol-20
❑ 95Sco-423
❑ 95ScoGolR-423
❑ 95ScoHaloG-HG68
❑ 95ScoPlaTS-423
❑ 95Sel-107
❑ 95SelArtP-107
❑ 95SelCer-69
❑ 95SelCerMG-69
❑ 95SP-61
❑ 95SPCha-52
❑ 95SPChaDC-52
❑ 95Spo-80
❑ 95SpoArtP-80
❑ 95SPSil-61
❑ 95SPSpeF-39
❑ 95StaClu-185
❑ 95StaCluFDI-185
❑ 95StaCluMO-6
❑ 95StaCluMOP-185
❑ 95StaCluSTWS-185
❑ 95StaCluVR-95
❑ 95StaCluVRMO-95
❑ 95Stu-50
❑ 95StuGolS-50
❑ 95Sum-31
❑ 95SumNthD-31
❑ 95Top-190
❑ 95TopCyb-108
❑ 95TopEmb-66
❑ 95TopEmbGI-66
❑ 95TopLeaL-LL41
❑ 95TopTra-157T
❑ 95UC3-72
❑ 95UC3ArtP-72
❑ 95Ult-384
❑ 95UltAllS-3
❑ 95UltAllSGM-3
❑ 95UltAwaW-12
❑ 95UltAwaWGM-12
❑ 95UltGolM-384
❑ 95UltLeaL-7
❑ 95UltLeaLGM-7
❑ 95UltOnBL-3
❑ 95UltOnBLGM-3
❑ 95UppDec-25
❑ 95UppDecED-25
❑ 95UppDecEDG-25
❑ 95UppDecSE-181
❑ 95UppDecSEG-181
❑ 95USPlaCMLA-11H
❑ 95Zen-18
❑ 96AstMot-3
❑ 96Baz-67
❑ 96Bow-29
❑ 96BowBes-49
❑ 96BowBesAR-49
❑ 96BowBesMI-2
❑ 96BowBesMIAR-2
❑ 96BowBesMIR-2
❑ 96BowBesR-49
❑ 96BowFoi-29
❑ 96Cir-135
❑ 96CirRav-135
❑ 96ColCho-159
❑ 96ColCho-274
❑ 96ColChoGS-159
❑ 96ColChoGS-274
❑ 96ColChoSS-159
❑ 96ColChoSS-274
❑ 96ColChoYMtP-6
❑ 96ColChoYMtP-6A
❑ 96ColChoYMtPGS-6
❑ 96ColChoYMtPGS-6A
❑ 96Don-472
❑ 96DonPreP-472
❑ 96EmoXL-196
❑ 96Fin-B238
❑ 96Fin-G355
❑ 96Fin-S112
❑ 96FinRef-B238
❑ 96FinRef-G355
❑ 96FinRef-S112
❑ 96Fla-275
❑ 96Fle-402
❑ 96FleTif-402
❑ 96Lea-207
❑ 96LeaLim-63
❑ 96LeaLimG-63
❑ 96LeaPre-77
❑ 96LeaPreP-77
❑ 96LeaPrePB-207
❑ 96LeaPrePG-207
❑ 96LeaPrePS-207
❑ 96LeaPreSG-72
❑ 96LeaPreSte-72
❑ 96LeaSig-29
❑ 96LeaSigPPG-29
❑ 96LeaSigPPP-29
❑ 96LibSpo-7
❑ 96MetUni-175
❑ 96MetUniP-175
❑ 96Pac-94
❑ 96PacPri-P31
❑ 96PacPriG-P31
❑ 96PanSti-57
❑ 96Pin-211
❑ 96PinAfi-25
❑ 96PinAfiAP-25
❑ 96PinAfiFPP-25
❑ 96PinArtP-111
❑ 96PinFirR-10
❑ 96PinFoil-211
❑ 96PinSta-111
❑ 96PinTeaP-2
❑ 96ProSta-12
❑ 96RedF-28
❑ 96Sco-88
❑ 96ScoDugC-A68
❑ 96ScoDugCAP-A68
❑ 96ScoRef-20
❑ 96Sel-147
❑ 96SelArtP-147
❑ 96SelCer-33
❑ 96SelCerAP-33
❑ 96SelCerCB-33
❑ 96SelCerCR-33
❑ 96SelCerMB-33
❑ 96SelCerMG-33
❑ 96SelCerMR-33
❑ 96SelTeaN-26
❑ 96SP-94
❑ 96Spo-37
❑ 96SpoArtP-37
❑ 96SpoDouT-2
❑ 96SPSpeFX-12
❑ 96SPSpeFXDC-12
❑ 96SPx-28
❑ 96SPxGol-28
❑ 96StaClu-186
❑ 96StaClu-298
❑ 96StaCluB&B-BB4
❑ 96StaCluEPB-298
❑ 96StaCluEPG-298
❑ 96StaCluEPS-298
❑ 96StaCluMM-MM4
❑ 96StaCluMO-5
❑ 96StaCluMOP-186
❑ 96StaCluMOP-298
❑ 96StaCluMOP-BB4
❑ 96StaCluMOP-MM4
❑ 96Stu-41
❑ 96StuPrePB-41
❑ 96StuPrePG-41
❑ 96StuPrePS-41
❑ 96Sum-139
❑ 96SumAbo&B-139
❑ 96SumArtP-139
❑ 96SumFoi-139
❑ 96SumPos-2
❑ 96TeaOut-8
❑ 96Top-9
❑ 96Top-306
❑ 96TopChr-9
❑ 96TopChr-122
❑ 96TopChrR-9
❑ 96TopChrR-122
❑ 96TopGal-58
❑ 96TopGalPPI-58
❑ 96TopLas-19
❑ 96TopPowB-9
❑ 96TopRoaW-RW3
❑ 96Ult-485
❑ 96UltGolM-485
❑ 96UltPriL-12
❑ 96UltPriLGM-12
❑ 96UppDec-345
❑ 96UppDecA-6
❑ 96UppDecPRE-R54
❑ 96UppDecPreR-R54
❑ 96Zen-71
❑ 96ZenArtP-71
❑ 96ZenMoz-25
❑ 97AstMot-3
❑ 97Bow-24
❑ 97BowBes-71
❑ 97BowBesAR-71
❑ 97BowBesMI-MI8
❑ 97BowBesMIAR-MI8
❑ 97BowBesMIARI-MI8
❑ 97BowBesMII-MI8
❑ 97BowBesMIR-MI8
❑ 97BowBesMIRI-MI8
❑ 97BowBesR-71
❑ 97BowChr-20
❑ 97BowChrI-20
❑ 97BowChrIR-20
❑ 97BowChrR-20
❑ 97BowInt-24
❑ 97Cir-362
❑ 97CirRav-362
❑ 97ColCho-350
❑ 97ColChoAC-20
❑ 97ColChoTBS-23
❑ 97ColChoTBSWH-23
❑ 97Don-14
❑ 97DonEli-38
❑ 97DonEliGS-38
❑ 97DonGolPP-14
❑ 97DonLim-48
❑ 97DonLim-144
❑ 97DonLimE-48
❑ 97DonLimE-144
❑ 97DonLimENG-48
❑ 97DonLimFotG-58
❑ 97DonPre-99
❑ 97DonPreCttC-99
❑ 97DonSig-76
❑ 97DonSigPPP-76
❑ 97DonSilPP-14
❑ 97E-X2-77
❑ 97E-X2Cred-77
❑ 97E-X2EssCre-77
❑ 97Fin-128
❑ 97Fin-327
❑ 97FinEmb-128
❑ 97FinEmb-327
❑ 97FinEmbR-128
❑ 97FinEmbR-327
❑ 97FinRef-128
❑ 97FinRef-327
❑ 97FlaShoLC-14
❑ 97FlaShoLeg0-14
❑ 97FlaShoLeg1-14
❑ 97FlaShoM-A14
❑ 97FlaShoM-B14
❑ 97FlaShoM-C14
❑ 97FlaShoR0-14
❑ 97FlaShoR1-14
❑ 97FlaShoR2-14
❑ 97Fle-342
❑ 97FleTif-342
❑ 97Lea-247
❑ 97LeaBanS-11
❑ 97LeaFraM-247
❑ 97LeaFraMDC-247
❑ 97MetUni-136
❑ 97NewPin-92
❑ 97NewPinAP-92
❑ 97NewPinMC-92
❑ 97NewPinPP-92
❑ 97Pac-314
❑ 97PacLigB-314
❑ 97PacPri-108
❑ 97PacPriLB-108
❑ 97PacPriP-108
❑ 97PacPriSL-SL10B
❑ 97PacSil-314
❑ 97PinCer-9
❑ 97PinCerMBla-9
❑ 97PinCerMBlu-9

❑ 97PinCerMG-9
❑ 97PinCerMR-9
❑ 97PinCerR-9
❑ 97PinFan-FF4
❑ 97PinIns-28
❑ 97PinInsCE-28
❑ 97PinInsDE-28
❑ 97PinTotCPB-9
❑ 97PinTotCPG-9
❑ 97PinTotCPR-9
❑ 97PinX-P-64
❑ 97PinX-PMoS-64
❑ 97Sco-235
❑ 97ScoArtPWB-235
❑ 97ScoPreS-235
❑ 97ScoShoS-235
❑ 97ScoShoSAP-235
❑ 97Sel-39
❑ 97SelArtP-39
❑ 97SelCom-39
❑ 97SelRegG-39
❑ 97SP-84
❑ 97SpoIll-100
❑ 97SpoIllEE-100
❑ 97StaClu-252
❑ 97StaCluMat-252
❑ 97StaCluMOP-252
❑ 97StaCluMOP-PL6
❑ 97StaCluPL-PL6
❑ 97StrAll-8
❑ 97Stu-70
❑ 97StuPrePG-70
❑ 97StuPrePS-70
❑ 97Top-85
❑ 97TopChr-32
❑ 97TopChrDD-DD5
❑ 97TopChrDDR-DD5
❑ 97TopChrR-32
❑ 97TopGal-46
❑ 97TopGalP-PP4
❑ 97TopGalPPI-46
❑ 97TopMem05-6
❑ 97TopSta-46
❑ 97TopSta97AS-AS11
❑ 97TopStaAM-46
❑ 97Ult-343
❑ 97UltGolME-343
❑ 97UltPlaME-343
❑ 97UppDec-143
❑ 97UppDec-367
❑ 98Bow-37
❑ 98BowBes-61
❑ 98BowBesAR-61
❑ 98BowBesMIF-MI13
❑ 98BowBesMIFAR-MI13
❑ 98BowBesMIFR-MI13
❑ 98BowBesR-61
❑ 98BowChr-37
❑ 98BowChrGA-37
❑ 98BowChrGAR-37
❑ 98BowChrI-37
❑ 98BowChrIR-37
❑ 98BowChrR-37
❑ 98BowGolA-37
❑ 98BowInt-37
❑ 98CirThu-224
❑ 98CirThuRav-224
❑ 98CirThuSupRav-224
❑ 98ColCho-130
❑ 98ColChoSQ-SQ56
❑ 98CroRoy-64
❑ 98CroRoyAS-16
❑ 98CroRoyDK-11
❑ 98Don-58
❑ 98Don-363
❑ 98DonCol-58
❑ 98DonColE-448
❑ 98DonColL-295
❑ 98DonColP-612
❑ 98DonColS-58
❑ 98DonCruG-78
❑ 98DonCruP-78
❑ 98DonCruR-78
❑ 98DonEli-48
❑ 98DonEliA-48
❑ 98DonEliS-48
❑ 98DonGolPP-58
❑ 98DonGolPP-363
❑ 98DonPre-62
❑ 98DonPreSeat-62
❑ 98DonPriCD-58
❑ 98DonPriCE-448
❑ 98DonPriCL-295
❑ 98DonPriCP-612
❑ 98DonProLO-15
❑ 98DonSig-10
❑ 98DonSigP-10
❑ 98DonSilPP-58
❑ 98DonSilPP-363
❑ 98E-X2-34
❑ 98E-X2ECFut-34
❑ 98E-X2ECNow-34
❑ 98Fin-149
❑ 98FinNo--149
❑ 98FinNo-R-149
❑ 98FinRef-149
❑ 98FlaShoLeg0-86
❑ 98FlaShoLeg1-86
❑ 98FlaShoLeg2-86
❑ 98FlaShoLeg3-86
❑ 98FlaShoLegM-86
❑ 98FlaShoR0-86
❑ 98FlaShoR1-86
❑ 98FlaShoR2-86
❑ 98FlaShoR3-86
❑ 98Fle-105
❑ 98FleVin'-30
❑ 98FleVin'C-30
❑ 98Lea-96
❑ 98LeaFraDA-96
❑ 98LeaFraF-96
❑ 98LeaFraM-96
❑ 98LeaFraM-96
❑ 98LeaFraMDC-96
❑ 98LeaFraMDC-96
❑ 98LeaFraMZ2-96
❑ 98LeaRS-58
❑ 98LeaRS-169
❑ 98LeaRSLHolo-58
❑ 98LeaRSLHolo-169
❑ 98LeaRSLMVP-12
❑ 98LeaRSLMVPPE-12
❑ 98LeaRSLong-58
❑ 98LeaRSLong-169
❑ 98LeaRSTicMas-7
❑ 98LeaRSTicMasDC-7
❑ 98LeaRTrue-58
❑ 98LeaRTrue-169
❑ 98MetUni-47
❑ 98MetUniPMG-47
❑ 98Pac-315
❑ 98PacAur-138
❑ 98PacInv-103
❑ 98PacInvInt-1N
❑ 98PacInvPBlue-103
❑ 98PacInvSilv-103
❑ 98PacInvTeam-12
❑ 98PacOme-107
❑ 98PacOmeR-107
❑ 98PacOnl-315
❑ 98PacOnlR-315
❑ 98PacOnlWC-315
❑ 98PacPar-169
❑ 98PacParC-169
❑ 98PacParG-169
❑ 98PacParHS-169
❑ 98PacParI-9
❑ 98PacParPB-169
❑ 98PacParR-169
❑ 98PacPlaB-315
❑ 98PacRedT-315
❑ 98PacSil-315
❑ 98PacTeaC-20
❑ 98Pin-50
❑ 98PinArtP-PP45
❑ 98PinIns-50
❑ 98PinInsCE-50
❑ 98PinInsDE-50
❑ 98PinInsSG-14AB
❑ 98PinInsSG-14CD
❑ 98PinInsSGS-14AB
❑ 98PinInsSGS-14CD
❑ 98PinMusC-PP45
❑ 98PinPer-63
❑ 98PinPerPP-63
❑ 98PinPlu-74
❑ 98PinPluAP-PP30
❑ 98PinPluGAP-PP30
❑ 98PinPluMAP-PP30
❑ 98PinPluTP-3
❑ 98PinPluTPG-3
❑ 98PinPluTPM-3
❑ 98PinPreP-50
❑ 98Revo-67
❑ 98RevoSS-67
❑ 98Sco-70
❑ 98ScoRT-42
❑ 98ScoRTSS-PP42
❑ 98ScoRTSSAP-PP42
❑ 98ScoRTSSAP1-PP42
❑ 98ScoSS-PP35
❑ 98ScoSSAP-PP35
❑ 98SkyDugA-20
❑ 98SkyDugAFF-FF6
❑ 98SkyDugAIA-20
❑ 98SP Aut-102
❑ 98SP Aut-SD4
❑ 98SP AutSD-SD4
❑ 98SP AutSDT-SD4
❑ 98SpoIll-12
❑ 98SpoIll-133
❑ 98SpoIllEE-12
❑ 98SpoIllEE-133
❑ 98SpoIllFE-12
❑ 98SpoIllFE-133
❑ 98SpoIllTaN-62
❑ 98SpoIllTaNEE-62
❑ 98SpoIllWSF-75
❑ 98SpoIllWSFEE-75
❑ 98SpoIllWSFFE-75
❑ 98SPxFin-88
❑ 98SPxFin-156
❑ 98SPxFinR-88
❑ 98SPxFinR-156
❑ 98SPxFinS-88
❑ 98SPxFinS-156
❑ 98StaCluFDI-49
❑ 98StaCluI-49
❑ 98StaCluOneK-49
❑ 98StaCluPP-49
❑ 98StaCluPWP-P5
❑ 98StaCluTIII-T12C
❑ 98StaCluTLme-T12C
❑ 98StaCluTLmo-T12C
❑ 98Stu-79
❑ 98StuGPP-79
❑ 98StuSPP-79
❑ 98Top-318
❑ 98TopChr-318
❑ 98TopChrC9-C4
❑ 98TopChrC9R-C4
❑ 98TopChrR-318
❑ 98TopClo9-C4
❑ 98TopDevR-318
❑ 98TopDia-318
❑ 98TopGal-82
❑ 98TopGalGP-82
❑ 98TopGalOPP-82
❑ 98TopGalPPI-82
❑ 98TopGalPPIA-82
❑ 98TopGolLabC1-5
❑ 98TopGolLabC1B-5
❑ 98TopGolLabC1One-5
❑ 98TopGolLabC1R-5
❑ 98TopGolLabC2-5
❑ 98TopGolLabC2B-5
❑ 98TopGolLabC2One-5
❑ 98TopGolLabC2R-5
❑ 98TopGolLabC3-5
❑ 98TopGolLabC3B-5
❑ 98TopGolLabC3One-5
❑ 98TopGolLabC3R-5
❑ 98TopMiniC-318
❑ 98TopOpeD-144
❑ 98TopSta-128
❑ 98TopStaB-128
❑ 98TopStaG-G9
❑ 98TopStaG-128
❑ 98TopStaGG-G9
❑ 98TopStaGGR-G9
❑ 98TopStaGR-128
❑ 98TopStaGS-G9
❑ 98TopStaPre-PP4
❑ 98TopStaS-128
❑ 98TopSup-26
❑ 98TopSup-26
❑ 98TopTek-12
❑ 98TopTekD-12
❑ 98UD3-78
❑ 98UD3-168
❑ 98UD3-258
❑ 98UD3DieCut-78
❑ 98UD3DieCut-168
❑ 98UD3DieCut-258
❑ 98Ult-23
❑ 98UltGolM-23
❑ 98UltMas-23
❑ 98UltPlaM-23
❑ 98UppDec-100
❑ 98UppDec10AP-30
❑ 98UppDec1APR-30
❑ 98UppDecAC-AS6
❑ 98UppDecR-40
❑ 98UppDecR-15
❑ 98UppDecRGKoG-G19
❑ 98UppDecRTC-TC40
❑ 98UppDecSF-61
❑ 98Zen-71
❑ 98Zen5 xx7-61
❑ 98Zen5x7GoldImp-61
❑ 98Zen5x7Imp-61
❑ 98ZenZ-G-71
❑ 98ZenZ-S-71
❑ 99199Fin-12
❑ 99Bow-251
❑ 99BowBes-25
❑ 99BowBesAR-25
❑ 99BowBesR-25
❑ 99BowGol-251
❑ 99BowInt-251
❑ 99CroRoyB-65
❑ 99CroRoyL-65
❑ 99CroRoyOD-65
❑ 99CroRoyPP-10
❑ 99CroRoyPPN-10
❑ 99DumSet-CB
❑ 99DumSet-CB
❑ 99E-X Cen-64
❑ 99E-X CenECFut-64
❑ 99E-X CenECNow-64
❑ 99FinDouF-DF4
❑ 99FinDouFDualR-DF4
❑ 99FinGolRef-12
❑ 99FinMil-M34
❑ 99FinRef-12
❑ 99FlaShoLeg1-50
❑ 99FlaShoLeg2-50
❑ 99FlaShoLeg3-50
❑ 99FlaShoLegM1-50
❑ 99FlaShoLegM2-50
❑ 99FlaShoLegM3-50
❑ 99FlaShoR1-50
❑ 99FlaShoR2-50
❑ 99FlaShoR3-50
❑ 99Fle-46
❑ 99FleBri-49
❑ 99FleBri2G-49
❑ 99FleBriBlu-49
❑ 99FleBriGol-49
❑ 99FleMys-90
❑ 99FleMysG-90
❑ 99FleMysM-90
❑ 99FleSta9-46
❑ 99FleVin'-46
❑ 99FleWarT-46
❑ 99MetUni-213
❑ 99MetUniGM-213
❑ 99MetUniPMG-213
❑ 99Pac-189
❑ 99PacAur-81
❑ 99PacAurOD-81
❑ 99PacCroC-123
❑ 99PacCroCPB-123
❑ 99PacGolCDC-28
❑ 99PacInv-66
❑ 99PacInvOD-66
❑ 99PacInvPB-66
❑ 99PacOme-104
❑ 99PacOmeC-104
❑ 99PacOmeDM-17
❑ 99PacOmeG-104
❑ 99PacOmePB-104
❑ 99PacPar-103
❑ 99PacParC-103
❑ 99PacParG-103
❑ 99PacParHoloGold-103
❑ 99PacParHS-103
❑ 99PacParOD-103
❑ 99PacParPB-17
❑ 99PacParPB-103
❑ 99PacParRed-103
❑ 99PacPlaB-189
❑ 99PacPri-68
❑ 99PacPriHB-68
❑ 99PacPriHG-68
❑ 99PacPriHM-68
❑ 99PacPriHP-68
❑ 99PacPriRed-68
❑ 99PacPriS-24
❑ 99PacPriS206-24
❑ 99PacPriS206R-24
❑ 99PacPriSP-24
❑ 99PacPriSV-24
❑ 99PacRed-189
❑ 99Pin-3
❑ 99Rev-63
❑ 99RevDiaL-17
❑ 99RevPremDate-63
❑ 99RevRet-63
❑ 99RevShaSS-63
❑ 99RevTri-24
❑ 99RevTri-24
❑ 99SkyMolM-96
❑ 99SkyMolMX-96
❑ 99SkyPre-151
❑ 99SkyPreR-151
❑ 99SkyThu-104
❑ 99SkyThuRant-104
❑ 99SkyThuRave-104
❑ 99SP Aut-38
❑ 99SP SigAutoG-CB
❑ 99SpoIll-37
❑ 99SpoIll-106
❑ 99SPSig-20
❑ 99SPx-43
❑ 99SPxFinR-43
❑ 99SPxFinS-43
❑ 99SPxStaF-SF14
❑ 99StaClu-25
❑ 99StaCluFDI-25
❑ 99StaCluOoaK-25
❑ 99StaCluPP-25
❑ 99StaCluTI-T6B
❑ 99StaCluTL-T6B
❑ 99StaCluTL-T6B
❑ 99ThuSkySupR-104
❑ 99Top-325
❑ 99TopBlaLC1-69
❑ 99TopBlaLC2-69
❑ 99TopBlaLC3-69
❑ 99TopChr-325
❑ 99TopChrR-325
❑ 99TopGal-76
❑ 99TopGalPP-76
❑ 99TopGalPPI-76
❑ 99TopGolL-69
❑ 99TopGolLC1-69
❑ 99TopGolLC2-69
❑ 99TopGolLOtO-69
❑ 99TopMVPP-325
❑ 99TopOpeD-114
❑ 99TopRedLC1-69
❑ 99TopRedLC2-69
❑ 99TopRedLC3-69
❑ 99TopSta-73
❑ 99TopSta'S-19
❑ 99TopSta'SG-19
❑ 99TopSta'SGDH-19
❑ 99TopSta1Foil-73
❑ 99TopStaFoil-73
❑ 99TopStaOS-73
❑ 99TopTek-11A
❑ 99TopTek-11B
❑ 99TopTekG-11A
❑ 99TopTekG-11B
❑ 99UD Cho-93
❑ 99UD ChoP-93
❑ 99UD ChoPCR-93
❑ 99UD Ion-30
❑ 99UD IonR-30
❑ 99UDHolo-26
❑ 99UDHoloAUsome-26
❑ 99Ult-145
❑ 99UltGolM-145
❑ 99UltMas-145
❑ 99UltPlaM-145
❑ 99UppDec-108
❑ 99UppDec10AT-X14
❑ 99UppDec10ATD-X14
❑ 99UppDec10ATHR-X14
❑ 99UppDec10ATT-X14
❑ 99UppDecBD-38
❑ 99UppDecBDD-38
❑ 99UppDecBDMN-M30
❑ 99UppDecBDMNE-M30
❑ 99UppDecBDQ-38
❑ 99UppDecBDT-38
❑ 99UppDecCL-83
❑ 99UppDecCLCC-83
❑ 99UppDecCLM-C43
❑ 99UppDecE-43
❑ 99UppDecE-158
❑ 99UppDecEFXG-43
❑ 99UppDecEFXG-158
❑ 99UppDecEL1-108
❑ 99UppDecEL2-108
❑ 99UppDecEPE-P15
❑ 99UppDecIP-I2
❑ 99UppDecIPD-I2
❑ 99UppDecIPHR-I2
❑ 99UppDecIPT-I2
❑ 99UppDecM-92
❑ 99UppDecMGS-92
❑ 99UppDecMHFS-92
❑ 99UppDecMP-92
❑ 99UppDecMSS-92
❑ 99UppDecO-10
❑ 99UppDecOSO-10
❑ 99UppDecR-39
❑ 99UppDecRG-39
❑ 99UppDecROSS-S6
❑ 99UppDecROSS-S6
❑ 99UppDecRP-39
❑ 99UppDecVtaT-V15
❑ 99UppDecVtaTD-V15
❑ 99UppDecVtaTQ-V15
❑ 99UppDecVtaTT-V15
❑ 99Vic-172

Biggs, Charles
❑ 31Zee-26
❑ 32Zee-29

Biggs, Doug
❑ 88BriTigP-1864

Biggus, Bengie
❑ 80BurBeeT-29

Bigham, Craig
❑ 88SpoIndP-1931

Bigham, David
❑ 89EliTwiS-4
❑ 90EliTwiS-4
❑ 91KenTwiC-12
❑ 91KenTwiP-2066
❑ 92VisOakC-6
❑ 92VisOakF-1004
❑ 93ForMyeMC-2
❑ 93ForMyeMF-2647
❑ 94ForMyeMC-2
❑ 94ForMyeMF-1158
❑ 96FreKeyB-26

Bigham, Scott
❑ 89RivRedWB-3
❑ 89RivRedWCLC-1
❑ 89RivRedWP-1396
❑ 90RivRedWB-3
❑ 90RivRedWCLC-8
❑ 90RivRedWP-2613

Bigler, Jeff
❑ 92SpaPhiC-16
❑ 92SpaPhiF-1274
❑ 93ClePhiC-2
❑ 94ClePhiC-5
❑ 94ClePhiF-2532
❑ 96AugGreB-5

Bigusiak, Mike
❑ 76CliPilT-2
❑ 86SanJosBP-3

Biittner, Larry David
❑ 71SenTealW-2
❑ 72OPC-122
❑ 72RanTeal-2
❑ 72Top-122
❑ 73OPC-249
❑ 73RanTeal-3
❑ 73SevTraC-6
❑ 73Top-249
❑ 75ExpPos-2
❑ 75OPC-543
❑ 75Top-543
❑ 75TopMin-543
❑ 76CubTri-1
❑ 76OPC-238
❑ 76SSP-336
❑ 76Top-238
❑ 77CubJewT-1
❑ 77Top-64
❑ 78SSP270-244
❑ 78Top-346
❑ 79OPC-224
❑ 79Top-433
❑ 80OPC-334
❑ 80Top-639
❑ 81Don-515
❑ 81Fle-314
❑ 81Top-718
❑ 81TopTra-736
❑ 82Don-43
❑ 82Fle-59
❑ 82RedCok-3
❑ 82Top-159
❑ 83Don-440
❑ 83Fle-586
❑ 83FleSta-16
❑ 83FleSti-215
❑ 83RanAffF-14
❑ 83Top-527
❑ 83TopTra-10T
❑ 84Don-342
❑ 84Fle-414
❑ 84Nes792-283
❑ 84Top-283
❑ 84TopTif-283
❑ 93RanKee-2

Biko, Tom
❑ 80OrlTwiT-3
❑ 82AmaGolST-14

Bilak, Paul

❑ 86PalSprAP-4
❑ 86PalSprAS-4
❑ 87PalSprP-6
Bilardello, Dann J.
❑ 83TopTra-11T
❑ 84Don-408
❑ 84Fle-464
❑ 84Nes792-424
❑ 84RedEnq-14
❑ 84Top-424
❑ 84TopSti-57
❑ 84TopTif-424
❑ 85Don-243
❑ 85Top-28
❑ 85TopTif-28
❑ 86BasStaB-11
❑ 86ExpPos-1
❑ 86ExpProPa-2
❑ 86Top-253
❑ 86TopTif-253
❑ 87Fle-313
❑ 87FleGlo-313
❑ 87OPC-217
❑ 87Top-577
❑ 87TopTif-577
❑ 87VanCanP-1618
❑ 88OmaRoyC-17
❑ 88OmaRoyP-1518
❑ 89BufBisC-13
❑ 89BufBisP-1677
❑ 90BufBisC-13
❑ 90BufBisP-375
❑ 90BufBisTI-2
❑ 90CMC-13
❑ 90OPC-682
❑ 90ProAAAF-490
❑ 90Top-682
❑ 90TopTif-682
❑ 91LasVegSLD-277
❑ 91LasVegSP-237
❑ 91LinDriAAA-277
❑ 91Sco-659
❑ 92Lea-348
❑ 92LeaBlaG-348
❑ 92PadCarJ-4
❑ 92PadMot-13
❑ 92PadSmo-4
❑ 92Sco-719
❑ 92StaClu-254
❑ 93NorTidF-2572
❑ 93PacSpa-256
Bilbert, Roy
❑ 91HagSunLD-230
Bilderback, Tyler
❑ 95BoiHawTI-6
❑ 97LakElsSG-7
Bilello, John
❑ 88BoiHawP-1605
❑ 88FreSunCLC-18
❑ 88FreSunP-1224
❑ 89BoiHawP-1997
❑ 89RenSilSCLC-241
Bilko, Steve (Steven Thomas)
❑ 47Exh-21
❑ 51Bow-265
❑ 52Top-287
❑ 53CarHunW-1
❑ 54Bow-206
❑ 54CarHunW-2
❑ 54Top-116
❑ 55Bow-88
❑ 55Top-93
❑ 55TopDouH-117
❑ 58RedEnq-5
❑ 58RedJayP-3
❑ 58Top-346
❑ 59DarFar-2
❑ 59Top-43
❑ 59TopVen-43
❑ 60Lea-106
❑ 60Top-396
❑ 61AngJayP-3
❑ 61Top-184
❑ 62AngJayP-2
❑ 62Jel-74
❑ 62Pos-74
❑ 62PosCan-74
❑ 62SalPlaC-17A
❑ 62SalPlaC-17B
❑ 62ShiPlaC-17
❑ 62Top-422
❑ 62TopStal-63
❑ 63Jel-24
❑ 63Pos-24
❑ 63RocRedWSP-2
❑ 79TCM50-177
❑ 83TopRep5-287
❑ 90DodTar-52
❑ 94TopArc1-116
❑ 94TopArc1G-116
Bill, Bob
❑ 79NewCoPT-4
❑ 83TriTriT-28
❑ 86TulDriTI-26
❑ 88WatPirP-33
Bill, Robert
❑ 94UtiBluSC-30
Billeci, Craig
❑ 91BatCliCB-6
❑ 91BatCliP-3488
Billingham, Jack
❑ 68Top-228
❑ 68TopVen-228
❑ 69OPC-92
❑ 69Top-92
❑ 69TopTeaP-10
❑ 70AstPho-1
❑ 70Top-701
❑ 71MLBOffS-74
❑ 71OPC-162
❑ 71Top-162
❑ 72Top-542
❑ 73OPC-89
❑ 73Top-89
❑ 74OPC-158
❑ 74Top-158
❑ 74TopSta-22
❑ 75OPC-235
❑ 75Top-235
❑ 75TopMin-235
❑ 76OPC-155
❑ 76RedKro-4
❑ 76SSP-23
❑ 76Top-155
❑ 77PepGloD-53
❑ 77RedCarP-21
❑ 77Top-512
❑ 78TigBurK-6
❑ 78TigTeal-3
❑ 78Top-47
❑ 79Top-388
❑ 80Top-603
❑ 85SpoIndGC-2
❑ 87AstShoSTw-2
❑ 87OscAstP-18
❑ 89SweBasG-43
❑ 90DodTar-53
❑ 90OscAstS-28
❑ 91OscAstP-700
❑ 92OscAstF-2547
❑ 93OscAstC-28
❑ 93OscAstF-644
❑ 93UppDecAH-11
❑ 94OscAstC-27
❑ 94OscAstF-1155
❑ 96KisCobB-2
❑ 97KisCob-28
❑ 98KisCobQ-4
Billingham, James
❑ 92OscAstC-28
Billings, Dick (Richard A.)
❑ 71OPC-729
❑ 71SenTealW-3
❑ 71Top-729
❑ 72OPC-148
❑ 72RanTeal-1
❑ 72Top-148
❑ 73OPC-94
❑ 73RanTeal-4
❑ 73Top-94
❑ 74OPC-466
❑ 74Top-466
❑ 75TulOil7-24
❑ 76SSP-288
❑ 86RanGreT-12
❑ 93RanKee-3
Billings, Haskell
❑ 94ConTSN-1313
❑ 94ConTSNB-1313
Billings, Josh (John A.)
❑ 24Zee-3
Billingsley, Brent
❑ 97MidLeaTP-11
❑ 98Bow-374
❑ 98BowChr-374
❑ 98BowChrGA-374
❑ 98BowChrGAR-374
❑ 98BowChrI-374
❑ 98BowChrIR-374
❑ 98BowChrR-374
❑ 98BowGolA-374
❑ 98BowInt-374
❑ 98PorSeaDQ-1
❑ 99JustheSAC-5
Billingsley, Marvin
❑ 93AshTouC-3
❑ 93AshTouF-2267
❑ 94OscAstC-3
❑ 94OscAstF-1129
Billingsley, Rod
❑ 89SpoIndSP-3
❑ 90WatDiaB-7
❑ 90WatDiaP-2380
Billmeyer, Mickey
❑ 86HagSunP-3
❑ 87MiaMarP-11
❑ 87PorChaRP-16
❑ 88MiaMarS-2
❑ 89ChaRanS-3
❑ 90QuaCitAGS-18
❑ 91CalLeLA-15
❑ 91MidAngOHP-5
❑ 91PalSprAP-2018
❑ 92EdmTraF-3541
❑ 92EdmTraS-168
❑ 92MidAngF-4030
❑ 92MidAngS-453
❑ 92SkyAA F-192
❑ 95AngMot-28
❑ 96AngMot-28
Billoni, Mike
❑ 87BufBisP-27
❑ 89BufBisC-1
Bills, Walter
❑ 92MedHatBJF-3202
❑ 92MedHatBJSP-14
Biltimier, Mike
❑ 93GreFalDSP-6
❑ 94BakDodC-2
❑ 95VerBeaDTI-3
Bilyeu, Aaron
❑ 90NebCor-4
Bingham, David
❑ 92IdaFalGF-3524
❑ 92IdaFalGSP-2
❑ 94HicCraC-3
❑ 94HicCraF-2179
Bingham, Mark
❑ 82DanSunF-5
Binkley, Brett
❑ 93YakBeaC-3
❑ 93YakBeaF-3874
❑ 94VerBeaDC-5
❑ 94VerBeaDF-62
❑ 95DurBulTI-3
Binks, George Eugene
❑ 47A'sTeal-3
❑ 50WorWidGV-21
❑ 83TCMPla1945-5
Binversie, Brian
❑ 94OneYanC-5
❑ 94OneYanF-3781
❑ 95GreBatTI-4
Biot, Charlie
❑ 92NegLeaRLI-5
❑ 95NegLeaL2-17
Birch, Brent
❑ 90ArkRaz-2
Birch, Brock
❑ 86EveGiaC-23
❑ 86EveGiaPC-2
❑ 87CliGiaP-20
Bird, Bill
❑ 90PitMetP-29
Bird, Billy
❑ 88LouRedBTI-52
❑ 89LouRedBTI-1
❑ 91LouRedTI-1
❑ 96LouRedB-5
❑ 98LouRedQ-36
Bird, David
❑ 88AlaGolTI-2
❑ 89WelPirP-5
❑ 90AugPirP-2456
❑ 90ProAaA-75
❑ 91SalBucC-14
❑ 91SalBucP-944
❑ 92CarMudF-1172
❑ 92CarMudS-126
❑ 92SkyAA F-59
Bird, Doug
❑ 74OPC-17
❑ 74RoyPos-2
❑ 74Top-17
❑ 75OPC-364
❑ 75RoyPos-1
❑ 75Top-364
❑ 75TopMin-364
❑ 76KanCitRP-1
❑ 76OPC-96
❑ 76RoyAaP-1
❑ 76SSP-180
❑ 76Top-96
❑ 77BurCheD-68
❑ 77OPC-191
❑ 77Top-556
❑ 78Roy-1
❑ 78SSP270-218
❑ 78Top-183
❑ 79PhiBurK-12
❑ 79Top-664
❑ 80Top-421
❑ 81Fle-106
❑ 81Top-516
❑ 81TopTra-737
❑ 82CubRedL-47
❑ 82Don-504
❑ 82Fle-586
❑ 82Top-273
❑ 83Don-48
❑ 83Fle-490
❑ 83Top-759
❑ 83TopTra-12T
❑ 84Fle-391
❑ 84Nes792-82
❑ 84Top-82
❑ 84TopTif-82
❑ 89PacSenL-90
❑ 90EliSenL-65
❑ 92YanWIZ8-11
Bird, Fred
❑ 86CarSchM-25
Bird, Larry
❑ 94TedWil-LP1
Bird, Oriole
❑ 79BalOriP-18
❑ 80BalOriP-22
❑ 81BalOriP-24
❑ 84BalOriP-42
❑ 86BalOriP-27
❑ 87BalOriP-43
❑ 88OriPos-42
❑ 89BalOriP-40
❑ 90BalOriP-30
❑ 91BalOriP-35
❑ 92BalOriP-38
❑ 94BalOriP-36
❑ 94MasMan-10
❑ 95BalOriP-51
❑ 96BalOriP-38
❑ 97BalOriP-35
Bird, Steven
❑ 88KinIndS-4
Birdie, BJ
❑ 93FunPacM-4
❑ 94MasMan-3
Birdsong, Tim
❑ 98BilMusTI-5
Birdt, Louis
❑ 93PocPosF-4200
❑ 93PocPosSP-23
Birkbeck, Mike
❑ 86VanCanP-3
❑ 87BrePol-40
❑ 87Don-33
❑ 87DonRoo-19
❑ 87FleUpd-5
❑ 87FleUpdG-5
❑ 87Lea-33
❑ 87Top-229
❑ 87TopTif-229
❑ 88BrePol-40
❑ 88BreTeal-3
❑ 88Don-49
❑ 88Sco-369
❑ 88ScoGlo-369
❑ 88Top-692
❑ 88TopTif-692
❑ 89Bow-132
❑ 89BowTif-132
❑ 89BrePol-40
❑ 89BreYea-40
❑ 89Don-501
❑ 89Fle-178
❑ 89FleGlo-178
❑ 89Sco-596
❑ 89Top-491
❑ 89TopTif-491
❑ 90BrePol-40
❑ 90CMC-46
❑ 90DenZepC-21
❑ 90DenZepP-617
❑ 90ProAAAF-642
❑ 90PubIntS-489
❑ 91CanIndP-972
❑ 92TidTidF-888
❑ 92TidTidS-552
❑ 93RicBraBB-21
❑ 93RicBraF-177
❑ 93RicBraP-9
❑ 93RicBraRC-6
❑ 93RicBraRC-6
❑ 94BreMilB-195
❑ 94RicBraF-2838
❑ 95NorTidTI-6
❑ 96SigRooOJ-3
❑ 96SigRooOJS-3
Birkel, Tony
❑ 85RedWinA-12
❑ 86RedWinA-24
Birkofer, Ralph
❑ 34BatR31-90
❑ 34DiaMatCSB-15
❑ 35DiaMatCS3T1-10
❑ 36NatChiFPR-9
❑ 90DodTar-901
Birmingham, Dode (Joseph L.)
❑ 08AmeLeaPC-3
❑ 08RosComP-22
❑ 09BriE97-2
❑ 09ColChiE-31
❑ 09SpoNewSM-101
❑ 09T206-29
❑ 10DomDisP-14
❑ 10SweCapPP-17
❑ 10W555-6
❑ 11HelSta-22
❑ 11PinT-5-622
❑ 11SpoLifM-39
❑ 11T205-17
❑ 12ColRedB-31
❑ 12ColTinT-31
❑ 12HasTriFT-7
❑ 12HasTriFT-8
❑ 12HasTriFT-72
❑ 12T207-14
❑ 13NatGamW-5
❑ 13TomBarW-4
❑ 14CraJacE-106
❑ 14PieStaT-11
❑ 15CraJacE-106
Birrell, Bob
❑ 79ElmPioRST-24
❑ 83PawRedST-1
Birrell, Simon
❑ 96DanBraB-7
❑ 97DanBraB-10
❑ 98DanBraQ-12
Birrer, Babe (Werner)
❑ 56BalOriP-21
❑ 56Top-84
❑ 58MonRoyF-4
❑ 59O'KAleMR-3
❑ 90DodTar-54
❑ 91OriCro-35
Birriel, Jose
❑ 86NewBriRSP-3
❑ 87NewBriRSP-24
❑ 88BlaYNPRWL-66
❑ 88EasLeaAP-19
❑ 88NewBriRSP-902
❑ 89BlaYNPRWL-72
❑ 89BlaYNPRWLU-25
❑ 89LynRedSS-2
Birtsas, Tim
❑ 82OneYanT-8
❑ 85DomLeaS-191
❑ 85FleUpd-6
❑ 86A'sMot-25
❑ 86Don-462
❑ 86Fle-412
❑ 86FleStiC-5
❑ 86Lea-227
❑ 87HunStaTI-3
❑ 87TacTigP-23
❑ 88FleUpd-82
❑ 88FleUpdG-82
❑ 88NasSouC-2
❑ 88NasSouP-477
❑ 88RedKah-48
❑ 88Top-501
❑ 88TopClo-17
❑ 88TopTif-501
❑ 89Fle-152
❑ 89FleGlo-152
❑ 89RedKah-48
❑ 89Sco-454
❑ 89Top-103
❑ 89TopTif-103
❑ 89UppDec-638
❑ 90Don-493
❑ 90Fle-414
❑ 90FleCan-414
❑ 90OPC-687
❑ 90RedKah-3
❑ 90Sco-408
❑ 90Top-687
❑ 90TopTif-687
❑ 90UppDec-137
❑ 91OPC-289
❑ 91Sco-648
❑ 91Top-289
❑ 91TopDesS-289
❑ 91TopMic-289
❑ 91TopTif-289
Biscan, Frank
❑ 46SeaSLP-5
Bisceglia, Dave
❑ 81WatRedT-20
Bisceglia, James
❑ 86SalAngC-90
❑ 87QuaCitAP-14
❑ 88PalSprAP-1458
❑ 89PalSprACLC-52
Bish, Brent
❑ 90SpoIndSP-10
❑ 91ChaRaiC-15
❑ 91ChaRaiP-100
❑ 92CalLeaACL-36
❑ 92HigDesMC-3
❑ 93RanCucQC-4
❑ 93RanCucQF-837
Bishop, Bennie
❑ 98MarPhiG-3
Bishop, Charles
❑ 52Par-98
❑ 53A'sTeal-5
❑ 53Top-186
❑ 54A'STEAI-3
❑ 55A'sRodM-3
❑ 55Top-96
❑ 55TopDouH-109
❑ 91TopArc1-186
Bishop, Craig
❑ 90BakDodCLC-243
❑ 90YakBeaTI-27
Bishop, Greg
❑ 89CarNewE-16
❑ 92MisStaB-50
Bishop, James
❑ 83KinBluJTI-1
❑ 86KnoBluJP-2
❑ 87WilBilP-8
❑ 88CedRapRP-1165
❑ 89MiaMirIS-2
❑ 91SalSpuC-9
❑ 91SalSpuP-2249
❑ 92BirBarF-2587
❑ 92BirBarS-78
❑ 92ClaFS7-239
Bishop, Josh
❑ 96BelSnaTI-4
❑ 96Bow-302
❑ 96BowFoi-302
❑ 97StoPor-2
Bishop, Max F.
❑ 25Exh-105
❑ 26Exh-105
❑ 28PorandAR-A4
❑ 28PorandAR-B4
❑ 28W56PlaC-C4
❑ 29ExhFou-28
❑ 29PorandAR-5
❑ 33Gou-61
❑ 33GouCanV-61
❑ 33RitCE-13S
❑ 33TatOrbSDR-187
❑ 33WorCig-10
❑ 34DiaStaR-6
❑ 35DiaMatCS3T1-11
❑ 35GouPuzR-6E
❑ 35GouPuzR-11G
❑ 35GouPuzR-13E
❑ 35GouPuzR-15E
❑ 70MetMusoAB-1
❑ 72TCMthe3-2
❑ 74A'sl92T-1
❑ 74CapPub-78
❑ 85BigLeaC3-7
❑ 88ConSer4-4
❑ 91ConTSN-183
❑ 94ConTSN-1149

□ 94ConTSNB-1149
Bishop, Mike (Michael D.)
□ 77QuaCitAT-4
□ 80ElPasDT-12
□ 81SalLakCGT-14
□ 82SpoIndT-10
□ 83TidTidT-6
□ 87AncGlaP-2
□ 91MetWIZ-38
Bishop, Teddy
□ 94BelMarC-6
□ 94BelMarF-3239
Bishop, Terry
□ 96MarPhiB-3
Bishop, Tim
□ 87OneYanP-28
□ 88PriWilYS-2
□ 97CapCitB-24
Bishop, William
□ 87OldJudN-31
Bison, Buster T.
□ 89BufBisC-12
□ 89BufBisP-1666
□ 92BufBisBS-28
□ 98BufBisG-4
Bisons, Buffalo
□ 88BufBisTI-9
□ 94OriofB-49
Bispo, Randy
□ 86SanJosBP-4
Bissant, John L.
□ 93NegLeaRL2-2
Bissonette, Del
□ 28LaPre-12
□ 28W56PlaC-S13
□ 29ExhFou-4
□ 29PorandAR-6
□ 31Exh-4
□ 36GouWidPPR-D2
□ 90DodTar-55
Bithorn, Hi
□ 42CubTeal-1
□ 43CubTeal-3
Bitker, Joe
□ 86BeaGolGP-2
□ 87LasVegSP-1
□ 88LasVegSC-1
□ 88LasVegSP-230
□ 89LasVegSC-1
□ 89LasVegSP-4
□ 90CMC-586
□ 90ProAAAF-132
□ 90TacTigC-9
□ 90TacTigP-85
□ 90TriAllGP-AAA47
□ 91Don-624
□ 91Fle-281
□ 91OklCit8P-171
□ 91TopDeb90-16
□ 91UppDec-797
□ 92Sco-743
□ 92Sco100RS-87
□ 93RanKee-72
Bitter, Mike
□ 89SanDieSAS-3
Bittiger, Jeff
□ 82JacMetT-1
□ 83TidTidT-13
□ 84TidTidT-13
□ 85IntLeaAT-20
□ 85MetTCM-37
□ 85TidTidT-8
□ 86PorBeaP-1
□ 87PorBeaP-1
□ 88ScoRoo-66T
□ 88ScoRooG-66T
□ 88VanCanC-1
□ 89Bow-60
□ 89BowTif-60
□ 89Sco-512
□ 89Top-209
□ 89TopTif-209
□ 89UppDec-509
□ 89VanCanC-1
□ 90AlbDukCm-2
□ 90AlbDukP-335
□ 90AlbDukTr-2
□ 90CMC-404
□ 90ProAAAF-56
□ 91ColSprSSLD-77
□ 91ColSprSSP-2176
□ 91LinDriAAA-77
□ 92HunStaF-3941
□ 92HunStaS-303
□ 98FarRedHM-3
Bivens, William E.
□ 87SprCarB-10
□ 88SprCarB-7
□ 89St.PetCS-3
□ 89TexLeaAGS-25
Bivin, Jim
□ 94ConTSN-1299
□ 94ConTSNB-1299
Bjerke, Jeff
□ 98FarRedHM-4
Bjorkman, George A.
□ 80ArkTraT-2
□ 80VenLeaS-79
□ 82LouRedE-1
□ 83ColAstT-1
□ 84IndIndTI-10
□ 84IndIndTI-20
□ 84Nes792-116
□ 84Top-116
□ 84TopTif-116
□ 85IndIndTI-20
□ 85RocRedWT-31
Bjornson, Craig
□ 92AshTouC-18
□ 92AubAstC-22
□ 92AubAstF-1344
□ 93QuaCitRBC-3
□ 93QuaCitRBF-90
Black Barons, Birmingham
□ 92NegLeaRLI-91
□ 92NegLeaRLI-92
□ 92NegLeaRLI-93
□ 93NegLeaRL2-52
□ 93NegLeaRL2-53
□ 93NegLeaRL2-75
□ 93NegLeaRL2-76
□ 93NegLeaRL2-77
□ 93NegLeaRL2-78
□ 93TedWilPC-4
Black Caps, Louisville
□ 93TedWilPC-13
Black Crackers, Atlanta
□ 93TedWilPC-1
Black Wolf, Madison
□ 98MadBlaW-1
Black Yankees, New York
□ 93TedWilPC-16
Black, Allen
□ 82QuaCitCT-2
Black, Bob
□ 89RicBraC-9
Black, Brett
□ 97BatCliTI-15
□ 98PieBolWM-4
Black, Bud (Harry)
□ 75OakOak2A-5
□ 80SanJosMJitB-4
□ 81LynSaiT-2
□ 83Don-322
□ 83Fle-107
□ 83Fle-644
□ 83OmaRoyT-2
□ 83RoyPos-3
□ 83Top-238
□ 84Don-130
□ 84Fle-343
□ 84Nes792-26
□ 84RoyPos-5
□ 84Top-26
□ 84TopSti-283
□ 84TopTif-26
□ 85Don-100
□ 85Fle-198
□ 85Lea-202
□ 85OPC-47
□ 85RoyTeal-4
□ 85Top-412
□ 85TopSti-275
□ 85TopTif-412
□ 86BasStaB-12
□ 86Don-374
□ 86Fle-4
□ 86Lea-170
□ 86OPC-319
□ 86RoyKitCD-7
□ 86RoyNatP-40
□ 86RoyTeal-4
□ 86Top-697
□ 86TopSti-261
□ 86TopTif-697
□ 87Don-404
□ 87Fle-365
□ 87FleGlo-365
□ 87OPC-315
□ 87Top-669
□ 87TopTif-669
□ 88Don-301
□ 88Fle-252
□ 88FleGlo-252
□ 88IndTeal-6
□ 88OPC-301
□ 88RoySmo-9
□ 88RoyTeal-4
□ 88SanDieS-3
□ 88SanDieS-4
□ 88SanDieSAAG-3
□ 88SanDieSAAG-4
□ 88Sco-313
□ 88ScoGlo-313
□ 88ScoRoo-11T
□ 88ScoRooG-11T
□ 88Top-301
□ 88TopTif-301
□ 88TopTra-16T
□ 88TopTraT-16T
□ 89Bow-82
□ 89BowTif-82
□ 89Don-556
□ 89IndTeal-5
□ 89OPC-5
□ 89SanDieSAG-3
□ 89SanDieSAG-4
□ 89Sco-404
□ 89Top-509
□ 89TopSti-209
□ 89TopTif-509
□ 89UppDec-466
□ 90Don-556
□ 90DonBesA-118
□ 90Fle-486
□ 90FleCan-486
□ 90IndTeal-6
□ 90Lea-451
□ 90OPC-144
□ 90PubIntS-554
□ 90Sco-197
□ 90Top-144
□ 90TopBig-223
□ 90TopSti-213
□ 90TopTif-144
□ 90UppDec-498
□ 91Bow-639
□ 91Don-719
□ 91FleUpd-128
□ 91GiaMot-7
□ 91GiaPacGaE-19
□ 91GiaSFE-3
□ 91Lea-312
□ 91OPC-292
□ 91OPCPre-9
□ 91ScoRoo-46T
□ 91StaClu-302
□ 91Stu-260
□ 91Top-292
□ 91TopDesS-292
□ 91TopMic-292
□ 91TopTif-292
□ 91TopTra-11T
□ 91TopTraT-11T
□ 91UltUpd-115
□ 91UppDec-799
□ 92Bow-692
□ 92Don-93
□ 92Fle-628
□ 92GiaMot-7
□ 92GiaPacGaE-6
□ 92Lea-3
□ 92LeaBlaG-3
□ 92OPC-774
□ 92Pin-202
□ 92Sco-358
□ 92StaClu-55
□ 92Top-774
□ 92TopGol-774
□ 92TopGolW-774
□ 92TopMic-774
□ 92UppDec-697
□ 93Bow-28
□ 93Don-50
□ 93Fle-151
□ 93GiaMot-22
□ 93GiaPos-5
□ 93GiaStaC-24
□ 93Lea-212
□ 93OPC-38
□ 93PacSpa-267
□ 93Pin-181
□ 93Sco-131
□ 93Sel-221
□ 93StaClu-624
□ 93StaCluFDI-624
□ 93StaCluMOP-624
□ 93Top-498
□ 93TopGol-498
□ 93TopInaM-498
□ 93TopInaR-498
□ 93TopMic-498
□ 93Ult-482
□ 93UppDec-229
□ 93UppDecGold-229
□ 94Don-64
□ 94Fle-683
□ 94Pin-140
□ 94PinArtP-140
□ 94PinMusC-140
□ 94Sco-176
□ 94ScoGolR-176
□ 94Top-89
□ 94TopGol-89
□ 94TopSpa-89
□ 95ColCho-263
□ 95ColChoGS-263
□ 95ColChoSS-263
□ 95FleUpd-40
□ 95Sco-115
□ 95ScoGolR-115
□ 95ScoPlaTS-115
□ 98BufBisG-5
Black, Carl
□ 98JohCCTI-3
Black, Don
□ 43A'STEAI-5
□ 45A'sTeal-3
□ 47IndTeal-1
□ 47IndVanPP-1
□ 48BluTin-28
□ 48IndTeal-3
□ 53IndPenCBP-4
□ 74CapPub-24
□ 76TayBow4-66
Black, Joe
□ 47PM1StaP1-12
□ 47PM1StaP1-13
□ 47PM1StaP1-14
□ 52Top-321
□ 53RedMan-NL4
□ 53SpoMagP-1
□ 53Top-81
□ 54NewYorJA-1
□ 54Top-98
□ 55DodGolS-9
□ 55Top-156
□ 56Kah-3
□ 56Top-178
□ 56TopPin-54
□ 57SeaPop-5
□ 74dod195T-4
□ 79DiaGre-271
□ 79TCM50-160
□ 83TopRep5-321
□ 89PacLegI-177
□ 89SweBasG-69
□ 90DodTar-56
□ 91DodRinP3-1
□ 91SweBasG-9
□ 91TopArc1-81
□ 92BazQua5A-13
□ 93ActPacA-143
□ 93TedWil-132
□ 93UppDecAH-12
□ 93UppDecAH-154
□ 94TopArc1-98
□ 94TopArc1G-98
□ 94UppDecAH-52
□ 94UppDecAH1-52
□ 95DodROY-3
□ 95TopArcBD-22
□ 95TopArcBD-44
□ 95TopArcBD-71
□ 95TopArcBD-103
□ 97NegLeaPC-10D
Black, Keith
□ 91HamRedC-23
□ 91HamRedP-4043
□ 92HamRedC-24
□ 92HamRedF-1596
□ 93SavCarC-4
□ 93SavCarF-691
□ 93SouAtlLAGF-45
□ 94St.PetCC-4
□ 94St.PetCF-2590
Black, Robbie
□ 89CarNewE-23
Black, Stephen
□ 91MelBusF-18
Blackaby, Ethan Allan
□ 68SeaPop-1
□ 75PhoGiaCK-25
□ 76PheGiaCr-NNO
□ 76PhoGiaCC-2
□ 77PhoGiaCC-3
□ 78PhoGiaC-1
□ 80PhoGiaVNB-24
□ 81PhoGiaVNB-27
□ 82PhoGiaVNB-11
□ 83PhoGiaBHN-26
Blackburn, J.D.
□ 94DavLipB-6
□ 95DavLipB-1
Blackburn, Jackie
□ 85Ft.MyeRT-24
Blackburn, James Ray
□ 49Bow-160
□ 51Bow-287
□ 79TCM50-259
Blackburn, Ron
□ 57JetPos-2
□ 58Top-459
□ 59Top-401
□ 60Top-209
Blackburne, Jim
□ 43A'STEAI-6
Blackburne, Lena (Russell)
□ 09T206-399
□ 10ChiE-12
□ 11PinT-5-770
□ 11SpoLifCW-36
□ 11SpoLifM-20
□ 11T205-18
□ 12T207-15
□ 42A'sTeal-4
□ 91ConTSNP-905
□ 93ConTSN-905
Blackerby, George (George F.)
□ 32Zee-50
□ 33Zee-77
Blackmon, Anthony
□ 87SalLakTTT-22
Blackmon, Kurt
□ 98MarPhiG-4
Blackmon, Tom
□ 80BatTroT-7
□ 83KnoBluJT-1
Blackmore, John
□ 98AubDouTI-3
Blackmun, Ben
□ 85BenPhiC-2
Blackshear, Steve
□ 87ReaPhiP-18
Blackwell, Barry
□ 85AncGlaPTI-4
□ 89KinIndS-3
Blackwell, Eric
□ 90GreFalDSP-14
□ 90YakBeaTI-30
□ 91VerBeaDP-786
□ 91YakBeaC-8
□ 91YakBeaP-4259
Blackwell, Ewell
□ 46SpoExcW-1-6
□ 47Exh-22A
□ 47Exh-22B
□ 47HomBon-3
□ 47PM1StaP1-15
□ 48BluTin-4
□ 48Bow-2
□ 49EurSta-77
□ 49Lea-39
□ 50AmeNut&CCP-1
□ 50Bow-63
□ 50RoyDes-9
□ 51Bow-24
□ 52BerRos-4
□ 52BerRos-20
□ 52RedMan-NL3
□ 52RoyPre-1
□ 52Top-344
□ 53Top-31
□ 55SeaPop-3
□ 76TayBow4-24
□ 79TCM50-119
□ 80MarExh-5
□ 82GSGalAG-22
□ 83TopRep5-344
□ 85TCMPla1-37
□ 89PacLegI-188
□ 91TopArc1-31
□ 92BazQua5A-18
Blackwell, Juan
□ 91Ft.LauYC-19
□ 91Ft.LauYP-2432
□ 92AlbYanF-2230
□ 92AlbYanSk-4
Blackwell, Larry
□ 86KenTwiP-2
□ 87OrlTwiP-26
□ 88VisOakCLC-159
□ 88VisOakP-83
□ 89OrlTwiB-11
□ 89OrlTwiP-1340
Blackwell, Orlando
□ 83CliGiaF-11
□ 84ShrCapFB-2
Blackwell, Richie
□ 94WelPirC-4
□ 94WelPirF-3483
Blackwell, Teddy
□ 89BurIndS-29
□ 90WatIndS-26
□ 91ColIndC-30
□ 92ColRedC-29
□ 93ColRedC-30
□ 93SouAtlLAGF-10
□ 94KinIndC-26
□ 97KinIndB-29
□ 98KinIndQ-29
Blackwell, Tim (Timothy P.)
□ 76SSP-415
□ 77ExpPos-5
□ 78OPC-223
□ 78Top-449
□ 80Top-153
□ 81CokTeaS-13
□ 81Don-559
□ 81Fle-304
□ 81OPC-43
□ 81Top-553
□ 81TopSupHT-22
□ 82Don-99
□ 82ExpHygM-1
□ 82ExpPos-1
□ 82Fle-587
□ 82Top-374
□ 82TopSti-28
□ 82TopTra-7T
□ 83Don-214
□ 83ExpPos-1
□ 83ExpStu-26
□ 83OPC-57
□ 83Top-57
□ 84PhoGiaC-241
□ 86FreGiaSB-1
□ 88PhoFirC-25
□ 89PitMetS-24
□ 90FloStaLAS-24
□ 90St.LucMS-28
□ 91ColMetPI-1
□ 91ColMetPPI-7
□ 91SouAtlLAGP-SAL12
□ 92ColMetC-26
□ 92ColMetF-312
□ 92ColMetPI-1
□ 96BowBayB-1
□ 98NewHavRM-1
□ 98NewHavRMA-1
Blackwell, Todd
□ 90RenSilSCLC-268
Blackwell, Tom
□ 88PhoFirP-53
Blades, Ray (Francis R.)
□ 21Exh-11
□ 25Exh-58
□ 26Exh-58
□ 27MidBre-4
□ 28Exh-30
□ 31CarMet-2
□ 47DodTeal-1
□ 48DodTeal-2
□ 54Top-243
□ 91ConTSN-130
□ 92ConTSN-646
□ 94TopArc1-243
□ 94TopArc1G-243
Bladow, Dave
□ 92EugEmeC-6
□ 92EugEmeF-3017
□ 93WilBluRF-1989
Bladt, Richard Alan
□ 74OPC-601
□ 74SyrChiTI-2
□ 74Top-601
□ 75SyrChiTI-NNO
□ 76SSP-444

❑ 76VenLeaS-103
❑ 77RocRedWM-9
❑ 92YanWIZ7-16

Blaeholder, George
❑ 32OrbPinNP-9
❑ 32OrbPinUP-6
❑ 33Gou-16
❑ 33GouCanV-16
❑ 33TatOrb-6
❑ 34DiaMatCSB-16
❑ 34DiaStaR-13
❑ 35AlDemDCR3-49
❑ 35DiaMatCS3T1-12
❑ 35GouPuzR-5D
❑ 35GouPuzR-6D
❑ 35GouPuzR-11F
❑ 35GouPuzR-13D
❑ 36GouWidPPR-A6
❑ 74CapPub-95
❑ 93ConTSN-742

Blaeholder, Harry
❑ 21Zee-88
❑ 22Zee-75

Blaine, James
❑ 93IdaFalBF-4023
❑ 93IdaFalBSP-16

Blaine, Tom
❑ 88ArkTraGS-8

Blair, Brian
❑ 93EriSaiC-2
❑ 93EriSaiF-3127
❑ 94ChaRivC-2
❑ 94ChaRivF-2680
❑ 96TulDriTI-3
❑ 97TulDriTI-3

Blair, Buddy (Louis Nathan)
❑ 42A'sTeal-5
❑ 83TCMPla1942-23

Blair, Dennis
❑ 72Dia-2
❑ 75ExpPos-3
❑ 75OPC-521
❑ 75Top-521
❑ 75TopMin-521
❑ 76OPC-642
❑ 76SSP-344
❑ 76Top-642
❑ 77OPC-189
❑ 77RocRedWM-23
❑ 77Top-593
❑ 78Top-466
❑ 79HawIslT-22
❑ 80HawIslT-9

Blair, Dirk
❑ 91PulBraC-17
❑ 91PulBraP-3996
❑ 92MacBraC-2
❑ 92MacBraF-258
❑ 93CarLeaAGF-36
❑ 93DurBulC-3
❑ 93DurBulF-477
❑ 93DurBulTI-35
❑ 94GreBraF-405
❑ 94GreBraTI-6
❑ 95AusFut-81
❑ 95BreBtaTI-43

Blair, Donny
❑ 93BelBreCB-2
❑ 93BelBreFI-1701
❑ 94StoPorC-3
❑ 94StoPorF-1684

Blair, Footsie (Clarence Vick)
❑ 30CubTeal-3
❑ 31CubTeal-3
❑ 79DiaGre-102

Blair, Garnett E.
❑ 91NegLeaRL-19
❑ 93NegLeaRL2-3
❑ 93TedWil-98
❑ 95NegLeaLI-19

Blair, Lonnie
❑ 91NegLeaRL-18
❑ 95NegLeaLI-18

Blair, Paul
❑ 65BalOriP-5
❑ 65Top-473
❑ 66BalOriP-4
❑ 66OPC-48
❑ 66Top-48
❑ 66TopVen-48
❑ 67BalOriP-13
❑ 67BalOriP-14
❑ 67BalOriP-15
❑ 67CokCapO-3
❑ 67OPC-153
❑ 67Top-153
❑ 67Top-319
❑ 67TopVen-218
❑ 68BalOriDPCP-2
❑ 68CokCapO-3
❑ 68DexPre-12
❑ 68OPC-135
❑ 68Top-135
❑ 68TopVen-135
❑ 69MilBra-27
❑ 69MLBOffS-1
❑ 69Top-506
❑ 69TopTeaP-5
❑ 70BalOriP-3
❑ 70DayDaiNM-157
❑ 70MLBOffS-146
❑ 70OPC-285
❑ 70Top-285
❑ 71BalOriP-3
❑ 71Kel-35
❑ 71MLBOffS-290
❑ 71OPC-53
❑ 71Top-53
❑ 71TopTat-45
❑ 72MilBra-33
❑ 72OriDMV-2
❑ 72OriPos-5
❑ 72Top-660
❑ 73BalOriP-7
❑ 73LinPor-8
❑ 73OPC-528
❑ 73OriJohP-6
❑ 73OriTeal-6
❑ 73Top-528
❑ 74OPC-92
❑ 74Top-92
❑ 74TopSta-123
❑ 75BalOriP-5
❑ 75Hos-12
❑ 75HosTwi-12
❑ 75OPC-275
❑ 75Top-275
❑ 75TopMin-275
❑ 76BalOriP-5
❑ 76OPC-473
❑ 76SSP-395
❑ 76Top-473
❑ 77BurCheD-39
❑ 77Top-313
❑ 77YanBurK-21
❑ 78SSP270-20
❑ 78Top-114
❑ 78YanBurK-22
❑ 78YanPhoA-3
❑ 78YanSSPD-20
❑ 79OPC-304
❑ 79Top-582
❑ 80OPC-149
❑ 80Top-281
❑ 81Ori6F-6
❑ 81TCM60I-311
❑ 84EveGiaC-19
❑ 86OriGreT-5
❑ 88CalLeaACLC-4
❑ 88SanJosGCLC-117
❑ 88SanJosGP-109
❑ 89PacSenL-76
❑ 89ShrCapP-1834
❑ 89T/MSenL-8
❑ 90CMC-308
❑ 90EliSenL-77
❑ 90ProAAAF-479
❑ 90RocRedWC-7
❑ 90RocRedWP-722
❑ 90WinSpiTI-4
❑ 91ChaKniLD-127
❑ 91ChaKniP-1694
❑ 91LinDriAA-127
❑ 91OriCro-36
❑ 92MCIAmb-8
❑ 92YanWIZ7-17
❑ 92YanWIZ8-12
❑ 93ActPacA-158
❑ 93MCIAmb-2
❑ 93OriCroASU-9
❑ 93UppDecAH-13
❑ 94BalOriP-4
❑ 94MCIAmb-7
❑ 94TedWil-8
❑ 94UppDecAH-197
❑ 94UppDecAH-211
❑ 94UppDecAH1-197
❑ 94UppDecAH1-211
❑ 95BalOriP-8
❑ 95MCIAmb-5
❑ 99SpollIGotG-56
❑ 99SpollIGotGA-7

Blair, Walter Allan
❑ 09RamT20-12
❑ 11MecDFT-4
❑ 11PinT-5-804
❑ 12HasTriFT-4
❑ 14CraJacE-126
❑ 14PieStaT-12
❑ 15CraJacE-126

Blair, William E.
❑ 87OldJudN-32

Blair, Willie
❑ 87DunBluJP-944
❑ 89SyrChiC-6
❑ 89SyrChiMB-2
❑ 89SyrChiP-805
❑ 90BluJayFS-3
❑ 90Bow-504
❑ 90BowTif-504
❑ 90ClaYel-T52
❑ 90DonRoo-29
❑ 90FleUpd-126
❑ 90Lea-449
❑ 90ScoRoo-88T
❑ 90TopTra-8T
❑ 90TopTraT-8T
❑ 91ColSprSSLD-78
❑ 91ColSprSSP-2177
❑ 91Don-267
❑ 91Fle-170
❑ 91LinDriAAA-78
❑ 91OPC-191
❑ 91Sco-57
❑ 91Sco100RS-19
❑ 91Top-191
❑ 91TopDeb90-17
❑ 91TopDesS-191
❑ 91TopMic-191
❑ 91TopTif-191
❑ 91UppDec-427
❑ 92Fle-106
❑ 92Sco-730
❑ 92StaClu-813
❑ 92TucTorF-478
❑ 92TucTorS-601
❑ 93Don-740
❑ 93Fla-36
❑ 93Fle-404
❑ 93FleFinE-23
❑ 93PacSpa-423
❑ 93RocUSPC-8C
❑ 93RocUSPC-10H
❑ 93TopTra-96T
❑ 93Ult-342
❑ 93UppDec-720
❑ 93UppDecGold-720
❑ 94Don-631
❑ 94Fle-434
❑ 94Pac-189
❑ 94RocPol-3
❑ 94Sco-118
❑ 94ScoGolR-118
❑ 94StaClu-348
❑ 94StaCluFDI-348
❑ 94StaCluGR-348
❑ 94StaCluMOP-348
❑ 94StaCluT-116
❑ 94StaCluTFDI-116
❑ 94Top-439
❑ 94TopGol-439
❑ 94TopSpa-439
❑ 94Ult-182
❑ 95Don-47
❑ 95DonPreP-47
❑ 95Fle-515
❑ 95PadMot-20
❑ 95StaClu-157
❑ 95StaCluFDI-157
❑ 95StaCluMOP-157
❑ 95StaCluSTWS-157
❑ 95Top-292
❑ 96Fle-561
❑ 96FleTif-561
❑ 96LeaSigA-25
❑ 96LeaSigAG-25
❑ 96LeaSigAS-25
❑ 96PadMot-26
❑ 96Sco-209
❑ 96Ult-555
❑ 96UltGolM-555
❑ 97Ult-496
❑ 97UltGolME-496
❑ 97UltPlaME-496
❑ 98CirThu-64
❑ 98CirThuRav-64
❑ 98CirThuSupRav-64
❑ 98ColCho-88
❑ 98ColCho-301
❑ 98DiaBacP-4
❑ 98DiaMcD-7
❑ 98Pac-83
❑ 98PacOnl-32
❑ 98PacOnlR-32
❑ 98PacOnlWC-32
❑ 98PacPlaB-83
❑ 98PacRedT-83
❑ 98PacSil-83
❑ 98Pin-133
❑ 98PinPlu-37
❑ 98PinPreP-133
❑ 98Sco-200
❑ 98StaCluFDI-314
❑ 98StaClul-314
❑ 98StaCluOneK-314
❑ 98StaCluPP-314
❑ 98Top-423
❑ 98TopChr-423
❑ 98TopChrR-423
❑ 98TopDevR-423
❑ 98TopDia-423
❑ 98TopMiniC-423
❑ 98Ult-456
❑ 98UltGolM-456
❑ 98UltMas-456
❑ 98UltPlaM-456
❑ 98UppDec-86
❑ 98UppDec-646
❑ 99UppDecEM-MC5
❑ 99UppDecEMFXG-MC5
❑ 99Vic-152

Blais, Jean-Marc
❑ 52LavPro-111

Blais, Mike
❑ 94LynRedSC-3
❑ 94LynRedSF-1884
❑ 95MicBatCTI-3
❑ 96TreThuB-7
❑ 97PawRedS-8
❑ 98TreThuM-28

Blake, Ben
❑ 92WatIndC-8
❑ 92WatIndF-3225

Blake, Bob
❑ 79WisRapTT-5

Blake, Casey
❑ 97DunBluJTI-3
❑ 98DunBluJSB-6
❑ 98DunBluJTI-5
❑ 99JustheSAC-6
❑ 99JustheSAD-5

Blake, Ed
❑ 52Top-144
❑ 83TopRep5-144

Blake, Sherriff (John Frederick)
❑ 23Zee-157
❑ 26Exh-18
❑ 30CubTeal-4
❑ 31CubTeal-4
❑ 92ConTSN-478

Blake, Todd
❑ 92JohCitCC-25
❑ 92JohCitCF-3106
❑ 93SprCarC-3
❑ 93SprCarF-1841
❑ 94SavCarC-8
❑ 94SavCarF-500

Blakely, Darren
❑ 99Bow-374
❑ 99BowGol-374
❑ 99BowInt-374
❑ 99TeaBesR-4
❑ 99TeaBesRFS-3
❑ 99TeaBesRG-4
❑ 99TeaBesRS-4

Blakely, Dave
❑ 85EveGiaC-1
❑ 86CliGiaP-2
❑ 87VisOakP-10

Blakely, Link (Lincoln H.)
❑ 33Zee-18
❑ 36GouWidPPR-D3

Blakeman, Todd
❑ 90EliTwiS-5
❑ 91KenTwiC-3
❑ 91KenTwiP-2080
❑ 92KenTwiC-8

Blakeney, Mo
❑ 98CapFeaCM-2

Blakesly, Jim
❑ 24Zee-122
❑ 25Zee-149

Blanchard, Doc
❑ 74NewYorNTDiS-25
❑ 74NewYorNTDiS-33

Blanchard, Johnny (John Edwin)
❑ 47StaPinP2-5
❑ 59Top-117
❑ 59TopVen-117
❑ 60Lea-89
❑ 60Top-283
❑ 61Pos-18
❑ 61Top-104
❑ 61TopStal-190
❑ 61Yan61RL-9
❑ 62Jel-11
❑ 62Pos-11
❑ 62PosCan-11
❑ 62Top-93
❑ 62TopVen-93
❑ 62YanJayP-3
❑ 63Jel-21
❑ 63Pos-21
❑ 63ReqKP-3
❑ 63Top-555
❑ 64ChatheY-2
❑ 64Top-118
❑ 64TopVen-118
❑ 65ChaTheY-1
❑ 65Top-388
❑ 66Top-268
❑ 66TopVen-268
❑ 78TCM60I-78
❑ 81TCM60I-382
❑ 81TCM60I-474
❑ 82ASAMicM-42
❑ 83Yan196-9
❑ 89SweBasG-92
❑ 91YanRinP11-7
❑ 92YanWIZ6-9
❑ 93UppDecS-11

Blanche, Al (Prosper A.)
❑ 34BatR31-83

Blanchette, Bill
❑ 92BoiHawC-11
❑ 92BoiHawF-3616
❑ 93BoiHawC-3
❑ 93BoiHawF-3904

Blanco, Alberto
❑ 94QuaCitRBC-4
❑ 94QuaCitRBF-526
❑ 95MidLeaA-3
❑ 95QuaCitRBTI-2
❑ 96QuaCitRB-8
❑ 97FloStaLTPB-13
❑ 97KisCob-4
❑ 98JacGenM-3

Blanco, Gil
❑ 65Top-566
❑ 67Top-303
❑ 92YanWIZ6-10

Blanco, Henry
❑ 90KisDodD-1
❑ 91GreFalDSP-5
❑ 92BakDodCLC-3
❑ 92UppDecML-201
❑ 93LinVenB-159
❑ 94SanAntMF-2474
❑ 94VenLinU-29
❑ 95LinVen-16
❑ 95LinVen-307
❑ 95LinVen-314
❑ 95LinVen-316
❑ 95LinVen-323
❑ 95SanAntMTI-48
❑ 96-97LinVen-145
❑ 96SanAntMB-1
❑ 97AlbDukGS-3
❑ 98MetUni-52
❑ 98MetUniPMG-52
❑ 98Spolll-163
❑ 98SpollIEE-163
❑ 98SpollIFE-163
❑ 98Ult-232
❑ 98UltGolM-232
❑ 98UltMas-232
❑ 98UltPlaM-232

Blanco, Ossie (Oswaldo C.)
❑ 76VenLeaS-128
❑ 80VenLeaS-192

Blanco, Pedro
❑ 92EliTwiF-3684
❑ 93EliTwiC-4
❑ 93EliTwiF-3426
❑ 93LinVenB-147

Blanco, Roger
❑ 96EveAquB-3
❑ 97DurBulTI-6

Blanco, Romauldo
❑ 73CedRapAT-22
❑ 75DubPacT-11
❑ 76VenLeaS-119

Bland, Lance
❑ 90SanBerSCLC-116

Bland, Nathan
❑ 93YakBeaC-4
❑ 93YakBeaF-3875
❑ 94BakDodC-3
❑ 94GreFalDSP-4
❑ 95BakBlaTI-11
❑ 96VerBeaDB-7
❑ 97SanAntMB-1
❑ 98SanAntMG-5
❑ 98SanAntMM-1

Blandford, Paul
❑ 96VerExpB-9

Blanding, Fritz (Fred)
❑ 11PinT-5-608
❑ 12T207-16
❑ 14CraJacE-109
❑ 15CraJacE-109

Blank, Matt
❑ 97VerExpB-9
❑ 98CapFeaCM-3
❑ 99Bow-428
❑ 99BowGol-428
❑ 99BowInt-428

Blanke, Scott
❑ 83CliGiaF-26

Blankenship, Bob
❑ 89BilMusP-2060
❑ 90BenBucL-11

Blankenship, Cliff
❑ 09AmeCarE90-1-8
❑ 09ObaT21-222
❑ 09RamT20-13
❑ 15Zee-74
❑ 16Zee-74

Blankenship, Kevin
❑ 84AriWilP-1
❑ 85DurBulT-3
❑ 86GreBraTI-4
❑ 87GreBraB-19
❑ 88GreBraB-16
❑ 88SouLeaAJ-28
❑ 89Don-658
❑ 89IowCubC-7
❑ 89IowCubP-1699
❑ 89TriAAAP-AAA44
❑ 89UppDec-762
❑ 90Bow-24
❑ 90BowTif-24
❑ 90CMC-78
❑ 90Fle-28
❑ 90FleCan-28
❑ 90IowCubC-3
❑ 90IowCubP-311
❑ 90ProAAAF-618
❑ 90Sco-646
❑ 90UppDec-47
❑ 91BufBisP-533
❑ 92OklCit8F-1907
❑ 92OklCit8S-303
❑ 92SkyAAAF-139

Blankenship, Lance
❑ 86MedA'sC-69
❑ 86ModA'sC-13
❑ 87HunStaTI-4
❑ 87ModA'sP-10
❑ 88TacTigC-11
❑ 88TacTigP-630
❑ 88TriAAAP-38
❑ 89Don-621
❑ 89Fle-2
❑ 89FleGlo-2
❑ 89Sco-641
❑ 89ScoHot1R-20
❑ 89TacTigC-12
❑ 89TacTigP-1539
❑ 89UppDec-15
❑ 90A'sMot-21
❑ 90Fle-1
❑ 90FleCan-1
❑ 90Hot50RS-8
❑ 90OPC-132
❑ 90Sco-536
❑ 90Sco100RS-82
❑ 90ScoYouS2-36
❑ 90Top-132

❑ 90TopBig-173
❑ 90TopTif-132
❑ 90UppDec-687
❑ 91A'sMot-21
❑ 91Don-701
❑ 91Fle-3
❑ 91OPC-411
❑ 91Sco-303
❑ 91SouOreAAP-SOA18
❑ 91StaClu-437
❑ 91Top-411
❑ 91TopDesS-411
❑ 91TopMic-411
❑ 91TopTif-411
❑ 92AthMot-21
❑ 92Don-768
❑ 92Fle-250
❑ 92Lea-410
❑ 92LeaBlaG-410
❑ 92OPC-386
❑ 92Sco-279
❑ 92StaClu-897
❑ 92Ult-418
❑ 92UppDec-749
❑ 93AthMot-22
❑ 93AthStaC-2
❑ 93Bow-273
❑ 93Don-23
❑ 93Fle-290
❑ 93Lea-221
❑ 93OPC-30
❑ 93PacSpa-562
❑ 93Pin-338
❑ 93StaClu-413
❑ 93StaCluFDI-413
❑ 93StaCluMOP-413
❑ 93Top-548
❑ 93TopGol-548
❑ 93TopInaM-548
❑ 93TopInaR-548
❑ 93TopMic-548
❑ 93Ult-253
❑ 93UppDec-108
❑ 93UppDecGold-108
❑ 94Don-401
❑ 94Fle-254
❑ 94Pac-445
❑ 94StaClu-341
❑ 94StaCluFDI-341
❑ 94StaCluGR-341
❑ 94StaCluMOP-341
❑ 94Top-17
❑ 94TopGol-17
❑ 94TopSpa-17
❑ 95Top-253

Blankenship, Ted
❑ 26Exh-73
❑ 27Exh-37
❑ 74CapPub-97
❑ 92ConTSN-457

Blanks, Daryl
❑ 88IdaFalBP-1834
❑ 89BurBraP-1621
❑ 89BurBraS-2
❑ 90BurBraB-23
❑ 90BurBraP-2362
❑ 90BurBraS-3

Blanks, Larvell
❑ 73OPC-609
❑ 73Top-609
❑ 75AtlBraP-2
❑ 75OPC-394
❑ 75Top-394
❑ 75TopMin-394
❑ 76IndTeal-1
❑ 76OPC-127
❑ 76SSP-8
❑ 76Top-127
❑ 76TopTra-127T
❑ 77IndTeal-2
❑ 77PepGloD-6
❑ 77Top-441
❑ 78IndTeal-2
❑ 78OPC-213
❑ 78Top-61
❑ 79Top-307
❑ 80Top-656
❑ 89PacSenL-206
❑ 89TopSenL-92
❑ 93RanKee-73

Blanton, Cy (Darrell)
❑ 34BatR31-88
❑ 34DiaStaR-57
❑ 35GouPuzR-8K
❑ 35GouPuzR-9K
❑ 36GouWidPPR-A7
❑ 36GouWidPPR-C3
❑ 36NatChiFPR-10
❑ 36R31PasP-2
❑ 36WorWidGV-3
❑ 37ExhFou-7
❑ 38ExhFou-7
❑ 39GouPreR303A-4
❑ 39WorWidGTP-4
❑ 74CapPub-82
❑ 91ConTSN-134

Blanton, Garrett
❑ 91HamRedC-16
❑ 91HamRedP-4049
❑ 93SavCarC-5
❑ 93SavCarF-697

Blaser, Mark
❑ 83GreHorT-16
❑ 85AlbYanT-14
❑ 86WesPalBEP-6

Blasingame, Don (Donald L.)
❑ 47Exh-23A
❑ 47Exh-23B
❑ 56Top-309
❑ 57Top-47
❑ 58CarJayP-1
❑ 58Top-199
❑ 59ArmCoi-5
❑ 59Top-491
❑ 60GiaJayP-2
❑ 60Top-397
❑ 61GiaJayP-2
❑ 61Pos-148A
❑ 61Pos-148B
❑ 61Top-294
❑ 61TopStaI-73
❑ 62Jel-117
❑ 62Pos-117
❑ 62PosCan-117
❑ 62RedEnq-1
❑ 62SalPlaC-103
❑ 62ShiPlaC-103
❑ 62Top-103
❑ 62TopVen-103
❑ 63Jel-126
❑ 63Kah-2
❑ 63Pos-126
❑ 63RedEnq-1
❑ 63RedFreBC-1
❑ 63Top-518
❑ 64Top-327
❑ 64TopVen-327
❑ 65OPC-21
❑ 65Top-21
❑ 66SenTeal-1
❑ 78TCM60I-84
❑ 79TCMJapPB-80
❑ 80Red196T-12

Blasingame, Kent
❑ 94ClePhiC-6
❑ 94ClePhiF-2538
❑ 94FloStaLAF-FSL31
❑ 95ReaPhiELC-5
❑ 95ReaPhiTI-29

Blasingame, Wade
❑ 65OPC-44
❑ 65Top-44
❑ 66BraPos-4
❑ 66Kah-5
❑ 66Top-355
❑ 66TopVen-355
❑ 67Ast-4
❑ 67BraPho-3
❑ 67CokCapB-14
❑ 67DexPre-23
❑ 67OPC-119
❑ 67Top-119
❑ 68CokCapA-7
❑ 68Top-507
❑ 69MilBra-28
❑ 69Top-308
❑ 71AstCok-2
❑ 71AstTeal-1
❑ 71OPC-79
❑ 71Top-79
❑ 72AstTeal-2
❑ 72Top-581
❑ 92YanWIZ7-18

Blasingim, Chad
❑ 94DavLipB-1

Blasingim, Joe
❑ 95BelGiaTI-37
❑ 96BelGiaTI-30

Blaske, Kevin
❑ 92ChaRanC-29

Blass, Steve
❑ 65OPC-232
❑ 65Top-232
❑ 66PirEasH-28
❑ 66Top-344
❑ 66TopVen-344
❑ 67CokCapPi-7
❑ 67PirTeal-3
❑ 67Top-562
❑ 67TopPirS-4
❑ 68PirKDK-28
❑ 68PirTeal-3
❑ 68Top-499
❑ 69Kah-B5
❑ 69OPC-104
❑ 69PirGre-3
❑ 69PirTeal-3
❑ 69Top-104
❑ 69TopSta-83
❑ 69TopSup-57
❑ 69TopTeaP-16
❑ 70OPC-396
❑ 70PirTeal-3
❑ 70Top-396
❑ 71MLBOffS-194
❑ 71OPC-143
❑ 71PirActP-13
❑ 71PirArc-2
❑ 71Top-143
❑ 72Kel-44
❑ 72MilBra-34
❑ 72OPC-229
❑ 72OPC-320
❑ 72PirTeal-1
❑ 72SevTraC-6
❑ 72Top-229
❑ 72Top-320
❑ 73Kel2D-11
❑ 73OPC-95
❑ 73SevTraC-7
❑ 73Top-95
❑ 74OPC-595
❑ 74Top-595
❑ 84OCoandSI-178
❑ 91UppDecS-13
❑ 93PirNatI-3
❑ 93UppDecAH-14
❑ 94UppDecAH-191
❑ 94UppDecAH1-191
❑ 97PirPos-2

Blasucci, Tony
❑ 85PriWilPT-18
❑ 86PriWilPP-3
❑ 87DayBeaAP-5
❑ 88BirBarB-2
❑ 89BirBarB-10
❑ 89BirBarP-94
❑ 90CalCanC-2
❑ 90CalCanP-644
❑ 90CMC-429
❑ 90ProAAAF-109

Blateric, Steve
❑ 73OPC-616
❑ 73Top-616
❑ 75CalAngP-4
❑ 75SalLakCC-19
❑ 92YanWIZ7-19

Blatnick, Johnny (John Louis)
❑ 49Bow-123

Blatt, Charles P.
❑ 88KimN18-3

Blattner, Buddy (Robert G.)
❑ 40SolHug-4
❑ 47TipTop-121
❑ 49EurSta-130
❑ 49PhiBul-6
❑ 75JohMiz-1
❑ 83Car194T-9
❑ 84TCMPla1-45

Blauser, Jeff
❑ 86DurBulP-2
❑ 87IntLeaAT-33
❑ 87RicBraC-2
❑ 87RicBraT-11
❑ 87SpoRoo2-48
❑ 88BobCamRB-6
❑ 88Don-513
❑ 88Fle-533
❑ 88FleGlo-533
❑ 88RicBraC-22
❑ 88RicBraP-18
❑ 88Sco-562
❑ 88ScoGlo-562
❑ 88ScoYouS2-14
❑ 88StaLinBra-3
❑ 89BraDub-5
❑ 89Don-592
❑ 89Fle-588
❑ 89FleGlo-588
❑ 89PanSti-41
❑ 89Sco-589
❑ 89Top-83
❑ 89TopBig-317
❑ 89TopTif-83
❑ 89UppDec-132
❑ 90Bow-15
❑ 90BowTif-15
❑ 90BraDubP-1
❑ 90BraDubS-2
❑ 90ClaBlu-123
❑ 90Don-271
❑ 90DonBesN-74
❑ 90Fle-576
❑ 90FleCan-576
❑ 90Lea-191
❑ 90OPC-251
❑ 90PanSti-217
❑ 90PublntS-109
❑ 90Sco-178
❑ 90Top-251
❑ 90TopBig-180
❑ 90TopSti-28
❑ 90TopTif-251
❑ 90UppDec-406
❑ 91BraDubP-4
❑ 91BraSubS-6
❑ 91Don-229
❑ 91Fle-683
❑ 91Lea-115
❑ 91OPC-623
❑ 91PanFreS-22
❑ 91Sco-52
❑ 91StaClu-377
❑ 91Top-623
❑ 91TopDesS-623
❑ 91TopMic-623
❑ 91TopTif-623
❑ 91Ult-2
❑ 91UppDec-382
❑ 92BraLykP-6
❑ 92BraLykS-7
❑ 92Don-228
❑ 92Fle-353
❑ 92Lea-147
❑ 92LeaBlaG-147
❑ 92OPC-199
❑ 92Pin-477
❑ 92Sco-362
❑ 92StaClu-168
❑ 92Top-199
❑ 92TopGol-199
❑ 92TopGolW-199
❑ 92TopMic-199
❑ 92Ult-159
❑ 92UppDec-370
❑ 93Bow-142
❑ 93BraFloA-3
❑ 93BraLykP-5
❑ 93BraLykS-6
❑ 93BraStaC-5
❑ 93Don-134
❑ 93Fla-2
❑ 93Fle-364
❑ 93Lea-86
❑ 93OPC-59
❑ 93PacSpa-333
❑ 93PanSti-183
❑ 93Pin-432
❑ 93Sco-142
❑ 93SP-56
❑ 93StaClu-436
❑ 93StaCluFDI-436
❑ 93StaCluMOP-436
❑ 93StuSil-8
❑ 93Top-552
❑ 93TopGol-552
❑ 93TopInaM-552
❑ 93TopInaR-552
❑ 93TopMic-552
❑ 93Ult-302
❑ 93UppDec-591
❑ 93UppDecGold-591
❑ 94Bow-517
❑ 94BraLykP-6
❑ 94BraLykS-6
❑ 94BraUSPC-1S
❑ 94BraUSPC-8H
❑ 94ColC-53
❑ 94ColChoGS-53
❑ 94ColChoSS-53
❑ 94Don-88
❑ 94Fin-27
❑ 94FinRef-27
❑ 94Fla-124
❑ 94Fle-354
❑ 94FleAllS-30
❑ 94FleExtB-200
❑ 94FUnPac-104
❑ 94Lea-194
❑ 94OPC-214
❑ 94Pac-4
❑ 94PanSti-143
❑ 94Pin-98
❑ 94PinArtP-98
❑ 94PinMusC-98
❑ 94PinRunC-RC29
❑ 94Sco-54
❑ 94ScoGolR-54
❑ 94ScoGolS-5
❑ 94Sel-14
❑ 94SP-48
❑ 94SPDieC-48
❑ 94Spo-111
❑ 94StaClu-229
❑ 94StaCluFDI-229
❑ 94StaCluGR-229
❑ 94StaCluMOP-229
❑ 94StaCluMOP-ST1
❑ 94StaCluST-ST1
❑ 94StaCluT-60
❑ 94StaCluTFDI-60
❑ 94Top-318
❑ 94Top-387
❑ 94TopBlaG-26
❑ 94TopGol-318
❑ 94TopGol-387
❑ 94TopSpa-318
❑ 94TopSpa-387
❑ 94TriPla-42
❑ 94TriPlaM-8
❑ 94Ult-150
❑ 94UppDec-324
❑ 94UppDecED-324
❑ 95ColCho-168
❑ 95ColChoGS-168
❑ 95ColChoSS-168
❑ 95Don-363
❑ 95DonPreP-363
❑ 95DonTopotO-182
❑ 95Fla-321
❑ 95Fle-302
❑ 95Lea-390
❑ 95Pac-3
❑ 95Pin-241
❑ 95PinArtP-241
❑ 95PinMusC-241
❑ 95Sco-440
❑ 95ScoGolR-440
❑ 95ScoPlaTS-440
❑ 95StaClu-136
❑ 95StaCluFDI-136
❑ 95StaCluMOP-136
❑ 95StaCluSTDW-B1T
❑ 95StaCluSTWS-136
❑ 95Top-414
❑ 95TopCyb-214
❑ 95Ult-346
❑ 95UltGolM-346
❑ 95UppDec-44
❑ 95UppDecED-44
❑ 95UppDecEDG-44
❑ 96BraFle-2
❑ 96ColCho-452
❑ 96ColChoGS-452
❑ 96ColChoSS-452
❑ 96Don-461
❑ 96DonPreP-461
❑ 96Fla-195
❑ 96Fle-287
❑ 96FleTif-287
❑ 96Pac-15
❑ 96Pin-89
❑ 96Sco-288
❑ 96ScoDugC-B13
❑ 96ScoDugCAP-B13
❑ 96StaClu-438
❑ 96StaCluEPB-438
❑ 96StaCluEPG-438
❑ 96StaCluEPS-438
❑ 96StaCluMOP-438
❑ 96Top-406
❑ 96Ult-152
❑ 96UltGolM-152
❑ 96UppDec-273
❑ 97Cir-94
❑ 97CirRav-94
❑ 97ColCho-267
❑ 97ColChoT-AB11
❑ 97Don-336
❑ 97DonGolPP-336
❑ 97DonLim-49
❑ 97DonLimE-49
❑ 97DonLimENG-49
❑ 97DonSilPP-336
❑ 97DonTea-27
❑ 97DonTeaSPE-27
❑ 97Fle-252
❑ 97FleTif-252
❑ 97Sco-434
❑ 97ScoArtPWB-434
❑ 97ScoResC-434
❑ 97ScoShoS-434
❑ 97ScoShoSAP-434
❑ 97StaClu-131
❑ 97StaCluMOP-131
❑ 97StrAll-9
❑ 97Top-419
❑ 97TopSta-45
❑ 97TopSta97AS-AS19
❑ 97TopStaAM-45
❑ 97Ult-546
❑ 97UltGolME-546
❑ 97UltPlaME-546
❑ 98BraSco-10
❑ 98BraScoP-10
❑ 98CirThu-185
❑ 98CirThuRav-185
❑ 98CirThuSupRav-185
❑ 98ColCho-33
❑ 98ColCho-331
❑ 98Don-262
❑ 98DonGolPP-262
❑ 98DonSilPP-262
❑ 98Fle-177
❑ 98Fle-497
❑ 98Pac-230
❑ 98PacAur-111
❑ 98PacOme-45
❑ 98PacOmeR-45
❑ 98PacOnl-137
❑ 98PacOnlR-137
❑ 98PacOnlWC-137
❑ 98PacPar-137
❑ 98PacParC-137
❑ 98PacParG-137
❑ 98PacParHS-137
❑ 98PacParPB-137
❑ 98PacParR-137
❑ 98PacPlaB-230
❑ 98PacRedT-230
❑ 98PacSil-230
❑ 98Pin-11
❑ 98PinArtP-PP11
❑ 98PinMusC-PP11
❑ 98PinPlu-162
❑ 98PinPreP-11
❑ 98Sco-135
❑ 98ScoSS-PP153
❑ 98ScoSSAP-PP153
❑ 98SP Aut-62
❑ 98SPxFin-258
❑ 98SPxFinR-258
❑ 98SPxFinS-258
❑ 98StaCluFDI-392
❑ 98StaCluI-392
❑ 98StaCluOneK-392
❑ 98StaCluPP-392
❑ 98Top-52
❑ 98TopChr-52
❑ 98TopChrC9-C6
❑ 98TopChrC9R-C6
❑ 98TopChrR-52
❑ 98TopClo9-C6
❑ 98TopDevR-52
❑ 98TopDia-52
❑ 98TopMiniC-52
❑ 98TopOpeD-31
❑ 98TopSta-96
❑ 98TopStaB-96
❑ 98TopStaG-96
❑ 98TopStaGR-96
❑ 98TopStaS-96
❑ 98Ult-388
❑ 98UltGolM-388
❑ 98UltMas-388
❑ 98UltPlaM-388
❑ 98UppDec-31
❑ 98UppDec-660
❑ 99Fle-348
❑ 99FleSta9-348
❑ 99FleWarT-348
❑ 99StaClu-189
❑ 99StaCluFDI-189

❑ 99StaCluOoaK-189
❑ 99StaCluPP-189
❑ 99Top-378
❑ 99TopChr-378
❑ 99TopChrR-378
❑ 99TopMVPP-378
❑ 99UppDec-58
❑ 99UppDec-336
❑ 99UppDecEL1-58
❑ 99UppDecEL1-336
❑ 99UppDecEL2-58
❑ 99UppDecEL2-336

Blaylock, Gary
❑ 59Top-539
❑ 84RoyPos-6
❑ 85RoyTeal-5

Blaylock, Marv (Marvin E.)
❑ 55Bow-292
❑ 57Top-224

Blaylock, Robert
❑ 59Top-211
❑ 64TulOil-1

Blaze, Bakersfield
❑ 95BakBlaTI-32

Blazier, Ron
❑ 90PriPatD-2
❑ 91BatCliCB-26
❑ 91BatCliP-3475
❑ 92SpaPhiC-10
❑ 92SpaPhiF-1255
❑ 93Bow-244
❑ 93ClaFS7-241
❑ 93ClePhiC-3
❑ 93ClePhiF-2675
❑ 93ExcFS7-83
❑ 93PhiStaC-23
❑ 94ClePhiC-7
❑ 94ClePhiF-2518
❑ 95ReaPhiELC-6
❑ 95ReaPhiTI-40
❑ 96Cir-163
❑ 96CirRav-163
❑ 96Exc-195
❑ 96ScrRedBB-7
❑ 97Fle-407
❑ 97FleTif-407
❑ 97Pac-373
❑ 97PacLigB-373
❑ 97PacSil-373
❑ 97PhiTeal-22
❑ 97Top-492
❑ 97Ult-247
❑ 97UltGolME-247
❑ 97UltPlaME-247

Bleazard, David
❑ 96MedHatBJTI-5
❑ 97HagSunB-3

Bledsoe, Randy
❑ 93JohCitCC-5
❑ 93JohCitCF-3669
❑ 94NewJerCC-3
❑ 94NewJerCF-3405

Blefary, Curt (Curtis LeRoy)
❑ 65BalOriP-6
❑ 65OPC-49
❑ 65Top-49
❑ 66BalOriP-5
❑ 66Baz-28
❑ 66Top-460
❑ 66TopRubI-9
❑ 67BalOriP-16
❑ 67Baz-28
❑ 67CokCapO-13
❑ 67DexPre-24
❑ 67OPC-180
❑ 67Top-180
❑ 67Top-521
❑ 67TopVen-227
❑ 68BalOriDPCP-3
❑ 68CokCapO-13
❑ 68DexPre-13
❑ 68Top-312
❑ 68TopVen-312
❑ 69MilBra-29
❑ 69MLBOffS-137
❑ 69Top-458
❑ 69TopSta-122
❑ 69TopSup-44
❑ 69TopTeaP-6
❑ 70MLBOffS-242
❑ 70OPC-297
❑ 70Top-297
❑ 70YanCliDP-3
❑ 70YanPhoS-4
❑ 71MLBOffS-483
❑ 71OPC-131
❑ 71Top-131
❑ 71YanCliDP-2
❑ 72MilBra-35
❑ 72Top-691
❑ 72Top-692
❑ 81Ori6F-7
❑ 81TCM60I-412
❑ 83FraBroR-23
❑ 87AstShoSTw-24
❑ 91OriCro-37
❑ 92YanWIZ7-20
❑ 94CarLeaA-DJ24

Blemenstock, Brad
❑ 98ModA'sG-3

Blemker, Ray
❑ 77FriOneYW-112

Bleser, Al
❑ 94BenRocC-29
❑ 96PorRocB-2
❑ 98PorRocG-2

Blessitt, Ike (Isiah)
❑ 75TucTorC-9
❑ 77HolMilT-1
❑ 89PacSenL-190
❑ 89TopSenL-20

Bleuberg, Jim
❑ 91JacSunP-142

Blevins, Brad
❑ 83QuaCitCT-8

Blevins, Greg
❑ 90ButCopKSP-2
❑ 91GasRanC-13
❑ 91GasRanP-2690

Blevins, Jeremy
❑ 96BesAutS-12
❑ 96BesAutSA-6
❑ 96BoiHawB-5
❑ 97BesAutAS-5
❑ 98GreBatM-2

Bligh, Ned (Edwin Forrest)
❑ 87OldJudN-33
❑ 94OriofB-31

Bliss, Bill (William)
❑ 91FroRowDP-45
❑ 91FroRowDPG-45
❑ 91FroRowDPS-45
❑ 91GenCubC-1
❑ 91GenCubP-4207
❑ 91PeoChiTI-34
❑ 92ClaFS7-218
❑ 92PeoChiC-4
❑ 92PeoChiTI-4
❑ 92StaCluD-17
❑ 92UppDecML-159
❑ 93PeoChiC-2
❑ 93PeoChiF-1075
❑ 93PeoChiTI-1
❑ 95SalAvaTI-25

Bliss, Elmer Ward
❑ 11SpoLifCW-37

Bliss, John J.A.
❑ 09AmeCarE90-1-9
❑ 09PC7HHB-4
❑ 09T206-30
❑ 11HelSta-167
❑ 11SpoLifM-263
❑ 13Zee-76
❑ 14Zee-127

Bliss, Roy
❑ 17Zee-60

Blizzard, Kevin
❑ 89GeoColC-2
❑ 89GeoColC-28

Blizzard, Mascot
❑ 96WatIndTI-NNO
❑ 97WatIndTI-7
❑ 98WatIndTI-3

Blobaum, Jeff
❑ 84PhoGiaC-19

Block, Bruno (James John)
❑ 10JuJuDE-4
❑ 11HelSta-6
❑ 11SpoLifM-21
❑ 12T207-17

Block, Cy (Seymour)
❑ 50WorWidGV-9
❑ 76TayBow4-111

Block, George
❑ 15Zee-97
❑ 16Zee-98

Block, Richard
❑ 79NewCoPT-19

Blocker, Terry
❑ 82JacMetT-20
❑ 84TidTidT-20
❑ 85IntLeaAT-16
❑ 85MetColP-17
❑ 85MetTCM-28
❑ 85TidTidT-19
❑ 86MetTCM-36
❑ 86TidTidP-2
❑ 87MetColP-25
❑ 87TidTidP-5
❑ 87TidTidT-19
❑ 89Fle-589
❑ 89FleGlo-589
❑ 89RicBraBC-3
❑ 89RicBraC-17
❑ 89RicBraTI-3
❑ 89Sco-605
❑ 89Top-76
❑ 89TopTif-76
❑ 89UppDec-399
❑ 91MetWIZ-39

Blohm, Pete
❑ 89AugPirP-516
❑ 89SouAtlLAGS-45
❑ 90DunBluJS-3
❑ 90KnoBluJB-3
❑ 90KnoBluJP-1246
❑ 90KnoBluJS-1
❑ 91KnoBluJLD-351
❑ 91LinDriAA-351
❑ 91SyrChiMB-3
❑ 91SyrChiP-2475
❑ 92SyrChiF-1959
❑ 92SyrChiMB-1
❑ 92SyrChiS-501
❑ 93SyrChiF-992

Blomberg, Ron (Ronald Mark)
❑ 70YanPhoS-5
❑ 72OPC-203
❑ 72Top-203
❑ 72YanSch-2
❑ 73LinPor-129
❑ 73NewYorSNM-5
❑ 73OPC-462
❑ 73SyrChiTI-3
❑ 73Top-462
❑ 73Yan-1
❑ 74Kel-54
❑ 74OPC-117
❑ 74SyrChiTI-1
❑ 74Top-117
❑ 74TopDecE-60
❑ 74TopSta-211
❑ 75OPC-68
❑ 75SyrChiTI-1
❑ 75Top-68
❑ 75TopMin-68
❑ 75YanSSP-4
❑ 76Hos-38
❑ 76HosTwi-38
❑ 76OPC-354
❑ 76SSP-450
❑ 76Top-354
❑ 77Top-543
❑ 78Hos-147
❑ 78SSP270-157
❑ 78Top-506
❑ 79OPC-17
❑ 79Top-42
❑ 88Top-663
❑ 88TopTif-663
❑ 92YanWIZ6-11
❑ 92YanWIZ7-21
❑ 94CarLeaA-DJ38
❑ 97FleMilDM-39
❑ 97FleMilDMR-39

Blomberg, Steve
❑ 76ShrCapT-16

Blomdahl, Ben
❑ 91NiaFalRC-19
❑ 91NiaFalRP-3625
❑ 92ClaFS7-99
❑ 92FayGenC-2
❑ 92FayGenF-2159
❑ 93Bow-207
❑ 93ClaFS7-158
❑ 93ClaGolF-51
❑ 93LonTigF-2297
❑ 94TolMudHF-1018
❑ 95TolMudHTI-7
❑ 96Sco-242
❑ 96TolMudHB-6
❑ 97BufBis-6
❑ 98BufBisG-6

Blondin, Strongman
❑ 88KimN18-4

Blood, Darin
❑ 95BelGiaTI-16
❑ 96Bow-380
❑ 96BowFoi-380
❑ 96Exc-240
❑ 96SanJosGB-17
❑ 97BesLimA-3
❑ 97Bow-192
❑ 97BowCerBlaIA-CA6
❑ 97BowCerBluIA-CA6
❑ 97BowCerGolIA-CA6
❑ 97BowChr-180
❑ 97BowChrI-180
❑ 97BowChrIR-180
❑ 97BowChrR-180
❑ 97BowInt-192
❑ 97ShrCap-6
❑ 97ShrCapB-6
❑ 97TexLeaTP-19
❑ 97Top-493
❑ 98BesPreA-3
❑ 98FreGriG-3
❑ 98SP MinPE-113
❑ 98SPMin-113

Bloodworth, Jimmy (James H.)
❑ 40PlaBal-189
❑ 49EurSta-78
❑ 50PhiPhil-2
❑ 51Bow-185
❑ 75Phi195T-3
❑ 79DiaGre-386
❑ 80Phi195T-3

Bloomer, Chris
❑ 97LetBlaDB-19
❑ 98SouBenSHM-15

Bloomfield, Clyde S.
❑ 64Top-532

Bloomfield, Jack (Gordon L.)
❑ 58SeaRalT-4
❑ 59SeaPop-3
❑ 74PadDea-4

Blosser, Doug
❑ 96LanLugB-7
❑ 97LanLugTS-3

Blosser, Greg
❑ 89HigSchPLS-21
❑ 90Bow-278
❑ 90BowTif-278
❑ 90CarLeaA-12
❑ 90LynRedSTI-1
❑ 90Sco-681
❑ 90TopTVRS-37
❑ 91Bow-115
❑ 91Cla/Bes-226
❑ 91LinDriAA-452
❑ 91NewBriRSLD-452
❑ 91NewBriRSP-363
❑ 91UppDec-70
❑ 92Bow-251
❑ 92ClaFS7-194
❑ 92NewBriRSF-445
❑ 92NewBriRSS-478
❑ 92SkyAA F-203
❑ 92UppDecML-260
❑ 93Bow-199
❑ 93ClaFS7-44
❑ 93ClaGolF-27
❑ 93ExcFS7-130
❑ 93FleFinE-170
❑ 93PawRedSDD-4
❑ 93PawRedSF-2419
❑ 93PawRedSTI-4
❑ 93Top-798
❑ 93TopGol-798
❑ 93TopInaM-798
❑ 93TopInaR-798
❑ 93TopMic-798
❑ 93Ult-506
❑ 94ColC-2
❑ 94ColChoGS-2
❑ 94ColChoSS-2
❑ 94Fin-402
❑ 94FinRef-402
❑ 94LeaLimR-30
❑ 94PawRedSDD-4
❑ 94Pin-245
❑ 94PinArtP-245
❑ 94PinMusC-245
❑ 94ScoRoo-RT162
❑ 94ScoRooGR-RT162
❑ 94Sel-190
❑ 94StaClu-172
❑ 94StaCluFDI-172
❑ 94StaCluGR-172
❑ 94StaCluMOP-172
❑ 94UppDec-5
❑ 94UppDecED-5
❑ 95PawRedSDD-6
❑ 95PawRedTI-33
❑ 95Sco-286
❑ 95ScoGolR-286
❑ 95ScoPlaTS-286
❑ 95TreThuTI-27
❑ 96RocRedWB-6
❑ 97St.PetDR-1
❑ 97St.PetDRUB-7
❑ 98DurBulTI-2

Blossom, Ray
❑ 21Zee-65

Blouin, Gary
❑ 86EugEmeC-45
❑ 87Ft.MyeRP-3

Blount, Bill
❑ 85SpoIndC-2
❑ 86ChaRaiP-3
❑ 87LasVegSP-16
❑ 88RivRedWCLC-230
❑ 88RivRedWP-1421

Blowers, Mike (Michael)
❑ 86JamExpP-1
❑ 87WesPalBEP-664
❑ 88JacExpB-16
❑ 88JacExpP-975
❑ 89IndIndC-14
❑ 89IndIndP-1221
❑ 90Bow-441
❑ 90BowTif-441
❑ 90ClaUpd-T5
❑ 90Don-656
❑ 90DonRoo-26
❑ 90Fle-438
❑ 90FleCan-438
❑ 90Lea-109
❑ 90Sco-624
❑ 90ScoYouS2-34
❑ 90TopDeb89-18
❑ 90TopTra-9T
❑ 90TopTraT-9T
❑ 90TopTVY-23
❑ 90UppDec-767
❑ 91Don-63
❑ 91OPC-691
❑ 91Sco-838
❑ 91Sco100RS-17
❑ 91Top-691
❑ 91TopDesS-691
❑ 91TopMic-691
❑ 91TopTif-691
❑ 91UppDec-730
❑ 92CalCanF-3739
❑ 92CalCanS-54
❑ 92SkyAAAF-23
❑ 92YanWIZ8-13
❑ 93FleFinE-264
❑ 93Lea-457
❑ 93MarMot-13
❑ 93PacSpa-618
❑ 93StaClu-144
❑ 93StaCluFDI-144
❑ 93StaCluMOP-144
❑ 94ColC-54
❑ 94ColChoGS-54
❑ 94ColChoSS-54
❑ 94Don-423
❑ 94Fin-183
❑ 94FinRef-183
❑ 94Fle-279
❑ 94Lea-218
❑ 94MarMot-17
❑ 94Pac-562
❑ 94Sco-521
❑ 94ScoGolR-521
❑ 94Sel-66
❑ 94StaClu-604
❑ 94StaCluFDI-604
❑ 94StaCluGR-604
❑ 94StaCluMOP-604
❑ 94StaCluMOP-ST26
❑ 94StaCluST-ST26
❑ 94Top-717
❑ 94TopGol-717
❑ 94TopSpa-717
❑ 94TriPla-123
❑ 94Ult-117
❑ 94UppDec-309
❑ 94UppDecED-309
❑ 95ColCho-284
❑ 95ColChoGS-284
❑ 95ColChoSS-284
❑ 95Don-46
❑ 95DonPreP-46
❑ 95DonTopotO-146
❑ 95Fla-79
❑ 95Fle-261
❑ 95Lea-289
❑ 95MarMot-10
❑ 95MarPac-22
❑ 95Pac-390
❑ 95Sco-531
❑ 95ScoGolR-531
❑ 95ScoPlaTS-531
❑ 95SP-191
❑ 95SPSil-191
❑ 95StaClu-494
❑ 95StaCluMOP-494
❑ 95StaCluSTDW-M26T
❑ 95StaCluSTDW-M494
❑ 95StaCluSTWS-494
❑ 95Top-348
❑ 95Ult-325
❑ 95UltGolM-325
❑ 95UppDecED-347
❑ 95UppDecEDG-347
❑ 96ColCho-313
❑ 96ColCho-586
❑ 96ColChoGS-313
❑ 96ColChoGS-586
❑ 96ColChoSS-313
❑ 96ColChoSS-586
❑ 96DodFle-1
❑ 96DodMot-10
❑ 96DodPol-3
❑ 96Don-148
❑ 96DonPreP-148
❑ 96EmoXL-204
❑ 96Fin-B215
❑ 96FinRef-B215
❑ 96Fla-286
❑ 96Fle-426
❑ 96FleTif-426
❑ 96FleUpd-U141
❑ 96FleUpdTC-U141
❑ 96LeaSigA-26
❑ 96LeaSigAG-26
❑ 96LeaSigAS-26
❑ 96MetUni-181
❑ 96MetUniP-181
❑ 96Pac-403
❑ 96Pin-55
❑ 96Pin-350
❑ 96PinFoil-350
❑ 96Sco-295
❑ 96ScoDugC-B20
❑ 96ScoDugCAP-B20
❑ 96StaClu-192
❑ 96StaCluMOP-192
❑ 96Top-419
❑ 96Ult-123
❑ 96Ult-492
❑ 96UltGolM-123
❑ 96UltGolM-492
❑ 96UppDec-359
❑ 97Fle-356
❑ 97Fle-545
❑ 97FleTif-356
❑ 97FleTif-545
❑ 97Top-192
❑ 97Ult-375
❑ 97UltGolME-375
❑ 97UltPlaME-375
❑ 97UppDecMP-P16
❑ 98A'sMot-25
❑ 98Fle-445
❑ 98PacOnl-524
❑ 98PacOnlR-524
❑ 98PacOnlWC-524
❑ 98Ult-333
❑ 98UltGolM-333
❑ 98UltMas-333
❑ 98UltPlaM-333
❑ 98UppDec-707
❑ 99Fle-326
❑ 99FleSta9-326
❑ 99FleWarT-326
❑ 99Pac-306
❑ 99PacPlaB-306
❑ 99PacRed-306
❑ 99Top-279
❑ 99TopChr-279
❑ 99TopChrR-279
❑ 99TopMVPP-279

Blue Jays, Dunedin
❑ 93DunBluJFFN-30

❑ 98DunBluJTI-NNO
Blue Jays, Knoxville
❑ 82KnoBluJT-1
Blue Jays, St. Catharines
❑ 92St.CatBJF-3403
❑ 93St.CatBJC-30
Blue Jays, Toronto
❑ 78OPC-58
❑ 78Top-626
❑ 79BluJayS-2
❑ 80OPC-300
❑ 81OPC-331
❑ 83FleSta-250
❑ 83FleSti-NNO
❑ 83FleSti-NNO
❑ 85BluJayFS-36
❑ 86BluJayFS-36
❑ 87SpoTeaL-5
❑ 88BluJayFS-35
❑ 88PanSti-468
❑ 88RedFolSB-118
❑ 89BluJayFS-36
❑ 90FleWaxBC-C13
❑ 90PubIntS-645
❑ 90RedFolSB-114
❑ 90TopMag-99
❑ 91PanCanT1-133
❑ 92BluJayMH-1
❑ 92BluJayMH-2
❑ 92BluJayMH-3
❑ 92BluJayMH-4
❑ 92BluJayMH-5
❑ 92BluJayMH-6
❑ 92BluJayMH-7
❑ 92BluJayMH-8
❑ 92BluJayMH-9
❑ 92BluJayMH-10
❑ 92BluJayMH-11
❑ 92BluJayMH-12
❑ 92BluJayMH-13
❑ 92BluJayMH-14
❑ 92BluJayMH-15
❑ 92BluJayMH-16
❑ 92KelFroFBB-1
❑ 92OPCBoxB-3
❑ 93BluJayDM-23
❑ 93BluJayDM-23A
❑ 94ImpProP-14
❑ 94Sco-330
❑ 94ScoGolR-330
❑ 95PacPriTL-14
❑ 95PanSti-151
❑ 96PanSti-163
❑ 99Vic-408
Blue, Lu (Luzerne Atwell)
❑ 19Zee-33
❑ 20Zee-42
❑ 21Nei-5
❑ 22E120-47
❑ 22W572-7
❑ 22W573-11
❑ 23WilChoV-10
❑ 26Exh-90
❑ 27AmeCarE126-54
❑ 28Exh-57
❑ 28StaPlaCE-3
❑ 29ExhFou-30
❑ 29PorandAR-7
❑ 31Exh-20
❑ 31W517-50
❑ 33ExhFou-10
❑ 46SpoExcW-1-10
❑ 81TigDetN-115
❑ 81TigSecNP-10
❑ 85BigLeaC3-15
❑ 90DodTar-57
❑ 94ConTSN-1229
❑ 94ConTSNB-1229
Blue, Vida
❑ 70OPC-21
❑ 70Top-21
❑ 71A'sPos-8
❑ 71MLBOffS-507
❑ 71OPC-544
❑ 71Top-544
❑ 72'sA'sPos-21
❑ 72Kel-9A
❑ 72Kel-9B
❑ 72OPC-92
❑ 72OPC-94
❑ 72OPC-96
❑ 72OPC-169
❑ 72OPC-170
❑ 72ProStaP-25
❑ 72SevTraC-7
❑ 72Top-92
❑ 72Top-94
❑ 72Top-96
❑ 72Top-169
❑ 72Top-170
❑ 72TopPos-8
❑ 73OPC-430
❑ 73Top-430
❑ 74OPC-290
❑ 74Top-290
❑ 74TopSta-222
❑ 75OPC-209
❑ 75OPC-510
❑ 75SSP42-12
❑ 75Top-209
❑ 75Top-510
❑ 75TopMin-209
❑ 75TopMin-510
❑ 76BlaDis-3
❑ 76BucDis-3
❑ 76CarDis-3
❑ 76CraDis-3
❑ 76DailsID-3
❑ 76Hos-20
❑ 76HosTwi-20
❑ 76IsaDis-3
❑ 76Kel-47A
❑ 76Kel-47B
❑ 76OPC-140
❑ 76OPC-200
❑ 76OrbDis-3
❑ 76RedBarD-3
❑ 76SafDis-3
❑ 76SSP-481
❑ 76Top-140
❑ 76Top-200
❑ 76TowCluD-3
❑ 77BurCheD-114
❑ 77Hos-52
❑ 77OPC-75
❑ 77RCColC-4
❑ 77Spo-6518
❑ 77Top-230
❑ 77TopCloS-4
❑ 78GiaTeal-4
❑ 78OPC-177
❑ 78RCColC-43
❑ 78Top-680
❑ 78WifBalD-4
❑ 79BasPat-3
❑ 79GiaPol-14
❑ 79Hos-74
❑ 79Kel-23
❑ 79OPC-49
❑ 79Top-110
❑ 79TopCom-33
❑ 80BurKinPHR-1
❑ 80GiaPol-14
❑ 80GiaTeal-2
❑ 80Kel-42
❑ 80OPC-14
❑ 80Top-30
❑ 80TopSup-59
❑ 81AllGamPI-166
❑ 81Don-433
❑ 81Fle-432
❑ 81FleStiC-63
❑ 81GiaTeal-3
❑ 81Kel-23
❑ 81OPC-310
❑ 81Top-310
❑ 81TopScr-108
❑ 81TopSti-239
❑ 82Don-4
❑ 82Don-222
❑ 82FBIDis-1
❑ 82Fle-384
❑ 82FleSta-61
❑ 82K-M-19
❑ 82Kel-63
❑ 82OPC-82
❑ 82OPC-267
❑ 82Roy-3
❑ 82SevSluC-3
❑ 82Top-430
❑ 82Top-431
❑ 82Top-576
❑ 82TopSti-111
❑ 82TopTra-8T
❑ 83Don-34
❑ 83Don-648
❑ 83Fle-106
❑ 83Fle-643
❑ 83FleSta-17
❑ 83FleSti-96
❑ 83OPC-178
❑ 83RoyPos-4
❑ 83Top-471
❑ 83Top-570
❑ 83TopFol-1
❑ 84GiaMot-25
❑ 84OCoandSI-145
❑ 85FleUpd-7
❑ 85GiaMot-10
❑ 85GiaPos-1
❑ 86Don-509
❑ 86Fle-533
❑ 86GiaMot-10
❑ 86GiaPos-3
❑ 86Lea-247
❑ 86Spo-132
❑ 86Spo-142
❑ 86SpoDecG-63
❑ 86Top-770
❑ 86TopTif-770
❑ 87A'sMot-7
❑ 87Don-362
❑ 87Fle-266
❑ 87FleGlo-266
❑ 87OPC-260
❑ 87RedFolSB-128
❑ 87Top-260
❑ 87TopTif-260
❑ 89PacLegI-198
❑ 89PacSenL-215
❑ 89T/MSenL-9
❑ 89TopSenL-48
❑ 90EliSenL-50
❑ 90EliSenL-121
❑ 90PacLeg-8
❑ 90SweBasG-89
❑ 91PacSenL-81
❑ 91SweBasG-10
❑ 92A'sUno7P-2
❑ 92A'sUno7P-4
❑ 92ActPacA-44
❑ 92MDAMVP-8
❑ 92UppDecHoB-H5
❑ 92UppDecHoB-H8
❑ 92UppDecHoB-AU5
❑ 92UppDecS-27
❑ 92UppDecS-33
❑ 93MCIAmb-1
❑ 93MetIma-2
❑ 93TedWil-43
❑ 93UppDecS-10
❑ 94UppDecAH-71
❑ 94UppDecAH1-71
❑ 95MCIAmb-1
❑ 99SpoIllGotG-61
❑ 99SpoIllGotGA-8
❑ 99SpoIllGotGC-22
Blueberg, James
❑ 86BelMarCr-120
❑ 87WauTimP-2
❑ 88CalLeaACLC-30
❑ 88SanBerSB-15
❑ 88SanBerSCLC-47
❑ 89SanBerSB-6
❑ 90CMC-795
❑ 90WilBilB-2
❑ 90WilBilP-1049
❑ 90WilBilS-1
❑ 91JacSunLD-328
❑ 91LinDriAA-328
Bluege, Ossie (Oswald Louis)
❑ 25Exh-121
❑ 26Exh-121
❑ 26SpoComoA-6
❑ 29ExhFou-31
❑ 31Exh-32
❑ 31SenTeaIPW-2
❑ 33Gou-113
❑ 33Gou-159
❑ 33GouCanV-83
❑ 34BatR31-105
❑ 34DiaStaR-71
❑ 35AlDemDCR3-61
❑ 36ExhFou-16
❑ 36NatChiFPR-11
❑ 36WorWidGV-87
❑ 38CloFotW-8
❑ 60SenUniMC-2
❑ 61Fle-93
❑ 75SenTCM1-3
❑ 75SenTCM1-39
❑ 79DiaGre-61
❑ 85BigLeaC3-53
❑ 91ConTSN-295
Bluege, Otto Adam
❑ 33WorCig(-7
❑ 94ConTSN-1305
❑ 94ConTSNB-1305
Bluepper, Mascot
❑ 92PadPolD-2
❑ 94MasMan-4
Blues, Cleveland
❑ 86JosHalC-6
Blues, Kansas City
❑ 38BasTabP-30
Bluestone, Brad
❑ 86EriCarP-4
❑ 87SprCarB-27
❑ 88SprCarB-27
❑ 90CMC-680
❑ 90LouRedBC-29
❑ 94St.PetCC-30
❑ 97JohCitCTI-4
❑ 98JohCCTI-4
Bluewinkle, Rocky
❑ 94WilBluRC-27
❑ 97WilBluR-30
❑ 98WilBluRC-25
Bluhm, Bill
❑ 87EveGiaC-25
❑ 88WatIndP-668
❑ 89RenSilSCLC-262
Bluhm, Brandon
❑ 91BurIndP-3290
❑ 92BurIndC-6
❑ 92BurIndF-1645
Blum, Brent
❑ 86AlbYanT-30
❑ 87AlbYanP-22
❑ 88PriWiIYS-3
Blum, Geoff
❑ 94StaCluDP-65
❑ 94StaCluDPFDI-65
❑ 94VerExpC-24
❑ 94VerExpF-3914
❑ 95Bow-245
❑ 95BowGolF-245
❑ 95Exc-220
❑ 95SPML-93
❑ 95UppDecML-126
❑ 95UppDecMLFS-126
❑ 96HarSenB-8
❑ 96HonShaHWB-24
Bluma, Jaime
❑ 94EugEmeC-1
❑ 94EugEmeF-3701
❑ 94SigRooDP-65
❑ 94SigRooDPS-65
❑ 95Bow-239
❑ 95BowGolF-239
❑ 95Exc-53
❑ 95WicWraTI-19
❑ 96BesAutSA-7
❑ 96Bow-147
❑ 96BowFoi-147
❑ 96Exc-55
❑ 96OmaRoyB-8
❑ 96Top-431
❑ 97Bow-98
❑ 97BowCerBlaIA-CA7
❑ 97BowCerBluIA-CA7
❑ 97BowCerGolIA-CA7
❑ 97BowChr-120
❑ 97BowChrI-120
❑ 97BowChrIR-120
❑ 97BowChrR-120
❑ 97BowInt-98
❑ 97Cir-264
❑ 97CirRav-264
❑ 97Fin-32
❑ 97FinRef-32
❑ 97Fle-111
❑ 97FleTif-111
❑ 97RoyPol-4
❑ 97SpoIll-2
❑ 97SpoIllEE-2
❑ 97StaCluM-M35
❑ 97StaCluMOP-M35
❑ 97TopAweI-AI1
❑ 97UppDec-479
❑ 98OmaRoyM-5
❑ 98WicWraM-1
Bluma, Jeff
❑ 90WicStaSGD-5
Blumberg, Rob
❑ 89St.CatBJP-2088
❑ 90MyrBeaBJP-2768
❑ 90ProAaA-89
❑ 90SouAtlLAS-27
❑ 91KanCouCC-4
❑ 91KanCouCP-2651
❑ 92HagSunS-252
Blume, David
❑ 81WauTimT-11
Blumenstock, Brad
❑ 96SouOreTI-12
❑ 97SouOreTB-19
Blumeyer, Rich
❑ 80WatIndT-33
Blundin, Barry
❑ 88BurIndP-1791
Bluthardt, Jay
❑ 88WatPirP-15
❑ 94SalBucF-2340
Bly, Derrick
❑ 97RocCub-9
❑ 98RocCubM-4
❑ 98RocCubTI-4
Blyleven, Bert
❑ 71MLBOffS-458
❑ 71OPC-26
❑ 71Top-26
❑ 72OPC-515
❑ 72Top-515
❑ 72TwiPos-1
❑ 72TwiTeal-1
❑ 73Kel2D-35
❑ 73LinPor-104
❑ 73OPC-199
❑ 73Top-199
❑ 74Kel-46
❑ 74OPC-98
❑ 74Top-98
❑ 74TopDecE-47
❑ 74TopSta-201
❑ 75Hos-74
❑ 75OPC-30
❑ 75Top-30
❑ 75TopMin-30
❑ 75TwiPos-2
❑ 75TwiTeal-2
❑ 76Hos-116
❑ 76Kel-11
❑ 76MinTwiP-1
❑ 76OPC-204
❑ 76OPC-235
❑ 76SSP-219
❑ 76Top-204
❑ 76Top-235
❑ 77BurCheD-22
❑ 77OPC-101
❑ 77Spo-4209
❑ 77Top-630
❑ 77TopCloS-5
❑ 78Hos-74
❑ 78Kel-53
❑ 78OPC-113
❑ 78RCColC-68
❑ 78Top-131
❑ 78WifBalD-5
❑ 79Hos-133
❑ 79OPC-155
❑ 79Top-308
❑ 80Kel-5
❑ 80OPC-238
❑ 80Top-457
❑ 81Don-135
❑ 81Fle-383
❑ 81OPC-294
❑ 81Top-554
❑ 81TopTra-738
❑ 82Don-111
❑ 82Fle-361
❑ 82FleSta-199
❑ 82Ind-5
❑ 82IndWhe-1
❑ 82OPC-164
❑ 82Top-559
❑ 82Top-685
❑ 82TopSti-173
❑ 83AllGamPI-73
❑ 83Don-589
❑ 83IndPos-6
❑ 83IndWhe-6
❑ 83OPC-280
❑ 83Top-280
❑ 83TopFol-1
❑ 84AllGamPI-164
❑ 84Don-129
❑ 84DonActAS-45
❑ 84DonCha-42
❑ 84Fle-536
❑ 84FunFooP-106
❑ 84Ind-5
❑ 84IndWhe-28
❑ 84Nes792-716
❑ 84Nes792-789
❑ 84OPC-126
❑ 84Top-716
❑ 84Top-789
❑ 84TopSti-261
❑ 84TopTif-716
❑ 84TopTif-789
❑ 85Don-4
❑ 85Don-224
❑ 85DonSupD-4
❑ 85Fle-440
❑ 85FleLimE-2
❑ 85FleStaS-81
❑ 85FleStaS-92
❑ 85FleStaS-112
❑ 85Ind-5
❑ 85IndPol-28
❑ 85Lea-4
❑ 85OPC-355
❑ 85SevCoi-G7
❑ 85Top-355
❑ 85TopGloS-17
❑ 85TopMin-355
❑ 85TopSti-247
❑ 85TopSup-35
❑ 85TopTif-355
❑ 86Don-649
❑ 86DonAll-52
❑ 86DonHig-31
❑ 86Fle-386
❑ 86FleMin-82
❑ 86FleSlu-1
❑ 86FleStiC-6
❑ 86Lea-88
❑ 86OPC-272
❑ 86QuaGra-21
❑ 86SevCoi-C10
❑ 86Spo-64
❑ 86Spo-103
❑ 86Spo-142
❑ 86Top-445
❑ 86Top3-D-1
❑ 86TopMinL-23
❑ 86TopSti-279
❑ 86TopSup-11
❑ 86TopTat-24
❑ 86TopTif-445
❑ 86TwiTeal-21
❑ 87Don-71
❑ 87DonOpeD-226
❑ 87Fle-536
❑ 87FleAwaW-3
❑ 87FleGlo-536
❑ 87FleMin-9
❑ 87FleStiC-10
❑ 87FleStiWBC-S3
❑ 87Lea-100
❑ 87OPC-25
❑ 87RedFolSB-101
❑ 87Spo-81
❑ 87SpoTeaP-17
❑ 87Top-25
❑ 87TopMinL-61
❑ 87TopSti-278
❑ 87TopTif-25
❑ 87TwiPos-3
❑ 87TwiTeal-19
❑ 88Don-71
❑ 88DonBasB-18
❑ 88Fle-4
❑ 88FleGlo-4
❑ 88FleStiC-41
❑ 88Lea-52
❑ 88OPC-295
❑ 88PanSti-132
❑ 88Sco-90
❑ 88ScoGlo-90
❑ 88Spo-92
❑ 88StaLinTw-3
❑ 88Top-295
❑ 88TopBig-180
❑ 88TopSti-20
❑ 88TopSti-276
❑ 88TopTif-295
❑ 88TwiMasBD-1
❑ 88TwiSmoC-6
❑ 88Woo-21
❑ 89Bow-41
❑ 89BowTif-41
❑ 89Don-119
❑ 89DonBasB-3
❑ 89DonTra-35
❑ 89Fle-105
❑ 89FleGlo-105
❑ 89FleUpd-12
❑ 89OPC-204
❑ 89Sco-215

❑ 89ScoRoo-17T
❑ 89Top-555
❑ 89TopBasT-96
❑ 89TopSti-285
❑ 89TopTif-555
❑ 89TopTra-11T
❑ 89TopTraT-11T
❑ 89UppDec-225
❑ 89UppDec-712
❑ 90AngSmo-2
❑ 90Bow-285
❑ 90BowTif-285
❑ 90ClaBlu-142
❑ 90Don-331
❑ 90DonBesA-4
❑ 90Fle-128
❑ 90FleAwaW-3
❑ 90FleBasM-2
❑ 90FleBasMC-2
❑ 90FleCan-128
❑ 90KayB-2
❑ 90Lea-63
❑ 90M.Vpin-14
❑ 90MLBBasB-96
❑ 90OPC-130
❑ 90PanSti-28
❑ 90PubIntS-366
❑ 90RedFolSB-5
❑ 90Sco-180
❑ 90Sco100S-12
❑ 90Spo-193
❑ 90Top-130
❑ 90TopBig-114
❑ 90TopMinL-7
❑ 90TopSti-165
❑ 90TopTif-130
❑ 90UppDec-527
❑ 90UppDecS-3
❑ 90Woo-7
❑ 91BasBesRB-1
❑ 91Don-453
❑ 91Fle-308
❑ 91OPC-615
❑ 91OPCBoxB-A
❑ 91Sco-235
❑ 91StaClu-175
❑ 91Stu-23
❑ 91Top-615
❑ 91TopDesS-615
❑ 91TopMic-615
❑ 91TopTif-615
❑ 91TopWaxBC-A
❑ 91UppDec-571
❑ 91Woo-7
❑ 92AngPol-3
❑ 92OPC-375
❑ 92Top-375
❑ 92TopGol-375
❑ 92TopGolW-375
❑ 92TopMic-375
❑ 93Fle-568
❑ 93PacSpa-41
❑ 93Pin-83
❑ 93Pin-296
❑ 93RanKee-74
❑ 93Sco-577
❑ 93Sel-252
❑ 93Top-48
❑ 93TopGol-48
❑ 93TopInaM-48
❑ 93TopInaR-48
❑ 93TopMic-48
❑ 95MCIAmb-9
❑ 96RanCup-2

Blyleven, Joe
❑ 78QuaCitAT-4

Blyleven, Todd
❑ 94BoiHawC-2
❑ 94BoiHawF-3343
❑ 95Exc-18
❑ 95LakElsSTI-4
❑ 95MidAngOHP-4

Blyth, Bert (Robert)
❑ 82IowCubT-14

Blythe, Billy
❑ 94StaCluDP-44
❑ 94StaCluDPFDI-44
❑ 95EugEmeTI-4
❑ 96MacBraB-2
❑ 97MacBra-20

Blyzka, Mike (Michael)
❑ 54OriEss-3
❑ 54Top-152
❑ 91OriCro-38
❑ 94TopArc1-152
❑ 94TopArc1G-152
❑ 97BalOriP-3

Boag, Jack
❑ 78St.PetCT-2

Boak, Chet (Chester Robert)
❑ 77FriOneYW-98

Boardman, Louis
❑ 09ObaT21-134

Boatman, John
❑ 92DavLipB-4
❑ 93DavLipB-2
❑ 94DavLipB-2
❑ 95DavLipB-2

Boatright, Dennis
❑ 83ButCopKT-1

Bobb, Jason
❑ 92GulCoaDF-3557
❑ 93ButCopKSP-18

Bobb, Randy (Mark Randall)
❑ 70OPC-429
❑ 70Top-429
❑ 71OPC-83
❑ 71Top-83

Bobbitt, Greg
❑ 93HunCubC-2
❑ 93HunCubF-3227
❑ 94MidLeaAF-MDW46
❑ 94PeoChiC-4
❑ 94PeoChiF-2258

Bobel, Jay
❑ 87SalAngP-3

Bobo, Elgin
❑ 91BoiHawC-10
❑ 91BoiHawP-3882
❑ 92BoiHawC-24
❑ 92BoiHawF-3635
❑ 92ClaFS7-448
❑ 92QuaCitRBC-17
❑ 92QuaCitRBF-812

Bobo, Paul
❑ 93DavLipB-3
❑ 94DavLipB-3

Bocachica, Hiram
❑ 94ClaUpdCotC-CC18
❑ 94SigRooDP-21
❑ 94SigRooDPS-21
❑ 95Bes-82
❑ 95SPML-91
❑ 95UppDecML-155
❑ 95UppDecML-224
❑ 95UppDecMLFS-155
❑ 95UppDecMLFS-224
❑ 96Exc-185
❑ 96WesPalBEB-21
❑ 97Bow-179
❑ 97BowBes-182
❑ 97BowBesAR-182
❑ 97BowBesMI-MI1
❑ 97BowBesMIAR-MI1
❑ 97BowBesMIARI-MI1
❑ 97BowBesMII-MI1
❑ 97BowBesMIR-MI1
❑ 97BowBesMIRI-MI1
❑ 97BowBesR-182
❑ 97BowChr-171
❑ 97BowChrI-171
❑ 97BowChrIR-171
❑ 97BowChrR-171
❑ 97BowInt-179
❑ 97EasLeaTPB-10
❑ 97HarSen-5
❑ 98arSenW1-5
❑ 98Bes-3
❑ 98BowGolA-196
❑ 98BowInt-196
❑ 98Don-324
❑ 98DonGolPP-324
❑ 98DonSilPP-324
❑ 98HarSenM-5
❑ 98SP MinPE-78
❑ 98SPMin-78
❑ 98UppDec-577

Boccabella, John D.
❑ 64Top-192
❑ 64TopVen-192
❑ 66Top-482
❑ 67CokCapC-5
❑ 67CubProPS-4
❑ 67DexPre-25
❑ 67Top-578
❑ 68Top-542
❑ 69MilBra-30
❑ 69Top-466
❑ 70ExpPos-15
❑ 70OPC-19
❑ 70Top-19
❑ 71ExpLaPR-2
❑ 71ExpPS-3
❑ 71MLBOffS-123
❑ 71OPC-452
❑ 71Top-452
❑ 72Dia-3
❑ 72OPC-159
❑ 72ProStaP-2
❑ 72Top-159
❑ 73OPC-592
❑ 73Top-592
❑ 74ExpWes-2
❑ 74OPC-253
❑ 74Top-253
❑ 74TopSta-52
❑ 75OPC-553
❑ 75Top-553
❑ 75TopMin-553
❑ 78TCM60I-291
❑ 92Nab-35

Bochesa, Greg
❑ 86WinHavRSP-4
❑ 87NewBriRSP-13
❑ 88NewBriRSP-900

Bochte, Bruce Anton
❑ 74SalLakCAC-96
❑ 75CalAngP-5
❑ 75OPC-392
❑ 75Top-392
❑ 75TopMin-392
❑ 76OPC-637
❑ 76SSP-200
❑ 76Top-637
❑ 77IndTeal-3
❑ 77MarPos-2
❑ 77Top-68
❑ 78Hos-81
❑ 78PapGinD-29
❑ 78SagDis-25
❑ 78TasDis-25
❑ 78Top-537
❑ 79Hos-123
❑ 79OPC-231
❑ 79Top-443
❑ 80Kel-59
❑ 80MarPos-6
❑ 80OPC-80
❑ 80Top-143
❑ 80TopSup-55
❑ 81AllGamPI-2
❑ 81Don-403
❑ 81Dra-25
❑ 81Fle-600
❑ 81FleStiC-8
❑ 81Kel-62
❑ 81MarPos-7
❑ 81MSAMinD-3
❑ 81OPC-18
❑ 81Squ-31
❑ 81Top-723
❑ 81TopScr-30
❑ 81TopSti-123
❑ 82Don-505
❑ 82Fle-505
❑ 82FleSta-222
❑ 82MarPos-6
❑ 82OnDecD-3
❑ 82OPC-224
❑ 82Top-224
❑ 82TopSti-232
❑ 83Don-127
❑ 83Fle-473
❑ 83FleSta-18
❑ 83FleSti-185
❑ 83OPC-28
❑ 83Top-28
❑ 83Top-711
❑ 83TopSti-111
❑ 84A'sMot-6
❑ 84FleUpd-13
❑ 85A'sMot-10
❑ 85Don-253
❑ 85Fle-416
❑ 85OPC-391
❑ 85Top-632
❑ 85TopSti-331
❑ 85TopTif-632
❑ 86A'sMot-10
❑ 86Don-400
❑ 86Fle-413
❑ 86FleMin-86
❑ 86FleStiC-7
❑ 86Lea-189
❑ 86OPC-378
❑ 86Top-378
❑ 86TopSti-170
❑ 86TopTat-6
❑ 86TopTif-378
❑ 87Fle-388
❑ 87FleGlo-388
❑ 87Top-496
❑ 87TopSti-169
❑ 87TopTif-496

Bochtler, Doug
❑ 90MidLeaASGS-4
❑ 90RocExpLC-2
❑ 90RocExpP-2694
❑ 91WesPalBEC-2
❑ 91WesPalBEP-1218
❑ 92HarSenF-452
❑ 92HarSenS-276
❑ 92SkyAA F-117
❑ 93Top-523
❑ 93TopGol-523
❑ 93TopInaM-523
❑ 93TopInaR-523
❑ 93TopMic-523
❑ 94AriFalLS-2
❑ 94LasVegSF-863
❑ 96LeaSigEA-9
❑ 96PadMot-18
❑ 97Fle-612
❑ 97FleTif-612
❑ 97PadMot-19

Bochy, Bruce Douglas
❑ 76DubPacT-4
❑ 77CocAstT-3
❑ 79AstPos-4
❑ 79Top-718
❑ 80Top-289
❑ 81Don-20
❑ 81Fle-69
❑ 81TidTidT-2
❑ 82TidTidT-6
❑ 84LasVegSC-225
❑ 84Nes792-571
❑ 84Top-571
❑ 84TopTif-571
❑ 85Don-505
❑ 85PadMot-12
❑ 85Top-324
❑ 85TopTif-324
❑ 86Don-551
❑ 86Top-608
❑ 86TopTif-608
❑ 87AstShoSPT-2
❑ 87Don-311
❑ 87Fle-411
❑ 87FleGlo-411
❑ 87Top-428
❑ 87TopTif-428
❑ 88LasVegSC-21
❑ 88LasVegSP-241
❑ 88Sco-469
❑ 88ScoGlo-469
❑ 88Top-31
❑ 88TopClo-12
❑ 88TopTif-31
❑ 89PacSenL-194
❑ 89RivRedWB-25
❑ 89RivRedWCLC-29
❑ 89RivRedWP-1405
❑ 89SpoIndSP-4
❑ 90EliSenL-51
❑ 90RivRedWB-22
❑ 90RivRedWCLC-24
❑ 91HigDesMC-29
❑ 91HigDesMP-2412
❑ 91MetWIZ-40
❑ 92WicWraF-3669
❑ 92WicWraS-649
❑ 93PadMot-28
❑ 94PadMot-28
❑ 95PadCHP-16
❑ 95PadMot-1
❑ 96PadMot-1
❑ 97PadMot-1
❑ 98PadMot-1

Bock, Doug
❑ 87EugEmeP-2656
❑ 88AppFoxP-157

Bock, Jeff
❑ 93DanBraC-3
❑ 93DanBraF-3608
❑ 94DurBulC-3
❑ 94DurBulF-320
❑ 94DurBulTI-3
❑ 95DurBulTI-4
❑ 96GreBraB-6
❑ 96GreBraTI-39

Bock, Paul
❑ 75AppFoxT-4
❑ 77CliDodT-2

Bockewitz, Stan
❑ 76WilTomT-3

Bockhorn, Glen
❑ 85GreBraTI-4
❑ 86BufBisP-1

Bockman, Eddie (Joseph E.)
❑ 47IndTeal-2
❑ 47IndVanPP-2
❑ 49Bow-195
❑ 49EurSta-153

Bockus, Randy
❑ 84ShrCapFB-3
❑ 86PhoFirP-3
❑ 87FleUpd-6
❑ 87FleUpdG-6
❑ 87GiaPos-2
❑ 87PhoFirP-3
❑ 88FleUpd-127
❑ 88FleUpdG-127
❑ 88PhoFirC-1
❑ 88PhoFirP-55
❑ 89BlaYNPRWL-58
❑ 89BlaYNPRWLU-65
❑ 89Bow-96
❑ 89BowTif-96
❑ 89TolMudHC-1
❑ 89TolMudHP-769
❑ 89Top-733
❑ 89TopTif-733
❑ 91EdmTraLD-155
❑ 91LinDriAAA-155

Boddicker, Mike
❑ 80RocRedWT-6
❑ 81RocRedWT-1
❑ 81RocRedWW-23
❑ 81Top-399
❑ 82RocRedWT-1
❑ 83OriPos-3
❑ 84AllGamPI-165
❑ 84BalOriP-3
❑ 84BalOriP-4
❑ 84Don-123
❑ 84Fle-1
❑ 84Fle-645
❑ 84FleSti-110
❑ 84FunFooP-121
❑ 84Nes792-191
❑ 84Nes792-426
❑ 84OriEng-1
❑ 84SevCoi-E9
❑ 84Top-191
❑ 84Top-426
❑ 84TopSti-13
❑ 84TopSti-375
❑ 84TopTif-191
❑ 84TopTif-426
❑ 85AllGamPI-74
❑ 85BalOriP-2
❑ 85Don-291
❑ 85Dra-34
❑ 85Fle-170
❑ 85FleStaS-80
❑ 85FleStaS-90
❑ 85Lea-109
❑ 85OPC-225
❑ 85OriHea-2
❑ 85SevCoi-E6
❑ 85SubDis-5
❑ 85ThoMcAD-5
❑ 85Top-225
❑ 85Top-709
❑ 85Top3-D-26
❑ 85TopGloS-4
❑ 85TopMin-225
❑ 85TopRubD-5
❑ 85TopSti-202
❑ 85TopSup-16
❑ 85TopTif-225
❑ 85TopTif-709
❑ 86BalOriHMP-2
❑ 86BalOriP-2
❑ 86Don-8
❑ 86Don-47
❑ 86DonSupD-8
❑ 86Fle-269
❑ 86FleMin-57
❑ 86Lea-8
❑ 86OPC-367
❑ 86SevCoi-E14
❑ 86Spo-104
❑ 86Spo-149
❑ 86Top-575
❑ 86TopSti-233
❑ 86TopTif-575
❑ 87BalOriP-5
❑ 87Don-125
❑ 87DonOpeD-140
❑ 87Fle-463
❑ 87FleGlo-463
❑ 87FleLeaL-2
❑ 87FleStiC-11
❑ 87Lea-76
❑ 87OPC-149
❑ 87OriFreB-52
❑ 87RedFolSB-40
❑ 87SevCoi-M8
❑ 87Spo-56
❑ 87SpoTeaP-21
❑ 87Top-455
❑ 87TopSti-227
❑ 87TopTif-455
❑ 88AlaGolAA70TI-23
❑ 88Don-89
❑ 88DonBasB-317
❑ 88Fle-556
❑ 88FleGlo-556
❑ 88FleStiC-1
❑ 88FleUpd-5
❑ 88FleUpdG-5
❑ 88OPC-281
❑ 88OriFreB-52
❑ 88OriPos-6
❑ 88PanSti-5
❑ 88Sco-67
❑ 88ScoGlo-67
❑ 88Spo-146
❑ 88StaLinO-2
❑ 88Top-725
❑ 88TopSti-231
❑ 88TopTif-725
❑ 89Bow-21
❑ 89BowTif-21
❑ 89ClaTraO-139
❑ 89Don-612
❑ 89DonBasB-297
❑ 89Fle-80
❑ 89FleGlo-80
❑ 89OPC-71
❑ 89Sco-549
❑ 89Spo-122
❑ 89Top-71
❑ 89TopBig-296
❑ 89TopSti-261
❑ 89TopTif-71
❑ 89TVSpoM-67
❑ 89UppDec-542
❑ 90Bow-267
❑ 90BowTif-267
❑ 90Don-280
❑ 90DonBesA-3
❑ 90Fle-267
❑ 90FleCan-267
❑ 90Lea-19
❑ 90OPC-652
❑ 90PanSti-20
❑ 90PubIntS-447
❑ 90RedSoxP-2
❑ 90Sco-31
❑ 90Top-652
❑ 90TopBig-258
❑ 90TopSti-258
❑ 90TopTif-652
❑ 90TopTVRS-7
❑ 90UppDec-652
❑ 91Bow-296
❑ 91Don-680
❑ 91Fle-85
❑ 91Lea-330
❑ 91OPC-303
❑ 91OPCPre-10
❑ 91OriCro-39
❑ 91PanCanT1-108
❑ 91RoyPol-3
❑ 91Sco-232
❑ 91ScoRoo-45T
❑ 91StaClu-400
❑ 91Stu-61
❑ 91Top-303
❑ 91TopDesS-303
❑ 91TopMic-303
❑ 91TopTif-303
❑ 91TopTra-12T
❑ 91TopTraT-12T
❑ 91UppDec-438
❑ 91UppDec-719
❑ 92Bow-132
❑ 92Don-176
❑ 92Fle-153

❑ 92HitTheBB-5
❑ 92Lea-268
❑ 92LeaBlaG-268
❑ 92OPC-106
❑ 92Pin-142
❑ 92RoyPol-3
❑ 92Sco-102
❑ 92StaClu-39
❑ 92Top-106
❑ 92TopGol-106
❑ 92TopGolW-106
❑ 92TopMic-106
❑ 92TriPla-12
❑ 92Ult-67
❑ 92UppDec-213
❑ 93CadDis-7
❑ 93Don-469
❑ 93Fle-616
❑ 93PacSpa-132
❑ 93RoyPol-4
❑ 93StaClu-192
❑ 93StaCluFDI-192
❑ 93StaCluMOP-192
❑ 93Top-239
❑ 93TopGol-239
❑ 93TopInaM-239
❑ 93TopInaR-239
❑ 93TopMic-239
❑ 93Ult-205
❑ 94BreMilB-284

Boddie, Eric
❑ 89BakDodCLC-193
❑ 90VerBeaDS-6

Boddie, Rod (Rodney)
❑ 88JamExpP-1905
❑ 89RocExpLC-4
❑ 90StaFS7-6
❑ 90WesPalBES-1

Bodell, Howard J.
❑ 52LavPro-81

Bodenhamer, Don
❑ 74GasRanT-5

Bodie, Keith
❑ 76WauMetT-5
❑ 79JacMetT-11
❑ 80ColAstT-18
❑ 86AubAstP-3
❑ 87AshTouP-4
❑ 88FloStaLAS-3
❑ 89CliGiaP-898
❑ 90SanBerSB-26
❑ 90SanBerSCLC-114
❑ 90SanBerSP-2649
❑ 91CalCanLD-74
❑ 91CalCanP-530
❑ 91LinDriAAA-74
❑ 92CalCanF-3745
❑ 92CalCanS-74
❑ 93CalCanF-1181
❑ 95PhoFirTI-31
❑ 97BakBlaB-27
❑ 97BakBlaTI-27

Bodie, Ping (Frank Stephan)
❑ 09MaxPubP-1
❑ 09ObaT21-48
❑ 09ObaT21-154
❑ 09SpoNewSM-81
❑ 10BisCoaLE99-1
❑ 11HelSta-7
❑ 12T207-18
❑ 14CraJacE-79
❑ 14TexTomE-6
❑ 14TexTomE-51
❑ 15CraJacE-79
❑ 15Zee-98
❑ 16Zee-99
❑ 17ColE13-16
❑ 17HolBreD-7
❑ 19W514-66
❑ 20W516-3
❑ 21E121So8-5
❑ 21KoBreWSI-28
❑ 22AmeCarE122-5
❑ 22W575-10
❑ 22Zee-144
❑ 23Zee-179
❑ 28ExhPCL-4
❑ 28Zee-126
❑ 81ConTSN-91

Boeckel, Tony (Norman Doxie)
❑ 21Nei-80
❑ 22E120-122
❑ 22W572-8
❑ 22W573-12
❑ 23WilChoV-11

Boehler, George
❑ 25Zee-18
❑ 27Zee-44
❑ 28Zee-65
❑ 29Zee-61
❑ 90DodTar-58

Boehling, John Joseph
❑ 14CraJacE-72
❑ 15CraJacE-72
❑ 17ColE13-17

Boehlow, Jason
❑ 92HunCubC-3
❑ 92HunCubF-3153

Boehmer, Len (Leonard J.)
❑ 69Top-519
❑ 69YanPhoS-37
❑ 81TCM60I-355
❑ 92YanWIZ6-12
❑ 92YanWIZ7-22

Boehringer, Brian
❑ 92ClaFS7-258
❑ 92SouBenWSC-1
❑ 92SouBenWSF-171
❑ 93FloStaLAF-21
❑ 93SarWhiSC-3
❑ 93SarWhiSF-1361
❑ 94AlbYanF-1430
❑ 94ClaGolF-193
❑ 94ExcFS7-35
❑ 95ColCliP-2
❑ 95ColCliTI-2
❑ 95Exc-90
❑ 95FleAllR-M3
❑ 96ColCliB-3
❑ 97Fle-606
❑ 97FleTif-606
❑ 98PacOnl-631
❑ 98PacOnlR-631
❑ 98PacOnlWC-631
❑ 98PadMot-20

Boelter, Tarry
❑ 79WisRapTT-14

Boemler, Bill
❑ 53MotCoo-63
❑ 53SanFraSTI-1

Boermans, Oswald
❑ 90IBAWorA-11

Boever, Dan
❑ 85CedRapRT-21
❑ 88NasSouC-15
❑ 88NasSouP-476
❑ 88NasSouTI-3
❑ 89CalCanC-12
❑ 89CalCanP-535
❑ 89CanIndB-7
❑ 89CanIndP-1325
❑ 89CanIndS-3
❑ 89CedRapRAB-33
❑ 90CedRapRDGB-33

Boever, Joe
❑ 83St.PetCT-1
❑ 86LouRedTI-6
❑ 87LouRedTI-5
❑ 88BlaYNPRWL-146
❑ 88BobCamRB-1
❑ 88Fle-534
❑ 88FleGlo-534
❑ 88RicBraC-9
❑ 88RicBraP-22
❑ 88Sco-542
❑ 88ScoGlo-542
❑ 88Top-627
❑ 88TopTif-627
❑ 88TriAAAP-34
❑ 89BraDub-6
❑ 89Don-168
❑ 89Top-586
❑ 89TopTif-586
❑ 90BraDubP-2
❑ 90BraDubS-3
❑ 90Don-357
❑ 90Fle-577
❑ 90FleCan-577
❑ 90Lea-349
❑ 90OPC-410
❑ 90PanSti-220
❑ 90PubIntS-110
❑ 90Sco-81
❑ 90SprCarDGB-14
❑ 90Top-410
❑ 90TopSti-34
❑ 90TopTif-410
❑ 90UppDec-408
❑ 91Bow-502
❑ 91Don-578
❑ 91Fle-387
❑ 91Lea-68
❑ 91OPC-159
❑ 91PhiMed-4
❑ 91StaClu-462
❑ 91Top-159
❑ 91TopDesS-159
❑ 91TopMic-159
❑ 91TopTif-159
❑ 91UppDec-430
❑ 92AstMot-13
❑ 92Don-493
❑ 92Fle-523
❑ 92Lea-491
❑ 92LeaBlaG-491
❑ 92OPC-696
❑ 92Sco-647
❑ 92StaClu-156
❑ 92StaClu-639
❑ 92StaCluECN-639
❑ 92Top-696
❑ 92TopGol-696
❑ 92TopGolW-696
❑ 92TopMic-696
❑ 92TopTra-12T
❑ 92TopTraG-12T
❑ 92UppDec-402
❑ 93AthMot-25
❑ 93AthStaC-15
❑ 93Don-504
❑ 93Fle-48
❑ 93PacSpa-119
❑ 93PacSpa-563
❑ 93Top-792
❑ 93TopGol-792
❑ 93TopInaM-792
❑ 93TopInaR-792
❑ 93TopMic-792
❑ 93UppDec-310
❑ 93UppDec-810
❑ 93UppDecGold-310
❑ 93UppDecGold-810
❑ 94FleUpd-41
❑ 94StaClu-458
❑ 94StaCluFDI-458
❑ 94StaCluGR-458
❑ 94StaCluMOP-458
❑ 94Top-467
❑ 94TopGol-467
❑ 94TopSpa-467
❑ 95Don-362
❑ 95DonPreP-362
❑ 95DonTopotO-71
❑ 95Fle-45
❑ 95Sco-203
❑ 95ScoGolR-203
❑ 95ScoPlaTS-203
❑ 95Top-457
❑ 95TopCyb-252
❑ 96ColCho-139
❑ 96ColChoGS-139
❑ 96ColChoSS-139
❑ 96Don-32
❑ 96DonPreP-32
❑ 96Fle-106
❑ 96FleTif-106
❑ 97CalCanB-8

Boffek, Scott
❑ 91VerBeaDC-19

Bogar, Tim
❑ 87LitFalMP-2397
❑ 89JacMetGS-3
❑ 90CMC-365
❑ 90ProAAAF-280
❑ 90TidTidC-14
❑ 90TidTidP-549
❑ 90TopTVM-36
❑ 91LinDriAA-626
❑ 91WilBilLD-626
❑ 91WilBilP-298
❑ 92TidTidF-903
❑ 92TidTidS-553
❑ 93Bow-326
❑ 93FleFinE-99
❑ 93Lea-525
❑ 93MetColP-26
❑ 93MetKah-23
❑ 93OPCPre-108
❑ 93SelRoo-54T
❑ 93SP-145
❑ 93StaClu-702
❑ 93StaCluFDI-702
❑ 93StaCluMOP-702
❑ 93TopTra-119T
❑ 94ColC-55
❑ 94ColChoGS-55
❑ 94ColChoSS-55
❑ 94Don-316
❑ 94Fin-354
❑ 94FinRef-354
❑ 94Fle-557
❑ 94Lea-99
❑ 94MetColP-5
❑ 94MetShuST-3
❑ 94Pac-395
❑ 94Sco-557
❑ 94ScoGolR-557
❑ 94Sel-104
❑ 94StaClu-170
❑ 94StaCluFDI-170
❑ 94StaCluGR-170
❑ 94StaCluMOP-170
❑ 94Top-509
❑ 94TopGol-509
❑ 94TopSpa-509
❑ 94Ult-234
❑ 94UppDec-101
❑ 94UppDecED-101
❑ 95MetColP-7
❑ 95Pac-276
❑ 96ColCho-619
❑ 96ColChoGS-619
❑ 96ColChoSS-619
❑ 96Don-16
❑ 96DonPreP-16
❑ 96Fle-473
❑ 96FleTif-473
❑ 96LeaSigEA-10
❑ 96MetKah-3
❑ 96MetKah-2
❑ 97Pac-359
❑ 97PacLigB-359
❑ 97PacSil-359
❑ 98PacInvGems-161
❑ 98PacOnl-316
❑ 98PacOnlR-316
❑ 98PacOnlWC-316
❑ 99StaClu-310
❑ 99StaCluFDI-310
❑ 99StaCluOoaK-310
❑ 99StaCluPP-310

Bogatyrev, Ilya
❑ 89EasLeaDDP-DD17
❑ 93Top-633
❑ 93TopGol-633
❑ 93TopInaM-633
❑ 93TopInaR-633
❑ 93TopMic-633

Bogener, Terry (Terrence W.)
❑ 79TulDriT-15
❑ 83Don-520
❑ 83OklCit8T-3
❑ 84WicAerRD-13
❑ 86ChaOriW-4
❑ 93RanKee-75

Boggess, Dusty
❑ 55Bow-297

Boggetto, Brad
❑ 91YakBeaC-20
❑ 91YakBeaP-4238

Boggs, Robert
❑ 96ForWayWB-4

Boggs, Tommy
❑ 76SacSolC-8
❑ 77Top-328
❑ 78Top-518
❑ 79RicBraT-22
❑ 79Top-384
❑ 81BraPol-40
❑ 81Don-597
❑ 81Fle-261
❑ 81Top-132
❑ 82BraBurKL-3
❑ 82Don-249
❑ 82Fle-430
❑ 82Top-61
❑ 83Don-349
❑ 83Fle-131
❑ 83Top-649
❑ 85OklCit8T-7
❑ 93RanKee-76

Boggs, Wade Anthony
❑ 81PawRedST-15
❑ 83AllGamPI-29
❑ 83Don-586
❑ 83Fle-179
❑ 83FleSta-19
❑ 83FleSti-64
❑ 83Top-498
❑ 83TopSti-308
❑ 84AllGamPI-119
❑ 84Don-26
❑ 84Don-26A
❑ 84Don-151
❑ 84DonActAS-22
❑ 84DonCha-16
❑ 84Dra-2
❑ 84Fle-392
❑ 84Fle-630
❑ 84FleSti-11
❑ 84FleSti-28
❑ 84FleSti-52
❑ 84FunFooP-43
❑ 84MilBra-1
❑ 84Nes792-30
❑ 84Nes792-131
❑ 84Nes792-786
❑ 84OCoandSI-6
❑ 84OCoandSI-226
❑ 84OPC-30
❑ 84RalPur-11
❑ 84SevCoi-E10
❑ 84Top-30
❑ 84Top-131
❑ 84Top-786
❑ 84TopCer-11
❑ 84TopGloS-8
❑ 84TopRubD-5
❑ 84TopSti-100
❑ 84TopSti-216
❑ 84TopStiB-7
❑ 84TopSup-7
❑ 84TopTif-30
❑ 84TopTif-131
❑ 84TopTif-786
❑ 85AllGamPI-29
❑ 85Don-172
❑ 85DonActA-38
❑ 85DonHig-49
❑ 85Fle-151
❑ 85Fle-160
❑ 85FleLimE-3
❑ 85FleStaS-6
❑ 85Lea-179
❑ 85OPC-350
❑ 85SevCoi-C8
❑ 85SevCoi-E7
❑ 85Top-350
❑ 85TopRubD-6
❑ 85TopSti-210
❑ 85TopTif-350
❑ 86BasStaB-13
❑ 86BurKinA-9
❑ 86Don-371
❑ 86DonAll-47
❑ 86DonAllB-PC7
❑ 86DonHig-11
❑ 86DonHig-13
❑ 86DorChe-18
❑ 86Dra-27
❑ 86Fle-341
❑ 86Fle-634
❑ 86Fle-639
❑ 86FleLeaL-1
❑ 86FleLimE-4
❑ 86FleMin-72
❑ 86FleSlu-2
❑ 86FleStiC-8
❑ 86FleStiWBC-S2
❑ 86FraGloT-1
❑ 86GenMilB-1A
❑ 86Lea-168
❑ 86MeaGolBB-1
❑ 86MeaGolM-1
❑ 86MeaGolSB-9
❑ 86MSAJifPD-2
❑ 86OPC-262
❑ 86OPCBoxB-B
❑ 86QuaGra-22
❑ 86SevCoi-C2
❑ 86SevCoi-E2
❑ 86SevCoi-S2
❑ 86SevCoi-W2
❑ 86Spo-3
❑ 86Spo-75
❑ 86Spo-180
❑ 86Spo-183
❑ 86Spo-184
❑ 86SpoDecG-68
❑ 86StaBog-1
❑ 86StaBog-2
❑ 86StaBog-3
❑ 86StaBog-4
❑ 86StaBog-5
❑ 86StaBog-6
❑ 86StaBog-7
❑ 86StaBog-8
❑ 86StaBog-9
❑ 86StaBog-10
❑ 86StaBog-11
❑ 86StaBog-12
❑ 86Top-510
❑ 86Top3-D-3
❑ 86TopGaloC-1
❑ 86TopGloS-26
❑ 86TopMinL-3
❑ 86TopSti-164
❑ 86TopSti-247
❑ 86TopSup-12
❑ 86TopTat-22
❑ 86TopTif-510
❑ 86TopWaxBC-B
❑ 86TruVal-30
❑ 86Woo-3
❑ 87BoaandB-31
❑ 87BurKinA-1
❑ 87ClaGam-60
❑ 87ClaUpdY-105
❑ 87Don-252
❑ 87DonAll-7
❑ 87DonHig-14
❑ 87DonHig-44
❑ 87DonOpeD-181
❑ 87DonP-7
❑ 87Dra-16
❑ 87Fle-29
❑ 87Fle-637
❑ 87FleBasA-3
❑ 87FleExcS-4
❑ 87FleGamW-5
❑ 87FleGlo-29
❑ 87FleGlo-637
❑ 87FleGlo-WS2
❑ 87FleHea-1
❑ 87FleLeaL-3
❑ 87FleMin-10
❑ 87FleSlu-4
❑ 87FleStiC-12
❑ 87FleStiWBC-S2
❑ 87FleWorS-2
❑ 87GenMilB-2A
❑ 87HosSti-19
❑ 87K-M-23
❑ 87KayB-4
❑ 87KeyFooD-13
❑ 87KraFoo-7
❑ 87Lea-193
❑ 87MandMSL-5
❑ 87MSAIceTD-13
❑ 87MSAJifPD-20
❑ 87OPC-150
❑ 87OurOwnTD-13
❑ 87RalPur-3
❑ 87RedFolSB-96
❑ 87RedSoxP-3
❑ 87RedSoxSAP-3
❑ 87SevCoi-E5
❑ 87SevCoi-M6
❑ 87Spo-2
❑ 87Spo-114
❑ 87Spo-197
❑ 87SpoDeaP-2
❑ 87SpoIIIS-1
❑ 87SpoRea-32
❑ 87SpoTeaP-9
❑ 87StaAwaW-4
❑ 87StaAwaW-5
❑ 87StuPan-15
❑ 87Top-150
❑ 87Top-608
❑ 87TopCoi-4
❑ 87TopGaloC-2
❑ 87TopGloA-15
❑ 87TopGloS-18
❑ 87TopMinL-41
❑ 87TopSti-148
❑ 87TopSti-253
❑ 87TopTif-150
❑ 87TopTif-608
❑ 87WeiMarD-13
❑ 87Woo-10
❑ 88ActPacT-1
❑ 88Baz-2
❑ 88CheBoy-22
❑ 88ClaBlu-214
❑ 88ClaRed-155
❑ 88Don-153
❑ 88DonAll-7
❑ 88DonAll-31
❑ 88DonBasB-65
❑ 88DonBonM-BC7

❑ 88DonPop-7
❑ 88DonTeaBRS-153
❑ 88Dra-4
❑ 88Fle-345
❑ 88FleAll-8
❑ 88FleAwaW-3
❑ 88FleBasA-2
❑ 88FleBasM-2
❑ 88FleExcS-4
❑ 88FleGlo-345
❑ 88FleHotS-2
❑ 88FleLeaL-2
❑ 88FleMin-4
❑ 88FleRecS-3
❑ 88FleSlu-2
❑ 88FleStiC-5
❑ 88FleSup-3
❑ 88FleTeaL-2
❑ 88GreBasS-5
❑ 88K-M-2
❑ 88KayB-2
❑ 88KeyFooD-1
❑ 88Lea-65
❑ 88MSAFanSD-8
❑ 88MSAIceTD-1
❑ 88MSAJifPD-2
❑ 88Nes-32
❑ 88OPC-200
❑ 88OurOwnTD-1
❑ 88PanSti-29
❑ 88PanSti-228
❑ 88Sco-2
❑ 88ScoBoxC-4
❑ 88ScoGlo-2
❑ 88Spo-50
❑ 88SpoGam-3
❑ 88StaBog-1
❑ 88StaBog-2
❑ 88StaBog-3
❑ 88StaBog-4
❑ 88StaBog-5
❑ 88StaBog-6
❑ 88StaBog-7
❑ 88StaBog-8
❑ 88StaBog-9
❑ 88StaBog-10
❑ 88StaBog-11
❑ 88StaBog-1
❑ 88StaBog-2
❑ 88StaBog-3
❑ 88StaBog-4
❑ 88StaBog-5
❑ 88StaBog-6
❑ 88StaBog-7
❑ 88StaBog-8
❑ 88StaBog-9
❑ 88StaBog-10
❑ 88StaBog-11
❑ 88StaBog/G-1
❑ 88StaBog/G-2
❑ 88StaBog/G-4
❑ 88StaBog/G-6
❑ 88StaBog/G-8
❑ 88StaBog/G-10
❑ 88StaLinAl-3
❑ 88StaLinRS-3
❑ 88TarPla-4
❑ 88TetTeaD-1
❑ 88Top-21
❑ 88Top-200
❑ 88Top-388
❑ 88TopBig-32
❑ 88TopClo-13
❑ 88TopCoi-4
❑ 88TopGaloC-3
❑ 88TopGloA-4
❑ 88TopGloS-51
❑ 88TopMinL-1
❑ 88TopRevLL-16
❑ 88TopRitTM-14
❑ 88TopSti-157
❑ 88TopSti-244
❑ 88TopStiB-40
❑ 88TopTif-21
❑ 88TopTif-200
❑ 88TopTif-388
❑ 88TopUKM-4
❑ 88TopUKMT-4
❑ 88WeiMarD-1
❑ 88Woo-13
❑ 89Baz-3
❑ 89Bow-32
❑ 89BowTif-32
❑ 89CadEllD-2
❑ 89ClaLigB-2
❑ 89ClaTraO-102
❑ 89Don-68
❑ 89DonAll-7
❑ 89DonBasB-140
❑ 89DonPop-7
❑ 89Fle-81
❑ 89Fle-633
❑ 89FleBasA-3
❑ 89FleBasM-3
❑ 89FleExcS-2
❑ 89FleForTR-1
❑ 89FleGlo-81
❑ 89FleGlo-633
❑ 89FleHeroB-2
❑ 89FleLeaL-2
❑ 89FleSup-4
❑ 89FleWaxBC-C2
❑ 89K-M-14
❑ 89KayB-1
❑ 89KeyFooD-7
❑ 89KinDis-3
❑ 89MasBreD-5
❑ 89MSAHolD-2
❑ 89MSAIceTD-7
❑ 89Nis-2
❑ 89OPC-184
❑ 89OurOwnTD-7
❑ 89PanSti-7
❑ 89PanSti-242
❑ 89PanSti-245
❑ 89PanSti-277
❑ 89RedFolSB-8
❑ 89Sco-175
❑ 89Sco-654A
❑ 89Sco-654B
❑ 89ScoHot1S-100
❑ 89Scomast-17
❑ 89Spo-100
❑ 89Spo-221
❑ 89SpoIllFKI-176
❑ 89TetTeaD-7
❑ 89Top-2
❑ 89Top-399
❑ 89Top-600
❑ 89TopBasT-57
❑ 89TopBatL-1
❑ 89TopBig-241
❑ 89TopCoi-32
❑ 89TopDouA-3
❑ 89TopGaloC-1
❑ 89TopGloA-4
❑ 89TopGloS-5
❑ 89TopHeaUT-11
❑ 89TopHilTM-2
❑ 89TopMinL-45
❑ 89TopSti-9
❑ 89TopSti-147
❑ 89TopSti-260
❑ 89TopStiB-7
❑ 89TopTif-2
❑ 89TopTif-399
❑ 89TopTif-600
❑ 89TopUKM-4
❑ 89TVSpoM-64
❑ 89TVSpoM-126
❑ 89UppDec-389
❑ 89UppDec-687
❑ 89UppDecS-1
❑ 89WeiMarD-7
❑ 89Woo-8
❑ 90AllBasT-3
❑ 90Bow-281
❑ 90BowTif-281
❑ 90ClaBlu-26
❑ 90Col-26
❑ 90Don-68
❑ 90Don-712A
❑ 90Don-712B
❑ 90DonBesA-86
❑ 90DonLeaS-21
❑ 90DonPre-11
❑ 90Fle-268
❑ 90Fle-632
❑ 90FleAwaW-4
❑ 90FleBasA-1
❑ 90FleBasAC-1
❑ 90FleBasM-3
❑ 90FleBasMC-3
❑ 90FleCan-268
❑ 90FleCan-632
❑ 90FleLeaL-4
❑ 90FleLeaLC-4
❑ 90FleLeaS-5
❑ 90GooHumICBLS-3
❑ 90Hot50PS-2
❑ 90K-M-19
❑ 90KayB-3
❑ 90KinDis-9
❑ 90Lea-51
❑ 90M.Vpin-9
❑ 90MLBBasB-68
❑ 90MSAIceTD-7
❑ 90OPC-387
❑ 90OPC-760
❑ 90OPCBoxB-A
❑ 90PanSti-19
❑ 90PanSti-199
❑ 90Pos-17
❑ 90PubIntS-277
❑ 90PubIntS-448
❑ 90RedFolSB-6
❑ 90RedSoxP-3
❑ 90Sco-245
❑ 90Sco-683A
❑ 90Sco-683B
❑ 90Sco-704
❑ 90Sco100S-80
❑ 90Spo-2
❑ 90StaLonJS-6
❑ 90StaLonJS-17
❑ 90StaLonJS-22
❑ 90Top-387
❑ 90Top-760
❑ 90TopAmeA-16
❑ 90TopBatL-1
❑ 90TopBig-77
❑ 90TopCoi-6
❑ 90TopDou-4
❑ 90TopGloA-15
❑ 90TopGloS-22
❑ 90TopHilHM-19
❑ 90TopMag-23
❑ 90TopMinL-3
❑ 90TopSti-8
❑ 90TopSti-156
❑ 90TopSti-253
❑ 90TopStiB-40
❑ 90TopTif-387
❑ 90TopTif-760
❑ 90TopTVA-20
❑ 90TopTVRS-22
❑ 90TopWaxBC-A
❑ 90UppDec-555
❑ 90UppDecS-4
❑ 90USPlaCA-11C
❑ 90WinDis-2
❑ 90Woo-8
❑ 91BasBesHM-2
❑ 91Bow-129
❑ 91CadEllD-4
❑ 91Cla1-T19
❑ 91Cla3-T3
❑ 91ClaGam-192
❑ 91Col-16
❑ 91Don-55
❑ 91Don-178
❑ 91Fle-86
❑ 91FouBal-30
❑ 91KinDis-11
❑ 91Lea-273
❑ 91LeaPre-14
❑ 91MajLeaCP-9
❑ 91MooSna-11
❑ 91OPC-450
❑ 91OPCPre-11
❑ 91PanCanT1-30
❑ 91PanFreS-169
❑ 91PanFreS-266
❑ 91PanSti-214
❑ 91RedFolS-9
❑ 91RedFolS-115
❑ 91RedSoxP-1
❑ 91Sco-12
❑ 91Sco-393
❑ 91Sco-889
❑ 91Sco100S-3
❑ 91ScoCoo-B1
❑ 91Sev3DCN-1
❑ 91SevCoi-NE1
❑ 91StaClu-170
❑ 91StaPinB-3
❑ 91Stu-11
❑ 91SunSee-2
❑ 91Top-450
❑ 91TopCraJI-29
❑ 91TopDesS-450
❑ 91TopGloA-4
❑ 91TopMic-450
❑ 91TopSta-3
❑ 91TopTif-450
❑ 91TopTriH-A2
❑ 91Ult-27
❑ 91UppDec-546
❑ 91UppDecFE-84F
❑ 91USPlaCA-WCO
❑ 92Bow-70
❑ 92Cla2-T63
❑ 92ClaGam-70
❑ 92ColAllG-7
❑ 92ColAllP-7
❑ 92Don-23
❑ 92Don-210
❑ 92DonCraJ2-29
❑ 92DonDiaK-DK9
❑ 92DonEli-9
❑ 92DonPre-1
❑ 92DonSupD-DK9
❑ 92Fle-32
❑ 92Fle-707
❑ 92FleCitTP-9
❑ 92FleTeaL-13
❑ 92Fre-14
❑ 92Hig5-6
❑ 92Hig5S-3
❑ 92KinDis-16
❑ 92LaKdec-1
❑ 92Lea-286
❑ 92LeaBlaG-286
❑ 92New-2
❑ 92OPC-10
❑ 92OPCPre-1
❑ 92PanSti-87
❑ 92PanSti-274
❑ 92PepDieM-21
❑ 92Pin-175
❑ 92Pin-282
❑ 92Pos-19
❑ 92RedFolS-14
❑ 92RedFolS-107
❑ 92RedSoxDD-2
❑ 92Sco-434
❑ 92Sco-660
❑ 92Sco-885
❑ 92Sco100S-30
❑ 92ScoProaG-4
❑ 92SpoIllFK1-178
❑ 92SpoStaCC-3
❑ 92StaClu-520
❑ 92StaCluD-18
❑ 92StaCluMO-2
❑ 92StaCluMO-3
❑ 92StaCluMP-1
❑ 92Stu-131
❑ 92StuHer-BC3
❑ 92StuPre-14
❑ 92Top-10
❑ 92Top-399
❑ 92TopGol-10
❑ 92TopGol-399
❑ 92TopGolW-10
❑ 92TopGolW-399
❑ 92TopKid-68
❑ 92TopMic-10
❑ 92TopMic-399
❑ 92TopMic-G10
❑ 92TriPla-211
❑ 92Ult-311
❑ 92UltAllS-4
❑ 92UppDec-443
❑ 92UppDec-646
❑ 92UppDecF-13
❑ 92UppDecFG-13
❑ 92UppDecTMH-10
❑ 92UppDecWB-T1
❑ 93Bow-399
❑ 93CadDis-8
❑ 93ColAllG-7
❑ 93DiaMar-13
❑ 93Don-619
❑ 93DonSpiotG-SG7
❑ 93Fin-90
❑ 93FinJum-90
❑ 93FinRef-90
❑ 93Fla-245
❑ 93Fle-554
❑ 93FleFinE-243
❑ 93FleFinEDT-1
❑ 93FunPac-206
❑ 93Lea-285
❑ 93LeaGolA-U5
❑ 93MetBak-1
❑ 93OPC-196
❑ 93OPCPre-49
❑ 93PacSpa-27
❑ 93PacSpa-552
❑ 93PanSti-152
❑ 93Pin-424
❑ 93Pin-476
❑ 93PinCoo-13
❑ 93PinCooD-13
❑ 93RedFolS-13
❑ 93Sco-592
❑ 93Sel-48
❑ 93SelRoo-17T
❑ 93SP-2
❑ 93StaClu-134
❑ 93StaClu-601
❑ 93StaCluFDI-134
❑ 93StaCluFDI-601
❑ 93StaCluM-15
❑ 93StaCluMOP-134
❑ 93StaCluMOP-601
❑ 93Stu-31
❑ 93Top-390
❑ 93TopGol-390
❑ 93TopInaM-390
❑ 93TopInaR-390
❑ 93TopMic-390
❑ 93TopTra-47T
❑ 93TriPla-143
❑ 93TriPla-258
❑ 93TriPlaG-GS3
❑ 93Ult-591
❑ 93UppDec-556
❑ 93UppDecCP-R2
❑ 93UppDecGold-556
❑ 93UppDecIC-WI20
❑ 93UppDecICJ-WI20
❑ 93UppDecOD-D5
❑ 93UppDecTAN-TN1
❑ 93YanStaC-5
❑ 94Bow-305
❑ 94BowBes-R42
❑ 94BowBesR-R42
❑ 94ColC-380
❑ 94ColChoGS-380
❑ 94ColChoSS-380
❑ 94Don-36
❑ 94DonAnn8-7
❑ 94DonSpeE-36
❑ 94Fin-173
❑ 94FinRef-173
❑ 94Fla-319
❑ 94Fle-226
❑ 94FleAllS-4
❑ 94FleExtB-128
❑ 94FUnPac-126
❑ 94KinDis-5
❑ 94Lea-257
❑ 94LeaL-54
❑ 94LeaLimGA-5
❑ 94OPC-193
❑ 94Pac-421
❑ 94PacSilP-9
❑ 94PacSilPC-9
❑ 94PanSti-99
❑ 94Pin-31
❑ 94PinArtP-31
❑ 94PinMusC-31
❑ 94ProMag-87
❑ 94Sco-101
❑ 94ScoGolR-101
❑ 94ScoGolS-50
❑ 94Sel-156
❑ 94SP-196
❑ 94SPDieC-196
❑ 94Spo-102
❑ 94StaClu-349
❑ 94StaCluFDI-349
❑ 94StaCluGR-349
❑ 94StaCluMOP-349
❑ 94StaCluT-204
❑ 94StaCluTFDI-204
❑ 94Stu-212
❑ 94Top-386
❑ 94Top-520
❑ 94Top-603
❑ 94TopGol-386
❑ 94TopGol-520
❑ 94TopGol-603
❑ 94TopPre-390
❑ 94TopSpa-386
❑ 94TopSpa-520
❑ 94TopSpa-603
❑ 94TriPla-272
❑ 94TriPlaM-9
❑ 94Ult-93
❑ 94UppDec-112
❑ 94UppDecAJ-8
❑ 94UppDecAJG-8
❑ 94UppDecED-112
❑ 95Baz-89
❑ 95BazRedH-RH18
❑ 95Bow-408
❑ 95BowBes-R26
❑ 95BowBesR-R26
❑ 95ClaPhoC-40
❑ 95ColCho-520
❑ 95ColChoGS-520
❑ 95ColChoSE-245
❑ 95ColChoSEGS-245
❑ 95ColChoSESS-245
❑ 95ColChoSS-520
❑ 95Don-355
❑ 95DonAll-AL5
❑ 95DonPreP-355
❑ 95DonTopotO-117
❑ 95Emo-59
❑ 95Fin-100
❑ 95FinRef-100
❑ 95Fla-63
❑ 95Fle-67
❑ 95FleAllS-4
❑ 95KinDis-3
❑ 95Lea-40
❑ 95Lea300C-11
❑ 95LeaCor-3
❑ 95LeaGreG-4
❑ 95LeaLim-105
❑ 95LeaLimIBP-3
❑ 95Pac-293
❑ 95PacGolP-6
❑ 95PacPri-95
❑ 95PanSti-57
❑ 95Pin-47
❑ 95PinArtP-47
❑ 95PinMusC-47
❑ 95Pos-1
❑ 95Sco-349
❑ 95Sco-560
❑ 95ScoGolR-349
❑ 95ScoGolR-560
❑ 95ScoHaloG-HG96
❑ 95ScoPlaTS-349
❑ 95ScoPlaTS-560
❑ 95Sel-16
❑ 95SelArtP-16
❑ 95SelCer-30
❑ 95SelCerMG-30
❑ 95SP-25
❑ 95SP-180
❑ 95SPCha-172
❑ 95SPChaDC-172
❑ 95Spo-107
❑ 95SpoArtP-107
❑ 95SpoDouT-4
❑ 95SPSil-25
❑ 95SPSil-180
❑ 95SPSpeF-14
❑ 95StaClu-85
❑ 95StaCluFDI-85
❑ 95StaCluMO-7
❑ 95StaCluMOP-85
❑ 95StaCluMOP-RL38
❑ 95StaCluRL-RL38
❑ 95StaCluSTWS-85
❑ 95StaCluVR-52
❑ 95StaCluVRMO-52
❑ 95Stu-46
❑ 95StuGolS-46
❑ 95Sum-65
❑ 95SumNthD-65
❑ 95Top-170
❑ 95Top-386
❑ 95TopCyb-100
❑ 95TopEmb-49
❑ 95TopEmbGI-49
❑ 95TopLeaL-LL3
❑ 95TopTra-158T
❑ 95UC3-30
❑ 95UC3ArtP-30
❑ 95Ult-80
❑ 95UltAllS-4
❑ 95UltAllSGM-4
❑ 95UltAwaW-4
❑ 95UltAwaWGM-4
❑ 95UltGolM-80
❑ 95UltOnBL-4
❑ 95UltOnBLGM-4
❑ 95UppDec-445
❑ 95UppDecED-445
❑ 95UppDecEDG-445
❑ 95UppDecPLL-R21
❑ 95UppDecPLLE-R21
❑ 95UppDecSE-10
❑ 95UppDecSEG-10
❑ 95USPlaCMLA-8D
❑ 95Zen-107
❑ 96Baz-34
❑ 96Bow-26
❑ 96BowBes-4

❑ 96BowBesAR-4
❑ 96BowBesMI-3
❑ 96BowBesMIAR-3
❑ 96BowBesMIR-3
❑ 96BowBesR-4
❑ 96BowFoi-26
❑ 96Cir-61
❑ 96CirBos-15
❑ 96CirRav-61
❑ 96Cla7/1PC-7
❑ 96ColCho-230
❑ 96ColCho-420
❑ 96ColChoGS-230
❑ 96ColChoGS-420
❑ 96ColChoSS-230
❑ 96ColChoSS-420
❑ 96ColChoYMtP-7
❑ 96ColChoYMtP-7A
❑ 96ColChoYMtPGS-7
❑ 96ColChoYMtPGS-7A
❑ 96DenHol-14
❑ 96Don-355
❑ 96Don-440
❑ 96DonHitL-14
❑ 96DonPreP-355
❑ 96DonPreP-440
❑ 96EmoXL-87
❑ 96Fin-B155
❑ 96Fin-B301
❑ 96FinRef-B155
❑ 96FinRef-B301
❑ 96Fla-125
❑ 96Fle-180
❑ 96FleTif-180
❑ 96FleUpd-U214
❑ 96FleUpd-1
❑ 96FleUpdTC-U214
❑ 96Lea-91
❑ 96LeaLim-61
❑ 96LeaLimG-61
❑ 96LeaPre-67
❑ 96LeaPreP-67
❑ 96LeaPrePB-91
❑ 96LeaPrePG-91
❑ 96LeaPrePS-91
❑ 96LeaPreSG-9
❑ 96LeaPreSte-9
❑ 96LeaSig-5
❑ 96LeaSigA-27
❑ 96LeaSigAG-27
❑ 96LeaSigAS-27
❑ 96LeaSigPPG-5
❑ 96LeaSigPPP-5
❑ 96MetUni-84
❑ 96MetUniP-84
❑ 96Pac-378
❑ 96PacCraC-CC2
❑ 96PacGolCD-DC20
❑ 96PacMil-M6
❑ 96PacPri-P118
❑ 96PacPriG-P118
❑ 96PacPriRHS-RH16
❑ 96PanSti-153
❑ 96Pin-215
❑ 96Pin-269
❑ 96Pin-334
❑ 96PinAfi-19
❑ 96PinAfiAP-19
❑ 96PinAfiFPP-19
❑ 96PinAfiSP-26
❑ 96PinArtP-115
❑ 96PinArtP-169
❑ 96PinArtP-199
❑ 96PinFan-13
❑ 96PinFoil-215
❑ 96PinFoil-269
❑ 96PinFoil-334
❑ 96PinSky-8
❑ 96PinSta-115
❑ 96PinSta-169
❑ 96PinSta-199
❑ 96ProSta-136
❑ 96Sco-345
❑ 96ScoDugC-B70
❑ 96ScoDugCAP-B70
❑ 96ScoRef-13
❑ 96Sel-1
❑ 96SelArtP-1
❑ 96SelCer-74
❑ 96SelCerAP-74
❑ 96SelCerCB-74
❑ 96SelCerCR-74
❑ 96SelCerIP-10
❑ 96SelCerMB-74
❑ 96SelCerMG-74
❑ 96SelCerMR-74
❑ 96SelEnF-15
❑ 96SelTeaN-6
❑ 96SP-131
❑ 96Spo-1
❑ 96SpoArtP-1
❑ 96SpoHitP-14
❑ 96SPSpeFX-18
❑ 96SPSpeFXDC-18
❑ 96SPx-44
❑ 96SPxGol-44
❑ 96StaClu-96
❑ 96StaCluEPB-96
❑ 96StaCluEPG-96
❑ 96StaCluEPS-96
❑ 96StaCluMM-MM5
❑ 96StaCluMO-6
❑ 96StaCluMOP-96
❑ 96StaCluMOP-MM5
❑ 96Stu-46
❑ 96StuPrePB-46
❑ 96StuPrePG-46
❑ 96StuPrePS-46
❑ 96Sum-149
❑ 96SumAbo&B-149
❑ 96SumArtP-149
❑ 96SumFoi-149
❑ 96SumHitI-7
❑ 96TeaOut-9
❑ 96Top-225
❑ 96Top-323
❑ 96TopChr-85
❑ 96TopChr-127
❑ 96TopChrMotG-11
❑ 96TopChrMotGR-11
❑ 96TopChrR-85
❑ 96TopChrR-127
❑ 96TopGal-84
❑ 96TopGalPPI-84
❑ 96TopLas-36
❑ 96TopMasotG-11
❑ 96Ult-98
❑ 96Ult-576
❑ 96UltGolM-98
❑ 96UltGolM-576
❑ 96UltOn-L-1
❑ 96UltOn-LGM-1
❑ 96UltPriL-5
❑ 96UltPriLGM-5
❑ 96UppDec-117
❑ 96UppDec-372
❑ 96UppDec-410
❑ 96UppDecA-7
❑ 96UppDecDD-DD27
❑ 96UppDecDDG-DD27
❑ 96UppDecDDS-DD27
❑ 96UppDecPRE-R23
❑ 96UppDecPreR-R23
❑ 96Zen-58
❑ 96ZenArtP-58
❑ 96ZenMoz-22
❑ 97Bow-58
❑ 97BowBes-57
❑ 97BowBesAR-57
❑ 97BowBesR-57
❑ 97BowChr-44
❑ 97BowChrI-44
❑ 97BowChrIR-44
❑ 97BowChrR-44
❑ 97BowInt-58
❑ 97Cir-27
❑ 97CirRav-27
❑ 97ColCho-177
❑ 97ColChoT-NY3
❑ 97Don-17
❑ 97Don-405
❑ 97DonEli-47
❑ 97DonEliGS-47
❑ 97DonGolPP-17
❑ 97DonGolPP-405
❑ 97DonLim-32
❑ 97DonLim-125
❑ 97DonLim-191
❑ 97DonLimE-32
❑ 97DonLimE-125
❑ 97DonLimE-191
❑ 97DonLimENG-32
❑ 97DonLimFotG-8
❑ 97DonPre-54
❑ 97DonPreCttC-54
❑ 97DonPrePM-11
❑ 97DonSig-77
❑ 97DonSigA-12
❑ 97DonSigAC-14
❑ 97DonSigAM-14
❑ 97DonSigPPP-77
❑ 97DonSilPP-17
❑ 97DonSilPP-405
❑ 97DonTea-121
❑ 97DonTeaSPE-121
❑ 97E-X2-31
❑ 97E-X2Cred-31
❑ 97E-X2EssCre-31
❑ 97E-X2Hall-6
❑ 97Fin-62
❑ 97FinRef-62
❑ 97FlaShoLC-163
❑ 97FlaShoLeg0-163
❑ 97FlaShoLeg1-163
❑ 97FlaShoM-A163
❑ 97FlaShoM-B163
❑ 97FlaShoM-C163
❑ 97FlaShoR0-163
❑ 97FlaShoR1-163
❑ 97FlaShoR2-163
❑ 97Fle-161
❑ 97FleDecoE-1
❑ 97FleDecoERT-1
❑ 97FleTif-161
❑ 97HigMinM-10
❑ 97Lea-1
❑ 97Lea-380
❑ 97LeaFraM-1
❑ 97LeaFraM-380
❑ 97LeaFraMDC-1
❑ 97LeaFraMDC-380
❑ 97MetUni-114
❑ 97NewPin-47
❑ 97NewPinAP-47
❑ 97NewPinMC-47
❑ 97NewPinPP-47
❑ 97Pac-147
❑ 97PacCar-12
❑ 97PacCarM-12
❑ 97PacGolCD-10
❑ 97PacLigB-147
❑ 97PacPri-49
❑ 97PacPriGA-GA8
❑ 97PacPriGotD-GD69
❑ 97PacPriLB-49
❑ 97PacPriP-49
❑ 97PacPriSL-SL4C
❑ 97PacSil-147
❑ 97PinCer-78
❑ 97PinCerMBla-78
❑ 97PinCerMBlu-78
❑ 97PinCerMG-78
❑ 97PinCerMR-78
❑ 97PinCerR-78
❑ 97PinIns-61
❑ 97PinInsCE-61
❑ 97PinInsDE-61
❑ 97PinTotCPB-78
❑ 97PinTotCPG-78
❑ 97PinTotCPR-78
❑ 97PinX-P-69
❑ 97PinX-PMoS-69
❑ 97Sco-167
❑ 97ScoArtPWB-167
❑ 97ScoHeaotO-17
❑ 97ScoPitP-13
❑ 97ScoPreS-167
❑ 97ScoShoS-167
❑ 97ScoShoSAP-167
❑ 97Sel-34
❑ 97SelArtP-34
❑ 97SelCom-34
❑ 97SelRegG-34
❑ 97SelToootT-17
❑ 97SelToootTMB-17
❑ 97SP-129
❑ 97SPSpeF-44
❑ 97SPSpxF-9
❑ 97SPSPxFA-9
❑ 97StaClu-217
❑ 97StaCluMat-217
❑ 97StaCluMOP-217
❑ 97Stu-47
❑ 97StuPrePG-47
❑ 97StuPrePS-47
❑ 97Top-8
❑ 97TopChr-4
❑ 97TopChrR-4
❑ 97TopGal-20
❑ 97TopGalPPI-20
❑ 97TopMemO5-7
❑ 97TopSta-57
❑ 97TopStaAM-57
❑ 97Ult-95
❑ 97UltFieC-3
❑ 97UltGolME-95
❑ 97UltPlaME-95
❑ 97UppDec-125
❑ 97YanSco-10
❑ 97YanScoPl-10
❑ 97YanScoPr-10
❑ 98Bow-249
❑ 98BowBes-74
❑ 98BowBesAR-74
❑ 98BowBesR-74
❑ 98BowChr-249
❑ 98BowChrGA-249
❑ 98BowChrGAR-249
❑ 98BowChrI-249
❑ 98BowChrIR-249
❑ 98BowChrR-249
❑ 98BowGolA-249
❑ 98BowInt-249
❑ 98CirThu-165
❑ 98CirThuRav-165
❑ 98CirThuSupRav-165
❑ 98ColCho-190
❑ 98ColCho-500
❑ 98CroRoy-131
❑ 98CroRoyDK-22
❑ 98CroRoyFoB-22
❑ 98CroRoyFoBA-22
❑ 98DevRayP-14
❑ 98Don-40
❑ 98Don-234
❑ 98DonCol-40
❑ 98DonColE-449
❑ 98DonColL-247
❑ 98DonColP-591
❑ 98DonColS-40
❑ 98DonCruG-35
❑ 98DonCruP-35
❑ 98DonCruR-35
❑ 98DonEli-49
❑ 98DonEliA-49
❑ 98DonEliS-49
❑ 98DonGolPP-40
❑ 98DonGolPP-234
❑ 98DonPre-41
❑ 98DonPreSeat-41
❑ 98DonPriCD-40
❑ 98DonPriCE-449
❑ 98DonPriCL-247
❑ 98DonPriCP-591
❑ 98DonSig-28
❑ 98DonSigAC-11
❑ 98DonSigAM-11
❑ 98DonSigP-28
❑ 98DonSilPP-40
❑ 98DonSilPP-234
❑ 98Fin-158
❑ 98FinNo--158
❑ 98FinNo-R-158
❑ 98FinRef-158
❑ 98Fle-372
❑ 98FleVin'-121
❑ 98FleVin'C-121
❑ 98Lea-48
❑ 98LeaCruG-35
❑ 98LeaCruP-35
❑ 98LeaCruR-35
❑ 98LeaFraDA-48
❑ 98LeaFraF-48
❑ 98LeaFraM-48
❑ 98LeaFraM-48
❑ 98LeaFraMDC-48
❑ 98LeaFraMDC-48
❑ 98LeaFraMZ2-48
❑ 98LeaHeaftH-4
❑ 98LeaHeaftHS-4
❑ 98LeaRS-14
❑ 98LeaRS-174
❑ 98LeaRSGAHSamp-18
❑ 98LeaRSGreAH-18
❑ 98LeaRSLHolo-14
❑ 98LeaRSLHolo-174
❑ 98LeaRSLong-14
❑ 98LeaRSLong-174
❑ 98LeaRTrue-14
❑ 98LeaRTrue-174
❑ 98Pac-144
❑ 98PacAur-79
❑ 98PacAurCube-18
❑ 98PacAurODLC-18
❑ 98PacAurPF-12
❑ 98PacAurPFC-12
❑ 98PacAurPFPB-12
❑ 98PacAurPFR-12
❑ 98PacAurPFS-12
❑ 98PacInv-50
❑ 98PacInvGems-71
❑ 98PacInvPBlue-50
❑ 98PacInvSilv-50
❑ 98PacInvTeam-30
❑ 98PacOme-229
❑ 98PacOmeFTF-6
❑ 98PacOmeOnIns-16
❑ 98PacOmeR-229
❑ 98PacOnl-704A
❑ 98PacOnl-704B
❑ 98PacOnl-725
❑ 98PacOnlR-704A
❑ 98PacOnlR-704B
❑ 98PacOnlR-725
❑ 98PacOnlWC-704A
❑ 98PacOnlWC-704B
❑ 98PacOnlWC-725
❑ 98PacPar-94
❑ 98PacParC-94
❑ 98PacParCB-10
❑ 98PacParCBPP-10
❑ 98PacParFC-18
❑ 98PacParG-94
❑ 98PacParHS-94
❑ 98PacParPB-94
❑ 98PacParR-94
❑ 98PacParTC-12
❑ 98PacPlaB-144
❑ 98PacRedT-144
❑ 98PacSil-144
❑ 98Pin-43
❑ 98PinArtP-PP40
❑ 98PinIns-55
❑ 98PinInsCE-55
❑ 98PinInsDE-55
❑ 98PinMusC-PP40
❑ 98PinPer-42
❑ 98PinPerPP-42
❑ 98PinPlu-132
❑ 98PinPluAP-PP43
❑ 98PinPluGAP-PP43
❑ 98PinPluMAP-PP43
❑ 98PinPreP-43
❑ 98PinSna-TBDR4
❑ 98Revo-138
❑ 98RevoShow-16
❑ 98RevoSS-138
❑ 98Sco-221
❑ 98ScoRT-174
❑ 98ScoRTSS-PP100
❑ 98ScoRTSSAP-PP100
❑ 98ScoRTSSAP1-PP100
❑ 98ScoSS-PP107
❑ 98ScoSSAP-PP107
❑ 98SkyDugA-83
❑ 98SkyDugAIA-83
❑ 98SP Aut-182
❑ 98SpoIllWSF-138
❑ 98SpoIllWSFEE-138
❑ 98SpoIllWSFFE-138
❑ 98SPxFin-324
❑ 98SPxFin-347
❑ 98SPxFinR-324
❑ 98SPxFinR-347
❑ 98SPxFinS-324
❑ 98SPxFinS-347
❑ 98StaCluFDI-320
❑ 98StaCluI-320
❑ 98StaCluOneK-320
❑ 98StaCluPP-320
❑ 98Stu-137
❑ 98StuGPP-137
❑ 98StuSPP-137
❑ 98Top-215
❑ 98TopChr-215
❑ 98TopChrHB-HB3
❑ 98TopChrHBR-HB3
❑ 98TopChrR-215
❑ 98TopDevR-215
❑ 98TopDia-215
❑ 98TopGal-3
❑ 98TopGalGP-3
❑ 98TopGalOPP-3
❑ 98TopGalPPI-3
❑ 98TopGalPPIA-3
❑ 98TopGolLabC1-59
❑ 98TopGolLabC1B-59
❑ 98TopGolLabC1One-59
❑ 98TopGolLabC1R-59
❑ 98TopGolLabC2-59
❑ 98TopGolLabC2B-59
❑ 98TopGolLabC2One-59
❑ 98TopGolLabC2R-59
❑ 98TopGolLabC3-59
❑ 98TopGolLabC3B-59
❑ 98TopGolLabC3One-59
❑ 98TopGolLabC3R-59
❑ 98TopHal-HB3
❑ 98TopMiniC-215
❑ 98TopOpeD-105
❑ 98TopSta-17
❑ 98TopStaB-17
❑ 98TopStaG-17
❑ 98TopStaGR-17
❑ 98TopStaS-17
❑ 98UD3-82
❑ 98UD3-172
❑ 98UD3-262
❑ 98UD3DieCut-82
❑ 98UD3DieCut-172
❑ 98UD3DieCut-262
❑ 98Ult-467
❑ 98UltGolM-467
❑ 98UltMas-467
❑ 98UltPlaM-467
❑ 98UltTop3-27
❑ 98UppDec-171
❑ 98UppDec-725
❑ 98UppDec10AP-34
❑ 98UppDec1APR-34
❑ 98UppDecR-6
❑ 98UppDecRTC-TC20
❑ 98YanSco-14
❑ 98YanScoP-14
❑ 99199Fin-246
❑ 99BowBes-7
❑ 99BowBesAR-7
❑ 99BowBesR-7
❑ 99CroRoyB-133
❑ 99CroRoyL-133
❑ 99CroRoyOD-133
❑ 99FinCom-C2
❑ 99FinComDualR-C2
❑ 99FinGolRef-246
❑ 99FinMil-M3
❑ 99FinRef-246
❑ 99FlaShoLeg1-128
❑ 99FlaShoLeg2-128
❑ 99FlaShoLeg3-128
❑ 99FlaShoLegM1-128
❑ 99FlaShoLegM2-128
❑ 99FlaShoLegM3-128
❑ 99FlaShoR1-128
❑ 99FlaShoR2-128
❑ 99FlaShoR3-128
❑ 99Fle-110
❑ 99FleMys-51
❑ 99FleMysG-51
❑ 99FleMysM-51
❑ 99FleSta9-110
❑ 99FleWarT-110
❑ 99MetUni-153
❑ 99MetUniGM-153
❑ 99MetUniPMG-153
❑ 99Pac-408
❑ 99PacAur-183
❑ 99PacAurOD-183
❑ 99PacCroC-272
❑ 99PacCroCPB-272
❑ 99PacCroCTC-28
❑ 99PacGolCDC-15
❑ 99PacInv-139
❑ 99PacInvOD-139
❑ 99PacInvPB-139
❑ 99PacOme-227
❑ 99PacOmeC-227
❑ 99PacOmeDD-10
❑ 99PacOmeG-227
❑ 99PacOmePB-227
❑ 99PacPar-224
❑ 99PacParC-224
❑ 99PacParG-224
❑ 99PacParHoloGold-224
❑ 99PacParHS-224
❑ 99PacParOD-224
❑ 99PacParPB-34
❑ 99PacParPB-224
❑ 99PacParRed-224
❑ 99PacParTC-28
❑ 99PacPlaB-408
❑ 99PacPri-138
❑ 99PacPriHB-138
❑ 99PacPriHG-138
❑ 99PacPriHM-138
❑ 99PacPriHP-138
❑ 99PacPriRed-138
❑ 99PacPriS-25
❑ 99PacPriS206-25
❑ 99PacPriS206R-25
❑ 99PacPriSP-25
❑ 99PacPriSV-25
❑ 99PacRed-408
❑ 99PacTeaC-12
❑ 99PacTim-9
❑ 99Rev-135
❑ 99RevPremDate-135

❑ 99RevRet-135
❑ 99RevShaSS-135
❑ 99SkyMolM-90
❑ 99SkyMolMX-90
❑ 99SkyPre-153
❑ 99SkyPreR-153
❑ 99SkyThu-239
❑ 99SkyThuRant-239
❑ 99SkyThuRave-239
❑ 99SpoIll-146
❑ 99SPSig-152
❑ 99SPx-75
❑ 99SPxFinR-75
❑ 99SPxFinS-75
❑ 99StaClu-10
❑ 99StaCluFDI-10
❑ 99StaCluOoaK-10
❑ 99StaCluPP-10
❑ 99ThuSkySupR-239
❑ 99Top-398
❑ 99TopBlaLC1-27
❑ 99TopBlaLC2-27
❑ 99TopBlaLC3-27
❑ 99TopChr-398
❑ 99TopChrR-398
❑ 99TopGal-25
❑ 99TopGalPP-25
❑ 99TopGalPPI-25
❑ 99TopGolL-27
❑ 99TopGolLC1-27
❑ 99TopGolLC2-27
❑ 99TopGolLOtO-27
❑ 99TopMVPP-398
❑ 99TopRedLC1-27
❑ 99TopRedLC2-27
❑ 99TopRedLC3-27
❑ 99TopSta-54
❑ 99TopSta1Foil-54
❑ 99TopStaFoil-54
❑ 99TopStaOS-54
❑ 99TopTek-9A
❑ 99TopTek-9B
❑ 99TopTekG-9A
❑ 99TopTekG-9B
❑ 99Ult-132
❑ 99UltGolM-132
❑ 99UltMas-132
❑ 99UltPlaM-132
❑ 99UppDec-210
❑ 99UppDec10AT-X15
❑ 99UppDec10ATD-X15
❑ 99UppDec10ATHR-X15
❑ 99UppDec10ATT-X15
❑ 99UppDecCL-60
❑ 99UppDecCLCC-60
❑ 99UppDecCLM-C92
❑ 99UppDecE-83
❑ 99UppDecEFXG-83
❑ 99UppDecEL1-210
❑ 99UppDecEL2-210
❑ 99UppDecM-199
❑ 99UppDecMGS-199
❑ 99UppDecMHFS-199
❑ 99UppDecMSS-199
❑ 99Vic-385
❑ 99Vic-454

Bogle, Bryan
❑ 94HunCubC-3
❑ 94HunCubF-3564
❑ 96HigDesMB-7
❑ 97BowBay-9
❑ 98BowBayM-5

Bogle, Sean
❑ 94WilCubF-3755
❑ 96RocCubTI-2

Bogott, Kurt
❑ 96DunBluJB-2
❑ 96DunBluJTI-2
❑ 96KnoSmoB-5

Bogues, Muggsy
❑ 91GasRanC-29

Bohanon, Brian
❑ 88ChaRanS-2
❑ 90Bow-489
❑ 90BowTif-489
❑ 90DonRoo-13
❑ 90FleUpd-122
❑ 90RanMot-13
❑ 90UppDec-731
❑ 91Sco100RS-53
❑ 91TopDeb90-18
❑ 92ClaGam-185
❑ 92DonRoo-11
❑ 92OklCit8F-1908
❑ 92OPC-149
❑ 92RanMot-18
❑ 92Sco-672
❑ 92StaClu-297
❑ 92Top-149
❑ 92TopGol-149
❑ 92TopGolW-149
❑ 92TopMic-149
❑ 92TulDriF-2686
❑ 93Don-27
❑ 93RanKee-395
❑ 93StaClu-154
❑ 93StaCluFDI-154
❑ 93StaCluMOP-154
❑ 93Top-638
❑ 93TopGol-638
❑ 93TopInaM-638
❑ 93TopInaR-638
❑ 93TopMic-638
❑ 93UppDec-380
❑ 93UppDecGold-380
❑ 94Fle-302
❑ 94OklCit8F-1488
❑ 94StaClu-55
❑ 94StaCluFDI-55
❑ 94StaCluGR-55
❑ 94StaCluMOP-55
❑ 94StaCluT-245
❑ 94StaCluTFDI-245
❑ 96BluJayOH-2
❑ 96Pac-317
❑ 97NorTid-7
❑ 97NorTidB-7
❑ 98PacOnl-472
❑ 98PacOnlR-472
❑ 98PacOnlWC-472
❑ 98UppDec-447
❑ 99Fle-327
❑ 99FleSta9-327
❑ 99FleWarT-327

Bohen, Leo
❑ 11Zee-22
❑ 12Zee-24

Bohlke, Scott
❑ 88DurBulS-2

Bohman, John
❑ 96GreFalDTI-2

Bohmbach, Jay
❑ 85RedWinA-5
❑ 86RedWinA-4

Bohmbach, Jim
❑ 85RedWinA-11
❑ 86RedWinA-16

Bohmbach, Kelly
❑ 85RedWinA-13
❑ 86RedWinA-13

Bohmbach, Lonnie
❑ 86RedWinA-23

Bohn, Matt
❑ 88CalLeaACLC-23

Bohne, Sammy Arthur
❑ 16Zee-100
❑ 19Zee-15
❑ 20Zee-122
❑ 21Exh-12
❑ 21Nei-67
❑ 22E120-166
❑ 23MapCriV-20
❑ 90DodTar-59

Bohnenkamp, Dave
❑ 89CliGiaP-880

Bohnet, Bob
❑ 79WisRapTT-13
❑ 80WatIndT-21
❑ 82HolMilT-14

Bohnet, John
❑ 80WatIndT-9
❑ 81ChaLooT-13
❑ 82ChaChaT-2
❑ 82Ind-6
❑ 84BufBisT-14

Bohringer, Helms
❑ 91BakDodCLC-24

Bohrofen, Brent
❑ 89OklSoo-6
❑ 90OklSoo-12
❑ 91HamRedC-22
❑ 91HamRedP-4050
❑ 92SavCarF-674

Boice, George
❑ 09ObaT21-9

Boigenzahn, Jeff
❑ 85RedWinA-21
❑ 86RedWinA-2

Boisclair, Bruce A.
❑ 74MetTeal-3
❑ 75TidTidTI-5
❑ 77MetDaiPA-4
❑ 77Top-399
❑ 78MetDaiPA-2
❑ 78Top-277
❑ 79OPC-68
❑ 79Top-148
❑ 80Top-654
❑ 91MetWIZ-41

Boitano, Danny
❑ 76OklCit8TI-16
❑ 79VanCanT-9
❑ 80Top-668
❑ 80VanCanT-14
❑ 81TidTidT-27
❑ 91MetWIZ-42
❑ 93RanKee-77
❑ 94BreMilB-196

Bojan, Tim
❑ 92SouOreAC-19
❑ 92SouOreAF-3406
❑ 93MadMusC-6
❑ 93MadMusF-1816
❑ 94WesMicWC-4
❑ 94WesMicWF-2289

Bojcun, Pat (Patrick)
❑ 91BatCliCB-21
❑ 91BatCliP-3476
❑ 92BatCliCB-7
❑ 92BatCliF-3255

Boka, Ben
❑ 93LetMouF-4151
❑ 93LetMouSP-3
❑ 94PitMetC-6
❑ 94PitMetF-3525

Bokek, Ken
❑ 76CliPilT-3

Bokelman, Dick
❑ 53Top-204
❑ 79TCM50-249
❑ 91TopArc1-204

Bokemeier, Matt
❑ 94HudValRC-1
❑ 94HudValRF-3390
❑ 96WesOahCHWB-41
❑ 97TexLeaTP-23
❑ 97TulDriTI-4

Boken, Bob (Robert A.)
❑ 33WorCig(-8
❑ 34Gou-74
❑ 72TCMthe3-3

Boker, John
❑ 96OgdRapTI-23

Boker, Mike
❑ 91BenBucCB-11
❑ 91BenBucP-3685
❑ 92CliGiaC-4
❑ 92CliGiaF-3589

Bolan, Bob
❑ 52LavPro-21

Bolanos, Marcos
❑ 94VenLinU-173

Bolar, Wendell
❑ 86BelMarCr-106
❑ 87WauTimP-9
❑ 88BoiHawP-1607

Bolden, Ed
❑ 91PomBlaBPB-23

Bolden, Jim
❑ 93NegLeaRL2-4

Boldt, Sean
❑ 92MarPhiC-3
❑ 92MarPhiF-3046

Bolek, Ken
❑ 78WatIndT-2
❑ 83ColAstT-23
❑ 86AshTouP-3
❑ 87OscAstP-6
❑ 88WatIndP-687
❑ 89KinIndS-25
❑ 90CanIndB-4
❑ 90CanIndP-1309
❑ 90CanIndS-20
❑ 91CanIndLD-99
❑ 91CanIndP-995
❑ 91LinDriAA-99
❑ 92IndFanC-30
❑ 94DayCubC-27
❑ 94DayCubF-2369

Bolen, Stew
❑ 27MidBre-25

Boles, Carl Theodore
❑ 63Top-428
❑ 81Gia196T-18

Boles, John
❑ 83AppFoxFr-25
❑ 85BufBisT-1
❑ 86OmaRoyP-2
❑ 86OmaRoyT-23

Boles, Kevin
❑ 98WilCubM-1

Boles, Walter
❑ 12Zee-2
❑ 13Zee-1
❑ 14Zee-3
❑ 15Zee-4
❑ 16Zee-2
❑ 17Zee-2
❑ 18Zee-1
❑ 19Zee-1

Boley, Joe (John Peter)
❑ 31Exh-27
❑ 74A's192T-2
❑ 94ConTSN-1141
❑ 94ConTSNB-1141

Bolger, Jim (James Cyril)
❑ 55Top-179
❑ 57Top-289
❑ 58Top-201
❑ 59Top-29
❑ 59TopVen-29
❑ 61UniOil-SD2

Bolick, Frank
❑ 76SanAntBTI-2

Bolick, Frank C.
❑ 88BelBreGS-4
❑ 89BelBre2S-1
❑ 89BelBreIS-1
❑ 89Sta-108
❑ 90CalLeaACLC-11
❑ 90CMC-713
❑ 90ProAaA-152
❑ 90StoPorB-7
❑ 90StoPorCLC-193
❑ 90StoPorP-2192
❑ 91Bow-534
❑ 91Cla/Bes-381
❑ 91JacSunLD-329
❑ 91JacSunP-154
❑ 91LinDriAA-329
❑ 92JacSunF-3712
❑ 92JacSunS-351
❑ 92OPC-473
❑ 92SkyAA F-148
❑ 92Top-473
❑ 92TopGol-473
❑ 92TopGolW-473
❑ 92TopMic-473
❑ 93Bow-296
❑ 93ExpPosN-5
❑ 93FleFinE-89
❑ 93Lea-231
❑ 93OPCPre-72
❑ 93PacSpa-530
❑ 93Pin-588
❑ 93StaClu-724
❑ 93StaCluFDI-724
❑ 93StaCluMOP-724
❑ 93Ult-412
❑ 93UppDec-531
❑ 93UppDecGold-531
❑ 94BufBisF-1843
❑ 94Don-63
❑ 94Pac-375
❑ 97MidAng-6
❑ 97VanCanB-7
❑ 98VanCanG-2

Bolin, Bobby
❑ 61Top-449
❑ 62Top-329
❑ 63Top-106
❑ 64Top-374
❑ 65Top-341
❑ 66OPC-61
❑ 66Top-61
❑ 66TopVen-61
❑ 67CokCapG-1
❑ 67Top-252
❑ 68DexPre-14
❑ 68OPC-169
❑ 68Top-169
❑ 68TopVen-169
❑ 69OPC-8
❑ 69Top-8
❑ 69Top-505A
❑ 69Top-505B
❑ 69TopSta-101
❑ 69TopTeaP-14
❑ 70BreMcD-2
❑ 70MLBOffS-266
❑ 70Top-574
❑ 71MLBOffS-314
❑ 71OPC-446
❑ 71Top-446
❑ 72MilBra-36
❑ 72OPC-266
❑ 72RedSoxTI-2
❑ 72Top-266
❑ 73LinPor-15
❑ 73OPC-541
❑ 73Top-541
❑ 74OPC-427
❑ 74Top-427
❑ 78TCM60I-109
❑ 81Gia196T-25
❑ 86BirBarTI-20
❑ 94BreMilB-197

Bolin, George
❑ 91MelBusF-10

Bolin, Stewart
❑ 37Zee-13

Boling, John
❑ 86AppFoxP-2
❑ 87BirBarB-12
❑ 88BirBarB-18

Bolinger, Monte
❑ 72CedRapCT-29

Bolivar, Flores
❑ 76VenLeaS-101
❑ 80VenLeaS-128
❑ 80VenLeaS-133
❑ 93LinVenB-82
❑ 95LinVen-35

Bolivar, Pape
❑ 97ForWayW-6
❑ 98ForMyeMTI-3

Bolke, Ken
❑ 93IndWUA-33

Bolling, Frank Elmore
❑ 55Bow-48A
❑ 55Bow-204A
❑ 55Bow-204B
❑ 57Top-325
❑ 58Top-95
❑ 59TigGraASP-4
❑ 59Top-280
❑ 60TigJayP-2
❑ 60Top-482
❑ 61Pos-41A
❑ 61Pos-41B
❑ 61Top-335
❑ 61TopStaI-145
❑ 62BraJayP-3
❑ 62Jel-146
❑ 62Pos-146
❑ 62PosCan-146
❑ 62SalPlaC-140
❑ 62ShiPlaC-140
❑ 62Top-130
❑ 62Top-211
❑ 62TopStaI-145
❑ 62TopVen-130
❑ 63BraJayP-2
❑ 63Fle-44
❑ 63Jel-149
❑ 63Pos-149
❑ 63SalMetC-18
❑ 63Top-570
❑ 64BraJayP-2
❑ 64Top-115
❑ 64TopVen-115
❑ 65BraTeal-2
❑ 65Kah-5
❑ 65OPC-269
❑ 65Top-269
❑ 66BraPos-5
❑ 66Kah-6
❑ 78AtlCon-4
❑ 78TCM60I-9
❑ 81TigDetN-103

Bolling, John Edward
❑ 79DiaGre-312
❑ 90DodTar-60

Bolling, Milt (Milton J.)
❑ 53RedSoxTI-1
❑ 53Top-280
❑ 54Bow-130
❑ 54Top-82
❑ 55Bow-48A
❑ 55Bow-48B
❑ 55Bow-204A
❑ 55Top-91
❑ 55TopDouH-91
❑ 56Top-315
❑ 57Top-131
❑ 58Top-188
❑ 79DiaGre-245
❑ 81RedSoxBG2S-6
❑ 91TopArc1-280
❑ 94TopArc1-82
❑ 94TopArc1G-82

Bollo, Greg
❑ 65Top-541
❑ 66Top-301
❑ 66TopVen-301
❑ 78TCM60I-30

Bollweg, Don (Donald R.)
❑ 47PM1StaP1-16
❑ 52Top-128
❑ 53Dor-120
❑ 54A'STEAI-4
❑ 54Bow-115
❑ 55A'sRodM-4
❑ 55Bow-54
❑ 83TopRep5-128

Bolognese, Keith
❑ 94DanBraC-2
❑ 94DanBraF-3537

Bolster, Bob
❑ 80GleFalWSBT-29
❑ 80GleFalWSCT-23

Bolt, James
❑ 86SanJosBP-5

Bolt, Michelle
❑ 91FreStaLBS-14

Bolton, Cliff (William C.)
❑ 31SenTealPW-3
❑ 34DiaStaR-47
❑ 34Gou-65
❑ 36GouWidPPR-A8
❑ 36NatChiFPR-12
❑ 36R31PasP-27
❑ 36WorWidGV-133
❑ 72TCMthe3-4
❑ 79DiaGre-71
❑ 92ConTSN-505

Bolton, Jacques
❑ 94WilCubC-29

Bolton, Rod
❑ 90UtiBluSP-14
❑ 91Cla/Bes-56
❑ 91FloStaLAP-FSL27
❑ 91SarWhiSC-1
❑ 91SarWhiSP-1104
❑ 92Bow-240
❑ 92ProFS7-45
❑ 92SkyAAAF-279
❑ 92TriA AAS-628
❑ 92UppDecML-117
❑ 92VanCanF-2713
❑ 92VanCanS-628
❑ 93Bow-471
❑ 93ExcFS7-150
❑ 93FleFinE-193
❑ 93LeaGolR-R12
❑ 93LeaGolRJ-R12
❑ 93Pin-580
❑ 93SelRoo-43T
❑ 93Ult-528
❑ 93UppDec-502
❑ 93UppDecGold-502
❑ 93WhiSoxK-4
❑ 93WhiSoxSC-3
❑ 94Bow-18
❑ 94Don-598
❑ 94Fle-77
❑ 94NasSouF-1243
❑ 94Pac-121
❑ 94Pin-130
❑ 94PinArtP-130
❑ 94PinMusC-130
❑ 94Sco-553
❑ 94ScoGolR-553
❑ 94StaClu-466
❑ 94StaCluFDI-466
❑ 94StaCluGR-466
❑ 94StaCluMOP-466
❑ 94StaCluT-131
❑ 94StaCluTFDI-131
❑ 94Top-766
❑ 94TopGol-766
❑ 94TopSpa-766
❑ 95NasSouTI-2
❑ 95Top-634
❑ 97IndInd-6
❑ 98IndIndQ-6

Bolton, Tom
❑ 80ElmPioRST-2
❑ 87IntLeaAT-22
❑ 87PawRedSP-62

❑ 87PawRedST-27
❑ 88Fle-346
❑ 88FleGlo-346
❑ 88PawRedSC-9
❑ 88PawRedSP-452
❑ 88Top-442
❑ 88TopTif-442
❑ 89Don-539
❑ 89PawRedSC-1
❑ 89PawRedSP-680
❑ 89PawRedSTI-3
❑ 89Sco-531
❑ 89Top-269
❑ 89TopTif-269
❑ 89TriAAAP-AAA17
❑ 89UppDec-545
❑ 90PawRedSDD-2
❑ 90PawRedSP-453
❑ 90ProAAAF-425
❑ 90TopTVRS-38
❑ 90UppDec-351
❑ 91Bow-114
❑ 91Don-609
❑ 91Fle-87
❑ 91Lea-47
❑ 91OPC-37
❑ 91RedSoxP-1
❑ 91RedSoxP-2
❑ 91Sco-781
❑ 91StaClu-588
❑ 91Top-37
❑ 91TopDesS-37
❑ 91TopMic-37
❑ 91TopTif-37
❑ 91Ult-28
❑ 91UppDec-86
❑ 92Fle-33
❑ 92OPC-708
❑ 92RedSoxDD-3
❑ 92Sco-99
❑ 92ScoProP-23
❑ 92ScoRoo-77T
❑ 92StaClu-561
❑ 92Top-708
❑ 92TopGol-708
❑ 92TopGolW-708
❑ 92TopMic-708
❑ 92UppDec-110
❑ 93PacSpa-442
❑ 93TigGat-3
❑ 93UppDec-633
❑ 93UppDecGold-633
❑ 94BalOriP-5
❑ 94ColC-56
❑ 94ColChoGS-56
❑ 94ColChoSS-56
❑ 94Pac-212
❑ 94RocRedWF-990
❑ 95NasSouTI-3
❑ 97TucTorB-1
❑ 98NasSouTI-5
❑ 98NasSouTISS-5

Boltz, Brian
❑ 90Bes-87
❑ 90GreBraB-7
❑ 90GreBraP-1122
❑ 90GreBraS-4
❑ 93GreBraF-341

Bomback, Mark
❑ 77HolMilT-2
❑ 79VanCanT-7
❑ 81Fle-323
❑ 81OPC-264
❑ 81Top-567
❑ 81TopTra-739
❑ 82Don-559
❑ 82Fle-610
❑ 82OPC-307
❑ 82Top-707
❑ 83SyrChiT-5
❑ 84SyrChiT-23
❑ 89PacSenL-39
❑ 91MetWIZ-43
❑ 94BreMilB-198

Bombard, Marc
❑ 86FloStaLAP-9
❑ 87TamTarP-8
❑ 88CedRapRP-1144
❑ 88MidLeaAGS-15
❑ 89CedRapRAB-28
❑ 89ElPasDGS-1
❑ 90CedRapRDGB-28
❑ 90EasLeaAP-EL29
❑ 90HarSenP-1208
❑ 90HarSenS-23
❑ 91CarMudLD-124
❑ 91CarMudP-1101
❑ 91LinDriAA-124
❑ 92BufBisBS-2
❑ 92BufBisF-338
❑ 92BufBisS-49
❑ 93IndIndF-1503
❑ 93TriAAAGF-7
❑ 94IndIndF-1824
❑ 95IndIndF-111
❑ 97ScrRedB-24
❑ 98ScrRedBQ-5

Bombard, Rich
❑ 82AubAstT-13
❑ 83DayBeaAT-3
❑ 86ColAstP-5
❑ 87CedRapRP-26
❑ 88ChaLooB-5
❑ 89ChaLooB-8
❑ 89ChaLooGS-2
❑ 91FayGenC-12
❑ 92LakTigC-28
❑ 92LakTigF-2294
❑ 93LakTigC-28
❑ 93LakTigF-1327
❑ 94TreThuF-2135
❑ 95JacSunTI-2
❑ 96LakTigB-2
❑ 97JacSun-26
❑ 98JacSunM-26

Bomgardner, Rich
❑ 89ColMetB-25
❑ 89ColMetGS-3

Bonacquista, Jeff
❑ 87AncGlaP-3

Bonanno, Rob
❑ 94BoiHawC-3
❑ 94BoiHawF-3344
❑ 95LakElsSTI-5
❑ 95MidAngTI-4
❑ 96MidAngOHP-4
❑ 97MidAng-7
❑ 98MidAngG-5
❑ 98MidAngO-5
❑ 98VanCanG-3

Bonaparte, Elijah
❑ 77SpaPhiT-17
❑ 81OklCit8T-3
❑ 82TolMudHT-19
❑ 83RocRedWT-19

Bonarigo, Nick
❑ 43CenFlo-2

Bonchek, Jeff
❑ 88BurIndP-1779
❑ 89MiaMirIS-3

Boncore, Steve
❑ 82VerBeaDT-13
❑ 83VerBeaDT-14

Bond, Aaron
❑ 98BesAutSS-4
❑ 98SavSanGM-4

Bond, Daven
❑ 86AubAstP-4
❑ 87AshTouP-6
❑ 88OscAstS-4
❑ 89OscAstS-2
❑ 90ColMudB-14
❑ 90ColMudP-1338
❑ 90ColMudS-5
❑ 91ColCliLD-102
❑ 91ColCliP-2
❑ 91ColCliP-589
❑ 91LinDriAAA-102
❑ 92JacSunS-352

Bond, David
❑ 87SpoIndP-16
❑ 88ChaRaiP-1196
❑ 89ChaRaiP-993

Bond, Doug
❑ 88BilMusP-1809

Bond, Jason
❑ 96EveAquB-4
❑ 97LanJet-6
❑ 98LanJetG-3

Bond, Michael
❑ 91BelMarCB-11
❑ 91BelMarP-3670
❑ 92BelMarCB-21
❑ 92BelMarF-1449
❑ 92JacSunF-3713

Bond, Walt (Walter F.)
❑ 60Top-552
❑ 61Top-334
❑ 62SalPlaC-208
❑ 62ShiPlaC-208
❑ 63Top-493
❑ 64Top-339
❑ 64TopVen-339
❑ 65AstJayP-4
❑ 65OPC-109
❑ 65Top-109
❑ 65TopEmbl-50
❑ 65TopTral-4
❑ 66Top-431
❑ 67AstTeal2-4
❑ 67Top-224
❑ 87AstSer1-4
❑ 87AstSer1-29

Bonds, Barry
❑ 86DonRoo-11
❑ 86FleUpd-14
❑ 86SpoRoo-13
❑ 86TopTra-11T
❑ 86TopTraT-11T
❑ 87ClaUpdY-113
❑ 87Don-361
❑ 87DonOpeD-163A
❑ 87DonOpeD-163B
❑ 87Fle-604
❑ 87FleGlo-604
❑ 87FleHotS-5
❑ 87Lea-219
❑ 87OPC-320
❑ 87SpoTeaP-18
❑ 87Top-320
❑ 87TopGloS-30
❑ 87TopSti-131
❑ 87TopTif-320
❑ 87ToyRoo-4
❑ 88Don-326
❑ 88DonBasB-17
❑ 88Fle-322
❑ 88FleGlo-322
❑ 88FleSup-4
❑ 88KinDis-11
❑ 88Lea-113
❑ 88OPC-267
❑ 88PanSti-376
❑ 88PirTeal-2
❑ 88RedFolSB-7
❑ 88Sco-265
❑ 88ScoGlo-265
❑ 88ScoYouS2-12
❑ 88Spo-119
❑ 88StaLinPi-2
❑ 88Top-231
❑ 88Top-450
❑ 88TopBig-89
❑ 88TopSti-135
❑ 88TopTif-231
❑ 88TopTif-450
❑ 88TopUKM-5
❑ 88TopUKMT-5
❑ 89Bow-426
❑ 89BowTif-426
❑ 89ClaTraO-117
❑ 89Don-92
❑ 89DonBasB-73
❑ 89Fle-202
❑ 89FleGlo-202
❑ 89FleHeroB-3
❑ 89OPC-263
❑ 89PanSti-172
❑ 89PirVerFJ-24
❑ 89RedFolSB-9
❑ 89Sco-127
❑ 89ScoHot1S-31
❑ 89Spo-146
❑ 89SpoIllFKI-229
❑ 89Top-620
❑ 89TopAme2C-5
❑ 89TopBasT-106
❑ 89TopBig-5
❑ 89TopSti-127
❑ 89TopStiB-46
❑ 89TopTif-620
❑ 89TopUKM-5
❑ 89TVSpoM-12
❑ 89UppDec-440
❑ 90Bow-181
❑ 90BowTif-181
❑ 90ClaBlu-82
❑ 90ClaYel-T68
❑ 90Don-126
❑ 90DonBesN-45
❑ 90Fle-461
❑ 90FleCan-461
❑ 90Lea-91
❑ 90M.Vpin-81
❑ 90MLBBasB-37
❑ 90OPC-220
❑ 90PanSti-322
❑ 90PirHomC-5
❑ 90PlaPri-1
❑ 90PubIntS-149
❑ 90RedFolSB-7
❑ 90Sco-4
❑ 90Sco100S-53
❑ 90ScoMcD-11
❑ 90Spo-143
❑ 90SunSee-9
❑ 90SupActM-19
❑ 90Top-220
❑ 90TopBig-128
❑ 90TopCoi-40
❑ 90TopDou-5
❑ 90TopMag-42
❑ 90TopMinL-70
❑ 90TopSti-9
❑ 90TopSti-123
❑ 90TopTif-220
❑ 90UppDec-227
❑ 90USPlaCA-13D
❑ 91Baz-1
❑ 91Bow-380
❑ 91Bow-513
❑ 91CadEllD-5
❑ 91Cla1-T81
❑ 91Cla2-T78
❑ 91ClaGam-195
❑ 91Col-26
❑ 91ColBon-1
❑ 91ColBon-2
❑ 91ColBon-3
❑ 91ColBon-4
❑ 91ColBon-5
❑ 91ColBon-6
❑ 91ColBon-7
❑ 91ColBon-8
❑ 91ColBon-9
❑ 91ColBon-10
❑ 91ColBon-11
❑ 91ColBon-12
❑ 91ColBon-xx
❑ 91Don-4
❑ 91Don-495
❑ 91Don-762
❑ 91DonEli-1
❑ 91DonGraS-5
❑ 91DonPre-10
❑ 91DonSupD-4
❑ 91Fle-33
❑ 91Fle-710
❑ 91FleAll-5
❑ 91FlePro-F1
❑ 91JimDea-4
❑ 91KinDis-21
❑ 91Lea-261
❑ 91Lea-364
❑ 91LeaPre-9
❑ 91MajLeaCP-57
❑ 91MooSna-3
❑ 91OPC-401
❑ 91OPC-570
❑ 91OPCPre-12
❑ 91PanCanT1-12
❑ 91PanCanT1-20
❑ 91PanCanT1-33
❑ 91PanCanT1-43
❑ 91PanCanT1-105
❑ 91PanFreS-119
❑ 91PanSti-114
❑ 91PepSup-7
❑ 91PetSta-16
❑ 91Pos-21
❑ 91PosCan-5
❑ 91Sco-330
❑ 91Sco-668
❑ 91Sco-868
❑ 91Sco-876
❑ 91Sco100S-26
❑ 91Sev3DCN-2
❑ 91SevCoi-F1
❑ 91SevCoi-T2
❑ 91SevCoi-NE2
❑ 91StaClu-220
❑ 91StaCluCM-3
❑ 91StaPinB-4
❑ 91Stu-222
❑ 91Top-401
❑ 91Top-570
❑ 91TopCraJI-19
❑ 91TopDesS-401
❑ 91TopDesS-570
❑ 91TopGaloC-2
❑ 91TopMic-401
❑ 91TopMic-570
❑ 91TopSta-4
❑ 91TopTif-401
❑ 91TopTif-570
❑ 91TopTriH-N9
❑ 91Ult-275
❑ 91Ult-391
❑ 91UltGol-1
❑ 91UppDec-94
❑ 91UppDec-154
❑ 91UppDecSS-SS5
❑ 91Woo-1
❑ 92Bow-60
❑ 92Bow-590
❑ 92Cla1-T16
❑ 92Cla1-NNO
❑ 92Cla2-T70
❑ 92ClaGam-155
❑ 92ColAllG-22
❑ 92ColAllP-22
❑ 92ColPro-3
❑ 92DenHol-20
❑ 92Don-243
❑ 92DonCraJ2-14
❑ 92DonPre-2
❑ 92Fle-550
❑ 92FleAll-3
❑ 92FleCitTP-23
❑ 92FleLumC-L8
❑ 92Fre-7
❑ 92Hig5-91
❑ 92Hig5S-4
❑ 92JimDea-2
❑ 92LaKdec-2
❑ 92Lea-275
❑ 92LeaBlaG-275
❑ 92MSABenSHD-18
❑ 92MVPPin-37
❑ 92OPC-380
❑ 92OPCPre-157
❑ 92PanSti-258
❑ 92PepDieM-29
❑ 92Pin-500
❑ 92PinSlu-4
❑ 92PinTeaP-8
❑ 92PirNatl-3
❑ 92Pos-15
❑ 92PosCan-9
❑ 92RedFolS-15
❑ 92Sco-555
❑ 92Sco-777
❑ 92Sco100S-26
❑ 92ScoImpP-55
❑ 92ScoProaG-15
❑ 92SpoIllFK1-157
❑ 92SpoIllFK1-562
❑ 92SpoStaCC-4
❑ 92StaClu-604
❑ 92StaClu-620
❑ 92StaCluECN-604
❑ 92StaCluECN-620
❑ 92StaCluMP-2
❑ 92Stu-82
❑ 92StuPre-15
❑ 92Top-380
❑ 92Top-390
❑ 92TopGol-380
❑ 92TopGol-390
❑ 92TopGolW-380
❑ 92TopGolW-390
❑ 92TopKid-21
❑ 92TopMcD-12
❑ 92TopMic-380
❑ 92TopMic-390
❑ 92TopMic-G380
❑ 92TriPla-116
❑ 92Ult-251
❑ 92UltAllS-16
❑ 92UltAwaW-11
❑ 92UppDec-134
❑ 92UppDec-711
❑ 92UppDec-721
❑ 92UppDecF-14
❑ 92UppDecFG-14
❑ 92UppDecHRH-HR21
❑ 92UppDecTMH-11
❑ 92UppDecWB-T2
❑ 93Ble-4
❑ 93Ble-5
❑ 93Ble-6
❑ 93Ble-7
❑ 93BlePro-1
❑ 93BlePro-2
❑ 93BlePro-3
❑ 93Bow-140
❑ 93Bow-702
❑ 93ClaGam-14
❑ 93ClaGolF-1
❑ 93ClaGolF-AU1
❑ 93ClaGolTP-3
❑ 93ColAllG-2
❑ 93DiaMar-14
❑ 93DiaMarA-2
❑ 93Don-678
❑ 93DonEli-31
❑ 93DonEliD-16
❑ 93DonEliS-13
❑ 93DonMasotG-14
❑ 93DonMVP-25
❑ 93DurPowP1-17
❑ 93Fin-103
❑ 93FinJum-103
❑ 93FinRef-103
❑ 93Fla-138
❑ 93Fle-112
❑ 93Fle-350
❑ 93FleAll-NL7
❑ 93FleAtl-2
❑ 93FleFinE-150
❑ 93FleFruotL-6
❑ 93FunPac-11
❑ 93FunPac-99
❑ 93FunPac-100
❑ 93FunPac-222
❑ 93FunPacA-AS7
❑ 93GiaMot-4
❑ 93GiaPos-6
❑ 93GiaPos-7
❑ 93GiaStaC-1
❑ 93HumDumC-49
❑ 93JimDea-10
❑ 93KinDis-1
❑ 93Lea-269
❑ 93LeaGolA-R16
❑ 93LeaGolA-U7
❑ 93MetBak-2
❑ 93OPC-46
❑ 93OPCPre-1
❑ 93OPCPreSP-14
❑ 93OPCPreSPF-14
❑ 93PacJugC-21
❑ 93PacSpa-607
❑ 93PanSti-165
❑ 93PanSti-243
❑ 93Pin-484
❑ 93Pin-504
❑ 93PinCoo-15
❑ 93PinCooD-15
❑ 93PinHomRC-4
❑ 93PinSlu-6
❑ 93PinTeaP-8
❑ 93Pos-15
❑ 93Pro22KGB-1
❑ 93RedFolS-14
❑ 93RedFolS-107
❑ 93Sco-482
❑ 93Sco-523
❑ 93Sco-560
❑ 93Sel-1
❑ 93SelChaS-7
❑ 93SelRoo-23T
❑ 93SelStaL-29
❑ 93SelStaL-40
❑ 93SelStaL-46
❑ 93SelStaL-52
❑ 93SP-10
❑ 93SPPlaP-PP2
❑ 93StaClu-51
❑ 93StaClu-51A
❑ 93StaClu-684
❑ 93StaClu-747
❑ 93StaCluFDI-51
❑ 93StaCluFDI-51A
❑ 93StaCluFDI-51B
❑ 93StaCluFDI-684
❑ 93StaCluFDI-747
❑ 93StaCluM-161
❑ 93StaCluMO-2
❑ 93StaCluMOP-51A
❑ 93StaCluMOP-51B
❑ 93StaCluMOP-684
❑ 93StaCluMOP-747
❑ 93StaCluMP-25
❑ 93StaCluU-1
❑ 93StaCluU-4
❑ 93StaCluU-5
❑ 93StaCluU-7
❑ 93StaCluU-10
❑ 93Stu-12
❑ 93StuSil-2
❑ 93StuSupoC-10
❑ 93Top-2
❑ 93Top-407
❑ 93TOPBLAG-1
❑ 93TopFulS-3

- ❑ 93TopGol-2
- ❑ 93TopGol-407
- ❑ 93TopInaM-2
- ❑ 93TopInaM-407
- ❑ 93TopInaR-2
- ❑ 93TopInaR-407
- ❑ 93TopMic-2
- ❑ 93TopMic-407
- ❑ 93TopPre-2
- ❑ 93TopTra-1T
- ❑ 93TriPlaG-GS1
- ❑ 93TriPlaLL-L1
- ❑ 93Ult-483
- ❑ 93UltAllS-6
- ❑ 93UltAwaW-7
- ❑ 93UltAwaW-24
- ❑ 93UltHomRK-6
- ❑ 93UltPer-1
- ❑ 93UppDec-210
- ❑ 93UppDec-471
- ❑ 93UppDec-476
- ❑ 93UppDec-486
- ❑ 93UppDec-567
- ❑ 93UppDecCP-R3
- ❑ 93UppDecDG-11
- ❑ 93UppDecFH-56
- ❑ 93UppDecGold-210
- ❑ 93UppDecGold-471
- ❑ 93UppDecGold-476
- ❑ 93UppDecGold-486
- ❑ 93UppDecGold-567
- ❑ 93UppDecHRH-HR6
- ❑ 93UppDecSH-HI5
- ❑ 93UppDecTriCro-TC1
- ❑ 93USPlaCA-10C
- ❑ 94Bow-135
- ❑ 94BowBes-R59
- ❑ 94BowBes-X97
- ❑ 94BowBesR-R59
- ❑ 94BowBesR-X97
- ❑ 94CarLeaA-DJ13
- ❑ 94ChuShoS-2
- ❑ 94ColC-311
- ❑ 94ColC-313
- ❑ 94ColC-316
- ❑ 94ColC-338
- ❑ 94ColC-610
- ❑ 94ColC-632
- ❑ 94ColChoGS-311
- ❑ 94ColChoGS-313
- ❑ 94ColChoGS-316
- ❑ 94ColChoGS-338
- ❑ 94ColChoGS-610
- ❑ 94ColChoGS-632
- ❑ 94ColChoHRA-HA3
- ❑ 94ColChoSS-311
- ❑ 94ColChoSS-313
- ❑ 94ColChoSS-316
- ❑ 94ColChoSS-338
- ❑ 94ColChoSS-610
- ❑ 94ColChoSS-632
- ❑ 94ColChoT-2
- ❑ 94ColChoT-11
- ❑ 94DenHol-6
- ❑ 94Don-349
- ❑ 94DonAwaWJ-1
- ❑ 94DonAwaWJ-4
- ❑ 94DonDiaK-DK1
- ❑ 94DonDiaKJ-DK1
- ❑ 94DonDom-A2
- ❑ 94DonDom-B7
- ❑ 94DonDomJ-A2
- ❑ 94DonDomJ-B7
- ❑ 94DonEli-44
- ❑ 94DonLonBL-9
- ❑ 94DonMVP-14
- ❑ 94DonPro-1
- ❑ 94DonPro-1SE
- ❑ 94DonSpeE-349
- ❑ 94DonSpiotG-2
- ❑ 94DonSpiotGJ-2
- ❑ 94Fin-230
- ❑ 94FinJum-230
- ❑ 94FinRef-230
- ❑ 94Fla-239
- ❑ 94FlaHotG-1
- ❑ 94FlaOutP-2
- ❑ 94Fle-684
- ❑ 94FleAllS-31
- ❑ 94FleAwaW-2
- ❑ 94FleExtB-383
- ❑ 94FleExtBGB-4
- ❑ 94FleLeaL-8
- ❑ 94FleLumC-2
- ❑ 94FleSun-5
- ❑ 94FleUpdDT-1
- ❑ 94FUnPac-25
- ❑ 94FUnPac-190
- ❑ 94FUnPac-194
- ❑ 94FUnPac-199
- ❑ 94FUnPac-212
- ❑ 94FUnPac-225
- ❑ 94FUnPac-226
- ❑ 94FUnPac-237
- ❑ 94GiaAMC-5
- ❑ 94GiaKTV-3
- ❑ 94GiaMot-3
- ❑ 94GiaSFC-2
- ❑ 94GiaTarBC-5
- ❑ 94GiaTeal-3
- ❑ 94GiaTeal-4
- ❑ 94GiaTeal-5
- ❑ 94GiaTeal-6
- ❑ 94GiaTeal-9
- ❑ 94GiaUSPC-1S
- ❑ 94GiaUSPC-7H
- ❑ 94KinDis-24
- ❑ 94Kra-17
- ❑ 94Lea-264
- ❑ 94LeaGam-8
- ❑ 94LeaGolS-2
- ❑ 94LeaL-156
- ❑ 94LeaLimGA-10
- ❑ 94LeaMVPC-N3
- ❑ 94LeaMVPCG-N3
- ❑ 94LeaPowB-3
- ❑ 94LeaSli-6
- ❑ 94LeaStaS-2
- ❑ 94O-PJumAF-3
- ❑ 94OPC-200
- ❑ 94OPCAllR-3
- ❑ 94OPCJumA-3
- ❑ 94OscMayR-17
- ❑ 94Pac-540
- ❑ 94Pac-655
- ❑ 94PacGolP-11
- ❑ 94PacSilP-28
- ❑ 94PacSilPC-28
- ❑ 94PanSti-12
- ❑ 94PanSti-13
- ❑ 94PanSti-261
- ❑ 94Pin-26
- ❑ 94PinArtP-26
- ❑ 94PinMusC-26
- ❑ 94PinRunC-RC23
- ❑ 94PinTeaP-7
- ❑ 94PinTheN-2
- ❑ 94PinTri-TR8
- ❑ 94Pos-11
- ❑ 94PosCan-11
- ❑ 94ProMag-121
- ❑ 94RedFolMI-29
- ❑ 94Sco-1
- ❑ 94Sco-632
- ❑ 94ScoCyc-TC16
- ❑ 94ScoGolR-1
- ❑ 94ScoGolR-632
- ❑ 94ScoGolS-1
- ❑ 94ScoSam-1
- ❑ 94ScoSam-1GR
- ❑ 94Sel-211
- ❑ 94SelCroC-CC6
- ❑ 94SelSki-SK6
- ❑ 94SP-90
- ❑ 94SPDieC-90
- ❑ 94Spo-91
- ❑ 94Spo-190
- ❑ 94SpoFanA-AS6
- ❑ 94SpoRooGGG-GG8
- ❑ 94SPPre-WR1
- ❑ 94StaClu-238
- ❑ 94StaClu-259
- ❑ 94StaClu-532
- ❑ 94StaCluDD-DD6
- ❑ 94StaCluF-F3
- ❑ 94StaCluFDI-238
- ❑ 94StaCluFDI-259
- ❑ 94StaCluFDI-532
- ❑ 94StaCluFJ-F3
- ❑ 94StaCluGR-238
- ❑ 94StaCluGR-259
- ❑ 94StaCluGR-532
- ❑ 94StaCluMO-24
- ❑ 94StaCluMOF-1
- ❑ 94StaCluMOP-238
- ❑ 94StaCluMOP-259
- ❑ 94StaCluMOP-532
- ❑ 94StaCluMOP-F3
- ❑ 94StaCluMOP-DD6
- ❑ 94StaCluP-238
- ❑ 94StaCluT-1
- ❑ 94StaCluTF-2
- ❑ 94StaCluTFDI-1
- ❑ 94Stu-83
- ❑ 94StuEdiC-1
- ❑ 94StuHer-1
- ❑ 94StuPro-83
- ❑ 94StuSerS-2
- ❑ 94StuSerSG-2
- ❑ 94SucSav-19
- ❑ 94TomPiz-3
- ❑ 94Top-390
- ❑ 94Top-605
- ❑ 94Top-700
- ❑ 94TopBlaG-27
- ❑ 94TopGol-390
- ❑ 94TopGol-605
- ❑ 94TopGol-700
- ❑ 94TopPre-2
- ❑ 94TopSpa-390
- ❑ 94TopSpa-605
- ❑ 94TopSpa-700
- ❑ 94TopSupS-5
- ❑ 94TriPla-102
- ❑ 94TriPlaBS-4
- ❑ 94TriPlaM-12
- ❑ 94TriPlaP-3
- ❑ 94Ult-286
- ❑ 94UltAllS-16
- ❑ 94UltAwaW-15
- ❑ 94UltAwaW-20
- ❑ 94UltHitM-3
- ❑ 94UltHomRK-7
- ❑ 94UltOnBL-2
- ❑ 94UltRBIK-7
- ❑ 94UppDec-38
- ❑ 94UppDec-280
- ❑ 94UppDec-400
- ❑ 94UppDecAJ-35
- ❑ 94UppDecAJG-35
- ❑ 94UppDecDC-W1
- ❑ 94UppDecED-38
- ❑ 94UppDecED-280
- ❑ 94UppDecED-400
- ❑ 94UppDecMLS-MM3
- ❑ 94UppDecMLSED-MM3
- ❑ 94USPlaCA-1C
- ❑ 94USPlaCA-11D
- ❑ 95Baz-20
- ❑ 95BazRedH-RH3
- ❑ 95Bow-376
- ❑ 95BowBes-R13
- ❑ 95BowBesR-R13
- ❑ 95ClaFanFPCP-1
- ❑ 95ClaPhoC-47
- ❑ 95ColCho-60
- ❑ 95ColCho-82
- ❑ 95ColCho-86
- ❑ 95ColChoCtA-2
- ❑ 95ColChoCtAGR-2
- ❑ 95ColChoCtG-CG3
- ❑ 95ColChoCtG-CG3B
- ❑ 95ColChoCtG-CG3C
- ❑ 95ColChoCtGE-3
- ❑ 95ColChoCtGG-CG3
- ❑ 95ColChoCtGG-CG3B
- ❑ 95ColChoCtGG-CG3C
- ❑ 95ColChoCtGGE-3
- ❑ 95ColChoGS-60
- ❑ 95ColChoGS-82
- ❑ 95ColChoGS-86
- ❑ 95ColChoSE-105
- ❑ 95ColChoSE-259
- ❑ 95ColChoSEGS-105
- ❑ 95ColChoSEGS-259
- ❑ 95ColChoSESS-105
- ❑ 95ColChoSESS-259
- ❑ 95ColChoSS-60
- ❑ 95ColChoSS-82
- ❑ 95ColChoSS-86
- ❑ 95Don-8
- ❑ 95DonAll-NL7
- ❑ 95DonBomS-3
- ❑ 95DonDom-7
- ❑ 95DonEli-56
- ❑ 95DonLonBL-7
- ❑ 95DonPreP-8
- ❑ 95DonTopotO-349
- ❑ 95Emo-192
- ❑ 95EmoMas-1
- ❑ 95EmoN-3
- ❑ 95Fin-192
- ❑ 95FinPowK-PK17
- ❑ 95FinRef-192
- ❑ 95Fla-207
- ❑ 95FlaHotG-2
- ❑ 95FlaHotN-3
- ❑ 95FlaOutP-3
- ❑ 95Fle-574
- ❑ 95FleAllF-6
- ❑ 95FleAllS-6
- ❑ 95FleLumC-3
- ❑ 95FleUpdDT-3
- ❑ 95FleUpdH-3
- ❑ 95FleUpdSL-2
- ❑ 95GiaMot-3
- ❑ 95KinDis-4
- ❑ 95Kra-18
- ❑ 95Lea-279
- ❑ 95LeaGolS-5
- ❑ 95LeaGreG-3
- ❑ 95LeaHeaftH-4
- ❑ 95LeaLim-11
- ❑ 95LeaLimG-4
- ❑ 95LeaLimIBP-15
- ❑ 95LeaLimL-2
- ❑ 95LeaOpeD-3
- ❑ 95NatPac-7
- ❑ 95Pac-373
- ❑ 95PacGolCDC-15
- ❑ 95PacGolP-13
- ❑ 95PacPri-120
- ❑ 95PanSti-73
- ❑ 95Pin-272
- ❑ 95Pin-299
- ❑ 95PinArtP-272
- ❑ 95PinArtP-299
- ❑ 95PinFan-24
- ❑ 95PinGatA-GA6
- ❑ 95PinMusC-272
- ❑ 95PinMusC-299
- ❑ 95PinPer-PP3
- ❑ 95PinPin-13
- ❑ 95PinPinR-13
- ❑ 95PinRedH-RH6
- ❑ 95PinTeaP-TP7
- ❑ 95PinWhiH-WH6
- ❑ 95PirCocP-19
- ❑ 95Pos-11
- ❑ 95PosCan-17
- ❑ 95RedFol-1
- ❑ 95Sco-30
- ❑ 95Sco-562
- ❑ 95ScoDouGC-GC3
- ❑ 95ScoGolR-30
- ❑ 95ScoGolR-562
- ❑ 95ScoHaloG-HG16
- ❑ 95ScoPlaTS-30
- ❑ 95ScoPlaTS-562
- ❑ 95ScoRul-SR9
- ❑ 95ScoRulJ-SR9
- ❑ 95Sel-46
- ❑ 95Sel-246
- ❑ 95SelArtP-46
- ❑ 95SelArtP-246
- ❑ 95SelBigS-BS9
- ❑ 95SelCer-1
- ❑ 95SelCerC-6
- ❑ 95SelCerGT-6
- ❑ 95SelCerMG-1
- ❑ 95SP-115
- ❑ 95SPCha-96
- ❑ 95SPChaDC-96
- ❑ 95SPChaDFC-9
- ❑ 95SPChaFCDC-9
- ❑ 95Spo-53
- ❑ 95Spo-170
- ❑ 95SpoArtP-53
- ❑ 95SpoArtP-170
- ❑ 95SpoDet-DE6
- ❑ 95SpoDouT-9
- ❑ 95SpoHamT-HT7
- ❑ 95SpoPro-PM10
- ❑ 95SPPlaP-PP2
- ❑ 95SPSil-115
- ❑ 95StaClu-271
- ❑ 95StaClu-509
- ❑ 95StaCluCC-CC27
- ❑ 95StaCluCT-19
- ❑ 95StaCluMO-8
- ❑ 95StaCluMOP-271
- ❑ 95StaCluMOP-509
- ❑ 95StaCluMOP-CC27
- ❑ 95StaCluMOP-PZ3
- ❑ 95StaCluMOP-RL30
- ❑ 95StaCluMOP-SS2
- ❑ 95StaCluMOP-VRE1
- ❑ 95StaCluPZ-PZ3
- ❑ 95StaCluRL-RL30
- ❑ 95StaCluSS-SS2
- ❑ 95StaCluSTWS-271
- ❑ 95StaCluSTWS-509
- ❑ 95StaCluVE-VRE1
- ❑ 95StaCluVR-136
- ❑ 95StaCluVRMO-136
- ❑ 95Stu-7
- ❑ 95StuGolS-7
- ❑ 95StuPlaS-7
- ❑ 95Sum-9
- ❑ 95Sum-179
- ❑ 95Sum-199
- ❑ 95SumBigB-BB6
- ❑ 95SumNthD-9
- ❑ 95SumNthD-179
- ❑ 95SumNthD-199
- ❑ 95TomPiz-20
- ❑ 95Top-100
- ❑ 95Top-388
- ❑ 95TopCyb-64
- ❑ 95TopCybSiR-1
- ❑ 95TopD3-24
- ❑ 95TopEmb-120
- ❑ 95TopEmbGI-120
- ❑ 95TopFinIns-7
- ❑ 95TopLeaL-LL8
- ❑ 95TopTra-3T
- ❑ 95TopTra-161T
- ❑ 95TopTraPB-3
- ❑ 95UC3-18
- ❑ 95UC3-128
- ❑ 95UC3ArtP-18
- ❑ 95UC3ArtP-128
- ❑ 95UC3CycS-CS5
- ❑ 95UC3InM-IM5
- ❑ 95Ult-442
- ❑ 95UltAllS-5
- ❑ 95UltAllSGM-5
- ❑ 95UltAwaW-15
- ❑ 95UltAwaWGM-15
- ❑ 95UltGolM-442
- ❑ 95UltHitM-4
- ❑ 95UltHitMGM-4
- ❑ 95UltHomRK-8
- ❑ 95UltHomRKGM-8
- ❑ 95UltOnBL-5
- ❑ 95UltOnBLGM-5
- ❑ 95UltPowP-5
- ❑ 95UltPowPGM-5
- ❑ 95UppDec-103
- ❑ 95UppDec-335
- ❑ 95UppDecED-103
- ❑ 95UppDecED-335
- ❑ 95UppDecEDG-103
- ❑ 95UppDecEDG-335
- ❑ 95UppDecPAW-H7
- ❑ 95UppDecPAWE-H7
- ❑ 95UppDecPC-MLB8
- ❑ 95UppDecPLL-R7
- ❑ 95UppDecPLL-R17
- ❑ 95UppDecPLLE-R7
- ❑ 95UppDecPLLE-R17
- ❑ 95UppDecSE-70
- ❑ 95UppDecSEG-70
- ❑ 95USPlaCMLA-4H
- ❑ 95USPlaCMLA-10C
- ❑ 95Zen-5
- ❑ 95ZenAllS-13
- ❑ 95ZenAllS-18
- ❑ 95ZenZ-6
- ❑ 96Baz-118
- ❑ 96Bow-78
- ❑ 96BowBes-10
- ❑ 96BowBesAR-10
- ❑ 96BowBesMI-6
- ❑ 96BowBesMIAR-6
- ❑ 96BowBesMIR-6
- ❑ 96BowBesP-BBP4
- ❑ 96BowBesPAR-BBP4
- ❑ 96BowBesPR-BBP4
- ❑ 96BowBesR-10
- ❑ 96BowFoi-78
- ❑ 96Cir-192
- ❑ 96Cir-197
- ❑ 96CirAcc-29
- ❑ 96CirBos-49
- ❑ 96CirRav-192
- ❑ 96CirRav-197
- ❑ 96ColCho-108
- ❑ 96ColCho-300
- ❑ 96ColCho-409
- ❑ 96ColChoCtG-CG23
- ❑ 96ColChoCtG-CG23B
- ❑ 96ColChoCtG-CG23C
- ❑ 96ColChoCtGE-CR23
- ❑ 96ColChoCtGG-CG23
- ❑ 96ColChoCtGG-CG23B
- ❑ 96ColChoCtGG-CG23C
- ❑ 96ColChoCtGGE-CR23
- ❑ 96ColChoGS-108
- ❑ 96ColChoGS-300
- ❑ 96ColChoGS-409
- ❑ 96ColChoSS-108
- ❑ 96ColChoSS-300
- ❑ 96ColChoSS-409
- ❑ 96ColChoYMtP-8
- ❑ 96ColChoYMtP-8A
- ❑ 96ColChoYMtPGS-8
- ❑ 96ColChoYMtPGS-8A
- ❑ 96DenHol-8
- ❑ 96DenHolGS-6
- ❑ 96DenHolGSAP-6
- ❑ 96Don-216
- ❑ 96DonDiaK-8
- ❑ 96DonHitL-10
- ❑ 96DonLonBL-1
- ❑ 96DonPowA-2
- ❑ 96DonPowADC-2
- ❑ 96DonPreP-216
- ❑ 96DonPurP-2
- ❑ 96DonRouT-2
- ❑ 96DonSam-2
- ❑ 96DonSho-2
- ❑ 96EmoLegoB-2
- ❑ 96EmoN-2
- ❑ 96EmoXL-286
- ❑ 96EmoXLD-2
- ❑ 96Fin-B146
- ❑ 96Fin-B240
- ❑ 96Fin-G105
- ❑ 96FinRef-B146
- ❑ 96FinRef-B240
- ❑ 96FinRef-G105
- ❑ 96Fla-384
- ❑ 96FlaDiaC-3
- ❑ 96FlaHotG-2
- ❑ 96FlaPow-2
- ❑ 96Fle-583
- ❑ 96FleChe-1
- ❑ 96FleGolM-2
- ❑ 96FleLumC-3
- ❑ 96FleTeaL-28
- ❑ 96FleTif-583
- ❑ 96FleUpd-U215
- ❑ 96FleUpd-U246
- ❑ 96FleUpd-2
- ❑ 96FleUpdH-4
- ❑ 96FleUpdSL-2
- ❑ 96FleUpdSS-2
- ❑ 96FleUpdTC-U215
- ❑ 96FleUpdTC-U246
- ❑ 96FleZon-2
- ❑ 96GiaMot-2
- ❑ 96Kin-23
- ❑ 96Lea-78
- ❑ 96LeaAllGMC-14
- ❑ 96LeaAllGMCG-14
- ❑ 96LeaLim-71
- ❑ 96LeaLimG-71
- ❑ 96LeaLimPC-9
- ❑ 96LeaPicP-12
- ❑ 96LeaPre-94
- ❑ 96LeaPreP-94
- ❑ 96LeaPrePB-78
- ❑ 96LeaPrePG-78
- ❑ 96LeaPrePS-78
- ❑ 96LeaPreSG-6
- ❑ 96LeaPreSP-6
- ❑ 96LeaPreSta-10
- ❑ 96LeaPreSte-6
- ❑ 96LeaSig-89
- ❑ 96LeaSigPPG-89
- ❑ 96LeaSigPPP-89
- ❑ 96LeaTotB-4
- ❑ 96LibSpo-16
- ❑ 96MetUni-241
- ❑ 96MetUniHM-2
- ❑ 96MetUniML-1
- ❑ 96MetUniP-241
- ❑ 96MetUniT-2
- ❑ 96Pac-202
- ❑ 96PacGolCD-DC36
- ❑ 96PacPri-P65
- ❑ 96PacPriFB-FB3
- ❑ 96PacPriG-P65
- ❑ 96PacPriRHS-RH15
- ❑ 96PanSti-107
- ❑ 96Pin-148
- ❑ 96Pin-199
- ❑ 96Pin-208
- ❑ 96Pin-260
- ❑ 96PinAfi-80
- ❑ 96PinAfiAP-80
- ❑ 96PinAfiFPP-80
- ❑ 96PinAfiR-14
- ❑ 96PinAfiR-17
- ❑ 96PinAfiR-19

❑ 96PinAfiR-22
❑ 96PinAfiR-23
❑ 96PinAfiR-24
❑ 96PinAfiSP-7
❑ 96PinArtP-75
❑ 96PinArtP-108
❑ 96PinArtP-160
❑ 96PinEssotG-18
❑ 96PinFan-16
❑ 96PinFirR-9
❑ 96PinFoil-208
❑ 96PinFoil-260
❑ 96PinPow-5
❑ 96PinSky-10
❑ 96PinSlu-4
❑ 96PinSta-75
❑ 96PinSta-108
❑ 96PinSta-160
❑ 96PinTeaP-5
❑ 96PinTeaS-12
❑ 96Pro-3
❑ 96ProMagA-14
❑ 96ProMagDM-20
❑ 96ProSta-52
❑ 96RedF-9
❑ 96SchDis-20
❑ 96Sco-340
❑ 96ScoAll-7
❑ 96ScoBigB-6
❑ 96ScoDiaA-6
❑ 96ScoDreT-6
❑ 96ScoDugC-B65
❑ 96ScoDugCAP-B65
❑ 96ScoGolS-15
❑ 96ScoNumG-5
❑ 96ScoPowP-13
❑ 96ScoRef-11
❑ 96ScoTitT-17
❑ 96Sel-101
❑ 96Sel-156
❑ 96SelArtP-101
❑ 96SelArtP-156
❑ 96SelCer-31
❑ 96SelCerAP-31
❑ 96SelCerCB-31
❑ 96SelCerCR-31
❑ 96SelCerIP-9
❑ 96SelCerMB-31
❑ 96SelCerMG-31
❑ 96SelCerMR-31
❑ 96SelCerSF-16
❑ 96SelClaTF-18
❑ 96SelEnF-6
❑ 96SelTeaN-18
❑ 96SP-166
❑ 96SPBasH-84
❑ 96SPMarM-MM8
❑ 96SPMarMDC-8
❑ 96Spo-5
❑ 96Spo-112
❑ 96SpoArtP-5
❑ 96SpoArtP-112
❑ 96SpoDouT-8
❑ 96SpoHitP-16
❑ 96SpoPowS-16
❑ 96SpoPro-16
❑ 96SPPreF-5
❑ 96SPSpeFX-25
❑ 96SPSpeFXDC-25
❑ 96SPx-51
❑ 96SPxBoufG-3
❑ 96SPxGol-51
❑ 96StaClu-202
❑ 96StaClu-402
❑ 96StaCluB&B-BB2
❑ 96StaCluEPB-402
❑ 96StaCluEPG-402
❑ 96StaCluEPS-402
❑ 96StaCluEWB-EW7
❑ 96StaCluEWG-EW7
❑ 96StaCluEWS-EW7
❑ 96StaCluMet-M2
❑ 96StaCluMM-MM7
❑ 96StaCluMO-7
❑ 96StaCluMOP-202
❑ 96StaCluMOP-402
❑ 96StaCluMOP-M2
❑ 96StaCluMOP-BB2
❑ 96StaCluMOP-MM7
❑ 96StaCluMOP-PC2
❑ 96StaCluMOP-PS14
❑ 96StaCluPC-PC2
❑ 96StaCluPS-PS14
❑ 96Stu-76
❑ 96StuHitP-7
❑ 96StuPrePB-76
❑ 96StuPrePG-76
❑ 96StuPrePS-76
❑ 96StuStaGS-10
❑ 96Sum-107
❑ 96SumAbo&B-107
❑ 96SumArtP-107
❑ 96SumBal-13
❑ 96SumBigB-5
❑ 96SumBigBM-5
❑ 96SumFoi-107
❑ 96SumPos-7
❑ 96TeaOut-10
❑ 96TeaOut-C94
❑ 96Top-10
❑ 96Top-300
❑ 96TopChr-10
❑ 96TopChr-119
❑ 96TopChrMotG-18
❑ 96TopChrMotGR-18
❑ 96TopChrR-10
❑ 96TopChrR-119
❑ 96TopChrWC-WC3
❑ 96TopChrWCR-WC3
❑ 96TopClaC-CC6
❑ 96TopGal-156
❑ 96TopGalPPI-156
❑ 96TopLas-37
❑ 96TopLasPC-10
❑ 96TopLasSS-2
❑ 96TopMasotG-18
❑ 96TopMysF-M13
❑ 96TopMysFR-M13
❑ 96TopPowB-10
❑ 96TopPro-NL3
❑ 96TopRoaW-RW4
❑ 96TopWreC-WC3
❑ 96Ult-290
❑ 96Ult-577
❑ 96UltCalttH-1
❑ 96UltCalttHGM-1
❑ 96UltChe-A2
❑ 96UltCheGM-A2
❑ 96UltDiaP-2
❑ 96UltDiaPGM-2
❑ 96UltGolM-290
❑ 96UltGolM-577
❑ 96UltHitM-2
❑ 96UltHitMGM-2
❑ 96UltHomRK-3
❑ 96UltHomRKGM-3
❑ 96UltHomRKR-3
❑ 96UltHomRKRGM-3
❑ 96UltOn-L-2
❑ 96UltOn-LGM-2
❑ 96UltPowP-2
❑ 96UltPowPGM-2
❑ 96UltPriL-15
❑ 96UltPriLGM-15
❑ 96UltPro-NNO
❑ 96UltRaw-2
❑ 96UltRawGM-2
❑ 96UltRBIK-4
❑ 96UltRBIKGM-4
❑ 96UltSeaC-1
❑ 96UltSeaCGM-1
❑ 96UltThu-2
❑ 96UltThuGM-2
❑ 96UppDec-195
❑ 96UppDec-373
❑ 96UppDecA-8
❑ 96UppDecDD-DD33
❑ 96UppDecDDG-DD33
❑ 96UppDecDDS-DD33
❑ 96UppDecG-GF3
❑ 96UppDecHC-HC12
❑ 96UppDecPD-PD2
❑ 96UppDecPHE-H33
❑ 96UppDecPRE-R32
❑ 96UppDecPRE-R43
❑ 96UppDecPRE-R55
❑ 96UppDecPreH-H33
❑ 96UppDecPreR-R32
❑ 96UppDecPreR-R43
❑ 96UppDecPreR-R55
❑ 96UppDecRCJ-2
❑ 96UppDecRipC-2
❑ 96UppDecRunP-RP3
❑ 96UppDecVJLS-VJ4
❑ 96Zen-29
❑ 96Zen-144
❑ 96ZenArtP-29
❑ 96ZenArtP-144
❑ 96ZenMoz-4
❑ 96ZenZ-14
❑ 97AriStaBG-6
❑ 97Bow-244
❑ 97BowBes-73
❑ 97BowBesAR-73
❑ 97BowBesJ-73
❑ 97BowBesJAR-73
❑ 97BowBesJR-73
❑ 97BowBesMI-MI5
❑ 97BowBesMIAR-MI5
❑ 97BowBesMIARI-MI5
❑ 97BowBesMII-MI5
❑ 97BowBesMIR-MI5
❑ 97BowBesMIRI-MI5
❑ 97BowBesP-3
❑ 97BowBesPAR-3
❑ 97BowBesPR-3
❑ 97BowBesR-73
❑ 97BowChr-69
❑ 97BowChrI-69
❑ 97BowChrIR-69
❑ 97BowChrR-69
❑ 97BowInt-244
❑ 97Cir-25
❑ 97CirBos-3
❑ 97CirLimA-3
❑ 97CirRav-25
❑ 97CirRavR-2
❑ 97CirSupB-3
❑ 97ColCho-225
❑ 97ColChoAC-24
❑ 97ColChoBS-14
❑ 97ColChoBSGS-14
❑ 97ColChoCtG-26A
❑ 97ColChoCtG-26B
❑ 97ColChoCtG-26C
❑ 97ColChoCtGE-CG26
❑ 97ColChoCtGIW-CG26
❑ 97ColChoNF-NF6
❑ 97ColChoPP-PP9
❑ 97ColChoPPG-PP9
❑ 97ColChoPPJ-PP9
❑ 97ColChoS-15
❑ 97ColChoSR-5
❑ 97ColChoTBS-40
❑ 97ColChoTBSWH-40
❑ 97ColChoTotT-T26
❑ 97CraJac-8
❑ 97DenHol-27
❑ 97Don-167
❑ 97Don-269
❑ 97Don-421
❑ 97Don-438
❑ 97DonArmaD-10
❑ 97DonEli-16
❑ 97DonEli-4
❑ 97DonEliGS-16
❑ 97DonEliLaL-7
❑ 97DonFraFea-7
❑ 97DonGolPP-167
❑ 97DonGolPP-269
❑ 97DonGolPP-421
❑ 97DonGolPP-438
❑ 97DonLim-6
❑ 97DonLim-89
❑ 97DonLim-123
❑ 97DonLimE-6
❑ 97DonLimE-89
❑ 97DonLimE-123
❑ 97DonLimENG-123
❑ 97DonLimFotG-10
❑ 97DonLimFotG-40
❑ 97DonPowA-16
❑ 97DonPowADC-16
❑ 97DonPre-94
❑ 97DonPre-182
❑ 97DonPreCttC-94
❑ 97DonPreCttC-182
❑ 97DonPrePM-17
❑ 97DonPreS-11
❑ 97DonPreSS-11
❑ 97DonPreTB-3
❑ 97DonPreTBG-3
❑ 97DonPreTF-3
❑ 97DonPreTP-3
❑ 97DonPreTPG-3
❑ 97DonRocL-11
❑ 97DonSig-30
❑ 97DonSigAC-15
❑ 97DonSigAM-15
❑ 97DonSigPPP-30
❑ 97DonSilPP-167
❑ 97DonSilPP-269
❑ 97DonSilPP-421
❑ 97DonSilPP-438
❑ 97DonTeaSMVP-12
❑ 97DonVxP1-25
❑ 97E-X2-95
❑ 97E-X2ACA-9
❑ 97E-X2Cred-95
❑ 97E-X2EssCre-95
❑ 97E-X2Hall-11
❑ 97Fin-1
❑ 97Fin-175
❑ 97Fin-313
❑ 97FinEmb-175
❑ 97FinEmb-313
❑ 97FinEmbR-175
❑ 97FinEmbR-313
❑ 97FinPro-1
❑ 97FinRef-1
❑ 97FinRef-175
❑ 97FinRef-313
❑ 97FlaShoHG-2
❑ 97FlaShoLC-25
❑ 97FlaShoLeg0-25
❑ 97FlaShoLeg1-25
❑ 97FlaShoM-A25
❑ 97FlaShoM-B25
❑ 97FlaShoM-C25
❑ 97FlaShoR0-25
❑ 97FlaShoR1-25
❑ 97FlaShoR2-25
❑ 97Fle-477
❑ 97Fle-698
❑ 97Fle-744
❑ 97FleBleB-2
❑ 97FleDecoE-2
❑ 97FleDecoERT-2
❑ 97FleDiaT-2
❑ 97FleGolM-1
❑ 97FleGouG-1
❑ 97FleGouGF-1
❑ 97FleHea-3
❑ 97FleLumC-4
❑ 97FleMilDM-4
❑ 97FleMilDMR-4
❑ 97FleNig&D-1
❑ 97FleSoaS-2
❑ 97FleSoaSG-2
❑ 97FleTeaL-28
❑ 97FleTif-477
❑ 97FleTif-698
❑ 97FleTif-744
❑ 97FleZon-3
❑ 97HigMinM-15
❑ 97HigMinM-16
❑ 97HigMinMCT-7
❑ 97HigMinMCT-8
❑ 97KinB-2
❑ 97Lea-65
❑ 97Lea-354
❑ 97LeaFraM-65
❑ 97LeaFraM-354
❑ 97LeaFraMDC-65
❑ 97LeaFraMDC-354
❑ 97LeaGet-8
❑ 97LeaGolS-16
❑ 97LeaLeaotN-1
❑ 97LeaStaS-11
❑ 97LeaWarT-3
❑ 97MetUni-242
❑ 97MetUniBF-3
❑ 97MetUniMF-3
❑ 97MetUniML-3
❑ 97NewPin-117
❑ 97NewPin-184
❑ 97NewPin-192
❑ 97NewPinAP-117
❑ 97NewPinAP-184
❑ 97NewPinAP-192
❑ 97NewPinIE-9
❑ 97NewPinKtP-6
❑ 97NewPinMC-117
❑ 97NewPinMC-184
❑ 97NewPinMC-192
❑ 97NewPinPP-117
❑ 97NewPinPP-184
❑ 97NewPinPP-192
❑ 97NewPinPP-I9D
❑ 97NewPinPP-K6
❑ 97Pac-440
❑ 97PacCar-36
❑ 97PacCarM-36
❑ 97PacCerCGT-12
❑ 97PacFirD-20
❑ 97PacGolCD-36
❑ 97PacLigB-440
❑ 97PacPri-147
❑ 97PacPriGA-GA32
❑ 97PacPriGotD-GD213
❑ 97PacPriLB-147
❑ 97PacPriP-147
❑ 97PacSil-440
❑ 97PacTriCD-20
❑ 97Pin-97
❑ 97PinArtP-PP97
❑ 97PinCar-12
❑ 97PinCer-1
❑ 97PinCerCMGT-12
❑ 97PinCerCT-12
❑ 97PinCerMBla-1
❑ 97PinCerMBlu-1
❑ 97PinCerMG-1
❑ 97PinCerMR-1
❑ 97PinCerR-1
❑ 97PinEpixGO-E22
❑ 97PinEpixPE-E22
❑ 97PinFan-FF10
❑ 97PinHom-13
❑ 97PinHom-14
❑ 97PinIns-60
❑ 97PinInsC-6
❑ 97PinInsCE-60
❑ 97PinInsDD-3
❑ 97PinInsDE-60
❑ 97PinInsFS-2
❑ 97PinMin-18
❑ 97PinMinB-18
❑ 97PinMinCB-18
❑ 97PinMinCG-18
❑ 97PinMinCGR-18
❑ 97PinMinCN-18
❑ 97PinMinCSS-18
❑ 97PinMinG-18
❑ 97PinMinS-18
❑ 97PinMusC-97
❑ 97PinPrePla-97
❑ 97PinTeaP-6
❑ 97PinTeaP-10
❑ 97PinTotCPB-1
❑ 97PinTotCPG-1
❑ 97PinTotCPR-1
❑ 97PinX-P-30
❑ 97PinX-PMoS-30
❑ 97PinX-PSfF-10
❑ 97PinX-PSfFU-10
❑ 97PreCon-15
❑ 97Sco-91
❑ 97Sco-504
❑ 97ScoArtPWB-91
❑ 97ScoArtPWB-504
❑ 97ScoBla-5
❑ 97ScoHigZ-6
❑ 97ScoPreS-91
❑ 97ScoResC-504
❑ 97ScoShoS-91
❑ 97ScoShoS-504
❑ 97ScoShoSAP-91
❑ 97ScoShoSAP-504
❑ 97ScoTitT-15
❑ 97Sel-26
❑ 97SelArtP-26
❑ 97SelCom-26
❑ 97SelRegG-26
❑ 97SelToootT-9
❑ 97SelToootTMB-9
❑ 97SP-160
❑ 97SPGamF-GF9
❑ 97SPInsI-20
❑ 97SPMarM-MM3
❑ 97SpoIll-121
❑ 97SpoIll-169
❑ 97SpoIllEE-121
❑ 97SpoIllEE-169
❑ 97SpoIllGS-20
❑ 97SPSpeF-3
❑ 97SPSpxF-4
❑ 97SPSPxFA-4
❑ 97SPx-43
❑ 97SPxBoufG-17
❑ 97SPxBro-43
❑ 97SPxCorotG-1
❑ 97SPxGol-43
❑ 97SPxGraF-43
❑ 97SPxSil-43
❑ 97SPxSte-43
❑ 97StaClu-15
❑ 97StaClu-386
❑ 97StaCluFR-F3
❑ 97StaCluFW-F3
❑ 97StaCluI-I5
❑ 97StaCluMat-15
❑ 97StaCluMOP-15
❑ 97StaCluMOP-386
❑ 97StaCluMOP-I5
❑ 97StaCluMOP-FB3
❑ 97StaCluMOP-PG4
❑ 97StaCluMOP-PL3
❑ 97StaCluPG-PG4
❑ 97StaCluPL-PL3
❑ 97StrAll-10
❑ 97Stu-59
❑ 97StuMasS-4
❑ 97StuMasS8-4
❑ 97StuPor8-14
❑ 97StuPrePG-59
❑ 97StuPrePS-59
❑ 97Top-1
❑ 97Top-465
❑ 97TopAll-AS12
❑ 97TopChr-1
❑ 97TopChrAS-AS12
❑ 97TopChrR-1
❑ 97TopChrSAR-AS12
❑ 97TopGal-42
❑ 97TopGalPMS-9
❑ 97TopGalPMSSS-9
❑ 97TopGalPPI-42
❑ 97TopHobM-HM16
❑ 97TopIntF-ILM1
❑ 97TopIntFR-ILM1
❑ 97TopMemO5-8
❑ 97TopScr-3
❑ 97TopScrT-3
❑ 97TopSta-42
❑ 97TopSta97AS-AS15
❑ 97TopStaAM-42
❑ 97TopSweS-SS4
❑ 97TopTeaT-TT7
❑ 97UD3-9
❑ 97UD3Marq-MA4
❑ 97Ult-290
❑ 97UltBasR-1
❑ 97UltChe-A2
❑ 97UltDiaP-2
❑ 97UltDouT-20
❑ 97UltFamGam-17
❑ 97UltFieC-4
❑ 97UltGolME-290
❑ 97UltHRK-2
❑ 97UltPlaME-290
❑ 97UltPowP-A2
❑ 97UltPowP-B12
❑ 97UltRBIK-4
❑ 97UltSeaC-3
❑ 97UltThu-1
❑ 97UltTop3-22
❑ 97UltTop3GM-22
❑ 97UppDec-152
❑ 97UppDec-170
❑ 97UppDec-215
❑ 97UppDec-323
❑ 97UppDecAG-AG17
❑ 97UppDecHC-HC11
❑ 97UppDecLDC-LD9
❑ 97UppDecMM-A8
❑ 97UppDecP-24
❑ 97UppDecPE-24
❑ 97UppDecPP-PP16
❑ 97UppDecPPJ-PP16
❑ 97UppDecRP-RP2
❑ 97UppDecSA-2
❑ 97UppDecSAG-2
❑ 97Zen-14
❑ 97Zen8x10-16
❑ 97Zen8x1D-16
❑ 98Bow-225
❑ 98BowBes-3
❑ 98BowBesAR-3
❑ 98BowBesMIF-MI18
❑ 98BowBesMIFAR-MI18
❑ 98BowBesMIFR-MI18
❑ 98BowBesR-3
❑ 98BowChr-225
❑ 98BowChrGA-225
❑ 98BowChrGAR-225
❑ 98BowChrI-225
❑ 98BowChrIR-225
❑ 98BowChrR-225
❑ 98BowGolA-225
❑ 98BowInt-225
❑ 98CirThu-75
❑ 98CirThuB-2
❑ 98CirThuRav-75
❑ 98CirThuRR-2
❑ 98CirThuSupRav-75
❑ 98CirThuTB-2
❑ 98ColCho-11
❑ 98ColCho-278
❑ 98ColCho-490
❑ 98ColChoB5-490
❑ 98ColChoCtG-CG30A
❑ 98ColChoCtG-CG30B
❑ 98ColChoCtG-CG30C
❑ 98ColChoCtGExch-CG30
❑ 98ColChoCtGIW-CG30

❑ 98ColChoER-ER25
❑ 98ColChoGJ5-278
❑ 98ColChoMBH-24
❑ 98ColChoRJ-SQ73
❑ 98ColChoS'-24
❑ 98ColChoSQ-SQ39
❑ 98ColChoSQ-SQ73
❑ 98ColChoSQDouble-15
❑ 98ColChoSQHR-15
❑ 98ColChoSQSingle-15
❑ 98ColChoSQTriple-15
❑ 98CroRoy-121
❑ 98CroRoyAS-20
❑ 98CroRoyDK-19
❑ 98CroRoyFoB-18
❑ 98CroRoyFoBA-18
❑ 98Don-37
❑ 98Don-347
❑ 98Don-414
❑ 98Don-416
❑ 98DonCol-37
❑ 98DonColE-416
❑ 98DonColE-533
❑ 98DonColL-371
❑ 98DonColP-569
❑ 98DonColP-735
❑ 98DonColS-37
❑ 98DonCruG-99
❑ 98DonCruP-99
❑ 98DonCruR-99
❑ 98DonDay-10
❑ 98DonDom-19
❑ 98DonEli-16
❑ 98DonEli-133
❑ 98DonEliA-16
❑ 98DonEliA-133
❑ 98DonEliC-23
❑ 98DonElil-19
❑ 98DonEliMC-23
❑ 98DonEliPN-8A
❑ 98DonEliPN-8B
❑ 98DonEliPN-8C
❑ 98DonEliPNDC-8A
❑ 98DonEliPNDC-8B
❑ 98DonEliPNDC-8C
❑ 98DonEliPNS-8A
❑ 98DonEliPNS-8B
❑ 98DonEliPNS-8C
❑ 98DonEliS-16
❑ 98DonEliS-133
❑ 98DonGolPP-37
❑ 98DonGolPP-347
❑ 98DonGolPP-414
❑ 98DonGolPP-416
❑ 98DonLonL-4
❑ 98DonPre-19
❑ 98DonPre-185
❑ 98DonPreGES-24
❑ 98DonPreGX-24
❑ 98DonPreGXDC-24
❑ 98DonPrePM-18
❑ 98DonPreSeat-19
❑ 98DonPreSeat-185
❑ 98DonPreTW-30
❑ 98DonPriCD-37
❑ 98DonPriCE-416
❑ 98DonPriCE-533
❑ 98DonPriCL-371
❑ 98DonPriCP-569
❑ 98DonPriCP-735
❑ 98DonProLO-9
❑ 98DonProLPI-3
❑ 98DonProLS-4
❑ 98DonSig-45
❑ 98DonSigAC-12
❑ 98DonSigAM-12
❑ 98DonSigP-45
❑ 98DonSilPP-37
❑ 98DonSilPP-347
❑ 98DonSilPP-414
❑ 98DonSilPP-416
❑ 98DonSonM9-3
❑ 98E-X2-2
❑ 98E-X2Cheap-14
❑ 98E-X2ECFut-2
❑ 98E-X2ECNow-2
❑ 98Fin-257
❑ 98FinCen-C7
❑ 98FinCenR-C7
❑ 98FinMysF1-M22
❑ 98FinMysF1-M25
❑ 98FinMysF1-M28
❑ 98FinMysF1-M29
❑ 98FinMysF2-M13
❑ 98FinMysF2-M16
❑ 98FinMysF2-M17
❑ 98FinMysF2R-M13
❑ 98FinMysF2R-M16
❑ 98FinMysF2R-M17
❑ 98FinMysFR-M22
❑ 98FinMysFR-M25
❑ 98FinMysFR-M28
❑ 98FinMysFR-M29
❑ 98FinNo--257
❑ 98FinNo-R-257
❑ 98FinOve-B6
❑ 98FinOveR-B6
❑ 98FinPowZ-P4
❑ 98FinRef-257
❑ 98FinStaS-SS20
❑ 98FinTheM-TM2
❑ 98FinTheMR-TM2
❑ 98FlaShoLeg0-36
❑ 98FlaShoLeg1-36
❑ 98FlaShoLeg2-36
❑ 98FlaShoLeg3-36
❑ 98FlaShoLegM-36
❑ 98FlaShoR0-36
❑ 98FlaShoR1-36
❑ 98FlaShoR2-36
❑ 98FlaShoR3-36
❑ 98Fle-300
❑ 98Fle-323
❑ 98Fle-577
❑ 98FleDecERT-2
❑ 98FleDecoE-2
❑ 98FleDiaS-2
❑ 98FleIn TC-IC2
❑ 98FleLumC-2
❑ 98FlePowG-3
❑ 98FleUpd-U4
❑ 98FleVin'-53
❑ 98FleVin'C-53
❑ 98FleZon-2
❑ 98GiaMot-2
❑ 98HamHel-4
❑ 98KinDis-2
❑ 98Lea-172
❑ 98LeaFraDA-172
❑ 98LeaFraF-172
❑ 98LeaFraM-172
❑ 98LeaFraM-172
❑ 98LeaFraMDC-172
❑ 98LeaFraMDC-172
❑ 98LeaFraMS-172
❑ 98LeaFraMZ2-172
❑ 98LeaHeaftH-5
❑ 98LeaHeaftHS-5
❑ 98LeaRS-44
❑ 98LeaRS-149
❑ 98LeaRS-182
❑ 98LeaRSCross-5
❑ 98LeaRSGAHSamp-14
❑ 98LeaRSGreAH-14
❑ 98LeaRSHRDerby-6
❑ 98LeaRSLHolo-44
❑ 98LeaRSLHolo-149
❑ 98LeaRSLHolo-182
❑ 98LeaRSLMVP-16
❑ 98LeaRSLMVPPE-16
❑ 98LeaRSLong-44
❑ 98LeaRSLong-149
❑ 98LeaRSLong-182
❑ 98LeaRSSOSamp-1
❑ 98LeaRSStaOva-1
❑ 98LeaRTrue-44
❑ 98LeaRTrue-149
❑ 98LeaRTrue-182
❑ 98LeaStaS-24
❑ 98LeaStaSDC-24
❑ 98MetUni-81
❑ 98MetUni-203
❑ 98MetUniPMG-81
❑ 98MetUniPMG-203
❑ 98Pac-437
❑ 98PacAur-195
❑ 98PacAurCube-15
❑ 98PacAurODLC-15
❑ 98PacAurPF-40
❑ 98PacAurPFC-40
❑ 98PacAurPFPB-40
❑ 98PacAurPFR-40
❑ 98PacAurPFS-40
❑ 98PacGolCDC-28
❑ 98PacHomRH-16
❑ 98PacInCage-15
❑ 98PacInv-142
❑ 98PacInvGems-217
❑ 98PacInvInt-6N
❑ 98PacInvPBlue-142
❑ 98PacInvPhoto-13
❑ 98PacInvSilv-142
❑ 98PacInvTeam-25
❑ 98PacOme-209
❑ 98PacOmeEP-20
❑ 98PacOmeEP1o1-20
❑ 98PacOmeOnIns-36
❑ 98PacOmeR-209
❑ 98PacOnl-655A
❑ 98PacOnl-655B
❑ 98PacOnl-676
❑ 98PacOnlR-655A
❑ 98PacOnlR-655B
❑ 98PacOnlR-676
❑ 98PacOnlWC-655A
❑ 98PacOnlWC-655B
❑ 98PacOnlWC-676
❑ 98PacPar-242
❑ 98PacParC-242
❑ 98PacParCB-8
❑ 98PacParCBPP-8
❑ 98PacParFC-15
❑ 98PacParG-242
❑ 98PacParHS-242
❑ 98PacParI-2
❑ 98PacParPB-242
❑ 98PacParR-242
❑ 98PacParSD-17
❑ 98PacParTC-30
❑ 98PacPlaB-437
❑ 98PacRedT-437
❑ 98PacSil-437
❑ 98PacTeaC-28
❑ 98Pin-23
❑ 98PinArtP-PP23
❑ 98PinEpixGE-E22
❑ 98PinEpixGP-E22
❑ 98PinEpixME-E22
❑ 98PinEpixMO-E22
❑ 98PinEpixMP-E22
❑ 98PinEpixPO-E22
❑ 98PinEpixPP-E22
❑ 98PinHitlH-5
❑ 98PinHitiHS-5
❑ 98PinIns-38
❑ 98PinInsCE-38
❑ 98PinInsDE-38
❑ 98PinInsSG-24AB
❑ 98PinInsSG-24CD
❑ 98PinInsSGS-24AB
❑ 98PinInsSGS-24CD
❑ 98PinMinB-3
❑ 98PinMinCB-3
❑ 98PinMinCBAP-3
❑ 98PinMinCGP-3
❑ 98PinMinCGPAP-3
❑ 98PinMinCN-3
❑ 98PinMinCNAP-3
❑ 98PinMinCSGR-3
❑ 98PinMinDC-3
❑ 98PinMinG-3
❑ 98PinMinMCSS-3
❑ 98PinMinS-3
❑ 98PinMusC-PP23
❑ 98PinPer-19
❑ 98PinPerBB-16
❑ 98PinPerBBSamp-16
❑ 98PinPerBBSO-16
❑ 98PinPerPP-19
❑ 98PinPerSftF-29
❑ 98PinPerSftFShop-2
❑ 98PinPlu-57
❑ 98PinPlu-200
❑ 98PinPluAE-22
❑ 98PinPluAEE-22
❑ 98PinPluAEP-22
❑ 98PinPluAP-PP24
❑ 98PinPluGAP-PP24
❑ 98PinPluLM-26
❑ 98PinPluMAP-PP24
❑ 98PinPluTP-8
❑ 98PinPluTPG-8
❑ 98PinPluTPM-8
❑ 98PinPluY-15
❑ 98PinPreP-23
❑ 98PinPreP-E22
❑ 98PinPreP-H5
❑ 98PreCon-2
❑ 98Revo-127
❑ 98RevoFP-20
❑ 98RevoShow-36
❑ 98RevoSS-127
❑ 98Sco-5
❑ 98ScoAllST-15
❑ 98ScoEpix-E22
❑ 98ScoFirP-11
❑ 98ScoLoaL-LL6
❑ 98ScoRT-10
❑ 98ScoRTSS-PP10
❑ 98ScoRTSSAP-PP10
❑ 98ScoRTSSAP1-PP10
❑ 98ScoSS-PP113
❑ 98ScoSSAP-PP113
❑ 98SkyDugA-46
❑ 98SkyDugADH-DH3
❑ 98SkyDugAFF-FF7
❑ 98SkyDugAIA-46
❑ 98SkyDugAS-SH1
❑ 98SP Aut-175
❑ 98SP Aut-SD20
❑ 98SP AutSD-SD20
❑ 98SP AutSDT-SD20
❑ 98SpollI-13
❑ 98SpollIEE-13
❑ 98SpollIFE-13
❑ 98SpollIODMP-OD26
❑ 98SpollITaN-49
❑ 98SpollITaN-63
❑ 98SpollITaNAotG-AG8
❑ 98SpollITaNEE-49
❑ 98SpollITaNEE-63
❑ 98SpollITaNRtC-RC1
❑ 98SpollIWSF-77
❑ 98SpollIWSFEE-77
❑ 98SpollIWSFFE-77
❑ 98SpollIWSFRJP-2
❑ 98SPxFin-49
❑ 98SPxFin-125
❑ 98SPxFin-164
❑ 98SPxFin-177
❑ 98SPxFin-233
❑ 98SPxFin-358
❑ 98SPxFinR-49
❑ 98SPxFinR-125
❑ 98SPxFinR-164
❑ 98SPxFinR-177
❑ 98SPxFinR-233
❑ 98SPxFinR-358
❑ 98SPxFinS-49
❑ 98SPxFinS-125
❑ 98SPxFinS-164
❑ 98SPxFinS-177
❑ 98SPxFinS-233
❑ 98SPxFinS-358
❑ 98StaCluBP-BP10
❑ 98StaCluFDI-43
❑ 98StaClul-43
❑ 98StaCluNC-NC12
❑ 98StaCluOneK-43
❑ 98StaCluPP-43
❑ 98StaCluRC-RC8
❑ 98StaCluTIII-T15A
❑ 98StaCluTLme-T15A
❑ 98StaCluTLmo-T15A
❑ 98Stu-98
❑ 98StuFF-16
❑ 98StuFFDC-16
❑ 98StuGPP-98
❑ 98StuHitPar-16
❑ 98StuPor8x10-18
❑ 98StuPor8x10GP-18
❑ 98StuSony99-3
❑ 98StuSPP-98
❑ 98Top-317
❑ 98TopChr-317
❑ 98TopChrC9-C7
❑ 98TopChrC9R-C7
❑ 98TopChrF-FB1
❑ 98TopChrFR-FB1
❑ 98TopChrHB-HB12
❑ 98TopChrHBR-HB12
❑ 98TopChrM-MS1
❑ 98TopChrMR-MS1
❑ 98TopChrR-317
❑ 98TopClo9-C7
❑ 98TopDevR-317
❑ 98TopDia-317
❑ 98TopEtc-ES2
❑ 98TopFla-FB1
❑ 98TopFocP-FP8
❑ 98TopGal-91
❑ 98TopGalGoH-GH3
❑ 98TopGalGoHJ-GH3
❑ 98TopGalGP-91
❑ 98TopGalOPP-91
❑ 98TopGalPG-PG10
❑ 98TopGalPPI-91
❑ 98TopGalPPIA-91
❑ 98TopGolLabC1-65
❑ 98TopGolLabC1B-65
❑ 98TopGolLabC1One-65
❑ 98TopGolLabC1R-65
❑ 98TopGolLabC2-65
❑ 98TopGolLabC2B-65
❑ 98TopGolLabC2One-65
❑ 98TopGolLabC2R-65
❑ 98TopGolLabC3-65
❑ 98TopGolLabC3B-65
❑ 98TopGolLabC3One-65
❑ 98TopGolLabC3R-65
❑ 98TopHal-HB12
❑ 98TopMil-MS1
❑ 98TopMiniC-317
❑ 98TopMysFB-M19
❑ 98TopMysFB-M19
❑ 98TopMysFBR-M19
❑ 98TopMysFBR-M19
❑ 98TopOpeD-143
❑ 98TopSta-145
❑ 98TopSta'S-5
❑ 98TopSta'SGH-5
❑ 98TopStaB-145
❑ 98TopStaG-G1
❑ 98TopStaG-145
❑ 98TopStaGG-G1
❑ 98TopStaGGR-G1
❑ 98TopStaGR-145
❑ 98TopStaGS-G1
❑ 98TopStaLB-L9
❑ 98TopStaLG-L9
❑ 98TopStaLGR-L9
❑ 98TopStaLS-L9
❑ 98TopStaS-145
❑ 98TopStaSteG-5
❑ 98TopSup-25
❑ 98TopSup-25
❑ 98TopTek-3
❑ 98TopTekD-3
❑ 98UD3-55
❑ 98UD3-145
❑ 98UD3-235
❑ 98UD3DieCut-55
❑ 98UD3DieCut-145
❑ 98UD3DieCut-235
❑ 98UD3PCBlowup-55
❑ 98Ult-50
❑ 98Ult-212
❑ 98Ult-500
❑ 98UltArtT-17
❑ 98UltBigS-8
❑ 98UltDial-15
❑ 98UltDiaP-14
❑ 98UltDouT-14
❑ 98UltFalC-15
❑ 98UltGolM-50
❑ 98UltGolM-212
❑ 98UltGolM-500
❑ 98UltMas-50
❑ 98UltMas-212
❑ 98UltMas-500
❑ 98UltNot-8
❑ 98UltPlaM-50
❑ 98UltPlaM-212
❑ 98UltPlaM-500
❑ 98UltPowP-9
❑ 98UltPriL-16
❑ 98UltTop3-1
❑ 98UppDec-144
❑ 98UppDec-505
❑ 98UppDec-625
❑ 98UppDec10AP-56
❑ 98UppDec1APR-56
❑ 98UppDecAC-AS18
❑ 98UppDecAG-AG15
❑ 98UppDecAGDC-AG15
❑ 98UppDecCD-CD29
❑ 98UppDecNP-NP34
❑ 98UppDecPN-PN50
❑ 98UppDecPN-PN51
❑ 98UppDecPN-PN52
❑ 98UppDecPN-PN53
❑ 98UppDecPN-PN54
❑ 98UppDecPN-PN55
❑ 98UppDecR-87
❑ 98UppDecR-10
❑ 98UppDecRBBop-BB30
❑ 98UppDecRGKoG-G30
❑ 98UppDecRQL-Q24
❑ 98UppDecRTC-TC50
❑ 98UppDecSFPD-PZ6
❑ 98UppDecSFPZOB-PZ6
❑ 98UppDecSFPZPD-PZ8
❑ 98UppDecSFPZSX-PZ6
❑ 98UppDecTMT-30
❑ 98UppDecTMTG-30
❑ 98UppDecU-16
❑ 98Zen-59
❑ 98Zen5 xx7-43
❑ 98Zen5x7GoldImp-43
❑ 98Zen5x7Imp-43
❑ 98ZenEpi-E22
❑ 98ZenZ-G-59
❑ 98ZenZ-S-59
❑ 99199Fin-84
❑ 99199Fin-112
❑ 99199Fin-276
❑ 99AllMysFR-M16
❑ 99Bow-34
❑ 99BowBes-58
❑ 99BowBesAR-58
❑ 99BowBesR-58
❑ 99BowChr-34
❑ 99BowChrG-34
❑ 99BowChrGR-34
❑ 99BowChrI-34
❑ 99BowChrIR-34
❑ 99BowChrR-34
❑ 99BowGol-34
❑ 99BowInt-34
❑ 99CroRoyB-123
❑ 99CroRoyL-123
❑ 99CroRoyMP-16
❑ 99CroRoyOD-123
❑ 99CroRoyPotG-21
❑ 99E-X Cen-24
❑ 99E-X CenECFut-24
❑ 99E-X CenECNow-24
❑ 99E-XCenFoF'-12
❑ 99E-XCenMotC-8
❑ 99FinFraR-FR9
❑ 99FinFraRR-FR9
❑ 99FinGolRef-84
❑ 99FinGolRef-112
❑ 99FinGolRef-276
❑ 99FinLeaI-L9
❑ 99FinMil-M6
❑ 99FinMil-M15
❑ 99FinMil-M22
❑ 99FinMil-M31
❑ 99FinPeelHyp-17
❑ 99FinPeelSpark-17
❑ 99FinPeeSS-17
❑ 99FinProF-PF15
❑ 99FinProF-PF30
❑ 99FinProF-PF47
❑ 99FinRef-84
❑ 99FinRef-112
❑ 99FinRef-276
❑ 99FinSplS-SS4
❑ 99FinSplSDR-SS4
❑ 99FinTeaFB-TF18
❑ 99FinTeaFBR-TF18
❑ 99FinTeaFG-TF18
❑ 99FinTeaFGR-TF18
❑ 99FinTeaFR-TF18
❑ 99FinTeaFRR-TF18
❑ 99FlaShoLeg1-25
❑ 99FlaShoLeg2-25
❑ 99FlaShoLeg3-25
❑ 99FlaShoLegM1-25
❑ 99FlaShoLegM2-25
❑ 99FlaShoLegM3-25
❑ 99FlaShoR1-25
❑ 99FlaShoR2-25
❑ 99FlaShoR3-25
❑ 99Fle-27
❑ 99FleBri-25
❑ 99FleBri2G-25
❑ 99FleBriBlu-25
❑ 99FleBriGol-25
❑ 99FleDatWD-1
❑ 99FleDiaM-1
❑ 99FleGolM-2
❑ 99FleMys-78
❑ 99FleMysG-78
❑ 99FleMysM-78
❑ 99FleSta9-27
❑ 99FleVin'-27
❑ 99FleWarT-27
❑ 99KinDis-2
❑ 99MetUni-43
❑ 99MetUni-246
❑ 99MetUni-297
❑ 99MetUniGM-43
❑ 99MetUniGM-246
❑ 99MetUniGM-297
❑ 99MetUniPMG-43
❑ 99MetUniPMG-246
❑ 99MetUniPMG-297
❑ 99Pac-378
❑ 99Pac-378A
❑ 99PacAur-169
❑ 99PacAurOD-169
❑ 99PacCroC-250
❑ 99PacCroCPB-250
❑ 99PacCroCTC-26

❑ 99PacDynaD-20
❑ 99PacDynaDT-20
❑ 99PacGolCDC-36
❑ 99PacInv-126
❑ 99PacInvOD-126
❑ 99PacInvPB-126
❑ 99PacOme-210
❑ 99PacOme5T-28
❑ 99PacOme5TT-28
❑ 99PacOmeC-210
❑ 99PacOmeDD-9
❑ 99PacOmeDM-29
❑ 99PacOmeEP-16
❑ 99PacOmeEP1o1-16
❑ 99PacOmeG-210
❑ 99PacOmeH'-16
❑ 99PacOmePB-210
❑ 99PacPar-208
❑ 99PacParC-208
❑ 99PacParG-208
❑ 99PacParHoloGold-208
❑ 99PacParHS-208
❑ 99PacParOD-208
❑ 99PacParPB-31
❑ 99PacParPB-208
❑ 99PacParRed-208
❑ 99PacParTC-26
❑ 99PacPlaB-378
❑ 99PacPlaB-378A
❑ 99PacPri-127
❑ 99PacPriHB-127
❑ 99PacPriHG-127
❑ 99PacPriHM-127
❑ 99PacPriHP-127
❑ 99PacPriRed-127
❑ 99PacPriS-26
❑ 99PacPriS206-26
❑ 99PacPriS206R-26
❑ 99PacPriSP-26
❑ 99PacPriSV-26
❑ 99PacRed-378
❑ 99PacRed-378A
❑ 99PacTeaC-30
❑ 99Pin-4
❑ 99Rev-124
❑ 99RevDiaL-30
❑ 99RevPremDate-124
❑ 99RevRet-124
❑ 99RevShaSS-124
❑ 99RevThoitS-16
❑ 99RevTri-19
❑ 99RevTri-19
❑ 99SkyMolM-122
❑ 99SkyMolMF-22
❑ 99SkyMolMFS-22
❑ 99SkyMolMFT-22
❑ 99SkyMolMX-122
❑ 99SkyPre-190
❑ 99SkyPre-285
❑ 99SkyPreR-190
❑ 99SkyPreR-285
❑ 99SkyThu-286
❑ 99SkyThuInD-ID2
❑ 99SkyThuRant-286
❑ 99SkyThuRave-286
❑ 99SP Aut-73
❑ 99SP Aut-129
❑ 99SP AutEF-E25
❑ 99SP AutHRC-HR14
❑ 99SP AutR-R25
❑ 99SP SigAuto-BB
❑ 99SP SigAutoG-BB
❑ 99SPAutHRCDC-HR14
❑ 99SpoIll-24
❑ 99SpoIll-118
❑ 99SpoIllH-14
❑ 99SPSig-38
❑ 99SPx-67
❑ 99SPxDom-FB15
❑ 99SPxFinR-67
❑ 99SPxFinS-67
❑ 99SPxPowE-PE24
❑ 99SPxPreS-PS25
❑ 99SPxStaF-SF23
❑ 99StaClu-280
❑ 99StaCluA-SCA3
❑ 99StaCluC-SCC17
❑ 99StaCluCR-SCC17
❑ 99StaCluFDI-280
❑ 99StaCluNC-NC5
❑ 99StaCluOoaK-280
❑ 99StaCluPP-280
❑ 99StaCluTI-T14C
❑ 99StaCluTL-T14C
❑ 99StaCluTL-T14C
❑ 99ThuSkySupR-286
❑ 99Top-395
❑ 99Top-455
❑ 99TopActF-1
❑ 99TopActFAU-1
❑ 99TopActFCU-1
❑ 99TopAllMF-M16
❑ 99TopAut-A10
❑ 99TopBlaLC1-99
❑ 99TopBlaLC2-99
❑ 99TopBlaLC3-99
❑ 99TopChr-395
❑ 99TopChr-455
❑ 99TopChrLotD-LD9
❑ 99TopChrLotDR-LD9
❑ 99TopChrR-395
❑ 99TopChrR-455
❑ 99TopChrRN-RN3
❑ 99TopChrRNR-RN3
❑ 99TopGal-77
❑ 99TopGal-111
❑ 99TopGalHer-TH15
❑ 99TopGalHerP-TH15
❑ 99TopGalPP-77
❑ 99TopGalPP-111
❑ 99TopGalPPI-77
❑ 99TopGalPPI-111
❑ 99TopGolL-99
❑ 99TopGolLC1-99
❑ 99TopGolLC2-99
❑ 99TopGolLOtO-99
❑ 99TopGolLRtA-RA10
❑ 99TopGolLRtAB-RA10
❑ 99TopGolLRtAOtO-RA10
❑ 99TopGolLRtAR-RA10
❑ 99TopLorotD-LD9
❑ 99TopMVPP-395
❑ 99TopMVPP-455
❑ 99TopOpeD-129
❑ 99TopOver-B7
❑ 99TopPowB-PB12
❑ 99TopPowBR-PB12
❑ 99TopRedLC1-99
❑ 99TopRedLC2-99
❑ 99TopRedLC3-99
❑ 99TopSta-14
❑ 99TopSta-163
❑ 99TopSta'S-14
❑ 99TopSta'SG-14
❑ 99TopSta'SGDH-14
❑ 99TopSta1Foil-14
❑ 99TopSta2Foil-14
❑ 99TopSta3Foil-14
❑ 99TopStaFoil-14
❑ 99TopStaFoil-163
❑ 99TopStaOS-14
❑ 99TopStaTS-14
❑ 99TopStaTS-14
❑ 99TopSupC-22
❑ 99TopSupCR-22
❑ 99TopTek-19A
❑ 99TopTek-19B
❑ 99TopTekG-19A
❑ 99TopTekG-19B
❑ 99UD Cho-140
❑ 99UD ChoMBH-B25
❑ 99UD ChoP-140
❑ 99UD ChoPCR-140
❑ 99UD ChoS-7
❑ 99UD ChoSD-7
❑ 99UD ChoSHR-7
❑ 99UD ChoST-7
❑ 99UD ChoYW-Y24
❑ 99UD Ion-51
❑ 99UD Ion-85
❑ 99UD IonC-C21
❑ 99UD IonR-51
❑ 99UD IonR-85
❑ 99UDHolo-52
❑ 99UDHoloAUsome-52
❑ 99UDHoloLau-L13
❑ 99UDHoloLauG-L13
❑ 99Ult-139
❑ 99UltGolM-139
❑ 99UltMas-139
❑ 99UltPlaM-139
❑ 99UltRBIK-4
❑ 99UltTheBook-8
❑ 99UppDec-481
❑ 99UppDec-531
❑ 99UppDec10AT-X7
❑ 99UppDec10ATD-X7
❑ 99UppDec10ATHR-X7
❑ 99UppDec10ATT-X7
❑ 99UppDecBD-73
❑ 99UppDecBDD-73
❑ 99UppDecBDDom-D26
❑ 99UppDecBDDomE-D26
❑ 99UppDecBDMN-M25
❑ 99UppDecBDMNE-M25
❑ 99UppDecBDQ-73
❑ 99UppDecBDT-73
❑ 99UppDecCf7-10
❑ 99UppDecCf7-57
❑ 99UppDecCf7-83
❑ 99UppDecCf7-C10
❑ 99UppDecCf7Cf7P-C10
❑ 99UppDecCf7LL-L5
❑ 99UppDecCG-CG2
❑ 99UppDecCGD-CG2
❑ 99UppDecCGHR-CG2
❑ 99UppDecCGT-CG2
❑ 99UppDecCL-34
❑ 99UppDecCL-52
❑ 99UppDecCLCC-34
❑ 99UppDecCLCC-52
❑ 99UppDecCLEM-EM10
❑ 99UppDecCLES-BB
❑ 99UppDecCLESC-BB
❑ 99UppDecCLM-C83
❑ 99UppDecCo7CE-10
❑ 99UppDecCo7CE-57
❑ 99UppDecCo7CE-83
❑ 99UppDecE-80
❑ 99UppDecE-148
❑ 99UppDecE-176
❑ 99UppDecEBPC-C-BB
❑ 99UppDecEDF-D11
❑ 99UppDecEDFFXG-D11
❑ 99UppDecEFXG-80
❑ 99UppDecEFXG-148
❑ 99UppDecEFXG-176
❑ 99UppDecEL1-481
❑ 99UppDecEL1-531
❑ 99UppDecEL2-481
❑ 99UppDecEL2-531
❑ 99UppDecEPE-P25
❑ 99UppDecF-F24
❑ 99UppDecFD-F24
❑ 99UppDecFQ-F24
❑ 99UppDecFT-F24
❑ 99UppDecIP-I3
❑ 99UppDecIPD-I3
❑ 99UppDecIPHR-I3
❑ 99UppDecIPT-I3
❑ 99UppDecM-183
❑ 99UppDecM-P15
❑ 99UppDecMGS-183
❑ 99UppDecMGUS-GUBB
❑ 99UppDecMHFS-183
❑ 99UppDecMP-183
❑ 99UppDecMSS-183
❑ 99UppDecMST-T9
❑ 99UppDecMST-S7
❑ 99UppDecO-4
❑ 99UppDecOAPoH-BB
❑ 99UppDecOMP-S6
❑ 99UppDecOSO-4
❑ 99UppDecOWP-R7
❑ 99UppDecR-74
❑ 99UppDecRDR-D13
❑ 99UppDecRDRL2-D13
❑ 99UppDecRG-74
❑ 99UppDecRP-74
❑ 99UppDecTE-T25
❑ 99UppDecTED-T25
❑ 99UppDecTEQ-T25
❑ 99UppDecTET-T25
❑ 99UppDecVtaT-V25
❑ 99UppDecVtaTD-V25
❑ 99UppDecVtaTQ-V25
❑ 99UppDecVtaTT-V25
❑ 99UppDecWY-W4
❑ 99UppDecWYD-W4
❑ 99UppDecWYHR-W4
❑ 99UppDecWYT-W4
❑ 99Vic-351
❑ 99Vic-352
❑ 99Vic-353
❑ 99Vic-356
❑ 99Vic-463

Bonds, Bobby

❑ 92ClaDraP-84
❑ 92ClaDraPFB-BC17
❑ 93ClaFS7-176
❑ 93WatDiaC-1
❑ 93WatDiaF-1780
❑ 94RanCucQC-6
❑ 94UppDecML-214
❑ 96SanJosGB-10
❑ 97SanJosG-1
❑ 98ShrCapM-2
❑ 98ShrCapWS-2

Bonds, Bobby Lee

❑ 69MilBra-31
❑ 69Top-630
❑ 70Gia-1
❑ 70GiaCheB-1
❑ 70MLBOffS-121
❑ 70OPC-425
❑ 70Top-425
❑ 71GiaTic-1
❑ 71MLBOffS-241
❑ 71OPC-295
❑ 71Top-295
❑ 71TopCoi-13
❑ 72GiaTeal-1
❑ 72MilBra-37
❑ 72Top-711
❑ 72Top-712
❑ 73Kel2D-8
❑ 73LinPor-157
❑ 73OPC-145
❑ 73Top-145
❑ 73TopCanL-6
❑ 74Kel-39
❑ 74LauAllG-73
❑ 74OPC-30
❑ 74Top-30
❑ 74TopDecE-36
❑ 74TopPuz-4
❑ 74TopSta-101
❑ 75Hos-145
❑ 75OPC-55
❑ 75SSPPuzB-3
❑ 75Top-55
❑ 75TopMin-55
❑ 75YanSSP-2
❑ 76Hos-18
❑ 76HosTwi-18
❑ 76OPC-2
❑ 76OPC-380
❑ 76SSP-439
❑ 76Top-2
❑ 76Top-380
❑ 76TopTra-380T
❑ 77BurCheD-124
❑ 77OPC-173
❑ 77RCColC-5
❑ 77Spo-8219
❑ 77Top-570
❑ 78Hos-42
❑ 78OPC-206
❑ 78RCColC-44
❑ 78SSP270-140
❑ 78Top-150
❑ 78WifBalD-6
❑ 79BasPat-4
❑ 79OPC-142
❑ 79Top-285
❑ 80BurKinPHR-23
❑ 80OPC-215
❑ 80Top-410
❑ 81Don-71A
❑ 81Don-71B
❑ 81Fle-548
❑ 81OPC-223
❑ 81Top-635
❑ 81TopTra-740
❑ 82Fle-588
❑ 82OPC-27
❑ 82Top-580
❑ 84GiaMot-12
❑ 84Ind-6
❑ 84IndWhe-NNO
❑ 85Ind-6
❑ 85IndPol-NNO
❑ 86IndOhH-NNO
❑ 86IndTeal-7
❑ 89PacSenL-128
❑ 89T/MSenL-10
❑ 89T/MSenL-119
❑ 89TopSenL-40
❑ 90EliSenL-109
❑ 90EliSenL-122
❑ 91MDAA-7
❑ 91SweBasG-11
❑ 91UppDecS-12
❑ 91UppDecS-19
❑ 92ActPacA-62
❑ 92UppDecF-53
❑ 92UppDecFG-53
❑ 92UppDecHH-HI1
❑ 92UppDecS-35
❑ 92YanWIZ7-23
❑ 92YanWIZA-4
❑ 93Bow-702
❑ 93GiaMot-28
❑ 93GiaPos-8
❑ 93MetIma-4
❑ 93RanKee-78
❑ 93StaCluU-3
❑ 93StaCluU-5
❑ 93TedWil-51
❑ 94GiaKTV-4
❑ 94GiaMot-28
❑ 94Yoo-2
❑ 95GiaMot-28
❑ 96GiaMot-28
❑ 97PhoFirDTTI-6

Bone, Pat

❑ 82OneYanT-10

Bones, Ricky (Ricardo)

❑ 86SpoIndC-163
❑ 87ChaRaiP-21
❑ 88BlaYNPRWL-99
❑ 88CalLeaACLC-41
❑ 88RivRedWCLC-208
❑ 88RivRedWP-1426
❑ 89BlaYNPRWL-106
❑ 89BlaYNPRWLU-42
❑ 89BlaYNPRWLU-54
❑ 89BlaYNPRWLU-64
❑ 89BlaYNPRWLU-71
❑ 89WicChaR-20
❑ 89WicStaR-16
❑ 89WicWraR-10
❑ 90TexLeaAGS-12
❑ 90WicWraRD-2
❑ 91Bow-643
❑ 91LasVegSLD-278
❑ 91LasVegSP-226
❑ 91LinDriAAA-278
❑ 92BrePol-4
❑ 92Cla2-T11
❑ 92ClaGam-60
❑ 92Don-545
❑ 92Fle-600
❑ 92Lea-500
❑ 92LeaBlaG-500
❑ 92OPC-711
❑ 92Sco-758
❑ 92StaClu-109
❑ 92Stu-192
❑ 92Top-711
❑ 92TopDeb91-17
❑ 92TopGol-711
❑ 92TopGolW-711
❑ 92TopMic-711
❑ 92TopTra-13T
❑ 92TopTraG-13T
❑ 92Ult-378
❑ 92UppDec-623
❑ 92UppDec-762
❑ 93BrePol-2
❑ 93Don-413
❑ 93Fle-247
❑ 93Lea-122
❑ 93OPC-33
❑ 93PacBeiA-9
❑ 93PacSpa-508
❑ 93Pin-393
❑ 93Sco-470
❑ 93StaClu-225
❑ 93StaCluFDI-225
❑ 93StaCluMOP-225
❑ 93Top-71
❑ 93TopGol-71
❑ 93TopInaM-71
❑ 93TopInaR-71
❑ 93TopMic-71
❑ 93Ult-568
❑ 93UppDec-328
❑ 93UppDecGold-328
❑ 94BreMilB-199
❑ 94BrePol-2
❑ 94BreTeal-1
❑ 94ColC-57
❑ 94ColChoGS-57
❑ 94ColChoSS-57
❑ 94Don-59
❑ 94Fin-293
❑ 94FinRef-293
❑ 94Fla-63
❑ 94Fle-174
❑ 94FleExtB-98
❑ 94Lea-222
❑ 94LeaL-42
❑ 94Pac-326
❑ 94Pin-123
❑ 94PinArtP-123
❑ 94PinMusC-123
❑ 94Sco-236
❑ 94ScoGolR-236
❑ 94SP-56
❑ 94SPDieC-56
❑ 94StaClu-398
❑ 94StaClu-564
❑ 94StaCluFDI-398
❑ 94StaCluFDI-564
❑ 94StaCluGR-398
❑ 94StaCluGR-564
❑ 94StaCluMOP-398
❑ 94StaCluMOP-564
❑ 94Stu-42
❑ 94Top-367
❑ 94TopGol-367
❑ 94TopSpa-367
❑ 94TriPla-51
❑ 94Ult-370
❑ 95ColCho-185
❑ 95ColChoGS-185
❑ 95ColChoSE-68
❑ 95ColChoSEGS-68
❑ 95ColChoSESS-68
❑ 95ColChoSS-185
❑ 95Don-143
❑ 95DonPreP-143
❑ 95DonTopotO-95
❑ 95Emo-52
❑ 95Fin-234
❑ 95FinRef-234
❑ 95Fla-50
❑ 95Fle-174
❑ 95FleTeaL-8
❑ 95Lea-388
❑ 95PacPri-74
❑ 95Pin-218
❑ 95PinArtP-218
❑ 95PinMusC-218
❑ 95Sco-98
❑ 95ScoGolR-98
❑ 95ScoPlaTS-98
❑ 95SP-163
❑ 95SPCha-163
❑ 95SPCha-166
❑ 95SPChaDC-163
❑ 95SPChaDC-166
❑ 95SPSil-163
❑ 95StaClu-199
❑ 95StaCluFDI-199
❑ 95StaCluMOP-199
❑ 95StaCluSTWS-199
❑ 95StaCluVR-105
❑ 95StaCluVRMO-105
❑ 95Top-35
❑ 95TopCyb-27
❑ 95Ult-62
❑ 95UltGolM-62
❑ 95UppDec-298
❑ 95UppDecED-298
❑ 95UppDecEDG-298
❑ 95UppDecSE-101
❑ 95UppDecSEG-101
❑ 96BrePol-1
❑ 96Cir-49
❑ 96CirRav-49
❑ 96ColCho-589
❑ 96ColChoGS-589
❑ 96ColChoSS-589
❑ 96Don-118
❑ 96DonPreP-118
❑ 96EmoXL-71
❑ 96Fin-B55
❑ 96FinRef-B55
❑ 96Fla-97
❑ 96Fle-141
❑ 96FleTif-141
❑ 96LeaSigA-28
❑ 96LeaSigAG-28
❑ 96LeaSigAS-28
❑ 96MetUni-68
❑ 96MetUniP-68
❑ 96Pac-345
❑ 96PacEstL-EL5
❑ 96PacPri-P108
❑ 96PacPriG-P108
❑ 96PanSti-192
❑ 96Sco-63
❑ 96StaClu-136
❑ 96StaCluMOP-136
❑ 96Top-396
❑ 96Ult-77
❑ 96UltGolM-77
❑ 96UppDec-362
❑ 97Ult-331
❑ 97UltGolME-331
❑ 97UltPlaME-331
❑ 97UppDec-97
❑ 98PacInvGems-51

❑ 98SalLakBO-11
Bonetti, Julio
❑ 93ConTSN-965
Bong, Jung
❑ 99Bow-310
❑ 99BowGol-310
❑ 99BowInt-310
Bongiovanni, Nino (Anthony)
❑ 33Zee-154
❑ 37Zee-43
❑ 38RedOraW-2
❑ 39OrcPhoAP-2
❑ 39RedTeal-2
❑ 77CinRedT-36
Bonham, Bill
❑ 72OPC-29
❑ 72Top-29A
❑ 72Top-29B
❑ 73LinPor-39
❑ 73OPC-328
❑ 73Top-328
❑ 74OPC-528
❑ 74Top-528
❑ 75OPC-85
❑ 75Top-85
❑ 75TopMin-85
❑ 76CubTri-2
❑ 76OPC-151
❑ 76SSP-303
❑ 76Top-151
❑ 77BurCheD-192
❑ 77CubJewT-2
❑ 77OPC-95
❑ 77Top-446
❑ 78Pep-5
❑ 78SSP270-112
❑ 78Top-276
❑ 79Kel-31
❑ 79OPC-182
❑ 79Top-354
❑ 80OPC-26
❑ 80RedEnq-42
❑ 80Top-47
❑ 81Fle-215A
❑ 81Fle-215B
❑ 81IndIndTI-13
❑ 81Top-712
❑ 86AubAstP-5
Bonham, Tiny (Ernie)
❑ 43MPR302-1-1
❑ 43YanSta-1
❑ 47TipTop-137
❑ 49Bow-77
❑ 49EurSta-154
❑ 85TCMPla1-41
❑ 92YanWIZA-5
Boni, Joel
❑ 82MadMusF-2
Bonifay, Ken
❑ 92AugPirC-18
❑ 92SalBucF-70
❑ 93CarLeaAGF-45
❑ 93SalBucC-1
❑ 93SalBucF-437
❑ 95LynHilTI-2
❑ 96CarMudB-17
❑ 97CarMudC-15
Bonifazio, Anthony
❑ 93LetMouF-4158
❑ 93LetMouSP-8
Bonikowski, Joe
❑ 61TwiCloD-4
❑ 62Top-592
Bonilla, Bobby
❑ 83AleDukT-16
❑ 86DonRoo-30
❑ 86FleUpd-15
❑ 86SpoRoo-26
❑ 86TopTra-12T
❑ 86TopTraT-12T
❑ 86WhiSoxC-26
❑ 87Don-558
❑ 87DonOpeD-167
❑ 87Fle-605
❑ 87FleGlo-605
❑ 87SpoTeaP-18
❑ 87Top-184
❑ 87TopTif-184
❑ 88ClaBlu-236
❑ 88Don-238
❑ 88DonBasB-33
❑ 88Fle-323
❑ 88FleBasA-3
❑ 88FleGlo-323
❑ 88FleHotS-3
❑ 88FleMin-103
❑ 88FleSlu-3
❑ 88FleStiC-114
❑ 88GreBasS-62
❑ 88Lea-188
❑ 88OPC-189
❑ 88PanSti-372
❑ 88PanSti-373
❑ 88PirTeal-3
❑ 88Sco-116
❑ 88ScoGlo-116
❑ 88ScoYouS2-9
❑ 88Spo-131
❑ 88StaLinPi-3
❑ 88TarPla-5
❑ 88Top-231
❑ 88Top-681
❑ 88TopBig-25
❑ 88TopCoi-37
❑ 88TopSti-129
❑ 88TopTif-231
❑ 88TopTif-681
❑ 89Bow-422
❑ 89BowTif-422
❑ 89CadEllD-3
❑ 89Don-2
❑ 89Don-151
❑ 89DonAll-39
❑ 89DonBasB-33
❑ 89DonPop-39
❑ 89DonSupD-2
❑ 89Fle-203
❑ 89Fle-637
❑ 89FleAll-1
❑ 89FleBasA-4
❑ 89FleGlo-203
❑ 89FleGlo-637
❑ 89MSAHolD-15
❑ 89Nis-15
❑ 89OPC-142
❑ 89PanSti-171
❑ 89PanSti-234
❑ 89PirVerFJ-25
❑ 89RedFolSB-10
❑ 89Sco-195
❑ 89ScoHot1S-42
❑ 89Spo-182
❑ 89SpollIFKI-181
❑ 89Top-388
❑ 89Top-440
❑ 89TopBasT-114
❑ 89TopBig-159
❑ 89TopCoi-5
❑ 89TopDouA-15
❑ 89TopGloA-15
❑ 89TopGloS-24
❑ 89TopMinL-30
❑ 89TopSti-131
❑ 89TopSti-158
❑ 89TopStiB-40
❑ 89TopTif-388
❑ 89TopTif-440
❑ 89TopUKM-6
❑ 89TVSpoM-10
❑ 89UppDec-578
❑ 90Bow-169
❑ 90BowTif-169
❑ 90ClaBlu-143
❑ 90ClaYel-T73
❑ 90Don-290
❑ 90DonBesN-70
❑ 90DOnBonM-BC16
❑ 90Fle-462
❑ 90FleBasA-2
❑ 90FleBasAC-2
❑ 90FleBasM-4
❑ 90FleBasMC-4
❑ 90FleCan-462
❑ 90GooHumICBLS-4
❑ 90Hot50PS-3
❑ 90KinDis-8
❑ 90Lea-196
❑ 90LeaPre-10
❑ 90M.Vpin-82
❑ 90MLBBasB-38
❑ 90MSAIceTD-11
❑ 90MSASupS-11
❑ 90OPC-273
❑ 90PanSti-325
❑ 90PirHomC-6
❑ 90PubIntS-150
❑ 90PubIntS-253
❑ 90Sco-170
❑ 90Sco100S-37
❑ 90Spo-195
❑ 90StaLonJS-5
❑ 90StaLonJS-31
❑ 90Top-273
❑ 90TopBig-208
❑ 90TopCoi-41
❑ 90TopDou-6
❑ 90TopMag-43
❑ 90TopMinL-71
❑ 90TopSti-129
❑ 90TopStiB-7
❑ 90TopTif-273
❑ 90TopTVA-59
❑ 90UppDec-16
❑ 90UppDec-366
❑ 90USPlaCA-11H
❑ 91Bow-381
❑ 91Bow-525
❑ 91CadEllD-6
❑ 91Cla2-T92
❑ 91Cla3-T4
❑ 91Cla3-NNO
❑ 91ClaGam-144
❑ 91DenHol-17
❑ 91Don-325
❑ 91DonGraS-2
❑ 91Fle-34
❑ 91Fle-711
❑ 91Lea-357
❑ 91MLBKeyC-1
❑ 91OPC-403
❑ 91OPC-750
❑ 91PanCanT1-18
❑ 91PanCanT1-50
❑ 91PanFreS-120
❑ 91PanSti-111
❑ 91PepSup-15
❑ 91Pos-14
❑ 91RedFolS-10
❑ 91Sco-315
❑ 91Sco-402
❑ 91Sco-670
❑ 91Sco100S-42
❑ 91StaClu-139
❑ 91StaCluP-6
❑ 91StaPinB-5
❑ 91StaPro-2
❑ 91Stu-223
❑ 91SunSee-3
❑ 91Top-403
❑ 91Top-750
❑ 91TopCraJ2-15
❑ 91TopDesS-403
❑ 91TopDesS-750
❑ 91TopMic-403
❑ 91TopMic-750
❑ 91TopSta-5
❑ 91TopTif-403
❑ 91TopTif-750
❑ 91TopTriH-N9
❑ 91Ult-276
❑ 91UppDec-152
❑ 91UppDecFE-99F
❑ 91UppDecSS-SS15
❑ 91USPlaCA-JKO
❑ 92Bow-235
❑ 92Cla2-T47
❑ 92ClaGam-176
❑ 92Don-427
❑ 92Don-610
❑ 92DonCraJ2-18
❑ 92DonUpd-U20
❑ 92Fle-551
❑ 92Fle-699
❑ 92FleAll-9
❑ 92FleTeaL-9
❑ 92FleUpd-101
❑ 92HitTheBB-6
❑ 92JimDea-16
❑ 92KinDis-5
❑ 92Lea-308
❑ 92Lea-463
❑ 92LeaBlaG-308
❑ 92LeaBlaG-463
❑ 92MetColP-2
❑ 92MetKah-25
❑ 92MSABenSHD-20
❑ 92OPC-160
❑ 92OPCPre-143
❑ 92PanSti-256
❑ 92Pin-310
❑ 92Pin-395
❑ 92PinSlu-6
❑ 92Pos-21
❑ 92RedFolS-16
❑ 92RedFolS-108
❑ 92RemUltP-P1
❑ 92RemUltP-P2
❑ 92RemUltP-P3
❑ 92RemUltP-P16
❑ 92RemUltP-P17
❑ 92RemUltP-P18
❑ 92Sco-225
❑ 92Sco100S-80
❑ 92ScoRoo-5T
❑ 92SpollIFK1-68
❑ 92SpoStaCC-5
❑ 92StaClu-608
❑ 92StaClu-780
❑ 92StaCluD-19
❑ 92StaCluECN-608
❑ 92Stu-61
❑ 92SunSee-16
❑ 92Top-160
❑ 92Top-392
❑ 92TopGol-160
❑ 92TopGol-392
❑ 92TopGolW-160
❑ 92TopGolW-392
❑ 92TopKid-22
❑ 92TopMcD-9
❑ 92TopMic-160
❑ 92TopMic-392
❑ 92TopTra-14T
❑ 92TopTraG-14T
❑ 92TriPlaG-GS1
❑ 92Ult-527
❑ 92UppDec-225
❑ 92UppDec-755
❑ 92UppDecF-15
❑ 92UppDecFG-15
❑ 93Bow-158
❑ 93ClaGam-15
❑ 93DiaMar-15
❑ 93Don-594
❑ 93Fin-66
❑ 93FinRef-66
❑ 93Fla-89
❑ 93Fle-84
❑ 93FleAtl-3
❑ 93FunPac-124
❑ 93Hos-3
❑ 93HumDumC-43
❑ 93Kra-16
❑ 93Lea-236
❑ 93MetBak-3
❑ 93MetColP-22
❑ 93MetKah-25
❑ 93OPC-15
❑ 93PacJugC-22
❑ 93PacSpa-192
❑ 93PacSpaGE-2
❑ 93PanSti-253
❑ 93Pin-43
❑ 93PinHomRC-41
❑ 93Pos-24
❑ 93PosCan-12
❑ 93RedFolS-15
❑ 93Sco-8
❑ 93ScoFra-21
❑ 93Sel-11
❑ 93SP-146
❑ 93StaClu-163
❑ 93StaCluFDI-163
❑ 93StaCluMOP-163
❑ 93Stu-16
❑ 93Top-52
❑ 93TopGol-52
❑ 93TopInaM-52
❑ 93TopInaR-52
❑ 93TopMic-52
❑ 93TopPreS-2
❑ 93TriPla-173
❑ 93TriPlaA-2
❑ 93Ult-422
❑ 93UppDec-275
❑ 93UppDec-484
❑ 93UppDec-826
❑ 93UppDecGold-275
❑ 93UppDecGold-484
❑ 93UppDecGold-826
❑ 93UppDecHRH-HR23
❑ 94Bow-128
❑ 94BowBes-R50
❑ 94BowBesR-R50
❑ 94ColC-58
❑ 94ColChoGS-58
❑ 94ColChoHRA-HA4
❑ 94ColChoSS-58
❑ 94DenHol-7
❑ 94Don-347
❑ 94DonDiaK-DK13
❑ 94DonDiaKJ-DK13
❑ 94DonMVP-9
❑ 94DonSpeE-347
❑ 94Fin-234
❑ 94FinJum-234
❑ 94FinRef-234
❑ 94Fla-407
❑ 94Fle-558
❑ 94FleAllS-32
❑ 94FleExtB-315
❑ 94FleTeaL-23
❑ 94FUnPac-127
❑ 94FUnPac-223
❑ 94Kra-18
❑ 94Lea-31
❑ 94LeaCleC-4
❑ 94LeaL-129
❑ 94MetColP-2
❑ 94MetShuST-4
❑ 94OPC-202
❑ 94OscMayR-18
❑ 94Pac-396
❑ 94PacAll-6
❑ 94PacGolP-17
❑ 94PanSti-215
❑ 94Pin-33
❑ 94PinArtP-33
❑ 94PinMusC-33
❑ 94Pos-10
❑ 94ProMag-91
❑ 94RedFolMI-6
❑ 94Sco-378
❑ 94ScoGolR-378
❑ 94ScoGolS-26
❑ 94Sel-238
❑ 94SP-115
❑ 94SPDieC-115
❑ 94Spo-49
❑ 94StaClu-59
❑ 94StaCluFDI-59
❑ 94StaCluGR-59
❑ 94StaCluMOP-59
❑ 94StaCluMOP-ST9
❑ 94StaCluST-ST9
❑ 94Stu-113
❑ 94SucSav-18
❑ 94TomPiz-4
❑ 94Top-730
❑ 94TopGol-730
❑ 94TopSpa-730
❑ 94TopSupS-6
❑ 94TriPla-141
❑ 94Ult-528
❑ 94UppDec-275
❑ 94UppDec-344
❑ 94UppDecAJ-41
❑ 94UppDecAJG-41
❑ 94UppDecED-275
❑ 94UppDecED-344
❑ 94USPlaCA-3C
❑ 95BalOriP-9
❑ 95Baz-36
❑ 95Bow-284
❑ 95BowBes-R11
❑ 95BowBesR-R11
❑ 95ColCho-320
❑ 95ColChoGS-320
❑ 95ColChoSE-145
❑ 95ColChoSEGS-145
❑ 95ColChoSESS-145
❑ 95ColChoSS-320
❑ 95Don-308
❑ 95DonDiaK-DK8
❑ 95DonPreP-308
❑ 95DonTopotO-5
❑ 95Emo-158
❑ 95Fin-104
❑ 95FinRef-104
❑ 95Fla-169
❑ 95Fle-365
❑ 95FleTeaL-23
❑ 95Lea-295
❑ 95LeaLim-15
❑ 95MetColP-2
❑ 95Pac-277
❑ 95PacGolP-23
❑ 95PacPri-90
❑ 95PanSti-51
❑ 95Pin-5
❑ 95PinArtP-5
❑ 95PinMusC-5
❑ 95RedFol-26
❑ 95Sco-424
❑ 95ScoGolR-424
❑ 95ScoHaloG-HG64
❑ 95ScoPlaTS-424
❑ 95Sel-47
❑ 95SelArtP-47
❑ 95SelCer-34
❑ 95SelCerMG-34
❑ 95SP-80
❑ 95SPCha-70
❑ 95SPChaDC-70
❑ 95Spo-18
❑ 95SpoArtP-18
❑ 95SPSil-80
❑ 95StaClu-118
❑ 95StaClu-312
❑ 95StaClu-504
❑ 95StaCluCC-CC7
❑ 95StaCluFDI-118
❑ 95StaCluMOP-118
❑ 95StaCluMOP-312
❑ 95StaCluMOP-504
❑ 95StaCluMOP-CC7
❑ 95StaCluSTWS-118
❑ 95StaCluSTWS-312
❑ 95StaCluSTWS-504
❑ 95StaCluVR-60
❑ 95StaCluVRMO-60
❑ 95Stu-105
❑ 95Sum-76
❑ 95SumNthD-76
❑ 95Top-502
❑ 95TopCyb-292
❑ 95TopD3-22
❑ 95TopEmb-38
❑ 95TopEmbGI-38
❑ 95UC3-34
❑ 95UC3ArtP-34
❑ 95UC3CycS-CS15
❑ 95Ult-195
❑ 95UltGolM-195
❑ 95UppDec-360
❑ 95UppDec-470
❑ 95UppDecED-360
❑ 95UppDecEDG-360
❑ 95UppDecSE-60
❑ 95UppDecSEG-60
❑ 95Zen-9
❑ 96BalOriP-5
❑ 96Baz-63
❑ 96Bow-39
❑ 96BowFoi-39
❑ 96ColCho-464
❑ 96ColChoGS-464
❑ 96ColChoSS-464
❑ 96ColChoYMtP-9
❑ 96ColChoYMtP-9A
❑ 96ColChoYMtPGS-9
❑ 96ColChoYMtPGS-9A
❑ 96Don-225
❑ 96DonPreP-225
❑ 96EmoXL-3
❑ 96Fin-B175
❑ 96FinRef-B175
❑ 96Fla-3
❑ 96Fle-5
❑ 96FleTif-5
❑ 96Lea-120
❑ 96LeaPrePB-120
❑ 96LeaPrePG-120
❑ 96LeaPrePS-120
❑ 96LeaPreSG-34
❑ 96LeaPreSte-34
❑ 96LeaSig-139
❑ 96LeaSigPPG-139
❑ 96LeaSigPPP-139
❑ 96MetKah-4
❑ 96MetMod-1
❑ 96MetTeal-1
❑ 96MetUni-3
❑ 96MetUniP-3
❑ 96MLBPin-5
❑ 96OriFle-4
❑ 96Pac-242
❑ 96PacEstL-EL6
❑ 96PacPri-P74
❑ 96PacPriG-P74
❑ 96PanSti-133
❑ 96Pin-30
❑ 96PinAfi-41
❑ 96PinAfiAP-41
❑ 96PinAfiFPP-41
❑ 96PinArtP-14
❑ 96PinSta-14
❑ 96ProMagDM-5
❑ 96ProSta-77
❑ 96Sco-167
❑ 96ScoDugC-A95
❑ 96ScoDugCAP-A95
❑ 96Sel-75
❑ 96SelArtP-75
❑ 96SelTeaN-20

❑ 96SP-32
❑ 96Spo-47
❑ 96SpoArtP-47
❑ 96StaClu-146
❑ 96StaCluEPB-146
❑ 96StaCluEPG-146
❑ 96StaCluEPS-146
❑ 96StaCluMOP-146
❑ 96Stu-27
❑ 96StuPrePB-27
❑ 96StuPrePG-27
❑ 96StuPrePS-27
❑ 96Sum-52
❑ 96SumAbo&B-52
❑ 96SumArtP-52
❑ 96SumFoi-52
❑ 96Top-329
❑ 96TopChr-131
❑ 96TopChrR-131
❑ 96TopGal-36
❑ 96TopGalPG-PG13
❑ 96TopGalPPI-36
❑ 96TopLas-20
❑ 96Ult-3
❑ 96UltGolM-3
❑ 96UltThu-3
❑ 96UltThuGM-3
❑ 96UppDec-279
❑ 97Bow-63
❑ 97BowInt-63
❑ 97Cir-231
❑ 97CirRav-231
❑ 97ColChoT-FM13
❑ 97ColChoU-U12
❑ 97Don-102
❑ 97DonEli-45
❑ 97DonEliGS-45
❑ 97DonGolPP-102
❑ 97DonLim-152
❑ 97DonLimE-152
❑ 97DonLimFotG-44
❑ 97DonPre-27
❑ 97DonPreCttC-27
❑ 97DonSig-88
❑ 97DonSigAC-16
❑ 97DonSigAM-16
❑ 97DonSigPPP-88
❑ 97DonSilPP-102
❑ 97Fin-199
❑ 97FinRef-199
❑ 97FlaShoLC-88
❑ 97FlaShoLeg0-88
❑ 97FlaShoLeg1-88
❑ 97FlaShoM-A88
❑ 97FlaShoM-B88
❑ 97FlaShoM-C88
❑ 97FlaShoR0-88
❑ 97FlaShoR1-88
❑ 97FlaShoR2-88
❑ 97Fle-3
❑ 97Fle-536
❑ 97FleTif-3
❑ 97FleTif-536
❑ 97Lea-262
❑ 97LeaFraM-262
❑ 97LeaFraMDC-262
❑ 97MarPac-4
❑ 97MetUni-170
❑ 97NewPin-28
❑ 97NewPinAP-28
❑ 97NewPinMC-28
❑ 97NewPinPP-28
❑ 97OriSco-6
❑ 97OriScoPl-6
❑ 97OriScoPr-6
❑ 97Pac-20
❑ 97PacLatotML-4
❑ 97PacLigB-20
❑ 97PacSil-20
❑ 97PinCer-77
❑ 97PinCerMBla-77
❑ 97PinCerMBlu-77
❑ 97PinCerMG-77
❑ 97PinCerMR-77
❑ 97PinCerR-77
❑ 97PinIns-53
❑ 97PinInsCE-53
❑ 97PinInsDE-53
❑ 97PinTotCPB-77
❑ 97PinTotCPG-77
❑ 97PinTotCPR-77
❑ 97PinX-P-107
❑ 97PinX-PMoS-107
❑ 97PinX-PSfF-11
❑ 97PinX-PSfFU-11
❑ 97Sco-123
❑ 97Sco-347
❑ 97ScoArtPWB-123
❑ 97ScoArtPWB-347
❑ 97ScoPreS-123
❑ 97ScoResC-347
❑ 97ScoShoS-123
❑ 97ScoShoS-347
❑ 97ScoShoSAP-123
❑ 97ScoShoSAP-347
❑ 97Sel-65
❑ 97SelArtP-65
❑ 97SelCom-65
❑ 97SelRegG-65
❑ 97SP-80
❑ 97SpoIll-82
❑ 97SpoIllEE-82
❑ 97StaClu-14
❑ 97StaCluMat-14
❑ 97StaCluMOP-14
❑ 97Stu-75
❑ 97StuPrePG-75
❑ 97StuPrePS-75
❑ 97Top-374
❑ 97TopChr-127
❑ 97TopChrR-127
❑ 97TopGal-16
❑ 97TopGalPPI-16
❑ 97TopSta-73
❑ 97TopStaAM-73
❑ 97Ult-360
❑ 97UltGolME-360
❑ 97UltPlaME-360
❑ 97UppDec-535
❑ 98CirThu-37
❑ 98CirThuRav-37
❑ 98CirThuSupRav-37
❑ 98ColCho-98
❑ 98CroRoy-69
❑ 98DodMot-3
❑ 98Don-142
❑ 98DonCol-142
❑ 98DonColE-461
❑ 98DonColL-203
❑ 98DonColP-651
❑ 98DonColS-142
❑ 98DonCruG-74
❑ 98DonCruP-74
❑ 98DonCruR-74
❑ 98DonEli-61
❑ 98DonEliA-61
❑ 98DonEliS-61
❑ 98DonGolPP-142
❑ 98DonPre-101
❑ 98DonPreSeat-101
❑ 98DonPriCD-142
❑ 98DonPriCE-461
❑ 98DonPriCL-203
❑ 98DonPriCP-651
❑ 98DonSig-78
❑ 98DonSigP-78
❑ 98DonSilPP-142
❑ 98Fle-458
❑ 98FleVin'-91
❑ 98FleVin'C-91
❑ 98Lea-3
❑ 98LeaFraDA-3
❑ 98LeaFraF-3
❑ 98LeaFraM-3
❑ 98LeaFraM-3
❑ 98LeaFraMDC-3
❑ 98LeaFraMDC-3
❑ 98LeaFraMZ2-3
❑ 98LeaRS-97
❑ 98LeaRSLHolo-97
❑ 98LeaRSLong-97
❑ 98LeaRTrue-97
❑ 98MetUni-22
❑ 98MetUniPMG-22
❑ 98Pac-296
❑ 98PacAur-129
❑ 98PacInCage-9
❑ 98PacInv-96
❑ 98PacInvGems-151
❑ 98PacInvPBlue-96
❑ 98PacInvSilv-96
❑ 98PacInvTeam-11
❑ 98PacLatotML-15
❑ 98PacOme-119
❑ 98PacOmeR-119
❑ 98PacOnl-361
❑ 98PacOnlR-361
❑ 98PacOnlWC-361
❑ 98PacPar-158
❑ 98PacParC-158
❑ 98PacParG-158
❑ 98PacParHS-158
❑ 98PacParl-6
❑ 98PacParPB-158
❑ 98PacParR-158
❑ 98PacPlaB-296
❑ 98PacRedT-296
❑ 98PacSil-296
❑ 98PacTeaC-19
❑ 98Pin-65
❑ 98PinArtP-PP58
❑ 98PinIns-73
❑ 98PinInsCE-73
❑ 98PinInsDE-73
❑ 98PinMusC-PP58
❑ 98PinPer-87
❑ 98PinPerPP-87
❑ 98PinPlu-150
❑ 98PinPreP-65
❑ 98Revo-73
❑ 98RevoSS-73
❑ 98ScoRT-97
❑ 98ScoRTSS-PP68
❑ 98ScoRTSSAP-PP68
❑ 98ScoRTSSAP1-PP68
❑ 98SP Aut-116
❑ 98SpoIll-14
❑ 98SpoIllEE-14
❑ 98SpoIllFE-14
❑ 98SpoIllWSF-132
❑ 98SpoIllWSFEE-132
❑ 98SpoIllWSFFE-132
❑ 98SPxFin-288
❑ 98SPxFinR-288
❑ 98SPxFinS-288
❑ 98StaCluFDI-157
❑ 98StaClul-157
❑ 98StaCluOneK-157
❑ 98StaCluPP-157
❑ 98Stu-75
❑ 98StuGPP-75
❑ 98StuSPP-75
❑ 98Top-356
❑ 98TopChr-356
❑ 98TopChrR-356
❑ 98TopDevR-356
❑ 98TopDia-356
❑ 98TopGal-87
❑ 98TopGalGP-87
❑ 98TopGalOPP-87
❑ 98TopGalPPI-87
❑ 98TopGalPPIA-87
❑ 98TopMiniC-356
❑ 98Ult-142
❑ 98Ult-298
❑ 98UltGolM-142
❑ 98UltGolM-298
❑ 98UltMas-142
❑ 98UltMas-298
❑ 98UltPlaM-142
❑ 98UltPlaM-298
❑ 98UppDec-375
❑ 98UppDec-691
❑ 99CroRoyB-90
❑ 99CroRoyL-90
❑ 99CroRoyOD-90
❑ 99Fle-358
❑ 99FleSta9-358
❑ 99FleWarT-358
❑ 99MetUni-155
❑ 99MetUniGM-155
❑ 99MetUniPMG-155
❑ 99Pac-215
❑ 99PacAur-118
❑ 99PacAurOD-118
❑ 99PacCroC-138
❑ 99PacCroC-31
❑ 99PacCroCPB-138
❑ 99PacInv-94
❑ 99PacInvOD-94
❑ 99PacInvPB-94
❑ 99PacPar-149
❑ 99PacParC-149
❑ 99PacParG-149
❑ 99PacParHoloGold-149
❑ 99PacParHS-149
❑ 99PacParOD-149
❑ 99PacParPB-149
❑ 99PacParRed-149
❑ 99PacPlaB-215
❑ 99PacPri-92
❑ 99PacPriHB-92
❑ 99PacPriHG-92
❑ 99PacPriHM-92
❑ 99PacPriHP-92
❑ 99PacPriRed-92
❑ 99PacRed-215
❑ 99SkyPre-25
❑ 99SkyPreR-25
❑ 99SkyThu-48
❑ 99SkyThuRant-48
❑ 99SkyThuRave-48
❑ 99StaClu-324
❑ 99StaCluFDI-324
❑ 99StaCluOoaK-324
❑ 99StaCluPP-324
❑ 99ThuSkySupR-48
❑ 99Top-282
❑ 99TopChr-282
❑ 99TopChrR-282
❑ 99TopMVPP-282
❑ 99Ult-32
❑ 99UltGolM-32
❑ 99UltMas-32
❑ 99UltPlaM-32
❑ 99UppDec-119
❑ 99UppDec-431
❑ 99UppDecEL1-119
❑ 99UppDecEL1-431
❑ 99UppDecEL2-119
❑ 99UppDecEL2-431
❑ 99Vic-259

Bonilla, Denny
❑ 96WisTimRB-7
❑ 97LanJet-7
❑ 98OrlRayM-2

Bonilla, Elin
❑ 98BatMucTI-2

Bonilla, George
❑ 85EveGiaC-2A
❑ 85EveGiaC-2B
❑ 86CliGiaP-3
❑ 88ShrCapP-1289
❑ 89ShrCapP-1855
❑ 90CMC-531
❑ 90PhoFirC-4
❑ 90PhoFirP-2
❑ 90ProAAAF-28

Bonilla, Juan G.
❑ 78WatIndT-3
❑ 80TacTigT-19
❑ 82Don-220
❑ 82Fle-567
❑ 82Top-464
❑ 83AllGamPI-100
❑ 83Don-346
❑ 83Fle-353
❑ 83PadTeal-2
❑ 83Top-563
❑ 84Don-234
❑ 84Fle-295
❑ 84Nes792-168
❑ 84OPC-168
❑ 84Top-168
❑ 84TopSti-152
❑ 84TopTif-168
❑ 85ColCliT-26
❑ 85IntLeaAT-26
❑ 86BalOriP-3
❑ 86TopTra-13T
❑ 86TopTraT-13T
❑ 87Fle-464
❑ 87FleGlo-464
❑ 87OPC-131
❑ 87Top-668
❑ 87TopTif-668
❑ 88ChaLooLTI-2
❑ 91OriCro-40
❑ 92YanWIZ8-14
❑ 98BluOriQ-12

Bonilla, Miguel
❑ 92WelPirC-2
❑ 92WelPirF-1314
❑ 93AugPirC-4
❑ 93AugPirF-1536
❑ 93LetMouF-4143
❑ 93LetMouSP-9

Bonilla, Welnis
❑ 95ButCopKtl-5

Bonin, Greg
❑ 88T/MUmp-56
❑ 89T/MUmp-54
❑ 90T/MUmp-52

Bonine, Eddie
❑ 83TucTorT-1
❑ 84TucTorC-64
❑ 85TucTorC-70
❑ 90GatCitPP-3363
❑ 90GatCitPSP-22

Bonitio, Arturo
❑ 77QuaCitAT-5

Bonitto, Arturo
❑ 78QuaCitAT-5

Bonk, Thomas
❑ 85GreHorT-5

Bonnano, Robert
❑ 96HilStaHWB-21

Bonneau, Britton
❑ 93HunCubC-3
❑ 93HunCubF-3240

Bonneau, Rob
❑ 88WytCubP-1976

Bonnell, Barry (Robert Barry)
❑ 78BraCok-1
❑ 78Hos-142
❑ 78Top-242
❑ 79Top-496
❑ 80OPC-331
❑ 80Top-632
❑ 81Don-272
❑ 81Fle-413
❑ 81OPC-82
❑ 81OPCPos-19
❑ 81Top-558
❑ 82BluJayS-2
❑ 82Don-432
❑ 82Fle-611
❑ 82OPC-99
❑ 82Top-99
❑ 82TopSti-251
❑ 82TopStiV-251
❑ 83AllGamPI-48
❑ 83Don-430
❑ 83Fle-425
❑ 83FleSti-109
❑ 83OPC-281
❑ 83Top-766
❑ 83TopSti-133
❑ 84Don-559
❑ 84Fle-149
❑ 84FleUpd-14
❑ 84MarMot-2
❑ 84Nes792-302
❑ 84OPC-302
❑ 84Top-302
❑ 84TopSti-370
❑ 84TopTif-302
❑ 84TopTra-14T
❑ 84TopTraT-14T
❑ 85Don-191
❑ 85Fle-485
❑ 85Lea-195
❑ 85MarMot-10
❑ 85OPC-107
❑ 85Top-423
❑ 85TopSti-342
❑ 85TopTif-423
❑ 86Fle-460
❑ 86MarMot-10
❑ 86OPC-119
❑ 86Top-119
❑ 86TopTif-119
❑ 91PacSenL-123
❑ 92Nab-6

Bonnelly, Richard
❑ 33Zee-44

Bonner, Al
❑ 12Zee-104

Bonner, Bob (Robert A.)
❑ 80RocRedWT-1
❑ 81RocRedWT-2
❑ 81RocRedWW-21
❑ 82Don-610
❑ 82Top-21
❑ 83Fle-53
❑ 83OriPos-4
❑ 83RocRedWT-14
❑ 84RocRedWT-13
❑ 91OriCro-41

Bonner, Frank J.
❑ 94OriTeal-1

Bonner, Jeff (Jeffry)
❑ 89CliGiaP-892
❑ 90CliGiaB-5
❑ 90CliGiaP-2560
❑ 91Cla/Bes-76
❑ 91SanJosGC-9
❑ 91SanJosGP-22

Bonner, Mark
❑ 82DanSunF-25
❑ 83RedPioT-4
❑ 85MidAngT-5

Bonnici, James
❑ 92BelMarCB-18
❑ 92BelMarF-1446
❑ 93RivPilCLC-4
❑ 94RivPilCLC-8
❑ 95Bes-42
❑ 95PorCitRTI-2
❑ 95SPML-149
❑ 96Bow-307
❑ 96BowFoi-307
❑ 96Exc-102
❑ 96TacRaiB-5
❑ 96Top-425
❑ 97BesAutAS-6
❑ 97TacRai-6
❑ 97Top-202

Bonura, Tony
❑ 86SalAngC-93

Bonura, Zeke (Henry John)
❑ 34BatR31-65
❑ 34BatR31-141
❑ 34DiaStaR-65
❑ 35DiaMatCS3T1-13
❑ 35ExhFou-10
❑ 35GouPuzR-8B
❑ 35GouPuzR-9B
❑ 36ExhFou-10
❑ 36GouBWR-2
❑ 36GouWidPPR-B3
❑ 36GouWidPPR-C4
❑ 36NatChiFPR-13
❑ 36OveCanR-5
❑ 36R31PasP-41
❑ 36SandSW-3
❑ 36WorWidGV-112
❑ 37ExhFou-10
❑ 37OPCBatUV-116
❑ 37WheBB14-1
❑ 37WheBB6-3
❑ 37WheBB7-29A
❑ 37WheBB9-1
❑ 38GouHeaU-252
❑ 38GouHeaU-276
❑ 38WheBB15-1
❑ 39GouPreR303A-5
❑ 39PlaBal-144
❑ 39WorWidGTP-5
❑ 39WorWidGV-3
❑ 40PlaBal-131
❑ 72TCMthe1-180
❑ 74TCMNic-17
❑ 76ChiGre-3
❑ 79DiaGre-139
❑ 82DiaCla-63
❑ 85WhiSoxC-0
❑ 88ConSer5-4
❑ 91ConTSN-237
❑ 93ConTSN-738

Book, Jeremy
❑ 98JohCCTI-5

Booker, Chris
❑ 97WilCubB-2
❑ 98RocCubM-5
❑ 98RocCubTI-5

Booker, Eric
❑ 90ProAaA-168
❑ 90SouOreAB-10
❑ 90SouOreAP-3429
❑ 91Cla/Bes-286
❑ 91ModA'sC-16
❑ 91ModA'sP-3101
❑ 92ClaFS7-34
❑ 92MadMusC-11
❑ 92MadMusF-1248
❑ 92ModA'sC-9

Booker, Greg
❑ 83LasVegSBHN-1
❑ 83PadTeal-3
❑ 84LasVegSC-218
❑ 85Fle-27
❑ 85PadMot-22
❑ 85Top-262
❑ 85TopTif-262
❑ 86LasVegSP-2
❑ 86Top-429
❑ 86TopTif-429
❑ 87TopTra-6T
❑ 87TopTraT-6T
❑ 88Don-311
❑ 88Fle-577
❑ 88FleGlo-577
❑ 88PadCok-51
❑ 88PadSmo-4
❑ 88Sco-447
❑ 88ScoGlo-447
❑ 88Top-727
❑ 88TopClo-14
❑ 88TopTif-727
❑ 89Sco-417
❑ 89Top-319
❑ 89TopBig-194

❑ 89TopTif-319
❑ 89UppDec-641
❑ 90CMC-536
❑ 90PhoFirC-9
❑ 90PhoFirP-3
❑ 90ProAAAF-29
❑ 90PubIntS-44
❑ 93CarLeaAGF-26
❑ 93KinIndC-29
❑ 93KinIndF-2264
❑ 93KinIndTI-30
❑ 94KinIndC-24
❑ 94KinIndF-2661
❑ 97PadMot-28
❑ 98PadMot-28

Booker, Kevin
❑ 92HunCubC-8
❑ 92HunCubF-3160
❑ 93GenCubC-5
❑ 93GenCubF-3189
❑ 94HicCraC-4
❑ 94HicCraF-2187

Booker, Rod
❑ 82OrlTwi8SCT-1
❑ 82TolMudHT-12
❑ 83ArkTraT-19
❑ 84LouRedR-12
❑ 86ArkTraP-2
❑ 86LouRedTI-7
❑ 87CarTeal-1
❑ 87FleUpd-7
❑ 87FleUpdG-7
❑ 87LouRedTI-6
❑ 88LouRedBTI-10
❑ 88StaLinCa-1
❑ 88Top-483
❑ 88TopTif-483
❑ 89LouRedBC-8
❑ 89LouRedBP-1264
❑ 89LouRedBTI-11
❑ 89TopBig-256
❑ 89UppDec-644
❑ 90PhiTas-2
❑ 91Fle-388
❑ 91OPC-186
❑ 91PhiMed-5
❑ 91Top-186
❑ 91TopDesS-186
❑ 91TopMic-186
❑ 91TopTif-186
❑ 92TucTorF-493
❑ 92TucTorS-602

Bool, Al (Albert)
❑ 26Zee-66
❑ 27Zee-45
❑ 28Zee-66

Boomer, Mascot
❑ 95TreThuTI-30
❑ 96TreThuB-30
❑ 97PitMet-30
❑ 98PitMetM-34
❑ 98TreThuM-30

Boone, Aaron
❑ 94BilMusF-3674
❑ 94BilMusSP-3
❑ 94SigRooDP-62
❑ 94SigRooDPS-62
❑ 94StaCluDP-10
❑ 94StaCluDPFDI-10
❑ 95Bes-65
❑ 95Bow-246
❑ 95BowGolF-246
❑ 95Exc-172
❑ 95ExcFirYP-4
❑ 95SPML-40
❑ 95SPMLA-5
❑ 95SPMLDtS-DS17
❑ 95Top-581
❑ 95UppDecML-95
❑ 95UppDecMLFS-95
❑ 96Bow-235
❑ 96BowFoi-235
❑ 96ChaLooB-7
❑ 96Exc-146
❑ 97Bow-139
❑ 97BowBes-125
❑ 97BowBesAR-125
❑ 97BowBesR-125
❑ 97BowChr-147
❑ 97BowChrI-147
❑ 97BowChrIR-147
❑ 97BowChrR-147
❑ 97BowInt-139
❑ 97ColCho-467
❑ 97Fle-754
❑ 97FleTif-754
❑ 97IndInd-7
❑ 97SP-7
❑ 97Top-204
❑ 98Bow-187
❑ 98BowChr-187
❑ 98BowChrGA-187
❑ 98BowChrGAR-187
❑ 98BowChrI-187
❑ 98BowChrIR-187
❑ 98BowChrR-187
❑ 98BowGolA-187
❑ 98BowInt-187
❑ 98CirThu-176
❑ 98CirThuRav-176
❑ 98CirThuSupRav-176
❑ 98ColCho-68
❑ 98Don-283
❑ 98DonColL-223
❑ 98DonColP-707
❑ 98DonGolPP-283
❑ 98DonPre-157
❑ 98DonPreSeat-157
❑ 98DonPriCL-223
❑ 98DonPriCP-707
❑ 98DonSigA-9
❑ 98DonSigAC-13
❑ 98DonSigAM-13
❑ 98DonSilPP-283
❑ 98Fle-37
❑ 98FleUpd-U16
❑ 98IndIndQ-22
❑ 98Lea-23
❑ 98LeaFraDA-23
❑ 98LeaFraF-23
❑ 98LeaFraM-23
❑ 98LeaFraM-23
❑ 98LeaFraMDC-23
❑ 98LeaFraMDC-23
❑ 98LeaFraMZ2-23
❑ 98MetUni-117
❑ 98MetUniPMG-117
❑ 98PacOmeRS-4
❑ 98PacOmeRST5-4
❑ 98PacOnl-186
❑ 98PacOnlR-186
❑ 98PacOnlWC-186
❑ 98PacPar-143
❑ 98PacParC-143
❑ 98PacParG-143
❑ 98PacParHS-143
❑ 98PacParPB-143
❑ 98PacParR-143
❑ 98PinPer-129
❑ 98PinPerPP-129
❑ 98PinPlu-102
❑ 98SP Aut-16
❑ 98SPxFin-22
❑ 98SPxFinR-22
❑ 98SPxFinS-22
❑ 98Stu-140
❑ 98StuGPP-140
❑ 98StuSPP-140
❑ 98Top-254
❑ 98TopChr-254
❑ 98TopChrR-254
❑ 98TopDevR-254
❑ 98TopDia-254
❑ 98TopMiniC-254
❑ 98Ult-226
❑ 98UltGolM-226
❑ 98UltMas-226
❑ 98UltPlaM-226
❑ 98UppDec-265
❑ 98UppDecBCP-BC29
❑ 98UppDecDS-DS48
❑ 98UppDecSF-146
❑ 99Fle-55
❑ 99FleSta9-55
❑ 99FleWarT-55
❑ 99MetUni-136
❑ 99MetUniGM-136
❑ 99MetUniPMG-136
❑ 99Pac-109
❑ 99PacAur-43
❑ 99PacAurOD-43
❑ 99PacPar-61
❑ 99PacParC-61
❑ 99PacParG-61
❑ 99PacParHoloGold-61
❑ 99PacParHS-61
❑ 99PacParOD-61
❑ 99PacParPB-61
❑ 99PacParRed-61
❑ 99PacPlaB-109
❑ 99PacPri-37
❑ 99PacPriHB-37
❑ 99PacPriHG-37
❑ 99PacPriHM-37
❑ 99PacPriHP-37
❑ 99PacPriRed-37
❑ 99PacPriS-60
❑ 99PacPriS206-60
❑ 99PacPriS206R-60
❑ 99PacRed-109
❑ 99SkyPre-131
❑ 99SkyPreR-131
❑ 99SkyThu-52
❑ 99SkyThuRant-52
❑ 99SkyThuRave-52
❑ 99StaClu-306
❑ 99StaCluFDI-306
❑ 99StaCluOoaK-306
❑ 99StaCluPP-306
❑ 99ThuSkySupR-52
❑ 99Vic-109

Boone, Antonio
❑ 91HamRedC-13
❑ 91HamRedP-4028
❑ 92HamRedC-9
❑ 92HamRedF-1580

Boone, Bob (Robert Raymond)
❑ 73LinPor-142
❑ 73OPC-613
❑ 73PhiTeal-2
❑ 73Top-613
❑ 74OPC-131
❑ 74PhiJohP-8
❑ 74Top-131
❑ 74TopSta-71
❑ 75OPC-351
❑ 75PhiPhiP-5
❑ 75PhiProPS-2
❑ 75Top-351
❑ 75TopMin-351
❑ 76OPC-67
❑ 76OPC-318
❑ 76PhiPhiP-3
❑ 76SSP-471
❑ 76Top-67
❑ 76Top-318
❑ 77BurCheD-164
❑ 77OPC-68
❑ 77RCColC-6
❑ 77Top-545
❑ 78Hos-29
❑ 78OPC-141
❑ 78RCColC-24
❑ 78SSP270-33
❑ 78Top-161
❑ 79BasPat-5
❑ 79Hos-113
❑ 79OPC-38
❑ 79PhiBurK-2
❑ 79PhiTeal-2
❑ 79Top-90
❑ 80OPC-246
❑ 80PhiBurK-2
❑ 80PhiBurK-2
❑ 80Top-470
❑ 81AllGamPI-129
❑ 81CokTeaS-97
❑ 81Don-262
❑ 81Fle-4
❑ 81FleStiC-79
❑ 81OPC-290
❑ 81Top-290
❑ 81TopSti-203
❑ 81TopSupHT-79
❑ 82Don-471
❑ 82Fle-240
❑ 82OPC-23
❑ 82OPC-392
❑ 82Top-615
❑ 82Top-616
❑ 82TopSti-77
❑ 82TopStiV-77
❑ 82TopTra-9T
❑ 83AllGamPI-37
❑ 83Don-192
❑ 83Fle-79
❑ 83FleSta-20
❑ 83FleSti-34
❑ 83OPC-366
❑ 83PhiPosGPaM-3
❑ 83Top-765
❑ 83TopSti-45
❑ 84AllGamPI-127
❑ 84AngSmo-3
❑ 84Don-158
❑ 84Fle-509
❑ 84Fle-637
❑ 84Nes792-520
❑ 84OPC-174
❑ 84Top-520
❑ 84TopSti-234
❑ 84TopTif-520
❑ 85AllGamPI-37
❑ 85AngSmo-3
❑ 85Don-230
❑ 85Fle-295
❑ 85OPC-348
❑ 85Top-133
❑ 85Top-348
❑ 85TopSti-228
❑ 85TopTif-133
❑ 85TopTif-348
❑ 86AngSmo-3
❑ 86Don-17
❑ 86Don-230
❑ 86DonSupD-17
❑ 86Fle-149
❑ 86Lea-17
❑ 86OPC-62
❑ 86Top-62
❑ 86TopSti-179
❑ 86TopTif-62
❑ 87Don-233
❑ 87DonHig-41
❑ 87Fle-73
❑ 87FleAwaW-4
❑ 87FleGlo-73
❑ 87Lea-202
❑ 87OPC-166
❑ 87Top-166
❑ 87Top-556
❑ 87TopSti-180
❑ 87TopTif-166
❑ 87TopTif-556
❑ 88AlaGolAA60TI-10
❑ 88AngSmo-9
❑ 88Don-305
❑ 88DonBasB-3
❑ 88Fle-485
❑ 88FleGlo-485
❑ 88Lea-151
❑ 88OPC-158
❑ 88OPCBoxB-D
❑ 88PanSti-39
❑ 88Sco-63
❑ 88ScoGlo-63
❑ 88Spo-212
❑ 88StaLinAn-1
❑ 88Top-498
❑ 88TopBig-30
❑ 88TopSti-5
❑ 88TopSti-182
❑ 88TopTif-498
❑ 88TopUKM-6
❑ 88TopUKMT-6
❑ 88TopWaxBC-D
❑ 89AngSmo-17
❑ 89Bow-119
❑ 89BowTif-119
❑ 89ClaTraP-187
❑ 89Don-170
❑ 89DonBasB-263
❑ 89DonTra-5
❑ 89Fle-469
❑ 89FleGlo-469
❑ 89FleUpd-36
❑ 89OPC-243
❑ 89PanSti-287
❑ 89Sco-233
❑ 89ScoHot1S-81
❑ 89ScoRoo-74T
❑ 89Spo-40
❑ 89Top-243
❑ 89Top-404
❑ 89TopBasT-135
❑ 89TopBig-269
❑ 89TopSti-175
❑ 89TopStiB-22
❑ 89TopTif-243
❑ 89TopTif-404
❑ 89TopTra-12T
❑ 89TopTraT-12T
❑ 89UppDec-119
❑ 89UppDec-767
❑ 90Bow-373
❑ 90BowTif-373
❑ 90Don-326
❑ 90DonBesA-50
❑ 90Fle-102
❑ 90FleAwaW-5
❑ 90FleCan-102
❑ 90Lea-46
❑ 90MLBBasB-107
❑ 90OPC-671
❑ 90PubIntS-278
❑ 90PubIntS-343
❑ 90RoyPos-3
❑ 90Sco-60
❑ 90Spo-40
❑ 90Top-671
❑ 90TopBig-268
❑ 90TopTif-671
❑ 90UppDec-271
❑ 91Don-356
❑ 91Fle-551
❑ 91UppDec-502
❑ 92TacTigS-549
❑ 94RedKah-33
❑ 94TedWil-72
❑ 94Yoo-3
❑ 96RoyPol-3
❑ 97RoyPol-5

Boone, Bret
❑ 88AlaGolTI-3
❑ 90TopMag-101
❑ 91Bow-261
❑ 91JacSunLD-330
❑ 91JacSunP-155
❑ 91LinDriAA-330
❑ 92Bow-511
❑ 92CalCanF-3740
❑ 92CalCanS-55
❑ 92DonRooP-BC2
❑ 92FleUpd-54
❑ 92LeaGolR-BC12
❑ 92ProFS7-142
❑ 92ScoRoo-104T
❑ 92SkyAAAF-24
❑ 92TriA AAS-55
❑ 92UppDec-771
❑ 93Bow-219
❑ 93ClaFS7-63
❑ 93Don-188
❑ 93Fle-304
❑ 93Lea-546
❑ 93MariStaClu-6
❑ 93OPC-13
❑ 93PacSpa-280
❑ 93Pin-243
❑ 93PinRooTP-5
❑ 93PinTea2-8
❑ 93Sco-335
❑ 93ScoProaG-3
❑ 93Sel-326
❑ 93SelChaR-21
❑ 93SelRoo-58T
❑ 93StaClu-532
❑ 93StaCluFDI-532
❑ 93StaCluMOP-532
❑ 93Top-808
❑ 93TopGol-808
❑ 93TopInaM-808
❑ 93TopInaR-808
❑ 93TopMic-808
❑ 93Toy-35
❑ 93TriPla-133
❑ 93Ult-266
❑ 93UppDec-65
❑ 93UppDecGold-65
❑ 93UppDecSH-HI6
❑ 94Bow-458
❑ 94ColC-59
❑ 94ColC-544
❑ 94ColChoGS-59
❑ 94ColChoGS-544
❑ 94ColChoSS-59
❑ 94ColChoSS-544
❑ 94Don-413
❑ 94Fin-386
❑ 94FinRef-386
❑ 94Fla-143
❑ 94Fle-280
❑ 94FleExtB-227
❑ 94FleUpd-114
❑ 94FUnPac-105
❑ 94Lea-233
❑ 94LeaL-94
❑ 94OPC-170
❑ 94PanSti-116
❑ 94Pin-510
❑ 94PinArtP-510
❑ 94PinMusC-510
❑ 94RedKah-1
❑ 94Sco-568
❑ 94ScoBoyoS-26
❑ 94ScoGolR-568
❑ 94ScoRoo-RT60
❑ 94ScoRooGR-RT60
❑ 94Sel-265
❑ 94SP-158
❑ 94SPDieC-158
❑ 94SpoRoo-14
❑ 94SpoRooAP-14
❑ 94SpoRooS-14
❑ 94StaClu-671
❑ 94StaCluFDI-671
❑ 94StaCluGR-671
❑ 94StaCluMOP-671
❑ 94Stu-167
❑ 94Top-659
❑ 94TopGol-659
❑ 94TopSpa-659
❑ 94TopTra-77T
❑ 94Ult-468
❑ 94UppDec-448
❑ 94UppDecED-448
❑ 94USPlaCR-8C
❑ 95Baz-49
❑ 95ColCho-427
❑ 95ColChoGS-427
❑ 95ColChoSE-198
❑ 95ColChoSEGS-198
❑ 95ColChoSESS-198
❑ 95ColChoSS-427
❑ 95Don-26
❑ 95DonPreP-26
❑ 95DonTopotO-208
❑ 95Emo-115
❑ 95Fin-54
❑ 95FinRef-54
❑ 95Fla-119
❑ 95Fle-429
❑ 95Lea-97
❑ 95LeaLim-22
❑ 95Pac-99
❑ 95PacGolP-29
❑ 95PacPri-32
❑ 95PanSti-44
❑ 95Pin-317
❑ 95PinArtP-317
❑ 95PinMusC-317
❑ 95PinUps-US27
❑ 95RedKah-3
❑ 95Sco-455
❑ 95ScoGolR-455
❑ 95ScoHaloG-HG95
❑ 95ScoPlaTS-455
❑ 95Sel-8
❑ 95SelArtP-8
❑ 95SP-44
❑ 95SPCha-37
❑ 95SPChaDC-37
❑ 95Spo-47
❑ 95SpoArtP-47
❑ 95SPSil-44
❑ 95SPSpeF-31
❑ 95StaClu-252
❑ 95StaCluFDI-252
❑ 95StaCluMOP-252
❑ 95StaCluSTDW-RE252
❑ 95StaCluSTWS-252
❑ 95StaCluVR-124
❑ 95StaCluVRMO-124
❑ 95Stu-139
❑ 95Sum-59
❑ 95SumNthD-59
❑ 95Top-113
❑ 95Top-385
❑ 95TopCyb-73
❑ 95TopD3-33
❑ 95TopEmb-18
❑ 95TopEmbGI-18
❑ 95Ult-363
❑ 95UltGolM-363
❑ 95UppDec-165
❑ 95UppDecED-165
❑ 95UppDecEDG-165
❑ 95UppDecPLL-R58
❑ 95UppDecPLLE-R58
❑ 95UppDecSE-164
❑ 95UppDecSEG-164
❑ 95UppDecSoaD-SD14
❑ 96Baz-47
❑ 96Cir-114
❑ 96CirRav-114
❑ 96ColCho-515
❑ 96ColChoGS-515
❑ 96ColChoSS-515
❑ 96Don-178
❑ 96DonPreP-178
❑ 96EmoXL-161
❑ 96Fin-S65
❑ 96FinRef-S65
❑ 96Fla-227
❑ 96Fle-334

❑ 96FleTif-334
❑ 96Lea-65
❑ 96LeaPrePB-65
❑ 96LeaPrePG-65
❑ 96LeaPrePS-65
❑ 96MetUni-147
❑ 96MetUniP-147
❑ 96Pac-35
❑ 96PacPri-P14
❑ 96PacPriG-P14
❑ 96PanSti-56
❑ 96Pin-235
❑ 96PinAfi-110
❑ 96PinAfiAP-110
❑ 96PinArtP-135
❑ 96PinFoil-235
❑ 96PinSta-135
❑ 96ProSta-105
❑ 96Sco-70
❑ 96ScoDugC-A58
❑ 96ScoDugCAP-A58
❑ 96Sel-88
❑ 96SelArtP-88
❑ 96SelTeaN-25
❑ 96SP-62
❑ 96StaClu-168
❑ 96StaCluEPB-168
❑ 96StaCluEPG-168
❑ 96StaCluEPS-168
❑ 96StaCluMOP-168
❑ 96Stu-62
❑ 96StuPrePB-62
❑ 96StuPrePG-62
❑ 96StuPrePS-62
❑ 96Sum-133
❑ 96SumAbo&B-133
❑ 96SumArtP-133
❑ 96SumFoi-133
❑ 96Top-162
❑ 96TopGal-119
❑ 96TopGalPG-PG4
❑ 96TopGalPPI-119
❑ 96Ult-174
❑ 96UltGolM-174
❑ 96UppDec-50
❑ 96UppDecPRE-R56
❑ 96UppDecPreR-R56
❑ 97Bow-50
❑ 97BowInt-50
❑ 97Cir-125
❑ 97CirRav-125
❑ 97ColCho-302
❑ 97Don-195
❑ 97DonGolPP-195
❑ 97DonSilPP-195
❑ 97FlaShoLC-86
❑ 97FlaShoLeg0-86
❑ 97FlaShoLeg1-86
❑ 97FlaShoM-A86
❑ 97FlaShoM-B86
❑ 97FlaShoM-C86
❑ 97FlaShoR0-86
❑ 97FlaShoR1-86
❑ 97FlaShoR2-86
❑ 97Fle-290
❑ 97FleTif-290
❑ 97Lea-163
❑ 97LeaFraM-163
❑ 97LeaFraMDC-163
❑ 97MetUni-44
❑ 97Pac-262
❑ 97PacLigB-262
❑ 97PacPri-90
❑ 97PacPriLB-90
❑ 97PacPriP-90
❑ 97PacSil-262
❑ 97Sco-63
❑ 97ScoArtPWB-63
❑ 97ScoPreS-63
❑ 97ScoShoS-63
❑ 97ScoShoSAP-63
❑ 97SP-51
❑ 97StaClu-170
❑ 97StaCluMOP-170
❑ 97Top-135
❑ 97TopChr-52
❑ 97TopChrR-52
❑ 97Ult-174
❑ 97UltGolME-174
❑ 97UltPlaME-174
❑ 97UppDec-340
❑ 98ColCho-343
❑ 98CroRoy-38
❑ 98Fle-528
❑ 98Pac-261
❑ 98PacOme-62
❑ 98PacOmeR-62
❑ 98PacOnl-187
❑ 98PacOnlR-187
❑ 98PacOnlWC-187
❑ 98PacPar-144
❑ 98PacParC-144
❑ 98PacParG-144
❑ 98PacParHS-144
❑ 98PacParPB-144
❑ 98PacParR-144
❑ 98PacPlaB-261
❑ 98PacRedT-261
❑ 98PacSil-261
❑ 98Revo-39
❑ 98RevoSS-39
❑ 98SkyDugA-11
❑ 98SkyDugAIA-11
❑ 98SPxFin-264
❑ 98SPxFinR-264
❑ 98SPxFinS-264
❑ 98StaCluFDI-240
❑ 98StaCluI-240
❑ 98StaCluOneK-240
❑ 98StaCluPP-240
❑ 98Top-232
❑ 98TopChr-232
❑ 98TopChrR-232
❑ 98TopDevR-232
❑ 98TopDia-232
❑ 98TopMiniC-232
❑ 98Ult-445
❑ 98UltGolM-445
❑ 98UltMas-445
❑ 98UltPlaM-445
❑ 98UppDec-336
❑ 99199Fin-157
❑ 99Bow-226
❑ 99BowGol-226
❑ 99BowInt-226
❑ 99FinGolRef-157
❑ 99FinRef-157
❑ 99FlaShoLeg1-107
❑ 99FlaShoLeg2-107
❑ 99FlaShoLeg3-107
❑ 99FlaShoLegM1-107
❑ 99FlaShoLegM2-107
❑ 99FlaShoLegM3-107
❑ 99FlaShoR1-107
❑ 99FlaShoR2-107
❑ 99FlaShoR3-107
❑ 99Fle-89
❑ 99FleSta9-89
❑ 99FleWarT-89
❑ 99Pac-110
❑ 99PacCroC-72
❑ 99PacCroCPB-72
❑ 99PacInv-11
❑ 99PacInvOD-11
❑ 99PacInvPB-11
❑ 99PacOme-18
❑ 99PacOmeC-18
❑ 99PacOmeG-18
❑ 99PacOmePB-18
❑ 99PacPar-20
❑ 99PacParC-20
❑ 99PacParG-20
❑ 99PacParHoloGold-20
❑ 99PacParHS-20
❑ 99PacParOD-20
❑ 99PacParPB-20
❑ 99PacParRed-20
❑ 99PacPlaB-110
❑ 99PacPriS-61
❑ 99PacPriS206-61
❑ 99PacPriS206R-61
❑ 99PacRed-110
❑ 99SkyMolMOA-3
❑ 99SkyThu-14
❑ 99SkyThuRant-14
❑ 99SkyThuRave-14
❑ 99StaClu-314
❑ 99StaCluFDI-314
❑ 99StaCluOoaK-314
❑ 99StaCluPP-314
❑ 99ThuSkySupR-14
❑ 99Top-170
❑ 99TopChr-170
❑ 99TopChrR-170
❑ 99TopMVPP-170
❑ 99TopOpeD-94
❑ 99Ult-51
❑ 99UltGolM-51
❑ 99UltMas-51
❑ 99UltPlaM-51
❑ 99UppDec-310
❑ 99UppDecEL1-310
❑ 99UppDecEL2-310
❑ 99Vic-39

Boone, Danny
❑ 79SalLakCGT-23B
❑ 81PadFamF-3
❑ 82Don-187
❑ 82Fle-568
❑ 82Top-407
❑ 83TucTorT-2
❑ 84VanCanC-36
❑ 85AncGlaPTI-5
❑ 90CMC-689
❑ 90El PasDAGTI-38
❑ 90ProAAAF-455
❑ 90RocRedWC-27
❑ 90RocRedWGC-15
❑ 90RocRedWP-698
❑ 91OriCro-42
❑ 91PacSenL-44
❑ 91Sco-715

Boone, Ike (Isaac Morgan)
❑ 26Zee-40
❑ 28Zee-89
❑ 29Zee-38
❑ 30Zee-45
❑ 36GouWidPPR-D4
❑ 87ConSer2-24
❑ 90DodTar-61

Boone, Luke (Lute Joseph)
❑ 14B18B-20
❑ 15SpoNewM-12

Boone, Ray (Raymond Otis)
❑ 49IndTeal-5
❑ 50IndNumN-4
❑ 50IndTeal-4
❑ 51Bow-54
❑ 51IndHag-1
❑ 51TopRedB-23
❑ 52Bow-214
❑ 52IndNumN-13
❑ 52Top-55
❑ 53BowC-79
❑ 53IndPenCBP-5
❑ 53Top-25
❑ 54Top-77
❑ 55RedMan-AL1
❑ 55RobGouS-11
❑ 55RobGouW-11
❑ 55Top-65
❑ 55TopDouH-113
❑ 56Top-6
❑ 56TopHocF-A7
❑ 56TopHocF-B9
❑ 56TopPin-36
❑ 57Top-102
❑ 58Top-185
❑ 59Top-252
❑ 60BraLaktL-3
❑ 60Top-281
❑ 76OPC-67
❑ 76Top-67
❑ 79TCM50-179
❑ 81TigDetN-84
❑ 81WhiSox1T-21
❑ 83TigAlKS-15
❑ 83TopRep5-55
❑ 85TCMPpl1-39
❑ 85Top-133
❑ 85TopTif-133
❑ 91TopArc1-25
❑ 92BazQua5A-6
❑ 93TedWil-36
❑ 93UppDecAH-15
❑ 94TopArc1-77
❑ 94TopArc1G-77
❑ 94UppDecAH-22
❑ 94UppDecAH1-22

Boone, Ron
❑ 75IowOakT-2

Bootay, Kevin
❑ 86SalRedBP-1
❑ 86TulDriTI-16
❑ 88TexLeaAGS-9
❑ 88TulDriTI-13
❑ 89ScrRedBC-24
❑ 89ScrRedBP-713

Booth, David
❑ 88PocGiaP-2098
❑ 89SanJosGB-10
❑ 89SanJosGCLC-228
❑ 89SanJosGP-440
❑ 89SanJosGS-2

Boothby, John
❑ 90WauTimS-4
❑ 91BriBanF-12
❑ 95AusFut-82
❑ 95AusFut-95

Booty, Josh
❑ 94Cla#1DPMF-DD5
❑ 94ClaUpdCotC-CC5
❑ 94SigRooDP-1
❑ 94SigRooDPS-1
❑ 95ActPacF-56
❑ 95ElmPioTI-1
❑ 95ElmPioUTI-1
❑ 95Exc-193
❑ 95KanCouCLTI-1
❑ 95KanCouCTI-35
❑ 95ScoDraP-DP5
❑ 95SigRooDDS-DD2
❑ 95SigRooDDSS-DD2
❑ 95SPML-63
❑ 95UppDecML-135
❑ 95UppDecML-219
❑ 95UppDecMLFS-135
❑ 95UppDecMLFS-219
❑ 95UppDecMLOP-OP11
❑ 96Bow-161
❑ 96BowFoi-161
❑ 96KanCouCTI-2
❑ 96KanCouCUTI-1
❑ 96KanCouCUTI-2
❑ 96MauStiHWB-22
❑ 97EasLeaTPB-22
❑ 97Lea-179
❑ 97LeaFraM-179
❑ 97LeaFraMDC-179
❑ 97PorSeaD-5
❑ 98Don-289
❑ 98DonGolPP-289
❑ 98DonSilPP-289
❑ 98Fle-524
❑ 98LeaRS-270
❑ 98LeaRSLHolo-270
❑ 98LeaRSLong-270
❑ 98LeaRTrue-270
❑ 98PacOme-94
❑ 98PacOmeR-94
❑ 98PacOnl-290
❑ 98PacOnlR-290
❑ 98PacOnlWC-290
❑ 98SpoIll-159
❑ 98SpoIllEE-159
❑ 98SpoIllFE-159
❑ 98UppDec-377
❑ 99MetUni-255
❑ 99MetUniGM-255
❑ 99MetUniPMG-255
❑ 99Ult-245
❑ 99UltGolM-245
❑ 99UltMas-245
❑ 99UltPlaM-245

Boozer, John
❑ 63Top-29A
❑ 63Top-29B
❑ 64PhiPhiB-5
❑ 64Top-16
❑ 64TopVen-16
❑ 65OPC-184
❑ 65Top-184
❑ 66Top-324
❑ 66TopVen-324
❑ 68OPC-173
❑ 68Top-173
❑ 68TopVen-173
❑ 69Top-599
❑ 89ChaLooLITI-3

Boras, Scott
❑ 77St.PetCT-17

Borbon, Ernie
❑ 82VerBeaDT-2
❑ 83AlbDukTc-21
❑ 84AlbDukCr-159
❑ 85DomLeaS-54

Borbon, Pedro
❑ 70OPC-358
❑ 70Top-358
❑ 71OPC-613
❑ 71Top-613
❑ 73OPC-492
❑ 73Top-492
❑ 74OPC-410
❑ 74Top-410
❑ 74TopSta-23
❑ 75OPC-157
❑ 75Top-157
❑ 75TopMin-157
❑ 76LinSup-101
❑ 76OPC-77
❑ 76RedParC-3
❑ 76SSP-24
❑ 76Top-77
❑ 77PepGloD-54
❑ 77Top-581
❑ 78OPC-199
❑ 78Pep-6
❑ 78SSP270-111
❑ 78Top-220
❑ 79OPC-164
❑ 79Top-326
❑ 80Top-627
❑ 89PacSenL-49
❑ 89T/MSenL-11
❑ 89TopSenL-77
❑ 90EliSenL-93
❑ 92UppDecS-14

Borbon, Pedro Jr.
❑ 90Bes-31
❑ 90BurBraB-1
❑ 90BurBraP-2340
❑ 90BurBraS-4
❑ 90DurBulUTI-2
❑ 90MidLeaASGS-58
❑ 90ProAaA-124
❑ 91DurBulC-10
❑ 91DurBulP-1536
❑ 92GreBraF-1148
❑ 92GreBraS-229
❑ 93Bow-226
❑ 93LimRocDWB-45
❑ 93RicBraBB-11
❑ 93RicBraF-178
❑ 93RicBraP-5
❑ 93RicBraRC-8
❑ 93RicBraRC-7
❑ 94BraUSPC-5C
❑ 94RicBraF-2839
❑ 94StaClu-233
❑ 94StaCluFDI-233
❑ 94StaCluGR-233
❑ 94StaCluMOP-233
❑ 94StaCluT-42
❑ 94StaCluTFDI-42
❑ 95FleUpd-89
❑ 96ColCho-391T
❑ 96ColCho-459
❑ 96ColChoGS-459
❑ 96ColChoSS-459
❑ 96Don-324
❑ 96DonPreP-324
❑ 96Fle-288
❑ 96FleTif-288
❑ 96LeaSigEA-12
❑ 96MLBPin-6
❑ 96Pac-3
❑ 97PacPriGotD-GD110
❑ 98Pac-231
❑ 98PacPlaB-231
❑ 98PacRedT-231
❑ 98PacSil-231
❑ 99DodPol-2

Borcherding, Mark
❑ 89BilMusP-2066
❑ 90CedRapRB-24
❑ 90ChaWheP-2232
❑ 91CedRapRC-2
❑ 91CedRapRP-2710
❑ 91Cla/Bes-372
❑ 91MidLeaAP-MWL21

Borchers, George
❑ 88SFHesCreN32-2

Borchers, Rick
❑ 79TacTugT-3
❑ 80TacTigT-21
❑ 82ChaLooT-20

Borchert, Shane
❑ 89CliGiaP-889
❑ 90MadMusB-27
❑ 91MadMusC-21
❑ 92RenSilSCLC-62

Bordagaray, Frenchy (Stanley)
❑ 32Zee-79
❑ 33Zee-28
❑ 36ExhFou-2
❑ 36GouBWR-3
❑ 36GouWidPPR-A9
❑ 36NatChiFPR-85
❑ 36R31PasP-28
❑ 38CloFotW-9
❑ 38RedOraW-3
❑ 39OrcPhoAP-3
❑ 39PlaBal-75
❑ 39RedTeal-3
❑ 42DodTeal-2
❑ 43DodTeal-2
❑ 77CinRedT-21
❑ 85BigLeaC3-86
❑ 90DodTar-62

Borden, Joe
❑ 63GadFunC-47

Border, Bob
❑ 78QuaCitAT-6
❑ 80ElPasDT-10

Border, Mark
❑ 82IdaFalAT-3

Borders, Charlie
❑ 75SpoIndC-4
❑ 76SacSolC-11

Borders, Ilya
❑ 92SpoIllFK1-768
❑ 97St.PauS-2

Borders, Pat
❑ 85KinBluJT-15
❑ 86KnoBluJP-3
❑ 87KnoBluJP-1513
❑ 88BluJayFS-4
❑ 88DonRoo-12
❑ 88FleUpd-65
❑ 88FleUpdG-65
❑ 88ScoRoo-99T
❑ 88ScoRooG-99T
❑ 88TopTra-17T
❑ 88TopTraT-17T
❑ 89BluJayFS-3
❑ 89Don-560
❑ 89Fle-227
❑ 89FleGlo-227
❑ 89OPC-343
❑ 89PanSti-464
❑ 89Sco-198
❑ 89ScoHot1R-91
❑ 89ScoYouSI-11
❑ 89Top-693
❑ 89TopSti-191
❑ 89TopTif-693
❑ 89UppDec-593
❑ 90BluJayFS-4
❑ 90Bow-521
❑ 90BowTif-521
❑ 90ClaYel-T39
❑ 90Don-560
❑ 90Fle-77
❑ 90FleCan-77
❑ 90Lea-343
❑ 90OPC-191
❑ 90PanSti-175
❑ 90PubIntS-510
❑ 90Sco-288
❑ 90Spo-45
❑ 90Top-191
❑ 90TopBig-60
❑ 90TopTif-191
❑ 90UppDec-113
❑ 91BluJayFS-3
❑ 91BluJayFS-4
❑ 91BluJayS-11
❑ 91Bow-14
❑ 91Don-317
❑ 91Fle-171
❑ 91Lea-23
❑ 91OPC-49
❑ 91PanFreS-335
❑ 91PanSti-156
❑ 91Sco-425
❑ 91StaClu-266
❑ 91Top-49A
❑ 91Top-49B
❑ 91TopDesS-49
❑ 91TopMic-49
❑ 91TopTif-49
❑ 91Ult-359
❑ 91UppDec-147
❑ 92BluJayP-2
❑ 92Bow-646
❑ 92Don-379
❑ 92Fle-325
❑ 92Lea-324
❑ 92LeaBlaG-324
❑ 92OPC-563
❑ 92PanSti-24
❑ 92Pin-421
❑ 92Sco-288
❑ 92StaClu-77
❑ 92Stu-253
❑ 92Top-563
❑ 92TopGol-563
❑ 92TopGolW-563
❑ 92TopMic-563
❑ 92Ult-144
❑ 92UppDec-140

❑ 93BluJayCP1-2
❑ 93BluJayCP1-5
❑ 93BluJayD-21
❑ 93BluJayD4-4
❑ 93BluJayDM-11
❑ 93BluJayDM-25
❑ 93BluJayDM-34
❑ 93BluJayDWS-8
❑ 93BluJayFS-3
❑ 93Bow-687
❑ 93DiaMar-16
❑ 93Don-115
❑ 93Fin-133
❑ 93FinRef-133
❑ 93Fla-288
❑ 93Fle-332
❑ 93HumDumC-23
❑ 93Lea-157
❑ 93OPC-58
❑ 93OPCWorC-2
❑ 93OPCWorSH-1
❑ 93PacSpa-321
❑ 93PanSti-25
❑ 93Pin-203
❑ 93PosCan-1
❑ 93Sco-642
❑ 93Sel-369
❑ 93SP-46
❑ 93StaClu-1
❑ 93StaCluFDI-1
❑ 93StaCluM-136
❑ 93StaCluMOP-1
❑ 93Stu-36
❑ 93Top-322
❑ 93TopGol-322
❑ 93TopInaM-322
❑ 93TopInaR-322
❑ 93TopMic-322
❑ 93TriPla-134
❑ 93Ult-287
❑ 93UltAwaW-21
❑ 93UppDec-149
❑ 93UppDecGold-149
❑ 94BluJayP-2
❑ 94BluJayUSPC-4C
❑ 94BluJayUSPC-12H
❑ 94Bow-441
❑ 94ColC-60
❑ 94ColChoGS-60
❑ 94ColChoSS-60
❑ 94Don-54
❑ 94Fin-266
❑ 94FinRef-266
❑ 94Fla-348
❑ 94Fle-325
❑ 94FleExtB-187
❑ 94Lea-179
❑ 94OPC-178
❑ 94OPCWorC-8
❑ 94Pac-633
❑ 94PanSti-135
❑ 94Pin-477
❑ 94PinArtP-477
❑ 94PinMusC-477
❑ 94PosCan-7
❑ 94Sco-343
❑ 94ScoGolR-343
❑ 94Sel-74
❑ 94StaClu-305
❑ 94StaCluFDI-305
❑ 94StaCluGR-305
❑ 94StaCluMOP-305
❑ 94StaCluT-165
❑ 94StaCluTFDI-165
❑ 94Stu-25
❑ 94Top-219
❑ 94TopGol-219
❑ 94TopSpa-219
❑ 94Ult-135
❑ 94UppDec-417
❑ 94UppDecED-417
❑ 95BluJayUSPC-5H
❑ 95BluJayUSPC-12C
❑ 95ColCho-146
❑ 95ColChoGS-146
❑ 95ColChoSS-146
❑ 95Don-499
❑ 95DonPreP-499
❑ 95Fla-263
❑ 95Fle-88
❑ 95FleUpd-44
❑ 95Lea-396
❑ 95Pac-436
❑ 95Sco-154
❑ 95ScoGolR-154
❑ 95ScoPlaTS-154
❑ 95StaClu-141
❑ 95StaClu-546
❑ 95StaCluFDI-141
❑ 95StaCluMOP-141
❑ 95StaCluMOP-546
❑ 95StaCluSTWS-141
❑ 95StaCluSTWS-546
❑ 95Top-424
❑ 95TopCyb-222
❑ 95TopTra-151T
❑ 95UppDec-417
❑ 95UppDecED-417
❑ 95UppDecEDG-417
❑ 96CarPol-3
❑ 96FleUpd-U184
❑ 96FleUpdTC-U184
❑ 96LeaSigEA-11
❑ 97BluJayS-42
❑ 97PacPriGotD-GD27
❑ 98PacOnl-213
❑ 98PacOnlR-213
❑ 98PacOnlWC-213

Bordi, Rich
❑ 81TacTigT-10
❑ 82SalLakCGT-4
❑ 82Top-531
❑ 83IowCubT-1
❑ 84CubChiT-2
❑ 84CubSev-42
❑ 85Don-289
❑ 85Fle-49
❑ 85FleUpd-8
❑ 85Lea-166
❑ 85Top-357
❑ 85TopTif-357
❑ 85TopTifT-7T
❑ 85TopTra-7T
❑ 85YanTCMP-8
❑ 86BalOriP-4
❑ 86Don-518
❑ 86Fle-101
❑ 86FleUpd-16
❑ 86Top-94
❑ 86TopTif-94
❑ 86TopTra-14T
❑ 86TopTraT-14T
❑ 87ColCliP-3
❑ 87ColCliP-18
❑ 87ColCliT-2
❑ 87Don-213
❑ 87Fle-465
❑ 87FleGlo-465
❑ 87Top-638
❑ 87TopTif-638
❑ 88TacTigC-1
❑ 88TacTigP-627
❑ 89TacTigC-1
❑ 89TacTigP-1544
❑ 90PhoFirP-4
❑ 90ProAAAF-30
❑ 91OriCro-43
❑ 92YanWIZ8-15

Bordick, Mike (Michael)
❑ 87ModA'sC-1
❑ 87ModA'sP-6
❑ 88HunStaTI-1
❑ 88SouLeaAJ-4
❑ 89TacTigC-23
❑ 89TacTigP-1565
❑ 90ProAAAF-145
❑ 90TacTigP-98
❑ 91Cla2-T58
❑ 91LinDriAAA-527
❑ 91Sco-339
❑ 91SouOreAAP-SOA34
❑ 91TacTigLD-527
❑ 91TopDeb90-19
❑ 92AthMot-20
❑ 92Bow-350
❑ 92Don-505
❑ 92Fle-251
❑ 92Lea-364
❑ 92LeaBlaG-364
❑ 92OPC-317
❑ 92OPCPre-5
❑ 92Pin-462
❑ 92Sco-681
❑ 92StaClu-272
❑ 92Top-317
❑ 92TopGol-317
❑ 92TopGolW-317
❑ 92TopMic-317
❑ 92Ult-419
❑ 92UppDec-727
❑ 93AthMot-7
❑ 93AthStaC-18
❑ 93Bow-401
❑ 93ClaGam-16
❑ 93Don-83
❑ 93Don-264
❑ 93DonSpiotG-SG1
❑ 93Fla-256
❑ 93Fle-291
❑ 93Lea-117
❑ 93OPC-57
❑ 93PacSpa-217
❑ 93PanSti-16
❑ 93Pin-85
❑ 93Sco-100
❑ 93Sel-208
❑ 93SP-37
❑ 93StaClu-80
❑ 93StaCluFDI-80
❑ 93StaCluMOP-80
❑ 93Top-639
❑ 93TopGol-639
❑ 93TopInaM-639
❑ 93TopInaR-639
❑ 93TopMic-639
❑ 93Toy-3
❑ 93TriPla-45
❑ 93TriPla-64
❑ 93Ult-254
❑ 93UppDec-189
❑ 93UppDecGold-189
❑ 94A'sMot-5
❑ 94Bow-576
❑ 94ColC-61
❑ 94ColChoGS-61
❑ 94ColChoSS-61
❑ 94Don-81
❑ 94Fin-81
❑ 94FinRef-81
❑ 94Fla-89
❑ 94Fle-255
❑ 94FleExtB-145
❑ 94Lea-128
❑ 94OPC-264
❑ 94Pac-446
❑ 94PanSti-107
❑ 94Pin-463
❑ 94PinArtP-463
❑ 94PinMusC-463
❑ 94Sco-491
❑ 94ScoGolR-491
❑ 94Sel-176
❑ 94StaClu-227
❑ 94StaCluFDI-227
❑ 94StaCluGR-227
❑ 94StaCluMOP-227
❑ 94StaCluMOP-ST25
❑ 94StaCluST-ST25
❑ 94Top-188
❑ 94TopGol-188
❑ 94TopSpa-188
❑ 94TriPla-1
❑ 94Ult-105
❑ 94UppDec-174
❑ 94UppDecED-174
❑ 95A'sCHP-6
❑ 95AthMot-10
❑ 95ColCho-127
❑ 95ColChoGS-127
❑ 95ColChoSS-127
❑ 95Don-148
❑ 95DonPreP-148
❑ 95DonTopotO-133
❑ 95Fin-176
❑ 95FinRef-176
❑ 95Fle-240
❑ 95Lea-81
❑ 95Pac-310
❑ 95Pin-219
❑ 95PinArtP-219
❑ 95PinMusC-219
❑ 95Sco-72
❑ 95ScoGolR-72
❑ 95ScoPlaTS-72
❑ 95StaClu-245
❑ 95StaCluFDI-245
❑ 95StaCluMOP-245
❑ 95StaCluSTWS-245
❑ 95Top-281
❑ 95TopCyb-153
❑ 95Ult-91
❑ 95UltGolM-91
❑ 95UppDec-281
❑ 95UppDecED-281
❑ 95UppDecEDG-281
❑ 96A'sMot-5
❑ 96ColCho-639
❑ 96ColChoGS-639
❑ 96ColChoSS-639
❑ 96Don-130
❑ 96DonPreP-130
❑ 96Fla-144
❑ 96Fle-204
❑ 96FleTif-204
❑ 96LeaSigA-29
❑ 96LeaSigAG-29
❑ 96LeaSigAS-29
❑ 96Pac-391
❑ 96Pin-358
❑ 96PinFoil-358
❑ 96SelCer-86
❑ 96SelCerAP-86
❑ 96SelCerCB-86
❑ 96SelCerCR-86
❑ 96SelCerMB-86
❑ 96SelCerMG-86
❑ 96SelCerMR-86
❑ 96SelTeaN-5
❑ 96StaClu-89
❑ 96StaCluMOP-89
❑ 96Sum-95
❑ 96SumAbo&B-95
❑ 96SumArtP-95
❑ 96SumFoi-95
❑ 96Ult-398
❑ 96UltGolM-398
❑ 96UppDec-166
❑ 96Zen-68
❑ 96ZenArtP-68
❑ 96ZenMoz-21
❑ 97BalOriP-4
❑ 97BalOriP-5
❑ 97Cir-120
❑ 97CirRav-120
❑ 97ColCho-274
❑ 97ColChoT-BO11
❑ 97DonTea-44
❑ 97DonTeaSPE-44
❑ 97Fle-185
❑ 97Fle-670
❑ 97FleTif-185
❑ 97FleTif-670
❑ 97Lea-297
❑ 97LeaFraM-297
❑ 97LeaFraMDC-297
❑ 97OriSun-5
❑ 97Pac-166
❑ 97PacLigB-166
❑ 97PacSil-166
❑ 97Sco-465
❑ 97ScoArtPWB-465
❑ 97ScoResC-465
❑ 97ScoShoS-465
❑ 97ScoShoSAP-465
❑ 97StaClu-115
❑ 97StaCluMOP-115
❑ 97Top-86
❑ 97Ult-370
❑ 97UltGolME-370
❑ 97UltPlaME-370
❑ 97UppDec-308
❑ 98ColCho-41
❑ 98Fle-539
❑ 98OriSco-10
❑ 98OriScoP-10
❑ 98Pac-22
❑ 98PacOnl-83
❑ 98PacOnlR-83
❑ 98PacOnlWC-83
❑ 98PacPlaB-22
❑ 98PacRedT-22
❑ 98PacSil-22
❑ 98PinSna-BO14
❑ 98Sco-156
❑ 98StaCluFDI-247
❑ 98StaCluI-247
❑ 98StaCluOneK-247
❑ 98StaCluPP-247
❑ 98Top-18
❑ 98TopChr-18
❑ 98TopChrR-18
❑ 98TopDevR-18
❑ 98TopDia-18
❑ 98TopMiniC-18
❑ 98UppDec-309
❑ 99Fle-342
❑ 99FleSta9-342
❑ 99FleWarT-342
❑ 99Pac-48
❑ 99PacPlaB-48
❑ 99PacRed-48
❑ 99Top-14
❑ 99TopChr-14
❑ 99TopChrR-14
❑ 99TopMVPP-14
❑ 99UppDec-45
❑ 99UppDecEL1-45
❑ 99UppDecEL2-45

Bordley, Bill
❑ 79PhoGiaVNB-7
❑ 80GiaTeal-3
❑ 80PhoGiaVNB-10

Boreani, Charles
❑ 27Zee-131
❑ 28Zee-149
❑ 29Zee-151

Borel, Jamie
❑ 94BriTigC-6
❑ 94BriTigF-3515
❑ 95FayGenTI-4
❑ 96LakTigB-7

Borg, Bjorn
❑ 82MonNew-2

Borg, Gary
❑ 86VisOakP-4
❑ 87OrlTwiP-16
❑ 88OrlTwiB-12
❑ 89CalLeaA-34
❑ 89StoPorB-18
❑ 89StoPorCLC-164
❑ 89StoPorP-396
❑ 89StoPorS-1

Borgatti, Mike
❑ 87HagSunP-1
❑ 88VirGenS-2
❑ 89WatDiaP-1793
❑ 89WatDiaS-1
❑ 90HagSunB-19
❑ 90HagSunP-1402
❑ 90HagSunS-2

Borges, Alex
❑ 97MacBra-19
❑ 98DanQ-C-18

Borges, Elio
❑ 98HicCraUO-8

Borges, Gary
❑ 96PitMetB-4

Borges, George
❑ 83MidCubT-15
❑ 84PriWilPT-33

Borges, Jose
❑ 89ButCopKSP-9

Borges, Reece
❑ 98KanCouC-4
❑ 98KanCouCCP-4

Borgese, Jeff
❑ 88CapCodPPaLP-20
❑ 90FreStaS-2
❑ 90MarPhiP-3201
❑ 90ProAaA-194

Borgmann, Bennie
❑ 40SolHug-5

Borgmann, Glenn D.
❑ 73OPC-284
❑ 73TacTwiC-2
❑ 73Top-284
❑ 74OPC-547
❑ 74Top-547
❑ 75OPC-127
❑ 75Top-127
❑ 75TopMin-127
❑ 75TwiPos-3
❑ 75TwiTeal-3
❑ 76OPC-498
❑ 76SSP-213
❑ 76Top-498
❑ 77Top-87
❑ 78Top-307
❑ 78TwiFriP-2
❑ 79Top-431
❑ 79TwiFriP-2
❑ 80Top-634
❑ 81Don-159
❑ 81Top-716

Borgogno, Mate
❑ 88NebCor-19
❑ 89AlaGol-17
❑ 90CliGiaUTI-U1
❑ 90EveGiaB-16
❑ 90EveGiaP-3132
❑ 91CliGiaC-11
❑ 91CliGiaP-839

Borhinger, Helms
❑ 90YakBeaTI-4

Boring, Richard
❑ 97LanLugTS-4

Boris, Paul
❑ 80NasSouTI-3
❑ 81ColCliP-31
❑ 81ColCliT-7
❑ 83TolMudHT-1
❑ 83Top-266
❑ 84RicBraT-4

Borja, Tony
❑ 33Zee-84
❑ 33Zee-103

Bork, Frank
❑ 64PirKDK-3
❑ 65Top-592
❑ 66OPC-123
❑ 66Top-123
❑ 66TopVen-123

Borkowski, Bob (Robert V.)
❑ 49PorBeaP-1
❑ 52Top-328
❑ 53Top-7
❑ 54Top-138
❑ 55Top-74
❑ 55TopDouH-63
❑ 83TopRep5-328
❑ 91TopArc1-7
❑ 94TopArc1-138
❑ 94TopArc1G-138
❑ 95TopArcBD-110

Borkowski, David
❑ 96FayGenB-7
❑ 97MidLeaTP-26
❑ 97WesMicW-5
❑ 98Bes-4
❑ 98JacSunM-1
❑ 98SouLeaTPG-2
❑ 98SP MinPE-55
❑ 98SP MinSTHPE-H28
❑ 98SPMin-55
❑ 98SPMinSTH-H28

Borland, Scott
❑ 83AleDukT-4
❑ 84PriWilPT-18
❑ 85PriWilPT-15

Borland, Toby
❑ 88MarPhiS-4
❑ 89SpaPhiP-1037
❑ 89SpaPhiS-2
❑ 90ClePhiS-2
❑ 90StaFS7-70
❑ 91Cla/Bes-336
❑ 91LinDriAA-502
❑ 91ReaPhiLD-502
❑ 91ReaPhiP-1363
❑ 92ScrRedBF-2440
❑ 92ScrRedBS-479
❑ 92SkyAAAF-217
❑ 92UppDecML-239
❑ 93ReaPhiF-289
❑ 94ScrRedBF-913
❑ 94SpoRoo-45
❑ 94SpoRooAP-45
❑ 94TopTra-5T
❑ 95Fla-176
❑ 95Fle-386
❑ 95Phi-3
❑ 95PhiMel-2
❑ 95Sel-214
❑ 95SelArtP-214
❑ 96ColCho-667
❑ 96ColChoGS-667
❑ 96ColChoSS-667
❑ 96Fle-492
❑ 96FleTif-492
❑ 96LeaSigA-30
❑ 96LeaSigAG-30
❑ 96LeaSigAS-30
❑ 96Pac-152
❑ 96PhiTeal-3
❑ 96Ult-517
❑ 96UltGolM-517
❑ 97PacPriGotD-GD181
❑ 98ReaPhiM-24
❑ 98ScrRedBQ-6

Borland, Tom
❑ 60Lea-26
❑ 60Top-117
❑ 60TopVen-117
❑ 61Top-419
❑ 75OakOak2A-6
❑ 89AstCol4S-6

Bormann, Mike
❑ 83DurBulT-16
❑ 85DurBulT-4

Borne, Matt
❑ 98HicCraUO-9
❑ 99TeaBesR-5
❑ 99TeaBesRG-5
❑ 99TeaBesRS-5

Bornyk, Matt
❑ 98YakBeaG-6
Borom, Red (Edward Jones)
❑ 76DalCon-3
Boros, Julius
❑ 68AtlOil-1
Boros, Steve (Stephen)
❑ 58Top-81A
❑ 58Top-81B
❑ 59Top-331
❑ 61TigJayP-1
❑ 61Top-348
❑ 61TopStal-146
❑ 62Jel-16
❑ 62Pos-16
❑ 62PosCan-16
❑ 62SalPlaC-50
❑ 62ShiPlaC-50
❑ 62TigJayP-1
❑ 62TigPosCF-2
❑ 62Top-62
❑ 62Top-72
❑ 62TopStal-42
❑ 62TopVen-62
❑ 62TopVen-72
❑ 63Jel-47
❑ 63Pos-47
❑ 63Top-532
❑ 64Top-131
❑ 64TopVen-131
❑ 65OPC-102
❑ 65RedEnq-2
❑ 65Top-102
❑ 75RoyPos-3
❑ 76KanCitRP-2
❑ 78TCM60I-88
❑ 81ExpPos-1
❑ 82ExpPos-2
❑ 83A'sGraG-14
❑ 83TopTra-13T
❑ 84A'sMot-1
❑ 84Nes792-531
❑ 84Top-531
❑ 84TopTif-531
❑ 86TopTra-15T
❑ 86TopTraT-15T
❑ 87Top-143
❑ 87TopTif-143
❑ 93RoyPol-27
❑ 95BalOriP-10
Boroski, Stan
❑ 83BelBreFr-28
❑ 86Ft.MyeRP-4
❑ 87Ft.MyeRP-2
Borowicz, Ray
❑ 88BurIndP-1801
Borowski, Bill
❑ 93CenValRC-28
❑ 94CenValRC-30
❑ 95SalAvaTI-26
❑ 96SalAvaB-29
❑ 97SalAva-5
❑ 98NewHavRM-3
❑ 98NewHavRMA-3
Borowski, Joe
❑ 91KanCouCC-2
❑ 91KanCouCP-2652
❑ 91KanCouCTI-3
❑ 92FreKeyC-23
❑ 92FreKeyF-1798
❑ 93FreKeyC-4
❑ 93FreKeyF-1017
❑ 94BowBayF-2406
❑ 94OriPro-9
❑ 95BowBayTI-12
❑ 95RocRedWTI-8
❑ 96RicBraB-7
❑ 96RicBraUB-4
❑ 97Fle-542
❑ 97FleTif-542
❑ 97Ult-530
❑ 97UltGolME-530
❑ 97UltPlaME-530
❑ 98ColCliD-3
❑ 98ColCliM-7
Borowski, Rich
❑ 83IdaFalAT-20
❑ 84MadMusP-23
Borowsky, Erez
❑ 83VisOakF-15
❑ 84VisOakT-3
❑ 85OrlTwiT-2
Borowy, Hank (Henry)
❑ 39ExhSal-4
❑ 43YanSta-2
❑ 49Bow-134
❑ 49EurSta-131
❑ 49PhiBul-7
❑ 49PhiLumPB-2
❑ 50Bow-177
❑ 51Bow-250
❑ 75Phi195T-4
❑ 80Phi195T-4
❑ 92YanWIZA-6
Borrego, Ramon
❑ 98ForWayW!-1
Borrelli, Dean
❑ 88SouOreAP-1705
❑ 89MadMusS-4
❑ 90ModA'sC-1
❑ 90ModA'sCLC-164
❑ 90ModA'sP-2214
❑ 91HunStaC-3
❑ 91HunStaLD-278
❑ 91HunStaP-1798
❑ 91HunStaTI-2
❑ 91LinDriAA-278
❑ 92HunStaF-3952
❑ 92HunStaS-304
❑ 93TacTigF-3034
❑ 94TacTigF-3177
Borrero, Richie
❑ 93UtiBluSC-5
❑ 93UtiBluSF-3535
❑ 97TreThuB-8
❑ 98TreThuM-8
Borriello, Sebby
❑ 82WisRapTF-13
Borrome, Edmundo
❑ 85DomLeaS-208
Borruel, Jeff
❑ 78CedRapGT-3
Borski, Jeff
❑ 91BelMarCB-23
❑ 91BelMarP-3655
❑ 91Cla/Bes-448
❑ 92JacSunF-3700
❑ 92SanBerC-7
❑ 92SanBerSF-944
❑ 93RivPilCLC-5
Borton, Babe (William Baker)
❑ 14Zee-128
❑ 18Zee-95
❑ 19Zee-125
Borucki, Ray
❑ 80PenPilBT-19
❑ 80PenPilCT-25
❑ 81ReaPhiT-18
Boryczewski, Marty
❑ 94LetMouF-3881
❑ 94LetMouSP-19
❑ 96LakTigB-8
Borzello, Aaire
❑ 91JohCitCC-3
Borzello, Mike
❑ 93GleFalRC-7
❑ 93GleFalRF-4005
❑ 94SavCarC-9
❑ 94SavCarF-507
Bosarge, Scott
❑ 91BelMarCB-15
❑ 91BelMarP-3667
Boscan, Jean
❑ 98DanBraQ-8
Bosch, Bryon
❑ 97BurIndG-3
Bosch, Don (Donald John)
❑ 68Top-572
❑ 69ExpFudP-3
❑ 69Top-578
❑ 70ExpPos-12
❑ 70OPC-527
❑ 70Top-527
❑ 72MilBra-38
❑ 91MetWIZ-44
Bosco, Joseph
❑ 90PeoChiTI-37
Bosco, Mike
❑ 89RenSilSCLC-253
Bosetti, Rick (Richard Alan)
❑ 76OklCit8TI-10
❑ 78Top-710
❑ 79BluJayBY-2
❑ 79OPC-279
❑ 79Top-542
❑ 80OPC-146
❑ 80Top-277
❑ 80TopSup-51
❑ 81Don-152
❑ 81OPC-46
❑ 81OPCPos-18
❑ 81Top-46
❑ 81TopTra-741
❑ 82Don-626
❑ 82Fle-88
❑ 82TacTigT-33
❑ 82Top-392
❑ 86BluJayGT-6
❑ 92Nab-16
❑ 92UppDecS-3
Bosio, Chris
❑ 83BelBreFr-27
❑ 86VanCanP-4
❑ 87BrePol-26
❑ 87BrePol-29
❑ 87Don-478
❑ 87DonRoo-20
❑ 87Fle-338
❑ 87FleGlo-338
❑ 87SpoRool-2
❑ 87Top-448
❑ 87TopTif-448
❑ 88BrePol-29
❑ 88BreTeal-4
❑ 88Don-117
❑ 88DonBasB-295
❑ 88Fle-156
❑ 88FleGlo-156
❑ 88OPC-137
❑ 88Sco-38
❑ 88ScoGlo-38
❑ 88ScoYouSI-4
❑ 88StaLinBre-1
❑ 88Top-137
❑ 88TopTif-137
❑ 89Bow-134
❑ 89BowTif-134
❑ 89BrePol-29
❑ 89BreYea-29
❑ 89Don-412
❑ 89DonBasB-109
❑ 89Fle-179
❑ 89FleGlo-179
❑ 89RedFolSB-11
❑ 89Sco-243
❑ 89Top-311
❑ 89TopTif-311
❑ 89UppDec-292
❑ 90Bow-389
❑ 90BowTif-389
❑ 90BreMilB-1
❑ 90BrePol-29
❑ 90ClaYel-T42
❑ 90Don-20
❑ 90Don-57
❑ 90DonBesA-9
❑ 90DonSupD-20
❑ 90El PasDAGTI-2
❑ 90Fle-316
❑ 90FleCan-316
❑ 90Lea-26
❑ 90OPC-597
❑ 90PanSti-99
❑ 90PubIntS-490
❑ 90RedFolSB-8
❑ 90Sco-283
❑ 90Spo-25
❑ 90Top-597
❑ 90TopBig-139
❑ 90TopMinL-19
❑ 90TopSti-205
❑ 90TopTif-597
❑ 90UppDec-293
❑ 91Bow-43
❑ 91BreMilB-4
❑ 91BrePol-3
❑ 91Don-160
❑ 91Fle-576
❑ 91Lea-518
❑ 91OPC-217
❑ 91Sco-43
❑ 91StaClu-164
❑ 91StaCluP-7
❑ 91Top-217
❑ 91TopDesS-217
❑ 91TopMic-217
❑ 91TopTif-217
❑ 91UppDec-529
❑ 92BrePol-5
❑ 92Don-471
❑ 92Hig5-66
❑ 92Lea-266
❑ 92LeaBlaG-266
❑ 92OPC-638
❑ 92PanSti-42
❑ 92Pin-367
❑ 92Sco-37
❑ 92StaClu-578
❑ 92Top-638
❑ 92TopGol-638
❑ 92TopGolW-638
❑ 92TopMic-638
❑ 92Ult-379
❑ 92UppDec-615
❑ 93Bow-191
❑ 93Don-499
❑ 93Fin-140
❑ 93FinRef-140
❑ 93Fla-267
❑ 93Fle-628
❑ 93FleFinE-265
❑ 93Lea-255
❑ 93MarDaiQ-3
❑ 93MariStaClu-28
❑ 93MarMot-20
❑ 93MSABenSPD-2
❑ 93OPC-60
❑ 93OPCPre-3
❑ 93PacSpa-619
❑ 93Pin-440
❑ 93Sco-616
❑ 93SelRoo-108T
❑ 93StaClu-79
❑ 93StaCluFDI-79
❑ 93StaCluMO-3
❑ 93StaCluMOP-79
❑ 93Stu-14
❑ 93Top-775
❑ 93TopGol-775
❑ 93TopInaM-775
❑ 93TopInaR-775
❑ 93TopMic-775
❑ 93TopTra-28T
❑ 93Ult-614
❑ 93UppDec-588
❑ 93UppDecGold-588
❑ 94Bow-613
❑ 94BreMilB-200
❑ 94ColC-391
❑ 94ColChoGS-391
❑ 94ColChoSS-391
❑ 94Don-546
❑ 94Fin-252
❑ 94FinRef-252
❑ 94Fla-99
❑ 94Fle-281
❑ 94FleExtB-161
❑ 94FleGolM-10
❑ 94FleGolMJ-10
❑ 94Lea-9
❑ 94MarMot-7
❑ 94OPC-134
❑ 94Pac-563
❑ 94Pin-372
❑ 94PinArtP-372
❑ 94PinMusC-372
❑ 94Sco-264
❑ 94Sco-316
❑ 94ScoGolR-264
❑ 94ScoGolR-316
❑ 94SP-103
❑ 94SPDieC-103
❑ 94StaClu-103
❑ 94StaCluFDI-103
❑ 94StaCluGR-103
❑ 94StaCluMOP-103
❑ 94Top-60
❑ 94TopGol-60
❑ 94TopSpa-60
❑ 94TriPla-124
❑ 94Ult-417
❑ 94UppDec-228
❑ 94UppDecED-228
❑ 95Don-529
❑ 95DonPreP-529
❑ 95Fle-262
❑ 95Lea-330
❑ 95MarMot-11
❑ 95MarPac-23
❑ 95Pac-391
❑ 95Pin-13
❑ 95PinArtP-13
❑ 95PinMusC-13
❑ 95StaClu-92
❑ 95StaCluFDI-92
❑ 95StaCluMOP-92
❑ 95StaCluSTDW-M92
❑ 95StaCluSTWS-92
❑ 95Top-320
❑ 95TopCyb-174
❑ 95Ult-99
❑ 95UltGolM-99
❑ 96ColCho-731
❑ 96ColChoGS-731
❑ 96ColChoSS-731
❑ 96Don-250
❑ 96DonPreP-250
❑ 96EmoXL-109
❑ 96Fla-156
❑ 96Fle-229
❑ 96FleTif-229
❑ 96LanJetB-7
❑ 96MarMot-11
❑ 96Pac-409
❑ 96Sco-417
❑ 96StaClu-413
❑ 96StaCluMOP-413
❑ 96Ult-124
❑ 96UltGolM-124
❑ 96UppDec-461
❑ 97MarSco-1
❑ 97MarScoPl-1
❑ 97MarScoPr-1
❑ 97Sco-18
❑ 97ScoArtPWB-18
❑ 97ScoPreS-18
❑ 97ScoShoS-18
❑ 97ScoShoSAP-18
Boskie, Shawn
❑ 87PeoChiP-8
❑ 89ChaKniTI-17
❑ 90ClaYel-T43
❑ 90CMC-76
❑ 90CubMar-3
❑ 90DonLeaS-31
❑ 90DonRoo-18
❑ 90FleUpd-7
❑ 90IowCubC-1
❑ 90IowCubP-312
❑ 90Lea-519
❑ 90ProAAAF-619
❑ 90ScoRoo-94T
❑ 90TopTra-10T
❑ 90TopTraT-10T
❑ 90TopTVCu-39
❑ 90UppDec-722
❑ 91CubMar-47
❑ 91CubVinL-6
❑ 91Don-241
❑ 91Fle-416
❑ 91Lea-221
❑ 91OPC-254
❑ 91Sco-59
❑ 91Sco100RS-4
❑ 91StaClu-521
❑ 91Stu-152
❑ 91Top-254
❑ 91TopDeb90-20
❑ 91TopDesS-254
❑ 91TopMic-254
❑ 91TopTif-254
❑ 91UppDec-471
❑ 92CubMar-47
❑ 92Fle-377
❑ 92Lea-162
❑ 92LeaBlaG-162
❑ 92OPC-229
❑ 92Pin-527
❑ 92Sco-713
❑ 92StaClu-284
❑ 92Top-229
❑ 92TopGol-229
❑ 92TopGolW-229
❑ 92TopMic-229
❑ 92TriPla-246
❑ 92Ult-466
❑ 93Don-500
❑ 93Fle-373
❑ 93IowCubF-2128
❑ 93StaClu-583
❑ 93StaCluFDI-583
❑ 93StaCluMOP-583
❑ 93Top-563
❑ 93TopGol-563
❑ 93TopInaM-563
❑ 93TopInaR-563
❑ 93TopMic-563
❑ 94Don-61
❑ 94Fle-380
❑ 94Pac-95
❑ 94PhiMel-3
❑ 94StaCluT-353
❑ 94StaCluTFDI-353
❑ 94Top-177
❑ 94TopGol-177
❑ 94TopSpa-177
❑ 94TopTra-53T
❑ 95AngMot-19
❑ 95FleUpd-65
❑ 96AngMot-17
❑ 96LeaSigEA-13
❑ 97BalOriP-6
❑ 97Fle-36
❑ 97FleTif-36
❑ 97PacPriGotD-GD2
Bosley, Rich
❑ 86BelBreP-2
Bosley, Thad (Thaddis)
❑ 75QuaCitAT-29
❑ 77SalLakCGC-9
❑ 78SSP270-141
❑ 78Top-619
❑ 79Top-127
❑ 80Top-412
❑ 81Don-162
❑ 81Fle-353
❑ 82Top-350
❑ 83CubThoAV-20
❑ 84CubChiT-3
❑ 84CubSev-27
❑ 84IowCubT-7
❑ 84Nes792-657
❑ 84Top-657
❑ 84TopTif-657
❑ 85CubLioP-2
❑ 85CubSev-27
❑ 85Don-388
❑ 85Top-432
❑ 85TopTif-432
❑ 86CubGat-27
❑ 86CubUno-2
❑ 86Don-483
❑ 86Fle-361
❑ 86Top-512
❑ 86TopTif-512
❑ 87Don-191
❑ 87Fle-555
❑ 87FleGlo-555
❑ 87FleUpd-8
❑ 87FleUpdG-8
❑ 87Top-58
❑ 87TopTif-58
❑ 87TopTra-7T
❑ 87TopTraT-7T
❑ 88Don-348
❑ 88Fle-253
❑ 88FleGlo-253
❑ 88RoyTeal-5
❑ 88Top-247
❑ 88TopTif-247
❑ 89UppDec-591
❑ 90RanMot-16
❑ 93RanKee-79
❑ 94BreMilB-201
Bosman, Dick
❑ 67Top-459
❑ 68Top-442
❑ 69SenTeal-2
❑ 69SenTeal8-4
❑ 69Top-607
❑ 70DayDaiNM-47
❑ 70MLBOffS-278
❑ 70OPC-68
❑ 70OPC-175
❑ 70SenPolY-1
❑ 70Top-68
❑ 70Top-175
❑ 70TopScr-6
❑ 70TopSup-22
❑ 71MLBOffS-530
❑ 71OPC-60
❑ 71SenPolP-1
❑ 71SenTealW-4
❑ 71Top-60
❑ 71TopCoi-70
❑ 71TopGreM-49
❑ 71TopSup-7
❑ 71TopTat-2
❑ 72MilBra-39
❑ 72OPC-365
❑ 72RanTeal-3
❑ 72Top-365
❑ 73OPC-640
❑ 73Top-640
❑ 73TopCanL-7
❑ 74OPC-465
❑ 74Top-465
❑ 75CleIndP-5
❑ 75Hos-114
❑ 75OPC-7

❑ 75OPC-354
❑ 75Top-7
❑ 75Top-354
❑ 75TopMin-7
❑ 75TopMin-354
❑ 76A'sPos-75
❑ 76OPC-298
❑ 76SSP-483
❑ 76Top-298
❑ 77Top-101
❑ 86BufBisP-2
❑ 89PacSenL-20
❑ 89RocRedWC-24
❑ 89RocRedWP-1641
❑ 89SweBasG-124
❑ 90CMC-681
❑ 90EliSenL-3
❑ 90ProAAAF-478
❑ 90RocRedWC-26
❑ 90RocRedWGC-35
❑ 90RocRedWP-721
❑ 91LinDriAAA-475
❑ 91RocRedWLD-475
❑ 91RocRedWP-1919
❑ 92BalOriP-4
❑ 93BalOriP-4
❑ 93RanKee-4
❑ 94BalOriP-6
❑ 95RanCra-4
❑ 96RanDr P-1
❑ 96RanMot-28
❑ 97RanDr P-1
❑ 97RanMot-28

Boss, David
❑ 89HamRedS-5
❑ 90HamRedB-8
❑ 90HamRedS-7

Boss, Harley (Elmer Harley)
❑ 37Zee-65

Bossy, Mike
❑ 93Pin-299

Bost, Heath
❑ 96AshTouB-8
❑ 97SalAva-8
❑ 98NewHavRM-2
❑ 98NewHavRMA-2

Bostic, Dwain
❑ 92ClaDraP-34
❑ 92ClaFS7-424
❑ 92GulCoaDF-3571
❑ 93GreFalDSP-23

Bostic, Jerry
❑ 75SpoIndC-17
❑ 76SacSolC-19

Bostic, Josh
❑ 95DavLipB-3

Bostic, Randy
❑ 94DavLipB-4
❑ 95DavLipB-4

Bostock, Jim
❑ 93SpoIndC-2
❑ 93SpoIndF-3597

Bostock, Lyman Sr.
❑ 91NegLeaRL-4
❑ 93TedWil-100
❑ 95NegLeaL2-2
❑ 95NegLeaLI-4

Bostock, Lyman W. Jr.
❑ 74TacTwiC-23
❑ 75TwiTeal-4
❑ 76MinTwiP-2
❑ 76OPC-263
❑ 76Top-263
❑ 77BurCheD-54
❑ 77Hos-102
❑ 77Kel-16A
❑ 77Kel-16B
❑ 77OPC-239
❑ 77Spo-5503
❑ 77Top-531
❑ 78AngFamF-4
❑ 78Hos-145
❑ 78Kel-46
❑ 78RCColC-69
❑ 78SSP270-195
❑ 78Top-655

Boston, D.J.
❑ 91MedHatBJP-4105
❑ 91MedHatBJSP-1
❑ 92St.CatBJC-11
❑ 92St.CatBJF-3392
❑ 93HagSunC-3
❑ 93HagSunF-1885
❑ 93SouAtlLAGF-24
❑ 94Bow-347
❑ 94BowBes-B50
❑ 94BowBesR-B50
❑ 94Cla-9
❑ 94ClaGolF-21
❑ 94DunBluJC-1
❑ 94DunBluJF-2567
❑ 94ExcAllF-9
❑ 94ExcFS7-139
❑ 94SP-2
❑ 94SPDieC-2
❑ 94Top-448
❑ 94TopGol-448
❑ 94TopSpa-448
❑ 94UppDecAHNIL-3
❑ 94UppDecML-94
❑ 94UppDecML-120
❑ 94UppDecML-259
❑ 95Exc-134
❑ 95KnoSmoF-46
❑ 95UppDecML-52
❑ 95UppDecMLFS-52
❑ 96BesAutSA-8
❑ 96CarMudB-18
❑ 96SyrChiTI-3
❑ 98ColSprSS-44

Boston, Daryl L.
❑ 82AppFoxFr-24
❑ 83GleFalWST-1
❑ 85Don-33
❑ 85FleUpd-9
❑ 85TopTifT-8T
❑ 85TopTra-8T
❑ 85WhiSoxC-8
❑ 86BufBisP-3
❑ 86Don-86
❑ 86Top-139
❑ 86TopTif-139
❑ 86WhiSoxC-8
❑ 87Don-137
❑ 87Fle-487
❑ 87FleGlo-487
❑ 87Top-482
❑ 87TopTif-482
❑ 87WhiSoxC-4
❑ 88BlaYNPRWLU-1
❑ 88Fle-393
❑ 88FleGlo-393
❑ 88Sco-582
❑ 88ScoGlo-582
❑ 88StaLinWS-3
❑ 88Top-739
❑ 88TopTif-739
❑ 88WhiSoxC-2
❑ 89Bow-70
❑ 89BowTif-70
❑ 89Don-455
❑ 89Fle-492
❑ 89FleGlo-492
❑ 89PanSti-311
❑ 89Sco-443
❑ 89Top-633
❑ 89TopTif-633
❑ 89UppDec-496
❑ 89WhiSoxC-6
❑ 90Bow-317
❑ 90BowTif-317
❑ 90DonBesN-135
❑ 90FleUpd-33
❑ 90Lea-514
❑ 90OPC-524
❑ 90PanSti-52
❑ 90PubIntS-384
❑ 90Sco-213
❑ 90ScoRoo-47T
❑ 90Top-524
❑ 90TopBig-54
❑ 90TopTif-524
❑ 90TopTra-11T
❑ 90TopTraT-11T
❑ 90UppDec-529
❑ 91Bow-476
❑ 91Don-210
❑ 91Fle-140
❑ 91Lea-202
❑ 91MetColP-7
❑ 91MetKah-8
❑ 91MetPerPA-7
❑ 91MetWIZ-45
❑ 91OPC-83
❑ 91PanFreS-84
❑ 91Sco-618
❑ 91StaClu-125
❑ 91StaCluP-8
❑ 91Stu-201
❑ 91Top-83
❑ 91TopDesS-83
❑ 91TopMic-83
❑ 91TopTif-83
❑ 91Ult-211
❑ 91UppDec-159
❑ 92Don-612
❑ 92Fle-495
❑ 92MetColP-11
❑ 92MetKah-6
❑ 92OPC-227
❑ 92Pin-343
❑ 92Sco-276
❑ 92StaClu-328
❑ 92Top-227
❑ 92TopGol-227
❑ 92TopGolW-227
❑ 92TopMic-227
❑ 92Ult-227
❑ 93Bow-528
❑ 93DiaMar-17
❑ 93Don-38
❑ 93Fle-85
❑ 93Lea-281
❑ 93PacSpa-193
❑ 93PanSti-254
❑ 93Pin-545
❑ 93RocStaC-12
❑ 93RocUSPC-6H
❑ 93RocUSPC-9C
❑ 93Sco-447
❑ 93StaClu-3
❑ 93StaClu-498
❑ 93StaCluFDI-3
❑ 93StaCluFDI-498
❑ 93StaCluMOP-3
❑ 93StaCluMOP-498
❑ 93Top-399
❑ 93TopGol-399
❑ 93TopInaM-399
❑ 93TopInaR-399
❑ 93TopMic-399
❑ 93TopTra-126T
❑ 93Ult-343
❑ 93UppDec-203
❑ 93UppDec-737
❑ 93UppDecGold-203
❑ 93UppDecGold-737
❑ 94ColC-62
❑ 94ColChoGS-62
❑ 94ColChoSS-62
❑ 94Fle-435
❑ 94Pac-190
❑ 94Sco-396
❑ 94ScoGolR-396
❑ 94ScoRoo-RT123
❑ 94ScoRooGR-RT123
❑ 94Top-106
❑ 94TopGol-106
❑ 94TopSpa-106
❑ 94TopTra-114T
❑ 95Top-114
❑ 98BriWhiSQ-2

Boswell, Dave
❑ 67CokCapTw-7
❑ 67DexPre-26
❑ 67Top-575
❑ 68Top-322
❑ 68TopVen-322
❑ 69Top-459
❑ 70MLBOffS-230
❑ 70OPC-70
❑ 70OPC-325
❑ 70Top-70
❑ 70Top-325
❑ 71MLBOffS-459
❑ 71OPC-675
❑ 71Top-675
❑ 72MilBra-40
❑ 72OriPos-6
❑ 78TwiFri-3
❑ 81TCM60I-403
❑ 91OriCro-44

Boswell, Ken (Kenneth G.)
❑ 68DexPre-15
❑ 69MetCit-2
❑ 69MetNewYDN-2
❑ 69MetTeal-3
❑ 69Top-402
❑ 69TopTeaP-24
❑ 70MetTeal-2
❑ 70MetTra-22A
❑ 70OPC-196
❑ 70OPC-214
❑ 70Top-196
❑ 70Top-214
❑ 71MetTealC-3
❑ 71MLBOffS-147
❑ 71OPC-492
❑ 71Top-492
❑ 72MetTeal-2
❑ 72MilBra-41
❑ 72OPC-305
❑ 72OPC-306
❑ 72Top-305
❑ 72Top-306
❑ 73MetTeal-1
❑ 73OPC-87
❑ 73Top-87
❑ 74MetDaiPA-14
❑ 74OPC-645
❑ 74Top-645
❑ 75AstPos-3
❑ 75OPC-479
❑ 75Top-479
❑ 75TopMin-479
❑ 76HouAstP-3
❑ 76OPC-379
❑ 76SSP-55
❑ 76Top-379
❑ 77Top-429
❑ 81TCM60I-312
❑ 87AstShoSPT-3
❑ 87Met196T-9
❑ 89MetRinP69-4
❑ 91MetWIZ-46
❑ 94Met69CCPP-8
❑ 94Met69CS-7
❑ 94Met69T-17

Boswell, Mike
❑ 87GenCubP-12
❑ 88PeoChiTI-6

Botelho, Derek
❑ 83OmaRoyT-3
❑ 84IowCubT-NNO
❑ 85IowCubT-13
❑ 87OmaRoyP-10
❑ 88LouRedBTI-11
❑ 90MarPhiP-3209
❑ 91ChaWheC-27
❑ 91ChaWheP-2903
❑ 91PacSenL-38
❑ 92ChaWheF-24
❑ 93WinSpiC-26
❑ 93WinSpiF-1585
❑ 94CarLeaAF-CAR45
❑ 94WinSpiC-27
❑ 94WinSpiF-288
❑ 97BurBeeB-28
❑ 98BurBeeM-28

Bothwell, Monte
❑ 77ModA'sC-14

Botkin, Alan
❑ 88CapCodPPaLP-81
❑ 89JohCitCS-3
❑ 90HamRedS-8
❑ 90SprCarB-5
❑ 91SprCarC-7
❑ 91SprCarP-733
❑ 92St.PetCC-24
❑ 92St.PetCF-2021
❑ 93St.PetCC-5
❑ 93St.PetCF-2619

Botkin, Mike
❑ 83DayBeaAT-24

Bottalico, Ricky (Rick)
❑ 92ClaFS7-262
❑ 92SpaPhiF-1256
❑ 93ClePhiC-4
❑ 93ClePhiF-2676
❑ 94Bow-496
❑ 94BowPre-7
❑ 94Cla-22
❑ 94ColC-653
❑ 94ColChoGS-653
❑ 94ColChoSS-653
❑ 94ExcFS7-243
❑ 94ExcLeaLF-3
❑ 94FleExtB-329
❑ 94FleExtBMLH-2
❑ 94LeaLimR-17
❑ 94OPC-204
❑ 94ScrRedBF-914
❑ 94SigRoo-3
❑ 94SigRooS-3
❑ 94Ult-541
❑ 94UppDec-6
❑ 94UppDecED-6
❑ 94UppDecML-148
❑ 94UppDecML-225
❑ 95Bow-275
❑ 95BowBes-R90
❑ 95BowBesR-R90
❑ 95ColCho-367
❑ 95ColChoGS-367
❑ 95ColChoSS-367
❑ 95Don-125
❑ 95DonPreP-125
❑ 95DonTopotO-299
❑ 95Emo-163
❑ 95Fla-388
❑ 95Fle-387
❑ 95Lea-327
❑ 95LeaGolR-8
❑ 95Phi-4
❑ 95PhiMel-3
❑ 95Pin-143
❑ 95PinArtP-143
❑ 95PinMusC-143
❑ 95Sco-280
❑ 95ScoGolR-280
❑ 95ScoPlaTS-280
❑ 95ScoRooDT-RDT12
❑ 95Stu-52
❑ 95Top-59
❑ 95UppDec-376
❑ 95UppDecED-376
❑ 95UppDecEDG-376
❑ 95UppDecSE-73
❑ 95UppDecSEG-73
❑ 96Cir-164
❑ 96CirRav-164
❑ 96ColCho-249
❑ 96ColChoGS-249
❑ 96ColChoSS-249
❑ 96Don-420
❑ 96DonPreP-420
❑ 96EmoXL-241
❑ 96Fla-329
❑ 96Fle-493
❑ 96FleTif-493
❑ 96Lea-61
❑ 96LeaPrePB-61
❑ 96LeaPrePG-61
❑ 96LeaPrePS-61
❑ 96LeaSigA-31
❑ 96LeaSigAG-31
❑ 96LeaSigAS-31
❑ 96MetUni-207
❑ 96MetUniP-207
❑ 96Pac-160
❑ 96PacPri-P50
❑ 96PacPriG-P50
❑ 96PhiTeal-4
❑ 96Pin-73
❑ 96Sco-445
❑ 96StaClu-169
❑ 96StaCluMOP-169
❑ 96Top-161
❑ 96TopGal-97
❑ 96TopGalPPI-97
❑ 96Ult-249
❑ 96UltGolM-249
❑ 96UppDec-428
❑ 97Bow-20
❑ 97BowChr-16
❑ 97BowChrI-16
❑ 97BowChrIR-16
❑ 97BowChrR-16
❑ 97BowInt-20
❑ 97Cir-230
❑ 97CirRav-230
❑ 97ColCho-192
❑ 97Fin-77
❑ 97FinRef-77
❑ 97Fle-408
❑ 97FleTif-408
❑ 97Lea-164
❑ 97LeaFraM-164
❑ 97LeaFraMDC-164
❑ 97MetUni-200
❑ 97Pac-374
❑ 97PacLigB-374
❑ 97PacSil-374
❑ 97PhiCopQ-3
❑ 97PhiTeal-52
❑ 97Pin-152
❑ 97PinArtP-PP152
❑ 97PinMusC-152
❑ 97PinPrePla-152
❑ 97Sco-61
❑ 97ScoArtPWB-61
❑ 97ScoPreS-61
❑ 97ScoShoS-61
❑ 97ScoShoSAP-61
❑ 97SP-136
❑ 97SpoIII-92
❑ 97SpoIIIEE-92
❑ 97StaClu-355
❑ 97StaCluMOP-355
❑ 97Top-14
❑ 97TopChr-8
❑ 97TopChrR-8
❑ 97TopGal-138
❑ 97TopGalPPI-138
❑ 97Ult-353
❑ 97UltGolME-353
❑ 97UltPlaME-353
❑ 97UppDec-135
❑ 98CirThu-242
❑ 98CirThuRav-242
❑ 98CirThuSupRav-242
❑ 98ColCho-204
❑ 98Fin-84
❑ 98FinNo--84
❑ 98FinNo-R-84
❑ 98FinRef-84
❑ 98Fle-173
❑ 98MetUni-13
❑ 98MetUniPMG-13
❑ 98Pac-376
❑ 98PacAur-169
❑ 98PacInv-123
❑ 98PacInvPBlue-123
❑ 98PacInvSilv-123
❑ 98PacInvTeam-21
❑ 98PacOme-180
❑ 98PacOmeR-180
❑ 98PacOnl-555
❑ 98PacOnlR-555
❑ 98PacOnlWC-555
❑ 98PacPar-210
❑ 98PacParC-210
❑ 98PacParG-210
❑ 98PacParHS-210
❑ 98PacParPB-210
❑ 98PacParR-210
❑ 98PacPlaB-376
❑ 98PacRedT-376
❑ 98PacSil-376
❑ 98PhiTeal-5
❑ 98Sco-160
❑ 98ScoSS-PP66
❑ 98ScoSSAP-PP66
❑ 98SkyDugA-36
❑ 98SkyDugAIA-36
❑ 98SP Aut-152
❑ 98SPxFin-306
❑ 98SPxFinR-306
❑ 98SPxFinS-306
❑ 98StaCluFDI-219
❑ 98StaCluI-219
❑ 98StaCluOneK-219
❑ 98StaCluPP-219
❑ 98Top-163
❑ 98TopChr-163
❑ 98TopChrR-163
❑ 98TopDevR-163
❑ 98TopDia-163
❑ 98TopMiniC-163
❑ 98TopOpeD-85
❑ 98Ult-36
❑ 98UltGolM-36
❑ 98UltMas-36
❑ 98UltPlaM-36
❑ 98UppDec-188
❑ 98UppDecSF-102
❑ 99Fle-351
❑ 99FleSta9-351
❑ 99FleWarT-351
❑ 99Pac-323
❑ 99PacPlaB-323
❑ 99PacRed-323
❑ 99Vic-328

Bottarini, John C.
❑ 33Zee-45

Bottenfield, Brian
❑ 92Ft.LauYF-2629

Bottenfield, Kent
❑ 87BurExpP-1071
❑ 88WesPalBES-4
❑ 89JacExpB-9
❑ 89JacExpP-163
❑ 90JacExpB-16
❑ 90JacExpP-1367
❑ 91IndIndLD-178
❑ 91IndIndP-455
❑ 91LinDriAAA-178
❑ 92Bow-478
❑ 92DonRoo-12
❑ 92IndIndF-1853
❑ 92IndIndS-178
❑ 92SkyAAAF-87
❑ 93Don-484
❑ 93ExpPosN-6

❑ 93FleFinE-90
❑ 93FleMajLP-B6
❑ 93OPCPre-64
❑ 93PacSpa-531
❑ 93Pin-617
❑ 93Sco-312
❑ 93StaClu-101
❑ 93StaCluFDI-101
❑ 93StaCluMOP-101
❑ 93Top-695
❑ 93TopGol-695
❑ 93TopInaM-695
❑ 93TopInaR-695
❑ 93TopMic-695
❑ 93Ult-62
❑ 93UppDec-635
❑ 93UppDecGold-635
❑ 94Don-528
❑ 94Fle-436
❑ 94RocPol-4
❑ 94StaCluT-108
❑ 94StaCluTFDI-108
❑ 94Top-589
❑ 94TopGol-589
❑ 94TopSpa-589
❑ 94Ult-183
❑ 95TolMudHTI-8
❑ 96IowCubB-7
❑ 98PacOnl-604
❑ 98PacOnlR-604
❑ 98PacOnlWC-604
❑ 99PacOme-192
❑ 99PacOmeC-192
❑ 99PacOmeG-192
❑ 99PacOmePB-192

Bottenfield, Keven
❑ 88BoiHawP-1628

Bottin, Andy
❑ 95EveAqaTI-2
❑ 96EveAquB-29
❑ 98EveAquG-20

Botting, Ralph
❑ 75QuaCitAT-2
❑ 76QuaCitAT-3
❑ 80SalLakCGT-1
❑ 80Top-663
❑ 80VenLeaS-168
❑ 81SalLakCGT-2
❑ 81Top-214
❑ 82OmaRoyT-2

Bottomley, Jim (James L.)
❑ 21Exh-13
❑ 23MapCriV-19
❑ 25Exh-59
❑ 26Exh-59
❑ 26SpoComoA-7
❑ 27Exh-30
❑ 27MidBre-5
❑ 28PorandAR-A5
❑ 28PorandAR-B5
❑ 28W56PlaC-C5
❑ 29ExhFou-15
❑ 29PorandAR-8
❑ 30UncJac-2
❑ 31CarMet-3
❑ 31Exh-15
❑ 33ButCanV-3
❑ 33DouDisP-6
❑ 33GeoCMil-6
❑ 33Gou-44
❑ 33GouCanV-44
❑ 33RitCE-11S
❑ 33TatOrbSDR-205
❑ 33WorCig-11
❑ 34BabRutG-5
❑ 34BatR31-8
❑ 34BatR31-115
❑ 34BatR31-179
❑ 34ButPreR-5
❑ 34DiaMatCSB-17
❑ 34DiaStaR-59
❑ 34ExhFou-4
❑ 35AlDemDCR3-108
❑ 35DiaMatCS3T1-14
❑ 35ExhFou-4
❑ 35GouPuzR-1H
❑ 35GouPuzR-3F
❑ 35GouPuzR-5B
❑ 35GouPuzR-6B
❑ 35GouPuzR-11K
❑ 35GouPuzR-13B
❑ 35GouPuzR-14F
❑ 35GouPuzR-15F
❑ 36NatChiFPR-100
❑ 36R31Pre-G2
❑ 36WorWidGV-85
❑ 40PlaBal-236
❑ 60Fle-45
❑ 61Fle-9
❑ 69Baz-7
❑ 72FleFamF-6
❑ 72LauGreF-13
❑ 74CapPub-65
❑ 75TCMAllG-2
❑ 76GrePlaG-12
❑ 76RowExh-2
❑ 76ShaPiz-142
❑ 77BobParHoF-6
❑ 77GalGloG-67
❑ 80PacLeg-64
❑ 80PerHaloFP-142
❑ 80SSPHOF-142
❑ 81DiaStaCD-119
❑ 82DiaCla-59
❑ 83CarGreT-1
❑ 90BasWit-83
❑ 90HOFStiB-26
❑ 90PerGreM-92
❑ 91ConTSN-22
❑ 91ConTSN-302
❑ 92CarMcD-1
❑ 92ConTSN-440
❑ 92ConTSN-645
❑ 92ConTSNCI-1
❑ 93ConTSN-909
❑ 94ConTSN-1004
❑ 94ConTSNB-1004
❑ 95ConTSNGJ-8

Bottoms, Derrick
❑ 92AubAstC-19
❑ 92AubAstF-1345

Botts, Jake
❑ 90KisDodD-2
❑ 91GreFalDSP-9
❑ 93YakBeaC-5
❑ 93YakBeaF-3876

Botz, Bob
❑ 77FriOneYW-41

Bouchee, Ed (Edward F.)
❑ 57Top-314
❑ 58PhiTeal-3
❑ 59Top-39
❑ 59TopVen-39
❑ 60PhiJayP-3
❑ 60Top-347
❑ 61CubJayP-5
❑ 61Top-196
❑ 61TopStal-5
❑ 62Jel-182
❑ 62Pos-182
❑ 62PosCan-182
❑ 62SalPlaC-116
❑ 62ShiPlaC-116
❑ 62Top-497
❑ 81TCM60I-328
❑ 91MetWIZ-47

Boucher, Denis
❑ 88MyrBeaBJP-1168
❑ 88SouAtlLAGS-23
❑ 89DunBluJS-1
❑ 90DunBluJS-2
❑ 91BluJayFS-4
❑ 91Bow-29
❑ 91DonRoo-45
❑ 91OPCPre-13
❑ 91SyrChiMB-4
❑ 91UppDec-761
❑ 92ColSprSSS-78
❑ 92Don-604
❑ 92Sco-848
❑ 92SkyAAAF-35
❑ 92StaClu-773
❑ 92StaCluNC-773
❑ 92TopDeb91-18
❑ 93Don-755
❑ 93Fle-405
❑ 93LasVegSF-936
❑ 93OPC-22
❑ 93Top-541
❑ 93TopGol-541
❑ 93TopInaM-541
❑ 93TopInaR-541
❑ 93TopMic-541
❑ 94ColC-541
❑ 94ColChoGS-541
❑ 94ColChoSS-541
❑ 94Fin-294
❑ 94FinRef-294
❑ 94OPC-236
❑ 94StaClu-545
❑ 94StaCluFDI-545
❑ 94StaCluGR-545
❑ 94StaCluMOP-545
❑ 94Top-164
❑ 94TopGol-164
❑ 94TopSpa-164

Boudreau, Jim
❑ 84MidCubT-4
❑ 86ChaOriW-5

Boudreau, Lou (Louis P.)
❑ 39ExhSal-5
❑ 41DouPlaR-131
❑ 43MPR302-1-2
❑ 46SpoExcW-2-2
❑ 47HomBon-4
❑ 47IndTeal-3
❑ 47IndVanPP-3
❑ 47PM1StaP1-17
❑ 47PM1StaP1-18
❑ 47PM1StaP1-19
❑ 48BluTin-22
❑ 48IndTeal-4
❑ 49Bow-11
❑ 49IndTeal-6
❑ 49IndVisEI-2
❑ 49IndVisEI-3
❑ 49IndVisEI-4
❑ 49Lea-106
❑ 49MPR302-2-100
❑ 50Bow-94
❑ 50IndNumN-5
❑ 50IndTeal-5
❑ 51Bow-62
❑ 53BowC-57
❑ 53IndPenCBP-6
❑ 53RedSoxTI-2
❑ 55A'sRodM-5
❑ 55A'sTeal-2
❑ 55Bow-89
❑ 56A'sPos-4
❑ 56A'sRodM-2
❑ 60Fle-16
❑ 61Fle-94
❑ 70SpoCarfCOP-12
❑ 73SevTraC-8
❑ 75TCMAllG-3
❑ 76A'sRodMC-4
❑ 76RowExh-5
❑ 76ShaPiz-115
❑ 76TayBow4-25
❑ 77GalGloG-19
❑ 78DexHaloFP-2
❑ 79DiaGre-291
❑ 79TCM50-287
❑ 80MarExhH-2
❑ 80PacLeg-79
❑ 80PerHaloFP-115
❑ 80PerHaloFPS-15
❑ 80SSPHOF-115
❑ 81RedSoxBG2S-7
❑ 82DiaCla-103
❑ 82GSGalAG-8
❑ 82OhiHaloF-16
❑ 83DonHOFH-12
❑ 83TCMPla1942-10
❑ 83YanYealT-18
❑ 84CubBriPC-9D
❑ 86IndGreT-3
❑ 86SpoDecG-17
❑ 87SpoRea-38
❑ 88PacLegl-106
❑ 89PacLegl-166
❑ 89PerCelP-7
❑ 89SweBasG-80
❑ 90PacLeg-9
❑ 90PerGreM-63
❑ 90SweBasG-31
❑ 91SweBasG-12
❑ 91TopArc1-304
❑ 92ActPacA-7
❑ 92ActPacA2-7G
❑ 92BazQua5A-19
❑ 92MVP-3
❑ 92MVP2H-11
❑ 93ActPacAC-7
❑ 93TedWil-32
❑ 93UppDecAH-16
❑ 93UppDecS-30
❑ 94UppDecAH-204
❑ 94UppDecAH1-204
❑ 95ConTSN-1425
❑ 95ConTSNP-1425
❑ 98SpollITaN-5
❑ 98SpollITaNEE-5

Boudreau, Tommy
❑ 91BelMarCB-3
❑ 91BelMarP-3679

Boudreaux, Corey
❑ 93Sou-5

Boudreaux, Eric
❑ 87ClePhiP-12
❑ 89ReaPhiB-19
❑ 89ReaPhiP-668
❑ 90CMC-227
❑ 90ReaPhiB-3
❑ 90ReaPhiP-1214
❑ 90ReaPhiS-7
❑ 90ScrRedBC-1

Boudreaux, Mascot
❑ 98NewOrlZM-26

Boughton, Mike
❑ 96AriBlaDB-10
❑ 97SouBenSH-9

Bouie, Tony
❑ 92AriWilP-2

Boulanger, Mike
❑ 97ForWayW-2
❑ 98ForMyeMTI-4

Bouldin, Carl
❑ 63Top-496
❑ 64Top-518

Boulo, Tyler
❑ 96IdaFalB-2

Boulware, Ben
❑ 94HicCraC-5
❑ 94HicCraF-2183
❑ 95Exc-27
❑ 96PriWilCB-5
❑ 98PriWilCASM-7

Bourbakis, Michael
❑ 95GreFalDTI-10
❑ 96GreFalDB-4
❑ 96GreFalDTI-3

Bourg, Art
❑ 21Zee-43

Bourgeois, Steve
❑ 93EveGiaC-5
❑ 93EveGiaF-3760
❑ 94CliLumC-5
❑ 94CliLumF-1971
❑ 96Bow-230
❑ 96BowFoi-230
❑ 96GiaMot-27
❑ 97ColSprSTI-2
❑ 98ColSprSS-33

Bourjos, Chris (Christopher)
❑ 77CedRapGT-22
❑ 79PhoGiaVNB-16
❑ 80PhoGiaVNB-11
❑ 80VenLeaS-70
❑ 81RocRedWT-21
❑ 81RocRedWW-3
❑ 81Top-502
❑ 83PorBeaT-14

Bourne, Kendrick
❑ 86ElmPioRSP-3
❑ 87ElmPioBC-6
❑ 87ElmPioRC-6
❑ 88WinHavRSS-5
❑ 89ClePhiS-3

Bourne, Tim
❑ 95StCatSTI-24

Bournigal, Rafael
❑ 89Sta-27
❑ 89VerBeaDS-3
❑ 90SanAntMGS-5
❑ 91VerBeaDC-17
❑ 91VerBeaDP-778
❑ 92AlbDukF-725
❑ 92AlbDukS-5
❑ 93AlbDukF-1466
❑ 93Don-10
❑ 93FleMajLP-B7
❑ 93Pin-279
❑ 93Sco-307
❑ 93StaClu-197
❑ 93StaCluFDI-197
❑ 93StaCluMOP-197
❑ 93Top-651
❑ 93TopGol-651
❑ 93TopInaM-651
❑ 93TopInaR-651
❑ 93TopMic-651
❑ 93Ult-50
❑ 94AlbDukF-847
❑ 94DodPol-3
❑ 94FleUpd-148
❑ 94Pac-303
❑ 94SpoRoo-138
❑ 94SpoRooAP-138
❑ 94StaClu-500
❑ 94StaCluFDI-500
❑ 94StaCluGR-500
❑ 94StaCluMOP-500
❑ 95ColCho-217
❑ 95ColChoGS-217
❑ 95ColChoSS-217
❑ 95DodPol-3
❑ 95Fla-152
❑ 95Fle-534
❑ 95Sco-472
❑ 95ScoGolR-472
❑ 95ScoPlaTS-472
❑ 95StaClu-116
❑ 95StaCluFDI-116
❑ 95StaCluMOP-116
❑ 95StaCluSTWS-116
❑ 95Top-628
❑ 95TopCyb-394
❑ 95UppDec-319
❑ 95UppDecED-319
❑ 95UppDecEDG-319
❑ 96A'sMot-26
❑ 96LeaSigEA-14
❑ 97A'sMot-13
❑ 97PacPriGotD-GD79
❑ 97Pin-148
❑ 97PinArtP-PP148
❑ 97PinMusC-148
❑ 97PinPrePla-148
❑ 97Sco-305
❑ 97ScoArtPWB-305
❑ 97ScoPreS-305
❑ 97ScoShoS-305
❑ 97ScoShoSAP-305
❑ 98A'sMot-12
❑ 98Pac-162
❑ 98PacOnl-525
❑ 98PacOnlR-525
❑ 98PacOnlWC-525
❑ 98PacPlaB-162
❑ 98PacRedT-162
❑ 98PacSil-162
❑ 99PacCroC-199
❑ 99PacCroCPB-199

Bourque, Pat (Patrick D.)
❑ 73OPC-605
❑ 73Top-605
❑ 74OPC-141
❑ 74Top-141
❑ 75OPC-502
❑ 75Top-502
❑ 75TopMin-502

Bouton, Jim
❑ 62Top-592
❑ 63RegKP-4
❑ 63Top-401
❑ 64ChatheY-3
❑ 64Top-4
❑ 64Top-219
❑ 64Top-470
❑ 64TopCoi-4
❑ 64TopCoi-138
❑ 64TopSta-45
❑ 64TopVen-4
❑ 64TopVen-219
❑ 64WheSta-7
❑ 65ChaTheY-2
❑ 65OPC-30
❑ 65OPC-137
❑ 65Top-30
❑ 65Top-137
❑ 65TopEmbl-25
❑ 65TopTral-5
❑ 66Top-276
❑ 66TopVen-276
❑ 67CokCapYM-V7
❑ 67DexPre-27
❑ 67Top-393
❑ 68Top-562
❑ 69PilPos-35
❑ 70DayDaiNM-81
❑ 73BooProC-3
❑ 73BooProC-14
❑ 73BooProC-22
❑ 77PilPosR-35
❑ 78TCM60I-77
❑ 83Pil69G-1
❑ 87AstShoSTw-3
❑ 88PacLegl-20
❑ 89SweBasG-66
❑ 90LitSunW-22
❑ 91FouBal-36
❑ 91SweBasG-123
❑ 92YanWIZ6-13
❑ 92YanWIZA-7
❑ 93TedWil-60
❑ 99SpollIGotG-47
❑ 99SpollIGotGA-9

Bouton, Tony
❑ 91GasRanC-1
❑ 91GasRanP-2678
❑ 92ChaRanC-11
❑ 92ChaRanF-2218

Bovee, Mike (Michael)
❑ 92AppFoxCB-18
❑ 92AppFoxFI-977
❑ 92UppDecML-212
❑ 93RocRoyC-3
❑ 93RocRoyF-704
❑ 94CarLeaAF-CAR14
❑ 94WilBluRC-1
❑ 94WilBluRF-290
❑ 95Bow-114
❑ 95Exc-54
❑ 95WicWraTI-38
❑ 96DouAllB-45
❑ 96SigRooOJTP-T2
❑ 96WicWraB-2
❑ 97MidAng-8
❑ 98VanCanG-4

Bovender, Andy
❑ 95AubAstTI-5
❑ 96QuaCitRB-9
❑ 97KisCob-5

Bowa, Larry (Lawrence Robert)
❑ 70OPC-539
❑ 70PhiTeal-1
❑ 70Top-539
❑ 71MLBOffS-169
❑ 71OPC-233
❑ 71PhiArcO-1
❑ 71Top-233
❑ 71TopTat-127
❑ 72Dia-55
❑ 72OPC-520
❑ 72Top-520
❑ 73LinPor-143
❑ 73OPC-119
❑ 73PhiTeal-3
❑ 73Top-119
❑ 74OPC-255
❑ 74PhiJohP-10
❑ 74Top-255
❑ 74TopDecE-70
❑ 74TopSta-72
❑ 75OPC-420
❑ 75PhiPhiP-6
❑ 75PhiProPS-3
❑ 75Top-420
❑ 75TopMin-420
❑ 76BlaDis-4
❑ 76BucDis-4
❑ 76CarDis-4
❑ 76CraDis-4
❑ 76DailsID-4
❑ 76Hos-145
❑ 76IsaDis-4
❑ 76OPC-145
❑ 76OrbDis-4
❑ 76PhiPhiP-4
❑ 76RedBarD-4
❑ 76SafDis-4
❑ 76SSP-464
❑ 76Top-145
❑ 76TowCluD-4
❑ 77BurCheD-170
❑ 77ChiWilD-5
❑ 77DailsID-5
❑ 77DetCaeD-5
❑ 77HolInnD-5
❑ 77Hos-62
❑ 77MSADis-5
❑ 77OPC-17
❑ 77RCColC-7
❑ 77SagDis-5
❑ 77sDis-5
❑ 77Top-310
❑ 77WenDis-5
❑ 77ZipDis-5
❑ 78Hos-71
❑ 78Kel-26
❑ 78OPC-68
❑ 78Pep-27
❑ 78RCColC-60
❑ 78SSP270-49
❑ 78Top-90
❑ 79BasPat-6
❑ 79Hos-134

❑ 79Kel-44
❑ 79OPC-104
❑ 79PhiBurK-15
❑ 79PhiTeal-3
❑ 79Top-210
❑ 80Kel-39
❑ 80OPC-330
❑ 80PhiBurK-7
❑ 80Top-630
❑ 80TopSup-34
❑ 81AllGamPI-109
❑ 81CokTeaS-98
❑ 81Don-142
❑ 81Fle-2
❑ 81Fle-645
❑ 81Fle-645B
❑ 81FleStiC-20
❑ 81FleStiC-43
❑ 81Kel-43
❑ 81OPC-120
❑ 81Top-120
❑ 81Top-403
❑ 81TopSti-201
❑ 81TopSupHT-80
❑ 82CubRedL-1
❑ 82Don-63
❑ 82Fle-241
❑ 82FleSta-56
❑ 82FleSta-107
❑ 82OPC-194
❑ 82OPC-374
❑ 82SevSluC-4
❑ 82Top-515
❑ 82Top-516
❑ 82TopSti-80
❑ 82TopTra-10T
❑ 83AllGamPI-109
❑ 83CubThoAV-1
❑ 83Don-435
❑ 83Fle-491
❑ 83FleSta-21
❑ 83FleSti-128
❑ 83OPC-305
❑ 83PhiPosGPaM-4
❑ 83Top-305
❑ 83TopFol-5
❑ 83TopSti-221
❑ 84CubChiT-4
❑ 84CubSev-1
❑ 84CubUno-7
❑ 84Don-239
❑ 84Fle-486
❑ 84FunFooP-126
❑ 84Nes792-705
❑ 84Nes792-757
❑ 84OPC-346
❑ 84Top-705
❑ 84Top-757
❑ 84TopSti-46
❑ 84TopTif-705
❑ 84TopTif-757
❑ 85AllGamPI-109
❑ 85CubLioP-1
❑ 85CubSev-1
❑ 85Don-361
❑ 85DonHig-7
❑ 85Fle-50
❑ 85OPC-56
❑ 85Top-484
❑ 85TopSti-45
❑ 85TopTif-484
❑ 86LasVegSP-3
❑ 86PhiGreT-9
❑ 87PadBohHB-10
❑ 87TopTra-8T
❑ 87TopTraT-8T
❑ 88PadCok-10
❑ 88PhiTas-31
❑ 88Top-284
❑ 88TopTif-284
❑ 89PhiTas-2
❑ 90PhiTas-34
❑ 91MetWIZ-48
❑ 91PhiMed-6
❑ 91UppDecS-17
❑ 92PhiMed-6
❑ 92UppDecS-24
❑ 93PhiMed-7
❑ 93TedWil-71
❑ 94PhiMed-3
❑ 95Phi-5
❑ 96PhiTeal-5
❑ 97AngMot-28
Bowden, James
❑ 84ButCopKT-3
Bowden, Mark
❑ 81CedRapRT-22
❑ 86ReaPhiP-3
❑ 87ReaPhiP-17
❑ 88RocRedWC-4
❑ 88RocRedWGCP-2
❑ 88RocRedWP-208
❑ 88RocRedWTI-4
❑ 90IowCubP-313
❑ 90ProAAAF-620
Bowden, Merritt
❑ 89AncGlaP-4
❑ 91EliTwiP-4310
Bowden, Steve
❑ 85BenPhiC-3
❑ 87HagSunP-15
❑ 88FreSunCLC-16
Bowen, Joe
❑ 94JohCitCC-4
❑ 94JohCitCF-3704
Bowen, John
❑ 89EriOriS-3
Bowen, Kenny
❑ 88MemChiB-5
❑ 89MemChiB-8
❑ 89MemChiP-1207
❑ 89MemChiS-2
Bowen, Mitch
❑ 93ElmPioC-3
❑ 93ElmPioF-3814
❑ 94BreCouMC-2
❑ 94BreCouMF-1
❑ 95BreCouMF-237
❑ 96BreCouMB-6
Bowen, Ryan
❑ 87AshTouP-5
❑ 88OscAstS-5
❑ 89ColMudB-18
❑ 89ColMudP-126
❑ 89ColMudS-4
❑ 90Bes-245
❑ 90CMC-603
❑ 90ProAAAF-186
❑ 90TucTorC-1
❑ 90TucTorP-196
❑ 91Bow-539
❑ 91LinDriAAA-604
❑ 91TucTorLD-604
❑ 91TucTorP-2205
❑ 91UppDecFE-45F
❑ 92Bow-401
❑ 92Cla1-T17
❑ 92ClaGam-117
❑ 92Don-671
❑ 92Lea-385
❑ 92LeaBlaG-385
❑ 92OPC-254
❑ 92OPCPre-28
❑ 92Pin-473
❑ 92ProFS7-225
❑ 92Sco-762
❑ 92StaClu-101
❑ 92Top-254
❑ 92TopDeb91-19
❑ 92TopGol-254
❑ 92TopGolW-254
❑ 92TopMic-254
❑ 92TucTorF-479
❑ 92Ult-488
❑ 92UppDec-354
❑ 93Don-372
❑ 93Fle-419
❑ 93FleFinE-53
❑ 93MarFloA-3
❑ 93MarlStaClu-16
❑ 93MarPub-5
❑ 93MarUppD-780
❑ 93MarUSPC-3S
❑ 93MarUSPC-9D
❑ 93PacSpa-455
❑ 93Pin-571
❑ 93StaClu-350
❑ 93StaCluFDI-350
❑ 93StaCluMOP-350
❑ 93TopTra-130T
❑ 93Ult-367
❑ 93UppDec-780
❑ 93UppDecGold-780
❑ 94ColC-63
❑ 94ColChoGS-63
❑ 94ColChoSS-63
❑ 94Don-407
❑ 94Fin-30
❑ 94FinRef-30
❑ 94Fle-462
❑ 94Lea-238
❑ 94MarTeal-2
❑ 94Pac-236
❑ 94Pin-117
❑ 94PinArtP-117
❑ 94PinMusC-117
❑ 94Sco-142
❑ 94ScoGolR-142
❑ 94Sel-59
❑ 94StaClu-345
❑ 94StaCluFDI-345
❑ 94StaCluGR-345
❑ 94StaCluMOP-345
❑ 94StaCluT-72
❑ 94StaCluTFDI-72
❑ 94Top-494
❑ 94TopGol-494
❑ 94TopSpa-494
❑ 94TriPla-132
❑ 94Ult-193
❑ 94UppDec-78
❑ 94UppDecED-78
❑ 95Don-236
❑ 95DonPreP-236
❑ 95Fle-326
Bowen, Sam (Samuel Thomas)
❑ 78PapGinD-6
❑ 81PawRedST-18
Bowens, Sam (Samuel Edward)
❑ 63RocRedWSP-3
❑ 64BalOriP-7
❑ 64BalOriP-8
❑ 64Top-201
❑ 64TopRooAB-3
❑ 64TopVen-201
❑ 65BalOriP-7
❑ 65BalOriP-12
❑ 65OPC-188
❑ 65Top-188
❑ 66BalOriP-6
❑ 66Top-412
❑ 67BalOriP-17
❑ 67CokCapO-12
❑ 67Top-491
❑ 68OPC-82
❑ 68Top-82
❑ 68TopVen-83
❑ 69MilBra-32
❑ 81Ori6F-8
❑ 81TCM60I-313
❑ 91OriCro-45
Bowens, Steve
❑ 83IdaFalAT-1
Bowerman, Frank E.
❑ 06GiaUllAFS-11
❑ 09RamT20-14
❑ 09T206-31
❑ 11SpoLifCW-38
❑ 67SpoHobFC-38
❑ 72ClaCar-65
❑ 98CamPepP-5
Bowers, Billy (Grover Bill)
❑ 52Par-6
Bowers, Blake
❑ 98ModA'sG-4
Bowers, Brent
❑ 90MedHatBJB-10
❑ 91MyrBeaHC-23
❑ 91MyrBeaHP-2957
❑ 92DunBluJC-6
❑ 92DunBluJF-2009
❑ 93Bow-407
❑ 93ClaFS7-169
❑ 93KnoSmoF-1261
❑ 94Cla-84
❑ 94KnoSmoF-1314
❑ 94UppDecML-38
❑ 95Bow-3
❑ 95SyrChiTI-3
❑ 96BowBayB-7
❑ 97ScrRedB-11
❑ 98NorTidP-4
❑ 98NorTidQ-4
Bowers, Cedrick
❑ 97ChaRivDG-7
❑ 97Top-470
❑ 98Bow-435
❑ 98BowChr-435
❑ 98BowChrGA-435
❑ 98BowChrGAR-435
❑ 98BowChrI-435
❑ 98BowChrIR-435
❑ 98BowChrR-435
❑ 98BowGolA-435
❑ 98BowInt-435
❑ 98St.PetDRM-5
❑ 98Top-501
❑ 98TopChr-501
❑ 98TopChrR-501
❑ 98TopDevR-501
❑ 98TopDia-501
❑ 98TopMiniC-501
Bowers, Jason
❑ 98DanBraQ-23
❑ 98JohCCTI-6
Bowers, Mickey
❑ 80LynSaiT-15
❑ 81LynSaiT-25
❑ 82LynSaiT-18
❑ 83ChaLooT-12
Bowers, R.J.
❑ 94QuaCitRBC-5
❑ 94QuaCitRBF-546
❑ 95MidLeaA-4
❑ 95QuaCitRBTI-3
❑ 96MidLeaAB-25
❑ 96QuaCitRB-10
Bowers, Shane
❑ 93EliTwiC-5
❑ 93EliTwiF-3408
❑ 94ForWayWC-3
❑ 94ForWayWF-2000
❑ 95Bes-31
❑ 95ForMyeMTI-2
❑ 95SPML-84
❑ 96Exc-76
❑ 96HarCitRCB-8
❑ 97NewBriRC-5
❑ 98MetUni-113
❑ 98MetUniPMG-113
❑ 98SalLakBO-12
❑ 98Ult-235
❑ 98UltGolM-235
❑ 98UltMas-235
❑ 98UltPlaM-235
Bowers, Stewart
❑ 79RedSoxEF-6
Bowers, Tom
❑ 58GiaSFCB-3
Bowie, Jim
❑ 86BelMarCr-102
❑ 87WauTimP-15
❑ 88CalLeaACLC-27
❑ 88SanBerSB-16
❑ 88SanBerSCLC-30
❑ 89CalCanC-17
❑ 89CalCanP-525
❑ 90Bes-258
❑ 90CMC-796
❑ 90WilBilB-3
❑ 90WilBilP-1067
❑ 90WilBilS-2
❑ 91JacSunLD-331
❑ 91JacSunP-156
❑ 91LinDriAA-331
❑ 92CalCanS-56
❑ 92JacSunF-3714
❑ 92SkyAA F-291
❑ 92SkyAAAF-25
❑ 93HunStaF-2087
❑ 94ExcFS7-117
❑ 94TacTigF-3181
❑ 95EdmTraTI-2
❑ 95Sco-598
❑ 95ScoGolR-598
❑ 95ScoPlaTS-598
❑ 96SigRooOJ-4
❑ 96SigRooOJS-4
❑ 97MobBayBB-7
Bowie, Micah
❑ 95DurBulTI-5
❑ 96DurBulBIB-2
❑ 98GreBraG-3
❑ 99Bow-294
❑ 99BowGol-294
❑ 99BowInt-294
❑ 99FlaShoLeg1-18
❑ 99FlaShoLeg2-18
❑ 99FlaShoLeg3-18
❑ 99FlaShoLegM1-18
❑ 99FlaShoLegM2-18
❑ 99FlaShoLegM3-18
❑ 99FlaShoR1-18
❑ 99FlaShoR2-18
❑ 99FlaShoR3-18
❑ 99FleBri-160
❑ 99FleBri2G-160
❑ 99FleBriBlu-160
❑ 99FleBriGol-160
❑ 99FleMysFI-4
❑ 99SkyMolMOA-9
❑ 99SkyPreA-5
❑ 99SkyPreABlue-5
❑ 99Top-428
❑ 99TopChr-428
❑ 99TopChrR-428
❑ 99TopMVPP-428
Bowlan, Mark
❑ 89HamRedS-4
❑ 91SprCarC-8
❑ 91SprCarP-734
Bowles, Brian
❑ 96MedHatBJTI-6
❑ 97DunBluJTI-4
❑ 97St.CatSB-9
Bowles, John
❑ 92HigSchPLS-13
❑ 94UtiBluSC-6
❑ 94UtiBluSF-3826
❑ 95MicBatCTI-4
❑ 96SarRedSB-9
Bowles, Justin
❑ 96SouOreTI-21
❑ 97ModA'sG-2
❑ 98HunStaTI-19
❑ 99Bow-89
❑ 99BowChr-89
❑ 99BowChrG-89
❑ 99BowChrGR-89
❑ 99BowChrI-89
❑ 99BowChrIR-89
❑ 99BowChrR-89
❑ 99BowGol-89
❑ 99BowInt-89
Bowlin, Allan
❑ 80ElmPioRST-3
Bowling, Robert
❑ 76VenLeaS-102
Bowling, Steve (Stephen S.)
❑ 75SacSolC-13
❑ 76SpoIndC-18
❑ 79IndIndTI-20
❑ 94BreMilB-202
Bowman, Alvah
❑ 19Zee-108
Bowman, Billy Joe
❑ 90AstMot-27
❑ 93AstMot-28
Bowman, Bob (Robert LeRoy)
❑ 47PM1StaP1-20
❑ 57Top-332
❑ 58PhiJayP-3
❑ 58Top-415
❑ 59Top-221
Bowman, Ernie (Ernest F.)
❑ 61TacBan-2
❑ 62Top-231
❑ 63Top-61
❑ 66Top-302
❑ 66TopVen-302
❑ 81Gia196T-17
❑ 81TCM60I-352
Bowman, General Manager (Don)
❑ 88PulBraP-1771
Bowman, Joe (Joseph Emil)
❑ 30Zee-102
❑ 31Zee-61
❑ 39PlaBal-128
❑ 40PlaBal-162
❑ 79DiaGre-357
❑ 94ConTSN-1224
❑ 94ConTSNB-1224
Bowman, Michael
❑ 89BriTigS-1
Bowman, Paul
❑ 94KinMetC-3
❑ 94KinMetF-3814
Bowman, Roger
❑ 55Bow-115
❑ 75Gia195T-2
Bowman, William
❑ 77St.PetCT-2
Bowness, Brian
❑ 96SouBenSHS-6
Bowring, Jason
❑ 98PitMetM-9
Bowrosen, Ricky
❑ 92UtiBluSC-13
❑ 93SouBenWSC-2
❑ 93SouBenWSF-1436
Bowser, Robert
❑ 95MarPhiTI-3
Bowsfield, Ted (Edward)
❑ 59Top-236
❑ 60Top-382
❑ 61Top-216
❑ 62Top-369
❑ 62TopStal-64
❑ 63Top-339
❑ 64Top-447
❑ 81RedSoxBG2S-8
Box, John
❑ 97PriDevR-18
❑ 98ChaRivDG-4
Box, Newt
❑ 80CedRapRT-2
Box, Shawn
❑ 96DayCubB-5
Boxberger, Rod
❑ 80ColAstT-12
❑ 81NasSouTI-1
❑ 83NasAngT-2
Boyan, Michael
❑ 88CapCodPPaLP-155
Boyce, Bob
❑ 82MiaMarT-14
Boyce, Joe
❑ 90EriSaiS-1
Boyce, Randy
❑ 78NewWayCT-3
❑ 79BurBeeT-19
Boyce, Tommy
❑ 88SalLakCTTI-10
❑ 89KenTwiS-1
❑ 89MiaMirIS-2
❑ 89Sta-141
❑ 90MiaMirIS-3
Boyd, Bert
❑ 95PeoChiTI-NNO
❑ 96PeoChiB-3
Boyd, Bob
❑ 26Zee-159
❑ 76QuaCitAT-4
❑ 77QuaCitAT-6
Boyd, Bob (Robert Richard)
❑ 53Top-257
❑ 54Bow-118
❑ 54Top-113
❑ 56BalOriP-20
❑ 56BalOriP-2
❑ 56BalOriP-3
❑ 56BalOriP-4
❑ 57Top-26
❑ 58BalOriP-3
❑ 58Hir-75
❑ 58OriJayP-1
❑ 58Top-279
❑ 59OriJayP-1
❑ 59Top-82
❑ 59TopVen-82
❑ 60Lea-13
❑ 60Top-207
❑ 61A'sTeal-1
❑ 61AthJayP-4
❑ 61Top-199
❑ 61TopStal-157
❑ 86NegLeaF-49
❑ 87NegLeaPD-9
❑ 91OriCro-46
❑ 91TopArc1-257
❑ 92NegLeaRLI-6
❑ 94CliLumC-30
❑ 94TopArc1-113
❑ 94TopArc1G-113
❑ 97NegLeaPC-3D
Boyd, Daryl
❑ 86WatPirP-4
❑ 89WesPalBES-4
Boyd, Frank John
❑ 93JusSo-1
Boyd, Gary Lee
❑ 70OPC-7
❑ 70Top-7
Boyd, Greg
❑ 90ArkRaz-29
❑ 93BenRocCB-3
❑ 93BenRocF-3275
❑ 93Top-621
❑ 93TopGol-621
❑ 93TopInaM-621
❑ 93TopInaR-621
❑ 93TopMic-621
Boyd, Jake (Jacob Henry)
❑ 87OldJudN-36
Boyd, Jason

❑ 94MarPhiC-4
❑ 94MarPhiF-3283
❑ 95PiePhiF-179
❑ 97EasLeaTPB-26
❑ 97ReaPhi-8
❑ 98TusSidM-6
Boyd, Oil Can (Dennis)
❑ 80ElmPioRST-4
❑ 83PawRedST-2
❑ 84Don-457
❑ 84Fle-393
❑ 85AllGamPI-75
❑ 85Don-151
❑ 85Fle-152
❑ 85Top-116
❑ 85TopTif-116
❑ 86BasStaB-14
❑ 86Don-50
❑ 86Fle-342
❑ 86FleStiC-9
❑ 86Lea-35
❑ 86OPC-259
❑ 86Spo-152
❑ 86Top-605
❑ 86TopMinL-4
❑ 86TopSti-249
❑ 86TopTat-16
❑ 86TopTif-605
❑ 87ClaGam-85
❑ 87Don-51
❑ 87Fle-30
❑ 87FleBasA-4
❑ 87FleExcS-5
❑ 87FleGlo-30
❑ 87Lea-248
❑ 87OPC-285
❑ 87RedFolSB-122
❑ 87RedSoxP-4
❑ 87RedSoxSAP-4
❑ 87SmoAmeL-2
❑ 87Spo-47
❑ 87SpoTeaP-9
❑ 87Top-285
❑ 87TopSti-249
❑ 87TopTif-285
❑ 88Don-462
❑ 88DonTeaBRS-462
❑ 88Fle-347
❑ 88FleGlo-347
❑ 88Lea-252
❑ 88PanSti-20
❑ 88Sco-121
❑ 88ScoGlo-121
❑ 88ScoSam-121
❑ 88StaLinRS-4
❑ 88Top-704
❑ 88TopClo-15
❑ 88TopTif-704
❑ 89Don-476
❑ 89Fle-82
❑ 89FleGlo-82
❑ 89OPC-326
❑ 89PanSti-269
❑ 89Sco-238
❑ 89Top-326
❑ 89TopTif-326
❑ 89UppDec-415
❑ 90Bow-102
❑ 90BowTif-102
❑ 90Don-633
❑ 90ExpPos-3
❑ 90FleUpd-26
❑ 90Lea-159
❑ 90OPC-544
❑ 90PubIntS-449
❑ 90Sco-137
❑ 90ScoRoo-24T
❑ 90Top-544
❑ 90TopTif-544
❑ 90TopTra-12T
❑ 90TopTraT-12T
❑ 90UppDec-484
❑ 90UppDec-749
❑ 91Bow-456
❑ 91ClaGam-9
❑ 91Don-194
❑ 91Fle-226
❑ 91Lea-167
❑ 91OPC-48
❑ 91PanFreS-147
❑ 91Sco-202
❑ 91StaClu-142
❑ 91Stu-193
❑ 91Top-48
❑ 91TopDesS-48
❑ 91TopMic-48
❑ 91TopTif-48
❑ 91Ult-197
❑ 91UppDec-359
❑ 91UppDecFE-51F
❑ 92Don-447
❑ 92OPC-428
❑ 92Sco-531
❑ 92StaClu-99
❑ 92Top-428
❑ 92TopGol-428
❑ 92TopGolW-428
❑ 92TopMic-428
❑ 92UppDec-559
❑ 93RanKee-80
Boyd, Quincy
❑ 95VerBeaDTI-4
Boyd, Randy
❑ 77SanJosMC-16
Boyd, Raymond
❑ 15Zee-26
❑ 16Zee-24
Boyer, Clete (Leroy)
❑ 47StaPinP2-6
❑ 56A'sPos-5
❑ 57Top-121
❑ 59Top-251
❑ 60Lea-46
❑ 60Top-109
❑ 60TopVen-109
❑ 61Pos-11
❑ 61Raw-3
❑ 61Top-19
❑ 61TopStaI-191
❑ 61Yan61RL-6
❑ 61YanJayP-2
❑ 62Jel-3
❑ 62Pos-3
❑ 62PosCan-3
❑ 62SalPlaC-80
❑ 62ShiPlaC-80
❑ 62Top-163
❑ 62Top-490
❑ 62TopStaI-84
❑ 62TopVen-163
❑ 62YanJayP-4
❑ 63Jel-14
❑ 63Kah-3
❑ 63Pos-14
❑ 63ReqKP-5
❑ 63Top-361
❑ 63YanJayP-2
❑ 64ChatheY-4
❑ 64Top-69
❑ 64TopVen-69
❑ 64YanJayP-2
❑ 65ChaTheY-3
❑ 65Top-475
❑ 66OPC-9
❑ 66Top-9
❑ 66TopVen-9
❑ 66YanTeaI-1
❑ 67BraIrvD-1
❑ 67BraPho-4
❑ 67CokCapB-13
❑ 67DexPre-28
❑ 67Top-328
❑ 68Baz-1
❑ 68BraPos-4
❑ 68CokCapB-13
❑ 68DexPre-16
❑ 68Kah-A4
❑ 68Kah-B9
❑ 68Top-518A
❑ 68Top-518B
❑ 68Top-550
❑ 69AtlBraBPPS-4
❑ 69Top-489
❑ 69TopSta-3
❑ 69TopTeaP-2
❑ 70OPC-206
❑ 70Top-206
❑ 71MLBOffS-4
❑ 71OPC-374
❑ 71Top-374
❑ 72MilBra-42
❑ 78GreBraT-4
❑ 81TCM60I-477
❑ 83Yan196-6
❑ 84A'sMot-27
❑ 85A'sMot-27
❑ 87ColCliP-25
❑ 87ColCliP-2
❑ 87ColCliT-24
❑ 88PacLegI-13
❑ 89Ft.LauYS-27
❑ 89PacSenL-149
❑ 89SweBasG-94
❑ 89T/MSenL-12
❑ 89TopSenL-4
❑ 90CMC-224
❑ 90ColCliC-24
❑ 90ColCliP-2
❑ 90ColCliP-693
❑ 90EliSenL-34
❑ 90PacLeg-10
❑ 90ProAAAF-343
❑ 90SweBasG-102
❑ 91ColCliP-NNO
❑ 91LinDriAAA-125
❑ 91PacSenL-43
❑ 91PacSenL-54
❑ 91SweBasG-109
❑ 91YanRinP11-12
❑ 92YanWIZ6-14
❑ 99SpoIllGotG-78
❑ 99SpoIllGotGA-10
Boyer, Cloyd
❑ 51Bow-228
❑ 52Top-280
❑ 53BowC-115
❑ 53CarHunW-3
❑ 53Top-60
❑ 55A'sRodM-6
❑ 55A'sRodM-7
❑ 55A'sTeaI-3
❑ 55Bow-149
❑ 76A'sRodMC-5
❑ 76VenLeaS-71
❑ 83RoyPos-5
❑ 83TopRep5-280
❑ 85SyrChiT-30
❑ 88PulBraP-1770
❑ 89IdaFalBP-2008
❑ 90PulBraB-28
❑ 90PulBraP-3113
❑ 91PulBraC-20
❑ 91PulBraP-4023
❑ 91TopArc1-60
❑ 92PulBraC-29
❑ 92PulBraF-3197
Boyer, Dave
❑ 78ArkTraT-3
Boyer, Ken (Kenton Lloyd)
❑ 47Exh-24
❑ 55CarHunW-2
❑ 55Top-125
❑ 56Top-14
❑ 56TopPin-46
❑ 57SwiFra-8
❑ 57Top-122
❑ 58CarJayP-2
❑ 58Top-350
❑ 59Baz-4
❑ 59HomRunD-4
❑ 59Top-325
❑ 59Top-557
❑ 60ArmCoi-4
❑ 60Baz-9
❑ 60CarJayP-1
❑ 60KeyChaI-8
❑ 60Lea-12
❑ 60Top-160
❑ 60Top-485
❑ 60TopVen-160
❑ 61Baz-14
❑ 61CarJayP-1
❑ 61Pos-171A
❑ 61Pos-171B
❑ 61SevElev-18
❑ 61Top-43
❑ 61Top-375
❑ 61Top-573
❑ 61TopStaI-85
❑ 62AurRec-3
❑ 62Baz-20
❑ 62CarJayP-1
❑ 62ExhStaB-5
❑ 62Jel-159
❑ 62Pos-159
❑ 62PosCan-159
❑ 62SalPlaC-167
❑ 62ShiPlaC-167
❑ 62Top-52
❑ 62Top-370
❑ 62Top-392
❑ 62TopBuc-10
❑ 62TopStaI-183
❑ 62TopVen-52
❑ 63CarJayP-1
❑ 63CarJayP-2
❑ 63ExhStaB-8
❑ 63Fle-60
❑ 63Jel-160
❑ 63Pos-160
❑ 63SalMetC-15
❑ 63Top-375
❑ 63TopStiI-6
❑ 64Baz-35
❑ 64CarTeaI-1
❑ 64Raw-1
❑ 64Top-11
❑ 64Top-160
❑ 64TopCoi-25
❑ 64TopCoi-145
❑ 64TopGia-57
❑ 64TopSta-61
❑ 64TopStaU-10
❑ 64TopTatI-26
❑ 64TopVen-11
❑ 64TopVen-160
❑ 64WheSta-8
❑ 65Baz-35
❑ 65CarJayP-1
❑ 65OldLonC-4
❑ 65OPC-6
❑ 65OPC-100
❑ 65OPC-135
❑ 65Top-6
❑ 65Top-100
❑ 65Top-135
❑ 65TopEmbI-47
❑ 65TopTraI-40
❑ 66MetTeaI-2
❑ 66Top-385
❑ 66TopRubI-10
❑ 67Baz-33
❑ 67CokCapYM-V28
❑ 67DexPre-29
❑ 67Kah-6A
❑ 67Kah-6B
❑ 67MetTeaI-2
❑ 67OPC-105
❑ 67Top-105
❑ 67TopVen-235
❑ 68Top-259
❑ 68TopActS-8A
❑ 68TopVen-259
❑ 69MilBra-33
❑ 69Top-379
❑ 71CarTeaI-4
❑ 71CarTeaI-3
❑ 74LauAllG-56
❑ 75OPC-202
❑ 75Top-202
❑ 75TopMin-202
❑ 75TulOil7-3
❑ 76GrePlaG-37
❑ 76TulOilGP-1
❑ 76UPIS-1
❑ 77RocRedWM-25
❑ 78CarTeaI-1
❑ 78TCM60I-67
❑ 79Car5-1
❑ 79Top-192
❑ 80Top-244
❑ 81TCM60I-414
❑ 82K-M-6
❑ 83CarGreT-3
❑ 88PacLegI-12
❑ 90DodTar-63
❑ 91MetWIZ-49
❑ 92CarMcD-29
❑ 93ActPacA-145
❑ 97TopMan-28
❑ 97TopManF-28
❑ 97TopManFR-27
Boyer, Leonard
❑ 66St.PetCTI-3
Boyer, Mickey
❑ 84IdaFalATI-4
❑ 89IdaFalBP-2008
Boyette, Tony
❑ 94PriRedC-4
❑ 94PriRedF-3263
❑ 97BurBeeB-3
Boykin, Tyrone
❑ 91BoiHawC-5
❑ 92QuaCitRBC-23
❑ 92QuaCitRBF-821
❑ 93PalSprAC-3
❑ 93PalSprAF-81
❑ 94MidAngF-2443
❑ 94MidAngOHP-2
❑ 95MidAngOHP-5
❑ 95MidAngTI-5
❑ 96MidAngB-7
❑ 96MidAngOHP-5
❑ 97LakElsSG-8
❑ 98CedRapKTI-3
Boylan, Brad
❑ 84SalLakCGC-193
❑ 86TolMudHP-2
❑ 87PorBeaP-24
❑ 88PorBeaP-648
Boyland, Dorian Scott
❑ 77ShrCapT-1
❑ 78ColCliT-2
❑ 79PorBeaT-7
❑ 80PorBeaT-2
❑ 80Top-683
❑ 81PorBeaT-8
❑ 82PhoGiaVNB-15
Boyle, Buzz (Ralph Francis)
❑ 34BabRutG-6
❑ 34ButPreR-6
❑ 34DiaMatCSB-18
❑ 72TCMthe3-94
❑ 74TCMNic-10
❑ 90DodTar-64
Boyle, Gary
❑ 76QuaCitAT-5
Boyle, Henry J.
❑ 87BucN28-38
❑ 87OldJudN-38
❑ 88WG1CarG-29
Boyle, Jack (John Anthony)
❑ 87OldJudN-37
Boyle, Jeff
❑ 93PocPosF-4212
❑ 93PocPosSP-1
Boyles, John
❑ 85CedRapRT-1
❑ 86VerRedP-2
❑ 89WauTimGS-6
Boyne, Bryan
❑ 76CedRapGT-6
Boynewicz, Jim
❑ 94BurBeeC-3
❑ 94BurBeeF-1072
Boynton, Paul
❑ 88KimN18-5
Boyzuick, Mike
❑ 91GreFalDSP-12
❑ 92BakDodCLC-4
❑ 92VerBeaDF-2881
❑ 93BelBreCB-3
❑ 93BelBreFI-1715
Boze, Marshall
❑ 91HelBreSP-5
❑ 92BelBreCB-6
❑ 92BelBreFI-395
❑ 93Bow-675
❑ 93ClaFS7-165
❑ 93StoPorC-2
❑ 93StoPorF-735
❑ 94ActPac-29
❑ 94Bow-37
❑ 94Cla-139
❑ 94ClaGolF-174
❑ 94ClaTriF-T43
❑ 94ExcFS7-78
❑ 94NewOrlZF-1461
❑ 94UppDecML-249
❑ 94UppDecMLPotYF-PY6
❑ 95SigRooOJ-7
❑ 95SigRooOJP-7
❑ 95SigRooOJPS-7
❑ 95SigRooOJS-7
❑ 96BrePol-2
❑ 97LasVegS1A-7
Bozich, Gary
❑ 81BirBarT-11
Braase, John
❑ 88GreFalDTI-14
❑ 90BakDodCLC-241
Braatz, Kim
❑ 95ColSilB-1
❑ 96ColSilB-2
Brabant, Dan
❑ 93BurIndC-5
❑ 93BurIndF-3287
❑ 94ColRedC-3
❑ 94ColRedF-433
❑ 95KinIndTI-5
❑ 96KenIndB-1
Brabender, Gene
❑ 66BalOriP-7
❑ 66Top-579
❑ 67BalOriP-18
❑ 67OPC-22
❑ 67Top-22
❑ 68OPC-163
❑ 68Top-163
❑ 68TopVen-163
❑ 69Top-393
❑ 70BreMcD-3
❑ 70BreMil-1
❑ 70OPC-289
❑ 70Top-289
❑ 71MLBOffS-340
❑ 71OPC-666
❑ 71Top-666
❑ 81Ori6F-9
❑ 83Pil69G-43
❑ 91OriCro-47
❑ 94BreMilB-203
Brabinski, Marek
❑ 90IdaFalBP-3268
Bracho, Alejandro
❑ 96-97LinVen-79
❑ 96GreBatB-6
Bracho, Darwin
❑ 96-97LinVen-182
Bracho, Didimo
❑ 96-97LinVen-129
Bracho, Jose
❑ 52Par-24
Brack, Gib (Gilbert Herman)
❑ 39PlaBal-127
❑ 72TCMthe3-101
Brackeen, Colin
❑ 98HagSunM-8
Bradbury, George
❑ 77LynMetT-5
Bradbury, Miah
❑ 88AlaGolTI-4
❑ 90MiaMirIS-1
❑ 91Cla/Bes-110
❑ 91MiaMirC-16
❑ 91MiaMirP-410
❑ 92PenPilC-3
❑ 92PenPilF-2935
❑ 93ExcFS7-220
❑ 93HarSenF-271
Braddock, Ron
❑ 66St.PetCTI-4
Braddy, Junior
❑ 96SarRedSB-10
Braddy, Leonard
❑ 84VisOakT-9
Brader, Tim
❑ 88BriTigP-1865
❑ 89FayGenP-1583
Bradford, Bill
❑ 53SanFraSTI-2
Bradford, Buddy (Charles W.)
❑ 68OPC-142
❑ 68Top-142
❑ 68TopVen-142
❑ 69MilBra-34
❑ 69OPC-97
❑ 69Top-97
❑ 69TopTeaP-11
❑ 69WhiSoxTI-4
❑ 70Ind-1
❑ 70MLBOffS-183
❑ 70OPC-299
❑ 70Top-299
❑ 70WhiSoxTI-3
❑ 71Ind-1
❑ 71MLBOffS-362
❑ 71OPC-552
❑ 71Top-552
❑ 72MilBra-43
❑ 74OPC-357
❑ 74Top-357
❑ 75OPC-504
❑ 75Top-504
❑ 75TopMin-504
❑ 76OPC-451
❑ 76SSP-281
❑ 76Top-451
Bradford, Chad
❑ 96HicCraB-3
❑ 98BirBarG-5
❑ 99Fle-377
❑ 99FleSta9-377
❑ 99FleWarT-377
Bradford, Chris
❑ 89AncBucTI-23
Bradford, Josh
❑ 96StCatSB-5
❑ 97DunBluJTI-5
❑ 98DunBluJSB-10

❑ 98DunBluJTI-6
Bradford, Larry
❑ 75LynRanT-5
❑ 78RicBraT-4
❑ 79RicBraT-17
❑ 80Top-675
❑ 81BraPol-34
❑ 81Don-584
❑ 81Fle-265
❑ 81Top-542
❑ 82Don-553
❑ 82Fle-431
❑ 82Top-271
❑ 83PorBeaT-24
❑ 85GreBraTI-5
Bradford, Mark
❑ 88BatCliP-1672
Bradford, Tony
❑ 94OrlCubF-1377
Bradford, Troy
❑ 88CapCodPPaLP-103
❑ 90AriWilP-1
❑ 90GenCubP-3030
❑ 90GenCubS-2
❑ 91CarLeaAP-CAR39
❑ 91WinSpiC-1
❑ 91WinSpiP-2820
❑ 92ChaKniF-2764
❑ 92PeoChiC-24
Bradford, Vincent
❑ 90BriTigP-3169
❑ 90BriTigS-2
❑ 90HigSchPLS-16
❑ 91BriTigC-15
❑ 91BriTigP-3617
Bradish, Mike
❑ 90UtiBluSP-29
❑ 92SalSpuC-23
❑ 93SarWhiSC-4
❑ 94PriWilCC-3
❑ 94PriWilCF-1926
Bradley, Bert
❑ 80WesHavWCT-10
❑ 81WesHavAT-3
❑ 82WesHavAT-2
❑ 83TacTigT-2
❑ 84TacTigC-92
❑ 85ColCliP-2
❑ 85ColCliT-2
❑ 87MadMusP-1
❑ 88MadMusP-4
❑ 90MadMusB-26
❑ 90MadMusP-2284
❑ 91HunStaC-17
❑ 91HunStaLD-300
❑ 91HunStaP-1812
❑ 91HunStaTI-24
❑ 91LinDriAA-300
❑ 92HunStaF-3965
❑ 92HunStaS-325
❑ 94TacTigF-3191
❑ 95WesMicWTI-17
❑ 96WesMicWB-2
❑ 97HunStaTI-3
❑ 98HunStaTI-7
Bradley, Bill (William J.)
❑ 03BreE10-11
❑ 04FanCraAL-6
❑ 05IndSouPSoCP-4
❑ 08AmeLeaPC-4
❑ 08RosComP-23
❑ 09AmeCarE90-1-10
❑ 09BriE97-3
❑ 09T206-32
❑ 09T206-33
❑ 10CouT21-81
❑ 10W555-7
❑ 11PinT-5-626
❑ 11SpoLifCW-39
❑ 11SpoLifCW-40
❑ 67SpoHobFC-43
❑ 74CapPub-77
Bradley, Byron
❑ 92GenCubF-1565
❑ 94DayCubF-2357
Bradley, David
❑ 91WelPirC-23
Bradley, Eric
❑ 90MyrBeaBJP-2769
Bradley, Fred
❑ 48WhiSoxTI-3
Bradley, Grin (George W.)
❑ 87OldJudN-40
❑ 90HOFStiB-1
Bradley, Hugh F.
❑ 11SpoLifM-40
❑ 12T207-19
Bradley, Kenny
❑ 92KinMetC-2
❑ 92KinMetF-1537
Bradley, Len
❑ 80GleFalWSBT-2
❑ 80GleFalWSCT-2
❑ 81GleFalWST-23
❑ 82EdmTraT-17
Bradley, London
❑ 92GenCubC-25
❑ 93ClaFS7-272
❑ 93PeoChiC-3
❑ 93PeoChiF-1089
❑ 93PeoChiTI-2
❑ 94DayCubC-3
Bradley, Mark
❑ 77LodDodT-2
❑ 82AlbDukTc-19
❑ 83DodPol-22
❑ 84Fle-581
❑ 84Nes792-316
❑ 84Top-316
❑ 84TopTif-316
❑ 90DodTar-65
❑ 91MetWIZ-50
Bradley, Mike
❑ 89AncBucTI-1
❑ 90SpoIndSP-18
❑ 91ChaRaiC-2
❑ 91ChaRaiP-88
Bradley, Milton
❑ 97Bow-145
❑ 97BowInt-145
❑ 97VerExpB-10
❑ 98Bow-372
❑ 98BowChr-372
❑ 98BowChrGA-372
❑ 98BowChrGAR-372
❑ 98BowChrI-372
❑ 98BowChrIR-372
❑ 98BowChrR-372
❑ 98BowGolA-372
❑ 98BowInt-372
❑ 98CapFeaCM-4
❑ 98SouAtlLPM-2
❑ 99BasAmeTP-16
❑ 99BasAmeTPG-16
❑ 99Bow-154
❑ 99BowChr-154
❑ 99BowChrG-154
❑ 99BowChrGR-154
❑ 99BowChrI-154
❑ 99BowChrIR-154
❑ 99BowChrR-154
❑ 99BowGol-154
❑ 99BowInt-154
Bradley, Nick (J. Nichols)
❑ 87OldJudN-39
Bradley, Otis
❑ 79CliDodT-7
Bradley, Paul
❑ 84ModA'sC-3
❑ 85ModA'sC-2
Bradley, Phil (Philip Poole)
❑ 83SalLakCGT-11
❑ 84FleUpd-15
❑ 84MarMot-24
❑ 84TopTra-15T
❑ 84TopTraT-15T
❑ 85Don-631
❑ 85Fle-486
❑ 85Lea-50
❑ 85MarMot-21
❑ 85OPC-69
❑ 85Top-449
❑ 85TopTif-449
❑ 86Don-22
❑ 86Don-191
❑ 86DonAll-41
❑ 86DonSupD-22
❑ 86Fle-461
❑ 86FleLimE-5
❑ 86FleMin-96
❑ 86FleStiC-10
❑ 86GenMilB-2B
❑ 86Lea-22
❑ 86MarMot-8
❑ 86MarPacNB-3
❑ 86OPC-305
❑ 86SevCoi-W11
❑ 86Spo-77
❑ 86Top-305
❑ 86TopGloS-54
❑ 86TopSti-217
❑ 86TopSup-13
❑ 86TopTat-14
❑ 86TopTif-305
❑ 87Don-270
❑ 87DonOpeD-122
❑ 87Fle-581
❑ 87FleGlo-581
❑ 87FleLeaL-4
❑ 87FleMin-11
❑ 87FleStiC-13
❑ 87GenMilB-3A
❑ 87HosSti-29
❑ 87Lea-200
❑ 87MarMot-6
❑ 87OPC-170
❑ 87Spo-89
❑ 87SpoTeaP-25
❑ 87StuPan-25
❑ 87Top-525
❑ 87TopMinL-70
❑ 87TopSti-221
❑ 87TopTif-525
❑ 88Don-243
❑ 88DonBasB-47
❑ 88Fle-369
❑ 88FleGlo-369
❑ 88FleUpd-107
❑ 88FleUpdG-107
❑ 88OPC-55
❑ 88PanSti-191
❑ 88PhiTas-4
❑ 88Sco-66
❑ 88ScoGlo-66
❑ 88ScoRoo-34T
❑ 88ScoRooG-34T
❑ 88Spo-93
❑ 88StaLinMa-1
❑ 88StaLinPh-3
❑ 88Top-55
❑ 88Top-519
❑ 88TopMinL-33
❑ 88TopSti-218
❑ 88TopTif-55
❑ 88TopTif-519
❑ 88TopTra-18T
❑ 88TopTraT-18T
❑ 89BalOriP-4
❑ 89Bow-17
❑ 89BowTif-17
❑ 89Don-369
❑ 89DonBasB-198
❑ 89DonTra-41
❑ 89Fle-563
❑ 89FleGlo-563
❑ 89FleUpd-1
❑ 89OPC-308
❑ 89OriFreB-16
❑ 89PanSti-154
❑ 89Sco-79
❑ 89ScoRoo-44T
❑ 89Top-608
❑ 89TopAme2C-6
❑ 89TopSti-113
❑ 89TopTif-608
❑ 89TopTra-13T
❑ 89TopTraT-13T
❑ 89UppDec-229
❑ 89UppDec-749
❑ 90Bow-261
❑ 90BowTif-261
❑ 90Don-259
❑ 90Fle-174
❑ 90FleCan-174
❑ 90Lea-138
❑ 90OPC-163
❑ 90PanSti-4
❑ 90PubIntS-575
❑ 90Sco-24
❑ 90Sco100S-36
❑ 90ScoRoo-44T
❑ 90Spo-95
❑ 90Top-163
❑ 90TopBatL-20
❑ 90TopBig-202
❑ 90TopMinL-2
❑ 90TopSti-241
❑ 90TopTif-163
❑ 90UppDec-194
❑ 91Don-646
❑ 91Fle-114
❑ 91OPC-717
❑ 91OriCro-48
❑ 91Sco-560
❑ 91SimandSMLBL-5
❑ 91Top-717
❑ 91TopDesS-717
❑ 91TopMic-717
❑ 91TopTif-717
❑ 91UppDec-641
❑ 92EdmTraF-3550
❑ 92ExpDonD-3B
Bradley, Rick
❑ 75PhoGiaC-7
❑ 77PhoGiaCC-4
❑ 77PhoGiaCP-3
❑ 77PhoGiaVNB-2
❑ 78PhoGiaC-2
❑ 79PhoGiaVNB-14
Bradley, Ryan
❑ 98BesNumOP-9
❑ 98FleUpd-U71
❑ 98TamYanM-6
❑ 99BasAmeTPBP-3
❑ 99Bow-145
❑ 99BowAut-BA42
❑ 99BowBes-122
❑ 99BowBesAR-122
❑ 99BowBesR-122
❑ 99BowChr-145
❑ 99BowChrG-145
❑ 99BowChrGR-145
❑ 99BowChrI-145
❑ 99BowChrIR-145
❑ 99BowChrR-145
❑ 99BowGol-145
❑ 99BowInt-145
❑ 99E-X Cen-120
❑ 99E-X CenECFut-120
❑ 99E-X CenECNow-120
❑ 99Fle-69
❑ 99FleBri-149
❑ 99FleBriBlu-149
❑ 99FleBriGol-149
❑ 99FleSta9-69
❑ 99FleWarT-69
❑ 99SkyThu-300
❑ 99SkyThuRant-300
❑ 99SkyThuRave-300
❑ 99SpoIll-71
❑ 99TeaBesRBG-3
❑ 99TeaBesRFS-13
❑ 99ThuSkySupR-300
Bradley, Scott W.
❑ 83NasSouTI-1
❑ 84ColCliP-2
❑ 84ColCliT-11
❑ 85Don-37
❑ 85YanTCMP-21
❑ 86BufBisP-4
❑ 86Don-396
❑ 86Top-481
❑ 86TopTif-481
❑ 87Don-440
❑ 87Fle-580
❑ 87FleBasA-5
❑ 87FleGlo-580
❑ 87MarMot-14
❑ 87SpoTeaP-25
❑ 87Top-376
❑ 87TopSti-217
❑ 87TopTif-376
❑ 88Don-147
❑ 88DonBasB-24
❑ 88Fle-370
❑ 88FleGlo-370
❑ 88Lea-75
❑ 88MarMot-14
❑ 88OPC-199
❑ 88PanSti-183
❑ 88RedFolSB-8
❑ 88Sco-151
❑ 88ScoGlo-151
❑ 88StaLinMa-2
❑ 88Top-762
❑ 88TopSti-222
❑ 88TopTif-762
❑ 89Bow-209
❑ 89BowTif-209
❑ 89Don-261
❑ 89Fle-540
❑ 89FleGlo-540
❑ 89MarMot-14
❑ 89OPC-279
❑ 89PanSti-432
❑ 89Sco-324
❑ 89Top-279
❑ 89TopSti-225
❑ 89TopTif-279
❑ 89UppDec-226
❑ 90Bow-483
❑ 90BowTif-483
❑ 90Don-581
❑ 90Fle-506
❑ 90FleCan-506
❑ 90Lea-404
❑ 90MarMot-25
❑ 90OPC-593
❑ 90PubIntS-427
❑ 90Sco-228
❑ 90Top-593
❑ 90TopBig-181
❑ 90TopSti-229
❑ 90TopTif-593
❑ 90UppDec-383
❑ 91Bow-239
❑ 91Don-287
❑ 91Fle-443
❑ 91Lea-99
❑ 91MarCouH-5
❑ 91OPC-38
❑ 91Sco-113
❑ 91ScoPro-113
❑ 91StaClu-252
❑ 91Top-38
❑ 91TopDesS-38
❑ 91TopMic-38
❑ 91TopTif-38
❑ 91Ult-332
❑ 91UppDec-130
❑ 92Don-713
❑ 92Fle-273
❑ 92OPC-608
❑ 92Sco-304
❑ 92StaClu-146
❑ 92Top-608
❑ 92TopGol-608
❑ 92TopGolW-608
❑ 92TopMic-608
❑ 92UppDec-390
❑ 92YanWIZ8-16
❑ 94ColSprSSF-736
Bradley, Tom
❑ 71OPC-588
❑ 71Top-588
❑ 72OPC-248
❑ 72Top-248
❑ 72WhiSoxTI1-4
❑ 73OPC-336
❑ 73Top-336
❑ 74OPC-455
❑ 74Top-455
❑ 74TopSta-102
❑ 75GiaTeal-2
❑ 75OPC-179
❑ 75PhoGiaCK-9
❑ 75Top-179
❑ 75TopMin-179
❑ 76OPC-644
❑ 76Top-644
❑ 76TucTorCa-16
❑ 76TusTorCr-35
Bradley, Wayne
❑ 75CedRapGT-28
Bradshaw, Craig
❑ 92IdaFalGF-3502
❑ 92IdaFalGSP-28
❑ 93DanBraC-4
❑ 93DanBraF-3609
Bradshaw, Joe
❑ 90DodTar-903
Bradshaw, Kevin
❑ 87LakTigP-7
❑ 88GleFalTP-934
❑ 89TolMudHC-19
❑ 89TolMudHP-783
❑ 91BriTigC-30
❑ 92TolMudHF-1058
❑ 92TolMudHS-600
❑ 93LakTigC-27
❑ 93LakTigF-1328
❑ 94BriTigC-28
❑ 94TreThuF-2136
Bradshaw, Terry
❑ 90HamRedB-23
❑ 91Cla/Bes-269
❑ 91SavCarC-23
❑ 91SavCarP-1664
❑ 91SouAtlLAGP-SAL41
❑ 92ProFS7-320
❑ 93ClaFS7-242
❑ 93St.PetCC-6
❑ 93St.PetCF-2639
❑ 94ArkTraF-3100
❑ 94Bow-648
❑ 94Cla-58
❑ 94ExcFS7-260
❑ 95Bow-71
❑ 95Exc-264
❑ 95FleUpd-154
❑ 95LouRedF-287
❑ 95Sum-164
❑ 95SumNthD-164
❑ 95Top-656
❑ 95UppDecML-35
❑ 95UppDecMLFS-35
❑ 96ColCho-282
❑ 96ColChoGS-282
❑ 96ColChoSS-282
❑ 96Don-422
❑ 96DonPreP-422
❑ 96LouRedB-11
❑ 96Sco-255
❑ 97LouRedB-11
❑ 97Pac-405
❑ 97PacLigB-405
❑ 97PacSil-405
❑ 98OmaRoyM-6
Brady, Brian
❑ 86MidAngP-2
❑ 87MidAngP-5
❑ 88EdmTraC-16
❑ 88EdmTraP-572
❑ 90CMC-539
❑ 90PhoFirC-12
❑ 90PhoFirP-16
❑ 90ProAAAF-42
❑ 90TopDeb89-19
Brady, Cliff (Clifford F.)
❑ 24Zee-115
❑ 25Zee-130
❑ 26Zee-160
❑ 27Zee-132
Brady, Dave
❑ 83RedPioT-6
Brady, Doug
❑ 91UtiBluSC-2
❑ 91UtiBluSP-3244
❑ 92ClaFS7-377
❑ 92SarWhiSCB-25
❑ 92SarWhiSF-211
❑ 92SouBenWSC-9
❑ 93SarWhiSC-5
❑ 93SarWhiSF-1374
❑ 94BirBarC-4
❑ 94BirBarF-626
❑ 95ARuFalLS-3
❑ 95NasSouTI-4
❑ 96NasSouB-9
Brady, Jim
❑ 56Top-126
❑ 77SalPirT-2
Brady, Lawrence
❑ 86WatPirP-5
Brady, Mike
❑ 89MyrBeaBJP-1477
❑ 90St.LucMS-1
❑ 91St.LucMP-702
❑ 91VerBeaDC-4
❑ 91VerBeaDP-765
❑ 92VerBeaDC-21
❑ 97St.CatSB-4
Brady, Pat
❑ 89SalSpuCLC-138
❑ 89SalSpuP-1815
❑ 90SanJosGB-4
❑ 90SanJosGCLC-31
❑ 90SanJosGP-2023
❑ 90SanJosGS-1
❑ 90SanJosGS-26
❑ 91ClePhiC-15
❑ 91ClePhiP-1626
❑ 91FloStaLAP-FSL6
❑ 92ClePhiC-22
❑ 92ClePhiF-2068
❑ 93ReaPhiF-306
❑ 94ScrRedBF-931
Brady, Steve (Stephen A.)
❑ 87OldJudN-41
❑ 88GandBCGCE-3
Bragan, Bobby (Robert R.)
❑ 40PhiTeal-5
❑ 41PhiTeal-5
❑ 43DodTeal-3
❑ 47DodTeal-2
❑ 47TipTop-91
❑ 48DodTeal-3
❑ 53MotCoo-4
❑ 56PirTeal-2

❑ 58IndTeal-2
❑ 59DarFar-3
❑ 60DodTeal-2
❑ 60Top-463
❑ 63Top-73
❑ 64BraJayP-3
❑ 64Top-506
❑ 65Top-346
❑ 66BraPos-6
❑ 66Top-476
❑ 79DiaGre-84
❑ 81TCM60I-410
❑ 85TCMPla1-26
❑ 90DodTar-66

Bragan, Jimmy
❑ 73ExpPos-1
❑ 89ChaLooLITI-4

Bragan, Peter
❑ 89JacExpB-23
❑ 96JacSunB-1

Bragg, Darren
❑ 92ClaFS7-213
❑ 92PenPilC-23
❑ 92PenPilF-2945
❑ 93ExcFS7-221
❑ 93JacSunF-2721
❑ 94LeaLimR-45
❑ 94MarMot-15
❑ 94SpoRoo-74
❑ 94SpoRooAP-74
❑ 94UppDecML-53
❑ 95ColCho-556T
❑ 95Don-496
❑ 95DonPreP-496
❑ 95Fla-299
❑ 95FleAllR-M4
❑ 95LinVen-145
❑ 95LinVen-270
❑ 95MarMot-15
❑ 95MarPac-24
❑ 95Sco-589
❑ 95ScoGolR-589
❑ 95ScoPlaTS-589
❑ 95SigRoo-9
❑ 95SigRooSig-9
❑ 95StaClu-561
❑ 95StaCluMOP-561
❑ 95StaCluSTWS-561
❑ 95TacRaiTI-5
❑ 95TopTra-87T
❑ 95UltGolMR-M5
❑ 95UppDec-238
❑ 95UppDecED-238
❑ 95UppDecEDG-238
❑ 95UppDecPAW-H36
❑ 95UppDecPAWE-H36
❑ 95UppDecSE-254
❑ 95UppDecSEG-254
❑ 96ColCho-314
❑ 96ColChoGS-314
❑ 96ColChoSS-314
❑ 96Fle-230
❑ 96FleTif-230
❑ 96LeaSigA-32
❑ 96LeaSigAG-32
❑ 96LeaSigAS-32
❑ 96MarMot-24
❑ 96TacRaiB-6
❑ 96Ult-407
❑ 96UltGolM-407
❑ 97ColCho-51
❑ 97Don-250
❑ 97DonGolPP-250
❑ 97DonSilPP-250
❑ 97DonTea-54
❑ 97DonTeaSPE-54
❑ 97Fle-17
❑ 97FleTif-17
❑ 97MetUni-18
❑ 97Pac-33
❑ 97PacLigB-33
❑ 97PacSil-33
❑ 97Pin-133
❑ 97PinArtP-PP133
❑ 97PinMusC-133
❑ 97PinPrePla-133
❑ 97RedSoxS-9
❑ 97RedSoxSPl-9
❑ 97RedSoxSPr-9
❑ 97Sco-188
❑ 97ScoArtPWB-188
❑ 97ScoPreS-188
❑ 97ScoShoS-188
❑ 97ScoShoSAP-188
❑ 97Top-354
❑ 97UppDec-314
❑ 98ColCho-47
❑ 98Fin-230
❑ 98FinNo--230
❑ 98FinNo-R-230
❑ 98FinRef-230
❑ 98Fle-55
❑ 98Pac-36
❑ 98PacOnl-108
❑ 98PacOnlR-108
❑ 98PacOnlWC-108
❑ 98PacPlaB-36
❑ 98PacRedT-36
❑ 98PacSil-36
❑ 98PinSna-BRS3
❑ 98RedSoxS-4
❑ 98RedSoxSP-4
❑ 98Sco-75
❑ 98StaCluFDI-194
❑ 98StaCluI-194
❑ 98StaCluOneK-194
❑ 98StaCluPP-194
❑ 98Top-178
❑ 98TopChr-178
❑ 98TopChrR-178
❑ 98TopDevR-178
❑ 98TopDia-178
❑ 98TopMiniC-178
❑ 98UppDec-45
❑ 98UppDecSF-27
❑ 99Fle-346
❑ 99FleSta9-346
❑ 99FleWarT-346
❑ 99Pac-63
❑ 99PacPlaB-63
❑ 99PacRed-63
❑ 99Top-92
❑ 99TopChr-92
❑ 99TopChrR-92
❑ 99TopMVPP-92
❑ 99UppDec-50
❑ 99UppDec-467
❑ 99UppDecEL1-50
❑ 99UppDecEL1-467
❑ 99UppDecEL2-50
❑ 99UppDecEL2-467
❑ 99Vic-332

Bragg, Luke Owen
❑ 98ChaRivDG-5

Bragga, Matt
❑ 94ButCopKSP-25

Braggs, Glenn
❑ 86SpoRoo-21
❑ 86VanCanP-5
❑ 87BrePol-26
❑ 87BreTeal-1
❑ 87Don-337
❑ 87DonOpeD-52
❑ 87Fle-339
❑ 87FleGlo-339
❑ 87SpoTeaP-19
❑ 87Top-622
❑ 87TopTif-622
❑ 88BrePol-26
❑ 88BreTeal-5
❑ 88Don-240
❑ 88DonBasB-15
❑ 88Fle-157
❑ 88FleGlo-157
❑ 88OPC-263
❑ 88PanSti-127
❑ 88Sco-59
❑ 88ScoGlo-59
❑ 88ScoYouS2-2
❑ 88StaLinBre-2
❑ 88Top-263
❑ 88Top-639
❑ 88TopSti-197
❑ 88TopTif-263
❑ 88TopTif-639
❑ 89Bow-145
❑ 89BowTif-145
❑ 89BreGar-12
❑ 89BrePol-26
❑ 89BreYea-26
❑ 89ClaTraP-169
❑ 89Don-103
❑ 89DonBasB-277
❑ 89Fle-180
❑ 89FleGlo-180
❑ 89OPC-271
❑ 89PanSti-375
❑ 89Sco-147
❑ 89Spo-29
❑ 89Top-718
❑ 89TopBig-204
❑ 89TopSti-196
❑ 89TopTif-718
❑ 89UppDec-504
❑ 90Bow-403
❑ 90BowTif-403
❑ 90BrePol-26
❑ 90Don-264
❑ 90El PasDAGTI-3
❑ 90Fle-317
❑ 90FleCan-317
❑ 90FleUpd-11
❑ 90Lea-466
❑ 90OPC-88
❑ 90PanSti-97
❑ 90PubIntS-491
❑ 90RedKah-4
❑ 90Sco-105
❑ 90ScoRoo-56T
❑ 90Top-88
❑ 90TopBig-10
❑ 90TopSti-206
❑ 90TopTif-88
❑ 90TopTra-13T
❑ 90TopTraT-13T
❑ 90UppDec-456
❑ 90UppDec-714
❑ 91Bow-669
❑ 91Don-253
❑ 91Fle-57
❑ 91Lea-362
❑ 91OPC-444
❑ 91RedKah-15
❑ 91RedPep-3
❑ 91Sco-18
❑ 91StaClu-187
❑ 91Top-444
❑ 91TopDesS-444
❑ 91TopMic-444
❑ 91TopTif-444
❑ 91Ult-88
❑ 91UppDec-631
❑ 92Don-363
❑ 92Fle-400
❑ 92OPC-197
❑ 92PanSti-268
❑ 92Pin-502
❑ 92RedKah-15
❑ 92Sco-393
❑ 92StaClu-13
❑ 92Top-197
❑ 92TopGol-197
❑ 92TopGolW-197
❑ 92TopMic-197
❑ 92TriPla-61
❑ 92Ult-185
❑ 92UppDec-341
❑ 94BreMilB-204

Brahms, Russ
❑ 82QuaCitCT-3

Brain, Dave (David Leonard)
❑ 09T206-400
❑ 11SpoLifCW-41

Brainard, Matthew
❑ 93BatCliCB-5
❑ 93BatCliF-3152
❑ 94SpaPhiF-1725
❑ 94SparPhiC-3

Brake, Greg
❑ 85MadMusP-4

Brakebill, Mark
❑ 89BelMarL-21
❑ 90PenPilS-4
❑ 91PenPilC-18
❑ 91PenPilP-383
❑ 92QuaCitRBC-24
❑ 92QuaCitRBF-815
❑ 93MidAngF-326
❑ 97MidAngOHP-2

Brakeley, Bill
❑ 89HelBreSP-9
❑ 90HelBreSP-27
❑ 91BelBreCB-1
❑ 91BelBreP-2094

Braley, Jeff (Jeffrey)
❑ 89BriTigS-2
❑ 90FayGenP-2397
❑ 90ProAaA-85
❑ 90SouAtlLAS-2
❑ 91FloStaLAP-FSL19
❑ 91LakTigC-1
❑ 91LakTigP-257
❑ 92LonTigF-624
❑ 92LonTigS-401
❑ 92SkyAA F-170
❑ 93LonTigF-2298

Brambilla, Mike
❑ 97SpoIndG-3

Brame, Erv (Ervin Beckham)
❑ 93ConTSN-959

Bramlett, Jeff
❑ 95GreFalDTI-27
❑ 96GreFalDB-5
❑ 96GreFalDTI-20
❑ 98SanBerS-4
❑ 98SanBerSTIS-4

Brammer, John
❑ 96WatIndTI-3
❑ 98KinIndQ-3

Bramon, Dudley
❑ 33WorCig(-9

Branca, Ralph
❑ 46DodTeal-3
❑ 46SpoExcW-1-11
❑ 47DodTeal-3
❑ 47Exh-25
❑ 47HomBon-5
❑ 47TipTop-92
❑ 48DodTeal-4
❑ 49Bow-194
❑ 49EurSta-30
❑ 50Bow-59
❑ 51Bow-56
❑ 51FisBakL-2
❑ 51R42SmaS-4
❑ 51TopBluB-20
❑ 52Bow-96
❑ 52TipTop-3
❑ 52Top-274
❑ 53BowBW-52
❑ 53ExhCan-8
❑ 74dod195T-6
❑ 76SSP-594
❑ 76TayBow4-26
❑ 79TCM50-32
❑ 83TopRep5-274
❑ 85TCMPhoC-15
❑ 85TCMPpl1-5
❑ 88DodRinP1-7A
❑ 89DodSmoG-51
❑ 90DodTar-67
❑ 90PacLeg-13
❑ 90SweBasG-133
❑ 91Bow-410
❑ 91SweBasG-14
❑ 91TopArc1-293
❑ 92ActPacA-41
❑ 92BazQua5A-7
❑ 93TedWil-8
❑ 95TopArcBD-17
❑ 95TopArcBD-58

Brancato, Al (Albert)
❑ 41DouPlaR-47
❑ 41PlaBal-43
❑ 42A'sTeal-6
❑ 79DiaGre-341
❑ 83TCMPla1945-22

Branch, Roy
❑ 75WatRoyT-5
❑ 80SpoIndT-7
❑ 89PacSenL-210
❑ 91PacSenL-57

Branconier, Paul
❑ 89SalDodTI-8
❑ 90AshTouC-2
❑ 90YakBeaTI-31
❑ 91AshTouP-560

Brand, Ron (Ronald George)
❑ 64Top-326
❑ 64TopVen-326
❑ 65AstJayP-5
❑ 65OPC-212
❑ 65Top-212
❑ 66Top-394
❑ 67CokCapAs-10
❑ 68CokCapA-10
❑ 68DexPre-17
❑ 68Top-317
❑ 68TopVen-317
❑ 69ExpPin-2
❑ 69Top-549
❑ 70ExpPos-16
❑ 70MLBOffS-63
❑ 70OPC-221
❑ 70Top-221
❑ 71ExpPS-4
❑ 71MLBOffS-124
❑ 71OPC-304
❑ 71Top-304
❑ 72MilBra-44
❑ 72Top-773
❑ 78TCM60I-41
❑ 87AstSer1-5
❑ 87AstShowSTh-27

Brandenburg, Mark
❑ 92ButCopKSP-8
❑ 93ChaRaiC-4
❑ 93ChaRaiF-1901
❑ 94ChaRanF-2490
❑ 94FloStaLAF-FSL1
❑ 95Exc-125
❑ 96FleUpd-U86
❑ 96FleUpdTC-U86
❑ 96LeaSigEA-15
❑ 96RanDr P-2
❑ 96RanFle-1
❑ 96RanMot-21

Brandon, Darrell
❑ 66Top-456
❑ 67CokCapRS-5
❑ 67OPC-117
❑ 67Top-117
❑ 67TopRedSS-2
❑ 68CokCapRS-5
❑ 68DexPre-18
❑ 68OPC-26
❑ 68RedSoxTI-2
❑ 68Top-26
❑ 68TopVen-26
❑ 69MilBra-35
❑ 69PilPos-37
❑ 69Top-301
❑ 72OPC-283
❑ 72Top-283
❑ 73OPC-326
❑ 73PhiTeal-4
❑ 73Top-326
❑ 77PilPosR-37
❑ 89PacSenL-44

Brandon, Jelani
❑ 94EugEmeC-2
❑ 94EugEmeF-3724
❑ 95SprSulTI-2

Brandow, Derek
❑ 91OklStaC-1
❑ 92OklStaC-1
❑ 92St.CatBJC-24
❑ 92St.CatBJF-3377
❑ 93HagSunC-4
❑ 93HagSunF-1870
❑ 94DunBluJC-4
❑ 94DunBluJF-2547
❑ 95KnoSmoF-33
❑ 96SyrChiTI-4
❑ 97SyrSkyCB-3

Brandt, Dutch/Lefty (Ed)
❑ 25Zee-131
❑ 30UncJac-3
❑ 32USCar*-28
❑ 33ButCre-2
❑ 33DouDisP-7
❑ 33Gou-50
❑ 33GouCanV-50
❑ 34BatR31-2
❑ 34BatR31-107
❑ 34DiaMatCSB-19
❑ 34ExhFou-1
❑ 34Gou-5
❑ 34GouCanV-62
❑ 34TarThoBD-3
❑ 35DiaMatCS3T1-15
❑ 35ExhFou-1
❑ 35GouPuzR-1J
❑ 35GouPuzR-3A
❑ 35GouPuzR-4E
❑ 35GouPuzR-7E
❑ 35GouPuzR-12E
❑ 35GouPuzR-14A
❑ 35GouPuzR-15A
❑ 36ExhFou-2
❑ 74CapPub-90
❑ 85BigLeaC3-44
❑ 90DodTar-68
❑ 91ConTSN-298

Brandt, Jackie (John George)
❑ 47Exh-26
❑ 57GiaJayP-2
❑ 58BalOriP-4
❑ 58BalOriP-5
❑ 59Top-297
❑ 60BalOriP-1
❑ 60OriJayP-1
❑ 60Top-53
❑ 60TopVen-53
❑ 61BalOriP-2
❑ 61Pos-76A
❑ 61Pos-76B
❑ 61Top-515
❑ 61TopMagR-27
❑ 61TopStal-98
❑ 62BalOriP-4
❑ 62Jel-31
❑ 62Pos-31
❑ 62PosCan-31
❑ 62SalPlaC-53A
❑ 62SalPlaC-53B
❑ 62ShiPlaC-53
❑ 62Top-165
❑ 62TopBuc-11
❑ 62TopStal-3
❑ 62TopVen-165
❑ 63BalOriP-6
❑ 63Jel-58
❑ 63Pos-58
❑ 63Top-65
❑ 64BalOriP-9
❑ 64OriJayP-4
❑ 64Top-399
❑ 65BalOriP-8
❑ 65OPC-33
❑ 65Top-33
❑ 66PhiTeal-2
❑ 66Top-383
❑ 67OPC-142
❑ 67Top-142
❑ 78TCM60I-33
❑ 91OriCro-49

Brandt, Randy
❑ 77SalPirT-3

Brandts, Mike
❑ 87SalSpuS-5

Branham, Luther H.
❑ 93NegLeaRL2-5

Brannan, Otis Owen
❑ 33Zee-2

Brannan, Ryan
❑ 97Bes-85
❑ 97Bow-332
❑ 97BowChr-228
❑ 97BowChrI-228
❑ 97BowChrIR-228
❑ 97BowChrR-228
❑ 97BowInt-332
❑ 97ClePhi-1
❑ 98Bow-127
❑ 98BowBes-159
❑ 98BowBesAR-159
❑ 98BowBesR-159
❑ 98BowChr-127
❑ 98BowChrGA-127
❑ 98BowChrGAR-127
❑ 98BowChrI-127
❑ 98BowChrIR-127
❑ 98BowChrR-127
❑ 98BowGolA-127
❑ 98BowInt-127
❑ 98ReaPhiUM-5
❑ 98ScrRedBQ-7
❑ 99Bow-197
❑ 99BowChr-197
❑ 99BowChrG-197
❑ 99BowChrGR-197
❑ 99BowChrI-197
❑ 99BowChrIR-197
❑ 99BowChrR-197
❑ 99BowGol-197
❑ 99BowInt-197
❑ 99SP TopP-19
❑ 99SP TopPPE-19

Brannon, Cliff
❑ 89HamRedS-6
❑ 90SavCarP-2080
❑ 91ArkTraLD-27
❑ 91ArkTraP-1298
❑ 91LinDriAA-27
❑ 92ArkTraF-1141
❑ 92ArkTraS-28
❑ 92SkyAA F-12

Brannon, Otis
❑ 30Zee-2
❑ 32Zee-2

Brannon, Paul
❑ 92SanBerC-25
❑ 92SanBerSF-960

Bransfield, Kitty (William)
❑ 08RosComP-136
❑ 09AmeCarE90-1-11
❑ 09AmeCarE90-1-12
❑ 09BriE97-4
❑ 09ColChiE-32

❑ 09RamT20-15
❑ 09T206-34
❑ 10NadE1-8
❑ 10SweCapPP-124
❑ 10W555-8
❑ 11PinT-5-305
❑ 11SpoLifCW-42
❑ 11SpoLifM-225
❑ 11T205-19
❑ 11TurRedT-82
❑ 12ColRedB-32
❑ 12ColTinT-32
❑ 67SpoHobFC-45
❑ 72ClaCar-90
❑ 94ConTSN-1193
❑ 94ConTSNB-1193

Branson, Jeff

❑ 88TopTra-19T
❑ 88TopTraT-19T
❑ 89CedRapRAB-20
❑ 89CedRapRB-1
❑ 89CedRapRP-928
❑ 89CedRapRS-1
❑ 89TopBig-69
❑ 90Bow-52
❑ 90BowTif-52
❑ 90CedRapRDGB-20
❑ 90ChaLooGS-6
❑ 91ChaLooLD-155
❑ 91ChaLooP-1965
❑ 91LinDriAA-155
❑ 92Bow-512
❑ 92DonRoo-13
❑ 92NasSouF-1836
❑ 92Pin-533
❑ 92StaClu-716
❑ 92StaCluECN-716
❑ 93Don-138
❑ 93Fle-31
❑ 93Lea-481
❑ 93PacSpa-399
❑ 93RedKah-3
❑ 93Sco-308
❑ 93StaClu-188
❑ 93StaCluFDI-188
❑ 93StaCluMOP-188
❑ 93Top-784
❑ 93TopGol-784
❑ 93TopInaM-784
❑ 93TopInaR-784
❑ 93TopMic-784
❑ 93Ult-27
❑ 93UppDec-642
❑ 93UppDecGold-642
❑ 93USPlaCR-6H
❑ 94ColC-64
❑ 94ColChoGS-64
❑ 94ColChoSS-64
❑ 94Don-642
❑ 94Fin-189
❑ 94FinRef-189
❑ 94Fle-405
❑ 94Pac-141
❑ 94RedKah-2
❑ 94Sco-225
❑ 94ScoGolR-225
❑ 94StaClu-20
❑ 94StaCluFDI-20
❑ 94StaCluGR-20
❑ 94StaCluMOP-20
❑ 94Top-368
❑ 94TopGol-368
❑ 94TopSpa-368
❑ 95Don-508
❑ 95DonPreP-508
❑ 95DonTopotO-209
❑ 95Fle-430
❑ 95RedKah-4
❑ 95Sco-535
❑ 95ScoGolR-535
❑ 95ScoPlaTS-535
❑ 95Top-198
❑ 96ColCho-516
❑ 96ColChoGS-516
❑ 96ColChoSS-516
❑ 96Don-267
❑ 96DonPreP-267
❑ 96Fla-228
❑ 96Fle-335
❑ 96FleTif-335
❑ 96LeaSigA-33
❑ 96LeaSigAG-33
❑ 96LeaSigAS-33
❑ 96Pac-46
❑ 96Ult-175
❑ 96UltGolM-175
❑ 96UppDec-52
❑ 97Fle-291
❑ 97FleTif-291
❑ 97Pac-263
❑ 97PacLigB-263
❑ 97PacSil-263
❑ 98PacOnl-214
❑ 98PacOnlR-214
❑ 98PacOnlWC-214

Brant, Marshall Lee

❑ 78TidTidT-5
❑ 79TidTidT-13
❑ 80ColCliP-33
❑ 80ColCliT-20
❑ 81ColCliP-33
❑ 81ColCliT-13
❑ 82ColCliP-33
❑ 82ColCliT-6
❑ 83ColCliT-16
❑ 92YanWIZ8-17

Brantley, Brian

❑ 98PorRocG-3

Brantley, Cliff

❑ 88ClePhiS-2
❑ 89ReaPhiB-11
❑ 89ReaPhiP-662
❑ 90ClePhiS-3
❑ 90ReaPhiS-8
❑ 91LinDriAA-503
❑ 91ReaPhiLD-503
❑ 91ReaPhiP-1364
❑ 92Bow-120
❑ 92Don-722
❑ 92Fle-662
❑ 92Lea-434
❑ 92LeaBlaG-434
❑ 92OPC-544
❑ 92PhiMed-7
❑ 92Pin-557
❑ 92ProFS7-299
❑ 92Sco-854
❑ 92StaClu-583
❑ 92Top-544
❑ 92TopDeb91-20
❑ 92TopGol-544
❑ 92TopGolW-544
❑ 92TopMic-544
❑ 92Ult-543
❑ 93Don-250
❑ 93Fle-486
❑ 93ScrRedBF-2538
❑ 93ScrRedBTI-3
❑ 93StaClu-253
❑ 93StaCluFDI-253
❑ 93StaCluMOP-253
❑ 93Top-773
❑ 93TopGol-773
❑ 93TopInaM-773
❑ 93TopInaR-773
❑ 93TopMic-773

Brantley, Jeff

❑ 86ShrCapP-1
❑ 87PhoFirP-28
❑ 87ShrCapP-13
❑ 88BlaYNPRWL-79
❑ 88PhoFirC-5
❑ 88PhoFirP-78
❑ 89DonRoo-41
❑ 89FleUpd-127
❑ 89GiaMot-17
❑ 89ScoRoo-101T
❑ 89TopTra-14T
❑ 89TopTraT-14T
❑ 90Don-466
❑ 90Fle-52
❑ 90FleCan-52
❑ 90GiaMot-25
❑ 90Hot50RS-9
❑ 90Lea-357
❑ 90OPC-703
❑ 90Sco-371
❑ 90Sco100RS-22
❑ 90ScoYouSI-24
❑ 90Top-703
❑ 90TopTif-703
❑ 90UppDec-358
❑ 90USPlaCA-3H
❑ 91Bow-620
❑ 91Cla2-T47
❑ 91ClaGam-143
❑ 91Don-319
❑ 91Fle-255
❑ 91GiaMot-25
❑ 91GiaPacGaE-7
❑ 91GiaSFE-4
❑ 91Lea-136
❑ 91MisStaB-5
❑ 91OPC-17
❑ 91PanFreS-75
❑ 91PanSti-70
❑ 91Sco-160
❑ 91SimandSMLBL-6
❑ 91StaClu-567
❑ 91Top-17
❑ 91TopDesS-17
❑ 91TopMic-17
❑ 91TopTif-17
❑ 91Ult-316
❑ 91UppDec-424
❑ 92Don-295
❑ 92Fle-629
❑ 92GiaMot-25
❑ 92GiaPacGaE-7
❑ 92Lea-56
❑ 92LeaBlaG-56
❑ 92OPC-491
❑ 92Pin-470
❑ 92Sco-157
❑ 92StaClu-294
❑ 92Stu-112
❑ 92Top-491
❑ 92TopGol-491
❑ 92TopGolW-491
❑ 92TopMic-491
❑ 92Ult-285
❑ 92UppDec-581
❑ 93Don-100
❑ 93Fle-152
❑ 93GiaMot-17
❑ 93GiaPos-9
❑ 93GiaStaC-14
❑ 93Lea-102
❑ 93OPC-65
❑ 93PacSpa-608
❑ 93Pin-512
❑ 93Sco-153
❑ 93StaClu-260
❑ 93StaCluFDI-260
❑ 93StaCluMOP-260
❑ 93Top-631
❑ 93TopGol-631
❑ 93TopInaM-631
❑ 93TopInaR-631
❑ 93TopMic-631
❑ 93TriPla-213
❑ 93Ult-128
❑ 93UppDec-581
❑ 93UppDecGold-581
❑ 94ColC-607
❑ 94ColChoGS-607
❑ 94ColChoSS-607
❑ 94Don-94
❑ 94Fla-365
❑ 94Fle-685
❑ 94FleExtB-228
❑ 94FleUpd-115
❑ 94Pac-541
❑ 94Pin-198
❑ 94PinArtP-198
❑ 94PinMusC-198
❑ 94RedKah-3
❑ 94StaClu-709
❑ 94StaCluFDI-709
❑ 94StaCluGR-709
❑ 94StaCluMOP-709
❑ 94Top-116
❑ 94TopGol-116
❑ 94TopSpa-116
❑ 94TopTra-37T
❑ 95ColCho-422
❑ 95ColChoGS-422
❑ 95ColChoSS-422
❑ 95Don-523
❑ 95DonPreP-523
❑ 95DonTopotO-210
❑ 95Fle-431
❑ 95Pac-100
❑ 95RedKah-5
❑ 95Top-236
❑ 95TopCyb-89
❑ 95Ult-142
❑ 95UltGolM-142
❑ 96ColCho-117
❑ 96ColChoGS-117
❑ 96ColChoSS-117
❑ 96Don-306
❑ 96DonPreP-306
❑ 96EmoXL-162
❑ 96Fla-229
❑ 96Fle-336
❑ 96FleTif-336
❑ 96Pac-39
❑ 96Sco-484
❑ 96StaClu-74
❑ 96StaClu-267
❑ 96StaCluMOP-74
❑ 96StaCluMOP-267
❑ 96Top-271
❑ 96Ult-176
❑ 96UltGolM-176
❑ 96UppDec-48
❑ 97Bow-60
❑ 97BowInt-60
❑ 97Cir-272
❑ 97CirRav-272
❑ 97ColCho-63
❑ 97ColCho-79
❑ 97Don-227
❑ 97DonGolPP-227
❑ 97DonSilPP-227
❑ 97Fin-147
❑ 97FinEmb-147
❑ 97FinEmbR-147
❑ 97FinRef-147
❑ 97Fle-292
❑ 97FleTif-292
❑ 97Lea-79
❑ 97LeaFraM-79
❑ 97LeaFraMDC-79
❑ 97MetUni-45
❑ 97Pac-264
❑ 97PacLigB-264
❑ 97PacPri-91
❑ 97PacPriLB-91
❑ 97PacPriP-91
❑ 97PacSil-264
❑ 97PhoFirDTTI-11
❑ 97Pin-62
❑ 97PinArtP-PP62
❑ 97PinMusC-62
❑ 97PinPrePla-62
❑ 97Sco-126
❑ 97ScoArtPWB-126
❑ 97ScoPreS-126
❑ 97ScoShoS-126
❑ 97ScoShoSAP-126
❑ 97StaClu-303
❑ 97StaCluMOP-303
❑ 97Top-188
❑ 97TopGal-65
❑ 97TopGalPPI-65
❑ 97Ult-175
❑ 97UltGolME-175
❑ 97UltPlaME-175
❑ 97UppDec-336
❑ 97UppDecAWJ-16
❑ 98Fle-488
❑ 98PacOnl-605
❑ 98PacOnlR-605
❑ 98PacOnlWC-605
❑ 98Top-378
❑ 98TopChr-378
❑ 98TopChrR-378
❑ 98TopDevR-378
❑ 98TopDia-378
❑ 98TopMiniC-378
❑ 98Ult-384
❑ 98UltGolM-384
❑ 98UltMas-384
❑ 98UltPlaM-384
❑ 99Top-162
❑ 99TopChr-162
❑ 99TopChrR-162
❑ 99TopMVPP-162

Brantley, Mickey

❑ 84ChaLooT-26
❑ 85CalCanC-88
❑ 86CalCanP-2
❑ 86Fle-651
❑ 86SpoRoo-45
❑ 87Don-656
❑ 87DonRoo-27
❑ 87Fle-582
❑ 87FleGlo-582
❑ 87MarMot-15
❑ 87SpoTeaP-25
❑ 87Top-347
❑ 87TopTif-347
❑ 88Don-610
❑ 88DonBasB-80
❑ 88Fle-371
❑ 88FleExcS-5
❑ 88FleGlo-371
❑ 88FleMin-51
❑ 88Lea-258
❑ 88MarMot-15
❑ 88PanSti-192
❑ 88Sco-213
❑ 88ScoGlo-213
❑ 88ScoYouS2-15
❑ 88StaLinMa-3
❑ 88Top-687
❑ 88TopTif-687
❑ 89ChaLooLITI-5
❑ 89Don-212
❑ 89Fle-541
❑ 89FleGlo-541
❑ 89MarMot-7
❑ 89OPC-369
❑ 89PanSti-439
❑ 89Sco-89
❑ 89Spo-6
❑ 89Top-568
❑ 89TopBig-38
❑ 89TopSti-219
❑ 89TopTif-568
❑ 89UppDec-550
❑ 90CalCanC-15
❑ 90CMC-442
❑ 90PubIntS-428
❑ 91DenZepLD-129
❑ 91DenZepP-133
❑ 91LinDriAAA-129
❑ 92TucTorS-603
❑ 93PhoFirF-1525
❑ 95BurBeeTI-34

Branyan, Russell

❑ 94BurIndC-3
❑ 94BurIndF-3801
❑ 96Bow-342
❑ 96BowFoi-342
❑ 96Exc-40
❑ 97Bes-56
❑ 97BesAutSBPP-39
❑ 97BesAutSC-8
❑ 97BesDiaB-20
❑ 97BesLum-2
❑ 97Bow-335
❑ 97BowBes-199
❑ 97BowBesAR-199
❑ 97BowBesMI-MI9
❑ 97BowBesMIAR-MI9
❑ 97BowBesMIARI-MI9
❑ 97BowBesMII-MI9
❑ 97BowBesMIR-MI9
❑ 97BowBesMIRI-MI9
❑ 97BowBesR-199
❑ 97BowChr-230
❑ 97BowChrI-230
❑ 97BowChrIR-230
❑ 97BowChrR-230
❑ 97BowInt-335
❑ 97CalLeaATI-28
❑ 97CarLeaTP-5
❑ 97KinIndB-3
❑ 97StaClu-190
❑ 97StaCluMOP-190
❑ 98AkrAerM-22
❑ 98Bes-5
❑ 98Bes-58
❑ 98Bow-293
❑ 98BowBes-136
❑ 98BowBesAR-136
❑ 98BowBesP-BP10
❑ 98BowBesPAR-BP10
❑ 98BowBesPR-BP10
❑ 98BowBesR-136
❑ 98BowCerBlueAU-25
❑ 98BowCerGA-25
❑ 98BowCerSA-25
❑ 98BowChr-293
❑ 98BowChrGA-293
❑ 98BowChrGAR-293
❑ 98BowChrI-293
❑ 98BowChrIR-293
❑ 98BowChrR-293
❑ 98BowGolA-293
❑ 98BowInt-293
❑ 98BowScoC-SC20
❑ 98ColCho-425
❑ 98ColChoPCR-425
❑ 98Don-290
❑ 98DonGolPP-290
❑ 98DonSigA-10
❑ 98DonSigAC-14
❑ 98DonSigAM-14
❑ 98DonSigSP-3
❑ 98DonSilPP-290
❑ 98EasLeaTPM-3
❑ 98LeaRCrusUP-129
❑ 98LeaRS-205
❑ 98LeaRSCrusUG-129
❑ 98LeaRSCrusUR-129
❑ 98LeaRSLHolo-205
❑ 98LeaRSLong-205
❑ 98LeaRTrue-205
❑ 98ScoRT-246
❑ 98ScoRTSS-PP139
❑ 98ScoRTSSAP-PP139
❑ 98ScoRTSSAP1-PP139
❑ 98SP Aut-30
❑ 98SP AutC-RB
❑ 98SP MinDTSPE-DS15
❑ 98SP MinPE-10
❑ 98SP MinPE-45
❑ 98SP MinSTHPE-H10
❑ 98SP SPTSC-RB
❑ 98SPMin-10
❑ 98SPMin-45
❑ 98SPMinDTS-DS15
❑ 98SPMinSTH-H10
❑ 98SPxFin-190
❑ 98SPxFin-239
❑ 98SPxFinR-190
❑ 98SPxFinR-239
❑ 98SPxFinS-190
❑ 98SPxFinS-239
❑ 98Stu-127
❑ 98StuGPP-127
❑ 98StuSPP-127
❑ 98Top-262
❑ 98TopChr-262
❑ 98TopChrR-262
❑ 98TopDevR-262
❑ 98TopDia-262
❑ 98TopMiniC-262
❑ 98UD3-22
❑ 98UD3-112
❑ 98UD3-202
❑ 98UD3DieCut-22
❑ 98UD3DieCut-112
❑ 98UD3DieCut-202
❑ 98UppDec-550
❑ 98UppDecDS-DS30
❑ 98UppDecR-109
❑ 98UppDecRNF-NF9
❑ 98UppDecRSotT-RB
❑ 99BasAmeTP-17
❑ 99BasAmeTPG-17
❑ 99Bow-148
❑ 99BowAut-BA14
❑ 99BowBes-141
❑ 99BowBesAR-141
❑ 99BowBesR-141
❑ 99BowChr-148
❑ 99BowChrG-148
❑ 99BowChrGR-148
❑ 99BowChrI-148
❑ 99BowChrIR-148
❑ 99BowChrR-148
❑ 99BowChrSC-SC16
❑ 99BowChrSCR-SC16
❑ 99BowGol-148
❑ 99BowInt-148
❑ 99BowScoC-SC16
❑ 99E-X Cen-111
❑ 99E-X CenECFut-111
❑ 99E-X CenECNow-111
❑ 99E-X CenEQ-4
❑ 99Fle-352
❑ 99FleBri-137
❑ 99FleBri2G-137
❑ 99FleBriBlu-137
❑ 99FleBriGol-137
❑ 99FleBriI-15
❑ 99FleSta9-352
❑ 99FleWarT-352
❑ 99SkyThu-259
❑ 99SkyThuRant-259
❑ 99SkyThuRave-259
❑ 99SP Aut-96
❑ 99SP AutC-RB
❑ 99SP AutCG-RB
❑ 99SP SigAuto-RB
❑ 99SP SigAutoG-RB
❑ 99SP TopP-8
❑ 99SP TopP-20
❑ 99SP TopPDtS-D4
❑ 99SP TopPGF-GF4
❑ 99SP TopPPE-8
❑ 99SP TopPPE-20
❑ 99SpoIll-55
❑ 99SPSig-18
❑ 99SPx-88
❑ 99SPxFinR-88
❑ 99SPxFinS-88
❑ 99ThuSkySupR-259
❑ 99UppDec-358
❑ 99UppDecEL1-358
❑ 99UppDecEL2-358

❑ 99UppDecMP-RB
❑ 99UppDecMSC-SC12
❑ 99Vic-114
Brashear, Kitty (Robert N.)
❑ 09ObaT21-65
❑ 09ObaT21-174
❑ 09ObaT21-406
❑ 10BisCoaLE99-2
❑ 12ObaPreT-155
Brashear, Roy Parks
❑ 09ObaT21-175
❑ 09ObaT21-341
❑ 09T206-401
❑ 11PacCoaBD-8
❑ 11Zee-108
❑ 12HomRunKE-79
❑ 12ObaPreT-90
❑ 12Zee-139
❑ 13Zee-133
❑ 14Zee-52
Brasher, Anthony
❑ 93AusFut-84
❑ 95AusFut-58
Brassil, Tom
❑ 85BeaGolGT-14
❑ 86BeaGolGP-3
❑ 87WicPilRD-19
❑ 88LasVegSC-23
❑ 88LasVegSP-238
❑ 89SpoIndSP-13
Brassington, Phil
❑ 93EugEmeC-5
❑ 93EugEmeF-3847
Braswell, Bryan
❑ 96AubDouB-1
❑ 97QuaCitRBB-4
❑ 98KisCobQ-9
Bratcher, Joe (Joseph W.)
❑ 25Zee-19
❑ 27Zee-46
❑ 28Zee-67
Brathwaite, Alonso
❑ 52LavPro-58
Bratlien, Erik
❑ 88BatCliP-1673
❑ 89BatCliP-1941
❑ 89ReaPhiS-3
Braun, Bart
❑ 77ModA'sC-15
❑ 79WatA'sT-4
❑ 81RedPioT-29
Braun, John Paul
❑ 65OPC-82
❑ 65Top-82
Braun, Randy
❑ 83DayBeaAT-17
❑ 86CalCanP-3
❑ 87CalCanP-2323
❑ 88JacExpB-21
❑ 88JacExpP-976
❑ 88SouLeaAJ-20
❑ 89IndIndC-16
❑ 89IndIndP-1213
❑ 90CMC-69
❑ 90IndIndC-19
❑ 90IndIndP-283
❑ 90ProAAAF-566
Braun, Steve (Stephen R.)
❑ 72OPC-244
❑ 72Top-244
❑ 72TwiPos-2
❑ 72TwiTeal-2
❑ 73LinPor-105
❑ 73OPC-16
❑ 73Top-16
❑ 74OPC-321
❑ 74Top-321
❑ 74TopSta-202
❑ 75Kel-41
❑ 75OPC-273
❑ 75Top-273
❑ 75TopMin-273
❑ 75TwiPos-4
❑ 75TwiTeal-5
❑ 76Hos-96
❑ 76OPC-183
❑ 76SSP-221
❑ 76Top-183
❑ 77ChiWilD-6
❑ 77DailsID-6
❑ 77DetCaeD-6
❑ 77HolInnD-6
❑ 77Hos-134
❑ 77MSADis-6
❑ 77OPC-123
❑ 77RCColC-8
❑ 77SagDis-6
❑ 77sDis-6
❑ 77Top-606
❑ 77TopCloS-6
❑ 77WenDis-6
❑ 77ZipDis-6
❑ 78RCColC-9
❑ 78Roy-2
❑ 78Top-422
❑ 79Top-502
❑ 80Top-9
❑ 81Car5x7-1
❑ 81Fle-427
❑ 82Don-418
❑ 82Fle-111
❑ 82Top-316
❑ 83Car-3
❑ 83Fle-3
❑ 83Top-734
❑ 84Car-3
❑ 84Car5x7-3
❑ 84Fle-320
❑ 84FleSti-42
❑ 84Nes792-227
❑ 84Top-227
❑ 84TopTif-227
❑ 85CarTeal-3
❑ 85Fle-221
❑ 85FleStaS-51
❑ 85Top-152
❑ 85TopTif-152
❑ 86CarKASD-4
❑ 86CarTeal-4
❑ 86Don-534
❑ 86Fle-27
❑ 86LouRedTI-5
❑ 86Top-631
❑ 86TopTif-631
❑ 88LouRedBTI-4
❑ 90TopTVCa-2
❑ 92WinHavRSC-29
Braunecker, Darek
❑ 91JamExpC-24
❑ 91JamExpP-3535
Brauning, Jeff
❑ 90SanJosGB-5
❑ 90SanJosGCLC-34
❑ 90SanJosGP-2015
❑ 90SanJosGS-2
Brave, Homer the
❑ 90BraDubS-13
❑ 92BraLykS-16
❑ 93BraLykS-14
❑ 94MasMan-7
Braves, Atlanta
❑ 66Top-326
❑ 66TopVen-326
❑ 67Top-477
❑ 68Top-221
❑ 68TopVen-221
❑ 69FleClоS-1
❑ 69FleCloS-27
❑ 69TopStaA-1
❑ 70OPC-472
❑ 70Top-472
❑ 71OPC-652
❑ 71Top-652
❑ 71TopTat-42
❑ 72OPC-21
❑ 72Top-21
❑ 73OPC-521
❑ 73OPCBTC-1
❑ 73Top-521
❑ 73TopBluTC-1
❑ 74OPC-483
❑ 74OPCTC-1
❑ 74Top-483
❑ 74TopStaA-1
❑ 74TopTeaC-1
❑ 78Top-551
❑ 83FleSta-225
❑ 83FleSti-NNO
❑ 83FleSti-NNO
❑ 87SpoTeaL-24
❑ 88PanSti-469
❑ 88RedFolSB-105
❑ 90PubIntS-628
❑ 90RedFolSB-130
❑ 93TedWilPC-2
❑ 94ImpProP-15
❑ 94Sco-647
❑ 94ScoGolR-647
❑ 95PacPriTL-15
❑ 95PanSti-139
❑ 95StaCluSTWS-R1L
❑ 95StaCluSTWS-R1W
❑ 96BraFle-19
❑ 96PanSti-6
❑ 96TopGalPG-PG15
❑ 97ColChoT-AB
❑ 99Vic-26
Braves, Boston
❑ 13FatT20-9
❑ 36R31Pre-G18
❑ 38BasTabP-29
❑ 48ExhTea-1
❑ 68LauWorS-11
❑ 70FleWorS-11
❑ 70FleWorS-45
❑ 71FleWorS-12
❑ 71FleWorS-46
❑ 80MarExh-32
❑ 86JosHalC-2
❑ 90KalTeaN-3
❑ 94OriofB-98
Braves, Bourne
❑ 88CapCodPB-26
Braves, Danville
❑ 98DanBraQ-31
Braves, Idaho Falls
❑ 88IdaFalBP-1833
❑ 97IdaFalBTI-32
Braves, Milwaukee
❑ 55BraGolS-1
❑ 56Top-95A
❑ 56Top-95B
❑ 56Top-95C
❑ 57Top-114
❑ 58Top-377A
❑ 58Top-377B
❑ 59Top-419
❑ 60Top-381
❑ 60TopTat-59
❑ 61Top-426
❑ 61TopMagR-18
❑ 62GuyPotCP-12
❑ 62Top-158
❑ 62TopVen-158
❑ 63GadFunC-58
❑ 63Top-503
❑ 64Top-132
❑ 64TopTatI-12
❑ 64TopVen-132
❑ 65Top-426
❑ 66TopRubI-112
❑ 71FleWorS-55
❑ 93TedWilPC-17
Braves, Pulaski
❑ 90PulBraP-3115
❑ 92PulBraC-30
❑ 92PulBraF-3199
Braves, Richmond
❑ 89RicBraP-818
❑ 92RicBraBB-26
❑ 93RicBraBB-NNO
Bravo, Angel (Angel Alfonso)
❑ 70DayDaiNM-74
❑ 70OPC-283
❑ 70Top-283
❑ 71MLBOffS-50
❑ 71OPC-538
❑ 71Top-538
❑ 76VenLeaS-115
Bravo, Danny
❑ 96WesPalBEB-22
❑ 98CapFeaCM-5
Bravo, Franklin
❑ 97AugGre-8
❑ 98AugGreM-18
❑ 98EriSeaWM-4
Bravo, Luis
❑ 79WisRapTT-17
❑ 80VenLeaS-14
❑ 83AlbA'sT-17
Braxton, Garland
❑ 30WhiSoxTI-4
❑ 74CapPub-83
❑ 91ConTSN-248
Braxton, Glenn
❑ 86AppFoxP-3
❑ 87PenWhiSP-16
❑ 89UtiBluSP-2
Bray, Chris
❑ 96BluOriB-6
Bray, Frank
❑ 96JacSunB-30
Bray, Notorris
❑ 95ButCopKtI-26
Bray, Scott
❑ 89SalLakTTI-23
Brazeau, Jay
❑ 90ColMetGS-29
Brazell, Don
❑ 78WauMetT-2
Brazill, Frank (Frank Leo)
❑ 23WilChoV-12
❑ 23Zee-62
❑ 24Zee-39
❑ 25Zee-132
❑ 26Zee-21
Brazle, Alpha
❑ 46SeaSLP-6
❑ 47TipTop-150
❑ 49Bow-126A
❑ 49Bow-126B
❑ 49EurSta-178
❑ 50Bow-126
❑ 51Bow-157
❑ 52Bow-134
❑ 52Top-228
❑ 53BowC-140
❑ 53CarHunW-2
❑ 54Bow-142
❑ 54CarHunW-3
❑ 55Bow-230
❑ 83Car194T-53
❑ 83CarGreT-11
❑ 83TopRep5-228
❑ 85TCMPpl1-1
Brazoban, Candido
❑ 93BriTigF-3639
❑ 94BriTigC-7
❑ 94BriTigF-3493
Brazoban, Melvin
❑ 98SavSanGM-5
Brea, Lesli
❑ 97EveAquG-3
❑ 98WisTimRM-3
Breadon, Sam
❑ 31CarMet-4
❑ 41CarW75-1
Bream, Scott
❑ 90ChaRaiP-2049
❑ 91ChaRaiC-16
❑ 91ChaRaiP-101
❑ 91Cla/Bes-184
❑ 91SpoIndC-23
❑ 91SpoIndP-3954
❑ 92WatDiaC-3
❑ 92WatDiaF-2148
❑ 93RanCucQC-5
❑ 93RanCucQF-842
❑ 94WicWraF-194
❑ 97JacSun-5
❑ 98JacSunM-3
Bream, Sid (Sidney Eugene)
❑ 82VerBeaDT-18
❑ 83AlbDukTc-15
❑ 84AlbDukCr-149
❑ 85Don-470
❑ 85Top-253
❑ 85TopTif-253
❑ 86Don-566
❑ 86Fle-604
❑ 86Top-589
❑ 86TopTif-589
❑ 87Don-79
❑ 87DonOpeD-168
❑ 87Fle-606
❑ 87FleExcS-6
❑ 87FleGlo-606
❑ 87FleMin-12
❑ 87FleSlu-5
❑ 87FleStiC-14
❑ 87Lea-239
❑ 87OPC-35
❑ 87SpoTeaP-18
❑ 87Top-35
❑ 87Top-131
❑ 87TopSti-126
❑ 87TopTif-35
❑ 87TopTif-131
❑ 88Don-188
❑ 88DonBasB-45
❑ 88Fle-324
❑ 88FleExcS-6
❑ 88FleGlo-324
❑ 88FleStiC-113
❑ 88OPC-304
❑ 88PanSti-370
❑ 88PirTeal-4
❑ 88Sco-260
❑ 88ScoGlo-260
❑ 88Spo-98
❑ 88StaLinPi-4
❑ 88Top-478
❑ 88TopBig-205
❑ 88TopSti-130
❑ 88TopTif-478
❑ 89Bow-419
❑ 89BowTif-419
❑ 89Don-252
❑ 89DonBasB-89
❑ 89Fle-204
❑ 89FleGlo-204
❑ 89OPC-126
❑ 89PanSti-169
❑ 89PirVerFJ-5
❑ 89Sco-48
❑ 89Top-126
❑ 89TopBig-106
❑ 89TopMinL-31
❑ 89TopSti-125
❑ 89TopTif-126
❑ 89UppDec-556
❑ 90Bow-175
❑ 90BowTif-175
❑ 90DodTar-69
❑ 90Don-329
❑ 90DonBesN-33
❑ 90Fle-463
❑ 90FleCan-463
❑ 90OPC-622
❑ 90PirHomC-7
❑ 90PubIntS-151
❑ 90Sco-423
❑ 90Top-622
❑ 90TopTif-622
❑ 90UppDec-250
❑ 91Bow-585
❑ 91BraDubP-5
❑ 91BraSubS-7
❑ 91Don-644
❑ 91Fle-35
❑ 91FleUpd-72
❑ 91Lea-379
❑ 91OPC-354
❑ 91PanFreS-115
❑ 91PanSti-119
❑ 91Sco-304
❑ 91ScoRoo-12T
❑ 91StaClu-427
❑ 91Stu-142
❑ 91Top-354
❑ 91TopDesS-354
❑ 91TopMic-354
❑ 91TopTif-354
❑ 91TopTra-13T
❑ 91TopTraT-13T
❑ 91UppDec-170
❑ 91UppDec-710
❑ 92Bow-356
❑ 92BraLykP-7
❑ 92BraLykS-8
❑ 92DenHol-7
❑ 92Don-202
❑ 92Fle-354
❑ 92Lea-242
❑ 92LeaBlaG-242
❑ 92OPC-770
❑ 92PanSti-162
❑ 92Pin-446
❑ 92RedFolS-17
❑ 92Sco-131
❑ 92StaClu-478
❑ 92Stu-2
❑ 92Top-770
❑ 92TopGol-770
❑ 92TopGolW-770
❑ 92TopMic-770
❑ 92TriPla-258
❑ 92Ult-160
❑ 92UppDec-495
❑ 93Bow-689
❑ 93BraFloA-4
❑ 93BraLykP-6
❑ 93BraLykS-7
❑ 93BraStaC-15
❑ 93Don-526
❑ 93Fle-2
❑ 93Lea-178
❑ 93OPC-84
❑ 93PacSpa-2
❑ 93PanSti-181
❑ 93Pin-204
❑ 93Sco-396
❑ 93Sel-382
❑ 93StaClu-151
❑ 93StaCluFDI-151
❑ 93StaCluMOP-151
❑ 93Stu-38
❑ 93Top-224
❑ 93TopGol-224
❑ 93TopInaM-224
❑ 93TopInaR-224
❑ 93TopMic-224
❑ 93Ult-4
❑ 93UppDec-104
❑ 93UppDecGold-104
❑ 94AstMot-10
❑ 94Don-118
❑ 94Fle-355
❑ 94FleUpd-140
❑ 94Pac-5
❑ 94ScoRoo-RT58
❑ 94ScoRooGR-RT58
❑ 94StaClu-79
❑ 94StaClu-655
❑ 94StaCluFDI-79
❑ 94StaCluFDI-655
❑ 94StaCluGR-79
❑ 94StaCluGR-655
❑ 94StaCluMOP-79
❑ 94StaCluMOP-655
❑ 94Top-528
❑ 94TopGol-528
❑ 94TopSpa-528
❑ 95ColCho-55
❑ 95ColChoGS-55
❑ 95ColChoSS-55
❑ 95Sco-240
❑ 95ScoGolR-240
❑ 95ScoPlaTS-240
❑ 95Top-19
Breard, Stan
❑ 43ParSpo-74
Breaux, Greg
❑ 88MarPhiS-5
Breazeale, Jim (James Leo)
❑ 71RicBraTI-4
❑ 73OPC-33
❑ 73Top-33
❑ 79AppFoxT-17
❑ 83MiaMarT-25
Brecheen, Harry
❑ 46SeaSLP-7
❑ 46SpoExcW-1-3
❑ 47Exh-27
❑ 47HomBon-6
❑ 49Bow-158
❑ 49EurSta-179
❑ 49Lea-158
❑ 50AmeNut&CCP-2
❑ 50Bow-90
❑ 51Bow-86
❑ 51FisBakL-3
❑ 51R42SmaS-8
❑ 51TopBluB-28
❑ 52Bow-176
❑ 52Top-263
❑ 53ExhCan-14
❑ 54OriEss-4
❑ 54Top-203
❑ 55OriEss-3
❑ 55Top-113
❑ 55TopDouH-73
❑ 56BalOriP-5
❑ 56Top-229
❑ 59OklTodML-19
❑ 60BalOriP-2
❑ 60Lea-132
❑ 60Top-455
❑ 63BalOriP-7
❑ 64BalOriP-10
❑ 65BalOriP-9
❑ 66BalOriP-8
❑ 67BalOriP-19
❑ 76TayBow4-27
❑ 79TCM50-166
❑ 81Ori6F-10
❑ 83Car194T-52
❑ 83CarGreT-9
❑ 83TopRep5-263
❑ 85TCMPpl1-2
❑ 92CarMcD-48
❑ 94TopArc1-203
❑ 94TopArc1G-203
Brecht, Mike
❑ 83PhoGiaBHN-17
Brechtel, Johnny
❑ 93Sou-3
Breckenridge, John
❑ 09ObaT21-64

❑ 09ObaT21-173
❑ 09ObaT21-340
❑ 11Zee-107
❑ 12ObaPreT-89
❑ 12Zee-138
❑ 13Zee-132
Breckinridge, E.L.
❑ 87OldJudN-42
Brede, Brent
❑ 90EliTwiS-6
❑ 91EliTwiP-4311
❑ 91KenTwiC-7
❑ 91KenTwiP-2087
❑ 92ClaFS7-147
❑ 92KenTwiC-19
❑ 92KenTwiF-615
❑ 93FloStaLAF-14
❑ 93ForMyeMC-3
❑ 93ForMyeMF-2666
❑ 94ClaGolF-65
❑ 94ForMyeMC-3
❑ 94ForMyeMF-1178
❑ 95HarCitRCTI-1
❑ 97Fle-689
❑ 97FleTif-689
❑ 97Ult-528
❑ 97UltGolME-528
❑ 97UltPlaME-528
❑ 98CirThu-277
❑ 98CirThuRav-277
❑ 98CirThuSupRav-277
❑ 98ColCho-294
❑ 98DiaBacP-21
❑ 98DiaMcD-8
❑ 98PacInvGems-63
❑ 98PacOnl-33
❑ 98PacOnlR-33
❑ 98PacOnlWC-33
❑ 98Top-471
❑ 98TopChr-471
❑ 98TopChrR-471
❑ 98TopDevR-471
❑ 98TopDia-471
❑ 98TopMiniC-471
❑ 98UppDec-641
❑ 99UppDec-29
❑ 99UppDecEL1-29
❑ 99UppDecEL2-29
Bree, Charlie
❑ 89PacSenL-217
Breeden, Danny (Daniel R.)
❑ 69Top-536
❑ 69TopTeaP-12
❑ 70OPC-36
❑ 70Top-36
❑ 71MLBOffS-27
Breeden, Hal (Harold Noel)
❑ 72Dia-4
❑ 72Top-684
❑ 73ExpPos-2
❑ 73OPC-173
❑ 73Top-173
❑ 74OPC-297
❑ 74Top-297
❑ 75ExpPos-4
❑ 75OPC-341
❑ 75Top-341
❑ 75TopMin-341
❑ 76SSP-329
Breeden, Joe
❑ 89MemChiB-25
❑ 89MemChiP-1193
❑ 90AppFoxBS-5
❑ 90AppFoxP-2111
❑ 91AppFoxCB-26
❑ 91AppFoxP-1731
Breeden, Scott
❑ 82IowCubT-26
❑ 83IowCubT-27
❑ 85CedRapRT-32
❑ 86RedTexG-NNO
❑ 87RedKah-NNO
❑ 88RedKah-NNO
❑ 89RedKah-xx
❑ 93St.CatBJC-27
❑ 96DunBluJB-28
❑ 96DunBluJTI-3
❑ 97SyrSkyCB-29
❑ 98SyrSkyG-5
Breeding, Marv (Marvin E.)
❑ 60BalOriP-3
❑ 60OriJayP-2
❑ 60Top-525
❑ 61BalOriP-3
❑ 61Pos-77A
❑ 61Pos-77B
❑ 61Top-321
❑ 61TopStal-99
❑ 62BalOriP-5
❑ 62Jel-28
❑ 62Pos-28
❑ 62PosCan-28
❑ 62SalPlaC-65A
❑ 62SalPlaC-65B
❑ 62ShiPlaC-65
❑ 62Top-6
❑ 62TopVen-6
❑ 63Top-149
❑ 83FraBroR-7
❑ 90DodTar-70
❑ 91OriCro-50
Breedlove, Larry R.
❑ 87SprCarB-21
Breen, Dick
❑ 09ObaT21-23
❑ 12ImpTobC-88
Breining, Fred
❑ 77ShrCapT-2
❑ 78ColCliT-3
❑ 79BufBisT-13
❑ 80PhoGiaVNB-9
❑ 81GiaTeal-4
❑ 82Don-186
❑ 82Fle-385
❑ 82Gia25tATI-3
❑ 82Top-144
❑ 83Don-503
❑ 83Fle-254
❑ 83FleSti-51
❑ 83GiaMot-7
❑ 83GiaPos-3
❑ 83Top-747
❑ 84Don-387
❑ 84ExpPos-2
❑ 84ExpStu-35
❑ 84Fle-367
❑ 84FleUpd-16
❑ 84Nes792-428
❑ 84Top-428
❑ 84TopTif-428
❑ 84TopTra-16T
❑ 84TopTraT-16T
❑ 85Fle-392
❑ 85IndIndTI-10
❑ 85OPC-36
❑ 85Top-36
❑ 85TopTif-36
❑ 86NasSouTI-2
Breitenbucher, Karl
❑ 87PocGiaTB-21
❑ 89CliGiaP-888
Breitenstein, Keith
❑ 94WelPirC-5
❑ 94WelPirF-3484
Breitenstein, Ted
❑ 09T206-479
❑ 10CouT21-5
❑ 98CamPepP-6
Bremer, Bernard
❑ 85AlbYanT-28
Bremigan, Nick
❑ 88T/MUmp-19
❑ 89T/MUmp-15
❑ 90T/MUmp-63
Brenegan, Sam (Olaf Selmer)
❑ 14Zee-53
Brenizer, Todd
❑ 77ReaPhiT-3
Brenly, Bob (Robert Earl)
❑ 77CedRapGT-2
❑ 80VenLeaS-19
❑ 81PhoGiaVNB-4
❑ 82Don-574
❑ 82Gia25tATI-4
❑ 82Top-171
❑ 83Don-377
❑ 83Fle-255
❑ 83GiaMot-6
❑ 83GiaPos-4
❑ 83Top-494
❑ 84Don-616
❑ 84Fle-368
❑ 84GiaPos-2
❑ 84Nes792-378
❑ 84Top-378
❑ 84TopSti-174
❑ 84TopTif-378
❑ 85AllGamPl-127
❑ 85Don-26
❑ 85Don-187
❑ 85DonSupD-26
❑ 85Fle-603
❑ 85GiaMot-7
❑ 85GiaPos-2
❑ 85Lea-26
❑ 85OPC-215
❑ 85Top-215
❑ 85TopGloS-3
❑ 85TopSti-158
❑ 85TopTif-215
❑ 86Don-323
❑ 86Fle-534
❑ 86GiaMot-5
❑ 86GiaPos-4
❑ 86Lea-194
❑ 86OPC-307
❑ 86Top-625
❑ 86TopSti-92
❑ 86TopTat-3
❑ 86TopTif-625
❑ 87Don-485
❑ 87DonOpeD-95
❑ 87Fle-267
❑ 87FleGlo-267
❑ 87GiaMot-4
❑ 87GiaPos-3
❑ 87OPC-125
❑ 87SpoTeaP-10
❑ 87Top-125
❑ 87Top-231
❑ 87TopSti-87
❑ 87TopTif-125
❑ 87TopTif-231
❑ 88Don-189
❑ 88Fle-77
❑ 88FleGlo-77
❑ 88GiaMot-4
❑ 88GiaPos-3
❑ 88OPC-69
❑ 88PanSti-419
❑ 88Sco-134A
❑ 88Sco-134B
❑ 88ScoGlo-134A
❑ 88ScoGlo-134B
❑ 88StaLinG-2
❑ 88Top-703
❑ 88TopBig-143
❑ 88TopSti-92
❑ 88TopTif-703
❑ 89BluJayFS-4
❑ 89Bow-249
❑ 89BowTif-249
❑ 89Don-453
❑ 89OPC-52
❑ 89Sco-395
❑ 89Top-52
❑ 89TopTif-52
❑ 89UppDec-479
❑ 92GiaMot-28
❑ 92GiaPacGaE-8
❑ 93GiaMot-28
❑ 93GiaPos-10
❑ 94GiaMot-28
❑ 95GiaMot-28
❑ 97PhoFirDTTI-20
Brennaman, Marty
❑ 93RedKah-4
Brennan, Addison
❑ 11PinT-5-311
❑ 14CraJacE-115
❑ 15CraJacE-115
Brennan, Bill (William)
❑ 85VerBeaDT-15
❑ 87AlbDukD-5
❑ 88AlbDukCm-6
❑ 88AlbDukP-250
❑ 88TriAAC-41
❑ 89AlbDukCm-1
❑ 89AlbDukP-65
❑ 89Don-589
❑ 89Sco-622
❑ 89ScoHot1R-9
❑ 89UppDec-16
❑ 90CMC-610
❑ 90DodTar-72
❑ 90ProAAAF-187
❑ 90TucTorC-8
❑ 90TucTorP-197
❑ 92TolMudHF-1032
❑ 92TolMudHS-577
❑ 94IowCubF-1270
❑ 94TopGol-395
Brennan, James D.
❑ 32OrbPinNP-92
❑ 34BatR31-178
❑ 34DiaMatCSB-20
❑ 35DiaMatCS3T1-16
Brennan, Shawn
❑ 93DanBraC-5
❑ 93DanBraF-3629
❑ 94IdaFalBF-3573
❑ 94IdaFalBSP-7
Brennan, Tom
❑ 80WauTimT-1
❑ 81ChaChaT-1
❑ 81WauTimT-5
❑ 83GleFalWST-12
Brennan, Tom (Thomas M.)
❑ 75OklCit8TI-5
❑ 77WatIndT-3A
❑ 77WatIndT-3B
❑ 79TacTugT-5
❑ 80TacTigT-12
❑ 80VenLeaS-229
❑ 81Top-451
❑ 82IndWhe-13
❑ 82Top-141
❑ 83Fle-403
❑ 83Top-524
❑ 84Don-102
❑ 84Fle-537
❑ 84Nes792-662
❑ 84Top-662
❑ 84TopTif-662
❑ 84WhiSoxTV-6
❑ 85DodCokP-5
❑ 85DomLeaS-20
❑ 90DodTar-71
Brenneman, Jim
❑ 77FriOneYW-21
❑ 81TCM60I-409
❑ 92YanWIZ6-15
Brennen, James
❑ 87DayBeaAP-9
Brenner, Bill
❑ 55SeaPop-4
❑ 56SeaPop-3
Brenner, Jack
❑ 52LavPro-11
Brenton, Lynn
❑ 17Zee-43
❑ 18Zee-36
❑ 20Zee-123
❑ 22Zee-22
❑ 23Zee-25
Brenzel, Bill (William R.)
❑ 28Zee-45
❑ 29Zee-39
❑ 30Zee-46
❑ 31Zee-27
❑ 94ConTSN-1302
❑ 94ConTSNB-1302
❑ 94TopGol-395
Breslin, Willie
❑ 87OldJudN-315
Bresnahan, Dave
❑ 86WatIndP-4
❑ 87WilBilP-14
Bresnahan, Roger P.
❑ 03WilCarE-2
❑ 06FanCraNL-5
❑ 08AmeCarE91-2
❑ 08RosComP-125
❑ 09AmeCarE90-1-13
❑ 09ColChiE-33A
❑ 09ColChiE-33B
❑ 09MaxPubP-20
❑ 09PC7HHB-5
❑ 09RamT20-16
❑ 09SpoNewSM-1
❑ 09T206-35
❑ 09T206-36
❑ 10CouT21-82
❑ 10CouT21-83
❑ 10CouT21-260
❑ 10DarChoE-4
❑ 10DomDisP-15
❑ 10E98-2
❑ 10JHDABE-2
❑ 10NadCarE-7
❑ 10NotCov-1
❑ 10PeoT21-6
❑ 10RedCroT-92
❑ 10SepAnoP-1
❑ 10SweCapPP-145A
❑ 10SweCapPP-145B
❑ 11HelSta-168
❑ 11L1L-129
❑ 11MecDFT-5
❑ 11PinT-5-357
❑ 11PloCanE-9
❑ 11S74Sil-117
❑ 11S81LarS-104
❑ 11SpoLifCW-43
❑ 11SpoLifM-264
❑ 11T205-20A
❑ 11T205-20B
❑ 11TurRedT-4
❑ 12ColRedB-33A
❑ 12ColRedB-33B
❑ 12ColTinT-33A
❑ 12ColTinT-33B
❑ 12HasTriFT-11
❑ 12HasTriFT-12
❑ 12HasTriFT-48B
❑ 12T207-20
❑ 13NatGamW-6
❑ 13TomBarW-5
❑ 14CraJacE-17
❑ 14FatPlaT-7
❑ 14PieStaT-13
❑ 15AmeCarE106-4
❑ 15CraJacE-17
❑ 15SpoNewM-16
❑ 15SpoNewP-1
❑ 15VicT21-2
❑ 16TanBraE-2
❑ 20MrsShePP-2
❑ 22MrsShePP-1
❑ 39PC7AlbHoF-29
❑ 48ExhHoF-2
❑ 50CalHOFW-6
❑ 53ArtHaloFP-6
❑ 60ExhWriH-4
❑ 60Fle-8
❑ 61Fle-10
❑ 72ClaCar-7
❑ 72ClaCar-66
❑ 72ClaCar-99
❑ 73TCMAllG-1
❑ 74CapPub-36
❑ 75FlePio-7
❑ 76ShaPiz-29
❑ 77GalGloG-179
❑ 80MarExhH-3
❑ 80PacLeg-102
❑ 80PerHaloFP-29
❑ 80SSPHOF-29
❑ 81ConTSN-74
❑ 84GalHaloFRL-29
❑ 89HOFStiB-55
❑ 92ConTSN-459
❑ 93ConTSN-871
Bressler, Rube (Raymond B.)
❑ 19W514-28
❑ 20RedWorCP-2
❑ 25Exh-25
❑ 26Exh-25
❑ 27Exh-13
❑ 76RedParC-4
❑ 90DodTar-73
❑ 91ConTSN-173
❑ 94ConTSN-1280
❑ 94ConTSNB-1280
Bressoud, Ed (Edward F.)
❑ 47PM1StaP1-21
❑ 57GiaJayP-3
❑ 58GiaSFCB-4
❑ 58Top-263
❑ 59Top-19
❑ 59TopVen-19
❑ 60GiaJayP-3
❑ 60Top-253
❑ 61Pos-152A
❑ 61Pos-152B
❑ 61Top-203
❑ 61TopStal-74
❑ 62RedSoxJP-1
❑ 62SalPlaC-182A
❑ 62SalPlaC-182B
❑ 62ShiPlaC-182
❑ 62Top-504
❑ 63Jel-78
❑ 63Pos-78
❑ 63Top-188
❑ 64RedSoxTI-1
❑ 64Top-352
❑ 64TopVen-352
❑ 65RedSoxTI-2
❑ 65Top-525
❑ 66Top-516
❑ 67CokCapYM-V29
❑ 67DexPre-30
❑ 67OPC-121
❑ 67Top-121
❑ 78TCM60I-39
❑ 78TCM60I-164
❑ 81RedSoxBG2S-72
❑ 91MetWIZ-51
Brester, Jason
❑ 95BelGiaTI-26
❑ 96BurBeeTI-3
❑ 96Top-237
❑ 97Bow-217
❑ 97BowChr-195
❑ 97BowChrI-195
❑ 97BowChrIR-195
❑ 97BowChrR-195
❑ 97BowInt-217
❑ 97CalLeaATI-2
❑ 97CalLeaTP-22
❑ 97SanJosG-3
❑ 98Bow-173
❑ 98BowCerBlueAU-40
❑ 98BowCerGA-40
❑ 98BowCerSA-40
❑ 98BowChr-173
❑ 98BowChrGA-173
❑ 98BowChrGAR-173
❑ 98BowChrI-173
❑ 98BowChrIR-173
❑ 98BowChrR-173
❑ 98BowGolA-173
❑ 98BowInt-173
❑ 98SP MinPE-111
❑ 98SPMin-111
Brett, George Howard
❑ 74RoyPos-3
❑ 75OPC-228
❑ 75RoyPos-2
❑ 75Top-228
❑ 75TopMin-228
❑ 76Hos-114
❑ 76KanCitRP-3
❑ 76OPC-19
❑ 76RoyAaP-2
❑ 76SSP-167
❑ 76SSP-589
❑ 76Top-19
❑ 77BurCheD-71
❑ 77ChiWilD-7
❑ 77DailsID-7
❑ 77DetCaeD-7
❑ 77HolInnD-7
❑ 77Hos-36
❑ 77Kel-6
❑ 77MSADis-7
❑ 77OPC-1
❑ 77OPC-170
❑ 77OPC-261
❑ 77PepGloD-32
❑ 77RCColC-9
❑ 77SagDis-7
❑ 77sDis-7
❑ 77Spo-3809
❑ 77SpoIIIAC-1
❑ 77Top-1
❑ 77Top-231
❑ 77Top-580
❑ 77Top-631
❑ 77TopCloS-7
❑ 77WenDis-7
❑ 77ZipDis-7
❑ 78Hos-27
❑ 78Kel-6
❑ 78OPC-215
❑ 78PapGinD-36
❑ 78Pep-28
❑ 78RCColC-23
❑ 78Roy-3
❑ 78SagDis-9
❑ 78SSP270-217
❑ 78TasDis-9
❑ 78Top-100
❑ 78WifBalD-7
❑ 79BasPat-7
❑ 79Hos-68
❑ 79Kel-50
❑ 79OPC-167
❑ 79RoyTeal-2
❑ 79Top-330
❑ 79TopCom-9
❑ 80BurKinPHR-13
❑ 80Kel-9
❑ 80OPC-235
❑ 80Top-450

❑ 80TopSup-14
❑ 80WilGloT-2
❑ 81AllGamPI-29
❑ 81CokTeaS-74
❑ 81Don-100
❑ 81Don-491
❑ 81Don-537
❑ 81Dra-5
❑ 81Fle-28
❑ 81Fle-655
❑ 81Fle-655B
❑ 81FleStiC-116
❑ 81FleStiC-127
❑ 81GeoBreP-1
❑ 81Kel-8
❑ 81MSAMinD-4
❑ 81OPC-113
❑ 81PerAll-10
❑ 81PerCreC-3
❑ 81RoyPol-2
❑ 81RoyProPS-4
❑ 81Squ-1
❑ 81Top-1
❑ 81Top-401
❑ 81Top-700
❑ 81TopScr-1
❑ 81TopSti-9
❑ 81TopSti-14
❑ 81TopSti-82
❑ 81TopSti-243
❑ 81TopSupN-3
❑ 82Don-15
❑ 82Don-34
❑ 82Dra-4
❑ 82FBIDis-2
❑ 82Fle-405
❑ 82FleSta-202
❑ 82FleSta-239
❑ 82K-M-38
❑ 82Kel-3
❑ 82OnDecD-4
❑ 82OPC-200
❑ 82OPC-201
❑ 82OPC-261
❑ 82PerAll-9
❑ 82PerAllG-9
❑ 82PerCreC-19
❑ 82PerCreCG-19
❑ 82Roy-4
❑ 82SevSluC-5
❑ 82SpoBre-5
❑ 82Squ-3
❑ 82Top-96
❑ 82Top-200
❑ 82Top-201
❑ 82Top-549
❑ 82TopSti-133
❑ 82TopSti-190
❑ 82WilSpoG-2
❑ 83AllGamPI-30
❑ 83Don-338
❑ 83DonActA-42
❑ 83Fle-108
❑ 83FleSta-22
❑ 83FleSti-98
❑ 83FunBal-1
❑ 83Kel-4
❑ 83Oco& SSBG-4
❑ 83OPC-3
❑ 83OPC-388
❑ 83PerAll-1
❑ 83PerAllG-1
❑ 83PerCreC-19
❑ 83PerCreCG-19
❑ 83RoyPol-2
❑ 83RoyPos-6
❑ 83Top-388
❑ 83Top-600
❑ 83TopFol-3
❑ 83TopGloS-31
❑ 83TopSti-76
❑ 84AllGamPI-120
❑ 84Don-53
❑ 84DonActAS-55
❑ 84DonCha-15
❑ 84Dra-3
❑ 84Fle-344
❑ 84Fle-638
❑ 84FleSti-36
❑ 84FunFooP-6
❑ 84MilBra-2
❑ 84MLBPen-9
❑ 84Nes792-399
❑ 84Nes792-500
❑ 84Nes792-710
❑ 84NesDreT-3
❑ 84OCoandSI-13
❑ 84OCoandSI-88
❑ 84OPC-212
❑ 84OPC-223
❑ 84RalPur-13
❑ 84RoyPos-7
❑ 84SevCoi-C5
❑ 84SevCoi-E5
❑ 84SevCoi-W5
❑ 84StaBre-1
❑ 84StaBre-2
❑ 84StaBre-3
❑ 84StaBre-4
❑ 84StaBre-5
❑ 84StaBre-6
❑ 84StaBre-7
❑ 84StaBre-8
❑ 84StaBre-9
❑ 84StaBre-10
❑ 84StaBre-11
❑ 84StaBre-12
❑ 84StaBre-13
❑ 84StaBre-14
❑ 84StaBre-15
❑ 84StaBre-16
❑ 84StaBre-17
❑ 84StaBre-18
❑ 84StaBre-19
❑ 84StaBre-20
❑ 84StaBre-21
❑ 84StaBre-22
❑ 84StaBre-23
❑ 84StaBre-24
❑ 84Top-399
❑ 84Top-500
❑ 84Top-710
❑ 84TopCer-13
❑ 84TopGaloC-1
❑ 84TopGloA-4
❑ 84TopGloS-12
❑ 84TopRubD-6
❑ 84TopSti-198
❑ 84TopSti-275
❑ 84TopSup-13
❑ 84TopTif-399
❑ 84TopTif-500
❑ 84TopTif-710
❑ 85AllGamPI-30
❑ 85Don-53
❑ 85DonActA-26
❑ 85DonHig-11
❑ 85DonHig-25
❑ 85Dra-4
❑ 85Fle-199
❑ 85FleLimE-4
❑ 85GenMilS-14
❑ 85Lea-176
❑ 85OPC-100
❑ 85RoyTeal-6
❑ 85SevCoi-C2
❑ 85SevCoi-E2
❑ 85SevCoi-G2
❑ 85Top-100
❑ 85Top-703
❑ 85Top3-D-4
❑ 85TopGloA-15
❑ 85TopRubD-7
❑ 85TopSti-188
❑ 85TopSti-268
❑ 85TopSup-46
❑ 85TopTif-100
❑ 85TopTif-703
❑ 86BasStaB-15
❑ 86BurKinA-20
❑ 86Don-53
❑ 86DonAll-12
❑ 86DonHig-3
❑ 86DonPop-12
❑ 86DorChe-1
❑ 86Dra-14
❑ 86Fle-5
❑ 86Fle-634
❑ 86FleAll-3
❑ 86FleLeaL-2
❑ 86FleLimE-6
❑ 86FleMin-1
❑ 86FleSlu-3
❑ 86FleStiC-11
❑ 86FleWaxBC-C2
❑ 86GenMilB-2C
❑ 86Lea-42
❑ 86MeaGolBB-2
❑ 86MeaGolM-2
❑ 86MeaGolSB-1
❑ 86MSAJifPD-4
❑ 86OPC-300
❑ 86OPCBoxB-C
❑ 86QuaGra-23
❑ 86RoyKitCD-20
❑ 86RoyNatP-5
❑ 86RoyTeal-5
❑ 86SevCoi-C2
❑ 86SevCoi-E2
❑ 86SevCoi-S2
❑ 86SevCoi-W2
❑ 86Spo-1
❑ 86Spo-52
❑ 86Spo-63
❑ 86Spo-179
❑ 86Spo-180
❑ 86Spo-186
❑ 86SpoDecG-64
❑ 86SpoIndC-160
❑ 86Top-300
❑ 86Top-714
❑ 86Top3-D-5
❑ 86TopGloA-4
❑ 86TopGloS-18
❑ 86TopMinL-18
❑ 86TopSti-3
❑ 86TopSti-16
❑ 86TopSti-23
❑ 86TopSti-157
❑ 86TopSti-256
❑ 86TopSup-14
❑ 86TopTat-6
❑ 86TopTif-300
❑ 86TopTif-714
❑ 86TopWaxBC-C
❑ 86TruVal-17
❑ 86Woo-4
❑ 87BoaandB-13
❑ 87ClaGam-47
❑ 87Don-15
❑ 87Don-54
❑ 87DonAll-27
❑ 87DonOpeD-206
❑ 87DonSupD-15
❑ 87Dra-14
❑ 87Fle-366
❑ 87FleGamW-6
❑ 87FleGlo-366
❑ 87FleHotS-6
❑ 87FleLeaL-5
❑ 87FleLimE-5
❑ 87FleMin-13
❑ 87FleRecS-1
❑ 87FleSlu-6
❑ 87FleStiC-15
❑ 87FleWaxBC-C3
❑ 87GenMilB-3B
❑ 87HosSti-24
❑ 87K-M-24
❑ 87KayB-5
❑ 87KraFoo-21
❑ 87Lea-15
❑ 87Lea-96
❑ 87MandMSL-14
❑ 87MSAJifPD-5
❑ 87OPC-126
❑ 87RedFolSB-111
❑ 87Spo-5
❑ 87Spo-114
❑ 87Spo-197
❑ 87SpoDeaP-4
❑ 87SpoSupD-12
❑ 87SpoTeaP-13
❑ 87StuPan-20
❑ 87Top-256
❑ 87Top-400
❑ 87TopCoi-5
❑ 87TopGloS-31
❑ 87TopMinL-57
❑ 87TopSti-254
❑ 87TopTif-256
❑ 87TopTif-400
❑ 88ClaBlu-248
❑ 88Don-102
❑ 88DonBasB-39
❑ 88Fle-254
❑ 88FleBasA-4
❑ 88FleGlo-254
❑ 88FleHotS-4
❑ 88FleStiC-30
❑ 88GreBasS-55
❑ 88K-M-3
❑ 88KinDis-7
❑ 88Lea-93
❑ 88MSAFanSD-2
❑ 88OPC-312
❑ 88PanSti-104
❑ 88RoySmo-20
❑ 88RoyTeal-6
❑ 88Sco-11
❑ 88ScoGlo-11
❑ 88Spo-150
❑ 88StaLinAl-4
❑ 88StaLinRo-2
❑ 88TarPla-6
❑ 88Top-141
❑ 88Top-700
❑ 88TopBig-157
❑ 88TopGloS-53
❑ 88TopSti-259
❑ 88TopStiB-41
❑ 88TopTif-141
❑ 88TopTif-700
❑ 88TopUKM-7
❑ 88TopUKMT-7
❑ 89Bow-121
❑ 89BowTif-121
❑ 89CadEllD-4
❑ 89CerSup-9
❑ 89ClaLigB-47
❑ 89Don-204
❑ 89DonAll-11
❑ 89DonBasB-7
❑ 89DonBonM-BC7
❑ 89Fle-277
❑ 89FleBasM-4
❑ 89FleGlo-277
❑ 89FleSup-5
❑ 89FleWaxBC-C3
❑ 89KayB-2
❑ 89MasBreD-9
❑ 89OPC-200
❑ 89OPCBoxB-A
❑ 89PanSti-355
❑ 89RedFolSB-12
❑ 89RoyTasD-1
❑ 89Sco-75
❑ 89Sco-75A
❑ 89ScoHot1S-4
❑ 89Scomast-11
❑ 89Spo-64
❑ 89SpoIllFKI-162
❑ 89Top-200
❑ 89TopBasT-52
❑ 89TopBatL-5
❑ 89TopBig-46
❑ 89TopCapC-9
❑ 89TopCoi-34
❑ 89TopGloS-14
❑ 89TopHilTM-3
❑ 89TopMinL-54
❑ 89TopSti-270
❑ 89TopStiB-1
❑ 89TopTif-200
❑ 89TopUKM-7
❑ 89TopWaxBC-A
❑ 89TVSpoM-105
❑ 89UppDec-215
❑ 89UppDec-689
❑ 90AllBasT-1
❑ 90Bow-382
❑ 90BowTif-382
❑ 90ClaUpd-T6
❑ 90Col-21
❑ 90Don-144
❑ 90DonBesA-35
❑ 90DonLeaS-1
❑ 90Fle-103
❑ 90Fle-621A
❑ 90Fle-621B
❑ 90FleBasM-5
❑ 90FleBasMC-5
❑ 90FleCan-103
❑ 90FleCan-621
❑ 90HOFStiB-93
❑ 90KayB-4
❑ 90Lea-178
❑ 90M.Vpin-43
❑ 90MLBBasB-101
❑ 90OPC-60
❑ 90OPCBoxB-B
❑ 90PanSti-91
❑ 90Pos-4
❑ 90PubIntS-344
❑ 90RedFolSB-9
❑ 90RoyPos-4
❑ 90Sco-140
❑ 90Sco100S-76
❑ 90ScoMcD-19
❑ 90Spo-214
❑ 90Top-60
❑ 90TopAmeA-2
❑ 90TopBatL-5
❑ 90TopHilHM-10
❑ 90TopMag-88
❑ 90TopSti-265
❑ 90TopTif-60
❑ 90TopWaxBC-B
❑ 90UppDec-124
❑ 90Woo-9
❑ 91BasBesHM-3
❑ 91Baz-10
❑ 91Bow-300
❑ 91Cla1-T46
❑ 91Cla2-T70
❑ 91ClaGam-137
❑ 91Col-28
❑ 91Don-201
❑ 91Don-396
❑ 91DonBonC-BC19
❑ 91DonEli-2
❑ 91Fle-552
❑ 91JimDea-12
❑ 91Lea-264
❑ 91Lea-335
❑ 91MajLeaCP-21
❑ 91MooSna-19
❑ 91OPC-2
❑ 91OPC-540
❑ 91OPCBoxB-B
❑ 91OPCPre-14
❑ 91PanCanT1-5
❑ 91PanFreS-276
❑ 91PanSti-224
❑ 91PetSta-13
❑ 91Pos-26
❑ 91PosCan-29
❑ 91RedFolS-11
❑ 91RoyPol-4
❑ 91Sco-120
❑ 91Sco-769
❑ 91Sco-853
❑ 91Sco100S-85
❑ 91ScoCoo-B5
❑ 91ScoPro-120
❑ 91SevCoi-F2
❑ 91SevCoi-M1
❑ 91SevCoi-NW1
❑ 91StaClu-159
❑ 91StaCluCM-2
❑ 91StaPinB-6
❑ 91Stu-62
❑ 91SunSee-4
❑ 91Top-2
❑ 91Top-540
❑ 91TopCraJI-15
❑ 91TopDesS-2
❑ 91TopDesS-540
❑ 91TopGaloC-3
❑ 91TopMic-2
❑ 91TopMic-540
❑ 91TopSta-6
❑ 91TopTif-2
❑ 91TopTif-540
❑ 91TopTriH-A7
❑ 91TopWaxBC-B
❑ 91Ult-144
❑ 91UppDec-525
❑ 91Woo-8
❑ 92Bow-500
❑ 92Cla2-T79
❑ 92ClaGam-81
❑ 92Don-143
❑ 92DonCraJ2-30
❑ 92DonMcD-3
❑ 92Fle-154
❑ 92Hig5-61
❑ 92HitTheBB-7
❑ 92JimDeaLL-1
❑ 92LaKdec-3
❑ 92Lea-255
❑ 92LeaBlaG-255
❑ 92LeaGolP-19
❑ 92LeaPre-19
❑ 92MooSna-21
❑ 92Mr.TurS-5
❑ 92New-3
❑ 92OPC-620
❑ 92OPCPre-114
❑ 92PanSti-102
❑ 92Pin-60
❑ 92Pin-282
❑ 92PinRool-3
❑ 92Pos-11
❑ 92RedFolS-18
❑ 92RoyPol-4
❑ 92Sco-650
❑ 92Sco100S-21
❑ 92ScoProP-14
❑ 92SevCoi-25
❑ 92SpoStaCC-6
❑ 92StaClu-150
❑ 92StaClu-609
❑ 92StaCluECN-609
❑ 92StaCluMO-4
❑ 92Stu-181
❑ 92Top-620
❑ 92TopGol-620
❑ 92TopGolW-620
❑ 92TopKid-105
❑ 92TopMcD-6
❑ 92TopMic-620
❑ 92TriPla-115
❑ 92Ult-68
❑ 92UppDec-444
❑ 92UppDecF-16
❑ 92UppDecFG-16
❑ 92UppDecTMH-12
❑ 93Bow-265
❑ 93ClaGam-17
❑ 93DiaMar-18
❑ 93DonEliD-15
❑ 93DonMVP-3
❑ 93DonPre-16
❑ 93DurPowP2-5
❑ 93Fin-63
❑ 93FinRef-63
❑ 93Fla-213
❑ 93Fle-236
❑ 93FleFinEDT-2
❑ 93FleFruotL-7
❑ 93FleGolM-A1
❑ 93FunPac-181
❑ 93GeoBre3H-1
❑ 93HumDumC-9
❑ 93JimDea-15
❑ 93KinDis-9
❑ 93Kra-4
❑ 93Lea-146
❑ 93LeaHeaftH-7
❑ 93OPC-50
❑ 93PacJugC-2
❑ 93PacSpa-133
❑ 93PanSti-110
❑ 93Pin-131
❑ 93Pin-294
❑ 93PinCoo-2
❑ 93PinCooD-2
❑ 93PinTri-1
❑ 93PinTri-2
❑ 93PinTri-3
❑ 93PinTri-4
❑ 93PinTri-5
❑ 93Pos-25
❑ 93RoyPol-5
❑ 93RoySta2-1
❑ 93RoyStaC-1
❑ 93Sco-57
❑ 93Sco-517
❑ 93Sel-78
❑ 93SP-227
❑ 93StaClu-424
❑ 93StaCluFDI-424
❑ 93StaClul-A2
❑ 93StaCluMO-4
❑ 93StaCluMOP-424
❑ 93StaCluMOP-MA2
❑ 93StaCluMP-13
❑ 93Stu-25
❑ 93StuHer-1
❑ 93Top-397
❑ 93TopGol-397
❑ 93TopInaM-397
❑ 93TopInaR-397
❑ 93TopMagJRC-3
❑ 93TopMic-397
❑ 93TopMic-P397
❑ 93TriPla-64
❑ 93TriPla-214
❑ 93Ult-206
❑ 93UppDec-54
❑ 93UppDec-56
❑ 93UppDec-SP5
❑ 93UppDecDG-24
❑ 93UppDecGold-54
❑ 93UppDecGold-56
❑ 93UppDecIC-WI22
❑ 93UppDecICJ-WI22
❑ 93UppDecOD-D6
❑ 93UppDecSH-HI7
❑ 93UppDecTAN-TN2
❑ 94ColC-65
❑ 94ColChoGS-65
❑ 94ColChoSS-65
❑ 94Don-107
❑ 94DonAnn8-3

❑ 94Fle-149
❑ 94FleGolM-6
❑ 94FleGolMJ-6
❑ 94StaClu-5
❑ 94StaCluFDI-5
❑ 94StaCluGR-5
❑ 94StaCluMOP-5
❑ 94Top-180
❑ 94TopGol-180
❑ 94TopPre-397
❑ 94TopSpa-180
❑ 94UppDecAH-20
❑ 94UppDecAH-123
❑ 94UppDecAH1-20
❑ 94UppDecAH1-123
❑ 94UppDecAHA-1
❑ 94UppDecTAE-80
❑ 95ColCho-49
❑ 95ColCho-54
❑ 95ColChoGS-49
❑ 95ColChoGS-54
❑ 95ColChoSS-49
❑ 95ColChoSS-54
❑ 95SP-3
❑ 95SPCha-101
❑ 95SPChaCP-CP5
❑ 95SPChaCPDC-CP5
❑ 95SPChaDC-101
❑ 95SPSil-3
❑ 95TomPiz-AU2
❑ 95UppDec-449
❑ 95UppDecED-449
❑ 95UppDecEDG-449
❑ 95UppDecSE-190
❑ 95UppDecSEG-190
❑ 96Pro-4
❑ 97DonSigSS-4
❑ 97HigMinMCT-9
❑ 97HigMinMCT-10
❑ 98DonSigSS-3
❑ 99UppDecCLJotC-GB
❑ 99UppDecR-90
❑ 99UppDecRG-90
❑ 99UppDecRI-GB
❑ 99UppDecRIL2-GB
❑ 99UppDecRP-90

Brett, Herbert
❑ 27Zee-133

Brett, Jason
❑ 98PitMetM-10

Brett, Ken (Kenneth Alvin)
❑ 69Top-476A
❑ 69Top-476B
❑ 70RedSoxCPPC-3
❑ 71MLBOffS-315
❑ 71OPC-89
❑ 71RedSoxA-2
❑ 71Top-89
❑ 72MilBra-45
❑ 72OPC-517
❑ 72Top-517
❑ 73LinPor-148
❑ 73OPC-444
❑ 73PhiTeal-5
❑ 73Top-444
❑ 74OPC-237
❑ 74Top-237
❑ 75Kel-52
❑ 75OPC-250
❑ 75PitPirP-1
❑ 75Top-250
❑ 75TopMin-250
❑ 76OPC-401
❑ 76SSP-569
❑ 76Top-401
❑ 76TopTra-401T
❑ 77Hos-65
❑ 77OPC-21
❑ 77Top-157
❑ 77Top-631
❑ 78AngFamF-5
❑ 78SSP270-192
❑ 78Top-682
❑ 79Top-557
❑ 80DodPol-34
❑ 80Top-521
❑ 81RedSoxBG2S-73
❑ 81Top-47
❑ 82Don-364
❑ 82Fle-406
❑ 82Top-397
❑ 85UtiBluST-24
❑ 90DodTar-74
❑ 90SweBasG-52
❑ 92YanWIZ7-24
❑ 93UppDecAH-17
❑ 94BreMilB-285
❑ 94UppDecAH-192
❑ 94UppDecAH1-192

Breuer, James
❑ 93GreFalDSP-29
❑ 94YakBeaC-2

Breuer, Marvin
❑ 40PlaBal-183
❑ 43YanSta-3
❑ 75YanDyn1T-3

Brevell, Bubba (Ron)
❑ 86KinEagP-2
❑ 88MiaMarS-3

Brewer, Bernie
❑ 92BreCarT-xx
❑ 94BrePol-1
❑ 94MasMan-1

Brewer, Billy
❑ 90JamExpP-15
❑ 92WesPalBEC-20
❑ 92WesPalBEF-2080
❑ 93Bow-561
❑ 93FleFinE-215
❑ 93OPCPre-99
❑ 93PacSpa-485
❑ 93Pin-606
❑ 93SelRoo-143T
❑ 93Ult-557
❑ 94Don-137
❑ 94Fle-150
❑ 94Pac-280
❑ 94Sco-564
❑ 94ScoGolR-564
❑ 94StaClu-490
❑ 94StaCluFDI-490
❑ 94StaCluGR-490
❑ 94StaCluMOP-490
❑ 94Top-123
❑ 94TopGol-123
❑ 94TopSpa-123
❑ 95ColCho-463
❑ 95ColChoGS-463
❑ 95ColChoSS-463
❑ 95Don-141
❑ 95DonPreP-141
❑ 95DonTopotO-83
❑ 95Fle-153
❑ 95Sco-140
❑ 95ScoGolR-140
❑ 95ScoPlaTS-140
❑ 95Top-439
❑ 95TopCyb-235
❑ 95Ult-54
❑ 95UltGolM-54
❑ 95UppDec-416
❑ 95UppDecED-416
❑ 95UppDecEDG-416
❑ 98PacOnl-556
❑ 98PacOnlR-556
❑ 98PacOnlWC-556
❑ 98PhiTeal-6

Brewer, Brad
❑ 97ButCopKB-3
❑ 97ButCopKK-3
❑ 98CedRapKTI-4

Brewer, Brett
❑ 94DanBraF-3543
❑ 95MacBraTI-1
❑ 95MacBraUTI-1

Brewer, Brian
❑ 93BluOriC-5
❑ 93BluOriF-4116
❑ 94AlbPolC-5
❑ 94AlbPolF-2228
❑ 94OriPro-10
❑ 96BowBayB-8

Brewer, Chet
❑ 78LauLonABS-23
❑ 87NegLeaPD-29
❑ 97NegLeaPC-9C

Brewer, Clint
❑ 98ChaAllCM-3

Brewer, Doug
❑ 94DanBraC-3

Brewer, Gay
❑ 68AtlOil-2

Brewer, Jim
❑ 61Top-317
❑ 61TopStal-6
❑ 62Top-191
❑ 62TopVen-191
❑ 63Top-309
❑ 64Top-553
❑ 65Top-416
❑ 66OPC-158
❑ 66Top-158
❑ 66TopVen-158
❑ 67CokCapD-7
❑ 67CokCapDA-7
❑ 67OPC-31
❑ 67Top-31
❑ 68Top-298
❑ 68TopVen-298
❑ 69MilBra-36
❑ 69Top-241
❑ 70Top-571
❑ 71Dod-3
❑ 71DodTic-3
❑ 71MLBOffS-98
❑ 71OPC-549
❑ 71Top-549
❑ 72MilBra-46
❑ 72OPC-151
❑ 72Top-151
❑ 73OPC-126
❑ 73Top-126
❑ 74Kel-14
❑ 74OPC-189
❑ 74Top-189
❑ 75CalAngP-6
❑ 75OPC-163
❑ 75Top-163
❑ 75TopMin-163
❑ 76OPC-459
❑ 76Top-459
❑ 77ExpPos-6
❑ 77OPC-198
❑ 78TCM60I-243
❑ 79ExpPos-4
❑ 87DodSmoA-3
❑ 88DodSmo-14
❑ 89DodSmoG-79
❑ 90DodTar-75
❑ 92DodStaTA-12

Brewer, John H.
❑ 48SomandK-2
❑ 49BowPCL-8
❑ 49SomandK-2

Brewer, Mark
❑ 91SalLakTP-3228
❑ 91SalLakTSP-26
❑ 96GreFalDTI-34
❑ 98VerBeaDM-2

Brewer, Matt
❑ 91Cla/Bes-420
❑ 91EveGiaC-21
❑ 91EveGiaP-3927
❑ 92ProFS7-359
❑ 92SanJosGC-1

Brewer, Mike
❑ 84OmaRoyT-9
❑ 85MaiGuiT-26
❑ 86OmaRoyP-3
❑ 86OmaRoyT-13

Brewer, Mudcat
❑ 94BenRocF-3600

Brewer, Nevin
❑ 93EugEmeC-6
❑ 93EugEmeF-3848
❑ 94RocRoyC-3
❑ 94RocRoyF-555
❑ 95Exc-55
❑ 95WilBluRTI-37

Brewer, Omar
❑ 88ChaRanS-3

Brewer, Rodney
❑ 88SprCarB-19
❑ 89ArkTraGS-3
❑ 90CMC-112
❑ 90LouRedBC-12
❑ 90LouRedBLBC-8
❑ 90LouRedBP-407
❑ 90ProAAAF-521
❑ 90TopTVCa-39
❑ 91Cla1-T92
❑ 91LinDriAAA-227
❑ 91LouRedLD-227
❑ 91LouRedP-2925
❑ 91LouRedTI-14
❑ 91TopDeb90-21
❑ 92LouRedF-1897
❑ 92LouRedS-253
❑ 92Sco-864
❑ 92SkyAAAF-123
❑ 92TriA AAS-253
❑ 93CarPol-3
❑ 93CarStaC-7
❑ 93FleMajLP-A17
❑ 93PacSpa-629
❑ 93StaClu-527
❑ 93StaCluFDI-527
❑ 93StaCluMOP-527
❑ 93Top-566
❑ 93TopGol-566
❑ 93TopInaM-566
❑ 93TopInaR-566
❑ 93TopMic-566
❑ 93UppDec-381
❑ 93UppDecGold-381
❑ 94Don-400
❑ 94Fle-629
❑ 94Sco-297
❑ 94ScoGolR-297
❑ 94StaCluT-326
❑ 94StaCluTFDI-326
❑ 97BufBis-7

Brewer, Ryan
❑ 97WilBluR-16
❑ 98WilBluRC-5

Brewer, Tom
❑ 47Exh-28
❑ 55Bow-178
❑ 55Top-83
❑ 55TopDouH-127
❑ 56Top-34
❑ 57Top-112
❑ 58RedSoxJP-1
❑ 58Top-220
❑ 59RedSoxJP-1
❑ 59Top-55
❑ 59Top-346
❑ 59TopVen-55
❑ 60RedSoxJP-1
❑ 60Top-439
❑ 61Pos-50A
❑ 61Pos-50B
❑ 61Top-434
❑ 61TopStal-108
❑ 62SalPlaC-4
❑ 62ShiPlaC-4
❑ 81RedSoxBG2S-9

Brewer, Tony (Anthony Bruce)
❑ 83AlbDukTc-20
❑ 84AlbDukCr-161
❑ 85AlbDukCr-152
❑ 85Don-31
❑ 87JapPlaB-42
❑ 90DodTar-76

Brewer, Woody (Sherwood)
❑ 93NegLeaRL2-6

Brewers, Helena
❑ 95HelBreTI-32
❑ 96HelBreTI-NNO

Brewers, Milwaukee
❑ 71OPC-698
❑ 71Top-698
❑ 71TopTat-61
❑ 72OPC-106
❑ 72Top-106
❑ 73OPC-127
❑ 73OPCBTC-13
❑ 73Top-127
❑ 73TopBluTC-13
❑ 74OPC-314
❑ 74OPCTC-13
❑ 74Top-314
❑ 74TopStaA-13
❑ 74TopTeaC-13
❑ 78Top-328
❑ 82BrePol-NNO
❑ 83BrePol-NNO0
❑ 83FleSta-237
❑ 83FleSti-NNO
❑ 83FleSti-NNO
❑ 84BrePol-NNO0
❑ 87BrePol-NNO0
❑ 87SpoTeaL-19
❑ 88BrePol-NNO
❑ 88PanSti-462
❑ 88RedFolSB-115
❑ 90PubIntS-644
❑ 90RedFolSB-123
❑ 91PanCanT1-126
❑ 92BreCarT-xx
❑ 94ImpProP-8
❑ 94Sco-324
❑ 94ScoGolR-324
❑ 95PacPriTL-8
❑ 95PanSti-155
❑ 96PanSti-195
❑ 99Vic-207

Brewers, Minors (Milwaukee)
❑ 38BasTabP-31

Brewington, Jamie
❑ 92EveGiaC-18
❑ 92EveGiaF-1677
❑ 93ClaGolF-159
❑ 93CliGiaC-5
❑ 93CliGiaF-2480
❑ 95UltGolMR-M6
❑ 96ColCho-38
❑ 96ColCho-660
❑ 96ColChoGS-38
❑ 96ColChoGS-660
❑ 96ColChoSS-38
❑ 96ColChoSS-660
❑ 96Don-495
❑ 96DonPreP-495
❑ 96Fle-584
❑ 96FleTif-584
❑ 96PhoFirB-10
❑ 96Top-331
❑ 96Ult-291
❑ 96UltGolM-291
❑ 96UppDec-193
❑ 96UppDecFSP-FS5

Brewington, Mike (Michael)
❑ 89WelPirP-6
❑ 90AugPirP-2476
❑ 90CMC-725
❑ 91SalBucC-10
❑ 91SalBucP-964

Brewster, Charlie (Charles L.)
❑ 43PhiTeal-3

Brewster, Rich
❑ 76QuaCitAT-6
❑ 77QuaCitAT-7
❑ 80ElPasDT-20

Brian, Braden
❑ 87JamExpP-2554

Brice, Alan
❑ 77FriOneYW-97

Brickell, Fred (George F.)
❑ 33Gou-38
❑ 33GouCanV-38
❑ 33RitCE-4D
❑ 35GouPuzR-6C
❑ 35GouPuzR-11E
❑ 35GouPuzR-13C
❑ 35GouPuzR-15C
❑ 93ConTSN-808

Brickell, Fritzie (Fritz D.)
❑ 61AngJayP-4
❑ 61MapLeaBH-2
❑ 61Top-333
❑ 81TCM60I-294

Brickey, Josh
❑ 89KinMetS-29
❑ 90KinMetS-30

Brickhouse, Jack
❑ 84CubBriPC-1H
❑ 89PacLegI-209

Brickler, Tim
❑ 93MisStaB-4

Bridenbaugh, Christian
❑ 98YakBeaG-7

Brideweser, Jim (James E.)
❑ 53BowC-136
❑ 54OriTeal-2
❑ 55Bow-151
❑ 56BalOriP-3
❑ 57Top-382
❑ 91OriCro-51
❑ 97BalOriP-4

Bridge, Eric
❑ 89FreStaBS-4

Bridge, Mark
❑ 85CloHSS-5

Bridgers, Brandon
❑ 93BluOriC-6
❑ 93BluOriF-4138
❑ 94AlbPolC-6
❑ 94AlbPolF-2248
❑ 94OriPro-11
❑ 94SouAtlLAF-SAL1

Bridges, Donnie
❑ 98Bow-306
❑ 98BowChr-306
❑ 98BowChrGA-306
❑ 98BowChrGAR-306
❑ 98BowChrI-306
❑ 98BowChrIR-306
❑ 98BowChrR-306
❑ 98BowGolA-306
❑ 98BowInt-306
❑ 98Top-489
❑ 98TopChr-489
❑ 98TopChrR-489
❑ 98TopDevR-489
❑ 98TopDia-489
❑ 98TopMiniC-489
❑ 98VerExpO-9

Bridges, Jason
❑ 88OneYanP-2045
❑ 89PriWilCS-1
❑ 90PriWilCTI-6

Bridges, Jim
❑ 85BurRanT-28

Bridges, Kary
❑ 94QuaCitRBC-6
❑ 94QuaCitRBF-539
❑ 95JacGenTI-19
❑ 96JacGenB-5
❑ 96TusTorB-4
❑ 98WesTenDJM-3

Bridges, Marshall
❑ 58UniOil-1
❑ 63ReqKP-6
❑ 64ChatheY-5
❑ 78TCM60I-48
❑ 80Red196T-41
❑ 92YanWIZ6-16

Bridges, Rocky (Everett L.)
❑ 50WorWidGV-1
❑ 52Top-239
❑ 53BowBW-32
❑ 54Bow-156
❑ 55Bow-136
❑ 56Top-324
❑ 57RedSoh-3
❑ 57Top-294
❑ 58SeaTeal-5
❑ 58SenJayP-1
❑ 58Top-274
❑ 59Top-318
❑ 60Lea-31
❑ 60TigJayP-3
❑ 60Top-22
❑ 60TopVen-22
❑ 61Top-508
❑ 62Jel-75
❑ 62Pos-75
❑ 62PosCan-75
❑ 74dod195T-5
❑ 74PhoGiaC-90
❑ 75PhoGiaCK-1
❑ 76PheGiaCr-26
❑ 76PhoGiaCa-6
❑ 76PhoGiaCC-3
❑ 76PhoGiaVNB-2
❑ 77PhoGiaCC-5
❑ 77PhoGiaCP-4
❑ 77PhoGiaVNB-3
❑ 78PhoGiaC-3
❑ 79PhoGiaVNB-5
❑ 80PhoGiaVNB-22
❑ 81PhoGiaVNB-25
❑ 82PhoGiaVNB-7
❑ 83TopRep5-239
❑ 84EveGiaC-28
❑ 84OCoandSI-117
❑ 85GiaMot-27
❑ 85GiaPos-3
❑ 86PriWilPP-4
❑ 87VanCanP-1605
❑ 88BufBisC-25
❑ 88BufBisP-1478
❑ 88BufBisTI-1
❑ 89SalBucS-25
❑ 90DodTar-77
❑ 90WelPirP-33
❑ 95TopArcBD-14
❑ 97PhoFirDTTI-12

Bridges, Thomas
❑ 33ButCanV-4
❑ 33Gou-199
❑ 33TatOrbSDR-177
❑ 33WorCig-12
❑ 34BatR31-9
❑ 34BatR31-81
❑ 34DiaStaR-5
❑ 34Gou-44
❑ 34GouCanV-87
❑ 34TarThoBD-4
❑ 34TigTeal-3
❑ 35GolMedFR-1
❑ 35GouPuzR-1D
❑ 35GouPuzR-2D
❑ 35GouPuzR-16D

❑ 35GouPuzR-17D
❑ 35WheBB1-4
❑ 36GouWidPPR-A10
❑ 36GouWidPPR-C5
❑ 36NatChiFPR-14
❑ 36WorWidGV-33
❑ 37OPCBatUV-133
❑ 37WheBB14-2
❑ 37WheBB7-29J
❑ 37WheBB9-2
❑ 38CloFotW-10
❑ 38ExhFou-12
❑ 39PlaBal-104
❑ 39TigSpo-3
❑ 41PlaBal-65
❑ 48SweSpoT-13
❑ 61Fle-95
❑ 70FleWorS-32
❑ 74CapPub-100
❑ 74TigTCM1AC-3
❑ 74TigTCM1AC-35
❑ 76TigOldTS-2
❑ 81TigDetN-56
❑ 81TigSecNP-15
❑ 82DiaCla-77
❑ 83ConMar-24
❑ 88ConAmeA-3
❑ 91ConTSN-180
❑ 93ConTSN-723
Bridges-Clements, Tony
❑ 88BasCitRS-9
❑ 89MemChiB-7
❑ 89MemChiP-1202
❑ 89MemChiS-3
❑ 91MemChiP-659
❑ 92BasCitRF-3850
❑ 92ClaFS7-237
❑ 92MemChiF-2430
❑ 92MemChiS-427
❑ 92SkyAA F-179
Bridgman, Mel
❑ 80PhiBul-23
Bridwell, Al (Albert H.)
❑ 08AmeCarE91-3
❑ 08AmeCarE91-38
❑ 09AmeCarE90-1-14
❑ 09ColChiE-34
❑ 09RamT20-17
❑ 09T206-37
❑ 09T206-38
❑ 10CouT21-84
❑ 10CouT21-85
❑ 10CouT21-261
❑ 10DarChoE-5
❑ 10DomDisP-16
❑ 10E101-6
❑ 10E12AmeCDCE125-6
❑ 10E98-3
❑ 10MelMinE-6
❑ 10NadCarE-8
❑ 10NadE1-9
❑ 10PeoT21-7A
❑ 10PeoT21-7B
❑ 10PeoT21-7C
❑ 10RedCroT-6
❑ 10RedCroT-172
❑ 10SepAnoP-2
❑ 10SweCapPP-108
❑ 11BasBatEU-4
❑ 11HelSta-77
❑ 11MecDFT-6
❑ 11PinT-5-259
❑ 11S74Sil-81
❑ 11SpoLifCW-44
❑ 11SpoLifM-205
❑ 11T205-21
❑ 11TurRedT-83
❑ 12ColRedB-34
❑ 12ColTinT-34
❑ 12HasTriFT-20
❑ 12HasTriFT-50A
❑ 14CraJacE-42
❑ 14PieStaT-14
❑ 15AmeCarE106-5
❑ 15CraJacE-42
❑ 16TanBraE-3
❑ 91ConTSN-170
Brief, Bunny (Anthony V.)
❑ 16Zee-75
❑ 17Zee-61
❑ 94ConTSN-1290
❑ 94ConTSNB-1290
Brier, Coe
❑ 83WisRapTF-1
Briggs, Anthony
❑ 94IdaFalBF-3574
❑ 95MacBraTI-2
❑ 96DurBulBlB-4
❑ 96DurBulBrB-5
❑ 96Exc-122
❑ 97DurBulTI-7
❑ 98RicBraQ-3
Briggs, Buttons (Herbert)
❑ 08IndPos-1
❑ 98CamPepP-7
Briggs, Dan (Daniel Lee)
❑ 74SalLakCAC-100
❑ 75SalLakCC-5
❑ 76SalLakCGC-20
❑ 77Top-592
❑ 79PadFamF-19
❑ 79Top-77
❑ 80Top-352
❑ 82OPC-102
❑ 82Top-102
❑ 82TopTra-11T
❑ 84ColCliP-3
❑ 84ColCliT-5
❑ 85ColCliP-3
❑ 85ColCliT-14
❑ 85IntLeaAT-33
Briggs, David
❑ 88SpoIndP-1938
❑ 89ChaRaiP-994
Briggs, John Edward
❑ 64PhiPhiB-6
❑ 64Top-482
❑ 65OPC-163
❑ 65Top-163
❑ 66Top-359
❑ 66TopVen-359
❑ 67CokCapPh-3
❑ 67DexPre-31
❑ 67PhiPol-3
❑ 67Top-268
❑ 68Top-284
❑ 68TopVen-284
❑ 69MilBra-37
❑ 69MLBOffS-173
❑ 69OPC-73
❑ 69Top-73
❑ 69TopSta-72
❑ 70MLBOffS-85
❑ 70PhiTeal-2
❑ 70Top-564
❑ 71MLBOffS-170
❑ 71OPC-297
❑ 71Top-297
❑ 72MilBra-47
❑ 72OPC-197
❑ 72Top-197
❑ 73LinPor-98
❑ 73OPC-71
❑ 73Top-71
❑ 74OPC-218
❑ 74Top-218
❑ 74TopSta-192
❑ 75Kel-16
❑ 75OPC-123
❑ 75Top-123
❑ 75TopMin-123
❑ 75TwiTeal-6
❑ 76OPC-373
❑ 76Top-373
❑ 81TCM60I-424
❑ 86BreGreT-6
❑ 94BreMilB-286
Briggs, John T.
❑ 59Top-177
❑ 59TopVen-177
❑ 60Top-376
Briggs, Ken
❑ 91SalSpuC-1
❑ 91SalSpuP-2246
Briggs, Kenny
❑ 83WauTimF-29
Briggs, Stoney
❑ 91MedHatBJP-4113
❑ 91MedHatBJSP-20
❑ 92MyrBeaHC-16
❑ 92MyrBeaHF-2209
❑ 93WatDiaC-6
❑ 93WatDiaF-1781
❑ 94RanCucQC-7
❑ 94RanCucQF-1649
❑ 95MemChiTI-6
❑ 95UppDecML-146
❑ 95UppDecMLFS-146
❑ 96MemChiB-8
❑ 97LasVegS1A-8
Briggs, Walter O.
❑ 81TigDetN-5
Bright, Brian
❑ 91ElmPioC-1
❑ 91ElmPioP-3281
❑ 92WinHavRSC-23
❑ 92WinHavRSF-1791
❑ 93FloStaLAF-13
❑ 93ForLauRSC-3
❑ 93ForLauRSFP-1608
❑ 94ClaGolF-64
❑ 94SarRedSC-5
❑ 94SarRedSF-1964
Bright, Don
❑ 74GasRanT-6
❑ 75AndRanT-43
❑ 76SanAntBTI-3
❑ 78TucTorC-21
Bright, Harry James
❑ 59Top-523
❑ 60Top-277
❑ 61Top-447
❑ 62Top-551
❑ 63Jel-95
❑ 63Pos-95
❑ 63RedEnq-2
❑ 63Top-304
❑ 64ChatheY-6
❑ 64Top-259
❑ 64TopVen-259
❑ 65Top-584
❑ 76TucTorCa-9
❑ 76TusTorCr-23
❑ 77PirTCM1WC-37
❑ 78TCM60I-214
❑ 85DurBulT-14
❑ 92YanWIZ6-17
Bright, Tom
❑ 77AppFoxT-2
Brightman, Al
❑ 54SeaPop-2
Brignac, Junior
❑ 97DanBraB-11
❑ 98EugEme-4
Briles, Nellie (Nelson)
❑ 64TulOil-2
❑ 65CarTeal-3
❑ 65Top-431
❑ 66Top-243
❑ 66TopVen-243
❑ 67Top-404
❑ 67TopVen-283
❑ 68OPC-153
❑ 68Top-153
❑ 68Top-540
❑ 68TopVen-153
❑ 69MilBra-38
❑ 69MLBOffS-208
❑ 69OPC-60
❑ 69Top-60
❑ 69TopSta-111
❑ 69TopTeaP-18
❑ 70MLBOffS-134
❑ 70OPC-435
❑ 70Top-435
❑ 71CarTeal-4
❑ 71MLBOffS-195
❑ 71OPC-257
❑ 71Pir-1
❑ 71PirActP-2
❑ 71Top-257
❑ 72CarTeal-1
❑ 72MilBra-48
❑ 72OPC-227
❑ 72Top-227
❑ 72Top-605
❑ 73OPC-303
❑ 73Top-303
❑ 74OPC-123
❑ 74RoyPos-4
❑ 74Top-123
❑ 74TopSta-81
❑ 74TopTra-123T
❑ 75OPC-495
❑ 75RoyPos-4
❑ 75Top-495
❑ 75TopMin-495
❑ 76OPC-569
❑ 76SSP-159
❑ 76Top-569
❑ 77Top-174
❑ 78BalOriP-2
❑ 78Top-717
❑ 79Top-262
❑ 81TCM60I-308
❑ 89SweBasG-79
❑ 91OriCro-52
❑ 93RanKee-81
❑ 93UppDecAH-18
❑ 94UppDecAH-27
❑ 94UppDecAH1-27
❑ 95PirCocP-10
Briley, Greg
❑ 86BelMarCr-107
❑ 87ChaLooB-17
❑ 88CalCanC-13
❑ 88CalCanP-799
❑ 88ScoRoo-74T
❑ 88ScoRooG-74T
❑ 89FleUpd-57
❑ 89ScoHot1R-54
❑ 89Top-781
❑ 89TopBig-247
❑ 89TopTif-781
❑ 89UppDec-770
❑ 90Baz-17
❑ 90Bow-482
❑ 90BowTif-482
❑ 90ClaBlu-54
❑ 90Don-463
❑ 90Fle-507
❑ 90FleCan-507
❑ 90Lea-391
❑ 90MarMot-14
❑ 90OPC-288
❑ 90PanSti-148
❑ 90Sco-303
❑ 90Sco100RS-60
❑ 90ScoYouSI-12
❑ 90Spo-43
❑ 90Top-288
❑ 90TopBig-35
❑ 90TopGloS-19
❑ 90TopRoo-4
❑ 90TopSti-226
❑ 90TopSti-320
❑ 90TopTif-288
❑ 90ToyRoo-5
❑ 90UppDec-455
❑ 91Bow-256
❑ 91Don-352
❑ 91Fle-444
❑ 91Lea-194
❑ 91MarCouH-4
❑ 91OPC-133
❑ 91Sco-494
❑ 91StaClu-130
❑ 91Top-133
❑ 91TopDesS-133
❑ 91TopMic-133
❑ 91TopTif-133
❑ 91UppDec-479
❑ 92Don-487
❑ 92Fle-274
❑ 92Lea-65
❑ 92LeaBlaG-65
❑ 92MarMot-15
❑ 92OPC-502
❑ 92PanSti-61
❑ 92Sco-387
❑ 92StaClu-228
❑ 92Top-502
❑ 92TopGol-502
❑ 92TopGolW-502
❑ 92TopMic-502
❑ 92Ult-120
❑ 92UppDec-369
❑ 93Don-695
❑ 93Fle-670
❑ 93FleFinE-54
❑ 93MarPub-6
❑ 93MarUppD-634
❑ 93MarUSPC-8S
❑ 93PacSpa-281
❑ 93StaClu-440
❑ 93StaCluFDI-440
❑ 93StaCluMOP-440
❑ 93Top-14
❑ 93TopGol-14
❑ 93ToplnaM-14
❑ 93ToplnaR-14
❑ 93TopMic-14
❑ 93TopTra-35T
❑ 93Ult-368
❑ 93UppDec-634
❑ 93UppDecGold-634
❑ 94ChaKniF-906
❑ 94VenLinU-48
❑ 95IndIndF-106
Briley, Paxton
❑ 92BoiHawC-25
❑ 92BoiHawF-3617
❑ 93StaCluM-158
Brilinski, Tyler
❑ 86ModA'sC-5
❑ 86ModA'sP-4
❑ 87HunStaTI-5
❑ 88TacTigC-12
❑ 88TacTigP-617
❑ 89TacTigC-13
❑ 89TacTigP-1561
Brill, Clinton
❑ 83AndBraT-26
Brill, Tim
❑ 78WatIndT-4
❑ 79SavBraT-6
Brill, Todd
❑ 88OneYanP-2042
Brillheart, Jim
❑ 47PadTeal-2
Brimhall, Bradley
❑ 90MadMusP-2260
❑ 90SouOreAB-22
❑ 90SouOreAP-3439
❑ 91MadMusC-5
❑ 91MadMusP-2122
❑ 92KanCouCTI-2
Brincks, Mark
❑ 93HicCraC-4
❑ 93HicCraF-1271
Bringhurst, Stewart
❑ 78WauMetT-3
Brink, Brad
❑ 87ClePhiP-23
❑ 88MaiPhiC-5
❑ 88MaiPhiP-289
❑ 88PhiTas-27
❑ 89ScrRedBP-721
❑ 92DonRoo-14
❑ 92PhiMed-38
❑ 92ReaPhiS-527
❑ 92ScrRedBS-484
❑ 92SkyAA F-227
❑ 93Sco-224
❑ 93ScrRedBF-2539
❑ 93ScrRedBTI-4
❑ 93Top-818
❑ 93TopGol-818
❑ 93ToplnaM-818
❑ 93ToplnaR-818
❑ 93TopMic-818
❑ 94PhiUSPC-2D
❑ 94PhiUSPC-9S
❑ 94PhoFirF-1512
❑ 95PhoFirTI-10
Brink, Craig
❑ 88OneYanP-2051
Brink, Jim
❑ 98SouOreTG-2
Brink, Mike
❑ 85CloHSS-6
Brinker, Bill (William H.)
❑ 09ObaT21-237
❑ 09ObaT21-407
❑ 12ObaPreT-156
Brinkley, Christie
❑ 96PinChrBC-PCB
Brinkley, Darryl
❑ 96RanCucQB-7
❑ 97MobBayBB-22
❑ 98NasSouTI-6
❑ 98NasSouTISS-6
Brinkley, Josh
❑ 96WesPalBEB-17
Brinkman, Chuck (Charles E.)
❑ 71OPC-13
❑ 71Top-13
❑ 72Top-786
❑ 73OPC-404
❑ 73Top-404
❑ 74OPC-641
❑ 74Top-641
Brinkman, Ed (Edwin A.)
❑ 63Top-479
❑ 64Top-46
❑ 64TopCoi-108
❑ 64TopGia-27
❑ 64TopVen-46
❑ 65Top-417
❑ 66SenTeal-2
❑ 66Top-251
❑ 66TopVen-251
❑ 67CokCapS-3
❑ 67DexPre-32
❑ 67SenPos-5
❑ 67SenTeal-2
❑ 67Top-311
❑ 68OPC-49
❑ 68SenTeal81/2-1
❑ 68Top-49A
❑ 68Top-49B
❑ 68TopVen-49
❑ 69MilBra-39
❑ 69MLBOffS-101
❑ 69OPC-153
❑ 69SenTeal-3
❑ 69SenTeal8-5
❑ 69SenTeal8-6
❑ 69Top-153
❑ 69TopFou-16
❑ 69TopSta-232
❑ 69TopTeaP-23
❑ 70MLBOffS-279
❑ 70SenPolY-2
❑ 70Top-711
❑ 71MLBOffS-385
❑ 71OPC-389
❑ 71Top-389
❑ 71TopCoi-46
❑ 72MilBra-49
❑ 72Top-535
❑ 73OPC-5
❑ 73TigJew-1
❑ 73Top-5
❑ 74OPC-138
❑ 74Top-138
❑ 74TopSta-171
❑ 75OPC-439
❑ 75St.LouCP-1
❑ 75Top-439
❑ 75TopMin-439
❑ 75YanSSP-3
❑ 76SSP-447
❑ 81PadFamF-4
❑ 81TigDetN-70
❑ 82BirBarT-24
❑ 84WhiSoxTV-8
❑ 92YanWIZ7-25
❑ 93RanKee-82
Brinkman, Greg
❑ 84ButCopKT-8
❑ 87SalSpuS-11
❑ 88VerMarP-957
❑ 89OrlTwiB-30
❑ 89VisOakP-1428
Brinkman, Joe
❑ 88T/MUmp-15
❑ 89T/MUmp-13
❑ 90T/MUmp-13
Brinkopf, Leon C.
❑ 77FriOneYW-18
Brinley, Earl
❑ 21Zee-89
Brinson, Hugh
❑ 86VenGulP-2
❑ 87DunBluJP-927
❑ 88KnoBluJB-24
Briones, Chris
❑ 95HudValRTI-15
❑ 96ChaRivTI-9607
❑ 98RanCucQG-5
❑ 98RanCucQG-5
Brisbin, Steve
❑ 75QuaCitAT-30
Brisco, Jamie
❑ 83EriCarT-9
❑ 84SavCarT-13
❑ 86StoPorP-2
❑ 87ElPasDP-10
❑ 88ElPasDB-4
Briscoe, John
❑ 90ModA'sC-2
❑ 90ModA'sCLC-150
❑ 90ModA'sP-2204
❑ 91HunStaLD-279
❑ 91LinDriAA-279
❑ 91ScoRoo-108T
❑ 92DonRoo-15
❑ 92SkyAAAF-235
❑ 92StaClu-681
❑ 92StaCluECN-681
❑ 92TacTigF-2495
❑ 92TacTigS-539
❑ 92TopDeb91-21
❑ 93HunStaF-2076
❑ 94A'sMot-27
❑ 95Fla-70
❑ 95Fle-241

❑ 95Top-435
❑ 95TopCyb-232
❑ 96LeaSigEA-16
Briskey, Dick
❑ 45CenFlo-2
Brison, Sam
❑ 76LauIndC-4
❑ 76LauIndC-11
❑ 76LauIndC-29
❑ 76LauIndC-37
Brissie, Lou
❑ 47Exh-29
❑ 48A'sTeal-2
❑ 49A'sTeal-6
❑ 49Bow-41
❑ 49Lea-31
❑ 49PhiBul-8
❑ 50A'sTeal-2
❑ 50A'sTeal-3
❑ 50Bow-48
❑ 50Dra-4
❑ 50RoyDes-8A
❑ 50RoyDes-8B
❑ 51Bow-155
❑ 51TopBluB-31
❑ 52Bow-79
❑ 52IndNumN-1
❑ 52NatTeaL-3
❑ 52RoyPre-2
❑ 52TipTop-4
❑ 52Top-270
❑ 53IndPenCBP-7
❑ 83TopRep5-270
❑ 85TCMPla1-45
Bristol, Dave
❑ 67OPC-21
❑ 67Top-21
❑ 68OPC-148
❑ 68Top-148
❑ 68TopVen-148
❑ 69Top-234
❑ 70BreMcD-4
❑ 70BreMil-2
❑ 70BreTeal-2
❑ 70Top-556
❑ 71BreTeal-2
❑ 71OPC-637
❑ 71Top-637
❑ 72Dia-5
❑ 72Top-602
❑ 73OPC-377
❑ 73Top-377
❑ 74OPC-531
❑ 74Top-531
❑ 75ExpPos-5
❑ 76AtlBraP-3
❑ 76OPC-631
❑ 76Top-631
❑ 77Top-442
❑ 79GiaPol-1
❑ 80GiaPol-1
❑ 80GiaTeal-1
❑ 80Top-499
❑ 81Don-436
❑ 81Top-686
❑ 84PhiTas-9
❑ 85PhiTas-3
❑ 85PhiTas-8
❑ 88PhiTas-29
❑ 89RedKah-xx
Bristow, Richie
❑ 90KinMetB-21
❑ 90KinMetS-3
❑ 91ColMetPI-12
❑ 91ColMetPPI-2
Briswalter, Andrew
❑ 09ObaT21-79
Brito, Adan
❑ 84IdaFalATI-5
Brito, Bernardo
❑ 81BatTroT-20
❑ 81WatIndT-31
❑ 83WatIndF-17
❑ 86IndTeal-8
❑ 86WatIndP-5
❑ 87WilBilP-23
❑ 88OrlTwiB-28
❑ 88SouLeaAJ-13
❑ 89PorBeaC-21
❑ 89PorBeaP-212
❑ 90CMC-575
❑ 90PorBeaC-23
❑ 90PorBeaP-190
❑ 90ProAAAF-260
❑ 91LinDriAAA-403
❑ 91PorBeaLD-403
❑ 91PorBeaP-1575
❑ 92PorBeaF-2677
❑ 92PorBeaS-402
❑ 92SkyAAAF-183
❑ 93LimRocDWB-79
❑ 93Pin-274
❑ 93PorBeaF-2392
❑ 93Sco-306
❑ 93TopGol-394
❑ 93TriAAAGF-46
❑ 94Fle-200
❑ 94Pac-350
❑ 94SalLakBF-827
❑ 94TriAAF-AAA15
Brito, Domingo
❑ 94MarPhiC-5
❑ 94MarPhiF-3300
❑ 95BatCliTI-4
❑ 95MarPhiTI-4
Brito, Frank
❑ 88BenBucL-6
Brito, Jorge
❑ 88ModA'sCLC-68
❑ 88ModA'sTI-17
❑ 89ModA'sCLC-282
❑ 90Bes-180
❑ 90HunStaB-13
❑ 91HunStaTI-3
❑ 91LinDriAAA-528
❑ 91TacTigLD-528
❑ 91TacTigP-2309
❑ 92HunStaF-3953
❑ 92TacTigS-527
❑ 94NewHavRF-1551
❑ 95FleUpd-165
❑ 96ColSprSSTI-3
❑ 96LeaSigEA-17
❑ 98LouRedQ-6
Brito, Jose Oscar
❑ 80WatRedT-12
❑ 81IndIndTI-11
❑ 82LouRedE-3
❑ 83LouRedR-14
❑ 85ChaO'sT-26
❑ 85RocRedWT-15
Brito, Juan
❑ 98CapCitBF5-3
❑ 98CapCitBM-3
❑ 98LanLugQ-14
❑ 98PitMetM-11
Brito, Luis
❑ 89MarPhiS-3
❑ 90PriPatD-3
❑ 91MarPhiC-13
❑ 91MarPhiP-3458
❑ 92ClePhiF-2061
❑ 92SpaPhiC-17
❑ 92SpaPhiF-1267
❑ 93SpaPhiC-6
❑ 93SpaPhiF-1060
❑ 94ClePhiC-8
❑ 94ClePhiF-2533
❑ 95ClePhiF-221
❑ 96DurBulBrB-26
❑ 97GreBraG-2
❑ 98CarMudM-15
Brito, Mario
❑ 87JamExpP-2557
❑ 88MidLeaAGS-45
❑ 88RocExpLC-2
❑ 90CMC-660
❑ 90JacExpB-17
❑ 90JacExpP-1368
❑ 91LinDriAAA-627
❑ 91VanCanLD-627
❑ 91VanCanP-1586
❑ 92HarSenF-453
❑ 92HarSenS-277
❑ 93HarSenF-261
❑ 93LimRocDWB-9
❑ 96ChaKniB-9
Brito, Tilson
❑ 93ClaFS7-273
❑ 93DunBluJC-2
❑ 93DunBluJF-1801
❑ 93DunBluJFFN-2
❑ 94KnoSmoF-1308
❑ 96FleUpd-U93
❑ 96FleUpdTC-U93
❑ 96LeaSigA-34
❑ 96LeaSigAG-34
❑ 96LeaSigAS-34
❑ 96SyrChiTI-5
❑ 96Ult-425
❑ 96UltGolM-425
❑ 97BluJayOH-2
❑ 97BluJayS-20
❑ 97Pac-213
❑ 97PacLigB-213
❑ 97PacSil-213
❑ 98TacRaiQ-7
Britt, Bob
❑ 88SpaPhiP-1046
Britt, Bryan
❑ 96NewJerCB-3
❑ 97PeoChi-3
❑ 98PriWilCQ-16
Britt, Doug
❑ 78ChaPirT-1
❑ 81BufBisT-3
❑ 82DayBeaAT-10
Britt, Ken
❑ 92HamRedC-16
❑ 92HamRedF-1581
❑ 93GleFalRC-8
❑ 93GleFalRF-3994
Britt, Patrick
❑ 87ModA'sC-2
❑ 87ModA'sP-21
Britt, Stephan
❑ 92DavLipB-5
❑ 92DavLipB-23
Brittain, Grant
❑ 90IdaFalBP-3251
❑ 90ProAaA-198
❑ 91MacBraC-17
❑ 91MacBraP-870
❑ 92DurBulC-10
❑ 92DurBulTI-9
Brittan, Corey
❑ 96PitMetB-7
❑ 97St.LucM-3
❑ 98St.LucMM-30
Britton, James Allan
❑ 64Top-94
❑ 64TopVen-94
❑ 68BraPos-5
❑ 68OPC-76
❑ 68Top-76
❑ 68TopVen-76
❑ 69OPC-154
❑ 69Top-154
❑ 69TopFou-3
❑ 70Top-646
❑ 71OPC-699
❑ 71Top-699
❑ 72MilBra-50
Britton, Jimmy W.
❑ 72OPC-351
❑ 72Top-351
Brixey, Dustin
❑ 95SprSulTI-3
❑ 96WilBluRB-23
❑ 97WicWra-12
Brizzolara, Tony
❑ 79RicBraT-25
❑ 80OPC-86
❑ 80RicBraT-7
❑ 80Top-156
❑ 80VenLeaS-108
❑ 81RicBraT-2
❑ 82RicBraT-2A
❑ 82RicBraT-2B
❑ 83RicBraT-2
❑ 84RicBraT-9
❑ 85IntLeaAT-11
❑ 85RicBraT-1
❑ 86BufBisP-5
❑ 90RicBra2ATI-5
Broaca, Johnny
❑ 34BatR31-192
❑ 72TCMthe3-5
❑ 75YanDyn1T-4
❑ 92ConTSN-517
❑ 94ConTSN-995
❑ 94ConTSNB-995
Broach, Donald
❑ 93PriRedC-2
❑ 93PriRedF-4191
❑ 94BilMusF-3681
❑ 94BilMusSP-10
❑ 96ChaLooB-8
Broadfoot, Scott
❑ 87EriCarP-15
❑ 88St.PetCS-2
❑ 89SprCarB-6
Broas, Rick
❑ 77NewCoPT-3
Broberg, Pete
❑ 71SenTealW-5
❑ 72OPC-64
❑ 72RanTeal-4
❑ 72Top-64
❑ 73Kel2D-41
❑ 73OPC-162
❑ 73RanTeal-5
❑ 73Top-162
❑ 74OPC-425
❑ 74Top-425
❑ 75OPC-542
❑ 75Top-542
❑ 75TopMin-542
❑ 76BreA&P-2
❑ 76CubTri-3
❑ 76Hos-74
❑ 76OPC-39
❑ 76SSP-245
❑ 76Top-39
❑ 76VenLeaS-29
❑ 77Hos-145
❑ 77OPC-55
❑ 77Top-409
❑ 78Top-722
❑ 79OPC-301
❑ 79Top-578
❑ 89TopSenL-87
❑ 93RanKee-5
❑ 94BreMilB-287
Brocail, Doug
❑ 86SpoIndC-162
❑ 87ChaRaiP-23
❑ 88ChaRaiP-1211
❑ 89WicStaR-13
❑ 89WicWraR-28
❑ 90WicWraRD-3
❑ 91LinDriAA-602
❑ 91WicWraLD-602
❑ 91WicWraP-2590
❑ 91WicWraRD-1
❑ 92DonRoo-16
❑ 92LasVegSF-2789
❑ 92LasVegSS-226
❑ 92SkyAAAF-110
❑ 93Don-418
❑ 93FleFinE-135
❑ 93LasVegSF-937
❑ 93Top-821
❑ 93TopGol-821
❑ 93TopInaM-821
❑ 93TopInaR-821
❑ 93TopMic-821
❑ 94Don-615
❑ 94Fle-657
❑ 94Lea-165
❑ 94Pac-518
❑ 94PadMot-25
❑ 94Top-579
❑ 94TopGol-579
❑ 94TopSpa-579
❑ 94TriPla-164
❑ 95AstMot-19
❑ 95FleUpd-139
❑ 96AstMot-20
❑ 96ColCho-358
❑ 96ColChoGS-358
❑ 96ColChoSS-358
❑ 96FleUpd-U138
❑ 96FleUpdTC-U138
❑ 96LeaSigEA-18
❑ 97Fle-556
❑ 97FleTif-556
❑ 97PacPriGotD-GD149
❑ 98PacOnl-264
❑ 98PacOnlR-264
❑ 98PacOnlWC-264
❑ 99Fle-347
❑ 99FleSta9-347
❑ 99FleWarT-347
Brock, Chris
❑ 92IdaFalGF-3503
❑ 92IdaFalGSP-19
❑ 93MacBraC-3
❑ 93MacBraF-1392
❑ 94ExcFS7-152
❑ 94GreBraF-406
❑ 94GreBraTI-7
❑ 95RicBraRC-2
❑ 95RicBraTI-2
❑ 96RicBraB-8
❑ 96RicBraRC-6
❑ 96RicBraUB-5
❑ 97RicBra-6
❑ 98FreGriG-4
Brock, Don
❑ 88PocGiaP-2073
❑ 89SanJosGB-6
❑ 89SanJosGCLC-210
❑ 89SanJosGP-442
❑ 89SanJosGS-3
❑ 90SanJosGB-18
❑ 90SanJosGCLC-50
❑ 90SanJosGP-2004
❑ 90SanJosGS-3
Brock, Greg (Gregory Allen)
❑ 82AlbDukTc-15
❑ 83DodPol-17
❑ 83DodPos-2
❑ 83Don-579
❑ 83Fle-203
❑ 83SevCoi-12
❑ 83TopTra-14T
❑ 84DodPol-9
❑ 84Don-296
❑ 84Fle-98
❑ 84Nes792-555
❑ 84OPC-242
❑ 84Top-555
❑ 84TopSti-376
❑ 84TopTif-555
❑ 85AllGamPI-91
❑ 85DodCokP-6
❑ 85Fle-368
❑ 85OPC-242
❑ 85Top-753
❑ 85TopMin-753
❑ 85TopTif-753
❑ 86BasStaB-16
❑ 86DodCokP-4
❑ 86DodPol-9
❑ 86DodUniOP-2
❑ 86Don-296
❑ 86Fle-125
❑ 86OPC-368
❑ 86Top-368
❑ 86TopSti-67
❑ 86TopTif-368
❑ 87BrePol-9
❑ 87BreTeal-2
❑ 87DonOpeD-50
❑ 87Fle-437
❑ 87FleGlo-437
❑ 87FleUpd-9
❑ 87FleUpdG-9
❑ 87OPC-26
❑ 87Top-26
❑ 87TopSti-68
❑ 87TopTif-26
❑ 87TopTra-9T
❑ 87TopTraT-9T
❑ 88BrePol-9
❑ 88BreTeal-6
❑ 88Don-337
❑ 88DonBasB-71
❑ 88Fle-158
❑ 88FleGlo-158
❑ 88Lea-148
❑ 88OPC-212
❑ 88PanSti-121
❑ 88Sco-234
❑ 88ScoGlo-234
❑ 88Spo-184
❑ 88StaLinBre-3
❑ 88Top-212
❑ 88TopBig-217
❑ 88TopTif-212
❑ 89Bow-143
❑ 89BowTif-143
❑ 89BreGar-11
❑ 89BrePol-9
❑ 89BreYea-9
❑ 89Don-57
❑ 89DonBasB-239
❑ 89Fle-181
❑ 89FleGlo-181
❑ 89OPC-163
❑ 89PanSti-371
❑ 89Sco-307
❑ 89Top-517
❑ 89TopBig-100
❑ 89TopSti-201
❑ 89TopTif-517
❑ 89UppDec-543
❑ 90Bow-395
❑ 90BowTif-395
❑ 90BreMilB-2
❑ 90DodTar-78
❑ 90Don-293
❑ 90DonBesA-142
❑ 90Fle-318
❑ 90FleCan-318
❑ 90Lea-454
❑ 90OPC-139
❑ 90PanSti-104
❑ 90PubIntS-492
❑ 90Sco-485
❑ 90Top-139
❑ 90TopBig-47
❑ 90TopSti-208
❑ 90TopTif-139
❑ 90UppDec-514
❑ 91Bow-41
❑ 91BrePol-4
❑ 91Don-572
❑ 91Fle-577
❑ 91OPC-663
❑ 91PanFreS-204
❑ 91RedFolS-12
❑ 91Sco-522
❑ 91StaClu-269
❑ 91Top-663
❑ 91TopDesS-663
❑ 91TopMic-663
❑ 91TopTif-663
❑ 91Ult-172
❑ 91UppDec-289
❑ 94BreMilB-288
Brock, Jim
❑ 89AriStaB-4
❑ 97AriStaBG-7
Brock, John Roy
❑ 98SouBenSHM-8
Brock, Lou (Louis Clark)
❑ 62Top-387
❑ 63CubJayP-3
❑ 63Top-472
❑ 64CubJayP-3
❑ 64Top-29
❑ 64TopCoi-97
❑ 64TopVen-29
❑ 65CarTeal-4
❑ 65Top-540
❑ 66CarTeal-1
❑ 66OPC-125
❑ 66Top-125
❑ 66TopVen-125
❑ 67OPC-63
❑ 67Top-63
❑ 67Top-285
❑ 67TopVen-307
❑ 68AtlOilPBCC-7
❑ 68Baz-15
❑ 68OPC-151
❑ 68Top-151
❑ 68Top-372
❑ 68Top-520
❑ 68TopVen-151
❑ 69KelPin-4
❑ 69MilBra-40
❑ 69MLBOffS-209
❑ 69MLBPin-36
❑ 69NabTeaF-3
❑ 69OPC-85
❑ 69OPC-165
❑ 69Top-85
❑ 69Top-165
❑ 69Top-428
❑ 69TopFou-4
❑ 69TopSta-112
❑ 69TopTeaP-18
❑ 69TraSta-31
❑ 70CarTeal-4
❑ 70DayDaiNM-88
❑ 70Kel-44
❑ 70MilBra-2
❑ 70MLBOffS-135
❑ 70OPC-330
❑ 70Top-330
❑ 70TopPos-4
❑ 70TopSup-11
❑ 71CarTeal-5
❑ 71CarTeal-5
❑ 71Kel-17
❑ 71MilDud-37
❑ 71MLBOffS-268
❑ 71OPC-625
❑ 71Top-625
❑ 71TopCoi-87
❑ 71TopGreM-27
❑ 71TopSup-25
❑ 72CarTeal-2
❑ 72Kel-48
❑ 72MilBra-51
❑ 72OPC-200
❑ 72SevTraC-8
❑ 72Top-200
❑ 73Kel2D-40
❑ 73LinPor-165
❑ 73OPC-64

❑ 73OPC-320
❑ 73SevTraC-9
❑ 73Top-64
❑ 73Top-320
❑ 73TopCanL-8
❑ 74GreHeroBP-2
❑ 74GreHeroBP-6
❑ 74OPC-60
❑ 74OPC-204
❑ 74Top-60
❑ 74Top-204
❑ 74TopDecE-20
❑ 74TopSta-111
❑ 75Hos-23
❑ 75HosTwi-23
❑ 75Kel-39
❑ 75OPC-2
❑ 75OPC-309
❑ 75OPC-540
❑ 75St.LouCP-2
❑ 75Top-2
❑ 75Top-309
❑ 75Top-540
❑ 75TopMin-2
❑ 75TopMin-309
❑ 75TopMin-540
❑ 76BlaDis-5
❑ 76BucDis-5
❑ 76CarDis-5
❑ 76CooPapB-2
❑ 76CraDis-5
❑ 76DailsID-5
❑ 76Hos-7
❑ 76HosTwi-7
❑ 76IsaDis-5
❑ 76Kel-40
❑ 76LauDiaJ-14
❑ 76OPC-10
❑ 76OPC-197
❑ 76OrbDis-5
❑ 76RedBarD-5
❑ 76SafDis-5
❑ 76SSP-275
❑ 76SSP-590
❑ 76St.LouCP-2
❑ 76Top-10
❑ 76Top-197
❑ 76TowCluD-5
❑ 77BurCheD-15
❑ 77Car5-2
❑ 77CarTeal-2
❑ 77ChiWilD-4
❑ 77DailsID-4
❑ 77DetCaeD-4
❑ 77GalGloG-269
❑ 77HolInnD-4
❑ 77Hos-32
❑ 77MSADis-4
❑ 77OPC-51
❑ 77RCColC-10
❑ 77SagDis-4
❑ 77sDis-4
❑ 77Spo-2416
❑ 77Top-355
❑ 77TopCloS-8
❑ 77WenDis-4
❑ 77ZipDis-4
❑ 78CarTeal-2
❑ 78Kel-7
❑ 78OPC-204
❑ 78OPC-236
❑ 78SagDis-6
❑ 78TasDis-6
❑ 78Top-1
❑ 78Top-170
❑ 78WifBalD-8
❑ 79BasPat-8
❑ 79Car5-2
❑ 79OPC-350
❑ 79Top-415
❑ 79Top-665
❑ 80MarExh-6
❑ 80PerHaloFP-190
❑ 80PerHaloFPS-55
❑ 80SSPHOF-195
❑ 80Top-1
❑ 81TCM60I-341
❑ 82BasCarN-9
❑ 82BasCarN-12
❑ 82TCMGreH-7
❑ 83KelCerB-13
❑ 84OCoandSI-75
❑ 84SpoDesPW-28
❑ 85DalNatCC-8
❑ 85Woo-5
❑ 86SpoDecG-59
❑ 86SpoDesJM-2
❑ 86TCMSupS-27
❑ 87K-M-13
❑ 88HouSho-10
❑ 89KahCoo-3
❑ 89Top-662
❑ 89TopBasT-26
❑ 89TopTif-662
❑ 90HOFStiB-86
❑ 90PacLeg-12
❑ 90PerGreM-66
❑ 90SweBasG-71
❑ 91Col-11
❑ 91Kel3D-10
❑ 91KelStaU-4
❑ 91LinDri-24
❑ 91SweBasG-13
❑ 91UppDec-636
❑ 91UppDec-636A
❑ 91UppDecHoB5-1
❑ 91UppDecS-6
❑ 91UppDecS-11
❑ 91UppDecS-14
❑ 91UppDecS-15
❑ 92ActPacA-2
❑ 92ActPacA2-2G
❑ 92CarMcD-30
❑ 92MVP-12
❑ 92MVP2H-6
❑ 92UppDecF-48
❑ 92UppDecFG-48
❑ 92UppDecHH-HI2
❑ 92UppDecHoB-H6
❑ 92UppDecHoB-H8
❑ 92UppDecHoB-AU6
❑ 92UppDecS-11
❑ 92UppDecS-33
❑ 92UppDecS-35
❑ 93ActPacAC-2
❑ 93FroRowB-1
❑ 93FroRowB-2
❑ 93FroRowB-3
❑ 93FroRowB-4
❑ 93FroRowB-5
❑ 93MetIma-5
❑ 93TedWil-86
❑ 93TedWilLC-2
❑ 93UppDecS-26
❑ 93Yoo-3
❑ 94UppDecAH-3
❑ 94UppDecAH-79
❑ 94UppDecAH-176
❑ 94UppDecAH-220
❑ 94UppDecAH1-3
❑ 94UppDecAH1-79
❑ 94UppDecAH1-176
❑ 94UppDecAH1-220
❑ 94UppDecS-2
❑ 97DonSigSS-5
❑ 97SpollICC-3
❑ 97St.VinHHS-3
❑ 98FanLouB-1
❑ 98FanLouB-2
❑ 98FanLouB-3
❑ 98FanLouB-4
❑ 98FanLouB-5
❑ 98SpollIAuto-1
❑ 98SpollITaN-6
❑ 98SpollITaNC-C1
❑ 98SpollITaNEE-6
❑ 98SpollITaNGS-17
❑ 98SpollIWSF-6
❑ 98SpollIWSFAE-6
❑ 98SpollIWSFAEG-6
❑ 98SpollIWSFEE-6
❑ 98SpollIWSFFE-6
❑ 98UppDecR-78
❑ 98UppDecRSotT-LB
❑ 99SpollIGotG-43
❑ 99SpollIGotGA-11
❑ 99SpollIGotGC-16

Brock, Norman
❑ 86FloStaLAP-10
❑ 86OscAstP-1
❑ 87ColAstP-24
❑ 88ColAstB-27
❑ 89CedRapRB-18
❑ 89CedRapRP-938
❑ 89CedRapRS-2

Brock, Russell
❑ 91SouOreAC-10
❑ 91SouOreAP-3832
❑ 92ProFS7-136
❑ 92RenSilSCLC-46
❑ 92StaCluD-20
❑ 93ModA'sC-4
❑ 93ModA'sF-790
❑ 94ExcFS7-118
❑ 94HunStaF-1324
❑ 94TacTigF-3167
❑ 95EdmTraTI-3

Brock, Tarrik
❑ 91BriTigC-6
❑ 91Cla/Bes-407
❑ 91FroRowDP-52
❑ 91FroRowDPG-52
❑ 91FroRowDPS-52
❑ 91HigSchPLS-8
❑ 92Bow-345
❑ 92FayGenC-6
❑ 92FayGenF-2180
❑ 92StaCluD-21
❑ 92UppDecML-189
❑ 93FayGenC-5
❑ 93FayGenF-140
❑ 94FloStaLAF-FSL13
❑ 94LakTigC-1
❑ 94LakTigF-3048
❑ 96LakTigB-9
❑ 97LanJet-8
❑ 98OrlRayM-3

Brocker, Gene (John)
❑ 49SomandK-26

Brockett, Lew
❑ 09ColChiE-35
❑ 11HelSta-39
❑ 11PinT-5-801
❑ 12ColRedB-35
❑ 12ColTinT-35
❑ 12ImpTobC-55

Brocki, Mike
❑ 87SanBerSP-16
❑ 88SanBerSB-26
❑ 88SanBerSCLC-40
❑ 89WilBilP-629
❑ 91PacSenL-92

Brocklander, Fred
❑ 88T/MUmp-38
❑ 89T/MUmp-36
❑ 90T/MUmp-34

Brockway, Kevin
❑ 86TriTriC-188

Broderick, Stan
❑ 83QuaCitCT-24

Brodie, John
❑ 74NewYorNTDiS-38

Brodie, Steve (Walter Scott)
❑ 94OriTeal-2

Brodowski, Dick
❑ 52Top-404
❑ 53Top-69
❑ 54Top-221
❑ 55Top-171
❑ 56Top-157
❑ 59Ind-1
❑ 59Kah-4
❑ 59Top-371
❑ 83TopRep5-404
❑ 91TopArc1-69
❑ 94TopArc1-221
❑ 94TopArc1G-221

Broersma, Eric
❑ 82OrlTwi8SCT-13
❑ 82OrlTwiT-3
❑ 83OrlTwiT-19
❑ 83TolMudHT-26
❑ 84TolMudHT-17
❑ 85TolMudHT-2
❑ 86TolMudHP-3
❑ 87TacTigP-11

Broglio, Ernie
❑ 59Top-296
❑ 60Lea-41
❑ 60Top-16
❑ 60TopVen-16
❑ 61Baz-16
❑ 61CarJayP-2
❑ 61Pos-179A
❑ 61Pos-179B
❑ 61Top-45
❑ 61Top-47
❑ 61Top-49
❑ 61Top-420
❑ 61Top-451
❑ 62CarJayP-2
❑ 62Jel-164
❑ 62Pos-164
❑ 62PosCan-164
❑ 62SalPlaC-132
❑ 62ShiPlaC-132
❑ 62Top-507
❑ 63CarJayP-3
❑ 63CarJayP-4
❑ 63Jel-165
❑ 63Pos-165
❑ 63Top-313
❑ 64Top-59
❑ 64TopCoi-95
❑ 64TopSta-77
❑ 64TopStaU-11
❑ 64TopVen-59
❑ 65CubJayP-4
❑ 65Top-565
❑ 66CubTeal-5
❑ 66Top-423
❑ 75OakOak2A-7
❑ 78TCM60I-18

Brogna, Dennis
❑ 81WatIndT-3
❑ 83MidCubT-6
❑ 84MidCubT-13
❑ 92MyrBeaHC-30
❑ 93HagSunC-28
❑ 94DunBluJC-30
❑ 95DunBluJTI-2
❑ 96DunBluJB-30
❑ 96DunBluJTI-4

Brogna, Rico
❑ 88BriTigP-1885
❑ 89Bow-102
❑ 89BowTif-102
❑ 89LakTigS-3
❑ 90Bow-351
❑ 90BowTif-351
❑ 90EasLeaAP-EL4
❑ 90LonTigP-1275
❑ 90ProAaA-30
❑ 91Bow-134
❑ 91Cla2-T12
❑ 91ClaGam-197
❑ 91LeaGolR-BC11
❑ 91LeaGolRNV-275
❑ 91LinDriAAA-580
❑ 91Sco-741
❑ 91TolMudHLD-580
❑ 91TolMudHP-1939
❑ 91UppDec-73
❑ 92Bow-256
❑ 92DonRoo-17
❑ 92FleUpd-19
❑ 92OPC-126
❑ 92ProFS7-63
❑ 92SkyAAAF-258
❑ 92TolMudHF-1049
❑ 92TolMudHS-578
❑ 92Top-126
❑ 92TopGol-126
❑ 92TopGolW-126
❑ 92TopMic-126
❑ 92UppDec-74
❑ 93ClaFS7-170
❑ 93Don-41
❑ 93FleMajLP-A15
❑ 93Pin-240
❑ 93Sco-114
❑ 93ScoBoyoS-17
❑ 93StaClu-530
❑ 93StaCluFDI-530
❑ 93StaCluMOP-530
❑ 93TolMudHF-1657
❑ 93Top-598
❑ 93TopGol-598
❑ 93TopInaM-598
❑ 93TopInaR-598
❑ 93TopMic-598
❑ 93UppDec-386
❑ 93UppDecGold-386
❑ 94FleUpd-156
❑ 94LeaLimR-2
❑ 94NorTidF-2925
❑ 95Baz-129
❑ 95Bow-414
❑ 95ColCho-314
❑ 95ColChoGS-314
❑ 95ColChoSS-314
❑ 95Don-525
❑ 95DonPreP-525
❑ 95DonTopotO-289
❑ 95Emo-159
❑ 95Fin-14
❑ 95FinRef-14
❑ 95Fla-170
❑ 95Fle-366
❑ 95FleRooS-2
❑ 95Lea-83
❑ 95LeaLim-162
❑ 95MetColP-8
❑ 95Pac-278
❑ 95Pin-265
❑ 95PinArtP-265
❑ 95PinFan-27
❑ 95PinMusC-265
❑ 95Sel-148
❑ 95SelArtP-148
❑ 95SelCer-31
❑ 95SelCerMG-31
❑ 95SigRoo-10
❑ 95SigRooSig-10
❑ 95SP-79
❑ 95Spo-103
❑ 95SpoArtP-103
❑ 95SPSil-79
❑ 95StaClu-170
❑ 95StaCluFDI-170
❑ 95StaCluMOP-170
❑ 95StaCluSTWS-170
❑ 95StaCluVR-88
❑ 95StaCluVRMO-88
❑ 95Stu-156
❑ 95Sum-69
❑ 95SumNthD-69
❑ 95Top-490
❑ 95TopCyb-281
❑ 95UC3-31
❑ 95UC3ArtP-31
❑ 95Ult-196
❑ 95UltGolM-196
❑ 95UppDec-121
❑ 95UppDecED-121
❑ 95UppDecEDG-121
❑ 95Zen-88
❑ 96Baz-50
❑ 96Bow-107
❑ 96BowFoi-107
❑ 96ColCho-224
❑ 96ColCho-397
❑ 96ColChoGS-224
❑ 96ColChoGS-397
❑ 96ColChoSS-224
❑ 96ColChoSS-397
❑ 96Don-274
❑ 96DonPreP-274
❑ 96EmoXL-228
❑ 96Fin-B116
❑ 96FinRef-B116
❑ 96Fla-316
❑ 96Fle-474
❑ 96FleTeaL-23
❑ 96FleTif-474
❑ 96Lea-129
❑ 96LeaPre-2
❑ 96LeaPreP-2
❑ 96LeaPrePB-129
❑ 96LeaPrePG-129
❑ 96LeaPrePS-129
❑ 96LeaSig-8
❑ 96LeaSigA-35
❑ 96LeaSigAG-35
❑ 96LeaSigAS-35
❑ 96LeaSigPPG-8
❑ 96LeaSigPPP-8
❑ 96MetKah-5
❑ 96MetKah-3
❑ 96MetUni-198
❑ 96MetUniP-198
❑ 96Pac-135
❑ 96PacPri-P46
❑ 96PacPriG-P46
❑ 96PanSti-26
❑ 96PinAfi-125
❑ 96PinAfiAP-125
❑ 96ProSta-74
❑ 96Sco-48
❑ 96ScoDugC-A41
❑ 96ScoDugCAP-A41
❑ 96Sel-46
❑ 96SelArtP-46
❑ 96SelCer-36
❑ 96SelCerAP-36
❑ 96SelCerCB-36
❑ 96SelCerCR-36
❑ 96SelCerMB-36
❑ 96SelCerMG-36
❑ 96SelCerMR-36
❑ 96SelTeaN-21
❑ 96SP-124
❑ 96Spo-32
❑ 96SpoArtP-32
❑ 96SpoDouT-12
❑ 96StaClu-367
❑ 96StaCluEPB-367
❑ 96StaCluEPG-367
❑ 96StaCluEPS-367
❑ 96StaCluMOP-367
❑ 96Stu-99
❑ 96StuPrePB-99
❑ 96StuPrePG-99
❑ 96StuPrePS-99
❑ 96Sum-143
❑ 96SumAbo&B-143
❑ 96SumArtP-143
❑ 96SumFoi-143
❑ 96Top-259
❑ 96TopChr-103
❑ 96TopChrR-103
❑ 96TopGal-122
❑ 96TopGalPPI-122
❑ 96Ult-240
❑ 96UltGolM-240
❑ 96UppDec-141
❑ 96Zen-17
❑ 96ZenArtP-17
❑ 96ZenMoz-24
❑ 97Bow-283
❑ 97BowInt-283
❑ 97Cir-29
❑ 97CirRav-29
❑ 97ColCho-420
❑ 97Don-153
❑ 97DonGolPP-153
❑ 97DonSilPP-153
❑ 97Fle-599
❑ 97FleTif-599
❑ 97NewPin-150
❑ 97NewPinAP-150
❑ 97NewPinMC-150
❑ 97NewPinPP-150
❑ 97Pac-360
❑ 97PacLigB-360
❑ 97PacSil-360
❑ 97PhiCopQ-4
❑ 97PhiTeal-2
❑ 97Pin-115
❑ 97PinArtP-PP115
❑ 97PinMusC-115
❑ 97PinPrePla-115
❑ 97Sco-60
❑ 97Sco-368
❑ 97ScoArtPWB-60
❑ 97ScoArtPWB-368
❑ 97ScoPreS-60
❑ 97ScoResC-368
❑ 97ScoShoS-60
❑ 97ScoShoS-368
❑ 97ScoShoSAP-60
❑ 97ScoShoSAP-368
❑ 97Top-289
❑ 97Ult-382
❑ 97UltGolME-382
❑ 97UltPlaME-382
❑ 98Bow-239
❑ 98BowChr-239
❑ 98BowChrGA-239
❑ 98BowChrGAR-239
❑ 98BowChrI-239
❑ 98BowChrIR-239
❑ 98BowChrR-239
❑ 98BowGolA-239
❑ 98BowInt-239
❑ 98CirThu-14
❑ 98CirThuRav-14
❑ 98CirThuSupRav-14
❑ 98ColCho-206
❑ 98Fin-155
❑ 98FinNo--155
❑ 98FinNo-R-155
❑ 98FinRef-155
❑ 98Fle-118
❑ 98Pac-377
❑ 98PacOme-181
❑ 98PacOmeR-181
❑ 98PacOnl-557
❑ 98PacOnlR-557
❑ 98PacOnlWC-557
❑ 98PacPlaB-377
❑ 98PacRedT-377
❑ 98PacSil-377
❑ 98PhiTeal-7
❑ 98SPxFin-114
❑ 98SPxFinR-114
❑ 98SPxFinS-114
❑ 98StaCluFDI-205
❑ 98StaCluI-205
❑ 98StaCluOneK-205
❑ 98StaCluPP-205
❑ 98Top-123
❑ 98TopChr-123
❑ 98TopChrR-123
❑ 98TopDevR-123

❑ 98TopDia-123
❑ 98TopMiniC-123
❑ 98Ult-391
❑ 98UltGolM-391
❑ 98UltMas-391
❑ 98UltPlaM-391
❑ 98UppDec-185
❑ 98UppDecSF-99
❑ 99199Fin-17
❑ 99FinGolRef-17
❑ 99FinRef-17
❑ 99FlaShoLeg1-138
❑ 99FlaShoLeg2-138
❑ 99FlaShoLeg3-138
❑ 99FlaShoLegM1-138
❑ 99FlaShoLegM2-138
❑ 99FlaShoLegM3-138
❑ 99FlaShoR1-138
❑ 99FlaShoR2-138
❑ 99FlaShoR3-138
❑ 99Fle-134
❑ 99FleSta9-134
❑ 99FleWarT-134
❑ 99MetUni-6
❑ 99MetUniGM-6
❑ 99MetUniPMG-6
❑ 99Pac-324
❑ 99PacPar-177
❑ 99PacParC-177
❑ 99PacParG-177
❑ 99PacParHoloGold-177
❑ 99PacParHS-177
❑ 99PacParOD-177
❑ 99PacParPB-177
❑ 99PacParRed-177
❑ 99PacPlaB-324
❑ 99PacRed-324
❑ 99SkyPre-13
❑ 99SkyPreR-13
❑ 99SkyThu-174
❑ 99SkyThuRant-174
❑ 99SkyThuRave-174
❑ 99SPSig-147
❑ 99StaClu-43
❑ 99StaCluFDI-43
❑ 99StaCluOoaK-43
❑ 99StaCluPP-43
❑ 99ThuSkySupR-174
❑ 99Top-321
❑ 99TopChr-321
❑ 99TopChrR-321
❑ 99TopMVPP-321
❑ 99Ult-92
❑ 99UltGolM-92
❑ 99UltMas-92
❑ 99UltPlaM-92
❑ 99UppDec-171
❑ 99UppDecEL1-171
❑ 99UppDecEL2-171
❑ 99UppDecM-160
❑ 99UppDecMGS-160
❑ 99UppDecMHFS-160
❑ 99UppDecMP-160
❑ 99UppDecMSS-160
❑ 99Vic-296

Brohamer, Jack (John A.)
❑ 73IndArtTC-2
❑ 73IndTeal-5
❑ 73OPC-181
❑ 73Top-181
❑ 74OPC-586
❑ 74Top-586
❑ 75CleIndP-6
❑ 75IndJB R-2
❑ 75OPC-552
❑ 75Top-552
❑ 75TopMin-552
❑ 76OPC-618
❑ 76SSP-518
❑ 76Top-618
❑ 76TopTra-618T
❑ 77BurCheD-78
❑ 77Top-293
❑ 77WhiSoxT-4
❑ 78PapGinD-3
❑ 78SSP270-166
❑ 78Top-416
❑ 79OPC-25
❑ 79Top-63
❑ 80Top-349
❑ 81Fle-393
❑ 81Top-462

Brohawn, Troy
❑ 94SigRooDP-80
❑ 94SigRooDPS-80
❑ 94StaCluDP-56
❑ 94StaCluDPFDI-56
❑ 97ShrCap-7
❑ 97ShrCapB-7
❑ 98FreGriG-5

Brohm, Jeff
❑ 90BurIndP-3019
❑ 91WatIndC-24
❑ 91WatIndP-3379

Bromby, Scott
❑ 88RocExpLC-3
❑ 89RocExpLC-5

Bromley, Jack
❑ 15Zee-27
❑ 18Zee-37
❑ 20Zee-78
❑ 20Zee-79
❑ 21Zee-90
❑ 22Zee-76

Bronkey, Jeff
❑ 87OrlTwiP-21
❑ 88VisOakCLC-166
❑ 88VisOakP-95
❑ 89OrlTwiB-12
❑ 89OrlTwiP-1337
❑ 91LinDriAAA-305
❑ 91OklCit8LD-305
❑ 91OklCit8P-172
❑ 92TulDriF-2687
❑ 92TulDriS-603
❑ 93FleFinE-277
❑ 93OklCit8F-1618
❑ 93RanKee-396
❑ 94BreMilB-289
❑ 94BrePol-3
❑ 94BreTeal-2
❑ 94Fla-64
❑ 94FleExtB-99
❑ 94FleUpd-52
❑ 94Pac-609
❑ 94TopGol-396

Bronson, Aaron
❑ 93DavLipB-25

Bronson, Ben
❑ 97WilBluR-11

Brookens, Andy
❑ 91EugEmeC-3
❑ 91EugEmeP-3731

Brookens, Casey
❑ 97RocCub-10

Brookens, Tim
❑ 75AndRanT-8

Brookens, Tom (Thomas D.)
❑ 77EvaTriT-4
❑ 80Top-416
❑ 81Don-6
❑ 81Fle-473
❑ 81Top-251
❑ 82Don-202
❑ 82Fle-263
❑ 82OPC-11
❑ 82Top-753
❑ 83Don-454
❑ 83Fle-327A
❑ 83Fle-327B
❑ 83FleSti-250
❑ 83TigPos-5
❑ 83Top-119
❑ 84Don-578
❑ 84Fle-78
❑ 84Nes792-14
❑ 84TigTeal-8
❑ 84TigWavP-8
❑ 84Top-14
❑ 84TopTif-14
❑ 85Don-593
❑ 85Fle-4
❑ 85TigCaiD-4
❑ 85TigWen-5
❑ 85Top-512
❑ 85TopTif-512
❑ 86Don-537
❑ 86Fle-223
❑ 86OPC-286
❑ 86TigCaiD-2
❑ 86Top-643
❑ 86TopTif-643
❑ 87Don-296
❑ 87Fle-145
❑ 87FleGlo-145
❑ 87OPC-232
❑ 87TigCaiD-1
❑ 87TigCok-17
❑ 87Top-713
❑ 87TopTif-713
❑ 88Don-107
❑ 88Fle-53
❑ 88FleGlo-53
❑ 88PanSti-93
❑ 88Sco-233
❑ 88ScoGlo-233
❑ 88StaLinTi-3
❑ 88TigPep-16
❑ 88TigPol-4
❑ 88Top-474
❑ 88TopTif-474
❑ 89Don-508
❑ 89DonTra-53
❑ 89Fle-130A
❑ 89Fle-130B
❑ 89FleGlo-130
❑ 89OPC-342
❑ 89PanSti-340
❑ 89Sco-269
❑ 89ScoRoo-73T
❑ 89Top-342
❑ 89TopSti-278
❑ 89TopTif-342
❑ 89UppDec-106
❑ 89YanScoNW-21
❑ 90Fle-439
❑ 90FleCan-439
❑ 90IndTeal-7
❑ 90Sco-297
❑ 90UppDec-138
❑ 91Don-658
❑ 91Fle-362
❑ 91OPC-268
❑ 91Sco-106
❑ 91Top-268
❑ 91TopDesS-268
❑ 91TopMic-268
❑ 91TopTif-268
❑ 91UppDec-102
❑ 92YanWIZ8-18

Brooks, Ali
❑ 97EriSeaWB-4

Brooks, Anthony
❑ 97DanBraB-12
❑ 98MacBraM-3

Brooks, Antone
❑ 95EugEmeTI-12
❑ 96DanBraB-8
❑ 96MacBraB-3
❑ 97GreBraG-3
❑ 98GreBraG-4

Brooks, Billy
❑ 87BakDodP-6
❑ 88BakDodCLC-250

Brooks, Bob
❑ 89CalLeaA-54
❑ 90CalLeaACLC-33
❑ 91CalLeLA-28

Brooks, Bobby (Robert)
❑ 70OPC-381
❑ 70Top-381
❑ 71OPC-633
❑ 71Top-633

Brooks, Brian Todd
❑ 87ChaRaiP-1
❑ 88RivRedWCLC-216
❑ 88RivRedWP-1410
❑ 89WicUpdR-12
❑ 89WicWraR-25

Brooks, Clarence
❑ 12Zee-3
❑ 13Zee-2
❑ 14Zee-4
❑ 15Zee-5
❑ 16Zee-101
❑ 18Zee-76
❑ 19Zee-83

Brooks, Craig
❑ 81BriRedST-1

Brooks, Damon
❑ 86AubAstP-6
❑ 87AubAstP-5

Brooks, Desi
❑ 86LynMetP-3
❑ 87LynMetP-6

Brooks, Eddie
❑ 94SigRooDP-87
❑ 94SigRooDPS-87
❑ 94StaCluDP-62
❑ 94StaCluDPFDI-62
❑ 96LynHilB-3

Brooks, Eric
❑ 89MyrBeaBJP-1460
❑ 91DunBluJC-12
❑ 91DunBluJP-208
❑ 92DunBluJC-4
❑ 92DunBluJF-2002
❑ 93DunBluJC-3
❑ 93DunBluJF-1798
❑ 93DunBluJFFN-3
❑ 94KnoSmoF-1305
❑ 95SyrChiTI-4

Brooks, Harvey
❑ 12HomRunKE-2
❑ 12HomRunKE-19
❑ 12Zee-25

Brooks, Herb
❑ 87SpoCubG-1

Brooks, Hubie (Hubert)
❑ 79JacMetT-3
❑ 80TidTidT-15
❑ 81Top-259
❑ 81TopTra-742
❑ 82Don-476
❑ 82Fle-522
❑ 82FleSta-81
❑ 82Kel-10
❑ 82MetPhoA-5
❑ 82OPC-266
❑ 82Top-246
❑ 82Top-494
❑ 82TopSti-68
❑ 83AllGamPI-118
❑ 83Don-49
❑ 83Fle-539
❑ 83FleSta-23
❑ 83OPC-134
❑ 83Top-134
❑ 83TopSti-261
❑ 84Don-607
❑ 84Fle-582
❑ 84JacMetF-3
❑ 84Nes792-368
❑ 84OPC-368
❑ 84Top-368
❑ 84TopSti-103
❑ 84TopTif-368
❑ 85AllGamPI-110
❑ 85Don-197
❑ 85ExpPos-3
❑ 85Fle-74
❑ 85FleUpd-10
❑ 85Lea-214
❑ 85OPC-222
❑ 85OPCPos-5
❑ 85Top-222
❑ 85TopMin-222
❑ 85TopSti-104
❑ 85TopTif-222
❑ 85TopTifT-9T
❑ 85TopTra-9T
❑ 86Don-55
❑ 86DonHig-15
❑ 86ExpProPa-1
❑ 86ExpProPo-3
❑ 86Fle-244
❑ 86FleLimE-7
❑ 86FleMin-52
❑ 86FleStiC-12
❑ 86GenMilB-6A
❑ 86Lea-44
❑ 86OPC-308
❑ 86Spo-187
❑ 86Top-555
❑ 86TopSti-77
❑ 86TopSup-15
❑ 86TopTat-13
❑ 86TopTif-555
❑ 87Don-17
❑ 87Don-88
❑ 87DonAll-48
❑ 87DonOpeD-91
❑ 87DonSupD-17
❑ 87ExpPos-2
❑ 87Fle-314
❑ 87FleGamW-7
❑ 87FleGlo-314
❑ 87FleLeaL-6
❑ 87FleMin-14
❑ 87FleStiC-16
❑ 87GenMilB-4A
❑ 87HosSti-4
❑ 87KayB-6
❑ 87KraFoo-42
❑ 87Lea-17
❑ 87Lea-142
❑ 87OPC-3
❑ 87RedFolSB-91
❑ 87Spo-18
❑ 87Spo-79
❑ 87Spo-197
❑ 87SpoTeaP-20
❑ 87StuPan-8
❑ 87Top-650
❑ 87TopCoi-27
❑ 87TopGloS-46
❑ 87TopSti-76
❑ 87TopTif-650
❑ 88Don-468
❑ 88DonAll-45
❑ 88DonBasB-12
❑ 88ExpPos-2
❑ 88Fle-179
❑ 88FleGlo-179
❑ 88GreBasS-17
❑ 88Lea-257
❑ 88MSAHosD-5
❑ 88OPC-50
❑ 88PanSti-328
❑ 88Sco-305
❑ 88ScoGlo-305
❑ 88Spo-187
❑ 88StaLinE-1
❑ 88Top-50
❑ 88Top-111
❑ 88TopBig-81
❑ 88TopSti-81
❑ 88TopStiB-10
❑ 88TopTif-50
❑ 88TopTif-111
❑ 88TopUKM-8
❑ 88TopUKMT-8
❑ 89Bow-367
❑ 89BowTif-367
❑ 89Don-220
❑ 89DonBasB-292
❑ 89ExpPos-3
❑ 89Fle-371
❑ 89FleBasM-5
❑ 89FleGlo-371
❑ 89OPC-221
❑ 89PanSti-123
❑ 89RedFolSB-13
❑ 89Sco-53
❑ 89Spo-96
❑ 89Top-485
❑ 89TopBasT-133
❑ 89TopBig-301
❑ 89TopMinL-21
❑ 89TopSti-72
❑ 89TopTif-485
❑ 89TopUKM-8
❑ 89TVSpoM-15
❑ 89UppDec-122
❑ 90Bow-100
❑ 90BowTif-100
❑ 90ClaBlu-129
❑ 90ClaYel-T75
❑ 90DodMot-10
❑ 90DodPol-21
❑ 90Don-130
❑ 90DonBesN-115
❑ 90Fle-341
❑ 90FleCan-341
❑ 90FleUpd-19
❑ 90Lea-16
❑ 90OPC-745
❑ 90PubIntS-169
❑ 90Sco-299
❑ 90ScoRoo-34T
❑ 90Top-745
❑ 90TopBig-262
❑ 90TopSti-77
❑ 90TopTif-745
❑ 90TopTra-14T
❑ 90TopTraT-14T
❑ 90UppDec-197
❑ 90UppDec-791
❑ 91BasBesHM-4
❑ 91Bow-461
❑ 91ClaGam-77
❑ 91Don-349
❑ 91Fle-195
❑ 91FleUpd-100
❑ 91Lea-295
❑ 91MetColP-12
❑ 91MetKah-7
❑ 91MetPerPA-8
❑ 91MetWIZ-52
❑ 91OPC-115
❑ 91OPCPre-15
❑ 91PanFreS-59
❑ 91PanSti-56
❑ 91RedFolS-13
❑ 91Sco-196
❑ 91ScoRoo-5T
❑ 91StaClu-325
❑ 91Top-115
❑ 91TopDesS-115
❑ 91TopMic-115
❑ 91TopTif-115
❑ 91TopTra-14T
❑ 91TopTraT-14T
❑ 91UltUpd-94
❑ 91UppDec-217
❑ 91UppDec-787
❑ 92AngPol-4
❑ 92Bow-97
❑ 92Don-64
❑ 92Fle-496
❑ 92Lea-378
❑ 92LeaBlaG-378
❑ 92OPC-457
❑ 92OPCPre-198
❑ 92PanSti-226
❑ 92Pin-449
❑ 92RedFolS-19
❑ 92Sco-107
❑ 92ScoRoo-69T
❑ 92StaClu-754
❑ 92Stu-142
❑ 92Top-457
❑ 92TopGol-457
❑ 92TopGolW-457
❑ 92TopMic-457
❑ 92TopTra-15T
❑ 92TopTraG-15T
❑ 92Ult-322
❑ 92UppDec-114
❑ 92UppDec-709
❑ 93CadDis-9
❑ 93Don-563
❑ 93RoyStaC-26
❑ 93UppDec-680
❑ 93UppDecGold-680
❑ 94Don-166
❑ 94Fle-151
❑ 94Sco-125
❑ 94ScoGolR-125
❑ 94StaClu-647
❑ 94StaCluFDI-647
❑ 94StaCluGR-647
❑ 94StaCluMOP-647
❑ 97AriStaBG-8

Brooks, Jacob
❑ 98ButCopKG-6

Brooks, Jeff
❑ 98LetBlaDG-5

Brooks, Jerry
❑ 88GreFalDTI-11
❑ 89BakDodCLC-203
❑ 89CalLeaA-18
❑ 90SanAntMGS-6
❑ 91AlbDukLD-2
❑ 91AlbDukP-1153
❑ 91LinDriAAA-2
❑ 91TriA AAGP-AAA1
❑ 92AlbDukF-733
❑ 92AlbDukS-6
❑ 93AlbDukF-1463
❑ 94AlbDukF-854
❑ 95IndIndF-97
❑ 96ChaKniB-10

Brooks, John
❑ 25Exh-19

Brooks, Kevin
❑ 88VirGenS-3

Brooks, Mandy (Jonathan J.)
❑ 29Zee-62

Brooks, Michael
❑ 73TacTwiC-3
❑ 75OklCit8TI-22
❑ 75SanAntBT-4
❑ 76BatRouCT-5
❑ 82RedPioT-1

Brooks, Monte
❑ 87SpoIndP-12
❑ 88ChaRaiP-1204
❑ 89RivRedWB-27
❑ 89RivRedWCLC-10
❑ 89RivRedWP-1417
❑ 90ChaRaiP-2048

Brooks, Rae
❑ 93RocRoyF-718
❑ 94HigDesMC-5
❑ 94HigDesMF-2792

Brooks, Ramy
❑ 90EugEmeGS-3
❑ 91EugEmeC-7
❑ 91EugEmeP-3728
❑ 92EugEmeC-7

❑ 92EugEmeF-3032
❑ 93RocRoyC-4
❑ 95WilBluRTI-22
❑ 96WilBluRB-4
❑ 97WicWra-25
Brooks, Rodney
❑ 88HamRedP-1740
Brooks, Trey
❑ 83MidCubT-16
❑ 84IowCubT-14
❑ 85IowCubT-3
❑ 86IowCubP-4
❑ 86StaoftFT-10
Brooks, Wes
❑ 94LynRedSC-4
❑ 94LynRedSF-1885
❑ 95TreThuTI-7
Broome, Corey
❑ 93NiaFalRF-3392
❑ 94FayGenF-2148
Broome, Curtis
❑ 94HicCraC-6
❑ 94HicCraF-2167
❑ 96PriWilCB-6
Broome, John
❑ 94WilCubC-3
❑ 94WilCubF-3756
Broome, Kim
❑ 89WelPirP-7
Brophy, E.J.
❑ 92MarPhiC-25
❑ 92MarPhiF-3057
❑ 93SpaPhiC-7
❑ 93SpaPhiF-1058
❑ 94ClePhiC-9
❑ 94ClePhiF-2530
❑ 95ScrRedBTI-2
Brosious, Frank
❑ 82BurRanF-8
❑ 82BurRanT-14
Brosius, Scott
❑ 88MadMusP-5
❑ 88MidLeaAGS-50
❑ 89HunStaB-12
❑ 90Bes-74
❑ 90HunStaB-15
❑ 91LinDriAAA-529
❑ 91TacTigLD-529
❑ 91TacTigP-2310
❑ 92AthMot-27
❑ 92Bow-527
❑ 92Cla1-T19
❑ 92Cla2-T5
❑ 92Don-591
❑ 92Fle-671
❑ 92Pin-274
❑ 92Sco-846
❑ 92TacTigF-2508
❑ 92TopDeb91-22
❑ 92Ult-420
❑ 92UppDec-312
❑ 93AthStaC-27
❑ 93Don-419
❑ 93PacSpa-218
❑ 93StaClu-62
❑ 93StaCluFDI-62
❑ 93StaCluMOP-62
❑ 93Top-796
❑ 93TopGol-796
❑ 93TopInaM-796
❑ 93TopInaR-796
❑ 93TopMic-796
❑ 93Ult-603
❑ 93UppDec-681
❑ 93UppDecGold-681
❑ 94A'sMot-26
❑ 94ColC-376
❑ 94ColChoGS-376
❑ 94ColChoSS-376
❑ 94Don-630
❑ 94Fin-396
❑ 94FinRef-396
❑ 94Fla-329
❑ 94Fle-256
❑ 94FleExtB-146
❑ 94Lea-208
❑ 94StaClu-164
❑ 94StaCluFDI-164
❑ 94StaCluGR-164
❑ 94StaCluMOP-164
❑ 94Top-74
❑ 94TopGol-74
❑ 94TopSpa-74
❑ 94UppDec-306
❑ 94UppDecED-306
❑ 95AthMot-27
❑ 95ColCho-126
❑ 95ColChoGS-126
❑ 95ColChoSS-126
❑ 95Don-548
❑ 95DonPreP-548
❑ 95DonTopotO-134
❑ 95Fla-71
❑ 95Fle-242
❑ 95Lea-204
❑ 95Sco-160
❑ 95ScoGolR-160
❑ 95ScoPlaTS-160
❑ 95Top-102
❑ 95Ult-315
❑ 95UltGolM-315
❑ 96A'sMot-7
❑ 96ColCho-239
❑ 96ColChoGS-239
❑ 96ColChoSS-239
❑ 96Don-218
❑ 96DonPreP-218
❑ 96Fla-145
❑ 96Fle-205
❑ 96FleTif-205
❑ 96LeaSigA-36
❑ 96LeaSigAG-36
❑ 96LeaSigAS-36
❑ 96Pac-386
❑ 96Sco-490
❑ 96SP-139
❑ 96StaClu-383
❑ 96StaCluMOP-383
❑ 96Ult-111
❑ 96UltGolM-111
❑ 96UppDec-165
❑ 96ZenMoz-21
❑ 97A'sMot-7
❑ 97Cir-269
❑ 97CirRav-269
❑ 97ColCho-183
❑ 97Don-188
❑ 97DonGolPP-188
❑ 97DonSilPP-188
❑ 97FlaShoLC-112
❑ 97FlaShoLeg0-112
❑ 97FlaShoLeg1-112
❑ 97FlaShoM-A112
❑ 97FlaShoM-B112
❑ 97FlaShoM-C112
❑ 97FlaShoR0-112
❑ 97FlaShoR1-112
❑ 97FlaShoR2-112
❑ 97Fle-186
❑ 97FleTif-186
❑ 97MetUni-128
❑ 97Pac-167
❑ 97PacLigB-167
❑ 97PacSil-167
❑ 97Pin-94
❑ 97PinArtP-PP94
❑ 97PinMusC-94
❑ 97PinPrePla-94
❑ 97Sco-97
❑ 97ScoArtPWB-97
❑ 97ScoPreS-97
❑ 97ScoShoS-97
❑ 97ScoShoSAP-97
❑ 97SpoIll-57
❑ 97SpoIllEE-57
❑ 97StaClu-142
❑ 97StaCluMOP-142
❑ 97Top-457
❑ 97Ult-361
❑ 97UltGolME-361
❑ 97UltPlaME-361
❑ 97UppDec-127
❑ 98Fle-471
❑ 98Pac-163
❑ 98PacOnl-496
❑ 98PacOnlR-496
❑ 98PacOnlWC-496
❑ 98PacPlaB-163
❑ 98PacRedT-163
❑ 98PacSil-163
❑ 98Pin-79
❑ 98PinPreP-79
❑ 98Top-405
❑ 98TopChr-405
❑ 98TopChrR-405
❑ 98TopDevR-405
❑ 98TopDia-405
❑ 98TopMiniC-405
❑ 98Ult-440
❑ 98UltGolM-440
❑ 98UltMas-440
❑ 98UltPlaM-440
❑ 98UppDec-704
❑ 98YanUppD-704
❑ 99199Fin-11
❑ 99E-X Cen-57
❑ 99E-X CenECFut-57
❑ 99E-X CenECNow-57
❑ 99FinGolRef-11
❑ 99FinRef-11
❑ 99FlaShoLeg1-87
❑ 99FlaShoLeg2-87
❑ 99FlaShoLeg3-87
❑ 99FlaShoLegM1-87
❑ 99FlaShoLegM2-87
❑ 99FlaShoLegM3-87
❑ 99FlaShoR1-87
❑ 99FlaShoR2-87
❑ 99FlaShoR3-87
❑ 99Fle-112
❑ 99FleSta9-112
❑ 99FleWarT-112
❑ 99MetUni-143
❑ 99MetUniGM-143
❑ 99MetUniPMG-143
❑ 99PacAur-125
❑ 99PacAurOD-125
❑ 99PacOme-158
❑ 99PacOmeC-158
❑ 99PacOmeG-158
❑ 99PacOmePB-158
❑ 99PacPriS-62
❑ 99PacPriS206-62
❑ 99PacPriS206R-62
❑ 99SkyPre-200
❑ 99SkyPreR-200
❑ 99SkyThu-56
❑ 99SkyThuRant-56
❑ 99SkyThuRave-56
❑ 99SP Aut-135
❑ 99SP SigAuto-SB
❑ 99SpoIll-2
❑ 99SPSig-112
❑ 99StaClu-106
❑ 99StaCluFDI-106
❑ 99StaCluOoaK-106
❑ 99StaCluPP-106
❑ 99ThuSkySupR-56
❑ 99Top-3
❑ 99Top-238
❑ 99TopChr-3
❑ 99TopChr-238
❑ 99TopChrR-3
❑ 99TopChrR-238
❑ 99TopMVPP-3
❑ 99TopOpeD-4
❑ 99TopSupC-36
❑ 99TopSupCR-36
❑ 99Ult-49
❑ 99UltGolM-49
❑ 99UltMas-49
❑ 99UltPlaM-49
❑ 99UppDec-437
❑ 99UppDec-529
❑ 99UppDecCf7-72
❑ 99UppDecCLM-C64
❑ 99UppDecCo7CE-72
❑ 99UppDecEL1-437
❑ 99UppDecEL1-529
❑ 99UppDecEL2-437
❑ 99UppDecEL2-529
❑ 99UppDecM-142
❑ 99UppDecMGS-142
❑ 99UppDecMHFS-142
❑ 99UppDecMP-142
❑ 99UppDecMSS-142
❑ 99Vic-266
❑ 99Vic-270
❑ 99YanFle-3
Brosnan, Jason
❑ 89GreFalDSP-10
❑ 90BakDodCLC-234
❑ 90CalLeaACLC-17
❑ 91LinDriAA-532
❑ 91SanAntMLD-532
❑ 92AlbDukS-7
❑ 92VerBeaDF-2866
❑ 93AusFut-2
❑ 93VerBeaDC-2
❑ 93VerBeaDF-2206
❑ 94SanAntMF-2459
❑ 96PorCitRB-7
❑ 98MidAngG-6
Brosnan, Jim
❑ 55Bow-229
❑ 57Top-155
❑ 58Top-342
❑ 59Top-194
❑ 59TopVen-194
❑ 60Lea-124
❑ 60Top-449
❑ 61Kah-5
❑ 61Top-513
❑ 61TopMagR-25
❑ 61TopStaI-15
❑ 62Jel-125
❑ 62Kah-2
❑ 62Pos-125
❑ 62PosCan-125
❑ 62RedEnq-2
❑ 62RedJayP-1
❑ 62Top-2
❑ 62TopVen-2
❑ 63RedEnq-3
❑ 63RedJayP-1
❑ 63Top-116
❑ 64WhiSoxI-3
❑ 80Red196T-30
❑ 90LitSunW-10
Brosnan, Timothy
❑ 87OldJudN-43
Bross, Terry
❑ 87LitFalMP-2382
❑ 88LitFalMP-15
❑ 89MetColP-23
❑ 89St.LucMS-2
❑ 90Bow-129
❑ 90BowTif-129
❑ 90Don-502
❑ 90JacMetGS-7
❑ 90MetColP-26
❑ 90TexLeaAGS-32
❑ 90TopTVM-37
❑ 91Don-34
❑ 91MetColP-24
❑ 91TidTidP-2501
❑ 92Fle-653
❑ 92LasVegSS-227
❑ 92Sco-763
❑ 92ScoRoo-21
❑ 92SkyAAAF-111
❑ 92TopDeb91-23
❑ 92UppDec-531
❑ 93PhoFirF-1507
❑ 94IndIndF-1801
Brothers, John
❑ 91PriRedC-25
❑ 91PriRedP-3505
❑ 93ClaFS7-159
❑ 93WesVirWC-3
❑ 93WesVirWF-2856
❑ 94WinSpiC-6
❑ 94WinSpiF-263
Broughton, Cal (Cecil C.)
❑ 87OldJudN-44
Brouhard, Mark Steven
❑ 80BreTeal-3
❑ 82BrePol-29
❑ 82Don-154
❑ 82Fle-135
❑ 82Top-517
❑ 83BreGar-3
❑ 83Don-532
❑ 83Fle-28
❑ 83Top-167
❑ 84BreGar-2
❑ 84BrePol-29
❑ 84Don-211
❑ 84Fle-195
❑ 84Nes792-528
❑ 84Top-528
❑ 84TopTif-528
❑ 85BreGar-2
❑ 85BrePol-29
❑ 85Don-149
❑ 85Fle-576
❑ 85Top-653
❑ 85TopTif-653
❑ 86OPC-21
❑ 86Top-473
❑ 86TopTif-473
❑ 92BreCarT-3
❑ 94BreMilB-290
Brousseau, Fernand
❑ 52LavPro-95
Brouthers, Dan (Dennis J.)
❑ 39PC7AlbHoF-30
❑ 50CalHOFW-7
❑ 74CapPub-28
❑ 75FlePio-6
❑ 76ShaPiz-30
❑ 76SSP188WS-12
❑ 77BobParHoF-7
❑ 80PerHaloFP-30
❑ 80SSPHOF-30
❑ 81TigDetN-80
❑ 84GalHaloFRL-30
❑ 87BucN28-28A
❑ 87BucN28-28B
❑ 87OldJudN-45
❑ 87ScrDC-11
❑ 87TobLit-3
❑ 88AugBecN-3
❑ 88GooN16-3
❑ 88SpoTimM-3
❑ 88WG1CarG-20
❑ 89DodSmoG-3
❑ 89EdgR.WG-2
❑ 89HOFStiB-7
❑ 89N526N7C-2
❑ 90BasWit-102
❑ 90DodTar-79
❑ 94OriofB-60
❑ 94OriTeal-3
❑ 95May-3A
❑ 95May-3B
Brovia, Joe (Joseph John)
❑ 48SomandK-11
❑ 52MotCoo-51
❑ 53MotCoo-18
❑ 75OakOak2A-8
❑ 77FriOneYW-3
Brovold, George
❑ 22Zee-119
Brow, Dennis
❑ 88PriWilYS-4
❑ 89PriWilCS-2
Brow, Scott
❑ 90St.CatBJP-3458
❑ 91DunBluJC-1
❑ 91DunBluJP-197
❑ 92DunBluJC-3
❑ 92DunBluJF-1990
❑ 93Bow-435
❑ 93FleFinE-286
❑ 93KnoSmoF-1241
❑ 94BluJayUSPC-8H
❑ 94BluJayUSPC-9S
❑ 94Pac-634
❑ 94ScoRoo-RT115
❑ 94ScoRooGR-RT115
❑ 94StaCluT-169
❑ 94StaCluTFDI-169
❑ 94Ult-435
❑ 95Pac-437
❑ 95SyrChiTI-5
❑ 96SyrChiTI-6
❑ 97RicBra-7
❑ 98DiaBacP-5
❑ 98PacOnl-34
❑ 98PacOnlR-34
❑ 98PacOnlWC-34
Brow, Steve
❑ 87Ft.LauYP-28
Browder, Bubba
❑ 88WytCubP-1987
Browder, Cameron
❑ 93IdaFalBF-4042
❑ 93IdaFalBSP-20
Brower, Bob
❑ 83BurRanF-11
❑ 83BurRanT-13
❑ 83TulDriT-13
❑ 85OklCit8T-21
❑ 86OklCit8P-1
❑ 87Don-651
❑ 87DonRoo-49
❑ 87FleUpd-10
❑ 87FleUpdG-10
❑ 87RanMot-18
❑ 87RanSmo-26
❑ 87SpoRool-3
❑ 87TopTra-10T
❑ 87TopTraT-10T
❑ 88Don-346
❑ 88Fle-461
❑ 88Fle-462A
❑ 88FleGlo-461
❑ 88OPC-252
❑ 88RanMot-18
❑ 88RanSmo-16
❑ 88RedFolSB-9
❑ 88Sco-236
❑ 88ScoGlo-236
❑ 88StaLinRa-1
❑ 88Top-252
❑ 88TopTif-252
❑ 88ToyRoo-2
❑ 89Bow-182
❑ 89BowTif-182
❑ 89Don-411
❑ 89Fle-514
❑ 89FleGlo-514
❑ 89Sco-344
❑ 89Top-754
❑ 89TopTif-754
❑ 89UppDec-439
❑ 90PubIntS-531
❑ 90TopTVY-37
❑ 92OklCit8F-1925
❑ 92OklCit8S-305
❑ 92YanWIZ8-19
❑ 93RanKee-83
Brower, Frank
❑ 25Zee-105
❑ 26Zee-132
Brower, Jim
❑ 94HudValRF-3374
❑ 95Bow-244
❑ 95BowGolF-244
❑ 97TulDriTI-5
❑ 98AkrAerM-6
Brown, Adam
❑ 88BakDodCLC-242
❑ 88CalLeaACLC-48
❑ 89SanAntMB-10
❑ 90AlbDukCm-14
❑ 90AlbDukP-347
❑ 90AlbDukTr-3
❑ 90CMC-416
❑ 90ProAAAF-68
❑ 90SanAntMGS-7
❑ 91FloStaLAP-FSL36
❑ 91VerBeaDC-14
❑ 91VerBeaDP-775
❑ 92SanAntMF-3977
❑ 92SanAntMS-557
❑ 93DayCubC-3
❑ 93DayCubF-861
❑ 94OrlCubF-1387
❑ 95ChaLooTI-2
Brown, Adrian
❑ 93LetMouF-4159
❑ 93LetMouSP-4
❑ 96CarMudB-5
❑ 96LynHilB-4
❑ 97BesLimA-4
❑ 97CarMudC-20
❑ 97Fle-759
❑ 97FleTif-759
❑ 97PirPos-3
❑ 97SouLeaTP-5
❑ 98BesPreA-4
❑ 98Fle-70
❑ 98Pac-391
❑ 98PacPar-218
❑ 98PacParC-218
❑ 98PacParG-218
❑ 98PacParHS-218
❑ 98PacParPB-218
❑ 98PacParR-218
❑ 98PacPlaB-391
❑ 98PacRedT-391
❑ 98PacSil-391
❑ 98Ult-354
❑ 98UltGolM-354
❑ 98UltMas-354
❑ 98UltPlaM-354
❑ 99Fle-333
❑ 99FleSta9-333
❑ 99FleWarT-333
❑ 99Pac-335
❑ 99PacCroC-217
❑ 99PacCroCPB-217
❑ 99PacPlaB-335
❑ 99PacRed-335
Brown, Alvin
❑ 91EliTwiP-4302
❑ 91KenTwiC-1
❑ 91KenTwiP-2077
❑ 93BriTigC-4
❑ 93BriTigF-3640
❑ 94FayGenC-4
❑ 94LakTigF-3027
❑ 97AlbDukUG-1
❑ 97SanAntMB-2
❑ 98SanAntMM-2
Brown, Andy
❑ 99199Fin-290
❑ 99Bow-130
❑ 99BowBes-181
❑ 99BowBesAR-181

❑ 99BowBesR-181
❑ 99BowChr-130
❑ 99BowChrG-130
❑ 99BowChrGR-130
❑ 99BowChrI-130
❑ 99BowChrIR-130
❑ 99BowChrR-130
❑ 99BowGol-130
❑ 99BowInt-130
❑ 99FinGolRef-290
❑ 99FinRef-290
❑ 99StaClu-160
❑ 99StaCluFDI-160
❑ 99StaCluOoaK-160
❑ 99StaCluPP-160
❑ 99Top-219
❑ 99TopChr-219
❑ 99TopChrR-219
❑ 99TopSta-79
❑ 99TopSta1Foil-79
❑ 99TopStaFoil-79
❑ 99TopStaOS-79
Brown, Anthony
❑ 90WelPirP-10
❑ 91AugPirP-817
❑ 91Cla/Bes-246
Brown, Armann
❑ 93ClaFS7-171
❑ 93EliTwiC-6
❑ 93EliTwiF-3427
❑ 93ForWayWC-2
❑ 93ForWayWF-1978
❑ 94ForWayWC-4
❑ 94ForWayWF-2021
❑ 96FtMyeMB-27
❑ 97NewBriRC-6
Brown, Big Bill (Willard)
❑ 87OldJudN-47
❑ 89SFHaCN-1
Brown, Bill (William Verna)
❑ 88AugBecN-4
❑ 88GandBCGCE-4
Brown, Billy (William James)
❑ 98HagSunM-9
❑ 98St.CatSM-26
Brown, Bob (Robert Murray)
❑ 33ButCanV-5
❑ 34Gou-81
❑ 94ConTSN-1281
❑ 94ConTSNB-1281
Brown, Bobby
❑ 97SpoIndG-4
Brown, Bobby (Robert W.)
❑ 47TipTop-48
❑ 47YanTeaT-3
❑ 48BluTin-9
❑ 48YanTeal-3
❑ 49Bow-19
❑ 49YanTeal-3
❑ 50Bow-101
❑ 50YanTeal-4
❑ 51BerRos-B6
❑ 51Bow-110
❑ 52BerRos-5
❑ 52Bow-105
❑ 76TayBow4-110
❑ 79DiaGre-18
❑ 85TCMPpl1-32
❑ 91SweBasG-15
❑ 92UppDecS-16
❑ 93TedWil-61
❑ 93UppDecAH-19
❑ 94UppDecAH-149
❑ 94UppDecAH1-149
Brown, Bobby (Rogers Lee)
❑ 78LodDodT-2
❑ 79ColCliT-27
❑ 79YanPicA-4
❑ 80Top-670
❑ 80YanPhoA-2
❑ 81Don-469
❑ 81Fle-95
❑ 81OPC-107
❑ 81Top-418
❑ 81YanPhoA-2
❑ 82Don-552
❑ 82Fle-30
❑ 82MarPos-7
❑ 82Top-791
❑ 82TopTra-12T
❑ 83LasVegSBHN-2
❑ 83Top-287
❑ 84Don-478
❑ 84Fle-296
❑ 84Nes792-261
❑ 84PadMot-14
❑ 84PadSmo-2
❑ 84Top-261
❑ 84TopSti-157
❑ 84TopTif-261
❑ 85Don-383
❑ 85Fle-28
❑ 85OPC-92
❑ 85PadMot-23
❑ 85Top-583
❑ 85TopTif-583
❑ 86Top-182
❑ 86TopTif-182
❑ 92YanWIZ7-26
❑ 92YanWIZ8-20
Brown, Brant
❑ 92ClaDraP-58
❑ 92FroRowDP-83
❑ 92FroRowDPG-83
❑ 92FroRowDPS-83
❑ 92PeoChiTI-5
❑ 93Bow-284
❑ 93ClaFS7-172
❑ 93StaCluM-194
❑ 94Bow-494
❑ 94Cla-128
❑ 94ExcFS7-163
❑ 94OrlCubF-1390
❑ 94SigRoo-2
❑ 94SigRooS-2
❑ 94UppDecML-134
❑ 94UppDecMLPotYF-PY8
❑ 95OrlCubF-15
❑ 96Cir-108
❑ 96CirRav-108
❑ 96IowCubB-8
❑ 97BowBes-173
❑ 97BowBesAR-173
❑ 97BowBesR-173
❑ 97Cir-128
❑ 97CirRav-128
❑ 97ColCho-291
❑ 97Don-149
❑ 97DonGolPP-149
❑ 97DonLim-118
❑ 97DonLimE-118
❑ 97DonLimENG-118
❑ 97DonPre-145
❑ 97DonPreCttC-145
❑ 97DonSilPP-149
❑ 97Fin-188
❑ 97FinRef-188
❑ 97Fle-273
❑ 97FleTif-273
❑ 97IowCub-6
❑ 97Lea-339
❑ 97LeaFraM-339
❑ 97LeaFraMDC-339
❑ 97MetUni-10
❑ 97NewPin-162
❑ 97NewPinAP-162
❑ 97NewPinMC-162
❑ 97NewPinPP-162
❑ 97Pac-246
❑ 97PacLigB-246
❑ 97PacSil-246
❑ 97Pin-156
❑ 97PinArtP-PP156
❑ 97PinMusC-156
❑ 97PinPrePla-156
❑ 97Sco-263
❑ 97Sco-482
❑ 97ScoArtPWB-263
❑ 97ScoArtPWB-482
❑ 97ScoPreS-263
❑ 97ScoResC-482
❑ 97ScoShoS-263
❑ 97ScoShoS-482
❑ 97ScoShoSAP-263
❑ 97ScoShoSAP-482
❑ 97StaClu-361
❑ 97StaCluM-M9
❑ 97StaCluMOP-361
❑ 97StaCluMOP-M9
❑ 97Ult-163
❑ 97UltGolME-163
❑ 97UltPlaME-163
❑ 97UppDec-241
❑ 98Bow-243
❑ 98BowChr-243
❑ 98BowChrGA-243
❑ 98BowChrGAR-243
❑ 98BowChrI-243
❑ 98BowChrIR-243
❑ 98BowChrR-243
❑ 98BowGolA-243
❑ 98BowInt-243
❑ 98CirThu-82
❑ 98CirThuRav-82
❑ 98CirThuSupRav-82
❑ 98PacOnl-138
❑ 98PacOnlR-138
❑ 98PacOnlWC-138
❑ 98PinSna-CC4
❑ 98PinSna-CC9
❑ 98Sco-121
❑ 98ScoRT-136
❑ 98ScoSS-PP51
❑ 98ScoSSAP-PP51
❑ 99Bow-279
❑ 99BowGol-279
❑ 99BowInt-279
❑ 99Fle-86
❑ 99FleSta9-86
❑ 99FleWarT-86
❑ 99Pac-81
❑ 99PacOme-185
❑ 99PacOmeC-185
❑ 99PacOmeG-185
❑ 99PacOmePB-185
❑ 99PacPar-183
❑ 99PacParC-183
❑ 99PacParG-183
❑ 99PacParHoloGold-183
❑ 99PacParHS-183
❑ 99PacParOD-183
❑ 99PacParPB-183
❑ 99PacParRed-183
❑ 99PacPlaB-81
❑ 99PacPriS-63
❑ 99PacPriS206-63
❑ 99PacPriS206R-63
❑ 99PacRed-81
❑ 99SkyThu-216
❑ 99SkyThuRant-216
❑ 99SkyThuRave-216
❑ 99StaClu-312
❑ 99StaCluFDI-312
❑ 99StaCluOoaK-312
❑ 99StaCluPP-312
❑ 99ThuSkySupR-216
❑ 99Top-47
❑ 99TopChr-47
❑ 99TopChrR-47
❑ 99TopMVPP-47
❑ 99UppDec-59
❑ 99UppDec-460
❑ 99UppDecEL1-59
❑ 99UppDecEL1-460
❑ 99UppDecEL2-59
❑ 99UppDecEL2-460
❑ 99Vic-310
Brown, Bryan
❑ 90LSUTigA-14
❑ 92WinHavRSC-18
❑ 92WinHavRSF-1792
❑ 93ForLauRSC-4
❑ 93ForLauRSFP-1609
Brown, Buster (Charles E.)
❑ 08RosComP-89
❑ 08RosComP-137
❑ 09AmeCarE90-1-15
❑ 11PinT-5-710
❑ 11SpoLifCW-45
❑ 11SpoLifM-136
❑ 15Zee-99
❑ 16Zee-102
❑ 17Zee-3
❑ 18Zee-2
❑ 19Zee-2
❑ 20Zee-4
Brown, Carmon
❑ 86DavLipB-5
Brown, Chad
❑ 92MedHatBJF-3203
❑ 92MedHatBJSP-2
❑ 93St.CatBJC-4
❑ 93St.CatBJF-3967
❑ 94DunBluJC-5
❑ 94DunBluJF-2548
❑ 95KnoSmoF-34
❑ 96KnoSmoB-6
❑ 96MauStiHWB-23
❑ 97SyrSkyCB-4
Brown, Charlie
❑ 92GulCoaYF-3780
❑ 94OneYanC-6
❑ 94OneYanF-3782
❑ 95GreBatTI-5
❑ 96TamYanY-5
❑ 97TamYan-6
Brown, Chris (John C.)
❑ 80CliGiaT-16
❑ 84PhoGiaC-23
❑ 85FleUpd-11
❑ 85GiaMot-18
❑ 85GiaPos-4
❑ 85TopTifT-10T
❑ 85TopTra-10T
❑ 86Don-553
❑ 86Fle-535
❑ 86FleLimE-8
❑ 86FleMin-108
❑ 86FleStiC-13
❑ 86GiaMot-18
❑ 86GiaPos-5
❑ 86KayB-2
❑ 86Lea-215
❑ 86OPC-383
❑ 86SevCoi-W13
❑ 86Spo-78
❑ 86Top-383
❑ 86TopGloS-10
❑ 86TopSti-85
❑ 86TopSti-311
❑ 86TopTat-18
❑ 86TopTif-383
❑ 87ClaGam-65
❑ 87Don-11
❑ 87Don-80
❑ 87DonAll-44
❑ 87DonOpeD-100
❑ 87DonSupD-11
❑ 87Fle-268
❑ 87FleGlo-268
❑ 87FleLeaL-7
❑ 87FleMin-15
❑ 87FleRecS-2
❑ 87FleUpd-11
❑ 87FleUpdG-11
❑ 87GiaMot-5
❑ 87GiaPos-4
❑ 87Lea-11
❑ 87Lea-236
❑ 87OPC-180
❑ 87Spo-13
❑ 87Spo-115
❑ 87SpoTeaP-10
❑ 87Top-180
❑ 87TopSti-86
❑ 87TopTif-180
❑ 88Don-483
❑ 88DonBasB-77
❑ 88Fle-578
❑ 88FleGlo-578
❑ 88Lea-221
❑ 88OPC-112
❑ 88PadCok-35
❑ 88PadSmo-5
❑ 88PanSti-408
❑ 88Sco-363
❑ 88ScoGlo-363
❑ 88Top-568
❑ 88TopBig-130
❑ 88TopSti-111
❑ 88TopTif-568
❑ 89Bow-106
❑ 89BowTif-106
❑ 89Don-183
❑ 89DonTra-9
❑ 89Fle-301
❑ 89FleGlo-301
❑ 89Sco-369
❑ 89Top-481
❑ 89TopSti-103
❑ 89TopTif-481
❑ 89UppDec-193
❑ 89UppDec-784
❑ 90PubIntS-469
❑ 98WilCubM-2
Brown, Clinton
❑ 33WorCig-13
❑ 34BatR31-82
❑ 34BatR31-189
❑ 39WhiSoxTI-3
❑ 40WhiSoxL-3
❑ 74CapPub-87
❑ 91ConTSN-132
Brown, Coach (Paul)
❑ 74NewYorNTDiS-40
Brown, Cory
❑ 93BluOriC-7
❑ 93BluOriF-4117
❑ 94AlbPolC-7
❑ 94AlbPolF-2229
❑ 94OriPro-12
Brown, Craig
❑ 83AleDukT-19
❑ 84PriWilPT-26
❑ 85NasPirT-4
❑ 86NasPirP-4
❑ 87HarSenP-8
❑ 98WatIndTI-4
Brown, Curt (Curtis)
❑ 81HolMilT-11
Brown, Curt S.
❑ 84ColCliP-1
❑ 84ColCliT-15
❑ 85ColCliP-4
❑ 85ColCliT-3
❑ 86IndIndTI-25
❑ 87IndIndTI-13
❑ 88ChaKniTI-24
❑ 88RocRedWGCP-4
❑ 92YanWIZ8-21
Brown, Dan
❑ 89SanDieSAS-4
❑ 91MarPhiC-26
❑ 91MarPhiP-3444
❑ 92ClePhiF-2047
❑ 92ProFS7-304
❑ 93SpaPhiC-8
❑ 93SpaPhiF-1049
❑ 94ClePhiC-10
❑ 94ClePhiF-2519
Brown, Dana
❑ 88CapCodPPaLP-95
❑ 89BatCliP-1932
❑ 90SpaPhiB-19
❑ 90SpaPhiP-2502
❑ 90SpaPhiS-2
❑ 91LinDriAA-504
❑ 91ReaPhiLD-504
❑ 91ReaPhiP-1380
Brown, Danny
❑ 90ArkRaz-3
Brown, Daren
❑ 89St.CatBJP-2073
❑ 90MyrBeaBJP-2770
❑ 91DunBluJC-2
❑ 91DunBluJP-198
❑ 92KnoBluJF-2981
❑ 92KnoBluJS-376
❑ 93KnoSmoF-1242
Brown, Darold
❑ 93DanBraC-6
❑ 93DanBraF-3610
❑ 94IdaFalBF-3575
❑ 94IdaFalBSP-8
❑ 97OrlRayB-5
❑ 98WesTenDJM-4
Brown, Darrell Wayne
❑ 80EvaTriT-11
❑ 84Fle-556
❑ 84MinTwiP-1
❑ 84Nes792-193
❑ 84Top-193
❑ 84TopSti-311
❑ 84TopTif-193
❑ 84TwiTeal-20
❑ 85Don-558
❑ 85Fle-270
❑ 85NasSouTI-2
❑ 85RocRedWT-11
❑ 85Top-767
❑ 85TopSti-306
❑ 85TopTif-767
Brown, Dave
❑ 78LauLonABS-27
❑ 89EriOriS-4
❑ 90NegLeaS-12
Brown, Dee (Dermal)
❑ 96BesAutS1RP-FR4
❑ 97Bes-71
❑ 97BesDiaB-11
❑ 97BesLimA-5
❑ 97Bow-311
❑ 97BowChr-215
❑ 97BowChrI-215
❑ 97BowChrIR-215
❑ 97BowChrR-215
❑ 97BowInt-311
❑ 97SpoIndG-5
❑ 97Top-272
❑ 98Bes-6
❑ 98BesAutPOY-2
❑ 98BesDiaBA-2
❑ 98BesFulCA-2
❑ 98BesNumOP-10
❑ 98BesPreA-5
❑ 98Bow-167
❑ 98BowBes-124
❑ 98BowBesAR-124
❑ 98BowBesR-124
❑ 98BowCerBlueAU-51
❑ 98BowCerGA-51
❑ 98BowCerSA-51
❑ 98BowChr-167
❑ 98BowChrGA-167
❑ 98BowChrGAR-167
❑ 98BowChrI-167
❑ 98BowChrIR-167
❑ 98BowChrR-167
❑ 98BowGolA-167
❑ 98BowInt-167
❑ 98BowScoC-SC15
❑ 98CarLeaTPQ-11
❑ 98DonSig-126
❑ 98DonSigP-126
❑ 98FleUpd-U75
❑ 98LeaRS-324
❑ 98LeaRSLHolo-324
❑ 98LeaRSLong-324
❑ 98LeaRTrue-324
❑ 98SP MinPE-65
❑ 98SP MinSTHPE-H13
❑ 98SPMin-65
❑ 98SPMinSTH-H13
❑ 98StaCluFDI-373
❑ 98StaCluI-373
❑ 98StaCluOneK-373
❑ 98StaCluPP-373
❑ 98Top-255
❑ 98TopChr-255
❑ 98TopChrR-255
❑ 98TopDevR-255
❑ 98TopDia-255
❑ 98TopMiniC-255
❑ 98WilBluRC-6
❑ 99Bow-298
❑ 99BowAut-BA47
❑ 99BowGol-298
❑ 99BowInt-298
❑ 99Fle-158
❑ 99FleSta9-158
❑ 99FleWarT-158
❑ 99SkyThu-166
❑ 99SkyThuRant-166
❑ 99SkyThuRave-166
❑ 99SP Aut-103
❑ 99SP SigAuto-DB
❑ 99SP SigAutoG-DB
❑ 99SP TopP-21
❑ 99SP TopPC-DB
❑ 99SP TopPGF-GF5
❑ 99SP TopPPE-21
❑ 99SpoIll-67
❑ 99SPSig-73
❑ 99SPx-98
❑ 99SPxFinR-98
❑ 99SPxFinS-98
❑ 99ThuSkySupR-166
❑ 99UD Cho-11
❑ 99UD ChoPCR-11
❑ 99UppDec-279
❑ 99UppDecEL1-279
❑ 99UppDecEL2-279
❑ 99UppDecM-102
❑ 99UppDecMGS-102
❑ 99UppDecMHFS-102
❑ 99UppDecMSS-102
Brown, Derek
❑ 98DelShoM-8
Brown, Deshon
❑ 92GulCoaRSP-7
Brown, Dick (Richard Ernest)
❑ 58IndTeal-3
❑ 58Top-456
❑ 59Top-61
❑ 59TopVen-61
❑ 60Top-256
❑ 61TigJayP-2
❑ 61Top-192
❑ 62Jel-21
❑ 62Pos-21
❑ 62PosCan-21
❑ 62SalPlaC-37
❑ 62ShiPlaC-37
❑ 62TigJayP-2
❑ 62TigPosCF-3
❑ 62Top-438
❑ 63BalOriP-8
❑ 63Jel-52

- 63Pos-52
- 63Top-112
- 64BalOriP-11
- 65BalOriP-10
- 78TCM60I-95
- 91OriCro-53
- 98TamYanM-7

Brown, Dickie
- 90BurIndP-3002
- 91ColIndC-10
- 91ColIndP-1477
- 92ColRedC-2
- 92ColRedF-2380
- 92KinIndC-5
- 93KinIndC-3
- 93KinIndF-2237
- 93KinIndTI-2
- 94HigDesMC-6
- 94HigDesMF-2779

Brown, Don
- 87CedRapRP-22
- 88GreHorP-1572
- 89CedRapRS-26
- 89ChaLooB-22
- 89ChaLooGS-6

Brown, Don PCL
- 22Zee-23
- 23Zee-26

Brown, Drew
- 94LetMouF-3884
- 94LetMouSP-23

Brown, Drummond Nic.
- 09ObaT21-66
- 09ObaT21-176
- 09ObaT21-238
- 09ObaT21-342
- 11Zee-109A
- 11Zee-109B
- 11Zee-109C
- 12HomRunKE-80
- 12ObaPreT-91
- 12Zee-140

Brown, Duane
- 90AshTouC-3
- 91AshTouP-561
- 92AshTouC-10
- 93OscAstC-5
- 93OscAstF-619

Brown, Eddie (Edward William)
- 21KoBreWSI-4
- 22W575-11
- 27AmeCarE126-44
- 27AmeCarE126-50
- 28Exh-1
- 90DodTar-80

Brown, Elliot
- 97ChaRivDG-8
- 98ChaRivDG-6

Brown, Elmer
- 90DodTar-81

Brown, Emil
- 95MidLeaA-5
- 95WesMicWTI-32
- 96ModA'sB-16
- 97ColCho-433
- 97FlaShoWotF-20
- 97Fle-571
- 97FleTif-571
- 97PirPos-4
- 97SpoIll-3
- 97SpoIllEE-3
- 97Ult-486
- 97UltGolME-486
- 97UltPlaME-486
- 98CarMudM-20
- 98Fle-165
- 98PacInvGems-192
- 98PacPar-219
- 98PacParC-219
- 98PacParG-219
- 98PacParHS-219
- 98PacParPB-219
- 98PacParR-219
- 98SouLeaTPG-6
- 98Ult-328
- 98UltGolM-328
- 98UltMas-328
- 98UltPlaM-328
- 99Pac-336
- 99PacPlaB-336
- 99PacPri-111
- 99PacPriHB-111
- 99PacPriHG-111
- 99PacPriHM-111
- 99PacPriHP-111
- 99PacPriRed-111
- 99PacRed-336
- 99SP SigAuto-EB
- 99SPSig-140
- 99UppDecM-165
- 99UppDecMGS-165
- 99UppDecMHFS-165
- 99UppDecMSS-165
- 99WesMicWAM-2

Brown, Eric
- 74CedRapAT-12
- 82IdaFalAT-4

Brown, Eric Gordon
- 95GreFalDTI-39
- 96YakBeaTI-12

Brown, Everett
- 14Zee-54

Brown, Fred Herbert
- 09ObaT21-35
- 09ObaT21-136

Brown, Gates (William James)
- 64Top-471
- 65OPC-19
- 65TigJayP-2
- 65Top-19
- 66Top-362
- 66TopVen-362
- 67OPC-134
- 67Top-134
- 68CokCapT-7
- 68TigDetFPB-1
- 68Top-583
- 69MilBra-41
- 69TigTealC-1
- 69Top-256
- 70OPC-98
- 70Top-98
- 71MLBOffS-386
- 71OPC-503
- 71Top-503
- 72MilBra-52
- 72OPC-187
- 72Top-187
- 73OPC-508
- 73TigJew-2
- 73Top-508
- 74OPC-389
- 74Tig-1
- 74Top-389
- 75DetTigP-4
- 75OPC-371
- 75Top-371
- 75TopMin-371
- 76SSP-371
- 78TigTeal-4
- 80VenLeaS-91
- 81TigDetN-106
- 83TigPos-6
- 84TigTeal-9
- 84TigWavP-9
- 86TigSpoD-18
- 88TigDom-1
- 89PacSenL-199
- 89T/MSenL-13

Brown, Gavin
- 96EugEmeB-3
- 97MacBra-7

Brown, George
- 05RotCP-3
- 06FanCraNL-6
- 09T206-39
- 09T206-40

Brown, Greg
- 78WauMetT-4
- 91BatCliCB-24
- 91BatCliP-3477
- 92SpaPhiF-1257
- 93ClePhiC-5
- 93ClePhiF-2677
- 93FloStaLAF-25
- 94ReaPhiF-2055

Brown, Greg ANN
- 97PirPos-5

Brown, Harry
- 23Zee-81
- 24Zee-59
- 25Zee-59
- 30Zee-115

Brown, Ike (Isaac)
- 70OPC-152
- 70Top-152
- 71MLBOffS-387
- 71OPC-669
- 71Top-669
- 72OPC-284
- 72Top-284
- 72TopCloT-3
- 73OPC-633
- 73TigJew-3
- 73Top-633
- 74OPC-409
- 74Top-409

Brown, J.B.
- 80AppFoxT-6
- 82GleFalWST-2
- 83GleFalWST-2

Brown, Jackie G.
- 57JetPos-3
- 71MLBOffS-531
- 71OPC-591
- 71SenTealW-6
- 71Top-591
- 72Dia-6
- 74OPC-89
- 74Top-89
- 75OPC-316
- 75RanPos-3
- 75Top-316
- 75TopMin-316
- 76OPC-301
- 76Top-301
- 77ExpPos-7
- 77OPC-36
- 77Top-147
- 78OPC-126
- 78Top-699
- 78TucTorC-39
- 86HawIsIP-1
- 87VanCanP-1599
- 88BufBisP-1479
- 89BufBisC-25
- 89BufBisP-1683
- 90BufBisP-390
- 90BufBisTI-3
- 90ProAAAF-505
- 91BufBisLD-50
- 91BufBisP-557
- 91LinDriAAA-50
- 92WhiSoxK-NNO
- 93RanKee-84
- 93WhiSoxK-30
- 94WhiSoxK-30

Brown, Jake (Jerald Ray)
- 75LafDriT-6

Brown, Jamie
- 97WatIndTI-8
- 98KinIndQ-4

Brown, Jarvis
- 87KenTwiP-14
- 88KenTwiP-1390
- 88MidLeaAGS-33
- 89VisOakCLC-106
- 89VisOakP-1437
- 90OrlSunRB-9
- 90OrlSunRP-1095
- 90OrlSunRS-3
- 91LinDriAAA-404
- 91PorBeaLD-404
- 91PorBeaP-1576
- 92Don-770
- 92Fle-669
- 92Pin-544
- 92ProFS7-92
- 92Sco-870
- 92ScoRoo-27
- 92StaClu-515
- 92TopDeb91-24
- 92Ult-394
- 93LasVegSF-955
- 94Fle-658
- 94Pac-519
- 94RicBraF-2858
- 94Sco-281
- 94ScoGolR-281
- 94StaCluT-36
- 94StaCluTFDI-36
- 95BowBayTI-4
- 97TucTorB-23

Brown, Jason
- 97YakBeaG-3
- 98VerBeaDM-17

Brown, Jeff
- 85AncGlaPTI-6
- 85Ft.MyeRT-14
- 87SanAntDTI-12
- 87VerBeaDP-16
- 88BakDodCLC-234
- 88CalLeaACLC-46
- 91ChaRaiC-3
- 91ChaRaiP-89
- 92BriTigC-2
- 92BriTigF-1400
- 92WatDiaC-8
- 92WatDiaF-2136
- 93RanCucQC-6
- 93RanCucQF-820
- 94ClaGolF-140

Brown, Jim
- 76QuaCitAT-7

Brown, Jim (James Nathaniel)
- 66AurSpoMK-1

Brown, Jimmy
- 90KisDodD-3
- 91NiaFalRC-2
- 91NiaFalRP-3639

Brown, Jimmy (James Roberson)
- 39PlaBal-132
- 40PlaBal-112
- 41CarW75-2
- 41DouPlaR-145
- 41PlaBal-12
- 83Car194T-1

Brown, John (James Murray)
- 67OPC-72
- 67Top-72
- 76BatTroTI-2

Brown, Jumbo (Walter G.)
- 28LaPre-19
- 33Gou-192
- 35DiaMatCS3T1-18
- 39PlaBal-124
- 40PlaBal-154
- 72TCMthe3-77
- 75YanDyn1T-5
- 92ConTSN-454

Brown, Keith
- 80AppFoxT-15
- 87CedRapRP-10
- 88ChaLooB-3
- 88NasSouTI-4
- 89CedRapRAB-32
- 89ChaLooLITI-6
- 89Don-115
- 89Fle-154
- 89FleGlo-154
- 89NasSouC-2
- 89NasSouP-1296
- 89NasSouTI-3
- 90CedRapRDGB-32
- 90CMC-134
- 90NasSouC-9
- 90NasSouP-224
- 90ProAAAF-536
- 91Fle-58
- 91LinDriAAA-253
- 91NasSouLD-253
- 91NasSouP-2149
- 92NasSouS-279
- 93OmaRoyF-1672
- 93TopGol-823

Brown, Ken
- 88PriWilYS-5

Brown, Kent
- 97IdaFalBTI-1

Brown, Kevin (James Kevin)
- 87Don-627
- 88BasAmeAAB-25
- 88TulDriTI-15
- 89Don-613
- 89DonBasB-256
- 89DonRoo-44
- 89Fle-641
- 89FleGlo-641
- 89FleUpd-63
- 89RanMot-18
- 89RanSmo-4
- 89ScoRoo-89T
- 89TopTra-15T
- 89TopTraT-15T
- 89UppDec-752
- 90Bow-488
- 90BowTif-488
- 90ClaYel-T41
- 90Don-343
- 90DonBesA-13
- 90Fle-291
- 90FleCan-291
- 90Lea-47
- 90OPC-136
- 90PanSti-168
- 90PubIntS-405
- 90RanMot-21
- 90Sco-210
- 90Sco100RS-28
- 90ScoYouSI-29
- 90Spo-73
- 90Top-136
- 90TopBig-261
- 90TopRoo-5
- 90TopSti-248
- 90TopTif-136
- 90ToyRoo-6
- 90TulDriDGB-32
- 90UppDec-123
- 91Bow-274
- 91Don-314
- 91Fle-282
- 91Lea-250
- 91OPC-584
- 91PanSti-208
- 91RanMot-21
- 91Sco-846
- 91StaClu-56
- 91Top-584
- 91TopDesS-584
- 91TopMic-584
- 91TopTif-584
- 91Ult-347
- 91UppDec-472
- 92Bow-191
- 92Don-55
- 92Fle-299
- 92Lea-326
- 92LeaBlaG-326
- 92OPC-297
- 92Pin-405
- 92RanMot-21
- 92RanTeal-2
- 92Sco-709
- 92ScoProaG-9
- 92Top-297
- 92TopGol-297
- 92TopGolW-297
- 92TopMic-297
- 92TriPla-226
- 92Ult-438
- 92UppDec-578
- 93Bow-685
- 93Don-377
- 93Fin-134
- 93FinRef-134
- 93Fla-277
- 93Fle-317
- 93FunPac-154
- 93Lea-202
- 93OPC-20
- 93PacSpa-306
- 93PanSti-79
- 93PanSti-156
- 93Pin-356
- 93RanKee-397
- 93RanStaC-20
- 93RedFolS-108
- 93Sco-146
- 93Sel-204
- 93SelAce-7
- 93SelStaL-62
- 93SelStaL-85
- 93SP-190
- 93StaClu-396
- 93StaCluFDI-396
- 93StaCluM-176
- 93StaCluMOP-396
- 93Stu-21
- 93Top-785
- 93TopComotH-14
- 93TopGol-785
- 93TopInaM-785
- 93TopInaR-785
- 93TopMic-785
- 93TriPla-252
- 93Ult-276
- 93UppDec-76
- 93UppDecGold-76
- 94Bow-325
- 94ColC-537
- 94ColChoGS-537
- 94ColChoSS-537
- 94Don-22
- 94DonSpeE-22
- 94Fin-257
- 94FinRef-257
- 94Fla-343
- 94Fle-303
- 94FleExtB-175
- 94FUnPac-41
- 94Lea-231
- 94OPC-205
- 94Pac-610
- 94Pin-71
- 94PinArtP-71
- 94PinMusC-71
- 94ProMag-131
- 94RanAllP-20
- 94RedFolMI-8
- 94Sco-99
- 94ScoGolR-99
- 94Sel-267
- 94Spo-132
- 94StaClu-382
- 94StaCluFDI-382
- 94StaCluGR-382
- 94StaCluMOP-382
- 94StaCluT-260
- 94StaCluTFDI-260
- 94Stu-151
- 94Top-345
- 94TopGol-345
- 94TopSpa-345
- 94TriPla-191
- 94TriPlaM-13
- 94Ult-126
- 94UppDec-487
- 94UppDecED-487
- 95BalOriP-11
- 95Bow-405
- 95ColCho-394
- 95ColCho-562T
- 95ColChoGS-394
- 95ColChoSS-394
- 95Don-207
- 95DonPreP-207
- 95Emo-2
- 95Fin-252
- 95FinRef-252
- 95Fla-219
- 95Fle-280
- 95FleUpd-4
- 95Pac-421
- 95Pin-231
- 95PinArtP-231
- 95PinMusC-231
- 95Sco-199
- 95ScoGolR-199
- 95ScoPlaTS-199
- 95Sel-228
- 95SelArtP-228
- 95StaClu-417
- 95StaClu-626
- 95StaCluMOP-417
- 95StaCluMOP-626
- 95StaCluSTWS-417
- 95StaCluSTWS-626
- 95StaCluVR-215
- 95StaCluVRMO-215
- 95Top-456
- 95Top-575
- 95TopCyb-349
- 95TopTra-148T
- 95Ult-332
- 95UltGolM-332
- 95UppDec-472
- 95UppDec-TC4
- 95UppDecSE-182
- 95UppDecSEG-182
- 95UppDecT-TC4
- 96Bow-176
- 96Cir-126
- 96CirRav-126
- 96ColCho-554
- 96ColChoGS-554
- 96ColChoSS-554
- 96Don-399
- 96DonPreP-399
- 96EmoXL-182
- 96Fin-B286
- 96FinRef-B286
- 96Fla-257
- 96Fle-6
- 96FleTif-6
- 96FleUpd-U131
- 96FleUpdTC-U131
- 96LeaSig-145
- 96LeaSigPPG-145
- 96LeaSigPPP-145
- 96Pac-244
- 96Sco-183
- 96TeaOut-11
- 96Top-376
- 96TopLas-115
- 96Ult-478
- 96UltGolM-478

❑ 96UppDec-495U
❑ 97Bow-45
❑ 97BowChr-36
❑ 97BowChrI-36
❑ 97BowChrIR-36
❑ 97BowChrIR-138
❑ 97BowChrR-36
❑ 97BowInt-45
❑ 97Cir-268
❑ 97CirRav-268
❑ 97ColCho-62
❑ 97ColCho-118
❑ 97ColChoT-FM8
❑ 97Don-81
❑ 97Don-431
❑ 97DonEli-97
❑ 97DonEliGS-97
❑ 97DonGolPP-81
❑ 97DonGolPP-431
❑ 97DonLim-143
❑ 97DonLim-152
❑ 97DonLimE-143
❑ 97DonLimE-152
❑ 97DonLimENG-143
❑ 97DonPre-72
❑ 97DonPreCttC-72
❑ 97DonSig-45
❑ 97DonSigAC-17
❑ 97DonSigAM-17
❑ 97DonSigPPP-45
❑ 97DonSilPP-81
❑ 97DonSilPP-431
❑ 97E-X2-71
❑ 97E-X2Cred-71
❑ 97E-X2EssCre-71
❑ 97Fin-25
❑ 97FinRef-25
❑ 97FlaShoLC-166
❑ 97FlaShoLeg0-166
❑ 97FlaShoLeg1-166
❑ 97FlaShoM-A166
❑ 97FlaShoM-B166
❑ 97FlaShoM-C166
❑ 97FlaShoR0-166
❑ 97FlaShoR1-166
❑ 97FlaShoR2-166
❑ 97Fle-325
❑ 97FleTif-325
❑ 97Lea-216
❑ 97Lea-381
❑ 97LeaFraM-216
❑ 97LeaFraM-381
❑ 97LeaFraMDC-216
❑ 97LeaFraMDC-381
❑ 97LeaGet-7
❑ 97MarPac-5
❑ 97MetUni-171
❑ 97NewPin-50
❑ 97NewPinAP-50
❑ 97NewPinMC-50
❑ 97NewPinPP-50
❑ 97Pac-297
❑ 97PacLigB-297
❑ 97PacPri-100
❑ 97PacPriLB-100
❑ 97PacPriP-100
❑ 97PacSil-297
❑ 97Pin-80
❑ 97PinArtP-PP80
❑ 97PinCar-18
❑ 97PinCer-85
❑ 97PinCerMBla-85
❑ 97PinCerMBlu-85
❑ 97PinCerMG-85
❑ 97PinCerMR-85
❑ 97PinCerR-85
❑ 97PinIns-26
❑ 97PinInsCE-26
❑ 97PinInsDE-26
❑ 97PinMusC-80
❑ 97PinPrePla-80
❑ 97PinTotCPB-85
❑ 97PinTotCPG-85
❑ 97PinTotCPR-85
❑ 97PinX-P-102
❑ 97PinX-PMoS-102
❑ 97Sco-127
❑ 97Sco-532
❑ 97ScoArtPWB-127
❑ 97ScoArtPWB-532
❑ 97ScoPreS-127
❑ 97ScoPreS-324
❑ 97ScoResC-532
❑ 97ScoShoS-127
❑ 97ScoShoS-532
❑ 97ScoShoSAP-127
❑ 97ScoShoSAP-532
❑ 97Sel-16
❑ 97SelArtP-16
❑ 97SelCom-16
❑ 97SelRegG-16
❑ 97SpoIll-32
❑ 97SpoIll-79
❑ 97SpoIllEE-32
❑ 97SpoIllEE-79
❑ 97StaClu-235
❑ 97StaCluMat-235
❑ 97StaCluMOP-235
❑ 97StrAll-11
❑ 97Stu-13
❑ 97StuPrePG-13
❑ 97StuPrePS-13
❑ 97Top-115
❑ 97TopChr-44
❑ 97TopChrR-44
❑ 97TopGal-18
❑ 97TopGalPPI-18
❑ 97TopSta-87
❑ 97TopStaAM-87
❑ 97Ult-193
❑ 97UltGolME-193
❑ 97UltPlaME-193
❑ 97UppDec-71
❑ 97UppDec-76
❑ 97UppDecAWJ-14
❑ 98BowBes-7
❑ 98BowBesAR-7
❑ 98BowBesR-7
❑ 98BowChr-280
❑ 98BowChrGA-280
❑ 98BowChrGAR-280
❑ 98BowChrI-280
❑ 98BowChrIR-280
❑ 98BowChrR-280
❑ 98CirThu-292
❑ 98CirThuRav-292
❑ 98CirThuSupRav-292
❑ 98ColCho-16
❑ 98ColCho-96
❑ 98ColCho-485
❑ 98Don-8
❑ 98Don-226
❑ 98DonCol-8
❑ 98DonColE-459
❑ 98DonColL-239
❑ 98DonColL-272
❑ 98DonColP-637
❑ 98DonColS-8
❑ 98DonCruG-75
❑ 98DonCruP-75
❑ 98DonCruR-75
❑ 98DonEli-59
❑ 98DonEliA-59
❑ 98DonEliS-59
❑ 98DonGolPP-8
❑ 98DonGolPP-226
❑ 98DonPre-87
❑ 98DonPreSeat-87
❑ 98DonPriCD-8
❑ 98DonPriCE-459
❑ 98DonPriCL-239
❑ 98DonPriCL-272
❑ 98DonPriCP-637
❑ 98DonSig-70
❑ 98DonSigP-70
❑ 98DonSilPP-8
❑ 98DonSilPP-226
❑ 98E-X2-72
❑ 98E-X2ECFut-72
❑ 98E-X2ECNow-72
❑ 98Fin-156
❑ 98FinNo--156
❑ 98FinNo-R-156
❑ 98FinRef-156
❑ 98FlaShoLeg0-82
❑ 98FlaShoLeg1-82
❑ 98FlaShoLeg2-82
❑ 98FlaShoLeg3-82
❑ 98FlaShoLegM-82
❑ 98FlaShoR0-82
❑ 98FlaShoR1-82
❑ 98FlaShoR2-82
❑ 98FlaShoR3-82
❑ 98Fle-27
❑ 98Fle-364
❑ 98FleVin'-25
❑ 98FleVin'-117
❑ 98FleVin'C-25
❑ 98FleVin'C-117
❑ 98Lea-39
❑ 98LeaFraDA-39
❑ 98LeaFraF-39
❑ 98LeaFraM-39
❑ 98LeaFraM-39
❑ 98LeaFraMDC-39
❑ 98LeaFraMDC-39
❑ 98LeaFraMS-39
❑ 98LeaFraMZ2-39
❑ 98LeaRS-87
❑ 98LeaRSLHolo-87
❑ 98LeaRSLong-87
❑ 98LeaRTrue-87
❑ 98MetUni-165
❑ 98MetUniPMG-165
❑ 98Pac-297
❑ 98PacAur-188
❑ 98PacInv-97
❑ 98PacInvGems-152
❑ 98PacInvPBlue-97
❑ 98PacInvSilv-97
❑ 98PacOme-202
❑ 98PacOmeR-202
❑ 98PacOnl-632
❑ 98PacOnlR-632
❑ 98PacOnlWC-632
❑ 98PacPar-234
❑ 98PacParC-234
❑ 98PacParG-234
❑ 98PacParHS-234
❑ 98PacParPB-234
❑ 98PacParR-234
❑ 98PacPlaB-297
❑ 98PacRedT-297
❑ 98PacSil-297
❑ 98Pin-116
❑ 98PinIns-49
❑ 98PinInsCE-49
❑ 98PinInsDE-49
❑ 98PinPer-83
❑ 98PinPerPP-83
❑ 98PinPlu-75
❑ 98PinPreP-116
❑ 98Sco-131
❑ 98ScoRT-208
❑ 98ScoRTSS-PP115
❑ 98ScoRTSSAP-PP115
❑ 98ScoRTSSAP1-PP115
❑ 98ScoSS-PP152
❑ 98ScoSSAP-PP152
❑ 98SkyDugA-45
❑ 98SkyDugAD-D2
❑ 98SkyDugAIA-45
❑ 98SP Aut-166
❑ 98SpoIll-15
❑ 98SpoIll-185
❑ 98SpoIllEE-15
❑ 98SpoIllEE-185
❑ 98SpoIllFE-15
❑ 98SpoIllFE-185
❑ 98SpoIllTaN-64
❑ 98SpoIllTaNEE-64
❑ 98SpoIllWSFEE-32
❑ 98SpoIllWSFFE-32
❑ 98SPxFin-315
❑ 98SPxFin-345
❑ 98SPxFinR-315
❑ 98SPxFinR-345
❑ 98SPxFinS-315
❑ 98SPxFinS-345
❑ 98StaCluFDI-331
❑ 98StaCluFDI-356
❑ 98StaCluI-331
❑ 98StaCluI-356
❑ 98StaCluOneK-331
❑ 98StaCluOneK-356
❑ 98StaCluPP-331
❑ 98StaCluPP-356
❑ 98Stu-180
❑ 98StuGPP-180
❑ 98StuSPP-180
❑ 98Top-6
❑ 98Top-266
❑ 98TopChr-6
❑ 98TopChr-266
❑ 98TopChrR-6
❑ 98TopChrR-266
❑ 98TopDevR-6
❑ 98TopDevR-266
❑ 98TopDia-6
❑ 98TopDia-266
❑ 98TopGal-80
❑ 98TopGalGP-80
❑ 98TopGalOPP-80
❑ 98TopGalPPI-80
❑ 98TopGalPPIA-80
❑ 98TopGolLabC1-1
❑ 98TopGolLabC1B-1
❑ 98TopGolLabC1One-1
❑ 98TopGolLabC1R-1
❑ 98TopGolLabC2-1
❑ 98TopGolLabC2B-1
❑ 98TopGolLabC2One-1
❑ 98TopGolLabC2R-1
❑ 98TopGolLabC3-1
❑ 98TopGolLabC3B-1
❑ 98TopGolLabC3One-1
❑ 98TopGolLabC3R-1
❑ 98TopMiniC-6
❑ 98TopMiniC-266
❑ 98TopOpeD-6
❑ 98TopSta-72
❑ 98TopStaB-72
❑ 98TopStaG-72
❑ 98TopStaGR-72
❑ 98TopStaS-72
❑ 98TopTek-71
❑ 98TopTekD-71
❑ 98Ult-32
❑ 98Ult-286
❑ 98UltGolM-32
❑ 98UltGolM-286
❑ 98UltMas-32
❑ 98UltMas-286
❑ 98UltPlaM-32
❑ 98UltPlaM-286
❑ 98UppDec-246
❑ 98UppDec-421
❑ 98UppDec-716
❑ 98UppDecR-83
❑ 98Zen-69
❑ 98Zen5 xx7-60
❑ 98Zen5x7GoldImp-60
❑ 98Zen5x7Imp-60
❑ 98ZenZ-G-69
❑ 98ZenZ-S-69
❑ 99199Fin-210
❑ 99Bow-280
❑ 99BowBes-63
❑ 99BowBesAR-63
❑ 99BowBesR-63
❑ 99BowGol-280
❑ 99BowInt-280
❑ 99CroRoyB-71
❑ 99CroRoyL-71
❑ 99CroRoyOD-71
❑ 99DodPol-3
❑ 99E-X Cen-88
❑ 99E-X CenECFut-88
❑ 99E-X CenECNow-88
❑ 99FinGolRef-210
❑ 99FinRef-210
❑ 99FlaShoLeg1-15
❑ 99FlaShoLeg2-15
❑ 99FlaShoLeg3-15
❑ 99FlaShoLegM1-15
❑ 99FlaShoLegM2-15
❑ 99FlaShoLegM3-15
❑ 99FlaShoR1-15
❑ 99FlaShoR2-15
❑ 99FlaShoR3-15
❑ 99Fle-106
❑ 99FleBri-111
❑ 99FleBri2G-111
❑ 99FleBriBlu-111
❑ 99FleBriGol-111
❑ 99FleMys-100
❑ 99FleMysG-100
❑ 99FleMysM-100
❑ 99FleSta9-106
❑ 99FleWarT-106
❑ 99MetUni-70
❑ 99MetUniGM-70
❑ 99MetUniPMG-70
❑ 99Pac-364
❑ 99PacAur-91
❑ 99PacAurOD-91
❑ 99PacCroC-238
❑ 99PacCroCPB-238
❑ 99PacInv-74
❑ 99PacInvOD-74
❑ 99PacInvPB-74
❑ 99PacOme-119
❑ 99PacOme5T-4
❑ 99PacOme5TT-4
❑ 99PacOmeC-119
❑ 99PacOmeG-119
❑ 99PacOmePB-119
❑ 99PacPar-115
❑ 99PacParC-115
❑ 99PacParG-115
❑ 99PacParHoloGold-115
❑ 99PacParHS-115
❑ 99PacParOD-115
❑ 99PacParPB-115
❑ 99PacParRed-115
❑ 99PacPlaB-364
❑ 99PacPri-122
❑ 99PacPriHB-122
❑ 99PacPriHG-122
❑ 99PacPriHM-122
❑ 99PacPriHP-122
❑ 99PacPriRed-122
❑ 99PacPriS-64
❑ 99PacPriS206-64
❑ 99PacPriS206R-64
❑ 99PacRed-364
❑ 99Pin-5
❑ 99Rev-69
❑ 99RevPremDate-69
❑ 99RevRet-69
❑ 99RevShaSS-69
❑ 99SkyMolM-84
❑ 99SkyMolMX-84
❑ 99SkyPre-211
❑ 99SkyPreR-211
❑ 99SkyThu-9
❑ 99SkyThuRant-9
❑ 99SkyThuRave-9
❑ 99SP Aut-43
❑ 99SP AutEF-E30
❑ 99SpoIll-154
❑ 99StaClu-320
❑ 99StaCluC-SCC8
❑ 99StaCluCR-SCC8
❑ 99StaCluFDI-320
❑ 99StaCluOoaK-320
❑ 99StaCluPP-320
❑ 99ThuSkySupR-9
❑ 99Top-285
❑ 99TopAll-AM27
❑ 99TopBlaLC1-48
❑ 99TopBlaLC2-48
❑ 99TopBlaLC3-48
❑ 99TopChr-285
❑ 99TopChrA-AE27
❑ 99TopChrAR-AE27
❑ 99TopChrR-285
❑ 99TopGal-74
❑ 99TopGalPP-74
❑ 99TopGalPPI-74
❑ 99TopGolL-48
❑ 99TopGolLC1-48
❑ 99TopGolLC2-48
❑ 99TopGolLOtO-48
❑ 99TopMVPP-285
❑ 99TopOpeD-127
❑ 99TopRedLC1-48
❑ 99TopRedLC2-48
❑ 99TopRedLC3-48
❑ 99TopSta-69
❑ 99TopSta1Foil-69
❑ 99TopStaFoil-69
❑ 99TopStaOS-69
❑ 99UD Cho-136
❑ 99UD ChoP-136
❑ 99UD ChoPCR-136
❑ 99UD Ion-50
❑ 99UD IonR-50
❑ 99UDHolo-31
❑ 99UDHoloAUsome-31
❑ 99Ult-90
❑ 99UltGolM-90
❑ 99UltMas-90
❑ 99UltPlaM-90
❑ 99UppDec-190
❑ 99UppDec-396
❑ 99UppDecBD-72
❑ 99UppDecBDD-72
❑ 99UppDecBDQ-72
❑ 99UppDecBDT-72
❑ 99UppDecCL-68
❑ 99UppDecCLCC-68
❑ 99UppDecCLM-C47
❑ 99UppDecEL1-190
❑ 99UppDecEL1-396
❑ 99UppDecEL2-190
❑ 99UppDecEL2-396
❑ 99UppDecM-103
❑ 99UppDecMGS-103
❑ 99UppDecMHFS-103
❑ 99UppDecMSS-103
❑ 99UppDecO-49
❑ 99UppDecOSO-49
❑ 99UppDecR-45
❑ 99UppDecRG-45
❑ 99UppDecRP-45
❑ 99UppDecTE-T13
❑ 99UppDecTED-T13
❑ 99UppDecTEQ-T13
❑ 99UppDecTET-T13
❑ 99Vic-198
❑ 99Vic-469

Brown, Kevin D.

❑ 86LynMetP-4
❑ 87SumBraP-7
❑ 87WicPilRD-21
❑ 88St.LucMS-3
❑ 88WicPilRD-32
❑ 89JacMetGS-26
❑ 89MetColP-24
❑ 89TidTidP-1962
❑ 90Bow-127
❑ 90BowTif-127
❑ 90CMC-353
❑ 90MetColP-27
❑ 90ProAAAF-266
❑ 90St.LucMS-2
❑ 90TidTidC-2
❑ 90TidTidP-535
❑ 90TopTVM-38
❑ 91Bow-49
❑ 91BreMilB-5
❑ 91BrePol-5
❑ 91Don-674
❑ 91Lea-475
❑ 91MetWIZ-53
❑ 91TopDeb90-22
❑ 92CalCanF-3726
❑ 92CalCanS-52
❑ 92Fle-174
❑ 92StaClu-123
❑ 93PhoFirF-1508
❑ 94BreMilB-291

Brown, Kevin L.

❑ 94HudValRC-2
❑ 94HudValRF-3386
❑ 94SigRooDP-48
❑ 94SigRooDPS-48
❑ 94StaCluDP-79
❑ 94StaCluDPFDI-79
❑ 94TopTra-129T
❑ 95Bow-32
❑ 95Exc-126
❑ 95SPML-161
❑ 96BesAutS-13
❑ 96BesAutSA-9
❑ 96BowFoi-176
❑ 96Exc-108
❑ 96TexLeaAB-3
❑ 96TulDriTI-4
❑ 97BesLimA-6
❑ 97Bow-124
❑ 97BowBesMI-MI4
❑ 97BowBesMIAR-MI4
❑ 97BowBesMIARI-MI4
❑ 97BowBesMII-MI4
❑ 97BowBesMIR-MI4
❑ 97BowBesMIRI-MI4
❑ 97BowCerBlaIA-CA8
❑ 97BowCerBluIA-CA8
❑ 97BowCerGolIA-CA8
❑ 97BowChr-138
❑ 97BowChrI-138
❑ 97BowChrR-138
❑ 97BowInt-124
❑ 97ColCho-12
❑ 97DonSigA-13
❑ 97DonSigAC-18
❑ 97DonSigAM-18
❑ 97MetUniMfG-2
❑ 97OklCit8-9
❑ 97PinIns-145
❑ 97PinInsCE-145
❑ 97PinInsDE-145
❑ 97Sel-129
❑ 97SelArtP-129
❑ 97SelCom-129
❑ 97SelRegG-129
❑ 97Top-205
❑ 97UppDec-473
❑ 98BesPreA-6
❑ 98Bow-280
❑ 98BowGolA-280
❑ 98BowInt-280
❑ 98Lea-73
❑ 98LeaFraDA-73
❑ 98LeaFraF-73
❑ 98LeaFraM-73
❑ 98LeaFraM-73
❑ 98LeaFraMDC-73
❑ 98LeaFraMDC-73
❑ 98LeaFraMZ2-73
❑ 98PacOmeRS-3
❑ 98PacOmeRST2-3
❑ 98PacOnl-752

❑ 98PacOnlR-752
❑ 98PacOnlWC-752
❑ 98PadMot-4
❑ 98Revo-122
❑ 98RevoSS-122
❑ 99UppDecE-48
❑ 99UppDecEFXG-48

Brown, Kurt
❑ 86AppFoxP-4
❑ 87PenWhiSP-26
❑ 88SouBenWSGS-13
❑ 88TamTarS-3
❑ 89SarWhiSS-1
❑ 90Bes-189
❑ 90BirBarB-2
❑ 90BirBarP-1111
❑ 91LinDriAAA-628
❑ 91VanCanLD-628
❑ 91VanCanP-1596

Brown, Larry
❑ 78LauLonABS-2
❑ 86NegLeaF-26
❑ 94TedWil-102

Brown, Larry Lesley
❑ 64Top-301
❑ 64TopVen-301
❑ 65Top-468
❑ 66IndVolC-3
❑ 66OPC-16
❑ 66Top-16
❑ 66TopVen-16
❑ 67CokCapI-3
❑ 67DexPre-33
❑ 67OPC-145
❑ 67Top-145
❑ 67TopVen-219
❑ 68Kah-B10
❑ 68Top-197
❑ 68TopVen-197
❑ 69MilBra-42
❑ 69MLBOffS-39
❑ 69Top-503
❑ 69TopSta-163
❑ 70Ind-2
❑ 70MLBOffS-194
❑ 70OPC-391
❑ 70Top-391
❑ 71MLBOffS-363
❑ 71OPC-539
❑ 71Top-539
❑ 72MilBra-53
❑ 72OPC-279
❑ 72Top-279
❑ 73BalOriP-8
❑ 73OriJohP-21
❑ 73OriTeal-7
❑ 81TCM60I-416
❑ 83LasVegSBHN-3
❑ 84LasVegSC-238
❑ 91OriCro-55
❑ 93RanKee-85

Brown, Leon
❑ 74PhoGiaC-82
❑ 75PhoGiaC-1
❑ 75PhoGiaCK-21
❑ 80OmaRoyP-3
❑ 91MetWIZ-54

Brown, Lindsay (John Lindsay)
❑ 90DodTar-82

Brown, Lloyd
❑ 31SenTealPW-4
❑ 35DiaMatCS3T1-17
❑ 90DodTar-83
❑ 91ConTSN-181

Brown, Mace
❑ 36R31PasP-3
❑ 39GouPreR303A-6
❑ 39WorWidGTP-6
❑ 40PlaBal-220
❑ 41DodTeal-1
❑ 42RedSoxTI-1
❑ 43RedSoxTI-1
❑ 46RedSoxTI-3
❑ 73Dod194T-2
❑ 75RedSox1T-3
❑ 75TCMGua-8
❑ 78DodTCM4-19
❑ 79DiaGre-359
❑ 90DodTar-84

Brown, Mark
❑ 81MiaOriT-4
❑ 83RocRedWT-2
❑ 84BalOriP-5
❑ 85TolMudHT-3
❑ 86ChaOriW-6
❑ 86TolMudHP-4
❑ 86Top-451
❑ 86TopTif-451
❑ 89EriOriS-28
❑ 91OriCro-56

Brown, Marty
❑ 86CedRapRT-14
❑ 87VerRedP-5
❑ 88NasSouC-18
❑ 88NasSouP-481
❑ 88NasSouTI-5
❑ 88TriAAAP-26
❑ 89CedRapRAB-29
❑ 89Fle-645
❑ 89FleGlo-645
❑ 89NasSouC-14
❑ 89NasSouP-1292
❑ 89NasSouTI-4
❑ 89ScoHot1R-70
❑ 90BalOriP-3
❑ 90CedRapRDGB-29
❑ 90DonRoo-39
❑ 90RocRedWGC-17
❑ 91ColSprSSLD-79
❑ 91ColSprSSP-2188
❑ 91LinDriAAA-79
❑ 91OriCro-57
❑ 98AugGreM-26

Brown, Matt
❑ 90EliTwiS-7
❑ 91Cla/Bes-93
❑ 91VisOakC-12
❑ 91VisOakP-1743
❑ 92VisOakC-16
❑ 92VisOakF-1017
❑ 93ForMyeMC-4
❑ 93ForMyeMF-2658

Brown, Michael
❑ 96LynHilB-5

Brown, Michael (Mike)
❑ 90WelPirP-2
❑ 91AugPirC-24
❑ 91AugPirP-809
❑ 91Cla/Bes-88
❑ 92AugPirF-243
❑ 93SalBucC-2
❑ 93VerBeaDC-3
❑ 94CarMudF-1584
❑ 94ExcFS7-251

Brown, Mike
❑ 77LynMetT-6
❑ 86OscAstP-2
❑ 87OscAstP-3
❑ 89KinIndS-26
❑ 91ColIndP-1504
❑ 91GreFalDSP-3
❑ 93CarLeaAGF-46
❑ 93SalBucF-438
❑ 93SouAtlLAGF-11
❑ 93VerBeaDF-2222
❑ 95CarMudF-163

Brown, Mike (Michael C.)
❑ 82SpoIndT-19
❑ 83TopTra-15T
❑ 84Don-42
❑ 84EdmTraC-117
❑ 84FleUpd-17
❑ 84Nes792-643
❑ 84Top-643
❑ 84TopTif-643
❑ 85AngSmo-4
❑ 85Don-207
❑ 85Fle-296
❑ 85Top-258
❑ 85TopTif-258
❑ 86Don-642
❑ 86Fle-605
❑ 86FleMin-117
❑ 86Lea-256
❑ 86PawRedSP-3
❑ 86Top-114
❑ 86TopTif-114
❑ 87Don-168
❑ 87Fle-607
❑ 87FleGlo-607
❑ 87RicBraC-42
❑ 87Top-341
❑ 87TopTif-341
❑ 88TolMudHC-24
❑ 88TolMudHP-611
❑ 88TolMudHP-NNO
❑ 89EdmTraC-18
❑ 89EdmTraP-558
❑ 92ColCliP-2
❑ 92ColCliS-125

Brown, Mike (Michael G.)
❑ 81HolMilT-8
❑ 84Don-517
❑ 84Fle-394
❑ 84Nes792-472
❑ 84Top-472
❑ 84TopTif-472
❑ 85Don-614
❑ 87CalCanP-2315
❑ 87Don-563
❑ 87Fle-583
❑ 87FleGlo-583
❑ 87RicBraT-27
❑ 87Top-271
❑ 87TopTif-271
❑ 88ColSprSSC-2
❑ 88ColSprSSP-1526
❑ 90PriWilCTI-1
❑ 90RenSilSCLC-286
❑ 91Ft.LauYC-29
❑ 91Ft.LauYP-2444
❑ 92ColRedC-27
❑ 92ColRedF-2407
❑ 92YakBeaF-3452
❑ 93ColRedC-27
❑ 93ColRedF-614
❑ 94CanIndF-3134

Brown, Mordecai
❑ 03WilCarE-3
❑ 06FanCraNL-7
❑ 07CubA.CDPP-1
❑ 07CubGFGCP-1
❑ 08AmeCarE91-4
❑ 08AmeCarE91-39
❑ 08RosComP-101
❑ 09AmeCarE90-1-16
❑ 09RamT20-18
❑ 09SpoNewSM-22
❑ 09T206-41
❑ 09T206-42
❑ 09T206-43
❑ 10ChiE-2
❑ 10CouT21-86
❑ 10CouT21-87
❑ 10CouT21-262
❑ 10DarChoE-6
❑ 10DomDisP-17
❑ 10E98-4
❑ 10RedCroT-93
❑ 10SepAnoP-3
❑ 10StaCarE-3
❑ 10SweCapPP-80A
❑ 10SweCapPP-80B
❑ 10W555-9
❑ 11BasBatEU-5
❑ 11DiaGumP-4
❑ 11HelSta-91
❑ 11MecDFT-28
❑ 11PinT-5-202
❑ 11PloCanE-10
❑ 11S74Sil-58
❑ 11SpoLifCW-46
❑ 11SpoLifM-167
❑ 11T205-22
❑ 11TurRedT-1
❑ 12HasTriFT-70B
❑ 12PhiCarE-5
❑ 14CraJacE-32
❑ 14FatPlaT-8
❑ 14PieStaT-15
❑ 15CraJacE-32
❑ 15SpoNewM-23
❑ 16BF2FP-66
❑ 16SpoNewM-17
❑ 37KelPepS-BB2
❑ 39PC7AlbHoF-56
❑ 50CalHOFW-8
❑ 50CubGreB-3
❑ 53ArtHaloFP-7
❑ 60ExhWriH-5
❑ 60Fle-9
❑ 61Fle-11
❑ 63BazA-13
❑ 67SpoHobFC-6
❑ 67SpoHobFC-34
❑ 67TopVen-173
❑ 68SCFOldT-30
❑ 72ClaCar-31
❑ 74CapPub-23
❑ 75FlePio-23
❑ 76ISCHooHA-9
❑ 76MotOldT-5
❑ 76ShaPiz-57
❑ 77BobParHoF-55
❑ 80PacLeg-71
❑ 80PerHaloFP-56
❑ 80SSPHOF-56
❑ 82TCMGreP-34
❑ 84CubBriPC-6H
❑ 87Cub190T-2
❑ 87HygAllG-6
❑ 89HOFStiB-60
❑ 90BasWit-89
❑ 92ConTSN-555
❑ 92CubOldS-4
❑ 93ConTSN-883
❑ 93CraJac-18
❑ 94ConTSNCI-37
❑ 94OriofB-90

Brown, Nate
❑ 96WesPalBEB-23

Brown, Ollie Lee
❑ 66Top-524
❑ 67CokCapG-2
❑ 67DexPre-34
❑ 67OPC-83
❑ 67Top-83
❑ 68Top-223
❑ 68TopVen-223
❑ 69MLBOffS-190
❑ 69OPC-149
❑ 69PadVol-1
❑ 69Top-149
❑ 69TopFou-8
❑ 69TopSta-92
❑ 69TopSup-63
❑ 69TopTeaP-12
❑ 70Kel-55
❑ 70MLBOffS-109
❑ 70OPC-130
❑ 70Top-130
❑ 70TopCanL-5
❑ 70TopPos-18
❑ 70TopSup-36
❑ 71MLBOffS-220
❑ 71OPC-505
❑ 71Top-505
❑ 71TopCoi-133
❑ 72MilBra-54
❑ 72PadPos-4
❑ 72Top-551
❑ 72Top-552
❑ 73OPC-526
❑ 73Top-526
❑ 74OPC-625
❑ 74Top-625
❑ 75OPC-596
❑ 75PhiPhiP-7
❑ 75Top-596
❑ 75TopMin-596
❑ 76OPC-223
❑ 76PhiPhiP-5
❑ 76SSP-466
❑ 76Top-223
❑ 77PadSchC-9
❑ 77Top-84
❑ 81TCM60I-368
❑ 86PadGreT-6
❑ 94BreMilB-292

Brown, Oscar Lee
❑ 71MLBOffS-5
❑ 71OPC-52
❑ 71Top-52
❑ 72OPC-516
❑ 72Top-516
❑ 73OPC-312
❑ 73Top-312

Brown, Paul
❑ 87ElmPioBC-34
❑ 87HawRai-28
❑ 88LynRedSS-2
❑ 90LynRedSTI-15
❑ 91WinHavRSC-2
❑ 91WinHavRSP-482

Brown, Paul D.
❑ 62Top-181
❑ 62TopVen-181
❑ 63Top-478
❑ 64Top-319
❑ 64TopVen-319

Brown, Randy
❑ 76WauMetT-6
❑ 77LynMetT-7
❑ 96TreThuB-20
❑ 97TreThuB-9

Brown, Randy J.
❑ 90ElmPioP-3
❑ 91Cla/Bes-131
❑ 91WinHavRSC-15
❑ 91WinHavRSP-495
❑ 92WinHavRSC-3
❑ 92WinHavRSF-1783
❑ 93CarLeaAGF-6
❑ 93LynRedSC-4
❑ 93LynRedSF-2521
❑ 94NewBriRSF-654
❑ 95PawRedSDD-7
❑ 95PawRedTI-25

Brown, Ray
❑ 94BilMusF-3675
❑ 94BilMusSP-4
❑ 94StaCluDP-78
❑ 94StaCluDPFDI-78
❑ 95Bow-236
❑ 95BowGolF-236
❑ 95Exc-173
❑ 95ExcFirYP-2
❑ 95Top-79
❑ 96BesAutS-14
❑ 96ChaLooB-9
❑ 96DouAllB-40
❑ 97Bow-303
❑ 97BowCerBlaIA-CA9
❑ 97BowCerBluIA-CA9
❑ 97BowCerGolIA-CA9
❑ 97BowInt-303
❑ 98WicWraM-2

Brown, Reggie
❑ 89HelBreSP-3

Brown, Renard
❑ 87StoPorP-9

Brown, Rick
❑ 86LitFalMP-4
❑ 87ColMetP-12
❑ 88St.LucMS-4

Brown, Rob
❑ 64TopRooAB-32
❑ 89SanDieSAS-5
❑ 90ChaRanS-2
❑ 91LinDriAA-576
❑ 91TulDriLD-576
❑ 91TulDriP-2765
❑ 91TulDriTI-2
❑ 92TulDriF-2688
❑ 92TulDriS-604
❑ 93OklCit8F-1619

Brown, Robert
❑ 85UtiBluST-17

Brown, Ron
❑ 91MisStaB-6
❑ 92MisStaB-5
❑ 93ElmPioC-4
❑ 93ElmPioF-3835
❑ 93MisStaB-5
❑ 94KanCouCC-6
❑ 94KanCouCF-173
❑ 94KanCouCTI-6
❑ 95BreCouMF-257
❑ 96PorSeaDB-9
❑ 97NorNav-9
❑ 97NorNavTI-4

Brown, Ronnie
❑ 89WytCubS-3

Brown, Roosevelt
❑ 94IdaFalBF-3596
❑ 94IdaFalBSP-1
❑ 95EugEmeTI-7
❑ 96KanCouCUTI-3
❑ 96MacBraB-22
❑ 99Bow-114
❑ 99BowAut-BA21
❑ 99BowBes-176
❑ 99BowBesAR-176
❑ 99BowBesR-176
❑ 99BowChr-114
❑ 99BowChrG-114
❑ 99BowChrGR-114
❑ 99BowChrI-114
❑ 99BowChrIR-114
❑ 99BowChrR-114
❑ 99BowGol-114
❑ 99BowInt-114
❑ 99E-X Cen-112
❑ 99E-X CenECFut-112
❑ 99E-X CenECNow-112
❑ 99E-X CenEQ-11
❑ 99FlaShoLeg1-26
❑ 99FlaShoLeg2-26
❑ 99FlaShoLeg3-26
❑ 99FlaShoLegM1-26
❑ 99FlaShoLegM2-26
❑ 99FlaShoLegM3-26
❑ 99FlaShoR1-26
❑ 99FlaShoR2-26
❑ 99FlaShoR3-26
❑ 99FlaShoWotF-13
❑ 99FleBri-175
❑ 99FleBri2G-175
❑ 99FleBriBlu-175
❑ 99FleBriGol-175
❑ 99SkyPreA-6
❑ 99SkyPreABlue-6
❑ 99SP TopP-22
❑ 99SP TopPPE-22
❑ 99Top-436
❑ 99TopChr-436
❑ 99TopChrR-436

Brown, Roy
❑ 27Zee-86

Brown, Sam (Samuel W.)
❑ 11SpoLifCW-47

Brown, Scott
❑ 79NaSouTI-5
❑ 80IndIndTI-17
❑ 81IndIndTI-19
❑ 82Fle-60
❑ 82Roy-5
❑ 82Top-351
❑ 83OmaRoyT-4
❑ 94VenLinU-115

Brown, Shawn
❑ 93NiaFalRF-3395
❑ 94LakTigC-3
❑ 94LakTigF-3042

Brown, Skinny (Hector Harold)
❑ 53RedSoxTI-3
❑ 53Top-184
❑ 54Top-172
❑ 55Bow-221
❑ 55Top-148
❑ 55TopDouH-85
❑ 56BalOriP-14
❑ 56BalOriP-7
❑ 57Top-194
❑ 58BalOriP-6
❑ 58Hir-18
❑ 58Top-381
❑ 59Top-487
❑ 60Top-89
❑ 60TopVen-89
❑ 61BalOriP-4
❑ 61Pos-78
❑ 61Top-46
❑ 61Top-218
❑ 62BalOriP-6
❑ 62Top-488
❑ 63Top-289
❑ 64Top-56
❑ 64TopVen-56
❑ 75OakOak2A-9
❑ 87AstSer1-6
❑ 91OriCro-54
❑ 91TopArc1-184
❑ 92YanWIZ6-18
❑ 94TopArc1-172
❑ 94TopArc1G-172
❑ 97BalOriP-5

Brown, Stacy
❑ 89BurIndS-3

Brown, Stanley
❑ 41DouPlaR-35

Brown, Steven E.
❑ 80ElPasDT-16
❑ 81SalLakCGT-3
❑ 82SpoIndT-1
❑ 85IndIndTI-24

Brown, Tab
❑ 89PulBraP-1899
❑ 90Bes-62
❑ 90CMC-828
❑ 90SumBraB-2
❑ 90SumBraP-2425

Brown, Terry M.
❑ 87BelBreP-15
❑ 89KenTwiP-1068
❑ 89KenTwiS-2

Brown, Thomas D.
❑ 76BatRouCT-6
❑ 89PacSenL-139

Brown, Tibor
❑ 92FroRowDP-62
❑ 92FroRowDPG-62
❑ 92FroRowDPS-62

Brown, Tim
❑ 88St.CatBJP-2007
❑ 89MyrBeaBJP-1465
❑ 90DunBluJS-4
❑ 91DunBluJC-3
❑ 91DunBluJP-199
❑ 92ClaFS7-158

❑ 92KnoBluJF-2982
❑ 92KnoBluJS-377
❑ 93SyrChiF-993
❑ 95SyrChiTI-6
Brown, Todd
❑ 86StoPorP-3
❑ 87ElPasDP-17
❑ 88DenZepC-19
❑ 88DenZepP-1278
❑ 94BluOriF-3574
❑ 98FreKeyM-5
Brown, Tom
❑ 78SanJosMMC-16
❑ 79TacTugT-2
❑ 80SyrChiT-8
❑ 80SyrChiTI-6
❑ 80VenLeaS-74
❑ 81SyrChiT-2
❑ 81SyrChiTI-4
❑ 89HagSunB-11
❑ 89HagSunP-283
❑ 89HagSunS-22
❑ 90HagSunB-5
❑ 90HagSunP-1432
❑ 90HagSunS-27
❑ 96OklCit8B-2
❑ 97OklCit8-2
❑ 98OklRedM-2
Brown, Tom (Thomas Michael)
❑ 47DodTeal-4
❑ 48DodTeal-5
❑ 49Bow-178
❑ 49EurSta-31
❑ 52Bow-236
❑ 52Top-281
❑ 53BowC-42
❑ 78ReaRem-1
❑ 83TopRep5-281
❑ 90DodTar-85
❑ 91DodRinP4-3
Brown, Tom (Thomas T.)
❑ 87BucN28-86
❑ 87OldJudN-46
❑ 88WG1CarG-1
❑ 89N526N7C-3
Brown, Tom (Thomas William)
❑ 64Top-311
❑ 64TopVen-311
Brown, Tony
❑ 86ReaPhiP-4
❑ 87ReaPhiP-2
❑ 88EasLeaAP-31
❑ 88ReaPhiP-867
❑ 89BlaYNPRWLU-1
❑ 89TidTidC-27
❑ 89TidTidP-1974
❑ 90Bes-298
❑ 90HunStaB-20
❑ 91AugPirC-23
❑ 92MidAngF-4036
❑ 92MidAngOHP-3
❑ 92MidAngS-455
Brown, Trent
❑ 97ChaRivDG-9
Brown, Vick
❑ 94GreBatF-482
❑ 94SouAtlLAF-SAL12
❑ 95GreBatTI-6
❑ 96TamYanY-6
❑ 97GreBatC-4
❑ 97TamYan-7
❑ 98NorNavQ-7
Brown, Willard
❑ 93BoiHawC-4
❑ 93BoiHawF-3905
❑ 94CedRapKC-4
❑ 95MidAngOHP-6
❑ 95MidAngTI-6
❑ 96MidAngOHP-6
❑ 97NegLeaPC-8S
Brown, Willard Jessie
❑ 90NegLeaS-7
❑ 94TedWil-101
Brown, Willie
❑ 92EriSaiC-1
❑ 92EriSaiF-1635
❑ 93LetMouF-4160
❑ 93LetMouSP-10
❑ 93StaCluM-54
❑ 93Top-497
❑ 93TopGol-497
❑ 93TopInaM-497
❑ 93TopInaR-497
❑ 93TopMic-497
❑ 94CedRapKF-1102
❑ 94KanCouCC-7
❑ 94KanCouCF-174
❑ 94KanCouCTI-7
❑ 94MidLeaAF-MDW35
❑ 95BreCouMF-258
Brown, Winston
❑ 61Top-391
❑ 89SprCarB-8
Brown, Zadrian
❑ 98BilMusTI-6
Browne, Byron
❑ 92BelBreCB-4
❑ 92BelBreFI-396
❑ 93StoPorC-3
❑ 93StoPorF-736
❑ 95ElPasDTI-2
❑ 96Bow-205
❑ 96BowFoi-205
Browne, Byron Ellis
❑ 66OPC-139
❑ 66Top-139
❑ 66TopVen-139
❑ 67CokCapC-18
❑ 67ProPizC-4
❑ 67Top-439
❑ 68Top-296
❑ 68TopVen-296
❑ 70OPC-388
❑ 70Top-388
❑ 71MLBOffS-171
❑ 71OPC-659
❑ 71Top-659
Browne, George Edward
❑ 08AmeCarE91-68
❑ 11PinT-5-567
❑ 11SpoLifCW-48
❑ 11TurRedT-84
Browne, Jerry
❑ 86TulDriTI-9A
❑ 87ClaUpdY-146
❑ 87Don-41
❑ 87DonOpeD-170
❑ 87DonRoo-29
❑ 87Fle-647
❑ 87FleGlo-647
❑ 87FleUpd-12
❑ 87FleUpdG-12
❑ 87Lea-41
❑ 87RanMot-22
❑ 87RanSmo-31
❑ 87SpoRool-4
❑ 87TopTra-11T
❑ 87TopTraT-11T
❑ 88Don-408
❑ 88Fle-462A
❑ 88Fle-462B
❑ 88FleGlo-462
❑ 88Lea-236
❑ 88OPC-139
❑ 88PanSti-201
❑ 88RanMot-22
❑ 88RanSmo-15
❑ 88Sco-278
❑ 88ScoGlo-278
❑ 88ScoYouS2-13
❑ 88StaLinRa-2
❑ 88Top-139
❑ 88TopBig-163
❑ 88TopRoo-21
❑ 88TopTif-139
❑ 88ToyRoo-3
❑ 89Bow-85
❑ 89BowTif-85
❑ 89Don-529
❑ 89DonBasB-280
❑ 89DonTra-44
❑ 89FleUpd-26
❑ 89IndTeal-6
❑ 89Top-532
❑ 89TopBig-236
❑ 89TopTif-532
❑ 89TopTra-16T
❑ 89TopTraT-16T
❑ 89UppDec-314
❑ 90Bow-332
❑ 90BowTif-332
❑ 90ClaBlu-53
❑ 90Don-138
❑ 90Fle-487
❑ 90FleCan-487
❑ 90IndTeal-8
❑ 90Lea-48
❑ 90OPC-442
❑ 90PanSti-54
❑ 90PubIntS-555
❑ 90Sco-52
❑ 90Spo-111
❑ 90Top-442
❑ 90TopBig-256
❑ 90TopCoi-7
❑ 90TopSti-210
❑ 90TopTif-442
❑ 90TulDriDGB-27
❑ 90UppDec-426
❑ 91Bow-71
❑ 91Don-162
❑ 91Fle-363
❑ 91IndFanC-5
❑ 91Lea-43
❑ 91OPC-76
❑ 91PanFreS-217
❑ 91Sco-481
❑ 91StaClu-25
❑ 91Top-76
❑ 91TopDesS-76
❑ 91TopMic-76
❑ 91TopTif-76
❑ 91Ult-108
❑ 91UppDec-116
❑ 92Fle-107
❑ 92FleUpd-47
❑ 92OPC-219
❑ 92Pin-208
❑ 92Sco-496
❑ 92StaClu-251
❑ 92Top-219
❑ 92TopGol-219
❑ 92TopGolW-219
❑ 92TopMic-219
❑ 92TopTra-16T
❑ 92TopTraG-16T
❑ 92TriPla-130
❑ 92Ult-48
❑ 92UppDec-340
❑ 93AthMot-13
❑ 93AthStaC-4
❑ 93Don-447
❑ 93Fle-292
❑ 93Lea-150
❑ 93OPC-234
❑ 93PacSpa-219
❑ 93PanSti-18
❑ 93Pin-391
❑ 93RanKee-86
❑ 93Sco-382
❑ 93StaClu-509
❑ 93StaCluFDI-509
❑ 93StaCluM-167
❑ 93StaCluMOP-509
❑ 93Top-383
❑ 93TopGol-383
❑ 93TopInaM-383
❑ 93TopInaR-383
❑ 93TopMic-383
❑ 93Ult-255
❑ 93UppDec-129
❑ 93UppDecGold-129
❑ 94ColC-448
❑ 94ColChoGS-448
❑ 94ColChoSS-448
❑ 94Fla-379
❑ 94Fle-257
❑ 94FleUpd-133
❑ 94Pin-489
❑ 94PinArtP-489
❑ 94PinMusC-489
❑ 94Sco-349
❑ 94ScoGolR-349
❑ 94ScoRoo-RT47
❑ 94ScoRooGR-RT47
❑ 94StaClu-683
❑ 94StaCluFDI-683
❑ 94StaCluGR-683
❑ 94StaCluMOP-683
❑ 94StaCluT-68
❑ 94StaCluTFDI-68
❑ 94Top-624
❑ 94TopGol-624
❑ 94TopSpa-624
❑ 94TopTra-16T
❑ 95ColCho-301
❑ 95ColChoGS-301
❑ 95ColChoSS-301
❑ 95Don-446
❑ 95DonPreP-446
❑ 95Fle-327
❑ 95Pac-168
❑ 95Sco-363
❑ 95ScoGolR-363
❑ 95ScoPlaTS-363
❑ 96ColCho-149
❑ 96ColChoGS-149
❑ 96ColChoSS-149
❑ 96Fle-382
❑ 96FleTif-382
Browne, Pidge (Prentice A.)
❑ 77FriOneYW-50
❑ 89AstCol4S-20
Brownell, Sam
❑ 97UCLBruTI-1
Brownholtz, Joe
❑ 92ChaRanF-2219
❑ 92GasRanC-8
❑ 93ChaRanC-3
❑ 93ChaRanF-1931
Browning, Frank
❑ 09ObaT21-49
❑ 09ObaT21-155
❑ 09ObaT21-322
❑ 11PacCoaBD-9
❑ 11Zee-83
❑ 12ObaPreT-71
Browning, Mike
❑ 82NasSouTI-2
❑ 83NasSouTI-2
❑ 84EdmTraC-114
❑ 86MiaMarP-3
❑ 87MiaMarP-15
❑ 88MiaMarS-4
❑ 89ColMudB-17
❑ 89ColMudP-122
❑ 89ColMudS-5
❑ 90ColMudB-20
❑ 90ColMudP-1339
❑ 90ColMudS-6
Browning, Pete (Louis R.)
❑ 87OldJudN-48
❑ 90DodTar-86
❑ 94OriofB-35
Browning, Tom
❑ 83TamTarT-5
❑ 84WicAerRD-5
❑ 85Don-634
❑ 85DonHig-43
❑ 85FleUpd-12
❑ 85TopTifT-11T
❑ 85TopTra-11T
❑ 86BasStaB-17
❑ 86Don-384
❑ 86Dra-37
❑ 86Fle-173
❑ 86FleMin-38
❑ 86FleSlu-4
❑ 86FleStiC-14
❑ 86FleWaxBC-C6
❑ 86KayB-3
❑ 86Lea-179
❑ 86RedTexG-32
❑ 86SevCoi-S15
❑ 86Spo-79
❑ 86Spo-185
❑ 86Top-652
❑ 86TopGloS-49
❑ 86TopMinL-40
❑ 86TopSti-141
❑ 86TopSti-313
❑ 86TopSup-16
❑ 86TopTat-10
❑ 86TopTif-652
❑ 87ClaGam-78
❑ 87Don-63
❑ 87DonOpeD-194
❑ 87Fle-194
❑ 87FleGlo-194
❑ 87Lea-138
❑ 87OPC-65
❑ 87RedKah-32
❑ 87SpoTeaP-4
❑ 87Top-65
❑ 87TopSti-137
❑ 87TopTif-65
❑ 88Don-63
❑ 88DonBasB-335
❑ 88Fle-228
❑ 88FleGlo-228
❑ 88RedKah-32
❑ 88Sco-132
❑ 88ScoGlo-132
❑ 88StaLinRe-2
❑ 88Top-577
❑ 88TopBig-96
❑ 88TopClo-18
❑ 88TopTif-577
❑ 89Bow-306
❑ 89BowTif-306
❑ 89ClaTraO-126
❑ 89Don-71
❑ 89DonBasB-62
❑ 89Fle-153
❑ 89Fle-629
❑ 89FleGlo-153
❑ 89FleGlo-629
❑ 89OPC-234
❑ 89PanSti-4
❑ 89PanSti-65
❑ 89RedKah-32
❑ 89Sco-554
❑ 89Sco-658
❑ 89ScoHot1S-61
❑ 89Spo-180
❑ 89Spo-222
❑ 89Top-234
❑ 89TopBig-14
❑ 89TopGloS-46
❑ 89TopMinL-6
❑ 89TopSti-7
❑ 89TopSti-141
❑ 89TopStiB-61
❑ 89TopTif-234
❑ 89TVSpoM-41
❑ 89UppDec-617
❑ 89UppDecS-3
❑ 89Woo-9
❑ 90Bow-43
❑ 90BowTif-43
❑ 90ClaUpd-T7
❑ 90Don-308
❑ 90DonBesN-27
❑ 90DonLeaS-54
❑ 90Fle-415
❑ 90FleCan-415
❑ 90Lea-110
❑ 90MLBBasB-20
❑ 90OPC-418
❑ 90PanSti-247
❑ 90PubIntS-23
❑ 90RedKah-5
❑ 90Sco-165
❑ 90Sco100S-33
❑ 90Spo-91
❑ 90Top-418
❑ 90TopBig-48
❑ 90TopSti-135
❑ 90TopTif-418
❑ 90UppDec-189
❑ 91Bow-684
❑ 91ClaGam-10
❑ 91Don-528
❑ 91Fle-59
❑ 91Lea-88
❑ 91OPC-151
❑ 91RedKah-32
❑ 91RedPep-4
❑ 91Sco-229
❑ 91Sco100S-32
❑ 91StaClu-235
❑ 91Stu-161
❑ 91Top-151
❑ 91TopDesS-151
❑ 91TopMic-151
❑ 91TopTif-151
❑ 91Ult-89
❑ 91UppDec-633
❑ 91USPlaCA-5S
❑ 92Bow-161
❑ 92Don-136
❑ 92Fle-401
❑ 92Lea-46
❑ 92LeaBlaG-46
❑ 92OPC-339
❑ 92Pin-101
❑ 92RedKah-32
❑ 92Sco-642
❑ 92StaClu-624
❑ 92StaCluD-22
❑ 92Top-339
❑ 92TopGol-339
❑ 92TopGolW-339
❑ 92TopMic-339
❑ 92Ult-186
❑ 92UppDec-461
❑ 93Don-190
❑ 93Fle-387
❑ 93Lea-359
❑ 93OPC-74
❑ 93PacSpa-79
❑ 93Pin-405
❑ 93RedKah-5
❑ 93Sco-404
❑ 93Sel-249
❑ 93Top-733
❑ 93TopGol-733
❑ 93TopInaM-733
❑ 93TopInaR-733
❑ 93TopMic-733
❑ 93TriPla-91
❑ 93Ult-325
❑ 93UppDec-270
❑ 93UppDecGold-270
❑ 94ColC-439
❑ 94ColChoGS-439
❑ 94ColChoSS-439
❑ 94Fin-337
❑ 94FinRef-337
❑ 94Fla-144
❑ 94Fle-406
❑ 94FleExtB-229
❑ 94Pac-142
❑ 94PanSti-161
❑ 94Pin-335
❑ 94PinArtP-335
❑ 94PinMusC-335
❑ 94RedKah-4
❑ 94Sco-168
❑ 94ScoGolR-168
❑ 94StaClu-433
❑ 94StaCluFDI-433
❑ 94StaCluGR-433
❑ 94StaCluMOP-433
❑ 94Top-619
❑ 94TopGol-619
❑ 94TopSpa-619
❑ 94Ult-469
❑ 95Sco-197
❑ 95ScoGolR-197
❑ 95ScoPlaTS-197
Browns, 19th C (St. Louis)
❑ 86JosHalC-13
Browns, St. Louis
❑ 13FatT20-7
❑ 36R31Pre-G27
❑ 38BasTabP-32
❑ 68LauWorS-41
❑ 70FleWorS-41
❑ 71FleWorS-42
❑ 93TedWilPC-20
❑ 96Bro194F-1
Brownson, Mark
❑ 95AshTouTI-17
❑ 96NewHavRB-6
❑ 97NewHavRB-15
❑ 98ColSprSS-32
❑ 99Fle-353
❑ 99FleSta9-353
❑ 99FleWarT-353
Broyles, Jason
❑ 90KisDodD-4
❑ 91YakBeaC-19
❑ 91YakBeaP-4239
Bruback, Matt
❑ 98WilCubM-3
Brubaker, Bill (Wilbur L.)
❑ 36GouBWR-4
❑ 36GouWidPPR-A11
❑ 39PlaBal-130
❑ 40PlaBal-166
❑ 72TCMthe3-6
❑ 94ConTSN-1133
❑ 94ConTSNB-1133
Brubaker, Bruce
❑ 65Top-493
❑ 67Top-276
❑ 90DodTar-904
❑ 94BreMilB-293
Brubaker, John
❑ 89OneYanP-2128
❑ 90Ft.LauYS-2
Brubaker, Ray
❑ 21Zee-24
❑ 22Zee-24
❑ 23Zee-27
❑ 24Zee-22
❑ 25Zee-20
❑ 26Zee-67
❑ 27Zee-47
❑ 28Zee-68
❑ 29Zee-63
❑ 30Zee-73
❑ 32Zee-51
❑ 33Zee-20
Brucato, Bob
❑ 89ChaRaiP-973
Bruce, Andy

❑ 91JohCitCC-5
❑ 91JohCitCP-3981
❑ 92ProFS7-325
❑ 92St.PetCF-2033
❑ 93MidLeaAGF-49
❑ 93SprCarC-4
❑ 93SprCarF-1856
❑ 94ArkTraF-3094
Bruce, Bob
❑ 60Top-118
❑ 60TopVen-118
❑ 61Top-83
❑ 62Col.45B-3
❑ 62Col45'JP-3
❑ 62Top-419
❑ 63Col45'P-3
❑ 63Col45'JP-2
❑ 63Top-24
❑ 64Col.45JP-2
❑ 64Top-282
❑ 64TopRooAB-3
❑ 64TopVen-282
❑ 65OPC-240
❑ 65Top-240
❑ 66OPC-64
❑ 66Top-64
❑ 66TopRubl-11
❑ 66TopVen-64
❑ 67AstTeal2-5
❑ 67BraPho-5
❑ 67CokCapB-11
❑ 67DexPre-35
❑ 67Top-417A
❑ 67Top-417B
❑ 87AstSer1-7
❑ 89AstCol4S-1
Bruce, Mo
❑ 98CapCitBF5-19
❑ 98CapCitBM-19
❑ 99Bow-325
❑ 99BowGol-325
❑ 99BowInt-325
Bruce, Rob
❑ 98KinIndQ-5
Bruce, Tim
❑ 93BelMarCB-5
❑ 93BelMarF-3197
❑ 94AppFoxC-3
❑ 94AppFoxFl-1044
Bruck, Tom
❑ 90BurBraB-5
❑ 90BurBraP-2341
❑ 90BurBraS-5
Brucker, Earle F. Jr.
❑ 30Zee-167
❑ 42A'sTeal-7
❑ 43A'STEAI-7
❑ 45A'sTeal-4
❑ 46A'sTeal-2
❑ 47A'sTeal-4
❑ 48A'sTeal-3
❑ 49A'sTeal-7
❑ 49PhiBul-9
❑ 79DiaGre-340
Brueggemann, Dean
❑ 96PorRocB-8
❑ 97AshTou-5
❑ 98AshTouM-3
Brueggemann, Jeff
❑ 80TolMudHT-18
❑ 83VisOakF-14
Brueggemann, Steve
❑ 85LitFalMT-3
Bruehl, Darin
❑ 89AubAstP-2179
Bruett, J.T. (Joseph T.)
❑ 88CapCodPPaLP-168
❑ 89KenTwiP-1074
❑ 89KenTwiS-3
❑ 90CalLeaACLC-13
❑ 90CMC-576
❑ 90PorBeaC-24
❑ 90ProAaA-154
❑ 90VisOakCLC-74
❑ 90VisOakP-2165
❑ 91LinDriAAA-405
❑ 91PorBeaLD-405
❑ 91PorBeaP-1577
❑ 92Bow-112
❑ 92DonRoo-18
❑ 92PorBeaF-2678
❑ 92PorBeaS-403
❑ 92SkyAAAF-184
❑ 93FleMajLP-B8
❑ 93PacSpa-519
❑ 93Pin-241
❑ 93Sco-275
❑ 93StaClu-397
❑ 93StaCluFDI-397
❑ 93StaCluMOP-397
❑ 93Top-309
❑ 93TopGol-309
❑ 93TopInaM-309
❑ 93TopInaR-309
❑ 93TopMic-309
❑ 93Ult-229
❑ 94SalLakBF-828
❑ 95OmaRoyTI-4
Brugo, Dale
❑ 91LynRedSC-1
Bruhert, Mike
❑ 78MetDaiPA-3
❑ 78TidTidT-6
❑ 79Top-172
❑ 79TucTorT-3
❑ 82ColCliP-25
❑ 82ColCliT-7
❑ 91MetWIZ-55
Bruins, UCLA
❑ 97UCLBruTI-31
Brumbaugh, Cliff
❑ 95HudValRTI-1
❑ 96Bow-156
❑ 96BowFoi-156
❑ 96ChaRivTI-9608
❑ 98TexLeaC-2
❑ 98TulDriTI-10
Brumfield, Harvey
❑ 87ClePhiP-9
❑ 88ReaPhiP-881
❑ 89ReaPhiB-20
❑ 89ReaPhiP-667
❑ 89ReaPhiS-4
Brumfield, Jacob
❑ 87Ft.MyeRP-33
❑ 88MemChiB-6
❑ 89MemChiB-3
❑ 89MemChiP-1188
❑ 89MemChiS-4
❑ 90BasCitRS-3
❑ 90FloStaLAS-26
❑ 90StaFS7-43
❑ 91LinDriAAA-327
❑ 91OmaRoyLD-327
❑ 91OmaRoyP-1045
❑ 92DonRoo-19
❑ 92Lea-499
❑ 92LeaBlaG-499
❑ 92NasSouF-1844
❑ 92OPC-591
❑ 92Pin-553
❑ 92Top-591
❑ 92TopGol-591
❑ 92TopGolW-591
❑ 92TopMic-591
❑ 92Ult-481
❑ 93IndIndF-1499
❑ 93PacSpa-80
❑ 93RedKah-6
❑ 93Sco-292
❑ 94Don-473
❑ 94Fle-407
❑ 94Pac-143
❑ 94RedKah-5
❑ 94StaClu-166
❑ 94StaCluFDI-166
❑ 94StaCluGR-166
❑ 94StaCluMOP-166
❑ 94Top-69
❑ 94TopGol-69
❑ 94TopSpa-69
❑ 95DonTopotO-313
❑ 95Fin-262
❑ 95FinRef-262
❑ 95Fle-473
❑ 95Lea-393
❑ 95Pac-101
❑ 95Pin-308
❑ 95PinArtP-308
❑ 95PinMusC-308
❑ 95PirFil-3
❑ 95Sco-93
❑ 95ScoGolR-93
❑ 95ScoPlaTS-93
❑ 95Sel-153
❑ 95SelArtP-153
❑ 95StaClu-553
❑ 95StaCluMOP-553
❑ 95StaCluSTWS-553
❑ 95TopTra-56T
❑ 96ColCho-683
❑ 96ColChoGS-683
❑ 96ColChoSS-683
❑ 96Don-247
❑ 96DonPreP-247
❑ 96Fle-515
❑ 96FleTif-515
❑ 96Pac-174
❑ 96Sco-151
❑ 96StaClu-341
❑ 96StaCluMOP-341
❑ 96Top-72
❑ 96Ult-261
❑ 96UltGolM-261
❑ 97BluJayOH-3
❑ 97BluJayS-18
❑ 97Cir-117
❑ 97CirRav-117
❑ 97Fle-234
❑ 97FleTif-234
❑ 97Pac-214
❑ 97PacLigB-214
❑ 97PacSil-214
❑ 98Pac-213
❑ 98PacPlaB-213
❑ 98PacRedT-213
❑ 98PacSil-213
❑ 99DodPol-4
Brumley, Duff
❑ 90JohCitCS-5
❑ 91HamRedC-10
❑ 91HamRedP-4029
❑ 92HamRedC-8
❑ 92HamRedF-1582
❑ 93FloStaLAF-42
❑ 93St.PetCC-7
❑ 93St.PetCF-2620
❑ 94Bow-73
❑ 94ExcFS7-261
❑ 94ExcLeaLF-5
❑ 94OklCit8F-1489
❑ 94Top-316
❑ 94TopGol-316
❑ 94TopSpa-316
❑ 94Ult-427
❑ 96ScrRedBB-8
❑ 96SigRooOJ-5
❑ 96SigRooOJS-5
Brumley, Mike (Anthony Michael)
❑ 86IowCubP-5
❑ 86StaoftFT-8
❑ 87IowCubTI-13
❑ 88Don-609
❑ 88LasVegSC-19
❑ 88LasVegSP-235
❑ 88TriAAAP-21
❑ 88TriAAC-35
❑ 89Don-302
❑ 89DonRoo-39
❑ 89Fle-302
❑ 89FleGlo-302
❑ 89FleUpd-30
❑ 89TigMar-12
❑ 89TopBig-324
❑ 90Don-533
❑ 90MarMot-26
❑ 90OPC-471
❑ 90Sco100RS-88
❑ 90Top-471
❑ 90TopTif-471
❑ 90UppDec-312
❑ 91Fle-445
❑ 91LinDriAAA-353
❑ 91PawRedSLD-353
❑ 91PawRedSP-45
❑ 91RedSoxP-3
❑ 91Sco-624
❑ 92OPC-407
❑ 92PawRedSF-929
❑ 92PawRedSS-353
❑ 92Sco-363
❑ 92TexLon-6
❑ 93TucTorF-3064
❑ 95TucTotTI-3
❑ 96TusTorB-5
❑ 97DunDonPPS-3
Brumley, Mike (Tony Mike)
❑ 58MonRoyF-6
❑ 59O'KAleMR-4
❑ 60DarFar-19
❑ 64Top-167
❑ 64TopRooAB-29
❑ 64TopVen-167
❑ 65Top-523
❑ 66OPC-29
❑ 66SenTeal-3
❑ 66Top-29
❑ 66TopVen-29
Brummer, Don
❑ 63RocRedWSP-4
Brummer, Glenn Edward
❑ 78ArkTraT-4
❑ 81Car5x7-2
❑ 82LouRedE-2
❑ 82Top-561
❑ 83Car-4
❑ 83Don-418
❑ 83Fle-4
❑ 83Top-311
❑ 84Car-4
❑ 84Car5x7-4
❑ 84Don-138
❑ 84Fle-321
❑ 84Nes792-152
❑ 84Top-152
❑ 84TopTif-152
❑ 85Don-290
❑ 85RanPer-7
❑ 86Fle-557
❑ 86HawIsIP-2
❑ 86Top-616
❑ 86TopTif-616
❑ 87CubCan-1
❑ 93RanKee-87
❑ 97ClePhi-28
❑ 98ClePhiM-29
❑ 98ClePhiUM-29
Brummer, Jeff
❑ 90YakBeaTI-7
Brummett, Greg
❑ 88AlaGolTI-5
❑ 89EveGiaS-26
❑ 90CliGiaB-7
❑ 90CliGiaP-2546
❑ 91CliGiaC-23
❑ 92SanJosGC-16
❑ 93FleFinE-151
❑ 93GiaStaC-28
❑ 94SalLakBF-808
Brummitt, Travis
❑ 98EugEme-5
Brunansky, Tom (Thomas A.)
❑ 80ElPasDT-17
❑ 81LonBeaPT-19
❑ 81SalLakCGT-21
❑ 82SpoIndT-20
❑ 82Top-653
❑ 82TopTra-13T
❑ 83AllGamPI-49
❑ 83Don-555
❑ 83Fle-607
❑ 83FleSta-24
❑ 83FleSti-138
❑ 83OPC-232
❑ 83Top-232
❑ 83TopSti-90
❑ 83TopSti-309
❑ 83TwiTeal-17
❑ 83TwiTeal-33
❑ 84AllGamPI-140
❑ 84Don-242
❑ 84Fle-557
❑ 84FunFooP-130
❑ 84MinTwiP-2
❑ 84Nes792-447
❑ 84OPC-98
❑ 84Top-447
❑ 84TopRubD-7
❑ 84TopSti-304
❑ 84TopTif-447
❑ 84TwiTeal-18
❑ 85AllGamPI-51
❑ 85Don-364
❑ 85Fle-271
❑ 85GenMilS-15
❑ 85Lea-36
❑ 85OPC-122
❑ 85Top-122
❑ 85TopGloS-39
❑ 85TopRubD-8
❑ 85TopSti-299
❑ 85TopSup-57
❑ 85TopTif-122
❑ 85Twi7-7
❑ 85TwiPos-1
❑ 85TwiTeal-1
❑ 85TwiTeal-19
❑ 86Don-24
❑ 86Don-192
❑ 86DonAll-44
❑ 86DonSupD-24
❑ 86Fle-387
❑ 86FleLimE-9
❑ 86FleMin-83
❑ 86FleStiC-15
❑ 86KayB-4
❑ 86Lea-24
❑ 86OPC-392
❑ 86SevCoi-C15
❑ 86Spo-80
❑ 86Top-565
❑ 86TopSti-276
❑ 86TopTat-18
❑ 86TopTif-565
❑ 86TwiTeal-17
❑ 87Don-194
❑ 87DonOpeD-222
❑ 87Fle-537
❑ 87FleGlo-537
❑ 87FleHotS-7
❑ 87FleStiC-17
❑ 87Lea-244
❑ 87OPC-261
❑ 87RedFolSB-75
❑ 87Spo-134
❑ 87SpoTeaP-17
❑ 87StuPan-22
❑ 87Top-776
❑ 87TopSti-280
❑ 87TopTif-776
❑ 87TwiPos-4
❑ 87TwiTeal-15
❑ 88CarSmo-25
❑ 88CarTeal-2
❑ 88Don-245
❑ 88DonBasB-19
❑ 88Fle-5
❑ 88FleGlo-5
❑ 88FleSlu-4
❑ 88FleStiC-42
❑ 88FleUpd-117
❑ 88FleUpdG-117
❑ 88OPC-375
❑ 88PanSti-142
❑ 88Sco-194
❑ 88ScoGlo-194
❑ 88ScoRoo-5T
❑ 88ScoRooG-5T
❑ 88Spo-194
❑ 88StaLinTw-4
❑ 88Top-375
❑ 88TopBig-211
❑ 88TopSti-15
❑ 88TopSti-275
❑ 88TopTif-375
❑ 88TopTra-20T
❑ 88TopTraT-20T
❑ 88TwiMasBD-12
❑ 89Bow-444
❑ 89BowTif-444
❑ 89CarSmo-1
❑ 89CarTeal-1
❑ 89ClaTraP-186
❑ 89Don-112
❑ 89DonBasB-187
❑ 89Fle-444
❑ 89FleGlo-444
❑ 89FleHeroB-4
❑ 89OPC-60
❑ 89PanSti-187
❑ 89RedFolSB-14
❑ 89Sco-184
❑ 89Spo-161
❑ 89Top-60
❑ 89Top-261
❑ 89TopBasT-152
❑ 89TopBig-54
❑ 89TopHilTM-4
❑ 89TopSti-41
❑ 89TopTif-60
❑ 89TopTif-261
❑ 89TopUKM-9
❑ 89TVSpoM-26
❑ 89UppDec-272
❑ 90Bow-202
❑ 90BowTif-202
❑ 90ClaBlu-119
❑ 90Don-399
❑ 90DonBesA-130
❑ 90El PasDAGTI-34
❑ 90Fle-242
❑ 90FleCan-242
❑ 90FleUpd-70
❑ 90Lea-447
❑ 90M.Vpin-97
❑ 90MLBBasB-31
❑ 90OPC-409
❑ 90PanSti-344
❑ 90PubIntS-211
❑ 90Sco-72
❑ 90ScoRoo-49T
❑ 90Top-409
❑ 90TopBig-94
❑ 90TopSti-45
❑ 90TopTif-409
❑ 90TopTra-15T
❑ 90TopTraT-15T
❑ 90TopTVCa-31
❑ 90UppDec-257
❑ 90UppDec-708
❑ 91Bow-125
❑ 91ClaGam-11
❑ 91Don-513
❑ 91Fle-88
❑ 91Lea-164
❑ 91OPC-675
❑ 91PanFreS-270
❑ 91RedFolS-14
❑ 91RedSoxP-2
❑ 91RedSoxP-4
❑ 91Sco-245
❑ 91SimandSMLBL-7
❑ 91StaClu-297
❑ 91Top-675
❑ 91TopDesS-675
❑ 91TopMic-675
❑ 91TopTif-675
❑ 91Ult-29
❑ 91UppDec-163
❑ 92Don-490
❑ 92Fle-34
❑ 92OPC-296
❑ 92PanSti-89
❑ 92Pin-314
❑ 92RedSoxDD-4
❑ 92Sco-46
❑ 92StaClu-464
❑ 92Top-296
❑ 92TopGol-296
❑ 92TopGolW-296
❑ 92TopMic-296
❑ 92Ult-12
❑ 92UppDec-543
❑ 93BrePol-3
❑ 93BreSen5-2
❑ 93Don-693
❑ 93Fle-555
❑ 93FleFinE-223
❑ 93Lea-226
❑ 93OPC-217
❑ 93OPCPre-34
❑ 93PacSpa-28
❑ 93Pin-534
❑ 93Sco-612
❑ 93Sel-210
❑ 93SelRoo-134T
❑ 93StaClu-625
❑ 93StaCluFDI-625
❑ 93StaCluMOP-625
❑ 93Top-532
❑ 93TopGol-532
❑ 93TopInaM-532
❑ 93TopInaR-532
❑ 93TopMic-532
❑ 93TriPla-217
❑ 93Ult-569
❑ 93UppDec-806
❑ 93UppDecGold-806
❑ 93UppDecHRH-HR26
❑ 94BreMilB-294
❑ 94BrePol-4
❑ 94BreTeal-3
❑ 94ColC-603
❑ 94ColChoGS-603
❑ 94ColChoSS-603
❑ 94Sco-423
❑ 94ScoGolR-423
❑ 94ScoRoo-RT127
❑ 94ScoRooGR-RT127
❑ 94SpoRoo-145
❑ 94SpoRooAP-145
❑ 94StaClu-661
❑ 94StaCluFDI-661
❑ 94StaCluGR-661
❑ 94StaCluMOP-661
❑ 95ColCho-413
❑ 95ColChoGS-413
❑ 95ColChoSS-413
❑ 95Don-359
❑ 95DonPreP-359
❑ 95Fle-24

❑ 95Sco-86
❑ 95ScoGolR-86
❑ 95ScoPlaTS-86

Brundage, Dave
❑ 87ClePhiP-20
❑ 88VerMarP-951
❑ 89WilBilP-642
❑ 89WilBilS-1
❑ 90WilBilS-3
❑ 91CalCanLD-53
❑ 91CalCanP-525
❑ 91LinDriAAA-53
❑ 92CalCanF-3742
❑ 92CalCanS-57
❑ 92SkyAAAF-26
❑ 93CalCanF-1182
❑ 94CalCanF-805
❑ 96LanJetB-1
❑ 98TacRaiQ-2

Brundin, Harold
❑ 33Zee-78

Brune, Jim
❑ 88BilMusP-1804
❑ 88CedRapRP-1154

Brunelle, Rodney
❑ 85BenPhiC-4
❑ 87ChaWheP-7
❑ 88ClePhiS-3

Brunenkant, Barry
❑ 84OklCit8T-15
❑ 85TulDriTI-14
❑ 86MaiGuiP-1
❑ 87BufBisP-5

Bruner, Clayton
❑ 96FayGenB-8
❑ 97BesGun-3
❑ 97WesMicW-6
❑ 98Bow-86
❑ 98BowChr-86
❑ 98BowChrGA-86
❑ 98BowChrGAR-86
❑ 98BowChrI-86
❑ 98BowChrIR-86
❑ 98BowChrR-86
❑ 98BowGolA-86
❑ 98BowInt-86
❑ 98JacSunM-4

Bruner, Roy
❑ 40PhiTeaI-6
❑ 41PhiTeaI-6

Brunet, George
❑ 58Top-139
❑ 63Top-538
❑ 64Top-322
❑ 64TopVen-322
❑ 65OPC-242
❑ 65Top-242
❑ 66AngDexP-1
❑ 66Top-393
❑ 67CokCapDA-31
❑ 67OPC-122
❑ 67Top-122
❑ 68Top-347
❑ 68TopVen-347
❑ 69MilBra-43
❑ 69MLBOffS-19
❑ 69MLBPin-3
❑ 69SenTeaI-4
❑ 69Top-645
❑ 69TopSta-141
❑ 69TopTeaP-17
❑ 70MLBOffS-267
❑ 70OPC-328
❑ 70Top-328
❑ 71MLBOffS-269
❑ 71OPC-73
❑ 71Top-73
❑ 72MilBra-55
❑ 91OriCro-58

Brunette, Justin
❑ 97NewJerCB-5

Brunk, Brenda
❑ 75WatRoyT-6

Brunk, Dave
❑ 75WatRoyT-6

Brunner, Clayton
❑ 97Bow-400
❑ 97BowChr-264
❑ 97BowChrI-264
❑ 97BowChrIR-264
❑ 97BowChrR-264
❑ 97BowInt-400

Brunner, Mike
❑ 95AubAstTI-11

Brunner, Tom
❑ 79ElmPioRST-26

Bruno, Joe
❑ 80PenPilBT-15
❑ 80PenPilCT-21
❑ 81ReaPhiT-20
❑ 87CedRapRP-12
❑ 88ChaLooB-17
❑ 88SouLeaAJ-37
❑ 89ChaLooB-21
❑ 89ChaLooGS-7
❑ 89SouLeaAJ-18
❑ 90ChaLooGS-7

Bruno, Julio
❑ 90ChaRaiB-5
❑ 90ChaRaiP-2046
❑ 90SpoIndSP-20
❑ 91Cla/Bes-367
❑ 91WatDiaC-15
❑ 91WatDiaP-1262
❑ 92ClaFS7-23
❑ 92HigDesMC-25
❑ 93Bow-546
❑ 93ClaFS7-173
❑ 93RanCucQC-1
❑ 93RanCucQF-838
❑ 94Bow-420
❑ 94Cla-17
❑ 94LasVegSF-876
❑ 94UppDecML-119
❑ 96LasVegSB-7
❑ 96MemChiB-9
❑ 97JacSun-6

Bruno, Paul
❑ 91Cla/Bes-343
❑ 91KenTwiC-23
❑ 91KenTwiP-2078

Bruno, Thomas
❑ 76OmaRoyTT-4
❑ 77OPC-32
❑ 78CarTeaI-3
❑ 78SprRedWK-16
❑ 79Top-724

Bruns, Aaron
❑ 94JohCitCC-30
❑ 96JohCitCTI-3
❑ 97PeoChi-30

Brunsberg, Arlo A.
❑ 77FriOneYW-24

Brunson, Bill
❑ 92PriRedF-3077

Brunson, Eddie
❑ 78NewWayCT-4
❑ 80HolMilT-7

Brunson, Matt
❑ 94ActPac-5
❑ 94Bow-28
❑ 94Cla-187
❑ 94ClaTriF-T28
❑ 94ColC-27
❑ 94ColChoGS-27
❑ 94ColChoSS-27
❑ 94FayGenC-1
❑ 94FayGenF-2151
❑ 94Pin-433
❑ 94PinArtP-433
❑ 94PinMusC-433
❑ 94Sco-532
❑ 94ScoGolR-532
❑ 94UppDec-296
❑ 94UppDec-547
❑ 94UppDecED-296
❑ 94UppDecED-547
❑ 94UppDecML-182
❑ 95Bow-195
❑ 95Exc-46
❑ 95FayGenTI-5
❑ 95UppDecML-39
❑ 95UppDecMLFS-39
❑ 96BreCouMB-7

Brunson, Will
❑ 92PriRedC-14
❑ 93WesVirWC-4
❑ 93WesVirWF-2857
❑ 94CarLeaAF-CAR46
❑ 94WinSpiC-7
❑ 94WinSpiF-264
❑ 95SanBerSTI-2
❑ 96SanAntMB-2
❑ 97AlbDukGS-4
❑ 98AlbDukG-2

Brunswick, Mark
❑ 85LitFalMT-13
❑ 86ColMetP-6
❑ 87LynMetP-25

Brunswick, Tom
❑ 77SpaPhiT-2

Bruske, James
❑ 87KinIndP-17
❑ 88WilBilP-1323
❑ 89KinIndS-4
❑ 90CanIndB-18
❑ 90CanIndP-1285
❑ 90CanIndS-1
❑ 90StaFS7-12
❑ 91CanIndLD-78
❑ 91CanIndP-973
❑ 91LinDriAA-78
❑ 92JacGenF-3992
❑ 93JacGenF-2100
❑ 93LinVenB-116
❑ 94ExcFS7-197
❑ 94TucTorF-753
❑ 97DodSco-9
❑ 97DodScoPl-9
❑ 97DodScoPr-9
❑ 97LasVegS1A-9
❑ 97Sco-209
❑ 97ScoArtPWB-209
❑ 97ScoPreS-209
❑ 97ScoShoS-209
❑ 97ScoShoSAP-209
❑ 98DodMot-26
❑ 98DodPol-1
❑ 98Pac-421
❑ 98PacOnl-362
❑ 98PacOnlR-362
❑ 98PacOnlWC-362
❑ 98PacPlaB-421
❑ 98PacRedT-421
❑ 98PacSil-421

Brusky, Brad
❑ 86CedRapRT-2
❑ 87VerRedP-1
❑ 88CedRapRP-1156
❑ 89WilBilP-644
❑ 89WilBilS-2

Brusstar, Warren
❑ 78SSP270-54
❑ 78Top-297
❑ 79PhiBurK-9
❑ 79Top-653
❑ 80Top-52
❑ 81OklCit8T-4
❑ 81Top-426
❑ 82Fle-242
❑ 82Top-647
❑ 83CubThoAV-41
❑ 84CubChiT-5
❑ 84CubSev-41
❑ 84Don-442
❑ 84Fle-487
❑ 84Nes792-304
❑ 84Top-304
❑ 84TopTif-304
❑ 85CubLioP-3
❑ 85CubSev-41
❑ 85Don-533
❑ 85Fle-51
❑ 85Top-189
❑ 85TopTif-189
❑ 86Don-555
❑ 86Fle-362
❑ 86Top-564
❑ 86TopTif-564
❑ 87SanJosBP-21
❑ 94SanBerSC-26
❑ 94SanBerSF-2775

Brust, Dave
❑ 90DurBulTI-20
❑ 91DurBulC-8
❑ 91DurBulP-1550

Brust, Jerry
❑ 76QuaCitAT-8

Brutcher, Lenny
❑ 90Bes-28
❑ 90MidLeaASGS-5
❑ 90SouBenWSB-1
❑ 90SouBenWSGS-1
❑ 91SarWhiSC-2
❑ 91SarWhiSP-1105
❑ 91UppDec-75

Bruton, Bill (William Haron)
❑ 47Exh-30
❑ 47PM1StaP1-22
❑ 53BraJohC-22
❑ 53BraMer-3
❑ 53BraSpiaS3-4
❑ 53BraSpiaS7-2
❑ 53Top-214
❑ 54Bow-224
❑ 54BraJohC-38
❑ 54BraSpiaSP-3
❑ 54Top-109
❑ 55Bow-11
❑ 55BraGolS-21
❑ 55BraJohC-38
❑ 55BraSpiaSD-3
❑ 55RobGouS-15
❑ 55RobGouW-15
❑ 56BraBilaBP-3
❑ 56Top-185
❑ 56YelBasP-8
❑ 57Bra8x1-2
❑ 57BraSpiaS4-3
❑ 57Top-48
❑ 58Top-355
❑ 59Top-165
❑ 59TopVen-165
❑ 60BraJayP-2
❑ 60BraLaktL-4
❑ 60BraSpiaS-3
❑ 60Top-37
❑ 60TopVen-37
❑ 61Pos-109A
❑ 61Pos-109B
❑ 61TigJayP-3
❑ 61Top-251
❑ 61TopStaI-39
❑ 62Jel-18
❑ 62PC7HFGSS-2
❑ 62Pos-18
❑ 62PosCan-18
❑ 62SalPlaC-92
❑ 62ShiPlaC-92
❑ 62Top-335
❑ 62TopStaI-43
❑ 63Jel-49
❑ 63Pos-49
❑ 63TigJayP-2
❑ 63Top-437
❑ 64TigJayP-2
❑ 64TigLid-2
❑ 64Top-98
❑ 64TopVen-98
❑ 78BraTCC-3
❑ 80Bra195T-42
❑ 81TigDetN-101
❑ 83Bra53F-38
❑ 84OCoandSI-112
❑ 91TopArc1-214
❑ 92BazQua5A-12
❑ 94TopArc1-109
❑ 94TopArc1G-109

Bryan, Billy (William Ronald)
❑ 63Top-236
❑ 64A's-1
❑ 65AthJayP-1
❑ 65OPC-51
❑ 65Top-51
❑ 66Top-332
❑ 66TopVen-332
❑ 67Top-601
❑ 68Top-498
❑ 78TCM60I-47
❑ 92YanWIZ6-19

Bryan, Ed
❑ 25Zee-150
❑ 26Zee-41
❑ 27Zee-21
❑ 28Zee-46
❑ 29Zee-104
❑ 30Zee-116
❑ 31Zee-80
❑ 33Zee-29

Bryan, Frank
❑ 85CloHSS-7
❑ 87NewOriP-9
❑ 87SanJosBP-9
❑ 88FreSunCLC-17
❑ 88FreSunP-1222
❑ 89PalSprACLC-47
❑ 89PalSprAP-487

Bryan, Leonardo
❑ 95BoiHawTI-8

Bryan, Rusty
❑ 89CarNewE-10

Bryand, Renay
❑ 88SpoIndP-1941
❑ 89ChaRaiP-996
❑ 90RivRedWB-4
❑ 90RivRedWCLC-13
❑ 90RivRedWP-2597
❑ 91HigDesMC-1
❑ 91HigDesMP-2384
❑ 91WicWraP-2591
❑ 92WicWraF-3651
❑ 92WicWraS-627
❑ 93WicWraF-2970

Bryans, Jason
❑ 91EugEmeC-27
❑ 91EugEmeP-3715

Bryant, Adam
❑ 94BilMusF-3661
❑ 94BilMusSP-14
❑ 95BilMusTI-11

Bryant, Allen
❑ 92NegLeaRLI-7

Bryant, Bobby
❑ 77LynMetT-8
❑ 79JacMetT-19
❑ 79TidTidT-21

Bryant, Chris
❑ 87IdaFalBP-12
❑ 93HunCubC-4
❑ 93HunCubF-3228
❑ 96FreKeyB-27
❑ 97FreKey-5
❑ 97WilCubB-3
❑ 98CarLeaAC-11
❑ 98FreKeyM-20

Bryant, Clay
❑ 35DiaMatCS3T1-19
❑ 36CubTeaI-1
❑ 36DiaMatCS3T2-1
❑ 58MonRoyF-5
❑ 59O'KAleMR-5
❑ 74OPC-521
❑ 74Top-521
❑ 79DiaGre-104

Bryant, Clint
❑ 97SalAva-9
❑ 98SalAvaC-6

Bryant, Craig
❑ 92ClaFS7-246
❑ 92SanBerC-13
❑ 92SanBerSF-961
❑ 93AppFoxCB-4
❑ 93AppFoxFI-2466

Bryant, Derek Roszell
❑ 77SanJosMC-4
❑ 80OgdA'sT-4
❑ 80Top-671
❑ 81TacTigT-9

Bryant, Don (Donald Ray)
❑ 67CokCapC-9
❑ 69Top-499
❑ 70OPC-473
❑ 70Top-473
❑ 74OPC-403
❑ 74Top-403
❑ 77Top-597

Bryant, Erick
❑ 87BelMarL-25
❑ 87BelMarTI-2
❑ 89WauTimGS-25

Bryant, Erwin
❑ 77BriRedST-1
❑ 81BriRedST-16

Bryant, Franklin S.
❑ 81VerBeaDT-3

Bryant, James
❑ 86ChaLooP-5
❑ 87ChaLooB-7

Bryant, John
❑ 82ChaRoyT-5
❑ 83ChaRoyT-15
❑ 86CedRapRT-23
❑ 87VerRedP-15

Bryant, Keith
❑ 89BelMarL-3

Bryant, Matt
❑ 98AugGreM-9

Bryant, Mike
❑ 80ElmPioRST-25

Bryant, Neil
❑ 82AmaGolST-15
❑ 83MidCubT-5

Bryant, Patrick
❑ 91Cla/Bes-57
❑ 91ColIndC-29
❑ 91ColIndP-1496
❑ 92ClaFS7-85
❑ 92ColRedC-3
❑ 92ColRedF-2402
❑ 92WatIndC-18
❑ 92WatIndF-3245
❑ 93ColRedC-4
❑ 93ColRedF-609
❑ 94CanIndF-3129
❑ 96CanIndB-7
❑ 97TreThuB-10
❑ 98PawRedSQ-8

Bryant, Phil
❑ 87GasRanP-7
❑ 88ChaRanS-4
❑ 89TulDriGS-6
❑ 89TulDriTI-4
❑ 90CMC-740
❑ 90TulDriP-1149

Bryant, Ralph
❑ 82VerBeaDT-21
❑ 83VerBeaDT-22
❑ 85AlbDukCr-161
❑ 85DomLeaS-183
❑ 86AlbDukP-2
❑ 86StaoftFT-17
❑ 87AlbDukD-25
❑ 87DodPol-24
❑ 87Don-587
❑ 87Fle-649
❑ 87FleGlo-649
❑ 87FleUpd-13
❑ 87FleUpdG-13
❑ 87SpoTeaP-14
❑ 87TopTra-12T
❑ 87TopTraT-12T
❑ 88Fle-510
❑ 88FleGlo-510
❑ 90DodTar-87
❑ 95LinVen-304
❑ 96MidAngB-8
❑ 96MidAngOHP-7

Bryant, Ron
❑ 70OPC-433
❑ 70Top-433
❑ 71MLBOffS-242
❑ 71OPC-621
❑ 71Top-621
❑ 72GiaTeaI-2
❑ 72OPC-185
❑ 72OPC-186
❑ 72Top-185
❑ 72Top-186
❑ 73LinPor-158
❑ 73OPC-298
❑ 73Top-298
❑ 74OPC-104
❑ 74OPC-205
❑ 74Top-104
❑ 74Top-205
❑ 74TopDecE-21
❑ 74TopSta-103
❑ 75OPC-265
❑ 75St.LouCP-3
❑ 75Top-265
❑ 75TopMin-265

Bryant, Scott
❑ 89CedRapRAB-30
❑ 90Bes-64
❑ 90Bow-59
❑ 90BowTif-59
❑ 90CedRapRB-1
❑ 90CedRapRDGB-30
❑ 90CedRapRP-2336
❑ 90CMC-877
❑ 90ProAaA-129
❑ 90Sco-667
❑ 91ChaLooLD-156
❑ 91ChaLooP-1970
❑ 91Cla/Bes-69
❑ 91LinDriAA-156
❑ 91UppDecFE-5F
❑ 92IowCubF-4059
❑ 92IowCubS-203
❑ 92SkyAAAF-97
❑ 93ClaFS7-126
❑ 93LinVenB-198
❑ 93LinVenB-296
❑ 93LinVenB-314
❑ 95EdmTraTI-4
❑ 97St.PauS-3

Bryant, Shawn
❑ 90BurIndP-3003
❑ 91KinIndC-2
❑ 91KinIndP-314
❑ 92ClaFS7-153
❑ 92KinIndC-1
❑ 92KinIndF-2467
❑ 93CanIndF-2832
❑ 94SalLakBF-809

Bryden, T.R. (Thomas R.)
❑ 82DanSunF-4
❑ 83RedPioT-7
❑ 85MidAngT-11
❑ 87EdmTraP-2081
❑ 87Top-387
❑ 87TopTif-387

❑ 88PorBeaC-3
❑ 88PorBeaP-663
Brye, Steve (Stephen Robert)
❑ 71OPC-391
❑ 71Top-391
❑ 72OPC-28
❑ 72Top-28
❑ 72TwiTeal-3
❑ 73LinPor-106
❑ 73OPC-353
❑ 73Top-353
❑ 74OPC-232
❑ 74Top-232
❑ 75OPC-151
❑ 75Top-151
❑ 75TopMin-151
❑ 75TwiPos-5
❑ 75TwiTeal-7
❑ 76MinTwiP-3
❑ 76OPC-519
❑ 76SSP-215
❑ 76Top-519
❑ 77Top-424
❑ 78Top-673
❑ 79HawIsIC-9
❑ 79HawIsIT-12
❑ 79Top-28
❑ 94BreMilB-295
Bryeans, Chris
❑ 82ChaRoyT-10
❑ 83ChaRoyT-5
Brynan, Charles
❑ 87OldJudN-49
Brynt, Chris
❑ 96RocCubTI-3
Brzezinski, George
❑ 88GenCubP-1657
Brzozoski, Marc
❑ 96PorRocB-9
Buba, Mark
❑ 77BriRedST-2
Bubalo, Mike
❑ 90BenBucL-8
❑ 91EveGiaP-3934
Bubrewicz, Tim
❑ 91ElmPioP-3262
Buccheri, James
❑ 88SouOreAP-1692
❑ 89MadMusS-5
❑ 89Sta-65
❑ 90ModA'sC-3
❑ 90ModA'sCLC-162
❑ 90ModA'sP-2217
❑ 91HunStaC-5
❑ 91HunStaLD-280
❑ 91HunStaP-1801
❑ 91HunStaTI-4
❑ 91LinDriAA-280
❑ 92HunStaS-305
❑ 92SkyAA F-128
❑ 93TacTigF-3044
❑ 94TacTigF-3185
❑ 97St.PetDRUB-8
❑ 98DurBulTI-3
Bucci, Carmen
❑ 95IdaFalBTI-5
❑ 96CliLumKTI-4
Bucci, Mike
❑ 76SanAntBTI-4
❑ 78TucTorC-15A
❑ 79TucTorT-5
❑ 80TacTigT-13
❑ 81ChaChaT-11
❑ 82WauTimF-12
❑ 83ChaLooT-9
❑ 85BurRanT-10
❑ 86SalRedBP-2
❑ 87BufBisP-26
❑ 88BurIndP-1786
Buccola, Vic
❑ 47SigOil-39
❑ 48SmiClo-16
Bucha, Johnny (John George)
❑ 52Top-19
❑ 53TigGle-2
❑ 54Bow-215
❑ 83TopRep5-19
Buchanan, Bob
❑ 81CedRapRT-23
❑ 82WatRedT-7
❑ 83IndIndTI-28
❑ 87MetColP-26
❑ 87TidTidP-26
❑ 87TidTidT-27
❑ 88OmaRoyC-3
❑ 88OmaRoyP-1514
❑ 89OmaRoyC-1
❑ 89OmaRoyP-1724
❑ 91LinDriAAA-328
❑ 91OmaRoyLD-328
❑ 91OmaRoyP-1027
❑ 92NasSouS-277
❑ 92SkyAAAF-131
Buchanan, Brian James
❑ 94ClaUpdCotC-CC20
❑ 94SigRooDP-23
❑ 94SigRooDPS-23
❑ 94StaCluDP-18
❑ 94StaCluDPFDI-18
❑ 95Bow-37
❑ 95Exc-91
❑ 95GreBatTI-7
❑ 95ScoDraP-DP18
❑ 95SelSurS-SS8
❑ 95SPML-117
❑ 95StaClu-111
❑ 95StaCluFDI-111
❑ 95StaCluMOP-111
❑ 95StaCluSTWS-111
❑ 95Top-28
❑ 95UppDecML-197
❑ 95UppDecMLFS-197
❑ 96TamYanY-7
❑ 97EasLeaTPB-19
❑ 97NorNav-10
❑ 97NorNavTI-5
❑ 98Bow-362
❑ 98BowChr-362
❑ 98BowChrGA-362
❑ 98BowChrGAR-362
❑ 98BowChrI-362
❑ 98BowChrIR-362
❑ 98BowChrR-362
❑ 98BowGolA-362
❑ 98BowInt-362
❑ 98SalLakBO-10
❑ 98Top-255
❑ 98TopChr-255
❑ 98TopChrR-255
❑ 98TopDevR-255
❑ 98TopDia-255
❑ 98TopMiniC-255
Buchanan, Brian Joseph
❑ 96Top-245
❑ 98OneYanG-3
Buchanan, Donald
❑ 52LavPro-12
Buchanan, Reggie
❑ 81BufBisT-25
Buchanan, Rob
❑ 88EugEmeB-13
❑ 89AppFoxP-868
❑ 89EugEmeB-21
Buchanan, Shawn
❑ 88NebCor-1
❑ 90NebCor-5
❑ 91UtiBluSC-5
❑ 91UtiBluSP-3252
❑ 92SarWhiSCB-17
❑ 92SarWhiSF-218
❑ 93SanBerSC-3
❑ 93SanBerSF-781
❑ 93SarWhiSF-1381
❑ 94SouBenSHC-4
❑ 94SouBenSHF-605
❑ 95PriWilCTI-5
Buchek, Jerry (Gerald Peter)
❑ 61UniOil-P3
❑ 62KahAtl-2
❑ 62Top-439
❑ 64Top-314
❑ 64TopVen-314
❑ 65CarTeal-5
❑ 65Top-397
❑ 66CarTeal-2
❑ 66Top-454
❑ 67Top-574
❑ 68Top-277
❑ 68TopVen-277
❑ 69MilBra-44
❑ 91MetWIZ-56
Bucher, Jim (James Quinter)
❑ 35DiaMatCS3T1-20
❑ 36NatChiFPR-5
❑ 36NatChiFPR-86
❑ 90DodTar-88
Buchheister, Bucky (Don)
❑ 72CedRapCT-4
❑ 73CedRapAT-9
❑ 74CedRapAT-28
❑ 75CedRapGT-18
❑ 76CedRapGT-7
❑ 77CedRapGT-19
❑ 78CedRapGT-5
❑ 79CedRapGT-29
❑ 80CedRapRT-21
❑ 81CedRapRT-20
❑ 82CedRapRT-27
❑ 83CedRapRT-26
❑ 84CedRapRT-19
❑ 85CedRapRT-28
❑ 86CedRapRT-27
❑ 88CedRapRP-1136
❑ 89CedRapRAB-34
❑ 89CedRapRB-24
❑ 89CedRapRP-931
❑ 90CedRapRDGB-34
Buchman, Tom
❑ 97ForWayW-7
Buchon, El
❑ 95LinVen-220
Buck, Bucky
❑ 88BenBucL-34
❑ 89BenBucL-30
Buckels, Gary
❑ 87SalAngP-2
❑ 88MidLeaAGS-25
❑ 88QuaCitAGS-28
❑ 89MidAngGS-6
❑ 90CMC-480
❑ 90EdmTraC-3
❑ 90EdmTraP-510
❑ 90ProAAAF-85
❑ 91EdmTraLD-156
❑ 91EdmTraP-1509
❑ 91LinDriAAA-156
❑ 93LouRedF-206
❑ 94LouRedF-2974
❑ 97PeoChi-29
❑ 98PeoChiM-28
Buckenberger, Albert
❑ 87OldJudN-50
Buckey, Mascot
❑ 90BenBucL-1
Buckeye, Garland
❑ 28StaPlaCE-4
❑ 93ConTSN-981
Buckeyes, Cleveland
❑ 92NegLeaRLI-95
❑ 93NegLeaRL2-89
❑ 93TedWilPC-8
Buckholz, Steven
❑ 88WatPirP-3
❑ 90SalBucS-2
❑ 91SalBucP-945
❑ 92CarMudF-1173
❑ 92CarMudS-127
Buckhorn, Glen
❑ 81DurBulT-11
Buckle, Larry
❑ 80CedRapRT-5
❑ 82WatRedT-2
Buckles, Bucky
❑ 94StaCluDP-72
❑ 94StaCluDPFDI-72
❑ 95Exc-127
❑ 95Top-369
❑ 97TulDriTI-6
Buckles, Matthew
❑ 95MarPhiTI-5
❑ 96MarPhiB-4
Buckley, Brandon
❑ 98AubDouTI-4
Buckley, Brian
❑ 81RedPioT-2
❑ 82HolMilT-2
❑ 84PriWilPT-10
Buckley, Dick (Richard D.)
❑ 87OldJudN-51
Buckley, Joe
❑ 89SpoIndSP-7
Buckley, Kevin John
❑ 82BurRanF-3
❑ 82BurRanT-15
❑ 83BurRanF-20
❑ 83BurRanT-2
❑ 83TulDriT-16
❑ 84OklCit8T-16
❑ 84TulDriTI-27
❑ 85MaiGuiT-15
❑ 86IndTeal-9
❑ 86MaiGuiP-2
❑ 87LasVegSP-8
❑ 90TulDriDGB-14
❑ 93RanKee-88
Buckley, Matt
❑ 93AusFut-48
❑ 94BoiHawC-4
❑ 94BoiHawF-3360
❑ 95AusFut-40
❑ 96BilMusTI-2
Buckley, Mike
❑ 81QuaCitCT-6
Buckley, Terrell
❑ 93ClaFS7-96
❑ 93MacBraC-4
❑ 93MacBraF-1405
Buckley, Tom
❑ 23Zee-124
❑ 24Zee-86
❑ 88SFHesCreN32-3
Buckley, Travis
❑ 90GasRanB-4
❑ 90GasRanP-2513
❑ 90GasRanS-3
❑ 90ProAaA-78
❑ 91ChaRanC-3
❑ 91ChaRanP-1307
❑ 92HarSenF-454
❑ 92HarSenS-278
❑ 92SkyAA F-118
❑ 93Top-732
❑ 93TopGol-732
❑ 93TopInaM-732
❑ 93TopInaR-732
❑ 93TopMic-732
❑ 94JacSunF-1404
❑ 95IndIndF-90
❑ 96ChaLooB-10
❑ 97VanCanB-8
❑ 98RicBraQ-4
Buckley, Troy
❑ 88CapCodPPaLP-170
❑ 89AncBucTI-11
❑ 90CalLeaACLC-15
❑ 90CMC-863
❑ 90VisOakCLC-75
❑ 90VisOakP-2157
❑ 91Cla/Bes-203
❑ 91VisOakC-13
❑ 91VisOakP-1744
❑ 92Ft.MyeMCB-19
❑ 92Ft.MyeMF-2748
❑ 93ClaGolF-64
❑ 93WinSpiC-5
❑ 93WinSpiF-1572
❑ 94ChaLooF-1360
Buckman, Tom
❑ 96BriWhiSB-11
❑ 97HicCraB-6
❑ 97HicCraRB-7
Buckmier, Jim
❑ 83AleDukT-29
❑ 84PriWilPT-2
Buckner, Bill (William J.)
❑ 70OPC-286
❑ 70Top-286
❑ 71Dod-2
❑ 71MLBOffS-99
❑ 71OPC-529
❑ 71Top-529
❑ 72OPC-114
❑ 72Top-114
❑ 73LinPor-92
❑ 73OPC-368
❑ 73Top-368
❑ 74OPC-505
❑ 74Top-505
❑ 74TopSta-41
❑ 75Hos-97
❑ 75Kel-32
❑ 75OPC-244
❑ 75Top-244
❑ 75TopMin-244
❑ 76LinSup-123
❑ 76OPC-253
❑ 76SSP-91
❑ 76Top-253
❑ 77BurCheD-195
❑ 77CubJewT-3
❑ 77Hos-54
❑ 77Top-27
❑ 78Hos-46
❑ 78OPC-127
❑ 78RCColC-70
❑ 78SSP270-264
❑ 78Top-473
❑ 78WifBalD-9
❑ 79Hos-27
❑ 79OPC-177
❑ 79Top-346
❑ 80OPC-75
❑ 80Top-135
❑ 81AllGamPI-91
❑ 81CokTeaS-14
❑ 81Don-482
❑ 81Dra-13
❑ 81Fle-292
❑ 81FleStiC-29
❑ 81MSAMinD-5
❑ 81OPC-202
❑ 81Squ-6
❑ 81Top-1
❑ 81Top-625
❑ 81TopScr-55
❑ 81TopSti-17
❑ 81TopSti-153
❑ 81TopSupHT-23
❑ 82CubRedL-22
❑ 82Don-403
❑ 82Dra-5
❑ 82Fle-589
❑ 82FleSta-96
❑ 82Kel-2
❑ 82OnDecD-5
❑ 82OPC-124
❑ 82Top-456
❑ 82Top-760
❑ 82TopSti-29
❑ 82TopStiV-29
❑ 83AllGamPI-91
❑ 83CubThoAV-22
❑ 83Don-14
❑ 83Don-99
❑ 83DonActA-7
❑ 83Dra-2
❑ 83Fle-492
❑ 83FleSta-25
❑ 83FleSti-132
❑ 83Kel-59
❑ 83OPC-250
❑ 83PerCreC-1
❑ 83PerCreCG-1
❑ 83Top-250
❑ 83TopGloS-24
❑ 83TopSti-223
❑ 84AllGamPI-1
❑ 84Don-117
❑ 84DonActAS-28
❑ 84DonCha-18
❑ 84Dra-4
❑ 84Fle-488
❑ 84FleUpd-18
❑ 84FunFooP-100
❑ 84Nes792-545
❑ 84OPC-96
❑ 84Top-545
❑ 84TopRubD-8
❑ 84TopSti-42
❑ 84TopSup-14
❑ 84TopTif-545
❑ 84TopTra-17T
❑ 84TopTraT-17T
❑ 85AllGamPI-1
❑ 85Don-416
❑ 85Fle-153
❑ 85Lea-254
❑ 85OPC-65
❑ 85SpoIndGC-3
❑ 85SubDis-6
❑ 85ThoMcAD-6
❑ 85Top-65
❑ 85TopMin-65
❑ 85TopRubD-9
❑ 85TopSti-214
❑ 85TopTif-65
❑ 86BasStaB-18
❑ 86Don-151
❑ 86Dra-17
❑ 86Fle-343
❑ 86FleStiC-16
❑ 86Lea-77
❑ 86OPC-239
❑ 86Spo-81
❑ 86Spo-140
❑ 86Top-443
❑ 86TopSti-252
❑ 86TopSup-17
❑ 86TopTat-14
❑ 86TopTif-443
❑ 86Woo-5
❑ 87BoaandB-14
❑ 87Don-462
❑ 87DonOpeD-183
❑ 87Fle-31
❑ 87FleGlo-31
❑ 87FleLimBC-C2
❑ 87Lea-241
❑ 87OPC-306
❑ 87RedSoxSAP-5
❑ 87Spo-70
❑ 87Top-764
❑ 87TopSti-250
❑ 87TopTif-764
❑ 88Don-456
❑ 88Fle-486
❑ 88FleGlo-486
❑ 88OPC-147
❑ 88RoyTeal-7
❑ 88Sco-591
❑ 88ScoGlo-591
❑ 88ScoRoo-36T
❑ 88ScoRooG-36T
❑ 88StaLinAn-2
❑ 88Top-147
❑ 88TopTif-147
❑ 89Fle-278
❑ 89FleGlo-278
❑ 89OPCBoxB-B
❑ 89Sco-214
❑ 89TopWaxBC-B
❑ 89UppDec-639
❑ 90DodTar-89
❑ 90Don-474
❑ 90PubIntS-345
❑ 90RedSoxP-4
❑ 90Sco-396
❑ 90TopTVRS-23
❑ 90UppDec-252
❑ 92UppDecS-26
❑ 93TedWil-20
❑ 93UppDecAH-20
❑ 94UppDecAH-189
❑ 94UppDecAH1-189
❑ 99SpoIllGotG-31
❑ 99SpoIllGotGA-12
Buckner, Jim
❑ 79TidTidT-10
❑ 79TolMudHT-14
❑ 80BufBisT-5
❑ 81OmaRoyT-20
Buckner, Rex
❑ 89MisStaB-5
❑ 90MisStaB-5
❑ 91MisStaB-7
❑ 92MisStaB-6
❑ 93MisStaB-6
Buckthorpe, David
❑ 91WavRedF-8
❑ 93AusFut-59
Bucz, Bruce
❑ 88VisOakCLC-171
❑ 90VisOakCLC-81
Bucz, Joseph
❑ 90VisOakCLC-83
Buczkowski, Matthew
❑ 96MarPhiB-5
Budaska, Mark David
❑ 79OgdA'sT-18
❑ 80OgdA'sT-7
❑ 81TacTigT-13
❑ 82Top-531
Buddie, Mike
❑ 92ClaDraP-77
❑ 92FroRowDP-13
❑ 92FroRowDPG-13
❑ 92FroRowDPS-13
❑ 92OneYanC-2
❑ 93ClaFS7-64
❑ 93GreHorC-3
❑ 93GreHorF-877
❑ 94TamYanC-3
❑ 94TamYanF-2373
❑ 95NorNavTI-36
❑ 96NorNavB-5
❑ 97ColCliB-7
❑ 97ColCliD-4
❑ 97NorNav-11
❑ 98ColCliD-4
❑ 98ColCliM-8
❑ 98PacOmeRS-8
❑ 98PacOmeRST5-8
❑ 98PacOnl-497
❑ 98PacOnlR-497
❑ 98PacOnlWC-497
Buddin, Don (Donald Thomas)

58RedSoxJP-2
58Top-297
59Top-32
59TopVen-32
60RedSoxJP-2
60Top-520
61Pos-53A
61Pos-53B
61Top-99
62Col45'HC-3
62Col45'JP-4
62Jel-59
62Pos-59
62PosCan-59
62SalPlaC-68A
62SalPlaC-68B
62ShiPlaC-68
62Top-332
81RedSoxBG2S-10
89AstCol4S-19

Budke, Todd
85VisOakT-17
86OrlTwiP-3

Budner, Scott
90SouOreAB-30
90SouOreAP-3450
91MadMusC-13
91MadMusP-2147
92RenSilSCLC-60

Budnick, Michael
47TipTop-122
75TCMGua-11

Budrewicz, Timothy
91ElmPioC-17
92WinSpiC-25
92WinSpiF-1199

Budz, Ed
94St.CatBJC-4
94St.CatBJF-3633

Budzinski, Mark
95WatIndTI-6
98AkrAerM-26

Buechele, Steve
82TulDriT-27
83TulDriT-22
84OklCit8T-13
85OklCit8T-17
86Don-544
86Fle-558
86RanPer-22
86Top-397
86TopTif-397
87Don-180
87DonOpeD-179
87Fle-121
87FleGlo-121
87OPC-176
87RanMot-7
87RanSmo-11
87Top-176
87TopSti-242
87TopTif-176
88Don-224
88DonBasB-312
88Fle-463
88FleGlo-463
88OPC-2
88PanSti-203
88PanSti-204
88RanMot-7
88RanSmo-12
88Sco-306
88ScoGlo-306
88StaLinRa-3
88Top-201
88Top-537
88TopBig-104
88TopSti-235
88TopTif-201
88TopTif-537
89Bow-232
89BowTif-232
89Don-174
89DonBasB-223
89Fle-515
89FleGlo-515
89OPC-83
89PanSti-453
89RanMot-8
89RanSmo-5
89Sco-368
89Top-729
89Top-732
89TopBig-156
89TopSti-250
89TopTif-729
89TopTif-732
89UppDec-418
90Bow-493
90BowTif-493
90Don-107
90Fle-292
90FleCan-292
90Lea-179
90OPC-279
90PanSti-169
90PubIntS-406
90RanMot-14
90Sco-221
90Top-279
90TopBig-63
90TopSti-251
90TopTif-279
90TulDriDGB-15
90UppDec-685
91Bow-268
91Don-357
91Fle-283
91OPC-464
91PanFreS-254
91PanSti-209
91RanMot-5
91Sco-257
91ScoRoo-77T
91StaClu-337
91Top-464
91TopDesS-464
91TopMic-464
91TopTif-464
91UppDec-650
92Bow-335
92ClaGam-66
92Don-699
92Fle-552
92Lea-91
92LeaBlaG-91
92OPC-622
92PanSti-254
92Pin-430
92PirNatI-4
92Sco-695
92ScoRoo-21T
92StaClu-405
92Stu-83
92Top-622
92TopGol-622
92TopGolW-622
92TopMic-622
92TriPla-50
92Ult-252
92UppDec-488
93Bow-608
93CubMar-3
93CubStaC-7
93Don-104
93Fla-13
93Fle-18
93Lea-106
93OPC-8
93PacSpa-53
93PanSti-206
93Pin-176
93RanKee-89
93Sco-97
93Sel-129
93SP-82
93StaClu-494
93StaCluFDI-494
93StaCluMOP-494
93Stu-8
93Top-74
93TopGol-74
93TopInaM-74
93TopInaR-74
93TopMic-74
93TriPla-79
93Ult-15
93UppDec-159
93UppDecGold-159
94Bow-522
94ColC-66
94ColChoGS-66
94ColChoSS-66
94Don-555
94Fin-51
94FinRef-51
94Fla-135
94Fle-381
94FleExtB-216
94Lea-180
94OPC-78
94Pac-96
94Pin-200
94PinArtP-200
94PinMusC-200
94ProMag-21
94Sco-346
94ScoGolR-346
94Sel-166
94StaClu-204
94StaCluFDI-204
94StaCluGR-204
94StaCluMOP-204
94StaCluT-333
94StaCluTFDI-333
94Stu-58
94Top-666
94TopGol-666
94TopSpa-666
94TriPla-71
94Ult-160
94UppDec-136
94UppDecED-136
95ColCho-203
95ColChoGS-203
95ColChoSS-203
95Don-186
95DonPreP-186
95Fla-330
95Fle-410
95Lea-71
95Pin-182
95PinArtP-182
95PinMusC-182
95Sco-389
95ScoGolR-389
95ScoPlaTS-389
95StaClu-181
95StaCluFDI-181
95StaCluMOP-181
95StaCluSTWS-181
95Stu-196
95Top-303
95TopCyb-163
95Ult-135
95UltGolM-135
95UppDec-312
95UppDecED-312
95UppDecEDG-312

Buelow, Fritz (Frederick W.)
03BreE10-12
05IndSouPSoCP-5

Bues, Art (Arthur F.)
09ObaT21-369
12ObaPreT-118

Buettemeyer, Kim
80WicAerT-3

Buetter, Bud
79RedSoxEF-6
79RedSoxEF-24

Buffamoyer, John
75BurBeeT-1
77HolMilT-3
78SpoIndC-20
80ChaO'sP-2
80ChaO'sW-2

Buffinton, Charlie (Charles G.)
87OldJudN-52
88AugBecN-5
88GandBCGCE-5
89EdgR.WG-3
90KalBatN-5

Buffolino, Rocco
87PocGiaTB-24
88FreSunCLC-24
88FreSunP-1231

Buford, Bobby
75LynRanT-6
76CliPilT-4

Buford, Damon
91Cla/Bes-198
91FreKeyC-23
91FreKeyP-2377
92Bow-224
92ClaFS7-120
92HagSunF-2567
92HagSunS-253
92SkyAA F-105
92UppDecML-51
92UppDecML-221
93BalOriP-5
93Bow-141
93ExcFS7-122
93FleFinE-157
93Lea-492
93RocRedWF-251
93SelRoo-149T
93StaClu-742
93StaCluFDI-742
93StaCluMOP-742
93Top-576
93TopGol-576
93TopInaM-576
93TopInaR-576
93TopMic-576
93TopTra-63T
93UppDec-691
93UppDecGold-691
94Don-605
94OriPro-13
94OriUSPC-6C
94OriUSPC-11H
94Pac-27
94Pin-423
94PinArtP-423
94PinMusC-423
94RocRedWF-1008
94RocRedWTI-4
94Sco-582
94ScoBoyoS-55
94ScoGolR-582
94SpoRoo-106
94SpoRooAP-106
94StaCluT-283
94StaCluTFDI-283
94Top-61
94TopGol-61
94TopSpa-61
94Ult-303
95Don-540
95DonPreP-540
95Fle-3
95Lea-24
96ColCho-739
96ColChoGS-739
96ColChoSS-739
96Don-544
96DonPreP-544
96Fle-475
96FleTif-475
96FleUpd-U87
96FleUpdTC-U87
96LeaSigA-37
96LeaSigAG-37
96LeaSigAS-37
96RanDr P-3
96RanFle-2
96RanMot-25
96Sco-482
96StaClu-393
96StaCluMOP-393
96Ult-418
96UltGolM-418
97Cir-80
97CirRav-80
97ColCho-487
97Fle-218
97FleTif-218
97NewPin-146
97NewPinAP-146
97NewPinMC-146
97NewPinPP-146
97RanDr P-2
97RanMot-18
97Sco-444
97ScoArtPWB-444
97ScoResC-444
97ScoShoS-444
97ScoShoSAP-444
97Stu-20
97StuPrePG-20
97StuPrePS-20
97Ult-308
97UltGolME-308
97UltPlaME-308
98PacInvGems-100
98PacOnl-109
98PacOnlR-109
98PacOnlWC-109
98PinSna-BRS16
99Fle-374
99FleSta9-374
99FleWarT-374

Buford, Don
87NewOriP-19
88HagSunS-3
89EasLeaDDP-DD38
89HagSunB-15
89HagSunP-277
89HagSunS-2
90HagSunP-1420
90HagSunS-3

Buford, Don (Donald Alvin)
64Top-368
64TopVen-368
64WhiSoxI-4
64WhiSoxTS-3
65OPC-81
65Top-81
66Top-465
66WhiSoxTI-4
67BalOriP-20
67BalOriP-21
67BalOriP-22
67BalOriP-23
67CokCapWS-6
67DexPre-36
67OPC-143
67ProPizC-5
67Top-143
67Top-232
67TopVen-258
68BalOriDPCP-4
68DexPre-19
68OPC-194
68Top-194
68TopVen-194
69MilBra-45
69MLBOffS-2
69Top-478
69TopSta-123
70BalOriP-4
70DayDaiNM-151
70MLBOffS-147
70OPC-305
70OPC-428
70Ori-2
70Top-305
70Top-428
71BalOriP-4
71MLBOffS-291
71OPC-29
71OPC-328
71OriCha-2
71Top-29
71Top-328
72MilBra-56
72OPC-370
72OriDMV-3
72OriPos-7
72Top-370
73OPC-183
73Top-183
74GreHeroBP-5
77SerSta-4
81TCM60I-299
84GiaPos-3
86IndIndTI-29
88OriFreB-2
88OriPos-7
90SouCalS-1
91FreKeyP-2382
91OriCro-59
92HagSunF-2570
92HagSunS-274
93BowBayF-2203
93UppDecAH-21
94BalOriP-7

Bug(Mascot), The
89SanBerSCLC-94
90SanBerSB-27
90SanBerSCLC-xxx
93SanBerSC-25
94SanBerSC-29
95SanBerSTI-32
96SanBerSB-30
97SanBerS-30
98SanBerS-30

Bugg, Jason
93IdaFalBF-4037
93IdaFalBSP-24
94HigDesMC-7
94HigDesMF-2795

Buggs, Doc (Ron)
77NewCoPT-4
78NewWayCT-5
79BurBeeT-9

Buggs, Michael J.
82AppFoxFr-26

Buhe, Tim
89KinMetS-2
90PitMetP-9

Buheller, Tim
86ElmPioRSP-4
87WinHavRSP-1
88LynRedSS-3
89LynRedSS-3

Buher, Brad
92DavLipB-6
93DavLipB-4
94DavLipB-5

Buhl, Bob
53BraJohC-4
53BraMer-4
53BraSpiaS3-5
53BraSpiaS7-3
54BraJohC-10
54BraMer-3
54BraSpiaSP-4
54Top-210
55Bow-43
55BraGolS-7
55BraJohC-10
55BraSpiaSD-4
56BraBilaBP-4
56Top-244
57Bra8x1-3
57BraSpiaS4-4
57Top-127
58Top-176
59Top-347
60BraLaktL-5
60BraSpiaS-4
60Top-230
60Top-374
61Pos-103A
61Pos-103B
61Top-145
61TopStal-40
62Jel-154
62Pos-154
62PosCan-154
62SalPlaC-117
62ShiPlaC-117
62Top-458A
62Top-458B
63CubJayP-4
63Top-175
64CubJayP-4
64Top-96
64TopVen-96
65CubJayP-5
65OPC-264
65Top-264
66OPC-185
66Top-185
66TopVen-185
67OPC-68
67Top-68
78BraTCC-4
80Bra195T-5
83Bra53F-10
87Bra195T-9
89SweBasG-21
94TopArc1-210
94TopArc1G-210

Buhner, Jay
87ColCliP-4
87ColCliP-15
87ColCliT-19
87IntLeaAT-2
88BlaYNPRWL-22
88ClaBlu-244
88ColCliC-23
88ColCliP-18
88ColCliP-329
88Don-545
88DonReaBY-545
88DonRoo-11
88ScoRoo-95T
88ScoRooG-95T
88Spo-223
88TopTra-21T
88TopTraT-21T
89Baz-4
89Bow-219
89BowTif-219
89CalCanC-13
89CalCanP-544
89Don-581
89DonBasB-136
89Fle-542
89FleGlo-542
89K-M-5
89OPC-223
89PanSti-440
89Sco-530
89ScoYouSI-6
89Spo-89
89Top-223
89TopBig-20
89TopCoi-35
89TopGloS-9

- ❑ 89TopRoo-5
- ❑ 89TopSti-319
- ❑ 89TopTif-223
- ❑ 89TopUKM-10
- ❑ 89ToyRoo-5
- ❑ 89TVSpoM-124
- ❑ 89UppDec-220
- ❑ 90Bow-477
- ❑ 90BowTif-477
- ❑ 90Don-448
- ❑ 90Fle-508
- ❑ 90FleCan-508
- ❑ 90Lea-114
- ❑ 90MarMot-7
- ❑ 90OPC-554
- ❑ 90Sco-521
- ❑ 90Top-554
- ❑ 90TopTif-554
- ❑ 90UppDec-534
- ❑ 91Bow-247
- ❑ 91Don-509
- ❑ 91DonGraS-6
- ❑ 91Fle-446
- ❑ 91Lea-62
- ❑ 91MarCouH-13
- ❑ 91OPC-154
- ❑ 91PanFreS-234
- ❑ 91PanSti-190
- ❑ 91Sco-125
- ❑ 91StaClu-153
- ❑ 91Top-154
- ❑ 91TopDesS-154
- ❑ 91TopMic-154
- ❑ 91TopTif-154
- ❑ 91UltUpd-49
- ❑ 91UppDec-128
- ❑ 92Bow-248
- ❑ 92Cla1-T20
- ❑ 92DenHol-23
- ❑ 92Don-61
- ❑ 92Fle-275
- ❑ 92Hig5-106
- ❑ 92Lea-128
- ❑ 92LeaBlaG-128
- ❑ 92MarMot-6
- ❑ 92OPC-327
- ❑ 92PanSti-59
- ❑ 92Pin-27
- ❑ 92Pin-305
- ❑ 92Sco-64
- ❑ 92ScoProP-6
- ❑ 92ScoProP-18
- ❑ 92StaClu-213
- ❑ 92Stu-231
- ❑ 92Top-327
- ❑ 92TopGol-327
- ❑ 92TopGolW-327
- ❑ 92TopMic-327
- ❑ 92Ult-121
- ❑ 92UppDec-441
- ❑ 92UppDecHRH-HR18
- ❑ 92YanWIZ8-22
- ❑ 93Bow-23
- ❑ 93Don-111
- ❑ 93Fin-124
- ❑ 93FinRef-124
- ❑ 93Fla-268
- ❑ 93Fle-305
- ❑ 93FunPac-112
- ❑ 93Lea-271
- ❑ 93MariStaClu-23
- ❑ 93MarMot-6
- ❑ 93OPC-40
- ❑ 93PacJugC-3
- ❑ 93PacSpa-282
- ❑ 93PanSti-65
- ❑ 93Pin-68
- ❑ 93PinHomRC-36
- ❑ 93Sco-172
- ❑ 93Sel-202
- ❑ 93SP-128
- ❑ 93StaClu-310
- ❑ 93StaCluFDI-310
- ❑ 93StaCluMO-5
- ❑ 93StaCluMOP-310
- ❑ 93Stu-52
- ❑ 93Top-718
- ❑ 93TopGol-718
- ❑ 93TopInaM-718
- ❑ 93TopInaR-718
- ❑ 93TopMic-718
- ❑ 93TriPla-231
- ❑ 93Ult-267
- ❑ 93UppDec-55
- ❑ 93UppDec-224
- ❑ 93UppDecGold-55
- ❑ 93UppDecGold-224
- ❑ 94Bow-557
- ❑ 94BowBes-R67
- ❑ 94BowBesR-R67
- ❑ 94ColC-424
- ❑ 94ColChoGS-424
- ❑ 94ColChoSS-424
- ❑ 94Don-369
- ❑ 94DonSpeE-369
- ❑ 94Fin-122
- ❑ 94FinRef-122
- ❑ 94Fla-336
- ❑ 94Fle-282
- ❑ 94FleExtB-162
- ❑ 94FUnPac-78
- ❑ 94Lea-131
- ❑ 94LeaL-65
- ❑ 94MarMot-6
- ❑ 94OPC-268
- ❑ 94Pac-564
- ❑ 94PanSti-117
- ❑ 94Pin-343
- ❑ 94PinArtP-343
- ❑ 94PinMusC-343
- ❑ 94PinRunC-RC17
- ❑ 94ProMag-126
- ❑ 94RedFolMI-7
- ❑ 94Sco-353
- ❑ 94ScoGolR-353
- ❑ 94Sel-79
- ❑ 94SP-104
- ❑ 94SPDieC-104
- ❑ 94Spo-18
- ❑ 94StaClu-299
- ❑ 94StaCluFDI-299
- ❑ 94StaCluGR-299
- ❑ 94StaCluMOP-299
- ❑ 94StaCluMOP-ST26
- ❑ 94StaCluST-ST26
- ❑ 94Stu-100
- ❑ 94Top-472
- ❑ 94TopGol-472
- ❑ 94TopSpa-472
- ❑ 94TriPla-125
- ❑ 94Ult-118
- ❑ 94UppDec-61
- ❑ 94UppDecED-61
- ❑ 95Baz-15
- ❑ 95Bow-362
- ❑ 95ColCho-290
- ❑ 95ColChoGS-290
- ❑ 95ColChoSE-124
- ❑ 95ColChoSEGS-124
- ❑ 95ColChoSESS-124
- ❑ 95ColChoSS-290
- ❑ 95Don-471
- ❑ 95DonPreP-471
- ❑ 95DonTopotO-147
- ❑ 95Emo-76
- ❑ 95Fin-105
- ❑ 95FinRef-105
- ❑ 95Fla-80
- ❑ 95Fle-263
- ❑ 95Lea-172
- ❑ 95LeaLim-13
- ❑ 95MarMot-6
- ❑ 95MarPac-13
- ❑ 95MarPac-25
- ❑ 95Pac-392
- ❑ 95PacPri-124
- ❑ 95PanSti-84
- ❑ 95Pin-234
- ❑ 95PinArtP-234
- ❑ 95PinMusC-234
- ❑ 95RedFol-34
- ❑ 95Sco-68
- ❑ 95ScoGolR-68
- ❑ 95ScoPlaTS-68
- ❑ 95Sel-38
- ❑ 95SelArtP-38
- ❑ 95SP-192
- ❑ 95SPCha-187
- ❑ 95SPChaDC-187
- ❑ 95SPSil-192
- ❑ 95StaClu-73
- ❑ 95StaCluFDI-73
- ❑ 95StaCluMOP-73
- ❑ 95StaCluMOP-SS3
- ❑ 95StaCluSS-SS3
- ❑ 95StaCluSTDW-M26T
- ❑ 95StaCluSTDW-M73
- ❑ 95StaCluSTWS-73
- ❑ 95StaCluVR-46
- ❑ 95StaCluVRMO-46
- ❑ 95Stu-114
- ❑ 95Top-25
- ❑ 95TopCyb-21
- ❑ 95TopEmb-65
- ❑ 95TopEmbGI-65
- ❑ 95Ult-326
- ❑ 95UltGolM-326
- ❑ 95UppDec-345
- ❑ 95UppDecED-345
- ❑ 95UppDecEDG-345
- ❑ 95UppDecSE-253
- ❑ 95UppDecSEG-253
- ❑ 96Baz-37
- ❑ 96Bow-9
- ❑ 96BowBes-62
- ❑ 96BowBesAR-62
- ❑ 96BowBesR-62
- ❑ 96BowFoi-9
- ❑ 96Cir-76
- ❑ 96CirBos-19
- ❑ 96CirRav-76
- ❑ 96ColCho-383T
- ❑ 96ColCho-730
- ❑ 96ColChoCtG-CG25
- ❑ 96ColChoCtG-CG25B
- ❑ 96ColChoCtG-CG25C
- ❑ 96ColChoCtGE-CR25
- ❑ 96ColChoCtGG-CG25
- ❑ 96ColChoCtGG-CG25B
- ❑ 96ColChoCtGG-CG25C
- ❑ 96ColChoCtGGE-CR25
- ❑ 96ColChoGS-730
- ❑ 96ColChoSS-730
- ❑ 96DenHol-7
- ❑ 96Don-141
- ❑ 96DonPreP-141
- ❑ 96EmoXL-110
- ❑ 96Fin-B237
- ❑ 96Fin-G164
- ❑ 96Fin-S353
- ❑ 96FinRef-B237
- ❑ 96FinRef-G164
- ❑ 96FinRef-S353
- ❑ 96Fla-157
- ❑ 96Fle-231
- ❑ 96FleTif-231
- ❑ 96Lea-113
- ❑ 96LeaLim-69
- ❑ 96LeaLimG-69
- ❑ 96LeaPre-103
- ❑ 96LeaPreP-103
- ❑ 96LeaPrePB-113
- ❑ 96LeaPrePG-113
- ❑ 96LeaPrePS-113
- ❑ 96LeaSig-86
- ❑ 96LeaSigEA-19
- ❑ 96LeaSigEACM-1
- ❑ 96LeaSigPPG-86
- ❑ 96LeaSigPPP-86
- ❑ 96MarMot-3
- ❑ 96MetUni-104
- ❑ 96MetUniP-104
- ❑ 96Pac-415
- ❑ 96PacPri-P129
- ❑ 96PacPriFB-FB4
- ❑ 96PacPriG-P129
- ❑ 96PanSti-228
- ❑ 96Pin-224
- ❑ 96PinAfi-46
- ❑ 96PinAfiAP-46
- ❑ 96PinAfiFPP-46
- ❑ 96PinArtP-124
- ❑ 96PinFoil-224
- ❑ 96PinSta-124
- ❑ 96ProSta-63
- ❑ 96Sco-323
- ❑ 96ScoDugC-B48
- ❑ 96ScoDugCAP-B48
- ❑ 96ScoPowP-3
- ❑ 96ScoTitT-18
- ❑ 96Sel-86
- ❑ 96SelArtP-86
- ❑ 96SelCer-84
- ❑ 96SelCerAP-84
- ❑ 96SelCerCB-84
- ❑ 96SelCerCR-84
- ❑ 96SelCerIP-9
- ❑ 96SelCerMB-84
- ❑ 96SelCerMG-84
- ❑ 96SelCerMR-84
- ❑ 96SP-173
- ❑ 96Spo-91
- ❑ 96Spo-120
- ❑ 96SpoArtP-91
- ❑ 96SpoArtP-120
- ❑ 96SpoPowS-24
- ❑ 96SPSpeFX-8
- ❑ 96SPSpeFXDC-8
- ❑ 96SPx-54
- ❑ 96SPxGol-54
- ❑ 96StaClu-211
- ❑ 96StaClu-333
- ❑ 96StaCluEPB-333
- ❑ 96StaCluEPG-333
- ❑ 96StaCluEPS-333
- ❑ 96StaCluMO-8
- ❑ 96StaCluMOP-211
- ❑ 96StaCluMOP-333
- ❑ 96StaCluMOP-PP14
- ❑ 96StaCluMOP-PS5
- ❑ 96StaCluPP-PP14
- ❑ 96StaCluPS-PS5
- ❑ 96Stu-98
- ❑ 96StuPrePB-98
- ❑ 96StuPrePG-98
- ❑ 96StuPrePS-98
- ❑ 96Sum-65
- ❑ 96SumAbo&B-65
- ❑ 96SumArtP-65
- ❑ 96SumFoi-65
- ❑ 96TeaOut-12
- ❑ 96Top-270
- ❑ 96TopChr-109
- ❑ 96TopChrR-109
- ❑ 96TopGal-16
- ❑ 96TopGalPPI-16
- ❑ 96TopLas-100
- ❑ 96TopLasPC-2
- ❑ 96TopPro-AL11
- ❑ 96TopRoaW-RW5
- ❑ 96Ult-408
- ❑ 96UltGolM-408
- ❑ 96UppDec-201
- ❑ 96UppDecDD-DD36
- ❑ 96UppDecDDG-DD36
- ❑ 96UppDecDDS-DD36
- ❑ 96UppDecPD-PD3
- ❑ 96UppDecPRE-R2
- ❑ 96UppDecPRE-R12
- ❑ 96UppDecPreR-R2
- ❑ 96UppDecPreR-R12
- ❑ 96UppDecRunP-RP4
- ❑ 96UppDecVJLS-VJ11
- ❑ 96Zen-48
- ❑ 96ZenArtP-48
- ❑ 97Bow-255
- ❑ 97BowBes-17
- ❑ 97BowBesAR-17
- ❑ 97BowBesR-17
- ❑ 97BowChr-78
- ❑ 97BowChrI-78
- ❑ 97BowChrIR-78
- ❑ 97BowChrR-78
- ❑ 97BowInt-255
- ❑ 97Cir-72
- ❑ 97CirRav-72
- ❑ 97ColCho-333
- ❑ 97ColCho-480
- ❑ 97ColChoBS-17
- ❑ 97ColChoBSGS-17
- ❑ 97ColChoCtG-27A
- ❑ 97ColChoCtG-27B
- ❑ 97ColChoCtG-27C
- ❑ 97ColChoCtGE-CG27
- ❑ 97ColChoCtGIW-CG27
- ❑ 97ColChoNF-NF13
- ❑ 97ColChoPP-PP7
- ❑ 97ColChoPPG-PP7
- ❑ 97ColChoPPJ-PP7
- ❑ 97ColChoS-9
- ❑ 97ColChoSR-6
- ❑ 97ColChoT-SM10
- ❑ 97ColChoTBS-42
- ❑ 97ColChoTBSWH-42
- ❑ 97Don-58
- ❑ 97DonEli-41
- ❑ 97DonEliGS-41
- ❑ 97DonGolPP-58
- ❑ 97DonLim-170
- ❑ 97DonLim-196
- ❑ 97DonLimE-170
- ❑ 97DonLimE-196
- ❑ 97DonLimENG-170
- ❑ 97DonLonL-7
- ❑ 97DonPre-63
- ❑ 97DonPreCttC-63
- ❑ 97DonSig-75
- ❑ 97DonSigAC-19
- ❑ 97DonSigAM-19
- ❑ 97DonSigPPP-75
- ❑ 97DonSilPP-58
- ❑ 97DonTea-138
- ❑ 97DonTeaSPE-138
- ❑ 97E-X2-39
- ❑ 97E-X2Cred-39
- ❑ 97E-X2EssCre-39
- ❑ 97Fin-35
- ❑ 97Fin-172
- ❑ 97Fin-282
- ❑ 97FinEmb-172
- ❑ 97FinEmb-282
- ❑ 97FinEmbR-172
- ❑ 97FinEmbR-282
- ❑ 97FinRef-35
- ❑ 97FinRef-172
- ❑ 97FinRef-282
- ❑ 97FlaShoLC-119
- ❑ 97FlaShoLeg0-119
- ❑ 97FlaShoLeg1-119
- ❑ 97FlaShoM-A119
- ❑ 97FlaShoM-B119
- ❑ 97FlaShoM-C119
- ❑ 97FlaShoR0-119
- ❑ 97FlaShoR1-119
- ❑ 97FlaShoR2-119
- ❑ 97Fle-202
- ❑ 97FleLumC-5
- ❑ 97FleTif-202
- ❑ 97Lea-102
- ❑ 97LeaFraM-102
- ❑ 97LeaFraMDC-102
- ❑ 97MarSco-7
- ❑ 97MarScoPl-7
- ❑ 97MarScoPr-7
- ❑ 97MetUni-143
- ❑ 97NewPin-55
- ❑ 97NewPinAP-55
- ❑ 97NewPinMC-55
- ❑ 97NewPinPP-55
- ❑ 97Pac-182
- ❑ 97PacCar-16
- ❑ 97PacCarM-16
- ❑ 97PacLigB-182
- ❑ 97PacPri-61
- ❑ 97PacPriLB-61
- ❑ 97PacPriP-61
- ❑ 97PacPriSL-SL6C
- ❑ 97PacSil-182
- ❑ 97Pin-195
- ❑ 97PinArtP-PP195
- ❑ 97PinCar-10
- ❑ 97PinCer-82
- ❑ 97PinCerMBla-82
- ❑ 97PinCerMBlu-82
- ❑ 97PinCerMG-82
- ❑ 97PinCerMR-82
- ❑ 97PinCerR-82
- ❑ 97PinIns-39
- ❑ 97PinInsCE-39
- ❑ 97PinInsDE-39
- ❑ 97PinInsFS-8
- ❑ 97PinMin-30
- ❑ 97PinMinB-30
- ❑ 97PinMinCB-30
- ❑ 97PinMinCG-30
- ❑ 97PinMinCGR-30
- ❑ 97PinMinCN-30
- ❑ 97PinMinCSS-30
- ❑ 97PinMinG-30
- ❑ 97PinMinS-30
- ❑ 97PinMusC-195
- ❑ 97PinPrePla-195
- ❑ 97PinTotCPB-82
- ❑ 97PinTotCPG-82
- ❑ 97PinTotCPR-82
- ❑ 97PinX-P-36
- ❑ 97PinX-PF&A-13
- ❑ 97PinX-PMoS-36
- ❑ 97PinX-PSfF-12
- ❑ 97PinX-PSfFU-12
- ❑ 97Sco-168
- ❑ 97Sco-513
- ❑ 97ScoArtPWB-168
- ❑ 97ScoArtPWB-513
- ❑ 97ScoHeaotO-8
- ❑ 97ScoPreS-168
- ❑ 97ScoResC-513
- ❑ 97ScoShoS-168
- ❑ 97ScoShoS-513
- ❑ 97ScoShoSAP-168
- ❑ 97ScoShoSAP-513
- ❑ 97ScoStaaD-7
- ❑ 97ScoTitT-13
- ❑ 97Sel-49
- ❑ 97SelArtP-49
- ❑ 97SelCom-49
- ❑ 97SelRegG-49
- ❑ 97SP-164
- ❑ 97SpollI-38
- ❑ 97SpollIEE-38
- ❑ 97SpollIGS-21
- ❑ 97SPSpeF-33
- ❑ 97SPSpxF-1
- ❑ 97SPSPxFA-1
- ❑ 97SPVinAu-5
- ❑ 97SPVinAu-6
- ❑ 97SPVinAu-7
- ❑ 97SPx-44
- ❑ 97SPxBro-44
- ❑ 97SPxGol-44
- ❑ 97SPxGraF-44
- ❑ 97SPxSil-44
- ❑ 97SPxSte-44
- ❑ 97StaClu-19
- ❑ 97StaClu-390
- ❑ 97StaCluMat-19
- ❑ 97StaCluMOP-19
- ❑ 97StaCluMOP-390
- ❑ 97StaCluMOP-PG5
- ❑ 97StaCluPG-PG5
- ❑ 97Stu-129
- ❑ 97StuPrePG-129
- ❑ 97StuPrePS-129
- ❑ 97Top-40
- ❑ 97TopChr-15
- ❑ 97TopChrDD-DD3
- ❑ 97TopChrDDR-DD3
- ❑ 97TopChrR-15
- ❑ 97TopGal-50
- ❑ 97TopGalPPI-50
- ❑ 97TopMem05-9
- ❑ 97TopSta-65
- ❑ 97TopStaAM-65
- ❑ 97UD3-7
- ❑ 97UltRBIK-5
- ❑ 97UppDec-177
- ❑ 97UppDecLDC-LD7
- ❑ 97UppDecP-25
- ❑ 97UppDecPE-25
- ❑ 97UppDecPP-PP4
- ❑ 97UppDecPPJ-PP4
- ❑ 97UppDecRP-RP11
- ❑ 97Zen-38
- ❑ 98Bow-250
- ❑ 98BowBes-9
- ❑ 98BowBesAR-9
- ❑ 98BowBesR-9
- ❑ 98BowChr-250
- ❑ 98BowChrGA-250
- ❑ 98BowChrGAR-250
- ❑ 98BowChrI-250
- ❑ 98BowChrIR-250
- ❑ 98BowChrR-250
- ❑ 98BowGolA-250
- ❑ 98BowInt-250
- ❑ 98CirThu-49
- ❑ 98CirThuRav-49
- ❑ 98CirThuSupRav-49
- ❑ 98CirThuTB-3
- ❑ 98ColCho-242
- ❑ 98ColChoCtG-CG12A
- ❑ 98ColChoCtG-CG12B
- ❑ 98ColChoCtG-CG12C
- ❑ 98ColChoCtGExch-CG12
- ❑ 98ColChoCtGIW-CG12
- ❑ 98ColChoRJ-242
- ❑ 98ColChoRJ-SQ71
- ❑ 98ColChoSQ-SQ71
- ❑ 98CroRoy-124
- ❑ 98Don-82
- ❑ 98DonCol-82
- ❑ 98DonColL-307
- ❑ 98DonColP-598
- ❑ 98DonColS-82
- ❑ 98DonCruG-43
- ❑ 98DonCruP-43
- ❑ 98DonCruR-43
- ❑ 98DonGolPP-82
- ❑ 98DonPre-48
- ❑ 98DonPreSeat-48
- ❑ 98DonPriCD-82
- ❑ 98DonPriCL-307
- ❑ 98DonPriCP-598
- ❑ 98DonSig-77
- ❑ 98DonSigAC-15
- ❑ 98DonSigAM-15
- ❑ 98DonSigP-77
- ❑ 98DonSilPP-82
- ❑ 98E-X2-35
- ❑ 98E-X2ECFut-35
- ❑ 98E-X2ECNow-35
- ❑ 98Fin-180
- ❑ 98FinNo--180
- ❑ 98FinNo-R-180
- ❑ 98FinPowZ-P13
- ❑ 98FinRef-180

❑ 98FlaShoLeg0-72
❑ 98FlaShoLeg1-72
❑ 98FlaShoLeg2-72
❑ 98FlaShoLeg3-72
❑ 98FlaShoLegM-72
❑ 98FlaShoR0-72
❑ 98FlaShoR1-72
❑ 98FlaShoR2-72
❑ 98FlaShoR3-72
❑ 98Fle-68
❑ 98Fle-324
❑ 98FleDiamInk-1
❑ 98FleVin'-54
❑ 98FleVin'C-54
❑ 98Lea-108
❑ 98LeaFraDA-108
❑ 98LeaFraF-108
❑ 98LeaFraM-108
❑ 98LeaFraM-108
❑ 98LeaFraMDC-108
❑ 98LeaFraMDC-108
❑ 98LeaFraMS-108
❑ 98LeaFraMZ2-108
❑ 98LeaRS-19
❑ 98LeaRSLHolo-19
❑ 98LeaRSLong-19
❑ 98LeaRTrue-19
❑ 98MarSco-6
❑ 98MarScoP-6
❑ 98MetUni-174
❑ 98MetUniPMG-174
❑ 98Pac-180
❑ 98PacAur-70
❑ 98PacHomRH-17
❑ 98PacInv-61
❑ 98PacInvPBlue-61
❑ 98PacInvSilv-61
❑ 98PacInvTeam-26
❑ 98PacOme-217
❑ 98PacOmeR-217
❑ 98PacOnl-679
❑ 98PacOnlR-679
❑ 98PacOnlWC-679
❑ 98PacPar-84
❑ 98PacParC-84
❑ 98PacParG-84
❑ 98PacParHS-84
❑ 98PacParI-21
❑ 98PacParPB-84
❑ 98PacParR-84
❑ 98PacPlaB-180
❑ 98PacRedT-180
❑ 98PacSil-180
❑ 98Pin-60
❑ 98PinArtP-PP53
❑ 98PinIns-102
❑ 98PinInsCE-102
❑ 98PinInsDE-102
❑ 98PinInsSG-4AB
❑ 98PinInsSG-4CD
❑ 98PinInsSGS-4AB
❑ 98PinInsSGS-4CD
❑ 98PinMusC-PP53
❑ 98PinPer-49
❑ 98PinPerPP-49
❑ 98PinPerSftF-3
❑ 98PinPreP-60
❑ 98PinSna-SM2
❑ 98PinSna-SM6
❑ 98Revo-131
❑ 98RevoSS-131
❑ 98Sco-82
❑ 98ScoRT-43
❑ 98ScoRTSS-PP43
❑ 98ScoRTSSAP-PP43
❑ 98ScoRTSSAP1-PP43
❑ 98ScoSS-PP37
❑ 98ScoSSAP-PP37
❑ 98SkyDugA-147
❑ 98SkyDugAAR-1
❑ 98SkyDugAIA-147
❑ 98SP Aut-178
❑ 98SP AutTrade-3
❑ 98SPAutGJ5x7-6
❑ 98SpoIll-16
❑ 98SpoIllC-C6
❑ 98SpoIllEE-16
❑ 98SpoIllFE-16
❑ 98SpoIllTaN-65
❑ 98SpoIllTaNEE-65
❑ 98SpoIllWSF-66
❑ 98SpoIllWSFEE-66
❑ 98SpoIllWSFFE-66
❑ 98SPxFin-37
❑ 98SPxFin-129
❑ 98SPxFinR-37
❑ 98SPxFinR-129
❑ 98SPxFinS-37
❑ 98SPxFinS-129
❑ 98StaCluFDI-20
❑ 98StaCluI-20
❑ 98StaCluOneK-20
❑ 98StaCluPP-20
❑ 98StaCluTIII-T3A
❑ 98StaCluTLme-T3A
❑ 98StaCluTLmo-T3A
❑ 98Stu-189
❑ 98StuGPP-189
❑ 98StuSPP-189
❑ 98Top-90
❑ 98TopChr-90
❑ 98TopChrR-90
❑ 98TopDevR-90
❑ 98TopDia-90
❑ 98TopGal-27
❑ 98TopGalGP-27
❑ 98TopGalOPP-27
❑ 98TopGalPPI-27
❑ 98TopGalPPIA-27
❑ 98TopGolLabC1-18
❑ 98TopGolLabC1B-18
❑ 98TopGolLabC1One-18
❑ 98TopGolLabC1R-18
❑ 98TopGolLabC2-18
❑ 98TopGolLabC2B-18
❑ 98TopGolLabC2One-18
❑ 98TopGolLabC2R-18
❑ 98TopGolLabC3-18
❑ 98TopGolLabC3B-18
❑ 98TopGolLabC3One-18
❑ 98TopGolLabC3R-18
❑ 98TopMiniC-90
❑ 98TopOpeD-44
❑ 98TopSta-74
❑ 98TopSta'S-6
❑ 98TopSta'SGH-6
❑ 98TopStaB-74
❑ 98TopStaG-74
❑ 98TopStaGR-74
❑ 98TopStaS-74
❑ 98TopStaSteG-6
❑ 98TopTek-81
❑ 98TopTekD-81
❑ 98UD3-33
❑ 98UD3-123
❑ 98UD3-213
❑ 98UD3DieCut-33
❑ 98UD3DieCut-123
❑ 98UD3DieCut-213
❑ 98Ult-135
❑ 98UltGolM-135
❑ 98UltMas-135
❑ 98UltPlaM-135
❑ 98UppDec-3
❑ 98UppDec-514
❑ 98UppDecAPA1-1
❑ 98UppDecAPA2-JB
❑ 98UppDecGHRC-29
❑ 98UppDecRBBop-BB15
❑ 98UppDecTMT-17
❑ 98UppDecTMTG-17
❑ 98Zen-48
❑ 98Zen5 xx7-63
❑ 98Zen5x7GoldImp-63
❑ 98Zen5x7Imp-63
❑ 98ZenZ-G-48
❑ 98ZenZ-S-48
❑ 99199Fin-152
❑ 99Bow-282
❑ 99BowGol-282
❑ 99BowInt-282
❑ 99FinGolRef-152
❑ 99FinRef-152
❑ 99Fle-75
❑ 99FleBri-80
❑ 99FleBri2G-80
❑ 99FleBriBlu-80
❑ 99FleBriGol-80
❑ 99FleSta9-75
❑ 99FleWarT-75
❑ 99MetUni-103
❑ 99MetUniGM-103
❑ 99MetUniPMG-103
❑ 99Pac-392
❑ 99PacAur-174
❑ 99PacAurOD-174
❑ 99PacInv-131
❑ 99PacInvOD-131
❑ 99PacInvPB-131
❑ 99PacOme-225
❑ 99PacOmeC-225
❑ 99PacOmeG-225
❑ 99PacOmePB-225
❑ 99PacPar-214
❑ 99PacParC-214
❑ 99PacParG-214
❑ 99PacParHoloGold-214
❑ 99PacParHS-214
❑ 99PacParOD-214
❑ 99PacParPB-214
❑ 99PacParRed-214
❑ 99PacPlaB-392
❑ 99PacPri-132
❑ 99PacPriHB-132
❑ 99PacPriHG-132
❑ 99PacPriHM-132
❑ 99PacPriHP-132
❑ 99PacPriRed-132
❑ 99PacRed-392
❑ 99SkyMolM-73
❑ 99SkyMolMX-73
❑ 99SkyPre-109
❑ 99SkyPreR-109
❑ 99SkyThu-112
❑ 99SkyThuRant-112
❑ 99SkyThuRave-112
❑ 99SPx-71
❑ 99SPxFinR-71
❑ 99SPxFinS-71
❑ 99StaClu-274
❑ 99StaCluC-CS6
❑ 99StaCluC-CS12
❑ 99StaCluC-CS17
❑ 99StaCluC-CS21
❑ 99StaCluFDI-274
❑ 99StaCluOoaK-274
❑ 99StaCluPP-274
❑ 99StaCluTI-T3A
❑ 99StaCluTL-T3A
❑ 99StaCluTL-T3A
❑ 99ThuSkySupR-112
❑ 99Top-376
❑ 99TopBlaLC1-41
❑ 99TopBlaLC2-41
❑ 99TopBlaLC3-41
❑ 99TopChr-376
❑ 99TopChrR-376
❑ 99TopGal-71
❑ 99TopGalPP-71
❑ 99TopGalPPI-71
❑ 99TopGolL-41
❑ 99TopGolLC1-41
❑ 99TopGolLC2-41
❑ 99TopGolLOtO-41
❑ 99TopMVPP-376
❑ 99TopOpeD-145
❑ 99TopRedLC1-41
❑ 99TopRedLC2-41
❑ 99TopRedLC3-41
❑ 99UD Cho-144
❑ 99UD ChoPCR-144
❑ 99Ult-77
❑ 99UltGolM-77
❑ 99UltMas-77
❑ 99UltPlaM-77
❑ 99UppDec-490
❑ 99UppDecBD-79
❑ 99UppDecBDD-79
❑ 99UppDecBDQ-79
❑ 99UppDecBDT-79
❑ 99UppDecEL1-490
❑ 99UppDecEL2-490
❑ 99UppDecR-78
❑ 99UppDecRG-78
❑ 99UppDecRP-78
❑ 99Vic-374

Buhner, Shawn
❑ 94BelMarC-7
❑ 94BelMarF-3241
❑ 96LanJetB-8
❑ 97LanJet-9
❑ 98OrlRayM-1

Buice, DeWayne
❑ 78CedRapGT-4
❑ 81WesHavAT-4
❑ 82TacTigT-1
❑ 83TacTigT-3
❑ 86MidAngP-3
❑ 87CalAngPPS-2
❑ 87DonRoo-6
❑ 87FleUpd-14
❑ 87FleUpdG-14
❑ 87SpoRoo2-26
❑ 87TopTra-13T
❑ 87TopTraT-13T
❑ 88AngSmo-7
❑ 88Don-58
❑ 88Fle-487
❑ 88FleGlo-487
❑ 88OPC-396
❑ 88Sco-376
❑ 88ScoGlo-376
❑ 88StaLinAn-3
❑ 88Top-649
❑ 88TopMinL-4
❑ 88TopRoo-4
❑ 88TopSti-180
❑ 88TopTif-649
❑ 88ToyRoo-4
❑ 88UppDecP-A1
❑ 88UppDecP-B1
❑ 88UppDecP-C1
❑ 89Sco-153
❑ 89SyrChiC-8
❑ 89SyrChiMB-3
❑ 89SyrChiP-811
❑ 89Top-147
❑ 89TopTif-147
❑ 89UppDec-147

Buirley, Matt
❑ 96VerExpB-10
❑ 98EriSeaWM-5

Buitimea, Martin
❑ 85MexCitTT-5

Buker, Cy
❑ 77FriOneYW-7

Buksa, Ken
❑ 88WatPirP-16

Bulkeley, Morgan G.
❑ 36Halof FP-3
❑ 39PC7AlbHoF-6
❑ 50CalHOFW-9
❑ 53ArtHaloFP-8
❑ 76ShaPiz-9
❑ 77BobParHoF-8
❑ 80PerHaloFP-6
❑ 80SSPHOF-6
❑ 84GalHaloFRL-9

Bull, Hornsby the
❑ 98TulDriTI-14

Bull, Wool E.
❑ 95DurBulTI-NNO
❑ 96HigDesMB-4
❑ 97HigDesMG-2

Bullard, Jason
❑ 91WelPirC-28
❑ 91WelPirP-3563
❑ 92CarMudF-1174
❑ 92CarMudS-128
❑ 96NorTidB-9
❑ 97BowBay-10
❑ 98RicBraQ-5

Bullard, Rocky (Larry)
❑ 76BatTroTI-3
❑ 78DunBluJT-2

Bullett, Scott
❑ 90WelPirP-11
❑ 91AugPirC-25
❑ 91AugPirP-818
❑ 91Cla/Bes-245
❑ 91SouAtlLAGP-SAL3
❑ 92Bow-321
❑ 92CarMudF-1191
❑ 92CarMudS-129
❑ 92ClaBluBF-BC4
❑ 92ClaFS7-42
❑ 92ClaRedB-BC4
❑ 92ProFS7-312
❑ 92SkyAA F-60
❑ 92StaClu-288
❑ 92TopDeb91-25
❑ 92Ult-551
❑ 93Bow-402
❑ 93BufBisF-529
❑ 93ClaFS7-127
❑ 93Lea-497
❑ 94Don-431
❑ 94IowCubF-1285
❑ 94Pac-493
❑ 94Top-584
❑ 94TopGol-584
❑ 94TopSpa-584
❑ 96Don-331
❑ 96DonPreP-331
❑ 96Fle-311
❑ 96FleTif-311
❑ 96LeaSigEA-20
❑ 96SigRooOJ-6
❑ 96SigRooOJS-6
❑ 96Ult-448
❑ 96UltGolM-448
❑ 97ColCho-53
❑ 97Pac-247
❑ 97PacLigB-247
❑ 97PacSil-247
❑ 97RocRedW-6

Bulling, Bud (Terry C.)
❑ 77OrlTwiT-3
❑ 78OrlTwiT-1
❑ 78Top-432
❑ 79SpoIndT-23
❑ 80SpoIndT-10
❑ 81MarPos-8
❑ 82Don-612
❑ 82MarPos-8
❑ 82Top-98
❑ 83Don-226
❑ 83Fle-630
❑ 83SalLakCGT-15
❑ 83Top-519

Bullinger, Jim
❑ 86GenCubP-1
❑ 87WinSpiP-10
❑ 88PitCubP-1367
❑ 89ChaKniTI-6
❑ 90WinSpiTI-17
❑ 91ChaKniLD-128
❑ 91ChaKniP-1681
❑ 91Cla/Bes-176
❑ 91LinDriAA-128
❑ 92DonRoo-20
❑ 92FleUpd-73
❑ 92IowCubS-204
❑ 92ScoRoo-101T
❑ 92SkyAAAF-98
❑ 92StaClu-714
❑ 92StaCluECN-714
❑ 92TopTra-17T
❑ 92TopTraG-17T
❑ 93CubStaC-26
❑ 93Don-556
❑ 93Fle-374
❑ 93IowCubF-2129
❑ 93Lea-31
❑ 93Sco-339
❑ 93Sel-285
❑ 93StaClu-118
❑ 93StaCluFDI-118
❑ 93StaCluMOP-118
❑ 93Top-101
❑ 93TopGol-101
❑ 93TopInaM-101
❑ 93TopInaR-101
❑ 93TopMic-101
❑ 93Toy-6
❑ 93UppDec-379
❑ 93UppDecGold-379
❑ 94FleUpd-107
❑ 94StaCluT-360
❑ 94StaCluTFDI-360
❑ 94TopGol-713
❑ 94TopSpa-713
❑ 95Don-239
❑ 95DonPreP-239
❑ 95DonTopotO-195
❑ 95Fla-111
❑ 95Fle-411
❑ 95Lea-341
❑ 95Pin-428
❑ 95PinArtP-428
❑ 95PinMusC-428
❑ 95Top-428
❑ 95TopCyb-226
❑ 95Ult-357
❑ 95UltGolM-357
❑ 96ColCho-79
❑ 96ColChoGS-79
❑ 96ColChoSS-79
❑ 96CubFle-2
❑ 96Don-185
❑ 96DonPreP-185
❑ 96EmoXL-151
❑ 96Fla-212
❑ 96Fle-312
❑ 96FleTif-312
❑ 96Pac-24
❑ 96Sco-128
❑ 96StaClu-53
❑ 96StaCluMOP-53
❑ 96Top-316
❑ 96Ult-163
❑ 96UltGolM-163
❑ 96UppDec-37
❑ 97ColCho-385
❑ 97Fle-587
❑ 97FleTif-587
❑ 97Ult-532
❑ 97UltGolME-532
❑ 97UltPlaME-532
❑ 98TacRaiQ-8
❑ 98Top-221
❑ 98TopChr-221
❑ 98TopChrR-221
❑ 98TopDevR-221
❑ 98TopDia-221
❑ 98TopMiniC-221
❑ 98UppDec-438

Bullinger, Kirk
❑ 92HamRedC-2
❑ 92HamRedF-1583
❑ 93MidLeaAGF-50
❑ 93SprCarC-5
❑ 93SprCarF-1842
❑ 94ExcFS7-262
❑ 94St.PetCC-5
❑ 94St.PetCF-2576
❑ 94Top-713
❑ 95HarSenTI-46
❑ 96HarSenB-9
❑ 97HarSen-6
❑ 99SpoIll-53

Bullinger, Matt
❑ 79WatIndT-1B
❑ 81ChaLooT-6
❑ 82JacMetT-2

Bullock, Craig
❑ 91ChaRaiC-17
❑ 91ChaRaiP-102
❑ 92ColMetC-18
❑ 92ColMetF-301
❑ 92ColMetPI-25
❑ 93CapCitBC-3
❑ 93CapCitBF-452
❑ 94St.LucMC-4
❑ 94St.LucMF-1186
❑ 95StLucMTI-8
❑ 96StLucMTI-17

Bullock, Derek
❑ 97LynHil-5

Bullock, Eric
❑ 82DayBeaAT-12
❑ 83ColAstT-9
❑ 85TucTorC-52
❑ 87TucTorP-19
❑ 88PorBeaC-17
❑ 88PorBeaP-640
❑ 89Fle-106
❑ 89FleGlo-106
❑ 89PhiTas-38
❑ 90CMC-67
❑ 90IndIndC-17
❑ 90IndIndP-285
❑ 90ProAAAF-568
❑ 91Bow-457
❑ 91ExpPos-2
❑ 91Lea-470
❑ 92Don-683
❑ 92ExpPos-5
❑ 92Fle-474
❑ 92IndIndF-1872
❑ 92Sco-661
❑ 92StaClu-659
❑ 93NorTidF-2580
❑ 96LasVegSB-4

Bullock, Josh
❑ 90NebCor-6
❑ 93JamExpC-4
❑ 93JamExpF-3318
❑ 94BurBeeC-4
❑ 94BurBeeF-1073

Bullock, Renaldo
❑ 92BelMarCB-26
❑ 92BelMarF-1455

Bullock, Wynn
❑ 75TopPho-104

Bulls, Dave
❑ 86PorBeaP-2

Bulls, Durham
❑ 90DurBulTI-1
❑ 92DurBulTI-NNO
❑ 93DurBulTI-5
❑ 95DurBulTI-NNO
❑ 95DurBulTI-NNO
❑ 96DurBulBrB-1

Bumagat, Noel
❑ 90IBAWorA-30

Bumbry, Al (Alonza B.)
❑ 73BalOriP-9
❑ 73BalOriP-10
❑ 73LinPor-9
❑ 73OPC-614
❑ 73OriJohP-1
❑ 73OriTeal-8
❑ 73Top-614
❑ 74OPC-137

❑ 74Top-137
❑ 75BalOriP-6
❑ 75OPC-358
❑ 75Top-358
❑ 75TopMin-358
❑ 76BalOriP-6
❑ 76OPC-307
❑ 76SSP-396
❑ 76Top-307
❑ 77BalOriP-2
❑ 77BurCheD-37
❑ 77Hos-90
❑ 77OPC-192
❑ 77Top-626
❑ 78BalOriP-3
❑ 78Top-188
❑ 79BalOriP-2
❑ 79Top-517
❑ 80OPC-36
❑ 80Top-65
❑ 81AllGamPI-48
❑ 81BalOriP-2
❑ 81Don-355
❑ 81Fle-172
❑ 81FleStiC-30
❑ 81OPC-34
❑ 81Top-425
❑ 81TopScr-29
❑ 81TopSti-35
❑ 82Don-153
❑ 82Fle-159
❑ 82FleSta-147
❑ 82OPC-265
❑ 82Top-265
❑ 82TopSti-141
❑ 83Don-383
❑ 83Fle-54
❑ 83FleSta-26
❑ 83FleSti-203
❑ 83OPC-272
❑ 83OriPos-5
❑ 83Top-655
❑ 83TopFol-5
❑ 84BalOriP-6
❑ 84Don-210
❑ 84Fle-2
❑ 84Nes792-319
❑ 84Top-319
❑ 84TopTif-319
❑ 85BalOriP-3
❑ 85Don-350
❑ 85Fle-171
❑ 85FleUpd-13
❑ 85PadMot-25
❑ 85Top-726
❑ 85TopSti-205
❑ 85TopTif-726
❑ 85TopTifT-12T
❑ 85TopTra-12T
❑ 86Fle-316
❑ 86Top-583
❑ 86TopTif-583
❑ 87ElmPioBC-29
❑ 87ElmPioRC-29
❑ 89PacSenL-47
❑ 89T/MSenL-14
❑ 89TopSenL-27
❑ 90EliSenL-94
❑ 90SweBasG-29
❑ 90TopTVRS-3
❑ 91OriCro-60
❑ 92RedSoxDD-5
❑ 93RedSoxP-3
❑ 93TedWil-82
❑ 93UppDecAH-22
❑ 94BowBayF-2429
❑ 94UppDecAH-73
❑ 94UppDecAH1-73
❑ 95BalOriP-12

Bumgarner, Jeff
❑ 86KenTwiP-3
❑ 87ColAstP-25
❑ 87OrlTwiP-1
❑ 88PorBeaC-4
❑ 88PorBeaP-659
❑ 89JacMetGS-10
❑ 90FreKeyTI-27
❑ 91HagSunP-2447
❑ 91LinDriAA-226
❑ 92HagSunS-254

Bump, Nate
❑ 98SalVol-3
❑ 99Bow-208
❑ 99BowChr-208
❑ 99BowChrG-208
❑ 99BowChrGR-208
❑ 99BowChrI-208
❑ 99BowChrIR-208
❑ 99BowChrR-208
❑ 99BowGol-208
❑ 99BowInt-208
❑ 99JustheS-12
❑ 99JustheSJB-12
❑ 99StaClu-159
❑ 99StaCluFDI-159
❑ 99StaCluOoaK-159
❑ 99StaCluPP-159
❑ 99TeaBesR-6
❑ 99TeaBesRFS-22
❑ 99TeaBesRG-6
❑ 99TeaBesRS-6
❑ 99Top-440
❑ 99TopChr-440
❑ 99TopChrR-440
❑ 99TopMVPP-440

Bumstead, Mark
❑ 78St.PetCT-3

Bunch, Melvin
❑ 93MidLeaAGF-17
❑ 93RocRoyC-5
❑ 93RocRoyF-705
❑ 94ClaGolF-195
❑ 94ExcFS7-65
❑ 94WilBluRC-2
❑ 94WilBluRF-291
❑ 95FleUpd-45
❑ 95OmaRoyTI-5
❑ 95TopTra-104T
❑ 96ColCho-168
❑ 96ColChoGS-168
❑ 96ColChoSS-168
❑ 96Don-164
❑ 96DonPreP-164
❑ 96OmaRoyB-9
❑ 96RoyPol-4
❑ 97HarSen-7

Bundy, Lorenzo
❑ 83AleDukT-31
❑ 84HawIslC-127
❑ 89IndIndC-17
❑ 89IndIndP-1223
❑ 90JacExpB-27
❑ 90JacExpP-1389
❑ 91SumFlyC-26
❑ 91SumFlyP-2351
❑ 92AlbPolCB-27
❑ 92AlbPolF-2321
❑ 93BurBeeC-26
❑ 93BurBeeF-173
❑ 94BurBeeC-26
❑ 94BurBeeF-1097
❑ 97BreCouMB-3

Bundy, Ryan
❑ 98St.CatSM-23
❑ 99TeaBesR-7
❑ 99TeaBesRFS-25
❑ 99TeaBesRG-7
❑ 99TeaBesRS-7

Bunge, Todd
❑ 86AncGlaPTI-4

Bunker, Wally
❑ 64BalOriP-12
❑ 64Top-201
❑ 64TopRooAB-33
❑ 64TopVen-201
❑ 65BalOriP-11
❑ 65OPC-9
❑ 65Top-9
❑ 65Top-290
❑ 66BalOriP-9
❑ 66BalOriP-10
❑ 66Top-499
❑ 67BalOriP-24
❑ 67BalOriP-25
❑ 67CokCapO-15
❑ 67DexPre-37
❑ 67Top-585
❑ 67TopVen-254
❑ 68CokCapO-15
❑ 68Top-489
❑ 69MLBOffS-56
❑ 69OPC-137
❑ 69RoySol-2
❑ 69Top-137
❑ 69TopFou-2
❑ 69TopSta-182
❑ 69TopTeaP-7
❑ 70DayDaiNM-23
❑ 70Kel-70
❑ 70MLBOffS-218
❑ 70OPC-266
❑ 70RoyTeal-4
❑ 70Top-266
❑ 70TopBoo-7
❑ 71MLBOffS-410
❑ 71OPC-528
❑ 71oySigST-2
❑ 71Top-528
❑ 72MilBra-57
❑ 81Ori6F-11
❑ 81TCM60I-408
❑ 91OriCro-61

Bunkley, Antuan
❑ 96ForWayWB-5
❑ 97HelBreB-5
❑ 98WesMicWM-4

Bunning, Jim
❑ 47StaPinP2-7
❑ 57Top-338
❑ 58Top-115
❑ 59TigGraASP-5
❑ 59Top-149
❑ 59TopVen-149
❑ 60Lea-144
❑ 60TigJayP-4
❑ 60Top-502
❑ 61Pos-39A
❑ 61Pos-39B
❑ 61TigJayP-4
❑ 61Top-46
❑ 61Top-50
❑ 61Top-490
❑ 61TopStal-147
❑ 62Jel-26
❑ 62Pos-26
❑ 62PosCan-26
❑ 62SalPlaC-13
❑ 62ShiPlaC-13
❑ 62TigJayP-3
❑ 62TigPosCF-4
❑ 62Top-57
❑ 62Top-59
❑ 62Top-460
❑ 62TopBuc-12
❑ 62TopStal-44
❑ 62TopVen-57
❑ 62TopVen-59
❑ 63BasMagM-12
❑ 63Jel-53
❑ 63Pos-53
❑ 63SalMetC-33
❑ 63TigJayP-3
❑ 63Top-8
❑ 63Top-10
❑ 63Top-218
❑ 63Top-365
❑ 63TopStil-7
❑ 64PhiJayP-3
❑ 64PhiPhiB-7
❑ 64PhiTeaS-1
❑ 64Top-6
❑ 64Top-265
❑ 64TopCoi-93
❑ 64TopGia-10
❑ 64TopVen-6
❑ 64TopVen-265
❑ 64WheSta-9
❑ 65Baz-21
❑ 65OldLonC-5
❑ 65OPC-20
❑ 65PhiJayP-3
❑ 65Top-20
❑ 65TopEmbl-17
❑ 65TopTral-6
❑ 66Baz-31
❑ 66PhiTeal-3
❑ 66Top-435
❑ 66TopRubl-12
❑ 67AshOil-1
❑ 67Baz-31
❑ 67CokCapA-15
❑ 67CokCapNLA-20
❑ 67CokCapPh-16
❑ 67DexPre-38
❑ 67DexPre-39
❑ 67PhiPol-2
❑ 67Top-238
❑ 67Top-560
❑ 67TopVen-274
❑ 68AtlOilPBCC-8
❑ 68Baz-7
❑ 68OPC-7
❑ 68OPC-9
❑ 68OPC-11
❑ 68PirKDK-14
❑ 68PirTeal-4
❑ 68Top-7
❑ 68Top-9
❑ 68Top-11
❑ 68Top-215
❑ 68TopActS-8A
❑ 68TopVen-7
❑ 68TopVen-9
❑ 68TopVen-11
❑ 68TopVen-215
❑ 69CitMetC-20
❑ 69MilBra-46
❑ 69MLBOffS-183
❑ 69OPC-175
❑ 69PirTeal-4
❑ 69Top-175
❑ 69TopFou-8
❑ 69TopSta-84
❑ 69TopTeaP-16
❑ 70DayDaiNM-77
❑ 70MLBOffS-86
❑ 70OPC-403
❑ 70Top-403
❑ 71MLBOffS-172
❑ 71OPC-574
❑ 71PhiArcO-2
❑ 71Top-574
❑ 71TopCoi-3
❑ 71TopGreM-43
❑ 72MilBra-58
❑ 74LauAllG-61
❑ 76LauDiaJ-10
❑ 76OklCit8TI-14
❑ 79DiaGre-397
❑ 80PerHaloFP-225
❑ 80PerHaloFPS-81
❑ 81TCM60I-454
❑ 81TigDetN-97
❑ 82TCMGreP-39
❑ 83PhiPosGM-4
❑ 83PhiPosGPaM-9
❑ 83TigAIKS-15
❑ 83TigAIKS-24
❑ 84OCoandSI-89
❑ 86SpoDesJM-14
❑ 86TigSpoD-13
❑ 88PacLegI-92
❑ 89SweBasG-7
❑ 90DodTar-90
❑ 90PacLeg-76
❑ 90PerGreM-97
❑ 91UppDecS-17
❑ 97FleMilDM-29
❑ 97FleMilDMR-29
❑ 97TopStaHRR-3
❑ 97TopStaRRAU-3
❑ 98SpollITaN-7
❑ 98SpollITaNEE-7

Bunting, John
❑ 80PhiBul-13

Buonantony, Rich
❑ 82QuaCitCT-4
❑ 86LouRedTI-8
❑ 87LouRedTI-7
❑ 88LouRedBC-7
❑ 88LouRedBP-445
❑ 88LouRedBTI-12
❑ 90ReaPhiS-9
❑ 91RenSilSCLC-19

Burba, Dave
❑ 88SanBerSB-17
❑ 88SanBerSCLC-49
❑ 89WilBilP-630
❑ 89WilBilS-25
❑ 90CalCanC-6
❑ 90CalCanP-645
❑ 90CMC-433
❑ 90ProAAAF-110
❑ 91Bow-263
❑ 91CalCanLD-54
❑ 91CalCanP-509
❑ 91DonRoo-12
❑ 91Fle-447
❑ 91LinDriAAA-54
❑ 91Sco-742
❑ 91TopDeb90-23
❑ 92Bow-190
❑ 92Cla1-T21
❑ 92Don-566
❑ 92GiaMot-26
❑ 92GiaPacGaE-9
❑ 92Lea-471
❑ 92LeaBlaG-471
❑ 92OPC-728
❑ 92OPCPre-160
❑ 92Pin-529
❑ 92Sco-611
❑ 92ScoRoo-51T
❑ 92StaClu-348
❑ 92StaClu-718
❑ 92Top-728
❑ 92TopGol-728
❑ 92TopGolW-728
❑ 92TopMic-728
❑ 92TopTra-18T
❑ 92TopTraG-18T
❑ 92Ult-587
❑ 93Don-128
❑ 93Fle-527
❑ 93GiaMot-18
❑ 93GiaPos-11
❑ 93LinVenB-28
❑ 93PacSpa-609
❑ 93StaClu-245
❑ 93StaCluFDI-245
❑ 93StaCluMOP-245
❑ 93Ult-484
❑ 93UppDec-809
❑ 93UppDecGold-809
❑ 94ColC-67
❑ 94ColChoGS-67
❑ 94ColChoSS-67
❑ 94Don-124
❑ 94Fla-443
❑ 94Fle-686
❑ 94GiaMot-25
❑ 94GiaTarBC-6
❑ 94GiaUSPC-5D
❑ 94GiaUSPC-12C
❑ 94Pac-542
❑ 94Sco-219
❑ 94ScoGolR-219
❑ 94StaCluT-8
❑ 94StaCluTFDI-8
❑ 94Top-433
❑ 94TopGol-433
❑ 94TopSpa-433
❑ 94Ult-287
❑ 95Don-495
❑ 95DonPreP-495
❑ 95Fle-575
❑ 95GiaMot-25
❑ 95StaClu-134
❑ 95StaCluFDI-134
❑ 95StaCluMOP-134
❑ 95StaCluSTWS-134
❑ 95Top-304
❑ 95Ult-240
❑ 95UltGolM-240
❑ 95UppDec-488
❑ 96ColCho-521
❑ 96ColChoGS-521
❑ 96ColChoSS-521
❑ 96Don-531
❑ 96DonPreP-531
❑ 96Fla-230
❑ 96Fle-337
❑ 96FleTif-337
❑ 96LeaSigEA-21
❑ 96Pac-45
❑ 96Ult-177
❑ 96UltGolM-177
❑ 96UppDec-311
❑ 97ColCho-304
❑ 97Fle-630
❑ 97FleTif-630
❑ 97Pac-265
❑ 97PacLigB-265
❑ 97PacSil-265
❑ 97StaClu-273
❑ 97StaCluMOP-273
❑ 97Ult-456
❑ 97UltGolME-456
❑ 97UltPlaME-456
❑ 98ColCho-348
❑ 98Fle-378
❑ 98Pac-262
❑ 98PacOnl-215
❑ 98PacOnlR-215
❑ 98PacOnlWC-215
❑ 98PacPar-145
❑ 98PacParC-145
❑ 98PacParG-145
❑ 98PacParHS-145
❑ 98PacParPB-145
❑ 98PacParR-145
❑ 98PacPlaB-262
❑ 98PacRedT-262
❑ 98PacSil-262
❑ 98PinPlu-163
❑ 98Top-239
❑ 98TopChr-239
❑ 98TopChrR-239
❑ 98TopDevR-239
❑ 98TopDia-239
❑ 98TopMiniC-239
❑ 98UppDec-338
❑ 99Fle-381
❑ 99FleSta9-381
❑ 99FleWarT-381
❑ 99Pac-124
❑ 99PacPlaB-124
❑ 99PacRed-124
❑ 99StaClu-194
❑ 99StaCluFDI-194
❑ 99StaCluOoaK-194
❑ 99StaCluPP-194
❑ 99Top-121
❑ 99TopChr-121
❑ 99TopChrR-121
❑ 99TopMVPP-121

Burbach, Bill
❑ 69Top-658
❑ 69YanPhoS-38
❑ 70OPC-167
❑ 70Top-167
❑ 70YanPhoS-6
❑ 71MLBOffS-484
❑ 71OPC-683
❑ 71Top-683
❑ 92YanWIZ6-20
❑ 92YanWIZ7-27

Burbank, Dennis
❑ 88CapCodPB-6
❑ 88CapCodPPaLP-151
❑ 91OklStaC-2
❑ 91OneYanP-4145
❑ 92ForLauYTI-2
❑ 92Ft.LauYF-2602

Burbrink, Nels (Nelson E.)
❑ 49AngTeal-5
❑ 49W725AngTI-4
❑ 56Top-27

Burch, Al (Albert William)
❑ 09ColChiE-37A
❑ 09T206-44
❑ 09T206-45
❑ 10JHDABE-3
❑ 11SpoLifM-151
❑ 12ColRedB-37A
❑ 12ColRedB-37B
❑ 12ColTinT-37A
❑ 12ColTinT-37B
❑ 67SpoHobFC-33
❑ 72ClaCar-25

Burch, Ernest W.
❑ 87OldJudN-53
❑ 88KimN18-6

Burch, John
❑ 12Zee-51

Burch, Matt
❑ 98SpoIndG-4
❑ 99Bow-107
❑ 99BowBes-197
❑ 99BowBesAR-197
❑ 99BowBesR-197
❑ 99BowChr-107
❑ 99BowChrG-107
❑ 99BowChrGR-107
❑ 99BowChrI-107
❑ 99BowChrIR-107
❑ 99BowChrR-107
❑ 99BowGol-107
❑ 99BowInt-107
❑ 99Top-216
❑ 99TopChr-216
❑ 99TopChrR-216

Burcham, Tim (Timothy)
❑ 86QuaCitAP-6
❑ 87PalSprP-21
❑ 88MidAngGS-6
❑ 89EdmTraC-5
❑ 89EdmTraP-553
❑ 89MidAngGS-7
❑ 90CMC-481
❑ 90EdmTraC-4
❑ 90EdmTraP-511
❑ 90ProAAAF-87
❑ 91EdmTraLD-157
❑ 91EdmTraP-1510
❑ 91LinDriAAA-157
❑ 93PalSprAC-4
❑ 93PalSprAF-61

Burchart, Kyle
❑ 96MedHatBJTI-7
❑ 97St.CatSB-10
❑ 98EriSeaWM-6

Burchart, Larry

❑ 69Top-597
❑ 70OPC-412
❑ 70Top-412
❑ 70WicAerM-3
Burchell, Fred
❑ 09RamT20-19
❑ 09T206-402
❑ 12ImpTobC-14
Burchers, Rick
❑ 81ChaLooT-18
Burchett, Kerry D.
❑ 81ArkTraT-10
Burckel, Brad
❑ 91MisStaB-8
Burda, Bob (Edward Robert)
❑ 61UniOil-P4
❑ 62KahAtl-3
❑ 69Top-392
❑ 70OPC-357
❑ 70Top-357
❑ 71CarTeal-6
❑ 71CarTeal-6
❑ 71OPC-541
❑ 71Top-541
❑ 72Top-734
❑ 94BreMilB-296
Burden, John
❑ 80WauTimT-2
❑ 81ChaLooT-2
❑ 83ChaLooT-20
❑ 86ChaLooP-6
❑ 87SalSpuS-29
Burdette, Freddie
❑ 64Top-408
Burdette, Lew
❑ 47Exh-31A
❑ 47Exh-31B
❑ 52Bow-244
❑ 53BowBW-51
❑ 53BraJohC-5
❑ 53BraMer-5
❑ 53BraSpiaS3-6
❑ 53BraSpiaS7-4
❑ 54Bow-192
❑ 54BraJohC-33
❑ 54BraSpiaSP-5
❑ 54RedMan-NL24
❑ 55Bow-70
❑ 55BraGolS-4
❑ 55BraJohC-33
❑ 55BraSpiaSD-5
❑ 56BraBilaBP-5
❑ 56Top-219
❑ 57Bra8x1-4
❑ 57BraSpiaS4-5
❑ 57Top-208
❑ 58BraJayP-3
❑ 58Top-10
❑ 58Top-289
❑ 59Top-440
❑ 60BraLaktL-6
❑ 60BraSpiaS-5
❑ 60KeyChal-9
❑ 60NuHi-35
❑ 60Top-70
❑ 60Top-230
❑ 60TopTat-7
❑ 60TopVen-70
❑ 61NuSco-408
❑ 61NuSco-435
❑ 61Pos-102A
❑ 61Pos-102B
❑ 61SevElev-24
❑ 61Top-47
❑ 61Top-320
❑ 62BraJayP-4
❑ 62ExhStaB-6
❑ 62Jel-153
❑ 62Pos-153
❑ 62PosCan-153
❑ 62SalPlaC-166
❑ 62ShiPlaC-166
❑ 62Top-380
❑ 62TopBuc-13
❑ 62TopStal-146
❑ 63BraJayP-3
❑ 63ExhStaB-9
❑ 63Jel-155
❑ 63Pos-155
❑ 63Top-429
❑ 64Top-523
❑ 65CubJayP-6
❑ 65OPC-64
❑ 65Top-64
❑ 66Top-299
❑ 66TopVen-299
❑ 67CokCapDA-22
❑ 67Top-265
❑ 68LauWorS-54
❑ 70FleWorS-54
❑ 73OPC-237
❑ 73Top-237A
❑ 73Top-237B
❑ 78BraTCC-5
❑ 78TCM60I-276
❑ 80Bra195T-6
❑ 83ASAWS-6
❑ 83Bra53F-33
❑ 87Bra195T-7
❑ 88PacLegI-68
❑ 91LinDri-15
❑ 91SweBasG-16
❑ 91TopArc1-310
❑ 92BazQua5A-13
❑ 93ActPacA-142
❑ 93MetIma-6
❑ 93TedWil-46
❑ 93UppDecAH-23
❑ 94UppDecAH-92
❑ 94UppDecAH1-92
Burdette, Ricky
❑ 77SpaPhiT-11
❑ 80AshTouT-24
Burdick, Kevin
❑ 87WatPirP-11
❑ 88SalBucS-3
❑ 89EasLeaDDP-DD22
❑ 89HarSenP-297
❑ 89HarSenS-4
❑ 89Sta-19
❑ 90BufBisC-16
❑ 90BufBisP-378
❑ 90BufBisTI-4
❑ 90CMC-16
❑ 90ProAAAF-493
❑ 91ColSprSSLD-80
❑ 91ColSprSSP-2189
❑ 91LinDriAAA-80
Burdick, Morgan
❑ 94BenRocF-3582
❑ 95AshTouTI-21
Burdick, Stacey
❑ 87MiaMarP-3
❑ 89FreKeyS-1
❑ 90Bes-255
❑ 90EasLeaAP-EL43
❑ 90HagSunB-17
❑ 90HagSunP-1403
❑ 90HagSunS-4
❑ 91HagSunLD-227
❑ 91HagSunP-2448
❑ 91LinDriAA-227
Burdick, William B.
❑ 87OldJudN-54
Burdock, Jack (John Joseph)
❑ 87BucN28-5
❑ 87OldJudN-55
❑ 90DodTar-91
Burdy, Mascot (B.J.)
❑ 91BluJayFS-35
Burelli, Luis
❑ 96-97LinVen-32
Burford, Kevin
❑ 98Bow-401
❑ 98BowChr-401
❑ 98BowChrGA-401
❑ 98BowChrGAR-401
❑ 98BowChrI-401
❑ 98BowChrIR-401
❑ 98BowChrR-401
❑ 98BowGolA-401
❑ 98BowInt-401
❑ 98CliLumG-2
❑ 98MidLeaPM-7
Burgen, Chris
❑ 88OklSoo-24
Burger, George
❑ 22Zee-120
❑ 24Zee-87
Burger, Rob
❑ 96PieBolWB-5
❑ 97ClePhi-2
❑ 98Bow-159
❑ 98BowChr-159
❑ 98BowChrGA-159
❑ 98BowChrGAR-159
❑ 98BowChrI-159
❑ 98BowChrIR-159
❑ 98BowChrR-159
❑ 98BowGolA-159
❑ 98BowInt-159
❑ 98ReaPhiM-8
❑ 98ReaPhiUM-6
Burgess, Bob
❑ 89WelPirP-34
❑ 90WelPirP-34
Burgess, Gus
❑ 80ElmPioRST-26
❑ 83PawRedST-20
❑ 84PawRedST-9
❑ 85PawRedST-1
Burgess, Kurt
❑ 86LakTigP-3
❑ 92MacBraC-23
❑ 92MacBraF-259
❑ 93DurBulC-4
❑ 93DurBulF-478
❑ 93DurBulTI-12
❑ 94HigDesMC-8
❑ 94HigDesMF-2780
❑ 95DurBulTI-6
Burgess, Smoky (Forrest H.)
❑ 49AngTeal-6
❑ 49EurSta-52
❑ 49W725AngTI-5
❑ 51Bow-317
❑ 52Bow-112
❑ 52Top-357
❑ 53BowC-28
❑ 53Top-10
❑ 54Bow-31
❑ 55Bow-209
❑ 55RobGouS-12
❑ 55RobGouW-12
❑ 56Kah-4
❑ 56RedBurB-3
❑ 56Top-192
❑ 57Kah-4
❑ 57RedSoh-4
❑ 57Top-228
❑ 58Kah-4
❑ 58RedEnq-6
❑ 58RedJayP-4
❑ 58Top-49
❑ 59Kah-5
❑ 59Top-432
❑ 60Kah-4
❑ 60KeyChal-10
❑ 60PirJayP-1
❑ 60PirTag-6
❑ 60Top-393
❑ 61Kah-6
❑ 61PirJayP-1
❑ 61Pos-138A
❑ 61Pos-138B
❑ 61Top-461
❑ 61TopStal-61
❑ 62Kah-3
❑ 62Pos-176
❑ 62PosCan-176
❑ 62SalPlaC-114
❑ 62ShiPlaC-114
❑ 62Top-389
❑ 62TopStal-173
❑ 63Fle-55
❑ 63Jel-144
❑ 63Kah-4
❑ 63PirIDL-2
❑ 63PirJayP-2
❑ 63Pos-144
❑ 63Top-18
❑ 63Top-425
❑ 64PirKDK-4
❑ 64Top-37
❑ 64TopVen-37
❑ 65OPC-198
❑ 65Top-198
❑ 66Top-354
❑ 66TopVen-354
❑ 67Top-506
❑ 72LauGreF-28
❑ 77GalGloG-6
❑ 77PirTCM1WC-9
❑ 78GreBraT-5
❑ 78TCM60I-1
❑ 79DiaGre-370
❑ 83TopRep5-357
❑ 85WhiSoxC-17
❑ 87Pir196T-6
❑ 88PulBraP-1750
❑ 89PacLegI-201
❑ 89SweBasG-32
❑ 90PacLeg-77
❑ 91TopArc1-10
❑ 92BazQua5A-9
❑ 93ActPacA-141
Burgess, Thomas R.
❑ 54CarHunW-4
❑ 79RicBraT-15
❑ 80ChaChaT-1
❑ 81TulDriT-20
❑ 82TulDriT-22
❑ 83OklCit8T-2
❑ 84OklCit8T-3
❑ 87GleFalTP-3
❑ 90TulDriDGB-28
Burgmeier, Tom
❑ 65SeaPop-2
❑ 66SeaPop-2
❑ 67SeaPop-2
❑ 69Top-558
❑ 70OPC-108
❑ 70RoyTeal-5
❑ 70Top-108
❑ 71MLBOffS-411
❑ 71OPC-431
❑ 71Top-431
❑ 72OPC-246
❑ 72oyTeal-2
❑ 72Top-246
❑ 73OPC-306
❑ 73Top-306
❑ 75OPC-478
❑ 75Top-478
❑ 75TopMin-478
❑ 75TwiTeal-8
❑ 76OPC-87
❑ 76SSP-206
❑ 76Top-87
❑ 77Top-398
❑ 78PapGinD-16
❑ 78Top-678
❑ 79OPC-272
❑ 79Top-524
❑ 80Top-128
❑ 81CokTeaS-1
❑ 81Don-97A
❑ 81Don-97B
❑ 81Fle-228
❑ 81OPC-320
❑ 81Top-320
❑ 81TopSupHT-1
❑ 82Don-361
❑ 82Fle-288
❑ 82RedSoxC-2
❑ 82Top-455
❑ 83A'sGraG-39
❑ 83Don-235
❑ 83Fle-180
❑ 83FleSti-59
❑ 83OPC-213
❑ 83Top-213
❑ 83TopFol-4
❑ 83TopTra-16T
❑ 84A'sMot-18
❑ 84Don-522
❑ 84Fle-439
❑ 84Nes792-33
❑ 84OPC-33
❑ 84Top-33
❑ 84TopTif-33
❑ 85Don-400
❑ 85Fle-417
❑ 93RocRoyC-29
❑ 93RocRoyF-732
❑ 94RocRoyC-29
❑ 94RocRoyF-582
❑ 95WilBluRTI-15
❑ 96WilBluRB-29
Burgo, Dale
❑ 88WinHavRSS-6
❑ 89LynRedSS-4
❑ 91LynRedSP-1190
Burgos, Carlos
❑ 92AppFoxFI-986
❑ 94EugEmeC-3
❑ 94EugEmeF-3715
❑ 95SprSulTI-4
Burgos, Enrique
❑ 87KnoBluJP-1510
❑ 88BlaYNPRWL-100
❑ 88SyrChiP-815
❑ 89DunBluJS-2
❑ 93OmaRoyF-1673
❑ 94OmaRoyF-1216
❑ 95PhoFirTI-47
Burgos, Francisco
❑ 89BlaYNPRWL-107
Burgos, John
❑ 87GasRanP-27
❑ 88BlaYNPRWL-163
❑ 89SavCarP-351
❑ 90ArkTraGS-6
❑ 91LinDriAA-505
❑ 91ReaPhiLD-505
❑ 91ReaPhiP-1365
❑ 94ChaLooF-1351
❑ 95ChaLooTI-3
Burgos, Paco
❑ 87SanJosBP-17
❑ 88ChaRanS-5
❑ 89ChaRanS-4
❑ 90TulDriP-1160
❑ 90TulDriTI-4
❑ 91LinDriAAA-306
❑ 91OklCit8LD-306
❑ 91OklCit8P-183
❑ 91TulDriTI-3
❑ 92AppFoxCB-12
❑ 92MemChiF-2424
❑ 92MemChiS-428
❑ 92SkyAA F-180
Burgos, Ricardo
❑ 98GreFalDG-3
Burguillos, Carlos
❑ 91NiaFalRC-17
❑ 91NiaFalRP-3644
❑ 92ClaFS7-101
❑ 92FayGenF-2181
❑ 93LakTigC-3
❑ 93LakTigF-1321
❑ 93LinVenB-211
❑ 94LakTigC-4
❑ 94LakTigF-3049
❑ 94VenLinU-232
❑ 95LinVen-51
❑ 96-97LinVen-101
Burgus, Travis
❑ 95ElmPioTI-2
❑ 95ElmPioUTI-2
❑ 96KanCouCTI-3
❑ 97PorSeaD-6
❑ 98PorSeaDQ-2
Burk, Mack Edwin
❑ 57Top-91
❑ 58Top-278
Burke, Alan
❑ 92BatCliCB-10
❑ 92BatCliF-3270
❑ 93ClaFS7-179
❑ 93SpaPhiC-9
❑ 93SpaPhiF-1065
❑ 94ClaGolF-163
❑ 94ClePhiC-11
❑ 94ClePhiF-2539
❑ 94ExcFS7-244
Burke, Bobby (Robert J.)
❑ 31SenTealPW-5
❑ 33Gou-71
❑ 34GouCanV-25
❑ 35GouPuzR-4C
❑ 35GouPuzR-7C
❑ 35GouPuzR-12C
❑ 92ConTSN-362
❑ 94ConTSN-1183
❑ 94ConTSNB-1183
Burke, Curtis
❑ 83DayBeaAT-25
❑ 85OscAstTI-22
Burke, Don
❑ 86JamExpP-2
❑ 87WesPalBEP-663
❑ 87WesPalBEP-675
Burke, Edward
❑ 95NewN566-177
❑ 98CamPepP-8
Burke, Glenn L.
❑ 75WatDodT-3
❑ 78SSP270-76
❑ 78Top-562
❑ 79OPC-78
❑ 79Top-163
❑ 90DodTar-92
Burke, Jamie
❑ 93BoiHawC-5
❑ 93BoiHawF-3906
❑ 94CedRapKC-5
❑ 94CedRapKF-1113
❑ 95LakElsSTI-6
❑ 96MidAngB-9
❑ 96VanCanB-6
❑ 98VanCanG-5
Burke, Jimmy (James Timothy)
❑ 09T206-403
❑ 10JuJuDE-5
❑ 11PinT-5-901
❑ 11PinT-5-906
❑ 11SpoLifCW-49
❑ 19W514-89
Burke, Joe
❑ 75RoyPos-5
❑ 76KanCitRP-4
❑ 92UppDecS-20
Burke, John C.
❑ 92BenRocCB-1
❑ 92BenRocF-1467
❑ 92ClaBluBF-BC29
❑ 92ClaDraP-79
❑ 92ClaFS7-412
❑ 92UppDecML-17
❑ 93Bow-388
❑ 93CenValRC-5
❑ 93CenValRF-2885
❑ 93ClaExp#PF-EP1
❑ 93ClaFS7-180
❑ 93ClaGolF-205
❑ 93ExcFS7-33
❑ 93StaClu-513
❑ 93StaCluFDI-513
❑ 93StaCluMOP-513
❑ 93UppDec-444
❑ 93UppDecGold-444
❑ 94Bow-226
❑ 94Bow-356
❑ 94BowBes-B11
❑ 94BowBesR-B11
❑ 94Cla-32
❑ 94ClaGolF-27
❑ 94ColSprSSF-725
❑ 94ExcFS7-184
❑ 94SigRoo-21
❑ 94SigRooHP-S1
❑ 94SigRooHPMP-S1
❑ 94SigRooHPMPS-S1
❑ 94SigRooHPS-S1
❑ 94SigRooS-21
❑ 94TedWil-119
❑ 94Top-780
❑ 94TopGol-780
❑ 94TopSpa-780
❑ 94Ult-477
❑ 94UppDecML-200
❑ 94UppDecMLPotYF-PY23
❑ 95Bow-73
❑ 96ColSprSSTI-4
❑ 96SalAvaB-23
❑ 97DonRatR-29
❑ 97Fle-664
❑ 97FleTif-664
❑ 97RocSco-15
❑ 97RocScoPl-15
❑ 97RocScoPr-15
❑ 97ScoPreS-274
Burke, Kevin
❑ 85NewOriT-24
❑ 87HagSunP-20
Burke, Leo Patrick
❑ 63Top-249
❑ 64Top-557
❑ 65OPC-202
❑ 65Top-202
❑ 91OriCro-62
Burke, Mark
❑ 97EugEmeB-21
❑ 98DanQ-C-14
Burke, Matt
❑ 90OklSoo-3
Burke, Mike (Michael E.)
❑ 86BakDodP-4
❑ 87VerBeaDP-25
Burke, Steve
❑ 77JacSunT-3
❑ 77MarPos-4
❑ 78Top-709
❑ 79SpoIndT-22
Burke, Stoney
❑ 94BelBreC-4
❑ 94BelBreFI-104
❑ 96LynHilB-6
Burke, Tim
❑ 82BufBisT-15
❑ 83ColCliT-7
❑ 83NasSouTI-3
❑ 84IndIndTI-23
❑ 85ExpPos-4
❑ 85FleUpd-14
❑ 86Don-421
❑ 86ExpPos-2
❑ 86ExpProPa-17

❑ 86Fle-245
❑ 86Lea-198
❑ 86OPC-258
❑ 86SevCoi-E15
❑ 86Top-258
❑ 86TopTif-258
❑ 87Don-222
❑ 87ExpPos-3
❑ 87Fle-315
❑ 87FleGlo-315
❑ 87Lea-205
❑ 87OPC-132
❑ 87SpoTeaP-20
❑ 87Top-624
❑ 87TopSti-78
❑ 87TopTif-624
❑ 88Don-98
❑ 88DonBasB-34
❑ 88ExpPos-3
❑ 88Fle-180
❑ 88FleGlo-180
❑ 88FleMin-87
❑ 88FleStiC-95
❑ 88Lea-84
❑ 88MSAHosD-2
❑ 88OPC-14
❑ 88Sco-187
❑ 88ScoGlo-187
❑ 88StaLinE-2
❑ 88Top-529
❑ 88TopTif-529
❑ 89Bow-360
❑ 89BowTif-360
❑ 89Don-274
❑ 89DonBasB-180
❑ 89ExpPos-4
❑ 89Fle-372
❑ 89FleGlo-372
❑ 89OPC-48
❑ 89PanSti-113
❑ 89RedFolSB-15
❑ 89Sco-228
❑ 89Spo-73
❑ 89Top-48
❑ 89TopSti-69
❑ 89TopTif-48
❑ 89UppDec-456
❑ 90Bow-103
❑ 90BowTif-103
❑ 90Don-334
❑ 90DonBesN-42
❑ 90ExpPos-4
❑ 90Fle-342
❑ 90FleBasA-3
❑ 90FleBasAC-3
❑ 90FleCan-342
❑ 90Lea-28
❑ 90OPC-195
❑ 90PanSti-294
❑ 90PublntS-170
❑ 90RedFolSB-10
❑ 90Sco-127
❑ 90Sco100S-34
❑ 90Spo-199
❑ 90Top-195
❑ 90TopBig-187
❑ 90TopMinL-61
❑ 90TopSti-72
❑ 90TopTif-195
❑ 90TopTVA-60
❑ 90UppDec-515
❑ 91Don-125
❑ 91Fle-227
❑ 91Lea-124
❑ 91MetPerPA-9
❑ 91OPC-715
❑ 91PanFreS-148
❑ 91RedFolS-15
❑ 91Sco-181
❑ 91StaClu-514
❑ 91Top-715
❑ 91TopDesS-715
❑ 91TopMic-715
❑ 91TopTif-715
❑ 91Ult-198
❑ 91UltUpd-95
❑ 91UppDec-215
❑ 91UppDecFE-70F
❑ 92Don-366
❑ 92Fle-497
❑ 92Lea-44
❑ 92LeaBlaG-44
❑ 92MetColP-10
❑ 92MetKah-44
❑ 92OPC-322
❑ 92Pin-471
❑ 92Sco-651
❑ 92StaClu-392
❑ 92Stu-62
❑ 92Top-322
❑ 92TopGol-322
❑ 92TopGolW-322
❑ 92TopMic-322
❑ 92TriPla-14
❑ 92Ult-228
❑ 92UppDec-433
❑ 93Fle-647
❑ 93Top-249
❑ 93TopGol-249
❑ 93TopInaM-249
❑ 93TopInaR-249
❑ 93TopMic-249
Burke, Todd
❑ 87VisOakP-18
Burke, Tom
❑ 77ChaPatT-1
Burke, Turk
❑ 88SFHesCreN32-4A
❑ 88SFHesCreN32-4B
Burke, William I.
❑ 09ColChiE-38A
❑ 09ColChiE-38B
❑ 11PinT-5-715
❑ 12ColRedB-38A
❑ 12ColRedB-38B
❑ 12ColTinT-38A
❑ 12ColTinT-38B
❑ 29Zee-105
Burkett, Howard
❑ 28Zee-27
❑ 29Zee-15
❑ 30Zee-3
Burkett, Jesse Cail
❑ 09RamT20-20
❑ 21KoBreWSI-5
❑ 22W575-12
❑ 39PC7AlbHoF-39
❑ 50CalHOFW-10
❑ 53ArtHaloFP-9
❑ 76ShaPiz-39
❑ 80PerHaloFP-39
❑ 80SSPHOF-39
❑ 81ConTSN-75
❑ 84GalHaloFRL-39
❑ 89HOFStiB-33
❑ 94OriofB-88
❑ 95ConTSN-1388
❑ 98CamPepP-9
Burkett, John
❑ 85FreGiaSB-22
❑ 86ShrCapP-2
❑ 87ShrCapP-14
❑ 87TexLeaAF-33
❑ 88Fle-651
❑ 88FleGlo-651
❑ 88PhoFirC-2
❑ 88PhoFirP-76
❑ 89PhoFirC-1
❑ 89PhoFirP-1483
❑ 90ClaYel-T6
❑ 90DonBesN-12
❑ 90DonRoo-51
❑ 90FleUpd-61
❑ 90GiaMot-26
❑ 90Lea-384
❑ 90PhoFirP-5
❑ 90ProAAAF-31
❑ 90ScoRoo-73T
❑ 90TopTra-16T
❑ 90TopTraT-16T
❑ 90UppDec-735
❑ 91Bow-637
❑ 91ClaGam-86
❑ 91Don-638
❑ 91Fle-256
❑ 91GiaMot-26
❑ 91GiaPacGaE-3
❑ 91GiaSFE-5
❑ 91Lea-56
❑ 91OPC-447
❑ 91PanFreS-74
❑ 91PanSti-78
❑ 91Sco-70
❑ 91Sco100RS-7
❑ 91SevCoi-NC1
❑ 91StaClu-119
❑ 91Stu-253
❑ 91Top-447
❑ 91TopDesS-447
❑ 91TopMic-447
❑ 91TopRoo-5
❑ 91TopTif-447
❑ 91Ult-317
❑ 91UppDec-577
❑ 92Don-257
❑ 92Fle-630
❑ 92GiaMot-5
❑ 92GiaPacGaE-10
❑ 92Lea-179
❑ 92LeaBlaG-179
❑ 92OPC-762
❑ 92Pin-292
❑ 92Pin-578
❑ 92Sco-522
❑ 92SpollIFK1-190
❑ 92StaClu-136
❑ 92Stu-113
❑ 92Top-762
❑ 92TopGol-762
❑ 92TopGolW-762
❑ 92TopMic-762
❑ 92Ult-286
❑ 92UppDec-148
❑ 93Bow-520
❑ 93DiaMar-19
❑ 93Don-156
❑ 93Fin-44
❑ 93FinRef-44
❑ 93Fla-139
❑ 93Fle-153
❑ 93GiaMot-7
❑ 93GiaPos-12
❑ 93GiaStaC-10
❑ 93Lea-342
❑ 93OPC-89
❑ 93PacSpa-268
❑ 93Pin-375
❑ 93Sco-174
❑ 93SP-110
❑ 93StaClu-412
❑ 93StaCluFDI-412
❑ 93StaCluMOP-412
❑ 93Stu-44
❑ 93Top-66
❑ 93TopGol-66
❑ 93TopInaM-66
❑ 93TopInaR-66
❑ 93TopMic-66
❑ 93Ult-129
❑ 93UppDec-160
❑ 93UppDecGold-160
❑ 94Bow-463
❑ 94BowBes-R28
❑ 94BowBesR-R28
❑ 94ColC-68
❑ 94ColC-306
❑ 94ColChoGS-68
❑ 94ColChoGS-306
❑ 94ColChoSS-68
❑ 94ColChoSS-306
❑ 94Don-13
❑ 94DonSpeE-13
❑ 94Fin-295
❑ 94FinRef-295
❑ 94Fla-240
❑ 94Fle-687
❑ 94FleAllS-33
❑ 94FleExtB-384
❑ 94FUnPac-82
❑ 94GiaAMC-6
❑ 94GiaKTV-5
❑ 94GiaMot-5
❑ 94GiaTarBC-7
❑ 94GiaTeal-7
❑ 94GiaUSPC-6D
❑ 94GiaUSPC-13C
❑ 94Lea-73
❑ 94LeaL-157
❑ 94OPC-19
❑ 94Pac-543
❑ 94PacSilP-19
❑ 94PacSilPC-19
❑ 94PanSti-14
❑ 94PanSti-262
❑ 94Pin-24
❑ 94PinArtP-24
❑ 94PinMusC-24
❑ 94ProMag-122
❑ 94Sco-5
❑ 94ScoGolR-5
❑ 94ScoGolS-21
❑ 94ScoSam-5
❑ 94ScoSam-5GR
❑ 94Sel-341
❑ 94SP-91
❑ 94SPDieC-91
❑ 94Spo-29
❑ 94StaClu-88
❑ 94StaCluFDI-88
❑ 94StaCluGR-88
❑ 94StaCluMO-32
❑ 94StaCluMOP-88
❑ 94StaCluT-28
❑ 94StaCluTFDI-28
❑ 94Top-213
❑ 94TopGol-213
❑ 94TopSpa-213
❑ 94TriPla-103
❑ 94Ult-587
❑ 94UppDec-403
❑ 94UppDecAJ-6
❑ 94UppDecAJG-6
❑ 94UppDecED-403
❑ 94USPlaCA-5S
❑ 95Bow-435
❑ 95ColCho-393
❑ 95ColCho-557T
❑ 95ColChoGS-393
❑ 95ColChoSS-393
❑ 95Don-233
❑ 95DonPreP-233
❑ 95DonTopotO-238
❑ 95Fin-198
❑ 95Fin-285
❑ 95FinRef-198
❑ 95FinRef-285
❑ 95Fla-350
❑ 95Fle-576
❑ 95FleUpd-94
❑ 95Lea-357
❑ 95Pac-374
❑ 95Pin-361
❑ 95PinArtP-361
❑ 95PinMusC-361
❑ 95SP-54
❑ 95SPSil-54
❑ 95StaClu-267
❑ 95StaClu-567
❑ 95StaCluFDI-267
❑ 95StaCluMOP-267
❑ 95StaCluMOP-567
❑ 95StaCluSTWS-267
❑ 95StaCluSTWS-567
❑ 95Top-491
❑ 95TopCyb-282
❑ 95TopTra-48T
❑ 95Ult-333
❑ 95UltGolM-333
❑ 95UppDec-353
❑ 95UppDecED-353
❑ 95UppDecEDG-353
❑ 96ColCho-556
❑ 96ColChoGS-556
❑ 96ColChoSS-556
❑ 96Don-116
❑ 96DonPreP-116
❑ 96EmoXL-183
❑ 96Fin-B107
❑ 96FinRef-B107
❑ 96Fla-258
❑ 96Fle-383
❑ 96FleTif-383
❑ 96MetUni-162
❑ 96MetUniP-162
❑ 96Pac-77
❑ 96PanSti-12
❑ 96Sco-427
❑ 96StaClu-71
❑ 96StaCluMOP-71
❑ 96Top-179
❑ 96Ult-196
❑ 96UltGolM-196
❑ 96UppDec-76
❑ 97Cir-162
❑ 97CirRav-162
❑ 97ColChoT-TR10
❑ 97ColChoU-U28
❑ 97Don-158
❑ 97Fin-73
❑ 97FinRef-73
❑ 97Fle-517
❑ 97FleTif-517
❑ 97Lea-243
❑ 97LeaFraM-243
❑ 97LeaFraMDC-243
❑ 97RanDr P-3
❑ 97RanMinM-1
❑ 97RanMot-21
❑ 97RanSco-14
❑ 97RanScoPl-14
❑ 97RanScoPr-14
❑ 97Sco-213
❑ 97ScoArtPWB-213
❑ 97ScoPreS-213
❑ 97ScoShoS-213
❑ 97ScoShoSAP-213
❑ 97StaClu-312
❑ 97StaCluMOP-312
❑ 97Top-27
❑ 97Ult-332
❑ 97UltGolME-332
❑ 97UltPlaME-332
❑ 97UppDec-507
❑ 98ColCho-244
❑ 98Fin-206
❑ 98FinNo--206
❑ 98FinNo-R-206
❑ 98FinRef-206
❑ 98Pac-198
❑ 98PacOnl-728
❑ 98PacOnlR-728
❑ 98PacOnlWC-728
❑ 98PacPar-102
❑ 98PacParC-102
❑ 98PacParG-102
❑ 98PacParHS-102
❑ 98PacParPB-102
❑ 98PacParR-102
❑ 98PacPlaB-198
❑ 98PacRedT-198
❑ 98PacSil-198
❑ 98PinSna-TR8
❑ 98StaCluFDI-62
❑ 98StaClul-62
❑ 98StaCluOneK-62
❑ 98StaCluPP-62
❑ 98Top-401
❑ 98TopChr-401
❑ 98TopChrR-401
❑ 98TopDevR-401
❑ 98TopDia-401
❑ 98TopMiniC-401
❑ 98Ult-451
❑ 98UltGolM-451
❑ 98UltMas-451
❑ 98UltPlaM-451
❑ 98UppDec-519
❑ 99Fle-369
❑ 99FleSta9-369
❑ 99FleWarT-369
❑ 99Pac-420
❑ 99PacPlaB-420
❑ 99PacRed-420
❑ 99Top-337
❑ 99TopChr-337
❑ 99TopChrR-337
❑ 99TopMVPP-337
Burkhart, Ken
❑ 46SeaSLP-8
❑ 47TipTop-151
❑ 83Car194T-59
Burkhart, Lance
❑ 97VerExpB-11
❑ 98VerExpO-19
Burkowatz, Jack
❑ 54SeaPop-3
❑ 55SeaPop-5
Burks, Ellis
❑ 86NewBriRSP-4
❑ 87DonRoo-5
❑ 87FleUpd-15
❑ 87FleUpdG-15
❑ 87PawRedSP-73
❑ 87PawRedST-22
❑ 87RedSoxP-5
❑ 87SpoRool-5
❑ 87TopTra-14T
❑ 87TopTraT-14T
❑ 88ClaBlu-229
❑ 88Don-174
❑ 88DonBasB-121
❑ 88DonTeaBRS-174
❑ 88Fle-348
❑ 88Fle-630
❑ 88FleGlo-348
❑ 88FleGlo-630
❑ 88FleSlu-5
❑ 88FleStiC-6
❑ 88KeyFooD-2
❑ 88Lea-174
❑ 88MSAIceTD-2
❑ 88OPC-269
❑ 88OurOwnTD-2
❑ 88PanSti-31
❑ 88RedFolSB-10
❑ 88Sco-472
❑ 88ScoGlo-472
❑ 88ScoYouSI-37
❑ 88Spo-144
❑ 88StaLinRS-5
❑ 88TetTeaD-2
❑ 88Top-269
❑ 88TopBig-80
❑ 88TopGloS-50
❑ 88TopRoo-2
❑ 88TopSti-250
❑ 88TopSti-310
❑ 88TopTif-269
❑ 88ToyRoo-5
❑ 88WeiMarD-2
❑ 89Bow-36
❑ 89BowTif-36
❑ 89ClaTraP-152
❑ 89ClaTraP-175
❑ 89Don-303
❑ 89DonBasB-9
❑ 89DonGraS-12
❑ 89Fle-83
❑ 89FleGlo-83
❑ 89Nis-3
❑ 89OPC-311
❑ 89PanSti-278
❑ 89Sco-9
❑ 89ScoHot1S-43
❑ 89Scomast-25
❑ 89Spo-191
❑ 89Top-785
❑ 89TopAme2C-7
❑ 89TopBig-259
❑ 89TopHeaUT-12
❑ 89TopSti-254
❑ 89TopTif-785
❑ 89TVSpoM-62
❑ 89UppDec-434
❑ 90Bow-280
❑ 90BowTif-280
❑ 90ClaUpd-T8
❑ 90Don-23
❑ 90Don-228
❑ 90DonBesA-30
❑ 90DonSupD-23
❑ 90Fle-269
❑ 90FleCan-269
❑ 90Lea-261
❑ 90OPC-155
❑ 90PanSti-21
❑ 90PublntS-450
❑ 90PublntS-594
❑ 90RedFolSB-11
❑ 90RedSoxP-5
❑ 90Sco-340
❑ 90Sco100S-16
❑ 90Spo-80
❑ 90Top-155
❑ 90TopBig-107
❑ 90TopCoi-8
❑ 90TopDou-7
❑ 90TopSti-259
❑ 90TopTif-155
❑ 90TopTVRS-28
❑ 90UppDec-343
❑ 90USPlaCA-7C
❑ 91Bow-109
❑ 91Bow-373
❑ 91ClaGam-12
❑ 91DenHol-1
❑ 91Don-235
❑ 91Fle-89
❑ 91Lea-121
❑ 91MajLeaCP-11
❑ 91OPC-70
❑ 91PanCanT1-114
❑ 91PanFreS-269
❑ 91PanSti-212
❑ 91RedSoxP-3
❑ 91RedSoxP-5
❑ 91Sco-8
❑ 91Sco100S-48
❑ 91StaClu-108
❑ 91StaCluCM-4
❑ 91Stu-12
❑ 91Top-70
❑ 91TopCraJ2-8
❑ 91TopDesS-70
❑ 91TopMic-70
❑ 91TopTif-70
❑ 91Ult-30
❑ 91UppDec-436
❑ 91UppDecSS-SS10
❑ 92Bow-570
❑ 92ClaGam-71
❑ 92Don-234
❑ 92Fle-35
❑ 92Lea-314
❑ 92LeaBlaG-314
❑ 92OPC-416

❑ 92PanSti-90
❑ 92Pin-26
❑ 92RedFolS-20
❑ 92RedSoxDD-6
❑ 92Sco-270
❑ 92Sco100S-83
❑ 92ScoImpP-78
❑ 92ScoProP-10
❑ 92SpoIllFK1-516
❑ 92StaClu-399
❑ 92Top-416
❑ 92TopGol-416
❑ 92TopGolW-416
❑ 92TopKid-70
❑ 92TopMic-416
❑ 92Ult-13
❑ 92UppDec-94
❑ 92UppDec-525
❑ 93Bow-231
❑ 93Don-33
❑ 93Fla-181
❑ 93Fle-176
❑ 93FleFinE-194
❑ 93Lea-252
❑ 93OPCPre-93
❑ 93PacSpa-29
❑ 93PacSpa-386
❑ 93PanSti-95
❑ 93Pin-46
❑ 93Sco-78
❑ 93Sel-68
❑ 93SelRoo-10T
❑ 93StaClu-187
❑ 93StaClu-607
❑ 93StaCluFDI-187
❑ 93StaCluFDI-607
❑ 93StaCluMOP-187
❑ 93StaCluMOP-607
❑ 93Stu-33
❑ 93Top-351
❑ 93TopGol-351
❑ 93TopInaM-351
❑ 93TopInaR-351
❑ 93TopMic-351
❑ 93TopTra-104T
❑ 93Ult-529
❑ 93UppDec-265
❑ 93UppDec-526
❑ 93UppDecGold-265
❑ 93UppDecGold-526
❑ 93WhiSoxK-5
❑ 93WhiSoxSC-27
❑ 94Bow-414
❑ 94BowBes-R72
❑ 94BowBesR-R72
❑ 94ColC-554
❑ 94ColChoGS-554
❑ 94ColChoSS-554
❑ 94Don-145
❑ 94Fin-275
❑ 94FinRef-275
❑ 94Fla-152
❑ 94Fle-78
❑ 94FleExtB-243
❑ 94FleUpd-122
❑ 94FUnPac-49
❑ 94Lea-242
❑ 94LeaL-101
❑ 94OPC-90
❑ 94Pac-122
❑ 94PanSti-45
❑ 94Pin-496
❑ 94PinArtP-496
❑ 94PinMusC-496
❑ 94ProMag-42
❑ 94RocPol-5
❑ 94Sco-431
❑ 94ScoGolR-431
❑ 94ScoRoo-RT4
❑ 94ScoRooCP-CP7
❑ 94ScoRooGR-RT4
❑ 94ScoRooS-RT4
❑ 94Sel-287
❑ 94SP-165
❑ 94SPDieC-165
❑ 94SpoRoo-20
❑ 94SpoRooAP-20
❑ 94SpoRooS-20
❑ 94StaClu-622
❑ 94StaCluFDI-622
❑ 94StaCluGR-622
❑ 94StaCluMOP-622
❑ 94StaCluT-115
❑ 94StaCluTFDI-115
❑ 94Stu-176
❑ 94Top-538
❑ 94TopGol-538
❑ 94TopSpa-538
❑ 94TopTra-18T
❑ 94TriPla-222
❑ 94Ult-478
❑ 94UppDec-483
❑ 94UppDecED-483
❑ 95ColCho-447
❑ 95ColChoGS-447
❑ 95ColChoSS-447
❑ 95Don-300
❑ 95DonPreP-300
❑ 95Fla-127
❑ 95Fle-516
❑ 95Lea-281
❑ 95Pac-133
❑ 95Pin-54
❑ 95PinArtP-54
❑ 95PinMusC-54
❑ 95RocPol-4
❑ 95Sco-370
❑ 95ScoGolR-370
❑ 95ScoHaloG-HG63
❑ 95ScoPlaTS-370
❑ 95Sel-127
❑ 95SelArtP-127
❑ 95Spo-11
❑ 95SpoArtP-11
❑ 95StaClu-443
❑ 95StaCluMOP-443
❑ 95StaCluSTWS-443
❑ 95StaCluVR-234
❑ 95StaCluVRMO-234
❑ 95Stu-153
❑ 95Top-235
❑ 95TopCyb-132
❑ 95Ult-152
❑ 95UltGolM-152
❑ 95UppDec-174
❑ 95UppDecED-174
❑ 95UppDecEDG-174
❑ 96Cir-121
❑ 96CirRav-121
❑ 96ColCho-534
❑ 96ColChoGS-534
❑ 96ColChoSS-534
❑ 96Don-70
❑ 96Don-71
❑ 96DonPreP-70
❑ 96EmoXL-173
❑ 96Fla-244
❑ 96Fle-361
❑ 96FleTif-361
❑ 96LeaSig-143
❑ 96LeaSigPPG-143
❑ 96LeaSigPPP-143
❑ 96Pac-55
❑ 96RocFle-3
❑ 96RocPol-5
❑ 96Sco-442
❑ 96SP-79
❑ 96TeaOut-13
❑ 96Top-123
❑ 96Ult-187
❑ 96UltGolM-187
❑ 96UppDec-323
❑ 97Bow-222
❑ 97BowBes-28
❑ 97BowBesAR-28
❑ 97BowBesR-28
❑ 97BowChr-52
❑ 97BowChrI-52
❑ 97BowChrIR-52
❑ 97BowChrR-52
❑ 97BowInt-222
❑ 97Cir-234
❑ 97CirRav-234
❑ 97ColCho-319
❑ 97ColChoAC-42
❑ 97ColChoPP-PP16
❑ 97ColChoPPG-PP16
❑ 97ColChoPPJ-PP16
❑ 97ColChoT-CR11
❑ 97Don-185
❑ 97DonEli-119
❑ 97DonEliGS-119
❑ 97DonGolPP-185
❑ 97DonLim-108
❑ 97DonLimE-108
❑ 97DonLimENG-108
❑ 97DonPre-31
❑ 97DonPreCttC-31
❑ 97DonSilPP-185
❑ 97DonTea-96
❑ 97DonTeaSPE-96
❑ 97E-X2-68
❑ 97E-X2Cred-68
❑ 97E-X2EssCre-68
❑ 97Fin-75
❑ 97Fin-290
❑ 97FinEmb-290
❑ 97FinEmbR-290
❑ 97FinRef-75
❑ 97FinRef-290
❑ 97FlaShoLC-179
❑ 97FlaShoLeg0-179
❑ 97FlaShoLeg1-179
❑ 97FlaShoM-A179
❑ 97FlaShoM-B179
❑ 97FlaShoM-C179
❑ 97FlaShoR0-179
❑ 97FlaShoR1-179
❑ 97FlaShoR2-179
❑ 97Fle-308
❑ 97FleLumC-6
❑ 97FleNig&D-2
❑ 97FleTeaL-18
❑ 97FleTif-308
❑ 97Lea-120
❑ 97LeaFraM-120
❑ 97LeaFraMDC-120
❑ 97MetUni-72
❑ 97NewPin-10
❑ 97NewPin-189
❑ 97NewPinAP-10
❑ 97NewPinAP-189
❑ 97NewPinMC-10
❑ 97NewPinMC-189
❑ 97NewPinPP-10
❑ 97NewPinPP-189
❑ 97Pac-280
❑ 97PacLigB-280
❑ 97PacPri-95
❑ 97PacPriLB-95
❑ 97PacPriP-95
❑ 97PacSil-280
❑ 97PacTriCD-15
❑ 97Pin-27
❑ 97PinArtP-PP27
❑ 97PinCer-88
❑ 97PinCerMBla-88
❑ 97PinCerMBlu-88
❑ 97PinCerMG-88
❑ 97PinCerMR-88
❑ 97PinCerR-88
❑ 97PinIns-120
❑ 97PinInsCE-120
❑ 97PinInsDE-120
❑ 97PinInsFS-7
❑ 97PinMusC-27
❑ 97PinPrePla-27
❑ 97PinTeaP-7
❑ 97PinTeaP-10
❑ 97PinTotCPB-88
❑ 97PinTotCPG-88
❑ 97PinTotCPR-88
❑ 97PinX-P-19
❑ 97PinX-PMoS-19
❑ 97PinX-PSfF-13
❑ 97PinX-PSfFU-13
❑ 97RocCok-3
❑ 97RocCok-4
❑ 97RocPol-3
❑ 97RocSco-4
❑ 97RocScoPl-4
❑ 97RocScoPr-4
❑ 97Sco-74
❑ 97ScoArtPWB-74
❑ 97ScoPreS-74
❑ 97ScoShoS-74
❑ 97ScoShoSAP-74
❑ 97Sel-81
❑ 97SelArtP-81
❑ 97SelCom-81
❑ 97SelRegG-81
❑ 97SP-66
❑ 97StaClu-199
❑ 97StaCluMat-199
❑ 97StaCluMOP-199
❑ 97Stu-50
❑ 97StuPrePG-50
❑ 97StuPrePS-50
❑ 97Top-146
❑ 97TopAll-AS14
❑ 97TopChr-56
❑ 97TopChrAS-AS14
❑ 97TopChrR-56
❑ 97TopChrSAR-AS14
❑ 97TopChrSB-3
❑ 97TopChrSBR-3
❑ 97TopGal-32
❑ 97TopGalPPI-32
❑ 97TopMem05-10
❑ 97TopSeaB-SB3
❑ 97TopSta-69
❑ 97TopStaAM-69
❑ 97UD3-12
❑ 97Ult-184
❑ 97UltGolME-184
❑ 97UltPlaME-184
❑ 97UppDec-349
❑ 98Bow-268
❑ 98BowBes-53
❑ 98BowBesAR-53
❑ 98BowBesR-53
❑ 98BowChr-268
❑ 98BowChrGA-268
❑ 98BowChrGAR-268
❑ 98BowChrI-268
❑ 98BowChrIR-268
❑ 98BowChrR-268
❑ 98BowGolA-268
❑ 98BowInt-268
❑ 98CirThu-255
❑ 98CirThuRav-255
❑ 98CirThuSupRav-255
❑ 98ColCho-86
❑ 98CroRoy-50
❑ 98Don-222
❑ 98DonGolPP-222
❑ 98DonSigAC-16
❑ 98DonSigAM-16
❑ 98DonSilPP-222
❑ 98Fin-236
❑ 98FinNo--236
❑ 98FinNo-R-236
❑ 98FinRef-236
❑ 98Fle-153
❑ 98FleUpd-U38
❑ 98LeaRS-112
❑ 98LeaRSLHolo-112
❑ 98LeaRSLong-112
❑ 98LeaRTrue-112
❑ 98MetUni-14
❑ 98MetUniPMG-14
❑ 98Pac-279
❑ 98PacAur-124
❑ 98PacInvTeam-9
❑ 98PacOme-80
❑ 98PacOmeR-80
❑ 98PacOnl-240
❑ 98PacOnlR-240
❑ 98PacOnlWC-240
❑ 98PacPar-152
❑ 98PacParC-152
❑ 98PacParG-152
❑ 98PacParHS-152
❑ 98PacParPB-152
❑ 98PacParR-152
❑ 98PacPlaB-279
❑ 98PacRedT-279
❑ 98PacSil-279
❑ 98PinInsSG-10AB
❑ 98PinInsSG-10CD
❑ 98PinInsSGS-10AB
❑ 98PinInsSGS-10CD
❑ 98PinPerSftF-30
❑ 98PinSna-CR15
❑ 98PinSna-CR18
❑ 98Revo-51
❑ 98RevoSS-51
❑ 98ScoRT-122
❑ 98ScoRTSS-PP77
❑ 98ScoRTSSAP-PP77
❑ 98ScoRTSSAP1-PP77
❑ 98SpoIll-17
❑ 98SpoIllEE-17
❑ 98SpoIllFE-17
❑ 98SpoIllTaN-66
❑ 98SpoIllTaNEE-66
❑ 98SPxFin-82
❑ 98SPxFinR-82
❑ 98SPxFinS-82
❑ 98StaCluFDI-4
❑ 98StaCluFDI-299
❑ 98StaCluI-4
❑ 98StaCluI-299
❑ 98StaCluOneK-4
❑ 98StaCluOneK-299
❑ 98StaCluPP-4
❑ 98StaCluPP-299
❑ 98Stu-173
❑ 98StuGPP-173
❑ 98StuSPP-173
❑ 98Top-310
❑ 98TopChr-310
❑ 98TopChrR-310
❑ 98TopDevR-310
❑ 98TopDia-310
❑ 98TopGal-24
❑ 98TopGalGP-24
❑ 98TopGalOPP-24
❑ 98TopGalPPI-24
❑ 98TopGalPPIA-24
❑ 98TopGolLabC1-51
❑ 98TopGolLabC1B-51
❑ 98TopGolLabC1One-51
❑ 98TopGolLabC1R-51
❑ 98TopGolLabC2-51
❑ 98TopGolLabC2B-51
❑ 98TopGolLabC2One-51
❑ 98TopGolLabC2R-51
❑ 98TopGolLabC3-51
❑ 98TopGolLabC3B-51
❑ 98TopGolLabC3One-51
❑ 98TopGolLabC3R-51
❑ 98TopMiniC-310
❑ 98TopOpeD-136
❑ 98TopSta-4
❑ 98TopStaB-4
❑ 98TopStaG-4
❑ 98TopStaGR-4
❑ 98TopStaS-4
❑ 98TopTek-53
❑ 98TopTekD-53
❑ 98Ult-29
❑ 98UltGolM-29
❑ 98UltMas-29
❑ 98UltPlaM-29
❑ 98UppDec-352
❑ 99199Fin-224
❑ 99CroRoyB-124
❑ 99CroRoyL-124
❑ 99CroRoyOD-124
❑ 99FinGolRef-224
❑ 99FinRef-224
❑ 99FlaShoLeg1-65
❑ 99FlaShoLeg2-65
❑ 99FlaShoLeg3-65
❑ 99FlaShoLegM1-65
❑ 99FlaShoLegM2-65
❑ 99FlaShoLegM3-65
❑ 99FlaShoR1-65
❑ 99FlaShoR2-65
❑ 99FlaShoR3-65
❑ 99Fle-73
❑ 99FleMys-60
❑ 99FleMysG-60
❑ 99FleMysM-60
❑ 99FleSta9-73
❑ 99FleWarT-73
❑ 99MetUni-226
❑ 99MetUniGM-226
❑ 99MetUniPMG-226
❑ 99Pac-379
❑ 99PacAur-170
❑ 99PacAurOD-170
❑ 99PacInv-127
❑ 99PacInvOD-127
❑ 99PacInvPB-127
❑ 99PacOme-211
❑ 99PacOmeC-211
❑ 99PacOmeG-211
❑ 99PacOmePB-211
❑ 99PacPar-209
❑ 99PacParC-209
❑ 99PacParG-209
❑ 99PacParHoloGold-209
❑ 99PacParHS-209
❑ 99PacParOD-209
❑ 99PacParPB-209
❑ 99PacParRed-209
❑ 99PacPlaB-379
❑ 99PacPri-128
❑ 99PacPriHB-128
❑ 99PacPriHG-128
❑ 99PacPriHM-128
❑ 99PacPriHP-128
❑ 99PacPriRed-128
❑ 99PacRed-379
❑ 99Rev-125
❑ 99RevPremDate-125
❑ 99RevRet-125
❑ 99RevShaSS-125
❑ 99SkyMolM-9
❑ 99SkyMolMX-9
❑ 99SkyThu-57
❑ 99SkyThuRant-57
❑ 99SkyThuRave-57
❑ 99SP Aut-74
❑ 99StaClu-183
❑ 99StaCluFDI-183
❑ 99StaCluOoaK-183
❑ 99StaCluPP-183
❑ 99ThuSkySupR-57
❑ 99Top-251
❑ 99TopChr-251
❑ 99TopChrR-251
❑ 99TopMVPP-251
❑ 99TopOpeD-151
❑ 99UD Cho-139
❑ 99UD ChoPCR-139
❑ 99UppDec-480
❑ 99UppDecCLM-C84
❑ 99UppDecEL1-480
❑ 99UppDecEL2-480
❑ 99UppDecM-184
❑ 99UppDecMGS-184
❑ 99UppDecMHFS-184
❑ 99UppDecMSS-184
❑ 99Vic-359

Burks, Robert E.
❑ 87OldJudN-56

Burks, Will
❑ 86DavLipB-6

Burleson, Rick (Richard P.)
❑ 75OPC-302
❑ 75Top-302
❑ 75TopMin-302
❑ 76Hos-44
❑ 76HosTwi-44
❑ 76LinSup-110
❑ 76OPC-29
❑ 76RedSox-1
❑ 76RedSoxSM-1
❑ 76SSP-410
❑ 76Top-29
❑ 77BurCheD-28
❑ 77Hos-68
❑ 77OPC-237
❑ 77Spo-8408
❑ 77Top-585
❑ 78OPC-37
❑ 78PapGinD-7
❑ 78SSP270-175
❑ 78Top-245
❑ 79BasPat-9
❑ 79OPC-57
❑ 79Top-125
❑ 80OPC-339
❑ 80Top-645
❑ 81AllGamPI-20
❑ 81Don-454
❑ 81Fle-225
❑ 81FleStiC-33
❑ 81Kel-49
❑ 81LonBeaPT-3A
❑ 81OPC-172
❑ 81Squ-13
❑ 81Top-455
❑ 81TopScr-37
❑ 81TopSti-52
❑ 81TopSupHT-56
❑ 81TopTra-743
❑ 82Don-342
❑ 82Fle-453
❑ 82FleSta-219
❑ 82Kel-44
❑ 82OPC-55
❑ 82Top-55
❑ 82TopSti-134
❑ 82TopSti-157
❑ 83Don-318
❑ 83Fle-80
❑ 83OPC-315
❑ 83Top-315
❑ 84AngSmo-4
❑ 84Fle-510
❑ 84Nes792-735
❑ 84OPC-376
❑ 84Top-735
❑ 84TopSti-238
❑ 84TopTif-735
❑ 86AngSmo-15
❑ 86TopTra-16T
❑ 86TopTraT-16T
❑ 87BalOriP-6
❑ 87DonOpeD-134
❑ 87Fle-74
❑ 87FleGlo-74
❑ 87OPC-152
❑ 87Top-579
❑ 87TopTif-579
❑ 91A'sMot-28
❑ 91OriCro-63
❑ 92RedSoxDD-7
❑ 93RedSoxP-4
❑ 95AngMot-28
❑ 96AngMot-28

❑ 97LanJet-1
❑ 98LanJetG-4
Burley, Rick
❑ 93EugEmeC-7
❑ 93EugEmeF-3849
❑ 93RocRoyC-6
❑ 93RocRoyF-706
❑ 94MidLeaAF-MDW20
❑ 94RocRoyC-4
❑ 94RocRoyF-556
Burley, Tony
❑ 82CedRapRT-16
❑ 83TamTarT-1
Burley, Travis
❑ 90MedHatBJB-4
Burlingame, Ben
❑ 91GenCubC-2
❑ 91GenCubP-4208
❑ 92WinSpiC-24
❑ 92WinSpiF-1200
❑ 93DayCubC-4
❑ 93DayCubF-851
❑ 93PeoChiTI-3
❑ 94OrlCubF-1378
❑ 95OrlCubF-2
❑ 96IowCubB-9
Burlingame, Dennis
❑ 88SouAtlLAGS-28
❑ 88SumBraP-393
❑ 89DurBullS-2
❑ 89DurBullS-2
❑ 89DurBulTI-2
❑ 91DurBulC-7
❑ 91DurBulP-1537
❑ 92GreBraF-1149
❑ 92GreBraS-230
❑ 92SkyAA F-98
❑ 92UppDecML-299
❑ 93GreBraF-342
❑ 93RicBraP-19
❑ 94HigDesMC-9
❑ 94HigDesMF-2781
❑ 97DurBulATI-4
Burlingame, Greg
❑ 87HawRai-22
❑ 89SanBerSB-5
❑ 89SanBerSCLC-70
Burlingame, Mark
❑ 77ForLauYS-26
Burmeister, Jerry
❑ 46SeaSLP-9
Burnau, Ben
❑ 89WauTimGS-10
Burne, Earle
❑ 93AusFut-37
Burnett, A.J.
❑ 98BesAutSS-5
❑ 99199Fin-289
❑ 99BasAmeTPA-4
❑ 99Bow-323
❑ 99Bow200RF-ROY3
❑ 99BowBes-155
❑ 99BowBesAR-155
❑ 99BowBesR-155
❑ 99BowGol-323
❑ 99BowInt-323
❑ 99DumSet-110
❑ 99E-X Cen-119
❑ 99E-X CenECFut-119
❑ 99E-X CenECNow-119
❑ 99FinGolRef-289
❑ 99FinRef-289
❑ 99FleBri-151
❑ 99FleBri2G-151
❑ 99FleBriBlu-151
❑ 99FleBriGol-151
❑ 99FleMys-110
❑ 99FleMysFI-5
❑ 99FleMysM-110
❑ 99FleMysP-3
❑ 99SkyMolM-114
❑ 99SkyMolMF-14
❑ 99SkyMolMFS-14
❑ 99SkyMolMFT-14
❑ 99SkyMolMX-114
❑ 99SkyPre-246
❑ 99SkyPre-246
❑ 99SkyPreA-7
❑ 99SkyPreABlue-7
❑ 99SkyPreR-246
❑ 99SkyPreR-246
❑ 99SP SigAuto-AJB
❑ 99SP SigAutoG-AJB
❑ 99SPSig-85
❑ 99TeaBesRA-4
❑ 99Top-437
❑ 99TopBlaLC1-34
❑ 99TopBlaLC2-34
❑ 99TopBlaLC3-34
❑ 99TopChr-437
❑ 99TopChrR-437
❑ 99TopGolL-34
❑ 99TopGolLC1-34
❑ 99TopGolLC2-34
❑ 99TopGolLOtO-34
❑ 99TopRedLC1-34
❑ 99TopRedLC2-34
❑ 99TopRedLC3-34
❑ 99TopSta-49
❑ 99TopSta1Foil-49
❑ 99TopSta2Foil-49
❑ 99TopStaFoil-49
❑ 99TopStaOS-49
❑ 99TopStaTS-49
❑ 99UppDec-278
❑ 99UppDecE-121
❑ 99UppDecEFXG-121
❑ 99UppDecEL1-278
❑ 99UppDecEL2-278
Burnett, John P.
❑ 35DiaMatCS3T1-21
Burnett, Johnny (John H.)
❑ 36GouWidPPR-D5
❑ 91ConTSN-82
❑ 92ConTSN-543
Burnett, Lance
❑ 88PocGiaP-2083
Burnett, Mickey
❑ 47SigOil-40
❑ 47SmiClo-17
Burnett, Ora
❑ 46RemBre-9
❑ 47RemBre-5
❑ 48AngTeal-6
❑ 49BowPCL-36
Burnett, Roger
❑ 91OneYanP-4160
❑ 92PriWilCC-12
❑ 92PriWilCF-154
❑ 93AusFut-35
❑ 93PriWilCC-2
❑ 93PriWilCF-661
❑ 94AlbYanF-1446
❑ 95NorNavTI-26
Burnett, William
❑ 88SFHesCreN32-5
Burnette, Wallace
❑ 56A'sPos-6
❑ 57Top-13
❑ 58Top-69
Burney, Wayne
❑ 74AlbDukTI-3
❑ 75AlbDukCa-10
Burnham, Elizabeth
❑ 95ColSilB-2
Burnham, Gary
❑ 97BatCliTI-1
❑ 98ClePhiM-3
Burnham, George W.
❑ 87OldJudN-57
Burnitz, Jeromy
❑ 88CapCodPPaLP-145
❑ 90ClaDraP-17
❑ 90PitMetP-31
❑ 91Bow-474
❑ 91Cla/Bes-68
❑ 91Cla1-T4
❑ 91ClaGolB-BC5
❑ 91LinDriAA-627
❑ 91Sco-380
❑ 91WilBilLD-627
❑ 91WilBilP-304
❑ 92Bow-189
❑ 92OPC-591
❑ 92ProFS7-280
❑ 92SkyAAAF-248
❑ 92TidTidF-908
❑ 92TidTidS-554
❑ 92Top-591
❑ 92TopGol-591
❑ 92TopGolW-591
❑ 92TopMic-591
❑ 92UppDec-65
❑ 92UppDecML-130
❑ 93Bow-622
❑ 93Don-787
❑ 93ExcFS7-69
❑ 93FlaWavotF-2
❑ 93FleFinE-100
❑ 93Lea-503
❑ 93NorTidF-2581
❑ 93SelRoo-85T
❑ 93SP-147
❑ 93Top-658
❑ 93TopGol-658
❑ 93TopInaM-658
❑ 93TopInaR-658
❑ 93TopMic-658
❑ 93TopTra-110T
❑ 93Ult-423
❑ 94Bow-512
❑ 94ColC-69
❑ 94ColChoGS-69
❑ 94ColChoSS-69
❑ 94Don-575
❑ 94Fin-15
❑ 94FinJum-15
❑ 94FinRef-15
❑ 94Fla-195
❑ 94Fle-559
❑ 94FleRooS-3
❑ 94FUnPac-81
❑ 94Lea-230
❑ 94MetColP-6
❑ 94MetShuST-2
❑ 94NorTidF-2931
❑ 94OPC-110
❑ 94Pac-397
❑ 94PanSti-216
❑ 94Pin-395
❑ 94PinArtP-395
❑ 94PinMusC-395
❑ 94PinNewG-NG23
❑ 94ProMag-94
❑ 94Sco-570
❑ 94ScoBoyoS-5
❑ 94ScoGolR-570
❑ 94Sel-282
❑ 94StaClu-201
❑ 94StaCluFDI-201
❑ 94StaCluGR-201
❑ 94StaCluMOP-201
❑ 94Top-122
❑ 94TopGol-122
❑ 94TopSpa-122
❑ 94TriPla-142
❑ 94Ult-235
❑ 94UppDec-190
❑ 94UppDecED-190
❑ 94USPlaCR-9C
❑ 95ActPacF-35
❑ 95ColCho-279
❑ 95ColChoGS-279
❑ 95ColChoSS-279
❑ 95Don-142
❑ 95DonPreP-142
❑ 95Fle-367
❑ 95Pac-279
❑ 95PacPri-91
❑ 95Pin-370
❑ 95Pin-381
❑ 95PinArtP-370
❑ 95PinArtP-381
❑ 95PinMusC-370
❑ 95PinMusC-381
❑ 95Sco-179
❑ 95ScoGolR-179
❑ 95ScoPlaTS-179
❑ 95Top-366
❑ 95TopCyb-194
❑ 96MetTeal-7
❑ 97BrePol-2
❑ 97ColCho-374
❑ 97Fle-125
❑ 97FleTif-125
❑ 97Pac-114
❑ 97PacLigB-114
❑ 97PacSil-114
❑ 97Sco-191
❑ 97ScoArtPWB-191
❑ 97ScoPreS-191
❑ 97ScoShoS-191
❑ 97ScoShoSAP-191
❑ 97Top-475
❑ 97Ult-309
❑ 97UltGolME-309
❑ 97UltPlaME-309
❑ 98Bow-282
❑ 98BowBes-2
❑ 98BowBesAR-2
❑ 98BowBesR-2
❑ 98BowChr-282
❑ 98BowChrGA-282
❑ 98BowChrGAR-282
❑ 98BowChrI-282
❑ 98BowChrIR-282
❑ 98BowChrR-282
❑ 98BowGolA-282
❑ 98BowInt-282
❑ 98CirThu-20
❑ 98CirThuRav-20
❑ 98CirThuSupRav-20
❑ 98ColCho-403
❑ 98CroRoy-73
❑ 98Fin-78
❑ 98FinNo--78
❑ 98FinNo-R-78
❑ 98FinRef-78
❑ 98Fle-222
❑ 98MetUni-183
❑ 98MetUniPMG-183
❑ 98Pac-113
❑ 98PacAur-150
❑ 98PacInv-40
❑ 98PacInvPBlue-40
❑ 98PacInvSilv-40
❑ 98PacInvTeam-15
❑ 98PacOme-130
❑ 98PacOmeR-130
❑ 98PacOnl-390
❑ 98PacOnlR-390
❑ 98PacOnlWC-390
❑ 98PacPar-183
❑ 98PacParC-183
❑ 98PacParG-183
❑ 98PacParHS-183
❑ 98PacParPB-183
❑ 98PacParR-183
❑ 98PacPlaB-113
❑ 98PacRedT-113
❑ 98PacSil-113
❑ 98Pin-49
❑ 98PinPreP-49
❑ 98Revo-78
❑ 98RevoSS-78
❑ 98Sco-264
❑ 98SkyDugA-27
❑ 98SkyDugAIA-27
❑ 98SP Aut-117
❑ 98SpoIllWSF-35
❑ 98SpoIllWSFEE-35
❑ 98SpoIllWSFFE-35
❑ 98SPxFin-293
❑ 98SPxFinR-293
❑ 98SPxFinS-293
❑ 98StaCluFDI-174
❑ 98StaCluI-174
❑ 98StaCluOneK-174
❑ 98StaCluPP-174
❑ 98Top-126
❑ 98TopChr-126
❑ 98TopChrR-126
❑ 98TopDevR-126
❑ 98TopDia-126
❑ 98TopGal-29
❑ 98TopGalGP-29
❑ 98TopGalOPP-29
❑ 98TopGalPPI-29
❑ 98TopGalPPIA-29
❑ 98TopGolLabC1-16
❑ 98TopGolLabC1B-16
❑ 98TopGolLabC1One-16
❑ 98TopGolLabC1R-16
❑ 98TopGolLabC2-16
❑ 98TopGolLabC2B-16
❑ 98TopGolLabC2One-16
❑ 98TopGolLabC2R-16
❑ 98TopGolLabC3-16
❑ 98TopGolLabC3B-16
❑ 98TopGolLabC3One-16
❑ 98TopGolLabC3R-16
❑ 98TopMiniC-126
❑ 98TopOpeD-62
❑ 98TopSta-42
❑ 98TopStaB-42
❑ 98TopStaG-42
❑ 98TopStaGR-42
❑ 98TopStaS-42
❑ 98TopTek-48
❑ 98TopTekD-48
❑ 98Ult-137
❑ 98UltGolM-137
❑ 98UltMas-137
❑ 98UltPlaM-137
❑ 98UppDec-405
❑ 98UppDecR-51
❑ 99199Fin-32
❑ 99Bow-227
❑ 99BowBes-8
❑ 99BowBesAR-8
❑ 99BowBesR-8
❑ 99BowGol-227
❑ 99BowInt-227
❑ 99CroRoyB-76
❑ 99CroRoyL-76
❑ 99CroRoyOD-76
❑ 99E-X Cen-50
❑ 99E-X CenECFut-50
❑ 99E-X CenECNow-50
❑ 99FinGolRef-32
❑ 99FinRef-32
❑ 99FlaShoLeg1-115
❑ 99FlaShoLeg2-115
❑ 99FlaShoLeg3-115
❑ 99FlaShoLegM1-115
❑ 99FlaShoLegM2-115
❑ 99FlaShoLegM3-115
❑ 99FlaShoR1-115
❑ 99FlaShoR2-115
❑ 99FlaShoR3-115
❑ 99Fle-25
❑ 99FleBri-74
❑ 99FleBri2G-74
❑ 99FleBriBlu-74
❑ 99FleBriGol-74
❑ 99FleMys-46
❑ 99FleMysG-46
❑ 99FleMysM-46
❑ 99FleSta9-25
❑ 99FleVin'-25
❑ 99FleWarT-25
❑ 99MetUni-107
❑ 99MetUniGM-107
❑ 99MetUniPMG-107
❑ 99Pac-230
❑ 99PacAur-97
❑ 99PacAurOD-97
❑ 99PacCroC-147
❑ 99PacCroCPB-147
❑ 99PacInv-80
❑ 99PacInvOD-80
❑ 99PacInvPB-80
❑ 99PacOme-129
❑ 99PacOmeC-129
❑ 99PacOmeG-129
❑ 99PacOmePB-129
❑ 99PacPar-124
❑ 99PacParC-124
❑ 99PacParG-124
❑ 99PacParHoloGold-124
❑ 99PacParHS-124
❑ 99PacParOD-124
❑ 99PacParPB-124
❑ 99PacParRed-124
❑ 99PacPlaB-230
❑ 99PacPri-78
❑ 99PacPriHB-78
❑ 99PacPriHG-78
❑ 99PacPriHM-78
❑ 99PacPriHP-78
❑ 99PacPriRed-78
❑ 99PacPriS-65
❑ 99PacPriS206-65
❑ 99PacPriS206R-65
❑ 99PacRed-230
❑ 99Rev-74
❑ 99RevPremDate-74
❑ 99RevRet-74
❑ 99RevShaSS-74
❑ 99SkyPre-49
❑ 99SkyPreR-49
❑ 99SkyThu-196
❑ 99SkyThuRant-196
❑ 99SkyThuRave-196
❑ 99SP Aut-46
❑ 99SP AutHRC-HR24
❑ 99SP SigAutoG-JB
❑ 99SPAutHRCDC-HR24
❑ 99SpoIll-101
❑ 99SPSig-31
❑ 99SPx-49
❑ 99SPxFinR-49
❑ 99SPxFinS-49
❑ 99StaClu-40
❑ 99StaCluFDI-40
❑ 99StaCluOoaK-40
❑ 99StaCluPP-40
❑ 99ThuSkySupR-196
❑ 99Top-401
❑ 99TopBlaLC1-79
❑ 99TopBlaLC2-79
❑ 99TopBlaLC3-79
❑ 99TopChr-401
❑ 99TopChrR-401
❑ 99TopGal-32
❑ 99TopGalPP-32
❑ 99TopGalPPI-32
❑ 99TopGolL-79
❑ 99TopGolLC1-79
❑ 99TopGolLC2-79
❑ 99TopGolLOtO-79
❑ 99TopMVPP-401
❑ 99TopOpeD-119
❑ 99TopRedLC1-79
❑ 99TopRedLC2-79
❑ 99TopRedLC3-79
❑ 99TopSta-68
❑ 99TopSta1Foil-68
❑ 99TopStaFoil-68
❑ 99TopStaOS-68
❑ 99UD Cho-101
❑ 99UD ChoPCR-101
❑ 99UD Ion-35
❑ 99UD IonR-35
❑ 99UDHolo-32
❑ 99UDHoloAUsome-32
❑ 99UppDec-129
❑ 99UppDecBD-45
❑ 99UppDecBDD-45
❑ 99UppDecBDQ-45
❑ 99UppDecBDT-45
❑ 99UppDecCf7-26
❑ 99UppDecCLM-C52
❑ 99UppDecCo7CE-26
❑ 99UppDecE-51
❑ 99UppDecEFXG-51
❑ 99UppDecEL1-129
❑ 99UppDecEL2-129
❑ 99UppDecM-116
❑ 99UppDecMGS-116
❑ 99UppDecMHFS-116
❑ 99UppDecMP-116
❑ 99UppDecMSS-116
❑ 99UppDecO-46
❑ 99UppDecOSO-46
❑ 99UppDecR-46
❑ 99UppDecRG-46
❑ 99UppDecRP-46
❑ 99Vic-210
Burnos, Jim
❑ 83WisRapTF-20
Burns, Britt
❑ 79KnoKnoST-6
❑ 81AllGamPI-75
❑ 81CokTeaS-25
❑ 81Don-279
❑ 81Fle-342A
❑ 81Fle-342B
❑ 81OPC-218
❑ 81Top-412
❑ 81TopSti-63
❑ 81TopSupHT-13
❑ 82Don-230
❑ 82Fle-339
❑ 82FleSta-189
❑ 82Top-44
❑ 83Don-23
❑ 83Don-193
❑ 83Fle-232
❑ 83FleSti-156
❑ 83Kel-43
❑ 83Top-541
❑ 83TopSti-48
❑ 83WhiSoxTV-40
❑ 84Don-424
❑ 84Fle-54
❑ 84Nes792-125
❑ 84OPC-125
❑ 84Top-125
❑ 84TopTif-125
❑ 84WhiSoxTV-7
❑ 85Don-257
❑ 85Fle-509
❑ 85OPC-338
❑ 85Top-338
❑ 85TopTif-338
❑ 85WhiSoxC-40
❑ 86Don-58
❑ 86Fle-200
❑ 86FleStiC-17
❑ 86OPC-174
❑ 86Spo-105
❑ 86Top-679
❑ 86TopMinL-10
❑ 86TopSti-292
❑ 86TopTif-679
❑ 86YanTCM-18
❑ 90TopTVY-38
❑ 94BreCouMC-25
❑ 95BreCouMF-262
❑ 96PorSeaDB-2
❑ 97PorSeaD-2
Burns, Casey
❑ 99Bow-439
❑ 99BowGol-439

❑ 99BowInt-439
Burns, Craig
❑ 72CedRapCT-23
Burns, Dan
❑ 83ElPasDT-1
Burns, Daren
❑ 88WytCubP-1985
Burns, Dennis
❑ 26Zee-91
Burns, Ed (Edward James)
❑ 11HelSta-111
❑ 15SpoNewM-17
❑ 16FleBreD-9
❑ 16SpoNewM-18
❑ 17ColE13-18
❑ 17HolBreD-8
Burns, George
❑ 19W514-24
❑ 20WalMaiW-7
❑ 21E121So8-6
❑ 21Nei-1
❑ 21Nei-70
❑ 23W503-39
❑ 74CapPub-69
❑ 75ShaPiz-7
❑ 80LauFamF-35
Burns, George Henry
❑ 16SpoNewM-19
❑ 17ColE13-19
❑ 17HolBreD-10
❑ 20GasAmeMBD-5
❑ 20NatCarE-8
❑ 20W516-10
❑ 21Exh-16
❑ 21Exh-17
❑ 22AmeCarE122-6
❑ 22E120-1
❑ 22W572-9
❑ 22W573-13
❑ 22W575-13
❑ 23WilChoV-13
❑ 26Exh-81
❑ 27Exh-41
❑ 27YorCarE-9
❑ 28StaPlaCE-5
❑ 28W502-9
❑ 28Yue-9
❑ 74A's192T-3
❑ 77Ind192T-2
❑ 91ConTSN-201
❑ 91ConTSN-309
❑ 94ConTSN-1153
❑ 94ConTSN-1272
❑ 94ConTSNB-1153
❑ 94ConTSNB-1272
❑ 95ConTSN-1359
Burns, George Joseph
❑ 14B18B-12A
❑ 14B18B-12B
❑ 14B18B-12C
❑ 14B18B-65
❑ 14FatPlaT-9
❑ 15SpoNewM-18
❑ 16BF2FP-76
❑ 16FleBreD-10
❑ 16SpoNewM-20
❑ 17ColE13-20
❑ 17HolBreD-9
❑ 20GasAmeMBD-27
❑ 20NatCarE-9
❑ 21E121So8-7
❑ 21Exh-14
❑ 21Exh-15
❑ 21KoBreWSI-6
❑ 22AmeCarE122-7
❑ 22E120-167
❑ 22W573-14
❑ 23W515-54
❑ 23WilChoV-14
❑ 27YorCarE-9
❑ 28Yue-9
❑ 30Zee-47
❑ 31Zee-28
❑ 33Zee-46
❑ 73SpoScoHC-4
❑ 91ConTSN-158
Burns, Gregory
❑ 85MadMusT-7
Burns, Ian
❑ 91DaiDolF-11
Burns, J.J.
❑ 92ChaRaiC-5
Burns, Jack (John Irving)
❑ 32OrbPinNP-64
❑ 32OrbPinUP-7
❑ 33Gou-198
❑ 33TatOrb-7
❑ 34BatR31-18
❑ 34DiaMatCSB-21
❑ 34DiaStaR-75
❑ 34ExhFou-15
❑ 34TarThoBD-5
❑ 35AlDemDCR3-41
❑ 35DiaMatCS3T1-22
❑ 35ExhFou-15
❑ 35GouPuzR-8C
❑ 35GouPuzR-9C
❑ 37GouThuMR-1
❑ 38GouFliMR-1A
❑ 38GouFliMR-1B
❑ 67SpoHobFC-21
❑ 85BigLeaC3-43
❑ 91ConTSN-131
Burns, James
❑ 83St.PetCT-16
Burns, Jerry
❑ 92ChaRaiF-113
Burns, Jim (James M.)
❑ 87OldJudN-59
Burns, Joe (Joseph James)
❑ 29Zee-64
❑ 45A'sTeal-5
Burns, John Joseph
❑ 34BatR31-191
Burns, Jonathan
❑ 94DavLipB-1
Burns, Kerry
❑ 83TriTriT-4
Burns, Kevin
❑ 96AubDouB-19
❑ 97QuaCitRBB-5
❑ 98KisCobQ-10
Burns, Michael
❑ 91BurAstC-24
❑ 91BurAstP-2804
❑ 92OscAstC-5
❑ 92OscAstF-2532
❑ 93OscAstC-6
❑ 93OscAstF-630
Burns, Oyster (Thomas P.)
❑ 74BroClu-1
❑ 87BucN28-1
❑ 87BucN28-19
❑ 87OldJudN-60
❑ 88GandBCGCE-6
❑ 88WG1CarG-11
❑ 90DodTar-905
Burns, Pat (Patrick)
❑ 98CapCitBF5-20
❑ 98CapCitBM-20
Burns, Sleepy (Bill)
❑ 09T206-46
❑ 11PinT-5-418
❑ 11TurRedT-85
❑ 88PacEigMO-17
❑ 88PacEigMO-18
Burns, Todd
❑ 85MadMusP-5
❑ 85MadMusT-8
❑ 86HunStaDJ-21
❑ 86SouLeaAJ-18
❑ 87HunStaTI-6
❑ 88FleUpd-52
❑ 88FleUpdG-52
❑ 88ScoRoo-106T
❑ 88ScoRooG-106T
❑ 88TacTigC-2
❑ 88TacTigP-632
❑ 89A'sMot-24
❑ 89ClaTraP-171
❑ 89Don-564
❑ 89Fle-3
❑ 89FleGlo-3
❑ 89PanSti-411
❑ 89Sco-465
❑ 89ScoHot1R-100
❑ 89ScoYouS2-4
❑ 89Spo-87
❑ 89Top-174
❑ 89TopBig-10
❑ 89TopTif-174
❑ 89UppDec-718
❑ 90A'sMot-20
❑ 90Don-446
❑ 90Fle-2
❑ 90FleCan-2
❑ 90Lea-458
❑ 90OPC-369
❑ 90PubIntS-299
❑ 90Sco-64
❑ 90Top-369
❑ 90TopTif-369
❑ 90UppDec-689
❑ 91A'sMot-20
❑ 91Bow-221
❑ 91Don-479
❑ 91Fle-4
❑ 91OPC-608
❑ 91Sco-41
❑ 91SouOreAAP-SOA30
❑ 91StaClu-207
❑ 91Top-608
❑ 91TopDesS-608
❑ 91TopMic-608
❑ 91TopTif-608
❑ 91Ult-243
❑ 91UppDec-405
❑ 92OklCit8S-306
❑ 92Sco-341
❑ 92SkyAAAF-140
❑ 93Don-641
❑ 93Fle-318
❑ 93PacSpa-307
❑ 93RanKee-398
❑ 93RanStaC-27
❑ 93StaClu-210
❑ 93StaCluFDI-210
❑ 93StaCluMOP-210
❑ 93Top-279
❑ 93TopGol-279
❑ 93TopInaM-279
❑ 93TopInaR-279
❑ 93TopMic-279
❑ 93UppDec-749
❑ 93UppDecGold-749
❑ 94CalCanF-781
Burns, Tom
❑ 85LynMetT-11
❑ 86TidTidP-3
❑ 87JacMetF-21
❑ 87MetColP-27
Burns, Tom (Thomas E.)
❑ 80BatTroT-8
❑ 81BatTroT-2
❑ 81WatIndT-7
❑ 83WauTimF-4
❑ 87OldJudN-61
❑ 88AugBecN-6A
❑ 88AugBecN-6B
Burns, William T.
❑ 15Zee-6
❑ 17Zee-21
Burns, Zavier
❑ 97EriSeaWB-5
❑ 98AugGreM-25
Burnside, Adrian
❑ 96GreFalDB-6
❑ 96GreFalDTI-4
❑ 97YakBeaG-4
❑ 98SanBerS-5
❑ 98SanBerSTIS-5
Burnside, Pete
❑ 58Top-211
❑ 59Top-354
❑ 60Top-261
❑ 61Pos-46
❑ 61SenJayP-1
❑ 61Top-507
❑ 62Top-207
❑ 63BalOriP-9
❑ 63Top-19
❑ 91OriCro-64
Burnside, Sheldon
❑ 80IndIndTI-3
❑ 80RedEnq-34
❑ 81Fle-220
Burr, Chris
❑ 92GulCoaRSP-2
❑ 93ChaRaiC-26
❑ 93ChaRaiF-1916
❑ 93ClaGolF-113
Burrell, Buster (Frank Andrew)
❑ 90DodTar-93
Burrell, Kevin
❑ 85LynMetT-14
❑ 86ShrCapP-3
❑ 87PhoFirP-8
❑ 88MemChiB-11
❑ 88SouLeaAJ-2
❑ 89OmaRoyC-10
❑ 89OmaRoyP-1733
❑ 90OmaRoyP-68
❑ 90ProAAAF-603
❑ 91LinDriAAA-329
❑ 91OmaRoyLD-329
❑ 91OmaRoyP-1037
Burrell, Leonard
❑ 11Zee-110
❑ 12HomRunKE-81
❑ 12Zee-141
Burrell, Pat
❑ 98ClePhiUM-4
❑ 99199Fin-131
❑ 99BasAmeTP-18
❑ 99BasAmeTPBP-5
❑ 99BasAmeTPG-18
❑ 99BasAmeTPSC-3
❑ 99Bow-175
❑ 99Bow200RF-ROY2
❑ 99BowBes-151
❑ 99BowBesAR-151
❑ 99BowBesFFMI-FF4
❑ 99BowBesFFMI-FF4
❑ 99BowBesFFMII-FF4
❑ 99BowBesMI-M10
❑ 99BowBesMIAR-M10
❑ 99BowBesMIR-M10
❑ 99BowBesR-151
❑ 99BowBesRLRA-RA1
❑ 99BowBesRLRGUB-RB1
❑ 99BowChr-175
❑ 99BowChrDA-DA9
❑ 99BowChrDAR-DA9
❑ 99BowChrG-175
❑ 99BowChrGR-175
❑ 99BowChrI-175
❑ 99BowChrIR-175
❑ 99BowChrR-175
❑ 99BowChrSC-SC3
❑ 99BowChrSCR-SC3
❑ 99BowGol-175
❑ 99BowInt-175
❑ 99BowScoC-SC3
❑ 99DumSet-134
❑ 99E-X Cen-104
❑ 99E-X CenECFut-104
❑ 99E-X CenECNow-104
❑ 99E-X CenEQ-3
❑ 99FinDouF-DF7
❑ 99FinDouFDualR-DF7
❑ 99FinFutF-FF1
❑ 99FinGolRef-131
❑ 99FinPeelHyp-20
❑ 99FinPeelSpark-20
❑ 99FinPeeSS-20
❑ 99FinRef-131
❑ 99FinSplS-SS14
❑ 99FinSplSDR-SS14
❑ 99FlaShoLeg1-23
❑ 99FlaShoLeg2-23
❑ 99FlaShoLeg3-23
❑ 99FlaShoLegM1-23
❑ 99FlaShoLegM2-23
❑ 99FlaShoLegM3-23
❑ 99FlaShoR1-23
❑ 99FlaShoR2-23
❑ 99FlaShoR3-23
❑ 99FlaShoWotF-14
❑ 99FleBri-140
❑ 99FleBri2G-140
❑ 99FleBriBlu-140
❑ 99FleBriGol-140
❑ 99FleMys-134
❑ 99FleMysFI-6
❑ 99FleMysM-134
❑ 99FleMysP-9
❑ 99SkyMolM-102
❑ 99SkyMolMF-2
❑ 99SkyMolMFS-2
❑ 99SkyMolMFT-2
❑ 99SkyMolMX-102
❑ 99SkyPre-248
❑ 99SkyPre-248
❑ 99SkyPreA-8
❑ 99SkyPreABlue-8
❑ 99SkyPreR-248
❑ 99SkyPreR-248
❑ 99SP SigAuto-PB
❑ 99SP SigAutoG-PB
❑ 99SP TopP-45
❑ 99SP TopPDtS-D22
❑ 99SP TopPPE-45
❑ 99SPSig-15
❑ 99StaClu-151
❑ 99StaCluFDI-151
❑ 99StaCluOoaK-151
❑ 99StaCluPP-151
❑ 99StaCluTI-T10C
❑ 99StaCluTL-T10C
❑ 99StaCluTL-T10C
❑ 99TeaBesR-81
❑ 99TeaBesRG-81
❑ 99TeaBesRS-81
❑ 99Top-444
❑ 99TopAut-A16
❑ 99TopBlaLC1-36
❑ 99TopBlaLC2-36
❑ 99TopBlaLC3-36
❑ 99TopChr-444
❑ 99TopChrR-444
❑ 99TopGal-141
❑ 99TopGalPP-141
❑ 99TopGalPPI-141
❑ 99TopGolL-36
❑ 99TopGolLC1-36
❑ 99TopGolLC2-36
❑ 99TopGolLOtO-36
❑ 99TopMVPP-444
❑ 99TopRedLC1-36
❑ 99TopRedLC2-36
❑ 99TopRedLC3-36
❑ 99TopSta-28
❑ 99TopSta-153
❑ 99TopSta1Foil-28
❑ 99TopSta2Foil-28
❑ 99TopStaBF-BF8
❑ 99TopStaBFFoil-BF8
❑ 99TopStaFoil-28
❑ 99TopStaFoil-153
❑ 99TopStaOS-28
❑ 99TopStaTS-28
❑ 99TopTek-36A
❑ 99TopTek-36B
❑ 99TopTekFP-F3
❑ 99TopTekG-36A
❑ 99TopTekG-36B
❑ 99UDHolo-45
❑ 99UDHoloAUsome-45
❑ 99UppDec-266
❑ 99UppDecCLM-C73
❑ 99UppDecE-109
❑ 99UppDecEFXG-109
❑ 99UppDecEL1-266
❑ 99UppDecEL2-266
❑ 99UppDecERE-R10
❑ 99UppDecEREFXG-R10
❑ 99UppDecEUA-PB
❑ 99UppDecM-157
❑ 99UppDecMGS-157
❑ 99UppDecMHFS-157
❑ 99UppDecMSC-SC7
❑ 99UppDecMSS-157
❑ 99UppDecRI-PB
❑ 99UppDecRIL2-PB
❑ 99UppDecROSS-S18
❑ 99UppDecROSS-S18
❑ 99Vic-291
Burrell, Scott
❑ 92UppDecML-71
Burress, Andy
❑ 95BilMusTI-1
❑ 96BilMusTI-3
❑ 98BurBeeM-3
Burress, Davey
❑ 76CliPilT-5
Burright, Larry
❑ 62DodVol-13
❑ 62Top-348
❑ 63MetJayP-1
❑ 63Top-174
❑ 81TCM60I-464
❑ 90DodTar-94
❑ 91MetWIZ-57
Burrill, Casey
❑ 93IdaFalBF-4035
❑ 93IdaFalBSP-23
Burris, Paul Robert
❑ 54BraJohC-29
❑ 55JetPos-2
❑ 83Bra53F-14
Burris, Pierre
❑ 91BilMusP-3765
❑ 91BilMusSP-2
Burris, Ray
❑ 74OPC-161
❑ 74Top-161
❑ 75OPC-566
❑ 75Top-566
❑ 75TopMin-566
❑ 76CubTri-4
❑ 76Hos-60
❑ 76HosTwi-60
❑ 76OPC-51
❑ 76Top-51
❑ 77BurCheD-194
❑ 77CubJewT-4
❑ 77Hos-67
❑ 77OPC-197
❑ 77Top-190
❑ 78SSP270-261
❑ 78Top-371
❑ 78WifBalD-10
❑ 79OPC-43
❑ 79Top-98
❑ 79YanPicA-5
❑ 80Top-364
❑ 81Don-524A
❑ 81Don-524B
❑ 81ExpPos-2
❑ 81Fle-328
❑ 81OPC-323
❑ 81Top-654
❑ 81TopTra-744
❑ 82Don-414
❑ 82ExpHygM-2
❑ 82ExpPos-3
❑ 82ExpZel-20
❑ 82Fle-184
❑ 82OPC-227
❑ 82Top-227
❑ 83Don-36
❑ 83ExpPos-2
❑ 83ExpStu-16
❑ 83Fle-277
❑ 83OPC-12
❑ 83Top-474
❑ 84A'sMot-22
❑ 84Don-331
❑ 84Fle-270
❑ 84FleUpd-19
❑ 84Nes792-552
❑ 84OPC-319
❑ 84Top-552
❑ 84TopTif-552
❑ 84TopTra-18T
❑ 84TopTraT-18T
❑ 85BrePol-48
❑ 85Don-218
❑ 85Fle-418
❑ 85FleUpd-15
❑ 85Lea-116
❑ 85OPC-238
❑ 85Top-758
❑ 85TopSti-328
❑ 85TopTif-758
❑ 85TopTifT-13T
❑ 85TopTra-13T
❑ 86CarTeal-5
❑ 86Don-107
❑ 86Fle-482
❑ 86Top-106
❑ 86TopTif-106
❑ 89HelBreSP-26
❑ 89TopSenL-108
❑ 90BreMilB-32
❑ 90BrePol-NNO
❑ 90EliSenL-18
❑ 91BreMilB-32
❑ 91BrePol-NNO
❑ 91MetWIZ-58
❑ 92RanMot-28
❑ 92YanWIZ7-28
❑ 93RanKee-90
❑ 94BreMilB-297
Burritt, Mike
❑ 92BurIndC-8
❑ 92BurIndF-1646
Burrough, Butch
❑ 92EliTwiC-7
❑ 92EliTwiF-3691
❑ 93ForMyeMF-2667
❑ 94AlbPolC-8
❑ 94AlbPolF-2249
Burroughs, Darren
❑ 80CarMudF-11
❑ 81ReaPhiT-4
❑ 82OklCit8T-23
❑ 83ReaPhiT-2
❑ 84LasVegSC-235
❑ 86BufBisP-6
❑ 88CalCanC-1
❑ 88CalCanP-780
Burroughs, Eric
❑ 90BilMusP-3233
Burroughs, Jeff (Jeffrey A.)
❑ 72OPC-191
❑ 72RanTeal-5
❑ 72Top-191

❑ 73LinPor-173
❑ 73OPC-489
❑ 73Top-489
❑ 74Kel-16
❑ 74OPC-223
❑ 74Top-223
❑ 74TopDecE-48
❑ 74TopSta-232
❑ 75Hos-94
❑ 75Kel-8
❑ 75OPC-212
❑ 75OPC-308
❑ 75OPC-470
❑ 75RanPos-4
❑ 75SSP42-27
❑ 75SSPPuzB-4
❑ 75Top-212
❑ 75Top-308
❑ 75Top-470
❑ 75TopMin-212
❑ 75TopMin-308
❑ 75TopMin-470
❑ 76BlaDis-6
❑ 76BucDis-6
❑ 76CarDis-6
❑ 76CraDis-6
❑ 76DailsID-6
❑ 76Hos-111
❑ 76IsaDis-6
❑ 76OPC-360
❑ 76OrbDis-6
❑ 76RedBarD-6
❑ 76SafDis-6
❑ 76Spo-4
❑ 76SSP-269
❑ 76Top-360
❑ 76TowCluD-6
❑ 77BurCheD-214
❑ 77ChiWilD-8
❑ 77DailsID-8
❑ 77DetCaeD-8
❑ 77HolInnD-8
❑ 77MSADis-8
❑ 77OPC-209
❑ 77PepGloD-58
❑ 77SagDis-8
❑ 77sDis-8
❑ 77Spo-4002
❑ 77Top-55
❑ 77WenDis-8
❑ 77ZipDis-8
❑ 78BraCok-2
❑ 78Hos-61
❑ 78Kel-15
❑ 78OPC-134
❑ 78Pep-29
❑ 78RCColC-25
❑ 78SagDis-4
❑ 78TasDis-4
❑ 78Top-130
❑ 78WifBalD-11
❑ 79BasPat-10
❑ 79Hos-20
❑ 79Kel-12
❑ 79OPC-124
❑ 79Top-245
❑ 80OPC-283
❑ 80Top-545
❑ 81Don-66
❑ 81Fle-245
❑ 81MarPol-1
❑ 81MarPos-9
❑ 81Top-20
❑ 81TopTra-745
❑ 82Don-379
❑ 82Fle-506
❑ 82FleSta-226
❑ 82K-M-25
❑ 82OPC-309
❑ 82Top-440
❑ 82TopSti-231
❑ 82TopStiV-231
❑ 82TopTra-14T
❑ 83Don-323
❑ 83Fle-515
❑ 83FleSta-27
❑ 83FleSti-186
❑ 83Top-648
❑ 84A'sMot-17
❑ 84Don-156
❑ 84DonCha-7
❑ 84Fle-440
❑ 84Nes792-354
❑ 84OPC-354
❑ 84Top-354
❑ 84TopSti-329
❑ 84TopTif-354
❑ 85BluJayFS-6
❑ 85Don-542
❑ 85FleUpd-16
❑ 85OPC-91
❑ 85Top-91
❑ 85Top-272
❑ 85TopMin-91
❑ 85TopTif-91
❑ 85TopTif-272
❑ 85TopTifT-14T
❑ 85TopTra-14T
❑ 86Fle-54
❑ 86OPC-168
❑ 86RanGreT-11
❑ 86Top-168
❑ 86TopTif-168
❑ 91UppDecS-6
❑ 92MCIAmb-9
❑ 92MDAMVP-9
❑ 93RanKee-6
❑ 93UppDecAH-24
❑ 93UppDecS-2
❑ 94RanAllP-2
❑ 94TedWil-86
❑ 99SpollIGotG-46
❑ 99SpollIGotGA-13

Burroughs, Kenny
❑ 89UtiBluSP-3
❑ 90YakBeaTI-8

Burroughs, Sean
❑ 99199Fin-277
❑ 99BasAmeTP-19
❑ 99BasAmeTPG-19
❑ 99Bow-345
❑ 99BowBes-157
❑ 99BowBesAR-157
❑ 99BowBesR-157
❑ 99BowGol-345
❑ 99BowInt-345
❑ 99FinGolRef-277
❑ 99FinRef-277

Burrows, John
❑ 44CubTeal-2

Burrows, Mike
❑ 95EveAqaTI-3
❑ 96EveAquB-5
❑ 97WisTimR-5
❑ 98LanJetG-5

Burrows, Terry
❑ 90ButCopKSP-5
❑ 91Cla/Bes-265
❑ 91GasRanC-2
❑ 91GasRanP-2679
❑ 92ChaRanC-25
❑ 92ClaFS7-65
❑ 93Bow-573
❑ 93ClaFS7-166
❑ 93OklCit8F-1620
❑ 94OklCit8F-1490
❑ 95FleUpd-81
❑ 95LinVen-219
❑ 95RanCra-5
❑ 97LasVegS1A-10

Burrus, Daryl
❑ 87BelMarTI-25

Burrus, Dick (Maurice L.)
❑ 25Exh-4
❑ 26Exh-3
❑ 94ConTSN-1238
❑ 94ConTSNB-1238

Burt, Chris
❑ 94HelBreF-3605
❑ 94HelBreSP-7
❑ 95BelBreTI-14
❑ 95MidLeaA-6
❑ 96StoPorB-23

Burton, Adam
❑ 93AusFut-94
❑ 93AusFut-114
❑ 95AusFut-55

Burton, Bob
❑ 89WauTimGS-4
❑ 90ColMetGS-27
❑ 90SouAtlLAS-48
❑ 91ColMetPI-4
❑ 92St.LucMCB-29

Burton, Chris
❑ 89IdaFalBP-2022
❑ 90IdaFalBP-3259
❑ 91Cla/Bes-163
❑ 91MiaMirC-27
❑ 91MiaMirP-420

Burton, Darren
❑ 91AppFoxCB-22
❑ 91AppFoxP-1727
❑ 91MidLeaAP-MWL1
❑ 92BasCitRC-23
❑ 92BasCitRF-3856
❑ 92Bow-424
❑ 92ClaFS7-20
❑ 92UppDecML-303
❑ 93Bow-181
❑ 93ClaFS7-99
❑ 93ClaGolF-81
❑ 93WilBluRC-4
❑ 93WilBluRF-2009
❑ 94Bow-639
❑ 94Cla-48
❑ 94MemChiF-368
❑ 94UppDecML-187
❑ 96OmaRoyB-10
❑ 97ScrRedB-22
❑ 98ScrRedBQ-8

Burton, Ellis N.
❑ 59Top-231
❑ 60Top-446
❑ 61MapLeaBH-3
❑ 63Top-262
❑ 64Top-269
❑ 64TopVen-269

Burton, Essex
❑ 92SouBenWSC-20
❑ 92SouBenWSF-182
❑ 93ExcFS7-151
❑ 93MidLeaAGF-20
❑ 93SouBenWSC-3
❑ 93SouBenWSF-1437
❑ 94CarLeaAF-CAR6
❑ 94PriWilCC-4
❑ 94PriWilCF-1927
❑ 96ReaPhiB-16
❑ 98PriWilCASM-17

Burton, Jaime
❑ 96SpoIndB-7

Burton, Jim
❑ 76OPC-471
❑ 76SSP-418
❑ 76Top-471
❑ 78SSP270-168

Burton, Ken
❑ 76CedRapGT-8

Burton, Michael
❑ 89FreStaBS-5
❑ 90Bes-268
❑ 90GasRanP-2526
❑ 90GasRanS-4
❑ 90ProAaA-99
❑ 90SouAtlLAS-3
❑ 91LinDriAA-577
❑ 91TulDriLD-577
❑ 91TulDriP-2777
❑ 91TulDriTI-4
❑ 92ChaRanC-2
❑ 92ChaRanF-2229

Burton, Steve
❑ 91GulCoaRSP-23
❑ 92GasRanC-21
❑ 92GasRanF-2258
❑ 93ChaRaiC-5
❑ 93ChaRaiF-1917

Burton, Terry
❑ 89TenTecGE-4

Burtschy, Ed
❑ 51A'sTeal-4
❑ 54A'STEAI-5
❑ 55A'sRodM-8
❑ 55Bow-120
❑ 57JetPos-4

Burtt, Dennis
❑ 81BriRedST-21
❑ 83PawRedST-3
❑ 84PawRedST-5
❑ 85IntLeaAT-39
❑ 85TolMudHT-4
❑ 86StaoftFT-24
❑ 86TwiTeal-12
❑ 87AlbDukD-6
❑ 88AlbDukCm-7
❑ 88AlbDukP-276
❑ 88BlaYNPRWL-180
❑ 89AlbDukCm-2
❑ 89AlbDukP-68
❑ 89BlaYNPRWL-22
❑ 90CMC-380
❑ 90ProAAAF-372
❑ 90TolMudHC-3
❑ 90TolMudHP-142
❑ 92Ft.MyeMCB-27
❑ 92Ft.MyeMF-2762
❑ 93NewBriRSF-1238
❑ 94NewBriRSF-667
❑ 98MadBlaW-22

Burwell, Bill
❑ 60Top-467
❑ 77PirTCM1WC-39

Burwell, Phil
❑ 83EriCarT-17

Busby, Jim (James F.)
❑ 51Bow-302
❑ 52BerRos-6
❑ 52Bow-68
❑ 52StaCalL-73F
❑ 52StaCalS-87D
❑ 52Top-309
❑ 53BowC-15
❑ 53Bri-1
❑ 53NorBreL-4
❑ 54Bow-8
❑ 54RedMan-AL2
❑ 55Bow-166
❑ 55DonWin-1
❑ 55RedMan-AL2
❑ 55RobGouS-8
❑ 55RobGouW-8
❑ 56BalOriP-8
❑ 56Top-330
❑ 57IndSoh-2
❑ 57Top-309
❑ 58Hir-68
❑ 58HirTes-2
❑ 58OriJayP-2
❑ 58Top-28
❑ 59Top-185
❑ 59TopVen-185
❑ 60Lea-11
❑ 60Top-232
❑ 61BalOriP-5
❑ 62SalPlaC-30
❑ 62ShiPlaC-30
❑ 67AstTeal2-6
❑ 68BraPos-6
❑ 73OPC-237
❑ 73Top-237A
❑ 73Top-237B
❑ 74OPC-634
❑ 74Top-634
❑ 75AtlBraP-5
❑ 77MarPos-3
❑ 77ShrCapT-3
❑ 77Top-597
❑ 79TCM50-66
❑ 83TopRep5-309
❑ 87AstSer1-30
❑ 91OriCro-65

Busby, Mike
❑ 91HigSchPLS-14
❑ 92SavCarF-653
❑ 93SavCarC-6
❑ 93SavCarF-678
❑ 93SouAtlLAGF-46
❑ 94ClaGolF-158
❑ 94ExcFS7-263
❑ 94St.PetCC-6
❑ 94St.PetCF-2577
❑ 95ArkTraTI-6
❑ 96Bow-345
❑ 96BowFoi-345
❑ 96Exc-226
❑ 96FleUpd-U185
❑ 96FleUpdTC-U185
❑ 96LeaSigA-38
❑ 96LeaSigAG-38
❑ 96LeaSigAS-38
❑ 96LouRedB-12
❑ 96Pin-392
❑ 96PinAfi-187
❑ 96PinAfiAP-187
❑ 96PinFoil-392
❑ 96Sum-192
❑ 96SumAbo&B-192
❑ 96SumArtP-192
❑ 96SumFoi-192
❑ 96Ult-543
❑ 96UltGolM-543
❑ 97LouRedB-12
❑ 98PacOmeRS-19
❑ 98PacOmeRST1-19
❑ 98PacOnl-606
❑ 98PacOnlR-606
❑ 98PacOnlWC-606

Busby, Paul Miller
❑ 43PhiTeal-4

Busby, Steve
❑ 73OPC-608
❑ 73Top-608
❑ 74OPC-365
❑ 74RoyPos-5
❑ 74Top-365
❑ 74TopSta-181
❑ 75Hos-124
❑ 75Kel-24
❑ 75OPC-7
❑ 75OPC-120
❑ 75RoyPos-6
❑ 75SSP42-39
❑ 75Top-7
❑ 75Top-120
❑ 75TopMin-7
❑ 75TopMin-120
❑ 76Hos-71
❑ 76KanCitRP-5
❑ 76Kel-33
❑ 76LauDiaJ-15
❑ 76OPC-260
❑ 76RoyAaP-3
❑ 76Spo-2
❑ 76SSP-183
❑ 76Top-260
❑ 78Top-336
❑ 80OmaRoyP-4
❑ 80Top-474
❑ 81Fle-33
❑ 86RoyGreT-9
❑ 90SouCalS-2
❑ 93RoySta2-2

Busby, Wayne
❑ 89SouBenWSGS-23
❑ 90SarWhiSS-2
❑ 91BirBarLD-52
❑ 91BirBarP-1458
❑ 91LinDriAA-52
❑ 92BirBarF-2588
❑ 92BirBarS-79
❑ 92SkyAA F-38

Busch, Ed (Edgar John)
❑ 45A'sTeal-6
❑ 83TCMPla1944-16

Busch, Gussie
❑ 81TCM60I-362

Busch, Mike
❑ 90GreFalDSP-3
❑ 91BakDodCLC-25
❑ 92ClaFS7-346
❑ 92SanAntMS-558
❑ 93AlbDukF-1467
❑ 94AlbDukF-848
❑ 94Bow-650
❑ 94ExcFS7-210
❑ 94ExcLeaLF-4
❑ 95SigRoo-11
❑ 95SigRooSig-11
❑ 96DodPol-4
❑ 97BufBis-8

Buschorn, Don
❑ 65Top-577

Bush, Chuck
❑ 91HelBreSP-26
❑ 92StoPorC-2
❑ 92StoPorF-27

Bush, Craig
❑ 92ElmPioC-5
❑ 92ElmPioF-1374
❑ 93UtiBluSC-6
❑ 93UtiBluSF-3526
❑ 94UtiBluSC-7
❑ 94UtiBluSF-3811
❑ 95MicBatCTI-5

Bush, Donie (Owen Joseph)
❑ 07TigACDPP-17
❑ 08IndPos-2
❑ 09AmeCarE90-1-17
❑ 09ColChiE-40
❑ 09SpoNewSM-25
❑ 09T206-47
❑ 09TigMorBBBP-3
❑ 09TigMorPWBPP-1
❑ 09TigTaCP-2
❑ 10JuJuDE-6
❑ 10PeoT21-8
❑ 11DiaGumP-5
❑ 11HelSta-27
❑ 11PinT-5-158
❑ 11PloCanE-11
❑ 11SpoLifM-54
❑ 12ColRedB-40
❑ 12ColTinT-40
❑ 12HasTriFT-9
❑ 14CraJacE-122
❑ 14TexTomE-7
❑ 15AmeCarE106-6
❑ 15CraJacE-122
❑ 15SpoNewM-20
❑ 16BF2FP-25
❑ 16SpoNewM-22
❑ 17ColE13-22
❑ 17HolBreD-11
❑ 19W514-30
❑ 21E121So8-8
❑ 21Exh-19
❑ 22AmeCarE122-8
❑ 22W575-14
❑ 30ChiEveAP-12
❑ 30WhiSoxTI-5
❑ 33WorCig(-11
❑ 33WorCig(-12
❑ 33WorCig(-13
❑ 61Fle-96
❑ 67SpoHobFC-50
❑ 76ISCHooHA-19
❑ 81TigDetN-38
❑ 81TigSecNP-5
❑ 86IndIndTI-2
❑ 94ConTSN-1234
❑ 94ConTSNB-1234

Bush, George W.
❑ 80PerHaloFP-F
❑ 92MegRut-149
❑ 92MegRutP-134

Bush, Guy T.
❑ 28StaPlaCE-6
❑ 28W56PlaC-S11
❑ 29PorandAR-9
❑ 31CubTeal-5
❑ 32CubTeal-1
❑ 32OrbPinNP-16
❑ 32OrbPinUP-8
❑ 33ButCre-3
❑ 33Gou-67
❑ 33GouCanV-67
❑ 33TatOrb-8
❑ 33TatOrbSDR-189
❑ 34BatR31-158
❑ 34DiaMatCSB-22
❑ 35ExhFou-7
❑ 35GouPuzR-1E
❑ 35GouPuzR-3C
❑ 35GouPuzR-5C
❑ 35GouPuzR-14C
❑ 36ExhFou-7
❑ 79DiaGre-356
❑ 82DiaCla-84
❑ 83ConMar-44
❑ 88ConNatA-2
❑ 91ConTSN-196

Bush, Homer
❑ 92ChaRaiC-16
❑ 92ChaRaiF-124
❑ 92ClaFS7-52
❑ 93AusFut-16
❑ 93MidLeaAGF-55
❑ 93WatDiaC-7
❑ 93WatDiaF-1772
❑ 94Bow-8
❑ 94ExcFS7-277
❑ 94RanCucQC-8
❑ 94RanCucQF-1643
❑ 95ActPacF-46
❑ 95AusFut-109
❑ 95Bow-174
❑ 95Exc-279
❑ 95MemChiTI-24
❑ 95SPML-138
❑ 95UppDecML-151
❑ 95UppDecMLFS-151
❑ 96BesAutS-15
❑ 96BesAutSA-10
❑ 96Bow-320
❑ 96BowFoi-320
❑ 96LasVegSB-8
❑ 97BesAutAS-7
❑ 97BesAutP-R3
❑ 97Bow-157
❑ 97BowCerBlaIA-CA10
❑ 97BowCerBluIA-CA10
❑ 97BowCerGolIA-CA10
❑ 97BowInt-157
❑ 97LasVegS1A-11
❑ 97Top-203
❑ 98Bow-166
❑ 98BowChr-166
❑ 98BowChrGA-166
❑ 98BowChrGAR-166
❑ 98BowChrI-166
❑ 98BowChrIR-166
❑ 98BowChrR-166
❑ 98BowGolA-166

❑ 98BowInt-166
❑ 98DonColE-473
❑ 98DonColL-395
❑ 98DonEli-73
❑ 98DonEliA-73
❑ 98DonEliS-73
❑ 98DonPriCE-473
❑ 98DonPriCL-395
❑ 98Fle-219
❑ 98Lea-196
❑ 98LeaFraDA-196
❑ 98LeaFraF-196
❑ 98LeaFraM-196
❑ 98LeaFraM-196
❑ 98LeaFraMDC-196
❑ 98LeaFraMDC-196
❑ 98LeaFraMZ2-196
❑ 98PacOmeRS-8
❑ 98PacOmeRST5-8
❑ 98PacOnl-498
❑ 98PacOnlR-498
❑ 98PacOnlWC-498
❑ 98PinIns-114
❑ 98PinInsCE-114
❑ 98PinInsDE-114
❑ 98PinPer-136
❑ 98PinPerPP-136
❑ 98Ult-228
❑ 98UltGolM-228
❑ 98UltMas-228
❑ 98UltPlaM-228
❑ 98Zen-96
❑ 98Zen5 xx7-78
❑ 98Zen5x7GoldImp-78
❑ 98Zen5x7Imp-78
❑ 98ZenZ-G-96
❑ 98ZenZ-S-96
❑ 99BowBes-147
❑ 99BowBesAR-147
❑ 99BowBesR-147
❑ 99PacOme-243
❑ 99PacOmeC-243
❑ 99PacOmeG-243
❑ 99PacOmePB-243
❑ 99UppDec-511
❑ 99UppDecEL1-511
❑ 99UppDecEL2-511
❑ 99Vic-415
❑ 99YanFle-16

Bush, Joe (Leslie Ambrose)
❑ 14FatPlaT-10
❑ 15CraJacE-166
❑ 15SpoNewM-19
❑ 16SpoNewM-21
❑ 17ColE13-21
❑ 20NatCarE-10
❑ 20WalMaiW-8
❑ 21E121So1-7
❑ 21Exh-18
❑ 21Nei-4
❑ 22E120-62
❑ 22W572-10
❑ 22W575-15
❑ 22WilPatV-5
❑ 23W501-34
❑ 23W503-1
❑ 23W515-27
❑ 27AmeCarE126-3
❑ 29CubCerICP-1
❑ 29Zee-84
❑ 68SCFOldT-12
❑ 92ConTSN-345
❑ 93CraJac-24
❑ 94ConTSN-1279
❑ 94ConTSNB-1279

Bush, Kalani
❑ 89GenCubP-1872

Bush, Randy (Robert Randall)
❑ 80TolMudHT-8
❑ 82OrlTwi8SCT-2
❑ 82TolMudHT-20
❑ 83TopTra-17T
❑ 83TwiTeal-18
❑ 84Don-513
❑ 84Fle-558
❑ 84MinTwiP-3
❑ 84Nes792-429
❑ 84OPC-84
❑ 84Top-429
❑ 84TopSti-314
❑ 84TopTif-429
❑ 84TwiTeal-19
❑ 85Don-633
❑ 85Fle-272
❑ 85Top-692
❑ 85TopTif-692
❑ 85TwiPos-2
❑ 85TwiTeal-2
❑ 85TwiTeal-20
❑ 86Fle-388
❑ 86OPC-214
❑ 86Top-214
❑ 86TopTif-214
❑ 86TwiTeal-18
❑ 87Don-441
❑ 87Fle-538
❑ 87FleGlo-538
❑ 87Top-364
❑ 87TopTif-364
❑ 87TwiPos-5
❑ 87TwiTeal-16
❑ 88Don-272
❑ 88Fle-6
❑ 88FleGlo-6
❑ 88FleGlo-WS2
❑ 88FleWorS-2
❑ 88PanSti-450
❑ 88Sco-292
❑ 88ScoGlo-292
❑ 88StaLinTw-5
❑ 88Top-73
❑ 88TopTif-73
❑ 88TwiMasBD-7
❑ 88TwiSmoC-9
❑ 89Bow-164
❑ 89BowTif-164
❑ 89Don-537
❑ 89DonBasB-214
❑ 89Fle-107
❑ 89FleGlo-107
❑ 89OPC-288
❑ 89PanSti-391
❑ 89Sco-212
❑ 89Top-577
❑ 89TopBig-282
❑ 89TopTif-577
❑ 89UppDec-158
❑ 90Bow-416
❑ 90BowTif-416
❑ 90Don-199
❑ 90Fle-370
❑ 90FleCan-370
❑ 90Lea-83
❑ 90OPC-747
❑ 90PanSti-109
❑ 90PublntS-324
❑ 90Sco-278
❑ 90Top-747
❑ 90TopBig-92
❑ 90TopSti-294
❑ 90TopTif-747
❑ 90UppDec-493
❑ 91DodPho-11
❑ 91Don-382
❑ 91Fle-605
❑ 91Lea-26
❑ 91OPC-124
❑ 91Sco-574
❑ 91Top-124
❑ 91TopDesS-124
❑ 91TopMic-124
❑ 91TopTif-124
❑ 91UltUpd-34
❑ 92Don-728
❑ 92Fle-198
❑ 92Lea-467
❑ 92LeaBlaG-467
❑ 92OPC-476
❑ 92Sco-377
❑ 92StaClu-84
❑ 92Top-476
❑ 92TopGol-476
❑ 92TopGolW-476
❑ 92TopMic-476
❑ 93Don-781
❑ 93Fle-638
❑ 93StaClu-645
❑ 93StaCluFDI-645
❑ 93StaCluMOP-645

Bush, Ricky
❑ 92MarPhiC-10
❑ 92MarPhiF-3058

Bush, Todd
❑ 91MiaHurBB-3

Busha, Rodney
❑ 90ButCopKSP-1

Bushart, John
❑ 95CedRapKTI-33

Bushell, James
❑ 91AdeGiaF-6

Bushelman, Jack (John)
❑ 12T207-21

Bushing, Chris
❑ 89PenPilS-2
❑ 90ProAaA-111
❑ 90RocExpLC-3
❑ 90RocExpP-2695
❑ 91WesPalBEC-3
❑ 91WesPalBEP-1219
❑ 92ReaPhiF-566
❑ 92ReaPhiS-528
❑ 93ChaLooF-2353
❑ 94NasSouF-1244

Bushman, Jon
❑ 98MarPhiG-5

Bushong, Doc (Albert John)
❑ 74BroClu-2
❑ 76SSP188WS-13
❑ 87BucN28-94
❑ 87LonJacN-1
❑ 87OldJudN-62A
❑ 87OldJudN-62B
❑ 87ScrDC-1
❑ 88SpoTimM-4
❑ 90DodTar-95
❑ 94OriofB-27

Busick, Warren
❑ 86DayBealP-3

Buskey, Tom (Michael T.)
❑ 74SyrChiTI-3
❑ 75CleIndP-7
❑ 75OPC-403
❑ 75Top-403
❑ 75TopMin-403
❑ 76IndTeal-2
❑ 76OklCit8TI-7
❑ 76OPC-178
❑ 76SSP-505
❑ 76Top-178
❑ 77IndTeal-4
❑ 77Top-236
❑ 79BluJayBY-3
❑ 79SyrChiTI-29
❑ 80OPC-265
❑ 80Top-506
❑ 81Don-270
❑ 92YanWIZ7-29

Busler, Matt
❑ 97WatIndTI-9
❑ 98WatIndTI-5

Buss, Scott
❑ 86ChaLooP-7
❑ 87KinIndP-5

Bussa, Todd
❑ 92FayGenC-11
❑ 92FayGenF-2160
❑ 93FayGenC-6
❑ 93FayGenF-122
❑ 94LakTigC-5
❑ 95KanCouCTI-39
❑ 95MidLeaA-7
❑ 97ModA'sG-3
❑ 98LynHilQ-3

Busse, Ray (Raymond Edward)
❑ 72OPC-101
❑ 72Top-101
❑ 73OPC-607
❑ 73Top-607
❑ 75IowOakT-3

Bustabad, Juan
❑ 83PawRedST-15
❑ 84PawRedST-25
❑ 85PawRedST-2
❑ 87SanAntDTI-9
❑ 88SanAntMB-12
❑ 89AlbDukCm-20
❑ 89AlbDukP-78
❑ 90YakBeaTI-5
❑ 93LetMouF-4165
❑ 93LetMouSP-24
❑ 98KanCouC-5
❑ 98KanCouCCP-5

Bustamante, Eddie
❑ 89FreStaBS-6

Bustamante, Rafael
❑ 87UtiBluSP-3
❑ 90Bes-201
❑ 90ChaWheB-14
❑ 90ChaWheP-2245
❑ 91ChaWheC-15
❑ 91ChaWheP-2892

Bustillos, Albert
❑ 89Sta-28
❑ 89VerBeaDS-4
❑ 91BakDodCLC-26
❑ 92AlbDukF-711
❑ 92SanAntMS-559
❑ 93AlbDukF-1452
❑ 94SanAntMF-2460
❑ 96ColSprSSTI-5

Bustos, Saul
❑ 94WilCubC-4
❑ 94WilCubF-3770
❑ 95RocCubTI-11
❑ 96DayCubB-6

Buszka, John
❑ 76BatTroTI-4
❑ 77WatIndT-4
❑ 78WatIndT-5

Butcher, Arthur
❑ 89BelBre2S-2
❑ 90BelBreB-20
❑ 90BelBreS-2
❑ 92SalSpuC-17

Butcher, Gary
❑ 81SanDieSC-1
❑ 81SanDieSC-20

Butcher, Hank (Henry Joseph)
❑ 12T207-22
❑ 12Zee-52

Butcher, Jason
❑ 92GreFalDSP-22
❑ 94YakBeaC-3
❑ 94YakBeaF-3839

Butcher, John
❑ 78AshTouT-2
❑ 79TulDriT-16
❑ 80ChaChaT-13
❑ 81Fle-635
❑ 81Top-41
❑ 82Top-418
❑ 83Don-37
❑ 83Fle-563
❑ 83RanAffF-29
❑ 83Top-534
❑ 84Don-220
❑ 84Fle-415
❑ 84FleUpd-20
❑ 84MinTwiP-4
❑ 84Nes792-299
❑ 84Top-299
❑ 84TopTif-299
❑ 84TopTra-19T
❑ 84TopTraT-19T
❑ 84TwiTeal-23
❑ 85Don-314
❑ 85Fle-273
❑ 85Lea-71
❑ 85OPC-356
❑ 85Top-741
❑ 85TopSti-305
❑ 85TopTif-741
❑ 85Twi7-5
❑ 85TwiPos-3
❑ 85TwiTeal-3
❑ 85TwiTeal-22
❑ 86Don-120
❑ 86Fle-389
❑ 86IndTeal-10
❑ 86Top-638
❑ 86TopTif-638
❑ 86TwiTeal-23
❑ 87Fle-245
❑ 87FleGlo-245
❑ 87Top-107
❑ 87TopTif-107
❑ 93RanKee-91

Butcher, Matthew
❑ 84VisOakT-17

Butcher, Max (A. Maxwell)
❑ 40PlaBal-222
❑ 74CapPub-103
❑ 90DodTar-96
❑ 93ConTSN-756
❑ 94ConTSN-1073
❑ 94ConTSNB-1073

Butcher, Mike
❑ 86EugEmeC-40
❑ 87AppFoxP-10
❑ 88BasCitRS-7
❑ 89MidAngGS-8
❑ 90MidAngGS-15
❑ 91LinDriAA-428
❑ 91MidAngLD-428
❑ 91MidAngOHP-6
❑ 91MidAngP-427
❑ 92EdmTraF-3534
❑ 92EdmTraS-153
❑ 92FleUpd-7
❑ 92SkyAAAF-75
❑ 93Don-665
❑ 93Fle-569
❑ 93PacSpa-364
❑ 93Pin-262
❑ 93Sco-277
❑ 93StaClu-407
❑ 93StaCluFDI-407
❑ 93StaCluMOP-407
❑ 93Top-104
❑ 93TopGol-104
❑ 93TopInaM-104
❑ 93TopInaR-104
❑ 93TopMic-104
❑ 94AngLAT-15
❑ 94AngMot-21
❑ 94ColC-436
❑ 94ColChoGS-436
❑ 94ColChoSS-436
❑ 94Don-52
❑ 94Fle-48
❑ 94Pac-71
❑ 94StaClu-78
❑ 94StaCluFDI-78
❑ 94StaCluGR-78
❑ 94StaCluMOP-78
❑ 94Top-236
❑ 94TopGol-236
❑ 94TopSpa-236
❑ 94Ult-20
❑ 95AngMot-21
❑ 95DonTopotO-31
❑ 95Top-368
❑ 96TacRaiB-7
❑ 98VanCanG-6

Butcher, Ryan
❑ 90GeoColC-1

Butcher, The
❑ 88BufBisP-1477

Buteaux, Shane
❑ 96SouBenSHS-7
❑ 97BirBarB-26
❑ 98BirBarG-6

Butera, Brian
❑ 80ElmPioRST-36

Butera, Sal (Salvatore P.)
❑ 77TacTwiDQ-5
❑ 79TolMudHT-8
❑ 80TwiPos-2
❑ 80VenLeaS-35
❑ 81Don-530
❑ 81Fle-570
❑ 81Top-243
❑ 81TwiPos-4
❑ 82Don-532
❑ 82Fle-548
❑ 82Top-676
❑ 82TwiPos-2
❑ 83TigPos-2
❑ 83Top-67
❑ 84IndIndTI-5
❑ 84IndIndTI-10
❑ 85ExpPos-5
❑ 85IndIndTI-15
❑ 86BasStaB-19
❑ 86OPC-261
❑ 86RedTexG-22
❑ 86Top-407
❑ 86TopTif-407
❑ 87Fle-195
❑ 87FleGlo-195
❑ 87Top-358
❑ 87TopTif-358
❑ 87TwiTeal-22
❑ 88Sco-361
❑ 88ScoGlo-361
❑ 88SyrChiC-16
❑ 88SyrChiP-826
❑ 88Top-772
❑ 88TopTif-772
❑ 89BluJayFS-5
❑ 89PacSenL-209
❑ 89SyrChiC-11
❑ 89SyrChiMB-4
❑ 89SyrChiP-802
❑ 89T/MSenL-15
❑ 89TopSenL-42
❑ 90OscAstS-27
❑ 91OscAstC-26
❑ 91OscAstP-700
❑ 92OscAstC-26
❑ 92OscAstF-2545
❑ 93JacGenF-2123
❑ 94JacGenF-231
❑ 95HarCitRCTI-2

Buther, Brad
❑ 94DavLipB-17

Butkus, Stan
❑ 76TulOilGP-4

Butland, Bill
❑ 42RedSoxTI-2
❑ 75RedSox1T-4

Butler, Adam
❑ 95EugEmeTI-22
❑ 96GreBraB-7
❑ 96GreBraTI-50
❑ 97GreBraG-4
❑ 98Bow-384
❑ 98BowChr-384
❑ 98BowChrGA-384
❑ 98BowChrGAR-384
❑ 98BowChrI-384
❑ 98BowChrIR-384
❑ 98BowChrR-384
❑ 98BowGolA-384
❑ 98BowInt-384
❑ 98Fle-431
❑ 98PacOnl-55
❑ 98PacOnlR-55
❑ 98PacOnlWC-55
❑ 98RicBraQ-6
❑ 98UppDec-571
❑ 99SpoIll-46

Butler, Allen
❑ 98GreBatM-3

Butler, Art (Arthur Edward)
❑ 15SpoNewM-21
❑ 16SpoNewM-23

Butler, Bill (W. J.)
❑ 69Top-619
❑ 70MLBOffS-219
❑ 70OPC-377
❑ 70RoyTeal-6
❑ 70Top-377
❑ 71MLBOffS-412
❑ 71OPC-681
❑ 71Top-681
❑ 72MilBra-59
❑ 75OPC-549
❑ 75Top-549
❑ 75TopMin-549
❑ 75TwiTeal-9
❑ 76OPC-619
❑ 76SSP-207
❑ 76TacTwiDQ-3
❑ 76Top-619
❑ 76VenLeaS-26
❑ 77TacTwiDQ-24A
❑ 78SSP270-61

Butler, Brent
❑ 96AppLeaAB-19
❑ 96HilStaHWB-11
❑ 96JohCitCTI-4
❑ 97Bes-93
❑ 97Bow-409
❑ 97BowChr-271
❑ 97BowChrI-271
❑ 97BowChrIR-271
❑ 97BowChrR-271
❑ 97BowInt-409
❑ 97MidLeaTP-18
❑ 97PeoChi-1
❑ 98Bes-7
❑ 98Bes-59
❑ 98BesAutSS-6
❑ 98Bow-154
❑ 98BowBes-142
❑ 98BowBesAR-142
❑ 98BowBesR-142
❑ 98BowChr-154
❑ 98BowChrGA-154
❑ 98BowChrGAR-154
❑ 98BowChrI-154
❑ 98BowChrIR-154
❑ 98BowChrR-154
❑ 98BowGolA-154
❑ 98BowInt-154
❑ 98CarLeaAC-28
❑ 98CarLeaTPQ-2
❑ 98PriWilCQ-17
❑ 98SP MinDTSPE-DS7
❑ 98SP MinPE-105
❑ 98SP SPTSC-BB
❑ 98SPMin-105
❑ 98SPMinDTS-DS7
❑ 98Top-260
❑ 98TopChr-260

- ❑ 98TopChrR-260
- ❑ 98TopDevR-260
- ❑ 98TopDia-260
- ❑ 98TopMiniC-260
- ❑ 99BasAmeTP-20
- ❑ 99BasAmeTPG-20
- ❑ 99Bow-108
- ❑ 99Bow-217
- ❑ 99BowChr-217
- ❑ 99BowChrG-217
- ❑ 99BowChrGR-217
- ❑ 99BowChrI-217
- ❑ 99BowChrIR-217
- ❑ 99BowChrR-217
- ❑ 99BowGol-108
- ❑ 99BowGol-217
- ❑ 99BowInt-108
- ❑ 99BowInt-217
- ❑ 99SP TopP-24
- ❑ 99SP TopPC-BB
- ❑ 99SP TopPGF-GF6
- ❑ 99SP TopPPE-24
- ❑ 99Top-212
- ❑ 99TopChr-212
- ❑ 99TopChrR-212

Butler, Brett Morgan

- ❑ 80AndBraT-26
- ❑ 81RicBraT-8
- ❑ 82BraBurKL-4
- ❑ 82BraPol-22
- ❑ 82Don-275
- ❑ 82Top-502
- ❑ 83BraPol-22
- ❑ 83Don-636
- ❑ 83Fle-132
- ❑ 83Top-364
- ❑ 84Don-141
- ❑ 84Fle-173
- ❑ 84FleUpd-21
- ❑ 84Ind-7
- ❑ 84IndWhe-2
- ❑ 84Nes792-77
- ❑ 84Top-77
- ❑ 84TopTif-77
- ❑ 84TopTra-20T
- ❑ 84TopTraT-20T
- ❑ 85AllGamPl-52
- ❑ 85Don-216
- ❑ 85DonActA-23
- ❑ 85Fle-441
- ❑ 85FleStaS-56
- ❑ 85Ind-7
- ❑ 85IndPol-2
- ❑ 85Lea-186
- ❑ 85OPC-241
- ❑ 85Top-637
- ❑ 85TopSti-246
- ❑ 85TopTif-637
- ❑ 86Don-12
- ❑ 86Don-102
- ❑ 86DonSupD-12
- ❑ 86Fle-581
- ❑ 86FleMin-114
- ❑ 86FleStiC-18
- ❑ 86IndOhH-2
- ❑ 86IndTeal-11
- ❑ 86Lea-12
- ❑ 86OPC-149
- ❑ 86SevCoi-C14
- ❑ 86Spo-26
- ❑ 86Top-149
- ❑ 86TopGloS-52
- ❑ 86TopMinL-12
- ❑ 86TopSti-206
- ❑ 86TopSup-18
- ❑ 86TopTat-9
- ❑ 86TopTif-149
- ❑ 87ClaGam-36
- ❑ 87Don-219
- ❑ 87DonOpeD-113
- ❑ 87Fle-246
- ❑ 87FleGlo-246
- ❑ 87FleHotS-8
- ❑ 87IndGat-2
- ❑ 87Lea-183
- ❑ 87OPC-197
- ❑ 87RedFolSB-79
- ❑ 87Spo-69
- ❑ 87SpoTeaP-3
- ❑ 87Top-723
- ❑ 87TopTif-723
- ❑ 88Don-279
- ❑ 88DonBasB-23
- ❑ 88Fle-603
- ❑ 88FleGlo-603
- ❑ 88FleUpd-128
- ❑ 88FleUpdG-128
- ❑ 88GiaMot-14
- ❑ 88GiaPos-4
- ❑ 88OPC-202
- ❑ 88PanSti-78
- ❑ 88Sco-122
- ❑ 88ScoGlo-122
- ❑ 88ScoRoo-3T
- ❑ 88ScoRooG-3T
- ❑ 88Spo-153
- ❑ 88StaLinG-3
- ❑ 88StaLinI-5
- ❑ 88Top-479
- ❑ 88TopBig-166
- ❑ 88TopSti-212
- ❑ 88TopTif-479
- ❑ 88TopTra-22T
- ❑ 88TopTraT-22T
- ❑ 89Bow-480
- ❑ 89BowTif-480
- ❑ 89ClaLigB-38
- ❑ 89Don-217
- ❑ 89DonBasB-274
- ❑ 89Fle-324
- ❑ 89FleGlo-324
- ❑ 89GiaMot-5
- ❑ 89OPC-241
- ❑ 89PanSti-220
- ❑ 89Sco-216
- ❑ 89Spo-31
- ❑ 89Top-241
- ❑ 89TopBasT-155
- ❑ 89TopBig-62
- ❑ 89TopCoi-6
- ❑ 89TopMinL-40
- ❑ 89TopSti-85
- ❑ 89TopTif-241
- ❑ 89TopUKM-11
- ❑ 89UppDec-218
- ❑ 90Bow-237
- ❑ 90BowTif-237
- ❑ 90Don-249
- ❑ 90DonBesN-139
- ❑ 90Fle-53
- ❑ 90FleCan-53
- ❑ 90GiaMot-7
- ❑ 90Lea-251
- ❑ 90M.Vpin-89
- ❑ 90MLBBasB-27
- ❑ 90OPC-571
- ❑ 90PanSti-365
- ❑ 90PubIntS-64
- ❑ 90RedFolSB-12
- ❑ 90RicBra2ATI-6
- ❑ 90Sco-236
- ❑ 90Sco100S-47
- ❑ 90Spo-136
- ❑ 90Top-571
- ❑ 90TopBig-259
- ❑ 90TopMinL-83
- ❑ 90TopSti-87
- ❑ 90TopTif-571
- ❑ 90UppDec-119
- ❑ 91Bow-597
- ❑ 91ClaGam-4
- ❑ 91DodMot-6
- ❑ 91DodPol-22
- ❑ 91DodSt.V-6
- ❑ 91Don-143
- ❑ 91Fle-257
- ❑ 91FleUpd-91
- ❑ 91Lea-411
- ❑ 91OPC-325
- ❑ 91OPCBoxB-C
- ❑ 91OPCPre-16
- ❑ 91PanCanT1-25
- ❑ 91PanCanT1-44
- ❑ 91PanCanT1-51
- ❑ 91PanFreS-72
- ❑ 91PanSti-75
- ❑ 91Sco-455
- ❑ 91ScoRoo-23T
- ❑ 91StaClu-389
- ❑ 91Stu-181
- ❑ 91Top-325
- ❑ 91TopDesS-325
- ❑ 91TopMic-325
- ❑ 91TopTif-325
- ❑ 91TopTra-15T
- ❑ 91TopTraT-15T
- ❑ 91TopWaxBC-C
- ❑ 91UltUpd-85
- ❑ 91UppDec-270
- ❑ 91UppDec-732
- ❑ 91USPlaCA-8S
- ❑ 92Bow-597
- ❑ 92ClaGam-32
- ❑ 92DodMot-2
- ❑ 92DodPol-22
- ❑ 92DodSmo-4292
- ❑ 92DodStaTA-30
- ❑ 92Don-369
- ❑ 92DonCraJ1-9
- ❑ 92DonDiaK-DK18
- ❑ 92DonSupD-DK18
- ❑ 92Fle-448
- ❑ 92Fle-702
- ❑ 92Hig5-51
- ❑ 92HitTheBB-8
- ❑ 92Lea-186
- ❑ 92LeaBlaG-186
- ❑ 92OPC-655
- ❑ 92OPCPre-145
- ❑ 92PanSti-197
- ❑ 92Pin-133
- ❑ 92Pin-619
- ❑ 92PinTeaP-9
- ❑ 92PosCan-8
- ❑ 92RedFolS-21
- ❑ 92Sco-465
- ❑ 92Sco-778
- ❑ 92ScoCokD-4
- ❑ 92StaClu-292
- ❑ 92StaCluD-23
- ❑ 92Stu-41
- ❑ 92StuPre-19
- ❑ 92SunSee-21
- ❑ 92Top-655
- ❑ 92TopGol-655
- ❑ 92TopGolPS-655
- ❑ 92TopGolW-655
- ❑ 92TopKid-49
- ❑ 92TopMic-655
- ❑ 92TopPreS-325
- ❑ 92TriPla-59
- ❑ 92TriPla-243
- ❑ 92Ult-209
- ❑ 92UppDec-307
- ❑ 93Bow-422
- ❑ 93DiaMar-20
- ❑ 93DodMot-3
- ❑ 93DodPol-2
- ❑ 93DodStaC-14
- ❑ 93Don-86
- ❑ 93Fin-6
- ❑ 93FinRef-6
- ❑ 93Fla-68
- ❑ 93Fle-59
- ❑ 93FleFruotL-8
- ❑ 93FunPac-87
- ❑ 93FunPac-210
- ❑ 93Hos-20
- ❑ 93KinDis-16
- ❑ 93Lea-230
- ❑ 93MilBonSS-17
- ❑ 93OPC-36
- ❑ 93PacSpa-143
- ❑ 93PanSti-218
- ❑ 93Pin-91
- ❑ 93Pin-487
- ❑ 93Sco-20
- ❑ 93ScoFra-19
- ❑ 93Sel-115
- ❑ 93SelStaL-54
- ❑ 93SP-91
- ❑ 93StaClu-216
- ❑ 93StaCluFDI-216
- ❑ 93StaCluMOP-216
- ❑ 93Stu-9
- ❑ 93Top-65
- ❑ 93TopGol-65
- ❑ 93TopInaM-65
- ❑ 93TopInaR-65
- ❑ 93TopMic-65
- ❑ 93TriPla-136
- ❑ 93Ult-51
- ❑ 93UppDec-259
- ❑ 93UppDecGold-259
- ❑ 94Bow-382
- ❑ 94Bow-622
- ❑ 94BowBes-R48
- ❑ 94BowBesR-R48
- ❑ 94ColC-70
- ❑ 94ColChoGS-70
- ❑ 94ColChoSS-70
- ❑ 94DodDaiN-8
- ❑ 94DodMot-6
- ❑ 94DodPol-4
- ❑ 94Don-543
- ❑ 94Fin-367
- ❑ 94FinRef-367
- ❑ 94Fla-393
- ❑ 94Fle-506
- ❑ 94Fle-711
- ❑ 94FleExtB-284
- ❑ 94FUnPac-72
- ❑ 94Lea-187
- ❑ 94LeaL-116
- ❑ 94OPC-215
- ❑ 94Pac-304
- ❑ 94PanSti-197
- ❑ 94Pin-369
- ❑ 94PinArtP-369
- ❑ 94PinMusC-369
- ❑ 94PinRunC-RC43
- ❑ 94Sco-46
- ❑ 94ScoCyc-TC1
- ❑ 94ScoCyc-TC14
- ❑ 94ScoGolR-46
- ❑ 94ScoGolS-28
- ❑ 94Sel-258
- ❑ 94SP-75
- ❑ 94SPDieC-75
- ❑ 94StaClu-121
- ❑ 94StaCluFDI-121
- ❑ 94StaCluGR-121
- ❑ 94StaCluMOP-121
- ❑ 94Stu-66
- ❑ 94Top-172
- ❑ 94TopGol-172
- ❑ 94TopSpa-172
- ❑ 94TriPla-82
- ❑ 94Ult-213
- ❑ 94UppDec-183
- ❑ 94UppDecED-183
- ❑ 94USPlaCA-2H
- ❑ 95Baz-80
- ❑ 95Bow-287
- ❑ 95ColCho-230
- ❑ 95ColCho-561T
- ❑ 95ColChoGS-230
- ❑ 95ColChoSE-87
- ❑ 95ColChoSEGS-87
- ❑ 95ColChoSESS-87
- ❑ 95ColChoSS-230
- ❑ 95Don-160
- ❑ 95Don-390
- ❑ 95DonPreP-160
- ❑ 95DonPreP-390
- ❑ 95DonTopotO-290
- ❑ 95Fin-32
- ❑ 95Fin-272
- ❑ 95FinRef-32
- ❑ 95FinRef-272
- ❑ 95Fla-381
- ❑ 95Fle-535
- ❑ 95FleUpd-110
- ❑ 95Lea-362
- ❑ 95LeaLim-42
- ❑ 95MetColP-9
- ❑ 95Pac-213
- ❑ 95PacPri-68
- ❑ 95Pin-401
- ❑ 95PinArtP-401
- ❑ 95PinMusC-401
- ❑ 95Sco-344
- ❑ 95ScoGolR-344
- ❑ 95ScoHaloG-HG103
- ❑ 95ScoPlaTS-344
- ❑ 95ScoYouTE-344T
- ❑ 95Sel-125
- ❑ 95SelArtP-125
- ❑ 95SP-82
- ❑ 95SPSil-82
- ❑ 95StaClu-242
- ❑ 95StaClu-629
- ❑ 95StaCluFDI-242
- ❑ 95StaCluMO-9
- ❑ 95StaCluMOP-242
- ❑ 95StaCluMOP-629
- ❑ 95StaCluSTDW-D242
- ❑ 95StaCluSTWS-242
- ❑ 95StaCluSTWS-629
- ❑ 95StaCluVR-121
- ❑ 95StaCluVRMO-121
- ❑ 95Stu-67
- ❑ 95Top-610
- ❑ 95TopCyb-378
- ❑ 95TopTra-41T
- ❑ 95Ult-394
- ❑ 95UltGolM-394
- ❑ 95UppDec-69
- ❑ 95UppDec-364
- ❑ 95UppDecED-69
- ❑ 95UppDecED-364
- ❑ 95UppDecEDG-69
- ❑ 95UppDecEDG-364
- ❑ 95UppDecSE-192
- ❑ 95UppDecSEG-192
- ❑ 96Cir-140
- ❑ 96CirRav-140
- ❑ 96ColCho-584
- ❑ 96ColChoGS-584
- ❑ 96ColChoSS-584
- ❑ 96DodFle-2
- ❑ 96DodMot-8
- ❑ 96DodPol-5
- ❑ 96Don-515
- ❑ 96DonPreP-515
- ❑ 96Fla-287
- ❑ 96Fle-427
- ❑ 96FleTif-427
- ❑ 96Lea-180
- ❑ 96LeaPrePB-180
- ❑ 96LeaPrePG-180
- ❑ 96LeaPrePS-180
- ❑ 96LeaSig-147
- ❑ 96LeaSigPPG-147
- ❑ 96LeaSigPPP-147
- ❑ 96MetKah-6
- ❑ 96Pac-112
- ❑ 96Sco-91
- ❑ 96StaClu-126
- ❑ 96StaCluEPB-126
- ❑ 96StaCluEPG-126
- ❑ 96StaCluEPS-126
- ❑ 96StaCluMOP-126
- ❑ 96Top-277
- ❑ 96TopChr-112
- ❑ 96TopChrR-112
- ❑ 96Ult-217
- ❑ 96UltGolM-217
- ❑ 96UppDec-357
- ❑ 97Cir-59
- ❑ 97CirRav-59
- ❑ 97ColCho-137
- ❑ 97ColChoT-LA2
- ❑ 97DodMot-8
- ❑ 97DodPol-3
- ❑ 97DodSco-13
- ❑ 97DodScoPl-13
- ❑ 97DodScoPr-13
- ❑ 97Don-191
- ❑ 97DonEli-103
- ❑ 97DonEliGS-103
- ❑ 97DonGolPP-191
- ❑ 97DonLim-91
- ❑ 97DonLimE-91
- ❑ 97DonLimENG-91
- ❑ 97DonSigA-14
- ❑ 97DonSigAC-20
- ❑ 97DonSigAM-20
- ❑ 97DonSilPP-191
- ❑ 97DonTea-112
- ❑ 97DonTeaSPE-112
- ❑ 97Fin-197
- ❑ 97FinRef-197
- ❑ 97FlaShoLC-175
- ❑ 97FlaShoLeg0-175
- ❑ 97FlaShoLeg1-175
- ❑ 97FlaShoM-A175
- ❑ 97FlaShoM-B175
- ❑ 97FlaShoM-C175
- ❑ 97FlaShoR0-175
- ❑ 97FlaShoR1-175
- ❑ 97FlaShoR2-175
- ❑ 97Fle-357
- ❑ 97FleTif-357
- ❑ 97Pac-326
- ❑ 97PacLigB-326
- ❑ 97PacSil-326
- ❑ 97Pin-70
- ❑ 97PinArtP-PP70
- ❑ 97PinIns-47
- ❑ 97PinInsCE-47
- ❑ 97PinInsDE-47
- ❑ 97PinMusC-70
- ❑ 97PinPrePla-70
- ❑ 97Sco-102
- ❑ 97ScoArtPWB-102
- ❑ 97ScoPreS-102
- ❑ 97ScoShoS-102
- ❑ 97ScoShoSAP-102
- ❑ 97Top-324
- ❑ 97TopChr-109
- ❑ 97TopChrR-109
- ❑ 97Ult-417
- ❑ 97UltGolME-417
- ❑ 97UltPlaME-417
- ❑ 97UppDec-90
- ❑ 98ColCho-143
- ❑ 98DodSco-5
- ❑ 98DodScoP-5
- ❑ 98Don-83
- ❑ 98DonCol-83
- ❑ 98DonColS-83
- ❑ 98DonGolPP-83
- ❑ 98DonPriCD-83
- ❑ 98DonSilPP-83
- ❑ 98PacInvGems-167
- ❑ 98Sco-76
- ❑ 98ScoSS-PP32
- ❑ 98ScoSSAP-PP32
- ❑ 98SpoIll-180
- ❑ 98SpoIllEE-180
- ❑ 98SpoIllFE-180
- ❑ 98Ult-9
- ❑ 98UltGolM-9
- ❑ 98UltMas-9
- ❑ 98UltPlaM-9
- ❑ 98UppDec-116

Butler, Cecil

- ❑ 62Top-239
- ❑ 63Top-201

Butler, Chris

- ❑ 89KinMetS-3
- ❑ 89Sta-181

Butler, Garrett

- ❑ 98ChaRivDG-7
- ❑ 98HudValR-3

Butler, Jason

- ❑ 91PulBraC-21
- ❑ 91PulBraP-3997
- ❑ 92MacBraC-15
- ❑ 92MacBraF-260
- ❑ 93MacBraC-5
- ❑ 93MacBraF-1393
- ❑ 94DurBulC-4
- ❑ 94DurBulF-321

Butler, John

- ❑ 90PeoChiTI-3

Butler, John Albert

- ❑ 09AmeCarE90-1-18
- ❑ 16Zee-3
- ❑ 29Zee-16
- ❑ 30Zee-24
- ❑ 90DodTar-97
- ❑ 90DodTar-906

Butler, Johnny (John S.)

- ❑ 09T206-404
- ❑ 11MecDFT-7
- ❑ 12ImpTobC-46

Butler, Johnny (John Stephen)

- ❑ 26Exh-9
- ❑ 27Exh-5

Butler, Kid (Willis E.)

- ❑ 12HomRunKE-33
- ❑ 12Zee-53
- ❑ 14Zee-102
- ❑ 20Zee-60
- ❑ 21Zee-44

Butler, Mark

- ❑ 83SanJosBC-11

Butler, Mick

- ❑ 86PalSprAP-5
- ❑ 86PalSprAS-17

Butler, Mike

- ❑ 92BoiHawC-20
- ❑ 92BoiHawF-3618
- ❑ 93PalSprAC-5
- ❑ 93PalSprAF-62
- ❑ 94LakElsSC-3
- ❑ 94LakElsSF-1655
- ❑ 95MidAngOHP-7
- ❑ 95MidAngTI-7

Butler, Rich

- ❑ 92MyrBeaHC-12
- ❑ 92MyrBeaHF-2210
- ❑ 93DunBluJC-4
- ❑ 93DunBluJF-1807
- ❑ 93DunBluJFFN-4
- ❑ 93FloStaLAF-7
- ❑ 94ClaGolF-54
- ❑ 94ExcFS7-140
- ❑ 94KnoSmoF-1315
- ❑ 95SigRooOJ-8
- ❑ 95SigRooOJP-8
- ❑ 95SigRooOJPS-8
- ❑ 95SigRooOJS-8
- ❑ 95SyrChiTI-7
- ❑ 97SyrSkyCB-5
- ❑ 98CirThu-48
- ❑ 98CirThuRav-48
- ❑ 98CirThuSupRav-48
- ❑ 98ColCho-432
- ❑ 98ColChoPCR-432
- ❑ 98DevRayP-21
- ❑ 98Don-273

❑ 98DonGolPP-273
❑ 98DonSilPP-273
❑ 98FlaShoWotF-11
❑ 98Fle-513
❑ 98LeaRCrusUP-107
❑ 98LeaRS-208
❑ 98LeaRSCrusUG-107
❑ 98LeaRSCrusUR-107
❑ 98LeaRSLHolo-208
❑ 98LeaRSLong-208
❑ 98LeaRTrue-208
❑ 98PacOmeRS-9
❑ 98PacOmeRST4-9
❑ 98PacOnl-705
❑ 98PacOnlR-705
❑ 98PacOnlWC-705
❑ 98PinSna-TBDR5
❑ 98SkyDugA-116
❑ 98SkyDugAIA-116
❑ 98SPxFin-206
❑ 98SPxFinR-206
❑ 98SPxFinS-206
❑ 98Top-468
❑ 98TopChr-468
❑ 98TopChrR-468
❑ 98TopDevR-468
❑ 98TopDia-468
❑ 98TopMiniC-468
❑ 98UppDec-566
❑ 98UppDecDS-DS41

Butler, Rob (Robert Frank John)
❑ 91St.CatBJC-8
❑ 91St.CatBJP-3406
❑ 92Bow-603
❑ 92ClaFS7-89
❑ 92DunBluJC-7
❑ 92DunBluJF-2010
❑ 92ProFS7-174
❑ 92UppDecML-315
❑ 93Bow-547
❑ 93ClaFisN-3
❑ 93ClaFS7-45
❑ 93ClaGolF-86
❑ 93ExcFS7-239
❑ 93ExcLeaLF-3
❑ 93SyrChiF-1009
❑ 93TopTra-15T
❑ 94BluJayUSPC-3D
❑ 94BluJayUSPC-11S
❑ 94ColC-71
❑ 94ColChoGS-71
❑ 94ColChoSS-71
❑ 94Don-558
❑ 94Fin-313
❑ 94FinRef-313
❑ 94Lea-17
❑ 94OPC-232
❑ 94Pac-635
❑ 94Pin-397
❑ 94PinArtP-397
❑ 94PinMusC-397
❑ 94ScoRoo-RT112
❑ 94ScoRooGR-RT112
❑ 94Sel-412
❑ 94SpoRoo-85
❑ 94SpoRooAP-85
❑ 94StaCluT-178
❑ 94StaCluTFDI-178
❑ 94SyrChiF-982
❑ 94SyrChiTI-4
❑ 94Top-361
❑ 94TopGol-361
❑ 94TopSpa-361
❑ 94UppDec-176
❑ 94UppDecED-176
❑ 95LinVen-166
❑ 95Pac-438
❑ 95ScrRedBTI-3
❑ 95Top-116
❑ 96ScrRedBB-9
❑ 97ScrRedB-9
❑ 98NewOrlZM-2

Butler, Todd
❑ 88BurIndP-1782
❑ 88OklSoo-17

Butterfield, Brian J.
❑ 82NasSouTI-3
❑ 86ColCliP-25
❑ 87OneYanP-14
❑ 89OneYanP-2098
❑ 90GreHorB-27
❑ 90GreHorP-2679
❑ 90GreHorS-26
❑ 92ForLauYC-23
❑ 92ForLauYTI-3
❑ 93AlbYanF-2178

Butterfield, Chris
❑ 89PitMetS-1
❑ 89Sta-157
❑ 90St.LucMS-3
❑ 91St.LucMC-10
❑ 91St.LucMP-715
❑ 92BinMetF-522
❑ 92BinMetS-52
❑ 92SkyAA F-22
❑ 93BinMetF-2345
❑ 95SanAntMTI-41

Butters, Dave
❑ 85PriWilPT-28

Butters, Tom
❑ 63Top-299
❑ 64PirKDK-5
❑ 64Top-74
❑ 64TopVen-74
❑ 65OPC-246
❑ 65Top-246

Butterworth, Gary
❑ 91MisStaB-9

Buttrum, Peter
❑ 93AusFut-26

Butts, David
❑ 87SumBraP-29
❑ 88DurBulS-3
❑ 89DurBulIS-3
❑ 89DurBullS-3
❑ 89DurBulTI-3

Butts, Randy
❑ 86EriCarP-5
❑ 87St.PetCP-24
❑ 88HamRedP-1735

Butts, Tom
❑ 82IowCubT-29

Butts, Tommy
❑ 78LauLonABS-11
❑ 97NegLeaPC-6H

Butz, Bryan
❑ 96LynHilB-30
❑ 97LynHil-30
❑ 98El PasDG-5

Buxbaum, Danny
❑ 95BoiHawTI-7
❑ 96Bow-272
❑ 96BowFoi-272
❑ 96Exc-23
❑ 96LakElsSB-15
❑ 97Bow-392
❑ 97BowChr-259
❑ 97BowChrI-259
❑ 97BowChrIR-259
❑ 97BowChrR-259
❑ 97BowInt-392
❑ 97MidAng-9
❑ 97TexAllM-6
❑ 98Bow-76
❑ 98BowChr-76
❑ 98BowChrGA-76
❑ 98BowChrGAR-76
❑ 98BowChrI-76
❑ 98BowChrIR-76
❑ 98BowChrR-76
❑ 98BowGolA-76
❑ 98BowInt-76
❑ 98MidAngG-7
❑ 98MidAngO-6

Buxowatz, Jack
❑ 52LavPro-92

Buxton, Buck (Ralph)
❑ 46RemBre-21
❑ 47RemBre-6
❑ 47SigOil-41
❑ 47SmiClo-11
❑ 48SigOil-2
❑ 48SmiClo-11
❑ 49RemBre-1

Buzard, Brian
❑ 90WicStaSGD-6
❑ 91WatIndC-2
❑ 91WatIndP-3357
❑ 92ColRedC-25

Buzas, Joe (Joseph John)
❑ 47CenFlo-2
❑ 97SalLakB-2

Buzhardt, John
❑ 58PhiTeal-4
❑ 59Top-118
❑ 59TopVen-118
❑ 60Top-549
❑ 61Top-3
❑ 61TopStal-49
❑ 62Jel-200
❑ 62Pos-200
❑ 62PosCan-200
❑ 62SalPlaC-129A
❑ 62SalPlaC-129B
❑ 62ShiPlaC-129
❑ 62Top-555
❑ 62WhiSoxTS-3
❑ 63Top-35
❑ 63WhiSoxTS-2
❑ 64Top-323
❑ 64TopVen-323
❑ 64WhiSoxI-5
❑ 64WhiSoxTS-4
❑ 65Top-458
❑ 66Top-245
❑ 66TopVen-245
❑ 67Ast-5
❑ 67CokCapWS-7
❑ 67OPC-178
❑ 67Top-178
❑ 68Top-403
❑ 81TCM60I-361
❑ 91OriCro-66

Buzzard, Buddy
❑ 87KenTwiP-7

Buzzard, Dale
❑ 89JamExpP-2130

Buzzell, Ron
❑ 95AubAstTI-2
❑ 96AubDouB-27
❑ 97BelSnaB-6

Buzzy, Mascot
❑ 97SalLakB-29
❑ 98SalLakBO-7

Byam, George
❑ 50WorWidGV-47

Byas, Michael
❑ 97SalVolG-6
❑ 98SanJosGQ-4

Byerly, Bud (Eldred)
❑ 52Top-161
❑ 58Top-72
❑ 60Top-371
❑ 61TacBan-3
❑ 83Car194T-54
❑ 83TopRep5-161

Byerly, Jim
❑ 92SouOreAC-18
❑ 92SouOreAF-3407

Byerly, Rod (Rodney)
❑ 89AugPirP-518
❑ 89WelPirP-8
❑ 90BurBraB-26
❑ 90BurBraP-2342
❑ 90BurBraS-6
❑ 90DurBulUTI-5

Byers, Bill (James W.)
❑ 09ColChiE-41

Byers, John William
❑ 12ColRedB-41
❑ 12ColTinT-41
❑ 12ImpTobC-74

Byers, Justin
❑ 98MadBlaW-24

Byers, MacGregor
❑ 96SouOreTI-8

Byers, Randell
❑ 86BeaGolGP-4
❑ 87LasVegSP-14
❑ 88Don-605
❑ 88Fle-653
❑ 88FleGlo-653
❑ 88LasVegSC-13
❑ 88LasVegSP-224
❑ 89LasVegSC-12
❑ 89LasVegSP-6
❑ 89LouRedBC-23
❑ 89LouRedBP-1245
❑ 89LouRedBTI-12

Byers, Scott
❑ 96BoiHawB-6

Byington, Jimmie
❑ 93EugEmeC-8
❑ 93EugEmeF-3866
❑ 94RocRoyC-5
❑ 94RocRoyF-570
❑ 95WilBluRTI-9
❑ 96WilBluRB-13
❑ 97WicWra-13
❑ 98WicWraM-13

Byington, John
❑ 88CapCodPPaLP-21
❑ 89BelBre2S-3
❑ 90BelBreB-15
❑ 90BelBreS-3
❑ 90Bes-254
❑ 90MidLeaASGS-6
❑ 91Cla/Bes-356
❑ 91ElPasDLD-177
❑ 91ElPasDP-2752
❑ 91LinDriAA-177
❑ 92ClaFS7-336
❑ 92ElPasDF-3926
❑ 92ElPasDS-201
❑ 92SkyAA F-90
❑ 92UppDecML-86
❑ 93ExcFS7-181
❑ 93NewOrlZF-977
❑ 94NewOrlZF-1474

Byler, Charles
❑ 19Zee-66
❑ 21Zee-92
❑ 22Zee-77
❑ 24Zee-4

Byram, Herbert
❑ 09ObaT21-306
❑ 11BigEatEU-3
❑ 11PacCoaBD-11
❑ 11Zee-64
❑ 12ObaPreT-55
❑ 12Zee-77

Byrd, Anthony
❑ 92KenTwiF-616
❑ 93ForWayWC-3
❑ 93ForWayWF-1979
❑ 93MidLeaAGF-5
❑ 94ExcFS7-91
❑ 94NasXprF-397
❑ 95HarCitRCTI-3
❑ 96HarCitRCB-9

Byrd, Ben
❑ 98BelSnaM-8

Byrd, Bill
❑ 86NegLeaF-52

Byrd, Brandon
❑ 98AubDouTI-5

Byrd, Felan
❑ 76CliPilT-6

Byrd, Harry
❑ 52A'sTeal-5
❑ 53A'sTeal-6
❑ 53BowC-38
❑ 53Top-131
❑ 54Bow-49
❑ 54NewYorJA-42
❑ 55Bow-159
❑ 55OriEss-4
❑ 58Top-154
❑ 79TCM50-172
❑ 91OriCro-67
❑ 91TopArc1-131
❑ 97BalOriP-6

Byrd, Isaac
❑ 96JohCitCTI-5

Byrd, James
❑ 90CarLeaA-13
❑ 90LynRedSTI-5
❑ 91LynRedSC-15
❑ 95TulDriTI-1
❑ 98Cha-26

Byrd, Jeff
❑ 75AndRanT-29
❑ 76SanAntBTI-5
❑ 78OPC-211
❑ 78SyrChiT-4
❑ 78Top-667

Byrd, Jim
❑ 89Sta-10
❑ 89WinHavRSS-2
❑ 91LynRedSP-1205
❑ 92PawRedSF-930
❑ 92WinHavRSC-9
❑ 93FleFinE-171
❑ 93PawRedSDD-5
❑ 93PawRedSF-2412
❑ 93PawRedSTI-5
❑ 94NewBriRSF-655

Byrd, Leland
❑ 77VisOakT-2

Byrd, Matt
❑ 93DanBraC-7
❑ 93DanBraF-3611
❑ 94DurBulC-5
❑ 94DurBulF-322
❑ 94DurBulTI-4
❑ 95DurBulTI-7
❑ 96Exc-123
❑ 96GreBraB-8
❑ 96GreBraTI-34
❑ 97GreBraG-5

Byrd, Paul
❑ 90LSUTigA-3
❑ 90LSUTigP-4
❑ 91LSUTigP-14
❑ 92Bow-349
❑ 92CanIndF-682
❑ 92CanIndS-102
❑ 92ClaFS7-37
❑ 92SkyAA F-47
❑ 92UppDecML-242
❑ 93Bow-233
❑ 93ChaKniF-535
❑ 93ClaFS7-156
❑ 93ExcFS7-158
❑ 94CanIndF-3107
❑ 95NorTidTI-7
❑ 96Fle-476
❑ 96FleTif-476
❑ 96MetKah-4
❑ 97PacPriGotD-GD172
❑ 98RicBraQ-7
❑ 99Fle-391
❑ 99FleSta9-391
❑ 99FleWarT-391

Byrd, Sammy (Samuel D.)
❑ 32OrbPinNP-96
❑ 33Gou-157
❑ 33GouCanV-86
❑ 34BatR31-56
❑ 34DiaStaR-84
❑ 35GouPuzR-4F
❑ 35GouPuzR-7F
❑ 35GouPuzR-12F
❑ 36GouWidPPR-A12
❑ 36NatChiFPR-15
❑ 91ConTSN-281

Byrdak, Tim
❑ 94EugEmeC-4
❑ 94EugEmeF-3702
❑ 94SigRooDP-88
❑ 94SigRooDPS-88
❑ 95Bes-25
❑ 95WilBluRTI-12
❑ 96Exc-56
❑ 96WicWraB-4
❑ 98WicWraM-17

Byrne, Bobby (Robert M.)
❑ 08RosComP-162
❑ 09ColChiE-42
❑ 09PC7HHB-6
❑ 09RamT20-21
❑ 09SpoNewSM-61
❑ 09T206-48
❑ 10CouT21-6
❑ 10CouT21-88
❑ 10CouT21-263
❑ 10DomDisP-18
❑ 10E12AmeCDCE125-7
❑ 10PirHerICP-3
❑ 10PirTipTD-13
❑ 10RedCroT-7
❑ 10RedCroT-94
❑ 10RedCroT-173
❑ 10SweCapPP-133
❑ 10W555-10
❑ 11E94-4
❑ 11HelSta-154
❑ 11MecDFT-8
❑ 11PinT-5-868
❑ 11PloCanE-12
❑ 11S74Sil-106
❑ 11SpoLifM-245
❑ 11T205-23
❑ 12ColRedB-42
❑ 12ColTinT-42
❑ 12HasTriFT-25A
❑ 12T207-23
❑ 14PieStaT-16
❑ 14TexTomE-8
❑ 15SpoNewM-22
❑ 16FleBreD-11
❑ 16SpoNewM-24
❑ 17ColE13-23

Byrne, Clayton
❑ 92KanCouCC-25
❑ 92KanCouCF-103
❑ 92KanCouCTI-3
❑ 93AlbPolCB-5
❑ 93AlbPolF-2036
❑ 93AusFut-69
❑ 93AusFut-113
❑ 93SouAtlLAGF-1
❑ 94ClaGolF-4
❑ 94FreKeyC-4
❑ 94FreKeyF-2626
❑ 94OriPro-14

Byrne, Earl
❑ 95RocCubTI-6
❑ 97OrlRayB-6
❑ 98IowCubQ-6

Byrne, T.J.
❑ 81HolMilT-4

Byrne, Tommy (Thomas Joseph)
❑ 43YanSta-4
❑ 47TipTop-49
❑ 49YanTeal-4
❑ 50YanTeal-5
❑ 51BerRos-D4
❑ 51Bow-73
❑ 51TopBluB-35
❑ 52Bow-61
❑ 52BroPenCB-1
❑ 52DixLid-2
❑ 52DixPre-2
❑ 52Top-241
❑ 53Bri-2
❑ 53Top-123
❑ 54SeaPop-4
❑ 55Bow-300
❑ 56Top-215
❑ 56YanJayP-3
❑ 56YanTeal-3
❑ 57Top-108
❑ 57YanJayP-3
❑ 79TCM50-198
❑ 83TopRep5-241
❑ 83YanASFY-5
❑ 85TCMPla1-31
❑ 91TopArc1-123
❑ 92YanWIZA-8

Byrnes, Chris
❑ 87OneYanP-20

Byrnes, Eric
❑ 97UCLBruTI-2
❑ 98SouOreTG-3
❑ 98VisOakG-3
❑ 99JustheS-13
❑ 99JustheSJB-13
❑ 99TeaBesR-8
❑ 99TeaBesRG-8
❑ 99TeaBesRS-8

Byrnes, Jim (James Joseph)
❑ 09ObaT21-36
❑ 13Zee-3

Byrnes, Milt (Milton John)
❑ 96Bro194F-3

Byron, Bill
❑ 73FleWilD-20
❑ 93ConTSN-731

Byron, Tim
❑ 82OneYanT-11
❑ 85AlbYanT-2

Bystrom, Marty
❑ 77SpaPhiT-3
❑ 80PhiBul-30
❑ 81Top-526
❑ 82Don-93
❑ 82Top-416
❑ 83Don-93
❑ 83Fle-154
❑ 83PhiTas-3
❑ 83Top-199
❑ 84Don-259
❑ 84Fle-24
❑ 84Nes792-511
❑ 84PhiTas-15
❑ 84Top-511
❑ 84TopTif-511
❑ 85Fle-122
❑ 85Top-284
❑ 85TopTif-284
❑ 86Don-591
❑ 86Fle-102
❑ 86Top-723
❑ 86TopTif-723
❑ 86YanTCM-5
❑ 87Ft.LauYP-2
❑ 88MaiPhiC-1
❑ 88MaiPhiP-292
❑ 92YanWIZ8-23

Ca, Adam
❑ 87SalLakTTT-19

Caballero, Ed
❑ 87GenCubP-18
❑ 88PeoChiTI-7
❑ 89WinSpiS-2
❑ 90WinSpiTI-18
❑ 91WinSpiC-2
❑ 91WinSpiP-2821

Caballero, Jose
❑ 82MiaMarT-8
Caballero, Putsy (Ralph J.)
❑ 49EurSta-132
❑ 49PhiBul-10
❑ 50PhiPhil-3
❑ 75Phi195T-5
❑ 80Phi195T-5
❑ 85TCMPla1-13
❑ 91JesHSA-4
Cabana, Gerry
❑ 52LavPro-37
Cabassa, Carlos
❑ 80PenPilBT-3
❑ 80PenPilCT-3
❑ 81ReaPhiT-9
Cabbage, Wayne
❑ 89CarNewE-5
Cabell, Billy
❑ 83CliGiaF-4
Cabell, Enos Milton
❑ 73BalOriP-11
❑ 73OPC-605
❑ 73OriTeal-9
❑ 73Top-605
❑ 75AstPos-4
❑ 75OPC-247
❑ 75Top-247
❑ 75TopMin-247
❑ 76HouAstP-4
❑ 76OPC-404
❑ 76SSP-61
❑ 76Top-404
❑ 77AstPho-3
❑ 77BurCheD-2
❑ 77Hos-94
❑ 77Top-567
❑ 78AstBurK-14
❑ 78AstPos-5
❑ 78Hos-9
❑ 78OPC-44
❑ 78Top-132
❑ 79AstPos-5
❑ 79AstTeal-3
❑ 79Hos-70
❑ 79OPC-269
❑ 79Top-515
❑ 80BurKinPHR-24
❑ 80OPC-201
❑ 80Top-385
❑ 81AllGamPI-92
❑ 81Don-138
❑ 81Fle-58
❑ 81FleStiC-36
❑ 81GiaTeal-5
❑ 81OPC-45
❑ 81Top-45
❑ 81TopTra-746
❑ 82Don-272
❑ 82Fle-386
❑ 82FleSta-64
❑ 82OPC-311
❑ 82Top-627
❑ 82TopSti-105
❑ 82TopStiV-105
❑ 82TopTra-15T
❑ 83Don-202
❑ 83Fle-328
❑ 83FleSta-28
❑ 83OPC-225
❑ 83TigPos-7
❑ 83Top-225
❑ 84AstMot-11
❑ 84AstPos-4
❑ 84Don-456
❑ 84Fle-79
❑ 84FleUpd-22
❑ 84Nes792-482
❑ 84Top-482
❑ 84TopSti-273
❑ 84TopTif-482
❑ 84TopTra-21T
❑ 84TopTraT-21T
❑ 85AllGamPI-92
❑ 85AstHouP-4
❑ 85AstMot-10
❑ 85Don-110
❑ 85Fle-346
❑ 85Lea-161
❑ 85Top-786
❑ 85TopSti-61
❑ 85TopTif-786
❑ 86DodCokP-5
❑ 86DodPol-23
❑ 86DodUniOP-3
❑ 86Don-418
❑ 86Fle-126
❑ 86Top-197
❑ 86TopTif-197
❑ 87AstShoSPO-4
❑ 87Fle-438
❑ 87FleGlo-438
❑ 87Top-509
❑ 87TopTif-509
❑ 90DodTar-98
❑ 91OriCro-68
❑ 94TedWil-35
Cabella, Jim
❑ 89BurIndS-27
Cabello, Bobby
❑ 86SalAngC-83
Cabral, Irene
❑ 91EriSaiC-3
❑ 91EriSaiP-4080
Cabral, Joaquin
❑ 91HunCubC-5
❑ 91HunCubP-3340
Cabreja, Alexis
❑ 95NorNavTI-23
Cabrera, Alex
❑ 93GenCubC-6
❑ 93GenCubF-3180
❑ 94PeoChiC-5
❑ 94PeoChiF-2273
❑ 95Exc-161
❑ 95LinVen-225
❑ 96-97LinVen-232
Cabrera, Basilio
❑ 87FayGenP-5
❑ 88LakTigS-4
❑ 89LakTigS-4
❑ 90LonTigP-1278
❑ 91LinDriAA-377
❑ 91LonTigLD-377
❑ 91LonTigP-1888
❑ 92LonTigF-643
❑ 92LonTigS-402
❑ 93BriTigC-28
❑ 94FayGenC-29
❑ 95FayGenTI-6
❑ 96LakTigB-3
Cabrera, Carlos
❑ 80UtiBluJT-3
❑ 80VenLeaS-55
❑ 93DunBluJF-1802
❑ 94HagSunC-3
❑ 94HagSunF-2736
❑ 94St.CatBJC-5
❑ 94St.CatBJF-3649
Cabrera, Francisco
❑ 86VenGulP-3
❑ 87MyrBeaBJP-1462
❑ 88BasAmeAAB-20
❑ 88DunBluJS-1
❑ 88SouLeaAJ-22
❑ 89FleUpd-68
❑ 89SyrChiC-20
❑ 89SyrChiMB-5
❑ 89SyrChiP-791
❑ 89TriAAAP-AAA16
❑ 90BraDubP-3
❑ 90BraDubS-4
❑ 90CMC-289
❑ 90Don-646
❑ 90FleUpd-2
❑ 90OPC-254
❑ 90ProAAAF-409
❑ 90RicBraC-13
❑ 90RicBraP-264
❑ 90RicBraTI-6
❑ 90ScoRoo-67T
❑ 90Top-254
❑ 90TopDeb89-20
❑ 90TopTif-254
❑ 90TriAAAC-16
❑ 90UppDec-64
❑ 91BraDubP-6
❑ 91BraSubS-8
❑ 91Don-341
❑ 91Fle-684
❑ 91OPC-693
❑ 91Sco-63
❑ 91Sco100RS-33
❑ 91Top-693
❑ 91TopDesS-693
❑ 91TopMic-693
❑ 91TopTif-693
❑ 91Ult-3
❑ 91UppDec-439
❑ 92BraLykP-8
❑ 92BraLykS-9
❑ 92Don-482
❑ 92Fle-355
❑ 92RicBraBB-21
❑ 92RicBraF-379
❑ 92RicBraRC-1
❑ 92Sco-581
❑ 92StaClu-797
❑ 92StaCluNC-797
❑ 93BraLykP-7
❑ 93BraLykS-8
❑ 93BraStaC-8
❑ 93Don-184
❑ 93Fle-365
❑ 93LimRocDWB-46
❑ 93OPC-383
❑ 93PacSpa-3
❑ 93PacSpaPI-1
❑ 93Sco-472
❑ 93StaCluM-172
❑ 93Top-769
❑ 93TopGol-769
❑ 93TopInaM-769
❑ 93TopInaR-769
❑ 93TopMic-769
❑ 93Ult-303
❑ 93UppDec-611
❑ 93UppDecGold-611
❑ 93UppDecSH-HI8
❑ 94Fle-356
❑ 94Pac-6
❑ 94Sco-222
❑ 94ScoGolR-222
❑ 97RicBraBC-14
Cabrera, Fremio
❑ 86WauTimP-2
Cabrera, Jairo
❑ 94BluOriC-2
❑ 94BluOriF-3565
Cabrera, Jolbert
❑ 91SumFlyP-2340
❑ 92AlbPolCB-7
❑ 92AlbPolF-2312
❑ 93BurBeeC-4
❑ 93BurBeeF-164
❑ 93MidLeaAGF-29
❑ 94WesPalBEC-4
❑ 94WesPalBEF-47
❑ 96HarSenB-10
❑ 97HarSen-8
❑ 98BufBisG-7
❑ 99SkyPre-228
❑ 99SkyPre-228
❑ 99SkyPreR-228
❑ 99SkyPreR-228
❑ 99SpoIll-55
Cabrera, Jose
❑ 92BurIndC-9
❑ 92BurIndF-1647
❑ 93ClaGolF-107
❑ 93ColRedC-5
❑ 93ColRedF-589
❑ 94KinIndC-2
❑ 94KinIndF-2634
❑ 97BufBis-9
❑ 98Don-249
❑ 98DonGolPP-249
❑ 98DonSilPP-249
❑ 98Fle-151
❑ 98PacOnl-317
❑ 98PacOnlR-317
❑ 98PacOnlWC-317
❑ 98Ult-403
❑ 98UltGolM-403
❑ 98UltMas-403
❑ 98UltPlaM-403
Cabrera, Juan
❑ 91BelBreCB-13
❑ 91BelBreP-2107
❑ 91SouOreAP-3852
Cabrera, Miguel
❑ 91AubAstP-4284
❑ 92AshTouC-17
Cabrera, Nasusel
❑ 88MadMusP-6
Cabrera, Orlando
❑ 96DelShoB-10
❑ 97Bes-77
❑ 97Bow-351
❑ 97BowChr-236
❑ 97BowChrI-236
❑ 97BowChrIR-236
❑ 97BowChrR-236
❑ 97BowInt-351
❑ 97FlaShoWotF-13
❑ 97Fle-675
❑ 97FleTif-675
❑ 97FloStaLTPB-30
❑ 97Ult-491
❑ 97UltGolME-491
❑ 97UltPlaME-491
❑ 98Bow-93
❑ 98BowBes-103
❑ 98BowBesAR-103
❑ 98BowBesR-103
❑ 98BowChr-93
❑ 98BowChrGA-93
❑ 98BowChrGAR-93
❑ 98BowChrI-93
❑ 98BowChrIR-93
❑ 98BowChrR-93
❑ 98BowGolA-93
❑ 98BowInt-93
❑ 98ColCho-108
❑ 98Don-277
❑ 98DonGolPP-277
❑ 98DonSigA-11
❑ 98DonSigAC-17
❑ 98DonSigAM-17
❑ 98DonSilPP-277
❑ 98Fle-178
❑ 98PacPar-192
❑ 98PacParC-192
❑ 98PacParG-192
❑ 98PacParHS-192
❑ 98PacParPB-192
❑ 98PacParR-192
❑ 98PinPlu-84
❑ 98Stu-66
❑ 98StuGPP-66
❑ 98StuSPP-66
❑ 98Top-366
❑ 98TopChr-366
❑ 98TopChrR-366
❑ 98TopDevR-366
❑ 98TopDia-366
❑ 98TopMiniC-366
❑ 98Ult-373
❑ 98UltGolM-373
❑ 98UltMas-373
❑ 98UltPlaM-373
❑ 98UppDec-439
❑ 99Fle-255
❑ 99FleSta9-255
❑ 99FleWarT-255
❑ 99MetUni-137
❑ 99MetUniGM-137
❑ 99MetUniPMG-137
❑ 99Pac-261
❑ 99PacAur-110
❑ 99PacAurOD-110
❑ 99PacCroC-168
❑ 99PacCroCPB-168
❑ 99PacOme-144
❑ 99PacOmeC-144
❑ 99PacOmeG-144
❑ 99PacOmePB-144
❑ 99PacPar-140
❑ 99PacParC-140
❑ 99PacParG-140
❑ 99PacParHoloGold-140
❑ 99PacParHS-140
❑ 99PacParOD-140
❑ 99PacParPB-140
❑ 99PacParRed-140
❑ 99PacPlaB-261
❑ 99PacRed-261
❑ 99SkyPre-212
❑ 99SkyPreR-212
❑ 99SkyThu-156
❑ 99SkyThuRant-156
❑ 99SkyThuRave-156
❑ 99ThuSkySupR-156
❑ 99Top-427
❑ 99TopChr-427
❑ 99TopChrR-427
❑ 99Ult-229
❑ 99UltGolM-229
❑ 99UltMas-229
❑ 99UltPlaM-229
❑ 99UppDec-421
❑ 99UppDecEL1-421
❑ 99UppDecEL2-421
❑ 99Vic-243
Cabrera, Ruben
❑ 76VenLeaS-169
❑ 80VenLeaS-113
Cabrera, Tony (Antonio)
❑ 84IdaFalATI-6
❑ 85ModA'sC-3
❑ 86MadMusP-4
❑ 86MadMusP-4
❑ 93BelMarCB-6
❑ 93BelMarF-3214
Cabrera, Victor
❑ 86ChaRaiP-4
Cacanindin, Lance
❑ 96HilStaHWB-NNO
Cacciatore, Frank
❑ 88AubAstP-1967
❑ 89TucTorC-24
❑ 89TucTorJP-2
❑ 89TucTorP-202
❑ 90AshTouC-26
❑ 90AshTouP-2764
❑ 91AshTouP-584
❑ 92OscAstC-29
❑ 92OscAstF-2546
❑ 93CliGiaC-27
❑ 93CliGiaF-2505
❑ 94ShrCapF-1623
❑ 97SanJosG-26
❑ 98ShrCapM-4
❑ 98ShrCapWS-4
Cacciatore, Paul
❑ 76WauMetT-7
❑ 77WauMetT-3
❑ 79JacMetT-10
Cacek, Craig Thomas
❑ 78ChaChaT-3
❑ 79PorBeaT-18
❑ 80PorBeaT-3
❑ 81PorBeaT-9
❑ 82SpoIndT-14
Caceres, Edgar
❑ 86WesPalBEP-7
❑ 87JacExpP-437
❑ 89SarWhiSS-2
❑ 90Bes-206
❑ 90BirBarB-7
❑ 90BirBarP-1395
❑ 92ElPasDF-3927
❑ 92ElPasDS-202
❑ 93ExcFS7-182
❑ 93LinVenB-167
❑ 93NewOrlZF-978
❑ 94OmaRoyF-1228
❑ 94VenLinU-49
❑ 95LinVen-19
❑ 96-97LinVen-139
❑ 97VanCanB-9
Caceres, Wilmy
❑ 98ChaAllCM-17
❑ 98SouAtlLPM-3
Caci, Bob
❑ 86BelBreP-3
Cacini, Ron
❑ 91AubAstP-4279
❑ 92AshTouC-13
Cadahia, Ben
❑ 81ChaRoyT-15
❑ 82ForMyeRT-4
Cadahia, Chino
❑ 80OrlTwiT-13
❑ 81TolMudHT-11
❑ 82OrlTwi8SCT-3
❑ 82OrlTwiT-15
❑ 83OrlTwiT-10
❑ 86DayBealP-4
❑ 86TulDriTI-12
❑ 91GulCoaRSP-30
❑ 92GulCoaRSP-30
Cadania, Aurelio
❑ 87GasRanP-3
Cadaret, Greg
❑ 84ModA'sC-4
❑ 85HunStaJ-34
❑ 86HunStaDJ-34
❑ 88A'sMot-26
❑ 88Don-528
❑ 88DonTeaBA-528
❑ 88ModA'sTI-35
❑ 88Top-328
❑ 88TopTif-328
❑ 89A'sMot-20
❑ 89Don-479
❑ 89Fle-4
❑ 89FleGlo-4
❑ 89Sco-340
❑ 89ScoRoo-69T
❑ 89Top-552
❑ 89TopTif-552
❑ 90Don-545
❑ 90Fle-440
❑ 90FleCan-440
❑ 90OPC-659
❑ 90PubIntS-300
❑ 90Top-659
❑ 90TopTif-659
❑ 90TopTVY-7
❑ 90UppDec-549
❑ 90YanScoNW-19
❑ 91Bow-157
❑ 91Don-236
❑ 91Fle-658
❑ 91Lea-415
❑ 91OPC-187
❑ 91Sco-188
❑ 91SouOreAAP-SOA8
❑ 91StaClu-536
❑ 91Top-187
❑ 91TopDesS-187
❑ 91TopMic-187
❑ 91TopTif-187
❑ 91Ult-229
❑ 91UppDec-343
❑ 92Bow-231
❑ 92Don-628
❑ 92Fle-222
❑ 92Lea-24
❑ 92LeaBlaG-24
❑ 92OPC-18
❑ 92Pin-402
❑ 92Sco-454
❑ 92StaClu-176
❑ 92Top-18
❑ 92TopGol-18
❑ 92TopGolW-18
❑ 92TopMic-18
❑ 92Ult-404
❑ 92UppDec-412
❑ 92YanWIZ8-24
❑ 93Don-610
❑ 93FleFinE-14
❑ 93PacSpa-204
❑ 93RedKah-7
❑ 93Top-478
❑ 93TopGol-478
❑ 93TopInaM-478
❑ 93TopInaR-478
❑ 93TopMic-478
❑ 94StaClu-585
❑ 94StaCluFDI-585
❑ 94StaCluGR-585
❑ 94StaCluMOP-585
❑ 94StaCluT-166
❑ 94StaCluTFDI-166
❑ 94Top-303
❑ 94TopGol-303
❑ 94TopSpa-303
❑ 96BufBisB-3
❑ 97BufBis-10
Caddell, Carl
❑ 96AppLeaAB-28
Cade, Jerry
❑ 58RedEnq-7
Cadian, Larry
❑ 89PorBeaC-7
Cadore, Leon
❑ 20NatCarE-11
❑ 21Exh-20
❑ 21Nei-97
❑ 22E120-136
❑ 22W572-11
❑ 23W503-35
❑ 23WilChoV-15
❑ 24Zee-123
❑ 61Top-403
❑ 72FleFamF-19
❑ 72LauGreF-37
❑ 90DodTar-99
❑ 90HOFStiB-22
Cadreau, William
❑ 13Zee-99
Cady, Hick (Forrest LeRoy)
❑ 11T205-191
❑ 12RedSoxBASP-1
❑ 12RedSoxBDASP-1
❑ 14CraJacE-87
❑ 15CraJacE-87
❑ 16BF2FP-2
❑ 16SpoNewM-25
❑ 17ColE13-24
Cady, Todd
❑ 94ElmPioC-2
❑ 94ElmPioF-3477
❑ 94SigRooDP-58
❑ 94SigRooDPS-58
❑ 95KanCouCTI-25
❑ 95MidLeaA-8
❑ 96BreCouMB-8
Cafaro, Cio
❑ 96HelBreTI-2

Cafaro, Rocco
❑ 94AlbPolC-9
❑ 94AlbPolF-2230
❑ 94OriPro-15
❑ 96BowBayB-9
❑ 97BowBay-11
❑ 97St.PetDRUB-9
Cafferty, Jason
❑ 96BatCliTI-13
Caffie, Joe (Joseph C.)
❑ 58Top-182
Caffrey, Bob
❑ 85Top-394
❑ 85TopTif-394
❑ 87WesPalBEP-661
❑ 88JacExpB-25
❑ 88JacExpP-979
❑ 88SouLeaAJ-19
Caffrey, Marty
❑ 76ForLauYS-16
Cage, Wayne Levell
❑ 76WilTomT-4
❑ 78IndTeal-3
❑ 78Top-706
❑ 79OPC-70
❑ 79TacTugT-26
❑ 79Top-150
❑ 80TacTigT-4
❑ 80Top-208
Cahill, Mark
❑ 80WauTimT-3
❑ 81LynSaiT-3
❑ 83ChaLooT-21
Cahill, Patsy (John F.P.)
❑ 87BucN28-39
❑ 87OldJudN-63
Caiazzo, Nick
❑ 97HelBreB-6
❑ 98BelSnaM-9
Cain, Aaron
❑ 82HawIslT-9
Cain, Bob
❑ 50Bow-236
❑ 51Bow-197
❑ 52Bow-19
❑ 52Top-349
❑ 53BowC-56
❑ 53Top-266
❑ 54Bow-195
❑ 54Top-61
❑ 75OakOak2A-10
❑ 79DiaGre-197
❑ 83TopRep5-349
❑ 91TopArc1-266
❑ 94TopArc1-61
❑ 94TopArc1G-61
Cain, Cal
❑ 86CedRapRT-19
❑ 87CedRapRP-18
Cain, Chance
❑ 93GleFalRC-9
❑ 93GleFalRF-3995
❑ 94MadHatC-3
❑ 94MadHatF-122
❑ 94MidLeaAF-MDW42
Cain, Jerald
❑ 83VerBeaDT-23
Cain, John
❑ 88RocExpLC-4
❑ 90RocExpLC-4
Cain, Les
❑ 69Top-324
❑ 71Kel-29
❑ 71MLBOffS-388
❑ 71OPC-101
❑ 71Top-101
❑ 72Top-783
❑ 73TigJew-4
Cain, Sugar (Merritt)
❑ 33RitCE-7D
❑ 35DiaMatCS3T1-23
❑ 93ConTSN-952
Cain, Tim
❑ 91BenBucCB-2
❑ 91BenBucP-3686
❑ 95TreThuTI-8
Cain, Travis
❑ 94DanBraC-4
❑ 94DanBraF-3522
❑ 95MacBraTI-3
❑ 96HudValRB-17
❑ 96WesOahCHWB-28
❑ 97St.PetDR-9
❑ 97St.PetDRUB-10
Caines, Art (Arturo)
❑ 89BriTigS-3
❑ 90FayGenP-2419
Caines, Franklyn
❑ 98MarPhiG-6
Cairncross, Cameron
❑ 91BriBanF-11
❑ 91ChaRaiC-4
❑ 91ChaRaiP-90
❑ 92WatDiaC-12
❑ 92WatDiaF-2137
❑ 93AusFut-23
❑ 93Bow-658
❑ 93RanCucQC-7
❑ 93RanCucQF-821
❑ 94Bow-644
❑ 94RanCucQC-9
❑ 94RanCucQF-1628
❑ 95AusFutGP-6
❑ 97RanCucQG-4
Cairo, Miguel
❑ 92GulCoaDF-3572
❑ 93VerBeaDC-4
❑ 93VerBeaDF-2224
❑ 94BakDodC-4
❑ 94VenLinU-47
❑ 95LinVen-9
❑ 95SanAntMTI-30
❑ 95Top-540
❑ 96-97LinVen-37
❑ 96-97LinVen-284
❑ 96SyrChiTI-7
❑ 97IowCub-7
❑ 97Pac-215
❑ 97PacLigB-215
❑ 97PacSil-215
❑ 98CirThu-209
❑ 98CirThuRav-209
❑ 98CirThuSupRav-209
❑ 98DevRayP-15
❑ 98Don-320
❑ 98DonGolPP-320
❑ 98DonSilPP-320
❑ 98Fle-568
❑ 98LeaRS-257
❑ 98LeaRSLHolo-257
❑ 98LeaRSLong-257
❑ 98LeaRTrue-257
❑ 98PacInvGems-127
❑ 98PacOme-230
❑ 98PacOmeR-230
❑ 98PacOmeRS-22
❑ 98PacOmeRST3-22
❑ 98PacOnl-706
❑ 98PacOnlR-706
❑ 98PacOnlWC-706
❑ 98PacPar-95
❑ 98PacParC-95
❑ 98PacParG-95
❑ 98PacParHS-95
❑ 98PacParPB-95
❑ 98PacParR-95
❑ 98Top-464
❑ 98TopChr-464
❑ 98TopChrR-464
❑ 98TopDevR-464
❑ 98TopDia-464
❑ 98TopMiniC-464
❑ 98UppDec-736
❑ 99Fle-140
❑ 99FleSta9-140
❑ 99FleWarT-140
❑ 99Pac-409
❑ 99PacCroC-273
❑ 99PacCroCPB-273
❑ 99PacOme-228
❑ 99PacOmeC-228
❑ 99PacOmeG-228
❑ 99PacOmePB-228
❑ 99PacPlaB-409
❑ 99PacRed-409
❑ 99SkyThu-208
❑ 99SkyThuRant-208
❑ 99SkyThuRave-208
❑ 99StaClu-173
❑ 99StaCluFDI-173
❑ 99StaCluOoaK-173
❑ 99StaCluPP-173
❑ 99ThuSkySupR-208
❑ 99Top-417
❑ 99TopChr-417
❑ 99TopChrR-417
❑ 99TopMVPP-417
❑ 99UppDec-211
❑ 99UppDecEL1-211
❑ 99UppDecEL2-211
❑ 99Vic-391
Cairo, Sergio
❑ 89BluOriS-6
❑ 90WauTimB-14
❑ 90WauTimP-2142
❑ 90WauTimS-5
❑ 91CarLeaAP-CAR6
❑ 91FreKeyC-24
❑ 91FreKeyP-2378
❑ 92HagSunF-2568
❑ 92HagSunS-255
❑ 93BirBarF-1204
❑ 93LimRocDWB-53
❑ 94TulDriF-254
❑ 94TulDriTI-2
Cajide, Al
❑ 76BatTroTI-5
❑ 78DayBeaAT-4
Cakora, Matt (Matthew)
❑ 87WytCubP-25
❑ 88ChaWheB-17
❑ 89ChaKniTI-20
❑ 89ChaWheB-22
❑ 89ChaWheP-1770
❑ 90MiaMirIS-2
Cala, Craig A.
❑ 88CapCodPPaLP-92
❑ 90SanJosGB-6
❑ 90SanJosGCLC-35
❑ 90SanJosGP-2022
❑ 90SanJosGS-4
Calandriello, Donato
❑ 98SouOreTG-4
Calarco, John
❑ 92SalLakTSP-23
Calcagno, Dan
❑ 91EveGiaP-3916
❑ 92CliGiaF-3600
❑ 92SanJosGC-11
❑ 93SanJosGC-4
❑ 93SanJosGF-12
❑ 94ElPasDF-3148
Calcaterra, Jeff
❑ 92GulCoaYF-3781
Calder, Joe
❑ 92AugPirC-23
❑ 92AugPirF-244
❑ 92UppDecML-101
❑ 93SalBucC-3
❑ 93SalBucF-439
Caldera, Eugene
❑ 18Zee-18
❑ 19Zee-67
Caldera, Jose V.
❑ 76VenLeaS-97
❑ 77BriRedST-3
❑ 80VenLeaS-262
Calderon, Henry
❑ 98SpoIndG-5
Calderon, Ivan
❑ 81WauTimT-26
❑ 82WauTimF-10
❑ 83ChaLooT-27
❑ 84SalLakCGC-173
❑ 85FleUpd-17
❑ 85MarMot-26
❑ 86Don-435
❑ 86Fle-462
❑ 86Lea-204
❑ 86MarMot-15
❑ 86OPC-382
❑ 86SevCoi-W13
❑ 86Top-382
❑ 86TopTif-382
❑ 87DonOpeD-230
❑ 87Fle-488
❑ 87FleGlo-488
❑ 87FleSlu-7
❑ 87TopTra-15T
❑ 87TopTraT-15T
❑ 87WhiSoxC-5
❑ 88Don-25
❑ 88Don-182
❑ 88DonBasB-25
❑ 88DonBonM-BC5
❑ 88DonSupD-25
❑ 88Fle-394
❑ 88FleBasM-4
❑ 88FleGlo-394
❑ 88FleLeaL-3
❑ 88FleMin-14
❑ 88FleStiC-14
❑ 88Lea-25
❑ 88Lea-175
❑ 88OPC-184
❑ 88PanSti-63
❑ 88Sco-607
❑ 88ScoGlo-607
❑ 88ScoYouS2-22
❑ 88Spo-166
❑ 88StaLinWS-4
❑ 88Top-184
❑ 88TopBig-63
❑ 88TopCoi-6
❑ 88TopMinL-7
❑ 88TopSti-285
❑ 88TopTif-184
❑ 88TopUKM-9
❑ 88TopUKMT-9
❑ 88WhiSoxC-3
❑ 88WhiSoxK-4
❑ 89BlaYNPRWL-108
❑ 89Bow-68
❑ 89BowTif-68
❑ 89Don-371
❑ 89DonBasB-193
❑ 89Fle-493
❑ 89FleGlo-493
❑ 89OPC-101
❑ 89RedFolSB-16
❑ 89Sco-331
❑ 89Top-656
❑ 89TopBig-289
❑ 89TopSti-297
❑ 89TopTif-656
❑ 89UppDec-650
❑ 89WhiSoxC-7
❑ 90Bow-316
❑ 90BowTif-316
❑ 90Don-294
❑ 90DonBesA-141
❑ 90Fle-529
❑ 90FleCan-529
❑ 90Lea-89
❑ 90OPC-569
❑ 90PanSti-47
❑ 90PubIntS-385
❑ 90RedFolSB-13
❑ 90Sco-94
❑ 90Spo-167
❑ 90Top-569
❑ 90TopBig-80
❑ 90TopCoi-9
❑ 90TopMinL-11
❑ 90TopSti-299
❑ 90TopTif-569
❑ 90UppDec-503
❑ 90WhiSoxC-1
❑ 91Bow-440
❑ 91Cla3-T5
❑ 91Don-203
❑ 91ExpPos-3
❑ 91Fle-115
❑ 91FleUpd-97
❑ 91Lea-338
❑ 91OPC-93
❑ 91OPCPre-17
❑ 91PanFreS-318
❑ 91PanSti-258
❑ 91Sco-254
❑ 91ScoRoo-6T
❑ 91StaClu-383
❑ 91Stu-194
❑ 91Top-93
❑ 91TopDesS-93
❑ 91TopMic-93
❑ 91TopTif-93
❑ 91TopTra-16T
❑ 91TopTraT-16T
❑ 91Ult-199
❑ 91UppDec-285
❑ 91UppDec-786
❑ 91UppDecFE-96F
❑ 91USPlaCA-13C
❑ 92Bow-179
❑ 92Don-48
❑ 92Don-431
❑ 92DonCraJ2-9
❑ 92ExpDonD-4
❑ 92ExpPos-7
❑ 92Fle-475
❑ 92Hig5-56
❑ 92Lea-283
❑ 92LeaBlaG-283
❑ 92OPC-775
❑ 92PanSti-208
❑ 92PanSti-287
❑ 92Pin-58
❑ 92RedFolS-109
❑ 92Sco-83
❑ 92Sco100S-61
❑ 92ScoProP-11
❑ 92ScoProP-22
❑ 92SevCoi-4
❑ 92StaClu-73
❑ 92StaCluD-24
❑ 92Stu-52
❑ 92Top-775
❑ 92TopGol-775
❑ 92TopGolW-775
❑ 92TopKid-7
❑ 92TopMic-775
❑ 92TriPla-196
❑ 92Ult-513
❑ 92UppDec-226
❑ 92UppDecHRH-HR24
❑ 92UppDecTMH-13
❑ 93Bow-663
❑ 93Don-196
❑ 93Fin-55
❑ 93FinRef-55
❑ 93Fle-71
❑ 93FleFinE-172
❑ 93Lea-242
❑ 93OPC-88
❑ 93OPCPre-105
❑ 93PacSpa-354
❑ 93PanSti-98
❑ 93Pin-150
❑ 93RedSoxP-5
❑ 93Sco-95
❑ 93Sel-125
❑ 93SelRoo-118T
❑ 93StaClu-119
❑ 93StaClu-647
❑ 93StaCluFDI-119
❑ 93StaCluFDI-647
❑ 93StaCluMOP-119
❑ 93StaCluMOP-647
❑ 93Top-540
❑ 93TopGol-540
❑ 93TopInaM-540
❑ 93TopInaR-540
❑ 93TopMic-540
❑ 93Ult-507
❑ 93UppDec-751
❑ 93UppDecGold-751
❑ 94Pin-192
❑ 94PinArtP-192
❑ 94PinMusC-192
❑ 97IndScoPr-4
Calderon, Jose
❑ 81BufBisT-16
❑ 84PorBeaC-207
❑ 85MaiGuiT-3
❑ 87ArkTraP-4
❑ 87LouRedTI-8
❑ 88BlaYNPRWL-164
❑ 89BlaYNPRWL-139
Calderon, Ricardo
❑ 95BelGiaTI-44
❑ 96BelGiaTI-17
Calderone, Jeff
❑ 90BurBraB-10
❑ 90BurBraP-2343
❑ 90BurBraS-7
Calderone, Sammy (Samuel F.)
❑ 50JJKCopP-2
❑ 53Top-260
❑ 54BraJohC-42
❑ 54Top-68
❑ 79TCM50-236
❑ 91TopArc1-260
❑ 94TopArc1-68
❑ 94TopArc1G-68
Caldwell, Bruce
❑ 90DodTar-100
Caldwell, David
❑ 94BurIndC-4
❑ 94BurIndF-3784
❑ 96KenIndB-2
❑ 97KinIndB-4
Caldwell, Earl W.
❑ 39WorWidGV-4
❑ 47TipTop-17
❑ 48WhiSoxTI-4
❑ 84TCMPla1-15
Caldwell, Mike (Ralph M.)
❑ 72PadPos-5
❑ 73OPC-182
❑ 73Top-182
❑ 74OPC-344
❑ 74Top-344
❑ 75Gia-1
❑ 75GiaTeal-3
❑ 75OPC-347
❑ 75Top-347
❑ 75TopMin-347
❑ 76OPC-157
❑ 76SanFraGP-4
❑ 76SSP-93
❑ 76Top-157
❑ 77Top-452
❑ 78Top-212
❑ 79Hos-14
❑ 79OPC-356
❑ 79Top-651
❑ 80BreTeal-4
❑ 80OPC-269
❑ 80Top-515
❑ 81Don-86
❑ 81Fle-512
❑ 81OPC-85
❑ 81Top-85
❑ 81TopSti-97
❑ 82BrePol-48
❑ 82Don-330
❑ 82Fle-136
❑ 82OPC-378
❑ 82Top-378
❑ 83BreGar-4
❑ 83BrePol-48
❑ 83Don-154
❑ 83Fle-29
❑ 83FleSti-21
❑ 83OPC-142
❑ 83Top-142
❑ 83TopSti-184
❑ 83TopSti-185
❑ 84AllGamPI-166
❑ 84BreGar-3
❑ 84BrePol-48
❑ 84Don-237
❑ 84Fle-196
❑ 84Nes792-605
❑ 84OPC-326
❑ 84Top-605
❑ 84TopTif-605
❑ 85Don-490
❑ 85Fle-577
❑ 85Top-419
❑ 85TopSti-289
❑ 85TopTif-419
❑ 86BreGreT-10
❑ 92BreCarT-4
❑ 92HelBreF-1733
❑ 92HelBreSP-24
❑ 93HelBreF-4113
❑ 93HelBreSP-28
❑ 94BreMilB-205
❑ 94HelBreF-3629
❑ 94HelBreSP-26
❑ 95BelBreTI-30
❑ 96El PasDB-2
❑ 97El PasDB-26
❑ 98LouRedQ-32
Caldwell, Ray (Raymond B.)
❑ 14CraJacE-129
❑ 15CraJacE-129
❑ 15SpoNewM-25
❑ 16FleBreD-12
❑ 16SpoNewM-27
❑ 74CapPub-86
❑ 77Ind192T-3
❑ 93ConTSN-705
Caldwell, Rich
❑ 84NewOriT-17
❑ 85ChaO'sT-19
Calero, Enrique
❑ 96SpoIndB-8
❑ 97TexAllM-7
❑ 97TexLeaTP-27
❑ 97WicWra-2
❑ 98Bes-8
❑ 98SP MinPE-66
❑ 98SPMin-66
❑ 98WicWraM-3
Calhoon, Greg
❑ 92StoPorC-25
Calhoun, Brad
❑ 77AppFoxT-3
Calhoun, Gary
❑ 90HelBreSP-29
❑ 91NiaFalRC-29
❑ 91NiaFalRP-3650
Calhoun, Jeff
❑ 83ColAstT-13
❑ 85AstMot-24
❑ 85FleUpd-18
❑ 86AstPol-19

❑ 86Don-426
❑ 86Fle-295
❑ 86Top-534
❑ 86TopTif-534
❑ 87Don-578
❑ 87Fle-52
❑ 87FleGlo-52
❑ 87MaiGuiP-14
❑ 87MaiGuiT-2
❑ 87Top-282
❑ 87TopTif-282
❑ 87TopTra-16T
❑ 87TopTraT-16T
❑ 88Don-509
❑ 88Fle-299
❑ 88FleGlo-299
❑ 88PhiTas-5
❑ 88StaLinPh-4
❑ 88Top-38
❑ 88TopTif-38
❑ 89UppDec-33
Calhoun, Ray
❑ 89GreFalDSP-30
❑ 90VerBeaDS-7
❑ 91FloStaLAP-FSL37
❑ 91VerBeaDC-5
❑ 91VerBeaDP-766
❑ 92SanAntMF-3968
❑ 92SanAntMS-560
Cali, Joe
❑ 97BurIndG-4
Caligiur, Fred
❑ 42A'sTeal-8
Calini, Ron
❑ 91AubAstC-11
Calise, Mike (Michael S.)
❑ 78ArkTraT-5
❑ 80ArkTraT-6
❑ 82LouRedE-4
❑ 83LouRedR-21
❑ 84RocRedWT-5
❑ 85TucTorC-63
Call, Keith
❑ 82MadMusF-26
❑ 83MadMusF-14
Call, Michael
❑ 93MidLeaAGF-21
❑ 93SouBenWSC-4
❑ 93SouBenWSF-1421
❑ 94CarLeaAF-CAR7
❑ 94PriWilCC-5
❑ 94PriWilCF-1913
❑ 95PriWilCTI-16
Callaghan, Marty (Martin F.)
❑ 21Nei-66
❑ 22E120-154
❑ 22W573-15
❑ 27Zee-134
❑ 32Zee-3
Callahan, Ben
❑ 82NasSouTI-4
❑ 83ColCliT-14
❑ 83NasSouTI-4
❑ 84NasSouTI-3
Callahan, Brian
❑ 88AriWilP-1
Callahan, C. H.
❑ 16Zee-125
❑ 17Zee-101
Callahan, Damon
❑ 94PriRedC-5
❑ 94PriRedF-3254
❑ 95BilMusTI-16
❑ 95Exc-174
❑ 97BurBeeB-4
Callahan, Dave
❑ 11PinT-5-619
❑ 99TeaBesR-9
❑ 99TeaBesRG-9
❑ 99TeaBesRS-9
Callahan, Harry
❑ 75TopPho-18
Callahan, Leo
❑ 90DodTar-107A
Callahan, Mike
❑ 83DayBeaAT-4
Callahan, Nixey (James J.)
❑ 03BreE10-13
❑ 09ColChiE-43
❑ 09SpoNewSM-77
❑ 10DomDisP-19
❑ 10SweCapPP-8
❑ 11HelSta-8
❑ 11PloCanE-13
❑ 11SpoLifCW-50
❑ 12ColRedB-43
❑ 12ColTinT-43
❑ 12T207-24
❑ 13NatGamW-7
❑ 13TomBarW-6
❑ 14CraJacE-111
❑ 14TexTomE-9
❑ 15SpoNewM-24
❑ 16FleBreD-13
❑ 16SpoNewM-26
❑ 95ConTSN-1351
Callahan, Pat (Patrick H.)
❑ 77ForLauYS-1
❑ 79WesHavYT-6
❑ 80NasSouTI-4
❑ 81ColCliP-23
❑ 81ColCliT-4
❑ 81NasSouTI-2
❑ 82NasSouTI-5
Callahan, Steve
❑ 89EveGiaS-3
❑ 89Sta-196
❑ 90CliGiaB-2
❑ 90CliGiaP-2545
❑ 91SanJosGC-14
❑ 91SanJosGP-2
❑ 92ModA'sC-13
❑ 92ModA'sF-3891
Callan, Brett
❑ 93AubAstC-3
❑ 93AubAstF-3446
❑ 94OscAstC-4
❑ 94OscAstF-1140
Callan, F
❑ 17Zee-22
Callari, Ray
❑ 91Cla/Bes-316
❑ 91RocExpC-17
❑ 91RocExpP-2052
Callas, Pete
❑ 87ChaWheP-6
❑ 88ClePhiS-4
Callaway, Frank B.
❑ 22E120-76
Callaway, Michael
❑ 97FloStaLTPB-19
❑ 97St.PetDR-10
Callaway, Mickey
❑ 96ButCopKB-11
❑ 98OrlRayM-4
Calley, Robert
❑ 85VisOakT-10
❑ 86VisOakP-5
Callier, Jeremy
❑ 98ButCopKG-7
Callihan, John
❑ 92YakBeaC-20
❑ 92YakBeaF-3456
Callis, Al
❑ 75CliPilT-27
Callison, Johnny (John W.)
❑ 47Exh-32
❑ 47StaPinP2-8
❑ 58PhiTeal-5
❑ 59OklTodML-18
❑ 59Top-119
❑ 59TopVen-119
❑ 60Lea-118
❑ 60PhiJayP-4
❑ 60Top-17
❑ 60TopVen-17
❑ 61Pos-123A
❑ 61Pos-123B
❑ 61Top-468
❑ 61TopStal-50
❑ 62Baz-18
❑ 62SalPlaC-204
❑ 62ShiPlaC-204
❑ 62Top-17
❑ 62TopStal-165
❑ 62TopVen-17
❑ 63Baz-15
❑ 63ExhStaB-10
❑ 63Fle-51
❑ 63Jel-179
❑ 63Pos-179
❑ 63SalMetC-26
❑ 63Top-434
❑ 63TopStil-8
❑ 64Baz-15
❑ 64PhiJayP-4
❑ 64PhiPhiB-8
❑ 64PhiTeaS-2
❑ 64Top-135
❑ 64TopCoi-50
❑ 64TopGia-36
❑ 64TopSta-80
❑ 64TopStaU-12
❑ 64TopTatl-27
❑ 64TopVen-135
❑ 65Baz-15
❑ 65OPC-4
❑ 65PhiJayP-4
❑ 65Top-4
❑ 65Top-310
❑ 65TopEmbl-32
❑ 65TopTral-41
❑ 66Baz-12
❑ 66OPC-52
❑ 66PhiTeal-4
❑ 66Top-52
❑ 66Top-230
❑ 66TopRubl-13
❑ 66TopVen-52
❑ 66TopVen-230
❑ 67Baz-12
❑ 67CokCapPh-4
❑ 67DexPre-40
❑ 67OPC-85
❑ 67OPCPapl-14
❑ 67PhiPol-4
❑ 67Top-85
❑ 67Top-309
❑ 67TopPos-14
❑ 67TopTesF-2
❑ 67TopVen-299
❑ 68AtlOilPBCC-9
❑ 68Top-415
❑ 68TopActS-4C
❑ 68TopActS-15C
❑ 69MilBra-47
❑ 69MLBOffS-174
❑ 69MLBPin-37
❑ 69OPC-133
❑ 69PhiTeal-2
❑ 69Top-133
❑ 69TopFou-6
❑ 69TopSta-73
❑ 69TopTeaP-8
❑ 69TraSta-59
❑ 70DayDaiNM-130
❑ 70MLBOffS-15
❑ 70OPC-375
❑ 70Top-375
❑ 71MLBOffS-28
❑ 71OPC-12
❑ 71Top-12
❑ 72MilBra-60
❑ 72OPC-364
❑ 72Top-364
❑ 72TopCloT-4
❑ 73OPC-535
❑ 73SyrChiTI-4
❑ 73Top-535
❑ 74LauAllG-64
❑ 78TCM60I-29
❑ 81WhiSox1T-14
❑ 83PhiPosGM-6
❑ 83PhiPosGPaM-1
❑ 92YanWIZ7-30
❑ 93ActPacA-146
❑ 93UppDecAH-25
❑ 94UppDecAH-198
❑ 94UppDecAH1-198
Callistro, Robby
❑ 91PocPioP-3774
❑ 91PocPioSP-2
Calloway, Michael
❑ 97St.PetDRUB-11
Calloway, Ron
❑ 97LetBlaDB-13
❑ 98HigDesMG-6
❑ 98MidLeaPM-23
❑ 98SouBenSHM-9
Calmus, Dick
❑ 64Top-231
❑ 64TopVen-231
❑ 68Top-427
❑ 90DodTar-101
Calmus, Lance
❑ 96WatIndTI-4
❑ 98AkrAerM-7
Calufetti, Larry
❑ 76WauMetT-8
Calui, Mark
❑ 92BelMarF-1447
Calvert, Art
❑ 87PriWilYP-8
❑ 88Ft.LauYS-3
❑ 89St.PetCS-4
❑ 89Sta-48
Calvert, Chris
❑ 85VisOakT-12
❑ 87VisOakP-13
❑ 88ClePhiS-5
❑ 88ReaPhiP-886
❑ 89EasLeaDDP-DD34
❑ 89ReaPhiB-21
❑ 89ReaPhiP-664
❑ 89ReaPhiS-5
Calvert, Klae
❑ 97LowSpiB-18
Calvert, Mark
❑ 81PhoGiaVNB-9
❑ 83GiaPos-5
❑ 83PhoGiaBHN-2
❑ 84PhoGiaC-2
❑ 85MaiGuiT-4
Calvert, Steve
❑ 92Min-4
Calvey, Jack
❑ 46SunBre-2
Calvi, Mark
❑ 92BelMarCB-19
Calvin, Derrick
❑ 93BenRocCB-4
❑ 93BenRocF-3257
Calvo, Jack (Jacinto)
❑ 14Zee-5
❑ 17Zee-83
Calzado, Francis
❑ 84EveGiaC-23
Calzado, Johnny
❑ 89JohCitCS-4
❑ 90SavCarP-2081
❑ 91Cla/Bes-79
❑ 91SprCarC-9
❑ 91SprCarP-754
Calzado, Lorenzo
❑ 89SavCarP-360
Camacho, Adulfo
❑ 85MexCitTT-18
Camacho, Dan
❑ 93GreFalDSP-22
❑ 94BakDodC-5
❑ 95SanBerSTI-3
❑ 96VerBeaDB-8
Camacho, Ernie
❑ 77ModA'sC-8
❑ 81Top-96
❑ 84Ind-8
❑ 84IndWhe-13
❑ 85Don-129
❑ 85Fle-442
❑ 85Ind-8
❑ 85IndPol-13
❑ 85Top-739
❑ 85TopSti-253
❑ 85TopTif-739
❑ 86Fle-582
❑ 86IndOhH-13
❑ 86IndTeal-12
❑ 86Top-509
❑ 86TopTif-509
❑ 87Don-350
❑ 87Fle-247
❑ 87FleGlo-247
❑ 87IndGat-13
❑ 87OPC-353
❑ 87Top-353
❑ 87TopSti-209
❑ 87TopTif-353
❑ 88AstMot-16
❑ 88TucTorP-189
❑ 89PhoFirC-6
❑ 89PhoFirP-1494
❑ 90Bow-229
❑ 90BowTif-229
❑ 90GiaMot-27
❑ 90LouRedBLBC-9
❑ 90TopTVCa-51
❑ 91PacSenL-132
Camacho, Joe
❑ 93RanKee-40
Camarena, Miguel
❑ 90HunCubP-3272
❑ 91HunCubC-6
❑ 91HunCubP-3326
Cambria, Fred
❑ 71OPC-27
❑ 71Top-27
❑ 72OPC-392
❑ 72Top-392
❑ 92SpoIndC-28
❑ 92SpoIndF-1311
Camelli, Hank (Henry R.)
❑ 47TipTop-77
Camelo, Pete
❑ 86JacExpT-6
❑ 87JacExpP-432
Cameron, Donald
❑ 09ObaT21-10
❑ 09ObaT21-97
Cameron, Ken
❑ 95NewJerCTI-4
❑ 96NewJerCB-4
❑ 97PeoChi-4
❑ 98PriWilCQ-18
Cameron, Mike
❑ 92UtiBluSC-6
❑ 93SouBenWSC-5
❑ 93SouBenWSF-1442
❑ 94PriWilCC-6
❑ 94PriWilCF-1932
❑ 96BirBarB-2
❑ 96Bow-264
❑ 96BowFoi-264
❑ 96ColCho-507
❑ 96ColChoGS-507
❑ 96ColChoSS-507
❑ 96Don-378
❑ 96DonPreP-378
❑ 96DouAllB-33
❑ 96FleUpd-U24
❑ 96FleUpdTC-U24
❑ 96UltGolP-4
❑ 96UltGolPHGM-4
❑ 97Bow-378
❑ 97BowBes-127
❑ 97BowBesAR-127
❑ 97BowBesR-127
❑ 97BowCerBlaIA-CA11
❑ 97BowCerBluIA-CA11
❑ 97BowCerGolIA-CA11
❑ 97BowChr-251
❑ 97BowChrl-251
❑ 97BowChrIR-251
❑ 97BowChrR-251
❑ 97BowInt-378
❑ 97Cir-123
❑ 97CirRav-123
❑ 97ColCho-74
❑ 97Don-234
❑ 97DonGolPP-234
❑ 97DonLim-126
❑ 97DonLimE-126
❑ 97DonPre-144
❑ 97DonPreCttC-144
❑ 97DonSig-87
❑ 97DonSigA-15
❑ 97DonSigAC-21
❑ 97DonSigAM-21
❑ 97DonSigPPP-87
❑ 97DonSilPP-234
❑ 97DonTea-69
❑ 97DonTeaSPE-69
❑ 97E-X2-13
❑ 97E-X2Cred-13
❑ 97E-X2EssCre-13
❑ 97Fle-58
❑ 97FleTif-58
❑ 97Lea-187
❑ 97LeaFraM-187
❑ 97LeaFraMDC-187
❑ 97MetUni-56
❑ 97PacPriGotD-GD28
❑ 97Pin-166
❑ 97PinArtP-PP166
❑ 97PinMusC-166
❑ 97PinPrePla-166
❑ 97ScoPreS-326
❑ 97Sel-112
❑ 97SelArtP-112
❑ 97SelCom-112
❑ 97SelRegG-112
❑ 97Top-201
❑ 97Ult-37
❑ 97UltGolME-37
❑ 97UltPlaME-37
❑ 97UppDec-238
❑ 97WhiSoxCM-1
❑ 97WhiSoxS-15
❑ 97WhiSoxSPl-15
❑ 97WhiSoxSPr-15
❑ 97WhiSoxTI-24
❑ 98CirThu-101
❑ 98CirThuRav-101
❑ 98CirThuSupRav-101
❑ 98ColCho-339
❑ 98ColChoSQ-SQ8
❑ 98Don-95
❑ 98DonCol-95
❑ 98DonCol-181
❑ 98DonColE-485
❑ 98DonColL-274
❑ 98DonColP-678
❑ 98DonColS-95
❑ 98DonColS-176
❑ 98DonCruG-16
❑ 98DonCruP-16
❑ 98DonCruR-16
❑ 98DonEli-85
❑ 98DonEliA-85
❑ 98DonEliS-85
❑ 98DonGolPP-95
❑ 98DonPre-128
❑ 98DonPreGES-26
❑ 98DonPreGX-26
❑ 98DonPreGXDC-26
❑ 98DonPreSeat-128
❑ 98DonPriCD-95
❑ 98DonPriCD-181
❑ 98DonPriCE-485
❑ 98DonPriCL-274
❑ 98DonPriCP-678
❑ 98DonRatR-6
❑ 98DonRatRM-6
❑ 98DonSigA-12
❑ 98DonSigAC-18
❑ 98DonSigAM-18
❑ 98DonSilPP-95
❑ 98Fin-31
❑ 98FinNo--31
❑ 98FinNo-R-31
❑ 98FinRef-31
❑ 98FlaShoLeg0-41
❑ 98FlaShoLeg1-41
❑ 98FlaShoLeg2-41
❑ 98FlaShoLeg3-41
❑ 98FlaShoLegM-41
❑ 98FlaShoR0-41
❑ 98FlaShoR1-41
❑ 98FlaShoR2-41
❑ 98FlaShoR3-41
❑ 98Fle-257
❑ 98FleRooS-1
❑ 98Lea-75
❑ 98LeaFraDA-75
❑ 98LeaFraF-75
❑ 98LeaFraM-75
❑ 98LeaFraM-75
❑ 98LeaFraMDC-75
❑ 98LeaFraMDC-75
❑ 98LeaFraMZ2-75
❑ 98LeaRS-114
❑ 98LeaRSLHolo-114
❑ 98LeaRSLong-114
❑ 98LeaRTrue-114
❑ 98MetUni-176
❑ 98MetUniPMG-176
❑ 98PacInvGems-29
❑ 98PacOme-54
❑ 98PacOmeR-54
❑ 98PacOnl-163
❑ 98PacOnlR-163
❑ 98PacOnlWC-163
❑ 98PinIns-46
❑ 98PinInsCE-46
❑ 98PinInsDE-46
❑ 98PinPer-100
❑ 98PinPerPP-100
❑ 98PinPlu-126
❑ 98PriWilCASM-18
❑ 98Sco-40
❑ 98ScoRT-108
❑ 98ScoRTSS-PP71
❑ 98ScoRTSSAP-PP71
❑ 98ScoRTSSAP1-PP71
❑ 98ScoSS-PP14
❑ 98ScoSSAP-PP14
❑ 98SP Aut-67
❑ 98SpoIll-18
❑ 98SpoIllEE-18
❑ 98SpoIllFE-18
❑ 98SPxFin-3
❑ 98SPxFinR-3
❑ 98SPxFinS-3
❑ 98StaCluFDI-11
❑ 98StaClul-11
❑ 98StaCluOneK-11
❑ 98StaCluPP-11
❑ 98Stu-50
❑ 98StuGPP-50
❑ 98StuSPP-50
❑ 98Top-41

❑ 98TopChr-41
❑ 98TopChrR-41
❑ 98TopDevR-41
❑ 98TopDia-41
❑ 98TopGal-110
❑ 98TopGalGP-110
❑ 98TopGalOPP-110
❑ 98TopGalPPI-110
❑ 98TopGalPPIA-110
❑ 98TopMiniC-41
❑ 98TopOpeD-26
❑ 98Ult-86
❑ 98UltBacttF-5
❑ 98UltGolM-86
❑ 98UltMas-86
❑ 98UltPlaM-86
❑ 98UppDec-59
❑ 98UppDecSF-38
❑ 98WhiSoxS-3
❑ 98WhiSoxSP-3
❑ 99199Fin-169
❑ 99CroRoyB-37
❑ 99CroRoyL-37
❑ 99CroRoyOD-37
❑ 99FinGolRef-169
❑ 99FinRef-169
❑ 99Fle-409
❑ 99FleBri-71
❑ 99FleBri2G-71
❑ 99FleBriBlu-71
❑ 99FleBriGol-71
❑ 99FleSta9-409
❑ 99FleWarT-409
❑ 99Pac-98
❑ 99PacInv-38
❑ 99PacInvOD-38
❑ 99PacInvPB-38
❑ 99PacOme-62
❑ 99PacOmeC-62
❑ 99PacOmeG-62
❑ 99PacOmePB-62
❑ 99PacPar-62
❑ 99PacParC-62
❑ 99PacParG-62
❑ 99PacParHoloGold-62
❑ 99PacParHS-62
❑ 99PacParOD-62
❑ 99PacParPB-62
❑ 99PacParRed-62
❑ 99PacPlaB-98
❑ 99PacRed-98
❑ 99Rev-37
❑ 99RevPremDate-37
❑ 99RevRet-37
❑ 99RevShaSS-37
❑ 99SkyMolM-91
❑ 99SkyMolMX-91
❑ 99StaClu-323
❑ 99StaCluFDI-323
❑ 99StaCluOoaK-323
❑ 99StaCluPP-323
❑ 99Top-173
❑ 99TopChr-173
❑ 99TopChrR-173
❑ 99TopMVPP-173
❑ 99UppDec-64
❑ 99UppDec-345
❑ 99UppDecEL1-64
❑ 99UppDecEL1-345
❑ 99UppDecEL2-64
❑ 99UppDecEL2-345
❑ 99Vic-107

Cameron, Paul
❑ 84ChaO'sT-5
❑ 85ChaO'sT-30
❑ 86ChaOriW-7
❑ 87ChaO'sW-NNO

Cameron, Ryan
❑ 98PorRocG-4

Cameron, Stanton
❑ 89PitMetS-2
❑ 90ColMetGS-25
❑ 90ColMetPPI-4
❑ 91St.LucMC-4
❑ 91St.LucMP-722
❑ 92FreKeyC-8
❑ 92FreKeyF-1818
❑ 93BowBayF-2199
❑ 93ClaGolF-62
❑ 93ExcFS7-123
❑ 94CarMudF-1592
❑ 94ExcFS7-2
❑ 94Top-79
❑ 94TopGol-79
❑ 94TopSpa-79
❑ 94UppDecML-84
❑ 97HigDesMG-3
❑ 97HigDesMUG-3
❑ 97HigDesMUG-17

Cameron, Tony
❑ 77ForLauYS-30

Cameron, Troy
❑ 97AppLeaTPB-1
❑ 97Bow-436
❑ 97BowChr-296
❑ 97BowChrI-296
❑ 97BowChrIR-296
❑ 97BowChrR-296
❑ 97BowInt-436
❑ 97DanBraB-3
❑ 97TopSta-121
❑ 97TopStaAM-121
❑ 98Bes-60
❑ 98BesNumOP-11
❑ 98Bow-135
❑ 98BowChr-135
❑ 98BowChrGA-135
❑ 98BowChrGAR-135
❑ 98BowChrI-135
❑ 98BowChrIR-135
❑ 98BowChrR-135
❑ 98BowGolA-135
❑ 98BowInt-135
❑ 98MacBraM-5
❑ 98SouAtlLPM-4
❑ 98Top-249
❑ 98TopChr-249
❑ 98TopChrR-249
❑ 98TopDevR-249
❑ 98TopDia-249
❑ 98TopMiniC-249
❑ 99Bow-213
❑ 99BowChr-213
❑ 99BowChrG-213
❑ 99BowChrGR-213
❑ 99BowChrI-213
❑ 99BowChrIR-213
❑ 99BowChrR-213
❑ 99BowGol-213
❑ 99BowInt-213
❑ 99TeaBesRFS-2

Camfield, Eric
❑ 96GreBatB-7
❑ 96TamYanY-8

Camilli, Dolph (Adolf Louis)
❑ 28Zee-127
❑ 29Zee-106
❑ 30Zee-117
❑ 31Zee-81
❑ 32Zee-80
❑ 33Zee-30
❑ 34BatR31-150
❑ 34DiaMatCSB-23
❑ 34Gou-91
❑ 36ExhFou-6
❑ 36GouBWR-5
❑ 36GouWidPPR-A13
❑ 36NatChiFPR-16
❑ 36NatChiFPR-101
❑ 36R31PasP-4
❑ 36SandSW-4
❑ 37ExhFou-6
❑ 37WheBB14-3
❑ 38CloFotW-11
❑ 38ExhFou-2
❑ 38WheBB10-16
❑ 39ExhSal-6A
❑ 39ExhSal-6B
❑ 39PlaBal-86
❑ 40DodTeal-1
❑ 40PlaBal-68
❑ 40WheM4-11
❑ 41DouPlaR-19
❑ 41PlaBal-51
❑ 42DodTeal-3
❑ 43DodTeal-4
❑ 43MPR302-1-3
❑ 47PM1StaP1-23
❑ 61Fle-97
❑ 73Dod194T-3
❑ 77TCMTheWY-64
❑ 78DodTCM4-11
❑ 79DiaGre-301
❑ 82TCMGreS-34
❑ 83TCMPla1943-31
❑ 85BigLeaC3-24
❑ 89DodSmoG-42
❑ 90DodTar-102
❑ 91DodRinP3-5

Camilli, Doug (Douglass J.)
❑ 61UniOil-SP1
❑ 62DodVol-23
❑ 62Top-594
❑ 63Top-196
❑ 64Top-249
❑ 64TopVen-249
❑ 65OPC-77
❑ 65Top-77
❑ 66Top-593
❑ 67SenPos-6
❑ 67Top-551
❑ 69SenTeal8-7
❑ 73OPC-131
❑ 73Top-131A
❑ 73Top-131B
❑ 85GreHorT-1
❑ 86GreHorP-3
❑ 87WinHavRSP-24
❑ 89WinHavRSS-28
❑ 90DodTar-103
❑ 90WinHavRSS-27

Camilli, Jason
❑ 94SigRooDP-39
❑ 94SigRooDPS-39
❑ 94StaCluDP-27
❑ 94StaCluDPFDI-27
❑ 95Top-540
❑ 96DelShoB-11
❑ 98JupHamQ-18

Camilli, Kevin
❑ 86GreHorP-4
❑ 88FayGenP-1099

Camilli, Lou (Louis Steven)
❑ 70WicAerM-4
❑ 71MLBOffS-364
❑ 71OPC-612
❑ 71Top-612

Camilo, Jose
❑ 97BreCouMB-4

Caminiti, Ken
❑ 85OscAstTI-17
❑ 86ColAstP-6
❑ 87SouLeaAJ-10
❑ 87SpoRoo2-37
❑ 88BlaYNPRWL-80
❑ 88ClaBlu-228
❑ 88Don-308
❑ 88Fle-441
❑ 88FleGlo-441
❑ 88OPC-64
❑ 88Sco-164
❑ 88ScoGlo-164
❑ 88ScoYouSI-29
❑ 88Spo-124
❑ 88StaLinAst-5
❑ 88Top-64
❑ 88TopSti-33
❑ 88TopTif-64
❑ 88ToyRoo-6
❑ 88TucTorC-11
❑ 88TucTorJP-3
❑ 88TucTorP-182
❑ 89AstLenH-21
❑ 89AstMot-25
❑ 89AstSmo-7
❑ 89Don-542
❑ 89DonBasB-262
❑ 89Top-369
❑ 89TopBig-210
❑ 89TopTif-369
❑ 89UppDec-141
❑ 90AstLenH-5
❑ 90AstMot-6
❑ 90Bow-73
❑ 90BowTif-73
❑ 90Don-424
❑ 90DonBesN-126
❑ 90Fle-225
❑ 90FleCan-225
❑ 90Lea-253
❑ 90MLBBasB-42
❑ 90OPC-531
❑ 90PanSti-260
❑ 90PubIntS-89
❑ 90Sco-76
❑ 90Spo-209
❑ 90Top-531
❑ 90TopBig-170
❑ 90TopSti-20
❑ 90TopTif-531
❑ 90TopTVA-37
❑ 90UppDec-122
❑ 91AstMot-6
❑ 91Bow-543
❑ 91Don-221
❑ 91Fle-500
❑ 91Lea-502
❑ 91OPC-174
❑ 91PanFreS-9
❑ 91PanSti-17
❑ 91Sco-186
❑ 91Sco-415
❑ 91SimandSMLBL-8
❑ 91StaClu-520
❑ 91Stu-174
❑ 91Top-174
❑ 91TopDesS-174
❑ 91TopMic-174
❑ 91TopTif-174
❑ 91TopTriH-N4
❑ 91Ult-133
❑ 91UppDec-180
❑ 92AstMot-6
❑ 92Bow-538
❑ 92DenHol-2
❑ 92Don-66
❑ 92Fle-427
❑ 92Hig5-38
❑ 92Lea-140
❑ 92LeaBlaG-140
❑ 92OPC-740
❑ 92PanSti-154
❑ 92Pin-43
❑ 92Sco-69
❑ 92ScoProP-20
❑ 92StaClu-142
❑ 92Stu-33
❑ 92Top-740
❑ 92TopGol-740
❑ 92TopGolW-740
❑ 92TopKid-45
❑ 92TopMic-740
❑ 92TriPla-78
❑ 92Ult-200
❑ 92UppDec-279
❑ 93AstMot-9
❑ 93AstStaC-4
❑ 93Bow-504
❑ 93DiaMar-21
❑ 93Don-140
❑ 93Fin-131
❑ 93FinRef-131
❑ 93Fla-59
❑ 93Fle-432
❑ 93FunPac-45
❑ 93Kra-17
❑ 93Lea-261
❑ 93MilBonSS-6
❑ 93OPC-81
❑ 93PanSti-173
❑ 93Pin-59
❑ 93Sco-40
❑ 93Sel-47
❑ 93SP-30
❑ 93StaClu-464
❑ 93StaCluFDI-464
❑ 93StaCluMOP-464
❑ 93Stu-143
❑ 93Top-448
❑ 93TopGol-448
❑ 93TopInaM-448
❑ 93TopInaR-448
❑ 93TopMic-448
❑ 93TriPla-61
❑ 93TriPla-149
❑ 93Ult-38
❑ 93UppDec-305
❑ 93UppDecGold-305
❑ 94AstMot-7
❑ 94Bow-230
❑ 94ColC-72
❑ 94ColChoGS-72
❑ 94ColChoSS-72
❑ 94Don-53
❑ 94Fin-191
❑ 94FinRef-191
❑ 94Fla-387
❑ 94Fle-486
❑ 94FleExtB-270
❑ 94FUnPac-137
❑ 94Lea-244
❑ 94LeaL-112
❑ 94Pac-260
❑ 94PanSti-191
❑ 94Pin-193
❑ 94PinArtP-193
❑ 94PinMusC-193
❑ 94Sco-342
❑ 94ScoGolR-342
❑ 94Sel-359
❑ 94SP-29
❑ 94SPDieC-29
❑ 94StaClu-322
❑ 94StaCluFDI-322
❑ 94StaCluGR-322
❑ 94StaCluMOP-322
❑ 94Stu-18
❑ 94SucSav-2
❑ 94Top-646
❑ 94TopGol-646
❑ 94TopSpa-646
❑ 94TriPla-23
❑ 94Ult-500
❑ 94UppDec-409
❑ 94UppDecED-409
❑ 95ColCho-354
❑ 95ColChoGS-354
❑ 95ColChoSE-39
❑ 95ColChoSEGS-39
❑ 95ColChoSESS-39
❑ 95ColChoSS-354
❑ 95Don-472
❑ 95DonPreP-472
❑ 95DonTopotO-338
❑ 95Emo-185
❑ 95Fin-182
❑ 95FinRef-182
❑ 95Fla-416
❑ 95Fle-454
❑ 95FleAllS-11
❑ 95FleUpd-181
❑ 95Lea-312
❑ 95LeaCor-4
❑ 95LeaLim-17
❑ 95PadCHP-10
❑ 95PadMot-3
❑ 95PanSti-55
❑ 95Pin-82
❑ 95PinArtP-82
❑ 95PinMusC-82
❑ 95Sco-56
❑ 95ScoGolR-56
❑ 95ScoHaloG-HG55
❑ 95ScoPlaTS-56
❑ 95Sel-225
❑ 95SelArtP-225
❑ 95SP-107
❑ 95SPCha-89
❑ 95SPChaDC-89
❑ 95Spo-132
❑ 95SpoArtP-132
❑ 95SPSil-107
❑ 95StaClu-91
❑ 95StaClu-621
❑ 95StaCluFDI-91
❑ 95StaCluMOP-91
❑ 95StaCluMOP-621
❑ 95StaCluSTWS-91
❑ 95StaCluSTWS-621
❑ 95StaCluVR-57
❑ 95StaCluVRMO-57
❑ 95Stu-115
❑ 95Top-105
❑ 95TopCyb-68
❑ 95TopTra-85T
❑ 95UC3-32
❑ 95UC3ArtP-32
❑ 95Ult-170
❑ 95UltGolM-170
❑ 95UppDec-370
❑ 95UppDecED-370
❑ 95UppDecEDG-370
❑ 95UppDecSE-267
❑ 95UppDecSEG-267
❑ 95Zen-60
❑ 96Baz-30
❑ 96Bow-73
❑ 96BowBes-11
❑ 96BowBesAR-11
❑ 96BowBesR-11
❑ 96BowFoi-73
❑ 96Cir-184
❑ 96CirRav-184
❑ 96ColCho-294
❑ 96ColCho-358
❑ 96ColCho-363
❑ 96ColChoCtG-CG22
❑ 96ColChoCtG-CG22B
❑ 96ColChoCtG-CG22C
❑ 96ColChoCtGE-CR22
❑ 96ColChoCtGG-CG22
❑ 96ColChoCtGG-CG22B
❑ 96ColChoCtGG-CG22C
❑ 96ColChoCtGGE-CR22
❑ 96ColChoGS-294
❑ 96ColChoGS-358
❑ 96ColChoGS-363
❑ 96ColChoSS-294
❑ 96ColChoSS-358
❑ 96ColChoSS-363
❑ 96Don-310
❑ 96DonPreP-310
❑ 96EmoXL-275
❑ 96Fin-B12
❑ 96FinRef-B12
❑ 96Fla-371
❑ 96Fle-562
❑ 96FleTif-562
❑ 96Lea-121
❑ 96LeaPre-75
❑ 96LeaPreP-75
❑ 96LeaPrePB-121
❑ 96LeaPrePG-121
❑ 96LeaPrePS-121
❑ 96LeaSig-106
❑ 96LeaSigEA-22
❑ 96LeaSigEACM-2
❑ 96LeaSigPPG-106
❑ 96LeaSigPPP-106
❑ 96MetUni-233
❑ 96MetUniP-233
❑ 96Pac-196
❑ 96PadMot-5
❑ 96PanSti-100
❑ 96Pin-106
❑ 96PinAfi-23
❑ 96PinAfiAP-23
❑ 96PinAfiFPP-23
❑ 96PinArtP-31
❑ 96PinSta-31
❑ 96ProSta-82
❑ 96Sco-338
❑ 96ScoDugC-B63
❑ 96ScoDugCAP-B63
❑ 96Sel-17
❑ 96SelArtP-17
❑ 96SelTeaN-22
❑ 96SP-158
❑ 96SPx-50
❑ 96SPxGol-50
❑ 96StaClu-77
❑ 96StaCluEPB-77
❑ 96StaCluEPG-77
❑ 96StaCluEPS-77
❑ 96StaCluEWB-EW5
❑ 96StaCluEWG-EW5
❑ 96StaCluEWS-EW5
❑ 96StaCluMOP-77
❑ 96Stu-129
❑ 96StuPrePB-129
❑ 96StuPrePG-129
❑ 96StuPrePS-129
❑ 96Sum-45
❑ 96SumAbo&B-45
❑ 96SumArtP-45
❑ 96SumFoi-45
❑ 96TeaOut-14
❑ 96Top-182
❑ 96TopChr-54
❑ 96TopChrR-54
❑ 96TopGal-34
❑ 96TopGalPPI-34
❑ 96TopLas-21
❑ 96Ult-282
❑ 96UltGolM-282
❑ 96UppDec-190
❑ 96UppDec-423
❑ 96UppDecVJLS-VJ8
❑ 97Bow-56
❑ 97BowBes-34
❑ 97BowBesAR-34
❑ 97BowBesBC-BC9
❑ 97BowBesBCAR-BC9
❑ 97BowBesBCR-BC9
❑ 97BowBesR-34
❑ 97BowChr-43
❑ 97BowChrI-43
❑ 97BowChrIR-43
❑ 97BowChrR-43
❑ 97BowInt-56
❑ 97Cir-385
❑ 97CirBos-4
❑ 97CirRav-385
❑ 97CirSupB-4
❑ 97ColCho-450
❑ 97ColChoAC-21
❑ 97ColChoBS-12
❑ 97ColChoBSGS-12
❑ 97ColChoCtG-25A
❑ 97ColChoCtG-25B
❑ 97ColChoCtG-25C
❑ 97ColChoCtGE-CG25
❑ 97ColChoCtGIW-CG25

❑ 97ColChoNF-NF8
❑ 97ColChoPP-PP14
❑ 97ColChoPPG-PP14
❑ 97ColChoPPJ-PP14
❑ 97ColChoS-29
❑ 97ColChoSR-7
❑ 97ColChoTotT-T24
❑ 97DenHol-26
❑ 97Don-173
❑ 97Don-446
❑ 97DonDom-19
❑ 97DonEli-83
❑ 97DonEliGS-83
❑ 97DonGolPP-173
❑ 97DonGolPP-446
❑ 97DonLim-50
❑ 97DonLim-132
❑ 97DonLimE-50
❑ 97DonLimE-132
❑ 97DonLimENG-50
❑ 97DonLimFotG-38
❑ 97DonPowA-12
❑ 97DonPowADC-12
❑ 97DonPre-81
❑ 97DonPre-181
❑ 97DonPreCttC-81
❑ 97DonPreCttC-181
❑ 97DonPrePM-14
❑ 97DonPreS-15
❑ 97DonPreSS-15
❑ 97DonPreXP-10B
❑ 97DonSig-91
❑ 97DonSigPPP-91
❑ 97DonSilPP-173
❑ 97DonSilPP-446
❑ 97DonVxP1-15
❑ 97E-X2-92
❑ 97E-X2Cred-92
❑ 97E-X2EssCre-92
❑ 97Fin-115
❑ 97Fin-161
❑ 97Fin-266
❑ 97FinEmb-115
❑ 97FinEmb-161
❑ 97FinEmbR-115
❑ 97FinEmbR-161
❑ 97FinRef-115
❑ 97FinRef-161
❑ 97FinRef-266
❑ 97FlaShoDC-3
❑ 97FlaShoLC-40
❑ 97FlaShoLeg0-40
❑ 97FlaShoLeg1-40
❑ 97FlaShoM-A40
❑ 97FlaShoM-B40
❑ 97FlaShoM-C40
❑ 97FlaShoR0-40
❑ 97FlaShoR1-40
❑ 97FlaShoR2-40
❑ 97Fle-457
❑ 97Fle-699
❑ 97FleHea-4
❑ 97FleMilDM-30
❑ 97FleMilDMR-30
❑ 97FleTif-457
❑ 97FleTif-699
❑ 97FleZon-4
❑ 97Lea-57
❑ 97Lea-392
❑ 97LeaBanS-10
❑ 97LeaDrefS-10
❑ 97LeaFraM-57
❑ 97LeaFraM-392
❑ 97LeaFraMDC-57
❑ 97LeaFraMDC-392
❑ 97LeaGet-16
❑ 97LeaLeaotN-3
❑ 97LeaStaS-13
❑ 97MetUni-217
❑ 97NewPin-52
❑ 97NewPinAP-52
❑ 97NewPinMC-52
❑ 97NewPinPP-52
❑ 97Pac-420
❑ 97PacCar-34
❑ 97PacCarM-34
❑ 97PacCerCGT-6
❑ 97PacGolCD-34
❑ 97PacLigB-420
❑ 97PacPri-142
❑ 97PacPriGA-GA30
❑ 97PacPriGotD-GD205
❑ 97PacPriLB-142
❑ 97PacPriP-142
❑ 97PacPriSL-SL12B
❑ 97PacSil-420
❑ 97PacTriCD-19
❑ 97PadMot-3
❑ 97Pin-84
❑ 97PinArtP-PP84
❑ 97PinCar-2
❑ 97PinCer-21
❑ 97PinCerCMGT-6
❑ 97PinCerCT-6
❑ 97PinCerMBla-21
❑ 97PinCerMBlu-21
❑ 97PinCerMG-21
❑ 97PinCerMR-21
❑ 97PinCerR-21
❑ 97PinFan-FF8
❑ 97PinIns-83
❑ 97PinIns-150
❑ 97PinInsC-21
❑ 97PinInsCE-83
❑ 97PinInsCE-150
❑ 97PinInsDD-2
❑ 97PinInsDE-83
❑ 97PinInsDE-150
❑ 97PinInsFS-3
❑ 97PinMin-22
❑ 97PinMinB-22
❑ 97PinMinCB-22
❑ 97PinMinCG-22
❑ 97PinMinCGR-22
❑ 97PinMinCN-22
❑ 97PinMinCSS-22
❑ 97PinMinG-22
❑ 97PinMinS-22
❑ 97PinMusC-84
❑ 97PinPrePla-84
❑ 97PinTeaP-3
❑ 97PinTeaP-10
❑ 97PinTotCPB-21
❑ 97PinTotCPG-21
❑ 97PinTotCPR-21
❑ 97PinX-P-56
❑ 97PinX-PF&A-15
❑ 97PinX-PMoS-56
❑ 97PinX-PSfF-14
❑ 97PinX-PSfFU-14
❑ 97Sco-21
❑ 97Sco-505
❑ 97ScoAllF-8
❑ 97ScoArtPWB-21
❑ 97ScoArtPWB-505
❑ 97ScoBla-14
❑ 97ScoHeaotO-27
❑ 97ScoPreS-21
❑ 97ScoResC-505
❑ 97ScoShoS-21
❑ 97ScoShoS-505
❑ 97ScoShoSAP-21
❑ 97ScoShoSAP-505
❑ 97Sel-36
❑ 97Sel-143
❑ 97SelArtP-36
❑ 97SelArtP-143
❑ 97SelCom-36
❑ 97SelCom-143
❑ 97SelRegG-36
❑ 97SelRegG-143
❑ 97SP-154
❑ 97SPInsI-21
❑ 97SpollI-35
❑ 97SpollI-118
❑ 97SpollIEE-35
❑ 97SpollIEE-118
❑ 97SPSpeF-25
❑ 97SPSpxF-3
❑ 97SPSPxFA-3
❑ 97SPx-41
❑ 97SPxBoufG-16
❑ 97SPxBro-41
❑ 97SPxGol-41
❑ 97SPxGraF-41
❑ 97SPxSil-41
❑ 97SPxSte-41
❑ 97StaClu-60
❑ 97StaClu-389
❑ 97StaClul-I9
❑ 97StaClul-I18
❑ 97StaCluMat-60
❑ 97StaCluMOP-60
❑ 97StaCluMOP-389
❑ 97StaCluMOP-I9
❑ 97StaCluMOP-I18
❑ 97StaCluMOP-PG12
❑ 97StaCluMOP-PL2
❑ 97StaCluPG-PG12
❑ 97StaCluPL-PL2
❑ 97StrAll-12
❑ 97Stu-10
❑ 97StuPrePG-10
❑ 97StuPrePS-10
❑ 97Top-262
❑ 97TopChr-93
❑ 97TopChrR-93
❑ 97TopGal-38
❑ 97TopGalPMS-3
❑ 97TopGalPMSSS-3
❑ 97TopGalPPI-38
❑ 97TopHobM-HM15
❑ 97TopMemO5-11
❑ 97TopSta-28
❑ 97TopSta97AS-AS8
❑ 97TopStaAM-28
❑ 97TopTeaT-TT2
❑ 97UD3-13
❑ 97UD3SupSign-1
❑ 97Ult-426
❑ 97UltGolME-426
❑ 97UltHitM-18
❑ 97UltLeaS-10
❑ 97UltPlaME-426
❑ 97UltTop3-24
❑ 97UltTop3GM-24
❑ 97UppDec-144
❑ 97UppDec-216
❑ 97UppDec-244
❑ 97UppDec-377
❑ 97UppDec-490
❑ 97UppDecAWJ-21
❑ 97UppDecHTH-HT12
❑ 97UppDecLDC-LD17
❑ 97UppDecP-22
❑ 97UppDecPE-22
❑ 97UppDecRP-RP22
❑ 97Zen-25
❑ 97Zen8x10-7
❑ 97Zen8x1D-7
❑ 98Bow-40
❑ 98BowBes-56
❑ 98BowBesAR-56
❑ 98BowBesR-56
❑ 98BowChr-40
❑ 98BowChrGA-40
❑ 98BowChrGAR-40
❑ 98BowChrI-40
❑ 98BowChrIR-40
❑ 98BowChrR-40
❑ 98BowGolA-40
❑ 98BowInt-40
❑ 98CirThu-223
❑ 98CirThuRav-223
❑ 98CirThuSupRav-223
❑ 98ColCho-225
❑ 98ColChoCtG-CG16A
❑ 98ColChoCtG-CG16B
❑ 98ColChoCtG-CG16C
❑ 98ColChoCtGExch-CG16
❑ 98ColChoCtGIW-CG16
❑ 98ColChoRJ-225
❑ 98ColChoSQ-SQ63
❑ 98Don-10
❑ 98Don-391
❑ 98DonCol-10
❑ 98DonColE-440
❑ 98DonColP-613
❑ 98DonColS-10
❑ 98DonCruG-98
❑ 98DonCruP-98
❑ 98DonCruR-98
❑ 98DonEli-40
❑ 98DonEliA-40
❑ 98DonEliS-40
❑ 98DonGolPP-10
❑ 98DonGolPP-391
❑ 98DonPre-63
❑ 98DonPreGES-19
❑ 98DonPreGX-19
❑ 98DonPreGXDC-19
❑ 98DonPreSeat-63
❑ 98DonPriCD-10
❑ 98DonPriCE-440
❑ 98DonPriCP-613
❑ 98DonSig-29
❑ 98DonSigAC-19
❑ 98DonSigAM-19
❑ 98DonSigP-29
❑ 98DonSigSB-4
❑ 98DonSilPP-10
❑ 98DonSilPP-391
❑ 98E-X2-62
❑ 98E-X2ECFut-62
❑ 98E-X2ECNow-62
❑ 98Fin-194
❑ 98FinNo--194
❑ 98FinNo-R-194
❑ 98FinRef-194
❑ 98FinStaS-SS23
❑ 98FlaShoLeg0-55
❑ 98FlaShoLeg1-55
❑ 98FlaShoLeg2-55
❑ 98FlaShoLeg3-55
❑ 98FlaShoLegM-55
❑ 98FlaShoR0-55
❑ 98FlaShoR1-55
❑ 98FlaShoR2-55
❑ 98FlaShoR3-55
❑ 98Fle-386
❑ 98FleVin'-118
❑ 98FleVin'C-118
❑ 98LeaCruG-98
❑ 98LeaCruP-98
❑ 98LeaCruR-98
❑ 98LeaRS-59
❑ 98LeaRS-168
❑ 98LeaRSLHolo-59
❑ 98LeaRSLHolo-168
❑ 98LeaRSLong-59
❑ 98LeaRSLong-168
❑ 98LeaRSTicMas-5
❑ 98LeaRSTicMasDC-5
❑ 98LeaRTrue-59
❑ 98LeaRTrue-168
❑ 98MetUni-166
❑ 98MetUniPMG-166
❑ 98Pac-422
❑ 98PacAur-189
❑ 98PacInv-137
❑ 98PacInvGems-208
❑ 98PacInvPBlue-137
❑ 98PacInvSilv-137
❑ 98PacInvTeam-24
❑ 98PacOme-203
❑ 98PacOmeR-203
❑ 98PacOnl-633
❑ 98PacOnlR-633
❑ 98PacOnlWC-633
❑ 98PacPar-235
❑ 98PacParC-235
❑ 98PacParG-235
❑ 98PacParHS-235
❑ 98PacParI-27
❑ 98PacParPB-235
❑ 98PacParR-235
❑ 98PacPlaB-422
❑ 98PacRedT-422
❑ 98PacSil-422
❑ 98PadMot-3
❑ 98Pin-16
❑ 98PinArtP-PP16
❑ 98PinIns-57
❑ 98PinInsCE-57
❑ 98PinInsDE-57
❑ 98PinInsSG-8AB
❑ 98PinInsSG-8CD
❑ 98PinInsSGS-8AB
❑ 98PinInsSGS-8CD
❑ 98PinMusC-PP16
❑ 98PinPer-64
❑ 98PinPerPP-64
❑ 98PinPerSftF-31
❑ 98PinPlu-114
❑ 98PinPluAP-PP36
❑ 98PinPluGAP-PP36
❑ 98PinPluMAP-PP36
❑ 98PinPreP-16
❑ 98Sco-115
❑ 98ScoRT-49
❑ 98ScoRTSS-PP49
❑ 98ScoRTSSAP-PP49
❑ 98ScoRTSSAP1-PP49
❑ 98ScoSS-PP149
❑ 98ScoSSAP-PP149
❑ 98SkyDugA-44
❑ 98SkyDugAG-G9
❑ 98SkyDugAIA-44
❑ 98SP Aut-165
❑ 98SpollI-19
❑ 98SpollI-136
❑ 98SpollIEE-19
❑ 98SpollIEE-136
❑ 98SpollIFE-19
❑ 98SpollIFE-136
❑ 98SpollITaN-67
❑ 98SpollITaNEE-67
❑ 98SpollIWSF-95
❑ 98SpollIWSFEE-95
❑ 98SpollIWSFFE-95
❑ 98SPxFin-122
❑ 98SPxFinR-122
❑ 98SPxFinS-122
❑ 98StaCluFDI-242
❑ 98StaClul-242
❑ 98StaCluNC-NC16
❑ 98StaCluOneK-242
❑ 98StaCluPP-242
❑ 98StaCluTIII-T13C
❑ 98StaCluTLme-T13C
❑ 98StaCluTLmo-T13C
❑ 98Stu-110
❑ 98StuGPP-110
❑ 98StuSPP-110
❑ 98Top-289
❑ 98TopChr-289
❑ 98TopChrR-289
❑ 98TopDevR-289
❑ 98TopDia-289
❑ 98TopGal-22
❑ 98TopGalGP-22
❑ 98TopGalOPP-22
❑ 98TopGalPPI-22
❑ 98TopGalPPIA-22
❑ 98TopGolLabC1-57
❑ 98TopGolLabC1B-57
❑ 98TopGolLabC1One-57
❑ 98TopGolLabC1R-57
❑ 98TopGolLabC2-57
❑ 98TopGolLabC2B-57
❑ 98TopGolLabC2One-57
❑ 98TopGolLabC2R-57
❑ 98TopGolLabC3-57
❑ 98TopGolLabC3B-57
❑ 98TopGolLabC3One-57
❑ 98TopGolLabC3R-57
❑ 98TopMiniC-289
❑ 98TopOpeD-116
❑ 98TopSta-115
❑ 98TopSta'S-7
❑ 98TopSta'SGH-7
❑ 98TopStaB-115
❑ 98TopStaG-115
❑ 98TopStaGR-115
❑ 98TopStaLB-L15
❑ 98TopStaLG-L15
❑ 98TopStaLGR-L15
❑ 98TopStaLS-L15
❑ 98TopStaS-115
❑ 98TopStaSteG-7
❑ 98TopTek-68
❑ 98TopTekD-68
❑ 98UD3-31
❑ 98UD3-121
❑ 98UD3-211
❑ 98UD3DieCut-31
❑ 98UD3DieCut-121
❑ 98UD3DieCut-211
❑ 98Ult-167
❑ 98UltGolM-167
❑ 98UltMas-167
❑ 98UltPlaM-167
❑ 98UppDec-142
❑ 98UppDec-210
❑ 98UppDec10AP-38
❑ 98UppDec1APR-38
❑ 98UppDecCD-CD27
❑ 98UppDecR-84
❑ 98UppDecRGKoG-G27
❑ 98UppDecRTC-TC48
❑ 98UppDecSF-115
❑ 98UppDecTMT-29
❑ 98UppDecTMTG-29
❑ 98Zen-74
❑ 98Zen5 xx7-53
❑ 98Zen5x7GoldImp-53
❑ 98Zen5x7Imp-53
❑ 98ZenZ-G-74
❑ 98ZenZ-S-74
❑ 99199Fin-190
❑ 99Bow-225
❑ 99BowGol-225
❑ 99BowInt-225
❑ 99CroRoyB-66
❑ 99CroRoyL-66
❑ 99CroRoyOD-66
❑ 99E-X Cen-78
❑ 99E-X CenECFut-78
❑ 99E-X CenECNow-78
❑ 99FinGolRef-190
❑ 99FinRef-190
❑ 99FlaShoLeg1-70
❑ 99FlaShoLeg2-70
❑ 99FlaShoLeg3-70
❑ 99FlaShoLegM1-70
❑ 99FlaShoLegM2-70
❑ 99FlaShoLegM3-70
❑ 99FlaShoR1-70
❑ 99FlaShoR2-70
❑ 99FlaShoR3-70
❑ 99Fle-26
❑ 99FleBri-122
❑ 99FleBri2G-122
❑ 99FleBriBlu-122
❑ 99FleBriGol-122
❑ 99FleMys-24
❑ 99FleMysFI-7
❑ 99FleMysG-24
❑ 99FleMysM-24
❑ 99FleSta9-26
❑ 99FleVin'-26
❑ 99FleWarT-26
❑ 99MetUni-57
❑ 99MetUniGM-57
❑ 99MetUniPMG-57
❑ 99Pac-365
❑ 99PacAur-82
❑ 99PacAurOD-82
❑ 99PacCroC-239
❑ 99PacCroCPB-239
❑ 99PacInv-67
❑ 99PacInvOD-67
❑ 99PacInvPB-67
❑ 99PacPar-104
❑ 99PacParC-104
❑ 99PacParG-104
❑ 99PacParHoloGold-104
❑ 99PacParHS-104
❑ 99PacParOD-104
❑ 99PacParPB-104
❑ 99PacParRed-104
❑ 99PacPlaB-365
❑ 99PacPriS-66
❑ 99PacPriS206-66
❑ 99PacPriS206R-66
❑ 99PacRed-365
❑ 99Rev-64
❑ 99RevPremDate-64
❑ 99RevRet-64
❑ 99RevShaSS-64
❑ 99SkyMolM-12
❑ 99SkyMolMX-12
❑ 99SkyPre-110
❑ 99SkyPreA-9
❑ 99SkyPreABlue-9
❑ 99SkyPreR-110
❑ 99SkyThu-134
❑ 99SkyThuRant-134
❑ 99SkyThuRave-134
❑ 99SP Aut-37
❑ 99SP AutHRC-HR36
❑ 99SPAutHRCDC-HR36
❑ 99SPxPowE-PE17
❑ 99StaClu-326
❑ 99StaCluFDI-326
❑ 99StaCluOoaK-326
❑ 99StaCluPP-326
❑ 99StaCluTI-T1B
❑ 99StaCluTL-T1B
❑ 99StaCluTL-T1B
❑ 99ThuSkySupR-134
❑ 99Top-375
❑ 99TopBlaLC1-52
❑ 99TopBlaLC2-52
❑ 99TopBlaLC3-52
❑ 99TopChr-375
❑ 99TopChrR-375
❑ 99TopGal-27
❑ 99TopGalPP-27
❑ 99TopGalPPI-27
❑ 99TopGolL-52
❑ 99TopGolLC1-52
❑ 99TopGolLC2-52
❑ 99TopGolLOtO-52
❑ 99TopMVPP-375
❑ 99TopRedLC1-52
❑ 99TopRedLC2-52
❑ 99TopRedLC3-52
❑ 99TopSta-117
❑ 99TopStaFoil-117
❑ 99UD ChoYW-Y23
❑ 99UDHolo-27
❑ 99UDHoloAUsome-27
❑ 99Ult-73
❑ 99UltGolM-73
❑ 99UltMas-73
❑ 99UltPlaM-73
❑ 99UppDec-191
❑ 99UppDec-381
❑ 99UppDecBD-70
❑ 99UppDecBDD-70
❑ 99UppDecBDQ-70
❑ 99UppDecBDT-70
❑ 99UppDecCf7-30
❑ 99UppDecCf7-C24
❑ 99UppDecCf7Cf7P-C24

❑ 99UppDecCf7LL-L17
❑ 99UppDecCLM-C40
❑ 99UppDecCo7CE-30
❑ 99UppDecE-44
❑ 99UppDecEFXG-44
❑ 99UppDecEL1-191
❑ 99UppDecEL1-381
❑ 99UppDecEL2-191
❑ 99UppDecEL2-381
❑ 99UppDecM-89
❑ 99UppDecMGS-89
❑ 99UppDecMHFS-89
❑ 99UppDecMSS-89
❑ 99UppDecR-37
❑ 99UppDecRG-37
❑ 99UppDecRP-37
❑ 99Vic-171

Cammack, Eric
❑ 97PitMet-8
❑ 98CapCitBF5-4
❑ 98CapCitBM-4

Camnitz, Howard (Samuel H.)
❑ 08RosComP-149
❑ 09AmeCarE90-1-19
❑ 09BriE97-5
❑ 09ColChiE-44
❑ 09T206-49
❑ 09T206-50
❑ 09T206-51
❑ 10CouT21-89
❑ 10CouT21-90
❑ 10CouT21-91
❑ 10DomDisP-20
❑ 10PirHerICP-4
❑ 10PirTipTD-8
❑ 10RedCroT-8
❑ 10RedCroT-95
❑ 10RedCroT-174
❑ 10SweCapPP-134A
❑ 10SweCapPP-134B
❑ 11HelSta-155
❑ 11L1L-124
❑ 11PinT-5-863
❑ 11S74Sil-107
❑ 11S81LarS-99
❑ 11SpoLifCW-51
❑ 11SpoLifM-246
❑ 11T205-24
❑ 11TurRedT-7
❑ 12ColRedB-44
❑ 12ColTinT-44
❑ 12HasTriFT-30A
❑ 12T207-25
❑ 14CraJacE-16
❑ 14PieStaT-17
❑ 14TexTomE-10
❑ 15CraJacE-16
❑ 15VicT21-3
❑ 72ClaCar-20

Camp, Jered
❑ 95HelBreTI-3
❑ 96BelSnaTI-5
❑ 96WatIndTI-5
❑ 98AkrAerM-8

Camp, Rick
❑ 77Top-475
❑ 78BraCok-3
❑ 78Top-349
❑ 79RicBraT-21
❑ 79Top-105
❑ 81BraPol-37
❑ 81Don-197
❑ 81Fle-246
❑ 81OPC-87
❑ 81Top-87
❑ 81TopSti-150
❑ 82BraBurKL-5
❑ 82BraPol-37
❑ 82Don-223
❑ 82Fle-432
❑ 82OPC-138
❑ 82Top-637
❑ 82TopSti-24
❑ 83AllGamPl-164
❑ 83BraPol-37
❑ 83Don-149
❑ 83Fle-133
❑ 83FleSti-82
❑ 83Top-207
❑ 84BraPol-37
❑ 84Don-165
❑ 84Fle-174
❑ 84Nes792-597
❑ 84OPC-136
❑ 84raPho-5
❑ 84Top-597
❑ 84TopTif-597
❑ 85BraHos-5
❑ 85BraPol-37
❑ 85Don-409
❑ 85Fle-321
❑ 85Lea-130
❑ 85OPC-167
❑ 85Top-491
❑ 85TopMin-491
❑ 85TopTif-491
❑ 86Don-385
❑ 86Fle-510
❑ 86Top-319
❑ 86TopTif-319

Camp, Scott
❑ 86OscAstP-3

Camp, Shawn
❑ 97IdaFalBTI-2
❑ 98CliLumG-3

Campa, Eric
❑ 90MadMusB-5

Campagno, Steve
❑ 82OneYanT-9

Campanella, Roy
❑ 47Exh-33
❑ 47PM1StaP1-24
❑ 47PM1StaP1-25
❑ 47PM1StaP1-26
❑ 47PM1StaP1-27
❑ 49Bow-84
❑ 49EurSta-32
❑ 50Bow-75
❑ 50Dra-6
❑ 51Bow-31
❑ 51R42SmaS-12
❑ 52BerRos-7
❑ 52Bow-44
❑ 52H-OInsOR-1
❑ 52StaCalL-79C
❑ 52StaCalS-91B
❑ 52TipTop-5
❑ 52Top-314
❑ 52Whe-5A
❑ 52Whe-5B
❑ 53BowC-46
❑ 53Dor-125
❑ 53ExhCan-20
❑ 53RedMan-NL5
❑ 53StaMey-2
❑ 53Top-27
❑ 54Bow-90
❑ 54NewYorJA-2
❑ 54RedMan-NL13
❑ 54Wil-1
❑ 55BigLealS-4
❑ 55Bow-22
❑ 55DaiQueS-4
❑ 55DodGolS-12
❑ 56Dod-5
❑ 56Top-101
❑ 57Top-210
❑ 57Top-400
❑ 58DodBelB-1
❑ 58DodJayP-2
❑ 59DodVol-2
❑ 59Top-550
❑ 60NuHi-29
❑ 61NuSco-429
❑ 61Top-480
❑ 63BasMagM-13
❑ 67TopVen-180
❑ 69EquSpoHoF-BB2
❑ 73HalofFPP-2
❑ 73SevTraC-10
❑ 74dod195T-7
❑ 75DodTCMA-2
❑ 75OPC-189
❑ 75OPC-191
❑ 75OPC-193
❑ 75Top-189
❑ 75Top-191
❑ 75Top-193
❑ 75TopMin-189
❑ 75TopMin-191
❑ 75TopMin-193
❑ 76GalBasGHoF-4
❑ 76ShaPiz-111
❑ 77BobParHoF-9
❑ 77GalGloG-5
❑ 77GalGloG-251
❑ 77Spo-6906
❑ 78DexHaloFP-3
❑ 78HalHalR-6
❑ 79TCM50-8
❑ 79TCM50-43
❑ 80DodGreT-11
❑ 80MarExhH-4
❑ 80PacLeg-90
❑ 80PerHaloFP-111
❑ 80SSPHOF-111
❑ 82BasCarN-13
❑ 82BasCarN-16
❑ 82DavHaloFB-3
❑ 82DiaCla-4
❑ 82TCMStaot5-8
❑ 83DonHOFH-39
❑ 83MLBPin-20
❑ 83Oco& SSBG-5
❑ 83TopRep5-314
❑ 84DodUniO-2
❑ 84OCoandSI-185
❑ 84OCoandSI-241
❑ 84SpoDesPW-22
❑ 86SpoDecG-33
❑ 86TCMSupS-35
❑ 87Dod195T-2
❑ 87HygAllG-7
❑ 87LeaSpeO*-H3
❑ 88DodRinP1-9A
❑ 88PacLegI-47
❑ 89DodSmoG-4
❑ 89HOFStiB-54
❑ 89PerCelP-8
❑ 90BasWit-30
❑ 90DodTar-104
❑ 90PerGreM-7
❑ 91PomBlaBPB-2
❑ 91TopArc1-27
❑ 92BazQua5A-20
❑ 92FroRowAH-2
❑ 93FroRowC-1
❑ 93FroRowC-2
❑ 93FroRowC-3
❑ 93FroRowC-4
❑ 93FroRowC-5
❑ 93FroRowCGS-1
❑ 93FroRowCGS-2
❑ 93FroRowCH-1
❑ 93TedWil-9
❑ 93TedWil-133
❑ 93TedWil-141
❑ 93TedWilM-1
❑ 93TedWilPC-21
❑ 93TedWilPC-22
❑ 93UppDecS-17
❑ 94UppDecAH-11
❑ 94UppDecAH-147
❑ 94UppDecAH-159
❑ 94UppDecAH1-11
❑ 94UppDecAH1-147
❑ 94UppDecAH1-159
❑ 95TopArcBD-19
❑ 95TopArcBD-40
❑ 95TopArcBD-84
❑ 95TopArcBD-122
❑ 95TopArcBD-149
❑ 97HigMinMM-15
❑ 97HigMinMM-17
❑ 97NegLeaPC-13S
❑ 97St.VinHHS-4
❑ 99SP SigLC-ROY
❑ 99UppDecCL-50
❑ 99UppDecCLCC-50
❑ 99UppDecCLLC-MO

Campaneris, Bert (Blanco D.)
❑ 64TopRooAB-21
❑ 65OPC-266
❑ 65Top-266
❑ 66Baz-44
❑ 66OPC-175
❑ 66Top-175
❑ 66TopRubI-14
❑ 66TopVen-175
❑ 67Baz-44
❑ 67CokCapAt-2
❑ 67DexPre-41
❑ 67OPCPapI-2
❑ 67Top-515
❑ 67TopPos-2
❑ 67TopTesF-3
❑ 67TopVen-197
❑ 68AtlOilPBCC-10
❑ 68Baz-3
❑ 68OPC-109
❑ 68Top-109
❑ 68TopActS-5A
❑ 68TopVen-109
❑ 69A'sJacitB-3
❑ 69MilBra-48
❑ 69MLBOffS-83
❑ 69Top-423
❑ 69Top-495
❑ 69Top-556
❑ 69TopSta-212
❑ 69TopSup-29
❑ 69TopTeaP-21
❑ 70DayDaiNM-48
❑ 70Kel-39
❑ 70MLBOffS-255
❑ 70OPC-205
❑ 70Top-205
❑ 70TopPos-23
❑ 71BazNumT-31
❑ 71BazUnn-4
❑ 71MLBOffS-508
❑ 71OPC-440
❑ 71Top-440
❑ 71TopCoi-64
❑ 71TopGreM-6
❑ 71TopSup-31
❑ 71TopTat-54
❑ 72MilBra-61
❑ 72OPC-75
❑ 72Top-75
❑ 73A'sPos-38
❑ 73LinPor-138
❑ 73OPC-64
❑ 73OPC-209
❑ 73OPC-295
❑ 73SevTraC-11
❑ 73Top-64
❑ 73Top-209
❑ 73Top-295
❑ 74GreHeroBP-5
❑ 74Kel-4
❑ 74OPC-155
❑ 74OPC-335
❑ 74OPC-474
❑ 74OPC-478
❑ 74Top-155
❑ 74Top-335
❑ 74Top-474
❑ 74Top-478
❑ 74TopDecE-46
❑ 74TopSta-223
❑ 75Hos-28
❑ 75HosTwi-28
❑ 75OPC-170
❑ 75SSP42-14
❑ 75Top-170
❑ 75TopMin-170
❑ 76A'sPos-76
❑ 76Hos-61
❑ 76OPC-580
❑ 76SSP-492
❑ 76Top-580
❑ 77BurCheD-19
❑ 77ChiWilD-9
❑ 77DailsID-9
❑ 77DetCaeD-9
❑ 77HolInnD-9
❑ 77Hos-149
❑ 77Kel-2
❑ 77MSADis-9
❑ 77OPC-74
❑ 77RCColC-11
❑ 77SagDis-9
❑ 77sDis-9
❑ 77Spo-6810
❑ 77Top-373
❑ 77WenDis-9
❑ 77ZipDis-9
❑ 78RanBurK-14
❑ 78RCColC-52
❑ 78SSP270-101
❑ 78Top-260
❑ 78TopZes-2
❑ 78WifBalD-12
❑ 79BasPat-11
❑ 79OPC-326
❑ 79Top-620
❑ 80OPC-264
❑ 80Top-505
❑ 81Don-50
❑ 81Fle-280
❑ 81LonBeaPT-20
❑ 81Top-410
❑ 82Don-593
❑ 82Fle-454
❑ 82Top-772
❑ 83ColCliT-17
❑ 83TopTra-18T
❑ 83YanPhoA-4
❑ 84Fle-120
❑ 84Nes792-139
❑ 84Nes792-711
❑ 84Nes792-714
❑ 84Top-139
❑ 84Top-711
❑ 84Top-714
❑ 84TopTif-139
❑ 84TopTif-711
❑ 84TopTif-714
❑ 86A'sGreT-3
❑ 87A'sMot-1
❑ 89PacLegI-157
❑ 89PacSenL-63
❑ 89T/MSenL-16
❑ 89TopSenL-32
❑ 90EliSenL-78
❑ 90HOFStiB-67
❑ 90PacLeg-15
❑ 90SweBasG-121
❑ 91KelLey-1
❑ 91SweBasG-110
❑ 92ActPacA-42
❑ 92MCIAmb-4
❑ 92UppDecS-27
❑ 92UppDecS-30
❑ 92YanWIZ8-25
❑ 93RanKee-92
❑ 93TedWil-44
❑ 93UppDecAH-26
❑ 94RanAllP-5
❑ 94UppDecAH-129
❑ 94UppDecAH-214
❑ 94UppDecAH1-129
❑ 94UppDecAH1-214
❑ 95MCIAmb-2
❑ 95SonGre-1
❑ 99SpoIllGotG-83
❑ 99SpoIllGotGA-14
❑ 99SpoIllGotGC-26

Campanis, Al (Alexander)
❑ 90DodTar-105
❑ 91FouBal-12

Campanis, Jim
❑ 88TopTra-23T
❑ 88TopTraT-23T
❑ 89SanBerSB-1
❑ 89SanBerSCLC-85
❑ 90PenPilS-5
❑ 91JacSunLD-332
❑ 91JacSunP-153
❑ 91LinDriAA-332
❑ 92Bow-144
❑ 92ClaFS7-328
❑ 92Don-647
❑ 92JacSunF-3709
❑ 92JacSunS-353
❑ 92OPC-58
❑ 92ProFS7-143
❑ 92SkyAA F-149
❑ 92Top-58
❑ 92TopGol-58
❑ 92TopGolW-58
❑ 92TopMic-58
❑ 92UppDecML-223
❑ 93ClaFS7-295
❑ 93JacSunF-2714

Campanis, Jim (James A.)
❑ 66SeaPop-3
❑ 67OPC-12
❑ 67Top-12
❑ 68Top-281
❑ 68TopVen-281
❑ 69RoyTeal-2
❑ 69Top-396
❑ 70RoyTeal-7
❑ 70Top-671
❑ 71MLBOffS-196
❑ 74OPC-513
❑ 74Top-513
❑ 90DodTar-106

Campas, Mike
❑ 89HamRedS-7
❑ 89Sta-105
❑ 90SprCarB-6
❑ 91St.PetCC-18
❑ 91St.PetCP-2281

Campau, Count (Charles C.)
❑ 87OldJudN-64

Campbell, Bill
❑ 73TacTwiC-4
❑ 74OPC-26
❑ 74Top-26
❑ 75OPC-226
❑ 75Top-226
❑ 75TopMin-226
❑ 75TwiPos-6
❑ 75TwiTeal-10
❑ 76MinTwiP-4
❑ 76OPC-288
❑ 76SSP-208
❑ 76Top-288
❑ 77OPC-8
❑ 77OPC-12
❑ 77RCColC-12
❑ 77Top-8
❑ 77Top-166
❑ 78Hos-107
❑ 78OPC-8
❑ 78OPC-87
❑ 78PapGinD-22
❑ 78RCColC-16
❑ 78SSP270-169
❑ 78Top-208
❑ 78Top-545
❑ 79OPC-195
❑ 79RedSoxTI-1
❑ 79Top-375
❑ 80Top-15
❑ 81Fle-240
❑ 81OPC-256
❑ 81Top-396
❑ 82CubRedL-39
❑ 82Don-487
❑ 82Fle-289
❑ 82Top-619
❑ 82TopTra-16T
❑ 83CubThoAV-39
❑ 83Don-504
❑ 83Fle-493
❑ 83FleSti-127
❑ 83Top-436
❑ 83TopFol-4
❑ 84Don-555
❑ 84Fle-489
❑ 84FleUpd-23
❑ 84Nes792-787
❑ 84PhiTas-16
❑ 84Top-787
❑ 84TopTif-787
❑ 84TopTra-22T
❑ 84TopTraT-22T
❑ 85CarTeal-4
❑ 85Don-163
❑ 85Fle-245
❑ 85FleUpd-19
❑ 85OPC-209
❑ 85PhiTas-9
❑ 85Top-209
❑ 85TopMin-209
❑ 85TopTif-209
❑ 85TopTifT-15T
❑ 85TopTra-15T
❑ 86CarTeal-6
❑ 86Don-571
❑ 86Fle-28
❑ 86FleUpd-17
❑ 86Top-112
❑ 86TopTif-112
❑ 86TopTra-17T
❑ 86TopTraT-17T
❑ 87Fle-146
❑ 87FleGlo-146
❑ 87OPC-362
❑ 87Top-674
❑ 87TopTif-674
❑ 89PacLegI-191
❑ 89PacSenL-34
❑ 89T/MSenL-17
❑ 89TopSenL-106
❑ 90EliSenL-95
❑ 91PacSenL-125
❑ 92DenZepF-2656
❑ 93NewOrlZF-987
❑ 94NewOrlZF-1484
❑ 96BelSnaTI-6

Campbell, Bruce D.
❑ 32OrbPinNP-34
❑ 32OrbPinUP-9
❑ 33TatOrb-9
❑ 34BatR31-152
❑ 34TarThoBD-6
❑ 35AlDemDCR3-46
❑ 35GouPuzR-8D
❑ 35GouPuzR-9D
❑ 36NatChiFPR-17
❑ 41PlaBal-37
❑ 79DiaGre-278
❑ 92ConTSN-539
❑ 93ConTSN-881
❑ 94ConTSN-1228
❑ 94ConTSNB-1228

Campbell, Camp
❑ 93BurIndC-6
❑ 93BurIndF-3288
❑ 94BurIndF-3785
❑ 94ColRedC-4
❑ 94ColRedF-434
Campbell, D.C
❑ 90DurBulTI-8
Campbell, Darrin
❑ 89SarWhiSS-3
❑ 90SarWhiSS-3
❑ 91BirBarLD-53
❑ 91BirBarP-1456
❑ 91LinDriAA-53
❑ 93RocRedWF-242
Campbell, Dave (David Alan)
❑ 78Top-402
❑ 79Top-9
Campbell, Dave (David W.)
❑ 69Top-324
❑ 70MLBOffS-110
❑ 70Top-639
❑ 71MLBOffS-221
❑ 71OPC-46
❑ 71Top-46
❑ 72OPC-384
❑ 72PadPos-6
❑ 72Top-384
❑ 73OPC-488
❑ 73PadDea-3
❑ 73Top-488
❑ 74OPC-556
❑ 74Top-556
❑ 77PadSchC-10A
❑ 77PadSchC-10B
❑ 78PadFamF-4
❑ 79PadFamF-33
❑ 84PadSmo-3
Campbell, Donovan
❑ 88IdaFalBP-1845
❑ 89BurBraP-1620
❑ 89BurBraS-3
❑ 92St.PetCC-7
Campbell, Gilly (William G.)
❑ 31Zee-13
❑ 32Zee-21
❑ 34BatR31-164
❑ 90DodTar-107B
Campbell, Greg
❑ 82BurRanF-26
❑ 83BurRanF-25
❑ 83BurRanT-28
❑ 84TulDriTI-NNO
❑ 85OklCit8T-14
❑ 86OklCit8P-2
Campbell, Jim (James A.)
❑ 81TigDetN-130
❑ 83TigAlKS-22
❑ 83TigAlKS-44
❑ 83TigAlKS-54
Campbell, Jim (James Marcus)
❑ 87EugEmeP-2654
❑ 88MemChiB-10
❑ 89Fle-646
❑ 89FleGlo-646
❑ 89MemChiB-17
❑ 89MemChiP-1194
❑ 89MemChiS-5
❑ 90Bes-311
❑ 90MemChiB-22
❑ 90MemChiP-1002
❑ 90MemChiS-3
❑ 90ProAaA-15
❑ 91SpoIndC-3
❑ 91SpoIndP-3938
❑ 91TopDeb90-24
❑ 92ClaFS7-267
❑ 92OmaRoyF-2954
❑ 93OmaRoyF-1674
Campbell, Jim (James R.)
❑ 62Col.45B-4
❑ 63Col45"P-4
❑ 63Top-373
❑ 64Top-303
❑ 64TopVen-303
❑ 89AstCol4S-13
Campbell, Keiver
❑ 91St.CatBJC-2
❑ 91St.CatBJP-3407
❑ 92St.CatBJC-14
❑ 92St.CatBJF-3397
Campbell, Kevin
❑ 87VerBeaDP-17
❑ 88VerBeaDS-2
❑ 89BakDodCLC-182
❑ 90SanAntMGS-8
❑ 90TexLeaAGS-16
❑ 91LinDriAAA-530
❑ 91TacTigLD-530
❑ 91TacTigP-2296
❑ 91TriA AAGP-AAA45
❑ 92DonRoo-21
❑ 92FleUpd-48
❑ 92Sco-855
❑ 92SkyAAAF-236
❑ 92StaClu-647
❑ 92StaCluECN-647
❑ 92TacTigS-528
❑ 92TopDeb91-26
❑ 92TopTra-19T
❑ 92TopTraG-19T
❑ 93Don-155
❑ 93Fle-660
❑ 93StaClu-235
❑ 93StaCluFDI-235
❑ 93StaCluMOP-235
❑ 93TacTigF-3025
❑ 93Top-236
❑ 93TopGol-236
❑ 93TopInaM-236
❑ 93TopInaR-236
❑ 93TopMic-236
❑ 94SalLakBF-810
Campbell, Mark
❑ 82DayBeaAT-17
Campbell, Mike
❑ 86CedRapRT-4
❑ 87CalCanP-2322
❑ 87TamTarP-21
❑ 88BlaYNPRWLU-2
❑ 88Don-30
❑ 88DonBasB-163
❑ 88DonRoo-2
❑ 88Fle-372
❑ 88FleGlo-372
❑ 88Lea-30
❑ 88MarMot-18
❑ 88StaLinMa-4
❑ 88Top-246
❑ 88TopTif-246
❑ 89Don-497
❑ 89Fle-543
❑ 89FleGlo-543
❑ 89MarMot-18
❑ 89Sco-568
❑ 89ScoHot1R-86
❑ 89ScoYouS2-30
❑ 89Top-143
❑ 89TopTif-143
❑ 89UppDec-337
❑ 90CMC-634
❑ 90ProAAAF-160
❑ 90VanCanC-7
❑ 90VanCanP-482
❑ 91TulDriTI-5
❑ 92OklCit8F-1909
❑ 92OklCit8S-307
❑ 93RanKee-93
❑ 94LasVegSF-864
❑ 95IowCubTI-5
❑ 96IowCubB-10
Campbell, Paul M.
❑ 42RedSoxTI-3
❑ 75RedSox1T-5
Campbell, Ron (Ronald T.)
❑ 67CokCapC-6
❑ 67Top-497
Campbell, Scott
❑ 90OklSoo-8
❑ 91JamExpC-8
❑ 91JamExpP-3550
❑ 92WesPalBEC-10
❑ 92WesPalBEF-2093
Campbell, Soup (Clarence)
❑ 40PlaBal-200
❑ 41DouPlaR-131
Campbell, Steve
❑ 82IdaFalAT-23
Campbell, Tedde
❑ 96EriSeaB-7
Campbell, Tim
❑ 95IdaFalBTI-29
❑ 96CliLumKTI-5
Campbell, Vin (Arthur V.)
❑ 09ColChiE-45
❑ 10PirTipTD-16
❑ 11PinT-5-869
❑ 11SpoLifM-247
❑ 12ColRedB-45
❑ 12ColTinT-45
❑ 15CraJacE-168
Campbell, William J.
❑ 08RosComP-113
❑ 09T206-52
❑ 10CouT21-7
❑ 10CouT21-92
❑ 72ClaCar-34
Campbell, Wylie
❑ 96BilMusTI-4
❑ 98BurBeeM-4
Camper, Cardell
❑ 76ArkTraT-1
❑ 78Top-711
❑ 91PacSenL-96
Campillo, Robert
❑ 92JamExpC-8
❑ 92JamExpF-1505
❑ 93HelBreF-4097
❑ 93HelBreSP-4
❑ 94HelBreF-3616
❑ 94HelBreSP-13
❑ 94NewOrlZF-1471
❑ 96StoPorB-24
Campisi, Sal
❑ 70CarTeal-6
❑ 70Top-716
❑ 71OPC-568
❑ 71Top-568
Campos, Frank
❑ 87WytCubP-24
❑ 88ChaWheB-24
❑ 89ChaWheB-23
❑ 89ChaWheP-1767
❑ 90SouBenWSGS-23
❑ 90UtiBluSP-15
❑ 91SouBenWSC-14
❑ 91SouBenWSP-2850
❑ 92BirBarF-2574
❑ 92SarWhiSCB-18
❑ 92UppDecML-180
❑ 93BirBarF-1186
❑ 93LinVenB-12
❑ 94VenLinU-70
❑ 95LinVen-234
❑ 96-97LinVen-247
Campos, Frank (Francisco J.)
❑ 52Top-307
❑ 53Top-51
❑ 83TopRep5-307
❑ 91TopArc1-51
Campos, Jesus
❑ 93JamExpC-5
❑ 93JamExpF-3337
❑ 94BurBeeF-1093
❑ 98arSenW1-7
❑ 98HarSenM-7
Campos, Marcos
❑ 80VenLeaS-238
Campos, Miguel
❑ 96-97LinVen-128
Campos, Rafael
❑ 89AshTouP-949
Campos, Tony
❑ 52LavPro-103
Campusano, Aribal
❑ 92LetMouSP-5
Campusano, Carlos
❑ 96BelSnaTI-7
❑ 97BakBlaB-24
❑ 97BakBlaTI-24
❑ 98SanJosGQ-26
Campusano, Genaro
❑ 90WelPirP-3
❑ 91AugPirC-29
❑ 91AugPirP-810
❑ 92SalBucC-9
Campusano, Nicholas
❑ 98HelBreM-8
Campusano, Sil (Silvestre)
❑ 86KnoBluJP-4
❑ 87IntLeaAT-24
❑ 87SyrChiP-1928
❑ 87SyrChiT-18
❑ 88BluJayFS-5
❑ 88DonRoo-42
❑ 88FleUpd-66
❑ 88FleUpdG-66
❑ 88ScoRoo-93T
❑ 88ScoRooG-93T
❑ 88TopTra-24T
❑ 88TopTraT-24T
❑ 89BluJayFS-6
❑ 89ClaTraO-137
❑ 89Don-584
❑ 89OPC-191
❑ 89Sco-473
❑ 89SyrChiC-21
❑ 89SyrChiMB-6
❑ 89SyrChiP-808
❑ 89Top-191
❑ 89TopTif-191
❑ 89UppDec-45
❑ 90ClaYel-T66
❑ 90PhiTas-3
❑ 91Fle-389
❑ 91OPC-618
❑ 91PhiMed-7
❑ 91Sco-847
❑ 91ScrRedBP-2549
❑ 91StaClu-484
❑ 91Top-618
❑ 91TopDesS-618
❑ 91TopMic-618
❑ 91TopTif-618
❑ 91UppDec-469
❑ 93LimRocDWB-81
Campusano, Teo
❑ 89AubAstP-2162
Cana, Nelson
❑ 96StoPorB-21
❑ 97StoPor-22
Canady, Chuckie
❑ 82BurRanF-16
❑ 82BurRanT-16
❑ 83TulDriT-14
❑ 84OklCit8T-17
❑ 85OklCit8T-29
❑ 90TulDriDGB-2
Canale, George
❑ 87StoPorP-18
❑ 88ElPasDB-5
❑ 89BlaYNPRWL-59
❑ 89DenZepC-19
❑ 89DenZepP-35
❑ 90Bow-392
❑ 90BowTif-392
❑ 90CMC-42
❑ 90DenZepC-17
❑ 90DenZepP-630
❑ 90Don-699
❑ 90El PasDAGTI-28
❑ 90Fle-641
❑ 90FleCan-641
❑ 90OPC-344
❑ 90OPC-538
❑ 90ProAAAF-655
❑ 90Sco-656
❑ 90Top-344
❑ 90Top-538
❑ 90TopDeb89-21
❑ 90TopTif-344
❑ 90UppDec-59
❑ 91DenZepLD-130
❑ 91DenZepP-128
❑ 91Fle-578
❑ 91LinDriAAA-130
❑ 91Sco100RS-27
❑ 93ChaKniF-548
❑ 94BreMilB-10
❑ 94MemChiF-362
❑ 95CarMudF-164
❑ 98NasSouTI-7
❑ 98NasSouTISS-7
Canan, Dick
❑ 86PeoChiP-2
❑ 87PeoChiP-5
❑ 89WinSpiS-3
❑ 90ChaKniTI-3
❑ 91ChaKniLD-129
❑ 91ChaKniP-1695
❑ 91LinDriAA-129
Canas, Nelson
❑ 76VenLeaS-60
❑ 95LinVen-212
❑ 96-97LinVen-189
Canate, William
❑ 90WatIndS-2
❑ 91KinIndC-23
❑ 91KinIndP-335
❑ 92ClaFS7-86
❑ 92ColRedC-4
❑ 92ColRedF-2403
❑ 93ClaGolF-11
❑ 93ExcFS7-159
❑ 93FleFinE-287
❑ 93LinVenB-188
❑ 93LinVenB-279
❑ 93LinVenB-321
❑ 93LinVenB-342
❑ 93PacSpa-650
❑ 93SouAtlLAIPI-15
❑ 93SouAtlLAPI-3
❑ 94BluJayUSPC-10C
❑ 94StaCluT-163
❑ 94StaCluTFDI-163
❑ 94SyrChiF-983
❑ 94SyrChiTI-5
❑ 94Top-124
❑ 94TopGol-124
❑ 94TopSpa-124
❑ 94VenLinU-102
❑ 95LinVen-177
❑ 95SyrChiTI-8
❑ 96-97LinVen-238
Canavan, Jimmy (James Edward)
❑ 87OldJudN-65
❑ 90DodTar-108
Cancel, Danny
❑ 91PeoChiP-1353
Cancel, David
❑ 96SouBenSHS-8
Cancel, Robinson
❑ 95HelBreTI-25
❑ 96BelSnaTI-8
❑ 97StoPor-23
❑ 98StoPorG-5
Cancel, Victor
❑ 88WytCubP-1980
❑ 89WytCubS-4
❑ 90GenCubP-3034
❑ 90GenCubS-3
❑ 90PeoChiTI-15
❑ 91PeoChiC-18
❑ 91PeoChiTI-23
Cancini, Ron
❑ 93QuaCitRBF-106
CancioBello, Anthony
❑ 97DanBraB-13
Candaele, Casey
❑ 85IndIndTI-25
❑ 86IndIndTI-33
❑ 87ClaUpdY-128
❑ 87Don-549
❑ 87DonRoo-33
❑ 87ExpPos-4
❑ 87FleUpd-16
❑ 87FleUpdG-16
❑ 87Spo-158
❑ 87SpoRool-6
❑ 87SpoTeaP-20
❑ 87TopTra-17T
❑ 87TopTraT-17T
❑ 88Don-179
❑ 88DonBasB-68
❑ 88ExpPos-4
❑ 88Fle-181
❑ 88FleGlo-181
❑ 88Lea-199
❑ 88MSAHosD-12
❑ 88OPC-87
❑ 88PanSti-329
❑ 88RedFolSB-11
❑ 88Sco-97
❑ 88ScoGlo-97
❑ 88ScoYouSI-34
❑ 88Spo-140
❑ 88StaLinE-3
❑ 88Top-431
❑ 88TopGloS-60
❑ 88TopRoo-11
❑ 88TopSti-77
❑ 88TopSti-305
❑ 88TopTif-431
❑ 88ToyRoo-7
❑ 89AstSmo-8
❑ 89TucTorC-16
❑ 89TucTorJP-3
❑ 89TucTorP-197
❑ 89UppDec-58
❑ 90AstLenH-6
❑ 90AstMot-25
❑ 90TopTra-17T
❑ 90TopTraT-17T
❑ 91AstMot-25
❑ 91Bow-559
❑ 91Don-324
❑ 91Fle-501
❑ 91Lea-114
❑ 91OPC-602
❑ 91PanFreS-8
❑ 91Sco-577
❑ 91StaClu-434
❑ 91Top-602
❑ 91TopDesS-602
❑ 91TopMic-602
❑ 91TopTif-602
❑ 91Ult-134
❑ 91UppDec-511
❑ 92AstMot-25
❑ 92Don-150
❑ 92Fle-428
❑ 92OPC-161
❑ 92PanSti-153
❑ 92Sco-147
❑ 92StaClu-178
❑ 92Top-161
❑ 92TopGol-161
❑ 92TopGolW-161
❑ 92TopMic-161
❑ 92Ult-489
❑ 92UppDec-387
❑ 93AstMot-24
❑ 93AstStaC-28
❑ 93Don-536
❑ 93Fle-49
❑ 93Lea-15
❑ 93OPC-105
❑ 93PacSpa-120
❑ 93PanSti-177
❑ 93StaClu-70
❑ 93StaCluFDI-70
❑ 93StaCluMOP-70
❑ 93Top-584
❑ 93TopGol-584
❑ 93TopInaM-584
❑ 93TopInaR-584
❑ 93TopMic-584
❑ 93UppDec-294
❑ 93UppDecGold-294
❑ 94IndIndF-1820
❑ 94Sco-285
❑ 94ScoGolR-285
❑ 96BufBisB-4
❑ 97BufBis-11
❑ 98NasSouTI-8
❑ 98NasSouTISS-8
Candelari, Rick
❑ 87BelMarL-1
❑ 89WauTimGS-21
Candelaria, Al
❑ 83AndBraT-9
❑ 85FreGiaSB-20
Candelaria, Ben
❑ 93MedHatBJF-3748
❑ 93MedHatBJSP-13
❑ 94St.CatBJC-6
❑ 94St.CatBJF-3656
❑ 95DunBluJTI-3
❑ 96KnoSmoB-7
❑ 97KnoSmo-6
❑ 97TexAllM-8
❑ 98SyrSkyG-4
Candelaria, John
❑ 75PitPirP-2
❑ 76BlaDis-7
❑ 76BucDis-7
❑ 76CarDis-7
❑ 76CraDis-7
❑ 76DailsID-7
❑ 76Hos-92
❑ 76IsaDis-7
❑ 76OPC-317
❑ 76OrbDis-7
❑ 76PirPos-1
❑ 76RedBarD-7
❑ 76SafDis-7
❑ 76SSP-563
❑ 76Top-317
❑ 76TowCluD-7
❑ 77BurCheD-188
❑ 77ChiWilD-10
❑ 77DailsID-10
❑ 77DetCaeD-10
❑ 77HolInnD-10
❑ 77Hos-80
❑ 77Kel-7
❑ 77MSADis-10
❑ 77OPC-59
❑ 77PepGloD-63
❑ 77PirPosP-1
❑ 77SagDis-10
❑ 77sDis-10
❑ 77Spo-3504
❑ 77Top-510

❑ 77WenDis-10
❑ 77ZipDis-10
❑ 78Hos-104
❑ 78Kel-18
❑ 78OPC-7
❑ 78OPC-221
❑ 78RCColC-72
❑ 78Top-190
❑ 78Top-207
❑ 79BasPat-12
❑ 79Hos-86
❑ 79Kel-34
❑ 79OPC-29
❑ 79Top-70
❑ 80OPC-332
❑ 80Top-635
❑ 81CokTeaS-110
❑ 81Don-374
❑ 81Fle-375
❑ 81OPC-265
❑ 81Top-265
❑ 82Don-297
❑ 82Fle-479
❑ 82OPC-3
❑ 82Top-425
❑ 83Don-549
❑ 83Fle-304
❑ 83FleSti-70
❑ 83OPC-127
❑ 83Top-291
❑ 83Top-755
❑ 83TopSti-282
❑ 84AllGamPI-75
❑ 84Don-357
❑ 84Fle-247
❑ 84FleSti-57
❑ 84FunFooP-50
❑ 84Nes792-330
❑ 84OPC-330
❑ 84Pir-3
❑ 84Top-330
❑ 84TopSti-127
❑ 84TopTif-330
❑ 85AllGamPI-165
❑ 85Don-430
❑ 85Fle-462
❑ 85FleStaS-98
❑ 85Lea-157
❑ 85OPC-50
❑ 85Pir-4
❑ 85Top-50
❑ 85TopSti-123
❑ 85TopTif-50
❑ 86AngSmo-16
❑ 86Don-499
❑ 86Fle-150
❑ 86OPC-140
❑ 86Spo-129
❑ 86Top-140
❑ 86TopTat-5
❑ 86TopTif-140
❑ 87AngSmo-1
❑ 87CalAngPPS-3
❑ 87Don-551
❑ 87Fle-75
❑ 87FleAwaW-5
❑ 87FleGlo-75
❑ 87FleLimBC-C3
❑ 87Lea-242
❑ 87OPC-313
❑ 87SmoAmeL-3
❑ 87Spo-148
❑ 87SpoTeaP-11
❑ 87Top-630
❑ 87TopTif-630
❑ 88Don-608
❑ 88DonBasB-20
❑ 88DonReaBY-NEW
❑ 88FleUpd-46
❑ 88FleUpdG-46
❑ 88Sco-293
❑ 88ScoGlo-293
❑ 88ScoRoo-40T
❑ 88ScoRooG-40T
❑ 88Top-546
❑ 88TopTif-546
❑ 88TopTra-25T
❑ 88TopTraT-25T
❑ 89Bow-171
❑ 89BowTif-171
❑ 89Don-192
❑ 89Fle-251
❑ 89FleGlo-251
❑ 89OPC-285
❑ 89PanSti-397
❑ 89Sco-246
❑ 89Spo-202
❑ 89Top-285
❑ 89TopSti-306
❑ 89TopTif-285
❑ 89UppDec-248
❑ 89YanScoNW-8
❑ 90KayB-5
❑ 90Lea-492
❑ 90OPC-485
❑ 90PubIntS-532
❑ 90ScoRoo-54T
❑ 90Top-485
❑ 90TopTif-485
❑ 90TopTra-18T
❑ 90TopTraT-18T
❑ 90UppDec-720
❑ 91DodMot-22
❑ 91DodPol-54
❑ 91DodSt.V-17
❑ 91FleUpd-92
❑ 91Lea-324
❑ 91MetWIZ-59
❑ 91OPC-777
❑ 91Sco-791
❑ 91ScoRoo-32T
❑ 91StaClu-538
❑ 91Top-777
❑ 91TopDesS-777
❑ 91TopMic-777
❑ 91TopTif-777
❑ 91TopTra-17T
❑ 91TopTraT-17T
❑ 91UppDecFE-40F
❑ 92DodMot-12
❑ 92DodPol-54
❑ 92DodSmo-5592
❑ 92Don-125
❑ 92Fle-449
❑ 92OPC-363
❑ 92Sco-350
❑ 92StaClu-164
❑ 92Top-363
❑ 92TopGol-363
❑ 92TopGolW-363
❑ 92TopMic-363
❑ 92Ult-500
❑ 92UppDec-482
❑ 92YanWIZ8-26
❑ 93Fle-443
❑ 93PacSpa-584
❑ 93PirHil-2
❑ 93PirNatl-4
❑ 93Sco-448
❑ 93Top-682
❑ 93TopGol-682
❑ 93TopInaM-682
❑ 93TopInaR-682
❑ 93TopMic-682
❑ 93UppDec-690
❑ 93UppDecGold-690
❑ 94CarLeaA-DJ3
❑ 95PirCocP-5
Candelaria, Jorge
❑ 88BlaYNPRWL-4
❑ 88OneYanP-2055
❑ 89BlaYNPRWL-171
❑ 89BoiHawP-1998
❑ 89RenSilSCLC-242
Candeleria, Vidal
❑ 98OneYanG-4
Candini, Mario
❑ 47SenGunBP-7
❑ 49RemBre-2
❑ 50PhiPhil-4
❑ 51Bow-255
Candiotti, Tom
❑ 81ElPasDT-22
❑ 84Don-393
❑ 84Fle-197
❑ 84Nes792-262
❑ 84Top-262
❑ 84TopTif-262
❑ 84VanCanC-32
❑ 86FleUpd-18
❑ 86IndOhH-49
❑ 86IndTeal-13
❑ 86TopTra-18T
❑ 86TopTraT-18T
❑ 87Don-342
❑ 87DonOpeD-104
❑ 87Fle-248
❑ 87FleGlo-248
❑ 87FleMin-16
❑ 87FleStiC-18
❑ 87IndGat-49
❑ 87Lea-81
❑ 87OPC-296
❑ 87SpoTeaP-3
❑ 87Top-463
❑ 87TopMinL-50
❑ 87TopSti-211
❑ 87TopTif-463
❑ 88Don-377
❑ 88DonBasB-112
❑ 88Fle-604
❑ 88FleGlo-604
❑ 88IndGat-49
❑ 88IndTeal-7
❑ 88OPC-123
❑ 88PanSti-69
❑ 88Sco-595
❑ 88ScoGlo-595
❑ 88Spo-37
❑ 88StaLinI-6
❑ 88Top-123
❑ 88TopBig-93
❑ 88TopTif-123
❑ 89Bow-80
❑ 89BowTif-80
❑ 89Don-256
❑ 89DonBasB-117
❑ 89Fle-399
❑ 89FleGlo-399
❑ 89IndTeal-7
❑ 89PanSti-317
❑ 89RedFolSB-17
❑ 89Sco-239
❑ 89Top-599
❑ 89TopBig-267
❑ 89TopSti-211
❑ 89TopTif-599
❑ 89UppDec-470
❑ 90Bow-324
❑ 90BowTif-324
❑ 90Don-256
❑ 90DonBesA-89
❑ 90El PasDAGTI-32
❑ 90Fle-488
❑ 90FleCan-488
❑ 90IndTeal-9
❑ 90Lea-55
❑ 90OPC-743
❑ 90PanSti-57
❑ 90PubIntS-556
❑ 90Sco-269
❑ 90Spo-126
❑ 90Top-743
❑ 90TopCoi-10
❑ 90TopSti-216
❑ 90TopTif-743
❑ 90UppDec-388
❑ 91BluJayS-28
❑ 91Bow-62
❑ 91ClaGam-54
❑ 91Don-115
❑ 91Fle-364
❑ 91FleUpd-64
❑ 91IndFanC-6
❑ 91Lea-79
❑ 91OPC-624
❑ 91PanFreS-223
❑ 91PanSti-174
❑ 91RedFolS-16
❑ 91Sco-488
❑ 91Sco100S-36
❑ 91ScoRoo-31T
❑ 91StaClu-405
❑ 91Stu-132
❑ 91Top-624
❑ 91TopDesS-624
❑ 91TopMic-624
❑ 91TopTif-624
❑ 91TopTra-18T
❑ 91TopTraT-18T
❑ 91Ult-109
❑ 91UltUpd-59
❑ 91UppDec-218
❑ 91UppDecFE-49F
❑ 92Bow-606
❑ 92DodMot-3
❑ 92DodPol-49
❑ 92DodSmo-4792
❑ 92Don-459
❑ 92Fle-326
❑ 92FleUpd-89
❑ 92Lea-409
❑ 92LeaBlaG-409
❑ 92OPC-38
❑ 92OPCPre-142
❑ 92Pin-459
❑ 92Pin-610
❑ 92Sco-575
❑ 92ScoRoo-68T
❑ 92StaClu-113
❑ 92StaClu-875
❑ 92StaCluNC-875
❑ 92Stu-42
❑ 92Top-38
❑ 92TopGol-38
❑ 92TopGolW-38
❑ 92TopMic-38
❑ 92TopTra-20T
❑ 92TopTraG-20T
❑ 92Ult-501
❑ 92UppDec-447
❑ 92UppDec-760
❑ 93Bow-322
❑ 93DodMot-11
❑ 93DodPol-3
❑ 93DodStaC-19
❑ 93Don-142
❑ 93Fin-132
❑ 93FinRef-132
❑ 93Fle-60
❑ 93Lea-487
❑ 93OPC-63
❑ 93PacSpa-497
❑ 93Pin-147
❑ 93Sco-175
❑ 93Sel-143
❑ 93StaClu-325
❑ 93StaCluFDI-325
❑ 93StaCluMOP-325
❑ 93Top-365
❑ 93TopComotH-22
❑ 93TopGol-365
❑ 93TopInaM-365
❑ 93TopInaR-365
❑ 93TopMic-365
❑ 93Ult-52
❑ 93UppDec-98
❑ 93UppDecGold-98
❑ 94Bow-126
❑ 94BreMilB-11
❑ 94ColC-402
❑ 94ColChoGS-402
❑ 94ColChoSS-402
❑ 94DodDaiN-5
❑ 94DodMot-15
❑ 94DodPol-5
❑ 94Don-521
❑ 94Fin-107
❑ 94FinRef-107
❑ 94Fla-394
❑ 94Fle-507
❑ 94FleExtB-285
❑ 94Lea-72
❑ 94Pac-305
❑ 94PanSti-198
❑ 94Pin-115
❑ 94PinArtP-115
❑ 94PinMusC-115
❑ 94ProMag-67
❑ 94Sco-203
❑ 94ScoGolR-203
❑ 94StaClu-32
❑ 94StaCluFDI-32
❑ 94StaCluGR-32
❑ 94StaCluMOP-32
❑ 94Top-211
❑ 94TopGol-211
❑ 94TopSpa-211
❑ 94Ult-514
❑ 94UppDec-260
❑ 94UppDecED-260
❑ 94USPlaCA-2S
❑ 95BluJayUSPC-9C
❑ 95ColCho-222
❑ 95ColChoGS-222
❑ 95ColChoSS-222
❑ 95DodMot-21
❑ 95DodPol-4
❑ 95Don-116
❑ 95DonPreP-116
❑ 95DonTopotO-263
❑ 95Fin-94
❑ 95FinRef-94
❑ 95Fle-536
❑ 95Lea-234
❑ 95Pin-441
❑ 95PinArtP-441
❑ 95PinMusC-441
❑ 95Sco-511
❑ 95ScoGolR-511
❑ 95ScoPlaTS-511
❑ 95StaClu-456
❑ 95StaCluMOP-456
❑ 95StaCluSTDW-D456
❑ 95StaCluSTWS-456
❑ 95StaCluVR-246
❑ 95StaCluVRMO-246
❑ 95Top-416
❑ 95TopCyb-216
❑ 95TopEmb-84
❑ 95TopEmbGI-84
❑ 95Ult-178
❑ 95UltGolM-178
❑ 96ColCho-179
❑ 96ColChoGS-179
❑ 96ColChoSS-179
❑ 96DodFle-3
❑ 96DodMot-14
❑ 96DodPol-6
❑ 96Don-94
❑ 96DonPreP-94
❑ 96EmoXL-205
❑ 96Fla-288
❑ 96Fle-428
❑ 96FleTif-428
❑ 96LeaSigA-39
❑ 96LeaSigAG-39
❑ 96LeaSigAS-39
❑ 96Pac-102
❑ 96StaClu-392
❑ 96StaCluEPB-392
❑ 96StaCluEPG-392
❑ 96StaCluEPS-392
❑ 96StaCluMOP-392
❑ 96Top-153
❑ 96Ult-493
❑ 96UltGolM-493
❑ 97Cir-321
❑ 97CirRav-321
❑ 97DodMot-13
❑ 97DodPol-4
❑ 97PacPriGotD-GD156
❑ 97StaClu-341
❑ 97StaCluMOP-341
❑ 97Top-91
❑ 98A'sMot-4
❑ 98ColCho-454
❑ 98Pac-326
❑ 98PacOnl-526
❑ 98PacOnlR-526
❑ 98PacOnlWC-526
❑ 98PacPar-77
❑ 98PacParC-77
❑ 98PacParG-77
❑ 98PacParHS-77
❑ 98PacParPB-77
❑ 98PacParR-77
❑ 98PacPlaB-326
❑ 98PacRedT-326
❑ 98PacSil-326
❑ 98PinPlu-105
❑ 98Top-188
❑ 98TopChr-188
❑ 98TopChrR-188
❑ 98TopDevR-188
❑ 98TopDia-188
❑ 98TopMiniC-188
❑ 98UppDec-709
❑ 99Pac-307
❑ 99PacPlaB-307
❑ 99PacRed-307
❑ 99StaClu-52
❑ 99StaCluFDI-52
❑ 99StaCluOoaK-52
❑ 99StaCluPP-52
❑ 99Top-319
❑ 99TopChr-319
❑ 99TopChrR-319
❑ 99TopMVPP-319
❑ 99UppDec-448
❑ 99UppDecEL1-448
❑ 99UppDecEL2-448
❑ 99Vic-288
Cane, Johnny
❑ 11PinT-5-204
Canefires, West Oahu
❑ 96WesOahCHWB-NNO
Caneira, John
❑ 75QuaCitAT-34
❑ 77SalLakCGC-18
❑ 78SalLakCGC-18
Caneman, Mascot
❑ 96WesOahCHWB-NNO
Canepa, Vincent
❑ 52LavPro-52
Canestro, Art
❑ 88OneYanP-2060
❑ 89OneYanP-2104
❑ 90PriWilCTI-7
❑ 91Ft.LauYC-2
❑ 91Ft.LauYP-2417
❑ 92SalLakTSP-28
Canfield, Carroll
❑ 22Zee-56
❑ 23Zee-82
❑ 25Zee-60
❑ 25Zee-61
❑ 26Zee-108
❑ 26Zee-109
❑ 28Zee-104
Cangelosi, John
❑ 83AppFoxFr-13
❑ 86DonHig-51
❑ 86DonRoo-51
❑ 86FleUpd-19
❑ 86SpoRoo-31
❑ 86TopTra-19T
❑ 86TopTraT-19T
❑ 86WhiSoxC-44
❑ 87Don-162
❑ 87Fle-489
❑ 87FleGlo-489
❑ 87Lea-251
❑ 87OPC-201
❑ 87SevCoi-C3
❑ 87Spo-157
❑ 87SpoTeaP-26
❑ 87Top-201
❑ 87TopMinL-49
❑ 87TopRoo-2
❑ 87TopSti-293
❑ 87TopTif-201
❑ 87TopTra-18T
❑ 87TopTraT-18T
❑ 88BlaYNPRWLU-24
❑ 88Don-435
❑ 88Fle-325
❑ 88FleGlo-325
❑ 88OPC-328
❑ 88PanSti-377
❑ 88PirTeal-5
❑ 88Sco-418
❑ 88ScoGlo-418
❑ 88StaLinPi-5
❑ 88Top-506
❑ 88TopTif-506
❑ 89PirVerFJ-44
❑ 89Sco-601
❑ 89Top-592
❑ 89TopTif-592
❑ 89UppDec-67
❑ 90Don-565
❑ 90OPC-29
❑ 90PirHomC-8
❑ 90Sco-367
❑ 90Top-29
❑ 90TopTif-29
❑ 90UppDec-370
❑ 91LinDriAAA-629
❑ 91VanCanLD-629
❑ 91VanCanP-1605
❑ 92Bow-442
❑ 92RanMot-27
❑ 92RanTeal-3
❑ 92Ult-439
❑ 93RanKee-94
❑ 94MetColP-7
❑ 96AstMot-22
❑ 96Fle-403
❑ 96FleTif-403
❑ 96LeaSigEA-23
❑ 97MarPac-6
❑ 98PacInvGems-153
❑ 98PacOnl-291
❑ 98PacOnlR-291
❑ 98PacOnlWC-291
❑ 99Pac-172
❑ 99PacPlaB-172
❑ 99PacRed-172
Cangemi, Jamie
❑ 87BelBreP-7
❑ 89BelBre2S-4
❑ 89StoPorB-6
❑ 89StoPorCLC-150
❑ 89StoPorP-389
❑ 89StoPorS-13
❑ 90StoPorB-21
❑ 90StoPorCLC-182
❑ 90StoPorP-2182
❑ 91StoPorC-1
❑ 91StoPorP-3025
Caniglia, Pete
❑ 52LavPro-45
Canino, Carlos
❑ 87WytCubP-23
❑ 88GenCubP-1655

Canizaro, Jay
❑ 92OklStaC-2
❑ 94SanJosGC-2
❑ 94SanJosGF-2822
❑ 95Bow-215
❑ 95SPML-146
❑ 96BesAutS-16
❑ 96BesAutSA-11
❑ 96Bow-126
❑ 96BowFoi-126
❑ 96ColCho-448
❑ 96ColChoGS-448
❑ 96ColChoSS-448
❑ 96Exc-241
❑ 96PhoFirB-11
❑ 96UppDec-247
❑ 97Bow-381
❑ 97BowCerBlaIA-CA12
❑ 97BowCerBluIA-CA12
❑ 97BowCerGolIA-CA12
❑ 97BowInt-381
❑ 97ColCho-227
❑ 97Fle-478
❑ 97FleTif-478
❑ 97PacPriGotD-GD214
❑ 97PhoFirTI-3
❑ 97Ult-291
❑ 97UltGolME-291
❑ 97UltPlaME-291
❑ 97UppDec-174
❑ 98ShrCapM-9
❑ 98ShrCapWS-9

Cannaday, Aaron
❑ 92WelPirC-3
❑ 92WelPirF-1325
❑ 93WelPirC-3
❑ 93WelPirF-3359
❑ 94AugGreC-2
❑ 94AugGreF-3011

Cannell, Rip (Virgin Wirt)
❑ 11SpoLifCW-52

Cannizzaro, Chris
❑ 86PawRedSP-4
❑ 87PawRedSP-77
❑ 87PawRedST-2
❑ 88PawRedSC-15
❑ 88PawRedSP-451
❑ 89PawRedSC-11
❑ 89PawRedSP-686
❑ 89PawRedSTI-4

Cannizzaro, Chris John
❑ 61Top-118
❑ 62Top-26
❑ 62TopVen-26
❑ 65MetJayP-3
❑ 65OPC-61
❑ 65Top-61
❑ 66Top-497
❑ 69OPC-131
❑ 69Top-131
❑ 69TopFou-24
❑ 70DayDaiNM-91
❑ 70OPC-329
❑ 70Top-329
❑ 71MLBOffS-222
❑ 71OPC-426
❑ 71Top-426
❑ 71TopCoi-109
❑ 71TopTat-46
❑ 72Top-759
❑ 75OPC-355
❑ 75Top-355
❑ 75TopMin-355
❑ 76AtlBraP-4
❑ 81RedPioT-28
❑ 82MetGal62-6
❑ 82RedPioT-25
❑ 90DodTar-109
❑ 91MetWIZ-60

Cannon, J.D.
❑ 95IndIndF-115

Cannon, J.J. (Joseph Jerome)
❑ 75DubPacT-15
❑ 78ChaChaT-4
❑ 79SyrChiT-7
❑ 79SyrChiTI-23
❑ 80OPC-118
❑ 80Top-221
❑ 81SyrChiT-17
❑ 81SyrChiTI-5
❑ 82KnoBluJT-18
❑ 83KinBluJTI-2
❑ 86KnoBluJP-5
❑ 87KnoBluJP-1519
❑ 89KnoBluJB-25
❑ 89KnoBluJP-1129
❑ 89KnoBluJS-24
❑ 90KnoBluJB-10
❑ 90KnoBluJP-1260
❑ 90KnoBluJS-25
❑ 91MedHatBJP-4117
❑ 91MedHatBJSP-26
❑ 92St.CatBJC-27
❑ 92St.CatBJF-3401
❑ 93St.CatBJC-25
❑ 93St.CatBJF-3989
❑ 94St.CatBJC-27
❑ 94St.CatBJF-3659
❑ 95StCatSTI-26
❑ 96HagSunB-27
❑ 97HagSunB-27
❑ 98KnoSG-1

Cannon, Jon
❑ 97RocCub-11

Cannon, Kevan
❑ 96MicBatCB-6
❑ 97SarRedS-3

Cannon, Robby
❑ 91BoiHawP-3894

Cannon, Scott
❑ 86KinEagP-3

Cannon, Stan
❑ 79WisRapTT-16

Cannon, Tim
❑ 83MiaMarT-22

Cannons, Prince William
❑ 90PriWilCTI-30

Cano, Felix
❑ 90IBAWorA-31

Cano, Jose
❑ 83AndBraT-8
❑ 84DurBulT-22
❑ 87OscAstP-27
❑ 88TucTorC-7
❑ 88TucTorJP-4
❑ 88TucTorP-171
❑ 89ColMudB-25
❑ 90AstLenH-7
❑ 90Bow-68
❑ 90BowTif-68
❑ 90ColMudB-25
❑ 90ColMudP-1340
❑ 90TopDeb89-22
❑ 90UppDec-43
❑ 93LimRocDWB-116

Canseco, Jose
❑ 83MadMusF-13
❑ 84ModA'sC-5
❑ 84TopPewB-4
❑ 84TopPewB-6
❑ 85HunStaJ-44
❑ 86A'sMot-9
❑ 86Don-39
❑ 86DonHig-55
❑ 86DonRoo-22
❑ 86Fle-649
❑ 86FleLeaL-3
❑ 86FleMin-87
❑ 86FleSlu-5
❑ 86FleStiC-19
❑ 86FleUpd-20
❑ 86SouLeaAJ-14
❑ 86Spo-178
❑ 86SpoRoo-11
❑ 86StaCan-1
❑ 86StaCan-2
❑ 86StaCan-3
❑ 86StaCan-4
❑ 86StaCan-5
❑ 86StaCan-6
❑ 86StaCan-7
❑ 86StaCan-8
❑ 86StaCan-9
❑ 86StaCan-10
❑ 86StaCan-11
❑ 86StaCan-12
❑ 86StaCan-13
❑ 86StaCan-14
❑ 86StaCan-15
❑ 86StaStiC-1
❑ 86StaStiC-2
❑ 86StaStiC-3
❑ 86StaStiC-4
❑ 86StaStiC-5
❑ 86StaStiC-6
❑ 86StaStiC-7
❑ 86StaStiC-8
❑ 86StaStiC-9
❑ 86StaStiC-10
❑ 86StaStiC-11
❑ 86StaStiC-12
❑ 86StaStiC-13
❑ 86StaStiC-14
❑ 86StaStiC-15
❑ 86TopTra-20T
❑ 86TopTraT-20T
❑ 87A'sMot-26
❑ 87A'sMot-27
❑ 87A'sSmoC-2
❑ 87ClaGam-46
❑ 87ClaUpdY-125
❑ 87Don-6
❑ 87Don-97
❑ 87DonAll-21
❑ 87DonHig-40
❑ 87DonOpeD-24
❑ 87DonSupD-6
❑ 87DonWaxBC-PC12
❑ 87Dra-4
❑ 87Fle-389
❑ 87Fle-625
❑ 87Fle-628
❑ 87Fle-633
❑ 87FleAwaW-6
❑ 87FleBasA-6
❑ 87FleExcS-7
❑ 87FleGamW-8
❑ 87FleGlo-389
❑ 87FleGlo-625
❑ 87FleGlo-628
❑ 87FleGlo-633
❑ 87FleHea-2
❑ 87FleHotS-9
❑ 87FleLeaL-8
❑ 87FleLimE-6
❑ 87FleMin-17
❑ 87FleRecS-3
❑ 87FleSlu-8
❑ 87FleStiC-19
❑ 87FleStiC-131
❑ 87GenMilB-3C
❑ 87HosSti-28
❑ 87KayB-7
❑ 87KeyFooD-17
❑ 87KraFoo-35
❑ 87Lea-6
❑ 87Lea-151
❑ 87MandMSL-10
❑ 87MSAIceTD-17
❑ 87OPC-247
❑ 87OurOwnTD-17
❑ 87RedFolSB-63
❑ 87SmoAmeL-1
❑ 87Spo-80
❑ 87Spo-90
❑ 87SpoTeaP-23
❑ 87StaAwaW-1
❑ 87StaAwaW-2
❑ 87StaAwaW-3
❑ 87StuPan-24
❑ 87Top-620
❑ 87TopCoi-6
❑ 87TopGaloC-3
❑ 87TopGloS-59
❑ 87TopMinL-68
❑ 87TopRoo-3
❑ 87TopSti-164
❑ 87TopSti-304
❑ 87TopTif-620
❑ 87ToyRoo-5
❑ 87WeiMarD-17
❑ 87Woo-12
❑ 88A'sMot-7
❑ 88A'sMot-28
❑ 88Baz-3
❑ 88ClaRed-165
❑ 88ClaRed-197
❑ 88Don-302
❑ 88DonBasB-22
❑ 88DonTeaBA-302
❑ 88Fle-276
❑ 88Fle-624
❑ 88FleAwaW-4
❑ 88FleBasA-5
❑ 88FleBasM-3
❑ 88FleExcS-7
❑ 88FleGlo-276
❑ 88FleGlo-624
❑ 88FleHotS-5
❑ 88FleLeaL-4
❑ 88FleMin-45
❑ 88FleRecS-4
❑ 88FleSlu-6
❑ 88FleStiC-54
❑ 88FleSup-5
❑ 88FleTeaL-3
❑ 88K-M-4
❑ 88KayB-3
❑ 88Lea-138
❑ 88Nes-37
❑ 88OPC-370
❑ 88PanSti-173
❑ 88Sco-45
❑ 88ScoGlo-45
❑ 88ScoYouSI-30
❑ 88Spo-201
❑ 88StaCan-1
❑ 88StaCan-2
❑ 88StaCan-3
❑ 88StaCan-4
❑ 88StaCan-5
❑ 88StaCan-6
❑ 88StaCan-7
❑ 88StaCan-8
❑ 88StaCan-9
❑ 88StaCan-10
❑ 88StaCan-11
❑ 88StaLinAs-2
❑ 88TarPla-7
❑ 88Top-370
❑ 88Top-759
❑ 88TopBig-13
❑ 88TopClo-71
❑ 88TopCoi-7
❑ 88TopGloS-55
❑ 88TopMinL-30
❑ 88TopSti-173
❑ 88TopStiB-48
❑ 88TopTif-370
❑ 88TopTif-759
❑ 88TopUKM-10
❑ 88TopUKMT-10
❑ 89A'sMot-7
❑ 89A'sMot-28
❑ 89A'sMotR-1
❑ 89A'sMotR-4
❑ 89Baz-5
❑ 89Bow-201
❑ 89BowTif-201
❑ 89CadEllD-5
❑ 89CerSup-12
❑ 89ClaLigB-3
❑ 89ClaTraO-103
❑ 89CMCCan-1
❑ 89CMCCan-2
❑ 89CMCCan-3
❑ 89CMCCan-4
❑ 89CMCCan-5
❑ 89CMCCan-6
❑ 89CMCCan-7
❑ 89CMCCan-8
❑ 89CMCCan-9
❑ 89CMCCan-10
❑ 89CMCCan-11
❑ 89CMCCan-12
❑ 89CMCCan-13
❑ 89CMCCan-14
❑ 89CMCCan-15
❑ 89CMCCan-16
❑ 89CMCCan-17
❑ 89CMCCan-18
❑ 89CMCCan-19
❑ 89CMCCan-20
❑ 89CMCCan-P1
❑ 89Don-91
❑ 89Don-643
❑ 89DonAll-2
❑ 89DonAll-30
❑ 89DonBasB-57
❑ 89DonBonM-BC5
❑ 89DonGraS-1
❑ 89DonPop-2
❑ 89Fle-5
❑ 89Fle-628
❑ 89Fle-634
❑ 89FleAll-2
❑ 89FleBasA-5
❑ 89FleBasM-6
❑ 89FleExcS-3
❑ 89FleGlo-5
❑ 89FleGlo-628
❑ 89FleGlo-634
❑ 89FleGlo-WS3
❑ 89FleHeroB-5
❑ 89FleLeaL-3
❑ 89FleSup-6
❑ 89FleWaxBC-C4
❑ 89FleWorS-3
❑ 89K-M-18
❑ 89KayB-3
❑ 89KeyFooD-18
❑ 89KinDis-17
❑ 89MasBreD-10
❑ 89ModA'sC-34
❑ 89MotCan-1
❑ 89MotCan-2
❑ 89MotCan-3
❑ 89MotCan-4
❑ 89MSAHolD-5
❑ 89MSAIceTD-18
❑ 89Nis-5
❑ 89OPC-389
❑ 89OurOwnTD-18
❑ 89PanSti-8
❑ 89PanSti-238
❑ 89PanSti-246
❑ 89PanSti-422
❑ 89PanSti-477
❑ 89PanSti-480
❑ 89RedFolSB-18
❑ 89Sco-1
❑ 89Sco-582
❑ 89Sco-655
❑ 89ScoHot1S-1
❑ 89Scomast-40
❑ 89Spo-1
❑ 89Spo-221
❑ 89SpoIllFKI-11
❑ 89TacTigP-1536
❑ 89TetTeaD-18
❑ 89Top-401
❑ 89Top-500
❑ 89TopAme2C-8
❑ 89TopBasT-60
❑ 89TopBig-190
❑ 89TopCapC-1
❑ 89TopCoi-29
❑ 89TopDouA-5
❑ 89TopGaloC-2
❑ 89TopGloA-6
❑ 89TopGloS-12
❑ 89TopHeaUT-18
❑ 89TopHilTM-5
❑ 89TopMinL-68
❑ 89TopSti-11
❑ 89TopSti-148
❑ 89TopSti-171
❑ 89TopStiB-13
❑ 89TopTif-401
❑ 89TopTif-500
❑ 89TopUKM-12
❑ 89TVSpoM-93
❑ 89TVSpoM-125
❑ 89TVSpoM-133
❑ 89UppDec-371
❑ 89UppDec-659A
❑ 89UppDec-659B
❑ 89UppDec-670
❑ 89WeiMarD-18
❑ 89Woo-1
❑ 89Woo-23
❑ 90A'sMot-6
❑ 90AllBasT-15
❑ 90BasWit-11
❑ 90Bow-460
❑ 90BowTif-460
❑ 90ClaBlu-22
❑ 90ClaYel-T32
❑ 90Col-25
❑ 90ColCan-1
❑ 90ColCan-2
❑ 90ColCan-3
❑ 90ColCan-4
❑ 90ColCan-5
❑ 90ColCan-6
❑ 90ColCan-7
❑ 90ColCan-8
❑ 90ColCan-9
❑ 90ColCan-10
❑ 90ColCan-11
❑ 90ColCan-12
❑ 90Don-125
❑ 90DonBesA-81
❑ 90DonLeaS-6
❑ 90Fle-3
❑ 90Fle-629
❑ 90FleAwaW-6
❑ 90FleBasA-4
❑ 90FleBasAC-4
❑ 90FleBasM-6
❑ 90FleBasMC-6
❑ 90FleCan-3
❑ 90FleCan-629
❑ 90FleLeaL-5
❑ 90FleLeaLC-5
❑ 90FleLeaS-4
❑ 90FleWorS-5
❑ 90FleWorS-10
❑ 90GooHumICBLS-5
❑ 90HOFStiB-95
❑ 90Hot50PS-4
❑ 90K-M-21
❑ 90Lea-108
❑ 90M.Vpin-72
❑ 90MLBBasB-78
❑ 90MotCan-1
❑ 90MotCan-2
❑ 90MotCan-3
❑ 90MotCan-4
❑ 90MSAIceTD-4
❑ 90OPC-250
❑ 90PanSti-142
❑ 90PepCan-1
❑ 90PepCan-2
❑ 90PepCan-3
❑ 90PepCan-4
❑ 90PepCan-5
❑ 90PepCan-6
❑ 90PepCan-7
❑ 90PepCan-8
❑ 90PepCan-9
❑ 90PepCan-10
❑ 90Pos-16
❑ 90PubIntS-279
❑ 90PubIntS-301
❑ 90RedFolSB-14
❑ 90Sco-375
❑ 90Sco-702
❑ 90Sco100S-5
❑ 90Spo-23
❑ 90SupActM-2
❑ 90Top-250
❑ 90TopAmeA-29
❑ 90TopBig-270
❑ 90TopDou-8
❑ 90TopGloS-31
❑ 90TopHeaU-18
❑ 90TopHilHM-7
❑ 90TopMag-21
❑ 90TopSti-177
❑ 90TopStiB-47
❑ 90TopTif-250
❑ 90TopTVA-11
❑ 90UppDec-66
❑ 90USPlaCA-WCO
❑ 90WinDis-8
❑ 90WonBreS-14
❑ 91A'sMot-6
❑ 91A'sSFE-2
❑ 91BasBesHRK-2
❑ 91BasBesRB-2
❑ 91Bow-227
❑ 91Bow-372
❑ 91CadEllD-7
❑ 91Cla2-T19
❑ 91Cla3-T6
❑ 91ClaGam-135
❑ 91Col-13
❑ 91Don-50A
❑ 91Don-50B
❑ 91Don-536
❑ 91DonEli-3
❑ 91DonGraS-4
❑ 91DonPre-11
❑ 91Fle-5
❑ 91FleAll-8
❑ 91FlePro-6
❑ 91FleWorS-3
❑ 91JimDea-19
❑ 91Lea-182
❑ 91MajLeaCP-38
❑ 91MooSna-1
❑ 91OPC-390
❑ 91OPC-700
❑ 91OPCPre-18
❑ 91PanCanT1-15
❑ 91PanCanT1-24
❑ 91PanCanT1-39
❑ 91PanFreS-173
❑ 91PanFreS-198
❑ 91PanSti-149
❑ 91PepSup-17
❑ 91PerGamC-1
❑ 91Pos-4
❑ 91RedFolS-17
❑ 91RedFolS-116
❑ 91Sco-1
❑ 91Sco-398
❑ 91Sco-441
❑ 91Sco-690
❑ 91Sco100S-1
❑ 91SevCoi-A6

❑ 91SevCoi-T3
❑ 91SevCoi-NC2
❑ 91SevCoi-NW2
❑ 91SevCoi-SC2
❑ 91SouOreAAP-SOA1
❑ 91SouOreAAP-SOA14
❑ 91SpoNSP-1
❑ 91StaClu-155
❑ 91StaCluMO-29
❑ 91StaPinB-7
❑ 91Stu-101
❑ 91Top-390
❑ 91Top-700
❑ 91TopCraJI-10
❑ 91TopDesS-390
❑ 91TopDesS-700
❑ 91TopGloA-8
❑ 91TopMic-390
❑ 91TopMic-700
❑ 91TopSta-7
❑ 91TopTif-390
❑ 91TopTif-700
❑ 91TopTriH-A11
❑ 91Ult-244
❑ 91UppDec-146
❑ 91UppDec-155
❑ 91UppDecSS-SS4
❑ 92A'sUno7P-1
❑ 92A'sUno7P-2
❑ 92AthMot-6
❑ 92Bow-600
❑ 92Cla1-T22
❑ 92Cla2-T3
❑ 92Cla2-NNO
❑ 92ClaGam-110
❑ 92ColAllG-21
❑ 92ColAllP-21
❑ 92ColPro-4
❑ 92DenHol-22
❑ 92Don-548
❑ 92DonCraJ1-25
❑ 92DonMcD-13
❑ 92Fle-252
❑ 92Fle-688
❑ 92FleAll-24
❑ 92FleCitTP-13
❑ 92FleLumC-L5
❑ 92FleTeaL-19
❑ 92FleUpd-59
❑ 92Fre-4
❑ 92Hig5-102
❑ 92Hig5S-5
❑ 92LaKdec-5
❑ 92Lea-267
❑ 92LeaBlaG-267
❑ 92LeaGolP-23
❑ 92LeaPre-23
❑ 92MSABenSHD-12
❑ 92MVPPin-25
❑ 92OPC-100
❑ 92OPCPre-24
❑ 92PanSti-19
❑ 92PanSti-144
❑ 92PepDieM-24
❑ 92Pin-130
❑ 92PinSlu-3
❑ 92Pos-25
❑ 92PosCan-16
❑ 92RedFolS-22
❑ 92RemUltP-P4
❑ 92RemUltP-P5
❑ 92RemUltP-P6
❑ 92RemUltP-P19
❑ 92Sco-500
❑ 92Sco100S-67
❑ 92ScoImpP-52
❑ 92ScoProaG-8
❑ 92ScoRoo-9T
❑ 92SevCoi-21
❑ 92SpoStaCC-7
❑ 92StaClu-370
❑ 92StaClu-597
❑ 92StaCluMP-3
❑ 92Stu-222
❑ 92StuHer-BC4
❑ 92SunSee-18
❑ 92Top-100
❑ 92Top-314
❑ 92Top-401
❑ 92TopGol-100
❑ 92TopGol-314
❑ 92TopGol-401
❑ 92TopGolW-100
❑ 92TopGolW-314
❑ 92TopGolW-401
❑ 92TopKid-115
❑ 92TopMcD-22
❑ 92TopMic-100
❑ 92TopMic-314
❑ 92TopMic-401
❑ 92TopMic-G100
❑ 92TriPla-214
❑ 92Ult-110
❑ 92Ult-133
❑ 92UppDec-196
❑ 92UppDec-333
❑ 92UppDec-640
❑ 92UppDec-649
❑ 92UppDecF-17
❑ 92UppDecFG-17
❑ 92UppDecHRH-HR1
❑ 92UppDecTMH-14
❑ 92UppDecWB-T3
❑ 93Bow-545
❑ 93CadDis-10
❑ 93ClaGam-18
❑ 93DiaMar-22
❑ 93Don-159
❑ 93DonLonBL-LL6
❑ 93DonMasotG-7
❑ 93DonPre-21
❑ 93DonSpiotG-SG5
❑ 93DurPowP2-19
❑ 93Fin-99
❑ 93FinJum-99
❑ 93FinRef-99
❑ 93Fla-278
❑ 93Fle-319
❑ 93FleFruotL-9
❑ 93FunPac-12
❑ 93FunPac-155
❑ 93Hos-10
❑ 93Lea-241
❑ 93LeaGolA-R9
❑ 93MetBak-22
❑ 93OPC-47
❑ 93OPCPre-81
❑ 93PacBeiA-14
❑ 93PacBeiA-15
❑ 93PacBeiA-27
❑ 93PacSpa-308
❑ 93PacSpaGE-13
❑ 93PacSpaPl-11
❑ 93PanSti-85
❑ 93Pin-49
❑ 93PinHomRC-10
❑ 93PinSlu-24
❑ 93RanKee-399
❑ 93RanStaC-28
❑ 93RedFolS-16
❑ 93Sco-13
❑ 93Sel-364
❑ 93SP-191
❑ 93StaClu-499
❑ 93StaCluFDI-499
❑ 93StaCluMOP-499
❑ 93StaCluMP-14
❑ 93Stu-47
❑ 93StuSupoC-2
❑ 93Top-500
❑ 93TopGol-500
❑ 93TopInaM-500
❑ 93TopInaR-500
❑ 93TopMic-500
❑ 93TriPla-243
❑ 93Ult-627
❑ 93UppDec-52
❑ 93UppDec-365
❑ 93UppDecCP-R4
❑ 93UppDecGold-52
❑ 93UppDecGold-365
❑ 93UppDecOD-D7
❑ 93UppDecTriCro-TC2
❑ 94Bow-600
❑ 94BowBes-R24
❑ 94BowBesR-R24
❑ 94ColC-560
❑ 94ColChoGS-560
❑ 94ColChoSS-560
❑ 94Don-372
❑ 94DonDom-A7
❑ 94DonDomJ-A7
❑ 94DonSpeE-372
❑ 94Fin-222
❑ 94FinJum-222
❑ 94FinRef-222
❑ 94Fla-344
❑ 94Fle-304
❑ 94FleExtB-176
❑ 94FleExtBGB-5
❑ 94FUnPac-133
❑ 94FUnPac-209
❑ 94Lea-249
❑ 94LeaL-70
❑ 94LeaMVPC-A3
❑ 94LeaMVPCG-A3
❑ 94OPC-169
❑ 94Pac-611
❑ 94PacAll-15
❑ 94PanSti-125
❑ 94Pin-306
❑ 94PinArtP-306
❑ 94PinMusC-306
❑ 94ProMag-132
❑ 94RedFolMI-8
❑ 94Sco-61
❑ 94ScoGolR-61
❑ 94Sel-276
❑ 94SP-146
❑ 94SPDieC-146
❑ 94SPHol-4
❑ 94SPHolDC-4
❑ 94Spo-141
❑ 94StaClu-171
❑ 94StaCluFDI-171
❑ 94StaCluGR-171
❑ 94StaCluMOP-171
❑ 94StaCluMOP-ST27
❑ 94StaCluST-ST27
❑ 94StaCluT-250
❑ 94StaCluTFDI-250
❑ 94Stu-152
❑ 94Top-80
❑ 94TopGol-80
❑ 94TopSpa-80
❑ 94TopSupS-7
❑ 94TriPla-192
❑ 94Ult-428
❑ 94UppDec-140
❑ 94UppDecAJ-34
❑ 94UppDecAJG-34
❑ 94UppDecED-140
❑ 94UppDecMLS-MM4
❑ 94UppDecMLSED-MM4
❑ 95Baz-42
❑ 95BazRedH-RH9
❑ 95Bow-417
❑ 95BowBes-R29
❑ 95BowBesR-R29
❑ 95ClaPhoC-7
❑ 95ColCho-415
❑ 95ColChoCtG-CG4
❑ 95ColChoCtG-CG4B
❑ 95ColChoCtG-CG4C
❑ 95ColChoCtGE-4
❑ 95ColChoCtGG-CG4
❑ 95ColChoCtGG-CG4B
❑ 95ColChoCtGG-CG4C
❑ 95ColChoCtGGE-4
❑ 95ColChoGS-415
❑ 95ColChoSE-185
❑ 95ColChoSEGS-185
❑ 95ColChoSESS-185
❑ 95ColChoSS-415
❑ 95Don-350
❑ 95DonBomS-4
❑ 95DonEli-59
❑ 95DonLonBL-6
❑ 95DonPreP-350
❑ 95DonTopotO-18
❑ 95Emo-9
❑ 95Fin-170
❑ 95FinRef-170
❑ 95Fla-226
❑ 95FlaOutP-4
❑ 95Fle-281
❑ 95FleLumC-4
❑ 95FleTeaL-13
❑ 95FleUpd-9
❑ 95FleUpdH-4
❑ 95Lea-391
❑ 95LeaGolS-12
❑ 95LeaLim-21
❑ 95LeaLimG-9
❑ 95LeaLimL-12
❑ 95LeaOpeD-7
❑ 95NatPac-9
❑ 95Pac-33
❑ 95PacGolCDC-5
❑ 95PacGolP-1
❑ 95PacLatD-6
❑ 95PacPri-134
❑ 95PanSti-92
❑ 95Pin-49
❑ 95PinArtP-49
❑ 95PinMusC-49
❑ 95RedFol-35
❑ 95Sco-4
❑ 95ScoGolR-4
❑ 95ScoHaloG-HG13
❑ 95ScoPlaTS-4
❑ 95ScoRul-SR11
❑ 95ScoRulJ-SR11
❑ 95ScoSam-4
❑ 95Sel-231
❑ 95SelArtP-231
❑ 95SelCerGT-12
❑ 95SP-130
❑ 95SPCha-127
❑ 95SPChaDC-127
❑ 95Spo-127
❑ 95SpoArtP-127
❑ 95SpoPro-PM8
❑ 95SPSil-130
❑ 95SPSpeF-1
❑ 95StaClu-214
❑ 95StaClu-347
❑ 95StaClu-630
❑ 95StaCluCC-CC10
❑ 95StaCluCT-6
❑ 95StaCluFDI-214
❑ 95StaCluMO-10
❑ 95StaCluMOP-214
❑ 95StaCluMOP-347
❑ 95StaCluMOP-630
❑ 95StaCluMOP-CC10
❑ 95StaCluMOP-RL8
❑ 95StaCluRL-RL8
❑ 95StaCluSTDW-RS347
❑ 95StaCluSTWS-214
❑ 95StaCluSTWS-347
❑ 95StaCluSTWS-630
❑ 95StaCluVR-183
❑ 95StaCluVRMO-183
❑ 95Stu-9
❑ 95StuGolS-9
❑ 95StuPlaS-9
❑ 95Sum-19
❑ 95Sum-185
❑ 95SumBigB-BB12
❑ 95SumNthD-19
❑ 95SumNthD-185
❑ 95SumSam-BB12
❑ 95Top-300
❑ 95TopCyb-161
❑ 95TopCybSiR-2
❑ 95TopFinIns-14
❑ 95TopLeaL-LL10
❑ 95TopTra-72T
❑ 95UC3-60
❑ 95UC3ArtP-60
❑ 95UC3CycS-CS9
❑ 95Ult-260
❑ 95UltGolM-260
❑ 95UltHitM-5
❑ 95UltHitMGM-5
❑ 95UltHomRK-4
❑ 95UltHomRKGM-4
❑ 95UppDec-158
❑ 95UppDecED-158
❑ 95UppDecEDG-158
❑ 95UppDecPAW-H30
❑ 95UppDecPAWE-H30
❑ 95UppDecPLL-R2
❑ 95UppDecPLL-R42
❑ 95UppDecPLLE-R2
❑ 95UppDecPLLE-R42
❑ 95UppDecSE-213
❑ 95UppDecSEG-213
❑ 95UppDecSoaD-SD10
❑ 95USPlaCMLA-7C
❑ 95Zen-56
❑ 96Baz-108
❑ 96Bow-23
❑ 96BowBes-57
❑ 96BowBesAR-57
❑ 96BowBesR-57
❑ 96BowFoi-23
❑ 96Cir-9
❑ 96CirBos-3
❑ 96CirRav-9
❑ 96ColCho-101
❑ 96ColCho-327
❑ 96ColCho-475
❑ 96ColChoCtG-CG5
❑ 96ColChoCtG-CG5B
❑ 96ColChoCtG-CG5C
❑ 96ColChoCtGE-CR5
❑ 96ColChoCtGG-CG5
❑ 96ColChoCtGG-CG5B
❑ 96ColChoCtGG-CG5C
❑ 96ColChoCtGGE-CR5
❑ 96ColChoGS-101
❑ 96ColChoGS-327
❑ 96ColChoGS-475
❑ 96ColChoSS-101
❑ 96ColChoSS-327
❑ 96ColChoSS-475
❑ 96ColChoYMtP-10
❑ 96ColChoYMtP-10A
❑ 96ColChoYMtPGS-10
❑ 96ColChoYMtPGS-10A
❑ 96Don-266
❑ 96DonPreP-266
❑ 96EmoN-3
❑ 96EmoXL-11
❑ 96Fin-B221
❑ 96Fin-G117
❑ 96FinRef-B221
❑ 96FinRef-G117
❑ 96Fla-15
❑ 96Fle-24
❑ 96FleRedS-2
❑ 96FleTif-24
❑ 96FleUpd-U216
❑ 96FleUpdTC-U216
❑ 96Lea-64
❑ 96LeaPre-86
❑ 96LeaPreP-86
❑ 96LeaPrePB-64
❑ 96LeaPrePG-64
❑ 96LeaPrePS-64
❑ 96LeaPreSG-47
❑ 96LeaPreSte-47
❑ 96LeaSig-105
❑ 96LeaSigPPG-105
❑ 96LeaSigPPP-105
❑ 96MetUni-12
❑ 96MetUniP-12
❑ 96Pac-246
❑ 96PacEstL-EL7
❑ 96PacGolCD-DC17
❑ 96PacHom-HP12
❑ 96PacMil-M4
❑ 96PacOctM-OM4
❑ 96PacPri-P78
❑ 96PacPriFB-FB5
❑ 96PacPriG-P78
❑ 96PacPriRHS-RH2
❑ 96PanSti-135
❑ 96Pin-36
❑ 96PinAfi-37
❑ 96PinAfiAP-37
❑ 96PinAfiFPP-37
❑ 96PinArtP-17
❑ 96PinSta-17
❑ 96ProMagA-2
❑ 96ProSta-107
❑ 96Sco-303
❑ 96ScoDugC-B28
❑ 96ScoDugCAP-B28
❑ 96Sel-91
❑ 96SelArtP-91
❑ 96SelCer-98
❑ 96SelCerAP-98
❑ 96SelCerCB-98
❑ 96SelCerCR-98
❑ 96SelCerMB-98
❑ 96SelCerMG-98
❑ 96SelCerMR-98
❑ 96SelTeaN-8
❑ 96SP-38
❑ 96Spo-94
❑ 96SpoArtP-94
❑ 96SPSpeFX-32
❑ 96SPSpeFXDC-32
❑ 96SPx-8
❑ 96SPxGol-8
❑ 96StaClu-223
❑ 96StaClu-342
❑ 96StaCluEPB-342
❑ 96StaCluEPG-342
❑ 96StaCluEPS-342
❑ 96StaCluMet-M3
❑ 96StaCluMOP-223
❑ 96StaCluMOP-342
❑ 96StaCluMOP-M3
❑ 96StaCluMOP-PP3
❑ 96StaCluPP-PP3
❑ 96Stu-53
❑ 96StuPrePB-53
❑ 96StuPrePG-53
❑ 96StuPrePS-53
❑ 96Sum-23
❑ 96SumAbo&B-23
❑ 96SumArtP-23
❑ 96SumFoi-23
❑ 96Top-362
❑ 96TopChr-146
❑ 96TopChrR-146
❑ 96TopChrWC-WC4
❑ 96TopChrWCR-WC4
❑ 96TopGal-33
❑ 96TopGalE-14
❑ 96TopGalPPI-33
❑ 96TopLas-38
❑ 96TopLasPC-11
❑ 96TopWreC-WC4
❑ 96Ult-15
❑ 96UltGolM-15
❑ 96UltHomRK-4
❑ 96UltHomRKGM-4
❑ 96UltHomRKR-4
❑ 96UltHomRKRGM-4
❑ 96UltThu-4
❑ 96UltThuGM-4
❑ 96UppDec-285
❑ 96UppDecPD-PD4
❑ 96UppDecRunP-RP5
❑ 96UppDecVJLS-VJ7
❑ 97A'sMot-3
❑ 97Bow-254
❑ 97BowBes-72
❑ 97BowBesAR-72
❑ 97BowBesR-72
❑ 97BowChr-77
❑ 97BowChrI-77
❑ 97BowChrIR-77
❑ 97BowChrR-77
❑ 97BowInt-254
❑ 97Cir-119
❑ 97CirRav-119
❑ 97ColCho-45
❑ 97ColCho-410
❑ 97ColChoCtG-23A
❑ 97ColChoCtG-23B
❑ 97ColChoCtG-23C
❑ 97ColChoCtGE-CG23
❑ 97ColChoCtGIW-CG23
❑ 97ColChoNF-NF3
❑ 97ColChoTBS-9
❑ 97ColChoTBSWH-9
❑ 97Don-54
❑ 97Don-277
❑ 97DonEli-52
❑ 97DonEliGS-52
❑ 97DonGolPP-54
❑ 97DonGolPP-277
❑ 97DonLim-17
❑ 97DonLim-168
❑ 97DonLimE-17
❑ 97DonLimE-168
❑ 97DonLimENG-17
❑ 97DonLonL-15
❑ 97DonPre-30
❑ 97DonPreCttC-30
❑ 97DonSig-57
❑ 97DonSigPPP-57
❑ 97DonSilPP-54
❑ 97DonSilPP-277
❑ 97E-X2-37
❑ 97E-X2Cred-37
❑ 97E-X2EssCre-37
❑ 97Fin-101
❑ 97Fin-284
❑ 97FinEmb-101
❑ 97FinEmb-284
❑ 97FinEmbR-101
❑ 97FinEmbR-284
❑ 97FinRef-101
❑ 97FinRef-284
❑ 97FlaShoLC-109
❑ 97FlaShoLeg0-109
❑ 97FlaShoLeg1-109
❑ 97FlaShoM-A109
❑ 97FlaShoM-B109
❑ 97FlaShoM-C109
❑ 97FlaShoR0-109
❑ 97FlaShoR1-109
❑ 97FlaShoR2-109
❑ 97Fle-18
❑ 97Fle-535
❑ 97FleTif-18
❑ 97FleTif-535
❑ 97HigMinM-20
❑ 97Lea-195
❑ 97Lea-206
❑ 97LeaFraM-195
❑ 97LeaFraM-206
❑ 97LeaFraMDC-195
❑ 97LeaFraMDC-206
❑ 97MetUni-19
❑ 97NewPin-15
❑ 97NewPinAP-15
❑ 97NewPinMC-15
❑ 97NewPinPP-15

❑ 97Pac-34
❑ 97PacCar-5
❑ 97PacCarM-5
❑ 97PacGolCD-6
❑ 97PacLatotML-5
❑ 97PacLigB-34
❑ 97PacPri-13
❑ 97PacPriLB-13
❑ 97PacPriP-13
❑ 97PacPriSH-SH2A
❑ 97PacSil-34
❑ 97Pin-25
❑ 97PinArtP-PP25
❑ 97PinCer-90
❑ 97PinCerMBla-90
❑ 97PinCerMBlu-90
❑ 97PinCerMG-90
❑ 97PinCerMR-90
❑ 97PinCerR-90
❑ 97PinIns-79
❑ 97PinInsCE-79
❑ 97PinInsDE-79
❑ 97PinMusC-25
❑ 97PinPrePla-25
❑ 97PinTotCPB-90
❑ 97PinTotCPG-90
❑ 97PinTotCPR-90
❑ 97PinX-P-12
❑ 97PinX-PMoS-12
❑ 97PinX-PSfF-15
❑ 97PinX-PSfFU-15
❑ 97RedSoxS-7
❑ 97RedSoxSPl-7
❑ 97RedSoxSPr-7
❑ 97Sco-170
❑ 97Sco-360
❑ 97ScoArtPWB-170
❑ 97ScoArtPWB-360
❑ 97ScoPreS-170
❑ 97ScoResC-360
❑ 97ScoShoS-170
❑ 97ScoShoS-360
❑ 97ScoShoSAP-170
❑ 97ScoShoSAP-360
❑ 97Sel-5
❑ 97SelArtP-5
❑ 97SelCom-5
❑ 97SelRegG-5
❑ 97SP-131
❑ 97SpoIll-166
❑ 97SpoIllEE-166
❑ 97SPSpeF-39
❑ 97SPSpxF-4
❑ 97SPSPxFA-4
❑ 97SPx-37
❑ 97SPxBro-37
❑ 97SPxGol-37
❑ 97SPxGraF-37
❑ 97SPxSil-37
❑ 97SPxSte-37
❑ 97StaClu-234
❑ 97StaCluMat-234
❑ 97StaCluMOP-234
❑ 97Stu-35
❑ 97StuPrePG-35
❑ 97StuPrePS-35
❑ 97Top-246
❑ 97TopChr-87
❑ 97TopChrR-87
❑ 97TopGal-8
❑ 97TopGalPPI-8
❑ 97TopMemO5-12
❑ 97TopSta-19
❑ 97TopStaAM-19
❑ 97Ult-12
❑ 97Ult-376
❑ 97UltDouT-2
❑ 97UltGolME-12
❑ 97UltGolME-376
❑ 97UltPlaME-12
❑ 97UltPlaME-376
❑ 97UppDec-24
❑ 97UppDecPP-PP18
❑ 97UppDecPPJ-PP18
❑ 98Bow-277
❑ 98BowChr-277
❑ 98BowChrGA-277
❑ 98BowChrGAR-277
❑ 98BowChrI-277
❑ 98BowChrIR-277
❑ 98BowChrR-277
❑ 98BowGolA-277
❑ 98BowInt-277
❑ 98CirThu-46
❑ 98CirThuRav-46
❑ 98CirThuSupRav-46
❑ 98ColCho-200
❑ 98ColCho-523
❑ 98ColChoER-ER20
❑ 98CroRoy-141
❑ 98CroRoyDK-25
❑ 98CroRoyHRF-10
❑ 98Don-125
❑ 98Don-198
❑ 98DonCol-125
❑ 98DonColL-308
❑ 98DonColP-596
❑ 98DonColS-125
❑ 98DonCruG-37
❑ 98DonCruP-37
❑ 98DonCruR-37
❑ 98DonGolPP-125
❑ 98DonGolPP-198
❑ 98DonPre-46
❑ 98DonPreSeat-46
❑ 98DonPriCD-125
❑ 98DonPriCL-308
❑ 98DonPriCP-596
❑ 98DonSilPP-125
❑ 98DonSilPP-198
❑ 98E-X2-40
❑ 98E-X2ECFut-40
❑ 98E-X2ECNow-40
❑ 98Fin-26
❑ 98FinNo--26
❑ 98FinNo-R-26
❑ 98FinRef-26
❑ 98Fle-66
❑ 98Fle-376
❑ 98FlePlaCS-1
❑ 98FleVin'-125
❑ 98FleVin'C-125
❑ 98Lea-109
❑ 98LeaFraDA-109
❑ 98LeaFraF-109
❑ 98LeaFraM-109
❑ 98LeaFraM-109
❑ 98LeaFraMDC-109
❑ 98LeaFraMDC-109
❑ 98LeaFraMS-109
❑ 98LeaFraMZ2-109
❑ 98LeaRS-60
❑ 98LeaRSLHolo-60
❑ 98LeaRSLong-60
❑ 98LeaRTrue-60
❑ 98MetUni-63
❑ 98MetUniPMG-63
❑ 98Pac-164
❑ 98PacAur-91
❑ 98PacAurPF-47
❑ 98PacAurPFC-47
❑ 98PacAurPFPB-47
❑ 98PacAurPFR-47
❑ 98PacAurPFS-47
❑ 98PacHomRH-6
❑ 98PacInv-57
❑ 98PacInvPBlue-57
❑ 98PacInvSilv-57
❑ 98PacInvTeam-20
❑ 98PacLatotML-29
❑ 98PacNes-15
❑ 98PacOme-244
❑ 98PacOmeR-244
❑ 98PacOnl-753
❑ 98PacOnlR-753
❑ 98PacOnlWC-753
❑ 98PacPar-110
❑ 98PacParC-110
❑ 98PacParG-110
❑ 98PacParHS-110
❑ 98PacParPB-110
❑ 98PacParR-110
❑ 98PacPlaB-164
❑ 98PacRedT-164
❑ 98PacSil-164
❑ 98PacTeaC-11
❑ 98Pin-59
❑ 98PinArtP-PP52
❑ 98PinMusC-PP52
❑ 98PinPer-47
❑ 98PinPerPP-47
❑ 98PinPerSftF-4
❑ 98PinPreP-59
❑ 98Revo-147
❑ 98RevoShow-19
❑ 98RevoSS-147
❑ 98ScoRT-118
❑ 98ScoRTSS-PP74
❑ 98ScoRTSSAP-PP74
❑ 98ScoRTSSAP1-PP74
❑ 98SP Aut-193
❑ 98SpoIll-20
❑ 98SpoIllC-C10
❑ 98SpoIllEE-20
❑ 98SpoIllFE-20
❑ 98SpoIllTaN-68
❑ 98SpoIllTaNEE-68
❑ 98SPxFin-328
❑ 98SPxFin-349
❑ 98SPxFinR-328
❑ 98SPxFinR-349
❑ 98SPxFinS-328
❑ 98SPxFinS-349
❑ 98StaCluFDI-325
❑ 98StaCluI-325
❑ 98StaCluOneK-325
❑ 98StaCluPP-325
❑ 98Stu-14
❑ 98StuGPP-14
❑ 98StuSPP-14
❑ 98Top-110
❑ 98TopChr-110
❑ 98TopChrR-110
❑ 98TopDevR-110
❑ 98TopDia-110
❑ 98TopMiniC-110
❑ 98TopOpeD-57
❑ 98TopSta-89
❑ 98TopStaB-89
❑ 98TopStaG-89
❑ 98TopStaGR-89
❑ 98TopStaS-89
❑ 98Ult-75
❑ 98Ult-308
❑ 98UltGolM-75
❑ 98UltGolM-308
❑ 98UltMas-75
❑ 98UltMas-308
❑ 98UltPlaM-75
❑ 98UltPlaM-308
❑ 98UppDec-745
❑ 98UppDec10AP-47
❑ 98UppDec1APR-47
❑ 98UppDecNP-NP4
❑ 98UppDecR-98
❑ 98UppDecRBBop-BB18
❑ 98UppDecRTC-TC25
❑ 98UppDecTMT-16
❑ 98UppDecTMTG-16
❑ 99199Fin-231
❑ 99Bow-266
❑ 99BowBes-43
❑ 99BowBesAR-43
❑ 99BowBesR-43
❑ 99BowEarR-ER10
❑ 99BowGol-266
❑ 99BowInt-266
❑ 99CroRoyB-134
❑ 99CroRoyL-134
❑ 99CroRoyOD-134
❑ 99DumSet-ER10
❑ 99E-X Cen-67
❑ 99E-X CenECFut-67
❑ 99E-X CenECNow-67
❑ 99FinGolRef-231
❑ 99FinMil-M19
❑ 99FinRef-231
❑ 99FlaShoLeg1-61
❑ 99FlaShoLeg2-61
❑ 99FlaShoLeg3-61
❑ 99FlaShoLegM1-61
❑ 99FlaShoLegM2-61
❑ 99FlaShoLegM3-61
❑ 99FlaShoR1-61
❑ 99FlaShoR2-61
❑ 99FlaShoR3-61
❑ 99Fle-338
❑ 99FleBri-112
❑ 99FleBri2G-112
❑ 99FleBriBlu-112
❑ 99FleBriGol-112
❑ 99FleGolYar-3
❑ 99FleMys-58
❑ 99FleMysFI-8
❑ 99FleMysG-58
❑ 99FleMysM-58
❑ 99FleSta9-338
❑ 99FleWarT-338
❑ 99MetUni-160
❑ 99MetUniGM-160
❑ 99MetUniPMG-160
❑ 99Pac-435
❑ 99Pac-435A
❑ 99PacAur-184
❑ 99PacAurOD-184
❑ 99PacCroC-291
❑ 99PacCroC-22
❑ 99PacCroCPB-291
❑ 99PacCroCTC-30
❑ 99PacCroCTM-20
❑ 99PacGolCDC-18
❑ 99PacInv-140
❑ 99PacInvOD-140
❑ 99PacInvPB-140
❑ 99PacOme-229
❑ 99PacOme5T-17
❑ 99PacOme5TT-17
❑ 99PacOmeC-229
❑ 99PacOmeDM-32
❑ 99PacOmeEP-19
❑ 99PacOmeEP1o1-19
❑ 99PacOmeG-229
❑ 99PacOmeH'-19
❑ 99PacOmePB-229
❑ 99PacPar-225
❑ 99PacParC-225
❑ 99PacParG-225
❑ 99PacParHoloGold-225
❑ 99PacParHS-225
❑ 99PacParOD-225
❑ 99PacParPB-225
❑ 99PacParRed-225
❑ 99PacPlaB-435
❑ 99PacPlaB-435A
❑ 99PacPri-146
❑ 99PacPriHB-146
❑ 99PacPriHG-146
❑ 99PacPriHM-146
❑ 99PacPriHP-146
❑ 99PacPriRed-146
❑ 99PacPriS-27
❑ 99PacPriS206-27
❑ 99PacPriS206R-27
❑ 99PacPriSP-27
❑ 99PacPriSV-27
❑ 99PacRed-435
❑ 99PacRed-435A
❑ 99PacTim-10
❑ 99Rev-136
❑ 99RevDiaL-33
❑ 99RevPremDate-136
❑ 99RevRet-136
❑ 99RevShaSS-136
❑ 99RevTri-29
❑ 99RevTri-29
❑ 99SkyMolM-2
❑ 99SkyMolMX-2
❑ 99SkyPre-191
❑ 99SkyPreA-10
❑ 99SkyPreABlue-10
❑ 99SkyPreR-191
❑ 99SkyThu-22
❑ 99SkyThuRant-22
❑ 99SkyThuRave-22
❑ 99SkyThuTur-TC1
❑ 99SP Aut-84
❑ 99SP AutHRC-HR7
❑ 99SP SigAuto-JOC
❑ 99SP SigAutoG-JOC
❑ 99SPAutHRCDC-HR7
❑ 99SpoIll-83
❑ 99SpoIllF4-6
❑ 99SpoIllF4E-6
❑ 99SPSig-67
❑ 99StaClu-32
❑ 99StaCluFDI-32
❑ 99StaCluOoaK-32
❑ 99StaCluPP-32
❑ 99ThuSkySupR-22
❑ 99Top-80
❑ 99TopAll-AM7
❑ 99TopChr-80
❑ 99TopChrA-AE7
❑ 99TopChrAR-AE7
❑ 99TopChrR-80
❑ 99TopGal-62
❑ 99TopGalPP-62
❑ 99TopGalPPI-62
❑ 99TopMVPP-80
❑ 99TopOpeD-45
❑ 99TopSta-31
❑ 99TopSta1Foil-31
❑ 99TopSta2Foil-31
❑ 99TopStaFoil-31
❑ 99TopStaOS-31
❑ 99TopStaTS-31
❑ 99UD ChoYW-Y29
❑ 99UDHolo-55
❑ 99UDHoloAUsome-55
❑ 99Ult-206
❑ 99UltGolM-206
❑ 99UltMas-206
❑ 99UltPlaM-206
❑ 99UltRBIK-29
❑ 99UppDec-222
❑ 99UppDec-499
❑ 99UppDecCf7-12
❑ 99UppDecCf7-47
❑ 99UppDecCL-69
❑ 99UppDecCLCC-69
❑ 99UppDecCLM-C90
❑ 99UppDecCo7CE-12
❑ 99UppDecCo7CE-47
❑ 99UppDecE-85
❑ 99UppDecE-153
❑ 99UppDecEFXG-85
❑ 99UppDecEFXG-153
❑ 99UppDecEL1-222
❑ 99UppDecEL1-499
❑ 99UppDecEL2-222
❑ 99UppDecEL2-499
❑ 99UppDecM-197
❑ 99UppDecMGS-197
❑ 99UppDecMHFS-197
❑ 99UppDecMSS-197
❑ 99UppDecR-80
❑ 99UppDecRG-80
❑ 99UppDecRP-80
❑ 99Vic-388

Canseco, Ozzie
❑ 83GreHorT-3
❑ 87MadMusP-3
❑ 87MadMusP-6
❑ 88MadMusP-7
❑ 88MidLeaAGS-51
❑ 89HunStaB-28
❑ 89UppDec-756
❑ 90Bes-162
❑ 90FleUpd-117
❑ 90HunStaB-21
❑ 90Lea-516
❑ 91MajLeaCP-41
❑ 91OPC-162
❑ 91Sco-346
❑ 91Top-162
❑ 91TopDeb90-25
❑ 91TopDesS-162
❑ 91TopMic-162
❑ 91TopTif-162
❑ 91UppDec-146
❑ 92LouRedF-1898
❑ 92LouRedS-254
❑ 92SkyAAAF-124
❑ 93Bow-164
❑ 93CarPol-4
❑ 93CarStaC-14
❑ 93ClaFS7-128
❑ 93Don-336
❑ 93LouRedF-226
❑ 93PacBeiA-27
❑ 93PacSpa-630
❑ 93Pin-272
❑ 93Sco-241
❑ 93ScoBoyoS-25
❑ 93StaClu-634
❑ 93StaCluFDI-634
❑ 93StaCluMOP-634
❑ 94NewOrlZF-1480

Cantillon, Pongo (Joe)
❑ 11PinT-5-951
❑ 11SpoLifCW-53

Canton, Michael
❑ 92ElmPioC-4
❑ 92ElmPioF-1387

Cantrell, Dave
❑ 89SalSpuCLC-129
❑ 89SalSpuP-1826

Cantrell, Derrick
❑ 92ClaDraP-111

Cantrell, Guy
❑ 90DodTar-110

Cantrelle, Lee
❑ 91OklStaC-3

Cantres, Jorge
❑ 90YakBeaTI-35

Cantu, Mike
❑ 91HamRedC-19
❑ 91HamRedP-4044
❑ 92St.PetCF-2034
❑ 93FloStaLAF-43
❑ 93St.PetCC-8
❑ 93St.PetCF-2632
❑ 94ClaGolF-169
❑ 94St.PetCC-7
❑ 94St.PetCF-2591

Cantwell, Ben
❑ 30SchR33-25
❑ 33Gou-139
❑ 33TatOrbSDR-168
❑ 34BatR31-96
❑ 34DiaMatCSB-24
❑ 34GouCanV-14
❑ 35DiaMatCS3T1-24
❑ 35GouPuzR-8L
❑ 35GouPuzR-9L
❑ 36SandSW-5
❑ 90DodTar-111
❑ 91ConTSN-211

Cantwell, Rob
❑ 88SpoIndP-1924
❑ 89WatDiaP-1780
❑ 89WatDiaS-2

Cantz, Bart (Bartholomew L.)
❑ 87OldJudN-66

Capel, Mike
❑ 84MidCubT-10
❑ 86PitCubP-3
❑ 87IowCubTI-4
❑ 88DonRoo-46
❑ 88IowCubC-1
❑ 88IowCubP-547
❑ 89Fle-643
❑ 89FleGlo-643
❑ 89IowCubC-1
❑ 89IowCubP-1706
❑ 89Top-767
❑ 89TopTif-767
❑ 90CMC-30
❑ 90DenZepC-5
❑ 90DenZepP-618
❑ 90ProAAAF-643
❑ 91LinDriAAA-605
❑ 91TucTorLD-605
❑ 91TucTorP-2206
❑ 92Fle-429
❑ 92Sco-687
❑ 92TexLon-7
❑ 92TucTorF-480
❑ 92TucTorS-604
❑ 93TucTorF-3052
❑ 94BreMilB-12

Capellan, Carlos
❑ 88KenTwiP-1396
❑ 89CalLeaA-6
❑ 89VisOakCLC-112
❑ 89VisOakP-1441
❑ 90CalLeaACLC-9
❑ 90VisOakCLC-71
❑ 90VisOakP-2159
❑ 91LinDriAA-477
❑ 91OrlSunRLD-477
❑ 91OrlSunRP-1854
❑ 93LimRocDWB-132

Capellan, Rene
❑ 97WesMicW-7
❑ 98LakTigM-14

Capello, Pete
❑ 87AppFoxP-4
❑ 88VirGenS-4
❑ 89AppFoxP-865

Capilla, Doug
❑ 76TulOilGP-7
❑ 76VenLeaS-25
❑ 78OPC-11
❑ 78SSP270-127
❑ 78Top-477
❑ 80Top-628
❑ 81Don-587
❑ 81Fle-309
❑ 81Top-136
❑ 82Top-537
❑ 82WicAerTI-3
❑ 89PacSenL-172

Capista, Aaron
❑ 98MicBatCM-8

Caple, Kyle
❑ 92KenTwiF-607

Caplinger, Roger
❑ 91HelBreSP-28
❑ 93HelBreSP-26

Capowski, Jim
❑ 78AshTouT-3
❑ 79TulDriT-4

Cappadona, Pete
❑ 86NewBriRSP-5

Cappuccio, Carmine
❑ 92UtiBluSC-5
❑ 93SarWhiSC-6
❑ 93SarWhiSF-1382
❑ 93SouBenWSC-6
❑ 94PriWilCC-7
❑ 94PriWilCF-1933
❑ 95NasSouTI-5
❑ 96NasSouB-10

Cappuzzello, George

❑ 77EvaTriT-5
❑ 78IndIndTI-15
❑ 79IndIndTI-16
❑ 81EvaTriT-2
❑ 82AstAstI-10
❑ 82Fle-264
❑ 82Top-137
❑ 82TucTorT-20
❑ 83Top-422
❑ 84ColCliP-4
❑ 84ColCliT-7

Capra, Buzz (Lee)
❑ 72OPC-141
❑ 72Top-141
❑ 75AtlBraP-6
❑ 75OPC-105
❑ 75OPC-311
❑ 75Top-105
❑ 75Top-311
❑ 75TopMin-105
❑ 75TopMin-311
❑ 76AtlBraP-5
❑ 76Hos-85
❑ 76OPC-153
❑ 76SSP-1
❑ 76Top-153
❑ 77Top-432
❑ 78Top-578
❑ 83AndBraT-6
❑ 86AppFoxP-5
❑ 87BurExpP-1087
❑ 88SpaPhiP-1047
❑ 88SpaPhiS-7
❑ 90SpaPhiB-26
❑ 90SpaPhiS-27
❑ 91MetWIZ-61
❑ 91SpaPhiC-29
❑ 91SpaPhiP-914
❑ 92SpaPhiC-24
❑ 92SpaPhiF-1281
❑ 93SpaPhiC-27
❑ 93SpaPhiF-1072
❑ 94SpaPhiF-1739
❑ 94SparPhiC-26
❑ 95PitMetTI-38
❑ 96PitMetB-2
❑ 98CapCitBF5-30
❑ 98CapCitBM-30

Capra, Nick Lee
❑ 79TulDriT-20
❑ 80TulDriT-8
❑ 83OklCit8T-4
❑ 84OklCit8T-11
❑ 85OklCit8T-25
❑ 86BufBisP-7
❑ 87OklCit8P-23
❑ 88OmaRoyC-12
❑ 88OmaRoyP-1499
❑ 89Fle-279
❑ 89FleGlo-279
❑ 89OmaRoyC-19
❑ 89OmaRoyP-1742
❑ 90CMC-166
❑ 90OklCit8C-16
❑ 90OklCit8P-443
❑ 90ProAAAF-689
❑ 91LinDriAAA-307
❑ 91OklCit8LD-307
❑ 91OklCit8P-190
❑ 92NasSouF-1845
❑ 92NasSouS-280
❑ 93EdmTraF-1148
❑ 93RanKee-95
❑ 94EdmTraF-2884
❑ 95ChaKniTI-7
❑ 96BriWhiSB-1
❑ 97BriWhiSB-25
❑ 98BriWhiSQ-1

Capriati, Jeff
❑ 91PacSenL-76

Caprillo, Matias
❑ 85MexCitTT-25

Capriotti, Jeff
❑ 96MemChiB-4

Captain, Shreveport Mascot
❑ 98ShrCapM-8
❑ 98ShrCapWS-8

Captains, Shreveport
❑ 76ShrCapT-NNO
❑ 86ShrCapP-28

Capusano, Genaro
❑ 91Cla/Bes-161

Caraballo, Felix
❑ 88MadMusP-8
❑ 88ModA'sTI-5
❑ 90RenSilSCLC-281

Caraballo, Gary
❑ 90AppFoxBS-6
❑ 90AppFoxP-2100
❑ 91AppFoxCB-15
❑ 91AppFoxP-1721
❑ 91Cla/Bes-211
❑ 91MidLeaAP-MWL2
❑ 92BasCitRC-19
❑ 92Bow-54
❑ 92UppDecML-289
❑ 93WilBluRC-5
❑ 93WilBluRF-2002
❑ 94MemChiF-363
❑ 95ForMyeMTI-3
❑ 96HarCitRCB-10

Caraballo, Ramon
❑ 85PhiTas-41
❑ 86PhiTas-NNO
❑ 87ClePhiP-11
❑ 88ClePhiS-6
❑ 90Bes-260
❑ 90BurBraB-4
❑ 90BurBraP-2360
❑ 90BurBraS-8
❑ 90MidLeaASGS-27
❑ 90ProAaA-131
❑ 91Bow-584
❑ 91Cla/Bes-376
❑ 91DurBulC-24
❑ 91DurBulP-1551
❑ 92DonRooP-BC13
❑ 92GreBraS-231
❑ 92ProFS7-187
❑ 92RicBraBB-11
❑ 92SkyAA F-99
❑ 92UppDecML-210
❑ 93BraStaC-30
❑ 93RicBraBB-2
❑ 93RicBraF-189
❑ 93RicBraP-12
❑ 93RicBraRC-2
❑ 93RicBraRC-8
❑ 93Top-451
❑ 93TopGol-451
❑ 93TopInaM-451
❑ 93TopInaR-451
❑ 93TopMic-451
❑ 94BraUSPC-10S
❑ 94Cla-133
❑ 94GreBraTI-8
❑ 94Pac-7
❑ 94Pin-260
❑ 94PinArtP-260
❑ 94PinMusC-260
❑ 94RicBraF-2851
❑ 94StaCluT-44
❑ 94StaCluTFDI-44
❑ 95LouRedF-280
❑ 97IowCub-8
❑ 97RicBraBC-13

Caraballo, Wilmer
❑ 85LynMetT-21
❑ 86LynMetP-5
❑ 87BirBarB-6

Carabba, Robbie
❑ 92AlbPolCB-10
❑ 92AlbPolF-2313

Carabello, Nelson
❑ 89WelPirP-9

Caraccioli, Lance
❑ 98YakBeaG-8

Caradonna, Brett
❑ 97Bow-425
❑ 97BowChr-285
❑ 97BowChrI-285
❑ 97BowChrIR-285
❑ 97BowChrR-285
❑ 97BowInt-425
❑ 97TopSta-117
❑ 97TopStaAM-117
❑ 98BesNumOP-12
❑ 98Bow-84
❑ 98BowChr-84
❑ 98BowChrGA-84
❑ 98BowChrGAR-84
❑ 98BowChrI-84
❑ 98BowChrIR-84
❑ 98BowChrR-84
❑ 98BowGolA-84
❑ 98BowInt-84
❑ 98HicCraM-7
❑ 98SouAtlLPM-5

Caranza, Pedro
❑ 93PocPosF-4213

Caravelli, Michael
❑ 96BreCouMB-9
❑ 97BreCouMB-5

Caraway, Pat
❑ 30WhiSoxTI-6

Caray, Harry
❑ 88PeoChiTI-8

Carballo, Gary
❑ 92ClaFS7-176

Carballo, Jay
❑ 90EugEmeGS-4

Carballo, Lee
❑ 88SalLakCTTI-28
❑ 88VirGenS-5

Carbo, Bernie (Bernardo)
❑ 70DayDaiNM-50
❑ 70OPC-36
❑ 70Top-36
❑ 71CarTeal-7
❑ 71MLBOffS-51
❑ 71OPC-478
❑ 71Top-478
❑ 72OPC-463
❑ 72Top-463
❑ 73LinPor-166
❑ 73OPC-171
❑ 73Top-171
❑ 74OPC-621
❑ 74Top-621
❑ 75OPC-379
❑ 75Top-379
❑ 75TopMin-379
❑ 76OPC-278
❑ 76SSP-411
❑ 76Top-278
❑ 77Top-159
❑ 78SSP270-185
❑ 78Top-524
❑ 79Car5-3
❑ 79Top-38
❑ 80Top-266
❑ 89PacSenL-45
❑ 89T/MSenL-18
❑ 89TopSenL-13
❑ 90EliSenL-96
❑ 92UppDecS-14
❑ 94BreMilB-108
❑ 94TedWil-2
❑ 94TedWilM-M33

Carbonnet, Mark
❑ 92ColRedF-2395

Carcione, Tom (Thomas)
❑ 88SouOreAP-1699
❑ 89MadMusS-6
❑ 89ModA'sC-19
❑ 90ModA'sC-4
❑ 90ModA'sCLC-167
❑ 90ModA'sP-2215
❑ 91HunStaC-6
❑ 91HunStaLD-281
❑ 91HunStaP-1799
❑ 91LinDriAA-281
❑ 92HunStaS-306
❑ 92ModA'sC-24
❑ 92ModA'sF-3902

Cardenal, Jose
❑ 65Top-374
❑ 66AngDexP-2
❑ 66Top-505
❑ 66TopRubl-15
❑ 67CokCapDA-29
❑ 67OPC-193
❑ 67Top-193
❑ 67TopVen-203
❑ 68OPC-102
❑ 68Top-102
❑ 68TopVen-102
❑ 69MilBra-49
❑ 69MLBOffS-40
❑ 69Top-325
❑ 69TopSta-164
❑ 69TopSup-15
❑ 69TopTeaP-13
❑ 69TraSta-5
❑ 70CarTeal-7
❑ 70DayDaiNM-93
❑ 70DayDaiNM-125
❑ 70MLBOffS-136
❑ 70Top-675
❑ 71CarTeal-7
❑ 71Kel-26
❑ 71MLBOffS-270
❑ 71OPC-435
❑ 71Top-435
❑ 72MilBra-62
❑ 72OPC-12
❑ 72Top-12
❑ 72Top-757
❑ 73LinPor-40
❑ 73OPC-393
❑ 73Top-393
❑ 74GreHeroBP-6
❑ 74OPC-185
❑ 74Top-185
❑ 74TopDecE-55
❑ 74TopSta-12
❑ 75Hos-65
❑ 75HosTwi-65
❑ 75Kel-29
❑ 75OPC-15
❑ 75Top-15
❑ 75TopMin-15
❑ 76BlaDis-8
❑ 76BucDis-8
❑ 76CarDis-8
❑ 76CraDis-8
❑ 76CubTri-5
❑ 76DailsID-8
❑ 76Hos-37
❑ 76HosTwi-37
❑ 76IsaDis-8
❑ 76OPC-430
❑ 76OrbDis-8
❑ 76RedBarD-8
❑ 76SafDis-8
❑ 76SSP-310
❑ 76Top-430
❑ 76TowCluD-8
❑ 76VenLeaS-117
❑ 76VenLeaS-241
❑ 77BurCheD-197
❑ 77ChiWilD-11
❑ 77DailsID-11
❑ 77DetCaeD-11
❑ 77HolInnD-11
❑ 77Hos-85
❑ 77MSADis-11
❑ 77OPC-127
❑ 77RCColC-13
❑ 77SagDis-11
❑ 77sDis-11
❑ 77Top-610
❑ 77TopCloS-9
❑ 77WenDis-11
❑ 77ZipDis-11
❑ 78Top-210
❑ 79PhiBurK-18
❑ 79Top-317
❑ 80Top-512
❑ 81Top-473
❑ 89PacLegI-149
❑ 89SweBasG-61
❑ 91MetWIZ-62
❑ 93RedKah-8
❑ 94BreMilB-109

Cardenas, Daniel
❑ 90YakBeaTI-10
❑ 91BakDodCLC-22

Cardenas, Epi
❑ 92WatIndC-14
❑ 92WatIndF-3240
❑ 93ColRedC-6
❑ 93ColRedF-602
❑ 93SouAtlLAGF-12
❑ 94KinIndC-3
❑ 94KinIndF-2650

Cardenas, Johnny
❑ 93BelMarCB-7
❑ 93BelMarF-3212
❑ 94RivPilCLC-22
❑ 95PorCitRTI-3
❑ 96OklCit8B-5
❑ 96PorCitRB-8
❑ 98BirBarG-7

Cardenas, Leo (Leonardo L.)
❑ 60Top-119
❑ 60TopVen-119
❑ 61Top-244
❑ 61TopStal-16
❑ 62Kah-4
❑ 62RedEnq-3
❑ 62RedJayP-2
❑ 62Top-381
❑ 63Jel-127
❑ 63Kah-5
❑ 63Pos-127
❑ 63RedEnq-4
❑ 63RedFreBC-2
❑ 63Top-203
❑ 64Kah-3
❑ 64RedJayP-1
❑ 64Top-72
❑ 64TopVen-72
❑ 65Kah-6
❑ 65RedEnq-3
❑ 65Top-437
❑ 66Kah-7
❑ 66RedVolC-1
❑ 66Top-370
❑ 66TopVen-370
❑ 67CokCapR-2
❑ 67DexPre-42
❑ 67Kah-7
❑ 67OPCPapI-10
❑ 67Top-325
❑ 67TopPos-10
❑ 67TopTesF-4
❑ 67TopVen-310
❑ 68Kah-A5
❑ 68Kah-B11
❑ 68OPC-23
❑ 68Top-23
❑ 68Top-480
❑ 68TopVen-23
❑ 69MilBra-50
❑ 69Top-265
❑ 69TopTeaP-15
❑ 69TwiTealC-2
❑ 70DayDaiNM-119
❑ 70MLBOffS-231
❑ 70OPC-245
❑ 70Top-245
❑ 70TwiSupV-2
❑ 71MLBOffS-460
❑ 71OPC-405
❑ 71Top-405
❑ 71TopCoi-148
❑ 71TopTat-62
❑ 72Kel-30
❑ 72MilBra-63
❑ 72Top-561
❑ 72Top-562
❑ 73IndTeal-6
❑ 73OPC-522
❑ 73Top-522
❑ 75OPC-518
❑ 75RanPos-5
❑ 75Top-518
❑ 75TopMin-518
❑ 76OPC-587
❑ 76SSP-261
❑ 76Top-587
❑ 78TCM60I-69
❑ 78TwiFri-27
❑ 80Red196T-14
❑ 83WisRapTF-15
❑ 86RedGreT-7
❑ 91UppDecS-9
❑ 93RanKee-96

Cardieri, Ron
❑ 82MiaMarT-9

Cardiff, Patsy
❑ 88KimN18-7

Cardin, Mark
❑ 95DavLipB-5

Cardinal, Randy (Conrad)
❑ 63Top-562

Cardinals, Cedar Rapids
❑ 72CedRapCT-30

Cardinals, Orleans
❑ 88CapCodPB-22

Cardinals, St Louis
❑ 13FatT20-16
❑ 36R31Pre-G28
❑ 38BasTabP-33
❑ 46SpoExcW-11-3
❑ 51TopTea-8
❑ 56Top-134
❑ 57Top-243
❑ 58Top-216
❑ 59Top-223
❑ 60Top-242
❑ 60TopTat-62
❑ 61Top-347
❑ 61TopMagR-16
❑ 62GuyPotCP-18
❑ 62Top-61
❑ 62TopVen-61
❑ 63Top-524
❑ 64Top-87
❑ 64TopTatI-18
❑ 64TopVen-87
❑ 65OPC-57
❑ 65Top-57
❑ 66Top-379
❑ 66TopRubl-119
❑ 67OPC-173
❑ 67Top-173
❑ 68LauWorS-27
❑ 68LauWorS-39
❑ 68LauWorS-41
❑ 68Top-497
❑ 69FleCloS-20
❑ 69FleCloS-28
❑ 69TopStaA-20
❑ 70FleWorS-27
❑ 70FleWorS-31
❑ 70FleWorS-39
❑ 70FleWorS-40
❑ 70FleWorS-41
❑ 70FleWorS-64
❑ 70FleWorS-65
❑ 70Top-549
❑ 71FleWorS-32
❑ 71FleWorS-40
❑ 71FleWorS-41
❑ 71FleWorS-42
❑ 71FleWorS-62
❑ 71FleWorS-65
❑ 71FleWorS-66
❑ 71OPC-308
❑ 71Top-308
❑ 71TopTat-126
❑ 72Top-688
❑ 73OPC-219
❑ 73OPCBTC-23
❑ 73Top-219
❑ 73TopBluTC-23
❑ 74Car193T-31
❑ 74OPC-36
❑ 74OPCTC-23
❑ 74Top-36
❑ 74TopStaA-23
❑ 74TopTeaC-23
❑ 78Top-479
❑ 83Car194T-67
❑ 83FleSta-245
❑ 83FleSti-NNO
❑ 83FleSti-NNO
❑ 86FleWaxBC-C5
❑ 87CarSmo-NNO
❑ 87SpoTeaL-12
❑ 87Top-181
❑ 87TopTif-181
❑ 88FleSupBC-C6
❑ 88FleWaxBC-C1
❑ 88PanSti-478
❑ 88RedFolSB-116
❑ 90FleWaxBC-C18
❑ 90PubIntS-633
❑ 90RedFolSB-118
❑ 94ImpProP-26
❑ 94Sco-658
❑ 94ScoGolR-658
❑ 95PacPriTL-26
❑ 95PanSti-141
❑ 96PanSti-77
❑ 99Vic-316

Cardinals, St. Petersburg
❑ 89St.PetCS-29

Cardona, Al
❑ 89AncBucTI-2

Cardona, Isbel
❑ 91MedHatBJP-4090
❑ 91MedHatBJSP-11
❑ 94CliLumC-6
❑ 94CliLumF-1972
❑ 94EveGiaC-2
❑ 94EveGiaF-3641
❑ 95LinVen-181
❑ 96-97LinVen-56

Cardona, James
❑ 91WelPirC-6
❑ 91WelPirP-3585

Cardona, Javier
❑ 95FayGenTI-7
❑ 96FayGenB-9
❑ 97LakTigB-10
❑ 98JacSunM-5

Cardona, Jose
❑ 90ButCopKSP-9
❑ 91GasRanC-3
❑ 91GasRanP-2680
❑ 93LinVenB-10
❑ 94VenLinU-77

Cardona, Ruben
❑ 95NewJerCTI-5

Cardona, Steve
❑ 97HicCraB-7

❑ 97HicCraRB-8
❑ 98HicCraM-8
❑ 98HicCraUO-11

Cardonna, Brett
❑ 98HicCraUO-10

Cardoz, Don
❑ 78RocRedWT-3

Cardwell, Buddy
❑ 77WauMetT-4

Cardwell, Don
❑ 57Top-374
❑ 58Top-372
❑ 59Top-314
❑ 60Top-384
❑ 61NuSco-410
❑ 61Pos-194A
❑ 61Pos-194B
❑ 61Top-393
❑ 61Top-564
❑ 62CubJayP-4
❑ 62Top-495
❑ 62TopBuc-14
❑ 62TopStal-106
❑ 63PirIDL-3
❑ 63Top-575
❑ 64PirKDK-6
❑ 64Top-417
❑ 65Top-502
❑ 66MetTeal-3
❑ 66PirEasH-43
❑ 66Top-235
❑ 66TopVen-235
❑ 67CokCapYM-V23
❑ 67MetTeal-3
❑ 67Top-555
❑ 68Top-437
❑ 69MetNewYDN-3
❑ 69MilBra-51
❑ 69OPC-193
❑ 69Top-193
❑ 69TopFou-2
❑ 70OPC-83
❑ 70Top-83
❑ 72MilBra-64
❑ 78TCM60I-89
❑ 79DiaGre-374
❑ 84CubBriPC-8D
❑ 89MetRinP69-6
❑ 90SweBasG-72
❑ 91MetWIZ-63
❑ 94Met69CCPP-9
❑ 94Met69CS-8
❑ 94Met69T-26

Cardwood, Alfredo
❑ 85OrlTwiT-15
❑ 86VisOakP-6
❑ 87WesPalBEP-655

Carek, Mark
❑ 98OneYanG-5

Carew, Jeff
❑ 91GulCoaRSP-17
❑ 92ButCopKSP-3
❑ 93ButCopKSP-16

Carew, Michelle
❑ 97LeaThoL-1

Carew, Rod (Rodney Cline)
❑ 67Top-569
❑ 67TwiTeal-3
❑ 68Baz-13
❑ 68DexPre-20
❑ 68OPC-80
❑ 68Top-80
❑ 68Top-363
❑ 68TopActS-7C
❑ 68TopGamI-29
❑ 68TopVen-80
❑ 68TopVen-363
❑ 69MilBra-52
❑ 69MLBOffS-65
❑ 69MLBPin-4
❑ 69OPCDec-3
❑ 69Top-419
❑ 69Top-510
❑ 69TopDec-12
❑ 69TopSta-192
❑ 69TopTeaP-15
❑ 69TwiTealC-3
❑ 70DayDaiNM-62
❑ 70Kel-47
❑ 70MilBra-4
❑ 70MLBOffS-232
❑ 70OPC-62
❑ 70OPC-290
❑ 70OPC-453
❑ 70Top-62
❑ 70Top-290
❑ 70Top-453
❑ 70TopPos-16
❑ 70TwiSupV-3
❑ 71MLBOffS-461
❑ 71OPC-210
❑ 71Top-210
❑ 71TopCoi-24
❑ 71TopTat-119
❑ 72EssCoi-2
❑ 72MilBra-65
❑ 72Top-695
❑ 72Top-696
❑ 73Kel2D-51
❑ 73LinPor-107
❑ 73OPC-61
❑ 73OPC-330
❑ 73SevTraC-12
❑ 73Top-61
❑ 73Top-330
❑ 73TopCanL-9
❑ 74GreHeroBP-3
❑ 74GreHeroBP-5
❑ 74Kel-30
❑ 74OPC-50
❑ 74OPC-201
❑ 74OPC-333
❑ 74Top-50
❑ 74Top-201
❑ 74Top-333
❑ 74TopDecE-32
❑ 74TopSta-203
❑ 75Hos-56
❑ 75Kel-33
❑ 75OPC-306
❑ 75OPC-600
❑ 75SSP42-32
❑ 75SSPPuzB-5
❑ 75Top-306
❑ 75Top-600
❑ 75TopMin-306
❑ 75TopMin-600
❑ 75TwiPos-7
❑ 76BlaDis-9
❑ 76BucDis-9
❑ 76CarDis-9
❑ 76CraDis-9
❑ 76DailsID-9
❑ 76Hos-33
❑ 76HosTwi-33
❑ 76IsaDis-9
❑ 76Kel-48
❑ 76MinTwiP-5
❑ 76OPC-192
❑ 76OPC-400
❑ 76OrbDis-9
❑ 76RedBarD-9
❑ 76SafDis-9
❑ 76SSP-214
❑ 76Top-192
❑ 76Top-400
❑ 76TowCluD-9
❑ 77BobParMBC-3
❑ 77BurCheD-51
❑ 77ChiWilD-12
❑ 77DailsID-12
❑ 77DetCaeD-12
❑ 77HolInnD-12
❑ 77Hos-9
❑ 77Kel-53
❑ 77MSADis-12
❑ 77OPC-143
❑ 77PepGloD-2
❑ 77RCColC-14
❑ 77SagDis-12
❑ 77sDis-12
❑ 77Spo-1007
❑ 77Spo-3101
❑ 77Top-120
❑ 77TopCloS-10
❑ 77WenDis-12
❑ 77ZipDis-12
❑ 78Hos-140
❑ 78Kel-29
❑ 78OPC-1
❑ 78OPC-230
❑ 78PapGinD-35
❑ 78Pep-30
❑ 78RCColC-48
❑ 78SagDis-8
❑ 78TasDis-8
❑ 78Top-201
❑ 78Top-580
❑ 78TwiFriP-3
❑ 78WifBalD-13
❑ 79BasPat-13
❑ 79Hos-38
❑ 79Kel-13
❑ 79OPC-151
❑ 79Top-1
❑ 79Top-300
❑ 79TopCom-11
❑ 80BurKinPHR-14
❑ 80Kel-60
❑ 80OPC-353
❑ 80PerHaloFP-207
❑ 80PerHaloFPS-70
❑ 80Top-700
❑ 80TopSup-12
❑ 81AllGamPI-3
❑ 81Don-49
❑ 81Don-169
❑ 81Don-537
❑ 81Dra-2
❑ 81Fle-268
❑ 81FleStiC-40
❑ 81Kel-26
❑ 81LonBeaPT-1
❑ 81MSAMinD-6
❑ 81OPC-100
❑ 81PerAll-11
❑ 81PerCreC-22
❑ 81Squ-9
❑ 81Top-100
❑ 81TopScr-18
❑ 81TopSti-49
❑ 81TopSupHT-57
❑ 81TopSupN-4
❑ 82Don-8
❑ 82Don-216
❑ 82Dra-6
❑ 82FBIDis-3
❑ 82Fle-455
❑ 82FleSta-217
❑ 82K-M-31
❑ 82Kel-51
❑ 82OnDecD-6
❑ 82OPC-36
❑ 82OPC-187
❑ 82OPC-363
❑ 82PerCreC-21
❑ 82PerCreCG-21
❑ 82SevSluC-6
❑ 82Top-276
❑ 82Top-500
❑ 82Top-501
❑ 82Top-547
❑ 82TopSti-131
❑ 82TopSti-160
❑ 83AllGamPI-2
❑ 83Don-90
❑ 83DonActA-38
❑ 83Dra-3
❑ 83Fle-81
❑ 83FleSta-29
❑ 83FleSti-26
❑ 83Kel-1
❑ 83Oco& SSBG-6
❑ 83OPC-200
❑ 83OPC-201
❑ 83OPC-386
❑ 83PerAll-2
❑ 83PerAllG-2
❑ 83PerCreC-20
❑ 83PerCreCG-20
❑ 83SevCoi-1
❑ 83Top-200
❑ 83Top-201
❑ 83Top-386
❑ 83Top-651
❑ 83TopFol-3
❑ 83TopFol-5
❑ 83TopGloS-29
❑ 83TopSti-39
❑ 84AllGamPI-91
❑ 84AngSmo-5
❑ 84Don-352
❑ 84DonCha-21
❑ 84Dra-5
❑ 84Fle-511
❑ 84Fle-629
❑ 84FleSti-12
❑ 84FleSti-54
❑ 84FleSti-103
❑ 84FunFooP-35
❑ 84MilBra-3
❑ 84Nes792-276
❑ 84Nes792-600
❑ 84Nes792-710
❑ 84Nes792-711
❑ 84OCoandSI-15
❑ 84OCoandSI-73
❑ 84OPC-26
❑ 84RalPur-17
❑ 84SevCoi-W8
❑ 84Top-276
❑ 84Top-600
❑ 84Top-710
❑ 84Top-711
❑ 84TopCer-17
❑ 84TopGaloC-2
❑ 84TopGloA-2
❑ 84TopGloS-26
❑ 84TopRubD-9
❑ 84TopSti-227
❑ 84TopStiB-11
❑ 84TopTif-276
❑ 84TopTif-600
❑ 84TopTif-710
❑ 84TopTif-711
❑ 85AllGamPI-2
❑ 85AngSmo-5
❑ 85AngStrH-4
❑ 85Don-85
❑ 85DonHig-31
❑ 85Fle-297
❑ 85FleLimE-5
❑ 85Lea-132
❑ 85OPC-300
❑ 85SevCoi-W6
❑ 85SubDis-7
❑ 85ThoMcAD-7
❑ 85Top-300
❑ 85TopGloA-13
❑ 85TopRubD-5
❑ 85TopSti-184
❑ 85TopSti-223
❑ 85TopTif-300
❑ 86AngGreT-1
❑ 86Don-280
❑ 86Fle-151
❑ 86Fle-629
❑ 86FleFutHoF-4
❑ 86FleLeaL-4
❑ 86FleStiC-20
❑ 86OPC-371
❑ 86SevCoi-W10
❑ 86Spo-69
❑ 86Spo-74
❑ 86Spo-106
❑ 86Spo-146
❑ 86Spo-180
❑ 86Spo-182
❑ 86Top-400
❑ 86TopGloS-16
❑ 86TopSti-4
❑ 86TopSti-176
❑ 86TopTif-400
❑ 86TwiGreT-2
❑ 86Woo-6
❑ 87K-M-14
❑ 87NesDreT-12
❑ 88GreBasS-48
❑ 88HouSho-7
❑ 89AngSmo-10
❑ 89TopBasT-25
❑ 90AGFA-7
❑ 90PacLeg-17
❑ 90PerGreM-77
❑ 90SweBasG-4
❑ 91Bow-1
❑ 91Bow-2
❑ 91Bow-3
❑ 91Bow-4
❑ 91Bow-5
❑ 91KelLey-2
❑ 91SweBasG-103
❑ 91TopRut-8
❑ 92KelAll-4
❑ 92MDAMVP-11
❑ 92Pin-584
❑ 93ActPacA-128
❑ 93ActPacA2-62G
❑ 93AngMot-28
❑ 93AngPol-4
❑ 93MetIma-7
❑ 93PacRya2S-242
❑ 93Yoo-4
❑ 94AngMot-28
❑ 94CarLeaA-DJ34
❑ 94TedWil-47
❑ 94TopSpa-L4
❑ 95AngMot-28
❑ 95JimDeaAG-1
❑ 96AngMot-28
❑ 97CalLot-1
❑ 97DonSigSS-6
❑ 97LeaThoL-1
❑ 97SpollICC-4
❑ 97St.VinHHS-5
❑ 98SpollITaN-8
❑ 98SpollITaNEE-8
❑ 98SpollITaNGS-22

Carey, Andy (Andrew Arthur)
❑ 47StaPinP2-9
❑ 53Top-188
❑ 54NewYorJA-43
❑ 54Top-105
❑ 55Top-20
❑ 55TopDouH-35
❑ 56Top-12
❑ 56YanJayP-4
❑ 56YanTeal-4
❑ 57Top-290
❑ 58Top-333
❑ 58YanJayP-3
❑ 59Top-45
❑ 59TopVen-45
❑ 60Top-196
❑ 60TopVen-196
❑ 60YanJayP-2
❑ 61A'sTeal-2
❑ 61Top-518
❑ 61TopStal-158
❑ 62DodVol-20
❑ 62Jel-52
❑ 62Pos-52
❑ 62PosCan-52
❑ 62SalPlaC-86A
❑ 62SalPlaC-86B
❑ 62ShiPlaC-86
❑ 62Top-418
❑ 79DiaGre-22
❑ 79TCM50-243
❑ 90DodTar-112
❑ 91TopArc1-188
❑ 92YanWIZ6-21
❑ 94TopArc1-105
❑ 94TopArc1G-105

Carey, Brooks M.
❑ 80ChaO'sP-3
❑ 80ChaO'sW-3
❑ 81RocRedWT-3
❑ 81RocRedWW-22
❑ 82IndIndTI-9

Carey, Frank
❑ 90Bes-67
❑ 90CliGiaB-4
❑ 90CliGiaP-2555
❑ 90MidLeaASGS-28
❑ 91LinDriAA-301
❑ 91ShrCapLD-301
❑ 91ShrCapP-1826

Carey, Jeff
❑ 82WesHavAT-3

Carey, Max George
❑ 10CouT21-8
❑ 11HelSta-156
❑ 12T207-26
❑ 14B18B-75A
❑ 14B18B-75B
❑ 14CraJacE-73
❑ 15CraJacE-73
❑ 15SpoNewM-26
❑ 16BF2FP-93
❑ 16SpoNewM-28
❑ 17ColE13-25
❑ 17HolBreD-12
❑ 19W514-22
❑ 20NatCarE-12
❑ 21E121So1-8
❑ 21E121So8-9A
❑ 21E121So8-9B
❑ 21Exh-21
❑ 21Nei-71
❑ 21OxfConE-3
❑ 22AmeCarE122-9
❑ 22E120-214
❑ 22W573-16
❑ 22W575-16
❑ 22WilPatV-28
❑ 23W501-86
❑ 23W503-53
❑ 23WilChoV-16
❑ 25Exh-50
❑ 26Exh-50
❑ 26SpoComoA-8
❑ 27AmeCarE126-32
❑ 27YorCarE-32
❑ 28Exh-6
❑ 28W502-32
❑ 28Yue-32
❑ 33WorCig-14
❑ 40PlaBal-178
❑ 53ArtHaloFP-10
❑ 61Fle-12
❑ 70SpoCarfCOP-16
❑ 72LauGreF-9
❑ 76RowExh-11
❑ 76ShaPiz-85
❑ 77BobParHoF-80
❑ 77GalGloG-103
❑ 77GalGloG-214
❑ 80LauFamF-12
❑ 80PerHaloFP-85
❑ 80SSPHOF-85
❑ 89DodSmoG-5
❑ 89HOFStiB-38
❑ 90BasWit-88
❑ 90DodTar-113
❑ 90PerGreM-50
❑ 91ConTSN-24
❑ 93ConTSN-797
❑ 94ConTSN-1232
❑ 94ConTSNB-1232

Carey, P.J.
❑ 87BelMarL-28
❑ 89BelMarL-30
❑ 91BilMusP-3770
❑ 91BilMusSP-28
❑ 92ChaWheF-23
❑ 92ChaWVWC-23
❑ 93CenValRF-2909
❑ 93SouAtlLAPI-4
❑ 94NewHavRF-1566
❑ 96AshTouB-2
❑ 96MauStiHWB-32

Carey, Paul
❑ 90MiaMirIS-3
❑ 91Cla/Bes-190
❑ 91HagSunLD-228
❑ 91HagSunP-2466
❑ 91LinDriAA-228
❑ 92ClaFS7-392
❑ 92FreKeyC-1
❑ 92RocRedWF-1949
❑ 93BalOriP-6
❑ 93ClaFS7-65
❑ 93FleFinE-158
❑ 93RocRedWF-246
❑ 94Don-465
❑ 94FreKeyC-5
❑ 94OriPro-16
❑ 94OriUSPC-3C
❑ 94Pac-28
❑ 94Pin-403
❑ 94PinArtP-403
❑ 94PinMusC-403
❑ 94RocRedWTI-5
❑ 94StaCluT-275
❑ 94StaCluTFDI-275
❑ 94Top-4
❑ 94TopGol-4
❑ 94TopSpa-4
❑ 95RocRedWTI-9
❑ 98SavSanGM-1

Carey, Pete
❑ 86Ft.MyeRP-5
❑ 87TamTarP-2

Carey, Scoops (George C.)
❑ 03BreE10-14
❑ 09T206-480

Carey, Tim
❑ 93LynRedSC-5
❑ 93LynRedSF-2518

Carey, Todd
❑ 92ElmPioC-9
❑ 92ElmPioF-1388
❑ 93ForLauRSC-5
❑ 93ForLauRSFP-1602
❑ 94LynRedSC-5
❑ 94LynRedSF-1897
❑ 95TreThuTI-28
❑ 96DouAllB-7
❑ 96TreThuB-21
❑ 97PawRedS-9
❑ 98NorTidQ-5
❑ 98PawRedSQ-9

Carey, Tom (Thomas Francis)
❑ 34BatR31-89
❑ 35DiaMatCS2-3
❑ 35DiaMatCS3T1-25
❑ 35DiaMatCS3T1-28
❑ 36DiaMatCS4-1
❑ 39PlaBal-62
❑ 40PlaBal-39
❑ 42RedSoxTI-4

❑ 75RedSox1T-6
❑ 93ConTSN-698
Carger, Ed
❑ 08AmeCarE91-69
Caribaldo, Chris
❑ 89AppFoxP-862
Caridad, Rolando
❑ 90UtiBluSP-16
❑ 91SouBenWSC-15
❑ 91SouBenWSP-2851
❑ 92SarWhiSCB-11
❑ 92SarWhiSF-199
❑ 94VenLinU-142
Caridad, Ron
❑ 90HigSchPLS-11
❑ 91EliTwiP-4293
❑ 92EliTwiC-21
❑ 92EliTwiF-3672
❑ 93ForWayWC-4
❑ 93ForWayWF-1959
❑ 94ForMyeMC-4
❑ 94ForMyeMF-1159
❑ 94VenLinU-145
❑ 96-97LinVen-82
Cariel, Rafael
❑ 76ShrCapT-20
❑ 76VenLeaS-150
Carillo, Matias
❑ 94ScoRoo-RT138
Carisch, Fred (Frederick B.)
❑ 11PinT-5-1065
Carisen, Robert
❑ 91MadMusC-25
Carista, Mike
❑ 85ElmPioT-3
❑ 86WinHavRSP-5
❑ 87GreHorP-5
❑ 88EasLeaAP-20
❑ 88NewBriRSP-909
❑ 89NewBriRSP-605
❑ 90NewBriRSB-12
❑ 90NewBriRSP-1311
❑ 90NewBriRSS-2
Carl, Jeff
❑ 83MemChiT-5
Carl, Todd
❑ 94BreCouMC-3
❑ 94ElmPioC-3
❑ 94ElmPioF-3465
❑ 95BreCouMF-238
❑ 96DayCubB-7
❑ 98MadBlaW-5
Carlesen, Donald
❑ 48AngTeal-7
❑ 49AngTeal-7
❑ 49W725AngTI-6
Carleton, Tex (James)
❑ 33WorCig-15
❑ 34BabRutG-7
❑ 34ButPreR-7
❑ 34DiaMatCSB-25
❑ 34Gou-48
❑ 34GouCanV-90
❑ 34TarThoBD-7
❑ 35DiaMatCS3T1-26
❑ 35GouPuzR-1A
❑ 35GouPuzR-2A
❑ 35GouPuzR-16A
❑ 35GouPuzR-17A
❑ 36CubTeal-2
❑ 36DiaMatCS3T2-2
❑ 40DodTeal-2
❑ 74Car193T-1
❑ 85BigLeaC3-80
❑ 87Car193T-8
❑ 90DodTar-114
❑ 92ConTSN-378
Carley, David
❑ 86AriWilP-1
❑ 87BelBreP-19
Carlin, Mike
❑ 89SpaPhiP-1035
❑ 89SpaPhiS-3
Carlisle, Matthew
❑ 86NegLeaF-85
Carlisle, Walter G.
❑ 09ObaT21-178
❑ 09ObaT21-344
❑ 11PacCoaBD-12
❑ 11Zee-111
❑ 12HomRunKE-82
❑ 12ObaPreT-93
❑ 12Zee-142
❑ 13Zee-134
❑ 14Zee-129
❑ 15Zee-123
Carlos, Cisco
❑ 68Top-287
❑ 68TopVen-287
❑ 69OPC-54
❑ 69Top-54
❑ 70OPC-487
❑ 70Top-487
❑ 72MilBra-66
Carlos, Gil
❑ 84IowCubT-20
Carlsen, Robert
❑ 91MadMusP-2137
❑ 92ChaWheF-14
Carlson, Bill
❑ 87CliGiaP-11
❑ 87PocGiaTB-13
❑ 88CliGiaP-700
❑ 89SanJosGB-9
❑ 89SanJosGCLC-229
❑ 89SanJosGP-439
❑ 89SanJosGS-4
❑ 90SalSpuCLC-131
❑ 90SalSpuP-2730
❑ 91SalSpuC-30
❑ 91SalSpuP-2250
Carlson, Bob
❑ 91EliTwiP-4294
❑ 92KenTwiC-21
❑ 92ProFS7-103
Carlson, Brad
❑ 80WisRapTT-21
Carlson, Dan
❑ 90EveGiaB-3
❑ 90EveGiaP-3119
❑ 91CliGiaC-1
❑ 91CliGiaP-826
❑ 92ClaFS7-183
❑ 92ShrCapF-3864
❑ 92ShrCapS-577
❑ 92SkyAA F-254
❑ 93ClaFS7-46
❑ 93ExcFS7-113
❑ 93GiaStaC-26
❑ 93PhoFirF-1509
❑ 94Bow-331
❑ 94PhoFirF-1513
❑ 95PhoFirTI-19
❑ 95Top-658
❑ 96PhoFirB-12
❑ 97Fle-654
❑ 97FleTif-654
❑ 97PhoFirDTTI-9
❑ 97PhoFirTI-4
❑ 98DevRayP-3
❑ 98PacOmeRS-22
❑ 98PacOmeRST3-22
Carlson, Garret
❑ 96BriWhiSB-12
Carlson, Hal
❑ 23WilChoV-17
❑ 28W513-75
❑ 29PorandAR-10
❑ 94ConTSN-1116
❑ 94ConTSNB-1116
Carlson, Jeff
❑ 98OneYanG-6
Carlson, Lynn
❑ 90WelPirP-19
❑ 91AugPirC-3
❑ 91AugPirP-796
Carlson, Tom
❑ 76CliPilT-7
Carlton, Andy
❑ 90St.CatBJP-3476
❑ 91MyrBeaHC-17
❑ 91MyrBeaHP-2951
Carlton, Scott
❑ 91SpaPhiC-1
❑ 91SpaPhiP-886
Carlton, Steve
❑ 65CarTeal-6
❑ 65Top-477
❑ 67OPC-146
❑ 67Top-146
❑ 68Top-408
❑ 69Top-255
❑ 70MLBOffS-137
❑ 70OPC-67
❑ 70OPC-220
❑ 70Top-67
❑ 70Top-220
❑ 71CarTeal-8
❑ 71CarTeal-8
❑ 71CarTeal-9
❑ 71MLBOffS-271
❑ 71OPC-55
❑ 71Top-55
❑ 71TopCoi-115
❑ 72CarTeal-3
❑ 72Dia-56
❑ 72MilBra-67
❑ 72OPC-93
❑ 72OPC-420
❑ 72Top-93
❑ 72Top-420
❑ 72Top-751
❑ 73Kel2D-7
❑ 73LinPor-144
❑ 73OPC-65
❑ 73OPC-66
❑ 73OPC-67
❑ 73OPC-300
❑ 73PhiTeal-6
❑ 73SevTraC-13
❑ 73Top-65
❑ 73Top-66
❑ 73Top-67
❑ 73Top-300
❑ 73TopCanL-10
❑ 73TopCom-4
❑ 73TopPin-4
❑ 74OPC-95
❑ 74PhiJohP-32
❑ 74Top-95
❑ 74TopDecE-5
❑ 74TopSta-73
❑ 75Hos-63
❑ 75OPC-185
❑ 75OPC-312
❑ 75PhiPhiP-8
❑ 75PhiProPS-4
❑ 75Top-185
❑ 75Top-312
❑ 75TopMin-185
❑ 75TopMin-312
❑ 76BlaDis-10
❑ 76BucDis-10
❑ 76CarDis-10
❑ 76CraDis-10
❑ 76DailsID-10
❑ 76IsaDis-10
❑ 76OPC-355
❑ 76OrbDis-10
❑ 76PhiPhiP-6
❑ 76RedBarD-10
❑ 76SafDis-10
❑ 76SSP-459
❑ 76Top-355
❑ 76TowCluD-10
❑ 77BurCheD-171
❑ 77ChiWilD-13
❑ 77DailsID-13
❑ 77DetCaeD-13
❑ 77HolInnD-13
❑ 77Hos-117
❑ 77Kel-57
❑ 77MSADis-13
❑ 77OPC-93
❑ 77SagDis-13
❑ 77sDis-13
❑ 77Spo-2702
❑ 77Top-110
❑ 77TopCloS-11
❑ 77WenDis-13
❑ 77ZipDis-13
❑ 78Hos-49
❑ 78Kel-1
❑ 78OPC-5
❑ 78OPC-170
❑ 78RCColC-71
❑ 78SSP270-29
❑ 78Top-205
❑ 78Top-540
❑ 78WifBalD-14
❑ 79BasPat-14
❑ 79Hos-71
❑ 79Kel-18
❑ 79OPC-9
❑ 79PhiBurK-4
❑ 79Top-25
❑ 80BurKinPHR-2
❑ 80Kel-14
❑ 80OPC-113
❑ 80PerHaloFP-217
❑ 80PerHaloFPS-77
❑ 80PhiBul-29
❑ 80PhiBurK-15
❑ 80Top-210
❑ 81AllGamPI-167
❑ 81CokTeaS-99
❑ 81Don-33
❑ 81Don-481
❑ 81Fle-6
❑ 81Fle-6B
❑ 81Fle-6C
❑ 81Fle-660
❑ 81Fle-660B
❑ 81FleStiC-85
❑ 81Kel-50
❑ 81MSAMinD-7
❑ 81OPC-203
❑ 81PerCreC-16
❑ 81Top-5
❑ 81Top-6
❑ 81Top-202
❑ 81Top-630
❑ 81TopScr-104
❑ 81TopSti-25
❑ 81TopSti-28
❑ 81TopSti-29
❑ 81TopSti-206
❑ 81TopSti-261
❑ 81TopSupHT-81
❑ 82Don-42
❑ 82FBIDis-4
❑ 82Fle-243
❑ 82Fle-632
❑ 82Fle-641
❑ 82FleSta-54
❑ 82FleSta-240
❑ 82FleSta-241
❑ 82Kel-27
❑ 82OnDecD-7
❑ 82OPC-68
❑ 82OPC-122
❑ 82PerCreC-10
❑ 82PerCreCG-10
❑ 82Top-1
❑ 82Top-480
❑ 82Top-481
❑ 82Top-636
❑ 82TopSti-75
❑ 82TopSti-129
❑ 83AllGamPI-165
❑ 83Don-16
❑ 83Don-219
❑ 83DonActA-24
❑ 83Fle-155
❑ 83FleSta-30
❑ 83FleSti-176
❑ 83Kel-45
❑ 83KelCerB-12
❑ 83OPC-70
❑ 83OPC-71
❑ 83OPC-384
❑ 83PerCreC-2
❑ 83PerCreCG-2
❑ 83PhiPosGM-9
❑ 83PhiPosGPaM-2
❑ 83PhiTas-4
❑ 83Top-70
❑ 83Top-71
❑ 83Top-229
❑ 83Top-406
❑ 83Top-705
❑ 83Top-706
❑ 83TopFol-1
❑ 83TopGloS-36
❑ 83TopSti-176
❑ 83TopSti-203
❑ 83TopSti-204
❑ 83TopSti-267
❑ 83TopTraBP-1
❑ 84Don-111
❑ 84DonActAS-24
❑ 84DonCha-38
❑ 84Fle-25
❑ 84Fle-642
❑ 84FleSti-78
❑ 84FleSti-101
❑ 84FunFooP-30
❑ 84MilBra-4
❑ 84MLBPen-12
❑ 84Nes792-1
❑ 84Nes792-4
❑ 84Nes792-136
❑ 84Nes792-395
❑ 84Nes792-706
❑ 84Nes792-707
❑ 84Nes792-708
❑ 84Nes792-780
❑ 84NesDreT-21
❑ 84OCoandSI-18
❑ 84OPC-214
❑ 84OPC-395
❑ 84PhiTas-5
❑ 84PhiTas-17
❑ 84RalPur-16
❑ 84SevCoi-E12
❑ 84StaCar-1
❑ 84StaCar-2
❑ 84StaCar-3
❑ 84StaCar-4
❑ 84StaCar-5
❑ 84StaCar-6
❑ 84StaCar-7
❑ 84StaCar-8
❑ 84StaCar-9
❑ 84StaCar-10
❑ 84StaCar-11
❑ 84StaCar-12
❑ 84StaCar-13
❑ 84StaCar-14
❑ 84StaCar-15
❑ 84StaCar-16
❑ 84StaCar-17
❑ 84StaCar-18
❑ 84StaCar-19
❑ 84StaCar-20
❑ 84StaCar-21
❑ 84StaCar-22
❑ 84StaCar-23
❑ 84StaCar-24
❑ 84Top-1
❑ 84Top-4
❑ 84Top-136
❑ 84Top-395
❑ 84Top-706
❑ 84Top-707
❑ 84Top-708
❑ 84Top-780
❑ 84TopCer-16
❑ 84TopGaloC-3
❑ 84TopGloS-27
❑ 84TopRubD-10
❑ 84TopSti-1
❑ 84TopSti-2
❑ 84TopSti-15
❑ 84TopSti-119
❑ 84TopSti-184
❑ 84TopSup-16
❑ 84TopTif-1
❑ 84TopTif-4
❑ 84TopTif-136
❑ 84TopTif-395
❑ 84TopTif-706
❑ 84TopTif-707
❑ 84TopTif-708
❑ 84TopTif-780
❑ 85Don-305
❑ 85DonActA-55
❑ 85Dra-35
❑ 85Fle-246
❑ 85FleLimE-6
❑ 85KASDis-1
❑ 85KitCloD-1
❑ 85Lea-113
❑ 85OPC-360
❑ 85PhiCIG-12
❑ 85PhiTas-9
❑ 85PhiTas-14
❑ 85SevCoi-E3
❑ 85SevCoi-S2
❑ 85SubDis-25
❑ 85ThoMcAD-25
❑ 85Top-360
❑ 85Top3-D-25
❑ 85TopMin-360
❑ 85TopRubD-10
❑ 85TopSti-112
❑ 85TopSup-24
❑ 85TopTif-360
❑ 85Woo-6
❑ 86BurKinA-6
❑ 86Don-183
❑ 86DonHig-35
❑ 86Fle-435
❑ 86FleFutHoF-2
❑ 86FleMin-91
❑ 86FleSluBC-M2
❑ 86FleStiC-21
❑ 86Lea-117
❑ 86MeaGolM-3
❑ 86OPC-120
❑ 86PhiKel-1
❑ 86PhiTas-32
❑ 86SevCoi-C8
❑ 86SevCoi-E8
❑ 86SevCoi-S8
❑ 86SevCoi-W8
❑ 86Spo-27
❑ 86Spo-70
❑ 86SpoDecG-54
❑ 86Top-120
❑ 86Top-246
❑ 86TopSti-116
❑ 86TopTat-3
❑ 86TopTif-120
❑ 86TopTif-246
❑ 87Don-617
❑ 87Fle-490
❑ 87Fle-635
❑ 87FleExcS-8
❑ 87FleGlo-490
❑ 87FleGlo-635
❑ 87FleUpd-17
❑ 87FleUpdG-17
❑ 87K-M-15
❑ 87OPC-271
❑ 87OPCBoxB-B
❑ 87Spo-200
❑ 87Top-718
❑ 87TopTif-718
❑ 87TopTra-19T
❑ 87TopTraT-19T
❑ 87TopWaxBC-B
❑ 87Woo-1
❑ 88Fle-7
❑ 88FleGlo-7
❑ 89SweBasG-95
❑ 89TopBasT-37
❑ 90AGFA-15
❑ 90BasWit-43
❑ 90HOFStiB-78
❑ 90PacLeg-16
❑ 90PerGreM-99
❑ 90PhiTas-30
❑ 90SweBasG-110
❑ 91Kel3D-8
❑ 91KelStaU-5
❑ 91LinDri-9
❑ 91MDAA-1
❑ 91SweBasG-17
❑ 92MVP-13
❑ 92MVP2H-7
❑ 92UppDecS-24
❑ 93TedWil-72
❑ 94Met69T-53
❑ 94UppDecAH-70
❑ 94UppDecAH-124
❑ 94UppDecAH-155
❑ 94UppDecAH1-70
❑ 94UppDecAH1-124
❑ 94UppDecAH1-155
❑ 94Yoo-4
❑ 96FanCar-1
❑ 96FanCar-2
❑ 96FanCar-3
❑ 96FanCar-4
❑ 96FanCar-5
❑ 96PinFan-31
❑ 97DonSigSS-7
❑ 99SpoIllGotG-32
❑ 99SpoIllGotGA-15
❑ 99SpoIllGotGC-25
❑ 99SpoIllGotGC-38
❑ 99SpoIllGotGC-47
❑ 99UppDecCL-30
❑ 99UppDecCLA-1970
❑ 99UppDecCLCC-30
❑ 99UppDecCLES-SC
❑ 99UppDecCLESC-SC
Carlucci, Dave
❑ 86BakDodP-5
Carlucci, Rich
❑ 81WatRedT-1
❑ 82IndIndTI-19
❑ 83IndIndTI-16
❑ 84RocRedWT-2
❑ 86SyrChiP-6
Carlucci, Tony
❑ 83TriTriT-14
Carlyle, Buddy
❑ 97SouAtlTPB-12
❑ 98BesAutSS-7
❑ 98Bow-315
❑ 98BowChr-315
❑ 98BowChrGA-315
❑ 98BowChrGAR-315
❑ 98BowChrI-315
❑ 98BowChrIR-315
❑ 98BowChrR-315
❑ 98BowGolA-315
❑ 98BowInt-315
❑ 98MobBayBTI-5
Carlyle, Cleo (Hiram Cleo)
❑ 29Zee-3
❑ 30Zee-4

❑ 31Zee-3
❑ 32Zee-4
❑ 33Zee-1

Carlyle, Kenny
❑ 92FayGenF-2161
❑ 92FroRowDP-6
❑ 92FroRowDPG-6
❑ 92FroRowDPS-6
❑ 93Bow-151
❑ 93ClaFS7-162
❑ 93ClaGolF-207
❑ 93LonTigF-2299
❑ 93StaCluM-116
❑ 94TreThuF-2113
❑ 95TolMudHTI-9
❑ 96JacSunB-6
❑ 97RicBra-8
❑ 98RicBraQ-8

Carlyle, Roy Edward
❑ 29Zee-65

Carman, Don
❑ 80PenPilBT-11
❑ 80PenPilCT-5
❑ 81ReaPhiT-8
❑ 82OklCit8T-24
❑ 83ReaPhiT-3
❑ 84PhiTas-41
❑ 84PorBeaC-204
❑ 85FleUpd-20
❑ 85PhiTas-9
❑ 85PhiTas-15
❑ 85TopTifT-16T
❑ 85TopTra-16T
❑ 86Don-427
❑ 86Fle-436
❑ 86FleStiC-22
❑ 86Lea-200
❑ 86PhiCIG-2
❑ 86PhiTas-42
❑ 86Top-532
❑ 86TopTif-532
❑ 87Don-432
❑ 87Fle-171
❑ 87FleGlo-171
❑ 87Lea-174
❑ 87OPC-355
❑ 87PhiTas-42
❑ 87Spo-108
❑ 87SpoTeaP-6
❑ 87Top-355
❑ 87TopSti-122
❑ 87TopTif-355
❑ 88Don-385
❑ 88DonBasB-72
❑ 88Fle-300
❑ 88FleGlo-300
❑ 88PhiTas-6
❑ 88Sco-401
❑ 88ScoGlo-401
❑ 88StaLinPh-5
❑ 88Top-415
❑ 88TopTif-415
❑ 89Bow-392
❑ 89BowTif-392
❑ 89Don-396
❑ 89Fle-564
❑ 89FleGlo-564
❑ 89OPC-154
❑ 89PanSti-146
❑ 89PhiTas-3
❑ 89Sco-222
❑ 89Top-154
❑ 89TopSti-121
❑ 89TopTif-154
❑ 89UppDec-409
❑ 90Don-604
❑ 90Fle-552
❑ 90FleCan-552
❑ 90OPC-731
❑ 90PhiTas-4
❑ 90PubIntS-233
❑ 90Top-731
❑ 90TopTif-731
❑ 90UppDec-420
❑ 91Don-377
❑ 91Fle-390
❑ 91OPC-282
❑ 91RedKah-36
❑ 91Sco-237
❑ 91Top-282
❑ 91TopDesS-282
❑ 91TopMic-282
❑ 91TopTif-282
❑ 91UppDec-288
❑ 92OklCit8F-1910
❑ 92TulDriF-2689
❑ 92TulDriS-616
❑ 93RanKee-97
❑ 94ScrRedBF-915

Carman, Fred
❑ 11Zee-84

Carmel, Duke (Leon James)
❑ 60Top-120
❑ 60TopVen-120
❑ 61UniOil-P5
❑ 63Top-544
❑ 64MetJayP-2
❑ 64Top-44
❑ 64TopCoi-81
❑ 64TopVen-44
❑ 65ChaTheY-4
❑ 65OPC-261
❑ 65Top-261
❑ 67BufBisJD-1
❑ 76Met63 S-2
❑ 91MetWIZ-64
❑ 92YanWIZ6-22

Carmichael, Al
❑ 85LynMetT-15
❑ 86LynMetP-6
❑ 87JacMetF-12

Carmichael, Harold
❑ 80PhiBul-7

Carmody, Brian
❑ 98RanCucQG-6
❑ 98RanCucQG-6

Carmody, Kevin
❑ 89BelBre2S-5
❑ 89BelBreIS-2
❑ 90StoPorB-20
❑ 90StoPorCLC-181
❑ 90StoPorP-2181

Carmona, Cesarin
❑ 96CliLumKTI-6
❑ 98RanCucQG-7
❑ 98RanCucQG-7

Carmona, Greg
❑ 89St.PetCS-5
❑ 90ArkTraGS-7
❑ 90TopTVCa-40
❑ 91ArkTraLD-28
❑ 91ArkTraP-1291
❑ 91Bow-392
❑ 91LinDriAA-28
❑ 91LouRedP-2920
❑ 91LouRedTI-21
❑ 92LouRedF-1892
❑ 92LouRedS-255
❑ 93LimRocDWB-74
❑ 93StoPorC-4

Carmona, Rafael
❑ 93BelMarCB-8
❑ 93BelMarF-3198
❑ 94RivPilCLC-17
❑ 95MarMot-19
❑ 95MarPac-26
❑ 96Bow-258
❑ 96BowFoi-258
❑ 96MarMot-14
❑ 97Pac-183
❑ 97PacLigB-183
❑ 97PacSil-183
❑ 97TacRai-7
❑ 98Pac-181
❑ 98PacPlaB-181
❑ 98PacRedT-181
❑ 98PacSil-181

Carmona, William
❑ 89MarPhiS-4
❑ 90MarPhiP-3181
❑ 91PocPioP-3795
❑ 91PocPioSP-27
❑ 92MarPhiC-21
❑ 92MarPhiF-3068
❑ 93SpaPhiC-10
❑ 94PriRedC-6
❑ 94PriRedF-3255

Carmuso, Mike
❑ 72CedRapCT-11

Carnegie, Olie
❑ 28LaPre-26

Carnelius, Brian
❑ 92LonTigS-403

Carnes, Matt
❑ 97AppLeaTPB-28
❑ 98ForWayW!-14

Carnes, Scott
❑ 77QuaCitAT-8
❑ 80ElPasDT-3
❑ 81SalLakCGT-17
❑ 82SpoIndT-15

Carnes, Shayne
❑ 98BatMucTI-3

Carnett, Eddie (Edwin E.)
❑ 43CenFlo-3
❑ 77TCMTheWY-63

Carnevale, Anthony
❑ 89AncGlaP-5

Carnevale, Dan
❑ 70RoyTeal-8

Carney, Bartt
❑ 97BowBay-12

Carney, Jack (John Joseph)
❑ 87OldJudN-67

Carney, Pat (Patrick J.)
❑ 11SpoLifCW-54

Carney, Ron
❑ 78AshTouT-4
❑ 79TulDriT-18
❑ 80AshTouT-14
❑ 81TulDriT-10

Caro, Joe
❑ 91BoiHawP-3900

Caro, Jorge
❑ 91BriTigC-2
❑ 91BriTigP-3611

Caroland, Kevin
❑ 89TenTecGE-6

Carone, Rick
❑ 94HicCraC-7
❑ 94HicCraF-2180
❑ 96PriWilCB-30

Carosielli, Marc
❑ 88WytCubP-1999

Carothers, Ron
❑ 91WavRedF-12
❑ 93AusFut-62
❑ 93AusFut-126
❑ 95AusFut-5
❑ 95AusFut-86

Carpenter, Brian
❑ 93ClaFS7-129
❑ 93GreFalDSP-27
❑ 93SavCarC-7
❑ 93SavCarF-679
❑ 94BakDodC-6
❑ 94St.PetCC-8
❑ 94St.PetCF-2578
❑ 96ArkTraB-7
❑ 97BinMetB-6

Carpenter, Bubba
❑ 90ArkRaz-4
❑ 92AlbYanF-2237
❑ 92AlbYanSk-5
❑ 93AlbYanF-2167
❑ 94AlbYanF-1452
❑ 95ColCliMCTI-23
❑ 95ColCliP-3
❑ 95ColCliTI-3
❑ 96ColCliB-4
❑ 97ColCliB-8
❑ 97ColCliD-5
❑ 98ColCliD-5
❑ 98ColCliM-9
❑ 98PriWilCASM-26

Carpenter, Chris
❑ 94MedHatBJF-3673
❑ 94MedHatBJSP-13
❑ 95Bes-49
❑ 95Bow-83
❑ 95BowBes-B74
❑ 95BowBesR-B74
❑ 95DunBluJTI-4
❑ 95Exc-135
❑ 95UppDecML-133
❑ 95UppDecMLFS-133
❑ 96Bow-185
❑ 96BowBes-129
❑ 96BowBesAR-129
❑ 96BowBesR-129
❑ 96BowFoi-185
❑ 96KnoSmoB-8
❑ 97Bes-20
❑ 97BluJayS-60
❑ 97Bow-158
❑ 97BowBes-184
❑ 97BowBesAR-184
❑ 97BowBesR-184
❑ 97BowChr-156
❑ 97BowChrI-156
❑ 97BowChrIR-156
❑ 97BowChrR-156
❑ 97BowInt-158
❑ 97Lea-329
❑ 97LeaFraM-329
❑ 97LeaFraMDC-329
❑ 97SyrSkyCB-6
❑ 98Bow-110
❑ 98BowChr-110
❑ 98BowChrGA-110
❑ 98BowChrGAR-110
❑ 98BowChrI-110
❑ 98BowChrIR-110
❑ 98BowChrR-110
❑ 98BowGolA-110
❑ 98BowInt-110
❑ 98ColCho-122
❑ 98Fle-71
❑ 98PacOnl-754
❑ 98PacOnlR-754
❑ 98PacOnlWC-754
❑ 98Top-442
❑ 98TopChr-442
❑ 98TopChrR-442
❑ 98TopDevR-442
❑ 98TopDia-442
❑ 98TopMiniC-442
❑ 98Ult-245
❑ 98UltGolM-245
❑ 98UltMas-245
❑ 98UltPlaM-245
❑ 98UppDec-287
❑ 98UppDecDS-DS42
❑ 99Fle-79
❑ 99FleBri-22
❑ 99FleBri2G-22
❑ 99FleBriBlu-22
❑ 99FleBriGol-22
❑ 99FleSta9-79
❑ 99FleWarT-79
❑ 99SkyThu-60
❑ 99SkyThuRant-60
❑ 99SkyThuRave-60
❑ 99ThuSkySupR-60
❑ 99Top-363
❑ 99TopChr-363
❑ 99TopChrR-363
❑ 99TopMVPP-363

Carpenter, Cris
❑ 87PanAmTUBI-34A
❑ 87PanAmTUBI-34B
❑ 87PanAmTURB-19
❑ 88DonRoo-50
❑ 88LouRedBC-8
❑ 88LouRedBP-428
❑ 88LouRedBTI-13
❑ 89CarTeal-2
❑ 89ClaTraP-185
❑ 89Don-39
❑ 89DonRoo-40
❑ 89FleUpd-117
❑ 89LouRedBTI-13
❑ 89ScoRoo-81T
❑ 89ScoYouS2-37
❑ 89Top-282
❑ 89TopBig-307
❑ 89TopTif-282
❑ 89UppDec-8
❑ 90CMC-103
❑ 90Don-634
❑ 90Fle-243
❑ 90FleCan-243
❑ 90Hot50RS-10
❑ 90LouRedBC-3
❑ 90LouRedBLBC-10
❑ 90LouRedBP-395
❑ 90OPC-443
❑ 90ProAAAF-509
❑ 90PubIntS-212
❑ 90Sco100RS-74
❑ 90Top-443
❑ 90TopTif-443
❑ 90TopTVCa-7
❑ 90UppDec-523
❑ 91Fle-628
❑ 91Lea-507
❑ 91OPC-518
❑ 91StaClu-499
❑ 91Top-518
❑ 91TopDesS-518
❑ 91TopMic-518
❑ 91TopTif-518
❑ 91UltUpd-105
❑ 92CarPol-2
❑ 92Don-79
❑ 92Fle-575
❑ 92OPC-147
❑ 92Sco-160
❑ 92StaClu-429
❑ 92Top-147
❑ 92TopGol-147
❑ 92TopGolW-147
❑ 92TopMic-147
❑ 92Ult-563
❑ 92UppDec-686
❑ 93Don-734
❑ 93Fle-420
❑ 93FleFinE-55
❑ 93MarlStaClu-11
❑ 93MarUppD-726
❑ 93MarUSPC-3C
❑ 93MarUSPC-13D
❑ 93PacSpa-456
❑ 93Pin-562
❑ 93RanKee-400
❑ 93Sco-633
❑ 93StaClu-706
❑ 93StaCluFDI-706
❑ 93StaCluMOP-706
❑ 93Top-629
❑ 93TopGol-629
❑ 93TopInaM-629
❑ 93TopInaR-629
❑ 93TopMic-629
❑ 93Ult-369
❑ 93UppDec-726
❑ 93UppDecGold-726
❑ 94ColC-73
❑ 94ColChoGS-73
❑ 94ColChoSS-73
❑ 94FleUpd-89
❑ 94Lea-261
❑ 94RanMagM-3
❑ 94StaClu-239
❑ 94StaCluFDI-239
❑ 94StaCluGR-239
❑ 94StaCluMOP-239
❑ 94StaCluT-259
❑ 94StaCluTFDI-259
❑ 94Top-317
❑ 94TopGol-317
❑ 94TopSpa-317
❑ 95Don-493
❑ 95DonPreP-493
❑ 95Fle-282
❑ 95LouRedF-271
❑ 95Pac-422
❑ 95Top-99
❑ 95Ult-107
❑ 95UltGolM-107
❑ 96LeaSigEA-24

Carpenter, Danny
❑ 87WytCubP-22

Carpenter, Doug
❑ 84GreHorT-9
❑ 85AlbYanT-20
❑ 86Ft.LauYP-3
❑ 87MiaMarP-7
❑ 89RenSilSCLC-254
❑ 90LakTigS-27
❑ 91LakTigC-10
❑ 91LakTigP-284

Carpenter, Glenn
❑ 83DayBeaAT-18
❑ 86TucTorP-4
❑ 87TucTorP-2
❑ 88TucTorC-12
❑ 88TucTorJP-5
❑ 88TucTorP-173

Carpenter, Hick (Warren W.)
❑ 87OldJudN-68
❑ 89EdgR.WG-4

Carpenter, Jay
❑ 90ArkRaz-5

Carpenter, Jerry
❑ 94BoiHawC-5
❑ 94BoiHawF-3357

Carpenter, John
❑ 45CenFlo-3

Carpenter, Justin
❑ 98OneYanG-7

Carpenter, Kevin
❑ 90JohCitCS-6

Carpenter, Matt
❑ 91MisStaB-10
❑ 92MisStaB-7
❑ 93MisStaB-7
❑ 94BenRocC-2
❑ 95WatIndTI-7

Carpenter, Mike
❑ 85RedWinA-25
❑ 86RedWinA-12

Carpenter, Paul
❑ 44CenFlo-2
❑ 47CenFlo-3

Carpenter, Rob
❑ 90KinMetB-10
❑ 90KinMetS-4
❑ 91ColMetPI-26

Carpenter, Terry
❑ 91FreStaLBS-1

Carpentier, Georges
❑ 52LaPat-2
❑ 52LavPro-54

Carpentier, Mike
❑ 95YakBeaTI-3
❑ 96SanBerSB-6
❑ 96VerBeaDB-9

Carpentier, Rob
❑ 91ColMetPPI-1
❑ 92St.LucMCB-12
❑ 92St.LucMF-1737
❑ 93St.LucMC-4
❑ 93St.LuMF-2912

Carper, Mark
❑ 88CapCodPPaLP-172
❑ 91FreKeyC-1
❑ 91FreKeyP-2355
❑ 92AlbYanF-2218
❑ 92HagSunS-256
❑ 93AlbYanF-2154
❑ 94ColCliF-2941
❑ 94ColCliP-2
❑ 95ColCliMCTI-7
❑ 95ColCliP-4
❑ 95ColCliTI-4
❑ 96ColCliB-5

Carpin, Frank
❑ 66OPC-71
❑ 66Top-71
❑ 66TopVen-71

Carpine, Bill
❑ 91CliGiaC-16
❑ 92CliGiaC-29
❑ 95PhoFirTI-NNO
❑ 96PhoFirB-5

Carpio, Jorge
❑ 82QuaCitCT-5
❑ 84MidCubT-6

Carr, Bobby
❑ 92GulCoaMF-3471
❑ 93KinMetC-4
❑ 93KinMetF-3788

Carr, Charlie (Charles Carbitt)
❑ 03BreE10-15
❑ 05IndSouPSoCP-6
❑ 08IndPos-3
❑ 09ColChiE-46A
❑ 09ColChiE-46B
❑ 09ColChiE-46C
❑ 09T206-405
❑ 11PinT-5-902
❑ 11SpoLifCW-55
❑ 12ColRedB-46A
❑ 12ColRedB-46B
❑ 12ColRedB-46C
❑ 12ColTinT-46A
❑ 12ColTinT-46B
❑ 12ColTinT-46C

Carr, Chuck
❑ 87BelMarTI-9
❑ 88MidLeaAGS-56
❑ 88WauTimGS-8
❑ 89JacMetGS-2
❑ 89TexLeaAGS-28
❑ 90FleUpd-34
❑ 90JacMetGS-24
❑ 91Fle-141
❑ 91MetColP-25
❑ 91MetWIZ-65
❑ 91TidTidP-2521
❑ 91TopDeb90-26
❑ 91UppDec-514
❑ 92ArkTraS-29
❑ 92LouRedF-1899
❑ 92Sco-857
❑ 92SkyAA F-13
❑ 92SpollIFK1-266
❑ 93Bow-474
❑ 93Don-124
❑ 93Don-762
❑ 93Fla-48
❑ 93Fle-421
❑ 93FleFinE-56
❑ 93Lea-541
❑ 93MarlStaClu-25
❑ 93MarPub-7
❑ 93MarUppD-590
❑ 93MarUSPC-6H
❑ 93MarUSPC-12D

❑ 93PacSpa-457
❑ 93Pin-618
❑ 93Sco-545
❑ 93SelRoo-37T
❑ 93SP-137
❑ 93StaClu-564
❑ 93StaCluFDI-564
❑ 93StaCluMOP-564
❑ 93Top-722
❑ 93TopGol-722
❑ 93TopInaM-722
❑ 93TopInaR-722
❑ 93TopMic-722
❑ 93Ult-370
❑ 93UppDec-590
❑ 93UppDecGold-590
❑ 94Bow-66
❑ 94BowBes-R66
❑ 94BowBesR-R66
❑ 94ColC-404
❑ 94ColChoGS-404
❑ 94ColChoSS-404
❑ 94Don-509
❑ 94Fin-8
❑ 94FinJum-8
❑ 94FinRef-8
❑ 94Fla-380
❑ 94Fle-463
❑ 94FleExtB-258
❑ 94FleExtBSYS-3
❑ 94FleLeaL-10
❑ 94FleRooS-4
❑ 94FUnPac-87
❑ 94FUnPac-198
❑ 94Lea-408
❑ 94LeaL-105
❑ 94MarTeal-3
❑ 94OPC-220
❑ 94Pac-237
❑ 94PanSti-180
❑ 94Pin-195
❑ 94PinArtP-195
❑ 94PinMusC-195
❑ 94Sco-512
❑ 94ScoBoyoS-31
❑ 94ScoGolR-512
❑ 94Sel-11
❑ 94SP-108
❑ 94SPDieC-108
❑ 94StaClu-29
❑ 94StaCluFDI-29
❑ 94StaCluGR-29
❑ 94StaCluMO-25
❑ 94StaCluMOP-29
❑ 94StaCluT-84
❑ 94StaCluTFDI-84
❑ 94Stu-107
❑ 94Top-653
❑ 94TopGol-653
❑ 94TopSpa-653
❑ 94TriPla-133
❑ 94Ult-194
❑ 94UltLeaL-8
❑ 94UltSecYS-6
❑ 94UppDec-202
❑ 94UppDecED-202
❑ 94USPlaCA-13H
❑ 94USPlaCR-1D
❑ 95Baz-69
❑ 95Bow-294
❑ 95ColCho-299
❑ 95ColChoGS-299
❑ 95ColChoSE-133
❑ 95ColChoSEGS-133
❑ 95ColChoSESS-133
❑ 95ColChoSS-299
❑ 95Don-192
❑ 95DonPreP-192
❑ 95DonTopotO-239
❑ 95Fin-70
❑ 95FinRef-70
❑ 95Fla-351
❑ 95Fle-328
❑ 95Lea-213
❑ 95Pac-169
❑ 95Pin-30
❑ 95PinArtP-30
❑ 95PinMusC-30
❑ 95Sco-224
❑ 95ScoGolR-224
❑ 95ScoPlaTS-224
❑ 95ScoSam-224
❑ 95StaClu-357
❑ 95StaClu-409
❑ 95StaCluMOP-357
❑ 95StaCluMOP-409
❑ 95StaCluMOP-SS4
❑ 95StaCluSS-SS4
❑ 95StaCluSTWS-357
❑ 95StaCluSTWS-409
❑ 95StaCluVR-187
❑ 95StaCluVRMO-187
❑ 95Stu-72
❑ 95Top-96
❑ 95TopCyb-63
❑ 95TopD3-52
❑ 95TopEmb-16
❑ 95TopEmbGI-16
❑ 96TopLeaL-LL20
❑ 95Ult-161
❑ 95UltGolM-161
❑ 95UppDec-352
❑ 95UppDecED-352
❑ 95UppDecEDG-352
❑ 95UppDecSE-116
❑ 95UppDecSEG-116
❑ 95USPlaCMLA-7H
❑ 96BrePol-3
❑ 96ColCho-593
❑ 96ColChoGS-593
❑ 96ColChoSS-593
❑ 96Don-236
❑ 96DonPreP-236
❑ 96EmoXL-72
❑ 96Fla-98
❑ 96Fle-142
❑ 96FleTif-142
❑ 96FleUpd-U45
❑ 96FleUpdTC-U45
❑ 96LeaSigEA-25
❑ 96Pac-70
❑ 96Sco-118
❑ 96Ult-362
❑ 96UltGolM-362
❑ 97BrePol-3
❑ 97Pac-115
❑ 97PacLigB-115
❑ 97PacSil-115
❑ 97Sco-436
❑ 97ScoArtPWB-436
❑ 97ScoResC-436
❑ 97ScoShoS-436
❑ 97ScoShoSAP-436
❑ 97Ult-427
❑ 97UltGolME-427
❑ 97UltPlaME-427
❑ 98Sco-4
❑ 98Top-350
❑ 98TopChr-350
❑ 98TopChrR-350
❑ 98TopDevR-350
❑ 98TopDia-350
❑ 98TopMiniC-350

Carr, Dustin
❑ 97HudValRB-2
❑ 98Bow-217
❑ 98BowChr-217
❑ 98BowChrGA-217
❑ 98BowChrGAR-217
❑ 98BowChrI-217
❑ 98BowChrIR-217
❑ 98BowChrR-217
❑ 98BowGolA-217
❑ 98BowInt-217
❑ 98St.PetDRM-19
❑ 98Top-500
❑ 98TopChr-500
❑ 98TopChrR-500
❑ 98TopDevR-500
❑ 98TopDia-500
❑ 98TopMiniC-500

Carr, Ernie
❑ 88GreFalDTI-4
❑ 89BakDodCLC-200
❑ 90SanAntMGS-9

Carr, Jeff
❑ 96WisTimRB-4
❑ 98WisTimRM-29

Carr, Jeremy
❑ 93EugEmeC-9
❑ 93EugEmeF-3860
❑ 94RocRoyC-6
❑ 94RocRoyF-571
❑ 95BakBlaTI-6
❑ 96HonShaHWB-11
❑ 96TexLeaAB-22
❑ 96WicWraB-6
❑ 97WicWra-20

Carr, Taylor
❑ 95FayGenTI-30

Carr, Terence
❑ 86SalAngC-95
❑ 87QuaCitAP-1
❑ 88QuaCitAGS-9
❑ 89RenSilSCLC-255
❑ 90PalSprACLC-203
❑ 90PalSprAP-2589

Carr, Tim
❑ 98PitMetM-12

Carrano, Rick
❑ 86MiaMarP-4

Carranza, Javier
❑ 83St.PetCT-2

Carranza, Pedro
❑ 94AshTouC-3
❑ 94AshTouF-1787
❑ 95AshTouTI-23

Carrara, Giovanni
❑ 91St.CatBJC-13
❑ 91St.CatBJP-3387
❑ 92DunBluJC-17
❑ 92MyrBeaHC-25
❑ 92ProFS7-175
❑ 93DunBluJC-5
❑ 93DunBluJF-1787
❑ 93DunBluJFFN-5
❑ 93LinVenB-21
❑ 93SouAtlLAPI-5
❑ 94KnoSmoF-1295
❑ 94VenLinU-124
❑ 95LinVen-186
❑ 95SyrChiTI-9
❑ 96-97LinVen-51
❑ 96FleUpd-U94
❑ 96FleUpdTC-U94
❑ 96SyrChiTI-8
❑ 96Ult-426
❑ 96UltGolM-426
❑ 97DonSigA-16
❑ 97DonSigAC-22
❑ 97DonSigAM-22
❑ 97RocRedW-7

Carrasco, Carlos
❑ 88BakDodCLC-251
❑ 89RenSilSCLC-243
❑ 90SalSpuCLC-127
❑ 90SalSpuP-2718
❑ 91SalSpuC-23
❑ 91SalSpuP-2235

Carrasco, Claudio
❑ 86WatIndP-5
❑ 87WatIndP-26
❑ 88WilBilP-1320
❑ 89QuaCitAB-23
❑ 89QuaCitAGS-29
❑ 89RenSilSCLC-259

Carrasco, Danny
❑ 98WatIndTI-6

Carrasco, Ernie
❑ 83EriCarT-22
❑ 84SavCarT-15
❑ 86ArkTraP-3

Carrasco, Hector
❑ 89KinMetS-4
❑ 90KinMetB-16
❑ 90KinMetS-5
❑ 91PitMetC-21
❑ 91PitMetP-3415
❑ 92AshTouC-24
❑ 93Bow-262
❑ 93ClaFS7-97
❑ 93KanCouCC-2
❑ 93KanCouCF-907
❑ 93KanCouCTI-1
❑ 94Bow-130
❑ 94BowBes-R89
❑ 94BowBesR-R89
❑ 94Fin-316
❑ 94FinRef-316
❑ 94Fla-145
❑ 94FleExtB-230
❑ 94FleExtBRS-3
❑ 94FleUpd-116
❑ 94LeaGolR-20
❑ 94LeaLimR-8
❑ 94RedKah-6
❑ 94ScoRoo-RT80
❑ 94ScoRooGR-RT80
❑ 94Sel-385
❑ 94SpoRoo-128
❑ 94SpoRooAP-128
❑ 94StaClu-552
❑ 94StaClu-634
❑ 94StaCluFDI-552
❑ 94StaCluFDI-634
❑ 94StaCluGR-552
❑ 94StaCluGR-634
❑ 94StaCluMOP-552
❑ 94StaCluMOP-634
❑ 94TopTra-91T
❑ 94Ult-470
❑ 94UppDec-511
❑ 94UppDecED-511
❑ 95Don-101
❑ 95DonPreP-101
❑ 95DonTopotO-211
❑ 95Fin-28
❑ 95FinRef-28
❑ 95Fla-337
❑ 95Fle-432
❑ 95FleRooS-3
❑ 95KanCouCLTI-2
❑ 95Lea-306
❑ 95Pac-102
❑ 95PacLatD-7
❑ 95Pin-26
❑ 95PinArtP-26
❑ 95PinMusC-26
❑ 95RedKah-6
❑ 95Sco-13
❑ 95ScoGolR-13
❑ 95ScoPlaTS-13
❑ 95StaClu-392
❑ 95StaCluMOP-392
❑ 95StaCluSTDW-RE392
❑ 95StaCluSTWS-392
❑ 95Top-447
❑ 95TopCyb-243
❑ 95Ult-143
❑ 95UltGolM-143
❑ 95UppDec-166
❑ 95UppDecED-166
❑ 95UppDecEDG-166
❑ 96Don-112
❑ 96DonPreP-112
❑ 96Fle-338
❑ 96FleTif-338
❑ 96IndIndB-7
❑ 96Pac-34
❑ 97Pac-266
❑ 97PacLigB-266
❑ 97PacSil-266
❑ 99PacCroC-158
❑ 99PacCroCPB-158

Carrasco, Jose
❑ 94BoiHawC-6
❑ 94BoiHawF-3345

Carrasco, Norman
❑ 82DanSunF-28
❑ 83RedPioT-5
❑ 85EdmTraC-22
❑ 86EdmTraP-2
❑ 87EdmTraP-2079
❑ 88MidAngGS-25
❑ 89TolMudHC-20
❑ 89TolMudHP-768

Carrasco, Troy
❑ 93EliTwiC-7
❑ 93EliTwiF-3409
❑ 94ForWayWC-5
❑ 94ForWayWF-2001
❑ 95ForMyeMTI-5
❑ 95SPML-86
❑ 96BesAutS-17
❑ 96HarCitRCB-11
❑ 97NewBriRC-7
❑ 98ForMyeMTI-5

Carrasquel, Alex
❑ 67TopVen-176
❑ 93ConTSN-956

Carrasquel, Chico (Alfonso)
❑ 47Exh-34A
❑ 47Exh-34B
❑ 47PM1StaP1-28
❑ 51Bow-60
❑ 51FisBakL-4
❑ 51R42SmaS-9
❑ 51TopBluB-26
❑ 52BerRos-8
❑ 52Bow-41
❑ 52DixLid-3
❑ 52DixPre-3
❑ 52StaCalL-73D
❑ 52StaCalS-87B
❑ 52Top-251
❑ 53BowC-54
❑ 53DixLid-2
❑ 53DixPre-2
❑ 53Dor-122
❑ 53ExhCan-4
❑ 54Bow-54
❑ 54RedMan-AL19
❑ 55Bow-173
❑ 55RedMan-AL23
❑ 55RobGouS-4
❑ 55RobGouW-4
❑ 56A'sPos-7
❑ 56BalOriP-9
❑ 56Top-230
❑ 57IndSoh-3
❑ 57IndTeal-3
❑ 57Top-67
❑ 58Hir-11
❑ 58IndTeal-4
❑ 58Top-55
❑ 59OriJayP-2
❑ 59Top-264
❑ 67TopVen-181
❑ 76VenLeaS-74
❑ 79TCM50-74
❑ 80VenLeaS-92
❑ 80VenLeaS-132
❑ 83TopRep5-251
❑ 85WhiSoxC-5
❑ 91OriCro-69
❑ 94TopSpa-L5

Carrasquel, Domingo
❑ 94HelBreF-3620
❑ 94HelBreSP-3
❑ 94VenLinU-110
❑ 95LinVen-172
❑ 96-97LinVen-46
❑ 96-97LinVen-196
❑ 96BelSnaTI-9

Carrasquel, Emilio
❑ 80VenLeaS-117
❑ 82BirBarT-22

Carrasquillo, Angel
❑ 88BenBucL-1

Carraway, Rod
❑ 82WatIndF-9
❑ 82WatIndT-14

Carreno, Amalio
❑ 87PriWilYP-19
❑ 88AlbYanP-1329
❑ 89ReaPhiS-6
❑ 90Bes-140
❑ 90ReaPhiB-5
❑ 90ReaPhiP-1213
❑ 90ReaPhiS-11
❑ 91LinDriAAA-481
❑ 91ScrRedBLD-481
❑ 91ScrRedBP-2532
❑ 92Sco-867
❑ 92TopDeb91-27
❑ 93LinVenB-71

Carreon, Cam (Camilo G.)
❑ 60Lea-88
❑ 60Top-121
❑ 60TopVen-121
❑ 61Top-509
❑ 61WhiSoxTS-3
❑ 62Top-178
❑ 62TopStal-23
❑ 62TopVen-178
❑ 62WhiSoxTS-4
❑ 63Top-308
❑ 63WhiSoxJP-1
❑ 63WhiSoxTS-3
❑ 64Top-421
❑ 64WhiSoxI-6
❑ 64WhiSoxTS-5
❑ 65Top-578
❑ 66BalOriP-11
❑ 66Top-513
❑ 81WhiSox1T-26
❑ 91OriCro-70

Carreon, Mark
❑ 83LynMetT-14A
❑ 84JacMetT-20
❑ 85TidTidT-25
❑ 86TidTidP-4
❑ 87IntLeaAT-12
❑ 87MetColP-28
❑ 87TidTidP-21
❑ 87TidTidT-20
❑ 88Fle-129
❑ 88FleGlo-129
❑ 88MetColP-15
❑ 88TidTidCa-14
❑ 88TidTidCM-22
❑ 88TidTidP-1588
❑ 88TriAAAP-39
❑ 88TriAAC-23
❑ 89Bow-389
❑ 89BowTif-389
❑ 89ClaLigB-84
❑ 89DonRoo-18
❑ 89Fle-29
❑ 89FleGlo-29
❑ 89MetColP-25
❑ 89MetKah-3
❑ 89ScoHot1R-16
❑ 89ScoRoo-108T
❑ 89TidTidC-14
❑ 89TidTidC-24
❑ 90ClaBlu-112
❑ 90Don-454
❑ 90Fle-198
❑ 90FleCan-198
❑ 90Hot50RS-11
❑ 90Lea-488
❑ 90MetColP-28
❑ 90MetKah-45
❑ 90OPC-434
❑ 90Sco-363
❑ 90Sco100RS-67
❑ 90ScoYouSI-17
❑ 90Top-434
❑ 90TopRoo-6
❑ 90TopTif-434
❑ 90TopTVM-30
❑ 90ToyRoo-7
❑ 90UppDec-135
❑ 91Don-731
❑ 91Fle-142
❑ 91MetColP-13
❑ 91MetKah-45
❑ 91MetPerPA-10
❑ 91MetWIZ-66
❑ 91OPC-764
❑ 91Sco-165
❑ 91StaClu-196
❑ 91Top-764
❑ 91TopDesS-764
❑ 91TopMic-764
❑ 91TopTif-764
❑ 92Bow-111
❑ 92Don-465
❑ 92Fle-498
❑ 92Lea-259
❑ 92LeaBlaG-259
❑ 92OPC-111
❑ 92OPCPre-88
❑ 92Pin-441
❑ 92Sco-19
❑ 92ScoProP-3
❑ 92ScoRoo-37T
❑ 92StaClu-678
❑ 92StaCluNC-678
❑ 92TigKro-4
❑ 92Top-111
❑ 92TopGol-111
❑ 92TopGolW-111
❑ 92TopMic-111
❑ 92TopTra-21T
❑ 92TopTraG-21T
❑ 92Ult-359
❑ 92UppDec-398
❑ 92UppDec-739
❑ 93Don-71
❑ 93Fle-604
❑ 93FleFinE-152
❑ 93GiaMot-15
❑ 93GiaPos-13
❑ 93GiaStaC-23
❑ 93PacSpa-104
❑ 93Pin-136
❑ 93Sco-366
❑ 93StaClu-680
❑ 93StaCluFDI-680
❑ 93StaCluMOP-680
❑ 93Top-567
❑ 93TopGol-567
❑ 93TopInaM-567
❑ 93TopInaR-567
❑ 93TopMic-567
❑ 93UppDec-570
❑ 93UppDecGold-570
❑ 94Fle-688
❑ 94GiaAMC-7
❑ 94GiaMot-27
❑ 94GiaTarBC-8
❑ 94GiaUSPC-4D
❑ 94GiaUSPC-11C
❑ 94Sco-132
❑ 94ScoGolR-132
❑ 94StaCluT-13
❑ 94StaCluTFDI-13
❑ 94Top-327
❑ 94TopGol-327
❑ 94TopSpa-327
❑ 94Ult-288
❑ 95Fle-577

❑ 95GiaMot-27
❑ 95Pac-375
❑ 95Sco-248
❑ 95ScoGolR-248
❑ 95ScoPlaTS-248
❑ 95Top-361
❑ 96ColCho-302
❑ 96ColChoGS-302
❑ 96ColChoSS-302
❑ 96Don-316
❑ 96DonPreP-316
❑ 96EmoXL-287
❑ 96Fla-385
❑ 96Fle-585
❑ 96FleTif-585
❑ 96GiaMot-8
❑ 96Pac-206
❑ 96Pin-317
❑ 96PinFoil-317
❑ 96Sco-147
❑ 96StaClu-318
❑ 96StaCluMOP-318
❑ 96Top-74
❑ 96Ult-292
❑ 96UltGolM-292
❑ 96UppDec-197
❑ 97Fle-76
❑ 97FleTif-76
❑ 97IndSco-12
❑ 97IndScoPl-12
❑ 97IndScoPr-12
❑ 97Sco-211
❑ 97ScoArtPWB-211
❑ 97ScoPreS-211
❑ 97ScoShoS-211
❑ 97ScoShoSAP-211
❑ 97Top-391
❑ 97Ult-47
❑ 97UltGolME-47
❑ 97UltPlaME-47
Carrera, Mahaly
❑ 93LinVenB-126
❑ 95LinVen-230
Carrick, William
❑ 03BreE10-16
❑ 07NewEveWS-1
Carrier, Brent
❑ 89TenTecGE-5
❑ 89TenTecGE-35
Carrigan, Bill (William F.)
❑ 09BriE97-6
❑ 09PhiCarE-2
❑ 09RamT20-22
❑ 09SpoNewSM-44
❑ 09T206-53
❑ 10DomDisP-21
❑ 10E-UOraBSC-4
❑ 10E12AmeCDCE125-8
❑ 10SweCapPP-1A
❑ 10SweCapPP-1B
❑ 11BasBatEU-6
❑ 11DiaGumP-6
❑ 11HelSta-1
❑ 11PinT-5-651
❑ 11S74Sil-1
❑ 11SpoLifCW-56
❑ 11SpoLifM-2
❑ 11T205-25
❑ 11TurRedT-86
❑ 12HasTriFT-10A
❑ 12HasTriFT-10B
❑ 12HasTriFT-24
❑ 12T207-27
❑ 12T207-28
❑ 13TomBarW-7
❑ 14CraJacE-27
❑ 14PieStaT-18
❑ 15CraJacE-27
❑ 16FleBreD-14
❑ 93ConTSN-828
❑ 94ConTSN-1056
❑ 94ConTSNB-1056
Carriger, Rick
❑ 87HagSunP-18
❑ 88JacExpB-1
❑ 88JacExpP-988
❑ 89JacExpB-19
❑ 89JacExpP-168
Carrigg, Mike
❑ 94OgdRapF-3740
❑ 94OgdRapSP-2
Carrillo, Joe
❑ 92JohCitCC-24
❑ 92JohCitCF-3107
❑ 93SavCarC-8
❑ 93SavCarF-680
Carrillo, Matias
❑ 86NasPirP-5
❑ 87SalBucP-10
❑ 88ElPasDB-12
❑ 89DenZepC-22
❑ 89DenZepP-49
❑ 91DenZepLD-131
❑ 91DenZepP-134
❑ 91LinDriAAA-131
❑ 92TopDeb91-28
❑ 93LinVenB-304
❑ 94BreMilB-110
❑ 94Pac-238
❑ 94ScoRooGR-RT138
❑ 94SpoRoo-108
❑ 94SpoRooAP-108
❑ 94StaClu-235
❑ 94StaCluFDI-235
❑ 94StaCluGR-235
❑ 94StaCluMOP-235
❑ 94Ult-490
❑ 95Don-255
❑ 95DonPreP-255
❑ 95Fle-329
❑ 95Pac-170
❑ 95Sco-159
❑ 95ScoGolR-159
❑ 95ScoPlaTS-159
Carrillo, Paul
❑ 85CloHSS-8
Carrion, German
❑ 92ChaRaiC-15
❑ 92ChaRaiF-125
❑ 93WatDiaC-8
Carrion, Jesus
❑ 86OscAstP-4
Carrion, Jorge
❑ 97Bow-421
❑ 97BowChr-281
❑ 97BowChrI-281
❑ 97BowChrIR-281
❑ 97BowChrR-281
❑ 97BowInt-421
❑ 98SavSanGM-6
Carrion, Leonel
❑ 76VenLeaS-199
❑ 80MemChiT-12
❑ 80VenLeaS-235
❑ 83MemChiT-15
❑ 84IndIndTI-3
❑ 86JacExpT-9
❑ 88ExpPos-5
❑ 93LinVenB-222
Carrisch, Frederick
❑ 15Zee-55
❑ 16Zee-47
Carrithers, Don
❑ 71MLBOffS-243
❑ 72Dia-7
❑ 72GiaTeal-3
❑ 72OPC-76
❑ 72Top-76
❑ 73OPC-651
❑ 73Top-651
❑ 74OPC-361
❑ 74Top-361
❑ 75ExpPos-6
❑ 75OPC-438
❑ 75Top-438
❑ 75TopMin-438
❑ 76ExpRed-3
❑ 76MonExpP-3
❑ 76OPC-312
❑ 76SSP-348
❑ 76Top-312
❑ 77OPC-18
❑ 77Top-579
❑ 78PhoGiaC-4
❑ 78Top-113
❑ 79PhoGiaVNB-11
Carrol, Jamey
❑ 96VerExpB-11
Carroll, Bob
❑ 75AndRanT-37
❑ 76AshTouT-5
❑ 77VisOakT-3
Carroll, Carson
❑ 83OrlTwiT-25
❑ 83WisRapTF-7
❑ 84VisOakT-15
❑ 86AlbYanT-3
❑ 87AlbYanP-14
Carroll, Chris
❑ 86Ft.LauYP-4
❑ 87Ft.LauYP-5
Carroll, Clay
❑ 65Top-461
❑ 66BraPos-7
❑ 66Top-307
❑ 66TopVen-307
❑ 67BraPho-6
❑ 67Top-219
❑ 68BraPos-7
❑ 68DexPre-21
❑ 68Top-412
❑ 69Kah-B6
❑ 69OPC-26
❑ 69Top-26
❑ 70DayDaiNM-71
❑ 70OPC-133
❑ 70Top-133
❑ 71MLBOffS-52
❑ 71OPC-394
❑ 71Top-394
❑ 72MilBra-68
❑ 72OPC-311
❑ 72OPC-312
❑ 72Top-311
❑ 72Top-312
❑ 73OPC-68
❑ 73OPC-195
❑ 73Top-68
❑ 73Top-195
❑ 74OPC-111
❑ 74Top-111
❑ 75OPC-345
❑ 75Top-345
❑ 75TopMin-345
❑ 76Kel-6A
❑ 76Kel-6B
❑ 76OPC-211
❑ 76SSP-25
❑ 76Top-211
❑ 76TopTra-211T
❑ 77Car5-3
❑ 77CarTeal-3
❑ 77Top-497
❑ 78Top-615
❑ 79VanCanT-14
❑ 86RedGreT-1
Carroll, Cliff (Samuel C.)
❑ 87BucN28-107
❑ 87OldJudN-69
Carroll, David
❑ 94MadHatC-4
❑ 94MadHatF-123
❑ 95PeoChiTI-25
❑ 97St.PetDR-11
❑ 97St.PetDRUB-12
❑ 98HunStaTI-17
❑ 98ModA'sG-5
Carroll, Dixie (Dorsey Lee)
❑ 21Zee-3
❑ 22Zee-2
❑ 23Zee-2
Carroll, Don
❑ 88GreFalDTI-12
❑ 89SalDodTI-9
❑ 90KisDodD-5
❑ 91BakDodCLC-27
❑ 91YakBeaC-18
❑ 91YakBeaP-4240
Carroll, Doug
❑ 97St.PetDR-12
❑ 97St.PetDRUB-13
Carroll, Ed
❑ 78HolMilT-3
❑ 79HolMilT-4
❑ 80HolMilT-19
Carroll, Frank
❑ 09ObaT21-11
❑ 09ObaT21-98
❑ 88SFHesCreN32-6
Carroll, Fred (Frederick H.)
❑ 87BucN28-87
❑ 87OldJudN-71
❑ 88WG1CarG-55
❑ 89EdgR.WG-4
Carroll, James
❑ 86MedA'sC-71
❑ 87MadMusP-4
❑ 87MadMusP-21
❑ 88MadMusP-9
❑ 88ModA'sTI-6
❑ 89ClePhiS-4
Carroll, Jamey
❑ 98JupHamQ-17
Carroll, Joe
❑ 78AshTouT-5
Carroll, Kevin
❑ 90ColMetGS-23
❑ 90ColMetPPI-2
❑ 91St.LucMC-12
❑ 91St.LucMP-713
❑ 92LynRedSC-17
❑ 92LynRedSF-2910
❑ 93NewBriRSF-1224
Carroll, Mark
❑ 98EveAquG-3
Carroll, Owen
❑ 28StaPlaCE-7
❑ 29PorandAR-11
❑ 33ButCanV-6
❑ 33DouDisP-8
❑ 33Gou-72
❑ 34BabRutG-8
❑ 34ButPreR-8
❑ 34DiaMatCSB-26
❑ 34GouCanV-46
❑ 72TCMthe3-99
❑ 90DodTar-115
❑ 92ConTSN-496
Carroll, Scrappy (John E.)
❑ 87OldJudN-70
Carroll, Shadow
❑ 12ImpTobC-39
Carroll, Steve
❑ 83IowCubT-24
❑ 85IowCubT-30
Carroll, Thomas M.
❑ 75OPC-507
❑ 75Top-507
❑ 75TopMin-507
❑ 76IndIndTI-12
❑ 76OPC-561
❑ 76Top-561
Carroll, Tim
❑ 80AppFoxT-22
Carroll, Tommy (Thomas E.)
❑ 55Top-158
❑ 56Top-139
❑ 57Top-164
❑ 59Top-513
Carruth, Jason
❑ 94LetMouF-3869
❑ 94LetMouSP-7
Carruth, Jim
❑ 76BatRouCT-7
Carruthers, Mike
❑ 70WicAerM-5
Carruthers, Robert
❑ 87BucN28-95
❑ 89EdgR.WG-3
❑ 94OriofB-39
Carsey, Kid (Wilfred)
❑ 90DodTar-908
Carsley, Jeff
❑ 78DunBluJT-3
Carson, Albert
❑ 09ObaT21-24
❑ 09ObaT21-345
❑ 11Zee-112B
❑ 11Zee-112C
❑ 12ObaPreT-94
Carson, Alexander
❑ 11Zee-112A
❑ 12HomRunKE-83
❑ 12Zee-143
❑ 13Zee-52
Carson, Clayton
❑ 26Zee-42
Carson, Harold
❑ 37Zee-44
Carson, Henry
❑ 83St.PetCT-3
❑ 86St.PetCP-5
Carson, Kit (Walter Lloyd)
❑ 36NatChiFPR-18
Carson, Paul
❑ 89MarPhiS-5
Carson, Ted
❑ 84SavCarT-23
Carstensen, Chris
❑ 77NewCoPT-5
❑ 78BurBeeT-7
Carswell, Frank W.
❑ 53TigGle-3
Cartagena, Jesus
❑ 90IBAWorA-35
Cartaya, Joel
❑ 86SalRedBP-3
❑ 87PorChaRP-21
❑ 88TulDriTI-16
❑ 89ChaRanS-5
❑ 93LinVenB-131
Cartaya, Luis
❑ 95LinVen-229
Cartelli, Doc (John)
❑ 85ModA'sC-28
❑ 86ModA'sC-26
❑ 86ModA'sP-5
❑ 87ModA'sC-25
❑ 87ModA'sP-22
Carter, Aaron
❑ 97SpoIndG-6
❑ 98LanLugQ-3
Carter, Andy
❑ 88SouAtlLAGS-27
❑ 88SpaPhiS-19
❑ 89ClePhiS-5
❑ 90ClePhiS-4
❑ 91LinDriAA-506
❑ 91ReaPhiLD-506
❑ 91ReaPhiP-1366
❑ 92ClePhiF-2048
❑ 92ReaPhiS-529
❑ 92SkyAA F-228
❑ 95ScrRedBTI-4
❑ 96PhoFirB-13
Carter, Bart
❑ 89MisStaB-6
❑ 97HudValRB-18
Carter, Bruce
❑ 86ClePhiP-2
❑ 86TriTriC-189
Carter, Bubba
❑ 92MisStaB-8
Carter, Cale
❑ 96LakElsSB-23
❑ 97CedRapK-2
Carter, Charley
❑ 98AubDouTI-6
Carter, Chris
❑ 93HelBreF-4098
❑ 93HelBreSP-20
❑ 97PriDevR-19
Carter, Cliff
❑ 91PomBlaBPB-23
Carter, David
❑ 90GatCitPP-3361
❑ 90GatCitPSP-4
❑ 91EriSaiC-14
❑ 91EriSaiP-4060
Carter, Dell
❑ 85ElmPioT-4
Carter, Dennis
❑ 87ArkTraP-1
❑ 88St.PetCS-3
❑ 89ArkTraGS-4
❑ 90CMC-110
❑ 90LouRedBC-10
❑ 90LouRedBP-414
❑ 90ProAAAF-528
Carter, Dick
❑ 60Top-466
Carter, Don
❑ 83MemChiT-7
❑ 84BufBisT-21
Carter, Dwight
❑ 75CliPilT-3
Carter, Eddie
❑ 87EriCarP-7
❑ 88SavCarP-354
❑ 89SavCarP-358
❑ 90St.PetCS-1
Carter, Fred
❑ 87Ft.LauYP-29
❑ 88RenSilSCLC-290
❑ 89PalSprACLC-45
❑ 89PalSprAP-479
Carter, Gary Edmund
❑ 70RelPam-1
❑ 73BooProC-17
❑ 75ExpPos-7
❑ 75IntLeaAT-21
❑ 75OPC-620
❑ 75Top-620
❑ 75TopMin-620
❑ 76ExpRed-4
❑ 76Hos-62
❑ 76Kel-34
❑ 76MonExpP-4
❑ 76OPC-441
❑ 76SSP-334
❑ 76Top-441
❑ 77BurCheD-154
❑ 77ExpPos-8
❑ 77Hos-41
❑ 77OPC-45
❑ 77Top-295
❑ 78ExpPos-2
❑ 78Hos-146
❑ 78OPC-135
❑ 78Top-120
❑ 79BasPat-15
❑ 79Hos-24
❑ 79OPC-270
❑ 79Top-520
❑ 80ExpPos-5
❑ 80OPC-37
❑ 80Top-70
❑ 80TopSup-52
❑ 81AllGamPI-130
❑ 81Don-90
❑ 81Dra-23
❑ 81Fle-142
❑ 81FleStiC-73
❑ 81OPC-6
❑ 81OPCPos-8
❑ 81PerAll-1
❑ 81PerCreC-32
❑ 81Top-660
❑ 81TopScr-66
❑ 81TopSti-184
❑ 81TopSti-259
❑ 82Don-2
❑ 82Don-114
❑ 82Dra-7
❑ 82ExpHygM-3
❑ 82ExpPos-4
❑ 82ExpZel-1
❑ 82ExpZel-6
❑ 82ExpZel-13
❑ 82ExpZel-16
❑ 82ExpZel-19
❑ 82FBIDis-5
❑ 82Fle-185
❑ 82Fle-635
❑ 82Fle-638
❑ 82FleSta-39
❑ 82Kel-24
❑ 82OPC-244
❑ 82OPC-344
❑ 82OPCPos-16
❑ 82PerAll-10
❑ 82PerAllG-10
❑ 82PerCreC-4
❑ 82PerCreCG-4
❑ 82SevSluC-7
❑ 82Squ-19
❑ 82Top-344
❑ 82Top-730
❑ 82TopSti-61
❑ 82TopSti-128
❑ 82TopSti-253
❑ 82TopStiV-61
❑ 83AllGamPI-129
❑ 83Don-340
❑ 83DonActA-58
❑ 83Dra-4
❑ 83ExpPos-3
❑ 83ExpStu-8
❑ 83Fle-278
❑ 83Fle-637
❑ 83Fle-638
❑ 83FleSta-31
❑ 83FleSti-262
❑ 83Kel-55
❑ 83OPC-314
❑ 83OPC-370
❑ 83PerAll-10
❑ 83PerAllG-10
❑ 83PerCreC-3
❑ 83PerCreCG-3
❑ 83Top-370
❑ 83Top-404
❑ 83TopGloS-20
❑ 83TopSti-178
❑ 83TopSti-255
❑ 83TopStiB-2
❑ 84AllGamPI-39
❑ 84Don-55
❑ 84DonCha-58
❑ 84Dra-6
❑ 84ExpPos-3
❑ 84ExpStu-15
❑ 84ExpStu-36
❑ 84Fle-271
❑ 84FunFooP-3
❑ 84MilBra-5
❑ 84Nes792-393
❑ 84Nes792-450
❑ 84OCoandSI-52

❑ 84OPC-366
❑ 84OPC-393
❑ 84RalPur-28
❑ 84SevCoi-C15
❑ 84Top-393
❑ 84Top-450
❑ 84TopCer-28
❑ 84TopGloA-20
❑ 84TopGloS-9
❑ 84TopRubD-11
❑ 84TopSti-90
❑ 84TopSti-183
❑ 84TopSup-18
❑ 84TopTif-393
❑ 84TopTif-450
❑ 85AllGamPI-128
❑ 85Don-55
❑ 85DonActA-57
❑ 85DonHig-21
❑ 85DonHig-47
❑ 85Dra-5
❑ 85Fle-393
❑ 85Fle-631
❑ 85Fle-632
❑ 85FleStaS-16
❑ 85FleStaS-26
❑ 85FleStaS-35
❑ 85FleUpd-21
❑ 85GenMilS-1
❑ 85Lea-241
❑ 85MetColP-23
❑ 85MetFanC-3
❑ 85MetTCM-18
❑ 85OPC-230
❑ 85PolMet-M2
❑ 85SevCoi-C9
❑ 85Top-230
❑ 85Top-719
❑ 85Top3-D-15
❑ 85TopGloA-9
❑ 85TopGloS-36
❑ 85TopMin-230
❑ 85TopRubD-11
❑ 85TopSti-83
❑ 85TopSti-180
❑ 85TopSti-192
❑ 85TopSup-13
❑ 85TopTif-230
❑ 85TopTif-719
❑ 85TopTifT-17T
❑ 85TopTra-17T
❑ 86BasStaB-20
❑ 86Don-68
❑ 86DorChe-3
❑ 86Dra-1
❑ 86Fle-76
❑ 86FleAll-4
❑ 86FleLeaL-5
❑ 86FleLimE-10
❑ 86FleMin-17
❑ 86FleSluBC-M3
❑ 86FleStiC-23
❑ 86FleWaxBC-C7
❑ 86GenMilB-4A
❑ 86Lea-63
❑ 86MetColP-3
❑ 86MetFanC-2
❑ 86MetTCM-13
❑ 86MetWorSC-2
❑ 86MSAJifPD-19
❑ 86OPC-170
❑ 86QuaGra-4
❑ 86SevCoi-E16
❑ 86Spo-28
❑ 86Spo-126
❑ 86Spo-137
❑ 86SpoDecG-72
❑ 86Top-170
❑ 86Top-708
❑ 86Top3-D-2
❑ 86TopGloS-23
❑ 86TopMinL-50
❑ 86TopSti-96
❑ 86TopSup-19
❑ 86TopTat-20
❑ 86TopTif-170
❑ 86TopTif-708
❑ 86TruVal-16
❑ 86Woo-7
❑ 87BoaandB-11
❑ 87BurKinA-2
❑ 87ClaGam-5
❑ 87Don-69
❑ 87DonAll-19
❑ 87DonOpeD-130
❑ 87DonP-19
❑ 87Dra-20
❑ 87Fle-4
❑ 87Fle-629
❑ 87Fle-634
❑ 87FleAll-2
❑ 87FleAwaW-7
❑ 87FleBasA-7
❑ 87FleExcS-9
❑ 87FleGamW-9
❑ 87FleGlo-4
❑ 87FleGlo-629
❑ 87FleGlo-634
❑ 87FleGlo-WS4
❑ 87FleMin-18
❑ 87FleStiC-20
❑ 87FleWorS-4
❑ 87GenMilB-5A
❑ 87HosSti-12
❑ 87K-M-25
❑ 87KayB-8
❑ 87KeyFooD-8
❑ 87Lea-109
❑ 87MandMSL-12
❑ 87MetColP-2
❑ 87MetFanC-1
❑ 87MSAIceTD-8
❑ 87OPC-20
❑ 87OurOwnTD-8
❑ 87RalPur-9
❑ 87RedFolSB-110
❑ 87SevCoi-E1
❑ 87SevCoi-M1
❑ 87Spo-50
❑ 87Spo-151
❑ 87SpoIllS-2
❑ 87SpoSupD-9
❑ 87SpoTeaP-2
❑ 87StaGarC-1
❑ 87StaGarC-2
❑ 87StaGarC-3
❑ 87StaGarC-4
❑ 87StaGarC-5
❑ 87StaGarC-6
❑ 87StaGarC-7
❑ 87StaGarC-8
❑ 87StaGarC-9
❑ 87StaGarC-10
❑ 87StaGarC-11
❑ 87StaGarC-12
❑ 87StaGarC-13
❑ 87StaGarC-14
❑ 87StuPan-1
❑ 87Top-20
❑ 87Top-331
❑ 87Top-602
❑ 87TopCoi-28
❑ 87TopGloA-9
❑ 87TopGloS-11
❑ 87TopMinL-20
❑ 87TopSti-14
❑ 87TopSti-22
❑ 87TopSti-101
❑ 87TopSti-158
❑ 87TopTif-20
❑ 87TopTif-331
❑ 87TopTif-602
❑ 87WeiMarD-8
❑ 87Woo-25
❑ 88CheBoy-10
❑ 88Don-199
❑ 88DonAll-41
❑ 88DonBasB-14
❑ 88DonPop-19
❑ 88DonTeaBM-199
❑ 88Dra-10
❑ 88Fle-130
❑ 88Fle-636
❑ 88FleGlo-130
❑ 88FleGlo-636
❑ 88FleStiWBC-S2
❑ 88GreBasS-37
❑ 88Lea-156
❑ 88MetColP-1
❑ 88MetFanC-8
❑ 88MetKah-8
❑ 88MSAJifPD-3
❑ 88Nes-26
❑ 88OPC-157
❑ 88PanSti-232
❑ 88PanSti-338
❑ 88Sco-325
❑ 88ScoBoxC-10
❑ 88ScoGlo-325
❑ 88Spo-28
❑ 88SpoGam-14
❑ 88StaGarC-1
❑ 88StaGarC-2
❑ 88StaGarC-3
❑ 88StaGarC-4
❑ 88StaGarC-5
❑ 88StaGarC-6
❑ 88StaGarC-7
❑ 88StaGarC-8
❑ 88StaGarC-9
❑ 88StaGarC-10
❑ 88StaGarC-11
❑ 88StaLinAl-5
❑ 88StaLinMe-3
❑ 88Top-530
❑ 88Top-579
❑ 88TopBig-37
❑ 88TopGloA-20
❑ 88TopGloS-7
❑ 88TopSti-105
❑ 88TopSti-152
❑ 88TopStiB-22
❑ 88TopTif-530
❑ 88TopTif-579
❑ 88TopUKM-11
❑ 88TopUKMT-11
❑ 89Bow-379
❑ 89BowTif-379
❑ 89CadEllD-6
❑ 89ClaLigB-64
❑ 89Don-53
❑ 89DonAll-41
❑ 89DonBasB-182
❑ 89DonPop-41
❑ 89Fle-30
❑ 89FleGlo-30
❑ 89FleSup-7
❑ 89KayB-4
❑ 89MetColP-3
❑ 89MetFanC-8
❑ 89MetKah-4
❑ 89OPC-324
❑ 89PanSti-136
❑ 89PanSti-228
❑ 89PAORelT-1
❑ 89RedFolSB-19
❑ 89Sco-240
❑ 89Spo-155
❑ 89Top-3
❑ 89Top-393
❑ 89Top-680
❑ 89TopBasT-76
❑ 89TopBig-325
❑ 89TopDouM-4
❑ 89TopGloA-20
❑ 89TopGloS-17
❑ 89TopSti-2
❑ 89TopSti-94
❑ 89TopSti-160
❑ 89TopStiB-55
❑ 89TopTif-3
❑ 89TopTif-393
❑ 89TopTif-680
❑ 89UppDec-390
❑ 89Woo-10
❑ 90BasWit-32
❑ 90Bow-236
❑ 90BowTif-236
❑ 90Don-147
❑ 90DonBesN-48
❑ 90DonLeaS-5
❑ 90Fle-199
❑ 90FleCan-199
❑ 90FleUpd-62
❑ 90GiaMot-3
❑ 90GiaSmo-3
❑ 90KayB-6
❑ 90Lea-134
❑ 90MLBBasB-17
❑ 90OPC-790
❑ 90PubIntS-128
❑ 90Sco-416
❑ 90ScoRoo-35T
❑ 90Top-790
❑ 90TopTif-790
❑ 90TopTra-19T
❑ 90TopTraT-19T
❑ 90UppDec-168
❑ 90UppDec-774
❑ 91BasBesRB-3
❑ 91Bow-598
❑ 91DodMot-16
❑ 91DodPho-9
❑ 91DodPol-12
❑ 91DodSt.V-2
❑ 91Don-151
❑ 91DonBonC-BC8
❑ 91Fle-258
❑ 91FleUpd-93
❑ 91Lea-457
❑ 91MetWIZ-67
❑ 91OPC-310
❑ 91OPCPre-19
❑ 91Sco-215
❑ 91ScoRoo-26T
❑ 91StaClu-424
❑ 91Stu-182
❑ 91Top-310
❑ 91TopDesS-310
❑ 91TopMic-310
❑ 91TopTif-310
❑ 91TopTra-19T
❑ 91TopTraT-19T
❑ 91UltUpd-86
❑ 91UppDec-176
❑ 91UppDec-758
❑ 92Bow-385
❑ 92Don-36
❑ 92DonUpd-U19
❑ 92ExpDonD-5
❑ 92ExpPos-6
❑ 92Fle-450
❑ 92Lea-442
❑ 92LeaBlaG-442
❑ 92OPC-45
❑ 92OPC-387
❑ 92OPC-389
❑ 92OPC-399
❑ 92OPC-402
❑ 92OPCPre-29
❑ 92PepDieM-12
❑ 92Pin-321
❑ 92Sco-489
❑ 92ScoRoo-59T
❑ 92StaClu-845
❑ 92StaCluMO-5
❑ 92StaCluNC-845
❑ 92Stu-53
❑ 92Top-45
❑ 92TopGol-45
❑ 92TopGolW-45
❑ 92TopMic-45
❑ 92TopTra-22T
❑ 92TopTraG-22T
❑ 92TriPla-26
❑ 92TriPlaP-5
❑ 92Ult-514
❑ 92UppDec-267
❑ 92UppDec-767
❑ 93Don-122
❑ 93ExpDonM-12
❑ 93Sel-55
❑ 93Top-205
❑ 93TopGol-205
❑ 93TopInaM-205
❑ 93TopInaR-205
❑ 93TopMic-205
❑ 93TopPreS-3
❑ 93UppDec-219
❑ 93UppDecGold-219
❑ 93UppDecS-27
❑ 94TedWil-50
❑ 94TedWil-136
❑ 95StoPop-2
❑ 95UppDecSHoB-8
❑ 99DumSet-GC
❑ 99DumSet-GC
❑ 99SpoIllGotG-21
❑ 99SpoIllGotGA-16
❑ 99SpoIllGotGC-41
❑ 99SpoIllGotGC-45
❑ 99UppDecR-105
❑ 99UppDecRG-105
❑ 99UppDecRP-105

Carter, Glenn

❑ 88BenBucL-21
❑ 89QuaCitAB-1
❑ 89QuaCitAGS-8
❑ 90MidAngGS-18
❑ 91Cla/Bes-305
❑ 91LinDriAA-429
❑ 91MidAngLD-429
❑ 91MidAngP-428
❑ 93El PasDF-2941
❑ 94NewBriRSF-643
❑ 94PawRedSDD-5

Carter, Herbert

❑ 82WisRapTF-10

Carter, Howard (John Howard)

❑ 89AriStaB-5

Carter, Jeff

❑ 85EveGialC-1
❑ 86CliGiaP-4
❑ 87JamExpP-2564
❑ 88RocExpLC-5
❑ 88ShrCapP-1291
❑ 89ShrCapP-1846
❑ 89TexLeaAGS-29
❑ 89WesPalBES-5
❑ 90Bes-316
❑ 90CMC-545
❑ 90JacExpB-18
❑ 90JacExpP-1369
❑ 90PhoFirC-18
❑ 90PhoFirP-17
❑ 90ProAaA-38
❑ 90ProAAAF-43
❑ 91Bow-348
❑ 91LinDriAAA-379
❑ 91LinDriAAA-630
❑ 91PhoFirLD-379
❑ 91PhoFirP-71
❑ 91VanCanLD-630
❑ 91VanCanP-1587
❑ 92Pin-280
❑ 92Sco-770
❑ 92SkyAAAF-237
❑ 92StaClu-381
❑ 92TacTigF-2509
❑ 92TacTigS-529
❑ 92TopDeb91-29
❑ 92VanCanF-2714
❑ 92VanCanS-630
❑ 93NasSouF-564
❑ 94SalLakBF-821
❑ 94VenLinU-267
❑ 95ChaKniTI-8
❑ 96ColSprSSTI-6
❑ 97ForWayW-4
❑ 98ForMyeMTI-6

Carter, Joe

❑ 83CubThoAV-33
❑ 83IowCubT-20
❑ 84Don-41
❑ 84IndWhe-30
❑ 84IowCubT-25
❑ 85Don-616
❑ 85Fle-443
❑ 85Ind-9
❑ 85IndPol-30
❑ 85Top-694
❑ 85TopTif-694
❑ 86Don-224
❑ 86DonHig-42
❑ 86Fle-583
❑ 86IndOhH-30
❑ 86IndTeal-14
❑ 86OPC-377
❑ 86Top-377
❑ 86TopSti-213
❑ 86TopTat-15
❑ 86TopTif-377
❑ 86WilGloT-1
❑ 87ClaUpdY-127
❑ 87Don-156
❑ 87DonOpeD-109
❑ 87Fle-249
❑ 87FleAwaW-8
❑ 87FleBasA-8
❑ 87FleGlo-249
❑ 87FleLeaL-9
❑ 87FleLimE-7
❑ 87FleMin-19
❑ 87FleStiC-21
❑ 87IndGat-30
❑ 87KayB-9
❑ 87KraFoo-15
❑ 87Lea-133
❑ 87MandMSL-16
❑ 87OPC-220
❑ 87RedFolSB-27
❑ 87SmoAmeL-5
❑ 87Spo-176
❑ 87SpoSupD-1
❑ 87SpoTeaP-3
❑ 87StuPan-18
❑ 87Top-220
❑ 87TopCoi-7
❑ 87TopGaloC-4
❑ 87TopGloS-16
❑ 87TopMinL-51
❑ 87TopSti-208
❑ 87TopTif-220
❑ 88Don-254
❑ 88DonBasB-56
❑ 88DonBonM-BC9
❑ 88Fle-605
❑ 88FleGlo-605
❑ 88FleMin-18
❑ 88FleSlu-7
❑ 88FleStiC-18
❑ 88FleSup-6
❑ 88GreBasS-56
❑ 88IndGat-30
❑ 88IndTeal-8
❑ 88KayB-4
❑ 88Lea-184
❑ 88Nes-36
❑ 88OPC-75
❑ 88OPCBoxB-I
❑ 88PanSti-72
❑ 88Sco-80
❑ 88ScoGlo-80
❑ 88Spo-5
❑ 88StaLinI-7
❑ 88Top-75
❑ 88Top-789
❑ 88TopBig-71
❑ 88TopCoi-8
❑ 88TopGloS-44
❑ 88TopRitTM-17
❑ 88TopSti-213
❑ 88TopStiB-49
❑ 88TopTif-75
❑ 88TopTif-789
❑ 88TopUKM-12
❑ 88TopUKMT-12
❑ 88TopWaxBC-I
❑ 89Bow-91
❑ 89BowTif-91
❑ 89CadEllD-7
❑ 89ClaLigB-11
❑ 89Don-83
❑ 89DonBasB-56
❑ 89DonBonM-BC3
❑ 89Fle-400
❑ 89FleExcS-4
❑ 89FleGlo-400
❑ 89FleHeroB-6
❑ 89IndTeal-8
❑ 89KinDis-8
❑ 89OPC-164
❑ 89PanSti-327
❑ 89RedFolSB-20
❑ 89Sco-213
❑ 89ScoHot1S-55
❑ 89Scomast-34
❑ 89Spo-104
❑ 89Top-420
❑ 89TopAme2C-9
❑ 89TopBasT-104
❑ 89TopBig-155
❑ 89TopCoi-36
❑ 89TopGloS-3
❑ 89TopHilTM-6
❑ 89TopSti-216
❑ 89TopStiB-14
❑ 89TopTif-420
❑ 89TopUKM-13
❑ 89TVSpoM-85
❑ 89UppDec-190
❑ 90Bow-220
❑ 90BowTif-220
❑ 90ClaBlu-138
❑ 90ClaUpd-T9
❑ 90Don-114
❑ 90DonBesN-72
❑ 90Fle-489
❑ 90FleCan-489
❑ 90FleUpd-55
❑ 90Hot50PS-5
❑ 90Lea-379
❑ 90LeaPre-2
❑ 90OPC-580
❑ 90PadCok-3
❑ 90PadMag-27
❑ 90PanSti-65
❑ 90Pos-30
❑ 90PubIntS-280
❑ 90PubIntS-557
❑ 90RedFolSB-15
❑ 90Sco-319
❑ 90Sco100S-59
❑ 90ScoRoo-19T
❑ 90Spo-120
❑ 90Top-580
❑ 90TopAmeA-27
❑ 90TopBig-245
❑ 90TopCoi-42
❑ 90TopDou-9
❑ 90TopGloS-33
❑ 90TopHilHM-28
❑ 90TopMag-58
❑ 90TopMinL-13
❑ 90TopSti-209

❑ 90TopStiB-48
❑ 90TopTif-580
❑ 90TopTra-20T
❑ 90TopTraT-20T
❑ 90TopTVA-43
❑ 90UppDec-53
❑ 90UppDec-375
❑ 90UppDec-754
❑ 90WicStaSGD-7
❑ 91BluJayFS-5
❑ 91BluJayFS-5
❑ 91BluJayS-1
❑ 91BluJayS-37
❑ 91Bow-11
❑ 91Cla1-T21
❑ 91Cla2-T98
❑ 91ClaGam-91
❑ 91ColJoeC-1
❑ 91ColJoeC-2
❑ 91ColJoeC-3
❑ 91ColJoeC-4
❑ 91ColJoeC-5
❑ 91ColJoeC-6
❑ 91ColJoeC-7
❑ 91ColJoeC-8
❑ 91ColJoeC-9
❑ 91ColJoeC-10
❑ 91ColJoeC-11
❑ 91ColJoeC-12
❑ 91ColJoeC-xx
❑ 91Don-298
❑ 91Don-409
❑ 91DonGraS-1
❑ 91Fle-525
❑ 91FleUpd-65
❑ 91Lea-353
❑ 91OPC-120
❑ 91OPCPre-20
❑ 91PanCanT1-19
❑ 91PanFreS-95
❑ 91PanSti-90
❑ 91Sco-9
❑ 91Sco100S-81
❑ 91ScoRoo-11T
❑ 91SpoNSP-1
❑ 91StaClu-513
❑ 91Stu-133
❑ 91Top-120
❑ 91TopDesS-120
❑ 91TopMic-120
❑ 91TopTif-120
❑ 91TopTra-20T
❑ 91TopTraT-20T
❑ 91TopTriH-A14
❑ 91Ult-360
❑ 91UppDec-226
❑ 91UppDec-765
❑ 91USPlaCA-4H
❑ 92BluJayP-3
❑ 92Bow-573
❑ 92Bow-667
❑ 92ClaGam-11
❑ 92ColAllG-12
❑ 92ColAllP-12
❑ 92ColPro-5A
❑ 92ColPro-5B
❑ 92DenHol-26
❑ 92Don-677
❑ 92Don-693
❑ 92DonCraJ2-21
❑ 92DonDiaK-DK3
❑ 92DonEli-10
❑ 92DonMcD-G2
❑ 92DonSupD-DK3
❑ 92Fle-327
❑ 92Fle-685
❑ 92Fle-703
❑ 92FleAll-21
❑ 92FleTeaL-14
❑ 92Fre-16
❑ 92Hig5-117
❑ 92Hig5S-6
❑ 92HitTheBB-9
❑ 92KinDis-24
❑ 92Lea-375
❑ 92LeaBlaG-375
❑ 92LeaGolP-26
❑ 92LeaPre-26
❑ 92MSABenSHD-2
❑ 92OPC-790
❑ 92OPCPre-194
❑ 92PanSti-29
❑ 92PepDieM-25
❑ 92Pin-148
❑ 92Pos-12
❑ 92RedFolS-23
❑ 92Sco-90
❑ 92Sco-435
❑ 92Sco100S-35
❑ 92SpollIFK1-254
❑ 92StaClu-10
❑ 92StaCluD-25
❑ 92Stu-254
❑ 92SunSee-12
❑ 92Top-402
❑ 92Top-790
❑ 92TopGol-402
❑ 92TopGol-790
❑ 92TopGolW-402
❑ 92TopGolW-790
❑ 92TopKid-89
❑ 92TopMcD-29
❑ 92TopMic-402
❑ 92TopMic-790
❑ 92TriPla-108
❑ 92Ult-145
❑ 92UppDec-224
❑ 92UppDecHRH-HR6
❑ 93BluJayCP1-3
❑ 93BluJayCP1-6
❑ 93BluJayD-6
❑ 93BluJayD4-5
❑ 93BluJayDM-22
❑ 93BluJayDM-32
❑ 93BluJayDWS-2
❑ 93BluJayFS-4
❑ 93Bow-575
❑ 93ClaGam-19
❑ 93ColAllG-19
❑ 93DenHol-4
❑ 93DiaMar-23
❑ 93Don-615
❑ 93Fin-94
❑ 93FinJum-94
❑ 93FinRef-94
❑ 93Fla-289
❑ 93Fle-333
❑ 93Fle-713
❑ 93FleAll-AL8
❑ 93FleFruotL-10
❑ 93FunPac-56
❑ 93HumDumC-20
❑ 93KinDis-13
❑ 93Lea-228
❑ 93LeaGolA-R8
❑ 93LeaGolA-U9
❑ 93MetBak-4
❑ 93OPC-83
❑ 93OPCPreSP-13
❑ 93OPCPreSPF-13
❑ 93OPCWorC-3
❑ 93PacSpa-322
❑ 93PanSti-31
❑ 93Pin-427
❑ 93PinCoo-21
❑ 93PinCooD-21
❑ 93PinHomRC-7
❑ 93PinSlu-4
❑ 93PinTeaP-10
❑ 93PosCan-4
❑ 93RedFolS-17
❑ 93RedFolS-109
❑ 93Sco-506
❑ 93Sco-575
❑ 93Sel-96
❑ 93SelChaS-20
❑ 93SelDufIP-1
❑ 93SelStaL-32
❑ 93SP-3
❑ 93SPPlaP-PP3
❑ 93StaClu-279
❑ 93StaClu-749
❑ 93StaCluFDI-279
❑ 93StaCluFDI-749
❑ 93StaCluM-74
❑ 93StaCluMO-6
❑ 93StaCluMO-7
❑ 93StaCluMOP-279
❑ 93StaCluMOP-749
❑ 93Stu-87
❑ 93StuSupoC-5
❑ 93Top-350
❑ 93Top-407
❑ 93TOPBLAG-26
❑ 93TopGol-350
❑ 93TopGol-407
❑ 93TopInaM-350
❑ 93TopInaM-407
❑ 93TopInaR-350
❑ 93TopInaR-407
❑ 93TopMic-350
❑ 93TopMic-407
❑ 93TriPla-123
❑ 93TriPlaA-30
❑ 93Ult-288
❑ 93UltHomRK-7
❑ 93UppDec-41
❑ 93UppDec-42
❑ 93UppDec-223
❑ 93UppDecCP-R5
❑ 93UppDecGold-41
❑ 93UppDecGold-42
❑ 93UppDecGold-223
❑ 93UppDecHRH-HR7
❑ 93USPlaCA-8C
❑ 94BluJayP-3
❑ 94BluJayUSPC-1H
❑ 94BluJayUSPC-6C
❑ 94BluJayUSPC-8S
❑ 94Bow-1
❑ 94BowBes-R16
❑ 94BowBesR-R16
❑ 94ChuShoS-8
❑ 94ColC-455
❑ 94ColChoGS-455
❑ 94ColChoSS-455
❑ 94Don-366
❑ 94DonAnn8-1
❑ 94DonDom-A5
❑ 94DonDomJ-A5
❑ 94DonSpeE-366
❑ 94Fin-207
❑ 94FinJum-207
❑ 94FinRef-207
❑ 94Fla-116
❑ 94FlaOutP-3
❑ 94Fle-326
❑ 94FleAllS-5
❑ 94FleExtB-188
❑ 94FleExtBGB-6
❑ 94FleSun-6
❑ 94FleUpdDT-2
❑ 94FUnPac-29
❑ 94FUnPac-227
❑ 94Lea-193
❑ 94LeaCleC-8
❑ 94LeaL-76
❑ 94LeaLimGA-13
❑ 94LeaMVPC-A4
❑ 94LeaMVPCG-A4
❑ 94LeaPowB-9
❑ 94LeaStaS-7
❑ 94O-PJumAF-23
❑ 94OPC-145
❑ 94OPCAllR-23
❑ 94OPCJumA-23
❑ 94OPCWorC-4
❑ 94Pac-636
❑ 94PacGolP-6
❑ 94PacPro-P2
❑ 94PanSti-136
❑ 94Pin-345
❑ 94PinArtP-345
❑ 94PinMusC-345
❑ 94PosCan-1
❑ 94PosCan-1G
❑ 94PosCan-NNO
❑ 94ProMag-137
❑ 94ProMag-AU137
❑ 94RedFolMI-30
❑ 94Sco-73
❑ 94Sco-625
❑ 94ScoGolR-73
❑ 94ScoGolR-625
❑ 94ScoGolS-31
❑ 94Sel-12
❑ 94SP-40
❑ 94SPDieC-40
❑ 94Spo-12
❑ 94Spo-183
❑ 94SpoMov-MM10
❑ 94SpoRooGGG-GG12
❑ 94StaClu-300
❑ 94StaClu-527
❑ 94StaCluFDI-300
❑ 94StaCluFDI-527
❑ 94StaCluGR-300
❑ 94StaCluGR-527
❑ 94StaCluMO-11
❑ 94StaCluMOP-300
❑ 94StaCluMOP-527
❑ 94StaCluT-151
❑ 94StaCluTFDI-151
❑ 94Stu-26
❑ 94StuHer-3
❑ 94StuSerS-5
❑ 94StuSerSG-5
❑ 94SucSav-5
❑ 94Top-645
❑ 94TopBlaG-4
❑ 94TopGol-645
❑ 94TopSpa-645
❑ 94TopSupS-8
❑ 94TriPla-32
❑ 94TriPlaN-4
❑ 94Ult-136
❑ 94UltCarA-1
❑ 94UltHomRK-6
❑ 94UltRBIK-3
❑ 94UppDec-91
❑ 94UppDecAJ-24
❑ 94UppDecAJG-24
❑ 94UppDecED-91
❑ 94UppDecMLS-MM5
❑ 94UppDecMLSED-MM5
❑ 95Baz-76
❑ 95BluJayB-5
❑ 95BluJayOH-4
❑ 95BluJayP-2
❑ 95BluJayUSPC-1D
❑ 95BluJayUSPC-6C
❑ 95Bow-297
❑ 95BowBes-R2
❑ 95BowBesR-R2
❑ 95ClaPhoC-56
❑ 95ColCho-59
❑ 95ColCho-150
❑ 95ColCho-529
❑ 95ColChoCtG-CG5
❑ 95ColChoCtG-CG5B
❑ 95ColChoCtG-CG5C
❑ 95ColChoCtGE-5
❑ 95ColChoCtGG-CG5
❑ 95ColChoCtGG-CG5B
❑ 95ColChoCtGG-CG5C
❑ 95ColChoCtGGE-5
❑ 95ColChoGS-59
❑ 95ColChoGS-150
❑ 95ColChoGS-529
❑ 95ColChoSE-54
❑ 95ColChoSEGS-54
❑ 95ColChoSESS-54
❑ 95ColChoSS-59
❑ 95ColChoSS-150
❑ 95ColChoSS-529
❑ 95Don-490
❑ 95Don-522
❑ 95DonAll-AL7
❑ 95DonBomS-6
❑ 95DonDiaK-DK9
❑ 95DonPreP-490
❑ 95DonPreP-522
❑ 95DonTopotO-172
❑ 95Emo-91
❑ 95Fin-163
❑ 95FinRef-163
❑ 95Fla-95
❑ 95FlaOutP-5
❑ 95Fle-89
❑ 95FleAllS-6
❑ 95FleLumC-5
❑ 95FleTeaL-14
❑ 95FleUpdH-5
❑ 95KinDis-5
❑ 95Kra-2
❑ 95Lea-10
❑ 95LeaGolS-8
❑ 95LeaLim-31
❑ 95LeaStaS-1
❑ 95Pac-439
❑ 95PacGolP-4
❑ 95PacPri-139
❑ 95PanSti-85
❑ 95Pin-52
❑ 95PinArtP-52
❑ 95PinMusC-52
❑ 95PinRedH-RH16
❑ 95PinWhiH-WH16
❑ 95PosCan-8
❑ 95RedFol-2
❑ 95Sco-357
❑ 95ScoGolR-357
❑ 95ScoHaloG-HG60
❑ 95ScoPlaTS-357
❑ 95Sel-80
❑ 95SelArtP-80
❑ 95SelCer-74
❑ 95SelCerMG-74
❑ 95SP-205
❑ 95SPCha-102
❑ 95SPCha-200
❑ 95SPChaCP-CP4
❑ 95SPChaCPDC-CP4
❑ 95SPChaDC-102
❑ 95SPChaDC-200
❑ 95Spo-120
❑ 95SpoArtP-120
❑ 95SPSil-205
❑ 95SPSpeF-24
❑ 95StaClu-215
❑ 95StaClu-281
❑ 95StaClu-523
❑ 95StaCluCC-CC26
❑ 95StaCluCT-8
❑ 95StaCluFDI-215
❑ 95StaCluMO-11
❑ 95StaCluMOP-215
❑ 95StaCluMOP-281
❑ 95StaCluMOP-523
❑ 95StaCluMOP-CC26
❑ 95StaCluMOP-PZ4
❑ 95StaCluMOP-RL25
❑ 95StaCluPZ-PZ4
❑ 95StaCluRL-RL25
❑ 95StaCluSTWS-215
❑ 95StaCluSTWS-281
❑ 95StaCluSTWS-523
❑ 95StaCluVR-144
❑ 95StaCluVRMO-144
❑ 95Stu-14
❑ 95StuGolS-14
❑ 95StuPlaS-14
❑ 95Sum-74
❑ 95Sum-188
❑ 95SumBigB-BB15
❑ 95SumNthD-74
❑ 95SumNthD-188
❑ 95Top-240
❑ 95TopCyb-133
❑ 95TopD3-55
❑ 95TopEmb-133
❑ 95TopEmbGI-133
❑ 95TopLeaL-LL37
❑ 95UC3-77
❑ 95UC3-146
❑ 95UC3ArtP-77
❑ 95UC3ArtP-146
❑ 95UC3CycS-CS20
❑ 95Ult-337
❑ 95UltGolM-337
❑ 95UltRBIK-2
❑ 95UltRBIKGM-2
❑ 95UppDec-39
❑ 95UppDecED-39
❑ 95UppDecEDG-39
❑ 95UppDecPLL-R12
❑ 95UppDecPLL-R31
❑ 95UppDecPLLE-R12
❑ 95UppDecPLLE-R31
❑ 95UppDecSE-200
❑ 95UppDecSEG-200
❑ 95UppDecSoaD-SD6
❑ 95USPlaCMLA-2C
❑ 95Zen-53
❑ 96Baz-91
❑ 96BluJayB-1
❑ 96BluJayOH-3
❑ 96Bow-81
❑ 96BowBes-28
❑ 96BowBesAR-28
❑ 96BowBesR-28
❑ 96BowFoi-81
❑ 96Cir-93
❑ 96CirBos-24
❑ 96CirRav-93
❑ 96ColCho-350
❑ 96ColCho-423
❑ 96ColChoCtG-CG30
❑ 96ColChoCtG-CG30B
❑ 96ColChoCtG-CG30C
❑ 96ColChoCtGG-CG30
❑ 96ColChoCtGG-CG30B
❑ 96ColChoCtGG-CG30C
❑ 96ColChoGS-350
❑ 96ColChoGS-423
❑ 96ColChoSS-350
❑ 96ColChoSS-423
❑ 96ColChoYMtP-11
❑ 96ColChoYMtP-11A
❑ 96ColChoYMtPGS-11
❑ 96ColChoYMtPGS-11A
❑ 96DenHol-23
❑ 96Don-192
❑ 96DonPreP-192
❑ 96EmoXL-129
❑ 96Fin-B315
❑ 96Fin-S143
❑ 96FinRef-B315
❑ 96FinRef-S143
❑ 96Fla-181
❑ 96Fle-268
❑ 96FleTeaL-14
❑ 96FleTif-268
❑ 96Lea-118
❑ 96LeaLim-76
❑ 96LeaLimG-76
❑ 96LeaPre-56
❑ 96LeaPreP-56
❑ 96LeaPrePB-118
❑ 96LeaPrePG-118
❑ 96LeaPrePS-118
❑ 96LeaPreSG-59
❑ 96LeaPreSte-59
❑ 96LeaSig-21
❑ 96LeaSigPPG-21
❑ 96LeaSigPPP-21
❑ 96LeaTotB-6
❑ 96MetUni-118
❑ 96MetUniP-118
❑ 96Pac-445
❑ 96PacPri-P141
❑ 96PacPriG-P141
❑ 96PanSti-162
❑ 96Pin-33
❑ 96Pin-162
❑ 96PinAfi-15
❑ 96PinAfiAP-15
❑ 96PinAfiFPP-15
❑ 96PinArtP-15
❑ 96PinArtP-89
❑ 96PinFan-29
❑ 96PinPow-15
❑ 96PinSta-15
❑ 96PinSta-89
❑ 96ProMagDM-25
❑ 96ProSta-18
❑ 96Sco-308
❑ 96ScoDugC-B33
❑ 96ScoDugCAP-B33
❑ 96Sel-47
❑ 96SelArtP-47
❑ 96SelCer-5
❑ 96SelCerAP-5
❑ 96SelCerCB-5
❑ 96SelCerCR-5
❑ 96SelCerMB-5
❑ 96SelCerMG-5
❑ 96SelCerMR-5
❑ 96SelTeaN-7
❑ 96SP-185
❑ 96Spo-85
❑ 96SpoArtP-85
❑ 96SPx-59
❑ 96SPxGol-59
❑ 96StaClu-129
❑ 96StaCluEPB-129
❑ 96StaCluEPG-129
❑ 96StaCluEPS-129
❑ 96StaCluMOP-129
❑ 96Stu-86
❑ 96StuPrePB-86
❑ 96StuPrePG-86
❑ 96StuPrePS-86
❑ 96Sum-130
❑ 96SumAbo&B-130
❑ 96SumArtP-130
❑ 96SumFoi-130
❑ 96TeaOut-15
❑ 96Top-115
❑ 96TopChr-31
❑ 96TopChrMotG-16
❑ 96TopChrMotGR-16
❑ 96TopChrR-31
❑ 96TopChrWC-WC5
❑ 96TopChrWCR-WC5
❑ 96TopGal-165
❑ 96TopGalPPI-165
❑ 96TopLas-3
❑ 96TopMasotG-16
❑ 96TopWreC-WC5
❑ 96Ult-143
❑ 96UltGolM-143
❑ 96UltRes-1
❑ 96UltResGM-1
❑ 96UltThu-5
❑ 96UltThuGM-5
❑ 96UppDec-215
❑ 96UppDecDD-DD40
❑ 96UppDecDDG-DD40
❑ 96UppDecDDS-DD40
❑ 96Zen-40
❑ 96ZenArtP-40
❑ 96ZenMoz-15
❑ 97BluJayB-1
❑ 97BluJayOH-4
❑ 97BluJayS-3

❑ 97BluJayS-40
❑ 97BluJayS-2
❑ 97Bow-271
❑ 97BowBes-90
❑ 97BowBesAR-90
❑ 97BowBesR-90
❑ 97BowChr-88
❑ 97BowChrI-88
❑ 97BowChrIR-88
❑ 97BowChrR-88
❑ 97BowInt-271
❑ 97Cir-273
❑ 97CirRav-273
❑ 97ColCho-505
❑ 97Don-5
❑ 97DonEli-61
❑ 97DonEliGS-61
❑ 97DonGolPP-5
❑ 97DonLim-96
❑ 97DonLim-183
❑ 97DonLimE-96
❑ 97DonLimE-183
❑ 97DonLimENG-96
❑ 97DonLimFotG-68
❑ 97DonPre-29
❑ 97DonPreCttC-29
❑ 97DonSig-64
❑ 97DonSigPPP-64
❑ 97DonSilPP-5
❑ 97E-X2-48
❑ 97E-X2Cred-48
❑ 97E-X2EssCre-48
❑ 97Fin-127
❑ 97Fin-338
❑ 97FinEmb-127
❑ 97FinEmb-338
❑ 97FinEmbR-127
❑ 97FinEmbR-338
❑ 97FinRef-127
❑ 97FinRef-338
❑ 97FlaShoLC-29
❑ 97FlaShoLeg0-29
❑ 97FlaShoLeg1-29
❑ 97FlaShoM-A29
❑ 97FlaShoM-B29
❑ 97FlaShoM-C29
❑ 97FlaShoR0-29
❑ 97FlaShoR1-29
❑ 97FlaShoR2-29
❑ 97Fle-235
❑ 97Fle-748
❑ 97FleMilDM-20
❑ 97FleMilDMR-20
❑ 97FleTif-235
❑ 97FleTif-748
❑ 97KinB-13
❑ 97Lea-11
❑ 97LeaFraM-11
❑ 97LeaFraMDC-11
❑ 97MetUni-181
❑ 97NewPin-72
❑ 97NewPinAP-72
❑ 97NewPinMC-72
❑ 97NewPinPP-72
❑ 97Pac-216
❑ 97PacLigB-216
❑ 97PacPri-72
❑ 97PacPriLB-72
❑ 97PacPriP-72
❑ 97PacSil-216
❑ 97Pin-24
❑ 97PinArtP-PP24
❑ 97PinCer-40
❑ 97PinCerMBla-40
❑ 97PinCerMBlu-40
❑ 97PinCerMG-40
❑ 97PinCerMR-40
❑ 97PinCerR-40
❑ 97PinIns-3
❑ 97PinInsCE-3
❑ 97PinInsDE-3
❑ 97PinMusC-24
❑ 97PinPrePla-24
❑ 97PinTotCPB-40
❑ 97PinTotCPG-40
❑ 97PinTotCPR-40
❑ 97PinX-P-115
❑ 97PinX-PMoS-115
❑ 97PinX-PSfF-16
❑ 97PinX-PSfFU-16
❑ 97Sco-247
❑ 97ScoArtPWB-247
❑ 97ScoPitP-9
❑ 97ScoPreS-247
❑ 97ScoShoS-247
❑ 97ScoShoSAP-247
❑ 97Sel-21
❑ 97SelArtP-21
❑ 97SelCom-21
❑ 97SelRegG-21
❑ 97SP-177
❑ 97SpoIll-39
❑ 97SpoIllEE-39
❑ 97StaClu-197
❑ 97StaCluMat-197
❑ 97StaCluMOP-197
❑ 97Stu-96
❑ 97StuPrePG-96
❑ 97StuPrePS-96
❑ 97Top-238
❑ 97TopChr-83
❑ 97TopChrR-83
❑ 97TopGal-31
❑ 97TopGalPPI-31
❑ 97TopIntF-ILM11
❑ 97TopIntFR-ILM11
❑ 97TopMem05-13
❑ 97TopSta-58
❑ 97TopStaAM-58
❑ 97Ult-141
❑ 97UltGolME-141
❑ 97UltPlaME-141
❑ 97UppDec-515
❑ 97UppDecPP-PP2
❑ 97UppDecPPJ-PP2
❑ 98CirThu-60
❑ 98CirThuRav-60
❑ 98CirThuSupRav-60
❑ 98ColCho-250
❑ 98ColCho-311
❑ 98Don-150
❑ 98Don-203
❑ 98DonCol-150
❑ 98DonColL-219
❑ 98DonColP-675
❑ 98DonColS-150
❑ 98DonGolPP-150
❑ 98DonGolPP-203
❑ 98DonPre-125
❑ 98DonPreSeat-125
❑ 98DonPriCD-150
❑ 98DonPriCL-219
❑ 98DonPriCP-675
❑ 98DonSigA-13
❑ 98DonSigAC-20
❑ 98DonSigAM-20
❑ 98DonSilPP-150
❑ 98DonSilPP-203
❑ 98Fin-166
❑ 98FinNo--166
❑ 98FinNo-R-166
❑ 98FinRef-166
❑ 98FlaShoLeg0-62
❑ 98FlaShoLeg1-62
❑ 98FlaShoLeg2-62
❑ 98FlaShoLeg3-62
❑ 98FlaShoLegM-62
❑ 98FlaShoR0-62
❑ 98FlaShoR1-62
❑ 98FlaShoR2-62
❑ 98FlaShoR3-62
❑ 98Fle-162
❑ 98Fle-511
❑ 98FleUpd-U95
❑ 98FleVin'-77
❑ 98FleVin'C-77
❑ 98Lea-19
❑ 98LeaFraDA-19
❑ 98LeaFraF-19
❑ 98LeaFraM-19
❑ 98LeaFraM-19
❑ 98LeaFraMDC-19
❑ 98LeaFraMDC-19
❑ 98LeaFraMZ2-19
❑ 98LeaRS-111
❑ 98LeaRSLHolo-111
❑ 98LeaRSLong-111
❑ 98LeaRTrue-111
❑ 98MetUni-29
❑ 98MetUniPMG-29
❑ 98Pac-214
❑ 98PacAur-11
❑ 98PacAurPF-29
❑ 98PacAurPFC-29
❑ 98PacAurPFPB-29
❑ 98PacAurPFR-29
❑ 98PacAurPFS-29
❑ 98PacInv-72
❑ 98PacInvGems-109
❑ 98PacInvPBlue-72
❑ 98PacInvSilv-72
❑ 98PacInvTeam-28
❑ 98PacOme-29
❑ 98PacOmeR-29
❑ 98PacOnl-84
❑ 98PacOnlR-84
❑ 98PacOnlWC-84
❑ 98PacPar-12
❑ 98PacParC-12
❑ 98PacParG-12
❑ 98PacParHS-12
❑ 98PacParPB-12
❑ 98PacParR-12
❑ 98PacPlaB-214
❑ 98PacRedT-214
❑ 98PacSil-214
❑ 98Pin-68
❑ 98PinArtP-PP61
❑ 98PinMusC-PP61
❑ 98PinPlu-51
❑ 98PinPreP-68
❑ 98PinSna-B06
❑ 98Revo-19
❑ 98RevoSS-19
❑ 98ScoRT-185
❑ 98ScoRTSS-PP103
❑ 98ScoRTSSAP-PP103
❑ 98ScoRTSSAP1-PP103
❑ 98SP Aut-54
❑ 98SpoIll-21
❑ 98SpoIllEE-21
❑ 98SpoIllFE-21
❑ 98SpoIllTaN-69
❑ 98SpoIllTaNEE-69
❑ 98SpoIllWSF-21
❑ 98SpoIllWSF-22
❑ 98SpoIllWSFEE-17
❑ 98SpoIllWSFEE-22
❑ 98SpoIllWSFFE-17
❑ 98SpoIllWSFFE-22
❑ 98SPxFin-252
❑ 98SPxFin-334
❑ 98SPxFinR-252
❑ 98SPxFinR-334
❑ 98SPxFinS-252
❑ 98SPxFinS-334
❑ 98StaCluFDI-382
❑ 98StaCluI-382
❑ 98StaCluOneK-382
❑ 98StaCluPP-382
❑ 98Stu-20
❑ 98StuGPP-20
❑ 98StuSPP-20
❑ 98Top-145
❑ 98TopChr-145
❑ 98TopChrR-145
❑ 98TopDevR-145
❑ 98TopDia-145
❑ 98TopMiniC-145
❑ 98TopOpeD-74
❑ 98Ult-165
❑ 98Ult-302
❑ 98UltGolM-165
❑ 98UltGolM-302
❑ 98UltMas-165
❑ 98UltMas-302
❑ 98UltPlaM-165
❑ 98UltPlaM-302
❑ 98UltTop3-29
❑ 98UppDec-240
❑ 98UppDec-653
❑ 98UppDecR-8
❑ 99Fle-107
❑ 99FleSta9-107
❑ 99FleWarT-107
❑ 99Pac-380
❑ 99PacPlaB-380
❑ 99PacRed-380
❑ 99StaClu-98
❑ 99StaCluFDI-98
❑ 99StaCluOoaK-98
❑ 99StaCluPP-98
❑ 99UppDecCLMS-HR9

Carter, John
❑ 92WelPirC-4
❑ 92WelPirF-1315
❑ 93ColRedC-7
❑ 93ColRedF-590
❑ 94Bow-663
❑ 94BowBes-B47
❑ 94BowBesR-B47
❑ 94CanIndF-3108
❑ 95Bow-190
❑ 95SigRooOJ-9
❑ 95SigRooOJP-9
❑ 95SigRooOJPS-9
❑ 95SigRooOJS-9
❑ 97CalCanB-9

Carter, Justin
❑ 98PorRocG-5

Carter, Lance
❑ 94EugEmeC-5
❑ 94EugEmeF-3703
❑ 95SprSulTI-5
❑ 96WilBluRB-18
❑ 98LanLugQ-4

Carter, Larry G.
❑ 89SalSpuCLC-126
❑ 89SalSpuP-1816
❑ 91ShrCapLD-302
❑ 91ShrCapP-1814

Carter, Larry L.
❑ 89BelBre2S-6
❑ 90BelBreB-4
❑ 90BelBreS-4
❑ 91BelBreCB-2
❑ 91BelBreP-2095
❑ 91LinDriAA-302
❑ 91MidLeaAP-MWL32
❑ 92PhoFirF-2815
❑ 92PhoFirS-378
❑ 92ProFS7-347
❑ 92SkyAA F-294
❑ 92SkyAAAF-174
❑ 92StoPorC-1
❑ 93Bow-168
❑ 93Don-76
❑ 93PhoFirF-1510
❑ 93Sco-300
❑ 93ScoBoyoS-18
❑ 98LanLugQ-29

Carter, Marlin
❑ 86NegLeaF-50
❑ 92NegLeaRLI-8
❑ 93TedWil-101

Carter, Michael
❑ 90HelBreSP-24
❑ 91BelBreCB-22
❑ 91BelBreP-2108
❑ 91Cla/Bes-214
❑ 91MidLeaAP-MWL33
❑ 92Bow-243
❑ 92ElPasDF-3933
❑ 92StoPorF-47
❑ 92UppDecML-270
❑ 93El PasDF-2962
❑ 94IowCubF-1286
❑ 95AusFut-9
❑ 95IowCubTI-6
❑ 96IowCubB-11

Carter, Nick (Paul Warren)
❑ 19W514-45

Carter, Paul
❑ 91PomBlaBPB-23

Carter, Quincy
❑ 97BesAll-11
❑ 97RocCub-12

Carter, Richard
❑ 87LakTigP-13
❑ 88LakTigS-6
❑ 89SanBerSB-3
❑ 89SanBerSCLC-68

Carter, Richie
❑ 86PalSprAP-6
❑ 86PalSprAS-14

Carter, Roger
❑ 97PriDevR-20

Carter, Ron
❑ 86MadMusP-5
❑ 86MadMusP-5
❑ 87SanBerSP-8

Carter, Shannon
❑ 98BluOriQ-14

Carter, Steve
❑ 87WatPirP-10
❑ 88AugPirP-385
❑ 89BufBisP-1665
❑ 89DonRoo-8
❑ 90Bow-179
❑ 90BowTif-179
❑ 90BufBisC-22
❑ 90BufBisP-385
❑ 90BufBisTI-5
❑ 90CMC-22
❑ 90OPC-482
❑ 90ProAAAF-500
❑ 90Top-482
❑ 90TopDeb89-23
❑ 90TopTif-482
❑ 90TriAllGP-AAA17
❑ 90UppDec-368
❑ 91Don-418
❑ 91IowCubLD-202
❑ 91IowCubP-1074
❑ 91LakTigC-8
❑ 91LinDriAAA-202
❑ 91Ult-374
❑ 92SkyAAAF-259
❑ 92TolMudHF-1053
❑ 92TolMudHS-579
❑ 93IndIndF-1500
❑ 94VenLinU-265

Carter, Tim
❑ 90HelBreSP-1
❑ 91BelBreCB-14
❑ 91BelBreP-2109
❑ 92StoPorC-6
❑ 92StoPorF-38

Carter, Tom
❑ 92ForLauYC-9
❑ 92ForLauYTI-4
❑ 92Ft.LauYF-2603
❑ 93PriWilCC-3
❑ 93PriWilCF-647
❑ 94AlbYanF-1431
❑ 95NorNavTI-5

Cartwright, Alan
❑ 84ElPasDT-19
❑ 86ElPasDP-5
❑ 87DenZepP-19
❑ 88ElPasDB-13

Cartwright, Alexander J.
❑ 36Halof FP-4
❑ 39PC7AlbHoF-15
❑ 50CalHOFW-11
❑ 53ArtHaloFP-11
❑ 76ShaPiz-15
❑ 77BobParHoF-10
❑ 80PerHaloFP-15
❑ 80SSPHOF-15
❑ 84GalHaloFRL-15
❑ 89HOFStiB-90
❑ 90BasWit-96
❑ 94OriofB-6
❑ 94UppDecTAE-2
❑ 94UppDecTAELD-LD2

Cartwright, Ed (Edward C.)
❑ 87OldJudN-72
❑ 95May-30

Cartwright, Joseph
❑ 22Zee-78

Cartwright, Mark
❑ 83VisOakF-16

Cartwright, Walter
❑ 13Zee-100
❑ 14Zee-103

Carty, Jorge
❑ 77ChaPatT-2

Carty, Rico (Ricardo Adolfo)
❑ 64Top-476
❑ 64TopRooAB-23
❑ 65Kah-7
❑ 65OPC-2
❑ 65Top-2
❑ 65Top-305
❑ 65TopTral-7
❑ 66BraPos-8
❑ 66OPC-153
❑ 66Top-153
❑ 66TopVen-153
❑ 67BraPho-7
❑ 67CokCapB-17
❑ 67Kah-8
❑ 67OPC-35
❑ 67Top-35
❑ 67Top-240
❑ 67TopVen-271
❑ 68BraPos-8
❑ 68CokCapB-17
❑ 68DexPre-22
❑ 68Top-455
❑ 69AtlBraBPPS-5
❑ 69MLBOffS-112
❑ 69Top-590
❑ 69TopTeaP-2
❑ 70AtlBraS-2
❑ 70DayDaiNM-40
❑ 70MLBOffS-3
❑ 70OPC-145
❑ 70Top-145
❑ 71AllBasA-5
❑ 71BazNumT-28
❑ 71BazUnn-7
❑ 71MilDud-38
❑ 71MLBOffS-557
❑ 71OPC-62
❑ 71OPC-270
❑ 71Top-62
❑ 71Top-270
❑ 71TopCoi-113
❑ 71TopGreM-3
❑ 71TopSup-29
❑ 71TopTat-89
❑ 72EssCoi-3
❑ 72Top-740
❑ 73OPC-435
❑ 73RanTeal-6
❑ 73Top-435
❑ 75CleIndP-8
❑ 75IndJB R-3
❑ 75OPC-655
❑ 75Top-655
❑ 75TopMin-655
❑ 76OPC-156
❑ 76SSP-519
❑ 76Top-156
❑ 77IndTeal-5
❑ 77OPC-114
❑ 77PepGloD-9
❑ 77Top-465
❑ 78BluJayP-3
❑ 78Top-305
❑ 79BluJayBY-4
❑ 79OPC-291
❑ 79Top-565
❑ 80OPC-25
❑ 80Top-46
❑ 91KelLey-3
❑ 91SweBasG-18
❑ 91UppDecS-6
❑ 92ActPacA-74
❑ 93RanKee-98
❑ 93UppDecAH-27
❑ 94TedWil-41
❑ 94UppDecAH-202
❑ 94UppDecAH-221
❑ 94UppDecAH1-202
❑ 94UppDecAH1-221

Caruso, Gene
❑ 93PocPosF-4201
❑ 93PocPosSP-3
❑ 94StoPorC-4
❑ 94StoPorF-1685
❑ 95ElPasDTI-3

Caruso, Joe
❑ 92LynRedSC-20
❑ 92LynRedSF-2899
❑ 92StaCluD-26
❑ 92UppDecML-111
❑ 93ClaFS7-47
❑ 93ExcFS7-131
❑ 93ExcLeaLF-15
❑ 93PawRedSDD-6
❑ 93PawRedSF-2400
❑ 93PawRedSTI-6
❑ 94NewBriRSF-644
❑ 97SpoIndG-7
❑ 98LanLugQ-16

Caruso, Mike
❑ 96BelGiaTI-16
❑ 97Bes-61
❑ 97Bow-304
❑ 97BowChr-211
❑ 97BowChrI-211
❑ 97BowChrIR-211
❑ 97BowChrR-211
❑ 97BowInt-304
❑ 97CalLeaTP-23
❑ 97SanJosG-2
❑ 98Bow-299
❑ 98BowBes-116
❑ 98BowBesAR-116
❑ 98BowBesMIF-MI4
❑ 98BowBesMIFAR-MI4
❑ 98BowBesMIFR-MI4
❑ 98BowBesR-116
❑ 98BowChr-299
❑ 98BowChrGA-299
❑ 98BowChrGAR-299
❑ 98BowChrI-299
❑ 98BowChrIR-299
❑ 98BowChrR-299
❑ 98BowGolA-299
❑ 98BowInt-299
❑ 98CirThu-67
❑ 98CirThuRav-67
❑ 98CirThuSupRav-67
❑ 98ColCho-426
❑ 98ColChoPCR-426
❑ 98CroRoy-34
❑ 98Don-238

- ❑ 98DonGolPP-238
- ❑ 98DonSilPP-238
- ❑ 98Fle-482
- ❑ 98LeaRS-244
- ❑ 98LeaRSLHolo-244
- ❑ 98LeaRSLong-244
- ❑ 98LeaRTrue-244
- ❑ 98PacOme-55
- ❑ 98PacOmeR-55
- ❑ 98PacOmeRST4-14
- ❑ 98PacOnl-164
- ❑ 98PacOnlR-164
- ❑ 98PacOnlWC-164
- ❑ 98RevoRooHH-9
- ❑ 98RevoRooHHG-9
- ❑ 98SkyDugA-97
- ❑ 98SkyDugAIA-97
- ❑ 98SP Aut-2
- ❑ 98SP MinDTSPE-DS17
- ❑ 98SP MinPE-35
- ❑ 98SP MinSTHPE-H3
- ❑ 98SPMin-35
- ❑ 98SPMinDTS-DS17
- ❑ 98SPMinSTH-H3
- ❑ 98SPxFin-181
- ❑ 98SPxFinR-181
- ❑ 98SPxFinS-181
- ❑ 98StaCluFDI-346
- ❑ 98StaClul-346
- ❑ 98StaCluOneK-346
- ❑ 98StaCluPP-346
- ❑ 98UD3-3
- ❑ 98UD3-93
- ❑ 98UD3-183
- ❑ 98UD3DieCut-3
- ❑ 98UD3DieCut-93
- ❑ 98UD3DieCut-183
- ❑ 98Ult-264
- ❑ 98UltGolM-264
- ❑ 98UltMas-264
- ❑ 98UltPlaM-264
- ❑ 98UltRoctS-4
- ❑ 98UppDec-567
- ❑ 98UppDecDS-DS54
- ❑ 98UppDecR-106
- ❑ 98UppDecRNF-NF5
- ❑ 99CroRoyB-32
- ❑ 99CroRoyL-32
- ❑ 99CroRoyOD-32
- ❑ 99FlaShoLeg1-96
- ❑ 99FlaShoLeg2-96
- ❑ 99FlaShoLeg3-96
- ❑ 99FlaShoLegM1-96
- ❑ 99FlaShoLegM2-96
- ❑ 99FlaShoLegM3-96
- ❑ 99FlaShoR1-96
- ❑ 99FlaShoR2-96
- ❑ 99FlaShoR3-96
- ❑ 99Fle-53
- ❑ 99FleBri-75
- ❑ 99FleBri2G-75
- ❑ 99FleBriBlu-75
- ❑ 99FleBriGol-75
- ❑ 99FleMys-15
- ❑ 99FleMysG-15
- ❑ 99FleMysM-15
- ❑ 99FleRooFla-4
- ❑ 99FleSta9-53
- ❑ 99FleWarT-53
- ❑ 99MetUni-174
- ❑ 99MetUniGM-174
- ❑ 99MetUniN-9
- ❑ 99MetUniPMG-174
- ❑ 99Pac-99
- ❑ 99PacAur-39
- ❑ 99PacAurOD-39
- ❑ 99PacCroC-65
- ❑ 99PacCroCPB-65
- ❑ 99PacOme-54
- ❑ 99PacOmeC-54
- ❑ 99PacOmeG-54
- ❑ 99PacOmePB-54
- ❑ 99PacPar-54
- ❑ 99PacParC-54
- ❑ 99PacParG-54
- ❑ 99PacParHoloGold-54
- ❑ 99PacParHS-54
- ❑ 99PacParOD-54
- ❑ 99PacParPB-54
- ❑ 99PacParRed-54
- ❑ 99PacPlaB-99
- ❑ 99PacPri-33
- ❑ 99PacPriHB-33
- ❑ 99PacPriHG-33
- ❑ 99PacPriHM-33
- ❑ 99PacPriHP-33
- ❑ 99PacPriRed-33
- ❑ 99PacPriS-67
- ❑ 99PacPriS206-67
- ❑ 99PacPriS206R-67
- ❑ 99PacRed-99
- ❑ 99SkyMolM-97
- ❑ 99SkyMolMX-97
- ❑ 99SkyPre-147
- ❑ 99SkyPreR-147
- ❑ 99SkyThu-71
- ❑ 99SkyThuRant-71
- ❑ 99SkyThuRave-71
- ❑ 99SP Aut-21
- ❑ 99SP SigAuto-MC
- ❑ 99SP SigAutoG-MC
- ❑ 99SPSig-65
- ❑ 99SPx-30
- ❑ 99SPxFinR-30
- ❑ 99SPxFinS-30
- ❑ 99StaClu-107
- ❑ 99StaCluFDI-107
- ❑ 99StaCluOoaK-107
- ❑ 99StaCluPP-107
- ❑ 99ThuSkySupR-71
- ❑ 99Top-84
- ❑ 99TopChr-84
- ❑ 99TopChrR-84
- ❑ 99TopMVPP-84
- ❑ 99TopOpeD-47
- ❑ 99TopSta-84
- ❑ 99TopSta1Foil-84
- ❑ 99TopStaFoil-84
- ❑ 99TopStaOS-84
- ❑ 99UD Cho-71
- ❑ 99UD ChoPCR-71
- ❑ 99Ult-129
- ❑ 99UltGolM-129
- ❑ 99UltMas-129
- ❑ 99UltPlaM-129
- ❑ 99UltWorP-4
- ❑ 99UppDec-65
- ❑ 99UppDecBD-95
- ❑ 99UppDecBDD-95
- ❑ 99UppDecBDQ-95
- ❑ 99UppDecBDT-95
- ❑ 99UppDecEL1-65
- ❑ 99UppDecEL2-65
- ❑ 99UppDecM-46
- ❑ 99UppDecMGS-46
- ❑ 99UppDecMHFS-46
- ❑ 99UppDecMSS-46
- ❑ 99Vic-95

Caruthers, Bob (Robert Lee)
- ❑ 76SSP188WS-1
- ❑ 87AllandGN-3
- ❑ 87LonJacN-2
- ❑ 87OldJudN-73
- ❑ 87OldJudN-74
- ❑ 87ScrDC-2
- ❑ 88GooN16-4
- ❑ 90DodTar-116

Caruthers, Clay
- ❑ 94BilMusF-3662
- ❑ 94BilMusSP-15
- ❑ 94SigRooDP-86
- ❑ 94SigRooDPS-86
- ❑ 94StaCluDP-58
- ❑ 94StaCluDPFDI-58
- ❑ 95Bow-54

Carvajal, Jhonny
- ❑ 93PriRedC-1
- ❑ 93PriRedF-4184
- ❑ 94ChaWheC-4
- ❑ 94ChaWheF-2709
- ❑ 95LinVen-41
- ❑ 96-97LinVen-111
- ❑ 96WesPalBEB-24
- ❑ 97HarSen-9
- ❑ 98arSenW1-6
- ❑ 98HarSenM-6

Carvajal, Jovina
- ❑ 90OneYanP-3375
- ❑ 91FloStaLAP-FSL12
- ❑ 91Ft.LauYC-25
- ❑ 91Ft.LauYP-2439
- ❑ 92ClaFS7-110
- ❑ 92ForLauYC-2
- ❑ 92ForLauYTI-5
- ❑ 92Ft.LauYF-2624
- ❑ 93PriWilCC-4
- ❑ 93PriWilCF-667
- ❑ 94CedRapKC-6
- ❑ 94CedRapKF-1120
- ❑ 95MidAngOHP-8
- ❑ 95MidAngTI-8
- ❑ 96Exc-24
- ❑ 97VanCanB-10
- ❑ 98VanCanG-7

Carvajal, Ramon
- ❑ 98JohCCTI-7

Carver, Billy Paul
- ❑ 87AubAstP-6
- ❑ 88AshTouP-1049
- ❑ 88SouAtlLAGS-4
- ❑ 89ColMudB-23
- ❑ 89OscAstS-3

Carver, Steve
- ❑ 95BatCliTI-5
- ❑ 96Exc-196
- ❑ 97EasLeaTPB-27
- ❑ 97ReaPhi-9
- ❑ 98Bow-433
- ❑ 98BowChr-433
- ❑ 98BowChrGA-433
- ❑ 98BowChrGAR-433
- ❑ 98BowChrl-433
- ❑ 98BowChrIR-433
- ❑ 98BowChrR-433
- ❑ 98BowGolA-433
- ❑ 98BowInt-433
- ❑ 98EasLeaTPM-4
- ❑ 98ReaPhiUM-7
- ❑ 98SP MinPE-97
- ❑ 98SPMin-97
- ❑ 99BasAmeTPA-5

Cary, Chuck
- ❑ 82BirBarT-9
- ❑ 83BirBarT-14
- ❑ 85NasSouTI-3
- ❑ 86FleUpd-21
- ❑ 86NasSouTI-3
- ❑ 87Don-461
- ❑ 87Fle-147
- ❑ 87FleGlo-147
- ❑ 87RicBraBC-1
- ❑ 87RicBraC-47
- ❑ 87RicBraT-1
- ❑ 87Top-171
- ❑ 87TopTif-171
- ❑ 88BlaYNPRWL-52
- ❑ 89ColCliC-7
- ❑ 89ColCliP-1
- ❑ 89ColCliP-745
- ❑ 89TopTra-17T
- ❑ 89TopTraT-17T
- ❑ 89UppDec-396
- ❑ 89YanScoNW-27
- ❑ 90ClaBlu-125
- ❑ 90Don-429
- ❑ 90Lea-50
- ❑ 90OPC-691
- ❑ 90PanSti-123
- ❑ 90Sco-393
- ❑ 90Top-691
- ❑ 90TopSti-315
- ❑ 90TopTif-691
- ❑ 90TopTVY-8
- ❑ 90UppDec-528
- ❑ 90YanScoNW-15
- ❑ 91Bow-176
- ❑ 91Don-179
- ❑ 91Fle-659
- ❑ 91Lea-66
- ❑ 91OPC-359
- ❑ 91PanFreS-331
- ❑ 91Sco-566
- ❑ 91StaClu-40
- ❑ 91StaCluP-9
- ❑ 91Top-359
- ❑ 91TopDesS-359
- ❑ 91TopMic-359
- ❑ 91TopTif-359
- ❑ 91UppDec-409
- ❑ 92YanWIZ8-27
- ❑ 93WhiSoxK-6

Cary, Jeff
- ❑ 80LynSaiT-12
- ❑ 81WauTimT-15
- ❑ 82MadMusF-31

Cary, Scott
- ❑ 47SenGunBP-2

Casado, Cancio
- ❑ 89MarPhiS-6

Casagrande, ,Tom
- ❑ 55Top-167

Casale, Jerry
- ❑ 59Top-456
- ❑ 60MacSta-5
- ❑ 60RedSoxJP-3
- ❑ 60Top-38
- ❑ 60TopVen-38
- ❑ 61Top-195
- ❑ 61TopStal-169
- ❑ 81RedSoxBG2S-11

Casano, Andy
- ❑ 88WatIndP-666
- ❑ 89KinIndS-5

Casanova, Paul (Ortiz P.)
- ❑ 67CokCapA-9
- ❑ 67CokCapAAm-35
- ❑ 67CokCapS-9
- ❑ 67DexPre-43
- ❑ 67OPC-115
- ❑ 67SenPos-7
- ❑ 67SenTeal-3
- ❑ 67Top-115
- ❑ 67TopVen-231
- ❑ 68Baz-1
- ❑ 68SenTeal-2
- ❑ 68Top-560
- ❑ 68TopActS-3C
- ❑ 68TopActS-14C
- ❑ 69MilBra-53
- ❑ 69MLBOffS-102
- ❑ 69NabTeaF-4
- ❑ 69SenTeal-5
- ❑ 69Top-486A
- ❑ 69Top-486B
- ❑ 69TopSta-233
- ❑ 69TopTeaP-23
- ❑ 70MLBOffS-280
- ❑ 70OPC-84
- ❑ 70SenPolY-3
- ❑ 70Top-84
- ❑ 71MLBOffS-532
- ❑ 71OPC-139
- ❑ 71SenPolP-2
- ❑ 71SenTealW-7
- ❑ 71Top-139
- ❑ 71TopCoi-146
- ❑ 72MilBra-69
- ❑ 72Top-591
- ❑ 73OPC-452
- ❑ 73Top-452
- ❑ 74OPC-272
- ❑ 74Top-272
- ❑ 75OPC-633
- ❑ 75Top-633
- ❑ 75TopMin-633
- ❑ 76LauIndC-24
- ❑ 89PacSenL-58
- ❑ 93HicCraC-27
- ❑ 94HicCraC-29
- ❑ 94HicCraF-2193

Casanova, Raul
- ❑ 92ColMetC-19
- ❑ 92ColMetF-299
- ❑ 92KinMetC-10
- ❑ 92KinMetF-1533
- ❑ 93WatDiaC-9
- ❑ 93WatDiaF-1770
- ❑ 94RanCucQC-10
- ❑ 94RanCucQF-1641
- ❑ 95Bow-91
- ❑ 95BowBes-B67
- ❑ 95BowBesR-B67
- ❑ 95ColCho-33
- ❑ 95ColChoGS-33
- ❑ 95ColChoSS-33
- ❑ 95Exc-280
- ❑ 95ExcAll-1
- ❑ 95MemChiTI-22
- ❑ 95Sel-197
- ❑ 95SelArtP-197
- ❑ 95SP-20
- ❑ 95SPML-141
- ❑ 95SPMLA-6
- ❑ 95SPSil-20
- ❑ 95UppDec-11
- ❑ 95UppDecED-11
- ❑ 95UppDecEDG-11
- ❑ 95UppDecML-20
- ❑ 95UppDecMLFS-20
- ❑ 95UppDecMLOP-OP24
- ❑ 95UppDecSE-131
- ❑ 95UppDecSEG-131
- ❑ 96BesAutS-18
- ❑ 96Bow-352
- ❑ 96BowFoi-352
- ❑ 96Exc-234
- ❑ 96LeaPre-143
- ❑ 96LeaPreP-143
- ❑ 96LeaSig-64
- ❑ 96LeaSigPPG-64
- ❑ 96LeaSigPPP-64
- ❑ 96TigHebN-20
- ❑ 96TolMudHB-7
- ❑ 96Zen-122
- ❑ 96ZenArtP-122
- ❑ 97Bow-399
- ❑ 97BowInt-399
- ❑ 97Cir-139
- ❑ 97CirRav-139
- ❑ 97Don-392
- ❑ 97DonEli-91
- ❑ 97DonEliGS-91
- ❑ 97DonGolPP-392
- ❑ 97DonLim-179
- ❑ 97DonLimE-179
- ❑ 97DonLimENG-179
- ❑ 97DonRatR-16
- ❑ 97DonSilPP-392
- ❑ 97Fle-95
- ❑ 97FleTif-95
- ❑ 97Lea-53
- ❑ 97LeaFraM-53
- ❑ 97LeaFraMDC-53
- ❑ 97Pac-85
- ❑ 97PacLigB-85
- ❑ 97PacPri-29
- ❑ 97PacPriLB-29
- ❑ 97PacPriP-29
- ❑ 97PacSil-85
- ❑ 97PinCer-122
- ❑ 97PinCerMBla-122
- ❑ 97PinCerMBlu-122
- ❑ 97PinCerMG-122
- ❑ 97PinCerMR-122
- ❑ 97PinCerR-122
- ❑ 97PinInsCE-138
- ❑ 97PinInsDE-138
- ❑ 97PinTotCPB-122
- ❑ 97PinTotCPG-122
- ❑ 97PinTotCPR-122
- ❑ 97Sco-28
- ❑ 97ScoArtPWB-28
- ❑ 97ScoPreS-28
- ❑ 97ScoShoS-28
- ❑ 97ScoShoSAP-28
- ❑ 97Sel-111
- ❑ 97SelArtP-111
- ❑ 97SelCom-111
- ❑ 97SelRegG-111
- ❑ 97StaClu-96
- ❑ 97StaCluMOP-96
- ❑ 97TolMudHB-8
- ❑ 97Ult-57
- ❑ 97UltGolME-57
- ❑ 97UltPlaME-57
- ❑ 97UppDec-474
- ❑ 98CirThu-160
- ❑ 98CirThuRav-160
- ❑ 98CirThuSupRav-160
- ❑ 98ColCho-183
- ❑ 98ColCho-368
- ❑ 98Don-220
- ❑ 98DonColP-684
- ❑ 98DonGolPP-220
- ❑ 98DonPre-134
- ❑ 98DonPreSeat-134
- ❑ 98DonPriCP-684
- ❑ 98DonSilPP-220
- ❑ 98Fle-519
- ❑ 98MetUni-149
- ❑ 98MetUniPMG-149
- ❑ 98Pac-84
- ❑ 98PacInv-30
- ❑ 98PacInvPBlue-30
- ❑ 98PacInvSilv-30
- ❑ 98PacOme-87
- ❑ 98PacOmeR-87
- ❑ 98PacOnl-265
- ❑ 98PacOnlR-265
- ❑ 98PacOnlWC-265
- ❑ 98PacPar-44
- ❑ 98PacParC-44
- ❑ 98PacParG-44
- ❑ 98PacParHS-44
- ❑ 98PacParPB-44
- ❑ 98PacParR-44
- ❑ 98PacPlaB-84
- ❑ 98PacRedT-84
- ❑ 98PacSil-84
- ❑ 98Sco-141
- ❑ 98ScoRT-104
- ❑ 98ScoSS-PP59
- ❑ 98ScoSSAP-PP59
- ❑ 98StaCluFDI-70
- ❑ 98StaClul-70
- ❑ 98StaCluOneK-70
- ❑ 98StaCluPP-70
- ❑ 98TolMudHQ-11
- ❑ 98Top-207
- ❑ 98TopChr-207
- ❑ 98TopChrR-207
- ❑ 98TopDevR-207
- ❑ 98TopDia-207
- ❑ 98TopMiniC-207
- ❑ 98Ult-106
- ❑ 98UltGolM-106
- ❑ 98UltMas-106
- ❑ 98UltPlaM-106
- ❑ 98UppDec-87
- ❑ 99Pac-158
- ❑ 99PacPlaB-158
- ❑ 99PacRed-158

Casarotti, Rich
- ❑ 88BurBraP-21
- ❑ 88MidLeaAGS-17
- ❑ 89DurBullS-4
- ❑ 89DurBullS-4
- ❑ 89DurBulTI-4
- ❑ 89Sta-68
- ❑ 90GreBraB-10
- ❑ 90GreBraP-1135
- ❑ 90GreBraS-5
- ❑ 91GreBraC-14
- ❑ 91GreBraLD-201
- ❑ 91GreBraP-3008
- ❑ 91LinDriAA-201
- ❑ 91RicBraBC-28
- ❑ 92ChaKniF-2776

Cascarella, Joe
- ❑ 29Zee-85
- ❑ 34BatR31-162
- ❑ 35DiaMatCS3T1-27
- ❑ 38RedOraW-4
- ❑ 39RedTeal-4

Case, Christopher
- ❑ 96MacBraB-4

Case, George W.
- ❑ 39GouPreR303A-7
- ❑ 39GouPreR303B-2
- ❑ 39PlaBal-138
- ❑ 39WorWidGTP-7
- ❑ 40PlaBal-15
- ❑ 41DouPlaR-75
- ❑ 41DouPlaR-87
- ❑ 41Gou-16
- ❑ 41PlaBal-69
- ❑ 46SpoExcW-1-9
- ❑ 47Exh-35
- ❑ 82DiaCla-75
- ❑ 83TCMPla1942-20

Case, Mike
- ❑ 92BenRocCB-8
- ❑ 92BenRocF-1484
- ❑ 93CenValRC-6
- ❑ 93CenValRF-2903
- ❑ 93TopInaM-661
- ❑ 93TopInaR-661
- ❑ 93TopMic-661
- ❑ 94NewHavRF-1553
- ❑ 95NewHavRTI-24

Casey, Dan
- ❑ 87BucN28-76
- ❑ 87OldJudN-75
- ❑ 88WG1CarG-48
- ❑ 90KalBatN-6

Casey, Doc (James Peter)
- ❑ 03BreE10-17
- ❑ 06FanCraNL-8
- ❑ 09T206-406
- ❑ 10E101-7
- ❑ 10MelMinE-7
- ❑ 10PeoT21-9
- ❑ 11SpoLifCW-57
- ❑ 90DodTar-117

Casey, Hugh
- ❑ 39PlaBal-151
- ❑ 40DodTeal-3
- ❑ 40PlaBal-148
- ❑ 42DodTeal-4
- ❑ 46DodTeal-4
- ❑ 46SpoExcW-2-7
- ❑ 47DodTeal-5
- ❑ 47Exh-36
- ❑ 47TipTop-93
- ❑ 48DodTeal-6
- ❑ 49Bow-179
- ❑ 49EurSta-155
- ❑ 73Dod194T-4
- ❑ 75DodTCMA-3
- ❑ 78DodTCM4-3
- ❑ 80DodGreT-8
- ❑ 80LauFamF-27
- ❑ 90DodTar-118

Casey, Joe (Joseph Felix)
❑ 10NadCarE-9
❑ 11PinT-5-166
Casey, Joe L
❑ 97St.CatSB-11
❑ 98HagSunM-10
Casey, Joie
❑ 88SalLakCTTI-NNO
Casey, Keith
❑ 90GatCitPP-3338
❑ 90GatCitPSP-5
Casey, Kim
❑ 87SalLakTTT-NNO
Casey, Mascot
❑ 95OmaRoyTI-29
❑ 96OmaRoyB-5
❑ 97OmaRoyB-7
❑ 98OmaRoyM-29
Casey, Mickey
❑ 91PomBlaBPB-23
Casey, Pat
❑ 83BeaGolGT-16
❑ 84BeaGolGT-16
❑ 85CalCanC-86
❑ 86CalCanP-4
❑ 87PorBeaP-7
Casey, Perle
❑ 09ObaT21-115
Casey, Philip
❑ 88KimN18-8
Casey, Ryan
❑ 94HunCubC-4
❑ 94HunCubF-3543
❑ 95RocCubTI-19
Casey, Sean
❑ 95WatIndTI-8
❑ 96CarLeaA1B-22
❑ 96CarLeaA2B-22
❑ 96KenIndB-3
❑ 96Top-25
❑ 96TopPowB-25
❑ 97AkrAer-6
❑ 97Bes-57
❑ 97BesAutSBPP-5
❑ 97Bow-367
❑ 97BowChr-245
❑ 97BowChrI-245
❑ 97BowChrIR-245
❑ 97BowChrR-245
❑ 97BowInt-367
❑ 97Top-202
❑ 98BesCasT-2
❑ 98BesCasT-3
❑ 98BesDiaB-10
❑ 98Bow-182
❑ 98BowChr-182
❑ 98BowChrGA-182
❑ 98BowChrGAR-182
❑ 98BowChrI-182
❑ 98BowChrIR-182
❑ 98BowChrR-182
❑ 98BowGolA-182
❑ 98BowInt-182
❑ 98CirThu-107
❑ 98CirThuRav-107
❑ 98CirThuSupRav-107
❑ 98ColCho-420
❑ 98ColChoPCR-420
❑ 98CroRoy-39
❑ 98Don-271
❑ 98DonGolPP-271
❑ 98DonSigA-14
❑ 98DonSigAC-21
❑ 98DonSigAM-21
❑ 98DonSilPP-271
❑ 98E-X2SD2001-9
❑ 98Fle-409
❑ 98FleProF-PF2
❑ 98FleVin'-86
❑ 98FleVin'C-86
❑ 98IndIndQ-23
❑ 98LeaRCrusUP-128
❑ 98LeaRS-280
❑ 98LeaRSCrusUG-128
❑ 98LeaRSCrusUR-128
❑ 98LeaRSLHolo-280
❑ 98LeaRSLong-280
❑ 98LeaRTrue-280
❑ 98PinPlu-122
❑ 98ScoRT-247
❑ 98ScoRTSS-PP140
❑ 98ScoRTSSAP-PP140
❑ 98ScoRTSSAP1-PP140
❑ 98SP Aut-17
❑ 98SP AutC-SC
❑ 98Stu-128
❑ 98StuGPP-128
❑ 98StuSPP-128
❑ 98Top-488
❑ 98TopChr-488
❑ 98TopChrR-488
❑ 98TopDevR-488
❑ 98TopDia-488
❑ 98TopMiniC-488
❑ 98UD3-19
❑ 98UD3-109
❑ 98UD3-199
❑ 98UD3DieCut-19
❑ 98UD3DieCut-109
❑ 98UD3DieCut-199
❑ 98Ult-351
❑ 98UltGolM-351
❑ 98UltMas-351
❑ 98UltPlaM-351
❑ 98UppDec-560
❑ 98UppDecDS-DS15
❑ 98UppDecR-26
❑ 99199Fin-88
❑ 99Bow-236
❑ 99BowBes-12
❑ 99BowBesAR-12
❑ 99BowBesR-12
❑ 99BowGol-236
❑ 99BowInt-236
❑ 99E-X Cen-51
❑ 99E-X CenECFut-51
❑ 99E-X CenECNow-51
❑ 99FinGolRef-88
❑ 99FinRef-88
❑ 99Fle-120
❑ 99FleMys-64
❑ 99FleMysFI-9
❑ 99FleMysG-64
❑ 99FleMysM-64
❑ 99FleSta9-120
❑ 99FleWarT-120
❑ 99MetUni-129
❑ 99MetUniGM-129
❑ 99MetUniPMG-129
❑ 99Pac-111
❑ 99PacAur-44
❑ 99PacAurOD-44
❑ 99PacCroC-73
❑ 99PacCroCPB-73
❑ 99PacOme-63
❑ 99PacOmeC-63
❑ 99PacOmeG-63
❑ 99PacOmePB-63
❑ 99PacPlaB-111
❑ 99PacPriS-68
❑ 99PacPriS206-68
❑ 99PacPriS206R-68
❑ 99PacRed-111
❑ 99Rev-38
❑ 99RevPremDate-38
❑ 99RevRet-38
❑ 99RevShaSS-38
❑ 99SkyMolM-24
❑ 99SkyMolMX-24
❑ 99SkyPre-121
❑ 99SkyPreR-121
❑ 99SkyThu-93
❑ 99SkyThuRant-93
❑ 99SkyThuRave-93
❑ 99SP Aut-24
❑ 99SP SigAuto-SC
❑ 99SPSig-135
❑ 99SPx-32
❑ 99SPxFinR-32
❑ 99SPxFinS-32
❑ 99StaClu-237
❑ 99StaCluFDI-237
❑ 99StaCluOoaK-237
❑ 99StaCluPP-237
❑ 99ThuSkySupR-93
❑ 99Top-402
❑ 99TopBlaLC1-56
❑ 99TopBlaLC2-56
❑ 99TopBlaLC3-56
❑ 99TopChr-402
❑ 99TopChrR-402
❑ 99TopGal-96
❑ 99TopGal-121
❑ 99TopGalPP-96
❑ 99TopGalPP-121
❑ 99TopGalPPI-96
❑ 99TopGalPPI-121
❑ 99TopGolL-56
❑ 99TopGolLC1-56
❑ 99TopGolLC2-56
❑ 99TopGolLOtO-56
❑ 99TopMVPP-402
❑ 99TopOpeD-125
❑ 99TopRedLC1-56
❑ 99TopRedLC2-56
❑ 99TopRedLC3-56
❑ 99UD Cho-73
❑ 99UD ChoPCR-73
❑ 99UD Ion-19
❑ 99UD IonR-19
❑ 99Ult-31
❑ 99UltGolM-31
❑ 99UltMas-31
❑ 99UltPlaM-31
❑ 99UppDec-70
❑ 99UppDecBD-24
❑ 99UppDecBDD-24
❑ 99UppDecBDQ-24
❑ 99UppDecBDT-24
❑ 99UppDecCLM-C22
❑ 99UppDecE-22
❑ 99UppDecEFXG-22
❑ 99UppDecEL1-70
❑ 99UppDecEL2-70
❑ 99UppDecM-55
❑ 99UppDecMGS-55
❑ 99UppDecMHFS-55
❑ 99UppDecMP-55
❑ 99UppDecMSS-55
❑ 99UppDecO-23
❑ 99UppDecOSO-23
❑ 99UppDecR-21
❑ 99UppDecRG-21
❑ 99UppDecRI-SC
❑ 99UppDecRIL2-SC
❑ 99UppDecRP-21
❑ 99Vic-108
Casey, Thomas
❑ 21Zee-4
Casey, Tim (Timothy)
❑ 86StoPorP-4
❑ 87ElPasDP-13
❑ 89HunStaB-14
❑ 90CMC-589
❑ 90ProAAAF-151
❑ 90TacTigC-12
❑ 90TacTigP-104
Cash, Bill
❑ 86NegLeaF-57
❑ 91NegLeaRL-2
❑ 92NegLeaRLI-9
❑ 95NegLeaLI-2
❑ 97NegLeaPC-2C
Cash, Dave (David)
❑ 69PirJacitB-2
❑ 70OPC-141
❑ 70Top-141
❑ 71MLBOffS-197
❑ 71OPC-582
❑ 71Pir-2
❑ 71PirActP-3
❑ 71Top-582
❑ 72OPC-125
❑ 72Top-125
❑ 73LinPor-145
❑ 73OPC-397
❑ 73Top-397
❑ 74OPC-198
❑ 74PhiJohP-16
❑ 74Top-198
❑ 75Hos-93
❑ 75Kel-48
❑ 75OPC-22
❑ 75PhiPhiP-9
❑ 75PhiProPS-5
❑ 75SSPPuzB-6
❑ 75Top-22
❑ 75TopMin-22
❑ 76BlaDis-11
❑ 76BucDis-11
❑ 76CarDis-11
❑ 76CraDis-11
❑ 76DailsID-11
❑ 76Hos-40
❑ 76HosTwi-40
❑ 76IsaDis-11
❑ 76Kel-16
❑ 76OPC-295
❑ 76OrbDis-11
❑ 76PhiPhiP-7
❑ 76RedBarD-11
❑ 76SafDis-11
❑ 76Spo-8
❑ 76SSP-465
❑ 76Top-295
❑ 76TowCluD-11
❑ 77BurCheD-162
❑ 77ChiWilD-14
❑ 77DailsID-14
❑ 77DetCaeD-14
❑ 77ExpPos-9
❑ 77HolInnD-14
❑ 77Hos-133
❑ 77MSADis-14
❑ 77OPC-180
❑ 77PepGloD-66
❑ 77RCColC-15
❑ 77SagDis-14
❑ 77sDis-14
❑ 77Top-649
❑ 77TopCloS-12
❑ 77WenDis-14
❑ 77ZipDis-14
❑ 78Hos-23
❑ 78OPC-18
❑ 78RCColC-6
❑ 78SagDis-17
❑ 78TasDis-17
❑ 78Top-495
❑ 78WifBalD-15
❑ 79BasPat-16
❑ 79ExpPos-5
❑ 79OPC-207
❑ 79Top-395
❑ 80OPC-3
❑ 80Top-14
❑ 81Don-121
❑ 81Fle-492
❑ 81PadFamF-5
❑ 81Top-707
❑ 86ExpGreT-2
❑ 88BatCliP-1663
❑ 89PacSenL-192
❑ 89ScrRedBC-6
❑ 89T/MSenL-19
❑ 89TopSenL-64
❑ 91PacSenL-58
❑ 91PacSenL-80
❑ 93ExpDonM-13
❑ 93ScrRedBF-2559
❑ 93ScrRedBTI-5
❑ 93UppDecAH-28
❑ 94ScrRedBF-936
❑ 95ScrRedBTI-5
❑ 96PhiTeal-6
❑ 97RocRedW-4
❑ 98RocRedWQ-4
Cash, Earl
❑ 85OscAstTI-4
❑ 86OscAstP-5
❑ 87ColAstP-19
Cash, Johnny
❑ 86DurBulP-3
Cash, Mike
❑ 75CedRapGT-15
❑ 78PhoGiaC-5
Cash, Norm (Norman Dalton)
❑ 47Exh-37
❑ 55DonWin-13
❑ 59Top-509
❑ 60Top-488
❑ 61Pos-40A
❑ 61Pos-40B
❑ 61TigJayP-5
❑ 61Top-95
❑ 61TopStal-148
❑ 62Baz-35
❑ 62ExhStaB-7
❑ 62Jel-14
❑ 62Pos-14A
❑ 62Pos-14B
❑ 62PosCan-14
❑ 62SalPlaC-72
❑ 62ShiPlaC-72
❑ 62TigJayP-4
❑ 62Top-51
❑ 62Top-250
❑ 62Top-466
❑ 62TopBuc-15
❑ 62TopStal-45
❑ 62TopVen-51
❑ 63BasMagM-14
❑ 63ExhStaB-11
❑ 63Jel-46
❑ 63Pos-46
❑ 63TigJayP-4
❑ 63Top-4
❑ 63Top-445
❑ 64Baz-20
❑ 64TigJayP-3
❑ 64TigLid-3
❑ 64Top-331
❑ 64Top-425
❑ 64TopCoi-79
❑ 64TopSta-49
❑ 64TopStaU-13
❑ 64TopTatl-28
❑ 64TopVen-331
❑ 65OPC-153
❑ 65TigJayP-3
❑ 65Top-153
❑ 66TigVolC-2
❑ 66Top-218
❑ 66Top-315
❑ 66TopVen-218
❑ 66TopVen-315
❑ 67CokCapTi-2
❑ 67DexPre-44
❑ 67TigDexP-1
❑ 67Top-216
❑ 67Top-540
❑ 67TopVen-198
❑ 68AtlOilPBCC-11
❑ 68CokCapT-2
❑ 68TigDetFPB-2
❑ 68Top-256
❑ 68TopVen-256
❑ 69MilBra-54
❑ 69MLBOffS-46
❑ 69OPC-80
❑ 69TigTeal-1
❑ 69TigTealC-2
❑ 69Top-80
❑ 69TopSta-171
❑ 69TopTeaP-1
❑ 70MLBOffS-205
❑ 70Top-611
❑ 71MLBOffS-389
❑ 71OPC-599
❑ 71Top-599
❑ 72MilBra-70
❑ 72OPC-90
❑ 72OPC-150
❑ 72SevTraC-9
❑ 72Top-90
❑ 72Top-150
❑ 73LinPor-68
❑ 73OPC-485
❑ 73TigJew-5
❑ 73Top-485
❑ 74OPC-367
❑ 74Top-367
❑ 74TopSta-172
❑ 75SSP42-38
❑ 78TCM60I-49
❑ 78TigDeaCS-13
❑ 81TigDetN-73A
❑ 81TigDetN-73B
❑ 81WhiSox1T-12
❑ 82TCMGreS-29
❑ 83MLBPin-3
❑ 83TigAlKS-19
❑ 83TigAlKS-22
❑ 83TigAlKS-24
❑ 85CirK-25
❑ 86TigSpoD-14
❑ 88TigDom-2
❑ 91FouBal-19
❑ 93ActPacA-147
❑ 94TedWil-29
❑ 94TedWilM-M29
❑ 97TopMan-36
❑ 97TopManF-36
❑ 97TopManFR-36
Cash, Ron (Ronald Forrest)
❑ 74OPC-600
❑ 74Tig-2
❑ 74Top-600
Cash, Timothy
❑ 88VerBeaDS-3
Cash, Todd
❑ 86CliGiaP-5
Cashen, Frank
❑ 92TopCas-1
Cashion, Jay Carl
❑ 09ColChiE-47
❑ 12ColRedB-47
❑ 12ColTinT-47
❑ 14CraJacE-62
Cashman, Joseph
❑ 59FleWil-32
Casian, Larry
❑ 88OrlTwiB-20
❑ 88SouLeaAJ-29
❑ 89PorBeaP-223
❑ 90CMC-555
❑ 90PorBeaC-3
❑ 90PorBeaP-170
❑ 90ProAAAF-240
❑ 91Bow-325
❑ 91Lea-481
❑ 91OPC-374
❑ 91Top-374
❑ 91TopDeb90-27
❑ 91TopDesS-374
❑ 91TopMic-374
❑ 91TopTif-374
❑ 92Fle-199
❑ 92PorBeaF-2660
❑ 92PorBeaS-404
❑ 92Sco100RS-94
❑ 92SkyAAAF-185
❑ 92TriA AAS-404
❑ 93Don-343
❑ 93FleFinE-233
❑ 93Lea-498
❑ 94Don-109
❑ 94Fle-201
❑ 94StaClu-479
❑ 94StaCluFDI-479
❑ 94StaCluGR-479
❑ 94StaCluMOP-479
❑ 94Top-543
❑ 94TopGol-543
❑ 94TopSpa-543
❑ 94Ult-84
❑ 96Fle-313
❑ 96FleTif-313
❑ 96LeaSigEA-26
Casillas, Adam
❑ 88GreHorP-1562
❑ 89CedRapRAB-18
❑ 89CedRapRB-14
❑ 89CedRapRP-922
❑ 89CedRapRS-3
❑ 89Sta-198
❑ 90CedRapRDGB-18
❑ 91LinDriAAA-254
❑ 91NasSouLD-254
❑ 91NasSouP-2168
❑ 92MemChiS-430
❑ 92OmaRoyF-2973
❑ 92SkyAA F-181
❑ 93MemChiF-385
Casillas, Uriel
❑ 98BatMucTI-4
Casimiro, Carlos
❑ 96AppLeaAB-2
❑ 96BluOriB-7
❑ 97DelSho-3
❑ 98FreKeyM-21
Caskill, Derrick
❑ 95HelBreTI-21
Casper, Brett
❑ 97SalVolG-7
Casper, Mike
❑ 98SpoIndG-6
Casper, Tim
❑ 91EveGiaC-13
❑ 91EveGiaP-3920
❑ 93SanJosGC-5
❑ 93SanJosGF-15
Cassel, Grahame
❑ 91ParPatF-9
Cassels, Chris
❑ 88BelBreGS-23
❑ 89StoPorB-19
❑ 89StoPorCLC-163
❑ 89StoPorP-392
❑ 89StoPorS-14
❑ 90CalLeaACLC-41
❑ 90StoPorB-14
❑ 90StoPorCLC-199
❑ 90StoPorP-2199
❑ 91HarSenLD-251
❑ 91HarSenP-638
❑ 91LinDriAA-251
Cassidy, Dave (David)
❑ 89AriStaB-6
❑ 89HamRedS-9
❑ 91St.PetCP-2266
❑ 92ArkTraF-1121
Cassidy, Hop (Howard)
❑ 79ColCliT-25
❑ 92ColCliP-2
❑ 94ColCliP-3
❑ 96ColCliB-1
Cassidy, Mike
❑ 91St.PetCC-2
Cassidy, Pete (Peter F.)
❑ 09T206-407

❑ 90DodTar-909
Cassidy, Reid
❑ 79WatIndT-15
Cassillas, Adam
❑ 90ChaLooGS-8
Cassini, Jack Dempsey
❑ 76BatTroTI-6
❑ 78HalHalR-12
Castaigne, Arcilio
❑ 80AndBraT-2
Castain, Maurice
❑ 83IdaFalAT-26
❑ 84MadMusP-22
Castain, Michael
❑ 97ModA'sG-4
Castaldo, Eric
❑ 96DanBraB-9
Castaldo, Gregg
❑ 92KanCouCTI-4
❑ 93FreKeyF-1031
❑ 94FreKeyC-6
❑ 94FreKeyF-2619
❑ 95BowBayTI-23
Castaldo, Joe
❑ 91HamRedC-1
❑ 91HamRedP-4030
Castaldo, Vince
❑ 90HelBreSP-16
❑ 91Cla/Bes-264
❑ 91StoPorC-19
❑ 91StoPorP-3036
❑ 92ElPasDF-3934
❑ 92ElPasDS-203
❑ 93OttLynF-2441
Castaneda, Hector
❑ 93BluOriC-8
❑ 93BluOriF-4127
❑ 94AlbPolC-10
❑ 94AlbPolF-2239
❑ 95BowBayTI-27
Castaneda, Michael
❑ 90IBAWorA-24
Castaneda, Nick
❑ 82AleDukT-13
❑ 83AleDukT-5
❑ 84PriWilPT-31
❑ 85MexCitTT-23
❑ 89OmaRoyC-13
❑ 89OmaRoyP-1722
❑ 91LinDriAAA-228
❑ 91LouRedLD-228
❑ 91LouRedP-2921
Castaneda, Robbie
❑ 91BenBucP-3687
Casteel, Brent
❑ 86WinSpiP-3
Casteel, Ricky
❑ 98BluOriQ-15
Castellano, John
❑ 98GreFalDG-4
Castellano, Miguel
❑ 90ButCopKSP-3
❑ 91GasRanC-16
❑ 91GasRanP-2693
❑ 92ChaRanC-14
❑ 92ChaRanF-2230
❑ 93ClaFS7-177
❑ 93LinVenB-118
❑ 93TulDriF-2737
❑ 93TulDriTI-3
❑ 94VenLinU-94
❑ 95LinVen-231
❑ 96-97LinVen-243
Castellano, Pedro
❑ 89Sta-163
❑ 89WytCubS-5
❑ 90MidLeaASGS-29
❑ 90PeoChiTI-8
❑ 90PeoChiTI-9
❑ 91CarLeaAP-CAR40
❑ 91Cla/Bes-173
❑ 91WinSpiC-17
❑ 91WinSpiP-2834
❑ 92Bow-271
❑ 92Bow-649
❑ 92DonRoo-22
❑ 92IowCubF-4057
❑ 92IowCubS-205
❑ 92ProFS7-204
❑ 92SkyAAAF-99
❑ 92UppDecML-133
❑ 93Bow-232
❑ 93ColSprSSF-3091
❑ 93Don-761
❑ 93ExcFS7-7
❑ 93FleFinE-24
❑ 93LinVenB-26
❑ 93TopTra-69T
❑ 94ColSprSSF-739
❑ 94Don-449
❑ 94Pac-191
❑ 94Pin-229
❑ 94PinArtP-229
❑ 94PinMusC-229
❑ 94StaCluT-97
❑ 94StaCluTFDI-97
❑ 94VenLinU-225
❑ 95LinVen-48
❑ 96-97LinVen-109
❑ 96ColSprSSTI-7
❑ 96FleUpd-U127
❑ 96FleUpdTC-U127
❑ 97ColSprSATTI-2
❑ 97SalLakB-10
Castelli, Bobby
❑ 98VerExpO-10
❑ 99TeaBesR-10
❑ 99TeaBesRG-10
❑ 99TeaBesRS-10
Castello, Brian
❑ 89SalSpuCLC-149
Caster, George
❑ 30Zee-48
❑ 32Zee-30
❑ 35DiaMatCS3T1-29
❑ 41BroW75-5
❑ 96Bro194F-31
Castiglia, Jim
❑ 42A'sTeal-9
Castiglione, Pete (Peter P.)
❑ 49EurSta-156
❑ 50Bow-201
❑ 50PirTeal-3
❑ 51Bow-17
❑ 52Bow-47
❑ 52DixLid-4
❑ 52DixPre-4
❑ 52Top-260
❑ 54Bow-174
❑ 83TopRep5-260
Castilla, Vinny (Vinicio)
❑ 90Bes-278
❑ 90CMC-727
❑ 90SouAtlLAS-28
❑ 90SumBraB-28
❑ 90SumBraP-2439
❑ 91GreBraC-15
❑ 91GreBraLD-202
❑ 91GreBraP-3009
❑ 91LinDriAA-202
❑ 91RicBraBC-29
❑ 92Fle-666
❑ 92ProFS7-183
❑ 92RicBraBB-2
❑ 92RicBraF-382
❑ 92RicBraRC-2
❑ 92RicBraS-427
❑ 92Sco-860
❑ 92SkyAAAF-195
❑ 92TopDeb91-30
❑ 93Bow-556
❑ 93Don-102
❑ 93Don-770
❑ 93Fle-406
❑ 93FleFinE-25
❑ 93JimDeaR-2
❑ 93Lea-495
❑ 93OPCPre-65
❑ 93PacJugC-23
❑ 93PacSpa-424
❑ 93RocStaC-23
❑ 93RocUSPC-4H
❑ 93RocUSPC-13C
❑ 93StaClu-547
❑ 93StaCluFDI-547
❑ 93StaCluMOP-547
❑ 93Stu-212
❑ 93TopTra-33T
❑ 93Ult-344
❑ 93UppDec-560
❑ 93UppDecGold-560
❑ 94ColC-74
❑ 94ColChoGS-74
❑ 94ColChoSS-74
❑ 94Don-549
❑ 94Fle-437
❑ 94Lea-214
❑ 94Pac-192
❑ 94PanSti-172
❑ 94Pin-191
❑ 94PinArtP-191
❑ 94PinMusC-191
❑ 94RocPol-6
❑ 94Sco-305
❑ 94ScoGolR-305
❑ 94StaClu-244
❑ 94StaCluFDI-244
❑ 94StaCluGR-244
❑ 94StaCluMOP-244
❑ 94StaCluMOP-ST4
❑ 94StaCluST-ST4
❑ 94StaCluT-92
❑ 94StaCluTFDI-92
❑ 94Top-163
❑ 94TopGol-163
❑ 94TopSpa-163
❑ 94USPlaCR-2C
❑ 95Don-181
❑ 95DonPreP-181
❑ 95DonTopotO-226
❑ 95Emo-124
❑ 95Fin-277
❑ 95FinRef-277
❑ 95Fla-128
❑ 95FleUpd-166
❑ 95Lea-230
❑ 95LeaLim-171
❑ 95LinVen-312
❑ 95Pac-134
❑ 95RocPol-5
❑ 95Sco-483
❑ 95ScoGolR-483
❑ 95ScoPlaTS-483
❑ 95SP-51
❑ 95SPCha-43
❑ 95SPChaDC-43
❑ 95SPSil-51
❑ 95StaClu-476
❑ 95StaCluMOP-476
❑ 95StaCluSTWS-476
❑ 95Top-552
❑ 95TopCyb-331
❑ 95UppDec-491
❑ 95Zen-106
❑ 96Baz-71
❑ 96Bow-60
❑ 96BowBes-67
❑ 96BowBesAR-67
❑ 96BowBesR-67
❑ 96BowFoi-60
❑ 96Cir-122
❑ 96CirRav-122
❑ 96ColCho-136
❑ 96ColCho-753
❑ 96ColChoCtG-CG15
❑ 96ColChoCtG-CG15B
❑ 96ColChoCtG-CG15C
❑ 96ColChoCtGE-CR15
❑ 96ColChoCtGG-CG15
❑ 96ColChoCtGG-CG15B
❑ 96ColChoCtGG-CG15C
❑ 96ColChoCtGGE-CR15
❑ 96ColChoGS-136
❑ 96ColChoGS-753
❑ 96ColChoSS-136
❑ 96ColChoSS-753
❑ 96Don-305
❑ 96DonPreP-305
❑ 96EmoXL-174
❑ 96Fin-S99
❑ 96FinRef-S99
❑ 96Fla-245
❑ 96Fle-362
❑ 96FleTif-362
❑ 96Lea-138
❑ 96LeaPrePB-138
❑ 96LeaPrePG-138
❑ 96LeaPrePS-138
❑ 96LeaPreSG-43
❑ 96LeaPreSte-43
❑ 96MetUni-155
❑ 96MetUniP-155
❑ 96Pac-58
❑ 96PacEstL-EL8
❑ 96PacGolCD-DC27
❑ 96PacHom-HP14
❑ 96PacPri-P20
❑ 96PacPriG-P20
❑ 96PanSti-88
❑ 96Pin-245
❑ 96PinAfi-81
❑ 96PinAfiAP-81
❑ 96PinAfiFPP-81
❑ 96PinArtP-145
❑ 96PinFoil-245
❑ 96PinSta-145
❑ 96ProSta-112
❑ 96RocFle-4
❑ 96RocPol-6
❑ 96Sco-74
❑ 96ScoDugC-A60
❑ 96ScoDugCAP-A60
❑ 96Sel-87
❑ 96SelArtP-87
❑ 96SP-76
❑ 96SPx-24
❑ 96SPxGol-24
❑ 96StaClu-5
❑ 96StaCluEPB-5
❑ 96StaCluEPG-5
❑ 96StaCluEPS-5
❑ 96StaCluMM-MM5
❑ 96StaCluMO-9
❑ 96StaCluMOP-5
❑ 96StaCluMOP-MM5
❑ 96Stu-16
❑ 96StuPrePB-16
❑ 96StuPrePG-16
❑ 96StuPrePS-16
❑ 96Sum-129
❑ 96SumAbo&B-129
❑ 96SumArtP-129
❑ 96SumFoi-129
❑ 96TeaOut-16
❑ 96Top-188
❑ 96TopChr-58
❑ 96TopChrR-58
❑ 96TopGal-113
❑ 96TopGalPPI-113
❑ 96TopLas-39
❑ 96Ult-188
❑ 96UltGolM-188
❑ 96UppDec-62
❑ 97Bow-28
❑ 97BowBes-80
❑ 97BowBesAR-80
❑ 97BowBesR-80
❑ 97BowChr-24
❑ 97BowChrI-24
❑ 97BowChrIR-24
❑ 97BowChrR-24
❑ 97BowInt-28
❑ 97BowIntB-BBI8
❑ 97BowIntBAR-BBI8
❑ 97BowIntBR-BBI8
❑ 97Cir-32
❑ 97CirRav-32
❑ 97ColCho-95
❑ 97ColChoAC-39
❑ 97ColChoCtG-15A
❑ 97ColChoCtG-15B
❑ 97ColChoCtG-15C
❑ 97ColChoCtGE-CG15
❑ 97ColChoCtGIW-CG15
❑ 97ColChoPP-PP15
❑ 97ColChoPPG-PP15
❑ 97ColChoPPJ-PP15
❑ 97ColChoT-CR2
❑ 97Don-78
❑ 97DonGolPP-78
❑ 97DonLim-14
❑ 97DonLimE-14
❑ 97DonLimENG-14
❑ 97DonPre-61
❑ 97DonPreCttC-61
❑ 97DonSilPP-78
❑ 97DonTea-93
❑ 97DonTeaSPE-93
❑ 97Fin-125
❑ 97Fin-213
❑ 97FinEmb-125
❑ 97FinEmbR-125
❑ 97FinRef-125
❑ 97FinRef-213
❑ 97FlaShoLC-165
❑ 97FlaShoLeg0-165
❑ 97FlaShoLeg1-165
❑ 97FlaShoM-A165
❑ 97FlaShoM-B165
❑ 97FlaShoM-C165
❑ 97FlaShoR0-165
❑ 97FlaShoR1-165
❑ 97FlaShoR2-165
❑ 97Fle-309
❑ 97FleTif-309
❑ 97Lea-155
❑ 97LeaFraM-155
❑ 97LeaFraMDC-155
❑ 97MetUni-73
❑ 97Pac-281
❑ 97PacLatotML-26
❑ 97PacLigB-281
❑ 97PacPri-97
❑ 97PacPriLB-97
❑ 97PacPriP-97
❑ 97PacPriSL-SL9C
❑ 97PacSil-281
❑ 97Pin-68
❑ 97PinArtP-PP68
❑ 97PinInsFS-10
❑ 97PinMusC-68
❑ 97PinPrePla-68
❑ 97PinX-P-21
❑ 97PinX-PMoS-21
❑ 97PinX-PSfF-17
❑ 97PinX-PSfFU-17
❑ 97RicBraBC-4
❑ 97RocPol-4
❑ 97RocSco-9
❑ 97RocScoPl-9
❑ 97RocScoPr-9
❑ 97Sco-183
❑ 97ScoArtPWB-183
❑ 97ScoPreS-183
❑ 97ScoShoS-183
❑ 97ScoShoSAP-183
❑ 97SP-63
❑ 97SpolII-109
❑ 97SpolIIEE-109
❑ 97SpolIIGS-13
❑ 97StaClu-221
❑ 97StaCluMat-221
❑ 97StaCluMOP-221
❑ 97Top-398
❑ 97TopChr-139
❑ 97TopChrR-139
❑ 97TopGal-107
❑ 97TopGalPG-PG12
❑ 97TopGalPPI-107
❑ 97TopSta-40
❑ 97TopStaAM-40
❑ 97UD3-14
❑ 97Ult-443
❑ 97UltGolME-443
❑ 97UltPlaME-443
❑ 97UppDec-197
❑ 97UppDec-351
❑ 98Bow-62
❑ 98BowBes-36
❑ 98BowBesAR-36
❑ 98BowBesR-36
❑ 98BowChr-62
❑ 98BowChrGA-62
❑ 98BowChrGAR-62
❑ 98BowChrI-62
❑ 98BowChrIR-62
❑ 98BowChrR-62
❑ 98BowGolA-62
❑ 98BowInt-62
❑ 98CirThu-188
❑ 98CirThuRav-188
❑ 98CirThuSupRav-188
❑ 98ColCho-85
❑ 98ColChoCtG-CG7A
❑ 98ColChoCtG-CG7B
❑ 98ColChoCtG-CG7C
❑ 98ColChoCtGExch-CG7
❑ 98ColChoCtGIW-CG7
❑ 98ColChoSQ-SQ80
❑ 98CroRoy-51
❑ 98CroRoyDK-9
❑ 98Don-79
❑ 98DonCol-79
❑ 98DonColL-263
❑ 98DonColP-650
❑ 98DonColS-79
❑ 98DonGolPP-79
❑ 98DonPre-100
❑ 98DonPreSeat-100
❑ 98DonPriCD-79
❑ 98DonPriCL-263
❑ 98DonPriCP-650
❑ 98DonSig-113
❑ 98DonSigP-113
❑ 98DonSilPP-79
❑ 98E-X2-63
❑ 98E-X2ECFut-63
❑ 98E-X2ECNow-63
❑ 98Fin-102
❑ 98FinNo--102
❑ 98FinNo-R-102
❑ 98FinRef-102
❑ 98FlaShoLeg0-93
❑ 98FlaShoLeg1-93
❑ 98FlaShoLeg2-93
❑ 98FlaShoLeg3-93
❑ 98FlaShoLegM-93
❑ 98FlaShoR0-93
❑ 98FlaShoR1-93
❑ 98FlaShoR2-93
❑ 98FlaShoR3-93
❑ 98Fle-255
❑ 98FleVin'-19
❑ 98FleVin'C-19
❑ 98Lea-64
❑ 98LeaFraDA-64
❑ 98LeaFraF-64
❑ 98LeaFraM-64
❑ 98LeaFraM-64
❑ 98LeaFraMDC-64
❑ 98LeaFraMDC-64
❑ 98LeaFraMZ2-64
❑ 98LeaRS-93
❑ 98LeaRSLHolo-93
❑ 98LeaRSLong-93
❑ 98LeaRTrue-93
❑ 98MetUni-39
❑ 98MetUniPMG-39
❑ 98Pac-280
❑ 98PacAur-125
❑ 98PacHomRH-9
❑ 98PacInv-91
❑ 98PacInvGems-143
❑ 98PacInvPBlue-91
❑ 98PacInvSilv-91
❑ 98PacInvTeam-9
❑ 98PacLatotML-12
❑ 98PacNes-9
❑ 98PacOme-81
❑ 98PacOmeR-81
❑ 98PacOnl-241
❑ 98PacOnlR-241
❑ 98PacOnlWC-241
❑ 98PacPar-153
❑ 98PacParC-153
❑ 98PacParG-153
❑ 98PacParHS-153
❑ 98PacParPB-153
❑ 98PacParR-153
❑ 98PacPlaB-280
❑ 98PacRedT-280
❑ 98PacSil-280
❑ 98Pin-34
❑ 98PinPer-110
❑ 98PinPerPP-110
❑ 98PinPerSftF-32
❑ 98PinPlu-135
❑ 98PinPreP-34
❑ 98Revo-52
❑ 98RevoFP-15
❑ 98RevoShow-27
❑ 98RevoSS-52
❑ 98Sco-97
❑ 98ScoRT-78
❑ 98ScoSS-PP43
❑ 98ScoSSAP-PP43
❑ 98SkyDugA-13
❑ 98SkyDugA-141
❑ 98SkyDugAIA-13
❑ 98SkyDugAIA-141
❑ 98SP Aut-84
❑ 98SpolII-22
❑ 98SpolII-147
❑ 98SpolIIEE-22
❑ 98SpolIIEE-147
❑ 98SpolIIFE-22
❑ 98SpolIIFE-147
❑ 98SpolIITaN-70
❑ 98SpolIITaNEE-70
❑ 98SpolIIWSF-102
❑ 98SpolIIWSFEE-102
❑ 98SpolIIWSFFE-102
❑ 98SPxFin-81
❑ 98SPxFin-216
❑ 98SPxFinHRH-HR8
❑ 98SPxFinR-81
❑ 98SPxFinR-216
❑ 98SPxFinS-81
❑ 98SPxFinS-216
❑ 98StaCluFDI-35
❑ 98StaCluI-35
❑ 98StaCluOneK-35
❑ 98StaCluPP-35
❑ 98StaCluTIII-T7A
❑ 98StaCluTLme-T7A
❑ 98StaCluTLmo-T7A
❑ 98Stu-47
❑ 98StuGPP-47
❑ 98StuSPP-47
❑ 98Top-172
❑ 98TopChr-172
❑ 98TopChrC9-C5
❑ 98TopChrC9R-C5

❑ 98TopChrR-172
❑ 98TopClo9-C5
❑ 98TopDevR-172
❑ 98TopDia-172
❑ 98TopGal-83
❑ 98TopGalGP-83
❑ 98TopGalOPP-83
❑ 98TopGalPPI-83
❑ 98TopGalPPIA-83
❑ 98TopGolLabC1-69
❑ 98TopGolLabC1B-69
❑ 98TopGolLabC1One-69
❑ 98TopGolLabC1R-69
❑ 98TopGolLabC2-69
❑ 98TopGolLabC2B-69
❑ 98TopGolLabC2One-69
❑ 98TopGolLabC2R-69
❑ 98TopGolLabC3-69
❑ 98TopGolLabC3B-69
❑ 98TopGolLabC3One-69
❑ 98TopGolLabC3R-69
❑ 98TopGolLP-PP1
❑ 98TopMiniC-172
❑ 98TopOpeD-92
❑ 98TopSta-111
❑ 98TopSta'S-8
❑ 98TopSta'SGH-8
❑ 98TopStaB-111
❑ 98TopStaG-111
❑ 98TopStaGR-111
❑ 98TopStaPre-PP3
❑ 98TopStaS-111
❑ 98TopStaSteG-8
❑ 98TopTek-38
❑ 98TopTekD-38
❑ 98UD3-36
❑ 98UD3-126
❑ 98UD3-216
❑ 98UD3DieCut-36
❑ 98UD3DieCut-126
❑ 98UD3DieCut-216
❑ 98Ult-55
❑ 98UltGolM-55
❑ 98UltMas-55
❑ 98UltPlaM-55
❑ 98UppDec-79
❑ 98UppDec-354
❑ 98UppDec10AP-37
❑ 98UppDec1APR-37
❑ 98UppDecNP-NP22
❑ 98UppDecRBBop-BB24
❑ 98UppDecSF-50
❑ 98UppDecTMT-27
❑ 98UppDecTMTG-27
❑ 99199Fin-3
❑ 99AllMysFR-M10
❑ 99Bow-22
❑ 99BowBes-51
❑ 99BowBesAR-51
❑ 99BowBesR-51
❑ 99BowChr-22
❑ 99BowChrG-22
❑ 99BowChrGR-22
❑ 99BowChrI-22
❑ 99BowChrIR-22
❑ 99BowChrR-22
❑ 99BowGol-22
❑ 99BowInt-22
❑ 99BowLatB-LB4
❑ 99BowPreProd-PP3
❑ 99CroRoyB-48
❑ 99CroRoyL-48
❑ 99CroRoyOD-48
❑ 99E-X Cen-63
❑ 99E-X CenECFut-63
❑ 99E-X CenECNow-63
❑ 99FinGolRef-3
❑ 99FinMil-M26
❑ 99FinPre-PP3
❑ 99FinProF-PF38
❑ 99FinRef-3
❑ 99FlaShoLeg1-52
❑ 99FlaShoLeg2-52
❑ 99FlaShoLeg3-52
❑ 99FlaShoLegM1-52
❑ 99FlaShoLegM2-52
❑ 99FlaShoLegM3-52
❑ 99FlaShoR1-52
❑ 99FlaShoR2-52
❑ 99FlaShoR3-52
❑ 99Fle-37
❑ 99FleBri-21
❑ 99FleBri2G-21
❑ 99FleBriBlu-21
❑ 99FleBriGol-21
❑ 99FleGolYar-4
❑ 99FleMys-6
❑ 99FleMysG-6
❑ 99FleMysM-6
❑ 99FleSta9-37
❑ 99FleVin'-37
❑ 99FleWarT-37
❑ 99MetUni-191
❑ 99MetUniGM-191
❑ 99MetUniPMG-191
❑ 99Pac-142
❑ 99Pac-142A
❑ 99PacAur-59
❑ 99PacAurOD-59
❑ 99PacCroC-94
❑ 99PacCroC-28
❑ 99PacCroCPB-94
❑ 99PacCroCTM-7
❑ 99PacInv-49
❑ 99PacInvOD-49
❑ 99PacInvPB-49
❑ 99PacOme-81
❑ 99PacOmeC-81
❑ 99PacOmeG-81
❑ 99PacOmePB-81
❑ 99PacPar-80
❑ 99PacParC-80
❑ 99PacParG-80
❑ 99PacParHoloGold-80
❑ 99PacParHS-80
❑ 99PacParOD-80
❑ 99PacParPB-80
❑ 99PacParRed-80
❑ 99PacPlaB-142
❑ 99PacPlaB-142A
❑ 99PacPri-50
❑ 99PacPriHB-50
❑ 99PacPriHG-50
❑ 99PacPriHM-50
❑ 99PacPriHP-50
❑ 99PacPriRed-50
❑ 99PacPriS-69
❑ 99PacPriS206-69
❑ 99PacPriS206R-69
❑ 99PacRed-142
❑ 99PacRed-142A
❑ 99Rev-49
❑ 99RevPremDate-49
❑ 99RevRet-49
❑ 99RevShaSS-49
❑ 99SkyMolM-30
❑ 99SkyMolMOA-5
❑ 99SkyMolMX-30
❑ 99SkyPre-51
❑ 99SkyPreR-51
❑ 99SkyThu-190
❑ 99SkyThuRant-190
❑ 99SkyThuRave-190
❑ 99SP AutHRC-HR21
❑ 99SP AutHRC-HR46
❑ 99SP SigAuto-VC
❑ 99SP SigAutoG-VC
❑ 99SPAutHRCDC-HR21
❑ 99SPAutHRCDC-HR46
❑ 99SpoIll-104
❑ 99SpoIllF4-7
❑ 99SpoIllF4E-7
❑ 99SPSig-75
❑ 99SPx-38
❑ 99SPxFinR-38
❑ 99SPxFinS-38
❑ 99SPxWinM-VC
❑ 99StaClu-9
❑ 99StaCluC-CS24
❑ 99StaCluC-CS31
❑ 99StaCluC-CS37
❑ 99StaCluC-CS41
❑ 99StaCluFDI-9
❑ 99StaCluNC-NC15
❑ 99StaCluOoaK-9
❑ 99StaCluPP-9
❑ 99StaCluTI-T12B
❑ 99StaCluTL-T12B
❑ 99StaCluTL-T12B
❑ 99ThuSkySupR-190
❑ 99Top-199
❑ 99Top-453
❑ 99TopAll-AM6
❑ 99TopAllMF-M10
❑ 99TopBlaLC1-68
❑ 99TopBlaLC2-68
❑ 99TopBlaLC3-68
❑ 99TopChr-199
❑ 99TopChr-453
❑ 99TopChrA-AE6
❑ 99TopChrAR-AE6
❑ 99TopChrR-199
❑ 99TopChrR-453
❑ 99TopGal-59
❑ 99TopGalPP-59
❑ 99TopGalPPI-59
❑ 99TopGolL-68
❑ 99TopGolLC1-68
❑ 99TopGolLC2-68
❑ 99TopGolLOtO-68
❑ 99TopMVPP-199
❑ 99TopMVPP-453
❑ 99TopOpeD-105
❑ 99TopPowB-PB9
❑ 99TopPowBR-PB9
❑ 99TopRedLC1-68
❑ 99TopRedLC2-68
❑ 99TopRedLC3-68
❑ 99TopSta-76
❑ 99TopSta'S-8
❑ 99TopSta'SG-8
❑ 99TopSta'SGDH-8
❑ 99TopSta1Foil-76
❑ 99TopStaFoil-76
❑ 99TopStaOS-76
❑ 99TopStaPre-PP2
❑ 99TopSupC-20
❑ 99TopSupCR-20
❑ 99UD Cho-83
❑ 99UD ChoPCR-83
❑ 99UD ChoYW-Y12
❑ 99Ult-50
❑ 99UltGolM-50
❑ 99UltMas-50
❑ 99UltPlaM-50
❑ 99UppDec-360
❑ 99UppDecBD-31
❑ 99UppDecBDD-31
❑ 99UppDecBDQ-31
❑ 99UppDecBDT-31
❑ 99UppDecCf7-17
❑ 99UppDecCf7-51
❑ 99UppDecCf7-C14
❑ 99UppDecCf7Cf7P-C14
❑ 99UppDecCL-86
❑ 99UppDecCLCC-86
❑ 99UppDecCLM-C29
❑ 99UppDecCo7CE-17
❑ 99UppDecCo7CE-51
❑ 99UppDecE-33
❑ 99UppDecE-156
❑ 99UppDecEBPC-C-VC
❑ 99UppDecEFXG-33
❑ 99UppDecEFXG-156
❑ 99UppDecEL1-360
❑ 99UppDecEL2-360
❑ 99UppDecIP-I26
❑ 99UppDecIPD-I26
❑ 99UppDecIPHR-I26
❑ 99UppDecIPT-I26
❑ 99UppDecM-70
❑ 99UppDecMGS-70
❑ 99UppDecMHFS-70
❑ 99UppDecMP-70
❑ 99UppDecMSS-70
❑ 99UppDecO-48
❑ 99UppDecOSO-48
❑ 99UppDecR-30
❑ 99UppDecRG-30
❑ 99UppDecRP-30
❑ 99Vic-134

Castillo, Ace
❑ 75QuaCitAT-27

Castillo, Albert
❑ 80VenLeaS-57

Castillo, Alberto
❑ 89KinMetS-5
❑ 90ColMetGS-19
❑ 90ColMetPPI-2
❑ 90PitMetP-23
❑ 91ColMetPI-10
❑ 91ColMetPPI-7
❑ 92St.LucMCB-15
❑ 92St.LucMF-1748
❑ 93St.LucMC-5
❑ 93St.LuMF-2924
❑ 94BinMetF-706
❑ 94Bow-23
❑ 94EveGiaC-3
❑ 94EveGiaF-3657
❑ 94StaCluDP-6
❑ 94StaCluDPFDI-6
❑ 95BelGiaTI-33
❑ 95NorTidTI-8
❑ 96NorTidB-10
❑ 96Pac-142
❑ 96UltGolP-2
❑ 96UltGolPGM-2
❑ 97PacPriGotD-GD173
❑ 98PacInvGems-181
❑ 98PacOnl-473
❑ 98PacOnlR-473
❑ 98PacOnlWC-473

Castillo, Axel
❑ 88BurIndP-1781

Castillo, Benny (Ben)
❑ 88BriTigP-1892
❑ 89FayGenP-1580
❑ 91SalLakTP-3222
❑ 91SalLakTSP-16
❑ 92ChaRanC-3
❑ 92ChaRanF-2236
❑ 93TulDriF-2745
❑ 93TulDriTI-4

Castillo, Bobby
❑ 79AlbDukTc-22
❑ 79Top-641
❑ 80DodPol-37
❑ 81Dod-4
❑ 81DodPol-37
❑ 81Don-298
❑ 81LonBeaPT-14
❑ 81Top-146
❑ 82Top-48
❑ 82TopTra-17T
❑ 82TwiPos-3
❑ 83Fle-608
❑ 83FleSta-32
❑ 83FleSti-139
❑ 83Top-327
❑ 83Top-771
❑ 83TwiTeal-23
❑ 84Don-436
❑ 84Fle-559
❑ 84MinTwiP-5
❑ 84Nes792-491
❑ 84OPC-329
❑ 84Top-491
❑ 84TopTif-491
❑ 84TwiTeal-24
❑ 85DodCokP-7
❑ 85DomLeaS-80
❑ 85Fle-274
❑ 85FleUpd-22
❑ 85Top-588
❑ 85TopTif-588
❑ 85TopTifT-18T
❑ 85TopTra-18T
❑ 86Fle-127
❑ 86Top-252
❑ 86TopTif-252
❑ 90DodTar-119

Castillo, Braulio
❑ 89BakDodCLC-202
❑ 89CalLeaA-9
❑ 90SanAntMGS-10
❑ 91Cla/Bes-307
❑ 91Cla2-T85
❑ 91LinDriAA-533
❑ 91SanAntMLD-533
❑ 91SanAntMP-2987
❑ 92Bow-104
❑ 92Don-753
❑ 92OPC-353
❑ 92ProFS7-245
❑ 92Sco-824
❑ 92ScoRoo-32
❑ 92ScrRedBF-2458
❑ 92ScrRedBS-480
❑ 92SkyAAAF-218
❑ 92StaClu-124
❑ 92Top-353
❑ 92TopDeb91-31
❑ 92TopGol-353
❑ 92TopGolW-353
❑ 92TopMic-353
❑ 92UppDec-21
❑ 93Don-386
❑ 93Fle-407
❑ 93LimRocDWB-80
❑ 93RocUSPC-5C
❑ 93RocUSPC-8S
❑ 93Sco-629
❑ 93Sel-340
❑ 93TucTorF-3072

Castillo, Carlos
❑ 91YakBeaC-23
❑ 91YakBeaP-4241
❑ 92BakDodCLC-5
❑ 92VisOakF-1005
❑ 95LakElsSTI-7
❑ 96LakElsSB-1
❑ 96MidAngB-10
❑ 96MidLeaAB-49
❑ 96SouBenSHS-9
❑ 97Fle-645
❑ 97FleTif-645
❑ 97Ult-503
❑ 97UltGolME-503
❑ 97UltPlaME-503
❑ 97WhiSoxTI-43
❑ 98PacOnl-165
❑ 98PacOnlR-165
❑ 98PacOnlWC-165
❑ 98Top-473
❑ 98TopChr-473
❑ 98TopChrR-473
❑ 98TopDevR-473
❑ 98TopDia-473
❑ 98TopMiniC-473
❑ 99PacCroC-66
❑ 99PacCroCPB-66
❑ 99SP SigAuto-CC
❑ 99SPSig-100

Castillo, Carmen (M. Carmelo)
❑ 79WatIndT-19
❑ 80WatIndT-27
❑ 81ChaLooT-16
❑ 82ChaChaT-19
❑ 82Ind-7
❑ 83Fle-404
❑ 83IndPos-7
❑ 84Ind-9
❑ 84IndWhe-8
❑ 85DomLeaS-129
❑ 85Don-590
❑ 85Fle-444
❑ 85Ind-10
❑ 85IndPol-8
❑ 85OPC-184
❑ 85Top-184
❑ 85TopSti-255
❑ 85TopTif-184
❑ 86Don-460
❑ 86Fle-584
❑ 86IndOhH-8
❑ 86IndTeal-15
❑ 86TopTra-21T
❑ 86TopTraT-21T
❑ 87Don-588
❑ 87Fle-250
❑ 87FleGlo-250
❑ 87IndGat-8
❑ 87Top-513
❑ 87TopTif-513
❑ 88Don-403
❑ 88Fle-606
❑ 88FleGlo-606
❑ 88IndGat-8
❑ 88IndTeal-9
❑ 88Sco-581
❑ 88ScoGlo-581
❑ 88StaLinI-8
❑ 88Top-341
❑ 88TopTif-341
❑ 89Don-374
❑ 89Fle-401
❑ 89FleGlo-401
❑ 89Sco-497
❑ 89ScoRoo-23T
❑ 89Top-637
❑ 89TopBig-91
❑ 89TopTif-637
❑ 89TopTra-18T
❑ 89TopTraT-18T
❑ 89UppDec-487
❑ 90Don-554
❑ 90Fle-371
❑ 90FleCan-371
❑ 90OPC-427
❑ 90Sco-123
❑ 90Top-427
❑ 90TopTif-427
❑ 90UppDec-281
❑ 91Fle-606
❑ 91OPC-266
❑ 91Sco-608
❑ 91Top-266
❑ 91TopDesS-266
❑ 91TopMic-266
❑ 91TopTif-266
❑ 93LimRocDWB-93

Castillo, Felipe
❑ 87GasRanP-1
❑ 88GasRanP-1008
❑ 89ChaRanS-6
❑ 89TulDriGS-7
❑ 89TulDriTI-5
❑ 90CMC-741
❑ 90TulDriP-1150
❑ 90TulDriTI-5

Castillo, Frank
❑ 87WytCubP-21
❑ 89WinSpiS-4
❑ 90ChaKniTI-20
❑ 91DonRoo-20
❑ 91IowCubLD-203
❑ 91LinDriAAA-203
❑ 91UppDecFE-27F
❑ 92CubMar-49
❑ 92Don-492
❑ 92Fle-378
❑ 92Lea-290
❑ 92LeaBlaG-290
❑ 92OPC-196
❑ 92OPCPre-159
❑ 92Pin-504
❑ 92Sco-399
❑ 92Sco100RS-61
❑ 92StaClu-65
❑ 92Top-196
❑ 92TopDeb91-32
❑ 92TopGol-196
❑ 92TopGolW-196
❑ 92TopMic-196
❑ 92Ult-467
❑ 92UppDec-526
❑ 93CubMar-4
❑ 93CubStaC-21
❑ 93Don-400
❑ 93Fle-375
❑ 93Lea-141
❑ 93PacBeiA-17
❑ 93PacSpa-54
❑ 93Pin-208
❑ 93Sco-462
❑ 93StaClu-346
❑ 93StaCluFDI-346
❑ 93StaCluMOP-346
❑ 93Top-533
❑ 93TopGol-533
❑ 93TopInaM-533
❑ 93TopInaR-533
❑ 93TopMic-533
❑ 93Ult-16
❑ 93UppDec-408
❑ 93UppDecGold-408
❑ 94ColC-454
❑ 94ColChoGS-454
❑ 94ColChoSS-454
❑ 94Don-91
❑ 94Fle-382
❑ 94Lea-217
❑ 94Pac-97
❑ 94StaClu-337
❑ 94StaCluFDI-337
❑ 94StaCluGR-337
❑ 94StaCluMOP-337
❑ 94StaCluT-341
❑ 94StaCluTFDI-341
❑ 94Top-399
❑ 94TopGol-399
❑ 94TopSpa-399
❑ 94UppDec-464
❑ 94UppDecED-464
❑ 95Fin-314
❑ 95FinRef-314
❑ 95FleUpd-125
❑ 95Top-358
❑ 96ColCho-494
❑ 96ColChoGS-494
❑ 96ColChoSS-494
❑ 96CubFle-3
❑ 96Don-319
❑ 96DonPreP-319
❑ 96EmoXL-152
❑ 96Fla-213
❑ 96Fle-314
❑ 96FleTif-314
❑ 96LeaSigA-40
❑ 96LeaSigAG-40
❑ 96LeaSigAS-40
❑ 96MetUni-138
❑ 96MetUniP-138
❑ 96Pac-28
❑ 96PacPri-P8
❑ 96PacPriG-P8
❑ 96Sco-217
❑ 96StaClu-252
❑ 96StaCluMOP-252
❑ 96Top-146
❑ 96TopGal-88
❑ 96TopGalPPI-88
❑ 96Ult-164
❑ 96UltGolM-164

❑ 96UppDec-299
❑ 97ColCho-67
❑ 97UppDec-327
❑ 98Pac-281
❑ 98PacOnl-266
❑ 98PacOnlR-266
❑ 98PacOnlWC-266
❑ 98PacPlaB-281
❑ 98PacRedT-281
❑ 98PacSil-281
❑ 98UppDec-677
❑ 99PacCroC-104
❑ 99PacCroCPB-104
Castillo, Humberto
❑ 95LinVen-259
Castillo, Jeff
❑ 88GreFalDTI-8
Castillo, Jose
❑ 98WesMicWM-5
Castillo, Juan 80's Minor Leaguer
❑ 80UtiBluJT-13
Castillo, Juan Brayas
❑ 80BurBeeT-22
❑ 81BurBeeT-20
❑ 83ElPasDT-10
❑ 84ElPasDT-16
❑ 85VanCanC-205
❑ 86BrePol-3
❑ 86FleUpd-22
❑ 87BrePol-3
❑ 87Don-249
❑ 87FleUpd-18
❑ 87FleUpdG-18
❑ 87TopTra-20T
❑ 87TopTraT-20T
❑ 88BrePol-3
❑ 88BreTeal-7
❑ 88Don-363
❑ 88Fle-159
❑ 88FleGlo-159
❑ 88OPC-362
❑ 88Sco-429
❑ 88ScoGlo-429
❑ 88StaLinBre-4
❑ 88Top-362
❑ 88TopBig-117
❑ 88TopClo-19
❑ 88TopTif-362
❑ 89Don-530
❑ 89Top-538
❑ 89TopBig-9
❑ 89TopTif-538
❑ 89UppDec-522
❑ 90ColSprSSP-41
❑ 90ProAAAF-222
❑ 91DenZepLD-132
❑ 91DenZepP-129
❑ 91LinDriAAA-132
❑ 94BreMilB-111
Castillo, Juan F.
❑ 90PitMetP-20
❑ 91ColMetPI-14
❑ 91ColMetPPI-3
❑ 91SouAtlLAGP-SAL13
❑ 92St.LucMCB-13
❑ 93BinMetF-2326
❑ 93Bow-538
❑ 93LinVenB-15
❑ 94BinMetF-697
❑ 94VenLinU-17
❑ 95ColCho-17
❑ 95ColChoGS-17
❑ 95ColChoSS-17
❑ 95LinVen-99
❑ 95SigRoo-12
❑ 95SigRooSig-12
❑ 95StaClu-389
❑ 95StaCluMOP-389
❑ 95StaCluSTWS-389
❑ 95UppDec-119
❑ 95UppDecED-119
❑ 95UppDecEDG-119
❑ 96-97LinVen-24
❑ 96TulDriTI-5
Castillo, Luis Antonio
❑ 95KanCouCLTI-3
❑ 95KanCouCTI-4
❑ 96BesAutS-19
❑ 96BesAutSA-12
❑ 96Bow-189
❑ 96BowBes-154
❑ 96BowBesAR-154
❑ 96BowBesMI-2
❑ 96BowBesMIAR-2
❑ 96BowBesMIR-2
❑ 96BowBesR-154
❑ 96BowFoi-189
❑ 96PorSeaDB-10
❑ 97Bow-150
❑ 97BowBes-138
❑ 97BowBesAR-138
❑ 97BowBesR-138
❑ 97BowCerBlaIA-CA13
❑ 97BowCerBluIA-CA13
❑ 97BowCerGolIA-CA13
❑ 97BowInt-150
❑ 97Cir-358
❑ 97CirRav-358
❑ 97ColCho-26
❑ 97ColChoT-FM1
❑ 97Don-316
❑ 97DonGolPP-316
❑ 97DonLim-21
❑ 97DonLimE-21
❑ 97DonLimENG-21
❑ 97DonPre-137
❑ 97DonPreCttC-137
❑ 97DonRatR-18
❑ 97DonSigA-17
❑ 97DonSigAC-23
❑ 97DonSigAM-23
❑ 97DonSilPP-316
❑ 97Fin-46
❑ 97FinRef-46
❑ 97Fle-326
❑ 97FleTif-326
❑ 97Lea-182
❑ 97LeaFraM-182
❑ 97LeaFraMDC-182
❑ 97MarPac-7
❑ 97Pac-298
❑ 97PacLigB-298
❑ 97PacSil-298
❑ 97Pin-160
❑ 97PinArtP-PP160
❑ 97PinMusC-160
❑ 97PinPrePla-160
❑ 97Sco-273
❑ 97ScoArtPWB-273
❑ 97ScoShoS-273
❑ 97ScoShoSAP-273
❑ 97SP-12
❑ 97StaClu-119
❑ 97StaCluM-M7
❑ 97StaCluMOP-119
❑ 97StaCluMOP-M7
❑ 97Top-267
❑ 97TopChr-95
❑ 97TopChrR-95
❑ 97TopGal-143
❑ 97TopGalPPI-143
❑ 97UD3-44
❑ 97UD3GenNex-GN3
❑ 97Ult-194
❑ 97UltGolME-194
❑ 97UltPlaME-194
❑ 97UppDec-223
❑ 98ChaKniQ-7
❑ 98Don-202
❑ 98DonColL-335
❑ 98DonColP-667
❑ 98DonGolPP-202
❑ 98DonPre-117
❑ 98DonPreSeat-117
❑ 98DonPriCL-335
❑ 98DonPriCP-667
❑ 98DonSilPP-202
❑ 98Lea-136
❑ 98LeaFraDA-136
❑ 98LeaFraF-136
❑ 98LeaFraM-136
❑ 98LeaFraM-136
❑ 98LeaFraMDC-136
❑ 98LeaFraMDC-136
❑ 98LeaFraMS-136
❑ 98LeaFraMZ2-136
❑ 98PorSeaD5AQ-4
❑ 98ScoRT-67
❑ 98Stu-197
❑ 98StuGPP-197
❑ 98StuSPP-197
❑ 99PacOme-96
❑ 99PacOmeC-96
❑ 99PacOmeG-96
❑ 99PacOmePB-96
Castillo, Luis T.
❑ 82WauTimF-16
❑ 87StoPorP-17
❑ 88ElPasDB-8
Castillo, Manny (Esteban M.)
❑ 76ArkTraT-2
❑ 78SprRedWK-9
❑ 80OmaRoyP-5
❑ 81OmaRoyT-15
❑ 81Top-66
❑ 82MarPos-9
❑ 83Don-253
❑ 83Fle-474
❑ 83Top-258
❑ 84Fle-607
❑ 84Nes792-562
❑ 84SyrChiT-24
❑ 84Top-562
❑ 84TopTif-562
Castillo, Marcos
❑ 98VerBeaDM-4
Castillo, Marino
❑ 93CliGiaC-6
❑ 93CliGiaF-2481
❑ 94SanJosGC-3
❑ 94SanJosGF-2808
Castillo, Marty (Martin H.)
❑ 80EvaTriT-19
❑ 81EvaTriT-11
❑ 82EvaTriT-11
❑ 82Fle-265
❑ 82Top-261
❑ 83EvaTriT-11
❑ 84Don-247
❑ 84Nes792-303
❑ 84TigTeal-10
❑ 84TigWavP-10
❑ 84Top-303
❑ 84TopTif-303
❑ 85Don-394
❑ 85Fle-5
❑ 85TigCaiD-5
❑ 85TigWen-6
❑ 85Top-461
❑ 85TopTif-461
❑ 86Top-788
❑ 86TopTif-788
❑ 89PacSenL-88
❑ 89TopSenL-10
❑ 90EliSenL-66
❑ 91PacSenL-2
Castillo, Neldy
❑ 76VenLeaS-105
Castillo, Roberto
❑ 81Fle-137
❑ 82Don-236
❑ 82Fle-2
❑ 83Don-102
❑ 90QuaCitAGS-8
❑ 93LinVenB-176
❑ 94VenLinU-190
❑ 95LinVen-139
Castillo, Tomas
❑ 80UtiBluJT-12
Castillo, Tony
❑ 96ColCho-749
❑ 96ColChoGS-749
❑ 96ColChoSS-749
❑ 96FleTif-269
❑ 96LeaSigEA-27
❑ 97PacPriGotD-GD29
❑ 98PacOnl-166
❑ 98PacOnlR-166
❑ 98PacOnlWC-166
Castillo, Tony (Anthony)
❑ 79HawIslC-27
❑ 79HawIslT-24
❑ 80HawIslT-21
❑ 81HawIslT-6
❑ 85KinBluJT-3
Castillo, Tony (Antonio Jose)
❑ 85IowCubT-1
❑ 87DunBluJP-934
❑ 88DunBluJS-2
❑ 89Bow-244
❑ 89BowTif-244
❑ 89DonRoo-12
❑ 90BraDubP-4
❑ 90Don-592
❑ 90OPC-620
❑ 90Top-620
❑ 90TopTif-620
❑ 90UppDec-551
❑ 91Fle-685
❑ 91LinDriAAA-428
❑ 91OPC-353
❑ 91RicBraBC-7
❑ 91RicBraLD-428
❑ 91RicBraP-2560
❑ 91RicBraTI-6
❑ 91Sco-582
❑ 91Top-353
❑ 91TopDesS-353
❑ 91TopMic-353
❑ 91TopTif-353
❑ 91UppDec-458
❑ 92Don-739
❑ 92Fle-499
❑ 92Sco-682
❑ 92TolMudHF-1033
❑ 92TolMudHS-580
❑ 93FleFinE-288
❑ 93LinVenB-2
❑ 94BluJayUSPC-4D
❑ 94BluJayUSPC-12S
❑ 94Don-601
❑ 94Fle-327
❑ 94Pac-637
❑ 94Sco-177
❑ 94ScoGolR-177
❑ 94StaClu-470
❑ 94StaCluFDI-470
❑ 94StaCluGR-470
❑ 94StaCluMOP-470
❑ 94StaCluT-167
❑ 94StaCluTFDI-167
❑ 94VenLinU-127
❑ 95BluJayOH-5
❑ 95Don-235
❑ 95DonPreP-235
❑ 95Fla-96
❑ 95Fle-90
❑ 95LinVen-185
❑ 95LinVen-273
❑ 95Pac-440
❑ 95Sco-219
❑ 95ScoGolR-219
❑ 95ScoPlaTS-219
❑ 96-97LinVen-50
❑ 96BluJayOH-4
❑ 96Don-347
❑ 96DonPreP-347
❑ 96Fle-269
❑ 96Pac-448
❑ 96Top-109
❑ 96Ult-144
❑ 96UltGolM-144
❑ 97WhiSoxTI-49
❑ 98Pac-53
❑ 98PacPlaB-53
❑ 98PacRedT-53
❑ 98PacSil-53
Castillo, William
❑ 76VenLeaS-27
Castillo, Wilson
❑ 98GreFalDG-5
Castino, John A.
❑ 77OrlTwiT-4
❑ 78OrlTwiT-2
❑ 79TwiFriP-3
❑ 80OPC-76
❑ 80Top-137
❑ 80TwiPos-3
❑ 81AllGamPI-30
❑ 81Don-488
❑ 81Dra-29
❑ 81Fle-554
❑ 81FleStiC-112
❑ 81OPC-304
❑ 81Squ-29
❑ 81Top-304
❑ 81TopScr-33
❑ 81TopSti-99
❑ 81TwiPos-5
❑ 82Don-256
❑ 82Fle-549
❑ 82FleSta-230
❑ 82Kel-29
❑ 82OPC-73
❑ 82Top-396
❑ 82Top-644
❑ 82TopSti-209
❑ 82TwiPos-4
❑ 83Don-303
❑ 83Fle-609
❑ 83OPC-93
❑ 83Top-93
❑ 83TopSti-89
❑ 83TwiTeal-1
❑ 84AllGamPI-121
❑ 84Don-4
❑ 84Don-4A
❑ 84Don-120
❑ 84DonActAS-7
❑ 84Fle-560
❑ 84MinTwiP-6
❑ 84Nes792-237
❑ 84OPC-237
❑ 84Top-237
❑ 84TopSti-307
❑ 84TopTif-237
❑ 84TwiTeal-1
❑ 85OPC-298
❑ 85Top-452
❑ 85TopMin-452
❑ 85TopTif-452
Castle, Don (Donald Hardy)
❑ 74SpoIndC-35
❑ 77WesHavYT-4
❑ 93RanKee-99
Castleberry, Kevin
❑ 88CapCodPPaLP-111
❑ 88OklSoo-8
❑ 89OklSoo-7
❑ 90DurBulTI-6
❑ 91MiaMirC-18
❑ 91MiaMirP-412
❑ 92BirBarF-2589
❑ 92SarWhiSCB-8
❑ 93El PasDF-2954
❑ 97OklCit8-10
Castleman, Clydell
❑ 36GouBWR-6
❑ 36GouWidPPR-A14
❑ 36GouWidPPR-A15
❑ 36WorWidGV-36
❑ 72TCMthe3-7
❑ 79DiaGre-47
Castleman, Foster E.
❑ 55GiaGolS-27
❑ 56BalOriP-10
❑ 56Top-271
❑ 57Top-237
❑ 58Top-416
❑ 79TCM50-225
❑ 91OriCro-71
Castleton, Roy
❑ 09ObaT21-80
❑ 09ObaT21-346
❑ 11Zee-113
❑ 12HomRunKE-84
❑ 12ObaPreT-95
❑ 12Zee-144
Castner, Rodger
❑ 87WatPirP-2
❑ 88WatPirP-4
Caston, Bernard
❑ 98St.PauSTI-1
Castor, John
❑ 91OklStaC-4
Castri, Andrea
❑ 98OneYanG-8
Castro, Al
❑ 97EugEmeB-22
❑ 98EugEme-6
Castro, Antionio
❑ 85MexCitTT-24
❑ 93CedRapKC-2
❑ 93CedRapKF-1744
❑ 96KanCouCTI-4
❑ 97BreCouMB-6
Castro, Bill
❑ 76OPC-293
❑ 76Top-293
❑ 77Top-528
❑ 78Top-448
❑ 79Top-133
❑ 80BreTeal-5
❑ 80Top-303
❑ 81Don-578
❑ 81Fle-517
❑ 81Top-271
❑ 82TacTigT-4
❑ 83Fle-109
❑ 83RoyPos-7
❑ 92BrePol-30
❑ 92YanWIZ8-28
❑ 94BreMilB-112
Castro, Dennis
❑ 96BreCouMB-10
Castro, Earnest
❑ 89WauTimGS-3
Castro, Edgar
❑ 82MiaMarT-15
❑ 88BlaYNPRWL-101
❑ 89BlaYNPRWL-109
Castro, Francisco
❑ 94GreFalDSP-8
Castro, Frank
❑ 85BeaGolGT-15
❑ 86BeaGolGP-5
Castro, Genaro
❑ 86LitFalMP-5
Castro, Guillermo
❑ 82DayBeaAT-1
❑ 83DayBeaAT-5
Castro, Jose
❑ 80CarMudF-2
❑ 81OklCit8T-24
❑ 82EdmTraT-2
❑ 85BufBisT-8
❑ 86SyrChiP-7
❑ 87SyrChiP-1945
❑ 87SyrChiT-12
❑ 88OmaRoyC-24
❑ 88OmaRoyP-1509
❑ 89OmaRoyC-14
❑ 89OmaRoyP-1731
❑ 90CMC-73
❑ 90IndIndC-23
❑ 90IndIndP-287
❑ 90JamExpP-29
❑ 90ProAAAF-570
❑ 91RocExpC-13
❑ 91RocExpP-2063
❑ 92EriSaiF-1643
❑ 93KanCouCC-27
❑ 93KanCouCF-932
❑ 93KanCouCTI-2
❑ 94PorSeaDF-693
❑ 94PorSeaDTI-5
❑ 95BreCouMF-263
❑ 96BreCouMB-2
❑ 97BreCouMB-7
❑ 97ModA'sG-5
❑ 98ModA'sG-7
Castro, Juan
❑ 91GreFalDSP-26
❑ 92BakDodCLC-6
❑ 93SanAntMF-3010
❑ 94SanAntMF-2475
❑ 95Exc-209
❑ 95WesMicWTI-4
❑ 96ColCho-21
❑ 96Fle-429
❑ 96FleTif-429
❑ 96Pac-113
❑ 97AlbDukUG-2
❑ 97DodMot-18
❑ 97DodPol-5
❑ 97Pac-327
❑ 97PacLigB-327
❑ 97PacSil-327
❑ 98DodMot-18
❑ 98DodPol-2
❑ 98PacInvGems-168
❑ 98PacOnl-363
❑ 98PacOnlR-363
❑ 98PacOnlWC-363
❑ 98PorRocG-6
❑ 99DodPol-5
Castro, Liliano
❑ 87FayGenP-21
❑ 88FayGenP-1101
Castro, Martires
❑ 98SavSanGM-7
Castro, Nelson
❑ 90KisDodD-6
❑ 91GreFalDSP-4
❑ 92BakDodCLC-7
❑ 93BakDodCLC-3
❑ 94BakDodC-7
❑ 94SanAntMF-2461
❑ 95SanAntMTI-27
❑ 97BoiHawG-3
❑ 98LakElsSG-3
Castro, Pablo
❑ 88St.CatBJP-2012
Castro, Rafael
❑ 98MarPhiG-7
Castro, Ramon
❑ 94ClaUpdCotC-CC15
❑ 94SigRooDP-17
❑ 94SigRooDPS-17
❑ 94StaCluDP-21
❑ 94StaCluDPFDI-21
❑ 95AubAstTI-30
❑ 95SelSurS-SS6
❑ 95SPML-66
❑ 95StaClu-115
❑ 95StaCluFDI-115
❑ 95StaCluMOP-115
❑ 95StaCluSTWS-115
❑ 95Top-313
❑ 95UppDecML-198

❑ 95UppDecMLFS-198
❑ 96BesAutS-20
❑ 96Bow-115
❑ 96BowFoi-115
❑ 96Exc-170
❑ 96MidLeaAB-26
❑ 96QuaCitRB-11
❑ 97FloStaLTPB-14
❑ 97KisCob-6
❑ 98BesAutSS-8
❑ 98JacGenM-4
❑ 98TexLeaTPG-5

Castro, Ruben
❑ 94EliTwiC-4
❑ 94EliTwiF-3738

Castro, Tony
❑ 91EugEmeC-1
❑ 91EugEmeP-3737

Cat, Al E
❑ 98ChaAllCM-31

Cat, Rally
❑ 96MicBatCB-30

Catalanotto, Frank
❑ 93BriTigC-5
❑ 93BriTigF-3657
❑ 94FayGenC-5
❑ 94FayGenF-2152
❑ 94SouAtlLAF-SAL11
❑ 95JacSunTI-3
❑ 95UppDecML-157
❑ 95UppDecMLFS-157
❑ 96DouAllB-30
❑ 96JacSunB-7
❑ 96SigRooOJ-7
❑ 96SigRooOJS-7
❑ 97TolMudHB-9
❑ 98BesAutSS-9
❑ 98ColCho-93
❑ 98Don-300
❑ 98DonGolPP-300
❑ 98DonSilPP-300
❑ 98Fle-212
❑ 98LeaRS-217
❑ 98LeaRSLHolo-217
❑ 98LeaRSLong-217
❑ 98LeaRTrue-217
❑ 98PacOmeRS-2
❑ 98PacOmeRST1-2
❑ 98PacOnl-267
❑ 98PacOnlR-267
❑ 98PacOnlWC-267
❑ 98PacPar-45
❑ 98PacParC-45
❑ 98PacParG-45
❑ 98PacParHS-45
❑ 98PacParPB-45
❑ 98PacParR-45
❑ 98PinPlu-66
❑ 98ScoRT-234
❑ 98ScoRTSS-PP127
❑ 98ScoRTSSAP-PP127
❑ 98ScoRTSSAP1-PP127
❑ 98SpoIll-168
❑ 98SpoIllEE-168
❑ 98SpoIllFE-168
❑ 98Stu-103
❑ 98StuGPP-103
❑ 98StuSPP-103
❑ 98Ult-293
❑ 98UltGolM-293
❑ 98UltMas-293
❑ 98UltPlaM-293
❑ 98UppDec-372
❑ 99Fle-378
❑ 99FleSta9-378
❑ 99FleWarT-378
❑ 99Pac-159
❑ 99PacPlaB-159
❑ 99PacRed-159

Cataline, Dan
❑ 81QuaCitCT-16
❑ 83VerBeaDT-24

Cater, Danny Anderson
❑ 64PhiPhiB-9
❑ 64Top-482
❑ 65OPC-253
❑ 65Top-253
❑ 66Top-398
❑ 67CokCapAt-17
❑ 67DexPre-45
❑ 67OPC-157
❑ 67Top-157
❑ 68Top-535
❑ 69A'sJacitB-4
❑ 69MilBra-55
❑ 69MLBOffS-84
❑ 69OPC-1
❑ 69OPC-44
❑ 69Top-1
❑ 69Top-44
❑ 69Top-556
❑ 69TopSta-213
❑ 69TopTeaP-21
❑ 69TraSta-12
❑ 70MLBOffS-243
❑ 70OPC-437
❑ 70Top-437
❑ 70YanCliDP-5
❑ 70YanPhoS-7
❑ 71Kel-30
❑ 71MilDud-3
❑ 71MLBOffS-485
❑ 71OPC-358
❑ 71Top-358
❑ 71TopCoi-14
❑ 71YanArcO-4
❑ 71YanCliDP-3
❑ 72MilBra-71
❑ 72RedSoxTI-3
❑ 72Top-676
❑ 72YanTeaI-1
❑ 73LinPor-16
❑ 73OPC-317
❑ 73Top-317
❑ 74OPC-543
❑ 74Top-543
❑ 75OPC-645
❑ 75St.LouCP-4
❑ 75Top-645
❑ 75TopMin-645
❑ 92YanWIZ7-31

Cater, Michael
❑ 92StoPorC-19

Cates, Tim
❑ 83MemChiT-11
❑ 85IndIndTI-8

Cathcart, Gary
❑ 86Ft.LauYP-5
❑ 87AlbYanP-9
❑ 88AlbYanP-1335

Cather, Mike
❑ 94ChaRanF-2491
❑ 95TulDriTI-3
❑ 96GreBraB-9
❑ 96GreBraTI-24
❑ 97GreBraG-6
❑ 98Don-264
❑ 98DonGolPP-264
❑ 98DonSilPP-264
❑ 98Fle-88
❑ 98PacOnl-56
❑ 98PacOnlR-56
❑ 98PacOnlWC-56

Cather, Ted (Theodore P.)
❑ 15CraJacE-145
❑ 21Zee-25
❑ 23Zee-28
❑ 24Zee-23
❑ 25Zee-21
❑ 80BraTCM1-27

Cathey, Joseph
❑ 97AubDouTI-20
❑ 98QuaCitRBG-2

Catlett, David
❑ 93IdaFalBF-4038
❑ 93IdaFalBSP-29
❑ 94Bow-666
❑ 94IdaFalBF-3591
❑ 94IdaFalBSP-16
❑ 94MacBraC-2
❑ 94MacBraF-2211
❑ 96RocCubTI-5
❑ 97RocCub-13

Cato, Keefe
❑ 81WatRedT-2
❑ 82WatRedT-3
❑ 83WatRedT-1
❑ 84WicAerRD-14
❑ 85LasVegSC-118
❑ 85Top-367
❑ 85TopTif-367
❑ 86OmaRoyP-4

Cato, Wayne
❑ 76CedRapGT-9
❑ 79CedRapGT-15
❑ 80CliGiaT-26

Catterson, Tom (Thomas H.)
❑ 90DodTar-910

Caudill, Bill
❑ 76ArkTraT-3
❑ 78SSP270-262
❑ 80Top-103
❑ 81Don-586
❑ 81Fle-306
❑ 81OPC-346
❑ 81Top-574
❑ 81TopSti-152
❑ 82Don-426
❑ 82Fle-590
❑ 82MarPos-10
❑ 82Top-303
❑ 82TopTra-18T
❑ 83AllGamPI-74
❑ 83Don-302
❑ 83Fle-475
❑ 83FleSta-33
❑ 83FleSti-179
❑ 83MarNal-1
❑ 83OPC-78
❑ 83Top-78
❑ 83TopSti-118
❑ 84A'sMot-12
❑ 84AllGamPI-167
❑ 84Don-118
❑ 84Fle-608
❑ 84FleSti-76
❑ 84FleUpd-24
❑ 84Nes792-769
❑ 84OPC-299
❑ 84Top-769
❑ 84TopSti-345
❑ 84TopTif-769
❑ 84TopTra-23T
❑ 84TopTraT-23T
❑ 85BluJayCC-2
❑ 85BluJayFS-7
❑ 85BluJayPLP-2
❑ 85Don-96
❑ 85Fle-419
❑ 85FleStaS-100
❑ 85FleUpd-23
❑ 85Lea-154
❑ 85OPC-275
❑ 85OPCPos-23
❑ 85Top-685
❑ 85TopMin-685
❑ 85TopSti-322
❑ 85TopTif-685
❑ 85TopTifT-19T
❑ 85TopTra-19T
❑ 86BluJayAF-5
❑ 86BluJayFS-5
❑ 86Don-317
❑ 86Fle-55
❑ 86GenMilB-3C
❑ 86OPC-207
❑ 86Top-435
❑ 86TopTif-435
❑ 87A'sMot-24
❑ 87Fle-221
❑ 87FleGlo-221
❑ 87OPC-156
❑ 87Top-733
❑ 87TopTif-733

Caughey, Wayne
❑ 77OrlTwiT-5
❑ 77TacTwiDQ-2A
❑ 79TolMudHT-11
❑ 80AlbDukTc-18
❑ 81AlbDukTc-14
❑ 82PorBeaT-12

Cauley, Chris
❑ 88TamTarS-4
❑ 89SarWhiSS-4

Caulfield, Tom
❑ 83EriCarT-23

Causey, Red (Cecil)
❑ 20GasAmeMBD-28
❑ 21E121So1-9
❑ 21E121So8-10
❑ 21KoBreWSI-7
❑ 22AmeCarE122-10
❑ 23W501-65

Causey, Wayne (James Wayne)
❑ 56BalOriP-2
❑ 61A'sTeal-3
❑ 61AthJayP-5
❑ 62SalPlaC-100
❑ 62ShiPlaC-100
❑ 62Top-496
❑ 63AthJayP-3
❑ 63Top-539
❑ 64A's-3
❑ 64AthJayP-1
❑ 64Top-75
❑ 64TopCoi-102
❑ 64TopCoi-161A
❑ 64TopCoi-161B
❑ 64TopGia-45
❑ 64TopSta-87
❑ 64TopStaU-14
❑ 64TopTatl-29
❑ 64TopVen-75
❑ 65AthJayP-2
❑ 65Top-425
❑ 65TopEmbl-21
❑ 65TopTral-8
❑ 66Top-366
❑ 66TopVen-366
❑ 67CokCapWS-8
❑ 67Top-286
❑ 68Top-522
❑ 69OPC-33
❑ 69Top-33
❑ 78TCM60I-8
❑ 91OriCro-72
❑ 97BalOriP-8

Causion, Bill
❑ 58JetPos-5

Cavalier, Kevin
❑ 87JamExpP-2563
❑ 88WesPalBES-5

Cavalli, Brian
❑ 90OklSoo-2
❑ 92OklStaC-3
❑ 93BoiHawC-6
❑ 93BoiHawF-3919

Cavallo, Gary
❑ 74SacSolC-51

Cavallo, Pablo
❑ 77NewCoPT-6
❑ 78NewWayCT-6

Cavanagh, Andy
❑ 98HelBreM-9

Cavanagh, Michael
❑ 92EveGiaC-21
❑ 92EveGiaF-1692
❑ 93CliGiaC-7
❑ 93CliGiaF-2491
❑ 94CliLumC-7
❑ 94CliLumF-1982

Cavanaugh, Andrew
❑ 97HelBreB-7

Cavanaugh, Marty
❑ 14B18B-13A
❑ 14B18B-13B
❑ 14B18B-13C

Cavarretta, Phil
❑ 34BatR31-101
❑ 35DiaMatCS3T1-30
❑ 36CubTeal-3
❑ 36DiaMatCS3T2-3
❑ 36GouWidPPR-A16
❑ 36OveCanR-6
❑ 36R31PasP-29
❑ 36R31PasP-31
❑ 36SandSW-6
❑ 36WorWidGV-54
❑ 38BasTabP-3
❑ 39CubTeal-2
❑ 39ExhSal-7
❑ 41CubTeal-1
❑ 41DouPlaR-103
❑ 42CubTeal-2
❑ 43CubTeal-4
❑ 44CubTeal-3
❑ 46SpoExcW-1-1A
❑ 47PM1StaP1-29
❑ 47TipTop-105
❑ 48KelPep*-BB1
❑ 49Bow-6
❑ 49EurSta-53
❑ 49Lea-168
❑ 50AmeNut&CCP-3
❑ 50Bow-195
❑ 51Bow-138
❑ 51R42SmaS-13
❑ 52Bow-126
❑ 52StaCalL-80F
❑ 52StaCalS-92A
❑ 52TipTop-6
❑ 52Top-295
❑ 53BowC-30
❑ 54Top-55
❑ 55Bow-282
❑ 62TigPosCF-5
❑ 74LauAllG-44
❑ 76ChiGre-4
❑ 76SSP-617
❑ 76TayBow4-41
❑ 81DiaStaCD-111
❑ 83TCMPla1943-35
❑ 83TopRep5-295
❑ 84CubBriPC-11C
❑ 84CubUno-3
❑ 89PacLegI-131
❑ 91TopArc1-295
❑ 92CubOldS-5
❑ 94TopArc1-55
❑ 94TopArc1G-55
❑ 94UppDecAH-46
❑ 94UppDecAH1-46

Cavazzoni, Ken
❑ 91PriRedC-5
❑ 91PriRedP-3519

Caveney, Ike (James C.)
❑ 19Zee-84
❑ 20Zee-103
❑ 21Exh-22
❑ 21Nei-116
❑ 21Zee-115
❑ 22E120-168
❑ 22W573-17
❑ 27Zee-48
❑ 28Zee-69
❑ 29Zee-125
❑ 30Zee-137
❑ 31Zee-99
❑ 32Zee-95
❑ 33Zee-104

Cavers, Mike
❑ 89FreKeyS-2
❑ 90HagSunB-25
❑ 90HagSunP-1404
❑ 90HagSunS-5

Cawhorn, Gerald
❑ 93WatIndC-3
❑ 93WatIndF-3567
❑ 94ColRedC-5
❑ 94ColRedF-448
❑ 94SouAtlLAF-SAL6
❑ 95KinIndTI-6
❑ 96KenIndB-4

Cayson, Tony
❑ 87BelMarL-3
❑ 87BelMarTI-20
❑ 89BelMarL-25

Cebuhar, John
❑ 88HamRedP-1721
❑ 89HamRedS-8

Ceccarelli, Art
❑ 55A'sRodM-9
❑ 55A'sTeal-4
❑ 56BalOriP-11
❑ 58Top-191
❑ 59Top-226
❑ 60Top-156
❑ 60TopVen-156
❑ 76A'sRodMC-6
❑ 91OriCro-73

Cecchetti, George
❑ 80WatIndT-20
❑ 81ChaLooT-14
❑ 82ChaLooT-14
❑ 83BufBisT-22
❑ 84BufBisT-2
❑ 85WatIndT-20
❑ 86MaiGuiP-3

Cecchini, Jim
❑ 86JacExpT-3

Cecena, Jose
❑ 86ReaPhiP-5
❑ 88DonRoo-6
❑ 88FleUpd-62
❑ 88FleUpdG-62
❑ 88RanMot-12
❑ 88TopTra-26T
❑ 88TopTraT-26T
❑ 89Fle-516
❑ 89FleGlo-516
❑ 89ScoHot1R-35
❑ 89Top-683
❑ 89TopTif-683
❑ 89UppDec-560
❑ 93CarMudF-2045
❑ 93CarMudTI-15
❑ 93RanKee-100

Cecere, Mike
❑ 93EveGiaC-6
❑ 93EveGiaF-3771

Ceci, Sam
❑ 74TacTwiC-15
❑ 76SpoIndC-3

Cecil, Rex
❑ 47CenFlo-4
❑ 49RemBre-3

Cecil, Timothy
❑ 90ChaWheB-12
❑ 90ChaWheP-2233
❑ 90CMC-708
❑ 91ChaWheC-1
❑ 91ChaWheP-2878
❑ 91Cla/Bes-262

Cedarblad, Brett
❑ 93AusFut-45

Cedarburg, John
❑ 91MisStaB-54

Cedeno, Andujar
❑ 89AshTouP-952
❑ 90Bes-72
❑ 90Bow-77
❑ 90BowTif-77
❑ 90CMC-811
❑ 90ColMudB-3
❑ 90ColMudP-1351
❑ 90ColMudS-7
❑ 90ProAaA-58
❑ 91Bow-563
❑ 91Cla1-T43
❑ 91ClaGam-200
❑ 91Fle-502
❑ 91LeaGolR-BC20
❑ 91LinDriAAA-606
❑ 91MajLeaCP-45
❑ 91OPC-646
❑ 91Sco-753
❑ 91ScoRoo-40
❑ 91StaClu-476
❑ 91StuPre-12
❑ 91Top-646
❑ 91TopDeb90-28
❑ 91TopDesS-646
❑ 91TopMic-646
❑ 91TopTif-646
❑ 91TucTorLD-606
❑ 91TucTorP-2218
❑ 91Ult-135
❑ 91UppDec-23
❑ 92AstMot-9
❑ 92Bow-9
❑ 92Cla1-T23
❑ 92Don-549
❑ 92Fle-430
❑ 92Lea-341
❑ 92LeaBlaG-341
❑ 92OPC-288
❑ 92OPCPre-156
❑ 92PanSti-155
❑ 92Pin-84
❑ 92PinTea2-33
❑ 92ProFS7-224
❑ 92Sco-599
❑ 92Sco100RS-65
❑ 92StaClu-310
❑ 92Stu-34
❑ 92Top-288
❑ 92TopGol-288
❑ 92TopGolW-288
❑ 92TopMic-288
❑ 92TriPla-68
❑ 92TucTorF-494
❑ 92Ult-201
❑ 92Ult-490
❑ 92UppDec-257
❑ 93AstMot-10
❑ 93AstStaC-20
❑ 93Bow-672
❑ 93Don-456
❑ 93Fla-60
❑ 93Fle-433
❑ 93Lea-108
❑ 93LimRocDWB-136
❑ 93LinVenB-300
❑ 93LinVenB-319
❑ 93OPC-129
❑ 93PacBeiA-24
❑ 93PacJugC-24
❑ 93PacSpa-121
❑ 93PanSti-172
❑ 93Pin-32
❑ 93Sco-127
❑ 93SP-31
❑ 93StaClu-207
❑ 93StaCluFDI-207
❑ 93StaCluMOP-207
❑ 93Top-553
❑ 93TopGol-553
❑ 93TopInaM-553
❑ 93TopInaR-553
❑ 93TopMic-553
❑ 93Ult-391

❑ 93UppDec-562
❑ 93UppDecGold-562
❑ 94AstMot-18
❑ 94Bow-558
❑ 94ColC-75
❑ 94ColChoGS-75
❑ 94ColChoSS-75
❑ 94Don-519
❑ 94Fin-97
❑ 94FinRef-97
❑ 94Fla-168
❑ 94Fle-487
❑ 94FleExtB-271
❑ 94Lea-260
❑ 94LeaL-113
❑ 94OPC-10
❑ 94Pac-261
❑ 94PanSti-192
❑ 94Pin-292
❑ 94PinArtP-292
❑ 94PinMusC-292
❑ 94ProMag-58
❑ 94Sco-104
❑ 94ScoGolR-104
❑ 94Sel-308
❑ 94StaClu-138
❑ 94StaCluFDI-138
❑ 94StaCluGR-138
❑ 94StaCluMOP-138
❑ 94Stu-19
❑ 94Top-11
❑ 94TopGol-11
❑ 94TopSpa-11
❑ 94TriPla-24
❑ 94Ult-204
❑ 94UppDec-354
❑ 94UppDecED-354
❑ 94VenLinU-57
❑ 95ColCho-351
❑ 95ColChoGS-351
❑ 95ColChoSS-351
❑ 95Don-530
❑ 95DonPreP-530
❑ 95DonTopotO-339
❑ 95Fin-231
❑ 95FinRef-231
❑ 95Fla-417
❑ 95Fle-455
❑ 95FleUpd-182
❑ 95Lea-373
❑ 95LeaLim-44
❑ 95LinVen-309
❑ 95Pac-183
❑ 95PadCHP-12
❑ 95PadMot-5
❑ 95Pin-366
❑ 95PinArtP-366
❑ 95PinMusC-366
❑ 95Sco-477
❑ 95ScoGolR-477
❑ 95ScoPlaTS-477
❑ 95Sel-229
❑ 95SelArtP-229
❑ 95StaClu-468
❑ 95StaClu-539
❑ 95StaCluMOP-468
❑ 95StaCluMOP-539
❑ 95StaCluSTWS-468
❑ 95StaCluSTWS-539
❑ 95StaCluVR-256
❑ 95StaCluVRMO-256
❑ 95Stu-130
❑ 95Top-464
❑ 95TopCyb-259
❑ 95TopTra-57T
❑ 95Ult-436
❑ 95UltGolM-436
❑ 95UppDec-373
❑ 95UppDecED-373
❑ 95UppDecEDG-373
❑ 95UppDecSE-268
❑ 95UppDecSEG-268
❑ 96ColCho-358
❑ 96ColCho-712
❑ 96ColChoGS-358
❑ 96ColChoGS-712
❑ 96ColChoSS-358
❑ 96ColChoSS-712
❑ 96Don-508
❑ 96DonPreP-508
❑ 96Fla-372
❑ 96Fle-563
❑ 96FleTif-563
❑ 96LeaSigA-41
❑ 96LeaSigAG-41
❑ 96LeaSigAS-41
❑ 96Pac-194
❑ 96PacPri-P60
❑ 96PacPriG-P60
❑ 96PadMot-12
❑ 96ProSta-83
❑ 96Sco-121
❑ 96StaClu-334
❑ 96StaCluMOP-334
❑ 96TigHebN-25
❑ 96Top-29
❑ 96Ult-556
❑ 96UltGolM-556
❑ 96UppDec-448
❑ 97Pin-145
❑ 97PinArtP-PP145
❑ 97PinMusC-145
❑ 97PinPrePla-145

Cedeno, Blas
❑ 91BriTigC-19
❑ 91BriTigP-3596
❑ 92BriTigC-3
❑ 92BriTigF-1401
❑ 93FayGenC-7
❑ 93FayGenF-123
❑ 93LinVenB-173
❑ 94LakTigF-3028
❑ 94TreThuF-2114
❑ 94VenLinU-229
❑ 95JacSunTI-4
❑ 95LinVen-62
❑ 96-97LinVen-121
❑ 96JacSunB-8
❑ 96LakTigB-10

Cedeno, Cesar
❑ 70AstPho-2
❑ 71AstCok-3
❑ 71AstTeal-2
❑ 71OPC-237
❑ 71Top-237
❑ 71TopSup-15
❑ 72AstTeal-3
❑ 72EssCoi-4
❑ 72OPC-65
❑ 72SevTraC-10
❑ 72Top-65
❑ 73Kel2D-13
❑ 73LinPor-80
❑ 73OPC-290
❑ 73SevTraC-14
❑ 73Top-290
❑ 74AstFouTIP-3
❑ 74OPC-200
❑ 74OPC-337
❑ 74Top-200
❑ 74Top-337
❑ 74TopSta-31
❑ 75AstPos-5
❑ 75Hos-17
❑ 75HosTwi-17
❑ 75OPC-590
❑ 75SSP42-26
❑ 75SSPPuzB-7
❑ 75Top-590
❑ 75TopMin-590
❑ 76BlaDis-12
❑ 76BucDis-12
❑ 76CarDis-12
❑ 76CraDis-12
❑ 76DailsID-12
❑ 76Hos-47
❑ 76HosTwi-47
❑ 76HouAstP-5
❑ 76IsaDis-12
❑ 76OPC-460
❑ 76OrbDis-12
❑ 76Raw-1
❑ 76RedBarD-12
❑ 76SafDis-12
❑ 76SSP-63
❑ 76Top-460
❑ 76TowCluD-12
❑ 77AstPho-4
❑ 77BurCheD-7
❑ 77ChiWilD-15
❑ 77DailsID-15
❑ 77DetCaeD-15
❑ 77HolInnD-15
❑ 77Hos-58
❑ 77MSADis-15
❑ 77OPC-131
❑ 77RCColC-16
❑ 77SagDis-15
❑ 77sDis-15
❑ 77Top-90
❑ 77TopCloS-13
❑ 77WenDis-15
❑ 77ZipDis-15
❑ 78AstBurK-18
❑ 78AstPos-6
❑ 78Hos-50
❑ 78OPC-226
❑ 78RCColC-51
❑ 78Top-650
❑ 78WifBalD-16
❑ 79AstPos-5
❑ 79AstTeal-4
❑ 79BasPat-17
❑ 79Hos-91
❑ 79OPC-294
❑ 79Top-570
❑ 80BurKinPHR-25
❑ 80Kel-36
❑ 80OPC-193
❑ 80Top-370
❑ 80TopSup-56
❑ 81AllGamPI-137
❑ 81AstPos-2
❑ 81CokTeaS-62
❑ 81Don-263
❑ 81Dra-20
❑ 81Fle-59
❑ 81FleStiC-35
❑ 81Kel-14
❑ 81MSAMinD-8
❑ 81OPC-190
❑ 81PerCreC-25
❑ 81Top-190
❑ 81TopScr-77
❑ 81TopSti-167
❑ 81TopSti-258
❑ 81TopSupHT-97
❑ 82Don-118
❑ 82Fle-213
❑ 82FleSta-41
❑ 82OnDecD-8
❑ 82OPC-48
❑ 82RedCok-4
❑ 82Top-640
❑ 82TopSti-47
❑ 82TopTra-19T
❑ 83AllGamPI-137
❑ 83Don-43
❑ 83Fle-587
❑ 83FleSta-34
❑ 83FleSti-221
❑ 83OPC-238
❑ 83RedYea-28
❑ 83Top-351
❑ 83Top-475
❑ 83TopFol-5
❑ 83TopSti-231
❑ 84Don-306
❑ 84Fle-465
❑ 84FunFooP-42
❑ 84Nes792-705
❑ 84Nes792-725
❑ 84OPC-191
❑ 84RedEnq-13
❑ 84Top-705
❑ 84Top-725
❑ 84TopSti-54
❑ 84TopTif-705
❑ 84TopTif-725
❑ 85Don-447
❑ 85Fle-531
❑ 85Lea-87
❑ 85OPC-54
❑ 85RedYea-1
❑ 85SubDis-26
❑ 85ThoMcAD-26
❑ 85Top-54
❑ 85TopSti-55
❑ 85TopTif-54
❑ 86AstGreT-6
❑ 86AstMot-11
❑ 86DodCokP-6
❑ 86Don-648
❑ 86Fle-29
❑ 86OPC-224
❑ 86Top-224
❑ 86TopTif-224
❑ 87AstShoSO-1
❑ 87AstShoSPO-5
❑ 87AstShoSTw-21
❑ 87AstShoSTw-26
❑ 87AstShoSTw-27
❑ 89PacSenL-62
❑ 89T/MSenL-20
❑ 89T/MSenL-118
❑ 89TopSenL-69
❑ 90DodTar-120
❑ 90EliSenL-79
❑ 90SweBasG-41
❑ 91KelLey-4
❑ 91LinDri-36
❑ 91PacSenL-40
❑ 91PacSenL-53
❑ 91SweBasG-104
❑ 91UppDecS-15
❑ 92ActPacA-29
❑ 92UppDecS-14
❑ 93QuaCitRBC-26
❑ 93QuaCitRBF-116
❑ 93TedWil-41
❑ 93UppDecAH-29
❑ 94QuaCitRBC-27
❑ 94QuaCitRBF-551
❑ 94UppDecAH-89
❑ 94UppDecAH1-89

Cedeno, Domingo
❑ 89MyrBeaBJP-1456
❑ 90DunBluJS-5
❑ 91KnoBluJLD-352
❑ 91KnoBluJP-1773
❑ 91LinDriAA-352
❑ 92KnoBluJF-2995
❑ 92KnoBluJS-378
❑ 93FleFinE-289
❑ 93Lea-486
❑ 93LimRocDWB-133
❑ 93SyrChiF-1002
❑ 94Don-455
❑ 94ScoRoo-RT105
❑ 94ScoRooGR-RT105
❑ 94SpoRoo-72
❑ 94SpoRooAP-72
❑ 94StaCluT-164
❑ 94StaCluTFDI-164
❑ 94Top-776
❑ 94TopGol-776
❑ 94TopSpa-776
❑ 94Ult-436
❑ 95BluJayOH-6
❑ 95LinVen-309
❑ 95Pac-441
❑ 95Sco-7
❑ 95ScoGolR-7
❑ 95ScoPlaTS-7
❑ 95Top-89
❑ 96BluJayOH-5
❑ 96ColCho-348
❑ 96ColChoGS-348
❑ 96ColChoSS-348
❑ 96Don-134
❑ 96DonPreP-134
❑ 96Fle-270
❑ 96FleTif-270
❑ 96LeaSigA-42
❑ 96LeaSigAG-42
❑ 96LeaSigAS-42
❑ 96Pac-439
❑ 96StaClu-295
❑ 96StaCluMOP-295
❑ 96Ult-427
❑ 96UltGolM-427
❑ 97PacPriGotD-GD30
❑ 97RanDr P-4
❑ 98Fle-93
❑ 98Pac-199
❑ 98PacOnl-729
❑ 98PacOnlR-729
❑ 98PacOnlWC-729
❑ 98PacPlaB-199
❑ 98PacRedT-199
❑ 98PacSil-199
❑ 98UppDec-522

Cedeno, Eduardo
❑ 93AshTouC-4
❑ 93AshTouF-2281
❑ 93AubAstC-4
❑ 93AubAstF-3450
❑ 94EugEmeC-26
❑ 94EugEmeF-3718
❑ 94RocRoyC-7
❑ 94RocRoyF-572
❑ 95SprSulTI-6
❑ 96WilBluRB-12

Cedeno, Jesus
❑ 97WesMicW-8
❑ 98LakTigM-20

Cedeno, Ramon
❑ 88AshTouP-1053
❑ 89OscAstS-4
❑ 90VisOakCLC-68
❑ 90VisOakP-2166

Cedeno, Roger
❑ 92GreFalDSP-19
❑ 93Bow-534
❑ 93ClaFS7-130
❑ 93DodStaC-24
❑ 93LinVenB-218
❑ 93LinVenB-277
❑ 93LinVenB-278
❑ 93SanAntMF-3015
❑ 93SP-272
❑ 94AlbDukF-855
❑ 94Bow-238
❑ 94BowBes-B17
❑ 94BowBesR-B17
❑ 94Cla-142
❑ 94ExcFS7-211
❑ 94UppDecML-25
❑ 94UppDecML-257
❑ 94UppDecMLPotYF-PY9
❑ 94UppDecMLT1PJF-TP1
❑ 94UppDecMLT1PMF-1
❑ 94VenLinU-53
❑ 95ActPacF-23
❑ 95Bow-104
❑ 95BowBes-B54
❑ 95BowBesR-B54
❑ 95Exc-210
❑ 95LinVen-1
❑ 95LinVen-315
❑ 95Sel-155
❑ 95SelArtP-155
❑ 95SelCer-93
❑ 95SelCerMG-93
❑ 95SP-67
❑ 95SPCha-2
❑ 95SPChaDC-2
❑ 95SPSil-67
❑ 95Sum-169
❑ 95SumNthD-169
❑ 95Top-651
❑ 95UppDec-228
❑ 95UppDecED-228
❑ 95UppDecEDG-228
❑ 95UppDecML-13
❑ 95UppDecML-107
❑ 95UppDecMLFS-13
❑ 95UppDecMLFS-107
❑ 95UppDecMLT1PF-7
❑ 95UppDecSE-170
❑ 95UppDecSEG-170
❑ 96-97LinVen-131
❑ 96-97LinVen-287
❑ 96Bow-80
❑ 96BowBes-115
❑ 96BowBesAR-115
❑ 96BowBesR-115
❑ 96BowFoi-80
❑ 96ColCho-12
❑ 96ColChoGS-12
❑ 96ColChoSS-12
❑ 96DodFle-4
❑ 96DodMot-27
❑ 96DodPol-7
❑ 96Don-337
❑ 96DonPreP-337
❑ 96Fin-B283
❑ 96FinRef-B283
❑ 96Fla-289
❑ 96FlePro-2
❑ 96FleUpd-U142
❑ 96FleUpdTC-U142
❑ 96Lea-216
❑ 96LeaPrePB-216
❑ 96LeaPrePG-216
❑ 96LeaPrePS-216
❑ 96LeaSigA-43
❑ 96LeaSigAG-43
❑ 96LeaSigAS-43
❑ 96MetUni-182
❑ 96MetUniP-182
❑ 96PanSti-90
❑ 96Pin-176
❑ 96PinAfi-182
❑ 96PinAfiAP-182
❑ 96Sco-233
❑ 96Spo-124
❑ 96SpoArtP-124
❑ 96StaClu-313
❑ 96StaCluMOP-313
❑ 96Stu-3
❑ 96StuPrePB-3
❑ 96StuPrePG-3
❑ 96StuPrePS-3
❑ 96Top-436
❑ 96TopGal-142
❑ 96TopGalPPI-142
❑ 96Ult-494
❑ 96UltGolM-494
❑ 96UltGolP-3
❑ 96UltGolPGM-3
❑ 96UppDecBCP-BC14
❑ 96UppDecPHE-H54
❑ 96UppDecPreH-H54
❑ 97AlbDukGS-5
❑ 97DodSco-6
❑ 97DodScoPl-6
❑ 97DodScoPr-6
❑ 97Don-74
❑ 97DonGolPP-74
❑ 97DonSilPP-74
❑ 97DonTea-108
❑ 97DonTeaSPE-108
❑ 97Fle-358
❑ 97FleTif-358
❑ 97Pac-328
❑ 97PacLigB-328
❑ 97PacSil-328
❑ 97Pin-46
❑ 97PinArtP-PP46
❑ 97PinMusC-46
❑ 97PinPrePla-46
❑ 97Sco-186
❑ 97ScoArtPWB-186
❑ 97ScoPreS-186
❑ 97ScoShoS-186
❑ 97ScoShoSAP-186
❑ 97StaClu-268
❑ 97StaCluMOP-268
❑ 97Top-126
❑ 97Ult-214
❑ 97UltGolME-214
❑ 97UltPlaME-214
❑ 98DodMot-14
❑ 98DodPol-3
❑ 98DodSco-7
❑ 98DodScoP-7
❑ 98Fle-418
❑ 98Pac-327
❑ 98PacOnl-364
❑ 98PacOnlR-364
❑ 98PacOnlWC-364
❑ 98PacPlaB-327
❑ 98PacRedT-327
❑ 98PacSil-327
❑ 98PinPlu-155
❑ 98PinSna-LAD6
❑ 98Sco-87
❑ 98Top-371
❑ 98TopChr-371
❑ 98TopChrR-371
❑ 98TopDevR-371
❑ 98TopDia-371
❑ 98TopMiniC-371
❑ 98Ult-430
❑ 98UltGolM-430
❑ 98UltMas-430
❑ 98UltPlaM-430
❑ 99Fle-384
❑ 99FleSta9-384
❑ 99FleWarT-384
❑ 99PacCroC-139
❑ 99PacCroCPB-139
❑ 99PacOme-151
❑ 99PacOmeC-151
❑ 99PacOmeG-151
❑ 99PacOmePB-151
❑ 99Top-71
❑ 99TopChr-71
❑ 99TopChrR-71
❑ 99TopMVPP-71
❑ 99UppDec-430
❑ 99UppDecEL1-430
❑ 99UppDecEL2-430

Cedeno, Vinicio
❑ 86MidAngP-4
❑ 87MidAngP-8
❑ 88MidAngGS-4
❑ 89MidAngGS-9

Cederblad, Brett
❑ 91DaiDolF-6
❑ 96TreThuB-8

Celis, Lucio
❑ 76VenLeaS-39
❑ 80VenLeaS-47

Censale, Silvio
❑ 93BatCliCB-6
❑ 93BatCliF-3136
❑ 95PiePhiF-180
❑ 97ReaPhi-10

Centala, Scott
❑ 88CapCodPPaLP-123
❑ 89EugEmeB-7
❑ 90Bes-29
❑ 90CMC-748
❑ 90MemChiB-14

□ 90MemChiP-1001
□ 90MemChiS-4
□ 90StaFS7-83
Centeno, Henry
□ 92AshTouC-3
□ 93LinVenB-146
□ 93QuaCitRBC-4
□ 93QuaCitRBF-107
□ 94OscAstC-5
□ 94OscAstF-1143
□ 95JacGenTI-20
□ 95LinVen-153
□ 96-97LinVen-211
Centeno, Jose
□ 93AshTouC-5
□ 93AshTouF-2268
□ 93LinVenB-256
□ 94VenLinU-30
□ 94VerExpC-6
□ 94VerExpF-3900
□ 95LinVen-22
□ 96-97LinVen-155
□ 96DelShoB-12
□ 96WesPalBEB-5
Centeno, Jose 70s
□ 75CliPilT-24
Cento, Tony
□ 86AppFoxP-6
□ 87PenWhiSP-28
Cepeda, Jose
□ 96Bow-347
□ 96BowFoi-347
□ 96LanLugB-8
□ 96MidLeaAB-36
□ 97WilBluR-4
□ 98WilBluRC-7
Cepeda, Malcom
□ 93EugEmeC-10
□ 94EugEmeC-6
□ 94EugEmeF-3719
□ 96BurBeeTI-15
□ 98BriBluM-6
Cepeda, Octavio
□ 86MacPirP-5
□ 87SalBucP-5
Cepeda, Orlando M.
□ 47Exh-38A
□ 47Exh-38B
□ 47PM1StaP1-30
□ 47PM1StaP1-31
□ 58GiaSFCB-5
□ 58Top-343
□ 59Baz-5
□ 59Top-390
□ 59Top-553
□ 60Baz-10
□ 60GiaJayP-4
□ 60Lea-128
□ 60Top-450
□ 60TopTat-8
□ 61GiaJayP-3
□ 61Pos-144A
□ 61Pos-144B
□ 61SevElev-20
□ 61Top-435
□ 61TopStal-75
□ 62BasPen-1
□ 62Baz-7
□ 62ExhStaB-8
□ 62GiaJayP-3
□ 62Jel-136
□ 62Pos-136
□ 62PosCan-136
□ 62SalPlaC-175
□ 62ShiPlaC-175
□ 62Top-40
□ 62Top-54
□ 62Top-390
□ 62Top-401
□ 62TopBuc-16
□ 62TopStal-195
□ 62TopVen-40
□ 62TopVen-54
□ 63BasMagM-15
□ 63Baz-22
□ 63ExhStaB-12
□ 63Fle-64
□ 63GiaJayP-2
□ 63Jel-101
□ 63Pos-101
□ 63SalMetC-13
□ 63Top-3
□ 63Top-520
□ 63TopStil-10
□ 64GiaJayP-1
□ 64Top-9
□ 64Top-306
□ 64Top-390
□ 64TopCoi-63
□ 64TopCoi-142
□ 64TopGia-55
□ 64TopSta-50
□ 64TopStaU-15
□ 64TopTatI-30
□ 64TopVen-9
□ 64TopVen-306
□ 64WheSta-10
□ 65OldLonC-6
□ 65OPC-4
□ 65Top-4
□ 65Top-360
□ 65TopEmbl-45
□ 65TopTral-9
□ 66OPC-132
□ 66Top-132
□ 66TopVen-132
□ 67OPC-20
□ 67OPCPapl-9
□ 67Top-20
□ 67TopGiaSU-13
□ 67TopPos-9
□ 67TopTesF-5
□ 67TopVen-291
□ 68AtlOilPBCC-12
□ 68Baz-6
□ 68OPC-3
□ 68Top-3
□ 68Top-200
□ 68Top-278
□ 68Top-362
□ 68TopActS-1A
□ 68TopActS-9B
□ 68TopActS-14A
□ 68TopGamI-32
□ 68TopPla-15
□ 68TopPos-12
□ 68TopVen-3
□ 68TopVen-200
□ 68TopVen-278
□ 68TopVen-362
□ 69AtlBraBPPS-6
□ 69MilBra-56
□ 69MLBOffS-113
□ 69MLBPin-38
□ 69Top-385
□ 69TopSta-113
□ 69TopTeaP-18
□ 70AtlBraS-3
□ 70MLBOffS-4
□ 70Top-555
□ 70TopBoo-13
□ 71BazNumT-33
□ 71BazUnn-6
□ 71MilDud-39
□ 71MLBOffS-7
□ 71OPC-605
□ 71Top-605
□ 71TopCoi-61
□ 71TopGreM-26
□ 71TopTat-17
□ 72EssCoi-5
□ 72MilBra-72
□ 72OPC-195
□ 72SevTraC-11
□ 72Top-195
□ 73LinPor-17
□ 73OPC-545
□ 73Top-545
□ 74Kel-24
□ 74OPC-83
□ 74RoyPos-6
□ 74Top-83
□ 74TopSta-132
□ 75OPC-205
□ 75Top-205
□ 75TopMin-205
□ 78AtlCon-5
□ 78TCM60I-50
□ 80GleFalWSBT-26
□ 80GleFalWSCT-25
□ 80VenLeaS-245
□ 81Gia196T-10
□ 82K-M-12
□ 82TCMGreS-33
□ 83MLBPin-21
□ 83TigAlKS-51
□ 84GiaMot-11
□ 84OCoandSI-162
□ 85CirK-24
□ 85TCMHomRC-2
□ 86SpoDecG-48
□ 88PacLegI-94
□ 89SweBasG-8
□ 90PacLeg-65
□ 90SweBasG-28
□ 91KelLey-5
□ 91SweBasG-105
□ 92ActPacA-66
□ 92CarMcD-26
□ 92GiaFanFFB-2
□ 92KodCelD-1
□ 92MDAMVP-5
□ 92MVP-14
□ 92MVP2H-13
□ 92UppDecS-7
□ 93TedWil-87
□ 93UppDecS-7
□ 93UppDecS-22
□ 93UppDecS-28
□ 94TopSpa-L6
□ 94UppDecAH-136
□ 94UppDecAH-215
□ 94UppDecAH1-136
□ 94UppDecAH1-215
□ 99SpollIGotG-58
□ 99SpollIGotGA-17
Cepeda, Rafael
□ 80VenLeaS-237
Cepeda, Wellington
□ 98SouBenSHM-16
Cephas, Ruben
□ 93HelBreF-4108
□ 93HelBreSP-3
Cepicky, Scott
□ 90Bes-173
□ 90MidLeaASGS-7
□ 90SouBenWSB-2
□ 90SouBenWSGS-2
□ 91Cla/Bes-86
□ 91FloStaLAP-FSL28
□ 91SarWhiSC-15
□ 91SarWhiSP-1118
□ 92BirBarF-2590
□ 92BirBarS-80
□ 92Bow-297
□ 92Bow-614
□ 92ClaFS7-30
□ 92ProFS7-44
□ 92SkyAA F-39
□ 92UppDecML-304
□ 93ExcFS7-152
□ 93LinVenB-63
□ 93NasSouF-574
Cerame, Mike
□ 89PulBraP-1903
□ 90PulBraB-29
□ 91PulBraC-30
□ 94OscAstC-29
Ceravolo, Steve
□ 93Sou-6
Cerefin, Mike
□ 85OscAstTI-5
Ceriani, Matt
□ 98HelBreM-10
Cerio, Steve
□ 92SprCarC-25
□ 92SprCarF-871
□ 93St.PetCC-9
□ 93St.PetCF-2629
□ 94St.PetCC-9
□ 94St.PetCF-2597
Cerny, Chris
□ 88BakDodCLC-252
□ 89BoiHawP-1999
Cerny, Mark
□ 89BilMusP-2054
□ 90EriSaiS-2
Cerny, Marty
□ 87PorChaRP-7
□ 88GasRanP-1016
□ 89MiaMirIS-4
□ 89MiaMirIS-3
Cerny, Scott
□ 86SalAngC-86
□ 87QuaCitAP-24
□ 88CalLeaACLC-33
□ 88PalSprACLC-101
□ 88PalSprAP-1440
□ 89MidAngGS-10
□ 90MidAngGS-8
Cerone, Rick (Richard Aldo)
□ 76SSP-516
□ 77OPC-76
□ 77Top-476
□ 78OPC-129
□ 78Top-469
□ 79BluJayBY-5
□ 79OPC-72
□ 79Top-152
□ 80OPC-311
□ 80Top-591
□ 80YanPhoA-3
□ 81AllGamPI-37
□ 81Don-346
□ 81Fle-83
□ 81FleStiC-88
□ 81OPC-335
□ 81Top-335
□ 81TopScr-28
□ 81TopSti-109
□ 81TopSti-248
□ 81TopSupHT-61
□ 82Don-199
□ 82Fle-31
□ 82FleSta-118
□ 82FleSta-238
□ 82OPC-45
□ 82Top-45
□ 82TopSti-218
□ 82YanPhoA-3
□ 83AllGamPI-38
□ 83Don-577
□ 83Fle-376
□ 83FleSta-35
□ 83FleSti-43
□ 83OPC-254
□ 83Top-254
□ 83YanPhoA-5
□ 83YanRoyRD-1
□ 84Don-492
□ 84Fle-121
□ 84Nes792-617
□ 84OPC-228
□ 84Top-617
□ 84TopTif-617
□ 85BraHos-6
□ 85BraPol-5
□ 85Don-274
□ 85Fle-123
□ 85FleUpd-24
□ 85OPC-337
□ 85Top-429
□ 85TopTif-429
□ 85TopTifT-20T
□ 85TopTra-20T
□ 86BluJayGT-8
□ 86BrePol-11
□ 86Don-310
□ 86Fle-511
□ 86FleUpd-23
□ 86OPC-203
□ 86Top-747
□ 86TopTif-747
□ 86TopTra-22T
□ 86TopTraT-22T
□ 87Fle-340
□ 87FleGlo-340
□ 87Top-129
□ 87TopTif-129
□ 87TopTra-21T
□ 87TopTraT-21T
□ 88Don-351
□ 88DonBasB-332
□ 88DonTeaBRS-NEW
□ 88Fle-203
□ 88FleGlo-203
□ 88FleUpd-6
□ 88FleUpdG-6
□ 88PanSti-151
□ 88Sco-486
□ 88ScoGlo-486
□ 88ScoRoo-21T
□ 88ScoRooG-21T
□ 88StaLinY-1
□ 88Top-561
□ 88TopClo-20
□ 88TopTif-561
□ 88TopTra-27T
□ 88TopTraT-27T
□ 89Don-398
□ 89DonBasB-308
□ 89Fle-84
□ 89FleGlo-84
□ 89OPC-96
□ 89Sco-396
□ 89Top-96
□ 89TopBig-119
□ 89TopTif-96
□ 89UppDec-152
□ 90Bow-435
□ 90BowTif-435
□ 90Don-305
□ 90Fle-270
□ 90FleCan-270
□ 90OPC-303
□ 90PubIntS-451
□ 90Sco-139
□ 90ScoRoo-63T
□ 90Top-303
□ 90TopSti-1
□ 90TopTif-303
□ 90TopTra-21T
□ 90TopTraT-21T
□ 90TopTVY-20
□ 90UppDec-405
□ 90YanScoNW-28
□ 91Bow-468
□ 91Fle-660
□ 91FleUpd-101
□ 91Lea-493
□ 91MetColP-26
□ 91MetKah-13
□ 91MetPerPA-11
□ 91OPC-237
□ 91Sco-580
□ 91ScoRoo-41T
□ 91StaClu-511
□ 91Top-237
□ 91TopDesS-237
□ 91TopMic-237
□ 91TopTif-237
□ 91TopTra-21T
□ 91TopTraT-21T
□ 91UltUpd-96
□ 92Don-335
□ 92ExpPos-8
□ 92Lea-523
□ 92LeaBlaG-523
□ 92OPC-643
□ 92OPCPre-90
□ 92PanSti-221
□ 92StaClu-705
□ 92StaCluNC-705
□ 92Top-643
□ 92TopGol-643
□ 92TopGolW-643
□ 92TopMic-643
□ 92YanWIZ8-29
□ 94BreMilB-113
Cerqueira, Jeff
□ 88CapCodPPaLP-83
Cerrud, Roberto
□ 80UtiBluJT-14
Cerutti, John
□ 83KnoBluJT-3
□ 84SyrChiT-31
□ 85SyrChiT-27
□ 86DonRoo-20
□ 86FleUpd-24
□ 86SpoRoo-36
□ 86SyrChiP-8
□ 86TopTra-23T
□ 86TopTraT-23T
□ 87BluJayFS-3
□ 87Don-442
□ 87Fle-222
□ 87FleGlo-222
□ 87Lea-210
□ 87OPC-282
□ 87SpoTeaP-5
□ 87SyrChi1A-9
□ 87Top-557
□ 87TopTif-557
□ 87ToyRoo-6
□ 88BluJayFS-6
□ 88Don-321
□ 88Fle-105
□ 88FleGlo-105
□ 88Lea-152
□ 88OPC-191
□ 88Sco-98
□ 88ScoGlo-98
□ 88Top-191
□ 88TopTif-191
□ 89BluJayFS-7
□ 89Bow-247
□ 89BowTif-247
□ 89Don-467
□ 89Fle-228
□ 89FleGlo-228
□ 89OPC-347
□ 89Sco-304
□ 89Top-347
□ 89TopTif-347
□ 89UppDec-129
□ 90BluJayFS-5
□ 90Bow-507
□ 90BowTif-507
□ 90Don-645
□ 90Fle-78
□ 90FleCan-78
□ 90Lea-27
□ 90OPC-211
□ 90PanSti-177
□ 90PubIntS-511
□ 90Sco-429
□ 90Spo-86
□ 90TigTeal-4
□ 90Top-211
□ 90TopSti-195
□ 90TopTif-211
□ 90UppDec-485
□ 91Bow-139
□ 91Don-467
□ 91Fle-172
□ 91FleUpd-22
□ 91Lea-270
□ 91OPC-687
□ 91Sco-786
□ 91ScoRoo-40T
□ 91StaClu-445
□ 91TigCok-55
□ 91Top-687A
□ 91Top-687B
□ 91TopDesS-687
□ 91TopMic-687B
□ 91TopTif-687
□ 91UppDec-585
□ 92Don-709
□ 92Fle-129
□ 92OPC-487
□ 92PawRedSF-915
□ 92PawRedSS-354
□ 92Sco-179
□ 92StaClu-71
□ 92Top-487
□ 92TopGol-487
□ 92TopGolW-487
□ 92TopMic-487
□ 92UppDec-487
□ 97DunDonPPS-4
Cerv, Bob (Robert Henry)
□ 47Exh-39A
□ 47Exh-39B
□ 53Top-210
□ 55Bow-306
□ 56A'sPos-8
□ 56Top-288
□ 56YanTeal-5
□ 57Top-269
□ 58JayPubA-3
□ 58Top-329
□ 59ArmCoi-6
□ 59Baz-6
□ 59HomRunD-5
□ 59Top-100
□ 59TopVen-100
□ 60A'sTeal-3
□ 60Baz-15
□ 60Top-415
□ 61AngJayP-5
□ 61Pos-13
□ 61Top-563
□ 61TopStal-170
□ 61Yan61RL-19
□ 62Top-169
□ 62TopVen-169
□ 79TCM50-162
□ 83Yan196-19
□ 91TopArc1-210
□ 91YanRinP13-6
□ 92YanWIZ6-23
Cervantes, Manny
□ 92ClaFS7-151
□ 92SanBerC-16
□ 92SanBerSF-962
□ 93ClaGolF-142
□ 93RivPilCLC-30
□ 94RivPilCLC-31
Cervantes, Pedro
□ 95YakBeaTI-4
□ 96GreFalDTI-5
□ 98SanBerS-6
□ 98SanBerSTIS-6
Cervantes, Raymond
□ 92EriSaiC-22
□ 92EriSaiF-1629
□ 94SanBerSC-2
□ 94SanBerSF-2764
Cesar, Dionys
□ 96SouOreTI-26
□ 97VisOakG-4
□ 98VisOakG-4
Cesari, Jeff

❑ 89GenCubP-1868
Cesarlo, Jim
❑ 83TriTriT-23
Cespedes, Angel
❑ 96PorRocB-10
Cespedes, Teodoro
❑ 89EveGiaS-4
Cey, Dan
❑ 97ForMyeM-6
❑ 98NewBriRCM-7
Cey, Ron (Ronald Charles)
❑ 72Top-761
❑ 73OPC-615
❑ 73Top-615
❑ 74OPC-315
❑ 74Top-315
❑ 74TopSta-42
❑ 75Hos-61
❑ 75HosTwi-61
❑ 75OPC-390
❑ 75Top-390
❑ 75TopMin-390
❑ 76BlaDis-13
❑ 76BucDis-13
❑ 76CarDis-13
❑ 76CraDis-13
❑ 76DailsID-13
❑ 76DodPos-3
❑ 76Hos-63
❑ 76IsaDis-13
❑ 76LinSup-117
❑ 76OPC-370
❑ 76OrbDis-13
❑ 76RedBarD-13
❑ 76SafDis-13
❑ 76SSP-75
❑ 76Top-370
❑ 76TowCluD-13
❑ 77BurCheD-153
❑ 77ChiWilD-16
❑ 77DailsID-16
❑ 77DetCaeD-16
❑ 77DodPho-1
❑ 77HolInnD-16
❑ 77Hos-89
❑ 77Kel-18
❑ 77MSADis-16
❑ 77OPC-199
❑ 77RCColC-17
❑ 77SagDis-16
❑ 77sDis-16
❑ 77Spo-3016
❑ 77Top-50
❑ 77TopCloS-14
❑ 77WenDis-16
❑ 77ZipDis-16
❑ 78Hos-93
❑ 78Kel-24
❑ 78OPC-130
❑ 78RCColC-19
❑ 78SSP270-62
❑ 78Top-630
❑ 78WifBalD-17
❑ 79BasPat-18
❑ 79DodBlu-2
❑ 79Hos-28
❑ 79OPC-94
❑ 79Top-190
❑ 80DodPol-10
❑ 80Kel-19
❑ 80OPC-267
❑ 80Top-510
❑ 81AllGamPI-118
❑ 81Dod-2
❑ 81Dod-5
❑ 81DodPol-10
❑ 81Don-296
❑ 81Fle-126A
❑ 81Fle-126B
❑ 81FleStiC-3
❑ 81LonBeaPT-4
❑ 81OPC-260
❑ 81Top-260
❑ 81TopScr-73
❑ 81TopSti-177
❑ 81TopSupHT-44
❑ 82DodPol-10
❑ 82DodUniOV-3
❑ 82DogBuiE-2
❑ 82Don-210
❑ 82Fle-3
❑ 82FleSta-3
❑ 82Kel-46
❑ 82OPC-216
❑ 82OPC-367
❑ 82Top-410
❑ 82Top-411
❑ 82TopSti-51
❑ 83AllGamPI-119
❑ 83CubThoAV-11
❑ 83Don-84
❑ 83DonActA-21
❑ 83Fle-204
❑ 83FleSta-36
❑ 83FleSti-122
❑ 83OPC-15
❑ 83Top-15
❑ 83TopFol-2
❑ 83TopSti-244
❑ 83TopTra-19T
❑ 84AllGamPI-28
❑ 84CubBriPC-JKO
❑ 84CubChiT-6
❑ 84CubSev-11
❑ 84CubUno-7
❑ 84DodUniO-8
❑ 84Don-361
❑ 84Dra-7
❑ 84Fle-490
❑ 84FunFooP-89
❑ 84Nes792-357
❑ 84OPC-357
❑ 84Top-357
❑ 84TopRubD-12
❑ 84TopSti-41
❑ 84TopTif-357
❑ 85AllGamPI-118
❑ 85CubLioP-4
❑ 85CubSev-11
❑ 85Don-320
❑ 85Dra-6
❑ 85Fle-52
❑ 85FleStaS-19
❑ 85Lea-84
❑ 85OPC-366
❑ 85Top-768
❑ 85TopSti-42
❑ 85TopTif-768
❑ 86CubGat-11
❑ 86CubUno-3
❑ 86Don-198
❑ 86Fle-363
❑ 86OPC-194
❑ 86Spo-130
❑ 86Top-669
❑ 86TopTif-669
❑ 87DodSmoA-4
❑ 87Fle-556
❑ 87FleGlo-556
❑ 87OPC-322
❑ 87OPCBoxB-C
❑ 87Top-581
❑ 87Top-767
❑ 87TopTif-581
❑ 87TopTif-767
❑ 87TopTra-22T
❑ 87TopTraT-22T
❑ 87TopWaxBC-C
❑ 88DodSmo-15
❑ 88DodSmo-21
❑ 88DodSmo-27
❑ 89DodSmoG-82
❑ 90DodTar-121
❑ 91DodUno7P-1
❑ 91DodUno7P-5
❑ 92DodStaTA-14
❑ 92UppDecS-15
❑ 93ActPacA-163
❑ 93Pin-480
❑ 93TedWil-10
❑ 93UppDecS-24
❑ 94UppDecAH-77
❑ 94UppDecAH1-77
Chabot, Kevin
❑ 97NewJerCB-6
Chacon, Elio R.
❑ 60Top-543
❑ 62MetJayP-2
❑ 62Top-256
❑ 62TopVen-199
❑ 80Red196T-15
❑ 82MetGal62-5
❑ 91MetWIZ-68
Chacon, Shawn
❑ 97AshTou-6
❑ 97Bow-349
❑ 97BowInt-349
❑ 98Bow-407
❑ 98BowChr-407
❑ 98BowChrGA-407
❑ 98BowChrGAR-407
❑ 98BowChrI-407
❑ 98BowChrIR-407
❑ 98BowChrR-407
❑ 98BowGolA-407
❑ 98BowInt-407
❑ 98CarLeaTPQ-14
❑ 98SalAvaC-7
Chacon, Troy
❑ 88CapCodPPaLP-183
Chadbourne, Chester
❑ 09ObaT21-289
❑ 11PacCoaBD-13
❑ 11Zee-45
❑ 12HomRunKE-34
❑ 12ObaPreT-38
❑ 12Zee-54
❑ 13Zee-53
❑ 17Zee-23
❑ 18Zee-97
❑ 19Zee-126
❑ 20Zee-136
❑ 21Zee-153
❑ 22Zee-145
❑ 23Zee-180
❑ 24Zee-124
Chadwick, Henry
❑ 36Halof FP-5
❑ 39PC7AlbHoF-16
❑ 50CalHOFW-12
❑ 53ArtHaloFP-12
❑ 76ShaPiz-16
❑ 77BobParHoF-11
❑ 77BobParMBC-23
❑ 80PerHaloFP-16
❑ 80SSPHOF-16
❑ 84GalHaloFRL-16
❑ 90LitSunW-2
❑ 94OriofB-11
❑ 94UppDecTAE-3
Chadwick, Ray
❑ 86EdmTraP-3
❑ 87CalAngPPS-4
❑ 87Don-505
❑ 88BirBarB-4
❑ 90CMC-177
❑ 90OmaRoyC-2
❑ 90OmaRoyP-58
❑ 90ProAAAF-593
Chadwick, Robert
❑ 86NewBriRSP-6
❑ 87NewBriRSP-9
❑ 87UtiBluSP-14
❑ 88NewBriRSP-893
Chafin, John
❑ 88UtiBluSP-14
❑ 91ElmPioC-23
❑ 91ElmPioP-3263
Chagnon, Leon
❑ 36GouWidPPR-D6
Chajin, David
❑ 91JohCitCP-3970
Chakales, Bob
❑ 52IndNumN-9
❑ 52Top-120
❑ 54OriTeal-3
❑ 55Bow-148
❑ 57Top-261
❑ 60MapLeaSF-2
❑ 61MapLeaBH-4
❑ 75TCM195CI-2
❑ 83TopRep5-120
❑ 91OriCro-74
❑ 97BalOriP-7
Chalk, Dave (David Lee)
❑ 74OPC-597
❑ 74Top-597
❑ 75CalAngP-7
❑ 75Hos-46
❑ 75HosTwi-46
❑ 75OPC-64
❑ 75Top-64
❑ 75TopMin-64
❑ 76Hos-59
❑ 76HosTwi-59
❑ 76OPC-52
❑ 76SSP-194
❑ 76Top-52
❑ 77BurCheD-119
❑ 77Top-315
❑ 78AngFamF-6
❑ 78SSP270-198
❑ 78Top-178
❑ 79OPC-362
❑ 79Top-682
❑ 80OPC-137
❑ 80Top-261
❑ 81Don-101
❑ 81Fle-35
❑ 82Don-590
❑ 82Fle-407
❑ 82Top-462
❑ 86AngGreT-4
❑ 93RanKee-101
Challinor, John
❑ 94YakBeaC-4
❑ 94YakBeaF-3840
❑ 95VerBeaDTI-5
Chalmers, George
❑ 12T207-29
❑ 14FatPlaT-11
❑ 15SpoNewM-27
❑ 16SpoNewM-29
Chamberlain, Bill
❑ 78WauMetT-5
Chamberlain, Craig
❑ 80OmaRoyP-6
❑ 80Top-417
❑ 81OmaRoyT-4
❑ 81Top-274
❑ 82PhoGiaVNB-12
❑ 83PhoGiaBHN-23
❑ 88ChaKniTI-12
Chamberlain, Elton
❑ 87OldJudN-76
Chamberlain, Harold
❑ 30Zee-74
Chamberlain, Joseph
❑ 32Zee-96
Chamberlain, Matt
❑ 93LSUTigM-11
❑ 93WelPirF-3348
❑ 94LSUTigMP-9
❑ 94SalBucC-4
❑ 94SalBucF-2316
Chamberlain, Tom
❑ 78St.PetCT-4
❑ 79ArkTraT-19A
Chamberlain, Wes (Wesley)
❑ 86AncGlaPTI-5
❑ 87WatPirP-12
❑ 88AugPirP-359
❑ 89BasAmeAPB-AA1
❑ 89EasLeaAP-5
❑ 89HarSenP-296
❑ 89HarSenS-5
❑ 89Sta-171
❑ 90BufBisC-23
❑ 90BufBisP-386
❑ 90BufBisTI-6
❑ 90CMC-23
❑ 90ProAAAF-501
❑ 91Bow-505
❑ 91Cla1-T80
❑ 91Cla3-T8
❑ 91ClaGam-92
❑ 91Don-423
❑ 91DonRoo-3
❑ 91Fle-391
❑ 91Lea-178
❑ 91OPC-603
❑ 91PhiMed-8
❑ 91Sco-713
❑ 91ScoRoo-14
❑ 91ScrRedBP-2550
❑ 91StaClu-317
❑ 91Stu-211
❑ 91Top-603A
❑ 91Top-603B
❑ 91TopDeb90-29
❑ 91TopDesS-603
❑ 91TopMic-603
❑ 91TopTif-603
❑ 91Ult-258
❑ 91UppDec-626
❑ 92Bow-412
❑ 92Cla2-T55
❑ 92ClaGam-63
❑ 92Don-384
❑ 92DonCraJ1-18
❑ 92Fle-524
❑ 92FleRooS-16
❑ 92Hig5-76
❑ 92JimDea-17
❑ 92Lea-453
❑ 92LeaBlaG-453
❑ 92OPC-14
❑ 92PhiMed-8
❑ 92Pin-36
❑ 92ProFS7-295
❑ 92Sco-384
❑ 92Sco100RS-25
❑ 92ScoImpP-11
❑ 92ScoProP-8
❑ 92ScrRedBF-2459
❑ 92StaClu-396
❑ 92Stu-72
❑ 92Top-14
❑ 92TopGol-14
❑ 92TopGolW-14
❑ 92TopMic-14
❑ 92Ult-239
❑ 92UppDec-347
❑ 93Bow-456
❑ 93Don-304
❑ 93Fle-99
❑ 93Lea-338
❑ 93OPC-45
❑ 93PacSpa-232
❑ 93PanSti-275
❑ 93PhiMed-8
❑ 93PhiStaC-13
❑ 93Pin-328
❑ 93RedFolS-18
❑ 93Sco-168
❑ 93Sel-217
❑ 93StaClu-34
❑ 93StaCluFDI-34
❑ 93StaCluMOP-34
❑ 93Stu-19
❑ 93Top-154
❑ 93TopGol-154
❑ 93TopInaM-154
❑ 93TopInaR-154
❑ 93TopMic-154
❑ 93Ult-85
❑ 93UppDec-267
❑ 93UppDecGold-267
❑ 94ColC-76
❑ 94ColChoGS-76
❑ 94ColChoSS-76
❑ 94Don-101
❑ 94Fin-123
❑ 94FinRef-123
❑ 94Fla-260
❑ 94Fle-584
❑ 94FleExtB-15
❑ 94FleUpd-10
❑ 94Lea-243
❑ 94OPC-27
❑ 94Pac-470
❑ 94PhiMed-4
❑ 94PhiUSPC-6S
❑ 94PhiUSPC-10D
❑ 94Pin-201
❑ 94PinArtP-201
❑ 94PinMusC-201
❑ 94Sco-438
❑ 94ScoGolR-438
❑ 94ScoRoo-RT25
❑ 94ScoRooGR-RT25
❑ 94Sel-67
❑ 94SpoRoo-81
❑ 94SpoRooAP-81
❑ 94StaClu-432
❑ 94StaCluFDI-432
❑ 94StaCluGR-432
❑ 94StaCluMOP-432
❑ 94StaCluT-238
❑ 94StaCluTFDI-238
❑ 94Top-419
❑ 94TopGol-419
❑ 94TopSpa-419
❑ 94Ult-542
❑ 94UppDec-148
❑ 94UppDecED-148
❑ 95Don-316
❑ 95DonPreP-316
❑ 95Fle-25
❑ 95Lea-82
❑ 95Pin-309
❑ 95PinArtP-309
❑ 95PinMusC-309
❑ 95Sco-510
❑ 95ScoGolR-510
❑ 95ScoPlaTS-510
❑ 95StaClu-458
❑ 95StaCluMOP-458
❑ 95StaCluSTWS-458
❑ 95StaCluVR-248
❑ 95StaCluVRMO-248
❑ 95Top-606
❑ 95TopCyb-376
❑ 95Ult-9
❑ 95UltGolM-9
❑ 96SyrChiTI-9
❑ 97NorTid-8
❑ 97NorTidB-8
Chamberlain, Wilt
❑ 74NewYorNTDiS-36
Chamberlin, Buck
❑ 79TolMudHT-13
❑ 80TolMudHT-14
❑ 81TolMudHT-2
❑ 82TolMudHT-24
Chambers, Al (Albert E.)
❑ 81LynSaiT-20
❑ 82SalLakCGT-5
❑ 83Don-649
❑ 83SalLakCGT-21
❑ 84SalLakCGC-188
❑ 85CalCanC-80
❑ 85Don-389
❑ 85Top-277
❑ 85TopTif-277
❑ 87ColAstP-1
Chambers, Carl
❑ 87WatIndP-17
Chambers, Cliff
❑ 47SigOil-23
❑ 49EurSta-157
❑ 50Bow-202
❑ 50PirTeal-4
❑ 51Bow-131
❑ 51FisBakL-5
❑ 51TopRedB-25
❑ 52Bow-14
❑ 52RedMan-NL4
❑ 52StaCalL-81C
❑ 52StaCalS-93C
❑ 52Top-68
❑ 53CarHunW-4
❑ 54Bow-126
❑ 79DiaGre-118
❑ 83TopRep5-68
Chambers, Jeff
❑ 89EliTwiS-31
Chambers, Mark
❑ 91PulBraC-11
❑ 91PulBraP-4017
❑ 92PulBraC-5
❑ 92PulBraF-3189
❑ 93BurIndC-7
❑ 93BurIndF-3306
❑ 93MacBraC-6
❑ 93MacBraF-1412
❑ 94BurIndC-5
❑ 94BurIndF-3802
Chambers, Scott
❑ 95YakBeaTI-5
❑ 96VerBeaDB-10
❑ 97VerBeaD-6
❑ 98VerBeaDM-5
Chambers, Travis
❑ 86ClePhiP-3
❑ 87IntLeaAT-37
❑ 87MaiGuiP-19
❑ 87MaiGuiT-3
❑ 88MaiPhiC-2
❑ 88MaiPhiP-283
❑ 89JacExpB-10
❑ 89JacExpP-162
❑ 90CMC-54
❑ 90IndIndC-4
❑ 90IndIndP-282
❑ 90ProAAAF-565
Chamblee, Jim
❑ 96MicBatCB-7
❑ 97MicBatC-8
❑ 98BowBes-197
❑ 98BowBesAR-197
❑ 98BowBesR-197
❑ 98TreThuM-9
❑ 98UppDec-588
Chambliss, Chris (Carroll C.)
❑ 70WicAerM-6
❑ 72OPC-142
❑ 72Top-142
❑ 73IndArtTC-3
❑ 73IndTeal-7
❑ 73LinPor-61
❑ 73OPC-11
❑ 73Top-11
❑ 74OPC-384
❑ 74Top-384
❑ 74TopDecE-15
❑ 74TopSta-162
❑ 75OPC-585
❑ 75Top-585
❑ 75TopMin-585
❑ 75YanSSP-14

- 76Hos-58
- 76HosTwi-58
- 76OPC-65
- 76SSP-434
- 76Top-65
- 77BurCheD-173
- 77Hos-98
- 77Kel-52
- 77OPC-49
- 77RCColC-18
- 77Top-220
- 77Top-276
- 77YanBurK-12
- 77YanNedC-1
- 78Hos-98
- 78Kel-13
- 78OPC-145
- 78RCColC-20
- 78SSP270-7
- 78Top-485
- 78WifBalD-18
- 78YanBurK-12
- 78YanPhoA-4
- 78YanSSPD-7
- 79BasPat-19
- 79Kel-37
- 79OPC-171
- 79Top-335
- 79YanBurK-12
- 79YanPicA-6
- 80OPC-328
- 80Top-625
- 81AllGamPI-93
- 81BraPol-10
- 81Don-219
- 81Fle-252
- 81FleStiC-81
- 81OPC-155
- 81Top-155
- 81TopSti-147
- 82BraBurKL-6
- 82BraPol-10
- 82Don-47
- 82Fle-433
- 82FleSta-70
- 82Kel-52
- 82OPC-320
- 82OPC-321
- 82SevSluC-8
- 82Top-320
- 82Top-321
- 82TopSti-17
- 82TopStiV-17
- 83AllGamPI-92
- 83BraPol-10
- 83Don-123
- 83Fle-134
- 83FleSta-37
- 83FleSti-86
- 83OPC-11
- 83Top-792
- 83TopSti-212
- 84AllGamPI-2
- 84BraPol-10
- 84Don-537
- 84DonActAS-29
- 84Fle-175
- 84FunFooP-123
- 84Nes792-50
- 84OPC-50
- 84raPho-6
- 84Top-50
- 84TopRubD-13
- 84TopSti-28
- 84TopTif-50
- 85BraHos-7
- 85BraPol-10
- 85Don-287
- 85Fle-322
- 85Lea-168
- 85OPC-187
- 85Top-518
- 85TopSti-29
- 85TopTif-518
- 86BraPol-10
- 86Don-618
- 86Fle-512
- 86Top-293
- 86TopTif-293
- 87Fle-513
- 87FleGlo-513
- 87OPC-204
- 87Top-777
- 87TopTif-777
- 89LonTigP-1378
- 91GreBraC-25
- 91GreBraLD-224
- 91GreBraP-3018
- 91LinDriAA-224
- 91UppDecS-6
- 92ActPacA-55
- 92RicBraBB-5
- 92RicBraF-391
- 92RicBraRC-3
- 92RicBraS-449
- 92YanWIZ7-32
- 92YanWIZ8-30
- 92YanWIZA-9
- 97FleMilDM-37
- 97FleMilDMR-37
- 97RicBraBC-26

Chambliss, Russ
- 98OneYanG-9

Champ, Jeff
- 89PenPilS-3

Champ, Mascot
- 96NasSouB-29
- 98VerExpO-6

Champagne, Andre
- 89OklSoo-8
- 90OklSoo-4

Champagne, Boo
- 86EugEmeC-44
- 87Ft.MyeRP-8

Champion, Billy
- 70OPC-149
- 70Top-149
- 71MLBOffS-173
- 71OPC-323
- 71Top-323
- 72Top-599
- 73OPC-74
- 73Top-74
- 74OPC-391
- 74Top-391
- 75Hos-118
- 75OPC-256
- 75Top-256
- 75TopMin-256
- 76OPC-501
- 76Top-501
- 93BenRocCB-29
- 93BenRocF-3284
- 94BreMilB-206
- 94NewHavRF-1567
- 95SalAvaTI-28
- 96SalAvaB-27
- 97BinMetB-2

Champion, Brian
- 88BurBraP-10
- 89DurBullS-5
- 89DurBullS-5
- 89DurBulTI-5
- 89Sta-69
- 90CarLeaA-31
- 90DurBulTI-3
- 90GreBraB-3
- 91Cla/Bes-177
- 91GreBraC-16
- 91GreBraLD-203
- 91GreBraP-3010
- 91LinDriAA-203

Champion, Jim
- 95ForMyeMTI-6

Champion, Keith
- 88SavCarP-337
- 89SavCarP-344
- 90SprCarB-26
- 92WatDiaC-26
- 92WatDiaF-2156
- 93RanCucQC-27
- 93RanCucQF-847
- 94WicWraF-205

Champion, Kirk
- 89SouBenWSGS-5
- 90SouBenWSB-27
- 90SouBenWSGS-28
- 91SouBenWSC-26
- 91SouBenWSP-2874
- 92SarWhiSCB-28
- 92SarWhiSF-226
- 93BirBarF-1209
- 94BirBarC-27
- 94BirBarF-639

Champion, Mike (Robert M.)
- 76HawIsIC-21
- 77PadSchC-11
- 77PadSchC-12
- 77Top-494
- 78PadFamF-5
- 78Top-683
- 79TacTugT-14
- 80TacTigT-16

Champion, Randall
- 83St.PetCT-14
- 87ArkTraP-8

Champlin, Kelly
- 91FreStaBS-2

Chance, Bob (Robert)
- 64Top-146
- 64TopRooAB-15
- 64TopVen-146
- 65Baz-18
- 65OPC-224
- 65Top-224
- 66SenTeal-4
- 66Top-564
- 67Top-349
- 69Top-523
- 69TopTeaP-17
- 78TCM60I-82

Chance, Dean
- 47Exh-40
- 62Top-194
- 62TopVen-194
- 63AngJayP-2
- 63AngJayP-3
- 63ExhStaB-13
- 63Jel-32
- 63Pos-32
- 63Top-6
- 63Top-355
- 64Top-32
- 64TopCoi-67
- 64TopGia-16
- 64TopVen-32
- 65AngMatSA-1
- 65Baz-5
- 65OldLonC-22
- 65OPC-7
- 65OPC-9
- 65OPC-11
- 65OPC-140
- 65Top-7
- 65Top-9
- 65Top-11
- 65Top-140
- 65TopEmbl-66
- 65TopTral-10
- 65TopTral-42
- 66AngDexP-3
- 66Baz-25
- 66Top-340
- 66TopRubl-16
- 66TopVen-340
- 67Baz-25
- 67CokCapTw-14
- 67DexPre-46
- 67Top-380
- 67TopGiaSU-12
- 67TopVen-217
- 67TwiTeal-4
- 67TwiTeal-5
- 68AtlOilPBCC-13
- 68Baz-10
- 68DexPre-23
- 68OPC-10
- 68OPC-12
- 68Top-10A
- 68Top-10B
- 68Top-12
- 68Top-255
- 68TopActS-4A
- 68TopActS-13A
- 68TopGamI-16
- 68TopPla-2
- 68TopPos-1
- 68TopVen-10
- 68TopVen-12
- 68TopVen-255
- 69MilBra-57
- 69MLBOffS-66
- 69MLBPin-5
- 69Top-620
- 69TopSta-193
- 69TopSup-21
- 69TopTeaP-15
- 69TwiTealC-4
- 70Kel-67
- 70MLBOffS-195
- 70Top-625
- 71MLBOffS-148
- 71OPC-36
- 71Top-36
- 72MilBra-73
- 78TCM60I-66
- 78TwiFri-4
- 80MarExh-7
- 82OhiHaloF-4
- 85AngStrH-5
- 86AngGreT-9
- 89AngSmo-2
- 89SweBasG-89
- 91MetWIZ-69
- 94SnaDeaC-1
- 94TedWil-14

Chance, Frank Leroy
- 03BreE10-18
- 03WilCarE-4
- 06FanCraNL-9
- 07CubA.CDPP-2
- 07CubGFGCP-2
- 08AmeCarE91-5
- 08AmeCarE91-40
- 08CubPos-1
- 08RosComP-102
- 09AmeCarE90-1-20
- 09ColChiE-48A
- 09ColChiE-48B
- 09MaxPubP-2
- 09PhiCarE-3
- 09RamT20-23
- 09SpoNewSM-8
- 09T206-54
- 09T206-55
- 09T206-56
- 09TigHMTP-8
- 10ChiE-3
- 10CouT21-9
- 10CouT21-93
- 10CouT21-94
- 10CouT21-95
- 10CouT21-96
- 10CouT21-264
- 10CouT21-265
- 10DomDisP-22
- 10E101-8
- 10E98-5
- 10JHDABE-4
- 10JuJuDE-7
- 10MelMinE-8
- 10NadCarE-10
- 10OrnOvaPP-2
- 10PeoT21-10
- 10RedCroT-9
- 10RedCroT-96
- 10RedCroT-175
- 10SepAnoP-6
- 10StaCarE-4
- 10SweCapPP-81A
- 10SweCapPP-81B
- 10W555-11
- 11BasBatEU-7
- 11DiaGumP-7
- 11E94-5
- 11HelSta-92
- 11JonKeyaAC-349
- 11MecDFT-9
- 11PinT-5-207
- 11S74Sil-59
- 11SpoLifCW-58
- 11SpoLifM-168
- 11T205-26
- 11TurRedT-47
- 12ColRedB-48A
- 12ColRedB-48B
- 12ColTinT-48A
- 12ColTinT-48B
- 12HasTriFT-13A
- 12HasTriFT-13B
- 12HasTriFT-13C
- 12HasTriFT-13D
- 12HasTriFT-13E
- 12HasTriFT-36B
- 12HasTriFT-36E
- 12T207-30
- 13LawSemC-1
- 13LawSemC-2
- 13NatGamW-8
- 13TomBarW-8
- 14B18B-21
- 14CraJacE-99
- 14FatPlaT-12
- 14NY NewFCP-1
- 14PieStaT-19
- 14PolGroW-3
- 14TexTomE-11
- 15SpoNewM-28
- 16Zee-4
- 17Zee-4
- 39PC7AlbHoF-40
- 40PlaBal-234
- 48ExhHoF-3
- 50CalHOFW-13
- 50CubGreB-4
- 53ArtHaloFP-13
- 60ExhWriH-6
- 60Fle-50
- 61Fle-98
- 63BazA-25
- 68LauWorS-5
- 69Baz-5
- 69Baz-11
- 70FleWorS-5
- 72ClaCar-5
- 72ClaCar-18
- 73FleWilD-2
- 74CapPub-17
- 76MotOldT-11
- 76ShaPiz-40
- 77BobParHoF-56
- 77GalGloG-161
- 80MarExhH-5
- 80PacLeg-84
- 80PerHaloFP-40
- 80SSPHOF-40
- 81ConTSN-12
- 84CubUno-7
- 84CubUno-8
- 84GalHaloFRL-40
- 87Cub190T-8
- 90PerGreM-40
- 92CubOldS-6
- 92YanWIZH-4
- 93ConTSN-819
- 93UppDecAH-30
- 93UppDecAH-148
- 93UppDecTR-9
- 94ConTSN-1166
- 94ConTSNB-1166
- 94OriofB-89
- 96PitPosH-2

Chance, Tony
- 86MacPirP-6
- 86PriWilPP-5
- 87SalBucP-25
- 88HarSenP-854
- 89UppDec-3
- 90CMC-319
- 90ProAAAF-470
- 90RocRedWC-19
- 90RocRedWGC-19
- 90RocRedWP-713
- 91LinDriAAA-451
- 91RocRedWLD-451
- 91RocRedWP-1913
- 92IowCubF-4060
- 92IowCubS-206
- 93IowCubF-2144

Chancey, Bailey
- 98St.LucMM-18

Chandler, Bob
- 90PadMag-16
- 91PadCok-1

Chandler, Chris
- 92St.CatBJC-21
- 92St.CatBJF-3393

Chandler, Ed
- 47DodTeal-6
- 52MotCoo-63
- 90DodTar-122

Chandler, George
- 85CloHSS-9

Chandler, Happy (A.B.)
- 49EurSta-1
- 50CalHOFW-14
- 75JohMiz-5
- 76TayBow4-80
- 80PerHaloFP-178
- 80PerHaloFPS-43
- 80SSPHOF-179
- 89HOFStiB-97
- 89PerCelP-9

Chandler, Jason
- 93PriRedC-3
- 93PriRedF-4168

Chandler, Ken
- 81WisRapTT-13

Chandler, Spud
- 33WorCig(-14
- 40PlaBal-181
- 43YanSta-5
- 46SpoExcW-3-2
- 47Exh-41
- 47YanTeaT-4
- 72TCMthe3-78
- 74TCMNic-3
- 75YanDyn1T-6
- 77TCMTheWY-55
- 79DiaGre-9
- 83TCMPla1943-1
- 83YanASFY-6
- 89PacLegI-136
- 92YanWIZA-10
- 93ConTSN-763
- 94ConTSN-1068
- 94ConTSNB-1068

Chandler, Steve
- 93OneYanF-3521

Chaney, Bruce
- 81BirBarT-16

Chaney, Darrel Lee
- 69Top-624
- 70DayDaiNM-133
- 70OPC-3
- 70Top-3
- 71MLBOffS-53
- 71OPC-632
- 71Top-632
- 72OPC-136
- 72Top-136
- 73OPC-507
- 73Top-507
- 74OPC-559
- 74Top-559
- 75OPC-581
- 75Top-581
- 75TopMin-581
- 76AtlBraP-6
- 76OPC-259
- 76SSP-33
- 76Top-259
- 76TopTra-259T
- 77BurCheD-216
- 77Hos-57
- 77OPC-134
- 77Top-384
- 78Top-443
- 79OPC-91
- 79Top-184

Chaney, Keith
- 91PulBraC-5
- 91PulBraP-4011

Chaney, Michael
- 96EriSeaB-8
- 97AugGre-9

Chang, Soon-Jo
- 90IBAWorA-3

Chant, Charlie (Charles J.)
- 75IntLeaASB-3
- 75PacCoaLAB-3
- 75TucTorC-8
- 75TucTorTI-2
- 76TulOilGP-20

Chantres, Carlos
- 98BirBarG-8
- 98WinWar-7

Chanye, Bruce
- 80WatIndT-18
- 83MidCubT-10

Chapa, Javier
- 95GreFalDTI-9

Chapin, Darrin
- 88Ft.LauYS-4
- 89AlbYanP-340
- 89AlbYanSt-3
- 89ColCliC-30
- 90AlbYanP-1029
- 90AlbYanSt-1
- 90CMC-220
- 90ColCliC-20
- 90ColCliP-668
- 90ProAaA-19
- 90ProAAAF-318
- 90StaFS7-51
- 91ColCliLD-103
- 91ColCliP-3
- 91ColCliP-590
- 91LinDriAAA-103
- 92Don-745
- 92ScrRedBF-2441
- 92ScrRedBS-481
- 92SkyAAAF-219
- 92TopDeb91-33
- 93LinVenB-264
- 94EdmTraF-2867

Chaplin, Tiny
- 33WorCig(-15
- 94ConTSN-1308
- 94ConTSNB-1308

Chapman, Ben (William B.)
- 30SchR33-40

❑ 30UncJac-4
❑ 32OrbPinNP-99
❑ 33Gou-191
❑ 33WorCig-16
❑ 34BabRutG-9
❑ 34BatR31-62
❑ 34BatR31-188
❑ 34ButPreR-9
❑ 34DiaStaR-38
❑ 34Gou-9
❑ 34GouCanV-51
❑ 36GouWidPPR-B4
❑ 36NatChiFPR-19
❑ 36NatChiFPR-87
❑ 36OveCanR-7
❑ 36WorWidGV-90
❑ 37OPCBatUV-130
❑ 38CloFotW-12
❑ 39GouPreR303A-8
❑ 39GouPreR303B-3
❑ 39WorWidGTP-8
❑ 41DouPlaR-73
❑ 46SpoExcW-2-12
❑ 52Top-391
❑ 75YanDyn1T-7
❑ 77GalGloG-197
❑ 79DiaGre-2
❑ 83BigLeaCOA-11
❑ 83ConMar-12
❑ 83TCMRut-1
❑ 83TopRep5-391
❑ 83YanASFY-7
❑ 88ConAmeA-4
❑ 88ConSer3-6
❑ 90DodTar-123
❑ 92YanWIZA-11
❑ 93ConTSN-688
❑ 94ConTSN-1081
❑ 94ConTSNB-1081
Chapman, Dan
❑ 88StoPorCLC-205
❑ 88StoPorP-751
❑ 89StoPorB-28
❑ 89StoPorCLC-174
❑ 89StoPorP-398
❑ 89StoPorS-23
Chapman, Dave
❑ 79AshTouT-7
Chapman, Eric
❑ 93WatIndC-4
❑ 93WatIndF-3574
Chapman, Glenn J.
❑ 90DodTar-911
Chapman, Jake
❑ 96SpoIndB-9
❑ 97WilBluR-17
❑ 98WilBluRC-8
Chapman, Jim
❑ 92MegRut-160
Chapman, Kelvin Keith
❑ 77WauMetT-5
❑ 79TidTidT-18
❑ 80TidTidT-18
❑ 81SyrChiT-13
❑ 81SyrChiTI-6
❑ 82TidTidT-2
❑ 83TidTidT-7
❑ 84TidTidT-27
❑ 85Don-626
❑ 85Fle-75
❑ 85MetColP-24
❑ 85MetTCM-22
❑ 85Top-751
❑ 85TopTif-751
❑ 86Top-492
❑ 86TopTif-492
❑ 91MetWIZ-70
Chapman, Ken
❑ 92YakBeaC-12
❑ 92YakBeaF-3457
Chapman, Mark
❑ 88BelBreGS-10
❑ 88MidLeaAGS-59
❑ 89ElPasDGS-4
❑ 90ElPasDGS-6
❑ 91ElPasDLD-178
❑ 91ElPasDP-2739
❑ 91LinDriAA-178
❑ 92HarSenF-455
❑ 92HarSenS-279
Chapman, Nathan
❑ 76ForLauYS-11
❑ 79ColCliT-22
❑ 80NasSouTI-5
❑ 81NasSouTI-3
❑ 82NasSouTI-6
Chapman, Ray (Raymond J.)
❑ 14B18B-2A
❑ 14B18B-2B
❑ 15SpoNewM-29
❑ 16BF2FP-22
❑ 16SpoNewM-30
❑ 17ColE13-26
❑ 74CapPub-66
❑ 77Ind192T-4
❑ 81ConTSN-52
❑ 94UppDecTAE-32
❑ 95ConTSNP-1464
Chapman, Ron
❑ 85AlbYanT-15
❑ 91WavRedF-13
Chapman, Sam (Samuel Blake)
❑ 40PlaBal-194
❑ 41DouPlaR-125
❑ 41PlaBal-44
❑ 46A'sTeal-3
❑ 46SpoExcW-3-7
❑ 47A'sTeal-5
❑ 48A'sTeal-4
❑ 49A'sTeal-8
❑ 49Bow-112
❑ 49Lea-26
❑ 49OlmStu-1
❑ 49PhiBul-11
❑ 50A'sTeal-4
❑ 50Bow-104
❑ 51A'sTeal-5
❑ 51Bow-9
❑ 51TopBluB-52
❑ 52MotCoo-33
❑ 52NatTeaL-4
❑ 52Top-391
❑ 76TayBow4-30
❑ 83TopRep5-391
❑ 85TCMPla1-20
Chapman, Scott
❑ 97AubDouTI-11
Chapman, Walker
❑ 95ForWayWTI-3
❑ 97ForMyeM-7
❑ 98ForMyeMTI-7
Chappas, Harry (Harold Perry)
❑ 78AppFoxT-5
❑ 79IowOakP-5
❑ 80Top-347
Chappell, Larry (Laverne A.)
❑ 18Zee-55
Chappelle, William
❑ 09T206-408
❑ 10CouT21-97
❑ 10CouT21-98
❑ 72ClaCar-119
Charboneau, Joe (Joseph)
❑ 80IndTeal-4
❑ 81AllGamPI-49
❑ 81Don-82A
❑ 81Don-82B
❑ 81Dra-21
❑ 81Fle-397
❑ 81Kel-54
❑ 81OPC-13
❑ 81Squ-32
❑ 81Top-13
❑ 81TopScr-12
❑ 81TopSti-66
❑ 82ChaSupJ-1
❑ 82ChaSupJ-2
❑ 82Don-363
❑ 82Fle-362
❑ 82FleSta-192
❑ 82Ind-8
❑ 82IndWhe-2
❑ 82OPC-211
❑ 82Top-630
❑ 83BufBisT-23
❑ 84PriWilPT-15
❑ 88ChaLooLTI-3
❑ 93MCIAmb-6
❑ 93UppDecAH-31
❑ 94UppDecAH-141
❑ 94UppDecAH1-141
Charbonneau, Marc
❑ 95GreFalDTI-13
❑ 96SavSanB-3
Charbonnet, Mark
❑ 89BurIndS-4
❑ 90RenSilSCLC-269
❑ 90WatIndS-3
❑ 91ColIndC-7
❑ 91ColIndP-1497
❑ 92ColRedC-13
❑ 93KinIndC-4
❑ 93KinIndF-2258
❑ 93KinIndTI-3
❑ 94WesPalBEC-5
❑ 94WesPalBEF-53
❑ 95HarSenTI-27
Charland, Colin
❑ 86SalAngC-76
❑ 87PalSprP-9
❑ 88CalLeaACLC-31
❑ 88PalSprACLC-85
❑ 88PalSprAP-1447
❑ 89EdmTraC-6
❑ 89EdmTraP-565
❑ 90Fle-640
❑ 90FleCan-640
❑ 90IndTeal-10
❑ 92CanIndF-683
❑ 92CanIndS-110
❑ 92SkyAA F-48
❑ 97MidAngOHP-3
Charles, Chappy (Raymond)
❑ 09PC7HHB-7
❑ 09T206-57
❑ 10CouT21-10
❑ 11SpoLifM-188
❑ 13Zee-101
❑ 14Zee-104
❑ 15Zee-100
Charles, Curtis
❑ 96BluOriB-8
❑ 97DelSho-4
❑ 98DelShoM-9
Charles, Domingo
❑ 93JohCitCC-6
❑ 93JohCitCF-3670
❑ 94JohCitCC-5
❑ 94JohCitCF-3689
Charles, Ed (Edwin)
❑ 52LavPro-19
❑ 62Top-595
❑ 63Jel-89
❑ 63Pos-89
❑ 63Top-67
❑ 64A's-2
❑ 64AthJayP-2
❑ 64Top-475
❑ 64TopCoi-117
❑ 64TopSta-1
❑ 64TopStaU-16
❑ 65AthJayP-3
❑ 65OPC-35
❑ 65Top-35
❑ 66Top-422
❑ 66TopRubI-17
❑ 67CokCapA-35
❑ 67CokCapAAm-25
❑ 67CokCapAt-3
❑ 67DexPre-47
❑ 67OPC-182
❑ 67Top-182
❑ 68Top-563
❑ 69MetTeal-4
❑ 69MilBra-58
❑ 69MLBOffS-164
❑ 69Top-245
❑ 69TopSta-62
❑ 69TopTeaP-24
❑ 70OPC-310
❑ 78TCM60I-25
❑ 89MetRinP69-5
❑ 90SweBasG-123
❑ 91MetWIZ-71
❑ 94Met69CCPP-10
❑ 94Met69CS-9
❑ 94Met69T-18
❑ 94UppDecAH-62
❑ 94UppDecAH1-62
❑ 96Met69Y-1
Charles, Ezzard
❑ 74NewYorNTDiS-5
Charles, Frank
❑ 91EveGiaC-11
❑ 91EveGiaP-3917
❑ 92ProFS7-357
❑ 94ChaRanF-2499
❑ 95TulDriTI-4
❑ 96TulDriTI-6
❑ 97TulDriTI-7
❑ 98ShrCapM-10
❑ 98ShrCapWS-10
Charles, Justin
❑ 94ElmPioC-4
❑ 94ElmPioF-3481
Charles, Steve
❑ 96StCatSB-6
Charleston, Oscar
❑ 74LauOldTBS-34
❑ 76LauIndC-30
❑ 76ShaPiz-152
❑ 80PerHaloFP-152
❑ 80SSPHOF-152
❑ 83ConMar-50
❑ 86NegLeaF-4
❑ 86NegLeaF-8
❑ 86NegLeaF-24
❑ 88ConNegA-2
❑ 88NegLeaD-7
❑ 90NegLeaS-36
❑ 91PomBlaBPB-9
❑ 91PomBlaBPB-18
❑ 93TedWil-102
❑ 94PomNegLB-10
❑ 95S.FExaNLT-9
❑ 97NegLeaPC-7H
Charleston, Porter
❑ 91PomBlaBPB-23
Charlton, Aaron
❑ 95BurBeeTI-25
Charlton, Norm
❑ 86VerRedP-3
❑ 87NasSouTI-2
❑ 88NasSouC-3
❑ 88NasSouP-488
❑ 88NasSouTI-6
❑ 88TriAAC-12
❑ 89Don-544
❑ 89Fle-155
❑ 89FleGlo-155
❑ 89RedKah-37
❑ 89Sco-646
❑ 89ScoYouS2-15
❑ 89Top-737
❑ 89TopTif-737
❑ 89UppDec-783
❑ 90Don-426
❑ 90Fle-416
❑ 90FleCan-416
❑ 90Lea-334
❑ 90OPC-289
❑ 90PubIntS-24
❑ 90RedKah-6
❑ 90Sco-248
❑ 90Top-289
❑ 90TopTif-289
❑ 90UppDec-566
❑ 91Bow-690
❑ 91Don-384
❑ 91Fle-60
❑ 91Lea-414
❑ 91OPC-309
❑ 91RedKah-37
❑ 91RedPep-5
❑ 91Sco-530
❑ 91StaClu-305
❑ 91Top-309
❑ 91TopDesS-309
❑ 91TopMic-309
❑ 91TopTif-309
❑ 91Ult-89
❑ 91Ult-90
❑ 91UppDec-394
❑ 92Don-102
❑ 92Fle-402
❑ 92Lea-120
❑ 92LeaBlaG-120
❑ 92OPC-649
❑ 92Pin-216
❑ 92RedKah-37
❑ 92Sco-267
❑ 92StaClu-530
❑ 92Stu-21
❑ 92Top-649
❑ 92TopGol-649
❑ 92TopGolW-649
❑ 92TopMic-649
❑ 92TriPla-163
❑ 92Ult-482
❑ 92UppDec-677
❑ 93Bow-655
❑ 93Don-238
❑ 93Fin-178
❑ 93FinRef-178
❑ 93Fla-269
❑ 93Fle-32
❑ 93FleFinE-266
❑ 93Lea-287
❑ 93MariStaClu-13
❑ 93MarMot-10
❑ 93OPC-98
❑ 93OPCPre-50
❑ 93PacSpa-620
❑ 93Pin-439
❑ 93Sco-375
❑ 93Sel-207
❑ 93SelRoo-96T
❑ 93SP-129
❑ 93StaClu-659
❑ 93StaCluFDI-659
❑ 93StaCluM-144
❑ 93StaCluMOP-659
❑ 93Top-57
❑ 93TopGol-57
❑ 93TopInaM-57
❑ 93TopInaR-57
❑ 93TopMic-57
❑ 93TopTra-123T
❑ 93Ult-615
❑ 93UppDec-663
❑ 93UppDecGold-663
❑ 94ColC-559
❑ 94ColChoGS-559
❑ 94ColChoSS-559
❑ 94Don-96
❑ 94Fle-283
❑ 94Pac-565
❑ 94PhiMed-5
❑ 94Pin-216
❑ 94PinArtP-216
❑ 94PinMusC-216
❑ 94Sco-549
❑ 94ScoGolR-549
❑ 95FleUpd-118
❑ 95Lea-359
❑ 95MarPac-27
❑ 95Phi-6
❑ 95PhiMel-4
❑ 96Cir-77
❑ 96CirRav-77
❑ 96ColCho-726
❑ 96ColChoGS-726
❑ 96ColChoSS-726
❑ 96Don-529
❑ 96DonPreP-529
❑ 96Fle-232
❑ 96FleTif-232
❑ 96LeaSigA-44
❑ 96LeaSigAG-44
❑ 96LeaSigAS-44
❑ 96MarMot-16
❑ 96Pac-402
❑ 96StaClu-423
❑ 96StaCluEPB-423
❑ 96StaCluEPG-423
❑ 96StaCluEPS-423
❑ 96StaCluMOP-423
❑ 96Top-392
❑ 96Ult-409
❑ 96UltGolM-409
❑ 96UppDec-203
❑ 97Cir-190
❑ 97CirRav-190
❑ 97ColCho-234
❑ 97ColChoT-SM5
❑ 97Fle-203
❑ 97FleTif-203
❑ 97Pac-184
❑ 97PacLigB-184
❑ 97PacSil-184
❑ 97Sco-331
❑ 97ScoArtPWB-331
❑ 97ScoResC-331
❑ 97ScoShoS-331
❑ 97ScoShoSAP-331
❑ 97StaClu-278
❑ 97StaCluMOP-278
❑ 97Top-199
❑ 97Ult-119
❑ 97UltGolME-119
❑ 97UltPlaME-119
❑ 97UppDecMP-P5
❑ 98PacOnl-85
❑ 98PacOnlR-85
❑ 98PacOnlWC-85
Charno, Joe
❑ 88AshTouP-1055
❑ 89AshTouP-962
Charpia, Billie Jo
❑ 95ColSilB-3
Charpia, Reed
❑ 89HelBreSP-16
Charry, Stephen
❑ 83MadMusF-2
Chartak, Mike (Michael G.)
❑ 96Bro194F-25
Charton, Pete (Frank)
❑ 64Top-459
❑ 66Top-329
❑ 66TopVen-329
Chase, Dave
❑ 80AndBraT-12
Chase, Hal (Harold Homer)
❑ 03WilCarE-5
❑ 08RosComP-43
❑ 09AmeCarE90-1-21
❑ 09ColChiE-49
❑ 09SpoNewSM-23
❑ 09T206-58
❑ 09T206-59
❑ 09T206-60
❑ 09T206-61
❑ 09T206-62
❑ 10CouT21-11
❑ 10CouT21-12
❑ 10CouT21-99
❑ 10CouT21-100
❑ 10CouT21-101
❑ 10CouT21-102
❑ 10CouT21-103
❑ 10CouT21-104
❑ 10CouT21-266
❑ 10CouT21-267
❑ 10CouT21-268
❑ 10DomDisP-23
❑ 10E-UOraBSC-5
❑ 10E101-9
❑ 10E102-3
❑ 10E98-6
❑ 10MelMinE-9
❑ 10NadCarE-11
❑ 10PeoT21-11A
❑ 10PeoT21-11B
❑ 10PeoT21-11C
❑ 10RedCroT-10
❑ 10RedCroT-176
❑ 10SepAnoP-7
❑ 10StaCarE-5
❑ 10SweCapPP-32A
❑ 10SweCapPP-32B
❑ 10W555-12
❑ 11BasBatEU-8
❑ 11DiaGumP-8
❑ 11HelSta-40
❑ 11MecDFT-46
❑ 11PinT-5-807
❑ 11PloCanE-14
❑ 11S74Sil-20
❑ 11SpoLifCW-59
❑ 11SpoLifM-75
❑ 11T205-27A
❑ 11T205-27B
❑ 11TurRedT-6
❑ 12ColRedB-49
❑ 12ColTinT-49
❑ 12HasTriFT-14A
❑ 12HasTriFT-14B
❑ 12HasTriFT-14C
❑ 12HasTriFT-15A
❑ 12HasTriFT-15B
❑ 12HasTriFT-16A
❑ 12HasTriFT-16B
❑ 12HasTriFT-16C
❑ 12HasTriFT-17
❑ 12HasTriFT-18
❑ 12HasTriFT-41A
❑ 12HasTriFT-41B
❑ 12HasTriFT-61B
❑ 13NatGamW-9
❑ 13TomBarW-9
❑ 14PieStaT-20
❑ 14PieStaT-21
❑ 14TexTomE-12
❑ 15AmeCarE106-7A
❑ 15AmeCarE106-7B
❑ 15CraJacE-99
❑ 16TanBraE-4
❑ 19W514-114
❑ 67SpoHobFC-35
❑ 67SpoHobFC-39
❑ 68SCFOldT-34
❑ 72ClaCar-103
❑ 74CapPub-67
❑ 75FlePio-22
❑ 75ShaPiz-13
❑ 77GalGloG-146
❑ 88ConSer4-5

❑ 91ConTSN-160
Chase, Ken
❑ 39PlaBal-59
❑ 40PlaBal-19
❑ 42RedSoxTI-5
❑ 43RedSoxTI-2
❑ 79DiaGre-59
Chase, Scott
❑ 89OneYanP-2107
Chasey, Mark
❑ 88UtiBluSP-4
❑ 89SouBenWSGS-21
❑ 90SarWhiSS-4
❑ 91BirBarLD-54
❑ 91BirBarP-1459
❑ 91LinDriAA-54
Chasin, David
❑ 91JohCitCC-22
Chasteen, Steve
❑ 83IdaFalAT-2
Chataing, Blanco
❑ 91PomBlaBPB-2
Chatham, Buster (Charles L.)
❑ 30Zee-103
❑ 94ConTSN-1287
❑ 94ConTSNB-1287
Chatman, Karl
❑ 96VerExpB-12
❑ 98CapFeaCM-6
Chatterton, Christopher
❑ 92BluOriC-14
❑ 92BluOriF-2353
❑ 93AlbPolCB-6
❑ 93AlbPolF-2018
Chauncey, Keathel
❑ 75AndRanT-9
❑ 76SanAntBTI-6
❑ 77TucTorC-12
❑ 78TucTorC-12
❑ 79TucTorT-19
❑ 80WesHavWCT-21A
❑ 81TolMudHT-19
Chavarria, David
❑ 92ButCopKSP-17
❑ 94HudValRF-3375
❑ 95ChaRivTI-18
❑ 97ArkTraB-1
Chavarria, Ossie (Oswaldo Q.)
❑ 67CokCapAt-6
❑ 67DexPre-48
❑ 67Top-344
❑ 67VanMouSO-3
Chavera, Arnie
❑ 96QuaCitRB-12
❑ 97QuaCitRBB-6
❑ 98KisCobQ-11
Chaves, Rafael
❑ 86ChaRaiP-5
❑ 92HigDesMC-23
❑ 93BowBayF-2182
❑ 93ClaGolF-56
❑ 94PorSeaDF-670
❑ 95LynHilTI-3
Chavez, Anthony
❑ 77RocRedWM-11
❑ 92BoiHawC-19
❑ 92BoiHawF-3619
❑ 93CedRapKC-3
❑ 93CedRapKF-1730
❑ 93MidLeaAGF-34
❑ 94LakElsSC-4
❑ 94LakElsSF-1656
❑ 95LakElsSTI-8
❑ 97MidAng-10
❑ 98VanCanG-8
Chavez, Carlos
❑ 92BluOriC-22
❑ 92BluOriF-2354
❑ 93AlbPolCB-7
❑ 93AlbPolF-2019
❑ 93BluOriC-9
❑ 93BluOriF-4118
❑ 94AlbPolC-11
❑ 94BluOriC-3
❑ 94BluOriF-3552
❑ 94OriPro-17
❑ 96BowBayB-10
❑ 96Exc-2
❑ 97PorSeaD-7
❑ 98El PasDG-6
Chavez, Devin
❑ 91HunCubC-7
❑ 91HunCubP-3341
Chavez, Eric (Ruben Eric)
❑ 92BluOriF-2364
❑ 93AlbPolCB-8
❑ 93AlbPolF-2031
❑ 93SouAtlLAGF-2
❑ 94ClaGolF-5
❑ 94ExcFS7-3
❑ 94FreKeyC-7
❑ 94FreKeyF-2620
❑ 94OriPro-18
❑ 96FreKeyB-3
❑ 97DelSho-7
Chavez, Eric Cesar
❑ 97Bes-37
❑ 97Bes-92
❑ 97BesDiaB-14
❑ 97BesLimA-7
❑ 97Bow-210
❑ 97BowChr-192
❑ 97BowChrI-192
❑ 97BowChrIR-192
❑ 97BowChrR-192
❑ 97BowInt-210
❑ 97CalLeaTP-28
❑ 97Top-479
❑ 97VisOakG-5
❑ 98AriFalLTP-9
❑ 98Bes-61
❑ 98BesAutPOY-3
❑ 98BesBet-3
❑ 98BesCor-3
❑ 98BesDiaBA-3
❑ 98BesFulCA-3
❑ 98BesNumOP-13
❑ 98BesPreA-7
❑ 98Bow-133
❑ 98Bow99ROYF-ROY5
❑ 98BowBes-185
❑ 98BowBesAR-185
❑ 98BowBesR-185
❑ 98BowCerBlueAU-55
❑ 98BowCerGA-55
❑ 98BowCerSA-55
❑ 98BowChr-133
❑ 98BowChrGA-133
❑ 98BowChrGAR-133
❑ 98BowChrI-133
❑ 98BowChrIR-133
❑ 98BowChrR-133
❑ 98BowGolA-133
❑ 98BowInt-133
❑ 98DonSig-128
❑ 98DonSigP-128
❑ 98FleUpd-U55
❑ 98HunStaTI-12
❑ 98LeaRS-326
❑ 98LeaRSLHolo-326
❑ 98LeaRSLong-326
❑ 98LeaRTrue-326
❑ 98SouLeaTPG-8
❑ 98SP MinDTSPE-DS2
❑ 98SP MinPE-89
❑ 98SP MinSTHPE-H2
❑ 98SP SPTSC-EC
❑ 98SPMin-89
❑ 98SPMinDTS-DS2
❑ 98SPMinSTH-H2
❑ 98Top-262
❑ 98TopChr-262
❑ 98TopChrR-262
❑ 98TopDevR-262
❑ 98TopDia-262
❑ 98TopMiniC-262
❑ 99199Fin-129
❑ 99199Fin-227
❑ 99199Fin-283
❑ 99Bow-330
❑ 99BowAut-BA69
❑ 99BowBes-101
❑ 99BowBesAR-101
❑ 99BowBesFFMI-FF3
❑ 99BowBesFFMI-FF3
❑ 99BowBesFFMII-FF3
❑ 99BowBesMI-M6
❑ 99BowBesMIAR-M6
❑ 99BowBesMIR-M6
❑ 99BowBesR-101
❑ 99BowBesRLRA-RA5
❑ 99BowBesRLRGUB-RB5
❑ 99BowBesRLRGWJ-RJ4
❑ 99BowChrDA-DA2
❑ 99BowChrDAR-DA2
❑ 99BowChrSC-SC5
❑ 99BowChrSCR-SC5
❑ 99BowGol-330
❑ 99BowInt-330
❑ 99BowScoC-SC5
❑ 99CroRoyB-101
❑ 99CroRoyL-101
❑ 99CroRoyOD-101
❑ 99DumSet-131
❑ 99E-X Cen-116
❑ 99E-X CenECFut-116
❑ 99E-X CenECNow-116
❑ 99E-X CenEQ-6
❑ 99FinDouF-DF5
❑ 99FinDouFDualR-DF5
❑ 99FinFutF-FF3
❑ 99FinGolRef-129
❑ 99FinGolRef-227
❑ 99FinGolRef-283
❑ 99FinRef-129
❑ 99FinRef-227
❑ 99FinRef-283
❑ 99FinSplS-SS12
❑ 99FinSplSDR-SS12
❑ 99FlaShoLeg1-33
❑ 99FlaShoLeg2-33
❑ 99FlaShoLeg3-33
❑ 99FlaShoLegM1-33
❑ 99FlaShoLegM2-33
❑ 99FlaShoLegM3-33
❑ 99FlaShoR1-33
❑ 99FlaShoR2-33
❑ 99FlaShoR3-33
❑ 99FlaShoWotF-9
❑ 99Fle-70
❑ 99Fle-577
❑ 99FleBri-130
❑ 99FleBri2G-130
❑ 99FleBriBlu-130
❑ 99FleBriGol-130
❑ 99FleBriI-9
❑ 99FleMys-131
❑ 99FleMysM-131
❑ 99FleMysP-1
❑ 99FleRooFla-5
❑ 99FleSta9-70
❑ 99FleSta9-577
❑ 99FleWarT-70
❑ 99FleWarT-577
❑ 99MetUni-261
❑ 99MetUniGM-261
❑ 99MetUniPMG-261
❑ 99Pac-308
❑ 99Pac-308A
❑ 99PacAur-133
❑ 99PacAurOD-133
❑ 99PacCroC-200
❑ 99PacCroCPB-200
❑ 99PacInv-105
❑ 99PacInvOD-105
❑ 99PacInvPB-105
❑ 99PacInvSH-13
❑ 99PacInvSH-13B
❑ 99PacOme-176
❑ 99PacOmeC-176
❑ 99PacOmeG-176
❑ 99PacOmePB-176
❑ 99PacPar-168
❑ 99PacParC-168
❑ 99PacParG-168
❑ 99PacParHoloGold-168
❑ 99PacParHS-168
❑ 99PacParOD-168
❑ 99PacParPB-25
❑ 99PacParPB-168
❑ 99PacParRed-168
❑ 99PacPlaB-308
❑ 99PacPlaB-308A
❑ 99PacPri-103
❑ 99PacPriHB-103
❑ 99PacPriHG-103
❑ 99PacPriHM-103
❑ 99PacPriHP-103
❑ 99PacPriRed-103
❑ 99PacPriS-70
❑ 99PacPriS206-70
❑ 99PacPriS206R-70
❑ 99PacRed-308
❑ 99PacRed-308A
❑ 99Rev-100
❑ 99RevPremDate-100
❑ 99RevRet-100
❑ 99RevShaSS-100
❑ 99SkyMolM-117
❑ 99SkyMolMF-17
❑ 99SkyMolMFS-17
❑ 99SkyMolMFT-17
❑ 99SkyMolMX-117
❑ 99SkyPre-264
❑ 99SkyPre-264
❑ 99SkyPreDD-1
❑ 99SkyPreR-264
❑ 99SkyPreR-264
❑ 99SkyThu-288
❑ 99SkyThuRant-288
❑ 99SkyThuRave-288
❑ 99SkyThuUnl-U3
❑ 99SP Aut-114
❑ 99SP AutC-EC
❑ 99SP AutCG-EC
❑ 99SP SigAuto-EC
❑ 99SP SigAutoG-EC
❑ 99SP TopP-6
❑ 99SP TopP-26
❑ 99SP TopPC-EC
❑ 99SP TopPDtS-D7
❑ 99SP TopPGF-GF7
❑ 99SP TopPPE-6
❑ 99SP TopPPE-26
❑ 99SpoIll-44
❑ 99SpoIllOTW-9
❑ 99SPSig-12
❑ 99SPx-111
❑ 99SPxFinR-111
❑ 99SPxFinS-111
❑ 99StaClu-166
❑ 99StaCluC-SCC36
❑ 99StaCluCR-SCC36
❑ 99StaCluFDI-166
❑ 99StaCluNC-NC18
❑ 99StaCluOoaK-166
❑ 99StaCluPP-166
❑ 99ThuSkySupR-288
❑ 99Top-250
❑ 99TopAll-AM14
❑ 99TopAut-A15
❑ 99TopBlaLC1-8
❑ 99TopBlaLC2-8
❑ 99TopBlaLC3-8
❑ 99TopChr-250
❑ 99TopChrA-AE14
❑ 99TopChrAR-AE14
❑ 99TopChrF1-FF8
❑ 99TopChrF1R-FF8
❑ 99TopChrR-250
❑ 99TopGal-135
❑ 99TopGalAuto-GA3
❑ 99TopGalPP-135
❑ 99TopGalPPI-135
❑ 99TopGolL-8
❑ 99TopGolLC1-8
❑ 99TopGolLC2-8
❑ 99TopGolLOtO-8
❑ 99TopMVPP-250
❑ 99TopRedLC1-8
❑ 99TopRedLC2-8
❑ 99TopRedLC3-8
❑ 99TopSta-12
❑ 99TopSta-160
❑ 99TopSta1Foil-12
❑ 99TopSta2Foil-12
❑ 99TopSta3Foil-12
❑ 99TopStaBF-BF2
❑ 99TopStaBFFoil-BF2
❑ 99TopStaFoil-12
❑ 99TopStaFoil-160
❑ 99TopStaOS-12
❑ 99TopStaTS-12
❑ 99TopStaTS-12
❑ 99TopTek-29A
❑ 99TopTek-29B
❑ 99TopTekFP-F1
❑ 99TopTekG-29A
❑ 99TopTekG-29B
❑ 99UD Cho-22
❑ 99UD ChoPCR-22
❑ 99UDHolo-43
❑ 99UDHoloAUsome-43
❑ 99Ult-249
❑ 99UltGolM-249
❑ 99UltMas-249
❑ 99UltPlaM-249
❑ 99UppDec-4
❑ 99UppDecBD-109
❑ 99UppDecBDD-109
❑ 99UppDecBDQ-109
❑ 99UppDecBDT-109
❑ 99UppDecCf7-43
❑ 99UppDecCL-110
❑ 99UppDecCLCC-110
❑ 99UppDecCLM-C69
❑ 99UppDecCo7CE-43
❑ 99UppDecE-94
❑ 99UppDecEBPC-C-EC
❑ 99UppDecEFXG-94
❑ 99UppDecEL1-4
❑ 99UppDecEL2-4
❑ 99UppDecEPE-P21
❑ 99UppDecERE-R2
❑ 99UppDecEREFXG-R2
❑ 99UppDecF-F19
❑ 99UppDecFD-F19
❑ 99UppDecFQ-F19
❑ 99UppDecFT-F19
❑ 99UppDecGJ-EC
❑ 99UppDecM-150
❑ 99UppDecMGS-150
❑ 99UppDecMHFS-150
❑ 99UppDecMP-EC
❑ 99UppDecMSC-SC11
❑ 99UppDecMSS-150
❑ 99UppDecO-65
❑ 99UppDecOSO-65
❑ 99UppDecR-61
❑ 99UppDecRG-61
❑ 99UppDecRP-61
❑ 99UppDecTE-T19
❑ 99UppDecTED-T19
❑ 99UppDecTEQ-T19
❑ 99UppDecTET-T19
❑ 99UppDecVtaT-V21
❑ 99UppDecVtaTD-V21
❑ 99UppDecVtaTQ-V21
❑ 99UppDecVtaTT-V21
❑ 99Vic-278
Chavez, Harold P.
❑ 20WalMaiW-9
❑ 23Zee-29
❑ 25Zee-22
Chavez, Joe
❑ 86BeaGolGP-6
❑ 88WicPilRD-NNO
❑ 89WicWraR-NNO
Chavez, Mark
❑ 96AriBlaDB-11
Chavez, Pedro
❑ 80VenLeaS-116
❑ 83BirBarT-21
❑ 86NasSouTI-4
❑ 87GleFalTP-21
❑ 88TolMudHC-17
❑ 88TolMudHP-601
❑ 93LinVenB-3
❑ 94VenLinU-160
❑ 95LinVen-157
Chavez, Rafael
❑ 88BlaYNPRWL-102
❑ 88CalLeaACLC-42
❑ 88RivRedWCLC-209
❑ 88RivRedWP-1429
❑ 89BlaYNPRWL-110
❑ 89WicStaR-25
❑ 89WicWraR-14
❑ 90WicWraRD-4
❑ 91LinDriAA-603
❑ 91WicWraLD-603
❑ 91WicWraP-2592
❑ 91WicWraRD-2
❑ 94PorSeaDTI-9
Chavez, Raul
❑ 91BurAstC-13
❑ 91BurAstP-2807
❑ 92AshTouC-8
❑ 93LinVenB-263
❑ 93OscAstC-7
❑ 93OscAstF-631
❑ 94JacGenF-219
❑ 94VenLinU-5
❑ 95JacGenTI-13
❑ 95LinVen-87
❑ 96-97LinVen-14
❑ 97PacPriGotD-GD167
❑ 98PacInvGems-177
❑ 98TacRaiQ-9
Chavez, Sam (Samuel)
❑ 88CedRapRP-1160
❑ 89SouBenWSGS-9
❑ 90HunStaB-3
Chavez, Steve
❑ 96IdaFalB-3
❑ 97Bow-327
❑ 97BowInt-327
❑ 97RanCucQG-5
Chech, Charles
❑ 08AmeCarE91-70
❑ 09RamT20-24
❑ 12HomRunKE-3
❑ 12Zee-4
❑ 14Zee-6
❑ 15Zee-137
❑ 19Zee-127
Checo, Pedro
❑ 89BriTigS-4
Checo, Robinson
❑ 97Bes-19
❑ 97BesAutSBPP-10
❑ 97BesGun-1
❑ 97BesIntB-IB5
❑ 97Fle-518
❑ 97FleTif-518
❑ 98Bow-335
❑ 98BowChr-335
❑ 98BowChrGA-335
❑ 98BowChrGAR-335
❑ 98BowChrI-335
❑ 98BowChrIR-335
❑ 98BowChrR-335
❑ 98BowGolA-335
❑ 98BowInt-335
❑ 98Don-301
❑ 98DonGolPP-301
❑ 98DonSilPP-301
❑ 98MetUniPMG-145
❑ 98PawRedSQ-10
❑ 98UppDec-319
Cheek, Carey
❑ 86PriWilPP-6
Cheek, Harry (Harry G.)
❑ 10JuJuDE-8
❑ 12Zee-78
❑ 13Zee-77
Cheek, Jeff
❑ 93St.CatBJC-5
❑ 93St.CatBJF-3968
❑ 94St.CatBJF-3634
Cheek, Patrick
❑ 90PriPatD-4
❑ 91BatCliCB-7
❑ 91BatCliP-3489
Cheek, Shawn
❑ 98Cha-13
❑ 98SavSanGM-8
Cheeks, Maurice
❑ 80PhiBul-24
Cheetham, Sean
❑ 90HigSchPLS-5
❑ 90HunCubP-3273
❑ 90ProAaA-185
❑ 91Bow-414
❑ 91Cla/Bes-231
❑ 91WinSpiC-3
❑ 91WinSpiP-2822
❑ 92ClaFS7-315
❑ 92WinSpiC-6
❑ 92WinSpiF-1201
Cheeves, Chief (Virgil)
❑ 21Nei-84
❑ 22E120-155
❑ 22W572-12
❑ 22W573-18
❑ 27AmeCarE126-23
Cheff, Tyler
❑ 94BurIndC-6
❑ 94BurIndF-3797
Chelette, Mark
❑ 80SanJosMJitB-5
❑ 81WauTimT-23
Chelini, Dan
❑ 83ButCopKT-2
Chelini, Italo
❑ 33Zee-19
❑ 34BatR31-114
Chen, Bruce
❑ 95DanBraTI-4
❑ 96EugEmeB-4
❑ 97Bow-212
❑ 97BowChr-194
❑ 97BowChrI-194
❑ 97BowChrIR-194
❑ 97BowChrR-194
❑ 97BowInt-212
❑ 97MacBra-1
❑ 98Bes-9
❑ 98Bes-62
❑ 98BesBet-4
❑ 98BesCor-4
❑ 98BesPro-2
❑ 98Bow-131
❑ 98BowBes-118
❑ 98BowBesAR-118
❑ 98BowBesR-118
❑ 98BowChr-131
❑ 98BowChrGA-131
❑ 98BowChrGAR-131

❑ 98BowChrI-131
❑ 98BowChrIR-131
❑ 98BowChrR-131
❑ 98BowGolA-131
❑ 98BowInt-131
❑ 98ColCho-418
❑ 98ColChoPCR-418
❑ 98Don-332
❑ 98DonGolPP-332
❑ 98DonSig-120
❑ 98DonSigA-15
❑ 98DonSigAC-22
❑ 98DonSigAM-22
❑ 98DonSigP-120
❑ 98DonSilPP-332
❑ 98FleUpd-U12
❑ 98GreBraG-5
❑ 98LeaRS-239
❑ 98LeaRSLHolo-239
❑ 98LeaRSLong-239
❑ 98LeaRTrue-239
❑ 98PinSna-AB15
❑ 98SouLeaTPG-28
❑ 98SP Aut-13
❑ 98SP MinPE-22
❑ 98SPMin-22
❑ 98SPxFin-191
❑ 98SPxFinR-191
❑ 98SPxFinS-191
❑ 98UD3-16
❑ 98UD3-106
❑ 98UD3-196
❑ 98UD3DieCut-16
❑ 98UD3DieCut-106
❑ 98UD3DieCut-196
❑ 98UppDec-575
❑ 98UppDecDS-DS35
❑ 99199Fin-137
❑ 99BasAmeTP-21
❑ 99BasAmeTPA-6
❑ 99BasAmeTPG-21
❑ 99Bow-71
❑ 99BowAut-BA62
❑ 99BowBes-106
❑ 99BowBesAR-106
❑ 99BowBesFFMI-FF10
❑ 99BowBesFFMI-FF10
❑ 99BowBesFFMII-FF10
❑ 99BowBesMI-M5
❑ 99BowBesMIAR-M5
❑ 99BowBesMIR-M5
❑ 99BowBesR-106
❑ 99BowChr-71
❑ 99BowChrDA-DA8
❑ 99BowChrDAR-DA8
❑ 99BowChrG-71
❑ 99BowChrGR-71
❑ 99BowChrI-71
❑ 99BowChrIR-71
❑ 99BowChrR-71
❑ 99BowChrSC-SC7
❑ 99BowChrSCR-SC7
❑ 99BowGol-71
❑ 99BowInt-71
❑ 99BowScoC-SC7
❑ 99E-X Cen-106
❑ 99E-X CenECFut-106
❑ 99E-X CenECNow-106
❑ 99E-XCenA-4
❑ 99FinGolRef-137
❑ 99FinRef-137
❑ 99Fle-54
❑ 99FleBri-138
❑ 99FleBri2G-138
❑ 99FleBriBlu-138
❑ 99FleBriGol-138
❑ 99FleSta9-54
❑ 99FleWarT-54
❑ 99Pac-27
❑ 99Pac-27A
❑ 99PacOme-28
❑ 99PacOmeC-28
❑ 99PacOmeG-28
❑ 99PacOmePB-28
❑ 99PacPlaB-27
❑ 99PacPlaB-27A
❑ 99PacRed-27
❑ 99PacRed-27A
❑ 99SkyThu-282
❑ 99SkyThuRant-282
❑ 99SkyThuRave-282
❑ 99SP AutC-BC
❑ 99SP AutCG-BC
❑ 99SP SigAuto-BC
❑ 99SP SigAutoG-BC
❑ 99SP TopP-10
❑ 99SP TopP-27
❑ 99SP TopPC-BC
❑ 99SP TopPDtS-D8
❑ 99SP TopPGF-GF8
❑ 99SP TopPPE-10
❑ 99SP TopPPE-27
❑ 99SpoIll-46
❑ 99SPSig-53
❑ 99SPx-84
❑ 99SPxFinR-84
❑ 99SPxFinS-84
❑ 99StaClu-170
❑ 99StaCluC-SCC40
❑ 99StaCluCR-SCC40
❑ 99StaCluFDI-170
❑ 99StaCluOoaK-170
❑ 99StaCluPP-170
❑ 99TeaBesRA-5
❑ 99TeaBesRBG-4
❑ 99ThuSkySupR-282
❑ 99Top-210
❑ 99TopChr-210
❑ 99TopChrR-210
❑ 99TopGal-140
❑ 99TopGalPP-140
❑ 99TopGalPPI-140
❑ 99TopSta-38
❑ 99TopSta1Foil-38
❑ 99TopSta2Foil-38
❑ 99TopStaFoil-38
❑ 99TopStaOS-38
❑ 99TopStaTS-38
❑ 99TopTekFP-F9
❑ 99UD Cho-5
❑ 99UD ChoPCR-5
❑ 99UDHoloUDA-BC
❑ 99Ult-242
❑ 99UltGolM-242
❑ 99UltMas-242
❑ 99UltPlaM-242
❑ 99UppDec-271
❑ 99UppDecBD-94
❑ 99UppDecBDD-94
❑ 99UppDecBDQ-94
❑ 99UppDecBDT-94
❑ 99UppDecE-114
❑ 99UppDecEFXG-114
❑ 99UppDecEL1-271
❑ 99UppDecEL2-271
❑ 99UppDecERE-R4
❑ 99UppDecEREFXG-R4
❑ 99UppDecMP-BC
❑ 99UppDecO-72
❑ 99UppDecOSO-72
❑ 99Vic-27

Chen, Chin-Feng
❑ 99BasAmeTP-22
❑ 99BasAmeTPG-22

Chenevey, Jim
❑ 88MadMusP-10
❑ 88MidLeaAGS-53

Cheney, Larry
❑ 11PinT-5-903
❑ 14CraJacE-89
❑ 14PolGroW-4
❑ 15CraJacE-89
❑ 15SpoNewM-30
❑ 16FleBreD-15
❑ 16SpoNewM-31
❑ 17ColE13-27
❑ 90DodTar-124

Cheney, Tom
❑ 47Exh-42
❑ 57Top-359
❑ 61Top-494
❑ 63ExhStaB-14
❑ 63Fle-27
❑ 63Jel-99
❑ 63Pos-99
❑ 64ChatheY-27
❑ 77PirTCM1WC-26
❑ 78TCM60I-85

Chergey, Dan
❑ 93ElmPioC-5
❑ 93ElmPioF-3815
❑ 94BreCouMC-4
❑ 94BreCouMF-2
❑ 94FloStaLAF-FSL26
❑ 95PorSeaDTI-2
❑ 96ChaKniB-11
❑ 97PorSeaD-8

Cherry, Gus
❑ 85OmaRoyT-6

Cherry, Joe
❑ 76LauIndC-15
❑ 76LauIndC-32

Cherry, Lamar
❑ 90HigSchPLS-3
❑ 91MarPhiC-12
❑ 91MarPhiP-3459
❑ 92BatCliCB-5
❑ 92BatCliF-3271
❑ 92SpaPhiC-15
❑ 92SpaPhiF-1275

Cherry, Michael
❑ 85VerBeaDT-23
❑ 86VerBeaDP-3

Cherry, Paul
❑ 83SprCarF-3
❑ 86ArkTraP-4
❑ 87LouRedTI-9
❑ 88TolMudHC-9
❑ 88TolMudHP-591

Chervinko, Paul
❑ 90DodTar-912

Chesbro, Jack
❑ 03BreE10-19
❑ 04FanCraAL-7
❑ 05RotCP-2
❑ 08RosComP-44
❑ 09T206-63
❑ 11SpoLifCW-60
❑ 39PC7AlbHoF-41
❑ 48ExhHoF-4
❑ 50CalHOFW-15
❑ 53ArtHaloFP-14
❑ 61Fle-13
❑ 61Top-407
❑ 63BazA-3
❑ 67SpoHobFC-51
❑ 68SCFOldT-10
❑ 69Baz-9
❑ 72FleFamF-39
❑ 72LauGreF-12
❑ 74CapPub-26
❑ 76ShaPiz-41
❑ 79Top-416
❑ 80PerHaloFP-41
❑ 80SSPHOF-41
❑ 82TCMGreP-19
❑ 84GalHaloFRL-41
❑ 85Woo-7
❑ 92YanWIZH-5
❑ 94OriofB-92

Cheshier, Casey
❑ 98EugEme-7

Cheshire, Donnie
❑ 78St.PetCT-5

Chesnes, Bob
❑ 49Bow-13
❑ 50Bow-70
❑ 85TCMPla1-18

Cheso, Reno
❑ 49SomandK-11
❑ 53MotCoo-33
❑ 53SanFraSTI-3

Chesterfield, Roy
❑ 31Zee-82

Chestnut, Troy
❑ 87KnoBluJP-1500

Chevalier, Bonel
❑ 89BelMarL-23
❑ 90BenBucL-7

Chevalier, Virgil
❑ 96Exc-11
❑ 96HilStaHWB-32
❑ 96MicBatCB-8
❑ 96MidLeaAB-42
❑ 97SarRedS-4

Chevez, Tony
❑ 78RocRedWT-4
❑ 79RocRedWT-19
❑ 91OriCro-75

Chevolek, Tom
❑ 80ElPasDT-5

Chew, Greg
❑ 94WelPirC-6
❑ 94WelPirF-3485

Chiaffredo, Paul
❑ 97St.CatSB-12
❑ 98DunBluJSB-9
❑ 98DunBluJTI-7

Chiamparino, Scott
❑ 88HunStaTI-2
❑ 88ModA'sCLC-64
❑ 88ModA'sTI-8
❑ 90CMC-580
❑ 90ProAAAF-133
❑ 90ScoRoo-108T
❑ 90TacTigC-3
❑ 90TacTigP-86
❑ 90TriAllGP-AAA49
❑ 91Bow-282
❑ 91Cla1-T84
❑ 91ClaGam-183
❑ 91Don-42
❑ 91DonPre-3
❑ 91Lea-401
❑ 91MajLeaCP-37
❑ 91OPC-676
❑ 91RanMot-14
❑ 91Sco-352A
❑ 91Sco-352B
❑ 91Sco100RS-14
❑ 91ScoRoo-29
❑ 91SouOreAAP-SOA25
❑ 91StaClu-384
❑ 91Stu-122
❑ 91Top-676
❑ 91TopDeb90-30
❑ 91TopDesS-676
❑ 91TopMic-676
❑ 91TopTif-676
❑ 91Ult-375
❑ 91UppDec-8
❑ 92OPC-277
❑ 92RanMot-14
❑ 92RanTeal-4
❑ 92Sco-688
❑ 92StaClu-896
❑ 92Top-277
❑ 92TopGol-277
❑ 92TopGolW-277
❑ 92TopMic-277
❑ 93Don-738
❑ 93Fle-422
❑ 93MarlStaClu-7
❑ 93RanKee-102
❑ 93Sco-386
❑ 93Top-64
❑ 93Top-711
❑ 93TopGol-64
❑ 93TopGol-711
❑ 93TopInaM-64
❑ 93TopInaM-711
❑ 93TopInaR-64
❑ 93TopInaR-711
❑ 93TopMic-64
❑ 93TopMic-711
❑ 93TriPla-63
❑ 94LasVegSF-865

Chiaramonte, Giuseppe
❑ 98BesAutSS-10
❑ 98SanJosGQ-2
❑ 99BasAmeTP-23
❑ 99BasAmeTPG-23
❑ 99Bow-395
❑ 99BowBes-190
❑ 99BowBesAR-190
❑ 99BowBesR-190
❑ 99BowGol-395
❑ 99BowInt-395
❑ 99JustheS-14
❑ 99JustheSJB-14
❑ 99StaClu-145
❑ 99StaCluFDI-145
❑ 99StaCluOoaK-145
❑ 99StaCluPP-145

Chick, Bruce
❑ 91CarLeaAP-CAR22
❑ 91Cla/Bes-13
❑ 91LynRedSC-20
❑ 91LynRedSP-1210
❑ 92NewBriRSF-446
❑ 92NewBriRSS-480
❑ 92SkyAA F-204
❑ 94NewBriRSF-661

Chickasaw, Chief
❑ 96MemChiB-5

Chicken, Chano
❑ 85MexCitTT-29

Chicken, Famous (San Diego)
❑ 79PadFamF-4
❑ 82Don-531A
❑ 82Don-531B
❑ 83Don-645
❑ 84Don-651
❑ 84PadSmo-4
❑ 85DalNatCC-7
❑ 92TriPla-138

Chicken, Kasey the KFC
❑ 97El PasDB-29
❑ 98El PasDG-7

Chicken, Nashua Angel
❑ 83NasAngT-27

Chiefs, Peoria
❑ 89PeoChiTI-14

Chiefs, Syracuse
❑ 87IntLeaAT-42
❑ 92SyrChiMB-31

Chiffer, Floyd
❑ 81HawIsIT-18
❑ 83Don-44
❑ 83Fle-354
❑ 83Top-298
❑ 85TolMudHT-32
❑ 87RicBraBC-2
❑ 87RicBraC-28
❑ 87RicBraT-2

Chikida, Honen
❑ 89SalSpuP-1812

Child, Casey
❑ 97BoiHawG-4
❑ 98CedRapKTI-5

Childers, Bob
❑ 88AlaGolTI-6

Childers, Chabon
❑ 92OklStaC-4

Childers, Jason
❑ 97HelBreB-8
❑ 98BelSnaM-6

Childers, Jeffrey
❑ 85BeaGolGT-1
❑ 88ModA'sTI-7
❑ 88WicPilRD-30

Childers, Matt
❑ 97HelBreB-9

Childers, Terry
❑ 93PitMetC-3
❑ 93PitMetF-3712

Childress, Billy
❑ 92HunCubF-3137
❑ 93HunCubC-5
❑ 93HunCubF-3229

Childress, Chip
❑ 83DurBulT-1
❑ 84DurBulT-13
❑ 85DurBulT-20
❑ 86GreBraTI-5

Childress, Rocky
❑ 85PhiTas-45
❑ 85PorBeaC-31
❑ 86PhiTas-50
❑ 87TucTorP-10
❑ 88Don-554
❑ 88Fle-442
❑ 88FleGlo-442
❑ 88Top-643
❑ 88TopTif-643
❑ 88TucTorC-8
❑ 88TucTorJP-6
❑ 88TucTorP-181
❑ 89TucTorC-1
❑ 89TucTorJP-4
❑ 89TucTorP-194
❑ 90CMC-354
❑ 90ProAAAF-267
❑ 90TidTidC-3
❑ 90TidTidP-536

Childress, Willie J.
❑ 87GreBraB-11

Childs, Cupid (Clarence A.)
❑ 87OldJudN-77
❑ 93JusSo-2
❑ 98CamPepP-10

Childs, Harry
❑ 29Zee-17
❑ 30Zee-25

Childs, Mike
❑ 79AshTouT-20

Chiles, Barry
❑ 90PulBraB-2
❑ 90PulBraP-3100
❑ 91MacBraC-1
❑ 91MacBraP-855
❑ 92DurBulC-20
❑ 92DurBulF-1092
❑ 92DurBulTI-34
❑ 93DurBulC-5
❑ 93DurBulF-479
❑ 93DurBulTI-34

Chiles, Bill
❑ 74HawIsIC-107

Chiles, Rich (Richard F.)
❑ 71AstTeal-3
❑ 72OPC-56
❑ 72Top-56
❑ 73OPC-617
❑ 73Top-617
❑ 78Top-193
❑ 78TwiFriP-4
❑ 79TacTugT-20
❑ 79Top-498
❑ 91MetWIZ-72
❑ 92CarMudF-1196
❑ 92CarMudS-150

Chimelis, Joel
❑ 88SouOreAP-1703
❑ 89ModA'sC-22
❑ 89ModA'sCLC-279
❑ 90ModA'sC-5
❑ 90RenSilSCLC-267
❑ 91HunStaC-7
❑ 91HunStaLD-282
❑ 91HunStaP-1802
❑ 91HunStaTI-5
❑ 91LinDriAA-282
❑ 92ClaFS7-446
❑ 92ShrCapF-3878
❑ 92ShrCapS-578
❑ 93Bow-464
❑ 93ClaFS7-161
❑ 93ExcFS7-114
❑ 93PhoFirF-1520
❑ 94ShrCapF-1611
❑ 95PhoFirTI-11
❑ 95Top-581

Chin, Chien Wei
❑ 90IBAWorA-13

Ching, Darcie
❑ 91HawWomS-1

Ching, Mo (Maurice)
❑ 83GreHorT-17
❑ 84GreHorT-22
❑ 86AlbYanT-18

Chinita, Clasico De La
❑ 96-97LinVen-126

Chiozza, Lou (Louis Peo)
❑ 34DiaMatCSB-27
❑ 34DiaStaR-80
❑ 35DiaMatCS2-4
❑ 35DiaMatCS3T1-31
❑ 38OurNatGPP-2
❑ 39PlaBal-58
❑ 40PlaBal-157
❑ 41Gou-3
❑ 94ConTSN-1074
❑ 94ConTSNB-1074

Chipman, Bob (Robert)
❑ 47TipTop-106
❑ 49Bow-184
❑ 49EurSta-54
❑ 50Bow-192
❑ 52Bow-228
❑ 52Top-388
❑ 83TCMPla1944-33
❑ 83TopRep5-388
❑ 90DodTar-125

Chireno, Manny
❑ 87BelBreP-24

Chirinos, Dario
❑ 76VenLeaS-195
❑ 80VenLeaS-232

Chism, Tom (Thomas R.)
❑ 78RocRedWT-5
❑ 79RocRedWT-18
❑ 81RocRedWT-4
❑ 81RocRedWW-24
❑ 82RocRedWT-21
❑ 83RocRedWT-23
❑ 91OriCro-76

Chisum, Dave
❑ 91BurIndP-3306
❑ 92WatIndC-16
❑ 92WatIndF-3246

Chitford, Erie
❑ 93StoPorF-755

Chiti, Dom
❑ 79SavBraT-1
❑ 85ChaO'sT-13
❑ 86RocRedWP-2
❑ 87RocRedWP-15
❑ 87RocRedWT-25
❑ 88RocRedWGCP-28
❑ 88RocRedWP-212
❑ 88RocRedWTI-5
❑ 92IndFanC-30
❑ 93IndWUA-33

Chiti, Harry Dominick
❑ 53BowC-7
❑ 55Bow-304

❑ 56A'sPos-9
❑ 56Top-179
❑ 58Top-119
❑ 59Top-79
❑ 59TopVen-79
❑ 60Top-339
❑ 61Top-269
❑ 61TopStal-149
❑ 62Top-253
❑ 79DiaGre-119
❑ 91MetWIZ-73
Chitren, Steve (Stephen)
❑ 86AncGlaPTI-6
❑ 87AncGlaP-4
❑ 89MedAthB-20
❑ 90Bes-279
❑ 90HunStaB-4
❑ 91A'sMot-27
❑ 91Bow-214
❑ 91Don-431
❑ 91Lea-486
❑ 91Sco-760
❑ 91SouOreAAP-SOA15
❑ 91TopDeb90-31
❑ 91Ult-376
❑ 91UppDec-753
❑ 92Bow-506
❑ 92Don-385
❑ 92Fle-253
❑ 92FleRooS-14
❑ 92Lea-32
❑ 92LeaBlaG-32
❑ 92OPC-379
❑ 92Pin-236
❑ 92Sco-202
❑ 92SkyAAAF-238
❑ 92StaClu-518
❑ 92TacTigF-2496
❑ 92TacTigS-530
❑ 92Top-379
❑ 92TopGol-379
❑ 92TopGolW-379
❑ 92TopMic-379
❑ 92UppDec-471
❑ 93HunStaF-2077
❑ 94BowBayF-2407
❑ 94OriPro-19
❑ 95RocRedWTI-10
Chittum, Nelson
❑ 60Top-296
❑ 63RocRedWSP-5
Chiyomaru, Akihiko
❑ 90GatCitPP-3339
❑ 90GatCitPSP-6
Chlan, Greg
❑ 75OmaRoyTI-4
Chlupsa, Bob
❑ 70CarTeal-8
❑ 71OPC-594
❑ 71Top-594
Chmil, Steve
❑ 83DurBulT-2
Cho, Jin Ho
❑ 98DonSig-136
❑ 98DonSigP-136
❑ 98LeaRS-315
❑ 98LeaRSLHolo-315
❑ 98LeaRSLong-315
❑ 98LeaRTrue-315
❑ 98TreThuM-27
❑ 99BasAmeTP-24
❑ 99BasAmeTPG-24
❑ 99FleBri-164
❑ 99FleBri2G-164
❑ 99FleBriBlu-164
❑ 99FleBriGol-164
❑ 99PacOme-39
❑ 99PacOmeC-39
❑ 99PacOmeG-39
❑ 99PacOmePB-39
❑ 99SP Aut-95
❑ 99SpoIll-65
❑ 99SPx-87
❑ 99SPxFinR-87
❑ 99SPxFinS-87
❑ 99UD Cho-2
❑ 99UD ChoPCR-2
❑ 99UppDec-5
❑ 99UppDecEL1-5
❑ 99UppDecEL2-5
❑ 99Vic-59
Choate, Don
❑ 60TacBan-3
❑ 61UniOil-P6
❑ 77FriOneYW-64
Choate, John
❑ 94WatIndC-4
❑ 94WatIndF-3950
❑ 95WatIndTI-9
Choate, Mark
❑ 90MedHatBJB-6
❑ 91MyrBeaHC-18
❑ 91MyrBeaHP-2952
❑ 92St.CatBJC-13
❑ 92St.CatBJF-3394
Choi, Ray
❑ 95BoiHawTI-9
❑ 97SarRedS-5
Cholowsky, Dan
❑ 91ClaDraP-35
❑ 91FroRowDP-5
❑ 91FroRowDPG-5
❑ 91FroRowDPS-5
❑ 92ClaFS7-370
❑ 92SavCarC-18
❑ 92SavCarF-667
❑ 92StaCluD-27
❑ 93Bow-488
❑ 93ClaGolF-95
❑ 93SouAtlLAPI-8
❑ 93SouAtlLAPI-6
❑ 93St.PetCC-10
❑ 93St.PetCF-2633
❑ 94ArkTraF-3095
❑ 94UppDecML-42
❑ 95ArkTraTI-7
❑ 97IowCub-9
❑ 98ColSprSS-21
Chorley, Dave
❑ 74SalLakCAC-94
Chouinard, Bobby
❑ 92KanCouCC-20
❑ 92KanCouCF-82
❑ 92KanCouCTI-5
❑ 92MidLeaATI-5
❑ 93ClaFS7-48
❑ 93ModA'sC-5
❑ 93ModA'sF-791
❑ 94ModA'sC-6
❑ 94ModA'sF-3058
❑ 95HunStaTI-7
❑ 96A'sMot-16
❑ 96BowBes-176
❑ 96BowBesAR-176
❑ 96BowBesR-176
❑ 97Fle-187
❑ 97FleTif-187
❑ 97Top-237
❑ 97Ult-110
❑ 97UltGolME-110
❑ 97UltPlaME-110
❑ 97UppDec-283
❑ 98LouRedQ-3
Chourio, Joe
❑ 76VenLeaS-211
Chozen, Myer
❑ 33Zee-21
Chris, Mike
❑ 80EvaTriT-5
❑ 80Top-666
❑ 81EvaTriT-3
❑ 82PhoGiaVNB-2
❑ 83GiaPos-6
❑ 85TacTigC-149
Chrisley, Neil (Barbra O.)
❑ 57Top-320
❑ 58SeaTeal-6
❑ 58Top-303
❑ 59Top-189
❑ 59TopVen-189
❑ 60Lea-117
❑ 60Top-273
❑ 62Top-308
Chrisman, Jim
❑ 91AppFoxCB-2
❑ 91AppFoxP-1708
❑ 92BasCitRC-10
❑ 92BasCitRF-3837
❑ 93WilBluRC-6
❑ 93WilBluRF-1990
Chrismon, Thad
❑ 95EugEmeTI-21
Christ, Michael
❑ 87ChaLooB-11
❑ 88CalCanC-6
Christenbury, Lloyd
❑ 23WilChoV-18
Christensen, Bruce R.
❑ 74PhoGiaC-86
❑ 75PhoGiaC-10
❑ 75PhoGiaCK-15
❑ 76PheGiaCr-17
❑ 76PhoGiaCa-2
❑ 76PhoGiaCC-5
❑ 76PhoGiaVNB-3
Christensen, Cuckoo (Walter)
❑ 29Zee-40
❑ 30Zee-49
Christensen, Jim
❑ 80WisRapTT-15
❑ 82TolMudHT-13
❑ 83TacTigT-30A
Christensen, John L.
❑ 84TidTidT-4
❑ 85MetColP-12
❑ 85MetTCM-31
❑ 86Don-360
❑ 86PawRedSP-5
❑ 86PawRedSP-6
❑ 86Top-287
❑ 86TopTif-287
❑ 87MarMot-27
❑ 87TopTra-23T
❑ 87TopTraT-23T
❑ 88CalCanC-17
❑ 88CalCanP-794
❑ 88Sco-419A
❑ 88Sco-419B
❑ 88ScoGlo-419A
❑ 88ScoGlo-419B
❑ 88Top-413
❑ 88TopTif-413
❑ 89Fle-108
❑ 89FleGlo-108
❑ 89PorBeaC-19
❑ 89PorBeaP-214
❑ 91MetWIZ-74
Christensen, McKay
❑ 94SigRooDP-6
❑ 94SigRooDPS-6
❑ 95Pin-167
❑ 95PinArtP-167
❑ 95PinMusC-167
❑ 95ScoDraP-DP1
❑ 95ScoSam-DP8
❑ 95SelSurS-SS7
❑ 95Top-473
❑ 97HicCraB-8
❑ 97HicCraRB-9
❑ 97SouAtlTPB-23
❑ 98WinWar-8
❑ 99DumSet-120
❑ 99FleMys-120
❑ 99FleMysM-120
❑ 99PacInv-34
❑ 99PacInvOD-34
❑ 99PacInvPB-34
Christenson, Gary
❑ 81OmaRoyT-5
Christenson, Kim
❑ 83AppFoxFr-4
❑ 84PriWilPT-25
❑ 85NasPirT-5
Christenson, Larry
❑ 74OPC-587
❑ 74Top-587
❑ 75OPC-551
❑ 75PhiPhiP-10
❑ 75Top-551
❑ 75TopMin-551
❑ 76OPC-634
❑ 76PhiPhiP-8
❑ 76SSP-460
❑ 76Top-634
❑ 77OPC-194
❑ 77Top-59
❑ 78OPC-17
❑ 78SSP270-47
❑ 78Top-247
❑ 79OPC-260
❑ 79PhiBurK-5
❑ 79Top-493
❑ 80OPC-89
❑ 80PhiBul-42
❑ 80PhiBurK-16
❑ 80Top-161
❑ 81Fle-8
❑ 81Top-346
❑ 82Don-219
❑ 82Fle-244
❑ 82Top-544
❑ 83Don-345
❑ 83Fle-156
❑ 83FleSta-38
❑ 83OPC-286
❑ 83PhiTas-5
❑ 83Top-668
❑ 84Nes792-252
❑ 84Top-252
❑ 84TopTif-252
Christenson, Ryan
❑ 97VisOakG-6
❑ 98A'sMot-20
❑ 98Bes-10
❑ 98Don-207
❑ 98DonGolPP-207
❑ 98DonSilPP-207
❑ 98JohCCTI-8
❑ 98LeaRCrusUP-115
❑ 98LeaRS-229
❑ 98LeaRSCrusUG-115
❑ 98LeaRSCrusUR-115
❑ 98LeaRSLHolo-229
❑ 98LeaRSLong-229
❑ 98LeaRTrue-229
❑ 98PacOme-174
❑ 98PacOmeR-174
❑ 98PacOmeRS-28
❑ 98PacOmeRST3-28
❑ 98PacOnl-527
❑ 98PacOnlR-527
❑ 98PacOnlWC-527
❑ 98SPxFin-193
❑ 98SPxFinR-193
❑ 98SPxFinS-193
❑ 98UppDec-547
❑ 98UppDecDS-DS32
❑ 99Fle-390
❑ 99FleSta9-390
❑ 99FleWarT-390
❑ 99Pac-309
❑ 99PacAur-134
❑ 99PacAurOD-134
❑ 99PacCroC-201
❑ 99PacCroCPB-201
❑ 99PacInv-106
❑ 99PacInvOD-106
❑ 99PacInvPB-106
❑ 99PacPar-169
❑ 99PacParC-169
❑ 99PacParG-169
❑ 99PacParHoloGold-169
❑ 99PacParHS-169
❑ 99PacParOD-169
❑ 99PacParPB-169
❑ 99PacParRed-169
❑ 99PacPlaB-309
❑ 99PacPriS-71
❑ 99PacPriS206-71
❑ 99PacPriS206R-71
❑ 99PacRed-309
❑ 99SkyThu-51
❑ 99SkyThuRant-51
❑ 99SkyThuRave-51
❑ 99ThuSkySupR-51
❑ 99Top-88
❑ 99TopMVPP-88
❑ 99UppDec-164
❑ 99UppDecEL1-164
❑ 99UppDecEL2-164
❑ 99UppDecM-153
❑ 99UppDecMGS-153
❑ 99UppDecMHFS-153
❑ 99UppDecMSS-153
❑ 99Vic-285
❑ 99WesMicWAM-4
Christian, C. V.
❑ 12PCLPin-3
❑ 24Zee-125
❑ 25Zee-151
❑ 26Zee-43
❑ 27Zee-22
Christian, Eddie
❑ 92FroRowDP-46
❑ 92FroRowDPG-46
❑ 92FroRowDPS-46
❑ 93KanCouCC-3
❑ 93KanCouCF-927
❑ 93KanCouCTI-3
❑ 93Top-683
❑ 93TopGol-683
❑ 93TopInaM-683
❑ 93TopInaR-683
❑ 93TopMic-683
❑ 94PorSeaDF-689
❑ 94PorSeaDTI-10
❑ 96MidAngOHP-8
❑ 98MidAngG-8
❑ 98MidAngO-7
Christian, Rick
❑ 86EriCarP-6
❑ 87EriCarP-1
❑ 88HamRedP-1724
❑ 89St.PetCS-6
❑ 90ArkTraGS-8
❑ 91ArkTraLD-29
❑ 91ArkTraP-1299
❑ 91LinDriAA-29
❑ 92LouRedS-256
Christian, Robert
❑ 69OPC-173
❑ 69Top-173
❑ 69TopFou-21
❑ 70OPC-51
❑ 70Top-51
Christian, Tyler
❑ 09ObaT21-12
❑ 09ObaT21-99
❑ 09ObaT21-270
❑ 11PacCoaBD-14
❑ 11Zee-23
❑ 12ObaPreT-19
❑ 12Zee-26
❑ 13Zee-26
❑ 14Zee-30
❑ 15Zee-28
Christiansen, Clay
❑ 82NasSouTI-7
❑ 83ColCliT-9
❑ 84ColCliP-5
❑ 84ColCliT-12
❑ 85ColCliP-5
❑ 85ColCliT-4
❑ 85Don-396
❑ 85Top-211
❑ 85TopTif-211
❑ 85YanTCMP-9
❑ 86AlbYanT-28
❑ 86ColCliP-3
❑ 86ColCliP-3
❑ 88TucTorP-179
❑ 92YanWIZ8-31
Christiansen, Jason
❑ 92AugPirC-7
❑ 92SalBucC-11
❑ 92SalBucF-55
❑ 93CarLeaAGF-47
❑ 93SalBucC-4
❑ 93SalBucF-422
❑ 94CarMudF-1570
❑ 95Fla-397
❑ 95FleUpd-146
❑ 95PirFil-4
❑ 95StaClu-596
❑ 95StaCluMOP-596
❑ 95StaCluSTWS-596
❑ 95UltGolMR-M7
❑ 96Fle-516
❑ 96FleTif-516
❑ 96LeaSigEA-28
❑ 96Pac-168
❑ 96PacPri-P56
❑ 96PacPriG-P56
❑ 97Pac-391
❑ 97PacLigB-391
❑ 97PacPriGotD-GD189
❑ 97PacSil-391
❑ 97PirPos-6
❑ 98Pac-392
❑ 98PacOnl-579
❑ 98PacOnlR-579
❑ 98PacOnlWC-579
❑ 98PacPlaB-392
❑ 98PacRedT-392
❑ 98PacSil-392
❑ 99Fle-345
❑ 99FleSta9-345
❑ 99FleWarT-345
❑ 99MetUni-192
❑ 99MetUniGM-192
❑ 99MetUniPMG-192
❑ 99SkyPre-178
❑ 99SkyPreR-178
❑ 99StaClu-298
❑ 99StaCluFDI-298
❑ 99StaCluOoaK-298
❑ 99StaCluPP-298
Christiansen, Jeff
❑ 89AncGlaP-6
Christiansen, Ryan
❑ 99TopChr-88
❑ 99TopChrR-88
Christianson, Alex
❑ 79WauTimT-19
Christianson, Robby
❑ 97EveAquG-4
Christman, Mark J.
❑ 46SeaSLP-10
❑ 46SpoExcW-2-8
❑ 49Bow-121
❑ 83TCMPla1944-2
❑ 96Bro194F-26
Christman, Scott
❑ 94Bow-211
❑ 94Cla-164
❑ 94ClaGolF-153
❑ 94ClaGolN1PLF-LP2
❑ 94Pin-266
❑ 94PinArtP-266
❑ 94PinMusC-266
❑ 94PriWilCC-8
❑ 94PriWilCF-1914
❑ 94Sco-548
❑ 94ScoGolR-548
❑ 95Bow-9
❑ 97BirBarB-7
Christman, Tim
❑ 96PorRocB-11
❑ 97AshTou-7
Christmas, Maurice
❑ 93ClaGolF-148
❑ 93DanBraC-8
❑ 93DanBraF-3612
❑ 94MacBraC-3
❑ 94MacBraF-2196
❑ 95DurBulTI-8
❑ 96MacBraB-5
Christmas, Steve (Stephen R.)
❑ 80WatRedT-3
❑ 81WatRedT-12
❑ 82IndIndTI-22
❑ 83TucTorT-12
❑ 85BufBisT-4
❑ 86CubGat-18
❑ 86IowCubP-6
Christmon, Drew
❑ 93BriTigC-6
❑ 93BriTigF-3659
❑ 94FayGenC-6
❑ 94FayGenF-2160
Christofferson, Bob
❑ 83TacTigT-25B
Christoperson, Dave
❑ 85RedWinA-7
❑ 86RedWinA-10
Christopher, Chris
❑ 93JohCitCC-7
❑ 93JohCitCF-3694
❑ 94SavCarC-10
❑ 94SavCarF-519
❑ 94SouAtlLAF-SAL48
Christopher, Fred
❑ 86BenPhiC-143
❑ 87SpaPhiP-27
❑ 88ClePhiS-7
❑ 89ClePhiS-6
❑ 89ReaPhiS-7
❑ 90ReaPhiP-1215
Christopher, Joe
❑ 61Top-82
❑ 63Top-217
❑ 64Top-546
❑ 65Baz-20
❑ 65ChaTheY-25
❑ 65MetPos-2
❑ 65Top-495
❑ 65TopEmbl-52
❑ 65TopTral-43
❑ 66Top-343
❑ 66TopVen-343
❑ 76Met63 S-3
❑ 77PirTCM1WC-14
❑ 78TCM60I-7
❑ 82MetGal62-17
❑ 91MetWIZ-75
Christopher, Lloyd
❑ 43CenFlo-4
❑ 44CenFlo-3
❑ 47SigOil-24
❑ 47TipTop-18
❑ 48SigOil-3
❑ 48SmiClo-5
❑ 49RemBre-4
❑ 50RemBre-3
Christopher, Mike
❑ 86Ft.LauYP-6
❑ 87Ft.LauYP-8
❑ 88AlbYanP-1337
❑ 89AlbYanB-22
❑ 89AlbYanP-321
❑ 89AlbYanSt-4
❑ 90AlbDukCm-1

❑ 90AlbDukP-336
❑ 90AlbDukTr-4
❑ 90CMC-403
❑ 90ProAAAF-57
❑ 91AlbDukLD-3
❑ 91AlbDukP-1134
❑ 91LinDriAAA-3
❑ 92Bow-374
❑ 92ColSprSSF-744
❑ 92ColSprSSS-80
❑ 92DonRoo-23
❑ 92Fle-654
❑ 92SkyAAAF-36
❑ 92StaClu-612
❑ 92StaCluECN-612
❑ 92TopDeb91-34
❑ 93IndWUA-5
❑ 93OPCPre-11
❑ 93PacSpa-408
❑ 93StaClu-308
❑ 93StaCluFDI-308
❑ 93StaCluMOP-308
❑ 93Top-786
❑ 93TopGol-786
❑ 93TopInaM-786
❑ 93TopInaR-786
❑ 93TopMic-786
❑ 94TolMudHF-1019
❑ 95TolMudHTI-10
❑ 97ColSprSATTI-13

Christopher, Russ
❑ 42A'sTeal-10
❑ 43A'STEAI-8
❑ 45A'sTeal-7
❑ 46A'sTeal-4
❑ 47A'sTeal-6
❑ 48IndTeal-5
❑ 74CapPub-10

Christopher, Terry
❑ 92BelBreCB-3
❑ 92BelBreFl-397

Christopher, Tyron
❑ 92GulCoaYF-3782

Christopherson, Eric
❑ 89AncGlaP-7
❑ 89SanDieSAS-6
❑ 90ClaDraP-19
❑ 90ClaYel-T87
❑ 90EveGiaB-13
❑ 90EveGiaP-3129
❑ 90ProAaA-170
❑ 90SanDieSA3-3
❑ 91Bow-635
❑ 91Cla/Bes-320
❑ 91CliGiaC-14
❑ 91CliGiaP-836
❑ 91MidLeaAP-MWL3
❑ 91Sco-672
❑ 92Bow-38
❑ 92ClaFS7-254
❑ 92ProFS7-354
❑ 92ShrCapF-3874
❑ 92ShrCapS-579
❑ 92SkyAA F-255
❑ 92UppDecML-128
❑ 93ExcFS7-115
❑ 94ShrCapF-1609
❑ 95PhoFirTI-16
❑ 98NorTidP-5
❑ 98NorTidQ-6

Christopherson, Gary
❑ 91BurAstC-14
❑ 91BurAstP-2808
❑ 92OscAstC-8
❑ 92OscAstF-2535

Christy, Al
❑ 83PeoSunF-19

Christy, Claude
❑ 53MotCoo-47

Chrysler, Clint
❑ 98EveAquG-4
❑ 98WisTimRM-4

Chue, Jose
❑ 79CedRapGT-18
❑ 80CliGiaT-3
❑ 81CliGiaT-7

Chueden, Chris
❑ 82MonNew-4

Chumas, Steve
❑ 83IdaFalAT-18

Chun, Bo
❑ 92VerBeaDF-2894

Chung, Lo-Kuo
❑ 90IBAWorA-34

Chung, Rocky
❑ 98SanBerS-7
❑ 98SanBerSTIS-7

Church, Bubba (Emory)
❑ 47Exh-43
❑ 50PhiPhil-5
❑ 51Bow-149
❑ 52Bow-40
❑ 52Top-323
❑ 53BowC-138
❑ 53Top-47
❑ 55Bow-273
❑ 75Phi195T-6
❑ 80Phi195T-6
❑ 83TopRep5-323
❑ 91TopArc1-47

Church, Dan
❑ 80AndBraT-1

Church, Donald
❑ 86BenPhiC-138

Church, Edwin
❑ 30Zee-50

Church, Hi (Hiram Lincoln)
❑ 19Zee-85

Church, Len
❑ 77FriOneYW-71

Churchill, James
❑ 82AleDukT-16

Churchill, Norman
❑ 77WatIndT-5
❑ 79QuaCitCT-27
❑ 80QuaCitCT-12

Churchill, Tim
❑ 88MarPhiS-6
❑ 89BatCliP-1919
❑ 89SpaPhiP-1053
❑ 89SpaPhiS-4
❑ 90SpaPhiB-14
❑ 90SpaPhiP-2496
❑ 90SpaPhiS-3

Churn, Chuck
❑ 59DarFar-4
❑ 59SeaPop-4
❑ 60DarFar-13
❑ 90DodTar-126

Chylak, Nestar
❑ 55Bow-283

Ciaglo, Paul
❑ 88CapCodPPaLP-6
❑ 89JamExpP-2135
❑ 90WesPalBES-2

Ciammachilli, Franco
❑ 77ReaPhiT-4

Ciampa, Mike
❑ 80ElmPioRST-27

Cianfrocco, Archi
❑ 87JamExpP-2539
❑ 88RocExpLC-6
❑ 89JacExpB-11
❑ 89JacExpP-160
❑ 90JacExpB-4
❑ 90JacExpP-1380
❑ 91HarSenLD-252
❑ 91HarSenP-632
❑ 91LinDriAA-252
❑ 92Bow-450
❑ 92DonRoo-24
❑ 92ExpPos-9
❑ 92Lea-493
❑ 92LeaBlaG-493
❑ 92Pin-510
❑ 92ScoRoo-99T
❑ 92StaClu-802
❑ 92StaCluECN-802
❑ 92TopTra-23T
❑ 92TopTraG-23T
❑ 92Ult-515
❑ 92UltAllR-4
❑ 92UppDec-772
❑ 92UppDecSR-SR5
❑ 93Don-246
❑ 93ExpColP7-2
❑ 93Fle-72
❑ 93OPC-112
❑ 93PacSpa-182
❑ 93Pin-349
❑ 93Sco-340
❑ 93SP-165
❑ 93StaClu-388
❑ 93StaCluFDI-388
❑ 93StaCluMOP-388
❑ 93Top-151
❑ 93TopGol-151
❑ 93TopInaM-151
❑ 93TopInaR-151
❑ 93TopMic-151
❑ 93Ult-63
❑ 93UppDec-736
❑ 93UppDecGold-736
❑ 94Bow-672
❑ 94ColC-77
❑ 94ColChoGS-77
❑ 94ColChoSS-77
❑ 94Don-493
❑ 94Fin-144
❑ 94FinRef-144
❑ 94Fla-232
❑ 94Fle-659
❑ 94FleExtB-371
❑ 94Lea-79
❑ 94PadMot-7
❑ 94Pin-331
❑ 94PinArtP-331
❑ 94PinMusC-331
❑ 94Sel-138
❑ 94StaClu-221
❑ 94StaCluFDI-221
❑ 94StaCluGR-221
❑ 94StaCluMOP-221
❑ 94Top-704
❑ 94TopGol-704
❑ 94TopSpa-704
❑ 94TriPla-165
❑ 94Ult-574
❑ 94UppDec-75
❑ 94UppDecED-75
❑ 96FleUpd-U196
❑ 96FleUpdTC-U196
❑ 96LeaSigEA-29
❑ 96PadMot-19
❑ 97ColCho-206
❑ 97Fle-458
❑ 97FleTif-458
❑ 97Pac-421
❑ 97PacLigB-421
❑ 97PacSil-421
❑ 97PadMot-22
❑ 97UppDec-167
❑ 98PadMot-21
❑ 98UppDec-206

Ciardi, Mark
❑ 86VanCanP-6
❑ 87BrePol-34
❑ 88DenZepC-9
❑ 88DenZepP-1272
❑ 88Top-417
❑ 88TopTif-417
❑ 94BreMilB-207

Cias, Darryl
❑ 80WesHavWCT-14
❑ 81WesHavAT-5
❑ 82TacTigT-11
❑ 83TacTigT-9
❑ 84Nes792-159
❑ 84Top-159
❑ 84TopTif-159
❑ 86SanJosBP-6

Ciccarella, Joe
❑ 89AlaGol-4
❑ 92ClaFS7-185
❑ 92UppDecML-99
❑ 92WinHavRSC-2
❑ 92WinHavRSF-1768
❑ 93Bow-551
❑ 93PawRedSDD-7
❑ 93PawRedSF-2401
❑ 93PawRedSTI-7
❑ 94NewBriRSF-645
❑ 95PawRedSDD-8
❑ 95PawRedTI-32
❑ 95SigRoo-13
❑ 95SigRooSig-13
❑ 95TreThuTI-16
❑ 96OrlCubB-5

Cicero, Joseph F.
❑ 45A'sTeal-8

Cicione, Mike
❑ 84EveGiaC-3

Cicotte, Al
❑ 57Top-398
❑ 58Top-382
❑ 59Top-57
❑ 59TopVen-57
❑ 60MapLeaSF-3
❑ 60Top-473
❑ 61Top-241
❑ 62Col45'HC-4
❑ 62Top-126
❑ 62TopVen-126
❑ 89AstCol4S-2

Cicotte, Eddie
❑ 09ColChiE-50
❑ 09PhiCarE-4
❑ 09RamT20-25
❑ 09T206-64
❑ 10DarChoE-7
❑ 10DomDisP-24
❑ 10E12AmeCDCE125-9
❑ 10JuJuDE-9
❑ 10SweCapPP-2
❑ 10W555-13
❑ 11BasBatEU-9
❑ 11E94-6
❑ 11HelSta-2
❑ 11MecDFT-47
❑ 11S74Sil-2
❑ 11SpoLifCW-61
❑ 11SpoLifM-3
❑ 11T205-28
❑ 12ColRedB-50
❑ 12ColTinT-50
❑ 12HasTriFT-46
❑ 12T207-31
❑ 14CraJacE-94
❑ 14PieStaT-22
❑ 15CraJacE-94
❑ 15SpoNewM-31
❑ 16SpoNewM-32
❑ 17ColE13-28
❑ 17HolBreD-14
❑ 18WhiSoxTI-3
❑ 19W514-82
❑ 20W516-21
❑ 74CapPub-33
❑ 75WhiSox1T-2
❑ 77GalGloG-175
❑ 77SerSta-5
❑ 87ConSer2-29
❑ 87SpoCubG-3
❑ 88LitSunBS-3
❑ 88PacEigMO-6
❑ 88PacEigMO-14
❑ 88PacEigMO-19
❑ 88PacEigMO-22
❑ 88PacEigMO-38
❑ 88PacEigMO-58
❑ 88PacEigMO-59
❑ 88PacEigMO-104
❑ 92Man191BSR-2
❑ 94ConTSN-1034
❑ 94ConTSN-1041
❑ 94ConTSNB-1034
❑ 94ConTSNB-1041

Cicotte, Greg
❑ 80BurBeeT-17

Ciczczon, Steve
❑ 89ColSprSSC-25

Cienscyzk, Frank
❑ 86A'sMot-26
❑ 90A'sMot-28
❑ 93AthMot-28

Ciesla, Dave
❑ 98BatMucTI-5

Ciesla, Theodore
❑ 90JamExpP-4
❑ 91RocExpC-18
❑ 91RocExpP-2053

Cieslak, Mark
❑ 85CedRapRT-2

Cifarelli, Gerard
❑ 89ChaRaiP-980

Cihocki, Al (Albert J.)
❑ 50WorWidGV-4

Cihocki, Ed (Edward J.)
❑ 33RitCE-8S
❑ 35DiaMatCS3T1-32

Cijntje, Sherwin
❑ 85NewOriT-13
❑ 86HagSunP-4
❑ 87ChaO'sW-2
❑ 88ChaKniTI-25
❑ 88RocRedWC-20
❑ 88RocRedWP-198
❑ 88RocRedWTI-6
❑ 89HagSunB-7
❑ 89HagSunS-3
❑ 89RocRedWC-15
❑ 89RocRedWP-1632

Cimino, Pete
❑ 66Top-563
❑ 67OPC-34
❑ 67Top-34
❑ 68OPC-143
❑ 68Top-143
❑ 68TopVen-143

Cimo, Matt
❑ 87ChaO'sW-15
❑ 88RocRedWC-11
❑ 88RocRedWGCP-5
❑ 88RocRedWP-203
❑ 88RocRedWTI-7
❑ 89ScrRedBC-14
❑ 89ScrRedBP-730

Cimoli, Gino Nicholas
❑ 50WorWidGV-22
❑ 52Par-70
❑ 57Top-319
❑ 58DodBelB-2
❑ 58DodJayP-3
❑ 58DodVol-2
❑ 58Hir-63
❑ 58Top-286
❑ 59Top-418
❑ 60Kah-5
❑ 60KeyChal-11
❑ 60Lea-142
❑ 60PirJayP-2
❑ 60Top-58
❑ 60TopVen-58
❑ 61Kah-7
❑ 61Pos-136A
❑ 61Pos-136B
❑ 61Top-165
❑ 61Top-309
❑ 62Jel-150
❑ 62Pos-150
❑ 62PosCan-150
❑ 62SalPlaC-148
❑ 62ShiPlaC-148
❑ 62Top-402
❑ 63Jel-88
❑ 63Pos-88
❑ 63Top-321
❑ 64Top-26
❑ 64TopVen-26
❑ 65Top-569
❑ 77PirTCM1WC-10
❑ 89DodSmoG-62
❑ 90DodTar-127
❑ 91DodRinP3-4
❑ 91OriCro-77

Cimorelli, Frank
❑ 89JohCitCS-5
❑ 90SprCarB-23
❑ 91SprCarC-10
❑ 91SprCarP-735
❑ 92MidLeaATI-6
❑ 92SprCarC-23
❑ 92SprCarF-861
❑ 93ArkTraF-2806
❑ 94Bow-223
❑ 94LouRedF-2975

Cina, Randy
❑ 88LynRedSS-4

Cindrich, Jeff
❑ 92GulCoaYF-3783
❑ 93GreHorC-4
❑ 93GreHorF-878
❑ 94TamYanC-4
❑ 94TamYanF-2374
❑ 95TamYanYI-2

Cinnella, Doug
❑ 87HagSunP-29
❑ 88FloStaLAS-4
❑ 88WesPalBES-6
❑ 89WesPalBES-6
❑ 90JacMetGS-15
❑ 91LinDriAAA-553
❑ 91TidTidLD-553
❑ 91TidTidP-2502

Cintron, Alex
❑ 98LetBlaDG-6

Cintron, Jose
❑ 94BoiHawC-7
❑ 94BoiHawF-3346
❑ 95CedRapKTI-10
❑ 96CedRapKTI-5
❑ 96MidLeaAB-16
❑ 98BriBluM-7

Ciocca, Eric
❑ 91SpoIndC-1
❑ 91SpoIndP-3939
❑ 92ChaRaiF-114

Cipaula, Julio
❑ 85DomLeaS-182

Cipolloni, Joe
❑ 86PhiTas-NNO
❑ 86PorBeaP-3
❑ 87MaiGuiP-18
❑ 87MaiGuiT-8
❑ 87PhiTas-23

Cipot, Ed
❑ 76WauMetT-9
❑ 78TidTidT-7
❑ 79TidTidT-14
❑ 80TidTidT-7
❑ 81TolMudHT-20
❑ 82GleFalWST-3

Cipres, Mark
❑ 83TriTriT-6

Ciprian, Francis
❑ 88ModA'sCLC-78
❑ 88ModA'sTI-18

Cipriani, Frank D.
❑ 61AthJayP-6
❑ 62Top-333

Ciravolo, John
❑ 97DanBraB-14

Cirbo, Dennis
❑ 78St.PetCT-6

Cirillo, Jeff
❑ 91HelBreSP-12
❑ 92BelBreCB-25
❑ 92BelBreFl-409
❑ 92MidLeaATI-7
❑ 93El PasDF-2955
❑ 93ExcFS7-183
❑ 94BreMilB-298
❑ 94ExcFS7-79
❑ 94NewOrlZF-1475
❑ 94StaClu-699
❑ 94StaCluFDI-699
❑ 94StaCluGR-699
❑ 94StaCluMOP-699
❑ 95ColCho-173
❑ 95ColChoGS-173
❑ 95ColChoSS-173
❑ 95Fla-269
❑ 95Fle-175
❑ 95Pac-228
❑ 95Pin-165
❑ 95PinArtP-165
❑ 95PinMusC-165
❑ 95Sco-599
❑ 95ScoGolR-599
❑ 95ScoPlaTS-599
❑ 95Sel-176
❑ 95SelArtP-176
❑ 95SelCer-131
❑ 95SelCerMG-131
❑ 95SigRooOJ-10
❑ 95SigRooOJP-10
❑ 95SigRooOJPS-10
❑ 95SigRooOJS-10
❑ 95StaClu-390
❑ 95StaCluMOP-390
❑ 95StaCluSTWS-390
❑ 95StaCluVR-249
❑ 95StaCluVRMO-249
❑ 95Sum-104
❑ 95SumNthD-104
❑ 95Top-544
❑ 95TopCyb-325
❑ 95UC3-105
❑ 95UC3ArtP-105
❑ 95Ult-294
❑ 95UltGolM-294
❑ 95UppDec-52
❑ 95UppDecED-52
❑ 95UppDecEDG-52
❑ 96BrePol-4
❑ 96Cir-50
❑ 96CirRav-50
❑ 96ColCho-188
❑ 96ColChoGS-188
❑ 96ColChoSS-188
❑ 96Don-326
❑ 96DonPreP-326
❑ 96Fla-99
❑ 96Fle-143
❑ 96FleTif-143
❑ 96LeaSig-27
❑ 96LeaSigA-45
❑ 96LeaSigAG-45
❑ 96LeaSigAS-45
❑ 96LeaSigPPG-27
❑ 96LeaSigPPP-27
❑ 96MetUni-69
❑ 96MetUniP-69
❑ 96Pac-341
❑ 96Pin-83
❑ 96Sco-397
❑ 96StaClu-65
❑ 96StaCluMOP-65
❑ 96TeaOut-17
❑ 96Top-282
❑ 96TopGal-121
❑ 96TopGalPPI-121
❑ 96Ult-78

❑ 96UltGolM-78
❑ 96UppDec-366
❑ 97Bow-31
❑ 97BowChr-27
❑ 97BowChrI-27
❑ 97BowChrIR-27
❑ 97BowChrR-27
❑ 97BowInt-31
❑ 97BrePol-4
❑ 97Cir-228
❑ 97CirRav-228
❑ 97ColCho-149
❑ 97Don-92
❑ 97DonGolPP-92
❑ 97DonLim-176
❑ 97DonLimE-176
❑ 97DonPre-36
❑ 97DonPreCttC-36
❑ 97DonSilPP-92
❑ 97E-X2-26
❑ 97E-X2Cred-26
❑ 97E-X2EssCre-26
❑ 97Fin-216
❑ 97FinRef-216
❑ 97FlaShoLC-126
❑ 97FlaShoLeg0-126
❑ 97FlaShoLeg1-126
❑ 97FlaShoM-A126
❑ 97FlaShoM-B126
❑ 97FlaShoM-C126
❑ 97FlaShoR0-126
❑ 97FlaShoR1-126
❑ 97FlaShoR2-126
❑ 97Fle-126
❑ 97Fle-735
❑ 97FleTif-126
❑ 97FleTif-735
❑ 97Lea-115
❑ 97LeaFraM-115
❑ 97LeaFraMDC-115
❑ 97MetUni-63
❑ 97Pac-116
❑ 97PacLigB-116
❑ 97PacPri-40
❑ 97PacPriLB-40
❑ 97PacPriP-40
❑ 97PacSil-116
❑ 97Pin-101
❑ 97PinArtP-PP101
❑ 97PinMusC-101
❑ 97PinPrePla-101
❑ 97PinX-P-48
❑ 97PinX-PMoS-48
❑ 97Sco-88
❑ 97ScoArtPWB-88
❑ 97ScoPreS-88
❑ 97ScoShoS-88
❑ 97ScoShoSAP-88
❑ 97SP-102
❑ 97SpoIll-152
❑ 97SpoIllEE-152
❑ 97StaClu-132
❑ 97StaCluMOP-132
❑ 97StrAll-13
❑ 97Stu-77
❑ 97StuPrePG-77
❑ 97StuPrePS-77
❑ 97Top-49
❑ 97TopChr-18
❑ 97TopChrR-18
❑ 97TopGal-136
❑ 97TopGalPPI-136
❑ 97TopSta-92
❑ 97TopStaAM-92
❑ 97Ult-74
❑ 97UltGolME-74
❑ 97UltPlaME-74
❑ 97UppDec-96
❑ 98Bow-45
❑ 98BowChr-45
❑ 98BowChrGA-45
❑ 98BowChrGAR-45
❑ 98BowChrI-45
❑ 98BowChrIR-45
❑ 98BowChrR-45
❑ 98BowGolA-45
❑ 98BowInt-45
❑ 98CirThu-156
❑ 98CirThuRav-156
❑ 98CirThuSupRav-156
❑ 98ColCho-150
❑ 98ColChoER-ER15
❑ 98CroRoy-74
❑ 98Don-183
❑ 98DonColL-321
❑ 98DonGolPP-183
❑ 98DonPriCL-321
❑ 98DonSilPP-183
❑ 98E-X2-41
❑ 98E-X2ECFut-41
❑ 98E-X2ECNow-41
❑ 98Fin-113
❑ 98FinNo--113
❑ 98FinNo-R-113
❑ 98FinRef-113
❑ 98FlaShoLeg0-96
❑ 98FlaShoLeg1-96
❑ 98FlaShoLeg2-96
❑ 98FlaShoLeg3-96
❑ 98FlaShoLegM-96
❑ 98FlaShoR0-96
❑ 98FlaShoR1-96
❑ 98FlaShoR2-96
❑ 98FlaShoR3-96
❑ 98Fle-94
❑ 98Lea-122
❑ 98LeaFraDA-122
❑ 98LeaFraF-122
❑ 98LeaFraM-122
❑ 98LeaFraM-122
❑ 98LeaFraMDC-122
❑ 98LeaFraMDC-122
❑ 98LeaFraMZ2-122
❑ 98MetUni-137
❑ 98MetUniPMG-137
❑ 98Pac-114
❑ 98PacInv-41
❑ 98PacInvPBlue-41
❑ 98PacInvSilv-41
❑ 98PacInvTeam-15
❑ 98PacOme-131
❑ 98PacOmeR-131
❑ 98PacOnl-391
❑ 98PacOnlR-391
❑ 98PacOnlWC-391
❑ 98PacPar-184
❑ 98PacParC-184
❑ 98PacParG-184
❑ 98PacParHS-184
❑ 98PacParPB-184
❑ 98PacParR-184
❑ 98PacPlaB-114
❑ 98PacRedT-114
❑ 98PacSil-114
❑ 98PacTeaC-8
❑ 98PinPlu-5
❑ 98SkyDugA-26
❑ 98SkyDugAIA-26
❑ 98SpoIll-23
❑ 98SpoIllEE-23
❑ 98SpoIllFE-23
❑ 98SpoIllWSF-47
❑ 98SpoIllWSFEE-47
❑ 98SpoIllWSFFE-47
❑ 98SPxFin-292
❑ 98SPxFinR-292
❑ 98SPxFinS-292
❑ 98StaCluFDI-47
❑ 98StaCluI-47
❑ 98StaCluOneK-47
❑ 98StaCluPP-47
❑ 98Stu-122
❑ 98StuGPP-122
❑ 98StuSPP-122
❑ 98Top-327
❑ 98TopChr-327
❑ 98TopChrR-327
❑ 98TopDevR-327
❑ 98TopDia-327
❑ 98TopGal-31
❑ 98TopGalGP-31
❑ 98TopGalOPP-31
❑ 98TopGalPPI-31
❑ 98TopGalPPIA-31
❑ 98TopMiniC-327
❑ 98TopOpeD-153
❑ 98TopSta-107
❑ 98TopStaB-107
❑ 98TopStaG-107
❑ 98TopStaGR-107
❑ 98TopStaS-107
❑ 98Ult-136
❑ 98UltGolM-136
❑ 98UltMas-136
❑ 98UltPlaM-136
❑ 98UppDec-406
❑ 98UppDecR-52
❑ 99199Fin-158
❑ 99Bow-33
❑ 99BowChr-33
❑ 99BowChrG-33
❑ 99BowChrGR-33
❑ 99BowChrI-33
❑ 99BowChrIR-33
❑ 99BowChrR-33
❑ 99BowGol-33
❑ 99BowInt-33
❑ 99CroRoyB-77
❑ 99CroRoyL-77
❑ 99CroRoyOD-77
❑ 99E-X Cen-48
❑ 99E-X CenECFut-48
❑ 99E-X CenECNow-48
❑ 99FinGolRef-158
❑ 99FinRef-158
❑ 99FlaShoLeg1-141
❑ 99FlaShoLeg2-141
❑ 99FlaShoLeg3-141
❑ 99FlaShoLegM1-141
❑ 99FlaShoLegM2-141
❑ 99FlaShoLegM3-141
❑ 99FlaShoR1-141
❑ 99FlaShoR2-141
❑ 99FlaShoR3-141
❑ 99Fle-74
❑ 99FleMys-73
❑ 99FleMysG-73
❑ 99FleMysM-73
❑ 99FleSta9-74
❑ 99FleWarT-74
❑ 99MetUni-117
❑ 99MetUniGM-117
❑ 99MetUniPMG-117
❑ 99Pac-231
❑ 99PacAur-98
❑ 99PacAurOD-98
❑ 99PacCroC-148
❑ 99PacCroCPB-148
❑ 99PacOme-130
❑ 99PacOmeC-130
❑ 99PacOmeG-130
❑ 99PacOmePB-130
❑ 99PacPar-125
❑ 99PacParC-125
❑ 99PacParG-125
❑ 99PacParHoloGold-125
❑ 99PacParHS-125
❑ 99PacParOD-125
❑ 99PacParPB-125
❑ 99PacParRed-125
❑ 99PacPlaB-231
❑ 99PacPri-79
❑ 99PacPriHB-79
❑ 99PacPriHG-79
❑ 99PacPriHM-79
❑ 99PacPriHP-79
❑ 99PacPriRed-79
❑ 99PacPriS-72
❑ 99PacPriS206-72
❑ 99PacPriS206R-72
❑ 99PacRed-231
❑ 99PacTeaC-23
❑ 99Rev-75
❑ 99RevPremDate-75
❑ 99RevRet-75
❑ 99RevShaSS-75
❑ 99SkyMolM-54
❑ 99SkyMolMX-54
❑ 99SkyPre-67
❑ 99SkyPreR-67
❑ 99SkyThu-169
❑ 99SkyThuRant-169
❑ 99SkyThuRave-169
❑ 99SP Aut-47
❑ 99SP SigAuto-JCI
❑ 99SP SigAutoG-JCI
❑ 99SpoIll-88
❑ 99SPSig-60
❑ 99StaClu-287
❑ 99StaCluFDI-287
❑ 99StaCluOoaK-287
❑ 99StaCluPP-287
❑ 99ThuSkySupR-169
❑ 99Top-89
❑ 99TopBlaLC1-37
❑ 99TopBlaLC2-37
❑ 99TopBlaLC3-37
❑ 99TopChr-89
❑ 99TopChrR-89
❑ 99TopGal-42
❑ 99TopGalPP-42
❑ 99TopGalPPI-42
❑ 99TopGolL-37
❑ 99TopGolLC1-37
❑ 99TopGolLC2-37
❑ 99TopGolLOtO-37
❑ 99TopMVPP-89
❑ 99TopOpeD-50
❑ 99TopRedLC1-37
❑ 99TopRedLC2-37
❑ 99TopRedLC3-37
❑ 99UD Cho-102
❑ 99UD ChoP-102
❑ 99UD ChoPCR-102
❑ 99Ult-199
❑ 99UltGolM-199
❑ 99UltMas-199
❑ 99UltPlaM-199
❑ 99UppDec-127
❑ 99UppDecBD-47
❑ 99UppDecBDD-47
❑ 99UppDecBDQ-47
❑ 99UppDecBDT-47
❑ 99UppDecE-50
❑ 99UppDecEFXG-50
❑ 99UppDecEL1-127
❑ 99UppDecEL2-127
❑ 99UppDecM-114
❑ 99UppDecMGS-114
❑ 99UppDecMHFS-114
❑ 99UppDecMP-114
❑ 99UppDecMSS-114
❑ 99UppDecR-47
❑ 99UppDecRG-47
❑ 99UppDecRP-47
❑ 99Vic-217

Cisar, George Joseph
❑ 90DodTar-913

Cisar, Mark
❑ 98LowSpiM-19

Cisarik, Brian
❑ 88SpoIndP-1940
❑ 89WicChaR-8
❑ 89WicStaR-5
❑ 89WicWraR-32
❑ 90WicWraRD-5
❑ 91LinDriAA-604
❑ 91WicWraLD-604
❑ 91WicWraP-2609
❑ 91WicWraRD-19

Cisco, Galen
❑ 61SeaPop-1
❑ 61UniOil-S1
❑ 62Top-301
❑ 63Top-93
❑ 64Top-202
❑ 64TopGia-47
❑ 64TopVen-202
❑ 65MetJayP-4
❑ 65Top-364
❑ 67Top-596
❑ 69OPC-211
❑ 69Top-211
❑ 71oySigST-3
❑ 73OPC-593
❑ 73Top-593
❑ 74RoyPos-7
❑ 74Top-166
❑ 75RoyPos-8
❑ 76KanCitRP-6
❑ 80ExpPos-6
❑ 82ExpPos-5
❑ 83ExpPos-4
❑ 83ExpStu-13
❑ 84ExpPos-4
❑ 84ExpStu-4
❑ 84ExpStu-38
❑ 88SyrChiC-25
❑ 88SyrChiP-818
❑ 89SyrChiC-24
❑ 89SyrChiP-799
❑ 90BluJayFS-6
❑ 91BluJayFS-6
❑ 91BluJayFS-6
❑ 91MetWIZ-76
❑ 93BluJayFS-5
❑ 95BluJayOH-7
❑ 96LasVegSB-3
❑ 97PhiTeal-42
❑ 98PhiTeal-8

Cisco, Jeff
❑ 86ChaRaiP-6

Cissell, Bill (Chalmer W.)
❑ 27Zee-67
❑ 28Exh-37
❑ 28PorandAR-C1
❑ 28PorandAR-D1
❑ 28StaPlaCE-8
❑ 29ExhFou-19
❑ 29PorandAR-12
❑ 30ChiEveAP-13
❑ 30WhiSoxTI-7
❑ 31Exh-19
❑ 31W517-5
❑ 32OrbPinNP-23
❑ 32OrbPinUP-10
❑ 33CraJacP-2
❑ 33Gou-26
❑ 33GouCanV-26
❑ 33TatOrb-10
❑ 33WorCig-17
❑ 34BatR31-13
❑ 34ExhFou-9
❑ 35AlDemDCR3-76
❑ 35GouPuzR-6E
❑ 35GouPuzR-11G
❑ 35GouPuzR-13E
❑ 35GouPuzR-15E
❑ 92ConTSN-411

Ciszczon, Steve
❑ 80TacTigT-26
❑ 83ChaChaT-21
❑ 85MaiGuiT-31
❑ 86MaiGuiP-4
❑ 88ColSprSSP-1539
❑ 89ColSprSSP-250

Ciszkowski, Jeff
❑ 84LitFalMT-16
❑ 86LynMetP-7
❑ 87LynMetP-13
❑ 88St.LucMS-5
❑ 89StoPorB-11
❑ 89StoPorCLC-154
❑ 89StoPorP-399
❑ 89StoPorS-17

Citarella, Ralph A.
❑ 81ArkTraT-18
❑ 82LouRedE-5
❑ 83LouRedR-16
❑ 84Car-5
❑ 84LouRedR-16
❑ 85Don-504
❑ 85PhiTas-46
❑ 85PorBeaC-44
❑ 86LouRedTI-9
❑ 86TacTigP-2
❑ 87HawIslP-6

Citari, Joe
❑ 86OmaRoyP-5
❑ 86OmaRoyT-14
❑ 87OmaRoyP-9
❑ 88OmaRoyC-21
❑ 88OmaRoyP-1519
❑ 89ReaPhiS-8

Citronnelli, Ed
❑ 87SalLakTTT-13

Civit, Xavier
❑ 94VerExpC-7
❑ 94VerExpF-3901
❑ 96DelShoB-13
❑ 98JupHamQ-6

Clabaugh, Moose (John W.)
❑ 37Zee-45
❑ 90DodTar-128

Clabo, Jason
❑ 98TenKry-7

Clack, Marvin
❑ 82AleDukT-12
❑ 83AleDukT-7

Clairmont, Guy
❑ 98FarRedHM-5

Clancey, Bill (William E.)
❑ 09T206-409

Clancy, Bill
❑ 12ColRedB-51

Clancy, Bud (John William)
❑ 28LaPre-21
❑ 28PorandAR-D2
❑ 29ExhFou-19
❑ 30WhiSoxTI-8
❑ 33Gou-32
❑ 33GouCanV-32
❑ 90DodTar-129
❑ 94ConTSN-1131
❑ 94ConTSNB-1131

Clancy, Jim
❑ 75AndRanT-32
❑ 76SanAntBTI-7
❑ 78BluJayP-4
❑ 78OPC-103
❑ 78Top-496
❑ 79BluJayBY-6
❑ 79OPC-61
❑ 79Top-131
❑ 80OPC-132
❑ 80Top-249
❑ 81Fle-412
❑ 81OPC-19
❑ 81OPCPos-21
❑ 81Top-19
❑ 81TopSti-143
❑ 82BluJayS-3
❑ 82Don-227
❑ 82Fle-612
❑ 82OPC-28
❑ 82Top-665
❑ 83Don-101
❑ 83Fle-426
❑ 83FleSta-39
❑ 83FleSti-108
❑ 83OPC-345
❑ 83Top-345
❑ 83TopSti-132
❑ 84BluJayFS-6
❑ 84Don-19
❑ 84Don-19A
❑ 84Don-119
❑ 84DonActAS-49
❑ 84Fle-150
❑ 84Nes792-575
❑ 84OPC-337
❑ 84Top-575
❑ 84TopSti-367
❑ 84TopTif-575
❑ 85BluJayFS-8
❑ 85Don-439
❑ 85Fle-101
❑ 85OPC-188
❑ 85Top-746
❑ 85TopTif-746
❑ 86BluJayAF-6
❑ 86BluJayFS-6
❑ 86Don-268
❑ 86Fle-56
❑ 86Lea-141
❑ 86OPC-213
❑ 86Top-96
❑ 86Top-412
❑ 86TopTif-96
❑ 86TopTif-412
❑ 87BluJayFS-5
❑ 87Don-639
❑ 87DonHig-11
❑ 87Fle-223
❑ 87FleGlo-223
❑ 87Lea-90
❑ 87OPC-122
❑ 87Spo-189
❑ 87Top-122
❑ 87TopSti-189
❑ 87TopTif-122
❑ 88BluJay5-3
❑ 88BluJayFS-7
❑ 88Don-74
❑ 88DonBasB-48
❑ 88Fle-106
❑ 88FleGlo-106
❑ 88Lea-73
❑ 88MSAHosD-13
❑ 88OPC-54
❑ 88Sco-530
❑ 88ScoGlo-530
❑ 88Spo-215
❑ 88StaLinBJ-4
❑ 88Top-54
❑ 88TopBig-258
❑ 88TopSti-184
❑ 88TopTif-54
❑ 89AstLenH-7
❑ 89AstMot-15
❑ 89AstSmo-9
❑ 89Bow-324
❑ 89BowTif-324
❑ 89Don-267
❑ 89DonBasB-206
❑ 89DonTra-32
❑ 89Fle-229
❑ 89FleGlo-229
❑ 89FleUpd-88
❑ 89OPC-219
❑ 89Sco-538
❑ 89ScoRoo-42T
❑ 89Top-219
❑ 89TopTif-219
❑ 89TopTra-19T
❑ 89TopTraT-19T
❑ 89UppDec-282
❑ 90AstLenH-8
❑ 90AstMot-23
❑ 90BluJayHS-4
❑ 90Don-69
❑ 90Fle-226

❑ 90FleCan-226
❑ 90OPC-648
❑ 90PublntS-90
❑ 90Sco-424
❑ 90Top-648
❑ 90TopTif-648
❑ 90UppDec-203
❑ 91AstMot-23
❑ 91Bow-554
❑ 91BraSubS-9
❑ 91UppDec-682
❑ 92Don-639
❑ 92OPC-279
❑ 92Sco-627
❑ 92Top-279
❑ 92TopGol-279
❑ 92TopGolW-279
❑ 92TopMic-279

Clapham, Mark
❑ 78OrlTwiT-3

Clapinski, Chris
❑ 93KanCouCC-4
❑ 93KanCouCF-921
❑ 93KanCouCTI-4
❑ 94BreCouMC-5
❑ 94BreCouMF-18
❑ 95PorSeaDTI-3
❑ 96PorSeaDB-11
❑ 97ChaKni-9
❑ 98ChaKniQ-8

Clapp, Steve
❑ 89TenTecGE-7

Clapp, Stubby
❑ 96JohCitCTI-6
❑ 98ArkTraH-3
❑ 98ArkTraM-5
❑ 98PriWilCASM-1
❑ 98TexLeaTPG-6

Clarey, Doug (Douglas W.)
❑ 77HolMilT-4

Clark, Al
❑ 51A'sTeal-6
❑ 52A'sTeal-6
❑ 88T/MUmp-24
❑ 89T/MUmp-22
❑ 90T/MUmp-21

Clark, Allie (Alfred A.)
❑ 48IndTeal-6
❑ 49Bow-150
❑ 49IndTeal-7
❑ 50Bow-233
❑ 50IndNumN-6
❑ 50IndTeal-6
❑ 51Bow-29
❑ 51IndHag-2
❑ 52Bow-130
❑ 52Top-278
❑ 53BowC-155
❑ 53IndPenCBP-8
❑ 83TopRep5-278
❑ 85TCMPla1-37

Clark, Anthony
❑ 86DayBealP-5

Clark, Bob (Robert H.)
❑ 74BroClu-4
❑ 87OldJudN-78

Clark, Bobby (Robert Cale)
❑ 76QuaCitAT-9
❑ 79SalLakCGT-12
❑ 80SalLakCGT-23
❑ 80Top-663
❑ 81Don-572
❑ 81Top-288
❑ 82Don-318
❑ 82Fle-456
❑ 82Top-74
❑ 83Don-444
❑ 83Fle-82
❑ 83Top-184
❑ 84BreGar-4
❑ 84BrePol-25
❑ 84Don-524
❑ 84Fle-512
❑ 84FleUpd-25
❑ 84Nes792-626
❑ 84Top-626
❑ 84TopTif-626
❑ 84TopTra-24T
❑ 84TopTraT-24T
❑ 85BreGar-3
❑ 85Don-481
❑ 85Fle-578
❑ 85Top-553
❑ 85TopTif-553
❑ 85VanCanC-204
❑ 86EdmTraP-4
❑ 86OPC-352
❑ 86Top-452
❑ 86TopTif-452
❑ 87TacTigP-4
❑ 90DodTar-130
❑ 94BreMilB-208
❑ 94BreMilB-299

Clark, Brady
❑ 97BurBeeB-1
❑ 98ChaLooG-4
❑ 99Bow-423
❑ 99BowGol-423
❑ 99BowInt-423

Clark, Brian
❑ 92MisStaB-9
❑ 93GreFalDSP-5
❑ 93MisStaB-8

Clark, Bryan Donald
❑ 77SalPirT-4
❑ 78ChaPirT-2
❑ 80SpoIndT-8
❑ 80VenLeaS-161
❑ 81MarPos-10
❑ 82Don-596
❑ 82Fle-507
❑ 82MarPos-11
❑ 82SalLakCGT-6
❑ 82Top-632
❑ 83Don-603
❑ 83Fle-476
❑ 83Top-789
❑ 84BluJayFS-7
❑ 84Don-562
❑ 84Fle-609
❑ 84FleUpd-26
❑ 84Nes792-22
❑ 84Top-22
❑ 84TopTif-22
❑ 84TopTra-25T
❑ 84TopTraT-25T
❑ 85IndPol-43
❑ 85MaiGuiT-5
❑ 85OPC-217
❑ 85Top-489
❑ 85TopMin-489
❑ 85TopTif-489
❑ 85TopTifT-21T
❑ 85TopTra-21T
❑ 86BufBisP-8
❑ 86MarGreT-11
❑ 89TacTigC-7
❑ 89TacTigP-1563
❑ 89TriAAAP-AAA39
❑ 90TriAAAC-41
❑ 96NewJerCB-5

Clark, Casey
❑ 77SalPirT-5
❑ 78ChaPirT-3

Clark, Chris
❑ 81HolMilT-9
❑ 82HolMilT-19
❑ 84EdmTraC-108
❑ 85EdmTraC-18

Clark, Chris Brian
❑ 96CliLumKTI-7
❑ 97CliLumG-3

Clark, Chris C.
❑ 97EriSeaWB-6

Clark, Dan
❑ 84ButCopKT-4

Clark, Danny (Daniel Curran)
❑ 21Exh-23
❑ 27MidBre-6

Clark, Dave
❑ 85WatIndT-15
❑ 86IndTeal-16
❑ 86MaiGuiP-5
❑ 87BufBisP-6
❑ 87Don-623
❑ 87Fle-644
❑ 87FleGlo-644
❑ 87IndGat-12
❑ 87Spo-118
❑ 88BlaYNPRWLU-47
❑ 88Don-473
❑ 88IndGat-25
❑ 88IndTeal-10
❑ 88RocExpLC-7
❑ 88Sco-633
❑ 88ScoGlo-633
❑ 88StaLinI-9
❑ 88Top-49
❑ 88TopTif-49
❑ 89Don-585
❑ 89Fle-402
❑ 89FleGlo-402
❑ 89IndTeal-9
❑ 89Top-574
❑ 89TopTif-574
❑ 89UppDec-517
❑ 90CubMar-4
❑ 90Don-492
❑ 90Fle-490
❑ 90FleCan-490
❑ 90OPC-339
❑ 90PublntS-558
❑ 90Sco-141
❑ 90Top-339
❑ 90TopTif-339
❑ 90TopTVCu-29
❑ 90UppDec-449
❑ 91Don-616
❑ 91Fle-417
❑ 91OPC-241
❑ 91Sco-542
❑ 91Top-241
❑ 91TopDesS-241
❑ 91TopMic-241
❑ 91TopTif-241
❑ 91UppDec-314
❑ 92BufBisBS-3
❑ 92BufBisF-332
❑ 92BufBisS-28
❑ 92Sco-657
❑ 93PirNatl-5
❑ 94ColC-78
❑ 94ColChoGS-78
❑ 94ColChoSS-78
❑ 94Fle-606
❑ 94Pac-494
❑ 94PirQui-2
❑ 94Sco-267
❑ 94ScoGolR-267
❑ 94StaClu-498
❑ 94StaCluFDI-498
❑ 94StaCluGR-498
❑ 94StaCluMOP-498
❑ 94TopTra-6T
❑ 95ColCho-386
❑ 95ColChoGS-386
❑ 95ColChoSS-386
❑ 95Don-265
❑ 95DonPreP-265
❑ 95DonTopotO-314
❑ 95Fin-52
❑ 95FinRef-52
❑ 95Fle-474
❑ 95Pac-341
❑ 95Pin-101
❑ 95PinArtP-101
❑ 95PinMusC-101
❑ 95PirFil-5
❑ 95Sco-161
❑ 95ScoGolR-161
❑ 95ScoPlaTS-161
❑ 95SP-97
❑ 95SPSil-97
❑ 95Top-585
❑ 95TopCyb-358
❑ 95Ult-212
❑ 95UltGolM-212
❑ 95UppDec-388
❑ 95UppDecED-388
❑ 95UppDecEDG-388
❑ 96ColCho-677
❑ 96ColChoGS-677
❑ 96ColChoSS-677
❑ 96Fle-517
❑ 96FleTif-517
❑ 96Pin-21
❑ 98PacInvGems-128
❑ 98PacOnl-318
❑ 98PacOnlR-318
❑ 98PacOnlWC-318

Clark, Dera
❑ 88BasCitRS-8
❑ 89MemChiB-18
❑ 89MemChiP-1199
❑ 89MemChiS-6
❑ 89Sta-40
❑ 90CMC-178
❑ 90OmaRoyC-3
❑ 90OmaRoyP-59
❑ 90ProAAAF-594
❑ 92OmaRoyF-2955
❑ 93OmaRoyF-1675
❑ 94RicBraF-2840
❑ 96MemChiB-10

Clark, Doug
❑ 90ArkRaz-26

Clark, Doug D.
❑ 98SalVol-4
❑ 99Bow-419
❑ 99BowGol-419
❑ 99BowInt-419
❑ 99TeaBesR-11
❑ 99TeaBesRG-11
❑ 99TeaBesRS-11

Clark, Dutch (Earl)
❑ 40WheM4-4

Clark, Earl (Bailey Earl)
❑ 33Gou-57
❑ 34GouCanV-41

Clark, Fred (Alfred Robert)
❑ 12PhiCarE-6

Clark, Garry
❑ 87ClePhiP-13
❑ 87SpaPhiP-7
❑ 88ClePhiS-8
❑ 90RenSilSCLC-284

Clark, Geoff
❑ 89SalDodTI-4
❑ 91YakBeaC-30

Clark, Glen Ester
❑ 77FriOneYW-67

Clark, Greg
❑ 98NewJerCM-5
❑ 99TeaBesR-12
❑ 99TeaBesRG-12
❑ 99TeaBesRS-12

Clark, Howie
❑ 93AlbPolCB-9
❑ 93BluOriC-10
❑ 93BluOriF-4131
❑ 94AlbPolC-12
❑ 94AlbPolF-2242
❑ 96BowBayB-11
❑ 97BowBay-13
❑ 98BowBayM-6
❑ 98RocRedWQ-7

Clark, Isaiah
❑ 86BelBreP-4
❑ 87StoPorP-11
❑ 88ModA'sTI-20
❑ 89RivRedWB-29
❑ 89RivRedWCLC-9
❑ 89RivRedWP-1404
❑ 90Bes-196
❑ 90CMC-720
❑ 90SanBerSB-7
❑ 90SanBerSCLC-103
❑ 90SanBerSP-2638

Clark, Jack Anthony
❑ 70RelPam-2
❑ 75LafDriT-13
❑ 76PheGiaCr-22
❑ 76PhoGiaCa-19
❑ 76PhoGiaCC-6
❑ 76PhoGiaVNB-4
❑ 77Gia-3
❑ 77GiaTeal-5
❑ 77Top-488
❑ 78GiaTeal-5
❑ 78Top-384
❑ 79BasPat-20
❑ 79GiaPol-22
❑ 79Hos-116
❑ 79Kel-40
❑ 79OPC-268
❑ 79Top-512
❑ 79TopCom-32
❑ 80GiaPol-22
❑ 80GiaTeal-4
❑ 80Kel-57
❑ 80OPC-93
❑ 80Top-167
❑ 80TopSup-54
❑ 81AllGamPI-138
❑ 81Don-315
❑ 81Dra-15
❑ 81Fle-433
❑ 81FleStiC-52
❑ 81MSAMinD-9
❑ 81OPC-30
❑ 81Squ-18
❑ 81Top-30
❑ 81TopScr-70
❑ 81TopSti-234
❑ 82Don-46
❑ 82Dra-8
❑ 82Fle-387
❑ 82FleSta-65
❑ 82Gia25tATI-5
❑ 82OnDecD-9
❑ 82Top-460
❑ 82TopSti-106
❑ 83AllGamPI-138
❑ 83Don-222
❑ 83DonActA-29
❑ 83Dra-5
❑ 83Fle-256
❑ 83FleSta-40
❑ 83FleSti-48
❑ 83GiaMot-2
❑ 83GiaPos-7
❑ 83Kel-48
❑ 83OPC-210
❑ 83Top-210
❑ 83TopGloS-32
❑ 83TopSti-162
❑ 83TopSti-300
❑ 84AllGamPI-46
❑ 84Don-7
❑ 84Don-7A
❑ 84Don-65
❑ 84DonActAS-31
❑ 84Fle-369
❑ 84FunFooP-19
❑ 84GiaMot-7
❑ 84GiaPos-4
❑ 84Nes792-690
❑ 84OPC-381
❑ 84Top-690
❑ 84TopRubD-14
❑ 84TopSti-167
❑ 84TopTif-690
❑ 85AllGamPI-136
❑ 85CarTeal-5
❑ 85Don-65
❑ 85DonActA-30
❑ 85Fle-604
❑ 85FleUpd-25
❑ 85KASDis-2
❑ 85KitCloD-2
❑ 85Lea-207
❑ 85OPC-208
❑ 85Top-740
❑ 85TopRubD-12
❑ 85TopSti-160
❑ 85TopTif-740
❑ 85TopTifT-22T
❑ 85TopTra-22T
❑ 86BasStaB-21
❑ 86CarIGAS-1
❑ 86CarKASD-9
❑ 86CarSchM-1
❑ 86CarTeal-7
❑ 86Don-168
❑ 86DonAll-23
❑ 86Fle-30
❑ 86FleLeaL-6
❑ 86FleMin-6
❑ 86FleStiC-24
❑ 86GenMilB-4B
❑ 86Lea-96
❑ 86OPC-350
❑ 86QuaGra-5
❑ 86SevCoi-S13
❑ 86Spo-107
❑ 86Top-350
❑ 86TopGloS-4
❑ 86TopMinL-59
❑ 86TopSti-50
❑ 86TopTat-19
❑ 86TopTif-350
❑ 87BoaandB-25
❑ 87CarSmo-13
❑ 87CarTeal-2
❑ 87ClaUpdY-148
❑ 87Don-111
❑ 87DonOpeD-67
❑ 87Fle-289
❑ 87FleGlo-289
❑ 87FleLimBC-C4
❑ 87FleSlu-9
❑ 87OPC-331
❑ 87SpoTeaP-12
❑ 87StuPan-11
❑ 87Top-520
❑ 87TopSti-52
❑ 87TopTif-520
❑ 88ClaBlu-205
❑ 88Don-15
❑ 88Don-183
❑ 88DonAll-33
❑ 88DonBasB-49
❑ 88DonPop-11
❑ 88DonReaBY-NEW
❑ 88DonSupD-15
❑ 88Fle-26
❑ 88FleAll-11
❑ 88FleBasA-6
❑ 88FleExcS-8
❑ 88FleGlo-26
❑ 88FleMin-39
❑ 88FleRecS-5
❑ 88FleSup-7
❑ 88FleUpd-47
❑ 88FleUpdG-47
❑ 88K-M-5
❑ 88KayB-5
❑ 88Lea-15
❑ 88Lea-181
❑ 88MSAJifPD-4
❑ 88Nes-17
❑ 88OPC-100
❑ 88PanSti-232
❑ 88PanSti-388
❑ 88RedFolSB-12
❑ 88Sco-100
❑ 88Sco-650
❑ 88ScoBoxC-11
❑ 88ScoGlo-100
❑ 88ScoGlo-650
❑ 88ScoRoo-1T
❑ 88ScoRooG-1T
❑ 88Spo-18
❑ 88SpoGam-25
❑ 88StaLinAl-6
❑ 88StaLinCa-2
❑ 88StaLinY-2
❑ 88Top-100
❑ 88Top-397
❑ 88TopBig-262
❑ 88TopClo-21
❑ 88TopCoi-9
❑ 88TopGaloC-4
❑ 88TopGloA-13
❑ 88TopGloS-41
❑ 88TopMinL-69
❑ 88TopRevLL-4
❑ 88TopRitTM-10
❑ 88TopSti-46
❑ 88TopSti-150
❑ 88TopStiB-1
❑ 88TopTif-100
❑ 88TopTif-397
❑ 88TopTra-28T
❑ 88TopTraT-28T
❑ 88TopUKM-13
❑ 88TopUKMT-13
❑ 89Bow-456
❑ 89BowTif-456
❑ 89ClaTraP-158
❑ 89Don-311
❑ 89DonBasB-98
❑ 89DonTra-2
❑ 89Fle-252
❑ 89FleGlo-252
❑ 89FleUpd-123
❑ 89KayB-5
❑ 89OPC-3
❑ 89PadCok-2
❑ 89PadMag-6
❑ 89PadPos-5
❑ 89RedFolSB-21
❑ 89Sco-25
❑ 89ScoHot1S-27
❑ 89ScoRoo-3T
❑ 89Spo-26
❑ 89Top-410
❑ 89TopBasT-65
❑ 89TopBig-240
❑ 89TopCapC-14
❑ 89TopCoi-7
❑ 89TopGloS-56
❑ 89TopMinL-65
❑ 89TopSti-308
❑ 89TopTif-410
❑ 89TopTra-20T
❑ 89TopTraT-20T
❑ 89TopUKM-14
❑ 89UppDec-346
❑ 89UppDec-773
❑ 90Bow-214
❑ 90BowTif-214
❑ 90Don-128
❑ 90DonBesN-109
❑ 90DonGraS-11
❑ 90Fle-152
❑ 90FleAwaW-8
❑ 90FleCan-152
❑ 90Lea-287
❑ 90M.Vpin-85
❑ 90MLBBasB-56

❑ 90OPC-90
❑ 90PadCok-4
❑ 90PadMag-18
❑ 90PanSti-348
❑ 90PubIntS-45
❑ 90RedFolSB-16
❑ 90Sco-20
❑ 90Spo-28
❑ 90Top-90
❑ 90TopAmeA-12
❑ 90TopBig-39
❑ 90TopHilHM-18
❑ 90TopMinL-78
❑ 90TopSti-104
❑ 90TopTif-90
❑ 90TopTVA-44
❑ 90UppDec-342
❑ 91Bow-122
❑ 91Cla2-T99
❑ 91ClaGam-154
❑ 91Don-618
❑ 91Fle-526
❑ 91FleUpd-4
❑ 91Lea-201
❑ 91OPC-650
❑ 91OPCPre-21
❑ 91PanFreS-91
❑ 91PanSti-98
❑ 91RedFolS-18
❑ 91RedSoxP-4
❑ 91RedSoxP-6
❑ 91Sco-523
❑ 91ScoRoo-4T
❑ 91StaClu-500
❑ 91Stu-13
❑ 91Top-650
❑ 91TopDesS-650
❑ 91TopMic-650
❑ 91TopTif-650
❑ 91TopTra-22T
❑ 91TopTraT-22T
❑ 91UltUpd-5
❑ 91UppDec-331
❑ 91UppDec-735
❑ 92Bow-233
❑ 92DenHol-5
❑ 92Don-169
❑ 92Fle-36
❑ 92Lea-366
❑ 92LeaBlaG-366
❑ 92OPC-207
❑ 92Pin-85
❑ 92RedFolS-24
❑ 92RedSoxDD-8
❑ 92Sco-318
❑ 92ScoProP-12
❑ 92StaClu-186
❑ 92Top-207
❑ 92TopGol-207
❑ 92TopGolW-207
❑ 92TopMic-207
❑ 92Ult-14
❑ 92UppDec-521
❑ 92UppDecHRH-HR14
❑ 92YanWIZ8-32
❑ 93Don-63
❑ 93Fle-556
❑ 93OPC-240
❑ 93Pin-221
❑ 93RedSoxWHP-7
❑ 93Sel-188
❑ 93StaClu-20
❑ 93StaCluFDI-20
❑ 93StaCluMOP-20
❑ 93Top-781
❑ 93TopGol-781
❑ 93TopInaM-781
❑ 93TopInaR-781
❑ 93TopMic-781
❑ 93Ult-148
❑ 97PhoFirDTTI-7
Clark, Jason
❑ 97HudValRB-22
Clark, Jeff
❑ 89PulBraP-1910
❑ 90BurBraB-16
❑ 90BurBraP-2363
❑ 90BurBraS-9
❑ 91DurBulC-20
❑ 91DurBulP-1558
Clark, Jerald
❑ 85SpoIndC-3
❑ 87WicPilRD-24
❑ 88LasVegSC-12
❑ 88LasVegSP-229
❑ 89Bow-462
❑ 89BowTif-462
❑ 89Don-599
❑ 89Fle-642
❑ 89FleGlo-642
❑ 89LasVegSC-13
❑ 89LasVegSP-10
❑ 89PadPos-6
❑ 89Sco-644
❑ 89Spo-179
❑ 89TriAAAP-AAA49
❑ 89UppDec-30
❑ 90ClaUpd-T10
❑ 90Don-593
❑ 90DonRoo-48
❑ 90Lea-510
❑ 90PubIntS-46
❑ 90Sco-660
❑ 90ScoYouS2-41
❑ 90TriAAAC-37
❑ 90UppDec-624
❑ 91Bow-658
❑ 91Don-74
❑ 91FleUpd-121
❑ 91Lea-265
❑ 91OPC-513
❑ 91PadMag-7
❑ 91PadMag-15B
❑ 91PadSmo-4
❑ 91Sco-242
❑ 91StaClu-468
❑ 91Top-513
❑ 91TopDesS-513
❑ 91TopMic-513
❑ 91TopTif-513
❑ 91UltUpd-110
❑ 91UppDec-624
❑ 92Bow-323
❑ 92Don-144
❑ 92Fle-601
❑ 92Lea-55
❑ 92LeaBlaG-55
❑ 92OPC-749
❑ 92PadCarJ-5
❑ 92PadMot-9
❑ 92PadPolD-4
❑ 92PadSmo-5
❑ 92Pin-48
❑ 92Sco-257
❑ 92StaClu-149
❑ 92Stu-102
❑ 92Top-749
❑ 92TopGol-749
❑ 92TopGolW-749
❑ 92TopMic-749
❑ 92Ult-275
❑ 92UppDec-292
❑ 93Bow-612
❑ 93Don-74
❑ 93Don-790
❑ 93Fla-37
❑ 93Fle-137
❑ 93FleFinE-26
❑ 93FunPac-175
❑ 93Lea-290
❑ 93OPC-44
❑ 93OPCPre-91
❑ 93PacSpa-425
❑ 93Pin-234
❑ 93PinExpOD-7
❑ 93RocStaC-13
❑ 93RocUSPC-7C
❑ 93RocUSPC-12H
❑ 93Sco-405
❑ 93SP-218
❑ 93StaClu-671
❑ 93StaCluFDI-671
❑ 93StaCluMOP-671
❑ 93Stu-41
❑ 93Top-194
❑ 93Top-565
❑ 93TopGol-194
❑ 93TopGol-565
❑ 93TopInaM-194
❑ 93TopInaM-565
❑ 93TopInaR-194
❑ 93TopInaR-565
❑ 93TopMic-194
❑ 93TopMic-565
❑ 93TriPla-126
❑ 93Ult-345
❑ 93UppDec-140
❑ 93UppDec-797
❑ 93UppDecGold-140
❑ 93UppDecGold-797
❑ 94ColC-79
❑ 94ColChoGS-79
❑ 94ColChoSS-79
❑ 94Don-136
❑ 94Fle-438
❑ 94Pac-193
❑ 94PanSti-173
❑ 94Pin-103
❑ 94PinArtP-103
❑ 94PinMusC-103
❑ 94Sco-362
❑ 94ScoGolR-362
❑ 94StaClu-98
❑ 94StaCluFDI-98
❑ 94StaCluGR-98
❑ 94StaCluMOP-98
❑ 94Top-77
❑ 94TopGol-77
❑ 94TopSpa-77
❑ 94Ult-184
❑ 95FleUpd-58
❑ 95StaClu-579
❑ 95StaCluMOP-579
❑ 95StaCluSTWS-579
❑ 95TopTra-118T
Clark, Jermaine
❑ 97EveAquG-5
❑ 98WisTimRM-15
Clark, Joe
❑ 97MidAng-28
Clark, John
❑ 96PorRocB-12
❑ 97PorRocG-4
Clark, Kevin
❑ 94UtiBluSC-8
❑ 94UtiBluSF-3822
❑ 96MicBatCB-9
❑ 96MidLeaAB-43
❑ 98HigDesMG-7
Clark, Kirby
❑ 96BatCliTI-8
❑ 97PieBolWB-6
❑ 98PieBolWM-5
Clark, Lefty (William Watson)
❑ 28W56PlaC-H1
❑ 32OrbPinNP-8
❑ 32OrbPinUP-11
❑ 32R33So2-407
❑ 33DouDisP-9
❑ 33Gou-17
❑ 33GouCanV-17
❑ 33TatOrb-11
❑ 34DiaMatCSB-28
❑ 35GouPuzR-1G
❑ 35GouPuzR-3E
❑ 35GouPuzR-5E
❑ 35GouPuzR-14E
❑ 36WorWidGV-86
❑ 90DodTar-131
Clark, Leroy
❑ 76DubPacT-5
Clark, Marcus
❑ 79WatIndT-18
Clark, Mark
❑ 87SumBraP-11
❑ 88HamRedP-1736
❑ 89SavCarP-370
❑ 90St.PetCS-2
❑ 90TopTVCa-41
❑ 91LouRedTI-2
❑ 92Bow-109
❑ 92DonRoo-25
❑ 92FleUpd-118
❑ 92LouRedS-257
❑ 92SkyAAAF-125
❑ 92TopDeb91-35
❑ 92Ult-564
❑ 92UppDec-702
❑ 92UppDec-773
❑ 93Don-152
❑ 93Fle-508
❑ 93IndWUA-6
❑ 93Lea-172
❑ 93Sco-320
❑ 93Sel-301
❑ 93StaClu-60
❑ 93StaCluFDI-60
❑ 93StaCluMOP-60
❑ 93Top-339
❑ 93TopGol-339
❑ 93TopInaM-339
❑ 93TopInaR-339
❑ 93TopMic-339
❑ 93UppDec-629
❑ 93UppDecGold-629
❑ 94ColC-538
❑ 94ColChoGS-538
❑ 94ColChoSS-538
❑ 94Don-656
❑ 94Fla-39
❑ 94Fle-101
❑ 94FleExtB-58
❑ 94Pac-167
❑ 94StaClu-207
❑ 94StaCluFDI-207
❑ 94StaCluGR-207
❑ 94StaCluMOP-207
❑ 94Top-696
❑ 94TopGol-696
❑ 94TopSpa-696
❑ 95ColCho-266
❑ 95ColChoGS-266
❑ 95ColChoSE-121
❑ 95ColChoSEGS-121
❑ 95ColChoSESS-121
❑ 95ColChoSS-266
❑ 95Don-156
❑ 95DonPreP-156
❑ 95Fle-133
❑ 95Lea-317
❑ 95Pin-183
❑ 95PinArtP-183
❑ 95PinMusC-183
❑ 95Sco-132
❑ 95ScoGolR-132
❑ 95ScoPlaTS-132
❑ 95StaClu-54
❑ 95StaCluFDI-54
❑ 95StaCluMOP-54
❑ 95StaCluSTWS-54
❑ 95Top-463
❑ 95TopCyb-258
❑ 95Ult-37
❑ 95UltGolM-37
❑ 95UppDec-93
❑ 95UppDecED-93
❑ 95UppDecEDG-93
❑ 96ColCho-529
❑ 96ColChoGS-529
❑ 96ColChoSS-529
❑ 96Don-510
❑ 96DonPreP-510
❑ 96Fin-B339
❑ 96FinRef-B339
❑ 96Fle-84
❑ 96FleTif-84
❑ 96FleUpd-U155
❑ 96FleUpdTC-U155
❑ 96LeaSigEA-30
❑ 96MetKah-5
❑ 97Cir-90
❑ 97CirRav-90
❑ 97ColCho-393
❑ 97Fin-68
❑ 97FinRef-68
❑ 97Fle-392
❑ 97FleTif-392
❑ 97Lea-310
❑ 97LeaFraM-310
❑ 97LeaFraMDC-310
❑ 97MetUni-191
❑ 97PacPriGotD-GD174
❑ 97Sco-364
❑ 97ScoArtPWB-364
❑ 97ScoResC-364
❑ 97ScoShoS-364
❑ 97ScoShoSAP-364
❑ 97StaClu-71
❑ 97StaCluMOP-71
❑ 97Top-5
❑ 97UppDec-431
❑ 98CirThu-142
❑ 98CirThuRav-142
❑ 98CirThuSupRav-142
❑ 98ColCho-327
❑ 98Fin-238
❑ 98FinNo--238
❑ 98FinNo-R-238
❑ 98FinRef-238
❑ 98Pac-248
❑ 98PacOnl-139
❑ 98PacOnlR-139
❑ 98PacOnlWC-139
❑ 98PacPlaB-248
❑ 98PacRedT-248
❑ 98PacSil-248
❑ 98PinSna-CC7
❑ 98StaCluFDI-51
❑ 98StaCluI-51
❑ 98StaCluOneK-51
❑ 98StaCluPP-51
❑ 98Top-403
❑ 98TopChr-403
❑ 98TopChrR-403
❑ 98TopDevR-403
❑ 98TopDia-403
❑ 98TopMiniC-403
❑ 98UppDec-323
❑ 99Fle-375
❑ 99FleSta9-375
❑ 99FleWarT-375
❑ 99Pac-82
❑ 99PacPlaB-82
❑ 99PacRed-82
❑ 99Top-118
❑ 99TopChr-118
❑ 99TopChrR-118
❑ 99TopMVPP-118
❑ 99UppDec-60
❑ 99UppDecEL1-60
❑ 99UppDecEL2-60
Clark, Mel (Melvin Earl)
❑ 53BowC-67
❑ 54Bow-175
❑ 55Bow-41
Clark, Mike J.
❑ 53CarHunW-5
❑ 53Top-193
❑ 91TopArc1-193
Clark, Pepper (Joshua B.)
❑ 09T206-410
Clark, Phil Benjamin
❑ 87FayGenP-23
❑ 88FloStaLAS-31
❑ 88LakTigS-7
❑ 89LonTigP-1383
❑ 90CMC-400
❑ 90ProAAAF-382
❑ 90TolMudHC-23
❑ 90TolMudHP-152
❑ 91Fle-332
❑ 91LinDriAAA-581
❑ 91Sco-756
❑ 91ScoRoo-7
❑ 91TolMudHLD-581
❑ 91TolMudHP-1934
❑ 92TolMudHS-581
❑ 92TopTra-24T
❑ 92TopTraG-24T
❑ 93Don-391
❑ 93FleFinE-136
❑ 93PadMot-21
❑ 93Pin-287
❑ 93Sel-335
❑ 93Top-802
❑ 93TopGol-802
❑ 93TopInaM-802
❑ 93TopInaR-802
❑ 93TopMic-802
❑ 93Ult-470
❑ 94ColC-426
❑ 94ColChoGS-426
❑ 94ColChoSS-426
❑ 94Don-130
❑ 94Fle-660
❑ 94Pac-520
❑ 94PadMot-5
❑ 94PanSti-254
❑ 94Pin-167
❑ 94PinArtP-167
❑ 94PinMusC-167
❑ 94Sco-241
❑ 94ScoGolR-241
❑ 94Sel-153
❑ 94StaClu-399
❑ 94StaCluFDI-399
❑ 94StaCluGR-399
❑ 94StaCluMOP-399
❑ 94Top-408
❑ 94TopGol-408
❑ 94TopSpa-408
❑ 94Ult-277
❑ 95Fle-557
❑ 95Pac-359
❑ 95PadMot-7
❑ 95Top-298
❑ 96Pac-187
❑ 96PawRedSDD-2
Clark, Philip J.
❑ 58Top-423
❑ 59Top-454
Clark, Randy
❑ 79QuaCitCT-14
Clark, Richard
❑ 97SalVolG-8
Clark, Rickey
❑ 70Top-586
❑ 71OPC-697
❑ 71Top-697
❑ 72OPC-462
❑ 72Top-462
❑ 73OPC-636
❑ 73Top-636
Clark, Rob
❑ 83TulDriT-4
❑ 84OklCit8T-2
❑ 85TulDriTI-27
❑ 86OklCit8P-3
❑ 90TulDriDGB-33
Clark, Rodney
❑ 85UtiBluST-13
Clark, Ron
❑ 96IowCubB-2
Clark, Ron (Ronald Bruce)
❑ 67OPC-137
❑ 67Top-137
❑ 67TwiTeal-6
❑ 68Top-589
❑ 69Top-561
❑ 70OPC-531
❑ 70Top-531
❑ 71MLBOffS-509
❑ 75IntLeaAT-13
❑ 76OklCit8TI-3
❑ 80CarMudF-17
❑ 80VenLeaS-260
❑ 81ReaPhiT-23
❑ 82OklCit8T-6
❑ 83KinBluJTI-3
❑ 83Pil69G-40
❑ 86ClePhiP-4
❑ 90WhiSoxC-30
❑ 92IndFanC-30
❑ 93IndWUA-33
❑ 94BreMilB-209
❑ 95IowCubTI-7
Clark, Roy
❑ 79TulDriT-24
❑ 80LynSaiT-20
❑ 81SpoIndT-6
❑ 82SalLakCGT-7
Clark, Russell
❑ 76WauMetT-10
❑ 77LynMetT-9
❑ 79JacMetT-20
❑ 79TidTidT-22
Clark, Skip
❑ 81MiaOriT-12
Clark, Spider (Owen F.)
❑ 87OldJudN-79
Clark, Stephen C.
❑ 80PerHaloFP-B
Clark, Terry
❑ 83ArkTraT-3
❑ 84LouRedR-24
❑ 86MidAngP-5
❑ 87EdmTraP-2082
❑ 88EdmTraC-1
❑ 88EdmTraP-569
❑ 89Don-607
❑ 89Fle-470
❑ 89FleGlo-470
❑ 89OPC-129
❑ 89Sco-566
❑ 89ScoHot1R-89
❑ 89Top-129
❑ 89TopTif-129
❑ 89TriAAAP-AAA27
❑ 89UppDec-234
❑ 90CMC-605
❑ 90ProAAAF-188
❑ 90TucTorC-3
❑ 90TucTorP-198
❑ 91LinDriAAA-607
❑ 91TucTorLD-607
❑ 91TucTorP-2207
❑ 92ColSprSSF-745
❑ 92ColSprSSS-81
❑ 94RicBraF-2841
❑ 94TriAAF-AAA41
❑ 94VenLinU-34
❑ 95BalOriP-13
❑ 95LinVen-32
❑ 96LeaSigEA-31
❑ 96RoyPol-5
❑ 97BufBis-12
❑ 98OklRedM-5
Clark, Tim
❑ 90BelBreS-5
❑ 90LSUTigP-14
❑ 91StoPorC-23

❑ 91StoPorP-3042
❑ 92SalLakTSP-8
❑ 93Bow-699
❑ 93HigDesMC-4
❑ 93HigDesMF-53
❑ 94ActPac-39
❑ 94Bow-343
❑ 94Bow-562
❑ 94BowBes-B51
❑ 94BowBesR-B51
❑ 94ClaGolF-94
❑ 94ExcFS7-189
❑ 94PorSeaDF-684
❑ 94PorSeaDTI-11
❑ 94Top-79
❑ 94TopGol-79
❑ 94TopSpa-79
❑ 94UppDecML-98
❑ 94UppDecML-106
❑ 95PorSeaDTI-4
❑ 98PorSeaD5AQ-18

Clark, Tom

❑ 90LitSunW-18

Clark, Tony Christopher

❑ 90BriTigP-3173
❑ 90BriTigS-3
❑ 90ProAaA-189
❑ 91NiaFalRC-13
❑ 91NiaFalRP-3645
❑ 92NiaFalRC-1
❑ 92NiaFalRF-3336
❑ 92UppDecML-182
❑ 94AriFalLS-3
❑ 94Bow-209
❑ 94BowBes-B62
❑ 94BowBesR-B62
❑ 94BowPre-8
❑ 94Cla-196
❑ 94TreThuF-2124
❑ 94UppDecML-57
❑ 95ActPacF-8
❑ 95Bow-253
❑ 95BowBes-B20
❑ 95BowBesR-B20
❑ 95BowGolF-253
❑ 95ColCho-16
❑ 95ColChoGS-16
❑ 95ColChoSS-16
❑ 95Exc-47
❑ 95ExcAll-2
❑ 95SP-16
❑ 95SPSil-16
❑ 95TolMudHTI-11
❑ 95Top-153
❑ 95UppDec-227
❑ 95UppDecED-227
❑ 95UppDecEDG-227
❑ 95UppDecML-70
❑ 95UppDecMLFS-70
❑ 95UppDecMLOP-OP10
❑ 96Bow-164
❑ 96BowFoi-164
❑ 96ColCho-543
❑ 96ColChoGS-543
❑ 96ColChoSS-543
❑ 96Don-407
❑ 96DonPreP-407
❑ 96Fin-B356
❑ 96FinRef-B356
❑ 96FlePro-3
❑ 96Lea-30
❑ 96LeaPre-114
❑ 96LeaPreP-114
❑ 96LeaPrePB-30
❑ 96LeaPrePG-30
❑ 96LeaPrePS-30
❑ 96LeaSig-87
❑ 96LeaSigPPG-87
❑ 96LeaSigPPP-87
❑ 96Pin-166
❑ 96PinArtP-93
❑ 96PinSam-166
❑ 96PinSta-93
❑ 96Sco-229
❑ 96Spo-123
❑ 96SpoArtP-123
❑ 96SpoRooJ-3
❑ 96StaClu-42
❑ 96StaCluMOP-42
❑ 96TigHebN-3
❑ 96TolMudHB-8
❑ 96Top-337
❑ 96TopGal-138
❑ 96TopGalPPI-138
❑ 96UppDec-327
❑ 96UppDecFSP-FS6
❑ 96UppDecPHE-H23
❑ 96UppDecPreH-H23
❑ 96Zen-106
❑ 96ZenArtP-106
❑ 97Bow-8
❑ 97BowBes-26
❑ 97BowBesAR-26
❑ 97BowBesR-26
❑ 97BowChr-6
❑ 97BowChrl-6
❑ 97BowChrIR-6
❑ 97BowChrR-6
❑ 97BowInt-8
❑ 97Cir-244
❑ 97CirRav-244
❑ 97ColCho-104
❑ 97Don-341
❑ 97DonEli-120
❑ 97DonEliGS-120
❑ 97DonEliTotC-9
❑ 97DonEliTotCDC-9
❑ 97DonFraFea-10
❑ 97DonGolPP-341
❑ 97DonLim-78
❑ 97DonLim-106
❑ 97DonLimE-78
❑ 97DonLimE-106
❑ 97DonLimENG-78
❑ 97DonLimFotG-14
❑ 97DonPre-110
❑ 97DonPreCttC-110
❑ 97DonRatR-13
❑ 97DonSig-4
❑ 97DonSigA-18
❑ 97DonSigAC-24
❑ 97DonSigAM-24
❑ 97DonSigNN-2
❑ 97DonSigPPP-4
❑ 97DonSilPP-341
❑ 97DonVxP1-7
❑ 97E-X2-20
❑ 97E-X2Cred-20
❑ 97E-X2EssCre-20
❑ 97E-X2SD2000-14
❑ 97Fin-129
❑ 97Fin-245
❑ 97FinEmb-129
❑ 97FinEmbR-129
❑ 97FinRef-129
❑ 97FinRef-245
❑ 97FlaShoLC-173
❑ 97FlaShoLeg0-173
❑ 97FlaShoLeg1-173
❑ 97FlaShoM-A173
❑ 97FlaShoM-B173
❑ 97FlaShoM-C173
❑ 97FlaShoR0-173
❑ 97FlaShoR1-173
❑ 97FlaShoR2-173
❑ 97Fle-96
❑ 97Fle-730
❑ 97FleTif-96
❑ 97FleTif-730
❑ 97Lea-42
❑ 97LeaFraM-42
❑ 97LeaFraMDC-42
❑ 97LeaGolS-28
❑ 97LeaLeaotN-15
❑ 97MetUni-108
❑ 97Pac-86
❑ 97PacLigB-86
❑ 97PacPri-30
❑ 97PacPriLB-30
❑ 97PacPriP-30
❑ 97PacSil-86
❑ 97Pin-110
❑ 97PinArtP-PP110
❑ 97PinCer-18
❑ 97PinCerMBla-18
❑ 97PinCerMBlu-18
❑ 97PinCerMG-18
❑ 97PinCerMR-18
❑ 97PinCerR-18
❑ 97PinIns-143
❑ 97PinInsCE-143
❑ 97PinInsDE-143
❑ 97PinMusC-110
❑ 97PinPrePla-110
❑ 97PinTotCPB-18
❑ 97PinTotCPG-18
❑ 97PinTotCPR-18
❑ 97PinTotCS-18
❑ 97PinX-P-39
❑ 97PinX-P-145
❑ 97PinX-PMoS-39
❑ 97PinX-PMoS-145
❑ 97PinX-PSfF-18
❑ 97PinX-PSfFU-18
❑ 97PreCon-22
❑ 97Sco-142
❑ 97ScoArtPWB-142
❑ 97ScoPreS-142
❑ 97ScoShoS-142
❑ 97ScoShoSAP-142
❑ 97Sel-193
❑ 97SelCom-193
❑ 97SP-71
❑ 97SpoIll-58
❑ 97SpoIll-137
❑ 97SpoIllEE-58
❑ 97SpoIllEE-137
❑ 97StaClu-263
❑ 97StaCluM-M5
❑ 97StaCluMOP-263
❑ 97StaCluMOP-M5
❑ 97Stu-100
❑ 97StuPrePG-100
❑ 97StuPrePS-100
❑ 97Top-406
❑ 97TopAwel-AI2
❑ 97TopChr-143
❑ 97TopChrR-143
❑ 97TopGal-166
❑ 97TopGalPPI-166
❑ 97TopStaFAS-FAS8
❑ 97Ult-58
❑ 97UltGolME-58
❑ 97UltPlaME-58
❑ 97UppDec-62
❑ 97Zen-10
❑ 98Bow-61
❑ 98BowBes-15
❑ 98BowBesA-15
❑ 98BowBesAAR-15
❑ 98BowBesAR-15
❑ 98BowBesAR-15
❑ 98BowBesR-15
❑ 98BowChr-61
❑ 98BowChrGA-61
❑ 98BowChrGAR-61
❑ 98BowChrl-61
❑ 98BowChrIR-61
❑ 98BowChrR-61
❑ 98BowChrR-41
❑ 98BowChrRR-41
❑ 98BowGolA-61
❑ 98BowInt-61
❑ 98CirThu-17
❑ 98CirThuRav-17
❑ 98CirThuSupRav-17
❑ 98ColCho-90
❑ 98ColChoCtG-CG4A
❑ 98ColChoCtG-CG4B
❑ 98ColChoCtG-CG4C
❑ 98ColChoCtGExch-CG4
❑ 98ColChoCtGIW-CG4
❑ 98ColChoMBH-14
❑ 98ColChoSQ-SQ66
❑ 98CroRoy-54
❑ 98Don-122
❑ 98Don-353
❑ 98Don-396
❑ 98DonCol-122
❑ 98DonColE-478
❑ 98DonColE-544
❑ 98DonColL-361
❑ 98DonColP-574
❑ 98DonColS-122
❑ 98DonCruG-23
❑ 98DonCruP-23
❑ 98DonCruR-23
❑ 98DonDay-2
❑ 98DonDom-2
❑ 98DonEli-78
❑ 98DonEli-144
❑ 98DonEliA-78
❑ 98DonEliA-144
❑ 98DonEliC-13
❑ 98DonEliMC-13
❑ 98DonEliS-78
❑ 98DonEliS-144
❑ 98DonGolPP-122
❑ 98DonGolPP-353
❑ 98DonGolPP-396
❑ 98DonLonL-19
❑ 98DonPre-24
❑ 98DonPreGES-25
❑ 98DonPreGX-25
❑ 98DonPreGXDC-25
❑ 98DonPreSeat-24
❑ 98DonPriCD-122
❑ 98DonPriCE-478
❑ 98DonPriCE-544
❑ 98DonPriCL-361
❑ 98DonPriCP-574
❑ 98DonProLS-19
❑ 98DonSig-66
❑ 98DonSigA-16
❑ 98DonSigAC-23
❑ 98DonSigAM-23
❑ 98DonSigP-66
❑ 98DonSigSB-5
❑ 98DonSigSP-4
❑ 98DonSilPP-122
❑ 98DonSilPP-353
❑ 98DonSilPP-396
❑ 98E-X2-23
❑ 98E-X2Cheap-9
❑ 98E-X2ECFut-23
❑ 98E-X2ECNow-23
❑ 98E-X2Sig2001-8
❑ 98Fin-20
❑ 98FinNo--20
❑ 98FinNo-R-20
❑ 98FinPowZ-P14
❑ 98FinRef-20
❑ 98FlaShoLeg0-22
❑ 98FlaShoLeg1-22
❑ 98FlaShoLeg2-22
❑ 98FlaShoLeg3-22
❑ 98FlaShoLegM-22
❑ 98FlaShoR0-22
❑ 98FlaShoR1-22
❑ 98FlaShoR2-22
❑ 98FlaShoR3-22
❑ 98Fle-17
❑ 98Fle-325
❑ 98Fle-578
❑ 98FlePowG-4
❑ 98FleVin'-23
❑ 98FleVin'C-23
❑ 98KinDis-3
❑ 98Lea-162
❑ 98LeaFraDA-162
❑ 98LeaFraF-162
❑ 98LeaFraM-162
❑ 98LeaFraM-162
❑ 98LeaFraMDC-162
❑ 98LeaFraMDC-162
❑ 98LeaFraMS-162
❑ 98LeaFraMZ2-162
❑ 98LeaRS-51
❑ 98LeaRS-179
❑ 98LeaRSHRDerby-4
❑ 98LeaRSLHolo-51
❑ 98LeaRSLHolo-179
❑ 98LeaRSLong-51
❑ 98LeaRSLong-179
❑ 98LeaRTrue-51
❑ 98LeaRTrue-179
❑ 98LeaStaRep-17
❑ 98LeaStaS-21
❑ 98LeaStaSDC-21
❑ 98MetUni-184
❑ 98MetUni-204
❑ 98MetUniPMG-184
❑ 98MetUniPMG-204
❑ 98Pac-85
❑ 98PacAur-37
❑ 98PacInv-31
❑ 98PacInvPBlue-31
❑ 98PacInvSilv-31
❑ 98PacInvTeam-10
❑ 98PacOme-88
❑ 98PacOmeR-88
❑ 98PacOnl-268
❑ 98PacOnl-287
❑ 98PacOnlR-268
❑ 98PacOnlR-287
❑ 98PacOnlWC-268
❑ 98PacOnlWC-287
❑ 98PacPar-46
❑ 98PacParC-46
❑ 98PacParG-46
❑ 98PacParHS-46
❑ 98PacParPB-46
❑ 98PacParR-46
❑ 98PacParTC-6
❑ 98PacPlaB-85
❑ 98PacRedT-85
❑ 98PacSil-85
❑ 98PacTeaC-6
❑ 98PinIns-109
❑ 98PinInsCE-109
❑ 98PinInsDE-109
❑ 98PinInsSG-22AB
❑ 98PinInsSG-22CD
❑ 98PinInsSGS-22AB
❑ 98PinInsSGS-22CD
❑ 98PinMinB-4
❑ 98PinMinCB-4
❑ 98PinMinCBAP-4
❑ 98PinMinCGP-4
❑ 98PinMinCGPAP-4
❑ 98PinMinCN-4
❑ 98PinMinCNAP-4
❑ 98PinMinCSGR-4
❑ 98PinMinDC-4
❑ 98PinMinG-4
❑ 98PinMinMCSS-4
❑ 98PinMinS-4
❑ 98PinPer-24
❑ 98PinPerBB-19
❑ 98PinPerBBSamp-19
❑ 98PinPerBBSO-19
❑ 98PinPerPP-24
❑ 98PinPerSftF-5
❑ 98PinPlu-30
❑ 98PinPluAP-PP17
❑ 98PinPluGAP-PP17
❑ 98PinPluMAP-PP17
❑ 98PinPluY-5
❑ 98Revo-55
❑ 98RevoSS-55
❑ 98Sco-266
❑ 98ScoRT-1
❑ 98ScoRTSS-PP1
❑ 98ScoRTSSAP-PP1
❑ 98ScoRTSSAP1-PP1
❑ 98ScoRTStarGaz-19
❑ 98SkyDugA-65
❑ 98SkyDugA-136
❑ 98SkyDugADH-DH5
❑ 98SkyDugAG-G10
❑ 98SkyDugAIA-65
❑ 98SkyDugAIA-136
❑ 98SP Aut-90
❑ 98SP AutC-TC
❑ 98SpoIll-24
❑ 98SpoIllEE-24
❑ 98SpoIllFE-24
❑ 98SpoIllODMP-OD11
❑ 98SpoIllTaN-71
❑ 98SpoIllTaNEE-71
❑ 98SpoIllWSF-46
❑ 98SpoIllWSFEE-46
❑ 98SpoIllWSFFE-46
❑ 98SPxFin-32
❑ 98SPxFin-85
❑ 98SPxFinR-32
❑ 98SPxFinR-85
❑ 98SPxFinS-32
❑ 98SPxFinS-85
❑ 98StaCluC-CS25
❑ 98StaCluC-CS26
❑ 98StaCluC-CS27
❑ 98StaCluFDI-33
❑ 98StaCluI-33
❑ 98StaCluOneK-33
❑ 98StaCluPP-33
❑ 98Stu-1
❑ 98StuGPP-1
❑ 98StuHitPar-17
❑ 98StuPor8x10-28
❑ 98StuPor8x10GP-28
❑ 98StuSPP-1
❑ 98Top-9
❑ 98TopBabB-BB7
❑ 98TopChr-9
❑ 98TopChrBB-BB7
❑ 98TopChrBBR-BB7
❑ 98TopChrR-9
❑ 98TopDevR-9
❑ 98TopDia-9
❑ 98TopGal-88
❑ 98TopGalGP-88
❑ 98TopGalOPP-88
❑ 98TopGalPPI-88
❑ 98TopGalPPIA-88
❑ 98TopGolLabC1-30
❑ 98TopGolLabC1B-30
❑ 98TopGolLabC1One-30
❑ 98TopGolLabC1R-30
❑ 98TopGolLabC2-30
❑ 98TopGolLabC2B-30
❑ 98TopGolLabC2One-30
❑ 98TopGolLabC2R-30
❑ 98TopGolLabC3-30
❑ 98TopGolLabC3B-30
❑ 98TopGolLabC3One-30
❑ 98TopGolLabC3R-30
❑ 98TopMiniC-9
❑ 98TopOpeD-8
❑ 98TopSta-20
❑ 98TopStaB-20
❑ 98TopStaG-20
❑ 98TopStaGR-20
❑ 98TopStaS-20
❑ 98TopSup-24
❑ 98TopSup-24
❑ 98TopTek-58
❑ 98TopTekD-58
❑ 98UD3-37
❑ 98UD3-127
❑ 98UD3-217
❑ 98UD3DieCut-37
❑ 98UD3DieCut-127
❑ 98UD3DieCut-217
❑ 98Ult-118
❑ 98UltBacttF-15
❑ 98UltBigS-15
❑ 98UltGolM-118
❑ 98UltMas-118
❑ 98UltNot-15
❑ 98UltPlaM-118
❑ 98UppDec-90
❑ 98UppDec-367
❑ 98UppDecR-35
❑ 98UppDecRBBop-BB10
❑ 98UppDecSF-55
❑ 98UppDecTMT-13
❑ 98UppDecTMTG-13
❑ 98Zen-62
❑ 98Zen5 xx7-55
❑ 98Zen5x7GoldImp-55
❑ 98Zen5x7Imp-55
❑ 98ZenZ-G-62
❑ 98ZenZ-S-62
❑ 99199Fin-10
❑ 99Bow-14
❑ 99BowBes-52
❑ 99BowBesAR-52
❑ 99BowBesR-52
❑ 99BowChr-14
❑ 99BowChrG-14
❑ 99BowChrGR-14
❑ 99BowChrl-14
❑ 99BowChrIR-14
❑ 99BowChrR-14
❑ 99BowGol-14
❑ 99BowInt-14
❑ 99CroRoyB-51
❑ 99CroRoyL-51
❑ 99CroRoyOD-51
❑ 99E-X Cen-84
❑ 99E-X CenECFut-84
❑ 99E-X CenECNow-84
❑ 99FinGolRef-10
❑ 99FinRef-10
❑ 99FlaShoLeg1-32
❑ 99FlaShoLeg2-32
❑ 99FlaShoLeg3-32
❑ 99FlaShoLegM1-32
❑ 99FlaShoLegM2-32
❑ 99FlaShoLegM3-32
❑ 99FlaShoR1-32
❑ 99FlaShoR2-32
❑ 99FlaShoR3-32
❑ 99Fle-16
❑ 99FleBri-17
❑ 99FleBri2G-17
❑ 99FleBriBlu-17
❑ 99FleBriGol-17
❑ 99FleMys-48
❑ 99FleMysG-48
❑ 99FleMysM-48
❑ 99FleSta9-16
❑ 99FleVin'-16
❑ 99FleWarT-16
❑ 99KinDis-4
❑ 99MetUni-183
❑ 99MetUniGM-183
❑ 99MetUniPMG-183
❑ 99Pac-160
❑ 99PacAur-65
❑ 99PacAurOD-65
❑ 99PacCroC-105
❑ 99PacCroCPB-105
❑ 99PacInv-54
❑ 99PacInvOD-54
❑ 99PacInvPB-54
❑ 99PacOme-87
❑ 99PacOmeC-87
❑ 99PacOmeG-87
❑ 99PacOmePB-87
❑ 99PacPar-87
❑ 99PacParC-87
❑ 99PacParG-87
❑ 99PacParHoloGold-87

- ❑ 99PacParHS-87
- ❑ 99PacParOD-87
- ❑ 99PacParPB-87
- ❑ 99PacParRed-87
- ❑ 99PacPlaB-160
- ❑ 99PacPri-55
- ❑ 99PacPriHB-55
- ❑ 99PacPriHG-55
- ❑ 99PacPriHM-55
- ❑ 99PacPriHP-55
- ❑ 99PacPriRed-55
- ❑ 99PacPriS-73
- ❑ 99PacPriS206-73
- ❑ 99PacPriS206R-73
- ❑ 99PacRed-160
- ❑ 99Rev-53
- ❑ 99RevPremDate-53
- ❑ 99RevRet-53
- ❑ 99RevShaSS-53
- ❑ 99SkyMolM-111
- ❑ 99SkyMolMF-11
- ❑ 99SkyMolMFS-11
- ❑ 99SkyMolMFT-11
- ❑ 99SkyMolMX-111
- ❑ 99SkyPre-206
- ❑ 99SkyPreR-206
- ❑ 99SkyThu-283
- ❑ 99SkyThuRant-283
- ❑ 99SkyThuRave-283
- ❑ 99SP Aut-33
- ❑ 99SP AutHRC-HR16
- ❑ 99SPAutHRCDC-HR16
- ❑ 99SpoIll-29
- ❑ 99SpoIll-148
- ❑ 99SPx-39
- ❑ 99SPxFinR-39
- ❑ 99SPxFinS-39
- ❑ 99SPxPowE-PE14
- ❑ 99SPxPreS-PS9
- ❑ 99StaClu-77
- ❑ 99StaCluFDI-77
- ❑ 99StaCluOoaK-77
- ❑ 99StaCluPP-77
- ❑ 99ThuSkySupR-283
- ❑ 99Top-292
- ❑ 99TopBlaLC1-4
- ❑ 99TopBlaLC2-4
- ❑ 99TopBlaLC3-4
- ❑ 99TopChr-292
- ❑ 99TopChrR-292
- ❑ 99TopGal-21
- ❑ 99TopGalPP-21
- ❑ 99TopGalPPI-21
- ❑ 99TopGolL-4
- ❑ 99TopGolLC1-4
- ❑ 99TopGolLC2-4
- ❑ 99TopGolLOtO-4
- ❑ 99TopMVPP-292
- ❑ 99TopOpeD-154
- ❑ 99TopRedLC1-4
- ❑ 99TopRedLC2-4
- ❑ 99TopRedLC3-4
- ❑ 99TopSta-82
- ❑ 99TopSta'S-20
- ❑ 99TopSta'SG-20
- ❑ 99TopSta'SGDH-20
- ❑ 99TopSta1Foil-82
- ❑ 99TopStaFoil-82
- ❑ 99TopStaOS-82
- ❑ 99TopTekP-PP3A
- ❑ 99UD Cho-85
- ❑ 99UD ChoPCR-85
- ❑ 99UD ChoS-24
- ❑ 99UD ChoSD-24
- ❑ 99UD ChoSHR-24
- ❑ 99UD ChoST-24
- ❑ 99UD ChoYW-Y13
- ❑ 99UD Ion-26
- ❑ 99UD IonR-26
- ❑ 99UDHolo-22
- ❑ 99UDHoloAUsome-22
- ❑ 99Ult-185
- ❑ 99UltGolM-185
- ❑ 99UltMas-185
- ❑ 99UltPlaM-185
- ❑ 99UppDec-93
- ❑ 99UppDecBD-32
- ❑ 99UppDecBDD-32
- ❑ 99UppDecBDDom-D20
- ❑ 99UppDecBDDomE-D20
- ❑ 99UppDecBDQ-32
- ❑ 99UppDecBDT-32
- ❑ 99UppDecCf7-21
- ❑ 99UppDecCf7-C18
- ❑ 99UppDecCf7Cf7P-C18
- ❑ 99UppDecCLM-C35
- ❑ 99UppDecCo7CE-21
- ❑ 99UppDecE-35
- ❑ 99UppDecE-162
- ❑ 99UppDecEBPC-C-TC
- ❑ 99UppDecEFXG-35
- ❑ 99UppDecEFXG-162
- ❑ 99UppDecEL1-93
- ❑ 99UppDecEL2-93
- ❑ 99UppDecEPE-P13
- ❑ 99UppDecIP-I7
- ❑ 99UppDecIPD-I7
- ❑ 99UppDecIPHR-I7
- ❑ 99UppDecIPT-I7
- ❑ 99UppDecM-80
- ❑ 99UppDecMGS-80
- ❑ 99UppDecMHFS-80
- ❑ 99UppDecMP-80
- ❑ 99UppDecMSS-80
- ❑ 99UppDecO-3
- ❑ 99UppDecOSO-3
- ❑ 99UppDecR-31
- ❑ 99UppDecRG-31
- ❑ 99UppDecRI-TC
- ❑ 99UppDecRIL2-TC
- ❑ 99UppDecRP-31
- ❑ 99UppDecVtaT-V13
- ❑ 99UppDecVtaTD-V13
- ❑ 99UppDecVtaTQ-V13
- ❑ 99UppDecVtaTT-V13
- ❑ 99Vic-143
- ❑ 99Vic-144

Clark, Will

- ❑ 84OCoandSI-208
- ❑ 86DonHig-1
- ❑ 86DonRoo-32
- ❑ 86FleSlu-6
- ❑ 86FleUpd-25
- ❑ 86GiaMot-7
- ❑ 86GiaPos-6
- ❑ 86SpoRoo-6
- ❑ 86StaCan-13
- ❑ 86TopTra-24T
- ❑ 86TopTraT-24T
- ❑ 87BurKinA-3
- ❑ 87Don-66
- ❑ 87DonOpeD-96
- ❑ 87Fle-269
- ❑ 87FleExcS-10
- ❑ 87FleGlo-269
- ❑ 87FleLimE-8
- ❑ 87FleSluBC-M2
- ❑ 87FleStiC-22
- ❑ 87GiaMot-2
- ❑ 87GiaPos-5
- ❑ 87Lea-144
- ❑ 87OPC-361
- ❑ 87RedFolSB-50
- ❑ 87Spo-95
- ❑ 87Spo-195
- ❑ 87SpoTeaP-10
- ❑ 87Top-420
- ❑ 87TopRoo-4
- ❑ 87TopSti-88
- ❑ 87TopTif-420
- ❑ 87ToyRoo-7
- ❑ 88ClaBlu-225
- ❑ 88Don-21
- ❑ 88Don-204
- ❑ 88DonBasB-79
- ❑ 88DonBonM-BC24
- ❑ 88DonSupD-21
- ❑ 88Dra-27
- ❑ 88Fle-78
- ❑ 88FleAwaW-5
- ❑ 88FleBasA-7
- ❑ 88FleBasM-5
- ❑ 88FleExcS-9
- ❑ 88FleGlo-78
- ❑ 88FleHotS-6
- ❑ 88FleLeaL-5
- ❑ 88FleMin-116
- ❑ 88FleRecS-6
- ❑ 88FleSlu-8
- ❑ 88FleStiC-126
- ❑ 88FleSup-8
- ❑ 88FleTeaL-4
- ❑ 88GiaMot-2
- ❑ 88GiaPos-6
- ❑ 88K-M-6
- ❑ 88KeyFooD-10
- ❑ 88Lea-21
- ❑ 88Lea-170
- ❑ 88MotWilC-1
- ❑ 88MotWilC-2
- ❑ 88MotWilC-3
- ❑ 88MotWilC-4
- ❑ 88MSAFanSD-12
- ❑ 88MSAIceTD-10
- ❑ 88MSAJifPD-5
- ❑ 88Nes-14
- ❑ 88OPC-350
- ❑ 88OurOwnTD-10
- ❑ 88PanSti-420
- ❑ 88PanSti-421
- ❑ 88Sco-27
- ❑ 88Sco-78
- ❑ 88Sco-84
- ❑ 88ScoGlo-27
- ❑ 88ScoGlo-78
- ❑ 88ScoGlo-84
- ❑ 88ScoYouSI-25
- ❑ 88Spo-9
- ❑ 88SpoGam-4
- ❑ 88StaCla-1
- ❑ 88StaCla-2
- ❑ 88StaCla-3
- ❑ 88StaCla-4
- ❑ 88StaCla-5
- ❑ 88StaCla-6
- ❑ 88StaCla-7
- ❑ 88StaCla-8
- ❑ 88StaCla-9
- ❑ 88StaCla-10
- ❑ 88StaCla-11
- ❑ 88StaLinG-4
- ❑ 88TarPla-8
- ❑ 88TetTeaD-10
- ❑ 88Top-350
- ❑ 88TopBig-9
- ❑ 88TopCoi-38
- ❑ 88TopRitTM-12
- ❑ 88TopSti-87
- ❑ 88TopTif-350
- ❑ 88TopUKM-14
- ❑ 88TopUKMT-14
- ❑ 88WeiMarD-10
- ❑ 89Bow-476
- ❑ 89BowTif-476
- ❑ 89CadEllD-8
- ❑ 89ClaLigB-18
- ❑ 89ClaTraO-150
- ❑ 89ClaTraP-180
- ❑ 89Don-249
- ❑ 89DonAll-33
- ❑ 89DonBasB-23
- ❑ 89DonBonM-BC22
- ❑ 89DonPop-33
- ❑ 89Fle-325
- ❑ 89Fle-631
- ❑ 89Fle-632
- ❑ 89FleAll-3
- ❑ 89FleBasA-6
- ❑ 89FleBasM-7
- ❑ 89FleExcS-5
- ❑ 89FleGlo-325
- ❑ 89FleGlo-631
- ❑ 89FleGlo-632
- ❑ 89FleHeroB-7
- ❑ 89FleLeaL-4
- ❑ 89FleSup-8
- ❑ 89FleWaxBC-C6
- ❑ 89GiaMot-2
- ❑ 89K-M-23
- ❑ 89KayB-6
- ❑ 89KeyFooD-4
- ❑ 89KinDis-22
- ❑ 89MotWilC-1
- ❑ 89MotWilC-2
- ❑ 89MotWilC-3
- ❑ 89MotWilC-4
- ❑ 89MSAIceTD-4
- ❑ 89OPC-321
- ❑ 89OurOwnTD-4
- ❑ 89PanSti-212
- ❑ 89PanSti-232
- ❑ 89RedFolSB-22
- ❑ 89Sco-450
- ❑ 89ScoHot1S-85
- ❑ 89Scomast-10
- ❑ 89Spo-170
- ❑ 89SpoIllFKI-70
- ❑ 89StaMit/C-1
- ❑ 89StaMit/C-3
- ❑ 89StaMit/C-5
- ❑ 89StaMit/C-7
- ❑ 89StaMit/C-9
- ❑ 89StaMit/C-11
- ❑ 89TetTeaD-4
- ❑ 89Top-660
- ❑ 89TopBasT-47
- ❑ 89TopBig-146
- ❑ 89TopCapC-19
- ❑ 89TopCoi-8
- ❑ 89TopDouA-13
- ❑ 89TopGaloC-3
- ❑ 89TopGloA-13
- ❑ 89TopGloS-11
- ❑ 89TopHeaUT-2
- ❑ 89TopHilTM-7
- ❑ 89TopMinL-41
- ❑ 89TopSti-88
- ❑ 89TopSti-159
- ❑ 89TopStiB-34
- ❑ 89TopTif-660
- ❑ 89TopUKM-15
- ❑ 89TVSpoM-49
- ❑ 89TVSpoM-131
- ❑ 89UppDec-155
- ❑ 89UppDec-678
- ❑ 89UppDecS-1
- ❑ 89WeiMarD-4
- ❑ 90AllBasT-18
- ❑ 90Bow-231
- ❑ 90BowIns-1
- ❑ 90BowInsL-1
- ❑ 90BowInsT-1
- ❑ 90BowTif-231
- ❑ 90BowTif-A1
- ❑ 90ClaBlu-6
- ❑ 90ClaBlu-87A
- ❑ 90ClaBlu-87B
- ❑ 90ClaBlu-150A
- ❑ 90ClaBlu-150B
- ❑ 90ClaUpd-T11
- ❑ 90ClaYel-T7
- ❑ 90Col-4
- ❑ 90ColPosWC-1
- ❑ 90ColPosWC-2
- ❑ 90ColPosWC-3
- ❑ 90ColPosWC-4
- ❑ 90ColPosWC-5
- ❑ 90ColPosWC-6
- ❑ 90ColPosWC-7
- ❑ 90ColPosWC-8
- ❑ 90ColWilC-1
- ❑ 90ColWilC-2
- ❑ 90ColWilC-3
- ❑ 90ColWilC-4
- ❑ 90ColWilC-5
- ❑ 90ColWilC-6
- ❑ 90ColWilC-7
- ❑ 90ColWilC-8
- ❑ 90ColWilC-9
- ❑ 90ColWilC-10
- ❑ 90ColWilC-11
- ❑ 90ColWilC-12
- ❑ 90Don-230
- ❑ 90Don-707A
- ❑ 90Don-707B
- ❑ 90DonBesN-24
- ❑ 90DonGraS-6
- ❑ 90DonLeaS-23
- ❑ 90DonPre-4
- ❑ 90Fle-54
- ❑ 90Fle-630A
- ❑ 90Fle-630B
- ❑ 90Fle-637
- ❑ 90FleAll-2
- ❑ 90FleAwaW-7
- ❑ 90FleBasA-5
- ❑ 90FleBasAC-5
- ❑ 90FleBasM-7
- ❑ 90FleBasMC-7
- ❑ 90FleCan-54
- ❑ 90FleCan-630
- ❑ 90FleCan-637
- ❑ 90FleLeaL-6
- ❑ 90FleLeaLC-6
- ❑ 90FleWorS-4
- ❑ 90FleWorS-10
- ❑ 90GiaMot-2
- ❑ 90GiaSmo-4
- ❑ 90GooHumICBLS-6
- ❑ 90Hot50PS-6
- ❑ 90K-M-1
- ❑ 90Lea-172
- ❑ 90Lea-444
- ❑ 90M.Vpin-90
- ❑ 90MLBBasB-28
- ❑ 90MotWilC-1
- ❑ 90MotWilC-2
- ❑ 90MotWilC-3
- ❑ 90MotWilC-4
- ❑ 90MSAHolD-11
- ❑ 90MSAIceTD-1
- ❑ 90OPC-100
- ❑ 90OPC-397
- ❑ 90PanSti-207
- ❑ 90PanSti-363
- ❑ 90Pos-7
- ❑ 90PubIntS-65
- ❑ 90PubIntS-254
- ❑ 90RedFolSB-17
- ❑ 90Sco-300
- ❑ 90Sco-684
- ❑ 90Sco-699
- ❑ 90Sco100S-30
- ❑ 90ScoMcD-1
- ❑ 90Spo-5
- ❑ 90StaCla-1
- ❑ 90StaCla-2
- ❑ 90StaCla-4
- ❑ 90StaCla-6
- ❑ 90StaCla-8
- ❑ 90StaCla-10
- ❑ 90SunSee-17
- ❑ 90Top-100
- ❑ 90Top-397
- ❑ 90TopAmeA-31
- ❑ 90TopBig-224
- ❑ 90TopCoi-43
- ❑ 90TopDou-10
- ❑ 90TopGloA-2
- ❑ 90TopGloS-52
- ❑ 90TopHeaU-2
- ❑ 90TopHilHM-2
- ❑ 90TopMag-11
- ❑ 90TopMinL-84
- ❑ 90TopSti-85
- ❑ 90TopSti-147
- ❑ 90TopStiB-1
- ❑ 90TopTif-100
- ❑ 90TopTif-397
- ❑ 90TopTVA-34
- ❑ 90UppDec-50
- ❑ 90UppDec-556
- ❑ 90USPlaCA-12D
- ❑ 90WonBreS-19
- ❑ 90Woo-24
- ❑ 91BasBesHM-5
- ❑ 91Bow-616
- ❑ 91CadEllD-8
- ❑ 91Cla2-T94
- ❑ 91Cla3-T9
- ❑ 91Cla3-NNO
- ❑ 91ClaGam-48
- ❑ 91DenHol-3
- ❑ 91Don-86
- ❑ 91Don-441
- ❑ 91Fle-259
- ❑ 91FlePro-2
- ❑ 91GiaMot-2
- ❑ 91GiaPacGaE-14
- ❑ 91GiaSFE-6
- ❑ 91JesHSA-8
- ❑ 91JimDea-1
- ❑ 91KinDis-15
- ❑ 91Lea-238
- ❑ 91LeaPre-12
- ❑ 91MajLeaCP-63
- ❑ 91MisStaB-11
- ❑ 91OPC-500
- ❑ 91OPCPre-22
- ❑ 91PanFreS-67
- ❑ 91PanFreS-158
- ❑ 91PanSti-79
- ❑ 91PetSta-20
- ❑ 91PlaWilC-21
- ❑ 91PlaWilC-22
- ❑ 91PlaWilC-23
- ❑ 91PlaWilC-24
- ❑ 91PlaWilC-25
- ❑ 91PlaWilC-39
- ❑ 91PlaWilC-40
- ❑ 91PlaWilC-41
- ❑ 91PlaWilC-42
- ❑ 91PlaWilC-43
- ❑ 91Pos-3
- ❑ 91PosCan-9
- ❑ 91RedFolS-19
- ❑ 91RedFolS-117
- ❑ 91Sco-7
- ❑ 91Sco-664
- ❑ 91Sco-871
- ❑ 91Sco-886
- ❑ 91Sco100S-4
- ❑ 91ScoCoo-B6
- ❑ 91SevCoi-NC3
- ❑ 91SilHol-5
- ❑ 91SimandSMLBL-9
- ❑ 91StaClu-5
- ❑ 91StaPinB-8
- ❑ 91Stu-254
- ❑ 91Top-500
- ❑ 91TopCraJI-35
- ❑ 91TopDesS-500
- ❑ 91TopGloA-13
- ❑ 91TopMic-500
- ❑ 91TopSta-8
- ❑ 91TopTif-500
- ❑ 91TopTriH-N11
- ❑ 91Ult-318
- ❑ 91UltGol-2
- ❑ 91UppDec-445
- ❑ 91UppDecFE-92F
- ❑ 91USPlaCA-WCO
- ❑ 92Bow-260
- ❑ 92Bow-673
- ❑ 92Cla1-T24
- ❑ 92Cla2-T37
- ❑ 92ClaGam-136
- ❑ 92ColAllG-2
- ❑ 92ColAllP-2
- ❑ 92ColPro-6
- ❑ 92DenHol-24
- ❑ 92Don-214
- ❑ 92Don-428
- ❑ 92DonCraJ1-14
- ❑ 92DonDiaK-DK2
- ❑ 92DonEli-11
- ❑ 92DonMcD-18
- ❑ 92DonPre-3
- ❑ 92DonSupD-DK2
- ❑ 92Fle-631
- ❑ 92Fle-699
- ❑ 92FleAll-13
- ❑ 92FleCitTP-22
- ❑ 92FleTeaL-8
- ❑ 92Fre-11
- ❑ 92GiaMot-2
- ❑ 92GiaPacGaE-11
- ❑ 92GiaPacGaE-12
- ❑ 92Hig5-126
- ❑ 92Hig5S-7
- ❑ 92Hig5S-31
- ❑ 92HitTheBB-10
- ❑ 92JimDea-7
- ❑ 92LaKdec-4
- ❑ 92Lea-241
- ❑ 92LeaBlaG-241
- ❑ 92LeaGolP-12
- ❑ 92LeaPre-12
- ❑ 92MooSna-8
- ❑ 92Mr.TurS-6
- ❑ 92MSABenSHD-17
- ❑ 92MVPPin-39
- ❑ 92New-4
- ❑ 92OPC-330
- ❑ 92OPCPre-146
- ❑ 92PanSti-212
- ❑ 92PanSti-281
- ❑ 92PepDieM-14
- ❑ 92Pin-122
- ❑ 92PinSlu-12
- ❑ 92PinTeaP-4
- ❑ 92Pos-14
- ❑ 92PosCan-3
- ❑ 92RedFolS-25
- ❑ 92RedFolS-110
- ❑ 92Sco-3
- ❑ 92Sco-773
- ❑ 92Sco-883
- ❑ 92Sco100S-24
- ❑ 92ScoImpP-51
- ❑ 92ScoProP-2
- ❑ 92SevCoi-20
- ❑ 92SpoIllFK1-86
- ❑ 92SpoStaCC-8
- ❑ 92StaClu-460
- ❑ 92StaClu-598
- ❑ 92StaCluD-28
- ❑ 92StaCluMP-4
- ❑ 92StaWilC-1
- ❑ 92StaWilC-2
- ❑ 92StaWilC-3
- ❑ 92StaWilC-4
- ❑ 92StaWilC-5
- ❑ 92StaWilC-6
- ❑ 92StaWilC-7
- ❑ 92StaWilC-8
- ❑ 92StaWilC-9
- ❑ 92StaWilC-10
- ❑ 92StaWilC-11
- ❑ 92Stu-114
- ❑ 92StuHer-BC8
- ❑ 92StuPre-11
- ❑ 92SunSee-8
- ❑ 92Top-330
- ❑ 92Top-386
- ❑ 92TopDaiQTU-2

❑ 92TopGol-330
❑ 92TopGol-386
❑ 92TopGolW-330
❑ 92TopGolW-386
❑ 92TopKid-58
❑ 92TopMcD-18
❑ 92TopMic-330
❑ 92TopMic-386
❑ 92TriPla-155
❑ 92Ult-287
❑ 92UltAllS-11
❑ 92UltAwaW-14
❑ 92UppDec-175
❑ 92UppDec-718
❑ 92UppDecF-18
❑ 92UppDecFG-18
❑ 92UppDecTMH-15
❑ 92UppDecWB-T4
❑ 93Bow-252
❑ 93DenHol-11
❑ 93DiaMar-24
❑ 93DiaMarP-2
❑ 93Don-446
❑ 93DonEli-S3
❑ 93DonMasotG-9
❑ 93DonMVP-13
❑ 93DonPre-11
❑ 93DonSpiotG-SG8
❑ 93DurPowP1-22
❑ 93Fin-108
❑ 93FinJum-108
❑ 93FinRef-108
❑ 93Fla-140
❑ 93FlaPro-1
❑ 93Fle-154
❑ 93FleAtl-4
❑ 93FleFruotL-11
❑ 93FleTeaL-NL1
❑ 93FunPac-13
❑ 93FunPac-101
❑ 93FunPacA-AS3
❑ 93GiaMot-2
❑ 93GiaPos-14
❑ 93GiaPos-15
❑ 93GiaStaC-9
❑ 93Hos-17
❑ 93Kra-18
❑ 93Lea-247
❑ 93LeaGolA-R11
❑ 93MetBak-23
❑ 93MilBonSS-7
❑ 93OPC-113
❑ 93OPCPreSP-12
❑ 93OPCPreSPF-12
❑ 93PacSpa-269
❑ 93PanSti-236
❑ 93Pin-16
❑ 93PinCoo-16
❑ 93PinCooD-16
❑ 93PinHomRC-38
❑ 93PinSlu-20
❑ 93Pos-2
❑ 93RedFolS-19
❑ 93RedFolS-110
❑ 93Sco-22
❑ 93ScoFra-26
❑ 93Sel-3
❑ 93SelStaL-17
❑ 93SP-111
❑ 93SPPlaP-PP4
❑ 93StaClu-562
❑ 93StaCluFDI-562
❑ 93StaCluI-B1
❑ 93StaCluM-139
❑ 93StaCluMOP-562
❑ 93StaCluMOP-MB1
❑ 93StaCluMP-15
❑ 93Stu-48
❑ 93Top-10
❑ 93TOPBLAG-2
❑ 93TopGol-10
❑ 93TopInaM-10
❑ 93TopInaR-10
❑ 93TopMic-10
❑ 93TriPla-107
❑ 93TriPlaA-11
❑ 93TriPlaN-4
❑ 93Ult-130
❑ 93UltAllS-2
❑ 93UppDec-315
❑ 93UppDec-471
❑ 93UppDec-476
❑ 93UppDec-576
❑ 93UppDecCP-R6
❑ 93UppDecGold-315
❑ 93UppDecGold-471
❑ 93UppDecGold-476
❑ 93UppDecGold-576
❑ 93UppDecIC-WI11
❑ 93UppDecICJ-WI11
❑ 93UppDecOD-D8
❑ 93UppDecTriCro-TC3
❑ 94BalParF-1
❑ 94Bow-485
❑ 94BowBes-R79
❑ 94BowBesR-R79
❑ 94ColC-540
❑ 94ColChoGS-540
❑ 94ColChoSS-540
❑ 94Don-38
❑ 94DonSpeE-38
❑ 94Fin-238
❑ 94FinJum-238
❑ 94FinRef-238
❑ 94Fla-108
❑ 94FlaHotG-2
❑ 94FlaHotN-3
❑ 94FlaInfP-2
❑ 94Fle-689
❑ 94FleExtB-177
❑ 94FleTeaL-28
❑ 94FleUpd-90
❑ 94FleUpdDT-3
❑ 94FUnPac-22
❑ 94GiaTeaI-9
❑ 94KelRusSWC-1
❑ 94Lea-404
❑ 94LeaGam-10
❑ 94LeaL-71
❑ 94LeaMVPC-A5
❑ 94LeaMVPCG-A5
❑ 94OPC-187
❑ 94Pac-544
❑ 94PanSti-263
❑ 94Pin-513
❑ 94PinArtP-513
❑ 94PinMusC-513
❑ 94Pos-22
❑ 94ProMag-134
❑ 94RanAllP-22
❑ 94RedFolMI-9
❑ 94Sco-10
❑ 94ScoGolR-10
❑ 94ScoRoo-RT1
❑ 94ScoRooCP-CP1
❑ 94ScoRooGR-RT1
❑ 94ScoRooS-RT1
❑ 94Sel-319
❑ 94SP-147
❑ 94SPDieC-147
❑ 94Spo-146
❑ 94SpoRoo-1
❑ 94SpoRooAP-1
❑ 94SpoRooS-1
❑ 94StaClu-203
❑ 94StaClu-666
❑ 94StaCluFDI-203
❑ 94StaCluFDI-666
❑ 94StaCluGR-203
❑ 94StaCluGR-666
❑ 94StaCluMOP-203
❑ 94StaCluMOP-666
❑ 94StaCluT-258
❑ 94StaCluTFDI-258
❑ 94Stu-153
❑ 94Top-240
❑ 94TopGol-240
❑ 94TopSpa-240
❑ 94TopSupS-9
❑ 94TopTra-115T
❑ 94TriPla-193
❑ 94Ult-429
❑ 94UppDec-350
❑ 94UppDecAJ-22
❑ 94UppDecAJG-22
❑ 94UppDecED-350
❑ 95Baz-32
❑ 95Bow-403
❑ 95BowBes-R22
❑ 95BowBesR-R22
❑ 95ClaFanFPCP-2
❑ 95ClaPhoC-54
❑ 95ColCho-400
❑ 95ColChoGS-400
❑ 95ColChoSE-184
❑ 95ColChoSEGS-184
❑ 95ColChoSESS-184
❑ 95ColChoSS-400
❑ 95Don-128
❑ 95DonDiaK-DK17
❑ 95DonPreP-128
❑ 95DonTopotO-157
❑ 95Emo-83
❑ 95Fin-123
❑ 95FinRef-123
❑ 95Fla-86
❑ 95Fle-283
❑ 95FleAllS-12
❑ 95FleUpdH-6
❑ 95Lea-167
❑ 95Lea300C-6
❑ 95LeaCor-5
❑ 95LeaLim-20
❑ 95LeaLimG-8
❑ 95LeaLimIBP-11
❑ 95LeaSli-6A
❑ 95LeaSli-6B
❑ 95NatPac-13
❑ 95Pac-423
❑ 95PacGolP-22
❑ 95PacPri-135
❑ 95PanSti-36
❑ 95Pin-269
❑ 95Pin-288
❑ 95PinArtP-269
❑ 95PinArtP-288
❑ 95PinFan-8
❑ 95PinGatA-GA11
❑ 95PinMusC-269
❑ 95PinMusC-288
❑ 95PinPer-PP11
❑ 95PinRedH-RH17
❑ 95PinWhiH-WH17
❑ 95Pos-16
❑ 95RanCra-6
❑ 95RedFol-35
❑ 95Sco-37
❑ 95Sco-570
❑ 95ScoGolR-37
❑ 95ScoGolR-570
❑ 95ScoHaloG-HG20
❑ 95ScoPlaTS-37
❑ 95ScoPlaTS-570
❑ 95ScoRul-SR19
❑ 95ScoRulJ-SR19
❑ 95Sel-99
❑ 95SelArtP-99
❑ 95SelBigS-BS6
❑ 95SelCer-11
❑ 95SelCerGT-9
❑ 95SelCerMG-11
❑ 95SP-200
❑ 95SPCha-103
❑ 95SPCha-189
❑ 95SPCha-194
❑ 95SPChaDC-103
❑ 95SPChaDC-189
❑ 95SPChaDC-194
❑ 95Spo-119
❑ 95SpoArtP-119
❑ 95SpoDouT-2
❑ 95SpoHamT-HT9
❑ 95SpoPro-PM11
❑ 95SPSil-200
❑ 95SPSpeF-21
❑ 95StaClu-131
❑ 95StaClu-522
❑ 95StaCluCT-15
❑ 95StaCluFDI-131
❑ 95StaCluMOP-131
❑ 95StaCluMOP-522
❑ 95StaCluMOP-RL18
❑ 95StaCluRL-RL18
❑ 95StaCluSTWS-131
❑ 95StaCluSTWS-522
❑ 95StaCluVR-67
❑ 95StaCluVRMO-67
❑ 95Stu-12
❑ 95StuGolS-12
❑ 95StuPlaS-12
❑ 95Sum-85
❑ 95Sum-182
❑ 95SumBigB-BB9
❑ 95SumNthD-85
❑ 95SumNthD-182
❑ 95Top-558
❑ 95TopCyb-334
❑ 95TopD3-21
❑ 95TopEmb-22
❑ 95TopEmbGI-22
❑ 95UC3-7
❑ 95UC3-132
❑ 95UC3ArtP-7
❑ 95UC3ArtP-132
❑ 95UC3CycS-CS10
❑ 95UC3InM-IM10
❑ 95Ult-108
❑ 95UltGolM-108
❑ 95UltOnBL-6
❑ 95UltOnBLGM-6
❑ 95UppDec-390
❑ 95UppDecED-390
❑ 95UppDecEDG-390
❑ 95UppDecPAW-H25
❑ 95UppDecPAWE-H25
❑ 95UppDecPLL-R43
❑ 95UppDecPLL-R51
❑ 95UppDecPLLE-R43
❑ 95UppDecPLLE-R51
❑ 95UppDecSE-39
❑ 95UppDecSEG-39
❑ 95USPlaCMLA-4D
❑ 95Zen-110
❑ 95ZenZ-13
❑ 96Baz-43
❑ 96Bow-108
❑ 96BowBes-77
❑ 96BowBesAR-77
❑ 96BowBesR-77
❑ 96BowFoi-108
❑ 96Cir-84
❑ 96CirBos-22
❑ 96CirRav-84
❑ 96ColCho-320
❑ 96ColChoGS-320
❑ 96ColChoSS-320
❑ 96Don-20
❑ 96DonHitL-3
❑ 96DonPreP-20
❑ 96EmoXL-120
❑ 96Fin-B149
❑ 96Fin-B193
❑ 96Fin-S62
❑ 96FinRef-B149
❑ 96FinRef-B193
❑ 96FinRef-S62
❑ 96Fla-167
❑ 96FlaHotG-3
❑ 96Fle-247
❑ 96FleTif-247
❑ 96FleUpdSL-3
❑ 96Lea-147
❑ 96LeaLim-68
❑ 96LeaLimG-68
❑ 96LeaPre-76
❑ 96LeaPreP-76
❑ 96LeaPrePB-147
❑ 96LeaPrePG-147
❑ 96LeaPrePS-147
❑ 96LeaPreSG-16
❑ 96LeaPreSte-16
❑ 96LeaSig-72
❑ 96LeaSigA-46
❑ 96LeaSigAG-46
❑ 96LeaSigAS-46
❑ 96LeaSigPPG-72
❑ 96LeaSigPPP-72
❑ 96MetUni-112
❑ 96MetUniP-112
❑ 96Pac-424
❑ 96PacGolCD-DC2
❑ 96PacPri-P135
❑ 96PacPriG-P135
❑ 96PanSti-231
❑ 96Pin-156
❑ 96Pin-213
❑ 96Pin-270
❑ 96Pin-302
❑ 96PinAfi-26
❑ 96PinAfiAP-26
❑ 96PinAfiFPP-26
❑ 96PinArtP-83
❑ 96PinArtP-113
❑ 96PinArtP-170
❑ 96PinArtP-186
❑ 96PinEssotG-16
❑ 96PinFirR-17
❑ 96PinFoil-213
❑ 96PinFoil-270
❑ 96PinFoil-302
❑ 96PinSky-9
❑ 96PinSta-83
❑ 96PinSta-113
❑ 96PinSta-170
❑ 96PinSta-186
❑ 96ProMagDM-23
❑ 96ProSta-97
❑ 96RanDr P-4
❑ 96RanFle-3
❑ 96RanMot-2
❑ 96Sco-1
❑ 96Sco-371
❑ 96ScoDugC-A1
❑ 96ScoDugC-B96
❑ 96ScoDugCAP-A1
❑ 96ScoDugCAP-B96
❑ 96ScoNumG-28
❑ 96ScoRef-15
❑ 96Sel-97
❑ 96SelArtP-97
❑ 96SelCer-11
❑ 96SelCerAP-11
❑ 96SelCerCB-11
❑ 96SelCerCR-11
❑ 96SelCerIP-12
❑ 96SelCerMB-11
❑ 96SelCerMG-11
❑ 96SelCerMR-11
❑ 96SelTeaN-14
❑ 96SP-177
❑ 96Spo-3
❑ 96SpoArtP-3
❑ 96StaClu-181
❑ 96StaClu-274
❑ 96StaCluEPB-274
❑ 96StaCluEPG-274
❑ 96StaCluEPS-274
❑ 96StaCluMeg-MH5
❑ 96StaCluMOP-181
❑ 96StaCluMOP-274
❑ 96StaCluMOP-MH5
❑ 96Stu-42
❑ 96StuPrePB-42
❑ 96StuPrePG-42
❑ 96StuPrePS-42
❑ 96Sum-105
❑ 96SumAbo&B-105
❑ 96SumArtP-105
❑ 96SumFoi-105
❑ 96TeaOut-18
❑ 96Top-299
❑ 96TopChr-118
❑ 96TopChrR-118
❑ 96TopGal-149
❑ 96TopGalPPI-149
❑ 96TopLas-40
❑ 96TopLasSS-9
❑ 96Ult-132
❑ 96UltGolM-132
❑ 96UltPriL-2
❑ 96UltPriLGM-2
❑ 96UltThu-6
❑ 96UltThuGM-6
❑ 96UppDec-207
❑ 96Zen-54
❑ 96ZenArtP-54
❑ 96ZenMoz-2
❑ 97Bow-36
❑ 97BowBes-48
❑ 97BowBesAR-48
❑ 97BowBesR-48
❑ 97BowChr-31
❑ 97BowChrI-31
❑ 97BowChrIR-31
❑ 97BowChrR-31
❑ 97BowInt-36
❑ 97Cir-328
❑ 97CirRav-328
❑ 97ColCho-241
❑ 97ColChoT-TR5
❑ 97Don-137
❑ 97DonEli-37
❑ 97DonEliGS-37
❑ 97DonGolPP-137
❑ 97DonLim-90
❑ 97DonLim-194
❑ 97DonLimE-90
❑ 97DonLimE-194
❑ 97DonLimENG-90
❑ 97DonPre-114
❑ 97DonPreCttC-114
❑ 97DonSig-17
❑ 97DonSigA-19
❑ 97DonSigAC-25
❑ 97DonSigAM-25
❑ 97DonSigPPP-17
❑ 97DonSilPP-137
❑ 97E-X2-45
❑ 97E-X2Cred-45
❑ 97E-X2EssCre-45
❑ 97Fin-44
❑ 97FinRef-44
❑ 97Fle-219
❑ 97FleTif-219
❑ 97HigMinM-25
❑ 97HigMinMCT-11
❑ 97HigMinMCT-12
❑ 97Lea-7
❑ 97LeaFraM-7
❑ 97LeaFraMDC-7
❑ 97MetUni-161
❑ 97NewPin-107
❑ 97NewPinAP-107
❑ 97NewPinMC-107
❑ 97NewPinPP-107
❑ 97Pac-197
❑ 97PacLigB-197
❑ 97PacPri-67
❑ 97PacPriLB-67
❑ 97PacPriP-67
❑ 97PacSil-197
❑ 97PinCer-97
❑ 97PinCerMBla-97
❑ 97PinCerMBlu-97
❑ 97PinCerMG-97
❑ 97PinCerMR-97
❑ 97PinCerR-97
❑ 97PinIns-24
❑ 97PinInsCE-24
❑ 97PinInsDD-14
❑ 97PinInsDE-24
❑ 97PinTotCPB-97
❑ 97PinTotCPG-97
❑ 97PinTotCPR-97
❑ 97PinX-P-65
❑ 97PinX-PMoS-65
❑ 97RanCup-1
❑ 97RanDr P-5
❑ 97RanMinM-2
❑ 97RanMot-2
❑ 97RanSco-2
❑ 97RanScoPl-2
❑ 97RanScoPr-2
❑ 97Sco-6
❑ 97Sco-539
❑ 97ScoArtPWB-6
❑ 97ScoArtPWB-539
❑ 97ScoHeaotO-1
❑ 97ScoPitP-11
❑ 97ScoPreS-6
❑ 97ScoResC-539
❑ 97ScoShoS-6
❑ 97ScoShoS-539
❑ 97ScoShoSAP-6
❑ 97ScoShoSAP-539
❑ 97Sel-94
❑ 97SelArtP-94
❑ 97SelCom-94
❑ 97SelRegG-94
❑ 97SP-172
❑ 97SpoIll-161
❑ 97SpoIll-175
❑ 97SpoIllEE-161
❑ 97SpoIllEE-175
❑ 97StaClu-49
❑ 97StaCluMat-49
❑ 97StaCluMOP-49
❑ 97Stu-93
❑ 97StuPrePG-93
❑ 97StuPrePS-93
❑ 97Top-387
❑ 97TopChr-133
❑ 97TopChrR-133
❑ 97TopGal-17
❑ 97TopGalPPI-17
❑ 97TopSta-66
❑ 97TopStaAM-66
❑ 97Ult-130
❑ 97UltDouT-10
❑ 97UltGolME-130
❑ 97UltPlaME-130
❑ 97UppDec-505
❑ 98Bow-253
❑ 98BowChr-253
❑ 98BowChrGA-253
❑ 98BowChrGAR-253
❑ 98BowChrI-253
❑ 98BowChrIR-253
❑ 98BowChrR-253
❑ 98BowGolA-253
❑ 98BowInt-253
❑ 98CirThu-266
❑ 98CirThuRav-266
❑ 98CirThuSupRav-266
❑ 98ColCho-515
❑ 98CroRoy-135
❑ 98Don-134
❑ 98DonCol-134
❑ 98DonColE-452
❑ 98DonColL-254
❑ 98DonColP-592
❑ 98DonColS-134
❑ 98DonCruG-45
❑ 98DonCruP-45
❑ 98DonCruR-45
❑ 98DonEli-52

- ❑ 98DonEliA-52
- ❑ 98DonEliS-52
- ❑ 98DonGolPP-134
- ❑ 98DonPre-42
- ❑ 98DonPreSeat-42
- ❑ 98DonPriCD-134
- ❑ 98DonPriCE-452
- ❑ 98DonPriCL-254
- ❑ 98DonPriCP-592
- ❑ 98DonSig-13
- ❑ 98DonSigA-17
- ❑ 98DonSigAC-24
- ❑ 98DonSigAM-24
- ❑ 98DonSigP-13
- ❑ 98DonSilPP-134
- ❑ 98Fin-68
- ❑ 98FinNo--68
- ❑ 98FinNo-R-68
- ❑ 98FinRef-68
- ❑ 98Fle-241
- ❑ 98Lea-55
- ❑ 98LeaFraDA-55
- ❑ 98LeaFraF-55
- ❑ 98LeaFraM-55
- ❑ 98LeaFraM-55
- ❑ 98LeaFraMDC-55
- ❑ 98LeaFraMDC-55
- ❑ 98LeaFraMS-55
- ❑ 98LeaFraMZ2-55
- ❑ 98LeaRS-22
- ❑ 98LeaRSLHolo-22
- ❑ 98LeaRSLong-22
- ❑ 98LeaRTrue-22
- ❑ 98MetUni-40
- ❑ 98MetUniPMG-40
- ❑ 98Pac-200
- ❑ 98PacAur-85
- ❑ 98PacInv-68
- ❑ 98PacInvPBlue-68
- ❑ 98PacInvSilv-68
- ❑ 98PacInvTeam-27
- ❑ 98PacOme-236
- ❑ 98PacOmeR-236
- ❑ 98PacOnl-730
- ❑ 98PacOnlR-730
- ❑ 98PacOnlWC-730
- ❑ 98PacPar-103
- ❑ 98PacParC-103
- ❑ 98PacParG-103
- ❑ 98PacParHS-103
- ❑ 98PacParI-50
- ❑ 98PacParPB-103
- ❑ 98PacParR-103
- ❑ 98PacPlaB-200
- ❑ 98PacRedT-200
- ❑ 98PacSil-200
- ❑ 98Pin-33
- ❑ 98PinArtP-PP33
- ❑ 98PinIns-67
- ❑ 98PinInsCE-67
- ❑ 98PinInsDE-67
- ❑ 98PinInsSG-18AB
- ❑ 98PinInsSG-18CD
- ❑ 98PinInsSGS-18AB
- ❑ 98PinInsSGS-18CD
- ❑ 98PinMusC-PP33
- ❑ 98PinPer-43
- ❑ 98PinPerPP-43
- ❑ 98PinPreP-33
- ❑ 98PinSna-TR4
- ❑ 98PinSna-TR16
- ❑ 98RanPinM-1
- ❑ 98Revo-141
- ❑ 98RevoSS-141
- ❑ 98ScoRT-190
- ❑ 98ScoRTSS-PP106
- ❑ 98ScoRTSSAP-PP106
- ❑ 98ScoRTSSAP1-PP106
- ❑ 98SP Aut-189
- ❑ 98SpoIll-25
- ❑ 98SpoIllEE-25
- ❑ 98SpoIllFE-25
- ❑ 98StaCluFDI-138
- ❑ 98StaCluI-138
- ❑ 98StaCluOneK-138
- ❑ 98StaCluPP-138
- ❑ 98Stu-6
- ❑ 98StuGPP-6
- ❑ 98StuSPP-6
- ❑ 98Top-316
- ❑ 98TopChr-316
- ❑ 98TopChrR-316
- ❑ 98TopDevR-316
- ❑ 98TopDia-316
- ❑ 98TopMiniC-316
- ❑ 98TopOpeD-142
- ❑ 98Ult-109
- ❑ 98UltGolM-109
- ❑ 98UltMas-109
- ❑ 98UltPlaM-109
- ❑ 98UppDec-229
- ❑ 98UppDecSF-128
- ❑ 98Zen-41
- ❑ 98ZenZ-G-41
- ❑ 98ZenZ-S-41
- ❑ 99199Fin-198
- ❑ 99Bow-257
- ❑ 99BowGol-257
- ❑ 99BowInt-257
- ❑ 99CroRoyB-19
- ❑ 99CroRoyL-19
- ❑ 99CroRoyOD-19
- ❑ 99E-X Cen-55
- ❑ 99E-X CenECFut-55
- ❑ 99E-X CenECNow-55
- ❑ 99FinGolRef-198
- ❑ 99FinRef-198
- ❑ 99Fle-78
- ❑ 99FleBri-115
- ❑ 99FleBri2G-115
- ❑ 99FleBriBlu-115
- ❑ 99FleBriGol-115
- ❑ 99FleMys-37
- ❑ 99FleMysG-37
- ❑ 99FleMysM-37
- ❑ 99FleSta9-78
- ❑ 99FleWarT-78
- ❑ 99MetUni-28
- ❑ 99MetUniGM-28
- ❑ 99MetUniPMG-28
- ❑ 99Pac-421
- ❑ 99PacAur-22
- ❑ 99PacAurOD-22
- ❑ 99PacCroC-281
- ❑ 99PacCroCPB-281
- ❑ 99PacInv-20
- ❑ 99PacInvOD-20
- ❑ 99PacInvPB-20
- ❑ 99PacOme-32
- ❑ 99PacOmeC-32
- ❑ 99PacOmeG-32
- ❑ 99PacOmePB-32
- ❑ 99PacPar-32
- ❑ 99PacParC-32
- ❑ 99PacParG-32
- ❑ 99PacParHoloGold-32
- ❑ 99PacParHS-32
- ❑ 99PacParOD-32
- ❑ 99PacParPB-32
- ❑ 99PacParRed-32
- ❑ 99PacPlaB-421
- ❑ 99PacPri-141
- ❑ 99PacPriHB-141
- ❑ 99PacPriHG-141
- ❑ 99PacPriHM-141
- ❑ 99PacPriHP-141
- ❑ 99PacPriRed-141
- ❑ 99PacPriS-74
- ❑ 99PacPriS206-74
- ❑ 99PacPriS206R-74
- ❑ 99PacRed-421
- ❑ 99Rev-20
- ❑ 99RevPremDate-20
- ❑ 99RevRet-20
- ❑ 99RevShaSS-20
- ❑ 99SkyMolM-31
- ❑ 99SkyMolMX-31
- ❑ 99SkyPre-83
- ❑ 99SkyPreR-83
- ❑ 99SkyThu-30
- ❑ 99SkyThuRant-30
- ❑ 99SkyThuRave-30
- ❑ 99SpoIll-170
- ❑ 99StaClu-332
- ❑ 99StaCluFDI-332
- ❑ 99StaCluOoaK-332
- ❑ 99StaCluPP-332
- ❑ 99ThuSkySupR-30
- ❑ 99Top-9
- ❑ 99TopChr-9
- ❑ 99TopChrR-9
- ❑ 99TopMVPP-9
- ❑ 99TopOpeD-6
- ❑ 99TopSta-111
- ❑ 99TopStaFoil-111
- ❑ 99UD Cho-150
- ❑ 99UD ChoP-150
- ❑ 99UD ChoPCR-150
- ❑ 99Ult-198
- ❑ 99UltGolM-198
- ❑ 99UltMas-198
- ❑ 99UltPlaM-198
- ❑ 99UppDec-216
- ❑ 99UppDec-317
- ❑ 99UppDecBD-87
- ❑ 99UppDecBDD-87
- ❑ 99UppDecBDQ-87
- ❑ 99UppDecBDT-87
- ❑ 99UppDecCL-78
- ❑ 99UppDecCLCC-78
- ❑ 99UppDecEL1-216
- ❑ 99UppDecEL1-317
- ❑ 99UppDecEL2-216
- ❑ 99UppDecEL2-317
- ❑ 99Vic-55

Clark, Willie
- ❑ 75WatRoyT-7

Clark, Willie (William Otis)
- ❑ 98CamPepP-11

Clarke, Bobby
- ❑ 80PhiBul-19

Clarke, Boileryard (William Jones)
- ❑ 03BreE10-20
- ❑ 98CamPepP-12

Clarke, Fred C.
- ❑ 03BreE10-21
- ❑ 06FanCraNL-10
- ❑ 08AmeCarE91-71
- ❑ 08RosComP-150
- ❑ 09AmeCarE90-1-22
- ❑ 09AmeCarE90-1-23
- ❑ 09ColChiE-53
- ❑ 09SpoNewSM-13
- ❑ 09T206-65
- ❑ 09T206-66
- ❑ 10DarChoE-8
- ❑ 10DomDisP-25
- ❑ 10E-UOraBSC-6
- ❑ 10E12AmeCDCE125-10
- ❑ 10E98-7
- ❑ 10NadE1-10
- ❑ 10PirAmeCE-2
- ❑ 10PirHerICP-5
- ❑ 10PirTipTD-3
- ❑ 10StaCarE-9
- ❑ 10SweCapPP-135A
- ❑ 10SweCapPP-135B
- ❑ 10W555-14
- ❑ 11BasBatEU-10
- ❑ 11HelSta-112
- ❑ 11HelSta-157
- ❑ 11JonKeyaAC-325
- ❑ 11MecDFT-8
- ❑ 11PinT-5-855
- ❑ 11PloCanE-15
- ❑ 11S74Sil-108
- ❑ 11SpoLifCW-62
- ❑ 11SpoLifM-248
- ❑ 11T205-29
- ❑ 11TurRedT-8
- ❑ 12ColRedB-52
- ❑ 12ColTinT-52
- ❑ 12ColTinT-54
- ❑ 12HasTriFT-14B
- ❑ 12HasTriFT-16B
- ❑ 12HasTriFT-20
- ❑ 12HasTriFT-25A
- ❑ 12HasTriFT-62
- ❑ 13NatGamW-10
- ❑ 13TomBarW-10
- ❑ 14CraJacE-70
- ❑ 14PieStaT-23
- ❑ 15CraJacE-70
- ❑ 39PC7AlbHoF-31
- ❑ 48ExhHoF-5
- ❑ 50CalHOFW-16
- ❑ 53ArtHaloFP-15
- ❑ 63BazA-26
- ❑ 73FleWilD-27
- ❑ 74CapPub-40
- ❑ 75TCMAllG-4
- ❑ 76GrePlaG-11
- ❑ 76ShaPiz-31
- ❑ 77GalGloG-164
- ❑ 80PerHaloFP-31
- ❑ 80SSPHOF-31
- ❑ 84GalHaloFRL-31
- ❑ 86ConSer1-53
- ❑ 93CraJac-13
- ❑ 94OriofB-85
- ❑ 96PitPosH-3

Clarke, Horace M.
- ❑ 66Top-547
- ❑ 67CokCapYM-V6
- ❑ 67DexPre-49
- ❑ 67OPC-169
- ❑ 67Top-169
- ❑ 68Top-263
- ❑ 68TopVen-263
- ❑ 68YanPhoS-62
- ❑ 69MilBra-59
- ❑ 69MLBOffS-73
- ❑ 69OPC-87
- ❑ 69Top-87
- ❑ 69TopSta-202
- ❑ 69TopTeaP-19
- ❑ 69YanMal-1
- ❑ 69YanPhoS-55
- ❑ 70MLBOffS-244
- ❑ 70Top-623
- ❑ 70YanCliDP-6
- ❑ 70YanPhoS-8
- ❑ 71MLBOffS-486
- ❑ 71OPC-715
- ❑ 71Top-715
- ❑ 71YanArcO-5
- ❑ 71YanCliDP-4
- ❑ 72MilBra-74
- ❑ 72OPC-387
- ❑ 72Top-387
- ❑ 73NewYorSNM-7
- ❑ 73OPC-198
- ❑ 73SyrChiTI-5
- ❑ 73Top-198
- ❑ 74OPC-529
- ❑ 74Top-529
- ❑ 92YanWIZ6-24
- ❑ 92YanWIZ7-33

Clarke, Jeff
- ❑ 91AppFoxCB-16
- ❑ 91AppFoxP-1722
- ❑ 92AppFoxCB-13
- ❑ 92AppFoxFI-990

Clarke, Josh (Joshua B.)
- ❑ 08RosComP-24
- ❑ 09T206-67

Clarke, Nig (Jay Austin)
- ❑ 09ColChiE-52
- ❑ 11PinT-5-604
- ❑ 11SpoLifCW-63
- ❑ 11SpoLifM-41
- ❑ 12ColRedB-54
- ❑ 13Zee-102
- ❑ 14Zee-105
- ❑ 15Zee-101

Clarke, Stan
- ❑ 83KnoBluJT-2
- ❑ 84BluJayFS-8
- ❑ 84SyrChiT-19
- ❑ 85SyrChiT-4
- ❑ 86StaoftFT-28
- ❑ 86SyrChiP-5
- ❑ 87CalCanP-2326
- ❑ 88TolMudHC-2
- ❑ 88TolMudHP-607
- ❑ 88Top-556
- ❑ 88TopTif-556
- ❑ 89BlaYNPRWL-90
- ❑ 89OmaRoyC-2
- ❑ 89OmaRoyP-1737
- ❑ 90CMC-104
- ❑ 90LouRedBC-4
- ❑ 90LouRedBLBC-11
- ❑ 90LouRedBP-396
- ❑ 90ProAAAF-510
- ❑ 90TopTVCa-42
- ❑ 91LinDriAAA-229
- ❑ 91LouRedLD-229

Clarke, Tim
- ❑ 82QuaCitCT-6

Clarke, Tommy (Thomas A.)
- ❑ 11MecDFT-10
- ❑ 11PinT-5-406
- ❑ 11SpoLifCW-64
- ❑ 11SpoLifM-189
- ❑ 12ColRedB-53
- ❑ 12ColTinT-53
- ❑ 12T207-32
- ❑ 15SpoNewM-32
- ❑ 16FleBreD-16
- ❑ 16SpoNewM-33
- ❑ 17ColE13-29

Clarke, William H.
- ❑ 87OldJudN-80
- ❑ 87OldJudN-81
- ❑ 95NewN566-201

Clarkin, Mike
- ❑ 86WinHavRSP-6
- ❑ 87NewBriRSP-1
- ❑ 88NewBriRSP-891

Clarkson, Buster
- ❑ 86NegLeaF-44

Clarkson, David
- ❑ 91WavRedF-14
- ❑ 93AusFut-89
- ❑ 95AusFut-62

Clarkson, John Gibson
- ❑ 53ArtHaloFP-16
- ❑ 68SCFOldT-4
- ❑ 75FlePio-26
- ❑ 76ShaPiz-91
- ❑ 77BobParHoF-12
- ❑ 80PerHaloFP-91
- ❑ 80SSPHOF-91
- ❑ 87AllandGN-4
- ❑ 87BucN28-20A
- ❑ 87BucN28-20B
- ❑ 87FouBasHN-2
- ❑ 87OldJudN-83
- ❑ 88AugBecN-7A
- ❑ 88AugBecN-7B
- ❑ 88GandBCGCE-7
- ❑ 88WG1CarG-2
- ❑ 89EdgR.WG-7
- ❑ 89N526N7C-4
- ❑ 93JusSo-3
- ❑ 94OriofB-47
- ❑ 95May-4

Clarkson, Walter
- ❑ 08AmeLeaPC-5
- ❑ 11SpoLifCW-65

Clary, Doug
- ❑ 76TulOilGP-5

Clary, Ellis
- ❑ 58SeaTeal-7
- ❑ 60Top-470
- ❑ 88ChaLooLTI-5
- ❑ 96Bro194F-20

Clary, Marty
- ❑ 85RicBraT-2
- ❑ 86Don-36
- ❑ 87IntLeaAT-34
- ❑ 87RicBraBC-3
- ❑ 87RicBraC-34
- ❑ 87RicBraT-3
- ❑ 88BobCamRB-11
- ❑ 88Fle-535
- ❑ 88FleGlo-535
- ❑ 88RicBraC-10
- ❑ 88RicBraP-11
- ❑ 89BraDub-8
- ❑ 89RicBraC-1
- ❑ 89RicBraP-826
- ❑ 89RicBraTI-4
- ❑ 90BraDubP-5
- ❑ 90Don-381
- ❑ 90Fle-578
- ❑ 90FleCan-578
- ❑ 90OPC-304
- ❑ 90Top-304
- ❑ 90TopTif-304
- ❑ 90UppDec-779
- ❑ 91Fle-686
- ❑ 91LinDriAAA-230
- ❑ 91LouRedLD-230
- ❑ 91LouRedP-2906
- ❑ 91OPC-582
- ❑ 91Top-582
- ❑ 91TopDesS-582
- ❑ 91TopMic-582
- ❑ 91TopTif-582
- ❑ 91UppDec-478

Claset, Gowell
- ❑ 33WorCig(-16

Classet, Gowell
- ❑ 28LaPre-16

Clatterbuck, Don
- ❑ 79NewCoPT-9

Claudio, Patricio
- ❑ 92BurIndC-21
- ❑ 92BurIndF-1668
- ❑ 93ColRedC-8
- ❑ 93ColRedF-610
- ❑ 93LimRocDWB-91
- ❑ 94KinIndC-4
- ❑ 94KinIndF-2655
- ❑ 96KenIndB-5

Claus, Marc
- ❑ 92KenTwiF-609
- ❑ 93ForWayWC-5
- ❑ 93ForWayWF-1973
- ❑ 94ForMyeMC-5
- ❑ 94ForMyeMF-1172

Claus, Todd
- ❑ 91BoiHawC-1
- ❑ 91BoiHawP-3885
- ❑ 92ClaFS7-226
- ❑ 92QuaCitRBC-2
- ❑ 92QuaCitRBF-816
- ❑ 93PalSprAC-6
- ❑ 93PalSprAF-75
- ❑ 95BoiHawTI-10
- ❑ 96BoiHawB-2
- ❑ 97CedRapK-3
- ❑ 97MidAngOHP-4
- ❑ 98MidAngG-9

Clausen, Todd
- ❑ 97St.PetDR-6

Claussen, Phil
- ❑ 87CubCan-2

Clawson, Chris
- ❑ 86AshTouP-4

Clawson, Ken
- ❑ 87PorChaRP-1

Claxton, Jimmy
- ❑ 16Zee-25

Clay, Billy
- ❑ 79NewCoPT-17

Clay, Dain Elmer
- ❑ 47PadTeal-3

Clay, Danny
- ❑ 83WisRapTF-16
- ❑ 85OrlTwiT-16
- ❑ 86TolMudHP-5
- ❑ 87PorBeaP-11
- ❑ 88BlaYNPRWL-53
- ❑ 88FleUpd-108
- ❑ 88FleUpdG-108
- ❑ 88MaiPhiP-297
- ❑ 89BlaYNPRWLU-13
- ❑ 89ScrRedBP-706
- ❑ 90CMC-52
- ❑ 90IndIndC-2
- ❑ 90IndIndP-284
- ❑ 90ProAAAF-567
- ❑ 90TopTVCu-40

Clay, Dave
- ❑ 82CedRapRT-26
- ❑ 82DurBulT-14
- ❑ 83DurBulT-17
- ❑ 85RicBraT-3
- ❑ 86ElPasDP-6
- ❑ 87DenZepP-1

Clay, Jeff
- ❑ 81CedRapRT-21
- ❑ 86SalRedBP-4

Clay, Ken
- ❑ 78SSP270-16
- ❑ 78Top-89
- ❑ 78YanPhoA-5
- ❑ 78YanSSPD-16
- ❑ 79OPC-225
- ❑ 79Top-434
- ❑ 80ColCliP-36
- ❑ 80Top-159
- ❑ 81Fle-633
- ❑ 81MarPol-8
- ❑ 81MarPos-11
- ❑ 81Top-305
- ❑ 81TopTra-747
- ❑ 82Fle-508
- ❑ 82Top-649
- ❑ 89PacSenL-72
- ❑ 92YanWIZ7-34
- ❑ 93RanKee-103

Claybrook, Steve
- ❑ 95BilMusTI-19

Clayton, Craig
- ❑ 91BelMarCB-13
- ❑ 91BelMarP-3671
- ❑ 92ClaFS7-114
- ❑ 92SanBerC-21
- ❑ 92SanBerSF-963
- ❑ 93RivPilCLC-6
- ❑ 94Bow-74
- ❑ 94JacSunF-1405
- ❑ 94RivPilCLC-2
- ❑ 96CliLumKTI-8

Clayton, Kenny
- ❑ 82BelBreFr-14
- ❑ 82IdaFalAT-22

Clayton, Royal
- ❑ 88CarLeaAS-4
- ❑ 88PriWilYS-6
- ❑ 89AlbYanB-6
- ❑ 89AlbYanP-318
- ❑ 89AlbYanSt-5
- ❑ 89Sta-96
- ❑ 90AlbDecGB-10
- ❑ 90AlbYanB-23

- 90AlbYanP-1030
- 90AlbYanSt-2
- 90Bes-287
- 90CMC-785
- 90EasLeaAP-EL13
- 90StaFS7-50
- 91ColCliLD-104
- 91ColCliP-4
- 91ColCliP-591
- 91LinDriAAA-104
- 92ColCliF-343
- 92ColCliP-3
- 92ColCliS-101
- 92SkyAAAF-44
- 93ColCliF-1102
- 93ColCliP-1
- 94ColCliF-2942
- 94ColCliP-4

Clayton, Royce

- 89Bow-472
- 89BowTif-472
- 89CliGiaP-895
- 90Bes-114
- 90CalLeaACLC-49
- 90CMC-855
- 90ProAaA-156
- 90SanJosGB-7
- 90SanJosGCLC-36
- 90SanJosGP-2018
- 90SanJosGS-5
- 90TopMag-73
- 91Bow-641
- 91Cla/Bes-251
- 91Cla3-T10
- 91ClaGolB-BC12
- 91ShrCapLD-303
- 91ShrCapP-1827
- 91UppDec-61
- 91UppDecFE-4F
- 92Bow-212
- 92Cla1-T25
- 92Cla2-T35
- 92ClaGam-179
- 92DEL-AU6
- 92Don-397
- 92DonCraJ2-10
- 92Fle-632
- 92GiaMot-4
- 92GiaPacGaE-13
- 92Lea-272
- 92LeaBlaG-272
- 92OPC-786
- 92OPCPre-39
- 92Pin-268
- 92PinRoo-26
- 92PinRool-15
- 92PinTea2-34
- 92ProFS7-343
- 92Sco-841
- 92ScoHotR-2
- 92ScoImpP-24
- 92ScoRoo-12
- 92StaClu-630
- 92StaCluNC-630
- 92Stu-115
- 92Top-786
- 92TopDeb91-36
- 92TopGol-786
- 92TopGolW-786
- 92TopMcD-38
- 92TopMic-786
- 92TriPla-123
- 92Ult-288
- 92UppDec-2
- 92UppDecF-5
- 92UppDecFG-5
- 92UppDecSR-SR6
- 93Bow-548
- 93ClaGam-20
- 93Don-208
- 93Fla-141
- 93Fle-155
- 93GiaMot-6
- 93GiaPos-16
- 93GiaStaC-4
- 93Lea-176
- 93OPC-138
- 93PacSpa-270
- 93PanSti-238
- 93Pin-321
- 93PinTea2-11
- 93Sco-157
- 93Sel-400
- 93SP-112
- 93StaClu-39
- 93StaCluFDI-39
- 93StaCluMOP-39
- 93Stu-94
- 93Top-542
- 93TopGol-542
- 93TopInaM-542
- 93TopInaR-542
- 93TopMic-542
- 93Toy-16
- 93TriPla-39
- 93Ult-131
- 93UppDec-151
- 93UppDecGold-151
- 93USPlaCR-10S
- 94Bow-519
- 94ColC-80
- 94ColChoGS-80
- 94ColChoSS-80
- 94Don-153
- 94Fin-28
- 94FinRef-28
- 94Fla-241
- 94Fle-690
- 94FleExtB-385
- 94GiaAMC-8
- 94GiaMot-4
- 94GiaTarBC-9
- 94GiaUSPC-7C
- 94GiaUSPC-13H
- 94Lea-381
- 94LeaL-158
- 94OPC-164
- 94Pac-545
- 94PanSti-264
- 94Pin-111
- 94PinArtP-111
- 94PinMusC-111
- 94Sco-448
- 94ScoGolR-448
- 94Sel-278
- 94SP-92
- 94SPDieC-92
- 94Spo-86
- 94StaClu-39
- 94StaCluFDI-39
- 94StaCluGR-39
- 94StaCluMOP-39
- 94StaCluT-2
- 94StaCluTFDI-2
- 94Stu-84
- 94Top-267
- 94TopGol-267
- 94TopSpa-267
- 94TriPla-104
- 94Ult-289
- 94UppDec-221
- 94UppDecED-221
- 95Bow-398
- 95ColCho-254
- 95ColChoGS-254
- 95ColChoSS-254
- 95Don-285
- 95DonPreP-285
- 95DonTopotO-350
- 95Emo-193
- 95Fin-134
- 95FinRef-134
- 95Fla-208
- 95Fle-578
- 95GiaMot-4
- 95Lea-33
- 95LeaLim-38
- 95Pac-376
- 95PanSti-65
- 95Pin-221
- 95PinArtP-221
- 95PinMusC-221
- 95Sco-413
- 95ScoGolR-413
- 95ScoPlaTS-413
- 95Sel-105
- 95SelArtP-105
- 95SelCer-81
- 95SelCerMG-81
- 95Spo-7
- 95SpoArtP-7
- 95StaClu-126
- 95StaCluFDI-126
- 95StaCluMOP-126
- 95StaCluSTWS-126
- 95Stu-194
- 95Sum-87
- 95SumNthD-87
- 95Top-67
- 95TopCyb-49
- 95TopEmb-31
- 95TopEmbGI-31
- 95UC3-88
- 95UC3ArtP-88
- 95Ult-443
- 95UltGolM-443
- 95UppDec-333
- 95UppDecED-333
- 95UppDecEDG-333
- 95UppDecSE-72
- 95UppDecSEG-72
- 95Zen-94
- 96CarPol-4
- 96Cir-176
- 96CirBos-45
- 96CirRav-176
- 96ColCho-303
- 96ColCho-787
- 96ColChoGS-303
- 96ColChoSS-303
- 96Don-235
- 96DonPreP-235
- 96EmoXL-263
- 96Fin-B306
- 96FinRef-B306
- 96Fla-356
- 96Fle-586
- 96FleTif-586
- 96FleUpd-U186
- 96FleUpdTC-U186
- 96MetUni-222
- 96MetUniP-222
- 96Pac-210
- 96PanSti-111
- 96Pin-329
- 96PinAfi-139
- 96PinAfiAP-139
- 96PinFoil-329
- 96Sco-386
- 96Sel-106
- 96SelArtP-106
- 96StaClu-141
- 96StaCluEPB-141
- 96StaCluEPG-141
- 96StaCluEPS-141
- 96StaCluMOP-141
- 96Sum-24
- 96SumAbo&B-24
- 96SumArtP-24
- 96SumFoi-24
- 96Top-61
- 96Ult-293
- 96Ult-544
- 96UltGolM-293
- 96UltGolM-544
- 96UppDec-198
- 96UppDec-507U
- 97CarPol-3
- 97Cir-256
- 97CirRav-256
- 97ColCho-439
- 97Don-217
- 97DonGolPP-217
- 97DonSilPP-217
- 97DonTea-159
- 97DonTeaSPE-159
- 97Fin-56
- 97FinRef-56
- 97FlaShoLC-135
- 97FlaShoLeg0-135
- 97FlaShoLeg1-135
- 97FlaShoM-A135
- 97FlaShoM-B135
- 97FlaShoM-C135
- 97FlaShoR0-135
- 97FlaShoR1-135
- 97FlaShoR2-135
- 97Fle-440
- 97FleTif-440
- 97Lea-51
- 97LeaFraM-51
- 97LeaFraMDC-51
- 97NewPin-103
- 97NewPinAP-103
- 97NewPinMC-103
- 97NewPinPP-103
- 97Pac-406
- 97PacLigB-406
- 97PacSil-406
- 97Sco-291
- 97ScoArtPWB-291
- 97ScoPreS-291
- 97ScoShoS-291
- 97ScoShoSAP-291
- 97StaClu-128
- 97StaCluMOP-128
- 97StrAll-14
- 97Top-18
- 97Ult-333
- 97UltGolME-333
- 97UltPlaME-333
- 97UppDec-467
- 98CarScoP-10
- 98CirThu-158
- 98CirThuRav-158
- 98CirThuSupRav-158
- 98ColCho-472
- 98Don-261
- 98DonGolPP-261
- 98DonSilPP-261
- 98Fin-34
- 98FinNo--34
- 98FinNo-R-34
- 98FinRef-34
- 98Fle-272
- 98FleUpd-U27
- 98Pac-406
- 98PacAur-180
- 98PacOme-194
- 98PacOmeR-194
- 98PacOnl-607
- 98PacOnlR-607
- 98PacOnlWC-607
- 98PacPar-227
- 98PacParC-227
- 98PacParG-227
- 98PacParHS-227
- 98PacParPB-227
- 98PacParR-227
- 98PacPlaB-406
- 98PacRedT-406
- 98PacSil-406
- 98Pin-21
- 98PinArtP-PP21
- 98PinMusC-PP21
- 98PinPreP-21
- 98PinSna-SLC10
- 98Sco-152
- 98ScoCar-10
- 98ScoSS-PP62
- 98ScoSSAP-PP62
- 98StaCluFDI-125
- 98StaCluI-125
- 98StaCluOneK-125
- 98StaCluPP-125
- 98Top-118
- 98TopChr-118
- 98TopChrR-118
- 98TopDevR-118
- 98TopDia-118
- 98TopMiniC-118
- 98Ult-271
- 98UltGolM-271
- 98UltMas-271
- 98UltPlaM-271
- 98UppDec-492
- 99199Fin-68
- 99FinGolRef-68
- 99FinRef-68
- 99Fle-398
- 99FleSta9-398
- 99FleWarT-398
- 99MetUni-175
- 99MetUniGM-175
- 99MetUniPMG-175
- 99Pac-422
- 99PacOme-234
- 99PacOmeC-234
- 99PacOmeG-234
- 99PacOmePB-234
- 99PacPar-232
- 99PacParC-232
- 99PacParG-232
- 99PacParHoloGold-232
- 99PacParHS-232
- 99PacParOD-232
- 99PacParPB-232
- 99PacParRed-232
- 99PacPlaB-422
- 99PacRed-422
- 99SkyPre-172
- 99SkyPreA-11
- 99SkyPreABlue-11
- 99SkyPreR-172
- 99SkyThu-59
- 99SkyThuRant-59
- 99SkyThuRave-59
- 99SP Aut-87
- 99SP SigAuto-RC
- 99SPSig-150
- 99StaClu-179
- 99StaCluFDI-179
- 99StaCluOoaK-179
- 99StaCluPP-179
- 99ThuSkySupR-59
- 99Top-339
- 99TopChr-339
- 99TopChrR-339
- 99TopMVPP-339
- 99Ult-205
- 99UltGolM-205
- 99UltMas-205
- 99UltPlaM-205
- 99UppDec-505
- 99UppDecEL1-505
- 99UppDecEL2-505
- 99UppDecM-207
- 99UppDecMGS-207
- 99UppDecMHFS-207
- 99UppDecMSS-207
- 99Vic-406

Clear, Bob

- 78AngFamF-7
- 87CalAngPPS-5

Clear, Mark

- 76QuaCitAT-10
- 77QuaCitAT-9
- 80Top-638
- 81Don-291
- 81Top-12
- 81TopTra-748
- 82Don-452
- 82Fle-290
- 82OPC-169
- 82RedSoxC-3
- 82Top-421
- 82TopSti-154
- 83Don-361
- 83Fle-181
- 83Fle-629
- 83FleSta-41
- 83FleSti-61
- 83OPC-162
- 83Top-162
- 83TopSti-36
- 84Don-611
- 84Fle-395
- 84Nes792-577
- 84OPC-148
- 84Top-577
- 84TopTif-577
- 85Don-538
- 85Fle-154
- 85Lea-32
- 85Top-207
- 85TopTif-207
- 86BrePol-25
- 86Don-493
- 86Fle-344
- 86FleUpd-26
- 86Top-349
- 86TopTif-349
- 86TopTra-25T
- 86TopTraT-25T
- 87BrePol-25
- 87BreTeal-3
- 87Don-355
- 87Fle-341
- 87FleBasA-9
- 87FleGlo-341
- 87FleStiC-23
- 87OPC-244
- 87Top-640
- 87TopSti-195
- 87TopTif-640
- 88BrePol-25
- 88BreTeal-8
- 88Don-372
- 88Fle-160
- 88FleGlo-160
- 88Sco-446
- 88ScoGlo-446
- 88Top-742
- 88TopClo-22
- 88TopTif-742
- 89Don-528
- 89Fle-182
- 89FleGlo-182
- 89Sco-430
- 89Top-63
- 89TopTif-63
- 90El PasDAGTI-37
- 94BreMilB-210

Cleary, James

- 08BufBisFJO-2

Cleary, Tony

- 79ElmPioRST-16
- 86PawRedSP-7
- 87PawRedSP-65
- 88PawRedSC-14
- 88PawRedSP-467
- 89PawRedSP-683
- 89PawRedSTI-5

Clelland, Rick

- 92AlbPolCB-14
- 92AlbPolF-2297
- 92ClaFS7-378
- 93BurBeeC-5
- 93BurBeeF-149
- 94BurBeeC-5
- 94BurBeeF-1074

Clem, Brad

- 92EriSaiC-23
- 92EriSaiF-1636

Clem, Brian

- 85CloHSS-10

Clem, John

- 86WauTimP-3
- 87SalSpuS-9

Clemens, Doug (Douglas H.)

- 67CokCapPh-5
- 67Top-489
- 78ReaRem-2

Clemens, Roger

- 84FleUpd-27
- 84OCoandSI-242
- 84PawRedST-22
- 85Don-273
- 85Fle-155
- 85FleStaS-123
- 85Lea-99
- 85Top-181
- 85TopTif-181
- 86Don-172
- 86DonHig-5
- 86DonHig-6
- 86DonHig-17
- 86DonHig-18
- 86DonHig-26
- 86Fle-345
- 86FleMin-73
- 86FleSlu-7
- 86OPC-98
- 86Top-661
- 86TopTif-661
- 87BurKinA-4
- 87ClaGam-84
- 87ClaUpdY-114
- 87Don-2
- 87Don-276
- 87DonAll-8
- 87DonAllB-PC14
- 87DonP-8
- 87DonSupD-2
- 87Dra-31
- 87Fle-32
- 87Fle-634
- 87Fle-640
- 87FleAll-11
- 87FleAwaW-9
- 87FleBasA-10
- 87FleExcS-11
- 87FleGamW-10
- 87FleGlo-32
- 87FleGlo-634
- 87FleGlo-640
- 87FleGlo-WS3
- 87FleHotS-10
- 87FleLeaL-10
- 87FleLimE-9
- 87FleMin-20
- 87FleRecS-4
- 87FleSlu-10
- 87FleStiC-24
- 87FleWorS-3
- 87GenMilB-2B
- 87KayB-10
- 87KeyFooD-2
- 87KraFoo-45
- 87Lea-2
- 87Lea-190
- 87MandMSL-7
- 87MSAIceTD-2
- 87MSAJifPD-12
- 87OPC-340
- 87OurOwnTD-2
- 87RalPur-10
- 87RedFolSB-70
- 87RedSoxP-6
- 87RedSoxSAP-6
- 87SevCoi-E8
- 87SevCoi-M10
- 87Spo-10
- 87Spo-111
- 87Spo-159

❑ 87Spo-196
❑ 87SpoDeaP-1
❑ 87SpoIllS-3
❑ 87SpoRea-12
❑ 87SpoTeaP-9
❑ 87StaCle-1
❑ 87StaCle-2
❑ 87StaCle-3
❑ 87StaCle-4
❑ 87StaCle-5
❑ 87StaCle-6
❑ 87StaCle-7
❑ 87StaCle-8
❑ 87StaCle-9
❑ 87StaCle-10
❑ 87StaCle-11
❑ 87StaCle-12
❑ 87StaCle2-1
❑ 87StaCle2-2
❑ 87StaCle2-3
❑ 87StaCle2-4
❑ 87StaCle2-5
❑ 87StuPan-15
❑ 87Top-1
❑ 87Top-340
❑ 87Top-614
❑ 87TopCoi-8
❑ 87TopGaloC-5
❑ 87TopGloA-21
❑ 87TopGloS-5
❑ 87TopMinL-42
❑ 87TopSti-2
❑ 87TopSti-3
❑ 87TopSti-154
❑ 87TopSti-244
❑ 87TopTif-1
❑ 87TopTif-340
❑ 87TopTif-614
❑ 87WeiMarD-2
❑ 87Woo-7
❑ 88Baz-4
❑ 88CheBoy-23
❑ 88ClaBlu-217
❑ 88ClaRed-158
❑ 88Don-51
❑ 88DonBasB-57
❑ 88DonTeaBRS-51
❑ 88Dra-30
❑ 88Fle-349
❑ 88FleAll-4
❑ 88FleAwaW-6
❑ 88FleBasA-8
❑ 88FleBasM-6
❑ 88FleExcS-10
❑ 88FleGlo-349
❑ 88FleHotS-7
❑ 88FleLeaL-6
❑ 88FleMin-5
❑ 88FleRecS-7
❑ 88FleSlu-9
❑ 88FleStiC-7
❑ 88FleSup-9
❑ 88FleTeaL-5
❑ 88GreBasS-47
❑ 88HouSho-13
❑ 88K-M-7
❑ 88KeyFooD-9
❑ 88KinDis-20
❑ 88Lea-56
❑ 88MSAIceTD-9
❑ 88MSAJifPD-6
❑ 88Nes-1
❑ 88OPC-70
❑ 88OurOwnTD-9
❑ 88PanSti-21
❑ 88RedFolSB-13
❑ 88Sco-110
❑ 88ScoGlo-110
❑ 88ScoYouS2-23
❑ 88Spo-207
❑ 88SpoGam-20
❑ 88StaCle-1
❑ 88StaCle-2
❑ 88StaCle-4
❑ 88StaCle-6
❑ 88StaCle-8
❑ 88StaCle-10
❑ 88StaLinAl-7
❑ 88StaLinRS-6
❑ 88TarPla-9
❑ 88TetTeaD-9
❑ 88Top-70
❑ 88Top-394
❑ 88TopBig-118
❑ 88TopClo-23
❑ 88TopClo-24
❑ 88TopCoi-2
❑ 88TopGaloC-5
❑ 88TopGloS-13
❑ 88TopMinL-2
❑ 88TopRevLL-28
❑ 88TopSti-251
❑ 88TopStiB-58
❑ 88TopTif-70
❑ 88TopTif-394
❑ 88TopUKM-15
❑ 88TopUKMT-15
❑ 88WeiMarD-9
❑ 88Woo-11
❑ 89Bow-26
❑ 89BowTif-26
❑ 89CadEllD-9
❑ 89CerSup-7
❑ 89ClaTraO-119
❑ 89Don-280
❑ 89DonAll-14
❑ 89DonBasB-65
❑ 89Fle-85
❑ 89FleBasA-7
❑ 89FleBasM-8
❑ 89FleExcS-6
❑ 89FleForTR-2
❑ 89FleGlo-85
❑ 89FleHeroB-8
❑ 89FleLeaL-5
❑ 89FleSup-9
❑ 89K-M-20
❑ 89KayB-7
❑ 89KeyFooD-8
❑ 89MSAHolD-16
❑ 89MSAIceTD-8
❑ 89Nis-16
❑ 89OPC-121
❑ 89OurOwnTD-8
❑ 89PanSti-249
❑ 89PanSti-270
❑ 89RedFolSB-23
❑ 89Sco-350
❑ 89Sco-350A
❑ 89ScoHot1S-90
❑ 89Scomast-20
❑ 89Spo-3
❑ 89SpoIllFKI-60
❑ 89TetTeaD-8
❑ 89Top-405
❑ 89Top-450
❑ 89TopBasT-58
❑ 89TopBig-42
❑ 89TopCapC-18
❑ 89TopCoi-37
❑ 89TopDouA-9
❑ 89TopGloS-23
❑ 89TopHilTM-8
❑ 89TopMinL-46
❑ 89TopSti-259
❑ 89TopStiB-25
❑ 89TopTif-405
❑ 89TopTif-450
❑ 89TopUKM-16
❑ 89TVSpoM-63
❑ 89UppDec-195
❑ 89WeiMarD-8
❑ 90AllBasT-8
❑ 90Bow-268
❑ 90BowTif-268
❑ 90ClaBlu-51
❑ 90Col-19
❑ 90Don-184
❑ 90DonBesA-58
❑ 90Fle-271
❑ 90Fle-627
❑ 90FleBasM-8
❑ 90FleBasMC-8
❑ 90FleCan-271
❑ 90FleCan-627
❑ 90FleWaxBC-C3
❑ 90Hot50PS-7
❑ 90Lea-12
❑ 90M.Vpin-10
❑ 90MLBBasB-69
❑ 90OPC-245
❑ 90PanSti-24
❑ 90Pos-2
❑ 90PubIntS-281
❑ 90PubIntS-452
❑ 90RedFolSB-18
❑ 90RedSoxP-6
❑ 90Sco-310
❑ 90Sco100S-79
❑ 90ScoMcD-18
❑ 90Spo-149
❑ 90SunSee-18
❑ 90Top-245
❑ 90TopBig-22
❑ 90TopDou-11
❑ 90TopMag-26
❑ 90TopMinL-4
❑ 90TopSti-255
❑ 90TopTif-245
❑ 90TopTVA-25
❑ 90TopTVRS-8
❑ 90UppDec-57
❑ 90UppDec-323
❑ 90USPlaCA-1S
❑ 90WinDis-3
❑ 90WonBreS-2
❑ 91BasBesAotM-4
❑ 91Bow-118
❑ 91CadEllD-9
❑ 91Cla1-T18
❑ 91Cla2-T65
❑ 91Cla2-T97
❑ 91ClaGam-149
❑ 91Col-1
❑ 91Don-9
❑ 91Don-81
❑ 91Don-395
❑ 91DonSupD-9
❑ 91Fle-90
❑ 91FleAll-10
❑ 91FlePro-9
❑ 91JimDea-18
❑ 91Lea-174
❑ 91Lea-488
❑ 91MajLeaCP-8
❑ 91MSAHolD-13
❑ 91OPC-530
❑ 91OPCPre-23
❑ 91PanCanT1-63
❑ 91PanCanT1-69
❑ 91PanCanT1-80
❑ 91PanCanT1-94
❑ 91PanFreS-271
❑ 91PanSti-215
❑ 91PepSup-6
❑ 91PetSta-3
❑ 91Pos-12
❑ 91PosCan-18
❑ 91RedFolS-20
❑ 91RedSoxP-5
❑ 91RedSoxP-7
❑ 91Sco-399
❑ 91Sco-655
❑ 91Sco-684
❑ 91Sco-850
❑ 91Sco100S-50
❑ 91Sev3DCN-3
❑ 91SevCoi-F3
❑ 91SevCoi-T4
❑ 91SevCoi-NE3
❑ 91SilHol-6
❑ 91StaClu-309
❑ 91StaCluMO-12
❑ 91StaPinB-9
❑ 91StaPro-3
❑ 91Stu-14
❑ 91StuPre-2
❑ 91Top-530
❑ 91TopCraJI-22
❑ 91TopDesS-530
❑ 91TopMic-530
❑ 91TopSta-9
❑ 91TopTif-530
❑ 91TopTriH-A2
❑ 91Ult-31
❑ 91UppDec-655
❑ 91USPlaCA-10H
❑ 92Bow-691
❑ 92Cla1-T26
❑ 92Cla1-NNO
❑ 92Cla2-T61
❑ 92ClaGam-189
❑ 92ColAllG-19
❑ 92ColAllP-19
❑ 92Don-244
❑ 92DonBonC-BC3
❑ 92DonCraJ1-17
❑ 92DonMcD-10
❑ 92Fle-37
❑ 92FleCitTP-6
❑ 92FleCle-1
❑ 92FleCle-2
❑ 92FleCle-3
❑ 92FleCle-4
❑ 92FleCle-5
❑ 92FleCle-6
❑ 92FleCle-7
❑ 92FleCle-8
❑ 92FleCle-9
❑ 92FleCle-10
❑ 92FleCle-11
❑ 92FleCle-12
❑ 92FleCle-13
❑ 92FleCle-14
❑ 92FleCle-15
❑ 92FleCle-AU0
❑ 92FleCle-NNO
❑ 92FleSmo'nH-S4
❑ 92Fre-2
❑ 92Hig5-7
❑ 92Hig5S-8
❑ 92JimDea-10
❑ 92KinDis-9
❑ 92LaKdec-6
❑ 92Lea-19
❑ 92LeaBlaG-19
❑ 92MooSna-4
❑ 92Mr.TurS-7
❑ 92MVPPin-5
❑ 92OPC-150
❑ 92OPCPre-105
❑ 92PacRyaTEI-200
❑ 92PanSti-92
❑ 92PanSti-146
❑ 92PepDieM-1
❑ 92Pin-95
❑ 92PinRool-4
❑ 92PinTeaP-1
❑ 92Pos-16
❑ 92PosCan-10
❑ 92RedFolS-26
❑ 92RedSoxDD-9
❑ 92Sco-21
❑ 92Sco-790
❑ 92Sco100S-74
❑ 92ScoCokD-5
❑ 92ScoImpP-57
❑ 92SevCoi-3
❑ 92SpoIllFK1-36
❑ 92SpoIllFK1-673
❑ 92SpoStaCC-9
❑ 92StaClu-80
❑ 92StaClu-593
❑ 92StaCluD-29
❑ 92StaCluMO-11
❑ 92Stu-132
❑ 92TexLon-8
❑ 92Top-150
❑ 92Top-405
❑ 92TopGol-150
❑ 92TopGol-405
❑ 92TopGolW-150
❑ 92TopGolW-405
❑ 92TopKid-67
❑ 92TopMcD-10
❑ 92TopMic-150
❑ 92TopMic-405
❑ 92TriPla-216
❑ 92Ult-15
❑ 92UltAwaW-6
❑ 92UppDec-545
❑ 92UppDec-641
❑ 92UppDecF-19
❑ 92UppDecFG-19
❑ 92UppDecTMH-16
❑ 93Bow-635
❑ 93CadDis-11
❑ 93ClaGam-21
❑ 93DiaMar-25
❑ 93Don-119
❑ 93DonDiaK-DK3
❑ 93DonMVP-15
❑ 93DonPre-13
❑ 93DurPowP1-1
❑ 93Fin-104
❑ 93FinJum-104
❑ 93FinRef-104
❑ 93Fla-160
❑ 93Fle-177
❑ 93Fle-348
❑ 93Fle-717
❑ 93FleAtl-5
❑ 93FleFruotL-12
❑ 93FleTeaL-AL4
❑ 93FunPac-14
❑ 93FunPac-23
❑ 93FunPac-29
❑ 93FunPac-161
❑ 93FunPac-162
❑ 93Hos-27
❑ 93HumDumC-3
❑ 93JimDea-7
❑ 93KinDis-21
❑ 93Kra-5
❑ 93Lea-279
❑ 93LeaGolA-R20
❑ 93LeaHeaftH-6
❑ 93MetBak-5
❑ 93MSABenSPD-12
❑ 93OPC-259
❑ 93OPCPreSP-18
❑ 93OPCPreSPF-18
❑ 93PacJugC-4
❑ 93PacSpa-30
❑ 93PanSti-90
❑ 93Pin-25
❑ 93PinCoo-18
❑ 93PinCooD-18
❑ 93Pos-4
❑ 93PosCan-3
❑ 93RedFolS-20
❑ 93RedSoxP-6
❑ 93RedSoxWHP-8
❑ 93Sco-7
❑ 93ScoFra-2
❑ 93Sel-14
❑ 93SelAce-1
❑ 93SelChaS-21
❑ 93SelDufIP-2
❑ 93SelStaL-62
❑ 93SelStaL-75
❑ 93SelStaL-79
❑ 93SelStaL-87
❑ 93SP-199
❑ 93StaClu-220
❑ 93StaClu-748
❑ 93StaCluFDI-220
❑ 93StaCluFDI-748
❑ 93StaCluM-97
❑ 93StaCluMOP-220
❑ 93StaCluMOP-748
❑ 93Stu-22
❑ 93StuHer-3
❑ 93Top-4
❑ 93Top-409
❑ 93TOPBLAG-27
❑ 93TopComotH-3
❑ 93TopFulS-15
❑ 93TopGol-4
❑ 93TopGol-409
❑ 93TopInaM-4
❑ 93TopInaM-409
❑ 93TopInaR-4
❑ 93TopInaR-409
❑ 93TopMic-4
❑ 93TopMic-409
❑ 93TriPla-118
❑ 93TriPlaA-14
❑ 93TriPlaN-2
❑ 93Ult-508
❑ 93UltStrK-1
❑ 93UppDec-48
❑ 93UppDec-135
❑ 93UppDec-630
❑ 93UppDecCP-R7
❑ 93UppDecDG-21
❑ 93UppDecFH-57
❑ 93UppDecGold-48
❑ 93UppDecGold-135
❑ 93UppDecGold-630
❑ 93UppDecOD-D9
❑ 93USPlaCA-11S
❑ 94Bow-475
❑ 94BowBes-R37
❑ 94BowBes-X100
❑ 94BowBesR-R37
❑ 94BowBesR-X100
❑ 94ChuHomS-13
❑ 94ChuHomSG-13
❑ 94ColC-322
❑ 94ColC-348
❑ 94ColC-550
❑ 94ColChoGS-322
❑ 94ColChoGS-348
❑ 94ColChoGS-550
❑ 94ColChoSS-322
❑ 94ColChoSS-348
❑ 94ColChoSS-550
❑ 94ColChoT-3
❑ 94Don-356
❑ 94Don-600
❑ 94DonSpeE-356
❑ 94Fin-217
❑ 94FinJum-217
❑ 94FinRef-217
❑ 94Fla-261
❑ 94Fle-26
❑ 94FleExtB-16
❑ 94FleExtBGB-7
❑ 94FleExtBPD-1
❑ 94FleSmo'nH-1
❑ 94FleSun-7
❑ 94FleUpdDT-4
❑ 94FUnPac-21
❑ 94FUnPac-207
❑ 94Lea-255
❑ 94LeaL-7
❑ 94O-PJumAF-18
❑ 94OPC-67
❑ 94OPCAllR-18
❑ 94OPCJumA-18
❑ 94OscMayR-3
❑ 94Pac-49
❑ 94PanSti-26
❑ 94Pin-25
❑ 94PinArtP-25
❑ 94PinMusC-25
❑ 94PinTheN-25
❑ 94ProMag-11
❑ 94RedFolMI-31
❑ 94Sco-25
❑ 94ScoGolR-25
❑ 94Sel-61
❑ 94SelCroC-CC3
❑ 94SP-152
❑ 94SPDieC-152
❑ 94SPHol-5
❑ 94SPHolDC-5
❑ 94Spo-15
❑ 94StaClu-534
❑ 94StaClu-650
❑ 94StaCluFDI-534
❑ 94StaCluFDI-650
❑ 94StaCluGR-534
❑ 94StaCluGR-650
❑ 94StaCluMOP-534
❑ 94StaCluMOP-650
❑ 94Stu-159
❑ 94SucSav-20
❑ 94Top-720
❑ 94TopGol-720
❑ 94TopSpa-720
❑ 94TopSupS-10
❑ 94TriPla-201
❑ 94Ult-11
❑ 94UppDec-450
❑ 94UppDecAJ-21
❑ 94UppDecAJG-21
❑ 94UppDecDC-E2
❑ 94UppDecED-450
❑ 95Baz-9
❑ 95Bow-293
❑ 95BowBes-R23
❑ 95BowBesR-R23
❑ 95ClaPhoC-9
❑ 95ColCho-410
❑ 95ColChoGS-410
❑ 95ColChoSE-190
❑ 95ColChoSEGS-190
❑ 95ColChoSESS-190
❑ 95ColChoSS-410
❑ 95DenHol-6
❑ 95Don-427
❑ 95DonPreP-427
❑ 95DonTopotO-19
❑ 95Emo-10
❑ 95Fin-185
❑ 95FinFlaT-FT2
❑ 95FinRef-185
❑ 95Fla-10
❑ 95Fle-26
❑ 95FleTeaL-2
❑ 95FleUpdH-7
❑ 95Lea-255
❑ 95LeaLim-48
❑ 95Pac-34
❑ 95PacPri-12
❑ 95PanSti-14
❑ 95Pin-2
❑ 95PinArtP-2
❑ 95PinFan-2
❑ 95PinGatA-GA13
❑ 95PinMusC-2
❑ 95PinRedH-RH18
❑ 95PinWhiH-WH18
❑ 95RedFol-3
❑ 95Sco-118
❑ 95ScoDouGC-GC7
❑ 95ScoGolR-118
❑ 95ScoHaloG-HG15
❑ 95ScoPlaTS-118
❑ 95Sel-72
❑ 95SelArtP-72
❑ 95SelCer-88
❑ 95SelCerMG-88
❑ 95SP-127

❑ 95SPCha-122
❑ 95SPChaDC-122
❑ 95Spo-51
❑ 95SpoArtP-51
❑ 95SPSil-127
❑ 95SPSpeF-2
❑ 95StaClu-10
❑ 95StaCluFDI-10
❑ 95StaCluMOP-10
❑ 95StaCluMOP-RL32
❑ 95StaCluRL-RL32
❑ 95StaCluSTDW-RS10
❑ 95StaCluSTWS-10
❑ 95StaCluVR-5
❑ 95StaCluVRMO-5
❑ 95Stu-16
❑ 95StuGolS-16
❑ 95StuPlaS-16
❑ 95Sum-41
❑ 95Sum-190
❑ 95SumNthD-41
❑ 95SumNthD-190
❑ 95Top-360
❑ 95TopCyb-192
❑ 95TopD3-9
❑ 95TopEmb-106
❑ 95TopEmbGI-106
❑ 95TopLeaL-LL23
❑ 95UC3-95
❑ 95UC3-141
❑ 95UC3ArtP-95
❑ 95UC3ArtP-141
❑ 95Ult-10
❑ 95UltGolM-10
❑ 95UltStrK-2
❑ 95UltStrKGM-2
❑ 95UppDec-159
❑ 95UppDec-J159
❑ 95UppDecA-1
❑ 95UppDecED-159
❑ 95UppDecEDG-159
❑ 95UppDecPC-MLB9
❑ 95UppDecSE-212
❑ 95UppDecSEG-212
❑ 95USPlaCMLA-10S
❑ 95Zen-91
❑ 96Baz-62
❑ 96Bow-89
❑ 96BowBes-33
❑ 96BowBesAR-33
❑ 96BowBesR-33
❑ 96BowFoi-89
❑ 96Cir-10
❑ 96CirRav-10
❑ 96ColCho-60
❑ 96ColCho-419
❑ 96ColChoGS-60
❑ 96ColChoGS-419
❑ 96ColChoSS-60
❑ 96ColChoSS-419
❑ 96Don-539
❑ 96DonPreP-539
❑ 96DonSho-4
❑ 96EmoXL-12
❑ 96Fin-S46
❑ 96FinRef-S46
❑ 96Fla-16
❑ 96Fle-25
❑ 96FleRedS-3
❑ 96FleSmo'H-2
❑ 96FleTif-25
❑ 96Kin-1
❑ 96Lea-69
❑ 96LeaLim-2
❑ 96LeaLimG-2
❑ 96LeaPre-19
❑ 96LeaPreP-19
❑ 96LeaPrePB-69
❑ 96LeaPrePG-69
❑ 96LeaPrePS-69
❑ 96LeaPreSG-63
❑ 96LeaPreSte-63
❑ 96LeaSig-28
❑ 96LeaSigEA-32
❑ 96LeaSigEACM-3
❑ 96LeaSigPPG-28
❑ 96LeaSigPPP-28
❑ 96MetUni-13
❑ 96MetUniP-13
❑ 96Pac-258
❑ 96PacPri-P79
❑ 96PacPriFT-FT3
❑ 96PacPriG-P79
❑ 96PanSti-136
❑ 96Pin-247
❑ 96PinAfi-9

❑ 96PinAfiAP-9
❑ 96PinAfiFPP-9
❑ 96PinAfiP-9
❑ 96PinArtP-147
❑ 96PinFoil-247
❑ 96PinSta-147
❑ 96Pro-5
❑ 96ProSta-110
❑ 96Sco-333
❑ 96ScoDugC-B58
❑ 96ScoDugCAP-B58
❑ 96Sel-20
❑ 96SelArtP-20
❑ 96SelCer-8
❑ 96SelCerAP-8
❑ 96SelCerCB-8
❑ 96SelCerCR-8
❑ 96SelCerIP-5
❑ 96SelCerMB-8
❑ 96SelCerMG-8
❑ 96SelCerMR-8
❑ 96SelTeaN-8
❑ 96SP-39
❑ 96SPMarM-MM19
❑ 96SPMarMDC-19
❑ 96Spo-58
❑ 96SpoArtP-58
❑ 96SPSpeFX-38
❑ 96SPSpeFXDC-38
❑ 96SPx-9
❑ 96SPxGol-9
❑ 96StaClu-25
❑ 96StaCluEPB-25
❑ 96StaCluEPG-25
❑ 96StaCluEPS-25
❑ 96StaCluMeg-MH8
❑ 96StaCluMet-M4
❑ 96StaCluMOP-25
❑ 96StaCluMOP-M4
❑ 96StaCluMOP-MH8
❑ 96Stu-11
❑ 96StuPrePB-11
❑ 96StuPrePG-11
❑ 96StuPrePS-11
❑ 96Sum-101
❑ 96Sum-152
❑ 96SumAbo&B-101
❑ 96SumAbo&B-152
❑ 96SumArtP-101
❑ 96SumArtP-152
❑ 96SumFoi-101
❑ 96SumFoi-152
❑ 96Top-197
❑ 96TopChr-65
❑ 96TopChrMotG-17
❑ 96TopChrMotGR-17
❑ 96TopChrR-65
❑ 96TopClaC-CC13
❑ 96TopGal-174
❑ 96TopGalPG-PG8
❑ 96TopGalPPI-174
❑ 96TopLas-52
❑ 96TopLasSS-10
❑ 96TopMasotG-17
❑ 96Ult-16
❑ 96UltGolM-16
❑ 96UppDec-20
❑ 96UppDec-374
❑ 96UppDecDD-DD11
❑ 96UppDecDDG-DD11
❑ 96UppDecDDS-DD11
❑ 96UppDecPHE-H11
❑ 96UppDecPreH-H11
❑ 96UppDecVJLS-VJ13
❑ 96Zen-83
❑ 96ZenArtP-83
❑ 96ZenMoz-9
❑ 97BluJayB-2
❑ 97BluJayCQI-1
❑ 97BluJayOH-5
❑ 97BluJayS-6
❑ 97BluJayS-31
❑ 97BluJayS-3
❑ 97Bow-64
❑ 97BowBes-86
❑ 97BowBesAR-86
❑ 97BowBesR-86
❑ 97BowChr-46
❑ 97BowChrI-46
❑ 97BowChrIR-46
❑ 97BowChrR-46
❑ 97BowInt-64
❑ 97Cir-21
❑ 97CirRav-21
❑ 97CleAaP-1
❑ 97CleTheF-1

❑ 97ColCho-61
❑ 97ColCho-500
❑ 97ColChoNF-NF17
❑ 97ColChoTBS-10
❑ 97ColChoTBSWH-10
❑ 97ColChoTotT-T30
❑ 97DenHol-13
❑ 97Don-27
❑ 97Don-273
❑ 97Don-428
❑ 97DonDom-11
❑ 97DonEli-40
❑ 97DonEliGS-40
❑ 97DonGolPP-27
❑ 97DonGolPP-273
❑ 97DonGolPP-428
❑ 97DonLim-110
❑ 97DonLim-124
❑ 97DonLim-165
❑ 97DonLimE-110
❑ 97DonLimE-124
❑ 97DonLimE-165
❑ 97DonLimENG-124
❑ 97DonPre-52
❑ 97DonPreCttC-52
❑ 97DonPreTB-4
❑ 97DonPreTBG-4
❑ 97DonPreTF-4
❑ 97DonPreTP-4
❑ 97DonPreTPG-4
❑ 97DonSig-11
❑ 97DonSigAC-26
❑ 97DonSigAM-26
❑ 97DonSigNN-3
❑ 97DonSigPPP-11
❑ 97DonSilPP-27
❑ 97DonSilPP-273
❑ 97DonSilPP-428
❑ 97DonTeaSMVP-17
❑ 97DonVxP1-48
❑ 97E-X2-49
❑ 97E-X2Cred-49
❑ 97E-X2EssCre-49
❑ 97E-X2Hall-7
❑ 97Fin-233
❑ 97Fin-344
❑ 97FinEmb-344
❑ 97FinEmbR-344
❑ 97FinRef-233
❑ 97FinRef-344
❑ 97FlaShoLC-21
❑ 97FlaShoLeg0-21
❑ 97FlaShoLeg1-21
❑ 97FlaShoM-A21
❑ 97FlaShoM-B21
❑ 97FlaShoM-C21
❑ 97FlaShoR0-21
❑ 97FlaShoR1-21
❑ 97FlaShoR2-21
❑ 97Fle-19
❑ 97Fle-569
❑ 97FleDecoE-3
❑ 97FleDecoERT-3
❑ 97FleMilDM-12
❑ 97FleMilDMR-12
❑ 97FleTif-19
❑ 97FleTif-569
❑ 97HigMinM-30
❑ 97HigMinM-31
❑ 97HigMinMCT-13
❑ 97HigMinMCT-14
❑ 97KinB-8
❑ 97Lea-208
❑ 97Lea-366
❑ 97LeaFraM-208
❑ 97LeaFraM-366
❑ 97LeaFraMDC-208
❑ 97LeaFraMDC-366
❑ 97LeaGet-11
❑ 97LeaGolS-13
❑ 97MetUni-20
❑ 97NewPin-21
❑ 97NewPinAP-21
❑ 97NewPinKtP-10
❑ 97NewPinMC-21
❑ 97NewPinPP-21
❑ 97NewPinPP-K10
❑ 97Pac-35
❑ 97PacLigB-35
❑ 97PacPri-14
❑ 97PacPriGotD-GD18
❑ 97PacPriLB-14
❑ 97PacPriP-14
❑ 97PacPriSH-SH2B
❑ 97PacSil-35
❑ 97PhiCopQ-5

❑ 97Pin-55
❑ 97PinAllFP-1
❑ 97PinArtP-PP55
❑ 97PinCar-13
❑ 97PinCer-39
❑ 97PinCer-138
❑ 97PinCerLI-11
❑ 97PinCerMBla-39
❑ 97PinCerMBla-138
❑ 97PinCerMBlu-39
❑ 97PinCerMBlu-138
❑ 97PinCerMG-39
❑ 97PinCerMG-138
❑ 97PinCerMR-39
❑ 97PinCerMR-138
❑ 97PinCerR-39
❑ 97PinCerR-138
❑ 97PinEpixPE-E17
❑ 97PinFan-FF19
❑ 97PinIns-36
❑ 97PinInsCE-36
❑ 97PinInsDD-15
❑ 97PinInsDE-36
❑ 97PinMusC-55
❑ 97PinPrePla-55
❑ 97PinTotCPB-39
❑ 97PinTotCPB-138
❑ 97PinTotCPG-39
❑ 97PinTotCPG-138
❑ 97PinTotCPR-39
❑ 97PinTotCPR-138
❑ 97PinTotCS-39
❑ 97PinX-P-54
❑ 97PinX-P-148
❑ 97PinX-PMoS-54
❑ 97PinX-PMoS-148
❑ 97PinX-PMW-20
❑ 97PinX-PMWG-20
❑ 97PinX-PMWS-20
❑ 97RedSoxS-8
❑ 97RedSoxSPI-8
❑ 97RedSoxSPr-8
❑ 97Sco-181
❑ 97Sco-430
❑ 97Sco-525
❑ 97ScoArtPWB-181
❑ 97ScoArtPWB-430
❑ 97ScoArtPWB-525
❑ 97ScoPreS-181
❑ 97ScoResC-430
❑ 97ScoResC-525
❑ 97ScoShoS-181
❑ 97ScoShoS-430
❑ 97ScoShoS-525
❑ 97ScoShoSAP-181
❑ 97ScoShoSAP-430
❑ 97ScoShoSAP-525
❑ 97Sel-24
❑ 97SelArtP-24
❑ 97SelCom-24
❑ 97SelRegG-24
❑ 97SelToootT-22
❑ 97SelToootTMB-22
❑ 97SP-180
❑ 97SPInsI-24
❑ 97SpoIll-30
❑ 97SpoIll-133
❑ 97SpoIll-171
❑ 97SpoIllEE-30
❑ 97SpoIllEE-133
❑ 97SpoIllEE-171
❑ 97SPSpeF-24
❑ 97SPSPxFA-5
❑ 97SPx-50
❑ 97SPxBro-50
❑ 97SPxGol-50
❑ 97SPxGraF-50
❑ 97SPxSil-50
❑ 97SPxSte-50
❑ 97StaClu-209
❑ 97StaCluI-I4
❑ 97StaCluMat-209
❑ 97StaCluMOP-209
❑ 97StaCluMOP-I4
❑ 97StrAll-15
❑ 97Stu-17
❑ 97StuPrePG-17
❑ 97StuPrePS-17
❑ 97Top-370
❑ 97TopChr-126
❑ 97TopChrR-126
❑ 97TopGal-41
❑ 97TopGalPPI-41
❑ 97TopMemO5-14
❑ 97TopSta-50
❑ 97TopStaAM-50

❑ 97TopStaP-PP2
❑ 97UD3-21
❑ 97Ult-13
❑ 97Ult-377
❑ 97UltGolME-13
❑ 97UltGolME-377
❑ 97UltPlaME-13
❑ 97UltPlaME-377
❑ 97UppDec-26
❑ 97UppDec-520
❑ 97UppDecAWJ-11
❑ 97UppDecMM-B8
❑ 97UppDecP-30
❑ 97UppDecPE-30
❑ 97UppDecSA-6
❑ 97UppDecSAG-6
❑ 97Zen-19
❑ 97Zen Z-Z-9
❑ 97Zen8x10-12
❑ 97Zen8x1D-12
❑ 98Bow-38
❑ 98BowBes-48
❑ 98BowBesAR-48
❑ 98BowBesR-48
❑ 98BowChr-38
❑ 98BowChrGA-38
❑ 98BowChrGAR-38
❑ 98BowChrI-38
❑ 98BowChrIR-38
❑ 98BowChrR-38
❑ 98BowGolA-38
❑ 98BowInt-38
❑ 98CirThu-21
❑ 98CirThuB-3
❑ 98CirThuLA-2
❑ 98CirThuQS-2
❑ 98CirThuRav-21
❑ 98CirThuRR-3
❑ 98CirThuSupRav-21
❑ 98ColCho-2
❑ 98ColCho-257
❑ 98ColCho-258
❑ 98ColCho-259
❑ 98ColCho-277
❑ 98ColCho-530
❑ 98ColChoB5-530
❑ 98ColChoCG-2
❑ 98ColChoER-ER28
❑ 98ColChoGJ5-277
❑ 98ColChoMBH-29
❑ 98ColChoRJ-2
❑ 98ColChoS'-29
❑ 98ColChoSQDouble-4
❑ 98ColChoSQHR-4
❑ 98ColChoSQSingle-4
❑ 98ColChoSQTriple-4
❑ 98CroRoy-142
❑ 98CroRoyFoB-25
❑ 98CroRoyFoBA-25
❑ 98CroRoyPotG-25
❑ 98Don-23
❑ 98Don-382
❑ 98Don-418
❑ 98DonCol-23
❑ 98DonColE-414
❑ 98DonColE-531
❑ 98DonColL-366
❑ 98DonColP-565
❑ 98DonColP-732
❑ 98DonColS-23
❑ 98DonCruG-48
❑ 98DonCruP-48
❑ 98DonCruR-48
❑ 98DonDiaK-14
❑ 98DonDiaKC-14
❑ 98DonDom-1
❑ 98DonEli-14
❑ 98DonEli-131
❑ 98DonEliA-14
❑ 98DonEliA-131
❑ 98DonEliC-21
❑ 98DonEliMC-21
❑ 98DonEliS-14
❑ 98DonEliS-131
❑ 98DonFANT-17
❑ 98DonFANTDC-17
❑ 98DonGolPP-23
❑ 98DonGolPP-382
❑ 98DonGolPP-418
❑ 98DonPre-15
❑ 98DonPre-182
❑ 98DonPreGB-14
❑ 98DonPreGES-8
❑ 98DonPreGoB-14
❑ 98DonPreGX-8
❑ 98DonPreGXDC-8

❑ 98DonPrePM-15
❑ 98DonPreSeat-15
❑ 98DonPreSeat-182
❑ 98DonPreTP-14
❑ 98DonPreTPD-7
❑ 98DonPreTPG-14
❑ 98DonPreTPS-14
❑ 98DonPreTW-3
❑ 98DonPriCD-23
❑ 98DonPriCE-414
❑ 98DonPriCE-531
❑ 98DonPriCL-366
❑ 98DonPriCP-565
❑ 98DonPriCP-732
❑ 98DonSig-21
❑ 98DonSigAC-25
❑ 98DonSigAM-25
❑ 98DonSigP-21
❑ 98DonSilPP-23
❑ 98DonSilPP-382
❑ 98DonSilPP-418
❑ 98E-X2-4
❑ 98E-X2DesCoop-4
❑ 98E-X2ECFut-4
❑ 98E-X2ECNow-4
❑ 98Fin-40
❑ 98FinMysF2-M9
❑ 98FinMysF2-M11
❑ 98FinMysF2-M12
❑ 98FinMysF2-M34
❑ 98FinMysF2R-M9
❑ 98FinMysF2R-M11
❑ 98FinMysF2R-M12
❑ 98FinMysF2R-M34
❑ 98FinNo--40
❑ 98FinNo-R-40
❑ 98FinOve-A7
❑ 98FinOveR-A7
❑ 98FinRef-40
❑ 98FinTheM-TM19
❑ 98FinTheMR-TM19
❑ 98FlaShoLeg0-21
❑ 98FlaShoLeg1-21
❑ 98FlaShoLeg2-21
❑ 98FlaShoLeg3-21
❑ 98FlaShoLegM-21
❑ 98FlaShoP1-10
❑ 98FlaShoR0-21
❑ 98FlaShoR1-21
❑ 98FlaShoR2-21
❑ 98FlaShoR3-21
❑ 98Fle-21
❑ 98Fle-301
❑ 98Fle-311
❑ 98Fle-579
❑ 98FleDecERT-3
❑ 98FleDecoE-3
❑ 98FleDiamInk-2
❑ 98FleDiaS-3
❑ 98FleDiaSCS-NNO
❑ 98FleDiaT-DT2
❑ 98FleIn TC-IC3
❑ 98FlePowG-5
❑ 98FleUpd-U3
❑ 98FleVin'-62
❑ 98FleVin'C-62
❑ 98FleZon-3
❑ 98KinDis-19
❑ 98Lea-167
❑ 98LeaCruG-48
❑ 98LeaCruP-48
❑ 98LeaCruR-48
❑ 98LeaFraDA-167
❑ 98LeaFraF-167
❑ 98LeaFraM-167
❑ 98LeaFraM-167
❑ 98LeaFraMDC-167
❑ 98LeaFraMDC-167
❑ 98LeaFraMS-167
❑ 98LeaFraMZ2-167
❑ 98LeaHeaftH-6
❑ 98LeaHeaftHS-6
❑ 98LeaRS-40
❑ 98LeaRS-158
❑ 98LeaRSExtM-7
❑ 98LeaRSExtMDC-7
❑ 98LeaRSGAHSamp-12
❑ 98LeaRSGreAH-12
❑ 98LeaRSLHolo-40
❑ 98LeaRSLHolo-158
❑ 98LeaRSLMVP-9
❑ 98LeaRSLMVPPE-9
❑ 98LeaRSLong-40
❑ 98LeaRSLong-158
❑ 98LeaRSSOSamp-8
❑ 98LeaRSStaOva-8

❑ 98LeaRSTicMas-14
❑ 98LeaRSTicMasDC-14
❑ 98LeaRTrue-40
❑ 98LeaRTrue-158
❑ 98MetUni-167
❑ 98MetUni-205
❑ 98MetUniPMG-167
❑ 98MetUniPMG-205
❑ 98Pac-215
❑ 98PacAur-92
❑ 98PacAurHC-19
❑ 98PacAurPF-21
❑ 98PacAurPFC-21
❑ 98PacAurPFPB-21
❑ 98PacAurPFR-21
❑ 98PacAurPFS-21
❑ 98PacCraCh-10
❑ 98PacGolCDC-35
❑ 98PacInv-73
❑ 98PacInvCCDB-10
❑ 98PacInvCCG-10
❑ 98PacInvCCG-10
❑ 98PacInvCCLB-10
❑ 98PacInvCCP-10
❑ 98PacInvCCR-10
❑ 98PacInvGems-110
❑ 98PacInvInt-14A
❑ 98PacInvPBlue-73
❑ 98PacInvPhoto-17
❑ 98PacInvSilv-73
❑ 98PacInvTeam-28
❑ 98PacOme-245
❑ 98PacOmeFTF-4
❑ 98PacOmeOnIns-19
❑ 98PacOmeR-245
❑ 98PacOnl-755
❑ 98PacOnl-780
❑ 98PacOnlR-755
❑ 98PacOnlR-780
❑ 98PacOnlWC-755
❑ 98PacOnlWC-780
❑ 98PacPar-111
❑ 98PacParC-111
❑ 98PacParG-111
❑ 98PacParHS-111
❑ 98PacParl-42
❑ 98PacParPB-111
❑ 98PacParR-111
❑ 98PacParTC-14
❑ 98PacPlaB-215
❑ 98PacRedT-215
❑ 98PacSil-215
❑ 98PacTeaC-14
❑ 98Pin-184
❑ 98PinArtP-PP87
❑ 98PinEpixME-E17
❑ 98PinEpixMO-E17
❑ 98PinEpixMP-E17
❑ 98PinEpixPO-E17
❑ 98PinEpixPP-E17
❑ 98PinEpixSE-E17
❑ 98PinEpixSO-E17
❑ 98PinEpixSP-E17
❑ 98PinIns-86
❑ 98PinInsBtN-13
❑ 98PinInsC-1
❑ 98PinInsCE-86
❑ 98PinInsCG-1
❑ 98PinInsDE-86
❑ 98PinInsSG-12AB
❑ 98PinInsSG-12CD
❑ 98PinInsSGS-12AB
❑ 98PinInsSGS-12CD
❑ 98PinMinB-5
❑ 98PinMinCB-5
❑ 98PinMinCBAP-5
❑ 98PinMinCGP-5
❑ 98PinMinCGPAP-5
❑ 98PinMinCN-5
❑ 98PinMinCNAP-5
❑ 98PinMinCSGR-5
❑ 98PinMinDC-5
❑ 98PinMinG-5
❑ 98PinMinMCSS-5
❑ 98PinMinMG-3
❑ 98PinMinMGC-3
❑ 98PinMinS-5
❑ 98PinMusC-PP87
❑ 98PinPer-15
❑ 98PinPerPP-15
❑ 98PinPlu-6
❑ 98PinPlu-194
❑ 98PinPluAE-16
❑ 98PinPluAEE-16
❑ 98PinPluAEP-16
❑ 98PinPluAP-PP3
❑ 98PinPluGAP-PP3
❑ 98PinPluLM-7
❑ 98PinPluMAP-PP3
❑ 98PinPluTP-12
❑ 98PinPluTPG-12
❑ 98PinPluTPM-12
❑ 98PinPowPJ-3
❑ 98PinPowPJS-3
❑ 98PinPreP-184
❑ 98PinPreP-E16
❑ 98PinPreP-S8
❑ 98PinPreP-S9
❑ 98PinPreP-S10
❑ 98PinPreP-S11
❑ 98PinPreP-S12
❑ 98PinPreP-S13
❑ 98PinSpe-8
❑ 98PinSpe-9
❑ 98PinSpe-10
❑ 98PinSpe-11
❑ 98PinSpe-12
❑ 98PinSpe-13
❑ 98PinUnc-184
❑ 98Revo-148
❑ 98RevoShow-20
❑ 98RevoSS-148
❑ 98Sco-49
❑ 98ScoAllST-17
❑ 98ScoEpix-E16
❑ 98ScoFirP-15
❑ 98ScoRT-8
❑ 98ScoRTComPla-8A
❑ 98ScoRTComPla-8B
❑ 98ScoRTComPla-8C
❑ 98ScoRTCPSamp-8A
❑ 98ScoRTCPSamp-8B
❑ 98ScoRTCPSamp-8C
❑ 98ScoRTSS-PP8
❑ 98ScoRTSSAP-PP8
❑ 98ScoRTSSAP1-PP8
❑ 98ScoSS-PP131
❑ 98ScoSSAP-PP131
❑ 98SkyDugA-88
❑ 98SkyDugA-138
❑ 98SkyDugAAR-2
❑ 98SkyDugAD-D8
❑ 98SkyDugAIA-88
❑ 98SkyDugAIA-138
❑ 98SP Aut-195
❑ 98SP Aut-SD35
❑ 98SP AutC-RC
❑ 98SP AutSD-SD35
❑ 98SP AutSDT-SD35
❑ 98SpollI-26
❑ 98SpollI-179
❑ 98SpollI-193
❑ 98SpollIEE-26
❑ 98SpollIEE-179
❑ 98SpollIEE-193
❑ 98SpollIFE-26
❑ 98SpollIFE-179
❑ 98SpollIFE-193
❑ 98SpollIODMP-OD30
❑ 98SpollITaN-53
❑ 98SpollITaN-72
❑ 98SpollITaNA-1
❑ 98SpollITaNAR-1
❑ 98SpollITaNC-C8
❑ 98SpollITaNEE-53
❑ 98SpollITaNEE-72
❑ 98SpollITaNRtC-RC2
❑ 98SpollIWSF-52
❑ 98SpollIWSFEE-52
❑ 98SpollIWSFFE-52
❑ 98SpollIWSFRJP-9
❑ 98SPxFin-140
❑ 98SPxFin-170
❑ 98SPxFin-180
❑ 98SPxFin-213
❑ 98SPxFinR-140
❑ 98SPxFinR-170
❑ 98SPxFinR-180
❑ 98SPxFinR-213
❑ 98SPxFinS-140
❑ 98SPxFinS-170
❑ 98SPxFinS-180
❑ 98SPxFinS-213
❑ 98StaCluC-CS31
❑ 98StaCluC-CS32
❑ 98StaCluC-CS33
❑ 98StaCluFDI-101
❑ 98StaClul-101
❑ 98StaCluNC-NC9
❑ 98StaCluOneK-101
❑ 98StaCluPP-101
❑ 98Stu-202
❑ 98StuFF-25
❑ 98StuFFDC-25
❑ 98StuGPP-202
❑ 98StuMast-5
❑ 98StuPor8x10-21
❑ 98StuPor8x10GP-21
❑ 98StuSPP-202
❑ 98Top-300
❑ 98Top-475
❑ 98TopChr-300
❑ 98TopChr-475
❑ 98TopChrHB-HB4
❑ 98TopChrHBR-HB4
❑ 98TopChrM-MS2
❑ 98TopChrMR-MS2
❑ 98TopChrR-300
❑ 98TopChrR-475
❑ 98TopDevR-300
❑ 98TopDevR-475
❑ 98TopDia-300
❑ 98TopDia-475
❑ 98TopFocP-FP9
❑ 98TopGal-40
❑ 98TopGalAG-AG3
❑ 98TopGalGP-40
❑ 98TopGalOPP-40
❑ 98TopGalPPI-40
❑ 98TopGalPPIA-40
❑ 98TopGolLabC1-21
❑ 98TopGolLabC1B-21
❑ 98TopGolLabC1One-21
❑ 98TopGolLabC1R-21
❑ 98TopGolLabC2-21
❑ 98TopGolLabC2B-21
❑ 98TopGolLabC2One-21
❑ 98TopGolLabC2R-21
❑ 98TopGolLabC3-21
❑ 98TopGolLabC3B-21
❑ 98TopGolLabC3One-21
❑ 98TopGolLabC3R-21
❑ 98TopHal-HB4
❑ 98TopMil-MS2
❑ 98TopMiniC-300
❑ 98TopMiniC-475
❑ 98TopOpeD-127
❑ 98TopSta-136
❑ 98TopSta'S-9
❑ 98TopSta'SGH-9
❑ 98TopStaB-136
❑ 98TopStaG-136
❑ 98TopStaGR-136
❑ 98TopStaS-136
❑ 98TopStaSteG-9
❑ 98TopSup-20
❑ 98TopSup-20
❑ 98TopTek-21
❑ 98TopTekD-21
❑ 98TopTekP-21
❑ 98UD3-80
❑ 98UD3-170
❑ 98UD3-260
❑ 98UD3DieCut-80
❑ 98UD3DieCut-170
❑ 98UD3DieCut-260
❑ 98Ult-3
❑ 98Ult-213
❑ 98Ult-492
❑ 98UltDial-14
❑ 98UltDouT-19
❑ 98UltGolM-3
❑ 98UltGolM-213
❑ 98UltGolM-492
❑ 98UltMas-3
❑ 98UltMas-213
❑ 98UltMas-492
❑ 98UltPlaM-3
❑ 98UltPlaM-213
❑ 98UltPlaM-492
❑ 98UltTop3-9
❑ 98UltWinN-18
❑ 98UppDec-17
❑ 98UppDec-137
❑ 98UppDec-451
❑ 98UppDec-530
❑ 98UppDec-534
❑ 98UppDec-603
❑ 98UppDec10AP-3
❑ 98UppDec1APR-3
❑ 98UppDec5x7-530
❑ 98UppDecAC-AS21
❑ 98UppDecAG-AG21
❑ 98UppDecAGDC-AG21
❑ 98UppDecCD-CD21
❑ 98UppDecR-99
❑ 98UppDecR-9
❑ 98UppDecRQL-Q11
❑ 98UppDecRTC-TC26
❑ 98UppDecSF-10
❑ 98UppDecU-9
❑ 98Zen-32
❑ 98Zen5 xx7-45
❑ 98Zen5x7GoldImp-45
❑ 98Zen5x7Imp-45
❑ 98ZenEpi-E16
❑ 98ZenZ-G-32
❑ 98ZenZ-S-32
❑ 98ZenZ-T-9
❑ 98ZenZ-T5x7-9
❑ 98ZenZ-TG-9
❑ 99199Fin-80
❑ 99199Fin-111
❑ 99199Fin-151
❑ 99199Fin-266
❑ 99AllMysFR-M31
❑ 99Bow-278
❑ 99BowBes-85
❑ 99BowBes-87
❑ 99BowBesAR-85
❑ 99BowBesAR-87
❑ 99BowBesR-85
❑ 99BowBesR-87
❑ 99BowGol-278
❑ 99BowInt-278
❑ 99CroRoyB-95
❑ 99CroRoyL-95
❑ 99CroRoyMP-10
❑ 99CroRoyOD-95
❑ 99CroRoyPotG-14
❑ 99CroRoyPP-14
❑ 99CroRoyPPN-14
❑ 99E-X Cen-18
❑ 99E-X CenECFut-18
❑ 99E-X CenECNow-18
❑ 99E-XCenFoF'-5
❑ 99E-XCenMotC-5
❑ 99FinCom-C3
❑ 99FinComDualR-C3
❑ 99FinGolRef-80
❑ 99FinGolRef-111
❑ 99FinGolRef-151
❑ 99FinGolRef-266
❑ 99FinPeelHyp-11
❑ 99FinPeelSpark-11
❑ 99FinPeeSS-11
❑ 99FinRef-80
❑ 99FinRef-111
❑ 99FinRef-151
❑ 99FinRef-266
❑ 99FinSplS-SS10
❑ 99FinSplSDR-SS10
❑ 99FinTeaFB-TF7
❑ 99FinTeaFBR-TF7
❑ 99FinTeaFG-TF7
❑ 99FinTeaFGR-TF7
❑ 99FinTeaFR-TF7
❑ 99FinTeaFRR-TF7
❑ 99FlaShoLeg1-21
❑ 99FlaShoLeg2-21
❑ 99FlaShoLeg3-21
❑ 99FlaShoLegM1-21
❑ 99FlaShoLegM2-21
❑ 99FlaShoLegM3-21
❑ 99FlaShoMoG-1
❑ 99FlaShoR1-21
❑ 99FlaShoR2-21
❑ 99FlaShoR3-21
❑ 99Fle-30
❑ 99FleBri-113
❑ 99FleBri2G-113
❑ 99FleBriBlu-113
❑ 99FleBriGol-113
❑ 99FleBriSS-13
❑ 99FleBriSSP-13
❑ 99FleDatWD-2
❑ 99FleDiaM-2
❑ 99FleGolM-3
❑ 99FleMys-63
❑ 99FleMysD-10
❑ 99FleMysG-63
❑ 99FleMysM-63
❑ 99FleSta9-30
❑ 99FleVin'-30
❑ 99FleWarT-30
❑ 99MetUni-206
❑ 99MetUni-296
❑ 99MetUniGM-206
❑ 99MetUniGM-296
❑ 99MetUniPMG-206
❑ 99MetUniPMG-296
❑ 99Pac-436
❑ 99Pac-436A
❑ 99PacAur-195
❑ 99PacAurOD-195
❑ 99PacCroC-292
❑ 99PacCroCPB-292
❑ 99PacGolCDC-19
❑ 99PacInv-99
❑ 99PacInvFP-11
❑ 99PacInvOD-99
❑ 99PacInvPB-99
❑ 99PacInvSH-11
❑ 99PacInvSH-11B
❑ 99PacOme-159
❑ 99PacOme5T-5
❑ 99PacOme5TT-5
❑ 99PacOmeC-159
❑ 99PacOmeDM-21
❑ 99PacOmeEP-11
❑ 99PacOmeEP1o1-11
❑ 99PacOmeG-159
❑ 99PacOmePB-159
❑ 99PacPar-158
❑ 99PacParC-158
❑ 99PacParG-158
❑ 99PacParHoloGold-158
❑ 99PacParHS-158
❑ 99PacParOD-158
❑ 99PacParPB-22
❑ 99PacParPB-158
❑ 99PacParRed-158
❑ 99PacParTC-20
❑ 99PacPlaB-436
❑ 99PacPlaB-436A
❑ 99PacPri-147
❑ 99PacPriHB-147
❑ 99PacPriHG-147
❑ 99PacPriHM-147
❑ 99PacPriHP-147
❑ 99PacPriRed-147
❑ 99PacPriS-2
❑ 99PacPriS206-2
❑ 99PacPriS206R-2
❑ 99PacPriSE-2
❑ 99PacPriSP-2
❑ 99PacPriSP-2
❑ 99PacPriSV-2
❑ 99PacRed-436
❑ 99PacRed-436A
❑ 99PacTeaC-14
❑ 99PacTim-11
❑ 99Rev-93
❑ 99RevDiaL-21
❑ 99RevPremDate-93
❑ 99RevRet-93
❑ 99RevShaSS-93
❑ 99RevTri-26
❑ 99RevTri-26
❑ 99SkyMolM-147
❑ 99SkyMolMF-47
❑ 99SkyMolMFS-47
❑ 99SkyMolMFT-47
❑ 99SkyMolMX-147
❑ 99SkyPre-111
❑ 99SkyPre-293
❑ 99SkyPreIN-14
❑ 99SkyPreR-111
❑ 99SkyPreR-293
❑ 99SkyPreSB-5
❑ 99SkyThu-265
❑ 99SkyThuInD-ID3
❑ 99SkyThuRant-265
❑ 99SkyThuRave-265
❑ 99SP Aut-60
❑ 99SP AutR-R30
❑ 99SpollI-14
❑ 99SpollI-15
❑ 99SpollI-16
❑ 99SpollI-19
❑ 99SpollI-23
❑ 99SpollI-162
❑ 99SpollIDD-2
❑ 99SpollIH-15
❑ 99SPx-57
❑ 99SPxFinR-57
❑ 99SPxFinS-57
❑ 99SPxPreS-PS26
❑ 99StaClu-96
❑ 99StaClu-319
❑ 99StaCluC-CS25
❑ 99StaCluC-CS31
❑ 99StaCluC-CS36
❑ 99StaCluC-CS41
❑ 99StaCluFDI-96
❑ 99StaCluFDI-319
❑ 99StaCluNC-NC8
❑ 99StaCluOoaK-96
❑ 99StaCluOoaK-319
❑ 99StaCluPP-96
❑ 99StaCluPP-319
❑ 99ThuSkySupR-265
❑ 99Top-1
❑ 99Top-203
❑ 99Top-232
❑ 99Top-334
❑ 99Top-445
❑ 99Top-460
❑ 99TopAll-AM25
❑ 99TopAllMF-M31
❑ 99TopAut-A1
❑ 99TopBlaLC1-95
❑ 99TopBlaLC2-95
❑ 99TopBlaLC3-95
❑ 99TopChr-1
❑ 99TopChr-203
❑ 99TopChr-232
❑ 99TopChr-334
❑ 99TopChr-445
❑ 99TopChr-460
❑ 99TopChrA-AE25
❑ 99TopChrAR-AE25
❑ 99TopChrR-1
❑ 99TopChrR-203
❑ 99TopChrR-232
❑ 99TopChrR-334
❑ 99TopChrR-445
❑ 99TopChrR-460
❑ 99TopChrRN-RN8
❑ 99TopChrRNR-RN8
❑ 99TopGal-31
❑ 99TopGal-115
❑ 99TopGalAG-AG3
❑ 99TopGalE-E4
❑ 99TopGalHer-TH4
❑ 99TopGalHerP-TH4
❑ 99TopGalPP-31
❑ 99TopGalPP-115
❑ 99TopGalPPI-31
❑ 99TopGalPPI-115
❑ 99TopGolL-95
❑ 99TopGolLC1-95
❑ 99TopGolLC2-95
❑ 99TopGolLOtO-95
❑ 99TopMVPP-1
❑ 99TopMVPP-334
❑ 99TopMVPP-445
❑ 99TopMVPP-460
❑ 99TopOpeD-2
❑ 99TopOpeD-161
❑ 99TopOver-A1
❑ 99TopPowB-PB19
❑ 99TopPowBR-PB19
❑ 99TopPre-PP1
❑ 99TopRecN-RN8
❑ 99TopRecNG-RN8
❑ 99TopRedLC1-95
❑ 99TopRedLC2-95
❑ 99TopRedLC3-95
❑ 99TopSta-18
❑ 99TopSta-154
❑ 99TopSta'S-12
❑ 99TopSta'SG-12
❑ 99TopSta'SGDH-12
❑ 99TopSta1Foil-18
❑ 99TopSta2Foil-18
❑ 99TopSta3Foil-18
❑ 99TopStaFoil-18
❑ 99TopStaFoil-154
❑ 99TopStaG-G2
❑ 99TopStaGFoil-G2
❑ 99TopStaOS-18
❑ 99TopStaTS-18
❑ 99TopStaTS-18
❑ 99TopSupC-1
❑ 99TopSupC-32
❑ 99TopSupCR-1
❑ 99TopSupCR-32
❑ 99TopTek-45A
❑ 99TopTek-45B
❑ 99TopTekG-45A
❑ 99TopTekG-45B
❑ 99TopTekT-T8
❑ 99UD Cho-41
❑ 99UD Cho-155
❑ 99UD ChoBU-5
❑ 99UD ChoBUCG-8
❑ 99UD ChoPCR-41
❑ 99UD ChoPCR-155
❑ 99UD ChoS-13
❑ 99UD ChoSD-13
❑ 99UD ChoSHR-13
❑ 99UD ChoST-13
❑ 99UD Ion-59
❑ 99UD Ion-89
❑ 99UD IonC-C15

❑ 99UD IonH-H15
❑ 99UD IonR-59
❑ 99UD IonR-89
❑ 99UDHolo-39
❑ 99UDHoloAUsome-39
❑ 99UDHoloFF-F6
❑ 99UDHoloFFG-F6
❑ 99UDHoloStar-S5
❑ 99UDHoloStarG-S5
❑ 99Ult-190
❑ 99UltGolM-190
❑ 99UltMas-190
❑ 99UltPlaM-190
❑ 99UppDec-223
❑ 99UppDec-440
❑ 99UppDec-532
❑ 99UppDec10AT-X30
❑ 99UppDec10ATD-X30
❑ 99UppDec10ATHR-X30
❑ 99UppDec10ATT-X30
❑ 99UppDecBD-88
❑ 99UppDecBDD-88
❑ 99UppDecBDDom-D21
❑ 99UppDecBDDomE-D21
❑ 99UppDecBDMN-M10
❑ 99UppDecBDMNE-M10
❑ 99UppDecBDQ-88
❑ 99UppDecBDT-88
❑ 99UppDecCG-CG1
❑ 99UppDecCGD-CG1
❑ 99UppDecCGHR-CG1
❑ 99UppDecCGT-CG1
❑ 99UppDecCL-53
❑ 99UppDecCLCC-53
❑ 99UppDecCLEM-EM5
❑ 99UppDecCLJotC-RC
❑ 99UppDecCLM-C66
❑ 99UppDecE-63
❑ 99UppDecEFXG-63
❑ 99UppDecEL1-223
❑ 99UppDecEL1-440
❑ 99UppDecEL1-532
❑ 99UppDecEL2-223
❑ 99UppDecEL2-440
❑ 99UppDecEL2-532
❑ 99UppDecEPE-P30
❑ 99UppDecEUR-U8
❑ 99UppDecF-F29
❑ 99UppDecFD-F29
❑ 99UppDecFQ-F29
❑ 99UppDecFT-F29
❑ 99UppDecIP-I4
❑ 99UppDecIPD-I4
❑ 99UppDecIPHR-I4
❑ 99UppDecIPT-I4
❑ 99UppDecM-144
❑ 99UppDecMGS-144
❑ 99UppDecMHFS-144
❑ 99UppDecMSS-144
❑ 99UppDecO-47
❑ 99UppDecOMP-S20
❑ 99UppDecOSO-47
❑ 99UppDecOWP-R5
❑ 99UppDecR-56
❑ 99UppDecRDR-D6
❑ 99UppDecRDRL2-D6
❑ 99UppDecRG-56
❑ 99UppDecRL-1
❑ 99UppDecROSS-S13
❑ 99UppDecROSS-S13
❑ 99UppDecRP-56
❑ 99UppDecRTA-T4
❑ 99UppDecRTAL2-T4
❑ 99UppDecTE-T30
❑ 99UppDecTED-T30
❑ 99UppDecTEQ-T30
❑ 99UppDecTET-T30
❑ 99UppDecVtaT-V30
❑ 99UppDecVtaTD-V30
❑ 99UppDecVtaTQ-V30
❑ 99UppDecVtaTT-V30
❑ 99UppDecWY-W5
❑ 99UppDecWYD-W5
❑ 99UppDecWYHR-W5
❑ 99UppDecWYT-W5
❑ 99Vic-268
❑ 99Vic-453

Clemens, Troy

❑ 90SprCarB-7
❑ 91RenSilSCLC-17
❑ 92SanJosGC-13
❑ 93SanJosGC-6
❑ 93SanJosGF-13
❑ 94SanJosGC-4
❑ 94SanJosGF-2819

Clement, Matt

❑ 95IdaFalBTI-31
❑ 95RanCucQT-31
❑ 96CliLumKTI-9
❑ 96MidLeaAB-18
❑ 97Bes-87
❑ 97Bow-207
❑ 97BowChr-190
❑ 97BowChrI-190
❑ 97BowChrIR-190
❑ 97BowChrR-190
❑ 97BowInt-207
❑ 97CalLeaATI-3
❑ 97CalLeaTP-16
❑ 97RanCucQUG-1
❑ 98Bes-63
❑ 98BesBet-5
❑ 98BesCor-5
❑ 98BesDiaB-13
❑ 98Bow-188
❑ 98Bow99ROYF-ROY4
❑ 98BowBes-113
❑ 98BowBesAR-113
❑ 98BowBesR-113
❑ 98BowChr-188
❑ 98BowChrGA-188
❑ 98BowChrGAR-188
❑ 98BowChrI-188
❑ 98BowChrIR-188
❑ 98BowChrR-188
❑ 98BowGolA-188
❑ 98BowInt-188
❑ 98BowScoC-SC6
❑ 98ColCho-429
❑ 98ColChoPCR-429
❑ 98Don-329
❑ 98DonGolPP-329
❑ 98DonSigA-18
❑ 98DonSigAC-26
❑ 98DonSigAM-26
❑ 98DonSilPP-329
❑ 98FleUpd-U74
❑ 98Las-6
❑ 98LeaRS-247
❑ 98LeaRSLHolo-247
❑ 98LeaRSLong-247
❑ 98LeaRTrue-247
❑ 98SP Aut-28
❑ 98SP MinPE-110
❑ 98SPMin-110
❑ 98SPxFin-209
❑ 98SPxFinR-209
❑ 98SPxFinS-209
❑ 98Top-264
❑ 98TopChr-264
❑ 98TopChrR-264
❑ 98TopDevR-264
❑ 98TopDia-264
❑ 98TopMiniC-264
❑ 98UD3-28
❑ 98UD3-118
❑ 98UD3-208
❑ 98UD3DieCut-28
❑ 98UD3DieCut-118
❑ 98UD3DieCut-208
❑ 98UppDec-595
❑ 98UppDecDS-DS22
❑ 98UppDecR-127
❑ 98UppDecRNF-NF27
❑ 99199Fin-138
❑ 99Bow-74
❑ 99BowBes-111
❑ 99BowBesAR-111
❑ 99BowBesR-111
❑ 99BowChr-74
❑ 99BowChrG-74
❑ 99BowChrGR-74
❑ 99BowChrI-74
❑ 99BowChrIR-74
❑ 99BowChrR-74
❑ 99BowChrSC-SC12
❑ 99BowChrSCR-SC12
❑ 99BowGol-74
❑ 99BowInt-74
❑ 99BowScoC-SC12
❑ 99CroRoyB-118
❑ 99CroRoyL-118
❑ 99CroRoyOD-118
❑ 99DumSet-147
❑ 99E-X Cen-107
❑ 99E-X CenECFut-107
❑ 99E-X CenECNow-107
❑ 99FinGolRef-138
❑ 99FinRef-138
❑ 99Fle-136
❑ 99FleBri-139
❑ 99FleBri2G-139
❑ 99FleBriBlu-139
❑ 99FleBriGol-139
❑ 99FleMys-147
❑ 99FleMysM-147
❑ 99FleSta9-136
❑ 99FleWarT-136
❑ 99MetUni-266
❑ 99MetUniGM-266
❑ 99MetUniPMG-266
❑ 99PacInv-121
❑ 99PacInvOD-121
❑ 99PacInvPB-121
❑ 99PacPar-204
❑ 99PacParC-204
❑ 99PacParG-204
❑ 99PacParHoloGold-204
❑ 99PacParHS-204
❑ 99PacParOD-204
❑ 99PacParPB-204
❑ 99PacParRed-204
❑ 99SkyMolM-74
❑ 99SkyMolMX-74
❑ 99SkyThu-66
❑ 99SkyThuRant-66
❑ 99SkyThuRave-66
❑ 99SP Aut-115
❑ 99SP SigAuto-MCI
❑ 99SP TopP-2
❑ 99SP TopP-28
❑ 99SP TopPC-MC
❑ 99SP TopPDtS-D9
❑ 99SP TopPGF-GF9
❑ 99SP TopPPE-2
❑ 99SP TopPPE-28
❑ 99SpoIll-60
❑ 99SPSig-111
❑ 99SPx-113
❑ 99SPxFinR-113
❑ 99SPxFinS-113
❑ 99TeaBesRBG-5
❑ 99ThuSkySupR-66
❑ 99TopSta-36
❑ 99TopSta1Foil-36
❑ 99TopSta2Foil-36
❑ 99TopStaBF-BF7
❑ 99TopStaBFFoil-BF7
❑ 99TopStaFoil-36
❑ 99TopStaOS-36
❑ 99TopStaTS-36
❑ 99Ult-248
❑ 99UltGolM-248
❑ 99UltMas-248
❑ 99UltPlaM-248
❑ 99UppDec-477
❑ 99UppDecBD-115
❑ 99UppDecBDD-115
❑ 99UppDecBDQ-115
❑ 99UppDecBDT-115
❑ 99UppDecE-78
❑ 99UppDecEFXG-78
❑ 99UppDecEL1-477
❑ 99UppDecEL2-477
❑ 99Vic-334

Clement, Wally (Wallace Oaks)

❑ 09AmeCarE90-1-24
❑ 90DodTar-914

Clemente, Edgard Velazquez

❑ 94AshTouC-22
❑ 94AshTouF-1796
❑ 95SalAvaTI-11
❑ 96Bow-351
❑ 96BowBes-132
❑ 96BowBesAR-132
❑ 96BowBesR-132
❑ 96BowFoi-351
❑ 96BowMinLP-15
❑ 97Bes-58
❑ 97Bow-211
❑ 97BowBes-140
❑ 97BowBesAR-140
❑ 97BowBesR-140
❑ 97BowChr-193
❑ 97BowChrI-193
❑ 97BowChrIR-193
❑ 97BowChrR-193
❑ 97BowInt-211
❑ 97ColSprSTI-26
❑ 97Top-491
❑ 98Bow-311
❑ 98BowBes-160
❑ 98BowBesAR-160
❑ 98BowBesR-160
❑ 98BowChr-311
❑ 98BowChrGA-311
❑ 98BowChrGAR-311
❑ 98BowChrI-311
❑ 98BowChrIR-311
❑ 98BowChrR-311
❑ 98BowGolA-311
❑ 98BowInt-311
❑ 98ColSprSS-12
❑ 98FleUpd-U72
❑ 99Fle-376
❑ 99FleBri-147
❑ 99FleBri2G-147
❑ 99FleBriBlu-147
❑ 99FleBriGol-147
❑ 99FleMysFI-10
❑ 99FleSta9-376
❑ 99FleWarT-376
❑ 99Pac-143
❑ 99Pac-143A
❑ 99PacAur-60
❑ 99PacAurOD-60
❑ 99PacCroC-95
❑ 99PacCroCPB-95
❑ 99PacPlaB-143
❑ 99PacPlaB-143A
❑ 99PacPri-51
❑ 99PacPriHB-51
❑ 99PacPriHG-51
❑ 99PacPriHM-51
❑ 99PacPriHP-51
❑ 99PacPriRed-51
❑ 99PacPriS-75
❑ 99PacPriS206-75
❑ 99PacPriS206R-75
❑ 99PacRed-143
❑ 99PacRed-143A
❑ 99SkyPreA-12
❑ 99SkyPreABlue-12
❑ 99SpoIll-66

Clemente, Joe

❑ 93MisStaB-9

Clemente, Roberto W.

❑ 47Exh-44
❑ 47PM1StaP1-32
❑ 55Top-164
❑ 56PirTeal-3
❑ 56Top-33
❑ 57Kah-5
❑ 57PirTeal-1
❑ 57Top-76
❑ 58Kah-5
❑ 58PirTeal-1
❑ 58Top-52A
❑ 58Top-52B
❑ 59Kah-6
❑ 59Top-478
❑ 59Top-543
❑ 60Baz-7
❑ 60Kah-6
❑ 60PirJayP-3
❑ 60PirTag-21
❑ 60Top-326
❑ 61Kah-8
❑ 61PirJayP-2
❑ 61PirRigF-1
❑ 61Pos-132A
❑ 61Pos-132B
❑ 61Top-41
❑ 61Top-388
❑ 62Baz-11
❑ 62ExhStaB-9
❑ 62Jel-173
❑ 62Kah-5
❑ 62Pos-173A
❑ 62Pos-173B
❑ 62PosCan-173
❑ 62SalPlaC-150
❑ 62ShiPlaC-150
❑ 62Top-10
❑ 62Top-52
❑ 62TopBuc-17
❑ 62TopStaI-174
❑ 62TopVen-10
❑ 62TopVen-52
❑ 63Baz-14
❑ 63ExhStaB-15
❑ 63Fle-56
❑ 63Jel-143
❑ 63Kah-6
❑ 63PirIDL-4
❑ 63PirJayP-3
❑ 63Pos-143
❑ 63SalMetC-23
❑ 63Top-18
❑ 63Top-540
❑ 63TopStiI-9
❑ 64Baz-14
❑ 64Kah-4
❑ 64PirKDK-7
❑ 64Top-7
❑ 64Top-440
❑ 64TopCoi-55
❑ 64TopCoi-150
❑ 64TopGia-11
❑ 64TopSta-27
❑ 64TopStaU-17
❑ 64TopVen-7
❑ 64WheSta-11
❑ 65Baz-14
❑ 65MacSta-1
❑ 65OPC-2
❑ 65OPC-160
❑ 65Top-2
❑ 65Top-160
❑ 65TopEmbI-19
❑ 65TopTraI-44
❑ 66Baz-26
❑ 66Kah-8
❑ 66PirEasH-21
❑ 66Top-215
❑ 66Top-300
❑ 66TopRubI-18
❑ 66TopVen-215
❑ 66TopVen-300
❑ 67Baz-26
❑ 67CokCapPi-18
❑ 67DexPre-50
❑ 67DexPre-51
❑ 67OPCPapI-11
❑ 67PirTeal-4
❑ 67Top-242
❑ 67Top-361
❑ 67Top-400
❑ 67TopGiaSU-7
❑ 67TopPirS-6
❑ 67TopPirS-27
❑ 67TopPos-11
❑ 67TopTesF-6
❑ 67TopVen-278
❑ 68AtlOilPBCC-14
❑ 68Baz-12
❑ 68DexPre-24
❑ 68OPC-1
❑ 68OPC-3
❑ 68OPC-150
❑ 68PirKDK-21
❑ 68PirTeal-5
❑ 68Top-1
❑ 68Top-3
❑ 68Top-150
❑ 68Top-374
❑ 68Top-480
❑ 68Top3-D-1
❑ 68TopActS-9C
❑ 68TopActS-12B
❑ 68TopGamI-6
❑ 68TopPla-16
❑ 68TopPos-6
❑ 68TopVen-1
❑ 68TopVen-3
❑ 68TopVen-150
❑ 69MilBra-60
❑ 69MLBOffS-184
❑ 69MLBPin-39
❑ 69NabTeaF-5
❑ 69OPC-50
❑ 69OPCDec-4
❑ 69PirGre-4
❑ 69PirTeal-5
❑ 69Top-50
❑ 69TopDec-27
❑ 69TopDecI-6
❑ 69TopSta-85
❑ 69TopSup-58
❑ 69TopTeaP-16
❑ 69TraSta-56
❑ 70DayDaiNM-32
❑ 70Kel-27
❑ 70MilBra-5
❑ 70MLBOffS-99
❑ 70OPC-61
❑ 70OPC-350
❑ 70PirTeal-4
❑ 70Top-61
❑ 70Top-350
❑ 70TopPos-21
❑ 70TopSup-12
❑ 70TraSta-5B
❑ 71AllBasA-6
❑ 71BazNumT-38
❑ 71BazUnn-11
❑ 71Kel-5
❑ 71MilDud-40
❑ 71MLBOffS-198
❑ 71MLBOffS-558
❑ 71OPC-630
❑ 71Pir-3
❑ 71PirActP-4
❑ 71PirArc-3
❑ 71Top-630
❑ 71TopCoi-71
❑ 71TopSup-37
❑ 71TopTat-79
❑ 72Dia-57
❑ 72Kel-49
❑ 72MilBra-75
❑ 72OPC-226
❑ 72OPC-309
❑ 72OPC-310
❑ 72PirTeal-2
❑ 72ProStaP-15
❑ 72SevTraC-12
❑ 72Top-226
❑ 72Top-309
❑ 72Top-310
❑ 72TopCloT-6
❑ 72TopPos-23
❑ 73OPC-50
❑ 73PicCle-1
❑ 73PicCle-2
❑ 73PicCle-3
❑ 73PicCle-4
❑ 73PicCle-5
❑ 73PicCle-6
❑ 73PicCle-7
❑ 73PicCle-8
❑ 73PicCle-9
❑ 73PicCle-10
❑ 73PicCle-11
❑ 73PicCle-12
❑ 73Top-50
❑ 74LauAllG-62
❑ 75OPC-204
❑ 75TCMAllG-5
❑ 75Top-204
❑ 75TopMin-204
❑ 76GalBasGHoF-5
❑ 76ShaPiz-135
❑ 76Spo-C
❑ 77BobParHoF-81
❑ 77GalGloG-41
❑ 77GalGloG-252
❑ 77PirTCM1WC-6
❑ 77SerSta-6
❑ 77Spo-3201
❑ 77Spo-6116
❑ 78DexHaloFP-4
❑ 78TCM60I-13
❑ 79TCM50-23
❑ 80LauFamF-21
❑ 80PacLeg-50
❑ 80PerHaloFP-135
❑ 80PirGreT-5
❑ 80SSPHOF-135
❑ 82BasCarN-10
❑ 82BHCRSpoL-8
❑ 82DiaCla-74
❑ 82K-M-10
❑ 82TCMGreH-4
❑ 82TCMStaot5-1
❑ 83DonHOFH-17
❑ 83KelCerB-7
❑ 83MLBPin-22
❑ 83Oco& SSBG-7
❑ 84OCoandSI-60
❑ 84OCoandSI-77
❑ 84OCoandSI-129
❑ 84SpoDesPW-3
❑ 84WilMay-19
❑ 86ChaRaiP-7
❑ 86PirGreT-7
❑ 86SpoDecG-43
❑ 86SpoDesJM-18
❑ 86TCM-1
❑ 86TCMSupS-6
❑ 87Don-612
❑ 87DonAllB-PUZ
❑ 87DonSupD-NNO
❑ 87DonWaxBC-PUZ
❑ 87HygAllG-8
❑ 87K-M-2
❑ 87Lea-163
❑ 87NesDreT-27
❑ 87Pir196T-4
❑ 87SpoRea-27
❑ 87Top-313
❑ 87TopTif-313
❑ 88GreBasS-73
❑ 89CMCBasG-1

❑ 89HOFStiB-46
❑ 89PacLegI-135
❑ 89SweBasG-125
❑ 89TopBasT-38
❑ 89USPLegSC-1
❑ 90AGFA-8
❑ 90Col-35
❑ 90PerGreM-32
❑ 90RinPosC-1
❑ 90RinPosC-2
❑ 90RinPosC-3
❑ 90RinPosC-4
❑ 90RinPosC-5
❑ 90RinPosC-6
❑ 90RinPosC-7
❑ 90RinPosC-8
❑ 90RinPosC-9
❑ 90RinPosC-10
❑ 90RinPosC-11
❑ 90RinPosC-12
❑ 90SweBasG-20
❑ 91BigLeaCC-1
❑ 91BigLeaCC-2
❑ 91BigLeaCC-3
❑ 91BigLeaCC-4
❑ 91BigLeaCC-5
❑ 91BigLeaCC-6
❑ 91BigLeaCC-7
❑ 91BigLeaCC-8
❑ 91BigLeaCC-9
❑ 91BigLeaCC-10
❑ 91BigLeaCC-11
❑ 91BigLeaCC-12
❑ 91BigLeaCC-13
❑ 91BigLeaCC-14
❑ 91BigLeaCC-15
❑ 91BigLeaCC-16
❑ 91BigLeaCC-17
❑ 91BigLeaCC-18
❑ 91BigLeaCC-19
❑ 91CadEIID-10
❑ 91HomCooC-7
❑ 91KelLey-6
❑ 91LinDri-39
❑ 91SweBasG-132
❑ 91USGamSBL-11C
❑ 91USGamSBL-11D
❑ 91USGamSBL-11H
❑ 91USGamSBL-11S
❑ 92PMGol-3
❑ 92RevLeg1-7
❑ 92RevLeg1-8
❑ 92RevLeg1-9
❑ 93ActPacA-119
❑ 93ActPacA2-53G
❑ 93Ble-8
❑ 93CadDis-12
❑ 93CitPriC-1
❑ 93CitPriC-2
❑ 93CitPriC-3
❑ 93CitPriC-4
❑ 93CitPriC-5
❑ 93CitPriC-6
❑ 93LegFoi-1
❑ 93TedWilM-11
❑ 93TedWilRC-1
❑ 93TedWilRC-2
❑ 93TedWilRC-3
❑ 93TedWilRC-4
❑ 93TedWilRC-5
❑ 93TedWilRC-6
❑ 93TedWilRC-7
❑ 93TedWilRC-8
❑ 93TedWilRC-9
❑ 93TedWilRC-10
❑ 93ZCle-1
❑ 93ZCle-2
❑ 93ZCle-3
❑ 93ZCle-4
❑ 93ZCle-5
❑ 93ZCle-6
❑ 93ZCle-7
❑ 93ZCle-8
❑ 93ZCle-9
❑ 93ZCle-10
❑ 94ActPac-67
❑ 94ActPac-68
❑ 94ActPac-69
❑ 94ActPac-70
❑ 94ActPac-71
❑ 94FanCle-1
❑ 94FanCle-2
❑ 94FanCle-3
❑ 94FanCle-4
❑ 94FanCle-5
❑ 94KelCle-1
❑ 94KelCle-2
❑ 94KelCle-3
❑ 94TopArc1-251
❑ 94TopArc1G-251
❑ 94UppDecTAE-72
❑ 94UppDecTAEGM-2
❑ 94WenCle-1
❑ 94Yoo-5
❑ 95PirCocP-2
❑ 95PirCocP-3
❑ 95TopArcBD-82
❑ 95TopLegot6M-8
❑ 97HigMinM-32
❑ 97St.VinHHS-6
❑ 98Top-21
❑ 98TopChr-21
❑ 98TopChrR-21
❑ 98TopCleF-1
❑ 98TopCleF-2
❑ 98TopCleF-3
❑ 98TopCleF-4
❑ 98TopCleF-5
❑ 98TopCleF-6
❑ 98TopCleF-7
❑ 98TopCleF-8
❑ 98TopCleF-9
❑ 98TopCleF-10
❑ 98TopCleF-11
❑ 98TopCleF-12
❑ 98TopCleF-13
❑ 98TopCleF-14
❑ 98TopCleF-15
❑ 98TopCleF-16
❑ 98TopCleF-17
❑ 98TopCleF-18
❑ 98TopCleF-19
❑ 98TopCleFR-1
❑ 98TopCleFR-2
❑ 98TopCleFR-3
❑ 98TopCleFR-4
❑ 98TopCleFR-5
❑ 98TopCleFR-6
❑ 98TopCleFR-7
❑ 98TopCleFR-8
❑ 98TopCleFR-9
❑ 98TopCleFR-10
❑ 98TopCleFR-11
❑ 98TopCleFR-12
❑ 98TopCleFR-13
❑ 98TopCleFR-14
❑ 98TopCleFR-15
❑ 98TopCleFR-16
❑ 98TopCleFR-17
❑ 98TopCleFR-18
❑ 98TopCleFR-19
❑ 98TopCleMMad-1
❑ 98TopCleMMad-2
❑ 98TopCleMMad-3
❑ 98TopCleMMad-4
❑ 98TopCleMMad-5
❑ 98TopCleMMad-6
❑ 98TopCleMMad-7
❑ 98TopCleMMad-8
❑ 98TopCleMMad-9
❑ 98TopCleMMad-10
❑ 98TopCleMMad-11
❑ 98TopCleMMad-12
❑ 98TopCleMMad-13
❑ 98TopCleMMad-14
❑ 98TopCleMMad-15
❑ 98TopCleMMad-16
❑ 98TopCleMMad-17
❑ 98TopCleMMad-18
❑ 98TopCleMMad-19
❑ 98TopCleMMad-20
❑ 98TopCleMMad-21
❑ 98TopCleMMad-22
❑ 98TopCleMMad-23
❑ 98TopCleMMad-24
❑ 98TopCleMMad-25
❑ 98TopCleMMad-26
❑ 98TopCleMMad-27
❑ 98TopCleMMad-28
❑ 98TopCleMMad-29
❑ 98TopCleMMad-30
❑ 98TopCleMMad-31
❑ 98TopCleMMad-32
❑ 98TopCleMMad-33
❑ 98TopCleMMad-34
❑ 98TopCleMMad-35
❑ 98TopCleMMad-36
❑ 98TopCleMMad-37
❑ 98TopCleMMad-38
❑ 98TopCleMMad-39
❑ 98TopCleMMad-40
❑ 98TopCleMMad-41
❑ 98TopCleMMad-42
❑ 98TopCleMMad-43
❑ 98TopCleMMad-44
❑ 98TopCleMMad-45
❑ 98TopCleMMad-46
❑ 98TopCleR-1
❑ 98TopCleR-2
❑ 98TopCleR-3
❑ 98TopCleR-4
❑ 98TopCleR-5
❑ 98TopCleR-6
❑ 98TopCleR-7
❑ 98TopCleR-8
❑ 98TopCleR-9
❑ 98TopCleR-10
❑ 98TopCleR-11
❑ 98TopCleR-12
❑ 98TopCleR-13
❑ 98TopCleR-14
❑ 98TopCleR-15
❑ 98TopCleR-16
❑ 98TopCleR-17
❑ 98TopCleR-18
❑ 98TopCleR-19
❑ 98TopCleS-1
❑ 98TopCleS-2
❑ 98TopCleS-3
❑ 98TopCleS-4
❑ 98TopCleS-5
❑ 98TopCleS-6
❑ 98TopCleS-7
❑ 98TopCleS-8
❑ 98TopCleS-9
❑ 98TopCleS-10
❑ 98TopCleS-11
❑ 98TopCleS-12
❑ 98TopCleS-13
❑ 98TopCleS-14
❑ 98TopCleS-15
❑ 98TopCleS-16
❑ 98TopCleS-17
❑ 98TopCleS-18
❑ 98TopCleS-19
❑ 98TopCleT-RC1
❑ 98TopCleT-RC2
❑ 98TopCleT-RC3
❑ 98TopCleT-RC4
❑ 98TopCleT-RC5
❑ 98TopCleTin-1
❑ 98TopCleTin-2
❑ 98TopCleTin-3
❑ 98TopCleTin-4
❑ 98TopDevR-21
❑ 98TopDia-21
❑ 98TopMiniC-21
❑ 98TopOpeD-21
❑ 98TopSup-21
❑ 99UppDecCL-20
❑ 99UppDecCL-123
❑ 99UppDecCLCC-20
❑ 99UppDecCLCC-123

Clements, Dave
❑ 83SprCarF-2
❑ 84ArkTraT-2
❑ 85LouRedR-14
❑ 86ArkTraP-5

Clements, Ed (Edward)
❑ 87OldJudN-84
❑ 89PacSenL-54

Clements, Jack (John T.)
❑ 74CapPub-81
❑ 87BucN28-77
❑ 88SpoTimM-5
❑ 88WG1CarG-49
❑ 90KalBatN-7
❑ 98CamPepP-13

Clements, Pat
❑ 85AngSmo-22
❑ 85FleUpd-26
❑ 85TopTifT-23T
❑ 85TopTra-23T
❑ 86Don-600
❑ 86Fle-606
❑ 86OPC-283
❑ 86Top-754
❑ 86TopTif-754
❑ 87Don-390
❑ 87Fle-608
❑ 87FleGlo-608
❑ 87Top-16
❑ 87TopTif-16
❑ 88ColCliC-1
❑ 88ColCliP-1
❑ 88ColCliP-318
❑ 88Don-52
❑ 88Fle-204
❑ 88FleGlo-204
❑ 88Sco-389
❑ 88ScoGlo-389
❑ 88StaLinY-3
❑ 88Top-484
❑ 88TopTif-484
❑ 89Bow-452
❑ 89BowTif-452
❑ 89LasVegSP-15
❑ 89PadPos-7
❑ 89Top-159
❑ 89TopTif-159
❑ 90Fle-153
❑ 90FleCan-153
❑ 90OPC-548
❑ 90Top-548
❑ 90TopTif-548
❑ 91LasVegSP-227
❑ 91PadSmo-5
❑ 92Bow-533
❑ 92Fle-602
❑ 92PadMot-23
❑ 92PadSmo-6
❑ 92Sco-714
❑ 92YanWIZ8-33
❑ 93RocRedWF-232

Clements, Tony
❑ 87EugEmeP-2667
❑ 91LinDriAA-403
❑ 91MemChiLD-403

Clements, Wes
❑ 83TucTorT-14
❑ 84TucTorC-53
❑ 85BelBreT-14
❑ 87GleFalTP-5
❑ 89PacSenL-176

Clemo, Scott
❑ 86JamExpP-3
❑ 87IndIndTI-28
❑ 88WesPalBES-7

Clemons, Chris
❑ 94SigRooDP-31
❑ 94SigRooDPS-31
❑ 95PriWilCTI-17
❑ 95Top-551
❑ 96PriWilCB-7
❑ 97Bow-330
❑ 97BowChr-226
❑ 97BowChrI-226
❑ 97BowChrIR-226
❑ 97BowChrR-226
❑ 97BowInt-330
❑ 98ColCho-63
❑ 98DiaBacP-1
❑ 98Fle-143
❑ 98Sco-96
❑ 98TusSidM-7
❑ 98UppDecDS-DS56
❑ 98WhiSoxS-6
❑ 98WhiSoxSP-6

Clemons, Lance
❑ 72OPC-372
❑ 72Top-372

Clemons, Mark
❑ 85KinBluJT-1
❑ 86OrlTwiP-4
❑ 87OrlTwiP-10
❑ 88JacExpB-8
❑ 88JacExpP-977

Clemons, Robert
❑ 12ColRedB-55
❑ 12ColTinT-55
❑ 13Zee-27

Clemons, Verne James
❑ 21Nei-85
❑ 22E120-227
❑ 22W573-19
❑ 23WilChoV-19

Clendenon, Donn Alvin
❑ 62Top-86
❑ 62TopVen-86
❑ 63Kah-7
❑ 63PirIDL-5
❑ 63PirJayP-4
❑ 63Top-477
❑ 64Kah-5
❑ 64PirKDK-8
❑ 64Top-163
❑ 64TopCoi-15
❑ 64TopSta-76
❑ 64TopStaU-18
❑ 64TopVen-163
❑ 65Kah-8
❑ 65Top-325
❑ 65TopEmbl-9
❑ 66OPC-99
❑ 66PirEasH-17
❑ 66Top-99
❑ 66Top-375
❑ 66TopVen-99
❑ 67CokCapPi-3
❑ 67DexPre-52
❑ 67PirTeal-5
❑ 67Top-266
❑ 67Top-535
❑ 67TopPirS-7
❑ 67TopPirS-30
❑ 68PirKDK-17
❑ 68PirTeal-6
❑ 68Top-344
❑ 68TopVen-344
❑ 69MetNewYDN-4
❑ 69MilBra-61
❑ 69OPC-208
❑ 69Top-208A
❑ 69Top-208B
❑ 69TopDecl-7
❑ 69TopFou-3
❑ 69TopSta-54
❑ 69TopTeaP-6
❑ 70DayDaiNM-142
❑ 70MetTeal-3
❑ 70MetTra-25C
❑ 70MLBOffS-74
❑ 70OPC-280
❑ 70OPC-306
❑ 70Top-280
❑ 70Top-306
❑ 71CarTeal-10
❑ 71MetTeal-3
❑ 71MetTealC-4
❑ 71MLBOffS-149
❑ 71OPC-115
❑ 71Top-115
❑ 71TopCoi-151
❑ 71TopSup-4
❑ 71TopTat-47
❑ 72CarTeal-4
❑ 72MilBra-76
❑ 72Top-671
❑ 78TCM60I-237
❑ 89Met196C-2
❑ 89MetRinP69-7
❑ 90SweBasG-82
❑ 91MetWIZ-77
❑ 91UppDecS-8
❑ 94Met69CCPP-11
❑ 94Met69CS-10
❑ 94Met69T-10
❑ 94Met69T-38
❑ 96Met69Y-2

Cleto, Ambioris
❑ 98EriSeaWM-7

Cleveland, Elmer E.
❑ 87OldJudN-85

Cleveland, Reggie
❑ 70Top-716
❑ 71CarTeal-9
❑ 71CarTeal-11
❑ 71OPC-216
❑ 71Top-216
❑ 72OPC-375
❑ 72Top-375
❑ 73OPC-104
❑ 73Top-104
❑ 74OPC-175
❑ 74Top-175
❑ 74TopSta-112
❑ 74TopTra-175T
❑ 75OPC-32
❑ 75Top-32
❑ 75TopMin-32
❑ 76OPC-419
❑ 76RedSoxSM-2
❑ 76Top-419
❑ 77OPC-111
❑ 77Top-613
❑ 78RanBurK-10
❑ 78SSP270-165
❑ 78Top-105
❑ 79OPC-103
❑ 79Top-209
❑ 80BreTeal-6
❑ 80Top-394
❑ 81Don-206
❑ 81Fle-523
❑ 81Top-576
❑ 82Don-456
❑ 82Fle-137
❑ 82Top-122
❑ 82Top-737
❑ 91PacSenL-61
❑ 91PacSenL-79
❑ 92St.CatBJC-28
❑ 93RanKee-104
❑ 93St.CatBJC-28
❑ 94BreMilB-211
❑ 94HagSunC-27
❑ 94HagSunF-2747
❑ 95HagSunF-85

Clevenger, Tex
❑ 58SeaTeal-8
❑ 58SenJayP-2
❑ 58Top-31
❑ 59SenTealW-4
❑ 59Top-298
❑ 60SenJayP-3
❑ 60Top-392
❑ 61Top-291
❑ 61Yan61RL-18
❑ 63Top-457
❑ 83Yan196-18
❑ 92YanWIZ6-25

Cleverly, Gary
❑ 75SanAntBT-5

Cliburn, Stan (Stanley Gene)
❑ 75QuaCitAT-5
❑ 76QuaCitAT-11
❑ 78SalLakCGC-14
❑ 82PorBeaT-10
❑ 83LynPirT-11
❑ 84HawIsIC-132
❑ 85HawIsIC-242
❑ 86EdmTraP-5
❑ 86EdmTraP-6
❑ 87RicBraC-29
❑ 87RicBraT-28
❑ 88BufBisC-24
❑ 88BufBisP-1480
❑ 88WatPirP-31
❑ 89AugPirP-514
❑ 89PacSenL-150
❑ 89SouAtlLAGS-1
❑ 89TopSenL-54
❑ 90SalBucS-25
❑ 91PacSenL-30
❑ 91PacSenL-51
❑ 91SalBucC-25
❑ 91SalBucP-968
❑ 92GasRanC-26
❑ 92GasRanF-2269
❑ 93TulDriF-2749
❑ 93TulDriTI-5
❑ 94TulDriF-258
❑ 94TulDriTI-26

Cliburn, Stewart
❑ 77SalPirT-6
❑ 79BufBisT-2
❑ 80PorBeaT-13
❑ 80VenLeaS-126
❑ 81BufBisT-9
❑ 83NasAngT-3
❑ 84EdmTraC-113
❑ 85DomLeaS-59
❑ 85EdmTraC-19
❑ 85FleUpd-27
❑ 86Don-301
❑ 86EdmTraP-7
❑ 86Fle-152
❑ 86SevCoi-W16
❑ 86Spo-177
❑ 86Top-179
❑ 86TopTif-179
❑ 87CalAngPPS-6
❑ 87Don-530
❑ 88AngSmo-19
❑ 89Don-462
❑ 89EdmTraC-7
❑ 89EdmTraP-566
❑ 89Fle-471
❑ 89FleGlo-471
❑ 89Sco-445
❑ 89Top-649
❑ 89TopTif-649
❑ 89UppDec-483
❑ 91PacSenL-29
❑ 91PacSenL-51
❑ 91PalSprAP-2034
❑ 92CalLeaACL-51
❑ 92PalSprAC-30
❑ 92PalSprAF-856
❑ 93EliTwiC-23

❑ 93EliTwiF-3431
❑ 94ForWayWC-27
❑ 94ForWayWF-2026
❑ 95ForWayWTI-27
❑ 96ForWayWB-28
❑ 97ForWayW-3
❑ 98ForMyeMTI-8
Clifford, Eric
❑ 95EveAqaTI-4
Clifford, James
❑ 92BelMarCB-22
❑ 92BelMarF-1450
❑ 93BelMarCB-9
❑ 93BelMarF-3215
❑ 94AppFoxC-4
❑ 94AppFoxFI-1059
❑ 96LanJetB-9
❑ 97LanJet-10
Clifford, Jeff
❑ 90SouOreAB-13
❑ 90SouOreAP-3440
Clifford, John
❑ 96AshTouB-9
❑ 97PorRocG-5
❑ 97SalAva-10
Clifford, Neal
❑ 37Zee-67
Clift, Harland Benton
❑ 36ExhFou-15
❑ 36NatChiFPR-115
❑ 36OveCanR-8
❑ 37ExhFou-15
❑ 37OPCBatUV-104
❑ 37WheBB9-3
❑ 38CloFotW-13
❑ 38ExhFou-15
❑ 39ExhSal-8
❑ 41BroW75-6
❑ 41DouPlaR-147
❑ 41Gou-2
❑ 41PlaBal-66
❑ 53SanFraSTI-4
❑ 77TCMTheWY-8
❑ 77TCMTheWY-60
❑ 79DiaGre-58
❑ 82DiaCla-109
❑ 83TCMPla1943-15
❑ 93DiaStaES-122
❑ 94ConTSN-1124
❑ 94ConTSNB-1124
Clifton, Flea (Herman Earl)
❑ 35DiaMatCS3T1-33
❑ 36GouWidPPR-B5
❑ 36WorWidGV-32
❑ 39WorWidGV-5
❑ 74TigTCM1AC-4
❑ 76TigOldTS-3
Clifton, Rodney
❑ 97SouOreTB-10
❑ 98ModA'sG-6
Clinatis, Mike
❑ 76CedRapGT-10
Cline, Monk (John)
❑ 87OldJudN-86
Cline, Pat
❑ 93HunCubC-6
❑ 93HunCubF-3237
❑ 95MidLeaA-9
❑ 95RocCubTI-23
❑ 96Bow-257
❑ 96BowFoi-257
❑ 96DayCubB-8
❑ 96Exc-136
❑ 97Bes-62
❑ 97Bow-164
❑ 97BowBes-123
❑ 97BowBesAR-123
❑ 97BowBesR-123
❑ 97BowChr-160
❑ 97BowChrI-160
❑ 97BowChrIR-160
❑ 97BowChrR-160
❑ 97BowInt-164
❑ 97ColCho-473
❑ 97FlaShoWotF-5
❑ 97Fle-674
❑ 97FleTif-674
❑ 97OrlRayB-7
❑ 97OrlRayB-30
❑ 97SouLeaTP-28
❑ 97Ult-544
❑ 97UltGolME-544
❑ 97UltPlaME-544
❑ 98Bes-11
❑ 98Bow-94
❑ 98BowChr-94
❑ 98BowChrGA-94
❑ 98BowChrGAR-94
❑ 98BowChrI-94
❑ 98BowChrIR-94
❑ 98BowChrR-94
❑ 98BowGolA-94
❑ 98BowInt-94
❑ 98Don-328
❑ 98DonGolPP-328
❑ 98DonSigA-19
❑ 98DonSigAC-27
❑ 98DonSigAM-27
❑ 98DonSilPP-328
❑ 98IowCubQ-7
❑ 98LeaRS-246
❑ 98LeaRSLHolo-246
❑ 98LeaRSLong-246
❑ 98LeaRTrue-246
❑ 98PinSna-CC14
❑ 98SP MinPE-32
❑ 98SPMin-32
❑ 98UppDec-259
❑ 99Bow-95
❑ 99BowChr-95
❑ 99BowChrG-95
❑ 99BowChrGR-95
❑ 99BowChrI-95
❑ 99BowChrIR-95
❑ 99BowChrR-95
❑ 99BowGol-95
❑ 99BowInt-95
❑ 99Top-209
❑ 99TopChr-209
❑ 99TopChrR-209
Cline, Steve
❑ 75CedRapGT-3
❑ 81CliGiaT-3
❑ 82CliGiaF-3
❑ 84ShrCapFB-4
❑ 88ShrCapP-1286
❑ 89ShrCapP-1837
❑ 90CliGiaB-10
❑ 90CliGiaP-2566
❑ 91CliGiaC-27
❑ 91CliGiaP-853
❑ 92ShrCapF-3888
❑ 93ShrCapF-2776
❑ 94ShrCapF-1624
❑ 95PhoFirTI-32
❑ 96OgdRapTI-32
Cline, Ty (Tyrone A.)
❑ 61Top-421
❑ 62Kah-6
❑ 62Top-362
❑ 62TopStal-32
❑ 63Jel-74
❑ 63Pos-74
❑ 63Top-414
❑ 64Top-171
❑ 64TopVen-171
❑ 65BraTeal-3
❑ 65OPC-63
❑ 65Top-63
❑ 66Top-306
❑ 66TopVen-306
❑ 67BraPho-8
❑ 67CokCapB-2
❑ 67DexPre-53
❑ 67Top-591
❑ 68Top-469
❑ 69MilBra-62
❑ 69MLBOffS-156
❑ 69Top-442
❑ 70DayDaiNM-99
❑ 70MLBOffS-64
❑ 70OPC-164
❑ 70Top-164
❑ 71MLBOffS-54
❑ 71OPC-199
❑ 71OPC-201
❑ 71OPC-319
❑ 71Top-199
❑ 71Top-201
❑ 71Top-319
❑ 72MilBra-77
❑ 78AtlCon-6
❑ 78TCM60I-149
❑ 78TCM60I-191
Clines, Gene (Eugene)
❑ 71OPC-27
❑ 71PirActP-14
❑ 71Top-27
❑ 72OPC-152
❑ 72Top-152
❑ 73OPC-333
❑ 73Top-333
❑ 74OPC-172
❑ 74Top-172
❑ 75MetSSP-17
❑ 75OPC-575
❑ 75Top-575
❑ 75TopMin-575
❑ 76CubTri-6
❑ 76OPC-417
❑ 76SSP-543
❑ 76Top-417
❑ 77CubJewT-5
❑ 77Top-237
❑ 78SSP270-253
❑ 78Top-639
❑ 79Top-171
❑ 88AstMot-27
❑ 89MarMot-27
❑ 89PacSenL-146
❑ 89T/MSenL-21
❑ 90MarMot-27
❑ 91MetWIZ-78
❑ 92MarMot-27
❑ 93RanKee-105
❑ 98GiaMot-28
Clinkscales, Sherard
❑ 92ClaDraP-22
❑ 92ClaFS7-414
❑ 92EugEmeC-1
❑ 92EugEmeF-3018
❑ 92FroRowDP-3
❑ 92FroRowDPG-3
❑ 92FroRowDPS-3
❑ 93ClaGolF-184
❑ 93RocRoyC-7
❑ 93RocRoyF-707
❑ 93StaCluM-6
❑ 93Top-706
❑ 93TopGol-706
❑ 93TopInaM-706
❑ 93TopInaR-706
❑ 93TopMic-706
❑ 94ClaGolF-146
Clinton, Barry
❑ 86ColCliP-21
Clinton, Bill
❑ 93TriPla-32
❑ 94UppDecTAE-78
Clinton, Jim (James)
❑ 89ButCopKSP-11
❑ 90GasRanB-24
❑ 90GasRanP-2527
❑ 90GasRanS-5
❑ 91ChaRanP-1320
❑ 92ChaRanC-15
❑ 92ChaRanF-2231
❑ 93ChaRanC-4
❑ 93TulDriF-2738
❑ 94TulDriF-249
❑ 94TulDriTI-3
❑ 95TulDriTI-5
Clinton, Lu (Luciean L.)
❑ 60Top-533
❑ 61UniOil-S2
❑ 62Top-457
❑ 63Fle-6
❑ 63Jel-82
❑ 63Pos-82
❑ 63Top-96
❑ 64Top-526
❑ 65OPC-229
❑ 65Top-229
❑ 67Top-426
❑ 81RedSoxBG2S-74
❑ 92YanWIZ6-26
Clipper, Chipper the
❑ 91BatCliCB-29
Clippers, Columbus
❑ 87IntLeaAT-39
❑ 88ColCliP-330
❑ 91ColCliP-613
Clisanchez, Gilberto
❑ 93LinVenB-44
❑ 94VenLinU-116
Cloherty, John
❑ 78DayBeaAT-5
Cloninger, Darin
❑ 85AlbYanT-3
Cloninger, Greg
❑ 88SumBraP-406
❑ 89BurBraP-1601
❑ 89BurBraS-4
Cloninger, Todd
❑ 86GenCubP-2
❑ 87WinSpiP-3
Cloninger, Tom
❑ 87OneYanP-33
Cloninger, Tony
❑ 62Top-63
❑ 62TopVen-63
❑ 63Jel-157
❑ 63Pos-157
❑ 63Top-367
❑ 64BraJayP-4
❑ 64Top-575
❑ 65Kah-9
❑ 65Top-520
❑ 66Baz-27
❑ 66BraPos-9
❑ 66Kah-9
❑ 66OPC-10
❑ 66Top-10
❑ 66Top-223
❑ 66TopRubI-19
❑ 66TopVen-10
❑ 66TopVen-223
❑ 67Baz-27
❑ 67BraPho-9
❑ 67CokCapB-5
❑ 67DexPre-54
❑ 67Kah-9
❑ 67Top-396
❑ 67Top-490
❑ 68BraPos-9
❑ 68CokCapB-5
❑ 68DexPre-25
❑ 68OPC-93
❑ 68Top-93
❑ 68TopVen-93
❑ 69Kah-B7
❑ 69MLBOffS-128
❑ 69Top-492
❑ 70DayDaiNM-97
❑ 70MLBOffS-26
❑ 70Top-705
❑ 71CarTeal-12
❑ 71MLBOffS-55
❑ 71OPC-218
❑ 71Top-218
❑ 72CarTeal-5
❑ 72Top-779
❑ 78AtlCon-7
❑ 78TCM60I-20
❑ 88AlbYanP-1353
❑ 90HOFStiB-70
❑ 91PacSenL-31
Clontz, Brad
❑ 92PulBraC-13
❑ 92PulBraF-3170
❑ 93ClaFS7-2
❑ 93DurBulC-6
❑ 93DurBulF-480
❑ 93DurBulTI-14
❑ 94Bow-641
❑ 94GreBraF-407
❑ 94GreBraTI-9
❑ 95Exc-148
❑ 95ExcLeaL-5
❑ 95Fin-247
❑ 95FinRef-247
❑ 95Fla-322
❑ 95FleAllR-M5
❑ 95Lea-319
❑ 95SigRooOJHP-HP2
❑ 95SigRooOJHPS-HP2
❑ 95StaClu-568
❑ 95StaCluMOP-568
❑ 95StaCluSTWS-568
❑ 95Sum-151
❑ 95SumNthD-151
❑ 95Top-369
❑ 95TopTra-132T
❑ 95UltGolMR-M8
❑ 95UppDec-245
❑ 95UppDecED-245
❑ 95UppDecEDG-245
❑ 96BraFle-3
❑ 96ColCho-454
❑ 96ColChoGS-454
❑ 96ColChoSS-454
❑ 96Don-288
❑ 96DonPreP-288
❑ 96Fla-196
❑ 96Fle-289
❑ 96FleTif-289
❑ 96Ult-153
❑ 96UltGolM-153
❑ 96UppDec-274
❑ 97Fle-253
❑ 97FleTif-253
❑ 97Top-224
❑ 98NorTidQ-7
Close, Casey
❑ 88ColCliC-21
❑ 88ColCliP-19
❑ 88ColCliP-325
❑ 90CalCanC-19
❑ 90CalCanP-661
❑ 90CMC-446
❑ 90ProAAAF-126
Clossen, Bill
❑ 86DurBulP-4
❑ 87PriWilYP-15
Closser, J.D.
❑ 99Bow-305
❑ 99BowGol-305
❑ 99BowInt-305
Closter, Alan
❑ 66Top-549
❑ 69OPC-114
❑ 69Top-114
❑ 69TopFou-24
❑ 72OPC-124
❑ 72Top-124
❑ 73OPC-634
❑ 73SyrChiTI-6
❑ 73Top-634
❑ 92YanWIZ7-35
Clothery, John
❑ 76DubPacT-6
Clotile, Mascot
❑ 98NewOrlZM-27
Cloud, David
❑ 94DavLipB-25
❑ 95DavLipB-6
Cloud, Tony
❑ 96BilMusTI-5
Cloude, Ken
❑ 96LanJetB-10
❑ 97Bow-396
❑ 97BowBes-162
❑ 97BowBesAR-162
❑ 97BowBesR-162
❑ 97BowChr-262
❑ 97BowChrI-262
❑ 97BowChrIR-262
❑ 97BowChrR-262
❑ 97BowInt-396
❑ 97SouLeaTP-22
❑ 97TexAllM-9
❑ 98Bow-172
❑ 98BowChr-172
❑ 98BowChrGA-172
❑ 98BowChrGAR-172
❑ 98BowChrI-172
❑ 98BowChrIR-172
❑ 98BowChrR-172
❑ 98BowGolA-172
❑ 98BowInt-172
❑ 98ColCho-104
❑ 98ColChoSQ-SQ14
❑ 98Don-269
❑ 98DonGolPP-269
❑ 98DonSigA-20
❑ 98DonSigAC-28
❑ 98DonSigAM-28
❑ 98DonSilPP-269
❑ 98Fle-282
❑ 98LeaRS-277
❑ 98LeaRSLHolo-277
❑ 98LeaRSLong-277
❑ 98LeaRTrue-277
❑ 98Pac-182
❑ 98PacInv-62
❑ 98PacInvPBlue-62
❑ 98PacInvSilv-62
❑ 98PacOme-218
❑ 98PacOmeR-218
❑ 98PacOnl-680
❑ 98PacOnlR-680
❑ 98PacOnlWC-680
❑ 98PacPlaB-182
❑ 98PacRedT-182
❑ 98PacSil-182
❑ 98PinSna-SM17
❑ 98SP Aut-181
❑ 98SpoIll-173
❑ 98SpoIllEE-173
❑ 98SpoIllFE-173
❑ 98SPxFin-4
❑ 98SPxFinR-4
❑ 98SPxFinS-4
❑ 98StaCluFDI-230
❑ 98StaCluI-230
❑ 98StaCluOneK-230
❑ 98StaCluPP-230
❑ 98Stu-67
❑ 98StuGPP-67
❑ 98StuSPP-67
❑ 98Top-369
❑ 98TopChr-369
❑ 98TopChrR-369
❑ 98TopDevR-369
❑ 98TopDia-369
❑ 98TopMiniC-369
❑ 98Ult-348
❑ 98UltGolM-348
❑ 98UltMas-348
❑ 98UltPlaM-348
❑ 98UppDec-282
❑ 98UppDecDS-DS58
❑ 99Fle-367
❑ 99FleSta9-367
❑ 99FleWarT-367
❑ 99Pac-393
❑ 99PacPlaB-393
❑ 99PacRed-393
❑ 99UppDec-202
❑ 99UppDecEL1-202
❑ 99UppDecEL2-202
Clough, Walt
❑ 53SanFraSTI-5
Clougherty, Pat
❑ 93BazTeaU-8
❑ 93TopTra-34T
Clowns, Indianapolis
❑ 92NegLeaRLI-76
❑ 92NegLeaRLI-99
❑ 93NegLeaRL2-92
❑ 93NegLeaRL2-93
Club, Lachine
❑ 28LaPre-2
Cluck, Bob
❑ 74CedRapAT-22
❑ 75DubPacT-10
❑ 76DubPacT-7
❑ 81TucTorT-5
❑ 84LasVegSC-239
❑ 85LasVegSC-110
❑ 90AstMot-27
❑ 91AstMot-28
❑ 92AstMot-27
❑ 93AstMot-28
❑ 96A'sMot-28
❑ 97A'sMot-28
Cluff, Paul
❑ 87BriYouC-14
❑ 89BoiHawP-2006
Clutterbuck, Bryan
❑ 82BelBreFr-20
❑ 83ElPasDT-15
❑ 84ElPasDT-5
❑ 85VanCanC-222
❑ 86VanCanP-7
❑ 87DenZepP-23
❑ 87Don-397
❑ 87Fle-342
❑ 87FleGlo-342
❑ 87Top-562
❑ 87TopTif-562
❑ 89BrePol-48
❑ 89TopTra-21T
❑ 89TopTraT-21T
❑ 90OPC-264
❑ 90Top-264
❑ 90TopTif-264
❑ 90UppDec-239
❑ 94BreMilB-212
Clyburn, Danny
❑ 92ClaDraP-32
❑ 92ClaFS7-422
❑ 92FroRowDP-18
❑ 92FroRowDPG-18
❑ 92FroRowDPS-18
❑ 93AugPirC-5
❑ 93AugPirF-1558
❑ 93Bow-542
❑ 93ClaFS7-98
❑ 93ClaGolF-194
❑ 93SouAtlLAGF-32
❑ 93StaCluM-12
❑ 94Bow-406
❑ 94CarLeaAF-CAR37
❑ 94Cla-12
❑ 94SalBucC-1
❑ 94SalBucF-2336
❑ 94UppDecML-76
❑ 94UppDecMLPotYF-PY19
❑ 95Exc-251
❑ 95SPML-16
❑ 95UppDecML-33
❑ 95UppDecMLFS-33

❑ 96BowBayB-12
❑ 96MauStiHWB-20
❑ 97Bow-315
❑ 97BowChr-217
❑ 97BowChrl-217
❑ 97BowChrIR-217
❑ 97BowChrR-217
❑ 97BowInt-315
❑ 97RocRedW-8
❑ 98Fle-284
❑ 98LeaRS-254
❑ 98LeaRSLHolo-254
❑ 98LeaRSLong-254
❑ 98LeaRTrue-254
❑ 98RocRedWQ-8
❑ 98UppDec-273
❑ 99Pac-49
❑ 99Pac-49A
❑ 99PacPlaB-49
❑ 99PacPlaB-49A
❑ 99PacRed-49
❑ 99PacRed-49A

Clyde, David
❑ 73LinPor-174
❑ 73RanTeal-7
❑ 74OPC-133
❑ 74Top-133
❑ 74TopSta-233
❑ 75OPC-12
❑ 75Top-12
❑ 75TopMin-12
❑ 76LauDiaJ-19
❑ 76SacSolC-21
❑ 77TucTorC-32
❑ 78IndTeal-4
❑ 79Top-399
❑ 80Top-697
❑ 93RanKee-106
❑ 99SpollIGotG-76
❑ 99SpollIGotGA-18

Clymer, Otis Edgar
❑ 08RosComP-76
❑ 09ColChiE-56
❑ 09MaxPubP-21
❑ 09RamT20-26
❑ 09SenBarP-1
❑ 11SpoLifCW-66
❑ 12ColRedB-56
❑ 12ColTinT-56

Clymer, William J.
❑ 09T206-411
❑ 19Zee-109

Coach, Calvin
❑ 94JohCitCC-6
❑ 94JohCitCF-3716

Coachman, Pete
❑ 86PalSprAP-7
❑ 86PalSprAS-22
❑ 87EdmTraP-2073
❑ 88EdmTraC-13
❑ 88EdmTraP-578
❑ 89EdmTraC-12
❑ 89EdmTraP-563
❑ 90CMC-497
❑ 90EdmTraC-20
❑ 90EdmTraP-522
❑ 90ProAAAF-98
❑ 91LinDriAAA-531
❑ 91Sco-344
❑ 91TacTigLD-531
❑ 91TacTigP-2311
❑ 91TopDeb90-32

Coakley, Andrew
❑ 08RosComP-114
❑ 08RosComP-179
❑ 09RamT20-27
❑ 11SpoLifCW-67
❑ 72ClaCar-67

Coan, Gil (Gilbert F.)
❑ 47SenGunBP-11
❑ 49Bow-90
❑ 49MPR302-2-114
❑ 50Bow-54
❑ 51Bow-18
❑ 52Bow-51
❑ 52RedMan-AL4
❑ 52Top-291
❑ 53BowC-34
❑ 53Bri-3
❑ 53Top-133
❑ 54Bow-40
❑ 54OriEss-5
❑ 54OriTeal-4
❑ 55Bow-78
❑ 55OriEss-5
❑ 79DiaGre-74
❑ 83TopRep5-291
❑ 85TCMPla1-34
❑ 88ChaLooLTI-6
❑ 91OriCro-78
❑ 91TopArc1-133
❑ 97BalOriP-9

Coates, Jim
❑ 55DonWin-14
❑ 59Top-525
❑ 60Lea-35
❑ 60Top-51
❑ 60TopVen-51
❑ 61Pos-17
❑ 61Top-531
❑ 61Yan61RL-16
❑ 62Top-553
❑ 63Top-237
❑ 66SeaPop-4
❑ 67SeaPop-3
❑ 67Top-401
❑ 68SeaPop-2
❑ 78TCM60I-217
❑ 78TCM60I-267
❑ 83Yan196-16
❑ 83YanASFY-8
❑ 91YanRinP11-5
❑ 92YanWIZ6-27
❑ 92YanWIZA-12

Coates, Thomas
❑ 91IdaFalBP-4339
❑ 91IdaFalBSP-6
❑ 92PulBraC-7
❑ 92PulBraF-3190
❑ 93DurBulC-7
❑ 93DurBulF-496
❑ 93DurBulTI-19

Coatney, Rick
❑ 81DurBulT-16
❑ 82DurBulT-15

Coats, Nathan
❑ 96WatIndTI-6

Cobb, Mark
❑ 87UtiBluSP-13
❑ 88SpaPhiS-20
❑ 89ClePhiS-7
❑ 89Sta-11

Cobb, Marvin
❑ 88OklSoo-16
❑ 89BenBucL-2
❑ 89OklSoo-9
❑ 90PalSprACLC-219
❑ 90PalSprAP-2570
❑ 91LinDriAA-430
❑ 91MidAngLD-430
❑ 91MidAngOHP-7
❑ 91MidAngP-429
❑ 92MidAngF-4019
❑ 92MidAngS-456
❑ 92SkyAA F-193

Cobb, Mickey
❑ 75OmaRoyTI-5

Cobb, Paul
❑ 75McCCob-11

Cobb, Trevor
❑ 93EliTwiC-8
❑ 93EliTwiF-3410
❑ 94EliTwiC-5
❑ 94EliTwiF-3722
❑ 95Exc-79
❑ 96FtMyeMB-28
❑ 97ForMyeM-8
❑ 98NewBriRCM-8

Cobb, Ty (Tyrus Raymond)
❑ 03WilCarE-6
❑ 07TigACDPP-1
❑ 07TigACDPP-18
❑ 08AmeLeaPC-6
❑ 08RosComP-31
❑ 09AmeCarE90-1-25
❑ 09ColChiE-57A
❑ 09ColChiE-57B
❑ 09MaxPubP-3
❑ 09PhiCarE-5
❑ 09SpoNewSM-5
❑ 09SpoNewSM-36
❑ 09T206-68
❑ 09T206-69
❑ 09T206-70
❑ 09T206-71
❑ 09TigHMTP-1
❑ 09TigMorBBBP-4
❑ 09TigMorPWBPP-2
❑ 09TigTaCP-3
❑ 09WolNewDTPP-1
❑ 09WolNewDTPP-2
❑ 09WWSmiP-1
❑ 10CouT21-13
❑ 10CouT21-105
❑ 10CouT21-106
❑ 10CouT21-269
❑ 10CouT21-270
❑ 10DarChoE-9
❑ 10DomDisP-26A
❑ 10DomDisP-26B
❑ 10E-UOraBSC-7
❑ 10E101-10
❑ 10E102-4
❑ 10E98-8
❑ 10JuJuDE-10
❑ 10MelMinE-10
❑ 10NadCarE-12
❑ 10NotCov-2
❑ 10OrnOvaPP-3
❑ 10PeoT21-12A
❑ 10PeoT21-12B
❑ 10PeoT21-12C
❑ 10RedCroT-11
❑ 10RedCroT-97
❑ 10SepAnoP-4
❑ 10SepAnoP-5
❑ 10StaCarE-6
❑ 10SweCapPP-22A
❑ 10SweCapPP-22B
❑ 10W555-15
❑ 11BasBatEU-11
❑ 11DiaGumP-9
❑ 11E94-7
❑ 11HelSta-28
❑ 11L1L-127
❑ 11MecDFT-11
❑ 11PinT-5-159
❑ 11PinT-5-169
❑ 11PinT-5-170
❑ 11PloCanE-16
❑ 11S74Sil-13
❑ 11S81LarS-102
❑ 11SpoLifCW-68
❑ 11SpoLifM-55
❑ 11T205-30
❑ 11TurRedT-9
❑ 12ColRedB-57A
❑ 12ColRedB-57B
❑ 12ColTinT-57A
❑ 12ColTinT-57B
❑ 12HasTriFT-2
❑ 12HasTriFT-37
❑ 12HasTriFT-39
❑ 12HasTriFT-75A
❑ 12HasTriFT-75B
❑ 12HasTriFT-75C
❑ 12T22SeroC-3
❑ 12VasSwe-1
❑ 13LawSemC-3
❑ 13NatGamW-11
❑ 13TomBarW-11
❑ 14B18B-14A
❑ 14B18B-14B
❑ 14B18B-14C
❑ 14CraJacE-30
❑ 14E&SP-2
❑ 14PieStaT-24
❑ 14PolGroW-5
❑ 14TexTomE-13
❑ 15AmeCarE106-8A
❑ 15AmeCarE106-8B
❑ 15CraJacE-30
❑ 15SpoNewP-2
❑ 15VicT21-4
❑ 16BF2FP-26
❑ 16FleBreD-17
❑ 16SpoNewM-38
❑ 16TanBraE-5
❑ 17ColE13-30
❑ 17HolBreD-15
❑ 19W514-43
❑ 20NatCarE-13
❑ 20W516-6
❑ 21E121So1-10A
❑ 21E121So1-10B
❑ 21E121So8-11A
❑ 21E121So8-11B
❑ 21Exh-24
❑ 21Nei-30
❑ 21OxfConE-4
❑ 22AmeCarE122-11
❑ 22E120-48
❑ 22W572-13
❑ 22W573-20
❑ 22W575-17
❑ 22WilPatV-46
❑ 23MapCriV-22
❑ 23W501-8
❑ 23W515-10
❑ 23W551-4
❑ 23WilChoV-20
❑ 24MrsShePP-2
❑ 25Exh-90
❑ 26Exh-91
❑ 26SpoComoA-9
❑ 27AmeCarE126-17
❑ 27Exh-53
❑ 27YorCarE-27
❑ 28StaPlaCE-9
❑ 28W502-27
❑ 28W512-3
❑ 28Yue-27
❑ 32USCar*-14
❑ 33SpoKin-1
❑ 36Halof FP-6
❑ 39PC7AlbHoF-1
❑ 48ExhHoF-6
❑ 50CalHOFW-17
❑ 51R42SmaS-14A
❑ 51R42SmaS-14B
❑ 53ArtHaloFP-17
❑ 58JayPubAG-1
❑ 60ExhWriH-7
❑ 60Fle-42
❑ 60NuHi-43
❑ 61Fle-1
❑ 61Fle-14
❑ 61GolPre-25
❑ 61NuSco-443
❑ 63BasMagM-16
❑ 63BazA-35
❑ 63GadFunC-11
❑ 63GadFunC-32
❑ 63HalofFB-1
❑ 67SpoHobFC-29
❑ 67TopVen-146
❑ 68LauWorS-6
❑ 68SCFOldT-9
❑ 68SpoMemAG-10
❑ 69Baz-7
❑ 69Baz-8
❑ 70FleWorS-6
❑ 70SpoCarfCOP-11
❑ 71FleWorS-6
❑ 72ClaCar-33
❑ 72FleFamF-15
❑ 72KelATG-15
❑ 72LauGreF-35
❑ 73FleWilD-35
❑ 73HalofFPP-3
❑ 73OPC-471
❑ 73OPC-475
❑ 73SevTraC-15
❑ 73Top-471
❑ 73Top-475
❑ 74CapPub-3
❑ 75FlePio-14
❑ 75McCCob-1
❑ 75McCCob-2
❑ 75McCCob-3
❑ 75McCCob-4
❑ 75McCCob-5
❑ 75McCCob-6
❑ 75McCCob-7
❑ 75McCCob-8
❑ 75McCCob-9
❑ 75McCCob-10
❑ 75McCCob-11
❑ 75McCCob-12
❑ 75McCCob-13
❑ 75McCCob-15
❑ 75McCCob-16
❑ 75McCCob-17
❑ 75McCCob-18
❑ 75McCCob-19
❑ 75McCCob-20
❑ 75TCMAllG-6
❑ 76MotOldT-3
❑ 76OPC-346
❑ 76RowExh-7
❑ 76ShaPiz-1
❑ 76TayBow4-113
❑ 76Top-346
❑ 77BobParHoF-13
❑ 77GalGloG-100
❑ 77GalGloG-136
❑ 77ShaPiz-19
❑ 78DexHaloFP-5
❑ 79Pew-2
❑ 79Top-411
❑ 79Top-414
❑ 80Lau300-4
❑ 80LauFamF-28
❑ 80MarExhH-6
❑ 80PacLeg-31
❑ 80PerHaloFP-1
❑ 80SSPHOF-2
❑ 80TigGreT-3
❑ 81ConTSN-1
❑ 81SpoHaloF-5
❑ 81TigDetN-17
❑ 81TigSecNP-1
❑ 82BHCRSpoL-1
❑ 82DavHaloFB-4
❑ 82DiaCla-39
❑ 82TCMGreH-14
❑ 83Don-653
❑ 83DonHOFH-1
❑ 84DonCha-26
❑ 84GalHaloFRL-1
❑ 84OCoandSI-86
❑ 84SpoDesPW-8
❑ 85FegMurCG-2
❑ 85UltBasC-1
❑ 85Woo-8
❑ 86ConSer1-2
❑ 86ConSer1-6
❑ 86ConSer1-24
❑ 86ConSer1-41
❑ 86TCM-5
❑ 86TigSpoD-1
❑ 87ConSer2-5
❑ 87HygAllG-9
❑ 87NesDreT-7
❑ 87SpoCubG-2
❑ 88ConHar-2
❑ 88ConSer4-6
❑ 88FriBasCM-3
❑ 88GreBasS-40
❑ 89CMCBasG-2
❑ 89HOFStiB-37
❑ 89PacLegI-117
❑ 89SpollIFKI-321
❑ 89SweBasG-2
❑ 89TopBasT-22
❑ 90BasWit-56
❑ 90HOFStiB-19
❑ 90PerGreM-12
❑ 90SweBasG-15
❑ 91CadEIID-11
❑ 91ConTSN-250
❑ 91ConTSNP-13
❑ 91ConTSNP-250
❑ 91ConTSNP-500
❑ 91FouBal-7
❑ 91HomCooC-4
❑ 91LinDri-48
❑ 91SweBasG-127
❑ 91USGamSBL-1C
❑ 91USGamSBL-1D
❑ 91USGamSBL-1H
❑ 91USGamSBL-1S
❑ 92ConTSN-425
❑ 92ConTSN-525
❑ 92ConTSNCI-10
❑ 92ConTSNGI-1000G
❑ 92MegRut-125
❑ 92Sco-878
❑ 92St.VinHHS-1
❑ 92WhiLegtL-1
❑ 92WhiPro-1
❑ 93ActPacA-88
❑ 93ActPacA2-22G
❑ 93CadDis-13
❑ 93CokCasI-TC1
❑ 93ConMasB-7
❑ 93ConTSN-796
❑ 93ConTSN-838
❑ 93CraJac-1
❑ 93Hoy-1
❑ 93SpeHOFI-2
❑ 93TedWil-125
❑ 93UppDecAH-32
❑ 93UppDecAH-145
❑ 93UppDecAH-146
❑ 93UppDecAH-160
❑ 93UppDecTR-2
❑ 93UppDecTR-6
❑ 93UppDecTR-7
❑ 93UppDecTR-8
❑ 94ConTSN-1000
❑ 94ConTSN-1011
❑ 94ConTSNB-1000
❑ 94ConTSNB-1011
❑ 94TedWil-30
❑ 94TedWilLC-LC11
❑ 94UppDecAH-30
❑ 94UppDecAH-106
❑ 94UppDecAH-174
❑ 94UppDecAH1-30
❑ 94UppDecAH1-106
❑ 94UppDecAH1-174
❑ 94UppDecAJ-44
❑ 94UppDecAJG-44
❑ 94UppDecTAE-11
❑ 94UppDecTAEGM-3
❑ 95ConTSNGJ-3
❑ 95UppDecSHoB-19
❑ 96BalHOF1C-1
❑ 96ColCho-501
❑ 96ColChoGS-501
❑ 96ColChoSS-501
❑ 99SpollIGotG-50
❑ 99SpollIGotGRB-9
❑ 99SpollIGotGRBG-9
❑ 99UppDecCL-3
❑ 99UppDecCL-130
❑ 99UppDecCLA-1900
❑ 99UppDecCLCC-3
❑ 99UppDecCLCC-130
❑ 99UppDecCLJotC-AC2
❑ 99UppDecCLLC-WJ

Coble, Drew
❑ 88T/MUmp-45
❑ 89T/MUmp-43
❑ 90T/MUmp-41

Coble, Tony
❑ 90HelBreSP-4

Cobleigh, Mike
❑ 89ModA'sC-5

Cobra, Alex
❑ 98AlbDukG-3

Coburn, Todd
❑ 96PieBolWB-6

Coca, Mark
❑ 95OdgRapTI-3

Cocanower, Jaime
❑ 81VanCanT-1
❑ 82VanCanT-20
❑ 84BrePol-47
❑ 84FleUpd-28
❑ 84TopTra-26T
❑ 84TopTraT-26T
❑ 85BreGar-4
❑ 85BrePol-47
❑ 85Don-455
❑ 85Fle-579
❑ 85Top-576
❑ 85TopSti-288
❑ 85TopTif-576
❑ 85VanCanC-210
❑ 86BrePol-47
❑ 86Don-393
❑ 86Fle-483
❑ 86Top-277
❑ 86TopTif-277
❑ 87AlbDukD-7
❑ 87Top-423
❑ 87TopTif-423
❑ 94BreMilB-213

Coccia, Dan
❑ 88MarPhiS-7

Cochran, Andrew
❑ 95DanBraTI-5
❑ 96EugEmeB-5

Cochran, Arnold
❑ 81BatTroT-1
❑ 81WatIndT-20

Cochran, Dave
❑ 84JacMetT-21

Cochran, Greg
❑ 79ColCliT-17
❑ 80ColCliP-27
❑ 80ColCliT-21
❑ 81ColCliP-27
❑ 81ColCliT-12
❑ 82ColCliP-27
❑ 82ColCliT-8

Cochran, Jamie
❑ 91JohCitCC-17
❑ 91JohCitCP-3971
❑ 92HamRedC-5
❑ 92HamRedF-1584
❑ 92ProFS7-327
❑ 93ExcFS7-97
❑ 93SavCarC-9
❑ 93SavCarF-681
❑ 93SouAtlLAGF-47
❑ 94ExcFS7-264
❑ 94ExcLeaLF-6

Cochrane, Charles
❑ 23Zee-83
❑ 24Zee-60
❑ 25Zee-62

Cochrane, Chris

❑ 94SouOreAC-2
❑ 94SouOreAF-3612
❑ 95WesMicWTI-36
❑ 96ModA'sB-9
Cochrane, Dave
❑ 83LynMetT-14B
❑ 86BirBarTI-11
❑ 87HawIsIP-13
❑ 87SevCoi-C5
❑ 87Spo-158
❑ 87SpoTeaP-26
❑ 88CalCanC-14
❑ 88CalCanP-785
❑ 89CalCanC-14
❑ 89CalCanP-542
❑ 90CalCanC-11
❑ 90CMC-438
❑ 90OPC-491
❑ 90Top-491
❑ 90TopTif-491
❑ 91CalCanLD-55
❑ 91CalCanP-518
❑ 91LinDriAAA-55
❑ 92Don-539
❑ 92Lea-398
❑ 92LeaBlaG-398
❑ 92MarMot-14
❑ 92Sco-461
❑ 92Sco100RS-70
❑ 92StaClu-69
❑ 92Ult-431
❑ 93Don-481
❑ 93Fle-671
❑ 93Top-288
❑ 93TopGol-288
❑ 93TopInaM-288
❑ 93TopInaR-288
❑ 93TopMic-288
Cochrane, Mickey (Gordon S.)
❑ 24Zee-40
❑ 26SpoComoA-10
❑ 28Exh-53
❑ 28StaPlaCE-10
❑ 28W56PlaC-JOK
❑ 29ExhFou-27
❑ 30SchR33-32
❑ 30UncJac-5
❑ 30W554-1
❑ 31Exh-28
❑ 31W517-37
❑ 31W517-54
❑ 32OrbPinNP-28
❑ 32OrbPinUP-12
❑ 32USCar*-12
❑ 33ButCanV-7
❑ 33ButCre-4
❑ 33DelR33-6
❑ 33DouDisP-10
❑ 33ExhFou-14
❑ 33Gou-76
❑ 33GouCanV-69
❑ 33TatOrb-12
❑ 33TatOrbSDR-155
❑ 33TatOrbSDR-186
❑ 33WorCig-18
❑ 34BabRutG-10
❑ 34BatR31-25
❑ 34ButPreR-10
❑ 34DiaStaR-9
❑ 34ExhFou-12
❑ 34ExhFou-14
❑ 34Gou-2
❑ 34GouCanV-59
❑ 34TigTeal-4
❑ 35AlDemDCR3-23
❑ 35AlDemDCR3-24
❑ 35ExhFou-12
❑ 35GolMedFR-2
❑ 35GouPreR-9
❑ 35GouPuzR-1D
❑ 35GouPuzR-2D
❑ 35GouPuzR-5A
❑ 35GouPuzR-6A
❑ 35GouPuzR-11J
❑ 35GouPuzR-13A
❑ 35GouPuzR-16D
❑ 35GouPuzR-17D
❑ 35WheBB1-5A
❑ 35WheBB1-5B
❑ 36ExhFou-12
❑ 36GouBWR-7
❑ 36GouWidPPR-A17
❑ 36NatChiFPR-90
❑ 36R31PasP-5
❑ 36R31Pre-G3
❑ 36WheBB3-2
❑ 36WorWidGV-45
❑ 37ExhFou-12
❑ 39PC7AlbHoF-50
❑ 40PlaBal-180
❑ 46SpoExcW-2-11
❑ 48ExhHoF-7
❑ 49LeaPre-2
❑ 50A'sTeal-5
❑ 50CalHOFW-18A
❑ 50CalHOFW-18B
❑ 51TopConMA-2
❑ 53ArtHaloFP-18
❑ 60Fle-24
❑ 60NuHi-19
❑ 61Fle-15
❑ 61GolPre-12
❑ 61NuSco-419
❑ 63BazA-34
❑ 63HalofFB-2
❑ 67TopVen-153
❑ 68SCFOldT-22
❑ 68SpoMemAG-7
❑ 69Baz-5
❑ 69Baz-8
❑ 71FleWorS-33
❑ 72KelATG-4
❑ 72TCMthe1-198
❑ 74A's192T-4
❑ 74CapPub-42
❑ 74Car193T-30
❑ 74TigTCM1AC-5
❑ 75TCMGua-16
❑ 76OPC-348
❑ 76RowExh-13
❑ 76ShaPiz-50
❑ 76TigOldTS-4
❑ 76Top-348
❑ 77BobParHoF-82
❑ 77GalGloG-61
❑ 77GalGloG-238
❑ 77ShaPiz-8
❑ 78TigDeaCS-14
❑ 80MarExhH-7
❑ 80PacLeg-38
❑ 80PerHaloFP-50
❑ 80SSPHOF-50
❑ 80TigGreT-11
❑ 81SpoHaloF-20
❑ 81TigDetN-3
❑ 81TigSecNP-22
❑ 83A'sGreT-8
❑ 83ConMar-7
❑ 84SpoDesPW-29
❑ 85BigLeaC3-13
❑ 86ConSer1-7
❑ 86SpoDecG-13
❑ 86TigSpoD-5
❑ 87HygAllG-10
❑ 87NesDreT-8
❑ 88ConAmeA-5
❑ 88ConSer3-7
❑ 89HOFStiB-56
❑ 89PacLegI-151
❑ 90SweBasG-3
❑ 91ConTSN-51
❑ 91ConTSN-266
❑ 91LinDri-49
❑ 91SweBasG-142
❑ 92ConTSN-432
❑ 92ConTSN-551
❑ 93ActPacA-98
❑ 93ActPacA2-32G
❑ 93ConMasB-5
❑ 93ConTSN-866
❑ 94ConTSN-1087
❑ 94ConTSN-1146
❑ 94ConTSNB-1087
❑ 94ConTSNB-1146
❑ 94TedWil-65
❑ 95MegRut-24
Cock, J.R.
❑ 91BenBucCB-1
❑ 91BenBucP-3688
Cockburn, J.C.
❑ 88KimN18-9
Cockman, Jim (James)
❑ 07NewEveWS-2
Cockrell, Alan
❑ 86ShrCapP-4
❑ 87PhoFirP-15
❑ 88PhoFirC-19
❑ 88PhoFirP-68
❑ 89PorBeaC-20
❑ 89PorBeaP-224
❑ 90CMC-475
❑ 90ColSprSSC-23
❑ 90ColSprSSP-49
❑ 90ProAAAF-230
❑ 90TriAllGP-AAA50
❑ 91CalCanLD-56
❑ 91CalCanP-526
❑ 91LinDriAAA-56
❑ 92ColSprSSF-753
❑ 92ColSprSSS-82
❑ 92OPC-591
❑ 92Top-591
❑ 92TopGol-591
❑ 92TopGolW-591
❑ 92TopMic-591
❑ 93ChaKniF-555
❑ 94NewHavRF-1554
❑ 96ColSprSSTI-8
❑ 97ColSprSATTI-21
❑ 98ColSprSS-31
Coco, Pascual
❑ 97St.CatSB-13
❑ 98St.CatSM-10
Cocreham, Gene
❑ 80BraTCM1-5
Codd, Tim
❑ 95HudValRTI-14
❑ 96ChaRivTI-9609
Codinach, Antonio
❑ 84VisOakT-19
Codington, Paul
❑ 18Zee-19
Codiroli, Chris
❑ 82WesHavAT-4
❑ 83TopTra-20T
❑ 84A'sMot-10
❑ 84Don-345
❑ 84Fle-441
❑ 84Nes792-61
❑ 84OPC-61
❑ 84Top-61
❑ 84TopSti-330
❑ 84TopTif-61
❑ 85A'sMot-9
❑ 85Don-462
❑ 85Fle-420
❑ 85Top-552
❑ 85TopSti-327
❑ 85TopTif-552
❑ 86A'sMot-15
❑ 86Don-278
❑ 86Fle-414
❑ 86Lea-151
❑ 86OPC-388
❑ 86Top-433
❑ 86TopSti-173
❑ 86TopTat-9
❑ 86TopTif-433
❑ 87Don-226
❑ 87Fle-390
❑ 87FleGlo-390
❑ 87Top-217
❑ 87TopTif-217
❑ 89Top-6
Cody, John
❑ 98OrlRayM-27
Cody, Ron
❑ 92BelMarCB-8
❑ 93AppFoxCB-5
❑ 93AppFoxFI-2452
Cody, Ryan
❑ 98MarPhiG-8
Cody, William
❑ 92BelMarF-1433
Coe, Keith
❑ 94BoiHawC-8
❑ 94BoiHawF-3347
❑ 95BoiHawTI-11
Coe, Ryan
❑ 96MidLeaAB-27
❑ 96QuaCitRB-13
❑ 97KisCob-7
Coentopp, Kevin
❑ 86SpoIndC-175
Cofer, Brian
❑ 90WatIndS-4
❑ 91CollndC-11
❑ 91CollndP-1478
❑ 92KinIndC-3
❑ 92KinIndF-2468
Coffee, Gary
❑ 96BesAutS-21
❑ 96Bow-225
❑ 96BowFoi-225
❑ 96Exc-57
❑ 96LanLugB-9
❑ 97WilBluR-5
Coffey, Jack (John Francis)
❑ 16Zee-103
Coffey, Mike
❑ 85CedRapRT-3
❑ 86ElmPioRSP-5
❑ 87WinHavRSP-11
Coffey, Stephen
❑ 90GenCubP-3047
❑ 90GenCubS-4
❑ 91PeoChiP-1346
Coffey, Todd
❑ 98BilMusTI-7
Coffie, Ivanon
❑ 97DelSho-9
❑ 98CarLeaTPQ-29
❑ 98FreKeyM-22
❑ 99SP SigAuto-IC
❑ 99SPSig-97
Coffman, Dick (Samuel R.)
❑ 28StaPlaCE-11
❑ 33Gou-101
❑ 34BatR31-92
❑ 34GouCanV-23
❑ 34TarThoBD-8
❑ 35DiaMatCS3T1-34
❑ 35GouPuzR-5D
❑ 35GouPuzR-6D
❑ 35GouPuzR-11F
❑ 35GouPuzR-13D
❑ 39PlaBal-24
❑ 40PlaBal-55
❑ 40PlaBal-140
❑ 72TCMthe3-8
❑ 91ConTSN-321
Coffman, George David
❑ 39PlaBal-147
❑ 41Gou-32
Coffman, Jim
❑ 82AmaGolST-12
Coffman, Kevin
❑ 85DurBulT-5
❑ 86DurBulP-5
❑ 87GreBraB-20
❑ 87SouLeaAJ-19
❑ 88BlaYNPRWL-54
❑ 88BobCamRB-21
❑ 88DonRoo-49
❑ 88Fle-536
❑ 88FleGlo-536
❑ 88TopTra-29T
❑ 88TopTraT-29T
❑ 89Bow-282
❑ 89BowTif-282
❑ 89OPC-44
❑ 89Top-488
❑ 89TopTif-488
❑ 91JacGenLD-555
❑ 91JacGenP-918
❑ 91LinDriAA-555
❑ 92GreBraS-232
❑ 92RicBraF-370
❑ 93CalCanF-1157
❑ 97RicBraBC-23
Coggin, Cliff
❑ 53SanFraSTI-6
Coggin, David
❑ 95MarPhiTI-6
❑ 96BesAutSA-13
❑ 96Bow-298
❑ 96BowFoi-298
❑ 96PieBolWB-7
❑ 96Top-431
❑ 97BesAutAS-8
❑ 97Bow-174
❑ 97BowCerBlaIA-CA14
❑ 97BowCerBluIA-CA14
❑ 97BowCerGolIA-CA14
❑ 97BowInt-174
❑ 97ClePhi-3
❑ 97FloStaLTPB-5
❑ 98Bow-160
❑ 98BowChr-160
❑ 98BowChrGA-160
❑ 98BowChrGAR-160
❑ 98BowChrI-160
❑ 98BowChrIR-160
❑ 98BowChrR-160
❑ 98BowGolA-160
❑ 98BowInt-160
❑ 98ReaPhiM-11
❑ 98ReaPhiUM-8
Coggins, Franklin
❑ 68OPC-96
❑ 68SenTeal-3
❑ 68Top-96
❑ 68TopVen-96
Coggins, Rich (Richard A.)
❑ 72OriPos-8
❑ 73BalOriP-12
❑ 73OPC-611
❑ 73OriJohP-2
❑ 73OriTeal-10
❑ 73Top-611
❑ 74OPC-353
❑ 74Top-353
❑ 75ExpPos-8
❑ 75OPC-167
❑ 75Top-167
❑ 75TopMin-167
❑ 76OPC-572
❑ 76SSP-446
❑ 76Top-572
❑ 91OriCro-79
❑ 92YanWIZ7-36
Coghen, Al
❑ 77WauMetT-6
❑ 78WauMetT-6
Coghill, Dave
❑ 80AndBraT-7
Cohane, Tim
❑ 64TopRooAB-4
Cohea, Dave
❑ 77CliDodT-3
❑ 82AlbDukTc-25
❑ 83AlbDukTc-24
Cohen, Alta (Albert)
❑ 90DodTar-132
Cohen, Andy (Andrew Howard)
❑ 28W56PlaC-H13
❑ 33Gou-52
❑ 33GouCanV-52
❑ 33WorCig(-17
❑ 33WorCig(-18
❑ 60Top-466
❑ 95ConTSN-1334
Cohen, David
❑ 98CapFeaCM-30
Cohen, Jim
❑ 92NegLeaK-13
❑ 92NegLeaRLI-10
❑ 95NegLeaL2-15
Cohen, John
❑ 88MisStaB-3
❑ 89MisStaB-7
❑ 90MisStaB-6
❑ 91Cla/Bes-78
❑ 91VisOakC-20
❑ 91VisOakP-1752
Cohen, Sid
❑ 28Zee-128
Cohen, Tony
❑ 87MacPirP-23
❑ 88AugPirP-380
Cohick, Emmitt
❑ 91QuaCitAC-23
❑ 91QuaCitAP-2642
❑ 92PalSprAC-21
❑ 92PalSprAF-852
❑ 93MidAngF-331
❑ 94MidAngF-2450
❑ 94MidAngOHP-3
❑ 95MidAngOHP-9
❑ 95MidAngTI-9
❑ 97MidAngOHP-5
Cohoon, Don
❑ 86WauTimP-4
❑ 88ChaWheB-18
❑ 89WinSpiS-5
Coimbre, Pancho (Francisco)
❑ 97NegLeaPC-8D
Coin, Mike
❑ 85BelBreT-5
Coker, Jimmie Goodwin
❑ 58PhiTeal-6
❑ 60PhiJayP-5
❑ 60Top-438
❑ 61Top-144
❑ 63Top-456
❑ 64Top-211
❑ 64TopVen-211
❑ 65OPC-192
❑ 65RedEnq-4
❑ 65Top-192
❑ 66Top-292
❑ 66TopVen-292
❑ 67OPC-158
❑ 67Top-158
Coker, Kerry
❑ 92DavLipB-7
❑ 93DavLipB-5
Coker, Kyle
❑ 92DavLipB-8
❑ 92DavLipB-23
Coker, Larry
❑ 88FayGenP-1084
Colangelo, Mike
❑ 98CedRapKTI-6
❑ 99SP TopP-70
❑ 99SP TopPPE-70
Colarusso, Sam
❑ 88CapCodPPaLP-105
❑ 89AncGlaP-8
Colavito, Rocky (Rocco D.)
❑ 47Exh-45A
❑ 47Exh-45B
❑ 55DonWin-15
❑ 57IndSoh-4
❑ 57IndTeal-4
❑ 57SwiFra-18
❑ 57Top-212
❑ 58HarSta-14
❑ 58IndTeal-5
❑ 58IndTeal-26
❑ 58Top-368
❑ 59Baz-7
❑ 59HomRunD-6
❑ 59Ind-2
❑ 59Kah-7
❑ 59Top-166
❑ 59Top-420
❑ 59Top-462
❑ 59TopVen-166
❑ 60ArmCoi-5
❑ 60Baz-30
❑ 60NuHi-68
❑ 60TigJayP-5
❑ 60Top-260
❑ 60Top-400
❑ 60TopTat-9
❑ 60TopTat-88
❑ 61Baz-17
❑ 61NuSco-468
❑ 61Pos-36A
❑ 61Pos-36B
❑ 61TigJayP-6
❑ 61Top-44
❑ 61Top-330
❑ 62AurRec-4
❑ 62Baz-42
❑ 62ExhStaB-10
❑ 62Pos-19
❑ 62PosCan-19
❑ 62SalPlaC-28
❑ 62ShiPlaC-28
❑ 62TigJayP-5
❑ 62TigPosCF-6
❑ 62Top-20
❑ 62Top-314
❑ 62Top-472
❑ 62TopBuc-18
❑ 62TopStal-46
❑ 62TopVen-20
❑ 63BasMagM-17
❑ 63Baz-33
❑ 63ExhStaB-16
❑ 63Jel-50
❑ 63Pos-50
❑ 63SalMetC-58
❑ 63TigJayP-5
❑ 63Top-4
❑ 63Top-240
❑ 63TopStil-11
❑ 64Baz-33
❑ 64Top-320
❑ 64TopCoi-46
❑ 64TopGia-9
❑ 64TopSta-65
❑ 64TopStaU-19
❑ 64TopTatl-31
❑ 64TopVen-320
❑ 65Baz-33
❑ 65OldLonC-23
❑ 65Top-380
❑ 65TopEmbl-46
❑ 65TopTral-45
❑ 66Baz-15
❑ 66IndTeal-3
❑ 66IndVolC-4
❑ 66OPC-150

❑ 66Top-150
❑ 66Top-220
❑ 66TopRubl-20
❑ 66TopVen-150
❑ 66TopVen-220
❑ 67Baz-15
❑ 67CokCapI-4
❑ 67DexPre-55
❑ 67OPC-109
❑ 67Top-109
❑ 67Top-580
❑ 68OPC-99
❑ 68Top-99
❑ 68TopVen-99
❑ 68YanPhoS-63
❑ 73OPC-449
❑ 73Top-449A
❑ 73Top-449B
❑ 77IndTeal-6
❑ 78IndTeal-5
❑ 78TigDeaCS-1
❑ 79TCM50-216
❑ 81TigDetN-99
❑ 82OhiHaloF-36
❑ 82TCMGreS-39
❑ 83RoyPos-8
❑ 83TigAlKS-19
❑ 84OCoandSI-12
❑ 84OCoandSI-181
❑ 85CirK-27
❑ 89SweBasG-126
❑ 90DodTar-133
❑ 90PacLeg-18
❑ 90SweBasG-119
❑ 91SweBasG-116
❑ 92ActPacA-65
❑ 92UppDecS-23
❑ 92YanWIZ6-28
❑ 93MetIma-8
❑ 93TedWil-33
❑ 94TedWil-146
❑ 97OhiLot-1

Colavito, Steve
❑ 88WatIndP-679

Colbern, Mike (Michael M.)
❑ 79IowOakP-6
❑ 79Top-704
❑ 80IowOakP-2A
❑ 80IowOakP-2B
❑ 80Top-664
❑ 81EdmTraRR-19
❑ 81Top-522
❑ 82RicBraT-22

Colbert, Craig
❑ 88CliGiaP-707
❑ 89ShrCapP-1844
❑ 89TexLeaAGS-30
❑ 90CMC-543
❑ 90PhoFirC-16
❑ 90PhoFirP-18
❑ 90ProAAAF-44
❑ 91LinDriAAA-380
❑ 91PhoFirLD-380
❑ 91PhoFirP-70
❑ 92DonRoo-26
❑ 92PhoFirF-2826
❑ 92StaClu-891
❑ 92StaCluECN-891
❑ 92Ult-588
❑ 93Fle-528
❑ 93GiaMot-21
❑ 93GiaPos-18
❑ 93GiaStaC-27
❑ 93PacSpa-610
❑ 93Sco-255
❑ 93Sel-338
❑ 93Top-91
❑ 93TopGol-91
❑ 93TopInaM-91
❑ 93TopInaR-91
❑ 93TopMic-91
❑ 94ChaKniF-897
❑ 96LasVegSB-9
❑ 97LasVegS1A-4
❑ 98Las-4

Colbert, Nate (Nathan)
❑ 66Top-596
❑ 69MilBra-63
❑ 69Top-408
❑ 70DayDaiNM-41
❑ 70MLBOffS-111
❑ 70OPC-11
❑ 70Top-11
❑ 70TopScr-7
❑ 71Kel-72
❑ 71MLBOffS-223
❑ 71OPC-235
❑ 71Top-235
❑ 71TopCoi-77
❑ 71TopGreM-28
❑ 71TopSup-22
❑ 71TopTat-3
❑ 72Kel-41
❑ 72MilBra-78
❑ 72PadPos-7
❑ 72SevTraC-13
❑ 72Top-571
❑ 72Top-572
❑ 73Kel2D-33
❑ 73LinPor-154
❑ 73OPC-340
❑ 73PadDea-4
❑ 73SevTraC-16
❑ 73Top-340
❑ 73TopCanL-11
❑ 73TopCom-5
❑ 73TopPin-5
❑ 74Kel-19
❑ 74OPC-125
❑ 74PadDea-5
❑ 74PadMcDD-3
❑ 74Top-125A
❑ 74Top-125B
❑ 74TopDecE-34
❑ 74TopSta-91
❑ 75DetTigP-5
❑ 75ExpPos-9
❑ 75Hos-76
❑ 75OPC-599
❑ 75Top-599
❑ 75TopMin-599
❑ 76LauDiaJ-16
❑ 76MonExpP-5
❑ 76OPC-495
❑ 76SSP-330
❑ 76Top-495
❑ 77PadSchC-13A
❑ 77PadSchC-13B
❑ 77PadSchC-14
❑ 77PadSchC-28
❑ 77Top-433
❑ 83PadTeal-4
❑ 86GreAmeSDFSB-1
❑ 86PadGreT-1
❑ 87AstShowSTh-4
❑ 87WicPiIRD-6
❑ 88WicPiIRD-17
❑ 89PadMag-12
❑ 89RivRedWB-24
❑ 89RivRedWCLC-27
❑ 89RivRedWP-1391
❑ 90HOFStiB-80
❑ 90RivRedWB-19
❑ 90RivRedWCLC-26
❑ 90RivRedWP-2622
❑ 93UppDecS-13
❑ 94TedWil-85

Colbert, Rick
❑ 81BriRedST-10
❑ 85TucTorC-59
❑ 87LouRedTI-10
❑ 88ArkTraGS-1
❑ 89SprCarB-27
❑ 90SavCarP-2084
❑ 91HamRedC-29
❑ 91HamRedP-4056
❑ 92SprCarC-27
❑ 92SprCarF-885
❑ 93CanIndF-2853

Colbert, Vince
❑ 71MLBOffS-365
❑ 71OPC-231
❑ 71Top-231
❑ 72OPC-84
❑ 72Top-84

Colborn, Jim
❑ 71MLBOffS-29
❑ 71OPC-38
❑ 71Top-38
❑ 72OPC-386
❑ 72Top-386
❑ 73LinPor-99
❑ 73OPC-408
❑ 73Top-408
❑ 74OPC-75
❑ 74Top-75
❑ 74TopDecE-49
❑ 74TopSta-193
❑ 75OPC-305
❑ 75Top-305
❑ 75TopMin-305
❑ 76BreA&P-3
❑ 76OPC-521
❑ 76SSP-226
❑ 76Top-521
❑ 77Top-331
❑ 78OPC-116
❑ 78SSP270-238
❑ 78Top-129
❑ 79OPC-137
❑ 79Top-276
❑ 85IowCubT-29
❑ 86BreGreT-9
❑ 86IowCubP-7
❑ 94BreMilB-214
❑ 94WesMicWC-26
❑ 94WesMicWF-2312
❑ 95WesMicWTI-48
❑ 96ModA'sB-27

Colbrunn, Greg
❑ 88MidLeaAGS-42
❑ 88RocExpLC-8
❑ 89WesPalBES-7
❑ 90Bes-5
❑ 90JacExpB-1
❑ 90JacExpP-1377
❑ 90ProAaA-53
❑ 91Bow-449
❑ 91Don-425
❑ 91OPC-91
❑ 91StaClu-215
❑ 91Top-91
❑ 91TopDesS-91
❑ 91TopMic-91
❑ 91TopTif-91
❑ 91UppDec-15
❑ 92Don-557
❑ 92FleUpd-96
❑ 92IndIndF-1864
❑ 93ClaGam-22
❑ 93Don-328
❑ 93ExpPosN-7
❑ 93Fla-79
❑ 93FleFinE-91
❑ 93FleMajLP-B3
❑ 93Lea-55
❑ 93OPC-137
❑ 93PanSti-225
❑ 93Pin-538
❑ 93Sco-271
❑ 93Sel-295
❑ 93StaClu-522
❑ 93StaCluFDI-522
❑ 93StaCluMOP-522
❑ 93Top-464
❑ 93TopGol-464
❑ 93TopInaM-464
❑ 93TopInaR-464
❑ 93TopMic-464
❑ 93Toy-74
❑ 93Ult-64
❑ 93UppDec-342
❑ 93UppDecGold-342
❑ 93USPlaCR-3H
❑ 94Don-93
❑ 94Fla-381
❑ 94Fle-534
❑ 94FleUpd-134
❑ 94Pin-474
❑ 94PinArtP-474
❑ 94PinMusC-474
❑ 94ScoRoo-RT92
❑ 94ScoRooGR-RT92
❑ 94Sel-387
❑ 94SpoRoo-146
❑ 94SpoRooAP-146
❑ 94Top-134
❑ 94TopGol-134
❑ 94TopSpa-134
❑ 94TopTra-47T
❑ 95ColCho-312
❑ 95ColChoGS-312
❑ 95ColChoSS-312
❑ 95Don-463
❑ 95DonPreP-463
❑ 95DonTopotO-240
❑ 95Emo-127
❑ 95Fla-136
❑ 95Fle-330
❑ 95Lea-116
❑ 95LeaLim-163
❑ 95Pac-171
❑ 95Pin-206
❑ 95PinArtP-206
❑ 95PinMusC-206
❑ 95Sco-97
❑ 95ScoGolR-97
❑ 95ScoPlaTS-97
❑ 95Sel-137
❑ 95SelArtP-137
❑ 95Spo-72
❑ 95SpoArtP-72
❑ 95StaClu-459
❑ 95StaCluMOP-459
❑ 95StaCluSTWS-459
❑ 95Sum-29
❑ 95SumNthD-29
❑ 95Top-476
❑ 95TopCyb-269
❑ 95Ult-378
❑ 95UltGolM-378
❑ 95UppDec-357
❑ 95UppDecED-357
❑ 95UppDecEDG-357
❑ 96Cir-127
❑ 96CirRav-127
❑ 96ColCho-152
❑ 96ColChoGS-152
❑ 96ColChoSS-152
❑ 96Don-133
❑ 96DonPreP-133
❑ 96EmoXL-184
❑ 96Fin-B176
❑ 96FinRef-B176
❑ 96Fla-259
❑ 96Fle-384
❑ 96FleTif-384
❑ 96Lea-40
❑ 96LeaPrePB-40
❑ 96LeaPrePG-40
❑ 96LeaPrePS-40
❑ 96MetUni-163
❑ 96MetUniP-163
❑ 96Pac-76
❑ 96PanSti-16
❑ 96Pin-66
❑ 96PinAfi-102
❑ 96PinAfiAP-102
❑ 96ProSta-70
❑ 96Sco-347
❑ 96ScoDugC-B72
❑ 96ScoDugCAP-B72
❑ 96Sel-138
❑ 96SelArtP-138
❑ 96SP-90
❑ 96StaClu-19
❑ 96StaCluMOP-19
❑ 96Sum-14
❑ 96SumAbo&B-14
❑ 96SumArtP-14
❑ 96SumFoi-14
❑ 96Top-408
❑ 96TopGal-77
❑ 96TopGalPPI-77
❑ 96Ult-197
❑ 96UltGolM-197
❑ 96UppDec-77
❑ 97Fin-269
❑ 97FinRef-269
❑ 97Fle-327
❑ 97Fle-621
❑ 97FleTif-327
❑ 97FleTif-621
❑ 97MetUni-172
❑ 97Pac-299
❑ 97PacLigB-299
❑ 97PacSil-299
❑ 97Sco-69
❑ 97Sco-357
❑ 97ScoArtPWB-69
❑ 97ScoArtPWB-357
❑ 97ScoPreS-69
❑ 97ScoResC-357
❑ 97ScoShoS-69
❑ 97ScoShoS-357
❑ 97ScoShoSAP-69
❑ 97ScoShoSAP-357
❑ 97StaClu-353
❑ 97StaCluMOP-353
❑ 97Top-294
❑ 97Ult-334
❑ 97UltGolME-334
❑ 97UltPlaME-334
❑ 98PacOnl-242
❑ 98PacOnlR-242
❑ 98PacOnlWC-242
❑ 98Pin-125
❑ 98PinPreP-125
❑ 98Ult-312
❑ 98UltGolM-312
❑ 98UltMas-312
❑ 98UltPlaM-312

Cole, Abdul
❑ 95KanCouCTI-20

Cole, Alex
❑ 86FloStaLAP-11
❑ 86St.PetCP-6
❑ 87ArkTraP-20
❑ 88LouRedBC-11
❑ 88LouRedBP-438
❑ 88LouRedBTI-14
❑ 89LouRedBC-21
❑ 89LouRedBP-1266
❑ 89LouRedBTI-14
❑ 89St.PetCS-7
❑ 90CMC-519
❑ 90Fle-244
❑ 90FleCan-244
❑ 90LasVegSC-16
❑ 90LasVegSP-133
❑ 90ProAAAF-21
❑ 90TriAAAC-14
❑ 90UppDec-751
❑ 91Bow-64
❑ 91Cla1-T36
❑ 91Don-383
❑ 91Fle-365
❑ 91IndFanC-7
❑ 91Lea-108
❑ 91OPC-421
❑ 91OPCPre-24
❑ 91PanCanT1-48
❑ 91PanFreS-222
❑ 91Sco-555
❑ 91Sco100RS-13
❑ 91StaClu-392
❑ 91Top-421
❑ 91TopDeb90-33
❑ 91TopDesS-421
❑ 91TopMic-421
❑ 91TopRoo-6
❑ 91TopTif-421
❑ 91TopTriH-A5
❑ 91ToyRoo-5
❑ 91Ult-110
❑ 91UppDec-654
❑ 92Bow-173
❑ 92Don-220
❑ 92Fle-108
❑ 92Hig5-44
❑ 92IndFanC-7
❑ 92Lea-307
❑ 92LeaBlaG-307
❑ 92OPC-170
❑ 92PanSti-50
❑ 92Pin-66
❑ 92Sco-463
❑ 92ScoProP-20
❑ 92StaClu-437
❑ 92Stu-165
❑ 92Top-170
❑ 92TopGol-170
❑ 92TopGolW-170
❑ 92TopMic-170
❑ 92TriPla-49
❑ 92Ult-345
❑ 92UppDec-197
❑ 93Bow-36
❑ 93CadDis-14
❑ 93Don-70
❑ 93Don-786
❑ 93Fin-12
❑ 93FinRef-12
❑ 93Fla-38
❑ 93Fle-408
❑ 93FleFinE-27
❑ 93Lea-312
❑ 93PacSpa-426
❑ 93Pin-556
❑ 93PinExpOD-8
❑ 93RocStaC-6
❑ 93RocUSPC-7H
❑ 93RocUSPC-12C
❑ 93Sco-400
❑ 93SP-219
❑ 93StaClu-458
❑ 93StaCluFDI-458
❑ 93StaCluMOP-458
❑ 93Stu-106
❑ 93Top-591
❑ 93TopGol-591
❑ 93TopInaM-591
❑ 93TopInaR-591
❑ 93TopMic-591
❑ 93TopPos-2
❑ 93TopPos-3
❑ 93Ult-346
❑ 93UppDec-538
❑ 93UppDecGold-538
❑ 94Fin-292
❑ 94FinRef-292
❑ 94Fla-312
❑ 94Fle-439
❑ 94FleExtB-115
❑ 94FleUpd-60
❑ 94Pac-194
❑ 94Pin-467
❑ 94PinArtP-467
❑ 94PinMusC-467
❑ 94Sco-336
❑ 94ScoGolR-336
❑ 94ScoRoo-RT50
❑ 94ScoRooGR-RT50
❑ 94SpoRoo-142
❑ 94SpoRooAP-142
❑ 94StaClu-584
❑ 94StaCluFDI-584
❑ 94StaCluGR-584
❑ 94StaCluMOP-584
❑ 94TopTra-12T
❑ 94Ult-386
❑ 95ColCho-492
❑ 95ColChoGS-492
❑ 95ColChoSS-492
❑ 95Don-304
❑ 95DonPreP-304
❑ 95DonTopotO-107
❑ 95Fin-139
❑ 95FinRef-139
❑ 95Fle-198
❑ 95Lea-361
❑ 95Pin-190
❑ 95PinArtP-190
❑ 95PinMusC-190
❑ 95Sco-404
❑ 95ScoGolR-404
❑ 95ScoPlaTS-404
❑ 95StaClu-207
❑ 95StaCluFDI-207
❑ 95StaCluMOP-207
❑ 95StaCluSTWS-207
❑ 95StaCluVR-108
❑ 95StaCluVRMO-108
❑ 95Top-331
❑ 95TopCyb-168
❑ 95Ult-73
❑ 95UltGolM-73
❑ 95USPlaCMLA-3H
❑ 96PawRedSDD-3

Cole, Bert
❑ 21Nei-28
❑ 22E120-49
❑ 22W573-21
❑ 23WilChoV-21
❑ 26Zee-44
❑ 29Zee-41
❑ 30Zee-51
❑ 31Zee-29
❑ 32Zee-31
❑ 33Zee-13
❑ 33Zee-105
❑ 33Zee-106

Cole, Butch
❑ 91AppFoxCB-23
❑ 91AppFoxP-1728
❑ 92BasCitRC-15
❑ 92BasCitRF-3857
❑ 93MemChiF-386

Cole, Chris
❑ 89BurIndS-5

Cole, David
❑ 52Bow-132
❑ 53BowBW-38
❑ 53BraJohC-6
❑ 83Bra53F-30

Cole, Dick (Richard Roy)
❑ 52MotCoo-35
❑ 53BraSpiaS3-7
❑ 54Bow-27
❑ 54Top-84
❑ 55Bow-28
❑ 56PirTeal-4
❑ 57Top-234
❑ 58UniOil-2
❑ 80Bra195T-29
❑ 94TopArc1-84
❑ 94TopArc1G-84

Cole, Doc
❑ 80ChaO'sP-4
❑ 80ChaO'sW-4

Cole, Eric
❑ 96AubDouB-21
❑ 97AubDouTI-2
❑ 98QuaCitRBG-3

Cole, Howard
❑ 90RenSilSCLC-283
Cole, Jason
❑ 94VerExpC-8
❑ 94VerExpF-3902
❑ 96DelShoB-14
❑ 96WesPalBEB-6
❑ 97GreBatB-9
❑ 98arSenW1-8
❑ 98HarSenM-8
Cole, Jim
❑ 93HelBreF-4085
❑ 93HelBreSP-19
❑ 94BelBreC-5
❑ 94BelBreFl-93
❑ 94MidLeaAF-MDW7
❑ 95Bow-187
❑ 95Exc-69
❑ 95SPML-79
❑ 95UppDecML-182
❑ 95UppDecMLFS-182
❑ 96Bow-195
❑ 96BowFoi-195
Cole, Joey
❑ 79QuaCitCT-13
Cole, King (Leonard)
❑ 09SpoNewSM-50
❑ 10ChiE-4
❑ 10DarChoE-10
❑ 10JuJuDE-11
❑ 11BasBatEU-12
❑ 11HelSta-93
❑ 11MecDFT-12
❑ 11PinT-5-203
❑ 11PloCanE-17
❑ 12T207-33
❑ 14B18B-22
Cole, Mark
❑ 88OklSoo-10
❑ 89OklSoo-10
❑ 90LakTigS-4
❑ 92StoPorC-20
❑ 92StoPorF-39
❑ 93StoPorF-749
Cole, Marvin
❑ 88WytCubP-1982
❑ 90PeoChiUTI-U5
❑ 91WinSpiC-18
❑ 91WinSpiP-2835
Cole, Michael
❑ 81WisRapTT-15
Cole, Popeye (Robert)
❑ 37Zee-66
❑ 88SumBraP-392
❑ 89BurBraP-1627
❑ 89BurBraS-5
❑ 90CarLeaA-30
❑ 90DurBulTI-12
❑ 91GreBraC-20
❑ 91GreBraLD-204
❑ 91GreBraP-3014
❑ 91LinDriAA-204
Cole, Rodger
❑ 85PhiTas-42
❑ 85PorBeaC-45
❑ 86IndIndTI-17
Cole, Stu (Stewart)
❑ 87EugEmeP-2652
❑ 89MemChiB-9
❑ 89MemChiP-1184
❑ 89MemChiS-7
❑ 89Sta-41
❑ 90MemChiB-4
❑ 90MemChiP-1014
❑ 90MemChiS-5
❑ 90StaFS7-84
❑ 91LinDriAAA-330
❑ 91OmaRoyLD-330
❑ 91OmaRoyP-1040
❑ 92OmaRoyF-2967
❑ 92OmaRoyS-328
❑ 92SkyAAAF-150
❑ 92StaClu-553
❑ 92TopDeb91-37
❑ 93ColSprSSF-3092
❑ 94ColSprSSF-740
❑ 96AshTouB-3
❑ 97SalAva-4
❑ 98NewHavRM-4
❑ 98NewHavRMA-4
Cole, Terry
❑ 95AshTouTI-NNO
Cole, Tim
❑ 78GreBraT-6
❑ 79SavBraT-20
❑ 82RicBraT-3
❑ 83DurBulT-18
Cole, Victor
❑ 89MemChiB-19
❑ 89MemChiP-1185
❑ 89MemChiS-8
❑ 90CMC-830
❑ 90MemChiB-20
❑ 90MemChiP-1006
❑ 90MemChiS-6
❑ 91LinDriAAA-331
❑ 91OmaRoyLD-331
❑ 91OmaRoyP-1028
❑ 92Bow-239
❑ 92BufBisF-316
❑ 92BufBisS-29
❑ 92DonRoo-27
❑ 92FleUpd-113
❑ 92SkyAAAF-13
❑ 93BufBisF-509
❑ 93Don-120
❑ 93Top-453
❑ 93TopGol-453
❑ 93TopInaM-453
❑ 93TopInaR-453
❑ 93TopMic-453
❑ 98WesTenDJM-5
Cole, Willis Russell
❑ 11PinT-5-755
Cole, Winston
❑ 76BatRouCT-8
❑ 77SalPirT-7
Coleman, Billy
❑ 33WorCig(-19
❑ 91OneYanP-4146
❑ 92GreHorC-14
❑ 92GreHorF-770
❑ 93GreHorC-5
❑ 93GreHorF-879
❑ 94AlbYanF-1432
❑ 94TamYanC-5
❑ 94TamYanF-2375
❑ 95NorNavTI-52
Coleman, Choo Choo (Clarence)
❑ 47Exh-46
❑ 61TopP-502
❑ 63ExhStaB-17
❑ 63Top-27
❑ 64MetJayP-3
❑ 64Top-251
❑ 64TopVen-251
❑ 66Top-561
❑ 76Met63 S-4
❑ 81TCM60I-298
❑ 82MetGal62-25
❑ 89TidTidC-5
❑ 91MetWIZ-79
Coleman, Curt (Curtis H.)
❑ 09ObaT21-224
❑ 09ObaT21-396
❑ 12ObaPreT-145
Coleman, Dale
❑ 90SanAntMGS-11
❑ 91SanAntMP-2967
❑ 91VerBeaDC-6
❑ 91VerBeaDP-767
Coleman, Dave (David Lee)
❑ 79TolMudHT-17
❑ 80ColCliP-17
❑ 80ColCliT-19
❑ 81ColCliP-17
❑ 81ColCliT-18
Coleman, DeWayne
❑ 86VisOakP-7
❑ 87WinSpiP-25
❑ 88ChaWheB-19
Coleman, Ed (Parke Edward)
❑ 30Zee-138
❑ 31Zee-62
❑ 34Gou-28
❑ 34GouCanV-76
❑ 35DiaMatCS3T1-35
❑ 35GouPuzR-8J
❑ 35GouPuzR-9J
❑ 93ConTSN-921
Coleman, Elliot
❑ 92NegLeaRLI-11
Coleman, Glenn
❑ 91BluOriC-14
❑ 91BluOriP-4139
Coleman, Gordy (Gordon C.)
❑ 47Exh-47
❑ 56RedBurB-4
❑ 59RedBurBP-3
❑ 60HenHouW-5
❑ 60Top-257
❑ 60UniOil-19
❑ 61Kah-9
❑ 61RedJayP-4
❑ 61Top-194
❑ 62Jel-116
❑ 62Kah-7
❑ 62Pos-116
❑ 62PosCan-116
❑ 62RedEnq-4
❑ 62RedJayP-3
❑ 62SalPlaC-110
❑ 62ShiPlaC-110
❑ 62Top-508
❑ 62TopStal-113
❑ 63Jel-125
❑ 63Kah-8
❑ 63Pos-125
❑ 63RedEnq-5
❑ 63RedFreBC-3
❑ 63RedJayP-2
❑ 63Top-90
❑ 64Raw-2
❑ 64RedJayP-2
❑ 64Top-577
❑ 65Kah-10
❑ 65RedEnq-5
❑ 65Top-289
❑ 66RedVolC-2
❑ 66Top-494
❑ 67CokCapR-3
❑ 67DexPre-56
❑ 67OPC-61
❑ 67Top-61
❑ 76RedParC-5
❑ 80Red196T-11
❑ 93UppDecS-8
Coleman, Guy
❑ 52LavPro-46
Coleman, Hampton
❑ 52LaPat-3
❑ 52Par-65
❑ 53ExhCan-52
Coleman, J. Dale
❑ 89VerBeaDS-5
Coleman, Jeff
❑ 85CloHSS-11
Coleman, Jerry (Gerald F.)
❑ 19Zee-86
❑ 47Exh-48
❑ 47PM1StaP1-33
❑ 47StaPinP2-10
❑ 47YanTeaT-5
❑ 49Bow-225
❑ 49YanTeal-5
❑ 50Bow-47
❑ 50Dra-26
❑ 50YanTeal-6
❑ 51BerRos-A6
❑ 51Bow-49
❑ 51R42SmaS-10
❑ 51TopRedB-18
❑ 52BerRos-9
❑ 52Bow-73
❑ 52StaCalL-70E
❑ 52StaCalS-84C
❑ 52Top-237
❑ 53Dor-126
❑ 54Bow-81
❑ 54NewYorJA-44
❑ 55Bow-99
❑ 55RobGouS-25
❑ 55RobGouW-25
❑ 56Top-316
❑ 56YanTeal-6
❑ 57Top-192
❑ 57YanJayP-4
❑ 67YanPhoS-99
❑ 77PadSchC-15
❑ 78PadFamF-6
❑ 79TCM50-36
❑ 80Top-356
❑ 83TopRep5-237
❑ 84PadSmo-5
❑ 87nsBasASD-2
❑ 90PadMag-8
❑ 91PadCok-2
❑ 91SweBasG-19
❑ 92YanWIZA-13
❑ 93UppDecAH-33
❑ 94UppDecAH-57
❑ 94UppDecAH1-57
Coleman, Joe H.
❑ 66TopVen-333
❑ 67OPC-167
❑ 67SenPos-8
❑ 67Top-167
❑ 68Top-573
❑ 69MilBra-64
❑ 69MLBOffS-103
❑ 69SenTeal-6
❑ 69SenTeal8-8
❑ 69Top-246
❑ 69TopSta-234
❑ 69TopTeaP-23
❑ 70MLBOffS-281
❑ 70OPC-127
❑ 70Top-127
❑ 71MLBOffS-390
❑ 71OPC-403
❑ 71Top-403
❑ 72Kel-18A
❑ 72Kel-18B
❑ 72MilBra-79
❑ 72OPC-96
❑ 72Top-96
❑ 72Top-640
❑ 73Kel2D-48
❑ 73OPC-120
❑ 73TigJew-6
❑ 73Top-120
❑ 74Kel-3
❑ 74OPC-240
❑ 74Tig-3
❑ 74Top-240
❑ 74TopDecE-53
❑ 74TopSta-173
❑ 75DetTigP-6
❑ 75Hos-60
❑ 75OPC-42
❑ 75Top-42
❑ 75TopMin-42
❑ 76DetTigP-2
❑ 76Hos-89
❑ 76OPC-68
❑ 76OPC-456
❑ 76SSP-358
❑ 76Top-68
❑ 76Top-456
❑ 77Top-219
❑ 78Top-554
❑ 79OPC-166
❑ 79PorBeaT-11
❑ 79Top-329
❑ 80SpoIndT-5
❑ 80Top-542
❑ 81SpoIndT-19
❑ 81TigDetN-126
❑ 82SpoIndT-25
❑ 83PeoSunF-29
❑ 89PacSenL-109
Coleman, Joe P.
❑ 47A'sTeal-7
❑ 48A'sTeal-5
❑ 49A'sTeal-9
❑ 49PhiBul-12
❑ 50A'sTeal-6
❑ 50Bow-141
❑ 51A'sTeal-7
❑ 51Bow-120
❑ 53A'sTeal-7
❑ 53Top-279
❑ 54OriEss-6
❑ 54OriTeal-5
❑ 54Top-156
❑ 55Bow-3
❑ 55OriEss-6
❑ 55RedMan-AL17
❑ 55RobGouS-20
❑ 55RobGouW-20
❑ 55Top-162
❑ 76OPC-68
❑ 76Top-68
❑ 91OriCro-80
❑ 91TopArc1-279
❑ 94TopArc1-156
❑ 94TopArc1G-156
❑ 97BalOriP-10
Coleman, John Francis
❑ 87BucN28-88
❑ 87OldJudN-88
❑ 88AugBecN-8
❑ 88GandBCGCE-8
❑ 88WG1CarG-56
❑ 93AusFut-30
Coleman, Ken
❑ 89UtiBluSP-4
❑ 92SarWhiSCB-2
❑ 92SarWhiSF-212
❑ 93SarWhiSC-7
❑ 94BirBarC-5
❑ 94BirBarF-627
❑ 95OrlCubF-16
Coleman, Matthew
❑ 89BriTigS-5
Coleman, Michael
❑ 95MicBatCTI-6
❑ 96HilStaHWB-17
❑ 96SarRedSB-11
❑ 96Top-438
❑ 97BesAutSBPP-18
❑ 97EasLeaTPB-28
❑ 97TreThuB-11
❑ 98Bow-415
❑ 98BowBes-155
❑ 98BowBesAR-155
❑ 98BowBesR-155
❑ 98BowChr-415
❑ 98BowChrGA-415
❑ 98BowChrGAR-415
❑ 98BowChrI-415
❑ 98BowChrIR-415
❑ 98BowChrR-415
❑ 98BowGolA-415
❑ 98BowInt-415
❑ 98CirThu-232
❑ 98CirThuRav-232
❑ 98CirThuSupRav-232
❑ 98Don-292
❑ 98DonGolPP-292
❑ 98DonSigA-21
❑ 98DonSigAC-29
❑ 98DonSigAM-29
❑ 98DonSilPP-292
❑ 98Fle-207
❑ 98LeaRS-255
❑ 98LeaRSLHolo-255
❑ 98LeaRSLong-255
❑ 98LeaRTrue-255
❑ 98PawRedSQ-11
❑ 98PinSna-BRS10
❑ 98ScoRT-134
❑ 98ScoRTSS-PP83
❑ 98ScoRTSSAP-PP83
❑ 98ScoRTSSAP1-PP83
❑ 98SpoIll-152
❑ 98SpoIllEE-152
❑ 98SpoIllFE-152
❑ 98SpoIllTaN-142
❑ 98SpoIllTaNEE-142
❑ 98Stu-198
❑ 98StuGPP-198
❑ 98StuSPP-198
❑ 98Top-484
❑ 98TopChr-484
❑ 98TopChrR-484
❑ 98TopDevR-484
❑ 98TopDia-484
❑ 98TopMiniC-484
❑ 98Ult-263
❑ 98UltGolM-263
❑ 98UltMas-263
❑ 98UltPlaM-263
❑ 98UltRoctS-7
❑ 98UppDec-278
Coleman, Paul
❑ 89HigSchPLS-10
❑ 89JohCitCS-6
❑ 90Bow-199
❑ 90BowTif-199
❑ 90CMC-842
❑ 90OPC-654
❑ 90SavCarP-2082
❑ 90Sco-662
❑ 90Top-654
❑ 90TopTif-654
❑ 90TopTVCa-43
❑ 91Bow-385
❑ 91SprCarP-755
Coleman, Ray (Raymond L.)
❑ 50Bow-250
❑ 51Bow-136
❑ 52Bow-201
❑ 52Top-211
❑ 52WhiSoxHDP-1
❑ 79DiaGre-194
❑ 83TopRep5-211
Coleman, Rickey
❑ 85BeaGolGT-2
Coleman, Rico
❑ 89SpoIndSP-24
❑ 90ChaRaiB-6
❑ 90ChaRaiP-2053
Coleman, Ronnie
❑ 91BurIndP-3314
❑ 92BurIndC-26
❑ 92BurIndF-1669
❑ 93BurIndC-8
❑ 93BurIndF-3310
Coleman, Scott
❑ 91MarPhiC-25
❑ 91MarPhiP-3445
❑ 92MarPhiC-13
❑ 92MarPhiF-3047
Coleman, Ty
❑ 80BurBeeT-14
Coleman, Vince
❑ 84LouRedR-20
❑ 85CarTeal-6
❑ 85DonHig-29
❑ 85DonHig-54
❑ 85FleUpd-28
❑ 85LouRedR-5
❑ 85TopTifT-24T
❑ 85TopTra-24T
❑ 86BasStaB-22
❑ 86CarIGAS-2
❑ 86CarKASD-1
❑ 86CarSchM-2
❑ 86CarTeal-8
❑ 86Don-181
❑ 86Don-651
❑ 86Fle-31
❑ 86Fle-636
❑ 86Fle-637
❑ 86FleLeaL-7
❑ 86FleLimE-11
❑ 86FleMin-7
❑ 86FleSluBC-M4
❑ 86FleStiC-25
❑ 86KayB-5
❑ 86Lea-115
❑ 86Lea-225
❑ 86OPC-370
❑ 86OPCBoxB-D
❑ 86QuaGra-3
❑ 86SevCoi-S9
❑ 86Spo-24
❑ 86Spo-136
❑ 86Spo-176
❑ 86Top-201
❑ 86Top-370
❑ 86TopGaloC-2
❑ 86TopGloS-21
❑ 86TopMinL-60
❑ 86TopSti-5
❑ 86TopSti-47
❑ 86TopSti-306
❑ 86TopSup-8
❑ 86TopTat-16
❑ 86TopTif-201
❑ 86TopTif-370
❑ 86TopWaxBC-D
❑ 87CarSmo-24
❑ 87CarTeal-3
❑ 87ClaGam-30
❑ 87Don-263
❑ 87DonHig-36
❑ 87DonOpeD-60
❑ 87Fle-290
❑ 87FleGlo-290
❑ 87FleLeaL-11
❑ 87FleLimE-10
❑ 87FleMin-21
❑ 87FleSluBC-M3
❑ 87FleStiC-25
❑ 87KayB-11
❑ 87KraFoo-18
❑ 87Lea-194
❑ 87OPC-119
❑ 87RedFolSB-8
❑ 87Spo-65
❑ 87Spo-152
❑ 87Spo-199
❑ 87SpoTeaP-12
❑ 87StuPan-11
❑ 87Top-590
❑ 87TopCoi-29
❑ 87TopGloS-38
❑ 87TopMinL-32
❑ 87TopSti-50
❑ 87TopTif-590
❑ 88Baz-5
❑ 88CarSmo-19
❑ 88CarTeal-3
❑ 88ClaBlu-223
❑ 88Don-293
❑ 88DonBasB-44

❑ 88Fle-27
❑ 88Fle-634
❑ 88FleBasM-7
❑ 88FleExcS-11
❑ 88FleGlo-27
❑ 88FleGlo-634
❑ 88FleGlo-WS6
❑ 88FleLeaL-7
❑ 88FleMin-106
❑ 88FleStiC-117
❑ 88FleWorS-6
❑ 88K-M-8
❑ 88KeyFooD-11
❑ 88Lea-128
❑ 88MSAIceTD-11
❑ 88MSAJifPD-7
❑ 88OPC-260
❑ 88OurOwnTD-11
❑ 88PanSti-394
❑ 88Sco-68
❑ 88Sco-652
❑ 88ScoGlo-68
❑ 88ScoGlo-652
❑ 88ScoYouS2-24
❑ 88Spo-67
❑ 88Spo-221
❑ 88StaLinCa-3
❑ 88TarPla-10
❑ 88TetTeaD-11
❑ 88Top-1
❑ 88Top-260
❑ 88TopBig-5
❑ 88TopMinL-70
❑ 88TopRevLL-3
❑ 88TopSti-4
❑ 88TopSti-47
❑ 88TopTif-1
❑ 88TopTif-260
❑ 88TopUKM-16
❑ 88TopUKMT-16
❑ 88WeiMarD-11
❑ 88Woo-2
❑ 89Baz-6
❑ 89Bow-443
❑ 89BowTif-443
❑ 89CadEllD-10
❑ 89CarSmo-2
❑ 89CarTeal-3
❑ 89Don-19
❑ 89Don-181
❑ 89DonAll-38
❑ 89DonBasB-19
❑ 89DonPop-38
❑ 89DonSupD-19
❑ 89Fle-445
❑ 89FleBasA-8
❑ 89FleExcS-7
❑ 89FleGlo-445
❑ 89FleLeaL-6
❑ 89OPC-90
❑ 89PanSti-188
❑ 89PanSti-229
❑ 89Sco-155
❑ 89ScoHot1S-86
❑ 89Scomast-35
❑ 89Spo-113
❑ 89Top-90
❑ 89TopBasT-141
❑ 89TopBig-124
❑ 89TopGloA-17
❑ 89TopMinL-34
❑ 89TopSti-43
❑ 89TopSti-154
❑ 89TopTif-90
❑ 89TVSpoM-28
❑ 89TVSpoM-132
❑ 89UppDec-253
❑ 90BasWit-45
❑ 90Baz-8
❑ 90Bow-198
❑ 90BowTif-198
❑ 90CarSmo-1
❑ 90ClaBlu-105
❑ 90Don-279
❑ 90DonBesN-138
❑ 90Fle-245
❑ 90FleAwaW-9
❑ 90FleCan-245
❑ 90HOFStiB-100
❑ 90KayB-7
❑ 90Lea-90
❑ 90MLBBasB-35
❑ 90MSAHolD-15
❑ 90OPC-6
❑ 90OPC-660
❑ 90PanSti-216
❑ 90PanSti-336
❑ 90PanSti-383
❑ 90PubIntS-213
❑ 90PubIntS-609
❑ 90RedFolSB-19
❑ 90Sco-260
❑ 90Sco100S-73
❑ 90Spo-142
❑ 90SprCarDGB-31
❑ 90Top-6
❑ 90Top-660
❑ 90TopBig-184
❑ 90TopDou-12
❑ 90TopMinL-73
❑ 90TopSti-4
❑ 90TopSti-39
❑ 90TopTif-6
❑ 90TopTif-660
❑ 90TopTVCa-32
❑ 90UppDec-68
❑ 90UppDec-223
❑ 90Woo-10
❑ 91BasBesRB-4
❑ 91Baz-12
❑ 91Bow-471
❑ 91CadElD-12
❑ 91Cla1-T91
❑ 91ClaGam-93
❑ 91Don-487
❑ 91Fle-629
❑ 91FleUpd-102
❑ 91Lea-427
❑ 91MetCol8-3
❑ 91MetColP-8
❑ 91MetKah-1
❑ 91MetPerPA-12
❑ 91OPC-160
❑ 91OPCPre-25
❑ 91PanCanT1-41
❑ 91PanFreS-35
❑ 91PanSti-35
❑ 91Pos-5
❑ 91RedFolS-21
❑ 91Sco-450
❑ 91ScoRoo-57T
❑ 91SimandSMLBL-10
❑ 91StaClu-498
❑ 91Stu-202
❑ 91Top-160
❑ 91TopDesS-160
❑ 91TopMic-160
❑ 91TopTif-160
❑ 91TopTra-23T
❑ 91TopTraT-23T
❑ 91TopTriH-N7
❑ 91Ult-212
❑ 91UppDec-461
❑ 91UppDec-768
❑ 92Bow-613
❑ 92CarMcD-42
❑ 92ClaGam-52
❑ 92Don-218
❑ 92Fle-500
❑ 92Lea-42
❑ 92LeaBlaG-42
❑ 92MetColP-12
❑ 92MetKah-1
❑ 92OPC-500
❑ 92PanSti-227
❑ 92Pin-39
❑ 92RedFolS-27
❑ 92Sco-95
❑ 92Sco100S-79
❑ 92ScoProP-24
❑ 92StaClu-40
❑ 92Stu-63
❑ 92Top-500
❑ 92TopGol-500
❑ 92TopGolW-500
❑ 92TopMic-500
❑ 92TriPla-208
❑ 92Ult-229
❑ 92UppDec-131
❑ 93Bow-186
❑ 93Don-618
❑ 93Fla-90
❑ 93Fle-467
❑ 93Lea-57
❑ 93MetColP-27
❑ 93MetKah-11
❑ 93PacSpa-194
❑ 93PanSti-252
❑ 93Pin-69
❑ 93Sco-650
❑ 93Sel-175
❑ 93SP-148
❑ 93StaClu-195
❑ 93StaCluFDI-195
❑ 93StaCluMOP-195
❑ 93Stu-56
❑ 93Top-765
❑ 93TopGol-765
❑ 93TopInaM-765
❑ 93TopInaR-765
❑ 93TopMic-765
❑ 93TriPla-14
❑ 93Ult-424
❑ 93UppDec-748
❑ 93UppDecGold-748
❑ 94Bow-499
❑ 94ColC-601
❑ 94ColChoGS-601
❑ 94ColChoSS-601
❑ 94Fin-326
❑ 94FinRef-326
❑ 94Fla-56
❑ 94FleExtB-84
❑ 94FleUpd-47
❑ 94Lea-240
❑ 94ScoRoo-RT12
❑ 94ScoRooGR-RT12
❑ 94Sel-369
❑ 94SpoRoo-24
❑ 94SpoRooAP-24
❑ 94StaClu-570
❑ 94StaCluFDI-570
❑ 94StaCluGR-570
❑ 94StaCluMOP-570
❑ 94TopTra-106T
❑ 94Ult-361
❑ 94UppDec-376
❑ 94UppDecED-376
❑ 95ColCho-458
❑ 95ColChoGS-458
❑ 95ColChoSS-458
❑ 95Don-118
❑ 95DonPreP-118
❑ 95DonTopotO-84
❑ 95Fle-154
❑ 95Lea-318
❑ 95MarPac-2
❑ 95MarPac-28
❑ 95Pac-198
❑ 95Sco-261
❑ 95ScoGolR-261
❑ 95ScoPlaTS-261
❑ 95StaClu-68
❑ 95StaCluFDI-68
❑ 95StaCluMO-12
❑ 95StaCluMOP-68
❑ 95StaCluSTWS-68
❑ 95StaCluVR-42
❑ 95StaCluVRMO-42
❑ 95Top-419
❑ 95TopCyb-219
❑ 95TopLeaL-LL42
❑ 95UppDecSE-52
❑ 95UppDecSEG-52
❑ 95USPlaCMLA-13H
❑ 96Don-496
❑ 96DonPreP-496
❑ 96EmoXL-163
❑ 96Fla-231
❑ 96Fle-233
❑ 96FleTif-233
❑ 96FleUpd-U117
❑ 96FleUpdTC-U117
❑ 96MetMod-2
❑ 96MetUni-105
❑ 96MetUniP-105
❑ 96Pac-413
❑ 96PanSti-229
❑ 96Sco-441
❑ 96Top-263
❑ 96Ult-458
❑ 96UltGolM-458
❑ 96VanCanB-7
❑ 97Ult-499
❑ 97UltGolME-499
❑ 97UltPlaME-499
❑ 98MemRedG-4

Coleman, W. Rip
❑ 57Top-354
❑ 59Top-51
❑ 59TopVen-51
❑ 60MapLeaSF-4
❑ 60Top-179
❑ 60TopVen-179
❑ 61MapLeaBH-5
❑ 91OriCro-81

Coles, Cad (Cadwallader R.)
❑ 09T206-481

Coles, Chuck (Charles Edward)
❑ 59RedEnq-3
❑ 59Top-120
❑ 59TopVen-120

Coles, Darnell
❑ 81WauTimT-19
❑ 83ChaLooT-1
❑ 84Don-630
❑ 84MarMot-26
❑ 84SalLakCGC-190
❑ 85CalCanC-96
❑ 85DomLeaS-26
❑ 85Don-118
❑ 85Top-108
❑ 85TopTif-108
❑ 86Don-557
❑ 86FleUpd-27
❑ 86Top-337
❑ 86TopTif-337
❑ 86TopTra-26T
❑ 86TopTraT-26T
❑ 87Don-47
❑ 87Don-230
❑ 87DonOpeD-215
❑ 87Fle-148
❑ 87FleGlo-148
❑ 87OPC-388
❑ 87SevCoi-D1
❑ 87SpoTeaP-15
❑ 87TigCaiD-2
❑ 87TigCok-14
❑ 87Top-411
❑ 87TopSti-271
❑ 87TopTif-411
❑ 88Don-572
❑ 88DonBasB-185
❑ 88OPC-46
❑ 88PirTeal-6
❑ 88Sco-554
❑ 88ScoGlo-554
❑ 88StaLinPi-6
❑ 88Top-46
❑ 88TopBig-255
❑ 88TopTif-46
❑ 89Bow-217
❑ 89BowTif-217
❑ 89Don-566
❑ 89DonBasB-163
❑ 89Fle-544
❑ 89FleGlo-544
❑ 89MarMot-23
❑ 89Sco-83
❑ 89Top-738
❑ 89TopBig-133
❑ 89TopTif-738
❑ 89UppDec-339
❑ 90Bow-480
❑ 90BowTif-480
❑ 90Don-212
❑ 90Fle-509
❑ 90FleCan-509
❑ 90MarMot-22
❑ 90OPC-232
❑ 90PanSti-145
❑ 90PubIntS-429
❑ 90Sco-62
❑ 90Top-232
❑ 90TopSti-227
❑ 90TopTif-232
❑ 90UppDec-311
❑ 91Fle-333
❑ 91LinDriAAA-381
❑ 91OPC-506
❑ 91PhoFirLD-381
❑ 91PhoFirP-79
❑ 91Sco-629
❑ 91Top-506
❑ 91TopDesS-506
❑ 91TopMic-506
❑ 91TopTif-506
❑ 92Bow-382
❑ 92NasSouS-281
❑ 92RedKah-26
❑ 93BluJayD-16
❑ 93BluJayFS-6
❑ 93Fle-388
❑ 93FleFinE-290
❑ 93PacSpa-651
❑ 93Sco-416
❑ 93SelRoo-105T
❑ 93UppDec-721
❑ 93UppDecGold-721
❑ 94BluJayUSPC-5S
❑ 94BluJayUSPC-12D
❑ 94Fle-328
❑ 94Sco-537
❑ 94ScoGolR-537
❑ 94StaCluT-162
❑ 94StaCluTFDI-162
❑ 94Ult-137
❑ 95Sco-35
❑ 95ScoGolR-35
❑ 95ScoPlaTS-35

Colescott, Rob
❑ 85LitFalMT-15
❑ 86LitFalMP-6
❑ 87ColMetP-27
❑ 88SavCarP-335
❑ 88SouAtlLAGS-24
❑ 89SprCarB-5

Coletta, Chris
❑ 75IntLeaAT-12
❑ 75IntLeaAT-27

Coletti, John
❑ 91BilMusSP-13

Coletti, Mike
❑ 91BilMusP-3745

Colina, Roberto
❑ 97St.PetDR-13
❑ 97St.PetDRUB-14
❑ 98St.PetDRM-20

Colina, Victor
❑ 76VenLeaS-140
❑ 80VenLeaS-202

Collard, Earl
❑ 29Zee-152
❑ 32Zee-81

Collazo, Alfonso
❑ 76VenLeaS-161

Collett, Mike
❑ 93BelMarCB-1
❑ 93BelMarF-3199
❑ 94BelMarC-8
❑ 94BelMarF-3225

Colletti, Manny
❑ 80WisRapTT-16
❑ 82OmaRoyT-15
❑ 82OrlTwi8SCT-4

Colley, Jay
❑ 88RocRedWP-220

Collie, Tim
❑ 96AugGreB-6

Collier, Anthony
❑ 89GreFalDSP-22
❑ 90StaFS7-20
❑ 90VerBeaDS-8
❑ 91BakDodCLC-20
❑ 91CalLeLA-17
❑ 92ClaFS7-204
❑ 92VerBeaDC-11
❑ 92VerBeaDF-2888
❑ 93SanAntMF-3016

Collier, Dan
❑ 92ElmPioC-2
❑ 92ElmPioF-1394
❑ 93UtiBluSC-1
❑ 93UtiBluSF-3545
❑ 94LynRedSC-6
❑ 94LynRedSF-1903
❑ 96TreThuB-23
❑ 97TulDriTI-8

Collier, Ervin
❑ 92KinMetC-20
❑ 92KinMetF-1523
❑ 93KinMetF-3789

Collier, Lou
❑ 93WelPirC-4
❑ 93WelPirF-3362
❑ 94AugGreC-1
❑ 94AugGreF-3014
❑ 94SouAtlLAF-SAL33
❑ 95Bow-5
❑ 95Exc-252
❑ 95LynHilTI-4
❑ 95SPML-134
❑ 96Bow-158
❑ 96BowFoi-158
❑ 96CarMudB-19
❑ 96DouAllB-38
❑ 97CalCanB-10
❑ 97ColCho-425
❑ 97DonLim-22
❑ 97DonLimE-22
❑ 97DonLimENG-22
❑ 97DonSigA-20
❑ 97DonSigAC-27
❑ 97DonSigAM-27
❑ 97PirPos-7
❑ 98Bow-412
❑ 98BowChr-412
❑ 98BowChrGA-412
❑ 98BowChrGAR-412
❑ 98BowChrI-412
❑ 98BowChrIR-412
❑ 98BowChrR-412
❑ 98BowGolA-412
❑ 98BowInt-412
❑ 98ColCho-208
❑ 98Don-71
❑ 98DonCol-71
❑ 98DonCol-201
❑ 98DonColE-514
❑ 98DonColL-264
❑ 98DonColS-71
❑ 98DonColS-196
❑ 98DonEli-114
❑ 98DonEliA-114
❑ 98DonEliS-114
❑ 98DonGolPP-71
❑ 98DonPriCD-71
❑ 98DonPriCD-201
❑ 98DonPriCE-514
❑ 98DonPriCL-264
❑ 98DonRatR-26
❑ 98DonRatRM-26
❑ 98DonSilPP-71
❑ 98Fle-46
❑ 98Lea-65
❑ 98LeaFraDA-65
❑ 98LeaFraF-65
❑ 98LeaFraM-65
❑ 98LeaFraM-65
❑ 98LeaFraMDC-65
❑ 98LeaFraMDC-65
❑ 98LeaFraMZ2-65
❑ 98LeaRS-259
❑ 98LeaRSLHolo-259
❑ 98LeaRSLong-259
❑ 98LeaRTrue-259
❑ 98MetUni-73
❑ 98MetUniPMG-73
❑ 98PacInvGems-193
❑ 98PacOme-188
❑ 98PacOmeR-188
❑ 98PacOmeRS-11
❑ 98PacOmeRST4-11
❑ 98PacOnl-580
❑ 98PacOnlR-580
❑ 98PacOnlWC-580
❑ 98PinIns-116
❑ 98PinInsCE-116
❑ 98PinInsDE-116
❑ 98Sco-246
❑ 98ScoRT-124
❑ 98Stu-114
❑ 98StuGPP-114
❑ 98StuSPP-114
❑ 98Ult-240
❑ 98UltGolM-240
❑ 98UltMas-240
❑ 98UltPlaM-240
❑ 98UppDec-197
❑ 98Zen-97
❑ 98Zen5 xx7-80
❑ 98Zen5x7GoldImp-80
❑ 98Zen5x7Imp-80
❑ 98ZenRooT-14
❑ 98ZenZ-G-97
❑ 98ZenZ-S-97
❑ 99Fle-392
❑ 99FleSta9-392
❑ 99FleWarT-392
❑ 99Pac-337
❑ 99PacPlaB-337
❑ 99PacRed-337

Collier, Slick
❑ 93KinMetC-5

Colligan, Edward
❑ 14Zee-106

Collins, Allen
❑ 86WesPalBEP-8
❑ 87WesPalBEP-666
❑ 88WesPalBES-8
❑ 90CanIndB-25
❑ 90CanIndP-1286
❑ 90CanIndS-2

Collins, Bill (William J.)
❑ 87OldJudN-89

Collins, Bill (William S.)
❑ 11PinT-5-704
❑ 12ImpTobC-34
❑ 90DodTar-915

Collins, Chris
❑ 86QuaCitAP-7

❑ 87MidAngP-4
❑ 88MidAngGS-7
Collins, Dave (David S.)
❑ 75CalAngP-8
❑ 75SalLakCC-2
❑ 76OPC-363
❑ 76SalLakCGC-19
❑ 76SSP-191
❑ 76Top-363
❑ 77OPC-248
❑ 77Top-431
❑ 78Pep-7
❑ 78SSP270-135
❑ 78Top-254
❑ 79Top-622
❑ 80RedEnq-29
❑ 80Top-73
❑ 81AllGamPI-139
❑ 81CokTeaS-38
❑ 81Don-185
❑ 81Fle-201
❑ 81OPC-175
❑ 81Top-175
❑ 81TopScr-84
❑ 81TopSti-162
❑ 81TopSupHT-32
❑ 82Don-169
❑ 82Fle-61
❑ 82FleSta-14
❑ 82OPC-349
❑ 82Top-595
❑ 82TopSti-33
❑ 82TopStiV-33
❑ 82TopTra-20T
❑ 82YanPhoA-4
❑ 83Don-234
❑ 83Fle-377
❑ 83FleSti-42
❑ 83MadMusF-3
❑ 83OPC-359
❑ 83Top-359
❑ 83TopTra-21T
❑ 84BluJayFS-9
❑ 84Don-650
❑ 84Fle-151
❑ 84Nes792-733
❑ 84OPC-38
❑ 84Top-733
❑ 84TopTif-733
❑ 85A'sMot-14
❑ 85AllGamPI-53
❑ 85Don-241
❑ 85Fle-102
❑ 85FleStaS-55
❑ 85FleUpd-29
❑ 85Lea-172
❑ 85OPC-164
❑ 85Top-463
❑ 85TopSti-363
❑ 85TopTif-463
❑ 85TopTifT-25T
❑ 85TopTra-25T
❑ 86Don-218
❑ 86Fle-415
❑ 86FleUpd-28
❑ 86OPC-271
❑ 86TigCaiD-3
❑ 86Top-271
❑ 86TopSti-172
❑ 86TopTif-271
❑ 86TopTra-27T
❑ 86TopTraT-27T
❑ 87Don-215
❑ 87Fle-149
❑ 87FleGlo-149
❑ 87SpoTeaP-20
❑ 87Top-148
❑ 87TopTif-148
❑ 88RedKah-22
❑ 88Sco-371
❑ 88ScoGlo-371
❑ 88StaLinRe-3
❑ 89Sco-267
❑ 89T/MSenL-22
❑ 89UppDec-351
❑ 90BluJayHS-5
❑ 90CarSmo-2
❑ 90TopTVCa-33
❑ 92YanWIZ8-34
Collins, Don
❑ 80TacTigT-5
❑ 82SprCarF-18
Collins, Eddie (Edw.T.)
❑ 42A'sTeal-11
Collins, Eddie (Edw.T.) Sr.
❑ 03WilCarE-7
❑ 08AmeCarE91-41
❑ 09AmeCarE90-1-26
❑ 09ColChiE-58
❑ 09PhiCarE-6
❑ 09RamT20-28
❑ 09SpoNewSM-16
❑ 09T206-72
❑ 10CouT21-107
❑ 10CouT21-108
❑ 10CouT21-109
❑ 10CouT21-271
❑ 10DarChoE-11
❑ 10DomDisP-27
❑ 10E101-11
❑ 10E102-5
❑ 10E12AmeCDCE125-11
❑ 10E98-9
❑ 10LuxCigPP-4
❑ 10MelMinE-11
❑ 10NadCarE-13
❑ 10NadE1-11
❑ 10NotCov-3
❑ 10PeoT21-13A
❑ 10PeoT21-13B
❑ 10PeoT21-13C
❑ 10RedCroT-12
❑ 10RedCroT-98
❑ 10RedCroT-177
❑ 10SepAnoP-8
❑ 10StaCarE-7
❑ 10SweCapPP-43A
❑ 10SweCapPP-43B
❑ 10W555-16
❑ 10W555-17
❑ 11A'sFirT20-4
❑ 11D35RocB-4
❑ 11DiaGumP-10
❑ 11HelSta-55
❑ 11L1L-125
❑ 11MecDFT-1
❑ 11PinT-5-511
❑ 11PinT-5-522
❑ 11PloCanE-18
❑ 11S74Sil-29
❑ 11S81LarS-100
❑ 11SpoLifCW-69
❑ 11SpoLifM-89
❑ 11T205-31A
❑ 11T205-31B
❑ 11TurRedT-87
❑ 12ColRedB-58
❑ 12ColTinT-58
❑ 12HasTriFT-6
❑ 12HasTriFT-25A
❑ 12HasTriFT-25B
❑ 12HasTriFT-25C
❑ 12T207-34
❑ 14CraJacE-7
❑ 14PieStaT-25
❑ 14PieStaT-26
❑ 14PolGroW-6
❑ 15AmeCarE106-9
❑ 15CraJacE-7
❑ 15SpoNewM-33
❑ 15SpoNewP-3
❑ 16BF2FP-9
❑ 16SpoNewM-34
❑ 16TanBraE-6
❑ 17ColE13-31
❑ 17HolBreD-16
❑ 18WhiSoxTI-4
❑ 19W514-25
❑ 20NatCarE-14
❑ 20W516-23
❑ 21E121So1-11
❑ 21E121So8-12
❑ 21Exh-25
❑ 21Nei-29
❑ 21OxfConE-5
❑ 22AmeCarE122-12
❑ 22E120-16
❑ 22W572-14
❑ 22W573-22
❑ 22W575-18
❑ 22WilPatV-35
❑ 23MapCriV-4
❑ 23W501-38
❑ 23W515-58
❑ 25Exh-73
❑ 26Exh-74
❑ 26SpoComoA-11
❑ 27AmeCarE126-16
❑ 27Exh-54
❑ 27YorCarE-47
❑ 28StaPlaCE-12
❑ 29A'sVil-1
❑ 31W517-52
❑ 32USCar*-1
❑ 33Gou-42
❑ 33GouCanV-42
❑ 36Halof FP-7
❑ 39PC7AlbHoF-18
❑ 48ExhHoF-8
❑ 50CalHOFW-19
❑ 51TopConMA-3
❑ 53ArtHaloFP-19
❑ 59FleWil-9
❑ 59FleWil-39
❑ 59FleWil-75
❑ 60ExhWriH-8
❑ 60Fle-20
❑ 61Fle-16
❑ 61GolPre-28
❑ 63BazA-41
❑ 63GadFunC-57
❑ 63HalofFB-23
❑ 69Baz-7
❑ 69Baz-8
❑ 71FleWorS-8
❑ 72FleFamF-18
❑ 72KelATG-10
❑ 72LauGreF-43
❑ 74A's192T-5
❑ 74A'sTCM1P-4
❑ 74CapPub-20
❑ 75FlePio-20
❑ 75WhiSox1T-3
❑ 76RowExh-13
❑ 76ShaPiz-17
❑ 76WhiSoxTAG-2
❑ 77BobParHoF-14
❑ 77GalGloG-111
❑ 77GalGloG-180
❑ 77GalGloG-182
❑ 77PhiFav-3
❑ 77ShaPiz-16
❑ 79RedSoxEF-16
❑ 80LauFamF-32
❑ 80PacLeg-26
❑ 80PerHaloFP-18
❑ 80SSPHOF-18
❑ 80WhiSoxGT-2
❑ 81ConTSN-39
❑ 81SpoHaloF-7
❑ 82DiaCla-29
❑ 82TCMGreH-29
❑ 83A'sGreT-2
❑ 84GalHaloFRL-17
❑ 85WhiSoxC-44
❑ 87ConSer2-27
❑ 87HygAllG-11
❑ 88ConSer5-5
❑ 88LitSunBS-10
❑ 88PacEigMO-8
❑ 88PacEigMO-99
❑ 89WhiSoxK-2
❑ 90BasWit-76
❑ 90PerGreM-45
❑ 91ConTSN-21
❑ 91ConTSN-312
❑ 92ConTSN-582
❑ 92Man191BSR-3
❑ 93ActPacA-89
❑ 93ActPacA2-23G
❑ 93CraJac-17
❑ 94ConTSN-1040
❑ 94ConTSN-1142
❑ 94ConTSNB-1040
❑ 94ConTSNB-1142
❑ 94TedWil-19
❑ 95ConTSN-1332
❑ 96PitPosH-4
❑ 99UppDecCL-24
❑ 99UppDecCLCC-24
Collins, Edward
❑ 95HelBreTI-20
❑ 96BelSnaTI-10
❑ 97BreCouMB-8
Collins, Franco
❑ 97BatCliTI-30
❑ 98PieBolWM-6
❑ 99BasAmeTP-25
❑ 99BasAmeTPG-25
Collins, Hub (George H.)
❑ 74BroClu-5
❑ 87OldJudN-90
Collins, Jeff
❑ 98SouOreTG-5
Collins, Jimmy (James Joseph)
❑ 03BreE10-22
❑ 04FanCraAL-8
❑ 04RedSoxUP-1
❑ 08AmeCarE91-6
❑ 08RosComP-56
❑ 09RamT20-29
❑ 09T206-412
❑ 11SpoLifCW-70
❑ 11T205-196
❑ 34ButPreR-11
❑ 36R31PasP-42
❑ 39PC7AlbHoF-32
❑ 50CalHOFW-20
❑ 51TopConMA-4
❑ 53ArtHaloFP-20
❑ 60ExhWriH-9
❑ 60Fle-25
❑ 61Fle-99
❑ 63BazA-23
❑ 67TopVen-155
❑ 68SCFOldT-15
❑ 76ShaPiz-32
❑ 77BobParHoF-15
❑ 80PerHaloFP-32
❑ 80SSPHOF-32
❑ 84GalHaloFRL-32
❑ 89HOFStiB-23
❑ 94OriofB-70
Collins, Joe (Joseph E.)
❑ 47StaPinP2-11
❑ 52BerRos-10
❑ 52Bow-181
❑ 52Top-202
❑ 53Dor-105
❑ 53Dor-105A
❑ 53Top-9
❑ 54NewYorJA-45
❑ 54Top-83
❑ 55Top-63
❑ 55TopDouH-65
❑ 56Top-21
❑ 56TopPin-28
❑ 56YanJayP-5
❑ 56YanTeal-7
❑ 57Top-295
❑ 79TCM50-21
❑ 82ASAMicM-19
❑ 83TopRep5-202
❑ 84FifNatC-6
❑ 91TopArc1-9
❑ 94TopArc1-83
❑ 94TopArc1G-83
Collins, Kenneth
❑ 95DanBraTI-6
Collins, Kevin M.
❑ 65Top-581
❑ 69MetTeal-5
❑ 69OPC-127
❑ 69Top-127
❑ 69TopFou-13
❑ 70Top-707
❑ 71OPC-553
❑ 71Top-553
❑ 91MetWIZ-80
Collins, Mike
❑ 92BilMusF-3361
❑ 92BilMusSP-14
❑ 94ButCopKSP-26
❑ 95SanBerSTI-28
❑ 96SanAntMB-27
❑ 97SanAntMB-30
❑ 98GreFalDG-6
❑ 98SanAntMM-30
Collins, Mrs. (Eddie)
❑ 79RedSoxEF-2
Collins, Pat (Tharon L.)
❑ 21Nei-35
❑ 22E120-92
❑ 22W573-23
❑ 27AmeCarE126-35
❑ 28Exh-49
❑ 29ExhFou-1
❑ 30Zee-168
❑ 75Yan192T-3
❑ 79Yan192T-5
❑ 84Yan192G-25
❑ 91ConTSN-118
Collins, Patrick T.
❑ 26Exh-97
Collins, Phil
❑ 32OrbPinNP-22
❑ 32OrbPinUP-13
❑ 33Gou-21
❑ 33GouCanV-21
❑ 33RitCE-13D
❑ 33TatOrb-13
❑ 34DiaMatCSB-30
❑ 35ExhFou-6
❑ 72TCMthe3-9
❑ 93ConTSN-785
Collins, Ray
❑ 11PinT-5-669
❑ 11SpoLifM-4
❑ 12RedSoxBDASP-2
❑ 15CraJacE-169
❑ 16FleBreD-18
Collins, Rip (Harry W.)
❑ 20GasAmeMBD-7
❑ 21E121So8-13
❑ 21KoBreWSI-29
❑ 22W575-19
❑ 94ConTSN-1261
❑ 94ConTSNB-1261
Collins, Rip (James A.)
❑ 31CarMet-5
❑ 34BabRutG-11
❑ 34BatR31-78
❑ 34BatR31-146
❑ 34DiaMatCSB-29
❑ 34Gou-51
❑ 35AlDemDCR3-125
❑ 35DiaMatCS3T1-36
❑ 35WheBB1-6
❑ 36DiaMatCS3T2-4
❑ 36NatChiFPR-20
❑ 36R31PasP-6
❑ 36SandSW-7
❑ 36WorWidGV-18
❑ 47PadTeal-4
❑ 74Car193T-2
❑ 81DiaStaCD-116
❑ 83ConMar-34
❑ 87Car193T-4
❑ 88ConNatA-3
❑ 92CarMcD-2
❑ 92ConTSN-656
❑ 94ConTSN-1237
❑ 94ConTSNB-1237
Collins, Ron
❑ 88EugEmeB-18
❑ 89EugEmeB-20
Collins, Scott
❑ 81BatTroT-19
Collins, Sean
❑ 89EugEmeB-24
❑ 90BasCitRS-4
Collins, Shano (John Francis)
❑ 11BasBatEU-13
❑ 11HelSta-9
❑ 11PinT-5-753
❑ 15SpoNewM-34
❑ 16BF2FP-10
❑ 16SpoNewM-35
❑ 17ColE13-32
❑ 18WhiSoxTI-5
❑ 20NatCarE-15
❑ 21Exh-26
❑ 22E120-2
❑ 22W572-15
❑ 23WilChoV-22
❑ 75WhiSox1T-4
❑ 79RedSoxEF-22
❑ 88PacEigMO-98
❑ 92Man191BSR-4
❑ 93ConTSN-745
❑ 94ConTSN-1042
❑ 94ConTSNB-1042
Collins, Sherman
❑ 89VerBeaDS-6
Collins, Stacey
❑ 91RocExpC-3
❑ 91RocExpP-2038
Collins, Terry
❑ 75AlbDukCa-8
❑ 80AlbDukTc-19
❑ 82VerBeaDT-26
❑ 84AlbDukCr-167
❑ 85AlbDukCr-156
❑ 85DomLeaS-43
❑ 86AlbDukP-3
❑ 87AlbDukD-1
❑ 88AlbDukCm-25
❑ 88AlbDukP-270
❑ 88TriAAAP-47
❑ 89BufBisC-24
❑ 89BufBisP-1668
❑ 90BufBisC-3
❑ 90BufBisP-389
❑ 90BufBisTI-7
❑ 90CMC-3
❑ 90ProAAAF-504
❑ 90TriAllGP-AAA36
❑ 91BufBisLD-49
❑ 91BufBisP-556
❑ 91LinDriAAA-49
❑ 92PirNatl-5
❑ 93PirNatl-6
❑ 94AstMot-1
❑ 95AstMot-1
❑ 96AstMot-1
❑ 97AngMot-1
Collins, Tim
❑ 85BenPhiC-5
Collins, Tony
❑ 86GenCubP-3
❑ 86PeoChiP-3
Collins, Zach
❑ 94IdaFalBF-3576
❑ 94IdaFalBSP-9
Collum, Gary
❑ 93PitMetC-4
❑ 93PitMetF-3723
❑ 94CapCitBC-2
❑ 94CapCitBF-1762
Collum, Jack
❑ 50WorWidGV-30
❑ 54Bow-204
❑ 55Bow-189
❑ 57Top-268
❑ 90DodTar-134
Colman, Frank Lloyd
❑ 52Par-9
Colmenares, Carlos
❑ 92MedHatBJF-3212
❑ 92MedHatBJSP-18
❑ 93MedHatBJF-3742
❑ 93MedHatBJSP-1
Colmenares, Luis
❑ 95AshTouTI-19
❑ 95LinVen-122
❑ 96-97LinVen-80
❑ 96SalAvaB-5
❑ 97SalAva-11
❑ 98SalAvaC-8
Colombino, Carlo
❑ 86AshTouP-5
❑ 87OscAstP-4
❑ 88ColAstB-19
❑ 88SouLeaAJ-10
❑ 89TucTorC-21
❑ 89TucTorJP-5
❑ 89TucTorP-206
❑ 91LinDriAAA-608
❑ 91TucTorLD-608
❑ 91TucTorP-2219
❑ 92CanIndF-695
❑ 92CanIndS-103
❑ 93ReaPhiF-299
❑ 96KenIndB-30
Colombino, Chris
❑ 90OscAstS-5
Colome, Jesus
❑ 99Bow-406
❑ 99BowGol-406
❑ 99BowInt-406
Colon, Angel
❑ 92WelPirC-6
❑ 92WelPirF-1328
Colon, Bartolo
❑ 94BurIndF-3786
❑ 95Bes-16
❑ 95Bow-22
❑ 95BowBes-B73
❑ 95BowBesR-B73
❑ 95KinIndTI-7
❑ 95SPML-45
❑ 95SPMLA-7
❑ 96BesAutSA-14
❑ 96Bow-312
❑ 96BowBes-100
❑ 96BowBesAR-100
❑ 96BowBesMI-9
❑ 96BowBesMIAR-9
❑ 96BowBesMIR-9
❑ 96BowBesR-100
❑ 96BowFoi-312
❑ 96BowMinLP-8
❑ 96CanIndB-8
❑ 96Exc-41
❑ 96ExcSeaC-2
❑ 96Top-428

❑ 97BesAutAS-9
❑ 97BesAutP-R4
❑ 97Bow-94
❑ 97BowBes-111
❑ 97BowBesAR-111
❑ 97BowBesP-19
❑ 97BowBesPAR-19
❑ 97BowBesPR-19
❑ 97BowBesR-111
❑ 97BowCerBlaIA-CA15
❑ 97BowCerBluIA-CA15
❑ 97BowCerGolIA-CA15
❑ 97BowChr-118
❑ 97BowChrI-118
❑ 97BowChrIR-118
❑ 97BowChrR-118
❑ 97BowInt-94
❑ 97ColCho-464
❑ 97Don-354
❑ 97DonGolPP-354
❑ 97DonLim-147
❑ 97DonLimE-147
❑ 97DonLimENG-147
❑ 97DonPre-161
❑ 97DonPreCttC-161
❑ 97DonRooDK-5
❑ 97DonRooDKC-5
❑ 97DonSigA-21
❑ 97DonSigAC-28
❑ 97DonSigAM-28
❑ 97DonSilPP-354
❑ 97DonTea-90
❑ 97DonTeaSPE-90
❑ 97Fin-275
❑ 97FinRef-275
❑ 97Fle-561
❑ 97FleTif-561
❑ 97Lea-326
❑ 97LeaFraM-326
❑ 97LeaFraMDC-326
❑ 97PinCer-131
❑ 97PinCerMBla-131
❑ 97PinCerMBlu-131
❑ 97PinCerMG-131
❑ 97PinCerMR-131
❑ 97PinCerR-131
❑ 97PinTotCPB-131
❑ 97PinTotCPG-131
❑ 97PinTotCPR-131
❑ 97Sel-113
❑ 97SelArtP-113
❑ 97SelCom-113
❑ 97SelRegG-113
❑ 97SP-8
❑ 97StaClu-192
❑ 97StaCluM-M24
❑ 97StaCluMOP-192
❑ 97StaCluMOP-M24
❑ 97Stu-146
❑ 97StuPrePG-146
❑ 97StuPrePS-146
❑ 97Top-386
❑ 97Ult-550
❑ 97UltGolME-550
❑ 97UltPlaME-550
❑ 97UppDec-529
❑ 98CirThu-225
❑ 98CirThuRav-225
❑ 98CirThuSupRav-225
❑ 98ColCho-74
❑ 98Don-109
❑ 98DonCol-109
❑ 98DonCol-188
❑ 98DonColE-492
❑ 98DonColL-287
❑ 98DonColS-109
❑ 98DonColS-183
❑ 98DonEli-92
❑ 98DonEliA-92
❑ 98DonEliS-92
❑ 98DonGolPP-109
❑ 98DonPriCD-109
❑ 98DonPriCD-188
❑ 98DonPriCE-492
❑ 98DonPriCL-287
❑ 98DonRatR-13
❑ 98DonRatRM-13
❑ 98DonSig-117
❑ 98DonSigP-117
❑ 98DonSilPP-109
❑ 98Fin-212
❑ 98FinNo--212
❑ 98FinNo-R-212
❑ 98FinRef-212
❑ 98Fle-155
❑ 98IndSco-14
❑ 98IndScoP-14
❑ 98Lea-88
❑ 98LeaFraDA-88
❑ 98LeaFraF-88
❑ 98LeaFraM-88
❑ 98LeaFraM-88
❑ 98LeaFraMDC-88
❑ 98LeaFraMDC-88
❑ 98LeaFraMZ2-88
❑ 98LeaRS-266
❑ 98LeaRSLHolo-266
❑ 98LeaRSLong-266
❑ 98LeaRTrue-266
❑ 98PacOnl-216
❑ 98PacOnlR-216
❑ 98PacOnlWC-216
❑ 98Pin-178
❑ 98PinArtP-PP81
❑ 98PinMusC-PP81
❑ 98PinPer-108
❑ 98PinPerPP-108
❑ 98PinPreP-178
❑ 98PinSna-CI5
❑ 98ScoRT-63
❑ 98ScoRTSS-PP56
❑ 98ScoRTSSAP-PP56
❑ 98ScoRTSSAP1-PP56
❑ 98StaCluFDI-58
❑ 98StaCluI-58
❑ 98StaCluOneK-58
❑ 98StaCluPP-58
❑ 98Stu-121
❑ 98StuGPP-121
❑ 98StuSPP-121
❑ 98Top-360
❑ 98TopChr-360
❑ 98TopChrR-360
❑ 98TopDevR-360
❑ 98TopDia-360
❑ 98TopMiniC-360
❑ 98UppDec-75
❑ 99199Fin-66
❑ 99Bow-255
❑ 99BowGol-255
❑ 99BowInt-255
❑ 99E-X Cen-58
❑ 99E-X CenECFut-58
❑ 99E-X CenECNow-58
❑ 99FinGolRef-66
❑ 99FinRef-66
❑ 99FlaShoLeg1-73
❑ 99FlaShoLeg2-73
❑ 99FlaShoLeg3-73
❑ 99FlaShoLegM1-73
❑ 99FlaShoLegM2-73
❑ 99FlaShoLegM3-73
❑ 99FlaShoR1-73
❑ 99FlaShoR2-73
❑ 99FlaShoR3-73
❑ 99Fle-56
❑ 99FleMysFI-11
❑ 99FleSta9-56
❑ 99FleWarT-56
❑ 99MetUni-176
❑ 99MetUniGM-176
❑ 99MetUniPMG-176
❑ 99Pac-125
❑ 99PacCroC-83
❑ 99PacCroC-7
❑ 99PacCroCPB-83
❑ 99PacPar-71
❑ 99PacParC-71
❑ 99PacParG-71
❑ 99PacParHoloGold-71
❑ 99PacParHS-71
❑ 99PacParOD-71
❑ 99PacParPB-71
❑ 99PacParRed-71
❑ 99PacPlaB-125
❑ 99PacPri-42
❑ 99PacPriHB-42
❑ 99PacPriHG-42
❑ 99PacPriHM-42
❑ 99PacPriHP-42
❑ 99PacPriRed-42
❑ 99PacRed-125
❑ 99SkyMolM-38
❑ 99SkyMolMX-38
❑ 99SkyPre-207
❑ 99SkyPreA-13
❑ 99SkyPreABlue-13
❑ 99SkyPreR-207
❑ 99SkyThu-98
❑ 99SkyThuRant-98
❑ 99SkyThuRave-98
❑ 99SP Aut-29
❑ 99SP SigAuto-BCO
❑ 99SpoIll-151
❑ 99SPSig-114
❑ 99StaClu-17
❑ 99StaCluFDI-17
❑ 99StaCluOoaK-17
❑ 99StaCluPP-17
❑ 99ThuSkySupR-98
❑ 99Top-40
❑ 99TopChr-40
❑ 99TopChrR-40
❑ 99TopGal-125
❑ 99TopGalPP-125
❑ 99TopGalPPI-125
❑ 99TopMVPP-40
❑ 99TopOpeD-23
❑ 99UD Cho-38
❑ 99UD ChoPCR-38
❑ 99UD Ion-23
❑ 99UD IonR-23
❑ 99Ult-15
❑ 99UltGolM-15
❑ 99UltMas-15
❑ 99UltPlaM-15
❑ 99UppDec-78
❑ 99UppDec-237
❑ 99UppDecEL1-78
❑ 99UppDecEL1-237
❑ 99UppDecEL2-78
❑ 99UppDecEL2-237
❑ 99UppDecM-61
❑ 99UppDecMGS-61
❑ 99UppDecMHFS-61
❑ 99UppDecMP-61
❑ 99UppDecMSS-61
❑ 99Vic-123

Colon, Charlie
❑ 88NebCor-2
❑ 90NebCor-7

Colon, Cris
❑ 87PorChaRP-22
❑ 88GasRanP-1005
❑ 89GasRanP-1014
❑ 89GasRanS-4
❑ 90ChaRanS-3
❑ 90SouAtlLAS-4
❑ 91ChaRanC-17
❑ 91ChaRanP-1321
❑ 91Cla/Bes-183
❑ 92Bow-405
❑ 92SkyAA F-266
❑ 92TulDriF-2700
❑ 92TulDriS-605
❑ 93Don-353
❑ 93LinVenB-150
❑ 93LinVenB-301
❑ 93LinVenB-319
❑ 93RanKee-107
❑ 93Sco-314
❑ 93Top-809
❑ 93TopGol-809
❑ 93TopInaM-809
❑ 93TopInaR-809
❑ 93TopMic-809
❑ 93TulDriF-2739
❑ 93TulDriTI-6
❑ 93UppDec-14
❑ 93UppDecGold-14
❑ 94ClaGolF-180
❑ 94IowCubF-1280
❑ 94UppDecML-197
❑ 94VenLinU-227
❑ 95IowCubTI-8
❑ 95LinVen-43
❑ 96-97LinVen-98

Colon, David
❑ 88BlaYNPRWL-103
❑ 88SumBraP-411
❑ 89BlaYNPRWL-111
❑ 90CMC-702
❑ 90WatDiaB-2
❑ 90WatDiaP-2389
❑ 91PalSprAP-2027
❑ 92PalSprAC-24
❑ 92PalSprAF-853

Colon, Dennis
❑ 92BurAstC-19
❑ 92BurAstF-553
❑ 93OscAstC-8
❑ 93OscAstF-634
❑ 94JacGenF-222
❑ 95JacGenTI-21
❑ 96JacGenB-6
❑ 98NorTidP-6

Colon, Felix
❑ 90WinHavRSS-2
❑ 91ElmPioC-2
❑ 91ElmPioP-3275
❑ 92WinHavRSF-1784
❑ 93LynRedSC-6
❑ 93LynRedSF-2522
❑ 94ExcFS7-19
❑ 94NewBriRSF-656

Colon, Hector
❑ 91JohCitCC-14
❑ 91JohCitCP-3988
❑ 92JohCitCC-22
❑ 92JohCitCF-3129
❑ 93SavCarC-10
❑ 93SavCarF-698
❑ 94MadHatC-5
❑ 94MadHatF-138

Colon, Jose
❑ 91BurIndP-3291

Colon, Julio
❑ 94GreFalDSP-5
❑ 95SanBerSTI-4
❑ 96VerBeaDB-11

Colon, Roman
❑ 98DanBraQ-7

Colon, Roque
❑ 92HunCubC-7
❑ 92HunCubF-3161

Colon, Tony
❑ 88BlaYNPRWLU-48
❑ 89GenCubP-1875

Colonels, Louisville
❑ 38BasTabP-34
❑ 86JosHalC-10

Colonials, Georgia
❑ 89GeoColC-33

Colpaert, Dick
❑ 73OPC-608
❑ 73Top-608

Colpitt, Mike
❑ 87SpaPhiP-28

Colquitt, Jason
❑ 98LakTigM-13

Colschen, Donna
❑ 76CliPilT-37

Colschen, Fritz
❑ 76CliPilT-37

Colson, Brent
❑ 92YakBeaF-3440
❑ 93BakDodCLC-4

Colson, Bruce
❑ 88CedRapRP-1145

Colson, Loyd
❑ 71OPC-111
❑ 71Top-111
❑ 92YanWIZ7-37

Colston, Frank
❑ 87MiaMarP-16
❑ 87SalLakTTT-18
❑ 88WauTimGS-24

Colt 45s, Houston
❑ 62GuyPotCP-8
❑ 63Top-312
❑ 89AstCol4S-29
❑ 93TedWilPC-10

Colton, Lawrence
❑ 68Top-348
❑ 68TopVen-348
❑ 69Top-454A
❑ 69Top-454B

Coltrin, Robert
❑ 17Zee-24

Coluccio, Bob (Robert P.)
❑ 74OPC-124
❑ 74Top-124
❑ 74TopSta-194
❑ 75OPC-456
❑ 75Top-456
❑ 75TopMin-456
❑ 76OPC-333
❑ 76SSP-150
❑ 76Top-333
❑ 78ChaChaT-5
❑ 94BreMilB-300

Columna, Jose
❑ 93DanBraC-9
❑ 93DanBraF-3623
❑ 94MacBraC-4
❑ 94MacBraF-2212

Colvard, Ben (Benny)
❑ 88BilMusP-1830
❑ 89CedRapRB-19
❑ 89CedRapRP-916
❑ 89CedRapRS-4
❑ 89Sta-197
❑ 90ChaLooGS-9
❑ 91ChaLooP-1971
❑ 92ChaLooF-3829
❑ 92ChaLooS-179
❑ 92ClaFS7-69

Colvin, Jeff
❑ 92DavLipB-9

Colwell, Ira
❑ 23Zee-30

Colyer, Steve
❑ 98YakBeaG-9
❑ 99Bow-387
❑ 99BowGol-387
❑ 99BowInt-387

Colzie, Rick
❑ 79WatIndT-20
❑ 80BatTroT-22
❑ 81WatIndT-2

Combe, Geoff
❑ 79IndIndTI-19
❑ 79NaSouTI-6
❑ 80IndIndTI-7
❑ 81IndIndTI-3
❑ 81Top-606
❑ 82EdmTraT-23
❑ 82Fle-62
❑ 82Top-351

Combs, Bobby
❑ 75AppFoxT-5
❑ 77AppFoxT-4

Combs, Chris
❑ 97EriSeaWB-7
❑ 98AugGreM-16

Combs, Earle Bryan
❑ 26Exh-98
❑ 28W502-21
❑ 28W513-86
❑ 28Yue-21
❑ 29ExhFou-25
❑ 29PorandAR-13
❑ 30SchR33-28
❑ 31Exh-25
❑ 31W517-1
❑ 32OrbPinNP-111
❑ 32USCar*-5
❑ 33Gou-103
❑ 33WorCig-20
❑ 34GouCanV-21
❑ 36GouWidPPR-A18
❑ 40PlaBal-124
❑ 43YanSta-6
❑ 46SpoExcW-3-8
❑ 50RedSoxTI-2
❑ 54Top-183
❑ 61Fle-17
❑ 72TCMthe3-10
❑ 75Yan192T-4
❑ 75YanDyn1T-8
❑ 76RowExh-2
❑ 76ShaPiz-116
❑ 77GalGloG-109
❑ 79Yan192T-6
❑ 80PacLeg-105
❑ 80PerHaloFP-116
❑ 80SSPHOF-116
❑ 82TCMGreH-32
❑ 84Yan192G-3
❑ 87Yan192T-6
❑ 91ConTSN-105
❑ 91ConTSN-262
❑ 92ConTSN-466
❑ 92ConTSN-583
❑ 92YanWIZH-6
❑ 93ConTSN-732
❑ 94TopArc1-183
❑ 94TopArc1G-183

Combs, Mark
❑ 87SanBerSP-9
❑ 88FreSunCLC-2

Combs, Merrill R.
❑ 48SigOil-4
❑ 48SmiClo-23
❑ 49RedSoxTI-2
❑ 52Top-18
❑ 54SeaPop-5
❑ 75RanPos-6
❑ 83TopRep5-18
❑ 93RanKee-108

Combs, Pat
❑ 87PanAmTUBI-25
❑ 87PanAmTURB-5
❑ 88TopTra-30T
❑ 88TopTraT-30T
❑ 89BasAmeAPB-AA10
❑ 89Bow-398
❑ 89BowTif-398
❑ 89ClePhiS-8
❑ 89ReaPhiP-676
❑ 89ReaPhiS-9
❑ 89Sta-12
❑ 89StaFutS-11
❑ 89StaFutS-12
❑ 89TopBig-227
❑ 90Bow-148
❑ 90BowTif-148
❑ 90ClaUpd-T12
❑ 90Don-44
❑ 90DonBesN-49
❑ 90DonRoo-3
❑ 90Fle-553
❑ 90FleCan-553
❑ 90Lea-78
❑ 90OPC-384
❑ 90PhiTas-5
❑ 90Sco-623
❑ 90ScoRooDT-B2
❑ 90ScoYouS2-4
❑ 90Top-384
❑ 90TopBig-136
❑ 90TopDeb89-24
❑ 90TopTif-384
❑ 90UppDec-763
❑ 90UppDecS-1
❑ 91Bow-498
❑ 91Cla2-T41
❑ 91ClaGam-94
❑ 91Don-60
❑ 91Fle-392
❑ 91Lea-32
❑ 91OPC-571
❑ 91PhiMed-9
❑ 91Sco-440
❑ 91Sco100RS-72
❑ 91StaClu-36
❑ 91StaCluP-10
❑ 91Top-571
❑ 91TopDesS-571
❑ 91TopMic-571
❑ 91TopRoo-7
❑ 91TopTif-571
❑ 91ToyRoo-6
❑ 91Ult-259
❑ 91UppDec-537
❑ 92Don-76
❑ 92Fle-525
❑ 92OPC-456
❑ 92PhiMed-39
❑ 92Sco-106
❑ 92ScrRedBF-2442
❑ 92ScrRedBS-482
❑ 92StaClu-443
❑ 92Top-456
❑ 92TopGol-456
❑ 92TopGolW-456
❑ 92TopMic-456
❑ 92TriPla-170
❑ 92UppDec-442
❑ 93ScrRedBF-2540
❑ 93ScrRedBTI-6
❑ 94ScrRedBF-916
❑ 98ScrRedB1ATI-5

Comeau, Drew
❑ 88CapCodPPaLP-124

Comeaux, Eddie
❑ 94HudValRC-3
❑ 94HudValRF-3397
❑ 95ChaRivTI-25

Comer, H. Wayne
❑ 66TolMudHTI-4
❑ 69PilPos-13
❑ 69PilWhe-1
❑ 69Top-346
❑ 70BreMcD-5
❑ 70BreMil-3
❑ 70MLBOffS-268
❑ 70OPC-323
❑ 70Top-323
❑ 77PilPosR-13
❑ 83Pil69G-42
❑ 88TigDom-3
❑ 94BreMilB-301

Comer, Scott
❑ 97PitMet-9

Comer, Steve
❑ 79Top-463
❑ 80Top-144
❑ 81Top-592
❑ 82Don-341
❑ 82Fle-314
❑ 82FleSta-177
❑ 82Top-16
❑ 82TopSti-242
❑ 83Don-163

- 83Fle-564
- 83Top-353
- 84IndWhe-31
- 85Top-788
- 85TopTif-788
- 86MaiGuiP-6
- 88OrlTwiB-7
- 93RanKee-109

Comimbre, Pancho (Francisco)
- 87NegLeaPD-38

Comiskey, Charlie (Charles A.)
- 09SpoNewSM-15
- 14CraJacE-23
- 15CraJacE-23
- 15SpoNewM-35
- 16BF2FP-11
- 16SpoNewM-36
- 18WhiSoxTI-1
- 36Halof FP-8
- 39PC7AlbHoF-19
- 50CalHOFW-21
- 53ArtHaloFP-21
- 61Fle-18
- 74CapPub-44
- 76ShaPiz-22
- 76SSP188WS-14
- 77BobParHoF-16
- 80PerHaloFP-20
- 80SSPHOF-19
- 84GalHaloFRL-22
- 87AllandGN-5
- 87BucN28-96
- 87ConSer2-26
- 87LonJacN-3
- 87OldJudN-91A
- 87OldJudN-91B
- 87ScrDC-3
- 88GandBCGCE-9
- 88LitSunBS-12
- 88PacEigMO-24
- 88PacEigMO-80
- 88SpoTimM-6
- 89EdgR.WG-5
- 92Man191BSR-5
- 94OriofB-71
- 95ConTSN-1397
- 95ConTSNP-1397

Commodores, Falmouth
- 88CapCodPB-27

Como, George
- 82HolMilT-25
- 83NasAngT-26
- 85NasPirT-28

Comoletti, Glenn
- 78St.PetCT-7

Comorosky, Adam A.
- 31Exh-13
- 33Gou-77
- 33GouCanV-70
- 33WorCig-21
- 34BatR31-44
- 34Gou-85
- 35GouPuzR-1H
- 35GouPuzR-3F
- 35GouPuzR-5B
- 35GouPuzR-6B
- 35GouPuzR-11K
- 35GouPuzR-13B
- 35GouPuzR-14F
- 35GouPuzR-15F
- 85BigLeaC3-42
- 91ConTSN-73

Compres, Fidel
- 87WatIndP-1
- 90ChaRanS-4
- 91ArkTraP-1276
- 91LinDriAAA-231
- 91LouRedLD-231
- 92ArkTraF-1122
- 92ArkTraS-30
- 92ClaFS7-331
- 92SkyAA F-14
- 93LimRocDWB-7
- 93LouRedF-207
- 94LasVegSF-866

Compton, Bruce
- 80QuaCitCT-20

Compton, Clint
- 92ChaRaiC-17
- 93RanCucQC-8
- 93RanCucQF-822

Compton, Clint (Robert Clinton)
- 73WicAerJPKB-3

Compton, Council
- 89PulBraP-1891

Compton, Kenny
- 86FreGiaSB-27

Compton, Mike (Michael Lynn)
- 71MLBOffS-174
- 71OPC-77
- 71Top-77
- 77SpaPhiT-19
- 80WatRedT-10

Compton, Pete (Anna S.)
- 19Zee-110
- 20Zee-61
- 21Zee-66
- 22Zee-57
- 23Zee-125

Compton, Scott
- 93YakBeaC-6
- 93YakBeaF-3894

Comstock, Brad
- 87EveGiaC-27
- 88FreSunCLC-25
- 88FreSunP-1226

Comstock, Keith
- 77QuaCitAT-10
- 80WesHavWCT-19B
- 81WesHavAT-6
- 82TacTigT-39
- 82WesHavAT-5
- 83BirBarT-22
- 84MinTwiP-7
- 84TolMudHT-16
- 84TwiTeal-16
- 87GiaPos-6
- 88Fle-579
- 88FleGlo-579
- 88LasVegSC-2
- 88LasVegSP-246
- 88Sco-438
- 88ScoGlo-438
- 88Top-778A
- 88Top-778B
- 88TopClo-25
- 88TopTif-778
- 89BirBarADB-5
- 89LasVegSC-2
- 89LasVegSP-14
- 90BirBarADB-5
- 90Bow-467
- 90BowTif-467
- 90Fle-510
- 90FleCan-510
- 90Lea-522
- 90MarMot-23
- 91Don-246
- 91MarCouH-20
- 91OPC-337
- 91Sco-502
- 91StaClu-556
- 91Top-337A
- 91Top-337B
- 91TopDesS-337
- 91TopMic-337
- 91TopTif-337
- 94EveGiaC-29
- 95BurBeeTI-33
- 96BurBeeTI-28
- 97SanJosG-27
- 98SalVol-5

Conaster, Clint
- 50W720HolS-5

Concello, Antoinette
- 40WheM4-11
- 41WheM5-17

Concepcion, Carlos
- 84ChaO'sT-6

Concepcion, Dave (David E.)
- 70DayDaiNM-59
- 71MLBOffS-56
- 71OPC-14
- 71Top-14
- 72OPC-267
- 72Top-267
- 72TopCloT-7
- 73OPC-554
- 73Top-554
- 74OPC-435
- 74Top-435
- 74TopSta-24
- 75Hos-47
- 75OPC-17
- 75Top-17
- 75TopMin-17
- 76Hos-128
- 76LinSup-98
- 76OPC-48
- 76RedIceL-2
- 76RedKro-5
- 76RedParC-6
- 76SSP-34
- 76Top-48
- 76VenLeaS-5
- 76VenLeaS-227
- 77BurCheD-200
- 77ChiWilD-17
- 77DaiIsID-17
- 77DetCaeD-17
- 77HolInnD-17
- 77Hos-95
- 77MSADis-17
- 77OPC-258
- 77PepGloD-47
- 77RCColC-19
- 77SagDis-17
- 77sDis-17
- 77Top-560
- 77WenDis-17
- 77ZipDis-17
- 78Hos-108
- 78OPC-220
- 78Pep-8
- 78RCColC-47
- 78SSP270-133
- 78Top-180
- 78WifBalD-19
- 79BasPat-21
- 79Hos-85
- 79OPC-234
- 79Top-450
- 80OPC-117
- 80RedEnq-13
- 80Top-220
- 81AllGamPI-110
- 81CokTeaS-39
- 81Don-181
- 81Fle-197
- 81FleStiC-101
- 81Kel-28
- 81OPC-83
- 81PerAll-2
- 81Top-375
- 81TopScr-95
- 81TopSti-161
- 81TopSupHT-33
- 82Don-421
- 82Fle-63
- 82Fle-630
- 82FleSta-15
- 82FleSta-109
- 82Kel-22
- 82OPC-86
- 82OPC-221
- 82OPC-340
- 82PerAll-11
- 82PerAllG-11
- 82RedCok-5
- 82Squ-15
- 82Top-340
- 82Top-660
- 82Top-661
- 82TopSti-37
- 82TopSti-124
- 82TopStiV-37
- 83AllGamPI-110
- 83Don-148
- 83DonActA-47
- 83Fle-588
- 83Fle-631
- 83FleSta-42
- 83FleSti-219
- 83Kel-57
- 83OPC-32
- 83OPC-102
- 83RedYea-13
- 83Top-400
- 83Top-720
- 83TopFol-5
- 83TopGloS-34
- 83TopSti-227
- 84AllGamPI-20
- 84Don-2
- 84Don-2A
- 84Don-121
- 84Fle-466
- 84FunFooP-23
- 84MilBra-6
- 84Nes792-55
- 84OCoandSI-55
- 84OPC-55
- 84RalPur-20
- 84RedEnq-5
- 84Top-55
- 84TopCer-20
- 84TopRubD-15
- 84TopSti-56
- 84TopTif-55
- 85AllGamPI-111
- 85Don-203
- 85DonHig-8
- 85Fle-532
- 85Lea-131
- 85OPC-21
- 85RedYea-2
- 85Top-515
- 85TopMin-515
- 85TopRubD-13
- 85TopSti-48
- 85TopTif-515
- 86BasStaB-23
- 86Don-243
- 86Fle-174
- 86GenMilB-5A
- 86OPC-195
- 86RedTexG-13
- 86Spo-131
- 86Spo-153
- 86Top-195
- 86Top-366
- 86TopSti-137
- 86TopTat-22
- 86TopTif-195
- 86TopTif-366
- 87Fle-196
- 87FleGlo-196
- 87OPC-193
- 87RedFolSB-12
- 87RedKah-13
- 87Top-731
- 87TopTif-731
- 88Don-329
- 88Fle-229
- 88FleGlo-229
- 88OPC-336
- 88PanSti-275
- 88RedKah-13
- 88Sco-210
- 88ScoGlo-210
- 88Spo-218
- 88StaLinRe-4
- 88Top-422
- 88TopBig-144
- 88TopTif-422
- 89Fle-156
- 89FleGlo-156
- 89Sco-166
- 89UppDec-196
- 91MDAA-6
- 93Pin-482
- 95LinVen-257
- 96-97LinVen-289
- 96-97LinVen-290
- 96-97LinVen-291
- 96-97LinVen-292
- 96-97LinVen-293
- 96-97LinVen-294
- 96-97LinVen-295
- 96-97LinVen-296
- 96-97LinVen-297
- 96Red76K-4

Concepcion, Onix
- 81OmaRoyT-16
- 82Roy-6
- 83Don-516
- 83Fle-110
- 83RoyPos-9
- 83Top-52
- 84Don-95
- 84Fle-345
- 84Nes792-247
- 84RoyPos-8
- 84Top-247
- 84TopTif-247
- 85AllGamPI-19
- 85Don-155
- 85Fle-200
- 85RoyTeal-7
- 85SubDis-8
- 85ThoMcAD-8
- 85Top-697
- 85TopTif-697
- 86Don-252
- 86Fle-6
- 86OPC-163
- 86RoyKitCD-5
- 86Top-596
- 86TopTif-596

Concepcion, Yamil
- 91PriRedC-19
- 91PriRedP-3520
- 92PriRedC-6
- 92PriRedF-3078
- 93PriRedC-4
- 93PriRedF-4185

Conde, Argenis
- 88SouBenWSGS-18
- 93LinVenB-18
- 94VenLinU-154
- 95LinVen-123
- 96-97LinVen-90

Conde, Ramon Luis
- 60DarFar-14
- 61UniOil-SP2
- 89BlaYNPRWL-30

Condon, Mike
- 97ButCopKB-4
- 97ButCopKK-4

Cone, David
- 82ChaRoyT-20
- 84MemChiT-25
- 85OmaRoyT-25
- 86OmaRoyP-6
- 86OmaRoyT-16
- 86RoyTeal-6
- 87Don-502
- 87DonRoo-35
- 87SpoRoo2-39
- 87TopTra-24T
- 87TopTraT-24T
- 88Don-653
- 88DonBasB-40
- 88DonTeaBM-653
- 88Fle-131
- 88FleGlo-131
- 88MetColP-16
- 88MetKah-44
- 88Sco-49
- 88ScoGlo-49
- 88StaCon-1
- 88StaCon-2
- 88StaCon-3
- 88StaCon-4
- 88StaCon-5
- 88StaCon-6
- 88StaCon-7
- 88StaCon-8
- 88StaCon-9
- 88StaCon-10
- 88StaCon-11
- 88StaLinMe-4
- 88Top-181
- 88TopTif-181
- 88ToyRoo-8
- 89Bow-375
- 89BowTif-375
- 89CadEllD-11
- 89ClaLigB-100
- 89ClaTraO-125
- 89Don-9
- 89Don-388
- 89DonAll-44
- 89DonBasB-96
- 89DonSupD-9
- 89Fle-31
- 89Fle-636
- 89FleBasA-9
- 89FleExcS-8
- 89FleGlo-31
- 89FleGlo-636
- 89FleHeroB-9
- 89FleLeaL-7
- 89FleWaxBC-C7
- 89KeyFooD-2
- 89MetColP-4
- 89MetFanC-44
- 89MetKah-5
- 89MSAHolD-19
- 89MSAIceTD-2
- 89Nis-19
- 89OPC-384
- 89OurOwnTD-2
- 89PanSti-129
- 89RedFolSB-24
- 89Sco-221
- 89ScoHot1S-2
- 89ScoYouSI-9
- 89Spo-51
- 89TetTeaD-2
- 89Top-710
- 89TopDouM-6
- 89TopGloS-6
- 89TopHilTM-9
- 89TopMinL-24
- 89TopSti-96
- 89TopStiB-58
- 89TopTif-710
- 89TopUKM-17
- 89TVSpoM-6
- 89UppDec-584
- 89WeiMarD-2
- 90Bow-125
- 90BowTif-125
- 90Don-265
- 90DonBesN-43
- 90Fle-200
- 90FleCan-200
- 90FleLeaL-7
- 90FleLeaLC-7
- 90Lea-40
- 90MetColP-12
- 90MetColP-1
- 90MetFanC-44
- 90MetKah-44
- 90MLBBasB-11
- 90OPC-30
- 90PanSti-301
- 90PublntS-129
- 90Sco-430
- 90Spo-201
- 90Top-30
- 90TopBig-11
- 90TopMinL-65
- 90TopSti-93
- 90TopTif-30
- 90TopTVM-8
- 90UppDec-224
- 91Bow-460
- 91Don-154
- 91Fle-143
- 91Lea-253
- 91MetCol8-6
- 91MetColP-14
- 91MetKah-17
- 91MetPerPA-13
- 91MetTro-1
- 91MetWIZ-81
- 91OPC-680
- 91PanCanT1-73
- 91PanSti-80
- 91Sco-409
- 91Sco-549
- 91SimandSMLBL-11
- 91StaClu-367
- 91StaCluMO-13
- 91Top-680
- 91TopDesS-680
- 91TopMic-680
- 91TopTif-680
- 91Ult-213
- 91UppDec-366
- 92Bow-238
- 92Cla1-T27
- 92Cla2-T45
- 92ClaGam-143
- 92Don-97
- 92Fle-501
- 92Fle-687
- 92FleSmo'nH-S3
- 92FleUpd-63
- 92Hig5-71
- 92LaKdec-7
- 92Lea-92
- 92LeaBlaG-92
- 92MetColP-6
- 92MetKah-17
- 92OPC-195
- 92OPCPre-175
- 92Pin-450
- 92Pin-590
- 92Pin-611
- 92Sco-680
- 92Sco-795
- 92Sco100S-16
- 92ScoImpP-90
- 92ScoRoo-27T
- 92SpoIllFK1-381
- 92SpoIllFK1-770
- 92StaClu-17
- 92Top-195
- 92TopGol-195
- 92TopGolW-195
- 92TopKid-16
- 92TopMic-195
- 92TriPla-35
- 92TriPla-64
- 92TriPlaP-8
- 92Ult-230

- ❑ 92UltAllS-19
- ❑ 92UppDec-364
- ❑ 92UppDecTMH-17
- ❑ 93BluJayD4-15
- ❑ 93Bow-97
- ❑ 93ClaGam-23
- ❑ 93Don-712
- ❑ 93Fin-115
- ❑ 93FinJum-115
- ❑ 93FinRef-115
- ❑ 93Fla-214
- ❑ 93Fle-691
- ❑ 93FleFlnE-216
- ❑ 93FunPac-179
- ❑ 93FunPac-182
- ❑ 93Lea-250
- ❑ 93OPC-107
- ❑ 93OPCPre-92
- ❑ 93OPCWorC-4
- ❑ 93PacSpa-486
- ❑ 93Pin-489
- ❑ 93Pin-544
- ❑ 93RoyPol-6
- ❑ 93RoyStaC-17
- ❑ 93Sco-654
- ❑ 93Sel-361
- ❑ 93SelRoo-18T
- ❑ 93SelStaL-77
- ❑ 93SP-228
- ❑ 93StaClu-703
- ❑ 93StaCluFDI-703
- ❑ 93StaCluM-154
- ❑ 93StaCluMOP-703
- ❑ 93Top-720
- ❑ 93TopGol-720
- ❑ 93TopInaM-720
- ❑ 93TopInaR-720
- ❑ 93TopMic-720
- ❑ 93TopTra-125T
- ❑ 93Ult-558
- ❑ 93UppDec-335
- ❑ 93UppDec-534
- ❑ 93UppDecGold-335
- ❑ 93UppDecGold-534
- ❑ 94Bow-593
- ❑ 94BowBes-R46
- ❑ 94BowBesR-R46
- ❑ 94ColC-81
- ❑ 94ColChoGS-81
- ❑ 94ColChoSS-81
- ❑ 94Don-194
- ❑ 94Fin-52
- ❑ 94FinPre-52P
- ❑ 94FinRef-52
- ❑ 94Fla-297
- ❑ 94Fle-152
- ❑ 94FleExtB-85
- ❑ 94FleExtBPD-3
- ❑ 94FleSmo'nH-2
- ❑ 94Lea-274
- ❑ 94LeaL-36
- ❑ 94OPC-260
- ❑ 94Pac-281
- ❑ 94Pin-325
- ❑ 94PinArtP-325
- ❑ 94PinMusC-325
- ❑ 94ProMag-63
- ❑ 94RedFolMI-19
- ❑ 94Sco-405
- ❑ 94ScoGolR-405
- ❑ 94Sel-76
- ❑ 94SP-171
- ❑ 94SPDieC-171
- ❑ 94Spo-39
- ❑ 94StaClu-292
- ❑ 94StaCluFDI-292
- ❑ 94StaCluGR-292
- ❑ 94StaCluMOP-292
- ❑ 94Stu-182
- ❑ 94Top-510
- ❑ 94TopGol-510
- ❑ 94TopSpa-510
- ❑ 94TriPla-232
- ❑ 94Ult-362
- ❑ 94UppDec-413
- ❑ 94UppDecED-413
- ❑ 95Baz-57
- ❑ 95BazRedH-RH12
- ❑ 95BluJayOH-8
- ❑ 95BluJayUSPC-9S
- ❑ 95Bow-407
- ❑ 95BowBes-R31
- ❑ 95BowBesR-R31
- ❑ 95ColCho-66
- ❑ 95ColCho-536T
- ❑ 95ColCho-TC2
- ❑ 95ColChoGS-66
- ❑ 95ColChoSE-210
- ❑ 95ColChoSEGS-210
- ❑ 95ColChoSESS-210
- ❑ 95ColChoSS-66
- ❑ 95Don-289
- ❑ 95DonDiaK-DK25
- ❑ 95DonDom-1
- ❑ 95DonMouM-2
- ❑ 95DonPreP-289
- ❑ 95DonTopotO-118
- ❑ 95Emo-92
- ❑ 95Fin-99
- ❑ 95FinRef-99
- ❑ 95Fla-43
- ❑ 95Fla-313
- ❑ 95Fle-155
- ❑ 95FleAllS-19
- ❑ 95FleAwaW-3
- ❑ 95FleTeaL-7
- ❑ 95FleUpd-29
- ❑ 95FleUpdDT-4
- ❑ 95Lea-339
- ❑ 95LeaChe-2
- ❑ 95LeaLim-59
- ❑ 95Pac-199
- ❑ 95PacPri-63
- ❑ 95PanSti-18
- ❑ 95PanSti-112
- ❑ 95Pin-270
- ❑ 95PinArtP-270
- ❑ 95PinMusC-270
- ❑ 95PosCan-12
- ❑ 95RedFol-21
- ❑ 95Sco-443
- ❑ 95ScoGolR-443
- ❑ 95ScoHaloG-HG93
- ❑ 95ScoHaloGYTE-HG93T
- ❑ 95ScoPlaTS-443
- ❑ 95ScoYouTE-443T
- ❑ 95Sel-111
- ❑ 95SelArtP-111
- ❑ 95SelCer-16
- ❑ 95SelCerMG-16
- ❑ 95SP-202
- ❑ 95SPCha-197
- ❑ 95SPChaDC-197
- ❑ 95Spo-26
- ❑ 95SpoArtP-26
- ❑ 95SPSil-202
- ❑ 95StaClu-204
- ❑ 95StaClu-216
- ❑ 95StaClu-620
- ❑ 95StaCluFDI-204
- ❑ 95StaCluFDI-216
- ❑ 95StaCluMOP-204
- ❑ 95StaCluMOP-216
- ❑ 95StaCluMOP-620
- ❑ 95StaCluSTWS-204
- ❑ 95StaCluSTWS-216
- ❑ 95StaCluSTWS-620
- ❑ 95StaCluVR-106
- ❑ 95StaCluVRMO-106
- ❑ 95Stu-33
- ❑ 95StuGolS-33
- ❑ 95Sum-80
- ❑ 95Sum-191
- ❑ 95SumNthD-80
- ❑ 95SumNthD-191
- ❑ 95SumSam-80
- ❑ 95TomPiz-2
- ❑ 95Top-5
- ❑ 95Top-392
- ❑ 95TopCyb-4
- ❑ 95TopEmb-98
- ❑ 95TopEmbGI-98
- ❑ 95TopTra-110T
- ❑ 95UC3-13
- ❑ 95UC3ArtP-13
- ❑ 95Ult-55
- ❑ 95UltAllS-6
- ❑ 95UltAllSGM-6
- ❑ 95UltAwaW-21
- ❑ 95UltAwaWGM-21
- ❑ 95UltGolM-55
- ❑ 95UppDec-178
- ❑ 95UppDec-288
- ❑ 95UppDec-495
- ❑ 95UppDecED-178
- ❑ 95UppDecED-288
- ❑ 95UppDecEDG-178
- ❑ 95UppDecEDG-288
- ❑ 95UppDecSE-198
- ❑ 95UppDecSEG-198
- ❑ 95USPlaCMLA-9S
- ❑ 95Zen-24
- ❑ 96Baz-58
- ❑ 96Bow-57
- ❑ 96BowFoi-57
- ❑ 96Cir-62
- ❑ 96CirRav-62
- ❑ 96ColCho-235
- ❑ 96ColChoGS-235
- ❑ 96ColChoSS-235
- ❑ 96Don-39
- ❑ 96DonPreP-39
- ❑ 96EmoXL-88
- ❑ 96Fin-B120
- ❑ 96FinRef-B120
- ❑ 96Fla-126
- ❑ 96Fle-181
- ❑ 96FleSmo'H-3
- ❑ 96FleTif-181
- ❑ 96Lea-154
- ❑ 96LeaLim-28
- ❑ 96LeaLimG-28
- ❑ 96LeaPre-26
- ❑ 96LeaPreP-26
- ❑ 96LeaPrePB-154
- ❑ 96LeaPrePG-154
- ❑ 96LeaPrePS-154
- ❑ 96LeaSig-103
- ❑ 96LeaSigPPG-103
- ❑ 96LeaSigPPP-103
- ❑ 96MetMod-3
- ❑ 96MetUni-85
- ❑ 96MetUniP-85
- ❑ 96Pac-374
- ❑ 96PacPriFT-FT8
- ❑ 96PanSti-158
- ❑ 96Pin-212
- ❑ 96PinAfi-12
- ❑ 96PinAfiAP-12
- ❑ 96PinAfiFPP-12
- ❑ 96PinArtP-112
- ❑ 96PinFoil-212
- ❑ 96PinSta-112
- ❑ 96ProSta-139
- ❑ 96Sco-176
- ❑ 96Sco-196
- ❑ 96Sco-364
- ❑ 96ScoDugC-A99
- ❑ 96ScoDugC-B89
- ❑ 96ScoDugCAP-A99
- ❑ 96ScoDugCAP-B89
- ❑ 96ScoRef-14
- ❑ 96Sel-66
- ❑ 96SelArtP-66
- ❑ 96SelCer-64
- ❑ 96SelCerAP-64
- ❑ 96SelCerCB-64
- ❑ 96SelCerCR-64
- ❑ 96SelCerIP-11
- ❑ 96SelCerMB-64
- ❑ 96SelCerMG-64
- ❑ 96SelCerMR-64
- ❑ 96SelTeaN-6
- ❑ 96SP-129
- ❑ 96Spo-24
- ❑ 96SpoArtP-24
- ❑ 96StaClu-151
- ❑ 96StaCluEPB-151
- ❑ 96StaCluEPG-151
- ❑ 96StaCluEPS-151
- ❑ 96StaCluMOF-3
- ❑ 96StaCluMOP-151
- ❑ 96Stu-58
- ❑ 96StuPrePB-58
- ❑ 96StuPrePG-58
- ❑ 96StuPrePS-58
- ❑ 96Sum-48
- ❑ 96SumAbo&B-48
- ❑ 96SumArtP-48
- ❑ 96SumFoi-48
- ❑ 96Top-124
- ❑ 96TopChr-33
- ❑ 96TopChrR-33
- ❑ 96TopGal-178
- ❑ 96TopGalPPI-178
- ❑ 96TopLas-116
- ❑ 96Ult-381
- ❑ 96UltGolM-381
- ❑ 96UppDec-405
- ❑ 96UppDecPHE-H12
- ❑ 96UppDecPreH-H12
- ❑ 96Zen-96
- ❑ 96ZenArtP-96
- ❑ 97Bow-253
- ❑ 97BowChr-76
- ❑ 97BowChrI-76
- ❑ 97BowChrIR-76
- ❑ 97BowChrR-76
- ❑ 97BowInt-253
- ❑ 97Cir-382
- ❑ 97CirRav-382
- ❑ 97ColCho-400
- ❑ 97ColChoT-NY13
- ❑ 97Don-70
- ❑ 97Don-435
- ❑ 97DonEli-124
- ❑ 97DonEliGS-124
- ❑ 97DonGolPP-70
- ❑ 97DonGolPP-435
- ❑ 97DonLim-2
- ❑ 97DonLimE-2
- ❑ 97DonLimENG-2
- ❑ 97DonPre-15
- ❑ 97DonPreCttC-15
- ❑ 97DonSilPP-70
- ❑ 97DonSilPP-435
- ❑ 97DonTea-125
- ❑ 97DonTeaSPE-125
- ❑ 97Fin-145
- ❑ 97FinEmb-145
- ❑ 97FinEmbR-145
- ❑ 97FinRef-145
- ❑ 97FlaShoLC-63
- ❑ 97FlaShoLeg0-63
- ❑ 97FlaShoLeg1-63
- ❑ 97FlaShoM-A63
- ❑ 97FlaShoM-B63
- ❑ 97FlaShoM-C63
- ❑ 97FlaShoR0-63
- ❑ 97FlaShoR1-63
- ❑ 97FlaShoR2-63
- ❑ 97Fle-162
- ❑ 97FleTif-162
- ❑ 97KinB-14
- ❑ 97Lea-234
- ❑ 97LeaFraM-234
- ❑ 97LeaFraMDC-234
- ❑ 97MetUni-115
- ❑ 97NewPin-14
- ❑ 97NewPinAP-14
- ❑ 97NewPinMC-14
- ❑ 97NewPinPP-14
- ❑ 97Pac-148
- ❑ 97PacLigB-148
- ❑ 97PacSil-148
- ❑ 97PinCar-10
- ❑ 97PinCer-34
- ❑ 97PinCerMBla-34
- ❑ 97PinCerMBlu-34
- ❑ 97PinCerMG-34
- ❑ 97PinCerMR-34
- ❑ 97PinCerR-34
- ❑ 97PinIns-1
- ❑ 97PinInsCE-1
- ❑ 97PinInsDE-1
- ❑ 97PinTotCPB-34
- ❑ 97PinTotCPG-34
- ❑ 97PinTotCPR-34
- ❑ 97PinX-P-60
- ❑ 97PinX-PMoS-60
- ❑ 97Sco-178
- ❑ 97ScoArtPWB-178
- ❑ 97ScoPreS-178
- ❑ 97ScoShoS-178
- ❑ 97ScoShoSAP-178
- ❑ 97Sel-6
- ❑ 97SelArtP-6
- ❑ 97SelCom-6
- ❑ 97SelRegG-6
- ❑ 97SP-123
- ❑ 97SpoIll-131
- ❑ 97SpoIllEE-131
- ❑ 97StaClu-231
- ❑ 97StaCluMat-231
- ❑ 97StaCluMOP-231
- ❑ 97StrAll-16
- ❑ 97Stu-25
- ❑ 97StuPrePG-25
- ❑ 97StuPrePS-25
- ❑ 97Top-360
- ❑ 97TopChr-123
- ❑ 97TopChrR-123
- ❑ 97TopGal-39
- ❑ 97TopGalPPI-39
- ❑ 97TopSta-75
- ❑ 97TopStaAM-75
- ❑ 97Ult-391
- ❑ 97UltGolME-391
- ❑ 97UltPlaME-391
- ❑ 97UppDec-264
- ❑ 97UppDec-382
- ❑ 97UppDec-438
- ❑ 97YanSco-12
- ❑ 97YanScoPI-12
- ❑ 97YanScoPr-12
- ❑ 98CirThu-145
- ❑ 98CirThuRav-145
- ❑ 98CirThuSupRav-145
- ❑ 98ColCho-446
- ❑ 98Don-60
- ❑ 98DonCol-60
- ❑ 98DonColL-226
- ❑ 98DonColP-641
- ❑ 98DonColS-60
- ❑ 98DonGolPP-60
- ❑ 98DonPre-91
- ❑ 98DonPreSeat-91
- ❑ 98DonPriCD-60
- ❑ 98DonPriCL-226
- ❑ 98DonPriCP-641
- ❑ 98DonSig-112
- ❑ 98DonSigA-22
- ❑ 98DonSigAC-30
- ❑ 98DonSigAM-30
- ❑ 98DonSigP-112
- ❑ 98DonSilPP-60
- ❑ 98Fin-71
- ❑ 98FinNo--71
- ❑ 98FinNo-R-71
- ❑ 98FinRef-71
- ❑ 98FlaShoLeg0-107
- ❑ 98FlaShoLeg1-107
- ❑ 98FlaShoLeg2-107
- ❑ 98FlaShoLeg3-107
- ❑ 98FlaShoLegM-107
- ❑ 98FlaShoR0-107
- ❑ 98FlaShoR1-107
- ❑ 98FlaShoR2-107
- ❑ 98FlaShoR3-107
- ❑ 98Fle-77
- ❑ 98Fle-302
- ❑ 98FleDecERT-4
- ❑ 98FleDecoE-4
- ❑ 98KinDis-20
- ❑ 98Lea-26
- ❑ 98LeaFraDA-26
- ❑ 98LeaFraF-26
- ❑ 98LeaFraM-26
- ❑ 98LeaFraM-26
- ❑ 98LeaFraMDC-26
- ❑ 98LeaFraMDC-26
- ❑ 98LeaFraMZ2-26
- ❑ 98LeaRS-91
- ❑ 98LeaRSLHolo-91
- ❑ 98LeaRSLong-91
- ❑ 98LeaRTrue-91
- ❑ 98MetUni-114
- ❑ 98MetUniPMG-114
- ❑ 98Pac-145
- ❑ 98PacOme-163
- ❑ 98PacOmeR-163
- ❑ 98PacOnl-499
- ❑ 98PacOnlR-499
- ❑ 98PacOnlWC-499
- ❑ 98PacPlaB-145
- ❑ 98PacRedT-145
- ❑ 98PacSil-145
- ❑ 98PinPlu-7
- ❑ 98PinSna-NYY12
- ❑ 98PinSna-NYY14
- ❑ 98Sco-56
- ❑ 98ScoRT-195
- ❑ 98ScoSS-PP25
- ❑ 98ScoSSAP-PP25
- ❑ 98SP Aut-144
- ❑ 98SpoIll-27
- ❑ 98SpoIllEE-27
- ❑ 98SpoIllFE-27
- ❑ 98SpoIllTaN-73
- ❑ 98SpoIllTaNEE-73
- ❑ 98SPxFin-106
- ❑ 98SPxFinR-106
- ❑ 98SPxFinS-106
- ❑ 98StaCluFDI-323
- ❑ 98StaCluI-323
- ❑ 98StaCluOneK-323
- ❑ 98StaCluPP-323
- ❑ 98Stu-94
- ❑ 98StuGPP-94
- ❑ 98StuSPP-94
- ❑ 98Top-391
- ❑ 98TopChr-391
- ❑ 98TopChrR-391
- ❑ 98TopDevR-391
- ❑ 98TopDia-391
- ❑ 98TopGal-33
- ❑ 98TopGalGP-33
- ❑ 98TopGalOPP-33
- ❑ 98TopGalPPI-33
- ❑ 98TopGalPPIA-33
- ❑ 98TopMiniC-391
- ❑ 98TopSta-88
- ❑ 98TopStaB-88
- ❑ 98TopStaG-88
- ❑ 98TopStaGR-88
- ❑ 98TopStaS-88
- ❑ 98UD3-61
- ❑ 98UD3-151
- ❑ 98UD3-241
- ❑ 98UD3DieCut-61
- ❑ 98UD3DieCut-151
- ❑ 98UD3DieCut-241
- ❑ 98Ult-119
- ❑ 98UltGolM-119
- ❑ 98UltMas-119
- ❑ 98UltPlaM-119
- ❑ 98UppDec-175
- ❑ 98UppDec10AP-5
- ❑ 98UppDec1APR-5
- ❑ 98UppDecSF-94
- ❑ 98YanSco-4
- ❑ 98YanScoP-4
- ❑ 98YanUppD-175
- ❑ 98YanUppDWSC-1
- ❑ 99199Fin-236
- ❑ 99Bow-66
- ❑ 99BowChr-66
- ❑ 99BowChrG-66
- ❑ 99BowChrGR-66
- ❑ 99BowChrI-66
- ❑ 99BowChrIR-66
- ❑ 99BowChrR-66
- ❑ 99BowGol-66
- ❑ 99BowInt-66
- ❑ 99FinGolRef-236
- ❑ 99FinRef-236
- ❑ 99FlaShoLeg1-99
- ❑ 99FlaShoLeg2-99
- ❑ 99FlaShoLeg3-99
- ❑ 99FlaShoLegM1-99
- ❑ 99FlaShoLegM2-99
- ❑ 99FlaShoLegM3-99
- ❑ 99FlaShoR1-99
- ❑ 99FlaShoR2-99
- ❑ 99FlaShoR3-99
- ❑ 99Fle-124
- ❑ 99FleBri-78
- ❑ 99FleBri2G-78
- ❑ 99FleBriBlu-78
- ❑ 99FleBriGol-78
- ❑ 99FleSta9-124
- ❑ 99FleWarT-124
- ❑ 99MetUni-148
- ❑ 99MetUniGM-148
- ❑ 99MetUniPMG-148
- ❑ 99Pac-289
- ❑ 99PacCroC-187
- ❑ 99PacCroCPB-187
- ❑ 99PacOme-160
- ❑ 99PacOmeC-160
- ❑ 99PacOmeG-160
- ❑ 99PacOmePB-160
- ❑ 99PacPar-159
- ❑ 99PacParC-159
- ❑ 99PacParG-159
- ❑ 99PacParHoloGold-159
- ❑ 99PacParHS-159
- ❑ 99PacParOD-159
- ❑ 99PacParPB-159
- ❑ 99PacParRed-159
- ❑ 99PacPlaB-289
- ❑ 99PacPri-97
- ❑ 99PacPriHB-97
- ❑ 99PacPriHG-97
- ❑ 99PacPriHM-97
- ❑ 99PacPriHP-97
- ❑ 99PacPriRed-97
- ❑ 99PacPriS-76
- ❑ 99PacPriS206-76
- ❑ 99PacPriS206R-76
- ❑ 99PacRed-289
- ❑ 99Pin-6
- ❑ 99SkyMolM-13
- ❑ 99SkyMolMX-13
- ❑ 99SkyPre-171
- ❑ 99SkyPreR-171
- ❑ 99SkyThu-236
- ❑ 99SkyThuRant-236
- ❑ 99SkyThuRave-236
- ❑ 99SpoIll-6
- ❑ 99SpoIll-14
- ❑ 99SpoIll-144
- ❑ 99StaClu-177
- ❑ 99StaCluC-SCC9
- ❑ 99StaCluCR-SCC9
- ❑ 99StaCluFDI-177

❑ 99StaCluOoaK-177
❑ 99StaCluPP-177
❑ 99ThuSkySupR-236
❑ 99Top-101
❑ 99TopChr-101
❑ 99TopChrR-101
❑ 99TopMVPP-101
❑ 99TopOpeD-59
❑ 99TopSta-98
❑ 99TopSta1Foil-98
❑ 99TopStaFoil-98
❑ 99TopStaOS-98
❑ 99UppDec-438
❑ 99UppDecCL-93
❑ 99UppDecCLCC-93
❑ 99UppDecEL1-438
❑ 99UppDecEL2-438
❑ 99YanFle-19

Confreda, Gene
❑ 83BeaGolGT-23
❑ 87AshTouP-3
❑ 88AshTouP-1076
❑ 90OscAstS-30

Congalton, Bunk (William M.)
❑ 09ColChiE-59A
❑ 09ColChiE-59B
❑ 09ColChiE-59C
❑ 09T206-413
❑ 11PinT-5-1064
❑ 11SpoLifCW-71
❑ 12ColRedB-59A
❑ 12ColRedB-59B
❑ 12ColRedB-59C
❑ 12ColTinT-59A
❑ 12ColTinT-59B
❑ 12ColTinT-59C

Conger, Jeff
❑ 92AugPirC-24
❑ 92AugPirF-250
❑ 92ClaFS7-16
❑ 93SalBucC-5
❑ 93SalBucF-444
❑ 94SalBucC-5
❑ 94SalBucF-2337
❑ 95LynHilTI-5
❑ 96CarMudB-23
❑ 97CarMudC-21

Conigliaro, Billy (William)
❑ 69Top-628
❑ 70DayDaiNM-118
❑ 70OPC-317
❑ 70RedSoxCPPC-4
❑ 70Top-317
❑ 71MLBOffS-316
❑ 71OPC-114
❑ 71RedSoxA-3
❑ 71RedSoxTI-2
❑ 71Top-114
❑ 72MilBra-80
❑ 72OPC-481
❑ 72Top-481
❑ 74OPC-545
❑ 74Top-545
❑ 81RedSoxBG2S-67
❑ 81RedSoxBG2S-76
❑ 94BreMilB-302

Conigliaro, Tony (Anthony)
❑ 47PM1StaP1-34
❑ 47PM1StaP1-35
❑ 64Top-287
❑ 64TopRooAB-25
❑ 64TopVen-287
❑ 65OPC-55
❑ 65RedSoxTI-3
❑ 65Top-55
❑ 65TopTral-11
❑ 66Baz-6
❑ 66RedSoxTI-2
❑ 66Top-218
❑ 66Top-380
❑ 66TopRubl-21
❑ 66TopVen-218
❑ 67Baz-6
❑ 67Top-280
❑ 67TopRedSS-3
❑ 67TopRedSS-30
❑ 67TopVen-245
❑ 68Baz-4
❑ 68OPC-140
❑ 68Top-140
❑ 68TopActS-8C
❑ 68TopVen-140
❑ 69RedSoxAO-2
❑ 69RedSoxTI-2
❑ 69RedSoxTI-2
❑ 69Top-330
❑ 69TopTeaP-3
❑ 70DayDaiNM-96
❑ 70OPC-340
❑ 70RedSoxCPPC-5
❑ 70Top-340
❑ 71AngJacitB-3
❑ 71BazNumT-45
❑ 71MLBOffS-342
❑ 71OPC-63
❑ 71OPC-105
❑ 71Top-63
❑ 71Top-105
❑ 71TopCoi-142
❑ 71TopTat-80
❑ 73BooProC-4
❑ 78TCM60I-206
❑ 81RedSoxBG2S-67
❑ 81RedSoxBG2S-75
❑ 92UppDecS-6
❑ 94TedWil-137

Conine, Jeff
❑ 88BasCitRS-10
❑ 89BasCitRS-6
❑ 90Bes-156
❑ 90CMC-743
❑ 90MemChiB-8
❑ 90MemChiP-1017
❑ 90MemChiS-7
❑ 90ProAaA-48
❑ 90StaFS7-85
❑ 91Bow-184
❑ 91Cla1-T47
❑ 91ClaGam-96
❑ 91Don-427
❑ 91Fle-553
❑ 91LinDriAAA-332
❑ 91OmaRoyLD-332
❑ 91OmaRoyP-1041
❑ 91OPCPre-26
❑ 91Sco-722
❑ 91ScoHotR-5
❑ 91ScoRoo-19
❑ 91StaClu-578
❑ 91Stu-63
❑ 91TopDeb90-34
❑ 91Ult-145
❑ 91UppDec-27
❑ 92DonRooP-BC3
❑ 92OmaRoyF-2968
❑ 92OmaRoyS-329
❑ 92Sco100RS-21
❑ 92SkyAAAF-151
❑ 92SpollIFK1-462
❑ 92StaClu-683
❑ 92TriA AAS-329
❑ 93Bow-670
❑ 93CadDis-15
❑ 93Don-101
❑ 93Don-765
❑ 93Fin-54
❑ 93FinRef-54
❑ 93Fla-49
❑ 93Fle-423
❑ 93FleFinE-57
❑ 93FunPac-119
❑ 93JimDeaR-3
❑ 93Lea-288
❑ 93MarFloA-8
❑ 93MarlStaClu-13
❑ 93MarPub-8
❑ 93MarUppD-754
❑ 93MarUSPC-5S
❑ 93MarUSPC-9C
❑ 93MarUSPC-11H
❑ 93OPCPre-119
❑ 93PacSpa-458
❑ 93Pin-479
❑ 93Pin-601
❑ 93PinExpOD-7
❑ 93Sco-402
❑ 93Sel-321
❑ 93SelChaR-12
❑ 93SelRooAR-1
❑ 93SP-138
❑ 93StaClu-340
❑ 93StaCluFDI-340
❑ 93StaCluMOP-340
❑ 93Stu-54
❑ 93Top-789
❑ 93TopGol-789
❑ 93TopInaM-789
❑ 93TopInaR-789
❑ 93TopMic-789
❑ 93TriPla-93
❑ 93Ult-371
❑ 93UltAllR-2
❑ 93UppDec-479
❑ 93UppDec-754
❑ 93UppDecGold-479
❑ 93UppDecGold-754
❑ 94Bow-383
❑ 94Bow-394
❑ 94BowBes-R34
❑ 94BowBesR-R34
❑ 94ColC-82
❑ 94ColChoGS-82
❑ 94ColChoSS-82
❑ 94Don-156
❑ 94Fin-4
❑ 94FinJum-4
❑ 94FinRef-4
❑ 94Fla-161
❑ 94Fle-464
❑ 94FleExtB-259
❑ 94FleExtBSYS-4
❑ 94FleRooS-5
❑ 94FUnPac-117
❑ 94Lea-41
❑ 94LeaL-106
❑ 94MarTeal-4
❑ 94OPC-238
❑ 94OPCDiaD-12
❑ 94OscMayR-19
❑ 94Pac-239
❑ 94PacSilP-23
❑ 94PacSilPC-23
❑ 94PanSti-181
❑ 94Pin-30
❑ 94PinArtP-30
❑ 94PinMusC-30
❑ 94ProMag-51
❑ 94Sco-484
❑ 94ScoBoyoS-1
❑ 94ScoGolR-484
❑ 94ScoGolS-30
❑ 94Sel-26
❑ 94SP-109
❑ 94SPDieC-109
❑ 94Spo-62
❑ 94StaClu-406
❑ 94StaCluFDI-406
❑ 94StaCluGR-406
❑ 94StaCluMO-50
❑ 94StaCluMOP-406
❑ 94StaCluT-90
❑ 94StaCluTFDI-90
❑ 94Stu-108
❑ 94Top-466
❑ 94TopGol-466
❑ 94TopSpa-466
❑ 94TriPla-134
❑ 94Ult-491
❑ 94UltSecYS-7
❑ 94UppDec-162
❑ 94UppDecED-162
❑ 94USPlaCR-7C
❑ 94USPlaCR-12H
❑ 95Baz-60
❑ 95Bow-390
❑ 95BowBes-R38
❑ 95BowBesR-R38
❑ 95ClaPhoC-28
❑ 95ColCho-305
❑ 95ColChoGS-305
❑ 95ColChoSE-134
❑ 95ColChoSEGS-134
❑ 95ColChoSESS-134
❑ 95ColChoSS-305
❑ 95Don-392
❑ 95DonDiaK-DK6
❑ 95DonPreP-392
❑ 95DonTopotO-241
❑ 95Emo-128
❑ 95Fin-148
❑ 95FinRef-148
❑ 95Fla-137
❑ 95Fle-331
❑ 95FleTeaL-19
❑ 95FleUpdSS-3
❑ 95Kra-19
❑ 95Lea-293
❑ 95LeaLim-41
❑ 95Pac-172
❑ 95PacGolP-28
❑ 95PacPri-55
❑ 95Pin-11
❑ 95PinArtP-11
❑ 95PinMusC-11
❑ 95Sco-54
❑ 95Sco-573
❑ 95ScoGolR-54
❑ 95ScoGolR-573
❑ 95ScoHaloG-HG28
❑ 95ScoPlaTS-54
❑ 95ScoPlaTS-573
❑ 95Sel-119
❑ 95SelArtP-119
❑ 95SelCer-58
❑ 95SelCerMG-58
❑ 95SP-53
❑ 95SPCha-45
❑ 95SPCha-49
❑ 95SPChaDC-45
❑ 95SPChaDC-49
❑ 95Spo-118
❑ 95SpoArtP-118
❑ 95SPSil-53
❑ 95StaClu-193
❑ 95StaClu-401
❑ 95StaCluFDI-193
❑ 95StaCluMO-13
❑ 95StaCluMOP-193
❑ 95StaCluMOP-401
❑ 95StaCluSTWS-193
❑ 95StaCluSTWS-401
❑ 95StaCluVR-101
❑ 95StaCluVRMO-101
❑ 95Stu-135
❑ 95Sum-25
❑ 95SumNthD-25
❑ 95TomPiz-21
❑ 95Top-130
❑ 95TopCyb-81
❑ 95TopD3-25
❑ 95TopEmb-86
❑ 95TopEmbGI-86
❑ 95TopFinIns-15
❑ 95Ult-379
❑ 95UltGolM-379
❑ 95UppDec-115
❑ 95UppDecED-115
❑ 95UppDecEDG-115
❑ 95UppDecSE-251
❑ 95UppDecSEG-251
❑ 95Zen-46
❑ 95ZenAllS-16
❑ 96Baz-53
❑ 96Bow-14
❑ 96BowBes-31
❑ 96BowBesAR-31
❑ 96BowBesR-31
❑ 96BowFoi-14
❑ 96Cir-128
❑ 96CirRav-128
❑ 96Cla7/1PC-4
❑ 96ColCho-555
❑ 96ColChoGS-555
❑ 96ColChoSS-555
❑ 96Don-463
❑ 96DonDiaK-21
❑ 96DonPreP-463
❑ 96EmoXL-185
❑ 96Fin-B265
❑ 96Fin-G100
❑ 96FinRef-B265
❑ 96FinRef-G100
❑ 96Fla-260
❑ 96Fle-385
❑ 96FleTeaL-19
❑ 96FleTif-385
❑ 96Lea-125
❑ 96LeaPrePB-125
❑ 96LeaPrePG-125
❑ 96LeaPrePS-125
❑ 96LeaPreSG-5
❑ 96LeaPreSte-5
❑ 96LeaSig-112
❑ 96LeaSigA-47
❑ 96LeaSigAG-47
❑ 96LeaSigAS-47
❑ 96LeaSigPPG-112
❑ 96LeaSigPPP-112
❑ 96MetUni-164
❑ 96MetUniP-164
❑ 96Pac-82
❑ 96PacPri-P24
❑ 96PacPriG-P24
❑ 96PanSti-14
❑ 96Pin-226
❑ 96Pin-300
❑ 96PinAfi-42
❑ 96PinAfiAP-42
❑ 96PinAfiFPP-42
❑ 96PinArtP-126
❑ 96PinArtP-184
❑ 96PinFoil-226
❑ 96PinFoil-300
❑ 96PinSta-126
❑ 96PinSta-184
❑ 96ProSta-67
❑ 96RedF-27
❑ 96Sco-9
❑ 96ScoDugC-A9
❑ 96ScoDugCAP-A9
❑ 96Sel-76
❑ 96SelArtP-76
❑ 96SP-89
❑ 96Spo-96
❑ 96SpoArtP-96
❑ 96StaClu-205
❑ 96StaClu-280
❑ 96StaCluEPB-280
❑ 96StaCluEPG-280
❑ 96StaCluEPS-280
❑ 96StaCluMO-10
❑ 96StaCluMOP-205
❑ 96StaCluMOP-280
❑ 96StaCluMOP-TSCA4
❑ 96StaCluTA-4
❑ 96Stu-8
❑ 96StuPrePB-8
❑ 96StuPrePG-8
❑ 96StuPrePS-8
❑ 96Sum-111
❑ 96SumAbo&B-111
❑ 96SumArtP-111
❑ 96SumFoi-111
❑ 96TeaOut-19
❑ 96Top-422
❑ 96TopChr-165
❑ 96TopChrR-165
❑ 96TopGal-15
❑ 96TopGalPG-PG6
❑ 96TopGalPPI-15
❑ 96TopLas-4
❑ 96Ult-198
❑ 96UltGolM-198
❑ 96UppDec-75
❑ 96UppDecPRE-R44
❑ 96UppDecPreR-R44
❑ 96ZenMoz-16
❑ 97Bow-265
❑ 97BowBes-18
❑ 97BowBesAR-18
❑ 97BowBesR-18
❑ 97BowInt-265
❑ 97Cir-110
❑ 97CirRav-110
❑ 97ColCho-113
❑ 97ColChoT-FM4
❑ 97Don-265
❑ 97Don-445
❑ 97DonEli-48
❑ 97DonEliGS-48
❑ 97DonGolPP-265
❑ 97DonGolPP-445
❑ 97DonLim-90
❑ 97DonLimE-90
❑ 97DonLimENG-90
❑ 97DonPre-117
❑ 97DonPreCttC-117
❑ 97DonSilPP-265
❑ 97DonSilPP-445
❑ 97Fin-164
❑ 97FinEmb-164
❑ 97FinEmbR-164
❑ 97FinRef-164
❑ 97FlaShoLC-159
❑ 97FlaShoLeg0-159
❑ 97FlaShoLeg1-159
❑ 97FlaShoM-A159
❑ 97FlaShoM-B159
❑ 97FlaShoM-C159
❑ 97FlaShoR0-159
❑ 97FlaShoR1-159
❑ 97FlaShoR2-159
❑ 97Fle-328
❑ 97FleTif-328
❑ 97Lea-251
❑ 97LeaFraM-251
❑ 97LeaFraMDC-251
❑ 97MarPac-8
❑ 97MetUni-173
❑ 97Pac-300
❑ 97PacLigB-300
❑ 97PacPri-101
❑ 97PacPriLB-101
❑ 97PacPriP-101
❑ 97PacSil-300
❑ 97Pin-117
❑ 97PinArtP-PP117
❑ 97PinIns-64
❑ 97PinInsCE-64
❑ 97PinInsDE-64
❑ 97PinMusC-117
❑ 97PinPrePla-117
❑ 97PinX-P-89
❑ 97PinX-PMoS-89
❑ 97Sco-4
❑ 97ScoArtPWB-4
❑ 97ScoPreS-4
❑ 97ScoShoS-4
❑ 97ScoShoSAP-4
❑ 97SP-74
❑ 97StaClu-9
❑ 97StaCluMat-9
❑ 97StaCluMOP-9
❑ 97Stu-33
❑ 97StuPrePG-33
❑ 97StuPrePS-33
❑ 97Top-159
❑ 97TopChr-62
❑ 97TopChrR-62
❑ 97TopGal-114
❑ 97TopGalPPI-114
❑ 97TopMem05-15
❑ 97TopSta-47
❑ 97TopStaAM-47
❑ 97TopStaASM-ASM2
❑ 97Ult-195
❑ 97UltGolME-195
❑ 97UltPlaME-195
❑ 97UppDec-359
❑ 98CirThu-55
❑ 98CirThuRav-55
❑ 98CirThuSupRav-55
❑ 98ColCho-391
❑ 98DonSigA-23
❑ 98DonSigAC-31
❑ 98DonSigAM-31
❑ 98Fle-374
❑ 98PacAur-42
❑ 98PacInvGems-154
❑ 98PacOme-113
❑ 98PacOmeR-113
❑ 98PinPlu-103
❑ 98ScoRT-59
❑ 98SP Aut-106
❑ 98StaCluFDI-400
❑ 98StaClul-400
❑ 98StaCluOneK-400
❑ 98StaCluPP-400
❑ 98Top-429
❑ 98TopChr-429
❑ 98TopChrR-429
❑ 98TopDevR-429
❑ 98TopDia-429
❑ 98TopMiniC-429
❑ 98Ult-372
❑ 98UltGolM-372
❑ 98UltMas-372
❑ 98UltPlaM-372
❑ 98UppDec-687
❑ 99Fle-356
❑ 99FleSta9-356
❑ 99FleWarT-356
❑ 99MetUni-104
❑ 99MetUniGM-104
❑ 99MetUniPMG-104
❑ 99Pac-201
❑ 99PacAur-85
❑ 99PacAurOD-85
❑ 99PacPar-108
❑ 99PacParC-108
❑ 99PacParG-108
❑ 99PacParHoloGold-108
❑ 99PacParHS-108
❑ 99PacParOD-108
❑ 99PacParPB-108
❑ 99PacParRed-108
❑ 99PacPlaB-201
❑ 99PacRed-201
❑ 99Top-393
❑ 99TopChr-393
❑ 99TopChrR-393
❑ 99TopMVPP-393
❑ 99Ult-115
❑ 99UltGolM-115
❑ 99UltMas-115
❑ 99UltPlaM-115

Conklin, Chip
❑ 82WauTimF-28
❑ 83WauTimF-11
❑ 84ModA'sC-6
❑ 85HunStaJ-17

Conkright, Dan
❑ 88BirBarB-21

Conlan, Jocko (John Bertrand)
❑ 35DiaMatCS3T1-37
❑ 55Bow-303
❑ 75TCMAllG-7
❑ 76GrePlaG-3
❑ 76ShaPiz-143
❑ 77GalGloG-87
❑ 80PacLeg-59
❑ 80PerHaloFP-143
❑ 80PerHaloFPS-24
❑ 80SSPHOF-143
❑ 85BigLeaC3-31
❑ 88T/MUmp-63
❑ 89HOFStiB-98
❑ 89PerCelP-10
❑ 94ConTSN-1196
❑ 94ConTSNB-1196
Conley, Bob
❑ 78WatIndT-6
Conley, Bob (Robert Burns)
❑ 59Top-121
❑ 59TopVen-121
Conley, Curt
❑ 93BenRocCB-5
❑ 93BenRocF-3258
❑ 94CenValRC-4
❑ 94CenValRF-3194
❑ 95SalAvaTI-12
Conley, Gene (D. Eugene)
❑ 53Top-215
❑ 54BraJohC-22
❑ 54BraSpiaSP-6
❑ 54Top-59
❑ 55BraGolS-6
❑ 55BraJohC-22
❑ 55BraSpiaSD-6
❑ 55Top-81
❑ 55TopDouH-33
❑ 56BraBilaBP-6
❑ 56Top-17
❑ 56TopPin-17
❑ 57BraSpiaS4-6
❑ 57Top-28
❑ 58Top-431
❑ 59Top-492
❑ 60ArmCoi-6
❑ 60Top-293
❑ 61Pos-124A
❑ 61Pos-124B
❑ 61Top-193
❑ 61TopStal-119
❑ 62RedSoxJP-2
❑ 62Top-187
❑ 62TopVen-187
❑ 63Top-216
❑ 64Top-571
❑ 80Bra195T-41
❑ 81RedSoxBG2S-77
❑ 90PacLeg-79
❑ 91TopArc1-215
❑ 94TopArc1-59
❑ 94TopArc1G-59
Conley, Greg
❑ 88SpoIndP-1922
❑ 89ChaRaiP-974
❑ 90WatDiaB-22
❑ 90WatDiaP-2381
❑ 91HigDesMC-15
❑ 91HigDesMP-2398
Conley, Matt
❑ 91SumFlyC-3
❑ 91SumFlyP-2326
❑ 92AlbPolCB-18
❑ 92AlbPolF-2298
Conley, Virgil
❑ 83TamTarT-2
❑ 84CedRapRT-8
❑ 85CedRapRT-4
❑ 86PenWhiSP-6
❑ 87PenWhiSP-27
❑ 88JacMetGS-11
Conlon, Charles M.
❑ 86ConSer1-59
❑ 86ConSer1-60
❑ 91ConTSN-327
❑ 94ConTSN-1266
❑ 94ConTSNB-1266
Conlon, Margie
❑ 86ConSer1-60
Conn, Gary
❑ 75BurBeeT-2
❑ 76BurBeeT-2
❑ 77HolMilT-5
Connacher, Kevin
❑ 98WinWar-9
Connally, Chris
❑ 98WilCubM-4
Connally, Fritzie Lee
❑ 81QuaCitCT-5
❑ 83IowCubT-13
❑ 84LasVegSC-224
❑ 85BalOriP-4
❑ 85FleUpd-30
❑ 91OriCro-82
Connally, Sarge (George)
❑ 32R33So2-406
❑ 33Gou-27
❑ 33GouCanV-27
❑ 34TarThoBD-9
❑ 67SpoHobFC-22
❑ 91ConTSN-247
Connel, Fred
❑ 21Zee-45
Connell, Brian
❑ 98HelBreM-11
Connell, Gene (Eugene J.)
❑ 98RocCubM-6
Connell, Jerry
❑ 97WilCubB-4
❑ 98RocCubTI-6
Connell, Lino
❑ 92BoiHawC-14
❑ 92BoiHawF-3636
❑ 93CedRapKC-4
❑ 93CedRapKF-1745
❑ 93LinVenB-206
❑ 95LinVen-50
❑ 96-97LinVen-102
Connell, Monty
❑ 89GeoColC-3
Connell, Pete (Peter J.)
❑ 87OldJudN-82
Connelly, Bill
❑ 53Top-126
❑ 79TCM50-60
❑ 91TopArc1-126
Connelly, Daron
❑ 86TriTriC-196
❑ 87CliGiaP-24
❑ 88SanJosGCLC-130
❑ 88SanJosGP-135
Connelly, David
❑ 86TriTriC-197
Connelly, Steve
❑ 96ModA'sB-24
❑ 97HunStaTI-4
Conner, Decomba
❑ 94PriRedC-1
❑ 94PriRedF-3275
❑ 95Bow-234
❑ 95BowGolF-234
❑ 95Exc-175
❑ 95ExcFirYP-6
❑ 96BesAutS-22
❑ 96Bow-215
❑ 96BowFoi-215
❑ 97JacSun-7
❑ 97LakTigB-11
❑ 98BowBayM-7
Conner, Greg
❑ 88SanJosGCLC-118
❑ 88SanJosGP-129
❑ 89ShrCapP-1839
Conner, Jeff
❑ 78QuaCitAT-7
❑ 81HolMilT-12
❑ 82HolMilT-3
❑ 83NasAngT-4
❑ 84EvaTriT-18
❑ 85NasSouTI-4
❑ 86NasSouTI-5
Conner, John
❑ 90AppFoxBS-7
❑ 90AppFoxP-2089
❑ 91BasCitRC-2
❑ 91BasCitRP-1389
❑ 91Cla/Bes-71
Conner, Scott
❑ 93AlbPolCB-10
❑ 93AlbPolF-2020
❑ 94FreKeyC-8
❑ 94FreKeyF-2605
❑ 95BowBayTI-32
❑ 96FreKeyB-4
❑ 98BriBluM-8
Connifer, Barney
❑ 17Zee-102
Connolly, Chris
❑ 91EugEmeC-29
❑ 91EugEmeP-3716
❑ 92AppFoxFI-978
❑ 93RocRoyC-8
❑ 93RocRoyF-708
❑ 94WilBluRC-3
❑ 94WilBluRF-292
❑ 95WilBluRTI-30
Connolly, Craig
❑ 90SouOreAB-20
❑ 90SouOreAP-3441
❑ 91MadMusC-6
❑ 91MadMusP-2123
❑ 92RenSilSCLC-37
❑ 93ModA'sC-6
❑ 93ModA'sF-792
Connolly, Ed (Edward J.)
❑ 65Top-543
Connolly, Edward Joseph Sr.
❑ 19Zee-87
❑ 34DiaMatCSB-31
Connolly, Joe (Joseph A.)
❑ 14B18B-47A
❑ 14B18B-47B
❑ 15CraJacE-155
❑ 15SpoNewM-36
❑ 16SpoNewM-37
❑ 20Zee-104
❑ 25Zee-86
❑ 26Zee-1
❑ 80BraTCM1-1
Connolly, Matt
❑ 91EriSaiC-16
❑ 91EriSaiP-4061
❑ 92VisOakC-4
❑ 92VisOakF-1006
❑ 93WesPalBEF-1331
❑ 96DouAllB-41
❑ 96OrlCubB-6
Connolly, Sean
❑ 96BriWhiSB-13
Connolly, Steve
❑ 87PocGiaTB-4
❑ 88CliGiaP-696
❑ 88MidLeaAGS-6
❑ 89ShrCapP-1830
❑ 90ShrCapP-1437
❑ 90ShrCapS-3
Connolly, Thomas H.
❑ 22Zee-121
❑ 50CalHOFW-22
❑ 53ArtHaloFP-22
❑ 76ShaPiz-67
❑ 77GalGloG-149
❑ 80PerHaloFP-65
❑ 80SSPHOF-65
❑ 89T/MUmp-63
❑ 92ConTSN-469
❑ 94ConTSN-1186
❑ 94ConTSNB-1186
❑ 94OriofB-72
Connor, Mark
❑ 84ColCliP-25
❑ 84ColCliT-21
❑ 85YanTCMP-1
❑ 90TopTVY-2
❑ 94KnoSmoF-1320
❑ 95KnoSmoF-56
Connor, Roger
❑ 74CapPub-5
❑ 76ShaPiz-153
❑ 77BobParHoF-83
❑ 80PerHaloFP-153
❑ 80SSPHOF-153
❑ 86OldJudN-1
❑ 87BucN28-64A
❑ 87BucN28-64B
❑ 87OldJudN-92A
❑ 87OldJudN-92B
❑ 88GandBCGCE-10
❑ 88WG1CarG-37
❑ 89EdgR.WG-5
❑ 89HOFStiB-9
❑ 89SFHaCN-2
❑ 90KalBatN-8
❑ 94OriofB-33
Connors, Billy
❑ 67ProPizC-6
❑ 67Top-272
❑ 82CubRedL-NNO
❑ 83CubThoAV-NNO
❑ 84CubChiT-7
❑ 84CubSev-NNO
❑ 85CubSev-NNO
❑ 86CubGat-NNO
❑ 87MarMot-28
❑ 90TopTVY-3
❑ 91CubMar-NNO
❑ 91MetWIZ-82
❑ 92CubMar-NNO
❑ 93CubMar-5
Connors, Chad
❑ 93BilMusF-3935
❑ 93BilMusSP-1
❑ 94ChaWheC-5
❑ 94ChaWheF-2693
Connors, Chuck (Kevin Joseph)
❑ 50WorWidGV-2
❑ 52MotCoo-4
❑ 77FriOneYW-2
❑ 80PacLeg-28
❑ 88DodRinP1-9B
❑ 88PacLegI-71
❑ 90DodTar-135
Connors, Greg
❑ 97EveAquG-6
❑ 98LanJetG-7
❑ 98WisTimRM-25
Connors, Jimmy (James Scott)
❑ 82MonNew-3
Connors, Merv (Mervyn James)
❑ 33Zee-53
Conquest, Tom
❑ 82IdaFalAT-5
❑ 83MadMusF-12
Conrad, Phil
❑ 48BabRutS-6
Conro, Pam
❑ 96ColSilB-3
Conroy, Bill (William G.)
❑ 42RedSoxTI-6
❑ 43RedSoxTI-3
❑ 46SunBre-4
Conroy, Brian
❑ 90CarLeaA-9
❑ 90LynRedSTI-16
❑ 91LinDriAA-453
❑ 91NewBriRSLD-453
❑ 91NewBriRSP-344
❑ 92NewBriRSF-425
❑ 92PawRedSS-355
❑ 92SkyAAAF-160
❑ 93Bow-579
❑ 93PawRedSDD-8
❑ 93PawRedSF-2402
❑ 93PawRedSTI-8
❑ 94PawRedSF-940
❑ 97DunDonPPS-5
Conroy, Daniel
❑ 96IdaFalB-4
Conroy, Mike
❑ 88StoPorP-752
❑ 89StoPorB-31
❑ 89StoPorS-28
Conroy, Tim
❑ 79WatA'sT-22
❑ 80WesHavWCT-22B
❑ 81WesHavAT-7
❑ 84A'sMot-24
❑ 84Don-340
❑ 84Fle-442
❑ 84Nes792-156
❑ 84Nes792-189
❑ 84Top-156
❑ 84Top-189
❑ 84TopTif-156
❑ 84TopTif-189
❑ 85A'sMot-16
❑ 85DomLeaS-12
❑ 85Don-156
❑ 85Fle-421
❑ 85Top-503
❑ 85TopTif-503
❑ 86CarSchM-3
❑ 86CarTeal-9
❑ 86FleUpd-29
❑ 86TopTra-28T
❑ 86TopTraT-28T
❑ 87CarTeal-4
❑ 87Fle-291
❑ 87FleGlo-291
❑ 87Top-338
❑ 87TopTif-338
❑ 88LouRedBC-5
❑ 88LouRedBTI-15
❑ 88Sco-384
❑ 88ScoGlo-384
❑ 88Top-658
❑ 88TopTif-658
❑ 89HarSenP-288
❑ 89HarSenS-6
❑ 93ButCopKSP-24
❑ 94HigDesMC-28
❑ 94HigDesMF-2805
Conroy, Wid (William E.)
❑ 08AmeCarE91-72
❑ 08RosComP-45
❑ 09ColChiE-60
❑ 09RamT20-30
❑ 09SenBarP-2
❑ 09T206-73
❑ 09T206-74
❑ 10DarChoE-12
❑ 10JHDABE-5
❑ 10RedCroT-13
❑ 10SenWasT-1
❑ 11HelSta-67
❑ 11PinT-5-563
❑ 11SpoLifCW-72
❑ 11SpoLifM-121
❑ 12ColRedB-60
❑ 12ColTinT-60
❑ 72ClaCar-6
Consolo, Billy (William A.)
❑ 53RedSoxTI-4
❑ 54Top-195
❑ 55Top-207
❑ 57Top-399
❑ 58Top-148
❑ 59SenTealW-5
❑ 59Top-112
❑ 59TopVen-112
❑ 60SenJayP-4
❑ 60Top-508
❑ 61Pos-100A
❑ 61Pos-100B
❑ 61Top-504
❑ 61TwiPetM-26
❑ 75OakOak2A-11
❑ 81RedSoxBG2S-12
❑ 83TigPos-8
❑ 84TigTeal-11
❑ 84TigWavP-11
❑ 88TigPep-NNO
❑ 89TigMar-NNO
❑ 90TigCok-28
❑ 90TigTeal-5
❑ 91TigCok-NNO
❑ 92TigKro-28
❑ 92TigTeal-6
❑ 94TopArc1-195
❑ 94TopArc1G-195
Constable, Jimmy
❑ 59Top-451
❑ 63Top-411
Constant, Andres
❑ 89FreKeyS-3
❑ 90FreKeyTI-25
❑ 91FreKeyC-2
❑ 91FreKeyP-2356
Constantinides, Nick
❑ 94BriTigC-8
❑ 94BriTigF-3494
Constantino, Kraig
❑ 92SpoIndC-16
❑ 92SpoIndF-1298
Consuegra, Sandy
❑ 51Bow-96
❑ 52Bow-143
❑ 53BowC-89
❑ 54Bow-166
❑ 55Bow-116
❑ 55RedMan-AL25
❑ 56Top-265
❑ 79TCM50-170
❑ 91OriCro-83
Conte, Mike (Michael)
❑ 89MedAthB-1
❑ 90MadMusP-2276
❑ 90ModA'sC-6
❑ 91HunStaC-4
❑ 91HunStaP-1808
❑ 91HunStaTI-6
❑ 92HunStaF-3959
❑ 92HunStaS-307
❑ 93SanBerSC-4
❑ 93SanBerSF-764
❑ 93SouOreAC-6
❑ 93SouOreAF-4055
Conti, Guy
❑ 86WatPirP-6
❑ 88BakDodCLC-263
❑ 89BakDodCLC-207
❑ 89CalLeaA-24
❑ 90GreFalDSP-29
❑ 92GreFalDSP-30
❑ 93BakDodCLC-29
❑ 94BakDodC-28
❑ 97SanAntMB-29
❑ 97TexAllM-34
❑ 98SanAntMM-29
Conti, Jason
❑ 96AriBlaDB-12
❑ 96HonShaHWB-6
❑ 97BowBes-196
❑ 97BowBesAR-196
❑ 97BowBesR-196
❑ 97SouBenSH-10
❑ 97Top-468
❑ 98Bow-174
❑ 98BowCerBlueAU-56
❑ 98BowCerGA-56
❑ 98BowCerSA-56
❑ 98BowChr-174
❑ 98BowChrGA-174
❑ 98BowChrGAR-174
❑ 98BowChrI-174
❑ 98BowChrIR-174
❑ 98BowChrR-174
❑ 98BowGolA-174
❑ 98BowInt-174
❑ 98TexLeaC-3
❑ 98Top-252
❑ 98TopChr-252
❑ 98TopChrR-252
❑ 98TopDevR-252
❑ 98TopDia-252
❑ 98TopMiniC-252
❑ 98TulDriTI-3
❑ 99Bow-162
❑ 99BowAut-BA19
❑ 99BowChr-162
❑ 99BowChrG-162
❑ 99BowChrGR-162
❑ 99BowChrI-162
❑ 99BowChrIR-162
❑ 99BowChrR-162
❑ 99BowGol-162
❑ 99BowInt-162
❑ 99SP SigAuto-JC
❑ 99SP SigAutoG-JC
❑ 99SPSig-58
Conti, Joe
❑ 88CapCodPPaLP-15
Contreras, Efrain
❑ 94NewJerCC-4
❑ 94NewJerCF-3429
❑ 95PeoChiTI-11
❑ 96StPetCB-6
Contreras, Frank
❑ 82MiaMarT-21
Contreras, Henry
❑ 81BurBeeT-15
❑ 93LinVenB-110
❑ 95LinVen-35
Contreras, Joaquin
❑ 85LitFalMT-22
❑ 86ColMetP-7
❑ 87JacMetF-15
❑ 87TexLeaAF-16
❑ 88JacMetGS-20
❑ 88MetColP-17
❑ 88TidTidCa-15
❑ 88TidTidCM-17
❑ 89BlaYNPRWL-23
❑ 89TidTidC-16
❑ 89TidTidP-1960
❑ 90ProAAAF-476
❑ 90RocRedWGC-25
❑ 90RocRedWP-719
❑ 91LinDriAAA-452
❑ 91RocRedWLD-452
❑ 96WisTimRB-3
Contreras, Nardi
❑ 75TidTidTI-6
❑ 77ReaPhiT-5
❑ 80IowOakP-3
❑ 81EdmTraRR-4
❑ 82EdmTraT-14
❑ 85BufBisT-2
❑ 87RicBraC-43
❑ 87RicBraT-22
❑ 88JacExpB-23

❑ 88JacExpP-969
❑ 88SouLeaAJ-40
❑ 89JacExpB-26
❑ 89JacExpP-173
❑ 89PacSenL-26
❑ 90JacExpB-26
❑ 90JacExpP-1392
❑ 91IndIndP-478
❑ 91LinDriAAA-200
❑ 94ColCliF-2968
❑ 94ColCliP-3

Contreras, Rafael
❑ 77ReaPhiT-6

Converse, Jim
❑ 90HigSchPLS-22
❑ 91PenPilC-2
❑ 92JacSunF-3701
❑ 92JacSunS-354
❑ 92SkyAA F-150
❑ 92UppDecML-259
❑ 93Bow-543
❑ 93CalCanF-1158
❑ 93ExcFS7-222
❑ 93FleFinE-267
❑ 93StaClu-683
❑ 93StaCluFDI-683
❑ 93StaCluMOP-683
❑ 93TopTra-40T
❑ 93Ult-616
❑ 94CalCanF-782
❑ 94Pac-566
❑ 94SpoRoo-54
❑ 94SpoRooAP-54
❑ 95Pac-393
❑ 95StaClu-324
❑ 95StaCluMOP-324
❑ 95StaCluSTWS-324
❑ 95TacRaiTI-6
❑ 96LeaSigEA-33
❑ 96RoyPol-6
❑ 98RocRedWQ-9

Converse, Mike
❑ 86CedRapRT-3
❑ 87TamTarP-3

Convertino, Phil
❑ 77ReaPhiT-7

Conway, Jack Clements
❑ 47IndTeal-4
❑ 47IndVanPP-4
❑ 48GiaTeal-1
❑ 92TexLon-9

Conway, James P.
❑ 87OldJudN-95

Conway, Jeff
❑ 94SpoIndC-4
❑ 94SpoIndF-3334

Conway, John
❑ 52Par-96

Conway, Keith
❑ 94MadHatC-6
❑ 94MadHatF-124
❑ 96StPetCB-7
❑ 97PriWilC-8

Conway, Pete (Peter J.)
❑ 87OldJudN-94

Conway, Rip (Richard D.)
❑ 87OldJudN-93

Conwright, Allen
❑ 18Zee-56
❑ 19Zee-68

Conyer, Darryl
❑ 99TeaBesR-13
❑ 99TeaBesRFS-1
❑ 99TeaBesRG-13
❑ 99TeaBesRS-13

Coogan, Dale Roger
❑ 50Bow-244
❑ 50PirTeal-5
❑ 52Top-87
❑ 83TopRep5-87

Coogan, Patrick
❑ 98PriWilCQ-4

Cook, Aaron
❑ 98PorRocG-7

Cook, Alan
❑ 12Zee-27
❑ 13Zee-28
❑ 14Zee-31
❑ 95OdgRapTI-4

Cook, Andy
❑ 88OneYanP-2041
❑ 89PriWilCS-3
❑ 90AlbYanB-2
❑ 90AlbYanP-1031
❑ 90AlbYanSt-3
❑ 90CMC-731
❑ 91AlbYanLD-1
❑ 91AlbYanP-999
❑ 91LinDriAA-1
❑ 92ColCliF-342
❑ 93Bow-124
❑ 93ColCliF-1103
❑ 93ColCliP-2
❑ 93FleFinE-244
❑ 94ColCliF-2943
❑ 94ColCliP-5
❑ 94Pin-257
❑ 94PinArtP-257
❑ 94PinMusC-257
❑ 94SalLakBF-811
❑ 95ColCliMCTI-18
❑ 95ColCliP-5
❑ 95ColCliTI-5
❑ 98PitMetM-13

Cook, Brian
❑ 90ArkRaz-6

Cook, Cliff (Raymond C.)
❑ 61Top-399
❑ 62RedEnq-5
❑ 62Top-41
❑ 62TopVen-41
❑ 63Top-566
❑ 80Red196T-20
❑ 81TCM60I-296
❑ 82MetGal62-4
❑ 91MetWIZ-83

Cook, Dennis
❑ 86FreGiaSB-16
❑ 87ShrCapP-4
❑ 88PhoFirC-3
❑ 88PhoFirP-80
❑ 89Don-646
❑ 89DonBasB-327
❑ 89Fle-652
❑ 89FleGlo-652
❑ 89FleUpd-104
❑ 89PanSti-207
❑ 89PhiTas-39
❑ 89PhoFirC-3
❑ 89PhoFirP-1482
❑ 89UppDec-779
❑ 90ClaBlu-80
❑ 90Don-193
❑ 90DonBesN-93
❑ 90Fle-554
❑ 90FleCan-554
❑ 90Hot50RS-12
❑ 90Lea-342
❑ 90OPC-633
❑ 90PanSti-320
❑ 90PhiTas-6
❑ 90Sco-545
❑ 90Sco100RS-75
❑ 90Top-633
❑ 90TopTif-633
❑ 90UppDec-71
❑ 91AlbDukLD-4
❑ 91DodPol-25
❑ 91Don-657
❑ 91Fle-196
❑ 91Lea-257
❑ 91LinDriAAA-4
❑ 91OPC-467
❑ 91StaClu-411
❑ 91Top-467
❑ 91TopDesS-467
❑ 91TopMic-467
❑ 91TopTif-467
❑ 91UppDec-612
❑ 92Bow-497
❑ 92Fle-451
❑ 92IndFanC-8
❑ 92Lea-503
❑ 92LeaBlaG-503
❑ 92Pin-493
❑ 92StaClu-887
❑ 92StaCluNC-887
❑ 92TexLon-10
❑ 92Ult-346
❑ 93Don-625
❑ 93Fle-214
❑ 93IndWUA-7
❑ 93Lea-193
❑ 93PacSpa-409
❑ 93StaClu-153
❑ 93StaCluFDI-153
❑ 93StaCluMOP-153
❑ 93Top-141
❑ 93TopGol-141
❑ 93TopInaM-141
❑ 93TopInaR-141
❑ 93TopMic-141
❑ 93UppDec-202
❑ 93UppDecGold-202
❑ 94FleUpd-23
❑ 94WhiSoxK-4
❑ 95Fle-112
❑ 96LeaSigEA-34
❑ 96RanDr P-5
❑ 96RanMot-24
❑ 98PacOnl-474
❑ 98PacOnlR-474
❑ 98PacOnlWC-474
❑ 99Fle-387
❑ 99FleSta9-387
❑ 99FleWarT-387

Cook, Derrick
❑ 98Cha-1

Cook, Doc (Luther Almus)
❑ 15SpoNewM-37
❑ 16Zee-26

Cook, Doug
❑ 81ChaRoyT-12
❑ 83ChaRoyT-16
❑ 84MemChiT-12
❑ 91IdaFalBP-4321

Cook, Fred
❑ 11PinT-5-1061

Cook, Glen
❑ 82BurRanF-23
❑ 82BurRanT-17
❑ 83BurRanF-12
❑ 83BurRanT-3
❑ 83TulDriT-2
❑ 84OklCit8T-22
❑ 85DomLeaS-128
❑ 85OklCit8T-8
❑ 86OklCit8P-4
❑ 86Top-502
❑ 86TopTif-502
❑ 87OklCit8P-14
❑ 93RanKee-110

Cook, Hayward
❑ 95KanCouCTI-42
❑ 96BreCouMB-11
❑ 97PorSeaD-9
❑ 98PorSeaDQ-23

Cook, Jake
❑ 95MicBatCTI-7

Cook, James
❑ 08IndPos-4
❑ 86KenTwiP-4

Cook, Jason
❑ 94AppFoxC-26
❑ 94AppFoxFI-1060
❑ 96LanJetB-11

Cook, Jeff
❑ 86PriWilPP-7
❑ 87HarSenP-10
❑ 88EasLeaAP-13
❑ 88HarSenP-835
❑ 89HarSenP-304
❑ 89HarSenS-7
❑ 90BufBisC-24
❑ 90BufBisP-387
❑ 90CMC-24
❑ 90ProAAAF-502

Cook, John
❑ 96AubDouB-17

Cook, Kenny
❑ 92GulCoaDF-3558
❑ 93YakBeaC-7
❑ 93YakBeaF-3877
❑ 94BakDodC-8

Cook, Kerry
❑ 83SanJosBC-13
❑ 86WesPalBEP-9

Cook, Kyle
❑ 93MisStaB-10

Cook, Larry
❑ 86PalSprAP-8
❑ 86PalSprAS-11

Cook, Lester
❑ 19Zee-128
❑ 20Zee-62
❑ 21Zee-67
❑ 22Zee-58
❑ 23Zee-84
❑ 25Zee-87
❑ 26Zee-2
❑ 27Zee-1
❑ 28Zee-3
❑ 32Zee-5

Cook, Mike
❑ 86MidAngP-6
❑ 87CalAngPPS-7
❑ 88EdmTraC-2
❑ 88EdmTraP-567
❑ 89Fle-472
❑ 89FleGlo-472
❑ 90CMC-556
❑ 90PorBeaC-4
❑ 90PorBeaP-171
❑ 90ProAAAF-241
❑ 90TriAllGP-AAA21
❑ 91CalCanLD-57
❑ 91LinDriAAA-57
❑ 92LouRedF-1881
❑ 92LouRedS-258
❑ 93LinVenB-307
❑ 93RocRedWF-233
❑ 94OriPro-20
❑ 94OriUSPC-2C
❑ 94StaCluT-289
❑ 94StaCluTFDI-289
❑ 94TopGol-791

Cook, Mitch
❑ 83QuaCitCT-9
❑ 86ColAstP-7
❑ 87ColAstP-9

Cook, O.J.
❑ 97EriSeaWB-8
❑ 98AugGreM-13

Cook, Paul
❑ 87OldJudN-96

Cook, Rodney
❑ 95ChaRivTI-4

Cook, Ron
❑ 88FayGenP-1096
❑ 89LakTigS-5
❑ 90LakTigS-5
❑ 90StaFS7-33
❑ 91LinDriAA-378
❑ 91LonTigLD-378

Cook, Ron W.
❑ 70AstPho-3
❑ 71MLBOffS-75
❑ 71OPC-583
❑ 71Top-583
❑ 72OPC-339
❑ 72Top-339
❑ 72TopCloT-8

Cook, Scott
❑ 94EveGiaC-5
❑ 94EveGiaF-3642

Cook, Stan
❑ 89BoiHawP-1982
❑ 90EriSaiS-3

Cook, Steve
❑ 93ButCopKSP-9
❑ 94CedRapKC-7
❑ 94CedRapKF-1114

Cook, Tim
❑ 79HolMilT-12
❑ 81ElPasDT-20
❑ 82VanCanT-12
❑ 83LasVegSBHN-4
❑ 84BeaGolGT-12

Cooke, Bobby
❑ 55DesMoiHB-4

Cooke, Dusty (Allan Lindsey)
❑ 34BatR31-148
❑ 35AlDemDCR3-78
❑ 38RedOraW-5
❑ 39OrcPhoAP-27
❑ 49PhiBul-13
❑ 75Phi195T-7
❑ 80Phi195T-7
❑ 92ConTSN-418

Cooke, Mitch
❑ 82QuaCitCT-7

Cooke, Scott
❑ 89MisStaB-8

Cooke, Steve
❑ 90WelPirP-20
❑ 91AugPirC-4
❑ 91AugPirP-797
❑ 92Bow-274
❑ 92BufBisBS-4
❑ 92CarMudS-130
❑ 92ClaFS7-43
❑ 92DonRoo-28
❑ 92SkyAA F-61
❑ 93Bow-514
❑ 93Don-150
❑ 93Fla-111
❑ 93FleMajLP-B16
❑ 93Lea-240
❑ 93OPCPre-19
❑ 93PacSpa-585
❑ 93Pin-260
❑ 93PirHil-3
❑ 93PirNatl-7
❑ 93Sco-296
❑ 93SelRoo-69T
❑ 93SP-183
❑ 93StaClu-726
❑ 93StaCluFDI-726
❑ 93StaCluMOP-726
❑ 93Top-716
❑ 93TopGol-716
❑ 93TopInaM-716
❑ 93TopInaR-716
❑ 93TopMic-716
❑ 93Ult-449
❑ 93UppDec-599
❑ 93UppDecGold-599
❑ 94Bow-434
❑ 94ColC-83
❑ 94ColChoGS-83
❑ 94ColChoSS-83
❑ 94Don-72
❑ 94Fin-19
❑ 94FinJum-19
❑ 94FinRef-19
❑ 94Fla-215
❑ 94Fle-607
❑ 94FleExtB-344
❑ 94FleExtBSYS-5
❑ 94FleRooS-6
❑ 94Lea-169
❑ 94OPC-85
❑ 94Pac-495
❑ 94PanSti-234
❑ 94Pin-93
❑ 94PinArtP-93
❑ 94PinMusC-93
❑ 94PirQui-3
❑ 94Sco-186
❑ 94ScoGolR-186
❑ 94Sel-130
❑ 94StaClu-47
❑ 94StaCluFDI-47
❑ 94StaCluGR-47
❑ 94StaCluMOP-47
❑ 94Top-72
❑ 94TopGol-72
❑ 94TopSpa-72
❑ 94TriPla-182
❑ 94Ult-255
❑ 94UppDec-132
❑ 94UppDecED-132
❑ 94USPlaCR-7S
❑ 95ColCho-378
❑ 95ColChoGS-378
❑ 95ColChoSS-378
❑ 95Don-196
❑ 95DonPreP-196
❑ 95Fla-185
❑ 95Fle-475
❑ 95Lea-77
❑ 95Pac-342
❑ 95Pin-194
❑ 95PinArtP-194
❑ 95PinMusC-194
❑ 95PirFil-6
❑ 95Sco-522
❑ 95ScoGolR-522
❑ 95ScoPlaTS-522
❑ 95StaClu-58
❑ 95StaCluFDI-58
❑ 95StaCluMOP-58
❑ 95StaCluSTWS-58
❑ 95Stu-144
❑ 95Top-197
❑ 95TopCyb-113
❑ 95Ult-213
❑ 95UltGolM-213
❑ 95UppDec-148
❑ 95UppDecED-148
❑ 95UppDecEDG-148
❑ 96LeaSigA-48
❑ 96LeaSigAG-48
❑ 96LeaSigAS-48
❑ 97ColCho-432
❑ 97PirPos-8
❑ 98Pac-393
❑ 98PacPlaB-393
❑ 98PacRedT-393
❑ 98PacSil-393
❑ 98Pin-106
❑ 98PinPreP-106
❑ 98Sco-204
❑ 98Top-39
❑ 98TopChr-39
❑ 98TopChrR-39
❑ 98TopDevR-39
❑ 98TopDia-39
❑ 98TopMiniC-39
❑ 98UppDec-666

Cookie, Mascot
❑ 89WicStaR-29
❑ 90WicWraRD-28

Cookson, Brent
❑ 91SouOreAC-11
❑ 91SouOreAP-3860
❑ 92CliGiaC-5
❑ 93SanJosGC-7
❑ 93SanJosGF-24
❑ 94ShrCapF-1618
❑ 94UppDecML-41
❑ 95OmaRoyTI-6
❑ 95PhoFirTI-12
❑ 96Pac-334
❑ 96PawRedSDD-4
❑ 98TusSidM-25

Coolbaugh, Mike
❑ 90MedHatBJB-1
❑ 91St.CatBJC-7
❑ 91St.CatBJP-3402
❑ 92St.CatBJC-3
❑ 92St.CatBJF-3395
❑ 93HagSunC-5
❑ 93HagSunF-1886
❑ 94DunBluJC-6
❑ 94DunBluJF-2563
❑ 95KnoSmoF-47
❑ 97HunStaTI-5
❑ 97TexAllM-10
❑ 98ColSprSS-17

Coolbaugh, Scott
❑ 88TexLeaAGS-12
❑ 88TulDriTI-18
❑ 89OklCit8C-21
❑ 89OklCit8P-1512
❑ 89TriAAAP-AAA26
❑ 90Bow-494
❑ 90BowTif-494
❑ 90ClaYel-T24
❑ 90Don-43
❑ 90DonRoo-32
❑ 90Fle-293
❑ 90FleCan-293
❑ 90FleSoaS-5
❑ 90Hot50RS-13
❑ 90Lea-363
❑ 90Sco-612
❑ 90Sco100RS-79
❑ 90Spo-180
❑ 90TopDeb89-25
❑ 90TopTra-22T
❑ 90TopTraT-22T
❑ 90TriAAAC-5
❑ 90TulDriDGB-1
❑ 90UppDec-42
❑ 91Bow-649
❑ 91FleUpd-122
❑ 91LasVegSLD-280
❑ 91LasVegSP-241
❑ 91Lea-397
❑ 91LinDriAAA-280
❑ 91OPC-277
❑ 91PadSmo-6
❑ 91Sco100RS-36
❑ 91StaClu-493
❑ 91Top-277
❑ 91TopDesS-277
❑ 91TopMic-277
❑ 91TopTif-277
❑ 91TopTra-24T
❑ 91TopTraT-24T
❑ 91UppDec-451
❑ 91UppDecFE-37F
❑ 92LasVegSS-228
❑ 92Sco-205
❑ 92SkyAAAF-112
❑ 92TexLon-11
❑ 93RanKee-111
❑ 93RocRedWF-247
❑ 94LouRedF-2985
❑ 94TriAAF-AAA36

Cooley, Chad
❑ 94LSUTig-11
❑ 94LSUTigMP-10

Cooley, Duff (Dick Gordon)
❑ 03BreE10-23
❑ 11SpoLifCW-73

Cooley, Fred
❑ 89MedAthB-9

❑ 90MadMusB-6
❑ 90MadMusP-2275
❑ 90MidLeaASGS-8
❑ 90ProAaA-126
❑ 91Cla/Bes-228
❑ 91HunStaC-8
❑ 91HunStaLD-283
❑ 91HunStaP-1803
❑ 91LinDriAA-283
❑ 91ModA'sP-3094
❑ 91SouOreAAP-SOA12
❑ 92OrlSunRS-502

Cooley, Jack
❑ 91PacSenL-90

Cooley, Shannon
❑ 96BatCliTI-11
❑ 97PieBolWB-7
❑ 98ClePhiM-4

Coombes, Melissa
❑ 94ColSilBC-1
❑ 95ColSilB-4
❑ 95ColSilB9-6
❑ 96ColSilB-4

Coombs, Bobby (Raymond)
❑ 34DiaMatCSB-32

Coombs, Daniel
❑ 65Top-553
❑ 66Top-414
❑ 67Ast-6
❑ 67AstTeal2-7
❑ 67Top-464
❑ 68Top-547
❑ 69Top-389
❑ 71OPC-126
❑ 71Top-126
❑ 71TopCoi-49
❑ 72OPC-91
❑ 72Top-91
❑ 87AstShoSO-2
❑ 87AstShoSTw-29

Coombs, Glenn
❑ 91WelPirC-25
❑ 91WelPirP-3564
❑ 92AugPirF-229

Coombs, Jack (John W.)
❑ 08RosComP-57
❑ 09ColChiE-62
❑ 09RamT20-31
❑ 09SpoNewSM-46
❑ 10E98-10
❑ 10JHDABE-6
❑ 10JuJuDE-12
❑ 10LuxCigPP-5
❑ 11MecDFT-13
❑ 11PinT-5-502
❑ 11PloCanE-19
❑ 11SpoLifCW-74
❑ 11SpoLifM-90
❑ 12ColRedB-62
❑ 12ColTinT-62
❑ 14TexTomE-14
❑ 15SpoNewM-38
❑ 16FleBreD-19
❑ 27YorCarE-31
❑ 39MobCooB-1
❑ 39MobCooB-2
❑ 39MobCooB-3
❑ 39MobCooB-4
❑ 39MobCooB-5
❑ 39MobCooB-6
❑ 70FleWorS-7
❑ 74A'sTCM1P-5
❑ 86ConSer1-40
❑ 90DodTar-136

Coombs, Mike
❑ 90HelBreSP-28

Comer, Ron (Ronald)
❑ 88CalLeaACLC-9
❑ 88ModA'sCLC-72
❑ 88ModA'sTI-21
❑ 90HunStaB-16
❑ 91BirBarLD-55
❑ 91BirBarP-1460
❑ 91LinDriAA-55
❑ 92SkyAAAF-280
❑ 92VanCanF-2727
❑ 92VanCanS-631
❑ 93BirBarF-1197
❑ 94AlbDukF-849
❑ 94ExcFS7-36
❑ 94TriAAF-AAA25
❑ 95DodPol-5
❑ 95Exc-211
❑ 95ExcAll-4
❑ 95Top-651
❑ 96Cir-54
❑ 96CirRav-54
❑ 96ColCho-602
❑ 96ColChoGS-602
❑ 96ColChoSS-602
❑ 96Don-526
❑ 96DonPreP-526
❑ 96Fin-B349
❑ 96FinRef-B349
❑ 96Fle-164
❑ 96FleTif-164
❑ 96Pin-177
❑ 96UppDec-128
❑ 97Cir-140
❑ 97CirRav-140
❑ 97ColCho-379
❑ 97Don-283
❑ 97DonGolPP-283
❑ 97DonLim-58
❑ 97DonLimE-58
❑ 97DonLimENG-58
❑ 97DonSig-48
❑ 97DonSigA-22
❑ 97DonSigAC-29
❑ 97DonSigAM-29
❑ 97DonSigPPP-48
❑ 97DonSilPP-283
❑ 97Fle-144
❑ 97FleTif-144
❑ 97Lea-159
❑ 97LeaFraM-159
❑ 97LeaFraMDC-159
❑ 97Pac-134
❑ 97PacLigB-134
❑ 97PacSil-134
❑ 97Sel-155
❑ 97SelCom-155
❑ 97Top-186
❑ 98CirThu-290
❑ 98CirThuRav-290
❑ 98CirThuSupRav-290
❑ 98ColCho-163
❑ 98Don-94
❑ 98DonCol-94
❑ 98DonColL-334
❑ 98DonColP-649
❑ 98DonColS-94
❑ 98DonGolPP-94
❑ 98DonPre-99
❑ 98DonPreSeat-99
❑ 98DonPriCD-94
❑ 98DonPriCL-334
❑ 98DonPriCP-649
❑ 98DonSilPP-94
❑ 98Fin-203
❑ 98FinNo--203
❑ 98FinNo-R-203
❑ 98FinRef-203
❑ 98Fle-233
❑ 98Lea-135
❑ 98LeaFraDA-135
❑ 98LeaFraF-135
❑ 98LeaFraM-135
❑ 98LeaFraM-135
❑ 98LeaFraMDC-135
❑ 98LeaFraMDC-135
❑ 98LeaFraMZ2-135
❑ 98Pac-130
❑ 98PacOnl-418
❑ 98PacOnlR-418
❑ 98PacOnlWC-418
❑ 98PacPlaB-130
❑ 98PacRedT-130
❑ 98PacSil-130
❑ 98Sco-52
❑ 98ScoRT-53
❑ 98ScoSS-PP16
❑ 98ScoSSAP-PP16
❑ 98SP Aut-124
❑ 98StaCluFDI-303
❑ 98StaClul-303
❑ 98StaCluOneK-303
❑ 98StaCluPP-303
❑ 98Stu-55
❑ 98StuGPP-55
❑ 98StuSPP-55
❑ 98Top-173
❑ 98TopChr-173
❑ 98TopChrR-173
❑ 98TopDevR-173
❑ 98TopDia-173
❑ 98TopMiniC-173
❑ 98UppDec-128
❑ 99Fle-88
❑ 99FleSta9-88
❑ 99FleWarT-88
❑ 99Pac-245
❑ 99PacOme-136
❑ 99PacOmeC-136
❑ 99PacOmeG-136
❑ 99PacOmePB-136
❑ 99PacPar-132
❑ 99PacParC-132
❑ 99PacParG-132
❑ 99PacParHoloGold-132
❑ 99PacParHS-132
❑ 99PacParOD-132
❑ 99PacParPB-132
❑ 99PacParRed-132
❑ 99PacPlaB-245
❑ 99PacRed-245
❑ 99SkyThu-18
❑ 99SkyThuRant-18
❑ 99SkyThuRave-18
❑ 99Spolll-91
❑ 99StaClu-134
❑ 99StaCluFDI-134
❑ 99StaCluOoaK-134
❑ 99StaCluPP-134
❑ 99ThuSkySupR-18
❑ 99Top-344
❑ 99TopChr-344
❑ 99TopChrR-344
❑ 99TopMVPP-344
❑ 99UppDec-414
❑ 99UppDecEL1-414
❑ 99UppDecEL2-414
❑ 99Vic-232

Coonan, Bill
❑ 86MedA'sC-58

Cooney, Ed
❑ 88CapCodPPaLP-14

Cooney, James E.
❑ 26Exh-19

Cooney, Jim
❑ 95ChaRivTI-24

Cooney, Jimmy (James Edward)
❑ 84CubBriPC-9H
❑ 87OldJudN-97

Cooney, Johnny (John Walter)
❑ 36OveCanR-9
❑ 36OveCanR-10
❑ 39PlaBal-85
❑ 40PlaBal-60
❑ 41DouPlaR-41
❑ 41PlaBal-50
❑ 43DodTeal-5
❑ 54BraJohC-28
❑ 55BraGolS-29
❑ 55BraJohC-28
❑ 60Top-458
❑ 79DiaGre-205
❑ 81WhiSox1T-45
❑ 83Bra53F-28
❑ 90DodTar-137
❑ 91ConTSN-94

Cooney, Kyle
❑ 94GreFalDSP-13
❑ 95VerBeaDTI-6
❑ 96MauStiHWB-21
❑ 96SanBerSB-7
❑ 97SanAntMB-13
❑ 98SanAntMG-6
❑ 98SanAntMM-13

Cooney, Phil (Phillip)
❑ 09ObaT21-209
❑ 09ObaT21-383
❑ 12ObaPreT-132

Cooney, Terry
❑ 88T/MUmp-21
❑ 89T/MUmp-19
❑ 90T/MUmp-18

Cooper, Arley Wilbur
❑ 16FleBreD-20
❑ 21E121So1-12
❑ 22W572-16

Cooper, Army (Alfred)
❑ 87NegLeaPD-11

Cooper, Bill
❑ 86LakTigP-4
❑ 87GleFalTP-8
❑ 88GleFalTP-933

Cooper, Brian
❑ 96LakElsSB-2
❑ 97LakElsSG-9
❑ 98MidAngG-10
❑ 98MidAngO-8
❑ 98TexLeaTPG-7
❑ 99Bow-422
❑ 99BowGol-422
❑ 99BowInt-422

Cooper, Cecil C.
❑ 72OPC-79
❑ 72Top-79
❑ 74OPC-523
❑ 74Top-523
❑ 75OPC-489
❑ 75Top-489
❑ 75TopMin-489
❑ 76OPC-78
❑ 76RedSoxSM-3
❑ 76SSP-404
❑ 76Top-78
❑ 77OPC-102
❑ 77Top-235
❑ 78Hos-119
❑ 78Kel-41
❑ 78OPC-71
❑ 78Top-154
❑ 79BasPat-22
❑ 79Hos-36
❑ 79OPC-163
❑ 79Top-325
❑ 80OPC-52
❑ 80Top-95
❑ 80TopSup-33
❑ 81AllGamPI-4
❑ 81Don-83
❑ 81Dra-16
❑ 81Fle-639
❑ 81FleStiC-16
❑ 81Kel-32
❑ 81MSAMinD-10
❑ 81OPC-356
❑ 81PerCreC-15
❑ 81Squ-30
❑ 81Top-3
❑ 81Top-555
❑ 81TopScr-2
❑ 81TopSti-10
❑ 81TopSti-13
❑ 81TopSti-93
❑ 81TopSti-241
❑ 81TopSupN-5
❑ 82BrePol-15
❑ 82Don-258
❑ 82Dra-9
❑ 82Fle-138
❑ 82FleSta-140
❑ 82Kel-60
❑ 82OnDecD-10
❑ 82OPC-167
❑ 82PerAll-2
❑ 82PerAllG-2
❑ 82PerCreC-18
❑ 82PerCreCG-18
❑ 82Squ-1
❑ 82Top-675
❑ 82Top-703
❑ 82TopSti-199
❑ 83AllGamPI-3
❑ 83BreGar-5
❑ 83BrePlaM-1
❑ 83BrePol-15
❑ 83Don-106
❑ 83DonActA-19
❑ 83Dra-6
❑ 83Fle-30
❑ 83FleSta-43
❑ 83FleSti-23
❑ 83Kel-28
❑ 83OPC-190
❑ 83PerCreC-21
❑ 83PerCreCG-21
❑ 83Top-190
❑ 83TopFol-3
❑ 83TopGloS-15
❑ 83TopSti-80
❑ 83TopSti-173
❑ 83TopSti-181
❑ 84AllGamPI-92
❑ 84BreGar-5
❑ 84BrePol-15
❑ 84Don-351
❑ 84DonCha-24
❑ 84Dra-8
❑ 84Fle-198
❑ 84FleSti-31
❑ 84FunFooP-48
❑ 84MilBra-7
❑ 84Nes792-133
❑ 84Nes792-420
❑ 84Nes792-710
❑ 84OPC-43
❑ 84RalPur-27
❑ 84SevCoi-C8
❑ 84Top-133
❑ 84Top-420
❑ 84Top-710
❑ 84TopCer-27
❑ 84TopGloS-34
❑ 84TopRubD-15
❑ 84TopSti-200A
❑ 84TopSti-291
❑ 84TopTif-133
❑ 84TopTif-420
❑ 84TopTif-710
❑ 85AllGamPI-3
❑ 85BreGar-5
❑ 85BrePol-15
❑ 85Don-170
❑ 85Fle-580
❑ 85Lea-246
❑ 85OPC-290
❑ 85SubDis-9
❑ 85ThoMcAD-9
❑ 85Top-290
❑ 85TopRubD-13
❑ 85TopSti-287
❑ 85TopTif-290
❑ 86BrePol-15
❑ 86Don-7
❑ 86Don-170
❑ 86DonAll-54
❑ 86DonAllB-PC9
❑ 86DonSupD-7
❑ 86Fle-484
❑ 86FleLimE-12
❑ 86FleMin-100
❑ 86FleStiC-26
❑ 86Lea-7
❑ 86MSAJayPCD-2
❑ 86OPC-385
❑ 86SevCoi-C15
❑ 86Spo-29
❑ 86Spo-145
❑ 86Spo-180
❑ 86Top-385
❑ 86TopSti-196
❑ 86TopSup-20
❑ 86TopTat-6
❑ 86TopTif-385
❑ 86Woo-8
❑ 87BoaandB-6
❑ 87BrePol-15
❑ 87BreTeal-4
❑ 87Don-363
❑ 87Fle-343
❑ 87FleAwaW-10
❑ 87FleGlo-343
❑ 87FleMin-22
❑ 87Lea-230
❑ 87OPC-10
❑ 87OPCBoxB-D
❑ 87RedFolSB-48
❑ 87Spo-169
❑ 87StuPan-21
❑ 87Top-10
❑ 87TopSti-198
❑ 87TopTif-10
❑ 87TopWaxBC-D
❑ 87Woo-2
❑ 88Fle-161
❑ 88FleGlo-161
❑ 88Sco-169
❑ 88ScoGlo-169
❑ 88Top-769
❑ 88TopClo-26
❑ 88TopTif-769
❑ 89PacSenL-42
❑ 89T/MSenL-23
❑ 91UppDecS-10
❑ 92BreCarT-5
❑ 92BreCarT-xx0
❑ 92UppDecS-9
❑ 93ActPacA-164
❑ 93TedWil-49
❑ 93UppDecAH-34
❑ 93UppDecS-9
❑ 94BreMilB-215
❑ 94BreMilB-303
❑ 94UppDecAH-21
❑ 94UppDecAH1-21

Cooper, Chris
❑ 87BriYouC-5

Cooper, Claude W.
❑ 18Zee-3
❑ 19Zee-3
❑ 19Zee-16
❑ 21Zee-26
❑ 22Zee-25
❑ 23Zee-31
❑ 23Zee-32
❑ 24Zee-24
❑ 25Zee-23
❑ 27Zee-87

Cooper, Craig
❑ 86SpoIndC-168
❑ 88WicPilRD-24
❑ 89WicUpdR-8
❑ 89WicWraR-34
❑ 90ElPasDGS-7
❑ 92CanIndS-104

Cooper, Darren
❑ 90MarPhiP-3200

Cooper, Dave
❑ 84AriWilP-2
❑ 87LakTigP-23
❑ 88TolMudHC-8
❑ 88TolMudHP-608
❑ 89LonTigP-1362

Cooper, David
❑ 94Top-761
❑ 94TopGol-761
❑ 94TopSpa-761

Cooper, Don
❑ 79WesHavYT-3
❑ 80NasSouTI-6
❑ 81TwiPos-6
❑ 82Fle-550
❑ 82TolMudHT-1
❑ 82Top-409
❑ 83SyrChiT-6
❑ 84ColCliP-6
❑ 84ColCliT-17
❑ 85ColCliP-6
❑ 85ColCliT-5
❑ 86SyrChiP-9
❑ 88SouBenWSGS-14
❑ 89SarWhiSS-25
❑ 90SarWhiSS-27
❑ 91PacSenL-22
❑ 91SarWhiSC-16
❑ 91SarWhiSP-1131
❑ 92BirBarF-2600
❑ 92BirBarS-100
❑ 92YanWIZ8-35
❑ 95WhiSoxK-31
❑ 96NasSouB-2

Cooper, Eric
❑ 98BilMusTI-8

Cooper, Gary Clifton
❑ 86AubAstP-7
❑ 87OscAstP-21
❑ 88ColAstB-21
❑ 89TucTorC-22
❑ 89TucTorJP-6
❑ 89TucTorP-184
❑ 90CMC-612
❑ 90HamRedB-19
❑ 90HamRedS-9
❑ 90ProAAAF-203
❑ 90TucTorC-10
❑ 90TucTorP-213
❑ 91LinDriAAA-609
❑ 91TriA AAGP-AAA51
❑ 91TucTorLD-609
❑ 91TucTorP-2224
❑ 92Don-774
❑ 92PinRool-3
❑ 92Sco-840
❑ 92ScoImpP-25
❑ 92ScoRoo-28
❑ 92SkyAAAF-270
❑ 92TopDeb91-38
❑ 92TriA AAS-605
❑ 92TucTorF-495
❑ 92TucTorS-605
❑ 93BufBisF-523
❑ 93ExcFS7-40
❑ 94IndIndF-1815
❑ 95JacSunTI-5

Cooper, Gary N.
❑ 74GasRanT-7
❑ 79SavBraT-2
❑ 81DurBulT-6

Cooper, Guy
❑ 19Zee-34
❑ 29Zee-86

Cooper, Jamie
❑ 87EveGiaC-9
❑ 88CliGiaP-715
❑ 88MidLeaAGS-4
❑ 89SanJosGB-3
❑ 89SanJosGCLC-230
❑ 89SanJosGP-458
❑ 89SanJosGS-5

❑ 89Sta-83
❑ 90ShrCapP-1457
❑ 90ShrCapS-4
❑ 91ShrCapP-1833
❑ 92PhoFirS-380
❑ 92SkyAAAF-179
Cooper, Jeff
❑ 91SalLakTP-3217
Cooper, Kent
❑ 84EveGiaC-7
Cooper, Mark
❑ 85KinBluJT-12
Cooper, Mort (Morton)
❑ 39PlaBal-131
❑ 40PlaBal-113
❑ 41CarW75-3
❑ 43MPR302-1-4
❑ 47Exh-49
❑ 47PM1StaP1-36
❑ 76TayBow4-78
❑ 83Car194T-40
❑ 83TCMPla1943-25
❑ 84TCMPla1-34
❑ 85BigLeaC3-64
❑ 87SpoRea-24
❑ 91ConTSN-301
❑ 92CarMcD-19
❑ 92ConTSN-624
Cooper, Neal
❑ 76DubPacT-8
Cooper, Paul
❑ 78DayBeaAT-6
Cooper, Scott
❑ 86ElmPioRSP-6
❑ 87GreHorP-10
❑ 88CarLeaAS-5
❑ 88LynRedSS-5
❑ 89BasAmeAPB-AA9
❑ 89NewBriRSP-609
❑ 89NewBriRSS-3
❑ 89Sta-126
❑ 90Bow-277
❑ 90BowTif-277
❑ 90ClaUpd-T13
❑ 90CMC-265
❑ 90PawRedSC-14
❑ 90PawRedSDD-3
❑ 90PawRedSP-467
❑ 90ProAAAF-439
❑ 90Sco-651
❑ 90TopTVRS-39
❑ 91Don-496
❑ 91Fle-91
❑ 91LinDriAAA-354
❑ 91PawRedSDD-3
❑ 91PawRedSLD-354
❑ 91PawRedSP-46
❑ 91TopDeb90-35
❑ 91TriA AAGP-AAA29
❑ 91UppDec-22
❑ 92Bow-129
❑ 92Cla1-T28
❑ 92ClaGam-142
❑ 92Don-570
❑ 92Lea-182
❑ 92LeaBlaG-182
❑ 92OPC-488
❑ 92Pin-252
❑ 92PinRoo-2
❑ 92ProFS7-16
❑ 92Sco-876
❑ 92Sco100RS-88
❑ 92ScoHotR-5
❑ 92ScoImpP-26
❑ 92ScoRoo-13
❑ 92StaClu-377
❑ 92Top-488
❑ 92TopGol-488
❑ 92TopGolW-488
❑ 92TopMic-488
❑ 92TriPla-180
❑ 92Ult-312
❑ 92UppDec-541
❑ 93Bow-467
❑ 93Don-135
❑ 93Fin-7
❑ 93FinRef-7
❑ 93Fla-161
❑ 93Fle-178
❑ 93Lea-175
❑ 93OPC-385
❑ 93OPCPre-13
❑ 93PacSpa-355
❑ 93PanSti-93
❑ 93Pin-330
❑ 93RedSoxP-7
❑ 93RedSoxWHP-9
❑ 93Sco-198
❑ 93Sel-302
❑ 93SP-200
❑ 93StaClu-368
❑ 93StaCluFDI-368
❑ 93StaCluMOP-368
❑ 93Stu-45
❑ 93Top-655
❑ 93TopGol-655
❑ 93TopInaM-655
❑ 93TopInaR-655
❑ 93TopMic-655
❑ 93Toy-29
❑ 93TriPla-25
❑ 93Ult-149
❑ 93UppDec-57
❑ 93UppDecGold-57
❑ 93USPlaCR-11D
❑ 94Bow-203
❑ 94ColC-84
❑ 94ColChoGS-84
❑ 94ColChoSS-84
❑ 94Don-417
❑ 94Fin-168
❑ 94FinPre-168P
❑ 94FinRef-168
❑ 94Fla-11
❑ 94Fle-27
❑ 94FleAllS-6
❑ 94FleExtB-17
❑ 94Lea-75
❑ 94LeaL-8
❑ 94OPC-4
❑ 94Pac-50
❑ 94PanSti-27
❑ 94Pin-72
❑ 94PinArtP-72
❑ 94PinMusC-72
❑ 94Sco-388
❑ 94ScoGolR-388
❑ 94Sel-39
❑ 94SP-153
❑ 94SPDieC-153
❑ 94StaClu-396
❑ 94StaCluFDI-396
❑ 94StaCluGR-396
❑ 94StaCluMOP-396
❑ 94Stu-160
❑ 94Top-235
❑ 94TopGol-235
❑ 94TopSpa-235
❑ 94TriPla-202
❑ 94Ult-313
❑ 94UppDec-502
❑ 94UppDecED-502
❑ 95ColCho-408
❑ 95ColCho-540T
❑ 95ColChoGS-408
❑ 95ColChoSE-192
❑ 95ColChoSEGS-192
❑ 95ColChoSESS-192
❑ 95ColChoSS-408
❑ 95Don-413
❑ 95DonDiaK-DK15
❑ 95DonPreP-413
❑ 95DonTopotO-325
❑ 95Fin-145
❑ 95Fin-244
❑ 95FinRef-145
❑ 95FinRef-244
❑ 95Fla-11
❑ 95Fla-406
❑ 95Fle-27
❑ 95FleAllS-11
❑ 95FleUpd-155
❑ 95Lea-155
❑ 95LeaLim-7
❑ 95Pac-35
❑ 95PacPri-13
❑ 95PanSti-58
❑ 95Pin-67
❑ 95PinArtP-67
❑ 95PinMusC-67
❑ 95Sco-427
❑ 95ScoGolR-427
❑ 95ScoPlaTS-427
❑ 95ScoYouTE-427T
❑ 95SP-99
❑ 95SPSil-99
❑ 95StaClu-328
❑ 95StaClu-614
❑ 95StaCluMOP-328
❑ 95StaCluMOP-614
❑ 95StaCluMOP-SS16
❑ 95StaCluSS-SS16
❑ 95StaCluSTWS-328
❑ 95StaCluSTWS-614
❑ 95Stu-169
❑ 95Sum-86
❑ 95SumNthD-86
❑ 95Top-4
❑ 95TopTra-138T
❑ 95Ult-261
❑ 95UltGolM-261
❑ 95UppDec-454
❑ 95UppDecSE-77
❑ 95UppDecSE-228
❑ 95UppDecSEG-77
❑ 95UppDecSEG-228
❑ 96ColCho-286
❑ 96ColChoGS-286
❑ 96ColChoSS-286
❑ 96Don-480
❑ 96DonPreP-480
❑ 96Fle-540
❑ 96FleTif-540
❑ 96Pac-215
❑ 96PanSti-79
❑ 96Sco-430
❑ 96StaClu-291
❑ 96StaCluMOP-291
❑ 96Top-371
❑ 96Ult-271
❑ 96UltGolM-271
❑ 97Ult-392
❑ 97UltGolME-392
❑ 97UltPlaME-392
❑ 98PacInvGems-52
Cooper, Tim
❑ 90TamYanD-1
❑ 91GreHorP-3064
❑ 92GreHorC-21
❑ 92GreHorF-785
❑ 93SanBerSC-5
❑ 93SanBerSF-777
❑ 94ClaGolF-148
❑ 94TamYanC-6
❑ 94TamYanF-2389
❑ 95TamYanYI-3
Cooper, Virgil
❑ 88UtiBluSP-15
❑ 89SouBenWSGS-10
Cooper, Walker (William W.)
❑ 41CarW75-4
❑ 43MPR302-1-5
❑ 46SpoExcW-2-1A
❑ 47Exh-50
❑ 48Bow-9
❑ 48GiaTeal-2
❑ 49Bow-117
❑ 49EurSta-79
❑ 49GiaTeal-2
❑ 50Bow-111
❑ 51Bow-135
❑ 51R42SmaS-11
❑ 52Bow-208
❑ 52DixLid-5
❑ 52DixPre-5
❑ 52Top-294
❑ 53BowBW-30
❑ 53BraJohC-14
❑ 53BraSpiaS3-8
❑ 53ExhCan-58
❑ 54DanDee-3
❑ 56Top-273
❑ 57Top-380
❑ 60Top-462
❑ 70SpoCarfCOP-26
❑ 76TayBow4-44
❑ 79DiaGre-168
❑ 79TCM50-69
❑ 83Bra53F-39
❑ 83Car194T-15
❑ 83TCMPla1943-24
❑ 83TopRep5-294
❑ 87SpoRea-24
❑ 92CarMcD-14
❑ 92ConTSN-633
Cooper, Wilbur
❑ 19W514-42
❑ 20NatCarE-16
❑ 20W516-19
❑ 20W52-6
❑ 21Exh-27
❑ 21Nei-57
❑ 22E120-215
❑ 22W573-24
❑ 23W501-80
❑ 27Zee-49
❑ 28Zee-70
❑ 77GalGloG-166
❑ 86PirGreT-10
Cope, Gary
❑ 91KisDodP-4175
❑ 92GreFalDSP-5
Cope, Robin
❑ 94AppFoxC-6
❑ 94AppFoxFl-1045
Copeland, Brandon
❑ 98CapCitBF5-26
❑ 98CapCitBM-26
Copeland, Mark
❑ 90AubAstB-24
Copley, Travis
❑ 98TenKry-8
Coplon, Mitch
❑ 82DayBeaAT-2
Copp, Bill
❑ 86WatPirP-7
❑ 87SalBucP-19
❑ 88HarSenP-853
Coppell, Shannon
❑ 89CliGiaP-902
Coppenbarger, Frank
❑ 77QuaCitAT-11
Copper Kings, Butte
❑ 95ButCopKtl-31
Copper, Jeff
❑ 91SalLakTSP-22
Coppeta, Greg
❑ 90NiaFalRP-16
❑ 91FayGenC-1
❑ 91FayGenP-1161
❑ 92LakTigC-12
❑ 93LakTigC-4
❑ 93LakTigF-1300
Coppinger, Rocky
❑ 94BluOriC-4
❑ 94BluOriF-3553
❑ 95Bes-1
❑ 95BesFra-F3
❑ 95BowBayTI-45
❑ 95SPML-18
❑ 96Bow-145
❑ 96BowBes-126
❑ 96BowBesAR-126
❑ 96BowBesR-126
❑ 96BowFoi-145
❑ 96Cir-3
❑ 96CirRav-3
❑ 96Exc-3
❑ 96ExcCli-2
❑ 96LeaPre-120
❑ 96LeaPreP-120
❑ 96RocRedWB-8
❑ 96Zen-119
❑ 96ZenArtP-119
❑ 97BalOriP-7
❑ 97BalOriP-8
❑ 97BowCerBlaIA-CA16
❑ 97BowCerBluIA-CA16
❑ 97BowCerGolIA-CA16
❑ 97Cir-291
❑ 97CirRav-291
❑ 97ColCho-2
❑ 97ColChoT-BO1
❑ 97Don-145
❑ 97DonGolPP-145
❑ 97DonPre-138
❑ 97DonPreCttC-138
❑ 97DonSilPP-145
❑ 97DonTea-36
❑ 97DonTeaSPE-36
❑ 97Fin-4
❑ 97FinRef-4
❑ 97FlaShoLC-108
❑ 97FlaShoLeg0-108
❑ 97FlaShoLeg1-108
❑ 97FlaShoM-A108
❑ 97FlaShoM-B108
❑ 97FlaShoM-C108
❑ 97FlaShoR0-108
❑ 97FlaShoR1-108
❑ 97FlaShoR2-108
❑ 97Fle-4
❑ 97FleTif-4
❑ 97MetUni-3
❑ 97OriSco-4
❑ 97OriScoPl-4
❑ 97OriScoPr-4
❑ 97Pac-21
❑ 97PacLigB-21
❑ 97PacSil-21
❑ 97Pin-175
❑ 97PinArtP-PP175
❑ 97PinMusC-175
❑ 97PinPrePla-175
❑ 97Sco-87
❑ 97ScoArtPWB-87
❑ 97ScoPreS-87
❑ 97ScoShoS-87
❑ 97ScoShoSAP-87
❑ 97SP-33
❑ 97StaClu-299
❑ 97StaCluMOP-299
❑ 97Top-311
❑ 97TopChr-105
❑ 97TopChrR-105
❑ 97TopGal-155
❑ 97TopGalPPI-155
❑ 97UD3-57
❑ 97UD3GenNex-GN11
❑ 97Ult-3
❑ 97UltGolME-3
❑ 97UltPlaME-3
❑ 97UppDec-225
❑ 97UppDecBCP-BC6
❑ 97UppDecTTS-TS16
❑ 98BowBayM-8
❑ 98PinSna-BO2
Coppock, Mark
❑ 90ArkRaz-30
Coppol, Carmen
❑ 77LynMetT-10
Coquillette, Trace
❑ 94BurBeeF-1087
❑ 94VerExpC-9
❑ 94VerExpF-3915
❑ 96WesPalBEB-25
❑ 98arSenW1-9
❑ 98EasLeaTPM-5
❑ 98HarSenM-9
Cora, Alex
❑ 97SanAntMB-15
❑ 97TexLeaTP-16
❑ 98BesAutSS-11
❑ 98BowBes-132
❑ 98BowBesAR-132
❑ 98BowBesR-132
❑ 98DodMot-22
❑ 98LeaRS-334
❑ 98LeaRSLHolo-334
❑ 98LeaRSLong-334
❑ 98LeaRTrue-334
❑ 98SanAntMM-15
❑ 98SP MinPE-69
❑ 98SPMin-69
❑ 99Pac-216
❑ 99PacCroC-140
❑ 99PacCroCPB-140
❑ 99PacPlaB-216
❑ 99PacRed-216
❑ 99SPx-100
❑ 99SPxFinR-100
❑ 99SPxFinS-100
❑ 99UppDecBD-104
❑ 99UppDecBDD-104
❑ 99UppDecBDQ-104
❑ 99UppDecBDT-104
Cora, Joey
❑ 85SpoIndC-4
❑ 86BeaGolGP-7
❑ 87DonOpeD-147
❑ 87PadBohHB-4
❑ 88BlaYNPRWL-104
❑ 88Fle-580
❑ 88FleGlo-580
❑ 88LasVegSC-18
❑ 88LasVegSP-234
❑ 88Sco-420
❑ 88ScoGlo-420
❑ 88Top-91
❑ 88TopClo-27
❑ 88TopTif-91
❑ 88TriAAAP-22
❑ 89BlaYNPRWL-112
❑ 89BlaYNPRWLU-49
❑ 89LasVegSC-14
❑ 89LasVegSP-23
❑ 90Bow-211
❑ 90BowTif-211
❑ 90Don-538
❑ 90Fle-154
❑ 90FleCan-154
❑ 90Lea-366
❑ 90ScoYouS2-14
❑ 90TriAAAC-33
❑ 90UppDec-601
❑ 91Fle-527
❑ 91FleUpd-11
❑ 91Lea-375
❑ 91Sco-253
❑ 91UppDec-291
❑ 91WhiSoxK-21
❑ 92Don-108
❑ 92Fle-76
❑ 92OPC-302
❑ 92PanSti-126
❑ 92Sco-326
❑ 92StaClu-535
❑ 92Top-302
❑ 92TopGol-302
❑ 92TopGolW-302
❑ 92TopMic-302
❑ 92Ult-334
❑ 92UppDec-359
❑ 92WhiSoxK-28
❑ 93Don-697
❑ 93Fla-182
❑ 93Fle-580
❑ 93Lea-461
❑ 93PacSpa-68
❑ 93Sco-454
❑ 93StaClu-54
❑ 93StaCluFDI-54
❑ 93StaCluMOP-54
❑ 93Top-122
❑ 93TopGol-122
❑ 93TopInaM-122
❑ 93TopInaR-122
❑ 93TopMic-122
❑ 93Ult-172
❑ 93UppDec-742
❑ 93UppDecGold-742
❑ 93WhiSoxK-7
❑ 93WhiSoxSC-6
❑ 94ColC-85
❑ 94ColChoGS-85
❑ 94ColChoSS-85
❑ 94Don-447
❑ 94Fin-146
❑ 94FinRef-146
❑ 94Fla-275
❑ 94Fle-79
❑ 94FleExtB-43
❑ 94Lea-175
❑ 94Pac-123
❑ 94PanSti-46
❑ 94Pin-318
❑ 94PinArtP-318
❑ 94PinMusC-318
❑ 94Sco-485
❑ 94ScoCyc-TC12
❑ 94ScoGolR-485
❑ 94Sel-132
❑ 94StaClu-100
❑ 94StaCluFDI-100
❑ 94StaCluGR-100
❑ 94StaCluMOP-100
❑ 94StaCluST-ST18
❑ 94StaCluT-143
❑ 94StaCluTFDI-143
❑ 94Top-478
❑ 94TopGol-478
❑ 94TopSpa-478
❑ 94Ult-32
❑ 94UppDec-371
❑ 94UppDecED-371
❑ 94WhiSoxK-5
❑ 95Don-33
❑ 95DonPreP-33
❑ 95DonTopotO-148
❑ 95Fin-311
❑ 95FinRef-311
❑ 95Fla-300
❑ 95Fle-113
❑ 95FleUpd-74
❑ 95MarMot-8
❑ 95MarPac-16
❑ 95MarPac-29
❑ 95Pac-84
❑ 95Sco-454
❑ 95ScoGolR-454
❑ 95ScoPlaTS-454
❑ 95StaClu-33
❑ 95StaClu-536
❑ 95StaCluFDI-33
❑ 95StaCluMOP-33
❑ 95StaCluMOP-536
❑ 95StaCluSTDW-M536
❑ 95StaCluSTWS-33
❑ 95StaCluSTWS-536
❑ 95StaCluVR-22
❑ 95StaCluVRMO-22
❑ 95Top-545
❑ 95TopCyb-326
❑ 95TopTra-125T
❑ 95Ult-27

- 95UltGolM-27
- 96ColCho-312
- 96ColChoGS-312
- 96ColChoSS-312
- 96Don-259
- 96DonPreP-259
- 96EmoXL-111
- 96Fla-158
- 96Fle-234
- 96FleTif-234
- 96LeaSigA-49
- 96LeaSigAG-49
- 96LeaSigAS-49
- 96MarMot-8
- 96MetUni-106
- 96MetUniP-106
- 96Pac-417
- 96PacPri-P130
- 96PacPriG-P130
- 96Sco-162
- 96StaClu-374
- 96StaCluMOP-374
- 96TeaOut-20
- 96Top-304
- 96Ult-125
- 96UltGolM-125
- 96UppDec-199
- 97Cir-390
- 97CirRav-390
- 97ColCho-233
- 97ColChoT-SM4
- 97Don-132
- 97DonGolPP-132
- 97DonSilPP-132
- 97DonTea-142
- 97DonTeaSPE-142
- 97Fle-204
- 97FleTif-204
- 97Lea-81
- 97LeaFraM-81
- 97LeaFraMDC-81
- 97MarSco-10
- 97MarScoPl-10
- 97MarScoPr-10
- 97Pac-185
- 97PacBaeS-5
- 97PacLatotML-18
- 97PacLigB-185
- 97PacPri-62
- 97PacPriLB-62
- 97PacPriP-62
- 97PacSil-185
- 97Pin-137
- 97PinArtP-PP137
- 97PinMusC-137
- 97PinPrePla-137
- 97Sco-201
- 97ScoArtPWB-201
- 97ScoPreS-201
- 97ScoShoS-201
- 97ScoShoSAP-201
- 97StaClu-149
- 97StaCluMOP-149
- 97StrAll-17
- 97Top-35
- 97TopSta-85
- 97TopStaAM-85
- 97Ult-120
- 97UltGolME-120
- 97UltPlaME-120
- 97UppDec-499
- 97UppDecMP-P1
- 98CirThu-199
- 98CirThuRav-199
- 98CirThuSupRav-199
- 98ColCho-239
- 98Don-255
- 98DonGolPP-255
- 98DonSilPP-255
- 98Fin-89
- 98FinNo--89
- 98FinNo-R-89
- 98FinRef-89
- 98Fle-34
- 98MarSco-10
- 98MarScoP-10
- 98Pac-183
- 98PacAur-71
- 98PacInv-63
- 98PacInvGems-89
- 98PacInvPBlue-63
- 98PacInvSilv-63
- 98PacLatotML-30
- 98PacNes-4B
- 98PacOme-219
- 98PacOmeR-219
- 98PacOnl-681
- 98PacOnlR-681
- 98PacOnlWC-681
- 98PacPar-85
- 98PacParC-85
- 98PacParG-85
- 98PacParHS-85
- 98PacParPB-85
- 98PacParR-85
- 98PacPlaB-183
- 98PacRedT-183
- 98PacSil-183
- 98PinPlu-18
- 98PinSna-SM4
- 98PinSna-SM5
- 98PinSnaS-8
- 98Sco-151
- 98ScoRT-68
- 98ScoSS-PP159
- 98ScoSSAP-PP159
- 98StaCluFDI-359
- 98StaClul-359
- 98StaCluOneK-359
- 98StaCluPP-359
- 98Top-143
- 98TopChr-143
- 98TopChrR-143
- 98TopDevR-143
- 98TopDia-143
- 98TopMiniC-143
- 98TopOpeD-72
- 98UppDec-222
- 98UppDecSF-124
- 99Fle-411
- 99FleSta9-411
- 99FleWarT-411
- 99Pac-126
- 99PacCroC-84
- 99PacCroCPB-84
- 99PacPlaB-126
- 99PacRed-126

Cora, Manny
- 92ChaRaiC-1
- 92ChaRaiF-126
- 92ClaFS7-53
- 92UppDecML-203
- 93SouAtlLAPl-12
- 93SouAtlLAPl-7
- 93WatDiaF-1773
- 94RivPilCLC-4
- 95PorCitRTI-4

Corbell, Charlie
- 85FreGiaSB-17
- 86ShrCapP-5
- 87MetColP-29
- 87PhoFirP-6
- 88TacTigC-3
- 88TacTigP-636

Corbell, Eric
- 91KinMetC-17
- 91KinMetP-3804

Corbett, Doug
- 79IndIndTI-12
- 80TwiPos-4
- 81Don-546
- 81Fle-555
- 81OPC-162
- 81Top-162
- 81TopSti-106
- 81TwiPos-7
- 82Don-53
- 82Fle-551
- 82FleSta-227
- 82OPC-157
- 82Top-560
- 82TopSti-210
- 82TopTra-21T
- 82TwiPos-5
- 83Fle-83
- 83Top-27
- 84EdmTraC-111
- 85AngSmo-18
- 85Don-474
- 85Fle-298
- 85Top-682
- 85TopTif-682
- 86AngSmo-8
- 86Top-234
- 86TopTif-234
- 87Don-333
- 87Fle-76
- 87FleGlo-76
- 87Top-359
- 87TopTif-359
- 89PacSenL-193
- 89T/MSenL-24
- 89TopSenL-114
- 90EliSenL-52
- 91OriCro-84

Corbett, Gene (Eugene Louis)
- 46SunBre-3
- 79DiaGre-305

Corbett, Joseph
- 16Zee-104

Corbett, Ray
- 81CedRapRT-8
- 82WatRedT-11
- 83IndIndTI-15
- 85RocRedWT-1
- 89CedRapRAB-25
- 90CedRapRDGB-25

Corbett, Sherman
- 86MidAngP-7
- 87CalAngPPS-8
- 87EdmTraP-2078
- 88BlaYNPRWL-147
- 88FleUpd-11
- 88FleUpdG-11
- 89Don-407
- 89EdmTraC-8
- 89EdmTraP-547
- 89Fle-473
- 89FleGlo-473
- 89Top-99
- 89TopTif-99
- 89ToyRoo-6
- 89UppDec-464
- 90CMC-482
- 90EdmTraC-5
- 90EdmTraP-512
- 90ProAAAF-88
- 91LinDriAA-431
- 91MidAngLD-431
- 91MidAngOHP-8
- 91MidAngP-430
- 92LonTigF-625
- 93TolMudHF-1644

Corbin, A. Ray
- 72OPC-66
- 72Top-66
- 72TwiPos-3
- 73OPC-411
- 73Top-411
- 74OPC-296
- 74Top-296
- 74TopSta-204
- 75OPC-78
- 75Top-78
- 75TopMin-78
- 75TwiPos-8
- 75TwiTeal-11
- 76OPC-474
- 76SSP-209
- 76Top-474
- 78TwiFri-28

Corbin, Archie
- 89ColMetB-5
- 89ColMetGS-7
- 90St.LucMS-4
- 91Cla/Bes-293
- 91LinDriAA-404
- 91MemChiLD-404
- 91MemChiP-646
- 92ClaFS7-180
- 92Don-400
- 92MemChiF-2410
- 92MemChiS-431
- 92ProFS7-75
- 92SkyAA F-182
- 92StaClu-473
- 92TopDeb91-39
- 93ClaGolF-125
- 93HarSenF-262
- 94BufBisF-1828
- 96RocRedWB-9
- 97RocRedW-9

Corbin, Ted
- 92ClaDraP-97
- 92FroRowDP-8
- 92FroRowDPG-8
- 92FroRowDPS-8
- 92Ft.MyeMCB-2
- 92Ft.MyeMF-2751
- 93ForMyeMC-5
- 93ForMyeMF-2660
- 94NasXprF-391

Corbitt, Claude E.
- 47RoyMon-1

Corbitt, Cord
- 91SpoIndC-19
- 91SpoIndP-3940

Corcino, Luis
- 86BurExpP-3
- 87Ft.MyeRP-22
- 88VirGenS-6

Corcoran, Larry (Lawrence J.)
- 86OldJudN-2
- 87OldJudN-98
- 88AugBecN-9
- 90KalBatN-9

Corcoran, Lori
- 83GleFalWST-23

Corcoran, Mickey (Michael J.)
- 12ColTinT-63
- 12ImpTobC-49

Corcoran, Tim (Timothy M.)
- 77EvaTriT-6
- 78TigBurK-20
- 78Top-515
- 79Top-272
- 80VenLeaS-31
- 81Don-367
- 81EvaTriT-18
- 81Fle-479
- 81Top-448
- 82OklCit8T-3
- 83PorBeaT-11
- 84PhiTas-34
- 85Don-381
- 85Fle-247
- 85PhiClG-6
- 85PhiTas-12
- 85PhiTas-34
- 85Top-302
- 85TopTif-302
- 86Don-381
- 86Fle-437
- 86MetColP-21
- 86MetTCM-43
- 86TidTidP-5
- 86Top-664
- 86TopTif-664
- 87MaiGuiT-24
- 88ReaPhiP-887
- 91MetWIZ-84

Corcoran, Tommy (Thomas W.)
- 03BreE10-24
- 06FanCraNL-11
- 12ColRedB-63
- 90DodTar-138
- 95May-5
- 98CamPepP-15

Cordani, Richard
- 88CapCodPPaLP-8
- 90LSUTigP-6
- 91LSUTigP-8

Cordeiro, Richard
- 52LavPro-6

Corder, Daniel
- 74WicAerODF-108

Cordero, Edward
- 93BriTigC-7
- 93BriTigF-3650
- 96DurBulBlB-26
- 96DurBulBrB-27
- 97DurBulTI-20

Cordero, Francisco
- 97WesMicW-9
- 98BesAutSS-12
- 98Bow-410
- 98BowBes-198
- 98BowBesAR-198
- 98BowBesR-198
- 98BowChr-410
- 98BowChrGA-410
- 98BowChrGAR-410
- 98BowChrl-410
- 98BowChrIR-410
- 98BowChrR-410
- 98BowGolA-410
- 98BowInt-410
- 98JacSunM-6
- 98SouLeaTPG-13
- 98UppDec-591
- 99SP TopP-30
- 99SP TopPC-FC
- 99SP TopPGF-GF29
- 99SP TopPPE-30
- 99WesMicWAM-5

Cordero, Jesus
- 99Bow-409
- 99BowGol-409
- 99BowInt-409

Cordero, Pablo
- 95BurBeeTI-26
- 96BurBeeTI-23

Cordero, Wilfredo (Wil)
- 88BlaYNPRWLU-15
- 88JamExpP-1895
- 89WesPalBES-8
- 90Bes-128
- 90CMC-682
- 90JacExpB-5
- 90JacExpP-1381
- 90TopMag-103
- 91Bow-436
- 91Cla2-T2
- 91IndIndLD-179
- 91IndIndP-466
- 91LeaGolR-BC3
- 91LeaGolRNV-267
- 91LinDriAAA-179
- 91UppDec-60
- 92Bow-194
- 92Don-2
- 92DonRooP-BC20
- 92FleUpd-97
- 92IndIndF-1865
- 92IndIndS-179
- 92OPC-551
- 92ProFS7-254
- 92ScoRoo-110T
- 92SkyAAAF-88
- 92Top-551
- 92TopGol-551
- 92TopGolW-551
- 92TopMic-551
- 92TriPla-179
- 92UppDec-16
- 93Bow-508
- 93Don-432
- 93ExpColP7-3
- 93ExpPosN-8
- 93Fin-123
- 93FinRef-123
- 93Fla-80
- 93Fle-73
- 93FunPac-1
- 93HumDumC-36
- 93Lea-37
- 93LeaGolR-R2
- 93LeaGolRJ-R2
- 93OPC-161
- 93OPCPre-29
- 93PacBeiA-25
- 93PacBeiA-26
- 93PacSpa-532
- 93PanSti-227
- 93Pin-280
- 93PinRooTP-7
- 93PinTea2-1
- 93Sco-334
- 93ScoProaG-1
- 93Sel-336
- 93SelChaR-18
- 93SelRoo-150T
- 93SP-101
- 93StaClu-361
- 93StaCluFDI-361
- 93StaCluMOP-361
- 93Stu-93
- 93Top-256
- 93TopGol-256
- 93TopInaM-256
- 93TopInaR-256
- 93TopMic-256
- 93Toy-90
- 93TriPla-27
- 93Ult-65
- 93UppDec-60
- 93UppDecDG-32
- 93UppDecGold-60
- 93USPlaCR-3S
- 94Bow-153
- 94ColC-395
- 94ColChoGS-395
- 94ColChoSS-395
- 94Don-545
- 94Fin-20
- 94FinJum-20
- 94FinRef-20
- 94Fla-187
- 94FleExtB-301
- 94FleExtBSYS-6
- 94FleUpd-152
- 94Lea-103
- 94OPC-252
- 94OPCDiaD-10
- 94Pac-376
- 94PanSti-208
- 94Pin-89
- 94PinArtP-89
- 94PinMusC-89
- 94PinNewG-NG7
- 94ProMag-82
- 94Sco-412
- 94ScoGolR-412
- 94Sel-81
- 94Spo-36
- 94StaClu-393
- 94StaCluFDI-393
- 94StaCluGR-393
- 94StaCluMO-46
- 94StaCluMOP-393
- 94Stu-76
- 94Top-21
- 94TopGol-21
- 94TopSpa-21
- 94TriPla-92
- 94Ult-224
- 94UppDec-97
- 94UppDecED-97
- 94USPlaCR-3C
- 94USPlaCR-6D
- 95Baz-95
- 95Bow-337
- 95ColCho-245
- 95ColChoGS-245
- 95ColChoSE-97
- 95ColChoSE-257
- 95ColChoSEGS-97
- 95ColChoSEGS-257
- 95ColChoSESS-97
- 95ColChoSESS-257
- 95ColChoSS-245
- 95Don-150
- 95DonDom-6
- 95DonPreP-150
- 95DonTopotO-278
- 95Emo-150
- 95Fin-40
- 95FinRef-40
- 95Fla-373
- 95Fle-346
- 95FleAllS-10
- 95Lea-128
- 95LeaLim-10
- 95Pac-264
- 95PacLatD-8
- 95PacPri-85
- 95PanSti-64
- 95Pin-346
- 95PinArtP-346
- 95PinFan-30
- 95PinMusC-346
- 95PinSam-US22
- 95PinUps-US22
- 95Sco-386
- 95ScoGolR-386
- 95ScoHaloG-HG105
- 95ScoPlaTS-386
- 95Sel-93
- 95SelArtP-93
- 95SelCer-6
- 95SelCerMG-6
- 95SP-74
- 95Spo-56
- 95SpoArtP-56
- 95SpoDouT-6
- 95SPSil-74
- 95StaClu-255
- 95StaCluFDI-255
- 95StaCluMOP-255
- 95StaCluSTWS-255
- 95StaCluVR-125
- 95StaCluVRMO-125
- 95Stu-186
- 95Sum-67
- 95SumNthD-67
- 95Top-108
- 95Top-387
- 95TopCyb-70
- 95TopD3-50
- 95TopEmb-85
- 95TopEmbGI-85
- 95UC3-2
- 95UC3ArtP-2
- 95Ult-188
- 95UltGolM-188
- 95UppDec-324
- 95UppDecED-324
- 95UppDecEDG-324
- 95UppDecSE-2
- 95UppDecSEG-2

❑ 95Zen-109
❑ 96ColCho-765
❑ 96Don-256
❑ 96DonPreP-256
❑ 96EmoXL-13
❑ 96Fla-17
❑ 96Fle-454
❑ 96FleRedS-4
❑ 96FleTif-454
❑ 96FleUpd-U11
❑ 96FleUpdTC-U11
❑ 96MetUni-14
❑ 96MetUniP-14
❑ 96Pac-131
❑ 96PacPri-P41
❑ 96PacPriG-P41
❑ 96PanSti-24
❑ 96Pin-11
❑ 96Pin-339
❑ 96PinAfi-121
❑ 96PinAfiAP-121
❑ 96PinArtP-8
❑ 96PinFoil-339
❑ 96PinSta-8
❑ 96ProSta-46
❑ 96Sco-344
❑ 96ScoDugC-B69
❑ 96ScoDugCAP-B69
❑ 96StaClu-327
❑ 96StaCluEPB-327
❑ 96StaCluEPG-327
❑ 96StaCluEPS-327
❑ 96StaCluMOP-327
❑ 96Sum-125
❑ 96SumAbo&B-125
❑ 96SumArtP-125
❑ 96SumFoi-125
❑ 96Top-413
❑ 96Ult-229
❑ 96Ult-312
❑ 96UltGolM-229
❑ 96UltGolM-312
❑ 96UppDec-282
❑ 97ColCho-52
❑ 97Fle-20
❑ 97FleTif-20
❑ 97NewPin-106
❑ 97NewPinAP-106
❑ 97NewPinMC-106
❑ 97NewPinPP-106
❑ 97Pac-36
❑ 97PacLigB-36
❑ 97PacSil-36
❑ 97RedSoxS-1
❑ 97RedSoxSPl-1
❑ 97RedSoxSPr-1
❑ 97Sco-57
❑ 97ScoArtPWB-57
❑ 97ScoPreS-57
❑ 97ScoShoS-57
❑ 97ScoShoSAP-57
❑ 97StaClu-332
❑ 97StaCluMOP-332
❑ 97Top-394
❑ 97Ult-431
❑ 97UltGolME-431
❑ 97UltPlaME-431
❑ 98BirBarG-9
❑ 98Pac-37
❑ 98PacPlaB-37
❑ 98PacRedT-37
❑ 98PacSil-37
❑ 98RedSoxS-12
❑ 98RedSoxSP-12
❑ 98Sco-211
❑ 98ScoSS-PP102
❑ 98ScoSSAP-PP102
❑ 99Fle-441
❑ 99FleSta9-441
❑ 99FleWarT-441
❑ 99Pac-100
❑ 99PacCroC-67
❑ 99PacCroCPB-67
❑ 99PacPlaB-100
❑ 99PacRed-100

Cordero, Willy E.
❑ 98SavSanGM-9

Cordido, Julio
❑ 97SalVolG-9

Cordner, Steve
❑ 83QuaCitCT-19

Cordoba, Wilfrido
❑ 82AleDukT-9
❑ 83LynPirT-2
❑ 84PriWilPT-13

Cordona, Javier
❑ 94JamJamC-5
❑ 94JamJamF-3966

Cordova, Antonio
❑ 80VenLeaS-190
❑ 82QuaCitCT-21
❑ 84MidCubT-2

Cordova, Francisco
❑ 96Fin-B343
❑ 96FinRef-B343
❑ 96FleUpd-U174
❑ 96FleUpdTC-U174
❑ 96LeaSigEA-35
❑ 97Cir-265
❑ 97CirRav-265
❑ 97ColCho-427
❑ 97Don-300
❑ 97DonGolPP-300
❑ 97DonLim-119
❑ 97DonLimE-119
❑ 97DonLimENG-119
❑ 97DonSilPP-300
❑ 97Fle-426
❑ 97FleTif-426
❑ 97MetUni-237
❑ 97Pac-392
❑ 97PacLigB-392
❑ 97PacPri-133
❑ 97PacPriLB-133
❑ 97PacPriP-133
❑ 97PacSil-392
❑ 97PirPos-9
❑ 97Sel-196
❑ 97SelCom-196
❑ 97StaClu-289
❑ 97StaCluMOP-289
❑ 97Top-118
❑ 97UppDec-158
❑ 98Bow-286
❑ 98BowChr-286
❑ 98BowChrGA-286
❑ 98BowChrGAR-286
❑ 98BowChrI-286
❑ 98BowChrIR-286
❑ 98BowChrR-286
❑ 98BowGolA-286
❑ 98BowInt-286
❑ 98CirThu-234
❑ 98CirThuRav-234
❑ 98CirThuSupRav-234
❑ 98ColCho-467
❑ 98Don-120
❑ 98DonCol-120
❑ 98DonColL-214
❑ 98DonColP-640
❑ 98DonColS-120
❑ 98DonCruG-89
❑ 98DonCruP-89
❑ 98DonCruR-89
❑ 98DonGolPP-120
❑ 98DonPre-90
❑ 98DonPreSeat-90
❑ 98DonPriCD-120
❑ 98DonPriCL-214
❑ 98DonPriCP-640
❑ 98DonSilPP-120
❑ 98Fin-261
❑ 98FinNo--261
❑ 98FinNo-R-261
❑ 98FinRef-261
❑ 98Fle-538
❑ 98Lea-14
❑ 98LeaFraDA-14
❑ 98LeaFraF-14
❑ 98LeaFraM-14
❑ 98LeaFraM-14
❑ 98LeaFraMDC-14
❑ 98LeaFraMDC-14
❑ 98LeaFraMZ2-14
❑ 98LeaRS-89
❑ 98LeaRSLHolo-89
❑ 98LeaRSLong-89
❑ 98LeaRTrue-89
❑ 98Pac-394
❑ 98PacInvGems-194
❑ 98PacOnl-581
❑ 98PacOnlR-581
❑ 98PacOnlWC-581
❑ 98PacPar-220
❑ 98PacParC-220
❑ 98PacParG-220
❑ 98PacParHS-220
❑ 98PacParPB-220
❑ 98PacParR-220
❑ 98PacPlaB-394
❑ 98PacRedT-394
❑ 98PacSil-394
❑ 98PinPlu-172
❑ 98Sco-8
❑ 98ScoRT-217
❑ 98SP Aut-154
❑ 98SpoIll-186
❑ 98SpoIllEE-186
❑ 98SpoIllFE-186
❑ 98StaCluFDI-166
❑ 98StaCluI-166
❑ 98StaCluOneK-166
❑ 98StaCluPP-166
❑ 98Stu-10
❑ 98StuGPP-10
❑ 98StuSPP-10
❑ 98Top-11
❑ 98Top-267
❑ 98TopChr-11
❑ 98TopChrR-11
❑ 98TopDevR-11
❑ 98TopDevR-267
❑ 98TopDia-11
❑ 98TopDia-267
❑ 98TopMiniC-11
❑ 98TopMiniC-267
❑ 98Ult-347
❑ 98UltGolM-347
❑ 98UltMas-347
❑ 98UltPlaM-347
❑ 98UppDec-192
❑ 98UppDec-532
❑ 99199Fin-53
❑ 99FinGolRef-53
❑ 99FinRef-53
❑ 99Fle-63
❑ 99FleSta9-63
❑ 99FleWarT-63
❑ 99Pac-338
❑ 99PacCroC-218
❑ 99PacCroCPB-218
❑ 99PacPlaB-338
❑ 99PacRed-338
❑ 99SkyThu-28
❑ 99SkyThuRant-28
❑ 99SkyThuRave-28
❑ 99StaClu-18
❑ 99StaCluFDI-18
❑ 99StaCluOoaK-18
❑ 99StaCluPP-18
❑ 99ThuSkySupR-28
❑ 99Top-177
❑ 99TopChr-177
❑ 99TopChrR-177
❑ 99TopMVPP-177
❑ 99TopOpeD-97
❑ 99TopSta-121
❑ 99TopStaFoil-121
❑ 99UppDec-177
❑ 99UppDecEL1-177
❑ 99UppDecEL2-177
❑ 99Vic-313

Cordova, Luis
❑ 92EriSaiC-25
❑ 92EriSaiF-1637
❑ 93LetMouF-4161
❑ 93LetMouSP-14

Cordova, Marty
❑ 89EliTwiS-5
❑ 92CalLeaACL-32
❑ 92UppDecML-115
❑ 92UppDecMLPotY-PY24
❑ 92VisOakC-14
❑ 92VisOakF-1026
❑ 93Bow-345
❑ 93ClaGolF-42
❑ 93ClaMVPF-3
❑ 93ExcFS7-198
❑ 93ExcLeaLF-4
❑ 93NasXprF-414
❑ 94AriFalLS-4
❑ 94Bow-544
❑ 94ExcFS7-92
❑ 94FleMajLP-6
❑ 94UppDecML-73
❑ 95Bow-183
❑ 95BowBes-R74
❑ 95BowBesR-R74
❑ 95ColCho-582T
❑ 95DonTopotO-108
❑ 95Emo-56
❑ 95EmoRoo-3
❑ 95Exc-80
❑ 95Fin-235
❑ 95FinRef-235
❑ 95Fla-278
❑ 95FlaWavotF-3
❑ 95Fle-199
❑ 95Lea-358
❑ 95LeaLim-26
❑ 95Sel-159
❑ 95SelArtP-159
❑ 95SelCer-114
❑ 95SelCerMG-114
❑ 95SigRooMR-MR1
❑ 95SigRooMRS-MR1
❑ 95SigRooOJSS-9
❑ 95SigRooOJSSS-9
❑ 95SP-23
❑ 95SPCha-8
❑ 95SPChaDC-8
❑ 95SPSil-23
❑ 95StaClu-538
❑ 95StaCluCB-CB9
❑ 95StaCluMOP-538
❑ 95StaCluMOP-CB9
❑ 95StaCluSTWS-538
❑ 95Sum-148
❑ 95SumNthD-148
❑ 95Top-639
❑ 95TopTra-45T
❑ 95UC3-118
❑ 95UC3ArtP-118
❑ 95UltGolMR-M9
❑ 95UppDec-250
❑ 95UppDecED-250
❑ 95UppDecEDG-250
❑ 95UppDecPAW-H40
❑ 95UppDecPAWE-H40
❑ 95UppDecSE-215
❑ 95UppDecSEG-215
❑ 95Zen-116
❑ 95ZenRooRC-12
❑ 96Baz-54
❑ 96Bow-91
❑ 96BowBes-44
❑ 96BowBesAR-44
❑ 96BowBesR-44
❑ 96BowFoi-91
❑ 96Cir-55
❑ 96CirRav-55
❑ 96ColCho-199
❑ 96ColCho-704
❑ 96ColCho-755
❑ 96ColChoGS-199
❑ 96ColChoGS-704
❑ 96ColChoGS-755
❑ 96ColChoSS-199
❑ 96ColChoSS-704
❑ 96ColChoSS-755
❑ 96Don-353
❑ 96DonPreP-353
❑ 96EmoRarB-2
❑ 96EmoXL-80
❑ 96Fin-B184
❑ 96Fin-B206
❑ 96Fin-G4
❑ 96FinRef-B184
❑ 96FinRef-B206
❑ 96FinRef-G4
❑ 96Fla-112
❑ 96Fle-165
❑ 96FleRooS-2
❑ 96FleTif-165
❑ 96FleUpd-U217
❑ 96FleUpdTC-U217
❑ 96Lea-31
❑ 96LeaLim-39
❑ 96LeaLimG-39
❑ 96LeaPre-54
❑ 96LeaPreP-54
❑ 96LeaPrePB-31
❑ 96LeaPrePG-31
❑ 96LeaPrePS-31
❑ 96LeaPreSG-70
❑ 96LeaPreSte-70
❑ 96LeaSig-141
❑ 96LeaSigA-50
❑ 96LeaSigAG-50
❑ 96LeaSigAS-50
❑ 96LeaSigPPG-141
❑ 96LeaSigPPP-141
❑ 96MetUni-75
❑ 96MetUniMFG-2
❑ 96MetUniP-75
❑ 96MetUniPP-2
❑ 96Pac-361
❑ 96Pac-368
❑ 96PacMil-M5
❑ 96PacPri-P113
❑ 96PacPriG-P113
❑ 96PanSti-201
❑ 96PanSti-246
❑ 96Pin-121
❑ 96PinAfi-141
❑ 96PinAfiAP-141
❑ 96PinArtP-30
❑ 96PinSta-30
❑ 96ProSta-128
❑ 96Sco-299
❑ 96Sco-511
❑ 96ScoDugC-B24
❑ 96ScoDugCAP-B24
❑ 96ScoFutF-11
❑ 96Sel-35
❑ 96SelArtP-35
❑ 96SelCer-43
❑ 96SelCerAP-43
❑ 96SelCerCB-43
❑ 96SelCerCR-43
❑ 96SelCerMB-43
❑ 96SelCerMG-43
❑ 96SelCerMR-43
❑ 96SelTeaN-19
❑ 96SigRooOJMC-RY1
❑ 96SigRooOJMC-RY2
❑ 96SigRooOJMC-RY3
❑ 96SigRooOJMC-RY4
❑ 96SigRooOJMC-RY5
❑ 96SP-113
❑ 96Spo-12
❑ 96SpoArtP-12
❑ 96SPx-38
❑ 96SPxGol-38
❑ 96StaClu-131
❑ 96StaClu-228
❑ 96StaCluEPB-131
❑ 96StaCluEPG-131
❑ 96StaCluEPS-131
❑ 96StaCluMO-47
❑ 96StaCluMOP-131
❑ 96StaCluMOP-228
❑ 96Stu-68
❑ 96StuPrePB-68
❑ 96StuPrePG-68
❑ 96StuPrePS-68
❑ 96Sum-90
❑ 96SumAbo&B-90
❑ 96SumArtP-90
❑ 96SumFoi-90
❑ 96TeaOut-21
❑ 96Top-187
❑ 96TopBroLL-6
❑ 96TopChr-57
❑ 96TopChrR-57
❑ 96TopGal-91
❑ 96TopGalPPI-91
❑ 96TopLas-41
❑ 96TopLasBS-10
❑ 96TopMysF-M5
❑ 96TopMysFR-M5
❑ 96TopPro-AL12
❑ 96Ult-88
❑ 96Ult-593
❑ 96UltFreF-2
❑ 96UltFreFGM-2
❑ 96UltGolM-88
❑ 96UltGolM-593
❑ 96UltRisS-2
❑ 96UltRisSGM-2
❑ 96UppDec-390
❑ 96UppDecBCP-BC5
❑ 96Zen-25
❑ 96ZenArtP-25
❑ 97Bow-269
❑ 97BowChr-87
❑ 97BowChrI-87
❑ 97BowChrIR-87
❑ 97BowChrR-87
❑ 97BowInt-269
❑ 97Cir-271
❑ 97CirRav-271
❑ 97ColCho-154
❑ 97Don-68
❑ 97DonEli-99
❑ 97DonEliGS-99
❑ 97DonGolPP-68
❑ 97DonLim-33
❑ 97DonLimE-33
❑ 97DonLimENG-33
❑ 97DonPre-130
❑ 97DonPreCttC-130
❑ 97DonSigA-23
❑ 97DonSigAC-30
❑ 97DonSigAM-30
❑ 97DonSilPP-68
❑ 97Fin-61
❑ 97FinRef-61
❑ 97FlaShoLC-102
❑ 97FlaShoLeg0-102
❑ 97FlaShoLeg1-102
❑ 97FlaShoM-A102
❑ 97FlaShoM-B102
❑ 97FlaShoM-C102
❑ 97FlaShoR0-102
❑ 97FlaShoR1-102
❑ 97FlaShoR2-102
❑ 97Fle-145
❑ 97FleTif-145
❑ 97Lea-63
❑ 97LeaFraM-63
❑ 97LeaFraMDC-63
❑ 97MetUni-209
❑ 97NewPin-138
❑ 97NewPinAP-138
❑ 97NewPinMC-138
❑ 97NewPinPP-138
❑ 97Pac-135
❑ 97PacLatotML-11
❑ 97PacLigB-135
❑ 97PacPri-44
❑ 97PacPriLB-44
❑ 97PacPriP-44
❑ 97PacSil-135
❑ 97Pin-149
❑ 97PinArtP-PP149
❑ 97PinIns-34
❑ 97PinInsCE-34
❑ 97PinInsDE-34
❑ 97PinMusC-149
❑ 97PinPrePla-149
❑ 97PinX-P-59
❑ 97PinX-PMoS-59
❑ 97Sco-34
❑ 97ScoArtPWB-34
❑ 97ScoPreS-34
❑ 97ScoShoS-34
❑ 97ScoShoSAP-34
❑ 97Sel-10
❑ 97SelArtP-10
❑ 97SelCom-10
❑ 97SelRegG-10
❑ 97SP-108
❑ 97SpoIll-147
❑ 97SpoIllEE-147
❑ 97StaClu-58
❑ 97StaCluC-CO9
❑ 97StaCluM-M16
❑ 97StaCluMat-58
❑ 97StaCluMOP-58
❑ 97StaCluMOP-M16
❑ 97Stu-61
❑ 97StuPrePG-61
❑ 97StuPrePS-61
❑ 97Top-435
❑ 97TopChr-154
❑ 97TopChrR-154
❑ 97TopGal-165
❑ 97TopGalPPI-165
❑ 97Ult-86
❑ 97UltDouT-6
❑ 97UltGolME-86
❑ 97UltPlaME-86
❑ 97UppDec-104
❑ 98Bow-36
❑ 98BowBes-40
❑ 98BowBesAR-40
❑ 98BowBesR-40
❑ 98BowChr-36
❑ 98BowChrGA-36
❑ 98BowChrGAR-36
❑ 98BowChrI-36
❑ 98BowChrIR-36
❑ 98BowChrR-36
❑ 98BowGolA-36
❑ 98BowInt-36
❑ 98CirThu-69
❑ 98CirThuRav-69
❑ 98CirThuSupRav-69
❑ 98ColCho-408
❑ 98CroRoy-77
❑ 98Don-251
❑ 98DonGolPP-251
❑ 98DonSilPP-251
❑ 98Fin-218
❑ 98FinNo--218
❑ 98FinNo-R-218
❑ 98FinRef-218
❑ 98Fle-479
❑ 98MetUni-128
❑ 98MetUniPMG-128
❑ 98Pac-131
❑ 98PacAur-51
❑ 98PacInv-45
❑ 98PacInvPBlue-45
❑ 98PacInvSilv-45

❑ 98PacInvTeam-16
❑ 98PacOme-140
❑ 98PacOmeR-140
❑ 98PacOnl-419
❑ 98PacOnlR-419
❑ 98PacOnlWC-419
❑ 98PacPar-61
❑ 98PacParC-61
❑ 98PacParG-61
❑ 98PacParHS-61
❑ 98PacParPB-61
❑ 98PacParR-61
❑ 98PacPlaB-131
❑ 98PacRedT-131
❑ 98PacSil-131
❑ 98Revo-82
❑ 98RevoSS-82
❑ 98ScoRT-100
❑ 98SkyDugA-71
❑ 98SkyDugAIA-71
❑ 98SP Aut-123
❑ 98SPxFin-96
❑ 98SPxFinR-96
❑ 98SPxFinS-96
❑ 98StaCluFDI-34
❑ 98StaCluI-34
❑ 98StaCluOneK-34
❑ 98StaCluPP-34
❑ 98Top-375
❑ 98TopChr-375
❑ 98TopChrR-375
❑ 98TopDevR-375
❑ 98TopDia-375
❑ 98TopGal-36
❑ 98TopGalGP-36
❑ 98TopGalOPP-36
❑ 98TopGalPPI-36
❑ 98TopGalPPIA-36
❑ 98TopMiniC-375
❑ 98TopSta-129
❑ 98TopStaB-129
❑ 98TopStaG-129
❑ 98TopStaGR-129
❑ 98TopStaS-129
❑ 98Ult-200
❑ 98UltGolM-200
❑ 98UltMas-200
❑ 98UltPlaM-200
❑ 98UppDec-414
❑ 99199Fin-222
❑ 99FinGolRef-222
❑ 99FinRef-222
❑ 99Fle-98
❑ 99FleSta9-98
❑ 99FleWarT-98
❑ 99MetUni-177
❑ 99MetUniGM-177
❑ 99MetUniPMG-177
❑ 99Pac-246
❑ 99PacAur-104
❑ 99PacAurOD-104
❑ 99PacCroC-159
❑ 99PacCroCPB-159
❑ 99PacOme-137
❑ 99PacOmeC-137
❑ 99PacOmeG-137
❑ 99PacOmePB-137
❑ 99PacPar-133
❑ 99PacParC-133
❑ 99PacParG-133
❑ 99PacParHoloGold-133
❑ 99PacParHS-133
❑ 99PacParOD-133
❑ 99PacParPB-133
❑ 99PacParRed-133
❑ 99PacPlaB-246
❑ 99PacPriS-77
❑ 99PacPriS206-77
❑ 99PacPriS206R-77
❑ 99PacRed-246
❑ 99SkyPre-163
❑ 99SkyPreR-163
❑ 99SkyThu-46
❑ 99SkyThuRant-46
❑ 99SkyThuRave-46
❑ 99StaClu-218
❑ 99StaCluFDI-218
❑ 99StaCluOoaK-218
❑ 99StaCluPP-218
❑ 99ThuSkySupR-46
❑ 99Top-312
❑ 99TopChr-312
❑ 99TopChrR-312
❑ 99TopMVPP-312
❑ 99Ult-89
❑ 99UltGolM-89
❑ 99UltMas-89
❑ 99UltPlaM-89
❑ 99UppDec-416
❑ 99UppDecEL1-416
❑ 99UppDecEL2-416
❑ 99Vic-230

Cordova, Rocky
❑ 78CliDodT-5
❑ 79LodDodT-7

Core, John
❑ 12HomRunKE-4
❑ 12Zee-5

Corey, Bryan
❑ 93BriTigF-3651
❑ 94JamJamC-6
❑ 94JamJamF-3970
❑ 96Exc-49
❑ 96FayGenB-10
❑ 97JacSun-8
❑ 98TusSidM-8
❑ 99SpoIll-51

Corey, Mark M.
❑ 79RocRedWT-15
❑ 79Top-701
❑ 80RocRedWT-5
❑ 80Top-661
❑ 81Fle-193
❑ 81RocRedWW-4
❑ 81Top-399
❑ 82EvaTriT-23
❑ 86JacExpT-20
❑ 87IndIndTI-30
❑ 89PacSenL-195
❑ 91OriCro-85
❑ 98BurBeeM-5

Corey, Mike
❑ 98EugEme-8

Corgan, Chuck (Charles H.)
❑ 90DodTar-916

Corhan, Roy George
❑ 12HomRunKE-63
❑ 12Zee-106
❑ 13Zee-103
❑ 14Zee-107
❑ 17Zee-84
❑ 19Zee-88
❑ 20Zee-105

Corkhill, Pop (John S.)
❑ 74BroClu-6
❑ 87OldJudN-99
❑ 89EdgR.WG-6
❑ 90DodTar-139

Corkins, Mike
❑ 70Top-573
❑ 71MLBOffS-224
❑ 71OPC-179
❑ 71Top-179
❑ 72PadPos-8
❑ 72Top-608
❑ 73OPC-461
❑ 73PadDea-5
❑ 73Top-461
❑ 74OPC-546
❑ 74PadDea-6
❑ 74PadTeal-3
❑ 74Top-546

Corley, Ken
❑ 98ButCopKG-8

Cormack, Terry
❑ 83DurBulT-3
❑ 84DurBulT-6
❑ 85DurBulT-21

Corman, Dave
❑ 85BeaGolGT-20
❑ 90HagSunDGB-5

Cormier, Eric
❑ 93UtiBluSC-7
❑ 93UtiBluSF-3527

Cormier, Rheal
❑ 89St.PetCS-8
❑ 90ArkTraGS-9
❑ 90LouRedBLBC-12
❑ 91Bow-396
❑ 91LouRedP-2907
❑ 91LouRedTI-5
❑ 92Bow-473
❑ 92Don-712
❑ 92FleUpd-119
❑ 92Lea-469
❑ 92LeaBlaG-469
❑ 92OPC-346
❑ 92ProFS7-315
❑ 92Sco-851
❑ 92StaClu-506
❑ 92Top-346
❑ 92TopDeb91-40
❑ 92TopGol-346
❑ 92TopGolW-346
❑ 92TopMic-346
❑ 92UppDec-574
❑ 93Bow-80
❑ 93CarPol-5
❑ 93CarStaC-18
❑ 93Don-228
❑ 93Fle-124
❑ 93Lea-209
❑ 93MSABenSPD-20
❑ 93OPC-34
❑ 93PacSpa-631
❑ 93Pin-360
❑ 93Sco-371
❑ 93StaClu-15
❑ 93StaCluFDI-15
❑ 93StaCluMOP-15
❑ 93Top-149
❑ 93TopGol-149
❑ 93TopInaM-149
❑ 93TopInaR-149
❑ 93TopMic-149
❑ 93Toy-21
❑ 93Ult-462
❑ 93UppDec-79
❑ 93UppDecGold-79
❑ 94CarPol-4
❑ 94ColC-481
❑ 94ColChoGS-481
❑ 94ColChoSS-481
❑ 94Don-622
❑ 94Fin-248
❑ 94FinRef-248
❑ 94Fla-224
❑ 94Fle-630
❑ 94FleExtB-357
❑ 94Lea-110
❑ 94Pac-587
❑ 94StaClu-437
❑ 94StaCluFDI-437
❑ 94StaCluGR-437
❑ 94StaCluMOP-437
❑ 94StaCluT-303
❑ 94StaCluTFDI-303
❑ 94Top-594
❑ 94TopGol-594
❑ 94TopSpa-594
❑ 94UppDec-422
❑ 94UppDecED-422
❑ 95ColCho-572T
❑ 95Don-352
❑ 95DonPreP-352
❑ 95Fle-495
❑ 95Lea-304
❑ 95Top-138
❑ 95TopTra-33T
❑ 96ColCho-61
❑ 96ColChoGS-61
❑ 96ColChoSS-61
❑ 96Don-97
❑ 96DonPreP-97
❑ 96ExpDis-6
❑ 96LeaSigA-51
❑ 96LeaSigAG-51
❑ 96LeaSigAS-51
❑ 97Fle-555
❑ 97FleTif-555
❑ 97Top-467
❑ 97Ult-371
❑ 97UltGolME-371
❑ 97UltPlaME-371

Cormier, Russ
❑ 89MedAthB-21
❑ 90ModA'sC-7
❑ 91HunStaC-9
❑ 91HunStaLD-284
❑ 91HunStaP-1788
❑ 91LinDriAA-284

Corn, Chris
❑ 94OneYanF-3783
❑ 95GreBatTI-8
❑ 96Exc-84
❑ 96TamYanY-9
❑ 98LynHilQ-4

Cornejo, Jesse
❑ 98HudValR-4

Cornejo, Mardie
❑ 78MetDaiPA-4
❑ 78TidTidT-8
❑ 91MetWIZ-85

Cornejo, Nate
❑ 99Bow-187
❑ 99BowBes-189
❑ 99BowBesAR-189
❑ 99BowBesR-189
❑ 99BowChr-187
❑ 99BowChrG-187
❑ 99BowChrGR-187
❑ 99BowChrI-187
❑ 99BowChrIR-187
❑ 99BowChrR-187
❑ 99BowGol-187
❑ 99BowInt-187
❑ 99StaClu-340
❑ 99StaCluFDI-340
❑ 99StaCluOoaK-340
❑ 99StaCluPP-340
❑ 99Top-440
❑ 99TopChr-440
❑ 99TopChrR-440
❑ 99TopMVPP-440

Cornelius, Brian
❑ 89NiaFalRP-4
❑ 90FayGenP-2420
❑ 91Cla/Bes-15
❑ 91FloStaLAP-FSL20
❑ 91LakTigC-23
❑ 91LakTigP-277
❑ 92LonTigF-644
❑ 92SkyAA F-171
❑ 93LonTigF-2320
❑ 98BriBluM-9

Cornelius, Jon
❑ 95BatCliTI-7
❑ 96PieBolWB-8
❑ 97ClePhi-4

Cornelius, Reid
❑ 89RocExpLC-6
❑ 90WesPalBES-3
❑ 91Bow-458
❑ 91Cla/Bes-52
❑ 91FloStaLAP-FSL42
❑ 91WesPalBEC-4
❑ 91WesPalBEP-1220
❑ 92ClaFS7-124
❑ 92HarSenS-280
❑ 92ProFS7-264
❑ 92SkyAA F-119
❑ 93HarSenF-263
❑ 94ExcFS7-223
❑ 94OttLynF-2894
❑ 95FleUpd-104
❑ 95NorTidTI-9
❑ 96BufBisB-5
❑ 97PorSeaD-10
❑ 98TusSidM-9

Cornelius, Willie
❑ 78LauLonABS-17

Cornell, Daren
❑ 90BelBreB-16

Cornell, David
❑ 92EugEmeF-3041

Cornell, Jeff
❑ 83PhoGiaBHN-7
❑ 84PhoGiaC-12
❑ 85PhoGiaC-200
❑ 85Top-514
❑ 85TopTif-514
❑ 86IowCubP-8

Cornett, Brad
❑ 92St.CatBJC-22
❑ 92St.CatBJF-3378
❑ 93AusFut-76
❑ 93HagSunC-6
❑ 93HagSunF-1871
❑ 93SouAtlLAGF-25
❑ 94ClaGolF-88
❑ 94ExcFS7-141
❑ 94KnoSmoF-1296
❑ 94SyrChiTI-6
❑ 95AusFut-107
❑ 95BluJayOH-9
❑ 95Fle-91
❑ 95Pac-442
❑ 95Ult-117
❑ 95UltGolM-117
❑ 98LouRedQ-18
❑ 98TusSidM-10

Cornish, Tim
❑ 92MarPhiC-14
❑ 92MarPhiF-3069
❑ 93MarPhiC-5
❑ 93MarPhiF-3482
❑ 95OdgRapTI-5

Cornutt, Terry
❑ 75LafDriT-23
❑ 76PheGiaCr-38
❑ 76PhoGiaCa-9
❑ 76PhoGiaCC-4
❑ 76PhoGiaVNB-5
❑ 77Gia-4
❑ 77GiaTeal-6
❑ 77PhoGiaVNB-4
❑ 78PhoGiaC-6
❑ 79PhoGiaVNB-15
❑ 80PhoGiaVNB-8

Corominas, Mike
❑ 95AubAstTI-18

Corona, John
❑ 90SprCarB-22
❑ 91St.PetCC-3
❑ 91St.PetCP-2267
❑ 93St.PetCC-11
❑ 93St.PetCF-2621
❑ 94ArkTraF-3083

Coronado, Osvaldo
❑ 95PitMetTI-27
❑ 97CapCitB-11
❑ 97St.LucM-4

Corps, Edwin
❑ 94SanJosGC-5
❑ 94SanJosGF-2809
❑ 96Exc-242
❑ 97ShrCap-8
❑ 97ShrCapB-8
❑ 98ShrCapM-11
❑ 98ShrCapWS-11

Corps, Erick
❑ 94MidLeaAF-MDW56
❑ 94SprSulC-4
❑ 94SprSulF-2041
❑ 95RanCucQT-5
❑ 97St.PetDR-14
❑ 98St.PetDRM-21

Corrado, Gary
❑ 77WauMetT-7

Corral, Ruben
❑ 96HagSunB-1

Corrales, Pat (Patrick)
❑ 65OPC-107
❑ 65Top-107
❑ 66OPC-137
❑ 66Top-137
❑ 66TopVen-137
❑ 67OPC-78
❑ 67Top-78
❑ 69Top-382
❑ 70DayDaiNM-46
❑ 70OPC-507
❑ 70Top-507
❑ 71MLBOffS-57
❑ 71OPC-293
❑ 71Top-293
❑ 72Top-705
❑ 72Top-706
❑ 73OPC-542
❑ 73PadDea-6
❑ 73Top-542
❑ 74HawIslC-105
❑ 74OPC-498
❑ 74Top-498
❑ 76VenLeaS-73
❑ 79Top-499
❑ 80Top-41
❑ 81Fle-623
❑ 83Don-626
❑ 83PhiTas-6
❑ 83Top-637
❑ 84Ind-10
❑ 84IndWhe-18
❑ 84Nes792-141
❑ 84Top-141
❑ 84TopTif-141
❑ 85Ind-11
❑ 85IndPol-18
❑ 85Top-119
❑ 85TopTif-119
❑ 86IndOhH-7
❑ 86IndTeal-17
❑ 86Top-699
❑ 86TopTif-699
❑ 87IndGat-7
❑ 87IndGat-NNO
❑ 87Top-268
❑ 87TopTif-268
❑ 88ChaLooLTI-4
❑ 88TolMudHC-25
❑ 88TolMudHP-590
❑ 90BraDubS-5
❑ 91BraSubS-10
❑ 92BraLykS-10
❑ 93BraLykS-9
❑ 93RanKee-112
❑ 94BraLykS-7

Correa, Amilcar
❑ 89WytCubS-6
❑ 90GenCubP-3051
❑ 90GenCubS-5
❑ 91PeoChiC-3
❑ 91PeoChiP-1334
❑ 91PeoChiTI-5
❑ 92WinSpiC-16
❑ 92WinSpiF-1202

Correa, Antonio
❑ 76VenLeaS-121

Correa, Edwin
❑ 83AppFoxFr-17
❑ 86DonRoo-4
❑ 86FleUpd-30
❑ 86RanPer-18
❑ 86SpoRoo-2
❑ 87ClaUpdY-143
❑ 87Don-57
❑ 87Fle-122
❑ 87FleGlo-122
❑ 87Lea-145
❑ 87OPC-334
❑ 87RanMot-19
❑ 87RanSmo-22
❑ 87Top-334
❑ 87TopTif-334
❑ 88Don-57
❑ 88Fle-464
❑ 88FleGlo-464
❑ 88PanSti-196
❑ 88RanSmo-18
❑ 88Sco-523
❑ 88ScoGlo-523
❑ 88Top-227
❑ 88TopClo-28
❑ 88TopTif-227
❑ 89RedFolSB-25
❑ 89UppDec-598
❑ 90VerBeaDS-9
❑ 93RanKee-113
❑ 93VerBeaDF-2207
❑ 95GreFalDTI-36
❑ 96SavSanB-1

Correa, Elvis
❑ 96GreFalDB-7
❑ 96GreFalDTI-6
❑ 97GreFalDTI-6
❑ 98VerBeaDM-6

Correa, Jorge
❑ 92AubAstC-26
❑ 92AubAstF-1346

Correa, Jose
❑ 92EliTwiC-16
❑ 92EliTwiF-3673
❑ 93ForWayWC-6
❑ 93ForWayWF-1960
❑ 94ForMyeMC-6
❑ 94ForMyeMF-1160
❑ 94VenLinU-177
❑ 96-97LinVen-87

Correa, Mickey
❑ 96DurBulBrB-12

Correa, Miguel
❑ 92IdaFalGF-3525
❑ 92IdaFalGSP-16
❑ 93MacBraC-7
❑ 93MacBraF-1413
❑ 93SouAtlLAGF-36
❑ 94GreBraF-424
❑ 95DurBulTI-9
❑ 98El PasDG-8

Correa, Ramser
❑ 89HelBreSP-15
❑ 90BelBreB-1
❑ 90Bes-24
❑ 92StoPorF-28
❑ 93StoPorC-5
❑ 94CanIndF-3109
❑ 95SanAntMTI-50
❑ 96SanAntMB-3
❑ 97VerBeaD-7

Correia, Rod
❑ 88SouOreAP-1702
❑ 89ModA'sC-23
❑ 89ModA'sCLC-277
❑ 90ModA'sC-8
❑ 90ModA'sCLC-163
❑ 90ModA'sP-2218
❑ 91HunStaTI-7
❑ 91TacTigP-2312
❑ 92MidAngF-4032
❑ 92MidAngOHP-4
❑ 92MidAngS-457
❑ 93AngStaCl-10
❑ 93ExcFS7-140
❑ 93FleFinE-179

❑ 93SelRoo-142T
❑ 93VanCanF-2603
❑ 94AngMot-10-
❑ 94Fle-49
❑ 94Pac-72
❑ 94Sco-594
❑ 94ScoGolR-594
❑ 94StaClu-352
❑ 94StaCluFDI-352
❑ 94StaCluGR-352
❑ 94StaCluMOP-352
❑ 94Top-532
❑ 94TopGol-532
❑ 94TopSpa-532
❑ 94Ult-21
❑ 94VanCanF-1868
❑ 95Pac-52
❑ 96HunStaTI-4
❑ 96Pac-263
❑ 97TreThuB-12

Correll, Vic (Victor C.)
❑ 75AtlBraP-7
❑ 75OPC-177
❑ 75Top-177
❑ 75TopMin-177
❑ 76AtlBraP-7
❑ 76OPC-608
❑ 76SSP-14
❑ 76Top-608
❑ 76VenLeaS-43
❑ 77Top-364
❑ 78IndIndTI-19
❑ 78Top-527
❑ 79Top-281
❑ 80RedEnq-9
❑ 80Top-419
❑ 81Top-628

Correnti, Chris
❑ 91BurAstC-28
❑ 92BurAstC-29
❑ 94LynRedSC-29
❑ 95TreThuTI-4

Corriden, John M. Jr.
❑ 43DodTeal-6
❑ 47YanTeaT-6
❑ 90DodTar-140

Corriden, John M. Sr.
❑ 32CubTeal-2
❑ 36CubTeal-4
❑ 39CubTeal-3
❑ 48BluTin-17
❑ 48YanTeal-4

Corridon, Frank
❑ 08RosComP-138
❑ 09AmeCarE90-1-27
❑ 09PC7HHB-8
❑ 11PinT-5-356
❑ 11SpoLifCW-75
❑ 11SpoLifM-265
❑ 11T205-32
❑ 12ImpTobC-17

Corrigan, Cory
❑ 93JohCitCC-8
❑ 93JohCitCF-3671
❑ 94SavCarC-11
❑ 94SavCarF-501
❑ 95PeoChiTI-23

Corrigan, Jack
❑ 97PinFan-PC4

Corrigan, Larry
❑ 75WatDodT-4

Corry, DeLynn
❑ 92HamRedC-29
❑ 92HamRedF-1585

Corsaro, Robby
❑ 89BatCliP-1945

Corsi, Jim (James)
❑ 83GreHorT-4
❑ 85GreHorT-16
❑ 86NewBriRSP-7
❑ 87HunStaTI-7
❑ 87ModA'sC-3
❑ 87ModA'sP-25
❑ 88TacTigC-7
❑ 88TacTigP-625
❑ 89Fle-649
❑ 89FleGlo-649
❑ 89ScoHot1R-36
❑ 89TacTigC-2
❑ 89TacTigP-1560
❑ 89Top-292
❑ 89TopTif-292
❑ 90Don-422
❑ 90Fle-4
❑ 90FleCan-4
❑ 90OPC-623
❑ 90Sco-553
❑ 90Top-623
❑ 90TopTif-623
❑ 90UppDec-521
❑ 91AstMot-21
❑ 91UltUpd-80
❑ 92Don-467
❑ 92Fle-431
❑ 92Sco-524
❑ 92TacTigS-531
❑ 93Don-741
❑ 93Fle-424
❑ 93FleFinE-58
❑ 93MarUSPC-8D
❑ 93MarUSPC-10H
❑ 93Top-753
❑ 93TopGol-753
❑ 93TopInaM-753
❑ 93TopInaR-753
❑ 93TopMic-753
❑ 94BreCouMF-3
❑ 95AthMot-25
❑ 95FleUpd-70
❑ 96A'sMot-18
❑ 96FleUpd-U72
❑ 96FleUpdTC-U72
❑ 96LeaSigEA-36
❑ 97Fle-188
❑ 97FleTif-188
❑ 98PacOnl-110
❑ 98PacOnlR-110
❑ 98PacOnlWC-110

Cort, Barry
❑ 75BurBeeT-3
❑ 78SpoIndC-18
❑ 79HolMilT-26
❑ 80HolMilT-4
❑ 94BreMilB-304

Cortes, David
❑ 97MacBra-21
❑ 98BesAutSS-13
❑ 98RicBraQ-9
❑ 99SP TopP-31
❑ 99SP TopPC-DC
❑ 99SP TopPPE-31

Cortes, Hernan
❑ 89BlaYNPRWL-172
❑ 89PenPilS-4
❑ 90Ft.LauYS-3
❑ 90StaFS7-39
❑ 91LinDriAA-628
❑ 91WilBilLD-628
❑ 91WilBilP-299

Cortez, Conde (Argenis)
❑ 87DayBeaAP-12
❑ 91BirBarLD-56
❑ 91BirBarP-1447
❑ 91LinDriAA-56

Cortez, Dave
❑ 87WicPilRD-18

Cortez, Sonny
❑ 98TenKry-9

Cortopassi, Tony
❑ 66SeaPop-5

Corujo, Rey
❑ 95BelGiaTI-10
❑ 96SanJosGB-7
❑ 97SanJosG-9

Corwin, Al (Elmer)
❑ 52Bow-121
❑ 53BowC-126
❑ 53BowC-149
❑ 54Bow-137
❑ 55Bow-122
❑ 55GiaGolS-10
❑ 75Gia195T-3
❑ 79TCM50-232

Corzo, Boanerge
❑ 96-97LinVen-127

Cosbey, Chris
❑ 98SouOreTG-6

Cosby, Bill
❑ 84WilMay-46

Cosby, Darin
❑ 88OklSoo-15
❑ 89OklSoo-11

Cosby, Rob
❑ 84EveGiaC-13A

Coscarart, Joe (Joseph M.)
❑ 30Zee-52
❑ 31Zee-30
❑ 32Zee-32
❑ 33Zee-20
❑ 33Zee-155
❑ 36GouBWR-8
❑ 36GouWidPPR-A19
❑ 37Zee-1

Coscarart, Pete (Peter J.)
❑ 39PlaBal-141
❑ 40DodTeal-4
❑ 40PlaBal-63
❑ 41DodTeal-2
❑ 47PadTeal-5
❑ 49BowPCL-21
❑ 78DodTCM4-12
❑ 79DiaGre-365
❑ 83TCMPla1945-33
❑ 89DodSmoG-46
❑ 90DodTar-141

Cosenza, Vincent
❑ 52LavPro-40

Cosey, Ray (Donald Ray)
❑ 79OgdA'sT-16
❑ 80OgdA'sT-2

Cosgrove, Mike
❑ 74AstFouTIP-4
❑ 75IowOakT-4
❑ 75OPC-96
❑ 75Top-96
❑ 75TopMin-96
❑ 76Hos-131
❑ 76HouAstP-6
❑ 76OPC-122
❑ 76Top-122
❑ 77Top-589
❑ 87AstShoSPT-3
❑ 98ForWayW!-15

Cosio, Raymundo
❑ 78CedRapGT-6
❑ 79CedRapGT-27

Cosman, Jeff
❑ 93PitMetC-5
❑ 93PitMetF-3699
❑ 94CapCitBC-3
❑ 94CapCitBF-1742
❑ 95StLucMTI-9

Cosman, Jim
❑ 67Top-384
❑ 70OPC-429
❑ 70Top-429
❑ 89MarPhiS-7

Cosme, Caonabo
❑ 98ModA'sG-8

Coss, Mike
❑ 91BluOriC-10
❑ 91BluOriP-4133
❑ 92FreKeyF-1810

Cossins, Tim
❑ 93EriSaiC-3
❑ 93EriSaiF-3119
❑ 94HudValRF-3387
❑ 95ChaRivUTIS-38
❑ 97TulDriTI-9

Costa, Tim
❑ 92MarPhiF-3048

Costa, Tony
❑ 92MarPhiC-6
❑ 93BatCliCB-7
❑ 93BatCliF-3137
❑ 94SpaPhiF-1712
❑ 94SparPhiC-4
❑ 95ClePhiF-209
❑ 96ReaPhiB-2
❑ 97ReaPhi-11
❑ 98ReaPhiM-7

Costas, Bob
❑ 89ChaLooLITI-7

Coste, Chris
❑ 98FarRedHM-6

Costell, Arnie
❑ 75DubPacT-28

Costello, Bob
❑ 83WisRapTF-14

Costello, Brian
❑ 89SalSpuP-1828
❑ 90CliGiaB-12
❑ 92SanJosGC-29
❑ 93MarPhiC-6
❑ 93MarPhiF-3487
❑ 94SpaPhiF-1734
❑ 94SparPhiC-5
❑ 95ClePhiF-227
❑ 97ClePhi-5
❑ 98ReaPhiUM-9

Costello, Bubba
❑ 93BakDodCLC-5
❑ 94VerBeaDF-63

Costello, Chris
❑ 92GulCoaDF-3559
❑ 93GreFalDSP-26
❑ 94VerBeaDC-6

Costello, Dan (Daniel F.)
❑ 15SpoNewM-39

Costello, Fred
❑ 88AshTouP-1063
❑ 89ColMudB-16
❑ 89ColMudP-129
❑ 89ColMudS-6
❑ 90Bes-218
❑ 90ColMudB-16
❑ 90ColMudP-1341
❑ 90ColMudS-8
❑ 91OscAstC-1
❑ 91OscAstP-673
❑ 92JacGenF-3993
❑ 92OscAstC-11
❑ 93JacGenF-2101
❑ 94PhoFirF-1514

Costello, John
❑ 83EriCarT-18
❑ 84SavCarT-4
❑ 85SprCarT-5
❑ 86St.PetCP-7
❑ 87ArkTraP-25
❑ 88FleUpd-118
❑ 88FleUpdG-118
❑ 88LouRedBC-1
❑ 88LouRedBP-440
❑ 88LouRedBTI-16
❑ 88ScoRoo-107T
❑ 88ScoRooG-107T
❑ 89CarSmo-3
❑ 89CarTeal-4
❑ 89ClaTraO-142
❑ 89Don-518
❑ 89Fle-446
❑ 89FleGlo-446
❑ 89PanSti-176
❑ 89Sco-534
❑ 89ScoHot1R-75
❑ 89Top-184
❑ 89TopTif-184
❑ 89UppDec-625
❑ 90Don-555
❑ 90ExpPos-5
❑ 90Fle-246
❑ 90FleCan-246
❑ 90OPC-36
❑ 90PublntS-214
❑ 90Sco-347
❑ 90SprCarDGB-10
❑ 90Top-36
❑ 90TopTif-36
❑ 90TopTVCa-8
❑ 90UppDec-486
❑ 91LasVegSLD-281
❑ 91LasVegSP-228
❑ 91LinDriAAA-281
❑ 91PadSmo-7
❑ 92Sco-614

Costello, Lou
❑ 93ActPacA-168
❑ 93ActPacA2-65G

Costello, Mike
❑ 86BeaGolGP-8
❑ 87WicPilRD-15
❑ 88WicPilRD-26
❑ 89DenZepC-5
❑ 89DenZepP-45
❑ 89ElPasDGS-5

Costello, T.J.
❑ 96SouOreTI-16

Costello, Tim
❑ 77VisOakT-4

Costic, Tim
❑ 90FreStaS-3
❑ 91FreStaBS-3
❑ 92EliTwiC-5
❑ 92EliTwiF-3692
❑ 93ForWayWC-7
❑ 93ForWayWF-1980
❑ 94ForWayWC-6
❑ 94ForWayWF-2014

Costner, Kevin
❑ 88BulDurM-1
❑ 88DurBulS-9B
❑ 88DurBulS-NNO
❑ 89DurBullS-29
❑ 89DurBullS-29

Costo, Tim
❑ 90ClaDraP-8
❑ 90KinIndTI-NNO
❑ 91Bow-79
❑ 91CanIndLD-79
❑ 91CanIndP-984
❑ 91Cla/Bes-389
❑ 91Cla/Bes-438
❑ 91Cla1-T38
❑ 91ClaGam-58
❑ 91LeaGolR-BC18
❑ 91LinDriAA-79
❑ 91LinDriP-79
❑ 91OPC-103
❑ 91Sco-680
❑ 91Top-103
❑ 91TopDesS-103
❑ 91TopMic-103
❑ 91TopTif-103
❑ 91UppDec-62
❑ 92Bow-489
❑ 92ChaLooF-3824
❑ 92ChaLooS-180
❑ 92ClaFS7-70
❑ 92DonRoo-29
❑ 92ProFS7-51
❑ 92SkyAA F-80
❑ 93Bow-314
❑ 93ClaFS7-160
❑ 93Don-270
❑ 93FleMajLP-A3
❑ 93IndIndF-1493
❑ 93Lea-529
❑ 93Pin-582
❑ 93Sco-265
❑ 93StaClu-390
❑ 93StaCluFDI-390
❑ 93StaCluMOP-390
❑ 93Top-577
❑ 93TopGol-577
❑ 93TopInaM-577
❑ 93TopInaR-577
❑ 93TopMic-577
❑ 93Toy-25
❑ 93Ult-326
❑ 93UppDec-11
❑ 93UppDecGold-11
❑ 94Bow-416
❑ 94ColC-86
❑ 94ColChoGS-86
❑ 94ColChoSS-86
❑ 94Don-561
❑ 94Fle-408
❑ 94Lea-53
❑ 94Pac-144
❑ 94Sco-552
❑ 94ScoBoyoS-48
❑ 94ScoGolR-552
❑ 94StaClu-119
❑ 94StaCluFDI-119
❑ 94StaCluGR-119
❑ 94StaCluMOP-119
❑ 94Top-513
❑ 94TopGol-513
❑ 94TopSpa-513
❑ 94UppDec-168
❑ 94UppDecED-168
❑ 96BufBisB-6
❑ 97LouRedB-13
❑ 98SyrSkyG-6

Cota, Chris
❑ 85MexCitTT-11
❑ 87DayBeaAP-20
❑ 89BenBucL-3

Cota, Francisco
❑ 83MiaMarT-4

Cota, Tim
❑ 87VisOakP-4

Cote, Brice
❑ 80ElmPioRST-5

Cotes, Eugenio
❑ 77SalPirT-8
❑ 79PorBeaT-10
❑ 79Top-723
❑ 85DomLeaS-168

Cotner, Andrew
❑ 91KinMetC-28
❑ 91KinMetP-3805
❑ 92KinMetC-22
❑ 92KinMetF-1524
❑ 93KinMetC-6
❑ 93KinMetF-3790
❑ 93St.LuMF-2913

Cotten, Jeremy
❑ 99TeaBesR-14
❑ 99TeaBesRG-14
❑ 99TeaBesRS-14

Cottier, Chuck (Charles K.)
❑ 55DonWin-16
❑ 60BraLaktL-7
❑ 60BraSpiaS-6
❑ 60Lea-138
❑ 60Top-417
❑ 61Pos-113
❑ 61SenJayP-2
❑ 61TigJayP-7
❑ 61Top-13
❑ 62Jel-66
❑ 62Pos-66
❑ 62PosCan-66
❑ 62SalPlaC-20
❑ 62ShiPlaC-20
❑ 62Top-27
❑ 62TopBuc-19
❑ 62TopStal-93
❑ 62TopVen-27
❑ 63Fle-28
❑ 63Jel-98
❑ 63Pos-98
❑ 63Top-219
❑ 64Top-397
❑ 67SeaPop-4
❑ 69Top-252
❑ 77QuaCitAT-12
❑ 78TCM60I-189
❑ 82MarPos-12
❑ 84MarMot-27
❑ 85MarMot-1
❑ 85Top-656
❑ 85TopTif-656
❑ 86Top-141
❑ 86TopTif-141
❑ 88CubDavB-NNO
❑ 89CubMar-NNO
❑ 90CubMar-28
❑ 90TopTVCu-3
❑ 91CubMar-NNO
❑ 91CubVinL-7
❑ 92CubMar-NNO
❑ 93CubMar-6
❑ 95BalOriP-14
❑ 97PhiTeal-3
❑ 98PhiTeal-9

Cotto, Hector
❑ 88MiaMarS-5

Cotto, Henry
❑ 81QuaCitCT-15
❑ 83IowCubT-21
❑ 84CubChiT-8
❑ 84CubSev-28
❑ 85Don-411
❑ 85Fle-53
❑ 85FleUpd-31
❑ 85Top-267
❑ 85TopTif-267
❑ 85YanTCMP-32
❑ 86YanTCM-31
❑ 87ColCliP-16
❑ 87ColCliT-20
❑ 87Top-174
❑ 87TopTif-174
❑ 88BlaYNPRWL-35
❑ 88DonBasB-51
❑ 88Fle-205
❑ 88FleGlo-205
❑ 88FleUpd-58
❑ 88FleUpdG-58
❑ 88MarMot-6
❑ 88OPC-172
❑ 88Sco-368
❑ 88ScoGlo-368
❑ 88ScoRoo-48T
❑ 88ScoRooG-48T
❑ 88StaLinMa-5
❑ 88Top-766
❑ 88TopBig-125
❑ 88TopTif-766
❑ 88TopTra-31T
❑ 88TopTraT-31T
❑ 89BlaYNPRWL-37
❑ 89BlaYNPRWLU-51
❑ 89BlaYNPRWLU-59
❑ 89Don-109
❑ 89Fle-545
❑ 89FleGlo-545
❑ 89MarMot-6
❑ 89OPC-207
❑ 89PanSti-441
❑ 89Sco-209
❑ 89Top-468
❑ 89TopBig-160
❑ 89TopSti-218
❑ 89TopTif-468
❑ 89UppDec-134
❑ 90Bow-476

❑ 90BowTif-476
❑ 90Don-644
❑ 90Fle-511
❑ 90FleCan-511
❑ 90MarMot-9
❑ 90OPC-31
❑ 90PubIntS-430
❑ 90Sco-161
❑ 90Top-31
❑ 90TopBig-156
❑ 90TopTif-31
❑ 90UppDec-207
❑ 91Bow-244
❑ 91Don-343
❑ 91Fle-448
❑ 91Lea-113
❑ 91MarCouH-18
❑ 91OPC-634
❑ 91PanFreS-232
❑ 91Sco-282
❑ 91StaClu-525
❑ 91Top-634
❑ 91TopDesS-634
❑ 91TopMic-634
❑ 91TopTif-634
❑ 91Ult-333
❑ 91UppDec-110
❑ 92Don-356
❑ 92Fle-276
❑ 92Lea-472
❑ 92LeaBlaG-472
❑ 92MarMot-9
❑ 92OPC-311
❑ 92Pin-342
❑ 92Sco-390
❑ 92StaClu-14
❑ 92Top-311
❑ 92TopGol-311
❑ 92TopGolW-311
❑ 92TopMic-311
❑ 92Ult-432
❑ 92UppDec-616
❑ 92YanWIZ8-36
❑ 93Don-705
❑ 93Fle-672
❑ 93MarMot-5
❑ 93MarPub-9
❑ 93PacSpa-283
❑ 93PanSti-64
❑ 93Pin-323
❑ 93StaClu-565
❑ 93StaCluFDI-565
❑ 93StaCluMOP-565
❑ 93Top-206
❑ 93TopGol-206
❑ 93TopInaM-206
❑ 93TopInaR-206
❑ 93TopMic-206
❑ 93TopTra-121T
❑ 93UppDec-411
❑ 93UppDecGold-411
❑ 94Don-184
❑ 94Fle-465
❑ 94Pac-240
❑ 94Sco-161
❑ 94ScoGolR-161
❑ 94Top-522
❑ 94TopGol-522
❑ 94TopSpa-522
❑ 96PorCitRB-2
❑ 97TacRai-3
❑ 98OrlRayM-24

Cotton, Joe
❑ 96BatCliTI-9
❑ 97BatCliTI-2
❑ 98PieBolWM-7

Cotton, John
❑ 89BurIndS-6
❑ 90WatIndS-5
❑ 91ColIndC-23
❑ 91ColIndP-1490
❑ 92KinIndC-16
❑ 92KinIndF-2482
❑ 92UppDecML-321
❑ 93CarLeaAGF-27
❑ 93KinIndC-5
❑ 93KinIndF-2259
❑ 93KinIndTI-4
❑ 94SprSulF-2048
❑ 95MemChiTI-7
❑ 96JacSunB-9
❑ 96TolMudHB-9
❑ 97BirBarB-19

Cottrell, Steve
❑ 84EveGiaC-8

Couch, Jack
❑ 21Zee-116

Couch, Johnny
❑ 15Zee-102
❑ 16Zee-105
❑ 19Zee-89
❑ 20Zee-109
❑ 26Zee-92
❑ 29Zee-126
❑ 94ConTSN-1297
❑ 94ConTSNB-1297

Couch, Richard
❑ 76AshTouT-12
❑ 77AshTouT-3

Couchee, Mike
❑ 82AmaGolST-16
❑ 85ChaO'sT-31
❑ 85LasVegSC-123
❑ 86TulDriTI-4
❑ 88QuaCitAGS-2
❑ 88SanDieS-5
❑ 88SanDieSAAG-5
❑ 89SanDieSAG-5

Couchman, Robert
❑ 11Zee-5

Cougar, Ozzie
❑ 93KanCouCC-30
❑ 93KanCouCTI-30
❑ 98KanCouC-6
❑ 98KanCouCCP-6
❑ 98NasSouTI-25

Coughenour, Cara
❑ 95ColSilB-5
❑ 96ColSilB-5

Coughlin, Bill (William P.)
❑ 03BreE10-25
❑ 07TigACDPP-2
❑ 08RosComP-32
❑ 09TigHMTP-2
❑ 09WolNewDTPP-3
❑ 11SpoLifCW-76

Coughlin, Kevin
❑ 90UtiBluSP-1
❑ 91SouBenWSC-9
❑ 91SouBenWSP-2868
❑ 92SarWhiSCB-19
❑ 93SarWhiSC-8
❑ 93SarWhiSF-1375
❑ 94BirBarC-6
❑ 94BirBarF-631
❑ 94ClaGolF-154
❑ 95UppDecML-105
❑ 95UppDecMLFS-105
❑ 96BesAutS-23
❑ 96BirBarB-24
❑ 96Exc-31
❑ 96ExcTL-2
❑ 96TreThuB-24
❑ 97ArkTraB-20

Coughlin, Red
❑ 85SyrChiT-24
❑ 86SyrChiP-10
❑ 87SyrChiT-33
❑ 88SyrChiP-819

Coughlon, Kevin
❑ 82MadMusF-7
❑ 84MadMusP-21
❑ 85ModA'sC-12

Coughtry, Marlan (James M.)
❑ 61SeaPop-2
❑ 61SeaPop-3
❑ 61UniOil-S3
❑ 62Top-595

Coulson, Robert
❑ 12T207-35

Coulson, Steven
❑ 77WesHavYT-5

Coulter, Chris
❑ 08IndPos-5
❑ 91BurIndP-3292

Coulter, Darrell
❑ 87UtiBluSP-19
❑ 88SpaPhiP-1029
❑ 88SpaPhiS-21
❑ 89SpaPhiP-1042
❑ 89SpaPhiS-5

Coulter, Roy
❑ 75AppFoxT-6
❑ 76AppFoxT-2
❑ 78AppFoxT-6

Coulter, Shannon
❑ 94EugEmeC-7
❑ 94EugEmeF-3720

Coulter, Tom (Thomas Lee)
❑ 66St.PetCTI-5

Coumbe, Fritz (Fred)
❑ 17ColE13-33
❑ 22Zee-96
❑ 23Zee-102
❑ 24Zee-76
❑ 25Zee-88
❑ 26Zee-3

Counsell, Craig
❑ 92BenRocCB-9
❑ 92BenRocF-1479
❑ 93CenValRC-7
❑ 93CenValRF-2897
❑ 94NewHavRF-1555
❑ 96Bow-194
❑ 96BowFoi-194
❑ 96ColSprSSTI-9
❑ 97ColSprSTI-3
❑ 98ColCho-101
❑ 98DonColL-206
❑ 98DonPriCL-206
❑ 98Fin-14
❑ 98FinNo--14
❑ 98FinNo-R-14
❑ 98FinRef-14
❑ 98Lea-6
❑ 98LeaFraDA-6
❑ 98LeaFraF-6
❑ 98LeaFraM-6
❑ 98LeaFraM-6
❑ 98LeaFraMDC-6
❑ 98LeaFraMDC-6
❑ 98LeaFraMZ2-6
❑ 98Pac-298
❑ 98PacInv-98
❑ 98PacInvPBlue-98
❑ 98PacInvSilv-98
❑ 98PacOme-95
❑ 98PacOmeR-95
❑ 98PacOnl-292
❑ 98PacOnlR-292
❑ 98PacOnlWC-292
❑ 98PacPlaB-298
❑ 98PacRedT-298
❑ 98PacSil-298
❑ 98SP Aut-94
❑ 98SPxFin-7
❑ 98SPxFinR-7
❑ 98SPxFinS-7
❑ 98StaCluFDI-196
❑ 98StaCluI-196
❑ 98StaCluOneK-196
❑ 98StaCluPP-196
❑ 98Top-343
❑ 98TopChr-343
❑ 98TopChrR-343
❑ 98TopDevR-343
❑ 98TopDia-343
❑ 98TopMiniC-343
❑ 98Ult-362
❑ 98UltGolM-362
❑ 98UltMas-362
❑ 98UltPlaM-362
❑ 98UppDec-271
❑ 99Pac-173
❑ 99PacAur-71
❑ 99PacAurOD-71
❑ 99PacPlaB-173
❑ 99PacRed-173
❑ 99Ult-108
❑ 99UltGolM-108
❑ 99UltMas-108
❑ 99UltPlaM-108
❑ 99UppDec-100
❑ 99UppDecEL1-100
❑ 99UppDecEL2-100
❑ 99Vic-164

Counts, Rick
❑ 78DunBluJT-4

Courtney, Bill
❑ 93SouOreAC-30

Courtney, Clint (Clinton D.)
❑ 53BowC-70
❑ 53NorBreL-5
❑ 53Top-127
❑ 54Bow-69
❑ 54DixLid-2
❑ 54OriEss-7
❑ 54OriTeal-6
❑ 55Bow-34
❑ 56Top-159
❑ 57Top-51
❑ 58SeaTeal-9
❑ 58SenJayP-3
❑ 58Top-92A
❑ 58Top-92B
❑ 59SenTealW-6
❑ 59Top-483
❑ 60Top-344
❑ 61A'sTeal-4
❑ 61SevElev-13
❑ 61Top-342
❑ 79TCM50-169
❑ 87AstSer1-30
❑ 91OriCro-86
❑ 91TopArc1-127
❑ 97BalOriP-11

Courtney, Ernie (Ernest E.)
❑ 09ColChiE-64
❑ 11SpoLifCW-77
❑ 12ColRedB-64
❑ 12ColTinT-64

Courtney, Harry
❑ 22E120-106
❑ 23Zee-126

Courtright, John
❑ 91BilMusP-3746
❑ 91BilMusSP-15
❑ 92ChaWheF-1
❑ 92ChaWVWC-14
❑ 93ChaLooF-2354
❑ 93SouAtlLAPI-8
❑ 94Bow-570
❑ 94ChaLooF-1352
❑ 95FleUpd-131

Cousins, Derryl
❑ 88T/MUmp-40
❑ 89T/MUmp-38
❑ 90T/MUmp-36

Couture, Mike
❑ 90HelBreSP-11
❑ 91StoPorC-15
❑ 91StoPorP-3043
❑ 92BelBreCB-10
❑ 92BelBreFl-418
❑ 92MidLeaATI-8
❑ 93StoPorC-6
❑ 93StoPorF-756

Coveleski, Harry
❑ 09ColChiE-65A
❑ 09T206-75
❑ 10W555-18
❑ 11TurRedT-88
❑ 12ColRedB-65A
❑ 12ColTinT-65A
❑ 12ColTinT-65B
❑ 14B18B-15A
❑ 14B18B-15B
❑ 14B18B-15C
❑ 15SpoNewM-40
❑ 16BF2FP-27
❑ 16SpoNewM-39
❑ 17ColE13-34
❑ 81TigDetN-39
❑ 81TigSecNP-12
❑ 94ConTSN-1172
❑ 94ConTSNB-1172

Coveleski, Stan
❑ 09ColChiE-65B
❑ 10StaCarE-8
❑ 11SpoLifM-280
❑ 12ColRedB-65B
❑ 15Zee-56
❑ 20NatCarE-17
❑ 20W52-14
❑ 21E121So1-13
❑ 21Exh-28
❑ 22E120-32
❑ 22W572-17
❑ 22W575-20
❑ 23W501-21
❑ 23W503-64
❑ 23WilChoV-23
❑ 25Exh-122
❑ 26Exh-122
❑ 26SpoComoA-12
❑ 27YorCarE-57
❑ 28StaPlaCE-13
❑ 28W502-57
❑ 28Yue-57
❑ 61Fle-100
❑ 70FleWorS-17
❑ 75SenTCM1-4
❑ 76ShaPiz-113
❑ 77GalGloG-118
❑ 77Ind192T-5
❑ 78DexHaloFP-6
❑ 79DiaGre-276
❑ 80PerHaloFP-112
❑ 80SSPHOF-112
❑ 82DiaCla-57
❑ 82OhiHaloF-24
❑ 88SouBenWSGS-28
❑ 92ConTSN-462
❑ 92YanWIZH-7
❑ 93ConTSN-707
❑ 94ConTSN-1172
❑ 94ConTSNB-1172
❑ 95ConTSN-1362

Coveney, Jim
❑ 89AshTouP-961
❑ 93AshTouC-26
❑ 93AshTouF-2295

Coveney, Patrick
❑ 84AriWilP-3
❑ 86ClePhiP-5
❑ 87DayBeaAP-13

Covert, Dave
❑ 77LynMetT-11

Covington, Kevin
❑ 98GreFalDG-7

Covington, Tex (William)
❑ 12T207-36

Covington, Wes (John W.)
❑ 56BraBilaBP-7
❑ 57BraSpiaS4-7
❑ 57Top-283
❑ 58BraJayP-4
❑ 58Top-140
❑ 59Top-290
❑ 59Top-565
❑ 60BraJayP-3
❑ 60BraLaktL-8
❑ 60Top-158
❑ 60TopVen-158
❑ 61Pos-108A
❑ 61Pos-108B
❑ 61Top-296
❑ 61TopStal-41
❑ 62SalPlaC-105
❑ 62ShiPlaC-105
❑ 62Top-157
❑ 62TopVen-157
❑ 63Jel-182
❑ 63Pos-182
❑ 63Top-529
❑ 64PhiPhiB-10
❑ 64Top-208
❑ 64TopVen-208
❑ 65Top-583
❑ 66OPC-52
❑ 66Top-52
❑ 66Top-484
❑ 66TopVen-52
❑ 78BraTCC-6
❑ 78TCM60I-132
❑ 80Bra195T-26
❑ 87Bra195T-6
❑ 90DodTar-142

Cowan, Billy Roland
❑ 64Top-192
❑ 64TopVen-192
❑ 65OPC-186
❑ 65Top-186
❑ 69Top-643
❑ 69YanPhoS-56
❑ 71MLBOffS-341
❑ 71OPC-614
❑ 71Top-614
❑ 72OPC-19
❑ 72Top-19
❑ 78TCM60I-282
❑ 91MetWIZ-86
❑ 92YanWIZ6-29

Cowan, Ed
❑ 77DayBealT-2

Cowan, Jed
❑ 96OgdRapTI-NNO

Cowan, Johnnie
❑ 92NegLeaRLI-12

Cowboys, Kansas City
❑ 86JosHalC-9

Cowens, Al (Alfred Edward)
❑ 74RoyPos-8
❑ 75OPC-437
❑ 75RoyPos-9
❑ 75Top-437
❑ 75TopMin-437
❑ 76Hos-28
❑ 76HosTwi-28
❑ 76KanCitRP-7
❑ 76OPC-648
❑ 76RoyAaP-4
❑ 76SSP-175
❑ 76SSP-589
❑ 76Top-648
❑ 77Top-262
❑ 78Hos-67
❑ 78Kel-5
❑ 78OPC-143
❑ 78RCColC-74
❑ 78Roy-4
❑ 78SSP270-240
❑ 78Top-46
❑ 79OPC-258
❑ 79Top-490
❑ 80OPC-174
❑ 80Top-330
❑ 81CokTeaS-50
❑ 81Don-369
❑ 81Fle-471
❑ 81OPC-123
❑ 81Top-123
❑ 82Don-207
❑ 82Fle-266
❑ 82MarPos-13
❑ 82OPC-103
❑ 82Top-575
❑ 82TopSti-182
❑ 82TopTra-22T
❑ 83AllGamPI-50
❑ 83Don-554
❑ 83Fle-477
❑ 83FleSti-184
❑ 83MarNal-2
❑ 83OPC-193
❑ 83Top-763
❑ 83TopSti-115
❑ 84Don-511
❑ 84Fle-610
❑ 84MarMot-19
❑ 84Nes792-622
❑ 84Top-622
❑ 84TopSti-344
❑ 84TopTif-622
❑ 85Don-196
❑ 85Fle-487
❑ 85Lea-239
❑ 85MarMot-6
❑ 85OPC-224
❑ 85SubDis-10
❑ 85ThoMcAD-10
❑ 85Top-224
❑ 85TopSti-333
❑ 85TopTif-224
❑ 86Don-389
❑ 86Fle-463
❑ 86Lea-184
❑ 86MarMot-6
❑ 86OPC-92
❑ 86Top-92
❑ 86TopTif-92
❑ 89PacSenL-145
❑ 89T/MSenL-25
❑ 93RoySta2-3

Cowger, Tracy
❑ 79AshTouT-2
❑ 80TulDriT-18
❑ 81TulDriT-2
❑ 82TulDriT-12
❑ 83OklCit8T-5
❑ 83TulDriT-17

Cowherd, Colin
❑ 97PorRocG-6

Cowley, Joe
❑ 78GreBraT-7
❑ 79SavBraT-15
❑ 82BraPol-38
❑ 83RicBraT-3
❑ 83Top-288
❑ 84ColCliP-7
❑ 84ColCliT-13
❑ 85Don-613
❑ 85Fle-124
❑ 85Lea-58
❑ 85Top-769
❑ 85TopSti-318
❑ 85TopTif-769
❑ 85YanTCMP-10
❑ 86BufBisP-9
❑ 86Don-608
❑ 86DonHig-44
❑ 86Fle-103
❑ 86FleUpd-31
❑ 86Top-427
❑ 86TopTif-427
❑ 86TopTra-29T
❑ 86TopTraT-29T
❑ 86WhiSoxC-40

❑ 87Don-552
❑ 87Fle-491
❑ 87FleGlo-491
❑ 87FleLeaL-12
❑ 87Lea-240
❑ 87PhiTas-39A
❑ 87Spo-196
❑ 87SpoTeaP-26
❑ 87Top-27
❑ 87TopSti-290
❑ 87TopTif-27
❑ 92YanWIZ8-37

Cowsill, Brendon
❑ 96BoiHawB-7
❑ 97CedRapK-4
❑ 98LakElsSG-4

Cox, Billy (William Richard)
❑ 47PM1StaP1-37
❑ 47PM1StaP1-38
❑ 47TipTop-138
❑ 48DodTeal-7
❑ 49Bow-73
❑ 49EurSta-33
❑ 50Bow-194
❑ 51Bow-224
❑ 51TopBluB-48
❑ 52Bow-152
❑ 52DixLid-6
❑ 52DixPre-6
❑ 52Top-232
❑ 53BowBW-60
❑ 53DixLid-3
❑ 53DixPre-3
❑ 53NorBreL-6
❑ 54Bow-26
❑ 54NewYorJA-3
❑ 54RedHeaF-4
❑ 54RedMan-NL2
❑ 55Bow-56
❑ 55OriEss-7
❑ 74dod195T-8
❑ 79TCM50-83
❑ 83TopRep5-232
❑ 84TCMPla1-41
❑ 90DodTar-143
❑ 91DodRinP2-11
❑ 91OriCro-87
❑ 95TopArcBD-13
❑ 95TopArcBD-64
❑ 95TopArcBD-85
❑ 97BalOriP-12

Cox, Bobby (Robert Joe)
❑ 68YanPhoS-83
❑ 69MilBra-65
❑ 69Top-237
❑ 69TopTeaP-19
❑ 69YanPhoS-39
❑ 75SyrChiTI-2
❑ 76VenLeaS-37
❑ 78Top-93
❑ 79Top-302
❑ 80Top-192
❑ 81BraPol-6
❑ 81Don-426
❑ 81Fle-247
❑ 81Top-675
❑ 83OPC-34
❑ 83Top-606
❑ 84BluJayFS-10
❑ 84Fle-653
❑ 84Nes792-202
❑ 84OPC-202
❑ 84Top-202
❑ 84TopTif-202
❑ 85BluJayFS-9
❑ 85OPC-135
❑ 85Top-411
❑ 85TopTif-411
❑ 86BluJayGT-12
❑ 86OPC-359
❑ 86Top-471
❑ 86TopTif-471
❑ 90BraDubS-6
❑ 90TopTra-23T
❑ 90TopTraT-23T
❑ 91BraDubP-7
❑ 91BraSubS-11
❑ 91OPC-759
❑ 91Top-759
❑ 91TopDesS-759
❑ 91TopMic-759
❑ 91TopTif-759
❑ 92BraLykP-9
❑ 92BraLykS-11
❑ 92OPC-489
❑ 92Top-489
❑ 92TopGol-489
❑ 92TopGolW-489
❑ 92TopMic-489
❑ 92YanWIZ6-30
❑ 93BluJayDM-15
❑ 93BraLykP-8
❑ 93BraLykS-10
❑ 93RedFolS-111
❑ 93Top-501
❑ 93TopGol-501
❑ 93TopInaM-501
❑ 93TopInaR-501
❑ 93TopMic-501
❑ 94BraLykP-7
❑ 94BraLykS-8
❑ 96UppDec-477

Cox, Boyce
❑ 89BriTigS-31
❑ 90BriTigS-30
❑ 96BriWhiSB-7
❑ 98BriWhiSQ-6

Cox, Brian
❑ 98EugEme-9

Cox, Carl
❑ 47SigOil-2
❑ 86VerBeaDP-4

Cox, Carter
❑ 87BriYouC-16

Cox, Chris
❑ 93DanBraC-10
❑ 93DanBraF-3624

Cox, Chuck
❑ 95BatCliTI-8
❑ 96PieBolWB-9

Cox, Danny
❑ 82SprCarF-12
❑ 83St.PetCT-4
❑ 84Car-6
❑ 84Car5x7-5
❑ 84Don-449
❑ 85CarTeal-7
❑ 85Don-571
❑ 85Fle-222
❑ 85Top-499
❑ 85TopTif-499
❑ 86BasStaB-24
❑ 86CarIGAS-3
❑ 86CarKASD-5
❑ 86CarSchM-4
❑ 86CarTeal-10
❑ 86Don-382
❑ 86Fle-32
❑ 86Lea-177
❑ 86OPC-294
❑ 86Spo-108
❑ 86Top-294
❑ 86TopMinL-61
❑ 86TopSti-48
❑ 86TopTif-294
❑ 87CarSmo-6
❑ 87CarTeal-5
❑ 87Don-553
❑ 87Fle-292
❑ 87FleExcS-12
❑ 87FleGlo-292
❑ 87Lea-160
❑ 87OPC-202
❑ 87SpoTeaP-12
❑ 87Top-621
❑ 87TopMinL-33
❑ 87TopTif-621
❑ 88CarSmo-2
❑ 88CarTeal-4
❑ 88Don-60
❑ 88DonBasB-75
❑ 88Fle-28
❑ 88FleGlo-28
❑ 88Lea-72
❑ 88LouRedBTI-17
❑ 88OPC-59
❑ 88PanSti-383
❑ 88Sco-415
❑ 88ScoGlo-415
❑ 88Spo-84
❑ 88StaLinCa-4
❑ 88Top-59
❑ 88TopBig-111
❑ 88TopTif-59
❑ 88Woo-27
❑ 89CarTeal-5
❑ 89Don-348
❑ 89Fle-447
❑ 89FleGlo-447
❑ 89OPC-158
❑ 89Sco-613
❑ 89Top-562
❑ 89TopTif-562
❑ 89UppDec-535
❑ 90CarSmo-3
❑ 90LouRedBLBC-13
❑ 90OPC-184
❑ 90PubIntS-215
❑ 90SprCarDGB-9
❑ 90Top-184
❑ 90TopTif-184
❑ 90TopTVCa-9
❑ 91Lea-350
❑ 91PhiMed-10
❑ 91TopTra-25T
❑ 91TopTraT-25T
❑ 92BufBisBS-5
❑ 92Don-614
❑ 92Fle-526
❑ 92OPC-791
❑ 92PhiMed-9
❑ 92Sco-568
❑ 92StaClu-351
❑ 92Top-791
❑ 92TopGol-791
❑ 92TopGolW-791
❑ 92TopMic-791
❑ 93BluJayD-3
❑ 93BluJayFS-7
❑ 93Don-466
❑ 93Fle-499
❑ 93FleFinE-291
❑ 94BluJayUSPC-3H
❑ 94BluJayUSPC-11C
❑ 94Don-114
❑ 94Fle-329
❑ 94Lea-87
❑ 94Sco-242
❑ 94ScoGolR-242
❑ 94StaCluT-152
❑ 94StaCluTFDI-152
❑ 94Top-582
❑ 94TopGol-582
❑ 94TopSpa-582
❑ 95BluJayOH-10
❑ 95BluJayUSPC-9H

Cox, Darren
❑ 87IdaFalBP-21

Cox, Darron
❑ 88CapCodPPaLP-97
❑ 88OklSoo-12
❑ 89BilMusP-2067
❑ 89OklSoo-12
❑ 90Bes-20
❑ 90ChaWheB-1
❑ 90ChaWheP-2243
❑ 90CMC-840
❑ 90SouAtlLAS-5
❑ 91CedRapRC-13
❑ 91CedRapRP-2720
❑ 92ChaLooF-3822
❑ 92ChaLooS-181
❑ 93ChaLooF-2363
❑ 94IowCubF-1278
❑ 95OrlCubF-13
❑ 95Top-646
❑ 96RicBraB-9
❑ 96RicBraRC-21
❑ 98DurBulTI-4

Cox, Dick (Elmer Joseph)
❑ 18Zee-57
❑ 19Zee-35
❑ 20Zee-43
❑ 21Zee-46
❑ 22E120-17
❑ 22W573-25
❑ 22Zee-40
❑ 24Zee-41
❑ 27AmeCarE126-5
❑ 27Zee-10
❑ 90DodTar-917

Cox, Doug
❑ 87BakDodP-13
❑ 88VerBeaDS-4

Cox, Frank Bernhardt
❑ 29Zee-153
❑ 30Zee-169
❑ 32Zee-113
❑ 33Zee-79

Cox, J. Casey
❑ 66Top-549
❑ 67CokCapS-7
❑ 67Top-414
❑ 68OPC-66
❑ 68Top-66A
❑ 68Top-66B
❑ 68TopVen-66
❑ 69SenTeal8-9
❑ 69Top-383
❑ 70OPC-281
❑ 70Top-281
❑ 71MLBOffS-533
❑ 71OPC-82
❑ 71SenTealW-8
❑ 71Top-82
❑ 72MilBra-81
❑ 72OPC-231
❑ 72RanTeal-6
❑ 72Top-231
❑ 73OPC-419
❑ 73Top-419
❑ 92YanWIZ7-38
❑ 93RanKee-7

Cox, Jeff (Jeffrey Linden)
❑ 79OgdA'sT-12
❑ 80OgdA'sT-19
❑ 81Don-230
❑ 81TacTigT-19
❑ 81Top-133
❑ 82EvaTriT-14
❑ 83OmaRoyT-14
❑ 86VerRedP-4
❑ 87VanCanP-1600
❑ 87WatPirP-30
❑ 88AugPirP-382
❑ 88ChaLooLTI-7
❑ 89MemChiB-24
❑ 89MemChiP-1195
❑ 89MemChiS-24
❑ 90MemChiB-26
❑ 90MemChiP-1025
❑ 90MemChiS-26
❑ 91LinDriAA-424
❑ 91MemChiLD-424
❑ 91MemChiP-669
❑ 92OmaRoyF-2977
❑ 92OmaRoyS-349
❑ 93OmaRoyF-1696
❑ 93TriAAAGF-41
❑ 94OmaRoyF-1238
❑ 94VenLinU-99
❑ 95LinVen-251
❑ 96GreBraB-1
❑ 96GreBraTI-43
❑ 98RicBraQ-1

Cox, Jim
❑ 85ElmPioT-5

Cox, Jim (James Charles)
❑ 72Dia-8
❑ 74OPC-600
❑ 74Top-600
❑ 76MonExpP-6
❑ 76SSP-325

Cox, John
❑ 86HunStaDJ-41

Cox, Larry Eugene
❑ 75PhiPhiP-11
❑ 76SSP-596
❑ 76TacTwiDQ-4
❑ 77Top-379
❑ 78SSP270-258
❑ 78Top-541
❑ 79Top-489
❑ 80OPC-63
❑ 80Top-116
❑ 81Don-285
❑ 81Fle-604
❑ 81Top-249
❑ 81TopTra-749
❑ 83QuaCitCT-2
❑ 85IowCubT-28
❑ 86IowCubP-9
❑ 87IowCubTI-22
❑ 88CubDavB-NNO
❑ 89CubMar-NNO
❑ 93RanKee-114

Cox, Robbie
❑ 76BatRouCT-9

Cox, Stan
❑ 86DavLipB-7

Cox, Steve
❑ 92ClaDraP-85
❑ 92FroRowDP-98
❑ 92FroRowDPG-98
❑ 92FroRowDPS-98
❑ 93Bow-653
❑ 93SouOreAC-1
❑ 93SouOreAF-4069
❑ 94WesMicWC-5
❑ 94WesMicWF-2302
❑ 95Bes-38
❑ 95ModA'sTI-4
❑ 95SPML-126
❑ 96ColCho-434
❑ 96ColChoGS-434
❑ 96ColChoSS-434
❑ 96Exc-97
❑ 96ExcAll-2
❑ 96Fla-146
❑ 96FlaWavotF-6
❑ 96FleUpd-U73
❑ 96FleUpdNH-4
❑ 96FleUpdTC-U73
❑ 96HunStaTI-5
❑ 96Top-424
❑ 96Ult-399
❑ 96UltGolM-399
❑ 96UltGolP-5
❑ 96UltGolPHGM-5
❑ 96UppDec-237
❑ 96UppDecFSP-FS7
❑ 97Bow-338
❑ 97BowInt-338
❑ 98DurBulTI-5
❑ 99WesMicWAM-6

Cox, Ted
❑ 91PeoChiTI-30

Cox, Ted (William Ted)
❑ 78IndTeal-6
❑ 78Top-706
❑ 79Top-79
❑ 80MarPos-7
❑ 80Top-252
❑ 80VenLeaS-215
❑ 81Don-283
❑ 81Fle-602
❑ 81SpoIndT-16

Cox, Terry
❑ 71OPC-559
❑ 71Top-559

Coy, Bert
❑ 09ObaT21-67
❑ 09ObaT21-179
❑ 09ObaT21-271
❑ 11Zee-24
❑ 12HomRunKE-20
❑ 12ObaPreT-20
❑ 12PCLPin-5
❑ 12Zee-28
❑ 13Zee-29
❑ 14Zee-79

Coyle, Bryan
❑ 94GreFalDSP-6
❑ 95YakBeaTI-6

Coyle, Clem
❑ 30Zee-118

Coyle, Rocky (Joseph)
❑ 84ModA'sC-8
❑ 86HunStaDJ-15
❑ 87KnoBluJP-1499
❑ 87SyrChiT-27

Cozzi, Dante
❑ 52LavPro-73

Cozzolino, Paul
❑ 82VerBeaDT-3

Crabb, James
❑ 13Zee-4
❑ 14Zee-7

Crabbe, Bruce
❑ 86PitCubP-4
❑ 87IowCubTI-12
❑ 88IowCubC-13
❑ 88IowCubP-550
❑ 89IowCubC-14
❑ 89IowCubP-1714
❑ 90CMC-290
❑ 90ProAAAF-410
❑ 90RicBraBC-5
❑ 90RicBraC-14
❑ 90RicBraP-265
❑ 90RicBraTI-7
❑ 91LinDriAAA-429
❑ 91RicBraBC-2
❑ 91RicBraLD-429
❑ 91RicBraP-2576
❑ 91RicBraTI-21
❑ 92SyrChiF-1973
❑ 92SyrChiMB-2
❑ 92SyrChiS-502
❑ 94ButCopKSP-27
❑ 95ColSilB-6
❑ 96ColSilB-6

Crable, George
❑ 90DodTar-918

Crabtree, Chris
❑ 91YakBeaC-24
❑ 91YakBeaP-4242

Crabtree, Estel C.
❑ 33WorCig-22
❑ 36WorWidGV-134
❑ 41CarW75-5
❑ 82OhiHaloF-45
❑ 83Car194T-6

Crabtree, Robert
❑ 96BelGiaTI-29
❑ 97BakBlaB-10
❑ 97BakBlaTI-10
❑ 98SanJosGQ-7

Crabtree, Tim
❑ 92ClaDraP-45
❑ 92ClaFS7-432
❑ 92FroRowDP-9
❑ 92FroRowDPG-9
❑ 92FroRowDPS-9
❑ 92St.CatBJC-23
❑ 92St.CatBJF-3379
❑ 93ClaFS7-66
❑ 93ClaGolF-208
❑ 93ExcFS7-240
❑ 93KnoSmoF-1243
❑ 93StaCluM-29
❑ 93Top-742
❑ 93TopGol-742
❑ 93TopInaM-742
❑ 93TopInaR-742
❑ 93TopMic-742
❑ 94SyrChiF-965
❑ 94SyrChiTI-7
❑ 95BluJayOH-11
❑ 95LinVen-182
❑ 95SyrChiTI-10
❑ 96BluJayOH-6
❑ 96Fle-271
❑ 96FleTif-271
❑ 96LeaSigEA-37
❑ 96Top-351
❑ 97BluJayB-3
❑ 97BluJayOH-6
❑ 97BluJayS-22
❑ 97Fle-236
❑ 97FleTif-236
❑ 97Top-129

Craddock, Walt
❑ 59Top-281

Cradle, Cobi
❑ 93PriRedC-5
❑ 93PriRedF-4192
❑ 94ChaWheC-6
❑ 94ChaWheF-2715
❑ 94SouAtlLAF-SAL39
❑ 95StLucMTI-10

Cradle, Rickey
❑ 92MedHatBJF-3218
❑ 92MedHatBJSP-15
❑ 93HagSunC-7
❑ 93HagSunF-1890
❑ 94DunBluJC-7
❑ 94DunBluJF-2568
❑ 95KnoSmoF-50
❑ 96DouAllB-27
❑ 96KnoSmoB-9
❑ 98TacRaiQ-10

Craft, Harry Francis
❑ 38CloFotW-14
❑ 38RedOraW-6
❑ 39OrcPhoAP-4
❑ 39PlaBal-65
❑ 39RedTeal-5
❑ 40PlaBal-79
❑ 41HarHarW-4
❑ 55A'sRodM-21
❑ 55A'sTeal-5
❑ 56A'sPos-10
❑ 58A'sJayP-1
❑ 62Col.45B-5
❑ 62Col45'JP-5
❑ 62Top-12
❑ 62TopVen-12
❑ 63Col45'JP-3
❑ 63Top-491
❑ 64Col.45JP-3
❑ 64Top-298
❑ 64TopVen-298
❑ 76A'sRodMC-7
❑ 76RedParC-7
❑ 77CinRedT-16
❑ 78TCM60I-244
❑ 79DiaGre-258
❑ 89AstCol4S-27

Craft, Mark

□ 90SouOreAB-16
□ 90SouOreAP-3442
Crafton, Kevin
□ 96NewJerCB-6
□ 97PeoChi-5
□ 98ArkTraM-6
Craghead, Howard
□ 28Zee-71
□ 29Zee-66
□ 30Zee-75
Craig, Benny
□ 98BurBeeM-6
Craig, Dale
□ 89WytCubS-7
□ 90WinSpiTI-8
□ 91GenCubC-3
□ 91GenCubP-4220
Craig, Dean
□ 78CliDodT-6
□ 79WauTimT-18
□ 82NasSouTI-8
Craig, Morris
□ 90HunCubP-3287
□ 91GenCubC-4
□ 91PeoChiP-1347
□ 92PeoChiC-23
Craig, Pete
□ 65Top-466
□ 66OPC-11
□ 66Top-11
□ 66TopVen-11
□ 67Top-459
Craig, Rodney Paul
□ 79SpoIndT-5
□ 80MarPos-8
□ 80Top-672
□ 81ChaChaT-19
□ 81Don-288
□ 81Fle-597
□ 81Top-282
□ 82Ind-9
□ 82IndWhe-14
□ 83ChaChaT-15
□ 83Don-515
□ 84MaiGuiT-19
Craig, Roger
□ 47Exh-51
□ 56Dod-6
□ 56Top-63
□ 57Top-173
□ 58DodTeal-4
□ 58Top-194
□ 59DodTeal-3
□ 60DodBelB-15
□ 60DodJayP-1
□ 60DodMor-2
□ 60DodPos-2
□ 60DodTeal-3
□ 60DodUniO-2
□ 60Lea-8
□ 60Top-62
□ 60TopVen-62
□ 61DodBelB-38
□ 61DodUniO-2
□ 61Top-543
□ 62MetJayP-3
□ 62SalPlaC-189
□ 62ShiPlaC-189
□ 62Top-183
□ 62TopBuc-20
□ 62TopStal-154
□ 62TopVen-183
□ 63ExhStaB-18
□ 63Fle-47
□ 63Jel-200
□ 63MetJayP-2
□ 63Pos-200
□ 63Top-197
□ 64Top-295
□ 64TopVen-295
□ 65RedEnq-6
□ 65Top-411
□ 66Top-543
□ 72PadPos-9
□ 74MetOriEB-3
□ 74OPC-31
□ 74Top-31
□ 76SSP-628
□ 77PadSchC-16
□ 78PadFamF-7
□ 78TCM60I-201
□ 79PadFamF-1
□ 79Top-479
□ 80MarExh-8
□ 81TCM60I-482
□ 82MetGal62-22
□ 83TigPos-9
□ 84TigTeal-12
□ 84TigWavP-12
□ 86GiaMot-1
□ 86GiaPos-7
□ 86Top-111
□ 86TopTif-111
□ 87GiaMot-1
□ 87GiaPos-7
□ 87Top-193
□ 87TopTif-193
□ 88DodRinP1-3B
□ 88GiaMot-1
□ 88GiaPos-7
□ 88Top-654
□ 88TopTif-654
□ 89GiaMot-1
□ 89PacLegI-145
□ 89Top-744
□ 89TopBasT-102
□ 89TopTif-744
□ 90DodTar-144
□ 90GiaMot-1
□ 90GiaSmo-5
□ 90K-M-33
□ 90OPC-351
□ 90Top-351
□ 90TopTif-351
□ 90TopTVA-66
□ 91GiaMot-1
□ 91GiaPacGaE-6
□ 91MetWIZ-87
□ 91OPC-579
□ 91Top-579
□ 91TopDesS-579
□ 91TopGloA-12
□ 91TopMic-579
□ 91TopTif-579
□ 92GiaMot-1
□ 92GiaPacGaE-14
□ 92OPC-109
□ 92Top-109
□ 92TopGol-109
□ 92TopGolW-109
□ 92TopMic-109
□ 95TopArcBD-111
□ 95TopArcBD-145
Craig, Tom
□ 82SyrChiT-25
□ 83SyrChiT-3
□ 84SyrChiT-3
Crain, Gregg
□ 91CedRapRC-29
Crall, Jim
□ 75AndRanT-18
Cram, Jerry
□ 71OPC-247
□ 71Top-247
□ 75TidTidTI-7
□ 76OmaRoyTT-5
□ 76SSP-559
□ 80OmaRoyP-7
□ 81OmaRoyT-2
□ 82OmaRoyT-26
□ 83OmaRoyT-25
□ 84OmaRoyT-13
□ 91MetWIZ-88
□ 98AshTouM-28
Cramer, Bill
□ 90RocExpLC-5
□ 90RocExpP-2698
□ 91WesPalBEC-15
□ 91WesPalBEP-1231
Cramer, Doc (Roger Maxwell)
□ 33ButCanV-8
□ 33RitCE-1C
□ 33WorCig-23
□ 34BatR31-53
□ 34DiaMatCSB-33
□ 34Gou-25
□ 34GouCanV-74
□ 35DiaMatCS3T1-38
□ 35GouPuzR-8J
□ 35GouPuzR-9J
□ 36GouWidPPR-B6
□ 38CloFotW-15
□ 39PlaBal-101
□ 40PlaBal-29
□ 72TCMthe3-11
□ 74A's192T-6
□ 77GalGloG-71
□ 79DiaGre-57
□ 81DiaStaCD-114
□ 81TigDetN-24
□ 82DiaCla-61
□ 83TCMPla1943-12
□ 89PacLegI-181
□ 92ConTSN-451
□ 93ConTSN-903
□ 94ConTSN-1154
□ 94ConTSNB-1154
Cramer, George
□ 35ExhFou-14
Cramer, Mike (Michael J.)
□ 75PhoGiaCK-26
Cramer, Rob
□ 86VisOakP-8
Crandall, Bob
□ 80ElmPioRST-33
Crandall, Del (Delmar W.)
□ 47Exh-52
□ 47StaPinP2-12
□ 50Bow-56
□ 50JJKCopP-3
□ 51Bow-20
□ 52Top-162
□ 53BraJohC-15
□ 53BraMer-6
□ 53BraSpiaS3-9
□ 53BraSpiaS7-5
□ 53Top-197
□ 54Bow-32
□ 54BraJohC-1
□ 54BraSpiaSP-7
□ 54RedMan-NL3
□ 54Top-12
□ 55ArmCoi-3
□ 55Bow-217
□ 55BraGolS-15
□ 55BraJohC-1
□ 55BraSpiaSD-7
□ 55RedMan-NL2
□ 56BraBilaBP-8
□ 56Top-175
□ 57Bra8x1-5
□ 57BraSpiaS4-8
□ 57Top-133
□ 58BraJayP-5
□ 58JayPubA-4
□ 58Top-351
□ 58Top-390
□ 59ArmCoi-7
□ 59Baz-8
□ 59Top-425
□ 59Top-567
□ 60ArmCoi-7
□ 60Baz-36
□ 60BraLaktL-9
□ 60BraSpiaS-7A
□ 60BraSpiaS-7B
□ 60KeyChal-12
□ 60MacSta-6
□ 60Top-170
□ 60Top-568
□ 60TopVen-170
□ 61Pos-110A
□ 61Pos-110B
□ 61Top-390
□ 61Top-583
□ 61TopDicG-2
□ 61TopStal-42
□ 62BraJayP-5
□ 62Top-351
□ 62Top-443
□ 62TopStal-147
□ 63BraJayP-4
□ 63Jel-153
□ 63Pos-153
□ 63SalMetC-11
□ 63Top-460
□ 64ChatheY-28
□ 64GiaJayP-2
□ 64Top-169
□ 64TopVen-169
□ 65OPC-68
□ 65Top-68
□ 66Top-339
□ 66TopVen-339
□ 73OPC-646
□ 73Top-646
□ 74Top-99
□ 75OPC-384
□ 75Top-384
□ 75TopMin-384
□ 78AtlCon-8
□ 78BraTCC-7
□ 78TCM60I-144
□ 79DiaGre-223
□ 79TCM50-68
□ 80AlbDukTc-23
□ 80Bra195T-25
□ 81AlbDukTc-25
□ 82AlbDukTc-24
□ 83AlbDukTc-23
□ 83Bra53F-1
□ 83TopRep5-162
□ 84Don-632
□ 84MarMot-1
□ 84Nes792-721
□ 84Top-721
□ 84TopTif-721
□ 86BraGreT-8
□ 88PacLegI-98
□ 89SweBasG-132
□ 91TopArc1-197
□ 92BazQua5A-4
□ 94TopArc1-12
□ 94TopArc1G-12
□ 96SanBerSB-1
□ 97SanBerS-1
Crandall, Doc (James Otis)
□ 09ColChiE-66
□ 09RamT20-32
□ 09T206-76
□ 09T206-77
□ 10CouT21-110
□ 10CouT21-111
□ 10DomDisP-28
□ 10NadE1-12
□ 10RedCroT-14
□ 10RedCroT-99
□ 10RedCroT-178
□ 10SweCapPP-109
□ 11HelSta-122
□ 11PinT-5-262
□ 11S74Sil-82
□ 11SpoLifCW-78
□ 11SpoLifM-206
□ 11T205-33
□ 12ColRedB-66
□ 12ColTinT-66
□ 12HasTriFT-48C
□ 12HasTriFT-74B
□ 12T207-37
□ 14CraJacE-67
□ 14PieStaT-27
□ 15CraJacE-67
□ 16Zee-27
□ 17Zee-5
□ 18Zee-4
□ 19Zee-4
□ 20Zee-5
□ 21Zee-5
□ 22Zee-3
□ 23Zee-3
□ 24Zee-5
□ 25Zee-2
□ 29Zee-107
□ 76ISCHooHA-17
Crandall, Ducky
□ 75LafDriT-29
Crandall, Karl
□ 17Zee-62
□ 18Zee-58
□ 19Zee-90
□ 20Zee-6
Crane, Cannonball (Edward N.)
□ 87OldJudN-100
□ 89SFHaCN-3
Crane, Gordy
□ 75SacSolC-18
Crane, John
□ 96BatCliTI-24
Crane, Rich
□ 89FreStaBS-7
□ 89GreFalDSP-3
□ 90BakDodCLC-235
Crane, Sam (Samuel Byren)
□ 22E120-137
□ 23Zee-158
□ 25Zee-133
□ 90DodTar-919
Crane, Sam (Samuel N.)
□ 87BucN28-109
□ 87OldJudN-101
Crane, Todd
□ 95BatCliTI-9
□ 96BatCliTI-3
□ 96PieBolWB-10
□ 97PieBolWB-8
□ 98ClePhiM-5
□ 98ClePhiUM-5
Cranford, Jay
□ 93AugPirC-6
□ 93AugPirF-1550
□ 94CarLeaAF-CAR38
□ 94SalBucC-6
□ 94SalBucF-2328
□ 95Bow-64
□ 95CarMudF-165
□ 96CarMudB-20
Cranford, Joey
□ 97ForMyeM-9
□ 98ForMyeMTI-9
Cranford, John
□ 92WelPirC-5
□ 92WelPirF-1329
Cranmer, Jim
□ 98SanAntMG-7
Cranston, William
□ 09T206-482
□ 10CouT21-14
Cravath, Gavvy (Clifford C.)
□ 09ColChiE-67
□ 09T206-414
□ 11PinT-5-761
□ 12ColRedB-67
□ 12ColTinT-67
□ 14CraJacE-82
□ 15CraJacE-82
□ 15SpoNewM-41
□ 16BF2FP-87
□ 16SpoNewM-40
□ 17ColE13-35
□ 17HolBreD-19
□ 19W514-11
□ 21Zee-93
□ 77PhiFav-16
□ 82TCMGreS-31
□ 83PhiPosGPaM-5
□ 91ConTSN-277
□ 93ConTSN-803
Craven, Britt
□ 91QuaCitAC-2
□ 91QuaCitAP-2619
Crawford, Carl
□ 99Bow-440
□ 99BowGol-440
□ 99BowInt-440
Crawford, Carlos
□ 91BurIndP-3293
□ 92ColRedC-6
□ 92ColRedF-2381
□ 93KinIndC-6
□ 93KinIndF-2238
□ 93KinIndTI-5
□ 94CanIndF-3110
□ 96PhiTeal-7
□ 96ScrRedBB-10
□ 97CarMudC-2
□ 98NasSouTI-9
□ 98NasSouTISS-9
Crawford, Glenn M.
□ 47RemBre-25
Crawford, Jack
□ 82DanSunF-8
□ 83PeoSunF-15
Crawford, Jerry
□ 88T/MUmp-28
□ 89T/MUmp-26
□ 90T/MUmp-25
Crawford, Jim
□ 74OPC-279
□ 74Top-279
□ 76DetTigP-3
□ 76OPC-428
□ 76SSP-47
□ 76Top-428
□ 76TopTra-428T
□ 77Top-69
□ 78TigTeal-6
□ 89GasRanP-1015
Crawford, Joe
□ 91KinMetC-16
□ 91KinMetP-3806
□ 92ColMetPI-39
□ 92ProFS7-290
□ 92St.LucMCB-5
□ 92St.LucMF-1739
□ 93St.LucMC-6
□ 93St.LuMF-2914
□ 94BinMetF-698
□ 94St.LucMC-5
□ 95BinMetTI-43
□ 96BinMetB-4
□ 96NorTidB-11
□ 97NorTid-9
□ 97NorTidB-9
Crawford, Johnny
□ 77ForLauYS-3
Crawford, Marty
□ 96BatCliTI-19
□ 97PieBolWB-9
Crawford, Pat (Clifford R.)
□ 33WorCig-24
□ 34DiaMatCSB-34
□ 74Car193T-3
□ 94ConTSN-1293
□ 94ConTSNB-1293
Crawford, Paxton
□ 96MicBatCB-10
□ 97SarRedS-6
□ 98TreThuM-10
□ 99SP TopP-32
□ 99SP TopPPE-32
Crawford, Rufus
□ 55Bow-121
Crawford, Sam (Samuel Earl)
□ 03WilCarE-8
□ 04FanCraAL-9
□ 07TigACDPP-3
□ 08RosComP-33
□ 09AmeCarE90-1-28
□ 09ColChiE-68
□ 09PhiCarE-7
□ 09SpoNewSM-31
□ 09T206-78
□ 09T206-79
□ 09TigHMTP-3
□ 09TigMorBBBP-5
□ 09TigMorPWBPP-3
□ 09TigTaCP-4
□ 09WolNewDTPP-4
□ 09WolNewDTPP-5
□ 10CouT21-112
□ 10CouT21-272
□ 10DarChoE-13
□ 10E-UOraBSC-8
□ 10E101-12
□ 10E102-6
□ 10MelMinE-12
□ 10NadCarE-14
□ 10NadE1-13
□ 10PeoT21-13
□ 10RedCroT-15
□ 10RedCroT-179
□ 10SepAnoP-9
□ 10W555-19
□ 11BasBatEU-14
□ 11E94-8
□ 11HelSta-29
□ 11MecDFT-11
□ 11PinT-5-156
□ 11SpoLifCW-79
□ 11SpoLifM-56
□ 11TurRedT-5
□ 12ColRedB-68
□ 12ColTinT-68
□ 12HasTriFT-5
□ 12HasTriFT-26
□ 12VasSwe-2
□ 13NatGamW-12
□ 13TomBarW-12
□ 14CraJacE-14
□ 14TexTomE-15
□ 15AmeCarE106-10
□ 15CraJacE-14
□ 15SpoNewM-42
□ 16BF2FP-28
□ 16SpoNewM-41
□ 16TanBraE-7
□ 17ColE13-36
□ 18Zee-5
□ 19W514-95
□ 20Zee-7
□ 21Zee-6
□ 53ArtHaloFP-23
□ 63GadFunC-40
□ 72ClaCar-37
□ 72FleFamF-27
□ 74CapPub-45
□ 75ShaPiz-9
□ 76ShaPiz-82
□ 77BobParHoF-17
□ 77GalGloG-140
□ 77GalGloG-267
□ 78DexHaloFP-7
□ 80PacLeg-55
□ 80PerHaloFP-82
□ 80SSPHOF-82

❑ 81ConTSN-98
❑ 81TigDetN-121
❑ 81TigSecNP-9
❑ 82DiaCla-27
❑ 85Woo-9
❑ 87ConSer2-30
❑ 87HygAllG-12
❑ 89HOFStiB-50
❑ 90BasWit-78
❑ 94ConTSN-1221
❑ 94ConTSNB-1221
❑ 96PitPosH-5
Crawford, Shag
❑ 89PacLegI-199
Crawford, Steve
❑ 82Don-564
❑ 82Fle-291
❑ 82RedSoxC-4
❑ 82Top-157
❑ 83PawRedST-4
❑ 83Top-419
❑ 84PawRedST-14
❑ 85Don-395
❑ 85Fle-156
❑ 85Top-661
❑ 85TopTif-661
❑ 86Don-416
❑ 86Fle-346
❑ 86Lea-193
❑ 86Top-91
❑ 86TopTif-91
❑ 87Don-399
❑ 87Fle-33
❑ 87FleGlo-33
❑ 87RedSoxP-7
❑ 87Top-589
❑ 87TopTif-589
❑ 88Fle-350
❑ 88FleGlo-350
❑ 88Sco-289
❑ 88ScoGlo-289
❑ 88Top-299
❑ 88TopTif-299
❑ 90Lea-494
❑ 90RoyPos-5
❑ 91Fle-554
❑ 91OPC-718
❑ 91RoyPol-5
❑ 91Sco-287
❑ 91Top-718
❑ 91TopDesS-718
❑ 91TopMic-718
❑ 91TopTif-718
❑ 92Sco-349
❑ 97SpoIndG-8
❑ 98WilBluRC-9
Crawford, Willie M.
❑ 65DodTeal-2
❑ 65Top-453
❑ 68Top-417
❑ 69Top-327
❑ 69TopTeaP-22
❑ 70Kel-26
❑ 70OPC-34
❑ 70Top-34
❑ 71Dod-4
❑ 71DodTic-4
❑ 71MLBOffS-100
❑ 71OPC-519
❑ 71Top-519
❑ 72Top-669
❑ 73LinPor-93
❑ 73OPC-639
❑ 73Top-639
❑ 74OPC-480
❑ 74Top-480
❑ 74TopSta-43
❑ 75OPC-186
❑ 75Top-186
❑ 75TopMin-186
❑ 76OPC-76
❑ 76SSP-84
❑ 76St.LouCP-3
❑ 76Top-76
❑ 77BurCheD-107
❑ 77Top-642
❑ 78TCM60I-157
❑ 78Top-507
❑ 85SpoIndGC-4
❑ 90DodTar-146
Crawfords, Pittsburgh
❑ 88NegLeaD-4
❑ 90PomBlaBNLP-2546
❑ 91PomBlaBPB-7
❑ 92NegLeaRLI-84
❑ 93NegLeaRL2-45
❑ 93NegLeaRL2-46
❑ 93NegLeaRL2-61
❑ 93NegLeaRL2-62
❑ 93NegLeaRL2-63
Creamer, Gerry
❑ 94SarRedSC-6
❑ 94SarRedSF-1942
Creamer, Robert
❑ 90LitSunW-14
Crede, Brad
❑ 96BatCliTI-26
❑ 97PieBolWB-10
❑ 97SouAtlTPB-27
Crede, Joe
❑ 97HicCraB-9
❑ 97HicCraRB-10
❑ 97SouAtlTPB-22
❑ 98CarLeaTPQ-17
❑ 98WinWar-10
❑ 99BasAmeTP-26
❑ 99BasAmeTPG-26
❑ 99BasAmeTPLM-2
❑ 99SP TopP-33
❑ 99SP TopPPE-33
❑ 99TopBlaLC1-62
❑ 99TopBlaLC2-62
❑ 99TopBlaLC3-62
❑ 99TopGolL-62
❑ 99TopGolLC1-62
❑ 99TopGolLC2-62
❑ 99TopGolLOtO-62
❑ 99TopRedLC1-62
❑ 99TopRedLC2-62
❑ 99TopRedLC3-62
Credeur, Todd
❑ 85AncGlaPTI-7
❑ 86AshTouP-6
❑ 87OscAstP-28
❑ 88OscAstS-6
❑ 89ColMudB-26
❑ 89OscAstS-5
❑ 90ColMudB-17
❑ 90ColMudP-1342
❑ 90ColMudS-9
Cree, Birdie (William F.)
❑ 09T206-80
❑ 10CouT21-15
❑ 10CouT21-113
❑ 10DomDisP-29
❑ 10RedCroT-16
❑ 10RedCroT-100
❑ 10RedCroT-180
❑ 10SweCapPP-33
❑ 11HelSta-41
❑ 11PinT-5-808
❑ 11SpoLifM-76
❑ 12HasTriFT-27
❑ 14TexTomE-16
❑ 15VicT21-5
Creech, Ed
❑ 90GatCitPSP-24
❑ 91JamExpC-28
❑ 91JamExpP-3561
Creed, Bennett
❑ 90MiaMirIS-30
Creek, Doug
❑ 91HamRedP-4031
❑ 93ArkTraF-2807
❑ 94Bow-3
❑ 94LouRedF-2976
❑ 95ArkTraTI-8
❑ 96FleUpd-U203
❑ 96FleUpdTC-U203
❑ 96GiaMot-17
❑ 96LeaSigEA-38
❑ 96Ult-565
❑ 96UltGolM-565
❑ 97PacPriGotD-GD215
❑ 97PhoFirTI-5
Creek, Ryan
❑ 94QuaCitRBC-7
❑ 94QuaCitRBF-527
❑ 95JacGenTI-1
❑ 96JacGenB-7
❑ 97JacGen-5
❑ 97JacGenS-2
Creekmore, Niles
❑ 87SalLakTTT-17
Creel, Keith
❑ 82OmaRoyT-3
❑ 83Don-574
❑ 83OmaRoyT-5
❑ 83RoyPos-10
❑ 84Fle-346
❑ 84OmaRoyT-15
❑ 85MaiGuiT-6
❑ 86IndTeal-18
❑ 86MaiGuiP-7
❑ 87OklCit8P-7
❑ 93RanKee-115
Creger, Bernie (Bernard Odell)
❑ 47TipTop-152
Creighton, James
❑ 94OriofB-17
Crema, Pat
❑ 92MedHatBJF-3204
❑ 92MedHatBJSP-4
Cremer, Rick
❑ 98GreBatM-4
❑ 98SouAtlLPM-6
Crenshaw, Ken
❑ 89PriPirS-28
Crespi, Creepy (Frank A.)
❑ 41CarW75-6
❑ 41DouPlaR-145
❑ 79DiaGre-159
❑ 83Car194T-20
Crespi, Dell
❑ 19Zee-91
Crespo, Cesar
❑ 98CapCitBF5-21
❑ 98CapCitBM-21
❑ 98SouAtlLPM-7
❑ 99BasAmeTP-27
❑ 99BasAmeTPG-27
Crespo, Felipe
❑ 91MedHatBJP-4106
❑ 91MedHatBJSP-22
❑ 92Bow-77
❑ 92MyrBeaHC-19
❑ 92MyrBeaHF-2202
❑ 93ClaFS7-274
❑ 93DunBluJC-6
❑ 93DunBluJF-1803
❑ 93DunBluJFFN-6
❑ 93FloStaLAF-8
❑ 94ClaGolF-55
❑ 94KnoSmoF-1309
❑ 95SPML-162
❑ 95SyrChiTI-11
❑ 96BluJayOH-7
❑ 96Bow-305
❑ 96BowFoi-305
❑ 96Fin-B217
❑ 96FinRef-B217
❑ 96Fla-182
❑ 96FleUpd-U95
❑ 96FleUpdTC-U95
❑ 96LeaSigA-52
❑ 96LeaSigAG-52
❑ 96LeaSigAS-52
❑ 96PinAfi-175
❑ 96PinAfiAP-175
❑ 96Sel-187
❑ 96SelArtP-187
❑ 96SelCer-130
❑ 96SelCerAP-130
❑ 96SelCerCB-130
❑ 96SelCerCR-130
❑ 96SelCerMB-130
❑ 96SelCerMG-130
❑ 96SelCerMR-130
❑ 96Sum-182
❑ 96SumAbo&B-182
❑ 96SumArtP-182
❑ 96SumFoi-182
❑ 96SyrChiTI-10
❑ 96Ult-428
❑ 96UltGolM-428
❑ 97BluJayOH-7
❑ 97BluJayS-55
❑ 97Fle-507
❑ 97FleTif-507
❑ 97Pac-217
❑ 97PacLigB-217
❑ 97PacSil-217
❑ 97Sco-426
❑ 97ScoArtPWB-426
❑ 97ScoResC-426
❑ 97ScoShoS-426
❑ 97ScoShoSAP-426
❑ 97SyrSkyCB-7
❑ 97Top-203
❑ 97UppDec-275
❑ 98Pac-216
❑ 98PacOnl-756
❑ 98PacOnlR-756
❑ 98PacOnlWC-756
❑ 98PacPlaB-216
❑ 98PacRedT-216
❑ 98PacSil-216
❑ 99Pac-437
❑ 99PacCroC-293
❑ 99PacCroCPB-293
❑ 99PacPlaB-437
❑ 99PacRed-437
Crespo, Michael
❑ 91ButCopKSP-7
❑ 91GasRanC-14
❑ 91GasRanP-2691
❑ 92GasRanC-3
❑ 92GasRanF-2255
❑ 93ChaRanC-5
❑ 93ChaRanF-1943
Cress, Missy
❑ 95ColSilB-7
❑ 96ColSilB-7
Cress, Robert
❑ 17Zee-63
Cresse, Mark
❑ 81Dod-6
❑ 81DodPol-NNO
❑ 83DodPol-NNO
❑ 84DodPol-NNO
❑ 85DodCokP-8
❑ 86DodCokP-7
❑ 86DodPol-NNO
❑ 87DodMot-27
❑ 87DodPol-29
❑ 88DodMot-28
❑ 89DodMot-27
❑ 89DodPol-1
❑ 90DodMot-28
❑ 90DodPol-NNO
❑ 91DodMot-28
❑ 91DodPho-3
❑ 91DodPol-NNO
❑ 92DodMot-28
❑ 92DodPol-NNO
❑ 93DodMot-28
❑ 93DodPol-30
❑ 94DodMot-28
❑ 94DodPol-30
❑ 95DodMot-28
❑ 95DodPol-30
❑ 96DodMot-28
❑ 96DodPol-8
❑ 97DodMot-28
❑ 97DodPol-30
❑ 98DodPol-30
Cressend, Jack
❑ 97SarRedS-7
❑ 98TreThuM-11
❑ 99Bow-103
❑ 99BowChr-103
❑ 99BowChrG-103
❑ 99BowChrGR-103
❑ 99BowChrI-103
❑ 99BowChrIR-103
❑ 99BowChrR-103
❑ 99BowGol-103
❑ 99BowInt-103
❑ 99Top-429
❑ 99TopChr-429
❑ 99TopChrR-429
❑ 99TopMVPP-429
Crew, Ken
❑ 86MemChiSTOS-2
❑ 86MemChiTOS-2
❑ 87MemChiB-8
❑ 87MemChiP-20
❑ 88ColAstB-6
Crews, Jason
❑ 96AriBlaDB-13
❑ 97SouBenSH-11
❑ 98HigDesMG-8
Crews, Larry
❑ 82CliGiaF-19
❑ 84ShrCapFB-5
❑ 85PhoGiaC-178
Crews, Tim
❑ 81BurBeeT-10
❑ 83ElPasDT-17
❑ 84ElPasDT-10
❑ 86ElPasDP-7
❑ 87AlbDukD-8
❑ 88AlbDukCm-8
❑ 88AlbDukP-264
❑ 88DodPol-27
❑ 88Don-464
❑ 88DonRoo-20
❑ 88Fle-511
❑ 88FleGlo-511
❑ 88Sco-641
❑ 88ScoGlo-641
❑ 88Spo-224
❑ 88Top-57
❑ 88TopTif-57
❑ 89DodMot-24
❑ 89DodPol-27
❑ 89DodStaSV-2
❑ 89Don-486
❑ 89PanSti-96
❑ 89Sco-505
❑ 89Top-22
❑ 89TopTif-22
❑ 89UppDec-611
❑ 90DodMot-26
❑ 90DodPol-52
❑ 90DodTar-147
❑ 90Don-550
❑ 90El PasDAGTI-29
❑ 90Fle-390
❑ 90FleCan-390
❑ 90OPC-551
❑ 90Sco-164
❑ 90Top-551
❑ 90TopTif-551
❑ 90UppDec-670
❑ 91DodMot-26
❑ 91DodPol-52
❑ 91Don-294
❑ 91Fle-197
❑ 91Lea-141
❑ 91OPC-737
❑ 91Sco-302
❑ 91StaClu-375
❑ 91Top-737
❑ 91TopDesS-737
❑ 91TopMic-737
❑ 91TopTif-737
❑ 91UltUpd-87
❑ 91UppDec-596
❑ 92DodMot-13
❑ 92DodPol-52
❑ 92DodSmo-5692
❑ 92Don-437
❑ 92Fle-452
❑ 92OPC-642
❑ 92Sco-238
❑ 92StaClu-349
❑ 92Top-642
❑ 92TopGol-642
❑ 92TopGolW-642
❑ 92TopMic-642
❑ 92Ult-502
❑ 92UppDec-687
❑ 93Fle-444
❑ 93Pin-554
Cribb, Buddy
❑ 89AlaGol-19
Crider, Jerry
❑ 69Top-491A
❑ 69Top-491B
❑ 71OPC-113
❑ 71Top-113
Cridland, Mark
❑ 98BelSnaM-10
Criger, Elmer
❑ 09ObaT21-81
❑ 09ObaT21-256
❑ 11Zee-6
❑ 12ObaPreT-5
Criger, Louis
❑ 03BreE10-26
❑ 04FanCraAL-10
❑ 04RedSoxUP-2
❑ 09AmeCarE90-1-29
❑ 09PC7HHB-10
❑ 09RamT20-33
❑ 09SpoNewSM-2
❑ 09T206-81
❑ 10E-UOraBSC-9
❑ 11BasBatEU-15
❑ 11SpoLifCW-80
❑ 11SpoLifM-77
❑ 11T205-34
❑ 11TurRedT-89
❑ 67SpoHobFC-8
Crills, Brad
❑ 94BluOriC-5
❑ 94BluOriF-3554
❑ 96HigDesMB-8
Crim, Chuck
❑ 83BelBreFr-22
❑ 84ElPasDT-6
❑ 85VanCanC-220
❑ 86VanCanP-8
❑ 87BrePol-32
❑ 87DonRoo-18
❑ 87FleUpd-19
❑ 87FleUpdG-19
❑ 87TopTra-25T
❑ 87TopTraT-25T
❑ 88BrePol-32
❑ 88BreTeal-9
❑ 88Don-355
❑ 88Fle-162
❑ 88FleGlo-162
❑ 88Sco-402
❑ 88ScoGlo-402
❑ 88StaLinBre-5
❑ 88Top-286
❑ 88TopTif-286
❑ 89Bow-136
❑ 89BowTif-136
❑ 89BrePol-32
❑ 89BreYea-32
❑ 89Don-617
❑ 89DonBasB-127
❑ 89Fle-183
❑ 89FleGlo-183
❑ 89OPC-99
❑ 89Sco-272
❑ 89Top-466
❑ 89TopTif-466
❑ 89UppDec-501
❑ 90BreMilB-3
❑ 90BrePol-32
❑ 90Don-221
❑ 90El PasDAGTI-7
❑ 90Fle-319
❑ 90FleCan-319
❑ 90Lea-58
❑ 90OPC-768
❑ 90PanSti-103
❑ 90PubIntS-493
❑ 90Sco-108
❑ 90Top-768
❑ 90TopTif-768
❑ 90UppDec-511
❑ 91Bow-51
❑ 91BreMilB-6
❑ 91BrePol-6
❑ 91Don-684
❑ 91Fle-579
❑ 91Lea-28
❑ 91OPC-644
❑ 91Sco-99
❑ 91StaClu-112
❑ 91Top-644
❑ 91TopDesS-644
❑ 91TopMic-644
❑ 91TopTif-644
❑ 91Ult-173
❑ 91UppDec-391
❑ 92Don-103
❑ 92Fle-175
❑ 92Lea-312
❑ 92LeaBlaG-312
❑ 92OPC-169
❑ 92Sco-22
❑ 92ScoProP-6
❑ 92ScoRoo-53T
❑ 92StaClu-823
❑ 92Top-169
❑ 92TopGol-169
❑ 92TopGolW-169
❑ 92TopMic-169
❑ 92UppDec-496
❑ 93AngMot-20
❑ 93AngStaCl-2
❑ 93Don-649
❑ 93Fle-570
❑ 93PacSpa-365
❑ 93Sco-455
❑ 93StaClu-327
❑ 93StaCluFDI-327
❑ 93StaCluMOP-327
❑ 93Top-499
❑ 93TopGol-499
❑ 93TopInaM-499
❑ 93TopInaR-499
❑ 93TopMic-499
❑ 94BreMilB-305
❑ 94FleUpd-108
❑ 95Fle-412
Crimian, Jack
❑ 53CarHunW-6
❑ 56A'sPos-11
❑ 56Top-319
❑ 57Top-297
Criminger, John
❑ 92BelBreFI-398
❑ 93StoPorC-7
❑ 93StoPorF-737
Crimmins, John

❑ 92ElmPioC-8
❑ 92ElmPioF-1384
Cripe, Dave (David Gordon)
❑ 76OmaRoyTT-6
❑ 83DayBeaAT-1
❑ 85OscAstTI-1
❑ 86ColAstP-8
Cripps, Bobby
❑ 96GreFalDB-8
❑ 96GreFalDTI-17
❑ 97GreFalDTI-7
❑ 98HagSunM-11
❑ 99SP TopP-34
❑ 99SP TopPPE-34
Criscione, Dave G.
❑ 74SpoIndC-33
❑ 75SpoIndC-12
❑ 76SacSolC-1
❑ 77RocRedWM-1
❑ 78RocRedWT-6
❑ 91OriCro-88
Criscola, Tony (Anthony P.)
❑ 47CenFlo-5
Crisler, Joel
❑ 77QuaCitAT-13
❑ 79SalLakCGT-15
❑ 80ElPasDT-11
Crisler, Thomas
❑ 81RedPioT-3
Crisp, Joe (Joseph Shelby)
❑ 13Zee-30
Crispin, Carlos
❑ 93AubAstC-5
❑ 93AubAstF-3451
Criss, Brian
❑ 97UCLBruTI-30
Criss, Dode
❑ 09ColChiE-69
❑ 09PC7HHB-9
❑ 09T206-82
❑ 11PinT-5-110
❑ 11SpoLifCW-81
❑ 11SpoLifM-107
❑ 12ColRedB-69
❑ 12ColTinT-69
❑ 67SpoHobFC-40
Criss, Matt
❑ 90WicStaSGD-8
Crist, Clark
❑ 81LynSaiT-28
❑ 81WauTimT-21
❑ 82LynSaiT-10
❑ 84ChaLooT-6
❑ 91AubAstC-24
❑ 91AubAstP-4291
❑ 92AubAstC-28
❑ 92AubAstF-1372
Crist, Jack
❑ 71RicBraTI-5
Cristelli, Pat
❑ 76SalLakCGC-10
❑ 77SalLakCGC-10
❑ 78SalLakCGC-10
Cristopher, Carlos
❑ 93BenRocCB-6
❑ 93BenRocF-3276
Criswell, Brian
❑ 85MadMusP-6
❑ 85MadMusT-9
❑ 86MadMusP-6
❑ 86MadMusP-6
❑ 87HunStaTI-8
❑ 88HunStaTI-3
Criswell, Tim
❑ 86DurBulP-6
❑ 87DurBulP-7
Critz, Hughie (Hugh Melville)
❑ 20WalMaiW-10
❑ 25Exh-26
❑ 26Exh-26
❑ 28Exh-13
❑ 28StaPlaCE-14
❑ 28W56PlaC-H2
❑ 29ExhFou-7
❑ 29PorandAR-14
❑ 30SchR33-46
❑ 31Exh-9
❑ 31W517-25
❑ 33ExhFou-5
❑ 33Gou-3
❑ 33Gou-238
❑ 33GouCanV-3
❑ 33RitCE-6C
❑ 33WorCig-25
❑ 34DiaMatCSB-35
❑ 34Gou-17
❑ 34GouCanV-72
❑ 35DiaMatCS3T1-39
❑ 35ExhFou-5
❑ 35GouPuzR-4A
❑ 35GouPuzR-7A
❑ 35GouPuzR-12A
❑ 61Fle-101
❑ 76RedParC-8
❑ 87ConSer2-10
❑ 88ConSer5-6
❑ 91ConTSN-290
Crnich, Jeff
❑ 89BelMarL-36
Croak, David
❑ 90MarPhiP-3188
Crockett, Claude
❑ 77St.PetCT-18
Crockett, J. W.
❑ 25Zee-106
❑ 26Zee-133
Crockett, Rusty
❑ 88PeoChiTI-9
❑ 89WinSpiS-6
❑ 90ChaKniTI-21
❑ 90TopTVCu-41
❑ 91ChaKniLD-130
❑ 91ChaKniP-1696
❑ 91LinDriAA-130
❑ 92ChaKniF-2777
❑ 92ChaKniS-151
Crofford, Kenny
❑ 93QuaCitRBC-28
❑ 94QuaCitRBC-28
Croft, Paul
❑ 78WisRapTT-2
❑ 90HagSunDGB-6
Crogan, Jack
❑ 87OldJudN-102
Croghan, Andy
❑ 89AlaGol-10
❑ 91OneYanP-4147
❑ 92GreHorC-5
❑ 92GreHorF-771
❑ 93PriWilCC-5
❑ 93PriWilCF-648
❑ 94AlbYanF-1433
❑ 95Exc-92
❑ 97NorNav-12
❑ 97NorNavTI-6
Croll, Ralph
❑ 18Zee-20
❑ 19Zee-17
Cromartie, Warren L.
❑ 76VenLeaS-86
❑ 77ExpPos-10
❑ 78OPC-117
❑ 78Top-468
❑ 79ExpPos-6
❑ 79OPC-32
❑ 79Top-76
❑ 80ExpPos-7
❑ 80OPC-102
❑ 80Top-180
❑ 81AllGamPI-140
❑ 81Don-332
❑ 81Fle-144
❑ 81FleStiC-92
❑ 81OPC-345
❑ 81OPCPos-5
❑ 81Top-345
❑ 81TopScr-78
❑ 81TopSti-188
❑ 82Don-340
❑ 82ExpHygM-4
❑ 82ExpPos-6
❑ 82ExpPos-7
❑ 82ExpZel-7
❑ 82ExpZel-18
❑ 82FBIDis-6
❑ 82Fle-186
❑ 82FleSta-33
❑ 82OPC-61
❑ 82OPC-94
❑ 82OPCPos-13
❑ 82Top-526
❑ 82Top-695
❑ 82TopSti-60
❑ 83AllGamPI-139
❑ 83Don-466
❑ 83ExpPos-5
❑ 83ExpStu-18
❑ 83Fle-279
❑ 83FleSta-44
❑ 83FleSti-261
❑ 83OPC-351
❑ 83Top-495
❑ 84Fle-272
❑ 84Nes792-287
❑ 84OPC-287
❑ 84Top-287
❑ 84TopTif-287
❑ 87JapPlaB-27
❑ 91Bow-315
❑ 91FleUpd-25
❑ 91Lea-458
❑ 91Stu-64
❑ 92Sco-637
❑ 93ExpDonM-14
❑ 93UppDecS-27
Crombie, Kevin
❑ 92NiaFalRC-19
❑ 92NiaFalRF-3316
❑ 93FayGenC-8
❑ 93FayGenF-124
Cromer, Brandon
❑ 92ClaDraP-25
❑ 92ClaFS7-416
❑ 92FroRowDP-36
❑ 92FroRowDPG-36
❑ 92FroRowDPS-36
❑ 92UppDecML-18
❑ 93ClaGolF-173
❑ 93St.CatBJC-6
❑ 93St.CatBJF-3979
❑ 93StaCluM-190
❑ 94HagSunC-4
❑ 94HagSunF-2737
❑ 95DunBluJTI-5
❑ 96KnoSmoB-10
❑ 98PorSeaDQ-16
Cromer, Burke
❑ 92IdaFalGF-3504
❑ 92IdaFalGSP-21
❑ 93DanBraC-11
❑ 93DanBraF-3613
Cromer, D.T.
❑ 92SouOreAC-7
❑ 92SouOreAF-3431
❑ 93MadMusC-7
❑ 93MadMusF-1834
❑ 94WesMicWC-6
❑ 94WesMicWF-2308
❑ 95ModA'sTI-5
❑ 96ModA'sB-7
❑ 97BesLimA-8
❑ 97Bow-177
❑ 97BowChr-169
❑ 97BowChrI-169
❑ 97BowChrIR-169
❑ 97BowChrR-169
❑ 97BowInt-177
❑ 97HunStaTI-6
❑ 97TexAllM-11
❑ 98BesPreA-8
❑ 99WesMicWAM-7
Cromer, Tripp
❑ 89HamRedS-10
❑ 90St.PetCS-3
❑ 91St.PetCC-19
❑ 91St.PetCP-2282
❑ 92ArkTraF-1135
❑ 92ArkTraS-31
❑ 92SkyAA F-15
❑ 93Bow-52
❑ 93LouRedF-220
❑ 93TriAAAGF-22
❑ 94Cla-56
❑ 94Don-419
❑ 94FleMajLP-7
❑ 94LouRedF-2986
❑ 94Pac-588
❑ 94Pin-425
❑ 94PinArtP-425
❑ 94PinMusC-425
❑ 94StaCluT-328
❑ 94StaCluTFDI-328
❑ 94Top-139
❑ 94TopGol-139
❑ 94TopSpa-139
❑ 94UppDec-113
❑ 94UppDecED-113
❑ 95FleUpd-156
❑ 95StaClu-602
❑ 95StaCluMOP-602
❑ 95StaCluSTWS-602
❑ 96ColCho-287
❑ 96ColChoGS-287
❑ 96ColChoSS-287
❑ 96Don-153
❑ 96DonPreP-153
❑ 96Fle-541
❑ 96FleTif-541
❑ 96LouRedB-13
❑ 96Pac-223
❑ 96Top-41
❑ 96Ult-272
❑ 96UltGolM-272
❑ 97AlbDukGS-6
❑ 98DodMot-27
❑ 98DodPol-4
❑ 98PacInvGems-169
❑ 99DodPol-6
Crompton, Herb (Herbert B.)
❑ 52LavPro-80
Cromwell, Brian
❑ 94DavLipB-6
❑ 95DavLipB-7
Cromwell, Nate
❑ 88MyrBeaBJP-1174
❑ 89DunBluJS-3
❑ 90CMC-816
❑ 90KnoBluJB-27
❑ 90KnoBluJP-1238
❑ 90KnoBluJS-2
❑ 91Cla/Bes-91
❑ 91KnoBluJLD-353
❑ 91KnoBluJP-1760
❑ 91LinDriAA-353
❑ 92KnoBluJF-2983
❑ 92KnoBluJS-379
❑ 93KnoSmoF-1244
❑ 93WicWraF-2971
❑ 94WicWraF-183
Cron, Chris
❑ 86DurBulP-7
❑ 87QuaCitAP-23
❑ 88CalLeaACLC-34
❑ 88PalSprACLC-102
❑ 88PalSprAP-1441
❑ 89MidAngGS-11
❑ 89TexLeaAGS-2
❑ 90CMC-498
❑ 90EdmTraC-21
❑ 90EdmTraP-523
❑ 90ProAAAF-99
❑ 91EdmTraLD-158
❑ 91EdmTraP-1521
❑ 91LinDriAAA-158
❑ 92Cla1-T29
❑ 92Don-698
❑ 92Fle-656
❑ 92Sco-847
❑ 92SkyAAAF-281
❑ 92TopDeb91-41
❑ 92VanCanF-2728
❑ 92VanCanS-632
❑ 93Fle-581
❑ 93NasSouF-575
❑ 94ChaKniF-900
❑ 96HicCraB-28
❑ 97HicCraB-1
❑ 97HicCraRB-1
❑ 98CarLeaAC-14
❑ 98WinWar-1
Crone, Bill
❑ 81LynSaiT-16
❑ 82LynSaiT-11
❑ 83SalLakCGT-18
❑ 84SalLakCGC-172
❑ 85CalCanC-93
❑ 86CalCanP-5
❑ 87TucTorP-4
Crone, Ray H.
❑ 54BraJohC-20
❑ 54BraSpiaSP-8
❑ 54Top-206
❑ 55BraGolS-14
❑ 55BraJohC-12
❑ 55Top-149
❑ 56Top-76
❑ 57BraSpiaS4-9
❑ 57Top-68
❑ 58GiaArmT-3
❑ 58GiaSFCB-6
❑ 58Top-272
❑ 80Bra195T-8
❑ 85NewOriT-18
❑ 94TopArc1-206
❑ 94TopArc1G-206
Cronin, Bill (William P.)
❑ 33Zee-7
❑ 37Zee-46
Cronin, Chuck
❑ 47SunBre-4
Cronin, James John
❑ 29Zee-87
❑ 30Zee-104
❑ 32Zee-82
❑ 90DodTar-148
❑ 94ConTSN-1158
❑ 94ConTSNB-1158
Cronin, Jeff
❑ 91DurBulC-5
❑ 91DurBulP-1538
Cronin, Joe (Joseph Edward)
❑ 30SchR33-37
❑ 30UncJac-6
❑ 31Exh-31
❑ 31SenTeaIPW-6
❑ 32USCar*-7
❑ 33ButCanV-9
❑ 33ButCre-5
❑ 33DouDisP-11
❑ 33GeoCMil-7
❑ 33Gou-63
❑ 33Gou-109
❑ 33Gou-189
❑ 33GouCanV-63
❑ 33RitCE-7H
❑ 33TatOrbSDR-176
❑ 33WorCig-26
❑ 34BabRutG-12
❑ 34BatR31-32
❑ 34BatR31-183
❑ 34ButPreR-12
❑ 34ExhFou-16
❑ 35AlDemDCR3-64
❑ 35ExhFou-9
❑ 35GouPuzR-6E
❑ 35GouPuzR-11G
❑ 35GouPuzR-13E
❑ 35GouPuzR-15E
❑ 36ExhFou-9
❑ 36GouWidPPR-A20
❑ 36GouWidPPR-B7
❑ 36NatChiFPR-21
❑ 36R31PasP-32
❑ 36R31Pre-G4
❑ 36SandSW-8
❑ 36WorWidGV-46
❑ 37ExhFou-9
❑ 37OPCBatUV-124
❑ 38CloFotW-16
❑ 38ExhFou-9
❑ 38OurNatGPP-3
❑ 39GouPreR303A-9
❑ 39GouPreR303B-4
❑ 39WorWidGTP-9
❑ 40PlaBal-134
❑ 40WheM4-7A
❑ 40WheM4-7B
❑ 41DouPlaR-59
❑ 41DouPlaR-81
❑ 41PlaBal-15
❑ 42RedSoxTI-7
❑ 43MPR302-1-6
❑ 43RedSoxTI-4
❑ 46RedSoxTI-4
❑ 47RedSoxTI-1
❑ 53ArtHaloFP-24
❑ 59FleWil-39
❑ 59FleWil-55
❑ 60SenUniMC-3
❑ 61GolPre-14
❑ 63HalofFB-3
❑ 67TopVen-164
❑ 72TCMthe1-179
❑ 72TCMthe3-12
❑ 73HalofFPP-4
❑ 75RedSox1T-7
❑ 75ShaPiz-6
❑ 76RowExh-16
❑ 76ShaPiz-80
❑ 77BobParHoF-84
❑ 77GalGloG-65
❑ 77GalGloG-198
❑ 79RedSoxEF-6
❑ 79RedSoxEF-24
❑ 80PacLeg-39
❑ 80PerHaloFP-80
❑ 80SSPHOF-80
❑ 81ConTSN-65
❑ 81SanDieSC-19
❑ 82DiaCla-51
❑ 82TCMGreH-40
❑ 83BigLeaCOA-14
❑ 83ConMar-14
❑ 83DonHOFH-20
❑ 85BigLeaC3-5
❑ 86ConSer1-9
❑ 86RedSoxGT-6
❑ 86SpoDecG-7
❑ 87HygAllG-13
❑ 87RedSox1T-1
❑ 88ConAmeA-6
❑ 89CMCMan-8
❑ 89HOFStiB-19
❑ 89PacLegI-167
❑ 91ConTSN-50
❑ 91ConTSN-314
❑ 92ConTSN-600
❑ 93ConTSN-676
❑ 93ConTSN-843
❑ 93DiaStaES-123
❑ 94ConTSN-1085
❑ 94ConTSNB-1085
Cronin, John J.
❑ 11SpoLifCW-82
Cronin, Pete
❑ 61SeaPop-4
Cronin, Shane
❑ 97CliLumG-4
❑ 98CliLumG-4
Cronk, Doug
❑ 89GasRanP-1013
❑ 89GasRanS-5
❑ 89SouAtlLAGS-29
❑ 89Sta-135
❑ 90ChaRanS-5
Cronkright, Dan
❑ 86PenWhiSP-7
Cronkright, Dave
❑ 87DayBeaAP-24
Crooks, John Charles
❑ 87OldJudN-103
Crosby, Bubba
❑ 99BasAmeTP-28
❑ 99BasAmeTPG-28
❑ 99Bow-408
❑ 99BowGol-408
❑ 99BowInt-408
❑ 99TeaBesR-15
❑ 99TeaBesRFS-11
❑ 99TeaBesRG-15
❑ 99TeaBesRS-15
Crosby, Ed (Edward C.)
❑ 70CarTeal-9
❑ 71CarTeal-13
❑ 71OPC-672
❑ 71Top-672
❑ 72CarTeal-6
❑ 73OPC-599
❑ 73Top-599
❑ 75CleIndP-9
❑ 76OPC-457
❑ 76SSP-520
❑ 76Top-457
❑ 76TulOilGP-9
❑ 78SanJosMMC-5
❑ 79SpoIndT-1
Crosby, Ken
❑ 75TulOil7-6
❑ 76OPC-593
❑ 76SSP-602
❑ 76Top-593
Crosby, Mike
❑ 92ColRedC-9
❑ 92ColRedF-2393
❑ 93Bow-177
❑ 93KinIndC-7
❑ 93KinIndF-2250
❑ 93KinIndTI-6
❑ 94CanIndF-3120
Crosby, Pat
❑ 86LitFalMP-7
Crosby, Todd
❑ 87SpaPhiP-15
❑ 88ClePhiS-9
❑ 89St.PetCS-9
❑ 89Sta-49
❑ 90CMC-124
❑ 90LouRedBC-24
❑ 90LouRedBLBC-14
❑ 90LouRedBP-408
❑ 90ProAAAF-522
❑ 90TopTVCa-44
❑ 91LinDriAAA-232
❑ 91LouRedLD-232
❑ 91LouRedP-2922
❑ 91LouRedTI-18
❑ 92ShrCapF-3879
❑ 92ShrCapS-580

Crosby, W. L.
❑ 25Zee-39
Crosetti, Frankie (Frank P.)
❑ 28Zee-129
❑ 29Zee-127
❑ 30Zee-139
❑ 31Zee-100
❑ 33Gou-217
❑ 33WorCig-27
❑ 34BatR31-182
❑ 34DiaStaR-86
❑ 35AlDemDCR3-7
❑ 36GouBWR-9
❑ 36GouWidPPR-A21
❑ 36NatChiFPR-22
❑ 36NatChiFPR-107
❑ 36R31Pre-L12
❑ 36SandSW-9
❑ 36WorWidGV-91
❑ 38OurNatGPP-4
❑ 39GouPreR303A-10
❑ 39WorWidGTP-10
❑ 39WorWidGV-6
❑ 41DouPlaR-113
❑ 43YanSta-7
❑ 47TipTop-50
❑ 47YanTeaT-7
❑ 48BluTin-24
❑ 48YanTeal-5
❑ 49YanTeal-6
❑ 50YanTeal-7
❑ 51R42SmaS-17
❑ 52Bow-252
❑ 52Top-384
❑ 53Dor-136
❑ 60Top-465
❑ 61Yan61RL-33
❑ 68Baz-13
❑ 69PilPos-21
❑ 70TwiTeal-3
❑ 75YanDyn1T-9
❑ 75YanDyn1T-51
❑ 75YanDyn1T-52
❑ 77PilPosR-21
❑ 81TCM60I-481
❑ 83Pil69G-20
❑ 83TCMPla1943-2
❑ 83TopRep5-384
❑ 83Yan196-NNO
❑ 88ConSer3-8
❑ 90PacLeg-19
❑ 90SweBasG-48
❑ 91SweBasG-20
❑ 92ActPacA-45
❑ 92YanWIZA-14
❑ 93UppDecAH-35
❑ 94UppDecAH-37
❑ 94UppDecAH1-37
Crosnoe, Cory
❑ 91PulBraC-6
❑ 91PulBraP-4012
❑ 92MacBraC-11
❑ 92MacBraF-272
Cross, Adam
❑ 95DanBraTI-7
❑ 96EugEmeB-6
❑ 97CliLumG-5
Cross, Bob
❑ 79NewCoPT-16
Cross, Jeff (Joffre)
❑ 46SeaSLP-11
❑ 47TipTop-153
❑ 83Car194T-2
Cross, Jesse
❑ 89MyrBeaBJP-1474
❑ 90DunBluJS-6
❑ 90FloStaLAS-27
❑ 90StaFS7-63
❑ 91KnoBluJLD-354
❑ 91KnoBluJP-1761
❑ 91LinDriAA-354
❑ 92KnoBluJF-2984
❑ 92SyrChiS-503
❑ 93SyrChiF-994
❑ 94ExcFS7-142
❑ 94SyrChiF-966
❑ 94SyrChiTI-8
Cross, Lave (LaFayette N.)
❑ 03BreE10-27
❑ 04FanCraAL-11
❑ 11SpoLifCW-83
❑ 87OldJudN-104
❑ 90DodTar-149
❑ 95May-6
❑ 98CamPepP-16
Cross, Mike
❑ 92FreKeyC-4
Cross, Monte (Montford M.)
❑ 03BreE10-28
❑ 04FanCraAL-12
❑ 09T206-415
❑ 11SpoLifCW-84
Crossan, Clay
❑ 96AriBlaDB-14
Crossley, Chad
❑ 95BoiHawTI-12
Crossley, William
❑ 87OldJudN-105
Croteau, Julie
❑ 92SpollIFK1-268
❑ 94ColSilBC-2
❑ 95ColSilB9-3
Crotty, Joe (Joseph P.)
❑ 87OldJudN-106A
❑ 87OldJudN-106B
Crouch, Bill
❑ 41CarW75-7
❑ 90DodTar-150
Crouch, Jack Albert
❑ 72TCMthe3-13
Crouch, Matt
❑ 86BurExpP-4
❑ 88MemChiB-8
❑ 89OmaRoyC-5
❑ 89OmaRoyP-1717
Crouch, Zach
❑ 85GreHorT-9
❑ 87NewBriRSP-2
❑ 88PawRedSC-6
❑ 88PawRedSP-457
❑ 89NewBriRSP-612
❑ 89NewBriRSS-4
❑ 90TopTVRS-40
Crough, Bill
❑ 41Gou-27
Crouse, Buck (Clyde E.)
❑ 28LaPre-25
❑ 30WhiSoxTI-9
❑ 92ConTSN-509
Croushore, Rich
❑ 93GleFalRC-10
❑ 93GleFalRF-3996
❑ 94MadHatC-7
❑ 94MadHatF-125
❑ 96ArkTraB-8
❑ 97ArkTraB-2
❑ 98FleUpd-U73
❑ 99Fle-397
❑ 99FleSta9-397
❑ 99FleWarT-397
Crouwel, Michael
❑ 92MarPhiC-2
❑ 92MarPhiF-3059
Crow, Bill
❑ 93EliTwiC-25
Crow, Dean
❑ 93BelMarCB-10
❑ 93BelMarF-3200
❑ 96PorCitRB-9
❑ 97Bow-365
❑ 97BowBes-146
❑ 97BowBesAR-146
❑ 97BowBesR-146
❑ 97BowInt-365
❑ 97TacRai-8
❑ 98BesAutSS-14
❑ 98TolMudHQ-12
Crow, Don (Donald Leroy)
❑ 80AlbDukTc-27
❑ 81AlbDukTc-13
❑ 82AlbDukTc-12
❑ 90DodTar-151
Crow, Gabby (Roger)
❑ 79QuaCitCT-4
❑ 80QuaCitCT-32
❑ 81QuaCitCT-32
❑ 82QuaCitCT-12
❑ 83QuaCitCT-1
Crowder, General (Alvin)
❑ 23Zee-159
❑ 31SenTealPW-7
❑ 33ButCanV-10
❑ 33Gou-95
❑ 33Gou-122
❑ 33GouCanV-71
❑ 33TatOrbSDR-185
❑ 33WorCig-28
❑ 34BabRutG-13
❑ 34BatR31-161
❑ 34ButPreR-13
❑ 34DiaMatCSB-36
❑ 34DiaStaR-93
❑ 34ExhFou-16
❑ 34Gou-15
❑ 34GouCanV-65
❑ 35DiaMatCS3T1-40
❑ 35GouPuzR-5F
❑ 35GouPuzR-6F
❑ 35GouPuzR-11H
❑ 35GouPuzR-13F
❑ 36R31PasP-46
❑ 60SenUniMC-4
❑ 61Fle-102
❑ 72TCMthe1-169
❑ 74TigTCM1AC-6
❑ 76TigOldTS-5
❑ 77GalGloG-187
❑ 83BigLeaCOA-3
❑ 83ConMar-19
❑ 88ConAmeA-7
❑ 91ConTSN-257
❑ 93ConTSN-682
❑ 94ConTSN-1277
❑ 94ConTSNB-1277
Crowe, George Daniel
❑ 52Top-360
❑ 53BraJohC-18
❑ 53BraSpiaS3-10
❑ 53Top-3
❑ 55BraJohC-39
❑ 56Top-254
❑ 57Kah-6
❑ 57Top-73
❑ 58Kah-6
❑ 58RedEnq-8
❑ 58RedJayP-5
❑ 58Top-12
❑ 59Top-337
❑ 60Top-419
❑ 61Top-52
❑ 83Bra53F-37
❑ 83TopRep5-360
❑ 91TopArc1-3
Crowe, Ron
❑ 88NebCor-3
❑ 89EveGiaS-5
❑ 89Sta-195
❑ 90Bes-170
❑ 90CliGiaB-21
❑ 90CliGiaP-2557
❑ 91SanJosGC-5
❑ 91SanJosGP-16
❑ 92ShrCapF-3875
❑ 92ShrCapS-581
❑ 93CliGiaC-8
❑ 93CliGiaF-2482
Crowell, James
❑ 95WatIndTI-10
❑ 97CalLeaATI-29
❑ 97KinIndB-5
❑ 98ChaLooG-5
Crowell, William
❑ 87OldJudN-107
Crowley, Bill
❑ 64TopRooAB-24
Crowley, Brian
❑ 89ButCopKSP-8
Crowley, Jim
❑ 91ElmPioC-3
❑ 91ElmPioP-3276
❑ 92LynRedSC-18
❑ 92LynRedSF-2912
❑ 93NewBriRSF-1227
❑ 94LynRedSC-7
❑ 94LynRedSF-1898
Crowley, Ray
❑ 78MemChiBC-2
❑ 79MemChiT-16
❑ 80MemChiT-11
Crowley, Terry
❑ 88SalBucS-4
❑ 89SalBucS-5
❑ 90CMC-762
❑ 90HarSenP-1198
❑ 90HarSenS-5
❑ 91CarMudLD-104
❑ 91CarMudP-1091
❑ 91LinDriAA-104
❑ 92CanIndF-696
Crowley, Terry (Terrence M.)
❑ 67BalOriP-26
❑ 70BalOriP-5
❑ 70OPC-121
❑ 70Top-121
❑ 71MLBOffS-292
❑ 71OPC-453
❑ 71Top-453
❑ 72OriPos-9
❑ 72Top-628
❑ 73BalOriP-13
❑ 73OPC-302
❑ 73OriJohP-11
❑ 73OriTeal-11
❑ 73Top-302
❑ 74OPC-648
❑ 74Top-648
❑ 74TopTra-648T
❑ 75OPC-447
❑ 75Top-447
❑ 75TopMin-447
❑ 76AtlBraP-8
❑ 76BalOriP-7
❑ 76OPC-491
❑ 76SSP-35
❑ 76Top-491
❑ 77RocRedWM-10
❑ 78BalOriP-4
❑ 79Top-91
❑ 80BalOriP-3
❑ 80Top-188
❑ 81BalOriP-3
❑ 81Don-507
❑ 81Fle-190
❑ 81OPC-342
❑ 81Top-543
❑ 82Don-383
❑ 82Fle-160
❑ 82Top-232
❑ 83Don-457
❑ 83ExpPos-6
❑ 83Fle-55
❑ 83Top-372
❑ 83TopTra-22T
❑ 84Nes792-732
❑ 84OPC-246
❑ 84Top-732
❑ 84TopTif-732
❑ 85BalOriP-5
❑ 87BalOriP-7
❑ 87OriFreB-10
❑ 88OriFreB-10
❑ 88OriPos-8
❑ 91DodPho-3
❑ 91OriCro-89
❑ 93OriCroASU-10
Crowley, William M.
❑ 87BucN28-49
Crownover, Derek
❑ 86DavLipB-8
Crowther, Brent
❑ 94BenRocC-3
❑ 94BenRocF-3583
❑ 95AshTouTI-31
❑ 95Bes-68
❑ 96Exc-151
❑ 96ExcCli-3
❑ 96NewHavRB-7
❑ 96SalAvaB-6
Crowther, John
❑ 94SigRooDP-53
❑ 94SigRooDPS-53
❑ 94St.CatBJC-7
❑ 94St.CatBJF-3635
❑ 94StaCluDP-33
❑ 94StaCluDPFDI-33
❑ 95HagSunF-60
❑ 95StCatSTI-5
❑ 96HagSunB-2
Cruise, Mark
❑ 94JohCitCC-7
❑ 94JohCitCF-3690
Cruise, Walt (Walton Edwin)
❑ 20NatCarE-18
❑ 21Exh-29
❑ 22E120-123
❑ 22W572-18
❑ 23WilChoV-24
❑ 95ConTSN-1410
Crum, George
❑ 83BurRanF-4
❑ 83BurRanT-14
❑ 85TulDriTI-4
❑ 86WatIndP-6
Crump, Jamie
❑ 90PulBraB-15
❑ 90PulBraP-3095
Crump, Jody
❑ 94JohCitCC-8
❑ 94JohCitCF-3691
Crumpler, Roy
❑ 21Zee-117
❑ 22Zee-41
❑ 23Zee-63
Crutcher, Dave
❑ 79TulDriT-19
❑ 80TulDriT-2
❑ 81TulDriT-15
Crutcher, Dick
❑ 80BraTCM1-22
Crutchfield, Jimmie (Jim)
❑ 78LauLonABS-35
❑ 86NegLeaF-29
❑ 91NegLeaRL-8
❑ 92NegLeaK-6
❑ 92NegLeaRLI-13
❑ 95NegLeaLI-8
Cruz, Andres
❑ 90MemChiB-23
❑ 90MemChiP-1003
❑ 90MemChiS-8
❑ 91LinDriAA-405
❑ 91MemChiLD-405
❑ 91MemChiP-647
❑ 97PriDevR-10
Cruz, Arcadio
❑ 77ChaPatT-3
Cruz, Bernardo
❑ 88SouBenWSGS-12
Cruz, Brian
❑ 94MacBraC-5
❑ 94MacBraF-2208
Cruz, Charlie
❑ 95EugEmeTI-5
❑ 96MacBraB-6
❑ 97DurBulTI-8
❑ 98GreBraG-6
Cruz, Cirilo
❑ 96EveAquB-6
❑ 97WisTimR-6
❑ 98LanJetG-6
Cruz, Daniel
❑ 90BriTigP-3162
❑ 90BriTigS-4
Cruz, Deivi
❑ 95BelGiaTI-7
❑ 96BurBeeTI-16
❑ 97Bow-346
❑ 97BowInt-346
❑ 97ColCho-338
❑ 97Don-388
❑ 97DonGolPP-388
❑ 97DonPre-166
❑ 97DonPreCttC-166
❑ 97DonSilPP-388
❑ 97Fle-591
❑ 97FleTif-591
❑ 97Lea-341
❑ 97LeaFraM-341
❑ 97LeaFraMDC-341
❑ 97PinX-P-136
❑ 97PinX-PMoS-136
❑ 97Sco-488
❑ 97ScoArtPWB-488
❑ 97ScoResC-488
❑ 97ScoShoS-488
❑ 97ScoShoSAP-488
❑ 97Sel-166
❑ 97SelCom-166
❑ 97Ult-512
❑ 97UltGolME-512
❑ 97UltPlaME-512
❑ 98CirThu-236
❑ 98CirThuRav-236
❑ 98CirThuSupRav-236
❑ 98ColCho-92
❑ 98Don-208
❑ 98DonGolPP-208
❑ 98DonSilPP-208
❑ 98Fle-172
❑ 98Pac-86
❑ 98PacInv-32
❑ 98PacInvPBlue-32
❑ 98PacInvSilv-32
❑ 98PacInvTeam-10
❑ 98PacOnl-269
❑ 98PacOnlR-269
❑ 98PacOnlWC-269
❑ 98PacPlaB-86
❑ 98PacRedT-86
❑ 98PacSil-86
❑ 98Revo-56
❑ 98RevoSS-56
❑ 98ScoRT-112
❑ 98StaCluFDI-119
❑ 98StaClul-119
❑ 98StaCluOneK-119
❑ 98StaCluPP-119
❑ 98Stu-52
❑ 98StuGPP-52
❑ 98StuSPP-52
❑ 98Top-97
❑ 98TopChr-97
❑ 98TopChrR-97
❑ 98TopDevR-97
❑ 98TopDia-97
❑ 98TopMiniC-97
❑ 98Ult-14
❑ 98UltGolM-14
❑ 98UltMas-14
❑ 98UltPlaM-14
❑ 98UppDec-359
❑ 99Fle-428
❑ 99FleSta9-428
❑ 99FleWarT-428
❑ 99Pac-161
❑ 99PacCroC-106
❑ 99PacCroCPB-106
❑ 99PacPlaB-161
❑ 99PacRed-161
❑ 99StaClu-41
❑ 99StaCluFDI-41
❑ 99StaCluOoaK-41
❑ 99StaCluPP-41
❑ 99Top-123
❑ 99TopChr-123
❑ 99TopChrR-123
❑ 99TopMVPP-123
❑ 99UppDec-94
❑ 99UppDecEL1-94
❑ 99UppDecEL2-94
Cruz, Edgar
❑ 97BurIndG-5
❑ 98ColRedSM-20
Cruz, Fausto
❑ 91ModA'sP-3095
❑ 92CalLeaACL-9
❑ 92RenSilSCLC-38
❑ 92UppDecML-157
❑ 93LimRocDWB-18
❑ 93LimRocDWB-141
❑ 93ModA'sC-7
❑ 93ModA'sF-806
❑ 94Bow-436
❑ 94Cla-45
❑ 94ExcFS7-119
❑ 94SpoRoo-112
❑ 94SpoRooAP-112
❑ 94TacTigF-3182
❑ 94Ult-406
❑ 95ColCho-128
❑ 95ColChoGS-128
❑ 95ColChoSS-128
❑ 95EdmTraTI-5
❑ 95Pin-146
❑ 95PinArtP-146
❑ 95PinMusC-146
❑ 95Sco-583
❑ 95ScoGolR-583
❑ 95ScoPlaTS-583
❑ 95Sel-216
❑ 95SelArtP-216
❑ 96ColCho-641
❑ 96ColChoGS-641
❑ 96ColChoSS-641
❑ 96TolMudHB-10
❑ 97PacPriGotD-GD40
❑ 97VanCanB-11
❑ 98VanCanG-9
Cruz, Georgie
❑ 83MemChiT-2
Cruz, Heity (Hector Dilan)
❑ 75TulOil7-1
❑ 76OPC-598
❑ 76St.LouCP-5
❑ 76Top-598
❑ 77Car5-4
❑ 77CarTeal-4
❑ 77Top-624
❑ 78SSP270-248
❑ 78Top-257
❑ 79GiaPol-9
❑ 79Top-436
❑ 80RedEnq-7
❑ 80Top-516
❑ 81Fle-206

❑ 81Top-52
❑ 81TopTra-750
❑ 82Don-57
❑ 82Fle-591
❑ 82OPC-364
❑ 82Top-663
❑ 91PacSenL-60

Cruz, Henry Acosta

❑ 74AlbDukCa-64
❑ 74AlbDukTI-4
❑ 76OPC-590
❑ 76SSP-85
❑ 76Top-590
❑ 78SSP270-152
❑ 78Top-316
❑ 80IowOakP-4
❑ 90DodTar-152

Cruz, Henry D'La

❑ 98WilCubM-8

Cruz, Ismael

❑ 89MarPhiS-8
❑ 90BatCliP-3071

Cruz, Ivan

❑ 89NiaFalRP-5b
❑ 90FloStaLAS-28
❑ 90LakTigS-6
❑ 90StaFS7-34
❑ 91Bow-153
❑ 91Cla/Bes-18
❑ 91LinDriAA-379
❑ 91LonTigLD-379
❑ 91LonTigP-1882
❑ 92Bow-170
❑ 92ClaFS7-171
❑ 92LonTigF-638
❑ 92LonTigS-404
❑ 92SkyAA F-172
❑ 92UppDecML-241
❑ 92UppDecMLPotY-PY23
❑ 93Bow-319
❑ 93ClaFS7-181
❑ 93ExcFS7-170
❑ 93TolMudHF-1658
❑ 93Top-423
❑ 93TopGol-423
❑ 93TopInaM-423
❑ 93TopInaR-423
❑ 93TopMic-423
❑ 94TolMudHF-1030
❑ 95JacSunTI-6
❑ 96ColCliB-6
❑ 97ColCliB-9
❑ 97ColCliD-6
❑ 98ColCliD-6
❑ 98ColCliM-10
❑ 98Don-137
❑ 98DonCol-137
❑ 98DonCol-204
❑ 98DonColS-137
❑ 98DonColS-199
❑ 98DonGolPP-137
❑ 98DonPriCD-137
❑ 98DonPriCD-204
❑ 98DonRatR-29
❑ 98DonRatRM-29
❑ 98DonSilPP-137

Cruz, J.J.

❑ 91EriSaiC-4
❑ 91EriSaiP-4071
❑ 92BatCliCB-6
❑ 92BatCliF-3268

Cruz, Jacob

❑ 94SigRooDP-30
❑ 94SigRooDPS-30
❑ 94StaCluDP-19
❑ 94StaCluDPFDI-19
❑ 95BowBes-B85
❑ 95BowBesR-B85
❑ 95SPML-144
❑ 95Top-521
❑ 96BesAutS-24
❑ 96BesAutSA-15
❑ 96Bow-273
❑ 96BowFoi-273
❑ 96Exc-243
❑ 96PhoFirB-14
❑ 96Top-438
❑ 97Bow-110
❑ 97BowCerBlaIA-CA17
❑ 97BowCerBluIA-CA17
❑ 97BowCerGolIA-CA17
❑ 97BowChr-130
❑ 97BowChrI-130
❑ 97BowChrIR-130
❑ 97BowChrR-130
❑ 97BowInt-110
❑ 97ColCho-9
❑ 97DonSigA-24
❑ 97DonSigAC-31
❑ 97DonSigAM-31
❑ 97PacPri-148
❑ 97PacPriGotD-GD216
❑ 97PacPriLB-148
❑ 97PacPriP-148
❑ 97PhoFirTI-6
❑ 97Sel-168
❑ 97SelCom-168
❑ 97StaClu-280
❑ 97StaCluM-M3
❑ 97StaCluMOP-280
❑ 97StaCluMOP-M3
❑ 97Top-220
❑ 97Ult-292
❑ 97UltGolME-292
❑ 97UltPlaME-292
❑ 97UppDec-232
❑ 98Bow-158
❑ 98BowCerBlueAU-50
❑ 98BowCerGA-50
❑ 98BowCerSA-50
❑ 98BowChr-158
❑ 98BowChrGA-158
❑ 98BowChrGAR-158
❑ 98BowChrI-158
❑ 98BowChrIR-158
❑ 98BowChrR-158
❑ 98BowGolA-158
❑ 98BowInt-158
❑ 98Don-303
❑ 98DonColE-504
❑ 98DonColL-386
❑ 98DonEli-104
❑ 98DonEliA-104
❑ 98DonEliS-104
❑ 98DonGolPP-303
❑ 98DonPriCE-504
❑ 98DonPriCL-386
❑ 98DonSigA-24
❑ 98DonSigAC-32
❑ 98DonSigAM-32
❑ 98DonSigSB-6
❑ 98DonSilPP-303
❑ 98FreGriG-6
❑ 98Lea-187
❑ 98LeaFraDA-187
❑ 98LeaFraF-187
❑ 98LeaFraM-187
❑ 98LeaFraM-187
❑ 98LeaFraMDC-187
❑ 98LeaFraMDC-187
❑ 98LeaFraMZ2-187
❑ 98LeaRS-281
❑ 98LeaRSLHolo-281
❑ 98LeaRSLong-281
❑ 98LeaRTrue-281
❑ 98Pac-438
❑ 98PacInv-143
❑ 98PacInvPBlue-143
❑ 98PacInvSilv-143
❑ 98PacPar-243
❑ 98PacParC-243
❑ 98PacParG-243
❑ 98PacParHS-243
❑ 98PacParPB-243
❑ 98PacParR-243
❑ 98PacPlaB-438
❑ 98PacRedT-438
❑ 98PacSil-438
❑ 98Pin-181
❑ 98PinArtP-PP84
❑ 98PinIns-118
❑ 98PinInsCE-118
❑ 98PinInsDE-118
❑ 98PinMusC-PP84
❑ 98PinPreP-181
❑ 98Sco-239
❑ 98ScoRT-159
❑ 98ScoRTSS-PP90
❑ 98ScoRTSSAP-PP90
❑ 98ScoRTSSAP1-PP90
❑ 98SpoIll-172
❑ 98SpoIllEE-172
❑ 98SpoIllFE-172
❑ 98StaCluFDI-42
❑ 98StaCluI-42
❑ 98StaCluOneK-42
❑ 98StaCluPP-42
❑ 98Stu-126
❑ 98StuGPP-126
❑ 98StuSPP-126
❑ 98Ult-426
❑ 98UltGolM-426
❑ 98UltMas-426
❑ 98UltPlaM-426
❑ 98Zen-83
❑ 98Zen5 xx7-77
❑ 98Zen5x7GoldImp-77
❑ 98Zen5x7Imp-77
❑ 98ZenRooT-7
❑ 98ZenZ-G-83
❑ 98ZenZ-S-83

Cruz, Javier

❑ 85MexCitTT-26

Cruz, Jesus

❑ 79CedRapGT-2

Cruz, Jose Dilan

❑ 71CarTeal-14
❑ 72CarTeal-7
❑ 72OPC-107
❑ 72Top-107
❑ 73OPC-292
❑ 73Top-292
❑ 74OPC-464
❑ 74Top-464
❑ 74TopSta-113
❑ 75AstPos-6
❑ 75OPC-514
❑ 75Top-514
❑ 75TopMin-514
❑ 76HouAstP-7
❑ 76OPC-321
❑ 76SSP-62
❑ 76Top-321
❑ 77AstPho-5
❑ 77BurCheD-9
❑ 77Hos-75
❑ 77Kel-50
❑ 77OPC-147
❑ 77Top-42
❑ 78AstBurK-17
❑ 78AstPos-7
❑ 78Hos-72
❑ 78Kel-16
❑ 78OPC-131
❑ 78Top-625
❑ 79AstPos-7
❑ 79AstTeal-5
❑ 79BasPat-23
❑ 79Hos-111
❑ 79OPC-143
❑ 79Top-289
❑ 80OPC-367
❑ 80Top-722
❑ 81AllGamPI-141
❑ 81AstPos-3
❑ 81CokTeaS-63
❑ 81Don-383
❑ 81Fle-60
❑ 81FleStiC-78
❑ 81OPC-105
❑ 81Top-105
❑ 81TopScr-83
❑ 81TopSti-169
❑ 81TopSupHT-98
❑ 82AstAstI-8
❑ 82AstPos-2
❑ 82Don-244
❑ 82Dra-10
❑ 82Fle-214
❑ 82FleSta-50
❑ 82OPC-325
❑ 82Top-325
❑ 82TopSti-44
❑ 83AllGamPI-140
❑ 83AstPos-3
❑ 83Don-41
❑ 83Fle-446
❑ 83FleSta-45
❑ 83FleSti-206
❑ 83OPC-327
❑ 83Top-585
❑ 83TopFol-5
❑ 83TopSti-242
❑ 84AllGamPI-47
❑ 84AstMot-8
❑ 84AstPos-5
❑ 84Don-182
❑ 84Fle-222
❑ 84FleSti-8
❑ 84FleSti-24
❑ 84FunFooP-129
❑ 84Nes792-66
❑ 84Nes792-422
❑ 84OCoandSI-198
❑ 84OPC-189
❑ 84SevCoi-W19
❑ 84Top-66
❑ 84Top-422
❑ 84TopRubD-16
❑ 84TopSti-65
❑ 84TopStiB-13
❑ 84TopTif-66
❑ 84TopTif-422
❑ 85AllGamPI-137
❑ 85AstHouP-2
❑ 85AstMot-4
❑ 85Don-20
❑ 85Don-304
❑ 85DonSupD-20
❑ 85Dra-7
❑ 85Fle-347
❑ 85Lea-20
❑ 85OPC-95
❑ 85SevCoi-C10
❑ 85SubDis-27
❑ 85ThoMcAD-27
❑ 85Top-95
❑ 85TopGloS-20
❑ 85TopMin-95
❑ 85TopRubD-14
❑ 85TopSti-59
❑ 85TopSup-34
❑ 85TopTif-95
❑ 86AstMilL-4
❑ 86AstMot-20
❑ 86AstPol-12
❑ 86AstTeal-3
❑ 86BasStaB-25
❑ 86Don-60
❑ 86DonAll-19
❑ 86Fle-296
❑ 86FleLeaL-8
❑ 86FleLimE-13
❑ 86FleMin-62
❑ 86FleStiC-27
❑ 86Lea-49
❑ 86OPC-96
❑ 86SevCoi-S13
❑ 86Spo-30
❑ 86Top-186
❑ 86Top-640
❑ 86TopSti-26
❑ 86TopTat-11
❑ 86TopTif-186
❑ 86TopTif-640
❑ 87AstMot-3
❑ 87AstPol-3
❑ 87AstShoSPT-4
❑ 87Don-85
❑ 87DonOpeD-13
❑ 87Fle-53
❑ 87FleBasA-11
❑ 87FleGlo-53
❑ 87FleStiC-26
❑ 87FleStiWBC-S4
❑ 87Lea-116
❑ 87OPC-343
❑ 87RedFolSB-95
❑ 87Spo-42
❑ 87Spo-152
❑ 87SpoTeaP-8
❑ 87Top-670
❑ 87TopSti-29
❑ 87TopTif-670
❑ 88DonReaBY-NEW
❑ 88Fle-443
❑ 88FleGlo-443
❑ 88GreBasS-10
❑ 88HouSho-14
❑ 88PanSti-299
❑ 88Sco-28
❑ 88ScoGlo-28
❑ 88StaLinAst-6
❑ 88Top-278
❑ 88TopTif-278
❑ 89PacSenL-188
❑ 89T/MSenL-26
❑ 89TopSenL-78
❑ 90EliSenL-53
❑ 90KisDodD-7
❑ 91PacSenL-36
❑ 92UppDecS-8
❑ 92YanWIZ8-38

Cruz, Jose Jr.

❑ 95Bes-129
❑ 95EveAqaTI-6
❑ 95SPML-110
❑ 95SPMLDtS-DS9
❑ 96Exc-103
❑ 96ExcFirYP-2
❑ 96LanJetB-12
❑ 96SigRooOJPP-P2
❑ 96SigRooOJPPS-P2
❑ 97Bes-7
❑ 97BesAll-10
❑ 97BesAutSBPP-13
❑ 97BesBetP-8
❑ 97BesCarCSP-2
❑ 97BesDiaB-8
❑ 97Bow-100
❑ 97BowBes-188
❑ 97BowBesA-188
❑ 97BowBesAAR-188
❑ 97BowBesAR-188
❑ 97BowBesBC-BC11
❑ 97BowBesBCAR-BC11
❑ 97BowBesBCR-BC11
❑ 97BowBesJ-188
❑ 97BowBesJAR-188
❑ 97BowBesJR-188
❑ 97BowBesMI-MI5
❑ 97BowBesMIAR-MI5
❑ 97BowBesMIARI-MI5
❑ 97BowBesMII-MI5
❑ 97BowBesMIR-MI5
❑ 97BowBesMIRI-MI5
❑ 97BowBesR-188
❑ 97BowCerBlaIA-CA18
❑ 97BowCerBluIA-CA18
❑ 97BowCerGolIA-CA18
❑ 97BowChr-122
❑ 97BowChrI-122
❑ 97BowChrIR-122
❑ 97BowChrR-122
❑ 97BowChrSHR-SHR10
❑ 97BowChrSHRR-SHR10
❑ 97BowInt-100
❑ 97BowIntB-BBI19
❑ 97BowIntBAR-BBI19
❑ 97BowIntBR-BBI19
❑ 97BowScoHR-10
❑ 97ColChoU-U27
❑ 97Don-396
❑ 97DonGolPP-396
❑ 97DonLim-18
❑ 97DonLim-196
❑ 97DonLimE-18
❑ 97DonLimE-196
❑ 97DonLimFotG-30
❑ 97DonSig-40
❑ 97DonSigA-25
❑ 97DonSigAC-32
❑ 97DonSigAM-32
❑ 97DonSigPPP-40
❑ 97DonSilPP-396
❑ 97DonTea-148
❑ 97DonTeaSPE-148
❑ 97DonVxP1-13
❑ 97Fin-337
❑ 97FinEmb-337
❑ 97FinEmbR-337
❑ 97FinRef-337
❑ 97FlaShoWotF-WF2
❑ 97Fle-589
❑ 97FleNewH-2
❑ 97FleTif-589
❑ 97HigMinM-33
❑ 97Lea-330
❑ 97LeaFraM-330
❑ 97LeaFraMDC-330
❑ 97PinCer-151
❑ 97PinCer-NNO
❑ 97PinX-P-126
❑ 97PinX-PMoS-126
❑ 97Sel-151
❑ 97SelCom-151
❑ 97SP-15
❑ 97SpoIll-4
❑ 97SpoIll-NNO
❑ 97SpoIllEE-4
❑ 97SPx-47
❑ 97SPxBro-47
❑ 97SPxGol-47
❑ 97SPxGraF-47
❑ 97SPxSil-47
❑ 97SPxSte-47
❑ 97TacRai-9
❑ 97TopStaFAS-FAS6
❑ 97Ult-551
❑ 97UltGolME-551
❑ 97UltPlaME-551
❑ 97UppDec-547
❑ 97UppDecMM-B9
❑ 97UppDecSA-19
❑ 97UppDecSAG-19
❑ 97Zen-47
❑ 98Bow-7
❑ 98BowBes-25
❑ 98BowBesA-25
❑ 98BowBesAAR-25
❑ 98BowBesAR-25
❑ 98BowBesAR-25
❑ 98BowBesMIF-MI8
❑ 98BowBesMIFAR-MI8
❑ 98BowBesMIFR-MI8
❑ 98BowBesR-25
❑ 98BowCerBlueAU-11
❑ 98BowCerGA-11
❑ 98BowCerSA-11
❑ 98BowChr-7
❑ 98BowChrGA-7
❑ 98BowChrGAR-7
❑ 98BowChrI-7
❑ 98BowChrIR-7
❑ 98BowChrR-7
❑ 98BowGolA-7
❑ 98BowInt-7
❑ 98CirThu-50
❑ 98CirThu-300
❑ 98CirThuB-4
❑ 98CirThuFT-1
❑ 98CirThuLA-3
❑ 98CirThuQS-3
❑ 98CirThuRav-50
❑ 98CirThuRR-4
❑ 98CirThuSupRav-50
❑ 98ColCho-7
❑ 98ColCho-270
❑ 98ColCho-525
❑ 98ColChoB5-525
❑ 98ColChoCG-7
❑ 98ColChoCtG-CG23A
❑ 98ColChoCtG-CG23B
❑ 98ColChoCtG-CG23C
❑ 98ColChoCtGExch-CG23
❑ 98ColChoCtGIW-CG23
❑ 98ColChoMBH-30
❑ 98ColChoRJ-7
❑ 98ColChoS'-30
❑ 98ColChoSQ-SQ10
❑ 98ColChoSQ-SQ81
❑ 98ColChoSQDouble-2
❑ 98ColChoSQHR-2
❑ 98ColChoSQSingle-2
❑ 98ColChoSQTriple-2
❑ 98Don-115
❑ 98Don-352
❑ 98Don-397
❑ 98DonCol-115
❑ 98DonCol-179
❑ 98DonColE-477
❑ 98DonColE-543
❑ 98DonColL-213
❑ 98DonColL-399
❑ 98DonColP-685
❑ 98DonColP-747
❑ 98DonColS-115
❑ 98DonColS-174
❑ 98DonCruG-51
❑ 98DonCruP-51
❑ 98DonCruR-51
❑ 98DonDom-16
❑ 98DonEli-77
❑ 98DonEli-143
❑ 98DonEliA-77
❑ 98DonEliA-143
❑ 98DonEliBttF-5
❑ 98DonEliBttFA-5
❑ 98DonEliC-12
❑ 98DonEliI-18
❑ 98DonEliMC-12
❑ 98DonEliS-77
❑ 98DonEliS-143
❑ 98DonFANT-4
❑ 98DonFANTDC-4
❑ 98DonGolPP-115
❑ 98DonGolPP-352
❑ 98DonGolPP-397
❑ 98DonPre-135
❑ 98DonPre-197
❑ 98DonPreGB-18
❑ 98DonPreGES-2
❑ 98DonPreGoB-18
❑ 98DonPreGX-2
❑ 98DonPreGXDC-2
❑ 98DonPrePM-25
❑ 98DonPreSeat-135
❑ 98DonPreSeat-197
❑ 98DonPreTP-18
❑ 98DonPreTPD-9
❑ 98DonPreTPG-18
❑ 98DonPreTPS-18
❑ 98DonPriCD-115
❑ 98DonPriCD-179
❑ 98DonPriCE-477

❑ 98DonPriCE-543
❑ 98DonPriCL-213
❑ 98DonPriCL-399
❑ 98DonPriCP-685
❑ 98DonPriCP-747
❑ 98DonProLS-18
❑ 98DonRatR-4
❑ 98DonRatRM-4
❑ 98DonRooDK-9
❑ 98DonRooDKC-9
❑ 98DonSig-23
❑ 98DonSigAC-33
❑ 98DonSigAM-33
❑ 98DonSigP-23
❑ 98DonSilPP-115
❑ 98DonSilPP-352
❑ 98DonSilPP-397
❑ 98DonSonM9-20
❑ 98E-X2-96
❑ 98E-X2Cheap-19
❑ 98E-X2DesCoop-12
❑ 98E-X2ECFut-96
❑ 98E-X2ECNow-96
❑ 98E-X2SD2001-2
❑ 98Fin-65
❑ 98FinCen-C6
❑ 98FinCenR-C6
❑ 98FinMysF1-M11
❑ 98FinMysF1-M15
❑ 93FinMysF1-M16
❑ 98FinMysF1-M17
❑ 98FinMysF2-M7
❑ 98FinMysF2-M10
❑ 98FinMysF2-M11
❑ 98FinMysF2R-M7
❑ 98FinMysF2R-M10
❑ 98FinMysF2R-M11
❑ 98FinMysFR-M11
❑ 98FinMysFR-M15
❑ 98FinMysFR-M16
❑ 98FinMysFR-M17
❑ 98FinNo--65
❑ 98FinNo-R-65
❑ 98FinOve-A6
❑ 98FinOveR-A6
❑ 98FinPowZ-P3
❑ 98FinRef-65
❑ 98FinStaS-SS15
❑ 98FinTheM-TM11
❑ 98FinTheMR-TM11
❑ 98FlaShoLeg0-6
❑ 98FlaShoLeg1-6
❑ 98FlaShoLeg2-6
❑ 98FlaShoLeg3-6
❑ 98FlaShoLegM-6
❑ 98FlaShoR0-6
❑ 98FlaShoR1-6
❑ 98FlaShoR2-6
❑ 98FlaShoR3-6
❑ 98Fle-275
❑ 98Fle-312
❑ 98Fle-326
❑ 98Fle-341
❑ 98Fle-571
❑ 98Fle-580
❑ 98FleDiamInk-3
❑ 98FleDiaS-4
❑ 98FleIn TC-IC4
❑ 98FleLumC-3
❑ 98FlePowG-6
❑ 98FleRooS-2
❑ 98FleVin'-63
❑ 98FleVin'C-63
❑ 98FleZon-4
❑ 98Lea-13
❑ 98Lea-200
❑ 98LeaFraDA-13
❑ 98LeaFraDA-200
❑ 98LeaFraF-13
❑ 98LeaFraF-200
❑ 98LeaFraM-13
❑ 98LeaFraM-200
❑ 98LeaFraM-13
❑ 98LeaFraM-200
❑ 98LeaFraMDC-13
❑ 98LeaFraMDC-200
❑ 98LeaFraMDC-13
❑ 98LeaFraMDC-200
❑ 98LeaFraMZ2-13
❑ 98LeaFraMZ2-200
❑ 98LeaRS-50
❑ 98LeaRS-180
❑ 98LeaRSFOSamp-19
❑ 98LeaRSFresh-19
❑ 98LeaRSHRDerby-5
❑ 98LeaRSLHolo-50
❑ 98LeaRSLHolo-180
❑ 98LeaRSLong-50
❑ 98LeaRSLong-180
❑ 98LeaRSTicMas-14
❑ 98LeaRSTicMasDC-14
❑ 98LeaRTrue-50
❑ 98LeaRTrue-180
❑ 98LeaStaRep-11
❑ 98LeaStaS-14
❑ 98LeaStaSDC-14
❑ 98MetUni-1
❑ 98MetUniAT-16
❑ 98MetUniDH-5
❑ 98MetUniPMG-1
❑ 98MetUniPP-4
❑ 98MetUniT-4
❑ 98MetUniUL-16
❑ 98Pac-217
❑ 98PacAur-93
❑ 98PacAurCube-20
❑ 98PacAurHC-20
❑ 98PacAurODLC-20
❑ 98PacAurPF-23
❑ 98PacAurPFC-23
❑ 98PacAurPFPB-23
❑ 98PacAurPFR-23
❑ 98PacAurPFS-23
❑ 98PacGolCDC-36
❑ 98PacInv-74
❑ 98PacInvGems-111
❑ 98PacInvInt-15A
❑ 98PacInvMiT-20
❑ 98PacInvPBlue-74
❑ 98PacInvPhoto-18
❑ 98PacInvSilv-74
❑ 98PacInvTeam-28
❑ 98PacLatotML-36
❑ 98PacOme-246
❑ 98PacOmeR-246
❑ 98PacOnl-757
❑ 98PacOnlR-757
❑ 98PacOnlWC-757
❑ 98PacPar-112
❑ 98PacParC-112
❑ 98PacParFC-20
❑ 98PacParG-112
❑ 98PacParHS-112
❑ 98PacParI-25
❑ 98PacParPB-112
❑ 98PacParR-112
❑ 98PacParSD-20
❑ 98PacPlaB-217
❑ 98PacRedT-217
❑ 98PacSil-217
❑ 98PacTeaC-14
❑ 98Pin-52
❑ 98PinArtP-PP47
❑ 98PinIns-91
❑ 98PinIns-149
❑ 98PinInsBtN-4
❑ 98PinInsC-2
❑ 98PinInsCE-91
❑ 98PinInsCE-149
❑ 98PinInsCG-2
❑ 98PinInsDE-91
❑ 98PinInsDE-149
❑ 98PinInsSG-9AB
❑ 98PinInsSG-9CD
❑ 98PinInsSG-13AB
❑ 98PinInsSG-13CD
❑ 98PinInsSGS-9AB
❑ 98PinInsSGS-9CD
❑ 98PinInsSGS-13AB
❑ 98PinInsSGS-13CD
❑ 98PinMinB-25
❑ 98PinMinCB-25
❑ 98PinMinCBAP-25
❑ 98PinMinCGP-25
❑ 98PinMinCGPAP-25
❑ 98PinMinCN-25
❑ 98PinMinCNAP-25
❑ 98PinMinCSGR-25
❑ 98PinMinDC-25
❑ 98PinMinG-25
❑ 98PinMinMCSS-25
❑ 98PinMinS-25
❑ 98PinMusC-PP47
❑ 98PinPer-26
❑ 98PinPerBB-18
❑ 98PinPerBBSamp-18
❑ 98PinPerBBSO-18
❑ 98PinPerLP-8
❑ 98PinPerPP-26
❑ 98PinPerSftF-6
❑ 98PinPlu-133
❑ 98PinPluAP-PP44
❑ 98PinPluGAP-PP44
❑ 98PinPluLM-14
❑ 98PinPluMAP-PP44
❑ 98PinPluY-10
❑ 98PinPreP-52
❑ 98Revo-149
❑ 98RevoSS-149
❑ 98Sco-233
❑ 98ScoNewS-NS11
❑ 98ScoRT-17
❑ 98ScoRT-256
❑ 98ScoRTComPla-4A
❑ 98ScoRTComPla-4B
❑ 98ScoRTComPla-4C
❑ 98ScoRTCPSamp-4A
❑ 98ScoRTCPSamp-4B
❑ 98ScoRTCPSamp-4C
❑ 98ScoRTSS-PP17
❑ 98ScoRTSS-PP149
❑ 98ScoRTSSAP-PP17
❑ 98ScoRTSSAP-PP149
❑ 98ScoRTSSAP1-PP17
❑ 98ScoRTSSAP1-PP149
❑ 98ScoRTStarGaz-15
❑ 98SelSelSamp-5
❑ 98SkyDugA-89
❑ 98SkyDugA-143
❑ 98SkyDugAAR-3
❑ 98SkyDugADH-DH20
❑ 98SkyDugAIA-89
❑ 98SkyDugAIA-143
❑ 98SP Aut-SD23
❑ 98SP AutC-JC
❑ 98SP AutSD-SD23
❑ 98SP AutSDT-SD23
❑ 98SpoIII-28
❑ 98SpoIIIAuto-2
❑ 98SpoIIIEC-EC10
❑ 98SpoIIIEE-28
❑ 98SpoIIIFE-28
❑ 98SpoIIITaN-54
❑ 98SpoIIITaN-74
❑ 98SpoIIITaNEE-54
❑ 98SpoIIITaNEE-74
❑ 98SpoIIITaNGS-14
❑ 98SpoIIIWSF-38
❑ 98SpoIIIWSFEE-38
❑ 98SpoIIIWSFFE-38
❑ 98SPxFin-10
❑ 98SPxFin-217
❑ 98SPxFin-330
❑ 98SPxFinR-10
❑ 98SPxFinR-217
❑ 98SPxFinR-330
❑ 98SPxFinS-10
❑ 98SPxFinS-217
❑ 98SPxFinS-330
❑ 98StaCluC-CS7
❑ 98StaCluC-CS10
❑ 98StaCluC-CS11
❑ 98StaCluFDI-255
❑ 98StaCluI-255
❑ 98StaCluOneK-255
❑ 98StaCluPP-255
❑ 98Stu-2
❑ 98StuFF-20
❑ 98StuFFDC-20
❑ 98StuGPP-2
❑ 98StuPor8x10-23
❑ 98StuPor8x10GP-23
❑ 98StuSony99-20
❑ 98StuSPP-2
❑ 98SyrSkyG-7
❑ 98Top-326
❑ 98TopBabB-BB4
❑ 98TopChr-326
❑ 98TopChrBB-BB4
❑ 98TopChrBBR-BB4
❑ 98TopChrR-326
❑ 98TopDevR-326
❑ 98TopDia-326
❑ 98TopFocP-FP3
❑ 98TopGal-35
❑ 98TopGalGoH-GH10
❑ 98TopGalGoHJ-GH10
❑ 98TopGalGP-35
❑ 98TopGalOPP-35
❑ 98TopGalPPI-35
❑ 98TopGalPPIA-35
❑ 98TopGolLabC1-85
❑ 98TopGolLabC1B-85
❑ 98TopGolLabC1One-85
❑ 98TopGolLabC1R-85
❑ 98TopGolLabC2-85
❑ 98TopGolLabC2B-85
❑ 98TopGolLabC2One-85
❑ 98TopGolLabC2R-85
❑ 98TopGolLabC3-85
❑ 98TopGolLabC3B-85
❑ 98TopGolLabC3One-85
❑ 98TopGolLabC3R-85
❑ 98TopMiniC-326
❑ 98TopMysFB-M6
❑ 98TopMysFB-M6
❑ 98TopMysFBR-M6
❑ 98TopMysFBR-M6
❑ 98TopOpeD-152
❑ 98TopSta-55
❑ 98TopSta'S-10
❑ 98TopSta'SGH-10
❑ 98TopStaB-55
❑ 98TopStaG-55
❑ 98TopStaGR-55
❑ 98TopStaS-55
❑ 98TopStaSteG-10
❑ 98TopSup-31
❑ 98TopSup-31
❑ 98TopTek-62
❑ 98TopTekD-62
❑ 98UD3-43
❑ 98UD3-133
❑ 98UD3-223
❑ 98UD3DieCut-43
❑ 98UD3DieCut-133
❑ 98UD3DieCut-223
❑ 98Ult-194
❑ 98Ult-487
❑ 98UltBacttF-9
❑ 98UltDial-13
❑ 98UltDiaP-15
❑ 98UltDouT-19
❑ 98UltGolM-194
❑ 98UltGolM-487
❑ 98UltKidG-9
❑ 98UltMas-194
❑ 98UltMas-487
❑ 98UltMilM-1
❑ 98UltNot-16
❑ 98UltPlaM-194
❑ 98UltPlaM-487
❑ 98UltPowP-10
❑ 98UltPriL-18
❑ 98UltTicS-9
❑ 98UltTop3-24
❑ 98UltWinN-11
❑ 98UppDec-14
❑ 98UppDec-525
❑ 98UppDec-623
❑ 98UppDecAC-AS4
❑ 98UppDecAG-AG23
❑ 98UppDecAGDC-AG23
❑ 98UppDecAPA3-JC
❑ 98UppDecBCP-BC13
❑ 98UppDecDS-DS13
❑ 98UppDecR-100
❑ 98UppDecRBBop-BB17
❑ 98UppDecRQL-Q10
❑ 98UppDecRSotT-JC
❑ 98UppDecRTC-TC27
❑ 98UppDecSF-7
❑ 98UppDecSFPD-PZ1
❑ 98UppDecSFPZSX-PZ1
❑ 98UppDecTMT-19
❑ 98UppDecTMTG-19
❑ 98UppDecU-4
❑ 98Zen-50
❑ 98Zen5 xx7-58
❑ 98Zen5x7GoldImp-58
❑ 98Zen5x7Imp-58
❑ 98ZenZ-G-50
❑ 98ZenZ-S-50
❑ 98ZenZ-T-12
❑ 98ZenZ-TG-12
❑ 99199Fin-228
❑ 99Bow-18
❑ 99BowBes-23
❑ 99BowBesAR-23
❑ 99BowBesR-23
❑ 99BowChr-18
❑ 99BowChrG-18
❑ 99BowChrGR-18
❑ 99BowChrI-18
❑ 99BowChrIR-18
❑ 99BowChrR-18
❑ 99BowGol-18
❑ 99BowInt-18
❑ 99CroRoyB-141
❑ 99CroRoyL-141
❑ 99CroRoyOD-141
❑ 99E-X Cen-71
❑ 99E-X CenECFut-71
❑ 99E-X CenECNow-71
❑ 99FinGolRef-228
❑ 99FinRef-228
❑ 99Fle-101
❑ 99FleMys-75
❑ 99FleMysG-75
❑ 99FleMysM-75
❑ 99FleSta9-101
❑ 99FleWarT-101
❑ 99MetUni-29
❑ 99MetUniGM-29
❑ 99MetUniPMG-29
❑ 99Pac-438
❑ 99PacAur-196
❑ 99PacAurOD-196
❑ 99PacCroC-294
❑ 99PacCroC-23
❑ 99PacCroCPB-294
❑ 99PacInv-147
❑ 99PacInvOD-147
❑ 99PacInvPB-147
❑ 99PacOme-244
❑ 99PacOmeC-244
❑ 99PacOmeG-244
❑ 99PacOmePB-244
❑ 99PacPar-242
❑ 99PacParC-242
❑ 99PacParG-242
❑ 99PacParHoloGold-242
❑ 99PacParHS-242
❑ 99PacParOD-242
❑ 99PacParPB-242
❑ 99PacParRed-242
❑ 99PacParTC-30
❑ 99PacPlaB-438
❑ 99PacPri-148
❑ 99PacPriHB-148
❑ 99PacPriHG-148
❑ 99PacPriHM-148
❑ 99PacPriHP-148
❑ 99PacPriRed-148
❑ 99PacPriS-78
❑ 99PacPriS206-78
❑ 99PacPriS206R-78
❑ 99PacRed-438
❑ 99Rev-145
❑ 99RevPremDate-145
❑ 99RevRet-145
❑ 99RevShaSS-145
❑ 99SkyMolM-56
❑ 99SkyMolMX-56
❑ 99SkyPre-122
❑ 99SkyPreR-122
❑ 99SkyThu-241
❑ 99SkyThuRant-241
❑ 99SkyThuRave-241
❑ 99SP Aut-89
❑ 99SPSig-105
❑ 99SPx-79
❑ 99SPxFinR-79
❑ 99SPxFinS-79
❑ 99SPxPreS-PS14
❑ 99StaClu-284
❑ 99StaCluFDI-284
❑ 99StaCluOoaK-284
❑ 99StaCluPP-284
❑ 99ThuSkySupR-241
❑ 99Top-386
❑ 99TopBlaLC1-64
❑ 99TopBlaLC2-64
❑ 99TopBlaLC3-64
❑ 99TopChr-386
❑ 99TopChrR-386
❑ 99TopGal-49
❑ 99TopGalPP-49
❑ 99TopGalPPI-49
❑ 99TopGolL-64
❑ 99TopGolLC1-64
❑ 99TopGolLC2-64
❑ 99TopGolLOtO-64
❑ 99TopMVPP-386
❑ 99TopOpeD-113
❑ 99TopRedLC1-64
❑ 99TopRedLC2-64
❑ 99TopRedLC3-64
❑ 99TopSta-129
❑ 99TopStaFoil-129
❑ 99UD Cho-153
❑ 99UD ChoPCR-153
❑ 99UD ChoYW-Y30
❑ 99UD Ion-60
❑ 99UD IonR-60
❑ 99Ult-23
❑ 99UltGolM-23
❑ 99UltMas-23
❑ 99UltPlaM-23
❑ 99UppDec-227
❑ 99UppDec-241
❑ 99UppDecBD-89
❑ 99UppDecBDD-89
❑ 99UppDecBDQ-89
❑ 99UppDecBDT-89
❑ 99UppDecCL-118
❑ 99UppDecCLCC-118
❑ 99UppDecCLM-C100
❑ 99UppDecEL1-227
❑ 99UppDecEL1-241
❑ 99UppDecEL2-227
❑ 99UppDecEL2-241
❑ 99UppDecIP-I5
❑ 99UppDecIPD-I5
❑ 99UppDecIPHR-I5
❑ 99UppDecIPT-I5
❑ 99UppDecM-217
❑ 99UppDecMGS-217
❑ 99UppDecMHFS-217
❑ 99UppDecMSS-217
❑ 99UppDecO-20
❑ 99UppDecOSO-20
❑ 99UppDecR-86
❑ 99UppDecRG-86
❑ 99UppDecRP-86
❑ 99UppDecWY-W6
❑ 99UppDecWYD-W6
❑ 99UppDecWYHR-W6
❑ 99UppDecWYT-W6
❑ 99Vic-411

Cruz, Juan-1

❑ 83MadMusF-21
❑ 84ModA'sC-14
❑ 85MidAngT-23

Cruz, Juan-2

❑ 92ChaRaiC-11
❑ 92SpoIndC-25
❑ 92SpoIndF-1305

Cruz, Julio

❑ 96TulDriTI-7

Cruz, Julio Luis

❑ 75QuaCitAT-8
❑ 77MarPos-5
❑ 78Top-687
❑ 79Hos-58
❑ 79OPC-305
❑ 79Top-583
❑ 80BurKinPHR-26
❑ 80MarPos-9
❑ 80OPC-16
❑ 80Top-32
❑ 81AllGamPI-10
❑ 81Don-163
❑ 81Fle-601
❑ 81MarPol-6
❑ 81MarPos-12
❑ 81OPC-121
❑ 81Top-397
❑ 81TopSti-126
❑ 82Don-50
❑ 82Fle-509
❑ 82FleSta-225
❑ 82MarPos-14
❑ 82OPC-130
❑ 82Top-130
❑ 82TopSti-114
❑ 82TopSti-235
❑ 83Don-379
❑ 83Fle-478
❑ 83OPC-113
❑ 83Top-414
❑ 83TopFol-5
❑ 83TopSti-112
❑ 83TopTra-23T
❑ 84AllGamPI-100
❑ 84Don-379
❑ 84Fle-55
❑ 84FleSti-95
❑ 84Nes792-257
❑ 84OPC-257
❑ 84Top-257
❑ 84TopSti-248
❑ 84TopTif-257
❑ 84WhiSoxTV-9
❑ 85AllGamPI-11
❑ 85Don-452
❑ 85Fle-510
❑ 85OPC-71
❑ 85Top-749
❑ 85TopSti-239
❑ 85TopTif-749
❑ 85WhiSoxC-12
❑ 86Don-257
❑ 86Fle-201
❑ 86OPC-14
❑ 86Top-14

❑ 86TopTif-14
❑ 86WhiSoxC-12
❑ 87Fle-492
❑ 87FleGlo-492
❑ 87OPC-53
❑ 87Top-790
❑ 87TopTif-790
❑ 89StoPorCLC-179
❑ 90SweBasG-88
❑ 91LinDri-32
❑ 91SweBasG-21
❑ 93UppDecS-14
Cruz, Luis
❑ 83WisRapTF-19
❑ 86PitCubP-5
❑ 87WinSpiP-9
❑ 88BlaYNPRWL-5
❑ 88CarLeaAS-26
❑ 88WinSpiS-2
❑ 89BlaYNPRWL-173
❑ 89ChaKniTI-8
❑ 89IowCubC-15
❑ 89IowCubP-1692
❑ 98ChaRivDG-10
❑ 98HudValR-5
❑ 98Top-500
❑ 98TopChr-500
❑ 98TopChrR-500
❑ 98TopDevR-500
❑ 98TopDia-500
❑ 98TopMiniC-500
Cruz, Nandi
❑ 90SarWhiSS-5
❑ 91DunBluJC-16
❑ 91DunBluJP-213
Cruz, Nelson
❑ 97BirBarB-13
❑ 98PriWilCASM-11
Cruz, Pablo
❑ 77SalPirT-9A
❑ 77SalPirT-9B
❑ 78SalPirT-2
Cruz, Rafael
❑ 86DayBealP-6
❑ 87GasRanP-13
Cruz, Ricardo
❑ 93GenCubC-7
❑ 93GenCubF-3176
Cruz, Ruben
❑ 91BurAstC-19
❑ 91BurAstP-2813
❑ 92OscAstC-22
❑ 92OscAstF-2541
❑ 93OscAstC-9
❑ 93OscAstF-635
Cruz, Todd Ruben
❑ 77ReaPhiT-8
❑ 80Top-492
❑ 80VenLeaS-258
❑ 81CokTeaS-26
❑ 81Fle-341
❑ 81Top-571
❑ 82MarPos-15
❑ 83AllGamPI-19
❑ 83Don-505
❑ 83Fle-479
❑ 83MarNal-3
❑ 83OPC-132
❑ 83OriPos-6
❑ 83Top-132
❑ 84BalOriP-7
❑ 84Don-148
❑ 84Fle-3
❑ 84Nes792-773
❑ 84Top-773
❑ 84TopTif-773
❑ 85Fle-172
❑ 85Top-366
❑ 85TopTif-366
❑ 86MarGreT-3
❑ 87SanBerSP-20
❑ 91OriCro-90
❑ 91PacSenL-147
❑ 91SalSpuC-5
❑ 91SalSpuP-2251
Cruz, Tommy
❑ 75IntLeaASB-4
❑ 75SpoIndC-8
❑ 76SacSolC-7
❑ 79ColCliT-13
Cruz, Tommy (Cirilio Dilan)
❑ 75PacCoaLAB-4
❑ 78TacYanC-44
❑ 92PenPilC-28
❑ 92PenPilF-2949
❑ 94AppFoxC-24
Cruz, Victor
❑ 78SyrChiT-5
❑ 79Top-714
❑ 80IndTeal-5
❑ 80OPC-54
❑ 80Top-99
❑ 81Don-321
❑ 81Fle-407
❑ 81OPC-252
❑ 81Top-252
❑ 81TopTra-751
❑ 82Fle-480
❑ 82Top-263
❑ 83OklCit8T-6
❑ 84OklCit8T-20
❑ 85DomLeaS-16
❑ 88PocGiaP-2089
❑ 93RanKee-116
Csefalvay, John
❑ 83ColAstT-3
❑ 84NasSouTI-4
Cub, Casey the
❑ 95RocCubTI-NNO
❑ 96RocCubTI-4
❑ 97RocCub-6
Cubanich, Creighton
❑ 91SouOreAC-23
Cubans, New York
❑ 93NegLeaRL2-94
❑ 93TedWilPC-4
Cubbage, Mike (Michael Lee)
❑ 74SpoIndC-39
❑ 75OPC-617
❑ 75RanPos-7
❑ 75SpoIndC-14
❑ 75Top-617
❑ 75TopMin-617
❑ 76MinTwiP-6
❑ 76OPC-615
❑ 76Top-615
❑ 77BurCheD-50
❑ 77Top-149
❑ 78Top-219
❑ 78TwiFriP-5
❑ 79OPC-187
❑ 79Top-362
❑ 79TwiFriP-4
❑ 80OPC-262
❑ 80Top-503
❑ 80TwiPos-5
❑ 81Don-492
❑ 81Fle-566
❑ 81Top-657
❑ 81TopTra-752
❑ 82Fle-523
❑ 82TidTidT-26
❑ 82Top-43
❑ 85LynMetT-1
❑ 86JacMetT-24
❑ 87TidTidP-12
❑ 87TidTidT-23
❑ 88TidTidCa-3
❑ 88TidTidCM-24
❑ 88TidTidP-1586
❑ 88TriAAAP-54
❑ 89TidTidC-21
❑ 89TidTidP-1947
❑ 90MetColP-29
❑ 90MetKah-4
❑ 90TopTVM-2
❑ 91MetColP-27
❑ 91MetKah-4
❑ 91MetPerPA-2
❑ 91MetWIZ-89
❑ 92MetColP-33
❑ 92MetKah-4
❑ 93RanKee-117
❑ 96MetKah-7
❑ 96MetKah-6
Cubbie, Mascot
❑ 96IowCubB-29
Cubee, Rich
❑ 89OmaRoyC-25
Cubillan, Darwin
❑ 95LinVen-128
❑ 96-97LinVen-84
❑ 98TamYanM-8
Cubs, Chicago
❑ 09MaxPubP-23
❑ 09SpoNewSM-53
❑ 13FatT20-11
❑ 36R31Pre-G24
❑ 36R31Pre-L15
❑ 38BasTabP-35
❑ 56Top-11A
❑ 56Top-11B
❑ 56Top-11C
❑ 57Top-183
❑ 58Top-327
❑ 59Top-304
❑ 60Top-513
❑ 60TopTat-56
❑ 61Top-122
❑ 61TopMagR-17
❑ 62GuyPotCP-3
❑ 62Top-552
❑ 63Top-222
❑ 64Top-237
❑ 64TopTatI-4
❑ 64TopVen-237
❑ 65OPC-91
❑ 65Top-91
❑ 66Top-204
❑ 66TopRubI-104
❑ 66TopVen-204
❑ 67Top-354
❑ 68LauWorS-3
❑ 68LauWorS-4
❑ 68LauWorS-7
❑ 68LauWorS-15
❑ 68LauWorS-26
❑ 68LauWorS-32
❑ 68LauWorS-35
❑ 69FleCloS-5
❑ 69FleCloS-29
❑ 69TopStaA-5
❑ 70FleWorS-3
❑ 70FleWorS-4
❑ 70FleWorS-15
❑ 70FleWorS-26
❑ 70Top-593
❑ 71FleWorS-4
❑ 71FleWorS-5
❑ 71FleWorS-27
❑ 71FleWorS-36
❑ 71OPC-502
❑ 71Top-502
❑ 71TopTat-51
❑ 72OPC-192
❑ 72Top-192
❑ 73FleWilD-1
❑ 73OPC-464
❑ 73OPCBTC-5
❑ 73Top-464
❑ 73TopBluTC-5
❑ 74OPC-211
❑ 74OPCTC-5
❑ 74Top-211
❑ 74TopStaA-5
❑ 74TopTeaC-5
❑ 78Top-302
❑ 82CubRedL-NNO
❑ 83CubThoAV-NNO
❑ 83FleSta-229
❑ 83FleSti-NNO
❑ 84CubBriPC-5D
❑ 84CubBriPC-5S
❑ 84CubBriPC-12C
❑ 85Fle-642
❑ 86JosHalC-4
❑ 87SpoTeaL-22
❑ 88PanSti-470
❑ 88RedFolSB-121
❑ 90FleWaxBC-C6
❑ 90PubIntS-632
❑ 90RedFolSB-122
❑ 91PanCanT1-120
❑ 93TedWilPC-5
❑ 94ImpProP-16
❑ 94Sco-648
❑ 94ScoGolR-648
❑ 95PacPriTL-16
❑ 95PanSti-142
❑ 96CubFle-19
❑ 96PanSti-45
❑ 99Vic-72
Cubs, Wytheville
❑ 87WytCubP-31
❑ 88WytCubP-2004
Cuccinello, Al (Alfred E.)
❑ 94ConTSN-1171
❑ 94ConTSNB-1171
Cuccinello, Tony (Anthony)
❑ 33Gou-99
❑ 33NatLeaAC-5
❑ 33WorCig-29
❑ 34BatR31-79
❑ 34DiaMatCSB-37
❑ 34DiaStaR-55
❑ 34TarThoBD-10
❑ 35AlDemDCR3-91
❑ 35DiaMatCS3T1-41
❑ 35ExhFou-2
❑ 36DiaMatCS4-2
❑ 36GouWidPPR-A22
❑ 38ExhFou-1
❑ 39ExhSal-9
❑ 39PlaBal-61
❑ 40PlaBal-61
❑ 49EurSta-80
❑ 55IndGolS-30
❑ 60Top-458
❑ 68TigDetFPB-3
❑ 72TCMthe3-14
❑ 74Bra193NLA-5
❑ 75TCM195CI-3
❑ 77GalGloG-223
❑ 79DiaGre-208
❑ 81WhiSox1T-44
❑ 83BigLeaCOA-28
❑ 89DodSmoG-37
❑ 89PacLegI-170
❑ 90DodTar-153
❑ 94ConTSN-1171
❑ 94ConTSNB-1171
❑ 95ConTSN-1391
Cucjen, Romy
❑ 85FreGiaSB-13
❑ 87ShrCapP-9
❑ 88ShrCapP-1293
❑ 89LouRedBC-15
❑ 89LouRedBP-1257
❑ 89LouRedBTI-15
❑ 90CMC-72
❑ 90IndIndC-22
❑ 90IndIndP-289
❑ 90ProAAAF-572
Cuddyer, Michael
❑ 98BesNumOP-14
❑ 98Bow-148
❑ 98BowChr-148
❑ 98BowChrGA-148
❑ 98BowChrGAR-148
❑ 98BowChrI-148
❑ 98BowChrIR-148
❑ 98BowChrR-148
❑ 98BowGolA-148
❑ 98BowInt-148
❑ 98ForWayW!-2
❑ 98MidLeaPM-9
❑ 98StaCluFDI-385
❑ 98StaCluI-385
❑ 98StaCluOneK-385
❑ 98StaCluPP-385
❑ 98Top-494
❑ 98TopChr-494
❑ 98TopChrR-494
❑ 98TopDevR-494
❑ 98TopDia-494
❑ 98TopMiniC-494
❑ 99BasAmeTP-29
❑ 99BasAmeTPA-7
❑ 99BasAmeTPG-29
❑ 99Bow-184
❑ 99BowAut-BA31
❑ 99BowBes-128
❑ 99BowBesAR-128
❑ 99BowBesR-128
❑ 99BowChr-184
❑ 99BowChrG-184
❑ 99BowChrGR-184
❑ 99BowChrI-184
❑ 99BowChrIR-184
❑ 99BowChrR-184
❑ 99BowGol-184
❑ 99BowInt-184
❑ 99SP TopP-35
❑ 99SP TopPPE-35
❑ 99TeaBesRA-6
❑ 99Top-426
❑ 99TopChr-426
❑ 99TopChrR-426
❑ 99TopMVPP-426
Cudjo, Lavell
❑ 89GreHorP-406
❑ 89SouAtlLAGS-34
❑ 90CedRapRB-9
❑ 90CedRapRP-2332
❑ 92LetMouSP-20
Cudworth, Jim (James A.)
❑ 87OldJudN-108
Cuellar, Bobby
❑ 75LynRanT-7
❑ 76SanAntBTI-8
❑ 77TucTorC-53
❑ 78TucTorC-46
❑ 79TacTugT-7
❑ 80TacTigT-6
❑ 80Top-665
❑ 81ChaChaT-2
❑ 84SalLakCGC-192
❑ 85CalCanC-84
❑ 86WauTimP-5
❑ 87WauTimP-1
❑ 88SanBerSB-27
❑ 88SanBerSCLC-54
❑ 89WilBilP-627
❑ 89WilBilS-3
❑ 90WilBilB-26
❑ 90WilBilP-1073
❑ 90WilBilS-26
❑ 91JacSunLD-350
❑ 91JacSunP-167
❑ 91LinDriAA-350
❑ 93RanKee-118
❑ 94CalCanF-806
❑ 95MarMot-28
❑ 96MarMot-28
Cuellar, Jose
❑ 94AppFoxC-7
❑ 94AppFoxFI-1056
Cuellar, Mike
❑ 80KnoBluJT-12
Cuellar, Mike Angel
❑ 59Top-518
❑ 60Top-398
❑ 65Top-337
❑ 66Top-566
❑ 67Ast-7
❑ 67AstTeal1-3
❑ 67BalOriP-27
❑ 67BalOriP-28
❑ 67CokCapAs-14
❑ 67OPC-97
❑ 67Top-97
❑ 67Top-234
❑ 67TopVen-318
❑ 68CokCapA-14
❑ 68DexPre-26
❑ 68Top-274
❑ 68TopActS-8C
❑ 68TopVen-274
❑ 69MilBra-66
❑ 69Top-453
❑ 69Top-532
❑ 70BalOriP-6
❑ 70DayDaiNM-56
❑ 70MLBOffS-148
❑ 70OPC-68
❑ 70OPC-70
❑ 70OPC-199
❑ 70Ori-3
❑ 70Top-70
❑ 70Top-199
❑ 70Top-590
❑ 70TopBoo-1
❑ 71BalOriP-5
❑ 71Kel-49
❑ 71MLBOffS-293
❑ 71OPC-69
❑ 71OPC-170
❑ 71OriCha-3
❑ 71Top-69
❑ 71Top-170
❑ 71TopCoi-150
❑ 71TopTat-128
❑ 72EssCoi-6
❑ 72Kel-27A
❑ 72Kel-27B
❑ 72MilBra-82
❑ 72OPC-70
❑ 72OriDMV-4
❑ 72OriPos-10
❑ 72Top-70
❑ 73BalOriP-16
❑ 73Kel2D-47
❑ 73OPC-470
❑ 73OriJohP-35
❑ 73OriTeal-12
❑ 73Top-470
❑ 74OPC-560
❑ 74Top-560
❑ 75BalOriP-7
❑ 75Hos-42
❑ 75OPC-410
❑ 75SSP42-24
❑ 75Top-410
❑ 75TopMin-410
❑ 76BalOriP-8
❑ 76Hos-121
❑ 76OPC-285
❑ 76OriEngCL-1
❑ 76SSP-375
❑ 76Top-285
❑ 77Top-162
❑ 86AstMot-5
❑ 87AstShoSO-3
❑ 87AstShoSTw-29
❑ 89PacSenL-46
❑ 89T/MSenL-27
❑ 91KelLey-7
❑ 91OriCro-91
Cuen, Eleno
❑ 73CedRapAT-24
❑ 75DubPacT-13
❑ 81PorBeaT-26
❑ 82BufBisT-14
Cuervo, Ed
❑ 78WauMetT-7
❑ 83ColAstT-2
Cuesta, Jamie
❑ 88BurBraP-17
❑ 89DurBullS-6
❑ 89DurBullS-6
❑ 89DurBulTI-6
Cueto, Manuel Melo
❑ 22Zee-122
Cuevas, Angelo
❑ 86LynMetP-8
❑ 88BlaYNPRWL-36
❑ 88JacMetGS-21
❑ 88TexLeaAGS-10
❑ 89BlaYNPRWL-38
❑ 89JacMetGS-14
Cuevas, Eduardo
❑ 94SprSulC-5
❑ 94SprSulF-2042
❑ 95RanCucQT-19
❑ 96CliLumKTI-10
Cuevas, Johnny
❑ 86SumBraP-4
❑ 87DurBulP-8
❑ 88SumBraP-397
❑ 89BurBraP-1597
❑ 89BurBraS-6
❑ 90DurBulTI-16
❑ 91GreBraC-11
❑ 91GreBraLD-205
❑ 91GreBraP-3005
❑ 91LinDriAA-205
❑ 92DurBulC-2
❑ 92DurBulF-1103
❑ 92DurBulTI-28
Cuevas, Rafael
❑ 78NewWayCT-7
Cuevas, Trent
❑ 95YakBeaTI-7
❑ 96GreFalDB-9
❑ 96GreFalDTI-21
❑ 98VerBeaDM-20
Cuitti, Art
❑ 75OakOak2A-12
Culberson, Calvain
❑ 88PulBraP-1760
❑ 89SumBraP-1101
❑ 92CedRapRC-24
❑ 92CedRapRF-1061
❑ 93ChaLooF-2355
❑ 94ChaLooF-1353
Culberson, Charles
❑ 85FreGiaSB-3
❑ 86FreGiaSB-25
❑ 87Ft.MyeRP-15
❑ 88MemChiB-17
❑ 91UtiBluSC-24
❑ 91UtiBluSP-3259
Culberson, Delbert Leon
❑ 46RedSoxTI-5
❑ 47RedSoxTI-2
❑ 47TipTop-1
❑ 75RedSox1T-8
Culberson, Don
❑ 92SouBenWSC-2
❑ 92SouBenWSF-172
❑ 93SouBenWSC-7
❑ 93SouBenWSF-1422
Culkar, Steve
❑ 87NewOriP-11
❑ 88VirGenS-7
❑ 89HagSunB-8
❑ 89HagSunP-276
❑ 89HagSunS-4
❑ 90HagSunB-16
❑ 90HagSunP-1405

❑ 90HagSunS-6
❑ 91HagSunP-2449
Cullen, Jack (John)
❑ 63Top-54A
❑ 63Top-54B
❑ 66OPC-31
❑ 66TolMudHTI-5
❑ 66Top-31
❑ 66TopVen-31
❑ 92YanWIZ6-31
Cullen, Mike
❑ 85KinBluJT-4
Cullen, Tim
❑ 67OPC-167
❑ 67SenPos-9
❑ 67Top-167
❑ 68Top-209
❑ 68TopVen-209
❑ 69Top-586
❑ 70Kel-30
❑ 70OPC-49
❑ 70Top-49
❑ 71MLBOffS-534
❑ 71OPC-566
❑ 71SenPolP-3
❑ 71SenTeaIW-9
❑ 71Top-566
❑ 72OPC-461
❑ 72Top-461
Cullenbine, Roy
❑ 41BroW75-7
❑ 79DiaGre-185
❑ 81TigDetN-43
❑ 83TCMPla1945-3
❑ 90DodTar-154
❑ 93ConTSN-849
Culler, Dick
❑ 47TipTop-78
❑ 83TCMPla1945-38
Cullers, Steve
❑ 85BurRanT-5
Cullop, Glen
❑ 92PriRedC-27
❑ 92PriRedF-2685
❑ 94ChaLooF-1354
Cullop, Henry Nick
❑ 19W514-59
❑ 29ExhFou-3
❑ 31Exh-7
❑ 33WorCig(-20
❑ 37Zee-52
❑ 82OhiHaloF-3
❑ 87ConSer2-11
❑ 88ConSer4-7
❑ 90DodTar-156
Cullop, Norman
❑ 20Zee-80
Culmer, Will
❑ 80PenPilBT-8
❑ 80PenPilCT-19
❑ 81ReaPhiT-21
❑ 82OklCit8T-25
❑ 83ChaChaT-16
❑ 83IndPos-8
❑ 83IndWhe-7
❑ 84MaiGuiT-14
Culmo, Kevin
❑ 96YakBeaTI-19
Culp, Bennie
❑ 43PhiTeaI-5
Culp, Brian
❑ 95SalAvaTI-13
❑ 96SalAvaB-7
Culp, Matt
❑ 95WatIndTI-11
Culp, Ray
❑ 60Lea-75
❑ 63Top-29A
❑ 63Top-29B
❑ 64PhiPhiB-11
❑ 64Top-412
❑ 64TopCoi-35
❑ 64TopSta-96
❑ 64TopStaU-20
❑ 64TopTatI-32
❑ 64WheSta-12
❑ 65Top-505
❑ 66OPC-4
❑ 66PhiTeaI-5
❑ 66Top-4
❑ 66TopVen-4
❑ 67CokCapC-7
❑ 67DexPre-57
❑ 67OPC-168
❑ 67Top-168
❑ 68CokCapRS-7
❑ 68Top-272
❑ 68TopVen-272
❑ 69MilBra-67
❑ 69MLBOffS-11
❑ 69RedSoxAO-3
❑ 69RedSoxTI-3
❑ 69Top-391
❑ 69TopSta-132
❑ 69TopSup-6
❑ 69TopTeaP-3
❑ 70Kel-35
❑ 70MLBOffS-158
❑ 70OPC-144
❑ 70RedSoxCPPC-6
❑ 70Top-144
❑ 71MilDud-4
❑ 71MLBOffS-317
❑ 71OPC-660
❑ 71RedSoxA-4
❑ 71RedSoxTI-3
❑ 71Top-660
❑ 71TopTat-103
❑ 72MilBra-83
❑ 72OPC-2
❑ 72Top-2
❑ 78TCM60I-197
❑ 81RedSoxBG2S-78
Culp, Wes
❑ 94DanBraC-5
❑ 94DanBraF-3523
❑ 95MacBraTI-4
❑ 98DanQ-C-7
Culpepper, Kevin
❑ 92KinMetC-25
❑ 93KinMetC-27
❑ 94KinMetC-28
Culver, George
❑ 65OPC-166
❑ 65Top-166
❑ 67Top-499
❑ 68Top-319
❑ 68TopVen-319
❑ 69Kah-B8
❑ 69Top-635
❑ 70AstPho-4
❑ 70CarTeaI-10
❑ 70OPC-92
❑ 70Top-92
❑ 71AstTeaI-4
❑ 71MLBOffS-76
❑ 71OPC-291
❑ 71Top-291
❑ 72AstTeaI-4
❑ 72MilBra-84
❑ 72Top-732
❑ 73OPC-242
❑ 73Top-242
❑ 74OPC-632
❑ 74Top-632
❑ 81ReaPhiT-24
❑ 83PorBeaT-12
❑ 84PorBeaC-215
❑ 86ReaPhiP-6
❑ 87AstShoSTw-4
❑ 87ReaPhiP-1
❑ 88MaiPhiC-23
❑ 88MaiPhiP-300
❑ 89ReaPhiS-26b
❑ 89ScrRedBP-724
❑ 90DodTar-155
❑ 90ReaPhiB-25
❑ 90ReaPhiP-1235
❑ 90ReaPhiS-28
❑ 93ScrRedBF-2558
❑ 93ScrRedBTI-7
❑ 93TriAAAGF-19
Culver, Lanell C.
❑ 83TamTarT-3
❑ 84CedRapRT-16
Cumberbatch, Abdiel
❑ 90TamYanD-2
❑ 92OneYanC-4
❑ 93GreHorC-6
❑ 93GreHorF-897
❑ 93OneYanC-5
❑ 93OneYanF-3515
❑ 94SanBerSF-2770
Cumberland, Chris
❑ 93OneYanC-6
❑ 93OneYanF-3495
❑ 94GreBatF-464
❑ 94SouAtlLAF-SAL13
❑ 95Bow-193
❑ 95Exc-93
❑ 96Bow-324
❑ 96BowFoi-324
❑ 96ColCliB-7
❑ 96SigRooOJ-8
❑ 96SigRooOJS-8
❑ 97GreBatC-5
❑ 97NorNav-13
❑ 97NorNavTI-7
Cumberland, John
❑ 69OPC-114
❑ 69Top-114
❑ 69TopFou-24
❑ 70YanPhoS-9
❑ 71MLBOffS-244
❑ 71OPC-108
❑ 71Top-108
❑ 72OPC-403
❑ 72Top-403
❑ 83LynMetT-13
❑ 85TidTidT-26
❑ 86TidTidP-6
❑ 87TidTidP-18
❑ 87TidTidT-24
❑ 88TidTidCa-2
❑ 88TidTidCM-25
❑ 88TidTidP-1579
❑ 90CMC-685
❑ 90ProAAAF-292
❑ 90TidTidC-28
❑ 90TidTidP-561
❑ 91LinDriAA-625
❑ 91WicWraLD-625
❑ 91WicWraP-2615
❑ 91WicWraRD-25
❑ 92YanWIZ6-32
❑ 92YanWIZ7-39
❑ 93LasVegSF-962
❑ 96PawRedSDD-5
❑ 97PawRedS-3
❑ 98PawRedSQ-3
Cummings, Audelle
❑ 89GreFalDSP-8
Cummings, Bob
❑ 79CedRapGT-32
❑ 80CliGiaT-24
❑ 84ShrCapFB-6
❑ 85PhoGiaC-197
Cummings, Brian
❑ 88BatCliP-1689
❑ 88BurBraP-12
❑ 89BatCliP-1943
❑ 89BurBraP-1618
❑ 89BurBraS-7
❑ 90DurBulTI-19
Cummings, Candy (William)
❑ 36Halof FP-9
❑ 39PC7AlbHoF-20
❑ 50CalHOFW-23
❑ 53ArtHaloFP-25
❑ 76ShaPiz-23
❑ 77BobParHoF-57
❑ 80PerHaloFP-19
❑ 80SSPHOF-20
❑ 84GalHaloFRL-23
❑ 89HOFStiB-64
❑ 90BasWit-60
❑ 94OriofB-23
Cummings, Dick
❑ 84IowCubT-21
❑ 85IowCubT-25
❑ 92GenCubC-29
Cummings, John
❑ 89AncGlaP-9
❑ 91SanBerSC-1
❑ 91SanBerSP-1977
❑ 92PenPilC-17
❑ 92PenPilF-2925
❑ 92UppDecML-179
❑ 93Bow-135
❑ 93ClaGolF-33
❑ 93ExcFS7-223
❑ 93ExcLeaLF-19
❑ 93FleFinE-268
❑ 93Lea-303
❑ 93MariStaClu-21
❑ 93MarMot-26
❑ 93OPCPre-69
❑ 93PacSpa-621
❑ 93Pin-595
❑ 93TopTra-129T
❑ 93Ult-617
❑ 93UppDec-503
❑ 93UppDecGold-503
❑ 94Don-126
❑ 94MarMot-18
❑ 94Top-443
❑ 94TopGol-443
❑ 94TopSpa-443
❑ 95Fle-264
❑ 96DodPol-9
❑ 96Fle-430
❑ 96FleTif-430
❑ 96LeaSigEA-39
❑ 97Fle-97
❑ 97FleTif-97
❑ 98BufBisG-8
Cummings, Midre
❑ 91Cla/Bes-318
❑ 91KenTwiC-24
❑ 91KenTwiP-2088
❑ 92ClaBluBF-BC13
❑ 92ClaFS7-240
❑ 92ClaRedB-BC13
❑ 92ProFS7-98
❑ 92SalBucC-1
❑ 92SalBucF-76
❑ 92UppDecML-41
❑ 92UppDecML-277
❑ 92UppDecMLPotY-PY18
❑ 92UppDecMLTPHF-TP1
❑ 93Bow-357
❑ 93Bow-598
❑ 93CarMudF-2066
❑ 93CarMudTI-22
❑ 93ClaFisN-12
❑ 93ClaGolF-76
❑ 93ClaYouG-YG1
❑ 93ExcFS7-90
❑ 93Top-616
❑ 93TopGol-616
❑ 93TopInaM-616
❑ 93TopInaR-616
❑ 93TopMic-616
❑ 93UppDec-440
❑ 93UppDecGold-440
❑ 94ActPac-12
❑ 94Bow-363
❑ 94Bow-630
❑ 94BowBes-B7
❑ 94BowBesR-B7
❑ 94BufBisF-1848
❑ 94Cla-87
❑ 94ClaCreotC-C22
❑ 94ColC-3
❑ 94ColChoGS-3
❑ 94ColChoSS-3
❑ 94Don-608
❑ 94FleMajLP-8
❑ 94LeaGolR-4
❑ 94LeaLimRP-3
❑ 94Pac-496
❑ 94SigRooDP-90
❑ 94SigRooDPS-90
❑ 94Top-787
❑ 94TopGol-787
❑ 94TopSpa-787
❑ 94TriPla-292
❑ 94UppDec-7
❑ 94UppDecED-7
❑ 95ColCho-384
❑ 95ColChoGS-384
❑ 95ColChoSS-384
❑ 95Don-193
❑ 95DonPreP-193
❑ 95Fla-398
❑ 95Fle-476
❑ 95Lea-171
❑ 95Pin-421
❑ 95PinArtP-421
❑ 95PinMusC-421
❑ 95PirFil-7
❑ 95Sel-165
❑ 95Sel-237
❑ 95SelArtP-165
❑ 95SelArtP-237
❑ 95SelCerPU-7
❑ 95SelCerPU9-7
❑ 95Spo-145
❑ 95SpoArtP-145
❑ 95StaClu-229
❑ 95StaCluFDI-229
❑ 95StaCluMOP-229
❑ 95StaCluSTWS-229
❑ 95StaCluVR-116
❑ 95StaCluVRMO-116
❑ 95Stu-178
❑ 95Sum-15
❑ 95SumNthD-15
❑ 95Top-78
❑ 95TopCyb-55
❑ 95UC3-117
❑ 95UC3ArtP-117
❑ 95Ult-214
❑ 95UltGolM-214
❑ 95UppDec-382
❑ 95UppDecED-382
❑ 95UppDecEDG-382
❑ 95UppDecSE-88
❑ 95UppDecSEG-88
❑ 95Zen-139
❑ 96ColCho-259
❑ 96ColCho-342
❑ 96ColChoGS-259
❑ 96ColChoGS-342
❑ 96ColChoSS-259
❑ 96ColChoSS-342
❑ 96Don-308
❑ 96DonPreP-308
❑ 96Fle-518
❑ 96FleTif-518
❑ 96Pac-181
❑ 96Sco-391
❑ 96StaClu-155
❑ 96StaCluMOP-155
❑ 97PirPos-10
❑ 97Sco-389
❑ 97ScoArtPWB-389
❑ 97ScoResC-389
❑ 97ScoShoS-389
❑ 97ScoShoSAP-389
❑ 97UppDec-207
❑ 97UppDec-458
❑ 98ColCho-203
❑ 98Fle-220
❑ 98PacInvGems-186
❑ 98UppDec-474
Cummings, Ron
❑ 84ModA'sC-7
Cummings, Ryan
❑ 97BoiHawG-5
❑ 98LakElsSG-5
Cummings, Steve
❑ 87DunBluJP-924
❑ 88KnoBluJB-20
❑ 88SouLeaAJ-27
❑ 89SyrChiC-7
❑ 89SyrChiMB-7
❑ 89SyrChiP-803
❑ 90CMC-329
❑ 90Don-698
❑ 90OPC-374
❑ 90ScoRoo-78T
❑ 90SyrChiC-3
❑ 90SyrChiMB-3
❑ 90Top-374
❑ 90TopDeb89-26
❑ 90TopTif-374
❑ 91ColSprSSLD-81
❑ 91ColSprSSP-2178
❑ 91LinDriAAA-81
❑ 92SkyAAAF-260
❑ 92TolMudHF-1034
❑ 92TolMudHS-582
Cummins, Jonathan
❑ 97HudValRB-21
❑ 98ChaRivDG-11
Cunha, Steve
❑ 91SalLakTP-3223
❑ 91SalLakTSP-11
Cunnane, Will
❑ 94KanCouCC-8
❑ 94KanCouCF-153
❑ 94KanCouCTI-8
❑ 95Bow-61
❑ 95Exc-194
❑ 95ExcLeaL-6
❑ 95KanCouCLTI-4
❑ 95PorSeaDTI-5
❑ 95SPML-59
❑ 95UppDecML-116
❑ 95UppDecMLFS-116
❑ 96Bow-239
❑ 96BowFoi-239
❑ 96PorSeaDB-12
❑ 97ColChoU-U23
❑ 97Fle-515
❑ 97FleTif-515
❑ 97PadMot-24
❑ 98ColCho-223
❑ 98Fle-181
❑ 98MetUni-101
❑ 98MetUniPMG-101
❑ 98Pac-423
❑ 98PacPlaB-423
❑ 98PacRedT-423
❑ 98PacSil-423
❑ 98PorSeaD5AQ-26
❑ 98Ult-18
❑ 98UltGolM-18
❑ 98UltMas-18
❑ 98UltPlaM-18
❑ 98UppDec-501
Cunningham, Bill
❑ 86WesPalBEP-10
❑ 87JacExpP-445
Cunningham, Bill Aloysius
❑ 19Zee-111
❑ 20NatCarE-19
❑ 21KoBreWSI-8
❑ 21Nei-112
❑ 21Zee-138
❑ 22E120-183
❑ 22W573-26
❑ 22W575-21
❑ 23W503-9
❑ 23W515-1
❑ 26Zee-110
Cunningham, Billy Kangaroo
❑ 80PhiBul-22
Cunningham, Bruce
❑ 27Zee-11
❑ 28Zee-28
Cunningham, Chip
❑ 85PriWilPT-5
Cunningham, Dave
❑ 55DesMoiHB-5
❑ 88AshTouP-1075
❑ 89WatDiaP-1795
❑ 89WatDiaS-3
Cunningham, Earl
❑ 89HigSchPLS-2
❑ 89WytCubS-8
❑ 90Bow-34
❑ 90BowTif-34
❑ 90OPC-134
❑ 90PeoChiCTI-1
❑ 90PeoChiCTI-2
❑ 90PeoChiCTI-3
❑ 90PeoChiCTI-4
❑ 90PeoChiTI-1
❑ 90PeoChiTI-2
❑ 90PeoChiTI-9
❑ 90Sco-670
❑ 90StaFS7-23
❑ 90Top-134
❑ 90TopTif-134
❑ 90TopTVCu-42
❑ 91Bow-420
❑ 91Cla/Bes-435
❑ 91PeoChiC-8
❑ 91PeoChiP-1354
❑ 91PeoChiTI-24
❑ 92Bow-81
❑ 92ClaFS7-316
❑ 92PeoChiC-1
❑ 92PeoChiTI-6
❑ 92ProFS7-208
❑ 92WinSpiC-2
❑ 93PeoChiTI-4
❑ 94LakElsSC-5
❑ 94LakElsSF-1675
❑ 95LakElsSTI-9
❑ 96AshTouB-10
Cunningham, Ellsworth
❑ 87OldJudN-109
Cunningham, Everett
❑ 88ButCopKSP-27
❑ 89GasRanP-1000
❑ 89GasRanS-6
❑ 89SouAtlLAGS-43
❑ 90ChaRanS-6
❑ 90FloStaLAS-29
❑ 90TulDriTI-6
❑ 91LinDriAA-578
❑ 91TulDriLD-578
❑ 91TulDriP-2766
❑ 91TulDriTI-6
Cunningham, George
❑ 20Zee-19
Cunningham, Joe (Joseph R.)
❑ 47Exh-53A
❑ 47Exh-53B
❑ 55Top-37
❑ 55TopDouH-37
❑ 57Top-304
❑ 58CarJayP-3
❑ 58Top-168
❑ 59Top-285
❑ 60Baz-27
❑ 60CarJayP-2
❑ 60Top-40

❑ 60Top-562
❑ 60TopTat-10
❑ 60TopVen-40
❑ 61CarJayP-3
❑ 61Pos-172A
❑ 61Pos-172B
❑ 61SevElev-19
❑ 61Top-520
❑ 62Jel-160
❑ 62Pos-160
❑ 62PosCan-160
❑ 62SalPlaC-173A
❑ 62SalPlaC-173B
❑ 62ShiPlaC-173
❑ 62Top-195
❑ 62TopVen-195
❑ 62WhiSoxTS-5
❑ 63ExhStaB-19
❑ 63Jel-35
❑ 63Pos-35
❑ 63Top-100
❑ 63WhiSoxJP-2
❑ 63WhiSoxTS-4
❑ 64Top-340
❑ 64TopVen-340
❑ 64WhiSoxI-7
❑ 64WhiSoxTS-6
❑ 65Top-496
❑ 65TopEmbl-63
❑ 66Top-531
❑ 79DiaGre-175
❑ 79TCM50-105
❑ 92CarMcD-33
❑ 98PriWilCQ-28

Cunningham, Joseph
❑ 87St.PetCP-8
❑ 88St.PetCS-4
❑ 89HamRedS-28
❑ 90JohCitCS-29
❑ 91JohCitCC-30
❑ 91JohCitCP-4172
❑ 93JohCitCC-30
❑ 94MadHatC-27
❑ 94MadHatF-149
❑ 95LouRedF-292
❑ 96LouRedB-2
❑ 97PeoChi-28

Cunningham, Kenn
❑ 89LakTigS-27
❑ 90BriTigP-3174
❑ 90BriTigS-27

Cunningham, O'Brian
❑ 91HigSchPLS-13
❑ 92LetMouSP-21

Cunningham, Scott
❑ 91OklStaC-5
❑ 92OklStaC-6
❑ 94NewJerCC-5
❑ 94NewJerCF-3406

Cunningham, Sean
❑ 87BurExpP-1091
❑ 88RocExpLC-9
❑ 89JacExpB-22
❑ 89JacExpP-158
❑ 90WesPalBES-31
❑ 91WesPalBEC-30

Cunningham, Shawn
❑ 88BenBucL-3
❑ 88BenBucL-33

Cunningham, Troy
❑ 89SpoIndSP-17
❑ 90ChaRaiB-7
❑ 90ChaRaiP-2034

Cunningham, Wm. J.
❑ 11PinT-5-553
❑ 12T207-38

Cuomo, Mario
❑ 94UppDecTAE-60

Cupit, Wayne
❑ 92AubAstC-23
❑ 92AubAstF-1347

Cupples, Michael
❑ 84IdaFalATI-7
❑ 85MadMusP-7
❑ 85MadMusT-10
❑ 86MadMusP-7
❑ 86MadMusP-7
❑ 87MadMusP-5
❑ 87MadMusP-16

Cuppy, Nig (George)
❑ 93JusSo-4
❑ 98CamPepP-17

Curbelo, Jorge
❑ 82MiaMarT-10

Curl, John
❑ 96DunBluJB-3
❑ 96DunBluJTI-5
❑ 96Exc-114
❑ 97DunBluJTI-6
❑ 97KnoSmo-7
❑ 98MobBayBTI-6

Curley, Tim
❑ 89PriPirS-3

Curnal, Jim
❑ 78TacYanC-19

Curnow, Robert
❑ 88SpoIndP-1939
❑ 89WatDiaP-1777
❑ 89WatDiaS-4
❑ 90ChaRaiB-8
❑ 90ChaRaiP-2042

Curran, Bud
❑ 79CedRapGT-14
❑ 88CedRapRP-1161

Curran, Dave
❑ 80HolMilT-22

Curran, Mike
❑ 75WesPalBES-15

Curran, Pat
❑ 75WatRoyT-8

Curran, Shawn
❑ 91ClaDraP-48
❑ 91FroRowDP-27
❑ 91FroRowDPG-27
❑ 91FroRowDPS-27
❑ 91HigSchPLS-25
❑ 92StaCluD-30
❑ 94OriPro-21

Curran, Tighe
❑ 94JohCitCC-9
❑ 94JohCitCF-3692
❑ 95PeoChiTI-9

Currence, Lafayette (Delaney)
❑ 76SSP-251
❑ 94BreMilB-306

Currens, Tim
❑ 97BriWhiSB-2
❑ 98HicCraM-9
❑ 98HicCraUO-12

Current, Matt
❑ 88MarPhiS-8
❑ 89MarPhiS-9
❑ 89Sta-143
❑ 90SpaPhiB-13
❑ 90SpaPhiP-2494
❑ 90SpaPhiS-4
❑ 91ClePhiC-13
❑ 91ClePhiP-1624

Currie, Brian
❑ 89BoiHawP-2000
❑ 90EriSaiS-4

Currie, Clarence
❑ 11SpoLifCW-85

Currier, Bryan
❑ 92EugEmeC-8
❑ 92EugEmeF-3019
❑ 93RocRoyC-9
❑ 93RocRoyF-709

Currier, Lenny
❑ 86AlbDukP-4
❑ 87AlbDukD-4
❑ 88AlbDukP-272

Currin, Wes
❑ 88SumBraP-395
❑ 89DurBullS-7
❑ 89DurBullS-7
❑ 89DurBulTI-7
❑ 89Sta-70

Curron, Bud
❑ 85CedRapRT-30

Curry, Clinton
❑ 83TriTriT-25

Curry, Dell
❑ 91GasRanC-27

Curry, G. Tony
❑ 60Top-541
❑ 61Pos-120A
❑ 61Pos-120B
❑ 61Top-262
❑ 61TopStal-51
❑ 67SeaPop-5
❑ 81TCM60I-452

Curry, Mike
❑ 98SpoIndG-7
❑ 99TeaBesR-16
❑ 99TeaBesRG-16
❑ 99TeaBesRS-16

Curry, Steve
❑ 80CarMudF-24
❑ 81RicBraT-17
❑ 86GreBraTI-6
❑ 86RicBraP-3
❑ 89BurBraP-1613
❑ 89BurBraS-29
❑ 90IdaFalBP-3262
❑ 91IdaFalBP-4344
❑ 91RicBraBC-43
❑ 92BurAstC-26
❑ 92BurAstF-563

Curry, Steve (Stephen T.)
❑ 86NewBriRSP-8
❑ 87PawRedSP-53
❑ 87PawRedST-3
❑ 88PawRedSC-7
❑ 88PawRedSP-468
❑ 88ScoRoo-81T
❑ 88ScoRooG-81T
❑ 88TriAAAP-31
❑ 89Fle-86
❑ 89FleGlo-86
❑ 89PanSti-267
❑ 89PawRedSC-2
❑ 89PawRedSP-691
❑ 89PawRedSTI-6
❑ 89ScoHot1R-53
❑ 89Top-471
❑ 89TopTif-471
❑ 90PawRedSDD-4
❑ 90PawRedSP-454
❑ 90ProAAAF-426
❑ 90TopTVRS-41
❑ 92MemChiF-2411
❑ 92MemChiS-432

Curtice, John
❑ 98BesNumOP-15
❑ 98Bow-87
❑ 98BowChr-87
❑ 98BowChrGA-87
❑ 98BowChrGAR-87
❑ 98BowChrI-87
❑ 98BowChrIR-87
❑ 98BowChrR-87
❑ 98BowGolA-87
❑ 98BowInt-87
❑ 98MicBatCM-9
❑ 98MidLeaPM-15
❑ 98Top-494
❑ 98TopChr-494
❑ 98TopChrR-494
❑ 98TopDevR-494
❑ 98TopDia-494
❑ 98TopMiniC-494
❑ 99Bow-166
❑ 99BowAut-BA53
❑ 99BowChr-166
❑ 99BowChrG-166
❑ 99BowChrGR-166
❑ 99BowChrI-166
❑ 99BowChrIR-166
❑ 99BowChrR-166
❑ 99BowGol-166
❑ 99BowInt-166
❑ 99SP TopP-36
❑ 99SP TopPPE-36

Curtis, Brandon
❑ 98St.PauSTI-2

Curtis, Chad
❑ 90MidLeaASGS-30
❑ 90QuaCitAGS-21
❑ 91EdmTraLD-159
❑ 91EdmTraP-1522
❑ 91LinDriAAA-159
❑ 91TriA AAGP-AAA13
❑ 92AngPol-5
❑ 92Bow-627
❑ 92Cla2-T96
❑ 92DonRoo-30
❑ 92DonUpd-U5
❑ 92FleUpd-8
❑ 92LeaGolR-BC1
❑ 92Pin-523
❑ 92PinRoo-29
❑ 92PinRooI-17
❑ 92PinTea2-40
❑ 92ProFS7-29
❑ 92ScoRoo-87T
❑ 92Stu-143
❑ 92TopTra-25T
❑ 92TopTraG-25T
❑ 92Ult-323
❑ 92UltAllR-6
❑ 92UppDec-774
❑ 93AngAdoF-1
❑ 93AngMot-12
❑ 93AngPol-7
❑ 93AngStaCl-23
❑ 93Bow-313
❑ 93DiaMar-26
❑ 93Don-93
❑ 93Fin-146
❑ 93FinRef-146
❑ 93Fla-170
❑ 93Fle-571
❑ 93FleRooS-RSB4
❑ 93Lea-227
❑ 93OPC-28
❑ 93OPCPre-2
❑ 93PacSpa-42
❑ 93PanSti-10
❑ 93Pin-411
❑ 93Sco-354
❑ 93Sel-290
❑ 93SelChaR-9
❑ 93SP-19
❑ 93StaClu-543
❑ 93StaCluFDI-543
❑ 93StaCluMOP-543
❑ 93Stu-2
❑ 93Top-699
❑ 93TopGol-699
❑ 93TopInaM-699
❑ 93TopInaR-699
❑ 93TopMic-699
❑ 93Toy-2
❑ 93TriPla-70
❑ 93TriPlaA-26
❑ 93Ult-159
❑ 93UppDec-235
❑ 93UppDecGold-235
❑ 93USPlaCA-2H
❑ 93USPlaCR-13S
❑ 94AngLAT-2
❑ 94AngMot-4
❑ 94Bow-179
❑ 94ColC-87
❑ 94ColChoGS-87
❑ 94ColChoSS-87
❑ 94Don-11
❑ 94DonSpeE-11
❑ 94Fin-358
❑ 94FinRef-358
❑ 94Fla-267
❑ 94Fle-50
❑ 94FleExtB-30
❑ 94FUnPac-114
❑ 94Lea-19
❑ 94LeaL-14
❑ 94OPC-98
❑ 94Pac-73
❑ 94PanSti-35
❑ 94Pin-282
❑ 94PinArtP-282
❑ 94PinMusC-282
❑ 94ProMag-16
❑ 94Sco-95
❑ 94ScoGolR-95
❑ 94ScoGolS-56
❑ 94Sel-345
❑ 94SP-22
❑ 94SPDieC-22
❑ 94Spo-119
❑ 94StaClu-295
❑ 94StaCluFDI-295
❑ 94StaCluGR-295
❑ 94StaCluMOP-295
❑ 94Stu-8
❑ 94Top-56
❑ 94TopGol-56
❑ 94TopSpa-56
❑ 94TriPla-11
❑ 94Ult-323
❑ 94UppDec-82
❑ 94UppDecED-82
❑ 94USPlaCA-8H
❑ 95Bow-340
❑ 95BowBes-R64
❑ 95BowBesR-R64
❑ 95ColCho-99
❑ 95ColCho-580T
❑ 95ColChoGS-99
❑ 95ColChoSE-32
❑ 95ColChoSEGS-32
❑ 95ColChoSESS-32
❑ 95ColChoSS-99
❑ 95Don-99
❑ 95DonPreP-99
❑ 95DonTopotO-72
❑ 95Emo-41
❑ 95Fin-179
❑ 95Fin-263
❑ 95FinRef-179
❑ 95FinRef-263
❑ 95Fla-16
❑ 95Fla-255
❑ 95Fle-219
❑ 95FleUpd-18
❑ 95Lea-297
❑ 95LeaLim-25
❑ 95Pac-53
❑ 95Pin-220
❑ 95PinArtP-220
❑ 95PinMusC-220
❑ 95Sco-392
❑ 95ScoGolR-392
❑ 95ScoPlaTS-392
❑ 95ScoYouTE-392T
❑ 95Sel-184
❑ 95SelArtP-184
❑ 95SP-152
❑ 95Spo-100
❑ 95SpoArtP-100
❑ 95SPSil-152
❑ 95StaClu-169
❑ 95StaClu-547
❑ 95StaCluFDI-169
❑ 95StaCluMOP-169
❑ 95StaCluMOP-547
❑ 95StaCluSTWS-169
❑ 95StaCluSTWS-547
❑ 95Stu-70
❑ 95Top-154
❑ 95TopCyb-92
❑ 95TopTra-21T
❑ 95Ult-266
❑ 95UltGolM-266
❑ 95UppDec-424
❑ 95UppDecED-424
❑ 95UppDecEDG-424
❑ 95UppDecSE-229
❑ 95UppDecSEG-229
❑ 96Baz-77
❑ 96ColCho-147
❑ 96ColChoGS-147
❑ 96ColChoSS-147
❑ 96Don-135
❑ 96DonDiaK-18
❑ 96DonPreP-135
❑ 96EmoXL-58
❑ 96Fin-B172
❑ 96FinRef-B172
❑ 96Fla-78
❑ 96Fle-107
❑ 96FleTif-107
❑ 96Lea-67
❑ 96LeaPrePB-67
❑ 96LeaPrePG-67
❑ 96LeaPrePS-67
❑ 96LeaSigA-53
❑ 96LeaSigAG-53
❑ 96LeaSigAS-53
❑ 96MetUni-56
❑ 96MetUniP-56
❑ 96Pac-313
❑ 96PacPri-P100
❑ 96PacPriG-P100
❑ 96PanSti-144
❑ 96Pin-118
❑ 96ProSta-121
❑ 96Sco-11
❑ 96ScoDugC-A11
❑ 96ScoDugCAP-A11
❑ 96SP-84
❑ 96StaClu-21
❑ 96StaCluB&B-BB9
❑ 96StaCluEPB-21
❑ 96StaCluEPG-21
❑ 96StaCluEPS-21
❑ 96StaCluMOP-21
❑ 96StaCluMOP-BB9
❑ 96Stu-95
❑ 96StuPrePB-95
❑ 96StuPrePG-95
❑ 96StuPrePS-95
❑ 96Sum-97
❑ 96SumAbo&B-97
❑ 96SumArtP-97
❑ 96SumFoi-97
❑ 96Top-202
❑ 96TopGal-85
❑ 96TopGalPPI-85
❑ 96Ult-57
❑ 96UltGolM-57
❑ 96UppDec-67
❑ 97Cir-326
❑ 97CirRav-326
❑ 97ColCho-314
❑ 97DodSco-11
❑ 97DodScoPI-11
❑ 97DodScoPr-11
❑ 97Fle-359
❑ 97FleTif-359
❑ 97Sco-239
❑ 97Sco-349
❑ 97ScoArtPWB-239
❑ 97ScoArtPWB-349
❑ 97ScoPreS-239
❑ 97ScoResC-349
❑ 97ScoShoS-239
❑ 97ScoShoS-349
❑ 97ScoShoSAP-239
❑ 97ScoShoSAP-349
❑ 97Top-449
❑ 97Ult-452
❑ 97UltGolME-452
❑ 97UltPlaME-452
❑ 97UppDec-344
❑ 98ColCho-179
❑ 98Fin-82
❑ 98FinNo--82
❑ 98FinNo-R-82
❑ 98FinRef-82
❑ 98Fle-112
❑ 98Pac-146
❑ 98PacOnl-500
❑ 98PacOnlR-500
❑ 98PacOnlWC-500
❑ 98PacPlaB-146
❑ 98PacRedT-146
❑ 98PacSil-146
❑ 98Sco-127
❑ 98StaCluFDI-207
❑ 98StaCluI-207
❑ 98StaCluOneK-207
❑ 98StaCluPP-207
❑ 98Top-406
❑ 98TopChr-406
❑ 98TopChrR-406
❑ 98TopDevR-406
❑ 98TopDia-406
❑ 98TopMiniC-406
❑ 98UppDec-461
❑ 98YanSco-11
❑ 98YanScoP-11
❑ 98YanUppD-461
❑ 99Fle-322
❑ 99FleSta9-322
❑ 99FleWarT-322
❑ 99Pac-290
❑ 99PacPlaB-290
❑ 99PacRed-290
❑ 99StaClu-208
❑ 99StaCluFDI-208
❑ 99StaCluOoaK-208
❑ 99StaCluPP-208
❑ 99Top-124
❑ 99TopChr-124
❑ 99TopChrR-124
❑ 99TopMVPP-124
❑ 99TopOpeD-72
❑ 99UppDec-441
❑ 99UppDecEL1-441
❑ 99UppDecEL2-441
❑ 99YanFle-26

Curtis, Chris
❑ 91ButCopKSP-10
❑ 92ClaFS7-327
❑ 92GasRanC-19
❑ 92GasRanF-2243
❑ 92StaCluD-31
❑ 93ChaRanC-6
❑ 94TulDriF-235
❑ 94TulDriTI-4
❑ 96OklCit8B-6
❑ 97BowBay-14
❑ 98RocRedWQ-10

Curtis, Cliff (Clinton)
❑ 11PinT-5-708
❑ 11SpoLifM-137
❑ 90DodTar-920

Curtis, Craig
❑ 90AshTouP-2753
❑ 91OscAstC-22
❑ 91OscAstP-696
❑ 92BurAstC-18
❑ 92BurAstF-554

Curtis, Ed
❑ 12ImpTobC-90

Curtis, Irvin
❑ 87OldJudN-110

Curtis, Jack P.
❑ 61Top-533
❑ 62CubJayP-5
❑ 62Top-372
❑ 66TolMudHTI-6

Curtis, John D.
❑ 72RedSoxTI-4
❑ 72Top-724
❑ 73LinPor-18
❑ 73OPC-143
❑ 73Top-143
❑ 74OPC-373
❑ 74Top-373
❑ 74TopTra-373T
❑ 75OPC-381
❑ 75St.LouCP-5
❑ 75Top-381
❑ 75TopMin-381
❑ 76OPC-239
❑ 76St.LouCP-4
❑ 76Top-239
❑ 77Top-324
❑ 78GiaTeal-6
❑ 78Top-486
❑ 79GiaPol-40
❑ 79Top-649
❑ 80Top-12
❑ 81Fle-491
❑ 81OPC-158
❑ 81Top-531
❑ 81TopSti-231
❑ 82Fle-569
❑ 82Top-219
❑ 83Don-170
❑ 83Fle-84
❑ 83Top-777
❑ 84AngSmo-6
❑ 84Fle-513
❑ 84Nes792-158
❑ 84Top-158
❑ 84TopTif-158
❑ 89PriPirS-4
❑ 90WelPirP-12
Curtis, Kevin
❑ 94OriPro-22
❑ 96BowBayB-13
Curtis, Matt
❑ 96BoiHawB-8
❑ 98MidAngG-11
❑ 98MidAngO-9
Curtis, Mike
❑ 86GenCubP-4
❑ 87WinSpiP-27
❑ 88HarSenP-843
❑ 90Bes-119
❑ 90CanIndB-26
❑ 90CanIndP-1287
❑ 90CanIndS-3
❑ 90CMC-733
❑ 90EasLeaAP-EL38
❑ 91CanIndLD-80
❑ 91CanIndP-974
❑ 91LinDriAA-80
Curtis, Randy
❑ 91PitMetC-6
❑ 91PitMetP-3434
❑ 92ClaFS7-80
❑ 92ColMetC-24
❑ 92ColMetF-307
❑ 92ColMetPI-13
❑ 92ColMetPI-31
❑ 93ClaFS7-131
❑ 93FloStaLAF-39
❑ 93St.LucMC-7
❑ 93St.LuMF-2932
❑ 94Bow-345
❑ 94ClaGolF-167
❑ 94ExcFS7-233
❑ 94LasVegSF-879
❑ 94UppDecML-65
❑ 94UppDecML-99
❑ 95SigRooOJ-11
❑ 95SigRooOJP-11
❑ 95SigRooOJPS-11
❑ 95SigRooOJS-11
❑ 96RanCucQB-8
❑ 97AkrAer-7
Curtwright, Guy
❑ 47Exh-54
Cusack, John
❑ 88PacEigMO-12
Cusack, Rocky
❑ 87LakTigP-12
❑ 88ChaKniTI-13
Cusey, Lee
❑ 92MadMusC-13
❑ 92MadMusF-1226
❑ 93AlbPolF-2021
Cushing, Steve
❑ 81BatTroT-4
❑ 81WatIndT-32
❑ 82WatIndF-15
❑ 82WatIndT-1
Cushman, Dwayne
❑ 97BurBeeB-5
Cushman, Ed
❑ 87BucN28-56
❑ 87OldJudN-111A
❑ 87OldJudN-111B
❑ 90KalBatN-10
Cusick, Anthony
❑ 87OldJudN-112
Cusick, Jack
❑ 52Bow-192
Cusson, Mario
❑ 82MonNew-5
Cust, Jack
❑ 98Bow-153
❑ 98BowChr-153
❑ 98BowChrGA-153
❑ 98BowChrGAR-153
❑ 98BowChrI-153
❑ 98BowChrIR-153
❑ 98BowChrR-153
❑ 98BowGolA-153
❑ 98BowInt-153
❑ 98LetBlaDG-7
❑ 98StaCluFDI-395
❑ 98StaCluI-395
❑ 98StaCluOneK-395
❑ 98StaCluPP-395
❑ 98Top-495
❑ 98TopChr-495
❑ 98TopChrR-495
❑ 98TopDevR-495
❑ 98TopDia-495
❑ 98TopMiniC-495
❑ 99Bow-73
❑ 99BowChr-73
❑ 99BowChrG-73
❑ 99BowChrGR-73
❑ 99BowChrI-73
❑ 99BowChrIR-73
❑ 99BowChrR-73
❑ 99BowGol-73
❑ 99BowInt-73
Cutchins, Todd
❑ 96PitMetB-8
❑ 98CapCitBF5-5
❑ 98CapCitBM-5
Cutler, Brad
❑ 75TacTwiK-16
Cutshall, Bill
❑ 86JacExpT-24
❑ 87NasSouTI-3
❑ 88OrlTwiB-27
Cutshall, Patrick
❑ 97AubDouTI-17
❑ 98QuaCitRBG-4
Cutshaw, George
❑ 09ObaT21-100
❑ 09ObaT21-272
❑ 10BisCoaLE99-7
❑ 11PacCoaBD-15
❑ 11Zee-25
❑ 12ObaPreT-21
❑ 14B18B-56
❑ 16FleBreD-21
❑ 17ColE13-37
❑ 17HolBreD-20
❑ 20NatCarE-20
❑ 21Exh-30
❑ 22E120-50
❑ 22W573-27
❑ 23WilChoV-25
❑ 25Zee-134
❑ 26Zee-161
❑ 90DodTar-157
Cutty, Fran
❑ 81ChaRoyT-11
❑ 82ForMyeRT-15
Cuyler, KiKi (Hazen)
❑ 25Exh-51
❑ 26Exh-51
❑ 26SpoComoA-13
❑ 26SpoNewSM-1
❑ 27Exh-25
❑ 28StaPlaCE-15
❑ 28W56PlaC-C1
❑ 29CubCerICP-2
❑ 29ExhFou-6
❑ 30ChiEveAP-2
❑ 30SchR33-3
❑ 30SchR33-29
❑ 30UncJac-7
❑ 31Exh-6
❑ 31W517-19
❑ 32CubTeal-3
❑ 32OrbPinNP-6
❑ 32OrbPinUP-14
❑ 33CraJacP-3
❑ 33DelR33-8
❑ 33Gou-23
❑ 33GouCanV-23
❑ 33RitCE-5C
❑ 33TatOrb-14
❑ 33TatOrbSDR-152
❑ 33WorCig-30
❑ 34DiaMatCSB-38
❑ 34DiaStaR-31A
❑ 34DiaStaR-31B
❑ 34Gou-90
❑ 35DiaMatCS3T1-42
❑ 35GouPuzR-1F
❑ 35GouPuzR-3D
❑ 35GouPuzR-14D
❑ 35GouPuzR-15D
❑ 36GouBWR-10
❑ 36GouWidPPR-A23
❑ 36NatChiFPR-91
❑ 36R31PasP-7
❑ 36R31PasP-37
❑ 36SandSW-10
❑ 36WorWidGV-55
❑ 37WheBB9-4
❑ 42CubTeal-25
❑ 43CubTeal-25
❑ 60Fle-75
❑ 61Fle-19
❑ 67SpoHobFC-9
❑ 71FleWorS-23
❑ 73FleWilD-14
❑ 76RowExh-9
❑ 76ShaPiz-109
❑ 77BobParHoF-85
❑ 77CubAllT-2
❑ 77GalGloG-72
❑ 80CubGreT-8
❑ 80PacLeg-92
❑ 80PerHaloFP-108
❑ 80SSPHOF-108
❑ 82DiaCla-54
❑ 89DodSmoG-6
❑ 90DodTar-158
❑ 91ConTSN-12
❑ 92ConTSN-587
❑ 92CubOldS-7
❑ 93ConTSN-741
❑ 94ConTSN-1096
❑ 94ConTSNB-1096
Cuyler, Milt
❑ 87FayGenP-8
❑ 88FloStaLAS-32
❑ 88LakTigS-8
❑ 89TolMudHC-21
❑ 89TolMudHP-787
❑ 90Bow-358
❑ 90BowTif-358
❑ 90CMC-398
❑ 90ProAAAF-390
❑ 90Sco-583A
❑ 90Sco-583B
❑ 90Sco100RS-84
❑ 90TigTeal-6
❑ 90TolMudHC-21
❑ 90TolMudHP-160
❑ 91Bow-141
❑ 91Cla1-T42
❑ 91ClaGam-191
❑ 91Don-40
❑ 91DonRoo-6
❑ 91Fle-334
❑ 91Lea-251
❑ 91OPC-684
❑ 91OPCPre-27
❑ 91StaClu-470
❑ 91Stu-51
❑ 91TigCok-22
❑ 91Top-684
❑ 91TopDeb90-36
❑ 91TopDesS-684
❑ 91TopMic-684
❑ 91TopTif-684
❑ 91UltUpd-22
❑ 91UppDec-556
❑ 92Bow-196
❑ 92ClaGam-87
❑ 92Don-232
❑ 92Fle-130
❑ 92FleRooS-7
❑ 92Lea-75
❑ 92LeaBlaG-75
❑ 92MVPPin-21
❑ 92OPC-522
❑ 92PanSti-110
❑ 92Pin-174
❑ 92PinTea2-44
❑ 92Sco-26
❑ 92Sco100RS-1
❑ 92ScoImpP-4
❑ 92StaClu-5
❑ 92Stu-171
❑ 92TigKro-5
❑ 92TigTeal-7
❑ 92Top-522
❑ 92TopGol-522
❑ 92TopGolW-522
❑ 92TopMic-522
❑ 92TriPla-100
❑ 92Ult-57
❑ 92UppDec-536
❑ 93Don-173
❑ 93Fle-224
❑ 93Lea-38
❑ 93PacSpa-105
❑ 93Pin-193
❑ 93RedFolS-21
❑ 93Sco-82
❑ 93Sel-166
❑ 93StaClu-156
❑ 93StaCluFDI-156
❑ 93StaCluMOP-156
❑ 93TigGat-4
❑ 93Top-429
❑ 93TopGol-429
❑ 93TopInaM-429
❑ 93TopInaR-429
❑ 93TopMic-429
❑ 93TriPla-44
❑ 93Ult-194
❑ 93UppDec-162
❑ 93UppDecGold-162
❑ 94Don-475
❑ 94Fle-125
❑ 94Pin-359
❑ 94PinArtP-359
❑ 94PinMusC-359
❑ 94Sco-79
❑ 95Don-274
❑ 95DonPreP-274
❑ 95Fle-46
❑ 95Pin-130
❑ 95PinArtP-130
❑ 95PinMusC-130
❑ 95Sco-259
❑ 95ScoGolR-259
❑ 95ScoPlaTS-259
❑ 95TolMudHTI-12
❑ 95Top-182
Cvejdlik, Kent
❑ 76WatRoyT-4
❑ 80OmaRoyP-8
Cyburt, Phil
❑ 78SalPirT-3
Cypret, Greg
❑ 80ColAstT-1
❑ 81TucTorT-1
❑ 82TucTorT-6
❑ 83TucTorT-15
❑ 84TucTorC-54
Czajkowski, Jim
❑ 87SumBraP-19
❑ 88DurBulS-4A
❑ 89DurBullS-8
❑ 89DurBullS-8
❑ 89DurBulTI-8
❑ 90HarSenP-1187
❑ 90HarSenS-6
❑ 91ElPasDLD-179
❑ 91ElPasDP-2740
❑ 91LinDriAA-179
❑ 92ElPasDF-3913
❑ 92ElPasDS-204
❑ 94ColSprSSF-726
❑ 96SyrChiTI-11
Czanstkowski, Tom
❑ 93AubAstC-6
❑ 93AubAstF-3433
❑ 94QuaCitRBC-8
❑ 94QuaCitRBF-528
Czarkowski, Mark
❑ 92JacSunF-3702
❑ 93CalCanF-1159
Czarnik, Chris
❑ 89BurBraP-1617
❑ 89BurBraS-8
❑ 89Sta-110
❑ 90DurBulTI-9
D'Acquisto, John (John F.)
❑ 74OPC-608
❑ 74Top-608A
❑ 74Top-608B
❑ 75GiaTeal-4
❑ 75OPC-372
❑ 75Top-372
❑ 75TopMin-372
❑ 76OPC-628
❑ 76SanFraGP-5
❑ 76SSP-94
❑ 76Top-628
❑ 77PadSchC-17
❑ 77Top-19
❑ 78PadFamF-8
❑ 79PadFamF-2
❑ 79Top-506
❑ 80Top-339
❑ 81Fle-163
❑ 81LonBeaPT-23
❑ 81OPC-204
❑ 81Top-427
❑ 82RicBraT-4
❑ 82Top-58
❑ 83Fle-516
❑ 89PacSenL-121
❑ 89TopSenL-31
❑ 93HolLeg-3
D'Alessandro, Marc
❑ 96AshTouB-11
❑ 97AshTou-8
D'Alessandro, Sal
❑ 85DurBulT-22
❑ 86GreBraTI-7
❑ 87RicBraBC-4
❑ 87RicBraC-10
❑ 88GreBraB-3
D'Alexander, Greg
❑ 90ArkRaz-10
❑ 90MiaMirIS-4
❑ 91MiaMirC-19
❑ 91MiaMirP-413
D'Amato, Brian
❑ 92ChaRaiC-8
❑ 92ChaRaiF-115
❑ 93WatDiaC-10
❑ 93WatDiaF-1760
❑ 94HigDesMC-10
❑ 94HigDesMF-2782
D'Ambrosia, Mark
❑ 94HunCubC-5
❑ 94HunCubF-3557
D'Amico, Jeff Charles
❑ 94Bow-205
❑ 94Bow-374
❑ 94BrePol-5
❑ 94Cla-173
❑ 94ClaGolF-2
❑ 94ClaGolN1PLF-LP3
❑ 94ClaGolREF-RE3
❑ 94SigRoo-30
❑ 94SigRooS-30
❑ 94Top-759
❑ 94TopGol-759
❑ 94TopSpa-759
❑ 95BelBreTI-9
❑ 95Bow-74
❑ 95BowBes-B47
❑ 95BowBesR-B47
❑ 95MidLeaA-11
❑ 95SPML-80
❑ 95Top-282
❑ 96BesAutS-25
❑ 96Bow-165
❑ 96BowBes-95
❑ 96BowBesAR-95
❑ 96BowBesR-95
❑ 96BowFoi-165
❑ 96El PasDB-7
❑ 96Exc-69
❑ 96Top-429
❑ 97Bow-55
❑ 97BowBes-113
❑ 97BowBesAR-113
❑ 97BowBesR-113
❑ 97BowCerBlaIA-CA19
❑ 97BowCerBluIA-CA19
❑ 97BowCerGolIA-CA19
❑ 97BowInt-55
❑ 97BrePol-5
❑ 97Cir-345
❑ 97CirRav-345
❑ 97ColCho-3
❑ 97DonRatR-7
❑ 97Fin-39
❑ 97FinRef-39
❑ 97Fle-127
❑ 97FleTif-127
❑ 97Lea-3
❑ 97LeaFraM-3
❑ 97LeaFraMDC-3
❑ 97MetUni-64
❑ 97Pin-159
❑ 97PinArtP-PP159
❑ 97PinMusC-159
❑ 97PinPrePla-159
❑ 97Sco-269
❑ 97ScoArtPWB-269
❑ 97ScoPreS-269
❑ 97ScoShoS-269
❑ 97ScoShoSAP-269
❑ 97SP-103
❑ 97StaClu-286
❑ 97StaCluM-M32
❑ 97StaCluMOP-286
❑ 97StaCluMOP-M32
❑ 97Top-39
❑ 97TopChr-14
❑ 97TopChrR-14
❑ 97TopGal-145
❑ 97TopGalPPI-145
❑ 97Ult-75
❑ 97UltGolME-75
❑ 97UltPlaME-75
❑ 97UppDec-227
❑ 97UppDecBCP-BC14
❑ 97UppDecTTS-TS17
❑ 98CirThu-218
❑ 98CirThuRav-218
❑ 98CirThuSupRav-218
❑ 98ColCho-155
❑ 98Fin-182
❑ 98FinNo--182
❑ 98FinNo-R-182
❑ 98FinRef-182
❑ 98PacInvGems-57
❑ 98ScoRT-73
❑ 98SP Aut-119
❑ 98StaCluFDI-204
❑ 98StaCluI-204
❑ 98StaCluOneK-204
❑ 98StaCluPP-204
❑ 98Top-385
❑ 98TopChr-385
❑ 98TopChrR-385
❑ 98TopDevR-385
❑ 98TopDia-385
❑ 98TopMiniC-385
❑ 98Ult-378
❑ 98UltGolM-378
❑ 98UltMas-378
❑ 98UltPlaM-378
❑ 98UppDec-122
❑ 98UppDecSF-75
D'Amico, Jeff Michael
❑ 95WesMicWTI-30
❑ 96ModA'sB-18
❑ 97ModA'sG-6
D'Amore, Louis
❑ 81CliGiaT-14
D'Andrea, Mike (Michael)
❑ 92PulBraC-25
❑ 92PulBraF-3171
❑ 93ExcFS7-1
❑ 93MacBraC-8
❑ 93MacBraF-1394
❑ 94DurBulC-6
❑ 94DurBulF-323
❑ 94DurBulTI-5
❑ 95BreBtaTI-46
D'Aquila, Tom
❑ 94BluOriC-7
❑ 94BluOriF-3575
❑ 96FreKeyB-5
D'Onofrio, Gary
❑ 83DayBeaAT-20
D'Vincenzo, Mark
❑ 86LitFalMP-8
Daal, Omar
❑ 92AlbDukF-712
❑ 92SanAntMS-561
❑ 93AlbDukF-1453
❑ 93Bow-42
❑ 93DodMot-15
❑ 93FleFinE-81
❑ 93LinVenB-37
❑ 94DodMot-19
❑ 94Fle-508
❑ 94Pac-306
❑ 94Top-29
❑ 94TopGol-29

❑ 94TopSpa-29
❑ 94Ult-214
❑ 94VenLinU-35
❑ 95DodMot-17
❑ 95DodPol-6
❑ 95Fle-537
❑ 95LinVen-21
❑ 95Pac-214
❑ 95Top-518
❑ 95TopCyb-239
❑ 95Ult-179
❑ 95UltGolM-179
❑ 96-97LinVen-153
❑ 96-97LinVen-280
❑ 96FleUpd-U147
❑ 96FleUpdTC-U147
❑ 96LeaSigEA-40
❑ 96Pac-115
❑ 97Pac-342
❑ 97PacLigB-342
❑ 97PacSil-342
❑ 98ColCho-298
❑ 98DiaBacP-6
❑ 98DiaMcD-9
❑ 98PacOnl-35
❑ 98PacOnlR-35
❑ 98PacOnlWC-35
❑ 98UppDec-639
❑ 99Fle-180
❑ 99FleSta9-180
❑ 99FleWarT-180
❑ 99Pac-18
❑ 99PacCroC-14
❑ 99PacCroCPB-14
❑ 99PacPlaB-18
❑ 99PacRed-18
❑ 99SkyThu-105
❑ 99SkyThuRant-105
❑ 99SkyThuRave-105
❑ 99StaClu-191
❑ 99StaCluFDI-191
❑ 99StaCluOoaK-191
❑ 99StaCluPP-191
❑ 99ThuSkySupR-105
❑ 99Top-384
❑ 99TopChr-384
❑ 99TopChrR-384
❑ 99TopMVPP-384
❑ 99UppDec-302
❑ 99UppDecEL1-302
❑ 99UppDecEL2-302
❑ 99Vic-25

Dabney, Fred
❑ 88UtiBluSP-16
❑ 89SouBenWSGS-11
❑ 90SarWhiSS-6
❑ 91SarWhiSC-3
❑ 91SarWhiSP-1106
❑ 92BirBarF-2575
❑ 92BirBarS-81
❑ 93NasSouF-565
❑ 94CanIndF-3111
❑ 95IowCubTI-9

Dabney, Ty
❑ 85EveGiaC-3
❑ 86FreGiaSB-19
❑ 87ShrCapP-3
❑ 87TexLeaAF-32
❑ 88PhoFirC-22
❑ 88PhoFirP-72

Daboll, Dennis
❑ 65Top-561

Dace, Derek
❑ 96AubDouB-15
❑ 98JacSunM-7

Dacko, Mark
❑ 81BirBarT-7
❑ 82EvaTriT-3
❑ 83EvaTriT-1
❑ 84EvaTriT-6

Dacosta, Bill
❑ 87OneYanP-11
❑ 88PriWilYS-7

Dacus, Barry
❑ 86PalSprAP-9
❑ 86PalSprAS-19
❑ 87MidAngP-28
❑ 88EdmTraC-10
❑ 88EdmTraP-568

Dade, Paul (Lonnie Paul)
❑ 74SalLakCAC-99
❑ 76SalLakCGC-18
❑ 78IndTeal-7
❑ 78Kel-14
❑ 78OPC-86
❑ 78Top-662
❑ 79OPC-3
❑ 79Top-13
❑ 80OPC-134
❑ 80Top-254
❑ 81PadFamF-6
❑ 81Top-496

Daedelow, Craig
❑ 97DelSho-14
❑ 98FreKeyM-24

Dafforn, Mike
❑ 88MarPhiS-9
❑ 89MarPhiS-10

Dafun, Kekoa
❑ 95BoiHawTI-13

Daggett, Jesse
❑ 98EriSeaWM-8

Dagley, Corey
❑ 98BatMucTI-6

Daglia, Peter
❑ 26Zee-68
❑ 27Zee-50
❑ 28Zee-72
❑ 29Zee-67
❑ 30Zee-76
❑ 32Zee-52
❑ 37Zee-68

Dagres, Angie (Angelo George)
❑ 91OriCro-92

Dahl, Greg
❑ 80ColAstT-11

Dahl, Jay
❑ 77FriOneYW-117

Dahle, Dave
❑ 52MotCoo-15

Dahlen, Bill (William F.)
❑ 03BreE10-29
❑ 05RotCP-4
❑ 06FanCraNL-12
❑ 08RosComP-90
❑ 09ColChiE-70
❑ 09T206-83
❑ 09T206-84
❑ 10DarChoE-14
❑ 10DomDisP-30
❑ 10E98-11
❑ 10JuJuDE-13
❑ 10SweCapPP-72
❑ 11HelSta-84
❑ 11PinT-5-265
❑ 11PloCanE-20
❑ 11S74Sil-51
❑ 11SpoLifCW-86
❑ 11SpoLifM-152
❑ 11T205-35
❑ 11TurRedT-11
❑ 12ColRedB-70
❑ 12ColTinT-70
❑ 12HasTriFT-43
❑ 12HasTriFT-76
❑ 13NatGamW-13
❑ 14PieStaT-28
❑ 72ClaCar-17
❑ 90DodTar-159
❑ 95May-31

Dahlgren, Babe (Ellsworth)
❑ 32Zee-33
❑ 33Zee-14
❑ 38CloFotW-17
❑ 39PlaBal-81
❑ 40PlaBal-3
❑ 41PlaBal-49
❑ 43PhiTeal-6
❑ 46SeaSLP-12
❑ 72TCMthe3-15
❑ 75YanDyn1T-10
❑ 79DiaGre-8
❑ 90DodTar-160

Dahse, David
❑ 84NewOriT-4

Daigle, Tim
❑ 94BluOriC-6
❑ 94BluOriF-3555

Dailey, Jason
❑ 93DanBraC-12
❑ 93DanBraF-3630
❑ 94IdaFalBF-3597
❑ 94IdaFalBSP-2

Dailey, Steve
❑ 91OklStaC-6
❑ 92OklStaC-7

Dailey, Vincent
❑ 87OldJudN-113

Dailey, William G.
❑ 63Top-391
❑ 63TwiJayP-4
❑ 63TwiVol-5
❑ 64Top-156
❑ 64TopVen-156

Daily, Con (Cornelius F.)
❑ 87OldJudN-116
❑ 90DodTar-922

Daily, Ed (Edward M.)
❑ 87BucN28-110
❑ 87OldJudN-114
❑ 88GandBCGCE-11

Dakin, Brian
❑ 90EveGiaB-17
❑ 90EveGiaP-3133

Dal Canton, Bruce (John B.)
❑ 69PirTeal-6
❑ 69Top-468A
❑ 69Top-468B
❑ 70OPC-52
❑ 70PirTeal-5
❑ 70Top-52
❑ 71MLBOffS-413
❑ 71OPC-168
❑ 71oySigST-4
❑ 71Top-168
❑ 72Top-717
❑ 73OPC-487
❑ 73Top-487
❑ 74OPC-308
❑ 74RoyPos-9
❑ 74Top-308
❑ 75AtlBraP-8
❑ 75OPC-472
❑ 75RoyPos-7
❑ 75Top-472
❑ 75TopMin-472
❑ 76AtlBraP-9
❑ 76OPC-486
❑ 76Top-486
❑ 77Top-114
❑ 77WhiSoxT-5
❑ 79KnoKnoST-18
❑ 82DurBulT-22
❑ 85IntLeaAT-23
❑ 85RicBraT-23
❑ 86RicBraP-4
❑ 89BraDub-7
❑ 91LinDriAAA-450
❑ 91RicBraBC-40
❑ 91RicBraLD-450
❑ 91RicBraP-2585
❑ 92RicBraF-392
❑ 92RicBraRC-4
❑ 92RicBraS-450
❑ 93RicBraF-202
❑ 93RicBraRC-2
❑ 94GreBraF-429
❑ 94GreBraTI-2
❑ 95BreBtaTI-39
❑ 96DurBulBIB-20
❑ 97GreBraG-7
❑ 98DanQ-C-29

Dale, Carl
❑ 94NewJerCC-6
❑ 94NewJerCF-3407
❑ 94SigRooDP-46
❑ 94SigRooDPS-46
❑ 94StaCluDP-30
❑ 94StaCluDPFDI-30
❑ 95MidLeaA-10
❑ 95PeoChiTI-40
❑ 96ModA'sB-6
❑ 97HunStaTI-7

Dale, Gene (Emmett Eugene)
❑ 15SpoNewM-43
❑ 16SpoNewM-42

Dale, Phil
❑ 86TamTarP-4
❑ 87CedRapRP-2
❑ 88ChaLooB-18
❑ 89CedRapRAB-22
❑ 89GreHorP-427
❑ 90CedRapRDGB-22
❑ 91IdaFalBP-4345
❑ 91WavRedF-xx
❑ 93AusFut-93
❑ 93AusFut-99
❑ 95AusFut-93
❑ 95AusFutSFP-SFFP9

Dale, Ron
❑ 93RanCucQF-823

Dalena, Pete
❑ 83NasSouTI-5
❑ 84ColCliP-8
❑ 84ColCliT-18
❑ 84NasSouTI-5
❑ 85ColCliP-7
❑ 85ColCliT-15
❑ 86ColCliP-4
❑ 86ColCliP-4
❑ 87ColCliP-5
❑ 87ColCliP-7
❑ 87ColCliT-12
❑ 88ColCliC-16
❑ 88ColCliP-14
❑ 88ColCliP-321
❑ 89ColSprSSC-12
❑ 89ColSprSSP-235
❑ 89TriAAAP-AAA36
❑ 90CMC-641
❑ 90ProAAAF-172
❑ 90TopDeb89-27
❑ 90VanCanC-14
❑ 90VanCanP-494
❑ 91HarSenP-643
❑ 91LinDriAA-275
❑ 93BurBeeC-27

Dalesandro, Mark
❑ 90BoiHawP-3324
❑ 90ProAaA-166
❑ 91Cla/Bes-259
❑ 91MidLeaAP-MWL25
❑ 91QuaCitAC-16
❑ 91QuaCitAP-2634
❑ 92CalLeaACL-38
❑ 92PalSprAC-20
❑ 92PalSprAF-846
❑ 93PalSprAC-7
❑ 93PalSprAF-72
❑ 94Sel-198
❑ 94TopTra-34T
❑ 94VanCanF-1866
❑ 95AngMot-10
❑ 95Pac-54
❑ 95Sco-278
❑ 95ScoGolR-278
❑ 95ScoPlaTS-278
❑ 96ColCliB-8
❑ 97IowCub-10
❑ 97MidAngOHP-6
❑ 98PacOmeRS-12
❑ 98PacOmeRST2-12
❑ 98PacOnl-758
❑ 98PacOnlR-758
❑ 98PacOnlWC-758
❑ 98SyrSkyG-8

Daley, Bill (William)
❑ 87BucN28-6
❑ 87OldJudN-115

Daley, Buddy (Leavitt Leo)
❑ 47Exh-55
❑ 56A'sPos-12
❑ 57IndTeal-5
❑ 58Top-222
❑ 59Top-263
❑ 60A'sJayP-2
❑ 60A'sTeal-4
❑ 60ArmCoi-8
❑ 60Baz-2
❑ 60Top-8
❑ 60TopTat-11
❑ 60TopVen-8
❑ 61A'sTeal-5
❑ 61AthJayP-7
❑ 61Baz-4
❑ 61Pos-83A
❑ 61Pos-83B
❑ 61Top-48
❑ 61Top-422
❑ 61TopStal-159
❑ 61TopStal-201
❑ 61Yan61RL-14
❑ 62SalPlaC-203
❑ 62ShiPlaC-203
❑ 62Top-376
❑ 62YanJayP-5
❑ 63Top-38
❑ 64Top-164
❑ 64TopVen-164
❑ 65OPC-262
❑ 65Top-262
❑ 78TCM60I-257
❑ 83Yan196-14
❑ 91YanRinP13-11
❑ 92YanWIZ6-33

Daley, Joe
❑ 21Zee-139
❑ 22Zee-123

Daley, Jud
❑ 90DodTar-923

Daley, Pete (Peter Harvey)
❑ 55Top-206
❑ 57Top-388
❑ 58Top-73
❑ 59Top-276
❑ 60Top-108
❑ 60TopVen-108
❑ 61Top-158
❑ 62TopStal-94
❑ 81RedSoxBG2S-13

Daley, Thomas
❑ 09ObaT21-82
❑ 09ObaT21-257
❑ 11PacCoaBD-16
❑ 11Zee-7
❑ 12HomRunKE-5
❑ 12ObaPreT-6
❑ 12Zee-6
❑ 25Zee-142

Dalkowski, Steve
❑ 63Top-496

Dallard, Eggie
❑ 91PomBlaBPB-23

Dallas, Gershon
❑ 90AshTouP-2759
❑ 91OscAstC-23
❑ 91OscAstP-697
❑ 92ColRedC-14
❑ 92ColRedF-2404

Dallessandro, Dom
❑ 41CubTeal-2
❑ 41DouPlaR-101
❑ 42CubTeal-3
❑ 43CubTeal-5
❑ 44CubTeal-4
❑ 48AngTeal-8
❑ 49BowPCL-9
❑ 77SerSta-7
❑ 78ReaRem-3
❑ 79DiaGre-109
❑ 83TCMPla1944-32

Dallimore, Brian
❑ 96AubDouB-6
❑ 97QuaCitRBB-7
❑ 98KisCobQ-12

Dallimore, Fred
❑ 97RocRedW-3

Dalrymple, Abner (Abner F.)
❑ 87OldJudN-117
❑ 88WG1CarG-57

Dalrymple, Clay (Clayton E.)
❑ 47StaPinP2-13
❑ 58PhiTeal-7
❑ 60Lea-143
❑ 60Top-523
❑ 61Top-299
❑ 61TopStal-52
❑ 62Jel-197
❑ 62Pos-197
❑ 62PosCan-197
❑ 62SalPlaC-141
❑ 62ShiPlaC-141
❑ 62Top-434
❑ 62TopStal-166
❑ 63Fle-52
❑ 63Jel-184
❑ 63Pos-184
❑ 63Top-192
❑ 64PhiJayP-5
❑ 64PhiPhiB-12
❑ 64PhiTeaS-3
❑ 64Top-191
❑ 64TopVen-191
❑ 65PhiJayP-5
❑ 65Top-372
❑ 66PhiTeal-6
❑ 66Top-202
❑ 66TopVen-202
❑ 67BalOriP-29
❑ 67CokCapPh-9
❑ 67DexPre-58
❑ 67OPC-53
❑ 67PhiPol-5
❑ 67Top-53
❑ 68Top-567
❑ 69MilBra-68
❑ 69OPC-151
❑ 69Top-151A
❑ 69Top-151B
❑ 69TopFou-12
❑ 69TopSta-74
❑ 70BalOriP-7
❑ 70OPC-319
❑ 70Ori-4
❑ 70Top-319
❑ 71BalOriP-6
❑ 71MLBOffS-294
❑ 71OPC-617
❑ 71Top-617
❑ 78TCM60I-203
❑ 91OriCro-93

Dalson, Kevin
❑ 89WytCubS-9

Dalton, Brian
❑ 94HelBreF-3606
❑ 94HelBreSP-10
❑ 95BelBreTI-5

Dalton, Dee
❑ 93JohCitCC-1
❑ 93JohCitCF-3685
❑ 94MadHatC-8
❑ 94MadHatF-139
❑ 96ArkTraB-9
❑ 97ArkTraB-14

Dalton, Harry
❑ 75CalAngP-9
❑ 82BrePol-NNO

Dalton, Jack
❑ 90DodTar-161

Dalton, Jed
❑ 95BoiHawTI-14
❑ 96CedRapKTI-6
❑ 97MidAng-11
❑ 98MidAngG-12
❑ 98MidAngO-10

Dalton, Mike
❑ 86PawRedSP-8
❑ 87PawRedSP-66
❑ 87PawRedST-4
❑ 88NewBriRSP-896
❑ 89NewBriRSP-607
❑ 89PawRedSTI-7
❑ 90CMC-275
❑ 90PawRedSC-24
❑ 90PawRedSDD-5
❑ 90PawRedSP-455
❑ 90ProAAAF-427
❑ 90TopTVRS-42
❑ 91LinDriAAA-582
❑ 91TigCok-42
❑ 91TolMudHLD-582
❑ 91TolMudHP-1923
❑ 92BufBisBS-6
❑ 92BufBisF-317
❑ 92BufBisS-30
❑ 92Fle-131
❑ 92Sco100RS-95
❑ 92TopDeb91-42
❑ 93BufBisF-510

Dalton, Rich
❑ 78OrlTwiT-4

Dalton, Talbot
❑ 16Zee-106

Daly, Bob
❑ 92GulCoaMF-3487
❑ 93KinMetC-7
❑ 93KinMetF-3800
❑ 95PitMetTI-17

Daly, Mark
❑ 81TidTidT-25

Daly, Sun (James J.)
❑ 87OldJudN-119

Daly, Tom (Thomas Peter)
❑ 03BreE10-30
❑ 22Zee-4
❑ 23Zee-4
❑ 23Zee-64
❑ 24Zee-42
❑ 25Zee-135
❑ 28LaPre-6
❑ 72ClaCar-94
❑ 74BroClu-7
❑ 75RedSox1T-9
❑ 79RedSoxEF-15
❑ 87FouBasHN-1
❑ 87OldJudN-118
❑ 88AugBecN-10
❑ 90DodTar-162
❑ 95May-32

Dalzachio, Paul
❑ 91ButCopKSP-6

Damascus, Horse
❑ 68AtlOil-5

Damaska, Jack

❑ 77FriOneYW-60
Damato, Joseph
❑ 49AngTeal-8
❑ 49W725AngTI-7
Damian, Len (Leonard)
❑ 86PeoChiP-4
❑ 87PitCubP-13
❑ 88IowCubC-2
❑ 88IowCubP-544
❑ 89IowCubC-2
❑ 89IowCubP-1705
❑ 90TopTVCu-43
Dammann, Bill
❑ 98CamPepP-18
Damon, John
❑ 83MemChiT-4
Damon, Johnny David
❑ 92ClaFS7-417
❑ 92UppDecML-1
❑ 92UppDecML-19
❑ 93ClaFS7-182
❑ 93ClaGolF-201
❑ 93RocRoyC-1
❑ 93RocRoyF-727
❑ 93SP-273
❑ 94ActPac-18
❑ 94Bow-373
❑ 94BowBes-B41
❑ 94BowBes-X96
❑ 94BowBesR-B41
❑ 94BowBesR-X96
❑ 94CarLeaAF-CAR15
❑ 94Cla-25
❑ 94ClaCreotC-C5
❑ 94ClaTriF-T37
❑ 94ColC-642
❑ 94ColChoGS-642
❑ 94ColChoSS-642
❑ 94ExcAllF-6
❑ 94ExcFS7-66
❑ 94SPDieC-3
❑ 94UppDec-546
❑ 94UppDecAHNIL-4
❑ 94UppDecED-546
❑ 94UppDecML-125
❑ 94UppDecML-252
❑ 94UppDecMLT1PJF-TP2
❑ 94UppDecMLT1PMF-2
❑ 94WilBluRC-4
❑ 94WilBluRF-311
❑ 95ActPacF-22
❑ 95Bow-254
❑ 95BowBes-B45
❑ 95BowBesR-B45
❑ 95BowGolF-254
❑ 95Exc-56
❑ 95ExcAll-7
❑ 95PinETA-4
❑ 95SigRooOP-OP2
❑ 95SigRooOPS-OP2
❑ 95Top-599
❑ 95UltGolMR-M10
❑ 95UppDecML-6
❑ 95UppDecML-162
❑ 95UppDecMLFS-6
❑ 95UppDecMLFS-162
❑ 95UppDecMLMLA-3
❑ 95UppDecMLOP-OP13
❑ 95UppDecMLT1PF-3
❑ 95WicWraTI-17
❑ 96Baz-125
❑ 96Bow-166
❑ 96BowBes-56
❑ 96BowBesAR-56
❑ 96BowBesR-56
❑ 96BowFoi-166
❑ 96Cir-44
❑ 96CirRav-44
❑ 96ColCho-10
❑ 96ColCho-411
❑ 96ColCho-650
❑ 96ColChoGS-10
❑ 96ColChoGS-411
❑ 96ColChoGS-650
❑ 96ColChoSS-10
❑ 96ColChoSS-411
❑ 96ColChoSS-650
❑ 96Don-60
❑ 96DonPreP-60
❑ 96EmoXL-65
❑ 96Fin-G102
❑ 96FinRef-G102
❑ 96Fla-87
❑ 96Fle-124
❑ 96FleRooS-3
❑ 96FleTif-124
❑ 96Lea-82
❑ 96LeaLim-24
❑ 96LeaLimG-24
❑ 96LeaPre-30
❑ 96LeaPreP-30
❑ 96LeaPrePB-82
❑ 96LeaPrePG-82
❑ 96LeaPrePS-82
❑ 96LeaPreSG-65
❑ 96LeaPreSte-65
❑ 96LeaSig-32
❑ 96LeaSigA-54
❑ 96LeaSigAG-54
❑ 96LeaSigAS-54
❑ 96LeaSigPPG-32
❑ 96LeaSigPPP-32
❑ 96MetUni-63
❑ 96MetUniP-63
❑ 96Pac-326
❑ 96PacGolCD-DC3
❑ 96PacPri-P105
❑ 96PacPriG-P105
❑ 96PanSti-190
❑ 96Pin-170
❑ 96Pin-277
❑ 96PinAfi-128
❑ 96PinAfiAP-128
❑ 96PinAfiSP-19
❑ 96PinArtP-96
❑ 96PinArtP-177
❑ 96PinFoil-277
❑ 96PinProS-4
❑ 96PinSta-96
❑ 96PinSta-177
❑ 96PinTeaS-11
❑ 96PinTeaT-2
❑ 96RoyPol-7
❑ 96Sco-29
❑ 96Sco-223
❑ 96Sco-382
❑ 96ScoDiaA-29
❑ 96ScoDugC-A103
❑ 96ScoDugC-B107
❑ 96ScoDugCAP-A103
❑ 96ScoDugCAP-B107
❑ 96ScoFutF-7
❑ 96Sel-37
❑ 96SelArtP-37
❑ 96SelCer-27
❑ 96SelCerAP-27
❑ 96SelCerCB-27
❑ 96SelCerCR-27
❑ 96SelCerIP-7
❑ 96SelCerMB-27
❑ 96SelCerMG-27
❑ 96SelCerMR-27
❑ 96SelCerSF-18
❑ 96SelClaTF-15
❑ 96SelEnF-23
❑ 96SelTeaN-17
❑ 96SigRooOJMR-M2
❑ 96SP-100
❑ 96Spo-15
❑ 96Spo-118
❑ 96SpoArtP-15
❑ 96SpoArtP-118
❑ 96SpoPowS-22
❑ 96SPSpeFX-22
❑ 96SPSpeFXDC-22
❑ 96SPx-31
❑ 96SPxGol-31
❑ 96StaClu-148
❑ 96StaClu-259
❑ 96StaCluEPB-148
❑ 96StaCluEPG-148
❑ 96StaCluEPS-148
❑ 96StaCluMOP-148
❑ 96StaCluMOP-259
❑ 96Stu-125
❑ 96StuPrePB-125
❑ 96StuPrePG-125
❑ 96StuPrePS-125
❑ 96Sum-124
❑ 96Sum-158
❑ 96SumAbo&B-124
❑ 96SumAbo&B-158
❑ 96SumArtP-124
❑ 96SumArtP-158
❑ 96SumBal-12
❑ 96SumFoi-124
❑ 96SumFoi-158
❑ 96SumPos-8
❑ 96Top-215
❑ 96TopChr-77
❑ 96TopChrR-77
❑ 96TopGal-93
❑ 96TopGalPG-PG7
❑ 96TopGalPPI-93
❑ 96TopLas-101
❑ 96Ult-352
❑ 96UltGolM-352
❑ 96UltGolP-4
❑ 96UltGolPGM-4
❑ 96UppDec-90
❑ 96UppDecBCP-BC2
❑ 96UppDecHC-HC8
❑ 96Zen-31
❑ 96ZenArtP-31
❑ 97Bow-287
❑ 97BowInt-287
❑ 97Cir-111
❑ 97CirRav-111
❑ 97ColCho-360
❑ 97DenHol-7
❑ 97Don-98
❑ 97DonGolPP-98
❑ 97DonLim-186
❑ 97DonLimE-186
❑ 97DonPre-102
❑ 97DonPreCttC-102
❑ 97DonSig-41
❑ 97DonSigPPP-41
❑ 97DonSilPP-98
❑ 97E-X2-24
❑ 97E-X2Cred-24
❑ 97E-X2EssCre-24
❑ 97Fin-122
❑ 97FinEmb-122
❑ 97FinEmbR-122
❑ 97FinRef-122
❑ 97FlaShoLC-22
❑ 97FlaShoLeg0-22
❑ 97FlaShoLeg1-22
❑ 97FlaShoM-A22
❑ 97FlaShoM-B22
❑ 97FlaShoM-C22
❑ 97FlaShoR0-22
❑ 97FlaShoR1-22
❑ 97FlaShoR2-22
❑ 97Fle-112
❑ 97FleTif-112
❑ 97Lea-229
❑ 97LeaFraM-229
❑ 97LeaFraMDC-229
❑ 97MetUni-91
❑ 97NewPin-97
❑ 97NewPinAP-97
❑ 97NewPinMC-97
❑ 97NewPinPP-97
❑ 97Pac-99
❑ 97PacLigB-99
❑ 97PacPri-35
❑ 97PacPriLB-35
❑ 97PacPriP-35
❑ 97PacSil-99
❑ 97PinCer-104
❑ 97PinCerMBla-104
❑ 97PinCerMBlu-104
❑ 97PinCerMG-104
❑ 97PinCerMR-104
❑ 97PinCerR-104
❑ 97PinTotCPB-104
❑ 97PinTotCPG-104
❑ 97PinTotCPR-104
❑ 97RoyPol-6
❑ 97Sco-3
❑ 97ScoArtPWB-3
❑ 97ScoPreS-3
❑ 97ScoShoS-3
❑ 97ScoShoSAP-3
❑ 97SP-90
❑ 97StaClu-333
❑ 97StaCluMOP-333
❑ 97Top-196
❑ 97TopChr-76
❑ 97TopChrR-76
❑ 97TopGal-169
❑ 97TopGalPPI-169
❑ 97TopIntF-ILM7
❑ 97TopIntFR-ILM7
❑ 97Ult-66
❑ 97UltGolME-66
❑ 97UltPlaME-66
❑ 97UppDec-390
❑ 97UppDecRSF-RS6
❑ 97UppDecTTS-TS18
❑ 97WicWra-30
❑ 98Bow-65
❑ 98BowChr-65
❑ 98BowChrGA-65
❑ 98BowChrGAR-65
❑ 98BowChrI-65
❑ 98BowChrIR-65
❑ 98BowChrR-65
❑ 98BowGolA-65
❑ 98BowInt-65
❑ 98CirThu-235
❑ 98CirThuRav-235
❑ 98CirThuSupRav-235
❑ 98ColCho-392
❑ 98ColChoER-ER13
❑ 98CroRoy-65
❑ 98Fin-144
❑ 98FinNo--144
❑ 98FinNo-R-144
❑ 98FinRef-144
❑ 98FlaShoLeg0-79
❑ 98FlaShoLeg1-79
❑ 98FlaShoLeg2-79
❑ 98FlaShoLeg3-79
❑ 98FlaShoLegM-79
❑ 98FlaShoR0-79
❑ 98FlaShoR1-79
❑ 98FlaShoR2-79
❑ 98FlaShoR3-79
❑ 98Fle-500
❑ 98FleVin'-98
❑ 98FleVin'C-98
❑ 98MetUni-177
❑ 98MetUniPMG-177
❑ 98Pac-101
❑ 98PacAur-43
❑ 98PacInv-36
❑ 98PacInvPBlue-36
❑ 98PacInvSilv-36
❑ 98PacInvTeam-13
❑ 98PacOme-114
❑ 98PacOmeR-114
❑ 98PacOnl-337
❑ 98PacOnlR-337
❑ 98PacOnlWC-337
❑ 98PacPar-53
❑ 98PacParC-53
❑ 98PacParG-53
❑ 98PacParHS-53
❑ 98PacParPB-53
❑ 98PacParR-53
❑ 98PacPlaB-101
❑ 98PacRedT-101
❑ 98PacSil-101
❑ 98PacTeaC-7
❑ 98PinIns-111
❑ 98PinInsCE-111
❑ 98PinInsDE-111
❑ 98Revo-69
❑ 98RevoSS-69
❑ 98ScoRT-192
❑ 98SkyDugA-69
❑ 98SkyDugAIA-69
❑ 98SP Aut-107
❑ 98SPxFin-284
❑ 98SPxFinR-284
❑ 98SPxFinS-284
❑ 98StaCluFDI-29
❑ 98StaCluI-29
❑ 98StaCluOneK-29
❑ 98StaCluPP-29
❑ 98Top-362
❑ 98TopChr-362
❑ 98TopChrR-362
❑ 98TopDevR-362
❑ 98TopDia-362
❑ 98TopGal-112
❑ 98TopGalGP-112
❑ 98TopGalOPP-112
❑ 98TopGalPPI-112
❑ 98TopGalPPIA-112
❑ 98TopMiniC-362
❑ 98TopSta-38
❑ 98TopStaB-38
❑ 98TopStaG-38
❑ 98TopStaGR-38
❑ 98TopStaS-38
❑ 98Ult-112
❑ 98UltGolM-112
❑ 98UltMas-112
❑ 98UltPlaM-112
❑ 98UppDec-390
❑ 98UppDecR-42
❑ 98Zen-53
❑ 98ZenZ-G-53
❑ 98ZenZ-S-53
❑ 99199Fin-204
❑ 99Bow-274
❑ 99BowGol-274
❑ 99BowInt-274
❑ 99CroRoyB-68
❑ 99CroRoyL-68
❑ 99CroRoyOD-68
❑ 99FinGolRef-204
❑ 99FinRef-204
❑ 99FlaShoLeg1-132
❑ 99FlaShoLeg2-132
❑ 99FlaShoLeg3-132
❑ 99FlaShoLegM1-132
❑ 99FlaShoLegM2-132
❑ 99FlaShoLegM3-132
❑ 99FlaShoR1-132
❑ 99FlaShoR2-132
❑ 99FlaShoR3-132
❑ 99Fle-64
❑ 99FleBri-47
❑ 99FleBri2G-47
❑ 99FleBriBlu-47
❑ 99FleBriGol-47
❑ 99FleMys-14
❑ 99FleMysG-14
❑ 99FleMysM-14
❑ 99FleSta9-64
❑ 99FleWarT-64
❑ 99MetUni-93
❑ 99MetUniGM-93
❑ 99MetUniPMG-93
❑ 99Pac-202
❑ 99PacAur-86
❑ 99PacAurOD-86
❑ 99PacCroC-130
❑ 99PacCroCPB-130
❑ 99PacInv-71
❑ 99PacInvOD-71
❑ 99PacInvPB-71
❑ 99PacOme-112
❑ 99PacOmeC-112
❑ 99PacOmeG-112
❑ 99PacOmePB-112
❑ 99PacPar-109
❑ 99PacParC-109
❑ 99PacParG-109
❑ 99PacParHoloGold-109
❑ 99PacParHS-109
❑ 99PacParOD-109
❑ 99PacParPB-109
❑ 99PacParRed-109
❑ 99PacPlaB-202
❑ 99PacPri-70
❑ 99PacPriHB-70
❑ 99PacPriHG-70
❑ 99PacPriHM-70
❑ 99PacPriHP-70
❑ 99PacPriRed-70
❑ 99PacRed-202
❑ 99Rev-66
❑ 99RevPremDate-66
❑ 99RevRet-66
❑ 99RevShaSS-66
❑ 99SkyMolM-87
❑ 99SkyMolMX-87
❑ 99SkyPre-164
❑ 99SkyPreR-164
❑ 99SkyThu-135
❑ 99SkyThuRant-135
❑ 99SkyThuRave-135
❑ 99SP Aut-41
❑ 99SP SigAuto-JDA
❑ 99SpoIll-129
❑ 99SPSig-144
❑ 99SPx-46
❑ 99SPxFinR-46
❑ 99SPxFinS-46
❑ 99StaClu-46
❑ 99StaCluFDI-46
❑ 99StaCluOoaK-46
❑ 99StaCluPP-46
❑ 99ThuSkySupR-135
❑ 99Top-45
❑ 99TopChr-45
❑ 99TopChrR-45
❑ 99TopGal-68
❑ 99TopGalPP-68
❑ 99TopGalPPI-68
❑ 99TopMVPP-45
❑ 99TopSta-137
❑ 99TopStaFoil-137
❑ 99UD Cho-96
❑ 99UD ChoP-96
❑ 99UD ChoPCR-96
❑ 99UD Ion-33
❑ 99UD IonR-33
❑ 99Ult-107
❑ 99UltGolM-107
❑ 99UltMas-107
❑ 99UltPlaM-107
❑ 99UppDec-114
❑ 99UppDecBD-41
❑ 99UppDecBDD-41
❑ 99UppDecBDQ-41
❑ 99UppDecBDT-41
❑ 99UppDecCLM-C46
❑ 99UppDecE-46
❑ 99UppDecEFXG-46
❑ 99UppDecEL1-114
❑ 99UppDecEL2-114
❑ 99UppDecM-101
❑ 99UppDecMGS-101
❑ 99UppDecMHFS-101
❑ 99UppDecMP-101
❑ 99UppDecMSS-101
❑ 99UppDecO-19
❑ 99UppDecOSO-19
❑ 99Vic-184
Dampeer, Kelly
❑ 97BurIndG-6
❑ 98WatIndTI-7
Dana, Derek
❑ 91EveGiaC-12
❑ 91EveGiaP-3918
❑ 92CliGiaC-14
❑ 92CliGiaF-3601
Danapilis, Eric
❑ 93NiaFalRF-3401
❑ 94ExcFS7-52
❑ 94FayGenC-7
❑ 94FayGenF-2153
❑ 95JacSunTI-7
Dancer, Faye
❑ 94TedWil-93
Dancy, Bill
❑ 76VenLeaS-207
❑ 80PenPiIBT-27
❑ 80PenPiICT-12
❑ 83ReaPhiT-23
❑ 85PorBeaC-35
❑ 87MaiGuiT-23
❑ 89ScrRedBC-25
❑ 89ScrRedBP-1208
❑ 90CMC-244
❑ 90ScrRedBC-18
❑ 90TriAllGP-AAA27
❑ 91LinDriAAA-499
❑ 91ScrRedBLD-499
❑ 91ScrRedBP-2555
❑ 92ClePhiF-2073
❑ 93ClePhiC-26
❑ 93ClePhiF-2699
❑ 94ReaPhiF-2078
❑ 95ReaPhiELC-7
❑ 96RicBraB-1
❑ 96RicBraRC-24
❑ 97RicBra-1
❑ 98ClePhiM-27
❑ 98ClePhiUM-27
Dando, Patrick
❑ 90ProAaA-191
❑ 90PulBraB-16
❑ 90PulBraP-3096
❑ 91DurBulC-18
❑ 91DurBulP-1552
❑ 92BasCitRC-3
❑ 92BasCitRF-3851
❑ 93WilBluRC-7
❑ 93WilBluRF-2003
Dandos, Mike
❑ 85EveGialC-2
Dandridge, Brad
❑ 93SpoIndC-3
❑ 94OgdRapF-3746
❑ 94OgdRapSP-15
❑ 95SanBerSTI-5
❑ 96SanAntMB-4
❑ 97VerBeaD-8
❑ 98AlbDukG-4
Dandridge, Hooks (Ray)
❑ 74LauOldTBS-26
❑ 78HalHalR-2
❑ 80PerHaloFP-197
❑ 80PerHaloFPS-60
❑ 80SSPHOF-199
❑ 86NegLeaF-7
❑ 87DonHig-18
❑ 88NegLeaD-17
❑ 89HOFStiB-26
❑ 89PerCelP-11
❑ 90NegLeaS-14
❑ 90PerGreM-34
❑ 91NegLeaRL-5
❑ 91PomBlaBPB-24
❑ 92FroRowD-1
❑ 92FroRowD-1AU

❑ 92FroRowD-2
❑ 92FroRowD-3
❑ 92FroRowD-4
❑ 92FroRowD-5
❑ 92NegLeaPL-4
❑ 93TedWil-103
❑ 93UppDecS-17
❑ 94PomNegLB-7
❑ 95NegLeaLI-5
❑ 95S.FExaNLT-10
❑ 97NegLeaPC-11S
Danek, Bill
❑ 86PeoChiP-5
❑ 87WinSpiP-5
Daneker, Pat
❑ 97BriWhiSB-1
❑ 98HicCraM-10
❑ 98HicCraUO-13
Danforth, Dave (David C.)
❑ 12T207-39
❑ 18WhiSoxTI-6
❑ 21E121So1-14
❑ 21Exh-31
❑ 21Nei-26
❑ 22E120-93
❑ 22W572-19
❑ 22W573-28
❑ 23W501-102
❑ 75WhiSox1T-5
❑ 92Man191BSR-6
❑ 93ConTSN-719
Danforth, Perry
❑ 76SpoIndC-11
❑ 77SpoIndC-7
Daniel, Chuck
❑ 88MisStaB-4
❑ 89MisStaB-9
❑ 90MisStaB-7
❑ 91MisStaB-12
❑ 92GenCubC-23
❑ 92GenCubF-1551
❑ 92MisStaB-10
❑ 93PeoChiC-4
❑ 93PeoChiF-1076
Daniel, Clay
❑ 85CedRapRT-5
❑ 86VerRedP-5
❑ 88HarSenP-860
❑ 90MiaMirIS-5
Daniel, Dave
❑ 82VerBeaDT-4
Daniel, Jake
❑ 90DodTar-924
Daniel, Jim
❑ 86ChaRaiP-8
❑ 86MemChiSTOS-3
❑ 86MemChiTOS-3
❑ 87ChaO'sW-11
❑ 88ChaKniTI-16
❑ 88RivRedWCLC-231
❑ 88RivRedWP-1412
❑ 89RivRedWB-28
❑ 89RivRedWP-1407
❑ 90RivRedWB-21
❑ 93RanCucQC-29
❑ 94RanCucQC-28
❑ 95RanCucQT-NNO
❑ 96RanCucQB-5
❑ 97RanCucQG-6
Daniel, Keith
❑ 90KisDodD-8
Daniel, Lee
❑ 90MedHatBJB-21
Daniel, Michael
❑ 91JamExpC-6
❑ 91JamExpP-3548
❑ 91OklStaC-7
❑ 92ClaFS7-302
❑ 92ProFS7-273
❑ 92WesPalBEC-23
❑ 92WesPalBEF-2090
❑ 93WesPalBEC-4
❑ 93WesPalBEF-1343
❑ 95LynHilTI-6
Daniel, Scott
❑ 91JamExpC-29
Daniel, Steve
❑ 85BurRanT-25
Daniels, B.A.
❑ 94ConTSN-1268
❑ 94ConTSNB-1268
Daniels, Bennie
❑ 55DonWin-17
❑ 58Top-392
❑ 59Top-122
❑ 59TopVen-122
❑ 60Lea-7
❑ 60Top-91
❑ 60TopVen-91
❑ 61SenJayP-3
❑ 61Top-368
❑ 62SalPlaC-42
❑ 62ShiPlaC-42
❑ 62Top-378
❑ 62TopBuc-21
❑ 62TopStal-95
❑ 63BasMagM-18
❑ 63Top-497
❑ 64Top-587
❑ 65OPC-129
❑ 65Top-129
❑ 66SenTeal-5
❑ 77PirTCM1WC-30
❑ 78TCM60I-145
Daniels, Bert (Bernard E.)
❑ 09ColChiE-71
❑ 10JuJuDE-14
❑ 11PinT-5-803
❑ 11PloCanE-21
❑ 12ColRedB-71
❑ 12ColTinT-71
❑ 12T207-40
Daniels, Dave
❑ 78AppFoxT-7
❑ 79AppFoxT-11
❑ 80AppFoxT-23
Daniels, David
❑ 96AugGreB-7
❑ 96EriSeaB-9
❑ 97AugGre-10
❑ 98LynHilQ-5
Daniels, Gary
❑ 90EriSaiS-5
Daniels, Greg
❑ 87MiaMarP-19
Daniels, Jack (Harold Jack)
❑ 53BowC-83
Daniels, Jerry
❑ 87EriCarP-23
❑ 88St.PetCS-5
Daniels, Jim
❑ 89RivRedWCLC-28
Daniels, John
❑ 94BelMarC-9
❑ 94BelMarF-3226
❑ 96LanJetB-13
❑ 97St.PetDR-15
❑ 97St.PetDRUB-15
❑ 98St.PetDRM-6
Daniels, Kal
❑ 83CedRapRF-17
❑ 83CedRapRT-22
❑ 86Don-27
❑ 86Fle-646
❑ 86RedTexG-28
❑ 86SpoRoo-43
❑ 87ClaUpdY-130
❑ 87Don-142
❑ 87DonOpeD-192
❑ 87Fle-197
❑ 87FleGlo-197
❑ 87FleLeaL-13
❑ 87RedKah-28
❑ 87SpoTeaP-4
❑ 87Top-466
❑ 87TopTif-466
❑ 87ToyRoo-8
❑ 88ClaRed-161
❑ 88Don-14
❑ 88Don-289
❑ 88DonBasB-6
❑ 88DonSupD-14
❑ 88Fle-230
❑ 88FleAwaW-7
❑ 88FleGlo-230
❑ 88FleMin-72
❑ 88FleStiC-82
❑ 88Lea-14
❑ 88Lea-150
❑ 88OPC-53
❑ 88PanSti-281
❑ 88RedFolSB-14
❑ 88RedKah-28
❑ 88Sco-86
❑ 88ScoGlo-86
❑ 88ScoYouSI-39
❑ 88Spo-112
❑ 88StaLinRe-5
❑ 88Top-622
❑ 88TopBig-48
❑ 88TopSti-139
❑ 88TopTif-622
❑ 89Bow-314
❑ 89BowTif-314
❑ 89CedRapRAB-2
❑ 89ClaLigB-74
❑ 89DodStaSV-4
❑ 89Don-198
❑ 89DonBasB-118
❑ 89DonBonM-BC18
❑ 89Fle-157
❑ 89FleGlo-157
❑ 89FleLeaL-8
❑ 89FleSup-10
❑ 89OPC-45
❑ 89PanSti-75
❑ 89RedFolSB-26
❑ 89RedKah-28
❑ 89Sco-7
❑ 89ScoRoo-48T
❑ 89Spo-52
❑ 89Top-45
❑ 89TopAme2C-10
❑ 89TopBasT-97
❑ 89TopBig-323
❑ 89TopMinL-7
❑ 89TopSti-144
❑ 89TopTif-45
❑ 89TVSpoM-42
❑ 89UppDec-160
❑ 90Bow-99
❑ 90BowTif-99
❑ 90CedRapRDGB-2
❑ 90ClaYel-T64
❑ 90DodMot-3
❑ 90DodPol-28
❑ 90DodTar-925
❑ 90Don-432
❑ 90DonBesN-127
❑ 90FleUpd-20
❑ 90Lea-313
❑ 90OPC-585
❑ 90PanSti-280
❑ 90PubIntS-25
❑ 90PubIntS-610
❑ 90Sco-490
❑ 90Top-585
❑ 90TopBig-238
❑ 90TopTif-585
❑ 90UppDec-603
❑ 91Bow-600
❑ 91ClaGam-14
❑ 91DodMot-3
❑ 91DodPho-10
❑ 91DodPol-28
❑ 91DodSt.V-8
❑ 91Don-336
❑ 91DonGraS-3
❑ 91Fle-198
❑ 91Lea-112
❑ 91MooSna-7
❑ 91OPC-245
❑ 91PanFreS-60
❑ 91PanSti-58
❑ 91RedFolS-22
❑ 91Sco-20
❑ 91Sco100S-53
❑ 91StaClu-116
❑ 91SunSee-5
❑ 91Top-245
❑ 91TopDesS-245
❑ 91TopMic-245
❑ 91TopTif-245
❑ 91Ult-160
❑ 91UppDec-166
❑ 92Bow-487
❑ 92ClaGam-125
❑ 92DenHol-14
❑ 92DodMot-14
❑ 92DodPol-28
❑ 92DodSmo-5792
❑ 92Don-343
❑ 92Fle-453
❑ 92OPC-767
❑ 92PanSti-198
❑ 92Pin-374
❑ 92Sco-110
❑ 92ScoRoo-70T
❑ 92StaClu-514
❑ 92Top-767
❑ 92TopGol-767
❑ 92TopGolW-767
❑ 92TopKid-51
❑ 92TopMic-767
❑ 92Ult-210
❑ 92UppDec-284
❑ 93PanSti-207
❑ 93Sel-181
❑ 93Top-128
❑ 93TopGol-128
❑ 93TopInaM-128
❑ 93TopInaR-128
❑ 93TopMic-128
Daniels, Lance
❑ 89BriTigS-6
Daniels, Law (Lawrence L.)
❑ 87OldJudN-120
Daniels, Lee
❑ 91MedHatBJP-4114
❑ 91MedHatBJSP-14
❑ 92St.CatBJC-9
❑ 92St.CatBJF-3380
❑ 94Bow-197
❑ 94DunBluJC-8
❑ 94DunBluJF-2549
❑ 94FloStaLAF-FSL5
❑ 96BowBes-117
❑ 96BowBesAR-117
❑ 96BowBesR-117
❑ 96GreBraB-10
❑ 96GreBraTI-10
❑ 97BesAutAS-10
Daniels, Moe
❑ 93CedRapKC-5
❑ 93CedRapKF-1750
❑ 94LakElsSC-6
❑ 94LakElsSF-1676
❑ 95LakElsSTI-10
❑ 95MidAngOHP-10
Daniels, Steve
❑ 80CedRapRT-24
Daniels, William
❑ 15Zee-29
Danies, Franklin
❑ 90IBAWorA-16
Dann, Tom
❑ 79NewCoPT-1
Danner, Andy
❑ 98ChaAllCM-4
Danner, Deon
❑ 91WelPirC-18
❑ 91WelPirP-3565
❑ 92AugPirC-8
❑ 92AugPirF-230
Danning, Harry (Harry)
❑ 36WorWidGV-22
❑ 38CloFotW-18
❑ 39PlaBal-18
❑ 39WorWidGV-7
❑ 40PlaBal-93
❑ 41DouPlaR-25
❑ 41DouPlaR-91
❑ 41PlaBal-7
❑ 43MPR302-1-7
Danning, Ike
❑ 26Zee-45
Danson, Roger
❑ 76BurBeeT-3
Dant, Larry
❑ 98WilCubM-5
Dantonio, Fats
❑ 90DodTar-921
❑ 91JesHSA-1
Dantzler, Eric
❑ 95BurBeeTI-27
Dantzler, Shawn
❑ 86ClePhiP-6
❑ 87ClePhiP-10
❑ 88ClePhiS-10
Danzig, Harold
❑ 09ObaT21-137
❑ 09ObaT21-307
❑ 11BigEatEU-4
❑ 11PacCoaBD-17
❑ 11Zee-65
❑ 12ObaPreT-56
Dapper, Cliff
❑ 50W720HolS-6
❑ 90DodTar-163
Darby, Mike
❑ 86WauTimP-6
❑ 87SalSpuS-17
Darcuiel, Faruq
❑ 96WisTimRB-8
Darcy, Pat (Patrick L.)
❑ 75OPC-615
❑ 75Top-615
❑ 75TopMin-615
❑ 76OPC-538
❑ 76SSP-26
❑ 76Top-538
Darden, Tony
❑ 94ElmPioC-5
❑ 94ElmPioF-3482
❑ 95KanCouCTI-8
❑ 96BreCouMB-12
❑ 97BreCouMB-9
❑ 98BinMetQ-10
Dare, Brian
❑ 89AncBucTI-3
❑ 90IdaFalBP-3241
Darensbourg, Vic
❑ 93KanCouCC-5
❑ 93KanCouCF-908
❑ 93KanCouCTI-5
❑ 94Bow-234
❑ 94Cla-15
❑ 94ExcFS7-190
❑ 94PorSeaDF-671
❑ 94PorSeaDTI-12
❑ 94SigRooDP-100
❑ 94SigRooDPS-100
❑ 95KanCouCLTI-5
❑ 95Top-649
❑ 97ChaKni-10
❑ 98Fle-408
❑ 98PacOnl-293
❑ 98PacOnlR-293
❑ 98PacOnlWC-293
❑ 99Fle-379
❑ 99FleSta9-379
❑ 99FleWarT-379
Dares, Darrin
❑ 90LSUTigA-15
Daringer, Cliff
❑ 09ObaT21-138
Darjean, John
❑ 98OneYanG-10
Dark, Alvin (Alvin Ralph)
❑ 47Exh-56A
❑ 47Exh-56B
❑ 47Exh-56C
❑ 47PM1StaP1-39
❑ 49Bow-67
❑ 49EurSta-6
❑ 49Lea-51
❑ 49MPR302-2-116
❑ 50Bow-64
❑ 50Dra-20
❑ 50RoyDes-18
❑ 51Bow-14
❑ 51R42SmaS-20
❑ 52BerRos-11
❑ 52Bow-34
❑ 52RoyPre-3
❑ 52StaCalL-78B
❑ 52StaCalS-90C
❑ 52Top-351
❑ 53BowC-19
❑ 53Top-109
❑ 54Bow-41
❑ 54NewYorJA-21
❑ 54RedHeaF-5
❑ 55Bow-2
❑ 55GiaGolS-19
❑ 56GiaJayP-2
❑ 56Top-148
❑ 57Top-98
❑ 58CarJayP-4
❑ 58Top-125
❑ 59OklTodML-17
❑ 59Top-502
❑ 60PhiJayP-6
❑ 60Top-472
❑ 61GiaJayP-4
❑ 61Top-220
❑ 62Top-322
❑ 63GiaJayP-3
❑ 63Top-258
❑ 64GiaJayP-3
❑ 64Top-529
❑ 66Top-433
❑ 67Top-389
❑ 68Top-237
❑ 68TopVen-237
❑ 69OPC-91
❑ 69Top-91
❑ 70Ind-3
❑ 70OPC-524
❑ 70RelPam-3
❑ 70Top-524
❑ 71Ind-2
❑ 71OPC-397
❑ 71Top-397
❑ 75Gia195T-4
❑ 75GiaAllT-1
❑ 75OPC-561
❑ 75Top-561
❑ 75TopMin-561
❑ 76GalBasGHoF-6
❑ 76SSP-488
❑ 77PadFamF-2
❑ 78Top-467
❑ 79TCM50-25
❑ 80GiaGreT-8
❑ 80PacLeg-80
❑ 81Gia196T-1
❑ 82GSGalAG-2
❑ 83TopRep5-351
❑ 84FifNatCT-3
❑ 85TCMPhoC-37
❑ 85TCMPpl1-11
❑ 86A'sGreT-12
❑ 87A'sMot-13
❑ 88PacLegI-28
❑ 89SweBasG-77
❑ 90PacLeg-69
❑ 91LinDri-23
❑ 91SweBasG-22
❑ 91TopArc1-109
❑ 92BazQua5A-15
❑ 93TedWil-52
❑ 93UppDecAH-36
Dark, David
❑ 92GenCubC-22
❑ 92GenCubF-1552
Darkis, Willie
❑ 83ReaPhiT-18
❑ 84PorBeaC-211
❑ 86GleFalTP-2
Darley, Ned
❑ 91MedHatBJP-4091
❑ 91MedHatBJSP-19
❑ 92St.CatBJC-8
❑ 92St.CatBJF-3381
❑ 93HagSunC-8
❑ 93HagSunF-1872
❑ 96HigDesMB-9
Darling, Dell (Dell Conrad)
❑ 87OldJudN-121
❑ 88KimN18-10
Darling, Gary
❑ 89T/MUmp-58
❑ 90T/MUmp-56
Darling, Ron (Ronald M.)
❑ 81TulDriT-18
❑ 82TidTidT-13
❑ 83TidTidT-1
❑ 84Don-30A
❑ 84Don-30B
❑ 84FleUpd-29
❑ 84MetFanC-2
❑ 84TopTra-27T
❑ 84TopTraT-27T
❑ 85Don-434
❑ 85Fle-76
❑ 85FleStaS-117
❑ 85Lea-256
❑ 85MetColP-20
❑ 85MetTCM-8
❑ 85OPC-138
❑ 85Top-415
❑ 85TopMin-415
❑ 85TopSti-105
❑ 85TopTif-415
❑ 86BasStaB-26
❑ 86Don-563
❑ 86DonAll-37
❑ 86Fle-77
❑ 86FleMin-18
❑ 86FleStiC-28
❑ 86KayB-6
❑ 86Lea-221
❑ 86MetColP-13
❑ 86MetFanC-3
❑ 86MetTCM-3
❑ 86MetWorSC-22
❑ 86OPC-225
❑ 86SevCoi-E14
❑ 86Spo-109
❑ 86Top-225
❑ 86TopSti-98
❑ 86TopTat-10
❑ 86TopTif-225
❑ 87BurKinA-6
❑ 87Don-192
❑ 87Dra-28
❑ 87Fle-5

❑ 87FleGlo-5
❑ 87FleGlo-WS5
❑ 87FleHotS-11
❑ 87FleLimBC-C1
❑ 87FleMin-23
❑ 87FleStiC-27
❑ 87FleWorS-5
❑ 87KeyFooD-3
❑ 87KraFoo-28
❑ 87Lea-85
❑ 87MetColP-11
❑ 87MetFanC-2
❑ 87MSAIceTD-3
❑ 87OPC-75
❑ 87OurOwnTD-3
❑ 87Spo-53
❑ 87SpoTeaP-2
❑ 87Top-75
❑ 87TopMinL-21
❑ 87TopSti-105
❑ 87TopTif-75
❑ 87WeiMarD-3
❑ 87Woo-26
❑ 88Don-6
❑ 88Don-76
❑ 88DonBasB-41
❑ 88DonSupD-6
❑ 88DonTeaBM-76
❑ 88Fle-132
❑ 88FleGlo-132
❑ 88FleSluBC-C1
❑ 88FleStiC-100
❑ 88Lea-6
❑ 88Lea-78
❑ 88MetColP-2
❑ 88MetKah-12
❑ 88OPC-38
❑ 88PanSti-335
❑ 88Sco-141
❑ 88ScoGlo-141
❑ 88Spo-73
❑ 88StaLinMe-5
❑ 88Top-685
❑ 88TopBig-85
❑ 88TopSti-98
❑ 88TopTif-685
❑ 89Bow-372
❑ 89BowTif-372
❑ 89Don-171
❑ 89DonBasB-41
❑ 89Fle-32
❑ 89FleGlo-32
❑ 89MetColP-5
❑ 89MetKah-6
❑ 89OPC-105
❑ 89PanSti-130
❑ 89Sco-180
❑ 89ScoHot1S-71
❑ 89Spo-32
❑ 89Top-105
❑ 89TopBasT-86
❑ 89TopBig-166
❑ 89TopDouM-7
❑ 89TopSti-100
❑ 89TopTif-105
❑ 89TVSpoM-2
❑ 89UppDec-159
❑ 90Don-289
❑ 90DonLeaS-29
❑ 90Fle-201
❑ 90FleCan-201
❑ 90Lea-304
❑ 90MetColP-13
❑ 90MetColP-2
❑ 90MetKah-15
❑ 90MLBBasB-14
❑ 90OPC-330
❑ 90PanSti-295
❑ 90PublntS-130
❑ 90Sco-446
❑ 90Top-330
❑ 90TopBig-113
❑ 90TopSti-98
❑ 90TopTif-330
❑ 90TopTVM-9
❑ 90TulDriDGB-18
❑ 90UppDec-241
❑ 91Bow-483
❑ 91Don-472
❑ 91Fle-144
❑ 91Lea-378
❑ 91MetColP-28
❑ 91MetKah-15
❑ 91MetWIZ-90
❑ 91OPC-735
❑ 91Sco-456
❑ 91StaClu-60
❑ 91Top-735
❑ 91TopDesS-735
❑ 91TopMic-735
❑ 91TopTif-735
❑ 91Ult-214
❑ 91UppDec-198
❑ 91UppDecFE-69F
❑ 92AthMot-24
❑ 92Bow-30
❑ 92Don-723
❑ 92Fle-254
❑ 92Lea-447
❑ 92LeaBlaG-447
❑ 92OPC-259
❑ 92Pin-378
❑ 92Sco-710
❑ 92StaClu-685
❑ 92StaCluECN-685
❑ 92Top-259
❑ 92TopGol-259
❑ 92TopGolW-259
❑ 92TopMic-259
❑ 92Ult-111
❑ 92UppDec-669
❑ 93AthMot-12
❑ 93AthStaC-14
❑ 93Bow-189
❑ 93Don-700
❑ 93Fle-661
❑ 93Lea-182
❑ 93OPC-82
❑ 93PacSpa-220
❑ 93PanSti-22
❑ 93Pin-199
❑ 93Sco-619
❑ 93Sel-10
❑ 93StaClu-305
❑ 93StaCluFDI-305
❑ 93StaCluMOP-305
❑ 93Top-182
❑ 93TopGol-182
❑ 93ToplnaM-182
❑ 93ToplnaR-182
❑ 93TopMic-182
❑ 93Ult-256
❑ 93UppDec-168
❑ 93UppDecGold-168
❑ 94A'sMot-16
❑ 94ColC-88
❑ 94ColChoGS-88
❑ 94ColChoSS-88
❑ 94Don-452
❑ 94Fin-243
❑ 94FinRef-243
❑ 94Fla-90
❑ 94Fle-258
❑ 94FleExtB-147
❑ 94Lea-57
❑ 94Pac-447
❑ 94Pin-90
❑ 94PinArtP-90
❑ 94PinMusC-90
❑ 94Sco-159
❑ 94ScoGolR-159
❑ 94StaClu-428
❑ 94StaCluFDI-428
❑ 94StaCluGR-428
❑ 94StaCluMOP-428
❑ 94Top-549
❑ 94TopGol-549
❑ 94TopSpa-549
❑ 94Ult-106
❑ 94UppDec-498
❑ 94UppDecED-498
❑ 95AthMot-6
❑ 95ColCho-136
❑ 95ColChoGS-136
❑ 95ColChoSS-136
❑ 95Don-13
❑ 95DonPreP-13
❑ 95Fla-72
❑ 95Fle-243
❑ 95Lea-112
❑ 95Pin-389
❑ 95PinArtP-389
❑ 95PinMusC-389
❑ 95Sco-381
❑ 95ScoGolR-381
❑ 95ScoPlaTS-381
❑ 95StaClu-142
❑ 95StaCluFDI-142
❑ 95StaCluMOP-142
❑ 95StaCluSTWS-142
❑ 95Top-16
❑ 95TopCyb-14
❑ 95Ult-92
❑ 95UltGolM-92
❑ 95UppDec-282
❑ 95UppDecED-282
❑ 95UppDecEDG-282

Darnbrough, William
❑ 87OldJudN-122

Darnell, Bob (Robert Jack)
❑ 55Bow-39
❑ 79TCM50-257
❑ 90DodTar-164
❑ 95TopArcBD-124

Darnell, Steve
❑ 76WauMetT-11

Darr, Mike
❑ 94BriTigF-3516
❑ 94SigRooDP-45
❑ 94SigRooDPS-45
❑ 94StaCluDP-25
❑ 94StaCluDPFDI-25
❑ 95FayGenTI-8
❑ 96Bow-247
❑ 96BowFoi-247
❑ 96LakTigB-11
❑ 97RanCucQG-7
❑ 98MobBayBTI-7
❑ 98SouLeaTPG-26
❑ 98UppDec-557
❑ 99BasAmeTPA-8
❑ 99Bow-393
❑ 99BowGol-393
❑ 99BowInt-393
❑ 99SP SigAutoG-MD
❑ 99SP TopP-37
❑ 99SP TopPC-MD
❑ 99SP TopPGF-GF11
❑ 99SP TopPPE-37
❑ 99SPSig-87
❑ 99SPx-115
❑ 99SPxFinR-115
❑ 99SPxFinS-115

Darr, Mike (Michael Edward)
❑ 78SyrChiT-6

Darr, Ryan
❑ 97JohCitCTI-5
❑ 98PeoChiM-4

Darrell, Tommy
❑ 96BoiHawB-9
❑ 97CedRapK-5
❑ 97MidLeaTP-5
❑ 98LakElsSG-6

Darretta, Dave
❑ 85BurRanT-9

Darrow, Darrell
❑ 75SalLakCC-9
❑ 76SalLakCGC-1
❑ 79SalLakCGT-17B

Darrow, George (George Oliver)
❑ 34Gou-87

Darula, Bobby
❑ 96OgdRapTI-36
❑ 98StoPorG-6

Darwin, Bobby (Arthur B.)
❑ 69Top-641
❑ 73LinPor-108
❑ 73OPC-228
❑ 73Top-228
❑ 74OPC-527
❑ 74Top-527
❑ 74TopSta-205
❑ 75Hos-98
❑ 75OPC-346
❑ 75Top-346
❑ 75TopMin-346
❑ 75TwiPos-9
❑ 76CubTri-7
❑ 76Hos-31
❑ 76HosTwi-31
❑ 76OPC-63
❑ 76SSP-247
❑ 76Top-63
❑ 76VenLeaS-213
❑ 77Top-617
❑ 90DodTar-165
❑ 94BreMilB-13

Darwin, Brian
❑ 94SouOreAC-3
❑ 94SouOreAF-3635

Darwin, Danny Wayne
❑ 78TucTorC-28
❑ 79Top-713
❑ 80Top-498
❑ 81Don-147
❑ 81Fle-632
❑ 81OPC-22
❑ 81Top-22
❑ 81TopSti-136
❑ 82Don-321
❑ 82Fle-315
❑ 82Top-298
❑ 82TopSti-237
❑ 83Don-289
❑ 83Fle-565
❑ 83FleSta-46
❑ 83FleSti-161
❑ 83RanAffF-44
❑ 83Top-609
❑ 83TopSti-121
❑ 84AllGamPI-168
❑ 84Don-544
❑ 84Fle-416
❑ 84Nes792-377
❑ 84RanJarP-44
❑ 84Top-377
❑ 84TopSti-359
❑ 84TopTif-377
❑ 85AllGamPI-76
❑ 85BrePol-18
❑ 85Don-98
❑ 85Fle-557
❑ 85FleUpd-32
❑ 85OPC-227
❑ 85Top-227
❑ 85TopSti-352
❑ 85TopTif-227
❑ 85TopTifT-26T
❑ 85TopTra-26T
❑ 86BrePol-18
❑ 86Don-149
❑ 86Fle-485
❑ 86Lea-75
❑ 86OPC-206
❑ 86Top-519
❑ 86TopSti-205
❑ 86TopTif-519
❑ 87AstMot-14
❑ 87AstPol-4
❑ 87Don-508
❑ 87Fle-54
❑ 87FleGlo-54
❑ 87OPC-157
❑ 87Top-157
❑ 87TopTif-157
❑ 88AstMot-14
❑ 88AstPol-7
❑ 88Don-358
❑ 88Fle-444
❑ 88FleGlo-444
❑ 88Sco-184
❑ 88ScoGlo-184
❑ 88StaLinAst-7
❑ 88Top-461
❑ 88TopTif-461
❑ 89AstLenH-13
❑ 89AstMot-13
❑ 89AstSmo-10
❑ 89Don-390
❑ 89Fle-354
❑ 89FleGlo-354
❑ 89Sco-553
❑ 89Top-719
❑ 89TopTif-719
❑ 89UppDec-97
❑ 90AstLenH-9
❑ 90AstMot-15
❑ 90Bow-66
❑ 90BowTif-66
❑ 90Don-561
❑ 90DonBesN-53
❑ 90Fle-227
❑ 90FleCan-227
❑ 90Lea-346
❑ 90OPC-64
❑ 90PublntS-91
❑ 90Sco-402
❑ 90Spo-83
❑ 90Top-64
❑ 90TopSti-14
❑ 90TopTif-64
❑ 90UppDec-305
❑ 91Bow-111
❑ 91Cla1-T44
❑ 91ClaGam-170
❑ 91Don-165
❑ 91Don-401
❑ 91Fle-503
❑ 91FleUpd-5
❑ 91Lea-405
❑ 91OPC-666
❑ 91OPCPre-28
❑ 91PanCanT1-65
❑ 91PanFreS-15
❑ 91PanSti-18
❑ 91RedSoxP-6
❑ 91RedSoxP-8
❑ 91Sco-51
❑ 91ScoRoo-24T
❑ 91StaClu-394
❑ 91Top-666
❑ 91TopDesS-666
❑ 91TopMic-666
❑ 91TopTif-666
❑ 91TopTra-26T
❑ 91TopTraT-26T
❑ 91UppDec-586
❑ 91UppDec-705
❑ 92Don-87
❑ 92Fle-38
❑ 92OPC-324
❑ 92RedSoxDD-10
❑ 92Sco-138
❑ 92StaClu-539
❑ 92Top-324
❑ 92TopGol-324
❑ 92TopGolW-324
❑ 92TopMic-324
❑ 92UppDec-678
❑ 93Don-647
❑ 93Fle-179
❑ 93Lea-455
❑ 93PacSpa-356
❑ 93RanKee-119
❑ 93RedSoxP-8
❑ 93RedSoxWHP-3
❑ 93StaClu-484
❑ 93StaCluFDI-484
❑ 93StaCluMOP-484
❑ 93Top-214
❑ 93TopGol-214
❑ 93ToplnaM-214
❑ 93ToplnaR-214
❑ 93TopMic-214
❑ 93Ult-150
❑ 93UppDec-220
❑ 93UppDecGold-220
❑ 94BreMilB-14
❑ 94ColC-89
❑ 94ColChoGS-89
❑ 94ColChoSS-89
❑ 94Don-469
❑ 94Fin-58
❑ 94FinRef-58
❑ 94Fla-12
❑ 94Fle-28
❑ 94FleExtB-18
❑ 94Lea-114
❑ 94Pac-51
❑ 94Pin-303
❑ 94PinArtP-303
❑ 94PinMusC-303
❑ 94Sco-192
❑ 94ScoGolR-192
❑ 94Sel-110
❑ 94StaClu-251
❑ 94StaCluFDI-251
❑ 94StaCluGR-251
❑ 94StaCluMOP-251
❑ 94Top-292
❑ 94TopGol-292
❑ 94TopSpa-292
❑ 94Ult-12
❑ 94UppDec-123
❑ 94UppDecED-123
❑ 95Sco-208
❑ 95ScoGolR-208
❑ 95ScoPlaTS-208
❑ 95StaClu-534
❑ 95StaCluMOP-534
❑ 95StaCluSTWS-534
❑ 96FleUpd-U175
❑ 96FleUpdTC-U175
❑ 97PacPriGotD-GD150
❑ 97WhiSoxTI-44
❑ 98GiaMot-21
❑ 98PacOnl-656
❑ 98PacOnlR-656
❑ 98PacOnlWC-656
❑ 99UppDec-195
❑ 99UppDecEL1-195
❑ 99UppDecEL2-195

Darwin, David
❑ 97WesMicW-10
❑ 98JacSunM-8

Darwin, Jeff
❑ 89BelMarL-4
❑ 90PenPilS-6
❑ 91Cla/Bes-51
❑ 91SanBerSC-2
❑ 91SanBerSP-1978
❑ 92PenPilC-16
❑ 92PenPilF-2926
❑ 93Bow-627
❑ 93JacSunF-2704
❑ 94CalCanF-783
❑ 95TacRaiTI-7
❑ 96NasSouB-11
❑ 96SigRooOJRS-R4
❑ 96SigRooOJRSS-R4
❑ 97Don-258
❑ 97DonGolPP-258
❑ 97DonSilPP-258
❑ 97Sco-314
❑ 97ScoArtPWB-314
❑ 97ScoArtPWB-315
❑ 97ScoPreS-314
❑ 97ScoShoS-314
❑ 97ScoShoSAP-314
❑ 97ScoShoSAP-315
❑ 97WhiSoxS-4
❑ 97WhiSoxSPl-4
❑ 97WhiSoxSPr-4
❑ 98FreGriG-7

Dascenzo, Doug
❑ 86WinSpiP-4
❑ 87PitCubP-23
❑ 88BlaYNPRWL-148
❑ 88IowCubC-19
❑ 88IowCubP-528
❑ 89Don-491
❑ 89Fle-420
❑ 89FleGlo-420
❑ 89IowCubC-20
❑ 89IowCubP-1702
❑ 89PanSti-47
❑ 89Sco-621
❑ 89ScoHot1R-4
❑ 89Spo-42
❑ 89Top-149
❑ 89TopTif-149
❑ 89UppDec-10
❑ 90CubMar-5
❑ 90OPC-762
❑ 90ScoYouS2-40
❑ 90Top-762
❑ 90TopTif-762
❑ 90TopTVCu-30
❑ 90UppDec-211
❑ 91CubMar-29
❑ 91CubVinL-8
❑ 91Don-749
❑ 91Fle-418
❑ 91Lea-483
❑ 91OPC-437
❑ 91Sco-209
❑ 91Top-437
❑ 91TopDesS-437
❑ 91TopMic-437
❑ 91TopTif-437
❑ 91Ult-60
❑ 92Bow-287
❑ 92CubMar-29
❑ 92Don-38
❑ 92Lea-51
❑ 92LeaBlaG-51
❑ 92OPC-509
❑ 92Pin-160
❑ 92Sco-319
❑ 92StaClu-252
❑ 92Stu-11
❑ 92Top-509
❑ 92TopGol-509
❑ 92TopGolW-509
❑ 92TopMic-509
❑ 92UppDec-239
❑ 93Bow-193
❑ 93Don-212
❑ 93Fle-376
❑ 93PacSpa-55
❑ 93PanSti-210
❑ 93Pin-555
❑ 93RanKee-401
❑ 93RanStaC-15
❑ 93Sco-446
❑ 93StaClu-664
❑ 93StaCluFDI-664
❑ 93StaCluMOP-664
❑ 93Top-211
❑ 93TopGol-211
❑ 93ToplnaM-211
❑ 93ToplnaR-211

❑ 93TopMic-211
❑ 93UppDec-64
❑ 93UppDec-739
❑ 93UppDecGold-64
❑ 93UppDecGold-739
❑ 94Pac-612
❑ 96LasVegSB-10
❑ 97LasVegS1A-12
❑ 98MobBayBTI-8

Dascoli, Frank
❑ 55Bow-291

DaSilva, Fernando
❑ 93BurBeeC-6
❑ 93BurBeeF-150
❑ 93ClaGolF-112
❑ 93JamExpC-6
❑ 93JamExpF-3319
❑ 94BurBeeC-6
❑ 94BurBeeF-1075
❑ 96WesPalBEB-7

DaSilva, Manny
❑ 94SouOreAC-4
❑ 94SouOreAF-3625
❑ 95WesMicWTI-25

Daspit, Jim (James)
❑ 90GreFalDSP-5
❑ 91BakDodCLC-21
❑ 92VerBeaDC-18
❑ 92VerBeaDF-2867
❑ 93SanAntMF-2997
❑ 93VerBeaDF-2208
❑ 94JacGenF-208
❑ 95Exc-200
❑ 95TucTotTI-4

Dasso, Frank (Francis J.)
❑ 47SigOil-3
❑ 47SigOil-59
❑ 49SolSunP-2

Dattola, Kevin
❑ 90SouOreAB-4
❑ 91Cla/Bes-115
❑ 91HunStaTI-8
❑ 91ModA'sC-25
❑ 91ModA'sP-3102
❑ 92HunStaF-3960
❑ 92HunStaS-308
❑ 93HunStaF-2093
❑ 93TacTigF-3045
❑ 97St.PauS-4

Datz, Jeff
❑ 82AubAstT-11
❑ 83DayBeaAT-15
❑ 86ColAstP-9
❑ 87ColAstP-2
❑ 88TucTorC-9
❑ 88TucTorJP-7
❑ 88TucTorP-187
❑ 89TolMudHC-11
❑ 89TolMudHP-761
❑ 90CMC-507
❑ 90ColCliC-19
❑ 90ColCliP-678
❑ 90ProAAAF-328
❑ 90TopDeb89-28
❑ 94WatIndC-28
❑ 94WatIndF-3954
❑ 96CanIndB-1
❑ 96WesOahCHWB-45
❑ 97AkrAer-1
❑ 98BufBisG-9

Daub, Dan
❑ 90DodTar-926

Daubach, Brian
❑ 91KinMetC-6
❑ 91KinMetP-3818
❑ 92PitMetC-15
❑ 92PitMetF-3302
❑ 94St.LucMC-6
❑ 94St.LucMF-1200
❑ 95BinMetTI-8
❑ 96BinMetB-5
❑ 97ChaKni-11
❑ 98ChaKniQ-9

Daubert, Jake (Jacob E.)
❑ 09ColChiE-72A
❑ 09ColChiE-72B
❑ 09SpoNewSM-94
❑ 11HelSta-85
❑ 11MecDFT-14
❑ 11PinT-5-460
❑ 11S74Sil-52
❑ 11T205-36
❑ 12ColRedB-72A
❑ 12ColRedB-72B
❑ 12ColTinT-72A
❑ 12ColTinT-72B
❑ 12HasTriFT-27
❑ 12T207-41
❑ 13NatGamW-14
❑ 13TomBarW-13
❑ 14B18B-57
❑ 14CraJacE-143
❑ 14PieStaT-29
❑ 15CraJacE-143
❑ 15SpoNewM-44
❑ 16BF2FP-60
❑ 16FleBreD-22
❑ 16SpoNewM-43
❑ 17ColE13-38
❑ 17HolBreD-21
❑ 19W514-68
❑ 20NatCarE-21
❑ 20RedWorCP-3
❑ 20WalMaiW-11
❑ 21E121So1-15
❑ 21E121So8-14
❑ 21Exh-32
❑ 21Nei-99
❑ 22AmeCarE122-13
❑ 22E120-169
❑ 22W572-20
❑ 22W575-22
❑ 22WilPatV-48
❑ 23W501-52
❑ 23W503-57
❑ 23WilChoV-26
❑ 75FlePio-24
❑ 87ConSer2-12
❑ 88PacEigMO-95
❑ 90DodTar-166
❑ 91ConTSN-307
❑ 93ConTSN-805
❑ 94ConTSN-1019
❑ 94ConTSNB-1019

Dauer, Edward
❑ 50W720HolS-27

Dauer, Rich (Richard F.)
❑ 76VenLeaS-136
❑ 77BalOriP-3
❑ 77Top-477
❑ 78BalOriP-5
❑ 78Top-237
❑ 79BalOriP-3
❑ 79Top-666
❑ 80OPC-56
❑ 80Top-102
❑ 81AllGamPI-11
❑ 81BalOriP-4
❑ 81Don-232
❑ 81Fle-182
❑ 81OPC-314
❑ 81Top-314
❑ 81TopSti-36
❑ 82BalOriP-1
❑ 82Don-257
❑ 82Fle-161
❑ 82OPC-8
❑ 82Top-8
❑ 82TopSti-147
❑ 83AllGamPI-10
❑ 83Don-455
❑ 83Fle-57
❑ 83FleSta-47
❑ 83FleSti-196
❑ 83OPC-192
❑ 83OriPos-7
❑ 83Top-579
❑ 83TopSti-27
❑ 84AllGamPI-101
❑ 84BalOriP-8
❑ 84Don-350
❑ 84Fle-4
❑ 84Nes792-723
❑ 84OPC-374
❑ 84OriEng-2
❑ 84Top-723
❑ 84TopSti-214
❑ 84TopTif-723
❑ 85BalOriP-6
❑ 85Don-106
❑ 85Fle-173
❑ 85OPC-58
❑ 85Top-494
❑ 85TopSti-203
❑ 85TopTif-494
❑ 86Fle-270
❑ 86OPC-251
❑ 86Top-251
❑ 86TopTif-251
❑ 87SanBerSP-7
❑ 89ColSprSSC-24
❑ 89ColSprSSP-242
❑ 89SanBerSB-28
❑ 90IndTeal-11
❑ 90SouCalS-3
❑ 91IndFanC-30
❑ 91OriCro-94
❑ 91PacSenL-105
❑ 92KanCouCTI-6
❑ 93OmaRoyF-1698

Daugherty, Jack
❑ 86JacExpT-25
❑ 87IndIndTI-10
❑ 88BlaYNPRWLU-16
❑ 88IndIndC-21
❑ 88IndIndP-521
❑ 89OklCit8C-13
❑ 89OklCit8P-1525
❑ 90Bow-503
❑ 90BowTif-503
❑ 90Don-461
❑ 90Fle-294
❑ 90FleCan-294
❑ 90Lea-521
❑ 90OPC-52
❑ 90RanMot-11
❑ 90Sco-564
❑ 90Sco100RS-61
❑ 90Top-52
❑ 90TopTif-52
❑ 90UppDec-614
❑ 91Bow-277
❑ 91Don-576
❑ 91Fle-284
❑ 91Lea-17
❑ 91OPC-622
❑ 91RanMot-11
❑ 91Sco-309
❑ 91StaClu-276
❑ 91Top-622
❑ 91TopDesS-622
❑ 91TopMic-622
❑ 91TopTif-622
❑ 91UppDec-284
❑ 92Don-569
❑ 92Fle-300
❑ 92OPC-344
❑ 92RanMot-11
❑ 92RanTeal-5
❑ 92Sco-622
❑ 92StaClu-634
❑ 92StaCluNC-634
❑ 92Top-344
❑ 92TopGol-344
❑ 92TopGolW-344
❑ 92TopMic-344
❑ 93Fle-682
❑ 93RanKee-120
❑ 93TucTorF-3065
❑ 94Sco-146
❑ 94ScoGolR-146
❑ 94SyrChiF-977
❑ 94SyrChiTI-9

Daugherty, Jim
❑ 90AshTouC-4
❑ 91AshTouP-562
❑ 91SouAtlLAGP-SAL1
❑ 92ProFS7-235

Daugherty, Keith
❑ 95DanBraTI-9
❑ 96MacBraB-16

Daugherty, Pat
❑ 90JamExpP-27

Daughterty, Mike
❑ 83SanJosBC-19

Daughtry, Dorian
❑ 87BelMarL-2
❑ 87BelMarTI-4
❑ 89SanBerSB-2
❑ 89SanBerSCLC-88

Dault, Donnie
❑ 93AubAstF-3434
❑ 96KisCobB-5

Dault, Raymond
❑ 93AubAstC-7

Daulton, Darren
❑ 83ReaPhiT-11
❑ 84PorBeaC-198
❑ 85FleUpd-33
❑ 85PhiTas-10
❑ 85PhiTas-24
❑ 85PorBeaC-42
❑ 86Don-477
❑ 86Fle-438
❑ 86PhiCIG-7
❑ 86PhiTas-10
❑ 86Top-264
❑ 86TopTif-264
❑ 87Don-262
❑ 87Fle-172
❑ 87FleGlo-172
❑ 87MaiGuiT-21
❑ 87OPC-57
❑ 87PhiTas-10
❑ 87Top-636
❑ 87TopTif-636
❑ 88Don-309
❑ 88PhiTas-7
❑ 88Sco-473
❑ 88ScoGlo-473
❑ 88StaLinPh-6
❑ 88Top-468
❑ 88TopTif-468
❑ 89Don-549
❑ 89DonBasB-128
❑ 89PhiTas-4
❑ 89Sco-413
❑ 89Top-187
❑ 89TopTif-187
❑ 89UppDec-448
❑ 90Bow-158
❑ 90BowTif-158
❑ 90Don-194
❑ 90DonBesN-20
❑ 90Fle-555
❑ 90FleCan-555
❑ 90Lea-369
❑ 90OPC-542
❑ 90PhiTas-7
❑ 90PubIntS-234
❑ 90Sco-389
❑ 90Top-542
❑ 90TopTif-542
❑ 90UppDec-418
❑ 91Bow-507
❑ 91ClaGam-81
❑ 91ClaGam-187
❑ 91Don-316
❑ 91Fle-393
❑ 91Lea-192
❑ 91OPC-89
❑ 91PanFreS-102
❑ 91PanSti-109
❑ 91PhiMed-11
❑ 91Sco-246
❑ 91StaClu-4
❑ 91Stu-212
❑ 91Top-89
❑ 91TopDesS-89
❑ 91TopMic-89
❑ 91TopTif-89
❑ 91Ult-260
❑ 91UppDec-408
❑ 92Bow-440
❑ 92Don-198
❑ 92Fle-527
❑ 92Lea-335
❑ 92LeaBlaG-335
❑ 92OPC-244
❑ 92PanSti-241
❑ 92PhiMed-10
❑ 92Pin-241
❑ 92Sco-506
❑ 92StaClu-529
❑ 92Stu-73
❑ 92StuHer-BC13
❑ 92Top-244
❑ 92TopGol-244
❑ 92TopGolW-244
❑ 92TopMic-244
❑ 92TriPla-143
❑ 92Ult-240
❑ 92UppDec-429
❑ 93Bow-160
❑ 93ClaGam-24
❑ 93ColAllG-6
❑ 93DiaMar-27
❑ 93Don-92
❑ 93DonDiaK-DK17
❑ 93DonEli-29
❑ 93DonEliS-11
❑ 93DonMVP-11
❑ 93DonPre-8
❑ 93Fin-171
❑ 93FinRef-171
❑ 93Fla-97
❑ 93FlaPro-2
❑ 93Fle-100
❑ 93Fle-352
❑ 93Fle-705
❑ 93Fle-715
❑ 93FleAll-NL9
❑ 93FleAtl-6
❑ 93FleFruotL-13
❑ 93FunPac-142
❑ 93FunPac-143
❑ 93FunPacA-AS2
❑ 93JimDea-5
❑ 93KinDis-10
❑ 93Kra-19
❑ 93Lea-95
❑ 93LeaGolA-R1
❑ 93LeaGolA-U2
❑ 93OPC-71
❑ 93OPCPre-12
❑ 93PacSpa-233
❑ 93PanSti-269
❑ 93PhiMed-9
❑ 93PhiStaC-1
❑ 93Pin-99
❑ 93PinHomRC-9
❑ 93PinTeaP-3
❑ 93Pos-18
❑ 93PosCan-10
❑ 93Sco-10
❑ 93Sco-526
❑ 93ScoFra-22
❑ 93Sel-13
❑ 93SelChaS-5
❑ 93SelDufIP-3
❑ 93SelStaL-34
❑ 93SP-11
❑ 93SPPlaP-PP5
❑ 93StaClu-313
❑ 93StaCluFDI-313
❑ 93StaCluM-91
❑ 93StaCluMOP-313
❑ 93Stu-51
❑ 93StuSupoC-7
❑ 93Top-180
❑ 93Top-408
❑ 93TOPBLAG-3
❑ 93TopFulS-13
❑ 93TopGol-180
❑ 93TopGol-408
❑ 93TopInaM-180
❑ 93TopInaM-408
❑ 93TopInaR-180
❑ 93TopInaR-408
❑ 93TopMic-180
❑ 93TopMic-408
❑ 93TriPla-7
❑ 93TriPla-229
❑ 93TriPlaA-5
❑ 93TriPlaLL-L5
❑ 93TriPlaP-7
❑ 93Ult-86
❑ 93UltAllS-1
❑ 93UltHomRK-9
❑ 93UppDec-137
❑ 93UppDec-485
❑ 93UppDec-498
❑ 93UppDec-829
❑ 93UppDecGold-137
❑ 93UppDecGold-485
❑ 93UppDecGold-498
❑ 93UppDecGold-829
❑ 93UppDecHRH-HR8
❑ 93UppDecIC-WI17
❑ 93UppDecICJ-WI17
❑ 93USPlaCA-3C
❑ 94Bow-140
❑ 94Bow-384
❑ 94BowBes-R11
❑ 94BowBesR-R11
❑ 94ColC-358
❑ 94ColChoGS-358
❑ 94ColChoSS-358
❑ 94Don-333
❑ 94DonPro-2
❑ 94DonSpeE-333
❑ 94Fin-220
❑ 94FinJum-220
❑ 94FinRef-220
❑ 94Fla-204
❑ 94FlaInfP-3
❑ 94Fle-585
❑ 94FleAllS-34
❑ 94FleExtB-330
❑ 94FleExtBGB-8
❑ 94FlePro-1
❑ 94FleSun-8
❑ 94FUnPac-140
❑ 94KinDis-4
❑ 94Lea-170
❑ 94LeaL-134
❑ 94LeaMVPC-N4
❑ 94LeaMVPCG-N4
❑ 94LeaPro-2
❑ 94LeaSli-3
❑ 94OPC-123
❑ 94Pac-471
❑ 94PacSilP-31
❑ 94PacSilPC-31
❑ 94PanSti-224
❑ 94PhiMed-6
❑ 94PhiMel-4
❑ 94PhiUSPC-8C
❑ 94PhiUSPC-13H
❑ 94Pin-91
❑ 94PinArtP-91
❑ 94PinMusC-91
❑ 94PinRunC-RC31
❑ 94Pos-9
❑ 94ProMag-101
❑ 94Sco-34
❑ 94ScoGolR-34
❑ 94ScoGolS-4
❑ 94Sel-9
❑ 94SP-134
❑ 94SPDieC-134
❑ 94Spo-128
❑ 94StaClu-450
❑ 94StaCluDD-DD12
❑ 94StaCluFDI-450
❑ 94StaCluGR-450
❑ 94StaCluMOP-450
❑ 94StaCluMOP-DD12
❑ 94StaCluT-237
❑ 94StaCluTFDI-237
❑ 94Stu-136
❑ 94Top-380
❑ 94Top-608
❑ 94TopBlaG-28
❑ 94TopGol-380
❑ 94TopGol-608
❑ 94TopSpa-380
❑ 94TopSpa-608
❑ 94TopSupS-11
❑ 94TriPla-171
❑ 94TriPlaM-2
❑ 94Ult-243
❑ 94Ult-P243
❑ 94UltPhiF-1
❑ 94UltPhiF-2
❑ 94UltPhiF-3
❑ 94UltPhiF-4
❑ 94UltPhiF-5
❑ 94UltPhiF-11
❑ 94UltPhiF-12
❑ 94UltPhiF-13
❑ 94UltPhiF-14
❑ 94UltPhiF-15
❑ 94UltPhiF-M1
❑ 94UltPhiF-M3
❑ 94UltPhiF-AU1
❑ 94UltRBIK-12
❑ 94UppDec-65
❑ 94UppDecAJ-7
❑ 94UppDecAJG-7
❑ 94UppDecED-65
❑ 95Baz-105
❑ 95Bow-326
❑ 95BowBes-R9
❑ 95BowBesR-R9
❑ 95ClaPhoC-43
❑ 95ColCho-370
❑ 95ColChoGS-370
❑ 95ColChoSE-171
❑ 95ColChoSEGS-171
❑ 95ColChoSESS-171
❑ 95ColChoSS-370
❑ 95DenHol-7
❑ 95Don-497
❑ 95DonDom-2
❑ 95DonPreP-497
❑ 95DonTopotO-300
❑ 95Emo-164
❑ 95Fin-164
❑ 95FinRef-164
❑ 95Fla-177
❑ 95FlaInfP-2
❑ 95Fle-388
❑ 95FleTeaL-24
❑ 95Lea-274
❑ 95LeaLim-99
❑ 95NatPac2-2
❑ 95Pac-326
❑ 95PacPri-105
❑ 95PanSti-21
❑ 95Phi-7
❑ 95PhiMel-5
❑ 95Pin-205

❑ 95PinArtP-205
❑ 95PinMusC-205
❑ 95Sco-432
❑ 95ScoGolR-432
❑ 95ScoHaloG-HG94
❑ 95ScoPlaTS-432
❑ 95Sel-44
❑ 95SelArtP-44
❑ 95SelCer-57
❑ 95SelCerMG-57
❑ 95SP-90
❑ 95SPCha-73
❑ 95SPCha-74
❑ 95SPChaDC-73
❑ 95SPChaDC-74
❑ 95Spo-27
❑ 95SpoArtP-27
❑ 95SPSil-90
❑ 95StaClu-237
❑ 95StaClu-263
❑ 95StaClu-505
❑ 95StaCluFDI-237
❑ 95StaCluFDI-263
❑ 95StaCluMOP-237
❑ 95StaCluMOP-263
❑ 95StaCluMOP-505
❑ 95StaCluMOP-RL19
❑ 95StaCluRL-RL19
❑ 95StaCluSTWS-237
❑ 95StaCluSTWS-263
❑ 95StaCluSTWS-505
❑ 95StaCluVR-131
❑ 95StaCluVRMO-131
❑ 95Stu-159
❑ 95Sum-70
❑ 95SumNthD-70
❑ 95Top-477
❑ 95TopCyb-270
❑ 95TopEmb-61
❑ 95TopEmbGI-61
❑ 95UC3-59
❑ 95UC3ArtP-59
❑ 95Ult-417
❑ 95UltGolM-417
❑ 95UppDec-380
❑ 95UppDecED-380
❑ 95UppDecEDG-380
❑ 95UppDecPLL-R50
❑ 95UppDecPLLE-R50
❑ 95UppDecSE-75
❑ 95UppDecSEG-75
❑ 95Zen-21
❑ 96Baz-39
❑ 96ColCho-398
❑ 96ColCho-671
❑ 96ColChoGS-398
❑ 96ColChoGS-671
❑ 96ColChoSS-398
❑ 96ColChoSS-671
❑ 96ColChoYMtP-12
❑ 96ColChoYMtP-12A
❑ 96ColChoYMtPGS-12
❑ 96ColChoYMtPGS-12A
❑ 96DenHol-27
❑ 96Don-395
❑ 96DonPreP-395
❑ 96EmoXL-242
❑ 96Fin-B136
❑ 96FinRef-B136
❑ 96Fla-330
❑ 96Fle-494
❑ 96FleTeaL-24
❑ 96FleTif-494
❑ 96Lea-196
❑ 96LeaPrePB-196
❑ 96LeaPrePG-196
❑ 96LeaPrePS-196
❑ 96LeaPreSG-36
❑ 96LeaPreSte-36
❑ 96MetUni-208
❑ 96MetUniP-208
❑ 96Pac-151
❑ 96PacPri-P51
❑ 96PacPriG-P51
❑ 96PanSti-36
❑ 96PhiTeal-8
❑ 96Pin-217
❑ 96PinAfi-32
❑ 96PinAfiAP-32
❑ 96PinAfiFPP-32
❑ 96PinArtP-117
❑ 96PinFan-30
❑ 96PinFoil-217
❑ 96PinSta-117
❑ 96ProSta-90
❑ 96Sco-12
❑ 96ScoDugC-A12
❑ 96ScoDugCAP-A12
❑ 96ScoGolS-21
❑ 96Sel-69
❑ 96SelArtP-69
❑ 96SelTeaN-10
❑ 96Spo-89
❑ 96SpoArtP-89
❑ 96StaClu-106
❑ 96StaCluEPB-106
❑ 96StaCluEPG-106
❑ 96StaCluEPS-106
❑ 96StaCluMOP-106
❑ 96Stu-52
❑ 96StuPrePB-52
❑ 96StuPrePG-52
❑ 96StuPrePS-52
❑ 96Sum-128
❑ 96SumAbo&B-128
❑ 96SumArtP-128
❑ 96SumFoi-128
❑ 96Top-85
❑ 96TopGal-148
❑ 96TopGalPPI-148
❑ 96TopLas-5
❑ 96Ult-250
❑ 96UltGolM-250
❑ 96UppDec-169
❑ 97Cir-143
❑ 97CirRav-143
❑ 97ColCho-193
❑ 97Don-287
❑ 97DonGolPP-287
❑ 97DonSilPP-287
❑ 97FlaShoLC-160
❑ 97FlaShoLeg0-160
❑ 97FlaShoLeg1-160
❑ 97FlaShoM-A160
❑ 97FlaShoM-B160
❑ 97FlaShoM-C160
❑ 97FlaShoR0-160
❑ 97FlaShoR1-160
❑ 97FlaShoR2-160
❑ 97Fle-669
❑ 97FleTif-669
❑ 97Lea-263
❑ 97LeaFraM-263
❑ 97LeaFraMDC-263
❑ 97PhiCopQ-6
❑ 97PhiTeal-10
❑ 97Sco-20
❑ 97ScoArtPWB-20
❑ 97ScoPreS-20
❑ 97ScoShoS-20
❑ 97ScoShoSAP-20
❑ 97SpoIll-40
❑ 97SpoIllEE-40
❑ 97SpoIllGS-18
❑ 97Ult-365
❑ 97UltGolME-365
❑ 97UltPlaME-365
❑ 97UppDec-455
❑ 98Fle-189
❑ 98Pac-299
❑ 98PacPlaB-299
❑ 98PacRedT-299
❑ 98PacSil-299
❑ 98Sco-139
❑ 98ScoSS-PP57
❑ 98ScoSSAP-PP57
❑ 98Top-218
❑ 98TopChr-218
❑ 98TopChrR-218
❑ 98TopDevR-218
❑ 98TopDia-218
❑ 98TopMiniC-218
❑ 98Ult-93
❑ 98UltGolM-93
❑ 98UltMas-93
❑ 98UltPlaM-93
❑ 98UppDec-378

Daunic, Willie
❑ 93MedHatBJF-3743
❑ 93MedHatBJSP-7
❑ 94St.CatBJC-8
❑ 94St.CatBJF-3650

Dauphin, Phil
❑ 90GenCubP-3036
❑ 90GenCubS-6
❑ 91MidLeaAP-MWL7
❑ 91PeoChiP-1355
❑ 91PeoChiTI-25
❑ 92ChaKniF-2782
❑ 92ChaKniS-152
❑ 92ClaFS7-60
❑ 92ProFS7-209
❑ 92SkyAA F-70
❑ 92UppDecML-305
❑ 93ClaFS7-3
❑ 93OrlCubF-2796
❑ 95HarSenTI-22

Dauphin, Philip J.
❑ 91PeoChiC-25
❑ 92Bow-169
❑ 93CubStaC-25

Dauss, Hooks (George August)
❑ 17ColE13-39
❑ 17HolBreD-22
❑ 21E121So1-16
❑ 21E121So8-15
❑ 21Exh-33
❑ 21Nei-18
❑ 22AmeCarE122-14
❑ 22E120-51
❑ 22W573-29
❑ 22W575-23
❑ 23MapCriV-11
❑ 23W501-111
❑ 23WilChoV-27
❑ 25Exh-91
❑ 26Exh-92
❑ 27Exh-46
❑ 76ISCHooHA-7
❑ 81TigDetN-74
❑ 88ConSer5-7
❑ 94ConTSN-1070
❑ 94ConTSNB-1070

Davalillo, David
❑ 95CedRapKTI-4
❑ 95LinVen-4
❑ 96-97LinVen-147
❑ 96CedRapKTI-7
❑ 96MidLeaAB-17
❑ 97LakElsSG-10
❑ 98LakElsSG-7

Davalillo, Pompeyo
❑ 76VenLeaS-109
❑ 80VenLeaS-182
❑ 93LinVenB-245
❑ 93LinVenB-316
❑ 94VenLinU-236
❑ 95LinVen-36
❑ 95LinVen-304
❑ 96-97LinVen-226

Davalillo, Vic (Victor J.)
❑ 63IndJayP-3
❑ 63Top-324
❑ 64IndJayP-3
❑ 64Kah-6
❑ 64Top-435
❑ 64TopCoi-86
❑ 64TopSta-100
❑ 64TopTatl-33
❑ 65ChaTheY-26
❑ 65Kah-11
❑ 65OldLonC-24
❑ 65OPC-128
❑ 65Top-128
❑ 66IndTeal-4
❑ 66IndVolC-5
❑ 66Kah-10
❑ 66Top-216
❑ 66Top-325
❑ 66TopRubI-22
❑ 66TopVen-216
❑ 66TopVen-325
❑ 67CokCapI-17
❑ 67DexPre-59
❑ 67OPC-69
❑ 67Top-69
❑ 67TopVen-190
❑ 68Top-397
❑ 69MilBra-70
❑ 69MLBOffS-20
❑ 69Top-275
❑ 69TopSta-142
❑ 69TopSup-9
❑ 69TopTeaP-17
❑ 70CarTeal-11
❑ 70MLBOffS-138
❑ 70OPC-256
❑ 70Top-256
❑ 71MLBOffS-199
❑ 71OPC-4
❑ 71PirActP-15
❑ 71Top-4
❑ 72MilBra-86
❑ 72Top-785
❑ 73OPC-163
❑ 73Top-163
❑ 74OPC-444
❑ 74Top-444
❑ 76VenLeaS-8
❑ 76VenLeaS-242
❑ 78SSP270-66
❑ 78Top-539
❑ 79Top-228
❑ 80VenLeaS-33
❑ 81Fle-132
❑ 90DodTar-167
❑ 95LinVen-280
❑ 95LinVen-281
❑ 95LinVen-283

DaVanon, Jeff
❑ 96WesMicWB-7
❑ 97VisOakG-7
❑ 98ModA'sG-9

DaVanon, Jerry (Frank G.)
❑ 69Top-637
❑ 71BalOriP-7
❑ 71OPC-32
❑ 71Top-32
❑ 75IowOakT-5
❑ 76HouAstP-9
❑ 76OPC-551
❑ 76Top-551
❑ 77Top-283
❑ 91OriCro-95

Davenport, Adell
❑ 87AncGlaP-5
❑ 89CliGiaP-882
❑ 90Bes-58
❑ 90CalLeaACLC-47
❑ 90CMC-715
❑ 90SanJosGB-8
❑ 90SanJosGCLC-39
❑ 90SanJosGP-2019
❑ 90SanJosGS-6
❑ 91CalLeLA-29
❑ 91SanJosGC-6
❑ 91SanJosGP-17
❑ 92ClaFS7-435
❑ 92ShrCapF-3880
❑ 92ShrCapS-582
❑ 92SkyAA F-256
❑ 93Bow-408
❑ 93ClaFS7-49
❑ 93ClaGolF-211
❑ 93ExcFS7-116
❑ 93GiaStaC-17
❑ 93PhoFirF-1521
❑ 93ShrCapF-2764
❑ 93Top-494
❑ 93TopGol-494
❑ 93TopInaM-494
❑ 93TopInaR-494
❑ 93TopMic-494
❑ 94NasXprF-392

Davenport, Dave (Arthur D.)
❑ 17HolBreD-23

Davenport, Gary
❑ 86FreGiaSB-2

Davenport, Jeff
❑ 98LetBlaDG-8

Davenport, Jim (James H.)
❑ 47PM1StaP1-40
❑ 58GiaSFCB-7
❑ 58Top-413
❑ 59Baz-9
❑ 59Top-198
❑ 60GiaJayP-5
❑ 60Top-154
❑ 60TopVen-154
❑ 61GiaJayP-5
❑ 61Pos-149A
❑ 61Pos-149B
❑ 61Top-55
❑ 61TopDicG-3
❑ 61TopStal-76
❑ 62GiaJayP-4
❑ 62Jel-134
❑ 62Pos-134
❑ 62PosCan-134
❑ 62SalPlaC-169
❑ 62ShiPlaC-169
❑ 62Top-9
❑ 62TopStal-196
❑ 62TopVen-9
❑ 63Fle-65
❑ 63GiaJayP-4
❑ 63Jel-104
❑ 63Pos-104
❑ 63SalMetC-19
❑ 63Top-388
❑ 64GiaJayP-4
❑ 64Top-82
❑ 64TopSta-63
❑ 64TopVen-82
❑ 65GiaTeal-1
❑ 65OPC-213
❑ 65Top-213
❑ 66OPC-176
❑ 66Top-176
❑ 66TopVen-176
❑ 67CokCapG-3
❑ 67DexPre-60
❑ 67Top-441
❑ 67TopVen-326
❑ 68DexPre-27
❑ 68Top-525
❑ 69MilBra-69
❑ 69OPC-102
❑ 69Top-102
❑ 69TopSta-102
❑ 69TopTeaP-14
❑ 70MLBOffS-122
❑ 70OPC-378
❑ 70Top-378
❑ 72MilBra-85
❑ 74PadDea-7
❑ 76SSP-626
❑ 78TCM60I-131
❑ 79GiaPol-12
❑ 79TCM50-288
❑ 80GiaPol-12
❑ 81Gia196T-13
❑ 82Gia25tATI-6
❑ 84GiaMot-6
❑ 85GiaMot-1
❑ 85GiaPos-5
❑ 85TopTifT-27T
❑ 85TopTra-27T
❑ 86PhiTas-2
❑ 87PhiTas-xx0
❑ 89IndTeal-28
❑ 89PacLegI-118
❑ 90TigTeal-7
❑ 91HamRedC-24
❑ 91HamRedP-4051
❑ 91TigCok-NNO
❑ 92UppDecS-7
❑ 93SanJosGC-27
❑ 93SanJosGF-28
❑ 93UppDecS-7
❑ 94SanJosGC-29
❑ 94SanJosGF-2834
❑ 96GiaMot-28
❑ 98FreGriG-8

Davenport, Joe
❑ 95HagSunF-61
❑ 96StCatSB-7
❑ 97HagSunB-4

Davenport, Neal
❑ 86CedRapRT-26
❑ 87TamTarP-23

Davenport, Scott
❑ 86AncGlaPTI-7

Daves, Eddie
❑ 78SprRedWK-11

Davey, Mike (Michael Gerard)
❑ 79SpoIndT-14
❑ 80PorBeaT-19

Davey, Tom
❑ 94MedHatBJF-3674
❑ 94MedHatBJSP-14
❑ 95StCatSTI-1
❑ 96HagSunB-3
❑ 97DunBluJTI-7
❑ 98KnoSG-2
❑ 99Bow-373
❑ 99BowGol-373
❑ 99BowInt-373
❑ 99SkyPre-259
❑ 99SkyPre-259
❑ 99SkyPreR-259
❑ 99SkyPreR-259

Daviault, Ray
❑ 61TacBan-4
❑ 77FriOneYW-105
❑ 91MetWIZ-91

David, Andre
❑ 82OrlTwi8SCT-5
❑ 82OrlTwiT-16
❑ 83TolMudHT-19
❑ 84TolMudHT-11
❑ 85TolMudHT-20
❑ 85Top-43
❑ 85TopTif-43
❑ 85TwiPos-4
❑ 85TwiTeal-16
❑ 86StaoftFT-23
❑ 86TolMudHP-7
❑ 87Don-519
❑ 87TidTidP-24
❑ 87TidTidT-12
❑ 88MetColP-18
❑ 88TidTidCa-7
❑ 88TidTidCM-18
❑ 88TidTidP-1596
❑ 89ElPasDGS-26
❑ 91KinMetC-24
❑ 91KinMetP-3829
❑ 92KinMetC-23
❑ 92KinMetF-1547
❑ 94St.LucMC-29
❑ 94St.LucMF-1212

David, Armin
❑ 86HunStaDJ-10

David, Brian
❑ 83WauTimF-6
❑ 86ChaLooP-8
❑ 87ChaLooB-23

David, Gerald
❑ 92ElmPioC-15

David, Greg
❑ 87DunBluJP-942
❑ 88MyrBeaBJP-1176
❑ 89MyrBeaBJP-1454
❑ 90TexLeaAGS-3
❑ 90WicWraRD-6
❑ 91LinDriAA-605
❑ 91WicWraLD-605
❑ 91WicWraP-2603
❑ 91WicWraRD-13
❑ 92MemChiF-2421
❑ 92MemChiS-433

David, House of
❑ 85TCMPhoC-30
❑ 93NegLeaRL2-96
❑ 94UppDecTAE-39

Davidsmeier, Dan
❑ 82ElPasDT-5
❑ 84VanCanC-29
❑ 85VanCanC-201
❑ 86VanCanP-9
❑ 87DenZepP-22

Davidson, Archer
❑ 63GadFunC-72

Davidson, Bob (Robert A.)
❑ 88T/MUmp-44
❑ 89T/MUmp-42
❑ 90T/MUmp-40

Davidson, Bobby
❑ 86AlbYanT-31
❑ 87PriWilYP-3
❑ 88AlbYanP-1334
❑ 89AlbYanB-3
❑ 89AlbYanP-327
❑ 89AlbYanSt-6
❑ 89Sta-97
❑ 90CMC-226
❑ 90ColCliC-26
❑ 90ColCliP-10
❑ 90ColCliP-669
❑ 90ProAAAF-319
❑ 90TopDeb89-29
❑ 90TopTVY-39
❑ 91LinDriAAA-233
❑ 91LouRedLD-233
❑ 91LouRedP-2908
❑ 92YanWIZ8-39

Davidson, Cleatus
❑ 94SigRooDP-37
❑ 94SigRooDPS-37
❑ 96ForWayWB-6
❑ 97ForWayW-8
❑ 98ForMyeMTI-10

Davidson, Grady
❑ 91WatIndC-3
❑ 91WatIndP-3358

Davidson, Harley
❑ 78HalHalR-11

Davidson, Jackie
❑ 86PitCubP-6
❑ 87IowCubTI-3
❑ 88PitCubP-1375
❑ 89ChaKniTI-19

Davidson, John
❑ 91KisDodP-4176

Davidson, Mark
❑ 85OrlTwiT-3
❑ 86TolMudHP-6
❑ 86TwiTeal-20

❑ 87DonOpeD-225
❑ 87DonRoo-22
❑ 87FleUpd-20
❑ 87FleUpdG-20
❑ 87TwiPos-6
❑ 87TwiTeal-18
❑ 88Don-519
❑ 88Fle-8
❑ 88FleGlo-8
❑ 88Sco-570
❑ 88ScoGlo-570
❑ 88StaLinTw-6
❑ 88Top-19
❑ 88TopClo-29
❑ 88TopTif-19
❑ 89Fle-109
❑ 89FleGlo-109
❑ 89PorBeaC-22
❑ 89PorBeaP-227
❑ 89Sco-107
❑ 89Top-451
❑ 89TopBig-320
❑ 89TopTif-451
❑ 89UppDec-577
❑ 90AstLenH-10
❑ 90AstMot-11
❑ 90OPC-267
❑ 90Top-267
❑ 90TopTif-267
❑ 91AstMot-11
❑ 91Don-540
❑ 91Fle-504
❑ 91Lea-143
❑ 91OPC-678
❑ 91StaClu-584
❑ 91Top-678
❑ 91TopDesS-678
❑ 91TopMic-678
❑ 91TopTif-678
❑ 91Ult-136
❑ 92ColSprSSF-763
❑ 92ColSprSSS-83
❑ 92Fle-432
❑ 92Sco-289
❑ 92TopGol-86
❑ 93ChaKniF-556
Davidson, Mike
❑ 88BriTigP-1871
❑ 89FayGenP-1593
Davidson, Paul
❑ 08IndPos-6
❑ 09T206-416
Davidson, Randy
❑ 78IndIndTI-24
❑ 79IndIndTI-13
❑ 81CedRapRT-19
❑ 82CedRapRT-25
Davidson, Rodney
❑ 93LetMouF-4144
❑ 93LetMouSP-2
Davidson, Scott
❑ 93MisStaB-11
Davidson, Ted (Thomas E.)
❑ 65OPC-243
❑ 65Top-243
❑ 66OPC-89
❑ 66Top-89
❑ 66TopVen-89
❑ 67Top-519
❑ 68OPC-48
❑ 68Top-48
❑ 68TopVen-48
Davidson, William J.
❑ 11PinT-5-453
❑ 11SpoLifM-153
Davie, Jerry (Gerald Lee)
❑ 59Top-256
❑ 60Top-301
Davies, Bob
❑ 52Whe-6A
❑ 52Whe-6B
❑ 98ForWayWI-16
Davies, Dan
❑ 85MiaHur-1
Davies, George
❑ 93JusSo-5
Davila, Jose (J.D.)
❑ 91SpoIndC-18
❑ 91SpoIndP-3941
❑ 92WatDiaC-10
❑ 92WatDiaF-2138
Davila, Vic
❑ 83ButCopKT-17
❑ 94HagSunC-5
❑ 94HagSunF-2738
❑ 95DunBluJTI-6
❑ 96DunBluJB-4
❑ 96DunBluJTI-6
Davin, D.
❑ 87OldJudN-123
Davino, Mike
❑ 89UtiBluSP-5
❑ 90SarWhiSS-7
❑ 91BirBarLD-57
❑ 91BirBarP-1448
❑ 91LinDriAA-57
Davins, Jim
❑ 86MacPirP-7
❑ 87KenTwiP-1
❑ 88PorBeaC-10
❑ 88PorBeaP-660
❑ 89PorBeaC-1
❑ 89PorBeaP-211
❑ 90CMC-61
❑ 90IndIndC-11
❑ 90IndIndP-286
❑ 90ProAAAF-569
❑ 91DenZepLD-133
❑ 91DenZepP-115
❑ 91LinDriAAA-133
Davis, Albert
❑ 97AugGre-26
Davis, Alvin
❑ 83ChaLooT-8
❑ 84FleUpd-30
❑ 84FunFooP-37
❑ 84MarMot-23
❑ 84TopTra-28T
❑ 84TopTraT-28T
❑ 85AllGamPI-4
❑ 85Don-18
❑ 85Don-69
❑ 85DonActA-16
❑ 85DonSupD-18
❑ 85Dra-8
❑ 85Fle-488
❑ 85FleLimE-7
❑ 85FleStaS-15
❑ 85GenMilS-16
❑ 85Lea-18
❑ 85MarMot-2
❑ 85OPC-145
❑ 85SevCoi-W7
❑ 85Top-145
❑ 85TopGaloC-2
❑ 85TopGloS-8
❑ 85TopRubD-15
❑ 85TopSti-332
❑ 85TopSti-368
❑ 85TopSup-6
❑ 85TopTif-145
❑ 86Don-69
❑ 86Fle-464
❑ 86FleLeaL-9
❑ 86FleMin-97
❑ 86FleSlu-8
❑ 86FleStiC-29
❑ 86KayB-7
❑ 86Lea-65
❑ 86MarMot-2
❑ 86MarPacNB-4
❑ 86OPC-309
❑ 86Spo-31
❑ 86Spo-74
❑ 86Top-440
❑ 86TopSti-218
❑ 86TopTat-12
❑ 86TopTif-440
❑ 86TruVal-21
❑ 87Don-75
❑ 87DonOpeD-115
❑ 87Fle-584
❑ 87FleExcS-13
❑ 87FleGlo-584
❑ 87FleMin-24
❑ 87FleRecS-5
❑ 87FleStiC-28
❑ 87KraFoo-37
❑ 87Lea-118
❑ 87MarMot-2
❑ 87OPC-235
❑ 87RedFolSB-71
❑ 87Spo-21
❑ 87SpoTeaP-25
❑ 87StuPan-25
❑ 87Top-235
❑ 87TopCoi-9
❑ 87TopSti-220
❑ 87TopTif-235
❑ 88Don-193
❑ 88DonBasB-107
❑ 88DonBonM-BC25
❑ 88Fle-373
❑ 88FleGlo-373
❑ 88FleRecS-8
❑ 88FleStiC-59
❑ 88FleSup-10
❑ 88GreBasS-78
❑ 88KayB-6
❑ 88KinDis-17
❑ 88Lea-196
❑ 88MarMot-2
❑ 88OPC-349
❑ 88PanSti-185
❑ 88Sco-83
❑ 88ScoGlo-83
❑ 88Spo-52
❑ 88StaLinMa-6
❑ 88Top-785
❑ 88TopBig-64
❑ 88TopCoi-10
❑ 88TopRitTM-24
❑ 88TopSti-219
❑ 88TopTif-785
❑ 88TopUKM-17
❑ 88TopUKMT-17
❑ 89Bow-215
❑ 89BowTif-215
❑ 89ChaLooLITI-8
❑ 89ClaLigB-81
❑ 89Don-345
❑ 89DonBasB-24
❑ 89DonBonM-BC25
❑ 89Fle-546
❑ 89FleGlo-546
❑ 89MarMot-2
❑ 89OPC-57
❑ 89PanSti-435
❑ 89PAORelT-2
❑ 89RedFolSB-27
❑ 89Sco-51
❑ 89ScoHot1S-78
❑ 89Spo-33
❑ 89Top-687
❑ 89TopBasT-59
❑ 89TopBig-218
❑ 89TopCoi-38
❑ 89TopMinL-72
❑ 89TopSti-227
❑ 89TopTif-687
❑ 89TopUKM-18
❑ 89TVSpoM-122
❑ 89UppDec-105
❑ 89UppDec-680
❑ 90Bow-479
❑ 90BowTif-479
❑ 90ClaBlu-136
❑ 90Don-109
❑ 90DonBesA-26
❑ 90DOnBonM-BC9
❑ 90Fle-512
❑ 90FleCan-512
❑ 90Hot50PS-8
❑ 90Lea-35
❑ 90M.Vpin-93
❑ 90MarMot-2
❑ 90MLBBasB-116
❑ 90OPC-373
❑ 90PanSti-149
❑ 90PubIntS-431
❑ 90Sco-205
❑ 90Sco100S-26
❑ 90Spo-112
❑ 90Top-373
❑ 90TopAmeA-26
❑ 90TopBig-315
❑ 90TopCoi-11
❑ 90TopDou-13
❑ 90TopHilHM-26
❑ 90TopMinL-33
❑ 90TopSti-220
❑ 90TopTif-373
❑ 90UppDec-364
❑ 91Bow-258
❑ 91DenHol-19
❑ 91Don-482
❑ 91Fle-449
❑ 91Lea-429
❑ 91MarCouH-14
❑ 91OPC-515
❑ 91PanSti-185
❑ 91Sco-482
❑ 91SevCoi-NW3
❑ 91SimandSMLBL-12
❑ 91StaClu-82
❑ 91Stu-111
❑ 91Top-515
❑ 91TopDesS-515
❑ 91TopMic-515
❑ 91TopTif-515
❑ 91Ult-334
❑ 91UppDec-457
❑ 92AngPol-6
❑ 92Bow-341
❑ 92Don-124
❑ 92Fle-277
❑ 92Lea-168
❑ 92LeaBlaG-168
❑ 92OPC-130
❑ 92OPCPre-183
❑ 92Pin-467
❑ 92Sco-76
❑ 92StaClu-90
❑ 92StaClu-617
❑ 92StaCluNC-617
❑ 92Top-130
❑ 92TopGol-130
❑ 92TopGolW-130
❑ 92TopMic-130
❑ 92Ult-324
❑ 92UppDec-386
Davis, Anthony
❑ 91PacSenL-95
❑ 93HolLeg-4
Davis, Ben
❑ 95Bes-111
❑ 95BowBes-X1
❑ 95BowBesR-X1
❑ 95IdaFalBTI-13
❑ 95IdaFalBTI-NNO
❑ 95IdaFalBTI-NNO
❑ 95TopTra-74T
❑ 96Bow-260
❑ 96BowBes-102
❑ 96BowBesAR-102
❑ 96BowBesMI-8
❑ 96BowBesMIAR-8
❑ 96BowBesMIR-8
❑ 96BowBesR-102
❑ 96BowFoi-260
❑ 96Exc-235
❑ 96ExcFirYP-3
❑ 96RanCucQB-10
❑ 96SigRooOJPP-P10
❑ 96SigRooOJPPS-P10
❑ 96Top-16
❑ 96TopPowB-16
❑ 97Bes-41
❑ 97Bow-193
❑ 97BowBes-110
❑ 97BowBesAR-110
❑ 97BowBesR-110
❑ 97BowCerBlaIA-CA20
❑ 97BowCerBluIA-CA20
❑ 97BowCerGolIA-CA20
❑ 97BowChr-181
❑ 97BowChrI-181
❑ 97BowChrIR-181
❑ 97BowChrR-181
❑ 97BowInt-193
❑ 97CalLeaTP-17
❑ 97RanCucQG-8
❑ 97Top-205
❑ 98AriFalLTP-15
❑ 98Bes-64
❑ 98Bow-142
❑ 98BowBes-166
❑ 98BowBesAR-166
❑ 98BowBesR-166
❑ 98BowCerBlueAU-41
❑ 98BowCerGA-41
❑ 98BowCerSA-41
❑ 98BowChr-142
❑ 98BowChrGA-142
❑ 98BowChrGAR-142
❑ 98BowChrI-142
❑ 98BowChrIR-142
❑ 98BowChrR-142
❑ 98BowGolA-142
❑ 98BowInt-142
❑ 98FleUpd-U22
❑ 98LeaRS-325
❑ 98LeaRSLHolo-325
❑ 98LeaRSLong-325
❑ 98LeaRTrue-325
❑ 98MobBayBTI-9
❑ 98SouLeaTPG-3
❑ 98SP MinPE-107
❑ 98SP MinSTHPE-H16
❑ 98SP SPTSC-BD
❑ 98SPMin-107
❑ 98SPMinSTH-H16
❑ 98Top-261
❑ 98TopChr-261
❑ 98TopChrR-261
❑ 98TopDevR-261
❑ 98TopDia-261
❑ 98TopMiniC-261
❑ 99BasAmeTP-30
❑ 99BasAmeTPG-30
❑ 99Bow-291
❑ 99BowAut-BA3
❑ 99BowBes-112
❑ 99BowBesAR-112
❑ 99BowBesR-112
❑ 99BowGol-291
❑ 99BowInt-291
❑ 99FlaShoWotF-10
❑ 99Fle-172
❑ 99FleBri-131
❑ 99FleBri2G-131
❑ 99FleBriBlu-131
❑ 99FleBriGol-131
❑ 99FleBriI-10
❑ 99FleSta9-172
❑ 99FleWarT-172
❑ 99MetUni-248
❑ 99MetUniGM-248
❑ 99MetUniPMG-248
❑ 99PacOme-201
❑ 99PacOmeC-201
❑ 99PacOmeG-201
❑ 99PacOmePB-201
❑ 99SkyThu-258
❑ 99SkyThuRant-258
❑ 99SkyThuRave-258
❑ 99SP SigAuto-BD
❑ 99SP SigAutoG-BD
❑ 99SP TopP-38
❑ 99SP TopPPE-38
❑ 99SpoIll-60
❑ 99SpoIllOTW-8
❑ 99SPSig-64
❑ 99SPx-114
❑ 99SPxFinR-114
❑ 99SPxFinS-114
❑ 99ThuSkySupR-258
❑ 99Top-208
❑ 99TopChr-208
❑ 99TopChrR-208
❑ 99Vic-335
Davis, Bill
❑ 82IdaFalAT-17
Davis, Bill (Arthur W.)
❑ 65Top-546
❑ 66OPC-44
❑ 66Top-44
❑ 66TopVen-44
❑ 67Top-253
❑ 68Top-432
❑ 69Top-304
❑ 69TopTeaP-12
Davis, Bo (Allen)
❑ 89BluOriS-7
❑ 90WauTimB-26
❑ 90WauTimP-2140
❑ 90WauTimS-6
❑ 91KanCouCC-21
❑ 91KanCouCP-2668
❑ 98YakBeaG-10
Davis, Bob (Robert Edward)
❑ 15Zee-57
❑ 56A'sPos-13
❑ 61Top-246
❑ 75HawIslC-3
❑ 75IntLeaASB-5
❑ 75PacCoaLAB-5
❑ 76OPC-472
❑ 76Top-472
❑ 76VenLeaS-107
❑ 77PadSchC-18
❑ 77Top-78
❑ 78PadFamF-9
❑ 78Top-713
❑ 80OPC-185
❑ 80Top-351
❑ 81Don-30
❑ 81Fle-428
❑ 81OPC-221
❑ 81SalLakCGT-26
❑ 81Top-221
❑ 86Ft.MyeRP-6
Davis, Brad
❑ 85Ft.MyeRT-3
Davis, Brad Earnest
❑ 85DalNatCC-12
Davis, Braz
❑ 87WytCubP-20
❑ 88ChaWheB-20
❑ 89PeoChiTI-2
Davis, Brent
❑ 92Min-5
Davis, Bret
❑ 85AncGlaPTI-8
❑ 86WauTimP-7
❑ 88JamExpP-1897
❑ 89RocExpLC-7
❑ 90WesPalBES-4
Davis, Brian
❑ 88TamTarS-5
❑ 89UtiBluSP-6
❑ 90ColMetGS-12
❑ 90ColMetPPI-5
❑ 90SouAtlLAS-29
❑ 91St.LucMP-723
Davis, Brock (Bryshear B.)
❑ 63Top-553
❑ 71OPC-576
❑ 71Top-576
❑ 72OPC-161
❑ 72Top-161
❑ 73OPC-366
❑ 73Top-366
❑ 94BreMilB-15
Davis, Butch (Wallace M.)
❑ 84Don-277
❑ 84RoyPos-9
❑ 85OmaRoyT-12
❑ 85Top-49
❑ 85TopTif-49
❑ 87VanCanP-1614
❑ 88ChaKniTI-3
❑ 89RocRedWC-22
❑ 89RocRedWP-1652
❑ 90AlbDukCm-22
❑ 90AlbDukP-357
❑ 90AlbDukTr-5
❑ 90CMC-424
❑ 90ProAAAF-78
❑ 90TriAAAC-21
❑ 91AlbDukLD-5
❑ 91AlbDukP-1154
❑ 91DodPho-11
❑ 91LinDriAAA-5
❑ 91OriCro-96
❑ 92SkyAAAF-224
❑ 92SyrChiF-1980
❑ 92SyrChiMB-3
❑ 92SyrChiS-504
❑ 92TriA AAS-503
❑ 93RanKee-402
❑ 93RanStaC-8
❑ 94OklCit8F-1502
❑ 94Pac-613
❑ 95RocRedWTI-43
❑ 96RocRedWB-4
Davis, Chili (Charles T.)
❑ 78CedRapGT-7
❑ 82Gia25tATI-7
❑ 82Top-171
❑ 82TopTra-23T
❑ 83AllGamPI-141
❑ 83Don-348
❑ 83Fle-257
❑ 83FleSti-53
❑ 83GiaMot-3
❑ 83GiaPos-3
❑ 83OPC-115
❑ 83Top-115
❑ 83TopSti-319
❑ 84AllGamPI-48
❑ 84Don-114
❑ 84Fle-370
❑ 84FunFooP-38
❑ 84GiaPos-5
❑ 84Nes792-494
❑ 84OPC-367
❑ 84Top-494
❑ 84TopSti-171
❑ 84TopTif-494
❑ 85AllGamPI-138
❑ 85Don-480
❑ 85Dra-9
❑ 85Fle-605
❑ 85FleStaS-10
❑ 85GiaMot-2
❑ 85GiaPos-6
❑ 85Lea-66
❑ 85OPC-245
❑ 85Top-245

❑ 85TopSti-162
❑ 85TopSup-40
❑ 85TopTif-245
❑ 86BasStaB-27
❑ 86Don-6
❑ 86Don-65
❑ 86DonSupD-6
❑ 86Fle-536
❑ 86FleMin-109
❑ 86GiaMot-2
❑ 86GiaPos-8
❑ 86Lea-6
❑ 86Spo-82
❑ 87Don-268
❑ 87DonAll-38
❑ 87DonOpeD-97
❑ 87Fle-270
❑ 87FleBasA-12
❑ 87FleGlo-270
❑ 87FleMin-25
❑ 87FleStiC-29
❑ 87GiaMot-3
❑ 87GiaPos-8
❑ 87KraFoo-46
❑ 87Lea-208
❑ 87OPC-162
❑ 87RedFolSB-76
❑ 87Spo-45
❑ 87SpoTeaP-10
❑ 87StuPan-13
❑ 87Top-672
❑ 87TopSti-95
❑ 87TopTif-672
❑ 88AngSmo-10
❑ 88Don-313
❑ 88Fle-79
❑ 88FleGlo-79
❑ 88FleUpd-12
❑ 88FleUpdG-12
❑ 88OPC-15
❑ 88Sco-605
❑ 88ScoGlo-605
❑ 88ScoRoo-28T
❑ 88ScoRooG-28T
❑ 88Spo-172
❑ 88StaLinAn-4
❑ 88StaLinG-5
❑ 88Top-15
❑ 88TopBig-235
❑ 88TopTif-15
❑ 88TopTra-32T
❑ 88TopTraT-32T
❑ 89Bow-50
❑ 89BowTif-50
❑ 89ClaLigB-80
❑ 89Don-449
❑ 89DonBasB-115
❑ 89Fle-474
❑ 89FleGlo-474
❑ 89FleLeaL-9
❑ 89OPC-103
❑ 89PanSti-296
❑ 89RedFolSB-28
❑ 89Sco-54
❑ 89Spo-129
❑ 89Top-525
❑ 89TopBasT-134
❑ 89TopBig-294
❑ 89TopSti-177
❑ 89TopTif-525
❑ 89UppDec-126
❑ 90AngSmo-3
❑ 90Bow-301
❑ 90BowTif-301
❑ 90Don-136
❑ 90DOnBonM-BC20
❑ 90Fle-129
❑ 90FleCan-129
❑ 90Lea-288
❑ 90OPC-765
❑ 90PanSti-39
❑ 90PublntS-367
❑ 90Sco-326
❑ 90Spo-21
❑ 90Top-765
❑ 90TopBig-280
❑ 90TopCoi-12
❑ 90TopSti-173
❑ 90TopTif-765
❑ 90UppDec-38
❑ 91Bow-331
❑ 91Cla3-T12
❑ 91DodPho-12
❑ 91Don-580
❑ 91Fle-309
❑ 91FleUpd-36
❑ 91Lea-374
❑ 91OPC-355
❑ 91PanSti-134
❑ 91Sco-803
❑ 91ScoRoo-70T
❑ 91StaClu-329
❑ 91Top-355
❑ 91TopDesS-355
❑ 91TopMic-355
❑ 91TopTif-355
❑ 91TopTra-27T
❑ 91TopTraT-27T
❑ 91UltUpd-35
❑ 91UppDec-339
❑ 91UppDec-722
❑ 92Bow-195
❑ 92ClaGam-92
❑ 92Don-115
❑ 92Fle-200
❑ 92Lea-395
❑ 92LeaBlaG-395
❑ 92OPC-118
❑ 92Pin-46
❑ 92Sco-94
❑ 92ScoCokD-6
❑ 92ScoProP-15
❑ 92ScoProP-25
❑ 92StaClu-18
❑ 92StaCluD-32
❑ 92Top-118
❑ 92TopGol-118
❑ 92TopGolW-118
❑ 92TopKid-113
❑ 92TopMic-118
❑ 92TriPla-27
❑ 92Ult-89
❑ 92UppDec-126
❑ 92UppDecHRH-HR12
❑ 93AngMot-6
❑ 93AngPol-6
❑ 93AngStaCl-3
❑ 93Bow-553
❑ 93DenHol-1
❑ 93Don-679
❑ 93Fla-171
❑ 93Fle-262
❑ 93FleFinE-180
❑ 93FunPac-38
❑ 93Lea-254
❑ 93OPC-52
❑ 93OPCPre-24
❑ 93PacSpa-366
❑ 93PanSti-131
❑ 93Pin-536
❑ 93Sco-583
❑ 93Sel-238
❑ 93SelRoo-124T
❑ 93SP-20
❑ 93StaClu-222
❑ 93StaClu-611
❑ 93StaCluFDI-222
❑ 93StaCluFDI-611
❑ 93StaCluMOP-222
❑ 93StaCluMOP-611
❑ 93Stu-32
❑ 93Top-455
❑ 93TopGol-455
❑ 93ToplnaM-455
❑ 93ToplnaR-455
❑ 93TopMic-455
❑ 93Ult-518
❑ 93UppDec-239
❑ 93UppDec-794
❑ 93UppDecGold-239
❑ 93UppDecGold-794
❑ 94AngLAT-1
❑ 94AngMot-14
❑ 94Bow-451
❑ 94ColC-491
❑ 94ColChoGS-491
❑ 94ColChoSS-491
❑ 94Don-82
❑ 94Fin-112
❑ 94FinRef-112
❑ 94Fla-268
❑ 94Fle-51
❑ 94FleExtB-31
❑ 94Lea-258
❑ 94LeaL-15
❑ 94OPC-143
❑ 94Pac-74
❑ 94Pin-458
❑ 94PinArtP-458
❑ 94PinMusC-458
❑ 94Sco-345
❑ 94ScoGolR-345
❑ 94Sel-283
❑ 94SP-23
❑ 94SPDieC-23
❑ 94StaClu-173
❑ 94StaCluFDI-173
❑ 94StaCluGR-173
❑ 94StaCluMOP-173
❑ 94Stu-9
❑ 94Top-265
❑ 94TopGol-265
❑ 94TopSpa-265
❑ 94TriPla-12
❑ 94Ult-324
❑ 94UppDec-74
❑ 94UppDecED-74
❑ 95AngCHP-8
❑ 95AngMot-5
❑ 95AngTeal-2
❑ 95Baz-87
❑ 95Bow-387
❑ 95BowBes-R3
❑ 95BowBesR-R3
❑ 95ColCho-101
❑ 95ColChoGS-101
❑ 95ColChoSE-31
❑ 95ColChoSEGS-31
❑ 95ColChoSESS-31
❑ 95ColChoSS-101
❑ 95Don-452
❑ 95Don-550
❑ 95DonDiaK-DK3
❑ 95DonPreP-452
❑ 95DonPreP-545
❑ 95DonPreP-550
❑ 95DonTopotO-32
❑ 95Emo-18
❑ 95Fin-149
❑ 95FinRef-149
❑ 95Fla-234
❑ 95Fle-220
❑ 95Lea-93
❑ 95LeaLim-134
❑ 95Pac-55
❑ 95PacPri-17
❑ 95PanSti-95
❑ 95Sco-14
❑ 95ScoGolR-14
❑ 95ScoHaloG-HG100
❑ 95ScoPlaTS-14
❑ 95Sel-117
❑ 95SelArtP-117
❑ 95SelCer-12
❑ 95SelCerMG-12
❑ 95SP-133
❑ 95SPCha-129
❑ 95SPCha-133
❑ 95SPChaDC-129
❑ 95SPChaDC-133
❑ 95Spo-111
❑ 95SpoArtP-111
❑ 95SPSil-133
❑ 95StaClu-133
❑ 95StaCluCC-CC8
❑ 95StaCluFDI-133
❑ 95StaCluMOP-133
❑ 95StaCluMOP-CC8
❑ 95StaCluSTWS-133
❑ 95StaCluVR-69
❑ 95StaCluVRMO-69
❑ 95Stu-158
❑ 95Sum-20
❑ 95SumNthD-20
❑ 95TomPiz-7
❑ 95Top-335
❑ 95TopCyb-182
❑ 95TopEmb-20
❑ 95TopEmbGI-20
❑ 95UC3-8
❑ 95UC3ArtP-8
❑ 95Ult-19
❑ 95UltGolM-19
❑ 95UppDec-17
❑ 95UppDecED-17
❑ 95UppDecEDG-17
❑ 95UppDecSE-263
❑ 95UppDecSEG-263
❑ 95Zen-16
❑ 96AngMot-2
❑ 96ColCho-70
❑ 96ColCho-331
❑ 96ColChoGS-70
❑ 96ColChoGS-331
❑ 96ColChoSS-70
❑ 96ColChoSS-331
❑ 96Don-122
❑ 96DonPreP-122
❑ 96EmoXL-24
❑ 96Fin-B123
❑ 96FinRef-B123
❑ 96Fla-34
❑ 96Fle-43
❑ 96FleTif-43
❑ 96Lea-27
❑ 96LeaPrePB-27
❑ 96LeaPrePG-27
❑ 96LeaPrePS-27
❑ 96LibSpo-8
❑ 96MetUni-24
❑ 96MetUniP-24
❑ 96Pac-276
❑ 96PanSti-208
❑ 96Pin-32
❑ 96PinAfi-13
❑ 96PinAfiAP-13
❑ 96PinAfiFPP-13
❑ 96PinArtP-58
❑ 96PinSta-58
❑ 96ProSta-5
❑ 96Sco-332
❑ 96ScoDugC-B57
❑ 96ScoDugCAP-B57
❑ 96Sel-93
❑ 96SelArtP-93
❑ 96SP-43
❑ 96Spo-46
❑ 96SpoArtP-46
❑ 96StaClu-222
❑ 96StaClu-311
❑ 96StaCluMOP-222
❑ 96StaCluMOP-311
❑ 96Stu-102
❑ 96StuPrePB-102
❑ 96StuPrePG-102
❑ 96StuPrePS-102
❑ 96Sum-22
❑ 96SumAbo&B-22
❑ 96SumArtP-22
❑ 96SumFoi-22
❑ 96Top-280
❑ 96TopChr-113
❑ 96TopChrMotG-10
❑ 96TopChrMotGR-10
❑ 96TopChrR-113
❑ 96TopGal-171
❑ 96TopGalPPI-171
❑ 96TopLas-102
❑ 96TopMasotG-10
❑ 96Ult-26
❑ 96UltGolM-26
❑ 96UppDec-293
❑ 97BowBes-56
❑ 97BowBesAR-56
❑ 97BowBesR-56
❑ 97Cir-248
❑ 97CirRav-248
❑ 97ColCho-358
❑ 97Don-88
❑ 97Don-282
❑ 97DonGolPP-88
❑ 97DonGolPP-282
❑ 97DonLim-17
❑ 97DonLimE-17
❑ 97DonLimENG-17
❑ 97DonSilPP-88
❑ 97DonSilPP-282
❑ 97Fin-250
❑ 97FinRef-250
❑ 97FlaShoLC-104
❑ 97FlaShoLeg0-104
❑ 97FlaShoLeg1-104
❑ 97FlaShoM-A104
❑ 97FlaShoM-B104
❑ 97FlaShoM-C104
❑ 97FlaShoR0-104
❑ 97FlaShoR1-104
❑ 97FlaShoR2-104
❑ 97Fle-37
❑ 97Fle-602
❑ 97FleTif-37
❑ 97FleTif-602
❑ 97Lea-207
❑ 97LeaFraM-207
❑ 97LeaFraMDC-207
❑ 97MetUni-92
❑ 97NewPin-7
❑ 97NewPinAP-7
❑ 97NewPinMC-7
❑ 97NewPinPP-7
❑ 97Pac-3
❑ 97PacLigB-3
❑ 97PacPri-1
❑ 97PacPriLB-1
❑ 97PacPriP-1
❑ 97PacSil-3
❑ 97PhoFirDTTI-8
❑ 97RoyPol-7
❑ 97Sco-11
❑ 97Sco-338
❑ 97ScoArtPWB-11
❑ 97ScoArtPWB-338
❑ 97ScoPitP-8
❑ 97ScoPreS-11
❑ 97ScoResC-338
❑ 97ScoShoS-11
❑ 97ScoShoS-338
❑ 97ScoShoSAP-11
❑ 97ScoShoSAP-338
❑ 97SP-87
❑ 97StaClu-85
❑ 97StaCluMOP-85
❑ 97Top-365
❑ 97TopChr-125
❑ 97TopChrR-125
❑ 97TopGal-9
❑ 97TopGalPPI-9
❑ 97TopSta-63
❑ 97TopStaAM-63
❑ 97Ult-24
❑ 97Ult-432
❑ 97UltGolME-24
❑ 97UltGolME-432
❑ 97UltPlaME-24
❑ 97UltPlaME-432
❑ 97UppDec-538
❑ 98CirThu-244
❑ 98CirThuRav-244
❑ 98CirThuSupRav-244
❑ 98ColCho-447
❑ 98DonColL-240
❑ 98DonPriCL-240
❑ 98Fin-250
❑ 98FinNo--250
❑ 98FinNo-R-250
❑ 98FinRef-250
❑ 98FlaShoLeg0-35
❑ 98FlaShoLeg1-35
❑ 98FlaShoLeg2-35
❑ 98FlaShoLeg3-35
❑ 98FlaShoLegM-35
❑ 98FlaShoR0-35
❑ 98FlaShoR1-35
❑ 98FlaShoR2-35
❑ 98FlaShoR3-35
❑ 98Fle-224
❑ 98Fle-363
❑ 98FleVin'-107
❑ 98FleVin'C-107
❑ 98Lea-40
❑ 98LeaFraDA-40
❑ 98LeaFraF-40
❑ 98LeaFraM-40
❑ 98LeaFraM-40
❑ 98LeaFraMDC-40
❑ 98LeaFraMDC-40
❑ 98LeaFraMZ2-40
❑ 98MetUni-129
❑ 98MetUniPMG-129
❑ 98Pac-102
❑ 98PacAur-57
❑ 98PacInvTeam-13
❑ 98PacOnl-501
❑ 98PacOnlR-501
❑ 98PacOnlWC-501
❑ 98PacPlaB-102
❑ 98PacRedT-102
❑ 98PacSil-102
❑ 98Pin-48
❑ 98PinPreP-48
❑ 98Sco-201
❑ 98ScoSS-PP95
❑ 98ScoSSAP-PP95
❑ 98SP Aut-139
❑ 98StaCluFDI-378
❑ 98StaClul-378
❑ 98StaCluOneK-378
❑ 98StaCluPP-378
❑ 98Top-40
❑ 98TopChr-40
❑ 98TopChrR-40
❑ 98TopDevR-40
❑ 98TopDia-40
❑ 98TopMiniC-40
❑ 98TopOpeD-25
❑ 98Ult-11
❑ 98Ult-260
❑ 98UltGolM-11
❑ 98UltGolM-260
❑ 98UltMas-11
❑ 98UltMas-260
❑ 98UltPlaM-11
❑ 98UltPlaM-260
❑ 98UppDec-106
❑ 98UppDec-703
❑ 98UppDec10AP-59
❑ 98UppDec1APR-59
❑ 98UppDecNP-NP15
❑ 98YanUppD-703
❑ 99Fle-362
❑ 99FleSta9-362
❑ 99FleWarT-362
❑ 99MetUni-118
❑ 99MetUniGM-118
❑ 99MetUniPMG-118
❑ 99PacOme-161
❑ 99PacOmeC-161
❑ 99PacOmeG-161
❑ 99PacOmePB-161
❑ 99Rev-94
❑ 99RevPremDate-94
❑ 99RevRet-94
❑ 99RevShaSS-94
❑ 99Top-347
❑ 99TopChr-347
❑ 99TopChrR-347
❑ 99TopMVPP-347
❑ 99UppDec-435
❑ 99UppDecEL1-435
❑ 99UppDecEL2-435
❑ 99YanFle-21

Davis, Chris

❑ 78St.PetCT-8
❑ 79ArkTraT-17
❑ 90ElmPioP-15
❑ 91ElmPioC-18
❑ 91ElmPioP-3264
❑ 92ProFS7-24
❑ 92WinHavRSC-1
❑ 93ForLauRSC-6
❑ 93ForLauRSFP-1588

Davis, Chuck

❑ 86NewBriRSP-9
❑ 87PawRedSP-74
❑ 87PawRedST-5

Davis, Clint

❑ 92SavCarC-7
❑ 92SavCarF-654
❑ 93FloStaLAF-44
❑ 93St.PetCC-12
❑ 93St.PetCF-2622
❑ 94Bow-564
❑ 94ClaGolF-170
❑ 94ExcFS7-265
❑ 94Ult-564
❑ 97OklCit8-11

Davis, Corbin

❑ 90MisStaB-8
❑ 91MisStaB-13

Davis, Courtney

❑ 90CliGiaUTI-U2
❑ 90EveGiaB-22
❑ 90EveGiaP-3138
❑ 91CliGiaP-845

Davis, Crash

❑ 89BulDurOS-1

Davis, Curt (Curtis Benton)

❑ 29Zee-128
❑ 30Zee-140
❑ 31Zee-101
❑ 32Zee-97
❑ 33Zee-107
❑ 34BatR31-97
❑ 36DiaMatCS3T2-5
❑ 36ExhFou-6
❑ 36GouWidPPR-A24
❑ 36WheBB4-1
❑ 40DodTeal-5
❑ 42DodTeal-5
❑ 43DodTeal-7
❑ 73Dod194T-5
❑ 74TCMNic-11
❑ 78DodTCM4-29
❑ 90DodTar-168
❑ 91ConTSN-282

Davis, D. K.

❑ 18Zee-39

Davis, Darwin

❑ 91KinMetC-3
❑ 91KinMetP-3819

Davis, Dick (Richard Earl)

❑ 77SpolndC-21
❑ 79Top-474
❑ 80BreTeal-7

❑ 80Top-553
❑ 81Don-528
❑ 81Fle-527
❑ 81Top-183
❑ 81TopTra-753
❑ 82Don-147
❑ 82Fle-245
❑ 82Top-352
❑ 82TopTra-24T
❑ 83Don-647
❑ 83Fle-305
❑ 83PorBeaT-16
❑ 83Top-667
❑ 87JapPlaB-18
❑ 94BreMilB-16

Davis, Dixie (Frank)

❑ 19W514-48
❑ 21E121So1-17
❑ 21Nei-36
❑ 22E120-94
❑ 22W573-30
❑ 22W575-24
❑ 23W501-3
❑ 23WilChoV-28

Davis, Doc (Dennis)

❑ 77SalPirT-10

Davis, Doug

❑ 98BesAutSS-15
❑ 98Cha-2

Davis, Doug (Douglas)

❑ 82BurRanF-22
❑ 82BurRanT-18
❑ 85MidAngT-14
❑ 86MidAngP-8
❑ 87MidAngP-10
❑ 88EdmTraC-18
❑ 88EdmTraP-559
❑ 89BelMarL-18
❑ 89EdmTraC-15
❑ 89EdmTraP-551
❑ 90CMC-495
❑ 90EdmTraC-18
❑ 90EdmTraP-519
❑ 90ProAAAF-95
❑ 91EdmTraLD-160
❑ 91EdmTraP-1518
❑ 91LinDriAAA-160
❑ 92Bow-490
❑ 92DonRoo-31
❑ 92OklCit8F-1916
❑ 92OklCit8S-308
❑ 92StaClu-692
❑ 92StaCluECN-692
❑ 93OklCit8F-1628
❑ 93RanKee-121
❑ 94OklCit8F-1496
❑ 96PitMetB-1
❑ 97PitMet-1
❑ 98CapCitBF5-30
❑ 98CapCitBM-30

Davis, Eddie

❑ 94Top-237
❑ 94TopGol-237
❑ 94TopSpa-237
❑ 95YakBeaTI-8
❑ 96SanBerSB-8
❑ 97SanAntMB-22
❑ 98SanAntMM-22

Davis, Eric (Eric Keith)

❑ 82CedRapRT-20
❑ 83WatRedT-15
❑ 84RedBor-44
❑ 84RedEnq-26
❑ 84WicAerRD-15
❑ 85Don-325
❑ 85Fle-533
❑ 85RedYea-3
❑ 85Top-627
❑ 85TopTif-627
❑ 86Don-164
❑ 86DonHig-30
❑ 86Fle-175
❑ 86OPC-85
❑ 86RedTexG-44
❑ 86SevCoi-S9
❑ 86Top-28
❑ 86Top-85
❑ 86TopTif-28
❑ 86TopTif-85
❑ 87ClaGam-21
❑ 87ClaUpdY-102
❑ 87ClaUpdY-150
❑ 87Don-22A
❑ 87Don-22B
❑ 87Don-265
❑ 87DonHig-3
❑ 87DonHig-8
❑ 87DonOpeD-197
❑ 87DonSupD-22
❑ 87Fle-198
❑ 87FleAwaW-11
❑ 87FleExcS-14
❑ 87FleGamW-11
❑ 87FleGlo-198
❑ 87FleHotS-12
❑ 87FleMin-26
❑ 87FleSlu-11
❑ 87FleStiC-30
❑ 87FleStiC-132
❑ 87GenMilB-6B
❑ 87HosSti-9
❑ 87KeyFooD-7
❑ 87KraFoo-10
❑ 87Lea-22
❑ 87Lea-179
❑ 87MSAIceTD-7
❑ 87OPC-228
❑ 87OurOwnTD-7
❑ 87RedKah-44
❑ 87Spo-22
❑ 87Spo-155
❑ 87Spo-199
❑ 87SpoIllS-4
❑ 87SpoSupD-18
❑ 87SpoTeaP-4
❑ 87StuPan-4
❑ 87Top-412
❑ 87TopCoi-30
❑ 87TopGloS-44
❑ 87TopMinL-4
❑ 87TopSti-136
❑ 87TopTif-412
❑ 87WeiMarD-7
❑ 88Baz-6
❑ 88CheBoy-2
❑ 88ClaBlu-201
❑ 88ClaBlu-213
❑ 88ClaRed-154
❑ 88Don-369
❑ 88DonAll-38
❑ 88DonBasB-62
❑ 88DonBonM-BC2
❑ 88DonPop-16
❑ 88Dra-24
❑ 88Fle-231
❑ 88Fle-637
❑ 88FleAll-7
❑ 88FleAwaW-8
❑ 88FleBasA-9
❑ 88FleBasM-8
❑ 88FleExcS-12
❑ 88FleGlo-231
❑ 88FleGlo-637
❑ 88FleHotS-8
❑ 88FleLeaL-8
❑ 88FleMin-73
❑ 88FleRecS-9
❑ 88FleSlu-10
❑ 88FleStiC-83
❑ 88FleStiWBC-S1
❑ 88FleSup-11
❑ 88FleTeaL-6
❑ 88GreBasS-32
❑ 88KayB-7
❑ 88KeyFooD-12
❑ 88KinDis-22
❑ 88Lea-149
❑ 88MSAFanSD-14
❑ 88MSAIceTD-12
❑ 88Nes-3
❑ 88OPC-150
❑ 88OPCBoxB-J
❑ 88OurOwnTD-12
❑ 88PanSti-235
❑ 88PanSti-282
❑ 88RedFolSB-15
❑ 88RedKah-44
❑ 88Sco-10
❑ 88Sco-649
❑ 88ScoBoxC-15
❑ 88ScoGlo-10
❑ 88ScoGlo-649
❑ 88ScoYouS2-10
❑ 88Spo-10
❑ 88SpoGam-5
❑ 88StaDav-1
❑ 88StaDav-2
❑ 88StaDav-4
❑ 88StaDav-6
❑ 88StaDav-8
❑ 88StaDav-10
❑ 88StaEriD-1
❑ 88StaEriD-2
❑ 88StaEriD-3
❑ 88StaEriD-4
❑ 88StaEriD-5
❑ 88StaEriD-6
❑ 88StaEriD-7
❑ 88StaEriD-8
❑ 88StaEriD-9
❑ 88StaEriD-10
❑ 88StaEriD-11
❑ 88StaEriD-12
❑ 88StaLinAl-8
❑ 88StaLinRe-6
❑ 88TarPla-11
❑ 88TetTeaD-12
❑ 88Top-150
❑ 88TopBig-20
❑ 88TopCoi-39
❑ 88TopGloA-17
❑ 88TopGloS-16
❑ 88TopMinL-46
❑ 88TopRitTM-3
❑ 88TopSti-141
❑ 88TopSti-146
❑ 88TopStiB-14
❑ 88TopTif-150
❑ 88TopUKM-18
❑ 88TopUKMT-18
❑ 88TopWaxBC-J
❑ 88WeiMarD-12
❑ 89Bow-316
❑ 89BowTif-316
❑ 89CadEllD-12
❑ 89CedRapRAB-1
❑ 89ClaLigB-9
❑ 89ClaTraO-109
❑ 89Don-80
❑ 89DonBasB-6
❑ 89Fle-158
❑ 89Fle-639
❑ 89FleBasM-9
❑ 89FleExcS-9
❑ 89FleGlo-158
❑ 89FleGlo-639
❑ 89FleHeroB-10
❑ 89FleLeaL-10
❑ 89FleSup-11
❑ 89KayB-8
❑ 89KeyFooD-11
❑ 89MSAHolD-7
❑ 89MSAIceTD-11
❑ 89Nis-7
❑ 89OPC-330
❑ 89OurOwnTD-11
❑ 89PanSti-76
❑ 89RedFolSB-29
❑ 89RedKah-44
❑ 89Sco-109
❑ 89ScoHot1S-58
❑ 89Scomast-18
❑ 89Spo-69
❑ 89SpoIllFKI-140
❑ 89TetTeaD-11
❑ 89Top-111
❑ 89Top-330
❑ 89TopAme2C-11
❑ 89TopBasT-51
❑ 89TopBig-273
❑ 89TopCapC-13
❑ 89TopCoi-9
❑ 89TopGloS-2
❑ 89TopHeaUT-21
❑ 89TopMinL-8
❑ 89TopSti-138
❑ 89TopStiB-47
❑ 89TopTif-111
❑ 89TopTif-330
❑ 89TopUKM-19
❑ 89TVSpoM-37
❑ 89UppDec-410
❑ 89UppDec-688
❑ 89WeiMarD-11
❑ 90Bow-58
❑ 90BowTif-58
❑ 90CedRapRDGB-1
❑ 90ClaBlu-11
❑ 90Col-28
❑ 90Don-233
❑ 90Don-695A
❑ 90Don-695B
❑ 90DonBesN-1
❑ 90DOnBonM-BC23
❑ 90Fle-417
❑ 90FleAwaW-10
❑ 90FleBasA-6
❑ 90FleBasAC-6
❑ 90FleBasM-9
❑ 90FleBasMC-9
❑ 90FleCan-417
❑ 90FleLeaL-8
❑ 90FleLeaLC-8
❑ 90FleWaxBC-C4
❑ 90GooHumICBLS-7
❑ 90Hot50PS-9
❑ 90Lea-189
❑ 90M.Vpin-27
❑ 90MLBBasB-22
❑ 90OPC-260
❑ 90OPC-402
❑ 90PanSti-209
❑ 90PanSti-246
❑ 90Pos-24
❑ 90PubIntS-26
❑ 90PubIntS-255
❑ 90RedFolSB-20
❑ 90RedKah-7
❑ 90Sco-185
❑ 90Sco100S-95
❑ 90Spo-97
❑ 90StaLonJS-3
❑ 90StaLonJS-38
❑ 90SunSee-21
❑ 90Top-260
❑ 90Top-402
❑ 90TopAmeA-28
❑ 90TopBig-72
❑ 90TopCoi-44
❑ 90TopDou-14
❑ 90TopGloA-7
❑ 90TopGloS-25
❑ 90TopHilHM-1
❑ 90TopMag-18
❑ 90TopMinL-53
❑ 90TopSti-134
❑ 90TopSti-149
❑ 90TopStiB-13
❑ 90TopTif-260
❑ 90TopTif-402
❑ 90TopTVA-38
❑ 90UppDec-116
❑ 91BasBesHRK-3
❑ 91Bow-686
❑ 91CadEllD-13
❑ 91Cla1-T34
❑ 91Cla3-T13
❑ 91ClaGam-136
❑ 91DenHol-4
❑ 91Don-84
❑ 91Fle-61
❑ 91FlePro-10
❑ 91FleWorS-1
❑ 91Lea-37
❑ 91MajLeaCP-70
❑ 91MSAHolD-2
❑ 91OPC-550
❑ 91OPCPre-29
❑ 91PanFreS-131
❑ 91PanSti-124
❑ 91PetSta-6
❑ 91RedKah-44
❑ 91RedPep-6
❑ 91Sco-137
❑ 91Sco-403
❑ 91Sco-669
❑ 91Sco-696
❑ 91Sco-863
❑ 91Sco100S-9
❑ 91SevCoi-SC6
❑ 91StaClu-37
❑ 91StaCluCM-5
❑ 91StaPinB-10
❑ 91Stu-162
❑ 91StuPre-11
❑ 91Top-550
❑ 91TopCraJI-16
❑ 91TopDesS-550
❑ 91TopMic-550
❑ 91TopSta-10
❑ 91TopTif-550
❑ 91TopTriH-N3
❑ 91Ult-91
❑ 91UppDec-355
❑ 91Woo-25
❑ 92Bow-671
❑ 92Cla2-T25
❑ 92ClaGam-161
❑ 92DodMot-4
❑ 92DodPol-33
❑ 92DodSmo-4392
❑ 92Don-503
❑ 92DonCraJ2-8
❑ 92Fle-403
❑ 92FleUpd-90
❑ 92Hig5-31
❑ 92Lea-430
❑ 92LeaBlaG-430
❑ 92New-5
❑ 92OPC-610
❑ 92OPCPre-129
❑ 92PanSti-267
❑ 92Pin-323
❑ 92Pin-602
❑ 92PinRool-1
❑ 92RedFolS-28
❑ 92Sco-44
❑ 92Sco100S-44
❑ 92ScoProP-13
❑ 92ScoRoo-62T
❑ 92SpoStaCC-10
❑ 92StaClu-660
❑ 92StaCluNC-660
❑ 92Stu-43
❑ 92Top-610
❑ 92TopGol-610
❑ 92TopGolW-610
❑ 92TopKid-38
❑ 92TopMic-610
❑ 92TopTra-26T
❑ 92TopTraG-26T
❑ 92Ult-503
❑ 92UppDec-125
❑ 92UppDec-756
❑ 92UppDecF-20
❑ 92UppDecFG-20
❑ 93Bow-450
❑ 93DiaMar-28
❑ 93DodMot-7
❑ 93DodPol-4
❑ 93DodStaC-20
❑ 93Don-482
❑ 93Fin-126
❑ 93FinRef-126
❑ 93Fle-445
❑ 93Lea-267
❑ 93OPC-87
❑ 93PacSpa-144
❑ 93PanSti-221
❑ 93Pin-429
❑ 93RedFolS-22
❑ 93Sco-570
❑ 93Sel-91
❑ 93SelRoo-92T
❑ 93SP-92
❑ 93StaClu-381
❑ 93StaCluFDI-381
❑ 93StaCluMOP-381
❑ 93Top-745
❑ 93TopGol-745
❑ 93TopInaM-745
❑ 93TopInaR-745
❑ 93TopMic-745
❑ 93TriPla-112
❑ 93Ult-53
❑ 93UppDec-477
❑ 93UppDec-595
❑ 93UppDecGold-477
❑ 93UppDecGold-595
❑ 94Bow-293
❑ 94ColC-563
❑ 94ColChoGS-563
❑ 94ColChoSS-563
❑ 94Don-618
❑ 94Fin-80
❑ 94FinRef-80
❑ 94Fla-46
❑ 94Fle-126
❑ 94FleExtB-71
❑ 94Lea-256
❑ 94OPC-226
❑ 94Pac-213
❑ 94PanSti-62
❑ 94Pin-388
❑ 94PinArtP-388
❑ 94PinMusC-388
❑ 94Sco-504
❑ 94ScoGolR-504
❑ 94Sel-273
❑ 94Spo-124
❑ 94StaClu-209
❑ 94StaCluFDI-209
❑ 94StaCluGR-209
❑ 94StaCluMOP-209
❑ 94Stu-189
❑ 94Top-488
❑ 94TopGol-488
❑ 94TopSpa-488
❑ 94TriPla-241
❑ 94Ult-354
❑ 94UppDec-261
❑ 94UppDecED-261
❑ 95Pin-338
❑ 95PinArtP-338
❑ 95PinMusC-338
❑ 95Sco-406
❑ 95ScoGolR-406
❑ 95ScoPlaTS-406
❑ 96Cir-115
❑ 96CirRav-115
❑ 96Fin-B222
❑ 96FinRef-B222
❑ 96FleUpd-U118
❑ 96FleUpdTC-U118
❑ 96TeaOut-22
❑ 96Ult-459
❑ 96UltGolM-459
❑ 96UppDec-491U
❑ 97BalOriP-9
❑ 97BalOriP-10
❑ 97Cir-175
❑ 97CirRav-175
❑ 97ColCho-276
❑ 97ColChoT-BO13
❑ 97Don-190
❑ 97Don-292
❑ 97DonGolPP-190
❑ 97DonGolPP-292
❑ 97DonLim-162
❑ 97DonLimE-162
❑ 97DonLimENG-162
❑ 97DonSilPP-190
❑ 97DonSilPP-292
❑ 97DonTea-39
❑ 97DonTeaSPE-39
❑ 97Fin-260
❑ 97FinRef-260
❑ 97Fle-293
❑ 97Fle-642
❑ 97FleTif-293
❑ 97FleTif-642
❑ 97Lea-313
❑ 97LeaFraM-313
❑ 97LeaFraMDC-313
❑ 97MetUni-46
❑ 97NewPin-143
❑ 97NewPinAP-143
❑ 97NewPinMC-143
❑ 97NewPinPP-143
❑ 97Pac-267
❑ 97PacLigB-267
❑ 97PacPri-92
❑ 97PacPriLB-92
❑ 97PacPriP-92
❑ 97PacSil-267
❑ 97Pin-6
❑ 97PinArtP-PP6
❑ 97PinMusC-6
❑ 97PinPrePla-6
❑ 97Sco-280
❑ 97Sco-356
❑ 97ScoArtPWB-280
❑ 97ScoArtPWB-356
❑ 97ScoPreS-280
❑ 97ScoResC-356
❑ 97ScoShoS-280
❑ 97ScoShoS-356
❑ 97ScoShoSAP-280
❑ 97ScoShoSAP-356
❑ 97StaClu-180
❑ 97StaCluMOP-180
❑ 97Top-218
❑ 97Ult-176
❑ 97Ult-383
❑ 97UltGolME-176
❑ 97UltGolME-383
❑ 97UltPlaME-176
❑ 97UltPlaME-383
❑ 97UppDec-44
❑ 97UppDec-306
❑ 98CirThu-270
❑ 98CirThuRav-270
❑ 98CirThuSupRav-270
❑ 98ColCho-45
❑ 98CroRoy-20
❑ 98DonColL-328
❑ 98DonPriCL-328
❑ 98Fin-93
❑ 98FinNo--93
❑ 98FinNo-R-93
❑ 98FinRef-93
❑ 98Fle-43
❑ 98Lea-129
❑ 98LeaFraDA-129
❑ 98LeaFraF-129
❑ 98LeaFraM-129

❑ 98LeaFraM-129
❑ 98LeaFraMDC-129
❑ 98LeaFraMDC-129
❑ 98LeaFraMZ2-129
❑ 98Pac-23
❑ 98PacInv-9
❑ 98PacInvPBlue-9
❑ 98PacInvSilv-9
❑ 98PacOme-30
❑ 98PacOmeR-30
❑ 98PacOnl-86
❑ 98PacOnlR-86
❑ 98PacOnlWC-86
❑ 98PacPar-13
❑ 98PacParC-13
❑ 98PacParG-13
❑ 98PacParHS-13
❑ 98PacParPB-13
❑ 98PacParR-13
❑ 98PacPlaB-23
❑ 98PacRedT-23
❑ 98PacSil-23
❑ 98PinPlu-77
❑ 98PinSna-B03
❑ 98ScoRT-144
❑ 98SpoIll-178
❑ 98SpoIllEE-178
❑ 98SpoIllFE-178
❑ 98SPxFin-253
❑ 98SPxFinR-253
❑ 98SPxFinS-253
❑ 98TopGal-111
❑ 98TopGalGP-111
❑ 98TopGalOPP-111
❑ 98TopGalPPI-111
❑ 98TopGalPPIA-111
❑ 98Ult-291
❑ 98UltGolM-291
❑ 98UltMas-291
❑ 98UltPlaM-291
❑ 98UppDec-39
❑ 98UppDec-424
❑ 98UppDecSF-24
❑ 99199Fin-189
❑ 99Bow-271
❑ 99BowGol-271
❑ 99BowInt-271
❑ 99DumSet-ED
❑ 99DumSet-ED
❑ 99FinGolRef-189
❑ 99FinRef-189
❑ 99Fle-146
❑ 99FleSta9-146
❑ 99FleWarT-146
❑ 99MetUni-119
❑ 99MetUniGM-119
❑ 99MetUniPMG-119
❑ 99Pac-50
❑ 99PacAur-152
❑ 99PacAurOD-152
❑ 99PacOme-193
❑ 99PacOmeC-193
❑ 99PacOmeG-193
❑ 99PacOmePB-193
❑ 99PacPar-190
❑ 99PacParC-190
❑ 99PacParG-190
❑ 99PacParHoloGold-190
❑ 99PacParHS-190
❑ 99PacParOD-190
❑ 99PacParPB-190
❑ 99PacParRed-190
❑ 99PacPlaB-50
❑ 99PacPriS-79
❑ 99PacPriS206-79
❑ 99PacPriS206R-79
❑ 99PacRed-50
❑ 99SkyMolM-25
❑ 99SkyMolMX-25
❑ 99SkyPre-68
❑ 99SkyPreR-68
❑ 99SkyThu-27
❑ 99SkyThuRant-27
❑ 99SkyThuRave-27
❑ 99StaClu-317
❑ 99StaCluFDI-317
❑ 99StaCluOoaK-317
❑ 99StaCluPP-317
❑ 99ThuSkySupR-27
❑ 99Top-153
❑ 99TopChr-153
❑ 99TopChrR-153
❑ 99TopGal-37
❑ 99TopGalPP-37
❑ 99TopGalPPI-37
❑ 99TopMVPP-153
❑ 99TopOpeD-88
❑ 99TopSta-110
❑ 99TopStaFoil-110
❑ 99Ult-114
❑ 99UltGolM-114
❑ 99UltMas-114
❑ 99UltPlaM-114
❑ 99UppDec-466
❑ 99UppDecE-75
❑ 99UppDecEFXG-75
❑ 99UppDecEL1-466
❑ 99UppDecEL2-466
❑ 99UppDecR-71
❑ 99UppDecRG-71
❑ 99UppDecRP-71
❑ 99Vic-331

Davis, Freddie
❑ 87SalAngP-28
❑ 89LynRedSS-5
❑ 90CarLeaA-10
❑ 90LynRedSTI-17
❑ 90WinHavRSS-3
❑ 91Cla/Bes-123
❑ 91LinDriAA-454
❑ 91NewBriRSLD-454
❑ 91NewBriRSP-345

Davis, Geff
❑ 86BurExpP-5
❑ 87WesPalBEP-678

Davis, George
❑ 76CliPilT-8
❑ 94ConTSN-1235
❑ 94ConTSNB-1235

Davis, George (George Allen)
❑ 15SpoNewM-45
❑ 33Gou-236

Davis, George (George Stacey)
❑ 03BreE10-31
❑ 07WhiSoxGWH-2
❑ 09AmeCarE90-1-31
❑ 09ColChiE-74
❑ 09T206-85
❑ 10JuJuDE-15
❑ 11HelSta-23
❑ 11PloCanE-22
❑ 11SpoLifCW-87
❑ 12ColRedB-74
❑ 72ClaCar-115
❑ 80BraTCM1-7
❑ 94DukCabN-1

Davis, Gerald
❑ 92ElmPioF-1395
❑ 98BriBluM-10

Davis, Gerrod
❑ 90KinMetB-3
❑ 92St.LucMCB-19

Davis, Gerry
❑ 88T/MUmp-52
❑ 89T/MUmp-50
❑ 90T/MUmp-48

Davis, Glenn
❑ 52Whe-7A
❑ 52Whe-7B
❑ 74NewYorNTDiS-25
❑ 97Bow-434
❑ 97BowChr-294
❑ 97BowChrI-294
❑ 97BowChrIR-294
❑ 97BowChrR-294
❑ 97BowInt-434
❑ 97TopSta-120
❑ 97TopStaAM-120
❑ 98AriFalLTP-21
❑ 98BesAutSS-16
❑ 98BesNumOP-16
❑ 98Bow-402
❑ 98BowChr-402
❑ 98BowChrGA-402
❑ 98BowChrGAR-402
❑ 98BowChrI-402
❑ 98BowChrIR-402
❑ 98BowChrR-402
❑ 98BowGolA-402
❑ 98BowInt-402
❑ 98SP MinPE-67
❑ 98SPMin-67
❑ 98Top-246
❑ 98TopChr-246
❑ 98TopChrR-246
❑ 98TopDevR-246
❑ 98TopDia-246
❑ 98TopMiniC-246
❑ 98VerBeaDM-25
❑ 99Bow-119
❑ 99BowChr-119
❑ 99BowChrG-119
❑ 99BowChrGR-119
❑ 99BowChrI-119
❑ 99BowChrIR-119
❑ 99BowChrR-119
❑ 99BowGol-119
❑ 99BowInt-119
❑ 99JustheS-15
❑ 99JustheSAC-7
❑ 99JustheSAD-6
❑ 99JustheSJB-15
❑ 99SP TopP-39
❑ 99SP TopPPE-39

Davis, Glenn (Glenn Earle)
❑ 82DayBeaAT-20
❑ 83ColAstT-11
❑ 84TucTorC-62
❑ 85AstHouP-20
❑ 85Fle-652
❑ 85TucTorC-65
❑ 86AstMilL-5
❑ 86AstPol-22
❑ 86AstTeal-4
❑ 86BasStaB-28
❑ 86Don-380
❑ 86Fle-297
❑ 86FleMin-63
❑ 86Lea-175
❑ 86OPC-389
❑ 86Spo-188
❑ 86Top-389
❑ 86TopGloS-59
❑ 86TopSti-29
❑ 86TopSti-314
❑ 86TopTat-18
❑ 86TopTif-389
❑ 87AstMot-10
❑ 87AstPol-23
❑ 87ClaGam-28
❑ 87ClaUpdY-107
❑ 87Don-61
❑ 87DonAll-42
❑ 87DonOpeD-16
❑ 87Fle-55
❑ 87Fle-636
❑ 87FleGamW-12
❑ 87FleGlo-55
❑ 87FleGlo-636
❑ 87FleLeaL-14
❑ 87FleLimE-11
❑ 87FleMin-27
❑ 87FleStiC-31
❑ 87FleStiWBC-S5
❑ 87KayB-12
❑ 87KraFoo-36
❑ 87Lea-115
❑ 87OPC-56
❑ 87RedFolSB-43
❑ 87Spo-17
❑ 87Spo-195
❑ 87SpoTeaP-8
❑ 87StuPan-5
❑ 87Top-560
❑ 87TopCoi-31
❑ 87TopGloS-4
❑ 87TopMinL-8
❑ 87TopSti-26
❑ 87TopTif-560
❑ 88AstMot-10
❑ 88AstPol-8
❑ 88ClaRed-182
❑ 88Don-184
❑ 88DonBasB-64
❑ 88Fle-445
❑ 88FleGlo-445
❑ 88FleMin-78
❑ 88FleSlu-11
❑ 88FleStiC-86
❑ 88FleSup-12
❑ 88HouSho-17
❑ 88Lea-186
❑ 88OPC-159
❑ 88PanSti-292
❑ 88Sco-460
❑ 88ScoGlo-460
❑ 88Spo-102
❑ 88StaLinAst-8
❑ 88Top-430
❑ 88TopBig-192
❑ 88TopSti-35
❑ 88TopTif-430
❑ 88TopUKM-19
❑ 88TopUKMT-19
❑ 89AstLenH-26
❑ 89AstMot-9
❑ 89AstSmo-11
❑ 89Bow-331
❑ 89BowTif-331
❑ 89CadEllD-13
❑ 89ClaLigB-17
❑ 89ClaTraP-168
❑ 89Don-25
❑ 89Don-236
❑ 89DonBasB-8
❑ 89DonSupD-25
❑ 89Fle-355
❑ 89FleBasM-10
❑ 89FleExcS-10
❑ 89FleGlo-355
❑ 89FleHeroB-11
❑ 89FleLeaL-11
❑ 89OPC-378
❑ 89PanSti-88
❑ 89RedFolSB-30
❑ 89Sco-164
❑ 89ScoHot1S-46
❑ 89Spo-137
❑ 89Top-579
❑ 89Top-765
❑ 89TopBasT-99
❑ 89TopBig-89
❑ 89TopCoi-10
❑ 89TopGloS-32
❑ 89TopHilTM-10
❑ 89TopSti-21
❑ 89TopStiB-35
❑ 89TopTif-579
❑ 89TopTif-765
❑ 89TopUKM-20
❑ 89TVSpoM-54
❑ 89UppDec-443
❑ 90AstLenH-11
❑ 90AstMot-2
❑ 90Bow-80
❑ 90BowTif-80
❑ 90ClaBlu-71
❑ 90Don-118
❑ 90DonBesN-65
❑ 90DOnBonM-BC21
❑ 90DonLeaS-22
❑ 90Fle-228
❑ 90FleBasA-7
❑ 90FleBasAC-7
❑ 90FleBasM-10
❑ 90FleBasMC-10
❑ 90FleCan-228
❑ 90FleLeaL-9
❑ 90FleLeaLC-9
❑ 90FleWaxBC-C5
❑ 90Hot50PS-10
❑ 90Lea-30
❑ 90M.Vpin-40
❑ 90MLBBasB-41
❑ 90OPC-50
❑ 90PanSti-258
❑ 90PubIntS-92
❑ 90RedFolSB-21
❑ 90Sco-272
❑ 90Sco100S-52
❑ 90Spo-19
❑ 90StaLonJS-15
❑ 90StaLonJS-30
❑ 90Top-50
❑ 90TopBig-122
❑ 90TopCoi-45
❑ 90TopDou-15
❑ 90TopGloS-3
❑ 90TopHilHM-22
❑ 90TopMinL-55
❑ 90TopSti-13
❑ 90TopStiB-2
❑ 90TopTif-50
❑ 90TopTVA-45
❑ 90UppDec-245
❑ 91BalOriP-4
❑ 91BasBesHRK-4
❑ 91Bow-83
❑ 91CadEllD-14
❑ 91Cla2-T6
❑ 91ClaGam-169
❑ 91Don-474
❑ 91Fle-505
❑ 91FleUpd-1
❑ 91Lea-398
❑ 91OPC-350
❑ 91OPCPre-30
❑ 91OriCro-496
❑ 91PanFreS-7
❑ 91PanSti-19
❑ 91PosCan-14
❑ 91RedFolS-23
❑ 91Sco-405
❑ 91Sco-830
❑ 91ScoRoo-7T
❑ 91SevCoi-A1
❑ 91SevCoi-F4
❑ 91SevCoi-T5
❑ 91StaClu-391
❑ 91StaPinB-11
❑ 91Stu-1
❑ 91SunSee-6
❑ 91Top-350
❑ 91TopDesS-350
❑ 91TopMic-350
❑ 91TopTif-350
❑ 91TopTra-28T
❑ 91TopTraT-28T
❑ 91Ult-14
❑ 91UppDec-81
❑ 91UppDec-535
❑ 91UppDec-757
❑ 92BalOriP-5
❑ 92Bow-428
❑ 92ClaGam-174
❑ 92Don-597
❑ 92Fle-4
❑ 92Lea-316
❑ 92LeaBlaG-316
❑ 92OPC-190
❑ 92Pin-138
❑ 92RedFolS-29
❑ 92Sco-615
❑ 92StaClu-808
❑ 92StaCluNC-808
❑ 92Stu-122
❑ 92Top-190
❑ 92TopGol-190
❑ 92TopGolW-190
❑ 92TopKid-65
❑ 92TopMic-190
❑ 92TriPla-60
❑ 92Ult-1
❑ 92UppDec-654
❑ 93Bow-1
❑ 93Don-163
❑ 93Fin-41
❑ 93FinRef-41
❑ 93Fle-164
❑ 93Lea-45
❑ 93OPC-69
❑ 93PacSpa-15
❑ 93Pin-217
❑ 93Sco-383
❑ 93Sel-378
❑ 93StaClu-326
❑ 93StaCluFDI-326
❑ 93StaCluMOP-326
❑ 93Top-485
❑ 93TopGol-485
❑ 93TopInaM-485
❑ 93TopInaR-485
❑ 93TopMic-485
❑ 93TriPla-73
❑ 93Ult-139
❑ 93UppDec-353
❑ 93UppDec-827
❑ 93UppDecGold-353
❑ 93UppDecGold-827
❑ 94OmaRoyF-1229

Davis, Grant
❑ 93MisStaB-12

Davis, Greg
❑ 90KisDodD-9
❑ 91GreFalDSP-15

Davis, Harry
❑ 84EveGiaC-5
❑ 86FreGiaSB-26
❑ 88ShrCapP-1299
❑ 89WilBilP-641
❑ 89WilBilS-4

Davis, Harry (Harry H.)
❑ 03BreE10-32
❑ 03WilCarE-9
❑ 04FanCraAL-13
❑ 08AmeCarE91-7
❑ 08AmeCarE91-42
❑ 08RosComP-58
❑ 09BriE97-7
❑ 09ColChiE-73
❑ 09RamT20-34
❑ 09SpoNewSM-58
❑ 09T206-86
❑ 09T206-87
❑ 10CouT21-114
❑ 10CouT21-115
❑ 10CouT21-273
❑ 10E101-13
❑ 10E12AmeCDCE125-12
❑ 10E98-12
❑ 10LuxCigPP-6
❑ 10MelMinE-13
❑ 10NadCarE-15
❑ 10NadE1-14
❑ 10PeoT21-14
❑ 10RedCroT-17
❑ 10RedCroT-101
❑ 10RedCroT-181
❑ 10W555-20
❑ 11A'sFirT20-5
❑ 11BasBatEU-16
❑ 11D35RocB-5
❑ 11DiaGumP-11
❑ 11E94-9
❑ 11PinT-5-514
❑ 11SpoLifCW-88
❑ 11SpoLifM-91
❑ 12ColRedB-73
❑ 12ColTinT-73
❑ 12PhiCarE-7
❑ 12T207-42
❑ 82TCMGreS-38

Davis, I.M.
❑ 25Exh-77
❑ 28Zee-90

Davis, J.J.
❑ 97Bow-437
❑ 97BowChr-297
❑ 97BowChrI-297
❑ 97BowChrIR-297
❑ 97BowChrR-297
❑ 97BowInt-437
❑ 97TopSta-122
❑ 97TopStaAM-122
❑ 98AugGreM-2
❑ 98BesNumOP-17
❑ 98Bow-141
❑ 98BowChr-141
❑ 98BowChrGA-141
❑ 98BowChrGAR-141
❑ 98BowChrI-141
❑ 98BowChrIR-141
❑ 98BowChrR-141
❑ 98BowGolA-141
❑ 98BowInt-141
❑ 98EriSeaWM-9
❑ 98SouAtlLPM-8
❑ 98StaCluFDI-383
❑ 98StaCluI-383
❑ 98StaCluOneK-383
❑ 98StaCluPP-383
❑ 98Top-492
❑ 98TopChr-492
❑ 98TopChrR-492
❑ 98TopDevR-492
❑ 98TopDia-492
❑ 98TopMiniC-492

Davis, Jacke (Jacke S.)
❑ 62Top-521
❑ 63Top-117

Davis, James David
❑ 97BurBeeB-6
❑ 97MidLeaTP-3
❑ 98ChaLooG-6

Davis, Jason
❑ 97CliLumG-6
❑ 97PieBolWB-11
❑ 98ReaPhiM-9
❑ 98ReaPhiUM-10

Davis, Jasper
❑ 09AmeCarE90-1-30

Davis, Jay
❑ 90KinMetS-6
❑ 91ColMetPI-24
❑ 91ColMetPPI-1
❑ 91SouAtlLAGP-SAL14
❑ 92St.LucMF-1760
❑ 93BinMetF-2346
❑ 93ExcFS7-70
❑ 94BinMetF-715
❑ 95BinMetTI-22
❑ 96TusTorB-20

Davis, Jeff
❑ 93EriSaiC-4
❑ 93EriSaiF-3105
❑ 94ChaRivC-3
❑ 94ChaRivF-2664
❑ 95Bes-46
❑ 95SPML-159
❑ 96Exc-109
❑ 96TulDriTI-8

❑ 97TexLeaTP-24
❑ 97TulDriTI-10

Davis, Jerry
❑ 90JohCitCS-7

Davis, Jerry (Gerald Edward)
❑ 82AmaGolST-5
❑ 83LasVegSBHN-5
❑ 84LasVegSC-222
❑ 85Don-162
❑ 85FleUpd-34
❑ 85PadMot-26
❑ 85TopTifT-28T
❑ 85TopTra-28T
❑ 86Don-429
❑ 86Fle-317
❑ 86Top-323
❑ 86TopTif-323
❑ 87TolMudHP-30
❑ 87TolMudHT-24

Davis, Jim (James Bennett)
❑ 52MotCoo-2
❑ 53MotCoo-46
❑ 55Top-68
❑ 55TopDouH-27
❑ 55TopTesS-1
❑ 56Top-102
❑ 57Top-273

Davis, Jody (Jody Richard)
❑ 79JacMetT-7
❑ 82CubRedL-7
❑ 82Don-225
❑ 82Fle-592
❑ 82Top-508
❑ 83AllGamPI-130
❑ 83CubThoAV-7
❑ 83Don-183
❑ 83Fle-494
❑ 83Top-542
❑ 83TopSti-226
❑ 84AllGamPI-40
❑ 84CubBriPC-9S
❑ 84CubChiT-9
❑ 84CubSev-7
❑ 84CubUno-6
❑ 84Don-433
❑ 84Fle-491
❑ 84FunFooP-51
❑ 84JacMetF-4
❑ 84Nes792-73
❑ 84OPC-73
❑ 84Top-73
❑ 84TopSti-43
❑ 84TopTif-73
❑ 85AllGamPI-129
❑ 85CubLioP-5
❑ 85CubSev-7
❑ 85Don-76
❑ 85DonActA-54
❑ 85Fle-54
❑ 85Lea-180
❑ 85OPC-384
❑ 85Top-384
❑ 85TopSti-37
❑ 85TopTif-384
❑ 86BasStaB-29
❑ 86CubGat-7
❑ 86CubUno-4
❑ 86Don-289
❑ 86Fle-364
❑ 86FleStiC-30
❑ 86MSAJayPCD-3
❑ 86OPC-176
❑ 86Top-767
❑ 86TopSti-58
❑ 86TopTat-13
❑ 86TopTif-767
❑ 87CubCan-3
❑ 87CubDavB-7
❑ 87Don-269
❑ 87DonAll-50
❑ 87DonOpeD-72
❑ 87Fle-557
❑ 87FleBasA-13
❑ 87FleGlo-557
❑ 87FleLeaL-15
❑ 87KraFoo-6
❑ 87Lea-48
❑ 87OPC-270
❑ 87RedFolSB-68
❑ 87SevCoi-C2
❑ 87SevCoi-M3
❑ 87SmoNatL-3A
❑ 87SmoNatL-3B
❑ 87Spo-170
❑ 87SpoTeaP-22
❑ 87StuPan-3
❑ 87Top-270
❑ 87TopSti-64
❑ 87TopTif-270
❑ 88CubDavB-7
❑ 88Don-119
❑ 88DonTeaBC-119
❑ 88Fle-414
❑ 88Fle-425A
❑ 88FleGlo-414
❑ 88Lea-69
❑ 88OPC-376
❑ 88PanSti-258
❑ 88PanSti-262
❑ 88Sco-551
❑ 88ScoGlo-551
❑ 88Spo-60
❑ 88StaLinAl-9
❑ 88StaLinCu-1
❑ 88Top-615
❑ 88TopSti-60
❑ 88TopStiB-23
❑ 88TopTif-615
❑ 89Bow-270
❑ 89BowTif-270
❑ 89BraDub-9
❑ 89Don-650
❑ 89DonBasB-58
❑ 89Fle-421
❑ 89FleGlo-421
❑ 89OPC-115
❑ 89RedFolSB-31
❑ 89Sco-173
❑ 89ScoRoo-64T
❑ 89Spo-187
❑ 89Top-115
❑ 89TopBig-3
❑ 89TopTif-115
❑ 89TopTra-22T
❑ 89TopTraT-22T
❑ 89TVSpoM-60
❑ 89UppDec-148
❑ 89UppDec-795
❑ 90Fle-579
❑ 90FleCan-579
❑ 90OPC-453
❑ 90PublntS-111
❑ 90Sco-328
❑ 90Top-453
❑ 90TopBig-26
❑ 90TopTif-453
❑ 90UppDec-429

Davis, Joe
❑ 89AncGlaP-10

Davis, Joel
❑ 86Don-623
❑ 86Fle-202
❑ 86TopTra-30T
❑ 86TopTraT-30T
❑ 86WhiSoxC-52
❑ 87Don-124
❑ 87Top-299
❑ 87TopTif-299
❑ 87WhiSoxC-6
❑ 88BlaYNPRWL-149
❑ 88Top-511
❑ 88TopTif-511
❑ 88VanCanC-2
❑ 88VanCanP-763
❑ 89ColSprSSC-7
❑ 89ColSprSSP-237

Davis, John
❑ 75OklCit8TI-23
❑ 88CapCodPPaLP-56
❑ 91LinDriAAA-430
❑ 91PeoChiTI-28
❑ 95GreFalDTI-4
❑ 96SavSanB-15
❑ 97SanBerS-5

Davis, John (John Humphrey)
❑ 52MotCoo-27

Davis, John Kirk
❑ 83ChaRoyT-17
❑ 86MemChiSTOS-4
❑ 86MemChiTOS-4
❑ 87OmaRoyP-19
❑ 88Don-594
❑ 88DonRoo-48
❑ 88Fle-255
❑ 88FleGlo-255
❑ 88FleUpd-15
❑ 88FleUpdG-15
❑ 88Sco-636
❑ 88ScoGlo-636
❑ 88Spo-224
❑ 88Top-672
❑ 88TopTif-672
❑ 88WhiSoxC-5
❑ 89Sco-608
❑ 89Top-162
❑ 89TopTif-162
❑ 89UppDec-548
❑ 89VanCanC-9
❑ 89VanCanP-582
❑ 91RicBraBC-6
❑ 91RicBraLD-430
❑ 91RicBraTI-22

Davis, Johnny
❑ 86NegLeaF-95

Davis, Joshua
❑ 96IdaFalB-5
❑ 98ModA'sG-10

Davis, Jumbo (James J.)
❑ 87OldJudN-124

Davis, Kane
❑ 94WelPirC-7
❑ 94WelPirF-3486
❑ 96LynHilB-7
❑ 97CarMudC-3

Davis, Keith
❑ 94SpoIndC-5
❑ 94SpoIndF-3314
❑ 96RanCucQB-9
❑ 97RanCucQG-9
❑ 98LakTigM-3

Davis, Kelvin
❑ 88EugEmeB-17

Davis, Kenny
❑ 87VisOakP-15
❑ 88VisOakCLC-145
❑ 88VisOakP-81

Davis, Kevin
❑ 83PeoSunF-3
❑ 83RedPioT-8
❑ 85MidAngT-18
❑ 87SalBucP-30
❑ 88EasLeaAP-14
❑ 88HarSenP-837
❑ 89BirBarB-6
❑ 89BirBarP-98
❑ 91LinDriAA-432
❑ 91MidAngLD-432
❑ 91MidAngOHP-9
❑ 91MidAngP-439
❑ 92SalSpuF-3762
❑ 93MidAngF-327
❑ 94MemChiF-364
❑ 97MidAngOHP-7

Davis, Kiddo (George Willis)
❑ 33RitCE-5D
❑ 35AlDemDCR3-83
❑ 36WorWidGV-17
❑ 92ConTSN-502

Davis, Lance
❑ 96BilMusTI-6
❑ 97BurBeeB-7
❑ 98BurBeeM-7

Davis, Larry
❑ 75TucTorTI-22
❑ 81TacTigT-1
❑ 82TacTigT-20
❑ 83TacTigT-22
❑ 86A'sMot-26
❑ 90A'sMot-28
❑ 94CarLeaA-DJ22

Davis, Lawrence
❑ 42A'sTeal-12

Davis, Lefty
❑ 90DodTar-1102

Davis, Mark (Mark Anthony)
❑ 84LitFalMT-22
❑ 86KenTwiP-5
❑ 87PenWhiSP-1
❑ 87SavCarP-12
❑ 88BirBarB-14
❑ 88BlaYNPRWL-23
❑ 88SumBraP-396
❑ 89BurBraP-1599
❑ 89BurBraS-9
❑ 89FleUpd-18
❑ 89VanCanC-22
❑ 89VanCanP-585
❑ 90MidAngGS-10
❑ 91EdmTraLD-161
❑ 91EdmTraP-1527
❑ 91LinDriAAA-161
❑ 92TopDeb91-43

Davis, Mark (Mark William)
❑ 80CarMudF-4
❑ 81OklCit8T-6
❑ 82OklCit8T-12
❑ 82Top-231
❑ 83PhoGiaBHN-20
❑ 84Don-201
❑ 84Fle-371
❑ 84GiaPos-6
❑ 84Nes792-343
❑ 84Top-343
❑ 84TopTif-343
❑ 85Don-553
❑ 85Fle-606
❑ 85GiaMot-20
❑ 85GiaPos-7
❑ 85Top-541
❑ 85TopTif-541
❑ 86Don-265
❑ 86Fle-537
❑ 86GiaMot-20
❑ 86GiaPos-9
❑ 86Top-138
❑ 86TopSti-91
❑ 86TopTif-138
❑ 87Don-313
❑ 87Fle-271
❑ 87FleGlo-271
❑ 87FleUpd-21
❑ 87FleUpdG-21
❑ 87GiaMot-14
❑ 87GiaPos-9
❑ 87Top-21
❑ 87TopTif-21
❑ 88Don-64
❑ 88DonBasB-98
❑ 88Fle-581
❑ 88FleGlo-581
❑ 88PadCok-48
❑ 88PadSmo-6
❑ 88Sco-391
❑ 88ScoGlo-391
❑ 88StaLinPa-2
❑ 88Top-482
❑ 88TopTif-482
❑ 89Bow-447
❑ 89BowTif-447
❑ 89Don-65
❑ 89DonAll-46
❑ 89DonBasB-133
❑ 89Fle-303
❑ 89Fle-635
❑ 89FleBasA-10
❑ 89FleGlo-303
❑ 89FleGlo-635
❑ 89OPC-59
❑ 89PadCok-3
❑ 89PadMag-13
❑ 89PadPos-8
❑ 89PanSti-193
❑ 89RedFolSB-32
❑ 89Sco-490
❑ 89ScoHot1S-62
❑ 89Spo-74
❑ 89Top-59
❑ 89TopAwaW-1
❑ 89TopSti-110
❑ 89TopStiB-64
❑ 89TopTif-59
❑ 89UppDec-268
❑ 90Baz-3
❑ 90Bow-369
❑ 90BowIns-2
❑ 90BowInsL-2
❑ 90BowInsT-2
❑ 90BowTif-369
❑ 90BowTif-A2
❑ 90ClaUpd-T14
❑ 90ClaUpd-NNO
❑ 90Don-302
❑ 90DonBesA-8
❑ 90Fle-155
❑ 90Fle-631
❑ 90FleAll-3
❑ 90FleCan-155
❑ 90FleCan-631
❑ 90FleUpd-101
❑ 90Hot50PS-11
❑ 90K-M-14
❑ 90Lea-468
❑ 90MSAHoID-6
❑ 90OPC-205
❑ 90OPC-407
❑ 90PanSti-215
❑ 90PanSti-352
❑ 90PublntS-47
❑ 90RedFolSB-22
❑ 90RoyPos-6
❑ 90Sco-259
❑ 90Sco100S-51
❑ 90ScoRoo-26T
❑ 90Spo-62
❑ 90StaSab-1
❑ 90StaSab-3
❑ 90StaSab-5
❑ 90StaSab-7
❑ 90StaSab-9
❑ 90StaSab-11
❑ 90Top-205
❑ 90Top-407
❑ 90TopBig-312
❑ 90TopCoi-34
❑ 90TopDou-16
❑ 90TopGaloC-1
❑ 90TopGloS-58
❑ 90TopMinL-79
❑ 90TopSti-102
❑ 90TopStiB-31
❑ 90TopTif-205
❑ 90TopTif-407
❑ 90TopTra-24T
❑ 90TopTraT-24T
❑ 90TopTVA-12
❑ 90UppDec-431
❑ 90UppDec-710
❑ 90Woo-4
❑ 91BasBesRB-5
❑ 91Bow-306
❑ 91ClaGam-15
❑ 91Don-560
❑ 91Fle-555
❑ 91Lea-16
❑ 91OPC-116
❑ 91RedFolS-24
❑ 91RoyPol-6
❑ 91Sco-136
❑ 91StaClu-136
❑ 91Top-116
❑ 91TopDesS-116
❑ 91TopMic-116
❑ 91TopTif-116
❑ 91UppDec-589
❑ 92Don-54
❑ 92Lea-163
❑ 92LeaBlaG-163
❑ 92OPC-766
❑ 92Pin-359
❑ 92RoyPol-5
❑ 92Sco-718
❑ 92SpoStaCC-11
❑ 92StaClu-212
❑ 92Top-766
❑ 92TopGol-766
❑ 92TopGolW-766
❑ 92TopMic-766
❑ 92TriPla-247
❑ 92Ult-369
❑ 92UppDec-607
❑ 93Don-52
❑ 93Pin-425
❑ 93StaClu-371
❑ 93StaCluFDI-371
❑ 93StaCluMOP-371
❑ 93Ult-437
❑ 94Don-657
❑ 94Fle-661
❑ 94Pac-521
❑ 94PadMot-10
❑ 94StaClu-497
❑ 94StaCluFDI-497
❑ 94StaCluGR-497
❑ 94StaCluMOP-497
❑ 97HigDesMUG-13
❑ 97TucTorB-2

Davis, Marty
❑ 91GulCoaRSP-18

Davis, Matt
❑ 91CliGiaC-12
❑ 91CliGiaP-840
❑ 92CalLeaACL-14
❑ 92SanJosGC-23
❑ 93ShrCapF-2765
❑ 94ElPasDF-3151

Davis, Melvin
❑ 93EveGiaC-7
❑ 93EveGiaF-3782
❑ 94CliLumC-8
❑ 94CliLumF-1993

Davis, Michael
❑ 82TacTigT-34
❑ 86TidTidP-7

Davis, Mike (Michael Dwayne)
❑ 79WatA'sT-15
❑ 81Don-470
❑ 81Fle-586
❑ 81SyrChiT-14
❑ 81TacTigT-11
❑ 81Top-364
❑ 82TidTidT-3
❑ 82Top-671
❑ 83A'sGraG-16
❑ 83PawRedST-16
❑ 83TopTra-24T
❑ 84A'sMot-5
❑ 84Don-298
❑ 84Fle-443
❑ 84Nes792-558
❑ 84PawRedST-7
❑ 84PawRedST-26
❑ 84Top-558
❑ 84TopSti-338
❑ 84TopTif-558
❑ 85A'sMot-7
❑ 85Don-223
❑ 85DonHig-3
❑ 85Fle-422
❑ 85TidTidT-23
❑ 85Top-778
❑ 85TopTif-778
❑ 86A'sMot-7
❑ 86Don-14
❑ 86Don-96
❑ 86DonSupD-14
❑ 86Fle-416
❑ 86FleLimE-14
❑ 86FleMin-88
❑ 86FleStiC-31
❑ 86Lea-14
❑ 86OPC-165
❑ 86Spo-83
❑ 86Top-165
❑ 86TopSti-166
❑ 86TopTat-4
❑ 86TopTif-165
❑ 87A'sSmoC-3
❑ 87Don-133
❑ 87DonOpeD-21
❑ 87Fle-391
❑ 87FleGlo-391
❑ 87FleLimE-12
❑ 87FleMin-28
❑ 87FleStiC-32
❑ 87SpoTeaP-23
❑ 87Top-83
❑ 87TopSti-168
❑ 87TopTif-83
❑ 88DodMot-12
❑ 88DodPol-37
❑ 88Don-281
❑ 88DonBasB-36
❑ 88Fle-277
❑ 88FleGlo-277
❑ 88OPC-217
❑ 88PanSti-174
❑ 88RedFolSB-16
❑ 88Sco-211
❑ 88ScoGlo-211
❑ 88ScoRoo-53T
❑ 88ScoRooG-53T
❑ 88Spo-206
❑ 88StaLinAs-3
❑ 88StaLinD-2
❑ 88Top-448
❑ 88TopBig-154
❑ 88TopSti-171
❑ 88TopTif-448
❑ 88TopTra-33T
❑ 88TopTraT-33T
❑ 89Bow-352
❑ 89BowTif-352
❑ 89BurIndS-7
❑ 89DodMot-12
❑ 89DodPol-11
❑ 89DodStaSV-5
❑ 89Don-316
❑ 89Fle-55
❑ 89FleGlo-55
❑ 89OPC-277
❑ 89PanSti-24
❑ 89Sco-376
❑ 89Top-277
❑ 89TopAme2C-12
❑ 89TopBig-225
❑ 89TopTif-277
❑ 89UppDec-146

❑ 89Woo-32
❑ 90DodTar-169
❑ 90Don-552
❑ 90Fle-391
❑ 90FleCan-391
❑ 90OPC-697
❑ 90PubIntS-3
❑ 90Sco-437
❑ 90Top-697
❑ 90TopTif-697
❑ 90UppDec-258
❑ 90WatIndS-6
❑ 91IndIndLD-180
❑ 91IndIndP-472
❑ 91LinDriAAA-180
❑ 97PitMet-10

Davis, Nick
❑ 89KinMetS-6
❑ 90ColMetGS-5
❑ 90ColMetPPI-6
❑ 91AshTouP-573
❑ 91Cla/Bes-49

Davis, Nicky
❑ 90AshTouC-12
❑ 90PitMetP-11

Davis, Odie (Odie Ernest)
❑ 79TucTorT-18
❑ 80ChaChaT-15
❑ 81ChaChaT-16
❑ 93RanKee-122

Davis, Pamela
❑ 95ColSilB-8
❑ 96ColSilB-8

Davis, Peaches (Ray)
❑ 38RedOraW-7
❑ 39OrcPhoAP-5
❑ 39PlaBal-123
❑ 77CinRedT-13

Davis, Pepper (Lavonne)
❑ 93TedWil-118

Davis, Phil
❑ 98LetBlaDG-9

Davis, Piper (Lorenzo)
❑ 53MotCoo-54
❑ 86NegLeaF-12
❑ 86NegLeaF-47
❑ 87NegLeaPD-37
❑ 92NegLeaRLI-15
❑ 93UppDecS-17
❑ 97NegLeaPC-4H

Davis, Ray
❑ 93SavCarC-11
❑ 93SavCarF-682
❑ 94MadHatC-9
❑ 94MadHatF-126
❑ 94MidLeaAF-MDW43
❑ 95ArkTraTI-9
❑ 96ArkTraB-10

Davis, Red
❑ 60TacBan-4
❑ 61TacBan-5
❑ 61UniOil-T10
❑ 76WilTomT-5

Davis, Reggie
❑ 96AriBlaDB-15
❑ 97HigDesMG-4

Davis, Rick
❑ 89SpoIndSP-11
❑ 90Bes-78
❑ 90RivRedWB-5
❑ 90RivRedWCLC-14
❑ 90RivRedWP-2598
❑ 91LinDriAA-606
❑ 91WicWraLD-606
❑ 91WicWraP-2593
❑ 91WicWraRD-3
❑ 92LasVegSF-2790
❑ 92LasVegSS-229
❑ 92SkyAAAF-113
❑ 93LasVegSF-938

Davis, Robert
❑ 89BriTigS-7

Davis, Robert PCL
❑ 14Zee-55
❑ 16Zee-28
❑ 17Zee-6

Davis, Ron (Ronald E.)
❑ 67Ast-8
❑ 67CokCapAs-3
❑ 67DexPre-61
❑ 67Top-298
❑ 68CokCapA-3
❑ 68DexPre-28
❑ 68OPC-21
❑ 68Top-21
❑ 68TopVen-21
❑ 69MilBra-71
❑ 69MLBOffS-185
❑ 69Top-553
❑ 69TopTeaP-12
❑ 70MLBOffS-100
❑ 87AstShoSTw-5

Davis, Ron (Ronald Gene)
❑ 79ColCliT-14
❑ 79YanPicA-8
❑ 80OPC-101
❑ 80Top-179
❑ 80YanPhoA-4
❑ 81Don-467
❑ 81Fle-86
❑ 81OPC-16
❑ 81Top-16
❑ 81YanPhoA-3
❑ 82Don-451
❑ 82Fle-32
❑ 82FleSta-117
❑ 82FleSta-242
❑ 82OPC-283
❑ 82Top-2
❑ 82Top-635
❑ 82TopTra-25T
❑ 82TwiPos-6
❑ 83Don-228
❑ 83Fle-610
❑ 83FleSta-48
❑ 83FleSti-133
❑ 83OPC-380
❑ 83Top-380
❑ 83TopSti-94
❑ 83TwiTeal-25
❑ 84AllGamPI-169
❑ 84Don-269
❑ 84Fle-561
❑ 84FleSti-75
❑ 84FunFooP-112
❑ 84MinTwiP-8
❑ 84Nes792-519
❑ 84OPC-101
❑ 84Top-519
❑ 84TopRubD-17
❑ 84TopSti-309
❑ 84TopTif-519
❑ 84TwiTeal-26
❑ 85Don-120
❑ 85Fle-275
❑ 85FleStaS-103
❑ 85OPC-78
❑ 85Top-430
❑ 85TopRubD-16
❑ 85TopSti-297
❑ 85TopTif-430
❑ 85Twi7-8
❑ 85TwiPos-5
❑ 85TwiTeal-29
❑ 86Don-364
❑ 86Fle-390
❑ 86OPC-265
❑ 86Top-265
❑ 86TopSti-281
❑ 86TopTat-18
❑ 86TopTif-265
❑ 86TwiTeal-27
❑ 87CubCan-4
❑ 87CubDavB-39
❑ 87Don-438
❑ 87Fle-558
❑ 87FleGlo-558
❑ 87OPC-383
❑ 87Top-383
❑ 87TopTif-383
❑ 89PhoFirP-1505
❑ 90ColCliP-9
❑ 90DodTar-170
❑ 91PacSenL-115
❑ 92YanWIZ7-40
❑ 92YanWIZ8-40
❑ 92YanWIZA-15
❑ 93HolLeg-5

Davis, Russ (Russell Stuart)
❑ 89Ft.LauYS-2
❑ 89OneYanP-2109
❑ 90CarLeaA-18
❑ 90PriWilCTI-8
❑ 91AlbYanLD-2
❑ 91AlbYanP-1014
❑ 91Cla/Bes-182
❑ 91LinDriAA-2
❑ 92AlbYanF-2231
❑ 92AlbYanSk-6
❑ 92ClaFS7-115
❑ 92SkyAA F-2
❑ 92UppDecML-132
❑ 93Bow-342
❑ 93ClaMVPF-9
❑ 93ColCliF-1115
❑ 93ColCliP-13
❑ 93ExcFS7-205
❑ 93ExcLeaLF-18
❑ 93FlaWavotF-3
❑ 93FleFinE-245
❑ 93SP-274
❑ 93Ult-592
❑ 94ActPac-13
❑ 94ActPacP-3
❑ 94Bow-109
❑ 94BowBes-B39
❑ 94BowBesR-B39
❑ 94Cla-143
❑ 94ColCliF-2956
❑ 94ColCliP-6
❑ 94ExcAllF-4
❑ 94ExcFS7-100
❑ 94Fle-227
❑ 94LeaGolR-8
❑ 94LeaLimR-5
❑ 94SigRoo-1
❑ 94SigRooHP-S2
❑ 94SigRooHPMP-S2
❑ 94SigRooHPMPS-S2
❑ 94SigRooHPS-S2
❑ 94SigRooS-1
❑ 94StaCluT-194
❑ 94StaCluTFDI-194
❑ 94Top-772
❑ 94TopGol-772
❑ 94TopSpa-772
❑ 94UppDecML-130
❑ 94UppDecML-155
❑ 95ActPac2G-13G
❑ 95ActPacF-9
❑ 95ActPacF-74
❑ 95Bow-428
❑ 95ColCho-524
❑ 95ColChoGS-524
❑ 95ColChoSE-18
❑ 95ColChoSEGS-18
❑ 95ColChoSESS-18
❑ 95ColChoSS-524
❑ 95ColCliMCTI-15
❑ 95Don-545
❑ 95Lea-300
❑ 95Pac-294
❑ 95Pin-414
❑ 95PinArtP-414
❑ 95PinMusC-414
❑ 95Sco-601
❑ 95ScoAi-AM6
❑ 95ScoGolR-601
❑ 95ScoPlaTS-601
❑ 95Sel-160
❑ 95SelArtP-160
❑ 95SelCer-104
❑ 95SelCerMG-104
❑ 95Spo-152
❑ 95SpoArtP-152
❑ 95SpoSam-152
❑ 95StaClu-359
❑ 95StaCluMOP-359
❑ 95StaCluSTWS-359
❑ 95Sum-162
❑ 95SumNthD-162
❑ 95Top-536
❑ 95UC3-110
❑ 95UC3ArtP-110
❑ 95UppDec-204
❑ 95UppDecED-204
❑ 95UppDecEDG-204
❑ 95Zen-132
❑ 96ColCho-723
❑ 96ColChoGS-723
❑ 96ColChoSS-723
❑ 96Don-241
❑ 96DonPreP-241
❑ 96EmoXL-112
❑ 96Fin-S295
❑ 96FinRef-S295
❑ 96Fla-159
❑ 96Fle-235
❑ 96FleTif-235
❑ 96FleUpd-U78
❑ 96FleUpdTC-U78
❑ 96LeaSigA-55
❑ 96LeaSigAG-55
❑ 96LeaSigAS-55
❑ 96MarMot-27
❑ 96Pin-349
❑ 96PinAfi-137
❑ 96PinAfiAP-137
❑ 96PinFoil-349
❑ 96Sco-129
❑ 96ScoDugC-A80
❑ 96ScoDugCAP-A80
❑ 96Sel-127
❑ 96SelArtP-127
❑ 96SP-174
❑ 96Stu-66
❑ 96StuPrePB-66
❑ 96StuPrePG-66
❑ 96StuPrePS-66
❑ 96Sum-30
❑ 96SumAbo&B-30
❑ 96SumArtP-30
❑ 96SumFoi-30
❑ 96Ult-99
❑ 96Ult-410
❑ 96UltGolM-99
❑ 96UltGolM-410
❑ 96UppDec-458
❑ 97Cir-159
❑ 97CirRav-159
❑ 97ColCho-484
❑ 97ColChoT-SM11
❑ 97Don-210
❑ 97DonGolPP-210
❑ 97DonLim-32
❑ 97DonLimE-32
❑ 97DonLimENG-32
❑ 97DonSigA-26
❑ 97DonSigAC-33
❑ 97DonSigAM-33
❑ 97DonSilPP-210
❑ 97Fle-205
❑ 97FleTif-205
❑ 97Lea-162
❑ 97LeaFraM-162
❑ 97LeaFraMDC-162
❑ 97Sco-437
❑ 97ScoArtPWB-437
❑ 97ScoResC-437
❑ 97ScoShoS-437
❑ 97ScoShoSAP-437
❑ 97StaClu-362
❑ 97StaCluMOP-362
❑ 97Top-193
❑ 97Ult-321
❑ 97UltGolME-321
❑ 97UltPlaME-321
❑ 97UppDecMP-P10
❑ 98CirThu-73
❑ 98CirThuRav-73
❑ 98CirThuSupRav-73
❑ 98ColCho-498
❑ 98Don-213
❑ 98DonColP-679
❑ 98DonGolPP-213
❑ 98DonPre-129
❑ 98DonPreSeat-129
❑ 98DonPriCP-679
❑ 98DonSigA-25
❑ 98DonSigAC-34
❑ 98DonSigAM-34
❑ 98DonSigSB-7
❑ 98DonSilPP-213
❑ 98Fle-209
❑ 98MarSco-12
❑ 98MarScoP-12
❑ 98MetUni-15
❑ 98MetUniPMG-15
❑ 98Pac-184
❑ 98PacOnl-682
❑ 98PacOnlR-682
❑ 98PacOnlWC-682
❑ 98PacPlaB-184
❑ 98PacRedT-184
❑ 98PacSil-184
❑ 98PinSna-SM3
❑ 98Sco-172
❑ 98ScoSS-PP74
❑ 98ScoSSAP-PP74
❑ 98SPxFin-319
❑ 98SPxFinR-319
❑ 98SPxFinS-319
❑ 98StaCluFDI-182
❑ 98StaCluI-182
❑ 98StaCluOneK-182
❑ 98StaCluPP-182
❑ 98Stu-207
❑ 98StuGPP-207
❑ 98StuSPP-207
❑ 98Top-202
❑ 98TopChr-202
❑ 98TopChrR-202
❑ 98TopDevR-202
❑ 98TopDia-202
❑ 98TopMiniC-202
❑ 98Ult-54
❑ 98UltGolM-54
❑ 98UltMas-54
❑ 98UltPlaM-54
❑ 98UppDec-227
❑ 99Fle-108
❑ 99FleSta9-108
❑ 99FleWarT-108
❑ 99Pac-394
❑ 99PacInv-134
❑ 99PacInvOD-134
❑ 99PacInvPB-134
❑ 99PacPlaB-394
❑ 99PacRed-394
❑ 99SkyThu-238
❑ 99SkyThuRant-238
❑ 99SkyThuRave-238
❑ 99ThuSkySupR-238
❑ 99Top-64
❑ 99TopChr-64
❑ 99TopChrR-64
❑ 99TopMVPP-64
❑ 99UppDec-203
❑ 99UppDecEL1-203
❑ 99UppDecEL2-203
❑ 99Vic-379

Davis, Sammy
❑ 78WatIndT-7
❑ 79WatIndT-10

Davis, Saul
❑ 92NegLeaRLI-14

Davis, Scott
❑ 90EugEmeGS-5

Davis, Spud (Virgil L.)
❑ 33Gou-210
❑ 33RitCE-9H
❑ 34DiaMatCSB-39
❑ 35AlDemDCR3-121
❑ 35DiaMatCS3T1-43
❑ 36GouWidPPR-A25
❑ 36SandSW-11
❑ 36WorWidGV-12
❑ 39PlaBal-37
❑ 40PlaBal-163
❑ 72TCMthe3-16
❑ 74Car193T-4
❑ 74TCMNic-19
❑ 82DiaCla-64
❑ 83ConMar-26
❑ 85BigLeaC3-56
❑ 86PhiGreT-4
❑ 87Car193T-9
❑ 88ConNatA-4
❑ 91ConTSN-269
❑ 93ConTSN-863
❑ 94ConTSN-1072
❑ 94ConTSNB-1072

Davis, Stan
❑ 77NewCoPT-7
❑ 78NewWayCT-8
❑ 79BurBeeT-21
❑ 81ElPasDT-6
❑ 82VanCanT-9
❑ 83ElPasDT-6
❑ 84ElPasDT-14

Davis, Steven K.
❑ 80SyrChiTI-7
❑ 86BluJayAF-7
❑ 86BluJayFS-7
❑ 87SyrChiT-2
❑ 88BlaYNPRWL-81
❑ 88BlaYNPRWLU-49
❑ 88SyrChiC-1
❑ 88SyrChiP-814
❑ 89ColSprSSC-1
❑ 89ColSprSSP-249
❑ 90AlbDukCm-4
❑ 90AlbDukP-337
❑ 90AlbDukTr-6
❑ 90CMC-406
❑ 90JacMetGS-28
❑ 90OPC-428
❑ 90ProAAAF-58
❑ 90Sco-187
❑ 90Top-428
❑ 90TopTif-428
❑ 91GenCubC-5
❑ 91GenCubP-4209
❑ 91LinDriAA-629
❑ 94BirBarC-30

Davis, Steven Michael
❑ 81SyrChiTI-7
❑ 87SyrChiP-1948
❑ 87TamTarP-19
❑ 88CedRapRP-1150
❑ 90SarWhiSS-29
❑ 91WilBilLD-629
❑ 91WilBilP-305

Davis, Storm (George)
❑ 83Don-619
❑ 83Fle-56
❑ 83OriPos-8
❑ 83Top-268
❑ 83TopSti-310
❑ 84BalOriP-9
❑ 84Don-585
❑ 84Fle-5
❑ 84FunFooP-120
❑ 84Nes792-140
❑ 84OPC-140
❑ 84OriEng-3
❑ 84Top-140
❑ 84TopTif-140
❑ 85Don-454
❑ 85Fle-174
❑ 85Lea-81
❑ 85OPC-73
❑ 85OriHea-3
❑ 85Top-599
❑ 85TopTif-599
❑ 86BalOriHMP-3
❑ 86BalOriP-5
❑ 86Don-169
❑ 86Fle-271
❑ 86Lea-99
❑ 86OPC-179
❑ 86Top-469
❑ 86TopSti-231
❑ 86TopTif-469
❑ 87Don-273
❑ 87Fle-466
❑ 87FleGlo-466
❑ 87FleUpd-22
❑ 87FleUpdG-22
❑ 87OPC-349
❑ 87PadBohHB-34
❑ 87Top-349
❑ 87TopSti-230
❑ 87TopTif-349
❑ 87TopTra-26T
❑ 87TopTraT-26T
❑ 88A'sMot-19
❑ 88Don-595
❑ 88DonBasB-282
❑ 88DonTeaBA-595
❑ 88Fle-278
❑ 88FleGlo-278
❑ 88Top-248
❑ 88TopTif-248
❑ 89A'sMot-18
❑ 89Bow-192
❑ 89BowTif-192
❑ 89Don-210
❑ 89Fle-6
❑ 89FleGlo-6
❑ 89PanSti-413
❑ 89Sco-248
❑ 89Top-701
❑ 89TopBig-121
❑ 89TopTif-701
❑ 89UppDec-153
❑ 90Bow-368
❑ 90BowTif-368
❑ 90ClaUpd-T15
❑ 90Don-479
❑ 90Fle-5
❑ 90FleCan-5
❑ 90FleUpd-102
❑ 90Lea-362
❑ 90OPC-606
❑ 90PubIntS-302
❑ 90Sco-266
❑ 90ScoRoo-21T
❑ 90Top-606
❑ 90TopMinL-26
❑ 90TopTif-606
❑ 90TopTra-25T
❑ 90TopTraT-25T
❑ 90UppDec-292
❑ 90UppDec-712
❑ 91Bow-293
❑ 91ClaGam-16
❑ 91Don-185
❑ 91Fle-556
❑ 91Lea-161
❑ 91OPC-22

❑ 91OriCro-97
❑ 91RoyPol-7
❑ 91Sco-511
❑ 91StaClu-67
❑ 91Stu-65
❑ 91Top-22
❑ 91TopDesS-22
❑ 91TopMic-22
❑ 91TopTif-22
❑ 91UltUpd-26
❑ 91UppDec-639
❑ 92BalOriP-6
❑ 92Don-529
❑ 92Fle-155
❑ 92Lea-465
❑ 92LeaBlaG-465
❑ 92OPC-556
❑ 92Pin-312
❑ 92Sco-264
❑ 92ScoRoo-34T
❑ 92StaClu-728
❑ 92Top-556
❑ 92TopGol-556
❑ 92TopGolW-556
❑ 92TopMic-556
❑ 92UppDec-499
❑ 93AthMot-18
❑ 93AthStaC-6
❑ 93Don-769
❑ 93Fle-541
❑ 93Lea-259
❑ 93PacSpa-564
❑ 93Sco-449
❑ 93StaClu-174
❑ 93StaCluFDI-174
❑ 93StaCluMOP-174
❑ 93Ult-604
❑ 93UppDec-746
❑ 93UppDecGold-746
❑ 94FleUpd-42
❑ 94Pac-214
❑ 94Top-682
❑ 94TopGol-682
❑ 94TopSpa-682
❑ 95Fle-47

Davis, Sweet Pea (Ernest)
❑ 66St.PetCTI-6

Davis, Ted
❑ 78AshTouT-6
❑ 79WauTimT-20
❑ 80TulDriT-4
❑ 81TulDriT-8
❑ 82JacMetT-3
❑ 83BirBarT-18

Davis, Tim
❑ 90ElmPioP-4
❑ 92TopTra-27T
❑ 92TopTraG-27T
❑ 93AppFoxCB-6
❑ 93AppFoxFI-2453
❑ 93ForLauRSC-7
❑ 93ForLauRSFP-1603
❑ 93MidLeaAGF-1
❑ 93StaCluM-103
❑ 94Bow-257
❑ 94ClaGolF-12
❑ 94ExcFS7-125
❑ 94Fla-100
❑ 94FleExtB-163
❑ 94FleExtBRS-4
❑ 94FleUpd-81
❑ 94LeaLimR-56
❑ 94MarMot-23
❑ 94SpoRoo-117
❑ 94SpoRooAP-117
❑ 94Top-167
❑ 94TopGol-167
❑ 94TopSpa-167
❑ 94Ult-418
❑ 94UppDec-512
❑ 94UppDecED-512
❑ 94UppDecML-224
❑ 95ColCho-281
❑ 95ColChoGS-281
❑ 95ColChoSS-281
❑ 95Don-179
❑ 95DonPreP-179
❑ 95Fle-265
❑ 95MarMot-9
❑ 95Pac-394
❑ 95Pin-142
❑ 95PinArtP-142
❑ 95PinMusC-142
❑ 95Sco-61
❑ 95ScoGolR-61
❑ 95ScoPlaTS-61
❑ 95StaClu-60
❑ 95StaCluFDI-60
❑ 95StaCluMOP-60
❑ 95StaCluSTWS-60
❑ 95Top-83
❑ 95TopCyb-59
❑ 95UppDec-344
❑ 95UppDecED-344
❑ 95UppDecEDG-344
❑ 96TacRaiB-8
❑ 97JohCitCTI-6
❑ 97TacRai-10

Davis, Tod (Thomas Oscar)
❑ 47SigOil-4
❑ 49PhiBul-14

Davis, Tom
❑ 49A'sTeal-10
❑ 76ForLauYS-6

Davis, Tommy
❑ 94SigRooDP-47
❑ 94SigRooDPS-47
❑ 94StaCluDP-22
❑ 94StaCluDPFDI-22
❑ 95Bow-115
❑ 95BowBes-B72
❑ 95BowBesR-B72
❑ 95Exc-3
❑ 95SPML-19
❑ 95Top-555
❑ 96BesAutS-26
❑ 96Bow-375
❑ 96BowBayB-14
❑ 96BowFoi-375
❑ 96Exc-4
❑ 97RocRedW-10
❑ 98BowBayM-9

Davis, Tommy (Herman Thomas)
❑ 59DarFar-5
❑ 60DodUniO-3
❑ 60Top-509
❑ 61DodBelB-12
❑ 61DodMor-1
❑ 61DodUniO-3
❑ 61Pos-165
❑ 61Raw-4
❑ 61Top-168
❑ 61TopStaI-25
❑ 62DodBelB-12
❑ 62DodVol-11
❑ 62Jel-105
❑ 62Pos-105
❑ 62PosCan-105
❑ 62SalPlaC-154A
❑ 62SalPlaC-154B
❑ 62ShiPlaC-154
❑ 62Top-358
❑ 63Baz-36
❑ 63DodJayP-2
❑ 63Fle-40
❑ 63Jel-117
❑ 63Pos-117
❑ 63Top-1
❑ 63Top-310
❑ 63TopStiI-12
❑ 64Baz-36
❑ 64DodHea-1
❑ 64Top-7
❑ 64Top-137
❑ 64Top-180
❑ 64TopCoi-57
❑ 64TopCoi-153
❑ 64TopGia-43
❑ 64TopRooAB-2
❑ 64TopSta-64
❑ 64TopStaU-21
❑ 64TopVen-7
❑ 64TopVen-137
❑ 64TopVen-180
❑ 64WheSta-13
❑ 65Baz-36
❑ 65DodJayP-2
❑ 65DodTeal-3
❑ 65Top-370
❑ 65TopEmbl-49
❑ 65TopTral-46
❑ 66DodVolT-1
❑ 66MetTeal-4
❑ 66OPC-75
❑ 66Top-75
❑ 66TopVen-75
❑ 67Baz-37
❑ 67CokCapYM-V30
❑ 67DexPre-62
❑ 67Kah-10
❑ 67MetPos-1
❑ 67MetTeal-4
❑ 67Top-370
❑ 67TopVen-332
❑ 68AtlOilPBCC-15
❑ 68Baz-10
❑ 68Top-265
❑ 68TopGamI-10
❑ 68TopPla-17
❑ 68TopVen-265
❑ 69MilBra-72
❑ 69MLBOffS-94
❑ 69OPC-135
❑ 69PilPos-6
❑ 69Top-135
❑ 69TopDec-15
❑ 69TopDecI-8
❑ 69TopFou-4
❑ 69TopSta-224
❑ 69TopSup-32
❑ 69TopTeaP-9
❑ 70AstTeal-1
❑ 70MilBra-6
❑ 70MLBOffS-38
❑ 70Top-559
❑ 71OPC-151
❑ 71Top-151
❑ 72MilBra-87
❑ 72OPC-41
❑ 72OPC-42
❑ 72Top-41
❑ 72Top-42
❑ 73BalOriP-17
❑ 73OriJohP-12
❑ 73OriTeal-13
❑ 73OriTeal-14
❑ 74Kel-43
❑ 74OPC-396
❑ 74Top-396
❑ 74TopSta-124
❑ 75BalOriP-8
❑ 75OPC-564
❑ 75SSP42-7
❑ 75Top-564
❑ 75TopMin-564
❑ 76OPC-149
❑ 76SSP-398
❑ 76Top-149
❑ 77PilPosR-6
❑ 77Top-362
❑ 78TCM60I-87
❑ 81MarPos-13
❑ 82Don-648
❑ 82TCMGreH-13
❑ 83Pil69G-14
❑ 87AstShowSTh-5
❑ 87DodSmoA-5
❑ 88BakDodCLC-265
❑ 88DodSmo-8
❑ 88PacLegI-83
❑ 89DodSmoG-70
❑ 90DodTar-171
❑ 91MetWIZ-92
❑ 91OriCro-98
❑ 92DodStaTA-2
❑ 93TedWil-11
❑ 93TedWilM-7
❑ 93TedWilPC-25
❑ 93UppDecAH-37
❑ 94UppDecAH-188
❑ 94UppDecAH1-188

Davis, Trench
❑ 82PorBeaT-19
❑ 84HawIsIC-139
❑ 85HawIsIC-238
❑ 86HawIsIP-3
❑ 87RicBraBC-5
❑ 87RicBraC-32
❑ 87RicBraT-17

Davis, Wayne
❑ 87MyrBeaBJP-1454
❑ 88DunBluJS-3

Davis, Wilbur
❑ 25Zee-63
❑ 26Zee-111

Davis, Willie (Willie Henry)
❑ 60DarFar-8
❑ 61DodBelB-3
❑ 61DodUniO-4
❑ 61Top-506
❑ 62DodBelB-3
❑ 62DodVol-7
❑ 62Jel-106
❑ 62Pos-106
❑ 62PosCan-106
❑ 62SalPlaC-161
❑ 62ShiPlaC-161
❑ 62Top-108
❑ 62TopVen-108
❑ 63DodJayP-3
❑ 63Jel-119
❑ 63Pos-119
❑ 63SalMetC-21
❑ 63Top-229
❑ 64DodHea-2
❑ 64Raw-3
❑ 64Top-68
❑ 64TopVen-68
❑ 65DodJayP-3
❑ 65DodTeal-4
❑ 65OldLonC-7
❑ 65Top-435
❑ 66Top-535
❑ 66TopRubI-23
❑ 67CokCapD-17
❑ 67CokCapDA-17
❑ 67DexPre-63
❑ 67DexPre-64
❑ 67OPC-160
❑ 67Top-160
❑ 67TopVen-319
❑ 68Top-208
❑ 68Top3-D-2
❑ 68TopVen-208
❑ 69MilBra-73
❑ 69MLBOffS-145
❑ 69MLBPin-40
❑ 69OPC-65
❑ 69Top-65
❑ 69TopSta-41
❑ 69TopSup-45
❑ 69TopTeaP-22
❑ 69TraSta-45
❑ 70MLBOffS-49
❑ 70OPC-390
❑ 70Top-390
❑ 70TopCanL-6
❑ 70TopPos-3
❑ 70TopSup-39
❑ 70TraSta-2B
❑ 71DodTic-5
❑ 71Kel-16
❑ 71MilDud-41
❑ 71MLBOffS-101
❑ 71OPC-585
❑ 71Top-585
❑ 71TopCoi-93
❑ 72Dia-9
❑ 72Dia-58
❑ 72Kel-3A
❑ 72Kel-3B
❑ 72MilBra-88
❑ 72OPC-390
❑ 72SevTraC-14
❑ 72Top-390
❑ 72TopCloT-9
❑ 72TopPos-12
❑ 73Kel2D-43
❑ 73OPC-35
❑ 73SevTraC-17
❑ 73Top-35
❑ 73TopCanL-12
❑ 73TopCom-6
❑ 73TopPin-6
❑ 74Kel-45
❑ 74OPC-165
❑ 74Top-165
❑ 74TopDecE-42
❑ 74TopSta-44
❑ 74TopTra-165T
❑ 75OPC-10
❑ 75SSP18-11
❑ 75St.LouCP-6
❑ 75Top-10
❑ 75TopMin-10
❑ 76OPC-265
❑ 76SSP-279
❑ 76Top-265
❑ 77PadSchC-19
❑ 77Top-603
❑ 78TCM60I-24
❑ 84DodUniO-3
❑ 87DodSmoA-6
❑ 88DodSmo-12
❑ 89DodSmoG-77
❑ 90DodTar-172
❑ 92DodStaTA-10
❑ 92Pin-591
❑ 93RanKee-123

Davison, Ashanti
❑ 98BluOriQ-19
❑ 98DelShoM-10

Davison, John
❑ 98WatIndTI-8

Davison, Mike (Michael Lynn)
❑ 71MLBOffS-245
❑ 71OPC-276
❑ 71Top-276

Davison, Nathan
❑ 91AdeGiaF-5
❑ 93AusFut-9

Davison, Scott
❑ 89JamExpP-2145
❑ 90RocExpLC-6
❑ 90RocExpP-2699
❑ 91WesPalBEC-19
❑ 91WesPalBEP-1235
❑ 94BelMarC-10
❑ 94BelMarF-3227
❑ 95Exc-114
❑ 95PorCitRTI-5
❑ 96TacRaiB-9

Davisson, Jay
❑ 83ReaPhiT-4
❑ 84PorBeaC-213
❑ 85PorBeaC-41

Dawes, Scott
❑ 95AusFut-33

Dawkins, Darryl
❑ 80PhiBul-18

Dawkins, Gookie
❑ 98BurBeeM-1
❑ 98MidLeaPM-3

Dawkins, Travis
❑ 98BesAutSS-17
❑ 99Bow-318
❑ 99BowGol-318
❑ 99BowInt-318

Dawkins, Walter
❑ 95BatCliTI-10
❑ 97ReaPhi-12
❑ 98ReaPhiM-13

Dawley, Bill
❑ 79NaSouTI-7
❑ 80IndIndTI-25
❑ 81IndIndTI-28
❑ 82IndIndTI-7
❑ 83AstPos-4
❑ 84AstMot-22
❑ 84AstPos-6
❑ 84Don-328
❑ 84Fle-223
❑ 84FleSti-108
❑ 84Nes792-248
❑ 84OPC-248
❑ 84Top-248
❑ 84TopSti-71
❑ 84TopTif-248
❑ 85AstMot-16
❑ 85Don-354
❑ 85Fle-348
❑ 85OPC-363
❑ 85Top-634
❑ 85TopMin-634
❑ 85TopTif-634
❑ 86AstMot-25
❑ 86Don-283
❑ 86Fle-298
❑ 86FleUpd-32
❑ 86Top-376
❑ 86TopTif-376
❑ 87CarSmo-9
❑ 87CarTeal-6
❑ 87Don-628
❑ 87Fle-493
❑ 87FleGlo-493
❑ 87FleUpd-23
❑ 87FleUpdG-23
❑ 87Top-54
❑ 87TopTif-54
❑ 88Don-331
❑ 88Fle-29
❑ 88FleGlo-29
❑ 88Sco-328
❑ 88ScoGlo-328
❑ 88Top-509
❑ 88TopTif-509
❑ 89TacTigC-5
❑ 89TacTigP-1555

Dawley, Joey
❑ 93BluOriC-11
❑ 93BluOriF-4119
❑ 94BluOriC-8
❑ 94BluOriF-3556
❑ 94OriPro-23

Dawsey, Jason
❑ 95HelBreTI-16
❑ 96BelSnaTI-11
❑ 97El PasDB-13
❑ 98StoPorG-7

Dawson, Andre (Andre Nolan)
❑ 77ExpPos-11
❑ 77ExpPos-12
❑ 77Top-473
❑ 78ExpPos-3
❑ 78OPC-180
❑ 78RCColC-73
❑ 78Top-72
❑ 79BasPat-24
❑ 79ExpPos-7
❑ 79OPC-179
❑ 79Top-348
❑ 80ExpPos-8
❑ 80OPC-124
❑ 80Top-235
❑ 81AllGamPI-142
❑ 81Don-212
❑ 81Fle-145
❑ 81FleStiC-123
❑ 81OPC-125
❑ 81OPCPos-6
❑ 81PerAll-3
❑ 81Top-125
❑ 81TopScr-90
❑ 81TopSti-187
❑ 82Don-88
❑ 82ExpHygM-5
❑ 82ExpPos-8
❑ 82ExpZel-4
❑ 82ExpZel-10
❑ 82ExpZel-14
❑ 82FBIDis-7
❑ 82Fle-187
❑ 82FleSta-35
❑ 82OPC-341
❑ 82OPC-379
❑ 82OPCPos-18
❑ 82PerAll-12
❑ 82PerAllG-12
❑ 82Squ-17
❑ 82Top-341
❑ 82Top-540
❑ 82TopSti-57
❑ 82TopSti-125
❑ 82TopStiV-57
❑ 83AllGamPI-142
❑ 83Don-518
❑ 83DonActA-9
❑ 83ExpPos-7
❑ 83ExpStu-4
❑ 83Fle-280
❑ 83FleSta-49
❑ 83FleSti-264
❑ 83OPC-173
❑ 83OPC-303
❑ 83PerAll-11
❑ 83PerAllG-11
❑ 83PerCreC-4
❑ 83PerCreCG-4
❑ 83Top-402
❑ 83Top-680
❑ 83TopSti-164
❑ 83TopSti-252
❑ 84AllGamPI-49
❑ 84Don-97
❑ 84DonActAS-18
❑ 84Dra-9
❑ 84ExpGla-1
❑ 84ExpPos-5
❑ 84ExpStu-11
❑ 84ExpStu-36
❑ 84ExpStu-37
❑ 84Fle-273
❑ 84FleSti-18
❑ 84FleSti-25
❑ 84FleSti-33
❑ 84FunFooP-22
❑ 84MilBra-8
❑ 84Nes792-200
❑ 84Nes792-392
❑ 84NesDreT-16
❑ 84OPC-200
❑ 84OPC-392
❑ 84RalPur-6
❑ 84SevCoi-C1
❑ 84SevCoi-E1
❑ 84SevCoi-W1
❑ 84Top-200
❑ 84Top-392
❑ 84TopCer-6

- ❑ 84TopGloA-18
- ❑ 84TopGloS-35
- ❑ 84TopRubD-6
- ❑ 84TopSti-92
- ❑ 84TopSti-181
- ❑ 84TopSup-20
- ❑ 84TopTif-200
- ❑ 84TopTif-392
- ❑ 85AllGamPl-139
- ❑ 85Don-421
- ❑ 85DonHig-41
- ❑ 85ExpPos-6
- ❑ 85Fle-394
- ❑ 85FleLimE-8
- ❑ 85GenMilS-2
- ❑ 85Lea-133
- ❑ 85OPC-133
- ❑ 85OPCPos-9
- ❑ 85SevCoi-S7
- ❑ 85Top-420
- ❑ 85TopRubD-7
- ❑ 85TopSti-86
- ❑ 85TopTif-420
- ❑ 86Don-25
- ❑ 86Don-87
- ❑ 86DonSupD-25
- ❑ 86ExpProPa-9
- ❑ 86ExpProPo-9
- ❑ 86Fle-246
- ❑ 86FleMin-53
- ❑ 86FleStiC-32
- ❑ 86GenMilB-6B
- ❑ 86Lea-25
- ❑ 86OPC-256
- ❑ 86SevCoi-E13
- ❑ 86Spo-66
- ❑ 86Spo-110
- ❑ 86Top-576
- ❑ 86Top-760
- ❑ 86TopSti-74
- ❑ 86TopTat-20
- ❑ 86TopTif-576
- ❑ 86TopTif-760
- ❑ 86TruVal-29
- ❑ 87BoaandB-10
- ❑ 87ClaUpdY-124
- ❑ 87CubCan-5
- ❑ 87CubDavB-8
- ❑ 87Don-458
- ❑ 87DonHig-28
- ❑ 87DonHig-31
- ❑ 87DonOpeD-70
- ❑ 87Fle-316
- ❑ 87FleGlo-316
- ❑ 87FleHotS-13
- ❑ 87FleSlu-12
- ❑ 87FleStiC-33
- ❑ 87FleUpd-24
- ❑ 87FleUpdG-24
- ❑ 87Lea-212
- ❑ 87OPC-345
- ❑ 87RedFolSB-13
- ❑ 87Spo-139
- ❑ 87SpoIllS-5
- ❑ 87StuPan-3
- ❑ 87Top-345
- ❑ 87TopSti-77
- ❑ 87TopTif-345
- ❑ 87TopTra-27T
- ❑ 87TopTraT-27T
- ❑ 88ActPacT-2
- ❑ 88CheBoy-18
- ❑ 88ClaBlu-216
- ❑ 88ClaRed-157
- ❑ 88CubDavB-8
- ❑ 88Don-9
- ❑ 88Don-269
- ❑ 88DonAll-36
- ❑ 88DonBasB-225
- ❑ 88DonBonM-BC10
- ❑ 88DonPop-14
- ❑ 88DonSupD-9
- ❑ 88DonTeaBC-269
- ❑ 88Dra-16
- ❑ 88Fle-415
- ❑ 88FleAll-6
- ❑ 88FleAwaW-9
- ❑ 88FleBasA-10
- ❑ 88FleBasM-9
- ❑ 88FleExcS-13
- ❑ 88FleGlo-415
- ❑ 88FleHotS-9
- ❑ 88FleLeaL-9
- ❑ 88FleMin-67
- ❑ 88FleRecS-10
- ❑ 88FleSlu-12
- ❑ 88FleStiC-79
- ❑ 88FleSup-13
- ❑ 88FleTeaL-7
- ❑ 88GreBasS-41
- ❑ 88K-M-9
- ❑ 88KayB-8
- ❑ 88KinDis-14
- ❑ 88Lea-9
- ❑ 88Lea-126
- ❑ 88MSAFanSD-15
- ❑ 88MSAJifPD-8
- ❑ 88Nes-9
- ❑ 88OPC-247
- ❑ 88PanSti-236
- ❑ 88PanSti-265
- ❑ 88RedFolSB-17
- ❑ 88Sco-4
- ❑ 88ScoBoxC-16
- ❑ 88ScoGlo-4
- ❑ 88Spo-3
- ❑ 88StaDaw-1
- ❑ 88StaDaw-2
- ❑ 88StaDaw-3
- ❑ 88StaDaw-4
- ❑ 88StaDaw-5
- ❑ 88StaDaw-6
- ❑ 88StaDaw-7
- ❑ 88StaDaw-8
- ❑ 88StaDaw-9
- ❑ 88StaDaw-10
- ❑ 88StaDaw-11
- ❑ 88StaLinAl-10
- ❑ 88StaLinCu-2
- ❑ 88TarPla-12
- ❑ 88Top-401
- ❑ 88Top-500
- ❑ 88TopBig-153
- ❑ 88TopCoi-33
- ❑ 88TopGaloC-6
- ❑ 88TopGloA-18
- ❑ 88TopGloS-1
- ❑ 88TopMinL-43
- ❑ 88TopRevLL-2
- ❑ 88TopRitTM-2
- ❑ 88TopSti-56
- ❑ 88TopSti-148
- ❑ 88TopStiB-13
- ❑ 88TopTif-401
- ❑ 88TopTif-500
- ❑ 88TopUKM-20
- ❑ 88TopUKMT-20
- ❑ 88Woo-8
- ❑ 89Bow-298
- ❑ 89BowTif-298
- ❑ 89CadEllD-14
- ❑ 89CerSup-2
- ❑ 89ClaLigB-37
- ❑ 89ColPosD-1
- ❑ 89ColPosD-2
- ❑ 89ColPosD-3
- ❑ 89ColPosD-4
- ❑ 89ColPosD-5
- ❑ 89ColPosD-6
- ❑ 89ColPosD-7
- ❑ 89ColPosD-8
- ❑ 89CubMar-8
- ❑ 89Don-167
- ❑ 89DonAll-36
- ❑ 89DonBasB-4
- ❑ 89DonBonM-BC8
- ❑ 89DonPop-36
- ❑ 89Fle-422
- ❑ 89FleBasA-11
- ❑ 89FleBasM-11
- ❑ 89FleExcS-11
- ❑ 89FleGlo-422
- ❑ 89FleHeroB-12
- ❑ 89FleLeaL-12
- ❑ 89FleSup-12
- ❑ 89KayB-9
- ❑ 89KeyFooD-14
- ❑ 89MSAIceTD-14
- ❑ 89OPC-10
- ❑ 89OurOwnTD-14
- ❑ 89PanSti-59
- ❑ 89PanSti-230
- ❑ 89RedFolSB-33
- ❑ 89Sco-2
- ❑ 89ScoHot1S-80
- ❑ 89Scomast-28
- ❑ 89Spo-95
- ❑ 89SpoIllFKI-52
- ❑ 89TetTeaD-14
- ❑ 89Top-4
- ❑ 89Top-10
- ❑ 89Top-391
- ❑ 89TopAme2C-13
- ❑ 89TopBasT-78
- ❑ 89TopBig-120
- ❑ 89TopCapC-10
- ❑ 89TopCoi-11
- ❑ 89TopDouA-17
- ❑ 89TopGloA-18
- ❑ 89TopHilTM-11
- ❑ 89TopMinL-3
- ❑ 89TopSti-5
- ❑ 89TopSti-54
- ❑ 89TopSti-156
- ❑ 89TopStiB-48
- ❑ 89TopTif-4
- ❑ 89TopTif-10
- ❑ 89TopTif-391
- ❑ 89TopUKM-21
- ❑ 89TVSpoM-21
- ❑ 89UppDec-205
- ❑ 89UppDecS-3
- ❑ 89WeiMarD-14
- ❑ 89Woo-11
- ❑ 90AllBasT-24
- ❑ 90Bow-39
- ❑ 90BowTif-39
- ❑ 90ClaBlu-85
- ❑ 90CubMar-6
- ❑ 90Don-223
- ❑ 90DonBesN-97
- ❑ 90DonLeaS-52
- ❑ 90Fle-29
- ❑ 90FleCan-29
- ❑ 90HOFStiB-96
- ❑ 90KayB-8
- ❑ 90Lea-177
- ❑ 90M.Vpin-17
- ❑ 90MLBBasB-54
- ❑ 90OPC-140
- ❑ 90OPCBoxB-C
- ❑ 90PanSti-240
- ❑ 90PubIntS-192
- ❑ 90PubIntS-256
- ❑ 90RedFolSB-23
- ❑ 90Sco-265
- ❑ 90Sco100S-74
- ❑ 90ScoMcD-10
- ❑ 90Spo-108
- ❑ 90Top-140
- ❑ 90TopAmeA-9
- ❑ 90TopBig-91
- ❑ 90TopDou-17
- ❑ 90TopGloS-41
- ❑ 90TopHilHM-15
- ❑ 90TopMag-65
- ❑ 90TopSti-47
- ❑ 90TopStiB-14
- ❑ 90TopTif-140
- ❑ 90TopTVCu-31
- ❑ 90TopWaxBC-C
- ❑ 90UppDec-73
- ❑ 90UppDec-357
- ❑ 90USPlaCA-9H
- ❑ 90Woo-11
- ❑ 91BasBesHRK-5
- ❑ 91Bow-429
- ❑ 91CadEllD-15
- ❑ 91Cla3-T14
- ❑ 91ClaGam-26
- ❑ 91CubMar-8
- ❑ 91CubVinL-9
- ❑ 91CubVinL-36
- ❑ 91DenHol-14
- ❑ 91Don-129
- ❑ 91Don-435
- ❑ 91DonEli-4
- ❑ 91Fle-419A
- ❑ 91Fle-419B
- ❑ 91Fle-713
- ❑ 91Lea-400
- ❑ 91MajLeaCP-67
- ❑ 91OPC-640
- ❑ 91OPCBoxB-D
- ❑ 91OPCPre-31
- ❑ 91PanFreS-49
- ❑ 91PanSti-41
- ❑ 91PepSup-2
- ❑ 91PosCan-7
- ❑ 91RedFolS-25
- ❑ 91RedFolS-118
- ❑ 91Sco-445
- ❑ 91Sco100S-87
- ❑ 91SevCoi-M2
- ❑ 91SimandSMLBL-13
- ❑ 91StaClu-310
- ❑ 91StaPinB-12
- ❑ 91Stu-153
- ❑ 91SunSee-14
- ❑ 91Top-640
- ❑ 91TopCraJ2-7
- ❑ 91TopDesS-640
- ❑ 91TopGloA-19
- ❑ 91TopMic-640
- ❑ 91TopSta-11
- ❑ 91TopTif-640
- ❑ 91TopWaxBC-D
- ❑ 91Ult-58
- ❑ 91UppDec-454
- ❑ 91UppDec-725
- ❑ 91UppDecFE-98F
- ❑ 91USPlaCA-11C
- ❑ 91Woo-9
- ❑ 92Bow-625
- ❑ 92Cla2-T24
- ❑ 92ClaGam-27
- ❑ 92CubMar-8
- ❑ 92Don-119
- ❑ 92Don-422
- ❑ 92DonPre-4
- ❑ 92Fle-379
- ❑ 92FleTeaL-20
- ❑ 92Hig5-27
- ❑ 92HitTheBB-12
- ❑ 92LaKdec-8
- ❑ 92Lea-183
- ❑ 92LeaBlaG-183
- ❑ 92MooSna-15
- ❑ 92MVPPin-41
- ❑ 92OPC-460
- ❑ 92OPCPre-45
- ❑ 92PanSti-186
- ❑ 92PanSti-285
- ❑ 92Pin-115
- ❑ 92RedFolS-30
- ❑ 32RedFolS-111
- ❑ 92Sco-75
- ❑ 92Sco100S-48
- ❑ 92ScoCokD-7
- ❑ 92ScoProP-19
- ❑ 92SpoStaCC-12
- ❑ 92StaClu-810
- ❑ 92StaCluD-33
- ❑ 92Stu-12
- ❑ 92StuHer-BC9
- ❑ 92Top-460
- ❑ 92TopGol-460
- ❑ 92TopGolW-460
- ❑ 92TopKid-2
- ❑ 92TopMcD-31
- ❑ 92TopMic-460
- ❑ 92TopMic-G460
- ❑ 92TriPla-113
- ❑ 92TriPla-174
- ❑ 92Ult-468
- ❑ 92UppDec-124
- ❑ 92UppDecHRH-HR9
- ❑ 93Bow-495
- ❑ 93CadDis-16
- ❑ 93DiaMar-29
- ❑ 93Don-632
- ❑ 93DurPowP1-3
- ❑ 93ExpDonM-2
- ❑ 93Fin-84
- ❑ 93FinJum-84
- ❑ 93FinRef-84
- ❑ 93Fla-162
- ❑ 93Fle-377
- ❑ 93FleFinE-173
- ❑ 93FleFinEDT-3
- ❑ 93FleFruotL-14
- ❑ 93FunPac-163
- ❑ 93Lea-310
- ❑ 93OPC-35
- ❑ 93OPCPre-18
- ❑ 93PacSpa-56
- ❑ 93PanSti-97
- ❑ 93Pin-497
- ❑ 93PinCoo-11
- ❑ 93PinCooD-11
- ❑ 93PinHomRC-16
- ❑ 93PinSlu-26
- ❑ 93RedSoxP-9
- ❑ 93RedSoxWHP-4
- ❑ 93Sco-552
- ❑ 93Sel-9
- ❑ 93SelRoo-11T
- ❑ 93SP-201
- ❑ 93StaClu-203
- ❑ 93StaClu-655
- ❑ 93StaCluFDI-203
- ❑ 93StaCluFDI-655
- ❑ 93StaCluMOP-203
- ❑ 93StaCluMOP-655
- ❑ 93Stu-104
- ❑ 93Top-265
- ❑ 93TOPBLAG-4
- ❑ 93TopGol-265
- ❑ 93TopInaM-265
- ❑ 93TopInaR-265
- ❑ 93TopMic-265
- ❑ 93TopPreS-4
- ❑ 93TopTra-92T
- ❑ 93TriPlaG-GS2
- ❑ 93Ult-509
- ❑ 93UppDec-308
- ❑ 93UppDec-777
- ❑ 93UppDec-832
- ❑ 93UppDecGold-308
- ❑ 93UppDecGold-777
- ❑ 93UppDecGold-832
- ❑ 94Bow-531
- ❑ 94ColC-412
- ❑ 94ColChoGS-412
- ❑ 94ColChoSS-412
- ❑ 94Don-448
- ❑ 94Fin-50
- ❑ 94FinRef-50
- ❑ 94Fla-13
- ❑ 94Fle-29
- ❑ 94FleExtB-19
- ❑ 94FUnPac-100
- ❑ 94Lea-142
- ❑ 94LeaL-9
- ❑ 94OPC-138
- ❑ 94Pac-52
- ❑ 94PanSti-28
- ❑ 94Pin-320
- ❑ 94PinArtP-320
- ❑ 94PinMusC-320
- ❑ 94ProMag-12
- ❑ 94Sco-471
- ❑ 94ScoGolR-471
- ❑ 94Sel-93
- ❑ 94SP-154
- ❑ 94SPDieC-154
- ❑ 94Spo-79
- ❑ 94StaClu-371
- ❑ 94StaCluFDI-371
- ❑ 94StaCluGR-371
- ❑ 94StaCluMOP-371
- ❑ 94Stu-161
- ❑ 94Top-595
- ❑ 94TopGol-595
- ❑ 94TopSpa-595
- ❑ 94TriPla-203
- ❑ 94Ult-13
- ❑ 94UppDec-96
- ❑ 94UppDecAJ-12
- ❑ 94UppDecAJG-12
- ❑ 94UppDecED-96
- ❑ 95ColCho-420
- ❑ 95ColCho-560T
- ❑ 95ColChoGS-420
- ❑ 95ColChoSE-195
- ❑ 95ColChoSEGS-195
- ❑ 95ColChoSESS-195
- ❑ 95ColChoSS-420
- ❑ 95Don-487
- ❑ 95DonPreP-487
- ❑ 95DonTopotO-242
- ❑ 95Emo-129
- ❑ 95Fin-330
- ❑ 95FinRef-330
- ❑ 95Fla-352
- ❑ 95Fle-28
- ❑ 95FleUpd-95
- ❑ 95Lea-316
- ❑ 95Pac-36
- ❑ 95Pin-318
- ❑ 95PinArtP-318
- ❑ 95PinMusC-318
- ❑ 95Sco-333
- ❑ 95ScoGolR-333
- ❑ 95ScoPlaTS-333
- ❑ 95ScoYouTE-333T
- ❑ 95SP-56
- ❑ 95SPCha-48
- ❑ 95SPChaDC-48
- ❑ 95SPSil-56
- ❑ 95StaClu-146
- ❑ 95StaClu-578
- ❑ 95StaCluFDI-146
- ❑ 95StaCluMOP-146
- ❑ 95StaCluMOP-578
- ❑ 95StaCluMOP-RL10
- ❑ 95StaCluRL-RL10
- ❑ 95StaCluSTWS-146
- ❑ 95StaCluSTWS-578
- ❑ 95StaCluVR-75
- ❑ 95StaCluVRMO-75
- ❑ 95TopTra-155T
- ❑ 95Ult-262
- ❑ 95UltGolM-262
- ❑ 95UppDec-160
- ❑ 95UppDec-350
- ❑ 95UppDecED-160
- ❑ 95UppDecED-350
- ❑ 95UppDecEDG-160
- ❑ 95UppDecEDG-350
- ❑ 95UppDecSE-250
- ❑ 95UppDecSEG-250
- ❑ 96ColCho-150
- ❑ 96ColChoGS-150
- ❑ 96ColChoSS-150
- ❑ 96Don-260
- ❑ 96DonPreP-260
- ❑ 96Fla-261
- ❑ 96Fle-386
- ❑ 96FleTif-386
- ❑ 96LeaLim-75
- ❑ 96LeaLimG-75
- ❑ 96LeaPre-100
- ❑ 96LeaPreP-100
- ❑ 96LeaSig-127
- ❑ 96LeaSigA-56
- ❑ 96LeaSigAG-56
- ❑ 96LeaSigAS-56
- ❑ 96LeaSigPPG-127
- ❑ 96LeaSigPPP-127
- ❑ 96Pac-75
- ❑ 96PacPri-P25
- ❑ 96PacPriG-P25
- ❑ 96Pin-86
- ❑ 96PinAfi-54
- ❑ 96PinAfiAP-54
- ❑ 96PinAfiFPP-54
- ❑ 96PinArtP-48
- ❑ 96PinSta-48
- ❑ 96Sco-51
- ❑ 96ScoDugC-A44
- ❑ 96ScoDugCAP-A44
- ❑ 96ScoRef-9
- ❑ 96Sel-79
- ❑ 96SelArtP-79
- ❑ 96SelCer-96
- ❑ 96SelCerAP-96
- ❑ 96SelCerCB-96
- ❑ 96SelCerCR-96
- ❑ 96SelCerMB-96
- ❑ 96SelCerMG-96
- ❑ 96SelCerMR-96
- ❑ 96SelTeaN-16
- ❑ 96SP-88
- ❑ 96Sum-148
- ❑ 96SumAbo&B-148
- ❑ 96SumArtP-148
- ❑ 96SumFoi-148
- ❑ 96Top-275
- ❑ 96Ult-199
- ❑ 96UltGolM-199
- ❑ 96UltThu-7
- ❑ 96UltThuGM-7
- ❑ 96UppDec-102
- ❑ 96UppDec-335
- ❑ 96Zen-44
- ❑ 96ZenArtP-44
- ❑ 97ColCho-115
- ❑ 97Don-142
- ❑ 97DonEli-109
- ❑ 97DonEliGS-109
- ❑ 97DonGolPP-142
- ❑ 97DonSilPP-142
- ❑ 97Fle-329
- ❑ 97FleTif-329
- ❑ 97PacPriGotD-GD140
- ❑ 97Pin-15
- ❑ 97PinArtP-PP15
- ❑ 97PinMusC-15
- ❑ 97PinPrePla-15
- ❑ 97Ult-196
- ❑ 97UltGolME-196
- ❑ 97UltPlaME-196
- ❑ 97UppDec-80
- ❑ 97UppDec-214
- ❑ 99DumSet-AD
- ❑ 99DumSet-AD
- ❑ 99SpoIllGotG-10
- ❑ 99SpoIllGotGA-19

Dawson, Charlie

- ❑ 94IdaFalBF-3587
- ❑ 94IdaFalBSP-14
- ❑ 95MacBraTI-5

Dawson, David

- ❑ 89BakDodCLC-180

Dawson, Dwayne

❑ 92AubAstC-20
❑ 92AubAstF-1348
❑ 93QuaCitRBC-5
❑ 93QuaCitRBF-91

Dawson, Gary
❑ 83MadMusF-24

Dawson, Joe
❑ 94ConTSN-1311
❑ 94ConTSNB-1311

Dawson, Larry
❑ 88AppFoxP-164

Dawson, Red (Lowell)
❑ 40WheM4-10
❑ 41WheM5-16

Dawson, Rexford
❑ 19Zee-129

Day, Boots (Charles F.)
❑ 70ExpPin-4
❑ 70Top-654
❑ 71ExpPS-5
❑ 71MLBOffS-125
❑ 71OPC-42
❑ 71Top-42
❑ 72OPC-254
❑ 72ProStaP-3
❑ 72Top-254
❑ 73OPC-307
❑ 73Top-307
❑ 74ExpWes-3
❑ 74OPC-589
❑ 74Top-589
❑ 77EvaTriT-7
❑ 97KinIndB-28
❑ 98PriWilCQ-30

Day, Dexter
❑ 83WatRedT-16
❑ 84CedRapRT-13

Day, George
❑ 91AppFoxCB-17
❑ 91AppFoxP-1723

Day, Kevin
❑ 89AshTouP-943

Day, Leon
❑ 78LauLonABS-5
❑ 80PerHaloFP-221
❑ 90NegLeaS-13
❑ 91NegLeaRL-6
❑ 92NegLeaK-1
❑ 92NegLeaRLI-16
❑ 93LeoDayCC-1
❑ 93UppDecS-17
❑ 94TedWil-103
❑ 94TedWil-NNO
❑ 95NegLeaL2-4
❑ 95NegLeaLI-6
❑ 95S.FExaNLT-6
❑ 97NegLeaPC-10H

Day, Mike
❑ 86WesPalBEP-11

Day, Ned
❑ 52Whe-8A
❑ 52Whe-8B

Day, Paul
❑ 88AugPirP-388

Day, Pea (Clyde Henry)
❑ 33WorCig(-21
❑ 78HalHalR-13
❑ 90DodTar-173

Day, Randy
❑ 86PhiTas-NNO
❑ 86PorBeaP-4
❑ 87SyrChiT-31

Day, Steve
❑ 77NewCoPT-8
❑ 93EveGiaC-8
❑ 93EveGiaF-3761
❑ 94CliLumC-9
❑ 94CliLumF-1973
❑ 94ExcFS7-287

Day, Tim
❑ 91AdeGiaF-4

Day, Zach
❑ 98TamYanM-9

Dayett, Brian (Brian Kelly)
❑ 79WesHavYT-4
❑ 80NasSouTI-7
❑ 81NasSouTI-4
❑ 82NasSouTI-9
❑ 83ColCliT-26
❑ 84ColCliP-9
❑ 84ColCliT-4
❑ 84Don-45
❑ 85CubLioP-6
❑ 85CubSev-24
❑ 85DomLeaS-185
❑ 85Don-152
❑ 85Fle-125
❑ 85FleUpd-35
❑ 85IowCubT-8
❑ 85Top-534
❑ 85TopTif-534
❑ 85TopTifT-29T
❑ 85TopTra-29T
❑ 86Top-284
❑ 86TopTif-284
❑ 87CubCan-6
❑ 87CubDavB-24
❑ 87DonOpeD-73
❑ 87FleUpd-25
❑ 87FleUpdG-25
❑ 87Top-369
❑ 87TopTif-369
❑ 88Don-416
❑ 88Fle-416
❑ 88FleGlo-416
❑ 88OPC-136
❑ 88Sco-205
❑ 88ScoGlo-205
❑ 88Top-136
❑ 88TopTif-136
❑ 92YanWIZ8-41

Dayle, Snookie
❑ 94TedWil-94

Dayley, Ken (Kenneth Grant)
❑ 81RicBraT-19
❑ 82BraBurKL-7
❑ 82Don-501
❑ 82RicBraT-25
❑ 83Don-375
❑ 83Fle-135
❑ 83RicBraT-4
❑ 83Top-314
❑ 84Don-199
❑ 84Fle-176
❑ 84Nes792-104
❑ 84Top-104
❑ 84TopTif-104
❑ 84TopTra-29T
❑ 84TopTraT-29T
❑ 85CarTeal-8
❑ 86CarKASD-2
❑ 86CarSchM-5
❑ 86CarTeal-11
❑ 86Don-303
❑ 86Fle-33
❑ 86OPC-202
❑ 86Top-607
❑ 86TopTif-607
❑ 87CarTeal-7
❑ 87Don-357
❑ 87Fle-293
❑ 87FleGlo-293
❑ 87Top-59
❑ 87TopTif-59
❑ 88CarSmo-3
❑ 88CarTeal-5
❑ 88Don-357
❑ 88DonBasB-299
❑ 88Fle-30
❑ 88FleGlo-30
❑ 88Sco-517
❑ 88ScoGlo-517
❑ 88StaLinCa-5
❑ 88Top-234
❑ 88TopTif-234
❑ 89Bow-428
❑ 89BowTif-428
❑ 89CarSmo-4
❑ 89CarTeal-6
❑ 89Don-299
❑ 89DonBasB-268
❑ 89Fle-448
❑ 89FleGlo-448
❑ 89OPC-396
❑ 89Top-409
❑ 89TopTif-409
❑ 89UppDec-114
❑ 90Bow-191
❑ 90BowTif-191
❑ 90CarSmo-4
❑ 90Don-281
❑ 90DonBesN-22
❑ 90Fle-247
❑ 90FleCan-247
❑ 90Lea-275
❑ 90OPC-561
❑ 90PubIntS-216
❑ 90RicBra2ATI-7
❑ 90Sco-556
❑ 90Top-561
❑ 90TopSti-36
❑ 90TopTif-561
❑ 90TopTVCa-10
❑ 90UppDec-280
❑ 91BluJayFS-7
❑ 91BluJayFS-7
❑ 91BluJayS-27
❑ 91Bow-27
❑ 91Don-735
❑ 91Fle-630
❑ 91OPC-41
❑ 91OPCPre-32
❑ 91Sco-607
❑ 91StaClu-552
❑ 91Stu-134
❑ 91Top-41
❑ 91TopDesS-41
❑ 91TopMic-41
❑ 91TopTif-41
❑ 91UppDec-628
❑ 91UppDec-781
❑ 92OPC-717
❑ 92Sco-685
❑ 92StaClu-137
❑ 92Top-717
❑ 92TopGol-717
❑ 92TopGolW-717
❑ 92TopMic-717
❑ 93BluJayD4-30
❑ 93BluJayFS-8

De Barr, Dennis
❑ 79WatA'sT-1

De La Cruz, Fernando
❑ 97CedRapK-6
❑ 97LakElsSG-12

De La Cruz, Miguel
❑ 85DomLeaS-206

De La Rosa, Rene
❑ 98GiaMot-27

De la Rosa, Tomas
❑ 97VerExpB-12
❑ 99BasAmeTP-32
❑ 99BasAmeTPG-32

De Leon, Erasmo
❑ 85DomLeaS-126

de los Santos, Eddy
❑ 97ChaRivDG-11
❑ 98St.PetDRM-22

De Los Santos, Luis
❑ 93LimRocDWB-19
❑ 98BesAutSS-46
❑ 98Bow-146
❑ 98BowChr-146
❑ 98BowChrGA-146
❑ 98BowChrGAR-146
❑ 98BowChrI-146
❑ 98BowChrIR-146
❑ 98BowChrR-146
❑ 98BowGolA-146
❑ 98BowInt-146

De Los Santos, Pintacora
❑ 85DomLeaS-31

De Los Santos, Valerio
❑ 96BelSnaTI-12
❑ 96MidLeaAB-10
❑ 97Bes-36
❑ 97Bow-319
❑ 97BowBes-179
❑ 97BowBesAR-179
❑ 97BowBesR-179
❑ 97BowInt-319
❑ 98El PasDG-9
❑ 98TexLeaTPG-8
❑ 99Fle-329
❑ 99FleSta9-329
❑ 99FleWarT-329
❑ 99PacCroC-149
❑ 99PacCroCPB-149
❑ 99SpoIll-47

De Wyre, Mike
❑ 85RedWinA-15
❑ 86RedWinA-22

Deabenderfer, Blaine
❑ 87MadMusP-6
❑ 87MadMusP-22

DeAbreu, Milton
❑ 97SalVolG-10

Deak, Brian
❑ 87SumBraP-26
❑ 88BurBraP-27
❑ 88MidLeaAGS-16
❑ 89DurBullS-9
❑ 89DurBullS-9
❑ 89DurBulTI-9
❑ 89Sta-71
❑ 90DurBulTI-4
❑ 91GreBraC-12
❑ 91GreBraLD-206
❑ 91GreBraP-3006
❑ 91LinDriAA-206
❑ 92RicBraBB-13
❑ 92RicBraF-380
❑ 92RicBraRC-5
❑ 92RicBraS-428
❑ 93CalCanF-1168
❑ 93MariStaClu-5
❑ 94LasVegSF-873
❑ 95LouRedF-277
❑ 97RicBraBC-8

Deak, Darrel
❑ 88AlaGolTI-7
❑ 89AlaGol-12
❑ 91JohCitCC-6
❑ 91JohCitCP-3982
❑ 92SprCarC-18
❑ 93ArkTraF-2817
❑ 93CarStaC-11
❑ 94Bow-620
❑ 94LouRedF-2987
❑ 95Exc-265
❑ 95LouRedF-281
❑ 95SigRoo-14
❑ 95SigRooSig-14
❑ 96LouRedB-14

Deakman, Josh
❑ 95BoiHawTI-15
❑ 96LakElsSB-3
❑ 97LakElsSG-11
❑ 98MidAngG-13
❑ 98MidAngO-11

Deal, Charlie (Charles Albert)
❑ 15SpoNewM-46
❑ 16SpoNewM-44
❑ 17ColE13-40
❑ 19W514-18
❑ 20GasAmeMBD-24
❑ 20NatCarE-22
❑ 21E121So8-16A
❑ 21E121So8-16B
❑ 21Exh-34
❑ 22AmeCarE122-15
❑ 22W575-25
❑ 22Zee-5
❑ 23WilChoV-29
❑ 23Zee-5
❑ 24Zee-126
❑ 25Zee-40
❑ 80BraTCM1-18

Deal, Cot (Ellis Fergason)
❑ 54CarHunW-6
❑ 54Top-192
❑ 60Top-459
❑ 78ColCliT-4
❑ 81OklCit8T-22
❑ 82OklCit8T-5
❑ 83AstPos-5
❑ 84AstMot-27
❑ 84AstPos-7
❑ 85AstMot-27
❑ 87AstShoSPT-32
❑ 94TopArc1-192
❑ 94TopArc1G-192

Deal, Jamon
❑ 92BelMarCB-7
❑ 92BelMarF-1434
❑ 93AppFoxCB-7
❑ 93AppFoxFI-2454

Deal, Lindsay
❑ 90DodTar-927

Dealey, Pat (Patrick E.)
❑ 87OldJudN-125

Dean, Aaron
❑ 97GreFalDTI-8
❑ 98GreFalDG-8
❑ 98SanBerS-8
❑ 98SanBerSTIS-8

Dean, Bob
❑ 73CedRapAT-5
❑ 75DubPacT-7

Dean, Brian
❑ 89CarNewE-3

Dean, Chris
❑ 92HigSchPLS-10
❑ 94BelMarC-12
❑ 94BelMarF-3242
❑ 95Exc-115
❑ 95ExcFirYP-3
❑ 96WisTimRB-9
❑ 97CalLeaATI-4
❑ 97LanJet-11
❑ 98OrlRayM-5

Dean, Chubby (Alfred Lovill)
❑ 40PlaBal-193

Dean, Daffy (Paul Dee)
❑ 34BatR31-143
❑ 34DiaMatCSB-41
❑ 35ExhFou-8
❑ 35GolMedFR-4
❑ 35WheBB1-8
❑ 35WheBB1-9
❑ 36ExhFou-8
❑ 39PlaBal-19
❑ 40PlaBal-156
❑ 59OklTodML-14
❑ 60NuHi-14
❑ 61NuSco-476
❑ 68LauWorS-31
❑ 72TCMthe3-17
❑ 74Car193T-5
❑ 74Car193T-6
❑ 74NewYorNTDiS-29
❑ 76TulOilGP-24
❑ 77Spo-7013
❑ 81ConTSN-22
❑ 85BigLeaC3-48
❑ 87Car193T-2
❑ 87SpoRea-17
❑ 88ConSer3-9
❑ 88WilMulP-3
❑ 92ConTSN-363
❑ 92ConTSN-631
❑ 93ConTSNP-1170
❑ 93DiaStaES-125
❑ 94ConTSN-1170
❑ 94ConTSNB-1170

Dean, Dizzy (Jay Hanna)
❑ 30SchR33-31
❑ 30SchR33-35
❑ 31CarMet-6
❑ 32OrbPinNP-14
❑ 32OrbPinUP-15
❑ 33ButCanV-11
❑ 33CraJacP-4
❑ 33GeoCMil-8
❑ 33Gou-223
❑ 33TatOrb-15
❑ 33TatOrbSDR-202
❑ 33WorCig-32
❑ 34BabRutG-14
❑ 34BatR31-64
❑ 34ButPreR-14
❑ 34DiaMatCSB-40
❑ 34Gou-6
❑ 34GouCanV-55
❑ 34WarBakSP-1
❑ 35DiaMatCS2-5
❑ 35DiaMatCS3T1-44
❑ 35ExhFou-8
❑ 35GolMedFR-3
❑ 35GouPuzR-1A
❑ 35GouPuzR-2A
❑ 35GouPuzR-16A
❑ 35GouPuzR-17A
❑ 35WheBB1-7
❑ 35WheBB1-8
❑ 36DiaMatCS3T2-6
❑ 36ExhFou-8
❑ 36R31Pre-G5
❑ 36WorWidGV-19
❑ 37ExhFou-8
❑ 38BasTabP-4
❑ 38ExhFou-3
❑ 38OurNatGPP-5
❑ 38WheBB10-13
❑ 39CubTeal-4
❑ 39ExhSal-10
❑ 39WorWidGV-8
❑ 41CubTeal-25
❑ 46SpoExcW-3-11
❑ 47PM1StaP1-41
❑ 50CalHOFW-24
❑ 51R42SmaS-21
❑ 53ArtHaloFP-26
❑ 59OklTodML-15
❑ 60KeyChal-13
❑ 60NuHi-14
❑ 61GolPre-8
❑ 61NuSco-476
❑ 63BasMagM-19
❑ 66CarCoi-1
❑ 68LauWorS-31
❑ 72TCMthe3-18
❑ 73HalofFP-5
❑ 73TCMAllG-2
❑ 74CapPub-92
❑ 74Car193T-5
❑ 74Car193T-7
❑ 74Car193T-28
❑ 74LauAllG-36
❑ 74NewYorNTDiS-9
❑ 74NewYorNTDiS-29
❑ 74TCMNic-8
❑ 75SpoHobBG-1
❑ 76RowExh-3
❑ 76ShaPiz-63
❑ 77BobParHoF-18
❑ 77GalGloG-52
❑ 80LauFamF-5
❑ 80MarExhH-8
❑ 80PacLeg-12
❑ 80PerHaloFP-66
❑ 80SSPHOF-66
❑ 81ConTSN-21
❑ 82DiaCla-12
❑ 82TCMGreP-36
❑ 83ConMar-45
❑ 83DonHOFH-29
❑ 84CubBriPC-4C
❑ 84OCoandSI-126
❑ 85FegMurCG-3
❑ 86ConSer1-10
❑ 86SpoDecG-14
❑ 87Car193T-1
❑ 87SpoRea-17
❑ 88ConNatA-5
❑ 88ConSer4-8
❑ 88GreBasS-27
❑ 88WilMulP-3
❑ 90BasWit-71
❑ 90PerGreM-18
❑ 90SweBasG-6
❑ 91ConTSN-3
❑ 91ConTSNP-34
❑ 91HomCooC-8
❑ 91LinDri-50
❑ 91SweBasG-138
❑ 91TopArc1-326
❑ 92CarMcD-15
❑ 92ConTSN-428
❑ 92ConTSN-635
❑ 92ConTSNCI-19
❑ 92St.VinHHS-2
❑ 93ActPacA-106
❑ 93ActPacA2-40G
❑ 93ConTSN-928
❑ 93ConTSNP-1170
❑ 93DiaStaES-124
❑ 93Hoy-2
❑ 93LegFoi-2
❑ 93SpeHOFI-5
❑ 93UppDecAH-38
❑ 94ConTSN-1109
❑ 94ConTSN-1170
❑ 94ConTSNB-1109
❑ 94ConTSNB-1170
❑ 94TedWil-82
❑ 94UppDecTAE-45
❑ 95MegRut-24
❑ 96NoiSatP-3

Dean, Greg
❑ 96HigDesMB-10

Dean, Jeff
❑ 83MiaMarT-11

Dean, Jimmy
❑ 93NegLeaRL2-7

Dean, John
❑ 77SalPirT-11A
❑ 77SalPirT-11B

Dean, Kevin
❑ 87WesPalBEP-660
❑ 88JacExpB-13
❑ 88JacExpP-984
❑ 89IndIndC-21
❑ 89IndIndP-1225
❑ 90CMC-625
❑ 90GreBraS-6
❑ 90ProAAAF-204
❑ 90TucTorC-23
❑ 90TucTorP-214
❑ 91JacGenLD-556
❑ 91JacGenP-936
❑ 91LinDriAA-556
❑ 92JacGenS-330

Dean, Mark

❑ 93GleFalRC-11
❑ 93GleFalRF-4009
❑ 94NewJerCF-3423
❑ 95PeoChiTI-5
Dean, Mike
❑ 98SalVol-6
❑ 99TeaBesR-17
❑ 99TeaBesRG-17
❑ 99TeaBesRS-17
Dean, Monroe
❑ 28Zee-73
❑ 29Zee-68
❑ 30Zee-77
❑ 31Zee-44
❑ 32Zee-53
Dean, Roger
❑ 85UtiBluST-9
Dean, Steve
❑ 90OklSoo-10
Dean, Tommy (Tommy Douglas)
❑ 69PadVol-2
❑ 69Top-641
❑ 70OPC-234
❑ 70Top-234
❑ 71MLBOffS-225
❑ 71OPC-364
❑ 71Top-364
❑ 90DodTar-174
DeAngelis, Steve
❑ 86ReaPhiP-7
❑ 87MaiGuiP-13
❑ 88PhiTas-27
❑ 88ReaPhiP-877
❑ 89QuaCitAB-29
❑ 89QuaCitAGS-26
❑ 90MidAngGS-3
Deardorff, Jeff
❑ 98BelSnaM-11
Deares, Greg
❑ 93GleFalRC-12
❑ 93GleFalRF-4017
DeArmas, Roly
❑ 80CarMudF-18
❑ 87ClePhiP-19
❑ 88MarPhiS-10
❑ 89MarPhiS-35
❑ 91MarPhiC-29
❑ 92MarPhiC-30
❑ 92MarPhiF-3075
❑ 93ClePhiC-27
❑ 94WhiSoxK-30
❑ 95WhiSoxK-31
❑ 98SouBenSHM-24
Dease, Don'l
❑ 90IdaFalBP-3247
Deasley, Pat (Thomas H.)
❑ 86OldJudN-3
❑ 87BucN28-65
❑ 87FouBasHN-3
❑ 87OldJudN-126
❑ 88AugBecN-11
❑ 88GandBCGCE-12
❑ 90KalBatN-11
DeBattista, Dan
❑ 77SalPirT-12
Debee, Rich
❑ 87MemChiP-11
❑ 89OmaRoyP-1739
❑ 90OmaRoyC-23
DeBerry, Hank (John Herman)
❑ 21Nei-101
❑ 22E120-138
❑ 22W572-21
❑ 22W573-31
❑ 25Exh-9
❑ 26SpoComoA-14
❑ 27AmeCarE126-30
❑ 29ExhFou-4
❑ 29PorandAR-15
❑ 31Zee-45
❑ 90DodTar-175
DeBerry, Joe
❑ 91BilMusP-3759
❑ 91BilMusSP-14
❑ 91FroRowDP-30
❑ 91FroRowDPG-30
❑ 91FroRowDPS-30
❑ 92CedRapRC-14
❑ 92CedRapRF-1076
❑ 92ClaFS7-46
❑ 92StaCluD-34
❑ 92UppDecML-126
❑ 93AlbYanF-2168
❑ 94AlbYanF-1453
❑ 95NorNavTI-17
❑ 95TamYanYI-4
❑ 96NorNavB-6
❑ 96StoPorB-13
❑ 97WicWra-21
DeBoer, Rob
❑ 94SouOreAC-5
❑ 94SouOreAF-3626
❑ 95WesMicWTI-18
❑ 96HunStaTI-6
❑ 96ModA'sB-8
❑ 97HunStaTI-8
❑ 98VisOakG-5
DeBoever, William
❑ 86JamExpP-4
DeBold, Rusty
❑ 85MiaHur-2
DeBord, Bob
❑ 83ChaRoyT-18
DeBottis, Marc
❑ 88SyrChiP-828
DeBrand, Genaro
❑ 90NiaFalRP-12
Debrand, Juan
❑ 93UtiBluSC-8
❑ 93UtiBluSF-3539
Debrand, Rafael
❑ 93St.CatBJC-7
❑ 93St.CatBJF-3985
Debrino, Rob
❑ 94ForWayWC-7
❑ 94ForWayWF-2002
❑ 95ForMyeMTI-8
DeBriyn, Norm
❑ 90ArkRaz-28
DeBruhl, Randy
❑ 93PriRedC-6
❑ 93PriRedF-4181
❑ 94ChaWheC-7
❑ 94ChaWheF-2705
Debus, Jon Eric
❑ 81VerBeaDT-4
❑ 84AlbDukCr-164
❑ 86AlbDukP-5
❑ 87AlbDukD-15
❑ 88AlbDukCm-15
❑ 88AlbDukP-269
❑ 89AlbDukCm-12
❑ 89AlbDukP-76
❑ 90SanAntMGS-3
❑ 91VerBeaDP-792
❑ 92GreFalDSP-29
❑ 93GreFalDSP-30
❑ 94VerBeaDC-27
❑ 94VerBeaDF-90
❑ 95VerBeaDTI-30
❑ 96MauStiHWB-31
❑ 96VerBeaDB-1
❑ 97AlbDukGS-22
❑ 98AlbDukG-5
DeBusschere, Dave (David A.)
❑ 63Top-54A
❑ 63Top-54B
❑ 63WhiSoxTS-5
❑ 64Top-247
❑ 64TopVen-247
❑ 64WhiSoxI-8
❑ 64WhiSoxTS-7
❑ 65Top-297
❑ 78TCM60I-246
DeButch, Mike
❑ 86BeaGolGP-9
❑ 87TexLeaAF-1
❑ 87WicPilRD-1
❑ 88WicPilRD-10
❑ 89JacMetGS-19
❑ 89TidTidP-1959
❑ 90CMC-366
❑ 90ProAAAF-281
❑ 90TidTidC-15
❑ 90TidTidP-550
❑ 90TopTVM-39
❑ 92LonTigF-639
❑ 92LonTigS-405
DeCanniere, Frank
❑ 13Zee-104
❑ 14Zee-130
❑ 15Zee-124
❑ 16Zee-126
❑ 17Zee-103
Decatur, Art (A.R.)
❑ 25Exh-10
❑ 27Exh-21
❑ 90DodTar-176
DeCelle, Mike
❑ 96ButCopKB-12
❑ 97ChaRivDG-10
❑ 97HudValRB-14
❑ 97Top-472
DeChavez, Oscar
❑ 83IdaFalAT-3
❑ 84ModA'sC-9
❑ 85ModA'sC-5
Decillis, Dean
❑ 88LakTigS-9
❑ 89LonTigP-1372
❑ 90CMC-397
❑ 90ProAAAF-384
❑ 90TolMudHC-20
❑ 90TolMudHP-154
❑ 91LinDriAA-380
❑ 91LonTigLD-380
❑ 91LonTigP-1883
❑ 92TolMudHF-1050
❑ 92TolMudHS-583
❑ 94TreThuF-2125
DeCinces, Doug (Douglas V.)
❑ 75BalOriP-9
❑ 75OPC-617
❑ 75Top-617
❑ 75TopMin-617
❑ 76BalOriP-9
❑ 76OPC-438
❑ 76SSP-387
❑ 76Top-438
❑ 77BalOriP-4
❑ 77BurCheD-44
❑ 77Hos-15
❑ 77OPC-228
❑ 77Top-216
❑ 78BalOriP-6
❑ 78Hos-10
❑ 78OPC-192
❑ 78Top-9
❑ 79BalOriP-4
❑ 79Hos-54
❑ 79OPC-217
❑ 79Top-421
❑ 80BalOriP-4
❑ 80OPC-322
❑ 80Top-615
❑ 81AllGamPI-31
❑ 81Don-352
❑ 81Fle-173
❑ 81Fle-195
❑ 81FleStiC-90
❑ 81OPC-188
❑ 81Top-188
❑ 82Don-279
❑ 82Fle-162
❑ 82FleSta-142
❑ 82OPC-174
❑ 82Top-564
❑ 82TopSti-142
❑ 82TopTra-26T
❑ 83AllGamPI-31
❑ 83Don-216
❑ 83Fle-85
❑ 83FleSta-50
❑ 83FleSti-30
❑ 83FraBroR-37
❑ 83OPC-341
❑ 83PerCreC-22
❑ 83PerCreCG-22
❑ 83SevCoi-7
❑ 83Top-341
❑ 83TopSti-46
❑ 83TopSti-155
❑ 83TopSti-171
❑ 84AllGamPI-122
❑ 84AngSmo-7
❑ 84Don-230
❑ 84DonActAS-6
❑ 84Fle-514
❑ 84FunFooP-73
❑ 84Nes792-790
❑ 84OPC-82
❑ 84Top-790
❑ 84TopSti-229
❑ 84TopTif-790
❑ 85AllGamPI-31
❑ 85AngSmo-6
❑ 85Don-2
❑ 85Don-179
❑ 85DonActA-51
❑ 85DonSupD-2
❑ 85Fle-299
❑ 85Lea-2
❑ 85OPC-111
❑ 85Top-111
❑ 85TopSti-222
❑ 85TopTif-111
❑ 86AngSmo-6
❑ 86Don-57
❑ 86DonHig-39
❑ 86DonWaxBC-PC6
❑ 86Fle-153
❑ 86OPC-257
❑ 86Spo-173
❑ 86Top-257
❑ 86TopSti-178
❑ 86TopTat-12
❑ 86TopTif-257
❑ 87AngSmo-17
❑ 87CalAngPPS-9
❑ 87Don-356
❑ 87DonOpeD-1
❑ 87Fle-77
❑ 87FleGlo-77
❑ 87FleHotS-14
❑ 87FleMin-29
❑ 87FleStiC-34
❑ 87OPC-22
❑ 87SevCoi-W1
❑ 87Spo-106
❑ 87SpoTeaP-11
❑ 87StuPan-16
❑ 87Top-22
❑ 87TopGloS-52
❑ 87TopSti-182
❑ 87TopTif-22
❑ 88Fle-31
❑ 88FleGlo-31
❑ 88OPC-141
❑ 88Sco-239
❑ 88ScoGlo-239
❑ 88Spo-185
❑ 88Top-446
❑ 88TopTif-446
❑ 89AngSmo-16
❑ 91LinDri-19
❑ 91OriCro-99
❑ 91SweBasG-23
❑ 93UppDecAH-39
❑ 94TedWil-15
DeCinces, Tim
❑ 96BluOriB-9
❑ 97DelSho-13
❑ 98FreKeyM-23
❑ 99BasAmeTP-31
❑ 99BasAmeTPG-31
Deck, Billy
❑ 96AppLeaAB-20
❑ 96JohCitCTI-7
❑ 97PeoChi-6
❑ 98PriWilCQ-19
Deck, Todd
❑ 85CloHSS-12
Decker, Edward
❑ 87OldJudN-127
Decker, Joe (George Henry)
❑ 71MLBOffS-30
❑ 71OPC-98
❑ 71Top-98
❑ 72Top-612
❑ 73OPC-311
❑ 73Top-311
❑ 74OPC-469
❑ 74Top-469
❑ 74TopSta-206
❑ 75Hos-96
❑ 75OPC-102
❑ 75Top-102
❑ 75TopMin-102
❑ 75TwiPos-10
❑ 75TwiTeal-12
❑ 76OPC-636
❑ 76SSP-210
❑ 76Top-636
❑ 78SanJosMMC-6
❑ 78TwiFri-29
❑ 79SpoIndT-12
❑ 82SalLakCGT-25
❑ 83SalLakCGT-10
❑ 89TopSenL-112
❑ 90NiaFalRP-29
❑ 91PacSenL-101
Decker, Marty (Dee Martin)
❑ 82OklCit8T-22
❑ 83PorBeaT-18
❑ 84LasVegSC-226
❑ 85LasVegSC-107
Decker, Steve
❑ 89SanJosGB-11
❑ 89SanJosGCLC-227
❑ 89SanJosGP-446
❑ 89SanJosGS-6
❑ 89Sta-84
❑ 90ProAaA-72
❑ 90ShrCapP-1445
❑ 90ShrCapS-5
❑ 90TexLeaAGS-24
❑ 90TopMag-55
❑ 91Bow-622
❑ 91Cla1-T7
❑ 91Cla2-T64
❑ 91Cla2-T100
❑ 91ClaGam-198
❑ 91Don-428
❑ 91Fle-260
❑ 91GiaMot-3
❑ 91GiaPacGaE-13
❑ 91GiaSFE-7
❑ 91Lea-441
❑ 91OPCPre-33
❑ 91Sco-710
❑ 91ScoAllF-2
❑ 91ScoHotR-8
❑ 91ScoRoo-12
❑ 91SevCoi-NC4
❑ 91StaClu-569
❑ 91Stu-260
❑ 91StuPre-16
❑ 91TopDeb90-37
❑ 91TopTra-29T
❑ 91TopTraT-29T
❑ 91Ult-319
❑ 91UppDec-25
❑ 92Don-389
❑ 92Fle-633
❑ 92OPC-593
❑ 92PanSti-211
❑ 92PhoFirF-2824
❑ 92PhoFirS-381
❑ 92Pin-63
❑ 92Sco-317
❑ 92Sco100RS-56
❑ 92SkyAAAF-175
❑ 92StaClu-417
❑ 92Top-593
❑ 92TopGol-593
❑ 92TopGolW-593
❑ 92TopMic-593
❑ 92TriA AAS-381
❑ 92Ult-289
❑ 92UppDec-173
❑ 93Don-260
❑ 93Don-768
❑ 93Fle-425
❑ 93MarlStaClu-15
❑ 93MarUppD-744
❑ 93MarUSPC-4S
❑ 93MarUSPC-8C
❑ 93PacSpa-459
❑ 93Pin-233
❑ 93Sco-653
❑ 93StaClu-692
❑ 93StaCluFDI-692
❑ 93StaCluMOP-692
❑ 93Top-544
❑ 93TopGol-544
❑ 93TopInaM-544
❑ 93TopInaR-544
❑ 93TopMic-544
❑ 93Ult-372
❑ 93UppDec-744
❑ 93UppDecGold-744
❑ 96GiaMot-24
❑ 97TacRai-11
❑ 98NasSouTI-10
❑ 98NasSouTISS-10
❑ 98NorTidP-7
❑ 98NorTidQ-8
Decksen, Robert
❑ 90BelBreB-26
DeClue, Jon
❑ 96MidAngB-11
❑ 96MidAngOHP-9
DeCordova, David
❑ 87St.PetCP-14
DeCosta, Bob
❑ 83VisOakF-8
DeDario, Joe
❑ 90NiaFalRP-31
Dede, Artie
❑ 90DodTar-928
Dedeaux, Rod (Raoul)
❑ 85Top-389
❑ 85TopTif-389
❑ 90DodTar-177
❑ 90SouCalS-4
Dedmon, Jeff (Jeffrey L.)
❑ 81DurBulT-17
❑ 82DurBulT-16
❑ 84raPho-7
❑ 84TopTra-30T
❑ 84TopTraT-30T
❑ 85Don-554
❑ 85Fle-323
❑ 85RicBraT-4
❑ 85Top-602
❑ 85TopTif-602
❑ 86BraPol-49
❑ 86Don-443
❑ 86Fle-513
❑ 86Top-129
❑ 86TopTif-129
❑ 87BraSmo-7
❑ 87Don-314
❑ 87Fle-514
❑ 87FleGlo-514
❑ 87Top-373
❑ 87TopTif-373
❑ 88Don-325
❑ 88Fle-537
❑ 88FleGlo-537
❑ 88IndGat-50
❑ 88Sco-498
❑ 88ScoGlo-498
❑ 88StaLinBra-4
❑ 88Top-469
❑ 88TopClo-31
❑ 88TopTif-469
❑ 89IndIndP-1214
Dedos, Felix
❑ 87WinHavRSP-2
❑ 89BlaYNPRWL-113
❑ 89WinHavRSS-3
Dedrick, James
❑ 91KanCouCC-5
❑ 91KanCouCP-2653
❑ 91KanCouCTI-4
❑ 92FreKeyC-15
❑ 93BowBayF-2183
❑ 94OriPro-24
❑ 94RocRedWF-991
❑ 94RocRedWTI-6
❑ 95BalOriP-15
❑ 95BowBayTI-28
❑ 95RocRedWTI-11
❑ 96BalOriP-6
❑ 96RocRedWB-10
❑ 98RicBraQ-10
Dedrick, Tim
❑ 92FreKeyF-1799
Deeble, Jon
❑ 93AusFut-53
❑ 95AusFut-21
❑ 95AusFut-89
Deer, Rob (Robert George)
❑ 79CedRapGT-28
❑ 80CliGiaT-20
❑ 84PhoGiaC-4
❑ 85Fle-648
❑ 85GiaMot-25
❑ 85GiaPos-8
❑ 86BrePol-45
❑ 86Fle-538
❑ 86FleUpd-33
❑ 86Top-249
❑ 86TopTif-249
❑ 86TopTra-31T
❑ 86TopTraT-31T
❑ 87BrePol-45
❑ 87BreTeal-5
❑ 87ClaGam-43
❑ 87ClaUpdY-141
❑ 87Don-274
❑ 87DonOpeD-57
❑ 87Fle-344
❑ 87FleBasA-14
❑ 87FleExcS-15
❑ 87FleGlo-344
❑ 87FleMin-30
❑ 87OPC-188
❑ 87Spo-172
❑ 87SpoTeaP-19
❑ 87Top-547
❑ 87TopCoi-10
❑ 87TopGloS-22
❑ 87TopMinL-59
❑ 87TopSti-194
❑ 87TopTif-547

❑ 88BrePol-45
❑ 88BreTeal-10
❑ 88Don-274
❑ 88DonBasB-109
❑ 88Fle-163
❑ 88FleGlo-163
❑ 88FleStiC-36
❑ 88OPC-33
❑ 88PanSti-128
❑ 88RedFolSB-18
❑ 88Sco-95
❑ 88ScoGlo-95
❑ 88Spo-183
❑ 88StaLinBre-6
❑ 88Top-33
❑ 88TopBig-151
❑ 88TopSti-198
❑ 88TopTif-33
❑ 89Bow-146
❑ 89BowTif-146
❑ 89BreGar-4
❑ 89BrePol-45
❑ 89BreYea-45
❑ 89ClaLigB-39
❑ 89Don-173
❑ 89DonBasB-71
❑ 89Fle-184
❑ 89FleGlo-184
❑ 89OPC-364
❑ 89PanSti-376
❑ 89RedFolSB-34
❑ 89Sco-72
❑ 89Spo-111
❑ 89Top-364
❑ 89Top-759
❑ 89TopBig-78
❑ 89TopSti-202
❑ 89TopTif-364
❑ 89TopTif-759
❑ 89UppDec-442
❑ 90Bow-401
❑ 90BowTif-401
❑ 90BreMilB-4
❑ 90BrePol-45
❑ 90Don-55
❑ 90Fle-320
❑ 90FleCan-320
❑ 90Lea-322
❑ 90MLBBasB-80
❑ 90OPC-615
❑ 90PanSti-102
❑ 90PubIntS-494
❑ 90RedFolSB-24
❑ 90Sco-390
❑ 90Spo-137
❑ 90TigTeal-8
❑ 90Top-615
❑ 90TopBig-74
❑ 90TopSti-204
❑ 90TopTif-615
❑ 90UppDec-176
❑ 91Bow-132
❑ 91Don-729
❑ 91Fle-580
❑ 91FleUpd-23
❑ 91Lea-237
❑ 91OPC-192
❑ 91PanFreS-209
❑ 91RedFolS-26
❑ 91Sco-248
❑ 91ScoRoo-47T
❑ 91StaClu-539
❑ 91Stu-52
❑ 91TigCok-44
❑ 91Top-192
❑ 91TopDesS-192
❑ 91TopMic-192
❑ 91TopTif-192
❑ 91TopTra-30T
❑ 91TopTraT-30T
❑ 91UppDec-272
❑ 91UppDec-726
❑ 92Bow-363
❑ 92Don-532
❑ 92Fle-132
❑ 92Lea-193
❑ 92LeaBlaG-193
❑ 92OPC-441
❑ 92PanSti-109
❑ 92Pin-348
❑ 92RedFolS-31
❑ 92Sco-56
❑ 92StaClu-92
❑ 92Stu-172
❑ 92TigKro-6
❑ 92TigTeal-8
❑ 92Top-441
❑ 92TopGol-441
❑ 92TopGolW-441
❑ 92TopMic-441
❑ 92Ult-58
❑ 92UppDec-294
❑ 93Bow-332
❑ 93Don-231
❑ 93DonLonBL-LL1
❑ 93DonSpiotG-SG10
❑ 93Fle-225
❑ 93Lea-246
❑ 93PacSpa-106
❑ 93PanSti-119
❑ 93Pin-167
❑ 93PinHomRC-15
❑ 93Sco-636
❑ 93Sel-186
❑ 93SelRoo-2T
❑ 93SP-235
❑ 93StaClu-357
❑ 93StaCluFDI-357
❑ 93StaCluMOP-357
❑ 93Stu-26
❑ 93TigGat-5
❑ 93Top-243
❑ 93TopGol-243
❑ 93TopInaM-243
❑ 93TopInaR-243
❑ 93TopMic-243
❑ 93TriPla-137
❑ 93Ult-195
❑ 93UppDec-217
❑ 93UppDecGold-217
❑ 93USPlaCA-5C
❑ 94BreMilB-114
❑ 94ColC-90
❑ 94ColChoGS-90
❑ 94ColChoSS-90
❑ 94Don-74
❑ 94Fle-30
❑ 94Sco-475
❑ 94ScoGolR-475
❑ 94StaClu-139
❑ 94StaCluFDI-139
❑ 94StaCluGR-139
❑ 94StaCluMOP-139
❑ 94Top-531
❑ 94TopGol-531
❑ 94TopSpa-531
❑ 96LasVegSB-11

Dees, Charlie (Charles Henry)
❑ 63AngJayP-4
❑ 64Top-159
❑ 64TopVen-159

DeFillippis, Art
❑ 75SpoIndC-20
❑ 76OPC-595
❑ 76SacSolC-12
❑ 76Top-595
❑ 77TacTwiDQ-19

DeFord, Logan
❑ 92MisStaB-11

DeFrancesco, Anthony
❑ 85GreHorT-25
❑ 86WinHavRSP-7
❑ 87NewBriRSP-15
❑ 88ChaLooB-7
❑ 88NasSouTI-7
❑ 89ChaLooB-3
❑ 89ChaLooGS-8
❑ 90ChaLooGS-10
❑ 90NasSouP-235
❑ 90ProAAAF-547
❑ 91LinDriAAA-255
❑ 91NasSouLD-255
❑ 91NasSouP-2159
❑ 92RenSilSCLC-39
❑ 92SouOreAC-30
❑ 93SouOreAF-4082
❑ 97VisOakG-8
❑ 98VisOakG-6

DeFreites, Art (Arturo S.)
❑ 76IndIndTI-4
❑ 77IndIndTI-20
❑ 78IndIndTI-22
❑ 80Top-677
❑ 85DomLeaS-155
❑ 91PacSenL-77

DeGerick, Mike
❑ 77FriOneYW-116

Degifico, Vince (Vincent)
❑ 87ElmPioBC-16
❑ 87ElmPioRC-16
❑ 89Sta-119
❑ 89WinHavRSS-4
❑ 90NewBriRSB-16
❑ 90NewBriRSP-1325
❑ 90NewBriRSS-3

DeGrasse, Tim
❑ 91HamRedC-2
❑ 91HamRedP-4032
❑ 92HamRedC-15
❑ 92HamRedF-1586
❑ 93SprCarC-6
❑ 93SprCarF-1843

Deguero, Jerry
❑ 86ModA'sP-6

DeHaan, Korwin
❑ 97EriSeaWB-9
❑ 98AugGreM-3
❑ 99Bow-420
❑ 99BowGol-420
❑ 99BowInt-420

Dehart, Casey
❑ 98BilMusTI-9

DeHart, Greg
❑ 78NewWayCT-9
❑ 79BurBeeT-20
❑ 80BurBeeT-6
❑ 83SanJosBC-25

DeHart, Rick
❑ 87BirBarB-28
❑ 92AlbPolCB-15
❑ 92AlbPolF-2299
❑ 93SanBerSC-6
❑ 93SanBerSF-765
❑ 94FloStaLAF-FSL51
❑ 94WesPalBEC-6
❑ 94WesPalBEF-31
❑ 95HarSenTI-33
❑ 96HarSenB-11
❑ 98PacOmeRS-25
❑ 98PacOmeRST1-25
❑ 98PacOnl-446
❑ 98PacOnlR-446
❑ 98PacOnlWC-446

Dehdashtion, Derek
❑ 92RocExpC-14
❑ 92RocExpF-2118

Deidel, Jim
❑ 92YanWIZ7-41

Deiley, Lou
❑ 87AshTouP-23
❑ 88OscAstS-7

Deisel, Pat
❑ 90DodTar-929

Deitrick, Jeremy
❑ 98MarPhiG-9

Deitz, Tim
❑ 86CedRapRT-5
❑ 88ChaLooB-15
❑ 89GreBraB-12
❑ 89GreBraP-1175
❑ 89GreBraS-5

Dejak, Tom
❑ 78DunBluJT-5
❑ 80KnoBluJT-16

DeJan, Mike
❑ 77CinRedT-40

DeJardin, Bobby (Bob)
❑ 88OneYanP-2044
❑ 89PriWilCS-4
❑ 90AlbYanB-14
❑ 90AlbYanP-1039
❑ 90Bes-212
❑ 91AlbYanLD-3
❑ 91AlbYanP-1015
❑ 91LinDriAA-3
❑ 92ColCliF-358
❑ 92ColCliP-16
❑ 92ColCliS-102
❑ 92OPC-179
❑ 92SkyAAAF-45
❑ 92Top-179
❑ 92TopGol-179
❑ 92TopGolW-179
❑ 92TopMic-179
❑ 93ColCliF-1116
❑ 94ColCliF-2957
❑ 94ColCliP-7
❑ 95RocRedWTI-12
❑ 98OneYanG-1

DeJardin, Brad
❑ 88AlaGolTI-8
❑ 91KinIndP-336
❑ 91SydWavF-13

Dejarld, John
❑ 90GreFalDSP-24

DeJean, Mike
❑ 92OneYanC-18
❑ 93ClaFS7-174
❑ 93GreHorC-7
❑ 93GreHorF-880
❑ 94FloStaLAF-FSL18
❑ 94TamYanC-7
❑ 94TamYanF-2376
❑ 95NorNavTI-33
❑ 96ColSprSSTI-10
❑ 96NewHavRB-8
❑ 98Don-268
❑ 98DonGolPP-268
❑ 98DonSilPP-268
❑ 98Fle-92
❑ 98Pac-282
❑ 98PacOnl-243
❑ 98PacOnlR-243
❑ 98PacOnlWC-243
❑ 98PacPlaB-282
❑ 98PacRedT-282
❑ 98PacSil-282

DeJesus, Eddy
❑ 97ButCopKB-5
❑ 97ButCopKK-5

DeJesus, Ivan
❑ 74AlbDukCa-68
❑ 74AlbDukTI-5
❑ 76CubTri-8
❑ 76SSP-76
❑ 77CubJewT-6
❑ 78OPC-158
❑ 78SSP270-256
❑ 78Top-152
❑ 79Hos-88
❑ 79OPC-209
❑ 79Top-398
❑ 80OPC-349
❑ 80Top-691
❑ 81AllGamPI-111
❑ 81CokTeaS-15
❑ 81Don-483A
❑ 81Don-483B
❑ 81Fle-297
❑ 81OPC-54
❑ 81Top-54
❑ 81TopScr-94
❑ 81TopSti-156
❑ 81TopSupHT-24
❑ 82Don-14
❑ 82Don-48
❑ 82Fle-593
❑ 82FleSta-95
❑ 82OPC-313
❑ 82Top-484
❑ 82TopSti-32
❑ 82TopTra-27T
❑ 83AllGamPI-111
❑ 83Don-399
❑ 83Fle-157
❑ 83FleSta-51
❑ 83FleSti-169
❑ 83OPC-233
❑ 83PhiTas-7
❑ 83Top-587
❑ 83TopSti-271
❑ 84AllGamPI-21
❑ 84Don-427
❑ 84Fle-26
❑ 84Nes792-279
❑ 84OPC-279
❑ 84PhiTas-29
❑ 84Top-279
❑ 84TopSti-121
❑ 84TopTif-279
❑ 85AllGamPI-112
❑ 85CarTeal-9
❑ 85Don-204
❑ 85Fle-248
❑ 85PhiTas-11
❑ 85SubDis-28
❑ 85ThoMcAD-28
❑ 85Top-791
❑ 85TopTif-791
❑ 85TopTifT-30T
❑ 85TopTra-30T
❑ 86CarTeal-12
❑ 86Don-449
❑ 86Fle-34
❑ 86Top-178
❑ 86TopTif-178
❑ 88BlaYNPRWL-165
❑ 89BlaYNPRWL-140
❑ 89TolMudHP-774
❑ 89UppDec-355
❑ 90DodTar-178
❑ 90EliSenL-4
❑ 90KisDodD-29
❑ 92SanBerC-27
❑ 92SanBerSF-228
❑ 92YanWIZ8-42
❑ 94OscAstC-28
❑ 94OscAstF-1156
❑ 96KisCobB-3

DeJesus, Javier
❑ 93EliTwiC-9
❑ 93EliTwiF-3411
❑ 94ForWayWC-8
❑ 94ForWayWF-2003
❑ 94MidLeaAF-MDW12
❑ 95Exc-81

DeJesus, Jorge
❑ 78NewWayCT-10
❑ 80BurBeeT-21

DeJesus, Jose
❑ 85Ft.MyeRT-12
❑ 85MexCitTT-19
❑ 86Ft.MyeRP-7
❑ 87MemChiB-9
❑ 87MemChiP-5
❑ 88BasAmeAAB-14
❑ 88BlaYNPRWL-37
❑ 88MemChiB-18
❑ 89BlaYNPRWL-39
❑ 89Don-558
❑ 89Fle-280
❑ 89FleGlo-280
❑ 89OmaRoyC-6
❑ 89OmaRoyP-1735
❑ 89UppDec-769
❑ 90Fle-104
❑ 90FleCan-104
❑ 90FleUpd-42
❑ 90Lea-415
❑ 90OPC-596
❑ 90ProAAAF-294
❑ 90Sco-587
❑ 90Sco100RS-95
❑ 90ScrRedBP-592
❑ 90Spo-131
❑ 90Top-596
❑ 90TopTif-596
❑ 90UppDec-255
❑ 91Don-596
❑ 91Fle-394
❑ 91Lea-200
❑ 91OPC-232
❑ 91PhiMed-12
❑ 91Sco-623
❑ 91Sco100RS-16
❑ 91StaClu-104
❑ 91Top-232
❑ 91TopDesS-232
❑ 91TopMic-232
❑ 91TopTif-232
❑ 91Ult-261
❑ 91UppDec-480
❑ 92Don-300
❑ 92Fle-528
❑ 92OPC-471
❑ 92Pin-172
❑ 92Sco-380
❑ 92Top-471
❑ 92TopGol-471
❑ 92TopGolW-471
❑ 92TopMic-471
❑ 92UppDec-631
❑ 94OmaRoyF-1217
❑ 95OmaRoyTI-7

DeJesus, Malvin
❑ 92NiaFalRC-4
❑ 92NiaFalRF-3329
❑ 93FayGenC-9
❑ 93FayGenF-134
❑ 93NiaFalRF-3396
❑ 94FayGenC-8
❑ 94FayGenF-2154

DeJesus, Tony
❑ 97EveAquG-7
❑ 98EveAquG-5

DeJohn, Mark (Mark Stephen)
❑ 75TidTidTI-8
❑ 80EvaTriT-2
❑ 80VenLeaS-114
❑ 81EvaTriT-13
❑ 83EvaTriT-24
❑ 87SavCarP-26
❑ 88SprCarB-26
❑ 89JohCitCS-24
❑ 90JohCitCS-28
❑ 91LinDriAAA-249
❑ 91LouRedLD-249
❑ 91LouRedP-2932
❑ 91LouRedTI-30
❑ 92LonTigF-648
❑ 92LonTigS-424

DeJonghe, Emile
❑ 39WorWidGV-9

Dejulio, Frank
❑ 80CedRapRT-15

DeKneef, Mike
❑ 91Cla/Bes-171
❑ 91WinHavRSC-17
❑ 91WinHavRSP-496
❑ 92NewBriRSF-440
❑ 92NewBriRSS-481

DeKraai, Brad
❑ 81BurBeeT-21
❑ 82BelBreFr-22

Del Guercio, Ted
❑ 55JetPos-3

Del Juego, Antes
❑ 80VenLeaS-218

Del Toro, Miguel
❑ 99SkyPre-238
❑ 99SkyPre-238
❑ 99SkyPreR-238
❑ 99SkyPreR-238

Dela Cuesta, Clara
❑ 91HawWomS-2

DeLa Maza, Roland
❑ 93WatIndC-5
❑ 93WatIndF-3552
❑ 94ColRedC-6
❑ 94ColRedF-435
❑ 95KinIndTI-8
❑ 96CanIndB-9

Dela, Fernando
❑ 96CedRapKTI-8

DelaCruz, Anthony
❑ 89BurIndS-8
❑ 89Sta-177

DeLaCruz, Carlos
❑ 87DayBeaAP-6
❑ 88UtiBluSP-17
❑ 89SouBenWSGS-12
❑ 90BirBarB-14
❑ 90BirBarP-1102
❑ 93LimRocDWB-32
❑ 96FayGenB-11

Delacruz, Fernando
❑ 96BoiHawB-10

DeLaCruz, Francisco
❑ 87SpoIndP-15
❑ 97NorNav-14
❑ 97TamYan-8

DeLaCruz, Gerry
❑ 77CliDodT-4

DeLaCruz, Hector
❑ 87DunBluJP-938
❑ 88KnoBluJB-8
❑ 88SyrChiC-18
❑ 89SyrChiMB-8
❑ 89SyrChiP-816
❑ 90CMC-346
❑ 90ProAAAF-363
❑ 90SyrChiC-20
❑ 90SyrChiMB-4
❑ 90SyrChiP-583

DeLaCruz, Lorenzo
❑ 93MedHatBJF-3749
❑ 93MedHatBJSP-20
❑ 94HagSunC-6
❑ 94HagSunF-2742
❑ 95KnoSmoF-51
❑ 96KnoSmoB-11
❑ 97BesLimA-9
❑ 97KnoSmo-8
❑ 97SyrSkyCB-8
❑ 98BesPreA-9

DeLaCruz, Marcelino
❑ 92ChaRaiC-9
❑ 92SpoIndC-26
❑ 92SpoIndF-1299

Delacruz, Narcisco
❑ 94MedHatBJF-3675
❑ 94MedHatBJSP-15
❑ 95StCatSTI-10

Delafield, Glenn
❑ 92GulCoaYF-3701

Delafield, Wil
❑ 94GreBatF-487
❑ 95GreBatTI-9
❑ 97GreBatC-6

Delahanty, Ed (Edward J.)
❑ 03BreE10-33

❑ 39PC7AlbHoF-33
❑ 50CalHOFW-25
❑ 53ArtHaloFP-27
❑ 63GadFunC-36
❑ 72FleFamF-38
❑ 72LauGreF-10
❑ 74CapPub-38
❑ 75FlePio-10
❑ 76ShaPiz-33
❑ 77PhiFav-15
❑ 80PerHaloFP-33
❑ 80SSPHOF-33
❑ 83PhiPosGPaM-5
❑ 84GalHaloFRL-33
❑ 87OldJudN-128
❑ 89HOFStiB-31
❑ 90BasWit-70
❑ 94DukCabN-2
❑ 94OriofB-74
❑ 95May-33

Delahanty, Frank (Frank G.)
❑ 08RosComP-77
❑ 09T206-417

Delahanty, Jim (James C.)
❑ 07TigACDPP-19
❑ 08AmeCarE91-73
❑ 09ColChiE-75
❑ 09T206-88
❑ 09TigTaCP-5
❑ 10DomDisP-31
❑ 10NadE1-15
❑ 10StaCarE-10
❑ 10SweCapPP-23
❑ 10W555-21
❑ 11BasBatEU-17
❑ 11HelSta-30
❑ 11PinT-5-152
❑ 11PloCanE-23
❑ 11S74Sil-14
❑ 11SpoLifCW-89
❑ 11SpoLifM-57
❑ 11T205-37
❑ 12ColRedB-75
❑ 12ColTinT-75
❑ 12HasTriFT-28
❑ 12HasTriFT-47
❑ 12PhiCarE-8
❑ 12T207-43
❑ 14CraJacE-81
❑ 14PieStaT-30
❑ 15CraJacE-81

Delahanty, Joseph
❑ 08RosComP-163
❑ 09PC7HHB-11
❑ 12ImpTobC-67
❑ 72ClaCar-95

DeLaHoya, Javier
❑ 89HigSchPLS-13
❑ 90VerBeaDS-10
❑ 90YakBeaTI-2
❑ 91BakDodCLC-18
❑ 92VerBeaDC-22
❑ 92VerBeaDF-2868
❑ 93SanAntMF-2998
❑ 94Bow-178
❑ 94PorSeaDF-672
❑ 94PorSeaDTI-13

DeLaHoz, Mike (Miguel A.)
❑ 61Top-191
❑ 62Top-123
❑ 62TopVen-123
❑ 63IndJayP-4
❑ 63Top-561
❑ 64Top-216
❑ 64TopVen-216
❑ 65BraTeal-4
❑ 65OPC-182
❑ 65Top-182
❑ 66BraPos-10
❑ 66Top-346
❑ 66TopVen-346
❑ 67BraPho-10
❑ 67Top-372

DeLaMata, Fred
❑ 87MiaMarP-21

DeLamaza, Roland
❑ 97BufBis-13
❑ 98OmaRoyM-7

Delancer, Julio
❑ 86KenTwiP-7

DeLancey, Bill (William P.)
❑ 34DiaStaR-81
❑ 35WheBB1-10
❑ 36WorWidGV-15
❑ 74Car193T-8
❑ 92ConTSN-625

Delaney, Art
❑ 25Zee-24
❑ 26Zee-69
❑ 31Zee-102
❑ 32Zee-54

Delaney, Donovan
❑ 94EugEmeC-8
❑ 94EugEmeF-3725
❑ 95WilBluRTI-40
❑ 96HonShaHWB-30
❑ 96WilBluRB-9
❑ 97WilBluR-12

Delaney, Sean
❑ 92AppFoxFI-3105
❑ 93RocRoyC-10
❑ 93RocRoyF-719
❑ 95SprSulTI-7
❑ 96WicWraB-15
❑ 97St.PauS-5

Delano, Mike
❑ 98WilCubM-6

DeLaNuez, Rex
❑ 89EliTwiS-24
❑ 90Bes-118
❑ 90KenTwiB-2
❑ 90KenTwiP-2305
❑ 90KenTwiS-8
❑ 91Cla/Bes-147
❑ 91VisOakC-21
❑ 91VisOakP-1753
❑ 92ClaFS7-199
❑ 92OrlSunRF-2857
❑ 92OrlSunRS-503
❑ 92SkyAA F-216
❑ 93NasXprF-415
❑ 95JacSunTI-8

Delany, Dennis
❑ 79ArkTraT-16
❑ 81ArkTraT-4

DeLao, Mike
❑ 85DurBulT-17
❑ 88FayGenP-1105
❑ 89LonTigP-1367
❑ 90EasLeaAP-EL48
❑ 91FayGenC-30

DeLaRosa, Benny
❑ 77ChaPatT-4
❑ 81BufBisT-6

DeLaRosa, Cesar
❑ 87SpaPhiP-24
❑ 88QuaCitAGS-23
❑ 89PalSprACLC-43
❑ 89PalSprAP-475

DeLaRosa, Domingo
❑ 87PocGiaTB-11
❑ 89CliGiaP-905

DeLaRosa, Elvis
❑ 94BriTigC-9
❑ 94BriTigF-3506

DeLaRosa, Francisco
❑ 89FreKeyS-4
❑ 90CMC-764
❑ 90HagSunB-23
❑ 90HagSunP-1406
❑ 90HagSunS-7
❑ 90ProAaA-3
❑ 90RocRedWGC-29
❑ 91LinDriAAA-453
❑ 91RocRedWLD-453
❑ 91RocRedWP-1895
❑ 92ColCliF-344
❑ 92ColCliP-4
❑ 92ColCliS-103
❑ 92StaClu-61
❑ 92TopDeb91-44
❑ 93ColCliF-1104
❑ 93ColCliP-3
❑ 93LimRocDWB-39
❑ 95LouRedF-272

DeLaRosa, Jesus
❑ 75IowOakT-10
❑ 80KnoBluJT-20
❑ 89PacSenL-57

DeLaRosa, Juan
❑ 88MyrBeaBJP-1175
❑ 89MyrBeaBJP-1458
❑ 90DunBluJS-7
❑ 91KnoBluJLD-355
❑ 91KnoBluJP-1779
❑ 91LinDriAA-355
❑ 92ClaFS7-436
❑ 92KnoBluJF-3002
❑ 92KnoBluJS-380
❑ 92UppDecML-73
❑ 93Bow-519
❑ 93ClaFS7-50
❑ 93ClaGolF-92
❑ 93ExcFS7-241
❑ 93LimRocDWB-28
❑ 93SyrChiF-1010
❑ 94SalLakBF-829

DeLaRosa, Maximo
❑ 86DurBulP-8
❑ 92BurIndC-30
❑ 92BurIndF-1670
❑ 93BurIndC-9
❑ 93BurIndF-3289
❑ 94ColRedC-7
❑ 94ColRedF-436
❑ 94SouAtlLAF-SAL7
❑ 95KinIndTI-9
❑ 96CanIndB-10
❑ 97BufBisB-14

DeLaRosa, Miguel
❑ 96ChaRivTI-9610

DeLaRosa, Nelson
❑ 82AleDukT-25
❑ 83AleDukT-23
❑ 85NasPirT-6

Delarosa, Tomas
❑ 98JupHamQ-19

Delarwelle, Chris
❑ 90Bes-229
❑ 91VisOakC-14
❑ 91VisOakP-1746
❑ 92OrlSunRF-2852
❑ 92ProFS7-96

Delas, Mickey
❑ 88BriTigP-1883
❑ 89FayGenP-1590

Delatori, Keola
❑ 98WilCubM-7
❑ 99TeaBesR-88
❑ 99TeaBesRG-88
❑ 99TeaBesRS-88

Delbianco, Ronnie
❑ 52LavPro-29

DeLeeuw, Karel
❑ 75WatRoyT-9
❑ 76WatRoyT-5

DeLeon, Elcilio
❑ 93LetMouF-4145
❑ 93LetMouSP-5
❑ 94WelPirC-8
❑ 94WelPirF-3487

DeLeon, Gerbacio
❑ 90MadMusB-14

DeLeon, Huascar
❑ 90BasCitRS-5
❑ 91BasCitRC-13
❑ 92BasCitRC-11

DeLeon, Jesus
❑ 87Ft.MyeRP-11
❑ 88AppFoxP-155
❑ 88MidLeaAGS-39

DeLeon, John
❑ 81MiaOriT-7

DeLeon, Jorge
❑ 98MicBatCM-10

DeLeon, Jose
❑ 94BelMarC-11
❑ 94BelMarF-3249
❑ 96JohCitCTI-8
❑ 97PeoChi-7
❑ 98PriWilCQ-5

DeLeon, Jose Chestaro
❑ 81BufBisT-4
❑ 82PorBeaT-1
❑ 84Don-628
❑ 84Fle-248
❑ 84Nes792-581
❑ 84Pir-4
❑ 84Top-581
❑ 84TopTif-581
❑ 85AllGamPI-166
❑ 85Don-308
❑ 85Fle-463
❑ 85OPC-385
❑ 85Pir-5
❑ 85Top-385
❑ 85TopTif-385
❑ 86Don-235
❑ 86Fle-607
❑ 86OPC-75
❑ 86Top-75
❑ 86TopTat-3
❑ 86TopTif-75
❑ 87Don-457
❑ 87Fle-494
❑ 87FleGlo-494
❑ 87Top-421
❑ 87TopTif-421
❑ 87WhiSoxC-7
❑ 88CarSmo-4
❑ 88CarTeal-6
❑ 88Don-59
❑ 88Fle-395
❑ 88FleGlo-395
❑ 88FleStiC-15
❑ 88FleUpd-119
❑ 88FleUpdG-119
❑ 88OPC-23
❑ 88Sco-508
❑ 88ScoGlo-508
❑ 88ScoRoo-7T
❑ 88ScoRooG-7T
❑ 88StaLinWS-5
❑ 88Top-634
❑ 88TopBig-194
❑ 88TopTif-634
❑ 88TopTra-34T
❑ 88TopTraT-34T
❑ 89Bow-431
❑ 89BowTif-431
❑ 89CarSmo-5
❑ 89CarTeal-7
❑ 89Don-437
❑ 89Fle-449
❑ 89FleGlo-449
❑ 89OPC-107
❑ 89PanSti-177
❑ 89RedFolSB-35
❑ 89Sco-115
❑ 89Top-107
❑ 89TopMinL-35
❑ 89TopTif-107
❑ 89UppDec-293
❑ 90Bow-186
❑ 90BowTif-186
❑ 90CarSmo-6
❑ 90Don-536
❑ 90DonBesN-59
❑ 90Fle-248
❑ 90FleAwaW-11
❑ 90FleCan-248
❑ 90Lea-485
❑ 90OPC-257
❑ 90PanSti-334
❑ 90PublntS-217
❑ 90RedFolSB-25
❑ 90Sco-309
❑ 90Spo-76
❑ 90Top-257
❑ 90TopBig-31
❑ 90TopGaloC-2
❑ 90TopMinL-74
❑ 90TopSti-38
❑ 90TopTif-257
❑ 90TopTVCa-11
❑ 90UppDec-697
❑ 91Bow-400
❑ 91CarPol-48
❑ 91Don-128
❑ 91Fle-631A
❑ 91Fle-631B
❑ 91Lea-190
❑ 91OPC-711
❑ 91Sco-221
❑ 91StaClu-455
❑ 91Top-711
❑ 91TopDesS-711
❑ 91TopMic-711
❑ 91TopTif-711
❑ 91Ult-288
❑ 91UppDec-220
❑ 92Bow-265
❑ 92CarPol-3
❑ 92Don-246
❑ 92Fle-576
❑ 92Lea-227
❑ 92LeaBlaG-227
❑ 92OPC-85
❑ 92PanSti-178
❑ 92Pin-341
❑ 92Sco-81
❑ 92StaClu-67
❑ 92Top-85
❑ 92TopGol-85
❑ 92TopGolW-85
❑ 92TopKid-30
❑ 92TopMic-85
❑ 92Ult-565
❑ 92UppDec-458
❑ 93Don-464
❑ 93Fle-487
❑ 93PacSpa-575
❑ 93PhiMed-10
❑ 93PhiStaC-25
❑ 93Ult-438
❑ 94FleUpd-24
❑ 94StaCluT-130
❑ 94StaCluTFDI-130
❑ 94WhiSoxK-6
❑ 95Don-126
❑ 95DonPreP-126
❑ 95Fle-114
❑ 95Pac-85
❑ 95WhiSoxK-5

DeLeon, Julio
❑ 87PorChaRP-20
❑ 97PriDevR-21

DeLeon, Luis (Luis Antonio)
❑ 80ArkTraT-7
❑ 80TacTigT-27
❑ 81ChaLooT-4
❑ 82ChaChaT-14
❑ 82Don-588
❑ 82Top-561
❑ 83ChaChaT-9
❑ 83Don-296
❑ 83Fle-355
❑ 83FleSta-52
❑ 83FleSti-224
❑ 83OPC-323
❑ 83PadTeal-5
❑ 83Top-323
❑ 84Don-162
❑ 84Fle-297
❑ 84Nes792-38
❑ 84PadMot-17
❑ 84PadSmo-6
❑ 84Top-38
❑ 84TopTif-38
❑ 85Don-406
❑ 85Fle-29
❑ 85PadMot-11
❑ 85SubDis-29
❑ 85ThoMcAD-29
❑ 85Top-689
❑ 85TopTif-689
❑ 86Fle-318
❑ 86Top-286
❑ 86TopTif-286
❑ 87BalOriP-8
❑ 87RocRedWP-16
❑ 87RocRedWT-2
❑ 88BlaYNPRWL-67
❑ 88TucTorC-10
❑ 88TucTorJP-8
❑ 88TucTorP-174
❑ 89BlaYNPRWL-73
❑ 89CalCanC-1
❑ 91OriCro-100

DeLeon, Paulo
❑ 73CedRapAT-13
❑ 74CedRapAT-27
❑ 75DubPacT-20

DeLeon, Pedro
❑ 86AshTouP-7
❑ 88OscAstS-8
❑ 89PriWilCS-5
❑ 89Sta-88

DeLeon, Pichy
❑ 84MaiGuiT-11

DeLeon, Rafael
❑ 86Ft.MyeRP-8

DeLeon, Reymundo
❑ 95EugEmeTI-19

DeLeon, Roberto
❑ 89SumBraP-1113
❑ 90Bes-166
❑ 90BurBraB-11
❑ 90BurBraP-2351
❑ 90BurBraS-10
❑ 92SpoIndC-12
❑ 92SpoIndF-1300
❑ 93WatDiaC-11
❑ 93WatDiaF-1774
❑ 94RanCucQC-11
❑ 94RanCucQF-1644
❑ 95MemChiTI-25

Deleon, Santos
❑ 94BelMarC-13
❑ 94BelMarF-3250

DeLeon, Yobanne
❑ 92AppFoxCB-16
❑ 92AppFoxFI-987
❑ 92BasCitRF-3848

Delgado, Alex
❑ 90WinHavRSS-4
❑ 91LynRedSC-16
❑ 91LynRedSP-1206
❑ 92WinHavRSF-1779
❑ 93ForLauRSC-8
❑ 93ForLauRSFP-1599
❑ 93LinVenB-121
❑ 93LinVenB-317
❑ 94VenLinU-215
❑ 95LinVen-47
❑ 95PawRedSDD-9
❑ 95PawRedTI-20
❑ 96-97LinVen-108
❑ 96TreThuB-16
❑ 96Ult-313
❑ 96UltGolM-313
❑ 97ChaKni-12
❑ 97Pac-37
❑ 97PacLigB-37
❑ 97PacSil-37
❑ 98SyrSkyG-9

Delgado, Ariel
❑ 97BoiHawG-6
❑ 98CedRapKTI-7

Delgado, Carlos
❑ 89St.CatBJP-2077
❑ 90ProAaA-184
❑ 90St.CatBJP-3454
❑ 91Cla/Bes-63
❑ 91MyrBeaHC-12
❑ 91MyrBeaHP-2946
❑ 91SouAtlLAGP-SAL37
❑ 92Bow-127
❑ 92ClaBluBF-BC6
❑ 92ClaFS7-90
❑ 92ClaRedB-BC6
❑ 92DunBluJC-20
❑ 92DunBluJF-2003
❑ 92ProFS7-170
❑ 92SyrChiMB-4
❑ 92UppDecML-50
❑ 92UppDecML-53
❑ 92UppDecML-264
❑ 92UppDecMLPotY-PY4
❑ 93Bow-379
❑ 93Bow-693
❑ 93ClaFisN-4
❑ 93ClaGolF-87
❑ 93ClaGolLF-5
❑ 93ClaInsC-1
❑ 93ClaMVPF-10
❑ 93ClaPla&MotYF-PM1
❑ 93ClaPro-2
❑ 93ClaYouG-YG2
❑ 93ExcAllF-6
❑ 93ExcFS7-242
❑ 93KnoSmoF-1252
❑ 93SP-275
❑ 93StaClu-520
❑ 93StaCluFDI-520
❑ 93StaCluMOP-520
❑ 93Top-701
❑ 93TopGol-701
❑ 93TopInaM-701
❑ 93TopInaR-701
❑ 93TopMic-701
❑ 93UppDec-425
❑ 93UppDecGold-425
❑ 94BluJayP-4
❑ 94BluJayUSPC-8D
❑ 94Bow-341
❑ 94Bow-637
❑ 94BowBes-R83
❑ 94BowBes-X105
❑ 94BowBesR-R83
❑ 94BowBesR-X105
❑ 94ColC-4
❑ 94ColChoGS-4
❑ 94ColChoSS-4
❑ 94Don-568
❑ 94Fin-423
❑ 94FinJum-423
❑ 94FinRef-423
❑ 94Fla-117
❑ 94FlaWavotF-A2
❑ 94FleAllR-M3
❑ 94FleExtB-189
❑ 94FleExtBRS-5
❑ 94FleMajLP-9
❑ 94FleUpd-96
❑ 94FUnPac-4
❑ 94LeaGolR-10
❑ 94LeaL-77
❑ 94LeaLimRP-4
❑ 94OPC-100

❑ 94OPCHotP-5
❑ 94Pin-413
❑ 94Pin-SR1
❑ 94PinArtP-413
❑ 94PinMusC-413
❑ 94PinNewG-NG18
❑ 94PinRooTP-1
❑ 94Sco-614
❑ 94ScoBoyoS-45
❑ 94ScoGolR-614
❑ 94ScoRoo-RT102
❑ 94ScoRooGR-RT102
❑ 94ScoRooS-RT102
❑ 94ScoRooSR-SU1
❑ 94Sel-193
❑ 94Sel-RY1
❑ 94SelRooS-RS4
❑ 94SP-41
❑ 94SPDieC-41
❑ 94SPHol-6
❑ 94SPHolDC-6
❑ 94SpoRoo-132
❑ 94SpoRooAP-132
❑ 94SpoRooRS-TR4
❑ 94StaClu-600
❑ 94StaClu-629
❑ 94StaCluFDI-600
❑ 94StaCluFDI-629
❑ 94StaCluGR-600
❑ 94StaCluGR-629
❑ 94StaCluMOP-600
❑ 94StaCluMOP-629
❑ 94StaCluT-168
❑ 94StaCluTFDI-168
❑ 94Stu-27
❑ 94Top-686
❑ 94TopGol-686
❑ 94TopSpa-686
❑ 94TriPla-296
❑ 94Ult-437
❑ 94UltAllR-2
❑ 94UltAllRJ-2
❑ 94UppDec-8
❑ 94UppDecED-8
❑ 94UppDecMLS-MM6
❑ 94UppDecMLSED-MM6
❑ 94UppDecNG-2
❑ 94UppDecNGED-2
❑ 95ActPac2G-4G
❑ 95ActPacF-6
❑ 95ActPacF-65
❑ 95Baz-124
❑ 95BluJayOH-12
❑ 95BluJayUSPC-8C
❑ 95Bow-431
❑ 95ColCho-147
❑ 95ColChoGS-147
❑ 95ColChoSE-52
❑ 95ColChoSEGS-52
❑ 95ColChoSESS-52
❑ 95ColChoSS-147
❑ 95Don-37
❑ 95DonPreP-37
❑ 95Fin-16
❑ 95FinPowK-PK4
❑ 95FinRef-16
❑ 95Fla-314
❑ 95Fle-92
❑ 95Lea-326
❑ 95LinVen-310
❑ 95LinVen-313
❑ 95Pac-443
❑ 95PacGolCDC-20
❑ 95PacGolP-12
❑ 95PacLatD-9
❑ 95PacPri-140
❑ 95Pin-277
❑ 95Pin-390
❑ 95PinArtP-277
❑ 95PinArtP-390
❑ 95PinMusC-277
❑ 95PinMusC-390
❑ 95PinNewB-NB7
❑ 95PinPin-4
❑ 95PinPinR-4
❑ 95PinTeaP-TP2
❑ 95PinUps-US6
❑ 95Sco-214
❑ 95ScoAi-AM12
❑ 95ScoGolR-214
❑ 95ScoHaloG-HG72
❑ 95ScoPlaTS-214
❑ 95ScoRul-SR29
❑ 95ScoRulJ-SR29
❑ 95Sel-56
❑ 95SelArtP-56
❑ 95SelCanM-CM8
❑ 95SelCerF-8
❑ 95SelCerPU-18
❑ 95SelCerPU9-18
❑ 95Spo-104
❑ 95SpoArtP-104
❑ 95SpoDouT-7
❑ 95StaClu-17
❑ 95StaCluFDI-17
❑ 95StaCluMOP-17
❑ 95StaCluSTWS-17
❑ 95StaCluVR-10
❑ 95StaCluVR-11
❑ 95StaCluVRMO-11
❑ 95Stu-43
❑ 95StuGolS-43
❑ 95Sum-28
❑ 95SumNewA-NA9
❑ 95SumNthD-28
❑ 95SyrChiTI-12
❑ 95Top-469
❑ 95TopCyb-263
❑ 95UC3-104
❑ 95UC3ArtP-104
❑ 95UC3CleS-CS7
❑ 95Ult-118
❑ 95UltGolM-118
❑ 95UppDec-38
❑ 95UppDecED-38
❑ 95UppDecEDG-38
❑ 95UppDecSE-199
❑ 95UppDecSEG-199
❑ 95Zen-14
❑ 96BluJayOH-8
❑ 96BowBes-63
❑ 96BowBesAR-63
❑ 96BowBesR-63
❑ 96Cir-94
❑ 96CirRav-94
❑ 96ColCho-352
❑ 96ColChoGS-352
❑ 96ColChoSS-352
❑ 96Don-360
❑ 96DonPreP-360
❑ 96EmoXL-130
❑ 96Fin-B30
❑ 96FinRef-B30
❑ 96Fle-272
❑ 96FleTif-272
❑ 96Lea-156
❑ 96LeaLim-16
❑ 96LeaLimG-16
❑ 96LeaPre-90
❑ 96LeaPreP-90
❑ 96LeaPrePB-156
❑ 96LeaPrePG-156
❑ 96LeaPrePS-156
❑ 96LeaPreSG-46
❑ 96LeaPreSte-46
❑ 96LeaSig-63
❑ 96LeaSigA-57
❑ 96LeaSigAG-57
❑ 96LeaSigAS-57
❑ 96LeaSigPPG-63
❑ 96LeaSigPPP-63
❑ 96Pac-436
❑ 96PacPri-P142
❑ 96PacPriG-P142
❑ 96PinAfi-143
❑ 96PinAfiAP-143
❑ 96ProSta-20
❑ 96Sco-139
❑ 96ScoDugC-A87
❑ 96ScoDugCAP-A87
❑ 96Sel-135
❑ 96SelArtP-135
❑ 96SelCer-77
❑ 96SelCerAP-77
❑ 96SelCerCB-77
❑ 96SelCerCR-77
❑ 96SelCerIP-18
❑ 96SelCerMB-77
❑ 96SelCerMG-77
❑ 96SelCerMR-77
❑ 96SP-181
❑ 96SPx-60
❑ 96SPxGol-60
❑ 96StaClu-346
❑ 96StaCluMOP-346
❑ 96Stu-57
❑ 96StuPrePB-57
❑ 96StuPrePG-57
❑ 96StuPrePS-57
❑ 96Sum-38
❑ 96SumAbo&B-38
❑ 96SumArtP-38
❑ 96SumFoi-38
❑ 96Ult-429
❑ 96UltGolM-429
❑ 96UppDec-470
❑ 96UppDecFSP-FS8
❑ 96Zen-62
❑ 96ZenArtP-62
❑ 96ZenMoz-15
❑ 97BluJayOH-8
❑ 97BluJayS-10
❑ 97BluJayS-4
❑ 97Bow-23
❑ 97BowBes-70
❑ 97BowBesAR-70
❑ 97BowBesR-70
❑ 97BowChr-19
❑ 97BowChrI-19
❑ 97BowChrIR-19
❑ 97BowChrR-19
❑ 97BowInt-23
❑ 97Cir-208
❑ 97CirRav-208
❑ 97ColCho-498
❑ 97ColChoNF-NF33
❑ 97Don-46
❑ 97DonEli-85
❑ 97DonEliGS-85
❑ 97DonGolPP-46
❑ 97DonLim-110
❑ 97DonLim-185
❑ 97DonLimE-110
❑ 97DonLimE-185
❑ 97DonLimENG-185
❑ 97DonPre-35
❑ 97DonPreCttC-35
❑ 97DonSig-36
❑ 97DonSigPPP-36
❑ 97DonSilPP-46
❑ 97Fin-57
❑ 97FinRef-57
❑ 97FlaShoLC-64
❑ 97FlaShoLeg0-64
❑ 97FlaShoLeg1-64
❑ 97FlaShoM-A64
❑ 97FlaShoM-B64
❑ 97FlaShoM-C64
❑ 97FlaShoR0-64
❑ 97FlaShoR1-64
❑ 97FlaShoR2-64
❑ 97Fle-237
❑ 97FleTif-237
❑ 97Lea-25
❑ 97LeaFraM-25
❑ 97LeaFraMDC-25
❑ 97MetUni-182
❑ 97NewPin-119
❑ 97NewPinAP-119
❑ 97NewPinMC-119
❑ 97NewPinPP-119
❑ 97Pac-210
❑ 97PacLigB-218
❑ 97PacPri-73
❑ 97PacPriLB-73
❑ 97PacPriP-73
❑ 97PacSil-218
❑ 97Pin-32
❑ 97PinArtP-PP32
❑ 97PinIns-90
❑ 97PinInsCE-90
❑ 97PinInsDE-90
❑ 97PinMusC-32
❑ 97PinPrePla-32
❑ 97PinX-PSfF-19
❑ 97PinX-PSfFU-19
❑ 97Sco-92
❑ 97ScoArtPWB-92
❑ 97ScoPreS-92
❑ 97ScoShoS-92
❑ 97ScoShoSAP-92
❑ 97Sel-76
❑ 97SelArtP-76
❑ 97SelCom-76
❑ 97SelRegG-76
❑ 97SP-179
❑ 97SpollI-59
❑ 97SpollIEE-59
❑ 97StaClu-204
❑ 97StaCluM-M8
❑ 97StaCluMat-204
❑ 97StaCluMOP-204
❑ 97StaCluMOP-M8
❑ 97Stu-49
❑ 97StuPrePG-49
❑ 97StuPrePS-49
❑ 97Top-92
❑ 97TopGal-149
❑ 97TopGalPPI-149
❑ 97Ult-142
❑ 97UltGolME-142
❑ 97UltPlaME-142
❑ 97UppDec-204
❑ 97UppDec-512
❑ 97UppDecRSF-RS17
❑ 97UppDecTTS-TS15
❑ 98Bow-235
❑ 98BowBes-86
❑ 98BowBesAR-86
❑ 98BowBesR-86
❑ 98BowChr-235
❑ 98BowChrGA-235
❑ 98BowChrGAR-235
❑ 98BowChrI-235
❑ 98BowChrIR-235
❑ 98BowChrR-235
❑ 98BowChrR-34
❑ 98BowChrRR-34
❑ 98BowGolA-235
❑ 98BowInt-235
❑ 98CirThu-170
❑ 98CirThuRav-170
❑ 98CirThuSupRav-170
❑ 98ColCho-265
❑ 98CroRoy-143
❑ 98Don-88
❑ 98DonCol-88
❑ 98DonColE-474
❑ 98DonColL-277
❑ 98DonColP-615
❑ 98DonColS-88
❑ 98DonCruG-49
❑ 98DonCruP-49
❑ 98DonCruR-49
❑ 98DonEli-74
❑ 98DonEliA-74
❑ 98DonEliS-74
❑ 98DonGolPP-88
❑ 98DonPre-65
❑ 98DonPreSeat-65
❑ 98DonPriCD-88
❑ 98DonPriCE-474
❑ 98DonPriCL-277
❑ 98DonPriCP-615
❑ 98DonSig-47
❑ 98DonSigP-47
❑ 98DonSilPP-88
❑ 98E-X2-78
❑ 98E-X2ECFut-78
❑ 98E-X2ECNow-78
❑ 98Fin-23
❑ 98FinNo--23
❑ 98FinNo-R-23
❑ 98FinRef-23
❑ 98FlaShoLeg0-74
❑ 98FlaShoLeg1-74
❑ 98FlaShoLeg2-74
❑ 98FlaShoLeg3-74
❑ 98FlaShoLegM-74
❑ 98FlaShoR0-74
❑ 98FlaShoR1-74
❑ 98FlaShoR2-74
❑ 98FlaShoR3-74
❑ 98Fle-4
❑ 98Lea-78
❑ 98LeaFraDA-78
❑ 98LeaFraF-78
❑ 98LeaFraM-78
❑ 98LeaFraM-78
❑ 98LeaFraMDC-78
❑ 98LeaFraMDC-78
❑ 98LeaFraMS-78
❑ 98LeaFraMZ2-78
❑ 98LeaRS-65
❑ 98LeaRSLHolo-65
❑ 98LeaRSLong-65
❑ 98LeaRTrue-65
❑ 98MetUni-164
❑ 98MetUniPMG-164
❑ 98Pac-218
❑ 98PacAur-94
❑ 98PacInv-75
❑ 98PacInvPBlue-75
❑ 98PacInvSilv-75
❑ 98PacOme-247
❑ 98PacOmeR-247
❑ 98PacOnl-759
❑ 98PacOnlR-759
❑ 98PacOnlWC-759
❑ 98PacPar-113
❑ 98PacParC-113
❑ 98PacParG-113
❑ 98PacParHS-113
❑ 98PacParPB-113
❑ 98PacParR-113
❑ 98PacPlaB-218
❑ 98PacRedT-218
❑ 98PacSil-218
❑ 98Pin-31
❑ 98PinArtP-PP31
❑ 98PinIns-90
❑ 98PinInsCE-90
❑ 98PinInsDE-90
❑ 98PinMusC-PP31
❑ 98PinPer-66
❑ 98PinPerPP-66
❑ 98PinPlu-108
❑ 98PinPreP-31
❑ 98Revo-150
❑ 98RevoSS-150
❑ 98Sco-60
❑ 98ScoRT-178
❑ 98ScoRTSS-PP102
❑ 98ScoRTSSAP-PP102
❑ 98ScoRTSSAP1-PP102
❑ 98ScoSam-60
❑ 98ScoSS-PP23
❑ 98ScoSSAP-PP23
❑ 98SP Aut-194
❑ 98SpollI-29
❑ 98SpollIEE-29
❑ 98SpollIFE-29
❑ 98SPxFin-138
❑ 98SPxFinR-138
❑ 98SPxFinS-138
❑ 98StaCluFDI-120
❑ 98StaCluI-120
❑ 98StaCluOneK-120
❑ 98StaCluPP-120
❑ 98Stu-154
❑ 98StuGPP-154
❑ 98StuSPP-154
❑ 98SyrSkyG-10
❑ 98Top-384
❑ 98TopChr-384
❑ 98TopChrR-384
❑ 98TopDevR-384
❑ 98TopDia-384
❑ 98TopGal-93
❑ 98TopGalGP-93
❑ 98TopGalOPP-93
❑ 98TopGalPPI-93
❑ 98TopGalPPIA-93
❑ 98TopGolLabC1-98
❑ 98TopGolLabC1B-98
❑ 98TopGolLabC1One-98
❑ 98TopGolLabC1R-98
❑ 98TopGolLabC2-98
❑ 98TopGolLabC2B-98
❑ 98TopGolLabC2One-98
❑ 98TopGolLabC2R-98
❑ 98TopGolLabC3-98
❑ 98TopGolLabC3B-98
❑ 98TopGolLabC3One-98
❑ 98TopGolLabC3R-98
❑ 98TopMiniC-384
❑ 98TopSta-13
❑ 98TopStaB-13
❑ 98TopStaG-13
❑ 98TopStaGR-13
❑ 98TopStaS-13
❑ 98TopTek-43
❑ 98TopTekD-43
❑ 98UD3-56
❑ 98UD3-146
❑ 98UD3-236
❑ 98UD3DieCut-56
❑ 98UD3DieCut-146
❑ 98UD3DieCut-236
❑ 98Ult-182
❑ 98UltGolM-182
❑ 98UltMas-182
❑ 98UltPlaM-182
❑ 98UppDec-241
❑ 98UppDecNP-NP30
❑ 98UppDecSF-135
❑ 98UppDecTMT-21
❑ 98UppDecTMTG-21
❑ 99199Fin-214
❑ 99Bow-269
❑ 99BowBes-46
❑ 99BowBesAR-46
❑ 99BowBesR-46
❑ 99BowGol-269
❑ 99BowInt-269
❑ 99CroRoyB-142
❑ 99CroRoyL-142
❑ 99CroRoyOD-142
❑ 99E-X Cen-38
❑ 99E-X CenECFut-38
❑ 99E-X CenECNow-38
❑ 99FinGolRef-214
❑ 99FinRef-214
❑ 99FlaShoLeg1-45
❑ 99FlaShoLeg2-45
❑ 99FlaShoLeg3-45
❑ 99FlaShoLegM1-45
❑ 99FlaShoLegM2-45
❑ 99FlaShoLegM3-45
❑ 99FlaShoR1-45
❑ 99FlaShoR2-45
❑ 99FlaShoR3-45
❑ 99Fle-47
❑ 99FleBri-26
❑ 99FleBri2G-26
❑ 99FleBriBlu-26
❑ 99FleBriGol-26
❑ 99FleMys-27
❑ 99FleMysG-27
❑ 99FleMysM-27
❑ 99FleSta9-47
❑ 99FleVin'-47
❑ 99FleWarT-47
❑ 99KinDis-20
❑ 99MetUni-44
❑ 99MetUniGM-44
❑ 99MetUniPMG-44
❑ 99Pac-439
❑ 99PacAur-197
❑ 99PacAurOD-197
❑ 99PacCroC-295
❑ 99PacCroCPB-295
❑ 99PacInv-148
❑ 99PacInvOD-148
❑ 99PacInvPB-148
❑ 99PacOme-245
❑ 99PacOmeC-245
❑ 99PacOmeG-245
❑ 99PacOmePB-245
❑ 99PacPar-243
❑ 99PacParC-243
❑ 99PacParG-243
❑ 99PacParHoloGold-243
❑ 99PacParHS-243
❑ 99PacParOD-243
❑ 99PacParPB-243
❑ 99PacParRed-243
❑ 99PacPlaB-439
❑ 99PacPri-149
❑ 99PacPriHB-149
❑ 99PacPriHG-149
❑ 99PacPriHM-149
❑ 99PacPriHP-149
❑ 99PacPriRed-149
❑ 99PacPriS-80
❑ 99PacPriS206-80
❑ 99PacPriS206R-80
❑ 99PacRed-439
❑ 99Rev-146
❑ 99RevPremDate-146
❑ 99RevRet-146
❑ 99RevShaSS-146
❑ 99SkyMolM-100
❑ 99SkyMolMX-100
❑ 99SkyPre-123
❑ 99SkyPreR-123
❑ 99SkyThu-210
❑ 99SkyThuRant-210
❑ 99SkyThuRave-210
❑ 99SP Aut-90
❑ 99SP AutHRC-HR12
❑ 99SP SigAuto-CD
❑ 99SPAutHRCDC-HR12
❑ 99SpollI-87
❑ 99SPSig-119
❑ 99SPx-80
❑ 99SPxFinR-80
❑ 99SPxFinS-80
❑ 99StaClu-271
❑ 99StaCluFDI-271
❑ 99StaCluOoaK-271
❑ 99StaCluPP-271
❑ 99ThuSkySupR-210
❑ 99Top-420
❑ 99TopBlaLC1-28
❑ 99TopBlaLC2-28
❑ 99TopBlaLC3-28
❑ 99TopChr-420
❑ 99TopChrR-420
❑ 99TopGal-16
❑ 99TopGalPP-16
❑ 99TopGalPPI-16
❑ 99TopGolL-28
❑ 99TopGolLC1-28
❑ 99TopGolLC2-28
❑ 99TopGolLOtO-28

❑ 99TopMVPP-420
❑ 99TopOpeD-109
❑ 99TopRedLC1-28
❑ 99TopRedLC2-28
❑ 99TopRedLC3-28
❑ 99TopSta-93
❑ 99TopSta'S-37
❑ 99TopSta'SG-37
❑ 99TopSta'SGDH-37
❑ 99TopSta1Foil-93
❑ 99TopStaFoil-93
❑ 99TopStaOS-93
❑ 99UD Cho-154
❑ 99UD ChoP-154
❑ 99UD ChoPCR-154
❑ 99UDHolo-60
❑ 99UDHoloAUsome-60
❑ 99UppDec-224
❑ 99UppDecCf7-14
❑ 99UppDecCf7-78
❑ 99UppDecCLM-C99
❑ 99UppDecCo7CE-14
❑ 99UppDecCo7CE-78
❑ 99UppDecE-89
❑ 99UppDecEFXG-89
❑ 99UppDecEL1-224
❑ 99UppDecEL2-224
❑ 99UppDecM-213
❑ 99UppDecMGS-213
❑ 99UppDecMHFS-213
❑ 99UppDecMSS-213
❑ 99UppDecR-88
❑ 99UppDecRG-88
❑ 99UppDecRP-88
❑ 99Vic-412

Delgado, Ernesto
❑ 96HagSunB-4
❑ 97HagSunB-5
❑ 98DunBluJTI-8

Delgado, Eugenio
❑ 92KanCouCTI-7

Delgado, Geno
❑ 93AlbPolCB-11
❑ 93AlbPolF-2032

Delgado, Jesus
❑ 93LinVenB-254
❑ 95LinVen-188
❑ 96-97LinVen-54

Delgado, Jose
❑ 94DanBraC-6
❑ 94DanBraF-3538
❑ 95MacBraTI-6
❑ 96MacBraB-17
❑ 97DurBulTI-21

Delgado, Juan
❑ 83DayBeaAT-19
❑ 85DomLeaS-86
❑ 86ColAstP-10
❑ 87OscAstP-22

Delgado, Luis (Luis Felipe)
❑ 78SanJosMMC-14

Delgado, Pablo
❑ 89GenCubP-1879
❑ 90HunCubP-3296

Delgado, Richard
❑ 91ElmPioC-19
❑ 91ElmPioP-3265
❑ 91WinHavRSC-29
❑ 93LinVenB-40

Delgado, Roberto
❑ 92CliGiaC-7
❑ 93LimRocDWB-130

Delgado, Tim
❑ 90GenCubP-3045
❑ 90MiaMirIS-4
❑ 91PeoChiC-4
❑ 91PeoChiP-1335
❑ 91PeoChiTI-6
❑ 92WinSpiC-14
❑ 92WinSpiF-1203
❑ 93DayCubC-5
❑ 93DayCubF-852
❑ 93FloStaLAF-30
❑ 93OrlCubF-2778
❑ 94ClaGolF-49

Delgado, Wilson
❑ 95BurBeeTI-1
❑ 96Bow-208
❑ 96BowFoi-208
❑ 96SanJosGB-4
❑ 97ColCho-454
❑ 97PhoFirTI-7
❑ 98Don-276
❑ 98DonGolPP-276
❑ 98DonSilPP-276
❑ 98FreGriG-9
❑ 98LeaRS-220
❑ 98LeaRSLHolo-220
❑ 98LeaRSLong-220
❑ 98LeaRTrue-220
❑ 98PinPlu-159
❑ 98Stu-171
❑ 98StuGPP-171
❑ 98StuSPP-171
❑ 98Ult-297
❑ 98UltGolM-297
❑ 98UltMas-297
❑ 98UltPlaM-297
❑ 99SpoIll-54

Delgatti, Scott
❑ 75ForLauYS-27
❑ 77ForLauYS-22

DelGreco, Bobby (Robert G.)
❑ 52Top-353
❑ 53Top-48
❑ 57Top-94
❑ 60Top-486
❑ 61Top-154
❑ 61TopStaI-53
❑ 62SalPlaC-16
❑ 62ShiPlaC-16
❑ 62Top-548
❑ 63Jel-91
❑ 63Pos-91
❑ 63Top-282
❑ 78TCM60I-259
❑ 83TopRep5-353
❑ 91TopArc1-48

Delhi, Lee
❑ 09ObaT21-83
❑ 09ObaT21-258
❑ 11PacCoaBD-18
❑ 11Zee-8
❑ 12ObaPreT-7
❑ 12Zee-107

DeLima, Rafael
❑ 86KenTwiP-8
❑ 87KenTwiP-6
❑ 88BasAmeAAB-15
❑ 88OrlTwiB-22
❑ 88SouLeaAJ-11
❑ 89PorBeaC-23
❑ 89PorBeaP-222
❑ 90CMC-574
❑ 90PorBeaC-22
❑ 90PorBeaP-191
❑ 90ProAAAF-261
❑ 91LinDriAA-478
❑ 91OrlSunRLD-478
❑ 91OrlSunRP-1861
❑ 92OrlSunRS-504
❑ 93LinVenB-140
❑ 94VenLinU-187
❑ 95LinVen-105
❑ 96-97LinVen-172

Delis, Juan
❑ 57SeaPop-6
❑ 58SeaRalT-5

Deliza, Juan
❑ 77ShrCapT-4

Delker, Edward
❑ 33ButCanV-12
❑ 34DiaMatCSB-42

Delkus, Pete
❑ 88KenTwiP-1398
❑ 88MidLeaAGS-35
❑ 89OrlTwiB-13
❑ 89OrlTwiP-1331
❑ 90CMC-557
❑ 90PorBeaC-5
❑ 90PorBeaP-172
❑ 90ProAAAF-242
❑ 91OrlSunRP-1843

Dell, Tim
❑ 88BatCliP-1674
❑ 89SpaPhiP-1052
❑ 89SpaPhiS-6
❑ 89Sta-54
❑ 90ClePhiS-5
❑ 91StoPorP-3026
❑ 92ElPasDF-3914
❑ 92ElPasDS-205
❑ 93El PasDF-2942

Dell, Wheezer (William George)
❑ 16FleBreD-23
❑ 17ColE13-41
❑ 19Zee-130
❑ 20WalMaiW-12
❑ 21Zee-154
❑ 22Zee-146

Dellaero, Jason
❑ 97Bow-440
❑ 97BowChr-300
❑ 97BowChrI-300
❑ 97BowChrIR-300
❑ 97BowChrR-300
❑ 97BowInt-440
❑ 97HicCraB-10
❑ 97TopSta-123
❑ 97TopStaAM-123
❑ 98BesNumOP-18
❑ 98Bow-124
❑ 98BowChr-124
❑ 98BowChrGA-124
❑ 98BowChrGAR-124
❑ 98BowChrI-124
❑ 98BowChrIR-124
❑ 98BowChrR-124
❑ 98BowGolA-124
❑ 98BowInt-124
❑ 98CarLeaTPQ-18
❑ 98SP MinPE-34
❑ 98SPMin-34
❑ 98StaCluFDI-389
❑ 98StaCluI-389
❑ 98StaCluOneK-389
❑ 98StaCluPP-389
❑ 98Top-249
❑ 98TopChr-249
❑ 98TopChrR-249
❑ 98TopDevR-249
❑ 98TopDia-249
❑ 98TopMiniC-249
❑ 98WinWar-11
❑ 99Bow-165
❑ 99BowChr-165
❑ 99BowChrG-165
❑ 99BowChrGR-165
❑ 99BowChrI-165
❑ 99BowChrIR-165
❑ 99BowChrR-165
❑ 99BowGol-165
❑ 99BowInt-165

Dellamano, Anthony
❑ 96HudValRB-23

DellaRatta, Pete
❑ 96SouOreTI-18
❑ 97ModA'sG-7
❑ 98VisOakG-24

Deller, Bob
❑ 90OneYanP-3388
❑ 91GreHorP-3071
❑ 92Ft.LauYF-2625
❑ 93PriWilCC-6
❑ 93PriWilCF-668

Deller, Tom
❑ 87AncGlaP-6
❑ 89WelPirP-10
❑ 90SalBucS-3

DelliCarri, Joe (Joseph)
❑ 88CapCodPPaLP-16
❑ 89PitMetS-3
❑ 90JacMetGS-9
❑ 90St.LucMS-5
❑ 91LinDriAA-630
❑ 91WilBilLD-630
❑ 91WilBilP-300
❑ 92BinMetF-523
❑ 92BinMetS-53
❑ 93NorTidF-2575
❑ 94TreThuF-2126
❑ 95BinMetTI-25

Dellucci, David
❑ 96FreKeyB-6
❑ 97BalOriP-11
❑ 97BowBay-15
❑ 98ColCho-417
❑ 98ColChoPCR-417
❑ 98CroRoy-6
❑ 98DiaBacP-22
❑ 98DiaMcD-10
❑ 98Don-258
❑ 98DonGolPP-258
❑ 98DonSilPP-258
❑ 98Fle-159
❑ 98LeaRS-212
❑ 98LeaRSLHolo-212
❑ 98LeaRSLong-212
❑ 98LeaRTrue-212
❑ 98MetUni-111
❑ 98MetUniPMG-111
❑ 98PacInvGems-10
❑ 98PacOmeRS-29
❑ 98PacOmeRST4-29
❑ 98PacOnl-36
❑ 98PacOnlR-36
❑ 98PacOnlWC-36
❑ 98SP Aut-26
❑ 98SPxFin-247
❑ 98SPxFinR-247
❑ 98SPxFinS-247
❑ 98Stu-212
❑ 98StuGPP-212
❑ 98StuSPP-212
❑ 98Top-409
❑ 98TopChr-409
❑ 98TopChrR-409
❑ 98TopDevR-409
❑ 98TopDia-409
❑ 98TopMiniC-409
❑ 98TusSidM-26
❑ 98Ult-223
❑ 98UltGolM-223
❑ 98UltMas-223
❑ 98UltPlaM-223
❑ 98UppDec-277
❑ 98UppDecDS-DS34
❑ 98UppDecR-102
❑ 98UppDecRNF-NF2
❑ 99Fle-205
❑ 99FleSta9-205
❑ 99FleWarT-205
❑ 99MetUni-92
❑ 99MetUniGM-92
❑ 99MetUniPMG-92
❑ 99Pac-19
❑ 99PacAur-8
❑ 99PacAurOD-8
❑ 99PacCroC-15
❑ 99PacCroCPB-15
❑ 99PacPar-19
❑ 99PacParC-19
❑ 99PacParG-19
❑ 99PacParHoloGold-19
❑ 99PacParHS-19
❑ 99PacParOD-19
❑ 99PacParPB-19
❑ 99PacParRed-19
❑ 99PacPlaB-19
❑ 99PacPri-7
❑ 99PacPriHB-7
❑ 99PacPriHG-7
❑ 99PacPriHM-7
❑ 99PacPriHP-7
❑ 99PacPriRed-7
❑ 99PacPriS-81
❑ 99PacPriS206-81
❑ 99PacPriS206R-81
❑ 99PacRed-19
❑ 99SkyPre-84
❑ 99SkyPreR-84
❑ 99StaClu-87
❑ 99StaCluFDI-87
❑ 99StaCluOoaK-87
❑ 99StaCluPP-87
❑ 99Top-165
❑ 99TopChr-165
❑ 99TopChrR-165
❑ 99TopMVPP-165
❑ 99TopOpeD-91
❑ 99UppDec-30
❑ 99UppDecBD-5
❑ 99UppDecBDD-5
❑ 99UppDecBDQ-5
❑ 99UppDecBDT-5
❑ 99UppDecEL1-30
❑ 99UppDecEL2-30
❑ 99UppDecM-14
❑ 99UppDecMGS-14
❑ 99UppDecMHFS-14
❑ 99UppDecMSS-14

Delmas, Bert
❑ 09ObaT21-2
❑ 09ObaT21-84
❑ 09ObaT21-259
❑ 10BisCoaLE99-8
❑ 11PacCoaBD-19
❑ 11Zee-9
❑ 12ObaPreT-8
❑ 90DodTar-930

Delmonico, Rod
❑ 95TenVolW-1
❑ 98TenKry-2

DeLoach, Bobby
❑ 87SavCarP-1
❑ 89SavCarP-346
❑ 90FloStaLAS-2
❑ 90St.PetCS-4
❑ 90StaFS7-62
❑ 91KnoBluJLD-356
❑ 91KnoBluJP-1780
❑ 91LinDriAA-356

DeLoach, Lee
❑ 89GreFalDSP-16

DeLoach, Rich
❑ 80QuaCitCT-27

Delock, Ike (Ivan Martin)
❑ 52Bow-250
❑ 52Top-329
❑ 55Bow-276
❑ 56Top-284
❑ 57Top-63
❑ 58Top-328
❑ 59Top-437
❑ 60RedSoxJP-4
❑ 60Top-336
❑ 61Top-268
❑ 61TopStaI-110
❑ 62Top-201
❑ 63Top-136
❑ 79DiaGre-241
❑ 81RedSoxBG2S-14
❑ 83TopRep5-329
❑ 91OriCro-101

DelOrbe, Chico
❑ 75LafDriT-1
❑ 85DomLeaS-211

DeLosSantos, Alberto
❑ 89PriPirS-5
❑ 91Cla/Bes-152
❑ 91SalBucC-5
❑ 91SalBucP-959
❑ 92CarMudF-1192
❑ 92CarMudS-131
❑ 92SkyAA F-62
❑ 93CarMudF-2067
❑ 93CarMudTI-24
❑ 93ClaFS7-132
❑ 93LimRocDWB-138

DeLosSantos, German
❑ 75CedRapGT-5
❑ 76CedRapGT-25

DeLosSantos, Luis
❑ 85Ft.MyeRT-28
❑ 86MemChiSTOS-5
❑ 86MemChiTOS-5
❑ 86SouLeaAJ-9
❑ 87OmaRoyP-25
❑ 88OmaRoyC-22
❑ 88OmaRoyP-1506
❑ 88TriAAAP-30
❑ 88TriAAC-2
❑ 89Don-562
❑ 89DonRoo-33
❑ 89Fle-646
❑ 89FleGlo-646
❑ 89FleUpd-37
❑ 89OmaRoyP-1729
❑ 89PanSti-347
❑ 89Sco-648
❑ 89ScoHot1R-52
❑ 89UppDec-12
❑ 90ClaBlu-9
❑ 90CMC-186
❑ 90Fle-105
❑ 90FleCan-105
❑ 90Hot50RS-14
❑ 90OmaRoyC-11
❑ 90OmaRoyP-70
❑ 90OPC-452
❑ 90ProAAAF-605
❑ 90Sco-659
❑ 90Sco100RS-100
❑ 90ScoRooDT-B4
❑ 90Top-452
❑ 90TopTif-452
❑ 90TriAAAC-2
❑ 91Bow-152
❑ 93EdmTraF-1142
❑ 97GreBatB-10
❑ 98EasLeaTPM-6
❑ 98NorNavQ-8
❑ 98TamYanM-10

DeLosSantos, Mariano
❑ 92AugPirC-14
❑ 92AugPirF-231
❑ 93CarLeaAGF-48
❑ 93LimRocDWB-10
❑ 93SalBucC-6
❑ 93SalBucF-423
❑ 94CarMudF-1571
❑ 95UppDecML-149
❑ 95UppDecMLFS-149
❑ 96CarMudB-2

DeLosSantos, Pedro
❑ 89AshTouP-951

DeLosSantos, Ramon
❑ 75IowOakT-11
❑ 84TacTigC-76

DeLosSantos, Reynoldo
❑ 91MarPhiC-5
❑ 91MarPhiP-3466
❑ 92BatCliCB-8
❑ 92BatCliF-3276
❑ 93SpaPhiC-11
❑ 93SpaPhiF-1066

Delpiano, Marc
❑ 89BurIndS-9
❑ 90WatIndS-7
❑ 93EriSaiC-28
❑ 93EriSaiF-3133
❑ 94HudValRC-27

DelPozo, Roberto
❑ 90SanBerSB-10
❑ 90SanBerSCLC-104
❑ 90SanBerSP-2643
❑ 91PenPilC-23
❑ 91PenPilP-388

DelRosario, Manny
❑ 83MiaMarT-18

DelRosario, Maximo
❑ 85DurBulT-6
❑ 87GreBraB-18
❑ 88GreBraB-17
❑ 89GreBraB-11
❑ 89GreBraP-1161
❑ 89GreBraS-6
❑ 90GreBraP-1123
❑ 90GreBraS-7

DelRosario, Sergio
❑ 83MiaMarT-6

Delsing, Jim (James Henry)
❑ 47SigOil-5
❑ 51Bow-279
❑ 52Bow-157
❑ 52Top-271
❑ 53BowBW-44
❑ 53TigGle-4
❑ 53Top-239
❑ 54Bow-55
❑ 54RedMan-AL24
❑ 54Top-111
❑ 55Bow-274
❑ 55Top-192
❑ 56Top-338
❑ 59Top-386
❑ 83TopRep5-271
❑ 91TopArc1-239
❑ 94TopArc1-111
❑ 94TopArc1G-111

DeLuca, Kurt
❑ 85LitFalMT-16
❑ 86ColMetP-8

Delucchi, Ron
❑ 86PriWilPP-8

DeLucia, Chris
❑ 95GreBatTI-31
❑ 96GreBatB-4
❑ 97GreBatB-5
❑ 97GreBatC-30
❑ 98GreBatM-30

DeLucia, Rich (Richard)
❑ 86BelMarCr-121
❑ 88SanBerSB-8
❑ 88SanBerSCLC-50
❑ 89WilBilP-649
❑ 89WilBilS-5
❑ 90Bes-228
❑ 90ProAaA-134
❑ 90SanBerSB-2
❑ 90SanBerSCLC-88
❑ 90SanBerSP-2626
❑ 90StaFS7-48
❑ 90WilBilS-4
❑ 91Bow-242
❑ 91Don-426
❑ 91DonRoo-2
❑ 91FleUpd-52
❑ 91Lea-222
❑ 91MarCouH-27
❑ 91Sco-728
❑ 91ScoRoo-37
❑ 91TopDeb90-38
❑ 91TopTra-31T
❑ 91TopTraT-31T
❑ 91UltUpd-50
❑ 91UppDec-727

❑ 92Bow-665
❑ 92Don-118
❑ 92Fle-278
❑ 92FleRooS-11
❑ 92Lea-155
❑ 92LeaBlaG-155
❑ 92OPC-686
❑ 92OPCPre-171
❑ 92Pin-388
❑ 92Sco-135
❑ 92Sco100RS-54
❑ 92ScoImpP-8
❑ 92StaClu-511
❑ 92Top-686
❑ 92TopGol-686
❑ 92TopGolW-686
❑ 92TopMic-686
❑ 92Ult-122
❑ 92UppDec-637
❑ 93Don-185
❑ 93Fle-673
❑ 93MarMot-18
❑ 93PacSpa-284
❑ 93StaClu-402
❑ 93StaCluFDI-402
❑ 93StaCluMOP-402
❑ 93Top-152
❑ 93TopGol-152
❑ 93TopInaM-152
❑ 93TopInaR-152
❑ 93TopMic-152
❑ 94IndIndF-1802
❑ 94Pac-567
❑ 96GiaMot-25
❑ 96LeaSigEA-41
❑ 97AngMot-27
❑ 98PacOnl-2
❑ 98PacOnlR-2
❑ 98PacOnlWC-2
DelVecchio, Jim
❑ 77CliDodT-5
DelVecchio, Nick
❑ 92OneYanC-19
❑ 93ClaFS7-175
❑ 93GreHorC-8
❑ 93GreHorF-890
❑ 93SouAtlLAGF-19
❑ 94ClaGolF-82
❑ 94ExcFS7-101
❑ 94TamYanC-8
❑ 94TamYanF-2390
❑ 95Bes-33
❑ 95NorNagUTI-47
❑ 95NorNavTI-47
❑ 95SPML-118
❑ 96ColCliB-9
❑ 96Exc-85
❑ 96SigRooOJTP-T7
Delyon, Gene
❑ 77HolMilT-6
Delzer, Ed
❑ 85MidAngT-22
❑ 86KinEagP-4
Delzine, Domingo
❑ 92GulCoaRSP-16
❑ 94ChaRivC-4
❑ 94ChaRivF-2665
DeMaestri, Joe (Joseph P.)
❑ 52Top-286
❑ 53A'sTeal-8
❑ 54A'STEAl-6
❑ 54Bow-147
❑ 55A'sRodM-10
❑ 55A'sRodM-11
❑ 55A'sTeal-6
❑ 55Bow-176
❑ 56A'sPos-14
❑ 56A'sRodM-3
❑ 56Top-161
❑ 57Top-44
❑ 58A'sJayP-2
❑ 58Top-62
❑ 59Top-64
❑ 59TopVen-64
❑ 60Lea-139
❑ 60Top-358
❑ 61Top-116
❑ 61Yan61RL-22
❑ 76A'sRodMC-8
❑ 79DiaGre-350
❑ 83TopRep5-286
❑ 83Yan196-22
❑ 91YanRinP13-12
❑ 92YanWIZ6-34
Deman, Lou
❑ 95NewJerCTI-6
❑ 96NewJerCB-7
Demaree, Al (Albert W.)
❑ 09SpoNewSM-98
❑ 10OrnOvaPP-4
❑ 14CraJacE-92
❑ 14FatPlaT-13
❑ 14TexTomE-17
❑ 15CraJacE-92
❑ 21Zee-140
❑ 94ConTSN-1216
❑ 94ConTSNB-1216
Demaree, Frank (Joseph F.)
❑ 15SpoNewM-47
❑ 16SpoNewM-45
❑ 31Zee-83
❑ 32CubTeal-4
❑ 32Zee-83
❑ 33Gou-224
❑ 34BatR31-166
❑ 36CubTeal-5
❑ 36DiaMatCS3T2-7
❑ 36R31PasP-31
❑ 36SandSW-12
❑ 37WheBB14-4
❑ 37WheBB7-29C
❑ 38CloFotW-19
❑ 38GouHeaU-244
❑ 38GouHeaU-268
❑ 38OurNatGPP-6
❑ 39PlaBal-34
❑ 40PlaBal-90
❑ 41PlaBal-58
❑ 83Car194T-23
❑ 91ConTSN-212
❑ 96Bro194F-10
DeMars, Billy (William L.)
❑ 48A'sTeal-6
❑ 50Bow-252
❑ 51Bow-43
❑ 52Par-8
❑ 73OPC-486
❑ 73PhiTeal-28
❑ 73Top-486A
❑ 73Top-486B
❑ 74OPC-119
❑ 74Top-119
❑ 75PhiPhiP-12
❑ 76PhiPhiP-9
❑ 78SSP270-45
❑ 82ExpPos-9
❑ 82ExpZel-9
❑ 83ExpPos-8
❑ 83ExpStu-11
❑ 84ExpPos-6
❑ 84ExpStu-3
❑ 86RedTexG-NNO
❑ 87RedKah-NNO
Dembowski, Steve
❑ 77Spo-8718
❑ 79NewCoPT-7
DeMeo, Bob M.
❑ 77ReaPhiT-9
❑ 81OklCit8T-21
DeMerit, John (John Stephen)
❑ 61Top-501
❑ 62SalPlaC-192
❑ 62ShiPlaC-192
❑ 62Top-4
❑ 62TopVen-4
❑ 78TCM60I-129
❑ 80Bra195T-12
❑ 91MetWIZ-93
DeMerit, Thomas
❑ 88VerBeaDS-5
DeMerritt, Martin
❑ 75BurBeeT-4
❑ 76DubPacT-9
❑ 88PhoFirC-25
❑ 88PhoFirP-67
❑ 89PhoFirC-7
❑ 89PhoFirP-1486
❑ 92EriSaiF-1643
❑ 93HigDesMC-27
❑ 93HigDesMF-58
❑ 94PorSeaDF-694
❑ 94PorSeaDTI-4
❑ 95OrlCubF-26
❑ 96OrlCubB-2
❑ 97IowCub-2
❑ 98IowCubQ-3
Demerson, Tim
❑ 90TamYanD-3
❑ 92ForLauYC-21
❑ 92ForLauYTI-6
❑ 92GreHorF-791
❑ 93SanBerSC-7
❑ 93SanBerSF-782
Demery, Larry (Lawrence C.)
❑ 75OPC-433
❑ 75PitPirP-3
❑ 75Top-433
❑ 75TopMin-433
❑ 76OPC-563
❑ 76PirPos-2
❑ 76SSP-564
❑ 76Top-563
❑ 77PirPosP-2
❑ 77Top-607
❑ 78Top-138
Demeter, Don (Donald Lee)
❑ 58Top-244
❑ 59OklTodML-16
❑ 59Top-324
❑ 60DodBelB-14
❑ 60DodJayP-2
❑ 60DodTeal-4
❑ 60DodUniO-4
❑ 60Top-234
❑ 61DodBelB-16
❑ 61Top-23
❑ 62Jel-195
❑ 62Pos-195
❑ 62PosCan-195
❑ 62SalPlaC-170
❑ 62ShiPlaC-170
❑ 62Top-146
❑ 62TopBuc-22
❑ 62TopStal-167
❑ 62TopVen-146
❑ 63Fle-53
❑ 63Jel-180
❑ 63Pos-180
❑ 63Top-268
❑ 64TigLid-4
❑ 64Top-58
❑ 64TopCoi-116
❑ 64TopVen-58
❑ 65TigJayP-4
❑ 65Top-429
❑ 66OPC-98
❑ 66TigVolC-3
❑ 66Top-98
❑ 66TopVen-98
❑ 67CokCapRS-3
❑ 67DexPre-65
❑ 67Top-572
❑ 67TopRedSS-4
❑ 78TCM60I-198
❑ 79DiaGre-324
❑ 79TCM50-237
❑ 90DodTar-179
Demeter, Steve (Stephen)
❑ 60MapLeaSF-5
❑ 61MapLeaBH-6
❑ 77FriOneYW-94
❑ 77SalPirT-13
❑ 79BufBisT-7
❑ 80BufBisT-16
❑ 87SalBucP-29
Demeter, Todd
❑ 85SprCarT-6
Demetral, Chris
❑ 91YakBeaC-7
❑ 91YakBeaP-4252
❑ 92BakDodCLC-8
❑ 93FloStaLAF-46
❑ 93VerBeaDC-1
❑ 93VerBeaDF-2225
❑ 94ClaGolF-184
❑ 94ExcFS7-212
❑ 94SanAntMF-2476
❑ 97AlbDukGS-7
Demetral, Scott
❑ 95OdgRapTI-6
Demetre, Doug
❑ 90OneYanP-3383
Demmitt, Ray (Charles R.)
❑ 09AmeCarE90-1-32
❑ 09ColChiE-76A
❑ 09ColChiE-76B
❑ 09ColChiE-76C
❑ 09T206-89
❑ 09T206-90
❑ 10CouT21-116
❑ 10PeoT21-15
❑ 11PinT-5-119
❑ 11SpoLifM-266
❑ 12ColRedB-76A
❑ 12ColRedB-76B
❑ 12ColRedB-76C
❑ 12ColTinT-76A
❑ 12ColTinT-76B
❑ 12ColTinT-76C
❑ 12ImpTobC-11
❑ 14B18B-16A
❑ 14B18B-16B
❑ 14B18B-16C
❑ 15AmeCarE106-11
❑ 15VicT21-6
❑ 16TanBraE-10
DeMola, Don (Donald John)
❑ 72Dia-10
❑ 75ExpPos-10
❑ 75OPC-391
❑ 75Top-391
❑ 75TopMin-391
❑ 76OPC-571
❑ 76Top-571
DeMontreville, Eugene
❑ 03BreE10-34
❑ 90DodTar-180
Demoran, Joe
❑ 43CenFlo-5
❑ 44CenFlo-4
❑ 45CenFlo-4
DeMorejon, Pete
❑ 96BriWhiSB-14
DeMoss, Bingo
❑ 74LauOldTBS-4
❑ 86NegLeaF-66
❑ 90NegLeaS-6
DeMoss, Dave
❑ 92GenCubC-21
❑ 92GenCubF-1571
DeMott, Ben
❑ 11PinT-5-620
Dempsay, Adam
❑ 87LakTigP-24
❑ 88GleFalTP-932
Dempsey, Con (Cornelius F.)
❑ 48SomandK-3
❑ 49SomandK-4
❑ 52Top-44
❑ 83TopRep5-44
Dempsey, Dalton
❑ 93WatIndC-6
Dempsey, Jack
❑ 32USCar*-22
❑ 66AurSpoMK-2
❑ 87SpoCubG-2
❑ 88KimN18-11
Dempsey, John
❑ 90JohCitCS-8
❑ 91JohCitCC-2
❑ 91JohCitCP-3979
❑ 91SprCarC-12
❑ 91SprCarP-744
❑ 92SavCarC-13
❑ 93WilBluRC-8
❑ 93WilBluRF-1999
❑ 94WilBluRC-5
❑ 94WilBluRF-302
Dempsey, John 70s
❑ 76BurBeeT-4
Dempsey, Mark (Mark S.)
❑ 81ShrCapT-11
❑ 82PhoGiaVNB-14
❑ 83PhoGiaBHN-21
Dempsey, Mike
❑ 25Zee-25
❑ 77BurBeeT-4
❑ 78HolMilT-4
Dempsey, Nick
❑ 98GreFalDG-9
Dempsey, Pat
❑ 77ModA'sC-9
❑ 79OgdA'sT-20
❑ 80OgdA'sT-22
❑ 80VenLeaS-159
❑ 81TacTigT-7
❑ 81Top-96
❑ 82TacTigT-26
❑ 84NasSouTI-6
❑ 85MaiGuiT-14
❑ 86TolMudHP-8
❑ 87PorBeaP-2
Dempsey, Pete
❑ 82SyrChiTI-8
Dempsey, Rick (John Rikard)
❑ 72Top-778
❑ 72TwiPos-4
❑ 74OPC-569
❑ 74SyrChiTI-4
❑ 74Top-569
❑ 75OPC-451
❑ 75SyrChiTI-3
❑ 75Top-451
❑ 75TopMin-451
❑ 75YanSSP-12
❑ 76BalOriP-10
❑ 76OPC-272
❑ 76SSP-438
❑ 76Top-272
❑ 77BalOriP-5
❑ 77Top-189
❑ 78BalOriP-7
❑ 78Top-367
❑ 79BalOriP-5
❑ 79Hos-73
❑ 79OPC-312
❑ 79Top-593
❑ 80OPC-51
❑ 80Top-91
❑ 81AllGamPI-38
❑ 81BalOriP-5
❑ 81Don-113
❑ 81Fle-177A
❑ 81Fle-177B
❑ 81OPC-132
❑ 81Top-615
❑ 81TopSti-38
❑ 82Don-77
❑ 82Fle-163
❑ 82FleSta-146
❑ 82OPC-262
❑ 82Top-489
❑ 83AllGamPI-39
❑ 83Don-329
❑ 83Fle-58
❑ 83OPC-138
❑ 83OriPos-9
❑ 83Top-138
❑ 83TopSti-30
❑ 84AllGamPI-128
❑ 84BalOriP-10
❑ 84Don-413
❑ 84Fle-6
❑ 84Fle-644
❑ 84FleSti-115
❑ 84Nes792-272
❑ 84OPC-272
❑ 84OriEng-4
❑ 84SevCoi-E21
❑ 84Top-272
❑ 84TopRubD-5
❑ 84TopSti-23
❑ 84TopSti-213
❑ 84TopTif-272
❑ 85AllGamPI-38
❑ 85BalOriP-7
❑ 85Don-332
❑ 85Fle-175
❑ 85OPC-94
❑ 85OriHea-4
❑ 85Top-521
❑ 85TopRubD-6
❑ 85TopSti-199
❑ 85TopTif-521
❑ 86BalOriHP-4
❑ 86BalOriP-6
❑ 86Don-106
❑ 86Fle-272
❑ 86OPC-358
❑ 86Spo-147
❑ 86Top-358
❑ 86Top-726
❑ 86TopSti-232
❑ 86TopTat-5
❑ 86TopTif-358
❑ 86TopTif-726
❑ 87Don-294
❑ 87Fle-467
❑ 87FleGlo-467
❑ 87FleUpd-26
❑ 87FleUpdG-26
❑ 87IndGat-24
❑ 87OPC-28
❑ 87RedFolSB-92
❑ 87Top-28
❑ 87TopSti-225
❑ 87TopTif-28
❑ 87TopTra-28T
❑ 87TopTraT-28T
❑ 88DodMot-15
❑ 88Sco-262
❑ 88ScoGlo-262
❑ 88ScoRoo-32T
❑ 88ScoRooG-32T
❑ 89Bow-343
❑ 89BowTif-343
❑ 89DodMot-15
❑ 89DodPol-10
❑ 89DodStaSV-12
❑ 89Don-432
❑ 89Sco-556
❑ 89Top-606
❑ 89TopBig-108
❑ 89TopTif-606
❑ 89UppDec-713
❑ 90DodMot-16
❑ 90DodPol-17
❑ 90DodTar-181
❑ 90Don-557
❑ 90DonLeaS-15
❑ 90Fle-392
❑ 90FleCan-392
❑ 90OPC-736
❑ 90PubIntS-4
❑ 90Sco-414
❑ 90Top-736
❑ 90TopTif-736
❑ 91BreMilB-7
❑ 91BrePol-7
❑ 91Lea-484
❑ 91OPC-427
❑ 91OriCro-102
❑ 91Sco-816
❑ 91StaClu-553
❑ 91Top-427
❑ 91TopDesS-427
❑ 91TopMic-427
❑ 91TopTif-427
❑ 92BalOriP-7
❑ 92YanWIZ7-42
❑ 93BakDodCLC-28
❑ 93OriCroASU-1
❑ 94AlbDukF-858
❑ 94BreMilB-115
❑ 97NorTid-1
❑ 97NorTidB-1
❑ 98NorTidP-8
❑ 98NorTidQ-32
Dempsey, Steve
❑ 93PocPosF-4202
❑ 93PocPosSP-4
❑ 93WatIndF-3553
Dempster, Kurt
❑ 88BilMusP-1828
❑ 89BilMusP-2053
❑ 89GreHorP-426
Dempster, Ryan
❑ 96Bow-140
❑ 96BowFoi-140
❑ 96ChaRivTI-9611
❑ 96KanCouCUTI-4
❑ 97BesAutAS-11
❑ 97BreCouMB-10
❑ 98PorSeaDQ-3
Demus, Joe
❑ 90ElmPioP-13
❑ 91WinHavRSC-11
❑ 91WinHavRSP-491
❑ 92NewBriRSF-436
❑ 92NewBriRSS-482
❑ 92WinHavRSF-1780
DeMuth, Dana
❑ 88T/MUmp-53
❑ 89T/MUmp-51
❑ 90T/MUmp-49
DeMuth, Don
❑ 89SpaPhiP-1056
Demyan, Kirk
❑ 93BelBreCB-4
❑ 93BelBreFl-1702
❑ 94CapCitBC-4
❑ 94CapCitBF-1743
Denbo, Gary
❑ 84CedRapRT-26
❑ 85CedRapRT-16
❑ 86VerRedP-6
❑ 87TamTarP-1
❑ 88CedRapRP-1143
❑ 89GreHorP-404
❑ 90CarLeaA-19
❑ 90PriWilCTI-2

❑ 91ColCliLD-125
❑ 91LinDriAAA-125
❑ 92GulCoaYF-3706
❑ 93GreHorF-904
❑ 94AlbYanF-1458
❑ 96NorNavB-2
Denbow, Don
❑ 94EveGiaC-6
❑ 94EveGiaF-3666
❑ 95BurBeeTI-2
❑ 96BurBeeTI-24
❑ 96MidLeaAB-13
❑ 97Bow-291
❑ 97BowChr-199
❑ 97BowChrI-199
❑ 97BowChrIR-199
❑ 97BowChrR-199
❑ 97BowInt-291
❑ 97CalLeaTP-24
❑ 97SanJosG-4
Denby, Darryl
❑ 83LynMetT-6
❑ 84JacMetT-19
❑ 86GreBraTI-8
Denehy, Bill (William F.)
❑ 67Top-581
❑ 68Top-526
❑ 91MetWIZ-94
Denevi, Mike
❑ 77JacSunT-4
Denkenberger, Ralph
❑ 88WatPirP-17
Denkinger, Don
❑ 76TCMUmp-2
❑ 88T/MUmp-8
❑ 89T/MUmp-6
❑ 90T/MUmp-6
Denman, Brian (Brian John)
❑ 81BriRedST-7
❑ 83PawRedST-5
❑ 84PawRedST-24
❑ 85NasSouTI-5
❑ 86NasSouTI-6
Denman, John
❑ 80ChaO'sP-5
❑ 80ChaO'sW-5
Denman, Ralph
❑ 93IdaFalBF-4043
❑ 93IdaFalBSP-14
❑ 94DanBraC-7
❑ 94DanBraF-3539
Denning, Wes
❑ 96DelShoB-15
Dennis, Brian
❑ 94WilCubC-5
❑ 94WilCubF-3767
❑ 95RocCubTI-24
Dennis, Don (Donald Ray)
❑ 65CarTeal-7
❑ 66OPC-142
❑ 66Top-142
❑ 66TopVen-142
❑ 67Top-259
Dennis, Eddie (Ed)
❑ 78DunBluJT-6
❑ 80KnoBluJT-14
❑ 82KnoBluJT-16
❑ 83KnoBluJT-16
❑ 86KnoBluJP-6
❑ 88St.CatBJP-2014
❑ 91PacSenL-71
Dennis, Les
❑ 96GreBatB-8
❑ 97TamYan-9
Dennis, Michael
❑ 91SydWavF-7
Dennis, Shane
❑ 94SpoIndC-6
❑ 94SpoIndF-3315
❑ 96MemChiB-11
❑ 96RanCucQB-11
Dennison, Brian
❑ 90ArkRaz-30
❑ 91HelBreSP-15
❑ 92BelBreCB-12
❑ 92BelBreFI-399
❑ 94BelBreC-6
❑ 94BelBreFI-94
Dennison, Jim
❑ 90ElmPioP-16
❑ 90WinHavRSS-5
❑ 91LynRedSC-2
❑ 91LynRedSP-1191
❑ 92LynRedSC-24
❑ 92LynRedSF-2900
Dennison, Scott
❑ 91JamExpC-10
❑ 91JamExpP-3551
❑ 92RocExpC-2
❑ 92RocExpF-2121
Denny, Jerry (Jeremiah D.)
❑ 87BucN28-40A
❑ 87BucN28-40B
❑ 87OldJudN-129
❑ 88SpoTimM-8
❑ 88WG1CarG-30
❑ 89EdgR.WG-8
Denny, John (John Allen)
❑ 75OPC-621
❑ 75St.LouCP-7
❑ 75Top-621
❑ 75TopMin-621
❑ 76OPC-339
❑ 76SSP-295
❑ 76St.LouCP-6
❑ 76Top-339
❑ 77BurCheD-14
❑ 77Car5-5
❑ 77CarTeal-5
❑ 77Hos-42
❑ 77OPC-7
❑ 77OPC-109
❑ 77Top-7
❑ 77Top-541
❑ 78CarTeal-4
❑ 78Hos-129
❑ 78RCColC-64
❑ 78Top-609
❑ 79Car5-4
❑ 79Hos-1
❑ 79Top-59
❑ 80IndTeal-6
❑ 80OPC-242
❑ 80Top-464
❑ 81Top-122
❑ 82Don-572
❑ 82Fle-363
❑ 82FleSta-194
❑ 82Ind-10
❑ 82IndWhe-22
❑ 82Top-773
❑ 83Don-237
❑ 83Fle-158
❑ 83PhiTas-8
❑ 83Top-211
❑ 84AllGamPI-76
❑ 84Don-407
❑ 84Fle-27
❑ 84FleSti-56
❑ 84FunFooP-49
❑ 84Nes792-17
❑ 84Nes792-135
❑ 84Nes792-637
❑ 84NesDreT-20
❑ 84PhiTas-18
❑ 84SevCoi-E19
❑ 84Top-17
❑ 84Top-135
❑ 84Top-637
❑ 84TopRubD-18
❑ 84TopSti-19
❑ 84TopSti-122
❑ 84TopSti-177
❑ 84TopSup-4
❑ 84TopTif-17
❑ 84TopTif-135
❑ 84TopTif-637
❑ 85AllGamPI-167
❑ 85Don-111
❑ 85Fle-249
❑ 85Lea-228
❑ 85OPC-325
❑ 85PhiCIG-13
❑ 85PhiTas-9
❑ 85PhiTas-16
❑ 85Top-325
❑ 85TopMin-325
❑ 85TopRubD-17
❑ 85TopSti-119
❑ 85TopTif-325
❑ 86BasStaB-30
❑ 86Don-204
❑ 86Fle-439
❑ 86FleUpd-34
❑ 86OPC-268
❑ 86RedTexG-40
❑ 86Spo-64
❑ 86Spo-132
❑ 86Spo-134
❑ 86Top-556
❑ 86TopTif-556
❑ 86TopTra-32T
❑ 86TopTraT-32T
❑ 87Don-329
❑ 87Fle-199
❑ 87FleGlo-199
❑ 87OPC-139
❑ 87Top-644
❑ 87TopTif-644
❑ 90SweBasG-116
❑ 93UppDecS-12
Densmore, James
❑ 33Zee-111
Denson, Drew (Andrew)
❑ 86DurBulP-9
❑ 87GreBraB-7
❑ 88GreBraB-9
❑ 88SouLeaAJ-17
❑ 89RicBraBC-4
❑ 89RicBraC-18
❑ 89RicBraP-847
❑ 89RicBraTI-5
❑ 90CMC-287
❑ 90ProAAAF-411
❑ 90RicBraC-11
❑ 90RicBraP-266
❑ 90RicBraTI-8
❑ 90TopDeb89-30
❑ 92VanCanF-2729
❑ 92VanCanS-637
❑ 93NasSouF-576
❑ 93TriAAAGF-34
❑ 94NasSouF-1255
❑ 94Pin-241
❑ 94PinArtP-241
❑ 94PinMusC-241
❑ 94TriAAF-AAA5
❑ 95IndIndF-100
Dent, Bucky (Russell Earl)
❑ 74OPC-582
❑ 74Top-582
❑ 75OPC-299
❑ 75SSPPuzB-8
❑ 75Top-299
❑ 75TopMin-299
❑ 76Hos-119
❑ 76OPC-154
❑ 76SSP-143
❑ 76Top-154
❑ 77BurCheD-81
❑ 77Hos-91
❑ 77OPC-122
❑ 77Top-29
❑ 77YanBurK-14
❑ 78Kel-2
❑ 78OPC-164
❑ 78SSP270-24
❑ 78Top-335
❑ 78YanBurK-15
❑ 78YanPhoA-6
❑ 78YanSSPD-24
❑ 79Hos-131
❑ 79OPC-254
❑ 79Top-485
❑ 79YanBurK-14
❑ 79YanPicA-9
❑ 80OPC-33
❑ 80Top-60
❑ 80YanPhoA-5
❑ 81AllGamPI-21
❑ 81Don-465
❑ 81Fle-80
❑ 81FleStiC-110
❑ 81Kel-7
❑ 81MSAMinD-11
❑ 81OPC-164
❑ 81PerAll-12
❑ 81Top-650
❑ 81TopSti-110
❑ 81TopSupHT-62
❑ 81YanPhoA-4
❑ 82Don-209
❑ 82Fle-33
❑ 82Fle-629
❑ 82OnDecD-11
❑ 82OPC-240
❑ 82OPC-241
❑ 82OPC-298
❑ 82Top-240
❑ 82Top-241
❑ 82Top-550
❑ 82YanPhoA-5
❑ 83Fle-566
❑ 83OPC-279
❑ 83RanAffF-7
❑ 83Top-565
❑ 83TopSti-122
❑ 84Don-300
❑ 84Fle-417
❑ 84Nes792-331
❑ 84OPC-331
❑ 84Top-331
❑ 84TopSti-362
❑ 84TopTif-331
❑ 87ColCliP-6
❑ 87ColCliP-1
❑ 87ColCliT-23
❑ 88ColCliC-25
❑ 88ColCliP-25
❑ 88ColCliP-306
❑ 89ColCliC-25
❑ 89ColCliP-25
❑ 89ColCliP-755
❑ 89ColCliP-757
❑ 89SweBasG-72
❑ 89TriAAAP-AAA21
❑ 90OPC-519
❑ 90Top-519
❑ 90TopTif-519
❑ 90TopTVY-1
❑ 92YanWIZ7-43
❑ 92YanWIZ8-43
❑ 92YanWIZA-16
❑ 93RanKee-124
❑ 93UppDecAH-40
❑ 94UppDecAH-18
❑ 94UppDecAH-28
❑ 94UppDecAH1-18
❑ 94UppDecAH1-28
❑ 95RanCra-7
❑ 96RanDr P-6
❑ 96RanMot-28
❑ 97FleMilDM-43
❑ 97FleMilDMR-43
❑ 97RanDr P-6
❑ 97RanMot-28
❑ 98SpoIllWSF-24
❑ 98SpoIllWSFEE-24
❑ 98SpoIllWSFFE-24
❑ 99UppDecCLES-BD
❑ 99UppDecCLESC-BD
❑ 99UppDecCLMS-HR6
❑ 99UppDecR-102
❑ 99UppDecRG-102
❑ 99UppDecRI-BD
❑ 99UppDecRIL2-BD
❑ 99UppDecRP-102
Dent, Darrell
❑ 96AppLeaAB-3
❑ 96BluOriB-10
❑ 97DelSho-10
❑ 98FreKeyM-27
Dent, Eddie
❑ 90DodTar-182
Dent, Elliott
❑ 15Zee-103
Dente, Sam (Samuel Joseph)
❑ 50Bow-107
❑ 51Bow-133
❑ 52Top-304
❑ 52WhiSoxHDP-2
❑ 53BowC-137
❑ 55IndGolS-23
❑ 75TCM195CI-4
❑ 79DiaGre-299
❑ 83TopRep5-304
❑ 85TCMPpl1-35
Denure, Matt
❑ 98BatMucTI-7
DePalo, Jim
❑ 79TCM50-82
DePaolo, Jimmy
❑ 77ForLauYS-25
DePastino, Joe
❑ 93UtiBluSC-9
❑ 93UtiBluSF-3540
❑ 94UtiBluSC-9
❑ 94UtiBluSF-3823
❑ 95MicBatCTI-8
❑ 96SarRedSB-12
❑ 97TreThuB-13
❑ 98Bow-375
❑ 98BowChr-375
❑ 98BowChrGA-375
❑ 98BowChrGAR-375
❑ 98BowChrI-375
❑ 98BowChrIR-375
❑ 98BowChrR-375
❑ 98BowGolA-375
❑ 98BowInt-375
❑ 98TreThuM-12
DePastino, Rich
❑ 87MyrBeaBJP-1456
❑ 88DunBluJS-5
❑ 89MyrBeaBJP-1628
❑ 90DunBluJS-8
DePaula, Sean
❑ 96BurIndB-3
❑ 97WatIndTI-10
❑ 98KinIndQ-6
DePew, Daren
❑ 88BoiHawP-1627
DePrimo, John
❑ 85GreHorT-28
Derdivannis, Kent
❑ 93PirNatI-8
Deremer, Scott
❑ 98MadBlaW-6
Derenches, Albert
❑ 97WisTimR-7
DeRicco, John
❑ 90GenCubP-3043
❑ 90GenCubS-8
Deriso, Phil
❑ 81BatTroT-8
Derksen, Rob
❑ 85BelBreT-25
❑ 86StoPorP-5
❑ 87StoPorP-2
❑ 88CalLeaACLC-18
❑ 88StoPorCLC-201
❑ 88StoPorP-721
❑ 89StoPorB-30
❑ 89StoPorCLC-177
❑ 89StoPorP-385
❑ 89StoPorS-25
❑ 90BelBreS-25
❑ 91BelBreCB-27
❑ 91BelBreP-2119
❑ 92ElPasDF-3938
❑ 92ElPasDS-225
❑ 93El PasDF-2967
❑ 94ElPasDF-3162
❑ 97SarRedS-27
Dermendziev, Tony
❑ 94AshTouC-4
❑ 94AshTouF-1793
Dernier, Bob (Robert E.)
❑ 80CarMudF-15
❑ 80VenLeaS-256
❑ 81OklCit8T-5
❑ 82Top-231
❑ 82TopTra-28T
❑ 83Don-189
❑ 83Fle-159
❑ 83OPC-43
❑ 83PhiTas-9
❑ 83Top-43
❑ 83TopSti-320
❑ 84CubBriPC-4S
❑ 84CubChiT-10
❑ 84CubSev-20
❑ 84CubUno-2
❑ 84Don-541
❑ 84Fle-28
❑ 84FleUpd-31
❑ 84FunFooP-127
❑ 84Nes792-358
❑ 84OPC-358
❑ 84Top-358
❑ 84TopTif-358
❑ 84TopTra-31T
❑ 84TopTraT-31T
❑ 85AllGamPI-140
❑ 85CubLioP-7
❑ 85CubSev-20
❑ 85Don-510
❑ 85Fle-55
❑ 85Lea-57
❑ 85OPC-334
❑ 85Top-589
❑ 85TopMin-589
❑ 85TopSti-38
❑ 85TopTif-589
❑ 86BasStaB-31
❑ 86CubGat-20
❑ 86CubUno-5
❑ 86Don-266
❑ 86Fle-365
❑ 86Lea-139
❑ 86MSAJayPCD-4
❑ 86OPC-188
❑ 86Top-188
❑ 86TopSti-63
❑ 86TopTif-188
❑ 87CubCan-7
❑ 87CubDavB-20
❑ 87Don-146
❑ 87DonOpeD-68
❑ 87Fle-559
❑ 87FleGlo-559
❑ 87OPC-138
❑ 87Top-715
❑ 87TopTif-715
❑ 88Don-392
❑ 88Fle-417
❑ 88FleGlo-417
❑ 88OPC-183
❑ 88PhiTas-8
❑ 88Sco-451
❑ 88ScoGlo-451
❑ 88ScoRoo-45T
❑ 88ScoRooG-45T
❑ 88StaLinCu-3
❑ 88StaLinPh-7
❑ 88Top-642
❑ 88TopTif-642
❑ 89Don-430
❑ 89Fle-565
❑ 89FleGlo-565
❑ 89PanSti-155
❑ 89PhiTas-5
❑ 89Sco-357
❑ 89Top-418
❑ 89TopBig-265
❑ 89TopTif-418
❑ 89UppDec-340
❑ 90OPC-204
❑ 90PubIntS-235
❑ 90Top-204
❑ 90TopTif-204
❑ 93MCIAmb-12
Derosa, Jeff
❑ 93ButCopKSP-5
DeRosa, Mark
❑ 96EugEmeB-7
❑ 97CalLeaATI-30
❑ 97CarLeaTP-21
❑ 97DurBulTI-22
❑ 98FleUpd-U52
❑ 98GreBraG-7
❑ 99BowBes-134
❑ 99BowBesAR-134
❑ 99BowBesR-134
❑ 99Fle-83
❑ 99FleSta9-83
❑ 99FleWarT-83
❑ 99PacOme-19
❑ 99PacOmeC-19
❑ 99PacOmeG-19
❑ 99PacOmePB-19
❑ 99Top-426
❑ 99TopChr-426
❑ 99TopChrR-426
❑ 99TopMVPP-426
DeRosa, Tom
❑ 77NewCoPT-9
❑ 78BurBeeT-8
DeRosa, Tony
❑ 75ForLauYS-9
❑ 80SyrChiTI-8
❑ 81SyrChiT-24
DeRosso, Tony
❑ 95MicBatCTI-9
❑ 96HilStaHWB-25
❑ 96SarRedSB-13
❑ 97TreThuB-14
Derotal, Francisco
❑ 94SpoIndC-7
❑ 94SpoIndF-3335
❑ 95RanCucQT-12
Derr, Jason
❑ 90GreFalDSP-15
Derrick, Claud (Claud Lester)
❑ 12T207-44
Derrick, Fred
❑ 13Zee-54
❑ 14Zee-56
❑ 15Zee-58
❑ 16Zee-48
Derringer, Paul
❑ 31CarMet-7
❑ 34BabRutG-15
❑ 34BatR31-190
❑ 34ButPreR-15
❑ 34DiaMatCSB-43

❑ 34Gou-84
❑ 35DiaMatCS3T1-45
❑ 35ExhFou-4
❑ 36ExhFou-4
❑ 36GouBWR-11
❑ 36GouWidPPR-A26
❑ 36NatChiFPR-23
❑ 36R31Pre-L1
❑ 36SandSW-13
❑ 36WorWidGV-66
❑ 37ExhFou-4
❑ 37GouThuMR-9
❑ 38BasTabP-5
❑ 38ExhFou-4
❑ 38GouFliMR-9A
❑ 38GouFliMR-9B
❑ 38RedOraW-8
❑ 39ExhSal-11
❑ 39GouPreR303A-11
❑ 39OrcPhoAP-6
❑ 39PlaBal-15
❑ 39RedTeal-6
❑ 39WorWidGTP-11
❑ 39WorWidGV-10
❑ 40PlaBal-74
❑ 40WheM4-7C
❑ 40WheM4-8B
❑ 41DouPlaR-7
❑ 41HarHarW-5
❑ 41PlaBal-4
❑ 43CubTeal-6
❑ 44CubTeal-5
❑ 60Fle-43
❑ 61Fle-20
❑ 77CinRedT-42
❑ 77GalGloG-74
❑ 77RedCarP-18
❑ 80PacLeg-113
❑ 82OhiHaloF-55
❑ 83TCMPla1945-23
❑ 85BigLeaC3-82
❑ 86RedGreT-3
❑ 86SpoDecG-14
❑ 91ConTSN-213

Derrington, Jim (Chas. J.)
❑ 58Top-129

Derryberry, Tim
❑ 82RocRedWT-9

Dersin, Eric
❑ 86AlbYanT-14

Dertli, Chuck
❑ 87WinSpiP-21

DeSa, Joe (Joseph)
❑ 79ArkTraT-10
❑ 82LouRedE-6
❑ 83LouRedR-7
❑ 85WhiSoxC-20
❑ 86BufBisP-10
❑ 86DeSCom-1
❑ 86Don-546
❑ 86Top-313
❑ 86TopTif-313

Desabrais, Mark D.
❑ 96IdaFalB-6

DeSalvo, Steve
❑ 85Ft.MyeRT-22
❑ 96GreBraTI-GM

DeSantis, Dominic
❑ 91MarPhiC-24
❑ 91MarPhiP-3446
❑ 92SpaPhiC-9
❑ 92SpaPhiF-1258
❑ 93ClePhiC-6
❑ 93ClePhiF-2678
❑ 94ClePhiF-2520

DeSanto, Tom
❑ 79ElmPioRST-27

DeSapio, Jim
❑ 88AubAstP-1968
❑ 89AubAstP-2172

Desautels, Gene (Eugene A.)
❑ 34DiaMatCSB-44
❑ 38CloFotW-20
❑ 39PlaBal-116
❑ 40PlaBal-28
❑ 53MotCoo-60
❑ 79DiaGre-387

Deschenes, Marc
❑ 95WatIndTI-12
❑ 98AkrAerM-9

DeSensi, Craig
❑ 95ButCopKtl-28

Desert, Harry
❑ 52Par-92

Deshaies, Jim
❑ 85ColCliP-8
❑ 85ColCliT-23
❑ 85IntLeaAT-34
❑ 85YanTCMP-11
❑ 86AstMilL-6
❑ 86AstPol-24
❑ 86DonHig-45
❑ 86DonRoo-34
❑ 86FleUpd-35
❑ 86SpoRoo-15
❑ 87AstMot-23
❑ 87AstPol-19
❑ 87ClaUpdY-137
❑ 87Don-184
❑ 87Fle-56
❑ 87FleGlo-56
❑ 87FleMin-31
❑ 87Lea-255
❑ 87Spo-156
❑ 87SpoTeaP-8
❑ 87Top-2
❑ 87Top-167
❑ 87TopGloS-20
❑ 87TopSti-1
❑ 87TopTif-2
❑ 87TopTif-167
❑ 87ToyRoo-9
❑ 88AstMot-23
❑ 88AstPol-9
❑ 88Don-85
❑ 88DonBasB-94
❑ 88Fle-446
❑ 88FleGlo-446
❑ 88Lea-96
❑ 88OPC-24
❑ 88PanSti-287
❑ 88Sco-354
❑ 88ScoGlo-354
❑ 88Spo-190
❑ 88Top-24
❑ 88TopSti-27
❑ 88TopTif-24
❑ 89AstLenH-11
❑ 89AstMot-22
❑ 89AstSmo-12
❑ 89Bow-320
❑ 89BowTif-320
❑ 89Don-241
❑ 89DonBasB-120
❑ 89Fle-356
❑ 89FleGlo-356
❑ 89OPC-341
❑ 89Sco-546
❑ 89Top-341
❑ 89TopBig-29
❑ 89TopTif-341
❑ 89UppDec-76
❑ 90AstLenH-12
❑ 90AstMot-12
❑ 90Bow-70
❑ 90BowTif-70
❑ 90Don-7
❑ 90Don-187
❑ 90DonBesN-4
❑ 90DonSupD-7
❑ 90Fle-229
❑ 90FleCan-229
❑ 90Lea-168
❑ 90OPC-225
❑ 90PanSti-267
❑ 90PubIntS-93
❑ 90RedFolSB-26
❑ 90Sco-154
❑ 90Spo-32
❑ 90Top-225
❑ 90TopBig-212
❑ 90TopSti-21
❑ 90TopTif-225
❑ 90UppDec-221
❑ 91AstMot-9
❑ 91Bow-541
❑ 91Don-652
❑ 91Fle-506
❑ 91Lea-49
❑ 91OPC-782
❑ 91PanSti-11
❑ 91Sco-193
❑ 91StaClu-262
❑ 91Stu-175
❑ 91Top-782
❑ 91TopDesS-782
❑ 91TopMic-782
❑ 91TopTif-782
❑ 91Ult-137
❑ 91UppDec-208
❑ 92Don-515
❑ 92LasVegSF-2791
❑ 92OPC-415
❑ 92PadPolD-5
❑ 92Sco-364
❑ 92Top-415
❑ 92TopGol-415
❑ 92TopGolW-415
❑ 92TopMic-415
❑ 92UppDec-297
❑ 92YanWIZ8-44
❑ 93Fla-234
❑ 93Fle-520
❑ 93FleFinE-234
❑ 93Lea-522
❑ 93Ult-580
❑ 93UppDec-648
❑ 93UppDecGold-648
❑ 94ColC-91
❑ 94ColC-437
❑ 94ColChoGS-91
❑ 94ColChoGS-437
❑ 94ColChoSS-91
❑ 94ColChoSS-437
❑ 94Fin-190
❑ 94FinRef-190
❑ 94Pin-301
❑ 94PinArtP-301
❑ 94PinMusC-301
❑ 95Pac-246
❑ 95ScrRedBTI-6

DeShields, Delino
❑ 88MidLeaAGS-44
❑ 88OPC-88
❑ 88RocExpLC-10
❑ 89BasAmeAPB-AA15
❑ 89JacExpB-15
❑ 89JacExpP-152
❑ 89SouLeaAJ-5
❑ 90Bow-119
❑ 90BowTif-119
❑ 90ClaBlu-55
❑ 90ClaYel-T95
❑ 90Don-42
❑ 90DonBesN-116
❑ 90DonLeaS-47
❑ 90DonRoo-6
❑ 90ExpPos-6
❑ 90Fle-653
❑ 90FleCan-653
❑ 90FleUpd-27
❑ 90Lea-193
❑ 90OPC-224
❑ 90Sco-645
❑ 90ScoYouS2-3
❑ 90Top-224
❑ 90TopBig-231
❑ 90TopMag-22
❑ 90TopTif-224
❑ 90UppDec-702
❑ 90UppDec-746
❑ 90UppDecS-2
❑ 91Baz-14
❑ 91Bow-445
❑ 91CadEllD-16
❑ 91Cla1-T61
❑ 91Cla2-T71
❑ 91ClaGam-134
❑ 91Don-11
❑ 91Don-555
❑ 91DonBonC-BC16
❑ 91DonSupD-11
❑ 91Fle-228
❑ 91Lea-139
❑ 91MajLeaCP-78
❑ 91OPC-432
❑ 91OPCPre-34
❑ 91PanFreS-140
❑ 91PanSti-69
❑ 91PosCan-1
❑ 91RedFolS-27
❑ 91Sco-545
❑ 91Sco100RS-55
❑ 91StaClu-194
❑ 91StaCluCM-6
❑ 91StaCluP-11
❑ 91StaPinB-13
❑ 91Stu-195
❑ 91Top-432
❑ 91TopCraJ2-35
❑ 91TopDeb90-39
❑ 91TopDesS-432
❑ 91TopMic-432
❑ 91TopRoo-8
❑ 91TopTif-432
❑ 91TopTriH-N6
❑ 91ToyRoo-7
❑ 91Ult-200
❑ 91UppDec-364
❑ 92Bow-47
❑ 92Cla2-T34
❑ 92ClaGam-38
❑ 92Don-277
❑ 92ExpDonD-6
❑ 92ExpPos-10
❑ 92Fle-476
❑ 92Hig5-57
❑ 92Lea-138
❑ 92LeaBlaG-138
❑ 92OPC-515
❑ 92OPCPre-163
❑ 92PanSti-203
❑ 92Pin-24
❑ 92PinTea2-22
❑ 92RedFolS-32
❑ 92Sco-16
❑ 92ScoCokD-8
❑ 92StaClu-505
❑ 92Stu-54
❑ 92Top-515
❑ 92TopGol-515
❑ 92TopGolW-515
❑ 92TopKid-9
❑ 92TopMic-515
❑ 92TriPla-209
❑ 92Ult-220
❑ 92UppDec-36
❑ 92UppDec-167
❑ 92UppDecF-4
❑ 92UppDecFG-4
❑ 93Bow-424
❑ 93ClaGam-25
❑ 93DiaMar-30
❑ 93Don-564
❑ 93DurPowP2-22
❑ 93ExpColP7-4
❑ 93ExpDonM-3
❑ 93Fin-168
❑ 93FinRef-168
❑ 93Fla-81
❑ 93Fle-74
❑ 93FleAll-NL2
❑ 93FleFruotL-15
❑ 93FunPac-94
❑ 93HumDumC-35
❑ 93Kra-21
❑ 93Lea-268
❑ 93LeaGolA-R5
❑ 93OPC-183
❑ 93OPCPre-7
❑ 93PacSpa-183
❑ 93PanSti-226
❑ 93Pin-121
❑ 93Pin-302
❑ 93PinTea2-12
❑ 93PinTeaP-5
❑ 93RedFolS-23
❑ 93Sco-145
❑ 93Sel-43
❑ 93SelStaL-59
❑ 93SP-102
❑ 93StaClu-78
❑ 93StaCluFDI-78
❑ 93StaCluMOP-78
❑ 93StaCluMP-2
❑ 93Stu-150
❑ 93Top-368
❑ 93TOPBLAG-5
❑ 93TopGol-368
❑ 93TopInaM-368
❑ 93TopInaR-368
❑ 93TopMic-368
❑ 93Toy-61
❑ 93TriPla-102
❑ 93Ult-66
❑ 93UppDec-142
❑ 93UppDec-454
❑ 93UppDec-481
❑ 93UppDecGold-142
❑ 93UppDecGold-454
❑ 93UppDecGold-481
❑ 93UppDecIC-WI10
❑ 93UppDecICJ-WI10
❑ 93USPlaCA-7H
❑ 94Bow-454
❑ 94BowBes-R39
❑ 94BowBesR-R39
❑ 94ColC-92
❑ 94ColC-524
❑ 94ColChoGS-92
❑ 94ColChoGS-524
❑ 94ColChoSS-92
❑ 94ColChoSS-524
❑ 94DodDaiN-6
❑ 94DodMot-3
❑ 94DodPol-6
❑ 94Don-350
❑ 94DonSpeE-350
❑ 94Fin-270
❑ 94FinRef-270
❑ 94Fla-395
❑ 94Fle-535
❑ 94FleExtB-286
❑ 94FleUpd-149
❑ 94FUnPac-94
❑ 94Kra-19
❑ 94Lea-277
❑ 94LeaL-117
❑ 94OPC-59
❑ 94Pac-377
❑ 94PanSti-209
❑ 94Pin-147
❑ 94PinArtP-147
❑ 94PinMusC-147
❑ 94ProMag-68
❑ 94Sco-38
❑ 94ScoGolR-38
❑ 94ScoRoo-RT6
❑ 94ScoRooCP-CP9
❑ 94ScoRooGR-RT6
❑ 94ScoRooS-RT6
❑ 94Sel-227
❑ 94SP-76
❑ 94SPDieC-76
❑ 94SpoRoo-6
❑ 94SpoRooAP-6
❑ 94StaClu-549
❑ 94StaCluFDI-549
❑ 94StaCluGR-549
❑ 94StaCluMOP-549
❑ 94Stu-67
❑ 94Top-109
❑ 94TopGol-109
❑ 94TopSpa-109
❑ 94TopTra-42T
❑ 94TriPla-83
❑ 94Ult-515
❑ 94UppDec-465
❑ 94UppDecED-465
❑ 94USPlaCA-4H
❑ 95Baz-39
❑ 95Bow-332
❑ 95ColCho-218
❑ 95ColChoGS-218
❑ 95ColChoSE-88
❑ 95ColChoSEGS-88
❑ 95ColChoSESS-88
❑ 95ColChoSS-218
❑ 95DodMot-9
❑ 95DodPol-7
❑ 95Don-71
❑ 95DonPreP-71
❑ 95DonTopotO-204
❑ 95Fin-74
❑ 95FinRef-74
❑ 95Fla-153
❑ 95Fle-538
❑ 95Lea-154
❑ 95LeaLim-161
❑ 95Pac-215
❑ 95PanSti-42
❑ 95Pin-102
❑ 95PinArtP-102
❑ 95PinMusC-102
❑ 95Sco-99
❑ 95ScoGolR-99
❑ 95ScoHaloG-HG39
❑ 95ScoPlaTS-99
❑ 95Sel-30
❑ 95SelArtP-30
❑ 95SP-68
❑ 95Spo-17
❑ 95SpoArtP-17
❑ 95SPSil-68
❑ 95StaClu-467
❑ 95StaCluMOP-467
❑ 95StaCluSTDW-D467
❑ 95StaCluSTWS-467
❑ 95StaCluVR-255
❑ 95StaCluVRMO-255
❑ 95Stu-90
❑ 95Top-9
❑ 95TopCyb-7
❑ 95TopEmb-53
❑ 95TopEmbGI-53
❑ 95Ult-395
❑ 95UltGolM-395
❑ 95UppDec-72
❑ 95UppDecED-72
❑ 95UppDecEDG-72
❑ 96ColCho-581
❑ 96ColChoGS-581
❑ 96ColChoSS-581
❑ 96DodFle-5
❑ 96DodMot-6
❑ 96DodPol-10
❑ 96Don-255
❑ 96DonPreP-255
❑ 96EmoXL-206
❑ 96Fin-B96
❑ 96FinRef-B96
❑ 96Fla-290
❑ 96Fle-431
❑ 96FleTif-431
❑ 96Lea-3
❑ 96LeaPrePB-3
❑ 96LeaPrePG-3
❑ 96LeaPrePS-3
❑ 96Pac-101
❑ 96ProSta-44
❑ 96Sco-446
❑ 96StaClu-50
❑ 96StaCluEPB-50
❑ 96StaCluEPG-50
❑ 96StaCluEPS-50
❑ 96StaCluMOP-50
❑ 96Stu-133
❑ 96StuPrePB-133
❑ 96StuPrePG-133
❑ 96StuPrePS-133
❑ 96Top-312
❑ 96Ult-495
❑ 96UltGolM-495
❑ 96UppDec-356
❑ 97CarPol-4
❑ 97Cir-56
❑ 97CirRav-56
❑ 97ColCho-438
❑ 97DodSco-4
❑ 97DodScoPl-4
❑ 97DodScoPr-4
❑ 97Don-130
❑ 97Don-285
❑ 97DonGolPP-130
❑ 97DonGolPP-285
❑ 97DonSilPP-130
❑ 97DonSilPP-285
❑ 97DonTea-163
❑ 97DonTeaSPE-163
❑ 97Fin-304
❑ 97FinEmb-304
❑ 97FinEmbR-304
❑ 97FinRef-304
❑ 97Fle-360
❑ 97Fle-636
❑ 97FleTif-360
❑ 97FleTif-636
❑ 97Lea-239
❑ 97LeaFraM-239
❑ 97LeaFraMDC-239
❑ 97Pac-329
❑ 97PacLigB-329
❑ 97PacSil-329
❑ 97Pin-95
❑ 97PinArtP-PP95
❑ 97PinMusC-95
❑ 97PinPrePla-95
❑ 97Sco-132
❑ 97Sco-343
❑ 97ScoArtPWB-132
❑ 97ScoArtPWB-343
❑ 97ScoPreS-132
❑ 97ScoResC-343
❑ 97ScoShoS-132
❑ 97ScoShoS-343
❑ 97ScoShoSAP-132
❑ 97ScoShoSAP-343
❑ 97StaClu-114
❑ 97StaCluMOP-114
❑ 97Top-285
❑ 97Ult-322
❑ 97UltGolME-322
❑ 97UltPlaME-322
❑ 98Bow-247
❑ 98BowChr-247
❑ 98BowChrGA-247
❑ 98BowChrGAR-247
❑ 98BowChrI-247
❑ 98BowChrIR-247
❑ 98BowChrR-247
❑ 98BowGolA-247
❑ 98BowInt-247
❑ 98CarScoP-12
❑ 98CirThu-227

❑ 98CirThuRav-227
❑ 98CirThuSupRav-227
❑ 98ColCho-476
❑ 98CroRoy-112
❑ 98Don-193
❑ 98DonColL-238
❑ 98DonGolPP-193
❑ 98DonPriCL-238
❑ 98DonSilPP-193
❑ 98Fin-107
❑ 98FinNo--107
❑ 98FinNo-R-107
❑ 98FinRef-107
❑ 98Fle-213
❑ 98Lea-38
❑ 98LeaFraDA-38
❑ 98LeaFraF-38
❑ 98LeaFraM-38
❑ 98LeaFraM-38
❑ 98LeaFraMDC-38
❑ 98LeaFraMDC-38
❑ 98LeaFraMZ2-38
❑ 98LeaRS-119
❑ 98LeaRSLHolo-119
❑ 98LeaRSLong-119
❑ 98LeaRTrue-119
❑ 98MetUni-138
❑ 98MetUniPMG-138
❑ 98Pac-407
❑ 98PacAur-181
❑ 98PacInvGems-202
❑ 98PacInvTeam-23
❑ 98PacOme-195
❑ 98PacOmeR-195
❑ 98PacOnl-608
❑ 98PacOnlR-608
❑ 98PacOnlWC-608
❑ 98PacPlaB-407
❑ 98PacRedT-407
❑ 98PacSil-407
❑ 98PinSna-SLC6
❑ 98PinSna-SLC8
❑ 98Revo-117
❑ 98RevoSS-117
❑ 98Sco-178
❑ 98ScoCar-12
❑ 98ScoRT-158
❑ 98ScoSS-PP136
❑ 98ScoSSAP-PP136
❑ 98SkyDugAFF-FF9
❑ 98SP Aut-159
❑ 98SPxFin-121
❑ 98SPxFinR-121
❑ 98SPxFinS-121
❑ 98StaCluFDI-48
❑ 98StaCluI-48
❑ 98StaCluOneK-48
❑ 98StaCluPP-48
❑ 98Stu-31
❑ 98StuGPP-31
❑ 98StuSPP-31
❑ 98Top-400
❑ 98TopChr-400
❑ 98TopChrR-400
❑ 98TopDevR-400
❑ 98TopDia-400
❑ 98TopGal-136
❑ 98TopGalGP-136
❑ 98TopGalOPP-136
❑ 98TopGalPPI-136
❑ 98TopGalPPIA-136
❑ 98TopMiniC-400
❑ 98TopSta-44
❑ 98TopStaB-44
❑ 98TopStaG-44
❑ 98TopStaGR-44
❑ 98TopStaS-44
❑ 98Ult-127
❑ 98UltGolM-127
❑ 98UltMas-127
❑ 98UltPlaM-127
❑ 98UppDec-487
❑ 99199Fin-223
❑ 99CroRoyB-20
❑ 99CroRoyL-20
❑ 99CroRoyOD-20
❑ 99FinGolRef-223
❑ 99FinRef-223
❑ 99Fle-308
❑ 99FleSta9-308
❑ 99FleWarT-308
❑ 99Pac-351
❑ 99PacOme-33
❑ 99PacOmeC-33
❑ 99PacOmeG-33
❑ 99PacOmePB-33
❑ 99PacPar-33
❑ 99PacParC-33
❑ 99PacParG-33
❑ 99PacParHoloGold-33
❑ 99PacParHS-33
❑ 99PacParOD-33
❑ 99PacParPB-33
❑ 99PacParRed-33
❑ 99PacPlaB-351
❑ 99PacPriS-82
❑ 99PacPriS206-82
❑ 99PacPriS206R-82
❑ 99PacRed-351
❑ 99SkyPre-69
❑ 99SkyPreR-69
❑ 99Top-327
❑ 99TopChr-327
❑ 99TopChrR-327
❑ 99TopMVPP-327
❑ 99TopSta-127
❑ 99TopStaFoil-127
❑ 99Ult-9
❑ 99UltGolM-9
❑ 99UltMas-9
❑ 99UltPlaM-9
❑ 99UppDec-183
❑ 99UppDec-319
❑ 99UppDecBD-81
❑ 99UppDecBDD-81
❑ 99UppDecBDQ-81
❑ 99UppDecBDT-81
❑ 99UppDecEL1-183
❑ 99UppDecEL1-319
❑ 99UppDecEL2-183
❑ 99UppDecEL2-319
❑ 99Vic-49

Deshong, Jimmie (James B.)
❑ 34Gou-96
❑ 35DiaMatCS3T1-46
❑ 35GouPuzR-8E
❑ 35GouPuzR-9E
❑ 38CloFotW-21
❑ 39PlaBal-10
❑ 79DiaGre-63

DeSilva, John
❑ 87BriYouC-6
❑ 89NiaFalRP-6
❑ 90FloStaLAS-30
❑ 90LakTigS-8
❑ 91Bow-148
❑ 91LinDriAA-381
❑ 91LonTigLD-381
❑ 91LonTigP-1869
❑ 92Bow-229
❑ 92SkyAAAF-269
❑ 92TolMudHF-1035
❑ 92TolMudHS-598
❑ 92UppDecML-137
❑ 93TolMudHF-1645
❑ 94AlbDukF-836
❑ 95LinVen-23
❑ 95RocRedWTI-13
❑ 96PawRedSDD-6

DeSimone, Jerry
❑ 82HawIsIT-7
❑ 83LasVegSBHN-6
❑ 84LasVegSC-223

Desimone, Ray
❑ 93EriSaiC-5
❑ 93EriSaiF-3122

DesJardins, Brad
❑ 89WatIndS-29

Desjarlais, Keith
❑ 81AppFoxT-3
❑ 82EdmTriT-7
❑ 83GleFalWST-13

Deskins, Casey
❑ 96YakBeaTI-50
❑ 97SanBerS-6
❑ 98SanAntMG-8

DeSonnaville, Erik
❑ 89CalLeaA-53

Desrosiers, Erik
❑ 96PriWilCB-8

Dessau, Rube (Frank Rolland)
❑ 09T206-418
❑ 11PinT-5-458
❑ 11SpoLifM-154
❑ 12ImpTobC-61
❑ 90DodTar-931

Dessellier, Chris
❑ 93ClaGolF-144

Dessens, Elmer
❑ 95Bes-93
❑ 95CarMudF-148
❑ 97PacPriGotD-GD190
❑ 98PacOnl-582
❑ 98PacOnlR-582
❑ 98PacOnlWC-582

Destrade, Orestes
❑ 82OneYanT-1
❑ 85AlbYanT-16
❑ 86ColCliP-5
❑ 86ColCliP-5
❑ 86StaoftFT-5
❑ 87ColCliP-7
❑ 87ColCliP-8
❑ 87ColCliT-13
❑ 87IntLeaAT-23
❑ 88BufBisC-20
❑ 88BufBisP-1486
❑ 88ScoRoo-110T
❑ 88ScoRooG-110T
❑ 89BufBisP-1687
❑ 89Top-27A
❑ 89Top-27B
❑ 89TopTif-27
❑ 90AlbDecGB-21
❑ 92YanWIZ8-45
❑ 93Bow-418
❑ 93DiaMar-31
❑ 93Fin-144
❑ 93FinRef-144
❑ 93Fla-50
❑ 93FleFinE-59
❑ 93Lea-304
❑ 93MarlStaClu-29
❑ 93MarPub-10
❑ 93MarUppD-524
❑ 93MarUSPC-7S
❑ 93MarUSPC-10D
❑ 93MarUSPC-11C
❑ 93OPCPre-32
❑ 93PacJugC-25
❑ 93PacSpa-460
❑ 93Pin-526
❑ 93PinExpOD-3
❑ 93SP-139
❑ 93StaClu-554
❑ 93StaCluFDI-554
❑ 93StaCluMOP-554
❑ 93Stu-97
❑ 93TopTra-11T
❑ 93Ult-373
❑ 93UppDec-479
❑ 93UppDec-524
❑ 93UppDecGold-479
❑ 93UppDecGold-524
❑ 94Bow-506
❑ 94ColC-397
❑ 94ColChoGS-397
❑ 94ColChoSS-397
❑ 94Don-212
❑ 94Fin-272
❑ 94FinRef-272
❑ 94Fla-162
❑ 94Fle-466
❑ 94Lea-191
❑ 94OPC-23
❑ 94Pac-241
❑ 94PacSilP-22
❑ 94PacSilPC-22
❑ 94PanSti-182
❑ 94Pin-373
❑ 94PinArtP-373
❑ 94PinMusC-373
❑ 94Sco-372
❑ 94ScoGolR-372
❑ 94Sel-150
❑ 94StaClu-387
❑ 94StaCluFDI-387
❑ 94StaCluGR-387
❑ 94StaCluMOP-387
❑ 94StaCluT-70
❑ 94StaCluTFDI-70
❑ 94Top-710
❑ 94TopGol-710
❑ 94TopSpa-710
❑ 94TriPla-135
❑ 94Ult-195
❑ 94UppDec-304
❑ 94UppDecED-304

Detherage, Bob (Robert W.)
❑ 75WatDodT-5
❑ 80OmaRoyP-9
❑ 81OmaRoyT-21

Detienne, David
❑ 98YakBeaG-11

Detmers, Kris
❑ 96ArkTraB-11
❑ 96Bow-160
❑ 96BowFoi-160
❑ 97Bow-342
❑ 97BowCerBlaIA-CA30
❑ 97BowCerBluIA-CA30
❑ 97BowCerGolIA-CA30
❑ 97BowInt-342
❑ 98ArkTraM-7

Dettmer, John
❑ 91TopTra-32T
❑ 91TopTraT-32T
❑ 92GasRanF-2244
❑ 92StaCluD-35
❑ 92TopDaiQTU-19
❑ 93ChaRanC-7
❑ 93ChaRanF-1932
❑ 94Bow-129
❑ 94BowBes-B68
❑ 94BowBesR-B68
❑ 94ExcFS7-131
❑ 94ExcLeaLF-7
❑ 94SigRooDP-91
❑ 94SigRooDPS-91
❑ 94TopTra-72T
❑ 94TulDriF-236
❑ 94TulDriTI-5
❑ 94UppDecML-235
❑ 95ColCho-403
❑ 95ColChoGS-403
❑ 95ColChoSS-403
❑ 95Lea-355
❑ 95StaClu-488
❑ 95StaCluMOP-488
❑ 95StaCluSTWS-488
❑ 95StaCluVR-268
❑ 95StaCluVRMO-268
❑ 95UppDec-152
❑ 95UppDecED-152
❑ 95UppDecEDG-152
❑ 96GreBraB-11
❑ 96RicBraUB-6
❑ 97St.PauS-6

Dettola, Kevin
❑ 92SkyAA F-129

Dettore, Tom (Thomas A.)
❑ 74WicAerODF-106
❑ 75OPC-469
❑ 75Top-469
❑ 75TopMin-469
❑ 76OPC-126
❑ 76Top-126
❑ 89PriPirS-27
❑ 91SalBucP-969
❑ 93BufBisF-533
❑ 94BufBisF-1853

Deutsch, John
❑ 89GreFalDSP-17
❑ 90BakDodCLC-249
❑ 90CalLeaACLC-3
❑ 91VerBeaDC-18
❑ 91VerBeaDP-779
❑ 92SanAntMF-3981
❑ 92SanAntMS-562
❑ 92SkyAA F-245
❑ 93PeoChiC-5
❑ 93PeoChiF-1090

Deutsch, Melvin
❑ 46RedSoxTI-6
❑ 92TexLon-12

Deutsch, Mike
❑ 89FreKeyS-5
❑ 90FreKeyTI-5

Devarez, Cesar
❑ 89BluOriS-8
❑ 90Bes-133
❑ 90WauTimB-17
❑ 90WauTimP-2130
❑ 90WauTimS-7
❑ 91CarLeaAP-CAR7
❑ 91FreKeyC-12
❑ 91FreKeyP-2366
❑ 92HagSunF-2559
❑ 92HagSunS-257
❑ 92SkyAA F-106
❑ 93FreKeyC-5
❑ 93FreKeyF-1028
❑ 93LimRocDWB-48
❑ 94BowBayF-2415
❑ 94OriPro-25
❑ 95Exc-4
❑ 95RocRedWTI-14
❑ 95UppDecML-160
❑ 95UppDecMLFS-160
❑ 96ColCho-466
❑ 96ColChoGS-466
❑ 96ColChoSS-466
❑ 96RocRedWB-11
❑ 96Sco-264
❑ 97Fle-5
❑ 97FleTif-5
❑ 97OrlRayB-8
❑ 97OrlRayB-29
❑ 97PacPriGotD-GD10

DeVaughan, Jeff
❑ 92SalLakTSP-4

Devens, Charlie
❑ 94ConTSN-1284
❑ 94ConTSNB-1284

Devereaux, Mike
❑ 87SanAntDTI-10
❑ 87TexLeaAF-28
❑ 88AlbDukCm-18
❑ 88AlbDukP-252
❑ 88BlaYNPRWL-181
❑ 88DodMot-27
❑ 88Don-546
❑ 88Fle-512
❑ 88FleGlo-512
❑ 88Sco-637
❑ 88ScoGlo-637
❑ 88TriAAAP-1
❑ 88TriAAC-36
❑ 89BalOriP-5
❑ 89ClaTraP-181
❑ 89Don-603
❑ 89DonBasB-326
❑ 89DonRoo-51
❑ 89DonTra-30
❑ 89Fle-56
❑ 89FleGlo-56
❑ 89FleUpd-2
❑ 89OriFreB-12
❑ 89ScoHot1R-11
❑ 89ScoYouS2-22
❑ 89TopTra-23T
❑ 89TopTraT-23T
❑ 89UppDec-68
❑ 90Bow-260
❑ 90BowTif-260
❑ 90DodTar-183
❑ 90Don-282
❑ 90Fle-175
❑ 90FleCan-175
❑ 90Lea-223
❑ 90OPC-127
❑ 90PanSti-12
❑ 90PubIntS-576
❑ 90Sco-232A
❑ 90Sco-232B
❑ 90Sco100RS-90
❑ 90Spo-114
❑ 90Top-127
❑ 90TopBig-178
❑ 90TopRoo-7
❑ 90TopTif-127
❑ 90ToyRoo-8
❑ 90UppDec-681
❑ 91BalOriP-5
❑ 91Bow-93
❑ 91Don-444
❑ 91Fle-469A
❑ 91Fle-469B
❑ 91Lea-138
❑ 91OPC-758
❑ 91OriCro-103
❑ 91PanFreS-245
❑ 91PanSti-196
❑ 91Sco-258
❑ 91StaClu-555
❑ 91Top-758
❑ 91TopDesS-758
❑ 91TopMic-758
❑ 91TopTif-758
❑ 91Ult-15
❑ 91UppDec-308
❑ 92BalOriP-8
❑ 92Bow-688
❑ 92Don-354
❑ 92Fle-5
❑ 92Hig5-1
❑ 92Lea-79
❑ 92LeaBlaG-79
❑ 92OPC-492
❑ 92PanSti-70
❑ 92Pin-165
❑ 92Sco-36
❑ 92StaClu-199
❑ 92Stu-123
❑ 92Top-492
❑ 92TopGol-492
❑ 92TopGolW-492
❑ 92TopMic-492
❑ 92Ult-2
❑ 92UppDec-209
❑ 93BalOriP-7
❑ 93BalOriP-8
❑ 93Bow-605
❑ 93Don-455
❑ 93Fin-74
❑ 93FinRef-74
❑ 93Fla-150
❑ 93Fle-165
❑ 93FunPac-132
❑ 93Lea-67
❑ 93OPC-93
❑ 93PacSpa-16
❑ 93PanSti-75
❑ 93Pin-400
❑ 93Sco-170
❑ 93Sel-170
❑ 93SelStaL-20
❑ 93SP-155
❑ 93StaClu-56
❑ 93StaCluFDI-56
❑ 93StaCluMOP-56
❑ 93Stu-55
❑ 93Top-741
❑ 93TOPBLAG-28
❑ 93TopGol-741
❑ 93TopInaM-741
❑ 93TopInaR-741
❑ 93TopMic-741
❑ 93Toy-8
❑ 93TriPla-34
❑ 93Ult-493
❑ 93UppDec-167
❑ 93UppDecGold-167
❑ 93UppDecHRH-HR14
❑ 94BalOriP-8
❑ 94Bow-403
❑ 94ColC-502
❑ 94ColChoGS-502
❑ 94ColChoSS-502
❑ 94Don-69
❑ 94Fin-117
❑ 94FinRef-117
❑ 94Fla-252
❑ 94Fle-3
❑ 94FleExtB-3
❑ 94Lea-154
❑ 94OPC-203
❑ 94OriPro-26
❑ 94OriUSPC-7S
❑ 94OriUSPC-12D
❑ 94Pac-29
❑ 94PanSti-19
❑ 94Pin-13
❑ 94PinArtP-13
❑ 94PinMusC-13
❑ 94Sco-386
❑ 94ScoGolR-386
❑ 94Sel-131
❑ 94StaClu-424
❑ 94StaCluFDI-424
❑ 94StaCluGR-424
❑ 94StaCluMOP-424
❑ 94StaCluT-299
❑ 94StaCluTFDI-299
❑ 94Stu-122
❑ 94Top-534
❑ 94TopGol-534
❑ 94TopSpa-534
❑ 94TriPla-153
❑ 94Ult-304
❑ 94UppDec-356
❑ 94UppDecED-356
❑ 95ColCho-583T
❑ 95Don-368
❑ 95DonPreP-368
❑ 95DonTopotO-46
❑ 95Fin-284
❑ 95FinRef-284
❑ 95Fla-242
❑ 95Fle-4
❑ 95FleUpd-34
❑ 95Lea-360
❑ 95Pac-20
❑ 95Pin-399
❑ 95PinArtP-399
❑ 95PinMusC-399
❑ 95Sco-476
❑ 95ScoGolR-476
❑ 95ScoPlaTS-476
❑ 95StaClu-282
❑ 95StaCluMOP-282
❑ 95StaCluSTWS-282

❑ 95StaCluVR-145
❑ 95StaCluVRMO-145
❑ 95Top-23
❑ 95TopCyb-19
❑ 95TopPre-PP7
❑ 95TopPreS-PP7
❑ 95TopTra-32T
❑ 95Ult-254
❑ 95UltGolM-254
❑ 95WhiSoxK-6
❑ 96BalOriP-7
❑ 96ColCho-379T
❑ 96ColCho-468
❑ 96ColChoGS-468
❑ 96ColChoSS-468
❑ 96Don-468
❑ 96DonPreP-468
❑ 96Fle-290
❑ 96FleTif-290
❑ 96FleUpd-U2
❑ 96FleUpdTC-U2
❑ 96MLBPin-7
❑ 96Sco-205
❑ 96Ult-303
❑ 96UltGolM-303
❑ 96UppDec-221
❑ 97RanDr P-7
❑ 97RanMot-12
❑ 97Sco-451
❑ 97ScoArtPWB-451
❑ 97ScoResC-451
❑ 97ScoShoS-451
❑ 97ScoShoSAP-451
❑ 97Ult-459
❑ 97UltGolME-459
❑ 97UltPlaME-459
❑ 98DodPol-5
❑ 98PacOnl-365
❑ 98PacOnlR-365
❑ 98PacOnlWC-365
Devereaux, Todd
❑ 88AriWilP-2
❑ 90Ft.LauYS-4
Devereux, Charles
❑ 93AlbPolCB-12
❑ 94FreKeyC-9
❑ 94FreKeyF-2606
Devers, Edgar
❑ 93SouBenWSC-8
❑ 93SouBenWSF-1443
Devich, John
❑ 83ButCopKT-24
Devil Rays, Tampa Bay
❑ 97Fle-750
❑ 97FleTif-750
❑ 98PinInsC-23
❑ 98PinInsCG-23
❑ 99Vic-382
Devil, Tasmanian
❑ 91UppDecCBP-2
Deville, Dan
❑ 89SpoIndSP-10
❑ 90RivRedWB-6
❑ 90RivRedWCLC-15
❑ 90RivRedWP-2599
❑ 91HigDesMC-2
❑ 91HigDesMP-2385
Devincenzo, John
❑ 80CarMudF-14
DeVincenzo, Rich
❑ 83AppFoxFr-7
❑ 86BirBarTI-27
Devine, Adrian (Paul Adrian)
❑ 70RelPam-4
❑ 74OPC-614
❑ 74Top-614
❑ 76AtlBraP-10
❑ 76VenLeaS-141
❑ 77Top-339
❑ 78Top-92
❑ 79Top-257
❑ 80Top-528
❑ 81Top-464
❑ 93RanKee-125
Devine, Joe
❑ 32Zee-34
Devine, Kevin
❑ 86VerBeaDP-5
❑ 87VerBeaDP-23
DeVitalus, Mario
❑ 20Zee-106
Devito, Fred
❑ 80WesHavWCT-13
DeViveiros, Bernie
❑ 30Zee-78
❑ 32Zee-84
❑ 33Zee-54
❑ 94ConTSN-1282
❑ 94ConTSNB-1282
Devlin, Art (Arthur M.)
❑ 03WilCarE-10
❑ 08AmeCarE91-8
❑ 08AmeCarE91-43
❑ 08RosComP-126
❑ 09ColChiE-77
❑ 09PhiCarE-8
❑ 09RamT20-35
❑ 09T206-91
❑ 10DomDisP-32
❑ 10E101-14
❑ 10E12AmeCDCE125-13
❑ 10MelMinE-14
❑ 10NadCarE-16
❑ 10SepAnoP-11
❑ 10SweCapPP-110
❑ 10W555-22
❑ 11BasBatEU-18
❑ 11E94-10
❑ 11HelSta-123
❑ 11PinT-5-254
❑ 11S74Sil-83
❑ 11SpoLifCW-90
❑ 11SpoLifM-207
❑ 11T205-38
❑ 11TurRedT-10
❑ 12ColRedB-77
❑ 12ColTinT-77
❑ 12HasTriFT-29A
❑ 12HasTriFT-29B
❑ 12HasTriFT-29C
❑ 12HasTriFT-29D
❑ 12HasTriFT-74A
❑ 12HasTriFT-74B
❑ 12HasTriFT-74C
❑ 12HasTriFT-74D
❑ 12HasTriFT-74E
❑ 12HasTriFT-74F
❑ 12T207-45
❑ 14Zee-32
❑ 72ClaCar-44
❑ 93UppDecTR-1
Devlin, Bob
❑ 84GreHorT-21
❑ 86WesPalBEP-12
❑ 87JacExpP-446
Devlin, Paul
❑ 88LynRedSS-6
❑ 89LynRedSS-6
Devlin, Steven
❑ 91BriBanF-4
Devlin, Tim (James H.)
❑ 87OldJudN-130
❑ 90KalBatN-12
Devoe, Dan
❑ 91KinIndC-29
❑ 92KinIndC-29
❑ 93CarLeaAGF-28
❑ 93KinIndC-30
❑ 93KinIndTI-29
❑ 96CanIndB-30
❑ 98AkrAerM-4
Devore, Josh (Joshua)
❑ 09BriE97-8
❑ 09ColChiE-78A
❑ 09ColChiE-78B
❑ 09T206-92
❑ 10CouT21-117
❑ 10CouT21-118
❑ 10DomDisP-33
❑ 10E12AmeCDCE125-14
❑ 10RedCroT-18
❑ 10RedCroT-100
❑ 10RedCroT-182
❑ 10SweCapPP-111
❑ 10W555-23
❑ 11BasBatEU-19
❑ 11E94-11
❑ 11HelSta-124
❑ 11PinT-5-256
❑ 11PloCanE-24
❑ 11S74Sil-84
❑ 11SpoLifM-208
❑ 11T205-39
❑ 12ColRedB-78A
❑ 12ColRedB-78B
❑ 12ColTinT-78A
❑ 12ColTinT-78B
❑ 12HasTriFT-48D
❑ 12T207-46
❑ 14CraJacE-47
❑ 14PieStaT-31
❑ 15CraJacE-47
❑ 16BF2FP-88
❑ 16SpoNewM-46
❑ 80BraTCM1-14
Devore, Ted
❑ 91ChaRaiC-5
❑ 91ChaRaiP-91
❑ 92HigDesMC-14
DeVormer, Al (Albert E.)
❑ 18Zee-96
❑ 19Zee-131
❑ 20Zee-137
❑ 21E121So1-18
❑ 21KoBreWSI-30
❑ 22E120-63
❑ 22W572-22
❑ 22W573-32
❑ 22W575-26
❑ 23W501-106
❑ 23W503-14
❑ 28W513-80
Devries, Andy
❑ 94HunCubC-6
❑ 94HunCubF-3544
Dewechter, Pat
❑ 85GreHorT-14
Deweerdt, Dan
❑ 88RocExpLC-11
Deweese, Brent
❑ 92MisStaB-13
❑ 93MisStaB-13
Dewett, Martin
❑ 94AshTouC-5
❑ 94AshTouF-1772
Dewey, Jason
❑ 97BoiHawG-7
❑ 98Bow-357
❑ 98BowChr-357
❑ 98BowChrGA-357
❑ 98BowChrGAR-357
❑ 98BowChrI-357
❑ 98BowChrIR-357
❑ 98BowChrR-357
❑ 98BowGolA-357
❑ 98BowInt-357
❑ 98LakElsSG-8
❑ 99Bow-109
❑ 99BowChr-109
❑ 99BowChrG-109
❑ 99BowChrGR-109
❑ 99BowChrI-109
❑ 99BowChrIR-109
❑ 99BowChrR-109
❑ 99BowGol-109
❑ 99BowInt-109
Dewey, Mark
❑ 87EveGiaC-32
❑ 88CliGiaP-711
❑ 89CalLeaA-43
❑ 89SanJosGB-7
❑ 89SanJosGCLC-211
❑ 89SanJosGP-448
❑ 89SanJosGS-7
❑ 89Sta-85
❑ 90ProAaA-65
❑ 90ShrCapP-1436
❑ 90ShrCapS-6
❑ 91LinDriAAA-382
❑ 91PhoFirLD-382
❑ 91PhoFirP-60
❑ 91Sco-371
❑ 91TidTidP-2503
❑ 91TopDeb90-40
❑ 92StaClu-817
❑ 92StaCluECN-817
❑ 92TidTidF-889
❑ 92TidTidS-564
❑ 93Fle-468
❑ 93MetColP-28
❑ 94ColC-584
❑ 94ColChoGS-584
❑ 94ColChoSS-584
❑ 94Don-102
❑ 94Fin-298
❑ 94FinRef-298
❑ 94Fla-216
❑ 94FleUpd-172
❑ 94Lea-82
❑ 94Pac-497
❑ 94PirQui-4
❑ 94Top-101
❑ 94TopGol-101
❑ 94TopSpa-101
❑ 95Don-129
❑ 95DonPreP-129
❑ 95Fle-477
❑ 95FleUpd-192
❑ 95GiaMot-19
❑ 95Sco-24
❑ 95ScoGolR-24
❑ 95ScoPlaTS-24
❑ 95Top-378
❑ 96GiaMot-19
❑ 96LeaSigEA-42
Dewey, Todd Alan
❑ 86DurBulP-10
❑ 87GreBraB-10
❑ 88BobCamRB-6
❑ 88RicBraC-11
❑ 88RicBraP-4
❑ 89DurBullS-10
❑ 89DurBullS-10
❑ 89DurBulTI-10
❑ 90DurBulTI-25
DeWillis, Jeff
❑ 88Sco-583
❑ 88ScoGlo-583
DeWitt, Matt
❑ 96JohCitCTI-9
❑ 97PeoChi-8
❑ 98BesAutSS-18
❑ 98CarLeaTPQ-3
❑ 98PriWilCQ-6
❑ 99SP TopP-40
❑ 99SP TopPPE-40
DeWitt, Scott
❑ 96KanCouCTI-5
❑ 97BreCouMB-11
❑ 98PorSeaDQ-4
DeWitt, William O.
❑ 41BroW75-8
❑ 63RedFreBC-4
DeWolf, Rob
❑ 85BelBreT-7
❑ 86StoPorP-6
❑ 87ElPasDP-6
❑ 88ElPasDB-14
❑ 89WicChaR-2
❑ 89WicChaR-8
❑ 89WicChaR-17
❑ 89WicUpdR-15
❑ 89WicUpdR-17
❑ 89WicWraR-9
DeWright, Wayne
❑ 78DunBluJT-7
Dews, Bobby (Robert)
❑ 64TulOil-3
❑ 82DurBulT-25
❑ 85BraPol-53
DeYoung, Dan
❑ 98Cha-3
DeYoung, Rob
❑ 86AncGlaPTI-8
❑ 87BurExpP-1094
❑ 88WesPalBES-9
❑ 89WesPalBES-9
Diagostino, Gary
❑ 89GeoColC-4
Dial, Bryan
❑ 85BurRanT-20
❑ 86SalRedBP-5
Dials, Lou
❑ 86NegLeaF-14
❑ 86NegLeaF-20
❑ 89NegLeaRP-9
❑ 92NegLeaRLI-17
Diamond Dog, Jake the
❑ 96KanCouCTI-14
Diamondbacks, Arizona
❑ 97Fle-749
❑ 97FleTif-749
❑ 98PinInsC-21
❑ 98PinInsCG-21
❑ 99Vic-15
Diar, Einar
❑ 93BurIndF-3300
Diaz, Alberto
❑ 89KinMetS-7
❑ 90ColMetGS-14
❑ 90ColMetPPI-2
❑ 91St.LucMC-9
❑ 91St.LucMP-716
Diaz, Alex
❑ 88BlaYNPRWL-68
❑ 88ColMetGS-14
❑ 89BlaYNPRWL-74
❑ 89BlaYNPRWLU-41
❑ 89St.LucMS-3
❑ 90CMC-374
❑ 90ProAAAF-286
❑ 90TidTidC-23
❑ 90TidTidP-555
❑ 90TopTVM-40
❑ 91IndIndLD-181
❑ 91IndIndP-473
❑ 91LinDriAAA-181
❑ 92DenZepF-2645
❑ 92DenZepS-126
❑ 93BrePol-4
❑ 93PacSpa-509
❑ 94BreMilB-116
❑ 94BreTeal-4
❑ 94Fla-65
❑ 94FleExtB-100
❑ 94FleUpd-53
❑ 94Lea-250
❑ 94Pac-327
❑ 94Pin-416
❑ 94PinArtP-416
❑ 94PinMusC-416
❑ 94ScoRoo-RT119
❑ 94ScoRooGR-RT119
❑ 94SpoRoo-73
❑ 94SpoRooAP-73
❑ 94Top-519
❑ 94TopGol-519
❑ 94TopSpa-519
❑ 95DonTopotO-149
❑ 95Fle-176
❑ 95MarMot-26
❑ 95MarPac-30
❑ 95Pac-229
❑ 95Sco-533
❑ 95ScoGolR-533
❑ 95ScoPlaTS-533
❑ 95Top-216
❑ 96Don-314
❑ 96DonPreP-314
❑ 96Fle-236
❑ 96FleTif-236
❑ 96LeaSigEA-43
❑ 96MarMot-21
❑ 96Pac-407
❑ 96TacRaiB-10
❑ 96Top-94
❑ 97OklCit8-12
❑ 97PacPriGotD-GD85
❑ 98GiaMot-25
❑ 98PacInvGems-101
Diaz, Alfredo
❑ 95LakElsSTI-11
❑ 96VanCanB-8
Diaz, Andres
❑ 90KisDodD-10
Diaz, Angel
❑ 89HelBreSP-2
❑ 98ButCopKG-9
Diaz, Armando
❑ 52LavPro-76
Diaz, Bo (Baudilio Jose)
❑ 76VenLeaS-78
❑ 78IndTeal-8
❑ 78Top-708
❑ 79Top-61
❑ 80IndTeal-7
❑ 80Top-483
❑ 80VenLeaS-95
❑ 81Don-517
❑ 81Fle-404
❑ 81Top-362
❑ 82Don-263
❑ 82Fle-364
❑ 82Fle-639
❑ 82FleSta-197
❑ 82OPC-258
❑ 82Top-258
❑ 82TopSti-176
❑ 82TopStiV-176
❑ 82TopTra-29T
❑ 83AllGamPI-131
❑ 83Don-147
❑ 83Fle-160
❑ 83Fle-637
❑ 83FleSta-53
❑ 83FleSti-177
❑ 83OPC-175
❑ 83PhiPosGPaM-3
❑ 83PhiTas-10
❑ 83Top-175
❑ 83Top-229
❑ 83TopSti-273
❑ 84AllGamPI-41
❑ 84Don-137
❑ 84Fle-29
❑ 84FleSti-118
❑ 84Nes792-535
❑ 84OPC-131
❑ 84PhiTas-25
❑ 84Top-535
❑ 84TopSti-120
❑ 84TopTif-535
❑ 85Fle-250
❑ 85OPC-219
❑ 85PhiTas-10
❑ 85PhiTas-25
❑ 85Top-737
❑ 85TopTif-737
❑ 86BasStaB-32
❑ 86Don-530
❑ 86Fle-176
❑ 86Lea-258
❑ 86OPC-253
❑ 86RedTexG-6
❑ 86Top-639
❑ 86TopTif-639
❑ 87Don-246
❑ 87DonHig-21
❑ 87DonOpeD-190
❑ 87Fle-200
❑ 87FleGlo-200
❑ 87FleMin-32
❑ 87OPC-41
❑ 87RedKah-6
❑ 87Top-41
❑ 87Top-281
❑ 87TopSti-142
❑ 87TopTif-41
❑ 88Don-186
❑ 88DonAll-47
❑ 88DonBasB-110
❑ 88Fle-232
❑ 88FleGlo-232
❑ 88Lea-191
❑ 88OPC-265
❑ 88PanSti-273
❑ 88RedKah-6
❑ 88Sco-206
❑ 88ScoGlo-206
❑ 88Spo-117
❑ 88StaLinRe-7
❑ 88Top-265
❑ 88TopSti-143
❑ 88TopTif-265
❑ 89Bow-307
❑ 89BowTif-307
❑ 89Don-242
❑ 89DonBasB-293
❑ 89Fle-159
❑ 89FleGlo-159
❑ 89OPC-201
❑ 89PanSti-71
❑ 89RedFolSB-36
❑ 89RedKah-6
❑ 89Sco-187
❑ 89Top-422
❑ 89TopSti-135
❑ 89TopTif-422
❑ 89UppDec-169
❑ 90Don-139
❑ 90PubIntS-27
❑ 90Sco-434
❑ 90UppDec-664
Diaz, Carlos (Carlos Antonio)
❑ 80SpoIndT-4
❑ 81RicBraT-13
❑ 82RicBraT-5
❑ 83Don-562
❑ 83Fle-540
❑ 84DodPol-27
❑ 84Don-600
❑ 84Fle-583
❑ 84FleUpd-32
❑ 84Nes792-524
❑ 84Top-524
❑ 84TopTif-524
❑ 84TopTra-32T
❑ 84TopTraT-32T
❑ 85DodCokP-9
❑ 85Fle-369
❑ 85Top-159
❑ 85TopTif-159
❑ 86DodCokP-9
❑ 86DodPol-27
❑ 86DodUniOP-4
❑ 86Don-348
❑ 86Fle-128
❑ 86Top-343

❑ 86TopTif-343
❑ 90DodTar-184
❑ 91MetWIZ-96
Diaz, Carlos Francisco
❑ 87DunBluJP-923
❑ 88KnoBluJB-12
❑ 89KnoBluJB-4
❑ 89KnoBluJP-1125
❑ 89KnoBluJS-2
❑ 90CMC-336
❑ 90SyrChiC-10
❑ 90SyrChiMB-5
❑ 91BriTigC-18
❑ 91BriTigP-3612
❑ 91DenZepLD-134
❑ 91DenZepP-124
❑ 91LinDriAAA-134
❑ 91TopDeb90-41
❑ 92MemChiF-2422
❑ 92MemChiS-434
❑ 92OmaRoyF-2963
❑ 93MemChiF-378
❑ 94MemChiF-360
Diaz, Cesar
❑ 91KinMetC-27
❑ 91KinMetP-3815
❑ 92ColMetPI-11
❑ 92PitMetC-11
❑ 92PitMetF-3298
❑ 93ExcFS7-71
❑ 93KinMetC-8
❑ 93KinMetF-3798
❑ 94CapCitBC-5
❑ 94CapCitBF-1753
❑ 94SouAtlLAF-SAL36
❑ 95LinVen-89
❑ 95StLucMTI-11
❑ 96-97LinVen-16
❑ 96StLucMTI-23
❑ 97DunBluJTI-8
Diaz, David
❑ 99TeaBesR-18
❑ 99TeaBesRG-18
❑ 99TeaBesRS-18
Diaz, Derek
❑ 85BelBreT-23
❑ 86ElPasDP-8
❑ 87ElPasDP-16
Diaz, Diogenes
❑ 98EriSeaWM-10
Diaz, Eddie
❑ 83WatIndF-4
❑ 91Sco-576
Diaz, Eddy
❑ 91BelMarCB-5
❑ 91BelMarP-3672
❑ 92SanBerC-20
❑ 92SanBerSF-964
❑ 93AppFoxFI-2467
❑ 93JacSunF-2716
❑ 93LinVenB-138
❑ 93MidLeaAGF-2
❑ 94ClaGolF-101
❑ 94JacSunF-1416
❑ 94VenLinU-15
❑ 95LinVen-78
❑ 95PorCitRTI-6
❑ 95Top-642
❑ 96-97LinVen-3
❑ 96-97LinVen-283
❑ 96TacRaiB-11
❑ 97BrePol-6
❑ 97TucTorB-16
❑ 98LouRedQ-8
Diaz, Edwin
❑ 94ChaRivC-5
❑ 94ChaRivF-2681
❑ 95Bow-129
❑ 96BesAutS-27
❑ 96Bow-233
❑ 96BowFoi-233
❑ 96Exc-110
❑ 96TexLeaAB-4
❑ 96TulDriTI-9
❑ 97Bow-201
❑ 97BowChr-187
❑ 97BowChrI-187
❑ 97BowChrIR-187
❑ 97BowChrR-187
❑ 97BowInt-201
❑ 97OklCit8-13
❑ 97TulDriTI-11
❑ 98Don-342
❑ 98DonGolPP-342
❑ 98DonSilPP-342
❑ 98LeaRS-294
❑ 98LeaRSLHolo-294
❑ 98LeaRSLong-294
❑ 98LeaRTrue-294
❑ 98PacOnl-37
❑ 98PacOnlR-37
❑ 98PacOnlWC-37
❑ 98PinSna-AD8
❑ 98Top-465
❑ 98TopChr-465
❑ 98TopChrR-465
❑ 98TopDevR-465
❑ 98TopDia-465
❑ 98TopMiniC-465
❑ 98TusSidM-19
❑ 98UppDec-554
Diaz, Einar
❑ 92BurIndC-28
❑ 92BurIndF-1662
❑ 93BurIndC-10
❑ 94ColRedC-8
❑ 94ColRedF-445
❑ 94SouAtlLAF-SAL8
❑ 95Exc-38
❑ 95KinIndTI-10
❑ 95Top-480
❑ 95UppDecML-53
❑ 95UppDecMLFS-53
❑ 96BesAutS-28
❑ 96BowBes-177
❑ 96BowBesAR-177
❑ 96BowBesR-177
❑ 96CanIndB-11
❑ 96Exc-42
❑ 97BufBis-15
❑ 97PacPriGotD-GD34
❑ 97UppDec-483
❑ 98BufBisG-10
❑ 99Fle-445
❑ 99FleSta9-445
❑ 99FleWarT-445
❑ 99PacCroC-85
❑ 99PacCroCPB-85
Diaz, Enrique
❑ 80WauTimT-15
❑ 81WauTimT-16
Diaz, Freddie
❑ 93BoiHawC-7
❑ 93BoiHawF-3921
❑ 94LakElsSC-7
❑ 94LakElsSF-1670
❑ 95MidAngOHP-11
❑ 97MidAng-12
Diaz, German
❑ 90GenCubP-3039
❑ 90GenCubS-9
❑ 91PeoChiC-16
❑ 91PeoChiP-1348
❑ 91PeoChiTI-16
❑ 92ClaFS7-219
❑ 92GenCubC-20
❑ 92GenCubF-1566
❑ 92PeoChiC-10
❑ 93WatIndC-7
❑ 93WatIndF-3554
Diaz, Jairo
❑ 96RocCubTI-6
Diaz, Javier
❑ 94AshTouF-1788
Diaz, Johnny
❑ 87ElmPioBC-22
❑ 87ElmPioRC-22
❑ 88WinHavRSS-7
❑ 89ElmPioP-2
Diaz, Jorge
❑ 83MadMusF-8
Diaz, Jose
❑ 87MyrBeaBJP-1437
❑ 88DunBluJS-4
❑ 88FloStaLAS-33
❑ 89KnoBluJB-5
❑ 89KnoBluJS-3
Diaz, Juan
❑ 98VerBeaDM-22
Diaz, Kiki
❑ 92ChaLooS-182
❑ 93OmaRoyF-1683
❑ 93OmaRoyF-1693
Diaz, Kiki (Edgar)
❑ 83BelBreFr-23
❑ 86VanCanP-10
❑ 87BrePol-2
❑ 88BlaYNPRWL-38
❑ 88DenZepC-18
❑ 88DenZepP-1256
❑ 89BlaYNPRWL-40
❑ 89DenZepC-12
❑ 89DenZepP-47
❑ 90BreMilB-5
❑ 90BrePol-2
❑ 90El PasDAGTI-16
❑ 90FleUpd-105
❑ 90Lea-335
❑ 90TopTra-26T
❑ 90TopTraT-26T
❑ 91Don-197
❑ 91Fle-581
❑ 91OPC-164
❑ 91Top-164
❑ 91TopDesS-164
❑ 91TopMic-164
❑ 91TopTif-164
❑ 91UppDec-286
❑ 92NasSouS-288
❑ 94BreMilB-216
❑ 94BreMilB-307
❑ 94ClaGolF-79
Diaz, Lino
❑ 93EugEmeC-11
❑ 93EugEmeF-3861
❑ 93MarPhiC-7
❑ 93MarPhiF-3488
❑ 94MarPhiC-6
❑ 94MarPhiF-3307
❑ 94MidLeaAF-MDW21
❑ 94RocRoyC-8
❑ 94RocRoyF-573
❑ 95Bes-24
❑ 95Exc-57
❑ 95Top-581
❑ 96BesAutSA-16
❑ 96Exc-58
❑ 96OmaRoyB-11
❑ 97BesAutAS-12
❑ 97WicWra-14
Diaz, Maikell
❑ 98DelShoM-11
Diaz, Mario
❑ 96ColCliB-10
Diaz, Mario Rafael
❑ 80WauTimT-14
❑ 81LynSaiT-17
❑ 82LynSaiT-12
❑ 84ChaLooT-25
❑ 86CalCanP-6
❑ 87CalCanP-2319
❑ 88BlaYNPRWL-39
❑ 88CalCanP-804
❑ 88Fle-649
❑ 88FleGlo-649
❑ 88FleUpd-59
❑ 88FleUpdG-59
❑ 88MarMot-21
❑ 89BlaYNPRWL-41
❑ 89Fle-547
❑ 89FleGlo-547
❑ 89MarMot-21
❑ 89PanSti-427
❑ 89Top-309
❑ 89TopTif-309
❑ 89UppDec-318
❑ 90CalCanP-655
❑ 90OPC-781
❑ 90ProAAAF-120
❑ 90PubIntS-432
❑ 90Top-781
❑ 90TopTif-781
❑ 91Lea-363
❑ 91MetWIZ-97
❑ 91RanMot-24
❑ 92CalCanS-58
❑ 92Don-149
❑ 92Fle-301
❑ 92OklCit8F-1919
❑ 93Lea-470
❑ 93OklCit8F-1631
❑ 93RanKee-126
❑ 94Don-73
❑ 94Fle-305
❑ 94Pac-614
❑ 94Sco-169
❑ 94ScoGolR-169
❑ 94StaCluT-71
❑ 94StaCluTFDI-71
❑ 95Sco-230
❑ 95ScoGolR-230
❑ 95ScoPlaTS-230
❑ 96Pac-69
Diaz, Miguel
❑ 97AppLeaTPB-24
❑ 97JohCitCTI-7
Diaz, Mike
❑ 80QuaCitCT-13
❑ 83IowCubT-11
❑ 85PhiTas-41
❑ 85PorBeaC-50
❑ 86SpoRoo-50
❑ 87Don-267
❑ 87Fle-609
❑ 87FleGlo-609
❑ 87SpoTeaP-18
❑ 87Top-469
❑ 87TopTif-469
❑ 88BlaYNPRWL-133
❑ 88Don-267
❑ 88Fle-326
❑ 88FleGlo-326
❑ 88OPC-239
❑ 88PanSti-378
❑ 88PirTeaI-7
❑ 88Sco-143
❑ 88ScoGlo-143
❑ 88StaLinPi-7
❑ 88Top-567
❑ 88TopTif-567
❑ 89Don-655
❑ 89Fle-494
❑ 89FleGlo-494
❑ 89Sco-603
❑ 89Top-142
❑ 89TopTif-142
❑ 89UppDec-606
Diaz, Rafael
❑ 90JamExpP-16
❑ 91RocExpC-4
❑ 91RocExpP-2039
❑ 92WesPalBEC-14
❑ 92WesPalBEF-2081
❑ 93PocPosF-4203
❑ 93PocPosSP-5
Diaz, Ralph
❑ 93HarSenF-264
❑ 94OttLynF-2895
Diaz, Remigio
❑ 90StoPorB-6
❑ 90StoPorCLC-192
❑ 90StoPorP-2191
❑ 91StoPorC-13
❑ 91StoPorP-3036
Diaz, Rich
❑ 83WatIndF-25
Diaz, Roberto
❑ 78NewWayCT-11
❑ 79BurBeeT-16
Diaz, Sandy
❑ 89EliTwiS-6
❑ 90EliTwiS-8
❑ 90KenTwiB-18
❑ 90KenTwiP-2287
❑ 90KenTwiS-2
❑ 91EliTwiP-4295
❑ 92KenTwiF-595
❑ 92ProFS7-104
Diaz, Steve
❑ 89BelBre2S-7
❑ 90StoPorB-3
❑ 90StoPorCLC-188
❑ 90StoPorP-2187
❑ 91BelBreCB-11
❑ 91BelBreP-2105
Diaz, Tony
❑ 84ButCopKT-9
❑ 88MiaMarS-6
❑ 89St.LucMS-4
Diaz, Victor
❑ 72CedRapCT-9
❑ 87MyrBeaBJP-1457
❑ 89BirBarB-4
❑ 89BirBarP-101
Diaz, William
❑ 86WauTimP-8
❑ 87SalSpuS-6
❑ 88SanBerSB-9
❑ 88SanBerSCLC-37
❑ 89WilBilP-640
❑ 89WilBilS-6
DiBartolomeo, Steve
❑ 90CarLeaA-52
❑ 90WinSpiTI-16
❑ 91ChaKniLD-131
❑ 91ChaKniP-1682
❑ 91LinDriAA-131
Dibble, Rob
❑ 85CedRapRT-6
❑ 86VerRedP-7
❑ 87NasSouTI-4
❑ 88BlaYNPRWL-55
❑ 88FleUpd-83
❑ 88FleUpdG-83
❑ 88NasSouC-4
❑ 88NasSouP-493
❑ 88NasSouTI-8
❑ 88ScoRoo-86T
❑ 88ScoRooG-86T
❑ 89Bow-305
❑ 89BowTif-305
❑ 89CedRapRAB-16
❑ 89ClaLigB-76
❑ 89Don-426
❑ 89DonBasB-334
❑ 89Fle-160
❑ 89FleGlo-160
❑ 89RedKah-49
❑ 89Sco-618
❑ 89Top-264
❑ 89TopTif-264
❑ 89UppDec-375
❑ 90Bow-42
❑ 90BowTif-42
❑ 90CedRapRDGB-16
❑ 90ClaBlu-43
❑ 90Don-189
❑ 90DonBesN-76
❑ 90Fle-418
❑ 90FleCan-418
❑ 90Lea-57
❑ 90OPC-46
❑ 90PanSti-249
❑ 90PubIntS-28
❑ 90RedKah-8
❑ 90Sco-277
❑ 90ScoYouS2-15
❑ 90Top-46
❑ 90TopTif-46
❑ 90UppDec-586
❑ 90USPlaCA-WCO
❑ 91Bow-667
❑ 91Cla1-T23
❑ 91Cla3-T15
❑ 91ClaGam-168
❑ 91Don-321
❑ 91Fle-62
❑ 91Lea-282
❑ 91OPC-662
❑ 91PanSti-128
❑ 91RedFolS-4
❑ 91RedKah-49
❑ 91RedPep-7
❑ 91Sco-17
❑ 91Sco-407
❑ 91StaClu-131
❑ 91Stu-163
❑ 91Top-662
❑ 91TopDesS-662
❑ 91TopMic-662
❑ 91TopTif-662
❑ 91Ult-92
❑ 91UppDec-635
❑ 91USPlaCA-10S
❑ 91Woo-23
❑ 92Bow-242
❑ 92Cla2-T76
❑ 92ClaGam-75
❑ 92Don-139
❑ 92Fle-404
❑ 92LaKdec-9
❑ 92Lea-69
❑ 92LeaBlaG-69
❑ 92New-6
❑ 92OPC-757
❑ 92OPCPre-53
❑ 92Pin-180
❑ 92PinTeaP-11
❑ 92RedKah-49
❑ 92Sco-455
❑ 92Sco-891
❑ 92Sco100S-41
❑ 92ScoImpP-71
❑ 92StaClu-584
❑ 92StaCluD-36
❑ 92Stu-22
❑ 92StuPre-12
❑ 92Top-757
❑ 92TopGol-757
❑ 92TopGolPS-757
❑ 92TopGolW-757
❑ 92TopKid-40
❑ 92TopMic-757
❑ 92TopPreS-131
❑ 92TriPla-257
❑ 92Ult-187
❑ 92UppDec-30
❑ 92UppDec-142
❑ 92UppDecF-21
❑ 92UppDecFG-21
❑ 93Bow-526
❑ 93ClaGam-26
❑ 93Don-322
❑ 93Fin-180
❑ 93FinRef-180
❑ 93Fla-25
❑ 93Fle-389
❑ 93FleFruotL-16
❑ 93FunPac-168
❑ 93Lea-280
❑ 93LeaGolA-R10
❑ 93MilBonSS-16
❑ 93OPC-122
❑ 93PacSpa-81
❑ 93PanSti-297
❑ 93Pin-101
❑ 93PinTeaP-B11
❑ 93RedFolS-24
❑ 93RedKah-9
❑ 93Sco-651
❑ 93Sel-65
❑ 93SelSam-65
❑ 93SP-208
❑ 93StaClu-369
❑ 93StaCluFDI-369
❑ 93StaCluMOP-369
❑ 93Top-470
❑ 93TopGol-470
❑ 93TopInaM-470
❑ 93TopInaR-470
❑ 93TopMic-470
❑ 93TriPla-52
❑ 93Ult-327
❑ 93UppDec-473
❑ 93UppDec-675
❑ 93UppDecGold-473
❑ 93UppDecGold-675
❑ 94ColC-93
❑ 94ColChoGS-93
❑ 94ColChoSS-93
❑ 94Don-451
❑ 94Fin-88
❑ 94FinRef-88
❑ 94Fle-409
❑ 94FleExtB-231
❑ 94Lea-166
❑ 94OPC-224
❑ 94Pac-145
❑ 94Pin-41
❑ 94PinArtP-41
❑ 94PinMusC-41
❑ 94RedKah-7
❑ 94Sco-114
❑ 94ScoGolR-114
❑ 94Sel-340
❑ 94Spo-14
❑ 94StaClu-202
❑ 94StaCluFDI-202
❑ 94StaCluGR-202
❑ 94StaCluMOP-202
❑ 94Top-183
❑ 94TopGol-183
❑ 94TopSpa-183
❑ 94TriPla-211
❑ 94Ult-471
❑ 94UppDec-308
❑ 94UppDecED-308
❑ 95Sco-530
❑ 95ScoGolR-530
❑ 95ScoPlaTS-530
❑ 95ScoYouTE-530T
❑ 95WhiSoxK-7
DiCeglio, Tom
❑ 85VisOakT-11
❑ 86KenTwiP-6
Dick, Bill
❑ 76BurBeeT-5
❑ 77BurBeeT-5
❑ 77HolMilT-7
❑ 78BurBeeT-9
❑ 78HolMilT-5
Dick, Ed
❑ 79TCM50-81
Dick, Ralph
❑ 88SanBerSB-14
❑ 88SanBerSCLC-53
❑ 89SanBerSB-11
❑ 89SanBerSCLC-90
Dicken, Rongie
❑ 92JohCitCC-5
❑ 92JohCitCF-3122
❑ 93JohCitCC-9
❑ 93JohCitCF-3686
Dickens, John
❑ 92EugEmeC-9
❑ 92EugEmeF-3020

❑ 93RocRoyC-11
❑ 93RocRoyF-710
❑ 94WilBluRC-6
❑ 94WilBluRF-293
❑ 95WilBluRTI-25

Dickerman, Leo
❑ 27Zee-51
❑ 90DodTar-932

Dickerson, Bobby (Bob)
❑ 87OneYanP-27
❑ 88Ft.LauYS-5
❑ 89AlbYanB-16
❑ 89AlbYanP-319
❑ 89AlbYanSt-7
❑ 90AlbYanB-15
❑ 90AlbYanP-1040
❑ 90AlbYanSt-4
❑ 91HagSunLD-229
❑ 91HagSunP-2461
❑ 91LinDriAA-229
❑ 92RocRedWF-1944
❑ 92RocRedWS-452
❑ 93RocRedWF-248
❑ 94FayGenC-9
❑ 94FayGenF-2161
❑ 96BluOriB-1

Dickerson, Jim
❑ 86PitCubP-7

Dickerson, Robert
❑ 92NiaFalRC-9
❑ 92NiaFalRF-3337
❑ 93NiaFalRF-3402

Dickey, Bill (William M.)
❑ 30SchR33-11
❑ 31Exh-25
❑ 32USCar*-6
❑ 33ButCanV-13
❑ 33ExhFou-13
❑ 33GeoCMil-9
❑ 33Gou-19
❑ 33GouCanV-19
❑ 33TatOrbSDR-161
❑ 33WorCig-33
❑ 34BabRutG-16
❑ 34BatR31-30
❑ 34BatR31-117
❑ 34ButPreR-16
❑ 34DiaStaR-11
❑ 34DiaStaR-103
❑ 34ExhFou-13
❑ 35ExhFou-13
❑ 35GouPuzR-4D
❑ 35GouPuzR-7D
❑ 35GouPuzR-12D
❑ 36GouWidPPR-A27
❑ 36NatChiFPR-109
❑ 36R31PasP-8
❑ 36SandSW-14
❑ 36WheBB5-9
❑ 36WorWidGV-34
❑ 37OPCBatUV-119
❑ 37WheBB6-1
❑ 38BasTabP-6
❑ 38CloFotW-22
❑ 38ExhFou-13
❑ 39ExhSal-12A
❑ 39ExhSal-12B
❑ 39GouPreR303A-12
❑ 39GouPreR303B-5
❑ 39PlaBal-30
❑ 39WorWidGTP-12
❑ 40PlaBal-7
❑ 40WheM4-3
❑ 41DouPlaR-65
❑ 41PlaBal-70
❑ 43MPR302-1-8
❑ 43YanSta-8
❑ 46SpoExcW-1-1B
❑ 47PM1StaP1-42
❑ 48SweSpoT-6
❑ 49YanTeal-7
❑ 50CalHOFW-26
❑ 50YanTeal-8
❑ 51Bow-290
❑ 51R42SmaS-22
❑ 52Top-400
❑ 53ArtHaloFP-28
❑ 60NuHi-34
❑ 60Top-465
❑ 61GolPre-27
❑ 61NuSco-434
❑ 63BazA-40
❑ 63HalofFB-4
❑ 67TopVen-140
❑ 68SCFOldT-7
❑ 68SpoMemAG-8
❑ 68YanPhoS-84
❑ 72TCMthe3-19
❑ 73SevTraC-18
❑ 75TCMGua-9
❑ 75YanAllTT-1
❑ 75YanDyn1T-12
❑ 75YanDyn1T-51
❑ 76RowExh-4
❑ 76ShaPiz-71
❑ 77GalGloG-68
❑ 77GalGloG-188
❑ 77ShaPiz-9
❑ 77TCMTheWY-55
❑ 80MarExhH-9
❑ 80PacLeg-44
❑ 80PerHaloFP-71
❑ 80PerHaloFPS-3
❑ 80SSPHOF-71
❑ 80YanGreT-8
❑ 81SanDieSC-18
❑ 81SanDieSC-19
❑ 82DiaCla-23
❑ 82TCMGreH-38
❑ 83BigLeaCOA-15
❑ 83ConMar-9
❑ 83DonHOFH-26
❑ 83TCMPla1942-3
❑ 83TopRep5-400
❑ 83YanASFY-9
❑ 83YanYealT-10
❑ 85FegMurCG-4
❑ 86SpoDecG-13
❑ 86TCM-16
❑ 87HygAllG-14
❑ 88ConAmeA-8
❑ 89PerCelP-12
❑ 90PerGreM-37
❑ 90YanMomPRP-7
❑ 92ConTSN-474
❑ 92MegRut-158
❑ 92YanWIZA-17
❑ 92YanWIZH-8
❑ 93ConTSN-755
❑ 93ConTSN-869
❑ 94ConTSN-1086
❑ 94ConTSNB-1086
❑ 94ConTSNCI-36
❑ 95ConTSNP-1475
❑ 95MegRut-5

Dickey, Chad
❑ 85CloHSS-13

Dickey, George W.
❑ 47TipTop-19
❑ 75TCMGua-13
❑ 85TCMPla1-14

Dickey, R.A.
❑ 97Bow-81
❑ 97BowChr-108
❑ 97BowChrl-108
❑ 97BowChrIR-108
❑ 97BowChrR-108
❑ 97BowInt-81
❑ 98Cha-6

Dickinson, Rodney
❑ 98EugEme-10

Dickman, Dave
❑ 89PulBraP-1888
❑ 89SumBraP-1100

Dickman, Geo. Emerson
❑ 39PlaBal-17
❑ 40PlaBal-37
❑ 41Gou-6
❑ 79DiaGre-228
❑ 94ConTSN-1167
❑ 94ConTSNB-1167

Dickman, Mark
❑ 85KinBluJT-5
❑ 86VenGulP-4

Dickshot, Johnny
❑ 79DiaGre-364
❑ 83TCMPla1945-16
❑ 94ConTSN-1286
❑ 94ConTSNB-1286

Dickson, Jason
❑ 95CedRapKTI-29
❑ 95SPML-28
❑ 96Bow-219
❑ 96BowFoi-219
❑ 96MidAngB-12
❑ 96VanCanB-9
❑ 97AngMot-20
❑ 97Bow-79
❑ 97BowBes-105
❑ 97BowBesAR-105
❑ 97BowBesR-105
❑ 97BowChr-106
❑ 97BowChrl-106
❑ 97BowChrIR-106
❑ 97BowChrR-106
❑ 97BowInt-79
❑ 97ColCho-254
❑ 97Don-371
❑ 97DonGolPP-371
❑ 97DonLim-52
❑ 97DonLim-198
❑ 97DonLimE-52
❑ 97DonLimE-198
❑ 97DonLimENG-52
❑ 97DonPre-158
❑ 97DonPreCttC-158
❑ 97DonSig-37
❑ 97DonSigA-27
❑ 97DonSigAC-34
❑ 97DonSigAM-34
❑ 97DonSigPPP-37
❑ 97DonSilPP-371
❑ 97DonTea-11
❑ 97DonTeaSPE-11
❑ 97Fle-38
❑ 97FleTif-38
❑ 97Lea-338
❑ 97LeaFraM-338
❑ 97LeaFraMDC-338
❑ 97NewPin-158
❑ 97NewPinAP-158
❑ 97NewPinMC-158
❑ 97NewPinPP-158
❑ 97Pin-134
❑ 97PinArtP-PP134
❑ 97PinCer-124
❑ 97PinCerMBla-124
❑ 97PinCerMBlu-124
❑ 97PinCerMG-124
❑ 97PinCerMR-124
❑ 97PinCerR-124
❑ 97PinMusC-134
❑ 97PinPrePla-134
❑ 97PinTotCPB-124
❑ 97PinTotCPG-124
❑ 97PinTotCPR-124
❑ 97PinX-P-130
❑ 97PinX-PMoS-130
❑ 97Sco-475
❑ 97ScoArtPWB-475
❑ 97ScoResC-475
❑ 97ScoShoS-475
❑ 97ScoShoSAP-475
❑ 97Sel-117
❑ 97SelArtP-117
❑ 97SelCom-117
❑ 97SelRegG-117
❑ 97SP-13
❑ 97Spolll-5
❑ 97SpolllEE-5
❑ 97StrAll-18
❑ 97TopSta-91
❑ 97TopStaAM-91
❑ 97Ult-451
❑ 97UltGolME-451
❑ 97UltGolP-7
❑ 97UltPlaME-451
❑ 97UppDec-522
❑ 98AngSco-5
❑ 98AngScoP-5
❑ 98Bow-6
❑ 98BowChr-6
❑ 98BowChrGA-6
❑ 98BowChrGAR-6
❑ 98BowChrl-6
❑ 98BowChrIR-6
❑ 98BowChrR-6
❑ 98BowGolA-6
❑ 98BowInt-6
❑ 98CirThu-269
❑ 98CirThuRav-269
❑ 98CirThuSupRav-269
❑ 98ColCho-24
❑ 98ColChoSQ-SQ3
❑ 98Don-15
❑ 98DonCol-15
❑ 98DonColL-340
❑ 98DonColP-672
❑ 98DonColS-15
❑ 98DonCruG-5
❑ 98DonCruP-5
❑ 98DonCruR-5
❑ 98DonGolPP-15
❑ 98DonPre-122
❑ 98DonPreSeat-122
❑ 98DonPriCD-15
❑ 98DonPriCL-340
❑ 98DonPriCP-672
❑ 98DonSigA-26
❑ 98DonSigAC-35
❑ 98DonSigAM-35
❑ 98DonSilPP-15
❑ 98E-X2-87
❑ 98E-X2ECFut-87
❑ 98E-X2ECNow-87
❑ 98Fin-46
❑ 98FinNo--46
❑ 98FinNo-R-46
❑ 98FinRef-46
❑ 98FlaShoLeg0-26
❑ 98FlaShoLeg1-26
❑ 98FlaShoLeg2-26
❑ 98FlaShoLeg3-26
❑ 98FlaShoLegM-26
❑ 98FlaShoR0-26
❑ 98FlaShoR1-26
❑ 98FlaShoR2-26
❑ 98FlaShoR3-26
❑ 98Fle-84
❑ 98FleRooS-3
❑ 98FleVin'-1
❑ 98FleVin'C-1
❑ 98Lea-141
❑ 98LeaFraDA-141
❑ 98LeaFraF-141
❑ 98LeaFraM-141
❑ 98LeaFraM-141
❑ 98LeaFraMDC-141
❑ 98LeaFraMDC-141
❑ 98LeaFraMZ2-141
❑ 98MetUni-130
❑ 98MetUniPMG-130
❑ 98Pac-3
❑ 98PacOnl-3
❑ 98PacOnlR-3
❑ 98PacOnlWC-3
❑ 98PacPlaB-3
❑ 98PacRedT-3
❑ 98PacSil-3
❑ 98PinPlu-10
❑ 98PinSna-AA1
❑ 98PinSna-AA18
❑ 98Sco-100
❑ 98ScoRT-188
❑ 98ScoRTSS-PP104
❑ 98ScoRTSSAP-PP104
❑ 98ScoRTSSAP1-PP104
❑ 98ScoSS-PP141
❑ 98ScoSSAP-PP141
❑ 98SkyDugA-51
❑ 98SkyDugAIA-51
❑ 98SP Aut-34
❑ 98Spolll-30
❑ 98SpolllEE-30
❑ 98SpolllFE-30
❑ 98SpolllTaN-75
❑ 98SpolllTaNEE-75
❑ 98SPxFin-51
❑ 98SPxFinR-51
❑ 98SPxFinS-51
❑ 98StaCluFDI-15
❑ 98StaClul-15
❑ 98StaCluOneK-15
❑ 98StaCluPP-15
❑ 98Stu-174
❑ 98StuGPP-174
❑ 98StuSPP-174
❑ 98Top-129
❑ 98TopChr-129
❑ 98TopChrR-129
❑ 98TopDevH-129
❑ 98TopDia-129
❑ 98TopGal-34
❑ 98TopGalGP-34
❑ 98TopGalOPP-34
❑ 98TopGalPPI-34
❑ 98TopGalPPIA-34
❑ 98TopMiniC-129
❑ 98TopOpeD-64
❑ 98Ult-186
❑ 98UltBactfF-13
❑ 98UltDouT-9
❑ 98UltGolM-186
❑ 98UltMas-186
❑ 98UltPlaM-186
❑ 98UppDec-21
❑ 98UppDecBCP-BC3
❑ 98UppDecSF-11
❑ 99Fle-341
❑ 99FleSta9-341
❑ 99FleWarT-341
❑ 99Pac-2
❑ 99PacPlaB-2
❑ 99PacRed-2
❑ 99Top-37
❑ 99TopChr-37
❑ 99TopChrR-37
❑ 99TopMVPP-37
❑ 99UppDec-294
❑ 99UppDecEL1-294
❑ 99UppDecEL2-294
❑ 99Vic-13

Dickson, Jim (James Edward)
❑ 64Top-524
❑ 65Top-286
❑ 66Top-201
❑ 66TopVen-201
❑ 67VanMouSO-4

Dickson, Ken
❑ 87AubAstP-21
❑ 88AshTouP-1050

Dickson, Lance
❑ 90AriWilP-2
❑ 90ChaKniTI-1
❑ 90ClaDraP-23
❑ 90ClaYel-T85
❑ 90GenCubP-3029
❑ 90GenCubS-10
❑ 90PeoChiUTI-U1
❑ 90ProAaA-173
❑ 91Bow-411
❑ 91Cla2-T55
❑ 91Don-424
❑ 91IowCubLD-204
❑ 91IowCubP-1053
❑ 91LinDriAAA-204
❑ 91OPC-114
❑ 91OPCPre-35
❑ 91Sco-385
❑ 91ScoRoo-24
❑ 91StaClu-44
❑ 91Stu-154
❑ 91Top-114
❑ 91TopDeb90-42
❑ 91TopDesS-114
❑ 91TopMic-114
❑ 91TopTif-114
❑ 91UppDec-9
❑ 91UppDecFE-3F
❑ 92Bow-316
❑ 92Don-421
❑ 92DonCraJ1-7
❑ 92IowCubS-207
❑ 92Pin-272
❑ 92ProFS7-199
❑ 92Sco100RS-96
❑ 92ScoImpP-85
❑ 92SkyAAAF-100
❑ 92StaClu-836
❑ 92StaCluNC-836
❑ 92TriPla-97
❑ 92UppDecML-74
❑ 93CubStaC-15
❑ 93DayCubC-6
❑ 93DayCubF-853
❑ 94IowCubF-1271
❑ 94StaCluT-352
❑ 94StaCluTFDI-352

Dickson, Murry (Murry Monroe)
❑ 46SeaSLP-13
❑ 47Exh-57
❑ 49Bow-8
❑ 49EurSta-158
❑ 50Bow-34
❑ 50PlrTeal-6
❑ 51Bow-167
❑ 51R42SmaS-23
❑ 51TopBluB-16
❑ 52Bow-59
❑ 52RedMan-NL5
❑ 52TipTop-7
❑ 52Top-266
❑ 53RedMan-NL22
❑ 54Bow-111
❑ 55Bow-236
❑ 56Top-211
❑ 57Top-71
❑ 58Top-349
❑ 59Top-23
❑ 59TopVen-23
❑ 79DiaGre-320
❑ 83Car194T-47
❑ 83TopRep5-266
❑ 85TCMPla1-1

Dickson, Walt (Walter R.)
❑ 11T205-40

Didier, Bob (Robert Daniel)
❑ 69AtlBraBPPS-7
❑ 69Top-611
❑ 70MLBOffS-5
❑ 70OPC-232
❑ 70Top-232
❑ 71MLBOffS-8
❑ 71OPC-432
❑ 71Top-432
❑ 73OPC-574
❑ 73Top-574
❑ 74OPC-482
❑ 74Top-482
❑ 75IowOakT-6
❑ 80VanCanT-11
❑ 81WesHavAT-1
❑ 82WesHavAT-26
❑ 83TacTigT-18
❑ 84A'sMot-27
❑ 85A'sMot-27
❑ 86A'sMot-27
❑ 87TucTorP-24
❑ 88TucTorC-24
❑ 88TucTorJP-9
❑ 88TucTorP-190
❑ 89MarMot-27
❑ 90MarMot-27
❑ 94SyrChiF-986
❑ 94SyrChiTI-10

Didion, Kristopher
❑ 96SpoIndB-10

Dieguez, Mike
❑ 94HunCubC-7
❑ 94HunCubF-3558
❑ 95PitMetTI-43

Diehl, Charles
❑ 52Whe-9A
❑ 52Whe-9B

Diehl, Greg
❑ 75ForLauYS-8
❑ 76ForLauYS-20

Diemido, Chet
❑ 87PenWhiSP-3
❑ 91SarWhiSP-1132

Dierderger, George
❑ 78WisRapTT-3
❑ 79WisRapTT-4

Diering, Bob
❑ 79WatIndT-22

Diering, Chuck (Charles E.)
❑ 47TipTop-154
❑ 49EurSta-180
❑ 50Bow-179
❑ 51Bow-158
❑ 52Bow-198
❑ 52NatTeaL-5
❑ 52Top-265
❑ 54OriEss-8
❑ 54OriTeal-7
❑ 55OriEss-8
❑ 55Top-105
❑ 55TopDouH-1
❑ 56BalOriP-26
❑ 56Top-19
❑ 56TopPin-1
❑ 79TCM50-51
❑ 83TopRep5-265
❑ 91OriCro-104
❑ 97BalOriP-13

Dierker, Larry (Lawrence E.)
❑ 65Top-409
❑ 66Top-228
❑ 66TopVen-228
❑ 67Ast-9
❑ 67AstTeal1-4
❑ 67AstTeal2-8
❑ 67CokCapAs-15
❑ 67DexPre-66
❑ 67Top-498
❑ 68CokCapA-15
❑ 68Top-565
❑ 69MLBOffS-138
❑ 69Top-411
❑ 69TopSta-32
❑ 69TopTeaP-6
❑ 70AstPho-5
❑ 70AstTeal-2
❑ 70DayDaiNM-17
❑ 70MLBOffS-39
❑ 70OPC-15
❑ 70Top-15

❑ 70TopPos-15
❑ 70TopSup-6
❑ 71AstCok-4
❑ 71AstTeal-5
❑ 71BazNumT-24
❑ 71BazUnn-33
❑ 71Kel-48
❑ 71MLBOffS-77
❑ 71OPC-540
❑ 71Top-540
❑ 71TopCoi-141
❑ 71TopGreM-32
❑ 71TopSup-30
❑ 71TopTat-48
❑ 72AstTeal-5
❑ 72MilBra-89
❑ 72OPC-155
❑ 72Top-155
❑ 73Kel2D-53
❑ 73OPC-375
❑ 73Top-375
❑ 73TopCanL-13
❑ 74AstFouTIP-2
❑ 74OPC-660
❑ 74Top-660
❑ 75AstPos-7
❑ 75OPC-49
❑ 75Top-49
❑ 75TopMin-49
❑ 76AstPosD-1
❑ 76Hos-25
❑ 76HosTwi-25
❑ 76HouAstP-8
❑ 76OPC-75
❑ 76Top-75
❑ 77Car5-6
❑ 77CarTeal-6
❑ 77Top-350
❑ 78Top-195
❑ 81Car5x7-3
❑ 82AstAstI-1
❑ 86AstMot-8
❑ 87AstSer1-8
❑ 87AstShoSO-4
❑ 87AstShowSTh-24
❑ 87AstShowSTh-26
❑ 87AstShowSTh-28
❑ 89SweBasG-78
❑ 93UppDecAH-41
❑ 97AstMot-1

Dietrich, Bill (William J.)
❑ 34DiaMatCSB-45
❑ 35DiaMatCS3T1-47
❑ 36NatChiFPR-24
❑ 36OveCanR-11
❑ 36OveCanR-12
❑ 39WhiSoxTI-4
❑ 40WhiSoxL-4
❑ 41Gou-9
❑ 47A'sTeal-8
❑ 72TCMthe3-89
❑ 83TCMPla1944-19
❑ 91ConTSN-133
❑ 92ConTSN-366

Dietrich, Jason
❑ 94BenRocC-4
❑ 94BenRocF-3584
❑ 96AshTouB-12
❑ 97SalAva-12

Dietrick, Pat (Patrick J.)
❑ 85MadMusP-9
❑ 85MadMusT-12
❑ 86MadMusP-8
❑ 86MadMusP-8
❑ 86ModA'sC-6
❑ 87HunStaTI-9
❑ 88HunStaTI-4
❑ 89TacTigC-24
❑ 89TacTigP-1553
❑ 90CMC-590
❑ 90ProAAAF-152
❑ 90TacTigC-13
❑ 90TacTigP-105

Dietz, Dick (Richard Allen)
❑ 62KahAtl-4
❑ 67Top-341
❑ 68OPC-104
❑ 68Top-104
❑ 68TopVen-104
❑ 69Top-293
❑ 69TopSta-103
❑ 69TopTeaP-14
❑ 70DayDaiNM-58
❑ 70Gia-2
❑ 70MLBOffS-123
❑ 70OPC-135
❑ 70Top-135
❑ 71GiaTic-2
❑ 71Kel-42
❑ 71MilDud-42
❑ 71MLBOffS-246
❑ 71OPC-545
❑ 71Top-545
❑ 71TopCoi-33
❑ 71TopTat-26
❑ 72MilBra-90
❑ 72OPC-295
❑ 72OPC-296
❑ 72Top-295
❑ 72Top-296
❑ 73OPC-442
❑ 73Top-442
❑ 84GiaMot-21
❑ 90DodTar-185
❑ 90SanJosGB-28
❑ 90SanJosGP-2027
❑ 90SanJosGS-28
❑ 91SanJosGC-25
❑ 91SanJosGP-28
❑ 92ShrCapF-3889
❑ 92ShrCapS-600
❑ 93SanJosGC-26
❑ 93SanJosGF-27
❑ 94SanJosGC-27
❑ 94SanJosGF-2833

Dietz, Don
❑ 87VerRedP-11

Dietz, Jim
❑ 89SanDieSAS-7

Dietz, Lloyd
❑ 43PhiTeal-7

Dietz, Steve
❑ 94FayGenC-10
❑ 94FayGenF-2155

Dietzman, Steve
❑ 93CliGiaC-29
❑ 94CliLumC-29
❑ 94CliLumF-1998

Diez, Scott
❑ 87MiaMarP-14
❑ 88FloStaLAS-5
❑ 88MiaMarS-7
❑ 90DurBulUTI-3

DiFelice, Mike
❑ 91HamRedC-15
❑ 91HamRedP-4041
❑ 92HamRedC-23
❑ 92HamRedF-1593
❑ 93SprCarC-7
❑ 93SprCarF-1853
❑ 94ArkTraF-3091
❑ 95ArkTraTI-10
❑ 96LouRedB-15
❑ 97ArkTraB-25
❑ 98CarScoP-7
❑ 98DevRayP-12
❑ 98Pac-408
❑ 98PacOnl-707
❑ 98PacOnlR-707
❑ 98PacOnlWC-707
❑ 98PacPlaB-408
❑ 98PacRedT-408
❑ 98PacSil-408
❑ 98PorRocG-8
❑ 98Sco-78
❑ 98ScoCar-7
❑ 98UppDec-198
❑ 99StaClu-308
❑ 99StaCluFDI-308
❑ 99StaCluOoaK-308
❑ 99StaCluPP-308

DiFilippo, John
❑ 94PriRedC-7
❑ 94PriRedF-3267

Diggle, Ron
❑ 75TidTidTI-9
❑ 77SpoIndC-16
❑ 78SpoIndC-3
❑ 79RocRedWT-14

Diggs, Tony
❑ 89HelBreSP-8
❑ 90HelBreSP-9
❑ 91BelBreCB-18
❑ 91BelBreP-2115
❑ 92ElPasDF-3935
❑ 92ElPasDS-206
❑ 92SkyAA F-91
❑ 93StoPorC-8
❑ 94ArkTraF-3101
❑ 96ArkTraB-12
❑ 96LouRedB-16
❑ 98PeoChiM-29

DiGiacomo, Kevin
❑ 92WatIndC-25
❑ 92WatIndF-3241

DiGioia, John
❑ 85SprCarT-7
❑ 86PalSprAP-10
❑ 86PalSprAS-7

DiGiovanna, Charlie
❑ 55DodGolS-31

Digirolama, Dave
❑ 83ButCopKT-3

Digrace, Jack
❑ 52LavPro-87

DiGrandi, Vince
❑ 90NebCor-8

DiHigo, Martin
❑ 74LauOldTBS-29
❑ 78DexHaloFP-8
❑ 80PerHaloFP-159
❑ 80SSPHOF-159
❑ 83ConMar-60
❑ 86NegLeaF-19
❑ 88ConNegA-3
❑ 88NegLeaD-10
❑ 89HOFStiB-63
❑ 89NegLeaRP-2
❑ 90NegLeaS-23
❑ 91PomBlaBPB-14
❑ 95NegLeaL2-5
❑ 95S.FExaNLT-7
❑ 97NegLeaPC-9S

DiLauro, Jack (Jack Edward)
❑ 70AstPho-6
❑ 70OPC-382
❑ 70Top-382
❑ 71MLBOffS-78
❑ 71OPC-677
❑ 71Top-677
❑ 87AstShowSTh-6
❑ 89MetRinP69-8
❑ 91MetWIZ-95
❑ 94Met69CCPP-12
❑ 94Met69CS-11
❑ 94Met69T-21

Dileso, Anthony
❑ 93IdaFalBF-4044
❑ 93IdaFalBSP-25

Dilks, Darren
❑ 84IndIndTI-27

Dill, Chip (Walter)
❑ 84AriWilP-4

Dillard, Don (David Donald)
❑ 59Top-123
❑ 59TopVen-123
❑ 60MapLeaSF-6
❑ 60Top-122
❑ 60TopVen-122
❑ 61Top-172
❑ 63Top-298

Dillard, Gordon
❑ 87HagSunP-25
❑ 88ChaKniTI-20
❑ 88RocRedWGCP-6
❑ 89ScrRedBC-7
❑ 89ScrRedBP-714
❑ 90BufBisC-2
❑ 90BufBisP-366
❑ 90CMC-2
❑ 90ProAAAF-481
❑ 91OriCro-105

Dillard, Jay
❑ 75LafDriT-18
❑ 76PhoGiaVNB-6

Dillard, Mike
❑ 87ElmPioRC-32

Dillard, Ron
❑ 81MiaOriT-1
❑ 82TulDriT-18
❑ 83BurRanF-14
❑ 83BurRanT-15

Dillard, Stephen B.
❑ 70RelPam-5
❑ 75IntLeaAT-22
❑ 76VenLeaS-151
❑ 77Top-142
❑ 78TigBurK-16
❑ 78TigTeal-7
❑ 78Top-597
❑ 79Top-217
❑ 80Top-452
❑ 81Don-502
❑ 81Fle-298
❑ 81Top-78
❑ 82Don-174
❑ 82EdmTraT-4
❑ 82Fle-594
❑ 82Top-324
❑ 88SouBenWSGS-15
❑ 89PacSenL-140
❑ 90EliSenL-35
❑ 91AubAstC-26
❑ 91AubAstP-4289
❑ 92AubAstC-27
❑ 92AubAstF-1370
❑ 93QuaCitRBC-25
❑ 93QuaCitRBF-115
❑ 94QuaCitRBC-25
❑ 94QuaCitRBF-550
❑ 95RocCubTI-NNO

Dillhoefer, Pickles (William)
❑ 19W514-71

Dillinger, Bob (Robert B.)
❑ 46SeaSLP-14
❑ 46SpoExcW-2-11
❑ 47Exh-58
❑ 48BluTin-14
❑ 49Bow-143A
❑ 49Bow-143B
❑ 49Lea-144
❑ 50A'sTeal-7
❑ 50Bow-105
❑ 51Bow-63
❑ 53MotCoo-61
❑ 76TayBow4-103
❑ 79DiaGre-195
❑ 85TCMPpl1-42

Dillinger, John
❑ 92FroRowDP-51
❑ 92FroRowDPG-51
❑ 92FroRowDPS-51
❑ 93ClaGolF-198
❑ 93LetMouF-4146
❑ 93LetMouSP-6
❑ 94AugGreC-3
❑ 94AugGreF-3000
❑ 95LynHilTI-7
❑ 96LynHilB-8
❑ 97CarMudC-4

Dillingham, Dan
❑ 94EugEmeC-9
❑ 94EugEmeF-3726

Dillingham, J.J.
❑ 94DavLipB-13

Dillman, Bill (William H.)
❑ 67BalOriP-30
❑ 67Top-558
❑ 68Top-466
❑ 69OPC-141
❑ 69Top-141
❑ 69TopFou-9
❑ 70OPC-386
❑ 70Top-386
❑ 91OriCro-106

Dillmore, Phillip
❑ 87KinIndP-6

Dillon, Chad
❑ 95ButCopKtl-7

Dillon, Jim (James)
❑ 90SouOreAB-11
❑ 90SouOreAP-3443
❑ 91MadMusC-7
❑ 91MadMusP-2124
❑ 91MidLeaAP-MWL40
❑ 92ModA'sC-21
❑ 92ModA'sF-3892

Dillon, Pop (Frank Edward)
❑ 03BreE10-35
❑ 03BreE10-36
❑ 09ObaT21-3
❑ 09ObaT21-85
❑ 09ObaT21-260
❑ 10BisCoaLE99-9
❑ 11PacCoaBD-20
❑ 11SpoLifCW-91
❑ 11Zee-10
❑ 12HomRunKE-6
❑ 12ObaPreT-9
❑ 12Zee-7
❑ 13Zee-5
❑ 14Zee-8
❑ 15Zee-7
❑ 90DodTar-186

Dillon, Steve (Stephen E.)
❑ 64Top-556
❑ 76Met63 S-5
❑ 91MetWIZ-98

Dilone, Juan
❑ 93SouOreAC-7
❑ 93SouOreAF-4070
❑ 94WesMicWC-7
❑ 94WesMicWF-2303
❑ 96ModA'sB-5
❑ 97ModA'sG-8
❑ 98SanJosGQ-22
❑ 99JustheS-16
❑ 99JustheSAC-8
❑ 99JustheSJB-16
❑ 99JustheSJP-4

Dilone, Miguel (Miguel Angel)
❑ 77PirPosP-3
❑ 78Top-705
❑ 79Hos-118
❑ 79OPC-256
❑ 79Top-487
❑ 80Top-541
❑ 81AllGamPI-50
❑ 81Don-441
❑ 81Fle-391
❑ 81FleStiC-86
❑ 81OPC-141
❑ 81Top-141
❑ 81TopSti-67
❑ 82Don-515
❑ 82Fle-365
❑ 82FleSta-196
❑ 82Ind-11
❑ 82IndWhe-23
❑ 82OPC-77
❑ 82Top-77
❑ 83Don-85
❑ 83Fle-405
❑ 83IndPos-9
❑ 83IndWhe-8
❑ 83Top-303
❑ 84ExpPos-7
❑ 84ExpStu-25
❑ 85DomLeaS-62
❑ 85Don-453
❑ 85Fle-395
❑ 85Lea-135
❑ 85OPC-178
❑ 85Top-178
❑ 85TopMin-178
❑ 85TopTif-178
❑ 93LimRocDWB-94
❑ 93LinVenB-316

Dilorenzo, Joe
❑ 52LavPro-30

DiMaggio, Dom (Dominic P.)
❑ 37Zee-69
❑ 41DouPlaR-107
❑ 41PlaBal-63
❑ 42RedSoxTI-8
❑ 46RedSoxTI-7
❑ 46SpoExcW-2-3
❑ 47Exh-59
❑ 47HomBon-9
❑ 47PM1StaP1-43
❑ 47PM1StaP1-44
❑ 47RedSoxTI-3
❑ 47TipTop-2
❑ 48RedSoxTI-2
❑ 49Bow-64
❑ 49Lea-75
❑ 49RedSoxTI-3
❑ 50Bow-3
❑ 50Dra-33
❑ 50RedSoxCL-3
❑ 50RedSoxTI-3
❑ 50RoyDes-4
❑ 51BerRos-A8
❑ 51R42SmaS-24
❑ 51TopRedB-20
❑ 52BerRos-12
❑ 52NatTeaL-6
❑ 52RedMan-AL5
❑ 52RoyPre-4
❑ 52StaCalL-71F
❑ 52StaCalS-85B
❑ 52Top-22
❑ 53ExhCan-23
❑ 53RedMan-AL22
❑ 53RedSoxTI-5
❑ 53Top-149
❑ 75RedSox1T-10
❑ 76TayBow4-28
❑ 79DiaGre-227
❑ 81RedSoxBG2S-15
❑ 82DiaCla-33
❑ 82GSGalAG-4
❑ 84TCMPla1-1
❑ 85TCMPhoC-40
❑ 87RedSox1T-5
❑ 91TopArc1-149
❑ 91UppDecS-4

DiMaggio, Joe (Joseph Paul)
❑ 33Zee-108
❑ 33Zee-109
❑ 35PebBea-2
❑ 36GouWidPPR-A117
❑ 36GouWidPPR-C6
❑ 36NatChiFPR-105
❑ 36OveCanR-13
❑ 36R31PasP-9
❑ 36R31Pre-L12
❑ 36WorWidGV-51
❑ 37ExhFou-13
❑ 37GouThuMR-4
❑ 37OPCBatUV-118
❑ 37WheBB14-5
❑ 37WheBB6-11
❑ 37WheBB7-29I
❑ 37WheBB8-3
❑ 37WheBB9-5
❑ 38BasTabP-7
❑ 38ExhFou-13
❑ 38GouFliMR-4A
❑ 38GouFliMR-4B
❑ 38GouHeaU-250
❑ 38GouHeaU-274
❑ 38OurNatGPP-7
❑ 38WheBB10-11
❑ 38WheBB15-2
❑ 39ExhSal-13
❑ 39GouPreR303A-13
❑ 39GouPreR303B-6
❑ 39OrcPhoAP-7
❑ 39PlaBal-26
❑ 39WorWidGTP-13
❑ 39WorWidGV-11
❑ 40PlaBal-1
❑ 40WheM4-2A
❑ 40WheM4-2B
❑ 41DouPlaR-63
❑ 41PlaBal-71
❑ 41WheM5-17
❑ 43MPR302-1-9
❑ 46SpoExcW-4-7
❑ 47HomBon-10
❑ 47PM1StaP1-45
❑ 47PM1StaP1-46
❑ 47PM1StaP1-47
❑ 47PM1StaP1-48
❑ 47PM1StaP1-49
❑ 47PM1StaP1-50
❑ 47YanTeaT-8
❑ 48BluTin-16
❑ 48SweSpoT-15
❑ 48YanTeal-6
❑ 49Lea-1
❑ 49MPR302-2-105
❑ 49YanTeal-8
❑ 50CalHOFW-27
❑ 50YanTeal-9
❑ 51BerRos-B5
❑ 51R42SmaS-25
❑ 52BerRos-13
❑ 53ArtHaloFP-29
❑ 53ExhCan-28
❑ 58JayPubAG-2
❑ 60NuHi-7
❑ 60NuHi-38
❑ 60RawGloT-5
❑ 61GolPre-9
❑ 61NuSco-438
❑ 61NuSco-467
❑ 63BasMagM-20
❑ 63GadFunC-33
❑ 63HalofFB-5
❑ 67TopVen-145
❑ 68LauWorS-36
❑ 69A'sJacitB-5
❑ 70Houof J-5
❑ 70SpoCarfCOP-10
❑ 70YanCliDP-13
❑ 72BowBanD-1
❑ 72LauGreF-1
❑ 72TCMthe3-20
❑ 73HalofFPP-6
❑ 73SyrChiTI-7
❑ 74LauAllG-39

□ 74SyrChiTI-5
□ 75McCCob-15
□ 75ShaPiz-1
□ 75SpoHobBG-2
□ 75TCMHouoJ-5
□ 75YanAllTT-2
□ 75YanDyn1T-11
□ 75YanDyn1T-51
□ 75YanDyn1T-53
□ 76GalBasGHoF-7
□ 76LauDiaJ-25
□ 76RowExh-4
□ 76ShaPiz-74
□ 76SSPYanOD-2
□ 76TayBow4-4
□ 76TayBow4-49
□ 77BobParHoF-19
□ 77BobParMBC-4
□ 77GalGloG-1
□ 77GalGloG-235
□ 77ShaPiz-24
□ 77Spo-208
□ 78DexHaloFP-9
□ 79DiaGre-1
□ 79TCM50-1
□ 80MarExhH-10
□ 80PacLeg-5
□ 80PerHaloFP-75
□ 80PerHaloFPS-5
□ 80SSPHOF-75
□ 80YanGreT-7
□ 81SanDieSC-14
□ 81SanDieSC-19
□ 81SpoHaloF-14
□ 82ASAMicM-67
□ 82BasCarN-8
□ 82BasCarN-18
□ 82DavHaloFB-5
□ 82DiaCla-1
□ 82GSGalAG-6
□ 82TCMGreH-3
□ 82TCMGreS-44
□ 82TCMStaot5-16
□ 83ASAJoeD-1
□ 83ASAJoeD-2
□ 83ASAJoeD-3
□ 83ASAJoeD-4
□ 83ASAJoeD-5
□ 83ASAJoeD-6
□ 83ASAJoeD-7
□ 83ASAJoeD-8
□ 83ASAJoeD-9
□ 83ASAJoeD-10
□ 83ASAJoeD-11
□ 83ASAJoeD-12
□ 83MLBPin-4
□ 83TCMPla1942-2
□ 83YanASFY-10
□ 83YanYealT-1
□ 84OCoandSI-50
□ 84SpoDesPW-5
□ 84TCMBruS-BS1
□ 84WilMay-44
□ 85BigLeaC3-17
□ 85CirK-31
□ 85SpoPro-1
□ 85TCMHomRC-3
□ 85TCMPla1-30
□ 85UltBasC-9
□ 86SpoDecG-20
□ 86SpoDesJM-11
□ 86TCM-8
□ 86TCMSupS-9
□ 86TCMSupS-18
□ 86TCMSupS-25
□ 87HygAllG-15
□ 88PacLegI-100
□ 88WilMulP-4
□ 89CMCMan-15
□ 89HOFStiB-39
□ 90BasWit-49
□ 90HOFStiB-39
□ 90YanMomPRP-12
□ 92ScoDiM-1
□ 92ScoDiM-2
□ 92ScoDiM-3
□ 92ScoDiM-4
□ 92ScoDiM-5
□ 92ScoDiM-AU0
□ 92ScoFacI-B12
□ 92ScoFacI-B13
□ 92ScoFacI-B14
□ 92YanWIZA-18
□ 92YanWIZH-9
□ 93DiaStaES-126
□ 93PinDiM-1
□ 93PinDiM-2
□ 93PinDiM-3
□ 93PinDiM-4
□ 93PinDiM-5
□ 93PinDiM-6
□ 93PinDiM-7
□ 93PinDiM-8
□ 93PinDiM-9
□ 93PinDiM-10
□ 93PinDiM-11
□ 93PinDiM-12
□ 93PinDiM-13
□ 93PinDiM-14
□ 93PinDiM-15
□ 93PinDiM-16
□ 93PinDiM-17
□ 93PinDiM-18
□ 93PinDiM-19
□ 93PinDiM-20
□ 93PinDiM-21
□ 93PinDiM-22
□ 93PinDiM-23
□ 93PinDiM-24
□ 93PinDiM-25
□ 93PinDiM-26
□ 93PinDiM-27
□ 93PinDiM-28
□ 93PinDiM-29
□ 93PinDiM-30
□ 93PinDiMA-1
□ 93PinDiMA-2
□ 93PinDiMA-3
□ 93PinDiMA-4
□ 93PinDiMA-5
□ 95SigRooOJ-JD1
□ 95SigRooOJS-JD1
□ 95SigRooOJTJD-1
□ 95SigRooOJTJD-2

DiMaggio, Vince (Vincent P.)
□ 33Zee-110
□ 38ExhFou-1
□ 39WorWidGV-12
□ 41PlaBal-61
□ 47SigOil-42
□ 72TCMthe1-201
□ 77CinRedT-1
□ 79DiaGre-211
□ 82DiaCla-58
□ 83TCMPla1942-38

DiMarco, Steven
□ 91EriSaiC-5
□ 91EriSaiP-4077
□ 91KanCouCC-15
□ 91KanCouCP-2662

DiMare, Gino
□ 91MiaHurBB-4
□ 93ForLauRSC-9
□ 93ForLauRSFP-1610

Dimartino, John
□ 52LavPro-43

Dimas, Rodolfo
□ 85MexCitTT-7

DiMascio, Dan
□ 87GleFalTP-22
□ 88EasLeaAP-6
□ 88GleFalTP-931
□ 89TolMudHC-17
□ 89TolMudHP-788

Dimeda, Jose
□ 91MacBraC-21

DiMichele, Frank
□ 86QuaCitAP-8
□ 87PalSprP-27
□ 88EdmTraP-565
□ 88MidAngGS-8
□ 89BlaYNPRWLU-5
□ 89MidAngGS-12
□ 90MidAngGS-22

Dimmel, Mike (Michael Wayne)
□ 75WatDodT-6
□ 78RocRedWT-7
□ 80ArkTraT-8
□ 91OriCro-107

Dimmick, Josh
□ 98AubDouTI-7

Dimuro, Ray
□ 91CalLeLA-53

Dina, Allen
□ 98PitMetM-14

Dineen, Bill (William H.)
□ 04FanCraAL-14
□ 04RedSoxUP-3
□ 09PC7HHB-12
□ 09RamT20-36
□ 09T206-93
□ 11SpoLifCW-92
□ 92ConTSN-374
□ 94ConTSN-1200
□ 94ConTSNB-1200

Dineen, Kerry (Kerry Michael)
□ 76SSP-452
□ 92YanWIZ7-44

Dinger, David
□ 00DavLipB-9

Dinger, Mascot
□ 94MasMan-5
□ 97RocPol-5

Dinges, Vance
□ 79DiaGre-307

Dingman, Craig
□ 97GreBatB-11
□ 98TamYanM-11

Dinkelmeyer, John
□ 75CliPilT-12

Dinneen, Bill (William H.)
□ 03BreE10-37

Dinnen, Kevin
□ 93BurIndC-11
□ 93BurIndF-3290

Dinyar, Eric
□ 94JamJamC-7
□ 94JamJamF-3958
□ 95FayGenTI-9
□ 96LakTigB-12
□ 97LakTigB-12

Dinzey, Amado
□ 75LynRanT-8

Dionne, Stephane
□ 97St.PauS-7
□ 98MadBlaW-23

Diorio, Mike
□ 93AubAstC-8
□ 93AubAstF-3435
□ 95QuaCitRBTI-4
□ 96KisCobB-6
□ 97JacGen-6
□ 97JacGenS-3
□ 98JacGenM-5

Diorio, Ron (Ronald M.)
□ 74OPC-599
□ 74Top-599A
□ 74Top-599B
□ 74Top-599C

DiPace, Danny
□ 98LanLugQ-17
□ 98SpoIndG-8
□ 98WilBluRC-10

DiPietro, Fred
□ 76CliPilT-9

DiPino, Frank M.
□ 78BurBeeT-10
□ 80HolMilT-12
□ 81VanCanT-17
□ 82Top-333
□ 82VanCanT-16
□ 83AstPos-6
□ 83TopTra-25T
□ 84AstMot-17
□ 84AstPos-8
□ 84Don-502
□ 84Fle-224
□ 84FleSti-72
□ 84Nes792-172
□ 84Top-172
□ 84TopSti-74
□ 84TopTif-172
□ 85AstHouP-21
□ 85AstMot-11
□ 85Don-232
□ 85Fle-349
□ 85OPC-376
□ 85Top-532
□ 85TopSti-66
□ 85TopTif-532
□ 86AstMilL-7
□ 86AstPol-25
□ 86Don-304
□ 86Fle-299
□ 86Top-26
□ 86TopTif-26
□ 87CubCan-8
□ 87CubDavB-33
□ 87Don-416
□ 87Fle-560
□ 87FleGlo-560
□ 87OPC-297
□ 87Top-662
□ 87TopTif-662
□ 88CubDavB-33
□ 88Don-570
□ 88DonBasB-205
□ 88DonTeaBC-570
□ 88Fle-418
□ 88FleGlo-418
□ 88Sco-413
□ 88ScoGlo-413
□ 88StaLinCu-4
□ 88Top-211
□ 88TopTif-211
□ 89Bow-434
□ 89BowTif-434
□ 89CarSmo-6
□ 89CarTeal-8
□ 89Don-393
□ 89Fle-423
□ 89FleGlo-423
□ 89FleUpd-118
□ 89Sco-146
□ 89Top-439
□ 89TopTif-439
□ 89TopTra-24T
□ 89TopTraT-24T
□ 89UppDec-61
□ 90Bow-187
□ 90BowTif-187
□ 90CarSmo-5
□ 90Don-518
□ 90Fle-249
□ 90FleCan-249
□ 90Lea-103
□ 90OPC-788
□ 90PubIntS-218
□ 90Sco-462
□ 90Top-788
□ 90TopTif-788
□ 90TopTVCa-12
□ 90UppDec-202
□ 91CarPol-35
□ 91Don-360
□ 91Fle-632
□ 91OPC-112
□ 91Sco-553
□ 91StaClu-439
□ 91Top-112
□ 91TopDesS-112
□ 91TopMic-112
□ 91TopTif-112
□ 91UppDec-350
□ 92StaClu-886
□ 92StaCluECN-886
□ 94BreMilB-217

DiPino, Paul
□ 90IdaFalBP-3254

DiPoto, Jerry
□ 89WatIndS-3
□ 90CarLeaA-36
□ 90KinIndTI-1
□ 91CanIndLD-81
□ 91CanIndP-975
□ 91LinDriAA-81
□ 92Bow-92
□ 92ColSprSSF-746
□ 92ColSprSSS-84
□ 92SkyAAAF-39
□ 93ChaKniF-536
□ 93FleFinE-199
□ 93TriAAAGF-36
□ 94Fle-102
□ 94Sco-278
□ 94ScoGolR-278
□ 94StaClu-380
□ 94StaCluFDI-380
□ 94StaCluGR-380
□ 94StaCluMOP-380
□ 94Top-767
□ 94TopGol-767
□ 94TopSpa-767
□ 95MetCoIP-10
□ 96Don-261
□ 96DonPreP-261
□ 96MetKah-8
□ 96MetKah-7
□ 98ColCho-82
□ 98Fle-225
□ 98PacOnl-244
□ 98PacOnlR-244
□ 98PacOnlWC-244
□ 98StaCluFDI-300
□ 98StaCluI-300
□ 98StaCluOneK-300
□ 98StaCluPP-300
□ 98UppDec-351
□ 99Fle-414
□ 99FleSta9-414
□ 99FleWarT-414
□ 99Top-171
□ 99TopChr-171
□ 99TopChrR-171
□ 99TopMVPP-171

Diprima, Giancarlo
□ 98HelBreM-12

Dirit, Nidio
□ 76VenLeaS-209

Disabato, Pat
□ 87LitFalMP-2383

DiSalvo, Pio
□ 77EvaTriT-8
□ 84TigWavP-13

DiSarcina, Gary
□ 88BenBucL-7
□ 89BasAmeAPB-AA30
□ 89MidAngGS-13
□ 89TexLeaAGS-4
□ 90Bow-290
□ 90BowTif-290
□ 90CMC-496
□ 90EdmTraC-19
□ 90EdmTraP-524
□ 90ProAAAF-100
□ 90ScoRoo-68T
□ 90TopDeb89-31
□ 90UppDec-761
□ 91EdmTraLD-162
□ 91EdmTraP-1523
□ 91LinDriAAA-162
□ 91Sco-768
□ 91Sco100RS-26
□ 92AngPol-7
□ 92Bow-159
□ 92Cla2-T8
□ 92Don-497
□ 92DonRoo-32
□ 92Fle-664
□ 92Lea-48
□ 92LeaBlaG-48
□ 92LeaGolP-30
□ 92LeaGolR-BC21
□ 92Pin-52
□ 92PinRoo-8
□ 92PinTea2-38
□ 92ScoRoo-25
□ 92StaClu-458
□ 92Stu-144
□ 92TopTra-28T
□ 92TopTraG-28T
□ 92TriPla-251
□ 92Ult-24
□ 92UltAllR-3
□ 92UppDec-726
□ 92UppDecSR-SR7
□ 93AngMot-2
□ 93AngPol-17
□ 93AngStaCl-27
□ 93Bow-145
□ 93DiaMar-32
□ 93Don-121
□ 93Fla-172
□ 93Fle-188
□ 93FleRooS-RSB5
□ 93Lea-260
□ 93OPC-80
□ 93PacSpa-43
□ 93PanSti-6
□ 93Pin-337
□ 93Sco-374
□ 93Sel-281
□ 93SP-21
□ 93StaClu-196
□ 93StaCluFDI-196
□ 93StaCluMOP-196
□ 93Stu-85
□ 93Top-157
□ 93TopGol-157
□ 93TopInaM-157
□ 93TopInaR-157
□ 93TopMic-157
□ 93TriPla-58
□ 93Ult-160
□ 93UppDec-230
□ 93UppDecGold-230
□ 93USPlaCR-13H
□ 94AngAdoF-1
□ 94AngLAT-4
□ 94AngMot-6
□ 94Bow-507
□ 94ColC-94
□ 94ColChoGS-94
□ 94ColChoSS-94
□ 94Don-478
□ 94Fin-171
□ 94FinRef-171
□ 94Fla-20
□ 94Fle-52
□ 94FleExtB-32
□ 94Lea-173
□ 94LeaL-16
□ 94Pac-75
□ 94PanSti-36
□ 94Pin-97
□ 94PinArtP-97
□ 94PinMusC-97
□ 94Sco-377
□ 94ScoGolR-377
□ 94Sel-226
□ 94StaClu-213
□ 94StaCluFDI-213
□ 94StaCluGR-213
□ 94StaCluMOP-213
□ 94Stu-10
□ 94Top-351
□ 94TopGol-351
□ 94TopSpa-351
□ 94TriPla-13
□ 94Ult-325
□ 94UppDec-165
□ 94UppDecED-165
□ 95AngCHP-4
□ 95AngMot-6
□ 95ColCho-97
□ 95ColChoGS-97
□ 95ColChoSS-97
□ 95Don-256
□ 95DonPreP-256
□ 95DonTopotO-33
□ 95Emo-19
□ 95Fla-17
□ 95Fle-221
□ 95Lea-367
□ 95Pac-56
□ 95PanSti-70
□ 95Pin-232
□ 95PinArtP-232
□ 95PinMusC-232
□ 95Sco-448
□ 95ScoGolR-448
□ 95ScoPlaTS-448
□ 95StaClu-338
□ 95StaCluMOP-338
□ 95StaCluSTWS-338
□ 95StaCluVR-177
□ 95StaCluVRMO-177
□ 95Stu-116
□ 95Top-12
□ 95TopCyb-10
□ 95Ult-267
□ 95UltGolM-267
□ 95UppDec-19
□ 95UppDecED-19
□ 95UppDecEDG-19
□ 96AngMot-7
□ 96ColCho-482
□ 96ColChoGS-482
□ 96ColChoSS-482
□ 96Don-31
□ 96DonPreP-31
□ 96Fla-35
□ 96Fle-44
□ 96FleTif-44
□ 96Lea-134
□ 96LeaPrePB-134
□ 96LeaPrePG-134
□ 96LeaPrePS-134
□ 96MetUni-25
□ 96MetUniP-25
□ 96Pac-271
□ 96Pin-320
□ 96PinFoil-320
□ 96ProSta-1
□ 96Sco-64
□ 96ScoDugC-A55
□ 96ScoDugCAP-A55
□ 96StaClu-36
□ 96StaCluMOP-36
□ 96Sum-114
□ 96SumAbo&B-114
□ 96SumArtP-114
□ 96SumFoi-114
□ 96Top-296
□ 96Ult-27
□ 96UltGolM-27
□ 96UppDec-27
□ 97AngMot-7
□ 97Cir-309
□ 97CirRav-309

❑ 97ColCho-263
❑ 97DonTea-15
❑ 97DonTeaSPE-15
❑ 97Fle-39
❑ 97FleTif-39
❑ 97MetUni-38
❑ 97Pac-4
❑ 97PacLigB-4
❑ 97PacPriGotD-GD3
❑ 97PacSil-4
❑ 97Sco-423
❑ 97ScoArtPWB-423
❑ 97ScoResC-423
❑ 97ScoShoS-423
❑ 97ScoShoSAP-423
❑ 97StaClu-93
❑ 97StaCluMOP-93
❑ 97Top-59
❑ 97UppDec-294
❑ 98AngSco-9
❑ 98AngScoP-9
❑ 98CirThu-83
❑ 98CirThuRav-83
❑ 98CirThuSupRav-83
❑ 98ColCho-281
❑ 98Fle-289
❑ 98Pac-4
❑ 98PacOme-2
❑ 98PacOmeR-2
❑ 98PacOnl-4
❑ 98PacOnlR-4
❑ 98PacOnlWC-4
❑ 98PacPar-2
❑ 98PacParC-2
❑ 98PacParG-2
❑ 98PacParHS-2
❑ 98PacParPB-2
❑ 98PacParR-2
❑ 98PacPlaB-4
❑ 98PacRedT-4
❑ 98PacSil-4
❑ 98Pin-110
❑ 98PinPreP-110
❑ 98PinSna-AA2
❑ 98PinSna-AA13
❑ 98Sco-167
❑ 98ScoRT-224
❑ 98StaCluFDI-128
❑ 98StaClul-128
❑ 98StaCluOneK-128
❑ 98StaCluPP-128
❑ 98Top-44
❑ 98TopChr-44
❑ 98TopChrR-44
❑ 98TopDevR-44
❑ 98TopDia-44
❑ 98TopMiniC-44
❑ 98Ult-360
❑ 98UltGolM-360
❑ 98UltMas-360
❑ 98UltPlaM-360
❑ 98UppDec-289
❑ 99Fle-370
❑ 99FleSta9-370
❑ 99FleWarT-370
❑ 99Pac-3
❑ 99PacCroC-2
❑ 99PacCroCPB-2
❑ 99PacPar-2
❑ 99PacParC-2
❑ 99PacParG-2
❑ 99PacParHoloGold-2
❑ 99PacParHS-2
❑ 99PacParOD-2
❑ 99PacParPB-2
❑ 99PacParRed-2
❑ 99PacPlaB-3
❑ 99PacPriS-83
❑ 99PacPriS206-83
❑ 99PacPriS206R-83
❑ 99PacRed-3
❑ 99StaClu-49
❑ 99StaCluFDI-49
❑ 99StaCluOoaK-49
❑ 99StaCluPP-49
❑ 99Top-163
❑ 99TopChr-163
❑ 99TopChrR-163
❑ 99TopMVPP-163
❑ 99UppDec-19
❑ 99UppDecEL1-19
❑ 99UppDecEL2-19

DiSarcina, Glenn
❑ 91UtiBluSC-16
❑ 91UtiBluSP-3245
❑ 92ClaFS7-259
❑ 92SouBenWSC-15
❑ 92SouBenWSF-183
❑ 93FloStaLAF-22
❑ 93SarWhiSC-1
❑ 93SarWhiSF-1376
❑ 94BirBarC-7
❑ 94BirBarF-628
❑ 94Bow-99
❑ 94ClaGolF-194
❑ 94UppDecML-247
❑ 96BirBarB-8
❑ 96NasSouB-12

Disher, Dan
❑ 87WauTimP-4
❑ 88SanBerSB-10
❑ 88SanBerSCLC-31

Disher, David
❑ 86BelMarCr-122

Dishington, Nate
❑ 94ClaGolF-104
❑ 96PeoChiB-8
❑ 97PriWilC-9
❑ 98ArkTraM-8
❑ 98PriWilCASM-3

Dishman, Glenn
❑ 93SpoIndC-1
❑ 93SpoIndF-3581
❑ 94ExcFS7-278
❑ 94WicWraF-184
❑ 95Bow-214
❑ 95BowBes-B84
❑ 95BowBesR-B84
❑ 95Exc-281
❑ 95ExcLeaL-7
❑ 95SPCha-16
❑ 95SPChaDC-16
❑ 95TopTra-107T
❑ 95UppDec-473
❑ 96ColCho-27
❑ 96ColChoGS-27
❑ 96ColChoSS-27
❑ 96Don-263
❑ 96DonPreP-263
❑ 96Fle-564
❑ 96FleTif-564
❑ 96LasVegSB-12
❑ 96StaClu-401
❑ 96StaCluMOP-401
❑ 96Top-410
❑ 96Ult-283
❑ 96UltGolM-283
❑ 96UppDec-186
❑ 97TolMudHB-10
❑ 98PacInvGems-46

Dishman, Rich
❑ 97EugEmeB-5
❑ 98MacBraM-2

Dishon, Chris
❑ 89PulBraP-1891

Dismuke, Jamie
❑ 91CedRapRC-17
❑ 91CedRapRP-2725
❑ 91Cla/Bes-368
❑ 92ChaWheF-15
❑ 92ChaWVWC-16
❑ 92ClaFS7-57
❑ 93ChaLooF-2365
❑ 93ClaGolF-185
❑ 93ExcFS7-17
❑ 94ExcFS7-173
❑ 94IndIndF-1816
❑ 94UppDecML-74
❑ 94VenLinU-266
❑ 95ChaLooTI-4
❑ 97ChaLoo-7

Dismukes, Dizzy (William)
❑ 87NegLeaPD-15
❑ 93NegLeaRL2-48

Distaso, Alec (Alec John)
❑ 69Top-602

Distefano, Benny
❑ 83LynPirT-19
❑ 84HawIslC-144
❑ 85Don-166
❑ 85HawIslC-231
❑ 85Top-162
❑ 85TopTif-162
❑ 86Don-78
❑ 86HawIslP-4
❑ 87Don-514
❑ 87Top-651
❑ 87TopTif-651
❑ 88BlaYNPRWL-150
❑ 88BufBisC-11
❑ 88BufBisP-1489
❑ 88BufBisTI-6
❑ 88TriAAAP-4
❑ 89BufBisC-11
❑ 89BufBisP-1682
❑ 89Fle-205
❑ 89FleGlo-205
❑ 89PirVerFJ-30
❑ 89TopTra-25T
❑ 89TopTraT-25T
❑ 90Fle-464
❑ 90FleCan-464
❑ 90PubIntS-152
❑ 91LinDriAAA-454
❑ 91RocRedWLD-454
❑ 91RocRedWP-1907
❑ 92AstMot-14
❑ 92Bow-414
❑ 92TucTorS-606
❑ 93OklCit8F-1636

Distel, George
❑ 24Zee-43

Ditmar, Art (Arthur J.)
❑ 54A'STEAI-7
❑ 55A'sRodM-12
❑ 55A'sTeal-7
❑ 55Bow-90
❑ 56A'sPos-15
❑ 56A'sRodM-4
❑ 56Top-258
❑ 57Top-132
❑ 58Top-354
❑ 59Top-374
❑ 60Lea-78
❑ 60MacSta-7
❑ 60Top-430
❑ 61Pos-16
❑ 61Top-46
❑ 61Top-48
❑ 61Top-510
❑ 61TopStal-192
❑ 61Yan61RL-20
❑ 61YanJayP-3
❑ 62Jel-100
❑ 62Pos-100
❑ 62PosCan-100
❑ 62SalPlaC-202
❑ 62ShiPlaC-202
❑ 62Top-246
❑ 76A'sRodMC-9
❑ 79TCM50-220
❑ 83Yan196-20
❑ 91YanRinP12-9
❑ 92YanWIZ6-35

Dittmar, Carl
❑ 28ExhPCL-5
❑ 28Zee-29
❑ 29Zee-18
❑ 30Zee-26
❑ 32Zee-22
❑ 33Zee-8

Dittmer, Jack (John D.)
❑ 53BraJohC-19
❑ 53BraMer-7
❑ 53BraSpiaS3-11
❑ 53BraSpiaS7-6
❑ 53Top-212
❑ 54Bow-48
❑ 54BraJohC-6
❑ 54BraSpiaSP-9
❑ 54Top-53
❑ 55Bow-212
❑ 55BraGolS-17
❑ 55BraJohC-6
❑ 55BraSpiaSD-8
❑ 57Top-282
❑ 59SeaPop-15
❑ 83Bra53F-6
❑ 91TopArc1-212
❑ 94TopArc1-53
❑ 94TopArc1G-53

Ditton, Julian
❑ 76CliPilT-10
❑ 77OrlTwiT-6

Divison, Julio
❑ 75LafDriT-20
❑ 91St.CatBJC-25
❑ 91St.CatBJP-3412

Dixon, Andrew
❑ 86EveGiaC-11
❑ 86EveGiaPC-3
❑ 88ShrCapP-1287

Dixon, Bryan
❑ 88St.CatBJP-2030

Dixon, Bubba
❑ 94SpoIndC-1
❑ 94SpoIndF-3316
❑ 95RanCucQT-16
❑ 96Exc-236
❑ 96MemChiB-12
❑ 97MobBayBB-18
❑ 98Las-7

Dixon, Colin
❑ 90WinHavRSS-6
❑ 91LinDriAA-455
❑ 91NewBriRSLD-455
❑ 91NewBriRSP-356
❑ 92NewBriRSF-439
❑ 92NewBriRSS-483
❑ 92SkyAA F-205
❑ 93NewBriRSF-1228
❑ 94SanBerSC-1
❑ 94SanBerSF-2765
❑ 95SalAvaTI-2
❑ 97DunDonPPS-6

Dixon, Dan
❑ 79AshTouT-23
❑ 79TulDriT-7

Dixon, Dee
❑ 87CliGiaP-15
❑ 89ShrCapP-1836
❑ 90ElPasDGS-8
❑ 90TexLeaAGS-9

Dixon, Dickie
❑ 91KenTwiC-13
❑ 91KenTwiP-2067
❑ 92VisOakC-3
❑ 92VisOakF-1007
❑ 93ForMyeMC-6
❑ 93ForMyeMF-2648

Dixon, Eddie
❑ 86WesPalBEP-13
❑ 87WesPalBEP-672
❑ 88JacExpB-6
❑ 88JacExpP-967
❑ 89JacExpB-5
❑ 89JacExpP-159
❑ 90CMC-60
❑ 90IndIndC-10
❑ 90IndIndP-288
❑ 90ProAAAF-571
❑ 91IndIndLD-182
❑ 91IndIndP-456
❑ 91LinDriAAA-182
❑ 92BufBisF-318
❑ 92BufBisS-31
❑ 93TucTorF-3053
❑ 94ChaLooF-1355

Dixon, Gary
❑ 95Exc-282

Dixon, Hal
❑ 55Bow-309

Dixon, Jim
❑ 94HicCraC-8
❑ 94HicCraF-2168
❑ 96PriWilCB-9

Dixon, John
❑ 55A'sRodM-13

Dixon, Ken
❑ 84BalOriP-11
❑ 84ChaO'sT-17
❑ 85BalOriP-8
❑ 85Don-270
❑ 85FleUpd-36
❑ 85OriHea-5
❑ 85TopTifT-31T
❑ 85TopTra-31T
❑ 86BalOriHMP-5
❑ 86BalOriP-7
❑ 86Don-148
❑ 86Fle-273
❑ 86Top-198
❑ 86TopTif-198
❑ 87BalOriP-9
❑ 87Don-171
❑ 87Fle-468
❑ 87FleGlo-468
❑ 87OriFreB-39
❑ 87Top-528
❑ 87TopTif-528
❑ 88Don-48
❑ 88Fle-557
❑ 88FleGlo-557
❑ 88Sco-411
❑ 88ScoGlo-411
❑ 88Top-676
❑ 88TopTif-676
❑ 91OriCro-108

Dixon, Leo
❑ 27MidBre-26

Dixon, Mason
❑ 90ColMudS-28

Dixon, Mike
❑ 81WatIndT-8

Dixon, Rap
❑ 74LauOldTBS-2
❑ 86NegLeaF-78
❑ 91PomBlaBPB-23

Dixon, Roger
❑ 90EliTwiS-9

Dixon, Ronn
❑ 82WauTimF-14
❑ 83WauTimF-7

Dixon, Seanelle
❑ 91HawWomS-3

Dixon, Sherry
❑ 56SeaPop-4

Dixon, Sonny (John Craig)
❑ 53Bri-4
❑ 55Bow-211
❑ 88ChaLooLTI-8

Dixon, Steve
❑ 89JohCitCS-8
❑ 90SavCarP-2061
❑ 91St.PetCC-4
❑ 91St.PetCP-2268
❑ 92ArkTraF-1123
❑ 92ArkTraS-32
❑ 92ClaFS7-13
❑ 93Bow-192
❑ 93ClaFS7-133
❑ 93LouRedF-208
❑ 94LouRedF-2977
❑ 94StaCluT-314
❑ 94StaCluTFDI-314
❑ 94Top-168
❑ 94TopGol-168
❑ 94TopSpa-168
❑ 94TriAAF-AAA37
❑ 95IowCubTI-10
❑ 96RocRedWB-12

Dixon, Tim
❑ 96WesPalBEB-8
❑ 97HarSen-10
❑ 98arSenW1-10
❑ 98HarSenM-10

Dixon, Tom (Thomas Earl)
❑ 75DubPacT-19
❑ 78AstPos-8
❑ 79AstPos-8
❑ 79OPC-186
❑ 79Top-361
❑ 80TidTidT-12
❑ 80Top-513
❑ 80VenLeaS-110
❑ 81TidTidT-14
❑ 82SyrChiT-2
❑ 82SyrChiTI-9
❑ 83WicAerDS-6
❑ 87AstShoSPT-4

Dixon, Troy
❑ 83BirBarT-23

Dixon, Tyrone
❑ 93NiaFalRF-3403

Dixon, Xavier
❑ 76SeaRaiC-4

Djakonow, Paul
❑ 75ShrCapT-1
❑ 76ShrCapT-9
❑ 77ShrCapT-5
❑ 79BufBisT-21
❑ 80BufBisT-10
❑ 82EvaTriT-15

Doak, Bill (William L.)
❑ 14B18B-83A
❑ 14B18B-83B
❑ 15SpoNewM-48
❑ 16SpoNewM-47
❑ 17ColE13-42
❑ 19W514-51
❑ 20NatCarE-23
❑ 21E121So1-19
❑ 21E121So8-17
❑ 21Exh-35
❑ 21Exh-36
❑ 21Nei-65
❑ 22AmeCarE122-16
❑ 22E120-228
❑ 22W572-23
❑ 22W573-33
❑ 22W575-27
❑ 23W501-78
❑ 23WilChoV-30
❑ 90DodTar-187

Doane, Walter
❑ 12HomRunKE-35
❑ 12Zee-55
❑ 13Zee-55
❑ 14Zee-57
❑ 15Zee-59
❑ 16Zee-127
❑ 17Zee-104

Dobbek, Dan (Daniel John)
❑ 55DonWin-18
❑ 59Top-124
❑ 59TopVen-124
❑ 60SenJayP-5
❑ 60Top-123
❑ 60TopVen-123
❑ 61Top-108
❑ 61TwiPetM-24
❑ 62Top-267

Dobbins, Joe
❑ 43CenFlo-6
❑ 44CenFlo-5
❑ 45CenFlo-5

Dobbs, Gary
❑ 78WisRapTT-4
❑ 79WisRapTT-15

Dobbs, John
❑ 11SpoLifCW-93
❑ 90DodTar-188

Dobbs, Victor
❑ 18Zee-77

Doberenz, Mark
❑ 82IdaFalAT-32
❑ 83IdaFalAT-33
❑ 84ModA'sC-25

Dobernic, Jess (Andrew J.)
❑ 49Bow-200
❑ 49EurSta-81
❑ 85TCMPla1-8

Dobie, Reggie
❑ 85LynMetT-5
❑ 86JacMetT-2
❑ 87MetColP-30
❑ 87TidTidP-3
❑ 87TidTidT-1
❑ 88BlaYNPRWLU-3
❑ 88MetColP-19
❑ 88TidTidP-1590
❑ 89CalCanC-5
❑ 89CalCanP-528

Dobis, Jason
❑ 98SouOreTG-7

Dobrolsky, Bill
❑ 92BelBreCB-19
❑ 92BelBreFl-407
❑ 92HelBreF-1717
❑ 92HelBreSP-5
❑ 93StoPorC-9
❑ 93StoPorF-746
❑ 94BelBreC-7
❑ 94BelBreFl-105
❑ 96El PasDB-8
❑ 97El PasDB-2

Dobson, Chuck (Charles T.)
❑ 66Top-588
❑ 67CokCapAt-14
❑ 67Top-438
❑ 68OPC-62
❑ 68Top-62
❑ 68TopVen-62
❑ 69A'sJacitB-6
❑ 69MilBra-74
❑ 69Top-397
❑ 70MLBOffS-256
❑ 70OPC-331
❑ 70Top-331
❑ 71Kel-32
❑ 71MLBOffS-510
❑ 71OPC-238
❑ 71Top-238
❑ 72MilBra-91
❑ 72OPC-523
❑ 72Top-523
❑ 75CalAngP-10
❑ 75OPC-635
❑ 75Top-635
❑ 75TopMin-635
❑ 77SalLakCGC-6

Dobson, Dwayne
❑ 98CedRapKTI-8

Dobson, Joe (Joseph Gordon)
❑ 42RedSoxTI-9
❑ 43RedSoxTI-5
❑ 46RedSoxTI-8

❑ 47Exh-60
❑ 47RedSoxTI-4
❑ 47TipTop-3
❑ 48RedSoxTI-3
❑ 49Bow-7
❑ 49RedSoxTI-4
❑ 50Bow-44
❑ 50RedSoxTI-4
❑ 51Bow-36
❑ 52Top-254
❑ 52WhiSoxHDP-3
❑ 53BowC-88
❑ 53RedMan-AL15
❑ 53Top-5
❑ 75RedSox1T-11
❑ 79DiaGre-284
❑ 82Bow195E-262
❑ 83TopRep5-254
❑ 91TopArc1-5

Dobson, Pat (Patrick E.)
❑ 67Top-526
❑ 68OPC-22
❑ 68TigDetFPB-4
❑ 68Top-22
❑ 68TopVen-22
❑ 69TigTealC-3
❑ 69Top-231
❑ 70MLBOffS-112
❑ 70OPC-421
❑ 70Top-421
❑ 71BalOriP-8
❑ 71MLBOffS-295
❑ 71OPC-547
❑ 71Top-547
❑ 72MilBra-92
❑ 72OPC-140
❑ 72OriPos-11
❑ 72Top-140
❑ 73OPC-34
❑ 73Top-34
❑ 74OPC-463
❑ 74SyrChiTI-6
❑ 74Top-463
❑ 75OPC-44
❑ 75SyrChiTI-4
❑ 75Top-44
❑ 75TopMin-44
❑ 75YanSSP-16
❑ 76OPC-296
❑ 76SSP-431
❑ 76Top-296
❑ 76TopTra-296T
❑ 77IndTeal-7
❑ 77PepGloD-8
❑ 77Top-618
❑ 78Top-575
❑ 80NasSouTI-8
❑ 83BrePol-NNO
❑ 84BrePol-NNO
❑ 88PadSmo-7
❑ 88TigDom-4
❑ 89PacSenL-87
❑ 89PacSenL-219
❑ 89PadPos-9
❑ 89T/MSenL-28
❑ 89TopSenL-96
❑ 90EliSenL-64
❑ 90PadMag-22
❑ 91OriCro-109
❑ 91PacSenL-9
❑ 92BreCarT-xx
❑ 92YanWIZ7-45
❑ 96BalOriP-8

Dobson, Scott
❑ 98VerExpO-11

Doby, Larry (Lawrence Eugene)
❑ 47Exh-61
❑ 47IndTeal-5
❑ 47PM1StaP1-51
❑ 47PM1StaP1-52
❑ 47PM1StaP1-53
❑ 48IndTeal-7
❑ 49Bow-233
❑ 49IndTeal-8
❑ 49IndVisEl-5
❑ 49Lea-138
❑ 49MPR302-2-124
❑ 50Bow-39
❑ 50IndNumN-7
❑ 50IndTeal-7
❑ 51Bow-151
❑ 51R42SmaS-18
❑ 51TopCurA-2
❑ 52BerRos-14
❑ 52Bow-115
❑ 52IndNumN-18
❑ 52RedMan-AL6
❑ 52StaCalL-74A
❑ 52StaCalS-88B
❑ 52Top-243
❑ 53BowC-40
❑ 53ExhCan-11
❑ 53IndPenCBP-9
❑ 54Bow-84
❑ 54DanDee-4
❑ 54Top-70
❑ 55ArmCoi-4
❑ 55BigLeaIS-5
❑ 55DaiQueS-5
❑ 55Ind-1
❑ 55IndGolS-15
❑ 55RedMan-AL18
❑ 56Top-250
❑ 56YelBasP-9
❑ 57Top-85
❑ 58Hir-17
❑ 58IndTeal-6
❑ 58Top-424
❑ 59Top-166
❑ 59Top-455
❑ 59TopVen-166
❑ 70SpoCarfCOP-2
❑ 72Dia-11
❑ 73ExpPos-3
❑ 73OPC-377
❑ 73Top-377
❑ 74OPC-531
❑ 74Top-531
❑ 75TCM195CI-5
❑ 76ExpRed-5
❑ 76MonExpP-7
❑ 78SSP270-153
❑ 79TCM50-27
❑ 80AppFoxT-26
❑ 81WhiSox1T-19
❑ 82CraJac-1
❑ 82TCMGreS-36
❑ 83TopRep5-243
❑ 84FifNatC-7
❑ 84OCoandSI-42
❑ 84OCoandSI-206
❑ 85TCMHomRC-4
❑ 85TCMPpl1-40
❑ 86IndGreT-7
❑ 88PacLegI-102
❑ 89SweBasG-115
❑ 90PacLeg-20
❑ 90SweBasG-43
❑ 91SweBasG-24
❑ 91TopArc1-333
❑ 92ActPacA-27
❑ 92MVP-4
❑ 92MVP2H-12
❑ 92UppDecS-18
❑ 93TedWil-134
❑ 93UppDecAH-42
❑ 93UppDecAH-153
❑ 94TopArc1-70
❑ 94TopArc1G-70
❑ 94UppDecAH-47
❑ 94UppDecAH1-47
❑ 97DenHol-30
❑ 97DonSigSS-8
❑ 97FanJacR-6
❑ 97NegLeaPC-8H
❑ 97OhiLot-2
❑ 97PinAllFP-2

Dockins, George
❑ 90DodTar-189

Dodd, Bill
❑ 88CedRapRP-1138
❑ 88MidLeaAGS-11
❑ 89ChaLooB-14
❑ 89ChaLooGS-9
❑ 90ChaLooGS-11
❑ 91ChaLooLD-157
❑ 91ChaLooP-1952
❑ 91LinDriAA-157

Dodd, Brian
❑ 89AriStaB-7

Dodd, Daniel
❑ 88St.CatBJP-2018
❑ 89MyrBeaBJP-1472

Dodd, Lance
❑ 82AleDukT-8

Dodd, Mike
❑ 75CedRapGT-22

Dodd, Rob
❑ 90ArkRaz-7
❑ 91BoiHawC-26
❑ 91BoiHawP-3869

Dodd, Robert
❑ 95ClePhiF-210
❑ 95ReaPhiELC-8
❑ 96ReaPhiB-3
❑ 97ReaPhi-13
❑ 98ScrRedBQ-9

Dodd, Scott
❑ 91BilMusP-3747
❑ 91BilMusSP-11
❑ 92CedRapRF-1062
❑ 98RanCucOG-8
❑ 98RanCucQG-8

Dodd, Tim
❑ 83TamTarT-7
❑ 84CedRapRT-11

Dodd, Tom
❑ 86ChaOriW-8
❑ 86SouLeaAJ-12
❑ 87ChaO'sW-8
❑ 87SouLeaAJ-6
❑ 88OmaRoyC-19
❑ 88OmaRoyP-1505
❑ 89OmaRoyC-11
❑ 89OmaRoyP-1727
❑ 90CalCanC-16
❑ 90CalCanP-662
❑ 90CMC-443
❑ 90ProAAAF-127
❑ 91OriCro-110

Dodd, Tommie
❑ 82NasSouTI-10

Dodge, Tom
❑ 91QuaCitAC-12
❑ 91QuaCitAP-2630
❑ 92PalSprAC-19
❑ 92PalSprAF-842
❑ 93PalSprAC-8
❑ 93PalSprAF-76

Dodgers, Brooklyn
❑ 13FatT20-10
❑ 36R31Pre-G20
❑ 38BasTabP-36
❑ 48ExhTea-3
❑ 48ExhTea-9
❑ 48ExhTea-13
❑ 48ExhTea-15
❑ 51TopTea-2
❑ 56Top-166
❑ 57Top-324
❑ 58Top-71
❑ 70FleWorS-38
❑ 70FleWorS-53
❑ 70OPC-411
❑ 71FleWorS-14
❑ 71FleWorS-39
❑ 71FleWorS-51
❑ 71FleWorS-54
❑ 71FleWorS-64
❑ 73Dod194T-20
❑ 86JosHalC-3
❑ 93TedWilPC-20
❑ 95TopArcBD-152

Dodgers, Great Falls
❑ 96GreFalDTI-NNO

Dodgers, Los Angeles
❑ 59Top-457
❑ 60Top-18
❑ 60TopTat-58
❑ 60TopVen-18
❑ 61Top-86
❑ 61TopMagR-13
❑ 62GuyPotCP-11
❑ 62Top-43
❑ 62TopVen-43
❑ 63Top-337
❑ 64Top-531
❑ 64TopTatI-11
❑ 65OPC-126
❑ 65Top-126
❑ 66Top-238
❑ 66TopRubI-111
❑ 66TopVen-238
❑ 67Top-503
❑ 68LauWorS-63
❑ 68OPC-168
❑ 68Top-168
❑ 68TopVen-168
❑ 69FleCloS-12
❑ 69FleCloS-30
❑ 69TopStaA-12
❑ 70FleWorS-62
❑ 70FleWorS-63
❑ 70Top-411
❑ 71FleWorS-61
❑ 71FleWorS-63
❑ 71FleWorS-64
❑ 71OPC-402
❑ 71Top-402
❑ 71TopTat-43
❑ 72OPC-522
❑ 72Top-522
❑ 73OPC-91
❑ 73OPCBTC-12
❑ 73Top-91
❑ 73TopBluTC-12
❑ 74OPC-643
❑ 74OPCTC-12
❑ 74Top-643
❑ 74TopStaA-12
❑ 74TopTeaC-12
❑ 78Top-259
❑ 80DodPol-NNO
❑ 81DodPol-NNO
❑ 82TopSti-255
❑ 82TopSti-256
❑ 83FleSta-235
❑ 83FleSti-NNO
❑ 83FleSti-NNO
❑ 86DodPol-NNO
❑ 87SpoTeaL-14
❑ 87Top-431
❑ 87TopTif-431
❑ 88PanSti-473
❑ 88RedFolSB-124
❑ 89FleGlo-WS12
❑ 89FleWaxBC-C9
❑ 89FleWorS-12
❑ 90PubIntS-623
❑ 90RedFolSB-111
❑ 94ImpProP-21
❑ 94Sco-653
❑ 94ScoGolR-653
❑ 95PacPriTL-21
❑ 95PanSti-132
❑ 96DodFle-19
❑ 96PanSti-93
❑ 97ColChoT-LA
❑ 99Vic-194

Dodgers, Newark
❑ 93NegLeaRL2-80

Dodig, Jeff
❑ 87IdaFalBP-25
❑ 88DurBulS-5

Dodson, Bo
❑ 89HelBreSP-17
❑ 89HigSchPLS-11
❑ 90CalLeaACLC-38
❑ 90ProAaA-150
❑ 90StoPorB-26
❑ 90StoPorCLC-190
❑ 90StoPorP-2189
❑ 91Bow-38
❑ 91CalLeLA-55
❑ 91Cla/Bes-358
❑ 91StoPorC-20
❑ 91StoPorP-3038
❑ 92ElPasDF-3928
❑ 92ElPasDS-207
❑ 92ProFS7-87
❑ 92SkyAA F-92
❑ 92UppDecML-311
❑ 93El PasDF-2956
❑ 94ExcFS7-80
❑ 94NewOrlZF-1476
❑ 95ElPasDTI-5
❑ 96PawRedSDD-7
❑ 98RocRedWQ-11

Dodson, Dan
❑ 94SanJosGC-30

Dodson, Jeremy
❑ 98SpoIndG-9
❑ 99TeaBesR-19
❑ 99TeaBesRG-19
❑ 99TeaBesRS-19

Dodson, Pat
❑ 84PawRedST-19
❑ 85PawRedST-3
❑ 86PawRedSP-9
❑ 87ClaGam-8
❑ 87Don-44
❑ 87Lea-44
❑ 87PawRedST-24
❑ 87SevCoi-E11
❑ 87Spo-118
❑ 87SpoTeaP-9
❑ 87Top-449
❑ 87TopTif-449
❑ 88PawRedSC-16
❑ 88PawRedSP-466
❑ 88Sco-352
❑ 88ScoGlo-352
❑ 90OklCit8P-437
❑ 90ProAAAF-683
❑ 91RoyPol-25

Doerr, Bobby (Robert P.)
❑ 36GouWidPPR-C7
❑ 38GouHeaU-258
❑ 38GouHeaU-282
❑ 39PlaBal-7
❑ 40PlaBal-38
❑ 41DouPlaR-105
❑ 41PlaBal-64
❑ 42RedSoxTI-10
❑ 43RedSoxTI-6
❑ 46RedSoxTI-9
❑ 46SpoExcW-2-1B
❑ 47Exh-62
❑ 47HomBon-11
❑ 47RedSoxTI-5
❑ 47TipTop-4
❑ 48RedSoxTI-4
❑ 49Bow-23
❑ 49Lea-83
❑ 49RedSoxTI-5
❑ 50AmeNut&CCP-4
❑ 50Bow-43
❑ 50Dra-13
❑ 50RedSoxCL-1
❑ 50RedSoxTI-5
❑ 51TopBluB-37
❑ 52BerRos-15
❑ 53ExhCan-24
❑ 60RawGloT-6
❑ 67TopVen-169
❑ 68RedSoxTI-3
❑ 70Houof J-6
❑ 74LauAllG-43
❑ 75RedSox1T-12
❑ 75ShaPiz-14
❑ 75TCMHouoJ-6
❑ 76TayBow4-1
❑ 79BluJayBY-7
❑ 79DiaGre-229
❑ 80PerHaloFP-194
❑ 80PerHaloFPS-58
❑ 80SSPHOF-192
❑ 81RedSoxBG2S-16
❑ 83MLBPin-5
❑ 85BigLeaC3-55
❑ 85TCMPla1-3
❑ 86DonHig-32
❑ 86RedSoxGT-5
❑ 87RedSox1T-3
❑ 88PacLegI-73
❑ 89HOFStiB-11
❑ 89PacLegI-150
❑ 89PerCelP-13
❑ 89SweBasG-110
❑ 89TopGloA-11
❑ 90PacLeg-21
❑ 90PerGreM-36
❑ 90SweBasG-96
❑ 91SweBasG-25
❑ 91UppDecS-4
❑ 91UppDecS-19
❑ 92ActPacA-8
❑ 92ActPacA2-8G
❑ 92ConTSN-467
❑ 93ActPacAC-8
❑ 93ConTSN-913
❑ 94TedWil-3

Doerr, Tim
❑ 76CliPilT-11

Doescher, Edward
❑ 12ImpTobC-50

Doezie, Troy
❑ 94OgdRapSP-10
❑ 94OgdRapSP-28
❑ 95NewJerCTI-7
❑ 97LanLugTS-5

Doffek, Scott
❑ 90YakBeaTI-15
❑ 91VerBeaDP-780
❑ 92SanAntMF-3982
❑ 92SanAntMS-563

Doggett, George
❑ 85LynMetT-26

Doggett, Jerry
❑ 59DodVol-14
❑ 60DodUniO-22
❑ 60DodUniO-23
❑ 61DodUniO-24
❑ 71DodTic-20

Doheny, Ed
❑ 11SpoLifCW-94

Doherty, John Harold
❑ 89NiaFalRP-7
❑ 90LakTigS-7
❑ 91LinDriAA-382
❑ 91LonTigLD-382
❑ 91LonTigP-1870
❑ 92Bow-518
❑ 92Cla2-T99
❑ 92DonRoo-33
❑ 92FleUpd-20
❑ 92LeaGolR-BC24
❑ 92Pin-513
❑ 92PinRoo-4
❑ 92ScoRoo-81T
❑ 92TigKro-7
❑ 92Ult-360
❑ 93Don-277
❑ 93Fla-200
❑ 93Fle-226
❑ 93Lea-534
❑ 93Pin-407
❑ 93Sco-353
❑ 93Sel-298
❑ 93TigGat-6
❑ 93Top-713
❑ 93TopGol-713
❑ 93TopInaM-713
❑ 93TopInaR-713
❑ 93TopMic-713
❑ 93Ult-196
❑ 93UppDec-757
❑ 93UppDecGold-757
❑ 93USPlaCR-7D
❑ 94ColC-442
❑ 94ColChoGS-442
❑ 94ColChoSS-442
❑ 94Don-78
❑ 94Fin-277
❑ 94FinRef-277
❑ 94Fla-47
❑ 94Fle-127
❑ 94FleExtB-72
❑ 94Lea-371
❑ 94Pac-219
❑ 94Pin-96
❑ 94PinArtP-96
❑ 94PinMusC-96
❑ 94Sco-531
❑ 94ScoGolR-531
❑ 94Sel-335
❑ 94StaClu-184
❑ 94StaCluFDI-184
❑ 94StaCluGR-184
❑ 94StaCluMOP-184
❑ 94Top-371
❑ 94TopGol-371
❑ 94TopSpa-371
❑ 94TriPla-242
❑ 94Ult-51
❑ 94UppDec-247
❑ 94UppDecED-247
❑ 95ColCho-477
❑ 95ColChoGS-477
❑ 95ColChoSS-477
❑ 95Don-312
❑ 95DonPreP-312
❑ 95Fla-37
❑ 95Fle-48
❑ 95Lea-9
❑ 95Sco-231
❑ 95ScoGolR-231
❑ 95ScoPlaTS-231
❑ 95StaClu-460
❑ 95StaCluMOP-460
❑ 95StaCluSTWS-460
❑ 95Stu-191
❑ 95Top-125
❑ 95Ult-284
❑ 95UltGolM-284
❑ 95UppDec-423
❑ 95UppDecED-423
❑ 95UppDecEDG-423
❑ 96Don-303
❑ 96DonPreP-303
❑ 96Fle-108
❑ 96FleTif-108
❑ 96PawRedSDD-8
❑ 96TreThuB-9

Doherty, John Michael
❑ 75CalAngP-11
❑ 75OPC-524
❑ 75SalLakCC-6
❑ 75Top-524
❑ 75TopMin-524

Doherty, Steve
❑ 97LetBlaDB-6

Dohne, Heriberto

❑ 88ModA'sCLC-76
Doi, Masahiro
❑ 79TCMJapPB-15
Doiron, Serge
❑ 91GenCubC-6
❑ 91GenCubP-4221
Dolan, Brett
❑ 96BelSnaTI-13
Dolan, Cozy
❑ 11SpoLifCW-95
❑ 14B18B-84A
❑ 14B18B-84B
❑ 23MapCriV-9
❑ 81ConTSN-41
❑ 90DodTar-190
❑ 98CamPepP-14
Dolan, John
❑ 88ElmPioC-7
❑ 89LynRedSS-7
Dolan, Tom (Thomas J.)
❑ 87OldJudN-131
Dold, John
❑ 93PriRedC-7
❑ 93PriRedF-4193
Dolejsi, Brad
❑ 91OklStaC-8
Dolejsi, Dale
❑ 94BriTigC-10
❑ 94BriTigF-3495
Dolf, Mike
❑ 76WilTomT-11
Doljack, Frank
❑ 33MrsShePP-3
❑ 34DiaMatCSB-46
❑ 34TigTeal-5
❑ 74TigTCM1AC-7
❑ 76TigOldTS-6
Doll, Chris
❑ 87BelMarL-24
❑ 88WauTimGS-4
Dollar, Toby
❑ 96GreFalDB-10
❑ 96GreFalDTI-7
❑ 98SanAntMG-9
Dolson, Andrew
❑ 91MedHatBJP-4092
❑ 91MedHatBJSP-17
❑ 92MedHatBJF-3205
❑ 92MedHatBJSP-8
❑ 93HagSunF-1873
❑ 94DunBluJC-9
❑ 94DunBluJF-2550
Doman, Roger
❑ 92St.CatBJC-7
❑ 92St.CatBJF-3382
❑ 93HagSunC-9
❑ 93HagSunF-1874
❑ 94DunBluJC-10
❑ 94DunBluJF-2551
❑ 95KnoSmoF-35
❑ 96DunBluJB-5
❑ 96DunBluJTI-7
❑ 97KnoSmo-9
❑ 98NasSouTI-11
❑ 98NasSouTISS-11
Dombrowski, Robert
❑ 89AriStaB-8
❑ 89BilMusP-2055
❑ 90CedRapRP-2328
Domecq, Ray
❑ 90MarPhiP-3192
❑ 91SpaPhiP-887
Domenichelli, Dom
❑ 59DarFar-6
Domenico, Brian
❑ 94SouOreAC-6
❑ 94SouOreAF-3613
Domingo, Placido
❑ 92PacSea-61
Domingo, Tyrone
❑ 92HigSchPLS-28
Dominguez, Frank
❑ 85MiaHur-3
❑ 89RenSilSCLC-256
❑ 90PalSprACLC-209
❑ 90PalSprAP-2580
❑ 91PalSprAP-2019
Dominguez, Johnny
❑ 93ElmPioC-6
Dominguez, Jose
❑ 85VisOakT-22
❑ 86OrlTwiP-5
❑ 88ShrCapP-1281
❑ 88TexLeaAGS-19
❑ 89ShrCapP-1854
Dominguez, Ken
❑ 87PanAmTUBI-NNO
❑ 90OneYanP-3390
❑ 92PriWilCC-28
❑ 92PriWilCF-165
❑ 93GreHorC-28
❑ 93OneYanC-27
❑ 93OneYanF-3520
❑ 94OneYanC-26
❑ 94OneYanF-3808
Dominico, Ron
❑ 84LitFalMT-26
❑ 85LitFalMT-4
Dominique, Andy
❑ 97BatCliTI-13
❑ 98PieBolWM-8
Domino, Robert
❑ 93PriRedC-8
❑ 93PriRedF-4182
❑ 94BilMusF-3673
❑ 94BilMusSP-2
Dominow, Eric
❑ 93EriSaiC-6
❑ 93EriSaiF-3123
Donaghue, Ray
❑ 77St.PetCT-15
❑ 78ArkTraT-6
Donahue, Chuck
❑ 86TamTarP-5
Donahue, Jack
❑ 87OldJudN-132
Donahue, Jiggs (John Augustus)
❑ 03BreE10-38
❑ 08AmeCarE91-74
❑ 11SpoLifCW-96
❑ 88SFHesCreN32-7
❑ 90KalBatN-13
Donahue, Jim (James A.)
❑ 87OldJudN-133
❑ 87OldJudN-134
Donahue, Margaret
❑ 31CubTeal-6
❑ 36CubTeal-6
Donahue, Matt
❑ 92EriSaiC-27
❑ 92EriSaiF-1611
❑ 93KanCouCC-6
❑ 93KanCouCF-909
❑ 93KanCouCTI-6
Donahue, Pat (Patrick W.)
❑ 09RamT20-37
❑ 11SpoLifM-5
Donahue, Red (Francis Rostell)
❑ 05IndSouPSoCP-7
Donahue, Tim
❑ 90RenSilSCLC-270
❑ 91ColIndC-24
❑ 91ColIndP-1491
❑ 92KinIndC-11
❑ 92KinIndF-2483
❑ 98CamPepP-19
Donald, Atley (Richard Atley)
❑ 40PlaBal-121
❑ 41PlaBal-38
❑ 43YanSta-9
❑ 75YanDyn1T-13
❑ 79DiaGre-12
❑ 95ConTSN-1413
Donald, Skip
❑ 95PitMetTI-NNO
Donald, Tremayne
❑ 90JohCitCS-9
❑ 92St.PetCC-19
❑ 92St.PetCF-2038
Donaldson, Bo
❑ 97BoiHawG-8
❑ 98LakElsSG-9
Donaldson, James
❑ 91SydWavF-20
Donaldson, John
❑ 78LauLonABS-28
❑ 86NegLeaF-77
❑ 90NegLeaS-8
❑ 94TedWil-104
Donaldson, John (John David)
❑ 67VanMouSO-5
❑ 68Top-244
❑ 68TopVen-244
❑ 69MilBra-75
❑ 69MLBOffS-85
❑ 69OPC-217
❑ 69Top-217
❑ 70MLBOffS-269
❑ 70OPC-418
❑ 70Top-418
❑ 72MilBra-93
❑ 83Pil69G-32
Donaldson, Rhodney
❑ 98KanCouC-7
❑ 98KanCouCCP-7
Donatelli, Andy
❑ 85UtiBluST-18
Donatelli, Augie
❑ 55Bow-313
Donati, John
❑ 92StaCluD-37
❑ 93BoiHawC-8
❑ 93BoiHawF-3922
❑ 94BoiHawC-9
❑ 94BoiHawF-3361
❑ 95Bow-233
❑ 95BowGolF-233
❑ 95CedRapKTI-25
❑ 95Exc-19
❑ 95MidLeaA-12
Donato, Dan
❑ 95GreBatTI-3
❑ 96BowBes-121
❑ 96BowBesAR-121
❑ 96BowBesR-121
❑ 96Exc-86
❑ 96NorNavB-7
❑ 97NorNav-15
❑ 97NorNavTI-8
Donavan, T.J.
❑ 98BatMucTI-8
Dondero, Leonard
❑ 31Zee-46
Done, Johnny
❑ 94WatIndC-5
❑ 94WatIndF-3926
❑ 96AriBlaDB-16
Donecq, Ray
❑ 91SpaPhiC-2
Donkey-Hokey, Mascot
❑ 96ButCopKB-8
Donlin, Mike (Michael J.)
❑ 03BreE10-39
❑ 06FanCraNL-13
❑ 06GiaUllAFS-2
❑ 08AmeCarE91-9
❑ 08AmeCarE91-44
❑ 08RosComP-127
❑ 09AmeCarE90-1-33
❑ 09RamT20-38
❑ 09T206-94
❑ 09T206-95
❑ 09T206-96
❑ 10CouT21-119
❑ 10CouT21-120
❑ 10CouT21-274
❑ 10RedCroT-19
❑ 10RedCroT-103
❑ 10RedCroT-183
❑ 11HelSta-158
❑ 11SpoLifCW-97
❑ 12ColRedB-79
❑ 12ColTinT-79
❑ 12HasTriFT-30A
❑ 12HasTriFT-30B
❑ 12HasTriFT-30C
❑ 12HasTriFT-30D
❑ 12HasTriFT-30E
❑ 12T207-47
❑ 75FlePio-25
❑ 92ConTSN-450
❑ 94ConTSN-1051
❑ 94ConTSNB-1051
Donnelly, Blix (Sylvester)
❑ 46SeaSLP-16
❑ 49Bow-145
❑ 49EurSta-133
❑ 49PhiBul-15
❑ 50Bow-176
❑ 50PhiPhil-6
❑ 51Bow-208
❑ 75Phi195T-8
❑ 76TayBow4-71
❑ 80Phi195T-8
❑ 83Car194T-60
Donnelly, Brendan
❑ 93GenCubC-8
❑ 93GenCubF-3166
❑ 96ChaLooB-11
❑ 97ChaLoo-8
❑ 98ChaLooG-7
Donnelly, Ed (Edward)
❑ 12T207-48
Donnelly, Jim (James B.)
❑ 87BucN28-111
❑ 87OldJudN-135
❑ 88WG1CarG-64
Donnelly, Rich
❑ 74GasRanT-8
❑ 76SacSolC-22
❑ 77TucTorC-14
❑ 78TucTorC-42
❑ 79TucTorT-8
❑ 83RanAffF-NNO
❑ 84RanJarP-NNO
❑ 85RanPer-NNO
❑ 88PirTeal-8
❑ 89PirVerFJ-39
❑ 90PirHomC-9
❑ 92PirNatI-6
❑ 93PirNatI-9
❑ 93RanKee-127
❑ 94PirQui-5
❑ 97MarPac-26
Donnelly, Robert
❑ 95NewJerCTI-8
❑ 96PeoChiB-9
❑ 97PriWilC-10
❑ 98St.PauSTI-3
Donnels, Chris
❑ 88ColMetGS-26
❑ 88St.LucMS-6
❑ 89St.LucMS-5
❑ 89Sta-116
❑ 90JacMetGS-12
❑ 90MetColP-30
❑ 90TopTVM-41
❑ 91Bow-465
❑ 91Cla3-T16
❑ 91Lea-447
❑ 91LinDriAAA-554
❑ 91MetColP-29
❑ 91ScoRoo-104T
❑ 91TidTidLD-554
❑ 91TidTidP-2516
❑ 91TriA AAGP-AAA47
❑ 91UppDecFE-61F
❑ 92Don-619
❑ 92MetColP-21
❑ 92OPC-376
❑ 92Pin-168
❑ 92ProFS7-275
❑ 92Sco-212
❑ 92Sco100RS-79
❑ 92ScoRoo-29
❑ 92SkyAAAF-249
❑ 92StaClu-353
❑ 92TidTidF-904
❑ 92TidTidS-555
❑ 92Top-376
❑ 92TopDeb91-45
❑ 92TopGol-376
❑ 92TopGolW-376
❑ 92TopMic-376
❑ 92UppDec-44
❑ 93AstMot-22
❑ 93AstStaC-23
❑ 93Don-747
❑ 93Fle-426
❑ 93PacSpa-475
❑ 93Top-238
❑ 93TopGol-238
❑ 93TopInaM-238
❑ 93TopInaR-238
❑ 93TopMic-238
❑ 94AstMot-16
❑ 94Fle-488
❑ 94Pac-262
❑ 94Sco-172
❑ 94ScoGolR-172
❑ 94StaClu-334
❑ 94StaCluFDI-334
❑ 94StaCluGR-334
❑ 94StaCluMOP-334
❑ 94Top-153
❑ 94TopGol-153
❑ 94TopSpa-153
❑ 95ColCho-107
❑ 95ColChoGS-107
❑ 95ColChoSS-107
Donofrio, Larry
❑ 80AshTouT-22
❑ 81AppFoxT-13
❑ 82GleFalWST-4
Donohoo, Chris
❑ 98LowSpiM-20
Donohue, J.A.
❑ 08AmeCarE91-75
Donohue, Jiggs (John F.)
❑ 07WhiSoxGWH-3
❑ 08RosComP-13
❑ 09T206-97
❑ 11T205-41
❑ 72ClaCar-118
Donohue, Jim (James A.)
❑ 87BucN28-57
Donohue, Jim (James T.)
❑ 60Top-124
❑ 60TopVen-124
❑ 61Top-151
❑ 62Top-498
Donohue, Pat
❑ 93JohCitCC-10
❑ 93JohCitCF-3687
Donohue, Pete (Peter J.)
❑ 21Nei-77
❑ 22E120-170
❑ 22W572-24
❑ 25Exh-27
❑ 26Exh-27
❑ 29PorandAR-16
❑ 31W517-26
❑ 91ConTSN-322
Donohue, Steve
❑ 79WesHavYT-19
❑ 82ColCliT-24
❑ 84ColCliT-21
Donohue, Tom (Thomas J.)
❑ 77SalLakCGC-8
❑ 78SalLakCGC-8
❑ 80Top-454
❑ 81Don-51A
❑ 81Don-51B
❑ 81Fle-281
❑ 81Top-621
Donovan, Bret
❑ 88CapCodPPaLP-165
❑ 92ClaFS7-322
❑ 92ElmPioC-3
❑ 92ElmPioF-1375
❑ 92WinHavRSC-22
❑ 93LynRedSC-7
❑ 93LynRedSF-2510
Donovan, Dick (Richard E.)
❑ 47Exh-63A
❑ 47Exh-63B
❑ 55Top-146
❑ 56Top-18
❑ 56TopPin-32
❑ 57Top-181
❑ 58Top-290
❑ 58WhiSoxJP-2
❑ 59Top-5
❑ 59TopVen-5
❑ 60Lea-72
❑ 60Top-199
❑ 60WhiSoxTS-4
❑ 61Baz-10
❑ 61Top-414
❑ 61TopStaI-202
❑ 62IndJayP-2
❑ 62Jel-73
❑ 62Kah-8
❑ 62Pos-73
❑ 62PosCan-73
❑ 62Top-15
❑ 62Top-55
❑ 62TopStaI-33
❑ 62TopVen-15
❑ 62TopVen-55
❑ 63Baz-10
❑ 63Fle-11
❑ 63IndJayP-5
❑ 63Jel-75
❑ 63Pos-75
❑ 63SalMetC-34
❑ 63Top-8
❑ 63Top-370
❑ 63TopStiI-13
❑ 64IndJayP-4
❑ 64Kah-7
❑ 79TCM50-34
❑ 81WhiSox1T-31
❑ 83Bra53F-20
Donovan, Gary
❑ 77BurBeeT-6
Donovan, Jack
❑ 81TucTorT-25
Donovan, Jack PCL
❑ 88SFHesCreN32-8
Donovan, Jerry
❑ 28Zee-130
❑ 29Zee-129
❑ 30Zee-141
❑ 31Zee-103
❑ 32Zee-98
❑ 33Zee-38
❑ 33Zee-85
Donovan, Mike (Michael B.)
❑ 80BurBeeT-3
Donovan, Patsy (Patrick J.)
❑ 03BreE10-40
❑ 04FanCraAL-15
❑ 11BasBatEU-20
❑ 11HelSta-31
❑ 11PinT-5-675
❑ 11SpoLifCW-98
❑ 11SpoLifM-6
❑ 90DodTar-191
❑ 98CamPepP-21
Donovan, Scot
❑ 94WatIndC-6
❑ 94WatIndF-3927
❑ 96KenIndB-6
Donovan, Wild Bill (William E.)
❑ 03WilCarE-11
❑ 07TigACDPP-4
❑ 07TigACDPP-20
❑ 08RosComP-34
❑ 08TigFreGWP-1
❑ 09AmeCarE90-1-34
❑ 09ColChiE-80
❑ 09RamT20-39
❑ 09T206-98
❑ 09T206-99
❑ 09TigHMTP-5
❑ 09TigHMTP-6
❑ 09TigHMTP-8
❑ 09TigMorBBBP-6
❑ 09TigMorPWBPP-4
❑ 09TigTaCP-6
❑ 09WolNewDTPP-6
❑ 09WolNewDTPP-19
❑ 10CouT21-16
❑ 10CouT21-121
❑ 10CouT21-275
❑ 10DarChoE-15
❑ 10E101-15
❑ 10E102-7
❑ 10MelMinE-15
❑ 10NadCarE-17
❑ 10PeoT21-17A
❑ 10PeoT21-17B
❑ 10StaCarE-11
❑ 10SweCapPP-24
❑ 10W555-24
❑ 11MecDFT-45
❑ 11PinT-5-160
❑ 11PloCanE-25
❑ 11SpoLifCW-99
❑ 11SpoLifM-58
❑ 11TurRedT-12
❑ 12ColRedB-80
❑ 12ColTinT-80
❑ 12PhiCarE-9
❑ 15AmeCarE106-12
❑ 15SpoNewM-49
❑ 16FleBreD-24
❑ 16SpoNewM-48
❑ 17ColE13-43
❑ 21E121So8-18
❑ 22AmeCarE122-17
❑ 22W575-28
❑ 23WilChoV-31
❑ 68SCFOldT-27
❑ 72ClaCar-77
❑ 81TigDetN-29
❑ 81TigSecNP-7
❑ 87ConSer2-13
❑ 90DodTar-192
Doody, Tom
❑ 96BatCliTI-32
Dooin, Red (Charles S.)
❑ 03WilCarE-12
❑ 06FanCraNL-14

❑ 08RosComP-139
❑ 08AmeCarE90-1-35
❑ 09ColChiE-79
❑ 09ColChiE-81
❑ 09SpoNewSM-43
❑ 09T206-100
❑ 10DomDisP-34
❑ 10E101-16
❑ 10E102-8
❑ 10E98-13
❑ 10LuxCigPP-7
❑ 10MelMinE-16
❑ 10NadCarE-18
❑ 10PeoT21-18A
❑ 10PeoT21-18B
❑ 10SepAnoP-12
❑ 10StaCarE-12
❑ 10SweCapPP-125A
❑ 10SweCapPP-125B
❑ 10W555-25
❑ 11DiaGumP-12
❑ 11HelSta-141
❑ 11L1L-126
❑ 11MecDFT-16
❑ 11PinT-5-303
❑ 11PloCanE-26
❑ 11S74Sil-98
❑ 11S81LarS-101
❑ 11SpoLifCW-100
❑ 11SpoLifM-226
❑ 11T205-42
❑ 11TurRedT-14
❑ 12ColRedB-81
❑ 12ColTinT-81
❑ 12HasTriFT-30D
❑ 12HasTriFT-31A
❑ 12HasTriFT-31B
❑ 12HasTriFT-31C
❑ 12HasTriFT-51
❑ 12PhiCarE-10
❑ 12T207-49
❑ 13NatGamW-15
❑ 13TomBarW-14
❑ 14CraJacE-38
❑ 14PieStaT-32
❑ 14TexTomE-18
❑ 15AmeCarE106-13
❑ 15CraJacE-38
❑ 15SpoNewM-50
❑ 16BF2FP-77
❑ 16SpoNewM-49
❑ 16TanBraE-8
❑ 16TanBraE-14
❑ 72ClaCar-38

Doolan, Blake
❑ 92BatCliCB-25
❑ 92BatCliF-3256
❑ 93SpaPhiC-12
❑ 93SpaPhiF-1050
❑ 94ClePhiC-12
❑ 94ClePhiF-2521
❑ 95ReaPhiELC-9
❑ 95ReaPhiTI-10
❑ 96Exc-197
❑ 96ScrRedBB-11

Doolan, Mickey (Michael J.)
❑ 06FanCraNL-15
❑ 08RosComP-140
❑ 09BriE97-9
❑ 09ColChiE-82
❑ 09T206-101
❑ 09T206-102
❑ 09T206-103
❑ 10CouT21-17
❑ 10CouT21-122
❑ 10CouT21-123
❑ 10CouT21-124
❑ 10CouT21-125
❑ 10CouT21-276
❑ 10CouT21-277
❑ 10DomDisP-35
❑ 10E-UOraBSC-10
❑ 10E101-17
❑ 10LuxCigPP-8
❑ 10MelMinE-17
❑ 10NadCarE-19
❑ 10PeoT21-19A
❑ 10PeoT21-19B
❑ 10RedCroT-20
❑ 10RedCroT-104
❑ 10RedCroT-105
❑ 10RedCroT-184
❑ 10RedCroT-185
❑ 10SweCapPP-126A
❑ 10SweCapPP-126B
❑ 10W555-26
❑ 11E94-12
❑ 11HelSta-142
❑ 11PinT-5-310
❑ 11S74Sil-99
❑ 11SpoLifCW-101
❑ 11SpoLifM-227
❑ 11T205-43
❑ 11TurRedT-90
❑ 12ColRedB-82
❑ 12ColTinT-82
❑ 12HasTriFT-31A
❑ 14CraJacE-120
❑ 14PieStaT-33
❑ 15AmeCarE106-14
❑ 15CraJacE-120
❑ 15SpoNewM-51
❑ 15VicT21-7
❑ 16SpoNewM-50
❑ 90DodTar-193

Dooley, Charles
❑ 87OldJudN-136

Dooley, Chris
❑ 96JohCitCTI-10

Dooley, Joseph
❑ 20Zee-107

Dooley, Marvin
❑ 89PriPirS-6

Dooner, Glenn
❑ 82TolMudHT-2

Doornenweerd, Dave
❑ 92Bow-146
❑ 92StaCluD-38
❑ 94SalBucC-7
❑ 94SalBucF-2317
❑ 96LakElsSB-4
❑ 96MidAngB-13

Dophied, Tracy
❑ 82AubAstT-12

Doprante, Luis
❑ 93ForLauRSC-28

Dopson, John
❑ 86IndIndTI-12
❑ 88DonRoo-43
❑ 88ExpPos-6
❑ 88FleUpd-99
❑ 88FleUpdG-99
❑ 88ScoRoo-88T
❑ 88ScoRooG-88T
❑ 89Bow-24
❑ 89BowTif-24
❑ 89ClaTraP-161
❑ 89Don-392
❑ 89DonBasB-177
❑ 89DonTra-7
❑ 89Fle-373
❑ 89FleGlo-373
❑ 89FleUpd-8
❑ 89OPC-251
❑ 89Sco-466
❑ 89ScoRoo-40T
❑ 89Top-251
❑ 89TopTif-251
❑ 89TopTra-26T
❑ 89TopTraT-26T
❑ 89UppDec-57
❑ 90Don-162
❑ 90Fle-272
❑ 90FleCan-272
❑ 90Lea-130
❑ 90OPC-733
❑ 90PanSti-18
❑ 90RedSoxP-7
❑ 90Sco-331
❑ 90ScoYouSI-26
❑ 90Top-733
❑ 90TopSti-260
❑ 90TopTif-733
❑ 90TopTVRS-9
❑ 90UppDec-671
❑ 91Don-193
❑ 91Fle-92
❑ 91OPC-94
❑ 91RedSoxP-9
❑ 91Sco-772
❑ 91Top-94
❑ 91TopDesS-94
❑ 91TopMic-94
❑ 91TopTif-94
❑ 91UppDec-88
❑ 92OPC-400
❑ 92PawRedSS-360
❑ 92StaClu-287
❑ 93Fle-557
❑ 93PacSpa-31
❑ 93RedSoxP-10
❑ 93RedSoxWHP-10
❑ 93StaClu-41
❑ 93StaCluFDI-41
❑ 93StaCluMOP-41
❑ 93Top-187
❑ 93TopGol-187
❑ 93TopInaM-187
❑ 93TopInaR-187
❑ 93TopMic-187
❑ 93Ult-151
❑ 93UppDec-409
❑ 93UppDecGold-409
❑ 94AngLAT-3
❑ 94AngMot-27
❑ 94ColC-443
❑ 94ColChoGS-443
❑ 94ColChoSS-443
❑ 94Don-104
❑ 94Fle-31
❑ 94Pac-53
❑ 94Sco-113
❑ 94ScoGolR-113
❑ 94StaClu-641
❑ 94StaCluFDI-641
❑ 94StaCluGR-641
❑ 94StaCluMOP-641
❑ 94Top-321
❑ 94TopGol-321
❑ 94TopSpa-321
❑ 97DunDonPPS-7

Doran, Bill
❑ 82TucTorT-7
❑ 83AstPos-7
❑ 83TopTra-26T
❑ 84AllGamPI-10
❑ 84AstMot-4
❑ 84AstPos-9
❑ 84Don-580
❑ 84Fle-225
❑ 84Nes792-198
❑ 84OPC-198
❑ 84Top-198
❑ 84TopSti-377
❑ 84TopTif-198
❑ 85AllGamPI-100
❑ 85AstHouP-1
❑ 85AstMot-8
❑ 85Don-84
❑ 85Fle-350
❑ 85OPC-299
❑ 85Top-684
❑ 85TopSti-68
❑ 85TopTif-684
❑ 86AstMilL-8
❑ 86AstPol-5
❑ 86AstTeaI-5
❑ 86BasStaB-33
❑ 86Don-10
❑ 86Don-110
❑ 86DonSupD-10
❑ 86Fle-300
❑ 86Lea-10
❑ 86OPC-57
❑ 86SevCoi-S14
❑ 86Top-57
❑ 86TopSti-25
❑ 86TopTat-19
❑ 86TopTif-57
❑ 87AstMot-4
❑ 87AstPol-5
❑ 87Don-286
❑ 87DonOpeD-11
❑ 87Fle-57
❑ 87FleGlo-57
❑ 87GenMilB-6C
❑ 87Lea-197
❑ 87OPC-243
❑ 87RedFolSB-69
❑ 87Spo-116
❑ 87Spo-162
❑ 87SpoTeaP-8
❑ 87Top-472
❑ 87TopMinL-9
❑ 87TopSti-31
❑ 87TopTif-472
❑ 88AstMot-4
❑ 88AstPol-10
❑ 88Don-235
❑ 88DonBasB-120
❑ 88Fle-447
❑ 88FleGlo-447
❑ 88FleLeaL-10
❑ 88FleStiC-87
❑ 88Lea-183
❑ 88Nes-19
❑ 88OPC-166
❑ 88PanSti-295
❑ 88Sco-52
❑ 88ScoGlo-52
❑ 88Spo-48
❑ 88StaLinAst-9
❑ 88Top-745
❑ 88TopBig-51
❑ 88TopSti-34
❑ 88TopTif-745
❑ 89AstLenH-8
❑ 89AstMot-4
❑ 89AstSmo-13
❑ 89Bow-329
❑ 89BowTif-329
❑ 89Don-306
❑ 89DonBasB-38
❑ 89Fle-357
❑ 89FleGlo-357
❑ 89OPC-226
❑ 89PanSti-89
❑ 89RedFolSB-37
❑ 89Sco-21
❑ 89Spo-57
❑ 89Top-226
❑ 89TopBig-168
❑ 89TopSti-16
❑ 89TopTif-226
❑ 89TopUKM-22
❑ 89UppDec-101
❑ 90AstLenH-13
❑ 90AstMot-7
❑ 90Bow-76
❑ 90BowTif-76
❑ 90Don-236
❑ 90DonBesN-102
❑ 90Fle-230
❑ 90FleCan-230
❑ 90Lea-161
❑ 90M.Vpin-41
❑ 90MLBBasB-44
❑ 90OPC-368
❑ 90PanSti-268
❑ 90PubIntS-94
❑ 90PubIntS-257
❑ 90Sco-182
❑ 90Sco100S-8
❑ 90Top-368
❑ 90TopBig-159
❑ 90TopSti-15
❑ 90TopTif-368
❑ 90UppDec-198
❑ 90UppDecS-1
❑ 91Bow-682
❑ 91Don-756
❑ 91Fle-63
❑ 91Lea-197
❑ 91OPC-577
❑ 91RedKah-19
❑ 91RedPep-8
❑ 91Sco-775
❑ 91SimandSMLBL-14
❑ 91StaClu-148
❑ 91Top-577
❑ 91TopDesS-577
❑ 91TopMic-577
❑ 91TopTif-577
❑ 91Ult-93
❑ 91UppDec-398
❑ 92Bow-234
❑ 92Don-293
❑ 92Fle-405
❑ 92Lea-231
❑ 92LeaBlaG-231
❑ 92OPC-136
❑ 92PanSti-263
❑ 92Pin-47
❑ 92RedKah-19
❑ 92Sco-77
❑ 92ScoProP-11
❑ 92StaClu-38
❑ 92Top-136
❑ 92TopGol-136
❑ 92TopGolW-136
❑ 92TopMic-136
❑ 92Ult-188
❑ 92UppDec-280
❑ 93BrePol-5
❑ 93Don-370
❑ 93Fle-390
❑ 93PacSpa-82
❑ 93Top-608
❑ 93TopGol-608
❑ 93TopInaM-608
❑ 93TopInaR-608
❑ 93TopMic-608
❑ 93Ult-28
❑ 93UppDec-107
❑ 93UppDecGold-107
❑ 94BreMilB-308

Doran, John (John F.)
❑ 87OldJudN-137

Doran, Mark
❑ 86PalSprAP-11
❑ 87MidAngP-21
❑ 88EdmTraC-24
❑ 88EdmTraP-570
❑ 89MidAngGS-14

Doran, Tom
❑ 11SpoLifCW-102

Dorante, Luis
❑ 87ElmPioBC-14
❑ 87ElmPioRC-14
❑ 88ElmPioC-12
❑ 89ElmPioP-3
❑ 90LynRedSTI-11
❑ 91WinHavRSC-12
❑ 91WinHavRSP-492
❑ 93ForLauRSFP-1614
❑ 93LinVenB-52
❑ 94VenLinU-75
❑ 98CapFeaCM-27

Dorencz, Mark
❑ 94QuaCitRBC-9
❑ 94QuaCitRBF-540

Dorgan, Charles
❑ 77CliDodT-6

Dorgan, Mike (Michael C.)
❑ 86OldJudN-4
❑ 87BucN28-66A
❑ 87BucN28-66B
❑ 87OldJudN-138
❑ 88AugBecN-12
❑ 90KalBatN-14

Dorish, Harry
❑ 47RedSoxTI-6
❑ 48RedSoxTI-5
❑ 51Bow-266
❑ 52Top-303
❑ 53Top-145
❑ 54Bow-86
❑ 54Top-110
❑ 55Bow-248
❑ 56BalOriP-15
❑ 56Top-167
❑ 68BraPos-10
❑ 79BufBisT-12
❑ 79DiaGre-240
❑ 80PorBeaT-14
❑ 83TopRep5-303
❑ 91OriCro-111
❑ 91TopArc1-145
❑ 94TopArc1-110
❑ 94TopArc1G-110
❑ 97BalOriP-14

Dorlarque, Aaron
❑ 89AncBucTI-4
❑ 92EugEmeC-10
❑ 92EugEmeF-3021
❑ 93RocRoyC-12
❑ 93RocRoyF-711
❑ 94MemChiF-350
❑ 95WicWraTI-17

Dorman, Charles
❑ 20Zee-20

Dorman, John
❑ 98KinIndQ-7

Dorn, Chris
❑ 89PitMetS-4
❑ 90ColMetGS-20
❑ 90ColMetPPI-5
❑ 91St.LucMC-22
❑ 91St.LucMP-703
❑ 92BinMetF-508
❑ 92BinMetS-54
❑ 93BinMetF-2327

Dorner, Gus (Augustus)
❑ 09RamT20-40
❑ 09T206-419
❑ 11SpoLifCW-103

Dorsett, Brian
❑ 84ModA'sC-10
❑ 85HunStaJ-22
❑ 85MadMusP-8
❑ 85MadMusT-11
❑ 86TacTigP-3
❑ 87TacTigP-22
❑ 88Fle-607
❑ 88FleGlo-607
❑ 89ColCliC-14
❑ 89ColCliP-12
❑ 89ColCliP-759
❑ 90ColCliP-18
❑ 90ColCliP-679
❑ 90ProAAAF-329
❑ 90TopTVY-40
❑ 90TriAllGP-AAA14
❑ 91LasVegSLD-279
❑ 91LasVegSP-238
❑ 91LinDriAAA-279
❑ 91PadSmo-8
❑ 91SouOreAAP-SOA16
❑ 92BufBisBS-7
❑ 92BufBisF-326
❑ 92BufBisS-32
❑ 92YanWIZ8-46
❑ 93IndIndF-1492
❑ 93TriAAAGF-8
❑ 94Pac-146
❑ 94RedKah-8
❑ 94Top-688
❑ 94TopGol-688
❑ 94TopSpa-688
❑ 95Don-549
❑ 95DonPreP-549
❑ 95Fla-120
❑ 95Fle-433
❑ 95IndIndF-98
❑ 95Pac-103
❑ 95Sco-252
❑ 95ScoGolR-252
❑ 95ScoPlaTS-252
❑ 95Ult-364
❑ 95UltGolM-364
❑ 97PacPriGotD-GD117

Dorsett, Cal
❑ 94ConTSN-1295
❑ 94ConTSNB-1295

Dorsey, Jim (James Edward)
❑ 75QuaCitAT-7
❑ 79SalLakCGT-14
❑ 80SalLakCGT-16
❑ 80VenLeaS-169
❑ 81PawRedST-9
❑ 81Top-214
❑ 83PawRedST-6
❑ 84PawRedST-6
❑ 85DomLeaS-127
❑ 93KinMetC-9
❑ 93KinMetF-3808
❑ 94PitMetC-7
❑ 94PitMetF-3533

Dorsey, Lee
❑ 90UtiBluSP-30

Doscher, Jack
❑ 90DodTar-194

Dose, Gary
❑ 97ForWayW-9

Doskocil, Darren
❑ 98St.PauSTI-4

Doss, Dennis
❑ 76BatTroTI-7
❑ 77WatIndT-6

Doss, Greg
❑ 88SavCarP-357

Doss, Jason
❑ 88WytCubP-1998
❑ 89ChaWheB-20
❑ 89ChaWheP-1765
❑ 90PeoChiTI-19
❑ 91PeoChiC-5
❑ 91PeoChiP-1336
❑ 91PeoChiTI-7
❑ 92WinSpiC-9
❑ 92WinSpiF-1204

Doss, Larry
❑ 87JamExpP-2546

Doss, Raymond
❑ 89WelPirP-11

Doss, Rick
❑ 79CedRapGT-10

Dostal, Bruce
❑ 88BakDodCLC-247
❑ 89VerBeaDS-7
❑ 90FloStaLAS-3
❑ 90VerBeaDS-11
❑ 91LinDriAA-507
❑ 91ReaPhiLD-507
❑ 91ReaPhiP-1381
❑ 92ReaPhiF-586
❑ 92ScrRedBS-483
❑ 92SkyAAAF-220
❑ 93ScrRedBTI-8
❑ 94RocRedWF-1009
❑ 94RocRedWTI-7

Doster, David

❑ 94ClePhiC-1
❑ 94ClePhiF-2534
❑ 94FloStaLAF-FSL32
❑ 95Exc-241
❑ 95ReaPhiELC-10
❑ 95ReaPhiTI-3
❑ 96BesAutS-29
❑ 96Bow-316
❑ 96BowFoi-316
❑ 96ColCho-444
❑ 96ColChoGS-444
❑ 96ColChoSS-444
❑ 96Exc-198
❑ 96Fla-331
❑ 96FlaWavotF-7
❑ 96FleUpd-U163
❑ 96FleUpdTC-U163
❑ 96ScrRedBB-12
❑ 96Ult-518
❑ 96UltGolM-518
❑ 96UppDec-265
❑ 97ColCho-194
❑ 97Don-162
❑ 97DonGolPP-162
❑ 97DonSilPP-162
❑ 97Pac-375
❑ 97PacLigB-375
❑ 97PacSil-375
❑ 97ScrRedB-1
❑ 97Ult-248
❑ 97UltGolME-248
❑ 97UltPlaME-248
❑ 98ScrRedBQ-10
Doster, Zach
❑ 87FayGenP-7
❑ 88FayGenP-1090
❑ 89MiaMirIS-5
Dotel, Angel
❑ 92BakDodCLC-9
❑ 93VerBeaDC-5
❑ 93VerBeaDF-2226
Dotel, Mariano
❑ 91MyrBeaHC-19
❑ 91MyrBeaHP-2953
❑ 92DunBluJC-12
❑ 92DunBluJF-2006
❑ 93HagSunC-10
❑ 93HagSunF-1887
Dotel, Melido
❑ 97GreFalDTI-9
❑ 98GreFalDG-10
❑ 98SanBerS-9
❑ 98SanBerSTIS-9
Dotel, Octavio
❑ 97BinMetB-7
❑ 97Bow-364
❑ 97BowChr-244
❑ 97BowChrI-244
❑ 97BowChrIR-244
❑ 97BowChrR-244
❑ 97BowInt-364
❑ 97CapCitB-1
❑ 98BesAutSS-19
❑ 98BinMetQ-11
❑ 98Bow-377
❑ 98BowChr-377
❑ 98BowChrGA-377
❑ 98BowChrGAR-377
❑ 98BowChrI-377
❑ 98BowChrIR-377
❑ 98BowChrR-377
❑ 98BowGolA-377
❑ 98BowInt-377
❑ 98EasLeaTPM-7
❑ 98NorTidQ-9
❑ 98SP MinPE-82
❑ 98SPMin-82
❑ 98UppDec-562
❑ 99BasAmeTP-33
❑ 99BasAmeTPG-33
❑ 99BasAmeTPSC-4
❑ 99Bow-188
❑ 99BowChr-188
❑ 99BowChrG-188
❑ 99BowChrGR-188
❑ 99BowChrI-188
❑ 99BowChrIR-188
❑ 99BowChrR-188
❑ 99BowGol-188
❑ 99BowInt-188
❑ 99BowPreProd-PP5
❑ 99PacOme-152
❑ 99PacOmeC-152
❑ 99PacOmeG-152
❑ 99PacOmePB-152
❑ 99SP SigAuto-OD
❑ 99SP SigAutoG-OD
❑ 99SPSig-30
❑ 99TeaBesRBG-6
❑ 99Top-211
❑ 99TopChr-211
❑ 99TopChrR-211
❑ 99Vic-250
Dotelson, Angel
❑ 91KisDodP-4200
Dotolo, C.L.
❑ 92CliGiaC-25
❑ 92CliGiaF-3603
❑ 93SanJosGF-16
❑ 94SanJosGC-6
❑ 94SanJosGF-2823
Dotson, Gene (J.)
❑ 78ArkTraT-7
❑ 79ArkTraT-8
❑ 83LouRedR-15
Dotson, Larry
❑ 81WatIndT-25
Dotson, Rich (Richard E.)
❑ 78KnoKnoST-3
❑ 79KnoKnoST-8
❑ 81AllGamPI-76
❑ 81CokTeaS-27
❑ 81Don-280
❑ 81Fle-356
❑ 81OPC-138
❑ 81Top-138
❑ 81TopSti-62
❑ 81TopSupHT-14
❑ 82Don-356
❑ 82Fle-340
❑ 82FleSta-186
❑ 82OPC-257
❑ 82Top-461
❑ 82TopSti-166
❑ 82TopStiV-166
❑ 83AllGamPI-75
❑ 83Don-319
❑ 83Fle-233
❑ 83OPC-46
❑ 83Top-46
❑ 83WhiSoxTV-34
❑ 84AllGamPI-170
❑ 84Don-180
❑ 84Fle-56
❑ 84FleSti-62
❑ 84Nes792-216
❑ 84Nes792-759
❑ 84OPC-24
❑ 84Top-216
❑ 84Top-759
❑ 84TopSti-241
❑ 84TopTif-216
❑ 84TopTif-759
❑ 84WhiSoxTV-10
❑ 85Don-3
❑ 85Don-302
❑ 85DonSupD-3
❑ 85Fle-511
❑ 85Lea-3
❑ 85OPC-364
❑ 85Top-364
❑ 85TopSti-233
❑ 85TopTif-364
❑ 85WhiSoxC-34
❑ 86Don-160
❑ 86Fle-203
❑ 86MSAJayPCD-5
❑ 86OPC-233
❑ 86Spo-133
❑ 86Top-156
❑ 86Top-612
❑ 86TopTif-156
❑ 86TopTif-612
❑ 86WhiSoxC-34
❑ 87Don-383
❑ 87DonOpeD-238
❑ 87Fle-495
❑ 87FleGlo-495
❑ 87FleMin-33
❑ 87OPC-211
❑ 87Top-720
❑ 87TopTif-720
❑ 87WhiSoxC-8
❑ 88Don-124
❑ 88DonBasB-52
❑ 88DonReaBY-NEW
❑ 88Fle-396
❑ 88FleGlo-396
❑ 88FleUpd-48
❑ 88FleUpdG-48
❑ 88OPC-209
❑ 88PanSti-53
❑ 88Sco-480
❑ 88ScoGlo-480
❑ 88ScoRoo-60T
❑ 88ScoRooG-60T
❑ 88StaLinWS-6
❑ 88Top-209
❑ 88TopSti-291
❑ 88TopTif-209
❑ 88TopTra-35T
❑ 88TopTraT-35T
❑ 89Don-277
❑ 89Fle-253
❑ 89FleGlo-253
❑ 89OPC-357
❑ 89PanSti-398
❑ 89Sco-278
❑ 89ScoRoo-80T
❑ 89Spo-194
❑ 89Top-511
❑ 89TopDouM-22
❑ 89TopSti-316
❑ 89TopTif-511
❑ 89UppDec-80
❑ 89YanScoNW-23
❑ 90OPC-169
❑ 90PublntS-533
❑ 90Sco-19
❑ 90Top-169
❑ 90TopTif-169
❑ 92YanWIZ8-47
❑ 93UppDecS-14
Dotter, Gary (Gary Richard)
❑ 65Top-421
Dotterer, Dutch (Henry John)
❑ 58RedEnq-9
❑ 58SeaRalT-6
❑ 58Top-396
❑ 59RedEnq-4
❑ 59RedShiBS-4
❑ 59Top-288
❑ 60RedJayP-2
❑ 60Top-21
❑ 60TopVen-21
❑ 61Top-332
❑ 61TopMagR-24
Dotterer, Tommy
❑ 61Top-332
Doty, Derrin
❑ 91WasVia-2
❑ 93BoiHawC-9
❑ 93BoiHawF-3927
❑ 94CedRapKC-8
❑ 94CedRapKF-1121
❑ 94MidLeaAF-MDW36
❑ 95AusFut-36
❑ 95LakElsSTI-12
❑ 96MidAngB-14
Doty, Sean
❑ 89BilMusP-2052
❑ 90BilMusP-3212
❑ 91ChaWheC-2
❑ 91ChaWheP-2879
❑ 92CedRapRC-25
❑ 92CedRapRF-1063
Dotzler, Mike
❑ 86DayBealP-7
❑ 87SalBucP-12
❑ 88OrlTwiB-21
❑ 89VisOakCLC-105
❑ 89VisOakP-1438
Doubleday, Abner
❑ 36Halof FP-31
❑ 39PC7AlbHoF-63
❑ 80PerHaloFP-A
❑ 90BasWit-108
❑ 94OriofB-1
Doubledays, Auburn
❑ 98AubDouTI-34
Doucet, Brandon
❑ 98HelBreM-13
Doucet, Eric
❑ 89BoiHawP-1983
Doucette, Darren
❑ 92HamRedC-22
❑ 92HamRedF-1598
❑ 93SavCarC-12
❑ 93SavCarF-692
❑ 94MadHatC-10
❑ 94MadHatF-140
Dougherty, Jeb
❑ 97BoiHawG-9
❑ 98CedRapKTI-9
Dougherty, Jim (James)
❑ 88CapCodPPaLP-55
❑ 92ClaFS7-351
❑ 92OscAstC-17
❑ 92OscAstF-2521
❑ 93ClaGolF-65
❑ 93ExcFS7-41
❑ 93JacGenF-2102
❑ 94ExcFS7-198
❑ 94TriAAF-AAA45
❑ 94TucTorF-754
❑ 94UppDecML-121
❑ 95AstMot-25
❑ 95Emo-137
❑ 95Fla-358
❑ 95FleAllR-M6
❑ 95StaClu-598
❑ 95StaCluMOP-598
❑ 95StaCluSTWS-598
❑ 96ColCho-561
❑ 96ColChoGS-561
❑ 96ColChoSS-561
❑ 96Fle-404
❑ 96FleTif-404
❑ 96Sco-232
❑ 96Top-76
❑ 96TusTorB-6
❑ 96Ult-486
❑ 96UltGolM-486
❑ 97NorTid-10
❑ 97NorTidB-10
Dougherty, Mark
❑ 83EriCarT-7
❑ 86ArkTraP-6
❑ 87LouRedTI-11
❑ 88LouRedBC-23
❑ 88LouRedBP-444
❑ 88LouRedBTI-18
Dougherty, Pat
❑ 04FanCraAL-16
❑ 07WhiSoxGWH-4
❑ 86BurExpP-6
Dougherty, Patsy (Patrick H.)
❑ 03BreE10-41
❑ 04RedSoxUP-4
❑ 09AmeCarE90-1-36
❑ 09ColChiE-83
❑ 09T206-104
❑ 09T206-105
❑ 10ChiE-13
❑ 10DarChoE-16
❑ 10DomDisP-36
❑ 10E101-18
❑ 10E102-9
❑ 10MelMinE-18
❑ 10NadCarE-20
❑ 10PeoT21-20
❑ 10RedCroT-21
❑ 10RedCroT-106
❑ 10RedCroT-186
❑ 10SweCapPP-9
❑ 11E94-13
❑ 11HelSta-10
❑ 11MecDFT-15
❑ 11PinT-5-752
❑ 11SpoLifCW-104
❑ 11SpoLifM-22
❑ 11T205-44A
❑ 11T205-44B
❑ 12ColRedB-83
❑ 12ColTinT-83
❑ 17Zee-85
❑ 72ClaCar-43
Dougherty, Tony
❑ 94WatIndC-7
❑ 94WatIndF-3928
❑ 96WesOahCHWB-32
❑ 97AkrAer-8
❑ 97EasLeaTPB-1
❑ 98AkrAerM-10
Doughty, Brian
❑ 93BelMarCB-11
❑ 93BelMarF-3201
❑ 94AppFoxC-8
❑ 94AppFoxFl-1046
❑ 98RanCucQG-9
❑ 98RanCucQG-9
Doughty, Jamie
❑ 85TulDriTI-9
❑ 86TulDriTI-11
Douglas, Charles
❑ 88BoiHawP-1624
Douglas, Dave
❑ 87HarSenP-16
Douglas, John
❑ 88OklSoo-7
❑ 89OklSoo-13
Douglas, John Franklin
❑ 90DodTar-933
Douglas, Ken
❑ 21Zee-7
❑ 30Zee-53
❑ 31Zee-104
❑ 33Zee-39
❑ 33Zee-55
❑ 33Zee-112
❑ 37Zee-32
Douglas, Klondike (William B.)
❑ 03BreE10-42
Douglas, Murray
❑ 93Sou-7
Douglas, Phil (Phillip B.)
❑ 13Zee-105
❑ 19W514-5
❑ 20W52-12
❑ 21E121So1-20
❑ 21E121So8-19
❑ 21KoBreWSI-9
❑ 22E120-184
❑ 22W575-29
❑ 23W501-74
❑ 90DodTar-195
❑ 91FouBal-9
Douglas, Preston
❑ 88UtiBluSP-27
Douglas, Steve
❑ 82OrlTwi8SCT-6
❑ 82OrlTwiT-17
Douglas, Whammy (Charles)
❑ 57JetPos-5
❑ 58JetPos-6
❑ 58Top-306
❑ 59Top-431
❑ 60SeaPop-3
Douglass, Ryan
❑ 98LanLugQ-5
Douglass, Sean
❑ 98BluOriQ-11
Douma, Todd
❑ 90PitMetP-13
❑ 91FloStaLAP-FSL30
❑ 91St.LucMC-24
❑ 91St.LucMP-704
❑ 92BinMetF-509
❑ 92BinMetS-55
❑ 92ProFS7-286
❑ 92SkyAA F-23
❑ 93BinMetF-2328
❑ 93ExcFS7-72
Dour, Brian
❑ 88CapCodPPaLP-64
❑ 89EveGiaS-6
❑ 90Bes-253
❑ 90SanJosGB-21
❑ 90SanJosGCLC-42
❑ 90SanJosGP-2009
❑ 90SanJosGS-7
❑ 91SanJosGC-15
❑ 91SanJosGP-3
❑ 93SanJosGC-10
❑ 93SanJosGF-1
Douris, John D.
❑ 91WelPirC-21
❑ 91WelPirP-3566
Douthit, Taylor (Taylor Lee)
❑ 27MidBre-7
❑ 28W56PlaC-C7
❑ 29ExhFou-16
❑ 29PorandAR-17
❑ 31Exh-16
❑ 33ExhFou-4
❑ 33Gou-40
❑ 33GouCanV-40
❑ 79DiaGre-152
❑ 85BigLeaC3-36
❑ 91ConTSN-264
❑ 94ConTSN-1214
❑ 94ConTSNB-1214
Dovalis, Alex
❑ 79WisRapTT-6
Dovey, Troy
❑ 89AshTouP-956
❑ 90AshTouP-2739
❑ 90OscAstS-6
❑ 91BurAstC-2
❑ 91BurAstP-2793
❑ 92OscAstF-2522
Dowd, Charlie
❑ 95NewHavRTI-NNO
❑ 96NewHavRB-30
❑ 97NewHavRB-3
❑ 98BriBluM-30
Dowd, Snooks
❑ 90DodTar-196
Dowell, Ken
❑ 83ReaPhiT-13
❑ 84PorBeaC-210
❑ 85PorBeaC-46
❑ 86PorBeaP-5
❑ 87FleUpd-27
❑ 87FleUpdG-27
❑ 87MaiGuiP-16
❑ 87MaiGuiT-10
❑ 88MetColP-20
❑ 88TidTidCa-8
❑ 88TidTidCM-14
❑ 88TidTidP-1595
❑ 89TidTidC-11
❑ 89TidTidP-1963
❑ 90CMC-298
❑ 90ProAAAF-412
❑ 90RicBraC-22
❑ 90RicBraP-267
❑ 90RicBraTI-9
Dowhower, Deron
❑ 93EliTwiF-3412
❑ 94EliTwiC-6
❑ 94EliTwiF-3723
❑ 95ForWayWTI-4
❑ 96FtMyeMB-29
Dowies, Butch
❑ 82DanSunF-10
Dowler, Dee
❑ 93GenCubC-9
❑ 93GenCubF-3181
❑ 94DayCubC-4
❑ 94DayCubF-2364
❑ 96OrlCubB-7
❑ 97IowCub-11
Dowless, Mike
❑ 81WatRedT-3
❑ 82IndIndTI-16
❑ 83IndIndTI-23
❑ 84CedRapRT-24
Dowling, Dave (David B.)
❑ 65OPC-116
❑ 65Top-116
❑ 66Top-482
❑ 67Top-272
❑ 88AlaGolAA60TI-12
Down, Rick
❑ 87CalAngPPS-10
❑ 90AlbYanP-1180
❑ 90AlbYanSt-24
❑ 91ColCliLD-124
❑ 91ColCliP-614
❑ 91LinDriAAA-124
❑ 92ColCliF-367
❑ 92ColCliS-124
❑ 94VenLinU-198
❑ 96BalOriP-9
Downey, Charles
❑ 90ArkRaz-8
Downey, Red (Alexander C.)
❑ 90DodTar-934
Downey, Tom (Thomas E.)
❑ 09ColChiE-84
❑ 09T206-106
❑ 09T206-107
❑ 10CouT21-126
❑ 10DomDisP-37
❑ 10SweCapPP-97A
❑ 10SweCapPP-97B
❑ 11HelSta-143
❑ 11MecDFT-17
❑ 11PinT-5-410
❑ 11S74Sil-73
❑ 11SpoLifCW-105
❑ 11SpoLifM-190
❑ 11T205-45
❑ 11TurRedT-91
❑ 12ColRedB-84
❑ 12ColTinT-84
❑ 12T207-50
❑ 14CraJacE-107
❑ 14PieStaT-34
❑ 15CraJacE-107
❑ 15VicT21-8
❑ 72ClaCar-40

Downhower, Deron
❑ 93EliTwiC-10
Downing, Al (Alphonso E.)
❑ 61Yan61RL-35
❑ 62Top-219
❑ 64ChatheY-7
❑ 64Top-86
❑ 64Top-219
❑ 64TopCoi-109
❑ 64TopVen-86
❑ 64TopVen-219
❑ 64YanJayP-3
❑ 65ChaTheY-5
❑ 65MacSta-2
❑ 65OPC-11
❑ 65Top-11
❑ 65Top-598
❑ 66Top-384
❑ 66YanTeal-2
❑ 67CokCapYM-V14
❑ 67DexPre-67
❑ 67Top-308
❑ 67TopVen-221
❑ 68Baz-12
❑ 68OPC-105
❑ 68Top-105
❑ 68TopActS-5A
❑ 68TopVen-105
❑ 68YanPhoS-64
❑ 69MilBra-76
❑ 69Top-292
❑ 70Top-584
❑ 71MLBOffS-102
❑ 71OPC-182
❑ 71Top-182
❑ 72MilBra-94
❑ 72OPC-93
❑ 72OPC-460
❑ 72Top-93
❑ 72Top-460
❑ 73OPC-324
❑ 73Top-324
❑ 74OPC-620
❑ 74Top-620
❑ 75OPC-498
❑ 75Top-498
❑ 75TopMin-498
❑ 76OPC-605
❑ 76SSP-66
❑ 76Top-605
❑ 81TCM60I-450
❑ 83YanASFY-11
❑ 90DodTar-197
❑ 91YanRinP11-4
❑ 92YanWIZ6-36
❑ 92YanWIZA-19
❑ 94BreMilB-309
Downing, Bradley
❑ 98ButCopKG-10
Downing, Brian (Brian Jay)
❑ 74OPC-601
❑ 74Top-601
❑ 75OPC-422
❑ 75Top-422
❑ 75TopMin-422
❑ 76OPC-23
❑ 76SSP-141
❑ 76Top-23
❑ 77Hos-138
❑ 77OPC-246
❑ 77Top-344
❑ 77WhiSoxT-6
❑ 78AngFamF-8
❑ 78Top-519
❑ 79Top-71
❑ 80OPC-315
❑ 80Top-602
❑ 80TopSup-49
❑ 81AllGamPI-39
❑ 81Don-410
❑ 81Fle-282
❑ 81LonBeaPT-8
❑ 81OPC-263
❑ 81Top-263
❑ 81TopSti-50
❑ 82Don-115
❑ 82Fle-457
❑ 82FleSta-215
❑ 82OPC-158
❑ 82Top-158
❑ 83AllGamPI-51
❑ 83Don-367
❑ 83Fle-86
❑ 83FleSta-54
❑ 83FleSti-35
❑ 83OPC-298
❑ 83Top-442
❑ 84AllGamPI-141
❑ 84AngSmo-8
❑ 84Don-423
❑ 84Fle-515
❑ 84Nes792-574
❑ 84OPC-135
❑ 84Top-574
❑ 84TopSti-236
❑ 84TopTif-574
❑ 85AllGamPI-54
❑ 85AngSmo-7
❑ 85Don-158
❑ 85Fle-300
❑ 85Lea-223
❑ 85OPC-374
❑ 85Top-374
❑ 85TopSti-224
❑ 85TopTif-374
❑ 86AngSmo-7
❑ 86BasStaB-34
❑ 86Don-108
❑ 86Fle-154
❑ 86Lea-39
❑ 86OPC-205
❑ 86Spo-154
❑ 86Top-772
❑ 86TopSti-183
❑ 86TopTat-14
❑ 86TopTif-772
❑ 87AngSmo-19
❑ 87CalAngPPS-11
❑ 87Don-86
❑ 87DonHig-5
❑ 87DonOpeD-9
❑ 87Fle-78
❑ 87FleBasA-15
❑ 87FleExcS-16
❑ 87FleGlo-78
❑ 87FleMin-34
❑ 87FleStiC-35
❑ 87OPC-88
❑ 87Spo-161
❑ 87SpoTeaP-11
❑ 87Top-782
❑ 87TopSti-178
❑ 87TopTif-782
❑ 88AngSmo-18
❑ 88Don-258
❑ 88DonBasB-27
❑ 88Fle-488
❑ 88FleGlo-488
❑ 88FleMin-10
❑ 88FleStiC-11
❑ 88Lea-203
❑ 88OPC-331
❑ 88PanSti-46
❑ 88RedFolSB-19
❑ 88Sco-44
❑ 88ScoGlo-44
❑ 88Spo-181
❑ 88StaLinAn-5
❑ 88Top-331
❑ 88TopBig-78
❑ 88TopMinL-5
❑ 88TopRevLL-23
❑ 88TopSti-181
❑ 88TopTif-331
❑ 89AngSmo-12
❑ 89Bow-53
❑ 89BowTif-53
❑ 89Don-254
❑ 89DonBasB-321
❑ 89Fle-475
❑ 89FleGlo-475
❑ 89OPC-17
❑ 89PanSti-288
❑ 89Sco-76
❑ 89Spo-117
❑ 89Top-17
❑ 89TopSti-178
❑ 89TopTif-17
❑ 89UppDec-485
❑ 90AngSmo-4
❑ 90Bow-294
❑ 90BowTif-294
❑ 90Don-10A
❑ 90Don-10B
❑ 90Don-352
❑ 90DonSupD-10
❑ 90Fle-130
❑ 90FleCan-130
❑ 90M.Vpin-15
❑ 90OPC-635
❑ 90PanSti-27
❑ 90PubIntS-368
❑ 90Sco-26
❑ 90Sco100S-46
❑ 90Spo-77
❑ 90Top-635
❑ 90TopSti-169
❑ 90TopTif-635
❑ 90UppDec-146
❑ 91Fle-310
❑ 91Lea-269
❑ 91OPC-255
❑ 91RanMot-17
❑ 91Sco-104
❑ 91ScoRoo-30T
❑ 91StaClu-348
❑ 91Top-255
❑ 91TopDesS-255
❑ 91TopMic-255
❑ 91TopTif-255
❑ 91TopTra-33T
❑ 91TopTraT-33T
❑ 91UltUpd-54
❑ 91UppDec-231A
❑ 91UppDec-231B
❑ 91UppDec-770
❑ 92Don-167
❑ 92Fle-302
❑ 92Lea-440
❑ 92LeaBlaG-440
❑ 92OPC-173
❑ 92Pin-368
❑ 92RanMot-17
❑ 92RanTeal-7
❑ 92Sco-579
❑ 92StaClu-494
❑ 92Top-173
❑ 92TopGol-173
❑ 92TopGolW-173
❑ 92TopMic-173
❑ 92Ult-440
❑ 92UppDec-483
❑ 93PanSti-88
❑ 93RanKee-128
Downing, Lance
❑ 98LetBlaDG-10
Downs, Brian
❑ 96HicCraB-4
❑ 97HicCraRB-11
❑ 98HicCraUO-14
Downs, Dorley
❑ 84PriWilPT-12
❑ 85NasPirT-7
❑ 86MacPirP-8
Downs, Jim
❑ 66TolMudHTI-7
Downs, John
❑ 91EugEmeC-22
❑ 91EugEmeP-3717
❑ 94WilBluRC-7
❑ 94WilBluRF-294
Downs, Kelly
❑ 82OklCit8T-21
❑ 83PorBeaT-9
❑ 84PorBeaC-201
❑ 85PhoGiaC-189
❑ 86PhoFirP-4
❑ 87Don-573
❑ 87Fle-272
❑ 87FleGlo-272
❑ 87GiaMot-17
❑ 87GiaPos-10
❑ 87SpoTeaP-10
❑ 87Top-438
❑ 87TopTif-438
❑ 88ClaRed-194
❑ 88Don-145
❑ 88DonBasB-106
❑ 88Fle-80
❑ 88FleGlo-80
❑ 88GiaMot-17
❑ 88GiaPos-8
❑ 88OPC-187
❑ 88PanSti-415
❑ 88Sco-27
❑ 88ScoGlo-27
❑ 88ScoYouSI-19
❑ 88Spo-203
❑ 88Top-629
❑ 88TopRoo-19
❑ 88TopTif-629
❑ 88ToyRoo-9
❑ 89Bow-465
❑ 89BowTif-465
❑ 89Don-367
❑ 89DonBasB-247
❑ 89Fle-326
❑ 89FleGlo-326
❑ 89GiaMot-4
❑ 89OPC-361
❑ 89PanSti-209
❑ 89Sco-124
❑ 89Spo-39
❑ 89Top-361
❑ 89TopBig-112
❑ 89TopSti-81
❑ 89TopTif-361
❑ 89UppDec-476
❑ 90Don-177
❑ 90Fle-55
❑ 90FleCan-55
❑ 90GiaMot-4
❑ 90GiaSmo-6
❑ 90OPC-17
❑ 90PubIntS-66
❑ 90Sco-534
❑ 90Top-17
❑ 90TopTif-17
❑ 90UppDec-699
❑ 91Bow-633
❑ 91Don-738
❑ 91Fle-261
❑ 91GiaMot-4
❑ 91GiaPacGaE-4
❑ 91OPC-733
❑ 91Sco-654
❑ 91StaClu-193
❑ 91Top-733
❑ 91TopDesS-733
❑ 91TopMic-733
❑ 91TopTif-733
❑ 91UltUpd-116
❑ 91UppDec-441
❑ 92Bow-343
❑ 92Don-303
❑ 92Fle-634
❑ 92GiaMot-21
❑ 92GiaPacGaE-15
❑ 92OPC-573
❑ 92Pin-492
❑ 92Sco-191
❑ 92StaClu-517
❑ 92Top-573
❑ 92TopGol-573
❑ 92TopGolW-573
❑ 92TopMic-573
❑ 92Ult-290
❑ 92UppDec-583
❑ 93AthMot-20
❑ 93Fle-662
❑ 93PacSpa-565
❑ 93UppDec-636
❑ 93UppDecGold-636
❑ 94Fle-259
Downs, Kirk
❑ 80BurBeeT-24
Downs, Paul
❑ 28Zee-47
Downs, Red (Jerome Willis)
❑ 07TigACDPP-5
❑ 09T206-420
❑ 09WolNewDTPP-7
❑ 11MecDFT-37
❑ 11PinT-5-1063
❑ 11SpoLifCW-106
❑ 13Zee-106
❑ 14Zee-108
❑ 15Zee-104
❑ 16Zee-107
❑ 17Zee-86
❑ 18Zee-78
❑ 90DodTar-198
Downs, Ron
❑ 88AugPirP-378
❑ 88SouAtlLAGS-5
❑ 89SalBucS-6
Doxtator, Melvil
❑ 52LavPro-74
Doyel, Dan
❑ 89SavCarP-347
❑ 90ArkTraGS-3
❑ 91St.PetCC-30
❑ 92St.PetCC-29
Doyle, Blake
❑ 77RocRedWM-8
❑ 78RocRedWT-8
❑ 79RocRedWT-4
❑ 80IndIndTI-20
Doyle, Brian (Brian Reed)
❑ 75LynRanT-9
❑ 78TacYanC-39A
❑ 79Top-710
❑ 79YanPicA-10
❑ 80ColCliP-2
❑ 80ColCliT-13
❑ 80Top-582
❑ 81Fle-104
❑ 81Top-159
❑ 81TopTra-754
❑ 82SyrChiT-16
❑ 82SyrChiTI-10
❑ 92YanWIZ7-46
❑ 92YanWIZ8-48
Doyle, Carl
❑ 36NatChiFPR-25
❑ 90DodTar-935
Doyle, Cornelius
❑ 87OldJudN-139
Doyle, Denny (Robert Dennis)
❑ 70OPC-539
❑ 70PhiTeal-3
❑ 70Top-539
❑ 71MLBOffS-175
❑ 71OPC-352
❑ 71Top-352
❑ 72Top-768
❑ 73OPC-424
❑ 73PhiTeal-7
❑ 73Top-424
❑ 74OPC-552
❑ 74Top-552
❑ 75CalAngP-12
❑ 75OPC-187
❑ 75SSP18-17
❑ 75Top-187
❑ 75TopMin-187
❑ 76Hos-107
❑ 76LinSup-107
❑ 76OPC-381
❑ 76RedSox-2
❑ 76RedSoxSM-4
❑ 76SSP-407
❑ 76Top-381
❑ 77AshTouT-4
❑ 77Top-336
❑ 78OPC-111
❑ 78Top-642
Doyle, Ian
❑ 91BurIndP-3294
❑ 92ColRedC-18
❑ 92ColRedF-2382
❑ 93CarLeaAGF-29
❑ 93ClaGolF-15
❑ 93KinIndC-8
❑ 93KinIndF-2239
❑ 93KinIndTI-7
❑ 93SouAtlLAPI-9
❑ 94CanIndF-3112
❑ 94ExcFS7-42
Doyle, Jack (John Joseph)
❑ 03BreE10-43
❑ 03BreE10-44
❑ 11SpoLifCW-108
❑ 72ClaCar-91
❑ 90DodTar-199
❑ 95NewN566-178
Doyle, James
❑ 11SpoLifCW-107
❑ 11SpoLifM-191
Doyle, Jeff (Jeffrey D.)
❑ 81ArkTraT-7
❑ 82LouRedE-7
❑ 03LouRedR-11
Doyle, Jesse
❑ 22Zee-147
❑ 23Zee-181
Doyle, Larry (Lawrence J.)
❑ 03WilCarE-13
❑ 08AmeCarE91-45
❑ 08RosComP-128
❑ 09ColChiE-85
❑ 09PhiCarE-9
❑ 09SpoNewSM-68
❑ 09T206-108A
❑ 09T206-108B
❑ 09T206-109
❑ 09T206-110
❑ 09T206-111
❑ 10CouT21-127
❑ 10CouT21-128
❑ 10CouT21-278
❑ 10CouT21-279
❑ 10DomDisP-38
❑ 10E101-19A
❑ 10E101-19B
❑ 10E102-10A
❑ 10E102-10B
❑ 10E12AmeCDCE125-15
❑ 10JuJuDE-16
❑ 10MelMinE-19A
❑ 10MelMinE-19B
❑ 10NadCarE-21A
❑ 10NadCarE-21B
❑ 10NadE1-16
❑ 10PeoT21-21A
❑ 10PeoT21-21B
❑ 10PeoT21-21C
❑ 10RedCroT-22
❑ 10RedCroT-23
❑ 10RedCroT-107
❑ 10RedCroT-108
❑ 10RedCroT-187
❑ 10RedCroT-188
❑ 10SweCapPP-112A
❑ 10SweCapPP-112B
❑ 11BasBatEU-21
❑ 11DiaGumP-13
❑ 11HelSta-125
❑ 11MecDFT-35
❑ 11PinT-5-260
❑ 11S74Sil-85
❑ 11SpoLifCW-109
❑ 11SpoLifM-209
❑ 11T205-46
❑ 11TurRedT-13
❑ 12ColRedB-85
❑ 12ColTinT-85
❑ 12HasTriFT-30B
❑ 12HasTriFT-32
❑ 12T207-51
❑ 14B18B-66
❑ 14CraJacE-4
❑ 14PieStaT-35
❑ 14PolGroW-7
❑ 14TexTomE-19
❑ 14TexTomE-52
❑ 15AmeCarE106-15
❑ 15CraJacE-4
❑ 15SpoNewM-52
❑ 16BF2FP-78
❑ 16FleBreD-25
❑ 16SpoNewM-51
❑ 17ColE13-44
❑ 19W514-81
❑ 20W516-13
❑ 20W52-3
❑ 72ClaCar-46
❑ 77GalGloG-157
❑ 91ConTSN-317
Doyle, Paul (Paul S.)
❑ 70OPC-277
❑ 70Top-277
❑ 72Top-629
Doyle, Rich
❑ 82WatIndF-23
❑ 82WatIndT-2
❑ 83BufBisT-3
❑ 84BufBisT-11
❑ 85WatIndT-6
❑ 86BeaGolGP-10
❑ 88SanBerSB-24
❑ 88SanBerSCLC-52
❑ 89CalCanC-7
❑ 89CalCanP-541
❑ 89EasLeaDDP-DD32
Doyle, Slow (Judd Bruce)
❑ 88FriBacCM-2
Doyle, Tim
❑ 91SouOreAC-4
❑ 91SouOreAP-3833
Doyle, Tom
❑ 86ColMetP-9
❑ 87ColMetP-23
❑ 88JacMetGS-7
❑ 88MarPhiS-11
❑ 90WatDiaB-26
❑ 90WatDiaP-2383
❑ 91ChaRaiC-18
❑ 91ChaRaiP-103
❑ 92JamExpC-3
❑ 92Min-6
❑ 93BurBeeC-7
❑ 93BurBeeF-165
❑ 93SpoIndC-4
❑ 93SpoIndF-3582
❑ 96ChaLooB-12
❑ 97ChaLoo-9

❑ 98ChaLooG-8
Dozier, D.J.
❑ 90FloStaLAS-4
❑ 90ScoRoo-97T
❑ 90St.LucMS-6
❑ 90StaFS7-9
❑ 90TopMag-47
❑ 91Bow-478
❑ 91Cla/Bes-387
❑ 91Cla2-T4
❑ 91ClaGam-89
❑ 91LinDriAA-631
❑ 91MetColP-30
❑ 91UppDec-3
❑ 91WilBilLD-631
❑ 91WilBilP-306
❑ 92Bow-219
❑ 92Don-20
❑ 92MetColP-22
❑ 92OPC-591
❑ 92ProFS7-282
❑ 92SkyAAAF-250
❑ 92TidTidF-909
❑ 92TidTidS-556
❑ 92Top-591
❑ 92TopGol-591
❑ 92TopGolW-591
❑ 92TopMic-591
❑ 93Don-90
❑ 93LasVegSF-956
Dozier, Tom
❑ 82SprCarF-15
❑ 83St.PetCT-5
❑ 84AlbA'sT-11
❑ 85HunStaJ-15
❑ 85TacTigC-145
❑ 86TacTigP-4
❑ 87TacTigP-1
❑ 88GreBraB-18
❑ 90SprCarDGB-8
Drabek, Doug
❑ 85AlbYanT-4
❑ 86ColCliP-6
❑ 86ColCliP-6
❑ 86DonRoo-31
❑ 86FleUpd-36
❑ 86StaoftFT-3
❑ 86YanTCM-6
❑ 87Don-251
❑ 87DonHig-32
❑ 87Fle-96
❑ 87FleGlo-96
❑ 87Top-283
❑ 87TopTif-283
❑ 87TopTra-29T
❑ 87TopTraT-29T
❑ 88Don-79
❑ 88DonBasB-73
❑ 88Fle-327
❑ 88FleGlo-327
❑ 88Lea-88
❑ 88OPC-143
❑ 88PirTeal-9
❑ 88RedFolSB-20
❑ 88Sco-51
❑ 88ScoGlo-51
❑ 88StaLinPi-8
❑ 88Top-591
❑ 88TopBig-124
❑ 88TopSti-134
❑ 88TopTif-591
❑ 89Bow-416
❑ 89BowTif-416
❑ 89Don-211
❑ 89DonBasB-17
❑ 89Fle-206
❑ 89FleGlo-206
❑ 89OPC-37
❑ 89PanSti-161
❑ 89PirVerFJ-15
❑ 89Sco-117
❑ 89ScoHot1S-87
❑ 89ScoYouSI-21
❑ 89Spo-27
❑ 89SpoIllFKI-266
❑ 89Top-478
❑ 89TopTif-478
❑ 89TVSpoM-11
❑ 89UppDec-597
❑ 90AlbDecGB-22
❑ 90Bow-164
❑ 90BowTif-164
❑ 90Don-92
❑ 90DonBesN-9
❑ 90Fle-465
❑ 90FleCan-465
❑ 90Lea-296
❑ 90M.Vpin-83
❑ 90OPC-197
❑ 90PanSti-332
❑ 90PirHomC-10
❑ 90PublntS-153
❑ 90RedFolSB-27
❑ 90Sco-505
❑ 90Top-197
❑ 90TopBig-185
❑ 90TopMag-87
❑ 90TopSti-130
❑ 90TopTif-197
❑ 90UppDec-422
❑ 91BasBesAotM-5
❑ 91Baz-4
❑ 91Bow-515
❑ 91Cla1-T82
❑ 91Cla2-T79
❑ 91ClaGam-167
❑ 91Col-29
❑ 91Don-269
❑ 91Don-411
❑ 91Don-750
❑ 91DonEli-5
❑ 91DonPre-2
❑ 91Fle-36
❑ 91Lea-516
❑ 91MajLeaCP-59
❑ 91MSAHolD-7
❑ 91OPC-405
❑ 91OPC-685
❑ 91PanCanT1-57
❑ 91PanCanT1-92
❑ 91PanFreS-122
❑ 91PanSti-116
❑ 91RedFolS-28
❑ 91Sco-472
❑ 91Sco-661
❑ 91Sco-878
❑ 91Sco100S-6
❑ 91StaClu-202
❑ 91StaCluCM-7
❑ 91StaPinB-14
❑ 91Stu-224
❑ 91StuPre-15
❑ 91Top-405
❑ 91Top-685
❑ 91TopCraJl-12
❑ 91TopDesS-405
❑ 91TopDesS-685
❑ 91TopGaloC-4
❑ 91TopMic-405
❑ 91TopMic-685
❑ 91TopTif-405
❑ 91TopTif-685
❑ 91Ult-277
❑ 91UltGol-3
❑ 91UppDec-278
❑ 91Woo-3
❑ 92Bow-465
❑ 92Cla2-T68
❑ 92ClaGam-67
❑ 92Don-209
❑ 92DonCraJ1-34
❑ 92Fle-553
❑ 92Hig5-92
❑ 92Lea-11
❑ 92LeaBlaG-11
❑ 92New-7
❑ 92OPC-440
❑ 92OPCPre-32
❑ 92PanSti-259
❑ 92Pin-96
❑ 92PirNatl-7
❑ 92Sco-115
❑ 92Sco100S-53
❑ 92ScoProP-23
❑ 92StaClu-170
❑ 92Stu-84
❑ 92Top-440
❑ 92TopGol-440
❑ 92TopGolW-440
❑ 92TopKid-24
❑ 92TopMic-440
❑ 92TriPla-106
❑ 92Ult-253
❑ 92UppDec-39
❑ 92UppDec-221
❑ 92UppDecTMH-18
❑ 92YanWIZ8-49
❑ 93AstMot-5
❑ 93AstStaC-1
❑ 93Bow-208
❑ 93Don-622
❑ 93DurPowP1-12
❑ 93Fin-127
❑ 93FinRef-127
❑ 93Fla-61
❑ 93Fle-500
❑ 93FleFinE-77
❑ 93FleFruotL-17
❑ 93FunPac-46
❑ 93JimDea-19
❑ 93KinDis-23
❑ 93Kra-20
❑ 93Lea-293
❑ 93LeaGolA-R20
❑ 93MetBak-6
❑ 93MSABenSPD-7
❑ 93OPC-72
❑ 93OPCPre-73
❑ 93PacSpa-476
❑ 93Pin-423
❑ 93Pin-485
❑ 93RedFolS-25
❑ 93Sco-580
❑ 93Sel-153
❑ 93SelAce-16
❑ 93SelRoo-97T
❑ 93SelStaL-65
❑ 93SP-32
❑ 93StaClu-167
❑ 93StaClu-672
❑ 93StaCluFDI-167
❑ 93StaCluFDI-672
❑ 93StaCluMOP-167
❑ 93StaCluMOP-672
❑ 93Stu-194
❑ 93Top-190
❑ 93TopComotH-26
❑ 93TopGol-190
❑ 93ToplnaM-190
❑ 93ToplnaR-190
❑ 93TopMic-190
❑ 93TopTra-94T
❑ 93TriPla-232
❑ 93Ult-392
❑ 93UppDec-475
❑ 93UppDec-664
❑ 93UppDecGold-475
❑ 93UppDecGold-664
❑ 94AstMot-14
❑ 94Bow-174
❑ 94ColC-95
❑ 94ColChoGS-95
❑ 94ColChoSS-95
❑ 94Don-632
❑ 94Fin-345
❑ 94FinRef-345
❑ 94Fla-388
❑ 94Fle-489
❑ 94FleExtB-272
❑ 94FleExtBPD-10
❑ 94FUnPac-138
❑ 94Lea-271
❑ 94LeaL-114
❑ 94OPC-248
❑ 94Pac-263
❑ 94PanSti-193
❑ 94Pin-104
❑ 94PinArtP-104
❑ 94PinMusC-104
❑ 94ProMag-60
❑ 94RedFolMI-2
❑ 94Sco-426
❑ 94ScoGolR-426
❑ 94Sel-349
❑ 94SP-30
❑ 94SPDieC-30
❑ 94Spo-17
❑ 94StaClu-408
❑ 94StaCluFDI-408
❑ 94StaCluGR-408
❑ 94StaCluMOP-408
❑ 94Stu-20
❑ 94Top-220
❑ 94TopGol-220
❑ 94TopSpa-220
❑ 94TriPla-25
❑ 94Ult-501
❑ 94UppDec-452
❑ 94UppDecED-452
❑ 95AstMot-11
❑ 95Baz-107
❑ 95Bow-307
❑ 95ColCho-116
❑ 95ColChoGS-116
❑ 95ColChoSE-37
❑ 95ColChoSEGS-37
❑ 95ColChoSESS-37
❑ 95ColChoSS-116
❑ 95Don-532
❑ 95DonMouM-6
❑ 95DonPreP-532
❑ 95DonTopotO-252
❑ 95Fin-135
❑ 95FinRef-135
❑ 95Fla-359
❑ 95Fle-456
❑ 95FleAllS-20
❑ 95FleTeaL-20
❑ 95Lea-321
❑ 95LeaLim-183
❑ 95Pac-184
❑ 95PacPri-60
❑ 95PanSti-2
❑ 95Pin-72
❑ 95PinArtP-72
❑ 95PinMusC-72
❑ 95Sco-378
❑ 95ScoGolR-378
❑ 95ScoHaloG-HG97
❑ 95ScoPlaTS-378
❑ 95Sel-129
❑ 95SelArtP-129
❑ 95SP-63
❑ 95SPCha-54
❑ 95SPChaDC-54
❑ 95Spo-15
❑ 95SpoArtP-15
❑ 95SPSil-63
❑ 95StaClu-224
❑ 95StaCluFDI-224
❑ 95StaCluMOP-224
❑ 95StaCluSTWS-224
❑ 95StaCluVR-113
❑ 95StaCluVRMO-113
❑ 95Stu-143
❑ 95Top-75
❑ 95TopCyb-52
❑ 95TopD3-44
❑ 95TopEmb-104
❑ 95TopEmbGl-104
❑ 95Ult-171
❑ 95UltGolM-171
❑ 95UppDec-26
❑ 95UppDecED-26
❑ 95UppDecEDG-26
❑ 95UppDecSE-180
❑ 95UppDecSEG-180
❑ 95USPlaCMLA-11S
❑ 96AstMot-7
❑ 96Baz-126
❑ 96Cir-136
❑ 96CirRav-136
❑ 96ColCho-565
❑ 96ColChoGS-565
❑ 96ColChoSS-565
❑ 96Don-142
❑ 96DonPreP-142
❑ 96EmoXL-197
❑ 96Fin-B181
❑ 96FinRef-B181
❑ 96Fla-276
❑ 96Fle-405
❑ 96FleTif-405
❑ 96Lea-161
❑ 96LeaPrePB-161
❑ 96LeaPrePG-161
❑ 96LeaPrePS-161
❑ 96LeaSigA-58
❑ 96LeaSigAG-58
❑ 96LeaSigAS-58
❑ 96MetUni-176
❑ 96MetUniP-176
❑ 96Pac-97
❑ 96PanSti-63
❑ 96ProSta-14
❑ 96Sco-109
❑ 96SP-93
❑ 96StaClu-127
❑ 96StaCluEPB-127
❑ 96StaCluEPG-127
❑ 96StaCluEPS-127
❑ 96StaCluMOP-127
❑ 96Top-105
❑ 96TopGal-18
❑ 96TopGalPPI-18
❑ 96TopLas-53
❑ 96Ult-207
❑ 96UltGolM-207
❑ 96UppDec-342
❑ 97Cir-305
❑ 97CirRav-305
❑ 97ColChoU-U6
❑ 97DonTea-68
❑ 97DonTeaSPE-68
❑ 97Fin-203
❑ 97FinRef-203
❑ 97FlaShoLC-178
❑ 97FlaShoLeg0-178
❑ 97FlaShoLeg1-178
❑ 97FlaShoM-A178
❑ 97FlaShoM-B178
❑ 97FlaShoM-C178
❑ 97FlaShoR0-178
❑ 97FlaShoR1-178
❑ 97FlaShoR2-178
❑ 97Fle-343
❑ 97Fle-534
❑ 97FleTif-343
❑ 97FleTif-534
❑ 97Pac-315
❑ 97PacLigB-315
❑ 97PacSil-315
❑ 97Sco-463
❑ 97ScoArtPWB-463
❑ 97ScoResC-463
❑ 97ScoShoS-463
❑ 97ScoShoSAP-463
❑ 97StaClu-107
❑ 97StaCluMOP-107
❑ 97Top-143
❑ 97Ult-444
❑ 97UltGolME-444
❑ 97UltPlaME-444
❑ 97WhiSoxTI-15
❑ 98ColCho-312
❑ 98Pac-54
❑ 98PacOnl-87
❑ 98PacOnlR-87
❑ 98PacOnlWC-87
❑ 98PacPlaB-54
❑ 98PacRedT-54
❑ 98PacSil-54
❑ 98Pin-82
❑ 98PinPreP-82
❑ 98Sco-107
❑ 98Top-235
❑ 98TopChr-235
❑ 98TopChrR-235
❑ 98TopDevR-235
❑ 98TopDia-235
❑ 98TopMiniC-235
❑ 98Ult-272
❑ 98UltGolM-272
❑ 98UltMas-272
❑ 98UltPlaM-272
❑ 98UppDec-61
❑ 98UppDec-651
❑ 98WhiSoxS-9
❑ 98WhiSoxSP-9
Drabinski, Marek
❑ 91MacBraC-14
❑ 91MacBraP-867
Drabowsky, Moe (Myron W.)
❑ 57Top-84
❑ 58Top-135
❑ 59Top-407
❑ 60CubJayP-5
❑ 60Lea-68
❑ 60Top-349
❑ 61Top-364
❑ 62RedEnq-6
❑ 62Top-331
❑ 64A's-4
❑ 64AthJayP-3
❑ 64Top-42
❑ 64TopSta-82
❑ 64TopTatl-34
❑ 64TopVen-42
❑ 65Top-439
❑ 66BalOriP-12
❑ 66Top-291
❑ 66TopVen-291
❑ 67BalOriP-31
❑ 67BalOriP-32
❑ 67CokCapO-16
❑ 67OPC-125
❑ 67OPC-151
❑ 67Top-125
❑ 67Top-151
❑ 68BalOriDPCP-5
❑ 68CokCapO-16
❑ 68DexPre-29
❑ 68Top-242
❑ 68TopVen-242
❑ 69MilBra-77
❑ 69MLBOffS-57
❑ 69RoySol-3
❑ 69RoyTeal-3
❑ 69Top-508
❑ 69TopSta-183
❑ 70BalOriP-8
❑ 70MLBOffS-220
❑ 70RoyTeal-9
❑ 70Top-653
❑ 71CarTeal-10
❑ 71CarTeal-15
❑ 71CarTeal-16
❑ 71MLBOffS-272
❑ 71OPC-685
❑ 71Top-685
❑ 72CarTeal-8
❑ 72MilBra-95
❑ 72Top-627
❑ 78TCM60I-121
❑ 81Ori6F-12
❑ 87BirBarB-3
❑ 88BirBarB-7
❑ 89PacLegI-215
❑ 89SweBasG-103
❑ 89VanCanC-25
❑ 89VanCanP-581
❑ 90CMC-175
❑ 90ProAAAF-184
❑ 90VanCanC-26
❑ 90VanCanP-506
❑ 91LinDriAAA-650
❑ 91OriCro-112
❑ 91VanCanP-1610
❑ 92HagSunF-2572
❑ 92HagSunS-275
❑ 93UppDecAH-43
❑ 93UppDecS-4
Draeger, Mark
❑ 95HudValRTI-26
❑ 96ChaRivTI-9612
❑ 96HudValRB-4
Drago, Dick (Richard A.)
❑ 69RoySol-4
❑ 69Top-662
❑ 70OPC-37
❑ 70RoyTeal-10
❑ 70Top-37
❑ 71MLBOffS-414
❑ 71OPC-752
❑ 71Top-752
❑ 72Kel-40A
❑ 72Kel-40B
❑ 72OPC-205
❑ 72Top-205
❑ 73OPC-392
❑ 73Top-392
❑ 74OPC-113
❑ 74Top-113
❑ 75OPC-333
❑ 75Top-333
❑ 75TopMin-333
❑ 76OPC-142
❑ 76SSP-422
❑ 76Top-142
❑ 77Top-426
❑ 78PapGinD-11
❑ 78SSP270-171
❑ 78Top-567
❑ 79OPC-2
❑ 79Top-12
❑ 80Top-271
❑ 81Don-336
❑ 81Fle-239
❑ 81MarPos-15
❑ 81OPC-332
❑ 81Top-647
❑ 81TopTra-755
❑ 82Fle-510
❑ 82Top-742
❑ 89T/MSenL-29
❑ 89TopSenL-17
❑ 91OriCro-113
❑ 93UppDecS-4
Dragon, Homer the
❑ 96ChaKniB-5
❑ 97ChaKni-2
❑ 98ChaKniQ-29
Drahman, Brian
❑ 87BelBreP-10
❑ 88StoPorCLC-186
❑ 88StoPorP-734
❑ 89ElPasDGS-6
❑ 90BirBarB-15
❑ 90BirBarP-1103
❑ 91Bow-363
❑ 91ScoRoo-81T
❑ 91WhiSoxK-50
❑ 92Fle-77
❑ 92OPC-231

❑ 92Sco-734
❑ 92Sco100RS-55
❑ 92StaClu-744
❑ 92StaCluNC-744
❑ 92Top-231
❑ 92TopDeb91-46
❑ 92TopGol-231
❑ 92TopGolW-231
❑ 92TopMic-231
❑ 92VanCanS-633
❑ 93Don-672
❑ 93NasSouF-566
❑ 93TriAAAGF-35
❑ 94EdmTraF-2868
❑ 94StaCluT-82
❑ 94StaCluTFDI-82
❑ 95ChaKniTI-9
❑ 97LasVegS1A-13

Drake, Delos (Delos Daniel)
❑ 12ColRedB-86
❑ 12ColTinT-86
❑ 12T207-52

Drake, H.P.
❑ 78LodDodT-3

Drake, Kevin
❑ 74CedRapAT-19
❑ 75DubPacT-29

Drake, Larry
❑ 45A'sTeal-9

Drake, Plunk (William)
❑ 78LauLonABS-8
❑ 86NegLeaF-69
❑ 87NegLeaPD-10

Drake, Sam
❑ 88CapCodPPaLP-131
❑ 89HelBreSP-22
❑ 90BelBreB-6
❑ 90BelBreS-6
❑ 91StoPorC-9
❑ 91StoPorP-3027

Drake, Sammy (Samuel H.)
❑ 62Top-162
❑ 62TopVen-162
❑ 91MetWIZ-99

Drake, Solly (Solomon L.)
❑ 57Top-159
❑ 59Top-406
❑ 90DodTar-200

Drake, Tex
❑ 85KinBluJT-26
❑ 86KinEagP-5
❑ 89RicBraP-819

Drake, Tom
❑ 73Dod194T-6
❑ 78DodTCM4-5
❑ 90DodTar-201

Dransfeldt, Kelly
❑ 96HudValRB-2
❑ 98Cha-17
❑ 98TexLeaC-4
❑ 99BasAmeTP-34
❑ 99BasAmeTPG-34
❑ 99Bow-312
❑ 99BowBes-162
❑ 99BowBesAR-162
❑ 99BowBesR-162
❑ 99BowGol-312
❑ 99BowInt-312
❑ 99DumSet-129
❑ 99FleMys-129
❑ 99FleMysM-129
❑ 99Rev-139
❑ 99RevPremDate-139
❑ 99RevRet-139
❑ 99RevShaSS-139
❑ 99SkyPre-262
❑ 99SkyPre-262
❑ 99SkyPreR-262
❑ 99SkyPreR-262
❑ 99TopBlaLC1-7
❑ 99TopBlaLC2-7
❑ 99TopBlaLC3-7
❑ 99TopGolL-7
❑ 99TopGolLC1-7
❑ 99TopGolLC2-7
❑ 99TopGolLOtO-7
❑ 99TopRedLC1-7
❑ 99TopRedLC2-7
❑ 99TopRedLC3-7
❑ 99UppDecE-103
❑ 99UppDecEFXG-103

Draper, Mike
❑ 88OneYanP-2059
❑ 89PriWilCS-6
❑ 90Ft.LauYS-5
❑ 91AlbYanLD-4
❑ 91AlbYanP-1000
❑ 91LinDriAA-4
❑ 92ColCliF-345
❑ 92ColCliP-5
❑ 92ColCliS-104
❑ 92DonRoo-34
❑ 92SkyAAAF-46
❑ 92TriAAAS-104
❑ 93Bow-482
❑ 93ExcFS7-206
❑ 93FleFinE-101
❑ 93LinVenB-248
❑ 93MetColP-29
❑ 93MetKah-47
❑ 93PacSpa-540
❑ 93StaClu-732
❑ 93StaCluFDI-732
❑ 93StaCluMOP-732
❑ 93Ult-425
❑ 94LasVegSF-867
❑ 94Pac-398

Dravecky, Dave (David F.)
❑ 79BufBisT-1
❑ 80BufBisT-4
❑ 82HawIsIT-20
❑ 83Fle-356
❑ 83PadTeal-6
❑ 83Top-384
❑ 84Don-8
❑ 84Don-8A
❑ 84Don-551
❑ 84Fle-298
❑ 84Nes792-290
❑ 84Nes792-366
❑ 84OPC-290
❑ 84PadMot-11
❑ 84PadSmo-7
❑ 84Top-290
❑ 84Top-366
❑ 84TopSti-155
❑ 84TopTif-290
❑ 84TopTif-366
❑ 85Don-112
❑ 85Fle-30
❑ 85OPC-32
❑ 85PadMot-8
❑ 85Top-530
❑ 85TopMin-530
❑ 85TopSti-154
❑ 85TopTif-530
❑ 86Don-162
❑ 86Fle-319
❑ 86Lea-92
❑ 86OPC-276
❑ 86PadFirPTB-1
❑ 86Top-735
❑ 86TopTif-735
❑ 87Don-187
❑ 87Fle-412
❑ 87FleGlo-412
❑ 87FleUpd-28
❑ 87FleUpdG-28
❑ 87OPC-62
❑ 87PadBohHB-43
❑ 87Top-470
❑ 87TopSti-107
❑ 87TopTif-470
❑ 88Don-485
❑ 88DonBasB-135
❑ 88Fle-81
❑ 88FleBasM-10
❑ 88FleGlo-81
❑ 88FleStiC-127
❑ 88GiaMot-9
❑ 88GiaPos-9
❑ 88Sco-564
❑ 88ScoGlo-564
❑ 88StaLinG-6
❑ 88Top-68
❑ 88TopTif-68
❑ 89Fle-327
❑ 89FleGlo-327
❑ 89GiaMot-9
❑ 89Top-601
❑ 89TopTif-601
❑ 89UppDec-39
❑ 90OPC-124
❑ 90PacLeg-80
❑ 90PanSti-360
❑ 90PanSti-386
❑ 90Sco-550
❑ 90Top-124
❑ 90TopTif-124
❑ 90UppDec-679
❑ 92SteDra-1
❑ 92SteDra-2
❑ 92SteDra-3
❑ 92SteDra-4
❑ 92SteDra-5
❑ 92SteDra-6
❑ 92SteDra-7
❑ 92SteDra-8
❑ 92SteDra-9
❑ 92SteDra-10
❑ 92SteDra-11
❑ 92SteDra-12
❑ 93TedWil-53
❑ 93UppDecAH-44
❑ 94UppDecAH-84
❑ 94UppDecAH1-84

Drawdy, Duke
❑ 76ForLauYS-2
❑ 77WesHavYT-6

Drees, Tom
❑ 86PenWhiSP-8
❑ 87DayBeaAP-4
❑ 88BirBarB-3
❑ 88SouLeaAJ-34
❑ 89BirBarADB-7
❑ 89TriAAAP-AAA29
❑ 89VanCanC-10
❑ 89VanCanP-588
❑ 90BirBarADB-7
❑ 90CMC-630
❑ 90Fle-644
❑ 90FleCan-644
❑ 90ProAAAF-161
❑ 90TriAllGP-AAA38
❑ 90UppDec-3
❑ 90VanCanC-3
❑ 90VanCanP-483
❑ 91LinDriAAA-631
❑ 91VanCanLD-631
❑ 91VanCanP-1588
❑ 92OklCit8S-309
❑ 92SkyAAAF-141
❑ 92TopDeb91-47
❑ 93PorBeaF-2378

Dreifort, Darren
❑ 91TopGolS-4
❑ 91TopTra-34T
❑ 91TopTraT-34T
❑ 92StaCluD-39
❑ 92TopTra-29T
❑ 92TopTraG-29T
❑ 93StaCluM-13
❑ 94DodMot-24
❑ 94DodPol-7
❑ 94LeaLimR-59
❑ 94Pin-540
❑ 94PinArtP-540
❑ 94PinMusC-540
❑ 94SP-3
❑ 95ColCho-226
❑ 95ColChoGS-226
❑ 95ColChoSE-6
❑ 95ColChoSEGS-6
❑ 95ColChoSESS-6
❑ 95ColChoSS-226
❑ 95Don-131
❑ 95DonPreP-131
❑ 95Fle-539
❑ 95LeaGolR-5
❑ 95Pac-216
❑ 95Sco-300
❑ 95ScoGolR-300
❑ 95ScoPlaTS-300
❑ 95Ult-180
❑ 95UltGolM-180
❑ 95UppDec-73
❑ 95UppDecED-73
❑ 95UppDecEDG-73
❑ 96LeaSigA-59
❑ 96LeaSigAG-59
❑ 96LeaSigAS-59
❑ 97DodMot-25
❑ 97DodPol-6
❑ 97DodSco-8
❑ 97DodScoPl-8
❑ 97DodScoPr-8
❑ 97DonRatR-28
❑ 97DonTea-120
❑ 97DonTeaSPE-120
❑ 97Fle-564
❑ 97FleTif-564
❑ 97Lea-303
❑ 97LeaFraM-303
❑ 97LeaFraMDC-303
❑ 97PacPriGotD-GD157
❑ 97Pin-50
❑ 97PinArtP-PP50
❑ 97PinMusC-50
❑ 97PinPrePla-50
❑ 97Sco-206
❑ 97ScoArtPWB-206
❑ 97ScoPreS-206
❑ 97ScoShoS-206
❑ 97ScoShoSAP-206
❑ 97Ult-464
❑ 97UltGolME-464
❑ 97UltPlaME-464
❑ 98DodMot-19
❑ 98DodPol-6
❑ 98Don-173
❑ 98DonGolPP-173
❑ 98DonSilPP-173
❑ 98Fle-460
❑ 98LeaRS-86
❑ 98LeaRSLHolo-86
❑ 98LeaRSLong-86
❑ 98LeaRTrue-86
❑ 98PacOnl-366
❑ 98PacOnlR-366
❑ 98PacOnlWC-366
❑ 98PinSna-LAD5
❑ 98UppDec-398
❑ 99DodPol-7
❑ 99Fle-96
❑ 99FleSta9-96
❑ 99FleWarT-96
❑ 99Pac-217
❑ 99PacPlaB-217
❑ 99PacRed-217
❑ 99SkyThu-44
❑ 99SkyThuRant-44
❑ 99SkyThuRave-44
❑ 99StaClu-12
❑ 99StaCluFDI-12
❑ 99StaCluOoaK-12
❑ 99StaCluPP-12
❑ 99ThuSkySupR-44
❑ 99Top-49
❑ 99TopChr-49
❑ 99TopChrR-49
❑ 99TopMVPP-49

Dreifort, Todd
❑ 90WicStaSGD-9
❑ 92JamExpC-7
❑ 92JamExpF-1512

Dreisbach, Bill
❑ 91PriRedC-12
❑ 91PriRedP-3517
❑ 92BilMusF-3357
❑ 92BilMusSP-22

Dreisewerd, Clem
❑ 75RedSox1T-13

Drell, Tom
❑ 88CapCodPB-1
❑ 88CapCodPPaLP-18
❑ 89AncGlaP-11
❑ 90NiaFalRP-17
❑ 91LakTigC-2
❑ 91LakTigP-258
❑ 92LakTigC-21

Drent, Brian
❑ 96SouBenSHS-10

Dresch, Michael
❑ 96BilMusTI-7

Drese, Ryan
❑ 98WatIndTI-9
❑ 99TeaBesR-20
❑ 99TeaBesRG-20
❑ 99TeaBesRS-20

Dressen, Chuck (Charles W.)
❑ 25Exh-28
❑ 26Exh-28
❑ 28StaPlaCE-16
❑ 29PorandAR-18
❑ 36NatChiFPR-95
❑ 36R31PasP-10
❑ 40PlaBal-72
❑ 47YanTeaT-9
❑ 48BluTin-8
❑ 48YanTeal-7
❑ 49RemBre-6
❑ 50RemBre-4
❑ 51Bow-259
❑ 52Bow-188
❑ 52Top-377
❑ 53BowC-124
❑ 53RedMan-NL1
❑ 53Top-50
❑ 55DonWin-2
❑ 56BraBilaBP-9
❑ 58DodTeal-5
❑ 59DodTeal-4
❑ 60BraJayP-4
❑ 60BraLaktL-10
❑ 60BraSpiaS-8
❑ 60Top-213
❑ 61Top-137
❑ 64TigJayP-4
❑ 64TigLid-5
❑ 64Top-443
❑ 65TigJayP-5
❑ 65Top-538
❑ 66OPC-187
❑ 66Top-187
❑ 66TopVen-187
❑ 74dod195T-9
❑ 78DodTCM4-43
❑ 79TCM50-56
❑ 83TigAlKS-29
❑ 83TopRep5-377
❑ 87ConSer2-31
❑ 88ConSer4-9
❑ 89DodSmoG-59
❑ 90DodTar-202
❑ 91DodRinP2-1
❑ 91TopArc1-50
❑ 92ConTSN-400
❑ 93ConTSN-832
❑ 94ConTSN-1120
❑ 94ConTSNB-1120
❑ 95TopArcBD-28
❑ 95TopArcBD-42

Dressendorfer, Kirk
❑ 88CapCodPPaLP-134
❑ 90ProAaA-163
❑ 90SouOreAB-3
❑ 90SouOreAP-3425
❑ 90TopMag-53
❑ 91A'sMot-19
❑ 91Bow-235
❑ 91Cla1-T77
❑ 91Cla2-T20
❑ 91ClaGam-159
❑ 91DonRoo-24
❑ 91FleUpd-50
❑ 91LeaGolR-BC13
❑ 91OPCPre-36
❑ 91ScoRoo-97T
❑ 91SouOreAAP-SOA11
❑ 91TopTra-35T
❑ 91TopTraT-35T
❑ 91UppDec-756
❑ 92Bow-91
❑ 92ClaGam-7
❑ 92Don-594
❑ 92OPC-716
❑ 92Pin-270
❑ 92Sco-728
❑ 92Sco100RS-37
❑ 92StaClu-806
❑ 92StaCluECN-806
❑ 92TexLon-13
❑ 92Top-716
❑ 92TopDeb91-48
❑ 92TopGol-716
❑ 92TopGolW-716
❑ 92TopMic-716
❑ 92TriPla-177
❑ 92UppDec-632
❑ 95ModA'sTI-6
❑ 97AlbDukGS-8

Dressler, Rob (Robert Alan)
❑ 75IntLeaASB-6
❑ 75LafDriT-16
❑ 75PacCoaLAB-6
❑ 75PhoGiaC-14
❑ 75PhoGiaCK-11
❑ 76OPC-599
❑ 76PheGiaCr-37
❑ 76PhoGiaCC-7
❑ 76SanFraGP-6
❑ 76Top-599
❑ 77Gia-5
❑ 77PhoGiaCC-6
❑ 77PhoGiaCP-5
❑ 77PhoGiaVNB-5
❑ 77Top-11
❑ 78PhoGiaC-7
❑ 79SpoIndT-19
❑ 80MarPos-10
❑ 80Top-366
❑ 81Don-406
❑ 81OPC-163
❑ 81Top-508

Drew, Bob
❑ 74WicAerODF-126
❑ 75LafDriT-25

Drew, Cameron
❑ 86AshTouP-8
❑ 87ColAstP-7
❑ 87SouLeaAJ-7
❑ 88TriAAAP-44
❑ 88TriAAC-37
❑ 88TucTorC-14
❑ 88TucTorJP-10
❑ 88TucTorP-188
❑ 89Bow-334
❑ 89BowTif-334
❑ 89ClaTraO-135
❑ 89Don-30
❑ 89Fle-640
❑ 89FleGlo-640
❑ 89Sco-643
❑ 89ScoHot1R-3
❑ 89Spo-225

Drew, J.D.
❑ 97St.PauS-8
❑ 98AriFalLTP-12
❑ 98ArkTra-32
❑ 98ArkTraH-1
❑ 98ArkTraH-2
❑ 98Bes-65
❑ 98BesBet-6
❑ 98BesCor-6
❑ 98BesDiaB-14
❑ 98BesNumOP-19
❑ 98BesPro-3
❑ 98DonSig-129
❑ 98DonSigP-129
❑ 98FleUpd-U100
❑ 98LeaRS-332
❑ 98LeaRSLHolo-332
❑ 98LeaRSLong-332
❑ 98LeaRTrue-332
❑ 98St.PauSTI-5
❑ 99AurOn DL-14
❑ 99AurPenF-14
❑ 99AurPenF-14
❑ 99AurPenFB-14
❑ 99AurPenFS-14
❑ 99AurSty-14
❑ 99BasAmeTPA-9
❑ 99CroRoyB-113
❑ 99CroRoyC2-6
❑ 99CroRoyCCDB-7
❑ 99CroRoyCCG-7
❑ 99CroRoyCCG-7
❑ 99CroRoyCCLB-7
❑ 99CroRoyCCP-7
❑ 99CroRoyCCP-7
❑ 99CroRoyCCR-7
❑ 99CroRoyL-113
❑ 99CroRoyMP-13
❑ 99CroRoyOD-113
❑ 99CroRoyPotG-18
❑ 99CroRoyPP-19
❑ 99CroRoyPPN-19
❑ 99DumSet-113
❑ 99DumSet-P113
❑ 99E-X Cen-105
❑ 99E-X CenECFut-105
❑ 99E-X CenECNow-105
❑ 99E-X CenEQ-2
❑ 99E-XCenA-1
❑ 99E-XCenA-B1
❑ 99E-XCenA-R1
❑ 99E-XCenFoF'-11
❑ 99FlaShoLeg1-6
❑ 99FlaShoLeg2-6
❑ 99FlaShoLeg3-6
❑ 99FlaShoLegM1-6
❑ 99FlaShoLegM2-6
❑ 99FlaShoLegM3-6
❑ 99FlaShoR1-6
❑ 99FlaShoR2-6
❑ 99FlaShoR3-6
❑ 99FlaShoWotF-3
❑ 99Fle-7
❑ 99Fle-578
❑ 99Fle-600
❑ 99Fle-P7
❑ 99FleBri-126
❑ 99FleBri-NNO
❑ 99FleBri2G-126
❑ 99FleBriBlu-126
❑ 99FleBriGol-126
❑ 99FleBril-3
❑ 99FleMys-113
❑ 99FleMys-P113

❑ 99FleMysFl-12
❑ 99FleMysFtG-2
❑ 99FleMysM-113
❑ 99FleMysP-2
❑ 99FleRooFla-6
❑ 99FleSta9-7
❑ 99FleSta9-578
❑ 99FleSta9-600
❑ 99FleVin'-7
❑ 99FleWarT-7
❑ 99FleWarT-578
❑ 99FleWarT-600
❑ 99MetUni-269
❑ 99MetUniGM-269
❑ 99MetUniN-6
❑ 99MetUniPMG-269
❑ 99MetUniSamp-NNOA
❑ 99MetUniSamp-NNO
❑ 99Pac-352
❑ 99Pac-352A
❑ 99PacAur-153
❑ 99PacAurOD-153
❑ 99PacCroC-227
❑ 99PacCroCITC-13
❑ 99PacCroCPB-227
❑ 99PacCroCTM-13
❑ 99PacDynaD-17
❑ 99PacDynaDT-17
❑ 99PacGolCDC-33
❑ 99PacInv-118
❑ 99PacInvDM-6
❑ 99PacInvFP-15
❑ 99PacInvGotG-6
❑ 99PacInvOD-118
❑ 99PacInvPB-118
❑ 99PacInvSF-14
❑ 99PacInvSF-14B
❑ 99PacInvSH-15
❑ 99PacInvSH-15B
❑ 99PacInvTA-14
❑ 99PacOme-194
❑ 99PacOme5T-9
❑ 99PacOme5TT-9
❑ 99PacOmeC-194
❑ 99PacOmeDM-25
❑ 99PacOmeG-194
❑ 99PacOmePB-194
❑ 99PacPar-191
❑ 99PacParC-191
❑ 99PacParFC-14
❑ 99PacParG-191
❑ 99PacParHoloGold-191
❑ 99PacParHS-191
❑ 99PacParOD-191
❑ 99PacParPB-28
❑ 99PacParPB-191
❑ 99PacParRed-191
❑ 99PacPlaB-352
❑ 99PacPlaB-352A
❑ 99PacPri-117
❑ 99PacPriAotG-15
❑ 99PacPriDG-15
❑ 99PacPriHB-117
❑ 99PacPriHG-117
❑ 99PacPriHM-117
❑ 99PacPriHP-117
❑ 99PacPriRed-117
❑ 99PacPriS-3
❑ 99PacPriS206-3
❑ 99PacPriS206R-3
❑ 99PacPriSE-3
❑ 99PacPriSP-3
❑ 99PacPriSP-3
❑ 99PacPriSV-3
❑ 99PacRed-352
❑ 99PacRed-352A
❑ 99Rev-114
❑ 99RevDiaL-26
❑ 99RevFouP-15
❑ 99RevPremDate-114
❑ 99RevRet-114
❑ 99RevShaSS-114
❑ 99RevThoitS-13
❑ 99RevTri-18
❑ 99RevTri-18
❑ 99SkyMolM-131
❑ 99SkyMolMF-31
❑ 99SkyMolMFS-31
❑ 99SkyMolMFT-31
❑ 99SkyMolMX-131
❑ 99SkyPre-252
❑ 99SkyPre-252
❑ 99SkyPre-294
❑ 99SkyPreA-14
❑ 99SkyPreABlue-14
❑ 99SkyPreDD-6
❑ 99SkyPreIN-13
❑ 99SkyPreR-252
❑ 99SkyPreR-252
❑ 99SkyPreR-294
❑ 99SkyThu-299
❑ 99SkyThuHip-H1
❑ 99SkyThuRant-299
❑ 99SkyThuRave-299
❑ 99SkyThuUnl-U4
❑ 99SkyThuwww-WB1
❑ 99SP Aut-117
❑ 99SP AutC-JD
❑ 99SP AutCG-JD
❑ 99SP AutEF-E28
❑ 99SP AutHRC-HR37
❑ 99SP AutR-R28
❑ 99SP SigAuto-JD
❑ 99SP SigAutoG-JD
❑ 99SP TopP-1
❑ 99SP TopP-51
❑ 99SP TopPDtS-D13
❑ 99SP TopPGF-GF13
❑ 99SP TopPPE-1
❑ 99SP TopPPE-51
❑ 99SPAutHRCDC-HR37
❑ 99SpoIll-48
❑ 99SpoIllOTW-1
❑ 99SpoIllOTW-NNO
❑ 99SPSig-3
❑ 99SPx-119
❑ 99SPxDom-FB19
❑ 99SPxFinR-119
❑ 99SPxFinS-119
❑ 99SPxPowE-PE28
❑ 99SPxPreS-PS4
❑ 99SPxStaF-SF27
❑ 99SPxWinM-JD
❑ 99TeaBesR-21
❑ 99TeaBesR-3
❑ 99TeaBesRA-7
❑ 99TeaBesRFS-18
❑ 99TeaBesRFS-20
❑ 99TeaBesRG-21
❑ 99TeaBesRS-21
❑ 99ThuSkySupR-299
❑ 99UD Cho-27
❑ 99UD ChoMBH-B29
❑ 99UD ChoPCR-27
❑ 99UD ChoYW-Y7
❑ 99UD Ion-55
❑ 99UD Ion-90
❑ 99UD IonC-C22
❑ 99UD IonH-H20
❑ 99UD IonN-N10
❑ 99UD IonR-55
❑ 99UD IonR-90
❑ 99UD IonWZ-WZ15
❑ 99UDHolo-49
❑ 99UDHoloAUsome-49
❑ 99UDHoloLau-L4
❑ 99UDHoloLauG-L4
❑ 99UDHoloUDA-JD
❑ 99Ult-241
❑ 99UltGolM-241
❑ 99UltMas-241
❑ 99UltPlaM-241
❑ 99UltWorP-14
❑ 99UppDec-10
❑ 99UppDec-522
❑ 99UppDecBD-117
❑ 99UppDecBDD-117
❑ 99UppDecBDQ-117
❑ 99UppDecBDT-117
❑ 99UppDecCf7-41
❑ 99UppDecCf7-90
❑ 99UppDecCf7-C30
❑ 99UppDecCf7Cf7P-C30
❑ 99UppDecCf7LL-L27
❑ 99UppDecCf7SftF-S6
❑ 99UppDecCL-101
❑ 99UppDecCLCC-101
❑ 99UppDecCLM-C77
❑ 99UppDecCo7CE-41
❑ 99UppDecCo7CE-90
❑ 99UppDecE-100
❑ 99UppDecE-143
❑ 99UppDecE2C-2K4
❑ 99UppDecEBPC-C-JD
❑ 99UppDecEDF-D15
❑ 99UppDecEDFFXG-D15
❑ 99UppDecEFXG-100
❑ 99UppDecEFXG-143
❑ 99UppDecEL1-10
❑ 99UppDecEL1-522
❑ 99UppDecEL2-10
❑ 99UppDecEL2-522
❑ 99UppDecEPE-P28
❑ 99UppDecERE-R1
❑ 99UppDecEREFXG-R1
❑ 99UppDecEUA-JD
❑ 99UppDecEUR-U7
❑ 99UppDecF-F22
❑ 99UppDecFD-F22
❑ 99UppDecFQ-F22
❑ 99UppDecFT-F22
❑ 99UppDecGJ-JD
❑ 99UppDecGJ-JDS
❑ 99UppDecM-170
❑ 99UppDecMD-D15
❑ 99UppDecMGS-170
❑ 99UppDecMGUS-GUJD
❑ 99UppDecMHFS-170
❑ 99UppDecMSC-SC1
❑ 99UppDecMSS-170
❑ 99UppDecMST-T13
❑ 99UppDecO-61
❑ 99UppDecOSO-61
❑ 99UppDecR-70
❑ 99UppDecRG-70
❑ 99UppDecROSS-S17
❑ 99UppDecROSS-S17
❑ 99UppDecRP-70
❑ 99UppDecRTA-T5
❑ 99UppDecRTAL2-T5
❑ 99UppDecTE-T23
❑ 99UppDecTED-T23
❑ 99UppDecTEQ-T23
❑ 99UppDecTET-T23
❑ 99UppDecVtaT-V28
❑ 99UppDecVtaTD-V28
❑ 99UppDecVtaTQ-V28
❑ 99UppDecVtaTT-V28
❑ 99Vic-317
❑ 99Vic-320

Drew, Tim
❑ 97BurIndG-7
❑ 98Bes-66
❑ 98BesNumOP-20
❑ 98ColRedSM-1
❑ 98KinIndQ-8
❑ 98SouAtlLPM-9
❑ 98Top-489
❑ 98TopChr-489
❑ 98TopChrR-489
❑ 98TopDevR-489
❑ 98TopDia-489
❑ 98TopMiniC-489
❑ 99BasAmeTP-35
❑ 99BasAmeTPA-10
❑ 99BasAmeTPG-35
❑ 99TeaBesRFS-20

Drewien, Dan
❑ 93SpoIndC-5
❑ 93SpoIndF-3583
❑ 94MidLeaAF-MDW57
❑ 94SprSulC-6
❑ 94SprSulF-2030
❑ 95RanCucQT-NNO

Drews, Karl (Karl August)
❑ 48YanTeal-8
❑ 49Bow-188
❑ 52Top-352
❑ 53BowC-113
❑ 53Top-59
❑ 54Bow-191
❑ 75OakOak2A-13
❑ 83TopRep5-352
❑ 91TopArc1-59

Drews, Matt
❑ 94Bow-53
❑ 94ColC-30
❑ 94ColChoGS-30
❑ 94ColChoSS-30
❑ 94OneYanC-1
❑ 94OneYanF-3784
❑ 94Pin-265
❑ 94PinArtP-265
❑ 94PinMusC-265
❑ 94Sco-506
❑ 94ScoGolR-506
❑ 94SigRoo-29
❑ 94SigRooS-29
❑ 94UppDecML-107
❑ 95Bes-35
❑ 95BesFra-F4
❑ 95Bow-21
❑ 95BowBes-B68
❑ 95BowBesR-B68
❑ 95Exc-94
❑ 95SPML-120
❑ 95SPMLDtS-DS18
❑ 95TamYanYI-5
❑ 95UppDecML-54
❑ 95UppDecMLFS-54
❑ 96Bow-183
❑ 96BowBes-131
❑ 96BowBesAR-131
❑ 96BowBesR-131
❑ 96BowFoi-183
❑ 96ColCliB-11
❑ 96Exc-87
❑ 96ExcSeaC-3
❑ 96Top-430
❑ 97JacSun-9
❑ 98TolMudHQ-13
❑ 99BasAmeTP-36
❑ 99BasAmeTPG-36

Dreyer, Darren
❑ 92GenCubC-19
❑ 92GenCubF-1553
❑ 94OrlCubF-1379

Dreyer, Steve
❑ 90ButCopKSP-10
❑ 91GasRanC-4
❑ 91GasRanP-2681
❑ 91SouAtlLAGP-SAL22
❑ 92ChaRanC-23
❑ 92ChaRanF-2220
❑ 92UppDecML-129
❑ 93RanKee-403
❑ 93TulDriF-2727
❑ 93TulDriTI-7
❑ 94ColC-5
❑ 94ColChoGS-5
❑ 94ColChoSS-5
❑ 94FleMajLP-10
❑ 94OklCit8F-1491
❑ 94RanMagM-4
❑ 94SpoRoo-77
❑ 94SpoRooAP-77
❑ 94StaCluT-244
❑ 94StaCluTFDI-244
❑ 94Top-193
❑ 94TopGol-193
❑ 94TopSpa-193
❑ 94Ult-430
❑ 94UppDec-9
❑ 94UppDecED-9
❑ 95Don-271
❑ 95DonPreP-271
❑ 95StaClu-477
❑ 95StaCluMOP-477
❑ 95StaCluSTWS-477
❑ 96OklCit8B-7

Dreyfuss, Barney
❑ 10PirTipTD-1

Drezek, Karl
❑ 88AppFoxP-148
❑ 88EugEmeB-21

Driessen, Dan (Daniel)
❑ 74OPC-341
❑ 74Top-341
❑ 74TopSta-25
❑ 75OPC-133
❑ 75Top-133
❑ 75TopMin-133
❑ 76LinSup-100
❑ 76OPC-514
❑ 76RedKro-6
❑ 76RedParC-9
❑ 76SSP-36
❑ 76Top-514
❑ 77BurCheD-199
❑ 77OPC-31
❑ 77PepGloD-45
❑ 77Top-23
❑ 78Hos-64
❑ 78OPC-84
❑ 78Pep-9
❑ 78RCColC-76
❑ 78SSP270-123
❑ 78Top-246
❑ 79BasPat-25
❑ 79Kel-26
❑ 79OPC-247
❑ 79Top-475
❑ 80OPC-173
❑ 80RedEnq-22
❑ 80Top-325
❑ 81AllGamPI-94
❑ 81CokTeaS-40
❑ 81Don-301
❑ 81Fle-205
❑ 81FleStiC-22
❑ 81OPC-14
❑ 81Top-655
❑ 81TopSti-164
❑ 81TopSupHT-34
❑ 82Don-248
❑ 82Fle-64
❑ 82Fle-630
❑ 82OPC-373
❑ 82RedCok-6
❑ 82Top-785
❑ 83AllGamPI-93
❑ 83Don-274
❑ 83Fle-589
❑ 83FleSta-55
❑ 83FleSti-217
❑ 83OPC-165
❑ 83RedYea-22
❑ 83Top-165
❑ 83TopSti-228
❑ 84AllGamPI-3
❑ 84Don-243
❑ 84Fle-467
❑ 84Nes792-585
❑ 84OPC-44
❑ 84RedEnq-2
❑ 84Top-585
❑ 84TopSti-55
❑ 84TopTif-585
❑ 85AllGamPI-93
❑ 85Don-619
❑ 85ExpPos-7
❑ 85Fle-396
❑ 85Lea-255
❑ 85OPC-285
❑ 85OPCPos-2
❑ 85Top-285
❑ 85TopSti-92
❑ 85TopTif-285
❑ 86Don-641
❑ 86Fle-539
❑ 86GiaMot-14
❑ 86Lea-255
❑ 86Top-65
❑ 86TopSti-89
❑ 86TopTat-14
❑ 86TopTif-65
❑ 87LouRedTI-12
❑ 88FleGlo-WS7
❑ 88FleWorS-7
❑ 89PacSenL-102
❑ 89PacSenL-105
❑ 89T/MSenL-30
❑ 89TopSenL-46
❑ 90EliSenL-67
❑ 91PacSenL-1

Driggers, Lee
❑ 90AugPirP-2480
❑ 91WelPirP-3591

Drill, Lew (Lewis L.)
❑ 03BreE10-45

Drilling, Robert
❑ 49SomandK-20

Drinkwater, Sean
❑ 92SpoIndC-15
❑ 92SpoIndF-1301
❑ 93RanCucQC-9
❑ 93RanCucQF-839
❑ 94ExcFS7-279
❑ 94WicWraF-195
❑ 95MemChiTI-26

Driscoll, Jim (James B.)
❑ 67VanMouSO-6
❑ 71OPC-317
❑ 71Top-317
❑ 72RanTeal-7
❑ 85WatIndT-19
❑ 86WatIndP-7
❑ 93RanKee-8

Driscoll, John
❑ 19Zee-5

Driscoll, Mary Ellen
❑ 85FreGiaSB-31

Driscoll, Milton
❑ 11Zee-11
❑ 12HomRunKE-7
❑ 12Zee-8
❑ 13Zee-6

Driscoll, Patrick
❑ 97BatCliTI-26

Driskell, Jeff
❑ 94JamJamC-8
❑ 94JamJamF-3967

Driskill, Travis
❑ 93WatIndC-8
❑ 93WatIndF-3555
❑ 94ColRedC-9
❑ 94ColRedF-437
❑ 95Exc-39
❑ 96CanIndB-12
❑ 96SigRooOJ-9
❑ 96SigRooOJS-9
❑ 97BufBis-16

Driver, Ron
❑ 77NewCoPT-10
❑ 78HolMilT-6
❑ 79HolMilT-11

Drizmala, Tom
❑ 83ChaRoyT-19

Drizos, Justin
❑ 96AshTouB-13
❑ 97HudValRB-26
❑ 97SalAva-13

Drohan, Bill
❑ 88EugEmeB-5
❑ 89AppFoxP-854
❑ 90BasCitRS-6

Droll, Jeff
❑ 92HelBreF-1708
❑ 92HelBreSP-9
❑ 93BelBreCB-5
❑ 93BelBreFI-1703
❑ 93HelBreF-4086
❑ 94HicCraC-1
❑ 94HicCraF-2169

Dromerhauser, Rob
❑ 85NewOriT-17
❑ 88MetColP-21
❑ 89MetColP-26
❑ 90MetColP-31
❑ 91MetColP-31

Droogsma, Tim
❑ 85RedWinA-4

Dropo, Walt (Walter)
❑ 47Exh-64
❑ 49SolSunP-3
❑ 50Bow-246
❑ 50RedSoxTI-6
❑ 51R42SmaS-19
❑ 51TopCurA-3
❑ 52Bow-169
❑ 52Top-235
❑ 53BowC-45
❑ 53RedMan-AL4
❑ 53TigGle-5
❑ 53Top-121
❑ 54Bow-7
❑ 54Top-18
❑ 55Bow-285
❑ 56Top-238
❑ 57Top-257
❑ 58Top-338
❑ 59RedEnq-5
❑ 59RedShiBS-5
❑ 59Top-158
❑ 59TopVen-158
❑ 60Top-79
❑ 60TopVen-79
❑ 61BalOriP-6
❑ 61Top-489
❑ 79TCM50-116
❑ 80LauFamF-36
❑ 81RedSoxBG2S-17
❑ 83FraBroR-8
❑ 83TopRep5-235
❑ 89SweBasG-108
❑ 90PacLeg-22
❑ 90SweBasG-57
❑ 91OriCro-114
❑ 91SweBasG-111
❑ 91TopArc1-121
❑ 92BazQua5A-20
❑ 94TopArc1-18
❑ 94TopArc1G-18

Droschak, Dave
❑ 83SprCarF-5

Drott, Dick (Richard Fred)
❑ 58Top-80
❑ 59Top-15
❑ 59TopVen-15
❑ 60Lea-76
❑ 60Top-27
❑ 60TopVen-27
❑ 61Top-231
❑ 79TCM50-64

Drucke, Louis
❑ 10DomDisP-39
❑ 10SweCapPP-113
❑ 11HelSta-126
❑ 11PinT-5-267
❑ 13Zee-78

Druhot, Carl
❑ 08IndPos-7

Drumheller, Albert
❑ 93OneYanC-7
❑ 93OneYanF-3496
❑ 94GreBatF-465
❑ 95TamYanYI-6
❑ 96TamYanY-10
❑ 97GreBatC-7
❑ 97RanCucQG-10
❑ 98MobBayBTI-10
Drumm, Doug
❑ 93EveGiaC-9
❑ 93EveGiaF-3782
Drummond, Tim
❑ 86PriWilPP-9
❑ 87VanCanP-1610
❑ 88TidTidCa-18
❑ 88TidTidCM-4
❑ 88TidTidP-1593
❑ 89MetColP-27
❑ 89TidTidC-1
❑ 89TidTidP-1952
❑ 90Don-510
❑ 90DonRoo-50
❑ 90FleUpd-107
❑ 90OPC-713
❑ 90ScoRoo-103T
❑ 90Top-713
❑ 90TopTif-713
❑ 91Don-694
❑ 91Fle-607
❑ 91LinDriAAA-406
❑ 91OPC-46
❑ 91PorBeaLD-406
❑ 91PorBeaP-1560
❑ 91Sco-76
❑ 91Sco100RS-95
❑ 91Top-46
❑ 91TopDesS-46
❑ 91TopMic-46
❑ 91TopTif-46
❑ 91UppDec-698
❑ 92HagSunF-2550
Drumright, Keith A.
❑ 78ChaChaT-6
❑ 79ChaChaT-1
❑ 80OmaRoyP-10
❑ 81TacTigT-17
❑ 82Don-616
❑ 82Fle-89
❑ 82TacTigT-29
❑ 82Top-673
Drumright, Mike
❑ 95Bes-119
❑ 96Exc-50
❑ 96JacSunB-10
❑ 97Bow-119
❑ 97BowBes-166
❑ 97BowBesAR-166
❑ 97BowBesR-166
❑ 97BowCerBlaIA-CA21
❑ 97BowCerBluIA-CA21
❑ 97BowCerGolIA-CA21
❑ 97BowChr-135
❑ 97BowChrI-135
❑ 97BowChrIR-135
❑ 97BowChrR-135
❑ 97BowInt-119
❑ 97JacSun-1
❑ 97SouLeaTP-16
❑ 97TolMudHB-11
❑ 98Bow-186
❑ 98BowBes-189
❑ 98BowBesAR-189
❑ 98BowBesR-189
❑ 98BowCerBlueAU-26
❑ 98BowCerGA-26
❑ 98BowCerSA-26
❑ 98BowChr-186
❑ 98BowChrGA-186
❑ 98BowChrGAR-186
❑ 98BowChrI-186
❑ 98BowChrIR-186
❑ 98BowChrR-186
❑ 98BowGolA-186
❑ 98BowInt-186
❑ 98LeaRS-267
❑ 98LeaRSLHolo-267
❑ 98LeaRSLong-267
❑ 98LeaRTrue-267
❑ 98SP MinPE-52
❑ 98SPMin-52
❑ 98TolMudHQ-14
❑ 99BasAmeTP-37
❑ 99BasAmeTPG-37
Druna, Roland
❑ 82ChaRoyT-17
Drury, Scott
❑ 88BatCliP-1668
Drysdale, Brooks
❑ 94CedRapKC-9
❑ 94CedRapKF-1103
❑ 94MidLeaAF-MDW37
❑ 96StoPorB-26
Drysdale, Don (Donald S.)
❑ 47Exh-65A
❑ 47Exh-65B
❑ 56Dod-7
❑ 57Top-18
❑ 58DodBelB-3
❑ 58DodJayP-4
❑ 58DodTeal-6
❑ 58DodVol-3
❑ 58HarSta-13
❑ 58Hir-55
❑ 58Top-25
❑ 59Baz-10
❑ 59DodMor-1
❑ 59DodPos-5
❑ 59DodTeal-5
❑ 59DodVol-3
❑ 59Top-262
❑ 59Top-387
❑ 60ArmCoi-9
❑ 60DodJayP-3
❑ 60DodMor-3
❑ 60DodPos-3
❑ 60DodTeal-5
❑ 60DodUniO-5
❑ 60KeyChal-14
❑ 60Pos-2
❑ 60Top-475
❑ 60Top-570
❑ 60TopTat-12
❑ 61Baz-26
❑ 61DodJayP-2
❑ 61DodMor-2
❑ 61DodUniO-5
❑ 61Pos-160A
❑ 61Pos-160B
❑ 61Top-45
❑ 61Top-49
❑ 61Top-260
❑ 61TopDicG-4
❑ 61TopStal-26
❑ 62AurRec-5
❑ 62DodBelB-53
❑ 62DodJayP-2
❑ 62DodVol-3
❑ 62Jel-110
❑ 62Pos-110
❑ 62PosCan-110
❑ 62Top-60
❑ 62Top-340
❑ 62Top-398
❑ 62TopBuc-23
❑ 62TopStal-133
❑ 62TopVen-60
❑ 63BasMagM-21
❑ 63Baz-17
❑ 63DodJayP-4
❑ 63ExhStaB-20
❑ 63Fle-41
❑ 63Jel-123
❑ 63Pos-123
❑ 63SalMetC-1
❑ 63Top-5
❑ 63Top-7
❑ 63Top-9
❑ 63Top-360
❑ 63Top-412
❑ 63TopStil-14
❑ 64DodHea-3
❑ 64Top-5
❑ 64Top-120
❑ 64TopCoi-34
❑ 64TopSta-79
❑ 64TopStaU-22
❑ 64TopVen-5
❑ 64TopVen-120
❑ 65DodJayP-4
❑ 65DodTeal-5
❑ 65OPC-8
❑ 65OPC-12
❑ 65OPC-260
❑ 65Top-8
❑ 65Top-12
❑ 65Top-260
❑ 65TopEmbl-15
❑ 65TopTral-47
❑ 66Baz-42
❑ 66DodVolT-2
❑ 66Top-223
❑ 66Top-430
❑ 66TopRubl-24
❑ 66TopVen-223
❑ 67Baz-42
❑ 67OPC-55
❑ 67OPCPapl-16
❑ 67Top-55
❑ 67TopGiaSU-11
❑ 67TopPos-16
❑ 67TopVen-295
❑ 68Baz-6
❑ 68Baz-15
❑ 68OPC-145
❑ 68Top-145
❑ 68TopActS-2C
❑ 68TopActS-11B
❑ 68TopActS-13C
❑ 68TopPla-18
❑ 68TopPos-7
❑ 68TopVen-145
❑ 69MLBPin-41
❑ 69Top-314
❑ 69Top-400
❑ 69TopDecl-9
❑ 69TopSta-42
❑ 69TopSup-46
❑ 69TopTeaP-22
❑ 72LauGreF-38
❑ 73BooProC-5
❑ 75CalAngP-13
❑ 75DodTCMA-4
❑ 76UPIS-2
❑ 77GalGloG-246
❑ 77Spo-7213
❑ 78TCM60I-3
❑ 79DiaGre-96
❑ 80PerHaloFP-186
❑ 80PerHaloFPS-51
❑ 80SSPHOF-187
❑ 82K-M-42
❑ 82TCMGreP-14
❑ 83MLBPin-23
❑ 84DodUniO-4
❑ 84SpoDesPW-9
❑ 84WilMay-35
❑ 86TCMSupS-22
❑ 87AstShoSO-26
❑ 87DodSmoA-7
❑ 88DodRinP1-8A
❑ 88DodSmo-11
❑ 88GreBasS-45
❑ 89CalLeaA-28
❑ 89DodSmoG-7
❑ 89TopBasT-39
❑ 90DodTar-203
❑ 90HOFStiB-73
❑ 90PacLeg-29
❑ 90SweBasG-62
❑ 90TopGloA-11
❑ 91Col-10
❑ 91DodUno7P-3
❑ 91LinDri-1
❑ 91SweBasG-26
❑ 92DodStaTA-3
❑ 93ActPacA-121
❑ 93ActPacA2-55G
❑ 93NabAllA-2
❑ 93TedWil-12
❑ 93TedWilM-6
❑ 95StoPop-3
❑ 95TopArcBD-112
❑ 95TopLegot6M-4
❑ 97CalLot-2
Drzayich, Emil
❑ 80CedRapRT-4
Duant, Rich
❑ 86LitFalMP-9
Duany, Claro
❑ 95NegLeaL2-22
Duarte, Luis
❑ 80BatTroT-16
❑ 81WatIndT-17
Duarte, Rene
❑ 90IBAWorA-22
❑ 98LakElsSG-10
Dube, Greg
❑ 85OscAstTI-6
❑ 87WilBilP-19
DuBeau, Jack
❑ 78WatIndT-8
Dubee, Rich
❑ 76WatRoyT-6
❑ 77DayBealT-3
❑ 84MemChiT-2
❑ 85OmaRoyT-11
❑ 86MemChiSTOS-6
❑ 86MemChiTOS-6
❑ 87MemChiB-3
❑ 88OmaRoyC-23
❑ 88OmaRoyP-1494
❑ 90CMC-198
❑ 90OmaRoyP-82
❑ 90ProAAAF-617
❑ 91RocExpC-16
❑ 91RocExpP-2064
❑ 92IndIndF-1876
❑ 93WesPalBEC-27
❑ 93WesPalBEF-1358
❑ 94EdmTraF-2891
Dubiel, Monk (Walter John)
❑ 47CenFlo-6
❑ 49EurSta-55
❑ 51Bow-283
❑ 52Top-164
❑ 83TopRep5-164
DuBois, Brian
❑ 86HagSunP-5
❑ 87HagSunP-4
❑ 88CarLeaAS-6
❑ 88VirGenS-8
❑ 89HagSunB-13
❑ 89HagSunP-274
❑ 89HagSunS-5
❑ 90Bow-349
❑ 90BowTif-349
❑ 90ClaUpd-T17
❑ 90Don-38
❑ 90DonRoo-4
❑ 90Fle-601
❑ 90FleCan-601
❑ 90HagSunDGB-7
❑ 90Lea-266
❑ 90OPC-413
❑ 90Sco-657
❑ 90TigCok-3
❑ 90Top-413
❑ 90TopBig-272
❑ 90TopDeb89-32
❑ 90TopTif-413
❑ 90UppDec-78
❑ 91Sco100RS-85
❑ 93FreKeyC-1
❑ 93FreKeyF-1018
❑ 94OriPro-27
❑ 94RocRedWF-992
❑ 95ScrRedBTI-7
DuBose, Brian
❑ 90BriTigP-3163
❑ 90BriTigS-5
❑ 91NiaFalRC-10
❑ 91NiaFalRP-3640
❑ 92ClaFS7-103
❑ 92FayGenC-5
❑ 92FayGenF-2174
❑ 93LakTigC-5
❑ 93LakTigF-1316
❑ 94TedWil-120
❑ 94TreThuF-2130
❑ 94UppDecML-142
❑ 94UppDecMLPotYF-PY25
❑ 97WesMicW-11
❑ 98LakTigM-25
DuBose, Eric
❑ 97VisOakG-9
❑ 98BesNumOP-21
❑ 98Bow-327
❑ 98BowChr-327
❑ 98BowChrGA-327
❑ 98BowChrGAR-327
❑ 98BowChrI-327
❑ 98BowChrIR-327
❑ 98BowChrR-327
❑ 98BowGolA-327
❑ 98BowInt-327
❑ 98HunStaTI-2
❑ 98VisOakG-7
❑ 99Bow-359
❑ 99BowGol-359
❑ 99BowInt-359
❑ 99JustheS-17
❑ 99JustheSJB-17
Dubuc, Jean (Jean J.)
❑ 09T206-112
❑ 10CouT21-18
❑ 10CouT21-129
❑ 10CouT21-280
❑ 10RedCroT-109
❑ 10RedCroT-189
❑ 15CraJacE-156
❑ 15SpoNewM-53
❑ 16BF2FP-29
❑ 16SpoNewM-52
❑ 17Zee-65
❑ 18Zee-59
❑ 20MrsShePP-3
Ducey, Rob
❑ 86VenGulP-5
❑ 87BluJayFS-6
❑ 87DonHig-39
❑ 87IntLeaAT-26
❑ 87SyrChiP-1943
❑ 87SyrChiT-19
❑ 88BluJayFS-8
❑ 88Fle-107
❑ 88FleGlo-107
❑ 88OPC-106
❑ 88Sco-629
❑ 88ScoGlo-629
❑ 88SyrChiC-14
❑ 88SyrChiP-825
❑ 88Top-438
❑ 88TopTif-438
❑ 89BluJayFS-8
❑ 89OPC-203
❑ 89PanSti-459
❑ 89ScoHot1R-7
❑ 89Top-203
❑ 89TopBig-280
❑ 89TopTif-203
❑ 89UppDec-721
❑ 90CMC-347
❑ 90OPC-619
❑ 90ProAAAF-364
❑ 90PublntS-512
❑ 90ScoYouSI-34
❑ 90SyrChiC-21
❑ 90SyrChiMB-6
❑ 90SyrChiP-584
❑ 90Top-619
❑ 90TopTif-619
❑ 90UppDec-464
❑ 91BluJayFS-8
❑ 91BluJayFS-8
❑ 91BluJayS-22
❑ 91Don-705
❑ 91LinDriAAA-502
❑ 91OPC-101
❑ 91Sco-821
❑ 91StaClu-374
❑ 91SyrChiLD-502
❑ 91SyrChiMB-5
❑ 91SyrChiP-2492
❑ 91Top-101
❑ 91TopDesS-101
❑ 91TopMic-101
❑ 91TopTif-101
❑ 91TriA AAGP-AAA43
❑ 92Don-466
❑ 92Fle-328
❑ 92OPC-739
❑ 92ProFS7-163
❑ 92Sco-609
❑ 92StaClu-422
❑ 92Top-739
❑ 92TopGol-739
❑ 92TopGolW-739
❑ 92TopMic-739
❑ 93BluJayD4-40
❑ 93Don-489
❑ 93OPC-55
❑ 93RanKee-404
❑ 93StaClu-69
❑ 93StaCluFDI-69
❑ 93StaCluMOP-69
❑ 93Top-293
❑ 93TopGol-293
❑ 93TopInaM-293
❑ 93TopInaR-293
❑ 93TopMic-293
❑ 93TriAAAGF-53
❑ 94OklCit8F-1503
❑ 94RanMagM-5
❑ 94StaCluT-257
❑ 94StaCluTFDI-257
❑ 94Top-618
❑ 94TopGol-618
❑ 94TopSpa-618
❑ 94TriAAF-AAA9
❑ 97TacRai-12
❑ 98PacInvGems-90
❑ 98PacOnl-683
❑ 98PacOnlR-683
❑ 98PacOnlWC-683
Duchalsky, James
❑ 23Zee-103
Duchin, David
❑ 90LynRedSTI-25
❑ 91LynRedSC-27
❑ 92LynRedSC-27
❑ 93LynRedSC-28
Duchscherer, Justin
❑ 98MicBatCM-11
Duck, Diamond
❑ 91RicBraTI-27
Duck, Dinger
❑ 90NiaFalRP-33
Duck, Kevin
❑ 98PorRocG-9
Duckett, Mahlon
❑ 86NegLeaF-40
❑ 91NegLeaRL-11
❑ 92NegLeaRLI-18
❑ 93TedWil-104
❑ 95NegLeaLI-11
Duckhorn, Steve
❑ 79CedRapGT-1
Duckins, George
❑ 46SeaSLP-15
Duckworth, Brandon
❑ 98PieBolWM-9
Duckworth, Jim (James R.)
❑ 78TCM60I-23
❑ 78TCM60I-151
Duda, Steve
❑ 93HelBreF-4087
❑ 94StoPorC-5
❑ 94StoPorF-1686
Dudeck, Dave
❑ 94LetMouF-3870
❑ 94LetMouSP-8
❑ 97GreBatB-12
Dudek, Steve
❑ 91JohCitCC-9
❑ 91JohCitCP-3983
❑ 92JohCitCC-4
❑ 92JohCitCF-3123
❑ 93SavCarC-13
❑ 93SavCarF-699
Dudley, Clise
❑ 90DodTar-204
Duenas, Alain
❑ 98BriWhiSQ-8
Duenas, Vernon
❑ 88ChaWheB-11
Duensing, Larry
❑ 80HawIsIT-3
❑ 81HawIsIT-20
❑ 82HawIsIT-25
❑ 84LasVegSC-244
Dues, Hal (Hal Joseph)
❑ 75WesPalBES-10
❑ 78ExpPos-4
❑ 79OPC-373
❑ 79Top-699
❑ 81OPC-71
❑ 81Top-71
Duey, Kody
❑ 86JamExpP-5
Duey, Kyle
❑ 90MedHatBJB-5
❑ 91MyrBeaHC-3
❑ 91MyrBeaHP-2937
❑ 92DunBluJC-22
❑ 92DunBluJF-1991
❑ 93KnoSmoF-1255
❑ 94SyrChiF-967
❑ 94SyrChiTI-11
Duezabou, Mel
❑ 47RemBre-20
❑ 47SigOil-43
❑ 47SmiClo-23
❑ 48SigOil-5
❑ 48SmiClo-14
❑ 49RemBre-5
❑ 50RemBre-5
Dufault, Monte
❑ 92KenTwiC-20
❑ 92KenTwiF-610
Duff, Cecil
❑ 28Zee-74
Duff, Dave
❑ 82JacMetT-12
Duff, Matt
❑ 98LynHilQ-6
Duff, Scott
❑ 90BilMusP-3213
❑ 91ChaWheC-3
❑ 91ChaWheP-2880
❑ 92CedRapRC-23

❑ 92CedRapRF-1064
❑ 93WinSpiC-6
❑ 93WinSpiF-1563
Duffalo, Jim
❑ 62Top-578
❑ 63Top-567
❑ 64Top-573
❑ 65OPC-159
❑ 65Top-159
❑ 78TCM60I-204
❑ 78TCM60I-248
❑ 80PhoGiaVNB-23
❑ 81Gia196T-22
❑ 81ShrCapT-13
Duffee, Charlie (Charles E.)
❑ 87OldJudN-140
Duffek, Tony
❑ 97OmaRoyB-32
Dufficy, Pat
❑ 96ColSilB-9
Duffie, John
❑ 77FriOneYW-29
❑ 90DodTar-936
Duffy, Allen
❑ 86GleFalTP-3
Duffy, Darrin
❑ 86MedA'sC-72
❑ 87HunStaTI-10
❑ 88ModA'sTI-22
❑ 89WinSpiS-7
❑ 90ChaKniTI-4
❑ 90TopTVCu-44
❑ 91PeoChiTI-33
❑ 92ChaKniS-153
❑ 92IowCubF-4058
Duffy, Frank (Frank Thomas)
❑ 71OPC-164
❑ 71Top-164
❑ 72Top-607
❑ 73IndTeal-8
❑ 73OPC-376
❑ 73Top-376
❑ 74OPC-81
❑ 74Top-81
❑ 74TopSta-163
❑ 75CleIndP-10
❑ 75IndJB R-4
❑ 75OPC-448
❑ 75Top-448
❑ 75TopMin-448
❑ 76Hos-115
❑ 76OPC-232
❑ 76SSP-521
❑ 76Top-232
❑ 77BurCheD-63
❑ 77IndTeal-8
❑ 77OPC-253
❑ 77PepGloD-18
❑ 77Top-542
❑ 78PapGinD-17
❑ 78SSP270-184
❑ 78Top-511
❑ 79OPC-47
❑ 79Top-106
Duffy, Hugh
❑ 06FanCraNL-16
❑ 09AmeCarE90-1-37
❑ 09T206-113
❑ 10SweCapPP-10A
❑ 10SweCapPP-10B
❑ 11PinT-5-768
❑ 11S74Sil-5
❑ 11SpoLifCW-110
❑ 11SpoLifM-23
❑ 11T205-47
❑ 23WilChoV-32
❑ 39PC7AlbHoF-34
❑ 48ExhHoF-9
❑ 50CalHOFW-28
❑ 53ArtHaloFP-30
❑ 63BazA-33
❑ 63GadFunC-49
❑ 69Baz-4
❑ 74CapPub-9
❑ 75TCMAllG-8
❑ 76ShaPiz-34
❑ 77GalGloG-147
❑ 80PerHaloFP-34
❑ 80SSPHOF-34
❑ 81ConTSN-18
❑ 84GalHaloFRL-34
❑ 87ConSer2-33
❑ 87OldJudN-141
❑ 90BasWit-67
❑ 90HOFStiB-8
❑ 92ConTSN-532
❑ 94ConTSN-1014
❑ 94ConTSNB-1014
❑ 94OriofB-75
❑ 95May-7
Duffy, Jim
❑ 97AubDouTI-25
❑ 97KisCob-8
❑ 98QuaCitRBG-5
Duffy, John
❑ 87GleFalTP-23
❑ 88TolMudHC-10
❑ 88TolMudHP-596
❑ 89MemChiB-2
❑ 89MemChiP-1181
❑ 89MemChiS-9
❑ 96LowSpiB-6
Duffy, Ryan
❑ 96AriBlaDB-17
Duffy, Tom
❑ 83VerBeaDT-2
Dugan, Joe (Joseph Anthony)
❑ 20NatCarE-24
❑ 20WalMaiW-13
❑ 21Exh-37
❑ 21Exh-38
❑ 21Exh-39
❑ 22E120-3
❑ 22W573-34
❑ 22W575-30
❑ 23W503-17
❑ 23W515-30
❑ 23WilChoV-33
❑ 27YorCarE-3A
❑ 27YorCarE-3B
❑ 28StaPlaCE-17
❑ 28W502-3
❑ 28W513-66
❑ 28Yue-3
❑ 29ExhFou-1
❑ 61Fle-103
❑ 75Yan192T-5
❑ 79DiaGre-3
❑ 79Yan192T-7
❑ 84Yan192G-20
❑ 88ConSer5-8
❑ 91ConTSN-112
❑ 94ConTSN-1059
❑ 94ConTSNB-1059
Dugan, Ken
❑ 86DavLipB-10
❑ 92DavLipB-10
❑ 93DavLipB-6
❑ 94DavLipB-7
❑ 95DavLipB-8
Dugan, Kurt
❑ 92DavLipB-11
❑ 93DavLipB-7
❑ 94DavLipB-8
❑ 95DavLipB-9
Dugan, Mike
❑ 86DavLipB-11
Dugan, Stanley
❑ 16Zee-76
❑ 17Zee-64
Dugas, Gus (Augustin J.)
❑ 36GouWidPPR-D7
Dugas, Shanie
❑ 81WatIndT-21
❑ 82ChaLooT-13
❑ 83BufBisT-15
❑ 84MaiGuiT-23
❑ 85MaiGuiT-17
❑ 87AlbDukD-18
❑ 88AlbDukCm-22
❑ 88AlbDukP-266
❑ 89AlbDukCm-13
❑ 89AlbDukP-85
Dugdale, Dan (Daniel E.)
❑ 87OldJudN-142
Duge, Don
❑ 40WheM4-2A
Dugey, Oscar (Oscar Joseph)
❑ 15CraJacE-60
❑ 15SpoNewM-54
❑ 16SpoNewM-53
❑ 80BraTCM1-13
Duggan, M.
❑ 33Zee-21A
❑ 33Zee-21B
❑ 33Zee-21C
Duggan, Tom
❑ 83WauTimF-21
❑ 86SalRedBP-6
Dugger, Bart
❑ 93BakDodCLC-31
❑ 94BakDodC-30
Dugger, Keith
❑ 91SpoIndC-30
❑ 93BenRocCB-30
❑ 96ColSprSSTI-11
❑ 97ColSprSTI-4
Dugger, Lonnie
❑ 81HolMilT-13
❑ 82HolMilT-4
Duggleby, Bill
❑ 11SpoLifCW-111
Dukart, Derek
❑ 94OneYanC-7
❑ 94OneYanF-3798
❑ 94StaCluDP-68
❑ 94StaCluDPFDI-68
❑ 95GreBatTI-10
❑ 96TamYanY-11
❑ 97TamYan-10
Duke, Andy
❑ 89BilMusP-2056
Duke, Darrick
❑ 93SpoIndC-6
❑ 93SpoIndF-3602
❑ 94SprSulC-7
❑ 94SprSulF-2049
Duke, Doug
❑ 87BurExpP-1073
❑ 88JacExpB-22
❑ 88JacExpP-970
❑ 89JacExpB-6
❑ 89JacExpP-167
Duke, Ed
❑ 86ColAstP-11
Duke, Jerome
❑ 86JamExpP-6
Duke, Kyle
❑ 90PenPilS-7
❑ 91BenBucCB-4
❑ 91BenBucP-3689
❑ 92SanBerC-4
❑ 92SanBerSF-945
❑ 94NewHavRF-1543
Duke, Martin F.
❑ 87OldJudN-143
Duke, Marvin
❑ 36WorWidGV-116
Duke, Richard
❑ 87IdaFalBP-6
Dukes, Jan (Jan Noble)
❑ 70OPC-154
❑ 70Top-154
❑ 93RanKee-9
Dukes, Kevin
❑ 82LynSaiT-3
❑ 83ChaLooT-19
Dukes, Tom (Thomas Earl)
❑ 68OPC-128
❑ 68Top-128
❑ 68TopVen-128
❑ 69Top-223
❑ 71BalOriP-9
❑ 71OPC-106
❑ 71Top-106
❑ 91OriCro-115
Dukes, Willie
❑ 90ElmPioP-9
❑ 90WinHavRSS-7
❑ 91WinHavRSC-13
❑ 91WinHavRSP-493
Duliba, Bob (Robert John)
❑ 60Lea-77
❑ 60Top-401
❑ 62KahAtl-5
❑ 62Top-149
❑ 62TopVen-149
❑ 63Top-97
❑ 64Top-441
❑ 66OPC-53
❑ 66Top-53
❑ 66TopVen-53
❑ 67Top-599
❑ 67VanMouSO-7
Dulin, James
❑ 11Zee-66
Dulin, Tim
❑ 86MiaMarP-5
❑ 87HagSunP-10
❑ 88ChaKniTI-5
❑ 88SouLeaAJ-9
❑ 89RocRedWC-20
❑ 89RocRedWP-1646
❑ 90CMC-316
❑ 90ProAAAF-465
❑ 90RocRedWC-16
❑ 90RocRedWGC-5
❑ 90RocRedWP-708
Dull, Darrell
❑ 83IdaFalAT-19
Dull, Mike
❑ 87BurExpP-1075
❑ 88WesPalBES-10
❑ 89JacExpB-7
❑ 89JacExpP-164
Dulom, Kirk
❑ 90Ft.LauYS-6
Dumas, Don
❑ 87SavCarP-21
Dumas, Michael
❑ 93BelBreCB-6
❑ 93BelBreFI-1716
❑ 94BelBreC-8
❑ 94BelBreFI-106
Dume, Mike
❑ 55JetPos-8
Dummies, Crash
❑ 94TulDriTI-30
❑ 95TulDriTI-30
❑ 96OklCit8B-25
❑ 96OklCit8B-26
❑ 96TulDriTI-29
❑ 97OklCit8-3
❑ 97OklCit8-16
❑ 97TulDriTI-29
Dumouchelle, Pat
❑ 81MiaOriT-8
❑ 84ChaO'sT-13
❑ 90HagSunDGB-8
Dumoulin, Dan
❑ 77IndIndTI-13
❑ 78IndIndTI-7
❑ 79IndIndTI-26
Dumovich, Martin
❑ 29Zee-69
❑ 30Zee-79
Dumovich, Nicholas
❑ 20Zee-8
❑ 21Zee-8
❑ 22Zee-6
❑ 25Zee-136
❑ 27Zee-23
Dunavan, Chad
❑ 93BelMarCB-12
❑ 93BelMarF-3222
❑ 94AppFoxFI-1066
Dunaway, Chris
❑ 98BluOriQ-6
Dunbar, Matt
❑ 88CapCodPPaLP-65
❑ 90OneYanP-3382
❑ 91GreHorP-3050
❑ 92PriWilCC-9
❑ 92PriWilCF-139
❑ 93CarLeaAGF-19
❑ 93PriWilCC-7
❑ 93PriWilCF-649
❑ 94AlbYanF-1434
❑ 94ColCliF-2944
❑ 94VenLinU-172
❑ 95ColCliP-6
❑ 95ColCliTI-6
❑ 95FleUpd-96
❑ 96NorNavB-8
❑ 98LouRedQ-23
❑ 98PriWilCASM-21
Dunbar, Tommy (Thomas Jerome)
❑ 82TulDriT-10
❑ 83OklCit8T-7
❑ 84Don-28
❑ 84OklCit8T-18
❑ 84RanJarP-13
❑ 85Don-159
❑ 85FleUpd-37
❑ 85RanPer-13
❑ 85Top-102
❑ 85TopTif-102
❑ 86Don-221
❑ 86OklCit8P-5
❑ 86Top-559
❑ 86TopTif-559
❑ 87VanCanP-1603
❑ 88BobCamRB-22
❑ 88GreBraB-21
❑ 89GreBraB-26
❑ 89GreBraP-1179
❑ 89GreBraS-7
❑ 90MemChiB-11
❑ 90MemChiP-1023
❑ 90MemChiS-9
❑ 90TulDriDGB-24
❑ 91LinDriAAA-333
❑ 91OmaRoyLD-333
❑ 91OmaRoyP-1046
❑ 93RanKee-129
❑ 94ChaLooF-1375
Duncan, Andres
❑ 91Cla/Bes-322
❑ 91CliGiaC-13
❑ 91CliGiaP-841
❑ 92SanJosGC-10
❑ 92UppDecML-215
❑ 93ShrCapF-2766
❑ 94NasXprF-393
❑ 95HarCitRCTI-4
Duncan, Carlos
❑ 97AppLeaTPB-15
❑ 98BatMucTI-9
Duncan, Chip
❑ 87WatPirP-6
❑ 88SalBucS-5
❑ 89SalBucS-7
❑ 90SalBucS-4
❑ 91CarMudLD-105
❑ 91CarMudP-1079
❑ 91LinDriAA-105
❑ 91ParPatF-18
❑ 92MemChiF-2412
❑ 95TulDriTI-6
Duncan, Courtney
❑ 97Bes-63
❑ 98Bow-423
❑ 98BowChr-423
❑ 98BowChrGA-423
❑ 98BowChrGAR-423
❑ 98BowChrI-423
❑ 98BowChrIR-423
❑ 98BowChrR-423
❑ 98BowGolA-423
❑ 98BowInt-423
❑ 98SouLeaTPG-4
❑ 98Top-259
❑ 98TopChr-259
❑ 98TopChrR-259
❑ 98TopDevR-259
❑ 98TopDia-259
❑ 98TopMiniC-259
❑ 98WesTenDJM-6
Duncan, Dave (David Edwin)
❑ 64Top-528
❑ 68Top-261
❑ 68TopVen-261
❑ 69OPC-68
❑ 69Top-68
❑ 69TopSta-214
❑ 70Top-678
❑ 71MLBOffS-511
❑ 71OPC-178
❑ 71Top-178
❑ 72OPC-17
❑ 72Top-17
❑ 73IndArtTC-4
❑ 73IndTeal-9
❑ 73OPC-337
❑ 73Top-337
❑ 74OPC-284
❑ 74Top-284
❑ 74TopSta-164
❑ 75BalOriP-10
❑ 75OPC-238
❑ 75OPC-626
❑ 75Top-238
❑ 75Top-626
❑ 75TopMin-238
❑ 75TopMin-626
❑ 76BalOriP-11
❑ 76OPC-49
❑ 76SSP-383
❑ 76Top-49
❑ 77Top-338
❑ 78IndTeal-9
❑ 80IndTeal-8
❑ 82MarPos-16
❑ 84WhiSoxTV-8
❑ 86A'sGreT-8
❑ 87A'sMot-8
❑ 87ModA'sC-A3
❑ 88A'sMot-27
❑ 89A'sMot-27
❑ 90A'sMot-27
❑ 91A'sMot-28
❑ 91OriCro-116
❑ 92AthMot-28
❑ 93AthMot-27
❑ 94A'sMot-28
❑ 95AthMot-28
Duncan, Devohn
❑ 94SpoIndC-8
❑ 94SpoIndF-3317
❑ 95Exc-283
Duncan, Doug
❑ 76SanAntBTI-9
❑ 77VisOakT-5
Duncan, Duke (C.)
❑ 78NewWayCT-12
❑ 79HolMilT-27
Duncan, Dunk (Frank)
❑ 86NegLeaF-118
❑ 87NegLeaPD-45
❑ 93NegLeaRL2-8
Duncan, Jeff
❑ 92MadMusC-3
❑ 92MadMusF-1240
Duncan, John
❑ 83WauTimF-26
Duncan, Lindy
❑ 81TulDriT-25
Duncan, Mariano
❑ 83VerBeaDT-16
❑ 85DodCokP-10
❑ 85DomLeaS-36
❑ 85FleUpd-38
❑ 85TopTifT-32T
❑ 85TopTra-32T
❑ 86DodCokP-8
❑ 86DodPol-25
❑ 86DodUniOP-5
❑ 86Don-128
❑ 86Fle-129
❑ 86FleLeaL-10
❑ 86FleMin-27
❑ 86FleStiC-33
❑ 86KayB-8
❑ 86Lea-50
❑ 86OPC-296
❑ 86SevCoi-W13
❑ 86Top-602
❑ 86TopTif-602
❑ 87DodMot-7
❑ 87DodPho-2
❑ 87DodPol-12
❑ 87Don-253
❑ 87DonOpeD-84
❑ 87Fle-439
❑ 87FleGlo-439
❑ 87OPC-199
❑ 87SevCoi-W2
❑ 87SpoTeaP-14
❑ 87Top-199
❑ 87TopMinL-13
❑ 87TopSti-74
❑ 87TopTif-199
❑ 88AlbDukCm-23
❑ 88AlbDukP-255
❑ 88DodPol-25
❑ 88Don-155
❑ 88Fle-513
❑ 88FleGlo-513
❑ 88OPC-181
❑ 88Sco-321
❑ 88ScoGlo-321
❑ 88StaLinD-3
❑ 88Top-481
❑ 88TopTif-481
❑ 89DodMot-26
❑ 89DodPol-15
❑ 90DodTar-205
❑ 90Don-684
❑ 90DonBesN-113
❑ 90FleUpd-12
❑ 90Lea-202
❑ 90OPC-234
❑ 90RedKah-9
❑ 90Sco-506
❑ 90Top-234
❑ 90TopBig-243
❑ 90TopTif-234
❑ 90UppDec-430
❑ 91Bow-675
❑ 91Don-309
❑ 91Fle-64
❑ 91Lea-494
❑ 91OPC-13
❑ 91PanFreS-128
❑ 91PanSti-123

❑ 91RedKah-7
❑ 91RedPep-9
❑ 91Sco-479
❑ 91StaClu-251
❑ 91Stu-164
❑ 91Top-13
❑ 91TopDesS-13
❑ 91TopMic-13
❑ 91TopTif-13
❑ 91Ult-94
❑ 91UppDec-112
❑ 92Don-540
❑ 92Fle-406
❑ 92FleUpd-109
❑ 92Lea-311
❑ 92LeaBlaG-311
❑ 92OPC-589
❑ 92PhiMed-11
❑ 92Pin-377
❑ 92Sco-352
❑ 92ScoRoo-54T
❑ 92StaClu-614
❑ 92Stu-74
❑ 92Top-589
❑ 92TopGol-589
❑ 92TopGolW-589
❑ 92TopMic-589
❑ 92TopTra-30T
❑ 92TopTraG-30T
❑ 92Ult-544
❑ 92UppDec-659
❑ 92UppDec-792
❑ 93Don-382
❑ 93Fla-98
❑ 93Fle-101
❑ 93Lea-187
❑ 93OPC-95
❑ 93PacSpa-234
❑ 93PanSti-272
❑ 93PhiMed-11
❑ 93PhiStaC-21
❑ 93Pin-218
❑ 93Sco-201
❑ 93Sel-151
❑ 93SelStaL-17
❑ 93SP-172
❑ 93StaClu-276
❑ 93StaCluFDI-276
❑ 93StaCluMOP-276
❑ 93Top-371
❑ 93TopGol-371
❑ 93TopInaM-371
❑ 93TopInaR-371
❑ 93TopMic-371
❑ 93Ult-87
❑ 93UppDec-201
❑ 93UppDecGold-201
❑ 94Bow-196
❑ 94ColC-429
❑ 94ColChoGS-429
❑ 94ColChoSS-429
❑ 94Don-614
❑ 94Fin-352
❑ 94FinRef-352
❑ 94Fla-411
❑ 94Fle-586
❑ 94FleExtB-331
❑ 94Lea-11
❑ 94LeaL-135
❑ 94LeaLimGA-4
❑ 94Pac-472
❑ 94PacAll-8
❑ 94PanSti-225
❑ 94PhiMed-7
❑ 94PhiMel-5
❑ 94PhiUSPC-4D
❑ 94PhiUSPC-11C
❑ 94Pin-479
❑ 94PinArtP-479
❑ 94PinMusC-479
❑ 94Sco-490
❑ 94ScoGolR-490
❑ 94Sel-271
❑ 94StaClu-54
❑ 94StaCluFDI-54
❑ 94StaCluGR-54
❑ 94StaCluMOP-54
❑ 94StaCluT-217
❑ 94StaCluTFDI-217
❑ 94Stu-137
❑ 94Top-663
❑ 94TopGol-663
❑ 94TopSpa-663
❑ 94TriPla-172
❑ 94Ult-543
❑ 94UppDec-181
❑ 94UppDecED-181
❑ 95ColCho-361
❑ 95ColChoGS-361
❑ 95ColChoSE-169
❑ 95ColChoSEGS-169
❑ 95ColChoSESS-169
❑ 95ColChoSS-361
❑ 95Don-341
❑ 95DonAll-NL4
❑ 95DonPreP-341
❑ 95DonTopotO-301
❑ 95Fle-389
❑ 95FleAllS-3
❑ 95KinDis-6
❑ 95Lea-266
❑ 95Pac-327
❑ 95PacPri-106
❑ 95Phi-8
❑ 95PhiMel-6
❑ 95Sco-350
❑ 95ScoGolR-350
❑ 95ScoPlaTS-350
❑ 95StaClu-27
❑ 95StaCluFDI-27
❑ 95StaCluMOP-27
❑ 95StaCluSTWS-27
❑ 95Top-103
❑ 95TopCyb-66
❑ 95Ult-418
❑ 95UltGolM-418
❑ 95UppDec-141
❑ 95UppDecED-141
❑ 95UppDecEDG-141
❑ 96Fle-339
❑ 96FleTif-339
❑ 96FleUpd-U58
❑ 96FleUpdTC-U58
❑ 96Pac-41
❑ 96Ult-382
❑ 96UltGolM-382
❑ 97Cir-179
❑ 97CirRav-179
❑ 97ColCho-406
❑ 97Fle-163
❑ 97FleTif-163
❑ 97Lea-311
❑ 97LeaFraM-311
❑ 97LeaFraMDC-311
❑ 97Pac-149
❑ 97PacLigB-149
❑ 97PacSil-149
❑ 97StaClu-117
❑ 97StaCluMOP-117
❑ 97Top-45
❑ 97Ult-433
❑ 97UltGolME-433
❑ 97UltPlaME-433
❑ 97UppDec-437
❑ 98Pac-219
❑ 98PacPlaB-219
❑ 98PacRedT-219
❑ 98PacSil-219

Duncan, Mark
❑ 94LetMouF-3885
❑ 94LetMouSP-24

Duncan, Michael
❑ 86ModA'sC-7
❑ 86ModA'sP-7
❑ 87ModA'sP-4

Duncan, Pat (Louis Baird)
❑ 20RedWorCP-4
❑ 20WalMaiW-14
❑ 21Exh-40
❑ 21Nei-109
❑ 22E120-171
❑ 22W572-25
❑ 23WilChoV-34
❑ 76RedParC-10
❑ 88PacEigMO-94
❑ 94ConTSN-1026
❑ 94ConTSNB-1026

Duncan, Rick
❑ 78OrlTwiT-5
❑ 79NaSouTI-8

Duncan, Robert
❑ 95DanBraTI-8

Duncan, Sean
❑ 96SouBenSHS-11
❑ 97QuaCitRBB-8
❑ 98KisCobQ-13

Duncan, Taylor M.
❑ 77RocRedWM-5
❑ 79Top-658
❑ 89PacSenL-70

Duncan, Tim
❑ 80ElmPioRST-20

Dunckel, Bill
❑ 92BoiHawC-23
❑ 92BoiHawF-3642

Dunckel, Keith
❑ 93WatDiaC-12

Duncun, John
❑ 86ChaLooP-9

Dundik, Alexander
❑ 89EasLeaDDP-DD10

Dundon, Gus
❑ 11SpoLifCW-112

Dunegan, James W. Jr.
❑ 71OPC-121
❑ 71Top-121

Dunham, Jim
❑ 72CedRapCT-10

Dunham, Patrick
❑ 98LanJetG-8

Dunivan, Kevin
❑ 92GulCoaRSP-4

Dunlap, Fred (Frederick C.)
❑ 76SSP188WS-6
❑ 87BucN28-29
❑ 87OldJudN-144
❑ 87ScrDC-12
❑ 88GooN16-5
❑ 88WG1CarG-58
❑ 94OriofB-56

Dunlap, Joe
❑ 86CedRapRT-15
❑ 87VerRedP-10
❑ 89CalCanC-18
❑ 89CalCanP-529
❑ 89EasLeaDDP-DD30

Dunlap, Paul
❑ 36WorWidGV-125

Dunlap, Travis
❑ 90PulBraB-3
❑ 90PulBraP-3099
❑ 91IdaFalBSP-11
❑ 92MacBraC-10
❑ 92MacBraF-261
❑ 94WilBluRC-8
❑ 94WilBluRF-295

Dunleavy, John E.
❑ 06FanCraNL-17
❑ 11SpoLifCW-113

Dunlop, Harry
❑ 70RoyTeal-11
❑ 71oySigST-5
❑ 72oyTeal-3
❑ 73OPC-593
❑ 73Top-593
❑ 74RoyPos-10
❑ 74Top-166
❑ 75RoyPos-10
❑ 80RedEnq-4
❑ 83LasVegSBHN-7
❑ 84PadMot-27
❑ 84PadSmo-8
❑ 85PadMot-27
❑ 91HelBreSP-30
❑ 92HelBreF-1732
❑ 92HelBreSP-26
❑ 93HelBreF-4112

Dunn, Adam
❑ 98BilMusTI-10
❑ 99Bow-369
❑ 99BowGol-369
❑ 99BowInt-369

Dunn, Alan
❑ 93GenCubF-3194
❑ 94PeoChiC-27
❑ 94PeoChiF-2284
❑ 95RocCubTI-NNO
❑ 96RocCubTI-7
❑ 98WesTenDJM-27

Dunn, Brian
❑ 89SanDieSAS-8
❑ 90PitMetP-12
❑ 91ColMetPI-19
❑ 91ColMetPPI-7

Dunn, Bubba
❑ 91BasCitRC-3
❑ 91BasCitRP-1390

Dunn, Geoff
❑ 91WavRedF-1

Dunn, Greg
❑ 82SprCarF-13
❑ 83SprCarF-14
❑ 85SprCarT-8
❑ 86LouRedTI-10

Dunn, J.
❑ 87OldJudN-145

Dunn, Jack (John Joseph)
❑ 03BreE10-46
❑ 09ColChiE-87
❑ 09T206-421
❑ 10CouT21-130
❑ 10CouT21-281
❑ 11SpoLifCW-114
❑ 11T205-188
❑ 12ColRedB-87
❑ 12ColTinT-87
❑ 12ImpTobC-19
❑ 18Zee-60
❑ 72ClaCar-39
❑ 90DodTar-206

Dunn, Jim (James William)
❑ 81ShrCapT-3

Dunn, Joe (Joseph Edward)
❑ 09RamT20-41
❑ 09T206-114
❑ 10CouT21-19

Dunn, Michael
❑ 95AusFut-50

Dunn, Nathan
❑ 92GreFalDSP-3
❑ 93YakBeaF-3888
❑ 97CliLumG-7
❑ 98RanCucQG-10
❑ 98RanCucQG-10

Dunn, Ron (Ronald Ray)
❑ 74WicAerODF-119
❑ 76SSP-322

Dunn, Ryan
❑ 97AubDouTI-21
❑ 98AubDouTI-8

Dunn, Steve
❑ 88QuaCitAGS-10
❑ 90PalSprACLC-220
❑ 90PalSprAP-2571

Dunn, Steve Robert
❑ 89EliTwiS-7
❑ 89KenTwiP-1073
❑ 89KenTwiS-4
❑ 89Sta-147
❑ 90Bes-152
❑ 90KenTwiB-1
❑ 90KenTwiP-2299
❑ 90KenTwiS-3
❑ 90MidLeaASGS-9
❑ 90StaFS7-55
❑ 91Cla/Bes-241
❑ 91VisOakC-15
❑ 91VisOakP-1747
❑ 92UppDecML-216
❑ 92VisOakC-19
❑ 92VisOakF-1019
❑ 93Bow-17
❑ 93ClaFS7-155
❑ 93ExcFS7-199
❑ 93NasXprF-407
❑ 94ExcFS7-93
❑ 94FleMajLP-11
❑ 94LeaLimR-14
❑ 94SalLakBF-822
❑ 94SpoRoo-43
❑ 94SpoRooAP-43
❑ 94Ult-387
❑ 94UppDecML-169
❑ 95ColCho-484
❑ 95ColChoGS-484
❑ 95ColChoSE-23
❑ 95ColChoSEGS-23
❑ 95ColChoSESS-23
❑ 95ColChoSS-484
❑ 95Don-106
❑ 95DonPreP-106
❑ 95Fle-200
❑ 95Pac-247
❑ 95Pin-157
❑ 95PinArtP-157
❑ 95PinMusC-157
❑ 95Sco-595
❑ 95ScoGolR-595
❑ 95ScoPlaTS-595
❑ 95Sel-157
❑ 95SelArtP-157
❑ 95SigRoo-15
❑ 95SigRooSig-15
❑ 95Spo-144
❑ 95SpoArtP-144
❑ 96BufBisB-7

Dunn, Todd
❑ 93BazTeaU-19
❑ 93TopTra-67T
❑ 94BelBreC-9
❑ 94BelBreFI-114
❑ 94Bow-657
❑ 94UppDec-528
❑ 94UppDecED-528
❑ 95Bow-189
❑ 95SPML-82
❑ 95UppDecML-141
❑ 95UppDecMLFS-141
❑ 96BesAutSA-17
❑ 96Bow-333
❑ 96BowFoi-333
❑ 96El PasDB-9
❑ 97Bow-101
❑ 97BowChr-123
❑ 97BowChrI-123
❑ 97BowChrIR-123
❑ 97BowChrR-123
❑ 97BowInt-101
❑ 97Sel-115
❑ 97SelArtP-115
❑ 97SelCom-115
❑ 97SelRegG-115
❑ 97TucTorB-24
❑ 97UppDec-476
❑ 98PacAur-151
❑ 98PacOme-132
❑ 98PacOmeR-132
❑ 98PacPar-185
❑ 98PacParC-185
❑ 98PacParG-185
❑ 98PacParHS-185
❑ 98PacParPB-185
❑ 98PacParR-185
❑ 98StaCluFDI-198
❑ 98StaCluI-198
❑ 98StaCluOneK-198
❑ 98StaCluPP-198
❑ 98Top-435
❑ 98TopChr-435
❑ 98TopChrR-435
❑ 98TopDevR-435
❑ 98TopDia-435
❑ 98TopMiniC-435
❑ 98Ult-305
❑ 98UltGolM-305
❑ 98UltMas-305
❑ 98UltPlaM-305
❑ 99BasAmeTP-38
❑ 99BasAmeTPG-38

Dunn, Yvon
❑ 58MonRoyF-7
❑ 59O'KAleMR-6

Dunne, Brian
❑ 95MarPhiTI-7

Dunne, Mike
❑ 85Top-395
❑ 85TopTif-395
❑ 86LouRedTI-11
❑ 87DonRoo-38
❑ 87FleUpd-29
❑ 87FleUpdG-29
❑ 87SpoRoo2-40
❑ 87TopTra-30T
❑ 87TopTraT-30T
❑ 87VanCanP-1612
❑ 88ClaBlu-237
❑ 88Don-390
❑ 88DonBasB-89
❑ 88Fle-328
❑ 88FleAwaW-10
❑ 88FleBasM-11
❑ 88FleGlo-328
❑ 88FleMin-104
❑ 88FleRecS-11
❑ 88FleStiC-115
❑ 88Lea-235
❑ 88OPC-224
❑ 88PanSti-367
❑ 88PirTeal-10
❑ 88Sco-432
❑ 88ScoGlo-432
❑ 88ScoYouSI-26
❑ 88Spo-171
❑ 88StaLinPi-9
❑ 88Top-619
❑ 88TopBig-236
❑ 88TopCoi-40
❑ 88TopGloS-19
❑ 88TopMinL-68
❑ 88TopRitTM-9
❑ 88TopRoo-16
❑ 88TopSti-132
❑ 88TopSti-307
❑ 88TopTif-619
❑ 88TopUKM-21
❑ 88TopUKMT-21
❑ 88ToyRoo-10
❑ 89Don-269
❑ 89Fle-207
❑ 89FleGlo-207
❑ 89OPC-165
❑ 89PanSti-162
❑ 89PirVerFJ-41
❑ 89Sco-285
❑ 89Top-165
❑ 89TopSti-130
❑ 89TopTif-165
❑ 89UppDec-518
❑ 90Lea-418
❑ 90OPC-522
❑ 90PadMag-19
❑ 90Top-522
❑ 90TopTif-522
❑ 91OPC-238
❑ 91Top-238
❑ 91TopDesS-238
❑ 91TopMic-238
❑ 91TopTif-238
❑ 92VanCanF-2715
❑ 92VanCanS-634
❑ 94ScrRedBF-917

Dunnegan, Steve
❑ 82DayBeaAT-11

Dunner, Mike
❑ 82CliGiaF-14

Dunning, Justin
❑ 98EveAquG-6

Dunning, Steve (Stephen John)
❑ 71Ind-3
❑ 71OPC-294
❑ 71Top-294
❑ 72Top-658
❑ 73OPC-53
❑ 73RanTeal-8
❑ 73Top-53
❑ 74SpoIndC-28
❑ 76ExpRed-6
❑ 78Top-647
❑ 93RanKee-130

Dunnum, Rick
❑ 88AubAstP-1969
❑ 89AshTouP-964
❑ 90OscAstS-7
❑ 91LinDriAA-508
❑ 91ReaPhiLD-508
❑ 91ReaPhiP-1367

Dunster, Don
❑ 86OscAstP-6
❑ 87OscAstP-19
❑ 88ColAstB-2

Dunston, Shawon
❑ 83QuaCitCT-20
❑ 84MidCubT-22
❑ 85CubLioP-8
❑ 85Don-39
❑ 85Fle-649
❑ 85Top-280
❑ 85TopTif-280
❑ 86BasStaB-35
❑ 86CubGat-12
❑ 86CubUno-6
❑ 86Don-311
❑ 86Fle-366
❑ 86FleMin-77
❑ 86FleStiC-34
❑ 86KayB-9
❑ 86Lea-181
❑ 86MSAJayPCD-6
❑ 86SevCoi-C13
❑ 86Spo-155
❑ 86Top-72
❑ 86TopTat-2
❑ 86TopTif-72
❑ 87CubCan-9
❑ 87CubDavB-12
❑ 87Don-119
❑ 87DonOpeD-76
❑ 87Fle-561
❑ 87FleGamW-13
❑ 87FleGlo-561
❑ 87FleMin-35
❑ 87FleRecS-6
❑ 87FleStiC-36
❑ 87Lea-128
❑ 87OPC-346
❑ 87RedFolSB-94
❑ 87SevCoi-C4
❑ 87Spo-79

❑ 87Spo-98
❑ 87SpoTeaP-22
❑ 87Top-346
❑ 87TopSti-59
❑ 87TopTif-346
❑ 88CubDavB-12
❑ 88Don-146
❑ 88DonBasB-37
❑ 88DonTeaBC-146
❑ 88Fle-419
❑ 88FleGlo-419
❑ 88Lea-70
❑ 88OPC-277
❑ 88PanSti-264
❑ 88Sco-529
❑ 88ScoGlo-529
❑ 88ScoYouS2-18
❑ 88Spo-163
❑ 88Top-171
❑ 88Top-695
❑ 88TopBig-225
❑ 88TopSti-65
❑ 88TopStiB-11
❑ 88TopTif-171
❑ 88TopTif-695
❑ 89Bow-294
❑ 89BowTif-294
❑ 89CadEllD-15
❑ 89CubMar-12
❑ 89Don-137
❑ 89DonAll-43
❑ 89DonBasB-93
❑ 89Fle-424
❑ 89FleGlo-424
❑ 89K-M-26
❑ 89OPC-140
❑ 89PanSti-58
❑ 89RedFolSB-38
❑ 89Sco-235
❑ 89Spo-190
❑ 89Top-140
❑ 89TopBig-233
❑ 89TopSti-49
❑ 89TopStiB-43
❑ 89TopTif-140
❑ 89TVSpoM-19
❑ 89UppDec-107
❑ 90Bow-38
❑ 90BowTif-38
❑ 90CubMar-7
❑ 90Don-49
❑ 90DonBesN-112
❑ 90Fle-30
❑ 90FleCan-30
❑ 90Lea-229
❑ 90M.Vpin-18
❑ 90MLBBasB-46
❑ 90OPC-415
❑ 90PanSti-236
❑ 90PubIntS-193
❑ 90Sco-169
❑ 90Top-415
❑ 90TopBig-62
❑ 90TopDou-18
❑ 90TopGloS-45
❑ 90TopSti-53
❑ 90TopStiB-10
❑ 90TopTif-415
❑ 90TopTVCu-22
❑ 90UppDec-231
❑ 90USPlaCA-10D
❑ 91Bow-424
❑ 91CadEllD-17
❑ 91ClaGam-27
❑ 91CubMar-12
❑ 91CubVinL-10
❑ 91Don-686
❑ 91Fle-420
❑ 91Lea-25
❑ 91OPC-765
❑ 91OPCPre-37
❑ 91PanFreS-46
❑ 91PanSti-47
❑ 91RedFolS-29
❑ 91Sco-201
❑ 91Sco-413
❑ 91Sco100S-45
❑ 91StaClu-3
❑ 91StaCluP-12
❑ 91StaPinB-15
❑ 91Stu-155
❑ 91Top-765
❑ 91TopCraJ2-23
❑ 91TopDesS-765
❑ 91TopMic-765
❑ 91TopTif-765
❑ 91Ult-59
❑ 91UppDec-111
❑ 92ClaGam-28
❑ 92CubMar-12
❑ 92Don-613
❑ 92Fle-380
❑ 92Lea-249
❑ 92LeaBlaG-249
❑ 92OPC-370
❑ 92OPCPre-125
❑ 92PanSti-185
❑ 92Pin-244
❑ 92Sco-634
❑ 92ScoImpP-70
❑ 92StaClu-540
❑ 92Top-370
❑ 92TopGol-370
❑ 92TopGolPS-370
❑ 92TopGolW-370
❑ 92TopKid-5
❑ 92TopMic-370
❑ 92TopPreS-3
❑ 92TriPla-160
❑ 92Ult-174
❑ 92UppDec-35
❑ 92UppDec-122
❑ 92UppDec-714
❑ 93CadDis-17
❑ 93CubStaC-9
❑ 93Don-268
❑ 93Fle-19
❑ 93MetBak-24
❑ 93OPC-62
❑ 93PacSpa-57
❑ 93PanSti-205
❑ 93Pin-89
❑ 93RedFolS-26
❑ 93Sco-26
❑ 93Sel-121
❑ 93StaClu-393
❑ 93StaCluFDI-393
❑ 93StaCluMOP-393
❑ 93Top-595
❑ 93TopGol-595
❑ 93TopInaM-595
❑ 93TopInaR-595
❑ 93TopMic-595
❑ 93TriPla-40
❑ 93Ult-17
❑ 93UppDec-101
❑ 93UppDecGold-101
❑ 94ColC-363
❑ 94ColChoGS-363
❑ 94ColChoSS-363
❑ 94Don-490
❑ 94Fin-368
❑ 94FinRef-368
❑ 94Fla-136
❑ 94FleExtB-217
❑ 94FleUpd-109
❑ 94Lea-316
❑ 94LeaL-89
❑ 94PanSti-152
❑ 94Pin-523
❑ 94PinArtP-523
❑ 94PinMusC-523
❑ 94ProMag-25
❑ 94Sel-136
❑ 94StaClu-576
❑ 94StaCluFDI-576
❑ 94StaCluGR-576
❑ 94StaCluMOP-576
❑ 94StaCluT-354
❑ 94StaCluTFDI-354
❑ 94Stu-59
❑ 94TopTra-46T
❑ 94Ult-454
❑ 94UppDec-477
❑ 94UppDecED-477
❑ 95Baz-34
❑ 95ColCho-204
❑ 95ColChoGS-204
❑ 95ColChoSE-82
❑ 95ColChoSEGS-82
❑ 95ColChoSESS-82
❑ 95ColChoSS-204
❑ 95Don-39
❑ 95DonPreP-39
❑ 95DonTopotO-196
❑ 95Emo-109
❑ 95Fin-140
❑ 95FinRef-140
❑ 95Fla-112
❑ 95Fle-413
❑ 95Lea-30
❑ 95LeaLim-120
❑ 95Pac-68
❑ 95Pin-4
❑ 95PinArtP-4
❑ 95PinMusC-4
❑ 95Sco-89
❑ 95ScoGolR-89
❑ 95ScoPlaTS-89
❑ 95Spo-89
❑ 95SpoArtP-89
❑ 95StaClu-29
❑ 95StaCluFDI-29
❑ 95StaCluMOP-29
❑ 95StaCluSTWS-29
❑ 95StaCluVR-19
❑ 95StaCluVRMO-19
❑ 95Stu-62
❑ 95Top-214
❑ 95TopCyb-122
❑ 95TopEmb-70
❑ 95TopEmbGI-70
❑ 95Ult-358
❑ 95UltGolM-358
❑ 95Zen-99
❑ 96Cir-193
❑ 96CirRav-193
❑ 96Don-429
❑ 96DonPreP-429
❑ 96EmoXL-288
❑ 96Fin-B219
❑ 96FinRef-B219
❑ 96Fla-386
❑ 96Fle-315
❑ 96FleTif-315
❑ 96FleUpd-U204
❑ 96FleUpdTC-U204
❑ 96GiaMot-11
❑ 96LeaSigA-60
❑ 96LeaSigAG-60
❑ 96LeaSigAS-60
❑ 96MetUni-139
❑ 96MetUniP-139
❑ 96Pac-26
❑ 96PanSti-44
❑ 96Pin-72
❑ 96Pin-354
❑ 96PinAfi-85
❑ 96PinAfiAP-85
❑ 96PinAfiFPP-85
❑ 96PinArtP-27
❑ 96PinFoil-354
❑ 96PinSta-27
❑ 96ProSta-37
❑ 96Sco-280
❑ 96ScoDugC-B5
❑ 96ScoDugCAP-B5
❑ 96Sel-129
❑ 96SelArtP-129
❑ 96StaClu-137
❑ 96StaCluEPB-137
❑ 96StaCluEPG-137
❑ 96StaCluEPS-137
❑ 96StaCluMOP-137
❑ 96Sum-63
❑ 96SumAbo&B-63
❑ 96SumArtP-63
❑ 96SumFoi-63
❑ 96Top-399
❑ 96TopChr-160
❑ 96TopChrR-160
❑ 96TopLas-22
❑ 96Ult-165
❑ 96Ult-566
❑ 96UltGolM-165
❑ 96UltGolM-566
❑ 96UppDec-457
❑ 97Cir-213
❑ 97CirRav-213
❑ 97ColCho-287
❑ 97Don-255
❑ 97DonGolPP-255
❑ 97DonSilPP-255
❑ 97Fle-479
❑ 97Fle-538
❑ 97FleTif-479
❑ 97FleTif-538
❑ 97Pac-441
❑ 97PacLigB-441
❑ 97PacSil-441
❑ 97Pin-51
❑ 97PinArtP-PP51
❑ 97PinMusC-51
❑ 97PinPrePla-51
❑ 97StaClu-306
❑ 97StaCluMOP-306
❑ 97Top-172
❑ 97Ult-293
❑ 97Ult-303
❑ 97UltGolME-293
❑ 97UltGolME-303
❑ 97UltPlaME-293
❑ 97UltPlaME-303
❑ 97UppDec-328
❑ 98Fle-218
❑ 98Fle-543
❑ 98PacOnl-217
❑ 98PacOnlR-217
❑ 98PacOnlWC-217
❑ 98Sco-212
❑ 98Top-414
❑ 98TopChr-414
❑ 98TopChrR-414
❑ 98TopDevR-414
❑ 98TopDia-414
❑ 98TopMiniC-414
❑ 98UppDec-668

Dunton, Kevin
❑ 86WesPalBEP-14

Dunwoody, Todd
❑ 95KanCouCTI-37
❑ 95MidLeaA-13
❑ 96BowBes-139
❑ 96BowBesAR-139
❑ 96BowBesR-139
❑ 96DouAllB-13
❑ 96Exc-161
❑ 96PorSeaDB-13
❑ 97Bow-90
❑ 97BowChr-114
❑ 97BowChrI-114
❑ 97BowChrIR-114
❑ 97BowChrR-114
❑ 97BowInt-90
❑ 97ChaKni-13
❑ 97ColChoU-U13
❑ 97Don-390
❑ 97DonGolPP-390
❑ 97DonLim-174
❑ 97DonLimE-174
❑ 97DonLimENG-174
❑ 97DonSigA-28
❑ 97DonSigAC-35
❑ 97DonSigAM-35
❑ 97DonSilPP-390
❑ 97Fle-652
❑ 97FleTif-652
❑ 97Lea-347
❑ 97LeaFraM-347
❑ 97LeaFraMDC-347
❑ 97Sel-189
❑ 97SelCom-189
❑ 97Ult-552
❑ 97UltGolME-552
❑ 97UltPlaME-552
❑ 98Bow-189
❑ 98BowBes-179
❑ 98BowBesAR-179
❑ 98BowBesR-179
❑ 98BowCerBlueAU-61
❑ 98BowCerGA-61
❑ 98BowCerSA-61
❑ 98BowChr-189
❑ 98BowChrGA-189
❑ 98BowChrGAR-189
❑ 98BowChrI-189
❑ 98BowChrIR-189
❑ 98BowChrR-189
❑ 98BowGolA-189
❑ 98BowInt-189
❑ 98ChaKniQ-10
❑ 98CirThu-162
❑ 98CirThuRav-162
❑ 98CirThuSupRav-162
❑ 98ColCho-118
❑ 98Don-114
❑ 98DonCol-114
❑ 98DonCol-185
❑ 98DonColE-487
❑ 98DonColP-705
❑ 98DonColS-114
❑ 98DonColS-180
❑ 98DonEli-87
❑ 98DonEliA-87
❑ 98DonEliS-87
❑ 98DonGolPP-114
❑ 98DonPre-155
❑ 98DonPreSeat-155
❑ 98DonPriCD-114
❑ 98DonPriCD-185
❑ 98DonPriCE-487
❑ 98DonPriCP-705
❑ 98DonRatR-10
❑ 98DonRatRM-10
❑ 98DonSigA-27
❑ 98DonSigAC-36
❑ 98DonSigAM-36
❑ 98DonSilPP-114
❑ 98E-X2SD2001-15
❑ 98Fle-290
❑ 98LeaRS-176
❑ 98LeaRSLHolo-176
❑ 98LeaRSLong-176
❑ 98LeaRTrue-176
❑ 98MetUni-30
❑ 98MetUniPMG-30
❑ 98PacPar-159
❑ 98PacParC-159
❑ 98PacParG-159
❑ 98PacParHS-159
❑ 98PacParPB-159
❑ 98PacParR-159
❑ 98Pin-165
❑ 98PinArtP-PP68
❑ 98PinMusC-PP68
❑ 98PinPreP-165
❑ 98PorSeaD5AQ-9
❑ 98Sco-237
❑ 98ScoRT-127
❑ 98ScoRTSS-PP78
❑ 98ScoRTSSAP-PP78
❑ 98ScoRTSSAP1-PP78
❑ 98SPxFin-19
❑ 98SPxFinR-19
❑ 98SPxFinS-19
❑ 98StaCluFDI-123
❑ 98StaCluI-123
❑ 98StaCluOneK-123
❑ 98StaCluPP-123
❑ 98Stu-65
❑ 98StuGPP-65
❑ 98StuSPP-65
❑ 98Top-263
❑ 98TopChr-263
❑ 98TopChrR-263
❑ 98TopDevR-263
❑ 98TopDia-263
❑ 98TopMiniC-263
❑ 98TopTek-36
❑ 98TopTekD-36
❑ 98Ult-41
❑ 98UltGolM-41
❑ 98UltMas-41
❑ 98UltPlaM-41
❑ 98UppDec-266
❑ 98UppDecBCP-BC17
❑ 98UppDecDS-DS18
❑ 98UppDecSF-147
❑ 99Fle-60
❑ 99FleSta9-60
❑ 99FleWarT-60
❑ 99Pac-174
❑ 99PacAur-72
❑ 99PacAurOD-72
❑ 99PacPar-93
❑ 99PacParC-93
❑ 99PacParG-93
❑ 99PacParHoloGold-93
❑ 99PacParHS-93
❑ 99PacParOD-93
❑ 99PacParPB-93
❑ 99PacParRed-93
❑ 99PacPlaB-174
❑ 99PacRed-174
❑ 99SkyThu-222
❑ 99SkyThuRant-222
❑ 99SkyThuRave-222
❑ 99StaClu-212
❑ 99StaCluFDI-212
❑ 99StaCluOoaK-212
❑ 99StaCluPP-212
❑ 99ThuSkySupR-222
❑ 99Top-82
❑ 99TopChr-82
❑ 99TopChrR-82
❑ 99TopMVPP-82
❑ 99UppDec-377
❑ 99UppDecEL1-377
❑ 99UppDecEL2-377
❑ 99UppDecM-87
❑ 99UppDecMGS-87
❑ 99UppDecMHFS-87
❑ 99UppDecMP-87
❑ 99UppDecMSS-87
❑ 99Vic-159

DuPlessis, Dave
❑ 92SalSpuC-21
❑ 92SalSpuF-3763
❑ 94WesPalBEC-7
❑ 94WesPalBEF-48

Dupree, Mike (Michael D.)
❑ 77Top-491
❑ 79HawIslT-19

Dupuy, Jerry
❑ 93MisStaB-14

Duquette, Bryan
❑ 83ElPasDT-5
❑ 84ElPasDT-11
❑ 85VanCanC-212
❑ 86VanCanP-11

Duquette, Chuck
❑ 88FayGenP-1089

Duran, Dan (Daniel James)
❑ 74GasRanT-9
❑ 75LynRanT-10
❑ 76SanAntBTI-10
❑ 80ChaChaT-12
❑ 93RanKee-131

Duran, Dave
❑ 81HolMilT-14
❑ 82HolMilT-5

Duran, Felipe
❑ 91BurIndP-3307
❑ 92ColRedC-24
❑ 92ColRedF-2396
❑ 93ColRedC-9
❑ 93ColRedF-603

Duran, Ignacio
❑ 90SavCarP-2072
❑ 91Cla/Bes-283
❑ 91SprCarC-13
❑ 91SprCarP-748
❑ 92SavCarF-668
❑ 93WatDiaC-13
❑ 93WatDiaF-1775
❑ 94SprSulC-8

Duran, Rick
❑ 79HolMilT-14

Duran, Roberto
❑ 92GulCoaDF-3560
❑ 93VerBeaDF-2209
❑ 93YakBeaC-8
❑ 93YakBeaF-3878
❑ 94BakDodC-9
❑ 95VerBeaDTI-7
❑ 96DunBluJB-6
❑ 96DunBluJTI-8
❑ 96Exc-174
❑ 97JacSun-10
❑ 98PacOmeRS-2
❑ 98PacOmeRST1-2
❑ 98PacOnl-270
❑ 98PacOnlR-270
❑ 98PacOnlWC-270
❑ 98StaCluFDI-222
❑ 98StaCluI-222
❑ 98StaCluOneK-222
❑ 98StaCluPP-222

Durant, Mike
❑ 91ClaDraP-42
❑ 91FroRowDP-17
❑ 91FroRowDPG-17
❑ 91FroRowDPS-17
❑ 92CalLeaACL-47
❑ 92ClaFS7-294
❑ 92StaCluD-40
❑ 92UppDecML-288
❑ 92VisOakC-21
❑ 92VisOakF-1018
❑ 93ClaFS7-152
❑ 93ClaGolF-43
❑ 93ExcFS7-200
❑ 93NasXprF-405
❑ 94SalLakBF-819
❑ 94UppDecML-161
❑ 96FleUpd-U51
❑ 96FleUpdTC-U51
❑ 97SalLakB-11

Durant, Richard
❑ 87ColMetP-25
❑ 88ColMetGS-3
❑ 89StoPorB-7
❑ 89StoPorCLC-155
❑ 89StoPorP-388
❑ 89StoPorS-19

Durazo, Erubiel
❑ 99Bow-380
❑ 99BowGol-380
❑ 99BowInt-380

Durbin, Blaine
❑ 12Zee-29

Durbin, Chad
❑ 97LanLugTS-6
❑ 98CarLeaTPQ-12

❑ 98WilBluRC-11

Duren, Ryne (Rinold George)

❑ 58Top-296
❑ 59Top-485
❑ 60Lea-22
❑ 60Top-204
❑ 60TopTat-13
❑ 61Pos-14
❑ 61Top-356
❑ 61Yan61RL-37
❑ 62AngJayP-3
❑ 62Jel-81
❑ 62Pos-81
❑ 62PosCan-81
❑ 62SalPlaC-46A
❑ 62SalPlaC-46B
❑ 62ShiPlaC-46
❑ 62Top-388
❑ 63BasMagM-22
❑ 63Top-17
❑ 63Top-231
❑ 64Top-173
❑ 64TopVen-173
❑ 65RedEnq-7
❑ 65Top-339
❑ 79TCM50-135
❑ 83YanASFY-12
❑ 89PacLegI-141
❑ 91OriCro-117
❑ 91YanRinP13-8
❑ 92YanWIZ6-37
❑ 92YanWIZA-20

Durham, Bull (Edward Fant)

❑ 34DiaMatCSB-47
❑ 34Gou-79
❑ 72TCMthe1-176

Durham, Bull (Louis)

❑ 08IndPos-8
❑ 09BriE97-10
❑ 09T206-115
❑ 10W555-27
❑ 72ClaCar-48
❑ 90DodTar-207

Durham, Chad

❑ 98HicCraM-11
❑ 98HicCraUO-15
❑ 99BasAmeTP-39
❑ 99BasAmeTPG-39

Durham, Don (Donald Gary)

❑ 73OPC-548
❑ 73Top-548
❑ 93RanKee-132

Durham, Joe (Joseph Vann)

❑ 56BalOriP-12
❑ 58Top-96
❑ 88OriPos-9
❑ 89BalOriP-6
❑ 90BalOriP-4
❑ 90HagSunB-6
❑ 90HagSunP-1433
❑ 90HagSunS-28
❑ 91HagSunLD-250
❑ 91HagSunP-2472
❑ 91LinDriAA-250
❑ 91OriCro-118
❑ 92HagSunF-2571
❑ 92HagSunS-275
❑ 92SkyAA F-109
❑ 93FreKeyC-27
❑ 93FreKeyF-1043
❑ 94FreKeyC-27
❑ 94FreKeyF-2631

Durham, Leon

❑ 78ArkTraT-8
❑ 81CokTeaS-16
❑ 81Don-427
❑ 81Fle-540
❑ 81OPC-321
❑ 81Top-321
❑ 81TopSupHT-25
❑ 81TopTra-756
❑ 82CubRedL-10
❑ 82Don-151
❑ 82Fle-595
❑ 82FleSta-94
❑ 82OPC-206
❑ 82Top-607
❑ 82TopSti-25
❑ 82TopStiV-25
❑ 83AllGamPI-143
❑ 83CubThoAV-10
❑ 83Don-477
❑ 83DonActA-55
❑ 83Fle-495
❑ 83FleSta-56
❑ 83FleSti-131
❑ 83Kel-27
❑ 83OPC-125
❑ 83Top-51
❑ 83Top-125
❑ 83TopSti-219
❑ 84AllGamPI-50
❑ 84CubBriPC-1S
❑ 84CubSev-10
❑ 84CubUno-7
❑ 84Don-5
❑ 84Don-5A
❑ 84Don-67
❑ 84Fle-492
❑ 84FunFooP-107
❑ 84MLBPen-11
❑ 84Nes792-565
❑ 84OPC-209
❑ 84Top-565
❑ 84TopRubD-19
❑ 84TopSti-40
❑ 84TopTif-565
❑ 85AllGamPI-94
❑ 85CubLioP-9
❑ 85CubSev-10
❑ 85Don-189
❑ 85DonActA-46
❑ 85Fle-56
❑ 85Lea-238
❑ 85OPC-330
❑ 85SevCoi-G8
❑ 85Top-330
❑ 85TopGloS-11
❑ 85TopMin-330
❑ 85TopRubD-18
❑ 85TopSti-36
❑ 85TopTif-330
❑ 86BasStaB-36
❑ 86CubGat-10
❑ 86CubUno-7
❑ 86Don-320
❑ 86Fle-367
❑ 86FleLeaL-11
❑ 86FleMin-78
❑ 86FleStiC-35
❑ 86Lea-190
❑ 86OPC-58
❑ 86Spo-111
❑ 86Top-460
❑ 86TopSti-60
❑ 86TopTat-4
❑ 86TopTif-460
❑ 87BoaandB-26
❑ 87CubCan-10
❑ 87CubDavB-10
❑ 87Don-242
❑ 87DonOpeD-74
❑ 87Fle-562
❑ 87FleGlo-562
❑ 87FleHotS-15
❑ 87Lea-125
❑ 87OPC-290
❑ 87RedFolSB-120
❑ 87SevCoi-C6
❑ 87Spo-185
❑ 87SpoTeaP-22
❑ 87StuPan-3
❑ 87Top-290
❑ 87TopSti-57
❑ 87TopTif-290
❑ 88Don-191
❑ 88DonTeaBC-191
❑ 88Fle-420
❑ 88FleGlo-420
❑ 88OPC-65
❑ 88PanSti-259
❑ 88RedKah-10
❑ 88Sco-378
❑ 88ScoGlo-378
❑ 88StaLinCu-5
❑ 88Top-65
❑ 88TopBig-42
❑ 88TopSti-63
❑ 88TopTif-65
❑ 89LouRedBC-16
❑ 89LouRedBP-1260
❑ 89LouRedBTI-16
❑ 89UppDec-354
❑ 96LakElsSB-28
❑ 97VanCanB-2
❑ 98VanCanG-10

Durham, Ray

❑ 91UtiBluSC-6
❑ 91UtiBluSP-3246
❑ 92SarWhiSF-219
❑ 93BirBarF-1198
❑ 94Cla-83
❑ 94ExcFS7-37
❑ 94FleExtB-44
❑ 94FleExtBMLH-3
❑ 94NasSouF-1256
❑ 94TriAAF-AAA6
❑ 94Ult-334
❑ 94UppDecML-59
❑ 95ActPac2G-3G
❑ 95ActPacF-32
❑ 95ActPacF-64
❑ 95Bow-251
❑ 95BowBes-R80
❑ 95BowBesR-R80
❑ 95BowGolF-251
❑ 95ColCho-3
❑ 95ColChoGS-3
❑ 95ColChoSS-3
❑ 95DonTopotO-47
❑ 95Emo-26
❑ 95EmoRoo-4
❑ 95Exc-28
❑ 95ExcAll-3
❑ 95Fin-292
❑ 95FinRef-292
❑ 95Fla-243
❑ 95FlaWavotF-4
❑ 95FleMajLP-5
❑ 95FleUpd-35
❑ 95FleUpdRU-2
❑ 95LeaLim-54
❑ 95Pin-416
❑ 95PinArtP-416
❑ 95PinMusC-416
❑ 95Sel-172
❑ 95SelArtP-172
❑ 95SelCer-110
❑ 95SelCerF-5
❑ 95SelCerMG-110
❑ 95SelCerPU-15
❑ 95SelCerPU9-15
❑ 95SelCerS-110
❑ 95SigRooOJSS-8
❑ 95SigRooOJSSS-8
❑ 95SigRooOP-OP3
❑ 95SigRooOPS-OP3
❑ 95SigRooP'P-P4
❑ 95SP-8
❑ 95SPCha-12
❑ 95SPChaDC-12
❑ 95SPSil-8
❑ 95StaClu-548
❑ 95StaCluCB-CB3
❑ 95StaCluMOP-548
❑ 95StaCluMOP-CB3
❑ 95StaCluSTWS-548
❑ 95Sum-165
❑ 95SumNewA-NA15
❑ 95SumNthD-165
❑ 95TopTra-11T
❑ 95TopTra-28T
❑ 95UC3-114
❑ 95UC3ArtP-114
❑ 95UltGolP-4
❑ 95UltGolPGM-4
❑ 95UppDec-235
❑ 95UppDecED-235
❑ 95UppDecEDG-235
❑ 95UppDecML-89
❑ 95UppDecMLFS-89
❑ 95UppDecPAW-H31
❑ 95UppDecPAWE-H31
❑ 95UppDecSE-153
❑ 95UppDecSEG-153
❑ 95WhiSoxK-8
❑ 95Zen-119
❑ 95ZenRooRC-8
❑ 96Baz-49
❑ 96Bow-2
❑ 96BowBes-68
❑ 96BowBesAR-68
❑ 96BowBesR-68
❑ 96BowFoi-2
❑ 96Cir-26
❑ 96CirRav-26
❑ 96ColCho-92
❑ 96ColChoGS-92
❑ 96ColChoSS-92
❑ 96Don-242
❑ 96DonPreP-242
❑ 96EmoXL-35
❑ 96Fin-S121
❑ 96FinRef-S121
❑ 96Fla-49
❑ 96Fle-64
❑ 96FleRooS-4
❑ 96FleTif-64
❑ 96Lea-51
❑ 96LeaLim-72
❑ 96LeaLimG-72
❑ 96LeaPre-107
❑ 96LeaPreP-107
❑ 96LeaPrePB-51
❑ 96LeaPrePG-51
❑ 96LeaPrePS-51
❑ 96LeaSigA-61
❑ 96LeaSigAG-61
❑ 96LeaSigAS-61
❑ 96MetUni-35
❑ 96MetUniP-35
❑ 96Pac-290
❑ 96PanSti-168
❑ 96Pin-299
❑ 96PinAfi-116
❑ 96PinAfiAP-116
❑ 96PinFoil-299
❑ 96Sco-37
❑ 96ScoDiaA-3
❑ 96ScoDugC-A35
❑ 96ScoDugCAP-A35
❑ 96Sel-89
❑ 96SelArtP-89
❑ 96SelCer-97
❑ 96SelCerAP-97
❑ 96SelCerCB-97
❑ 96SelCerCR-97
❑ 96SelCerMB-97
❑ 96SelCerMG-97
❑ 96SelCerMR-97
❑ 96SP-61
❑ 96Spo-49
❑ 96SpoArtP-49
❑ 96StaClu-7
❑ 96StaClu-232
❑ 96StaCluEPB-7
❑ 96StaCluEPG-7
❑ 96StaCluEPS-7
❑ 96StaCluMOP-7
❑ 96StaCluMOP-232
❑ 96Stu-87
❑ 96StuPrePB-87
❑ 96StuPrePG-87
❑ 96StuPrePS-87
❑ 96Sum-5
❑ 96SumAbo&B-5
❑ 96SumArtP-5
❑ 96SumFoi-5
❑ 96TeaOut-23
❑ 96Top-173
❑ 96TopGal-96
❑ 96TopGalPPI-96
❑ 96TopLas-103
❑ 96Ult-36
❑ 96UltGolM-36
❑ 96UppDec-40
❑ 96WhiSoxF-4
❑ 96Zen-46
❑ 96ZenArtP-46
❑ 96ZenMoz-3
❑ 97Bow-270
❑ 97BowInt-270
❑ 97Cir-2
❑ 97CirRav-2
❑ 97ColCho-295
❑ 97ColChoT-CW9
❑ 97Don-156
❑ 97DonEli-73
❑ 97DonEliGS-73
❑ 97DonGolPP-156
❑ 97DonLim-12
❑ 97DonLimE-12
❑ 97DonLimENG-12
❑ 97DonPre-67
❑ 97DonPreCttC-67
❑ 97DonSilPP-156
❑ 97DonTea-65
❑ 97DonTeaSPE-65
❑ 97E-X2-14
❑ 97E-X2Cred-14
❑ 97E-X2EssCre-14
❑ 97Fin-301
❑ 97FinEmb-301
❑ 97FinEmbR-301
❑ 97FinRef-301
❑ 97FlaShoLC-148
❑ 97FlaShoLeg0-148
❑ 97FlaShoLeg1-148
❑ 97FlaShoM-A148
❑ 97FlaShoM-B148
❑ 97FlaShoM-C148
❑ 97FlaShoR0-148
❑ 97FlaShoR1-148
❑ 97FlaShoR2-148
❑ 97Fle-59
❑ 97FleTif-59
❑ 97Lea-114
❑ 97LeaFraM-114
❑ 97LeaFraMDC-114
❑ 97MetUni-57
❑ 97Pac-51
❑ 97PacLigB-51
❑ 97PacSil-51
❑ 97Pin-108
❑ 97PinArtP-PP108
❑ 97PinIns-46
❑ 97PinInsCE-46
❑ 97PinInsDE-46
❑ 97PinMusC-108
❑ 97PinPrePla-108
❑ 97PinX-P-62
❑ 97PinX-PMoS-62
❑ 97Sco-158
❑ 97ScoArtPWB-158
❑ 97ScoPreS-158
❑ 97ScoShoS-158
❑ 97ScoShoSAP-158
❑ 97SP-48
❑ 97StaClu-293
❑ 97StaCluM-M4
❑ 97StaCluMOP-293
❑ 97StaCluMOP-M4
❑ 97Stu-22
❑ 97StuPrePG-22
❑ 97StuPrePS-22
❑ 97Top-215
❑ 97TopChr-80
❑ 97TopChrR-80
❑ 97TopGal-163
❑ 97TopGalPPI-163
❑ 97Ult-38
❑ 97UltGolME-38
❑ 97UltPlaME-38
❑ 97UppDec-329
❑ 97WhiSoxCM-2
❑ 97WhiSoxS-7
❑ 97WhiSoxSPl-7
❑ 97WhiSoxSPr-7
❑ 97WhiSoxTI-5
❑ 98CirThu-216
❑ 98CirThuRav-216
❑ 98CirThuSupRav-216
❑ 98ColCho-340
❑ 98CroRoy-35
❑ 98DonColL-273
❑ 98DonPriCL-273
❑ 98Fin-191
❑ 98FinNo--191
❑ 98FinNo-R-191
❑ 98FinRef-191
❑ 98Fle-156
❑ 98Lea-74
❑ 98LeaFraDA-74
❑ 98LeaFraF-74
❑ 98LeaFraM-74
❑ 98LeaFraM-74
❑ 98LeaFraMDC-74
❑ 98LeaFraMDC-74
❑ 98LeaFraMZ2-74
❑ 98MetUni-202
❑ 98MetUniPMG-202
❑ 98Pac-55
❑ 98PacAur-23
❑ 98PacOme-56
❑ 98PacOmeR-56
❑ 98PacOnl-167
❑ 98PacOnlR-167
❑ 98PacOnlWC-167
❑ 98PacPar-28
❑ 98PacParC-28
❑ 98PacParG-28
❑ 98PacParHS-28
❑ 98PacParPB-28
❑ 98PacParR-28
❑ 98PacPlaB-55
❑ 98PacRedT-55
❑ 98PacSil-55
❑ 98Pin-77
❑ 98PinPreP-77
❑ 98Revo-35
❑ 98RevoSS-35
❑ 98Sco-149
❑ 98ScoRT-140
❑ 98ScoSS-PP111
❑ 98ScoSSAP-PP111
❑ 98SPxFin-260
❑ 98SPxFinR-260
❑ 98SPxFinS-260
❑ 98StaCluFDI-339
❑ 98StaCluI-339
❑ 98StaCluOneK-339
❑ 98StaCluPP-339
❑ 98Top-383
❑ 98TopChr-383
❑ 98TopChrR-383
❑ 98TopDevR-383
❑ 98TopDia-383
❑ 98TopGal-37
❑ 98TopGalGP-37
❑ 98TopGalOPP-37
❑ 98TopGalPPI-37
❑ 98TopGalPPIA-37
❑ 98TopMiniC-383
❑ 98TopSta-27
❑ 98TopStaB-27
❑ 98TopStaG-27
❑ 98TopStaGR-27
❑ 98TopStaS-27
❑ 98Ult-94
❑ 98UltGolM-94
❑ 98UltMas-94
❑ 98UltPlaM-94
❑ 98UppDec-57
❑ 98UppDecSF-36
❑ 98WhiSoxS-12
❑ 98WhiSoxSP-12
❑ 99199Fin-64
❑ 99Bow-40
❑ 99BowBes-17
❑ 99BowBesAR-17
❑ 99BowBesR-17
❑ 99BowChr-40
❑ 99BowChrG-40
❑ 99BowChrGR-40
❑ 99BowChrI-40
❑ 99BowChrIR-40
❑ 99BowChrR-40
❑ 99BowGol-40
❑ 99BowInt-40
❑ 99CroRoyB-33
❑ 99CroRoyL-33
❑ 99CroRoyOD-33
❑ 99FinGolRef-64
❑ 99FinRef-64
❑ 99FlaShoLeg1-137
❑ 99FlaShoLeg2-137
❑ 99FlaShoLeg3-137
❑ 99FlaShoLegM1-137
❑ 99FlaShoLegM2-137
❑ 99FlaShoLegM3-137
❑ 99FlaShoR1-137
❑ 99FlaShoR2-137
❑ 99FlaShoR3-137
❑ 99Fle-87
❑ 99FleBri-87
❑ 99FleBri2G-87
❑ 99FleBriBlu-87
❑ 99FleBriGol-87
❑ 99FleMys-72
❑ 99FleMysG-72
❑ 99FleMysM-72
❑ 99FleSta9-87
❑ 99FleWarT-87
❑ 99MetUni-185
❑ 99MetUniGM-185
❑ 99MetUniPMG-185
❑ 99Pac-101
❑ 99PacAur-40
❑ 99PacAurOD-40
❑ 99PacInv-35
❑ 99PacInvOD-35
❑ 99PacInvPB-35
❑ 99PacOme-55
❑ 99PacOmeC-55
❑ 99PacOmeG-55
❑ 99PacOmePB-55
❑ 99PacPar-55
❑ 99PacParC-55
❑ 99PacParG-55
❑ 99PacParHoloGold-55
❑ 99PacParHS-55
❑ 99PacParOD-55
❑ 99PacParPB-55
❑ 99PacParRed-55
❑ 99PacPlaB-101
❑ 99PacRed-101
❑ 99Rev-32
❑ 99RevPremDate-32
❑ 99RevRet-32
❑ 99RevShaSS-32
❑ 99SkyMolM-32
❑ 99SkyMolMX-32

❑ 99SkyPre-165
❑ 99SkyPreR-165
❑ 99SkyThu-96
❑ 99SkyThuRant-96
❑ 99SkyThuRave-96
❑ 99SP SigAuto-RD
❑ 99SPSig-148
❑ 99StaClu-76
❑ 99StaCluFDI-76
❑ 99StaCluOoaK-76
❑ 99StaCluPP-76
❑ 99ThuSkySupR-96
❑ 99Top-6
❑ 99TopChr-6
❑ 99TopChrR-6
❑ 99TopMVPP-6
❑ 99TopOpeD-5
❑ 99TopSta-139
❑ 99TopStaFoil-139
❑ 99Ult-106
❑ 99UltGolM-106
❑ 99UltMas-106
❑ 99UltPlaM-106
❑ 99UppDec-66
❑ 99UppDecCLM-C20
❑ 99UppDecEL1-66
❑ 99UppDecEL2-66
❑ 99UppDecM-49
❑ 99UppDecMGS-49
❑ 99UppDecMHFS-49
❑ 99UppDecMP-49
❑ 99UppDecMSS-49
❑ 99UppDecR-20
❑ 99UppDecRG-20
❑ 99UppDecRP-20
❑ 99Vic-96

Durham, Shane
❑ 87AncGlaP-7

Durkac, Bo
❑ 97HigDesMG-5

Durkin, Chris
❑ 91AubAstC-19
❑ 91AubAstP-4285
❑ 91Cla/Bes-410
❑ 91FroRowDP-8
❑ 91FroRowDPG-8
❑ 91FroRowDPS-8
❑ 92AshTouC-21
❑ 92ClaFS7-15
❑ 92StaCluD-41
❑ 92UppDecML-177
❑ 93QuaCitRBC-6
❑ 93QuaCitRBF-111
❑ 94OscAstC-6
❑ 94OscAstF-1149
❑ 96VerBeaDB-12
❑ 97SanAntMB-23
❑ 98SanAntMM-23

Durkin, Marty (Martin)
❑ 88CapCodPPaLP-128
❑ 89WatIndS-4
❑ 90MiaMirIS-6
❑ 90MiaMirIS-5
❑ 91WesPalBEC-25
❑ 91WesPalBEP-1240
❑ 92WinHavRSF-1785
❑ 93ForLauRSC-10
❑ 93ForLauRSFP-1604

Durkovic, Peter
❑ 96FayGenB-12
❑ 97LakTigB-13
❑ 98JacSunM-9

Durney, Bill
❑ 88PalSprACLC-115
❑ 88PalSprAP-1462
❑ 89BenBucL-29

Durning, Dick
❑ 90DodTar-937

Durocher, Francois
❑ 86OscAstP-7

Durocher, Jayson
❑ 94VerExpF-3903
❑ 96WesPalBEB-9

Durocher, Leo (Leo Ernest)
❑ 29ExhFou-26
❑ 31Exh-7
❑ 33Gou-147
❑ 33GouCanV-74
❑ 33WorCig-34
❑ 34BabRutG-17
❑ 34BatR31-156
❑ 34ButPreR-17
❑ 34DiaMatCSB-48
❑ 34Gou-7
❑ 34GouCanV-69
❑ 35AlDemDCR3-129
❑ 35DiaMatCS3T1-48
❑ 36WorWidGV-25
❑ 37KelPepS-BB3
❑ 38ExhFou-2
❑ 39PlaBal-6
❑ 40DodTeal-6
❑ 40WheM4-1B
❑ 41DouPlaR-141
❑ 42DodTeal-6
❑ 43DodTeal-8
❑ 46DodTeal-5
❑ 48BluTin-2A
❑ 48BluTin-2B
❑ 48DodTeal-8
❑ 48GiaTeal-3
❑ 49EurSta-102
❑ 49GiaTeal-3
❑ 50Bow-220
❑ 51Bow-233
❑ 52Bow-146
❑ 52RedMan-NL1
❑ 52Top-315
❑ 53BowC-55
❑ 55GiaGolS-2
❑ 66CubTeal-6
❑ 67Top-481
❑ 68Top-321
❑ 68TopVen-321
❑ 69CubPho-4
❑ 69OPC-147
❑ 69Top-147
❑ 69TopFou-12
❑ 70OPC-291
❑ 70Top-291
❑ 71OPC-609
❑ 71Top-609
❑ 72Top-576
❑ 73Dod194T-7
❑ 73OPC-624
❑ 73Top-624
❑ 74Car193T-9
❑ 74Car193T-28
❑ 74Car193T-29
❑ 75Gia195T-33
❑ 75Gia195T-34
❑ 78DodTCM4-37
❑ 79DiaGre-85
❑ 79TCM50-201
❑ 80PacLeg-40
❑ 80PerHaloFP-218
❑ 83Car194T-30
❑ 83TopRep5-315
❑ 84CubUno-8
❑ 84OCoandSI-187
❑ 84WilMay-4
❑ 85BigLeaC3-6
❑ 86ConSer1-11
❑ 87AstShoSTw-21
❑ 87Car193T-6
❑ 88ConSer3-10
❑ 88DodRinP1-4C
❑ 88DodRinP1-6C
❑ 88PacLegI-27
❑ 89DodSmoG-39
❑ 90DodTar-208
❑ 90PerGreM-103
❑ 91TopArc1-309
❑ 92BazQua5A-5
❑ 93DiaStaES-127

Duross, Gabe
❑ 93GenCubC-10
❑ 93GenCubF-3182
❑ 94MidLeaAF-MDW47
❑ 94PeoChiC-6
❑ 94PeoChiF-2274
❑ 95Exc-162
❑ 95OrlCubF-17
❑ 96OrlCubB-8

Durrett, Red
❑ 43ParSpo-75
❑ 90DodTar-938

Durrington, Trent
❑ 95AusFut-53
❑ 95BoiHawTI-16
❑ 96BoiHawB-11
❑ 97LakElsSG-13
❑ 98MidAngG-14
❑ 98MidAngO-12

Durrman, Jim
❑ 81WesHavAT-8
❑ 83AlbA'sT-9

Durrwacher, Doug
❑ 93BilMusF-3954
❑ 94BilMusF-3676
❑ 94BilMusSP-5

Durso, Joe
❑ 93St.CatBJC-8
❑ 93St.CatBJF-3977
❑ 94HagSunC-7
❑ 94HagSunF-2733
❑ 95PriWilCTI-13

Durst, Cedric
❑ 24Zee-6
❑ 33Zee-2
❑ 75Yan192T-6
❑ 79Yan192T-8
❑ 84Yan192G-15
❑ 91ConTSN-108

DuRussel, Scott
❑ 91NiaFalRP-3626
❑ 92NiaFalRC-18
❑ 92NiaFalRF-3317

Duryea, Jesse (James Whitney)
❑ 87OldJudN-146

Dusak, Erv (Ervin Frank)
❑ 46SeaSLP-17
❑ 47TipTop-155
❑ 51Bow-310
❑ 52Top-183
❑ 79TCM50-122
❑ 83Car194T-10
❑ 83TopRep5-183
❑ 85TCMPla1-23

Dusan, Gene
❑ 75OklCit8TI-21
❑ 77WatIndT-7
❑ 79TacTugT-24
❑ 80TacTigT-23
❑ 82JacMetT-22
❑ 84WicAerRD-22
❑ 86CedRapRT-25
❑ 90BenBucL-2

Dusan, John
❑ 92BenRocCB-28

Duser, Carl
❑ 55JetPos-4

Dustal, Bob (Robert Andrew)
❑ 63Top-299

Dutch, John
❑ 95MicBatCTI-10

Duty, Darrell
❑ 89AncGlaP-12

Duva, Brian
❑ 94WatIndC-8
❑ 94WatIndF-3951

Duval, Mickey (Michael)
❑ 79IndIndTI-27
❑ 82MadMusF-34

DuVall, Brad
❑ 88HamRedP-1722
❑ 89Bow-430
❑ 89BowTif-430
❑ 89SprCarB-4
❑ 90St.PetCS-5
❑ 90TopTVCa-45

Duvall, Michael
❑ 96KanCouCTI-6
❑ 97BreCouMB-12
❑ 98BesAutSS-20
❑ 98PorSeaD5AQ-28
❑ 99PacOme-233
❑ 99PacOmeC-233
❑ 99PacOmeG-233
❑ 99PacOmePB-233
❑ 99SpoIll-50

Duverge, Salvador
❑ 96AshTouB-14
❑ 97AshTou-9
❑ 97SalAva-U1
❑ 98SalAvaC-9

Dwight, Pee Wee (Edward Joseph)
❑ 87NegLeaPD-4

Dworak, John
❑ 52LavPro-61

Dwyer, Frank (John Francis)
❑ 87OldJudN-147
❑ 98CamPepP-22

Dwyer, Greg
❑ 98QuaCitRBG-6

Dwyer, Jim (James Edward)
❑ 75ExpPos-11
❑ 75OPC-429
❑ 75St.LouCP-8
❑ 75Top-429
❑ 75TopMin-429
❑ 76ExpRed-7
❑ 76MonExpP-8
❑ 76OPC-94
❑ 76SSP-341
❑ 76Top-94
❑ 78CarTeal-5
❑ 78Top-644
❑ 79Top-236
❑ 80Top-576
❑ 81BalOriP-6
❑ 81Don-577
❑ 81Fle-235
❑ 81OPC-184
❑ 81Top-184
❑ 81TopTra-757
❑ 82Don-611
❑ 82Fle-164
❑ 82Top-359
❑ 83Don-583
❑ 83Fle-59
❑ 83OriPos-10
❑ 83Top-718
❑ 84BalOriP-12
❑ 84Don-454
❑ 84Fle-7
❑ 84FleSti-117
❑ 84Nes792-473
❑ 84Top-473
❑ 84TopTif-473
❑ 85Fle-176
❑ 85OriHea-6
❑ 85Top-56
❑ 85TopTif-56
❑ 86BalOriHMP-6
❑ 86BalOriP-8
❑ 86Don-413
❑ 86Fle-274
❑ 86OPC-339
❑ 86Top-653
❑ 86TopTif-653
❑ 87BalOriP-10
❑ 87Don-418
❑ 87Fle-469
❑ 87FleGlo-469
❑ 87OriFreB-9
❑ 87Top-246
❑ 87TopTif-246
❑ 88Don-459
❑ 88Fle-558
❑ 88FleGlo-558
❑ 88OriFreB-9
❑ 88OriPos-10
❑ 88Sco-229
❑ 88ScoGlo-229
❑ 88StaLinO-3
❑ 88Top-521
❑ 88TopClo-32
❑ 88TopTif-521
❑ 89DonBasB-311
❑ 90Don-484
❑ 90PubIntS-325
❑ 91LinDriAAA-425
❑ 91MetWIZ-100
❑ 91OriCro-119
❑ 91PacSenL-118
❑ 91PorBeaLD-425
❑ 91PorBeaP-1582
❑ 92KenTwiC-25
❑ 92KenTwiF-620
❑ 93ForWayWC-26
❑ 93ForWayWF-1984
❑ 94ForWayWC-26
❑ 94ForWayWF-2025
❑ 95HarCitRCTI-5
❑ 96HarCitRCB-3

Dwyer, Scott
❑ 79WatIndT-16

Dybzinski, Jerry (Jerome M.)
❑ 78WatIndT-9
❑ 79TacTugT-13
❑ 80IndTeal-9
❑ 81Don-438
❑ 81Fle-399
❑ 81OPC-198
❑ 81Top-198
❑ 82Don-647
❑ 82Fle-366
❑ 82Ind-12
❑ 82IndWhe-3
❑ 82Top-512
❑ 83Don-576
❑ 83Fle-406
❑ 83IndPos-10
❑ 83Top-289
❑ 83TopTra-27T
❑ 84Don-160
❑ 84Fle-57
❑ 84Nes792-619
❑ 84Top-619
❑ 84TopTif-619
❑ 84WhiSoxTV-11
❑ 85Fle-512
❑ 85HawIslC-250
❑ 85Top-52
❑ 85TopTif-52
❑ 86CalCanP-7

Dyce, George
❑ 89NasSouTI-27

Dyck, Jim (James Robert)
❑ 53BowC-111
❑ 53NorBreL-7
❑ 53Top-177
❑ 54Bow-85
❑ 56BalOriP-6
❑ 56Top-303
❑ 57HygMea-3
❑ 57SeaPop-7
❑ 58SeaRalT-7
❑ 59SeaPop-16
❑ 91OriCro-120
❑ 91TopArc1-177
❑ 97BalOriP-15

Dye, Jermaine
❑ 94Bow-433
❑ 94MacBraC-6
❑ 94MacBraF-2217
❑ 94SouAtlLAF-SAL43
❑ 95Bes-52
❑ 95Bow-206
❑ 95BowBes-B21
❑ 95BowBesR-B21
❑ 95BreBtaTI-24
❑ 95Exc-149
❑ 95SPML-11
❑ 95SPMLA-8
❑ 95UppDecML-93
❑ 95UppDecMLFS-93
❑ 96BesAutSA-18
❑ 96Bow-132
❑ 96BowBes-127
❑ 96BowBesAR-127
❑ 96BowBesR-127
❑ 96BowFoi-132
❑ 96Cir-98
❑ 96CirRav-98
❑ 96ColCho-437
❑ 96ColChoGS-437
❑ 96ColChoSS-437
❑ 96EmoXL-139
❑ 96Exc-124
❑ 96Fin-G324
❑ 96FinRef-G324
❑ 96Fla-197
❑ 96FlaWavotF-8
❑ 96FleUpd-U104
❑ 96FleUpdNH-5
❑ 96FleUpdTC-U104
❑ 96LeaLimR-5
❑ 96LeaLimRG-5
❑ 96LeaPre-123
❑ 96LeaPreP-123
❑ 96LeaSig-88
❑ 96LeaSigEA-44
❑ 96LeaSigEACM-4
❑ 96LeaSigPPG-88
❑ 96LeaSigPPP-88
❑ 96MLBPin-8
❑ 96Pin-375
❑ 96PinAfi-178
❑ 96PinAfiAP-178
❑ 96PinFoil-375
❑ 96PinProS-15
❑ 96RicBraB-10
❑ 96RicBraRC-9
❑ 96RicBraUB-7
❑ 96Sel-188
❑ 96SelArtP-188
❑ 96SelCer-107
❑ 96SelCerAP-107
❑ 96SelCerCB-107
❑ 96SelCerCR-107
❑ 96SelCerMB-107
❑ 96SelCerMG-107
❑ 96SelCerMR-107
❑ 96SigRooOJRS-R1
❑ 96SigRooOJRSS-R1
❑ 96SP-19
❑ 96Sum-191
❑ 96SumAbo&B-191
❑ 96SumArtP-191
❑ 96SumFoi-191
❑ 96Top-439
❑ 96Ult-438
❑ 96UltGolM-438
❑ 96UltGolP-6
❑ 96UltGolPHGM-6
❑ 96UppDec-249
❑ 96Zen-108
❑ 96ZenArtP-108
❑ 96ZenDiaC-6
❑ 96ZenDiaCP-6
❑ 97BowBes-89
❑ 97BowBesAR-89
❑ 97BowBesR-89
❑ 97BraSco-7
❑ 97BraScoPl-7
❑ 97BraScoPr-7
❑ 97Cir-225
❑ 97CirRav-225
❑ 97ColCho-28
❑ 97Don-111
❑ 97DonEli-26
❑ 97DonEliGS-26
❑ 97DonGolPP-111
❑ 97DonLim-186
❑ 97DonLimE-186
❑ 97DonPre-83
❑ 97DonPreCttC-83
❑ 97DonSigA-29
❑ 97DonSigAC-36
❑ 97DonSigAM-36
❑ 97DonSilPP-111
❑ 97E-X2-25
❑ 97E-X2Cred-25
❑ 97E-X2EssCre-25
❑ 97E-X2SD2000-9
❑ 97Fin-16
❑ 97FinRef-16
❑ 97FlaShoLC-41
❑ 97FlaShoLeg0-41
❑ 97FlaShoLeg1-41
❑ 97FlaShoM-A41
❑ 97FlaShoM-B41
❑ 97FlaShoM-C41
❑ 97FlaShoR0-41
❑ 97FlaShoR1-41
❑ 97FlaShoR2-41
❑ 97Fle-254
❑ 97Fle-525
❑ 97FleRooS-4
❑ 97FleTif-254
❑ 97FleTif-525
❑ 97Lea-211
❑ 97LeaFraM-211
❑ 97LeaFraMDC-211
❑ 97MetUni-27
❑ 97MetUniPP-2
❑ 97NewPin-144
❑ 97NewPinAP-144
❑ 97NewPinMC-144
❑ 97NewPinPP-144
❑ 97Pac-231
❑ 97PacLigB-231
❑ 97PacPri-77
❑ 97PacPriLB-77
❑ 97PacPriP-77
❑ 97PacSil-231
❑ 97Pin-86
❑ 97PinArtP-PP86
❑ 97PinCer-15
❑ 97PinCerMBla-15
❑ 97PinCerMBlu-15
❑ 97PinCerMG-15
❑ 97PinCerMR-15
❑ 97PinCerR-15
❑ 97PinIns-100
❑ 97PinInsCE-100
❑ 97PinInsDE-100
❑ 97PinMusC-86
❑ 97PinPrePla-86
❑ 97PinTotCPB-15
❑ 97PinTotCPG-15
❑ 97PinTotCPR-15
❑ 97PinX-P-63
❑ 97PinX-PMoS-63
❑ 97Sco-141
❑ 97ScoArtPWB-141
❑ 97ScoPreS-141
❑ 97ScoShoS-141
❑ 97ScoShoSAP-141
❑ 97Sel-70
❑ 97SelArtP-70
❑ 97SelCom-70
❑ 97SelRegG-70
❑ 97SelRooR-8

❑ 97SelToootT-8
❑ 97SelToootTMB-8
❑ 97SpollI-60
❑ 97SpollIEE-60
❑ 97StaClu-351
❑ 97StaCluC-CO3
❑ 97StaCluMOP-351
❑ 97Stu-119
❑ 97StuHarH-14
❑ 97StuPrePG-119
❑ 97StuPrePS-119
❑ 97Top-239
❑ 97TopAwel-AI3
❑ 97TopChr-84
❑ 97TopChrR-84
❑ 97TopGal-170
❑ 97TopGalPPI-170
❑ 97UD3-59
❑ 97UD3GenNex-GN9
❑ 97Ult-151
❑ 97Ult-324
❑ 97UltGolME-151
❑ 97UltGolME-324
❑ 97UltPlaME-151
❑ 97UltPlaME-324
❑ 97UltRooR-2
❑ 97UppDec-12
❑ 97UppDecBCP-BC9
❑ 97UppDecTTS-TS2
❑ 98Don-155
❑ 98DonCol-155
❑ 98DonColS-155
❑ 98DonGolPP-155
❑ 98DonPriCD-155
❑ 98DonSilPP-155
❑ 98Pac-103
❑ 98PacAur-44
❑ 98PacInv-37
❑ 98PacInvPBlue-37
❑ 98PacInvSilv-37
❑ 98PacInvTeam-13
❑ 98PacOnl-338
❑ 98PacOnlR-338
❑ 98PacOnlWC-338
❑ 98PacPar-54
❑ 98PacParC-54
❑ 98PacParG-54
❑ 98PacParHS-54
❑ 98PacParPB-54
❑ 98PacParR-54
❑ 98PacPlaB-103
❑ 98PacRedT-103
❑ 98PacSil-103
❑ 98PacTeaC-7
❑ 98PinPlu-79
❑ 98ScoRT-152
❑ 98StaCluFDI-301
❑ 98StaCluI-301
❑ 98StaCluOneK-301
❑ 98StaCluPP-301
❑ 98UppDec-391
❑ 99Pac-203
❑ 99PacAur-87
❑ 99PacAurOD-87
❑ 99PacOme-113
❑ 99PacOmeC-113
❑ 99PacOmeG-113
❑ 99PacOmePB-113
❑ 99PacPlaB-203
❑ 99PacRed-203
❑ 99Rev-67
❑ 99RevPremDate-67
❑ 99RevRet-67
❑ 99RevShaSS-67
❑ 99Vic-193

Dye, Mark
❑ 82IdaFalAT-18

Dye, Scott
❑ 80WatRedT-8
❑ 81TidTidT-15
❑ 82JacMetT-4
❑ 83TidTidT-14

Dye, Steve
❑ 89ModA'sC-9
❑ 89ModA'sCLC-269

Dyer, Duffy (Don Robert)
❑ 69Top-624
❑ 70Top-692
❑ 71MetTeal-4
❑ 71MLBOffS-150
❑ 71OPC-136
❑ 71Top-136
❑ 72Dia-12
❑ 72OPC-127
❑ 72Top-127
❑ 73LinPor-110
❑ 73OPC-493
❑ 73Top-493
❑ 74MetDaiPA-4
❑ 74OPC-536
❑ 74Top-536
❑ 75OPC-538
❑ 75PitPirP-4
❑ 75Top-538
❑ 75TopMin-538
❑ 76OPC-88
❑ 76SSP-581
❑ 76Top-88
❑ 77BurCheD-185
❑ 77PirPosP-4
❑ 77Top-318
❑ 78Top-637
❑ 79ExpPos-8
❑ 79Top-286
❑ 80OPC-232
❑ 80Top-446
❑ 81Don-7A
❑ 81Don-7B
❑ 81Top-196
❑ 83CubThoAV-NNO
❑ 86ElPasDP-9
❑ 87ElPasDP-14
❑ 88BlaYNPRWLU-31
❑ 88DenZepC-25
❑ 88DenZepP-1264
❑ 89BrePol-NNO
❑ 89MetRinP69-9
❑ 90BreMilB-32
❑ 90BrePol-NNO
❑ 90El PasDAGTI-20
❑ 91BreMilB-32
❑ 91BrePol-NNO
❑ 91MetWIZ-101
❑ 92BrePol-30
❑ 94Met69CCPP-13
❑ 94Met69CS-12
❑ 94Met69T-22
❑ 96A'sMot-28
❑ 97A'sMot-28
❑ 98A'sMot-28

Dyer, Eddie
❑ 46SeaSLP-18
❑ 46SpoExcW-1-5
❑ 49EurSta-181
❑ 83Car194T-63
❑ 84OCoandSI-148
❑ 92ConTSN-618

Dyer, Hal
❑ 87ChaWheP-14
❑ 93MedHatBJSP-3753
❑ 93MedHatBJSP-24
❑ 94MedHatBJF-3698
❑ 94MedHatBJSP-28

Dyer, John
❑ 78GreBraT-8

Dyer, Linton
❑ 88AppFoxP-143
❑ 89AppFoxP-867
❑ 90BasCitRS-7

Dyer, Mike
❑ 87KenTwiP-11
❑ 88OrlTwiB-9
❑ 89PorBeaC-8
❑ 89PorBeaP-228
❑ 90CMC-558
❑ 90Don-640
❑ 90Fle-372
❑ 90FleCan-372
❑ 90OPC-576
❑ 90PorBeaC-6
❑ 90PorBeaP-173
❑ 90ProAAAF-243
❑ 90Sco-571
❑ 90Top-576
❑ 90TopDeb89-33
❑ 90TopTif-576
❑ 90UppDec-374
❑ 93IowCubF-2130
❑ 94BufBisF-1829
❑ 95PirFil-8
❑ 95Top-136
❑ 97RicBra-9

Dyes, Andy
❑ 76VenLeaS-193
❑ 78SyrChiT-7
❑ 79HawIsIC-28
❑ 79HawIsIT-5
❑ 80HawIsIT-24

Dyess, Todd
❑ 96FreKeyB-7
❑ 97FreKey-6

Dygert, Jimmy (James Henry)
❑ 08RosComP-59
❑ 09AmeCarE90-1-38
❑ 09BriE97-11
❑ 09T206-116
❑ 10LuxCigPP-9
❑ 10NadE1-17
❑ 10SweCapPP-44
❑ 10W555-28
❑ 11A'sFirT20-6
❑ 11D35RocB-6
❑ 11MecDFT-18
❑ 11PinT-5-509
❑ 11S74Sil-30
❑ 11SpoLifCW-115
❑ 11SpoLifM-92
❑ 11T205-48
❑ 11TurRedT-92
❑ 12ImpTobC-45

Dyke, Bill
❑ 89KnoBluJP-1120

Dykes, Jimmy (James Joseph)
❑ 20NatCarE-25A
❑ 20NatCarE-25B
❑ 21Exh-41
❑ 22E120-77
❑ 22W572-26
❑ 23WilChoV-35
❑ 25Exh-106
❑ 26Exh-107
❑ 27YorCarE-51
❑ 29A'sVil-2
❑ 29ExhFou-28
❑ 29PorandAR-19
❑ 31Exh-27
❑ 31W517-22
❑ 32OrbPinNP-11
❑ 32OrbPinUP-16
❑ 32R33So2-410
❑ 33DelR33-18
❑ 33DouDisP-12
❑ 33GeoCMil-10
❑ 33Gou-6
❑ 33GouCanV-6
❑ 33RitCE-5H
❑ 33TatOrb-16
❑ 33TatOrbSDR-167
❑ 33WorCig-35
❑ 34BatR31-29
❑ 34BatR31-159
❑ 34DiaStaR-42
❑ 34WarBakSP-2
❑ 35AlDemDCR3-17
❑ 35ExhFou-10
❑ 35GouPuzR-1I
❑ 35GouPuzR-2F
❑ 35GouPuzR-16F
❑ 35GouPuzR-17F
❑ 36ExhFou-10
❑ 36GouBWR-12
❑ 36GouWidPPR-A28
❑ 36GouWidPPR-B8
❑ 36GouWidPPR-C8
❑ 36NatChiFPR-99
❑ 36NatChiFPR-107
❑ 36R31Pre-G6
❑ 36WorWidGV-1
❑ 37ExhFou-10
❑ 38CloFotW-23
❑ 40PlaBal-187
❑ 40WhiSoxL-5
❑ 47SigOil-6
❑ 49A'sTeal-11
❑ 49PhiBul-16
❑ 50A'sTeal-8
❑ 51A'sTeal-8
❑ 51Bow-226
❑ 52A'sTeal-7
❑ 52Bow-98
❑ 53A'sTeal-9
❑ 53BowC-31
❑ 54OriEss-9
❑ 58RedEnq-10
❑ 60Top-214
❑ 61Kah-10
❑ 61Top-222
❑ 74A's192T-7
❑ 76ChiGre-5
❑ 77GalGloG-120
❑ 77GalGloG-201
❑ 77PhiFav-9
❑ 78TCM60I-224
❑ 82GSGalAG-12
❑ 83BigLeaCOA-5
❑ 87ConSer2-37
❑ 88ConSer4-10
❑ 91ConTSN-92
❑ 91TopArc1-281
❑ 93ConTSN-678
❑ 93ConTSN-848
❑ 94ConTSN-1150
❑ 94ConTSNB-1150
❑ 97BalOriP-16

Dykhoff, Radhames
❑ 96FreKeyB-8
❑ 97BowBay-16
❑ 97CarLeaTP-19
❑ 98BowBayM-10

Dykstra, Kevin
❑ 90CalLeaACLC-32

Dykstra, Lenny (Len)
❑ 83LynMetT-15
❑ 84JacMetT-18
❑ 85MetTCM-32
❑ 85TidTidT-20
❑ 86BasStaB-37
❑ 86Don-482
❑ 86Fle-78
❑ 86MetColP-15
❑ 86MetTCM-24
❑ 86MetWorSC-4
❑ 86OPC-53
❑ 86Top-53
❑ 86TopTif-53
❑ 87ClaGam-2
❑ 87Don-611
❑ 87Fle-6
❑ 87FleGlo-6
❑ 87FleLimE-13
❑ 87Lea-88
❑ 87MetColP-3
❑ 87MetFanC-3
❑ 87OPC-295
❑ 87SevCoi-E4
❑ 87SevCoi-M5
❑ 87Spo-58
❑ 87SpoTeaP-2
❑ 87Top-295
❑ 87TopSti-13
❑ 87TopSti-21
❑ 87TopSti-98
❑ 87TopTif-295
❑ 87Woo-23
❑ 88Don-364
❑ 88DonBasB-264
❑ 88DonTeaBM-364
❑ 88Fle-133
❑ 88FleGlo-133
❑ 88Lea-135
❑ 88MetColP-3
❑ 88MetKah-4
❑ 88OPC-299
❑ 88PanSti-345
❑ 88Sco-370
❑ 88ScoGlo-370
❑ 88ScoYouS2-19
❑ 88Spo-106
❑ 88StaLinMe-6
❑ 88Top-655
❑ 88TopBig-203
❑ 88TopMinL-59
❑ 88TopTif-655
❑ 89ClaLigB-36
❑ 89Don-353
❑ 89DonBasB-159
❑ 89Fle-33
❑ 89FleGlo-33
❑ 89FleUpd-105
❑ 89MetColP-6
❑ 89OPC-349
❑ 89PanSti-138
❑ 89PhiTas-40
❑ 89Sco-84
❑ 89ScoRoo-28T
❑ 89Spo-123
❑ 89Top-435
❑ 89TopBig-41
❑ 89TopDouM-12
❑ 89TopSti-90
❑ 89TopTif-435
❑ 89TopTra-27T
❑ 89TopTraT-27T
❑ 89UppDec-369
❑ 90Bow-152
❑ 90BowTif-152
❑ 90ClaUpd-T18
❑ 90Don-313
❑ 90DonBesN-118
❑ 90Fle-556
❑ 90FleCan-556
❑ 90Lea-262
❑ 90M.Vpin-77
❑ 90MLBBasB-5
❑ 90OPC-515
❑ 90PanSti-313
❑ 90PhiTas-8
❑ 90PubIntS-131
❑ 90RedFolSB-28
❑ 90Sco-427
❑ 90ScoMcD-14
❑ 90Spo-156
❑ 90SupActM-18
❑ 90Top 515
❑ 90TopBig-300
❑ 90TopMag-32
❑ 90TopSti-118
❑ 90TopTif-515
❑ 90UppDec-472
❑ 90USPlaCA-9D
❑ 91BasBesHM-6
❑ 91Bow-501
❑ 91Cla1-T78
❑ 91ClaGam-133
❑ 91Col-8
❑ 91Don-7
❑ 91Don-410
❑ 91Don-434
❑ 91Don-523
❑ 91Don-744
❑ 91DonSupD-7
❑ 91Fle-395A
❑ 91Fle-395B
❑ 91Lea-163
❑ 91LeaPre-8
❑ 91MajLeaCP-60
❑ 91MetWIZ-102
❑ 91MooSna-18
❑ 91OPC-345
❑ 91PanCanT1-4
❑ 91PanCanT1-26
❑ 91PanFreS-108
❑ 91PanFreS-163
❑ 91PanSti-103
❑ 91PepSup-16
❑ 91PhiMed-13
❑ 91Pos-8
❑ 91PosCan-6
❑ 91RedFolS-30
❑ 91RedFolS-119
❑ 91Sco-250
❑ 91Sco-867
❑ 91Sco100S-11
❑ 91Sev3DCN-4
❑ 91SevCoi-NE4
❑ 91StaClu-150
❑ 91StaPinB-16
❑ 91Stu-213
❑ 91SunSee-9
❑ 91Top-345
❑ 91TopCraJl-21
❑ 91TopDesS-345
❑ 91TopGloA-18
❑ 91TopMic-345
❑ 91TopSta-12
❑ 91TopTif-345
❑ 91TopTriH-N8
❑ 91Ult-262
❑ 91UppDec-97
❑ 91UppDec-267
❑ 92Bow-635
❑ 92Cla1-T30
❑ 92Cla2-T51
❑ 92ClaGam-152
❑ 92Don-57
❑ 92DonCraJ2-13
❑ 92DonMcD-8
❑ 92Fle-529
❑ 92FleTeaL-10
❑ 92Hig5-77
❑ 92LaKdec-10
❑ 92Lea-504
❑ 92LeaBlaG-504
❑ 92MVPPin-38
❑ 92OPC-200
❑ 92OPCPre-184
❑ 92PanSti-247
❑ 92PhiMed-12
❑ 92Pin-12
❑ 92RedFolS-33
❑ 92Sco-560
❑ 92Sco100S-86
❑ 92ScoImpP-74
❑ 92SevCoi-8
❑ 92SpollIFK1-236
❑ 92SpoStaCC-13
❑ 92StaClu-470
❑ 92Stu-75
❑ 92Top-200
❑ 92TopGol-200
❑ 92TopGolW-200
❑ 92TopKid-17
❑ 92TopMic-200
❑ 92TriPla-94
❑ 92Ult-241
❑ 92UppDec-246
❑ 93Bow-300
❑ 93CadDis-18
❑ 93DiaMar-33
❑ 93Don-544
❑ 93Fin-177
❑ 93FinRef-177
❑ 93Fla-99
❑ 93Fle-488
❑ 93FunPac-144
❑ 93HumDumC-44
❑ 93Lea-59
❑ 93OPC-119
❑ 93PacSpa-235
❑ 93PanSti-274
❑ 93PhiMed-12
❑ 93PhiStaC-15
❑ 93Pin-45
❑ 93Pin-477
❑ 93RedFolS-27
❑ 93Sco-30
❑ 93Sel-59
❑ 93SP-173
❑ 93StaClu-477
❑ 93StaCluFDI-477
❑ 93StaCluMOP-477
❑ 93Stu-101
❑ 93Top-740
❑ 93TopGol-740
❑ 93TopInaM-740
❑ 93TopInaR-740
❑ 93TopMic-740
❑ 93TriPla-185
❑ 93Ult-439
❑ 93UppDec-69
❑ 93UppDec-485
❑ 93UppDecGold-69
❑ 93UppDecGold-485
❑ 94Bow-440
❑ 94BowBes-R47
❑ 94BowBesR-R47
❑ 94CarLeaA-DJ8
❑ 94ChuHomS-8
❑ 94ChuHomSG-8
❑ 94ColC-345
❑ 94ColC-369
❑ 94ColChoGS-345
❑ 94ColChoGS-369
❑ 94ColChoSS-345
❑ 94ColChoSS-369
❑ 94ColChoT-4
❑ 94DenHol-8
❑ 94Don-373
❑ 94DonDom-B9
❑ 94DonDomJ-B9
❑ 94DonMVP-10
❑ 94DonSpeE-373
❑ 94DonSpiotG-10
❑ 94DonSpiotGJ-10
❑ 94Fin-237
❑ 94FinJum-237
❑ 94FinRef-237
❑ 94Fla-205
❑ 94FlaOutP-4
❑ 94Fle-587
❑ 94FleExtB-332
❑ 94FleExtBGB-9
❑ 94FleLeaL-9
❑ 94FleSun-9
❑ 94FleTeaL-24
❑ 94FUnPac-69
❑ 94FUnPac-191
❑ 94KinDis-15
❑ 94Kra-20
❑ 94Lea-97
❑ 94LeaGam-2
❑ 94LeaGolS-5
❑ 94LeaL-136
❑ 94OPC-168
❑ 94OscMayR-20
❑ 94Pac-473
❑ 94PacSilP-33
❑ 94PacSilPC-33
❑ 94PanSti-226
❑ 94PhiMed-8
❑ 94PhiMel-6
❑ 94PhiUSPC-1H
❑ 94PhiUSPC-2C

❑ 94PhiUSPC-5S
❑ 94Pin-34
❑ 94PinArtP-34
❑ 94PinMusC-34
❑ 94PinRunC-RC24
❑ 94PinTeaP-6
❑ 94PinTheN-17
❑ 94PinTri-TR6
❑ 94Pos-20
❑ 94PosCan-16
❑ 94ProMag-102
❑ 94Sco-60
❑ 94Sco-624
❑ 94ScoCyc-TC8
❑ 94ScoGolR-60
❑ 94ScoGolR-624
❑ 94ScoGolS-17
❑ 94Sel-89
❑ 94SelCroC-CC1
❑ 94SelSam-CC1
❑ 94SelSki-SK3
❑ 94SP-135
❑ 94SPDieC-135
❑ 94Spo-1
❑ 94Spo-191
❑ 94SpoFanA-AS7
❑ 94SpoMov-MM12
❑ 94SpoSam-1
❑ 94StaClu-165
❑ 94StaCluFDI-165
❑ 94StaCluGR-165
❑ 94StaCluMO-13
❑ 94StaCluMOP-165
❑ 94StaCluT-211
❑ 94StaCluTF-3
❑ 94StaCluTFDI-211
❑ 94Stu-138
❑ 94Top-388
❑ 94Top-635
❑ 94TopBlaG-29
❑ 94TopGol-388
❑ 94TopGol-635
❑ 94TopSpa-388
❑ 94TopSpa-635
❑ 94TopSupS-12
❑ 94TriPla-173
❑ 94TriPlaM-12
❑ 94TriPlaP-8
❑ 94Ult-544
❑ 94UltAllS-17
❑ 94UltLeaL-7
❑ 94UltOnBL-3
❑ 94UppDec-172
❑ 94UppDecDC-E3
❑ 94UppDecED-172
❑ 95Baz-90
❑ 95Bow-366
❑ 95BowBes-R41
❑ 95BowBesR-R41
❑ 95ClaPhoC-44
❑ 95ColCho-365
❑ 95ColChoGS-365
❑ 95ColChoSE-170
❑ 95ColChoSEGS-170
❑ 95ColChoSESS-170
❑ 95ColChoSS-365
❑ 95Don-209
❑ 95DonDiaK-DK18
❑ 95DonPreP-209
❑ 95DonTopotO-302
❑ 95Emo-165
❑ 95Fin-92
❑ 95FinRef-92
❑ 95Fla-178
❑ 95Fle-390
❑ 95FleUpdH-8
❑ 95KinDis-7
❑ 95Kra-20
❑ 95Lea-141
❑ 95LeaLim-180
❑ 95Pac-328
❑ 95PacPri-107
❑ 95PanSti-72
❑ 95Phi-9
❑ 95PhiMel-7
❑ 95Pin-246
❑ 95PinArtP-246
❑ 95PinFan-26
❑ 95PinMusC-246
❑ 95Pos-15
❑ 95RedFol-29
❑ 95Sco-22
❑ 95ScoGolR-22
❑ 95ScoHaloG-HG21
❑ 95ScoPlaTS-22
❑ 95Sel-92
❑ 95SelArtP-92
❑ 95SelCer-60
❑ 95SelCerMG-60
❑ 95SP-87
❑ 95SPCha-78
❑ 95SPChaDC-78
❑ 95Spo-42
❑ 95SpoArtP-42
❑ 95SPSil-87
❑ 95StaClu-317
❑ 95StaClu-442
❑ 95StaCluCC-CC25
❑ 95StaCluMOP-317
❑ 95StaCluMOP-442
❑ 95StaCluMOP-CC25
❑ 95StaCluSTWS-317
❑ 95StaCluSTWS-442
❑ 95StaCluVR-233
❑ 95StaCluVRMO-233
❑ 95Stu-44
❑ 95StuGolS-44
❑ 95Sum-34
❑ 95SumNthD-34
❑ 95TomPiz-22
❑ 95Top-120
❑ 95TopCyb-76
❑ 95TopD3-56
❑ 95TopEmb-131
❑ 95TopEmbGI-131
❑ 95TopTra-162T
❑ 95UC3-63
❑ 95UC3ArtP-63
❑ 95Ult-203
❑ 95UltGolM-203
❑ 95UppDec-140
❑ 95UppDecED-140
❑ 95UppDecEDG-140
❑ 95UppDecSE-206
❑ 95UppDecSEG-206
❑ 95Zen-68
❑ 96Baz-10
❑ 96Bow-61
❑ 96BowBes-82
❑ 96BowBesAR-82
❑ 96BowBesR-82
❑ 96BowFoi-61
❑ 96ColCho-251
❑ 96ColChoGS-251
❑ 96ColChoSS-251
❑ 96Don-167
❑ 96DonPreP-167
❑ 96EmoXL-243
❑ 96Fin-B50
❑ 96FinRef-B50
❑ 96Fla-332
❑ 96Fle-495
❑ 96FleTif-495
❑ 96Lea-54
❑ 96LeaPre-82
❑ 96LeaPreP-82
❑ 96LeaPrePB-54
❑ 96LeaPrePG-54
❑ 96LeaPrePS-54
❑ 96LeaPreSG-30
❑ 96LeaPreSte-30
❑ 96LeaSig-97
❑ 96LeaSigPPG-97
❑ 96LeaSigPPP-97
❑ 96LibSpo-17
❑ 96MetUni-209
❑ 96MetUniP-209
❑ 96Pac-161
❑ 96PacPri-P52
❑ 96PacPriG-P52
❑ 96PanSti-33
❑ 96PhiTeal-9
❑ 96Pin-232
❑ 96PinAfi-53
❑ 96PinAfiAP-53
❑ 96PinAfiFPP-53
❑ 96PinArtP-132
❑ 96PinFoil-232
❑ 96PinSta-132
❑ 96RedF-5
❑ 96Sco-67
❑ 96ScoDugC-A57
❑ 96ScoDugCAP-A57
❑ 96Sel-144
❑ 96SelArtP-144
❑ 96SelCer-72
❑ 96SelCerAP-72
❑ 96SelCerCB-72
❑ 96SelCerCR-72
❑ 96SelCerMB-72
❑ 96SelCerMG-72
❑ 96SelCerMR-72
❑ 96SelTeaN-10
❑ 96SP-141
❑ 96Spo-17
❑ 96SpoArtP-17
❑ 96StaClu-17
❑ 96StaCluEPB-17
❑ 96StaCluEPG-17
❑ 96StaCluEPS-17
❑ 96StaCluMM-MM8
❑ 96StaCluMOP-17
❑ 96StaCluMOP-MM8
❑ 96Stu-126
❑ 96StuPrePB-126
❑ 96StuPrePG-126
❑ 96StuPrePS-126
❑ 96Sum-92
❑ 96SumAbo&B-92
❑ 96SumArtP-92
❑ 96SumFoi-92
❑ 96Top-261
❑ 96TopChr-104
❑ 96TopChrR-104
❑ 96TopGal-30
❑ 96TopGalPPI-30
❑ 96TopLas-104
❑ 96Ult-519
❑ 96UltGolM-519
❑ 96UppDec-430
❑ 96Zen-43
❑ 96ZenArtP-43
❑ 97ColCho-196
❑ 97Fle-409
❑ 97FleTif-409
❑ 97Pac-376
❑ 97PacLigB-376
❑ 97PacPri-128
❑ 97PacPriLB-128
❑ 97PacPriP-128
❑ 97PacSil-376
❑ 97Pin-66
❑ 97PinArtP-PP66
❑ 97PinMusC-66
❑ 97PinPrePla-66
❑ 97Sco-435
❑ 97ScoArtPWB-435
❑ 97ScoResC-435
❑ 97ScoShoS-435
❑ 97ScoShoSAP-435
❑ 97Top-413
❑ 97UppDec-453
❑ 98Pac-378
❑ 98PacInvTeam-21
❑ 98PacPlaB-378
❑ 98PacRedT-378
❑ 98PacSil-378
❑ 98Ult-441
❑ 98UltGolM-441
❑ 98UltMas-441
❑ 98UltPlaM-441
❑ 99DumSet-LD
❑ 99DumSet-LD

Dylar, Charles
❑ 20Zee-81

Dyson, Ted (Theodore Timothy)
❑ 88PalSprACLC-103
❑ 88PalSprAP-1453

Dyt, Darren
❑ 98JohCCTI-9

Dzafic, Bernie
❑ 88ElmPioC-5
❑ 89LynRedSS-27
❑ 89WinHavRSS-5
❑ 92WinHavRSF-1769
❑ 93NewBriRSF-1212
❑ 94LynRedSC-8
❑ 94LynRedSF-1886

Dziadkowiec, Andy
❑ 87MyrBeaBJP-1461
❑ 89DunBluJS-4
❑ 90CMC-351
❑ 90KnoBluJB-17
❑ 90KnoBluJS-3
❑ 90ProAAAF-353
❑ 90SyrChiC-25
❑ 90SyrChiP-573
❑ 91MiaMirC-17
❑ 91MiaMirP-411
❑ 92BinMetF-519
❑ 92BinMetS-56
❑ 93BinMetF-2336

Eaddy, Brad
❑ 94GreFalDSP-22
❑ 95BakBlaTI-12

Eaddy, Deon
❑ 98WilCubM-9

Eaddy, Don
❑ 77FriOneYW-54

Eaddy, Keith
❑ 92BluOriC-13
❑ 92BluOriF-2370
❑ 93AlbPolCB-13
❑ 93AlbPolF-2037
❑ 94FreKeyF-2627
❑ 94OriPro-28

Eady, Gerald
❑ 97EveAquG-8
❑ 98WisTimRM-21

Eagan, Truck (Charles)
❑ 09ColChiE-88
❑ 09ObaT21-68
❑ 12ColRedB-88
❑ 12ColTinT-88

Eagar, Brad
❑ 87AncGlaP-8
❑ 87BriYouC-18
❑ 89MedAthB-7

Eagar, Steve
❑ 86LakTigP-5

Eagelston, Chris
❑ 86HagSunP-6

Eagles, Brooklyn
❑ 93NegLeaRL2-81

Eagles, Carson Newman
❑ 89CarNewE-NNO

Eagles, Newark
❑ 91PomBlaBPB-4
❑ 92NegLeaRLI-97
❑ 93NegLeaRL2-82

Eaglin, Mike
❑ 93IdaFalBF-4039
❑ 93IdaFalBSP-7
❑ 94MacBraC-7
❑ 94MacBraF-2213
❑ 95MacBraTI-7
❑ 96CarLeaA1B-13
❑ 96CarLeaA2B-13
❑ 96DurBulBIB-29
❑ 96DurBulBrB-29
❑ 97GreBraG-8
❑ 98GreBraG-8

Eakes, Steven
❑ 82RedPioT-2
❑ 83RedPioT-9

Eakle, Jim
❑ 77PadSchC-20

Ealy, Tom (Thomas)
❑ 85EveGiaC-4
❑ 86CliGiaP-6
❑ 86TriTriC-200
❑ 87CliGiaP-12
❑ 88CliGiaP-718
❑ 89SanJosGB-14
❑ 89SanJosGCLC-231
❑ 89SanJosGP-434
❑ 89SanJosGS-8
❑ 90ShrCapP-1454
❑ 90ShrCapS-7
❑ 91LinDriAA-304
❑ 91ShrCapLD-304
❑ 91ShrCapP-1834
❑ 92LakTigC-23
❑ 92LakTigF-2290

Ealy, Tracey
❑ 90JohCitCS-10
❑ 91SavCarC-24
❑ 91SavCarP-1665
❑ 92EugEmeC-11
❑ 92EugEmeF-3042
❑ 93CliGiaC-9
❑ 93CliGiaF-2500
❑ 94SanJosGC-7
❑ 94SanJosGF-2828

Eaman, Bob
❑ 89LonTigP-1359

Earl, Scottie
❑ 83BirBarT-17
❑ 84EvaTriT-14
❑ 85Don-491
❑ 85NasSouTI-6
❑ 86NasSouTI-7
❑ 87TolMudHP-1
❑ 87TolMudHT-10
❑ 88NasSouC-19
❑ 88NasSouP-471
❑ 88NasSouTI-9
❑ 89BirBarADB-8
❑ 90BirBarADB-8

Earle, Billy (William)
❑ 87OldJudN-148
❑ 90DodTar-209

Earley, Arnie (Arnold Carl)
❑ 61SeaPop-5
❑ 67Top-388
❑ 78TCM60I-209
❑ 81RedSoxBG2S-18

Earley, Bill
❑ 83IowCubT-2
❑ 84IowCubT-2
❑ 85OklCit8T-30
❑ 86LouRedTI-12
❑ 87LouRedTI-13
❑ 88WytCubP-1989
❑ 89ChaWheB-24
❑ 89ChaWheP-1754
❑ 90WinSpiTI-28
❑ 91WinSpiC-21
❑ 91WinSpiP-2846
❑ 92ChaKniF-2787
❑ 92ChaKniS-175
❑ 93IowCubF-2149
❑ 94IowCubF-1291
❑ 95IowCubTI-11
❑ 96IowCubB-4

Early, Jake (Jacob Willard)
❑ 46SpoExcW-2-9
❑ 49Bow-106
❑ 49Lea-61
❑ 85TCMPla1-33
❑ 93ConTSN-749

Earnshaw, George (George L.)
❑ 30SchR33-13
❑ 30UncJac-8
❑ 31W517-8
❑ 32OrbPinNP-38
❑ 32OrbPinUP-17
❑ 32USCar*-29
❑ 33ButCre-6
❑ 33DouDisP-13
❑ 33RitCE-3H
❑ 33TatOrb-17
❑ 33TatOrbSDR-169
❑ 33WorCig-36
❑ 34BabRutG-18
❑ 34ButPreR-18
❑ 34ExhFou-10
❑ 34Gou-41
❑ 34GouCanV-93
❑ 35DiaMatCS3T1-49
❑ 35GouPuzR-1I
❑ 35GouPuzR-2F
❑ 35GouPuzR-16F
❑ 35GouPuzR-17F
❑ 36NatChiFPR-85
❑ 36R31PasP-28
❑ 40PlaBal-233
❑ 72TCMthe3-21
❑ 74A's192T-8
❑ 90DodTar-210
❑ 91ConTSN-88
❑ 94ConTSN-1137
❑ 94ConTSNB-1137
❑ 95ConTSN-1338

Easler, Mike (Michael A.)
❑ 75AstPos-8
❑ 75IowOakT-7
❑ 76TulOilGP-6
❑ 77ColCliT-4
❑ 78ColCliT-5
❑ 78Top-710
❑ 80Top-194
❑ 80VenLeaS-259
❑ 81AllGamPI-143
❑ 81CokTeaS-111
❑ 81Don-256
❑ 81Fle-372
❑ 81OPC-92
❑ 81Top-92
❑ 81TopScr-81
❑ 81TopSti-212
❑ 82Don-221
❑ 82Fle-481
❑ 82FleSta-74
❑ 82Kel-49
❑ 82OPC-235
❑ 82Top-235
❑ 82TopSti-84
❑ 83AllGamPI-144
❑ 83Don-221
❑ 83Fle-306
❑ 83FleSta-57
❑ 83FleSti-80
❑ 83OPC-385
❑ 83Top-385
❑ 84Don-444
❑ 84Fle-249
❑ 84FleUpd-33
❑ 84Nes792-589
❑ 84OPC-353
❑ 84Top-589
❑ 84TopSti-137
❑ 84TopTif-589
❑ 84TopTra-33T
❑ 84TopTraT-33T
❑ 85AllGamPI-55
❑ 85Don-213
❑ 85Fle-157
❑ 85FleStaS-46
❑ 85Lea-206
❑ 85OPC-349
❑ 85Top-686
❑ 85TopSti-213
❑ 85TopTif-686
❑ 86Don-395
❑ 86Fle-347
❑ 86FleUpd-37
❑ 86Top-477
❑ 86TopSti-255
❑ 86TopTat-21
❑ 86TopTif-477
❑ 86TopTra-33T
❑ 86TopTraT-33T
❑ 86YanTCM-45
❑ 87AstShowSTh-7
❑ 87Don-277
❑ 87DonOpeD-155
❑ 87Fle-97
❑ 87FleAll-7
❑ 87FleGlo-97
❑ 87Lea-192
❑ 87OPC-135
❑ 87PhiTas-34
❑ 87Spo-92
❑ 87Top-135
❑ 87TopSti-295
❑ 87TopTif-135
❑ 88Fle-206
❑ 88FleGlo-206
❑ 88OPC-9
❑ 88Sco-220
❑ 88ScoGlo-220
❑ 88StaLinY-4
❑ 88Top-741
❑ 88TopTif-741
❑ 89TopSenL-80
❑ 90EliSenL-19
❑ 90MiaMirIS-28
❑ 90MiaMirIS-26
❑ 92BrePol-30
❑ 92YanWIZ8-50
❑ 93RedSoxP-11

Easley, Damion
❑ 89BenBucL-16
❑ 90MidLeaASGS-31
❑ 90QuaCitAGS-24
❑ 91Cla/Bes-121
❑ 91LinDriAA-433
❑ 91MidAngLD-433
❑ 91MidAngOHP-10
❑ 91MidAngP-440
❑ 92Bow-672
❑ 92EdmTraF-3544
❑ 92EdmTraS-154
❑ 92FleUpd-9
❑ 92SkyAAAF-76
❑ 93AngAdoF-2
❑ 93AngMot-26
❑ 93AngPol-13
❑ 93AngStaCl-21
❑ 93Bow-257
❑ 93Don-457
❑ 93Fla-173
❑ 93Fle-189
❑ 93Lea-286
❑ 93OPC-104
❑ 93PacSpa-367
❑ 93PanSti-7
❑ 93Pin-227
❑ 93Sco-222
❑ 93Sel-328
❑ 93SP-22
❑ 93StaClu-6
❑ 93StaCluFDI-6
❑ 93StaCluMOP-6
❑ 93Stu-142
❑ 93Top-184
❑ 93TopGol-184
❑ 93TopInaM-184

❑ 93TopInaR-184
❑ 93TopMic-184
❑ 93Toy-43
❑ 93TriPla-103
❑ 93Ult-161
❑ 93UppDec-377
❑ 93UppDecGold-377
❑ 94AngLAT-18
❑ 94Bow-563
❑ 94ColC-505
❑ 94ColChoGS-505
❑ 94ColChoSS-505
❑ 94Don-112
❑ 94Fin-332
❑ 94FinRef-332
❑ 94Fla-269
❑ 94Fle-53
❑ 94FleExtB-33
❑ 94Lea-86
❑ 94OPC-9
❑ 94Pac-76
❑ 94PanSti-37
❑ 94Pin-340
❑ 94PinArtP-340
❑ 94PinMusC-340
❑ 94Sco-17
❑ 94ScoGolR-17
❑ 94Sel-222
❑ 94StaClu-124
❑ 94StaCluFDI-124
❑ 94StaCluGR-124
❑ 94StaCluMOP-124
❑ 94Stu-11
❑ 94Top-418
❑ 94TopGol-418
❑ 94TopSpa-418
❑ 94TriPla-14
❑ 94Ult-326
❑ 94UppDec-66
❑ 94UppDecED-66
❑ 95AngCHP-5
❑ 95AngMot-20
❑ 95ColCho-96
❑ 95ColChoGS-96
❑ 95ColChoSS-96
❑ 95Don-7
❑ 95DonPreP-7
❑ 95DonTopotO-34
❑ 95Fle-222
❑ 95Lea-4
❑ 95Pac-57
❑ 95PacLatD-10
❑ 95Sco-447
❑ 95ScoGolR-447
❑ 95ScoPlaTS-447
❑ 95StaClu-325
❑ 95StaCluMOP-325
❑ 95StaCluSTWS-325
❑ 95Top-306
❑ 95Ult-20
❑ 95UltGolM-20
❑ 96Don-403
❑ 96DonPreP-403
❑ 96Fle-45
❑ 96FleTif-45
❑ 96Pac-272
❑ 96PacPri-P84
❑ 96PacPriG-P84
❑ 97ColCho-339
❑ 97Fle-672
❑ 97FleTif-672
❑ 97Sco-439
❑ 97ScoArtPWB-439
❑ 97ScoResC-439
❑ 97ScoShoS-439
❑ 97ScoShoSAP-439
❑ 97Ult-330
❑ 97UltGolME-330
❑ 97UltPlaME-330
❑ 98CirThu-102
❑ 98CirThuRav-102
❑ 98CirThuSupRav-102
❑ 98ColCho-369
❑ 98CroRoy-55
❑ 98Don-182
❑ 98DonGolPP-182
❑ 98DonSilPP-182
❑ 98Fin-116
❑ 98FinNo--116
❑ 98FinNo-R-116
❑ 98FinRef-116
❑ 98Fle-76
❑ 98MetUni-48
❑ 98MetUniPMG-48
❑ 98Pac-87
❑ 98PacOnl-271
❑ 98PacOnlR-271
❑ 98PacOnlWC-271
❑ 98PacPlaB-87
❑ 98PacRedT-87
❑ 98PacSil-87
❑ 98Pin-103
❑ 98PinPreP-103
❑ 98Revo-57
❑ 98RevoSS-57
❑ 98SP Aut-89
❑ 98SPxFin-272
❑ 98SPxFinR-272
❑ 98SPxFinS-272
❑ 98StaCluFDI-297
❑ 98StaCluI-297
❑ 98StaCluOneK-297
❑ 98StaCluPP-297
❑ 98Top-147
❑ 98TopChr-147
❑ 98TopChrR-147
❑ 98TopDevR-147
❑ 98TopDia-147
❑ 98TopGolLabC1-40
❑ 98TopGolLabC1B-40
❑ 98TopGolLabC1One-40
❑ 98TopGolLabC1R-40
❑ 98TopGolLabC2-40
❑ 98TopGolLabC2B-40
❑ 98TopGolLabC2One-40
❑ 98TopGolLabC2R-40
❑ 98TopGolLabC3-40
❑ 98TopGolLabC3B-40
❑ 98TopGolLabC3One-40
❑ 98TopGolLabC3R-40
❑ 98TopMiniC-147
❑ 98TopOpeD-76
❑ 98Ult-163
❑ 98UltGolM-163
❑ 98UltMas-163
❑ 98UltPlaM-163
❑ 98UppDec-84
❑ 98UppDecR-36
❑ 98UppDecSF-52
❑ 99199Fin-63
❑ 99CroRoyB-52
❑ 99CroRoyL-52
❑ 99CroRoyOD-52
❑ 99FinGolRef-63
❑ 99FinRef-63
❑ 99FlaShoLeg1-82
❑ 99FlaShoLeg2-82
❑ 99FlaShoLeg3-82
❑ 99FlaShoLegM1-82
❑ 99FlaShoLegM2-82
❑ 99FlaShoLegM3-82
❑ 99FlaShoR1-82
❑ 99FlaShoR2-82
❑ 99FlaShoR3-82
❑ 99Fle-103
❑ 99FleBri-36
❑ 99FleBri2G-36
❑ 99FleBriBlu-36
❑ 99FleBriGol-36
❑ 99FleSta9-103
❑ 99FleWarT-103
❑ 99MetUni-219
❑ 99MetUniGM-219
❑ 99MetUniPMG-219
❑ 99Pac-162
❑ 99PacAur-66
❑ 99PacAurOD-66
❑ 99PacCroC-107
❑ 99PacCroCPB-107
❑ 99PacInv-55
❑ 99PacInvOD-55
❑ 99PacInvPB-55
❑ 99PacOme-88
❑ 99PacOmeC-88
❑ 99PacOmeG-88
❑ 99PacOmePB-88
❑ 99PacPar-88
❑ 99PacParC-88
❑ 99PacParG-88
❑ 99PacParHoloGold-88
❑ 99PacParHS-88
❑ 99PacParOD-88
❑ 99PacParPB-88
❑ 99PacParRed-88
❑ 99PacParTC-11
❑ 99PacPlaB-162
❑ 99PacPri-56
❑ 99PacPriHB-56
❑ 99PacPriHG-56
❑ 99PacPriHM-56
❑ 99PacPriHP-56
❑ 99PacPriRed-56
❑ 99PacPriS-84
❑ 99PacPriS206-84
❑ 99PacPriS206R-84
❑ 99PacRedB-162
❑ 99PacTeaC-6
❑ 99Rev-54
❑ 99RevPremDate-54
❑ 99RevRet-54
❑ 99RevShaSS-54
❑ 99SkyPre-192
❑ 99SkyPreA-15
❑ 99SkyPreABlue-15
❑ 99SkyPreR-192
❑ 99SkyThu-75
❑ 99SkyThuRant-75
❑ 99SkyThuRave-75
❑ 99SP SigAuto-DEA
❑ 99SpoIll-165
❑ 99SPSig-145
❑ 99StaClu-222
❑ 99StaCluFDI-222
❑ 99StaCluOoaK-222
❑ 99StaCluPP-222
❑ 99ThuSkySupR-75
❑ 99Top-73
❑ 99TopChr-73
❑ 99TopChrR-73
❑ 99TopMVPP-73
❑ 99TopOpeD-41
❑ 99TopSta-149
❑ 99TopStaFoil-149
❑ 99UD Cho-86
❑ 99UD ChoP-86
❑ 99UD ChoPCR-86
❑ 99Ult-147
❑ 99UltGolM-147
❑ 99UltMas-147
❑ 99UltPlaM-147
❑ 99UppDec-95
❑ 99UppDecBD-33
❑ 99UppDecBDD-33
❑ 99UppDecBDQ-33
❑ 99UppDecBDT-33
❑ 99UppDecEL1-95
❑ 99UppDecEL2-95
❑ 99UppDecM-79
❑ 99UppDecMGS-79
❑ 99UppDecMHFS-79
❑ 99UppDecMP-79
❑ 99UppDecMSS-79
❑ 99Vic-147

Easley, Logan
❑ 83GreHorT-5
❑ 85AlbYanT-5
❑ 86AlbYanT-17
❑ 86AlbYanT-32
❑ 88BufBisC-1
❑ 88BufBisP-1490
❑ 90AlbDecGB-5
❑ 90DenZepP-619
❑ 90ProAAAF-644

Easley, Mike
❑ 90RenSilSCLC-266
❑ 91CarLeaAP-CAR12
❑ 91KinIndC-15
❑ 91KinIndP-327
❑ 92ShrCapF-3881
❑ 92ShrCapS-583

Eason, Greg
❑ 80AshTouT-26

Eason, Mal
❑ 90DodTar-939
❑ 92ConTSN-375

Eason, R. Clay
❑ 97BatCliTI-12
❑ 98PieBolWM-10

Eason, Samuel
❑ 95ReaPhiTI-13

Eason, Tommy
❑ 91BatCliCB-3
❑ 91BatCliP-3485
❑ 92ClaFS7-263
❑ 92SpaPhiF-1265
❑ 93ClaGolF-135
❑ 93ExcFS7-84
❑ 94ClePhiC-13
❑ 94ClePhiF-2535
❑ 95ReaPhiELC-11
❑ 96Exc-199

Easter, Dick
❑ 84IowCubT-4

Easter, Luke (Luscious Luke)
❑ 47Exh-66
❑ 47PM1StaP1-54
❑ 50IndNumN-8
❑ 50IndTeal-8
❑ 51Bow-258
❑ 51IndHag-3
❑ 51TopRedB-26
❑ 52Bow-95
❑ 52IndNumN-12
❑ 52Top-24
❑ 53BowC-104
❑ 53ExhCan-2
❑ 53IndPenCBP-10
❑ 53Top-2
❑ 54Bow-116
❑ 54DanDee-5
❑ 54Top-23
❑ 63RocRedWSP-6
❑ 75TCM195CI-6
❑ 79TCM50-80
❑ 83TopRep5-24
❑ 86NegLeaF-83
❑ 91TopArc1-2
❑ 92BazQua5A-6
❑ 94TopArc1-23
❑ 94TopArc1G-23

Easterly, Jamie (James M.)
❑ 75AtlBraP-9
❑ 75OPC-618
❑ 75Top-618
❑ 75TopMin-618
❑ 76OPC-511
❑ 76Top-511
❑ 76VenLeaS-179
❑ 78Top-264
❑ 79RicBraT-11
❑ 79Top-684
❑ 82BrePol-28
❑ 82Don-623
❑ 82Fle-139
❑ 82Top-122
❑ 83BrePol-28
❑ 83Don-280
❑ 83Fle-31
❑ 83Top-528
❑ 83TopTra-28T
❑ 84Fle-538
❑ 84Ind-11
❑ 84IndWhe-36
❑ 84Nes792-367
❑ 84Top-367
❑ 84TopSti-258
❑ 84TopTif-367
❑ 85Fle-445
❑ 85Ind-12
❑ 85IndPol-36
❑ 85Top-764
❑ 85TopTif-764
❑ 86Don-582
❑ 86Fle-585
❑ 86IndOhH-36
❑ 86IndTeal-19
❑ 86Top-31
❑ 86TopTif-31
❑ 87IndGat-11
❑ 89PacSenL-189
❑ 89T/MSenL-31
❑ 90EliSenL-54
❑ 94BreMilB-17

Easterly, Ted (Theodore H.)
❑ 09T206-117
❑ 11PinT-5-610
❑ 12T207-53
❑ 14CraJacE-117
❑ 15CraJacE-117
❑ 18Zee-40

Easterwood, Roy
❑ 44CubTeal-6

Eastley, Frank
❑ 09ObaT21-50
❑ 09ObaT21-157
❑ 19Zee-112

Eastman, Doug
❑ 88CedRapRP-1153
❑ 89CedRapRB-20
❑ 89CedRapRP-923
❑ 89CedRapRS-5

Easton, Eric
❑ 98ButCopKG-11

Eastwick, Rawly (Rawlins J.)
❑ 75OPC-621
❑ 75Top-621
❑ 75TopMin-621
❑ 76OPC-469
❑ 76RedIceL-3
❑ 76RedKro-7
❑ 76Top-469
❑ 77Car5-7
❑ 77OPC-8
❑ 77OPC-140
❑ 77PepGloD-55
❑ 77Top-8
❑ 77Top-45
❑ 78Top-405
❑ 78YanBurK-11
❑ 79BasPat-26
❑ 79Top-271
❑ 80Top-692
❑ 82Fle-596
❑ 82Top-117
❑ 92YanWIZ7-47

Eatinger, Michael
❑ 90Bes-222
❑ 90MidLeaASGS-10
❑ 90SouBenWSB-18
❑ 90SouBenWSGS-3
❑ 92SarWhiSCB-9
❑ 92SarWhiSF-213

Eaton, Adam
❑ 97BesLimA-10
❑ 97Bow-363
❑ 97BowChr-243
❑ 97BowChrI-243
❑ 97BowChrIR-243
❑ 97BowChrR-243
❑ 97BowInt-363
❑ 97PieBolWB-12
❑ 97Top-479
❑ 98BesPreA-10
❑ 98Bow-116
❑ 98BowChr-116
❑ 98BowChrGA-116
❑ 98BowChrGAR-116
❑ 98BowChrI-116
❑ 98BowChrIR-116
❑ 98BowChrR-116
❑ 98BowGolA-116
❑ 98BowInt-116
❑ 98ClePhiM-6
❑ 98ClePhiUM-6
❑ 99SP TopP-42
❑ 99SP TopPPE-42

Eaton, Craig
❑ 76WatRoyT-7
❑ 77DayBealT-4
❑ 80SalLakCGT-3
❑ 80VenLeaS-125
❑ 81SalLakCGT-4
❑ 82SpoIndT-2
❑ 83EvaTriT-2
❑ 84IndIndTI-8

Eaton, Dann
❑ 91SprCarC-14
❑ 91SprCarP-736

Eaton, Tommy
❑ 80ChaO'sP-6
❑ 80ChaO'sW-6
❑ 81RocRedWT-5
❑ 81RocRedWW-19

Eave, Gary
❑ 87DurBulP-19
❑ 88BobCamRB-18
❑ 88RicBraC-5
❑ 88RicBraP-26
❑ 89RicBraBC-5
❑ 89RicBraC-2
❑ 89RicBraP-828
❑ 89RicBraTI-6
❑ 90Bow-471
❑ 90BowTif-471
❑ 90Don-713
❑ 90Sco-621
❑ 91JacSunLD-333
❑ 91JacSunP-143
❑ 91LinDriAA-333

Eaves, Dan
❑ 94FreKeyC-28

Ebanks, Weddison
❑ 90EugEmeGS-6

Ebbert, Chad
❑ 96CliLumKTI-11
❑ 96IdaFalB-7

Ebbetts, Charlie
❑ 90DodTar-940

Ebel, Brian
❑ 89HagSunB-16
❑ 89HagSunP-284

Ebel, Dino
❑ 89VerBeaDS-8
❑ 90VerBeaDS-12
❑ 91AdeGiaF-7
❑ 91BakDodCLC-19
❑ 91SanAntMP-2981
❑ 92BakDodCLC-31
❑ 93BakDodCLC-30
❑ 94BakDodC-29
❑ 95SanBerSTI-29
❑ 96SanAntMB-28
❑ 97SanBerS-3
❑ 98GreFalDG-11

Eberle, Greg
❑ 89PeoChiTI-27

Eberle, Mike
❑ 87NewOriP-24
❑ 88CarLeaAS-7
❑ 88HagSunS-4
❑ 89HagSunB-12
❑ 89HagSunP-270
❑ 89HagSunS-6
❑ 90Bes-199
❑ 90HagSunB-4
❑ 90HagSunP-1415
❑ 90HagSunS-8
❑ 91LinDriAAA-455
❑ 91RocRedWLD-455
❑ 91RocRedWP-1905

Eberly, Ryan
❑ 90TamYanD-4

Ebersberger, Randy
❑ 82CliGiaF-24

Ebert, Derrin
❑ 95MacBraTI-8
❑ 95MacBraUTI-2
❑ 96BesAutS-30
❑ 96DurBulBIB-6
❑ 96DurBulBrB-7
❑ 96Exc-125
❑ 97GreBraG-9
❑ 97TexAllM-35
❑ 98RicBraQ-11
❑ 99SkyPreA-16
❑ 99SkyPreABlue-16

Ebert, Scott
❑ 88PocGiaP-2080
❑ 89EveGiaS-7
❑ 90CliGiaUTI-U3
❑ 90EveGiaP-3118

Eberwein, Kevin
❑ 99Bow-405
❑ 99BowGol-405
❑ 99BowInt-405

Ebright, Chris
❑ 88CapCodPPaLP-33
❑ 88OklSoo-3
❑ 89GenCubP-1876
❑ 89OklSoo-14
❑ 90PeoChiTI-16
❑ 91CarLeaAP-CAR41
❑ 91WinSpiC-23
❑ 91WinSpiP-3840
❑ 92ChaKniF-2778
❑ 92ChaKniS-154
❑ 92SkyAA F-71
❑ 93OrlCubF-2790

Ebright, Hi (Hiram C.)
❑ 87OldJudN-149

Eby, Michael
❑ 96FayGenB-13

Eccles, John
❑ 85AncGlaPTI-9
❑ 87OrlTwiP-4
❑ 88CalLeaACLC-38
❑ 88VisOakCLC-150
❑ 88VisOakP-84
❑ 89OrlTwiP-1351
❑ 90OrlSunRB-2
❑ 90OrlSunRP-1086
❑ 90OrlSunRS-4

Eccleston, Tom
❑ 86WauTimP-9
❑ 87SalSpuS-14

Echemendia, Bert (Idaiberto)
❑ 88JamExpP-1906
❑ 89Sta-33
❑ 89WesPalBES-10

Echenique, O.
❑ 80VenLeaS-194

Echevarria, Angel
❑ 92BenRocCB-10
❑ 92BenRocF-1485
❑ 93CenValRC-8
❑ 93CenValRF-2904
❑ 94Bow-610
❑ 94CenValRC-5
❑ 94CenValRF-3214
❑ 95NewHavRTI-29
❑ 96ColSprSSTI-12

❑ 96Exc-152
❑ 96Top-439
❑ 97ColSprSTI-5
❑ 97DonLim-59
❑ 97DonLimE-59
❑ 97DonLimENG-59
❑ 97Lea-169
❑ 97LeaFraM-169
❑ 97LeaFraMDC-169
❑ 97StaClu-194
❑ 97StaCluMOP-194
❑ 98ColSprSS-11

Echevarria, Francisco
❑ 84EveGiaC-17

Echevarria, Robert
❑ 87ElmPioBC-7
❑ 87ElmPioRC-7

Echeverria, Phil
❑ 90AriWilP-3
❑ 92AriWilP-3

Echols, Mandell
❑ 95HudValRTI-8

Echols, Tony
❑ 76WauMetT-12

Echols, Tracy
❑ 89MisStaB-10
❑ 90MisStaB-9

Eckard, Paul
❑ 91EveGiaC-29

Eckelman, Alex
❑ 97JohCitCTI-8
❑ 98PeoChiM-5
❑ 99BasAmeTP-40
❑ 99BasAmeTPG-40

Eckersley, Dennis (Dennis Lee)
❑ 76Hos-137
❑ 76IndTeal-3
❑ 76Kel-19
❑ 76OPC-98
❑ 76OPC-202
❑ 76SSP-506
❑ 76Top-98
❑ 76Top-202
❑ 77BurCheD-58
❑ 77ChiWilD-18
❑ 77DailsID-18
❑ 77DetCaeD-18
❑ 77HollnnD-18
❑ 77Hos-106
❑ 77IndTeal-9
❑ 77MSADis-18
❑ 77OPC-15
❑ 77PepGloD-13
❑ 77SagDis-18
❑ 77sDis-18
❑ 77Spo-5007
❑ 77Spo-8415
❑ 77Top-525
❑ 77WenDis-18
❑ 77ZipDis-18
❑ 78Hos-78
❑ 78OPC-138
❑ 78PapGinD-5
❑ 78SSP270-178
❑ 78Top-122
❑ 78WifBalD-20
❑ 79Hos-145
❑ 79Kel-9
❑ 79OPC-16
❑ 79RedSoxTI-2
❑ 79Top-40
❑ 80OPC-169
❑ 80Top-320
❑ 81AllGamPI-77
❑ 81CokTeaS-2
❑ 81Don-96
❑ 81Fle-226
❑ 81FleStiC-34
❑ 81OPC-109
❑ 81Top-620
❑ 81TopSti-48
❑ 81TopSupHT-2
❑ 82Don-30
❑ 82Fle-292
❑ 82FleSta-165
❑ 82OPC-287
❑ 82PerAll-1
❑ 82PerAllG-1
❑ 82RedSoxC-5
❑ 82Top-490
❑ 83AllGamPI-76
❑ 83Don-487
❑ 83Fle-182
❑ 83Fle-629
❑ 83FleSta-58
❑ 83FleSti-63
❑ 83OPC-270
❑ 83Top-270
❑ 83TopSti-34
❑ 84CubChiT-11
❑ 84CubSev-43
❑ 84Don-639
❑ 84Fle-396
❑ 84FleUpd-34
❑ 84Nes792-745
❑ 84OPC-218
❑ 84Top-745
❑ 84TopSti-224
❑ 84TopTif-745
❑ 84TopTra-34T
❑ 84TopTraT-34T
❑ 85AllGamPI-168
❑ 85CubLioP-10
❑ 85CubSev-43
❑ 85Don-442
❑ 85Fle-57
❑ 85OPC-163
❑ 85Top-163
❑ 85TopTif-163
❑ 86BasStaB-38
❑ 86CubGat-43
❑ 86CubUno-8
❑ 86Don-239
❑ 86Fle-368
❑ 86Lea-113
❑ 86OPC-199
❑ 86Spo-129
❑ 86Top-538
❑ 86TopSti-62
❑ 86TopTat-2
❑ 86TopTif-538
❑ 87Don-365
❑ 87Fle-563
❑ 87FleGlo-563
❑ 87FleUpd-30
❑ 87FleUpdG-30
❑ 87OPC-381
❑ 87SevCoi-C8
❑ 87SpoTeaP-22
❑ 87Top-459
❑ 87TopSti-63
❑ 87TopTif-459
❑ 87TopTra-31T
❑ 87TopTraT-31T
❑ 88A'sMot-10
❑ 88Don-349
❑ 88DonBasB-43
❑ 88DonTeaBA-349
❑ 88Fle-279
❑ 88FleGlo-279
❑ 88FleSlu-13
❑ 88OPC-72
❑ 88Sco-104
❑ 88ScoGlo-104
❑ 88StaLinAs-4
❑ 88TarPla-13
❑ 88Top-72
❑ 88TopSti-170
❑ 88TopTif-72
❑ 89A'sMot-10
❑ 89Bow-190
❑ 89BowTif-190
❑ 89CadEllD-16
❑ 89ClaLigB-90
❑ 89Don-67
❑ 89DonAll-16
❑ 89DonBasB-134
❑ 89Fle-7
❑ 89FleAll-4
❑ 89FleBasA-12
❑ 89FleGlo-7
❑ 89FleHeroB-13
❑ 89OPC-370
❑ 89PanSti-12
❑ 89PanSti-414
❑ 89RedFolSB-39
❑ 89Sco-276
❑ 89ScoHot1S-16
❑ 89Spo-101
❑ 89Spo-222
❑ 89SpollIFKI-197
❑ 89Top-370
❑ 89TopBasT-128
❑ 89TopDouA-11
❑ 89TopGaloC-4
❑ 89TopGloS-16
❑ 89TopHilTM-12
❑ 89TopMinL-69
❑ 89TopSti-167
❑ 89TopStiB-31
❑ 89TopTif-370
❑ 89TopUKM-23
❑ 89TVSpoM-96
❑ 89UppDec-289
❑ 89UppDec-664
❑ 89Woo-20
❑ 90A'sMot-7
❑ 90Bow-451
❑ 90BowTif-451
❑ 90Don-210
❑ 90DonBesA-12
❑ 90Fle-6
❑ 90FleCan-6
❑ 90FleLeaL-11
❑ 90FleLeaLC-11
❑ 90K-M-29
❑ 90KayB-9
❑ 90Lea-29
❑ 90LeaPre-3
❑ 90M.Vpin-73
❑ 90MLBBasB-75
❑ 90OPC-670
❑ 90PanSti-137
❑ 90PublntS-282
❑ 90PublntS-303
❑ 90RedFolSB-29
❑ 90Sco-315
❑ 90Spo-170
❑ 90Top-670
❑ 90TopBig-50
❑ 90TopDou-19
❑ 90TopGloS-53
❑ 90TopHeaU-4
❑ 90TopMinL-27
❑ 90TopSti-182
❑ 90TopStiB-64
❑ 90TopTif-670
❑ 90TopTVA-13
❑ 90UppDec-513
❑ 90USPlaCA-8C
❑ 91A'sMot-7
❑ 91A'sSFE-3
❑ 91BasBesAotM-6
❑ 91Bow-237
❑ 91Cla2-T18
❑ 91ClaGam-126
❑ 91Don-270
❑ 91Fle-6
❑ 91Lea-285
❑ 91OPC-250
❑ 91OPCPre-38
❑ 91PanCanT1-86
❑ 91PanFreS-200
❑ 91PanSti-148
❑ 91RedFolS-31
❑ 91Sco-485
❑ 91Sco100S-73
❑ 91SevCoi-NC5
❑ 91StaClu-332
❑ 91Stu-102
❑ 91Top-250
❑ 91TopDesS-250
❑ 91TopMic-250
❑ 91TopTif-250
❑ 91Ult-245
❑ 91UppDec-172
❑ 91USPlaCA-10D
❑ 92AthMot-7
❑ 92Bow-431
❑ 92ClaGam-8
❑ 92ColAllG-17
❑ 92ColAllP-17
❑ 92Don-147
❑ 92DonCraJ1-1
❑ 92DonPre-5
❑ 92Fle-255
❑ 92Hig5-103
❑ 92Hig5S-9
❑ 92Lea-100
❑ 92LeaBlaG-100
❑ 92OPC-738
❑ 92OPCPre-188
❑ 92PanSti-22
❑ 92PepDieM-7
❑ 92Pin-25
❑ 92PinTeaP-11
❑ 92Sco-190
❑ 92Sco100S-56
❑ 92SpollIFK1-152
❑ 92StaClu-190
❑ 92StaCluD-42
❑ 92Stu-223
❑ 92Top-738
❑ 92TopGol-738
❑ 92TopGolW-738
❑ 92TopKid-119
❑ 92TopMic-738
❑ 92TriPla-195
❑ 92Ult-421
❑ 92UppDec-331
❑ 92UppDecTMH-19
❑ 93AthMot-4
❑ 93AthStaC-1
❑ 93Bow-485
❑ 93ClaGam-27
❑ 93DiaMar-34
❑ 93DiaMarP-3
❑ 93Don-215
❑ 93Don-396
❑ 93DonEli-25
❑ 93DonEliS-7
❑ 93DonPre-19
❑ 93DonSpiotG-SG4
❑ 93DurPowP2-23
❑ 93Fin-100
❑ 93FinJum-100
❑ 93FinRef-100
❑ 93Fla-257
❑ 93Fle-293
❑ 93Fle-717
❑ 93FleAtl-7
❑ 93FleFruotL-18
❑ 93FleGolM-B1
❑ 93FlePro-A2
❑ 93FunPac-49
❑ 93Hos-11
❑ 93Kra-6
❑ 93Lea-72
❑ 93LeaGolA-R10
❑ 93MetBak-25
❑ 93MSABenSPD-1
❑ 93OPC-106
❑ 93OPCPreSP-22
❑ 93OPCPreSPF-22
❑ 93PacSpa-221
❑ 93PanSti-13
❑ 93PanSti-157
❑ 93PanSti-161
❑ 93PanSti-162
❑ 93Pin-100
❑ 93Pin-474
❑ 93PinCoo-6
❑ 93PinCooD-6
❑ 93RedFolS-112
❑ 93Sco-21
❑ 93Sco-481
❑ 93Sco-483
❑ 93Sco-509
❑ 93Sco-513
❑ 93Sco-540
❑ 93ScoFra-11
❑ 93ScoGolDT-9
❑ 93Sel-38
❑ 93SelChaS-24
❑ 93SelDufIP-4
❑ 93SelStaL-67
❑ 93SP-38
❑ 93StaClu-291
❑ 93StaClu-461
❑ 93StaCluFDI-291
❑ 93StaCluFDI-461
❑ 93StaCluM-179
❑ 93StaCluMOP-291
❑ 93StaCluMOP-461
❑ 93Stu-1
❑ 93Top-155
❑ 93Top-411
❑ 93TOPBLAG-29
❑ 93TopComotH-1
❑ 93TopGol-155
❑ 93TopGol-411
❑ 93ToplnaM-155
❑ 93ToplnaM-411
❑ 93ToplnaR-155
❑ 93ToplnaR-411
❑ 93TopMagJRC-1
❑ 93TopMic-155
❑ 93TopMic-411
❑ 93TopMic-P155
❑ 93TriPla-9
❑ 93TriPlaLL-L1
❑ 93TriPlaLL-L2
❑ 93TriPlaP-9
❑ 93Ult-257
❑ 93UltAwaW-23
❑ 93UltEck-1
❑ 93UltEck-2
❑ 93UltEck-3
❑ 93UltEck-4
❑ 93UltEck-5
❑ 93UltEck-6
❑ 93UltEck-7
❑ 93UltEck-8
❑ 93UltEck-9
❑ 93UltEck-10
❑ 93UltEck-11
❑ 93UltEck-12
❑ 93UltEck-P1
❑ 93UltEck-AU0
❑ 93UppDec-271
❑ 93UppDec-487
❑ 93UppDec-489
❑ 93UppDec-814
❑ 93UppDecCP-R8
❑ 93UppDecGold-271
❑ 93UppDecGold-487
❑ 93UppDecGold-489
❑ 93UppDecGold-814
❑ 93UppDecOD-D10
❑ 93UppDecTAN-TN10
❑ 94A'sMot-4
❑ 94Bow-520
❑ 94ColC-495
❑ 94ColChoGS-495
❑ 94ColChoSS-495
❑ 94Don-16
❑ 94DonSpeE-16
❑ 94Fin-206
❑ 94FinJum-206
❑ 94FinRef-206
❑ 94Fla-91
❑ 94Fle-260
❑ 94FleExtB-148
❑ 94FUnPac-43
❑ 94KinDis-8
❑ 94Kra-2
❑ 94Lea-234
❑ 94LeaL-59
❑ 94OPC-144
❑ 94Pac-448
❑ 94PanSti-108
❑ 94Pin-32
❑ 94PinArtP-32
❑ 94PinMusC-32
❑ 94ProMag-96
❑ 94RedFolMI-18
❑ 94Sco-109
❑ 94ScoGolR-109
❑ 94Sel-245
❑ 94Spo-50
❑ 94StaClu-125
❑ 94StaCluFDI-125
❑ 94StaCluGR-125
❑ 94StaCluMOP-125
❑ 94StaCluP-125
❑ 94Stu-1
❑ 94Top-465
❑ 94TopGol-465
❑ 94TopSpa-465
❑ 94TriPla-2
❑ 94Ult-407
❑ 94UltFir-5
❑ 94UppDec-365
❑ 94UppDecED-365
❑ 95AthMot-4
❑ 95Baz-21
❑ 95Bow-426
❑ 95BowBes-R58
❑ 95BowBesR-R58
❑ 95ColCho-134
❑ 95ColChoGS-134
❑ 95ColChoSE-44
❑ 95ColChoSEGS-44
❑ 95ColChoSESS-44
❑ 95ColChoSS-134
❑ 95Don-511
❑ 95DonPreP-511
❑ 95DonTopotO-135
❑ 95Emo-70
❑ 95Fin-155
❑ 95FinRef-155
❑ 95Fla-293
❑ 95Fle-244
❑ 95FleTeaL-11
❑ 95FleUpdDT-5
❑ 95Lea-352
❑ 95LeaLim-109
❑ 95Pac-311
❑ 95Pin-251
❑ 95PinArtP-251
❑ 95PinMusC-251
❑ 95RedFol-28
❑ 95Sco-408
❑ 95ScoGolR-408
❑ 95ScoHaloG-HG87
❑ 95ScoPlaTS-408
❑ 95Sel-140
❑ 95SelArtP-140
❑ 95SP-187
❑ 95SPCha-104
❑ 95SPCha-182
❑ 95SPChaDC-104
❑ 95SPChaDC-182
❑ 95Spo-116
❑ 95SpoArtP-116
❑ 95SPSil-187
❑ 95StaClu-72
❑ 95StaCluFDI-72
❑ 95StaCluMOP-72
❑ 95StaCluMOP-RL16
❑ 95StaCluRL-RL16
❑ 95StaCluSTWS-72
❑ 95StaCluVR-45
❑ 95StaCluVRMO-45
❑ 95Stu-129
❑ 95Sum-99
❑ 95SumNthD-99
❑ 95Top-45
❑ 95TopCyb-34
❑ 95TopD3-11
❑ 95UC3-52
❑ 95UC3ArtP-52
❑ 95Ult-316
❑ 95UltGolM-316
❑ 95UppDec-34
❑ 95UppDecED-34
❑ 95UppDecEDG-34
❑ 95UppDecSE-243
❑ 95UppDecSEG-243
❑ 95UppDecSoaD-SD9
❑ 95Zen-27
❑ 96Baz-42
❑ 96Bow-64
❑ 96BowFoi-64
❑ 96CarPol-5
❑ 96ColCho-245
❑ 96ColChoGS-245
❑ 96ColChoSS-245
❑ 96Don-406
❑ 96DonPreP-406
❑ 96EmoXL-264
❑ 96Fin-G198
❑ 96Fin-S54
❑ 96FinRef-G198
❑ 96FinRef-S54
❑ 96Fla-357
❑ 96Fle-206
❑ 96FleTif-206
❑ 96FleUpd-U187
❑ 96FleUpdTC-U187
❑ 96Lea-2
❑ 96LeaPrePB-2
❑ 96LeaPrePG-2
❑ 96LeaPrePS-2
❑ 96LeaPreSG-56
❑ 96LeaPreSte-56
❑ 96LeaSig-144
❑ 96LeaSigPPG-144
❑ 96LeaSigPPP-144
❑ 96MetUni-99
❑ 96MetUniP-99
❑ 96MLBPin-9
❑ 96Pac-393
❑ 96PanSti-215
❑ 96Pin-210
❑ 96PinAfi-55
❑ 96PinAfiAP-55
❑ 96PinAfiFPP-55
❑ 96PinArtP-110
❑ 96PinFoil-210
❑ 96PinSta-110
❑ 96Sco-324
❑ 96ScoDugC-B49
❑ 96ScoDugCAP-B49
❑ 96Sel-111
❑ 96SelArtP-111
❑ 96SP-153
❑ 96StaClu-130
❑ 96StaClu-261
❑ 96StaCluEPB-130
❑ 96StaCluEPG-130
❑ 96StaCluEPS-130
❑ 96StaCluMet-M5
❑ 96StaCluMOP-130
❑ 96StaCluMOP-261
❑ 96StaCluMOP-M5
❑ 96Stu-32
❑ 96StuPrePB-32
❑ 96StuPrePG-32
❑ 96StuPrePS-32
❑ 96Top-368
❑ 96TopChr-150
❑ 96TopChrMotG-1
❑ 96TopChrMotGR-1
❑ 96TopChrR-150

❑ 96TopGal-176
❑ 96TopGalPPI-176
❑ 96TopLas-54
❑ 96TopMasotG-1
❑ 96Ult-112
❑ 96Ult-545
❑ 96UltGolM-112
❑ 96UltGolM-545
❑ 96UppDec-101
❑ 96UppDec-375
❑ 96UppDec-416
❑ 96UppDec-442
❑ 97Bow-46
❑ 97BowBes-60
❑ 97BowBesAR-60
❑ 97BowBesR-60
❑ 97BowChr-37
❑ 97BowChrl-37
❑ 97BowChrlR-37
❑ 97BowChrR-37
❑ 97BowInt-46
❑ 97CarPol-5
❑ 97Cir-240
❑ 97CirRav-240
❑ 97ColCho-201
❑ 97Don-214
❑ 97DonGolPP-214
❑ 97DonLim-86
❑ 97DonLimE-86
❑ 97DonLimENG-86
❑ 97DonSilPP-214
❑ 97DonTea-158
❑ 97DonTeaSPE-158
❑ 97E-X2-97
❑ 97E-X2Cred-97
❑ 97E-X2EssCre-97
❑ 97E-X2Hall-17
❑ 97Fin-163
❑ 97FinEmb-163
❑ 97FinEmbR-163
❑ 97FinRef-163
❑ 97FlaShoLC-167
❑ 97FlaShoLeg0-167
❑ 97FlaShoLeg1-167
❑ 97FlaShoM-A167
❑ 97FlaShoM-B167
❑ 97FlaShoM-C167
❑ 97FlaShoR0-167
❑ 97FlaShoR1-167
❑ 97FlaShoR2-167
❑ 97Fle-441
❑ 97FleTif-441
❑ 97Lea-288
❑ 97LeaFraM-288
❑ 97LeaFraMDC-288
❑ 97MetUni-229
❑ 97Pac-407
❑ 97PacCar-33
❑ 97PacCarM-33
❑ 97PacLigB-407
❑ 97PacPri-137
❑ 97PacPriLB-137
❑ 97PacPriP-137
❑ 97PacSil-407
❑ 97Sco-98
❑ 97ScoArtPWB-98
❑ 97ScoPreS-98
❑ 97ScoShoS-98
❑ 97ScoShoSAP-98
❑ 97SP-151
❑ 97StaClu-239
❑ 97StaCluMat-239
❑ 97StaCluMOP-239
❑ 97Stu-74
❑ 97StuPrePG-74
❑ 97StuPrePS-74
❑ 97Top-388
❑ 97TopChr-134
❑ 97TopChrR-134
❑ 97TopGal-43
❑ 97TopGalPPI-43
❑ 97TopSta-34
❑ 97TopStaAM-34
❑ 97Ult-269
❑ 97UltGolME-269
❑ 97UltPlaME-269
❑ 97UppDec-159
❑ 98CarScoP-3
❑ 98CirThu-116
❑ 98CirThuRav-116
❑ 98CirThuSupRav-116
❑ 98ColCho-318
❑ 98Don-204
❑ 98DonGolPP-204
❑ 98DonSilPP-204
❑ 98Fle-514
❑ 98FleVin'-80
❑ 98FleVin'C-80
❑ 98MetUni-118
❑ 98MetUniPMG-118
❑ 98Pac-409
❑ 98PacInv-132
❑ 98PacInvGems-203
❑ 98PacInvPBlue-132
❑ 98PacInvSilv-132
❑ 98PacInvTeam-23
❑ 98PacOme-36
❑ 98PacOmeR-36
❑ 98PacOnl-111
❑ 98PacOnlR-111
❑ 98PacOnlWC-111
❑ 98PacPlaB-409
❑ 98PacRedT-409
❑ 98PacSil-409
❑ 98PacTeaC-26
❑ 98Pin-138
❑ 98PinPlu-88
❑ 98PinPreP-138
❑ 98Sco-31
❑ 98ScoAllST-20
❑ 98ScoCar-3
❑ 98ScoSS-PP11
❑ 98ScoSSAP-PP11
❑ 98SP Aut-59
❑ 98SpoIll-31
❑ 98SpoIllEE-31
❑ 98SpoIllFE-31
❑ 98SPxFin-256
❑ 98SPxFinR-256
❑ 98SPxFinS-256
❑ 98StaCluFDI-362
❑ 98StaClul-362
❑ 98StaCluOneK-362
❑ 98StaCluPP-362
❑ 98Top-200
❑ 98TopChr-200
❑ 98TopChrHB-HB5
❑ 98TopChrHBR-HB5
❑ 98TopChrM-MS3
❑ 98TopChrMR-MS3
❑ 98TopChrR-200
❑ 98TopDevR-200
❑ 98TopDia-200
❑ 98TopHal-HB5
❑ 98TopMil-MS3
❑ 98TopMiniC-200
❑ 98TopOpeD-100
❑ 98UD3-68
❑ 98UD3-158
❑ 98UD3-248
❑ 98UD3DieCut-68
❑ 98UD3DieCut-158
❑ 98UD3DieCut-248
❑ 98Ult-146
❑ 98Ult-409
❑ 98UltGolM-146
❑ 98UltGolM-409
❑ 98UltMas-146
❑ 98UltMas-409
❑ 98UltPlaM-146
❑ 98UltPlaM-409
❑ 98UppDec-138
❑ 98UppDec-200
❑ 98UppDec-654
❑ 98UppDec10AP-10
❑ 98UppDec1APR-10
❑ 98UppDecCD-CD22
❑ 98UppDecR-1
❑ 99DumSet-DE
❑ 99DumSet-DE
❑ 99Fle-52
❑ 99FleSta9-52
❑ 99FleWarT-52
❑ 99Pac-64
❑ 99PacCroC-44
❑ 99PacCroCPB-44
❑ 99PacPlaB-64
❑ 99PacPriS-85
❑ 99PacPriS206-85
❑ 99PacPriS206R-85
❑ 99PacRed-64
❑ 99SpoIll-32
❑ 99UppDec-51
❑ 99UppDec10AT-X11
❑ 99UppDec10ATD-X11
❑ 99UppDec10ATHR-X11
❑ 99UppDec10ATT-X11
❑ 99UppDecEL1-51
❑ 99UppDecEL2-51

Eckert, Chas
❑ 23Zee-65
❑ 24Zee-44
❑ 25Zee-152
❑ 26Zee-46
❑ 27Zee-24
❑ 28Zee-48

Eckfords, Brooklyn
❑ 94OriofB-9

Eckhardt, Ox
❑ 29Zee-154
❑ 33Zee-22
❑ 90DodTar-211

Eckhardt, Tom
❑ 89IdaFalBP-2030

Eckstein, David
❑ 97LowSpiB-7
❑ 99Bow-421
❑ 99BowGol-421
❑ 99BowInt-421

Eckstrom, Wayne
❑ 85RedWinA-3

Economy, Scott
❑ 88BilMusP-1814
❑ 89CedRapRB-9
❑ 89CedRapRP-921
❑ 89CedRapRS-6
❑ 90CedRapRP-2317

Eddie, Steve
❑ 93BilMusF-3952
❑ 93BilMusSP-7
❑ 94ChaWheC-8
❑ 94ChaWheF-2710
❑ 97ChaLoo-10
❑ 98ChaLooG-9

Eddings, Jay
❑ 87WytCubP-19
❑ 88ChaWheB-12
❑ 89ChaWheB-21
❑ 89ChaWheP-1766
❑ 89PeoChiTI-6
❑ 90PeoChiTI-21

Eddings, Jeff
❑ 94GreFalDSP-23

Eddins, Glenn
❑ 79ElmPioRST-6
❑ 81BriRedST-18

Eddy, Chris
❑ 92ClaDraP-57
❑ 92EugEmeC-12
❑ 92EugEmeF-3022
❑ 92FroRowDP-56
❑ 92FroRowDPG-56
❑ 92FroRowDPS-56
❑ 93Bow-477
❑ 93ClaFS7-109
❑ 93RoyStaC-27
❑ 93StaCluM-82
❑ 93WilBluRC-9
❑ 93WilBluRF-1991
❑ 94ExcFS7-67
❑ 94MemChiF-351
❑ 94UppDecML-58
❑ 95OmaRoyTI-8
❑ 96WicWraB-23
❑ 97TulDriTI-12

Eddy, Don (Donald Eugene)
❑ 72OPC-413
❑ 72Top-413

Eddy, Jim
❑ 90RocExpLC-7
❑ 90RocExpP-2691
❑ 91WesPalBEC-5
❑ 91WesPalBEP-1221

Eddy, Martin
❑ 88BurIndP-1775

Eddy, Steve (Steven Allen)
❑ 76QuaCitAT-12
❑ 80SalLakCGT-17

Edelen, Joe (Benny Joe)
❑ 77St.PetCT-24
❑ 78ArkTraT-9
❑ 80ArkTraT-1
❑ 82Fle-65
❑ 83IndIndTI-8

Eden, Bill
❑ 94BenRocC-5
❑ 94BenRocF-3585
❑ 95AshTouUTI-16
❑ 96NewHavRB-9

Eden, Mike (Edward Michael)
❑ 75PhoGiaC-11
❑ 75PhoGiaCK-16
❑ 76PheGiaCr-19
❑ 76PhoGiaCa-14
❑ 76PhoGiaCC-8
❑ 78SSP270-136
❑ 79RocRedWT-9
❑ 80RocRedWT-12

Edenfield, Ken
❑ 90BoiHawP-3308
❑ 91Cla/Bes-260
❑ 91QuaCitAC-3
❑ 91QuaCitAP-2620
❑ 92MidAngF-4020
❑ 92MidAngOHP-5
❑ 92PalSprAC-13
❑ 93MidAngF-315
❑ 94VanCanF-1857
❑ 96LeaSigEA-45
❑ 97ColCliB-10
❑ 97MidAngOHP-8

Edens, Larry
❑ 94WilCubC-6
❑ 94WilCubF-3776

Edens, Tom
❑ 83ButCopKT-4
❑ 86JacMetT-4
❑ 87TidTidP-9
❑ 87TidTidT-2
❑ 88TidTidCa-19
❑ 88TidTidCM-5
❑ 88TidTidP-1581
❑ 89TidTidC-2
❑ 89TidTidP-1956
❑ 90BreMilB-6
❑ 90CMC-29
❑ 90DenZepC-4
❑ 90DenZepP-620
❑ 90ProAAAF-645
❑ 91Don-590
❑ 91Fle-582
❑ 91LinDriAAA-407
❑ 91MetWIZ-103
❑ 91OPC-118
❑ 91PorBeaLD-407
❑ 91PorBeaP-1561
❑ 91Sco-78
❑ 91Sco100RS-2
❑ 91Top-118
❑ 91TopDesS-118
❑ 91TopMic-118
❑ 91TopTif-118
❑ 91TriA AAGP-AAA35
❑ 91UppDec-616
❑ 92FleUpd-39
❑ 92Sco-720
❑ 92StaClu-662
❑ 92StaCluNC-662
❑ 93AstMot-27
❑ 93Don-729
❑ 93Fle-434
❑ 93FleFinE-78
❑ 93Sco-450
❑ 94AstMot-12
❑ 94BreMilB-18
❑ 94BreMilB-310
❑ 94Don-456
❑ 94Fla-169
❑ 94FleUpd-141
❑ 94Pac-264
❑ 94Top-427
❑ 94TopGol-427
❑ 94TopSpa-427
❑ 96RocRedWB-13
❑ 98PorRocG-10

Edgar, Dwaine
❑ 94OneYanC-8
❑ 94OneYanF-3785

Edge, Alvin
❑ 76BurBeeT-6
❑ 78BurBeeT-11

Edge, Butch (Claude Lee) Jr.
❑ 75BurBeeT-5
❑ 76BurBeeT-7
❑ 78SyrChiT-8
❑ 79SyrChiT-9
❑ 79SyrChiTI-19
❑ 80OPC-329
❑ 80RicBraT-3
❑ 80Top-674
❑ 81RicBraT-11
❑ 82PorBeaT-2

Edge, Greg
❑ 86ClePhiP-7
❑ 87ReaPhiP-4
❑ 88EasLeaAP-32
❑ 88ReaPhiP-880
❑ 89ElPasDGS-21
❑ 89ReaPhiB-16
❑ 89ReaPhiP-666
❑ 90ElPasDGS-9
❑ 91CarMudLD-106
❑ 91CarMudP-1092
❑ 91LinDriAA-106
❑ 92CarMudS-132

Edge, Tim
❑ 90WelPirP-16
❑ 91SalBucC-1
❑ 91SalBucP-955
❑ 92SalBucC-19
❑ 92SalBucF-66
❑ 93CarMudF-2057
❑ 93CarMudTI-1
❑ 94CarMudF-1582
❑ 95CarMudF-159
❑ 96CarMudB-13
❑ 97CalCanB-11
❑ 98NasSouTI-12
❑ 98NasSouTISS-12

Edgerton, Bill
❑ 67VanMouSO-8
❑ 83Pil69G-3

Ediger, Lance
❑ 78NewWayCT-13

Edington, Jacob
❑ 19Zee-132
❑ 20Zee-138

Edison, Thomas Alva
❑ 75McCCob-12

Edler, Dave (David Delmar)
❑ 80SpoIndT-15
❑ 81Fle-610
❑ 81MarPol-7
❑ 81MarPos-16
❑ 82OmaRoyT-16
❑ 82Top-711
❑ 83Top-622

Edmendsen, Chris
❑ 92LetMouSP-7

Edmonds, Bobby Joe
❑ 89ReaPhiB-17
❑ 89ReaPhiP-673
❑ 89ReaPhiS-10

Edmonds, Jim
❑ 88BenBucL-10
❑ 89QuaCitAB-27
❑ 89QuaCitAGS-6
❑ 90CalLeaACLC-6
❑ 91PalSprAP-2028
❑ 92ClaFS7-343
❑ 92MidAngF-4037
❑ 92MidAngOHP-6
❑ 92MidAngS-458
❑ 92SkyAA F-194
❑ 93ExcFS7-141
❑ 93FlaWavotF-4
❑ 93FleFinE-181
❑ 93Top-799
❑ 93TopGol-799
❑ 93TopInaM-799
❑ 93TopInaR-799
❑ 93TopMic-799
❑ 93Ult-519
❑ 93VanCanF-2609
❑ 94AngLAT-5
❑ 94AngMot-16
❑ 94Bow-423
❑ 94ColC-517
❑ 94ColChoGS-517
❑ 94ColChoSS-517
❑ 94Fla-21
❑ 94Fle-54
❑ 94FleExtB-34
❑ 94LeaLimR-49
❑ 94Pin-394
❑ 94PinArtP-394
❑ 94PinMusC-394
❑ 94ScoRoo-RT160
❑ 94ScoRooGR-RT160
❑ 94ScoRooSR-SU18
❑ 94Sel-198
❑ 94SpoRoo-104
❑ 94SpoRooAP-104
❑ 94StaClu-603
❑ 94StaCluFDI-603
❑ 94StaCluGR-603
❑ 94StaCluMOP-603
❑ 94Top-404
❑ 94TopGol-404
❑ 94TopSpa-404
❑ 94Ult-327
❑ 95AngCHP-9
❑ 95AngMot-8
❑ 95ColCho-98
❑ 95ColChoGS-98
❑ 95ColChoSS-98
❑ 95Don-223
❑ 95DonPreP-223
❑ 95DonTopotO-35
❑ 95Fin-17
❑ 95FinRef-17
❑ 95Fla-235
❑ 95Fle-223
❑ 95Lea-26
❑ 95LeaLim-178
❑ 95Pac-58
❑ 95PacPri-18
❑ 95Pin-65
❑ 95PinArtP-65
❑ 95PinMusC-65
❑ 95Sco-253
❑ 95ScoGolR-253
❑ 95ScoHaloG-HG52
❑ 95ScoPlaTS-253
❑ 95Sel-40
❑ 95SelArtP-40
❑ 95SelCer-51
❑ 95SelCerMG-51
❑ 95SPCha-131
❑ 95SPChaDC-131
❑ 95StaClu-40
❑ 95StaCluFDI-40
❑ 95StaCluMOP-40
❑ 95StaCluSTWS-40
❑ 95StaCluVR-29
❑ 95StaCluVRMO-29
❑ 95Top-183
❑ 95TopCyb-104
❑ 95TopD3-29
❑ 95Ult-21
❑ 95UltGolM-21
❑ 95UppDec-268
❑ 95UppDecED-268
❑ 95UppDecEDG-268
❑ 95Zen-73
❑ 96AngMot-6
❑ 96Baz-83
❑ 96Bow-99
❑ 96BowBes-22
❑ 96BowBesAR-22
❑ 96BowBesR-22
❑ 96BowFoi-99
❑ 96Cir-18
❑ 96CirRav-18
❑ 96ColCho-71
❑ 96ColChoCtG-CG7
❑ 96ColChoCtG-CG7B
❑ 96ColChoCtG-CG7C
❑ 96ColChoCtGE-CR7
❑ 96ColChoCtGG-CG7
❑ 96ColChoCtGG-CG7B
❑ 96ColChoCtGG-CG7C
❑ 96ColChoCtGGE-CR7
❑ 96ColChoGS-71
❑ 96ColChoSS-71
❑ 96Don-227
❑ 96DonPowA-8
❑ 96DonPowADC-8
❑ 96DonPreP-227
❑ 96EmoXL-25
❑ 96Fin-B216
❑ 96Fin-G83
❑ 96FinRef-B216
❑ 96FinRef-G83
❑ 96Fla-36
❑ 96Fle-46
❑ 96FleTeaL-3
❑ 96FleTif-46
❑ 96FleTomL-2
❑ 96FleUpd-U218
❑ 96FleUpdTC-U218
❑ 96Lea-89
❑ 96LeaLim-58
❑ 96LeaLimG-58
❑ 96LeaPre-70
❑ 96LeaPreP-70
❑ 96LeaPrePB-89
❑ 96LeaPrePG-89
❑ 96LeaPrePS-89
❑ 96LeaPreSG-44
❑ 96LeaPreSte-44
❑ 96LeaSig-46
❑ 96LeaSigA-62
❑ 96LeaSigAG-62
❑ 96LeaSigAS-62
❑ 96LeaSigPPG-46
❑ 96LeaSigPPP-46
❑ 96MetUni-26
❑ 96MetUniML-2
❑ 96MetUniP-26

❑ 96MetUniPP-3
❑ 96Pac-262
❑ 96PacPri-P85
❑ 96PacPriG-P85
❑ 96PanSti-212
❑ 96Pin-145
❑ 96Pin-221
❑ 96PinAfi-123
❑ 96PinAfiAP-123
❑ 96PinArtP-72
❑ 96PinArtP-121
❑ 96PinFoil-221
❑ 96PinPow-8
❑ 96PinSta-72
❑ 96PinSta-121
❑ 96Sco-4
❑ 96Sco-359
❑ 96ScoDiaA-20
❑ 96ScoDugC-A4
❑ 96ScoDugC-B84
❑ 96ScoDugCAP-A4
❑ 96ScoDugCAP-B84
❑ 96ScoDugCSamp-4
❑ 96ScoNumG-15
❑ 96ScoSam-4
❑ 96Sel-65
❑ 96SelArtP-65
❑ 96SelCer-75
❑ 96SelCerAP-75
❑ 96SelCerCB-75
❑ 96SelCerCR-75
❑ 96SelCerIP-4
❑ 96SelCerMB-75
❑ 96SelCerMG-75
❑ 96SelCerMR-75
❑ 96SelTeaN-23
❑ 96SP-50
❑ 96Spo-22
❑ 96SpoArtP-22
❑ 96SPSpeFX-6
❑ 96SPSpeFXDC-6
❑ 96SPx-11
❑ 96SPxGol-11
❑ 96StaClu-206
❑ 96StaClu-276
❑ 96StaCluEPB-276
❑ 96StaCluEPG-276
❑ 96StaCluEPS-276
❑ 96StaCluMO-11
❑ 96StaCluMOP-206
❑ 96StaCluMOP-276
❑ 96StaCluMOP-PS15
❑ 96StaCluPS-PS15
❑ 96Stu-75
❑ 96StuPrePB-75
❑ 96StuPrePG-75
❑ 96StuPrePS-75
❑ 96Sum-55
❑ 96SumAbo&B-55
❑ 96SumArtP-55
❑ 96SumFoi-55
❑ 96SumPos-8
❑ 96TeaOut-24
❑ 96Top-171
❑ 96TopChr-50
❑ 96TopChrR-50
❑ 96TopGal-109
❑ 96TopGalPPI-109
❑ 96TopLas-6
❑ 96TopMysF-M11
❑ 96TopMysFR-M11
❑ 96TopPro-AL13
❑ 96TopRoaW-RW6
❑ 96Ult-28
❑ 96Ult-594
❑ 96UltFreF-3
❑ 96UltFreFGM-3
❑ 96UltGolM-28
❑ 96UltGolM-594
❑ 96UltRBIK-5
❑ 96UltRBIKGM-5
❑ 96UltRisS-3
❑ 96UltRisSGM-3
❑ 96UppDec-30
❑ 96UppDecPRE-R13
❑ 96UppDecPreR-R13
❑ 96UppDecVJLS-VJ16
❑ 96Zen-26
❑ 96Zen-146
❑ 96ZenArtP-26
❑ 96ZenArtP-146
❑ 96ZenMoz-7
❑ 96ZenZ-16
❑ 97AngMot-5
❑ 97Bow-251
❑ 97BowBes-19
❑ 97BowBesAR-19
❑ 97BowBesR-19
❑ 97BowChr-74
❑ 97BowChrI-74
❑ 97BowChrIR-74
❑ 97BowChrR-74
❑ 97BowInt-251
❑ 97Cir-97
❑ 97CirRav-97
❑ 97ColCho-255
❑ 97ColChoTBS-12
❑ 97ColChoTBSWH-12
❑ 97Don-2
❑ 97Don-419
❑ 97DonEli-28
❑ 97DonEliGS-28
❑ 97DonGolPP-2
❑ 97DonGolPP-419
❑ 97DonLim-138
❑ 97DonLim-180
❑ 97DonLimE-138
❑ 97DonLimE-180
❑ 97DonLimENG-138
❑ 97DonPre-116
❑ 97DonPreCttC-116
❑ 97DonPreXP-6B
❑ 97DonSig-24
❑ 97DonSigA-30
❑ 97DonSigAC-37
❑ 97DonSigAM-37
❑ 97DonSigPPP-24
❑ 97DonSilPP-2
❑ 97DonSilPP-419
❑ 97DonTea-1
❑ 97DonTeaSPE-1
❑ 97DonVxP1-35
❑ 97E-X2-1
❑ 97E-X2Cred-1
❑ 97E-X2EssCre-1
❑ 97Fin-165
❑ 97FinEmb-165
❑ 97FinEmbR-165
❑ 97FinRef-165
❑ 97FlaShoLC-125
❑ 97FlaShoLeg0-125
❑ 97FlaShoLeg1-125
❑ 97FlaShoM-A125
❑ 97FlaShoM-B125
❑ 97FlaShoM-C125
❑ 97FlaShoR0-125
❑ 97FlaShoR1-125
❑ 97FlaShoR2-125
❑ 97Fle-40
❑ 97FleTeaL-3
❑ 97FleTif-40
❑ 97Lea-231
❑ 97Lea-396
❑ 97LeaFraM-231
❑ 97LeaFraM-396
❑ 97LeaFraMDC-231
❑ 97LeaFraMDC-396
❑ 97LeaWarT-18
❑ 97MetUni-39
❑ 97NewPin-122
❑ 97NewPinAP-122
❑ 97NewPinMC-122
❑ 97NewPinPP-122
❑ 97Pac-5
❑ 97PacLigB-5
❑ 97PacPri-2
❑ 97PacPriGotD-GD4
❑ 97PacPriLB-2
❑ 97PacPriP-2
❑ 97PacSil-5
❑ 97PinCer-100
❑ 97PinCerMBla-100
❑ 97PinCerMBlu-100
❑ 97PinCerMG-100
❑ 97PinCerMR-100
❑ 97PinCerR-100
❑ 97PinIns-115
❑ 97PinInsCE-115
❑ 97PinInsDE-115
❑ 97PinTotCPB-100
❑ 97PinTotCPG-100
❑ 97PinTotCPR-100
❑ 97PinX-P-81
❑ 97PinX-PMoS-81
❑ 97PinX-PSfF-20
❑ 97PinX-PSfFU-20
❑ 97Sco-402
❑ 97ScoArtPWB-402
❑ 97ScoHeaotO-33
❑ 97ScoResC-402
❑ 97ScoShoS-402
❑ 97ScoShoSAP-402
❑ 97Sel-84
❑ 97SelArtP-84
❑ 97SelCom-84
❑ 97SelRegG-84
❑ 97SP-19
❑ 97SpoIll-164
❑ 97SpoIllEE-164
❑ 97StaClu-226
❑ 97StaCluMat-226
❑ 97StaCluMOP-226
❑ 97Stu-126
❑ 97StuPrePG-126
❑ 97StuPrePS-126
❑ 97Top-75
❑ 97TopChr-28
❑ 97TopChrR-28
❑ 97TopGal-93
❑ 97TopGalPPI-93
❑ 97TopSta-18
❑ 97TopStaAM-18
❑ 97Ult-25
❑ 97UltDouT-3
❑ 97UltGolME-25
❑ 97UltPlaME-25
❑ 97UppDec-291
❑ 98AngSco-11
❑ 98AngScoP-11
❑ 98Bow-226
❑ 98BowBes-13
❑ 98BowBesAR-13
❑ 98BowBesR-13
❑ 98BowChr-226
❑ 98BowChrGA-226
❑ 98BowChrGAR-226
❑ 98BowChrI-226
❑ 98BowChrIR-226
❑ 98BowChrR-226
❑ 98BowGolA-226
❑ 98BowInt-226
❑ 98CirThu-220
❑ 98CirThuRav-220
❑ 98CirThuSupRav-220
❑ 98ColCho-285
❑ 98ColChoSQ-SQ62
❑ 98CroRoy-2
❑ 98CroRoyPotG-1
❑ 98Don-44
❑ 98Don-393
❑ 98DonCol-44
❑ 98DonColE-438
❑ 98DonColL-314
❑ 98DonColP-607
❑ 98DonColS-44
❑ 98DonCruG-3
❑ 98DonCruP-3
❑ 98DonCruR-3
❑ 98DonEli-38
❑ 98DonEliA-38
❑ 98DonEliS-38
❑ 98DonGolPP-44
❑ 98DonGolPP-393
❑ 98DonLonL-18
❑ 98DonPre-57
❑ 98DonPreSeat-57
❑ 98DonPriCD-44
❑ 98DonPriCE-438
❑ 98DonPriCL-314
❑ 98DonPriCP-607
❑ 98DonSig-50
❑ 98DonSigP-50
❑ 98DonSilPP-44
❑ 98DonSilPP-393
❑ 98E-X2-46
❑ 98E-X2ECFut-46
❑ 98E-X2ECNow-46
❑ 98Fin-213
❑ 98FinNo--213
❑ 98FinNo-R-213
❑ 98FinRef-213
❑ 98FlaShoLeg0-50
❑ 98FlaShoLeg1-50
❑ 98FlaShoLeg2-50
❑ 98FlaShoLeg3-50
❑ 98FlaShoLegM-50
❑ 98FlaShoR0-50
❑ 98FlaShoR1-50
❑ 98FlaShoR2-50
❑ 98FlaShoR3-50
❑ 98Fle-217
❑ 98FleDiaSCS-NNO
❑ 98Lea-115
❑ 98LeaCruG-3
❑ 98LeaCruP-3
❑ 98LeaCruR-3
❑ 98LeaFraDA-115
❑ 98LeaFraF-115
❑ 98LeaFraM-115
❑ 98LeaFraM-115
❑ 98LeaFraMDC-115
❑ 98LeaFraMDC-115
❑ 98LeaFraMZ2-115
❑ 98LeaRS-25
❑ 98LeaRSLHolo-25
❑ 98LeaRSLong-25
❑ 98LeaRTrue-25
❑ 98MetUni-23
❑ 98MetUniPMG-23
❑ 98Pac-5
❑ 98PacAur-2
❑ 98PacAurPF-39
❑ 98PacAurPFC-39
❑ 98PacAurPFPB-39
❑ 98PacAurPFR-39
❑ 98PacAurPFS-39
❑ 98PacInv-2
❑ 98PacInvGems-1
❑ 98PacInvPBlue-2
❑ 98PacInvSilv-2
❑ 98PacInvTeam-1
❑ 98PacOme-3
❑ 98PacOmeR-3
❑ 98PacOnl-5
❑ 98PacOnl-26
❑ 98PacOnlR-5
❑ 98PacOnlR-26
❑ 98PacOnlWC-5
❑ 98PacOnlWC-26
❑ 98PacPar-3
❑ 98PacParC-3
❑ 98PacParG-3
❑ 98PacParHS-3
❑ 98PacParI-23
❑ 98PacParPB-3
❑ 98PacParR-3
❑ 98PacPlaB-5
❑ 98PacRedT-5
❑ 98PacSil-5
❑ 98PacTeaC-1
❑ 98Pin-87
❑ 98PinIns-64
❑ 98PinInsCE-64
❑ 98PinInsDE-64
❑ 98PinInsSG-16AB
❑ 98PinInsSG-16CD
❑ 98PinInsSGS-16AB
❑ 98PinInsSGS-16CD
❑ 98PinPer-58
❑ 98PinPerPP-58
❑ 98PinPerSftF-7
❑ 98PinPlu-161
❑ 98PinPluAP-PP52
❑ 98PinPluGAP-PP52
❑ 98PinPluMAP-PP52
❑ 98PinPreP-87
❑ 98PinSna-AA8
❑ 98PinSna-AA17
❑ 98Revo-2
❑ 98RevoSS-2
❑ 98Sco-186
❑ 98ScoRT-11
❑ 98ScoRTSS-PP11
❑ 98ScoRTSSAP-PP11
❑ 98ScoRTSSAP1-PP11
❑ 98ScoSS-PP86
❑ 98ScoSSAP-PP86
❑ 98SkyDugA-49
❑ 98SkyDugAIA-49
❑ 98SP Aut-32
❑ 98SpoIll-32
❑ 98SpoIll-138
❑ 98SpoIllEE-32
❑ 98SpoIllEE-138
❑ 98SpoIllFE-32
❑ 98SpoIllFE-138
❑ 98SpoIllTaN-76
❑ 98SpoIllTaNEE-76
❑ 98SpoIllWSF-37
❑ 98SpoIllWSFEE-37
❑ 98SpoIllWSFFE-37
❑ 98SPxFin-52
❑ 98SPxFinR-52
❑ 98SPxFinS-52
❑ 98StaCluFDI-12
❑ 98StaCluI-12
❑ 98StaCluOneK-12
❑ 98StaCluPP-12
❑ 98StaCluPWP-P2
❑ 98Stu-117
❑ 98StuGPP-117
❑ 98StuSPP-117
❑ 98Top-75
❑ 98TopChr-75
❑ 98TopChrR-75
❑ 98TopDevR-75
❑ 98TopDia-75
❑ 98TopGal-121
❑ 98TopGalGP-121
❑ 98TopGalOPP-121
❑ 98TopGalPPI-121
❑ 98TopGalPPIA-121
❑ 98TopGolLabC1-47
❑ 98TopGolLabC1B-47
❑ 98TopGolLabC1One-47
❑ 98TopGolLabC1R-47
❑ 98TopGolLabC2-47
❑ 98TopGolLabC2B-47
❑ 98TopGolLabC2One-47
❑ 98TopGolLabC2R-47
❑ 98TopGolLabC3-47
❑ 98TopGolLabC3B-47
❑ 98TopGolLabC3One-47
❑ 98TopGolLabC3R-47
❑ 98TopMiniC-75
❑ 98TopMysF-ILM14
❑ 98TopMysFR-ILM14
❑ 98TopOpeD-38
❑ 98TopSta-14
❑ 98TopStaB-14
❑ 98TopStaG-14
❑ 98TopStaGR-14
❑ 98TopStaS-14
❑ 98TopTek-20
❑ 98TopTekD-20
❑ 98UD3-46
❑ 98UD3-136
❑ 98UD3-226
❑ 98UD3DieCut-46
❑ 98UD3DieCut-136
❑ 98UD3DieCut-226
❑ 98Ult-24
❑ 98UltGolM-24
❑ 98UltMas-24
❑ 98UltPlaM-24
❑ 98UppDec-295
❑ 98UppDecR-1
❑ 98Zen-77
❑ 98Zen5 xx7-52
❑ 98Zen5x7GoldImp-52
❑ 98Zen5x7Imp-52
❑ 98ZenZ-G-77
❑ 98ZenZ-S-77
❑ 99199Fin-155
❑ 99Bow-9
❑ 99BowBes-6
❑ 99BowBesAR-6
❑ 99BowBesR-6
❑ 99BowChr-9
❑ 99BowChrG-9
❑ 99BowChrGR-9
❑ 99BowChrI-9
❑ 99BowChrIR-9
❑ 99BowChrR-9
❑ 99BowGol-9
❑ 99BowInt-9
❑ 99BowLatB-LB6
❑ 99CroRoyB-1
❑ 99CroRoyL-1
❑ 99CroRoyOD-1
❑ 99FinGolRef-155
❑ 99FinRef-155
❑ 99FlaShoLeg1-76
❑ 99FlaShoLeg2-76
❑ 99FlaShoLeg3-76
❑ 99FlaShoLegM1-76
❑ 99FlaShoLegM2-76
❑ 99FlaShoLegM3-76
❑ 99FlaShoR1-76
❑ 99FlaShoR2-76
❑ 99FlaShoR3-76
❑ 99Fle-80
❑ 99FleBri-116
❑ 99FleBri2G-116
❑ 99FleBriBlu-116
❑ 99FleBriGol-116
❑ 99FleSta9-80
❑ 99FleWarT-80
❑ 99MetUni-2
❑ 99MetUniGM-2
❑ 99MetUniPMG-2
❑ 99Pac-4
❑ 99PacAur-2
❑ 99PacAurOD-2
❑ 99PacCroC-3
❑ 99PacCroCPB-3
❑ 99PacInv-1
❑ 99PacInvOD-1
❑ 99PacInvPB-1
❑ 99PacOme-2
❑ 99PacOmeC-2
❑ 99PacOmeG-2
❑ 99PacOmePB-2
❑ 99PacPar-3
❑ 99PacParC-3
❑ 99PacParG-3
❑ 99PacParHoloGold-3
❑ 99PacParHS-3
❑ 99PacParOD-3
❑ 99PacParPB-3
❑ 99PacParRed-3
❑ 99PacPlaB-4
❑ 99PacPri-2
❑ 99PacPriHB-2
❑ 99PacPriHG-2
❑ 99PacPriHM-2
❑ 99PacPriHP-2
❑ 99PacPriRed-2
❑ 99PacPriS-28
❑ 99PacPriS206-28
❑ 99PacPriS206R-28
❑ 99PacPriSP-28
❑ 99PacPriSV-28
❑ 99PacRed-4
❑ 99Rev-1
❑ 99RevPremDate-1
❑ 99RevRet-1
❑ 99RevShaSS-1
❑ 99SkyMolM-44
❑ 99SkyMolMX-44
❑ 99SkyPre-193
❑ 99SkyPreR-193
❑ 99SkyThu-33
❑ 99SkyThuRant-33
❑ 99SkyThuRave-33
❑ 99SP Aut-2
❑ 99SpoIll-105
❑ 99StaClu-4
❑ 99StaCluFDI-4
❑ 99StaCluOoaK-4
❑ 99StaCluPP-4
❑ 99ThuSkySupR-33
❑ 99Top-130
❑ 99TopBlaLC1-63
❑ 99TopBlaLC2-63
❑ 99TopBlaLC3-63
❑ 99TopChr-130
❑ 99TopChrR-130
❑ 99TopGal-79
❑ 99TopGalPP-79
❑ 99TopGalPPI-79
❑ 99TopGolL-63
❑ 99TopGolLC1-63
❑ 99TopGolLC2-63
❑ 99TopGolLOtO-63
❑ 99TopMVPP-130
❑ 99TopOpeD-76
❑ 99TopRedLC1-63
❑ 99TopRedLC2-63
❑ 99TopRedLC3-63
❑ 99TopSta-131
❑ 99TopStaFoil-131
❑ 99Ult-183
❑ 99UltGolM-183
❑ 99UltMas-183
❑ 99UltPlaM-183
❑ 99UppDec-297
❑ 99UppDecBD-3
❑ 99UppDecBDD-3
❑ 99UppDecBDQ-3
❑ 99UppDecBDT-3
❑ 99UppDecEL1-297
❑ 99UppDecEL2-297
❑ 99UppDecM-7
❑ 99UppDecMGS-7
❑ 99UppDecMHFS-7
❑ 99UppDecMSS-7
❑ 99Vic-14

Edmonds, Stan

❑ 82WauTimF-4

Edmondson, Bobby

❑ 75WatRoyT-10

Edmondson, Brian

❑ 91BriTigC-26
❑ 91BriTigP-3597
❑ 92FayGenC-3
❑ 92FayGenF-2162
❑ 92StaCluD-43
❑ 93Bow-291
❑ 93FloStaLAF-17
❑ 93LakTigC-6
❑ 93LakTigF-1301
❑ 94Bow-265
❑ 94ExcFS7-53
❑ 94TreThuF-2115
❑ 96BinMetB-6

❑ 97NorTid-11
❑ 97NorTidB-11
❑ 98Fle-508
❑ 98PacOmeRS-10
❑ 98PacOmeRST1-10
❑ 98PacOnl-57
❑ 98PacOnlR-57
❑ 98PacOnlWC-57
Edmondson, Gavin
❑ 92GulCoaDF-3568
❑ 93AusFut-68
❑ 93AusFut-106
❑ 93BakDodCLC-6
❑ 95AusFut-60
Edmondson, Paul (Paul M.)
❑ 70OPC-414
❑ 70Top-414
Edmondson, Tracy
❑ 97CapCitB-16
Edsell, Geoff
❑ 93BoiHawC-10
❑ 93BoiHawF-3907
❑ 94CedRapKC-10
❑ 94CedRapKF-1104
❑ 94MidLeaAF-MDW38
❑ 95LakElsSTI-13
❑ 96Exc-25
❑ 96MidAngB-15
❑ 96MidAngOHP-10
❑ 96VanCanB-10
❑ 97VanCanB-12
❑ 98VanCanG-11
Eduardo, Hector
❑ 77St.PetCT-21
❑ 78St.PetCT-9
❑ 79ArkTraT-19B
❑ 81EdmTraRR-13
Edwards, Allen
❑ 82MadMusF-17
❑ 83AlbA'sT-2
Edwards, Bobby
❑ 88SalLakCTTI-11
Edwards, Bruce (Charles B.)
❑ 46SpoExcW-2-10
❑ 47Exh-67
❑ 47HomBon-12
❑ 47TipTop-94
❑ 48BluTin-26
❑ 48Bow-43
❑ 48DodTeal-9
❑ 49Bow-206
❑ 49EurSta-34
❑ 50Bow-165
❑ 51Bow-116
❑ 51TopBluB-42
❑ 52Bow-88
❑ 52Top-224
❑ 76TayBow4-29
❑ 83TopRep5-224
❑ 89DodSmoG-52
❑ 90DodTar-212
❑ 91DodRinP4-6
Edwards, Chuck
❑ 89JohCitCS-9
Edwards, Dave (David L.)
❑ 77TacTwiDQ-3
❑ 79TwiFriP-5
❑ 80Top-657
❑ 80TwiPos-6
❑ 81Don-595A
❑ 81Don-595B
❑ 81Fle-568
❑ 81PadFamF-7
❑ 81Top-386
❑ 81TopTra-758
❑ 82Don-247
❑ 82Top-151
❑ 83Don-565
❑ 83Fle-357
❑ 83Top-94
❑ 87PocGiaTB-17
❑ 88PocGiaP-2084
❑ 90EveGiaB-28
❑ 97HigDesMG-6
Edwards, Doc (Howard R.)
❑ 62Top-594
❑ 63Top-296
❑ 64A's-5
❑ 64AthJayP-4
❑ 64Top-174
❑ 64TopVen-174
❑ 65AthJayP-4
❑ 65OPC-239
❑ 65Top-239
❑ 79RocRedWT-10
❑ 80RocRedWT-13
❑ 81RocRedWT-22
❑ 81RocRedWW-5
❑ 81TCM60I-426
❑ 82ChaChaT-23
❑ 83ChaChaT-22
❑ 84MaiGuiT-10
❑ 85IntLeaAT-24
❑ 85MaiGuiT-29
❑ 86IndOhH-NNO
❑ 86IndTeal-20
❑ 87IndGat-NNO
❑ 88IndGat-32
❑ 88IndTeal-11
❑ 88Top-374
❑ 88TopTif-374
❑ 89IndTeal-10
❑ 89Top-534
❑ 89TopTif-534
❑ 90MetColP-32
❑ 90MetKah-32
❑ 90TopTVM-3
❑ 91MetColP-32
❑ 91MetKah-32
❑ 91MetPerPA-3
❑ 92BufBisBS-8
❑ 92BufBisF-339
❑ 92BufBisS-50
❑ 92YanWIZ6-38
❑ 94BufBisF-1852
Edwards, Glenn
❑ 85WatIndT-5
Edwards, Hank (Henry Albert)
❑ 47IndTeal-6
❑ 47IndVanPP-5
❑ 48IndTeal-8
❑ 49Bow-136
❑ 49EurSta-56
❑ 49Lea-72
❑ 50Bow-169
❑ 52Bow-141
❑ 52NatTeaL-7
❑ 52Top-176
❑ 53Top-90
❑ 79DiaGre-296
❑ 83TCMPla1943-7
❑ 83TopRep5-176
❑ 90DodTar-213
❑ 91TopArc1-90
Edwards, Jay
❑ 93ClePhiF-2694
❑ 94ReaPhiF-2074
Edwards, Jeff
❑ 86AshTouP-9
❑ 86AubAstP-8
❑ 87AlbDukD-9
❑ 87AshTouP-25
❑ 87SanBerSP-3
❑ 88ColAstB-16
❑ 89CanIndP-1316
❑ 89CanIndS-4
❑ 89EasLeaDDP-DD41
❑ 90CMC-458
❑ 90ColSprSSC-6
❑ 92GulCoaMF-3499
❑ 93PitMetC-26
❑ 93PitMetF-3727
Edwards, Jerome
❑ 90PriPatD-5
❑ 91BatCliCB-12
❑ 91BatCliP-3495
❑ 92SpaPhiC-2
❑ 92SpaPhiF-1276
❑ 93ClePhiC-7
Edwards, Jim
❑ 30Zee-80
❑ 93ConTSN-985
Edwards, Johnny (John Alban)
❑ 56RedBurB-5
❑ 62Kah-9
❑ 62RedEnq-7
❑ 62SalPlaC-191
❑ 62ShiPlaC-191
❑ 62Top-302
❑ 62TopStal-114
❑ 63Jel-132
❑ 63Kah-9
❑ 63Pos-132
❑ 63RedEnq-6
❑ 63RedFreBC-5
❑ 63Top-178
❑ 64Kah-8
❑ 64Top-507
❑ 64WheSta-14
❑ 65Kah-12
❑ 65MacSta-3
❑ 65RedEnq-8
❑ 65Top-418
❑ 66Kah-11
❑ 66RedVolC-3
❑ 66Top-507
❑ 67CokCapR-10
❑ 67DexPre-68
❑ 67Kah-11
❑ 67Top-202
❑ 68Top-558
❑ 69MLBOffS-139
❑ 69OPC-186
❑ 69Top-186
❑ 69TopFou-22
❑ 69TopSta-33
❑ 69TopTeaP-6
❑ 70AstPho-7
❑ 70AstTeal-3
❑ 70MLBOffS-40
❑ 70OPC-339
❑ 70Top-339
❑ 71AstCok-5
❑ 71AstTeal-6
❑ 71MLBOffS-79
❑ 71OPC-44
❑ 71Top-44
❑ 72AstTeal-6
❑ 72MilBra-96
❑ 72OPC-416
❑ 72Top-416
❑ 73OPC-519
❑ 73Top-519
❑ 74AstFouTIP-2
❑ 74OPC-635
❑ 74Top-635
❑ 80Red196T-23
❑ 82AstAstI-1
❑ 84OCoandSI-183
❑ 86AstGreT-8
❑ 87AstShoSO-5
❑ 87AstShoSTw-27
❑ 87AstShowSTh-29
❑ 91UppDecS-9
Edwards, Jon
❑ 96WatIndTI-7
❑ 97KinIndB-6
❑ 98KinIndQ-9
Edwards, Jovon
❑ 86BakDodP-6
❑ 87SalSpuS-16
❑ 88St.LucMS-7
Edwards, Lamont
❑ 96MarPhiB-6
❑ 97PieBolWB-13
❑ 98BriBluM-11
Edwards, Larry
❑ 77BurBeeT-7
❑ 78BurBeeT-12
❑ 79BurBeeT-1
❑ 80AndBraT-5
❑ 81GleFalWST-24
❑ 82GleFalWST-16
Edwards, Marshall L.
❑ 78HolMilT-7
❑ 79VanCanT-4
❑ 80VanCanT-19
❑ 82Fle-140
❑ 82Top-333
❑ 83BreGar-6
❑ 83BrePol-16
❑ 83Don-406
❑ 83Fle-32
❑ 83Top-582
❑ 84Don-490
❑ 84Nes792-167
❑ 84Top-167
❑ 84TopTif-167
❑ 84VanCanC-47
❑ 88TopClo-33
❑ 92BreCarT-6
❑ 94BreMilB-19
Edwards, Mel
❑ 91SpoIndP-3955
Edwards, Michael Donald
❑ 96BurIndB-19
❑ 97BurIndG-8
❑ 98ColRedSM-14
Edwards, Mike
❑ 91ButCopKSP-9
❑ 92ClaFS7-310
❑ 92GasRanC-12
❑ 92GasRanF-2259
❑ 93ChaRanC-8
❑ 93ChaRanF-1947
❑ 94TulDriF-250
❑ 94TulDriTI-6
❑ 95TulDriTI-7
Edwards, Mike (Michael L.)
❑ 75ShrCapT-2
❑ 76ShrCapT-11
❑ 77ColCliT-5
❑ 79Top-201
❑ 79Top-613
❑ 80OPC-158
❑ 80Top-301
❑ 81Don-497
Edwards, Otis
❑ 91WatIndC-25
❑ 91WatIndP-3380
Edwards, Randy
❑ 94AshTouC-6
❑ 94AshTouF-1794
Edwards, Ryan
❑ 90BilMusP-3223
❑ 91CedRapRC-3
❑ 91CedRapRP-2711
❑ 92CedRapRC-27
❑ 92CedRapRF-1065
Edwards, Samuel
❑ 90PriPatD-6
❑ 91MarPhiC-23
❑ 91MarPhiP-3447
❑ 92MarPhiC-23
❑ 92MarPhiF-3049
Edwards, Todd
❑ 86MiaMarP-6
❑ 90HelBreSP-19
❑ 91BelBreCB-19
❑ 91BelBreP-2116
❑ 91SalLakTP-3224
❑ 91SalLakTSP-4
❑ 92GenCubC-18
❑ 92GenCubF-1554
Edwards, Wayne
❑ 86PenWhiSP-9
❑ 87DayBeaAP-15
❑ 88BirBarB-1
❑ 88BlaYNPRWL-24
❑ 89BasAmeAPB-AA22
❑ 89BirBarADB-9
❑ 89BirBarB-21
❑ 89BirBarP-110
❑ 89SouLeaAJ-16
❑ 90BirBarADB-9
❑ 90Bow-309
❑ 90BowTif-309
❑ 90DonRoo-17
❑ 90Fle-652
❑ 90FleCan-652
❑ 90FleUpd-83
❑ 90Lea-352
❑ 90ScoRoo-85T
❑ 90TopDeb89-34
❑ 90TopTra-27T
❑ 90TopTraT-27T
❑ 90UppDec-762
❑ 90WhiSoxC-2
❑ 90WhiSoxC-28
❑ 91Bow-364
❑ 91Don-327
❑ 91Fle-116
❑ 91Lea-454
❑ 91OPC-751
❑ 91Sco-66
❑ 91Sco100RS-10
❑ 91StaClu-129
❑ 91Top-751
❑ 91TopDesS-751
❑ 91TopMic-751
❑ 91TopTif-751
❑ 91UppDec-697
❑ 91WhiSoxK-45
❑ 92OPC-404
❑ 92StaClu-674
❑ 92SyrChiF-1960
❑ 92SyrChiMB-5
❑ 92SyrChiS-505
❑ 94TolMudHF-1020
❑ 95BakBlaTI-13
Eenhoorn, Robert
❑ 90OneYanP-3384
❑ 90ProAaA-182
❑ 91Bow-172
❑ 91PriWilCC-16
❑ 91PriWilCP-1432
❑ 91UppDecFE-16F
❑ 92Bow-278
❑ 92ClaFS7-229
❑ 92ForLauYC-4
❑ 92ForLauYTI-7
❑ 92Ft.LauYF-2617
❑ 92ProFS7-121
❑ 92UppDecML-326
❑ 93AlbYanF-2169
❑ 93Bow-567
❑ 93ClaFS7-68
❑ 93YanStaC-25
❑ 94Bow-277
❑ 94ClaGolF-9
❑ 94ColCliF-2958
❑ 94ColCliP-8
❑ 94ExcFS7-102
❑ 94ScoRoo-RT103
❑ 94ScoRooGR-RT103
❑ 94SpoRoo-78
❑ 94SpoRooAP-78
❑ 94UppDec-514
❑ 94UppDecED-514
❑ 94UppDecML-143
❑ 95ColCliP-7
❑ 95ColCliTI-7
❑ 95Don-34
❑ 95DonPreP-34
❑ 95Pin-152
❑ 95PinArtP-152
❑ 95PinMusC-152
❑ 95Sco-281
❑ 95ScoGolR-281
❑ 95ScoPlaTS-281
❑ 96ColCho-228
❑ 96ColCho-330
❑ 96ColChoGS-228
❑ 96ColChoGS-330
❑ 96ColChoSS-228
❑ 96ColChoSS-330
❑ 96ColCliB-12
❑ 97UppDec-190
❑ 97VanCanB-13
❑ 98NorTidP-9
❑ 98NorTidQ-10
Effrig, Mark
❑ 83ElPasDT-7
❑ 84ElPasDT-1
Egan, Dick (Richard Wallis)
❑ 11PinT-5-416
❑ 63Top-169
❑ 64Top-572
❑ 66Top-536
❑ 67Top-539
❑ 81TCM60I-434
❑ 89RanMot-27
❑ 89RanSmo-6
❑ 90CMC-172
❑ 90DodTar-214
❑ 90OklCit8C-22
❑ 90OklCit8P-449
❑ 91ButCopKSP-30
❑ 93RanKee-133
Egan, Jack
❑ 94ConTSN-1185
❑ 94ConTSNB-1185
Egan, Joe (Richard Joseph)
❑ 09T206-118
❑ 11SpoLifCW-116
❑ 11SpoLifM-192
❑ 11T205-49
❑ 12HasTriFT-15A
❑ 12HasTriFT-71
❑ 14PieStaT-36
❑ 16FleBreD-26
Egan, Tom (Thomas Patrick)
❑ 65Top-486
❑ 66Top-263
❑ 66TopVen-263
❑ 67OPC-147
❑ 67Top-147
❑ 68SeaPop-3
❑ 69Top-407
❑ 70MLBOffS-171
❑ 70OPC-4
❑ 70Top-4
❑ 71OPC-537
❑ 71Top-537
❑ 72MilBra-97
❑ 72OPC-207
❑ 72Top-207
❑ 72WhiSoxTI1-5
❑ 73OPC-648
❑ 73Top-648
❑ 75CalAngP-14
❑ 75OPC-88
❑ 75Top-88
❑ 75TopMin-88
❑ 77WauMetT-24
Egawa, Suguru
❑ 87JapPlaB-25
Egenes, Mike
❑ 98QuaCitRBG-6
Eggert, David
❑ 92JamExpC-25
❑ 92JamExpF-1492
❑ 93BurBeeC-8
❑ 93BurBeeF-151
❑ 94WesPalBEC-8
❑ 94WesPalBEF-32
Eggertsen, Todd
❑ 86PalSprAP-12
❑ 86PalSprAS-16
❑ 87PalSprP-29
❑ 88MidAngGS-9
Eggleston, Brian
❑ 98JupHamQ-4
Eggleston, Darren
❑ 87WytCubP-18
❑ 88ChaWheB-10
Eggleston, Scott
❑ 91SpoIndC-17
❑ 91SpoIndP-3942
❑ 92SpoIndC-20
❑ 92SpoIndF-1285
❑ 93BatCliCB-8
❑ 93BatCliF-3138
❑ 94SpaPhiF-1713
❑ 94SparPhiC-6
Eggleston, Skip
❑ 88GenCubP-1639
Eggleston, Wayne
❑ 92ButCopKSP-24
❑ 93ChaRaiC-6
❑ 93ChaRaiF-1918
Egins, Paul C. III
❑ 88BurBraP-30
❑ 89BurBraP-1625
Egloff, Bruce
❑ 87WatIndP-15
❑ 89WatIndS-5
❑ 90Bes-251
❑ 90CanIndB-20
❑ 90CanIndP-1288
❑ 90ProAaA-11
❑ 91Bow-78
❑ 91IndFanC-8
❑ 92ColSprSSF-747
❑ 92Sco-751
❑ 92StaClu-503
❑ 92TopDeb91-49
Ehardt, Rube
❑ 90DodTar-941
Ehler, Dan
❑ 94KanCouCC-9
❑ 94KanCouCF-154
❑ 94KanCouCTI-9
❑ 94Top-751
❑ 94TopGol-751
❑ 94TopSpa-751
❑ 95BreCouMF-239
❑ 96BreCouMB-13
Ehmann, Kurt
❑ 92ClaDraP-83
❑ 92EveGiaC-23
❑ 93SanJosGC-11
❑ 93SanJosGF-17
❑ 93StaCluM-70
❑ 94ClaGolF-150
❑ 94ExcFS7-288
❑ 94ShrCapF-1612
❑ 94UppDecML-141
❑ 95PhoFirTI-6
❑ 96PhoFirB-15
❑ 97SanJosG-10
Ehmig, Greg
❑ 88SalLakCTTI-14
Ehmke, Howard (Howard J.)
❑ 14Zee-9
❑ 20WalMaiW-15
❑ 21Exh-42
❑ 21Exh-43
❑ 22E120-52
❑ 22W573-35
❑ 23Lec-1
❑ 23WilChoV-36
❑ 25Exh-65
❑ 28Exh-54

- 29PorandAR-20
- 61Fle-21
- 74A's192T-9
- 88ConSer5-9
- 92ConTSN-357
- 93ConTSN-759
- 94ConTSN-1135
- 94ConTSNB-1135

Ehret, Red (Philip S.)
- 87OldJudN-150

Ehrhard, Jim
- 88Ft.LauYS-6

Ehrhard, Rod
- 87OneYanP-23
- 88OneYanP-2072
- 89PriWilCS-7
- 90Ft.LauYS-7

Eibey, Scott
- 96AppLeaAB-4
- 96BluOriB-11
- 97DelSho-1
- 98BowBayM-11

Eichelberger, Juan T.
- 79HawIslC-13
- 79HawIslT-21
- 80HawIslT-4
- 80VenLeaS-193
- 81AllGamPI-168
- 81Top-478
- 82Don-422A
- 82Don-422B
- 82Fle-570
- 82Top-366
- 82Top-614
- 82TopSti-97
- 82TopStiV-97
- 83Don-247
- 83Don-422
- 83Fle-358
- 83IndPos-12
- 83IndWhe-9
- 83OPC-168
- 83Top-168
- 83TopTra-29T
- 84Don-398
- 84Fle-539
- 84Nes792-226
- 84Top-226
- 84TopTif-226
- 86RicBraP-5
- 87RicBraBC-6
- 87RicBraC-15
- 87RicBraT-4
- 88RicBraC-6
- 88RicBraP-10
- 89PacSenL-175
- 89T/MSenL-32
- 89TopSenL-123
- 90EliSenL-20
- 91PacSenL-119
- 94AppFoxC-23
- 94AppFoxFI-1070
- 96LanJetB-3

Eicher, Mike
- 92SprCarC-17
- 92SprCarF-881
- 93SprCarC-8
- 93SprCarF-1862

Eichhorn, Dave
- 86AlbDukP-6
- 87SanAntDTI-20
- 88SanAntMB-13
- 89AlbDukCm-6
- 89AlbDukP-61

Eichhorn, Mark A.
- 82SyrChiT-3
- 82SyrChiTI-11
- 83SyrChiT-7
- 84SyrChiT-18
- 86BluJayFS-8
- 86DonRoo-13
- 86FleUpd-38
- 86SpoRoo-38
- 86TopTra-34T
- 86TopTraT-34T
- 87BluJayFS-7
- 87Don-321
- 87Fle-224
- 87FleGamW-14
- 87FleGlo-224
- 87FleHotS-16
- 87FleMin-36
- 87FleStiC-37
- 87Lea-173
- 87Lea-229
- 87OPC-371
- 87Spo-194
- 87SpoTeaP-5
- 87SyrChi1A-11
- 87Top-371
- 87TopGloS-49
- 87TopRoo-5
- 87TopSti-187
- 87TopTif-371
- 87ToyRoo-10
- 88BluJay5-4
- 88BluJayFS-9
- 88Don-121
- 88Fle-108
- 88FleGlo-108
- 88FleMin-60
- 88Lea-74
- 88MSAHosD-18
- 88OPC-116
- 88PanSti-212
- 88Sco-198
- 88ScoGlo-198
- 88Spo-210
- 88StaLinBJ-5
- 88Top-749
- 88TopBig-208
- 88TopRevLL-30
- 88TopTif-749
- 89BraDub-10
- 89Fle-230
- 89FleGlo-230
- 89OPC-274
- 89RicBraP-825
- 89Sco-152
- 89Top-274
- 89TopBig-188
- 89TopTif-274
- 90Fle-580
- 90FleCan-580
- 90FleUpd-77
- 90Lea-472
- 90OPC-513
- 90Top-513
- 90TopTif-513
- 90TopTra-28T
- 90TopTraT-28T
- 90TriAAAC-26
- 91AngSmo-16
- 91Don-318
- 91Fle-311
- 91OPC-129
- 91Sco-504
- 91Top-129
- 91TopDesS-129
- 91TopMic-129
- 91TopTif-129
- 91UppDec-519
- 92Don-181
- 92Fle-55
- 92Lea-97
- 92LeaBlaG-97
- 92OPC-435
- 92Pin-353
- 92Sco-221
- 92StaClu-857
- 92StaCluNC-857
- 92Top-435
- 92TopGol-435
- 92TopGolW-435
- 92TopMic-435
- 92UppDec-287
- 93BluJayD-15
- 93BluJayD4-16
- 93BluJayFS-9
- 93FleFinE-292
- 93StaClu-617
- 93StaCluFDI-617
- 93StaCluMOP-617
- 94BalOriP-9
- 94Don-144
- 94Fle-330
- 94FleUpd-1
- 94OriPro-29
- 94Pac-638
- 94Pin-511
- 94PinArtP-511
- 94PinMusC-511
- 94Sco-266
- 94ScoGolR-266
- 94StaCluT-282
- 94StaCluTFDI-282
- 95BalOriP-16
- 95BluJayUSPC-7C
- 95Don-475
- 95DonPreP-475
- 95Fle-5
- 95Sco-532
- 95ScoGolR-532
- 95ScoPlaTS-532
- 95Top-563
- 95TopCyb-339
- 96AngMot-18
- 96LeaSigEA-46
- 98DurBulTI-6

Eierman, John
- 91ElmPioC-4
- 91ElmPioP-3282
- 92LynRedSC-2
- 92LynRedSF-2918
- 93LynRedSC-8
- 93LynRedSF-2529
- 94LynRedSC-9
- 94LynRedSF-1904

Eiffert, Michael
- 92BenRocCB-11
- 92BenRocF-1468
- 93BenRocCB-7
- 93BenRocF-3259
- 93CenValRC-9
- 93CenValRF-2886

Eiland, Dave
- 87OneYanP-17
- 88AlbYanP-1336
- 88EasLeaAP-1
- 89ColCliC-8
- 89ColCliP-2
- 89ColCliP-750
- 89Don-481
- 89Top-8
- 89TopTif-8
- 90AlbDecGB-26
- 90CMC-202
- 90ColCliC-2
- 90ColCliP-13
- 90ColCliP-670
- 90ProAAAF-320
- 90Sco-652
- 90TopTVY-41
- 91Don-354
- 91Fle-661
- 91Lea-184
- 91OPC-611
- 91Sco-826
- 91StaClu-477
- 91Top-611
- 91TopDesS-611
- 91TopMic-611
- 91TopTif-611
- 92Fle-223
- 92Lea-488
- 92LeaBlaG-488
- 92OPC-406
- 92PadMot-10
- 92PadPolD-6
- 92PadSmo-7
- 92Sco-679
- 92StaClu-133
- 92StaClu-879
- 92StaCluMO-6
- 92StaCluNC-879
- 92Ult-575
- 92YanWIZ8-51
- 93PadMot-7
- 93UppDec-709
- 93UppDecGold-709
- 94ColCliF-2945
- 94ColCliP-9
- 95ColCliP-8
- 95ColCliTI-8
- 96LouRedB-17
- 97ColCliB-11
- 97ColCliD-7
- 98DurBulTI-7

Eilers, Dave (David Louis)
- 66Top-534
- 78TCM60I-245
- 91MetWIZ-104

Einerston, Darrell
- 96GreBatB-9
- 97TamYan-11

Einertson, Darrell
- 98NorNavQ-9

Einstein, Charles
- 90LitSunW-11

Einterfeldt, Todd
- 81TidTidT-7

Eischen, Joey (Joe)
- 89ButCopKSP-13
- 90GasRanB-6
- 90GasRanP-2514
- 90GasRanS-6
- 91ChaRanC-4
- 91ChaRanP-1308
- 92ClaFS7-303
- 92WesPalBEC-18
- 92WesPalBEF-2082
- 93Bow-240
- 93ClaFS7-134
- 93HarSenF-265
- 94Bow-528
- 94BowBes-B77
- 94BowBesR-B77
- 94Cla-96
- 94ClaGolF-137
- 94ColC-656
- 94ColChoGS-656
- 94ColChoSS-656
- 94ExcFS7-224
- 94ExcLeaLF-8
- 94FleExtB-302
- 94FleExtBMLH-4
- 94OttLynF-2896
- 94SigRoo-10
- 94SigRooS-10
- 94Ult-522
- 94UppDec-10
- 94UppDecED-10
- 94UppDecML-77
- 94UppDecML-152
- 95ColCho-241
- 95ColChoGS-241
- 95ColChoSS-241
- 95DodMot-25
- 95Don-115
- 95DonPreP-115
- 95Fle-347
- 95Pin-162
- 95PinArtP-162
- 95PinMusC-162
- 95Sel-211
- 95SelArtP-211
- 96DodMot-16
- 96DodPol-11
- 96Fle-432
- 96FleTif-432
- 96LeaSigA-63
- 96LeaSigAG-63
- 96LeaSigAS-63
- 97PacPriGotD-GD41
- 98IndIndQ-7

Eisenhower, Dwight D.
- 85TCMPhoC-3
- 94UppDecTAE-59

Eisenman, Charles
- 47PadTeal-6

Eisenreich, Charlie
- 87AppFoxP-15

Eisenreich, Jim (James M.)
- 81WisRapTT-21
- 82TwiPos-7
- 83Top-197
- 83TwiTeal-2
- 83TwiTeal-31
- 84MinTwiP-9
- 84TwiTeal-2
- 87MemChiB-21
- 87MemChiP-27
- 88Don-343
- 88OPC-348
- 88RoySmo-26
- 88RoyTeal-8
- 88Sco-456
- 88ScoGlo-456
- 88StaLinRo-3
- 88Top-348
- 88TopTif-348
- 89DonBasB-306
- 89FleUpd-38
- 89Sco-594
- 89TopTra-28T
- 89TopTraT-28T
- 89UppDec-44
- 90Bow-374
- 90BowTif-374
- 90Don-238
- 90DonBesA-120
- 90Fle-106
- 90FleCan-106
- 90Lea-278
- 90OPC-246
- 90PanSti-80
- 90PubIntS-346
- 90RoyPos-7
- 90Sco-179
- 90Spo-166
- 90Top-246
- 90TopBig-234
- 90TopSti-271
- 90TopTif-246
- 90UppDec-294
- 91Bow-304
- 91Don-448
- 91Fle-557
- 91OPC-707
- 91PanFreS-280
- 91PanSti-229
- 91RoyPol-8
- 91Sco-154
- 91StaClu-373
- 91Top-707
- 91TopDesS-707
- 91TopMic-707
- 91TopTif-707
- 91Ult-146
- 91UppDec-658
- 92Don-297
- 92Fle-156
- 92Hig5-62
- 92Lea-295
- 92LeaBlaG-295
- 92OPC-469
- 92Pin-468
- 92RoyPol-6
- 92Sco-158
- 92StaClu-409
- 92Top-469
- 92TopGol-469
- 92TopGolW-469
- 92TopMic-469
- 92TriPla-140
- 92Ult-69
- 92UppDec-539
- 93Don-722
- 93Fla-100
- 93Fle-617
- 93FleFinE-109
- 93Lea-507
- 93PacSpa-576
- 93PanSti-104
- 93PhiMed-13
- 93PhiStaC-7
- 93Sco-551
- 93Sel-241
- 93StaClu-224
- 93StaCluFDI-224
- 93StaCluMOP-224
- 93Top-22
- 93TopGol-22
- 93TopInaM-22
- 93TopInaR-22
- 93TopMic-22
- 93Ult-440
- 93UppDec-800
- 93UppDecGold-800
- 94ColC-388
- 94ColChoGS-388
- 94ColChoSS-388
- 94Don-548
- 94Fla-206
- 94Fle-588
- 94Lea-176
- 94Pac-474
- 94PanSti-227
- 94PhiMed-9
- 94PhiMel-7
- 94PhiUSPC-6D
- 94PhiUSPC-11D
- 94PhiUSPC-13S
- 94Pin-149
- 94PinArtP-149
- 94PinMusC-149
- 94Sel-213
- 94StaClu-27
- 94StaCluFDI-27
- 94StaCluGR-27
- 94StaCluMOP-27
- 94StaCluT-224
- 94StaCluTFDI-224
- 94Top-504
- 94TopGol-504
- 94TopSpa-504
- 94Ult-545
- 94UppDec-157
- 94UppDecED-157
- 95ColCho-366
- 95ColChoGS-366
- 95ColChoSS-366
- 95Don-211
- 95DonPreP-211
- 95DonTopotO-303
- 95Fla-179
- 95Fle-391
- 95Lea-149
- 95Pac-329
- 95Phi-10
- 95PhiMel-8
- 95Sco-362
- 95ScoGolR-362
- 95ScoPlaTS-362
- 95StaClu-209
- 95StaCluFDI-209
- 95StaCluMOP-209
- 95StaCluSTWS-209
- 95StaCluVR-110
- 95StaCluVRMO-110
- 95Top-326
- 95Ult-204
- 95UltGolM-204
- 96Cir-165
- 96CirRav-165
- 96ColCho-649
- 96ColChoGS-649
- 96ColChoSS-649
- 96Don-470
- 96DonPreP-470
- 96EmoXL-244
- 96Fla-333
- 96Fle-496
- 96FleTif-496
- 96LeaSigA-64
- 96LeaSigAG-64
- 96LeaSigAS-64
- 96MetUni-210
- 96MetUniP-210
- 96Pac-164
- 96PanSti-40
- 96PhiTeal-10
- 96ProSta-86
- 96Sco-125
- 96StaClu-281
- 96StaCluMOP-281
- 96Top-66
- 96Ult-251
- 96UltGolM-251
- 96UppDec-171
- 97ColCho-191
- 97ColCho-342
- 97Don-180
- 97DonGolPP-180
- 97DonSilPP-180
- 97Fle-410
- 97Fle-604
- 97FleTif-410
- 97FleTif-604
- 97MarPac-9
- 97MetUni-174
- 97Pac-377
- 97PacLigB-377
- 97PacSil-377
- 97Pin-23
- 97PinArtP-PP23
- 97PinMusC-23
- 97PinPrePla-23
- 97Sco-452
- 97ScoArtPWB-452
- 97ScoResC-452
- 97ScoShoS-452
- 97ScoShoSAP-452
- 97Top-161
- 97Ult-249
- 97Ult-367
- 97UltGolME-249
- 97UltGolME-367
- 97UltPlaME-249
- 97UltPlaME-367
- 97UppDec-133
- 98ColCho-374
- 98DodMot-10
- 98Pac-300
- 98PacOnl-367
- 98PacOnlR-367
- 98PacOnlWC-367
- 98PacPlaB-300
- 98PacRedT-300
- 98PacSil-300
- 98Top-67
- 98TopChr-67
- 98TopChrR-67
- 98TopDevR-67
- 98TopDia-67
- 98TopMiniC-67
- 98UppDec-381
- 99UppDec-120
- 99UppDecEL1-120
- 99UppDecEL2-120

Eisenstat, Harry
- 40PlaBal-204
- 90DodTar-215

Eisinger, John
❑ 77ModA'sC-21
Eissens, Simon
❑ 91PerHeaF-1
❑ 95AusFut-57
Eiterman, Tom
❑ 90CalLeaACLC-39
❑ 90RenSilSCLC-263
❑ 91CarLeaAP-CAR13
❑ 91KinIndC-25
❑ 91KinIndP-337
❑ 92CanIndF-700
❑ 92CanIndS-105
Eklund, Troy
❑ 89ButCopKSP-16
❑ 90GasRanB-12
❑ 90GasRanP-2532
❑ 90GasRanS-7
Ekman, Rich
❑ 91PocPioP-3775
❑ 91PocPioSP-9
el Himmo, Oyendo
❑ 80VenLeaS-135
Elam, Brett
❑ 96AshTouB-15
❑ 97SalAva-14
Elam, Scott
❑ 82KnoBluJT-2
❑ 83KinBluJTI-4
Elam, Todd
❑ 88BatCliP-1682
❑ 89SpaPhiP-1028
❑ 89SpaPhiS-7
❑ 90ClePhiS-6
Elarton, Scott
❑ 94SigRooDP-24
❑ 94SigRooDPS-24
❑ 95Bow-242
❑ 95BowBes-B37
❑ 95BowBesR-B37
❑ 95BowGolF-242
❑ 95ColCho-32
❑ 95ColChoGS-32
❑ 95ColChoSS-32
❑ 95Exc-201
❑ 95Pin-171
❑ 95PinArtP-171
❑ 95PinMusC-171
❑ 95QuaCitRBTI-5
❑ 95ScoDraP-DP8
❑ 95SPML-67
❑ 95StaClu-108
❑ 95StaCluFDI-108
❑ 95StaCluMOP-108
❑ 95StaCluSTWS-108
❑ 95Top-510
❑ 96Bow-281
❑ 96BowBes-112
❑ 96BowBesAR-112
❑ 96BowBesR-112
❑ 96BowFoi-281
❑ 96KisCobB-7
❑ 97Bow-355
❑ 97BowCerBlaIA-CA22
❑ 97BowCerBluIA-CA22
❑ 97BowCerGolIA-CA22
❑ 97BowChr-240
❑ 97BowChrI-240
❑ 97BowChrIR-240
❑ 97BowChrR-240
❑ 97BowInt-355
❑ 97JacGen-7
❑ 97JacGenS-4
❑ 97TexAllM-36
❑ 97TexLeaTP-8
❑ 98Bes-12
❑ 98Bow-211
❑ 98BowBes-151
❑ 98BowBesAR-151
❑ 98BowBesR-151
❑ 98BowCerBlueAU-24
❑ 98BowCerGA-24
❑ 98BowCerSA-24
❑ 98BowChr-211
❑ 98BowChrGA-211
❑ 98BowChrGAR-211
❑ 98BowChrI-211
❑ 98BowChrIR-211
❑ 98BowChrR-211
❑ 98BowGolA-211
❑ 98BowInt-211
❑ 98Don-330
❑ 98DonGolPP-330
❑ 98DonSigAC-37
❑ 98DonSigAM-37
❑ 98DonSilPP-330
❑ 98FleUpd-U42
❑ 98LeaRS-242
❑ 98LeaRSLHolo-242
❑ 98LeaRSLong-242
❑ 98LeaRTrue-242
❑ 98NewOrlZM-3
❑ 98SP Aut-6
❑ 98SP MinPE-62
❑ 98SPMin-62
❑ 98Stu-25
❑ 98StuGPP-25
❑ 98StuSPP-25
❑ 98UppDec-569
❑ 98UppDecDS-DS11
❑ 99Bow-93
❑ 99BowChr-93
❑ 99BowChrG-93
❑ 99BowChrGR-93
❑ 99BowChrI-93
❑ 99BowChrIR-93
❑ 99BowChrR-93
❑ 99BowGol-93
❑ 99BowInt-93
❑ 99Fle-94
❑ 99FleSta9-94
❑ 99FleWarT-94
❑ 99MetUniN-3
❑ 99PacInv-68
❑ 99PacInvOD-68
❑ 99PacInvPB-68
❑ 99SkyThu-165
❑ 99SkyThuRant-165
❑ 99SkyThuRave-165
❑ 99ThuSkySupR-165
❑ 99Top-299
❑ 99TopChr-299
❑ 99TopChrR-299
❑ 99TopMVPP-299
❑ 99UltWorP-8
❑ 99UppDec-382
❑ 99UppDecEL1-382
❑ 99UppDecEL2-382
❑ 99UppDecEM-MC6
❑ 99UppDecEMFXG-MC6
❑ 99Vic-178
Elberfeld, Kid (Norman A.)
❑ 03BreE10-47
❑ 03BreE10-48
❑ 04FanCraAL-17
❑ 08RosComP-46
❑ 09ColChiE-89A
❑ 09ColChiE-89B
❑ 09ColChiE-89C
❑ 09RamT20-42
❑ 09T206-119
❑ 09T206-120
❑ 09T206-121
❑ 10CouT21-131
❑ 10CouT21-132
❑ 10CouT21-282
❑ 10DarChoE-17
❑ 10RedCroT-24
❑ 10RedCroT-110
❑ 10RedCroT-190
❑ 10SweCapPP-57A
❑ 10SweCapPP-57B
❑ 11MecDFT-19
❑ 11PinT-5-558
❑ 11S74Sil-38
❑ 11SpoLifCW-117
❑ 11SpoLifM-122
❑ 11T205-50
❑ 11TurRedT-15
❑ 12ColRedB-89A
❑ 12ColRedB-89B
❑ 12ColRedB-89C
❑ 12ColTinT-89A
❑ 12ColTinT-89B
❑ 12ColTinT-89C
❑ 12HasTriFT-33
❑ 12HasTriFT-34
❑ 14PieStaT-37
❑ 15VicT21-9
❑ 72ClaCar-64
❑ 89ChaLooLITI-9
❑ 90DodTar-216
❑ 92ConTSN-557
Elder, Isaac
❑ 89JamExpP-2147
❑ 90RocExpLC-8
❑ 90RocExpP-2706
Elder, Rick
❑ 99Bow-102
❑ 99BowBes-196
❑ 99BowBesAR-196
❑ 99BowBesR-196
❑ 99BowChr-102
❑ 99BowChrG-102
❑ 99BowChrGR-102
❑ 99BowChrI-102
❑ 99BowChrIR-102
❑ 99BowChrR-102
❑ 99BowGol-102
❑ 99BowInt-102
❑ 99JustheS-18
❑ 99JustheSAC-9
❑ 99JustheSAD-7
❑ 99JustheSJB-18
❑ 99StaClu-154
❑ 99StaCluFDI-154
❑ 99StaCluOoaK-154
❑ 99StaCluPP-154
❑ 99Top-217
❑ 99TopChr-217
❑ 99TopChrR-217
Elders, Mike
❑ 76CliPilT-12
Eldred, Cal (Calvin)
❑ 89BelBre2S-8
❑ 90Bes-61
❑ 90Bow-387
❑ 90BowTif-387
❑ 90CMC-866
❑ 90ElPasDGS-10
❑ 90ProAaA-138
❑ 90Sco-669
❑ 90StoPorB-1
❑ 90StoPorCLC-174
❑ 90StoPorP-2178
❑ 91Bow-56
❑ 91DenZepLD-135
❑ 91DenZepP-116
❑ 91LinDriAAA-135
❑ 92Bow-299
❑ 92Cla1-T31
❑ 92ClaGam-126
❑ 92DenZepF-2631
❑ 92DenZepS-127
❑ 92Don-718
❑ 92Fle-679
❑ 92Lea-2
❑ 92LeaBlaG-2
❑ 92OPC-433
❑ 92Pin-249
❑ 92PinTea2-36
❑ 92ProFS7-81
❑ 92Sco-834
❑ 92ScoHotR-1
❑ 92ScoImpP-89
❑ 92ScoRoo-33
❑ 92SkyAAAF-61
❑ 92StaClu-327
❑ 92Top-433
❑ 92TopDeb91-50
❑ 92TopGol-433
❑ 92TopGolW-433
❑ 92TopMic-433
❑ 92TriPla-213
❑ 92Ult-380
❑ 92UppDec-477
❑ 93Bow-127
❑ 93BrePol-6
❑ 93ClaGam-28
❑ 93Don-131
❑ 93Fin-147
❑ 93FinRef-147
❑ 93Fla-223
❑ 93Fle-248
❑ 93FleRooS-RSA2
❑ 93FunPac-70
❑ 93HumDumC-10
❑ 93Lea-34
❑ 93LeaFas-16
❑ 93OPC-85
❑ 93OPCPre-4
❑ 93Pin-2
❑ 93PinTea2-2
❑ 93Sco-368
❑ 93Sel-296
❑ 93SelAce-21
❑ 93SelChaR-15
❑ 93SP-64
❑ 93StaClu-475
❑ 93StaCluFDI-475
❑ 93StaCluMOP-475
❑ 93Stu-6
❑ 93Top-590
❑ 93TopGol-590
❑ 93TopInaM-590
❑ 93TopInaR-590
❑ 93TopMic-590
❑ 93Toy-80
❑ 93TriPla-18
❑ 93Ult-218
❑ 93UppDec-375
❑ 93UppDecGold-375
❑ 93USPlaCR-13C
❑ 94Bow-393
❑ 94BreMilB-20
❑ 94BrePol-6
❑ 94BreTeal-5
❑ 94ColC-606
❑ 94ColChoGS-606
❑ 94ColChoSS-606
❑ 94DenHol-9
❑ 94Don-89
❑ 94Fin-288
❑ 94FinRef-288
❑ 94Fla-66
❑ 94Fle-175
❑ 94FleExtB-101
❑ 94FUnPac-166
❑ 94Lea-267
❑ 94OPC-179
❑ 94Pac-328
❑ 94Pin-19
❑ 94PinArtP-19
❑ 94PinMusC-19
❑ 94RedFolMI-28
❑ 94Sco-449
❑ 94ScoGolR-449
❑ 94Sel-347
❑ 94SP-57
❑ 94SPDieC-57
❑ 94Spo-107
❑ 94StaClu-329
❑ 94StaCluFDI-329
❑ 94StaCluGR-329
❑ 94StaCluMOP-329
❑ 94StaCluMOP-ST22
❑ 94StaCluST-ST22
❑ 94Top-45
❑ 94TopGol-45
❑ 94TopSpa-45
❑ 94TriPla-52
❑ 94Ult-73
❑ 94UppDec-431
❑ 94UppDecED-431
❑ 95Bow-361
❑ 95ColCho-175
❑ 95ColChoGS-175
❑ 95ColChoSE-69
❑ 95ColChoSEGS-69
❑ 95ColChoSESS-69
❑ 95ColChoSS-175
❑ 95Don-536
❑ 95DonPreP-536
❑ 95Emo-53
❑ 95Fin-63
❑ 95FinRef-63
❑ 95Fla-51
❑ 95Fle-177
❑ 95Lea-34
❑ 95Pac-230
❑ 95Pin-377
❑ 95PinArtP-377
❑ 95PinMusC-377
❑ 95RedFol-23
❑ 95Sco-393
❑ 95ScoGolR-393
❑ 95ScoPlaTS-393
❑ 95Sel-149
❑ 95SelArtP-149
❑ 95SP-164
❑ 95SPSil-164
❑ 95StaClu-20
❑ 95StaCluFDI-20
❑ 95StaCluMOP-20
❑ 95StaCluSTWS-20
❑ 95StaCluVR-14
❑ 95StaCluVRMO-14
❑ 95Stu-174
❑ 95Top-580
❑ 95TopCyb-354
❑ 95TopD3-10
❑ 95TopEmb-29
❑ 95TopEmbGI-29
❑ 95Ult-295
❑ 95UltGolM-295
❑ 95UppDec-53
❑ 95UppDecED-53
❑ 95UppDecEDG-53
❑ 95UppDecSE-235
❑ 95UppDecSEG-235
❑ 96BrePol-5
❑ 96ColCho-592
❑ 96ColChoGS-592
❑ 96ColChoSS-592
❑ 96Don-333
❑ 96DonPreP-333
❑ 96StaClu-312
❑ 96StaCluMOP-312
❑ 96Top-335
❑ 97Cir-70
❑ 97CirRav-70
❑ 97ColCho-143
❑ 97Fle-578
❑ 97FleTif-578
❑ 97PacPriGotD-GD54
❑ 97Sco-404
❑ 97ScoArtPWB-404
❑ 97ScoResC-404
❑ 97ScoShoS-404
❑ 97ScoShoSAP-404
❑ 97StaClu-318
❑ 97StaCluMOP-318
❑ 97Top-424
❑ 97Ult-315
❑ 97UltGolME-315
❑ 97UltPlaME-315
❑ 97UppDec-408
❑ 98Pac-115
❑ 98PacOnl-392
❑ 98PacOnlR-392
❑ 98PacOnlWC-392
❑ 98PacPlaB-115
❑ 98PacRedT-115
❑ 98PacSil-115
❑ 98Pin-130
❑ 98PinPreP-130
❑ 98SP Aut-118
❑ 98StaCluFDI-215
❑ 98StaCluI-215
❑ 98StaCluOneK-215
❑ 98StaCluPP-215
❑ 98Top-187
❑ 98TopChr-187
❑ 98TopChrR-187
❑ 98TopDevR-187
❑ 98TopDia-187
❑ 98TopMiniC-187
❑ 98Ult-259
❑ 98UltGolM-259
❑ 98UltMas-259
❑ 98UltPlaM-259
❑ 98UppDec-121
❑ 98UppDecSF-74
❑ 99Top-135
❑ 99TopChr-135
❑ 99TopChrR-135
❑ 99TopMVPP-135
❑ 99Ult-171
❑ 99UltGolM-171
❑ 99UltMas-171
❑ 99UltPlaM-171
Eldred, Ross
❑ 16Zee-77
❑ 18Zee-41
❑ 19Zee-50
❑ 20Zee-63
❑ 22Zee-124
❑ 23Zee-160
❑ 24Zee-116
❑ 25Zee-137
❑ 26Zee-162
❑ 27Zee-135
❑ 28Zee-150
Eldredge, Ted
❑ 87BelMarL-23
❑ 88SanBerSB-11
❑ 88SanBerSCLC-41
❑ 89WauTimGS-9
Eldridge, Brian
❑ 89AncGlaP-13
❑ 90AriWilP-4
❑ 93MadMusC-8
❑ 93MadMusF-1826
❑ 94ModA'sC-7
❑ 94ModA'sF-3068
Eldridge, Rodney
❑ 90HamRedB-20
❑ 90HamRedS-10
❑ 91Cla/Bes-180
❑ 91SavCarC-16
❑ 91SavCarP-1657
❑ 92St.PetCC-15
Elenes, Larry
❑ 74CedRapAT-23
Elerman, John
❑ 92ClaFS7-388
Eley, Orville
❑ 23Zee-33
Elguezabal, Jose
❑ 78SanJosMMC-7
Elia, Lee (Lee Constantine)
❑ 66Top-529
❑ 67Top-406
❑ 68Top-561
❑ 69Top-312
❑ 75IntLeaAT-8
❑ 75IntLeaAT-26
❑ 77ReaPhiT-10
❑ 81TCM60I-428
❑ 82CubRedL-4
❑ 83CubThoAV-NNO
❑ 83Don-614
❑ 83Top-456
❑ 84PorBeaC-200
❑ 85PhiTas-4
❑ 85PhiTas-8
❑ 86PhiTas-4
❑ 87PhiTas-xx0
❑ 87TopTra-32T
❑ 87TopTraT-32T
❑ 88ChaLooLTI-9
❑ 88PhiTas-9A
❑ 88PhiTas-9B
❑ 88PhiTas-32
❑ 88Top-254
❑ 88TopTif-254
❑ 90ClePhiS-26
❑ 91ClePhiC-18
❑ 91ClePhiP-1638
❑ 92ScrRedBF-2462
❑ 92ScrRedBS-499
❑ 93MarMot-28
❑ 94MarMot-28
❑ 95MarMot-28
❑ 96MarMot-28
❑ 98ScrRedB1ATI-6
Elias, Javier
❑ 97ButCopKB-6
❑ 97ButCopKK-6
Elick, Jason
❑ 90VisOakCLC-84
Elite Giants, Baltimore
❑ 92NegLeaRLI-98
❑ 93NegLeaRL2-51
❑ 93NegLeaRL2-87
❑ 93NegLeaRL2-88
❑ 93TedWilPC-1
Elite Giants, Nashville
❑ 93NegLeaRL2-50
❑ 93NegLeaRL2-86
Elizabeth, Queen
❑ 84WilMay-39
Elkin, Rick
❑ 80BatTroT-15
❑ 81BatTroT-11
Elkins, Mark
❑ 89TenTecGE-8
Ellam, Roy
❑ 09ColChiE-90
❑ 09T206-483
❑ 10CouT21-20
❑ 12ColRedB-90
❑ 12ColTinT-90
Eller, Hod (Horace Owen)
❑ 19W514-38
❑ 20RedWorCP-5
❑ 22Zee-26
❑ 23Zee-34
❑ 88PacEigMO-93
❑ 92ConTSN-352
❑ 94ConTSN-1027
❑ 94ConTSNB-1027
Ellerbe, Frank (Francis R.)
❑ 21Nei-51
❑ 22E120-95
❑ 22W573-36
❑ 23WilChoV-37
Elli, Rocky
❑ 88ColMetGS-4
❑ 90JacMetGS-22
❑ 91LinDriAAA-482
❑ 91ScrRedBLD-482
❑ 91ScrRedBP-2533
❑ 92ClePhiF-2049
❑ 94SarRedSC-7
❑ 94SarRedSF-1943
Ellingsen, H. Bruce
❑ 75OklCit8TI-6
❑ 75OPC-288
❑ 75Top-288
❑ 75TopMin-288

Elliot, Corey
❑ 84VisOakT-7
Elliot, David
❑ 96BelSnaTI-14
Elliot, Dawan
❑ 97EriSeaWB-10
Elliot, Greg
❑ 92AubAstC-2
❑ 92AubAstF-1359
Elliot, Larry (Lawrence L.)
❑ 61ColJet-1
❑ 63Top-407
❑ 64Top-536
❑ 67OPC-23
❑ 67Top-23
❑ 67VanMouSO-9
❑ 68SeaPop-4
❑ 91MetWIZ-105
Elliot, Paul
❑ 91ParPatF-2
Elliot, Rowdy
❑ 90DodTar-942
Elliot, Terry
❑ 86AncGlaPTI-9
❑ 88St.PetCS-6
❑ 89St.PetCS-10
Elliott, Bob (Robert I.)
❑ 39ExhSal-14
❑ 47HomBon-13
❑ 48BluTin-38
❑ 48Bow-1
❑ 49Bow-58
❑ 49EurSta-7
❑ 49Lea-65
❑ 50AmeNut&CCP-5
❑ 50Bow-20
❑ 50Dra-35
❑ 51Bow-66
❑ 51R42SmaS-28
❑ 51TopBluB-32
❑ 52BerRos-16
❑ 52Top-14
❑ 53ExhCan-26
❑ 60A's-3
❑ 60A'sJayP-3
❑ 60Top-215
❑ 76TayBow4-22
❑ 83TCMPla1942-37
❑ 83TopRep5-14
Elliott, Carter
❑ 18Zee-42
❑ 25Zee-138
Elliott, Claude
❑ 08IndPos-9
❑ 11SpoLifCW-118
Elliott, Clay
❑ 79SavBraT-11
Elliott, Dave
❑ 95HelBreTI-5
❑ 97BelSnaB-10
❑ 98StoPorG-8
Elliott, Dawan
❑ 98AugGreM-7
❑ 98EriSeaWM-11
Elliott, Donnie
❑ 88MarPhiS-12
❑ 89BatCliP-1925
❑ 90SpaPhiB-16
❑ 90SpaPhiP-2482
❑ 90SpaPhiS-5
❑ 91SpaPhiC-3
❑ 91SpaPhiP-888
❑ 92ClaFS7-369
❑ 92GreBraF-1150
❑ 93Bow-58
❑ 93RicBraBB-18
❑ 93RicBraF-179
❑ 93RicBraP-8
❑ 93RicBraRC-11
❑ 93RicBraRC-9
❑ 94Bow-255
❑ 94ColC-655
❑ 94ColChoGS-655
❑ 94ColChoSS-655
❑ 94Fla-435
❑ 94FleUpd-184
❑ 94SpoRoo-53
❑ 94SpoRooAP-53
❑ 94TopTra-17T
❑ 95Don-104
❑ 95DonPreP-104
❑ 95Fla-199
❑ 95Fle-558
❑ 95Pac-360
❑ 95Ult-437
❑ 95UltGolM-437
❑ 96ScrRedBB-13
❑ 98TexLeaC-5
Elliott, Frank
❑ 15Zee-30
❑ 15Zee-31
❑ 16Zee-29
Elliott, Glenn
❑ 43CenFlo-7
❑ 44CenFlo-6
❑ 45CenFlo-6
❑ 49EurSta-8
Elliott, Greg
❑ 93AshTouC-6
❑ 93AshTouF-2282
❑ 93ClaGolF-155
❑ 93SouAtlLAGF-29
❑ 94OscAstC-7
❑ 94OscAstF-1144
Elliott, Harold
❑ 13Zee-135
❑ 14Zee-146
❑ 16Zee-30
❑ 19Zee-18
Elliott, Harry (Harry Lewis)
❑ 55CarHunW-3
❑ 55Top-137
Elliott, Howard
❑ 21Zee-68
❑ 22Zee-42
Elliott, Jim
❑ 26Zee-163
❑ 33Gou-132
❑ 34DiaMatCSB-49
❑ 34GouCanV-6
❑ 90SpoIndSP-11
Elliott, John
❑ 86AshTouP-10
❑ 87OscAstP-17
❑ 88ColAstB-13
Elliott, Jumbo (James Thomas)
❑ 28W513-64
❑ 33RitCE-11C
❑ 90DodTar-217
Elliott, Kevin
❑ 98HagSunM-4
Elliott, Mark
❑ 78CliDodT-7
❑ 79CliDodT-1
Elliott, Paul
❑ 96HagSunB-29
❑ 97KnoSmo-2
❑ 98HagSunM-3
Elliott, Randy (Randy Lee)
❑ 75HawIsIC-4
❑ 77GiaTeal-7
❑ 78Top-719
❑ 97SouOreTB-29
Elliott, Zach
❑ 95MarPhiTI-8
❑ 96Exc-200
❑ 96PieBolWB-11
❑ 97ClePhi-6
Ellis, Bruce
❑ 87BriYouC-20
Ellis, Bull
❑ 91UtiBluSP-3233
Ellis, Dock (Dock Phillip)
❑ 69PirJacitB-3
❑ 69PirTeal-7
❑ 69Top-286
❑ 70PirTeal-6
❑ 70Top-551
❑ 71MLBOffS-200
❑ 71OPC-2
❑ 71PirActP-5
❑ 71Top-2
❑ 71TopCoi-99
❑ 72OPC-179
❑ 72OPC-180
❑ 72PirTeal-3
❑ 72Top-179
❑ 72Top-180
❑ 73OPC-575
❑ 73Top-575
❑ 74OPC-145
❑ 74Top-145
❑ 74TopSta-82
❑ 75OPC-385
❑ 75PitPirP-5
❑ 75Top-385
❑ 75TopMin-385
❑ 76OPC-528
❑ 76Top-528
❑ 76TopTra-528T
❑ 77Kel-4
❑ 77Kel-16A
❑ 77OPC-146
❑ 77Top-71
❑ 78RanBurK-6
❑ 78SSP270-96
❑ 78Top-209
❑ 79Top-691
❑ 80OPC-64
❑ 80Top-117
❑ 89PacSenL-15
❑ 89T/MSenL-33
❑ 89TopSenL-116
❑ 90EliSenL-5
❑ 91FouBal-21
❑ 91MetWIZ-106
❑ 92YanWIZ7-48
❑ 93RanKee-134
❑ 94TedWil-76
Ellis, Doug
❑ 87MacPirP-15
Ellis, Jim
❑ 91MisStaB-14
❑ 92MisStaB-12
Ellis, Jim Russell
❑ 77FriOneYW-28
Ellis, John
❑ 96HudValRB-6
❑ 98Cha-11
Ellis, John (John Charles)
❑ 69YanPhoS-57
❑ 70OPC-516
❑ 70Top-516
❑ 70YanCliDP-10
❑ 70YanPhoS-10
❑ 71MLBOffS-487
❑ 71OPC-263
❑ 71Top-263
❑ 71YanArcO-6
❑ 71YanCliDP-5
❑ 72OPC-47
❑ 72OPC-48
❑ 72Top-47
❑ 72Top-48
❑ 72YanTeal-2
❑ 73IndTeal-10
❑ 73LinPor-62
❑ 73OPC-656
❑ 73Top-656
❑ 74OPC-128
❑ 74Top-128
❑ 74TopSta-165
❑ 75CleIndP-11
❑ 75Hos-54
❑ 75OPC-605
❑ 75Top-605
❑ 75TopMin-605
❑ 76Hos-27
❑ 76HosTwi-27
❑ 76OPC-383
❑ 76SSP-515
❑ 76Top-383
❑ 76TopTra-383T
❑ 77Top-36
❑ 78RanBurK-3
❑ 78SSP270-100
❑ 78Top-438
❑ 79Top-539
❑ 80Top-283
❑ 81Don-26A
❑ 81Don-26B
❑ 81Top-339
❑ 82Don-642
❑ 82Fle-316
❑ 82Top-177
❑ 92YanWIZ6-39
❑ 92YanWIZ7-49
❑ 93RanKee-135
Ellis, K.J.
❑ 93HunCubF-3241
Ellis, Kevin
❑ 93HunCubC-1
❑ 94PeoChiC-7
❑ 94PeoChiF-2275
❑ 96DayCubB-9
❑ 97OrlRayB-9
❑ 98IowCubQ-8
Ellis, Paul
❑ 90HamRedB-13
❑ 90HamRedS-11
❑ 91Cla/Bes-81
❑ 91FloStaLAP-FSL34
❑ 91St.PetCC-15
❑ 91St.PetCP-2278
❑ 92ClaFS7-278
❑ 92St.PetCC-5
❑ 92St.PetCF-2030
❑ 93ArkTraF-2814
❑ 93Bow-336
❑ 93ClaFS7-69
❑ 93ClaGolF-97
❑ 94ArkTraF-3092
❑ 95ArkTraTI-12
❑ 96ArkTraB-13
Ellis, Rob (Robert Walter)
❑ 74SacSolC-61
❑ 75SacSolC-11
❑ 76SpoIndC-6
❑ 76SSP-240
❑ 77SpoIndC-24
❑ 79TacTugT-23
❑ 80PorBeaT-5
❑ 89AncGlaP-14
❑ 91EveGiaP-3933
❑ 93HolLeg-6
❑ 94BreMilB-21
❑ 98NewBriRCM-3
Ellis, Robert
❑ 91UtiBluSC-7
❑ 92SouBenWSC-3
❑ 93FloStaLAF-23
❑ 93SarWhiSC-9
❑ 93SarWhiSF-1364
❑ 94ActPac-51
❑ 94Bow-183
❑ 94Cla-29
❑ 94ExcFS7-38
❑ 94NasSouF-1245
❑ 94UppDec-25
❑ 94UppDecML-139
❑ 96NasSouB-13
❑ 96VanCanB-11
❑ 97VanCanB-14
❑ 98LouRedQ-30
Ellis, Rube (George W.)
❑ 09AmeCarE90-1-39
❑ 09ColChiE-92
❑ 10JuJuDE-17
❑ 10NadCarE-22
❑ 11PinT-5-352
❑ 11SpoLifCW-119
❑ 11SpoLifM-267
❑ 12ColRedB-92
❑ 12ColTinT-92
❑ 12T207-54
❑ 13Zee-7
❑ 14Zee-10
❑ 15Zee-8
❑ 16Zee-5
❑ 17Zee-87
❑ 18Zee-6
❑ 19Zee-6
❑ 20Zee-9
❑ 21Zee-9
❑ 72ClaCar-106
Ellis, Rufus
❑ 86FloStaLAP-12
❑ 86Ft.MyeRP-9
❑ 87Ft.MyeRP-18
❑ 88ChaRanS-6
Ellis, Sammy (Samuel Joseph)
❑ 63RedEnq-7
❑ 63Top-29A
❑ 63Top-29B
❑ 64Top-33
❑ 64TopVen-33
❑ 65Kah-13
❑ 65RedEnq-9
❑ 65Top-507
❑ 66Kah-12
❑ 66RedVolC-4
❑ 66Top-250
❑ 66TopRubl-25
❑ 66TopVen-250
❑ 67Kah-12A
❑ 67Kah-12B
❑ 67OPC-176
❑ 67Top-176
❑ 67TopVen-279
❑ 68Top-453
❑ 69OPC-32
❑ 69Top-32
❑ 77ForLauYS-17
❑ 78TCM60I-293
❑ 80ColCliP-NNO
❑ 80ColCliT-14
❑ 81ColCliP-NNO
❑ 81ColCliT-26
❑ 82ColCliP-NNO
❑ 82ColCliT-24
❑ 83YanPhoA-3
❑ 86YanTCM-40
❑ 90WhiSoxC-30
❑ 91WhiSoxK-NNO
❑ 92CubMar-NNO
❑ 93MarMot-28
❑ 94MarMot-28
Ellis, Terry
❑ 88MisStaB-5
Ellis, Tim
❑ 88GenCubP-1643
❑ 90KinIndTI-26
❑ 90WatIndS-8
Ellison, Bert
❑ 21Zee-118
❑ 22Zee-97
❑ 23Zee-127
❑ 23Zee-128
❑ 24Zee-88
❑ 25Zee-107
❑ 26Zee-134
❑ 27Zee-110
Ellison, Darold
❑ 80BatTroT-18
Ellison, Jeff
❑ 76DubPacT-10
❑ 77CocAstT-5
❑ 98GreBatM-5
Ellison, Paul
❑ 88SpaPhiS-22
❑ 89SpaPhiP-1041
❑ 89SpaPhiS-8
Ellison, Skeeter
❑ 96DanBraB-10
Ellsworth, Ben
❑ 90JohCitCS-11
❑ 91HamRedC-25
❑ 91HamRedP-4045
❑ 92SavCarC-5
❑ 92SavCarF-669
❑ 93SprCarC-9
❑ 93SprCarF-1857
❑ 94SavCarC-12
❑ 94SavCarF-514
Ellsworth, Dick (Richard C.)
❑ 60Top-125
❑ 60TopVen-125
❑ 61CubJayP-6
❑ 61Top-427
❑ 61TopStal-7
❑ 61WilSpoGH828-1-1
❑ 62Top-264
❑ 62TopStal-107
❑ 63Top-399
❑ 64Baz-28
❑ 64CubJayP-5
❑ 64Top-1
❑ 64Top-220
❑ 64TopCoi-56
❑ 64TopGia-17
❑ 64TopSta-5
❑ 64TopStaU-23
❑ 64TopTatl-35
❑ 64TopVen-1
❑ 64TopVen-220
❑ 65CubJayP-7
❑ 65OPC-165
❑ 65Top-165
❑ 65TopEmbl-67
❑ 66CubTeal-7
❑ 66Top-447
❑ 66TopRubl-26
❑ 67CokCapPh-7
❑ 67PhiPol-6
❑ 67ProPizC-7
❑ 67Top-359
❑ 68CokCapRS-14
❑ 68DexPre-30
❑ 68Top-406
❑ 69MilBra-78
❑ 69MLBOffS-12
❑ 69Top-605
❑ 70MLBOffS-196
❑ 70OPC-59
❑ 70Top-59
❑ 71MLBOffS-435
❑ 71OPC-309
❑ 71Top-309
❑ 72MilBra-98
❑ 81RedSoxBG2S-79
❑ 94BreMilB-117
Ellsworth, Floyd
❑ 26Zee-164
❑ 29Zee-155
❑ 30Zee-170
❑ 31Zee-117
❑ 32Zee-114
❑ 33Zee-86
Ellsworth, Fred
❑ 28Zee-151
Ellsworth, Steve
❑ 86NewBriRSP-10
❑ 87PawRedSP-67
❑ 87PawRedST-6
❑ 88DonRoo-54
❑ 88DonTeaBRS-NEW
❑ 88ScoRoo-83T
❑ 88ScoRooG-83T
❑ 89PawRedSC-7
❑ 89PawRedSP-704
❑ 89PawRedSTI-8
❑ 89Top-299
❑ 89TopTif-299
Elmore, Jason
❑ 96EriSeaB-10
Elmore, Mike
❑ 87NewOriP-16
Elpin, Ralph
❑ 81WatIndT-33
❑ 82WatIndF-12
❑ 82WatIndT-3
Elrod, Greg
❑ 85CloHSS-14
Elsbecker, Andy
❑ 92HunCubC-16
❑ 92HunCubF-3138
Elsbernd, David
❑ 92UtiBluSC-23
❑ 93HicCraC-5
❑ 93HicCraF-1272
❑ 94HicCraC-9
❑ 94HicCraF-2170
Elsea, Dottie
❑ 89KinMetS-30
❑ 90KinMetS-29
Elsh, Eugene
❑ 26Zee-93
Elster, Kevin
❑ 84LitFalMT-19
❑ 85LynMetT-19
❑ 86JacMetT-13
❑ 86MetWorSC-18
❑ 87Don-635
❑ 87Fle-7
❑ 87FleGlo-7
❑ 87IntLeaAT-6
❑ 87MetColP-31
❑ 87TidTidP-32
❑ 87TidTidT-13
❑ 88ClaRed-190
❑ 88Don-37
❑ 88DonBasB-70
❑ 88DonRoo-34
❑ 88DonTeaBM-37
❑ 88FleUpd-104
❑ 88FleUpdG-104
❑ 88Lea-37
❑ 88MetColP-22
❑ 88MetFanC-21
❑ 88MetKah-21
❑ 88Sco-624
❑ 88ScoGlo-624
❑ 88ScoYouS2-40
❑ 88SpoGam-24
❑ 88Top-8
❑ 88TopTif-8
❑ 89Bow-383
❑ 89BowTif-383
❑ 89ClaLigB-75
❑ 89Don-289
❑ 89DonBasB-97
❑ 89Fle-34
❑ 89FleGlo-34
❑ 89MetColP-7
❑ 89MetKah-7
❑ 89PanSti-127
❑ 89Sco-130
❑ 89Spo-71
❑ 89TidTidC-15
❑ 89Top-356
❑ 89TopBig-16
❑ 89TopRoo-6
❑ 89TopTif-356
❑ 89ToyRoo-7
❑ 89UppDec-269
❑ 90Bow-137

❑ 90BowTif-137
❑ 90Don-152
❑ 90DonBesN-31
❑ 90Fle-202
❑ 90FleCan-202
❑ 90Lea-8
❑ 90MetColP-7
❑ 90MetFanC-21
❑ 90MetKah-21
❑ 90MLBBasB-12
❑ 90OPC-734
❑ 90PanStl-296
❑ 90PubIntS-132
❑ 90Sco-443
❑ 90Spo-118
❑ 90Top-734
❑ 90TopBig-143
❑ 90TopSti-2
❑ 90TopSti-97
❑ 90TopTif-734
❑ 90TopTVM-23
❑ 90UppDec-187
❑ 91Bow-469
❑ 91Don-304
❑ 91Fle-145
❑ 91Lea-305
❑ 91MetColP-15
❑ 91MetKah-21
❑ 91MetPerPA-14
❑ 91MetWIZ-107
❑ 91OPC-134
❑ 91PanFreS-82
❑ 91RedFolS-32
❑ 91Sco-633
❑ 91StaClu-149
❑ 91Top-134
❑ 91TopDesS-134
❑ 91TopMic-134
❑ 91TopTif-134
❑ 91Ult-215
❑ 91UppDec-101
❑ 92Don-307
❑ 92Fle-502
❑ 92MetColP-13
❑ 92MetKah-15
❑ 92OPC-251
❑ 92PanSti-225
❑ 92Pin-89
❑ 92Sco-103
❑ 92StaClu-201
❑ 92Top-251
❑ 92TopGol-251
❑ 92TopGolW-251
❑ 92TopMic-251
❑ 92TriPla-66
❑ 92Ult-231
❑ 92UppDec-385
❑ 93Fle-469
❑ 93PacSpa-195
❑ 96Cir-85
❑ 96CirRav-85
❑ 96FleUpd-U88
❑ 96FleUpdTC-U88
❑ 96RanDr P-7
❑ 96RanFle-4
❑ 96RanMot-12
❑ 97Cir-34
❑ 97CirRav-34
❑ 97ColCho-238
❑ 97ColCho-426
❑ 97Don-150
❑ 97Don-333
❑ 97DonGolPP-150
❑ 97DonGolPP-333
❑ 97DonSilPP-150
❑ 97DonSilPP-333
❑ 97Fin-225
❑ 97FinRef-225
❑ 97Fle-220
❑ 97Fle-660
❑ 97FleTif-220
❑ 97FleTif-660
❑ 97Lea-106
❑ 97Lea-213
❑ 97LeaFraM-106
❑ 97LeaFraM-213
❑ 97LeaFraMDC-106
❑ 97LeaFraMDC-213
❑ 97NewPin-156
❑ 97NewPinAP-156
❑ 97NewPinMC-156
❑ 97NewPinPP-156
❑ 97Pac-198
❑ 97PacLigB-198
❑ 97PacSil-198
❑ 97Pin-67
❑ 97PinArtP-PP67
❑ 97PinMusC-67
❑ 97PinPrePla-67
❑ 97PirPos-11
❑ 97RanSco-5
❑ 97RanScoPl-5
❑ 97RanScoPr-5
❑ 97Sco-73
❑ 97Sco-346
❑ 97ScoArtPWB-73
❑ 97ScoArtPWB-346
❑ 97ScoPreS-73
❑ 97ScoResC-346
❑ 97ScoShoS-73
❑ 97ScoShoS-346
❑ 97ScoShoSAP-73
❑ 97ScoShoSAP-346
❑ 97SP-141
❑ 97SpoIll-107
❑ 97SpoIllEE-107
❑ 97StaClu-138
❑ 97StaCluMOP-138
❑ 97Top-61
❑ 97Ult-131
❑ 97Ult-394
❑ 97UltGolME-131
❑ 97UltGolME-394
❑ 97UltPlaME-131
❑ 97UltPlaME-394
❑ 97UppDec-461
❑ 98ColCho-514
❑ 98Don-179
❑ 98DonGolPP-179
❑ 98DonSilPP-179
❑ 98Fle-399
❑ 98PacInvGems-195
❑ 98PacOnl-731
❑ 98PacOnlR-731
❑ 98PacOnlWC-731
❑ 98PinSna-TR5
❑ 98StaCluFDI-179
❑ 98StaCluI-179
❑ 98StaCluOneK-179
❑ 98StaCluPP-179
❑ 98Top-198
❑ 98TopChr-198
❑ 98TopChrR-198
❑ 98TopDevR-198
❑ 98TopDia-198
❑ 98TopMiniC-198
❑ 98Ult-385
❑ 98UltGolM-385
❑ 98UltMas-385
❑ 98UltPlaM-385
❑ 98UppDec-195
❑ 98UppDec-518

Elston, Carey
❑ 89BurIndS-10

Elston, Curt
❑ 12ImpTobC-23

Elston, Don (Donald Ray)
❑ 57Top-376
❑ 58Top-363
❑ 59Top-520
❑ 60CubJayP-6
❑ 60Top-233
❑ 61CubJayP-7
❑ 61Pos-200A
❑ 61Pos-200B
❑ 61Top-169
❑ 61TopStaI-8
❑ 62CubJayP-6
❑ 62Jel-190
❑ 62Pos-190
❑ 62PosCan-190
❑ 62SalPlaC-101
❑ 62ShiPlaC-101
❑ 62Top-446
❑ 63CubJayP-5
❑ 63Top-515
❑ 64Top-111
❑ 64TopVen-111
❑ 65Top-436
❑ 78TCM60I-143
❑ 84CubUno-9
❑ 90DodTar-218

Elston, Guy
❑ 82NasSouTI-11
❑ 83ColCliT-13
❑ 84MaiGuiT-13

Elvee, (Mascot)
❑ 97LasVegS1A-30
❑ 98Las-8

Elvira, Narciso
❑ 88StoPorCLC-183
❑ 88StoPorP-748
❑ 89StoPorS-6
❑ 91Bow-47
❑ 91DenZepLD-136
❑ 91DenZepP-117
❑ 91LinDriAAA-136
❑ 91TopDeb90-43
❑ 91UppDec-13
❑ 92OklCit8F-1911
❑ 92OklCit8S-323
❑ 94BreMilB-118
❑ 97AlbDukGS-9

Elway, John
❑ 82OneYanT-13

Elwert, William
❑ 11PinT-5-1111

Ely, Bones
❑ 90DodTar-943
❑ 98CamPepP-23

Embree, Alan
❑ 90BurIndP-3004
❑ 91ColIndC-12
❑ 91ColIndP-1479
❑ 92Bow-387
❑ 92KinIndC-17
❑ 92KinIndF-2469
❑ 93Bow-389
❑ 93Don-333
❑ 93FleMajLP-A5
❑ 93Pin-593
❑ 93ScoBoyoS-20
❑ 93StaClu-379
❑ 93StaCluFDI-379
❑ 93StaCluMOP-379
❑ 93Top-742
❑ 93TopGol-742
❑ 93TopInaM-742
❑ 93TopInaR-742
❑ 93TopMic-742
❑ 93Toy-59
❑ 93UppDec-12
❑ 93UppDecGold-12
❑ 94CanIndF-3113
❑ 94UppDecML-22
❑ 95Bow-110
❑ 96ColCho-526
❑ 96ColChoGS-526
❑ 96ColChoSS-526
❑ 96Fle-85
❑ 96FleTif-85
❑ 96Sco-246
❑ 97ColCho-268
❑ 97Fle-676
❑ 97FleTif-676
❑ 97PacPriGotD-GD35
❑ 97Ult-445
❑ 97UltGolME-445
❑ 97UltPlaME-445
❑ 98PacOnl-58
❑ 98PacOnlR-58
❑ 98PacOnlWC-58

Embree, Red (Charles W.)
❑ 47IndTeal-7
❑ 47IndVanPP-6
❑ 48YanTeal-9
❑ 52MotCoo-22
❑ 79DiaGre-289

Embry, Bryon
❑ 97DanBraB-15
❑ 98MacBraM-4

Embry, Todd
❑ 90WatDiaB-4
❑ 90WatDiaP-2370

Embser, Rich
❑ 85SprCarT-2
❑ 86ArkTraP-7

Emeralds, Eugene
❑ 92EugEmeC-30
❑ 92EugEmeF-3649

Emerick, Chris
❑ 90GatCitPP-3357
❑ 90GatCitPSP-7

Emerson, Scott
❑ 92BluOriC-15
❑ 92BluOriF-2355
❑ 93AlbPolCB-14
❑ 93AlbPolF-2022
❑ 94FreKeyC-10
❑ 94FreKeyF-2607
❑ 94OriPro-30

Emery, Cal (Calvin Wayne)
❑ 77FriOneYW-73
❑ 79WatIndT-24
❑ 80WatIndT-30
❑ 81ChaChaT-24
❑ 89VanCanC-21
❑ 89VanCanP-572

Emiliano, James
❑ 96AshTouB-16

Emm, Art
❑ 90ColMetGS-17
❑ 90ColMetPPI-1

Emmer, Frank
❑ 25Zee-139

Emmerich, William P.
❑ 49AngTeal-9
❑ 49W725AngTI-8

Emmerke, R.
❑ 87OldJudN-151

Emmett, John
❑ 94HelBreSP-28

Emmons, Scott
❑ 97TamYan-12
❑ 98NorNavQ-10

Emoto, Kouichi
❑ 90SalSpuCLC-121
❑ 90SalSpuP-2715

Emoto, Takenori
❑ 79TCMJapPB-87

Empting, Mike
❑ 83CliGiaF-15

Emslie, Bob
❑ 94ConTSN-1203
❑ 94ConTSNB-1203

Enard, Tony
❑ 95ElmPioTI-3
❑ 95ElmPioUTI-3
❑ 96BreCouMB-14
❑ 96KanCouCTI-7

Enatsu, Yutaka
❑ 79TCMJapPB-27

Enberg, Dick
❑ 75CalAngP-15

Encarcion, Miguel
❑ 76BurBeeT-8

Encarnacion, Angelo
❑ 91WelPirC-10
❑ 91WelPirP-3574
❑ 92AugPirF-241
❑ 93CarLeaAGF-49
❑ 93SalBucC-8
❑ 93SalBucF-434
❑ 94CarMudF-1583
❑ 95PirFil-9
❑ 96ColCho-681
❑ 96ColChoGS-681
❑ 96ColChoSS-681
❑ 96Don-5
❑ 96DonPreP-5
❑ 96Fle-519
❑ 96FleTif-519
❑ 96Pac-179
❑ 96Ult-262
❑ 96UltGolM-262
❑ 97LasVegS1A-14
❑ 97PacPriGotD-GD191

Encarnacion, Anito
❑ 93RanCucQC-10
❑ 93RanCucQF-834
❑ 95CedRapKTI-26

Encarnacion, Bienvenido
❑ 97ButCopKB-7
❑ 97ButCopKK-7
❑ 98ButCopKG-12

Encarnacion, Juan
❑ 94BriTigC-11
❑ 94BriTigF-3517
❑ 94FayGenC-11
❑ 94FayGenF-2162
❑ 95Bes-20
❑ 95BowBes-B49
❑ 95BowBesR-B49
❑ 95FayGenTI-10
❑ 95SPML-53
❑ 96Bow-268
❑ 96BowFoi-268
❑ 96Exc-51
❑ 96LakTigB-13
❑ 97Bes-64
❑ 97BesAutSBPP-41
❑ 97BesWhe-2
❑ 97Bow-406
❑ 97BowChr-269
❑ 97BowChrI-269
❑ 97BowChrIR-269
❑ 97BowChrR-269
❑ 97BowInt-406
❑ 97JacSun-3
❑ 97Sel-133
❑ 97SelArtP-133
❑ 97SelCom-133
❑ 97SelRegG-133
❑ 97SouLeaTP-18
❑ 97TexAllM-13
❑ 97TopSta-101
❑ 97TopStaAM-101
❑ 98Bow-297
❑ 98BowBes-134
❑ 98BowBesAR-134
❑ 98BowBesMIF-MI7
❑ 98BowBesMIFAR-MI7
❑ 98BowBesMIFR-MI7
❑ 98BowBesR-134
❑ 98BowCerBlueAU-57
❑ 98BowCerGA-57
❑ 98BowCerSA-57
❑ 98BowChr-297
❑ 98BowChrGA-297
❑ 98BowChrGAR-297
❑ 98BowChrI-297
❑ 98BowChrIR-297
❑ 98BowChrR-297
❑ 98BowGolA-297
❑ 98BowInt-297
❑ 98BowScoC-SC16
❑ 98CirThu-274
❑ 98CirThuFT-2
❑ 98CirThuRav-274
❑ 98CirThuSupRav-274
❑ 98ColCho-106
❑ 98ColChoSQ-SQ18
❑ 98Don-333
❑ 98DonColE-501
❑ 98DonColL-384
❑ 98DonColP-698
❑ 98DonEli-101
❑ 98DonEliA-101
❑ 98DonEliS-101
❑ 98DonGolPP-333
❑ 98DonPre-148
❑ 98DonPreGES-9
❑ 98DonPreGX-9
❑ 98DonPreGXDC-9
❑ 98DonPreSeat-148
❑ 98DonPriCE-501
❑ 98DonPriCL-384
❑ 98DonPriCP-698
❑ 98DonSig-87
❑ 98DonSigA-28
❑ 98DonSigAM-38
❑ 98DonSigP-87
❑ 98DonSigSB-8
❑ 98DonSigSP-5
❑ 98DonSilPP-333
❑ 98E-X2SD2001-6
❑ 98FlaShoLeg0-18
❑ 98FlaShoLeg1-18
❑ 98FlaShoLeg2-18
❑ 98FlaShoLeg3-18
❑ 98FlaShoLegM-18
❑ 98FlaShoR0-18
❑ 98FlaShoR1-18
❑ 98FlaShoR2-18
❑ 98FlaShoR3-18
❑ 98FlaShoWotF-4
❑ 98Fle-258
❑ 98Lea-185
❑ 98LeaFraDA-185
❑ 98LeaFraF-185
❑ 98LeaFraM-185
❑ 98LeaFraM-185
❑ 98LeaFraMDC-185
❑ 98LeaFraMDC-185
❑ 98LeaFraMZ2-185
❑ 98LeaRCrusUP-111
❑ 98LeaRS-237
❑ 98LeaRSCrusUG-111
❑ 98LeaRSCrusUR-111
❑ 98LeaRSFOSamp-13
❑ 98LeaRSFresh-13
❑ 98LeaRSLHolo-237
❑ 98LeaRSLong-237
❑ 98LeaRTrue-237
❑ 98Pin-180
❑ 98PinArtP-PP83
❑ 98PinIns-127
❑ 98PinInsCE-127
❑ 98PinInsDE-127
❑ 98PinMusC-PP83
❑ 98PinPer-126
❑ 98PinPerPP-126
❑ 98PinPlu-90
❑ 98PinPluAP-PP33
❑ 98PinPluGAP-PP33
❑ 98PinPluMAP-PP33
❑ 98PinPreP-180
❑ 98ScoRT-245
❑ 98ScoRTSS-PP138
❑ 98ScoRTSSAP-PP138
❑ 98ScoRTSSAP1-PP138
❑ 98SkyDugA-100
❑ 98SkyDugAIA-100
❑ 98SP Aut-14
❑ 98SP MinPE-6
❑ 98SPMin-6
❑ 98SpoIll-157
❑ 98SpoIllEE-157
❑ 98SpoIllFE-157
❑ 98SpoIllTaN-143
❑ 98SpoIllTaNEE-143
❑ 98SPxFin-21
❑ 98SPxFinR-21
❑ 98SPxFinS-21
❑ 98StaCluBPP-BP6
❑ 98StaCluFDI-135
❑ 98StaCluI-135
❑ 98StaCluITW-W1
❑ 98StaCluOneK-135
❑ 98StaCluPP-135
❑ 98Stu-206
❑ 98StuGPP-206
❑ 98StuSPP-206
❑ 98TolMudHQ-15
❑ 98Top-258
❑ 98TopChr-258
❑ 98TopChrR-258
❑ 98TopChrRC-R9
❑ 98TopChrRCRef-R9
❑ 98TopDevR-258
❑ 98TopDia-258
❑ 98TopMiniC-258
❑ 98TopRooCla-R9
❑ 98UD3-24
❑ 98UD3-114
❑ 98UD3-204
❑ 98UD3DieCut-24
❑ 98UD3DieCut-114
❑ 98UD3DieCut-204
❑ 98Ult-396
❑ 98UltGolM-396
❑ 98UltMas-396
❑ 98UltPlaM-396
❑ 98UltRoctS-8
❑ 98UppDec-286
❑ 98UppDecBCP-BC22
❑ 98UppDecDS-DS49
❑ 98UppDecREP-6
❑ 98Zen-88
❑ 98Zen5 xx7-71
❑ 98Zen5x7GoldImp-71
❑ 98Zen5x7Imp-71
❑ 98ZenRooT-2
❑ 98ZenZ-G-88
❑ 98ZenZ-S-88
❑ 99Bow-139
❑ 99BowBes-143
❑ 99BowBesAR-143
❑ 99BowBesR-143
❑ 99BowChr-139
❑ 99BowChrG-139
❑ 99BowChrGR-139
❑ 99BowChrI-139
❑ 99BowChrIR-139
❑ 99BowChrR-139
❑ 99BowGol-139
❑ 99BowInt-139
❑ 99DumSet-JE
❑ 99DumSet-JE
❑ 99E-X Cen-80
❑ 99E-X CenECFut-80
❑ 99E-X CenECNow-80
❑ 99FlaShoLeg1-47
❑ 99FlaShoLeg2-47
❑ 99FlaShoLeg3-47
❑ 99FlaShoLegM1-47
❑ 99FlaShoLegM2-47
❑ 99FlaShoLegM3-47
❑ 99FlaShoR1-47
❑ 99FlaShoR2-47
❑ 99FlaShoR3-47
❑ 99FlaShoWotF-4
❑ 99Fle-38
❑ 99Fle-579
❑ 99FleBri-68
❑ 99FleBri2G-68
❑ 99FleBriBlu-68
❑ 99FleBriGol-68
❑ 99FleBriI-4
❑ 99FleMys-76
❑ 99FleMysFI-13
❑ 99FleMysG-76

❑ 99FleMysM-76
❑ 99FleRooFla-7
❑ 99FleSta9-38
❑ 99FleSta9-579
❑ 99FleVin'-38
❑ 99FleWarT-38
❑ 99FleWarT-579
❑ 99Pac-163
❑ 99PacOme-89
❑ 99PacOmeC-89
❑ 99PacOmeG-89
❑ 99PacOmePB-89
❑ 99PacPlaB-163
❑ 99PacRed-163
❑ 99SkyMolM-51
❑ 99SkyMolMX-51
❑ 99SkyPre-194
❑ 99SkyPreA-18
❑ 99SkyPreABlue-18
❑ 99SkyPreR-194
❑ 99SkyThu-249
❑ 99SkyThuRant-249
❑ 99SkyThuRave-249
❑ 99SkyThuUnl-U5
❑ 99SP SigAuto-JE
❑ 99SP SigAutoG-JE
❑ 99SpoIll-109
❑ 99SPSig-72
❑ 99SPx-93
❑ 99SPxFinR-93
❑ 99SPxFinS-93
❑ 99StaClu-291
❑ 99StaCluFDI-291
❑ 99StaCluOoaK-291
❑ 99StaCluPP-291
❑ 99ThuSkySupR-249
❑ 99Top-397
❑ 99TopChr-397
❑ 99TopChrR-397
❑ 99TopGal-147
❑ 99TopGalPP-147
❑ 99TopGalPPI-147
❑ 99TopMVPP-397
❑ 99UDHolo-23
❑ 99UDHoloAUsome-23
❑ 99Ult-164
❑ 99UltGolM-164
❑ 99UltMas-164
❑ 99UltPlaM-164
❑ 99UppDec-372
❑ 99UppDecCLM-C36
❑ 99UppDecE-38
❑ 99UppDecEFXG-38
❑ 99UppDecEL1-372
❑ 99UppDecEL2-372
❑ 99UppDecM-81
❑ 99UppDecMGS-81
❑ 99UppDecMHFS-81
❑ 99UppDecMP-81
❑ 99UppDecMSS-81
❑ 99UppDecR-32
❑ 99UppDecRG-32
❑ 99UppDecRP-32
❑ 99Vic-145

Encarnacion, Juan Minors
❑ 90AshTouP-2760

Encarnacion, Luis
❑ 86WatIndP-8
❑ 87WilBilP-5
❑ 88MemChiB-12
❑ 89MemChiB-20
❑ 89MemChiP-1187
❑ 89MemChiS-10
❑ 89SouLeaAJ-22
❑ 90CMC-179
❑ 90OmaRoyC-4
❑ 90OmaRoyP-60
❑ 90ProAAAF-595
❑ 91LinDriAAA-334
❑ 91OmaRoyLD-334
❑ 91OmaRoyP-1029
❑ 91TopDeb90-44
❑ 93LimRocDWB-1

Encarnacion, Mario
❑ 96WesMicWB-8
❑ 97CalLeaTP-14
❑ 97ModA'sG-9
❑ 98Bes-13
❑ 98HunStaTI-15
❑ 99Bow-171
❑ 99BowChr-171
❑ 99BowChrG-171
❑ 99BowChrGR-171
❑ 99BowChrI-171
❑ 99BowChrIR-171
❑ 99BowChrR-171
❑ 99BowGol-171
❑ 99BowInt-171
❑ 99E-X Cen-114
❑ 99E-X CenECFut-114
❑ 99E-X CenECNow-114
❑ 99FlaShoLeg1-36
❑ 99FlaShoLeg2-36
❑ 99FlaShoLeg3-36
❑ 99FlaShoLegM1-36
❑ 99FlaShoLegM2-36
❑ 99FlaShoLegM3-36
❑ 99FlaShoR1-36
❑ 99FlaShoR2-36
❑ 99FlaShoR3-36
❑ 99FleBri-174
❑ 99FleBri2G-174
❑ 99FleBriBlu-174
❑ 99FleBriGol-174
❑ 99SkyPreA-17
❑ 99SkyPreABlue-17
❑ 99SP TopP-43
❑ 99SP TopPPE-43
❑ 99WesMicWAM-8

Endebrock, Kurt
❑ 91SouOreAC-25
❑ 91SouOreAP-3853
❑ 92SouOreAC-27
❑ 92SouOreAF-3432

Ender, Scott
❑ 81CedRapRT-24

Enders, Trevor
❑ 97ChaRivDG-12
❑ 98St.PetDRM-7

Endicott, Bill
❑ 46SeaSLP-19
❑ 83Car194T-36

Engel, Bob
❑ 88T/MUmp-5
❑ 89T/MUmp-3
❑ 90T/MUmp-3

Engel, Joe
❑ 88ChaLooLTI-10

Engel, Steve
❑ 86Don-510
❑ 86IowCubP-10
❑ 88ArkTraGS-3

Engelhardt, Jim
❑ 68SeaPop-5

Engelkin, Gary
❑ 88JacExpB-28
❑ 88JacExpP-990
❑ 89JamExpP-2149

Engelmeyer, Bob
❑ 77DayBeaIT-5

Engeln, William
❑ 55Bow-301

England, Dave
❑ 82ArkTraT-23
❑ 83ArkTraT-25
❑ 92HelBreF-1709
❑ 92HelBreSP-4

Engle, Beau
❑ 97CapCitB-13

Engle, Dave (Ralph David)
❑ 79TolMudHT-7
❑ 80TolMudHT-15
❑ 80VenLeaS-10
❑ 81Top-328
❑ 81TwiPos-8
❑ 82Don-102
❑ 82Fle-552
❑ 82Top-738
❑ 82TwiPos-8
❑ 83Don-646
❑ 83Top-294
❑ 83TwiTeal-14
❑ 83TwiTeal-32
❑ 84Don-598
❑ 84Fle-562
❑ 84MinTwiP-10
❑ 84Nes792-463
❑ 84Top-463
❑ 84TopSti-313
❑ 84TopTif-463
❑ 84TwiTeal-15
❑ 85Don-72
❑ 85Fle-276
❑ 85Lea-173
❑ 85OPC-199
❑ 85Top-667
❑ 85TopSti-298
❑ 85TopTif-667
❑ 85TwiPos-6
❑ 85TwiTeal-5
❑ 85TwiTeal-15
❑ 86Don-438
❑ 86Fle-391
❑ 86FleUpd-39
❑ 86Top-43
❑ 86TopTif-43
❑ 87ExpPos-5
❑ 88ExpPos-7
❑ 88OPC-196
❑ 88Sco-617
❑ 88ScoGlo-617
❑ 88Top-196
❑ 88TopTif-196
❑ 89BrePol-25
❑ 90OklCit8P-435
❑ 90ProAAAF-681
❑ 91LinDriAAA-625
❑ 91TucTorLD-625
❑ 91TucTorP-2229
❑ 92TucTorF-505
❑ 92TucTorS-625
❑ 93TucTorF-3077
❑ 94BreMilB-218
❑ 94TucTorF-778
❑ 96JacGenB-1

Engle, Eleanor
❑ 91TopArc1-332

Engle, Hack (Arthur Clyde)
❑ 07NewEveWS-3
❑ 09AmeCarE90-1-40
❑ 09ColChiE-94A
❑ 09ColChiE-94B
❑ 09T206-122
❑ 10CouT21-21
❑ 10DomDisP-40
❑ 10PeoT21-22
❑ 10SweCapPP-3A
❑ 10SweCapPP-3B
❑ 11HelSta-3
❑ 11PinT-5-661
❑ 11SpoLifM-7
❑ 11T205-51
❑ 12ColRedB-94A
❑ 12ColRedB-94B
❑ 12ColTinT-94A
❑ 12ColTinT-94B
❑ 12HasTriFT-35
❑ 12HasTriFT-64
❑ 12T207-55
❑ 14PieStaT-38
❑ 15AmeCarE106-16
❑ 86ConSer1-14

Engle, Rick
❑ 79MemChiT-14

Engle, Scott
❑ 84AriWilP-5

Engle, Tom
❑ 89HigSchPLS-3
❑ 89KinMetS-8
❑ 90KinMetB-22
❑ 90KinMetS-7
❑ 91ColMetPI-5
❑ 91ColMetPI-31
❑ 91ColMetPPI-5
❑ 92ColMetPI-29
❑ 93CapCitBC-4
❑ 93CapCitBF-453
❑ 93PitMetC-6
❑ 93PitMetF-3700
❑ 94Bow-70
❑ 94CapCitBC-6
❑ 94CapCitBF-1744
❑ 95BinMetTI-46

Englehart, Bill
❑ 84GreHorT-26

Englehart, Scott
❑ 92EriSaiC-12
❑ 92EriSaiF-1612

Engleka, Matt
❑ 96FayGenB-14

English, Gil
❑ 90DodTar-219

English, Jim
❑ 80AppFoxT-16

English, Maddy
❑ 94TedWil-95

English, Woody (Elwood G.)
❑ 28Exh-9
❑ 28StaPlaCE-18
❑ 29ExhFou-6
❑ 29PorandAR-21
❑ 30ChiEveAP-3
❑ 30CubTeal-5
❑ 30SchR33-18
❑ 31CubTeal-7
❑ 31Exh-6
❑ 32CubTeal-5
❑ 32OrbPinNP-32A
❑ 32OrbPinNP-32B
❑ 32OrbPinUP-18
❑ 33ExhFou-3
❑ 33Gou-135
❑ 33NatLeaAC-2
❑ 33TatOrb-18
❑ 33TatOrbSDR-156
❑ 33TatOrbSDR-193
❑ 34DiaMatCSB-50
❑ 34DiaMatCSB-51
❑ 34ExhFou-3
❑ 34Gou-4
❑ 34GouCanV-11
❑ 34GouCanV-50
❑ 35DiaMatCS3T1-50
❑ 35GouPuzR-1F
❑ 35GouPuzR-3D
❑ 35GouPuzR-14D
❑ 35GouPuzR-15D
❑ 36CubTeal-7
❑ 36SandSW-15
❑ 37ExhFou-2
❑ 72TCMthe3-22
❑ 72TCMthe3-23
❑ 74Bra193NLA-2
❑ 77GalGloG-210
❑ 79DiaGre-86
❑ 83BigLeaCOA-24
❑ 90DodTar-944
❑ 93ConTSN-689
❑ 94ConTSN-1240
❑ 94ConTSNB-1240

Englishby, Steve
❑ 73CedRapAT-18
❑ 78DayBeaAT-7

Englund, Tim
❑ 86KnoBluJP-7
❑ 87KnoBluJP-1501

Engram, Duane
❑ 86PenWhiSP-10

Engram, Graylyn
❑ 87DayBeaAP-21

Ennen, Chuck
❑ 85CloHSS-15

Ennis, Alan
❑ 84NewOriT-8

Ennis, Del (Delmar)
❑ 46SpoExcW-3-3
❑ 47Exh-68
❑ 47HomBon-14
❑ 47PM1StaP1-55
❑ 49EurSta-134
❑ 49Lea-49
❑ 49MPR302-2-109
❑ 49PhiBul-17
❑ 49PhiLumPB-3
❑ 50Bow-31
❑ 50Dra-21
❑ 50JJKCopP-4
❑ 50PhiPhil-7
❑ 51BerRos-A10
❑ 51Bow-4
❑ 51R42SmaS-29
❑ 51TopBluB-4
❑ 52BerRos-17
❑ 52Bow-76
❑ 52NatTeaL-8
❑ 52Top-223
❑ 53BowC-103
❑ 53ExhCan-60
❑ 53RedMan-NL17
❑ 54Bow-127
❑ 54Wil-2
❑ 55BigLeaIS-6
❑ 55Bow-17
❑ 55DaiQueS-6
❑ 56Top-220
❑ 57Top-260
❑ 58CarJayP-5
❑ 58Top-60A
❑ 58Top-60B
❑ 59RedEnq-6
❑ 59RedShiBS-6
❑ 59Top-255
❑ 75Phi195T-9
❑ 75TCMGua-7
❑ 76TayBow4-14
❑ 77PhiFav-11
❑ 79TCM50-18
❑ 80Phi195T-9
❑ 81WhiSox1T-17
❑ 83PhiPosGM-2
❑ 83PhiPosGPaM-6
❑ 83TopRep5-223
❑ 84TCMPla1-36
❑ 86PhiGreT-3
❑ 87Phi195T-6
❑ 89PacLegI-121
❑ 89SweBasG-19
❑ 93UppDecAH-45
❑ 94TedWil-73
❑ 94UppDecAH-32
❑ 94UppDecAH1-32

Ennis, Russ
❑ 25Zee-3

Ennis, Wayne
❑ 94PriRedC-8
❑ 94PriRedF-3268

Enno, Clayton
❑ 89SalDodTI-10

Enochs, Chris
❑ 98Bow-184
❑ 98BowChr-184
❑ 98BowChrGA-184
❑ 98BowChrGAR-184
❑ 98BowChrI-184
❑ 98BowChrIR-184
❑ 98BowChrR-184
❑ 98BowGolA-184
❑ 98BowInt-184
❑ 98HunStaTI-21
❑ 98SouLeaTPG-27
❑ 98SP MinPE-94
❑ 98SPMin-94
❑ 98StaCluFDI-387
❑ 98StaCluI-387
❑ 98StaCluOneK-387
❑ 98StaCluPP-387
❑ 99BasAmeTP-41
❑ 99BasAmeTPG-41
❑ 99Bow-204
❑ 99BowChr-204
❑ 99BowChrG-204
❑ 99BowChrGR-204
❑ 99BowChrI-204
❑ 99BowChrIR-204
❑ 99BowChrR-204
❑ 99BowGol-204
❑ 99BowInt-204
❑ 99SP TopP-44
❑ 99SP TopPC-CE
❑ 99SP TopPGF-GF12
❑ 99SP TopPPE-44
❑ 99Top-210
❑ 99TopChr-210
❑ 99TopChrR-210

Enos, Dave
❑ 82ReaPhiT-13

Enos, Eric
❑ 88BatCliP-1671

Enright, George (George A.)
❑ 82QuaCitCT-26
❑ 84MidCubT-15

Enriquez, Graciano
❑ 91BelBreCB-20
❑ 91BelBreP-2117
❑ 92BelBreCB-17
❑ 92BelBreFI-419

Enriquez, Martin
❑ 82WauTimF-15
❑ 83WauTimF-5

Ens, Jewel
❑ 92ConTSN-499

Ensberg, Morgan
❑ 98AubDouTI-9
❑ 99TeaBesR-22
❑ 99TeaBesRG-22
❑ 99TeaBesRS-22

Enyart, Terry (Terry Gene)
❑ 79OgdA'sT-1
❑ 80OgdA'sT-8

Enzmann, Johnny
❑ 90DodTar-220

Ephan, Larry
❑ 94ChaRivC-6
❑ 94ChaRivF-2676

Epley, Daren
❑ 89KinIndS-6
❑ 90CanIndB-5
❑ 90CanIndP-1296
❑ 90CanIndS-4
❑ 91CanIndLD-82
❑ 91CanIndP-985
❑ 91LinDriAA-82
❑ 92ColSprSSS-85
❑ 92SkyAAAF-37
❑ 93TulDriF-2746
❑ 93TulDriTI-8

Eppard, Jim
❑ 84AlbA'sT-24
❑ 85ModA'sC-13
❑ 86TacTigP-5
❑ 87EdmTraP-2061
❑ 88EdmTraC-21
❑ 88EdmTraP-558
❑ 88Fle-645
❑ 88FleGlo-645
❑ 88FleUpd-13
❑ 88FleUpdG-13
❑ 89EdmTraC-14
❑ 89EdmTraP-548
❑ 89Fle-476
❑ 89FleGlo-476
❑ 89Sco-607
❑ 89Top-42
❑ 89TopTif-42
❑ 89UppDec-614
❑ 90CMC-339
❑ 90ProAAAF-356
❑ 90SyrChiC-13
❑ 90SyrChiMB-7
❑ 90SyrChiP-576
❑ 91SouOreAAP-SOA27
❑ 92IndIndF-1873
❑ 92IndIndS-180
❑ 94CenValRC-29
❑ 94CenValRF-3219
❑ 98PorRocG-11

Epperly, Al
❑ 79DiaGre-110
❑ 90DodTar-221

Epperly, Tom
❑ 76TacTwiDQ-5
❑ 77OrlTwiT-7

Epperson, Chad
❑ 92GulCoaMF-3483
❑ 93KinMetC-10
❑ 93KinMetF-3799
❑ 94St.LucMC-7
❑ 94St.LucMF-1197
❑ 95StLucMTI-12
❑ 97SarRedS-8
❑ 98TreThuM-13

Epple, Tom
❑ 82SprCarF-8
❑ 83St.PetCT-6

Epps, Hal
❑ 45A'sTeal-10
❑ 96Bro194F-35

Epps, Riley
❑ 86SalRedBP-7

Epps, Scott
❑ 90ArkRaz-9
❑ 93PriWilCF-658
❑ 94TamYanC-9
❑ 94TamYanF-2385
❑ 95NorNavTI-11

Epstein, Mike (Michael P.)
❑ 67BalOriP-33
❑ 67SenPos-10
❑ 67Top-204
❑ 68SenTeal-4
❑ 68Top-358
❑ 68TopVen-358
❑ 69MilBra-79
❑ 69MLBOffS-104
❑ 69SenTeal-7
❑ 69SenTeal8-10
❑ 69Top-461A
❑ 69Top-461B
❑ 69Top-539
❑ 69TopSta-235
❑ 69TopTeaP-23
❑ 69TraSta-25
❑ 70DayDaiNM-98
❑ 70Kel-24
❑ 70MLBOffS-282
❑ 70OPC-235
❑ 70SenPolY-4
❑ 70Top-235
❑ 70TopBoo-12
❑ 71Kel-34
❑ 71MLBOffS-535
❑ 71OPC-655
❑ 71Top-655
❑ 71TopCoi-126
❑ 72MilBra-99
❑ 72Top-715
❑ 73OPC-38
❑ 73Top-38
❑ 73TopCanL-14

❑ 74OPC-650
❑ 74Top-650
❑ 74TopSta-142
❑ 78TCM60I-261
❑ 91OriCro-121
❑ 93HelBreSP-27
❑ 93RanKee-136
Erardi, Joe (Joseph G.)
❑ 77HolMilT-8
Erautt, Eddie (Edward L.S.)
❑ 49EurSta-82
❑ 52Top-171
❑ 53Top-226
❑ 83TopRep5-171
❑ 91TopArc1-226
Erautt, Joe (Joseph M.)
❑ 52MotCoo-43
❑ 54SeaPop-6
Erb, Gerry
❑ 77NewCoPT-11
Erb, Mike
❑ 87SalAngP-24
❑ 88PalSprACLC-86
❑ 88PalSprAP-1443
❑ 89QuaCitAB-10
❑ 89QuaCitAGS-14
❑ 90CMC-483
❑ 90EdmTraC-6
❑ 90EdmTraP-513
❑ 90ProAAAF-89
❑ 91EdmTraLD-154
❑ 91EdmTraP-1511
❑ 91LinDriAAA-154
❑ 92JacSunS-369
Erdahl, Jay Michael
❑ 82WauTimF-21
Erdman, Brad
❑ 90GenCubP-3033
❑ 90GenCubS-11
❑ 90PeoChiTI-4
❑ 91MidLeaAP-MWL8
❑ 91PeoChiC-10
❑ 91PeoChiP-1344
❑ 91PeoChiTI-14
❑ 92ClaFS7-317
❑ 92WinSpiC-11
❑ 92WinSpiF-1210
❑ 93OrlCubF-2787
❑ 93PeoChiF-1087
❑ 94DayCubC-5
❑ 94DayCubF-2355
❑ 94FloStaLAF-FSL33
❑ 96IowCubB-12
Erdos, Todd
❑ 93SpoIndC-7
❑ 93SpoIndF-3584
❑ 93WatDiaC-14
❑ 93WatDiaF-1761
❑ 95IdaFalBTI-25
❑ 96RanCucQB-12
❑ 97MobBayBB-23
❑ 97SouLeaTP-27
❑ 97TexAllM-37
❑ 98ColCliD-7
❑ 98ColCliM-11
❑ 98Don-243
❑ 98DonGolPP-243
❑ 98DonSilPP-243
❑ 98Fle-123
❑ 98LeaRS-215
❑ 98LeaRSLHolo-215
❑ 98LeaRSLong-215
❑ 98LeaRTrue-215
❑ 98Stu-36
❑ 98StuGPP-36
❑ 98StuSPP-36
Ereu, William
❑ 80VenLeaS-61
❑ 93LinVenB-102
❑ 95LinVen-190
Erhard, Barney
❑ 91BelMarCB-9
❑ 91BelMarP-3673
❑ 92BelMarCB-23
❑ 92BelMarF-1451
Erhardt, Herb
❑ 88OneYanP-2046
❑ 89Ft.LauYS-3
❑ 90PriWilCTI-9
❑ 91ChaWheC-16
❑ 91ChaWheP-2893
Ericks, John
❑ 89Bow-433
❑ 89BowTif-433
❑ 89SavCarP-371
❑ 89SouAtlLAGS-36
❑ 90ArkTraGS-10
❑ 90Bow-190
❑ 90BowTif-190
❑ 90St.PetCS-6
❑ 90TopTVCa-46
❑ 91ArkTraLD-30
❑ 91ArkTraP-1277
❑ 91Bow-393
❑ 91Cla/Bes-287
❑ 91LinDriAA-30
❑ 91UppDec-57
❑ 92ArkTraF-1124
❑ 92ArkTraS-33
❑ 92Bow-48
❑ 92ClaFS7-332
❑ 92SkyAA F-16
❑ 94SalBucC-8
❑ 94SalBucF-2318
❑ 96Don-265
❑ 96DonPreP-265
❑ 96Fla-344
❑ 96Fle-520
❑ 96FleTif-520
❑ 96LeaSigEA-47
❑ 96StaClu-355
❑ 96StaCluMOP-355
❑ 96Ult-263
❑ 96UltGolM-263
❑ 97Cir-376
❑ 97CirRav-376
❑ 97Fle-539
❑ 97FleTif-539
❑ 97PirPos-12
❑ 97Ult-325
❑ 97UltGolME-325
❑ 97UltPlaME-325
Erickson, Corey
❑ 96PitMetB-9
❑ 97BesBetP-7
❑ 97Bow-380
❑ 97BowInt-380
❑ 97St.LucM-5
❑ 98St.LucMM-22
Erickson, Don
❑ 89BelBreIS-3
Erickson, Eric G.
❑ 16Zee-108
❑ 17Zee-88
❑ 23WilChoV-38
❑ 82CliGiaF-22
❑ 86FreGiaSB-14
❑ 87LynMetP-7
Erickson, Greg
❑ 92ForLauYTI-8
❑ 93CarLeaAGF-20
❑ 93PriWilCC-8
❑ 93PriWilCF-662
❑ 94AlbYanF-1447
❑ 94TamYanC-10
❑ 94TamYanF-2391
Erickson, Hal (Harold J.)
❑ 53TigGle-6
Erickson, Hank (Henry Nels)
❑ 36GouWidPPR-D8
❑ 98KanCouCCP-8
Erickson, Matt
❑ 98KanCouC-8
❑ 98MidLeaPM-12
Erickson, Paul
❑ 41CubTeal-3
❑ 42CubTeal-4
❑ 43CubTeal-7
❑ 44CubTeal-7
Erickson, Roger F.
❑ 78TwiFriP-6
❑ 79Hos-94
❑ 79OPC-34
❑ 79Top-81
❑ 79TwiFriP-6
❑ 80Top-256
❑ 80TwiPos-7
❑ 81Don-549
❑ 81Fle-561
❑ 81OPC-80
❑ 81Top-434
❑ 81TopSti-105
❑ 81TwiPos-9
❑ 82Don-303
❑ 82Fle-553
❑ 82Top-153
❑ 82TopSti-211
❑ 82TopStiV-211
❑ 82TopTra-30T
❑ 82TwiPos-9
❑ 82YanPhoA-1
❑ 83Fle-378
❑ 83Top-539
❑ 87SanJosBP-23
❑ 89LouRedBC-3
❑ 89LouRedBP-1242
❑ 89LouRedBTI-17
❑ 90SprCarB-27
❑ 91PacSenL-98
❑ 91SprCarC-29
❑ 91SprCarP-760
❑ 91TopTriH-A9
❑ 92YanWIZ8-52
Erickson, Scott
❑ 90Bes-106
❑ 90ButCopKSP-13
❑ 90OrlSunRB-16
❑ 90OrlSunRP-1077
❑ 90OrlSunRS-5
❑ 90ProAaA-41
❑ 90TopMag-62
❑ 90TopTra-29T
❑ 90TopTraT-29T
❑ 91Bow-335
❑ 91Cla2-T16
❑ 91Cla3-T17
❑ 91Cla3-NNO
❑ 91ClaGam-160
❑ 91DodPho-13
❑ 91Don-767
❑ 91Fle-608
❑ 91GasRanC-5
❑ 91GasRanP-2682
❑ 91Lea-527
❑ 91OPC-234
❑ 91Sco-812
❑ 91StaClu-560
❑ 91Stu-83
❑ 91Top-234
❑ 91TopDeb90-45
❑ 91TopDesS-234
❑ 91TopMic-234
❑ 91TopTif-234
❑ 91UltUpd-36
❑ 91UppDec-522
❑ 92Bow-53
❑ 92ClaGam-93
❑ 92Don-463
❑ 92DonCraJ2-33
❑ 92DonDiaK-DK21
❑ 92DonSupD-DK21
❑ 92Fle-201
❑ 92Fle-693
❑ 92FleAll-10
❑ 92FleSmo'nH-S6
❑ 92Fre-5
❑ 92Hig5-82
❑ 92Hig5S-10
❑ 92KinDis-23
❑ 92Lea-166
❑ 92LeaBlaG-166
❑ 92LeaGolP-21
❑ 92LeaPre-21
❑ 92MVPPin-8
❑ 92OPC-605
❑ 92Pin-106
❑ 92PinTea2-60
❑ 92Pos-18
❑ 92RedFolS-34
❑ 92RemUltP-P10
❑ 92RemUltP-P11
❑ 92RemUltP-P12
❑ 92Sco-60
❑ 92Sco-438
❑ 92Sco-889
❑ 92Sco100S-2
❑ 92ScoImpP-13
❑ 92StaClu-110
❑ 92Stu-202
❑ 92SunSee-23
❑ 92Top-605
❑ 92TopGol-605
❑ 92TopGolW-605
❑ 92TopKid-110
❑ 92TopMic-605
❑ 92TriPla-3
❑ 92Ult-90
❑ 92UppDec-89
❑ 92UppDec-146
❑ 92UppDecTMH-20
❑ 93Bow-425
❑ 93ClaGam-29
❑ 93Don-211
❑ 93Fin-142
❑ 93FinRef-142
❑ 93Fle-263
❑ 93FunPac-192
❑ 93Lea-142
❑ 93OPC-77
❑ 93PacSpa-169
❑ 93PanSti-123
❑ 93Pin-163
❑ 93RedFolS-28
❑ 93Sco-206
❑ 93Sel-253
❑ 93SP-245
❑ 93StaClu-443
❑ 93StaCluFDI-443
❑ 93StaCluMOP-443
❑ 93Top-90
❑ 93TopGol-90
❑ 93TopInaM-90
❑ 93TopInaR-90
❑ 93TopMic-90
❑ 93TriPla-33
❑ 93Ult-230
❑ 93UppDec-397
❑ 93UppDecGold-397
❑ 94ColC-96
❑ 94ColChoGS-96
❑ 94ColChoSS-96
❑ 94Don-437
❑ 94Fin-166
❑ 94FinPre-166P
❑ 94FinRef-166
❑ 94Fla-73
❑ 94Fle-202
❑ 94FleExtB-116
❑ 94Lea-227
❑ 94Pac-351
❑ 94Pin-361
❑ 94PinArtP-361
❑ 94PinMusC-361
❑ 94Sco-461
❑ 94ScoGolR-461
❑ 94Sel-171
❑ 94SP-184
❑ 94SPDieC-184
❑ 94StaClu-637
❑ 94StaCluFDI-637
❑ 94StaCluGR-637
❑ 94StaCluMOP-637
❑ 94Top-365
❑ 94TopGol-365
❑ 94TopSpa-365
❑ 94TriPla-252
❑ 94Ult-85
❑ 94UppDec-503
❑ 94UppDecED-503
❑ 95BalOriP-17
❑ 95ColCho-483
❑ 95ColChoGS-483
❑ 95ColChoSE-225
❑ 95ColChoSEGS-225
❑ 95ColChoSESS-225
❑ 95ColChoSS-483
❑ 95Don-161
❑ 95DonPreP-161
❑ 95DonTopotO-6
❑ 95Fla-279
❑ 95Fle-201
❑ 95Lea-287
❑ 95Pac-248
❑ 95Pin-335
❑ 95PinArtP-335
❑ 95PinMusC-335
❑ 95Sco-27
❑ 95ScoGolR-27
❑ 95ScoPlaTS-27
❑ 95StaClu-429
❑ 95StaCluMOP-429
❑ 95StaCluSTWS-429
❑ 95StaCluVR-225
❑ 95StaCluVRMO-225
❑ 95Stu-166
❑ 95Top-617
❑ 95TopCyb-385
❑ 95Ult-301
❑ 95UltGolM-301
❑ 95UppDec-428
❑ 95UppDec-471
❑ 95UppDecED-428
❑ 95UppDecEDG-428
❑ 95UppDecSE-83
❑ 95UppDecSEG-83
❑ 96BalOriP-10
❑ 96ColCho-57
❑ 96ColChoGS-57
❑ 96ColChoSS-57
❑ 96Don-311
❑ 96DonPreP-311
❑ 96Fla-4
❑ 96Fle-7
❑ 96FleTif-7
❑ 96OriFle-5
❑ 96Pac-231
❑ 96Sco-401
❑ 96StaClu-51
❑ 96StaCluMOP-51
❑ 96Ult-4
❑ 96UltGolM-4
❑ 96UppDec-13
❑ 97BalOriP-12
❑ 97Cir-245
❑ 97CirRav-245
❑ 97ColCho-37
❑ 97ColChoT-BO2
❑ 97Fle-6
❑ 97FleTif-6
❑ 97Pac-22
❑ 97PacLigB-22
❑ 97PacSil-22
❑ 97Sco-400
❑ 97ScoArtPWB-400
❑ 97ScoResC-400
❑ 97ScoShoS-400
❑ 97ScoShoSAP-400
❑ 97StaClu-291
❑ 97StaCluMOP-291
❑ 97Top-347
❑ 97UppDec-307
❑ 98CirThu-192
❑ 98CirThuRav-192
❑ 98CirThuSupRav-192
❑ 98ColCho-44
❑ 98Don-242
❑ 98DonGolPP-242
❑ 98DonSilPP-242
❑ 98Fin-104
❑ 98FinNo--104
❑ 98FinNo-R-104
❑ 98FinRef-104
❑ 98OriSco-11
❑ 98OriScoP-11
❑ 98Pac-24
❑ 98PacOnl-88
❑ 98PacOnlR-88
❑ 98PacOnlWC-88
❑ 98PacPlaB-24
❑ 98PacRedT-24
❑ 98PacSil-24
❑ 98Pin-152
❑ 98PinPreP-152
❑ 98PinSna-BO10
❑ 98Sco-161
❑ 98ScoSS-PP67
❑ 98ScoSSAP-PP67
❑ 98SpoIll-33
❑ 98SpoIllEE-33
❑ 98SpoIllFE-33
❑ 98SpoIllTaN-77
❑ 98SpoIllTaNEE-77
❑ 98StaCluFDI-283
❑ 98StaCluI-283
❑ 98StaCluOneK-283
❑ 98StaCluPP-283
❑ 98Top-416
❑ 98TopChr-416
❑ 98TopChrR-416
❑ 98TopDevR-416
❑ 98TopDia-416
❑ 98TopMiniC-416
❑ 98Ult-379
❑ 98UltGolM-379
❑ 98UltMas-379
❑ 98UltPlaM-379
❑ 98UppDec-34
❑ 98UppDecSF-21
❑ 99199Fin-202
❑ 99Bow-26
❑ 99BowChr-26
❑ 99BowChrG-26
❑ 99BowChrGR-26
❑ 99BowChrI-26
❑ 99BowChrIR-26
❑ 99BowChrR-26
❑ 99BowGol-26
❑ 99BowInt-26
❑ 99FinGolRef-202
❑ 99FinRef-202
❑ 99Fle-296
❑ 99FleBri-84
❑ 99FleBri2G-84
❑ 99FleBriBlu-84
❑ 99FleBriGol-84
❑ 99FleSta9-296
❑ 99FleWarT-296
❑ 99Pac-51
❑ 99PacAur-23
❑ 99PacAurOD-23
❑ 99PacCroC-35
❑ 99PacCroCPB-35
❑ 99PacPlaB-51
❑ 99PacRed-51
❑ 99SkyThu-214
❑ 99SkyThuRant-214
❑ 99SkyThuRave-214
❑ 99SpoIll-143
❑ 99StaClu-27
❑ 99StaCluFDI-27
❑ 99StaCluOoaK-27
❑ 99StaCluPP-27
❑ 99ThuSkySupR-214
❑ 99Top-174
❑ 99TopChr-174
❑ 99TopChrR-174
❑ 99TopMVPP-174
❑ 99Ult-105
❑ 99UltGolM-105
❑ 99UltMas-105
❑ 99UltPlaM-105
❑ 99UppDec-47
❑ 99UppDecEL1-47
❑ 99UppDecEL2-47
❑ 99Vic-51
Erickson, Steve
❑ 87OneYanP-8
❑ 88Ft.LauYS-7
❑ 89Ft.LauYS-4
Erickson, Tim
❑ 87WauTimP-28
Ericson, Mark
❑ 88KenTwiP-1394
Ericson, Mike
❑ 89AncGlaP-15
❑ 90MiaMirIS-7
❑ 91MiaMirC-6
❑ 91MiaMirP-400
❑ 92VisOakC-8
❑ 92VisOakF-1008
❑ 93CenValRC-10
❑ 93CenValRF-2887
❑ 94NewHavRF-1544
Erikson, Greg
❑ 92Ft.LauYF-2618
Ermer, Cal (Calvin C.)
❑ 68Top-206
❑ 68TopVen-206
❑ 70BreMcD-6
❑ 70BreMil-4
❑ 74TacTwiC-4
❑ 75TacTwiK-10
❑ 76TacTwiDQ-6
❑ 79TolMudHT-3
❑ 80TolMudHT-3
❑ 81TolMudHT-1
❑ 82TolMudHT-23
❑ 83TolMudHT-23
❑ 84TolMudHT-6
❑ 85TolMudHT-26
❑ 88ChaLooLTI-12
Ermis, Chris
❑ 91MedHatBJP-4093
❑ 91MedHatBJSP-5
Erskine, Carl (Carl Daniel)
❑ 47PM1StaP1-56
❑ 51Bow-260
❑ 52Bow-70
❑ 52Top-250
❑ 53BowC-12
❑ 53Bri-30
❑ 53Dor-124
❑ 54Bow-10
❑ 54NewYorJA-4
❑ 54RedHeaF-6
❑ 54RedMan-NL4
❑ 54StaMey-2
❑ 54Wil-3
❑ 55Bow-170
❑ 55DodGolS-3
❑ 55RedMan-NL14
❑ 55StaMey-2
❑ 56Dod-8
❑ 56Top-233
❑ 57Top-252
❑ 58DodTeal-7
❑ 58DodVol-4
❑ 58Top-258
❑ 59DodTeal-6
❑ 59DodVol-4

❑ 59Top-217
❑ 60NuHi-69
❑ 61NuSco-469
❑ 70FleWorS-50
❑ 74dod195T-13
❑ 76SSP-594
❑ 77SerSta-8
❑ 79DiaGre-99
❑ 79TCM50-146
❑ 81SanDieSC-7
❑ 83TopRep5-250
❑ 84FifNatCT-4
❑ 84OCoandSI-74
❑ 86TCMSupS-1
❑ 87Dod195T-9
❑ 88DodRinP1-1C
❑ 88DodRinP1-11B
❑ 88PacLegI-75
❑ 89DodSmoG-60
❑ 89SweBasG-44
❑ 90DodTar-222
❑ 90PacLeg-14
❑ 90SweBasG-36
❑ 91SweBasG-27
❑ 91TopArc1-308
❑ 92ActPacA-54
❑ 92BazQua5A-11
❑ 93TedWil-13
❑ 93UppDecAH-46
❑ 94UppDecAH-187
❑ 94UppDecAH1-187
❑ 95TopArcBD-15
❑ 95TopArcBD-61
❑ 95TopArcBD-86
❑ 95TopArcBD-133
❑ 95TopArcBD-157

Erstad, Darin

❑ 95ARuFalLS-4
❑ 95Bes-128
❑ 95BesFra-F1
❑ 95LakElsSTI-14
❑ 95SPML-25
❑ 95SPML-100
❑ 95SPMLDtS-DS11
❑ 96Cir-19
❑ 96CirRav-19
❑ 96Exc-26
❑ 96ExcFirYP-4
❑ 96LeaLimR-2
❑ 96LeaLimRG-2
❑ 96LeaSig-94
❑ 96LeaSigEA-48
❑ 96LeaSigEACM-5
❑ 96LeaSigPPG-94
❑ 96LeaSigPPP-94
❑ 96SigRooOJPP-P1
❑ 96SigRooOJPPS-P1
❑ 96SP-4
❑ 96UppDecDD-DD12
❑ 96UppDecDD-DD12G
❑ 96UppDecDD-DD12S
❑ 96UppDecDDG-DD12
❑ 96UppDecDDS-DD12
❑ 96VanCanB-12
❑ 96Zen-130
❑ 96ZenArtP-130
❑ 96ZenDiaC-16
❑ 96ZenDiaCP-16
❑ 97AngMot-10
❑ 97Bow-92
❑ 97BowBes-115
❑ 97BowBesAR-115
❑ 97BowBesBC-BC13
❑ 97BowBesBCAR-BC13
❑ 97BowBesBCR-BC13
❑ 97BowBesR-115
❑ 97BowCerBlaIA-CA23
❑ 97BowCerBluIA-CA23
❑ 97BowCerGolIA-CA23
❑ 97BowChr-116
❑ 97BowChrI-116
❑ 97BowChrIR-116
❑ 97BowChrR-116
❑ 97BowChrSHR-SHR8
❑ 97BowChrSHRR-SHR8
❑ 97BowInt-92
❑ 97BowScoHR-8
❑ 97Cir-241
❑ 97CirEmeA-241
❑ 97CirEmeAR-AU1
❑ 97CirRav-241
❑ 97ColCho-5
❑ 97Don-356
❑ 97DonEli-58
❑ 97DonEliGS-58
❑ 97DonEliTotC-8
❑ 97DonEliTotCDC-8
❑ 97DonFraFea-2
❑ 97DonGolPP-356
❑ 97DonLim-27
❑ 97DonLim-71
❑ 97DonLim-198
❑ 97DonLimE-27
❑ 97DonLimE-71
❑ 97DonLimE-198
❑ 97DonLimENG-71
❑ 97DonLimFotG-26
❑ 97DonPre-133
❑ 97DonPreCttC-133
❑ 97DonRatR-24
❑ 97DonRooDK-8
❑ 97DonRooDKC-8
❑ 97DonSig-67
❑ 97DonSigA-31
❑ 97DonSigAC-38
❑ 97DonSigAM-38
❑ 97DonSigPPP-67
❑ 97DonSilPP-356
❑ 97DonTea-10
❑ 97DonTeaSPE-10
❑ 97DonVxP1-1
❑ 97E-X2-2
❑ 97E-X2Cred-2
❑ 97E-X2EmeAuto-2
❑ 97E-X2EmeAutoR-AU1
❑ 97E-X2EssCre-2
❑ 97E-X2SD2000-6
❑ 97Fin-37
❑ 97Fin-276
❑ 97FinEmb-276
❑ 97FinEmbR-276
❑ 97FinRef-37
❑ 97FinRef-276
❑ 97FlaShoLC-39
❑ 97FlaShoLeg0-39
❑ 97FlaShoLeg1-39
❑ 97FlaShoM-A39
❑ 97FlaShoM-B39
❑ 97FlaShoM-C39
❑ 97FlaShoR0-39
❑ 97FlaShoR1-39
❑ 97FlaShoR2-39
❑ 97Fle-41
❑ 97FleNewH-3
❑ 97FleRooS-5
❑ 97FleTif-41
❑ 97Lea-149
❑ 97Lea-399
❑ 97LeaFraM-149
❑ 97LeaFraM-399
❑ 97LeaFraMDC-149
❑ 97LeaFraMDC-399
❑ 97LeaGolS-25
❑ 97LeaLeaotN-14
❑ 97MetUni-40
❑ 97MetUniEA-AU1
❑ 97MetUniEAR-AU1
❑ 97NewPin-115
❑ 97NewPinAP-115
❑ 97NewPinMC-115
❑ 97NewPinPP-115
❑ 97Pac-6
❑ 97PacLigB-6
❑ 97PacPri-3
❑ 97PacPriLB-3
❑ 97PacPriP-3
❑ 97PacSil-6
❑ 97Pin-161
❑ 97Pin-199
❑ 97PinArtP-PP161
❑ 97PinArtP-PP199
❑ 97PinCar-16
❑ 97PinCer-31
❑ 97PinCerMBla-31
❑ 97PinCerMBlu-31
❑ 97PinCerMG-31
❑ 97PinCerMR-31
❑ 97PinCerR-31
❑ 97PinIns-110
❑ 97PinInsCE-110
❑ 97PinInsDD-19
❑ 97PinInsDE-110
❑ 97PinMusC-161
❑ 97PinMusC-199
❑ 97PinPrePla-161
❑ 97PinPrePla-199
❑ 97PinTotCPB-31
❑ 97PinTotCPG-31
❑ 97PinTotCPR-31
❑ 97PinX-P-82
❑ 97PinX-PF&A-12
❑ 97PinX-PMoS-82
❑ 97PreCon-23
❑ 97Sco-24
❑ 97Sco-506
❑ 97ScoArtPWB-24
❑ 97ScoArtPWB-506
❑ 97ScoHeaotO-31
❑ 97ScoPreS-24
❑ 97ScoResC-506
❑ 97ScoShoS-24
❑ 97ScoShoS-506
❑ 97ScoShoSAP-24
❑ 97ScoShoSAP-506
❑ 97Sel-100
❑ 97SelArtP-100
❑ 97SelCom-100
❑ 97SelRegG-100
❑ 97SelRooR-16
❑ 97SelToootT-11
❑ 97SelToootTMB-11
❑ 97SP-17
❑ 97SpollI-61
❑ 97SpollIEE-61
❑ 97SPSpeF-42
❑ 97SPx-2
❑ 97SPxBro-2
❑ 97SPxGol-2
❑ 97SPxGraF-2
❑ 97SPxSil-2
❑ 97SPxSte-2
❑ 97StaClu-248
❑ 97StaCluMat-248
❑ 97StaCluMOP-248
❑ 97Stu-162
❑ 97StuHarH-23
❑ 97StuPrePG-162
❑ 97StuPrePS-162
❑ 97TopGal-147
❑ 97TopGalPPI-147
❑ 97TopMem05-51
❑ 97TopStaFAS-FAS7
❑ 97UD3-45
❑ 97UD3GenNex-GN6
❑ 97Ult-26
❑ 97UltAutE-4
❑ 97UltGolME-26
❑ 97UltPlaME-26
❑ 97UltRooR-3
❑ 97UppDec-230
❑ 97UppDecBCP-BC8
❑ 97UppDecRSF-RS4
❑ 97UppDecTTS-TS9
❑ 97Zen-36
❑ 98AngSco-4
❑ 98AngScoP-4
❑ 98Bow-47
❑ 98BowBes-49
❑ 98BowBesAR-49
❑ 98BowBesR-49
❑ 98BowChr-47
❑ 98BowChrGA-47
❑ 98BowChrGAR-47
❑ 98BowChrI-47
❑ 98BowChrIR-47
❑ 98BowChrR-47
❑ 98BowGolA-47
❑ 98BowInt-47
❑ 98CirThu-281
❑ 98CirThuRav-281
❑ 98CirThuSupRav-281
❑ 98ColCho-25
❑ 98ColChoSQ-SQ61
❑ 98CroRoy-3
❑ 98Don-67
❑ 98Don-348
❑ 98Don-399
❑ 98DonCol-67
❑ 98DonColE-483
❑ 98DonColL-357
❑ 98DonColP-570
❑ 98DonColP-736
❑ 98DonColS-67
❑ 98DonCruG-4
❑ 98DonCruP-4
❑ 98DonCruR-4
❑ 98DonDiaK-8
❑ 98DonDiaKC-8
❑ 98DonDom-3
❑ 98DonEli-83
❑ 98DonEliA-83
❑ 98DonEliS-83
❑ 98DonGolPP-67
❑ 98DonGolPP-348
❑ 98DonGolPP-399
❑ 98DonPre-20
❑ 98DonPre-186
❑ 98DonPreGES-17
❑ 98DonPreGX-17
❑ 98DonPreGXDC-17
❑ 98DonPrePM-19
❑ 98DonPreSeat-20
❑ 98DonPreSeat-186
❑ 98DonPriCD-67
❑ 98DonPriCE-483
❑ 98DonPriCL-357
❑ 98DonPriCP-570
❑ 98DonPriCP-736
❑ 98DonSig-26
❑ 98DonSigA-29
❑ 98DonSigAC-38
❑ 98DonSigAM-39
❑ 98DonSigP-26
❑ 98DonSilPP-67
❑ 98DonSilPP-348
❑ 98DonSilPP-399
❑ 98E-X2-93
❑ 98E-X2ECFut-93
❑ 98E-X2ECNow-93
❑ 98Fin-224
❑ 98FinNo--224
❑ 98FinNo-R-224
❑ 98FinRef-224
❑ 98FlaShoLeg0-30
❑ 98FlaShoLeg1-30
❑ 98FlaShoLeg2-30
❑ 98FlaShoLeg3-30
❑ 98FlaShoLegM-30
❑ 98FlaShoR0-30
❑ 98FlaShoR1-30
❑ 98FlaShoR2-30
❑ 98FlaShoR3-30
❑ 98Fle-354
❑ 98FleVin'-64
❑ 98FleVin'C-64
❑ 98Lea-158
❑ 98LeaCruG-4
❑ 98LeaCruP-4
❑ 98LeaCruR-4
❑ 98LeaFraDA-158
❑ 98LeaFraF-158
❑ 98LeaFraM-158
❑ 98LeaFraM-158
❑ 98LeaFraMDC-158
❑ 98LeaFraMDC-158
❑ 98LeaFraMS-158
❑ 98LeaFraMZ2-158
❑ 98LeaRCMLHDSamp-17
❑ 98LeaRS-45
❑ 98LeaRS-181
❑ 98LeaRSGreHit-17
❑ 98LeaRSLHolo-45
❑ 98LeaRSLHolo-181
❑ 98LeaRSLong-45
❑ 98LeaRSLong-181
❑ 98LeaRSMLHD-17
❑ 98LeaRSTicMas-18
❑ 98LeaRSTicMasDC-18
❑ 98LeaRTrue-45
❑ 98LeaRTrue-181
❑ 98MetUni-157
❑ 98MetUniAT-11
❑ 98MetUniPMG-157
❑ 98MetUniPP-8
❑ 98MetUniT-11
❑ 98MetUniUL-11
❑ 98Pac-6
❑ 98PacAur-3
❑ 98PacAurPF-44
❑ 98PacAurPFC-44
❑ 98PacAurPFPB-44
❑ 98PacAurPFR-44
❑ 98PacAurPFS-44
❑ 98PacInv-3
❑ 98PacInvPBlue-3
❑ 98PacInvSilv-3
❑ 98PacInvTeam-1
❑ 98PacOme-4
❑ 98PacOmeR-4
❑ 98PacOnl-6
❑ 98PacOnlR-6
❑ 98PacOnlWC-6
❑ 98PacPar-4
❑ 98PacParC-4
❑ 98PacParG-4
❑ 98PacParHS-4
❑ 98PacParPB-4
❑ 98PacParR-4
❑ 98PacPlaB-6
❑ 98PacRedT-6
❑ 98PacSil-6
❑ 98Pin-30
❑ 98PinArtP-PP30
❑ 98PinIns-1
❑ 98PinInsCE-1
❑ 98PinInsDE-1
❑ 98PinInsSG-16AB
❑ 98PinInsSG-16CD
❑ 98PinInsSGS-16AB
❑ 98PinInsSGS-16CD
❑ 98PinMusC-PP30
❑ 98PinPer-20
❑ 98PinPerPP-20
❑ 98PinPlu-177
❑ 98PinPluAP-PP58
❑ 98PinPluGAP-PP58
❑ 98PinPluMAP-PP58
❑ 98PinPreP-30
❑ 98PinSna-AA15
❑ 98Revo-3
❑ 98RevoSS-3
❑ 98Sco-93
❑ 98ScoComP-6A
❑ 98ScoComP-6B
❑ 98ScoComP-6C
❑ 98ScoComPG-6A
❑ 98ScoComPG-6B
❑ 98ScoComPG-6C
❑ 98ScoRT-22
❑ 98ScoRTSS-PP22
❑ 98ScoRTSSAP-PP22
❑ 98ScoRTSSAP1-PP22
❑ 98ScoSS-PP41
❑ 98ScoSSAP-PP41
❑ 98SkyDugAAR-4
❑ 98SP Aut-33
❑ 98SP AutC-DE
❑ 98SpollI-34
❑ 98SpollIEE-34
❑ 98SpollIFE-34
❑ 98SpollITaN-78
❑ 98SpollITaNEE-78
❑ 98SPxFin-53
❑ 98SPxFinR-53
❑ 98SPxFinS-53
❑ 98StaCluFDI-105
❑ 98StaCluI-105
❑ 98StaCluOneK-105
❑ 98StaCluPP-105
❑ 98Stu-58
❑ 98StuGPP-58
❑ 98StuHitPar-19
❑ 98StuPor8x10-32
❑ 98StuPor8x10GP-32
❑ 98StuSPP-58
❑ 98Top-288
❑ 98TopBabB-BB5
❑ 98TopChr-288
❑ 98TopChrBB-BB5
❑ 98TopChrBBR-BB5
❑ 98TopChrR-288
❑ 98TopDevR-288
❑ 98TopDia-288
❑ 98TopGal-113
❑ 98TopGalGP-113
❑ 98TopGalOPP-113
❑ 98TopGalPPI-113
❑ 98TopGalPPIA-113
❑ 98TopGolLabC1-61
❑ 98TopGolLabC1B-61
❑ 98TopGolLabC1One-61
❑ 98TopGolLabC1R-61
❑ 98TopGolLabC2-61
❑ 98TopGolLabC2B-61
❑ 98TopGolLabC2One-61
❑ 98TopGolLabC2R-61
❑ 98TopGolLabC3-61
❑ 98TopGolLabC3B-61
❑ 98TopGolLabC3One-61
❑ 98TopGolLabC3R-61
❑ 98TopMiniC-288
❑ 98TopOpeD-115
❑ 98TopSta-79
❑ 98TopStaB-79
❑ 98TopStaG-79
❑ 98TopStaGR-79
❑ 98TopStaPre-PP2
❑ 98TopStaS-79
❑ 98TopTek-35
❑ 98TopTekD-35
❑ 98UD3-8
❑ 98UD3-98
❑ 98UD3-188
❑ 98UD3DieCut-8
❑ 98UD3DieCut-98
❑ 98UD3DieCut-188
❑ 98Ult-164
❑ 98Ult-493
❑ 98UltArtT-11
❑ 98UltBacttF-4
❑ 98UltDouT-9
❑ 98UltGolM-164
❑ 98UltGolM-493
❑ 98UltKidG-5
❑ 98UltMas-164
❑ 98UltMas-493
❑ 98UltPlaM-164
❑ 98UltPlaM-493
❑ 98UltPriL-11
❑ 98UltTop3-8
❑ 98UltWinN-5
❑ 98UppDec-22
❑ 98UppDecBCP-BC4
❑ 98UppDecR-2
❑ 98UppDecRBBop-BB1
❑ 98UppDecRQL-Q1
❑ 98UppDecSF-12
❑ 98Zen-37
❑ 98Zen5 xx7-33
❑ 98Zen5x7GoldImp-33
❑ 98Zen5x7Imp-33
❑ 98ZenZ-G-37
❑ 98ZenZ-S-37
❑ 99199Fin-1
❑ 99199Fin-113
❑ 99199Fin-269
❑ 99Bow-42
❑ 99BowBes-47
❑ 99BowBesAR-47
❑ 99BowBesR-47
❑ 99BowChr-42
❑ 99BowChrG-42
❑ 99BowChrGR-42
❑ 99BowChrI-42
❑ 99BowChrIR-42
❑ 99BowChrR-42
❑ 99BowGol-42
❑ 99BowInt-42
❑ 99CroRoyB-2
❑ 99CroRoyL-2
❑ 99CroRoyOD-2
❑ 99E-X Cen-22
❑ 99E-X CenECFut-22
❑ 99E-X CenECNow-22
❑ 99FinDouF-DF3
❑ 99FinDouFDualR-DF3
❑ 99FinGolRef-1
❑ 99FinGolRef-113
❑ 99FinGolRef-269
❑ 99FinPre-PP1
❑ 99FinRef-1
❑ 99FinRef-113
❑ 99FinRef-269
❑ 99FinTeaFB-TF8
❑ 99FinTeaFBR-TF8
❑ 99FinTeaFG-TF8
❑ 99FinTeaFGR-TF8
❑ 99FinTeaFR-TF8
❑ 99FinTeaFRR-TF8
❑ 99FlaShoLeg1-16
❑ 99FlaShoLeg2-16
❑ 99FlaShoLeg3-16
❑ 99FlaShoLegM1-16
❑ 99FlaShoLegM2-16
❑ 99FlaShoLegM3-16
❑ 99FlaShoR1-16
❑ 99FlaShoR2-16
❑ 99FlaShoR3-16
❑ 99Fle-113
❑ 99FleBri-100
❑ 99FleBri2G-100
❑ 99FleBriBlu-100
❑ 99FleBriGol-100
❑ 99FleMys-88
❑ 99FleMysD-8
❑ 99FleMysG-88
❑ 99FleMysM-88
❑ 99FleSta9-113
❑ 99FleWarT-113
❑ 99MetUni-178
❑ 99MetUni-236
❑ 99MetUni-276
❑ 99MetUniGM-178
❑ 99MetUniGM-236
❑ 99MetUniGM-276
❑ 99MetUniPM-5
❑ 99MetUniPMG-178
❑ 99MetUniPMG-236
❑ 99MetUniPMG-276
❑ 99Pac-5
❑ 99PacAur-3
❑ 99PacAurOD-3
❑ 99PacCroC-4
❑ 99PacCroCPB-4
❑ 99PacCroCTC-1
❑ 99PacGolCDC-1

❑ 99PacInv-2
❑ 99PacInvOD-2
❑ 99PacInvPB-2
❑ 99PacOme-3
❑ 99PacOmeC-3
❑ 99PacOmeDM-1
❑ 99PacOmeG-3
❑ 99PacOmePB-3
❑ 99PacPar-4
❑ 99PacParC-4
❑ 99PacParG-4
❑ 99PacParHoloGold-4
❑ 99PacParHS-4
❑ 99PacParOD-4
❑ 99PacParPB-1
❑ 99PacParPB-4
❑ 99PacParRed-4
❑ 99PacPlaB-5
❑ 99PacPri-3
❑ 99PacPriAotG-1
❑ 99PacPriDG-1
❑ 99PacPriHB-3
❑ 99PacPriHG-3
❑ 99PacPriHM-3
❑ 99PacPriHP-3
❑ 99PacPriRed-3
❑ 99PacPriS-29
❑ 99PacPriS206-29
❑ 99PacPriS206R-29
❑ 99PacPriSP-29
❑ 99PacPriSV-29
❑ 99PacRed-5
❑ 99PacTeaC-1
❑ 99Rev-2
❑ 99RevPremDate-2
❑ 99RevRet-2
❑ 99RevShaSS-2
❑ 99SkyMolM-104
❑ 99SkyMolMF-4
❑ 99SkyMolMFS-4
❑ 99SkyMolMFT-4
❑ 99SkyMolMX-104
❑ 99SkyPre-26
❑ 99SkyPreR-26
❑ 99SkyThu-272
❑ 99SkyThuRant-272
❑ 99SkyThuRave-272
❑ 99SP Aut-3
❑ 99SP SigAuto-DE
❑ 99SP SigAutoG-DE
❑ 99SpoIll-121
❑ 99SpoIllH-16
❑ 99SPSig-16
❑ 99SPx-12
❑ 99SPxFinR-12
❑ 99SPxFinS-12
❑ 99StaClu-171
❑ 99StaCluC-SCC10
❑ 99StaCluCR-SCC10
❑ 99StaCluFDI-171
❑ 99StaCluNC-NC7
❑ 99StaCluOoaK-171
❑ 99StaCluPP-171
❑ 99ThuSkySupR-272
❑ 99Top-140
❑ 99TopAut-A13
❑ 99TopBlaLC1-85
❑ 99TopBlaLC2-85
❑ 99TopBlaLC3-85
❑ 99TopChr-140
❑ 99TopChrLotD-LD11
❑ 99TopChrLotDR-LD11
❑ 99TopChrNB-NB1
❑ 99TopChrNBR-NB1
❑ 99TopChrR-140
❑ 99TopGal-17
❑ 99TopGalE-E17
❑ 99TopGalPP-17
❑ 99TopGalPPI-17
❑ 99TopGolL-85
❑ 99TopGolLC1-85
❑ 99TopGolLC2-85
❑ 99TopGolLOtO-85
❑ 99TopLorotD-LD11
❑ 99TopMVPP-140
❑ 99TopNewB-NB1
❑ 99TopOpeD-83
❑ 99TopPre-PP5
❑ 99TopRedLC1-85
❑ 99TopRedLC2-85
❑ 99TopRedLC3-85
❑ 99TopSta-21
❑ 99TopSta-166
❑ 99TopSta'S-13
❑ 99TopSta'SG-13
❑ 99TopSta'SGDH-13
❑ 99TopSta1Foil-21
❑ 99TopSta2Foil-21
❑ 99TopStaFoil-21
❑ 99TopStaFoil-166
❑ 99TopStaOS-21
❑ 99TopStaPre-PP3
❑ 99TopStaTS-21
❑ 99TopTek-28A
❑ 99TopTek-28B
❑ 99TopTekG-28A
❑ 99TopTekG-28B
❑ 99UD Cho-47
❑ 99UD ChoPCR-47
❑ 99UD Ion-2
❑ 99UD IonR-2
❑ 99Ult-36
❑ 99UltGolM-36
❑ 99UltMas-36
❑ 99UltPlaM-36
❑ 99UltRBIK-8
❑ 99UltThu-5
❑ 99UppDec-20
❑ 99UppDecBD-1
❑ 99UppDecBDD-1
❑ 99UppDecBDMN-M17
❑ 99UppDecBDMNE-M17
❑ 99UppDecBDQ-1
❑ 99UppDecBDT-1
❑ 99UppDecCf7-29
❑ 99UppDecCf7-C23
❑ 99UppDecCf7Cf7P-C23
❑ 99UppDecCf7LL-L25
❑ 99UppDecCL-115
❑ 99UppDecCLCC-115
❑ 99UppDecCLM-C3
❑ 99UppDecCo7CE-29
❑ 99UppDecE-1
❑ 99UppDecEFXG-1
❑ 99UppDecEL1-20
❑ 99UppDecEL2-20
❑ 99UppDecEPE-P2
❑ 99UppDecF-F1
❑ 99UppDecFD-F1
❑ 99UppDecFQ-F1
❑ 99UppDecFT-F1
❑ 99UppDecGJ-DE
❑ 99UppDecM-5
❑ 99UppDecMGS-5
❑ 99UppDecMHFS-5
❑ 99UppDecMP-5
❑ 99UppDecMSS-5
❑ 99UppDecMST-T10
❑ 99UppDecO-30
❑ 99UppDecOSO-30
❑ 99UppDecRI-DE
❑ 99UppDecRIL2-DE
❑ 99UppDecVtaT-V2
❑ 99UppDecVtaTD-V2
❑ 99UppDecVtaTQ-V2
❑ 99UppDecVtaTT-V2
❑ 99Vic-4
❑ 99Vic-8

Ervin, Chris
❑ 91BelBreCB-21

Ervin, Kent
❑ 96IdaFalB-8
❑ 97IdaFalBTI-3

Erving, Julius
❑ 80PhiBul-20

Erwin, David
❑ 97WatIndTI-11

Erwin, Mat
❑ 95ElmPioTI-4
❑ 95ElmPioUTI-4

Erwin, Scott
❑ 88CapCodPPaLP-78
❑ 89MedAthB-5
❑ 90ModA'sC-9
❑ 90ModA'sCLC-149
❑ 90ModA'sP-2205
❑ 91ModA'sP-3079
❑ 92ClaFS7-135
❑ 92HunStaF-3942
❑ 92HunStaS-309
❑ 92SkyAA F-130
❑ 92UppDecML-92

Erwin, Terry
❑ 75BurBeeT-6

Erwin, Tex (Ross Emil)
❑ 09AmeCarE90-1-54
❑ 10DomDisP-41
❑ 10SweCapPP-73
❑ 11HelSta-98
❑ 11PinT-5-466
❑ 11SpoLifM-155
❑ 12T207-56
❑ 90DodTar-223

Esasky, Nick (Nicholas A.)
❑ 80WatRedT-21
❑ 81IndIndTI-15
❑ 82IndIndTI-4
❑ 83IndIndTI-5
❑ 84Don-602
❑ 84Fle-468
❑ 84Nes792-192
❑ 84OPC-192
❑ 84RedEnq-7
❑ 84Top-192
❑ 84TopSti-378
❑ 84TopTif-192
❑ 85Don-121
❑ 85Fle-534
❑ 85IndIndTI-35
❑ 85OPC-253
❑ 85RedYea-4
❑ 85Top-779
❑ 85TopSti-51
❑ 85TopTif-779
❑ 86BasStaB-39
❑ 86Don-286
❑ 86Fle-177
❑ 86Lea-162
❑ 86OPC-201
❑ 86RedTexG-12
❑ 86Top-677
❑ 86TopTif-677
❑ 87Don-166
❑ 87Fle-201
❑ 87FleGlo-201
❑ 87OPC-13
❑ 87RedKah-12
❑ 87Top-13
❑ 87TopTif-13
❑ 88Don-413
❑ 88DonBasB-118
❑ 88Fle-233
❑ 88FleGlo-233
❑ 88Lea-240
❑ 88OPC-364
❑ 88PanSti-274
❑ 88RedKah-12
❑ 88Sco-163
❑ 88ScoGlo-163
❑ 88StaLinRe-8
❑ 88Top-364
❑ 88TopBig-167
❑ 88TopSti-137
❑ 88TopTif-364
❑ 89Bow-31
❑ 89BowTif-31
❑ 89Don-189
❑ 89DonBasB-284
❑ 89DonTra-18
❑ 89Fle-161
❑ 89FleGlo-161
❑ 89FleUpd-9
❑ 89OPC-262
❑ 89PanSti-72
❑ 89Sco-64
❑ 89ScoRoo-37T
❑ 89Top-554
❑ 89TopBig-316
❑ 89TopSti-134
❑ 89TopTif-554
❑ 89TopTra-29T
❑ 89TopTraT-29T
❑ 89UppDec-299
❑ 89UppDec-757
❑ 90Bow-20
❑ 90BowTif-20
❑ 90BraDubP-6
❑ 90BraDubS-7
❑ 90Don-303
❑ 90DonBesN-13
❑ 90Fle-273
❑ 90FleCan-273
❑ 90FleLeaL-10
❑ 90FleLeaLC-10
❑ 90FleUpd-3
❑ 90Lea-164
❑ 90OPC-206
❑ 90PanSti-26
❑ 90PublntS-453
❑ 90Sco-91
❑ 90ScoRoo-3T
❑ 90Spo-72
❑ 90Top-206
❑ 90TopBig-251
❑ 90TopMinL-5
❑ 90TopSti-263
❑ 90TopTif-206
❑ 90TopTra-30T
❑ 90TopTraT-30T
❑ 90UppDec-463
❑ 90UppDec-758
❑ 91BraDubP-8
❑ 91BraSubS-12
❑ 91Fle-687
❑ 91OPC-418
❑ 91SimandSMLBL-15
❑ 91Stu-143
❑ 91Top-418
❑ 91TopDesS-418
❑ 91TopMic-418
❑ 91TopTif-418
❑ 92BraLykP-10
❑ 92OPC-405
❑ 92StaClu-497
❑ 97RicBraBC-24

Escalante, Jimmy
❑ 93BluOriQ-16

Escalera, Carlos
❑ 86BelBreP-5
❑ 86EugEmeC-30
❑ 87AppFoxP-6
❑ 88BasCitRS-11
❑ 88BlaYNPRWL-69
❑ 88FloStaLAS-34
❑ 89BlaYNPRWLU-34
❑ 89MemChiB-10
❑ 89MemChiP-1182
❑ 89MemChiS-11

Escalera, Nino
❑ 77FriOneYW-10

Escalera, Ruben
❑ 87StoPorP-14
❑ 88BlaYNPRWL-134
❑ 88CalLeaACLC-17
❑ 88StoPorCLC-200
❑ 88StoPorP-735
❑ 89BlaYNPRWL-6
❑ 89ElPasDGS-27
❑ 90CMC-49
❑ 90DenZepC-24
❑ 90DenZepP-637
❑ 90ElPasDGS-11
❑ 90ProAAAF-662
❑ 91ElPasDLD-180
❑ 91ElPasDP-2759
❑ 91LinDriAA-180
❑ 92NasSouS-283
❑ 93LinVenB-320

Escalet, Roberto
❑ 94HelBreF-3621
❑ 94HelBreSP-1

Escalona, Felix
❑ 98AubDouTI-10

Escamilla, Jaime
❑ 94HudValRC-4
❑ 94HudValRF-3376
❑ 95ChaRivTI-9
❑ 95Exc-128

Escamilla, Roman
❑ 96SpoIndB-11
❑ 97WilBluR-1
❑ 98WicWraM-9

Escandon, Emiliano
❑ 95SpoIndTI-4
❑ 96LanLugB-10
❑ 97WilBluR-6
❑ 98CarLeaAC-17
❑ 98WilBluRC-12

Escarrega, Acosta (Ernesto)
❑ 83Don-291
❑ 83Fle-234

Eschen, Jim
❑ 77EvaTriT-9
❑ 89KinMetS-26
❑ 90PitMetP-25
❑ 91LinDriAA-650
❑ 91WilBilLD-650
❑ 91WilBilP-310

Escobar, Alex
❑ 98CapCitBF5-27
❑ 98CapCitBM-27
❑ 99199Fin-145
❑ 99BasAmeTPA-11
❑ 99BasAmeTPSC-5
❑ 99Bow-214
❑ 99Bow200RF-ROY5
❑ 99BowAut-BA9
❑ 99BowBes-167
❑ 99BowBesAR-167
❑ 99BowBesR-167
❑ 99BowChr-214
❑ 99BowChrG-214
❑ 99BowChrGR-214
❑ 99BowChrI-214
❑ 99BowChrIR-214
❑ 99BowChrR-214
❑ 99BowGol-214
❑ 99BowInt-214
❑ 99FinGolRef-145
❑ 99FinRef-145
❑ 99JustheS-19
❑ 99JustheSJB-19
❑ 99JustheSJN-1
❑ 99JustheSJN-4
❑ 99SP TopP-5
❑ 99SP TopP-78
❑ 99SP TopPPE-5
❑ 99SP TopPPE-78
❑ 99TeaBesRA-8
❑ 99TeaBesRBW-1
❑ 99Top-206
❑ 99TopChrQ-206
❑ 99TopChrR-206
❑ 99TopSta-33
❑ 99TopSta1Foil-33
❑ 99TopSta2Foil-33
❑ 99TopStaFoil-33
❑ 99TopStaOS-33
❑ 99TopStaTS-33

Escobar, Angel
❑ 85FreGiaSB-4
❑ 86ShrCapP-7
❑ 87PhoFirP-7
❑ 88PhoFirC-14
❑ 88PhoFirP-63
❑ 89HunStaB-25
❑ 93LinVenB-115
❑ 94VenLinU-218

Escobar, Gustavo
❑ 98JohCCTI-10

Escobar, John
❑ 88MarPhiS-13
❑ 89BatCliP-1940
❑ 90SpaPhiB-15
❑ 90SpaPhiP-2497
❑ 90SpaPhiS-6
❑ 91ClePhiC-16
❑ 91ClePhiP-1627
❑ 92ReaPhiF-580
❑ 92ReaPhiS-530
❑ 93ReaPhiF-300

Escobar, Jose
❑ 80UtiBluJT-15
❑ 80VenLeaS-51
❑ 83KinBluJTI-5
❑ 87SyrChiP-1944
❑ 87SyrChiT-13
❑ 88KnoBluJB-13
❑ 89SyrChiMB-9
❑ 90CMC-341
❑ 90ProAAAF-357
❑ 90SyrChiC-15
❑ 90SyrChiMB-8
❑ 90SyrChiP-577
❑ 91Bow-74
❑ 91IndFanC-9
❑ 92TopDeb91-51

Escobar, Juan
❑ 95LinVen-190

Escobar, Kelvim
❑ 95LinVen-189
❑ 96-97LinVen-55
❑ 96DunBluJB-7
❑ 96DunBluJTI-9
❑ 96DunBluJUTI-1
❑ 97Bes-48
❑ 97Bow-394
❑ 97BowChr-260
❑ 97BowChrI-260
❑ 97BowChrIR-260
❑ 97BowChrR-260
❑ 97BowInt-394
❑ 97Sel-178
❑ 97SelCom-178
❑ 98CirThu-132
❑ 98CirThuRav-132
❑ 98CirThuSupRav-132
❑ 98ColCho-109
❑ 98Fin-59
❑ 98FinNo--59
❑ 98FinNo-R-59
❑ 98FinRef-59
❑ 98Fle-106
❑ 98FleRooS-4
❑ 98MetUni-158
❑ 98MetUniPMG-158
❑ 98PacOnl-760
❑ 98PacOnlR-760
❑ 98PacOnlWC-760
❑ 98StaCluFDI-140
❑ 98StaCluI-140
❑ 98StaCluOneK-140
❑ 98StaCluPP-140
❑ 98SyrSkyG-11
❑ 98Top-346
❑ 98TopChr-346
❑ 98TopChrR-346
❑ 98TopDevR-346
❑ 98TopDia-346
❑ 98TopMiniC-346
❑ 98Ult-166
❑ 98UltGolM-166
❑ 98UltMas-166
❑ 98UltPlaM-166
❑ 98UppDec-239
❑ 99Fle-143
❑ 99FleSta9-143
❑ 99FleWarT-143
❑ 99PacCroC-296
❑ 99PacCroCPB-296
❑ 99SkyThu-223
❑ 99SkyThuRant-223
❑ 99SkyThuRave-223
❑ 99ThuSkySupR-223
❑ 99UppDec-515
❑ 99UppDecEL1-515
❑ 99UppDecEL2-515
❑ 99Vic-418

Escobar, Oscar
❑ 86VenGulP-6
❑ 87MyrBeaBJP-1436
❑ 88SalBucS-6
❑ 93LinVenB-137

Escobar, Rodney
❑ 90WicStaSGD-10

Escobar, Ruben
❑ 98WatIndTI-10

Escribano, Eddie
❑ 83MadMusF-17

Eshelman, Vaughn
❑ 91BluOriC-7
❑ 91BluOriP-4120
❑ 91KanCouCTI-5
❑ 92Bow-318
❑ 92StaCluD-44
❑ 93FreKeyC-6
❑ 93FreKeyF-1019
❑ 94Bow-431
❑ 94BowBayF-2408
❑ 94OriPro-31
❑ 95BowBes-R76
❑ 95BowBesR-R76
❑ 95ColCho-573T
❑ 95Emo-11
❑ 95Fin-254
❑ 95FinRef-254
❑ 95Fla-227
❑ 95FlaWavotF-5
❑ 95FleUpd-10
❑ 95SelCer-113
❑ 95SelCerMG-113
❑ 95SigRoo-16
❑ 95SigRooOJSS-7
❑ 95SigRooOJSSS-7
❑ 95SigRooSig-16
❑ 95StaClu-623
❑ 95StaCluMOP-623
❑ 95StaCluSTWS-623
❑ 95Sum-113
❑ 95SumNthD-113
❑ 95TopTra-92T
❑ 95UC3-108
❑ 95UC3ArtP-108
❑ 95UltGolMR-M11
❑ 95UppDec-481
❑ 95Zen-115
❑ 96ColCho-62
❑ 96ColChoGS-62
❑ 96ColChoSS-62
❑ 96Don-29
❑ 96DonPreP-29
❑ 96Fle-26
❑ 96FleRedS-5
❑ 96FleTif-26
❑ 96Pac-250
❑ 96Sco-472
❑ 97PacPriGotD-GD19
❑ 97PawRedS-10

Eskew, Dan
❑ 88SouOreAP-1711
❑ 89ModA'sC-10
❑ 90Bes-51
❑ 90HunStaB-5

❑ 91HunStaTI-9
❑ 91LinDriAAA-532
❑ 91TacTigLD-532
❑ 91TacTigP-2297

Eskins, Mark
❑ 88IdaFalBP-1856

Esmay, Tim
❑ 89AriStaB-5

Esmond, Jimmy (James J.)
❑ 09ColChiE-95
❑ 12ColRedB-95
❑ 12ColTinT-95

Espada, Angel
❑ 95DanBraTI-10
❑ 96EugEmeB-8
❑ 97PitMet-11
❑ 98CapCitBF5-22
❑ 98CapCitBM-22

Espada, Joe
❑ 96SouOreTI-28
❑ 99WesMicWAM-9

Espada, Josue
❑ 97CalLeaTP-29
❑ 98HunStaTI-22

Esper, Duke (Charles)
❑ 94OriTeal-4

Espinal, Jose
❑ 97RocCub-14

Espinal, Josue
❑ 88SouOreAP-1700

Espinal, Juan
❑ 94SprSulC-9
❑ 94SprSulF-2043
❑ 97SarRedS-9

Espinal, Mendy
❑ 87CedRapRP-9

Espinal, Sergio
❑ 86GenCubP-5
❑ 87PeoChiP-4
❑ 88PeoChiTI-10

Espinal, Willie (Bill)
❑ 89JohCitCS-11
❑ 90ProAaA-76
❑ 90SavCarP-2062
❑ 91SprCarC-15
❑ 91SprCarP-737

Espino, Fernando
❑ 97EveAquG-9
❑ 98WisTimRM-22

Espino, Francisco
❑ 87WytCubP-17
❑ 88GenCubP-1648
❑ 89GenCubP-1860
❑ 89PeoChiTI-3

Espino, Jose
❑ 98JohCCTI-11

Espino, Juan
❑ 76ForLauYS-29
❑ 77ForLauYS-29
❑ 79WesHavYT-24
❑ 80ColCliT-28
❑ 81ColCliP-29
❑ 81ColCliT-15
❑ 82ColCliP-29
❑ 82ColCliT-23
❑ 83ColCliT-3
❑ 84Don-92
❑ 84MaiGuiT-17
❑ 85ColCliP-9
❑ 85ColCliT-11
❑ 85DomLeaS-161
❑ 85IntLeaAT-32
❑ 86ColCliP-7
❑ 86ColCliP-7
❑ 86StaoftFT-4
❑ 87ColCliP-8
❑ 87ColCliP-4
❑ 87ColCliT-10
❑ 87Top-239
❑ 87TopTif-239
❑ 88BobCamRB-9
❑ 88RicBraC-20
❑ 88RicBraP-7
❑ 92YanWIZ8-53

Espinosa, Nino (Anulfo A.)
❑ 75TidTidTI-10
❑ 77MetDaiPA-5
❑ 77Top-376
❑ 78MetDaiPA-5
❑ 78Top-197
❑ 79OPC-292
❑ 79PhiBurK-11
❑ 79Top-566
❑ 80OPC-233
❑ 80PhiBurK-17
❑ 80Top-447
❑ 81Fle-20
❑ 81Top-405
❑ 85DomLeaS-49
❑ 89TidTidC-7
❑ 91MetWIZ-108

Espinosa, Philip
❑ 87AncGlaP-9

Espinosa, Ramon
❑ 92WelPirC-7
❑ 92WelPirF-1336
❑ 93AugPirC-7
❑ 93AugPirF-1559
❑ 94CarMudF-1593
❑ 95CarMudF-171
❑ 97BinMetB-8
❑ 97CarMudC-22

Espinosa, Santiago
❑ 86SalAngC-98
❑ 87QuaCitAP-4
❑ 87SalAngP-18

Espinosa, Wendee
❑ 96ColSilB-10

Espinoza, Alvaro
❑ 80VenLeaS-24
❑ 82WisRapTF-7
❑ 83VisOakF-23
❑ 84TolMudHT-3
❑ 85TolMudHT-15
❑ 85TwiPos-7
❑ 85TwiTeal-1
❑ 86TolMudHP-9
❑ 87PorBeaP-14
❑ 87Top-529
❑ 87TopTif-529
❑ 88ColCliC-15
❑ 88ColCliP-15
❑ 88ColCliP-320
❑ 89DonBasB-161
❑ 89FleUpd-47
❑ 89TopTra-30T
❑ 89TopTraT-30T
❑ 89YanScoNW-3
❑ 90Bow-431
❑ 90BowTif-431
❑ 90Don-245
❑ 90DonBesA-123
❑ 90Fle-441
❑ 90FleCan-441
❑ 90Lea-240
❑ 90OPC-791
❑ 90PanSti-121
❑ 90Sco-101
❑ 90Top-791
❑ 90TopBig-8
❑ 90TopSti-311
❑ 90TopTif-791
❑ 90TopTVY-24
❑ 90UppDec-163
❑ 90YanScoNW-4
❑ 91Bow-163
❑ 91Don-226
❑ 91Fle-662
❑ 91Lea-198
❑ 91OPC-28
❑ 91PanFreS-327
❑ 91PanSti-269
❑ 91Sco-127
❑ 91StaClu-242
❑ 91StaCluP-13
❑ 91Top-28
❑ 91TopDesS-28
❑ 91TopMic-28
❑ 91TopTif-28
❑ 91Ult-230
❑ 91UppDec-204
❑ 92ColSprSSF-757
❑ 92ColSprSSS-86
❑ 92Don-474
❑ 92Fle-224
❑ 92OPC-243
❑ 92PanSti-138
❑ 92Sco-41
❑ 92StaClu-527
❑ 92Top-243
❑ 92TopGol-243
❑ 92TopGolW-243
❑ 92TopMic-243
❑ 92Ult-100
❑ 92UppDec-119
❑ 92UppDecS-1
❑ 92YanWIZ8-54
❑ 93FleFinE-200
❑ 93IndWUA-8
❑ 93PacBeiA-6
❑ 93PacSpa-410
❑ 94Fle-103
❑ 94Pac-168
❑ 94Sco-141
❑ 94ScoGolR-141
❑ 94StaClu-461
❑ 94StaCluFDI-461
❑ 94StaCluGR-461
❑ 94StaCluMOP-461
❑ 94Top-726
❑ 94TopGol-726
❑ 94TopSpa-726
❑ 94VenLinU-26
❑ 95Don-303
❑ 95DonPreP-303
❑ 95Fle-134
❑ 95LinVen-79
❑ 95Pac-119
❑ 96-97LinVen-2
❑ 96Fle-86
❑ 96FleTif-86
❑ 96LeaSigEA-49
❑ 96Pac-305
❑ 97ColSprSATTI-16
❑ 97Fle-393
❑ 97FleTif-393
❑ 97Pac-361
❑ 97PacLigB-361
❑ 97PacSil-361
❑ 97StaClu-314
❑ 97StaCluMOP-314
❑ 98PinSnaS-9

Espinoza, Andres
❑ 85LitFalMT-17
❑ 86QuaCitAP-10
❑ 87PalSprP-31
❑ 93LinVenB-154
❑ 94VenLinU-14
❑ 95LinVen-83
❑ 96-97LinVen-18

Espinoza, Carlos
❑ 90GatCitPP-3343

Espinoza, Jose
❑ 92GulCoaMF-3488

Espinoza, Roberto
❑ 80VenLeaS-9
❑ 93LinVenB-191
❑ 96-97LinVen-28

Espinoza-Watson, Laura
❑ 96ColSilB-11

Espinsosa, Santiago
❑ 86QuaCitAP-9

Esposito, Nick
❑ 83TriTriT-9

Esposito, Sammy (Samuel)
❑ 57Top-301
❑ 58Top-425
❑ 59Top-438
❑ 60Top-31
❑ 60TopVen-31
❑ 61Top-323
❑ 61WhiSoxTS-4
❑ 62Top-586
❑ 63Top-181
❑ 79DiaGre-145
❑ 81WhiSox1T-11

Epstein, Ian
❑ 95WesMicWTI-29

Espy, Cecil (Cecil Edward)
❑ 81AppFoxT-14
❑ 82VerBeaDT-22
❑ 86HawIslP-5
❑ 87OklCit8P-16
❑ 88BlaYNPRWL-56
❑ 88DonRoo-9
❑ 88Fle-465
❑ 88FleGlo-465
❑ 88RanMot-13
❑ 88ScoRoo-73T
❑ 88ScoRooG-73T
❑ 88TopTra-36T
❑ 88TopTraT-36T
❑ 89Baz-7
❑ 89Bow-236
❑ 89BowTif-236
❑ 89ClaTraO-143
❑ 89Don-292
❑ 89DonBasB-335
❑ 89Fle-517
❑ 89FleGlo-517
❑ 89K-M-6
❑ 89PanSti-443
❑ 89RanMot-12
❑ 89RanSmo-7
❑ 89Sco-401
❑ 89ScoYouS2-10
❑ 89Top-221
❑ 89TopBig-36
❑ 89TopGloS-59
❑ 89TopRoo-7
❑ 89TopSti-240
❑ 89TopSti-320
❑ 89TopTif-221
❑ 89ToyRoo-8
❑ 89UppDec-92
❑ 90Bow-502
❑ 90BowTif-502
❑ 90DodTar-224
❑ 90Don-260
❑ 90Fle-295
❑ 90FleCan-295
❑ 90OPC-496
❑ 90PubIntS-407
❑ 90RanMot-25
❑ 90Sco-69
❑ 90Top-496
❑ 90TopBig-37
❑ 90TopMinL-36
❑ 90TopSti-249
❑ 90TopTif-496
❑ 90UppDec-371
❑ 91BufBisLD-27
❑ 91BufBisP-551
❑ 91LinDriAAA-27
❑ 92Don-678
❑ 92PirNatI-8
❑ 92Sco-673
❑ 92StaClu-95
❑ 92Ult-552
❑ 93RanKee-137

Espy, Duane
❑ 75SacSolC-7
❑ 77SpoIndC-1
❑ 78SpoIndC-1
❑ 79BurBeeT-17
❑ 80BurBeeT-10
❑ 84ShrCapFB-7
❑ 86PhoFirP-5
❑ 87PhoFirP-22
❑ 88SanJosGCLC-141
❑ 88SanJosGP-125
❑ 89CalLeaA-49
❑ 89SanJosGB-28
❑ 89SanJosGCLC-235
❑ 89SanJosGP-453
❑ 89SanJosGS-27
❑ 90CMC-551
❑ 90PhoFirC-24
❑ 90PhoFirP-27
❑ 90ProAAAF-53
❑ 91LinDriAAA-399
❑ 91PhoFirLD-399
❑ 91PhoFirP-83
❑ 93PhoFirF-1533
❑ 94PhoFirF-1536

Espy, Nate
❑ 98MarPhiG-10

Esquer, Dave (David)
❑ 87NewOriP-1
❑ 89QuaCitAB-7
❑ 89QuaCitAGS-25
❑ 90PalSprACLC-204
❑ 90PalSprAP-2583

Esquer, Mercedes
❑ 83KnoBluJT-4

Essegian, Chuck (Charles A.)
❑ 58Top-460
❑ 59Top-278
❑ 60DodBelB-11
❑ 60DodTeal-6
❑ 60DodUniO-6
❑ 60Top-166
❑ 60TopVen-166
❑ 61Top-384
❑ 62Jel-45
❑ 62Pos-45
❑ 62PosCan-45
❑ 62Top-379
❑ 63Jel-71
❑ 63Pos-71
❑ 63Top-103
❑ 70FleWorS-56
❑ 90DodTar-225
❑ 91OriCro-122

Esser, Mark (Mark Gerald)
❑ 78AppFoxT-8
❑ 80GleFalWSBT-14
❑ 80GleFalWSCT-5

Essian, Jim (James Sarkis)
❑ 75PhiProPS-6
❑ 76SSP-142
❑ 77Top-529
❑ 77WhiSoxJT-3
❑ 77WhiSoxT-7
❑ 78Top-98
❑ 79OPC-239
❑ 79Top-458
❑ 80OPC-179
❑ 80Top-341
❑ 81CokTeaS-28
❑ 81Don-503
❑ 81Fle-593
❑ 81Top-178
❑ 81TopTra-759
❑ 82Don-369
❑ 82Fle-341
❑ 82MarPos-17
❑ 82Top-269
❑ 82TopTra-31T
❑ 83Don-478
❑ 83IndPos-11
❑ 83IndWhe-10
❑ 83Top-646
❑ 83TopSti-117
❑ 83TopTra-30T
❑ 84A'sMot-19
❑ 84Don-629
❑ 84Fle-540
❑ 84FleUpd-35
❑ 84Nes792-737
❑ 84Top-737
❑ 84TopTif-737
❑ 84TopTra-35T
❑ 84TopTraT-35T
❑ 85Fle-423
❑ 85Top-472
❑ 85TopTif-472
❑ 86WinSpiP-7
❑ 87PitCubP-4
❑ 88BlaYNPRWL-97
❑ 88EasLeaAP-47
❑ 88PitCubP-1360
❑ 89ChaKniTI-2
❑ 90CMC-99
❑ 90IowCubC-24
❑ 90IowCubP-333
❑ 90ProAAAF-640
❑ 91CubMar-41
❑ 91IowCubLD-224
❑ 91IowCubP-1076
❑ 91LinDriAAA-224
❑ 91TopTra-36T
❑ 91TopTraT-36T
❑ 96NorNavB-1

Essick, William
❑ 18Zee-98
❑ 19Zee-133
❑ 20Zee-139
❑ 21Zee-155
❑ 22Zee-148
❑ 23Zee-182
❑ 24Zee-127
❑ 25Zee-153

Estalella, Bobby
❑ 93MarPhiC-8
❑ 93MarPhiF-3476
❑ 94SpaPhiF-1726
❑ 94SparPhiC-7
❑ 95ClePhiF-218
❑ 95ReaPhiELC-12
❑ 96BesAutS-31
❑ 96BesAutSA-19
❑ 96Bow-248
❑ 96BowFoi-248
❑ 96DouAllB-11
❑ 96Exc-201
❑ 96ReaPhiB-13
❑ 97Bow-375
❑ 97BowBes-163
❑ 97BowBesAR-163
❑ 97BowBesR-163
❑ 97BowCerBlaIA-CA24
❑ 97BowCerBluIA-CA24
❑ 97BowCerGolIA-CA24
❑ 97BowChr-249
❑ 97BowChrI-249
❑ 97BowChrIR-249
❑ 97BowChrR-249
❑ 97BowInt-375
❑ 97Cir-367
❑ 97CirRav-367
❑ 97DonSigA-32
❑ 97DonSigAC-39
❑ 97DonSigAM-39
❑ 97Fle-411
❑ 97FleTif-411
❑ 97Pac-378
❑ 97PacLigB-378
❑ 97PacSil-378
❑ 97ScrRedB-17
❑ 97Top-205
❑ 97UppDec-287
❑ 98BesDiaB-15
❑ 98Bow-88
❑ 98BowChr-88
❑ 98BowChrGA-88
❑ 98BowChrGAR-88
❑ 98BowChrI-88
❑ 98BowChrIR-88
❑ 98BowChrR-88
❑ 98BowGolA-88
❑ 98BowInt-88
❑ 98CirThu-208
❑ 98CirThuRav-208
❑ 98CirThuSupRav-208
❑ 98ColCho-201
❑ 98Don-310
❑ 98DonCol-200
❑ 98DonColE-496
❑ 98DonColL-379
❑ 98DonColP-717
❑ 98DonColS-195
❑ 98DonEli-96
❑ 98DonEliA-96
❑ 98DonEliS-96
❑ 98DonGolPP-310
❑ 98DonPre-167
❑ 98DonPreSeat-167
❑ 98DonPriCD-200
❑ 98DonPriCE-496
❑ 98DonPriCL-379
❑ 98DonPriCP-717
❑ 98DonRatR-25
❑ 98DonRatRM-25
❑ 98DonSigA-30
❑ 98DonSigAC-39
❑ 98DonSigAM-40
❑ 98DonSigSB-9
❑ 98DonSilPP-310
❑ 98E-X2SD2001-4
❑ 98E-X2Sig2001-15
❑ 98Fle-29
❑ 98Lea-180
❑ 98LeaFraDA-180
❑ 98LeaFraF-180
❑ 98LeaFraM-180
❑ 98LeaFraM-180
❑ 98LeaFraMDC-180
❑ 98LeaFraMDC-180
❑ 98LeaFraMZ2-180
❑ 98LeaRCrusUP-125
❑ 98LeaRS-274
❑ 98LeaRSCrusUG-125
❑ 98LeaRSCrusUR-125
❑ 98LeaRSLHolo-274
❑ 98LeaRSLong-274
❑ 98LeaRTrue-274
❑ 98Pac-379
❑ 98PacPar-211
❑ 98PacParC-211
❑ 98PacParG-211
❑ 98PacParHS-211
❑ 98PacParPB-211
❑ 98PacParR-211
❑ 98PacPlaB-379
❑ 98PacRedT-379
❑ 98PacSil-379
❑ 98PhiTeal-10
❑ 98Pin-171
❑ 98PinArtP-PP74
❑ 98PinIns-34
❑ 98PinInsCE-34
❑ 98PinInsDE-34
❑ 98PinMusC-PP74
❑ 98PinPer-135
❑ 98PinPerPP-135
❑ 98PinPreP-171
❑ 98Sco-249
❑ 98ScoRT-169
❑ 98ScoRTSS-PP98
❑ 98ScoRTSSAP-PP98
❑ 98ScoRTSSAP1-PP98
❑ 98ScrRedBQ-11
❑ 98SpoIll-169
❑ 98SpoIllEE-169
❑ 98SpoIllFE-169
❑ 98StaCluBPP-BP5
❑ 98StaCluFDI-350

❑ 98StaClul-350
❑ 98StaCluOneK-350
❑ 98StaCluPP-350
❑ 98Stu-101
❑ 98StuGPP-101
❑ 98StuSPP-101
❑ 98Ult-407
❑ 98UltGolM-407
❑ 98UltMas-407
❑ 98UltPlaM-407
❑ 99Fle-424
❑ 99FleSta9-424
❑ 99FleWarT-424
❑ 99Pac-325
❑ 99PacCroC-212
❑ 99PacCroCPB-212
❑ 99PacPlaB-325
❑ 99PacRed-325
❑ 99StaClu-114
❑ 99StaCluFDI-114
❑ 99StaCluOoaK-114
❑ 99StaCluPP-114
❑ 99UppDec-450
❑ 99UppDecEL1-450
❑ 99UppDecEL2-450
Estalella, Roberto M.
❑ 41BroW75-9
❑ 43A'STEAI-9
❑ 45A'sTeal-11
Estavil, Mauricio
❑ 95PiePhiF-181
Esteban, Felipe
❑ 87VerBeaDP-21
❑ 88VerBeaDS-6
Estelle, Dick (Richard H.)
❑ 65OPC-282
❑ 65Top-282
❑ 66Top-373
Estep, Chad
❑ 93DavLipB-8
❑ 94DavLipB-9
❑ 95DavLipB-10
Estep, Chris
❑ 87AncGlaP-10
❑ 88WatPirP-18
❑ 89AugPirP-499
❑ 90CarLeaA-25
❑ 90SalBucS-5
❑ 91CarMudLD-107
❑ 91CarMudP-1097
❑ 91LinDriAA-107
❑ 92CarMudS-133
❑ 92CedRapRF-1082
❑ 92ChaLooF-3830
Estep, Richie
❑ 94DavLipB-19
❑ 95DavLipB-11
Estepa, Ramon
❑ 80SanJosMJitB-6
❑ 81LynSaiT-21
❑ 82LynSaiT-14
❑ 83ChaLooT-5
❑ 84ChaLooT-2
Estepan, Rafael
❑ 80CliGiaT-18
Esterbrook, Dude (Thomas J.)
❑ 86OldJudN-5
❑ 87BucN28-58
❑ 87OldJudN-152
❑ 88GandBCGCE-13
❑ 88SpoTimM-10
❑ 88WG1CarG-31
❑ 90DodTar-226
❑ 90KalBatN-15
❑ 94OriofB-64
Esterday, Henry
❑ 87OldJudN-153
Estes, Doc (Frank)
❑ 77OrlTwiT-8
❑ 78OrlTwiT-6
❑ 80OrlTwiT-9
❑ 81TolMudHT-21
❑ 85IntLeaAT-8
❑ 85RicBraT-18
❑ 86RicBraP-6
❑ 87SyrChiP-1949
❑ 87SyrChiT-22
Estes, Eric
❑ 97FreKey-7
❑ 98BowBayM-12
Estes, Joel
❑ 84AriWilP-6
❑ 86AriWilP-2
❑ 86AubAstP-9
❑ 87OscAstP-20
❑ 89ColMudP-128
❑ 89ColMudS-7
❑ 90Bes-97
❑ 90SanJosGB-17
❑ 90SanJosGCLC-45
❑ 90SanJosGP-2007
❑ 90SanJosGS-8
Estes, Marc
❑ 86MiaMarP-7
Estes, Mark
❑ 89GeoColC-5
❑ 90GeoColC-2
Estes, Shawn
❑ 91BelMarCB-29
❑ 91BelMarP-3656
❑ 91Cla/Bes-429
❑ 91ClaDraP-8
❑ 91HigSchPLS-11
❑ 92BelMarCB-1
❑ 92BelMarF-1435
❑ 92Bow-151
❑ 92OPC-624
❑ 92ProFS7-146
❑ 92StaCluD-45
❑ 92Top-624
❑ 92TopGol-624
❑ 92TopGolW-624
❑ 92TopMic-624
❑ 92UppDecML-164
❑ 93AppFoxCB-1
❑ 93AppFoxFI-2455
❑ 93Bow-275
❑ 93ClaFS7-70
❑ 93ClaGolF-191
❑ 93ExcFS7-224
❑ 93MariStaClu-30
❑ 94Bow-473
❑ 95ARuFalLS-5
❑ 95Bow-205
❑ 96Bow-173
❑ 96BowFoi-173
❑ 96ColCho-722
❑ 96ColChoGS-722
❑ 96ColChoSS-722
❑ 96Fle-587
❑ 96FleTif-587
❑ 96PhoFirB-16
❑ 96Sco-496
❑ 96Spo-134
❑ 96SpoArtP-134
❑ 97Cir-142
❑ 97CirRav-142
❑ 97Don-140
❑ 97DonGolPP-140
❑ 97DonLim-80
❑ 97DonLimE-80
❑ 97DonLimENG-80
❑ 97DonSig-78
❑ 97DonSigA-33
❑ 97DonSigAC-40
❑ 97DonSigAM-40
❑ 97DonSigPPP-78
❑ 97DonSilPP-140
❑ 97Fle-480
❑ 97FleTif-480
❑ 97Lea-50
❑ 97LeaFraM-50
❑ 97LeaFraMDC-50
❑ 97MetUni-243
❑ 97Pac-442
❑ 97PacLigB-442
❑ 97PacSil-442
❑ 97Sco-270
❑ 97ScoArtPWB-270
❑ 97ScoPreS-270
❑ 97ScoShoS-270
❑ 97ScoShoSAP-270
❑ 97StaClu-370
❑ 97StaCluMOP-370
❑ 97StrAll-19
❑ 97TopSta-32
❑ 97TopStaAM-32
❑ 97Ult-294
❑ 97UltGolME-294
❑ 97UltPlaME-294
❑ 98Bow-29
❑ 98BowChr-29
❑ 98BowChrGA-29
❑ 98BowChrGAR-29
❑ 98BowChrl-29
❑ 98BowChrIR-29
❑ 98BowChrR-29
❑ 98BowGolA-29
❑ 98BowInt-29
❑ 98CirThu-289
❑ 98CirThuRav-289
❑ 98CirThuSupRav-289
❑ 98ColCho-235
❑ 98ColChoSQ-SQ29
❑ 98Don-27
❑ 98DonCol-27
❑ 98DonColE-494
❑ 98DonColL-210
❑ 98DonColP-656
❑ 98DonColS-27
❑ 98DonCruG-100
❑ 98DonCruP-100
❑ 98DonCruR-100
❑ 98DonEli-94
❑ 98DonEliA-94
❑ 98DonEliS-94
❑ 98DonGolPP-27
❑ 98DonPre-106
❑ 98DonPreSeat-106
❑ 98DonPriCD-27
❑ 98DonPriCE-494
❑ 98DonPriCL-210
❑ 98DonPriCP-656
❑ 98DonSilPP-27
❑ 98E-X2-59
❑ 98E-X2ECFut-59
❑ 98E-X2ECNow-59
❑ 98Fin-123
❑ 98FinNo--123
❑ 98FinNo-R-123
❑ 98FinRef-123
❑ 98FlaShoLeg0-120
❑ 98FlaShoLeg1-120
❑ 98FlaShoLeg2-120
❑ 98FlaShoLeg3-120
❑ 98FlaShoLegM-120
❑ 98FlaShoR0-120
❑ 98FlaShoR1-120
❑ 98FlaShoR2-120
❑ 98FlaShoR3-120
❑ 98Fle-246
❑ 98GiaMot-3
❑ 98Lea-10
❑ 98LeaFraDA-10
❑ 98LeaFraF-10
❑ 98LeaFraM-10
❑ 98LeaFraM-10
❑ 98LeaFraMDC-10
❑ 98LeaFraMDC-10
❑ 98LeaFraMS-10
❑ 98LeaFraMZ2-10
❑ 98MetUni-185
❑ 98MetUniPMG-185
❑ 98Pac-439
❑ 98PacAur-196
❑ 98PacInv-144
❑ 98PacInvPBlue-144
❑ 98PacInvSilv-144
❑ 98PacOme-210
❑ 98PacOmeR-210
❑ 98PacOnl-657
❑ 98PacOnlR-657
❑ 98PacOnlWC-657
❑ 98PacPar-244
❑ 98PacParC-244
❑ 98PacParG-244
❑ 98PacParHS-244
❑ 98PacParPB-244
❑ 98PacParR-244
❑ 98PacPlaB-439
❑ 98PacRedT-439
❑ 98PacSil-439
❑ 98Pin-5
❑ 98PinArtP-PP5
❑ 98PinIns-59
❑ 98PinInsCE-59
❑ 98PinInsDE-59
❑ 98PinMusC-PP5
❑ 98PinPer-88
❑ 98PinPerPP-88
❑ 98PinPreP-5
❑ 98Sco-35
❑ 98ScoRT-154
❑ 98ScoRTSS-PP88
❑ 98ScoRTSSAP-PP88
❑ 98ScoRTSSAP1-PP88
❑ 98ScoSS-PP124
❑ 98ScoSSAP-PP124
❑ 98SkyDugA-48
❑ 98SkyDugAIA-48
❑ 98SP Aut-171
❑ 98SpollI-35
❑ 98SpollIEE-35
❑ 98SpollIFE-35
❑ 98SpollIWSF-40
❑ 98SpollIWSFEE-40
❑ 98SpollIWSFFE-40
❑ 98SPxFin-127
❑ 98SPxFinR-127
❑ 98SPxFinS-127
❑ 98StaCluFDI-111
❑ 98StaClul-111
❑ 98StaCluOneK-111
❑ 98StaCluPP-111
❑ 98Stu-74
❑ 98StuGPP-74
❑ 98StuSPP-74
❑ 98Top-171
❑ 98TopChr-171
❑ 98TopChrR-171
❑ 98TopDevR-171
❑ 98TopDia-171
❑ 98TopGal-96
❑ 98TopGalGP-96
❑ 98TopGalOPP-96
❑ 98TopGalPPI-96
❑ 98TopGalPPIA-96
❑ 98TopMiniC-171
❑ 98TopOpeD-91
❑ 98TopSta-28
❑ 98TopStaB-28
❑ 98TopStaG-28
❑ 98TopStaGR-28
❑ 98TopStaS-28
❑ 98Ult-37
❑ 98UltGolM-37
❑ 98UltMas-37
❑ 98UltPlaM-37
❑ 98UppDec-215
❑ 98UppDecSF-119
❑ 99Fle-395
❑ 99FleSta9-395
❑ 99FleWarT-395
❑ 99MetUni-18
❑ 99MetUniGM-18
❑ 99MetUniPMG-18
❑ 99SkyPre-27
❑ 99SkyPreR-27
❑ 99SkyThu-88
❑ 99SkyThuRant-88
❑ 99SkyThuRave-88
❑ 99StaClu-116
❑ 99StaCluFDI-116
❑ 99StaCluOoaK-116
❑ 99StaCluPP-116
❑ 99ThuSkySupR-88
❑ 99Top-297
❑ 99TopChr-297
❑ 99TopChrR-297
❑ 99TopMVPP-297
❑ 99Ult-184
❑ 99UltGolM-184
❑ 99UltMas-184
❑ 99UltPlaM-184
❑ 99UppDec-196
❑ 99UppDecEL1-196
❑ 99UppDecEL2-196
❑ 99Vic-363
Estevez, Bernado
❑ 76ForLauYS-7
Estevez, Carlos
❑ 92Ft.MyeMCB-13
❑ 92Ft.MyeMF-2752
❑ 92KenTwiC-6
Estevez, Domingo
❑ 98St.CatSM-4
Estevez, Juan
❑ 88BriTigP-1866
Estrada, Asdrubal
❑ 93LinVenB-145
❑ 94VenLinU-106
❑ 95LinVen-196
❑ 96-97LinVen-175
Estrada, Chuck (Charles L.)
❑ 60BalOriP-4
❑ 60Top-126
❑ 60TopVen-126
❑ 61BalOriP-7
❑ 61Baz-13
❑ 61Pos-73
❑ 61Top-48
❑ 61Top-395
❑ 61TopStal-100
❑ 62BalOriP-7
❑ 62Jel-36
❑ 62Pos-36
❑ 62PosCan-36
❑ 62SalPlaC-212
❑ 62ShiPlaC-212
❑ 62Top-560
❑ 62TopBuc-24
❑ 62TopStal-4
❑ 63BalOriP-10
❑ 63Top-465
❑ 64BalOriP-13
❑ 64OriJayP-5
❑ 64Top-263
❑ 64TopVen-263
❑ 65SeaPop-3
❑ 65Top-378
❑ 66SeaPop-6
❑ 67Top-537
❑ 73OPC-549
❑ 73Top-549
❑ 78PadFamF-10
❑ 79PadFamF-16
❑ 81PadFamF-8
❑ 82ChaChaT-24
❑ 85TacTigC-129
❑ 86TacTigP-6
❑ 87TacTigP-12
❑ 88TacTigP-623
❑ 89TacTigC-9
❑ 89TacTigP-1564
❑ 90ProAAAF-158
❑ 90TacTigP-111
❑ 91MetWIZ-109
❑ 91OriCro-123
❑ 93RanKee-138
❑ 93SanBerSC-23
❑ 93SanBerSF-787
❑ 94CenValRC-27
❑ 94CenValRF-3220
❑ 95NewHavRTI-23
Estrada, Eduardo
❑ 86NewBriRSP-11
❑ 87NewBriRSP-25
❑ 88EasLeaAP-21
❑ 88NewBriRSP-903
❑ 89NewBriRSS-1
❑ 89PawRedSC-23
❑ 89PawRedSP-698
Estrada, Francisco
❑ 91MetWIZ-110
Estrada, Horacio
❑ 97El PasDB-14
❑ 98El PasDG-11
❑ 98LouRedQ-15
❑ 98TexLeaTPG-9
Estrada, Jay
❑ 87SpoIndP-5
❑ 88ChaRaiP-1213
❑ 89RivRedWB-4
❑ 89RivRedWCLC-21
❑ 89RivRedWP-1409
❑ 90RivRedWB-7
❑ 90RivRedWCLC-16
❑ 90RivRedWP-2600
❑ 91HigDesMC-3
❑ 91HigDesMP-2386
Estrada, Johnny
❑ 97BatCliTI-6
❑ 98PieBolWM-11
Estrada, Josue
❑ 94BurBeeC-7
❑ 94BurBeeF-1094
❑ 94ClaGolF-71
❑ 94Top-741
❑ 94TopGol-741
❑ 94TopSpa-741
❑ 97VisOakG-10
Estrada, Luis
❑ 79AppFoxT-16
❑ 80AppFoxT-1
❑ 81GleFalWST-1
Estrada, Manny (Manuel)
❑ 78SanJosMMC-22
❑ 79SpoIndT-25
❑ 80LynSaiT-13
❑ 81SpoIndT-2
❑ 82SalLakCGT-23
❑ 83SalLakCGT-25
❑ 84ButCopKT-1
Estrada, Osmani
❑ 94ChaRanF-2502
❑ 95TulDriTI-8
❑ 96OklCit8B-8
❑ 97OklCit8-14
Estrada, Pete (Peter)
❑ 88ElmPioC-8
❑ 89WinHavRSS-6
❑ 90LynRedSTI-18
❑ 91LinDriAA-456
❑ 91NewBriRSLD-456
❑ 91NewBriRSP-346
❑ 92LynRedSC-3
❑ 92LynRedSF-2901
Estrella, Leoncio
❑ 97PitMet-12
❑ 98CapCitBF5-6
❑ 98CapCitBM-6
Estrella, Luis
❑ 96BelGiaTI-28
❑ 98SanJosGQ-3
Etchandy, Curt
❑ 76AppFoxT-3
Etchebarren, Andy
❑ 66BalOriP-13
❑ 66OPC-27
❑ 66Top-27
❑ 66TopVen-27
❑ 67BalOriP-34
❑ 67BalOriP-35
❑ 67BalOriP-36
❑ 67BalOriP-37
❑ 67CokCapO-9
❑ 67DexPre-69
❑ 67Top-457
❑ 68AtlOilPBCC-16
❑ 68BalOriDPCP-6
❑ 68CokCapO-9
❑ 68DexPre-31
❑ 68Top-204
❑ 68TopVen-204
❑ 69MilBra-80
❑ 69MLBOffS-3
❑ 69Top-634
❑ 70BalOriP-9
❑ 70DayDaiNM-158
❑ 70MLBOffS-149
❑ 70OPC-201
❑ 70OPC-213
❑ 70Ori-5
❑ 70Top-201
❑ 70Top-213
❑ 71BalOriP-10
❑ 71MLBOffS-296
❑ 71OPC-501
❑ 71OriCha-4
❑ 71Top-501
❑ 72MilBra-100
❑ 72OPC-26
❑ 72OriPos-12
❑ 72Top-26
❑ 73BalOriP-18
❑ 73OPC-618
❑ 73OriJohP-8
❑ 73OriTeal-15
❑ 73Top-618
❑ 74OPC-488
❑ 74Top-488
❑ 75OPC-583
❑ 75Top-583
❑ 75TopMin-583
❑ 76OPC-129
❑ 76Top-129
❑ 77Top-454
❑ 78Top-313
❑ 81Ori6F-13
❑ 84BrePol-NNO
❑ 85BrePol-NNO
❑ 86BrePol-8
❑ 87BrePol-NNO
❑ 88BrePol-NNO
❑ 88BreTeal-11
❑ 89BrePol-NNO
❑ 90BreMilB-32
❑ 90BrePol-NNO
❑ 91BreMilB-32
❑ 91BrePol-NNO
❑ 91OriCro-124
❑ 93BluOriC-12
❑ 94BluOriC-23
❑ 94BluOriF-3578
❑ 94BreMilB-311
❑ 94TedWil-9
❑ 96BalOriP-11
❑ 98BluOriQ-1
Etchebarren, Ray
❑ 84BeaGolGT-24
Etheredge, Jeff
❑ 89BatCliP-1917
Etheridge, Bobby (Bobby L.)
❑ 68OPC-126
❑ 68Top-126
❑ 68TopVen-126
❑ 69Top-604
❑ 70OPC-107
❑ 70Top-107
Etheridge, Haden
❑ 90ArkRaz-12

Etheridge, Josh
❑ 98PorRocG-12
Etheridge, Roger
❑ 92PriRedC-9
❑ 92PriRedF-3079
❑ 93PriRedC-9
❑ 93PriRedF-4169
❑ 93WesVirWC-5
❑ 93WesVirWF-2858
❑ 94ChaWheC-9
❑ 94ChaWheF-2694
❑ 95BreBtaTI-18
❑ 96GreBraB-12
❑ 96GreBraTI-43
Etherton, Seth
❑ 98MidAngO-13
❑ 99BasAmeTPA-12
❑ 99Bow-81
❑ 99BowBes-187
❑ 99BowBesAR-187
❑ 99BowBesR-187
❑ 99BowChr-81
❑ 99BowChrG-81
❑ 99BowChrGR-81
❑ 99BowChrI-81
❑ 99BowChrIR-81
❑ 99BowChrR-81
❑ 99BowGol-81
❑ 99BowInt-81
❑ 99SP TopP-55
❑ 99SP TopPPE-55
❑ 99StaClu-344
❑ 99StaCluFDI-344
❑ 99StaCluOoaK-344
❑ 99StaCluPP-344
❑ 99TeaBesRA-9
❑ 99Top-216
❑ 99TopChr-216
❑ 99TopChrR-216
Ethiopian Clowns, Miami
❑ 93NegLeaRL2-91
Etler, Todd
❑ 92ClaDraP-54
❑ 92FroRowDP-63
❑ 92FroRowDPG-63
❑ 92FroRowDPS-63
❑ 92HigSchPLS-7
❑ 92PriRedC-1
❑ 92PriRedF-3080
❑ 93BilMusF-3936
❑ 93BilMusSP-5
❑ 93StaCluM-68
❑ 94ChaWheC-10
❑ 94ChaWheF-2695
❑ 94SouAtlLAF-SAL40
❑ 97BurBeeB-8
❑ 98ChaLooG-10
Etohandy, Curt
❑ 78AppFoxT-9
Etten, Nick (Nicholas R.)
❑ 41DouPlaR-123
❑ 43YanSta-10
❑ 48SigOil-6
❑ 48SmiClo-4
❑ 77TCMTheWY-55
❑ 79DiaGre-337
Ettles, Mark
❑ 89NiaFalRP-8
❑ 90LakTigS-9
❑ 91LakTigC-3
❑ 91LakTigP-259
❑ 92WicWraF-3652
❑ 92WicWraS-628
❑ 93AusFut-112
❑ 93AusFut-131
❑ 93FleFinE-137
❑ 93LasVegSF-939
❑ 95AusFut-16
❑ 95AusFutSFP-SFFP7
Etzweiler, Dan
❑ 88MyrBeaBJP-1177
Eubanks, Craig
❑ 91ChaRaiC-6
❑ 91ChaRaiP-92
Eubanks, John
❑ 08IndPos-10
Eubanks, Larry
❑ 76DubPacT-11
❑ 77CocAstT-6
Eufemia, Frank
❑ 83VisOakF-11
❑ 85TolMudHT-6
❑ 86Don-513
❑ 86Fle-392
❑ 86TolMudHP-10
❑ 86Top-236
❑ 86TopTif-236
❑ 86TwiTeal-19
Eusebio, Ralph
❑ 93HunCubC-7
❑ 93HunCubF-3248
Eusebio, Tony
❑ 88OscAstS-9
❑ 89ColMudB-15
❑ 89ColMudP-125
❑ 89ColMudS-8
❑ 90Bes-112
❑ 90ColMudB-5
❑ 90ColMudP-1350
❑ 90ColMudS-10
❑ 90StaFS7-15
❑ 91JacGenLD-557
❑ 91JacGenP-928
❑ 91LinDriAA-557
❑ 92ClaFS7-338
❑ 92JacGenS-331
❑ 92Sco-858
❑ 92SkyAA F-140
❑ 92StaClu-546
❑ 92TopDeb91-52
❑ 93AstStaC-29
❑ 93ExcFS7-42
❑ 93LimRocDWB-16
❑ 93TucTorF-3061
❑ 94AstMot-24
❑ 94ExcFS7-199
❑ 94FleUpd-142
❑ 94LeaLimR-51
❑ 94Pin-537
❑ 94PinArtP-537
❑ 94PinMusC-537
❑ 94ScoRoo-RT116
❑ 94ScoRooGR-RT116
❑ 94Sel-192
❑ 94SpoRoo-93
❑ 94SpoRooAP-93
❑ 94StaClu-690
❑ 94StaCluFDI-690
❑ 94StaCluGR-690
❑ 94StaCluMOP-690
❑ 94Ult-502
❑ 95AstMot-12
❑ 95ColCho-114
❑ 95ColChoGS-114
❑ 95ColChoSS-114
❑ 95Don-445
❑ 95DonPreP-445
❑ 95DonTopotO-253
❑ 95Fla-145
❑ 95Fle-457
❑ 95Pac-185
❑ 95PacLatD-11
❑ 95PacPri-61
❑ 95Sco-133
❑ 95ScoGolR-133
❑ 95ScoPlaTS-133
❑ 95Top-454
❑ 95TopCyb-250
❑ 95Ult-385
❑ 95UltGolM-385
❑ 95UppDec-24
❑ 95UppDecED-24
❑ 95UppDecEDG-24
❑ 96AstMot-18
❑ 96ColCho-563
❑ 96ColChoGS-563
❑ 96ColChoSS-563
❑ 96Don-200
❑ 96DonPreP-200
❑ 96EmoXL-198
❑ 96Fla-277
❑ 96Fle-406
❑ 96FleTif-406
❑ 96MetUni-177
❑ 96MetUniP-177
❑ 96Pac-93
❑ 96PacPri-P32
❑ 96PacPriG-P32
❑ 96Sco-102
❑ 96StaClu-218
❑ 96StaClu-347
❑ 96StaCluEPB-347
❑ 96StaCluEPG-347
❑ 96StaCluEPS-347
❑ 96StaCluMOP-218
❑ 96StaCluMOP-347
❑ 96Top-46
❑ 96Ult-208
❑ 96UltGolM-208
❑ 96UppDec-344
❑ 97AstMot-12
❑ 97Fle-344
❑ 97FleTif-344
❑ 97Pac-316
❑ 97PacLigB-316
❑ 97PacSil-316
❑ 97Ult-335
❑ 97UltGolME-335
❑ 97UltPlaME-335
❑ 98PacInvGems-162
❑ 98PacOnl-319
❑ 98PacOnlR-319
❑ 98PacOnlWC-319
❑ 99PacCroC-124
❑ 99PacCroCPB-124
Evangelista, Alberto
❑ 93IdaFalBF-4024
❑ 93IdaFalBSP-1
❑ 94DanBraC-8
❑ 94DanBraF-3524
❑ 95MacBraTI-9
Evangelista, George
❑ 91GulCoaRSP-19
❑ 92ClaFS7-84
❑ 92Ft.MyeMCB-3
❑ 92Ft.MyeMF-2753
❑ 93ChaRanC-9
❑ 93ChaRanF-1948
Evans, Al (Alfred Hubert)
❑ 46SpoExcW-4-3
❑ 47Exh-69
❑ 47SenGunBP-2
❑ 49Bow-132A
❑ 49Bow-132B
❑ 49Lea-22
❑ 50Bow-144
❑ 51Bow-38
❑ 52Top-152
❑ 83TopRep5-152
❑ 84TCMPla1-11
Evans, Barry (Barry Steven)
❑ 79PadFamF-14
❑ 81Fle-499
❑ 81OPC-72
❑ 81Top-72
❑ 82Don-271
❑ 82Fle-571
❑ 82Top-541
❑ 83ColCliT-19
❑ 85MaiGuiT-18
❑ 86MaiGuiP-8
❑ 92YanWIZ8-55
Evans, Bart
❑ 92EugEmeC-13
❑ 92EugEmeF-3023
❑ 93RocRoyC-13
❑ 93RocRoyF-712
❑ 94CarLeaAF-CAR16
❑ 94WilBluRC-9
❑ 94WilBluRF-296
❑ 95Bow-35
❑ 95Exc-58
❑ 95SigRoo-17
❑ 95SigRooSig-17
❑ 95UppDecML-56
❑ 95UppDecMLFS-56
❑ 95WicWraTI-37
❑ 95WilBluRTI-19
❑ 96WicWraB-24
❑ 97WilBluR-18
Evans, Bill
❑ 54SeaPop-7
Evans, Billy (William L.)
❑ 09SpoNewSM-38
❑ 21Exh-44
❑ 61Fle-22
❑ 76ShaPiz-136
❑ 77GalGloG-134
❑ 78DexHaloFP-10
❑ 80PerHaloFP-136
❑ 80SSPHOF-136
❑ 89HOFStiB-100
❑ 92ConTSN-472
❑ 94ConTSN-1210
❑ 94ConTSNB-1210
Evans, Brad
❑ 96JohCitCTI-11
Evans, Brent
❑ 92ButCopKSP-10
Evans, Brian
❑ 89ChaRanS-7
❑ 90GasRanB-13
❑ 90GasRanP-2515
❑ 90GasRanS-8
❑ 90ProAaA-81
Evans, Bubba (Rick)
❑ 76AppFoxT-4
❑ 77ChaPatT-5
❑ 79BufBisT-9
❑ 80BufBisT-8
❑ 89GeoColC-6
Evans, Chris
❑ 97St.PauS-9
❑ 98St.PauSTI-6
Evans, Darrell
❑ 70Top-621
❑ 72OPC-171
❑ 72OPC-172
❑ 72Top-171
❑ 72Top-172
❑ 73LinPor-2
❑ 73OPC-374
❑ 73Top-374
❑ 74BraPhoC-3
❑ 74OPC-140
❑ 74Top-140
❑ 74TopDecE-2
❑ 74TopSta-3
❑ 75AtlBraP-10
❑ 75Hos-3
❑ 75HosTwi-3
❑ 75OPC-475
❑ 75Top-475
❑ 75TopMin-475
❑ 76AtlBraP-11
❑ 76Hos-24
❑ 76HosTwi-24
❑ 76OPC-81
❑ 76SSP-9
❑ 76Top-81
❑ 77Gia-6
❑ 77GiaTeal-8
❑ 77Top-571
❑ 78GiaTeal-7
❑ 78Hos-54
❑ 78Top-215
❑ 79GiaPol-41
❑ 79Hos-33
❑ 79OPC-215
❑ 79Top-410
❑ 80GiaPol-41
❑ 80GiaTeal-5
❑ 80OPC-81
❑ 80Top-145
❑ 81AllGamPI-119
❑ 81Don-192
❑ 81Fle-436A
❑ 81Fle-436B
❑ 81OPC-69
❑ 81Top-648
❑ 81TopSti-235
❑ 82Don-398
❑ 82Fle-388
❑ 82Gia25tATI-8
❑ 82OPC-17
❑ 82Top-17
❑ 82TopSti-112
❑ 83Don-251
❑ 83Fle-258
❑ 83GiaMot-9
❑ 83GiaPos-10
❑ 83OPC-329
❑ 83Top-448
❑ 83TopFol-2
❑ 83TopSti-305
❑ 84AllGamPI-93
❑ 84Don-431
❑ 84Fle-372
❑ 84FleSti-3
❑ 84FleUpd-36
❑ 84FunFooP-117
❑ 84GiaMot-27
❑ 84Nes792-325
❑ 84OPC-325
❑ 84TigFarJ-2
❑ 84TigTeal-13
❑ 84TigWavP-14
❑ 84Top-325
❑ 84TopGloS-11
❑ 84TopSti-163
❑ 84TopTif-325
❑ 84TopTra-36T
❑ 84TopTraT-36T
❑ 85AllGamPI-32
❑ 85Don-227
❑ 85DonHig-51
❑ 85Fle-6
❑ 85Lea-215
❑ 85OPC-319
❑ 85SevCoi-D3
❑ 85TigCaiD-6
❑ 85TigWen-7
❑ 85Top-792
❑ 85TopTif-792
❑ 86Don-369
❑ 86Fle-224
❑ 86FleStiC-36
❑ 86OPC-103
❑ 86QuaGra-24
❑ 86SevCoi-C15
❑ 86Spo-183
❑ 86Spo-189
❑ 86TigCaiD-4
❑ 86Top-515
❑ 86Top3-D-7
❑ 86TopGaloC-3
❑ 86TopGloS-60
❑ 86TopMinL-13
❑ 86TopSti-165
❑ 86TopSti-269
❑ 86TopSup-21
❑ 86TopTat-4
❑ 86TopTif-515
❑ 86Woo-9
❑ 87Don-398
❑ 87DonOpeD-210
❑ 87Fle-150
❑ 87FleGlo-150
❑ 87FleLeaL-16
❑ 87OPC-265
❑ 87SevCoi-D2
❑ 87Spo-132
❑ 87SpoTeaP-15
❑ 87TigCaiD-6
❑ 87TigCok-13
❑ 87Top-265
❑ 87TopSti-264
❑ 87TopTif-265
❑ 88Don-250
❑ 88DonBasB-35
❑ 88Fle-54
❑ 88FleGlo-54
❑ 88KayB-9
❑ 88KinDis-12
❑ 88Lea-173
❑ 88OPC-390
❑ 88OPCBoxB-E
❑ 88PanSti-89
❑ 88PanSti-90
❑ 88PanSti-441
❑ 88Sco-75
❑ 88ScoGlo-75
❑ 88Spo-188
❑ 88StaLinTi-4
❑ 88TigPep-41
❑ 88TigPol-5
❑ 88Top-630
❑ 88TopBig-82
❑ 88TopMinL-10
❑ 88TopSti-8
❑ 88TopSti-265
❑ 88TopTif-630
❑ 88TopWaxBC-E
❑ 88Woo-3
❑ 89Bow-275
❑ 89BowTif-275
❑ 89Don-533
❑ 89OPCBoxB-C
❑ 89Sco-171
❑ 89ScoRoo-65T
❑ 89TopTra-31T
❑ 89TopTraT-31T
❑ 89TopWaxBC-C
❑ 89UppDec-394
❑ 90Fle-581
❑ 90FleCan-581
❑ 90KayB-10
❑ 90OPC-55
❑ 90OPCBoxB-D
❑ 90PubIntS-112
❑ 90RicBra2ATI-8
❑ 90Sco-302
❑ 90Top-55
❑ 90TopSti-31
❑ 90TopTif-55
❑ 90TopWaxBC-D
❑ 90UppDec-143
❑ 91UppDecS-6
❑ 92SanAntMF-3989
❑ 92UppDecS-4
❑ 93TedWil-37
❑ 94UppDecAH-196
❑ 94UppDecAH1-196
❑ 98WilBluRC-13
❑ 99SpoIllGotG-68
❑ 99SpoIllGotGA-20
Evans, Dave
❑ 90CMC-839
❑ 90SanBerSB-5
❑ 90SanBerSCLC-97
❑ 90SanBerSP-2627
❑ 91JacSunLD-334
❑ 91JacSunP-144
❑ 91LinDriAA-334
❑ 94JacSunF-1406
❑ 95JacGenTI-2
❑ 96TusTorB-7
❑ 98CarMudM-2
Evans, Dickie
❑ 49W725AngTI-31
Evans, Dr. (Richard)
❑ 82IowCubT-32
Evans, Duane
❑ 82LynMetT-13
Evans, Dwight (Dwight Michael)
❑ 73LinPor-19
❑ 73OPC-614
❑ 73Top-614
❑ 74OPC-351
❑ 74Top-351
❑ 75Hos-18
❑ 75HosTwi-18
❑ 75Kel-38
❑ 75OPC-255
❑ 75Top-255
❑ 75TopMin-255
❑ 76Hos-87
❑ 76LinSup-104
❑ 76OPC-575
❑ 76RedSox-3
❑ 76RedSoxSM-5
❑ 76SSP-408
❑ 76Top-575
❑ 77BurCheD-30
❑ 77Hos-21
❑ 77OPC-259
❑ 77Top-25
❑ 78PapGinD-24
❑ 78SSP270-181
❑ 78Top-695
❑ 79BasPat-27
❑ 79Hos-64
❑ 79Kel-41
❑ 79OPC-73
❑ 79Top-155
❑ 80OPC-210
❑ 80Top-405
❑ 81CokTeaS-3
❑ 81Don-458
❑ 81Fle-232
❑ 81OPC-275
❑ 81Top-275
❑ 81TopSupHT-3
❑ 82Don-7
❑ 82Don-109
❑ 82Dra-11
❑ 82Fle-293
❑ 82Fle-642
❑ 82FleSta-167
❑ 82Kel-45
❑ 82OPC-355
❑ 82RedSoxC-6
❑ 82Top-162
❑ 82Top-355
❑ 82TopSti-4
❑ 82TopSti-135
❑ 82TopSti-153
❑ 83AllGamPI-52
❑ 83Don-452
❑ 83DonActA-2
❑ 83Dra-7
❑ 83Fle-183
❑ 83FleSta-59
❑ 83FleSti-69
❑ 83OPC-135
❑ 83Top-135
❑ 83TopSti-38
❑ 84AllGamPI-142
❑ 84Don-395
❑ 84Fle-397
❑ 84FunFooP-62
❑ 84Nes792-720
❑ 84OCoandSI-57
❑ 84OPC-244
❑ 84Top-720
❑ 84TopRubD-13
❑ 84TopSti-219
❑ 84TopTif-720
❑ 85AllGamPI-56
❑ 85Don-294

❑ 85DonActA-15
❑ 85Dra-10
❑ 85Fle-158
❑ 85FleStaS-40
❑ 85Lea-150
❑ 85OPC-271
❑ 85SevCoi-E8
❑ 85Top-580
❑ 85TopMin-580
❑ 85TopRubD-19
❑ 85TopSti-212
❑ 85TopSup-33
❑ 85TopTif-580
❑ 86Don-249
❑ 86Dra-2
❑ 86Fle-348
❑ 86FleMin-74
❑ 86Lea-127
❑ 86OPC-60
❑ 86SevCoi-E13
❑ 86Spo-32
❑ 86Top-60
❑ 86Top-396
❑ 86TopMinL-5
❑ 86TopSti-251
❑ 86TopSup-22
❑ 86TopTat-13
❑ 86TopTif-60
❑ 86TopTif-396
❑ 86Woo-10
❑ 87BoaandB-7
❑ 87Don-129
❑ 87DonHig-33
❑ 87DonOpeD-184
❑ 87Fle-34
❑ 87FleGlo-34
❑ 87FleGlo-WS9
❑ 87FleLeaL-17
❑ 87FleMin-37
❑ 87FleStiC-38
❑ 87FleWorS-9
❑ 87Lea-57
❑ 87OPC-368
❑ 87RedSoxP-8
❑ 87RedSoxSAP-7
❑ 87Spo-128
❑ 87SpoTeaP-9
❑ 87Top-3
❑ 87Top-645
❑ 87TopSti-4
❑ 87TopSti-20
❑ 87TopSti-251
❑ 87TopTif-3
❑ 87TopTif-645
❑ 87Woo-21
❑ 88Don-16
❑ 88Don-216
❑ 88DonAll-23
❑ 88DonBasB-84
❑ 88DonSupD-16
❑ 88DonTeaBRS-216
❑ 88Dra-9
❑ 88Fle-351
❑ 88FleAwaW-11
❑ 88FleBasM-12
❑ 88FleGlo-351
❑ 88FleLeaL-11
❑ 88FleMin-6
❑ 88FleStiC-8
❑ 88FleWaxBC-C2
❑ 88KayB-10
❑ 88Lea-16
❑ 88Lea-171
❑ 88OPC-221
❑ 88PanSti-25
❑ 88RedFolSB-21
❑ 88Sco-65
❑ 88ScoGlo-65
❑ 88Spo-137
❑ 88StaLinRS-7
❑ 88Top-470
❑ 88TopBig-6
❑ 88TopCoi-11
❑ 88TopCoi-42
❑ 88TopGloS-21
❑ 88TopMinL-3
❑ 88TopRevLL-24
❑ 88TopSti-245
❑ 88TopStiB-50
❑ 88TopTif-470
❑ 88TopUKM-22
❑ 88TopUKMT-22
❑ 89Bow-35
❑ 89BowTif-35
❑ 89ClaLigB-44
❑ 89Don-240
❑ 89DonBasB-121
❑ 89Fle-87
❑ 89FleExcS-12
❑ 89FleGlo-87
❑ 89KayB-10
❑ 89OPC-205
❑ 89PanSti-279
❑ 89RedFolSB-40
❑ 89Sco-193
❑ 89ScoHot1S-8
❑ 89Spo-204
❑ 89SpoIllFKI-288
❑ 89Top-205
❑ 89TopBasT-109
❑ 89TopBig-193
❑ 89TopGloS-36
❑ 89TopMinL-47
❑ 89TopSti-252
❑ 89TopStiB-15
❑ 89TopTif-205
❑ 89TopUKM-24
❑ 89TVSpoM-65
❑ 89UppDec-366
❑ 90Bow-279
❑ 90BowTif-279
❑ 90ClaBlu-77
❑ 90Don-122
❑ 90DonBesA-102
❑ 90DonGraS-5
❑ 90Fle-274
❑ 90FleCan-274
❑ 90KayB-11
❑ 90Lea-235
❑ 90OPC-375
❑ 90PanSti-17
❑ 90PubIntS-454
❑ 90RedSoxP-8
❑ 90Sco-3
❑ 90Sco100S-54
❑ 90Spo-217
❑ 90Top-375
❑ 90TopAmeA-4
❑ 90TopBig-1
❑ 90TopHilHM-23
❑ 90TopSti-257
❑ 90TopTif-375
❑ 90TopTVA-28
❑ 90TopTVRS-29
❑ 90UppDec-112
❑ 90Woo-12
❑ 91BalOriP-6
❑ 91BasBesHRK-6
❑ 91Bow-103
❑ 91Don-122
❑ 91Fle-93
❑ 91FleUpd-2
❑ 91Lea-266
❑ 91OPC-155
❑ 91OPCBoxB-E
❑ 91OPCPre-39
❑ 91OriCro-497
❑ 91PanSti-213
❑ 91Sco-225
❑ 91Sco100S-99
❑ 91ScoRoo-62T
❑ 91SevCoi-A2
❑ 91StaClu-351
❑ 91Stu-2
❑ 91Top-155A
❑ 91Top-155B
❑ 91TopDesS-155
❑ 91TopMic-155
❑ 91TopTif-155
❑ 91TopTra-37T
❑ 91TopTraT-37T
❑ 91TopWaxBC-E
❑ 91UltUpd-1
❑ 91UppDec-549
❑ 91UppDec-776
❑ 91Woo-10
❑ 92Don-502
❑ 92Fle-6
❑ 92OPC-705
❑ 92PanSti-69
❑ 92Sco-150
❑ 92StaClu-463
❑ 92Top-705
❑ 92TopGol-705
❑ 92TopGolW-705
❑ 92TopMic-705
❑ 92TriPla-67
❑ 92Ult-3
❑ 92UppDec-248
❑ 93Pin-303
❑ 94RocPol-27

Evans, Evan
❑ 14Zee-58
❑ 15Zee-60
❑ 17Zee-66

Evans, Felix
❑ 92NegLeaRLI-19

Evans, Frank
❑ 85LouRedR-3
❑ 91NegLeaRL-23
❑ 95NegLeaLI-23

Evans, Freeman
❑ 75AndRanT-42
❑ 76CliPilT-13

Evans, Gary
❑ 82BelBreFr-17

Evans, Glenn
❑ 92EliTwiC-19
❑ 92EliTwiF-3693
❑ 92KenTwiC-5

Evans, Godfrey
❑ 75WesPalBES-12
❑ 78MemChiBC-3
❑ 79MemChiT-24

Evans, Jamie
❑ 91AubAstC-7
❑ 91AubAstP-4268
❑ 92AshTouC-12
❑ 93QuaCitRBC-7
❑ 93QuaCitRBF-92
❑ 94OscAstC-8
❑ 94OscAstF-1130

Evans, Jason
❑ 92UtiBluSC-11
❑ 93HicCraC-6
❑ 93HicCraF-1283
❑ 94MidLeaAF-MDW26
❑ 94SouBenSHC-5
❑ 94SouBenSHF-606
❑ 96PriWilCB-10
❑ 97BirBarB-11
❑ 98TenKry-10

Evans, Jim
❑ 77CliDodT-7
❑ 88T/MUmp-13
❑ 89T/MUmp-11
❑ 90T/MUmp-11

Evans, Joe
❑ 77Ind192T-6
❑ 93ConTSN-949

Evans, John
❑ 79BurBeeT-15
❑ 80BurBeeT-25
❑ 81ElPasDT-21
❑ 82TacTigT-16

Evans, Keith
❑ 98JupHamQ-7

Evans, Kyle
❑ 95HudValRTI-3

Evans, Lee
❑ 97AugGre-17
❑ 97EriSeaWB-11
❑ 97SouAtlTPB-3
❑ 98AugGreM-20

Evans, Matt
❑ 92BriTigC-18
❑ 92BriTigF-1417
❑ 93FayGenC-10
❑ 93FayGenF-135
❑ 94LakTigC-6
❑ 94LakTigF-3043

Evans, Michael
❑ 91SouOreAC-18
❑ 91SouOreAP-3834
❑ 95WilBluRTI-21
❑ 96WilBluRB-3
❑ 97WilBluR-2

Evans, Mike
❑ 82WauTimF-22
❑ 84ChaLooT-1A
❑ 87EriCarP-17
❑ 88HamRedP-1734
❑ 89HamRedS-29
❑ 90SprCarB-28
❑ 91SprCarC-30
❑ 92SprCarC-29
❑ 93EugEmeC-12
❑ 93EugEmeF-3867
❑ 93SprCarC-30
❑ 98WicWraM-10

Evans, Park
❑ 90MisStaB-10
❑ 91MisStaB-15
❑ 92MisStaB-14

Evans, Pat
❑ 94WatIndC-9
❑ 94WatIndF-3939
❑ 96KenIndB-7
❑ 97KinIndB-7

Evans, Phil
❑ 89SalLakTTI-25

Evans, Randy
❑ 80GleFalWSBT-4
❑ 80GleFalWSCT-15
❑ 81GleFalWST-2

Evans, Red (Russell Edison)
❑ 39PlaBal-159
❑ 90DodTar-227

Evans, Rickey
❑ 78SalPirT-4

Evans, Rob
❑ 87TidTidP-29

Evans, Roy
❑ 90DodTar-945

Evans, Scott
❑ 87MiaMarP-4
❑ 87NewOriP-23
❑ 88HagSunS-5

Evans, Sean
❑ 92AugPirC-10
❑ 92SalBucF-56
❑ 93SalBucC-9
❑ 93SalBucF-425
❑ 94CarLeaAF-CAR39
❑ 94SalBucC-9
❑ 95CarMudF-149

Evans, Stanley
❑ 92MarPhiC-29
❑ 92MarPhiF-3070
❑ 93SouAtlLAGF-52
❑ 93SpaPhiC-13
❑ 93SpaPhiF-1067
❑ 94ClaGolF-35
❑ 94ClePhiC-14
❑ 94ClePhiF-2540
❑ 95ClePhiF-228
❑ 97BatCliTI-27

Evans, Steve (Louis Richard)
❑ 09ColChiE-96
❑ 09PC7HHB-13
❑ 09T206-123
❑ 10CouT21-133
❑ 10DomDisP-42
❑ 10RedCroT-191
❑ 10SweCapPP-146
❑ 11HelSta-169
❑ 11PinT-5-353
❑ 11S74Sil-118
❑ 11SpoLifM-268
❑ 11T205-52
❑ 12ColRedB-96
❑ 12ColTinT-96
❑ 12HasTriFT-67A
❑ 12T207-57
❑ 14CraJacE-128
❑ 14PieStaT-39
❑ 15CraJacE-128
❑ 74CapPub-22

Evans, Tim
❑ 92OscAstF-2536
❑ 93MidLeaAGF-46
❑ 93QuaCitRBC-8
❑ 93QuaCitRBF-112
❑ 94JacGenF-228

Evans, Tom
❑ 92ClaDraP-108
❑ 92HigSchPLS-24
❑ 92MedHatBJSP-24
❑ 93HagSunC-11
❑ 93HagSunF-1888
❑ 93StaCluM-79
❑ 95Bow-52
❑ 95DunBluJTI-7
❑ 96Bow-171
❑ 96BowFoi-171
❑ 96KnoSmoB-12
❑ 97SyrSkyCB-9
❑ 98Bow-341
❑ 98BowChr-341
❑ 98BowChrGA-341
❑ 98BowChrGAR-341
❑ 98BowChrI-341
❑ 98BowChrIR-341
❑ 98BowChrR-341
❑ 98BowGolA-341
❑ 98BowInt-341
❑ 98ColCho-113
❑ 98Don-250
❑ 98DonGolPP-250
❑ 98DonSilPP-250
❑ 98Fle-61
❑ 98LeaRS-245
❑ 98LeaRSLHolo-245
❑ 98LeaRSLong-245
❑ 98LeaRTrue-245
❑ 98SP MinPE-126
❑ 98SPMin-126
❑ 98SpoIll-176
❑ 98SpoIllEE-176
❑ 98SpoIllFE-176
❑ 98SyrSkyG-12
❑ 98UppDec-283
❑ 99Fle-177
❑ 99FleSta9-177
❑ 99FleWarT-177
❑ 99MetUni-7
❑ 99MetUniGM-7
❑ 99MetUniPMG-7
❑ 99Pac-440
❑ 99Pac-440A
❑ 99PacPlaB-440
❑ 99PacPlaB-440A
❑ 99PacRed-440
❑ 99PacRed-440A
❑ 99SkyThu-152
❑ 99SkyThuRant-152
❑ 99SkyThuRave-152
❑ 99SpoIll-45
❑ 99ThuSkySupR-152
❑ 99Top-367
❑ 99TopChr-367
❑ 99TopChrR-367
❑ 99TopMVPP-367

Evans, Tony
❑ 83TamTarT-4

Evans, Tory
❑ 89SanBerSCLC-65

Evans, Van
❑ 85PriWilPT-25
❑ 86KinEagP-6

Evaschuk, Brad
❑ 88St.CatBJP-2010

Eveline, Billy (William)
❑ 86AppFoxP-7
❑ 87DayBeaAP-18
❑ 88TamTarS-6
❑ 89QuaCitAB-26
❑ 89QuaCitAGS-30

Evenhus, Jason
❑ 94OgdRapF-3729
❑ 94OgdRapSP-5

Everett, Adam
❑ 99199Fin-135
❑ 99Bow-77
❑ 99BowBes-178
❑ 99BowBesAR-178
❑ 99BowBesR-178
❑ 99BowChr-77
❑ 99BowChrG-77
❑ 99BowChrGR-77
❑ 99BowChrI-77
❑ 99BowChrIR-77
❑ 99BowChrR-77
❑ 99BowGol-77
❑ 99BowInt-77
❑ 99FinGolRef-135
❑ 99FinRef-135
❑ 99StaClu-345
❑ 99StaCluFDI-345
❑ 99StaCluOoaK-345
❑ 99StaCluPP-345
❑ 99TeaBesR-23
❑ 99TeaBesRFS-5
❑ 99TeaBesRG-23
❑ 99TeaBesRS-23
❑ 99Top-443
❑ 99TopChr-443
❑ 99TopChrR-443
❑ 99TopMVPP-443

Everett, Carl
❑ 90ClaDraP-10
❑ 90HigSchPLS-13
❑ 90TamYanD-5
❑ 91Bow-156
❑ 91GreHorP-3072
❑ 91OPC-113
❑ 91Sco-386
❑ 91SouAtlLAGP-SAL25
❑ 91Top-113
❑ 91TopDesS-113
❑ 91TopMic-113
❑ 91TopTif-113
❑ 92Bow-258
❑ 92ForLauYTI-9
❑ 92Ft.LauYF-2626
❑ 92ProFS7-124
❑ 92UppDecML-56
❑ 92UppDecML-155
❑ 93Bow-94
❑ 93ClaFS7-183
❑ 93ExcFS7-207
❑ 93HigDesMC-1
❑ 93HigDesMF-54
❑ 93MarlStaClu-30
❑ 93SP-276
❑ 93TopTra-74T
❑ 94Bow-318
❑ 94BowBes-B56
❑ 94BowBesR-B56
❑ 94ColC-6
❑ 94ColChoGS-6
❑ 94ColChoSS-6
❑ 94Don-241
❑ 94EdmTraF-2885
❑ 94LeaLimR-31
❑ 94Pin-252
❑ 94PinArtP-252
❑ 94PinMusC-252
❑ 94Sco-601
❑ 94ScoGolR-601
❑ 94Sel-393
❑ 94SP-110
❑ 94SPDieC-110
❑ 94Spo-168
❑ 94StaCluT-73
❑ 94StaCluTFDI-73
❑ 94Top-781
❑ 94TopGol-781
❑ 94TopSpa-781
❑ 94TriAAF-AAA29
❑ 94UppDec-11
❑ 94UppDecED-11
❑ 95Bow-20
❑ 95ColCho-318
❑ 95ColChoGS-318
❑ 95ColChoSS-318
❑ 95Fla-382
❑ 95FlaWavotF-6
❑ 95FleUpd-111
❑ 95Lea-397
❑ 95MetColP-11
❑ 95NorTidTI-10
❑ 95Pac-173
❑ 95Pin-368
❑ 95PinArtP-368
❑ 95PinMusC-368
❑ 95Sel-142
❑ 95SelArtP-142
❑ 95Sum-73
❑ 95SumNthD-73
❑ 96ColCho-219
❑ 96ColChoGS-219
❑ 96ColChoSS-219
❑ 96Don-312
❑ 96DonPreP-312
❑ 96EmoXL-229
❑ 96Fla-317
❑ 96Fle-477
❑ 96FleRooS-5
❑ 96FleTif-477
❑ 96Lea-136
❑ 96LeaPrePB-136
❑ 96LeaPrePG-136
❑ 96LeaPrePS-136
❑ 96MetKah-8
❑ 96MetUni-199
❑ 96MetUniP-199
❑ 96Pac-139
❑ 96PanSti-31
❑ 96Pin-77
❑ 96Sco-188
❑ 96StaClu-58
❑ 96StaCluMOP-58
❑ 96Top-281
❑ 96Ult-241
❑ 96UltGolM-241
❑ 96UppDec-137
❑ 97Fle-623
❑ 97FleTif-623
❑ 97Lea-300
❑ 97LeaFraM-300
❑ 97LeaFraMDC-300
❑ 97Pac-362
❑ 97PacLigB-362
❑ 97PacSil-362
❑ 97Sco-438
❑ 97ScoArtPWB-438
❑ 97ScoResC-438
❑ 97ScoShoS-438
❑ 97ScoShoSAP-438
❑ 97Sel-200
❑ 97SelCom-200
❑ 98CirThu-59

❑ 98CirThuRav-59
❑ 98CirThuSupRav-59
❑ 98ColCho-383
❑ 98Fin-41
❑ 98FinNo--41
❑ 98FinNo-R-41
❑ 98FinRef-41
❑ 98Fle-531
❑ 98MetUni-159
❑ 98MetUniPMG-159
❑ 98Pac-363
❑ 98PacOnl-320
❑ 98PacOnlR-320
❑ 98PacOnlWC-320
❑ 98PacPlaB-363
❑ 98PacRedT-363
❑ 98PacSil-363
❑ 98Pin-124
❑ 98PinPreP-124
❑ 98Sco-109
❑ 98ScoSS-PP44
❑ 98ScoSSAP-PP44
❑ 98Top-157
❑ 98TopChr-157
❑ 98TopChrR-157
❑ 98TopDevR-157
❑ 98TopDia-157
❑ 98TopMiniC-157
❑ 98Ult-10
❑ 98Ult-331
❑ 98UltGolM-10
❑ 98UltGolM-331
❑ 98UltMas-10
❑ 98UltMas-331
❑ 98UltPlaM-10
❑ 98UltPlaM-331
❑ 98UppDec-684
❑ 99Fle-126
❑ 99FleSta9-126
❑ 99FleWarT-126
❑ 99Pac-190
❑ 99PacPlaB-190
❑ 99PacRed-190
❑ 99SkyThu-140
❑ 99SkyThuRant-140
❑ 99SkyThuRave-140
❑ 99StaClu-202
❑ 99StaCluFDI-202
❑ 99StaCluOoaK-202
❑ 99StaCluPP-202
❑ 99ThuSkySupR-140
❑ 99Top-137
❑ 99TopChr-137
❑ 99TopChrR-137
❑ 99TopMVPP-137
❑ 99Ult-22
❑ 99UltGolM-22
❑ 99UltMas-22
❑ 99UltPlaM-22
❑ 99UppDec-388
❑ 99UppDecEL1-388
❑ 99UppDecEL2-388
❑ 99Vic-177

Everett, Conrad
❑ 80WisRapTT-10

Everett, Matt
❑ 98WatIndTI-11

Everett, Smokey
❑ 81WisRapTT-3
❑ 82OrlTwiT-4

Everingham, Matt
❑ 91SydWavF-3
❑ 93AusFut-33
❑ 95AusFut-38

Everly, Bill
❑ 97YakBeaG-5
❑ 98VerBeaDM-7

Evers, Bill
❑ 83GreHorT-28
❑ 86CliGiaP-7
❑ 87CliGiaP-17
❑ 88CliGiaP-712
❑ 89ShrCapP-1838
❑ 90ShrCapP-1458
❑ 90ShrCapS-25
❑ 90TexLeaAGS-37
❑ 91LinDriAA-324
❑ 91ShrCapLD-324
❑ 91ShrCapP-1838
❑ 92PhoFirF-2837
❑ 92PhoFirS-399
❑ 93GreHorC-27
❑ 93GreHorF-903
❑ 93SouAtlLAGF-20
❑ 94AlbYanF-1457
❑ 95ColCliMCTI-1
❑ 95ColCliP-9
❑ 95ColCliTI-9
❑ 97St.PetDR-2
❑ 97St.PetDRUB-2
❑ 98DurBulTI-8

Evers, Hoot (Walter Arthur)
❑ 47Exh-70
❑ 47TipTop-31
❑ 49Bow-42
❑ 49Lea-78
❑ 49MPR302-2-123
❑ 50Bow-41
❑ 51Bow-23
❑ 51FisBakL-6
❑ 51TopCurA-4
❑ 52Bow-111
❑ 52StaCalL-71H
❑ 52StaCalL-72C
❑ 52StaCalS-86B
❑ 52Top-222
❑ 53BowC-25
❑ 53RedSoxTI-6
❑ 54Bow-18
❑ 55OriEss-9
❑ 56BalOriP-29
❑ 76TayBow4-55
❑ 79TCM50-264
❑ 81RedSoxBG2S-19
❑ 81TigDetN-44
❑ 83TopRep5-222
❑ 85TCMPla1-27
❑ 91OriCro-125
❑ 91TopArc1-291

Evers, Johnny (John Joseph)
❑ 07CubA.CDPP-3
❑ 07CubGFGCP-3
❑ 08AmeCarE91-10
❑ 08AmeCarE91-46
❑ 08RosComP-103
❑ 09ColChiE-97
❑ 09MaxPubP-4
❑ 09MaxPubP-20
❑ 09PhiCarE-10
❑ 09RamT20-43
❑ 09SpoNewSM-26
❑ 09T206-124
❑ 09T206-125
❑ 09T206-126
❑ 10ChiE-5
❑ 10CouT21-22
❑ 10CouT21-134
❑ 10CouT21-283
❑ 10DarChoE-18
❑ 10DomDisP-43
❑ 10E101-20
❑ 10E102-11
❑ 10E98-14
❑ 10MelMinE-20
❑ 10NadCarE-23
❑ 10NotCov-4
❑ 10OrnOvaPP-5
❑ 10PeoT21-23A
❑ 10PeoT21-23B
❑ 10RedCroT-111
❑ 10RedCroT-192
❑ 10SepAnoP-10
❑ 10StaCarE-13
❑ 10SweCapPP-82
❑ 10W555-29
❑ 11BasBatEU-22
❑ 11DiaGumP-14
❑ 11E94-14
❑ 11HelSta-94
❑ 11JonKeyaAC-348
❑ 11L1L-134
❑ 11MecDFT-9
❑ 11PinT-5-201
❑ 11PloCanE-27
❑ 11S74Sil-60
❑ 11S81LarS-109
❑ 11SpoLifCW-120
❑ 11SpoLifM-169
❑ 11T205-53
❑ 11TurRedT-16
❑ 12ColRedB-97
❑ 12ColTinT-97
❑ 12HasTriFT-36A
❑ 12HasTriFT-36B
❑ 12HasTriFT-36C
❑ 12HasTriFT-36D
❑ 12HasTriFT-36E
❑ 13NatGamW-16
❑ 13TomBarW-15
❑ 14CraJacE-18
❑ 14PieStaT-40
❑ 14TexTomE-20
❑ 15AmeCarE106-17
❑ 15CraJacE-18
❑ 15SpoNewM-55
❑ 16BF2FP-52
❑ 16FleBreD-27
❑ 16SpoNewM-54
❑ 16TanBraE-9
❑ 17ColE13-45
❑ 17HolBreD-27
❑ 21E121So8-20A
❑ 21E121So8-20B
❑ 22AmeCarE122-18
❑ 22W575-31
❑ 23WilChoV-39
❑ 37KelPepS-BB4
❑ 39PC7AlbHoF-42
❑ 40PlaBal-174
❑ 48ExhHoF-10
❑ 50CalHOFW-29
❑ 50CubGreB-5
❑ 53ArtHaloFP-31
❑ 60ExhWriH-10
❑ 60Fle-57
❑ 61Fle-23
❑ 63HalofFB-24
❑ 68LauWorS-5
❑ 68SCFOldT-6
❑ 69Baz-6
❑ 69Baz-7
❑ 69EquSpoHoF-BB3
❑ 70FleWorS-5
❑ 72ClaCar-79
❑ 72FleFamF-7
❑ 74CapPub-41
❑ 75FlePio-17
❑ 76ShaPiz-42
❑ 77BobParHoF-86
❑ 77GalGloG-159
❑ 78DexHaloFP-11
❑ 80BraTCM1-12
❑ 80BraTCM1-21
❑ 80BraTCM1-32
❑ 80MarExhH-11
❑ 80PerHaloFP-42
❑ 80SSPHOF-42
❑ 81ConTSN-13
❑ 84CubUno-7
❑ 84GalHaloFRL-42
❑ 87Cub190T-9
❑ 90PerGreM-40
❑ 91ConTSN-15
❑ 92CubOldS-8
❑ 93ConTSN-818
❑ 93ConTSN-892
❑ 93CraJac-11
❑ 93UppDecAH-47
❑ 93UppDecAH-147
❑ 93UppDecAH-148
❑ 94ConTSN-1165
❑ 94ConTSNB-1165
❑ 94UppDecTAE-27
❑ 96PitPosH-6

Evers, Troy
❑ 87Ft.LauYP-4
❑ 88AlbYanP-1340
❑ 90WilBilB-4
❑ 90WilBilP-1050
❑ 90WilBilS-5

Eversgerd, Bryan
❑ 89JohCitCS-10
❑ 91SavCarC-3
❑ 91SavCarP-1644
❑ 92ProFS7-321
❑ 92St.PetCC-12
❑ 92St.PetCF-2022
❑ 93ArkTraF-2808
❑ 94Bow-244
❑ 94Fla-427
❑ 94FleUpd-178
❑ 94ScoRoo-RT141
❑ 94ScoRooGR-RT141
❑ 94SpoRoo-121
❑ 94SpoRooAP-121
❑ 94TopTra-71T
❑ 95Don-317
❑ 95DonPreP-317
❑ 95Fle-496
❑ 95StaClu-411
❑ 95StaCluMOP-411
❑ 95StaCluSTWS-411
❑ 95StaCluVR-210
❑ 95StaCluVRMO-210
❑ 95Top-481
❑ 95TopCyb-273
❑ 96OklCit8B-9
❑ 98MemRedG-5

Eversgerd, Randy
❑ 98HagSunM-12
❑ 98St.CatSM-11

Everson, Darin
❑ 98MadBlaW-7

Everson, Greg (Gregory)
❑ 88FloStaLAS-35
❑ 88LakTigS-10
❑ 89LonTigP-1380
❑ 90MemChiB-15
❑ 90MemChiP-1005
❑ 90MemChiS-10
❑ 91LinDriAAA-335
❑ 91OmaRoyLD-335
❑ 91OmaRoyP-1030

Ewan, Bry
❑ 98EugEme-11
❑ 98MacBraM-7

Ewart, Ron
❑ 86WinSpiP-8

Ewell, Doc
❑ 88AstMot-28
❑ 89AstMot-28
❑ 90AstMot-28
❑ 92AstMot-28

Ewell, Jim
❑ 56A'sPos-16
❑ 60A'sTeal-5

Ewell, Mark
❑ 75WesPalBES-5

Ewing, Bill
❑ 76QuaCitAT-13
❑ 79SalLakCGT-13

Ewing, Buck (William)
❑ 36Halof FP-10
❑ 39PC7AlbHoF-21
❑ 50CalHOFW-30
❑ 53ArtHaloFP-32
❑ 67SpoHobFC-14
❑ 73TCMAllG-3
❑ 74CapPub-13
❑ 75FlePio-3
❑ 76ShaPiz-24
❑ 77BobParHoF-20
❑ 77BobParMBC-23
❑ 80PerHaloFP-21
❑ 80SSPHOF-21
❑ 84GalHaloFRL-24
❑ 86OldJudN-6
❑ 87BucN28-67A
❑ 87BucN28-67B
❑ 87OldJudN-155
❑ 87OldJudN-156
❑ 88AllandGN-1
❑ 88AllandGN-1
❑ 88AugBecN-13
❑ 88GandBCGCE-14
❑ 88SpoTimM-9
❑ 88WG1CarG-38
❑ 89EdgR.WG-1
❑ 89HOFStiB-57
❑ 89SFHaCN-4
❑ 90BasWit-68
❑ 90KalBatN-16
❑ 94OriofB-76
❑ 95May-8A
❑ 95May-8B
❑ 98CamPepP-24

Ewing, Don
❑ 93HolLeg-11

Ewing, Jim
❑ 84EveGiaC-10B

Ewing, Justin
❑ 90MisStaB-11
❑ 93MisStaB-15

Ewing, Long Bob (George L.)
❑ 06FanCraNL-18
❑ 08RosComP-115
❑ 09RamT20-44
❑ 09T206-127
❑ 11PinT-5-312
❑ 11S74Sil-100
❑ 11SpoLifCW-121
❑ 11SpoLifM-228
❑ 11T205-54
❑ 72ClaCar-93

Ewing, Long John (John)
❑ 03WilCarE-14
❑ 87OldJudN-154

Ewing, Sam (Samuel James)
❑ 77OPC-221
❑ 78BluJayP-5
❑ 78OPC-112
❑ 78SyrChiT-9
❑ 78Top-344
❑ 79OPC-271
❑ 79TCMJapPB-34
❑ 79Top-521
❑ 81AppFoxT-28

Excelsiors, Brooklyn
❑ 94OriofB-12

Expos, Burlington
❑ 86BurExpP-28

Expos, Jacksonville
❑ 87JacExpP-457
❑ 88JacExpP-993
❑ 89JacExpB-29
❑ 89JacExpP-178
❑ 90JacExpB-30
❑ 90JacExpP-1390

Expos, Montreal
❑ 69FleCloS-14
❑ 69FleCloS-31
❑ 69TopStaA-14
❑ 70OPC-509
❑ 70Top-509
❑ 71OPC-674
❑ 71Top-674
❑ 71TopTat-8
❑ 72Top-582
❑ 73OPC-576
❑ 73OPCBTC-15
❑ 73Top-576
❑ 73TopBluTC-15
❑ 74OPC-508
❑ 74OPCTC-15
❑ 74Top-508
❑ 74TopStaA-15
❑ 74TopTeaC-15
❑ 78OPC-207
❑ 78Top-244
❑ 80OPC-249
❑ 81OPC-268
❑ 83FleSta-239
❑ 83FleSti-NNO
❑ 83FleSti-NNO
❑ 84ExpStu-39
❑ 87SpoTeaL-20
❑ 87Top-381
❑ 87TopTif-381
❑ 88PanSti-474
❑ 88RedFolSB-128
❑ 90PubIntS-631
❑ 90RedFolSB-115
❑ 91PanCanT1-121
❑ 91PanCanT1-129
❑ 93TedWilPC-15
❑ 94ImpProP-22
❑ 94Sco-654
❑ 94ScoGolR-654
❑ 94VerExpC-29B
❑ 95PacPriTL-22
❑ 95PanSti-130
❑ 95UppDecC-1A
❑ 96PanSti-21
❑ 99Vic-234

Expos, Rockford
❑ 90RocExpLC-30

Expos, West Palm Beach
❑ 75WesPalBES-4A

Eyre, Scott
❑ 92ButCopKSP-18
❑ 93Bow-277
❑ 93ChaRaiC-1
❑ 93ChaRaiF-1902
❑ 93ClaFS7-100
❑ 93SouAtlLAGF-6
❑ 94ClaGolF-29
❑ 94ExcFS7-132
❑ 94UppDecML-48
❑ 95UppDecML-137
❑ 95UppDecMLFS-137
❑ 96BirBarB-14
❑ 97BirBarB-4
❑ 97TexAllM-14
❑ 98ColCho-61
❑ 98Fle-197
❑ 98PacOnl-168
❑ 98PacOnlR-168
❑ 98PacOnlWC-168
❑ 98SpoIll-154
❑ 98SpoIllEE-154
❑ 98SpoIllFE-154
❑ 98UppDec-329

Eyrich, George
❑ 43PhiTeal-8
❑ 78ReaRem-4

Ezell, Glenn
❑ 73TacTwiC-5
❑ 74PhoGiaC-89
❑ 82AmaGolST-23
❑ 83RanAffF-NNO
❑ 84RanJarP-NNO
❑ 85RanPer-NNO
❑ 86VenGulP-7
❑ 87KnoBluJP-1516
❑ 88OmaRoyC-25
❑ 88OmaRoyP-1503
❑ 90RoyPos-8
❑ 91RoyPol-26
❑ 92RoyPol-27
❑ 93RanKee-139
❑ 93RoyPol-27
❑ 95ModA'sTI-7
❑ 96TigHebN-28
❑ 97TolMudHB-2

Faatz, Jay
❑ 87OldJudN-157
❑ 88SpoTimM-11

Fabbro, Arthur
❑ 52Par-55
❑ 53ExhCan-45

Faber, Dick
❑ 52MotCoo-28

Faber, Red (Urban)
❑ 15SpoNewM-56
❑ 16BF2FP-12
❑ 16SpoNewM-55
❑ 17ColE13-46
❑ 17HolBreD-28
❑ 18WhiSoxTI-7
❑ 19W514-69
❑ 20NatCarE-26
❑ 21E121So1-21
❑ 21E121So8-21A
❑ 21E121So8-21B
❑ 21Exh-45
❑ 21Nei-14
❑ 22AmeCarE122-19
❑ 22E120-18
❑ 22W572-27
❑ 22W573-37
❑ 22W575-32
❑ 23W501-48
❑ 23W515-60
❑ 23WilChoV-40
❑ 27AmeCarE126-6
❑ 27YorCarE-4
❑ 28W502-4
❑ 28Yue-4
❑ 29PorandAR-22
❑ 30ChiEveAP-14
❑ 30WhiSoxTI-10
❑ 33Gou-79
❑ 33GouCanV-54
❑ 40PlaBal-230
❑ 48WhiSoxTI-5
❑ 61Fle-24
❑ 68SCFOldT-28
❑ 71FleWorS-15
❑ 75TCMAllG-9
❑ 75WhiSox1T-6
❑ 76ChiGre-12
❑ 76GrePlaG-20
❑ 76RowExh-1
❑ 76ShaPiz-96
❑ 77GalGloG-121
❑ 78DexHaloFP-12
❑ 80PerHaloFP-96
❑ 80SSPHOF-96
❑ 85WhiSoxC-24
❑ 88PacEigMO-96
❑ 89HOFStiB-61
❑ 91ConTSN-41
❑ 91ConTSNP-710
❑ 92ConTSN-483
❑ 92Man191BSR-7
❑ 93ConTSN-710
❑ 94ConTSN-1251
❑ 94ConTSNB-1251
❑ 94ConTSNCI-26

Fabregas, Jorge
❑ 91ClaDraP-30
❑ 91MiaHurBB-5
❑ 92Bow-8
❑ 92ClaFS7-359
❑ 92PalSprAC-18
❑ 92PalSprAF-843
❑ 92StaCluD-46
❑ 92UppDecML-329
❑ 93AngStaCl-8

- ❑ 93Bow-5
- ❑ 93ClaFS7-184
- ❑ 93ClaGolF-31
- ❑ 93MidAngF-324
- ❑ 94AngMot-26
- ❑ 94Bow-171
- ❑ 94ExcFS7-24
- ❑ 94Fla-270
- ❑ 94FleAllR-M4
- ❑ 94FleUpd-16
- ❑ 94LeaLimR-72
- ❑ 94ScoRoo-RT110
- ❑ 94ScoRooGR-RT110
- ❑ 94Sel-398
- ❑ 94SpoRoo-58
- ❑ 94SpoRooAP-58
- ❑ 94TopTra-62T
- ❑ 94UppDec-515
- ❑ 94UppDecED-515
- ❑ 94UppDecML-14
- ❑ 94VanCanF-1867
- ❑ 95ColCho-91
- ❑ 95ColChoGS-91
- ❑ 95ColChoSS-91
- ❑ 95Don-276
- ❑ 95DonPreP-276
- ❑ 95Pac-59
- ❑ 95PacPri-19
- ❑ 95Pin-136
- ❑ 95PinArtP-136
- ❑ 95PinMusC-136
- ❑ 95Sco-288
- ❑ 95ScoGolR-288
- ❑ 95ScoPlaTS-288
- ❑ 95ScoSam-288
- ❑ 95Top-493
- ❑ 95TopCyb-283
- ❑ 95UppDec-269
- ❑ 95UppDecED-269
- ❑ 95UppDecEDG-269
- ❑ 95UppDecSE-128
- ❑ 96AngMot-16
- ❑ 96ColCho-483
- ❑ 96ColChoGS-483
- ❑ 96ColChoSS-483
- ❑ 96Don-452
- ❑ 96DonPreP-452
- ❑ 96FleUpd-U20
- ❑ 96FleUpdTC-U20
- ❑ 96LeaSigEA-50
- ❑ 96Pac-267
- ❑ 96Sco-185
- ❑ 96Ult-29
- ❑ 96UltGolM-29
- ❑ 97Fle-42
- ❑ 97FleTif-42
- ❑ 97MidAngOHP-9
- ❑ 97Pac-7
- ❑ 97PacLigB-7
- ❑ 97PacSil-7
- ❑ 97Top-47
- ❑ 97WhiSoxCM-3
- ❑ 97WhiSoxTI-12
- ❑ 98CirThu-194
- ❑ 98CirThuRav-194
- ❑ 98CirThuSupRav-194
- ❑ 98ColCho-64
- ❑ 98ColCho-289
- ❑ 98DiaBacP-13
- ❑ 98DiaMcD-11
- ❑ 98Fle-74
- ❑ 98Fle-464
- ❑ 98Pac-56
- ❑ 98PacOme-13
- ❑ 98PacOmeR-13
- ❑ 98PacOnl-38
- ❑ 98PacOnlR-38
- ❑ 98PacOnlWC-38
- ❑ 98PacPar-122
- ❑ 98PacParC-122
- ❑ 98PacParG-122
- ❑ 98PacParHS-122
- ❑ 98PacParPB-122
- ❑ 98PacParR-122
- ❑ 98PacPlaB-56
- ❑ 98PacRedT-56
- ❑ 98PacSil-56
- ❑ 98Pin-92
- ❑ 98PinPreP-92
- ❑ 98PinSna-AD13
- ❑ 98Sco-229
- ❑ 98ScoRT-179
- ❑ 98StaCluFDI-306
- ❑ 98StaCluI-306
- ❑ 98StaCluOneK-306
- ❑ 98StaCluPP-306
- ❑ 98Top-367
- ❑ 98TopChr-367
- ❑ 98TopChrR-367
- ❑ 98TopDevR-367
- ❑ 98TopDia-367
- ❑ 98TopMiniC-367
- ❑ 98Ult-462
- ❑ 98UltGolM-462
- ❑ 98UltMas-462
- ❑ 98UltPlaM-462
- ❑ 98UppDec-642
- ❑ 98WhiSoxS-15
- ❑ 98WhiSoxSP-15

Fabri, Isidro
- ❑ 86NegLeaF-73
- ❑ 89NegLeaRP-6

Fabrique, Bunny
- ❑ 19Zee-113
- ❑ 90DodTar-228

Fabrizio, Kurt
- ❑ 80ChaO'sP-7
- ❑ 80ChaO'sW-7

Faccio, John
- ❑ 89BelBreIS-4
- ❑ 89Sta-4

Faccio, Luis
- ❑ 85BenPhiC-6
- ❑ 88PriWilYS-8
- ❑ 89BlaYNPRWL-75
- ❑ 89SprCarB-7
- ❑ 90SavCarP-2063
- ❑ 91St.PetCC-6
- ❑ 91St.PetCP-2269
- ❑ 93ArkTraF-2809

Face, Elroy
- ❑ 53Top-246
- ❑ 54Top-87
- ❑ 56PirTeal-5
- ❑ 56Top-13
- ❑ 57Kah-7
- ❑ 57Top-166
- ❑ 58Hir-59
- ❑ 58Kah-7
- ❑ 58Top-74
- ❑ 59Kah-8
- ❑ 59Top-339
- ❑ 59Top-428
- ❑ 60El RoyFM-1
- ❑ 60Kah-7
- ❑ 60KeyChal-15
- ❑ 60Lea-16
- ❑ 60PirJayP-4
- ❑ 60PirTag-26
- ❑ 60Top-20
- ❑ 60Top-115
- ❑ 60TopTat-14
- ❑ 60TopTat-89
- ❑ 60TopVen-20
- ❑ 60TopVen-115
- ❑ 61Kah-11
- ❑ 61PirJayP-3
- ❑ 61Pos-133
- ❑ 61Top-250
- ❑ 61Top-310
- ❑ 61Top-370
- ❑ 61TopStal-62
- ❑ 62Jel-177
- ❑ 62Pos-177
- ❑ 62PosCan-177
- ❑ 62SalPlaC-174
- ❑ 62ShiPlaC-174
- ❑ 62Top-210
- ❑ 62Top-423
- ❑ 62TopStal-175
- ❑ 63BasMagM-23
- ❑ 63Fle-57
- ❑ 63Jel-147
- ❑ 63PirIDL-6
- ❑ 63PirJayP-5
- ❑ 63Pos-147
- ❑ 63Top-409
- ❑ 64PirKDK-9
- ❑ 64Top-539
- ❑ 65Top-347
- ❑ 66PirEasH-26
- ❑ 66Top-461
- ❑ 67CokCapPi-14
- ❑ 67OPC-49
- ❑ 67PirTeal-6
- ❑ 67Top-49
- ❑ 67TopPirS-8
- ❑ 67TopVen-336
- ❑ 68PirKDK-26
- ❑ 68PirTeal-7
- ❑ 68Top-198
- ❑ 68TopVen-198
- ❑ 69OPC-207
- ❑ 69Top-207
- ❑ 69TopFou-16
- ❑ 70ExpPos-1
- ❑ 72LauGreF-26
- ❑ 74NewYorNTDiS-21
- ❑ 77PirTCM1WC-21
- ❑ 78TCM60I-5
- ❑ 80PirGreT-11
- ❑ 82TCMGreP-12
- ❑ 86PirGreT-11
- ❑ 87McDCoi-1
- ❑ 87Pir196T-7
- ❑ 89PacLegI-178
- ❑ 89SweBasG-51
- ❑ 90HOFStiB-58
- ❑ 91SweBasG-28
- ❑ 91TopArc1-246
- ❑ 92ActPacA-26
- ❑ 92BazQua5A-19
- ❑ 92UppDecS-19
- ❑ 93UppDecAH-48
- ❑ 94TedWil-77
- ❑ 94TopArc1-87
- ❑ 94TopArc1G-87
- ❑ 94UppDecAH-59
- ❑ 94UppDecAH1-59

Facione, Chris
- ❑ 93BriTigC-8
- ❑ 93BriTigF-3660
- ❑ 94FayGenC-12
- ❑ 94FayGenF-2163

Faedo, Len
- ❑ 80OrlTwiT-10
- ❑ 81ChaChaT-12
- ❑ 82Top-766
- ❑ 82TwiPos-10
- ❑ 83Fle-611
- ❑ 83Top-671
- ❑ 83TwiTeal-8
- ❑ 84EvaTriT-10
- ❑ 84Fle-563
- ❑ 84MinTwiP-11
- ❑ 84Nes792-84
- ❑ 84Top-84
- ❑ 84TopSti-310
- ❑ 84TopTif-84
- ❑ 84TwiTeal-9

Faeth, Tony
- ❑ 21Zee-69

Fagan, Everett
- ❑ 43A'STEAI-10
- ❑ 47A'sTeal-9

Fagan, Pete
- ❑ 87St.PetCP-26
- ❑ 91SavCarC-4
- ❑ 92SavCarC-25
- ❑ 93St.PetCC-30
- ❑ 95ArkTraTI-11
- ❑ 96ArkTraB-4
- ❑ 97ArkTraB-29

Fagan, William
- ❑ 87OldJudN-158

Faggett, Ethan
- ❑ 95MicBatCTI-11
- ❑ 95MidLeaA-14
- ❑ 96SarRedSB-14
- ❑ 97SarRedS-10

Fagley, Dan
- ❑ 96BreCouMB-15

Fagnano, Phil
- ❑ 87UtiBluSP-29
- ❑ 88SpaPhiP-1032

Fagnant, Ray
- ❑ 90WinHavRSS-8
- ❑ 91LinDriAA-457
- ❑ 91NewBriRSLD-457
- ❑ 91NewBriRSP-354

Faherty, Sean
- ❑ 83AleDukT-18
- ❑ 84PriWilPT-3

Fahey, Bill
- ❑ 72OPC-334
- ❑ 72Top-334
- ❑ 73OPC-186
- ❑ 73Top-186
- ❑ 74OPC-558
- ❑ 74SpoIndC-34
- ❑ 74Top-558
- ❑ 75OPC-644
- ❑ 75RanPos-8
- ❑ 75Top-644
- ❑ 75TopMin-644
- ❑ 76OPC-436
- ❑ 76SSP-259
- ❑ 76Top-436
- ❑ 77Top-511
- ❑ 78SSP270-97
- ❑ 78Top-388
- ❑ 78TucTorC-14
- ❑ 79PadFamF-17
- ❑ 80OPC-23
- ❑ 80Top-44
- ❑ 81Don-361
- ❑ 81Fle-490
- ❑ 81Top-653
- ❑ 81TopTra-760
- ❑ 82Top-286
- ❑ 83Don-281
- ❑ 83TigPos-10
- ❑ 83Top-196
- ❑ 85TulDriTI-28
- ❑ 86GiaMot-28
- ❑ 86GiaPos-10
- ❑ 87GiaMot-27
- ❑ 87GiaPos-11
- ❑ 88GiaMot-27
- ❑ 88GiaPos-10
- ❑ 89GiaMot-28
- ❑ 89Top-351
- ❑ 89TopTif-351
- ❑ 90GiaMot-21
- ❑ 90GiaSmo-7
- ❑ 91GiaMot-27
- ❑ 93RanKee-10

Fahr, Gerald
- ❑ 52Par-23

Fahrow, Bryant
- ❑ 75QuaCitAT-4

Failla, Paul
- ❑ 94SigRooDP-59
- ❑ 94SigRooDPS-59
- ❑ 94StaCluDP-36
- ❑ 94StaCluDPFDI-36
- ❑ 95CedRapKTI-13
- ❑ 95MidLeaA-15
- ❑ 96LakElsSB-16
- ❑ 97CalLeaATI-5
- ❑ 97LakElsSG-14

Fain, Ferris
- ❑ 47A'sTeal-10
- ❑ 47Exh-71A
- ❑ 47Exh-71B
- ❑ 47PM1StaP1-57
- ❑ 48A'sTeal-7
- ❑ 48Bow-21
- ❑ 49A'sTeal-12
- ❑ 49Bow-9
- ❑ 49MPR302-2-107
- ❑ 49OlmStu-2
- ❑ 49PhiBul-18
- ❑ 50A'sTeal-9
- ❑ 50Bow-13
- ❑ 50RoyDes-24
- ❑ 51A'sTeal-9
- ❑ 51TopRedB-3
- ❑ 52A'sTeal-8
- ❑ 52BerRos-18
- ❑ 52Bow-154
- ❑ 52DixLid-7
- ❑ 52DixPre-7
- ❑ 52NatTeaL-9
- ❑ 52RedMan-AL7
- ❑ 52RoyPre-5
- ❑ 52StaCalL-76B
- ❑ 52StaCalS-89B
- ❑ 52TipTop-8
- ❑ 52Top-21
- ❑ 53DixLid-4
- ❑ 53DixPre-4
- ❑ 53Top-24
- ❑ 54Bow-214
- ❑ 54RedHeaF-7
- ❑ 54RedMan-AL22
- ❑ 54Top-27
- ❑ 54Wil-4
- ❑ 55Top-11
- ❑ 55TopDouH-115
- ❑ 77PhiFav-8
- ❑ 82TCMGreH-43
- ❑ 83TopRep5-21
- ❑ 85TCMPla1-22
- ❑ 91TopArc1-24
- ❑ 92BazQua5A-3
- ❑ 94TopArc1-27
- ❑ 94TopArc1G-27

Faino, Jeff
- ❑ 92ClaDraP-109
- ❑ 92ElmPioF-1376
- ❑ 93LynRedSC-9
- ❑ 93LynRedSF-2511
- ❑ 94LynRedSC-10
- ❑ 94LynRedSF-1887
- ❑ 95BowBayTI-29

Fairchild, Glenn
- ❑ 86WatIndP-6
- ❑ 87WatIndP-25
- ❑ 88KinIndS-5

Faircloth, Chad
- ❑ 97SalVolG-11

Faircloth, Kevin
- ❑ 94YakBeaC-5
- ❑ 94YakBeaF-3856
- ❑ 95SanBerSTI-6
- ❑ 97SanBerS-21

Faircloth, Wayne
- ❑ 93HicCraC-7
- ❑ 93HicCraF-1280
- ❑ 94SouBenSHF-596

Fairey, Jim
- ❑ 68Top-228
- ❑ 68TopVen-228
- ❑ 69MLBOffS-157
- ❑ 69OPC-117
- ❑ 69Top-117
- ❑ 69TopFou-22
- ❑ 71ExpPS-6
- ❑ 71MLBOffS-126
- ❑ 71OPC-474
- ❑ 71Top-474
- ❑ 72Dia-13
- ❑ 72ProStaP-4
- ❑ 72Top-653
- ❑ 73OPC-429
- ❑ 73Top-429
- ❑ 74TacTwiC-24
- ❑ 75HawIsIC-7
- ❑ 76HawIsIC-15
- ❑ 81TCM60I-334
- ❑ 85SpoIndGC-5
- ❑ 90DodTar-229

Fairfax, Kenny
- ❑ 93WelPirC-5
- ❑ 93WelPirF-3349

Fairley, Craig
- ❑ 90NebCor-9

Fairly, Pat
- ❑ 92GenCubC-17
- ❑ 92GenCubF-1567

Fairly, Ron
- ❑ 59DodTeal-7
- ❑ 59Top-125
- ❑ 59TopVen-125
- ❑ 60DarFar-21
- ❑ 60DodJayP-4
- ❑ 60Top-321
- ❑ 61DodUniO-7
- ❑ 61Top-492
- ❑ 62DodBelB-6
- ❑ 62DodJayP-3
- ❑ 62DodVol-12
- ❑ 62Top-375
- ❑ 62TopStal-134
- ❑ 63DodJayP-5
- ❑ 63Jel-116
- ❑ 63Pos-116
- ❑ 63Top-105
- ❑ 64DodHea-4
- ❑ 64Top-138
- ❑ 64Top-490
- ❑ 64TopCoi-54
- ❑ 64TopVen-138
- ❑ 65DodJayP-5
- ❑ 65DodTeal-6
- ❑ 65OldLonC-8
- ❑ 65OPC-196
- ❑ 65Top-196
- ❑ 65TopEmbl-2
- ❑ 66Baz-20
- ❑ 66DodVolT-3
- ❑ 66Top-330
- ❑ 66TopRubl-27
- ❑ 66TopVen-330
- ❑ 67Baz-20
- ❑ 67CokCapD-3
- ❑ 67CokCapDA-3
- ❑ 67DexPre-70
- ❑ 67OPC-94
- ❑ 67Top-94
- ❑ 68AtlOilPBCC-17
- ❑ 68Top-510
- ❑ 68Top3-D-3
- ❑ 69ExpPin-3
- ❑ 69MilBra-81
- ❑ 69MLBOffS-146
- ❑ 69MLBPin-42
- ❑ 69OPC-122
- ❑ 69Top-122
- ❑ 69TopFou-5
- ❑ 69TopSta-43
- ❑ 69TopTeaP-22
- ❑ 70ExpPin-5
- ❑ 70MLBOffS-65
- ❑ 70Top-690
- ❑ 70TopPos-10
- ❑ 71ExpLaPR-3
- ❑ 71ExpPS-7
- ❑ 71MLBOffS-127
- ❑ 71OPC-315
- ❑ 71Top-315
- ❑ 71TopCoi-83
- ❑ 72Dia-14
- ❑ 72MilBra-101
- ❑ 72OPC-405
- ❑ 72Top-405
- ❑ 73ExpPos-4
- ❑ 73OPC-125
- ❑ 73Top-125
- ❑ 74Kel-27
- ❑ 74OPC-146
- ❑ 74Top-146
- ❑ 74TopSta-53
- ❑ 75OPC-270
- ❑ 75St.LouCP-9
- ❑ 75Top-270
- ❑ 75TopMin-270
- ❑ 76OPC-375
- ❑ 76SSP-276
- ❑ 76St.LouCP-7
- ❑ 76Top-375
- ❑ 77Top-127
- ❑ 78AngFamF-9
- ❑ 78OPC-40
- ❑ 78SSP270-205
- ❑ 78Top-85
- ❑ 79Top-580
- ❑ 81TCM60I-324
- ❑ 86ExpGreT-1
- ❑ 90DodTar-230
- ❑ 90SouCalS-5
- ❑ 92Nab-19

Fairman, Andy
- ❑ 91HelBreSP-16
- ❑ 92BelBreCB-20
- ❑ 92BelBreFI-410
- ❑ 93StoPorC-10
- ❑ 93StoPorF-750
- ❑ 94StoPorC-6
- ❑ 94StoPorF-1699

Fajardo, Alejandro
- ❑ 97BatCliTI-8
- ❑ 98PieBolWM-12

Fajardo, Hector
- ❑ 91AugPirC-5
- ❑ 91AugPirP-798
- ❑ 91SouAtlLAGP-SAL4
- ❑ 92Bow-22
- ❑ 92Cla1-T32
- ❑ 92Don-419
- ❑ 92Pin-573
- ❑ 92PinRool-2
- ❑ 92ProFS7-311
- ❑ 92Sco-842
- ❑ 92ScoRoo-23
- ❑ 92TopDeb91-53
- ❑ 93PacSpa-309
- ❑ 93RanKee-140
- ❑ 93StaClu-430
- ❑ 93StaCluFDI-430
- ❑ 93StaCluMOP-430
- ❑ 94ScoRoo-RT132
- ❑ 94ScoRooGR-RT132
- ❑ 94SpoRoo-37
- ❑ 94SpoRooAP-37
- ❑ 95Don-244
- ❑ 95DonPreP-244
- ❑ 95Pac-424
- ❑ 95PacLatD-12
- ❑ 95Pin-437
- ❑ 95PinArtP-437
- ❑ 95PinMusC-437
- ❑ 95RanCra-8
- ❑ 95StaClu-374
- ❑ 95StaCluMOP-374
- ❑ 95StaCluSTWS-374
- ❑ 95StaCluVR-197
- ❑ 95StaCluVRMO-197
- ❑ 95Top-184

Falciglia, Tony
- ❑ 96NewJerCB-8
- ❑ 97PriWilC-11

Falco, Chris
- ❑ 90FreStaS-4
- ❑ 91FreStaBS-4

❑ 91JamExpC-9
❑ 91JamExpP-3552
❑ 92RocExpC-23
❑ 92RocExpF-2122
Falcon, Edwin
❑ 96GreFalDTI-18
❑ 97GreFalDTI-10
❑ 98LowSpiM-5
Falcone, Dave
❑ 84ChaO'sT-16
❑ 85RocRedWT-4
❑ 86ChaOriW-9
❑ 87ChaO'sW-36
❑ 87SouLeaAJ-1
❑ 90HagSunDGB-9
Falcone, Pete
❑ 72GiaTeal-4
❑ 75Gia-2
❑ 75GiaTeal-5
❑ 76OPC-524
❑ 76St.LouCP-8
❑ 76Top-524
❑ 76TopTra-524T
❑ 77BurCheD-12
❑ 77Car5-8
❑ 77CarTeal-7
❑ 77Hos-24
❑ 77OPC-177
❑ 77Top-205
❑ 78CarTeal-6
❑ 78Top-669
❑ 79OPC-36
❑ 79Top-87
❑ 80Top-401
❑ 81Don-395
❑ 81Fle-327
❑ 81OPC-117
❑ 81Top-117
❑ 82Don-380
❑ 82Fle-524
❑ 82MetPhoA-6
❑ 82Top-326
❑ 83BraPol-33
❑ 83Don-182
❑ 83Fle-541
❑ 83Top-764
❑ 83TopTra-31T
❑ 84BraPol-33
❑ 84Don-385
❑ 84Fle-177
❑ 84Nes792-521
❑ 84OPC-51
❑ 84raPho-8
❑ 84Top-521
❑ 84TopTif-521
❑ 85Top-618
❑ 85TopTif-618
❑ 89PacSenL-208
❑ 89TopSenL-56
❑ 90EliSenL-55
❑ 91MetWIZ-111
❑ 91PacSenL-110
Falk, Bibb A.
❑ 21E121So1-22
❑ 21Exh-46
❑ 21Nei-15
❑ 22E120-19
❑ 22W572-28
❑ 22W573-38
❑ 22W575-33
❑ 23W501-41
❑ 23WilChoV-41
❑ 25Exh-74
❑ 26Exh-75
❑ 27YorCarE-39
❑ 28Exh-38
❑ 28StaPlaCE-19
❑ 28W502-39
❑ 28Yue-39
❑ 29ExhFou-22
❑ 31Exh-22
❑ 61Fle-104
❑ 92ConTSN-518
Falk, Chet
❑ 27MidBre-27
❑ 30Zee-171
Falkenborg, Brian
❑ 97DelSho-6
❑ 97SouAtlTPB-15
❑ 98CarLeaTPQ-30
❑ 98FreKeyM-1
❑ 99BasAmeTPA-13
Falkenburg, Cy (Frederick)
❑ 11MecDFT-20
❑ 11PinT-5-605
❑ 11SpoLifCW-122
❑ 11SpoLifM-42
❑ 14CraJacE-20
❑ 15CraJacE-20
❑ 19Zee-114
Falkner, Richard
❑ 88BurIndP-1773
❑ 89KinIndS-7
❑ 89Sta-75
❑ 90KinIndTI-18
Fallentine, Ernest
❑ 19Zee-36
Fallon, George
❑ 49W72HolS-2
❑ 50W720HolS-7
❑ 83Car194T-24
❑ 90DodTar-231
Fallon, Robert
❑ 80AppFoxT-2
❑ 81GleFalWST-3
❑ 82GleFalWST-17
❑ 85BufBisT-17
❑ 85FleUpd-39
Falls, Bobby
❑ 86ColAstP-12
Falls, Curtis
❑ 94LetMouF-3871
❑ 94LetMouSP-9
Falteisek, Steven
❑ 92JamExpF-1493
❑ 94WesPalBEC-9
❑ 94WesPalBEF-33
❑ 95HarSenTI-17
❑ 98PacPar-193
❑ 98PacParC-193
❑ 98PacParG-193
❑ 98PacParHS-193
❑ 98PacParPB-193
❑ 98PacParR-193
Falzone, Jim
❑ 87MiaMarP-2
Fana, Alberto
❑ 95BatCliTI-11
Fancher, Terry
❑ 89MisStaB-11
Fancher, Tim
❑ 89MisStaB-12
Fandozzi, Mike
❑ 52LavPro-15
Faneyte, Ricky (Rikkert)
❑ 90IBAWorA-39
❑ 90IBAWorA-47
❑ 91CliGiaC-22
❑ 92SanJosGC-7
❑ 92UppDecML-116
❑ 93PhoFirF-1526
❑ 94Bow-51
❑ 94Cla-125
❑ 94ColC-97
❑ 94ColChoGS-97
❑ 94ColChoSS-97
❑ 94LeaLimR-40
❑ 94PhoFirF-1531
❑ 94ScoRoo-RT111
❑ 94ScoRooGR-RT111
❑ 94Sel-401
❑ 94SpoRoo-125
❑ 94SpoRooAP-125
❑ 94Top-790
❑ 94TopGol-790
❑ 94TopSpa-790
❑ 95ColChoGS-260
❑ 95ColChoSS-260
❑ 95PhoFirTI-39
❑ 95Pin-138
❑ 95PinArtP-138
❑ 95PinMusC-138
❑ 95Sco-282
❑ 95ScoGolR-282
❑ 95ScoPlaTS-282
❑ 95Sel-33
❑ 95SelArtP-33
❑ 95SigRoo-18
❑ 95SigRooSig-18
❑ 95Spo-158
❑ 95SpoArtP-158
❑ 96OklCit8B-10
❑ 96Pac-201
❑ 96Sco-36
Fang, Wild
❑ 95RocRedWTI-47
Fanio, Jeff
❑ 92ElmPioC-21
Fannin, Cliff
❑ 47TipTop-62
❑ 49Bow-120
❑ 49Lea-123
❑ 50Bow-106
❑ 51Bow-244
❑ 51TopBluB-36
❑ 52Top-285
❑ 53Top-203
❑ 83TopRep5-285
❑ 91TopArc1-203
Fanning, Charles
❑ 11Zee-85
❑ 12Zee-108
❑ 13Zee-107
❑ 14Zee-109
❑ 15Zee-105
❑ 16Zee-109
Fanning, Jim
❑ 82Don-492
❑ 82ExpHygM-6
❑ 82ExpPos-10
❑ 85OPC-267
❑ 85Top-759
❑ 85TopTif-759
❑ 86ExpGreT-12
Fanning, Steve
❑ 88HamRedP-1739
❑ 89SavCarP-363
❑ 90ArkTraGS-11
❑ 91ArkTraLD-31
❑ 91ArkTraP-1292
❑ 91LinDriAA-31
❑ 92ArkTraF-1136
❑ 92ArkTraS-34
❑ 93ArkTraF-2818
❑ 94LouRedF-2988
Fanok, Harry
❑ 62KahAtl-6
❑ 63Top-54A
❑ 63Top-54B
❑ 64Top-262
❑ 64TopVen-262
Fanovich, Frank
❑ 49EurSta-83
❑ 52Par-84
❑ 53A'sTeal-10
❑ 54OriEss-10
Fansler, Stan
❑ 85NasPirT-8
❑ 86HawIslP-7
❑ 87VanCanP-1604
❑ 88BufBisC-2
❑ 88BufBisP-1469
❑ 91CarMudLD-102
❑ 91CarMudP-1080
❑ 91LinDriAA-102
❑ 92CarMudF-1175
❑ 92CarMudS-134
❑ 92SkyAA F-63
❑ 96VerExpB-2
Fantauzzi, John
❑ 93ClaFS7-185
❑ 93WatDiaC-15
❑ 93WatDiaF-1776
❑ 94MidLeaAF-MDW58
❑ 94SprSulC-1
❑ 94SprSulF-2044
❑ 95AshTouTI-29
❑ 96SalAvaB-8
Fanucchi, Paul
❑ 90NebCor-10
Fanzone, Carmen
❑ 73OPC-139
❑ 73Top-139
❑ 74OPC-484
❑ 74Top-484
❑ 75OPC-363
❑ 75Top-363
❑ 75TopMin-363
Faraci, Joe
❑ 66TolMudHTI-8
Farfan, David
❑ 95BoiHawTI-17
Fargas, Hector
❑ 93SpoIndC-8
❑ 93SpoIndF-3585
❑ 94SprSulC-10
Faria, Joe
❑ 47SmiClo-25
Farias, Tom
❑ 77BriRedST-4
Faries, Paul
❑ 87SpoIndP-17
❑ 88CalLeaACLC-43
❑ 88RivRedWCLC-217
❑ 88RivRedWP-1422
❑ 89TexLeaAGS-7
❑ 89WicChaR-5
❑ 89WicStaR-18
❑ 89WicUpdR-3
❑ 89WicWraR-22
❑ 90CMC-517
❑ 90LasVegSC-14
❑ 90LasVegSP-128
❑ 90ProAAAF-16
❑ 90TriAllGP-AAA8
❑ 91Bow-664
❑ 91DonRoo-16
❑ 91Fle-528
❑ 91MajLeaCP-55
❑ 91PadCok-3
❑ 91PadMag-20
❑ 91PadSmo-9
❑ 91Sco-711
❑ 91StaClu-557
❑ 91Stu-243
❑ 91TopDeb90-46
❑ 91Ult-302
❑ 91UppDec-751
❑ 92Fle-603
❑ 92LasVegSF-2799
❑ 92LasVegSS-230
❑ 92OPC-162
❑ 92Pin-332
❑ 92Sco-509
❑ 92Sco100RS-22
❑ 92StaClu-513
❑ 92Top-162
❑ 92TopGol-162
❑ 92TopGolW-162
❑ 92TopMic-162
❑ 92TriA AAS-230
❑ 92UppDec-310
❑ 93PhoFirF-1522
❑ 93TriAAAGF-26
❑ 94GiaUSPC-2H
❑ 94GiaUSPC-9S
❑ 94PhoFirF-1525
❑ 94TriAAF-AAA40
❑ 95EdmTraTI-6
❑ 96IowCubB-13
❑ 98TolMudHQ-16
Fariss, Monty
❑ 88ButCopKSP-22
❑ 88TulDriTI-3
❑ 89Bow-233
❑ 89BowTif-233
❑ 89Top-177
❑ 89TopTif-177
❑ 89TulDriGS-8
❑ 89TulDriTI-6
❑ 90Bow-500
❑ 90BowTif-500
❑ 90CMC-799
❑ 90TulDriP-1161
❑ 90TulDriTI-7
❑ 91Bow-285
❑ 91Cla3-T18
❑ 91Don-455
❑ 91LinDriAAA-308
❑ 91OklCit8LD-308
❑ 91OklCit8P-184
❑ 91TriA AAGP-AAA25
❑ 92ClaGam-107
❑ 92DonRoo-35
❑ 92Fle-668
❑ 92Lea-354
❑ 92LeaBlaG-354
❑ 92OklCit8F-1926
❑ 92OPC-138
❑ 92Pin-560
❑ 92PinRoo-14
❑ 92PinTea2-74
❑ 92ProFS7-152
❑ 92RanMot-24
❑ 92Sco-772
❑ 92ScoRoo-30
❑ 92StaClu-803
❑ 92StaCluNC-803
❑ 92Top-138
❑ 92TopDeb91-54
❑ 92TopGol-138
❑ 92TopGolW-138
❑ 92TopMic-138
❑ 92Ult-441
❑ 92UppDec-462
❑ 93Don-245
❑ 93Don-753
❑ 93Fle-427
❑ 93Lea-320
❑ 93MarlStaClu-19
❑ 93MarUppD-717
❑ 93MarUSPC-3H
❑ 93MarUSPC-13C
❑ 93PacSpa-461
❑ 93RanKee-141
❑ 93Sco-432
❑ 93StaClu-535
❑ 93StaCluFDI-535
❑ 93StaCluMOP-535
❑ 93Top-575
❑ 93TopGol-575
❑ 93TopInaM-575
❑ 93TopInaR-575
❑ 93TopMic-575
❑ 93TopTra-111T
❑ 93Ult-374
❑ 93UppDec-717
❑ 93UppDecGold-717
❑ 93USPlaCR-7H
❑ 94EdmTraF-2886
Farkas, Ron
❑ 78SprRedWK-2
❑ 82IndIndTI-24
Farley, Bob
❑ 60TacBan-5
❑ 61TacBan-6
❑ 61UniOil-T34
❑ 62Top-426
❑ 62WhiSoxTS-6
Farley, Brian
❑ 83EriCarT-10
❑ 87SprCarB-20
Farley, Cordell
❑ 96JohCitCTI-12
❑ 98PriWilCQ-20
❑ 99BasAmeTP-42
❑ 99BasAmeTPG-42
❑ 99TeaBesRBW-2
Farley, Joe
❑ 96BriWhiSB-15
❑ 96HicCraB-5
❑ 97HicCraB-11
❑ 97HicCraRB-12
❑ 97SalVolG-12
❑ 98SalVol-7
❑ 98WinWar-12
Farlow, Kevin
❑ 90SpoIndSP-23
❑ 91WatDiaC-16
❑ 91WatDiaP-1263
❑ 92WatDiaC-1
❑ 92WatDiaF-2149
Farmar, Damon
❑ 83QuaCitCT-25
❑ 85ModA'sC-20
❑ 86HunStaDJ-18
❑ 87MidAngP-14
❑ 98WilCubM-30
Farmer, Al
❑ 86SalRedBP-8
Farmer, Billy
❑ 70OPC-444
❑ 70Top-444
Farmer, Bryan Pierce
❑ 87GreBraB-16
❑ 88GreBraB-13
❑ 89RicBraBC-6
❑ 89RicBraC-8
❑ 89RicBraP-834
❑ 89RicBraTI-7
Farmer, Craig
❑ 94LetMouF-3872
❑ 94LetMouSP-10
Farmer, Ed
❑ 70WicAerM-7
❑ 72OPC-116
❑ 72Top-116
❑ 73IndTeal-11
❑ 73OPC-272
❑ 73Top-272
❑ 74OPC-506
❑ 74Top-506
❑ 77RocRedWM-18
❑ 78SpoIndC-22
❑ 80Top-702
❑ 81CokTeaS-29
❑ 81Don-40
❑ 81Fle-339
❑ 81FleStiC-114
❑ 81OPC-36
❑ 81Top-36
❑ 81TopScr-54
❑ 81TopSti-64
❑ 81TopSupHT-15
❑ 82Don-482
❑ 82Fle-342
❑ 82OPC-328
❑ 82Top-328
❑ 82TopTra-32T
❑ 83Don-471
❑ 83Fle-161
❑ 83PhiTas-11
❑ 83Top-459
❑ 83TopFol-4
❑ 84TacTigC-247
❑ 86HawIslP-8
❑ 91OriCro-126
❑ 93RanKee-142
❑ 94BreMilB-22
Farmer, Floyd
❑ 17Zee-44
❑ 18Zee-61
Farmer, Gordon
❑ 88AubAstP-1970
❑ 89AshTouP-953
❑ 91OscAstC-2
❑ 91OscAstP-674
Farmer, Howard
❑ 87JamExpP-2561
❑ 88MidLeaAGS-46
❑ 88RocExpLC-12
❑ 89BasAmeAPB-AA20
❑ 89JacExpB-12
❑ 89JacExpP-155
❑ 90Bow-107
❑ 90BowTif-107
❑ 90CMC-53
❑ 90IndIndC-3
❑ 90IndIndP-290
❑ 90ProAAAF-573
❑ 90ScoRoo-91T
❑ 90UppDec-753
❑ 91Don-734
❑ 91MajLeaCP-79
❑ 91OPCPre-40
❑ 91Sco-718
❑ 91Sco100RS-20
❑ 91TopDeb90-47
❑ 91UppDec-362
❑ 92Don-779
❑ 92IndIndF-1854
❑ 92IndIndS-181
❑ 92StaClu-367
Farmer, Jon
❑ 95KanCouCTI-41
Farmer, Ken
❑ 86LitFalMP-10
Farmer, Kevin
❑ 87SpoIndP-14
❑ 88RivRedWCLC-218
❑ 88RivRedWP-1408
❑ 89RivRedWB-5
❑ 89RivRedWCLC-7
❑ 89RivRedWP-1412
Farmer, Michael
❑ 91SouAtlLAGP-SAL43
❑ 91SpaPhiC-23
❑ 91SpaPhiP-908
❑ 92ClePhiC-8
❑ 93Bow-624
❑ 94UppDecML-37
Farmer, Mike
❑ 90MarPhiP-3182
❑ 92ClaFS7-75
❑ 92ClePhiF-2069
❑ 93ClaFS7-186
❑ 93ReaPhiF-290
❑ 94CenValRC-6
❑ 94CenValRF-3195
❑ 95NewHavRTI-27
❑ 97ColSprSTI-6
❑ 98ColSprSS-40
Farmer, Randy
❑ 91KinMetC-13
❑ 91KinMetP-3820
❑ 92ColMetC-14
❑ 92ColMetF-302
❑ 92ColMetPI-6
Farmer, Reggie
❑ 87SpoIndP-11
❑ 88ChaRaiP-1216
❑ 89WatDiaP-1796
❑ 89WatDiaS-5
❑ 90RivRedWB-8
❑ 90RivRedWCLC-9
❑ 90RivRedWP-2618
❑ 91HigDesMC-24
❑ 91HigDesMP-2407
Farmer, William
❑ 87OldJudN-159
Farner, Matt
❑ 94ClaGolF-68
❑ 94Top-203
❑ 94TopGol-203

❑ 94TopSpa-203
Farnham, Gregg
❑ 98St.PauSTI-7
Farnsworth, Jeff
❑ 96EveAquB-7
❑ 97Bow-186
❑ 97BowInt-186
❑ 98SP MinPE-115
❑ 98SPMin-115
Farnsworth, Kyle
❑ 96RocCubTI-8
❑ 97FloStaLTPB-7
❑ 98WesTenDJM-7
❑ 99Bow-317
❑ 99BowGol-317
❑ 99BowInt-317
❑ 99SkyPre-225
❑ 99SkyPre-225
❑ 99SkyPreDD-2
❑ 99SkyPreR-225
❑ 99SkyPreR-225
❑ 99SP TopP-46
❑ 99SP TopPPE-46
❑ 99UppDecE-99
❑ 99UppDecEFXG-99
❑ 99UppDecROSS-S29
❑ 99UppDecROSS-S29
❑ 99Vic-73
Farnsworth, Mark
❑ 82ChaRoyT-23
❑ 83ChaRoyT-26
❑ 85Ft.MyeRT-21
❑ 86Ft.MyeRP-10
❑ 87Ft.MyeRP-31
❑ 90BasCitRS-31
❑ 95OmaRoyTI-9
❑ 96OmaRoyB-4
❑ 97OmaRoyB-4
Farnsworth, Ross
❑ 90KisDodD-11
❑ 91GreFalDSP-11
❑ 92BakDodCLC-10
Farnsworth, Troy
❑ 98NewJerCM-6
Faron, Robert J.
❑ 87SprCarB-11
❑ 88ArkTraGS-9
❑ 90SprCarDGB-21
Farr, Jim
❑ 79AshTouT-6
❑ 80TulDriT-7
❑ 83OklCit8T-22
❑ 84PhoGiaC-9
❑ 93RanKee-143
Farr, Mark
❑ 95ElmPioTI-5
❑ 95ElmPioUTI-5
Farr, Michael
❑ 86WatIndP-7
❑ 87KinIndP-15
❑ 88WilBilP-1307
Farr, Steve
❑ 78ChaPirT-4
❑ 80BufBisT-7
❑ 81BufBisT-18
❑ 82BufBisT-13
❑ 84IndWhe-27
❑ 84MaiGuiT-4
❑ 85Don-653
❑ 85Fle-446
❑ 85Top-664
❑ 85TopTif-664
❑ 86Don-588
❑ 86Fle-7
❑ 86RoyNatP-26
❑ 86RoyTeal-7
❑ 86TopTra-35T
❑ 86TopTraT-35T
❑ 87Don-301
❑ 87Fle-367
❑ 87FleGlo-367
❑ 87OPC-216
❑ 87Top-473
❑ 87TopSti-255
❑ 87TopTif-473
❑ 88Don-378
❑ 88Fle-256
❑ 88FleGlo-256
❑ 88RoySmo-10
❑ 88RoyTeal-9
❑ 88Sco-466
❑ 88ScoGlo-466
❑ 88Top-222
❑ 88TopTif-222
❑ 89Bow-114
❑ 89BowTif-114
❑ 89Don-356
❑ 89DonBasB-151
❑ 89Fle-281
❑ 89FleGlo-281
❑ 89OPC-356
❑ 89PanSti-349
❑ 89RoyTasD-12
❑ 89Sco-183
❑ 89Top-507
❑ 89TopSti-272
❑ 89TopTif-507
❑ 89UppDec-308
❑ 90Bow-366
❑ 90BowTif-366
❑ 90Don-356
❑ 90Fle-107
❑ 90FleCan-107
❑ 90OPC-149
❑ 90PubIntS-347
❑ 90RedFolSB-30
❑ 90RoyPos-9
❑ 90Sco-356
❑ 90Top-149
❑ 90TopSti-270
❑ 90TopTif-149
❑ 90UppDec-680
❑ 91Bow-168
❑ 91Don-365
❑ 91Fle-558
❑ 91Lea-348
❑ 91OPC-301
❑ 91Sco-172
❑ 91ScoRoo-21T
❑ 91StaClu-419
❑ 91Stu-92
❑ 91Top-301
❑ 91TopDesS-301
❑ 91TopMic-301
❑ 91TopTif-301
❑ 91TopTra-38T
❑ 91TopTraT-38T
❑ 91UppDec-660
❑ 91UppDec-717
❑ 92Bow-622
❑ 92Don-735
❑ 92Fle-225
❑ 92Lea-20
❑ 92LeaBlaG-20
❑ 92OPC-46
❑ 92Pin-206
❑ 92Sco-47
❑ 92StaClu-793
❑ 92StaCluNC-793
❑ 92Top-46
❑ 92TopGol-46
❑ 92TopGolW-46
❑ 92TopMic-46
❑ 92Ult-405
❑ 92UppDec-48
❑ 93Bow-539
❑ 93Don-21
❑ 93Fle-276
❑ 93Lea-504
❑ 93OPC-27
❑ 93PacSpa-553
❑ 93Pin-196
❑ 93Sco-162
❑ 93Sel-172
❑ 93SP-263
❑ 93StaClu-176
❑ 93StaCluFDI-176
❑ 93StaCluMOP-176
❑ 93Top-717
❑ 93TopGol-717
❑ 93TopInaM-717
❑ 93TopInaR-717
❑ 93TopMic-717
❑ 93Ult-593
❑ 93UppDec-410
❑ 93UppDecGold-410
❑ 93YanStaC-7
❑ 94ColC-514
❑ 94ColChoGS-514
❑ 94ColChoSS-514
❑ 94Don-531
❑ 94Fin-348
❑ 94FinRef-348
❑ 94Fle-228
❑ 94Lea-270
❑ 94Sco-535
❑ 94ScoGolR-535
❑ 94ScoRoo-RT70
❑ 94ScoRooGR-RT70
❑ 94StaClu-593
❑ 94StaCluFDI-593
❑ 94StaCluGR-593
❑ 94StaCluMOP-593
❑ 94Top-641
❑ 94TopGol-641
❑ 94TopSpa-641
❑ 94UppDec-467
❑ 94UppDecED-467
❑ 95ColCho-414
❑ 95ColChoGS-414
❑ 95ColChoSS-414
❑ 95Sco-186
❑ 95ScoGolR-186
❑ 95ScoPlaTS-186
Farraez, Jesus
❑ 96AubDouB-7
❑ 98KisCobQ-14
Farrar, Sid
❑ 87BucN28-78
❑ 87OldJudN-160
❑ 88WG1CarG-50
❑ 90KalBatN-17
Farrar, Terry
❑ 91BluOriC-4
❑ 91BluOriP-4121
❑ 91KanCouCTI-6
❑ 92FreKeyC-18
❑ 92FreKeyF-1800
❑ 93BowBayF-2184
❑ 94Bow-78
Farreaz, Jesus
❑ 97QuaCitRBB-9
Farrell, Doc (Edward S.)
❑ 26Exh-33
❑ 29ExhFou-1
❑ 30CubTeal-6
❑ 31Zee-14
❑ 33Gou-148
❑ 33GouCanV-73
❑ 91ConTSN-324
Farrell, Duke (Charles A.)
❑ 03BreE10-49
❑ 04RedSoxUP-5
❑ 87OldJudN-162
❑ 90DodTar-233
Farrell, Jim
❑ 95MicBatCTI-12
❑ 97TexAllM-15
❑ 97TreThuB-15
❑ 98PawRedSQ-12
Farrell, John A.
❑ 87BucN28-112A
❑ 87BucN28-112B
❑ 87OldJudN-161
❑ 94OriofB-54
Farrell, John Edward
❑ 85WatIndT-21
❑ 86WatIndP-9
❑ 87BufBisP-15
❑ 88ClaBlu-239
❑ 88Don-42
❑ 88DonBasB-117
❑ 88Fle-608
❑ 88FleGlo-608
❑ 88IndGat-52
❑ 88IndTeal-12
❑ 88Lea-42
❑ 88Sco-620
❑ 88ScoBoxC-T6
❑ 88ScoGlo-620
❑ 88ScoYouSI-33
❑ 88Spo-132
❑ 88StaLinI-10
❑ 88Top-533
❑ 88TopBig-213
❑ 88TopClo-34
❑ 88TopTif-533
❑ 89Bow-74
❑ 89BowTif-74
❑ 89Don-320
❑ 89DonBasB-285
❑ 89Fle-403
❑ 89FleGlo-403
❑ 89IndTeal-11
❑ 89OPC-227
❑ 89PanSti-318
❑ 89Sco-266
❑ 89Spo-37
❑ 89Top-227
❑ 89TopBig-135
❑ 89TopSti-214
❑ 89TopTif-227
❑ 89UppDec-468
❑ 90Don-232
❑ 90DonBesA-19
❑ 90Fle-491
❑ 90FleCan-491
❑ 90IndTeal-12
❑ 90Lea-22
❑ 90OPC-32
❑ 90PanSti-53
❑ 90PubIntS-559
❑ 90Sco-103
❑ 90Top-32
❑ 90TopBig-237
❑ 90TopSti-217
❑ 90TopTif-32
❑ 90UppDec-570
❑ 91Bow-02
❑ 91Don-106
❑ 91Fle-366
❑ 91IndFanC-12
❑ 91OPC-664
❑ 91Sco-50
❑ 91StaClu-185
❑ 91Stu-42
❑ 91Top-664
❑ 91TopDesS-664
❑ 91TopMic-664
❑ 91TopTif-664
❑ 91Ult-111
❑ 91UppDec-692
❑ 92AugPirC-1
❑ 92ClaFS7-17
❑ 92StaClu-693
❑ 92StaCluECN-693
❑ 93AngMot-21
❑ 93AngStaCl-20
❑ 93UppDec-689
❑ 93UppDecGold-689
❑ 94Pac-77
Farrell, John Sebastian
❑ 11SpoLifCW-123
Farrell, Jon
❑ 88CapCodPPaLP-76
❑ 91Cla/Bes-422
❑ 91ClaDraP-20
❑ 91FroRowDP-12
❑ 91FroRowDPG-12
❑ 91FroRowDPP-1
❑ 91FroRowDPS-12
❑ 91WelPirC-1
❑ 91WelPirP-3575
❑ 92AugPirF-251
❑ 92Bow-393
❑ 92OPC-9
❑ 92Pin-299
❑ 92ProFS7-313
❑ 92Sco-804
❑ 92StaCluD-47
❑ 92Top-9
❑ 92TopGol-9
❑ 92TopGolW-9
❑ 92TopMic-9
❑ 92UppDec-69
❑ 92UppDecML-108
❑ 93ExcFS7-91
❑ 93SalBucC-10
❑ 93SalBucF-445
❑ 94SalBucC-10
❑ 94SalBucF-2338
❑ 94UppDecML-171
❑ 94VanCanF-1858
❑ 95CarMudF-172
❑ 96CarMudB-22
Farrell, Kerby
❑ 57IndTeal-6
❑ 73TacTwiC-6
Farrell, Mike
❑ 76AppFoxT-5
❑ 92CalLeaACL-15
❑ 92ElPasDF-3915
❑ 92GulCoaMF-3489
❑ 92StoPorC-21
❑ 92StoPorF-29
❑ 93Bow-211
❑ 93ClaFS7-187
❑ 93ExcFS7-184
❑ 93KinMetC-11
❑ 93KinMetF-3801
❑ 93NewOrlZF-964
❑ 94St.LucMC-8
❑ 94St.LucMF-1201
Farrell, Turk (Dick)
❑ 47Exh-72
❑ 58Hir-43
❑ 58PhiJayP-4
❑ 58Top-76A
❑ 58Top-76B
❑ 59Top-175
❑ 59TopVen-175
❑ 60PhiJayP-7
❑ 60Top-103
❑ 60TopVen-103
❑ 61DodUniO-6
❑ 61Pos-115A
❑ 61Pos-115B
❑ 61Top-522
❑ 61TopStal-54
❑ 62Col.45B-6
❑ 62Col45'HC-5
❑ 62Col45'JP-6
❑ 62SalPlaC-184
❑ 62ShiPlaC-184
❑ 62Top-304
❑ 62TopBuc-25
❑ 62TopStal-125
❑ 63Baz-8
❑ 63Col45"P-5
❑ 63Col45'JP-4
❑ 63ExhStaB-21
❑ 63Fle-38
❑ 63Jel-192
❑ 63Pos-192
❑ 63SalMetC-2
❑ 63Top-9
❑ 63Top-277
❑ 63TopStil-15
❑ 64Baz-8
❑ 64Col.45JP-4
❑ 64Top-560
❑ 64TopCoi-91
❑ 64TopGia-22
❑ 64TopSta-98
❑ 64TopStaU-24
❑ 65OldLonC-9
❑ 65OPC-80
❑ 65Top-80
❑ 66Top-377
❑ 66TopRubI-28
❑ 67AstTeal2-9
❑ 67CokCapAs-16
❑ 67DexPre-71
❑ 67OPC-190
❑ 67Top-190
❑ 68Top-217
❑ 68TopVen-217
❑ 69MilBra-82
❑ 69Top-531
❑ 78TCM60I-202
❑ 78TCM60I-256
❑ 82AstAstI-1
❑ 86AstMot-1
❑ 87AstSer1-9
❑ 87AstSer1-27
❑ 87AstShoSO-6
❑ 89AstCol4S-8
❑ 90DodTar-232
Farris, Ed
❑ 97SouOreTB-5
❑ 98SouOreTG-8
Farris, Mark
❑ 94ClaUpdCotC-CC10
❑ 94SigRooDP-11
❑ 94SigRooDPS-11
❑ 94StaCluDP-85
❑ 94StaCluDPFDI-85
❑ 94TopTra-87T
❑ 94WelPirC-1
❑ 94WelPirF-3502
❑ 95Bow-125
❑ 95ColCho-41
❑ 95ColChoGS-41
❑ 95ColChoSS-41
❑ 95Exc-253
❑ 95SelSurS-SS3
❑ 95StaClu-106
❑ 95StaCluFDI-106
❑ 95StaCluMOP-106
❑ 95StaCluSTWS-106
❑ 95Top-363
❑ 96AugGreB-8
❑ 96HonShaHWB-10
❑ 97LynHil-6
❑ 98CarMudM-12
Farrish, Keoki
❑ 90GreFalDSP-8
❑ 91YakBeaC-9
❑ 91YakBeaP-4260
❑ 92VerBeaDC-2
❑ 92VerBeaDF-2890
Farrow, Doug
❑ 82IdaFalAT-6
Farrow, James
❑ 93GenCubC-11
❑ 93GenCubF-3167
❑ 96AugGreB-9
Farsaci, Dave
❑ 91EugEmeC-17
❑ 91EugEmeP-3718
Farson, Bryan
❑ 94StaCluDP-54
❑ 94StaCluDPFDI-54
❑ 95LynHilTI-8
Farson, George
❑ 78HolMilT-8
❑ 79HolMilT-8
❑ 80PenPilCT-11
Farwell, Fred
❑ 87BakDodP-20
Fasano, Sal
❑ 93EugEmeC-13
❑ 93EugEmeF-3858
❑ 94MidLeaAF-MDW22
❑ 94RocRoyC-1
❑ 94RocRoyF-567
❑ 95Bow-230
❑ 95BowGolF-230
❑ 95Exc-59
❑ 95SigRooOJ-12
❑ 95SigRooOJP-12
❑ 95SigRooOJPS-12
❑ 95SigRooOJS-12
❑ 95SPML-71
❑ 95UppDecML-145
❑ 95UppDecMLFS-145
❑ 95WicWraTI-33
❑ 96Bow-308
❑ 96BowFoi-308
❑ 96Exc-59
❑ 96Fin-B307
❑ 96FinRef-B307
❑ 96FleUpd-U39
❑ 96FleUpdTC-U39
❑ 96LeaSigA-65
❑ 96LeaSigAG-65
❑ 96LeaSigAS-65
❑ 96Pin-370
❑ 96PinAfi-166
❑ 96PinAfiAP-166
❑ 96PinFoil-370
❑ 96Sel-177
❑ 96SelArtP-177
❑ 96SelCer-105
❑ 96SelCerAP-105
❑ 96SelCerCB-105
❑ 96SelCerCR-105
❑ 96SelCerMB-105
❑ 96SelCerMG-105
❑ 96SelCerMR-105
❑ 96Sum-169
❑ 96SumAbo&B-169
❑ 96SumArtP-169
❑ 96SumFoi-169
❑ 96Ult-353
❑ 96UltGolM-353
❑ 96UppDec-260
❑ 97Sco-70
❑ 97ScoArtPWB-70
❑ 97ScoPreS-70
❑ 97ScoShoS-70
❑ 97ScoShoSAP-70
❑ 97WicWra-24
❑ 98PacOnl-339
❑ 98PacOnlR-339
❑ 98PacOnlWC-339
❑ 99Fle-382
❑ 99FleSta9-382
❑ 99FleWarT-382
Fascher, Stan
❑ 86AshTouP-11
❑ 87OscAstP-11
Fassero, Jeff
❑ 85SprCarT-9
❑ 86FloStaLAP-13
❑ 86St.PetCP-8
❑ 87ArkTraP-6
❑ 88ArkTraGS-5
❑ 88BlaYNPRWL-82
❑ 89LouRedBC-4
❑ 89LouRedBP-1246
❑ 89LouRedBTI-18
❑ 90CanIndB-19
❑ 90CanIndP-1289
❑ 90CanIndS-5
❑ 91DonRoo-28
❑ 91IndIndLD-183
❑ 91IndIndP-457
❑ 91LinDriAAA-183
❑ 91TopTra-39T
❑ 91TopTraT-39T
❑ 92Don-717
❑ 92ExpDonD-7

❑ 92ExpPos-11
❑ 92Fle-477
❑ 92FleRooS-5
❑ 92OPC-423
❑ 92OPCPre-119
❑ 92Sco-738
❑ 92StaClu-469
❑ 92Top-423
❑ 92TopDeb91-55
❑ 92TopGol-423
❑ 92TopGolW-423
❑ 92TopMic-423
❑ 92Ult-516
❑ 92UppDec-685
❑ 93Don-642
❑ 93ExpPosN-9
❑ 93Fla-82
❑ 93Fle-459
❑ 93Lea-91
❑ 93OPC-192
❑ 93PacSpa-533
❑ 93Top-178
❑ 93TopGol-178
❑ 93TopInaM-178
❑ 93TopInaR-178
❑ 93TopMic-178
❑ 93UppDec-609
❑ 93UppDecGold-609
❑ 94ColC-98
❑ 94ColChoGS-98
❑ 94ColChoSS-98
❑ 94Don-123
❑ 94Fin-250
❑ 94FinRef-250
❑ 94Fla-401
❑ 94Fle-536
❑ 94FleExtB-303
❑ 94Lea-181
❑ 94Pac-378
❑ 94Sco-261
❑ 94ScoGolR-261
❑ 94Sel-124
❑ 94StaClu-379
❑ 94StaCluFDI-379
❑ 94StaCluGR-379
❑ 94StaCluMOP-379
❑ 94Top-554
❑ 94TopGol-554
❑ 94TopSpa-554
❑ 94TriPla-93
❑ 94Ult-225
❑ 94UppDec-192
❑ 94UppDecED-192
❑ 95ColCho-246
❑ 95ColChoGS-246
❑ 95ColChoSS-246
❑ 95Don-310
❑ 95DonPreP-310
❑ 95DonTopotO-279
❑ 95Emo-151
❑ 95Fin-291
❑ 95FinRef-291
❑ 95Fla-374
❑ 95Fle-348
❑ 95Lea-53
❑ 95Pac-265
❑ 95Pin-99
❑ 95PinArtP-99
❑ 95PinMusC-99
❑ 95Sco-101
❑ 95ScoGolR-101
❑ 95ScoPlaTS-101
❑ 95SP-72
❑ 95SPCha-64
❑ 95SPChaDC-64
❑ 95SPSil-72
❑ 95StaClu-117
❑ 95StaCluFDI-117
❑ 95StaCluMOP-117
❑ 95StaCluSTWS-117
❑ 95Top-603
❑ 95TopCyb-374
❑ 95Ult-189
❑ 95UltGolM-189
❑ 95UppDec-327
❑ 95UppDecED-327
❑ 95UppDecEDG-327
❑ 95USPlaCMLA-8S
❑ 96Don-492
❑ 96DonPreP-492
❑ 96EmoXL-220
❑ 96ExpDis-7
❑ 96Fla-304
❑ 96Fle-455
❑ 96FleTif-455
❑ 96LeaSigA-66
❑ 96LeaSigAG-66
❑ 96LeaSigAS-66
❑ 96Pac-132
❑ 96Sco-411
❑ 96SP-123
❑ 96StaClu-296
❑ 96StaCluEPB-296
❑ 96StaCluEPG-296
❑ 96StaCluEPS-296
❑ 96StaCluMOP-296
❑ 96Top-269
❑ 96Ult-230
❑ 96UltGolM-230
❑ 96UppDec-397
❑ 97Cir-323
❑ 97CirRav-323
❑ 97ColCho-482
❑ 97ColChoT-SM12
❑ 97Don-305
❑ 97Don-436
❑ 97DonGolPP-305
❑ 97DonGolPP-436
❑ 97DonLim-159
❑ 97DonLimE-159
❑ 97DonLimENG-159
❑ 97DonSigA-34
❑ 97DonSigAC-41
❑ 97DonSigAM-41
❑ 97DonSilPP-305
❑ 97DonSilPP-436
❑ 97DonTea-146
❑ 97DonTeaSPE-146
❑ 97Fle-377
❑ 97Fle-682
❑ 97FleTif-377
❑ 97FleTif-682
❑ 97Lea-256
❑ 97LeaFraM-256
❑ 97LeaFraMDC-256
❑ 97MetUni-144
❑ 97NewPin-124
❑ 97NewPinAP-124
❑ 97NewPinMC-124
❑ 97NewPinPP-124
❑ 97Pac-343
❑ 97PacLigB-343
❑ 97PacSil-343
❑ 97Pin-10
❑ 97PinArtP-PP10
❑ 97PinIns-41
❑ 97PinInsCE-41
❑ 97PinInsDE-41
❑ 97PinMusC-10
❑ 97PinPrePla-10
❑ 97PinX-P-100
❑ 97PinX-PMoS-100
❑ 97Sco-414
❑ 97ScoArtPWB-414
❑ 97ScoResC-414
❑ 97ScoShoS-414
❑ 97ScoShoSAP-414
❑ 97Sel-175
❑ 97SelCom-175
❑ 97SpoIll-41
❑ 97SpoIllEE-41
❑ 97StaClu-100
❑ 97StaCluMOP-100
❑ 97Stu-80
❑ 97StuPrePG-80
❑ 97StuPrePS-80
❑ 97Top-335
❑ 97Ult-228
❑ 97Ult-326
❑ 97UltGolME-228
❑ 97UltGolME-326
❑ 97UltPlaME-228
❑ 97UltPlaME-326
❑ 97UppDecMP-P13
❑ 98CirThu-262
❑ 98CirThuRav-262
❑ 98CirThuSupRav-262
❑ 98ColCho-494
❑ 98Don-101
❑ 98DonCol-101
❑ 98DonColL-306
❑ 98DonColS-101
❑ 98DonGolPP-101
❑ 98DonPriCD-101
❑ 98DonPriCL-306
❑ 98DonSigA-31
❑ 98DonSigAC-40
❑ 98DonSigAM-41
❑ 98DonSigSB-10
❑ 98DonSilPP-101
❑ 98Fin-94
❑ 98FinNo--94
❑ 98FinNo-R-94
❑ 98FinRef-94
❑ 98Fle-553
❑ 98Lea-107
❑ 98LeaFraDA-107
❑ 98LeaFraF-107
❑ 98LeaFraM-107
❑ 98LeaFraMP-107
❑ 98LeaFraMDC-107
❑ 98LeaFraMDC-107
❑ 98LeaFraMZ2-107
❑ 98MarSco-3
❑ 98MarScoP-3
❑ 98Pac-185
❑ 98PacOnl-684
❑ 98PacOnlR-684
❑ 98PacOnlWC-684
❑ 98PacPar-86
❑ 98PacParC-86
❑ 98PacParG-86
❑ 98PacParHS-86
❑ 98PacParPB-86
❑ 98PacParR-86
❑ 98PacPlaB-185
❑ 98PacRedT-185
❑ 98PacSil-185
❑ 98Pin-96
❑ 98PinPreP-96
❑ 98PinSna-SM16
❑ 98Sco-20
❑ 98ScoRT-111
❑ 98ScoSS-PP6
❑ 98ScoSSAP-PP6
❑ 98SpoIll-36
❑ 98SpoIllEE-36
❑ 98SpoIllFE-36
❑ 98StaCluFDI-143
❑ 98StaCluI-143
❑ 98StaCluOneK-143
❑ 98StaCluPP-143
❑ 98Top-342
❑ 98TopChr-342
❑ 98TopChrR-342
❑ 98TopDevR-342
❑ 98TopDia-342
❑ 98TopMiniC-342
❑ 98UppDec-223
❑ 98UppDecSF-126
❑ 99Fle-393
❑ 99FleSta9-393
❑ 99FleWarT-393
❑ 99Pac-395
❑ 99PacAur-175
❑ 99PacAurOD-175
❑ 99PacCroC-260
❑ 99PacCroCPB-260
❑ 99PacPar-215
❑ 99PacParC-215
❑ 99PacParG-215
❑ 99PacParHoloGold-215
❑ 99PacParHS-215
❑ 99PacParOD-215
❑ 99PacParPB-215
❑ 99PacParRed-215
❑ 99PacPlaB-395
❑ 99PacRed-395
❑ 99StaClu-109
❑ 99StaCluFDI-109
❑ 99StaCluOoaK-109
❑ 99StaCluPP-109
❑ 99Top-117
❑ 99TopChr-117
❑ 99TopChrR-117
❑ 99TopMVPP-117
❑ 99TopOpeD-69
❑ 99UppDec-204
❑ 99UppDecEL1-204
❑ 99UppDecEL2-204
❑ 99Vic-376

Fast, Darcy
❑ 72OPC-457
❑ 72Top-457

Faszholz, John
❑ 55CarHunW-4

Fatheree, Danny
❑ 98AubDouTI-11

Faul, Bill
❑ 63Top-558
❑ 64Top-236
❑ 64TopVen-236
❑ 66Top-322
❑ 66TopVen-322

Faulk, Jim (James)
❑ 88RocExpLC-13
❑ 90FloStaLAS-5
❑ 90StaFS7-7
❑ 90WesPalBES-5

Faulk, Kelly
❑ 80PenPilBT-6
❑ 80PenPilCT-13
❑ 81ReaPhiT-2
❑ 82ReaPhiT-2
❑ 85ColCliP-10
❑ 85ColCliT-6
❑ 86ColCliP-8
❑ 86ColCliP-8
❑ 87IndIndTI-24

Faulk, Paul
❑ 94OneYanC-28

Faulkner, Craig
❑ 87LSUTigP-2
❑ 88HagSunS-6
❑ 89HagSunB-14
❑ 89HagSunP-266
❑ 89HagSunS-7
❑ 90CMC-742
❑ 90HagSunB-10
❑ 90HagSunP-1421
❑ 90HagSunS-9
❑ 90LSUTigGM-6
❑ 91ElPasDLD-181
❑ 91ElPasDP-2750
❑ 91LinDriAA-181
❑ 92ElPasDF-3924
❑ 92ElPasDS-208
❑ 92SkyAA F-93
❑ 93ArkTraF-2819
❑ 94OriPro-32
❑ 94RocRedWF-1000
❑ 94RocRedWTI-8
❑ 95BowBayTI-47

Faulkner, Jim
❑ 90DodTar-234

Faulkner, Neil
❑ 94HunCubC-8
❑ 94HunCubF-3545
❑ 95RocCubTI-34

Faurot, Adam
❑ 96OgdRapTI-2
❑ 97BelSnaB-11
❑ 98El PasDG-12

Faurot, Scott
❑ 90YakBeaTI-21

Fauske, Josh
❑ 96HicCraB-6
❑ 97HicCraB-12
❑ 98HicCraM-12
❑ 98HicCraUO-16

Faust, Jason
❑ 97SouOreTB-15
❑ 98SouOreTG-9
❑ 98VisOakG-8

Faust, Nancy
❑ 84WhiSoxTV-12
❑ 85WhiSoxC-NNO
❑ 86WhiSoxC-NNO
❑ 87WhiSoxC-9
❑ 88WhiSoxC-6
❑ 89WhiSoxC-29

Fava, Andres
❑ 85AncGlaPTI-10

Favre, Mike
❑ 98HigDesMG-9

Faw, Brian
❑ 90TamYanD-6
❑ 91GreHorP-3051
❑ 92ForLauYC-19
❑ 92ForLauYTI-10
❑ 92Ft.LauYF-2604
❑ 93AlbYanF-2155
❑ 94AlbYanF-1435
❑ 95NorNavTI-22

Fay, May
❑ 08AllLadBC-2

Faye, Eddie
❑ 15Zee-75

Fayne, Jeff
❑ 89JohCitCS-13
❑ 90HamRedS-12
❑ 91SprCarC-16
❑ 91SprCarP-756

Fazekas, Robert
❑ 88CapCodPPaLP-160
❑ 90NiaFalRP-18
❑ 91FayGenC-9
❑ 91FayGenP-1162

Fazio, Ernie
❑ 63Col45"P-6
❑ 63Col45"P-17
❑ 78TCM60I-215

Fazzini, Frank
❑ 86BelBreP-6

Fazzio, Daryl
❑ 80WatIndT-14

Fears, Tom
❑ 52Whe-10A
❑ 52Whe-10B

Febles, Carlos
❑ 96LanLugB-11
❑ 97CarLeaTP-14
❑ 97WilBluR-7
❑ 98Bow-353
❑ 98BowChr-353
❑ 98BowChrGA-353
❑ 98BowChrGAR-353
❑ 98BowChrI-353
❑ 98BowChrIR-353
❑ 98BowChrR-353
❑ 98BowGolA-353
❑ 98BowInt-353
❑ 98FleUpd-U46
❑ 98TexLeaTPG-10
❑ 98WicWraM-25
❑ 99Bow-133
❑ 99BowBes-126
❑ 99BowBesAR-126
❑ 99BowBesR-126
❑ 99BowChr-133
❑ 99BowChrG-133
❑ 99BowChrGR-133
❑ 99BowChrI-133
❑ 99BowChrIR-133
❑ 99BowChrR-133
❑ 99BowGol-133
❑ 99BowInt-133
❑ 99CroRoyB-69
❑ 99CroRoyL-69
❑ 99CroRoyOD-69
❑ 99DumSet-121
❑ 99E-X Cen-109
❑ 99E-X CenECFut-109
❑ 99E-X CenECNow-109
❑ 99Fle-194
❑ 99FleBri-143
❑ 99FleBri2G-143
❑ 99FleBriBlu-143
❑ 99FleBriGol-143
❑ 99FleMys-121
❑ 99FleMysM-121
❑ 99FleSta9-194
❑ 99FleWarT-194
❑ 99PacCroC-131
❑ 99PacCroCPB-131
❑ 99PacInv-72
❑ 99PacInvOD-72
❑ 99PacInvPB-72
❑ 99PacOme-114
❑ 99PacOmeC-114
❑ 99PacOmeG-114
❑ 99PacOmePB-114
❑ 99PacPar-110
❑ 99PacParC-110
❑ 99PacParG-110
❑ 99PacParHoloGold-110
❑ 99PacParHS-110
❑ 99PacParOD-110
❑ 99PacParPB-110
❑ 99PacParRed-110
❑ 99Rev-68
❑ 99RevPremDate-68
❑ 99RevRet-68
❑ 99RevShaSS-68
❑ 99SkyPre-231
❑ 99SkyPre-231
❑ 99SkyPreDD-7
❑ 99SkyPreR-231
❑ 99SkyPreR-231
❑ 99SkyThu-106
❑ 99SkyThuRant-106
❑ 99SkyThuRave-106
❑ 99SP SigAuto-CF
❑ 99SP SigAutoG-CF
❑ 99SPSig-49
❑ 99TeaBesRBW-3
❑ 99ThuSkySupR-106
❑ 99UppDec-282
❑ 99UppDecE-125
❑ 99UppDecEFXG-125
❑ 99UppDecEL1-282
❑ 99UppDecEL2-282
❑ 99UppDecR-40
❑ 99UppDecRG-40
❑ 99UppDecRP-40
❑ 99Vic-182

Feder, Mike
❑ 76WauMetT-25

Federici, Rick
❑ 78ChaPirT-5
❑ 80BufBisT-3

Federico, Gustavo
❑ 89HelBreSP-14

Federico, Joe
❑ 87AncGlaP-11
❑ 88HamRedP-1738
❑ 88NebCor-20
❑ 89St.PetCS-11
❑ 90Bes-93
❑ 90SprCarB-8
❑ 91St.PetCC-20
❑ 91St.PetCP-2283

Federoff, Al
❑ 53MotCoo-62
❑ 58SeaRalT-8

Fedor, Chris
❑ 84GreHorT-11

Fedor, Fritz
❑ 82BelBreFr-9
❑ 83BelBreFr-24
❑ 86BurExpP-7
❑ 87KinIndP-10

Feeley, James
❑ 82MadMusF-20

Feeley, Peter
❑ 91NiaFalRC-16
❑ 91NiaFalRP-3646
❑ 92NiaFalRC-5
❑ 92NiaFalRF-3330
❑ 93FayGenC-11
❑ 93FayGenF-136

Feffee, Theo
❑ 97CedRapK-7

Fehrenbach, Todd
❑ 95BilMusTI-10

Feinburg, Ken
❑ 77CedRapGT-5
❑ 78CedRapGT-8

Feist, Ken
❑ 91EveGiaC-9
❑ 91EveGiaP-3928
❑ 92CliGiaC-6
❑ 92CliGiaF-3608

Felch, Jim
❑ 94DanBraC-9
❑ 94DanBraF-3544

Felda, Brian
❑ 75CedRapGT-13

Felden, Keith
❑ 88UtiBluSP-18
❑ 89MiaMirIS-6

Felder, Kenny
❑ 92ClaDraP-9
❑ 92ClaDraPFB-BC9
❑ 92HelBreF-1726
❑ 92HelBreSP-2
❑ 93BelBreCB-7
❑ 93BelBreFI-1722
❑ 93Bow-563
❑ 93ClaFS7-275
❑ 93ExcFS7-185
❑ 93StaCluM-99
❑ 93Top-723
❑ 93TopGol-723
❑ 93TopInaM-723
❑ 93TopInaR-723
❑ 93TopMic-723
❑ 94Bow-421
❑ 94Cla-127
❑ 94StoPorC-7
❑ 94StoPorF-1705
❑ 95ElPasDTI-6
❑ 95SigRoo-19
❑ 95SigRooSig-19
❑ 95UppDecML-121
❑ 95UppDecMLFS-121

Felder, Mike
❑ 83ElPasDT-9
❑ 84ElPasDT-23
❑ 85VanCanC-211
❑ 86BrePol-16
❑ 86Don-634
❑ 87BrePol-16
❑ 87Don-295
❑ 87Top-352
❑ 87TopTif-352
❑ 88BlaYNPRWL-117
❑ 88BrePol-16
❑ 88BreTeal-12
❑ 88Don-397
❑ 88Fle-164
❑ 88FleGlo-164
❑ 88Sco-388
❑ 88ScoGlo-388
❑ 88StaLinBre-7
❑ 88Top-718

❑ 88TopClo-35
❑ 88TopTif-718
❑ 89BrePol-16
❑ 89Top-263
❑ 89TopTif-263
❑ 89UppDec-252
❑ 90BreMilB-7
❑ 90BrePol-16
❑ 90Don-609
❑ 90El PasDAGTI-12
❑ 90Fle-321
❑ 90FleCan-321
❑ 90Lea-480
❑ 90OPC-159
❑ 90PubIntS-495
❑ 90Sco-268
❑ 90Top-159
❑ 90TopTif-159
❑ 90UppDec-178
❑ 91Don-535
❑ 91Fle-583
❑ 91FleUpd-129
❑ 91GiaMot-15
❑ 91GiaPacGaE-28
❑ 91Lea-445
❑ 91OPC-44
❑ 91Sco-97
❑ 91StaClu-307
❑ 91Top-44
❑ 91TopDesS-44
❑ 91TopMic-44
❑ 91TopTif-44
❑ 91UltUpd-117
❑ 91UppDec-395
❑ 92Bow-93
❑ 92Don-182
❑ 92Fle-635
❑ 92GiaMot-15
❑ 92GiaPacGaE-16
❑ 92OPC-697
❑ 92Pin-311
❑ 92Sco-251
❑ 92StaClu-194
❑ 92Top-697
❑ 92TopGol-697
❑ 92TopGolW-697
❑ 92TopMic-697
❑ 92Ult-291
❑ 92UppDec-288
❑ 93Bow-247
❑ 93Fle-529
❑ 93FleFinE-269
❑ 93Lea-248
❑ 93MariStaClu-29
❑ 93MarMot-9
❑ 93PacSpa-622
❑ 93Pin-148
❑ 93Sco-621
❑ 93SelRoo-106T
❑ 93StaClu-675
❑ 93StaCluFDI-675
❑ 93StaCluMOP-675
❑ 93Top-466
❑ 93TopGol-466
❑ 93TopInaM-466
❑ 93TopInaR-466
❑ 93TopMic-466
❑ 93Ult-618
❑ 93UppDec-186
❑ 93UppDec-714
❑ 93UppDecGold-186
❑ 93UppDecGold-714
❑ 94AstMot-11
❑ 94BreMilB-23
❑ 94ColC-361
❑ 94ColChoGS-361
❑ 94ColChoSS-361
❑ 94Don-155
❑ 94Fle-284
❑ 94Lea-348
❑ 94Pac-568
❑ 94Pin-352
❑ 94PinArtP-352
❑ 94PinMusC-352
❑ 94Sco-411
❑ 94ScoGolR-411
❑ 94StaClu-555
❑ 94StaCluFDI-555
❑ 94StaCluGR-555
❑ 94StaCluMOP-555
❑ 94Top-569
❑ 94TopGol-569
❑ 94TopSpa-569
❑ 95Fle-458
❑ 98BriBluM-12

Feledyk, Kristian

❑ 95AusFutSFP-SFFP8

Felice, Jason

❑ 83TamTarT-8
❑ 86JacMetT-20
❑ 87TidTidP-7

Feliciano, Felix

❑ 80UtiBluJT-5

Feliciano, Jesus

❑ 98YakBeaG-12

Feliciano, Pedro

❑ 95GreFalDTI-2
❑ 96GreFalDB-11
❑ 96GreFalDTI-8
❑ 98VerBeaDM-8

Felitz, Bill

❑ 89JohCitCS-12

Felix, Albert

❑ 92ChaRanC-9

Felix, Antonio

❑ 89AugPirP-510
❑ 90SalBucS-6

Felix, Chris

❑ 94HigDesMC-30

Felix, Gus

❑ 90DodTar-946

Felix, Junior

❑ 87MyrBeaBJP-1455
❑ 88KnoBluJB-2
❑ 88SouLeaAJ-24
❑ 89DonBasB-199
❑ 89DonRoo-55
❑ 89FleUpd-69
❑ 89ScoRoo-83T
❑ 89SyrChiC-19
❑ 89SyrChiMB-10
❑ 89SyrChiP-810
❑ 89TopTra-32T
❑ 89TopTraT-32T
❑ 89UppDec-743
❑ 89UppDecS-2
❑ 90BluJayFS-7
❑ 90BluJayHS-5
❑ 90BluJayHS-6
❑ 90Bow-522
❑ 90BowTif-522
❑ 90ClaBlu-50
❑ 90Don-70
❑ 90DonBesA-70
❑ 90Fle-79
❑ 90FleCan-79
❑ 90FleSoaS-9
❑ 90Hot50RS-15
❑ 90Lea-422
❑ 90OPC-347
❑ 90PanSti-377
❑ 90Sco-258
❑ 90Sco100RS-18
❑ 90ScoYouSI-9
❑ 90Spo-186
❑ 90Top-347
❑ 90TopBig-210
❑ 90TopDeb89-35
❑ 90TopRoo-8
❑ 90TopSti-188
❑ 90TopTif-347
❑ 90ToyRoo-9
❑ 90UppDec-106
❑ 91AngSmo-2
❑ 91Bow-201
❑ 91Cla2-T48
❑ 91ClaGam-190
❑ 91Don-323
❑ 91Fle-173
❑ 91Lea-435
❑ 91OPC-543
❑ 91OPCPre-41
❑ 91PanFreS-342
❑ 91Sco-203
❑ 91ScoRoo-20T
❑ 91StaClu-457
❑ 91Top-543
❑ 91TopDesS-543
❑ 91TopMic-543
❑ 91TopTif-543
❑ 91TopTra-40T
❑ 91TopTraT-40T
❑ 91UppDec-192
❑ 91UppDec-711
❑ 92AngPol-8
❑ 92Bow-404
❑ 92Don-217
❑ 92Lea-118
❑ 92LeaBlaG-118
❑ 92OPC-189
❑ 92PanSti-9
❑ 92Pin-220
❑ 92Sco-519
❑ 92StaClu-141
❑ 92Top-189
❑ 92TopGol-189
❑ 92TopGolW-189
❑ 92TopMic-189
❑ 92TriPla-168
❑ 92Ult-325
❑ 92UppDec-303
❑ 93Bow-122
❑ 93ClaGam-30
❑ 93Don-197
❑ 93Don-771
❑ 93Fin-173
❑ 93FinRef-173
❑ 93Fle-190
❑ 93FleFinE-60
❑ 93Lea-333
❑ 93MarlStaClu-8
❑ 93MarUppD-771
❑ 93MarUSPC-6C
❑ 93MarUSPC-9H
❑ 93MarUSPC-12S
❑ 93OPC-128
❑ 93PacSpa-462
❑ 93Pin-515
❑ 93PinExpOD-9
❑ 93Sco-425
❑ 93Sel-28
❑ 93StaClu-457
❑ 93StaCluFDI-457
❑ 93StaCluMOP-457
❑ 93Stu-181
❑ 93Top-77
❑ 93TopGol-77
❑ 93TopInaM-77
❑ 93TopInaR-77
❑ 93TopMic-77
❑ 93Ult-375
❑ 93UppDec-157
❑ 93UppDec-771
❑ 93UppDecGold-157
❑ 93UppDecGold-771
❑ 94ColC-364
❑ 94ColChoGS-364
❑ 94ColChoSS-364
❑ 94Fla-48
❑ 94FleUpd-43
❑ 94ScoRoo-RT44
❑ 94ScoRooGR-RT44
❑ 94StaClu-660
❑ 94StaCluFDI-660
❑ 94StaCluGR-660
❑ 94StaCluMOP-660
❑ 94TopTra-89T
❑ 95Don-309
❑ 95DonPreP-309
❑ 95Fle-49
❑ 95Pac-150
❑ 95Pin-42
❑ 95PinArtP-42
❑ 95PinMusC-42
❑ 95Sco-18
❑ 95ScoGolR-18
❑ 95ScoPlaTS-18
❑ 95StaClu-154
❑ 95StaCluFDI-154
❑ 95StaCluMOP-154
❑ 95StaCluSTWS-154
❑ 95StaCluVR-80
❑ 95StaCluVRMO-80
❑ 95Top-68
❑ 95TopCyb-135
❑ 95Ult-45
❑ 95UltGolM-45
❑ 95UppDecSE-98
❑ 95UppDecSEG-98

Felix, Lauro

❑ 93ModA'sC-8
❑ 93ModA'sF-807
❑ 94ModA'sC-8
❑ 94ModA'sF-3069
❑ 95ElPasDTI-7
❑ 96El PasDB-10
❑ 97El PasDB-3

Felix, Miguel

❑ 98HicCraM-13

Felix, Nathanael

❑ 90TamYanD-7

Felix, Nick

❑ 87BelMarL-22
❑ 89WauTimGS-16
❑ 90SanBerSCLC-92
❑ 91ChaRanC-5
❑ 91ChaRanP-1309
❑ 93WicWraF-2972

Felix, Paul

❑ 83WisRapTF-6
❑ 85OrlTwiT-4
❑ 86GleFalTP-4
❑ 87GleFalTP-19
❑ 88TolMudHC-20
❑ 88TolMudHP-600

Felix, Pedro

❑ 95BelGiaTI-3
❑ 96BurBeeTI-20
❑ 97BakBlaB-7
❑ 97BakBlaTI-7

Felix, Ruben

❑ 95BelBreTI-11

Feliz, Adolfo

❑ 81WatRedT-13
❑ 82CedRapRT-15
❑ 83TamTarT-9
❑ 83WatRedT-11

Feliz, Bienvenido

❑ 96WatIndTI-8

Feliz, Janiero

❑ 90WelPirP-5

Feliz, Pedro

❑ 98ShrCapM-12
❑ 98ShrCapWS-12

Feller, Bob (Robert)

❑ 36GouWidPPR-C9
❑ 37ExhFou-11
❑ 37GouThuMR-8
❑ 37OPCBatUV-120
❑ 37WheBB8-4
❑ 37WheBB9-6
❑ 38BasTabP-8
❑ 38DixLid-2
❑ 38DixLidP-2
❑ 38ExhFou-11
❑ 38GouFliMR-8A
❑ 38GouFliMR-8B
❑ 38GouHeaU-264
❑ 38GouHeaU-288
❑ 38OurNatGPP-8
❑ 38WheBB10-1
❑ 39ExhSal-15A
❑ 39ExhSal-15B
❑ 39GouPreR303A-14
❑ 39GouPreR303B-7
❑ 39WorWidGTP-14
❑ 40WheM4-1A
❑ 40WheM4-6B
❑ 41DouPlaR-77
❑ 41WheM5-15
❑ 43MPR302-1-10
❑ 46SpoExcW-3-1B
❑ 47HomBon-15
❑ 47IndTeal-8
❑ 47IndVanPP-7A
❑ 47IndVanPP-7B
❑ 47PM1StaP1-58
❑ 47PM1StaP1-59
❑ 48BluTin-43
❑ 48Bow-5
❑ 48IndTeal-9
❑ 48SweSpoT-19
❑ 48ThoMcAF-1
❑ 49Bow-27
❑ 49IndTeal-9
❑ 49IndVisEl-6
❑ 49Lea-93
❑ 49MPR302-2-103
❑ 50Bow-6
❑ 50IndNumN-9
❑ 50IndTeal-9
❑ 51Bow-30
❑ 51R42SmaS-31
❑ 51TopRedB-22
❑ 51Whe-1
❑ 52BerRos-19
❑ 52Bow-43
❑ 52DixLid-8
❑ 52DixPre-8
❑ 52IndNumN-5
❑ 52RedMan-AL8
❑ 52StaCalL-74E
❑ 52StaCalS-88B
❑ 52Top-88
❑ 52Whe-11A
❑ 52Whe-11B
❑ 53ArtHaloFP-33
❑ 53BowC-114
❑ 53ExhCan-17
❑ 53IndPenCBP-11
❑ 53Top-54
❑ 54Bow-132
❑ 54DanDee-6
❑ 54Wil-5
❑ 55Bow-134
❑ 55IndCarBL-1
❑ 55IndGolS-5
❑ 56Top-200
❑ 60Fle-26
❑ 60NuHi-60
❑ 61Fle-25
❑ 61NuSco-460
❑ 63BasMagM-24
❑ 63GadFunC-61
❑ 63HalofFB-6
❑ 67TopVen-160
❑ 68LauWorS-45
❑ 69EquSpoHoF-BB4
❑ 70SpoCarfCOP-4
❑ 72LauGreF-44
❑ 73HalofFPP-7
❑ 73SevTraC-19
❑ 74TCMNic-1
❑ 75SpoHobBG-3
❑ 75TCM195Cl-7
❑ 76GalBasGHoF-8
❑ 76GrePlaG-1
❑ 76RowExh-5
❑ 76ShaPiz-87
❑ 76TayBow4-11
❑ 77BobParHoF-21
❑ 77GalGloG-12
❑ 79BasGre-74
❑ 79DiaGre-285
❑ 79TCM50-28
❑ 80PacLeg-53
❑ 80PerHaloFP-87
❑ 80PerHaloFPS-8
❑ 80SSPHOF-87
❑ 81SpoHaloF-22
❑ 81WatIndT-34
❑ 82BasCarN-8
❑ 82BasCarN-15
❑ 82CraJac-2
❑ 82DavHaloFB-6
❑ 82DiaCla-47
❑ 82OhiHaloF-5
❑ 82TCMGreP-1
❑ 82TCMStaot5-4
❑ 83ASABobF-1
❑ 83ASABobF-2
❑ 83ASABobF-3
❑ 83ASABobF-4
❑ 83ASABobF-5
❑ 83ASABobF-6
❑ 83ASABobF-7
❑ 83ASABobF-8
❑ 83ASABobF-9
❑ 83ASABobF-10
❑ 83ASABobF-11
❑ 83ASABobF-12
❑ 83DonHOFH-36
❑ 83MLBPin-6
❑ 83TopRep5-88
❑ 84OCoandSI-53
❑ 84SpoDesPW-10
❑ 84TCMPla1-17
❑ 85BigLeaC3-67
❑ 85TCMPhoC-6
❑ 86SpoDecG-16
❑ 87HygAllG-16
❑ 87NesDreT-20
❑ 88GreBasS-75
❑ 88PacLegI-101
❑ 89HOFStiB-62
❑ 89PacLegI-156
❑ 89SweBasG-75
❑ 90BasWit-13
❑ 90Col-36
❑ 90PacLeg-85
❑ 90PerGreM-83
❑ 90SweBasG-60
❑ 91ConTSN-35
❑ 91HomCooC-6
❑ 91LinDri-43
❑ 91SweBasG-145
❑ 91TopArc1-54
❑ 92BazQua5A-7
❑ 92ConTSN-370
❑ 92ConTSNCI-23
❑ 92MCIAmb-14
❑ 92PacRyaTEI-135
❑ 92St.VinHHS-3
❑ 92UppDecS-17
❑ 93ActPacA-110
❑ 93ActPacA2-44G
❑ 93ConTSN-933
❑ 93DiaStaES-128
❑ 93MCIAmb-5
❑ 93PinDiM-11
❑ 93UppDecS-3
❑ 93UppDecS-30
❑ 93Yoo-5
❑ 94TedWil-25
❑ 94TedWilLC-LC12
❑ 94UppDecTAE-48
❑ 95ConTSN-1337
❑ 95ConTSNCMP-1435
❑ 95ConTSNP-1337
❑ 95MrTurBG-1
❑ 95StoPop-4
❑ 97FleMilDM-13
❑ 97FleMilDMR-13
❑ 97TopStaHRR-4
❑ 97TopStaRRAU-4
❑ 98SpollITaN-9
❑ 98SpollITaNEE-9
❑ 98UppDecR-28
❑ 98UppDecRSotT-BF
❑ 99SpollIGotG-19
❑ 99SpollIGotGA-21
❑ 99TopHaloFC-HOF9
❑ 99UppDecCL-36
❑ 99UppDecCLCC-36
❑ 99UppDecCLES-BF
❑ 99UppDecCLESC-BF

Fellows, Mark

❑ 82MadMusF-14
❑ 83AlbA'sT-3

Felsch, Happy (Oscar)

❑ 15SpoNewM-57
❑ 16SpoNewM-56
❑ 16TanBraE-10
❑ 17ColE13-47
❑ 17HolBreD-29
❑ 18WhiSoxTI-8
❑ 19W514-3
❑ 75WhiSox1T-7
❑ 88LitSunBS-7
❑ 88PacEigMO-10
❑ 88PacEigMO-41
❑ 88PacEigMO-55
❑ 88PacEigMO-76
❑ 88PacEigMO-109
❑ 92Man191BSR-8
❑ 94ConTSN-1042
❑ 94ConTSNB-1042

Felske, John

❑ 73OPC-45
❑ 73OPC-332
❑ 73Top-45
❑ 73Top-332
❑ 77SpoIndC-26
❑ 78SpoIndC-26
❑ 79VanCanT-20
❑ 82ReaPhiT-22
❑ 83PorBeaT-13
❑ 84PhiTas-10
❑ 85PhiTas-2
❑ 85PhiTas-8
❑ 85TopTifT-33T
❑ 85TopTra-33T
❑ 86PhiTas-7
❑ 86Top-621
❑ 86TopTif-621
❑ 87PhiTas-7
❑ 87Top-443
❑ 87TopTif-443
❑ 94BreMilB-24

Felston, Anthony

❑ 97ForWayW-10
❑ 98ForMyeMTI-11

Felt, Jim

❑ 82AleDukT-24
❑ 83AleDukT-22
❑ 84PriWilPT-5

Felt, Rich

❑ 82VerBeaDT-5
❑ 83VerBeaDT-3

Felton, Fred

❑ 88BatCliP-1686

Felton, Terry

❑ 77OrlTwiT-9A
❑ 77OrlTwiT-9B
❑ 79TolMudHT-9
❑ 80TolMudHT-7
❑ 80TwiPos-8
❑ 81TolMudHT-4
❑ 82TwiPos-11
❑ 83Don-354
❑ 83Fle-612
❑ 83TolMudHT-2
❑ 83Top-181

Felton, Todd

❑ 88SpaPhiP-1043

Felts, Albert

❑ 12Zee-109
Fendrick, Dave
❑ 74GasRanT-10
Fennell, Barry
❑ 97WilCubB-5
❑ 98RocCubM-7
❑ 98RocCubTI-7
Fennell, Jason
❑ 97BriWhiSB-16
❑ 98BriWhiSQ-9
Fennell, Mike
❑ 82OneYanT-14
❑ 83GreHorT-18
❑ 85AlbYanT-26
❑ 89TopTra-37T
❑ 89TopTraT-37T
Fennelly, Francis
❑ 87OldJudN-163
Fenner, Robert
❑ 33WorCig(-22
Feno, Quinn
❑ 92ElmPioC-11
❑ 92ElmPioF-1396
Fenton, Cary
❑ 94VerExpC-10
❑ 94VerExpF-3916
Fenton, John
❑ 26Zee-70
❑ 27Zee-52
❑ 28Zee-75
❑ 29Zee-70
❑ 31Zee-63
❑ 33Zee-113
Fenus, Justin
❑ 96MarPhiB-7
❑ 97BatCliTI-19
❑ 98PieBolWM-13
Fenwick, Bob
❑ 72AstTeal-7
❑ 72Top-679
❑ 73OPC-567
❑ 73Top-567
Feola, Larry (Lawrence)
❑ 75CliPilT-13
❑ 87SanJosBP-22
Feramisco, Derek
❑ 97JohCitCTI-9
❑ 98PeoChiM-6
Ferens, Stan
❑ 46SeaSLP-20
Ferguson, Alex
❑ 21KoBreWSI-31
❑ 22W575-34
❑ 27AmeCarE126-40
❑ 75SenTCM1-5
❑ 75SenTCM1-40
❑ 90DodTar-235
❑ 93ConTSN-793
Ferguson, Bruce
❑ 78WauMetT-8
Ferguson, Charles
❑ 87BucN28-79
❑ 87OldJudN-164
❑ 87TobLit-4
❑ 88GandBCGCE-15
❑ 90KalBatN-18
Ferguson, Fergy
❑ 83TamTarT-10
Ferguson, George Cecil
❑ 06GiaUllAFS-3
❑ 08RosComP-91
❑ 09ColChiE-98
❑ 09RamT20-45
❑ 09T206-128
❑ 10DomDisP-44
❑ 10JuJuDE-18
❑ 10SweCapPP-66
❑ 11PinT-5-714
❑ 11SpoLifCW-124
❑ 11SpoLifM-138
❑ 11T205-55
❑ 12ColRedB-98
❑ 12ColTinT-98
❑ 72ClaCar-19
Ferguson, Greg
❑ 88SouOreAP-1708
Ferguson, Jeff
❑ 96HarCitRCB-12
❑ 97NewBriRC-8
❑ 98SalLakBO-13
Ferguson, Jim (James)
❑ 82OneYanT-15
❑ 87SalLakTTT-6
❑ 88SavCarP-348
❑ 89SavCarP-354
❑ 90SavCarP-2075
❑ 91JamExpC-23
❑ 91JamExpP-3536
❑ 92AlbPolCB-2
❑ 92JamExpC-10
❑ 92JamExpF-1494
Ferguson, Joe
❑ 72Top-616
❑ 73LinPor-94
❑ 73OPC-621
❑ 73Top-621
❑ 74OPC-86
❑ 74Top-86
❑ 74TopDecE-67
❑ 74TopSta-45
❑ 75OPC-115
❑ 75Top-115
❑ 75TopMin-115
❑ 76DodPos-4
❑ 76LinSup-121
❑ 76OPC-329
❑ 76SSP-81
❑ 76St.LouCP-9
❑ 76Top-329
❑ 77BurCheD-8
❑ 77OPC-107
❑ 77Top-573
❑ 78AstBurK-2
❑ 78Hos-109
❑ 78Top-226
❑ 79Top-671
❑ 80DodPol-13
❑ 80OPC-29
❑ 80Top-51
❑ 81Dod-7
❑ 81DodPol-13
❑ 81Don-177
❑ 81Fle-124
❑ 81LonBeaPT-21
❑ 81Top-711
❑ 82Top-514
❑ 83Don-604
❑ 83Fle-87
❑ 83Top-416
❑ 86RanPer-NNO
❑ 87AstShoSPT-5
❑ 87AstShoSPT-6
❑ 87RanMot-28
❑ 87RanSmo-24
❑ 88DodMot-28
❑ 89DodMot-27
❑ 89DodPol-1
❑ 90DodMot-28
❑ 90DodPol-NNO
❑ 90DodTar-236
❑ 91DodMot-28
❑ 91DodPol-NNO
❑ 92DodMot-28
❑ 92DodPol-NNO
❑ 93DodMot-28
❑ 93DodPol-30
❑ 93RanKee-144
❑ 94DodMot-28
❑ 94DodPol-30
❑ 96HigDesMB-1
❑ 97BowBay-1
❑ 98BowBayM-1
Ferguson, Mark
❑ 83AlbA'sT-4
❑ 84GreHorT-19
❑ 84ModA'sC-11
❑ 85AlbYanT-6
Ferguson, Mike
❑ 82CedRapRT-8
Ferguson, Ryan
❑ 96MarPhiB-8
Ferguson, Shane
❑ 92GulCoaYF-3784
Ferlenda, Greg
❑ 86SalRedBP-9
❑ 86TulDriTI-15
❑ 88KinIndS-6
❑ 89CanIndB-14
❑ 89CanIndS-5
❑ 89KinIndS-8
❑ 90CarLeaA-35
❑ 90KinIndTI-19
❑ 92WatIndC-27
❑ 92WatIndF-3251
Ferm, Ed
❑ 88BriTigP-1886
❑ 90LakTigS-10
❑ 91Cla/Bes-289
❑ 91LakTigC-4
❑ 91LakTigP-260
Fermaint, Mike
❑ 91PenPilC-19
❑ 91PenPilP-384
Fermin, Carlos
❑ 90BriTigP-3149
❑ 90BriTigS-6
❑ 91Cla/Bes-374
❑ 91FayGenC-18
❑ 91FayGenP-1177
❑ 92NiaFalRC-17
❑ 92NiaFalRF-3331
❑ 93LakTigC-7
❑ 93LakTigF-1317
❑ 93LimRocDWB-108
❑ 94LakTigC-7
❑ 95JacSunTI-9
Fermin, Felix
❑ 84PriWilPT-16
❑ 85NasPirT-9
❑ 86HawIslP-9
❑ 87HarSenP-6
❑ 88BufBisC-21
❑ 88BufBisP-1465
❑ 88Don-144
❑ 88Fle-643
❑ 88FleGlo-643
❑ 88PirTeal-11
❑ 88StaLinPi-10
❑ 88Top-547
❑ 88TopTif-547
❑ 88TriAAC-5
❑ 89Don-565
❑ 89DonBasB-229
❑ 89DonTra-33
❑ 89Fle-208
❑ 89FleGlo-208
❑ 89FleUpd-27
❑ 89IndTeal-12
❑ 89Sco-620
❑ 89ScoRoo-78T
❑ 89Top-303
❑ 89TopTif-303
❑ 89TopTra-33T
❑ 89TopTraT-33T
❑ 89UppDec-88
❑ 90Bow-334
❑ 90BowTif-334
❑ 90Don-191
❑ 90Fle-492
❑ 90FleCan-492
❑ 90IndTeal-13
❑ 90OPC-722
❑ 90PanSti-60
❑ 90PublntS-560
❑ 90Sco-256
❑ 90ScoYouSI-6
❑ 90Top-722
❑ 90TopTif-722
❑ 90UppDec-409
❑ 91Don-537
❑ 91Fle-367
❑ 91IndFanC-10
❑ 91Lea-137
❑ 91OPC-193
❑ 91PanFreS-219
❑ 91Sco-139
❑ 91StaClu-238
❑ 91Top-193
❑ 91TopDesS-193
❑ 91TopMic-193
❑ 91TopTif-193
❑ 91Ult-112
❑ 91UppDec-104
❑ 92Don-242
❑ 92Fle-109
❑ 92IndFanC-9
❑ 92OPC-632
❑ 92PanSti-48
❑ 92Pin-152
❑ 92Sco-148
❑ 92StaClu-102
❑ 92Top-632
❑ 92TopGol-632
❑ 92TopGolW-632
❑ 92TopMic-632
❑ 92Ult-49
❑ 92UppDec-160
❑ 93Don-597
❑ 93Fle-591
❑ 93IndWUA-9
❑ 93Lea-215
❑ 93LimRocDWB-107
❑ 93LinVenB-309
❑ 93OPC-90
❑ 93PacBeiA-6
❑ 93PacSpa-95
❑ 93PanSti-50
❑ 93Pin-331
❑ 93Sel-256
❑ 93StaClu-139
❑ 93StaCluFDI-139
❑ 93StaCluMOP-139
❑ 93Top-462
❑ 93TopGol-462
❑ 93TopInaM-462
❑ 93TopInaR-462
❑ 93TopMic-462
❑ 93Ult-184
❑ 93UppDec-615
❑ 93UppDecGold-615
❑ 94ColC-387
❑ 94ColChoGS-387
❑ 94ColChoSS-387
❑ 94Don-573
❑ 94Fin-271
❑ 94FinRef-271
❑ 94Fla-101
❑ 94Fle-104
❑ 94FleExtB-164
❑ 94FleUpd-82
❑ 94MarMot-5
❑ 94Pac-169
❑ 94PanSti-56
❑ 94Pin-102
❑ 94PinArtP-102
❑ 94PinMusC-102
❑ 94Sco-107
❑ 94ScoGolR-107
❑ 94ScoRoo-RT37
❑ 94ScoRooGR-RT37
❑ 94Sel-324
❑ 94StaClu-81
❑ 94StaClu-675
❑ 94StaCluFDI-81
❑ 94StaCluFDI-675
❑ 94StaCluGR-81
❑ 94StaCluGR-675
❑ 94StaCluMOP-81
❑ 94StaCluMOP-675
❑ 94Top-36
❑ 94TopGol-36
❑ 94TopSpa-36
❑ 94TopTra-99T
❑ 94Ult-42
❑ 94UppDec-389
❑ 94UppDecED-389
❑ 95ColCho-289
❑ 95ColChoGS-289
❑ 95ColChoSS-289
❑ 95Don-409
❑ 95DonPreP-409
❑ 95Fle-266
❑ 95Lea-146
❑ 95MarMot-24
❑ 95MarPac-31
❑ 95Pac-395
❑ 95PacPri-125
❑ 95Sco-106
❑ 95ScoGolR-106
❑ 95ScoPlaTS-106
❑ 95StaClu-421
❑ 95StaCluMOP-421
❑ 95StaCluSTDW-M421
❑ 95StaCluSTWS-421
❑ 95StaCluVR-219
❑ 95StaCluVRMO-219
❑ 95Top-234
❑ 95TopCyb-131
❑ 95Ult-327
❑ 95UltGolM-327
❑ 96Fle-237
❑ 96FleTif-237
❑ 96Top-67
Fermin, Miguel
❑ 93CedRapKC-6
❑ 93CedRapKF-1731
❑ 93LimRocDWB-97
Fermin, Pompilio
❑ 76CliPilT-14
Fermin, Ramon
❑ 92MadMusC-2
❑ 92MadMusF-1227
❑ 93ModA'sC-9
❑ 93ModA'sF-793
❑ 94ModA'sC-9
❑ 94ModA'sF-3059
❑ 95Bow-123
❑ 95HunStaTI-8
❑ 96JacSunB-11
❑ 97TolMudHB-12
Fernandes, Eddie
❑ 47SunBre-5
Fernandes, Jamie
❑ 95ButCopKtl-8
Fernandez, Alex
❑ 90Bes-250
❑ 90Bes-321
❑ 90ClaDraP-4
❑ 90ClaYel-T99
❑ 90FleUpd-84
❑ 90TopMag-40
❑ 91Baz-5
❑ 91Bow-351
❑ 91Cla2-T7
❑ 91ClaGam-184
❑ 91Don-59
❑ 91Fle-117
❑ 91Lea-296
❑ 91OPC-278
❑ 91OPCPre-42
❑ 91Sco-382
❑ 91Sco100RS-66
❑ 91SevCoi-F5
❑ 91SevCoi-M9
❑ 91StaClu-147
❑ 91Stu-31
❑ 91Top-278
❑ 91TopCraJ2-36
❑ 91TopDeb90-48
❑ 91TopDesS-278
❑ 91TopGolS-1
❑ 91TopMic-278
❑ 91TopTif-278
❑ 91UltUpd-14
❑ 91UppDec-645
❑ 91WhiSoxK-32
❑ 91WhiSoxK-NNO
❑ 91Woo-11
❑ 92Bow-201
❑ 92ClaGam-95
❑ 92Don-191
❑ 92Fle-78
❑ 92Lea-85
❑ 92LeaBlaG-85
❑ 92MVPPin-10
❑ 92OPC-755
❑ 92Pin-30
❑ 92Sco-82
❑ 92ScoProP-9
❑ 92ScoProP-21
❑ 92StaClu-467
❑ 92Stu-152
❑ 92Top-755
❑ 92TopGol-755
❑ 92TopGolW-755
❑ 92TopMic-755
❑ 92TriPla-74
❑ 92Ult-335
❑ 92UppDec-551
❑ 92WhiSoxK-32
❑ 93Don-139
❑ 93Fin-27
❑ 93FinRef-27
❑ 93Fla-183
❑ 93Fle-201
❑ 93Lea-41
❑ 93OPC-53
❑ 93PacSpa-69
❑ 93PacSpaPl-12
❑ 93Pin-383
❑ 93Sco-412
❑ 93SP-253
❑ 93StaClu-552
❑ 93StaCluFDI-552
❑ 93StaCluMOP-552
❑ 93Top-41
❑ 93TopGol-41
❑ 93TopInaM-41
❑ 93TopInaR-41
❑ 93TopMic-41
❑ 93Ult-173
❑ 93UppDec-362
❑ 93UppDecGold-362
❑ 93WhiSoxK-8
❑ 93WhiSoxSC-23
❑ 94Bow-239
❑ 94ColC-99
❑ 94ColChoGS-99
❑ 94ColChoSS-99
❑ 94Don-582
❑ 94Fin-26
❑ 94FinPre-26P
❑ 94FinRef-26
❑ 94Fla-30
❑ 94Fle-80
❑ 94FleExtB-45
❑ 94FUnPac-54
❑ 94Lea-268
❑ 94OPC-6
❑ 94Pac-124
❑ 94PacAll-19
❑ 94Pin-289
❑ 94PinArtP-289
❑ 94PinMusC-289
❑ 94Sco-153
❑ 94ScoGolR-153
❑ 94Sel-311
❑ 94SP-190
❑ 94SPDieC-190
❑ 94Spo-3
❑ 94StaClu-583
❑ 94StaCluFDI-583
❑ 94StaCluGR-583
❑ 94StaCluMOP-583
❑ 94StaCluT-142
❑ 94StaCluTFDI-142
❑ 94Stu-204
❑ 94Top-599
❑ 94TopGol-599
❑ 94TopSpa-599
❑ 94TriPla-263
❑ 94Ult-33
❑ 94UppDec-43
❑ 94UppDec-231
❑ 94UppDecED-43
❑ 94UppDecED-231
❑ 94WhiSoxK-7
❑ 95Baz-72
❑ 95Bow-313
❑ 95ColCho-506
❑ 95ColChoGS-506
❑ 95ColChoSE-234
❑ 95ColChoSEGS-234
❑ 95ColChoSESS-234
❑ 95ColChoSS-506
❑ 95Don-259
❑ 95DonPreP-259
❑ 95DonTopotO-48
❑ 95Fin-125
❑ 95FinRef-125
❑ 95Fla-244
❑ 95Fle-115
❑ 95Lea-69
❑ 95Pac-86
❑ 95Pin-359
❑ 95PinArtP-359
❑ 95PinMusC-359
❑ 95Sel-115
❑ 95SelArtP-115
❑ 95SP-141
❑ 95SPCha-141
❑ 95SPChaDC-141
❑ 95Spo-35
❑ 95SpoArtP-35
❑ 95SPSil-141
❑ 95StaClu-272
❑ 95StaCluMOP-272
❑ 95StaCluSTWS-272
❑ 95StaCluVR-137
❑ 95StaCluVRMO-137
❑ 95Stu-76
❑ 95Sum-2
❑ 95SumNthD-2
❑ 95Top-163
❑ 95TopCyb-98
❑ 95TopEmb-45
❑ 95TopEmbGI-45
❑ 95TopPre-PP9
❑ 95TopPreS-PP9
❑ 95UC3-17
❑ 95UC3ArtP-17
❑ 95Ult-28
❑ 95UltGolM-28
❑ 95UppDec-434
❑ 95UppDecED-434
❑ 95UppDecEDG-434
❑ 95UppDecSE-19
❑ 95UppDecSEG-19
❑ 95WhiSoxK-9
❑ 95Zen-2
❑ 96Cir-27
❑ 96CirRav-27
❑ 96ColCho-93
❑ 96ColChoGS-93
❑ 96ColChoSS-93
❑ 96Don-504
❑ 96DonPreP-504
❑ 96EmoXL-36
❑ 96Fin-B154
❑ 96FinRef-B154
❑ 96Fla-50
❑ 96Fle-65
❑ 96FleTif-65

❑ 96Lea-39
❑ 96LeaPre-65
❑ 96LeaPreP-65
❑ 96LeaPrePB-39
❑ 96LeaPrePG-39
❑ 96LeaPrePS-39
❑ 96LeaSigA-67
❑ 96LeaSigAG-67
❑ 96LeaSigAS-67
❑ 96MetUni-36
❑ 96MetUniP-36
❑ 96Pac-278
❑ 96PacPri-P88
❑ 96PacPriG-P88
❑ 96PanSti-167
❑ 96Pin-40
❑ 96PinAfi-84
❑ 96PinAfiAP-84
❑ 96PinAfiFPP-84
❑ 96ProSta-135
❑ 96Sco-286
❑ 96ScoDugC-B11
❑ 96ScoDugCAP-B11
❑ 96Sel-100
❑ 96SelArtP-100
❑ 96SelTeaN-27
❑ 96SP-59
❑ 96StaClu-304
❑ 96StaCluEPB-304
❑ 96StaCluEPG-304
❑ 96StaCluEPS-304
❑ 96StaCluMOP-304
❑ 96Sum-147
❑ 96SumAbo&B-147
❑ 96SumArtP-147
❑ 96SumFoi-147
❑ 96Top-194
❑ 96TopChr-62
❑ 96TopChrR-62
❑ 96TopGal-23
❑ 96TopGalPPI-23
❑ 96TopLas-117
❑ 96Ult-37
❑ 96UltGolM-37
❑ 96UppDec-42
❑ 96WhiSoxF-5
❑ 97Bow-278
❑ 97BowBes-41
❑ 97BowBesAR-41
❑ 97BowBesR-41
❑ 97BowInt-278
❑ 97Cir-392
❑ 97CirRav-392
❑ 97ColCho-344
❑ 97ColChoT-FM10
❑ 97Don-32
❑ 97Don-433
❑ 97DonEli-142
❑ 97DonEliGS-142
❑ 97DonGolPP-32
❑ 97DonGolPP-433
❑ 97DonLim-80
❑ 97DonLimE-80
❑ 97DonLimENG-80
❑ 97DonPre-19
❑ 97DonPreCttC-19
❑ 97DonSilPP-32
❑ 97DonSilPP-433
❑ 97Fin-285
❑ 97FinEmb-285
❑ 97FinEmbR-285
❑ 97FinRef-285
❑ 97FlaShoLC-133
❑ 97FlaShoLeg0-133
❑ 97FlaShoLeg1-133
❑ 97FlaShoM-A133
❑ 97FlaShoM-B133
❑ 97FlaShoM-C133
❑ 97FlaShoR0-133
❑ 97FlaShoR1-133
❑ 97FlaShoR2-133
❑ 97Fle-60
❑ 97Fle-563
❑ 97FleTif-60
❑ 97FleTif-563
❑ 97Lea-245
❑ 97LeaFraM-245
❑ 97LeaFraMDC-245
❑ 97MarPac-10
❑ 97MetUni-58
❑ 97NewPin-141
❑ 97NewPinAP-141
❑ 97NewPinMC-141
❑ 97NewPinPP-141
❑ 97Pac-52
❑ 97PacLigB-52
❑ 97PacPri-20
❑ 97PacPriLB-20
❑ 97PacPriP-20
❑ 97PacSil-52
❑ 97Pin-13
❑ 97PinArtP-PP13
❑ 97PinIns-118
❑ 97PinInsCE-118
❑ 97PinInsDE-118
❑ 97PinMusC-13
❑ 97PinPrePla-13
❑ 97PinX-P-75
❑ 97PinX-PMoS-75
❑ 97Sco-232
❑ 97Sco-341
❑ 97Sco-531
❑ 97ScoArtPWB-232
❑ 97ScoArtPWB-341
❑ 97ScoArtPWB-531
❑ 97ScoPreS-232
❑ 97ScoResC-341
❑ 97ScoResC-531
❑ 97ScoShoS-232
❑ 97ScoShoS-341
❑ 97ScoShoS-531
❑ 97ScoShoSAP-232
❑ 97ScoShoSAP-341
❑ 97ScoShoSAP-531
❑ 97Sel-91
❑ 97SelArtP-91
❑ 97SelCom-91
❑ 97SelRegG-91
❑ 97SP-78
❑ 97SpoIll-80
❑ 97SpoIllEE-80
❑ 97StaClu-228
❑ 97StaCluMat-228
❑ 97StaCluMOP-228
❑ 97Stu-52
❑ 97StuPrePG-52
❑ 97StuPrePS-52
❑ 97Top-355
❑ 97TopChr-120
❑ 97TopChrR-120
❑ 97TopGal-60
❑ 97TopGalPPI-60
❑ 97Ult-358
❑ 97UltGolME-358
❑ 97UltPlaME-358
❑ 97UppDec-536
❑ 97WhiSoxS-11
❑ 97WhiSoxSPl-11
❑ 97WhiSoxSPr-11
❑ 98CirThu-70
❑ 98CirThuRav-70
❑ 98CirThuSupRav-70
❑ 98ColCho-378
❑ 98Don-73
❑ 98DonCol-73
❑ 98DonColL-339
❑ 98DonColS-73
❑ 98DonGolPP-73
❑ 98DonPriCD-73
❑ 98DonPriCL-339
❑ 98DonSilPP-73
❑ 98Fin-56
❑ 98FinNo--56
❑ 98FinNo-R-56
❑ 98FinRef-56
❑ 98Fle-89
❑ 98Lea-140
❑ 98LeaFraDA-140
❑ 98LeaFraF-140
❑ 98LeaFraM-140
❑ 98LeaFraM-140
❑ 98LeaFraMDC-140
❑ 98LeaFraMDC-140
❑ 98LeaFraMZ2-140
❑ 98Pac-301
❑ 98PacPlaB-301
❑ 98PacRedT-301
❑ 98PacSil-301
❑ 98Pin-155
❑ 98PinPreP-155
❑ 98Sco-150
❑ 98ScoSS-PP112
❑ 98ScoSSAP-PP112
❑ 98SpoIll-37
❑ 98SpoIllEE-37
❑ 98SpoIllFE-37
❑ 98SpoIllTaN-79
❑ 98SpoIllTaNEE-79
❑ 98StaCluFDI-267
❑ 98StaCluI-267
❑ 98StaCluOneK-267
❑ 98StaCluPP-267
❑ 98Top-149
❑ 98TopChr-149
❑ 98TopChrR-149
❑ 98TopDevR-149
❑ 98TopDia-149
❑ 98TopMiniC-149
❑ 98TopOpeD-77
❑ 98UppDec-94
❑ 98UppDecSF-58
❑ 99Fle-406
❑ 99FleSta9-406
❑ 99FleWarT-406
❑ 99PacCroC-112
❑ 99PacCroCPB-112
❑ 99PacOme-97
❑ 99PacOmeC-97
❑ 99PacOmeG-97
❑ 99PacOmePB-97
❑ 99UppDec-378
❑ 99UppDecEL1-378
❑ 99UppDecEL2-378
❑ 99Vic-160

Fernandez, Antonio
❑ 94SpoIndC-9
❑ 94SpoIndF-3328
❑ 96HilStaHWB-8
❑ 96RanCucQB-13
❑ 97StoPor-10

Fernandez, Chico (Humberto)
❑ 55Bow-270
❑ 56Dod-9
❑ 57Top-305
❑ 58Hir-16
❑ 58HirTes-3
❑ 58PhiJayP-5
❑ 58Top-348
❑ 59Top-452
❑ 60Top-314
❑ 61Top-112
❑ 61TopStaI-150
❑ 62Jel-17
❑ 62Pos-17
❑ 62PosCan-17
❑ 62SalPlaC-3
❑ 62ShiPlaC-3
❑ 62TigJayP-6
❑ 62Top-173
❑ 62TopVen-173
❑ 63TigJayP-6
❑ 63Top-278
❑ 67BalOriP-38
❑ 79TCM50-274
❑ 88CedRapRP-1141
❑ 90DodTar-237
❑ 91MetWIZ-113
❑ 91OriCro-127
❑ 95TopArcBD-138

Fernandez, Chris
❑ 87TamTarP-22

Fernandez, Dan
❑ 89SanJosGB-8
❑ 89SanJosGCLC-232
❑ 89SanJosGP-441
❑ 89SanJosGS-9
❑ 90SanJosGB-12
❑ 90SanJosGCLC-40
❑ 90SanJosGP-2012
❑ 90SanJosGS-9
❑ 91SanJosGC-1
❑ 91SanJosGP-12
❑ 92ShrCapF-3876
❑ 92ShrCapS-584
❑ 93ShrCapF-2763
❑ 94PhoFirF-1522

Fernandez, Daniel
❑ 95JacSunTI-10

Fernandez, Fernando
❑ 94BenRocC-6
❑ 94BenRocF-3586

Fernandez, Frank
❑ 66TolMudHTI-9
❑ 66Top-584
❑ 68Top-214
❑ 68TopVen-214
❑ 68YanPhoS-65
❑ 68YanPhoS-85
❑ 69Top-557
❑ 70OPC-82
❑ 70Top-82
❑ 71MLBOffS-512
❑ 71OPC-468
❑ 71Top-468
❑ 72MilBra-102
❑ 92YanWIZ6-40

Fernandez, James
❑ 88St.PetCS-7

Fernandez, Jared
❑ 94UtiBluSC-10
❑ 96TreThuB-10
❑ 97TreThuB-16
❑ 98TreThuM-14

Fernandez, Jose
❑ 89HamRedS-11
❑ 89St.PetCS-12
❑ 90ArkTraGS-12
❑ 90St.PetCS-7
❑ 91ArkTraLD-32
❑ 91ArkTraLD-33
❑ 91ArkTraP-1288
❑ 91ArkTraP-1293
❑ 91HunCubC-8
❑ 91HunCubP-3346
❑ 91LinDriAA-32
❑ 91LinDriAA-33
❑ 91LouRedP-2926
❑ 91LouRedTI-15
❑ 92ArkTraF-1132
❑ 92LouRedS-260
❑ 92LouRedS-261
❑ 92SkyAAAF-126
❑ 93ReaPhiF-297
❑ 94LouRedF-2983
❑ 96DelShoB-16
❑ 98arSenW1-11
❑ 98HarSenM-11
❑ 99BowBes-186
❑ 99BowBesAR-186
❑ 99BowBesR-186
❑ 99Top-434
❑ 99TopChr-434
❑ 99TopChrR-434
❑ 99TopMVPP-434

Fernandez, Jose Maria
❑ 86NegLeaF-72
❑ 89NegLeaRP-12

Fernandez, Julio
❑ 89CliGiaP-900
❑ 91BelMarCB-17
❑ 91BelMarP-3680
❑ 92SanBerC-19

Fernandez, Luis
❑ 93PriRedC-10
❑ 93PriRedF-4170

Fernandez, Mike
❑ 91EliTwiP-4305
❑ 92KenTwiC-24
❑ 92KenTwiF-611
❑ 93ForMyeMC-7
❑ 93ForMyeMF-2661
❑ 94NasXprF-394

Fernandez, Nanny (Froilan)
❑ 47TipTop-79
❑ 50PirTeal-7
❑ 50RoyDes-23
❑ 54SeaPop-8

Fernandez, Omar
❑ 95GreFalDTI-7

Fernandez, Osvaldo
❑ 94RivPilCLC-12
❑ 95Bes-43
❑ 95PorCitRTI-7
❑ 96ColCho-424
❑ 96ColChoGS-424
❑ 96ColChoSS-424
❑ 96EmoXL-289
❑ 96Exc-104
❑ 96Fla-387
❑ 96FlaWavotF-9
❑ 96FleUpd-U205
❑ 96FleUpdTC-U205
❑ 96GiaMot-9
❑ 96LeaPre-132
❑ 96LeaPreP-132
❑ 96Pin-382
❑ 96PinAfi-183
❑ 96PinAfiAP-183
❑ 96PinFoil-382
❑ 96Sel-175
❑ 96SelArtP-175
❑ 96SelCer-116
❑ 96SelCerAP-116
❑ 96SelCerCB-116
❑ 96SelCerCR-116
❑ 96SelCerMB-116
❑ 96SelCerMG-116
❑ 96SelCerMR-116
❑ 96SP-3
❑ 96SPSpeFX-47
❑ 96SPSpeFXDC-47
❑ 96SPx-53
❑ 96SPxGol-53
❑ 96Stu-123
❑ 96StuPrePB-123
❑ 96StuPrePG-123
❑ 96StuPrePS-123
❑ 96Ult-567
❑ 96UltGolM-567
❑ 96UppDec-243
❑ 96UppDecPHE-H41
❑ 96UppDecPreH-H41
❑ 96ZenMoz-4
❑ 97Cir-183
❑ 97CirRav-183
❑ 97ColCho-214
❑ 97Don-30
❑ 97DonGolPP-30
❑ 97DonSilPP-30
❑ 97Fle-549
❑ 97FleTif-549
❑ 97Lea-154
❑ 97LeaFraM-154
❑ 97LeaFraMDC-154
❑ 97Pac-443
❑ 97PacLatotML-36
❑ 97PacLigB-443
❑ 97PacPri-149
❑ 97PacPriLB-149
❑ 97PacPriP-149
❑ 97PacSil-443
❑ 97Pin-150
❑ 97PinArtP-PP150
❑ 97PinMusC-150
❑ 97PinPrePla-150
❑ 97Sco-300
❑ 97ScoArtPWB-300
❑ 97ScoPreS-300
❑ 97ScoShoS-300
❑ 97ScoShoSAP-300
❑ 97UppDec-186
❑ 97UppDec-497
❑ 98PacInvGems-218
❑ 98UppDec-506

Fernandez, Ramon
❑ 96OgdRapTI-38
❑ 97HelBreB-10

Fernandez, Reynaldo
❑ 88OneYanP-2053
❑ 88PriWilYS-9

Fernandez, Richard
❑ 96-97LinVen-252

Fernandez, Rolando
❑ 90HunCubP-3297
❑ 91PeoChiC-19
❑ 91PeoChiP-1356
❑ 91PeoChiTI-26
❑ 92WinSpiC-12
❑ 92WinSpiF-1218

Fernandez, Rudy
❑ 92NegLeaRLI-20
❑ 95NegLeaL2-12

Fernandez, Sid
❑ 82VerBeaDT-6
❑ 84Don-44
❑ 84TidTidT-2
❑ 85Don-563
❑ 85Fle-77
❑ 85MetColP-6
❑ 85MetTCM-9
❑ 85OPC-390
❑ 85TidTidT-3
❑ 85Top-649
❑ 85TopTif-649
❑ 86BasStaB-40
❑ 86Don-625
❑ 86Fle-79
❑ 86KayB-10
❑ 86Lea-242
❑ 86MetColP-20
❑ 86MetTCM-4
❑ 86MetWorSC-24
❑ 86Top-104
❑ 86TopMinL-51
❑ 86TopTif-104
❑ 87ClaGam-74
❑ 87Don-323
❑ 87DonAll-26
❑ 87DonHig-4
❑ 87Fle-8
❑ 87Fle-629
❑ 87FleBasA-16
❑ 87FleGlo-8
❑ 87FleGlo-629
❑ 87FleSlu-13
❑ 87Lea-93
❑ 87MetColP-12
❑ 87OPC-337
❑ 87Spo-63
❑ 87SpoTeaP-2
❑ 87Top-570
❑ 87TopMinL-22
❑ 87TopSti-97
❑ 87TopTif-570
❑ 88Don-118
❑ 88DonAll-58
❑ 88DonTeaBM-118
❑ 88Fle-134
❑ 88FleBasM-13
❑ 88FleGlo-134
❑ 88FleStiC-101
❑ 88Lea-63
❑ 88MetColP-23
❑ 88MetFanC-50
❑ 88MetKah-50
❑ 88OPC-30
❑ 88PanSti-336
❑ 88RedFolSB-22
❑ 88Sco-615
❑ 88ScoGlo-615
❑ 88Spo-177
❑ 88StaLinMe-7
❑ 88Top-30
❑ 88TopSti-103
❑ 88TopStiB-28
❑ 88TopTif-30
❑ 89Bow-377
❑ 89BowTif-377
❑ 89Don-471
❑ 89Fle-35
❑ 89FleGlo-35
❑ 89MetColP-28
❑ 89MetKah-8
❑ 89OPC-34
❑ 89Sco-268
❑ 89Top-790
❑ 89TopBig-276
❑ 89TopMinL-25
❑ 89TopTif-790
❑ 89UppDec-168
❑ 90Bow-131
❑ 90BowTif-131
❑ 90DodTar-238
❑ 90Don-572
❑ 90DonBesN-105
❑ 90Fle-203
❑ 90FleCan-203
❑ 90K-M-11
❑ 90Lea-66
❑ 90M.Vpin-63
❑ 90MetColP-14
❑ 90MetColP-3
❑ 90MetFanC-50
❑ 90MetKah-50
❑ 90OPC-480
❑ 90PanSti-299
❑ 90PubIntS-133
❑ 90Sco-18
❑ 90Spo-113
❑ 90Top-480
❑ 90TopBig-155
❑ 90TopCoi-46
❑ 90TopDou-20
❑ 90TopMinL-66
❑ 90TopSti-92
❑ 90TopStiB-28
❑ 90TopTif-480
❑ 90TopTVA-61
❑ 90TopTVM-10
❑ 90UppDec-261
❑ 91Bow-462
❑ 91Don-97
❑ 91Fle-146
❑ 91MetColP-16
❑ 91MetKah-50
❑ 91MetPerPA-15
❑ 91MetWIZ-112
❑ 91OPC-230
❑ 91PepSidF-1
❑ 91PepSidF-2
❑ 91Sco-180
❑ 91StaClu-225
❑ 91StaCluP-14
❑ 91Top-230
❑ 91TopDesS-230
❑ 91TopMic-230
❑ 91TopTif-230
❑ 91Ult-216
❑ 91UppDec-242
❑ 92Bow-296
❑ 92Don-719
❑ 92Fle-503
❑ 92Lea-519

❑ 92LeaBlaG-519
❑ 92MetColP-14
❑ 92MetKah-50
❑ 92OPC-382
❑ 92Pin-509
❑ 92Sco-675
❑ 92StaClu-655
❑ 92Top-382
❑ 92TopGol-382
❑ 92TopGolW-382
❑ 92TopMic-382
❑ 92Ult-528
❑ 92UppDec-671
❑ 93Bow-214
❑ 93Don-566
❑ 93Fin-5
❑ 93FinRef-5
❑ 93Fle-86
❑ 93Lea-2
❑ 93MetColP-30
❑ 93MetKah-50
❑ 93OPC-42
❑ 93PacSpa-196
❑ 93PanSti-248
❑ 93Pin-500
❑ 93Sco-556
❑ 93Sel-243
❑ 93StaClu-351
❑ 93StaCluFDI-351
❑ 93StaCluMOP-351
❑ 93Top-188
❑ 93TopComotH-24
❑ 93TopGol-188
❑ 93TopInaM-188
❑ 93TopInaR-188
❑ 93TopMic-188
❑ 93Ult-72
❑ 93UppDec-361
❑ 93UppDecGold-361
❑ 93USPlaCA-3S
❑ 94BalOriP-10
❑ 94Bow-571
❑ 94ColC-511
❑ 94ColChoGS-511
❑ 94ColChoSS-511
❑ 94Don-396
❑ 94ElSidPog-1
❑ 94ElSidPog-2
❑ 94ElSidPog-3
❑ 94ElSidPog-4
❑ 94ElSidPog-5
❑ 94Fin-379
❑ 94FinRef-379
❑ 94Fla-253
❑ 94Fle-560
❑ 94FleExtB-4
❑ 94FleUpd-2
❑ 94Lea-246
❑ 94OPC-63
❑ 94OriPro-33
❑ 94OriUSPC-4H
❑ 94Pac-399
❑ 94Pin-483
❑ 94PinArtP-483
❑ 94PinMusC-483
❑ 94Sco-182
❑ 94ScoGolR-182
❑ 94ScoRoo-RT51
❑ 94ScoRooGR-RT51
❑ 94Sel-353
❑ 94SpoRoo-2
❑ 94SpoRooAP-2
❑ 94StaClu-579
❑ 94StaCluFDI-579
❑ 94StaCluGR-579
❑ 94StaCluMOP-579
❑ 94StaCluT-273
❑ 94StaCluTFDI-273
❑ 94Top-615
❑ 94TopGol-615
❑ 94TopSpa-615
❑ 94TopTra-28T
❑ 94Ult-305
❑ 94UppDec-433
❑ 94UppDecED-433
❑ 95BalOriP-18
❑ 95ColCho-344
❑ 95ColChoGS-344
❑ 95ColChoSS-344
❑ 95Don-270
❑ 95DonPreP-270
❑ 95Fla-220
❑ 95Fle-6
❑ 95Lea-353
❑ 95Pin-88
❑ 95PinArtP-88
❑ 95PinMusC-88
❑ 95Sco-182
❑ 95ScoGolR-182
❑ 95ScoPlaTS-182
❑ 95StaClu-188
❑ 95StaCluFDI-188
❑ 95StaCluMOP-188
❑ 95StaCluSTWS-188
❑ 95Top-507
❑ 95TopCyb-296
❑ 95Ult-2
❑ 95UltGolM-2
❑ 96ColCho-648
❑ 96ColChoGS-648
❑ 96ColChoSS-648
❑ 96EmoXL-245
❑ 96Fla-334
❑ 96Fle-497
❑ 96FleTif-497
❑ 96Pac-155
❑ 96PhiTeal-11
❑ 96Sco-215
❑ 96StaClu-122
❑ 96StaCluMOP-122
❑ 96Ult-520
❑ 96UltGolM-520
❑ 96UppDec-427
❑ 97AstMot-16
❑ 97Fle-666
❑ 97FleTif-666
❑ 97StaClu-319
❑ 97StaCluMOP-319
❑ 97Top-299
❑ 97Ult-525
❑ 97UltGolME-525
❑ 97UltPlaME-525

Fernandez, Tony
❑ 82SyrChiT-17
❑ 82SyrChiTI-12
❑ 83SyrChiT-16
❑ 84BluJayFS-11
❑ 84Don-32
❑ 84Fle-152
❑ 84SyrChiT-9
❑ 85AllGamPI-20
❑ 85BluJayFS-10
❑ 85Don-390
❑ 85Fle-103
❑ 85Lea-91
❑ 85OPC-48
❑ 85OPCPos-16
❑ 85Top-48
❑ 85TopTif-48
❑ 86BluJayAF-8
❑ 86BluJayFS-9
❑ 86Don-119
❑ 86Fle-57
❑ 86FleMin-14
❑ 86FleStiC-37
❑ 86GenMilB-3D
❑ 86KayB-11
❑ 86Lea-45
❑ 86OPC-241
❑ 86Spo-112
❑ 86Top-241
❑ 86TopSti-194
❑ 86TopTat-15
❑ 86TopTif-241
❑ 87BluJayFS-8
❑ 87ClaGam-57
❑ 87Don-72
❑ 87DonAll-35
❑ 87DonOpeD-35
❑ 87Fle-225
❑ 87FleAll-3
❑ 87FleAwaW-12
❑ 87FleGlo-225
❑ 87FleMin-38
❑ 87FleRecS-7
❑ 87FleStiC-39
❑ 87GenMilB-1C
❑ 87Lea-106
❑ 87OPC-329
❑ 87RedFolSB-29
❑ 87Spo-113
❑ 87Spo-187
❑ 87SpoTeaP-5
❑ 87StuPan-27
❑ 87SyrChi1A-12
❑ 87Top-485
❑ 87TopMinL-75
❑ 87TopSti-191
❑ 87TopTif-485
❑ 88Baz-7
❑ 88BluJay5-5
❑ 88BluJayFS-10
❑ 88Don-12
❑ 88Don-319
❑ 88DonAll-25
❑ 88DonBasB-87
❑ 88DonSupD-12
❑ 88Fle-109
❑ 88Fle-635
❑ 88FleBasM-14
❑ 88FleGlo-109
❑ 88FleGlo-635
❑ 88FleHotS-10
❑ 88FleMin-61
❑ 88FleStiC-72
❑ 88FleSupBC-C3
❑ 88Lea-12
❑ 88Lea-133
❑ 88MSAHosD-21
❑ 88OPC-290
❑ 88PanSti-222
❑ 88Sco-20
❑ 88Sco-651
❑ 88ScoGlo-20
❑ 88ScoGlo-651
❑ 88ScoYouS2-6
❑ 88Spo-26
❑ 88StaLinBJ-6
❑ 88Top-290
❑ 88TopBig-187
❑ 88TopCoi-12
❑ 88TopGloS-15
❑ 88TopSti-193
❑ 88TopStiB-43
❑ 88TopTif-290
❑ 88TopUKM-23
❑ 88TopUKMT-23
❑ 89BluJayFS-9
❑ 89Bow-254
❑ 89BowTif-254
❑ 89ClaTraO-115
❑ 89Don-206
❑ 89DonBasB-48
❑ 89Fle-231
❑ 89FleGlo-231
❑ 89FleSup-13
❑ 89OPC-170
❑ 89PanSti-470
❑ 89RedFolSB-41
❑ 89Sco-57
❑ 89ScoHot1S-53
❑ 89Spo-93
❑ 89Top-170
❑ 89TopBasT-146
❑ 89TopBig-157
❑ 89TopCoi-39
❑ 89TopGloS-52
❑ 89TopMinL-76
❑ 89TopSti-189
❑ 89TopStiB-10
❑ 89TopTif-170
❑ 89TopUKM-25
❑ 89TVSpoM-80
❑ 89UppDec-139
❑ 90BluJayFS-8
❑ 90BluJayHS-5
❑ 90Bow-524
❑ 90BowTif-524
❑ 90Don-149
❑ 90DonBesA-113
❑ 90Fle-80
❑ 90Fle-634
❑ 90FleAwaW-12
❑ 90FleBasA-9
❑ 90FleBasAC-9
❑ 90FleBasM-11
❑ 90FleBasMC-11
❑ 90FleCan-80
❑ 90FleCan-634
❑ 90Lea-53
❑ 90M.Vpin-106
❑ 90OPC-685
❑ 90PanSti-176
❑ 90PubIntS-283
❑ 90PubIntS-513
❑ 90RedFolSB-31
❑ 90Sco-89
❑ 90Spo-6
❑ 90Top-685
❑ 90TopBatL-16
❑ 90TopBig-165
❑ 90TopDou-21
❑ 90TopMinL-42
❑ 90TopSti-11
❑ 90TopSti-194
❑ 90TopStiB-43
❑ 90TopTif-685
❑ 90UppDec-130
❑ 91Bow-642
❑ 91CadElID-19
❑ 91Cla2-T45
❑ 91ClaGam-161
❑ 91Don-524
❑ 91Fle-174
❑ 91FleUpd-123
❑ 91Lea-315
❑ 91OPC-320
❑ 91OPCPre-43
❑ 91PadMag-27
❑ 91PadSmo-10
❑ 91PanFreS-339
❑ 91PanSti-152
❑ 91RedFolS-33
❑ 91Sco-432
❑ 91ScoRoo-66T
❑ 91StaClu-515
❑ 91Stu-244
❑ 91Top-320
❑ 91TopDesS-320
❑ 91TopMic-320
❑ 91TopTif-320
❑ 91TopTra-41T
❑ 91TopTraT-41T
❑ 91UltUpd-111
❑ 91UppDec-126
❑ 91UppDec-754
❑ 92Bow-293
❑ 92ColAllG-24
❑ 92ColAllP-24
❑ 92Don-362
❑ 92Fle-604
❑ 92Hig5-121
❑ 92Lea-187
❑ 92LeaBlaG-187
❑ 92OPC-60
❑ 92PadCarJ-6
❑ 92PadMot-8
❑ 92PadPolD-7
❑ 92PadPolD-30
❑ 92PadSmo-8
❑ 92PanSti-235
❑ 92Pin-137
❑ 92Sco-645
❑ 92StaClu-203
❑ 92Stu-103
❑ 92Top-60
❑ 92TopGol-60
❑ 92TopGolW-60
❑ 92TopKid-57
❑ 92TopMic-60
❑ 92TriPla-102
❑ 92TriPla-165
❑ 92Ult-276
❑ 92UppDec-272
❑ 93Bow-18
❑ 93ClaGam-31
❑ 93Don-674
❑ 93Fin-36
❑ 93FinRef-36
❑ 93Fle-470
❑ 93FleFinE-293
❑ 93FunPac-125
❑ 93Lea-273
❑ 93MetColP-31
❑ 93MetKah-1
❑ 93OPC-70
❑ 93OPCPre-20
❑ 93PacSpa-541
❑ 93PacSpaGE-3
❑ 93PanSti-249
❑ 93Pin-533
❑ 93RedFolS-113
❑ 93Sco-572
❑ 93Sel-93
❑ 93SelRoo-19T
❑ 93SP-47
❑ 93StaClu-644
❑ 93StaCluFDI-644
❑ 93StaCluM-32
❑ 93StaCluMOP-644
❑ 93Stu-98
❑ 93Top-465
❑ 93TopGol-465
❑ 93TopInaM-465
❑ 93TopInaR-465
❑ 93TopMic-465
❑ 93TopTra-9T
❑ 93Ult-426
❑ 93UppDec-672
❑ 93UppDecGold-672
❑ 94ColC-619
❑ 94ColChoGS-619
❑ 94ColChoSS-619
❑ 94Don-172
❑ 94Fla-366
❑ 94Fle-331
❑ 94FleUpd-117
❑ 94Lea-266
❑ 94OPCWorC-9
❑ 94Pac-639
❑ 94PanSti-137
❑ 94Pin-427
❑ 94PinArtP-427
❑ 94PinMusC-427
❑ 94RedKah-9
❑ 94Sco-62
❑ 94ScoCyc-TC13
❑ 94ScoGolR-62
❑ 94ScoRoo-RT39
❑ 94ScoRooGR-RT39
❑ 94Sel-310
❑ 94SpoRoo-44
❑ 94SpoRooAP-44
❑ 94StaClu-214
❑ 94StaCluFDI-214
❑ 94StaCluGR-214
❑ 94StaCluMOP-214
❑ 94Top-702
❑ 94TopGol-702
❑ 94TopSpa-702
❑ 94TopTra-127T
❑ 94TriPlaM-7
❑ 94UppDec-437
❑ 94UppDecED-437
❑ 95BluJayUSPC-4D
❑ 95BluJayUSPC-11C
❑ 95ColCho-514
❑ 95ColChoGS-514
❑ 95ColChoSS-514
❑ 95DonTopotO-119
❑ 95Fin-283
❑ 95FinRef-283
❑ 95Fla-283
❑ 95Fle-434
❑ 95FleUpd-25
❑ 95Lea-340
❑ 95Pac-104
❑ 95Sco-123
❑ 95ScoGolR-123
❑ 95ScoPlaTS-123
❑ 95Sel-188
❑ 95SelArtP-188
❑ 95StaClu-221
❑ 95StaClu-544
❑ 95StaCluFDI-221
❑ 95StaCluMOP-221
❑ 95StaCluMOP-544
❑ 95StaCluSTWS-221
❑ 95StaCluSTWS-544
❑ 95TopTra-70T
❑ 95Ult-308
❑ 95UltGolM-308
❑ 95UppDec-441
❑ 95UppDecED-441
❑ 95UppDecEDG-441
❑ 96ColCho-232
❑ 96ColChoGS-232
❑ 96ColChoSS-232
❑ 96Don-51
❑ 96DonPreP-51
❑ 96Fle-182
❑ 96FleTif-182
❑ 96Pac-380
❑ 96StaClu-427
❑ 96StaCluMOP-427
❑ 96Top-27
❑ 97BluJayS-45
❑ 97ColCho-309
❑ 97Lea-308
❑ 97LeaFraM-308
❑ 97LeaFraMDC-308
❑ 97PacPriGotD-GD70
❑ 97Sco-462
❑ 97ScoArtPWB-462
❑ 97ScoResC-462
❑ 97ScoShoS-462
❑ 97ScoShoSAP-462
❑ 98ColCho-527
❑ 98IndSco-13
❑ 98IndScoP-13
❑ 98Pac-68
❑ 98PacOnl-761
❑ 98PacOnlR-761
❑ 98PacOnlWC-761
❑ 98PacPlaB-68
❑ 98PacRedT-68
❑ 98PacSil-68
❑ 98Sco-224
❑ 98Top-58
❑ 98TopChr-58
❑ 98TopChrR-58
❑ 98TopDevR-58
❑ 98TopDia-58
❑ 98TopMiniC-58
❑ 98Ult-364
❑ 98UltGolM-364
❑ 98UltMas-364
❑ 98UltPlaM-364
❑ 98UppDec-425
❑ 98UppDec-743
❑ 99Fle-368
❑ 99FleSta9-368
❑ 99FleWarT-368
❑ 99Pac-441
❑ 99PacCroC-297
❑ 99PacCroCPB-297
❑ 99PacOme-246
❑ 99PacOmeC-246
❑ 99PacOmeG-246
❑ 99PacOmePB-246
❑ 99PacPar-244
❑ 99PacParC-244
❑ 99PacParG-244
❑ 99PacParHoloGold-244
❑ 99PacParHS-244
❑ 99PacParOD-244
❑ 99PacParPB-244
❑ 99PacParRed-244
❑ 99PacPlaB-441
❑ 99PacRed-441
❑ 99Top-196
❑ 99TopChr-196
❑ 99TopChrR-196
❑ 99TopMVPP-196
❑ 99UppDec-516
❑ 99UppDecEL1-516
❑ 99UppDecEL2-516

Ferran, Alex
❑ 89WatIndS-6
❑ 90RenSilSCLC-265

Ferran, George
❑ 86ShrCapP-8
❑ 87PhoFirP-4

Ferrand, Ray
❑ 93Sou-8

Ferrand, Thomas
❑ 96MarPhiB-9

Ferrante, Joe
❑ 82DayBeaAT-3

Ferrara, Al
❑ 64Top-337
❑ 64TopVen-337
❑ 65Top-331
❑ 66Top-487
❑ 67CokCapD-18
❑ 67CokCapDA-18
❑ 67Top-557
❑ 68OPC-34
❑ 68Top-34
❑ 68TopVen-34
❑ 69MLBOffS-191
❑ 69NabTeaF-6
❑ 69PadVol-3
❑ 69Top-452A
❑ 69Top-452B
❑ 69TopDec-30
❑ 69TopSta-93
❑ 70MLBOffS-113
❑ 70OPC-345
❑ 70Top-345
❑ 70TopBoo-23
❑ 71MLBOffS-226
❑ 71OPC-214
❑ 71Top-214
❑ 71TopCoi-25
❑ 72MilBra-103
❑ 81TCM60I-330
❑ 90DodTar-239

Ferrarese, Don
❑ 55Top-185
❑ 56BalOriP-19
❑ 56Top-266
❑ 57Top-146
❑ 58Top-469
❑ 59Top-247
❑ 60Top-477
❑ 61Top-558
❑ 62Top-547
❑ 75OakOak2A-14
❑ 91OriCro-128

Ferraro, Carl
❑ 86ChaRaiP-9

Ferraro, Mike
❑ 66TolMudHTI-10
❑ 68Top-539
❑ 69OPC-83

❑ 69PilPos-17
❑ 69Top-83
❑ 72Top-613
❑ 75ForLauYS-2
❑ 76ForLauYS-17
❑ 77PilPosR-17
❑ 77WesHavYT-7
❑ 78TacYanC-1
❑ 79YanPicA-11
❑ 81TCM60I-436
❑ 81YanPhoA-1
❑ 82YanPhoA-2
❑ 83IndPos-13
❑ 83IndWhe-11
❑ 83Pil69G-36
❑ 83TopTra-32T
❑ 84RoyPos-10
❑ 85RoyTeal-8
❑ 90TopTVY-4
❑ 92YanWIZ6-41
❑ 93BalOriP-9
❑ 94BreMilB-25
Ferraro, Vincent
❑ 84VisOakT-5
Ferrebee, Anthony
❑ 87IdaFalBP-2
Ferreira, Jose (Arturo J.)
❑ 84IdaFalATI-8
❑ 85MadMusP-10
❑ 85MadMusT-13
Ferreira, Marcos
❑ 95LinVen-33
Ferreira, Tony
❑ 82ForMyeRT-11
❑ 84OmaRoyT-3
❑ 85OmaRoyT-10
❑ 86StaoftFT-35
❑ 86TidTidP-8
❑ 87CalCanP-2328
❑ 88AlbYanP-1339
❑ 90CMC-183
❑ 90OmaRoyC-8
❑ 90OmaRoyP-61
❑ 90ProAAAF-596
❑ 92WinHavRSC-7
❑ 92WinHavRSF-1786
❑ 93ForLauRSC-11
❑ 93ForLauRSFP-1605
Ferreiras, Sal
❑ 86PriWilPP-10
Ferrell, Della
❑ 88KimN18-12
Ferrell, Frank
❑ 75CedRapGT-21
Ferrell, Rick
❑ 31Exh-30
❑ 33ButCanV-14
❑ 33ExhFou-15
❑ 33Gou-197
❑ 33WorCig-37
❑ 34BabRutG-19
❑ 34BatR31-10
❑ 34BatR31-126
❑ 34ButPreR-19
❑ 34DiaMatCSB-52
❑ 34DiaStaR-48
❑ 34ExhFou-9
❑ 35ExhFou-9
❑ 35GouPuzR-8G
❑ 35GouPuzR-9G
❑ 36ExhFou-9
❑ 36GouBWR-13
❑ 36GouWidPPR-A29
❑ 36GouWidPPR-A118
❑ 36NatChiFPR-97
❑ 36R31PasP-50
❑ 36SandSW-17
❑ 37ExhFou-9
❑ 37KelPepS-BB5
❑ 37OPCBatUV-132
❑ 38ExhFou-16
❑ 39PlaBal-39
❑ 40PlaBal-21
❑ 41BroW75-10
❑ 47SenGunBP-6
❑ 61Fle-105
❑ 77GalGloG-199
❑ 79DiaGre-179
❑ 80PerHaloFP-187
❑ 80PerHaloFPS-52
❑ 80SSPHOF-189
❑ 81ConTSN-49
❑ 83BigLeaCOA-17
❑ 83TCMPla1944-20
❑ 85BigLeaC3-27
❑ 89PerCelP-14
❑ 90PacLeg-23
❑ 90PerGreM-70
❑ 90SweBasG-86
❑ 91SweBasG-29
❑ 92ConTSN-471
❑ 93ConTSN-674
❑ 93ConTSN-861
❑ 93FroRowRF-1
❑ 93FroRowRF-2
❑ 93FroRowRF-3
❑ 93FroRowRF-4
❑ 93FroRowRF-5
❑ 93TedWil-2
❑ 93UppDecAH-49
❑ 94ConTSN-994
❑ 94ConTSN-1169
❑ 94ConTSNB-994
❑ 94ConTSNB-1169
❑ 94UppDecAH-142
❑ 94UppDecAH1-142
Ferrell, Wes
❑ 30SchR33-21
❑ 30UncJac-9
❑ 31Exh-21
❑ 33ButCre-7
❑ 33CraJacP-5
❑ 33DouDisP-14
❑ 33ExhFou-11
❑ 33GeoCMil-11
❑ 33Gou-218
❑ 33TatOrbSDR-162
❑ 33WorCig-38
❑ 34BatR31-12
❑ 34BatR31-174
❑ 34DiaMatCSB-53
❑ 34DiaStaR-94
❑ 34ExhFou-11
❑ 35GouPuzR-8G
❑ 35GouPuzR-9G
❑ 36GouWidPPR-A30
❑ 36GouWidPPR-A118
❑ 36NatChiFPR-97
❑ 36R31Pre-L2
❑ 36WorWidGV-40
❑ 37OPCBatUV-138
❑ 38ExhFou-16
❑ 61Fle-26
❑ 72TCMthe3-85
❑ 72TCMthe3-115
❑ 75YanDyn1T-14
❑ 77GalGloG-189
❑ 79RedSoxEF-4
❑ 81ConTSN-50
❑ 82TCMGreP-21
❑ 83BigLeaCOA-19
❑ 88ConSer3-11
❑ 90DodTar-240
❑ 90HOFStiB-30
❑ 91ConTSN-198
❑ 92ConTSN-361
❑ 92ConTSN-446
❑ 92MegRut-148
❑ 94ConTSN-1169
❑ 94ConTSNB-1169
Ferrer, Eduardo
❑ 96BoiHawB-12
Ferrer, Gavriel
❑ 80VenLeaS-198
Ferrer, Sergio
❑ 74TacTwiC-17
❑ 76OklCit8TI-2
❑ 78MetDaiPA-27
❑ 78TidTidT-9
❑ 79Top-397
❑ 80TidTidT-5
❑ 80Top-619
❑ 81IndIndTI-31
❑ 89PacSenL-2
❑ 90EliSenL-110
❑ 91MetWIZ-114
Ferretti, Sam
❑ 88WatIndP-680
❑ 89CanIndP-1307
❑ 89KinIndS-9
❑ 90Bes-309
❑ 90CanIndB-7
❑ 90CanIndP-1297
❑ 90CanIndS-6
❑ 91CanIndLD-83
❑ 91CanIndP-986
❑ 91LinDriAA-83
❑ 92HagSunF-2561
❑ 92HagSunS-258
❑ 93BowBayF-2194
Ferreyra, Raul
❑ 77IndIndTI-19
❑ 78IndIndTI-21
❑ 78SSP270-130
❑ 79NaSouTI-9
Ferrick, Tom
❑ 47SenGunBP-3
❑ 51Bow-182
❑ 58RedEnq-11
❑ 60Top-461
❑ 79DiaGre-330
Ferrier, Ross
❑ 94PitMetC-8
❑ 94PitMetF-3534
❑ 95StLucMTI-13
Ferris, Bob
❑ 76QuaCitAT-14
❑ 78SalLakCGC-19
❑ 79SalLakCGT-10
❑ 80SalLakCGT-24
❑ 81SalLakCGT-5
Ferris, Boo (David)
❑ 39ExhSal-16
❑ 46RedSoxTI-10
❑ 46SpoExcW-3-1A
❑ 47RedSoxTI-7
❑ 47TipTop-5
❑ 48RedSoxTI-6
❑ 49Bow-211
❑ 49RedSoxTI-6
❑ 50AmeNut&CCP-6
❑ 75RedSox1T-14
❑ 76TayBow4-101
❑ 84TCMPla1-2
❑ 87RedSox1T-7
Ferris, Hobe (Albert)
❑ 03BreE10-50
❑ 04FanCraAL-18
❑ 04RedSoxUP-6
❑ 08RosComP-67
❑ 09ColChiE-99
❑ 09RamT20-46
❑ 09T206-129
❑ 11PinT-5-117
❑ 11SpoLifCW-125
❑ 12ColRedB-99
❑ 12ColTinT-99
Ferro, Bob
❑ 83WisRapTF-11
Ferroni, Frank
❑ 81MiaOriT-14
Ferry, John
❑ 11HelSta-159
❑ 12T207-58
Ferry, Mike
❑ 90BilMusP-3214
❑ 90ProAaA-195
❑ 91CedRapRC-4
❑ 91CedRapRP-2712
❑ 92CedRapRC-7
❑ 92CedRapRF-1066
❑ 92MidLeaATI-9
❑ 93ChaLooF-2356
❑ 94Bow-486
❑ 94ExcFS7-174
❑ 94IndIndF-1803
❑ 95ChaLooTI-5
Ferson, Alexander
❑ 87OldJudN-165
Ferst, Larry
❑ 78CliDodT-8
❑ 79CliDodT-28
Ferullo, Matt
❑ 95PitMetTI-47
❑ 96PitMetB-10
Fesh, Sean
❑ 93AshTouC-7
❑ 93AshTouF-2269
❑ 94OscAstC-9
❑ 94OscAstF-1131
❑ 96RanCucQB-14
❑ 97BinMetB-9
Fessenden, Wallace
❑ 87OldJudN-166
Festa, Chris
❑ 96LowSpiB-7
❑ 97MicBatC-9
Fette, Lou
❑ 33WorCig(-23
❑ 38BasTabP-9
❑ 38CloFotW-24
❑ 38WheBB10-10
❑ 38WheBB11-1
❑ 79DiaGre-210
❑ 90DodTar-241
Fetters, Mike (Michael Lee)
❑ 86SalAngC-97
❑ 87PalSprP-26
❑ 88MidAngGS-10
❑ 89EdmTraC-9
❑ 90Bow-286
❑ 90BowTif-286
❑ 90CMC-484
❑ 90Don-35
❑ 90EdmTraC-7
❑ 90EdmTraP-514
❑ 90Fle-131
❑ 90FleCan-131
❑ 90OPC-14
❑ 90ProAAAF-90
❑ 90Top-14
❑ 90TopDeb89-36
❑ 90TopTif-14
❑ 90UppDec-742
❑ 91Don-565
❑ 91EdmTraLD-163
❑ 91EdmTraP-1512
❑ 91Fle-312
❑ 91LinDriAAA-163
❑ 91OPC-477
❑ 91Sco-497
❑ 91Sco100RS-74
❑ 91StaClu-228
❑ 91Top-477
❑ 91TopDesS-477
❑ 91TopMic-477
❑ 91TopTif-477
❑ 91UppDec-696
❑ 92BrePol-6
❑ 92Don-491
❑ 92Fle-56
❑ 92Lea-460
❑ 92LeaBlaG-460
❑ 92OPC-602
❑ 92Sco-606
❑ 92Sco100RS-38
❑ 92StaClu-696
❑ 92Top-602
❑ 92TopGol-602
❑ 92TopGolW-602
❑ 92TopMic-602
❑ 93BrePol-7
❑ 93Don-573
❑ 93Fle-249
❑ 93OPC-109
❑ 93PacSpa-510
❑ 93Sco-420
❑ 93Sel-174
❑ 93StaClu-633
❑ 93StaCluFDI-633
❑ 93StaCluMOP-633
❑ 93Top-527
❑ 93TopGol-527
❑ 93TopInaM-527
❑ 93TopInaR-527
❑ 93TopMic-527
❑ 93UppDec-193
❑ 93UppDecGold-193
❑ 94BreMilB-26
❑ 94BrePol-7
❑ 94BreTeal-6
❑ 94Don-603
❑ 94Fla-303
❑ 94Fle-176
❑ 94Sco-200
❑ 94ScoGolR-200
❑ 94Top-159
❑ 94TopGol-159
❑ 94TopSpa-159
❑ 95ColCho-183
❑ 95ColChoGS-183
❑ 95ColChoSS-183
❑ 95Don-503
❑ 95DonPreP-503
❑ 95DonTopotO-96
❑ 95Fle-178
❑ 95Pac-231
❑ 95Top-339
❑ 95Ult-63
❑ 95UltGolM-63
❑ 96BrePol-6
❑ 96ColCho-191
❑ 96ColChoGS-191
❑ 96ColChoSS-191
❑ 96Don-173
❑ 96DonPreP-173
❑ 96Fin-B29
❑ 96FinRef-B29
❑ 96Fla-100
❑ 96Fle-144
❑ 96FleTif-144
❑ 96LeaSigEA-51
❑ 96StaClu-47
❑ 96StaCluMOP-47
❑ 96Top-142
❑ 96Ult-79
❑ 96UltGolM-79
❑ 97BrePol-7
❑ 97Cir-285
❑ 97CirRav-285
❑ 97ColCho-146
❑ 97Fin-184
❑ 97FinRef-184
❑ 97Fle-128
❑ 97FleTif-128
❑ 97Pac-117
❑ 97PacLigB-117
❑ 97PacSil-117
❑ 97Pin-69
❑ 97PinArtP-PP69
❑ 97PinMusC-69
❑ 97PinPrePla-69
❑ 97StaClu-143
❑ 97StaCluMOP-143
❑ 97Top-84
❑ 97Ult-438
❑ 97UltGolME-438
❑ 97UltPlaME-438
❑ 97UppDec-403
❑ 98A'sMot-19
❑ 98ColCho-152
❑ 98Fle-520
❑ 98PacInvGems-58
❑ 98PacOnl-528
❑ 98PacOnlR-528
❑ 98PacOnlWC-528
❑ 98Top-381
❑ 98TopChr-381
❑ 98TopChrR-381
❑ 98TopDevR-381
❑ 98TopDia-381
❑ 98TopMiniC-381
❑ 98Ult-269
❑ 98UltGolM-269
❑ 98UltMas-269
❑ 98UltPlaM-269
❑ 98UppDec-708
Fetty, Pat
❑ 92BelBreCB-23
❑ 92BelBreFI-400
❑ 93StoPorC-11
❑ 93StoPorF-738
Fetzer, John E.
❑ 81TigDetN-81
❑ 83TigAlKS-39
❑ 83TigAlKS-44
Feuerstein, David
❑ 96AshTouB-17
❑ 97SalAva-15
❑ 98NewHavRM-5
❑ 98NewHavRMA-5
Fewster, Chick (Wilson)
❑ 20GasAmeMBD-8
❑ 20NatCarE-27A
❑ 20NatCarE-27B
❑ 21E121So1-23
❑ 21E121So8-22
❑ 21KoBreWSI-32
❑ 22W575-35
❑ 22WilPatV-29
❑ 23W501-120
❑ 25Exh-81
❑ 26Exh-12
❑ 27Exh-6
❑ 28LaPre-5
❑ 90DodTar-242
❑ 95ConTSN-1424
Fiacco, Charlie
❑ 90GenCubP-3035
❑ 90GenCubS-12
Fiala, Mike
❑ 86BakDodP-7
❑ 93SanBerSF-774
Fiala, Neil
❑ 78St.PetCT-10
❑ 79ArkTraT-13
❑ 82IndIndTI-29
Fiala, Walter
❑ 52LaPat-4
❑ 52Par-67
❑ 53ExhCan-48
Fichman, Mal
❑ 88BoiHawP-1632
❑ 90EriSaiS-29
❑ 91RenSilSCLC-29
Fichman, Mike
❑ 79NewCoPT-6
Fichter, Bob
❑ 75TopPho-128
Fick, Barry
❑ 85CedRapRT-7
Fick, Chris
❑ 96ArkTraB-14
❑ 97HigDesMG-7
Fick, Chuck
❑ 82WesHavAT-11
❑ 90EliSenL-111
❑ 91PacSenL-93
Fick, Robert
❑ 97WesMicW-12
❑ 98Bow-200
❑ 98BowChr-200
❑ 98BowChrGA-200
❑ 98BowChrGAR-200
❑ 98BowChrI-200
❑ 98BowChrIR-200
❑ 98BowChrR-200
❑ 98BowGolA-200
❑ 98BowInt-200
❑ 98JacSunM-10
❑ 98SouLeaTPG-21
❑ 98SP MinPE-54
❑ 98SP SPTSC-RF
❑ 98SPMin-54
❑ 98Top-487
❑ 98TopChr-487
❑ 98TopChrR-487
❑ 98TopDevR-487
❑ 98TopDia-487
❑ 98TopMiniC-487
❑ 99BasAmeTPA-14
❑ 99Bow-99
❑ 99BowAut-BA26
❑ 99BowChr-99
❑ 99BowChrG-99
❑ 99BowChrGR-99
❑ 99BowChrI-99
❑ 99BowChrIR-99
❑ 99BowChrR-99
❑ 99BowGol-99
❑ 99BowInt-99
❑ 99DumSet-119
❑ 99E-X Cen-110
❑ 99E-X CenECFut-110
❑ 99E-X CenECNow-110
❑ 99Fle-241
❑ 99FleBri-132
❑ 99FleBri2G-132
❑ 99FleBriBlu-132
❑ 99FleBriGol-132
❑ 99FleMys-119
❑ 99FleMysM-119
❑ 99FleSta9-241
❑ 99FleWarT-241
❑ 99MetUni-249
❑ 99MetUniGM-249
❑ 99MetUniPMG-249
❑ 99SkyThu-132
❑ 99SkyThuRant-132
❑ 99SkyThuRave-132
❑ 99SP SigAuto-ROB
❑ 99SpoIll-68
❑ 99SPSig-92
❑ 99SPx-92
❑ 99SPxFinR-92
❑ 99SPxFinS-92
❑ 99ThuSkySupR-132
❑ 99Top-208
❑ 99TopChr-208
❑ 99TopChrR-208
❑ 99UD Cho-12
❑ 99UD ChoPCR-12
❑ 99UppDec-268
❑ 99UppDecEL1-268
❑ 99UppDecEL2-268
❑ 99UppDecO-78
❑ 99UppDecOSO-78
❑ 99WesMicWAM-10
Ficklin, Winston
❑ 81WatIndT-29
❑ 82WatIndF-19
❑ 82WatIndT-15
❑ 83WatIndF-18
❑ 85WatIndT-4
❑ 86WatIndP-10
❑ 87WilBilP-3
❑ 88PorBeaC-18
❑ 88PorBeaP-652
❑ 89IowCubC-21
❑ 89IowCubP-1711
Fidge, Darren
❑ 93AusFut-1
❑ 94EliTwiC-7

❑ 94EliTwiF-3724
❑ 95Exc-82
❑ 95ForWayWTI-5
❑ 97ForWayW-11

Fidler, Andy
❑ 89KinMetS-9
❑ 90PitMetP-19
❑ 91ColMetPPI-1

Fidrych, Mark
❑ 76DetTigP-4
❑ 77BurCheD-92
❑ 77ChiWilD-19
❑ 77DailsID-19
❑ 77DetCaeD-19
❑ 77HolInnD-19
❑ 77Hos-46
❑ 77Kel-26
❑ 77MSADis-19
❑ 77OPC-7
❑ 77OPC-115
❑ 77PepGloD-30
❑ 77RCColC-20
❑ 77SagDis-19
❑ 77sDis-19
❑ 77Spo-1811
❑ 77TigBurK-1
❑ 77Top-7
❑ 77Top-265
❑ 77TopCloS-15
❑ 77WenDis-19
❑ 77ZipDis-19
❑ 78OPC-235
❑ 78PapGinD-32
❑ 78SagDis-22
❑ 78TasDis-22
❑ 78TigBurK-4
❑ 78TigTeal-8
❑ 78Top-45
❑ 78WifBalD-21
❑ 79BasPat-28
❑ 79Hos-77
❑ 79OPC-329
❑ 79Top-625
❑ 80EvaTriT-6
❑ 80OPC-231
❑ 80Top-445
❑ 81Don-8
❑ 81EvaTriT-4
❑ 81Fle-462
❑ 81OPC-150
❑ 81TigDetN-6
❑ 81Top-150
❑ 83PawRedST-7
❑ 84OCoandSI-192
❑ 88PacLegI-62
❑ 90SweBasG-122
❑ 91UppDecS-5
❑ 92ActPacA-25
❑ 92UppDecS-8
❑ 93UppDecAH-50
❑ 93UppDecS-9
❑ 93UppDecS-24
❑ 94TedWil-31
❑ 94UppDecAH-178
❑ 94UppDecAH1-178
❑ 99SpoIllGotG-88
❑ 99SpoIllGotGA-22
❑ 99SpoIllGotGC-35

Fiedler, Mark
❑ 86LitFalMP-11

Fiegel, Todd
❑ 91KinMetC-15
❑ 91KinMetP-3807
❑ 92ColMetC-11
❑ 92ColMetF-288
❑ 92ColMetPI-18
❑ 92ColMetPI-30
❑ 92ProFS7-291
❑ 93St.LucMC-8
❑ 93St.LuMF-2915
❑ 94St.LucMF-1187

Field, Greg
❑ 77OrlTwiT-10
❑ 79PorBeaT-3
❑ 83RicBraT-5
❑ 84TolMudHT-18

Field, James
❑ 09ColChiE-100
❑ 12ColRedB-100
❑ 12ColTinT-100

Field, Nate
❑ 98VerExpO-12

Fieldbinder, Mick
❑ 96HelBreTI-3
❑ 97CalLeaATI-6
❑ 97StoPor-4
❑ 98ForMyeMTI-12

Fielder, Cecil
❑ 84OCoandSI-209
❑ 86BluJayAF-9
❑ 86BluJayFS-10
❑ 86Don-512
❑ 86Fle-653
❑ 86OPC-386
❑ 86Top-386
❑ 86TopTif-386
❑ 87BluJayFS-9
❑ 87FleUpd-31
❑ 87FleUpdG-31
❑ 87OPC-178
❑ 87Top-178
❑ 87TopTif-178
❑ 88BluJayFS-11
❑ 88Don-565
❑ 88Fle-110
❑ 88FleGlo-110
❑ 88OPC-21
❑ 88Sco-399
❑ 88ScoGlo-399
❑ 88StaLinBJ-7
❑ 88Top-618
❑ 88TopTif-618
❑ 89Don-442
❑ 89Fle-232
❑ 89FleGlo-232
❑ 89OPC-224
❑ 89Sco-120
❑ 89SpoIllFKI-205
❑ 89Top-541
❑ 89TopTif-541
❑ 89UppDec-364
❑ 90Bow-357
❑ 90BowTif-357
❑ 90ClaYel-T94
❑ 90DonBesA-133
❑ 90DonLeaS-26
❑ 90FleUpd-95
❑ 90Lea-165
❑ 90ScoMcD-16
❑ 90ScoRoo-9T
❑ 90StaFie-1
❑ 90StaFie-2
❑ 90StaFie-3
❑ 90StaFie-4
❑ 90StaFie-5
❑ 90StaFie-6
❑ 90StaFie-7
❑ 90StaFie-8
❑ 90StaFie-9
❑ 90StaFie-10
❑ 90StaFie-11
❑ 90SupActM-7
❑ 90TigCok-4
❑ 90TigTeal-9
❑ 90TopBig-313
❑ 90TopMag-28
❑ 90TopTra-31T
❑ 90TopTraT-31T
❑ 90UppDec-786
❑ 90UppDecS-2
❑ 90USPlaCA-13S
❑ 90WinDis-4
❑ 91BasBesHRK-7
❑ 91Baz-8
❑ 91Bow-136
❑ 91Bow-367
❑ 91CadEllD-18
❑ 91Cla1-T41
❑ 91Cla2-T69
❑ 91ClaGam-127
❑ 91Col-14
❑ 91DenHol-2
❑ 91Don-3
❑ 91Don-397
❑ 91Don-451
❑ 91DonBonC-BC5
❑ 91DonEli-6
❑ 91DonGraS-7
❑ 91DonSupD-3
❑ 91Fle-335
❑ 91Fle-709
❑ 91FleAll-4
❑ 91JimDea-21
❑ 91KinDis-14
❑ 91Lea-106
❑ 91LeaPre-18
❑ 91MajLeaCP-32
❑ 91MooSna-24
❑ 91MSAHolD-17
❑ 91OPC-386
❑ 91OPC-720
❑ 91OPCPre-44
❑ 91PanCanT1-13
❑ 91PanCanT1-21
❑ 91PanCanT1-37
❑ 91PanCanT1-54
❑ 91PanFreS-288
❑ 91PanSti-232
❑ 91PepSup-10
❑ 91PetSta-11
❑ 91Pos-23
❑ 91PosCan-19
❑ 91RedFolS-34
❑ 91Sco-168
❑ 91Sco-395
❑ 91Sco-693
❑ 91Sco-770
❑ 91Sco100S-88
❑ 91SevCoi-F6
❑ 91SevCoi-M3
❑ 91SpoNSP-1
❑ 91StaClu-186
❑ 91StaCluCM-8
❑ 91StaCluMO-29
❑ 91StaPinB-17
❑ 91Stu-53
❑ 91SunSee-8
❑ 91TigCok-45
❑ 91TigPol-3
❑ 91Top-386
❑ 91Top-720
❑ 91TopCraJI-31
❑ 91TopDesS-386
❑ 91TopDesS-720
❑ 91TopGaloC-5
❑ 91TopMic-386
❑ 91TopMic-720
❑ 91TopSta-13
❑ 91TopTif-386
❑ 91TopTif-720
❑ 91TopTriH-A6
❑ 91Ult-121
❑ 91Ult-392
❑ 91UppDec-83
❑ 91UppDec-244
❑ 91UppDecFE-82F
❑ 91UppDecSS-SS12
❑ 91USPlaCA-12D
❑ 92Bow-90
❑ 92Cla1-T33
❑ 92Cla2-T73
❑ 92ClaGam-129
❑ 92DenHol-13
❑ 92Don-27
❑ 92Don-206
❑ 92DonCraJ1-22
❑ 92DonMcD-20
❑ 92Fle-133
❑ 92Fle-692
❑ 92Fle-705
❑ 92FleCitTP-7
❑ 92FleLumC-L1
❑ 92FleTeaL-6
❑ 92FleUpdH-4
❑ 92Hig5-46
❑ 92Hig5S-11
❑ 92HitTheBB-13
❑ 92JimDea-15
❑ 92KinDis-17
❑ 92LaKdec-11
❑ 92Lea-153
❑ 92LeaBlaG-153
❑ 92LeaGolP-18
❑ 92LeaPre-18
❑ 92MooSna-10
❑ 92Mr.TurS-8
❑ 92MSABenSHD-1
❑ 92MVPPin-20
❑ 92OPC-425
❑ 92OPCPre-70
❑ 92PanSti-105
❑ 92PanSti-144
❑ 92PanSti-272
❑ 92PepDieM-13
❑ 92Pin-4
❑ 92PinSlu-1
❑ 92Pos-13
❑ 92PosCan-12
❑ 92RedFolS-35
❑ 92RedFolS-112
❑ 92Sco-50
❑ 92Sco-431
❑ 92Sco100S-66
❑ 92ScoImpP-60
❑ 92SevCoi-19
❑ 92SpoStaCC-14
❑ 92StaClu-250
❑ 92StaClu-599
❑ 92StaCluD-48
❑ 92StaCluMP-5
❑ 92Stu-173
❑ 92TigKro-8
❑ 92TigTeal-10
❑ 92Top-397
❑ 92Top-425
❑ 92TopGol-397
❑ 92TopGol-425
❑ 92TopGolW-397
❑ 92TopGolW-425
❑ 92TopKid-76
❑ 92TopMcD-1
❑ 92TopMic-397
❑ 92TopMic-425
❑ 92TopMic-G397
❑ 92TriPla-29
❑ 92Ult-59
❑ 92UppDec-96
❑ 92UppDec-255
❑ 92UppDec-647
❑ 92UppDecF-22
❑ 92UppDecFG-22
❑ 92UppDecHRH-HR2
❑ 92UppDecTMH-21
❑ 92UppDecWB-T5
❑ 93Bow-475
❑ 93ClaGam-32
❑ 93DenHol-25
❑ 93DiaMar-35
❑ 93Don-541
❑ 93DonDiaK-DK15
❑ 93DonEli-34
❑ 93DonEliS-16
❑ 93DonLonBL-LL13
❑ 93DonMVP-17
❑ 93DonPre-15
❑ 93DonSpiotG-SG10
❑ 93DurPowP1-23
❑ 93Fin-111
❑ 93FinJum-111
❑ 93FinRef-111
❑ 93Fla-201
❑ 93Fle-227
❑ 93Fle-345
❑ 93Fle-711
❑ 93Fle-714
❑ 93FleAll-AL5
❑ 93FleAtl-8
❑ 93FleFruotL-19
❑ 93FlePro-B3
❑ 93FunPac-185
❑ 93FunPac-186
❑ 93Hos-16
❑ 93HumDumC-8
❑ 93JimDea-12
❑ 93KinDis-11
❑ 93Kra-7
❑ 93Lea-283
❑ 93LeaGolA-R3
❑ 93MetBak-7
❑ 93OPC-51
❑ 93OPCPre-96
❑ 93PacSpa-107
❑ 93PanSti-114
❑ 93Pin-26
❑ 93PinCoo-28
❑ 93PinCooD-28
❑ 93PinHomRC-3
❑ 93PinSlu-3
❑ 93Pos-10
❑ 93RedFolS-29
❑ 93Sco-31
❑ 93ScoFra-6
❑ 93Sel-20
❑ 93SelChaS-13
❑ 93SelDufIP-5
❑ 93SelStaL-27
❑ 93SelStaL-31
❑ 93SP-236
❑ 93SPPlaP-PP6
❑ 93StaClu-503
❑ 93StaCluFDI-503
❑ 93StaCluMOP-503
❑ 93Stu-37
❑ 93TigGat-7
❑ 93Top-80
❑ 93TOPBLAG-30
❑ 93TopGol-80
❑ 93TopInaM-80
❑ 93TopInaR-80
❑ 93TopMic-80
❑ 93TriPla-5
❑ 93TriPlaA-15
❑ 93TriPlaLL-L5
❑ 93TriPlaP-5
❑ 93Ult-548
❑ 93UltHomRK-3
❑ 93UppDec-46
❑ 93UppDec-499
❑ 93UppDec-564
❑ 93UppDecCP-R9
❑ 93UppDecGold-46
❑ 93UppDecGold-499
❑ 93UppDecGold-564
❑ 93UppDecHRH-HR3
❑ 93UppDecIC-WI23
❑ 93UppDecICJ-WI23
❑ 93UppDecOD-D11
❑ 93USPlaCA-12C
❑ 94Bow-69
❑ 94BowBes-R32
❑ 94BowBesR-R32
❑ 94CarLeaA-DJ2
❑ 94ChuShoS-9
❑ 94ColC-100
❑ 94ColC-352
❑ 94ColChoGS-100
❑ 94ColChoGS-352
❑ 94ColChoHRA-HA5
❑ 94ColChoSS-100
❑ 94ColChoSS-352
❑ 94ColChoT-13
❑ 94DenHol-10
❑ 94Don-27
❑ 94DonDiaK-DK22
❑ 94DonDiaKJ-DK22
❑ 94DonDom-A1
❑ 94DonDomJ-A1
❑ 94DonLonBL-1
❑ 94DonMVP-20
❑ 94DonSpeE-27
❑ 94Fin-219
❑ 94FinJum-219
❑ 94FinRef-219
❑ 94Fla-49
❑ 94Fle-128
❑ 94FleAllS-7
❑ 94FleExtB-73
❑ 94FleExtBGB-10
❑ 94FleSun-10
❑ 94FleTeaL-6
❑ 94FUnPac-45
❑ 94Kra-3
❑ 94Lea-50
❑ 94LeaCleC-5
❑ 94LeaL-31
❑ 94LeaMVPC-A6
❑ 94LeaMVPCG-A6
❑ 94LeaPowB-7
❑ 94O-PJumAF-20
❑ 94OPC-126
❑ 94OPCAllR-20
❑ 94OPCJumA-20
❑ 94OscMayR-4
❑ 94Pac-215
❑ 94PacSilP-18
❑ 94PacSilPC-18
❑ 94PanSti-63
❑ 94Pin-10
❑ 94PinArtP-10
❑ 94PinMusC-10
❑ 94PinSam-10
❑ 94Pos-17
❑ 94ProMag-46
❑ 94RedFolMI-10
❑ 94Sco-393
❑ 94ScoGolR-393
❑ 94ScoGolS-40
❑ 94Sel-233
❑ 94SP-176
❑ 94SPDieC-176
❑ 94SPHol-7
❑ 94SPHolDC-7
❑ 94Spo-78
❑ 94SpoMov-MM3
❑ 94SpoRooGGG-GG10
❑ 94StaClu-25
❑ 94StaClu-535
❑ 94StaCluFDI-25
❑ 94StaCluFDI-535
❑ 94StaCluGR-25
❑ 94StaCluGR-535
❑ 94StaCluMO-34
❑ 94StaCluMOP-25
❑ 94StaCluMOP-535
❑ 94Stu-190
❑ 94SucSav-14
❑ 94TomPiz-18
❑ 94Top-190
❑ 94TopBlaG-5
❑ 94TopGol-190
❑ 94TopSpa-190
❑ 94TopSupS-13
❑ 94TriPla-243
❑ 94TriPlaBS-2
❑ 94TriPlaN-1
❑ 94Ult-52
❑ 94UltRBIK-5
❑ 94UppDec-220
❑ 94UppDec-286
❑ 94UppDecAJ-23
❑ 94UppDecAJG-23
❑ 94UppDecDC-E4
❑ 94UppDecED-220
❑ 94UppDecED-286
❑ 94UppDecMLS-MM7
❑ 94UppDecMLSED-MM7
❑ 95Baz-12
❑ 95BluJayUSPC-4C
❑ 95BluJayUSPC-13H
❑ 95Bow-416
❑ 95BowBes-R28
❑ 95BowBesR-R28
❑ 95ClaPhoC-26
❑ 95ColCho-51
❑ 95ColCho-470
❑ 95ColChoCtG-CG6
❑ 95ColChoCtG-CG6B
❑ 95ColChoCtG-CG6C
❑ 95ColChoCtGE-6
❑ 95ColChoCtGG-CG6
❑ 95ColChoCtGG-CG6B
❑ 95ColChoCtGG-CG6C
❑ 95ColChoCtGGE-6
❑ 95ColChoGS-51
❑ 95ColChoGS-470
❑ 95ColChoSE-220
❑ 95ColChoSEGS-220
❑ 95ColChoSESS-220
❑ 95ColChoSS-51
❑ 95ColChoSS-470
❑ 95DenHol-8
❑ 95Don-109
❑ 95DonBomS-5
❑ 95DonPreP-109
❑ 95DonTopotO-73
❑ 95Emo-42
❑ 95EmoN-4
❑ 95Fin-124
❑ 95FinPowK-PK18
❑ 95FinRef-124
❑ 95Fla-38
❑ 95FlaInfP-3
❑ 95Fle-50
❑ 95FleTeaL-6
❑ 95FleUpdH-9
❑ 95Kra-3
❑ 95Lea-63
❑ 95LeaCor-2
❑ 95LeaLim-139
❑ 95LeaLimL-15
❑ 95Pac-151
❑ 95PacGolP-31
❑ 95PacPri-48
❑ 95PanSti-40
❑ 95Pin-184
❑ 95PinArtP-184
❑ 95PinFan-6
❑ 95PinMusC-184
❑ 95RedFol-18
❑ 95Sco-398
❑ 95ScoGolR-398
❑ 95ScoHaloG-HG82
❑ 95ScoPlaTS-398
❑ 95Sel-96
❑ 95SelArtP-96
❑ 95SelCer-47
❑ 95SelCerMG-47
❑ 95SP-155
❑ 95SPCha-151
❑ 95SPCha-155
❑ 95SPChaDC-151
❑ 95SPChaDC-155
❑ 95Spo-82
❑ 95SpoArtP-82
❑ 95SPPlaP-PP10
❑ 95SPSil-155
❑ 95StaClu-309
❑ 95StaClu-515
❑ 95StaCluCC-CC28
❑ 95StaCluMO-14
❑ 95StaCluMOP-309
❑ 95StaCluMOP-515
❑ 95StaCluMOP-CC28
❑ 95StaCluMOP-PZ5
❑ 95StaCluMOP-RL31
❑ 95StaCluPZ-PZ5

❑ 95StaCluRL-RL31
❑ 95StaCluSTWS-309
❑ 95StaCluSTWS-515
❑ 95StaCluVR-164
❑ 95StaCluVRMO-164
❑ 95Stu-45
❑ 95StuGolS-45
❑ 95Sum-57
❑ 95SumNthD-57
❑ 95TomPiz-8
❑ 95Top-220
❑ 95TopCyb-124
❑ 95TopEmb-76
❑ 95TopEmbGI-76
❑ 95TopLeaL-LL35
❑ 95UC3-47
❑ 95UC3ArtP-47
❑ 95Ult-46
❑ 95UltGolM-46
❑ 95UltHomRK-5
❑ 95UltHomRKGM-5
❑ 95UppDec-425
❑ 95UppDecC-1B
❑ 95UppDecED-425
❑ 95UppDecEDG-425
❑ 95UppDecPC-MLB5
❑ 95UppDecPLL-R13
❑ 95UppDecPLL-R32
❑ 95UppDecPLLE-R13
❑ 95UppDecPLLE-R32
❑ 95UppDecSE-95
❑ 95UppDecSEG-95
❑ 95UppDecSoaD-SD12
❑ 95USPlaCMLA-4C
❑ 95Zen-15
❑ 96Baz-93
❑ 96Bow-100
❑ 96BowBes-5
❑ 96BowBesAR-5
❑ 96BowBesR-5
❑ 96BowFoi-100
❑ 96Cir-63
❑ 96CirRav-63
❑ 96ColCho-103
❑ 96ColCho-140
❑ 96ColCho-422
❑ 96ColChoCtG-CG17
❑ 96ColChoCtG-CG17B
❑ 96ColChoCtG-CG17C
❑ 96ColChoCtGE-CR17
❑ 96ColChoCtGG-CG17
❑ 96ColChoCtGG-CG17B
❑ 96ColChoCtGG-CG17C
❑ 96ColChoCtGGE-CR17
❑ 96ColChoGS-103
❑ 96ColChoGS-140
❑ 96ColChoGS-422
❑ 96ColChoSS-103
❑ 96ColChoSS-140
❑ 96ColChoSS-422
❑ 96ColChoYMtP-13
❑ 96ColChoYMtP-13A
❑ 96ColChoYMtPGS-13
❑ 96ColChoYMtPGS-13A
❑ 96DenHol-18
❑ 96Don-434
❑ 96DonLonBL-5
❑ 96DonPreP-434
❑ 96EmoXL-59
❑ 96Fin-B344
❑ 96Fin-G290
❑ 96Fin-S84
❑ 96FinRef-B344
❑ 96FinRef-G290
❑ 96FinRef-S84
❑ 96Fla-79
❑ 96Fle-109
❑ 96FleTif-109
❑ 96FleUpd-U219
❑ 96FleUpdH-5
❑ 96FleUpdTC-U219
❑ 96Lea-6
❑ 96LeaLim-45
❑ 96LeaLimG-45
❑ 96LeaPre-85
❑ 96LeaPreP-85
❑ 96LeaPrePB-6
❑ 96LeaPrePG-6
❑ 96LeaPrePS-6
❑ 96LeaPreSG-76
❑ 96LeaPreSte-76
❑ 96LeaSig-12
❑ 96LeaSigPPG-12
❑ 96LeaSigPPP-12
❑ 96MetUni-57
❑ 96MetUniP-57
❑ 96Pac-321
❑ 96PacGolCD-DC32
❑ 96PacPri-P101
❑ 96PacPriG-P101
❑ 96PanSti-146
❑ 96Pin-144
❑ 96Pin-246
❑ 96PinAfi-11
❑ 96PinAfiAP-11
❑ 96PinAfiFPP-11
❑ 96PinArtP-71
❑ 96PinArtP-146
❑ 96PinFan-23
❑ 96PinFoil-246
❑ 96PinPow-18
❑ 96PinSlu-18
❑ 96PinSta-71
❑ 96PinSta-146
❑ 96ProMagDM-14
❑ 96ProSta-125
❑ 96RedF-26
❑ 96Sco-76
❑ 96Sco-357
❑ 96ScoDugC-A62
❑ 96ScoDugC-B82
❑ 96ScoDugCAP-A62
❑ 96ScoDugCAP-B82
❑ 96ScoRef-16
❑ 96ScoTitT-12
❑ 96Sel-39
❑ 96SelArtP-39
❑ 96SelCer-63
❑ 96SelCerAP-63
❑ 96SelCerCB-63
❑ 96SelCerCR-63
❑ 96SelCerIP-19
❑ 96SelCerMB-63
❑ 96SelCerMG-63
❑ 96SelCerMR-63
❑ 96SelTeaN-13
❑ 96SP-81
❑ 96Spo-55
❑ 96SpoArtP-55
❑ 96SPx-26
❑ 96SPxGol-26
❑ 96StaClu-95
❑ 96StaCluEPB-95
❑ 96StaCluEPG-95
❑ 96StaCluEPS-95
❑ 96StaCluMOP-95
❑ 96StaCluMOP-PP8
❑ 96StaCluPP-PP8
❑ 96Stu-54
❑ 96StuPrePB-54
❑ 96StuPrePG-54
❑ 96StuPrePS-54
❑ 96Sum-49
❑ 96SumAbo&B-49
❑ 96SumArtP-49
❑ 96SumFoi-49
❑ 96TeaOut-25
❑ 96Top-393
❑ 96TopChr-157
❑ 96TopChrR-157
❑ 96TopChrWC-WC6
❑ 96TopChrWCR-WC6
❑ 96TopGal-160
❑ 96TopGalPPI-160
❑ 96TopLas-105
❑ 96TopLasPC-12
❑ 96TopPro-AL4
❑ 96TopWreC-WC6
❑ 96Ult-58
❑ 96UltChe-B2
❑ 96UltCheGM-B2
❑ 96UltGolM-58
❑ 96UltThu-8
❑ 96UltThuGM-8
❑ 96UppDec-70
❑ 96UppDecPD-PD5
❑ 96UppDecPRE-R14
❑ 96UppDecPreR-R14
❑ 96Zen-36
❑ 96ZenArtP-36
❑ 97Bow-276
❑ 97BowBes-2
❑ 97BowBesAR-2
❑ 97BowBesR-2
❑ 97BowInt-276
❑ 97Cir-243
❑ 97CirRav-243
❑ 97ColCho-408
❑ 97ColChoCtG-22A
❑ 97ColChoCtG-22B
❑ 97ColChoCtG-22C
❑ 97ColChoCtGE-CG22
❑ 97ColChoCtGIW-CG22
❑ 97ColChoNF-NF37
❑ 97ColChoT-NY11
❑ 97Don-157
❑ 97DonEli-54
❑ 97DonEliGS-54
❑ 97DonEliPtT-7
❑ 97DonEliPtT-9
❑ 97DonEliPtTA-7
❑ 97DonEliPtTA-9
❑ 97DonGolPP-157
❑ 97DonLim-47
❑ 97DonLimE-47
❑ 97DonLimENG-47
❑ 97DonLonL-13
❑ 97DonPre-3
❑ 97DonPreCttC-3
❑ 97DonSilPP-157
❑ 97DonTea-130
❑ 97DonTeaSPE-130
❑ 97E-X2-32
❑ 97E-X2Cred-32
❑ 97E-X2EssCre-32
❑ 97Fin-322
❑ 97Fin-340
❑ 97FinEmb-322
❑ 97FinEmb-340
❑ 97FinEmbR-322
❑ 97FinEmbR-340
❑ 97FinRef-322
❑ 97FinRef-340
❑ 97FlaShoLC-176
❑ 97FlaShoLeg0-176
❑ 97FlaShoLeg1-176
❑ 97FlaShoM-A176
❑ 97FlaShoM-B176
❑ 97FlaShoM-C176
❑ 97FlaShoR0-176
❑ 97FlaShoR1-176
❑ 97FlaShoR2-176
❑ 97Fle-164
❑ 97FleTif-164
❑ 97HigMinM-35
❑ 97Lea-64
❑ 97LeaFraM-64
❑ 97LeaFraMDC-64
❑ 97MetUni-116
❑ 97NewPin-30
❑ 97NewPinAP-30
❑ 97NewPinMC-30
❑ 97NewPinPP-30
❑ 97Pac-150
❑ 97PacLigB-150
❑ 97PacPri-50
❑ 97PacPriLB-50
❑ 97PacPriP-50
❑ 97PacSil-150
❑ 97PacTriCD-7
❑ 97Pin-1
❑ 97PinArtP-PP1
❑ 97PinIns-86
❑ 97PinInsCE-86
❑ 97PinInsDE-86
❑ 97PinMusC-1
❑ 97PinPrePla-1
❑ 97PinX-P-11
❑ 97PinX-PMoS-11
❑ 97PinX-PSfF-21
❑ 97PinX-PSfFU-21
❑ 97Sco-8
❑ 97ScoArtPWB-8
❑ 97ScoPreS-8
❑ 97ScoShoS-8
❑ 97ScoShoSAP-8
❑ 97ScoTitT-18
❑ 97Sel-52
❑ 97SelArtP-52
❑ 97SelCom-52
❑ 97SelRegG-52
❑ 97SP-124
❑ 97SPSpxF-2
❑ 97SPSPxFA-2
❑ 97StaClu-211
❑ 97StaCluMat-211
❑ 97StaCluMOP-211
❑ 97Stu-132
❑ 97StuPrePG-132
❑ 97StuPrePS-132
❑ 97Top-411
❑ 97TopChr-146
❑ 97TopChrR-146
❑ 97TopGal-14
❑ 97TopGalPPI-14
❑ 97TopSta-29
❑ 97TopStaAM-29
❑ 97Ult-96
❑ 97UltGolME-96
❑ 97UltPlaME-96
❑ 97UppDec-252
❑ 97UppDec-445
❑ 97YanSco-2
❑ 97YanScoPl-2
❑ 97YanScoPr-2
❑ 98CirThu-29
❑ 98CirThuRav-29
❑ 98CirThuSupRav-29
❑ 98ColCho-282
❑ 98Don-218
❑ 98DonGolPP-218
❑ 98DonSilPP-218
❑ 98Fin-262
❑ 98FinNo--262
❑ 98FinNo-R-262
❑ 98FinRef-262
❑ 98Fle-451
❑ 98Pac-147
❑ 98PacAur-4
❑ 98PacOme-5
❑ 98PacOmeR-5
❑ 98PacOnl-7
❑ 98PacOnlR-7
❑ 98PacOnlWC-7
❑ 98PacPar-5
❑ 98PacParC-5
❑ 98PacParG-5
❑ 98PacParHS-5
❑ 98PacParPB-5
❑ 98PacParR-5
❑ 98PacPlaB-147
❑ 98PacRedT-147
❑ 98PacSil-147
❑ 98PinPerSftF-8
❑ 98PinPlu-125
❑ 98PinSna-AA14
❑ 98Sco-199
❑ 98ScoSS-PP94
❑ 98ScoSSAP-PP94
❑ 98SP Aut-36
❑ 98SPxFin-241
❑ 98SPxFinR-241
❑ 98SPxFinS-241
❑ 98StaCluFDI-372
❑ 98StaCluI-372
❑ 98StaCluOneK-372
❑ 98StaCluPP-372
❑ 98Stu-70
❑ 98StuGPP-70
❑ 98StuSPP-70
❑ 98Top-374
❑ 98TopChr-374
❑ 98TopChrR-374
❑ 98TopDevR-374
❑ 98TopDia-374
❑ 98TopMiniC-374
❑ 98Ult-207
❑ 98Ult-417
❑ 98UltGolM-207
❑ 98UltGolM-417
❑ 98UltMas-207
❑ 98UltMas-417
❑ 98UltPlaM-207
❑ 98UltPlaM-417
❑ 98UppDec-173
❑ 98UppDec-631
❑ 98YanSco-13
❑ 98YanScoP-13
❑ 99PacPar-245
❑ 99PacParC-245
❑ 99PacParG-245
❑ 99PacParHoloGold-245
❑ 99PacParHS-245
❑ 99PacParOD-245
❑ 99PacParPB-245
❑ 99PacParRed-245

Fields, Bruce
❑ 82BirBarT-11
❑ 83SanJosBC-14
❑ 86NasSouTI-8
❑ 87Don-47
❑ 87IntLeaAT-14
❑ 87Lea-47
❑ 87TolMudHP-14
❑ 87TolMudHT-9
❑ 88MarMot-16
❑ 89BirBarADB-10
❑ 89CalCanC-19
❑ 89CalCanP-534
❑ 89ScoHot1R-43
❑ 89Top-556
❑ 89TopTif-556
❑ 89UppDec-238
❑ 90BirBarADB-10
❑ 90CMC-591
❑ 90ProAAAF-153
❑ 90TacTigC-14
❑ 90TacTigP-106
❑ 90TriAAAC-36
❑ 91RicBraBC-24
❑ 91RicBraP-2580
❑ 91RicBraTI-5
❑ 92LonTigF-649
❑ 92LonTigS-425
❑ 93TolMudHF-1668
❑ 94TolMudHF-1041
❑ 97WesMicW-1
❑ 98WesMicWM-2

Fields, John James
❑ 87OldJudN-167

Fields, Red (Wilmer)
❑ 52Par-21
❑ 91NegLeaRL-17
❑ 93NegLeaRL2-9
❑ 95NegLeaL2-8
❑ 95NegLeaLI-17
❑ 97NegLeaPC-NNO

Fiene, Lou
❑ 09T206-130
❑ 09T206-131

Fiepke, Scott
❑ 86NasPirP-6

Fier, Mike
❑ 90GatCitPP-3350
❑ 90GatCitPSP-9

Fierbaugh, Randy
❑ 79HawIsIC-22

Fierro, John
❑ 80PenPilBT-24
❑ 80PenPilCT-10
❑ 86PeoChiP-6
❑ 87CubCan-11

Fife, Dan
❑ 73TacTwiC-7
❑ 74OPC-421
❑ 74TacTwiC-6
❑ 74Top-421

Figga, Michael
❑ 90TamYanD-8
❑ 91PriWilCC-14
❑ 91PriWilCP-1430
❑ 92ForLauYC-10
❑ 92ForLauYTI-11
❑ 92Ft.LauYF-2614
❑ 93AusFut-36
❑ 93AusFut-105
❑ 93SanBerSC-8
❑ 94FloStaLAF-FSL19
❑ 94TamYanC-11
❑ 94TamYanF-2386
❑ 95AusFut-17
❑ 95Bes-34
❑ 95NorNavTI-46
❑ 96ColCliB-13
❑ 96Exc-88
❑ 96NorNavB-9
❑ 96Top-432
❑ 97ColCliB-12
❑ 97ColCliD-8
❑ 98ColCliD-8
❑ 98ColCliM-12
❑ 99SkyMolM-129
❑ 99SkyMolMF-29
❑ 99SkyMolMFS-29
❑ 99SkyMolMFT-29
❑ 99SkyMolMX-129

Figgins, Chone
❑ 98PorRocG-13

Figueroa, Alexis
❑ 89WatDiaP-1774
❑ 89WatDiaS-6

Figueroa, Bien (Bienvenido)
❑ 86EriCarP-7
❑ 87SprCarB-22
❑ 88ArkTraGS-6
❑ 89LouRedBC-17
❑ 89LouRedBP-1262
❑ 89LouRedBTI-19
❑ 90CMC-117
❑ 90LouRedBC-17
❑ 90LouRedBLBC-15
❑ 90LouRedBP-409
❑ 90ProAAAF-523
❑ 90TopTVCa-47
❑ 91LinDriAAA-234
❑ 91LouRedLD-234
❑ 91LouRedP-2923
❑ 91LouRedTI-20
❑ 92DonRoo-36
❑ 92LouRedF-1893
❑ 92LouRedS-262
❑ 93LimRocDWB-5
❑ 93LouRedF-221
❑ 93Pin-263
❑ 93Sco-281
❑ 93StaClu-304
❑ 93StaCluFDI-304
❑ 93StaCluMOP-304
❑ 93Top-690
❑ 93TopGol-690
❑ 93TopInaM-690
❑ 93TopInaR-690
❑ 93TopMic-690
❑ 94OttLynF-2903
❑ 97BowBay-3
❑ 98BowBayM-3

Figueroa, Danny
❑ 93Top-704
❑ 93TopGol-704
❑ 93TopInaM-704
❑ 93TopInaR-704
❑ 93TopMic-704
❑ 94AshTouC-7
❑ 94AshTouF-1789
❑ 95AshTouTI-3

Figueroa, Ed
❑ 75CalAngP-16
❑ 75OPC-476
❑ 75Top-476
❑ 75TopMin-476
❑ 76OPC-27
❑ 76SSP-190
❑ 76Top-27
❑ 76TopTra-27T
❑ 77Kel-42
❑ 77OPC-164
❑ 77Top-195
❑ 77YanBurK-5
❑ 78SSP270-9
❑ 78Top-365
❑ 78TopZes-3
❑ 78YanBurK-5
❑ 78YanPhoA-7
❑ 78YanSSPD-9
❑ 79OPC-13
❑ 79Top-35
❑ 79YanBurK-11
❑ 79YanPicA-12
❑ 80OPC-288
❑ 80Top-555
❑ 80YanPhoA-6
❑ 81Fle-624
❑ 81TacTigT-32
❑ 81Top-245
❑ 82TacTigT-10
❑ 89PacSenL-75
❑ 89T/MSenL-34
❑ 89TopSenL-43
❑ 90EliSenL-80
❑ 91KelLey-8
❑ 92YanWIZ7-50
❑ 92YanWIZ8-56
❑ 93RanKee-145

Figueroa, Eduardo Jr
❑ 98HelBreM-14
❑ 98TenKry-11

Figueroa, Fernando
❑ 87PriWilYP-22
❑ 88BlaYNPRWL-6
❑ 88Ft.LauYS-8
❑ 89BlaYNPRWL-174
❑ 89MiaMirIS-4
❑ 90WilBilB-5
❑ 90WilBilP-1051
❑ 90WilBilS-6
❑ 91JacSunLD-335
❑ 91JacSunP-145
❑ 91LinDriAA-335
❑ 92JacSunF-3703
❑ 92JacSunS-355

Figueroa, Franky
❑ 97AppLeaTPB-19
❑ 98DelShoM-12
❑ 99BasAmeTP-43
❑ 99BasAmeTPG-43

Figueroa, Jesus
❑ 75ForLauYS-22
❑ 76ForLauYS-1
❑ 77WesHavYT-8
❑ 80WicAerT-9
❑ 81Don-556A
❑ 81Don-556B
❑ 81Top-533
❑ 85DomLeaS-210
❑ 87PocGiaTB-25

Figueroa, Jose
❑ 97SouOreTB-2
Figueroa, Juan
❑ 98BriWhiSQ-10
Figueroa, Julio
❑ 96VerExpB-13
Figueroa, Luis
❑ 97WisTimR-8
❑ 98CarMudM-13
❑ 98WisTimRM-16
❑ 99SP TopP-108
❑ 99SP TopPPE-108
Figueroa, Matt
❑ 90AriWilP-5
❑ 91JamExpC-22
❑ 91JamExpP-3537
Figueroa, Nelson
❑ 97BesLimA-11
❑ 97BinMetB-10
❑ 97Bow-178
❑ 97BowCerBlaIA-CA90
❑ 97BowCerBluIA-CA90
❑ 97BowCerGolIA-CA90
❑ 97BowChr-170
❑ 97BowChrI-170
❑ 97BowChrIR-170
❑ 97BowChrR-170
❑ 97BowInt-178
❑ 97CapCitB-2
❑ 97StaClu-184
❑ 97StaCluMOP-184
❑ 97Top-494
❑ 98BesPreA-11
❑ 98BinMetQ-12
❑ 99SP TopP-47
❑ 99SP TopPPE-47
Figueroa, Ray
❑ 88GenCubP-1637
Figueroa, Rich
❑ 80CliGiaT-23
❑ 81CliGiaT-28
Figueroa, Vic
❑ 86ModA'sP-8
Filbeck, Ryan
❑ 93ElmPioC-7
❑ 93ElmPioF-3816
❑ 94KanCouCC-10
❑ 94KanCouCF-155
❑ 94KanCouCTI-10
Filchner, Duane
❑ 96MidLeaAB-57
❑ 96WesMicWB-9
❑ 97VisOakG-11
❑ 98VisOakG-9
Filer, Thomas
❑ 79WesHavYT-11
❑ 80NasSouTI-9
❑ 81ColCliT-24
❑ 82IowCubT-15
❑ 83IowCubT-3
❑ 83Top-508
❑ 84IowCubT-28
❑ 85DomLeaS-152
❑ 85SyrChiT-6
❑ 86BluJayFS-11
❑ 86Don-439
❑ 86Fle-58
❑ 86Lea-211
❑ 86OPC-312
❑ 86Top-312
❑ 86TopTif-312
❑ 88BreTeal-13
❑ 88DenZepC-10
❑ 88DenZepP-1257
❑ 88TopTra-37T
❑ 88TopTraT-37T
❑ 89Fle-185
❑ 89FleGlo-185
❑ 89Top-419
❑ 89TopTif-419
❑ 90Bow-385
❑ 90BowTif-385
❑ 90BreMilB-8
❑ 90BrePol-28
❑ 90BreYea-1
❑ 90Don-687
❑ 90Fle-322
❑ 90FleCan-322
❑ 92TidTidF-890
❑ 93NorTidF-2562
❑ 94BreMilB-119
❑ 97GreBatB-2
❑ 98GreBatM-27
Filippi, James
❑ 86AppFoxP-8
❑ 87SanBerSP-10

Filkins, Les
❑ 80VenLeaS-131
❑ 81EvaTriT-19
❑ 82EvaTriT-19
Fillingim, Dana
❑ 21Exh-47
❑ 22E120-124
Fillmore, Joe
❑ 86NegLeaF-59
❑ 92NegLeaRLI-21
Filosa, Brian
❑ 92SouBenWSC-14
❑ 92SouBenWSF-184
❑ 92UtiBluSC-12
Filotei, Bobby
❑ 90BilMusP-3227
❑ 91CedRapRP-2726
Filson, Matt
❑ 92YakBeaC-22
❑ 92YakBeaF-3461
❑ 93BakDodCLC-7
Filson, Pete
❑ 82ColCliP-30
❑ 82ColCliT-9
❑ 82TolMudHT-26
❑ 83TwiTeal-16
❑ 84Don-194
❑ 84Fle-564
❑ 84MinTwiP-12
❑ 84Nes792-568
❑ 84Top-568
❑ 84TopTif-568
❑ 84TwiTeal-17
❑ 85Don-607
❑ 85Fle-277
❑ 85Top-97
❑ 85TopTif-97
❑ 85TwiPos-8
❑ 85TwiTeal-6
❑ 85TwiTeal-18
❑ 86BufBisP-11
❑ 86Don-436
❑ 86Fle-393
❑ 86Top-122
❑ 86TopTif-122
❑ 86TwiTeal-16
❑ 87ColCliP-9
❑ 87ColCliP-25
❑ 87ColCliT-3
❑ 90CMC-184
❑ 90OmaRoyC-9
❑ 90OmaRoyP-62
❑ 90ProAAAF-597
❑ 90TriAllGP-AAA23
❑ 91BasCitRC-30
❑ 91BasCitRP-1414
❑ 92BasCitRC-26
❑ 92BasCitRF-3862
❑ 92YanWIZ8-57
❑ 95GreBatTI-28
❑ 96PorRocB-3
❑ 98DurBulTI-9
Filter, Rusty
❑ 89SanDieSAS-9
❑ 90SanDieSA3-4
❑ 90St.CatBJP-3468
Fimple, Jack
❑ 81WatIndT-18
❑ 82VerBeaDT-14
❑ 83AlbDukTc-11
❑ 84AlbDukCr-146
❑ 84DodPol-31
❑ 84Don-372
❑ 84Fle-99
❑ 84HawIslC-146
❑ 84Nes792-263
❑ 84Top-263
❑ 84TopTif-263
❑ 85AlbDukCr-163
❑ 86AlbDukP-7
❑ 87CalAngPPS-12
❑ 87EdmTraP-2083
❑ 90DodTar-243
Finch, Joel
❑ 77BriRedST-6
❑ 79Top-702
❑ 80Top-662
❑ 81PawRedST-1
Finch, Steve
❑ 77AshTouT-5
❑ 79TulDriT-6
❑ 81SpoIndT-11
❑ 82SalLakCGT-8
❑ 84EdmTraC-106
❑ 85MidAngT-13
❑ 86EdmTraP-8

Fincher, Matt
❑ 89GeoColC-7
❑ 90GeoColC-3
Fincher, William
❑ 17Zee-45
Findlay, Bill
❑ 88GasRanP-997
Fine, Andrea
❑ 87SalSpuS-7
Fine, Tom
❑ 89PenPilS-5
❑ 90VisOakCLC-61
❑ 90VisOakP-2147
Fine, Tommy
❑ 47RedSoxTI-8
❑ 48SomandK-4
Fingers, Bob
❑ 87ModA'sC-26
❑ 87ModA'sP-18
Fingers, Rollie
❑ 69Top-597
❑ 70OPC-502
❑ 70Top-502
❑ 71MLBOffS-513
❑ 71OPC-384
❑ 71Top-384
❑ 72OPC-241
❑ 72Top-241
❑ 73A'sPos-36
❑ 73LinPor-139
❑ 73OPC-84
❑ 73Top-84
❑ 74OPC-212
❑ 74Top-212
❑ 75A'sPos-60
❑ 75Hos-52
❑ 75HosTwi-52
❑ 75Kel-55
❑ 75OPC-21
❑ 75OPC-463
❑ 75OPC-466
❑ 75SSPPuzB-9
❑ 75Top-21
❑ 75Top-463
❑ 75Top-466
❑ 75TopMin-21
❑ 75TopMin-463
❑ 75TopMin-466
❑ 76Hos-104
❑ 76OPC-405
❑ 76SSP-480
❑ 76Top-405
❑ 77A'sPos-85
❑ 77BurCheD-133
❑ 77ChiWilD-20
❑ 77DailsID-20
❑ 77DetCaeD-20
❑ 77HolInnD-20
❑ 77Hos-137
❑ 77Kel-51
❑ 77MSADis-20
❑ 77OPC-52
❑ 77PadSchC-21A
❑ 77PadSchC-21B
❑ 77RCColC-21
❑ 77SagDis-20
❑ 77sDis-20
❑ 77Spo-1409
❑ 77Top-523
❑ 77WenDis-20
❑ 77ZipDis-20
❑ 78Hos-144
❑ 78OPC-8
❑ 78OPC-201
❑ 78PadFamF-11
❑ 78RCColC-34
❑ 78Top-140
❑ 78Top-208
❑ 78WifBalD-22
❑ 79BasPat-29
❑ 79OPC-203
❑ 79PadFamF-24
❑ 79Top-8
❑ 79Top-390
❑ 80BurKinPHR-3
❑ 80OPC-343
❑ 80PerHaloFP-212
❑ 80PerHaloFPS-73
❑ 80Top-651
❑ 81AllGamPI-78
❑ 81Don-2
❑ 81Fle-485
❑ 81FleStiC-47
❑ 81OPC-229
❑ 81PadFamF-9
❑ 81Top-8

❑ 81Top-229
❑ 81TopSti-31
❑ 81TopTra-761
❑ 82BrePol-34
❑ 82Don-28
❑ 82FBIDis-8
❑ 82Fle-141
❑ 82Fle-644
❑ 82FleSta-132
❑ 82K-M-40
❑ 82Kel-7
❑ 82OPC-44
❑ 82OPC-176
❑ 82PerCreC-16
❑ 82PerCreCG-16
❑ 82SevSluC-9
❑ 82Squ-11
❑ 82Top-168
❑ 82Top-585
❑ 82Top-586
❑ 82TopSti-16
❑ 82TopSti-198
❑ 83BreGar-7
❑ 83BrePlaM-2
❑ 83BrePol-34
❑ 83Don-2
❑ 83Don-78
❑ 83DonActA-33
❑ 83Fle-33
❑ 83FleSta-60
❑ 83FleSti-13
❑ 83Kel-2
❑ 83OPC-35
❑ 83OPC-36
❑ 83PerCreC-23
❑ 83PerCreCG-23
❑ 83Top-35
❑ 83Top-36
❑ 83TopFol-4
❑ 83TopSti-79
❑ 83TopStiB-6
❑ 84BreGar-6
❑ 84BrePol-34
❑ 84Don-A
❑ 84DonCha-45
❑ 84Fle-199
❑ 84FunFooP-10
❑ 84Nes792-495
❑ 84Nes792-717
❑ 84Nes792-718
❑ 84OCoandSI-72
❑ 84OCoandSI-188
❑ 84OPC-283
❑ 84Top-495
❑ 84Top-717
❑ 84Top-718
❑ 84TopGaloC-4
❑ 84TopTif-495
❑ 84TopTif-717
❑ 84TopTif-718
❑ 85BreGar-6
❑ 85BrePol-34
❑ 85Don-292
❑ 85DonActA-36
❑ 85DonHig-2
❑ 85Fle-581
❑ 85Lea-190
❑ 85OPC-182
❑ 85Top-750
❑ 85TopSti-285
❑ 85TopTif-750
❑ 85Woo-10
❑ 86A'sGreT-11
❑ 86BreGreT-11
❑ 86Don-229
❑ 86Fle-486
❑ 86OPC-185
❑ 86PadGreT-11
❑ 86SevCoi-C11
❑ 86Spo-65
❑ 86Spo-130
❑ 86Spo-146
❑ 86Top-185
❑ 86TopSti-198
❑ 86TopTif-185
❑ 87A'sMot-10
❑ 88PacLegI-103
❑ 89PacSenL-161
❑ 89PadMag-8
❑ 89T/MSenL-35
❑ 89TopSenL-65
❑ 90AGFA-18
❑ 90BasWit-51
❑ 90EliSenL-21
❑ 90EliSenL-123
❑ 90PerGreM-74

❑ 91Kel3D-7
❑ 91PacSenL-126
❑ 91SweBasG-30
❑ 91UppDecS-10
❑ 92BreCarT-7
❑ 92LegSpoF-RF1
❑ 92LegSpoF-RF2
❑ 92LegSpoF-RF3
❑ 92MDAMVP-15
❑ 92PhoFilHoF-1
❑ 92UppDecF-45
❑ 92UppDecFG-45
❑ 92UppDecHH-HI3
❑ 92UppDecHoB-H7
❑ 92UppDecHoB-H8
❑ 92UppDecHoB-AU7
❑ 92UppDecS-17
❑ 92UppDecS-18
❑ 92UppDecS-25
❑ 92UppDecS-27
❑ 92UppDecS-33
❑ 92UppDecS-34
❑ 92Zip-3
❑ 93ActPacA-130
❑ 93ActPacA2-64G
❑ 93FroRowF-1
❑ 93FroRowF-2
❑ 93FroRowF-3
❑ 93FroRowF-4
❑ 93FroRowF-5
❑ 94BreMilB-120
❑ 94BreMilB-312
❑ 94BreSen-2
❑ 94TedWil-66
❑ 94UppDecS-3
❑ 97CalLot-3
❑ 97TopStaHRR-5
❑ 97TopStaRRAU-5
❑ 98SpoIllAuto-3
❑ 98SpoIllTaN-10
❑ 98SpoIllTaNEE-10
❑ 98SpoIllWSFMC-5
❑ 98UppDecR-71
❑ 98UppDecRSotT-RF
❑ 99SP SigAuto-ROL
❑ 99SpoIllGotG-69
❑ 99SpoIllGotGA-23
❑ 99SpoIllGotGC-40
❑ 99SPSig-173
❑ 99UppDecR-100
❑ 99UppDecRG-100
❑ 99UppDecRI-RF
❑ 99UppDecRIL2-RF
❑ 99UppDecRP-100
Finigan, Jim
❑ 54A'STEAI-8
❑ 55A'sRodM-14
❑ 55A'sTeal-8
❑ 55ArmCoi-5
❑ 55RobGouS-17
❑ 55RobGouW-17
❑ 55Top-14
❑ 55TopDouH-49
❑ 56A'sPos-17
❑ 56A'sRodM-5
❑ 56BalOriP-13
❑ 56Top-22
❑ 56TopPin-12
❑ 57Top-248
❑ 58Top-136
❑ 59Top-47
❑ 59TopVen-47
❑ 76A'sRodMC-10
❑ 79TCM50-128
❑ 91OriCro-129
Finigan, Kevin
❑ 87BurExpP-1079
❑ 88JamExpP-1915
Fink, Eric
❑ 84PriWilPT-11
Fink, Mark
❑ 96HelBreTI-4
❑ 98FarRedHM-7
Finken, Steve
❑ 88GreFalDTI-15
❑ 89BakDodCLC-205
❑ 89CalLeaA-22
❑ 90SanAntMGS-12
❑ 91LinDriAA-534
❑ 91SanAntMLD-534
❑ 91SanAntMP-2982
❑ 92ShrCapS-592
❑ 92SkyAA F-257
Finlayson, Mike
❑ 75WesPalBES-23
❑ 79MemChiT-12

Finley, Bob
❑ 45CenFlo-7
❑ 83TCMPla1944-45
Finley, Brian
❑ 83BelBreFr-18
❑ 86ElPasDP-10
❑ 88ChaLooB-13
❑ 90ChaLooGS-12
Finley, Charles
❑ 91FouBal-17
Finley, Chris
❑ 93Sou-9
Finley, Chuck
❑ 86QuaCitAP-11
❑ 87AngSmo-6
❑ 87CalAngPPS-13
❑ 87Don-407
❑ 87Fle-79
❑ 87FleGlo-79
❑ 87Top-446
❑ 87TopTif-446
❑ 88AngSmo-15
❑ 88Don-530
❑ 88DonBasB-283
❑ 88Fle-489
❑ 88FleGlo-489
❑ 88StaLinAn-6
❑ 88Top-99
❑ 88TopBig-254
❑ 88TopTif-99
❑ 89Bow-37
❑ 89BowTif-37
❑ 89Don-226
❑ 89DonBasB-333
❑ 89Fle-477
❑ 89FleGlo-477
❑ 89Sco-503
❑ 89Top-708
❑ 89TopBig-76
❑ 89TopTif-708
❑ 89UppDec-632
❑ 90AngSmo-5
❑ 90Bow-289
❑ 90BowTif-289
❑ 90Don-344
❑ 90DonBesA-103
❑ 90Fle-132
❑ 90FleCan-132
❑ 90K-M-28
❑ 90Lea-162
❑ 90OPC-147
❑ 90PanSti-32
❑ 90PublntS-369
❑ 90Sco-380
❑ 90Sco100S-24
❑ 90Spo-172
❑ 90Top-147
❑ 90TopBig-319
❑ 90TopCoi-13
❑ 90TopDou-22
❑ 90TopMinL-8
❑ 90TopSti-171
❑ 90TopStiB-62
❑ 90TopTif-147
❑ 90TopTVA-14
❑ 90UppDec-667
❑ 90USPlaCA-9S
❑ 90WinDis-5
❑ 91AngSmo-9
❑ 91BasBesAotM-7
❑ 91Bow-196
❑ 91Cla1-T95
❑ 91Cla3-T20
❑ 91Don-26
❑ 91Don-692
❑ 91DonSupD-26
❑ 91Fle-313
❑ 91Lea-45
❑ 91LeaPre-15
❑ 91OPC-395
❑ 91OPC-505
❑ 91PanCanT1-70
❑ 91PanFreS-187
❑ 91PanSti-135
❑ 91RedFolS-35
❑ 91Sco-100
❑ 91Sco100S-90
❑ 91StaClu-81
❑ 91Stu-24
❑ 91SunSee-7
❑ 91Top-395
❑ 91Top-505
❑ 91TopCraJ2-12
❑ 91TopDesS-395
❑ 91TopDesS-505
❑ 91TopMic-395

❑ 91TopMic-505
❑ 91TopTif-395
❑ 91TopTif-505
❑ 91TopTriH-A3
❑ 91Ult-44
❑ 91UppDec-31
❑ 91UppDec-437
❑ 92AngPol-9
❑ 92Bow-32
❑ 92ClaGam-1
❑ 92Don-255
❑ 92Fle-57
❑ 92Hig5-12
❑ 92Lea-450
❑ 92LeaBlaG-450
❑ 92OPC-247
❑ 92OPCPre-155
❑ 92Pin-42
❑ 92Sco-585
❑ 92Sco100S-6
❑ 92SpollIFK1-72
❑ 92StaClu-315
❑ 92Stu-145
❑ 92Top-247
❑ 92TopGol-247
❑ 92TopGolW-247
❑ 92TopKid-94
❑ 92TopMic-247
❑ 92TriPla-91
❑ 92Ult-25
❑ 92UppDec-244
❑ 93AngMot-3
❑ 93AngPol-19
❑ 93AngStaCl-16
❑ 93Bow-385
❑ 93Don-225
❑ 93Fin-72
❑ 93FinRef-72
❑ 93Fla-174
❑ 93Fle-191
❑ 93FunPac-39
❑ 93HumDumC-4
❑ 93Lea-292
❑ 93OPC-153
❑ 93PacSpa-44
❑ 93Pin-201
❑ 93Sco-158
❑ 93Sel-198
❑ 93SP-23
❑ 93StaClu-301
❑ 93StaCluFDI-301
❑ 93StaCluMOP-301
❑ 93Top-605
❑ 93TopGol-605
❑ 93TopInaM-605
❑ 93TopInaR-605
❑ 93TopMic-605
❑ 93TriPla-169
❑ 93Ult-162
❑ 93UppDec-53
❑ 93UppDec-77
❑ 93UppDecGold-53
❑ 93UppDecGold-77
❑ 94AngLAT-11
❑ 94AngMot-9
❑ 94Bow-67
❑ 94ColC-515
❑ 94ColChoGS-515
❑ 94ColChoSS-515
❑ 94Don-363
❑ 94DonSpeE-363
❑ 94Fin-143
❑ 94FinRef-143
❑ 94Fla-22
❑ 94Fle-55
❑ 94FleExtB-35
❑ 94FleExtBPD-5
❑ 94Lea-394
❑ 94OPC-158
❑ 94Pac-78
❑ 94Pin-38
❑ 94PinArtP-38
❑ 94PinMusC-38
❑ 94ProMag-19
❑ 94Sco-151
❑ 94ScoGolR-151
❑ 94Sel-291
❑ 94Spo-21
❑ 94StaClu-211
❑ 94StaCluFDI-211
❑ 94StaCluGR-211
❑ 94StaCluMOP-211
❑ 94Top-381
❑ 94TopGol-381
❑ 94TopSpa-381
❑ 94TriPla-15
❑ 94Ult-328
❑ 94UppDec-314
❑ 94UppDecED-314
❑ 95AngCHP-2
❑ 95AngMot-9
❑ 95Baz-19
❑ 95Bow-298
❑ 95ColCho-102
❑ 95ColChoGS-102
❑ 95ColChoSE-34
❑ 95ColChoSEGS-34
❑ 95ColChoSESS-34
❑ 95ColChoSS-102
❑ 95Don-477
❑ 95DonPreP-477
❑ 95DonTopotO-36
❑ 95Emo-20
❑ 95Fin-87
❑ 95FinRef-87
❑ 95Fla-18
❑ 95Fle-224
❑ 95FleTeaL-3
❑ 95Lea-67
❑ 95LeaLim-111
❑ 95Pac-60
❑ 95Pin-17
❑ 95PinArtP-17
❑ 95PinMusC-17
❑ 95RedFol-12
❑ 95Sco-134
❑ 95ScoGolR-134
❑ 95ScoPlaTS-134
❑ 95SP-134
❑ 95SPCha-132
❑ 95SPChaDC-132
❑ 95SPSil-134
❑ 95SPSpeF-5
❑ 95StaClu-441
❑ 95StaCluMOP-441
❑ 95StaCluSTWS-441
❑ 95StaCluVR-232
❑ 95StaCluVRMO-232
❑ 95Stu-132
❑ 95Top-455
❑ 95TopCyb-251
❑ 95TopEmb-48
❑ 95TopEmbGI-48
❑ 95TopLeaL-LL48
❑ 95Ult-268
❑ 95UltGolM-268
❑ 95UppDec-21
❑ 95UppDecED-21
❑ 95UppDecEDG-21
❑ 95UppDecSE-264
❑ 95UppDecSEG-264
❑ 96AngMot-9
❑ 96Baz-103
❑ 96Cir-20
❑ 96CirRav-20
❑ 96ColCho-485
❑ 96ColChoGS-485
❑ 96ColChoSS-485
❑ 96Don-147
❑ 96DonPreP-147
❑ 96EmoXL-26
❑ 96Fin-B89
❑ 96FinRef-B89
❑ 96Fla-37
❑ 96Fle-47
❑ 96FleSmo'H-4
❑ 96FleTif-47
❑ 96Lea-5
❑ 96LeaPrePB-5
❑ 96LeaPrePG-5
❑ 96LeaPrePS-5
❑ 96MetUni-27
❑ 96MetUniP-27
❑ 96Pac-275
❑ 96PanSti-213
❑ 96Sco-410
❑ 96SP-46
❑ 96StaClu-120
❑ 96StaCluEPB-120
❑ 96StaCluEPG-120
❑ 96StaCluEPS-120
❑ 96StaCluMOP-120
❑ 96Top-192
❑ 96TopGal-25
❑ 96TopGalPPI-25
❑ 96TopLas-118
❑ 96Ult-30
❑ 96UltGolM-30
❑ 96UppDec-291
❑ 96UppDecPHE-H15
❑ 96UppDecPreH-H15
❑ 97AngMot-9
❑ 97Cir-393
❑ 97CirRav-393
❑ 97ColCho-256
❑ 97Don-260
❑ 97DonGolPP-260
❑ 97DonSilPP-260
❑ 97DonTea-7
❑ 97DonTeaSPE-7
❑ 97Fin-53
❑ 97FinRef-53
❑ 97Fle-43
❑ 97FleTif-43
❑ 97Lea-87
❑ 97LeaFraM-87
❑ 97LeaFraMDC-87
❑ 97MetUni-41
❑ 97NewPin-134
❑ 97NewPinAP-134
❑ 97NewPinMC-134
❑ 97NewPinPP-134
❑ 97Pac-8
❑ 97PacLigB-8
❑ 97PacSil-8
❑ 97Sco-75
❑ 97ScoArtPWB-75
❑ 97ScoPreS-75
❑ 97ScoShoS-75
❑ 97ScoShoSAP-75
❑ 97SP-21
❑ 97StaClu-102
❑ 97StaCluMOP-102
❑ 97Top-336
❑ 97Ult-27
❑ 97UltGolME-27
❑ 97UltPlaME-27
❑ 97UppDec-295
❑ 98AngSco-13
❑ 98AngScoP-13
❑ 98Bow-245
❑ 98BowChr-245
❑ 98BowChrGA-245
❑ 98BowChrGAR-245
❑ 98BowChrI-245
❑ 98BowChrIR-245
❑ 98BowChrR-245
❑ 98BowGolA-245
❑ 98BowInt-245
❑ 98CirThu-179
❑ 98CirThuRav-179
❑ 98CirThuSupRav-179
❑ 98ColCho-27
❑ 98Fin-164
❑ 98FinNo--164
❑ 98FinNo-R-164
❑ 98FinRef-164
❑ 98Fle-562
❑ 98MetUni-7
❑ 98MetUniPMG-7
❑ 98Pac-7
❑ 98PacAur-5
❑ 98PacInv-4
❑ 98PacInvPBlue-4
❑ 98PacInvSilv-4
❑ 98PacOme-6
❑ 98PacOmeR-6
❑ 98PacOnl-8
❑ 98PacOnlR-8
❑ 98PacOnlWC-8
❑ 98PacPar-6
❑ 98PacParC-6
❑ 98PacParG-6
❑ 98PacParHS-6
❑ 98PacParPB-6
❑ 98PacParR-6
❑ 98PacPlaB-7
❑ 98PacRedT-7
❑ 98PacSil-7
❑ 98Pin-136
❑ 98PinPreP-136
❑ 98PinSna-AA16
❑ 98Revo-4
❑ 98RevoSS-4
❑ 98Sco-205
❑ 98ScoSS-PP97
❑ 98ScoSSAP-PP97
❑ 98SP Aut-31
❑ 98SpollI-38
❑ 98SpollIEE-38
❑ 98SpollIFE-38
❑ 98SpollIWSF-139
❑ 98SpollIWSFEE-139
❑ 98SpollIWSFFE-139
❑ 98SPxFin-242
❑ 98SPxFinR-242
❑ 98SPxFinS-242
❑ 98StaCluFDI-261
❑ 98StaCluI-261
❑ 98StaCluOneK-261
❑ 98StaCluPP-261
❑ 98Top-152
❑ 98TopChr-152
❑ 98TopChrR-152
❑ 98TopDevR-152
❑ 98TopDia-152
❑ 98TopMiniC-152
❑ 98TopSta-41
❑ 98TopStaB-41
❑ 98TopStaG-41
❑ 98TopStaGR-41
❑ 98TopStaS-41
❑ 98Ult-12
❑ 98UltGolM-12
❑ 98UltMas-12
❑ 98UltPlaM-12
❑ 98UppDec-23
❑ 98UppDecSF-13
❑ 99199Fin-58
❑ 99Bow-62
❑ 99BowChr-62
❑ 99BowChrG-62
❑ 99BowChrGR-62
❑ 99BowChrI-62
❑ 99BowChrIR-62
❑ 99BowChrR-62
❑ 99BowGol-62
❑ 99BowInt-62
❑ 99FinGolRef-58
❑ 99FinRef-58
❑ 99Fle-141
❑ 99FleSta9-141
❑ 99FleWarT-141
❑ 99MetUni-45
❑ 99MetUniGM-45
❑ 99MetUniPMG-45
❑ 99Pac-6
❑ 99PacOme-4
❑ 99PacOmeC-4
❑ 99PacOmeG-4
❑ 99PacOmePB-4
❑ 99PacPar-5
❑ 99PacParC-5
❑ 99PacParG-5
❑ 99PacParHoloGold-5
❑ 99PacParHS-5
❑ 99PacParOD-5
❑ 99PacParPB-5
❑ 99PacParRed-5
❑ 99PacPlaB-6
❑ 99PacPri-4
❑ 99PacPriHB-4
❑ 99PacPriHG-4
❑ 99PacPriHM-4
❑ 99PacPriHP-4
❑ 99PacPriRed-4
❑ 99PacRed-6
❑ 99SkyPre-179
❑ 99SkyPreR-179
❑ 99SkyThu-94
❑ 99SkyThuRant-94
❑ 99SkyThuRave-94
❑ 99SpolII-176
❑ 99StaClu-254
❑ 99StaCluFDI-254
❑ 99StaCluOoaK-254
❑ 99StaCluPP-254
❑ 99ThuSkySupR-94
❑ 99Top-278
❑ 99TopChr-278
❑ 99TopChrR-278
❑ 99TopMVPP-278
❑ 99UD Cho-48
❑ 99UD ChoP-48
❑ 99UD ChoPCR-48
❑ 99Ult-163
❑ 99UltGolM-163
❑ 99UltMas-163
❑ 99UltPlaM-163
❑ 99UppDec-22
❑ 99UppDecEL1-22
❑ 99UppDecEL2-22
❑ 99Vic-12

Finley, David

❑ 88ModA'sCLC-70
❑ 88ModA'sTI-23

Finley, John

❑ 98WicWraM-20

Finley, Steve

❑ 87NewOriP-21
❑ 88BlaYNPRWL-83
❑ 88HagSunS-7
❑ 88RocRedWGCP-7
❑ 88TriAAAP-29
❑ 88TriAAC-21
❑ 89BalOriP-7
❑ 89Bow-15
❑ 89BowTif-15
❑ 89DonRoo-47
❑ 89FleUpd-3
❑ 89OriFreB-10
❑ 89RocRedWP-1639
❑ 89ScoRoo-95T
❑ 89UppDec-742
❑ 90BalOriP-5
❑ 90Don-215
❑ 90Fle-176
❑ 90FleCan-176
❑ 90HagSunDGB-10
❑ 90Lea-329
❑ 90OPC-349
❑ 90Sco-339
❑ 90Sco100RS-58
❑ 90ScoYouSI-11
❑ 90Top-349
❑ 90TopDeb89-37
❑ 90TopTif-349
❑ 90UppDec-602
❑ 91AstMot-2
❑ 91Bow-561
❑ 91Don-355
❑ 91Fle-470
❑ 91FleUpd-88
❑ 91Lea-231
❑ 91OPC-212
❑ 91OriCro-130
❑ 91PanFreS-244
❑ 91Sco-266
❑ 91StaClu-376
❑ 91Stu-176
❑ 91Top-212
❑ 91TopDesS-212
❑ 91TopMic-212
❑ 91TopTif-212
❑ 91TopTra-42T
❑ 91TopTraT-42T
❑ 91UltUpd-81
❑ 91UppDec-330
❑ 91UppDec-794
❑ 92AstMot-2
❑ 92Bow-574
❑ 92Don-197
❑ 92Fle-433
❑ 92Lea-66
❑ 92LeaBlaG-66
❑ 92OPC-86
❑ 92PanSti-157
❑ 92Pin-19
❑ 92Sco-176
❑ 92StaClu-29
❑ 92Stu-35
❑ 92Top-86
❑ 92TopGol-86
❑ 92TopGolW-86
❑ 92TopKid-46
❑ 92TopMic-86
❑ 92TriPla-26
❑ 92TriPla-43
❑ 92TriPlaP-5
❑ 92Ult-202
❑ 92UppDec-368
❑ 93AstMot-2
❑ 93AstStaC-10
❑ 93Bow-96
❑ 93ClaGam-33
❑ 93Don-192
❑ 93Fin-9
❑ 93FinRef-9
❑ 93Fla-62
❑ 93Fle-50
❑ 93FunPac-47
❑ 93Lea-325
❑ 93OPC-154
❑ 93PacSpa-122
❑ 93PanSti-174
❑ 93Pin-172
❑ 93RedFolS-30
❑ 93Sco-65
❑ 93Sel-88
❑ 93SelStaL-23
❑ 93SelStaL-60
❑ 93SP-33
❑ 93StaClu-556
❑ 93StaCluFDI-556
❑ 93StaCluMOP-556
❑ 93Top-148
❑ 93TopGol-148
❑ 93TopInaM-148
❑ 93TopInaR-148
❑ 93TopMic-148
❑ 93TriPla-203
❑ 93Ult-39
❑ 93UppDec-231
❑ 93UppDecGold-231
❑ 93USPlaCA-5H
❑ 94AstMot-8
❑ 94Bow-502
❑ 94ColC-523
❑ 94ColChoGS-523
❑ 94ColChoSS-523
❑ 94Don-402
❑ 94Fin-31
❑ 94FinPre-31P
❑ 94FinRef-31
❑ 94Fla-389
❑ 94Fle-490
❑ 94FleExtB-273
❑ 94FUnPac-91
❑ 94Lea-383
❑ 94OPC-129
❑ 94Pac-265
❑ 94PanSti-194
❑ 94Pin-351
❑ 94PinArtP-351
❑ 94PinMusC-351
❑ 94Sco-364
❑ 94ScoCyc-TC12
❑ 94ScoGolR-364
❑ 94Sel-362
❑ 94Spo-135
❑ 94StaClu-308
❑ 94StaCluFDI-308
❑ 94StaCluGR-308
❑ 94StaCluMOP-308
❑ 94StaCluMOP-ST6
❑ 94StaCluST-ST6
❑ 94Stu-21
❑ 94Top-580
❑ 94TopGol-580
❑ 94TopSpa-580
❑ 94TriPla-26
❑ 94Ult-503
❑ 94UppDec-346
❑ 94UppDecED-346
❑ 95ColCho-349
❑ 95ColChoGS-349
❑ 95ColChoSS-349
❑ 95Don-25
❑ 95DonPreP-25
❑ 95DonTopotO-340
❑ 95Emo-186
❑ 95Fin-194
❑ 95FinRef-194
❑ 95Fla-418
❑ 95Fle-459
❑ 95FleUpd-183
❑ 95Lea-320
❑ 95LeaLim-164
❑ 95Pac-186
❑ 95PadCHP-11
❑ 95PadMot-14
❑ 95Pin-114
❑ 95PinArtP-114
❑ 95PinMusC-114
❑ 95Sco-397
❑ 95ScoGolR-397
❑ 95ScoPlaTS-397
❑ 95SP-108
❑ 95SPSil-108
❑ 95StaClu-18
❑ 95StaCluFDI-18
❑ 95StaCluMOP-18
❑ 95StaCluMOP-551
❑ 95StaCluSTWS-18
❑ 95StaCluSTWS-551
❑ 95StaCluVR-12
❑ 95StaCluVRMO-12
❑ 95Stu-133
❑ 95Top-626
❑ 95TopCyb-393
❑ 95TopTra-91T
❑ 95Ult-172
❑ 95UltGolM-172
❑ 95UppDec-371
❑ 95UppDecED-371
❑ 95UppDecEDG-371
❑ 95UppDecSE-269
❑ 95UppDecSEG-269
❑ 96Baz-66
❑ 96Cir-185
❑ 96CirRav-185
❑ 96ColCho-358
❑ 96ColCho-696
❑ 96ColChoGS-358
❑ 96ColChoGS-696

❑ 96ColChoSS-358
❑ 96ColChoSS-696
❑ 96Don-66
❑ 96DonPreP-66
❑ 96EmoXL-276
❑ 96Fin-S160
❑ 96FinRef-S160
❑ 96Fla-373
❑ 96Fle-565
❑ 96FleTif-565
❑ 96Lea-12
❑ 96LeaPrePB-12
❑ 96LeaPrePG-12
❑ 96LeaPrePS-12
❑ 96MetUni-234
❑ 96MetUniP-234
❑ 96Pac-192
❑ 96PadMot-7
❑ 96PanSti-103
❑ 96Pin-6
❑ 96Sco-287
❑ 96ScoDugC-B12
❑ 96ScoDugCAP-B12
❑ 96SP-163
❑ 96StaClu-378
❑ 96StaCluEPB-378
❑ 96StaCluEPG-378
❑ 96StaCluEPS-378
❑ 96StaCluMO-12
❑ 96StaCluMOP-378
❑ 96Top-139
❑ 96TopChr-38
❑ 96TopChrR-38
❑ 96TopGal-9
❑ 96TopGalPPI-9
❑ 96Ult-557
❑ 96UltGolM-557
❑ 96UppDec-449
❑ 97BowBes-15
❑ 97BowBesAR-15
❑ 97BowBesR-15
❑ 97Cir-254
❑ 97CirRav-254
❑ 97ColCho-209
❑ 97ColChoAC-33
❑ 97Don-60
❑ 97DonEli-144
❑ 97DonEliGS-144
❑ 97DonGolPP-60
❑ 97DonLim-66
❑ 97DonLimE-66
❑ 97DonLimENG-66
❑ 97DonPre-65
❑ 97DonPreCttC-65
❑ 97DonSilPP-60
❑ 97Fin-314
❑ 97FinEmb-314
❑ 97FinEmbR-314
❑ 97FinRef-314
❑ 97FlaShoLC-96
❑ 97FlaShoLeg0-96
❑ 97FlaShoLeg1-96
❑ 97FlaShoM-A96
❑ 97FlaShoM-B96
❑ 97FlaShoM-C96
❑ 97FlaShoR0-96
❑ 97FlaShoR1-96
❑ 97FlaShoR2-96
❑ 97Fle-459
❑ 97FleTif-459
❑ 97KinB-27
❑ 97Lea-100
❑ 97LeaFraM-100
❑ 97LeaFraMDC-100
❑ 97MetUni-218
❑ 97NewPin-58
❑ 97NewPinAP-58
❑ 97NewPinMC-58
❑ 97NewPinPP-58
❑ 97Pac-422
❑ 97PacLigB-422
❑ 97PacPri-143
❑ 97PacPriLB-143
❑ 97PacPriP-143
❑ 97PacSil-422
❑ 97PadMot-7
❑ 97PinIns-121
❑ 97PinInsCE-121
❑ 97PinInsDE-121
❑ 97PinX-P-50
❑ 97PinX-PMoS-50
❑ 97Sco-279
❑ 97ScoArtPWB-279
❑ 97ScoPreS-279
❑ 97ScoShoS-279
❑ 97ScoShoSAP-279
❑ 97Sel-90
❑ 97SelArtP-90
❑ 97SelCom-90
❑ 97SelRegG-90
❑ 97SP-156
❑ 97SpoIll-120
❑ 97SpoIllEE-120
❑ 97StaClu-24
❑ 97StaCluMat-24
❑ 97StaCluMOP-24
❑ 97StrAll-20
❑ 97Top-189
❑ 97TopChr-73
❑ 97TopChrR-73
❑ 97TopGal-76
❑ 97TopGalPPI-76
❑ 97Ult-280
❑ 97UltGolME-280
❑ 97UltPlaME-280
❑ 97UppDec-165
❑ 97UppDec-376
❑ 98Bow-252
❑ 98BowBes-71
❑ 98BowBesAR-71
❑ 98BowBesR-71
❑ 98BowChr-252
❑ 98BowChrGA-252
❑ 98BowChrGAR-252
❑ 98BowChrI-252
❑ 98BowChrIR-252
❑ 98BowChrR-252
❑ 98BowGolA-252
❑ 98BowInt-252
❑ 98CirThu-12
❑ 98CirThuRav-12
❑ 98CirThuSupRav-12
❑ 98ColCho-479
❑ 98Don-205
❑ 98DonGolPP-205
❑ 98DonSilPP-205
❑ 98Fin-220
❑ 98FinNo--220
❑ 98FinNo-R-220
❑ 98FinRef-220
❑ 98FlaShoLeg0-101
❑ 98FlaShoLeg1-101
❑ 98FlaShoLeg2-101
❑ 98FlaShoLeg3-101
❑ 98FlaShoLegM-101
❑ 98FlaShoR0-101
❑ 98FlaShoR1-101
❑ 98FlaShoR2-101
❑ 98FlaShoR3-101
❑ 98Fle-198
❑ 98KinDis-27
❑ 98MetUni-64
❑ 98MetUniPMG-64
❑ 98Pac-424
❑ 98PacAur-190
❑ 98PacInv-138
❑ 98PacInvPBlue-138
❑ 98PacInvSilv-138
❑ 98PacInvTeam-24
❑ 98PacOme-204
❑ 98PacOmeR-204
❑ 98PacOnl-634
❑ 98PacOnlR-634
❑ 98PacOnlWC-634
❑ 98PacPar-236
❑ 98PacParC-236
❑ 98PacParG-236
❑ 98PacParHS-236
❑ 98PacParPB-236
❑ 98PacParR-236
❑ 98PacPlaB-424
❑ 98PacRedT-424
❑ 98PacSil-424
❑ 98PadMot-8
❑ 98Pin-24
❑ 98PinArtP-PP24
❑ 98PinMusC-PP24
❑ 98PinPlu-158
❑ 98PinPreP-24
❑ 98Revo-123
❑ 98RevoSS-123
❑ 98Sco-55
❑ 98ScoRT-117
❑ 98ScoRTSS-PP73
❑ 98ScoRTSSAP-PP73
❑ 98ScoRTSSAP1-PP73
❑ 98ScoSS-PP19
❑ 98ScoSSAP-PP19
❑ 98SP Aut-168
❑ 98SpoIll-39
❑ 98SpoIllEE-39
❑ 98SpoIllFE-39
❑ 98SpoIllTaN-80
❑ 98SpoIllTaNEE-80
❑ 98StaCluFDI-60
❑ 98StaCluI-60
❑ 98StaCluOneK-60
❑ 98StaCluPP-60
❑ 98Stu-211
❑ 98StuGPP-211
❑ 98StuSPP-211
❑ 98Top-330
❑ 98TopChr-330
❑ 98TopChrR-330
❑ 98TopDevR-330
❑ 98TopDia-330
❑ 98TopGal-139
❑ 98TopGalGP-139
❑ 98TopGalOPP-139
❑ 98TopGalPPI-139
❑ 98TopGalPPIA-139
❑ 98TopGolLabC1-36
❑ 98TopGolLabC1B-36
❑ 98TopGolLabC1One-36
❑ 98TopGolLabC1R-36
❑ 98TopGolLabC2-36
❑ 98TopGolLabC2B-36
❑ 98TopGolLabC2One-36
❑ 98TopGolLabC2R-36
❑ 98TopGolLabC3-36
❑ 98TopGolLabC3B-36
❑ 98TopGolLabC3One-36
❑ 98TopGolLabC3R-36
❑ 98TopMiniC-330
❑ 98TopOpeD-157
❑ 98TopSta-31
❑ 98TopStaB-31
❑ 98TopStaG-31
❑ 98TopStaGR-31
❑ 98TopStaS-31
❑ 98Ult-117
❑ 98UltDouT-12
❑ 98UltGolM-117
❑ 98UltMas-117
❑ 98UltPlaM-117
❑ 98UppDec-208
❑ 98UppDec-251
❑ 98UppDecSF-113
❑ 99199Fin-226
❑ 99Bow-228
❑ 99BowGol-228
❑ 99BowInt-228
❑ 99CroRoyB-7
❑ 99CroRoyL-7
❑ 99CroRoyOD-7
❑ 99E-X Cen-59
❑ 99E-X CenECFut-59
❑ 99E-X CenECNow-59
❑ 99FinGolRef-226
❑ 99FinRef-226
❑ 99FlaShoLeg1-117
❑ 99FlaShoLeg2-117
❑ 99FlaShoLeg3-117
❑ 99FlaShoLegM1-117
❑ 99FlaShoLegM2-117
❑ 99FlaShoLegM3-117
❑ 99FlaShoR1-117
❑ 99FlaShoR2-117
❑ 99FlaShoR3-117
❑ 99Fle-170
❑ 99FleBri-108
❑ 99FleBri2G-108
❑ 99FleBriBlu-108
❑ 99FleBriGol-108
❑ 99FleSta9-170
❑ 99FleWarT-170
❑ 99MetUni-164
❑ 99MetUniGM-164
❑ 99MetUniPMG-164
❑ 99Pac-366
❑ 99PacAur-9
❑ 99PacAurOD-9
❑ 99PacCroC-240
❑ 99PacCroCPB-240
❑ 99PacInv-6
❑ 99PacInvOD-6
❑ 99PacInvPB-6
❑ 99PacOme-11
❑ 99PacOmeC-11
❑ 99PacOmeG-11
❑ 99PacOmePB-11
❑ 99PacPar-13
❑ 99PacParC-13
❑ 99PacParG-13
❑ 99PacParHoloGold-13
❑ 99PacParHS-13
❑ 99PacParOD-13
❑ 99PacParPB-13
❑ 99PacParRed-13
❑ 99PacPlaB-366
❑ 99PacRed-366
❑ 99Rev-6
❑ 99RevPremDate-6
❑ 99RevRet-6
❑ 99RevShaSS-6
❑ 99SkyMolM-39
❑ 99SkyMolMX-39
❑ 99SkyPre-70
❑ 99SkyPreR-70
❑ 99SkyThu-235
❑ 99SkyThuRant-235
❑ 99SkyThuRave-235
❑ 99StaClu-313
❑ 99StaCluFDI-313
❑ 99StaCluOoaK-313
❑ 99StaCluPP-313
❑ 99ThuSkySupR-235
❑ 99Top-253
❑ 99TopChr-253
❑ 99TopChrR-253
❑ 99TopMVPP-253
❑ 99TopSta-128
❑ 99TopStaFoil-128
❑ 99UppDec-303
❑ 99UppDecEL1-303
❑ 99UppDecEL2-303
❑ 99UppDecM-9
❑ 99UppDecMGS-9
❑ 99UppDecMHFS-9
❑ 99UppDecMSS-9
❑ 99Vic-21

Finley, Tom
❑ 91PomBlaBPB-23

Finn, John
❑ 89AriStaB-9
❑ 89BelBre2S-9
❑ 90StoPorB-11
❑ 90StoPorCLC-196
❑ 90StoPorP-2196
❑ 91CalLeLA-30
❑ 91StoPorC-18
❑ 91StoPorP-3044
❑ 92ClaFS7-96
❑ 92ElPasDF-3929
❑ 92ElPasDS-209
❑ 92UppDecML-141
❑ 93NewOrlZF-979
❑ 98BirBarG-10

Finn, Michael
❑ 88SFHesCreN32-9

Finn, Mickey (Neal)
❑ 25Zee-154
❑ 26Zee-47
❑ 27Zee-25
❑ 28ExhPCL-7
❑ 28Zee-49
❑ 29Zee-42
❑ 33DouDisP-15
❑ 90DodTar-244

Finneran, Joseph
❑ 19Zee-134
❑ 22Zee-125

Finnerty, Keith
❑ 96NewJerCB-9

Finney, Hal
❑ 72TCMthe3-24

Finney, Lou
❑ 33RitCE-8H
❑ 35AlDemDCR3-57
❑ 35DiaMatCS3T1-51
❑ 36GouWidPPR-A31
❑ 36WorWidGV-64
❑ 38CloFotW-25
❑ 40PlaBal-197
❑ 41PlaBal-30
❑ 42RedSoxTI-11
❑ 74A's192T-10
❑ 92ConTSN-512

Finney, Mark
❑ 91BenBucCB-5
❑ 91BenBucP-3690

Finnieston, Adam R.
❑ 96LanLugB-12

Finnvold, Gar
❑ 90ElmPioP-17
❑ 91Cla/Bes-192
❑ 91LynRedSC-3
❑ 91LynRedSP-1192
❑ 92ClaFS7-195
❑ 92NewBriRSF-426
❑ 92NewBriRSS-484
❑ 92SkyAA F-206
❑ 93PawRedSDD-9
❑ 93PawRedSF-2403
❑ 93PawRedSTI-9
❑ 94Bow-231
❑ 94Fla-262
❑ 94FleUpd-11
❑ 94LeaLimR-68
❑ 94PawRedSDD-6
❑ 94PawRedSF-941
❑ 94SigRooDP-92
❑ 94SigRooDPS-92
❑ 94TopTra-96T
❑ 95Don-283
❑ 95DonPreP-283
❑ 95Fle-29
❑ 95Lea-130
❑ 95PawRedSDD-10
❑ 95PawRedTI-NNO
❑ 95Sco-580
❑ 95ScoGolR-580
❑ 95ScoPlaTS-580
❑ 95Top-92
❑ 96PawRedSDD-9

Finzer, Kory
❑ 91AubAstC-27

Fiore, Mike
❑ 85MiaHur-4
❑ 87PanAmTUBI-20
❑ 87PanAmTURB-6
❑ 88TopTra-38T
❑ 88TopTraT-38T
❑ 89SprCarB-1
❑ 89TopBig-8
❑ 90St.PetCS-8
❑ 91ArkTraLD-34
❑ 91ArkTraP-1294
❑ 91LinDriAA-34

Fiore, Mike Gary Joseph
❑ 69RoyTeal-4
❑ 69Top-376
❑ 69TopTeaP-7
❑ 70RoyTeal-12
❑ 70Top-709
❑ 71MLBOffS-318
❑ 71OPC-287
❑ 71Top-287
❑ 72MilBra-104
❑ 72OPC-199
❑ 72RedSoxTI-5
❑ 72Top-199
❑ 77RocRedWM-16
❑ 78ColCliT-6
❑ 91OriCro-131

Fiore, Tom
❑ 86KenTwiP-9

Fiore, Tony
❑ 92MarPhiC-22
❑ 92MarPhiF-3050
❑ 93BatCliCB-9
❑ 93BatCliF-3139
❑ 94SpaPhiF-1714
❑ 94SparPhiC-8
❑ 95ClePhiF-211
❑ 97ReaPhi-14
❑ 98ScrRedBQ-12

Fiorillo, Nicholas
❑ 80WatRedT-1
❑ 82WatRedT-10
❑ 83TamTarT-27

Firebird, Phineas T.
❑ 95PhoFirTI-0
❑ 96PhoFirB-29
❑ 97PhoFirTI-29

Firebirds, Phoenix
❑ 95PhoFirTI-NNO
❑ 96PhoFirB-1
❑ 97PhoFirTI-30

Fireovid, Steve
❑ 81HawIsIT-12
❑ 82HawIsIT-13
❑ 83LasVegSBHN-8
❑ 84PorBeaC-214
❑ 85BufBisT-18
❑ 86CalCanP-8
❑ 87Fle-653
❑ 87SpoTeaP-25
❑ 87SyrChiP-1933
❑ 87SyrChiT-30
❑ 87Top-357
❑ 87TopTif-357
❑ 88OmaRoyC-4
❑ 88OmaRoyP-1513
❑ 89OmaRoyC-3
❑ 89OmaRoyP-1718
❑ 90CMC-51
❑ 90IndIndC-1
❑ 90IndIndP-292
❑ 90ProAAAF-575
❑ 91BufBisLD-28
❑ 91BufBisP-534
❑ 91LinDriAAA-28
❑ 92Bow-334
❑ 92OklCit8F-1912
❑ 93OklCit8F-1621
❑ 93RanKee-146

Firestone, Roy
❑ 97FleFir-1
❑ 98CroRoyFoB-26
❑ 98CroRoyFoB-26A
❑ 98CroRoyFoBA-26

Firova, Dan
❑ 80SpoIndT-22
❑ 86CalCanP-9
❑ 89UppDec-32

Firsich, Steve
❑ 91BluOriC-20
❑ 91BluOriP-4122
❑ 92KanCouCC-24
❑ 92KanCouCF-83
❑ 92KanCouCTI-8

Fisch, Elbert
❑ 29Zee-156
❑ 30Zee-172

Fischback, Bruce
❑ 86KinEagP-7

Fischer, Bill (William Charles)
❑ 15SpoNewM-58
❑ 16SpoNewM-57
❑ 17ColE13-48
❑ 19W514-27
❑ 27Zee-68
❑ 59SenTealW-7
❑ 60TopVen-76
❑ 63AthJayP-4
❑ 67DexPre-72
❑ 72LauGreF-47
❑ 80RedEnq-6
❑ 90DodTar-947
❑ 90HOFStiB-64
❑ 94RicBraF-2863
❑ 95RicBraTI-27
❑ 96RicBraB-2
❑ 97RicBra-2
❑ 98RicBraQ-28

Fischer, Brad
❑ 82MadMusF-19
❑ 83MadMusF-31
❑ 84MadMusP-1
❑ 85HunStaJ-25
❑ 86HunStaDJ-25
❑ 87HunStaTI-11
❑ 88TacTigP-622
❑ 89TacTigC-25
❑ 89TacTigP-1551
❑ 90ProAAAF-157
❑ 90TacTigP-110
❑ 96A'sMot-28
❑ 97A'sMot-28
❑ 98A'sMot-28

Fischer, Carl
❑ 31SenTealPW-9
❑ 34DiaMatCSB-54
❑ 35DiaMatCS3T1-52
❑ 43CenFlo-8
❑ 44CenFlo-7
❑ 45CenFlo-8
❑ 74TigTCM1AC-8
❑ 76TigOldTS-7
❑ 92ConTSN-409
❑ 93DiaStaES-129

Fischer, Dan
❑ 80OmaRoyP-11
❑ 81OmaRoyT-7
❑ 82OmaRoyT-4

Fischer, Hank
❑ 63Top-554
❑ 64Top-218
❑ 64TopVen-218
❑ 65BraTeal-5
❑ 65Top-585
❑ 66Top-381
❑ 67CokCapRS-15
❑ 67Top-342
❑ 67TopRedSS-5

Fischer, Jeff
❑ 86FloStaLAP-14
❑ 86WesPalBEP-15
❑ 87IndIndTI-15
❑ 88IndIndC-6
❑ 88IndIndP-503
❑ 89AlbDukCm-3
❑ 89AlbDukP-86

❑ 90AlbDukCm-3
❑ 90AlbDukP-338
❑ 90AlbDukTr-7
❑ 90CMC-405
❑ 90DodTar-948
❑ 90ProAAAF-59
❑ 90Sco-654
❑ 93BurBeeC-28
❑ 93BurBeeF-174
❑ 94BurBeeC-27
❑ 94BurBeeF-1099
❑ 96WesPalBEB-3
Fischer, Mark
❑ 97BesAutSBPP-29
❑ 98Bes-14
❑ 98BesNumOP-22
❑ 98MicBatCM-12
❑ 98MidLeaPM-16
❑ 99BasAmeTPA-15
❑ 99JustheSAC-10
❑ 99TeaBesRA-10
Fischer, Mike
❑ 99TeaBesR-24
❑ 99TeaBesRG-24
❑ 99TeaBesRS-24
Fischer, Todd
❑ 82IdaFalAT-7
❑ 83MadMusF-4
❑ 84AlbA'sT-12
❑ 86EdmTraP-9
❑ 87CalAngPPS-14
Fischer, Tom
❑ 89Bow-20
❑ 89BowTif-20
❑ 89LynRedSS-8
❑ 90CMC-806
❑ 90NewBriRSB-2
❑ 90NewBriRSP-1312
❑ 90NewBriRSS-4
❑ 91Cla/Bes-306
❑ 91LinDriAA-458
❑ 91NewBriRSLD-458
❑ 91NewBriRSP-347
❑ 92PawRedSF-916
❑ 92PawRedSS-356
❑ 93NewBriRSF-1213
❑ 97DunDonPPS-8
Fischer, William C.
❑ 58Top-56
❑ 59Top-230
❑ 60Top-76
❑ 61Top-553
❑ 63Top-301
❑ 64Top-409
❑ 90TopTVRS-4
Fischetti, Art
❑ 75WatDodT-7
Fischlin, Mike
❑ 78ChaChaT-7
❑ 79ChaChaT-6
❑ 79Top-718
❑ 80TucTorT-17
❑ 81ChaChaT-13
❑ 82IndWhe-15
❑ 83Don-489
❑ 83Fle-407
❑ 83IndPos-14
❑ 83IndWhe-12
❑ 83Top-182
❑ 84Fle-541
❑ 84Ind-12
❑ 84IndWhe-22
❑ 84Nes792-689
❑ 84Top-689
❑ 84TopTif-689
❑ 85Don-495
❑ 85Fle-447
❑ 85Ind-13
❑ 85IndPol-22
❑ 85Top-41
❑ 85TopTif-41
❑ 86FleUpd-40
❑ 86Top-283
❑ 86TopTif-283
❑ 86YanTCM-23
❑ 87Fle-98
❑ 87FleGlo-98
❑ 87RicBraBC-7
❑ 87RicBraC-18
❑ 87RicBraT-12
❑ 87Top-434
❑ 87TopTif-434
❑ 88BobCamRB-12
❑ 88GreBraB-23
❑ 89MyrBeaBJP-1466
❑ 90MyrBeaBJP-2792
❑ 90SouAtlLAS-47
❑ 92YanWIZ8-58
Fish, Steve
❑ 97BoiHawG-10
❑ 98CedRapKTI-10
Fishel, John
❑ 86FloStaLAP-15
❑ 86OscAstP-8
❑ 87ColAstP-12
❑ 88FleUpd-88
❑ 88FleUpdG-88
❑ 88TucTorC-19
❑ 88TucTorJP-11
❑ 88TucTorP-178
❑ 89ColCliC-18
❑ 89ColCliP-20
❑ 89ColCliP-735
❑ 89Don-443
❑ 89Fle-358
❑ 89FleGlo-358
❑ 89PanSti-80
❑ 89ScoHot1R-42
❑ 90CMC-214
❑ 90ColCliC-14
❑ 90ColCliP-6
❑ 90ColCliP-689
❑ 90ProAAAF-339
❑ 90TopTVY-42
Fisher, Anthony
❑ 98SavSanGM-10
Fisher, Brian
❑ 77NewCoPT-12
Fisher, Brian K.
❑ 82DurBulT-17
❑ 84RicBraT-20
❑ 85ColCliP-11
❑ 85ColCliT-7
❑ 85FleUpd-40
❑ 85YanTCMP-40
❑ 86Don-492
❑ 86Fle-104
❑ 86KayB-12
❑ 86SevCoi-E15
❑ 86Spo-177
❑ 86Top-584
❑ 86TopGloS-30
❑ 86TopSti-312
❑ 86TopTat-2
❑ 86TopTif-584
❑ 86YanTCM-7
❑ 87Don-340
❑ 87Fle-99
❑ 87FleGlo-99
❑ 87FleUpd-32
❑ 87FleUpdG-32
❑ 87OPC-316
❑ 87SpoTeaP-18
❑ 87Top-316
❑ 87TopTif-316
❑ 87TopTra-33T
❑ 87TopTraT-33T
❑ 88Don-415
❑ 88DonBasB-101
❑ 88Fle-329
❑ 88FleGlo-329
❑ 88Lea-244
❑ 88OPC-193
❑ 88PanSti-368
❑ 88PirTeal-12
❑ 88Sco-130
❑ 88ScoGlo-130
❑ 88StaLinPi-11
❑ 88Top-193
❑ 88TopBig-159
❑ 88TopTif-193
❑ 89Bow-415
❑ 89BowTif-415
❑ 89Don-126
❑ 89Fle-209
❑ 89FleGlo-209
❑ 89OPC-303
❑ 89PirVerFJ-54
❑ 89RedFolSB-42
❑ 89Sco-24
❑ 89Top-423
❑ 89TopTif-423
❑ 89UppDec-69
❑ 90CMC-626
❑ 90OPC-666
❑ 90ProAAAF-189
❑ 90PubIntS-154
❑ 90Sco-547
❑ 90Top-666
❑ 90TopTif-666
❑ 90TucTorC-24
❑ 90TucTorP-199
❑ 90UppDec-97
❑ 91DenZepLD-137
❑ 91DenZepP-118
❑ 91LinDriAAA-137
❑ 92NasSouF-1826
❑ 92NasSouS-278
❑ 92YanWIZ8-59
❑ 93Fle-674
❑ 93PhoFirF-1511
Fisher, Chauncey
❑ 90DodTar-949
Fisher, Curt
❑ 77LynMetT-12
Fisher, David
❑ 92MarPhiC-20
❑ 92MarPhiF-3064
❑ 93ClePhiC-8
❑ 93ClePhiF-2688
❑ 94ReaPhiF-2067
❑ 95ReaPhiELC-13
❑ 95ReaPhiTI-6
❑ 96ReaPhiB-17
❑ 96ScrRedBB-14
Fisher, Eddie
❑ 60TacBan-6
❑ 60Top-23
❑ 60TopVen-23
❑ 61Top-161
❑ 61Top-366
❑ 62WhiSoxTS-7
❑ 63Top-6
❑ 63Top-223
❑ 63WhiSoxTS-6
❑ 64Top-66
❑ 64TopVen-66
❑ 64WhiSoxI-9
❑ 64WhiSoxTS-8
❑ 65Top-328
❑ 66BalOriP-14
❑ 66Baz-47
❑ 66OPC-85
❑ 66Top-85
❑ 66Top-222
❑ 66TopRubI-29
❑ 66TopVen-85
❑ 66TopVen-222
❑ 67BalOriP-39
❑ 67CokCapO-14
❑ 67DexPre-73
❑ 67Top-434
❑ 68Top-418
❑ 69Top-315
❑ 69TopSta-143
❑ 70OPC-156
❑ 70Top-156
❑ 71MLBOffS-343
❑ 71OPC-631
❑ 71Top-631
❑ 72Top-689
❑ 73OPC-439
❑ 73Top-439
❑ 81Ori6F-14
❑ 91OriCro-132
Fisher, Fritz (Frederick)
❑ 64Top-312
❑ 64TopVen-312
❑ 66Top-209
❑ 66TopVen-209
Fisher, Glen
❑ 15Zee-61
❑ 77BriRedST-5
❑ 79CedRapGT-13
❑ 81ShrCapT-6
❑ 82RedPioT-20
Fisher, Gus
❑ 09ObaT21-25
❑ 09ObaT21-116
❑ 12HomRunKE-36
❑ 12Zee-56
❑ 13Zee-56
❑ 14Zee-59
❑ 16Zee-49
❑ 17Zee-46
❑ 18Zee-43
❑ 19Zee-51
❑ 21Zee-47
Fisher, Jack H.
❑ 58BalOriP-7
❑ 60BalOriP-5
❑ 60OriJayP-3
❑ 60Top-46
❑ 60Top-399
❑ 60TopVen-46
❑ 61BalOriP-8
❑ 61SevElev-5
❑ 61Top-463
❑ 62BalOriP-8
❑ 62Top-203
❑ 63Top-474
❑ 64Top-422
❑ 65MetJayP-5
❑ 65MetPos-3
❑ 65OPC-93
❑ 65Top-93
❑ 66MetTeal-5
❑ 66MetVolC-3
❑ 66Top-316
❑ 66TopRubI-30
❑ 66TopVen-316
❑ 67CokCapYM-V32
❑ 67DexPre-74
❑ 67Kah-13
❑ 67MetPos-2
❑ 67MetTeal-5
❑ 67Top-533
❑ 68Top-444
❑ 69Top-318
❑ 70Top-684
❑ 81TCM60I-478
❑ 89ColMetB-23
❑ 89ColMetGS-2
❑ 90ColMetGS-2
❑ 90ColMetPPI-6
❑ 91MetWIZ-115
❑ 91OriCro-133
Fisher, Kyle
❑ 89AugPirP-521
Fisher, Louis
❑ 96BluOriB-12
Fisher, Pete
❑ 99TeaBesR-25
❑ 99TeaBesRG-25
❑ 99TeaBesRS-25
Fisher, Ray
❑ 11HelSta-42
❑ 11PinT-5-120
❑ 11T205-56
❑ 12ColRedB-101
❑ 12ColTinT-101
❑ 12T207-59
❑ 12T207-60
❑ 14CraJacE-102
❑ 14PieStaT-41
❑ 15CraJacE-102
❑ 15SpoNewM-59
❑ 16FleBreD-28
❑ 16SpoNewM-58
❑ 17ColE13-49
❑ 20RedWorCP-6
❑ 88PacEigMO-92
❑ 93ConTSN-702
Fisher, Robert
❑ 09ObaT21-180
❑ 12ImpTobC-43
❑ 19Zee-135
❑ 20Zee-140
❑ 90DodTar-245
Fisher, Ryan
❑ 96AugGreB-10
❑ 97EriSeaWB-12
Fisher, Showboat (George)
❑ 75SenTCM1-6
Fisher, Tom Chalmers
❑ 11SpoLifCW-126
Fisher, Tom Gene
❑ 77FriOneYW-37
❑ 91OriCro-134
Fisk, Carlton
❑ 72OPC-79
❑ 72RedSoxTI-6
❑ 72Top-79
❑ 73Kel2D-27
❑ 73LinPor-20
❑ 73OPC-193
❑ 73SevTraC-20
❑ 73Top-193
❑ 73TopCanL-15
❑ 74Kel-5
❑ 74OPC-105
❑ 74OPC-331
❑ 74Top-105
❑ 74Top-331
❑ 74TopDecE-64
❑ 74TopSta-133
❑ 75Hos-143
❑ 75OPC-80
❑ 75Top-80
❑ 75TopMin-80
❑ 76BlaDis-14
❑ 76BucDis-14
❑ 76CarDis-14
❑ 76CraDis-14
❑ 76DailsID-14
❑ 76Hos-64
❑ 76IsaDis-14
❑ 76LinSup-109
❑ 76OPC-365
❑ 76OrbDis-14
❑ 76RedBarD-14
❑ 76RedSox-4
❑ 76RedSoxSM-6
❑ 76SafDis-14
❑ 76SSP-403
❑ 76Top-365
❑ 76TowCluD-14
❑ 77BurCheD-33
❑ 77ChiWilD-21
❑ 77DailsID-21
❑ 77DetCaeD-21
❑ 77HolInnD-21
❑ 77Hos-104
❑ 77MSADis-21
❑ 77OPC-137
❑ 77PepGloD-22
❑ 77SagDis-21
❑ 77sDis-21
❑ 77Spo-5613
❑ 77Top-640
❑ 77WenDis-21
❑ 77ZipDis-21
❑ 78OPC-210
❑ 78PapGinD-25
❑ 78SSP270-180
❑ 78Top-270
❑ 78WifBalD-23
❑ 79BasPat-30
❑ 79Hos-106
❑ 79OPC-360
❑ 79Top-680
❑ 80Kel-41
❑ 80OPC-20
❑ 80Top-40
❑ 81AllGamPI-40
❑ 81Don-335
❑ 81Dra-32
❑ 81Fle-224
❑ 81FleStiC-58
❑ 81MSAMinD-12
❑ 81OPC-116
❑ 81PerAll-13
❑ 81Top-480
❑ 81TopSti-46
❑ 81TopSupHT-4
❑ 81TopTra-762
❑ 82Don-20
❑ 82Don-495
❑ 82Dra-12
❑ 82Fle-343
❑ 82Fle-632
❑ 82FleSta-183
❑ 82Kel-25
❑ 82OnDecD-12
❑ 82OPC-58
❑ 82OPC-110
❑ 82OPC-111
❑ 82PerAll-3
❑ 82PerAllG-3
❑ 82SevSluC-10
❑ 82Squ-8
❑ 82Top-110
❑ 82Top-111
❑ 82Top-554
❑ 82TopSti-138
❑ 82TopSti-170
❑ 83AllGamPI-40
❑ 83Don-104
❑ 83DonActA-43
❑ 83Fle-235
❑ 83Fle-638
❑ 83FleSta-61
❑ 83FleSti-148
❑ 83FleSti-153
❑ 83Kel-56
❑ 83OPC-20
❑ 83OPC-393
❑ 83Top-20
❑ 83Top-393
❑ 83TopGloS-17
❑ 83TopSti-54
❑ 83TopSti-177
❑ 83WhiSoxTV-72
❑ 84AllGamPI-129
❑ 84Don-302
❑ 84DonCha-52
❑ 84Fle-58
❑ 84FleSti-39
❑ 84FunFooP-72
❑ 84MilBra-9
❑ 84MLBPen-10
❑ 84Nes792-216
❑ 84Nes792-560
❑ 84OCoandSI-47
❑ 84OPC-127
❑ 84RalPur-33
❑ 84SevCoi-C12
❑ 84Top-216
❑ 84Top-560
❑ 84TopCer-33
❑ 84TopGloS-40
❑ 84TopRubD-9
❑ 84TopSti-243
❑ 84TopSup-15
❑ 84TopTif-216
❑ 84TopTif-560
❑ 84WhiSoxTV-13
❑ 85AllGamPI-39
❑ 85Don-208
❑ 85Fle-513
❑ 85GenMilS-17
❑ 85Lea-155
❑ 85OPC-49
❑ 85Top-1
❑ 85Top-770
❑ 85TopRubD-5
❑ 85TopSti-243
❑ 85TopTif-1
❑ 85TopTif-770
❑ 85WhiSoxC-72
❑ 86BasStaB-41
❑ 86Don-366
❑ 86DonAll-17
❑ 86DonPop-17
❑ 86Fle-204
❑ 86Fle-643
❑ 86FleLeaL-12
❑ 86FleLimE-15
❑ 86FleMin-43
❑ 86FleStiC-38
❑ 86FleWaxBC-C8
❑ 86GenMilB-2D
❑ 86Lea-163
❑ 86MeaGolBB-3
❑ 86MeaGolSB-13
❑ 86MSAJayPCD-7
❑ 86OPC-290
❑ 86OPCBoxB-E
❑ 86SevCoi-C12
❑ 86Spo-67
❑ 86Spo-125
❑ 86SpoDecG-62
❑ 86Top-290
❑ 86Top-719
❑ 86TopGloA-9
❑ 86TopGloS-28
❑ 86TopMinL-11
❑ 86TopSti-162
❑ 86TopSti-286
❑ 86TopSup-23
❑ 86TopTat-23
❑ 86TopTif-290
❑ 86TopTif-719
❑ 86TopWaxBC-E
❑ 86WhiSoxC-72
❑ 87ClaGam-41
❑ 87Don-247
❑ 87DonOpeD-232
❑ 87Fle-496
❑ 87FleGlo-496
❑ 87FleRecS-8
❑ 87GenMilB-3D
❑ 87Lea-199
❑ 87OPC-164
❑ 87RedFolSB-41
❑ 87SevCoi-C7
❑ 87Spo-140
❑ 87SpoTeaP-26
❑ 87StuPan-17
❑ 87Top-756
❑ 87TopSti-288
❑ 87TopTif-756
❑ 87WhiSoxC-10
❑ 88Don-260
❑ 88DonBasB-67
❑ 88Fle-397
❑ 88FleAwaW-12
❑ 88FleGlo-397
❑ 88KinDis-18
❑ 88Lea-208
❑ 88Nes-38
❑ 88OPC-385
❑ 88PanSti-55
❑ 88PanSti-91

❑ 88RedFolSB-23
❑ 88Sco-592
❑ 88ScoGlo-592
❑ 88Spo-43
❑ 88StaLinAl-11
❑ 88StaLinWS-7
❑ 88TarPla-14
❑ 88Top-321
❑ 88Top-385
❑ 88TopBig-197
❑ 88TopMinL-8
❑ 88TopSti-290
❑ 88TopTif-321
❑ 88TopTif-385
❑ 88WhiSoxC-8
❑ 88WhiSoxK-2
❑ 89Bow-62
❑ 89BowTif-62
❑ 89CadEllD-17
❑ 89Don-7
❑ 89Don-101
❑ 89DonBasB-11
❑ 89DonSupD-7
❑ 89Fle-495
❑ 89FleGlo-495
❑ 89KayB-11
❑ 89OPC-46
❑ 89PanSti-304
❑ 89RedFolSB-43
❑ 89Sco-449
❑ 89ScoHot1S-39
❑ 89Scomast-9
❑ 89Spo-219
❑ 89SpollIFKI-171
❑ 89Top-695
❑ 89TopBasT-151
❑ 89TopBig-24
❑ 89TopCoi-40
❑ 89TopDouA-8
❑ 89TopSti-299
❑ 89TopStiB-23
❑ 89TopTif-695
❑ 89TopUKM-26
❑ 89UppDec-609
❑ 89WhiSoxC-8
❑ 89WhiSoxK-3
❑ 90AllBasT-21
❑ 90Bow-314
❑ 90BowTif-314
❑ 90ClaBlu-116
❑ 90Don-58
❑ 90DonBesA-5
❑ 90DOnBonM-BC19
❑ 90DonLeaS-49
❑ 90Fle-530
❑ 90FleAwaW-13
❑ 90FleCan-530
❑ 90GooHumICBLS-8
❑ 90Hot50PS-12
❑ 90KayB-12
❑ 90Lea-10
❑ 90Lea-174
❑ 90M.Vpin-23
❑ 90OPC-392
❑ 90OPC-420
❑ 90PanSti-44
❑ 90PubIntS-284
❑ 90PubIntS-386
❑ 90RedFolSB-32
❑ 90Sco-290
❑ 90Sco100S-70
❑ 90ScoMcD-4
❑ 90Spo-204
❑ 90Top-392
❑ 90Top-420
❑ 90TopBig-176
❑ 90TopDou-23
❑ 90TopGloS-46
❑ 90TopHilHM-29
❑ 90TopMag-41
❑ 90TopSti-303
❑ 90TopStiB-55
❑ 90TopTif-392
❑ 90TopTif-420
❑ 90TopTVA-8
❑ 90UppDec-367
❑ 90WhiSoxC-3
❑ 90WhiSoxC-29
❑ 90WhiSoxK-1
❑ 90Woo-13
❑ 91BasBesRB-6
❑ 91Bow-345
❑ 91CadEllD-20
❑ 91Cla3-T21
❑ 91ClaGam-51
❑ 91Don-108
❑ 91DonBonC-BC6
❑ 91Fle-118
❑ 91KinDis-22
❑ 91Lea-384
❑ 91LeaPre-16
❑ 91MajLeaCP-14
❑ 91OPC-3
❑ 91OPC-170
❑ 91OPC-393
❑ 91OPCBoxB-F
❑ 91OPCPre-45
❑ 91PanFreS-311
❑ 91PanSti-255
❑ 91PetSta-7
❑ 91RedFolS-36
❑ 91Sco-265
❑ 91Sco-421
❑ 91Sco100S-41
❑ 91SevCoi-M4
❑ 91StaClu-180
❑ 91StaCluCM-9
❑ 91StaCluMO-14
❑ 91StaPinB-18
❑ 91Stu-32
❑ 91Top-3
❑ 91Top-170
❑ 91Top-393
❑ 91TopCraJ2-2
❑ 91TopDesS-3
❑ 91TopDesS-170
❑ 91TopDesS-393
❑ 91TopMic-3
❑ 91TopMic-170
❑ 91TopMic-393
❑ 91TopSta-14
❑ 91TopTif-3
❑ 91TopTif-170
❑ 91TopTif-393
❑ 91TopTriH-A4
❑ 91TopWaxBC-F
❑ 91Ult-72
❑ 91UppDec-29
❑ 91UppDec-643
❑ 91UppDec-677
❑ 91USPlaCA-2D
❑ 91WhiSoxK-72
❑ 91WhiSoxK-NNO0
❑ 91Woo-12
❑ 92Bow-585
❑ 92ClaGam-96
❑ 92Don-543
❑ 92Fle-79
❑ 92FleTeaL-4
❑ 92Hig5-16
❑ 92JimDeaLL-2
❑ 92Lea-303
❑ 92LeaBlaG-303
❑ 92Mr.TurS-9
❑ 92OPC-630
❑ 92OPCPre-86
❑ 92PacSea-60
❑ 92PanSti-124
❑ 92PepDieM-11
❑ 92Pin-361
❑ 92RedFolS-36
❑ 92RedFolS-113
❑ 92Sco-72
❑ 92Sco100S-72
❑ 92ScoFacI-B8
❑ 92ScoProP-17
❑ 92SpoStaCC-15
❑ 92StaClu-480
❑ 92StaCluD-49
❑ 92StuHer-BC2
❑ 92Top-630
❑ 92TopGol-630
❑ 92TopGolW-630
❑ 92TopMcD-15
❑ 92TopMic-630
❑ 92TriPla-149
❑ 92Ult-33
❑ 92UppDec-571
❑ 92WhiSoxK-72
❑ 93Bow-175
❑ 93CadDis-19
❑ 93Don-519
❑ 93Fin-125
❑ 93FinRef-125
❑ 93Fle-582
❑ 93FleFinEDT-4
❑ 93Lea-284
❑ 93MetBak-26
❑ 93OPC-78
❑ 93PacSpa-70
❑ 93PanSti-135
❑ 93Pin-301
❑ 93Pin-421
❑ 93Pin-475
❑ 93PinCoo-4
❑ 93PinCooD-4
❑ 93Sco-579
❑ 93Sel-76
❑ 93StaClu-221
❑ 93StaCluFDI-221
❑ 93StaCluMO-8
❑ 93StaCluMOP-221
❑ 93Top-230
❑ 93TopGol-230
❑ 93TopInaM-230
❑ 93TopInaR-230
❑ 93TopMic-230
❑ 93TopPre-230
❑ 93Ult-530
❑ 93UppDec-272
❑ 93UppDecGold-272
❑ 93WhiSoxSC-16
❑ 96IllLot-2
❑ 97DonSigSS-9
❑ 97FleMilDM-41
❑ 97FleMilDMR-41
❑ 98SpollIWSF-23
❑ 98SpollIWSFEE-23
❑ 98SpollIWSFFE-23
❑ 98UppDecR-21
❑ 98UppDecRSotT-CF
❑ 99UppDecCLES-CF
❑ 99UppDecCLESC-CF
❑ 99UppDecCLMS-HR4

Fisk, Don
❑ 77ForLauYS-23

Fister, Corby
❑ 90IdaFalBP-3256

Fithian, Grant
❑ 95GreBatTI-11
❑ 96NorNavB-10
❑ 97NorNav-16
❑ 97NorNavTI-9
❑ 98NorNavQ-11

Fitterer, Leo
❑ 28Zee-4

Fitterer, Scott
❑ 95StCatSTI-12
❑ 96DunBluJB-8
❑ 96DunBluJTI-10
❑ 96HagSunB-5

Fittery, Paul
❑ 15Zee-76
❑ 16Zee-78
❑ 18Zee-7
❑ 21Zee-70
❑ 22Zee-59
❑ 23Zee-85

Fitzer, Doug
❑ 91Cla/Bes-362
❑ 91SanBerSC-3
❑ 91SanBerSP-1979
❑ 92PenPilC-11
❑ 92PenPilF-2927
❑ 94RivPilCLC-27

Fitzgerald, Barry
❑ 93MarPhiC-9
❑ 93MarPhiF-3477

Fitzgerald, Brian
❑ 96EveAquB-8
❑ 97WisTimR-9
❑ 98LanJetG-9

Fitzgerald, Dave
❑ 89BelBre2S-10
❑ 89BelBrelS-5
❑ 90CalLeaACLC-54
❑ 90StoPorB-17
❑ 90StoPorCLC-178
❑ 90StoPorP-2177
❑ 91HelBreSP-18
❑ 91StoPorC-11
❑ 92ElPasDS-210

Fitzgerald, Ed
❑ 47SigOil-60
❑ 47SunBre-6
❑ 49Bow-109A
❑ 49Bow-109B
❑ 49EurSta-159
❑ 50Bow-178
❑ 52Bow-180
❑ 52Top-236
❑ 53Bri-5
❑ 54Bow-168
❑ 55Bow-208
❑ 55DonWin-3
❑ 56Top-198
❑ 57Top-22
❑ 57Top-367
❑ 58SeaTeal-10
❑ 58Top-236
❑ 59Top-33
❑ 59TopVen-33
❑ 60Top-423
❑ 83TopRep5-236

Fitzgerald, Jason
❑ 98Bow-162
❑ 98BowChr-162
❑ 98BowChrGA-162
❑ 98BowChrGAR-162
❑ 98BowChrI-162
❑ 98BowChrIR-162
❑ 98BowChrR-162
❑ 98BowGolA-162
❑ 98BowInt-162
❑ 98ColRedSM-22
❑ 98SouAtlLPM-10

Fitzgerald, John
❑ 09ObaT21-38
❑ 09ObaT21-139
❑ 09ObaT21-308
❑ 11BigEatEU-5
❑ 11Zee-67
❑ 12ObaPreT-57
❑ 12Zee-79

Fitzgerald, Justin
❑ 13Zee-57
❑ 14Zee-110
❑ 15Zee-106
❑ 16Zee-110
❑ 17Zee-89
❑ 19Zee-92
❑ 20Zee-108
❑ 21Zee-119
❑ 22Zee-98

Fitzgerald, Kevin
❑ 86EveGiaC-1
❑ 86EveGiaPC-4

Fitzgerald, Matthew
❑ 06GiaUllAFS-4
❑ 09ColChiE-102
❑ 12ColRedB-102
❑ 12ColTinT-102

Fitzgerald, Mike P.
❑ 85SprCarT-11
❑ 87ArkTraP-21
❑ 87TexLeaAF-26
❑ 88LouRedBC-18
❑ 88LouRedBP-427
❑ 88LouRedBTI-19
❑ 89LouRedBC-18
❑ 89LouRedBP-1259
❑ 89LouRedBTI-20
❑ 90ArkTraGS-13
❑ 90SprCarDGB-34

Fitzgerald, Mike R.
❑ 82TidTidT-4
❑ 83TidTidT-2
❑ 84Don-482
❑ 84FleUpd-37
❑ 84TopTra-37T
❑ 84TopTraT-37T
❑ 85AllGamPI-130
❑ 85Don-238
❑ 85ExpPos-8
❑ 85Fle-78
❑ 85FleUpd-41
❑ 85OPC-104
❑ 85OPCPos-1
❑ 85Top-104
❑ 85TopSti-108
❑ 85TopSti-372
❑ 85TopTif-104
❑ 85TopTifT-34T
❑ 85TopTra-34T
❑ 86Don-97
❑ 86ExpPos-3
❑ 86ExpProPa-26
❑ 86ExpProPo-7
❑ 86Fle-247
❑ 86GenMilB-6C
❑ 86Lea-32
❑ 86OPC-313
❑ 86Top-503
❑ 86TopTif-503
❑ 87Don-345
❑ 87ExpPos-6
❑ 87Fle-317
❑ 87FleGlo-317
❑ 87GenMilB-4B
❑ 87Lea-222
❑ 87OPC-212
❑ 87SmoNatL-14
❑ 87SpoTeaP-20
❑ 87Top-212
❑ 87TopTif-212
❑ 88Don-159
❑ 88ExpPos-8
❑ 88Fle-182
❑ 88FleGlo-182
❑ 88Lea-81
❑ 88MSAHosD-6
❑ 88OPC-386
❑ 88PanSti-322
❑ 88Sco-318
❑ 88ScoGlo-318
❑ 88StaLinE-4
❑ 88Top-674
❑ 88TopSti-78
❑ 88TopTif-674
❑ 89Don-456
❑ 89ExpPos-5
❑ 89Fle-374
❑ 89FleGlo-374
❑ 89OPC-23
❑ 89Sco-511
❑ 89Top-23
❑ 89TopTif-23
❑ 89UppDec-133
❑ 90Don-392
❑ 90ExpPos-7
❑ 90Fle-343
❑ 90FleCan-343
❑ 90OPC-484
❑ 90PubIntS-171
❑ 90Sco-361
❑ 90Top-484
❑ 90TopBig-84
❑ 90TopTif-484
❑ 90UppDec-558
❑ 91Bow-453
❑ 91Don-82
❑ 91ExpPos-4
❑ 91Fle-229
❑ 91MetWIZ-116
❑ 91OPC-317
❑ 91PanFreS-138
❑ 91Sco-198
❑ 91StaClu-128
❑ 91Stu-196
❑ 91Top-317
❑ 91TopDesS-317
❑ 91TopMic-317
❑ 91TopTif-317
❑ 91Ult-201
❑ 91UppDec-516
❑ 92Bow-186
❑ 92Fle-478
❑ 92Lea-371
❑ 92LeaBlaG-371
❑ 92OPC-761
❑ 92Sco-667
❑ 92StaClu-844
❑ 92StaCluNC-844
❑ 92Top-761
❑ 92TopGol-761
❑ 92TopGolW-761
❑ 92TopMic-761
❑ 92TopTra-31T
❑ 92TopTraG-31T
❑ 92UppDec-210
❑ 93Don-757
❑ 93NewOrlZF-975
❑ 93PacSpa-45

Fitzgerald, Ray
❑ 33WorCig(-24

Fitzgerald, Richard
❑ 52LavPro-100

Fitzmaurice, Shaun
❑ 71RicBraTI-6
❑ 77FriOneYW-113
❑ 91MetWIZ-117

Fitzmorris, Al
❑ 70OPC-241
❑ 70RoyTeal-13
❑ 70Top-241
❑ 71OPC-564
❑ 71oySigST-6
❑ 71Top-564
❑ 72OPC-349
❑ 72oyTeal-4
❑ 72Top-349
❑ 72TopCloT-10
❑ 73OPC-643
❑ 73Top-643
❑ 74OPC-191
❑ 74RoyPos-11
❑ 74Top-191
❑ 75OPC-24
❑ 75RoyPos-11
❑ 75Top-24
❑ 75TopMin-24
❑ 76Hos-8
❑ 76HosTwi-8
❑ 76KanCitRP-8
❑ 76OPC-144
❑ 76RoyAaP-5
❑ 76SSP-160
❑ 76Top-144
❑ 77IndTeal-10
❑ 77Top-449
❑ 78IndTeal-10
❑ 78Top-227
❑ 79HawIslC-19
❑ 79HawIslT-17
❑ 79Top-638

Fitzpatrick, Dan
❑ 84NewOriT-7
❑ 86BelBreP-7
❑ 87StoPorP-6
❑ 88CalLeaACLC-11
❑ 88StoPorCLC-187
❑ 88StoPorP-745
❑ 89StoPorB-12
❑ 89StoPorCLC-151
❑ 89StoPorP-395

Fitzpatrick, David
❑ 91KisDodP-4177
❑ 92GreFalDSP-16
❑ 93HicCraC-8
❑ 93HicCraF-1273
❑ 94SouBenSHC-6
❑ 94SouBenSHF-587

Fitzpatrick, Edward
❑ 11MecDFT-21
❑ 12ImpTobC-70
❑ 97BatCliTI-9

Fitzpatrick, Gary
❑ 83LynPirT-27

Fitzpatrick, John
❑ 31Zee-64
❑ 32Zee-72
❑ 33Zee-23
❑ 49W72HolS-3
❑ 50W720HolS-8
❑ 54Top-213
❑ 94TopArc1-213
❑ 94TopArc1G-213

Fitzpatrick, Ken
❑ 94RocRoyC-9
❑ 94RocRoyF-557
❑ 95SprSulTI-8

Fitzpatrick, Luke
❑ 98HicCraM-14
❑ 98HicCraUO-17

Fitzpatrick, Mike
❑ 89EasLeaDDP-DD48

Fitzpatrick, Rob (Robert)
❑ 90JamExpP-2
❑ 91Cla/Bes-254
❑ 91RocExpC-14
❑ 91RocExpP-2049
❑ 92WesPalBEC-4
❑ 92WesPalBEF-2091
❑ 93HarSenF-272
❑ 94Bow-256
❑ 94HarSenF-2095
❑ 95HarSenTI-14

Fitzpatrick, Will
❑ 93PocPosF-4214
❑ 93PocPosSP-8
❑ 94BelBreC-10
❑ 94BelBreFI-107
❑ 94MidLeaAF-MDW8

Fitzsimmons, Freddie (Fred)
❑ 28PorandAR-A6
❑ 28PorandAR-B6
❑ 28W56PlaC-D13
❑ 29PorandAR-23
❑ 31Exh-10
❑ 33ExhFou-5
❑ 33Gou-130
❑ 33Gou-235
❑ 34BatR31-72
❑ 34DiaMatCSB-55
❑ 34GouCanV-20
❑ 35DiaMatCS3T1-53
❑ 35GouPuzR-8A
❑ 35GouPuzR-8M
❑ 36DiaMatCS4-3
❑ 36SandSW-16
❑ 36WorWidGV-14
❑ 39PlaBal-110
❑ 40DodTeal-7
❑ 40PlaBal-65

❑ 41DouPlaR-143
❑ 43DodTeal-9
❑ 49GiaTeal-4
❑ 52Bow-234
❑ 60Top-462
❑ 72TCMthe3-25
❑ 73Dod194T-8
❑ 75Gia195T-33
❑ 77GalGloG-75
❑ 78DodTCM4-20
❑ 79DiaGre-29
❑ 82TCMGreP-41
❑ 85BigLeaC3-62
❑ 90DodTar-246
❑ 91ConTSN-260
❑ 94ConTSN-1117
❑ 94ConTSNB-1117

Fitzsimmons, Hadley
❑ 72TCMthe3-25

Fitzsimmons, Tom
❑ 90DodTar-950

Fix, Greg
❑ 86SalAngC-91
❑ 87QuaCitAP-17

Flach, Jason
❑ 96EugEmeB-23
❑ 97EugEmeB-6
❑ 98DanQ-C-13

Flack, Max
❑ 15SpoNewM-60
❑ 16SpoNewM-59
❑ 21E121So1-24
❑ 22E120-156
❑ 22W573-39
❑ 23W501-118
❑ 23WilChoV-42
❑ 25Exh-60

Flacon, Bobby
❑ 75WatRoyT-11

Flagg, Paul
❑ 92GulCoaDF-3578

Flagstead, Ira
❑ 19W514-1
❑ 20NatCarE-28
❑ 21E121So1-25
❑ 21Exh-48
❑ 22E120-53
❑ 22W573-40
❑ 23W501-7
❑ 25Exh-66
❑ 26Exh-65
❑ 27Exh-33
❑ 27YorCarE-21
❑ 28Exh-33
❑ 28StaPlaCE-20
❑ 31Zee-65
❑ 87ConSer2-34
❑ 91ConTSN-291

Flaherty, Bernie
❑ 93ElmPioC-28
❑ 93ElmPioF-3840

Flaherty, Ed
❑ 21Zee-120

Flaherty, John F.
❑ 55Bow-272

Flaherty, John Timothy
❑ 88ElmPioC-13
❑ 89WinHavRSS-7
❑ 90CMC-262
❑ 90PawRedSC-11
❑ 90PawRedSDD-6
❑ 90PawRedSP-464
❑ 90ProAAAF-436
❑ 90TopTVRS-43
❑ 91LinDriAA-459
❑ 91NewBriRSLD-459
❑ 91NewBriRSP-355
❑ 91PawRedSDD-4
❑ 92DonRoo-37
❑ 92Lea-439
❑ 92LeaBlaG-439
❑ 92TopTra-32T
❑ 92TopTraG-32T
❑ 92Ult-313
❑ 93Don-561
❑ 93PacSpa-32
❑ 93PawRedSDD-10
❑ 93PawRedSF-2410
❑ 93PawRedSTI-10
❑ 93RedSoxP-12
❑ 93Sco-278
❑ 94Don-596
❑ 94Pin-443
❑ 94PinArtP-443
❑ 94PinMusC-443
❑ 94Sco-313
❑ 94ScoGolR-313
❑ 94TolMudHF-1028
❑ 94Top-197
❑ 94TopGol-197
❑ 94TopSpa-197
❑ 95DonTopotO-74
❑ 95FleUpd-19
❑ 95Top-334
❑ 96ColCho-141
❑ 96ColChoGS-141
❑ 96ColChoSS-141
❑ 96Don-300
❑ 96DonPreP-300
❑ 96Fle-110
❑ 96FleTif-110
❑ 96LeaSigEA-52
❑ 96MetUni-58
❑ 96MetUniP-58
❑ 96Pac-314
❑ 96PanSti-148
❑ 96Sco-424
❑ 96StaClu-397
❑ 96StaCluMOP-397
❑ 96Top-291
❑ 96Ult-59
❑ 96UltGolM-59
❑ 97Cir-83
❑ 97CirRav-83
❑ 97ColCho-446
❑ 97Fle-460
❑ 97FleTif-460
❑ 97PadMot-9
❑ 97Pin-141
❑ 97PinArtP-PP141
❑ 97PinMusC-141
❑ 97PinPrePla-141
❑ 97StaClu-348
❑ 97StaCluMOP-348
❑ 97Top-412
❑ 97Ult-281
❑ 97UltGolME-281
❑ 97UltPlaME-281
❑ 97UppDec-491
❑ 98ColCho-509
❑ 98DevRayP-13
❑ 98Pac-425
❑ 98PacOnl-708
❑ 98PacOnlR-708
❑ 98PacOnlWC-708
❑ 98PacPar-96
❑ 98PacParC-96
❑ 98PacParG-96
❑ 98PacParHS-96
❑ 98PacParPB-96
❑ 98PacParR-96
❑ 98PacPlaB-425
❑ 98PacRedT-425
❑ 98PacSil-425
❑ 98PinPlu-146
❑ 98PinSna-TBDR3
❑ 98Top-62
❑ 98Top-460
❑ 98TopChr-62
❑ 98TopChr-460
❑ 98TopChrR-62
❑ 98TopChrR-460
❑ 98TopDevR-62
❑ 98TopDevR-460
❑ 98TopDia-62
❑ 98TopDia-460
❑ 98TopMiniC-62
❑ 98TopMiniC-460
❑ 98UppDec-737
❑ 99Top-4
❑ 99TopChr-4
❑ 99TopChrR-4
❑ 99TopMVPP-4

Flaherty, Patrick
❑ 09ColChiE-103A
❑ 09ColChiE-103B
❑ 11SpoLifCW-127
❑ 12ColRedB-103A
❑ 12ColRedB-103B
❑ 12ColTinT-103A
❑ 12ColTinT-103B

Flaherty, Tim
❑ 97SalVolG-13

Flammang, Chris
❑ 80SanJosMJitB-7
❑ 81SpoIndT-1

Flammini, Bert
❑ 55DesMoiHB-6

Flanagan, Dan
❑ 90CliGiaUTI-U4
❑ 90EveGiaB-4
❑ 90EveGiaP-3120
❑ 91CliGiaC-2
❑ 91CliGiaP-827
❑ 92CalLeaACL-7
❑ 92SanJosGC-12

Flanagan, James
❑ 09T206-422

Flanagan, Mike
❑ 76BalOriP-12
❑ 76OPC-589
❑ 76Top-589
❑ 77Spo-10201
❑ 77Top-106
❑ 78BalOriP-8
❑ 78Hos-134
❑ 78OPC-231
❑ 78Top-341
❑ 79BalOriP-6
❑ 79Kel-48
❑ 79OPC-76
❑ 79Top-160
❑ 80BalOriP-5
❑ 80Kel-3
❑ 80OPC-335
❑ 80Top-205
❑ 80Top-640
❑ 81AllGamPI-79
❑ 81Don-234
❑ 81Fle-171
❑ 81FleStiC-56
❑ 81Kel-60
❑ 81OPC-10
❑ 81Top-10
❑ 82BalOriP-2
❑ 82Don-329
❑ 82Fle-165
❑ 82FleSta-145
❑ 82OPC-153
❑ 82Top-520
❑ 82TopSti-148
❑ 82TopStiV-148
❑ 83AllGamPI-77
❑ 83Don-105
❑ 83Fle-60
❑ 83FleSta-62
❑ 83FleSti-193
❑ 83OPC-172
❑ 83OriPos-11
❑ 83Top-445
❑ 83TopSti-25
❑ 84BalOriP-13
❑ 84Don-169
❑ 84Fle-8
❑ 84FleSti-63
❑ 84Nes792-295
❑ 84OPC-295
❑ 84OriEng-5
❑ 84Top-295
❑ 84TopSti-12
❑ 84TopSti-210
❑ 84TopTif-295
❑ 85BalOriP-9
❑ 85Don-88
❑ 85Fle-177
❑ 85Lea-175
❑ 85OPC-46
❑ 85OriHea-7
❑ 85Top-780
❑ 85TopMin-780
❑ 85TopSti-207
❑ 85TopTif-780
❑ 86BalOriHMP-7
❑ 86Don-576
❑ 86Fle-275
❑ 86Spo-59
❑ 86Top-365
❑ 86TopTif-365
❑ 87BalOriP-11
❑ 87Don-459
❑ 87Fle-470
❑ 87FleGlo-470
❑ 87OPC-112
❑ 87OriFreB-46
❑ 87Top-748
❑ 87TopTif-748
❑ 88BluJayFS-12
❑ 88Don-636
❑ 88DonBasB-272
❑ 88FleUpd-67
❑ 88FleUpdG-67
❑ 88OPC-164
❑ 88Sco-427
❑ 88ScoGlo-427
❑ 88Top-623
❑ 88TopTif-623
❑ 89BluJayFS-10
❑ 89Bow-241
❑ 89BowTif-241
❑ 89Don-324
❑ 89DonBasB-316
❑ 89Fle-233
❑ 89FleGlo-233
❑ 89OPC-139
❑ 89RedFolSB-44
❑ 89Sco-475
❑ 89Top-139
❑ 89TopBasT-108
❑ 89TopBig-243
❑ 89TopSti-190
❑ 89TopTif-139
❑ 89UppDec-385
❑ 90Don-324
❑ 90Fle-81
❑ 90FleCan-81
❑ 90OPC-78
❑ 90PubIntS-514
❑ 90Sco-67
❑ 90Top-78
❑ 90TopTif-78
❑ 90UppDec-483
❑ 91BalOriP-7
❑ 91Lea-479
❑ 91OriCro-135
❑ 91ScoRoo-2T
❑ 91StaCluMO-10
❑ 92BalOriP-9
❑ 92Don-196
❑ 92Fle-7
❑ 92OPC-218
❑ 92Pin-475
❑ 92Sco-333
❑ 92Sco-427
❑ 92StaClu-30
❑ 92Top-218
❑ 92TopGol-218
❑ 92TopGolW-218
❑ 92TopMic-218
❑ 92UppDec-380
❑ 93StaClu-123
❑ 93StaCluFDI-123
❑ 93StaCluMOP-123
❑ 93Top-381
❑ 93TopGol-381
❑ 93TopInaM-381
❑ 93TopInaR-381
❑ 93TopMic-381
❑ 95BalOriP-19

Flanders, Craig
❑ 75WatRoyT-12

Flanigan, Steve
❑ 96AugGreB-11

Flanigan, Thomas
❑ 87OldJudN-169

Flannelly, Tim
❑ 91OneYanP-4161
❑ 92GreHorC-3
❑ 92GreHorF-786
❑ 92ProFS7-128
❑ 92StaCluD-50
❑ 93PriWilCC-9
❑ 93PriWilCF-663

Flannery, John
❑ 76QuaCitAT-15
❑ 79KnoKnoST-10
❑ 81EdmTraRR-11
❑ 82BirBarT-15

Flannery, Kevin
❑ 81AppFoxT-4
❑ 82AppFoxFr-21
❑ 83TolMudHT-3

Flannery, Tim
❑ 80HawIsIT-19
❑ 80Top-685
❑ 81Fle-493A
❑ 81Fle-493B
❑ 81HawIsIT-1
❑ 81Top-579
❑ 82Don-61
❑ 82Fle-572
❑ 82Top-249
❑ 83Don-472
❑ 83Fle-359
❑ 83FleSti-226
❑ 83PadTeal-7
❑ 83Top-38
❑ 84Don-202
❑ 84Fle-299
❑ 84Nes792-674
❑ 84PadMot-12
❑ 84PadSmo-9
❑ 84Top-674
❑ 84TopTif-674
❑ 85Don-551
❑ 85Fle-31
❑ 85PadMot-20
❑ 85Top-182
❑ 85TopTif-182
❑ 86Don-383
❑ 86Fle-320
❑ 86OPC-387
❑ 86PadFirPTB-2
❑ 86Top-413
❑ 86TopSti-112
❑ 86TopTif-413
❑ 87Don-287
❑ 87Fle-413
❑ 87FleGlo-413
❑ 87OPC-52
❑ 87PadBohHB-11
❑ 87Top-763
❑ 87TopSti-114
❑ 87TopTif-763
❑ 88Don-328
❑ 88Fle-582
❑ 88FleGlo-582
❑ 88OPC-262
❑ 88PadCok-11
❑ 88PadSmo-8
❑ 88PanSti-404
❑ 88Sco-483
❑ 88ScoGlo-483
❑ 88Top-513
❑ 88TopSti-108
❑ 88TopTif-513
❑ 89Bow-457
❑ 89BowTif-457
❑ 89Don-364
❑ 89PadCok-4
❑ 89PadMag-15
❑ 89PadPos-10
❑ 89Sco-513
❑ 89Top-379
❑ 89TopBig-174
❑ 89TopTif-379
❑ 89UppDec-603
❑ 90PubIntS-48
❑ 93SpoIndC-28
❑ 93SpoIndF-3606
❑ 94RanCucQC-26
❑ 94RanCucQF-1651
❑ 96PadMot-28
❑ 97PadMot-28
❑ 98PadMot-28

Flannigan, R
❑ 19Zee-93

Flashkamper, Ray
❑ 23Zee-129
❑ 24Zee-89
❑ 26Zee-135

Flater, John
❑ 09ColChiE-104
❑ 09ObaT21-273
❑ 11Zee-26
❑ 12ColRedB-104
❑ 12ColTinT-104
❑ 12HomRunKE-8
❑ 12ObaPreT-22
❑ 12PCLPin-6
❑ 12Zee-9

Flath, Daniel
❑ 90SarWhiSS-30

Flavin, John
❑ 77FriOneYW-61

Fleck, Will
❑ 97DanBraB-16
❑ 98MacBraM-6

Fleet, Joe
❑ 91WatIndC-4
❑ 91WatIndP-3359
❑ 93KinIndC-9
❑ 93KinIndF-2240
❑ 93KinIndTI-8

Fleet, Kenyatta
❑ 92ColRedC-26
❑ 92ColRedF-2383

Fleetham, Ben
❑ 94VerExpF-3904
❑ 96DelShoB-17
❑ 96WesPalBEB-10
❑ 97HarSen-11

Fleetwood, Tony
❑ 96WatIndTI-9

Fleharty, Earle
❑ 14Zee-131

Fleischer, Herb
❑ 52LavPro-47

Fleita, Oneri
❑ 89FreKeyS-6
❑ 90WauTimP-2145
❑ 91KanCouCC-28
❑ 91KanCouCP-2675
❑ 92FreKeyC-28
❑ 92FreKeyF-1823

Fleming, Bill
❑ 91PacSenL-84

Fleming, Bill (Leslie Fletchard)
❑ 42CubTeal-5
❑ 43CubTeal-8
❑ 44CubTeal-8

Fleming, Carlton
❑ 92ClaDraP-98
❑ 92OneYanC-5
❑ 93CarLeaAGF-21
❑ 93PriWilCC-10
❑ 93PriWilCF-664
❑ 94AlbYanF-1448
❑ 95NorNavTI-19
❑ 96NorNavB-11

Fleming, Dave
❑ 90Bes-57
❑ 90TopMag-92
❑ 91Bow-249
❑ 91Cla/Bes-284
❑ 91JacSunLD-336
❑ 91JacSunP-146
❑ 91LinDriAA-336
❑ 92Bow-624
❑ 92Cla1-T34
❑ 92ClaGam-163
❑ 92Don-404
❑ 92DonRooP-BC4
❑ 92FleUpd-55
❑ 92JimDeaRS-6
❑ 92Lea-494
❑ 92LeaBlaG-494
❑ 92MarMot-17
❑ 92OPC-192
❑ 92Pin-275
❑ 92PinRoo-13
❑ 92PinRooI-14
❑ 92ProFS7-141
❑ 92ScoRoo-85T
❑ 92StaClu-814
❑ 92StaCluECN-814
❑ 92Top-192
❑ 92TopDeb91-56
❑ 92TopGol-192
❑ 92TopGolW-192
❑ 92TopMic-192
❑ 92UppDec-4
❑ 92UppDecSR-SR8
❑ 93Bow-487
❑ 93ClaGam-34
❑ 93Don-243
❑ 93Fin-196
❑ 93FinRef-196
❑ 93Fle-306
❑ 93FleAll-AL11
❑ 93FleRooS-RSA5
❑ 93FunPac-113
❑ 93MariStaClu-8
❑ 93MarMot-2
❑ 93OPC-67
❑ 93PacSpa-285
❑ 93PanSti-57
❑ 93Pin-5
❑ 93PinTea2-23
❑ 93Pos-1
❑ 93Sco-356
❑ 93Sel-271
❑ 93SelAce-23
❑ 93SelChaR-20
❑ 93SelChaS-22
❑ 93SP-130
❑ 93StaClu-358
❑ 93StaCluFDI-358
❑ 93StaCluMOP-358
❑ 93Top-45
❑ 93Top-410
❑ 93TopComotH-13
❑ 93TopGol-45
❑ 93TopGol-410
❑ 93TopInaM-45
❑ 93TopInaM-410
❑ 93TopInaR-45
❑ 93TopInaR-410
❑ 93TopMic-45
❑ 93TopMic-410
❑ 93TopPreS-5
❑ 93Toy-77
❑ 93TriPla-99
❑ 93Ult-268
❑ 93UppDec-141

❑ 93UppDecGold-141
❑ 93USPlaCR-1D
❑ 94Bow-117
❑ 94ColC-101
❑ 94ColChoGS-101
❑ 94ColChoSS-101
❑ 94Don-183
❑ 94Fin-172
❑ 94FinRef-172
❑ 94Fla-102
❑ 94Fle-285
❑ 94FleExtB-165
❑ 94FUnPac-135
❑ 94Lea-149
❑ 94MarMot-10
❑ 94OPC-183
❑ 94Pac-569
❑ 94Pin-158
❑ 94PinArtP-158
❑ 94PinMusC-158
❑ 94Sco-135
❑ 94ScoGolR-135
❑ 94Sel-173
❑ 94StaClu-409
❑ 94StaCluFDI-409
❑ 94StaCluGR-409
❑ 94StaCluMOP-409
❑ 94Top-415
❑ 94TopGol-415
❑ 94TopSpa-415
❑ 94TriPla-126
❑ 94Ult-119
❑ 94UppDec-246
❑ 94UppDecED-246
❑ 95ColCho-293
❑ 95ColChoGS-293
❑ 95ColChoSS-293
❑ 95Don-373
❑ 95DonPreP-373
❑ 95Fle-267
❑ 95Lea-37
❑ 95MarMot-3
❑ 95Pac-396
❑ 95Sco-212
❑ 95ScoGolR-212
❑ 95ScoPlaTS-212
❑ 95StaClu-487
❑ 95StaCluMOP-487
❑ 95StaCluSTWS-487
❑ 95StaCluVR-267
❑ 95StaCluVRMO-267
❑ 95Top-482
❑ 95TopCyb-274
❑ 95Ult-100
❑ 95UltGolM-100
❑ 95UppDec-348
❑ 95UppDecED-348
❑ 95UppDecEDG-348

Fleming, Emar
❑ 98SavSanGM-11

Fleming, Hap
❑ 91MisStaB-16
❑ 92MisStaB-15
❑ 93MisStaB-16

Fleming, Henry
❑ 87WytCubP-15

Fleming, Jack
❑ 77DayBealT-6
❑ 80TucTorT-7

Fleming, Jim
❑ 88OklSoo-4
❑ 89OklSoo-3
❑ 91JamExpP-3561
❑ 92JamExpC-27
❑ 92JamExpF-1517

Fleming, John
❑ 97LetBlaDB-20

Fleming, Keith
❑ 87StoPorP-20
❑ 88StoPorCLC-185
❑ 88StoPorP-725
❑ 89ElPasDGS-7
❑ 90BelBreB-25
❑ 90BelBreS-7

Fleming, Les
❑ 47IndTeal-9
❑ 47IndVanPP-8
❑ 49EurSta-160
❑ 76TayBow4-67

Fleming, Paul
❑ 82WisRapTF-8

Fleming, Ricky
❑ 86EveGiaPC-5

Flener, Huck
❑ 90St.CatBJP-3470
❑ 91MyrBeaHC-4
❑ 91MyrBeaHP-2938
❑ 92DunBluJC-24
❑ 92DunBluJF-1992
❑ 92ProFS7-173
❑ 93KnoSmoF-1246
❑ 94Pac-640
❑ 94StaCluT-177
❑ 94StaCluTFDI-177
❑ 94SyrChiF-968
❑ 94SyrChiTI-12
❑ 94Top-39
❑ 94TopGol-39
❑ 94TopSpa-39
❑ 94VenLinU-128
❑ 95SyrChiTI-13
❑ 96SyrChiTI-12
❑ 97BluJayS-52
❑ 97Fle-238
❑ 97FleTif-238
❑ 97SyrSkyCB-10
❑ 98BufBisG-11

Flesher, Jay
❑ 89GeoColC-8

Fleshman, Richard
❑ 75ForLauYS-10
❑ 77WesHavYT-9

Fletcher, Arthur
❑ 09SpoNewSM-99
❑ 09T206-132
❑ 10CouT21-23
❑ 11HelSta-127
❑ 11S74Sil-86
❑ 11SpoLifM-210
❑ 11T205-57
❑ 12HasTriFT-29C
❑ 12HasTriFT-48E
❑ 12T207-61
❑ 14B18B-67
❑ 14FatPlaT-14
❑ 14PieStaT-42
❑ 14PolGroW-8
❑ 15SpoNewM-61
❑ 16SpoNewM-60
❑ 17ColE13-50
❑ 17HolBreD-30
❑ 19W514-14
❑ 20NatCarE-29
❑ 20W516-14
❑ 20W52-5
❑ 21Exh-49
❑ 21Nei-107
❑ 22E120-197
❑ 22W573-41
❑ 23W503-30
❑ 40PlaBal-125
❑ 43YanSta-11
❑ 61Fle-106
❑ 75YanDyn1T-15
❑ 77GalGloG-183
❑ 79Yan192T-9
❑ 84Yan192G-21
❑ 87ConSer2-32
❑ 88ConSer4-11
❑ 91ConTSN-117
❑ 92ConTSN-490

Fletcher, Bob
❑ 89GreFalDSP-27
❑ 89SarWhiSS-5
❑ 90VerBeaDS-13

Fletcher, Darrin
❑ 88SanAntMB-15
❑ 89AlbDukCm-18
❑ 89AlbDukP-58
❑ 90AlbDukCm-15
❑ 90AlbDukP-348
❑ 90AlbDukTr-8
❑ 90CMC-417
❑ 90DodTar-951
❑ 90ProAAAF-69
❑ 90Sco-622
❑ 90TopDeb89-38
❑ 90TriAllGP-AAA44
❑ 91Bow-496
❑ 91Cla2-T5
❑ 91Don-47
❑ 91FleUpd-107
❑ 91LinDriAAA-483
❑ 91OPC-9
❑ 91PhiMed-14
❑ 91ScrRedBLD-483
❑ 91ScrRedBP-2541
❑ 91Top-9
❑ 91TopDesS-9
❑ 91TopMic-9
❑ 91TopTif-9
❑ 91Ult-377
❑ 91UppDec-428
❑ 92Bow-609
❑ 92Don-319
❑ 92ExpDonD-8
❑ 92ExpPos-12
❑ 92Fle-530
❑ 92IndIndF-1861
❑ 92Lea-264
❑ 92LeaBlaG-264
❑ 92OPC-159
❑ 92OPCPre-41
❑ 92Sco-193
❑ 92ScoRoo-64T
❑ 92Top-159
❑ 92TopGol-159
❑ 92TopGolW-159
❑ 92TopMic-159
❑ 92TopTra-33T
❑ 92TopTraG-33T
❑ 92Ult-517
❑ 92UppDec-108
❑ 93Bow-620
❑ 93CadDis-20
❑ 93Don-378
❑ 93ExpPosN-10
❑ 93Fle-460
❑ 93Lea-165
❑ 93OPC-64
❑ 93PacSpa-184
❑ 93PanSti-224
❑ 93Sco-216
❑ 93SP-103
❑ 93StaClu-272
❑ 93StaCluFDI-272
❑ 93StaCluMOP-272
❑ 93Top-665
❑ 93TopGol-665
❑ 93TopInaM-665
❑ 93TopInaR-665
❑ 93TopMic-665
❑ 93Ult-67
❑ 93UppDec-614
❑ 93UppDecGold-614
❑ 94Bow-612
❑ 94ColC-102
❑ 94ColChoGS-102
❑ 94ColChoSS-102
❑ 94Don-152
❑ 94Fin-137
❑ 94FinRef-137
❑ 94Fla-188
❑ 94Fle-537
❑ 94FleExtB-304
❑ 94Lea-118
❑ 94Pac-379
❑ 94Pin-205
❑ 94PinArtP-205
❑ 94PinMusC-205
❑ 94Sco-436
❑ 94ScoGolR-436
❑ 94Sel-168
❑ 94StaClu-42
❑ 94StaCluFDI-42
❑ 94StaCluGR-42
❑ 94StaCluMOP-42
❑ 94Top-412
❑ 94TopGol-412
❑ 94TopSpa-412
❑ 94TriPla-94
❑ 94Ult-226
❑ 94UppDec-459
❑ 94UppDecED-459
❑ 95ColCho-243
❑ 95ColChoGS-243
❑ 95ColChoSS-243
❑ 95Don-40
❑ 95DonPreP-40
❑ 95DonTopotO-280
❑ 95Fin-156
❑ 95FinRef-156
❑ 95Fla-375
❑ 95Fle-349
❑ 95Lea-133
❑ 95Pac-266
❑ 95PanSti-22
❑ 95Sco-387
❑ 95ScoGolR-387
❑ 95ScoPlaTS-387
❑ 95StaClu-192
❑ 95StaCluFDI-192
❑ 95StaCluMOP-192
❑ 95StaCluSTWS-192
❑ 95StaCluVR-100
❑ 95StaCluVRMO-100
❑ 95Top-255
❑ 95TopCyb-140
❑ 95Ult-190
❑ 95UltGolM-190
❑ 96ColCho-614
❑ 96ColChoGS-614
❑ 96ColChoSS-614
❑ 96Don-58
❑ 96DonPreP-58
❑ 96EmoXL-221
❑ 96ExpDis-8
❑ 96Fin-B94
❑ 96FinRef-B94
❑ 96Fla-305
❑ 96Fle-456
❑ 96FleTif-456
❑ 96LeaSigA-68
❑ 96LeaSigAG-68
❑ 96LeaSigAS-68
❑ 96MetUni-190
❑ 96MetUniP-190
❑ 96ProSta-47
❑ 96Sco-97
❑ 96StaClu-345
❑ 96StaCluEPB-345
❑ 96StaCluEPG-345
❑ 96StaCluEPS-345
❑ 96StaCluMOP-345
❑ 96Top-127
❑ 96Ult-231
❑ 96UltGolM-231
❑ 96UppDec-391
❑ 97Cir-145
❑ 97CirRav-145
❑ 97ColCho-387
❑ 97Fin-187
❑ 97FinRef-187
❑ 97Fle-378
❑ 97FleTif-378
❑ 97MetUni-153
❑ 97PacPriGotD-GD168
❑ 97Pin-135
❑ 97PinArtP-PP135
❑ 97PinMusC-135
❑ 97PinPrePla-135
❑ 97StaClu-360
❑ 97StaCluMOP-360
❑ 97Top-265
❑ 97Ult-229
❑ 97UltGolME-229
❑ 97UltPlaME-229
❑ 97UppDec-426
❑ 98CirThu-119
❑ 98CirThuRav-119
❑ 98CirThuSupRav-119
❑ 98ColCho-522
❑ 98Fle-63
❑ 98Fle-559
❑ 98Pac-344
❑ 98PacOnl-762
❑ 98PacOnlR-762
❑ 98PacOnlWC-762
❑ 98PacPlaB-344
❑ 98PacRedT-344
❑ 98PacSil-344
❑ 98PinPlu-145
❑ 98StaCluFDI-249
❑ 98StaCluI-249
❑ 98StaCluOneK-249
❑ 98StaCluPP-249
❑ 98Top-451
❑ 98TopChr-451
❑ 98TopChrR-451
❑ 98TopDevR-451
❑ 98TopDia-451
❑ 98TopMiniC-451
❑ 98UppDec-746
❑ 99Fle-400
❑ 99FleSta9-400
❑ 99FleWarT-400
❑ 99Pac-442
❑ 99PacPlaB-442
❑ 99PacRed-442
❑ 99StaClu-244
❑ 99StaCluFDI-244
❑ 99StaCluOoaK-244
❑ 99StaCluPP-244
❑ 99Top-187
❑ 99TopChr-187
❑ 99TopChrR-187
❑ 99TopMVPP-187
❑ 99UppDec-225
❑ 99UppDecEL1-225
❑ 99UppDecEL2-225
❑ 99UppDecM-214
❑ 99UppDecMGS-214
❑ 99UppDecMHFS-214
❑ 99UppDecMSS-214

Fletcher, David
❑ 90MedHatBJB-17

Fletcher, Dennis
❑ 90ProAaA-77
❑ 90SavCarP-2064
❑ 91SprCarC-17
❑ 91SprCarP-738
❑ 92St.PetCC-2
❑ 92St.PetCF-2023

Fletcher, Don
❑ 76CliPilT-15
❑ 91PacSenL-103

Fletcher, Elburt
❑ 36GouWidPPR-C10
❑ 39PlaBal-69
❑ 40PlaBal-103
❑ 41DouPlaR-149
❑ 41Gou-26
❑ 41PlaBal-62
❑ 46SpoExcW-3-10
❑ 47TipTop-139
❑ 49EurSta-9
❑ 76TayBow4-72
❑ 79DiaGre-361
❑ 83TCMPla1943-32
❑ 95ConTSN-1373

Fletcher, Guy (Van)
❑ 46SunBre-5
❑ 47SigOil-61
❑ 47SigOil-76
❑ 47SunBre-7
❑ 54SeaPop-9
❑ 55SeaPop-6

Fletcher, Mitch
❑ 80TulDriT-26

Fletcher, Paul
(Edward Paul)
❑ 88MarPhiS-14
❑ 89BatCliP-1921
❑ 90SpaPhiB-2
❑ 90SpaPhiP-2483
❑ 90SpaPhiS-7
❑ 91Cla/Bes-111
❑ 91ClePhiC-2
❑ 91ClePhiP-1613
❑ 92EugEmeC-14
❑ 92EugEmeF-3024
❑ 92ReaPhiF-567
❑ 92ReaPhiS-535
❑ 93Bow-272
❑ 93ClaFS7-79
❑ 93ScrRedBF-2541
❑ 93ScrRedBTI-9
❑ 94ScrRedBF-918
❑ 95ScrRedBTI-8
❑ 97IowCub-12
❑ 98SyrSkyG-13

Fletcher, Rob
❑ 90WesPalBES-6
❑ 91ModA'sC-4
❑ 91ModA'sP-3096

Fletcher, Scott
❑ 80VenLeaS-158
❑ 82Don-554
❑ 82IowCubT-2
❑ 83WhiSoxTV-1
❑ 84Don-452
❑ 84Fle-59
❑ 84Nes792-364
❑ 84Top-364
❑ 84TopSti-250
❑ 84TopTif-364
❑ 84WhiSoxTV-14
❑ 85Don-330
❑ 85Fle-514
❑ 85Top-78
❑ 85TopSti-240
❑ 85TopTif-78
❑ 85WhiSoxC-1
❑ 86BasStaB-42
❑ 86Don-282
❑ 86DonHig-28
❑ 86Fle-205
❑ 86FleUpd-41
❑ 86OPC-187
❑ 86RanPer-1
❑ 86Top-187
❑ 86TopTif-187
❑ 86TopTra-36T
❑ 86TopTraT-36T
❑ 87ClaUpdY-118
❑ 87Don-304
❑ 87DonOpeD-171
❑ 87Fle-123
❑ 87FleAwaW-13
❑ 87FleGlo-123
❑ 87Lea-226
❑ 87RanMot-6
❑ 87RanSmo-13
❑ 87Spo-113
❑ 87Spo-136
❑ 87SpoTeaP-1
❑ 87Top-462
❑ 87TopSti-237
❑ 87TopTif-462
❑ 88Don-11
❑ 88Don-180
❑ 88DonBasB-32
❑ 88DonSupD-11
❑ 88Fle-466
❑ 88FleGlo-466
❑ 88FleMin-54
❑ 88FleStiC-63
❑ 88Lea-11
❑ 88Lea-155
❑ 88OPC-345
❑ 88PanSti-154
❑ 88PanSti-206
❑ 88RanMot-6
❑ 88RanSmo-10
❑ 88RedFolSB-24
❑ 88Sco-251
❑ 88ScoGlo-251
❑ 88Spo-77
❑ 88StaLinRa-4
❑ 88Top-345
❑ 88TopBig-19
❑ 88TopSti-241
❑ 88TopTif-345
❑ 89Bow-230
❑ 89BowTif-230
❑ 89CadEllD-18
❑ 89Don-142
❑ 89DonBasB-167
❑ 89Fle-518
❑ 89FleGlo-518
❑ 89FleSup-14
❑ 89OPC-295
❑ 89PanSti-454
❑ 89RanMot-13
❑ 89RanSmo-8
❑ 89Sco-78
❑ 89ScoRoo-47T
❑ 89Spo-185
❑ 89Top-295
❑ 89TopBig-205
❑ 89TopSti-246
❑ 89TopTif-295
❑ 89TVSpoM-120
❑ 89UppDec-420
❑ 90Bow-319
❑ 90BowTif-319
❑ 90Don-455
❑ 90DonBesA-88
❑ 90Fle-531
❑ 90FleCan-531
❑ 90Lea-141
❑ 90OPC-565
❑ 90PanSti-43
❑ 90PubIntS-408
❑ 90Sco-58
❑ 90Spo-220
❑ 90Top-565
❑ 90TopBig-207
❑ 90TopSti-307
❑ 90TopTif-565
❑ 90UppDec-310
❑ 90WhiSoxC-4
❑ 90WhiSoxK-5
❑ 91Bow-359
❑ 91Don-276
❑ 91Fle-119
❑ 91Lea-306
❑ 91OPC-785
❑ 91PanFreS-313
❑ 91Sco-36
❑ 91StaClu-30
❑ 91Stu-33
❑ 91Top-785
❑ 91TopDesS-785
❑ 91TopMic-785
❑ 91TopTif-785
❑ 91Ult-73
❑ 91UppDec-321
❑ 91WhiSoxK-7
❑ 92Bow-7
❑ 92BrePol-7
❑ 92Fle-80
❑ 92FleUpd-34
❑ 92Lea-234
❑ 92LeaBlaG-234
❑ 92OPC-648

❑ 92Sco-203
❑ 92StaClu-116
❑ 92StaClu-792
❑ 92StaCluNC-792
❑ 92Stu-193
❑ 92Top-648
❑ 92TopGol-648
❑ 92TopGolW-648
❑ 92TopMic-648
❑ 92TopTra-34T
❑ 92TopTraG-34T
❑ 92Ult-381
❑ 92UppDec-186
❑ 93Bow-383
❑ 93Don-631
❑ 93Fla-163
❑ 93Fle-629
❑ 93FleFinE-174
❑ 93Lea-344
❑ 93OPC-133
❑ 93OPCPre-48
❑ 93PacSpa-357
❑ 93Pin-495
❑ 93RanKee-147
❑ 93RedSoxP-13
❑ 93RedSoxWHP-5
❑ 93Sco-632
❑ 93Sel-140
❑ 93SelRoo-98T
❑ 93StaClu-112
❑ 93StaClu-623
❑ 93StaCluFDI-112
❑ 93StaCluFDI-623
❑ 93StaCluMOP-112
❑ 93StaCluMOP-623
❑ 93Top-97
❑ 93TopGol-97
❑ 93TopInaM-97
❑ 93TopInaR-97
❑ 93TopMic-97
❑ 93Ult-510
❑ 93UppDec-523
❑ 93UppDecGold-523
❑ 94Bow-503
❑ 94BreMilB-121
❑ 94ColC-103
❑ 94ColChoGS-103
❑ 94ColChoSS-103
❑ 94Don-134
❑ 94Fin-181
❑ 94FinRef-181
❑ 94Fle-32
❑ 94Lea-422
❑ 94Pac-54
❑ 94PanSti-29
❑ 94Pin-146
❑ 94PinArtP-146
❑ 94PinMusC-146
❑ 94Sco-367
❑ 94ScoGolR-367
❑ 94StaClu-198
❑ 94StaCluFDI-198
❑ 94StaCluGR-198
❑ 94StaCluMOP-198
❑ 94Top-169
❑ 94TopGol-169
❑ 94TopSpa-169
❑ 94Ult-14
❑ 95Don-449
❑ 95DonPreP-449
❑ 95Sco-166
❑ 95ScoGolR-166
❑ 95ScoPlaTS-166
❑ 97ChaRivDG-13
Fletcher, Tom
❑ 77FriOneYW-84
Fletschock, Justin
❑ 98FarRedHM-8
Flick, Elmer
❑ 03BreE10-51
❑ 04FanCraAL-19
❑ 05IndSouPSoCP-8
❑ 08AmeLeaPC-7
❑ 09ColChiE-105A
❑ 09ColChiE-105B
❑ 09T206-133
❑ 11PinT-5-613
❑ 11SpoLifM-43
❑ 12ColRedB-105A
❑ 12ColRedB-105B
❑ 12ColTinT-105A
❑ 12ColTinT-105B
❑ 53ArtHaloFP-34
❑ 74CapPub-72
❑ 76ShaPiz-92
❑ 78DexHaloFP-13
❑ 80PerHaloFP-92
❑ 80SSPHOF-92
❑ 84OCoandSI-168
❑ 89HOFStiB-53
Flick, Lew
❑ 63GadFunC-25
Flinn, Geoff
❑ 89ButCopKSP-15
Flinn, John
❑ 77RocRedWM-12
❑ 79Top-701
❑ 81Top-659
❑ 81VanCanT-21
❑ 82RocRedWT-2
❑ 83RocRedWT-3
❑ 85ChaO'sT-24
❑ 86ChaOriW-10
❑ 87ChaO'sW-25
❑ 91OriCro-136
❑ 94BreMilB-122
Flinn, Mike
❑ 82MadMusF-4
Flint, Frank S.
❑ 87BucN28-21
❑ 87OldJudN-170
❑ 88AugBecN-14
❑ 88GandBCGCE-16
❑ 88WG1CarG-12
Floethe, Chris
❑ 72OPC-268
❑ 72Top-268
Flohr, Adam
❑ 98HudValR-6
Flood, Curt
❑ 58Top-464
❑ 59Top-353
❑ 60CarJayP-3
❑ 60Lea-141
❑ 60Top-275
❑ 61CarJayP-4
❑ 61Pos-178A
❑ 61Pos-178B
❑ 61Top-438
❑ 61TopStaI-86
❑ 62CarJayP-3
❑ 62Jel-166
❑ 62Pos-166
❑ 62PosCan-166
❑ 62SalPlaC-139
❑ 62ShiPlaC-139
❑ 62Top-590
❑ 63CarJayP-5
❑ 63CarJayP-6
❑ 63Jel-162
❑ 63Pos-162
❑ 63Top-505
❑ 64CarTeal-2
❑ 64Top-103
❑ 64TopCoi-65
❑ 64TopSta-28
❑ 64TopTatI-36
❑ 64TopVen-103
❑ 65CarJayP-2
❑ 65CarTeal-8
❑ 65Top-415
❑ 66CarTeal-3
❑ 66OPC-60
❑ 66Top-60
❑ 66TopRubI-31
❑ 66TopVen-60
❑ 67OPC-63
❑ 67Top-63
❑ 67Top-245
❑ 67TopVen-276
❑ 68Baz-11
❑ 68OPC-180
❑ 68Top-180
❑ 68Top3-D-4
❑ 68TopVen-180
❑ 69KelPin-5
❑ 69MilBra-83
❑ 69MLBOffS-210
❑ 69MLBPin-43
❑ 69OPCDec-5
❑ 69Top-164
❑ 69Top-426
❑ 69Top-540
❑ 69TopDec-28
❑ 69TopSta-114
❑ 69TopSup-59
❑ 69TopTeaP-18
❑ 70Kel-48
❑ 70MLBOffS-87
❑ 70OPC-360
❑ 70Top-360
❑ 71MLBOffS-536
❑ 71OPC-535
❑ 71Top-535
❑ 71TopSup-41
❑ 72MilBra-105
❑ 78TCM60I-240
❑ 84OCoandSI-169
❑ 89PacSenL-220
❑ 89T/MSenL-1
❑ 90EliSenL-1
❑ 92ActPacA-72
❑ 92CarMcD-32
❑ 93TedWil-88
❑ 93UppDecAH-51
❑ 93UppDecS-26
❑ 94UppDecTAE-71
❑ 94UppDecTAELD-LD14
Flood, Thomas J.
❑ 87OldJudN-171
Flood, Tim
❑ 90DodTar-247
❑ 98CamPepP-26
Flora, Kevin
❑ 87SalAngP-22
❑ 88QuaCitAGS-5
❑ 89QuaCitAB-6
❑ 89QuaCitAGS-11
❑ 90MidAngGS-24
❑ 91Cla/Bes-19
❑ 91LinDriAA-434
❑ 91MidAngLD-434
❑ 91MidAngOHP-11
❑ 91MidAngP-441
❑ 92Bow-283
❑ 92EdmTraF-3545
❑ 92EdmTraS-156
❑ 92ProFS7-33
❑ 92SkyAAAF-77
❑ 92TopDeb91-57
❑ 92UppDecML-96
❑ 93ClaFS7-4
❑ 93Top-521
❑ 93TopGol-521
❑ 93TopInaM-521
❑ 93TopInaR-521
❑ 93TopMic-521
❑ 94Cla-144
❑ 95Sel-171
❑ 95SelArtP-171
❑ 96NorTidB-12
Florence, Donald
❑ 88WinHavRSS-8
❑ 89WinHavRSS-8
❑ 90NewBriRSB-10
❑ 90NewBriRSP-1313
❑ 90NewBriRSS-5
❑ 91LinDriAA-460
❑ 91NewBriRSLD-460
❑ 91NewBriRSP-348
❑ 92NewBriRSF-427
❑ 92NewBriRSS-485
❑ 93PawRedSDD-11
❑ 93PawRedSF-2404
❑ 93PawRedSTI-11
❑ 93TriAAAGF-31
❑ 94PawRedSDD-7
❑ 94PawRedSF-942
❑ 95NorTidTI-11
❑ 96RocRedWB-14
Florence, Paul
❑ 36WorWidGV-117
Flores, Adalberto
❑ 76BurBeeT-9
❑ 77NewCoPT-13
Flores, Alex
❑ 87GreHorP-18
Flores, Benito
❑ 98LowSpiM-21
Flores, Bert (Norberto)
❑ 77BurBeeT-8
❑ 85VerBeaDT-12
❑ 86BakDodP-8
Flores, Eric
❑ 95GreFalDTI-26
❑ 96YakBeaTI-23
❑ 97YakBeaG-6
Flores, Gil
❑ 76SalLakCGC-22
❑ 77SalLakCGC-5
❑ 78AngFamF-10
❑ 78SalLakCGC-6
❑ 78SSP270-209
❑ 78Top-268
❑ 80TidTidT-6
❑ 80Top-478
❑ 81TidTidT-11
❑ 82TidTidT-7
❑ 83TidTidT-22
❑ 84TidTidT-7
❑ 91MetWIZ-118
Flores, Ignacio
❑ 97SanAntMB-3
❑ 97TexAllM-38
❑ 98AlbDukG-6
❑ 98SanAntMM-3
Flores, Javier
❑ 97SouOreTB-3
❑ 98VisOakG-10
Flores, Jesse
❑ 80KnoBluJT-8
❑ 87SalAngP-31
Flores, Jesse (Sandoval)
❑ 43A'STEAI-11
❑ 45A'sTeal-12
❑ 46A'sTeal-5
❑ 47A'sTeal-11
❑ 50IndTeal-10
❑ 51IndHag-4
Flores, Joe
❑ 92KinMetF-1538
❑ 93CapCitBC-5
Flores, Jose
❑ 85GreHorT-23
❑ 86GreHorP-5
❑ 90AshTouC-13
❑ 90AubAstB-6
❑ 90AubAstP-3411
❑ 91AshTouP-574
❑ 92AshTouC-2
❑ 92KinMetC-21
❑ 92PitMetF-3303
❑ 93CapCitBF-465
❑ 93OscAstC-10
❑ 93OscAstF-636
❑ 94BatCliC-4
❑ 94BatCliF-3452
❑ 94JacGenF-223
❑ 95ClePhiF-222
❑ 95GreFalDTI-3
❑ 97ScrRedB-21
❑ 98ScrRedBQ-13
Flores, Juan
❑ 90HelBreSP-3
❑ 91StoPorC-22
❑ 91StoPorP-3034
Flores, Miguel
❑ 90BurIndP-3013
❑ 91CarLeaAP-CAR14
❑ 91KinIndC-16
❑ 91KinIndP-328
❑ 92CanIndF-697
❑ 92CanIndS-106
❑ 92ProFS7-55
❑ 92SkyAA F-49
❑ 92UppDecML-140
❑ 93CanIndF-2845
❑ 94ChaKniF-901
Flores, Ozzie
❑ 98LowSpiM-6
Flores, Pedro
❑ 96GreFalDB-12
❑ 96GreFalDTI-9
❑ 97GreFalDTI-11
❑ 98SanBerS-10
❑ 98SanBerSTIS-10
Flores, Willi
❑ 80VenLeaS-38
❑ 82WisRapTF-21
Florez, Tim
❑ 91EveGiaC-10
❑ 91EveGiaP-3921
❑ 92CliGiaC-22
❑ 93ShrCapF-2767
❑ 94ShrCapF-1613
❑ 97PhoFirTI-8
❑ 98TusSidM-20
Florie, Bryce
❑ 89ChaRaiP-983
❑ 90Bes-130
❑ 90WatDiaB-3
❑ 90WatDiaP-2371
❑ 91WatDiaC-3
❑ 91WatDiaP-1250
❑ 92HigDesMC-20
❑ 93WicWraF-2973
❑ 94Bow-316
❑ 94ExcFS7-280
❑ 94LasVegSF-868
❑ 95Bow-93
❑ 95Fla-200
❑ 95FleUpd-184
❑ 95PadMot-27
❑ 95Pin-147
❑ 95PinArtP-147
❑ 95PinMusC-147
❑ 95Top-657
❑ 95Ult-438
❑ 95UltGolM-438
❑ 96ColCho-292
❑ 96ColChoGS-292
❑ 96ColChoSS-292
❑ 96Don-86
❑ 96DonPreP-86
❑ 96Fle-566
❑ 96FleTif-566
❑ 96LeaSigEA-53
❑ 96PadMot-27
❑ 97BrePol-8
❑ 98PacOnl-272
❑ 98PacOnlR-272
❑ 98PacOnlWC-272
Flower, George
❑ 86WesPalBEP-16
Flowers, Bennett
❑ 53RedSoxTI-7
❑ 55Bow-254
Flowers, Doug
❑ 91KanCouCC-29
Flowers, Jake (D'Arcy)
❑ 25Zee-26
❑ 29ExhFou-3
❑ 31CarMet-8
❑ 31Exh-3
❑ 33Gou-151
❑ 33GouCanV-81
❑ 74CapPub-73
❑ 90DodTar-248
Flowers, Kim
❑ 85EveGiaC-5A
❑ 85EveGiaC-5B
❑ 87CliGiaP-16
❑ 88FreSunCLC-11
❑ 88FreSunP-1223
Flowers, Larry
❑ 90GeoColC-4
Flowers, Perry
❑ 86CliGiaP-8
Flowers, Wes
❑ 90DodTar-952
Flowers, Willie
❑ 78NewWayCT-14
Floyd, Bobby (Robert)
❑ 67BalOriP-40
❑ 69Top-597
❑ 70OPC-101
❑ 70Top-101
❑ 71MLBOffS-415
❑ 71OPC-646
❑ 71Top-646
❑ 72OPC-273
❑ 72oyTeal-5
❑ 72Top-273
❑ 72TopCloT-11
❑ 74OPC-41
❑ 74Top-41
❑ 75OmaRoyTI-6
❑ 80LynSaiT-4
❑ 81LynSaiT-24
❑ 82SalLakCGT-24
❑ 83SalLakCGT-24
❑ 84SalLakCGC-191
❑ 85CalCanC-78
❑ 86LynMetP-9
❑ 91OriCro-137
Floyd, Chad
❑ 98ForWayW!-29
Floyd, Chris
❑ 88MyrBeaBJP-1173
Floyd, Cliff
❑ 91ClaDraP-11
❑ 91FroRowDP-49
❑ 91FroRowDPG-49
❑ 91FroRowDPS-49
❑ 91HigSchPLS-19
❑ 92AlbPolCB-22
❑ 92AlbPolF-2314
❑ 92Bow-678
❑ 92ClaBluBF-BC19
❑ 92ClaFS7-380
❑ 92ClaRedB-BC19
❑ 92OPC-186
❑ 92Pin-296
❑ 92Sco-801
❑ 92StaCluD-51
❑ 92Top-186
❑ 92TopGol-186
❑ 92TopGolW-186
❑ 92TopMic-186
❑ 92UppDecML-63
❑ 92UppDecML-267
❑ 92UppDecMLPotY-PY10
❑ 92UppDecMLTPHF-TP2
❑ 93Bow-128
❑ 93Bow-354
❑ 93ClaFisN-17
❑ 93ClaGolF-72
❑ 93ClaInsC-2
❑ 93ClaYouG-YG3
❑ 93ExcFS7-58
❑ 93ExcLeaLF-7
❑ 93FlaWavotF-5
❑ 93FleFinE-92
❑ 93HarSenF-274
❑ 93SouAtlLAIPI-1
❑ 93SouAtlLAIPI-18
❑ 93SouAtlLAPI-10
❑ 93SP-277
❑ 93Top-576
❑ 93TopGol-576
❑ 93TopInaM-576
❑ 93TopInaR-576
❑ 93TopMic-576
❑ 93Ult-413
❑ 93UppDec-431
❑ 93UppDecGold-431
❑ 94Bow-200
❑ 94Bow-340
❑ 94BowBes-R87
❑ 94BowBesR-R87
❑ 94BowPre-5
❑ 94ColC-7
❑ 94ColC-337
❑ 94ColChoGS-7
❑ 94ColChoGS-337
❑ 94ColChoSS-7
❑ 94ColChoSS-337
❑ 94ColChoT-15
❑ 94Don-651
❑ 94Fin-427
❑ 94FinJum-427
❑ 94FinRef-427
❑ 94Fla-189
❑ 94Fle-538
❑ 94FleExtB-305
❑ 94FleExtBRS-6
❑ 94FleRooS-7
❑ 94FUnPac-2
❑ 94FUnPac-205
❑ 94LeaGolR-18
❑ 94LeaL-124
❑ 94LeaLimRP-5
❑ 94OPC-223
❑ 94OPCHotP-1
❑ 94Pac-380
❑ 94Pin-392
❑ 94PinArtP-392
❑ 94PinMusC-392
❑ 94PinNewG-NG10
❑ 94PinNewG-PNG10
❑ 94PinPowS-PS19
❑ 94PinRooTP-7
❑ 94Sco-587
❑ 94ScoBoyoS-60
❑ 94ScoGolR-587
❑ 94ScoRoo-RT76
❑ 94ScoRooGR-RT76
❑ 94ScoRooSR-SU8
❑ 94Sel-185
❑ 94SelRooS-RS1
❑ 94SelSam-RS1
❑ 94SigRooCF-B1
❑ 94SigRooCF-B2
❑ 94SigRooCF-B3
❑ 94SigRooCF-B4
❑ 94SigRooCF-B5
❑ 94SigRooCFS-B1
❑ 94SigRooCFS-B2
❑ 94SigRooCFS-B3
❑ 94SigRooCFS-B4
❑ 94SigRooCFS-B5
❑ 94SigRooP-1
❑ 94SP-83
❑ 94SPDieC-83
❑ 94SPHol-8
❑ 94SPHolDC-8
❑ 94Spo-173
❑ 94Spo-NNO
❑ 94SpoRooRS-TR12
❑ 94SPPre-ER2
❑ 94StaClu-127
❑ 94StaCluFDI-127
❑ 94StaCluGR-127
❑ 94StaCluMOP-127

❑ 94Stu-77
❑ 94TedWil-154
❑ 94TedWil-155
❑ 94TedWil-156
❑ 94TedWil-157
❑ 94Top-259
❑ 94TopGol-259
❑ 94TopSpa-259
❑ 94TopSupS-14
❑ 94TriPla-289
❑ 94Ult-227
❑ 94UltAllR-3
❑ 94UltAllRJ-3
❑ 94UltRisS-4
❑ 94UppDec-12
❑ 94UppDecDC-E5
❑ 94UppDecED-12
❑ 94UppDecMLS-MM8
❑ 94UppDecMLSED-MM8
❑ 94UppDecNG-3
❑ 94UppDecNGED-3
❑ 95Baz-125
❑ 95Bow-394
❑ 95ColCho-240
❑ 95ColChoGS-240
❑ 95ColChoSE-100
❑ 95ColChoSEGS-100
❑ 95ColChoSESS-100
❑ 95ColChoSS-240
❑ 95Don-212
❑ 95DonPreP-212
❑ 95Emo-152
❑ 95Fin-23
❑ 95FinRef-23
❑ 95Fla-161
❑ 95FlaTodS-3
❑ 95Fle-350
❑ 95FleUpdSS-4
❑ 95Lea-184
❑ 95Pac-267
❑ 95PacPri-86
❑ 95PanSti-101
❑ 95Pin-8
❑ 95Pin-281
❑ 95PinArtP-8
❑ 95PinArtP-281
❑ 95PinGatA-GA18
❑ 95PinMusC-8
❑ 95PinMusC-281
❑ 95PinRedH-RH24
❑ 95PinWhiH-WH24
❑ 95Sco-401
❑ 95ScoAi-AM11
❑ 95ScoGolR-401
❑ 95ScoHaloG-HG83
❑ 95ScoPlaTS-401
❑ 95ScoRul-SR17
❑ 95ScoRulJ-SR17
❑ 95Sel-58
❑ 95SelArtP-58
❑ 95SelCanM-CM1
❑ 95SelCer-79
❑ 95SelCerMG-79
❑ 95SelCerPU-1
❑ 95SelCerPU9-1
❑ 95Spo-19
❑ 95SpoArtP-19
❑ 95SpoDet-DE8
❑ 95StaClu-164
❑ 95StaCluFDI-164
❑ 95StaCluMOP-164
❑ 95StaCluSTWS-164
❑ 95StaCluVR-87
❑ 95StaCluVRMO-87
❑ 95Stu-26
❑ 95StuGolS-26
❑ 95Sum-52
❑ 95SumNewA-NA1
❑ 95SumNthD-52
❑ 95Top-462
❑ 95TopCyb-257
❑ 95TopEmb-4
❑ 95TopEmbGI-4
❑ 95UC3CleS-CS8
❑ 95UC3CleS-PCS8
❑ 95Ult-402
❑ 95UltAllR-1
❑ 95UltAllRGM-1
❑ 95UltGolM-402
❑ 95UltSecYS-1
❑ 95UltSecYSGM-1
❑ 95UppDec-80
❑ 95UppDecED-80
❑ 95UppDecEDG-80
❑ 95UppDecSE-1
❑ 95UppDecSEG-1
❑ 96ColCho-211
❑ 96ColChoGS-211
❑ 96ColChoSS-211
❑ 96Don-388
❑ 96DonPreP-388
❑ 96EmoXL-222
❑ 96Fla-306
❑ 96Fle-457
❑ 96FleTif-457
❑ 96Lea-4
❑ 96LeaPrePB-4
❑ 96LeaPrePG-4
❑ 96LeaPrePS-4
❑ 96MetUni-191
❑ 96MetUniP-191
❑ 96Pac-126
❑ 96Pin-91
❑ 96PinAfi-145
❑ 96PinAfiAP-145
❑ 96PinArtP-34
❑ 96PinSta-34
❑ 96Sco-89
❑ 96ScoDugC-A69
❑ 96ScoDugCAP-A69
❑ 96SelTeaN-24
❑ 96Top-334
❑ 96Ult-503
❑ 96Ult-595
❑ 96UltGolM-503
❑ 96UltGolM-595
❑ 96UltRisS-4
❑ 96UltRisSGM-4
❑ 96UppDec-146
❑ 96UppDec-392
❑ 97Cir-209
❑ 97CirRav-209
❑ 97E-X2-72
❑ 97E-X2Cred-72
❑ 97E-X2EssCre-72
❑ 97Fle-379
❑ 97Fle-679
❑ 97FleTif-379
❑ 97FleTif-679
❑ 97Lea-250
❑ 97LeaFraM-250
❑ 97LeaFraMDC-250
❑ 97MarPac-11
❑ 97MetUni-154
❑ 97NewPin-11
❑ 97NewPinAP-11
❑ 97NewPinMC-11
❑ 97NewPinPP-11
❑ 97Pac-344
❑ 97PacLigB-344
❑ 97PacSil-344
❑ 97Sco-14
❑ 97ScoArtPWB-14
❑ 97ScoPreS-14
❑ 97ScoShoS-14
❑ 97ScoShoSAP-14
❑ 97Top-444
❑ 97Ult-372
❑ 97UltGolME-372
❑ 97UltPlaME-372
❑ 97UppDec-427
❑ 98CirThu-243
❑ 98CirThuRav-243
❑ 98CirThuSupRav-243
❑ 98ColCho-377
❑ 98CroRoy-57
❑ 98Fin-80
❑ 98FinNo--80
❑ 98FinNo-R-80
❑ 98FinRef-80
❑ 98Fle-487
❑ 98FleVin'-92
❑ 98FleVin'C-92
❑ 98LeaRS-128
❑ 98LeaRSLHolo-128
❑ 98LeaRSLong-128
❑ 98LeaRTrue-128
❑ 98PacInvGems-155
❑ 98PacOme-102
❑ 98PacOmeR-102
❑ 98PacOnl-294
❑ 98PacOnlR-294
❑ 98PacOnlWC-294
❑ 98Revo-60
❑ 98RevoSS-60
❑ 98SPxFin-279
❑ 98SPxFinR-279
❑ 98SPxFinS-279
❑ 98StaCluFDI-110
❑ 98StaCluI-110
❑ 98StaCluOneK-110
❑ 98StaCluPP-110
❑ 98TopSta-59
❑ 98TopStaB-59
❑ 98TopStaG-59
❑ 98TopStaGR-59
❑ 98TopStaS-59
❑ 98UppDec-374
❑ 98UppDecR-37
❑ 99199Fin-181
❑ 99Bow-222
❑ 99BowBes-11
❑ 99BowBesAR-11
❑ 99BowBesR-11
❑ 99BowGol-222
❑ 99BowInt-222
❑ 99CroRoyB-57
❑ 99CroRoyL-57
❑ 99CroRoyOD-57
❑ 99E-X Cen-76
❑ 99E-X CenECFut-76
❑ 99E-X CenECNow-76
❑ 99FinGolRef-181
❑ 99FinRef-181
❑ 99FlaShoLeg1-71
❑ 99FlaShoLeg2-71
❑ 99FlaShoLeg3-71
❑ 99FlaShoLegM1-71
❑ 99FlaShoLegM2-71
❑ 99FlaShoLegM3-71
❑ 99FlaShoR1-71
❑ 99FlaShoR2-71
❑ 99FlaShoR3-71
❑ 99Fle-93
❑ 99FleMys-16
❑ 99FleMysG-16
❑ 99FleMysM-16
❑ 99FleSta9-93
❑ 99FleWarT-93
❑ 99MetUni-94
❑ 99MetUniGM-94
❑ 99MetUniPMG-94
❑ 99Pac-175
❑ 99PacAur-73
❑ 99PacAurOD-73
❑ 99PacCroC-113
❑ 99PacCroCPB-113
❑ 99PacInv-59
❑ 99PacInvOD-59
❑ 99PacInvPB-59
❑ 99PacOme-98
❑ 99PacOmeC-98
❑ 99PacOmeG-98
❑ 99PacOmePB-98
❑ 99PacPar-94
❑ 99PacParC-94
❑ 99PacParG-94
❑ 99PacParHoloGold-94
❑ 99PacParHS-94
❑ 99PacParOD-94
❑ 99PacParPB-94
❑ 99PacParRed-94
❑ 99PacPlaB-175
❑ 99PacPri-60
❑ 99PacPriHB-60
❑ 99PacPriHG-60
❑ 99PacPriHM-60
❑ 99PacPriHP-60
❑ 99PacPriRed-60
❑ 99PacPriS-86
❑ 99PacPriS206-86
❑ 99PacPriS206R-86
❑ 99PacRed-175
❑ 99SkyMolM-45
❑ 99SkyMolMX-45
❑ 99SkyPre-79
❑ 99SkyPreR-79
❑ 99SkyThu-193
❑ 99SkyThuRant-193
❑ 99SkyThuRave-193
❑ 99SP Aut-36
❑ 99SpoIll-172
❑ 99StaClu-279
❑ 99StaCluC-CS5
❑ 99StaCluC-CS11
❑ 99StaCluC-CS17
❑ 99StaCluC-CS21
❑ 99StaCluFDI-279
❑ 99StaCluOoaK-279
❑ 99StaCluPP-279
❑ 99ThuSkySupR-193
❑ 99Top-296
❑ 99TopBlaLC1-21
❑ 99TopBlaLC2-21
❑ 99TopBlaLC3-21
❑ 99TopChr-296
❑ 99TopChrR-296
❑ 99TopGal-82
❑ 99TopGalPP-82
❑ 99TopGalPPI-82
❑ 99TopGolL-21
❑ 99TopGolLC1-21
❑ 99TopGolLC2-21
❑ 99TopGolLOtO-21
❑ 99TopMVPP-296
❑ 99TopOpeD-136
❑ 99TopRedLC1-21
❑ 99TopRedLC2-21
❑ 99TopRedLC3-21
❑ 99TopSta-72
❑ 99TopSta1Foil-72
❑ 99TopStaFoil-72
❑ 99TopStaOS-72
❑ 99UD Cho-89
❑ 99UD ChoPCR-89
❑ 99Ult-101
❑ 99UltGolM-101
❑ 99UltMas-101
❑ 99UltPlaM-101
❑ 99UppDec-101
❑ 99UppDecEL1-101
❑ 99UppDecEL2-101
❑ 99UppDecM-88
❑ 99UppDecMGS-88
❑ 99UppDecMHFS-88
❑ 99UppDecMP-88
❑ 99UppDecMSS-88
❑ 99Vic-158

Floyd, D.J.
❑ 90EriSaiS-6

Floyd, Spanky
❑ 94HelBreF-3623

Floyd, Stan
❑ 77ChaPatT-6

Floyd, Tony
❑ 88SouOreAP-1707
❑ 91SouOreAAP-SOA5

Flury, Pat
❑ 93EugEmeC-14
❑ 93EugEmeF-3850
❑ 94RocRoyC-10
❑ 94RocRoyF-558
❑ 95SprSulTI-9
❑ 96HonShaHWB-34
❑ 96WilBluRB-19
❑ 97WicWra-7

Flynn, Bob
❑ 75AppFoxT-7
❑ 76AppFoxT-6

Flynn, David
❑ 88CapCodPPaLP-13

Flynn, Errol
❑ 88PulBraP-1758

Flynn, John Anthony
❑ 10E12AmeCDCE125-16
❑ 10PirTipTD-22
❑ 10SweCapPP-136
❑ 11BasBatEU-23
❑ 11PinT-5-851
❑ 11S74Sil-109
❑ 11SpoLifCW-128
❑ 11SpoLifM-249
❑ 11T205-58

Flynn, R. Doug
❑ 76OPC-518
❑ 76SSP-37
❑ 76Top-518
❑ 77BobParMBC-5
❑ 77Top-186
❑ 78MetDaiPA-6
❑ 78Top-453
❑ 79Hos-81
❑ 79OPC-116
❑ 79Top-229
❑ 80OPC-32
❑ 80Top-58
❑ 81AllGamPI-100
❑ 81CokTeaS-86
❑ 81Don-394
❑ 81Fle-330
❑ 81OPC-311
❑ 81Top-634
❑ 81TopScr-93
❑ 81TopSti-192
❑ 81TopSupHT-74
❑ 82Don-427
❑ 82ExpPos-11
❑ 82Fle-525
❑ 82FleSta-87
❑ 82OPC-302
❑ 82Top-302
❑ 82TopSti-70
❑ 82TopTra-33T
❑ 83AllGamPI-101
❑ 83Don-240
❑ 83ExpPos-9
❑ 83ExpStu-7
❑ 83Fle-282
❑ 83OPC-169
❑ 83Top-169
❑ 84Don-254
❑ 84ExpPos-8
❑ 84ExpStu-29
❑ 84Fle-274
❑ 84Nes792-749
❑ 84OPC-262
❑ 84Top-749
❑ 84TopSti-97
❑ 84TopTif-749
❑ 85Don-463
❑ 85Fle-397
❑ 85Lea-257
❑ 85OPC-112
❑ 85Top-554
❑ 85TopMin-554
❑ 85TopSti-93
❑ 85TopTif-554
❑ 86TigCaiD-5
❑ 86Top-436
❑ 86TopTif-436
❑ 91MetWIZ-119
❑ 92MCIAmb-3
❑ 93RanKee-148
❑ 94MCIAmb-10
❑ 94MCIAmb-S1
❑ 95MCIAmb-4
❑ 97St.LucM-6

Flynn, Tom
❑ 28Zee-105
❑ 29Zee-108
❑ 30Zee-119
❑ 31Zee-84
❑ 33Zee-31

Fobbs, Larry
❑ 78LodDodT-4
❑ 81AlbDukTc-15
❑ 82AlbDukTc-16

Foderaro, Kevin
❑ 94JohCitCC-10
❑ 94JohCitCF-3693
❑ 96PeoChiB-10

Fodge, Gene
❑ 55DesMoiHB-7
❑ 58Top-449

Fogarty, James
❑ 87BucN28-80
❑ 87OldJudN-173
❑ 88AllandGN-2
❑ 88AllandGN-2
❑ 88WG1CarG-51
❑ 89EdgR.WG-6
❑ 90KalBatN-19
❑ 90KalBatN-20

Fogg, Josh
❑ 98HicCraUO-18
❑ 99TeaBesR-26
❑ 99TeaBesRFS-6
❑ 99TeaBesRG-26
❑ 99TeaBesRS-26

Fogg, Kevin
❑ 76BatRouCT-10

Foggie, Cornell
❑ 89WatIndS-7

Fogler, Seth
❑ 89MiaMirIS-21
❑ 90MiaMirIS-29

Fohl, Lee
❑ 23MapCriV-5
❑ 23WilChoV-43

Foiles, Hank
❑ 52Par-85
❑ 53Top-252
❑ 55IndGolS-20
❑ 56PirTeal-6
❑ 57Top-104
❑ 58Hir-71
❑ 58Kah-8
❑ 58PirTeal-2
❑ 58Top-4
❑ 59Top-294
❑ 60Top-77
❑ 60TopVen-77
❑ 61BalOriP-9
❑ 61Top-277
❑ 62Top-112
❑ 62TopVen-112
❑ 63RedEnq-8
❑ 63Top-326
❑ 64Top-554
❑ 91OriCro-138
❑ 91TopArc1-252

Foit, Jim
❑ 83TulDriT-20

Fojas, Francisco
❑ 79CedRapGT-9
❑ 97JohCitCTI-29

Foldman, Hal (Harry)
❑ 49SomandK-29

Folers, Ken
❑ 97St.CatSB-14

Foley, Bill
❑ 77NewCoPT-14
❑ 78BurBeeT-13
❑ 79HolMilT-3
❑ 82ElPasDT-6

Foley, Doc
❑ 66TolMudHTI-11

Foley, Jack
❑ 83TamTarT-11

Foley, Jim
❑ 87AncGlaP-12
❑ 88ModA'sTI-9
❑ 89MadMusS-8
❑ 90CliGiaP-2549

Foley, Keith
❑ 86WesPalBEP-17
❑ 87SalSpuS-1
❑ 88VerMarP-948

Foley, Mark
❑ 87PenWhiSP-4

Foley, Martin
❑ 87SpaPhiP-17
❑ 88SpaPhiP-1038
❑ 88SpaPhiS-23
❑ 89ReaPhiB-15
❑ 89ReaPhiP-672
❑ 89ReaPhiS-11
❑ 90ReaPhiB-16
❑ 90ReaPhiP-1226
❑ 90ReaPhiS-12

Foley, Marv
❑ 77AppFoxT-5
❑ 78KnoKnoST-4
❑ 81Don-399
❑ 81EdmTraRR-18
❑ 81Top-646
❑ 83Don-652
❑ 83Top-409
❑ 84RanJarP-30
❑ 85Don-500
❑ 85Top-621
❑ 85TopTif-621
❑ 86BirBarTI-23
❑ 88BlaYNPRWL-1
❑ 88TamTarS-10B
❑ 89VanCanC-23
❑ 89VanCanP-573
❑ 90CMC-632
❑ 90ProAAAF-183
❑ 90TriAllGP-AAA39
❑ 90VanCanC-5
❑ 90VanCanP-505
❑ 91LinDriAAA-649
❑ 91PacSenL-23
❑ 91VanCanLD-649
❑ 91VanCanP-1609
❑ 92ChaKniF-2786
❑ 92ChaKniS-174
❑ 93IowCubF-2148
❑ 93RanKee-149
❑ 95RocRedWTI-41
❑ 96RocRedWB-2
❑ 97RocRedW-2
❑ 98RocRedWQ-2

Foley, Rick
❑ 79SalLakCGT-18B
❑ 80SalLakCGT-15
❑ 81HolMilT-15
❑ 82SpoIndT-3

Foley, Tom (Thomas)
❑ 80WatRedT-19
❑ 81IndIndTI-7
❑ 82IndIndTI-20
❑ 84Don-81
❑ 84Nes792-632
❑ 84RedEnq-6
❑ 84Top-632
❑ 84TopTif-632
❑ 85Don-569
❑ 85Fle-535
❑ 85RedYea-5
❑ 85Top-107
❑ 85TopTif-107
❑ 86Don-549
❑ 86Fle-440
❑ 86PhiTas-11

❑ 86Top-466
❑ 86TopTif-466
❑ 87Don-504
❑ 87ExpPos-7
❑ 87Fle-318
❑ 87FleGlo-318
❑ 87OPC-78
❑ 87Top-78
❑ 87TopTif-78
❑ 88Don-303
❑ 88ExpPos-9
❑ 88Fle-183
❑ 88FleGlo-183
❑ 88Lea-143
❑ 88MSAHosD-3
❑ 88OPC-251
❑ 88Sco-159
❑ 88ScoGlo-159
❑ 88StaLinE-5
❑ 88Top-251
❑ 88TopTif-251
❑ 89Don-342
❑ 89DonBasB-314
❑ 89ExpPos-6
❑ 89Fle-375
❑ 89FleGlo-375
❑ 89OPC-159
❑ 89PanSti-121
❑ 89Sco-405
❑ 89Top-529
❑ 89TopBig-261
❑ 89TopTif-529
❑ 89UppDec-441
❑ 90Bow-120
❑ 90BowTif-120
❑ 90Don-274
❑ 90ExpPos-8
❑ 90Fle-344
❑ 90FleCan-344
❑ 90Lea-292
❑ 90OPC-341
❑ 90PanSti-292
❑ 90PubIntS-172
❑ 90Sco-32
❑ 90Top-341
❑ 90TopBig-58
❑ 90TopTif-341
❑ 90UppDec-489
❑ 91Don-180
❑ 91ExpPos-5
❑ 91Fle-230
❑ 91OPC-773
❑ 91Sco-526
❑ 91StuPre-13
❑ 91Top-773
❑ 91TopDesS-773
❑ 91TopMic-773
❑ 91TopTif-773
❑ 91UppDec-381
❑ 92Don-538
❑ 92ExpPos-13
❑ 92Lea-372
❑ 92LeaBlaG-372
❑ 92OPC-666
❑ 92Sco-486
❑ 92StaClu-19
❑ 92Top-666
❑ 92TopGol-666
❑ 92TopGolW-666
❑ 92TopMic-666
❑ 92TriPla-2
❑ 92Ult-221
❑ 92UppDec-492
❑ 93Don-727
❑ 93MilBonSS-13
❑ 93PacSpa-586
❑ 93PirNatI-10
❑ 94Don-132
❑ 94Fle-608
❑ 94Lea-335
❑ 94PirQui-6
❑ 94StaClu-142
❑ 94StaCluFDI-142
❑ 94StaCluGR-142
❑ 94StaCluMOP-142
❑ 95Fle-478
❑ 96ButCopKB-3

Folga, Mike
❑ 85PriWilPT-12
❑ 87PeoChiP-26

Folger, Ken
❑ 92SalLakTSP-16

Foli, Ernie
❑ 67VanMouSO-10

Foli, Tim
❑ 71OPC-83
❑ 71Top-83
❑ 72Dia-15
❑ 72ProStaP-5
❑ 72Top-707
❑ 72Top-708
❑ 73OPC-19
❑ 73Top-19
❑ 73TopCanL-16
❑ 74ExpWes-4
❑ 74OPC-217
❑ 74Top-217
❑ 74TopDecE-19
❑ 74TopSta-54
❑ 75ExpPos-12
❑ 75Hos-9
❑ 75HosTwi-9
❑ 75OPC-149
❑ 75Top-149
❑ 75TopMin-149
❑ 76ExpRed-8
❑ 76MonExpP-9
❑ 76OPC-397
❑ 76SSP-328
❑ 76Top-397
❑ 77BurCheD-156
❑ 77GiaTeal-9
❑ 77OPC-162
❑ 77Top-76
❑ 78MetDaiPA-7
❑ 78OPC-169
❑ 78Top-167
❑ 79OPC-213
❑ 79Top-403
❑ 80OPC-131
❑ 80Top-246
❑ 81AllGamPI-112
❑ 81CokTeaS-112
❑ 81Don-13
❑ 81Fle-379
❑ 81OPC-38
❑ 81Top-501
❑ 82Don-376
❑ 82Fle-482
❑ 82FleSta-75
❑ 82OPC-97
❑ 82Top-618
❑ 82TopSti-88
❑ 82TopTra-34T
❑ 83AllGamPI-20
❑ 83Don-342
❑ 83Fle-88
❑ 83OPC-319
❑ 83Top-738
❑ 84AllGamPI-109
❑ 84Don-474
❑ 84Fle-516
❑ 84FleUpd-38
❑ 84Nes792-342
❑ 84OPC-342
❑ 84Top-342
❑ 84TopTif-342
❑ 84TopTra-38T
❑ 84TopTraT-38T
❑ 85Fle-126
❑ 85Pir-6
❑ 85Top-271
❑ 85Top-456
❑ 85TopTif-271
❑ 85TopTif-456
❑ 86ExpGreT-3
❑ 86RanLit-1
❑ 86RanPer-NNO
❑ 87RanMot-28
❑ 87RanSmo-29
❑ 91MetWIZ-120
❑ 92BrePol-30
❑ 92YanWIZ8-60
❑ 93RanKee-150

Folkers, Brandon
❑ 97JohCitCTI-10
❑ 98NewJerCM-7

Folkers, Ken
❑ 98DunBluJSB-13

Folkers, Rich
❑ 71OPC-648
❑ 71Top-648
❑ 73OPC-649
❑ 73Top-649
❑ 74OPC-417
❑ 74Top-417
❑ 75OPC-98
❑ 75PadDea-1
❑ 75Top-98
❑ 75TopMin-98
❑ 76OPC-611
❑ 76SSP-114
❑ 76Top-611
❑ 77SpoIndC-28
❑ 77Top-372
❑ 91MetWIZ-121
❑ 93St.PetCC-28
❑ 93St.PetCF-2645
❑ 94BreMilB-123
❑ 94St.PetCC-29
❑ 94St.PetCF-2603
❑ 96StPetCB-2
❑ 97ArkTraB-27

Followell, Vern
❑ 81EvaTriT-14
❑ 82EvaTriT-18
❑ 85TucTorC-57

Folmar, Ryan
❑ 98AshTouM-4

Fonceca, Chad
❑ 96BilMusTI-8

Fondy, Dee
❑ 52Bow-231
❑ 52Top-359
❑ 53BowBW-5
❑ 54Bow-173
❑ 54RedHeaF-8
❑ 55Bow-224
❑ 56Top-112
❑ 57Top-42
❑ 58Kah-9
❑ 58RedEnq-12
❑ 58Top-157
❑ 59SeaPop-17
❑ 79TCM50-47
❑ 83TopRep5-359

Fong, Steve
❑ 87SalLakTTT-21

Fonseca, Angel
❑ 82WauTimF-25

Fonseca, Dave
❑ 80CliGiaT-13

Fonseca, Lew
❑ 20WalMaiW-16
❑ 29ExhFou-21
❑ 29PorandAR-24
❑ 30W554-2
❑ 31Exh-22
❑ 31W517-48
❑ 32OrbPinNP-20
❑ 32OrbPinUP-19
❑ 33ButCanV-15
❑ 33DouDisP-16
❑ 33Gou-43
❑ 33GouCanV-43
❑ 33TatOrb-19
❑ 33TatOrbSDR-184
❑ 34BabRutG-20
❑ 34ButPreR-20
❑ 34DiaMatCSB-56
❑ 34DiaStaR-7
❑ 37KelPepS-BB6
❑ 61Fle-27
❑ 82OhiHaloF-61
❑ 91ConTSN-283

Font, Franklin
❑ 97WilCubB-6
❑ 98RocCubM-8
❑ 98RocCubTI-8

Fontaine, Tom
❑ 98DelShoM-13

Fontanes, Ruben
❑ 97LetBlaDB-21

Fontenot, Joe
❑ 95BelGiaTI-12
❑ 95Bes-118
❑ 96Exc-244
❑ 96SanJosGB-16
❑ 97Bes-30
❑ 97Bow-202
❑ 97BowBes-155
❑ 97BowBesAR-155
❑ 97BowBesR-155
❑ 97BowCerBlaIA-CA25
❑ 97BowCerBluIA-CA25
❑ 97BowCerGolIA-CA25
❑ 97BowChr-188
❑ 97BowChrI-188
❑ 97BowChrIR-188
❑ 97BowChrR-188
❑ 97BowInt-202
❑ 97ShrCap-1
❑ 97ShrCapB-1
❑ 97TexLeaTP-20
❑ 98Bow-358
❑ 98BowChr-358
❑ 98BowChrGA-358
❑ 98BowChrGAR-358
❑ 98BowChrI-358
❑ 98BowChrIR-358
❑ 98BowChrR-358
❑ 98BowGolA-358
❑ 98BowInt-358
❑ 98EasLeaTPM-8
❑ 98PorSeaDQ-5
❑ 98SP MinPE-112
❑ 98SPMin-112
❑ 99BasAmeTP-44
❑ 99BasAmeTPG-44
❑ 99Bow-153
❑ 99BowAut-BA39
❑ 99BowChr-153
❑ 99BowChrG-153
❑ 99BowChrGR-153
❑ 99BowChrI-153
❑ 99BowChrIR-153
❑ 99BowChrR-153
❑ 99BowGol-153
❑ 99BowInt-153
❑ 99SpoIll-57
❑ 99Top-404
❑ 99TopChr-404
❑ 99TopChrR-404
❑ 99TopMVPP-404

Fontenot, Ray
❑ 82NasSouTI-12
❑ 83ColCliT-5
❑ 83YanPhoA-1
❑ 84Don-370
❑ 84Fle-122
❑ 84Nes792-19
❑ 84Top-19
❑ 84TopTif-19
❑ 85CubLioP-11
❑ 85CubSev-31
❑ 85Don-248
❑ 85Fle-127
❑ 85FleUpd-42
❑ 85Top-507
❑ 85TopTif-507
❑ 85TopTifT-35T
❑ 85TopTra-35T
❑ 86CubGat-31
❑ 86CubUno-9
❑ 86Don-361
❑ 86Fle-369
❑ 86Top-308
❑ 86TopTif-308
❑ 87Top-124
❑ 87TopTif-124
❑ 87TucTorP-12
❑ 92YanWIZ8-61

Fontes, Brad
❑ 88ButCopKSP-24
❑ 89KenTwiP-1062
❑ 89KenTwiS-5

Fontes, Brian
❑ 93BoiHawC-11
❑ 93BoiHawF-3908

Fonville, Chad
❑ 92ClaFS7-449
❑ 92EveGiaC-28
❑ 92EveGiaF-1695
❑ 93ClaGolF-160
❑ 93CliGiaF-2495
❑ 93MidLeaAGF-38
❑ 94ClaGolF-41
❑ 94ExcFS7-289
❑ 95ARuFalLS-6
❑ 95FleUpd-105
❑ 95TopTra-82T
❑ 95UltGolMR-M12
❑ 95UppDec-462
❑ 96ColCho-181
❑ 96ColCho-655
❑ 96ColChoGS-181
❑ 96ColChoGS-655
❑ 96ColChoSS-181
❑ 96ColChoSS-655
❑ 96DodFle-6
❑ 96DodMot-23
❑ 96DodPol-12
❑ 96Don-289
❑ 96DonPreP-289
❑ 96Fin-B140
❑ 96FinRef-B140
❑ 96Fle-433
❑ 96FleTif-433
❑ 96LeaSigA-69
❑ 96LeaSigAG-69
❑ 96LeaSigAS-69
❑ 96Pac-106
❑ 96PanSti-91
❑ 96Sco-213
❑ 96StaClu-31
❑ 96StaCluEPB-31
❑ 96StaCluEPG-31
❑ 96StaCluEPS-31
❑ 96StaCluMOP-31
❑ 96Top-402
❑ 96Ult-218
❑ 96UltGolM-218
❑ 96UppDec-93
❑ 96UppDecFSP-FS9
❑ 97AlbDukGS-10
❑ 97DodPol-7

Fonville, Charlie
❑ 84ButCopKT-10

Foor, Jim
❑ 72OPC-257
❑ 72Top-257
❑ 75TulOil7-20

Foote, Barry
❑ 72Dia-16
❑ 72Dia-17
❑ 74OPC-603
❑ 74Top-603
❑ 75ExpPos-13
❑ 75Hos-39
❑ 75OPC-229
❑ 75Top-229
❑ 75TopMin-229
❑ 76ExpRed-9
❑ 76MonExpP-10
❑ 76OPC-42
❑ 76Top-42
❑ 77BurCheD-157
❑ 77ExpPos-13
❑ 77OPC-207
❑ 77Top-612
❑ 78SSP270-40
❑ 78Top-513
❑ 79Top-161
❑ 80OPC-208
❑ 80Top-398
❑ 81Don-558
❑ 81Fle-313
❑ 81OPC-305
❑ 81Top-492
❑ 81TopSti-154
❑ 81TopTra-763
❑ 81YanPhoA-5
❑ 82Don-83
❑ 82Fle-34
❑ 82Top-706
❑ 82YanPhoA-1
❑ 83Top-697
❑ 85AlbYanT-23
❑ 86ColCliP-21
❑ 86ColCliP-9
❑ 86StaoftFT-2
❑ 87MyrBeaBJP-1441
❑ 89KnoBluJB-28
❑ 89KnoBluJP-1128
❑ 89SouLeaAJ-24
❑ 90WhiSoxC-30
❑ 91WhiSoxK-NNO
❑ 92MetColP-34
❑ 92MetKah-26
❑ 92YanWIZ8-62

Foote, Derek
❑ 94DanBraC-10
❑ 94DanBraF-3534
❑ 96MacBraB-13
❑ 97DurBulTI-23

Foran, John
❑ 96FayGenB-15
❑ 97WesMicW-13
❑ 98RanCucQG-11
❑ 98RanCucQG-11

Forbes, Andre
❑ 78GreBraT-9

Forbes, Cameron
❑ 97DelSho-12
❑ 98FreKeyM-8

Forbes, Kevin
❑ 97VerExpB-13

Forbes, P.J.
❑ 90BoiHawP-3320
❑ 90WicStaSGD-11
❑ 91PalSprAP-2022
❑ 92ClaFS7-376
❑ 92QuaCitRBC-18
❑ 92QuaCitRBF-817
❑ 93MidAngF-328
❑ 94ExcFS7-25
❑ 94VanCanF-1869
❑ 96VanCanB-13
❑ 97MidAngOHP-10
❑ 97RocRedW-11
❑ 98RocRedWQ-12

Forbes, Willie
❑ 88ChaRaiP-1193

Ford, Allen
❑ 91MedHatBJP-4094

Ford, Ben
❑ 96Exc-89
❑ 96GreBatB-10
❑ 97TamYan-13
❑ 98Bow-382
❑ 98BowChr-382
❑ 98BowChrGA-382
❑ 98BowChrGAR-382
❑ 98BowChrI-382
❑ 98BowChrIR-382
❑ 98BowChrR-382
❑ 98BowGolA-382
❑ 98BowInt-382
❑ 98Don-274
❑ 98DonGolPP-274
❑ 98DonSilPP-274
❑ 98LeaRS-207
❑ 98LeaRSLHolo-207
❑ 98LeaRSLong-207
❑ 98LeaRTrue-207
❑ 98PinSna-AD15
❑ 98Top-469
❑ 98TopChr-469
❑ 98TopChrR-469
❑ 98TopDevR-469
❑ 98TopDia-469
❑ 98TopMiniC-469
❑ 98TusSidM-11
❑ 99Fle-343
❑ 99FleSta9-343
❑ 99FleWarT-343
❑ 99SpoIll-51

Ford, Brian
❑ 95BatCliTI-12
❑ 96PieBolWB-12

Ford, Calvin
❑ 89WytCubS-15
❑ 90HunCubP-3298

Ford, Curt
❑ 83SprCarF-6
❑ 84ArkTraT-16
❑ 85LouRedR-13
❑ 86Fle-648
❑ 86LouRedTI-13
❑ 87CarSmo-21
❑ 87CarTeal-8
❑ 87Don-454
❑ 87Fle-294
❑ 87FleGlo-294
❑ 87Top-399
❑ 87TopTif-399
❑ 88CarSmo-20
❑ 88CarTeal-7
❑ 88Don-417
❑ 88Fle-32
❑ 88FleGlo-32
❑ 88PanSti-395
❑ 88Sco-288
❑ 88ScoGlo-288
❑ 88StaLinCa-6
❑ 88Top-612
❑ 88TopClo-36
❑ 88TopSti-23
❑ 88TopTif-612
❑ 88Woo-28
❑ 89Bow-408
❑ 89BowTif-408
❑ 89Fle-450
❑ 89FleGlo-450
❑ 89PhiTas-6
❑ 89Top-132
❑ 89TopTif-132
❑ 89UppDec-309
❑ 90Don-694
❑ 90Fle-557
❑ 90FleCan-557
❑ 90OPC-39
❑ 90PhiTas-9
❑ 90Sco-183
❑ 90SprCarDGB-30
❑ 90Top-39
❑ 90TopTif-39
❑ 90UppDec-490
❑ 91LinDriAAA-583
❑ 91TolMudHLD-583
❑ 91TolMudHP-1943
❑ 92LouRedF-1900
❑ 95ChaKniTI-10

Ford, Dale
❑ 88T/MUmp-23
❑ 89T/MUmp-21

❑ 89T/MUmp-60
❑ 90T/MUmp-20
Ford, Dan (Darnell)
❑ 75TwiPos-11
❑ 75TwiTeal-13
❑ 76MinTwiP-7
❑ 76OPC-313
❑ 76SSP-216
❑ 76Top-313
❑ 77BurCheD-48
❑ 77Hos-121
❑ 77OPC-104
❑ 77Top-555
❑ 77TopCloS-16
❑ 78Hos-18
❑ 78OPC-34
❑ 78Top-275
❑ 78TwiFriP-7
❑ 79OPC-201
❑ 79Top-385
❑ 80OPC-7
❑ 80Top-20
❑ 81AllGamPI-51
❑ 81Don-54
❑ 81Fle-273
❑ 81LonBeaPT-7
❑ 81OPC-303
❑ 81Top-422
❑ 82Don-468
❑ 82Fle-458
❑ 82FleSta-216
❑ 82OPC-134
❑ 82Top-134
❑ 82TopSti-163
❑ 82TopTra-35T
❑ 83Don-509
❑ 83Fle-61
❑ 83OPC-357
❑ 83OriPos-12
❑ 83Top-683
❑ 84BalOriP-14
❑ 84Don-367
❑ 84Fle-9
❑ 84Nes792-530
❑ 84OPC-349
❑ 84Top-530
❑ 84TopSti-212
❑ 84TopTif-530
❑ 85Don-489
❑ 85Fle-178
❑ 85Top-252
❑ 85TopTif-252
❑ 86Top-753
❑ 86TopTif-753
❑ 91OriCro-139
Ford, Dave
❑ 77RocRedWM-6
❑ 79RocRedWT-20
❑ 80BalOriP-6
❑ 80Top-661
❑ 81Don-552
❑ 81Fle-192
❑ 81Top-706
❑ 82Don-597
❑ 82Fle-166
❑ 82Top-174
❑ 83RocRedWT-4
❑ 84TacTigC-94
❑ 91OriCro-140
Ford, Doug
❑ 47CenFlo-7
Ford, Eric
❑ 94UtiBluSC-11
❑ 94UtiBluSF-3832
Ford, Gervise
❑ 85DalNatCC-12
Ford, Hod (Horace E.)
❑ 21Nei-111
❑ 22E120-125
❑ 22W573-42
❑ 27AmeCarE126-57
❑ 29ExhFou-8
❑ 29PorandAR-25
❑ 31Exh-8
❑ 33Gou-24
❑ 33GouCanV-24
❑ 90DodTar-249
❑ 93ConTSN-923
Ford, Jack
❑ 96PriWilCB-11
Ford, Jason
❑ 96PorRocB-13
Ford, Ken
❑ 82AleDukT-23
❑ 83LynPirT-20
❑ 85NasPirT-10
❑ 86NasPirP-7
Ford, Ondra
❑ 86EugEmeC-33
❑ 89AppFoxP-859
Ford, Randy
❑ 82KnoBluJT-3
Ford, Rick
❑ 76BurBeeT-10
❑ 77BurBeeT-9
❑ 77HolMilT-9
❑ 78CliDodT-9
Ford, Russ
❑ 09ColChiE-106
❑ 09SpoNewSM-49
❑ 09T206-134
❑ 10CouT21-135
❑ 10DomDisP-45
❑ 10E98-15
❑ 10JuJuDE-19
❑ 10RedCroT-25
❑ 10RedCroT-112
❑ 10RedCroT-193
❑ 10SweCapPP-34A
❑ 10SweCapPP-34B
❑ 10W555-30
❑ 11HelSta-43
❑ 11L1L-115
❑ 11MecDFT-30
❑ 11PloCanE-28
❑ 11S74Sil-21
❑ 11S81LarS-90
❑ 11SpoLifM-78
❑ 11T205-59A
❑ 11T205-59B
❑ 12ColRedB-106
❑ 12ColTinT-106
❑ 12HasTriFT-38A
❑ 12HasTriFT-38B
❑ 12HasTriFT-67B
❑ 12HasTriFT-68A
❑ 12HasTriFT-68B
❑ 14CraJacE-83
❑ 14PieStaT-43
❑ 14PieStaT-44
❑ 15CraJacE-83
❑ 15VicT21-10
❑ 95ConTSN-1369
Ford, Rusty
❑ 86BeaGolGP-11
❑ 87LasVegSP-9
❑ 88WicPilRD-41
Ford, Scott
❑ 86DavLipB-12
Ford, Steve
❑ 90YakBeaTI-20
Ford, Stewart
❑ 90PulBraB-4
❑ 90PulBraP-3098
❑ 91PulBraC-18
❑ 91PulBraP-3998
❑ 92IdaFalGF-3505
❑ 92IdaFalGSP-25
Ford, Ted
❑ 71OPC-612
❑ 71Top-612
❑ 72OPC-24
❑ 72RanTeal-8
❑ 72Top-24
❑ 73OPC-299
❑ 73Top-299
❑ 74OPC-617
❑ 74Top-617
❑ 93RanKee-11
Ford, Whitey (Edward C.)
❑ 47Exh-73A
❑ 47Exh-73B
❑ 47Exh-73C
❑ 47PM1StaP1-60
❑ 47StaPinP2-14
❑ 51BerRos-D5
❑ 51Bow-1
❑ 53BowC-153
❑ 53Dor-115
❑ 53Top-207
❑ 54Bow-177
❑ 54NewYorJA-46
❑ 54RedMan-AL16
❑ 54Top-37
❑ 55ArmCoi-6
❑ 55Bow-59
❑ 55RedMan-AL3
❑ 56Top-240
❑ 56YanJayP-6
❑ 56YanTeal-8
❑ 57Top-25
❑ 57YanJayP-5
❑ 58JayPubA-5
❑ 58Top-320
❑ 58YanJayP-4
❑ 59ArmCoi-8
❑ 59Top-430
❑ 59Yoo-2
❑ 60ArmCoi-10
❑ 60Top-35
❑ 60TopTat-15
❑ 60TopVen-35
❑ 60YanJayP-3
❑ 61Pos-6A
❑ 61Pos-6B
❑ 61Top-160
❑ 61Top-311
❑ 61Top-586
❑ 61TopStal-193
❑ 61Yan61RL-11
❑ 61YanJayP-4
❑ 62AurRec-6
❑ 62Baz-41
❑ 62ExhStaB-11
❑ 62Jel-9
❑ 62Pos-9
❑ 62PosCan-9A
❑ 62PosCan-9B
❑ 62SalPlaC-8
❑ 62ShiPlaC-8
❑ 62Top-57
❑ 62Top-59
❑ 62Top-235
❑ 62Top-310
❑ 62Top-315
❑ 62Top-475
❑ 62TopBuc-26
❑ 62TopStal-85
❑ 62TopVen-57
❑ 62TopVen-59
❑ 62YanJayP-6
❑ 63BasMagM-25
❑ 63ExhStaB-22
❑ 63Jel-19
❑ 63Pos-19
❑ 63ReqKP-7
❑ 63Top-6
❑ 63Top-142
❑ 63Top-446
❑ 63YanJayP-3
❑ 64ChatheY-8
❑ 64Top-4
❑ 64Top-380
❑ 64TopCoi-139
❑ 64TopGia-7
❑ 64TopVen-4
❑ 64WheSta-15
❑ 64YanJayP-4
❑ 65ChaTheY-6
❑ 65Top-330
❑ 66DexPre-1
❑ 66OPC-160
❑ 66Top-160
❑ 66TopRubl-32
❑ 66TopVen-160
❑ 66YanTeal-3
❑ 67NasHeaF-1
❑ 67OPC-5
❑ 67Top-5
❑ 67TopVen-178
❑ 68LauWorS-58
❑ 70FleWorS-58
❑ 71FleWorS-59
❑ 74NewYorNTDiS-18
❑ 74SyrChiTI-30
❑ 75SSP42-33
❑ 75SyrChiTI-5
❑ 75TCMAllG-10
❑ 75YanAllTT-3
❑ 76GalBasGHoF-9
❑ 76ShaPiz-144
❑ 76UPIS-3
❑ 77GalGloG-25
❑ 78TCM60I-21
❑ 79BasGre-73
❑ 80PerHaloFP-144
❑ 80PerHaloFPS-25
❑ 80SSPHOF-144
❑ 80YanGreT-10
❑ 81TCM60I-450
❑ 82ASAMicM-66
❑ 82ASAMicM-67
❑ 82CraJac-3
❑ 82DiaCla-83
❑ 82TCMGreP-3
❑ 83MLBPin-7
❑ 83TigAlKS-16
❑ 83Yan196-11
❑ 83YanASFY-13
❑ 83YanASFY-14
❑ 83YanYealT-17
❑ 84FifNatCT-6
❑ 84OCoandSI-5
❑ 84WilMay-24
❑ 85GeoSteM-3
❑ 85Woo-11
❑ 86SpoDecG-44
❑ 86SpoDesJM-24
❑ 86TCMSupS-9
❑ 87HygAllG-17
❑ 87NesDreT-21
❑ 87Yan196T-7
❑ 89BowInsT-3
❑ 89BowRepl-3
❑ 89BowTif-R3
❑ 89HOFStiB-70
❑ 89KahCoo-4
❑ 89PacLegI-210
❑ 89SweBasG-50
❑ 89TopBasT-31
❑ 89YanCitAG-1
❑ 90AGFA-16
❑ 90PerGreM-5
❑ 90SweBasG-8
❑ 91MDAA-10
❑ 91TopArc1-207
❑ 91YanRinP13-10
❑ 92BazQua5A-12
❑ 92FroRowF-1
❑ 92FroRowF-1AU
❑ 92FroRowF-2
❑ 92FroRowF-3
❑ 92FroRowF-4
❑ 92FroRowF-5
❑ 92PinMan-25
❑ 92St.VinHHS-4
❑ 92YanWIZ6-42
❑ 92YanWIZA-21
❑ 92YanWIZH-10
❑ 93ActPacA-116
❑ 93ActPacA2-50G
❑ 93Ble-9
❑ 93TedWil-62
❑ 93UppDecAH-52
❑ 93UppDecAH-140
❑ 93UppDecAH-152
❑ 93UppDecAH-158
❑ 93Yoo-6
❑ 94TopArc1-37
❑ 94TopArc1G-37
❑ 94UppDecAH-146
❑ 94UppDecAH-157
❑ 94UppDecAH1-146
❑ 94UppDecAH1-157
❑ 95EagBalL-6
❑ 95SPCha-105
❑ 95SPChaDC-105
❑ 95UppDecSHoB-1
❑ 98SpoIllWSFAE-5
❑ 98SpoIllWSFAEG-5
❑ 98TopStaRR-2
❑ 98TopStaRRA-2
❑ 99TopHaloFC-HOF8
Fordham, Tom
❑ 93SarWhiSF-1362
❑ 94HicCraC-10
❑ 94HicCraF-2171
❑ 94SouAtlLAF-SAL21
❑ 95Bes-13
❑ 95BowBes-B79
❑ 95BowBesR-B79
❑ 95PriWilCTI-18
❑ 95SPML-37
❑ 96BesAutSA-20
❑ 96BirBarB-13
❑ 96Bow-292
❑ 96BowFoi-292
❑ 96Exc-32
❑ 97BesAutAS-13
❑ 97BesAutP-R5
❑ 97Bow-117
❑ 97BowCerBlaIA-CA26
❑ 97BowCerBluIA-CA26
❑ 97BowCerGolIA-CA26
❑ 97BowInt-117
❑ 98ColCho-114
❑ 98PacOmeRS-14
❑ 98PacOmeRST4-14
❑ 98PacOnl-169
❑ 98PacOnlR-169
❑ 98PacOnlWC-169
❑ 98PriWilCASM-12
❑ 98UppDec-288
Fordyce, Brook
❑ 89KinMetS-10
❑ 89Sta-191
❑ 90ColMetGS-22
❑ 90ColMetPPI-4
❑ 90SouAtlLAS-30
❑ 91Cla/Bes-220
❑ 91ClaGolB-BC10
❑ 91ColMetPPI-7
❑ 91FloStaLAP-FSL31
❑ 91St.LucMC-11
❑ 91St.LucMP-714
❑ 91UppDec-64
❑ 92BinMetF-520
❑ 92BinMetS-57
❑ 92Bow-56
❑ 92ClaFS7-25
❑ 92ProFS7-285
❑ 92SkyAA F-24
❑ 92UppDecML-287
❑ 93Bow-333
❑ 93ClaFS7-135
❑ 93ExcFS7-73
❑ 93NorTidF-2573
❑ 93Top-701
❑ 93TopGol-701
❑ 93TopInaM-701
❑ 93TopInaR-701
❑ 94Bow-540
❑ 94Cla-193
❑ 94NorTidF-2923
❑ 94SigRoo-9
❑ 94SigRooS-9
❑ 94Top-785
❑ 94TopGol-785
❑ 94TopSpa-785
❑ 94UppDecML-19
❑ 95MetColP-12
❑ 96IndIndB-8
❑ 98Pac-263
❑ 98PacOnl-188
❑ 98PacOnlR-188
❑ 98PacOnlWC-188
❑ 98PacPlaB-263
❑ 98PacRedT-263
❑ 98PacSil-263
Fore, Chuck L.
❑ 78SyrChiT-10
❑ 79SyrChiT-14
❑ 80KnoBluJT-1
❑ 81SyrChiT-3
❑ 81SyrChiTI-8
❑ 83RicBraT-6
Foreman, Dave
❑ 87AncGlaP-40
Foreman, Francis
❑ 87OldJudN-174
Foreman, Toby
❑ 91BelMarCB-21
❑ 91BelMarP-3657
Forer, Daniel Lynn
❑ 81VerBeaDT-5
Forgeur, Freddy
❑ 79QuaCitCT-21
Forgione, Chris
❑ 85VisOakT-9
❑ 86VisOakP-9
❑ 87KenTwiP-22
❑ 88OrlTwiB-16
Forkerway, Trey
❑ 96DayCubB-10
❑ 97OrlRayB-10
❑ 98WesTenDJM-8
Forkner, Tim
❑ 93AubAstC-9
❑ 93AubAstF-3452
❑ 94MidLeaAF-MDW51
❑ 94QuaCitRBC-10
❑ 94QuaCitRBF-541
❑ 96JacGenB-8
❑ 96TexLeaAB-5
❑ 97JacGen-8
❑ 97JacGenS-5
Fornasiere, Bob
❑ 92Min-20
Forney, Jeff
❑ 87TamTarP-25
❑ 88CedRapRP-1151
❑ 88MidLeaAGS-10
❑ 90ChaLooGS-13
Forney, Rick
❑ 92KanCouCC-22
❑ 92KanCouCF-84
❑ 92KanCouCTI-9
❑ 92MidLeaATI-10
❑ 93CarLeaAGF-1
❑ 93FreKeyC-7
❑ 93FreKeyF-1020
❑ 94Bow-327
❑ 94BowBayF-2409
❑ 94Cla-55
❑ 94ExcFS7-4
❑ 94OriPro-34
❑ 95BowBayTI-43
❑ 95RocRedWTI-15
Fornieles, Mike
❑ 54Top-154
❑ 55Bow-266
❑ 56BalOriP-32
❑ 57Top-116
❑ 58Top-361
❑ 59Top-473
❑ 60Top-54
❑ 60TopVen-54
❑ 61Top-113
❑ 62Top-512
❑ 62TopStal-12
❑ 63Top-28
❑ 79TCM50-132
❑ 81RedSoxBG2S-20
❑ 91OriCro-141
❑ 94TopArc1-154
❑ 94TopArc1G-154
Forrest, Chris
❑ 87St.PetCP-15
❑ 89BoiHawP-2001
Forrest, Joel
❑ 87MacPirP-3
❑ 88AugPirP-381
❑ 88WatPirP-5
Forrester, Gary
❑ 89SalDodTI-11
❑ 90BakDodCLC-251
❑ 91QuaCitAP-2635
Forrester, Tom
❑ 86BirBarTI-15
❑ 87HawIsIP-7
❑ 88BirBarB-12
❑ 89BirBarADB-11
❑ 89VanCanC-20
❑ 89VanCanP-597
❑ 90BirBarADB-11
❑ 90SouBenWSB-19
❑ 90SouBenWSGS-4
Forry, Dewey
❑ 75WatDodT-8
Forsch, Ken
❑ 70AstPho-8
❑ 71AstTeal-7
❑ 71OPC-102
❑ 71Top-102
❑ 72AstTeal-8
❑ 72OPC-394
❑ 72Top-394
❑ 73OPC-589
❑ 73Top-589
❑ 74OPC-91
❑ 74Top-91
❑ 75AstPos-9
❑ 75OPC-357
❑ 75Top-357
❑ 75TopMin-357
❑ 76HouAstP-10
❑ 76OPC-357
❑ 76SSP-48
❑ 76Top-357
❑ 77AstPho-6
❑ 77BurCheD-4
❑ 77OPC-78
❑ 77Spo-7423
❑ 77Top-21
❑ 77Top-632
❑ 78AstBurK-8
❑ 78AstPos-9
❑ 78Kel-50
❑ 78Top-181
❑ 79AstPos-9
❑ 79AstTeal-6
❑ 79Hos-51
❑ 79OPC-276
❑ 79Top-534
❑ 80OPC-337
❑ 80Top-642
❑ 81AllGamPI-80
❑ 81Don-141
❑ 81Don-261A
❑ 81Fle-52
❑ 81LonBeaPT-12
❑ 81OPC-269
❑ 81Top-269
❑ 81TopTra-764
❑ 82Don-393

❑ 82Fle-459
❑ 82FleSta-221
❑ 82OPC-385
❑ 82Top-276
❑ 82Top-385
❑ 82TopSti-159
❑ 83AllGamPI-78
❑ 83Don-164
❑ 83Fle-89
❑ 83FleSta-64
❑ 83FleSti-28
❑ 83OPC-346
❑ 83Top-625
❑ 84AngSmo-9
❑ 84Don-280
❑ 84Fle-517
❑ 84Nes792-765
❑ 84OPC-193
❑ 84Top-765
❑ 84TopSti-237
❑ 84TopTif-765
❑ 85AngSmo-8
❑ 85Fle-301
❑ 85OPC-141
❑ 85Top-442
❑ 85TopTif-442
❑ 86AstMot-14
❑ 86Fle-155
❑ 87AstShoSO-7
❑ 87AstShoSPO-6
❑ 87AstShowSTh-26
❑ 90SweBasG-37

Forsch, Robert
❑ 75OPC-51
❑ 75St.LouCP-10
❑ 75Top-51
❑ 75TopMin-51
❑ 76OPC-426
❑ 76SSP-294
❑ 76St.LouCP-10
❑ 76Top-426
❑ 77Car5-9
❑ 77CarTeal-8
❑ 77Spo-7423
❑ 77Top-381
❑ 77Top-632
❑ 78CarTeal-7
❑ 78Hos-3
❑ 78OPC-83
❑ 78Top-58
❑ 79Car5-5
❑ 79Kel-38
❑ 79OPC-117
❑ 79Top-230
❑ 80OPC-279
❑ 80Top-535
❑ 81Car5x7-4
❑ 81CokTeaS-121
❑ 81Don-69
❑ 81Fle-537
❑ 81OPC-140
❑ 81Top-140
❑ 82Don-91
❑ 82Fle-112
❑ 82FleSta-22
❑ 82OPC-34
❑ 82Top-186
❑ 82Top-775
❑ 82TopSti-90
❑ 83Car-5
❑ 83Don-64
❑ 83Fle-5
❑ 83FleSta-63
❑ 83FleSti-11
❑ 83OPC-197
❑ 83Top-415
❑ 83TopSti-289
❑ 84Car-7
❑ 84Car5x7-6
❑ 84Don-168
❑ 84Fle-322
❑ 84Fle-639
❑ 84Nes792-5
❑ 84Nes792-75
❑ 84OPC-75
❑ 84Top-5
❑ 84Top-75
❑ 84TopSti-288A
❑ 84TopTif-5
❑ 84TopTif-75
❑ 85CarTeal-10
❑ 85Fle-223
❑ 85OPC-137
❑ 85Top-631
❑ 85TopTif-631
❑ 86CarIGAS-4
❑ 86CarKASD-6
❑ 86CarSchM-6
❑ 86CarTeal-13
❑ 86Don-353
❑ 86Fle-35
❑ 86Spo-129
❑ 86Top-66
❑ 86Top-322
❑ 86TopTif-66
❑ 86TopTif-322
❑ 87CarSmo-7
❑ 87CarTeal-9
❑ 87Don-540
❑ 87Fle-295
❑ 87FleAwaW-14
❑ 87FleGlo-295
❑ 87FleStiC-40
❑ 87Lea-161
❑ 87OPC-257
❑ 87Spo-191
❑ 87SpoTeaP-12
❑ 87Top-257
❑ 87TopSti-47
❑ 87TopTif-257
❑ 88CarSmo-5
❑ 88CarTeal-8
❑ 88Don-111
❑ 88Fle-33
❑ 88FleGlo-33
❑ 88PanSti-384
❑ 88Sco-264
❑ 88ScoGlo-264
❑ 88Spo-199
❑ 88Top-586
❑ 88TopClo-37
❑ 88TopTif-586
❑ 89AstLenH-23
❑ 89AstMot-11
❑ 89AstSmo-14
❑ 89Don-118
❑ 89Sco-525
❑ 89Top-163
❑ 89TopTif-163
❑ 90Fle-231
❑ 90FleCan-231
❑ 90PubIntS-95
❑ 90Sco-219
❑ 92CarMcD-51
❑ 99SpollIGotG-48
❑ 99SpollIGotGA-24

Forster, Guillermo
❑ 73CedRapAT-4
❑ 74CedRapAT-20

Forster, Scott
❑ 94StaCluDP-46
❑ 94StaCluDPFDI-46
❑ 94VerExpF-3905
❑ 96HarSenB-12
❑ 97HarSen-12
❑ 98JupHamQ-29

Forster, Terry
❑ 72Top-539
❑ 72WhiSox-3
❑ 72WhiSoxTI1-6
❑ 73OPC-129
❑ 73Top-129
❑ 74OPC-310
❑ 74Top-310
❑ 74TopSta-153
❑ 75OPC-137
❑ 75OPC-313
❑ 75Top-137
❑ 75Top-313
❑ 75TopMin-137
❑ 75TopMin-313
❑ 76Hos-14
❑ 76HosTwi-14
❑ 76OPC-437
❑ 76SSP-157
❑ 76Top-437
❑ 77PirPosP-5
❑ 77Top-271
❑ 78SSP270-68
❑ 78Top-347
❑ 79DodBlu-3
❑ 79OPC-7
❑ 79Top-23
❑ 80DodPol-51
❑ 80Top-605
❑ 81Dod-3
❑ 81Dod-8
❑ 81DodPol-51
❑ 81Fle-119
❑ 81LonBeaPT-16
❑ 81Top-104
❑ 82DodPol-51
❑ 82DodPos-1
❑ 82DodUniOV-4
❑ 82Don-362
❑ 82Fle-4
❑ 82Top-444
❑ 83BraPol-51
❑ 83Don-453
❑ 83Fle-205
❑ 83Top-583
❑ 83TopFol-4
❑ 83TopTra-33T
❑ 84BraPol-51
❑ 84Fle-178
❑ 84Nes792-791
❑ 84OPC-109
❑ 84raPho-9
❑ 84Top-791
❑ 84TopTif-791
❑ 85BraHos-8
❑ 85BraPol-51
❑ 85Fle-324
❑ 85OPC-248
❑ 85Top-248
❑ 85TopMin-248
❑ 85TopTif-248
❑ 86AngSmo-23
❑ 86Don-432
❑ 86Fle-514
❑ 86FleUpd-42
❑ 86Lea-202
❑ 86Top-363
❑ 86TopTif-363
❑ 86TopTra-37T
❑ 86TopTraT-37T
❑ 87Fle-80
❑ 87FleGlo-80
❑ 87Top-652
❑ 87TopTif-652
❑ 90DodTar-250

Forster, Tom
❑ 87BucN28-52
❑ 87OldJudN-175
❑ 87OldJudN-177

Forsythe, Frank
❑ 18Zee-44

Fortaleza, Ray
❑ 84GreHorT-2

Fortenberry, Jim
❑ 86ClePhiP-8
❑ 86FloStaLAP-16
❑ 87ReaPhiP-21

Fortin, Blaine
❑ 96StCatSB-8

Fortin, Troy
❑ 94EliTwiC-8
❑ 94EliTwiF-3735
❑ 95Exc-83
❑ 95ForWayWTI-13
❑ 96FtMyeMB-30
❑ 97ForMyeM-10
❑ 97NewBriRC-9
❑ 98NewBriRCM-9

Fortinberry, Bill
❑ 80PorBeaT-12

Fortugno, Tim
❑ 86BelMarCr-115
❑ 87SalSpuS-26
❑ 88ReaPhiP-876
❑ 89RenSilSCLC-244
❑ 89StoPorS-7
❑ 90BelBreB-7
❑ 90BelBreS-8
❑ 91ElPasDLD-182
❑ 91ElPasDP-2741
❑ 91LinDriAA-182
❑ 92DonRoo-38
❑ 92EdmTraF-3535
❑ 92EdmTraS-157
❑ 92SkyAAAF-78
❑ 93Don-299
❑ 93Fle-572
❑ 93OttLynF-2429
❑ 93Sco-262
❑ 93StaClu-231
❑ 93StaCluFDI-231
❑ 93StaCluMOP-231
❑ 93Top-320
❑ 93TopGol-320
❑ 93TopInaM-320
❑ 93TopInaR-320
❑ 93TopMic-320
❑ 93Ult-163
❑ 94ChaLooF-1356
❑ 94FleUpd-118
❑ 94RedKah-10
❑ 95Fle-435
❑ 95FleUpd-36
❑ 95WhiSoxK-10
❑ 97ScrRedB-6

Fortuna, Mike
❑ 89SalBucS-8
❑ 89WelPirP-12

Fortune, Grehsam
❑ 94ButCopKSP-19

Fortune, Steve
❑ 79ElmPioRST-9

Fosnow, Gerald
❑ 65Top-529

Foss, Larry
❑ 77FriOneYW-106
❑ 91MetWIZ-122

Fossa, Dick
❑ 88CalLeaACLC-24

Fossas, Tony
❑ 80AshTouT-7
❑ 81TulDriT-16A
❑ 83TulDriT-3
❑ 84OklCit8T-12
❑ 85OklCit8T-10
❑ 86EdmTraP-10
❑ 87EdmTraP-2080
❑ 88OklCit8C-9
❑ 88OklCit8P-34
❑ 89DenZepC-3
❑ 89DenZepP-55
❑ 90BrePol-36
❑ 90Don-457
❑ 90Fle-323
❑ 90FleCan-323
❑ 90OPC-34
❑ 90Sco-567
❑ 90Top-34
❑ 90TopTif-34
❑ 91Lea-276
❑ 91OPC-747
❑ 91RedSoxP-10
❑ 91Sco-634
❑ 91Top-747
❑ 91TopDesS-747
❑ 91TopMic-747
❑ 91TopTif-747
❑ 92Don-645
❑ 92OPC-249
❑ 92RedSoxDD-11
❑ 92Sco-389
❑ 92StaClu-144
❑ 92Top-249
❑ 92TopGol-249
❑ 92TopGolW-249
❑ 92TopMic-249
❑ 92UppDec-503
❑ 93Don-195
❑ 93Fle-180
❑ 93PacSpa-358
❑ 93RanKee-151
❑ 93RedSoxP-14
❑ 93StaClu-247
❑ 93StaCluFDI-247
❑ 93StaCluMOP-247
❑ 94BreMilB-124
❑ 94Pac-55
❑ 94StaClu-26
❑ 94StaCluFDI-26
❑ 94StaCluGR-26
❑ 94StaCluMOP-26
❑ 94Top-378
❑ 94TopGol-378
❑ 94TopSpa-378
❑ 95Fle-30
❑ 95Pac-37
❑ 95Top-119
❑ 96CarPol-6
❑ 96Fle-542
❑ 96FleTif-542
❑ 96LeaSigEA-54
❑ 96Pac-220
❑ 97CarPol-6
❑ 97PacPriGotD-GD198
❑ 97StaClu-367
❑ 97StaCluMOP-367
❑ 98PacOnl-685
❑ 98PacOnlR-685
❑ 98PacOnlWC-685

Fosse, Ray
❑ 69Top-244
❑ 70DayDaiNM-102a
❑ 70Ind-4
❑ 70OPC-184
❑ 70Top-184
❑ 71Ind-4
❑ 71Kel-39
❑ 71MilDud-5
❑ 71MLBOffS-366
❑ 71OPC-125
❑ 71Top-125
❑ 71TopCoi-42
❑ 71TopSup-51
❑ 71TopTat-129
❑ 72OPC-470
❑ 72SevTraC-15
❑ 72Top-470
❑ 72TopPos-4
❑ 73A'sPos-30
❑ 73Kel2D-18
❑ 73OPC-226
❑ 73Top-226
❑ 73TopCanL-17
❑ 74A'sPos-46
❑ 74OPC-420
❑ 74Top-420
❑ 75OPC-486
❑ 75Top-486
❑ 75TopMin-486
❑ 76IndTeal-4
❑ 76OPC-554
❑ 76SSP-500
❑ 76Top-554
❑ 76TopTra-554T
❑ 77BurCheD-62
❑ 77Hos-122
❑ 77IndTeal-11
❑ 77OPC-39
❑ 77PepGloD-17
❑ 77Top-267
❑ 78Hos-57
❑ 78Top-415
❑ 79Top-51
❑ 80Top-327
❑ 86TopRos-68
❑ 86TopRos-69
❑ 91UppDecS-5
❑ 94BreMilB-219

Foster, Alan
❑ 69Top-266
❑ 70OPC-369
❑ 70Top-369
❑ 71MLBOffS-367
❑ 71OPC-207
❑ 71Top-207
❑ 72OPC-521
❑ 72Top-521
❑ 73OPC-543
❑ 73Top-543
❑ 74OPC-442
❑ 74Top-442
❑ 75OPC-296
❑ 75Top-296
❑ 75TopMin-296
❑ 76OPC-266
❑ 76SSP-115
❑ 76Top-266
❑ 77Top-108
❑ 81TCM60I-465
❑ 85SpoIndGC-6
❑ 90DodTar-251

Foster, Bob
❑ 79LodDodT-17

Foster, Bryan
❑ 88BelBreGS-12
❑ 89StoPorB-21
❑ 89StoPorCLC-171
❑ 89StoPorP-393
❑ 89StoPorS-20

Foster, Bud
❑ 46RemBre-15
❑ 47RemBre-9
❑ 47SigOil-44
❑ 48SigOil-7
❑ 49RemBre-7

Foster, Clifton
❑ 92SouOreAC-24
❑ 92SouOreAF-3408
❑ 93MadMusC-9
❑ 93MadMusF-1817

Foster, Doug
❑ 78CliDodT-10

Foster, Edward Lee
❑ 09T206-484
❑ 11MecDFT-49
❑ 11SpoLifM-123
❑ 21E121So8-23

Foster, Elmer
❑ 87OldJudN-176A
❑ 87OldJudN-176B
❑ 88WG1CarG-39
❑ 89SFHaCN-5
❑ 90KalBatN-21

Foster, George
❑ 24Zee-25
❑ 71OPC-276
❑ 71Top-276
❑ 72OPC-256
❑ 72Top-256
❑ 73OPC-202
❑ 73OPC-399
❑ 73Top-202
❑ 73Top-399
❑ 74OPC-646
❑ 74Top-646
❑ 75OPC-87
❑ 75Top-87
❑ 75TopMin-87
❑ 76Hos-106
❑ 76LinSup-95
❑ 76OPC-179
❑ 76RedIceL-4
❑ 76RedKro-8
❑ 76SSP-44
❑ 76Top-179
❑ 77BurCheD-201
❑ 77ChiWilD-22
❑ 77DailsID-22
❑ 77DetCaeD-22
❑ 77HolInnD-22
❑ 77Hos-40
❑ 77Kel-1
❑ 77MSADis-22
❑ 77OPC-3
❑ 77OPC-120
❑ 77PepGloD-48
❑ 77RCColC-22
❑ 77RedCarP-10
❑ 77SagDis-22
❑ 77sDis-22
❑ 77Spo-4517
❑ 77SpollIAC-2
❑ 77Top-3
❑ 77Top-347
❑ 77WenDis-22
❑ 77ZipDis-22
❑ 78Hos-2
❑ 78Kel-10
❑ 78OPC-2
❑ 78OPC-3
❑ 78OPC-70
❑ 78Pep-10
❑ 78RCColC-13
❑ 78SSP270-113
❑ 78Top-202
❑ 78Top-203
❑ 78Top-500
❑ 78WifBalD-24
❑ 79BasPat-31
❑ 79Hos-107
❑ 79Kel-32
❑ 79OPC-316
❑ 79Top-2
❑ 79Top-3
❑ 79Top-600
❑ 80BurKinPHR-15
❑ 80Kel-50
❑ 80OPC-209
❑ 80RedEnq-15
❑ 80Top-400
❑ 80TopSup-24
❑ 81AllGamPI-144
❑ 81CokTeaS-41
❑ 81Don-65
❑ 81Dra-18
❑ 81Fle-202A
❑ 81Fle-202B
❑ 81Fle-216
❑ 81FleStiC-41
❑ 81Kel-1
❑ 81OPC-200
❑ 81PerAll-4
❑ 81PerCreC-9
❑ 81Squ-2
❑ 81Top-200
❑ 81TopScr-65
❑ 81TopSti-159
❑ 81TopSupHT-35
❑ 82Don-274
❑ 82Dra-13
❑ 82Fle-66
❑ 82Fle-630
❑ 82FleSta-12
❑ 82K-M-32
❑ 82Kel-56
❑ 82MetPhoA-7
❑ 82OPC-177
❑ 82OPC-336
❑ 82OPC-342
❑ 82RegGloT-1

❑ 82SevSluC-11
❑ 82Squ-18
❑ 82Top-342A
❑ 82Top-342B
❑ 82Top-700
❑ 82Top-701
❑ 82TopSti-40
❑ 82TopSti-126
❑ 82TopTra-36T
❑ 83AllGamPl-145
❑ 83Don-6
❑ 83Don-427
❑ 83Dra-8
❑ 83Fle-542
❑ 83FleSta-65
❑ 83FleSti-239
❑ 83Kel-22
❑ 83OPC-80
❑ 83Top-80
❑ 83TopFol-2
❑ 83TopSti-263
❑ 84AllGamPl-51
❑ 84Don-312
❑ 84DonCha-2
❑ 84Fle-584
❑ 84FunFooP-46
❑ 84MetFanC-3
❑ 84Nes792-350
❑ 84OCoandSl-193
❑ 84OPC-350
❑ 84Top-350
❑ 84TopRubD-20
❑ 84TopSti-105
❑ 84TopTif-350
❑ 85AllGamPl-141
❑ 85Don-603
❑ 85Fle-79
❑ 85Lea-42
❑ 85MetColP-26
❑ 85MetFanC-4
❑ 85MetTCM-33
❑ 85OPC-170
❑ 85PolMet-M1
❑ 85Top-170
❑ 85TopMin-170
❑ 85TopRubD-20
❑ 85TopSti-99
❑ 85TopTif-170
❑ 86Don-116
❑ 86Fle-80
❑ 86GenMilB-4C
❑ 86MetColP-12
❑ 86MetTCM-25
❑ 86OPC-69
❑ 86Spo-68
❑ 86Spo-126
❑ 86Spo-131
❑ 86Spo-139
❑ 86Top-680
❑ 86TopSti-100
❑ 86TopTif-680
❑ 86Woo-11
❑ 89PacLegl-173
❑ 89PacSenL-114
❑ 89T/MSenL-36
❑ 89T/MSenL-119
❑ 89TopSenL-1
❑ 90EliSenL-112
❑ 90EliSenL-124
❑ 90PacLeg-72
❑ 90SweBasG-97
❑ 91LinDri-37
❑ 91MDAA-8
❑ 91MetWIZ-123
❑ 91SweBasG-112
❑ 91UppDecS-12
❑ 92ActPacA-61
❑ 92MDAMVP-10
❑ 92UppDecS-14
❑ 93Metlma-9
❑ 93TedWil-29
❑ 93TedWilM-17
❑ 93TedWilPC-25
❑ 93UppDecAH-53
❑ 93UppDecS-15
❑ 93UppDecS-22
❑ 93UppDecS-24
❑ 94UppDecAH-182
❑ 94UppDecAH1-182
❑ 95MCIAmb-16
❑ 95SonGre-2
❑ 96Red76K-5
❑ 97OhiLot-3
❑ 99SpollIGotG-16
❑ 99SpollIGotGA-25

Foster, Jeff
❑ 94BurBeeC-8

Foster, Jim
❑ 93BluOriC-13
❑ 93BluOriF-4128
❑ 94AlbPolC-1
❑ 94AlbPolF-2240
❑ 94ExcFirYPF-1
❑ 94ExcFS7-5
❑ 94OriPro-35
❑ 94SouAtlLAF-SAL2
❑ 96FreKeyB-10
❑ 97CalLeaATI-31
❑ 97FreKey-8
❑ 98BowBayM-13

Foster, John
❑ 82WisRapTF-19

Foster, Julio
❑ 92UtiBluSC-9

Foster, Ken
❑ 81WisRapTT-16
❑ 82OrlTwiT-18
❑ 83OrlTwiT-11
❑ 86SanJosBP-7

Foster, Kevin
❑ 89RocExpLC-8
❑ 90WesPalBES-7
❑ 91SumFlyC-4
❑ 91SumFlyP-2327
❑ 92WesPalBEF-2083
❑ 93JacSunF-2705
❑ 94LeaLimR-19
❑ 94PhiUSPC-8H
❑ 94StaCluT-236
❑ 94StaCluTFDI-236
❑ 94Top-786
❑ 94TopGol-786
❑ 94TopSpa-786
❑ 94TopTra-79T
❑ 95ColCho-214
❑ 95ColChoGS-214
❑ 95ColChoSS-214
❑ 95Don-296
❑ 95DonPreP-296
❑ 95DonTopotO-197
❑ 95Fin-24
❑ 95FinRef-24
❑ 95Fla-331
❑ 95Fle-414
❑ 95FleRooS-4
❑ 95Lea-45
❑ 95Pac-69
❑ 95Pin-393
❑ 95PinArtP-393
❑ 95PinMusC-393
❑ 95StaClu-461
❑ 95StaCluMOP-461
❑ 95StaCluSTWS-461
❑ 95StaCluVR-250
❑ 95StaCluVRMO-250
❑ 95Top-412
❑ 95TopCyb-212
❑ 95Ult-136
❑ 95UltGolM-136
❑ 95UppDec-314
❑ 95UppDecED-314
❑ 95UppDecEDG-314
❑ 95UppDecSE-121
❑ 95UppDecSEG-121
❑ 96ColCho-82
❑ 96ColChoGS-82
❑ 96ColChoSS-82
❑ 96CubFle-4
❑ 96Don-294
❑ 96DonPreP-294
❑ 96EmoXL-153
❑ 96Fla-214
❑ 96Fle-316
❑ 96FleTif-316
❑ 96LeaSigA-70
❑ 96LeaSigAG-70
❑ 96LeaSigAS-70
❑ 96Pac-22
❑ 96Sco-92
❑ 96StaClu-326
❑ 96StaCluMOP-326
❑ 96Top-62
❑ 96Ult-166
❑ 96UltGolM-166
❑ 96UppDec-34
❑ 97ColCho-288
❑ 98ColCho-54
❑ 98PacInvGems-129
❑ 98Pin-104
❑ 98PinPreP-104
❑ 98PinSna-CC8
❑ 98PinSna-CC10
❑ 98Top-127
❑ 98TopChr-127
❑ 98TopChrR-127
❑ 98TopDevR-127
❑ 98TopDia-127
❑ 98TopMiniC-127
❑ 98UppDec-53
❑ 98UppDecSF-32

Foster, Kid (Edward C.)
❑ 14B18B-39
❑ 15SpoNewM-62
❑ 16BF2FP-46
❑ 16SpoNewM-61
❑ 17ColE13-51
❑ 22AmeCarE122-20
❑ 22W575-36

Foster, Kris
❑ 95YakBeaTI-9
❑ 96SanBerSB-9
❑ 97VerBeaD-9
❑ 98VerBeaDM-9

Foster, Lamar
❑ 89MarPhiS-11
❑ 90MarPhiP-3179
❑ 91BatCliCB-8
❑ 91BatCliP-3490

Foster, Larry
❑ 77FriOneYW-86

Foster, Leo
❑ 74OPC-607
❑ 74Top-607
❑ 75OPC-418
❑ 75TidTidTI-11
❑ 75Top-418
❑ 75TopMin-418
❑ 77MetDaiPA-1
❑ 77Top-458
❑ 78Top-229
❑ 91MetWIZ-124

Foster, Lindsay
❑ 87MyrBeaBJP-1449
❑ 88DunBluJS-6
❑ 89CanIndB-15
❑ 89CanIndP-1304
❑ 89CanIndS-6
❑ 90KinIndTI-14
❑ 91BirBarLD-58
❑ 91BirBarP-1461
❑ 91LinDriAA-58
❑ 92BirBarF-2591
❑ 92BirBarS-82

Foster, Mark
❑ 93MarPhiC-10
❑ 93MarPhiF-3464
❑ 94SpaPhiF-1715
❑ 94SparPhiC-9
❑ 95ReaPhiTI-12
❑ 96ReaPhiB-4
❑ 97ReaPhi-15

Foster, Otis
❑ 77BriRedST-7

Foster, Paul
❑ 87FayGenP-16
❑ 88LakTigS-11

Foster, Quincy
❑ 98KanCouC-9
❑ 98KanCouCCP-9

Foster, Randy
❑ 87OneYanP-21
❑ 88PriWilYS-10

Foster, Roy
❑ 71MLBOffS-368
❑ 71OPC-107
❑ 71Top-107
❑ 72OPC-329
❑ 72Top-329
❑ 72TopCloT-12
❑ 89TidTidC-2

Foster, Rube (Andrew)
❑ 74LauOldTBS-35
❑ 80PerHaloFP-174
❑ 80SSPHOF-175
❑ 83ConMar-55
❑ 84OCoandSl-139
❑ 86NegLeaF-18
❑ 87NegLeaPD-25
❑ 88ConNegA-4
❑ 88NegLeaD-1
❑ 90NegLeaS-16
❑ 91ConTSN-138
❑ 91PomBlaBPB-27
❑ 94TedWil-105
❑ 94UppDecTAE-31
❑ 95S.FExaNLT-11
❑ 97NegLeaPC-SJKO

Foster, Rube (George)
❑ 09ColChiE-107
❑ 12ColRedB-107
❑ 12ColTinT-107
❑ 17HolBreD-31

Foster, Russ
❑ 91PacSenL-75

Foster, Steve (Stephen)
❑ 88BilMusP-1818
❑ 89CedRapRB-2
❑ 89CedRapRP-936
❑ 89CedRapRS-7
❑ 89Sta-194
❑ 90ChaLooGS-14
❑ 91ChaLooLD-158
❑ 91ChaLooP-1953
❑ 91LinDriAA-158
❑ 92Cla1-T35
❑ 92Don-420
❑ 92FleUpd-80
❑ 92NasSouF-1827
❑ 92OPC-528
❑ 92ProFS7-216
❑ 92StaClu-826
❑ 92StaCluECN-826
❑ 92Top-528
❑ 92TopDeb91-58
❑ 92TopGol-528
❑ 92TopGolW-528
❑ 92TopMic-528
❑ 93Don-666
❑ 93Fle-33
❑ 93Sco-284
❑ 93Top-193
❑ 93TopGol-193
❑ 93ToplnaM-193
❑ 93ToplnaR-193
❑ 93TopMic-193
❑ 93Ult-328
❑ 94Pac-147
❑ 94RedKah-11

Foster, Willie
❑ 74LauOldTBS-5
❑ 80PerHaloFP-226
❑ 90NegLeaS-24

Fothergill, Bob (Robert)
❑ 28Exh-45
❑ 28StaPlaCE-21
❑ 30WhiSoxTI-11
❑ 79RedSoxEF-9
❑ 81TigDetN-85
❑ 81TigSecNP-11
❑ 85BigLeaC3-63
❑ 91ConTSN-72

Foucault, Steve
❑ 73RanTeal-9
❑ 74OPC-294
❑ 74Top-294
❑ 75OPC-283
❑ 75RanPos-9
❑ 75Top-283
❑ 75TopMin-283
❑ 76OPC-303
❑ 76SSP-252
❑ 76Top-303
❑ 77Top-459
❑ 78TigBurK-10
❑ 78TigTeal-9
❑ 78Top-68
❑ 92BelBreCB-29
❑ 92BelBreFI-423
❑ 93BelBreCB-27
❑ 93BelBreFI-1727
❑ 93RanKee-152
❑ 94BelBreC-28
❑ 94BelBreFI-119
❑ 95HudValRTI-29

Foulk, Leon
❑ 52Par-15

Foulke, Keith
❑ 94EveGiaC-7
❑ 94EveGiaF-3643
❑ 96DouAllB-55
❑ 96TexLeaAB-6
❑ 97Bow-317
❑ 97BowChr-219
❑ 97BowChrl-219
❑ 97BowChrIR-219
❑ 97BowChrR-219
❑ 97BowInt-317
❑ 97Fle-760
❑ 97FleTif-760
❑ 97PhoFirTI-9
❑ 98Fle-276
❑ 98PacOnl-170
❑ 98PacOnlR-170
❑ 98PacOnlWC-170
❑ 98StaCluFDI-270
❑ 98StaClul-270
❑ 98StaCluOneK-270
❑ 98StaCluPP-270
❑ 98Ult-227
❑ 98UltGolM-227
❑ 98UltMas-227
❑ 98UltPlaM-227
❑ 98UppDec-333

Foulks, Brian
❑ 96GreFalDB-13
❑ 96GreFalDTI-28

Fournier, Bruce
❑ 79WatA'sT-19
❑ 80OgdA'sT-16
❑ 80WesHavWCT-5
❑ 81WesHavAT-10

Fournier, Jacques F.
❑ 12T207-62
❑ 15SpoNewM-63
❑ 16SpoNewM-62
❑ 17ColE13-52
❑ 17HolBreD-32
❑ 17Zee-7
❑ 18Zee-8
❑ 19Zee-7
❑ 21Exh-50
❑ 21Exh-51
❑ 22E120-229
❑ 22W573-43
❑ 23WilChoV-44
❑ 25Exh-11
❑ 26Exh-10
❑ 26SpoComoA-15
❑ 73SpoScoHC-5
❑ 90DodTar-252
❑ 92ConTSN-541
❑ 95ConTSN-1381

Fournier, John
❑ 09ObaT21-140

Foussianes, George
❑ 83BirBarT-11
❑ 85TulDriTI-6
❑ 89BirBarADB-12
❑ 90BirBarADB-12

Foutz, Dave
❑ 74BroClu-8
❑ 76SSP188WS-2
❑ 87BucN28-97
❑ 87LonJacN-4
❑ 87OldJudN-178A
❑ 87OldJudN-178B
❑ 87ScrDC-4
❑ 89EdgR.WG-9
❑ 90DodTar-253
❑ 95May-9
❑ 95NewN566-181

Fowble, Greg
❑ 87AriWilP-2
❑ 88AriWilP-3

Fowler, Ben
❑ 96DanBraB-11
❑ 98ColRedSM-21

Fowler, Derek
❑ 97UCLBruTI-3

Fowler, Dick
❑ 42A'sTeal-13
❑ 46A'sTeal-6
❑ 47A'sTeal-12
❑ 47Exh-74
❑ 48A'sTeal-8
❑ 49A'sTeal-13
❑ 49Bow-171
❑ 49OlmStu-3
❑ 49PhiBul-19
❑ 50A'sTeal-10
❑ 50Bow-214
❑ 51A'sTeal-10
❑ 52A'sTeal-9
❑ 52Bow-190
❑ 52Top-210
❑ 83TopRep5-210

Fowler, Don
❑ 80CarMudF-5
❑ 81TacTigT-14
❑ 82TacTigT-2
❑ 84ColCliP-10
❑ 84ColCliT-6
❑ 84NasSouTI-7
❑ 89WatDiaP-1792
❑ 89WatDiaS-7

Fowler, Dwayne
❑ 91PulBraC-19
❑ 91PulBraP-3999

Fowler, Eddie
❑ 89WytCubS-10

Fowler, J. Art
❑ 55Top-3
❑ 55TopDouH-79
❑ 56Kah-5
❑ 56Top-47
❑ 56TopPin-55
❑ 57Top-233
❑ 58SeaRalT-9
❑ 59Top-508
❑ 62Top-128
❑ 62TopVen-128
❑ 63Top-454A
❑ 63Top-454B
❑ 64Top-349
❑ 64TopVen-349
❑ 73OPC-323
❑ 73Top-323
❑ 74OPC-379
❑ 74Top-379
❑ 75RanPos-10
❑ 79YanPicA-13
❑ 90DodTar-254
❑ 93RanKee-153

Fowler, Jesse
❑ 26Zee-71

Fowler, John
❑ 89BluOriS-9
❑ 90WauTimB-21
❑ 90WauTimP-2134
❑ 90WauTimS-8
❑ 94TedWil-106

Fowler, Maleke
❑ 96BluOriB-13
❑ 97DelSho-15
❑ 98FreKeyM-28

Fowler, Mike
❑ 88DurBulS-6
❑ 89DurBullS-11
❑ 89DurBulIS-11
❑ 89DurBulTI-11

Fowler, Yale
❑ 89GreFalDSP-13
❑ 90YakBeaTI-32

Fowlkes, Alan Kim
❑ 81ShrCapT-7
❑ 82Gia25tATI-9
❑ 83Don-46
❑ 83Fle-259
❑ 83Top-543
❑ 84PhoGiaC-16
❑ 86EdmTraP-11
❑ 88RenSilSCLC-268

Fowlkes, David
❑ 76BatTroTI-8
❑ 77WatIndT-8

Fox, Andy
❑ 89HigSchPLS-8
❑ 90Bes-263
❑ 90CMC-825
❑ 90GreHorB-16
❑ 90GreHorP-2668
❑ 90GreHorS-1
❑ 90SouAtlLAS-6
❑ 90TopTVY-43
❑ 91CarLeaAP-CAR30
❑ 91Cla/Bes-132
❑ 91PriWilCC-17
❑ 91PriWilCP-1433
❑ 92PriWilCC-2
❑ 92PriWilCF-155
❑ 93AlbYanF-2170
❑ 93ClaFS7-71
❑ 94AlbYanF-1449
❑ 94AlbYanTI-1
❑ 94AriFalLS-5
❑ 95ColCliP-10
❑ 95ColCliTI-10
❑ 95NorNavTI-51
❑ 96Bow-275
❑ 96BowFoi-275
❑ 96Fin-S272
❑ 96FinRef-S272
❑ 96FleUpd-U59
❑ 96FleUpdNH-6
❑ 96FleUpdTC-U59
❑ 96Sel-194
❑ 96SelArtP-194
❑ 96Ult-383
❑ 96UltGolM-383
❑ 97ColCliB-13
❑ 97ColCliD-9
❑ 97PacPriGotD-GD71
❑ 97Sco-250

❑ 97ScoArtPWB-250
❑ 97ScoPreS-250
❑ 97ScoShoS-250
❑ 97ScoShoSAP-250
❑ 97YanSco-15
❑ 97YanScoPl-15
❑ 97YanScoPr-15
❑ 98DiaBacP-17
❑ 98DiaMcD-12
❑ 98PacOnl-39
❑ 98PacOnlR-39
❑ 98PacOnlWC-39
❑ 98PriWilCASM-27
❑ 99Fle-236
❑ 99FleSta9-236
❑ 99FleWarT-236
❑ 99StaClu-129
❑ 99StaCluFDI-129
❑ 99StaCluOoaK-129
❑ 99StaCluPP-129
❑ 99Top-183
❑ 99TopChr-183
❑ 99TopChrR-183
❑ 99TopMVPP-183

Fox, Blane
❑ 87LakTigP-22
❑ 88FloStaLAS-36
❑ 88LakTigS-12
❑ 89ColMudB-14
❑ 89ColMudP-143
❑ 89ColMudS-9
❑ 91LinDriAA-461
❑ 91NewBriRSLD-461
❑ 91NewBriRSP-364

Fox, Brian
❑ 97LetBlaDB-7

Fox, Chad
❑ 92ClaDraP-100
❑ 92PriRedC-13
❑ 92PriRedF-3081
❑ 93ClaFS7-101
❑ 93ExcFS7-18
❑ 93WesVirWC-1
❑ 93WesVirWF-2859
❑ 94CarLeaAF-CAR47
❑ 94WinSpiC-8
❑ 94WinSpiF-265
❑ 95ChaLooTI-6
❑ 95UppDecML-138
❑ 95UppDecMLFS-138
❑ 96RicBraB-11
❑ 96RicBraRC-7
❑ 98Don-336
❑ 98DonGolPP-336
❑ 98DonSilPP-336
❑ 98Fle-147
❑ 98PacOnl-393
❑ 98PacOnlR-393
❑ 98PacOnlWC-393
❑ 98Ult-144
❑ 98UltGolM-144
❑ 98UltMas-144
❑ 98UltPlaM-144
❑ 99Fle-385
❑ 99FleSta9-385
❑ 99FleWarT-385

Fox, Charlie
❑ 70Gia-3
❑ 71GiaTic-3
❑ 71OPC-517
❑ 71Top-517
❑ 72GiaTeal-5
❑ 72OPC-129
❑ 72Top-129
❑ 73OPC-252
❑ 73Top-252A
❑ 73Top-252B
❑ 74OPC-78
❑ 74Top-78

Fox, Dan
❑ 89KenTwiP-1085
❑ 89KenTwiS-26
❑ 90KenTwiB-29
❑ 90KenTwiS-27
❑ 91KenTwiC-21
❑ 92KenTwiC-27
❑ 93ForWayWC-28
❑ 94ForWayWC-30

Fox, Eric
❑ 85AncGlaPTI-11
❑ 87ChaLooB-16
❑ 88VerMarP-945
❑ 89HunStaB-9
❑ 90CMC-592
❑ 90ProAAAF-154
❑ 90TacTigC-15
❑ 90TacTigP-107
❑ 91LinDriAAA-533
❑ 91TacTigLD-533
❑ 91TacTigP-2317
❑ 92DonRoo-39
❑ 92HunStaF-3961
❑ 92ScoRoo-88T
❑ 92TacTigS-532
❑ 93Don-287
❑ 93Fle-663
❑ 93LinVenB-321
❑ 93PacSpa-566
❑ 93Pin-567
❑ 93Sco-352
❑ 93Sel-313
❑ 93StaClu-131
❑ 93StaCluFDI-131
❑ 93StaCluMOP-131
❑ 93TacTigF-3046
❑ 93Top-46
❑ 93TopGol-46
❑ 93TopInaM-46
❑ 93TopInaR-46
❑ 93TopMic-46
❑ 93Ult-605
❑ 93UppDec-781
❑ 93UppDecGold-781
❑ 93USPlaCR-2C
❑ 94TacTigF-3186
❑ 98ColRedSM-27

Fox, Howie (Howard)
❑ 49EurSta-84
❑ 50Bow-80
❑ 51Bow-180
❑ 52Bow-125
❑ 52NatTeaL-10
❑ 52Top-209
❑ 53BowC-158
❑ 53Top-22
❑ 54OriEss-11
❑ 54OriTeal-8
❑ 54Top-246
❑ 83TCMPla1945-41
❑ 83TopRep5-209
❑ 91OriCro-142
❑ 91TopArc1-22
❑ 94TopArc1-246
❑ 94TopArc1G-246
❑ 97BalOriP-17

Fox, Jason
❑ 98HelBreM-15

Fox, Kenneth
❑ 86JamExpP-7

Fox, Mike
❑ 87St.PetCP-11
❑ 89ArkTraGS-5

Fox, Nellie (Jacob Nelson)
❑ 47Exh-75
❑ 47PM1StaP1-61
❑ 49A'sTeal-14
❑ 49PhiBul-20
❑ 51Bow-232
❑ 52BasPho-2
❑ 52BerRos-4
❑ 52BerRos-20
❑ 52Bow-21
❑ 52DixLid-9
❑ 52DixPre-9
❑ 52RedMan-AL9
❑ 52StaCalL-73G
❑ 52StaCalS-87C
❑ 52WhiSoxHDP-4
❑ 53BowC-18
❑ 53DixLid-5
❑ 53DixPre-5
❑ 53NorBreL-8
❑ 53RedMan-AL5
❑ 54Bow-6
❑ 54RedHeaF-9
❑ 54RedMan-AL3
❑ 54Wil-6
❑ 55Bow-33
❑ 55DonWin-19
❑ 55RedMan-AL4
❑ 56Top-118
❑ 56YelBasP-11
❑ 57SwiFra-7
❑ 57Top-38
❑ 58HarSta-10
❑ 58JayPubA-6
❑ 58JayPubS-3
❑ 58Top-400
❑ 58Top-479
❑ 58WhiSoxJP-3
❑ 59ArmCoi-9
❑ 59Baz-11
❑ 59Top-30
❑ 59Top-408
❑ 59Top-556
❑ 59TopVen-30
❑ 59WilSpoG-3
❑ 60ArmCoi-11
❑ 60Baz-25
❑ 60KeyChal-16
❑ 60NuHi-72
❑ 60Top-100
❑ 60Top-429
❑ 60Top-555
❑ 60TopTat-16
❑ 60TopVen-100
❑ 60WhiSoxJP-2
❑ 60WhiSoxTS-5
❑ 61ChePat-3
❑ 61NuSco-472
❑ 61Pos-20A
❑ 61Pos-20B
❑ 61Top-30
❑ 61Top-477
❑ 61Top-570
❑ 61WhiSoxTS-5
❑ 62ExhStaB-12
❑ 62Jel-47
❑ 62Pos-47
❑ 62PosCan-47
❑ 62SalPlaC-12
❑ 62ShiPlaC-12
❑ 62Top-73
❑ 62TopBuc-27
❑ 62TopStal-24
❑ 62TopVen-73
❑ 62WhiSoxJP-3
❑ 62WhiSoxTS-8
❑ 63BasMagM-26
❑ 63ExhStaB-23
❑ 63Jel-36
❑ 63Pos-36
❑ 63Top-525
❑ 63WhiSoxTS-7
❑ 64Top-81
❑ 64Top-205
❑ 64TopGia-13
❑ 64TopVen-81
❑ 64TopVen-205
❑ 64WheSta-16
❑ 65AstJayP-6
❑ 65Top-485
❑ 67AstTeal2-10
❑ 69SenTeal8-11
❑ 74LauAllG-58
❑ 75OPC-197
❑ 75Top-197
❑ 75TopMin-197
❑ 76ChiGre-6
❑ 76LauDiaJ-24
❑ 77SerSta-9
❑ 79TCM50-15
❑ 80LauFamF-7
❑ 80PacLeg-68
❑ 81WhiSox1T-2
❑ 82GSGalAG-13
❑ 82TCMStaot5-11
❑ 83MLBPin-8
❑ 83TigAlKS-20
❑ 84OCoandSI-78
❑ 84OCoandSI-231
❑ 85WhiSoxC-12
❑ 86SpoDecG-37
❑ 87AstSer1-10
❑ 87AstSer1-25
❑ 87AstSer1-27
❑ 87AstShoSTw-6
❑ 87NesDreT-13
❑ 88GreBasS-25
❑ 88PacLegI-57
❑ 89WhiSoxK-2
❑ 90PerGreM-101
❑ 91TopArc1-331
❑ 92BazQua5A-17
❑ 92Zip-9
❑ 93ActPacA-139
❑ 93RanKee-41
❑ 94TedWil-20
❑ 97WhiSoxTI-2

Fox, Nickie
❑ 94TedWil-96

Fox, Pete (Ervin)
❑ 34BatR31-175
❑ 34Gou-70
❑ 34TigTeal-6
❑ 35AlDemDCR3-25
❑ 35GouPreR-10
❑ 35GouPuzR-8F
❑ 35GouPuzR-9F
❑ 36GouWidPPR-A32
❑ 36GouWidPPR-B9
❑ 36GouWidPPR-C11
❑ 36NatChiFPR-26
❑ 36R31PasP-30
❑ 36SandSW-18
❑ 36WorWidGV-30
❑ 38GouHeaU-242
❑ 38GouHeaU-266
❑ 39PlaBal-80
❑ 40PlaBal-43
❑ 42RedSoxTI-12
❑ 43RedSoxTI-7
❑ 74TigTCM1AC-9
❑ 76ISCHooHA-15
❑ 76TigOldTS-8
❑ 78TigDeaCS-2
❑ 81DiaStaCD-110
❑ 81TigDetN-110
❑ 81TigSecNP-27
❑ 91ConTSN-197

Fox, Terry
❑ 61Top-459
❑ 62TigPosCF-7
❑ 62Top-196
❑ 62TopVen-196
❑ 63Top-44
❑ 64Top-387
❑ 65Top-576
❑ 66Top-472
❑ 67OPC-181
❑ 67Top-181

Foxen, Bill
❑ 11S74Sil-61
❑ 11SpoLifCW-129
❑ 11SpoLifM-229
❑ 11T205-60
❑ 12HasTriFT-13A

Foxes, Appleton
❑ 83AppFoxFr-15
❑ 83AppFoxFr-16
❑ 88AppFoxP-165

Foxover, David
❑ 91DaiDolF-4
❑ 93AusFut-21

Foxx, Jimmie (James Emory)
❑ 28PorandAR-A7
❑ 28PorandAR-B7
❑ 28W56PlaC-JOK
❑ 29ExhFou-27
❑ 29PorandAR-26
❑ 30UncJac-10
❑ 30W554-3
❑ 31Exh-28
❑ 31W517-21
❑ 32OrbPinNP-18
❑ 32OrbPinUP-20
❑ 32R33So2-xx
❑ 32USCar*-23
❑ 33ButCanV-16A
❑ 33ButCanV-16B
❑ 33ButCre-8
❑ 33DelR33-21
❑ 33DouDisP-17
❑ 33ExhFou-14
❑ 33GeoCMil-12
❑ 33Gou-29
❑ 33Gou-154
❑ 33GouCanV-29
❑ 33GouCanV-85
❑ 33RitCE-10S
❑ 33TatOrb-20
❑ 33TatOrbSDR-153
❑ 33WorCig-39
❑ 34BabRutG-21
❑ 34BabRutG-22
❑ 34BatR31-28
❑ 34BatR31-144
❑ 34ButPreR-21A
❑ 34ButPreR-21B
❑ 34DiaStaR-64
❑ 34ExhFou-14
❑ 34Gou-1
❑ 34GouCanV-58
❑ 34WarBakSP-3
❑ 35ExhFou-14
❑ 35GouPuzR-1B
❑ 35GouPuzR-2B
❑ 35GouPuzR-16B
❑ 35GouPuzR-17B
❑ 35WheBB1-11
❑ 36ExhFou-9
❑ 36GouWidPPR-B10
❑ 36NatChiFPR-90
❑ 36OveCanR-14
❑ 36R31PasP-43
❑ 36R31Pre-G7
❑ 36R31Pre-L3
❑ 36SandSW-19
❑ 36WheBB3-3
❑ 36WheBB5-4
❑ 36WorWidGV-47
❑ 37ExhFou-9
❑ 37GouThuMR-12
❑ 37OPCBatUV-106
❑ 38BasTabP-10
❑ 38DixLid-3
❑ 38DixLidP-3
❑ 38ExhFou-9
❑ 38GouFliMR-12A
❑ 38GouFliMR-12B
❑ 38GouHeaU-249
❑ 38GouHeaU-273
❑ 38OurNatGPP-9
❑ 38WheBB11-2
❑ 39ExhSal-17
❑ 39GouPreR303A-15
❑ 39GouPreR303B-8
❑ 39PC7AlbHoF-59
❑ 39WheBB12-5
❑ 39WorWidGTP-15
❑ 40PlaBal-133
❑ 40WheM4-3
❑ 41DouPlaR-59
❑ 41PlaBal-13
❑ 41WheM5-14
❑ 42RedSoxTI-13
❑ 43MPR302-1-11
❑ 44CubTeal-9
❑ 46SpoExcW-1-4
❑ 50CalHOFW-31
❑ 53ArtHaloFP-35
❑ 59FleWil-11
❑ 60Fle-53
❑ 61Fle-28
❑ 61GolPre-22
❑ 61SevElev-27
❑ 63HalofFB-7
❑ 67TopVen-163
❑ 70SpoCarfCOP-13
❑ 71FleWorS-28
❑ 72FleFamF-16
❑ 72LauGreF-19
❑ 72TCMthe3-120
❑ 73FleWilD-41
❑ 73TCMAllG-4
❑ 74A's192T-11
❑ 74CapPub-51
❑ 74LauAllG-35
❑ 75SpoHobBG-4
❑ 75TCMAllG-11
❑ 76GalBasGHoF-10
❑ 76RowExh-6
❑ 76ShaPiz-59
❑ 76TayBow4-48
❑ 77BobParHoF-87
❑ 77GalGloG-57
❑ 77GalGloG-184
❑ 77PhiFav-6
❑ 77ShaPiz-13
❑ 79RedSoxEF-11
❑ 79RedSoxEF-18
❑ 79RedSoxEF-20
❑ 79RedSoxEF-25
❑ 80Lau300-21
❑ 80LauFamF-23
❑ 80MarExhH-12
❑ 80PacLeg-16
❑ 80PerHaloFP-59
❑ 80SSPHOF-59
❑ 81ConTSN-80
❑ 81SpoHaloF-10
❑ 82BHCRSpoL-4
❑ 82DavHaloFB-7
❑ 82DiaCla-85
❑ 82TCMGreS-20
❑ 83A'sGreT-1
❑ 83BigLeaCOA-12
❑ 83ConMar-1
❑ 83DonHOFH-13
❑ 84OCoandSI-142
❑ 85BigLeaC3-61
❑ 85CirK-7
❑ 85FegMurCG-5
❑ 86BigLeaC-7
❑ 86ConSer1-12
❑ 86RedSoxGT-4
❑ 86SpoDecG-2
❑ 87HygAllG-18
❑ 87NesDreT-11
❑ 88ConAmeA-9
❑ 88ConSer5-10
❑ 90BasWit-61
❑ 90SweBasG-101
❑ 91ConTSN-2
❑ 91ConTSN-303
❑ 91LinDri-44
❑ 91SweBasG-143
❑ 91USGamSBL-6C
❑ 91USGamSBL-6D
❑ 91USGamSBL-6H
❑ 91USGamSBL-6S
❑ 92ConTSN-526
❑ 92ConTSN-560
❑ 92ConTSNCI-16
❑ 92TVSpoMF5HRC-3
❑ 93ActPacA-100
❑ 93ActPacA2-34G
❑ 93ConTSN-917
❑ 93TedWil-123
❑ 93UppDecAH-54
❑ 94ConTSN-1083
❑ 94ConTSN-1152
❑ 94ConTSNB-1083
❑ 94ConTSNB-1152
❑ 94TedWil5C-5
❑ 94UppDecAH-58
❑ 94UppDecAH-169
❑ 94UppDecAH1-58
❑ 94UppDecAH1-169
❑ 94UppDecTAE-42
❑ 95ConTSNGJ-4
❑ 95MegRut-3
❑ 99SP SigLC-XX
❑ 99SpoIllGotG-1
❑ 99UppDecAP-JF
❑ 99UppDecCL-15
❑ 99UppDecCLCC-15
❑ 99UppDecCLLC-XX

Foy, Joe
❑ 66RedSoxTI-3
❑ 66Top-456
❑ 67CokCapRS-6
❑ 67DexPre-75
❑ 67Top-331
❑ 67TopRedSS-6
❑ 67TopVen-208
❑ 68CokCapRS-6
❑ 68DexPre-32
❑ 68Top-387
❑ 69MilBra-84
❑ 69MLBOffS-58
❑ 69OPC-93
❑ 69RoySol-5
❑ 69RoyTeal-5
❑ 69Top-93
❑ 69TopDec-22B
❑ 69TopDecl-10
❑ 69TopSta-184
❑ 69TopSup-22
❑ 69TopTeaP-7
❑ 70DayDaiNM-136
❑ 70MetTeal-4
❑ 70MLBOffS-75
❑ 70OPC-138
❑ 70Top-138
❑ 71MLBOffS-537
❑ 71OPC-706
❑ 71SenPolP-4
❑ 71Top-706
❑ 72MilBra-106
❑ 81RedSoxBG2S-80
❑ 81TCM60I-321
❑ 91MetWIZ-125

Foytack, Paul
❑ 53TigGle-7
❑ 57Top-77
❑ 58Top-282
❑ 59TigGraASP-6
❑ 59Top-233
❑ 60TigJayP-6
❑ 60Top-364
❑ 61Pos-62A
❑ 61Pos-62B
❑ 61Top-171
❑ 62Top-349
❑ 63TigJayP-7
❑ 63Top-327
❑ 64Top-149
❑ 64TopVen-149
❑ 81TCM60I-323

Fracchia, Don
❑ 56SeaPop-5

Frace, Ryan
❑ 96BatCliTI-21

Frachiseur, Zach
❑ 98EugEme-12
Fragasso, Jerry
❑ 94SpoIndC-27
Frailing, Ken
❑ 74OPC-605
❑ 74Top-605
❑ 75OPC-436
❑ 75Top-436
❑ 75TopMin-436
❑ 76SSP-305
❑ 78KnoKnoST-5
Fralick, Bob
❑ 90MiaMirIS-28
❑ 90MiaMirIS-27
❑ 91MiaMirC-30
❑ 91MiaMirP-424
Frambach, Fred
❑ 14Zee-60
Frame, Mike (Michael)
❑ 89GreFalDSP-2
❑ 90BakDodCLC-236
France, Aaron
❑ 94WelPirC-9
❑ 94WelPirF-3488
❑ 96LynHilB-9
❑ 98LynHilQ-7
France, Todd
❑ 86StoPorP-7
❑ 87StoPorP-5
Franceschi, Sean
❑ 90EugEmeGS-7
Franchi, Kevin
❑ 86MacPirP-9
❑ 87SalBucP-1
Franchuk, Orv
❑ 90BoiHawP-3332
❑ 91BoiHawP-3901
❑ 93BoiHawC-28
❑ 93BoiHawF-3933
❑ 95EdmTraTI-7
Francia, David
❑ 96BatCliTI-23
❑ 97PieBolWB-14
❑ 97SouAtlTPB-28
❑ 98ClePhiM-7
❑ 98ClePhiUM-7
❑ 98ReaPhiUM-11
Francingues, Ken
❑ 80WisRapTT-9
Francis, Earl
❑ 61Top-54
❑ 62Top-252
❑ 63PirIDL-7
❑ 63Top-303
❑ 64Top-117
❑ 64TopVen-117
❑ 77PirTCM1WC-27
❑ 78TCM60I-226
Francis, Harry
❑ 81RedPioT-13
❑ 82HolMilT-20
❑ 83NasAngT-12
Francis, Ray
❑ 21Zee-141
Francis, Scott
❑ 91PulBraC-22
❑ 91PulBraP-4000
❑ 92MacBraF-262
Francis, Todd
❑ 83WauTimF-14
Francis, Tommy
❑ 83MiaMarT-23
Francisco, David
❑ 93MadMusC-10
❑ 93MadMusF-1835
❑ 93MidLeaAGF-12
❑ 94ModA'sC-10
❑ 94ModA'sF-3070
❑ 95HunStaTI-9
❑ 96HunStaTI-7
Francisco, Rene
❑ 89GenCubP-1862
❑ 90PeoChiTI-17
Francisco, Vicente
❑ 91SouOreAC-22
❑ 91SouOreAP-3854
❑ 92MadMusC-25
❑ 92MadMusF-1241
❑ 93MadMusC-11
❑ 93MadMusF-1827
❑ 94WesMicWC-8
❑ 94WesMicWF-2304
❑ 95WesMicWTI-13
Franco, John
❑ 82AlbDukTc-2
❑ 84FleUpd-39
❑ 84RedEnq-24
❑ 84WicAerRD-19
❑ 85Don-164
❑ 85Fle-536
❑ 85FleStaS-120
❑ 85RedYea-6
❑ 85Top-417
❑ 85TopTif-417
❑ 86Don-487
❑ 86Fle-178
❑ 86FleStiC-39
❑ 86KayB-13
❑ 86Lea-240
❑ 86OPC-54
❑ 86RedTexG-31
❑ 86Spo-156
❑ 86Top-54
❑ 86TopSti-142
❑ 86TopTat-7
❑ 86TopTif-54
❑ 87ClaGam-100
❑ 87Don-289
❑ 87DonAll-22
❑ 87Fle-202
❑ 87Fle-631
❑ 87FleBasA-17
❑ 87FleGlo-202
❑ 87FleGlo-631
❑ 87FleLeaL-18
❑ 87FleLimE-14
❑ 87FleSlu-14
❑ 87FleStiC-41
❑ 87Lea-178
❑ 87OPC-305
❑ 87RedFolSB-116
❑ 87RedKah-31
❑ 87Spo-192
❑ 87SpoTeaP-4
❑ 87Top-305
❑ 87TopMinL-5
❑ 87TopSti-138
❑ 87TopTif-305
❑ 88Don-123
❑ 88DonAll-53
❑ 88DonBasB-54
❑ 88Fle-234
❑ 88Fle-627
❑ 88FleGlo-234
❑ 88FleGlo-627
❑ 88FleMin-74
❑ 88FleRecS-12
❑ 88FleStiC-84
❑ 88Lea-79
❑ 88Nes-8
❑ 88OPC-341
❑ 88PanSti-271
❑ 88RedKah-31
❑ 88Sco-535
❑ 88ScoGlo-535
❑ 88Spo-195
❑ 88StaLinRe-9
❑ 88Top-81
❑ 88Top-730
❑ 88TopBig-232
❑ 88TopCoi-41
❑ 88TopMinL-47
❑ 88TopSti-142
❑ 88TopStiB-32
❑ 88TopTif-81
❑ 88TopTif-730
❑ 88TopUKM-24
❑ 88TopUKMT-24
❑ 89Bow-301
❑ 89BowTif-301
❑ 89CadEllD-19
❑ 89Don-233
❑ 89DonBasB-166
❑ 89Fle-162
❑ 89FleGlo-162
❑ 89FleHeroB-14
❑ 89FleLeaL-13
❑ 89OPC-290
❑ 89PanSti-66
❑ 89RedFolSB-45
❑ 89RedKah-31
❑ 89Sco-575
❑ 89ScoHot1S-97
❑ 89Spo-176
❑ 89SpoIllFKI-64
❑ 89Top-290
❑ 89TopBasT-130
❑ 89TopCoi-12
❑ 89TopDouA-23
❑ 89TopGaloC-5
❑ 89TopMinL-9
❑ 89TopSti-4
❑ 89TopSti-136
❑ 89TopStiB-65
❑ 89TopTif-290
❑ 89TopUKM-27
❑ 89TVSpoM-43
❑ 89UppDec-407
❑ 89Woo-12
❑ 90Bow-128
❑ 90BowTif-128
❑ 90ClaBlu-86
❑ 90ClaUpd-T19
❑ 90Don-14
❑ 90Don-124
❑ 90DonBesN-92
❑ 90DonSupD-14
❑ 90Fle-419
❑ 90FleCan-419
❑ 90FleUpd-35
❑ 90FleWaxBC-C7
❑ 90Hot50PS-13
❑ 90Lea-356
❑ 90MetColP-2
❑ 90MetKah-31
❑ 90OPC-120
❑ 90PanSti-244
❑ 90PubIntS-29
❑ 90PubIntS-258
❑ 90RedFolSB-33
❑ 90Sco-273
❑ 90Sco100S-49
❑ 90ScoMcD-7
❑ 90ScoRoo-15T
❑ 90Spo-138
❑ 90Top-120
❑ 90TopBig-264
❑ 90TopHeaU-11
❑ 90TopMinL-54
❑ 90TopSti-144
❑ 90TopTif-120
❑ 90TopTra-32T
❑ 90TopTraT-32T
❑ 90TopTVM-11
❑ 90UppDec-139
❑ 90UppDec-709
❑ 90USPlaCA-7H
❑ 91Bow-475
❑ 91Cla1-T65
❑ 91ClaGam-125
❑ 91Don-322
❑ 91Fle-147
❑ 91Fle-712
❑ 91Lea-437
❑ 91MetCol8-4
❑ 91MetColP-3
❑ 91MetKah-31
❑ 91MetPerPA-16
❑ 91MetTro-2
❑ 91MetWIZ-126
❑ 91OPC-407
❑ 91OPC-510
❑ 91PanCanT1-81
❑ 91PanSti-87
❑ 91Sco-14
❑ 91Sco100S-29
❑ 91StaClu-22
❑ 91Stu-203
❑ 91Top-407
❑ 91Top-510
❑ 91TopDesS-407
❑ 91TopDesS-510
❑ 91TopGaloC-6
❑ 91TopMic-407
❑ 91TopMic-510
❑ 91TopTif-407
❑ 91TopTif-510
❑ 91Ult-217
❑ 91UppDec-290
❑ 92Bow-546
❑ 92Don-186
❑ 92Fle-504
❑ 92Lea-174
❑ 92LeaBlaG-174
❑ 92MetColP-15
❑ 92MetKah-31
❑ 92OPC-690
❑ 92OPCPre-73
❑ 92Pin-64
❑ 92PinTeaP-12
❑ 92Sco-605
❑ 92Sco100S-57
❑ 92ScoImpP-61
❑ 92StaClu-565
❑ 92Stu-64
❑ 92Top-690
❑ 92TopGol-690
❑ 92TopGolW-690
❑ 92TopKid-13
❑ 92TopMic-690
❑ 92TriPla-64
❑ 92TriPla-182
❑ 92TriPlaP-8
❑ 92Ult-529
❑ 92UppDec-514
❑ 93Bow-298
❑ 93Don-146
❑ 93Fin-191
❑ 93FinRef-191
❑ 93Fle-471
❑ 93Lea-112
❑ 93MetColP-32
❑ 93MetKah-31
❑ 93OPC-68
❑ 93PacSpa-197
❑ 93Pin-216
❑ 93Pin-310
❑ 93Sco-139
❑ 93Sel-167
❑ 93SelChaS-11
❑ 93StaClu-316
❑ 93StaCluFDI-316
❑ 93StaCluMOP-316
❑ 93Stu-70
❑ 93Top-25
❑ 93TopGol-25
❑ 93TopInaM-25
❑ 93TopInaR-25
❑ 93TopMic-25
❑ 93TriPla-90
❑ 93Ult-73
❑ 93UppDec-321
❑ 93UppDecGold-321
❑ 94Bow-184
❑ 94ColC-414
❑ 94ColChoGS-414
❑ 94ColChoSS-414
❑ 94Don-98
❑ 94Fin-170
❑ 94FinRef-170
❑ 94Fla-196
❑ 94Fle-561
❑ 94FleExtB-316
❑ 94Lea-144
❑ 94LeaL-130
❑ 94MetColP-8
❑ 94MetShuST-4
❑ 94OPC-256
❑ 94Pac-400
❑ 94Pin-368
❑ 94PinArtP-368
❑ 94PinMusC-368
❑ 94Sco-122
❑ 94ScoGolR-122
❑ 94StaClu-339
❑ 94StaCluFDI-339
❑ 94StaCluGR-339
❑ 94StaCluMOP-339
❑ 94Top-481
❑ 94TopGol-481
❑ 94TopSpa-481
❑ 94UppDec-323
❑ 94UppDecED-323
❑ 95Baz-48
❑ 95ColCho-329
❑ 95ColChoGS-329
❑ 95ColChoSE-151
❑ 95ColChoSEGS-151
❑ 95ColChoSESS-151
❑ 95ColChoSS-329
❑ 95Don-346
❑ 95DonPreP-346
❑ 95DonTopotO-291
❑ 95Fin-131
❑ 95FinRef-131
❑ 95Fla-383
❑ 95Fle-368
❑ 95Lea-225
❑ 95MetColP-3
❑ 95Pac-280
❑ 95PacPri-92
❑ 95PanSti-121
❑ 95Pin-402
❑ 95PinArtP-402
❑ 95PinMusC-402
❑ 95Sco-457
❑ 95ScoGolR-457
❑ 95ScoPlaTS-457
❑ 95StaClu-189
❑ 95StaCluFDI-189
❑ 95StaCluMO-15
❑ 95StaCluMOP-189
❑ 95StaCluSTWS-189
❑ 95StaCluVR-98
❑ 95StaCluVRMO-98
❑ 95Top-280
❑ 95Top-394
❑ 95TopCyb-152
❑ 95Ult-411
❑ 95UltGolM-411
❑ 95UltLeaL-10
❑ 95UltLeaLGM-10
❑ 95UppDec-122
❑ 95UppDecED-122
❑ 95UppDecEDG-122
❑ 96Cir-155
❑ 96CirRav-155
❑ 96ColCho-220
❑ 96ColChoGS-220
❑ 96ColChoSS-220
❑ 96Don-128
❑ 96DonPreP-128
❑ 96EmoXL-230
❑ 96Fin-S174
❑ 96FinRef-S174
❑ 96Fla-318
❑ 96Fle-478
❑ 96FleTif-478
❑ 96LeaSigA-71
❑ 96LeaSigAG-71
❑ 96LeaSigAS-71
❑ 96LibSpo-13
❑ 96MetKah-9
❑ 96MetKah-9
❑ 96MetTeal-3
❑ 96Pac-134
❑ 96PacPri-P47
❑ 96PacPriG-P47
❑ 96Sco-290
❑ 96ScoDugC-B15
❑ 96ScoDugCAP-B15
❑ 96StaClu-114
❑ 96StaClu-266
❑ 96StaCluEPB-114
❑ 96StaCluEPG-114
❑ 96StaCluEPS-114
❑ 96StaCluMOP-114
❑ 96StaCluMOP-266
❑ 96Top-155
❑ 96TopGal-48
❑ 96TopGalPPI-48
❑ 96Ult-511
❑ 96UltGolM-511
❑ 96UppDec-400
❑ 97Cir-281
❑ 97CirRav-281
❑ 97ColCho-171
❑ 97DonLim-30
❑ 97DonLimE-30
❑ 97DonLimENG-30
❑ 97Fin-288
❑ 97FinEmb-288
❑ 97FinEmbR-288
❑ 97FinRef-288
❑ 97Fle-394
❑ 97FleTif-394
❑ 97MetUni-192
❑ 97Pac-363
❑ 97PacLigB-363
❑ 97PacSil-363
❑ 97SP-121
❑ 97StaClu-373
❑ 97StaCluMOP-373
❑ 97Top-227
❑ 97TopGal-35
❑ 97TopGalPPI-35
❑ 97TopSta-86
❑ 97TopStaAM-86
❑ 97Ult-237
❑ 97UltGolME-237
❑ 97UltPlaME-237
❑ 97UppDec-119
❑ 98CirThu-231
❑ 98CirThuRav-231
❑ 98CirThuSupRav-231
❑ 98ColCho-173
❑ 98DonSigA-32
❑ 98DonSigAC-41
❑ 98DonSigAM-42
❑ 98Fin-229
❑ 98FinNo--229
❑ 98FinNo-R-229
❑ 98FinRef-229
❑ 98Fle-188
❑ 98Pac-364
❑ 98PacAur-163
❑ 98PacInv-120
❑ 98PacInvPBlue-120
❑ 98PacInvSilv-120
❑ 98PacOnl-475
❑ 98PacOnlR-475
❑ 98PacOnlWC-475
❑ 98PacPar-202
❑ 98PacParC-202
❑ 98PacParG-202
❑ 98PacParHS-202
❑ 98PacParPB-202
❑ 98PacParR-202
❑ 98PacPlaB-364
❑ 98PacRedT-364
❑ 98PacSil-364
❑ 98PinSna-NYM11
❑ 98SP Aut-133
❑ 98SPxFin-103
❑ 98SPxFinR-103
❑ 98SPxFinS-103
❑ 98StaCluFDI-5
❑ 98StaCluI-5
❑ 98StaCluOneK-5
❑ 98StaCluPP-5
❑ 98Top-306
❑ 98TopChr-306
❑ 98TopChrR-306
❑ 98TopDevR-306
❑ 98TopDia-306
❑ 98TopMiniC-306
❑ 98TopOpeD-133
❑ 98Ult-276
❑ 98UltGolM-276
❑ 98UltMas-276
❑ 98UltPlaM-276
❑ 98UppDec-164
❑ 98UppDec10AP-12
❑ 98UppDec1APR-12
❑ 98UppDecSF-88
❑ 99Fle-416
❑ 99FleSta9-416
❑ 99FleWarT-416
❑ 99MetUni-8
❑ 99MetUniGM-8
❑ 99MetUniPMG-8
❑ 99Pac-276
❑ 99PacCroC-179
❑ 99PacCroCPB-179
❑ 99PacPlaB-276
❑ 99PacRed-276
❑ 99SkyPre-28
❑ 99SkyPreR-28
❑ 99StaClu-22
❑ 99StaCluFDI-22
❑ 99StaCluOoaK-22
❑ 99StaCluPP-22
❑ 99Top-275
❑ 99TopChr-275
❑ 99TopChrR-275
❑ 99TopMVPP-275
❑ 99UppDec-146
❑ 99UppDecEL1-146
❑ 99UppDecEL2-146
Franco, Julio
❑ 80PenPilBT-21
❑ 80PenPilCT-17
❑ 81ReaPhiT-17
❑ 82OklCit8T-11
❑ 83Don-525
❑ 83IndPos-15
❑ 83IndWhe-13
❑ 83TopTra-34T
❑ 84AllGamPI-110
❑ 84Don-216
❑ 84Fle-542
❑ 84FleSti-111
❑ 84Ind-13
❑ 84IndWhe-14
❑ 84Nes792-48
❑ 84OPC-48
❑ 84Top-48
❑ 84TopRubD-13
❑ 84TopSti-379
❑ 84TopTif-48
❑ 85AllGamPI-21
❑ 85Don-94
❑ 85Fle-448
❑ 85Ind-14
❑ 85IndPol-14
❑ 85Lea-213
❑ 85OPC-237
❑ 85Top-237
❑ 85TopMin-237
❑ 85TopRubD-19
❑ 85TopSti-245
❑ 85TopTif-237
❑ 86Don-216
❑ 86Fle-586

❑ 86FleLeaL-13
❑ 86FleLimE-16
❑ 86FleMin-115
❑ 86FleSlu-9
❑ 86FleStiC-40
❑ 86IndOhH-14
❑ 86IndTeal-21
❑ 86KayB-14
❑ 86Lea-93
❑ 86OPC-391
❑ 86Spo-33
❑ 86Top-391
❑ 86TopSti-211
❑ 86TopTat-1
❑ 86TopTif-391
❑ 87Don-131
❑ 87DonOpeD-111
❑ 87Fle-251
❑ 87FleGlo-251
❑ 87FleLeaL-19
❑ 87FleLimE-15
❑ 87FleMin-39
❑ 87FleStiC-42
❑ 87IndGat-14
❑ 87Lea-131
❑ 87OPC-160
❑ 87RedFolSB-1
❑ 87Spo-84
❑ 87SpoTeaP-3
❑ 87StuPan-18
❑ 87Top-160
❑ 87TopSti-210
❑ 87TopTif-160
❑ 88ClaRed-187
❑ 88Don-10
❑ 88Don-156
❑ 88DonBasB-168
❑ 88DonSupD-10
❑ 88Fle-609
❑ 88FleAwaW-13
❑ 88FleBasA-11
❑ 88FleBasM-15
❑ 88FleExcS-14
❑ 88FleGlo-609
❑ 88FleHotS-11
❑ 88FleLeaL-12
❑ 88FleMin-19
❑ 88FleRecS-13
❑ 88FleStiC-19
❑ 88FleTeaL-8
❑ 88GreBasS-66
❑ 88IndGat-14
❑ 88IndTeal-13
❑ 88Lea-10
❑ 88Lea-71
❑ 88MSAFanSD-10
❑ 88OPC-49
❑ 88PanSti-77
❑ 88RedFolSB-25
❑ 88Sco-60
❑ 88ScoGlo-60
❑ 88ScoYouS2-7
❑ 88Spo-58
❑ 88StaLinI-11
❑ 88Top-683
❑ 88TopBig-135
❑ 88TopSti-207
❑ 88TopTif-683
❑ 89Bow-228
❑ 89BowTif-228
❑ 89CadEllD-20
❑ 89Don-310
❑ 89DonBasB-32
❑ 89DonTra-31
❑ 89Fle-404
❑ 89FleAll-5
❑ 89FleGlo-404
❑ 89FleUpd-64
❑ 89MasBreD-11
❑ 89OPC-55
❑ 89PanSti-325
❑ 89RanMot-3
❑ 89RanSmo-9
❑ 89Sco-11
❑ 89ScoHot1S-36
❑ 89Scomast-29
❑ 89ScoRoo-35T
❑ 89Spo-149
❑ 89Top-55
❑ 89Top-398
❑ 89TopBatL-14
❑ 89TopBig-288
❑ 89TopDouA-2
❑ 89TopSti-208
❑ 89TopStiB-4
❑ 89TopTif-55
❑ 89TopTif-398
❑ 89TopTra-34T
❑ 89TopTraT-34T
❑ 89UppDec-186
❑ 89UppDec-793
❑ 90Bow-497
❑ 90BowTif-497
❑ 90ClaBlu-67
❑ 90Don-142
❑ 90Don-701A
❑ 90Don-701B
❑ 90DonBesA-112
❑ 90DOnBonM-BC14
❑ 90DonLeaS-17
❑ 90Fle-296
❑ 90FleBasA-8
❑ 90FleBasAC-8
❑ 90FleCan-296
❑ 90K-M-18
❑ 90Lea-205
❑ 90M.Vpin-102
❑ 90OPC-386
❑ 90OPC-550
❑ 90PanSti-163
❑ 90PanSti-201
❑ 90PubIntS-285
❑ 90PubIntS-409
❑ 90RanMot-10
❑ 90RedFolSB-34
❑ 90Sco-160
❑ 90Sco100S-84
❑ 90ScoMcD-3
❑ 90Spo-158
❑ 90Top-386
❑ 90Top-550
❑ 90TopAmeA-21
❑ 90TopBatL-11
❑ 90TopBig-205
❑ 90TopDou-24
❑ 90TopGloA-14
❑ 90TopGloS-35
❑ 90TopMag-70
❑ 90TopMinL-37
❑ 90TopSti-159
❑ 90TopSti-243
❑ 90TopStiB-37
❑ 90TopTif-386
❑ 90TopTif-550
❑ 90TopTVA-2
❑ 90UppDec-82
❑ 90UppDec-103
❑ 90USPlaCA-JKO
❑ 90WinDis-6
❑ 91Bow-265
❑ 91Bow-368
❑ 91CadEllD-21
❑ 91Don-192
❑ 91Fle-285
❑ 91Lea-228
❑ 91OPC-387
❑ 91OPC-775
❑ 91PanFreS-253
❑ 91PanSti-210
❑ 91RanMot-10
❑ 91Sco-392
❑ 91Sco-493
❑ 91Sco100S-84
❑ 91SevCoi-T6
❑ 91StaClu-173
❑ 91StaCluMO-15
❑ 91Stu-123
❑ 91Top-387
❑ 91Top-775
❑ 91TopDesS-387
❑ 91TopDesS-775
❑ 91TopMic-387
❑ 91TopMic-775
❑ 91TopTif-387
❑ 91TopTif-775
❑ 91TopTriH-A13
❑ 91Ult-348
❑ 91UppDec-227
❑ 91UppDecSS-SS1
❑ 91USPlaCA-6H
❑ 92Bow-206
❑ 92Cla1-T36
❑ 92ClaGam-157
❑ 92Don-741
❑ 92DonCraJ2-27
❑ 92DonDiaK-DK4
❑ 92DonSupD-DK4
❑ 92Fle-303
❑ 92Fle-690
❑ 92FleAll-18
❑ 92Fre-3
❑ 92Hig5-111
❑ 92Hig5S-12
❑ 92LaKdec-12
❑ 92Lea-119
❑ 92LeaBlaG-119
❑ 92MSABenSHD-9
❑ 92New-8
❑ 92OPC-490
❑ 92OPCPre-15
❑ 92PanSti-76
❑ 92PanSti-145
❑ 92Pin-150
❑ 92PinRool-5
❑ 92RanMot-10
❑ 92RanTeal-6
❑ 92Sco-108
❑ 92Sco-432
❑ 92Sco100S-38
❑ 92StaClu-440
❑ 92StaCluD-52
❑ 92Stu-241
❑ 92Top-398
❑ 92Top-490
❑ 92TopGol-398
❑ 92TopGol-490
❑ 92TopGolW-398
❑ 92TopGolW-490
❑ 92TopKid-129
❑ 92TopMcD-27
❑ 92TopMic-398
❑ 92TopMic-490
❑ 92TriPla-83
❑ 92Ult-131
❑ 92UppDec-241
❑ 93Bow-657
❑ 93Don-451
❑ 93Fin-161
❑ 93FinRef-161
❑ 93Fla-279
❑ 93Fle-320
❑ 93Lea-27
❑ 93LinVenB-22
❑ 93OPC-73
❑ 93PacBeiA-3
❑ 93PacBeiA-13
❑ 93PacBeiA-14
❑ 93PacSpa-310
❑ 93PacSpaPI-13
❑ 93PanSti-82
❑ 93Pin-104
❑ 93RanKee-405
❑ 93RanStaC-25
❑ 93Sco-394
❑ 93Sel-58
❑ 93SP-192
❑ 93StaClu-651
❑ 93StaCluFDI-651
❑ 93StaCluMOP-651
❑ 93Stu-103
❑ 93Top-670
❑ 93TopGol-670
❑ 93TopInaM-670
❑ 93TopInaR-670
❑ 93TopMic-670
❑ 93TriPla-148
❑ 93Ult-277
❑ 93UppDec-656
❑ 93UppDecGold-656
❑ 94Bow-399
❑ 94BowBes-R74
❑ 94BowBesR-R74
❑ 94ColC-415
❑ 94ColChoGS-415
❑ 94ColChoSS-415
❑ 94Don-481
❑ 94Fin-278
❑ 94FinRef-278
❑ 94Fla-276
❑ 94Fle-306
❑ 94FleExtB-46
❑ 94FleUpd-25
❑ 94Lea-364
❑ 94LeaL-21
❑ 94OPC-142
❑ 94Pac-615
❑ 94PanSti-126
❑ 94Pin-520
❑ 94PinArtP-520
❑ 94PinMusC-520
❑ 94ProMag-30
❑ 94RanAllP-17
❑ 94RanAllP-18
❑ 94RanAllP-19
❑ 94Sco-413
❑ 94ScoGolR-413
❑ 94ScoRoo-RT29
❑ 94ScoRooGR-RT29
❑ 94Sel-288
❑ 94SP-191
❑ 94SPDieC-191
❑ 94SpoRoo-41
❑ 94SpoRooAP-41
❑ 94StaClu-680
❑ 94StaCluFDI-680
❑ 94StaCluGR-680
❑ 94StaCluMOP-680
❑ 94StaCluT-147
❑ 94StaCluTFDI-147
❑ 94Stu-205
❑ 94Top-260
❑ 94TopGol-260
❑ 94TopSpa-260
❑ 94TopTra-25T
❑ 94Ult-335
❑ 94UppDec-57
❑ 94UppDecED-57
❑ 94VenLinU-158
❑ 94WhiSoxK-8
❑ 95ColChoSE-231
❑ 95ColChoSEGS-231
❑ 95ColChoSESS-231
❑ 95Don-328
❑ 95DonPreP-328
❑ 95Fle-116
❑ 95Pac-87
❑ 95PacPri-28
❑ 95Sco-70
❑ 95ScoGolR-70
❑ 95ScoHaloG-HG42
❑ 95ScoPlaTS-70
❑ 95StaClu-248
❑ 95StaCluCT-5
❑ 95StaCluFDI-248
❑ 95StaCluMO-16
❑ 95StaCluMOP-248
❑ 95StaCluMOP-RL21
❑ 95StaCluRL-RL21
❑ 95StaCluSTWS-248
❑ 95StaCluVR-122
❑ 95StaCluVRMO-122
❑ 95Top-135
❑ 95TopCyb-83
❑ 95TopLeaL-LL13
❑ 95UltRBIK-5
❑ 95UltRBIKGM-5
❑ 96ColCho-770
❑ 96EmoXL-47
❑ 96Fin-B314
❑ 96FinRef-B314
❑ 96Fla-65
❑ 96FleUpd-U31
❑ 96FleUpdTC-U31
❑ 96LeaSigA-72
❑ 96LeaSigAG-72
❑ 96LeaSigAS-72
❑ 96Pin-347
❑ 96PinAfi-60
❑ 96PinAfiAP-60
❑ 96PinAfiFPP-60
❑ 96PinChrBC-15
❑ 96PinFoil-347
❑ 96Sel-120
❑ 96SelArtP-120
❑ 96Stu-82
❑ 96StuPrePB-82
❑ 96StuPrePG-82
❑ 96StuPrePS-82
❑ 96Ult-341
❑ 96UltGolM-341
❑ 96UppDec-492U
❑ 97Cir-101
❑ 97CirRav-101
❑ 97ColCho-87
❑ 97ColChoT-CI3
❑ 97Don-330
❑ 97DonGolPP-330
❑ 97DonSilPP-330
❑ 97DonTea-89
❑ 97DonTeaSPE-89
❑ 97Fin-291
❑ 97FinEmb-291
❑ 97FinEmbR-291
❑ 97FinRef-291
❑ 97Fle-77
❑ 97FleTif-77
❑ 97IndSco-5
❑ 97IndScoPl-5
❑ 97IndScoPr-5
❑ 97IndScoU-5
❑ 97IndScoUTC-5
❑ 97Lea-236
❑ 97LeaFraM-236
❑ 97LeaFraMDC-236
❑ 97MetUni-80
❑ 97Pac-68
❑ 97PacLatotML-8
❑ 97PacLigB-68
❑ 97PacSil-68
❑ 97Sco-139
❑ 97ScoArtPWB-139
❑ 97ScoPreS-139
❑ 97ScoShoS-139
❑ 97ScoShoSAP-139
❑ 97StaClu-65
❑ 97StaCluMOP-65
❑ 97Stu-131
❑ 97StuPrePG-131
❑ 97StuPrePS-131
❑ 97Top-241
❑ 97TopChr-85
❑ 97TopChrR-85
❑ 97TopGal-40
❑ 97TopGalPPI-40
❑ 97Ult-48
❑ 97UltGolME-48
❑ 97UltPlaME-48
❑ 97UppDec-51
❑ 98PacInvTeam-15

Franco, Matt (Matthew)

❑ 87WytCubP-16
❑ 89ChaWheB-11
❑ 89ChaWheP-1748
❑ 89SouAtlLAGS-14
❑ 90PeoChiTI-11
❑ 91Cla/Bes-134
❑ 91WinSpiC-19
❑ 91WinSpiP-2836
❑ 92ChaKniF-2779
❑ 92ChaKniS-155
❑ 93OrlCubF-2791
❑ 94ActPac-46
❑ 94Cla-141
❑ 94ClaTriF-T13
❑ 94ExcFS7-164
❑ 94IowCubF-1281
❑ 94UppDecML-242
❑ 95IowCubTI-12
❑ 96ColCho-492
❑ 96ColChoGS-492
❑ 96ColChoSS-492
❑ 96Fle-317
❑ 96FleTif-317
❑ 96NorTidB-13
❑ 97NorTid-12
❑ 97NorTidB-12
❑ 98ColCho-177
❑ 98PacOnl-476
❑ 98PacOnlR-476
❑ 98PacOnlWC-476
❑ 98StaCluFDI-172
❑ 98StaCluI-172
❑ 98StaCluOneK-172
❑ 98StaCluPP-172
❑ 98UppDec-443
❑ 99Top-268
❑ 99TopChr-268
❑ 99TopChrR-268
❑ 99TopMVPP-268

Franco, Raul

❑ 98KanCouC-10
❑ 98KanCouCCP-10

Francois, Manny

❑ 85VerBeaDT-5
❑ 87VerBeaDP-11
❑ 88SanAntMB-14
❑ 89SanAntMB-2
❑ 90CanIndB-8
❑ 90CanIndP-1298

Francona, Terry

❑ 80MemChiT-13
❑ 82Don-627
❑ 82ExpHygM-7
❑ 82ExpPos-12
❑ 82ExpZel-5
❑ 82ExpZel-11
❑ 82Fle-188
❑ 82OPC-118
❑ 82OPCPos-19
❑ 82Top-118
❑ 83Don-592
❑ 83ExpPos-10
❑ 83ExpStu-14
❑ 83Fle-281
❑ 83OPC-267
❑ 83Top-267
❑ 83TopSti-321
❑ 84Don-463
❑ 84ExpPos-9
❑ 84ExpStu-18
❑ 84Fle-275
❑ 84Nes792-496
❑ 84OPC-89
❑ 84Top-496
❑ 84TopTif-496
❑ 85Don-132
❑ 85Fle-398
❑ 85Lea-245
❑ 85OPC-258
❑ 85Top-134
❑ 85Top-578
❑ 85TopSti-88
❑ 85TopTif-134
❑ 85TopTif-578
❑ 86CubGat-16
❑ 86Don-401
❑ 86Fle-248
❑ 86FleUpd-43
❑ 86IowCubP-11
❑ 86Lea-191
❑ 86OPC-374
❑ 86Top-374
❑ 86TopSti-80
❑ 86TopTif-374
❑ 86TopTra-38T
❑ 86TopTraT-38T
❑ 87DonOpeD-193
❑ 87Fle-564
❑ 87FleGlo-564
❑ 87OPC-294
❑ 87RedKah-10
❑ 87Top-785
❑ 87TopTif-785
❑ 87TopTra-34T
❑ 87TopTraT-34T
❑ 88ColSprSSC-20
❑ 88ColSprSSP-1541
❑ 88IndTeal-14
❑ 88Sco-297A
❑ 88Sco-297B
❑ 88ScoGlo-297A
❑ 88ScoGlo-297B
❑ 88StaLinRe-10
❑ 88Top-686
❑ 88TopTif-686
❑ 89BlaYNPRWL-125
❑ 89BlaYNPRWLU-46
❑ 89BrePol-30
❑ 89Sco-597
❑ 89Top-31
❑ 89TopTif-31
❑ 89TopTra-35T
❑ 89TopTraT-35T
❑ 89UppDec-536
❑ 90BrePol-30
❑ 90LouRedBLBC-16
❑ 90OPC-214
❑ 90Sco-216
❑ 90Top-214
❑ 90TopTif-214
❑ 90TopTVCa-48
❑ 90UppDec-180
❑ 92SouBenWSC-24
❑ 92SouBenWSF-193
❑ 93BirBarF-1207
❑ 93LinVenB-273
❑ 94BirBarC-26
❑ 94BirBarF-637
❑ 94BreMilB-220
❑ 96BirBarB-30
❑ 97PhiCopQ-7
❑ 97PhiTeal-7
❑ 98PhiTeal-11

Francona, Tito (John)

❑ 47Exh-76
❑ 56BalOriP-18
❑ 56BalOriP-14
❑ 57Top-184
❑ 58Top-316
❑ 58WhiSoxJP-4
❑ 59Top-268
❑ 60IndJayP-1
❑ 60Kah-8
❑ 60Top-30
❑ 60Top-260
❑ 60TopTat-17
❑ 60TopVen-30
❑ 61Kah-12
❑ 61Pos-64A
❑ 61Pos-64B
❑ 61Top-503
❑ 61TopStal-134
❑ 62ExhStaB-13
❑ 62IndJayP-3
❑ 62Jel-40

❑ 62Kah-10
❑ 62Pos-40
❑ 62PosCan-40
❑ 62SalPlaC-15
❑ 62ShiPlaC-15
❑ 62Top-97
❑ 62TopBuc-28
❑ 62TopStal-34
❑ 62TopVen-97
❑ 63BasMagM-27
❑ 63ExhStaB-24
❑ 63Fle-12
❑ 63IndJayP-6
❑ 63Jel-67
❑ 63Pos-67
❑ 63Top-248
❑ 63Top-392
❑ 64ChatheY-29
❑ 64IndJayP-5
❑ 64Top-583
❑ 65CarTeal-10
❑ 65OPC-256
❑ 65Top-256
❑ 66OPC-163
❑ 66Top-163
❑ 66TopVen-163
❑ 67Top-443
❑ 68BraPos-11
❑ 68CokCapB-2
❑ 68Top-527
❑ 69MilBra-85
❑ 69Top-398
❑ 69TopSta-4
❑ 69TopTeaP-2
❑ 70MLBOffS-257
❑ 70Top-663
❑ 72MilBra-107
❑ 78TCM60I-205
❑ 78TCM60I-231
❑ 85Top-134
❑ 85TopTif-134
❑ 89PacLegI-133
❑ 89SweBasG-76
❑ 91OriCro-143
❑ 94BreMilB-221

Franek, Ken
❑ 88CalLeaACLC-49

Franek, Tom
❑ 93BatCliCB-1
❑ 93BatCliF-3140
❑ 94SpaPhiF-1716
❑ 94SparPhiC-10

Franjul, Miguel
❑ 78CliDodT-11
❑ 79LodDodT-15

Frank, Mike
❑ 98ChaLooG-11
❑ 98FleUpd-U90
❑ 98IndIndQ-29
❑ 98LeaRS-313
❑ 98LeaRSLHolo-313
❑ 98LeaRSLong-313
❑ 98LeaRTrue-313
❑ 98SouLeaTPG-17
❑ 99Bow-87
❑ 99BowChr-87
❑ 99BowChrG-87
❑ 99BowChrGR-87
❑ 99BowChrI-87
❑ 99BowChrIR-87
❑ 99BowChrR-87
❑ 99BowGol-87
❑ 99BowInt-87
❑ 99Fle-151
❑ 99FleSta9-151
❑ 99FleWarT-151
❑ 99MetUni-251
❑ 99MetUniGM-251
❑ 99MetUniN-10
❑ 99MetUniPMG-251
❑ 99SkyThu-206
❑ 99SkyThuRant-206
❑ 99SkyThuRave-206
❑ 99ThuSkySupR-206
❑ 99Top-205
❑ 99TopChr-205
❑ 99TopChrR-205
❑ 99Ult-237
❑ 99UltGolM-237
❑ 99UltMas-237
❑ 99UltPlaM-237
❑ 99UltWorP-10

Frankhouse, Fred
❑ 33Gou-131
❑ 33WorCig-40
❑ 34BatR31-75
❑ 34DiaMatCSB-57
❑ 34DiaStaR-62
❑ 34GouCanV-19
❑ 35GouPuzR-4E
❑ 35GouPuzR-7E
❑ 35GouPuzR-12E
❑ 39PlaBal-70
❑ 79DiaGre-79
❑ 90DodTar-255
❑ 92ConTSN-498
❑ 93ConTSN-725
❑ 94ConTSN-1110
❑ 94ConTSNB-1110

Franklin, Ben
❑ 96PinFan-BF1

Franklin, Bo
❑ 94IdaFalBF-3598

Franklin, Elliott
❑ 76BurBeeT-11

Franklin, Glen
❑ 80MemChiT-10
❑ 82WatRedT-17
❑ 83IndIndTI-24

Franklin, James
❑ 93EriSaiC-7
❑ 93EriSaiF-3106
❑ 95DanBraTI-11

Franklin, Jason
❑ 97PorRocG-7
❑ 98PorRocG-14

Franklin, Jay
❑ 89ButCopKSP-17
❑ 90GasRanB-11
❑ 90GasRanP-2516
❑ 90GasRanS-9
❑ 92GasRanF-2245
❑ 93DayCubC-7
❑ 93DayCubF-854
❑ 94DayCubC-6
❑ 94DayCubF-2344

Franklin, Jeff
❑ 78WauMetT-9

Franklin, Joel
❑ 93PriRedC-11
❑ 93PriRedF-4171
❑ 94BilMusF-3663
❑ 94BilMusSP-16

Franklin, Micah
❑ 90KinMetB-7
❑ 90KinMetS-8
❑ 91PitMetC-12
❑ 91PitMetP-3428
❑ 92BilMusF-3367
❑ 92BilMusSP-10
❑ 93ExcFS7-19
❑ 93WesVirWC-6
❑ 93WesVirWF-2876
❑ 94WinSpiC-1
❑ 94WinSpiF-283
❑ 95Bes-92
❑ 95Bow-39
❑ 95Emo-173
❑ 95SigRoo-20
❑ 95SigRooSig-20
❑ 95SPML-136
❑ 95UppDecML-57
❑ 95UppDecMLFS-57
❑ 96Exc-216
❑ 96FlePro-4
❑ 96TolMudHB-11
❑ 96UltGolP-5
❑ 96UltGolPGM-5
❑ 97LouRedB-14
❑ 98IowCubQ-9

Franklin, Murray
❑ 50W720HolS-9

Franklin, Ryan
❑ 93BelMarCB-13
❑ 93BelMarF-3202
❑ 94AppFoxC-9
❑ 94AppFoxFI-1047
❑ 94RivPilCLC-21
❑ 95PorCitRTI-8
❑ 96DouAllB-31
❑ 96PorCitRB-10
❑ 98TacRaiQ-11

Franklin, Tony
❑ 76IndIndTI-23
❑ 79RocRedWT-7
❑ 89SarWhiSS-25
❑ 90SarWhiSS-26
❑ 91BirBarLD-74
❑ 91BirBarP-1469
❑ 91LinDriAA-74
❑ 92BirBarF-2598
❑ 92BirBarS-99
❑ 93SouBenWSF-1446

Franklin, Wayne
❑ 96YakBeaTI-16
❑ 98VerBeaDM-10

Franko, Kris
❑ 93EveGiaC-10
❑ 93EveGiaF-3763
❑ 94ExcFS7-290
❑ 94SanJosGC-8
❑ 94SanJosGF-2810

Franko, Phil
❑ 82WisRapTF-18
❑ 83VisOakF-5

Frankovich, Mitchell
❑ 33Zee-24
❑ 37Zee-14

Franks, Herman
❑ 40DodTeal-8
❑ 43ParSpo-76
❑ 48A'sTeal-9
❑ 52Top-385
❑ 60RawGloT-7
❑ 65GiaTeal-2
❑ 65OPC-32
❑ 65Top-32
❑ 66Top-537
❑ 67OPC-116
❑ 67Top-116
❑ 68Top-267
❑ 68TopVen-267
❑ 70Houof J-7
❑ 73Dod194T-9
❑ 75Gia195T-33
❑ 75TCMHouoJ-7
❑ 76CubTri-9
❑ 77TCMTheWY-46
❑ 77Top-518
❑ 78DodTCM4-24
❑ 78SSP270-268
❑ 78Top-234
❑ 79Top-551
❑ 83TopRep5-385
❑ 90DodTar-256

Franks, Lance
❑ 97JohCitCTI-11
❑ 98PeoChiM-7

Fraraccio, Dan
❑ 93SouBenWSF-1438
❑ 94PriWilCC-9
❑ 94PriWilCF-1928
❑ 95PriWilCTI-6
❑ 96PriWilCB-12
❑ 97St.PetDR-16
❑ 97St.PetDRUB-16
❑ 98BriBluM-13

Frascatore, John
❑ 91HamRedC-3
❑ 91HamRedP-4033
❑ 92SavCarC-8
❑ 92SavCarF-655
❑ 93SprCarC-10
❑ 93SprCarF-1844
❑ 94ArkTraF-3084
❑ 94BowBes-B81
❑ 94BowBesR-B81
❑ 95FleUpd-157
❑ 95LouRedF-273
❑ 95Top-656
❑ 96Bow-206
❑ 96BowFoi-206
❑ 96ColCho-692
❑ 96ColChoGS-692
❑ 96ColChoSS-692
❑ 96LouRedB-18
❑ 96Sco-267
❑ 96SigRooOJ-10
❑ 96SigRooOJS-10
❑ 96Top-298
❑ 98Pac-410
❑ 98PacOnl-609
❑ 98PacOnlR-609
❑ 98PacOnlWC-609
❑ 98PacPlaB-410
❑ 98PacRedT-410
❑ 98PacSil-410

Frascatore, Steve
❑ 94NewJerCC-7
❑ 94NewJerCF-3408
❑ 95NewJerCTI-9

Fraser, Chick
❑ 06FanCraNL-19
❑ 11SpoLifCW-130

Fraser, Gretchen
❑ 52Whe-12A
❑ 52Whe-12B

Fraser, Jeff
❑ 97NewBriRC-10

Fraser, Joe
❑ 96ForWayWB-7
❑ 97VerExpB-14

Fraser, Ron
❑ 85MiaHur-5
❑ 87PanAmTUBI-NNO
❑ 91MiaHurBB-6
❑ 92TopDaiQTU-33
❑ 92TopTra-35T
❑ 92TopTraG-35T

Fraser, Willie (Will)
❑ 86PalSprAP-13
❑ 86PalSprAS-9
❑ 87AngSmo-7
❑ 87CalAngPPS-15
❑ 87Don-40
❑ 87DonRoo-9
❑ 87Fle-646
❑ 87FleGlo-646
❑ 87FleUpd-33
❑ 87FleUpdG-33
❑ 87Lea-40
❑ 87SpoRoo2-27
❑ 87TopTra-35T
❑ 87TopTraT-35T
❑ 88AngSmo-14
❑ 88Don-135
❑ 88Fle-490
❑ 88FleGlo-490
❑ 88OPC-363
❑ 88Sco-394
❑ 88ScoGlo-394
❑ 88StaLinAn-7
❑ 88Top-363
❑ 88TopBig-183
❑ 88TopTif-363
❑ 89Don-567
❑ 89Fle-478
❑ 89FleGlo-478
❑ 89Sco-157
❑ 89Top-679
❑ 89TopBig-272
❑ 89TopTif-679
❑ 89UppDec-613
❑ 90AngSmo-6
❑ 90Don-587
❑ 90Fle-133
❑ 90FleCan-133
❑ 90OPC-477
❑ 90PubIntS-370
❑ 90Sco-358
❑ 90Top-477
❑ 90TopTif-477
❑ 90UppDec-85
❑ 91Bow-6
❑ 91Don-379
❑ 91Fle-314
❑ 91OPC-784
❑ 91OPCPre-46
❑ 91Sco-96
❑ 91StaClu-496
❑ 91Top-784
❑ 91TopDesS-784
❑ 91TopMic-784
❑ 91TopTif-784
❑ 91UppDec-699
❑ 92Don-755
❑ 92EdmTraF-3536
❑ 92EdmTraS-158
❑ 92Sco-721
❑ 92StaClu-33
❑ 93TolMudHF-1646
❑ 94EdmTraF-2869

Frash, Roger
❑ 82LynMetT-12

Frasier, Brad
❑ 94DavLipB-10
❑ 95DavLipB-12

Frasier, Vic
❑ 74TigTCM1AC-10
❑ 93ConTSN-982

Frassa, Bob
❑ 88BriTigP-1867

Fraticelli, Carl
❑ 90VisOakCLC-66
❑ 90VisOakP-2160

Frattare, Lanny
❑ 88PirTeal-13
❑ 93PirNatl-11
❑ 97PirPos-13

Frauenhoffer, Mike
❑ 90GreFalDSP-21

Frawley, Liam
❑ 97VerExpB-5
❑ 98VerExpO-4

Frazee, Harry
❑ 87SpoCubG-2

Frazier, Brad
❑ 92EriSaiC-3
❑ 92EriSaiF-1613
❑ 93KanCouCC-7
❑ 93KanCouCF-910
❑ 93KanCouCTI-7

Frazier, Carlos
❑ 98SalVol-8

Frazier, Foy
❑ 28Zee-76
❑ 29Zee-71
❑ 31Zee-105
❑ 32Zee-99

Frazier, Fred
❑ 74SyrChiTI-7
❑ 75IntLeaAT-15
❑ 75IntLeaAT-20
❑ 77SalLakCGC-2
❑ 78KnoKnoST-6
❑ 79IowOakP-7
❑ 80IowOakP-5

Frazier, George
❑ 76BurBeeT-12
❑ 77HolMilT-10
❑ 78SprRedWK-23
❑ 79Car5-6
❑ 79Top-724
❑ 80Top-684
❑ 81Don-310
❑ 82Don-584
❑ 82Fle-35
❑ 82Top-349
❑ 82YanPhoA-6
❑ 83Don-535
❑ 83Fle-379
❑ 83Top-123
❑ 83YanPhoA-6
❑ 84CubChiT-12
❑ 84CubSev-39
❑ 84Don-591
❑ 84Fle-123
❑ 84FleUpd-40
❑ 84Ind-14
❑ 84Nes792-539
❑ 84OPC-139
❑ 84Top-539
❑ 84TopTif-539
❑ 84TopTra-39T
❑ 84TopTraT-39T
❑ 85CubLioP-12
❑ 85CubSev-39
❑ 85Don-167
❑ 85Fle-58
❑ 85OPC-19
❑ 85Top-19
❑ 85TopTif-19
❑ 86CubGat-39
❑ 86CubUno-10
❑ 86Don-411
❑ 86Fle-370
❑ 86Top-431
❑ 86TopTif-431
❑ 87Don-564
❑ 87Fle-539
❑ 87FleGlo-539
❑ 87Top-207
❑ 87TopTif-207
❑ 87TwiPos-7
❑ 87TwiTeal-13
❑ 88Don-443
❑ 88Fle-9
❑ 88FleGlo-9
❑ 88Sco-332
❑ 88ScoGlo-332
❑ 88Top-709
❑ 88TopTif-709
❑ 92YanWIZ8-63

Frazier, Harold
❑ 98St.PauSTI-8

Frazier, Joe (Joseph F.)
❑ 55CarHunW-5
❑ 55Top-89
❑ 55TopDouH-83
❑ 56BalOriP-36
❑ 56Top-141
❑ 60DarFar-22
❑ 75TidTidTI-12
❑ 76OPC-531
❑ 76SSP-610
❑ 76Top-531
❑ 77Top-259
❑ 82LouRedE-8
❑ 91OriCro-144

Frazier, Keith
❑ 37Zee-70
❑ 45CenFlo-9

Frazier, Ken
❑ 81CliGiaT-18

Frazier, Lou
❑ 87AshTouP-7
❑ 88OscAstS-10
❑ 89ColMudB-12
❑ 89ColMudP-145
❑ 89ColMudS-10
❑ 90LonTigP-1276
❑ 91LinDriAA-383
❑ 91LonTigLD-383
❑ 91LonTigP-1889
❑ 92LonTigF-645
❑ 92LonTigS-406
❑ 92SkyAA F-173
❑ 93ExcFS7-171
❑ 93ExpPosN-11
❑ 93FleFinE-93
❑ 93Lea-515
❑ 93SelRoo-49T
❑ 94Don-524
❑ 94Fle-539
❑ 94Pac-381
❑ 94Sco-577
❑ 94ScoGolR-577
❑ 94Sel-263
❑ 94StaClu-517
❑ 94StaCluFDI-517
❑ 94StaCluGR-517
❑ 94StaCluMOP-517
❑ 94Top-192
❑ 94TopGol-192
❑ 94TopSpa-192
❑ 94USPlaCR-9D
❑ 95ColCho-242
❑ 95ColChoGS-242
❑ 95ColChoSS-242
❑ 95Don-388
❑ 95DonPreP-388
❑ 95Sco-135
❑ 95ScoGolR-135
❑ 95ScoPlaTS-135
❑ 95StaClu-15
❑ 95StaCluFDI-15
❑ 95StaCluMOP-15
❑ 95StaCluSTWS-15
❑ 95Top-441
❑ 95TopCyb-237
❑ 96ColCho-742
❑ 96ColChoGS-742
❑ 96ColChoSS-742
❑ 96LeaSigEA-55
❑ 96RanDr P-8
❑ 98PacOnl-171
❑ 98PacOnlR-171
❑ 98PacOnlWC-171

Frazier, Ron
❑ 88CapCodPPaLP-90
❑ 90OneYanP-3376
❑ 91GreHorP-3052
❑ 92PriWilCC-21
❑ 92PriWilCF-140
❑ 93CarLeaAGF-22
❑ 93PriWilCC-11
❑ 93PriWilCF-650
❑ 94Bow-541
❑ 94ColCliF-2946
❑ 94ColCliP-10
❑ 95ColCliP-11
❑ 95ColCliTI-11
❑ 96ChaLooB-13

Frazier, Shawn
❑ 86SumBraP-5

Frazier, Terance
❑ 89FreStaBS-8
❑ 92SouOreAC-8
❑ 92SouOreAF-3423
❑ 93ModA'sC-10
❑ 93ModA'sF-811
❑ 94ModA'sC-11
❑ 94ModA'sF-3074

Frazier, Tyrone
❑ 95SpoIndTI-5

Fredbird, Mascot
❑ 93FunPacM-3
❑ 94MasMan-6
❑ 96CarPol-7
❑ 97CarPol-7

Frederick, Charlie
❑ 84ChaO'sT-3
❑ 85ChaO'sT-29
❑ 86ChaOriW-11

❑ 87ChaO'sW-NNO
Frederick, Chuck
❑ 90EugEmeGS-8
Frederick, Jim
❑ 89GeoColC-9
Frederick, John
❑ 23Zee-104
❑ 24Zee-77
❑ 25Zee-89
❑ 26Zee-4
❑ 27Zee-2
❑ 28PorandAR-A8
❑ 28PorandAR-B8
❑ 34DiaMatCSB-58
❑ 34Gou-47
❑ 34GouCanV-85
❑ 35AlDemDCR3-99
❑ 37Zee-47
❑ 83ConMar-38
❑ 85Woo-12
❑ 88ConNatA-6
❑ 90DodTar-257
❑ 90HOFStiB-34
Frederiksen, Kelly
❑ 90GatCitPP-3359
❑ 90GatCitPSP-10
Fredlund, Jay
❑ 79ElmPioRST-2
❑ 81BriRedST-15
Fredrickson, Scott
❑ 90SpoIndSP-16
❑ 91WatDiaC-4
❑ 91WatDiaP-1251
❑ 92SkyAA F-278
❑ 92WicWraF-3653
❑ 92WicWraS-629
❑ 93FleFinE-28
❑ 93Top-489
❑ 93TopGol-489
❑ 93TopInaM-489
❑ 93TopInaR-489
❑ 93TopMic-489
❑ 96ColSprSSTI-13
Fredymond, Juan
❑ 85DurBulT-23
❑ 86DurBulP-11
❑ 87DurBulP-21
❑ 88SumBraP-409
Freeberger, George
❑ 92BluOriC-20
❑ 92BluOriF-2362
Freeburg, Larry
❑ 82CedRapRT-11
Freeburg, Ryan
❑ 92BenRocCB-4
❑ 92BenRocF-1486
❑ 93SanBerSC-9
❑ 93SanBerSF-778
❑ 93StaCluM-46
❑ 93Top-616
❑ 93TopGol-616
❑ 93TopInaM-616
❑ 93TopInaR-616
❑ 93TopMic-616
❑ 94CenValRC-7
❑ 94CenValRF-3206
Freed, Dan (Daniel)
❑ 88JamExpP-1899
❑ 89RocExpLC-9
❑ 90FloStaLAS-6
❑ 90StaFS7-8
❑ 90WesPalBES-8
❑ 91HarSenLD-253
❑ 91HarSenP-617
❑ 91LinDriAA-253
❑ 92LonTigF-626
❑ 92LonTigS-407
Freed, Roger
❑ 70OPC-477
❑ 70Top-477
❑ 71MLBOffS-176
❑ 71OPC-362
❑ 71PhiArcO-3
❑ 71Top-362
❑ 72OPC-69
❑ 72Top-69
❑ 77Car5-10
❑ 77CarTeaI-9
❑ 78CarTeaI-8
❑ 78Top-504
❑ 79Car5-7
❑ 79Top-111
❑ 80Top-418
❑ 91OriCro-145
❑ 93UppDecS-11
Freehan, Bill
❑ 63Top-466
❑ 64TigJayP-5
❑ 64TigLid-6
❑ 64Top-407
❑ 64TopCoi-87
❑ 64TopGia-30
❑ 64TopSta-68
❑ 64TopTatI-37
❑ 65ChaTheY-27
❑ 65TigJayP-6
❑ 65Top-390
❑ 65TopEmbI-41
❑ 65TopTraI-12
❑ 66OPC-145
❑ 66TigVolC-4
❑ 66Top-145
❑ 66TopRubI-33
❑ 66TopVen-145
❑ 67CokCapTi-9
❑ 67DexPre-76
❑ 67OPC-48
❑ 67TigDexP-2
❑ 67Top-48
❑ 67TopVen-212
❑ 68AtlOilPBCC-18
❑ 68Baz-2
❑ 68CokCapT-9
❑ 68DexPre-33
❑ 68Kah-A6
❑ 68Kah-B12
❑ 68TigDetFPB-5
❑ 68Top-375
❑ 68Top-470
❑ 68TopActS-11A
❑ 68TopGamI-11
❑ 69MilBra-86
❑ 69MLBOffS-47
❑ 69MLBPin-6
❑ 69NabTeaF-7
❑ 69OPCDec-6
❑ 69TigTeaI-2
❑ 69TigTeaIC-4
❑ 69Top-390
❑ 69Top-431
❑ 69TopDec-10
❑ 69TopSta-172
❑ 69TopSup-18
❑ 69TopTeaP-1
❑ 70DayDaiNM-109
❑ 70Kel-57
❑ 70MilBra-7
❑ 70MLBOffS-206
❑ 70OPC-335
❑ 70OPC-465
❑ 70Top-335
❑ 70Top-465
❑ 70TopBoo-6
❑ 70TopSup-7
❑ 71BazNumT-37
❑ 71BazUnn-10
❑ 71MilDud-6
❑ 71MLBOffS-391
❑ 71OPC-575
❑ 71Top-575
❑ 71TopCoi-38
❑ 71TopGreM-22
❑ 71TopSup-12
❑ 71TopTat-95
❑ 72Kel-31A
❑ 72Kel-31B
❑ 72MilBra-108
❑ 72OPC-120
❑ 72Top-120
❑ 73LinPor-69
❑ 73OPC-460
❑ 73SevTraC-21
❑ 73TigJew-7
❑ 73Top-460
❑ 73TopCanL-18
❑ 73TopCom-7
❑ 73TopPin-7
❑ 74OPC-162
❑ 74Tig-4
❑ 74Top-162
❑ 74TopSta-174
❑ 75DetTigP-7
❑ 75Hos-120
❑ 75OPC-397
❑ 75Top-397
❑ 75TopMin-397
❑ 76DetTigP-5
❑ 76Hos-6
❑ 76HosTwi-6
❑ 76OPC-540
❑ 76Top-540
❑ 77BurCheD-94
❑ 77Top-22
❑ 78TCM60I-285
❑ 78TigDeaCS-16
❑ 81TigDetN-72
❑ 83TigAlKS-33
❑ 86SpoDecG-49
❑ 86TigSpoD-17
❑ 88PacLegI-93
❑ 88TigDom-5
❑ 89SweBasG-106
❑ 91UppDecS-22
❑ 93ActPacA-150
Freehill, Mike
❑ 94BoiHawC-10
❑ 94BoiHawF-3348
❑ 95CedRapKTI-23
❑ 95MidLeaA-16
❑ 96MidAngB-16
❑ 96MidAngOHP-11
❑ 96TexLeaAB-23
❑ 97MidAng-13
Freehling, Rick
❑ 92EriSaiC-21
❑ 92EriSaiF-1638
❑ 93SanBerSF-783
Freel, Ryan
❑ 95StCatSTI-17
❑ 96DunBluJB-9
❑ 96DunBluJTI-11
❑ 97KnoSmo-10
❑ 98KnoSG-3
Freeland, Dean
❑ 85BelBreT-15
❑ 86CliGiaP-9
❑ 87ShrCapP-5
❑ 88ShrCapP-1285
❑ 89ShrCapP-1852
❑ 90ElPasDGS-22
❑ 91JacGenLD-558
❑ 91LinDriAA-558
❑ 91TucTorP-2208
Freeman, Alex
❑ 26Zee-72
Freeman, Brad
❑ 98NewJerCM-8
❑ 99TeaBesR-27
❑ 99TeaBesRG-27
❑ 99TeaBesRS-27
Freeman, Buck (James J.)
❑ 03BreE10-52
❑ 04FanCraAL-20
❑ 04RedSoxUP-7
❑ 08RosComP-79
❑ 09RamT20-47
❑ 09T206-423
❑ 11PinT-5-1103
❑ 12ColRedB-109
❑ 12ColTinT-109
Freeman, Choo
❑ 99199Fin-295
❑ 99Bow-115
❑ 99BowBes-152
❑ 99BowBesAR-152
❑ 99BowBesR-152
❑ 99BowChr-115
❑ 99BowChrG-115
❑ 99BowChrGR-115
❑ 99BowChrI-115
❑ 99BowChrIR-115
❑ 99BowChrR-115
❑ 99BowGol-115
❑ 99BowInt-115
❑ 99FinGolRef-295
❑ 99FinRef-295
❑ 99StaClu-153
❑ 99StaCluFDI-153
❑ 99StaCluOoaK-153
❑ 99StaCluPP-153
❑ 99Top-219
❑ 99TopChr-219
❑ 99TopChrR-219
❑ 99TopGal-145
❑ 99TopGalPP-145
❑ 99TopGalPPI-145
❑ 99TopSta-47
❑ 99TopSta1Foil-47
❑ 99TopSta2Foil-47
❑ 99TopStaFoil-47
❑ 99TopStaOS-47
❑ 99TopStaTS-47
Freeman, Chris
❑ 95KnoSmoF-36
❑ 95TenVolW-2
❑ 96KnoSmoB-13
❑ 97KnoSmo-11
Freeman, Clarence
❑ 88KimN18-13
Freeman, Clem
❑ 82WatRedT-6
❑ 83TamTarT-12
Freeman, Harvey
❑ 22Zee-43
Freeman, Hersh (Herschel)
❑ 53RedSoxTI-8
❑ 55Bow-290
❑ 56Kah-6
❑ 56Top-242
❑ 57Kah-8
❑ 57RedSoh-5
❑ 57Top-32
❑ 58RedEnq-13
❑ 58Top-27
❑ 79TCM50-120
Freeman, Jimmy
❑ 73OPC-610
❑ 73Top-610
❑ 76TulOilGP-10
Freeman, Julius
❑ 87OldJudN-179
Freeman, LaVell
❑ 86ElPasDP-11
❑ 87ElPasDP-1
❑ 87TexLeaAF-25
❑ 88DenZepC-20
❑ 88DenZepP-1277
❑ 88TriAAAP-12
❑ 88TriAAC-10
❑ 89DenZepC-14
❑ 89DenZepP-48
❑ 89UppDec-788
❑ 90CMC-394
❑ 90El PasDAGTI-31
❑ 90ProAAAF-391
❑ 90TolMudHC-17
❑ 90TolMudHP-161
❑ 90TopDeb89-39
❑ 94BreMilB-222
Freeman, Mark
❑ 59SeaPop-18
❑ 59Top-532
❑ 79TCM50-265
Freeman, Marty
❑ 86GleFalTP-5
Freeman, Marvin
❑ 86ReaPhiP-8
❑ 87Don-576
❑ 87Fle-651
❑ 87FleGlo-651
❑ 87MaiGuiP-12
❑ 87MaiGuiT-4
❑ 87PhiTas-48
❑ 87SpoRooP-4
❑ 87SpoTeaP-6
❑ 88BlaYNPRWL-118
❑ 88MaiPhiC-4
❑ 88MaiPhiP-279
❑ 89Don-631
❑ 89Fle-566
❑ 89FleGlo-566
❑ 89ScoHot1R-34
❑ 89ScrRedBC-1
❑ 89Top-634
❑ 89TopTif-634
❑ 90CMC-228
❑ 90OPC-103
❑ 90ProAAAF-295
❑ 90PubIntS-236
❑ 90ScrRedBC-2
❑ 90ScrRedBP-593
❑ 90Top-103
❑ 90TopTif-103
❑ 91BraDubP-9
❑ 91BraSubS-13
❑ 91Don-619
❑ 91FleUpd-73
❑ 92BraLykP-11
❑ 92BraLykS-12
❑ 92Don-603
❑ 92Fle-356
❑ 92Lea-110
❑ 92LeaBlaG-110
❑ 92OPC-68
❑ 92Sco-307
❑ 92StaClu-264
❑ 92Top-68
❑ 92TopGol-68
❑ 92TopGolW-68
❑ 92TopMic-68
❑ 92Ult-458
❑ 92UppDec-491
❑ 93BraLykP-9
❑ 93BraLykS-11
❑ 93BraStaC-24
❑ 93Don-662
❑ 93Fle-366
❑ 93Lea-11
❑ 93PacSpa-4
❑ 93StaClu-309
❑ 93StaCluFDI-309
❑ 93StaCluMOP-309
❑ 93Top-583
❑ 93TopGol-583
❑ 93TopInaM-583
❑ 93TopInaR-583
❑ 93TopMic-583
❑ 93Ult-304
❑ 93UppDec-519
❑ 93UppDecGold-519
❑ 94ColC-618
❑ 94ColChoGS-618
❑ 94ColChoSS-618
❑ 94Fin-327
❑ 94FinRef-327
❑ 94Fla-372
❑ 94Fle-357
❑ 94FleUpd-123
❑ 94RocPol-7
❑ 94ScoRoo-RT48
❑ 94ScoRooGR-RT48
❑ 94StaClu-701
❑ 94StaCluFDI-701
❑ 94StaCluGR-701
❑ 94StaCluMOP-701
❑ 94StaCluT-106
❑ 94StaCluTFDI-106
❑ 94Top-374
❑ 94TopGol-374
❑ 94TopSpa-374
❑ 94TopTra-49T
❑ 94Ult-479
❑ 95ColCho-444
❑ 95ColChoGS-444
❑ 95ColChoSE-204
❑ 95ColChoSEGS-204
❑ 95ColChoSESS-204
❑ 95ColChoSS-444
❑ 95Don-226
❑ 95DonPreP-226
❑ 95Fin-31
❑ 95FinRef-31
❑ 95Fla-129
❑ 95Fle-517
❑ 95Lea-259
❑ 95Pac-135
❑ 95PacPri-44
❑ 95PanSti-9
❑ 95Pin-432
❑ 95PinArtP-432
❑ 95PinMusC-432
❑ 95Sco-407
❑ 95ScoGolR-407
❑ 95ScoPlaTS-407
❑ 95StaClu-388
❑ 95StaCluMOP-388
❑ 95StaCluSTWS-388
❑ 95StaCluVR-204
❑ 95StaCluVRMO-204
❑ 95Top-465
❑ 95TopCyb-260
❑ 95Ult-373
❑ 95UltGolM-373
❑ 95UppDec-176
❑ 95UppDecED-176
❑ 95UppDecEDG-176
❑ 95UppDecSE-238
❑ 95UppDecSEG-238
❑ 96LeaSigA-73
❑ 96LeaSigAG-73
❑ 96LeaSigAS-73
❑ 96RocPol-7
❑ 96Top-93
Freeman, Pete
❑ 87WatPirP-9
❑ 88AugPirP-367
❑ 90MarPhiP-3193
Freeman, Rick
❑ 89EliTwiS-8
Freeman, Ricky
❑ 94HunCubC-9
❑ 94HunCubF-3559
❑ 95RocCubTI-31
❑ 96DayCubB-11
❑ 97OrlRayB-11
Freeman, Scott
❑ 90YakBeaTI-28
❑ 91Cla/Bes-357
❑ 91VerBeaDC-7
❑ 91VerBeaDP-768
❑ 92BakDodCLC-11
❑ 93VerBeaDF-2210
Freeman, Sean
❑ 94JamJamC-9
❑ 94JamJamF-3971
❑ 96JacSunB-12
Freeman, Terrance
❑ 96SouOreTI-22
❑ 97EriSeaWB-13
❑ 98AugGreM-17
Freer, Mike
❑ 91OscAstC-27
❑ 92OscAstC-27
❑ 93OscAstC-29
❑ 95JacGenTI-27
❑ 96JacGenB-27
Freese, Gene
❑ 55Top-205
❑ 56PirTeaI-7
❑ 56RedBurB-6
❑ 56Top-46
❑ 58Top-293
❑ 59RedBurBP-4
❑ 59Top-472
❑ 60Lea-140
❑ 60MacSta-8
❑ 60Top-435
❑ 60TopTat-18
❑ 60WhiSoxJP-3
❑ 60WhiSoxTS-6
❑ 61Kah-13
❑ 61Pos-30A
❑ 61Pos-30B
❑ 61Top-175
❑ 61TopStaI-17
❑ 62Jel-118
❑ 62Kah-11
❑ 62Pos-118
❑ 62PosCan-118
❑ 62RedEnq-8
❑ 62SalPlaC-137
❑ 62ShiPlaC-137
❑ 62Top-205
❑ 62TopStaI-115
❑ 63Fle-33
❑ 63Kah-10
❑ 63RedEnq-9
❑ 63Top-133
❑ 64PirKDK-10
❑ 64Top-266
❑ 64TopVen-266
❑ 65Top-492
❑ 66Top-319
❑ 66TopVen-319
❑ 79DiaGre-322
❑ 80Red196T-10
❑ 81TCM60I-304
Freese, George
❑ 55Bow-84
Fregin, Doug
❑ 82TolMudHT-27
Fregosi, Jim
❑ 85SprCarT-3
❑ 86St.PetCP-9
❑ 87ArkTraP-11
❑ 88ArkTraGS-16
❑ 89WesPalBES-11
❑ 91BenBucCB-12
❑ 91BenBucP-3711
Fregosi, Jim Louis
❑ 62Top-209
❑ 63AngJayP-5
❑ 63Top-167
❑ 64Baz-22
❑ 64Top-97
❑ 64TopCoi-98
❑ 64TopCoi-128
❑ 64TopGia-18
❑ 64TopSta-60
❑ 64TopStaU-25
❑ 64TopTatI-38
❑ 64TopVen-97
❑ 65AngMatSA-2
❑ 65Baz-22
❑ 65OldLonC-25
❑ 65OPC-210
❑ 65Top-210
❑ 65TopEmbI-39
❑ 65TopTraI-13
❑ 66AngDexP-4
❑ 66Baz-19
❑ 66OPC-5
❑ 66Top-5
❑ 66TopRubI-34

❑ 66TopVen-5
❑ 67Baz-19
❑ 67CokCapA-8
❑ 67CokCapAAm-24
❑ 67CokCapDA-30
❑ 67Top-385
❑ 67TopGiaSU-9
❑ 67TopVen-244
❑ 68AtlOilPBCC-19
❑ 68Baz-9
❑ 68DexPre-34
❑ 68OPC-170
❑ 68Top-170
❑ 68Top-367
❑ 68TopActS-9A
❑ 68TopGamI-33
❑ 68TopPla-3
❑ 68TopPos-4
❑ 68TopVen-170
❑ 68TopVen-367
❑ 69AngJacitB-3
❑ 69CitMetC-7
❑ 69MilBra-87
❑ 69MLBOffS-21
❑ 69MLBPin-7
❑ 69NabTeaF-8
❑ 69Top-365
❑ 69TopDec-5
❑ 69TopDecI-11
❑ 69TopSta-144
❑ 69TopSup-7
❑ 69TopTeaP-17
❑ 69TraSta-14
❑ 70DayDaiNM-94
❑ 70Kel-36
❑ 70MilBra-8
❑ 70MLBOffS-172
❑ 70Top-570
❑ 70TopCanL-7
❑ 70TopSup-30
❑ 70TraSta-14B
❑ 71AngJacitB-4
❑ 71BazNumT-25
❑ 71BazUnn-13
❑ 71Kel-64A
❑ 71Kel-64B
❑ 71Kel-64C
❑ 71Kel-64D
❑ 71MilDud-7
❑ 71MLBOffS-344
❑ 71OPC-360
❑ 71Top-360
❑ 71TopCoi-136
❑ 71TopGreM-16
❑ 71TopTat-18
❑ 71TopTat-19
❑ 72MetTeal-7
❑ 72MilBra-109
❑ 72OPC-115
❑ 72OPC-346
❑ 72Top-115
❑ 72Top-346
❑ 72Top-755
❑ 72TopCloT-13
❑ 73LinPor-175
❑ 73MetTeal-2
❑ 73NewYorSNM-11
❑ 73OPC-525
❑ 73Top-525
❑ 74Top-196
❑ 74TopSta-234
❑ 75OPC-339
❑ 75RanPos-11
❑ 75Top-339
❑ 75TopMin-339
❑ 76OPC-635
❑ 76SSP-262
❑ 76Top-635
❑ 77PirPosP-6
❑ 78TCM60I-170
❑ 78Top-323
❑ 79Top-424
❑ 80Top-214
❑ 81Don-414
❑ 81Fle-274
❑ 81LonBeaPT-26
❑ 81Top-663
❑ 83LouRedR-1
❑ 84LouRedR-1
❑ 85AngStrH-6
❑ 85LouRedR-1
❑ 86AngGreT-3
❑ 86LouRedTI-1
❑ 86TopTra-39T
❑ 86TopTraT-39T
❑ 87Top-318
❑ 87TopTif-318
❑ 87WhiSoxC-11
❑ 88Top-714
❑ 88TopTif-714
❑ 88WhiSoxC-7
❑ 89AngSmo-3
❑ 89Top-414
❑ 89TopTif-414
❑ 91MDAA-15
❑ 91MetWIZ-127
❑ 91TopTra-43T
❑ 91TopTraT-43T
❑ 92OPC-669
❑ 92PhiMed-13
❑ 92Top-669
❑ 92TopGol-669
❑ 92TopGolW-669
❑ 92TopMic-669
❑ 93PhiMed-14
❑ 93RanKee-154
❑ 93TedWil-18
❑ 93Top-510
❑ 93TopGol-510
❑ 93TopInaM-510
❑ 93TopInaR-510
❑ 93TopMic-510
❑ 93UppDecAH-55
❑ 94PhiMed-10
❑ 95Phi-11
❑ 96PhiTeal-12

Fregoso, Dan
❑ 92BluOriC-4
❑ 92BluOriF-2356

Freigau, Howard
❑ 21Exh-52
❑ 25Exh-20
❑ 26Exh-20
❑ 90DodTar-953

Freiling, Howard
❑ 88VerBeaDS-7
❑ 89JacMetGS-18
❑ 90JacMetGS-11
❑ 91ColMetPI-3
❑ 92PitMetC-20
❑ 92PitMetF-3311
❑ 93PitMetC-25
❑ 93PitMetF-3726
❑ 94PitMetC-25
❑ 94PitMetF-3538
❑ 97BinMetB-3
❑ 98St.LucMM-26

Freire, Alejandro
❑ 95MidLeaA-17
❑ 95QuaCitRBTI-6
❑ 96-97LinVen-10
❑ 96KisCobB-8
❑ 97LakTigB-14
❑ 98JacSunM-11

Freisleben, Dave
❑ 74OPC-599
❑ 74PadDea-8
❑ 74PadTeal-4
❑ 74Top-599A
❑ 74Top-599B
❑ 74Top-599C
❑ 75OPC-37
❑ 75Top-37
❑ 75TopMin-37
❑ 76HawIsIC-16
❑ 76OPC-217
❑ 76SSP-116
❑ 76Top-217
❑ 77PadSchC-22A
❑ 77PadSchC-22B
❑ 77Top-407
❑ 78PadFamF-12
❑ 78Top-594
❑ 79BluJayBY-8
❑ 79Top-168
❑ 80OPC-199
❑ 80Top-382
❑ 89ButCopKSP-30

Freitag, Dusty
❑ 92RocExpC-26
❑ 92RocExpF-2119

Freitas, Antonio
❑ 29Zee-109
❑ 30Zee-120
❑ 31Zee-85
❑ 32Zee-85
❑ 36GouWidPPR-A33
❑ 37Zee-53
❑ 40SolHug-6
❑ 46SunBre-6
❑ 47SigOil-62
❑ 47SunBre-8
❑ 49BowPCL-11
❑ 72TCMthe3-26
❑ 79DiaGre-255

Freitas, Jeremy
❑ 98SpoIndG-10

Freitas, Joe
❑ 96NewJerCB-10
❑ 97MidLeaTP-19
❑ 97PeoChi-9

Freitas, Mike
❑ 90PitMetP-24
❑ 91ColMetPI-23
❑ 91ColMetPPI-2
❑ 92St.LucMCB-7
❑ 92St.LucMF-1740
❑ 93ClaGolF-170
❑ 95MemChiTI-12
❑ 96MemChiB-13

French, Anton
❑ 11Zee-86
❑ 95PeoChiTI-18
❑ 96DurBulBIB-15
❑ 96Top-437
❑ 97DunBluJTI-9
❑ 97KnoSmo-12
❑ 98LanJetG-10

French, Charlie
❑ 11PinT-5-751
❑ 12ImpTobC-25

French, Jim
❑ 69TopFou-6
❑ 71RicBraTI-7

French, Kevin
❑ 90NebCor-11

French, Larry
❑ 28Zee-91
❑ 34BatR31-132
❑ 34Gou-29
❑ 34GouCanV-79
❑ 36CubTeal-8
❑ 36DiaMatCS3T2-8
❑ 36SandSW-20
❑ 38CloFotW-26
❑ 39CubTeal-5
❑ 41CubTeal-4
❑ 41DouPlaR-1
❑ 42DodTeal-7
❑ 75TCMLarFP-1
❑ 75TCMLarFP-2
❑ 75TCMLarFP-3
❑ 75TCMLarFP-4
❑ 75TCMLarFP-5
❑ 75TCMLarFP-6
❑ 76ChiGre-7
❑ 77CubAllT-3
❑ 78DodTCM4-4
❑ 79DiaGre-360
❑ 80CubGreT-4
❑ 83ConMar-47
❑ 83TCMPla1942-30
❑ 85BigLeaC3-68
❑ 88ConNatA-7
❑ 90DodTar-258
❑ 92ConTSN-416
❑ 95ConTSN-1340

French, Lee
❑ 89CarNewE-6

French, Ray
❑ 19Zee-69
❑ 20WalMaiW-17
❑ 21Zee-156
❑ 22Zee-149
❑ 23Zee-183
❑ 26Zee-112
❑ 27Zee-88
❑ 28ExhPCL-31
❑ 28Zee-106
❑ 29Zee-110
❑ 30Zee-121
❑ 31Zee-86
❑ 33Zee-32

French, Richard J.
❑ 66Top-333
❑ 66TopVen-333
❑ 69OPC-199
❑ 69Top-199
❑ 70Top-617
❑ 71MLBOffS-538
❑ 71OPC-399
❑ 71Top-399

French, Ron
❑ 90JohCitCS-12
❑ 91HamRedC-27
❑ 91HamRedP-4052
❑ 92HamRedC-7
❑ 92HamRedF-1605
❑ 93SavCarC-14
❑ 93SavCarF-700

French, Steve
❑ 84ButCopKT-11

French, Walter
❑ 30Zee-105
❑ 33Gou-177
❑ 74A's192T-12
❑ 79DiaGre-329
❑ 92ConTSN-397
❑ 94ConTSN-1143
❑ 94ConTSNB-1143

Frese, Nate
❑ 98WilCubM-10
❑ 99TeaBesR-28
❑ 99TeaBesRG-28
❑ 99TeaBesRS-28

Frew, Mike
❑ 85BelBreT-16
❑ 86StoPorP-8
❑ 87StoPorP-15

Frey, Benjamin R.
❑ 34BabRutG-23
❑ 34ButPreR-22
❑ 34DiaMatCSB-59
❑ 36R31PasP-11
❑ 81DiaStaCD-109
❑ 92ConTSN-381

Frey, Eric
❑ 77NewCoPT-15

Frey, Jim
❑ 67BalOriP-41
❑ 70BalOriP-10
❑ 71BalOriP-11
❑ 72OriPos-13
❑ 73BalOriP-19
❑ 73OPC-136
❑ 73OriTeal-16
❑ 73Top-136A
❑ 73Top-136B
❑ 74OPC-306
❑ 74Top-306
❑ 75BalOriP-11
❑ 76BalOriP-13
❑ 78BalOriP-9
❑ 79BalOriP-7
❑ 80Top-66
❑ 81Don-464
❑ 81Top-667
❑ 82MetPhoA-28
❑ 84CubBriPC-7S
❑ 84CubChiT-13
❑ 84CubSev-NNO
❑ 84CubUno-8
❑ 84CubUno-10
❑ 84CubUno-12
❑ 84Nes792-51
❑ 84Top-51
❑ 84TopTif-51
❑ 85CubLioP-13
❑ 85CubSev-NNO
❑ 85Top-241
❑ 85TopTif-241
❑ 86RoyGreT-12
❑ 86Top-231
❑ 86TopTif-231

Frey, Lonny (Linus R.)
❑ 34DiaMatCSB-60
❑ 34Gou-89
❑ 35DiaMatCS3T1-54
❑ 35GouPuzR-1G
❑ 35GouPuzR-3E
❑ 35GouPuzR-5E
❑ 35GouPuzR-14E
❑ 36DiaMatCS3T2-9
❑ 36GouWidPPR-A34
❑ 38CloFotW-27
❑ 38RedOraW-9
❑ 39OrcPhoAP-8
❑ 39OrcPhoAP-28
❑ 39PlaBal-161
❑ 39RedTeal-7
❑ 40PlaBal-76
❑ 41DouPlaR-5
❑ 41HarHarW-6
❑ 72TCMthe3-97
❑ 76RedParC-11
❑ 77CinRedT-32
❑ 79DiaGre-81
❑ 81DiaStaCD-117
❑ 83TCMPla1942-36
❑ 90DodTar-259
❑ 93ConTSN-812

Frey, Steve
❑ 85AlbYanT-7
❑ 87AlbYanP-23
❑ 87Ft.LauYP-3
❑ 88MetColP-24
❑ 88TidTidCa-20
❑ 88TidTidCM-6
❑ 88TidTidP-1602
❑ 89ExpPos-7
❑ 89IndIndC-3
❑ 89IndIndP-1218
❑ 89MetColP-29
❑ 90ExpPos-9
❑ 90Fle-649
❑ 90FleCan-649
❑ 90FleUpd-28
❑ 90OPC-91
❑ 90Top-91
❑ 90TopDeb89-40
❑ 90TopTif-91
❑ 91Bow-451
❑ 91Don-292
❑ 91ExpPos-6
❑ 91Fle-231
❑ 91Lea-153
❑ 91OPC-462
❑ 91PanFreS-154
❑ 91Sco-436
❑ 91Top-462
❑ 91TopDesS-462
❑ 91TopMic-462
❑ 91TopTif-462
❑ 91Ult-202
❑ 91UppDec-397
❑ 92Don-660
❑ 92Fle-479
❑ 92Lea-418
❑ 92LeaBlaG-418
❑ 92OPC-174
❑ 92StaClu-572
❑ 92Top-174
❑ 92TopGol-174
❑ 92TopGolW-174
❑ 92TopMic-174
❑ 92Ult-222
❑ 93AngMot-22
❑ 93AngStaCl-12
❑ 93Don-533
❑ 93Fle-573
❑ 93Lea-488
❑ 93PacSpa-368
❑ 93Top-728
❑ 93TopGol-728
❑ 93TopInaM-728
❑ 93TopInaR-728
❑ 93TopMic-728
❑ 93UppDec-750
❑ 93UppDecGold-750
❑ 94Don-142
❑ 94Fle-56
❑ 94FleUpd-192
❑ 94GiaAMC-9
❑ 94GiaMot-18
❑ 94GiaTarBC-10
❑ 94Pin-185
❑ 94PinArtP-185
❑ 94PinMusC-185
❑ 94Sco-250
❑ 94ScoGolR-250
❑ 94StaCluT-26
❑ 94StaCluTFDI-26
❑ 94Top-503
❑ 94TopGol-503
❑ 94TopSpa-503
❑ 94Ult-22
❑ 95Fle-579
❑ 95MarMot-22
❑ 95Top-201
❑ 96PhiTeal-13
❑ 97VanCanB-15
❑ 98PawRedSQ-13

Frias, Hanley
❑ 92GulCoaRSP-12
❑ 93ChaRaiC-7
❑ 93ChaRaiF-1919
❑ 94HigDesMC-11
❑ 94HigDesMF-2796
❑ 96TulDriTI-10
❑ 97OklCit8-15
❑ 98ColCho-243
❑ 98Don-252
❑ 98DonGolPP-252
❑ 98DonSilPP-252
❑ 98LeaRS-256
❑ 98LeaRSLHolo-256
❑ 98LeaRSLong-256
❑ 98LeaRTrue-256
❑ 98Pac-201
❑ 98PacPlaB-201
❑ 98PacRedT-201
❑ 98PacSil-201
❑ 98Stu-148
❑ 98StuGPP-148
❑ 98StuSPP-148

Frias, Israel
❑ 89BluOriS-10
❑ 90BenBucL-25

Frias, Joe
❑ 91SpoIndC-27
❑ 91SpoIndP-3956

Frias, Ovidio
❑ 97HicCraRB-13

Frias, Pepe (Jesus M.)
❑ 72Dia-18
❑ 73OPC-607
❑ 73Top-607
❑ 74OPC-468
❑ 74Top-468
❑ 75ExpPos-14
❑ 75OPC-496
❑ 75Top-496
❑ 75TopMin-496
❑ 76ExpRed-10
❑ 76MonExpP-11
❑ 76OPC-544
❑ 76SSP-331
❑ 76Top-544
❑ 77ExpPos-14
❑ 77OPC-225
❑ 77Top-199
❑ 78OPC-171
❑ 78Top-654
❑ 79OPC-146
❑ 79Top-294
❑ 80OPC-48
❑ 80Top-87
❑ 81Dod-9
❑ 81DodPol-36
❑ 81Fle-134
❑ 81LonBeaPT-25
❑ 89PacSenL-106
❑ 90DodTar-260
❑ 91CliGiaC-18
❑ 92SanJosGC-21
❑ 93RanKee-155

Friberg, Barney (A. Bernhardt)
❑ 26Exh-42
❑ 29ExhFou-11
❑ 31Exh-12
❑ 33Gou-105
❑ 34GouCanV-10
❑ 91ConTSN-297

Fric, Sean
❑ 93HunCubC-8
❑ 93HunCubF-3249
❑ 94PeoChiC-8
❑ 94PeoChiF-2278
❑ 94WilCubC-7
❑ 94WilCubF-3777

Fricano, Marion
❑ 53A'sTeal-11
❑ 53Top-199
❑ 54A'STEAI-9
❑ 54Bow-3
❑ 54Top-124
❑ 55A'sRodM-15
❑ 55Bow-316
❑ 57HygMea-4
❑ 57SeaPop-8
❑ 91TopArc1-199
❑ 94TopArc1-124
❑ 94TopArc1G-124

Frick, Ford
❑ 49EurSta-2
❑ 59FleWil-48
❑ 59Top-1
❑ 59TopVen-1
❑ 60Fle-74
❑ 61Fle-29
❑ 76ShaPiz-117
❑ 78DexHaloFP-14
❑ 80PerHaloFP-117
❑ 80SSPHOF-117
❑ 95ConTSN-1395

Frick, James
❑ 11T205-192
❑ 12Zee-30

Frick, Tod
❑ 91SouOreAP-3848

Fricke, Dave
❑ 90KinMetB-28
❑ 90KinMetS-28
❑ 92ColMetC-29

❑ 92ColMetPl-32
Fridley, Jim
❑ 52Top-399
❑ 53Top-187
❑ 54OriEss-12
❑ 54OriTeal-9
❑ 59RedEnq-7
❑ 72TopTes5-4
❑ 83TopRep5-399
❑ 91OriCro-146
❑ 91TopArc1-187
❑ 97BalOriP-18
Fridman, Jason
❑ 91ElmPioC-5
Friedel, Chuck
❑ 84LitFalMT-5
Friederich, Mike
❑ 85OscAstTI-7
❑ 86ColAstP-13
Friedholm, Scott
❑ 98St.PetDRM-17
Friedland, Michael
❑ 90JamExpP-12
❑ 91RocExpC-19
❑ 91RocExpP-2054
Friedman, Jason
❑ 90ElmPioP-5
❑ 90WinHavRSS-9
❑ 91ElmPioP-3277
❑ 92LynRedSC-6
❑ 92LynRedSF-2913
❑ 93ExcFS7-132
❑ 94FloStaLAF-FSL17
❑ 94SarRedSC-8
❑ 94SarRedSF-1955
❑ 95BowBayTI-39
❑ 96PorCitRB-11
Friedrich, Steve
❑ 96MidLeaAB-50
❑ 96SouBenSHS-12
Friel, Bill
❑ 03BreE10-53
❑ 09ColChiE-110
❑ 11PinT-5-1051
❑ 11PinT-5-1052
❑ 11SpoLifCW-131
❑ 12ColRedB-110
❑ 12ColTinT-110
Friend, Bob
❑ 47Exh-77
❑ 52Bow-191
❑ 52Top-233
❑ 53BowC-16
❑ 54Bow-43
❑ 54DanDee-7
❑ 55Bow-57
❑ 56PirTeal-8
❑ 56Top-221
❑ 56YelBasP-10
❑ 57Kah-9
❑ 57Top-150
❑ 58Hir-24
❑ 58HirTes-4
❑ 58JayPubA-7
❑ 58Kah-10
❑ 58PirTeal-3
❑ 58Top-315
❑ 58Top-334
❑ 58Top-492
❑ 59Kah-9
❑ 59Top-428
❑ 59Top-460
❑ 59Top-569
❑ 60Kah-9
❑ 60KeyChal-17
❑ 60Lea-53
❑ 60PirJayP-5
❑ 60PirTag-19
❑ 60Top-437
❑ 61Kah-14
❑ 61PirJayP-4
❑ 61PirRigF-2
❑ 61Pos-125A
❑ 61Pos-125B
❑ 61Top-45
❑ 61Top-270
❑ 61Top-585
❑ 62Jel-178
❑ 62Kah-12
❑ 62Pos-178
❑ 62PosCan-178
❑ 62SalPlaC-157
❑ 62ShiPlaC-157
❑ 62Top-520
❑ 62TopBuc-29
❑ 62TopStal-176
❑ 63BasMagM-28
❑ 63Jel-145
❑ 63Kah-11
❑ 63PirIDL-8
❑ 63PirJayP-6
❑ 63Pos-145
❑ 63Top-450
❑ 64Baz-6
❑ 64Kah-9
❑ 64PirKDK-11
❑ 64Top-1
❑ 64Top-20
❑ 64TopCoi-77
❑ 64TopGia-28
❑ 64TopSta-66
❑ 64TopStaU-26
❑ 64TopTatl-39
❑ 64TopVen-1
❑ 64TopVen-20
❑ 65Kah-14
❑ 65OldLonC-10
❑ 65Top-392
❑ 66Top-519
❑ 77PirTCM1WC-18
❑ 77PirTCM1WC-42
❑ 78TCM60I-160
❑ 79DiaGre-375
❑ 83TopRep5-233
❑ 84OCoandSI-224
❑ 87Pir196T-8
❑ 88PacLegI-78
❑ 89SweBasG-86
❑ 91MetWIZ-128
❑ 91TopArc1-298
❑ 92BazQua5A-22
❑ 92YanWIZ6-43
Friend, Owen
❑ 50Bow-189
❑ 51Bow-101
❑ 52Top-160
❑ 53TigGle-8
❑ 54Bow-212
❑ 55Bow-256
❑ 83TopRep5-160
Frierson, John
❑ 83MiaMarT-19
Frierson, Mike
❑ 80WauTimT-19
Friesen, Rob
❑ 87FayGenP-26
Frietas, Richard
❑ 33Zee-47
Frill, John E.
❑ 09ColChiE-111
❑ 09T206-135
❑ 11SpoLifM-282
❑ 12ColRedB-111
❑ 12ColTinT-111
Frink, Keith
❑ 88WauTimGS-7
Frisch, Frankie (Frank)
❑ 20NatCarE-30
❑ 21E121So1-26
❑ 21E121So8-24
❑ 21Exh-53
❑ 21KoBreWSI-10
❑ 21Nei-62
❑ 21OxfConE-6
❑ 22E120-185
❑ 22W572-29
❑ 22W573-44
❑ 22W575-37
❑ 22WilPatV-24
❑ 23Lec-2
❑ 23W501-62
❑ 23W501-105
❑ 23W503-21
❑ 23W515-14
❑ 23WilChoV-45
❑ 25Exh-33
❑ 26Exh-34
❑ 27MidBre-8
❑ 27YorCarE-50
❑ 28Exh-31
❑ 28PorandAR-A9
❑ 28PorandAR-B9
❑ 28StaPlaCE-22
❑ 28W502-50
❑ 28W512-8
❑ 28Yue-50
❑ 29ExhFou-15
❑ 29PorandAR-27
❑ 30SchR33-4
❑ 30UncJac-11
❑ 31CarMet-9
❑ 31Exh-15
❑ 31W517-16
❑ 32R33So2-419
❑ 32USCar*-30
❑ 33ButCre-9
❑ 33CraJacP-6
❑ 33DouDisP-18
❑ 33ExhFou-8
❑ 33GeoCMil-13
❑ 33Gou-49
❑ 33GouCanV-49
❑ 33NatLeaAC-11
❑ 33RitCE-3S
❑ 33RitCE-7S
❑ 33WorCig-41
❑ 33WorCig-42
❑ 34BabRutG-24
❑ 34BatR31-33
❑ 34BatR31-173
❑ 34ButPreR-23
❑ 34DiaMatCSB-61
❑ 34DiaStaR-17
❑ 34ExhFou-8
❑ 34Gou-13
❑ 34GouCanV-64
❑ 34WarBakSP-4
❑ 35AlDemDCR3-123
❑ 35DiaMatCS2-6
❑ 35DiaMatCS3T1-55
❑ 35ExhFou-8
❑ 35GolMedFR-5
❑ 35GouPuzR-1A
❑ 35GouPuzR-2A
❑ 35GouPuzR-16A
❑ 35GouPuzR-17A
❑ 35WheBB1-12
❑ 36DiaMatCS4-4
❑ 36ExhFou-8
❑ 36GouWidPPR-A35
❑ 36NatChiFPR-27
❑ 36R31Pre-G8
❑ 36SandSW-21
❑ 36WorWidGV-107
❑ 39PC7AlbHoF-51
❑ 40PlaBal-167
❑ 46SpoExcW-2-4
❑ 48ExhHoF-11
❑ 49GiaTeal-5
❑ 50Bow-229
❑ 50CalHOFW-32
❑ 51Bow-282
❑ 51R42SmaS-32
❑ 53ArtHaloFP-36
❑ 61Fle-30
❑ 61GolPre-19
❑ 64TopRooAB-4
❑ 66CarCoi-7
❑ 67TopVen-165
❑ 68LauWorS-19
❑ 72TCMthe3-27
❑ 74Bra193NLA-11
❑ 74Car193T-10
❑ 75GiaAllT-2
❑ 76MotOldT-7
❑ 76RowExh-3
❑ 76ShaPiz-51
❑ 77BobParHoF-58
❑ 77GalGloG-53
❑ 77GalGloG-207
❑ 78DexHaloFP-15
❑ 80GiaGreT-6
❑ 80PacLeg-46
❑ 80PerHaloFP-51
❑ 80SSPHOF-51
❑ 81ConTSN-23
❑ 81SpoHaloF-16
❑ 82DavHaloFB-8
❑ 82DiaCla-14
❑ 82TCMGreH-37
❑ 83BigLeaCOA-29
❑ 83ConMar-41
❑ 83TCMPla1945-34
❑ 85FegMurCG-6
❑ 85Woo-13
❑ 86ConSer1-14
❑ 87Car193T-5
❑ 87HygAllG-19
❑ 88ConNatA-8
❑ 88ConSer5-11
❑ 89HOFStiB-13
❑ 89PacLegI-113
❑ 90PerGreM-57
❑ 91ConTSN-11
❑ 91ConTSN-305
❑ 91ConTSNP-664
❑ 92CarMcD-7
❑ 92ConTSN-634
❑ 92ConTSNAP-664G
❑ 93ConTSN-664
❑ 93ConTSN-835
❑ 94ConTSN-1091
❑ 94ConTSN-1233
❑ 94ConTSNB-1091
❑ 94ConTSNB-1233
❑ 95MegRut-24
Frisella, Danny (Dan)
❑ 68OPC-191
❑ 68Top-191
❑ 68TopVen-191
❑ 69Top-343
❑ 71MetTeal-5
❑ 71MetTealA-2
❑ 71MLBOffS-151
❑ 71OPC-104
❑ 71Top-104
❑ 72OPC-293
❑ 72OPC-294
❑ 72Top-293
❑ 72Top-294
❑ 72TopCloT-14
❑ 73OPC-432
❑ 73Top-432
❑ 74OPC-71
❑ 74Top-71
❑ 75OPC-343
❑ 75PadDea-7
❑ 75Top-343
❑ 75TopMin-343
❑ 76OPC-32
❑ 76SSP-117
❑ 76St.LouCP-11
❑ 76Top-32
❑ 77Top-278
❑ 81TCM60I-470
❑ 89TidTidC-1
❑ 91MetWIZ-129
❑ 94BreMilB-27
Frisk, John
❑ 09ObaT21-193
❑ 09ObaT21-330
❑ 12ObaPreT-133
Frisz, Paul
❑ 76ISCHooHA-26
Fritsch, Ted Sr.
❑ 77FriOneYW-8
Fritz, Charles
❑ 09T206-485
❑ 10CouT21-24
❑ 94IdaFalBF-3577
❑ 94IdaFalBSP-10
Fritz, Greg
❑ 91UtiBluSC-19
❑ 91UtiBluSP-3234
❑ 92SalSpuC-2
❑ 93SouBenWSC-9
❑ 93SouBenWSF-1423
Fritz, James Michael
❑ 97BatCliTI-16
❑ 98PieBolWM-14
Fritz, John
❑ 88BenBucL-20
❑ 88PalSprACLC-87
❑ 88PalSprAP-1445
❑ 90PalSprACLC-221
❑ 90PalSprAP-2572
❑ 91MelBusF-7
❑ 91MiaMirC-7
❑ 91MiaMirP-401
❑ 92QuaCitRBC-10
❑ 92QuaCitRBF-801
❑ 93ExcFS7-142
❑ 93ExcLeaLF-5
❑ 93MidAngF-316
❑ 94ExcFS7-26
❑ 94MidAngOHP-4
❑ 94VanCanF-1859
❑ 97MidAngOHP-11
Frobel, Doug
❑ 78ChaPirT-6
❑ 81BufBisT-22
❑ 82PorBeaT-20
❑ 84Don-38
❑ 84Nes792-264
❑ 84Pir-5
❑ 84Top-264
❑ 84TopTif-264
❑ 85Fle-464
❑ 85Top-587
❑ 85TopSti-128
❑ 85TopTif-587
❑ 86BasStaB-43
❑ 86TidTidP-9
❑ 87BufBisP-7
❑ 89BirBarB-7
❑ 89BirBarP-105
Frock, Sam
❑ 10SepAnoP-13
❑ 11PinT-5-716
❑ 11SpoLifM-139
❑ 12ImpTobC-13
Froemming, Bruce
❑ 88T/MUmp-11
❑ 89T/MUmp-9
❑ 90T/MUmp-9
Frohwirth, Todd
❑ 86ClePhiP-9
❑ 87PhiTas-52
❑ 87ReaPhiP-19
❑ 88DonRoo-3
❑ 88Fle-301
❑ 88FleGlo-301
❑ 88MaiPhiC-10
❑ 88MaiPhiP-296
❑ 88PhiTas-10
❑ 88Top-378
❑ 88TopTif-378
❑ 89Don-587
❑ 89Fle-567
❑ 89FleGlo-567
❑ 89PhiTas-7
❑ 89Sco-647
❑ 89ScoHot1R-14
❑ 89Top-542
❑ 89TopTif-542
❑ 90CMC-250
❑ 90Don-631
❑ 90OPC-69
❑ 90ProAAAF-296
❑ 90ScrRedBC-24
❑ 90ScrRedBP-594
❑ 90Top-69
❑ 90TopTif-69
❑ 90UppDec-443
❑ 91BalOriP-8
❑ 91LinDriAAA-456
❑ 91RocRedWLD-456
❑ 91RocRedWP-1896
❑ 92BalOriP-10
❑ 92Don-317
❑ 92FleUpd-1
❑ 92OPC-158
❑ 92Pin-411
❑ 92ProFS7-3
❑ 92Sco-534
❑ 92StaClu-358
❑ 92Top-158
❑ 92TopGol-158
❑ 92TopGolW-158
❑ 92TopMic-158
❑ 92TopPreS-18
❑ 92Ult-302
❑ 92UppDec-318
❑ 93Don-513
❑ 93Fle-166
❑ 93PacSpa-342
❑ 93StaClu-445
❑ 93StaCluFDI-445
❑ 93StaCluMOP-445
❑ 93Top-415
❑ 93TopGol-415
❑ 93TopInaM-415
❑ 93TopInaR-415
❑ 93TopMic-415
❑ 93Ult-494
❑ 93UppDec-191
❑ 93UppDecGold-191
❑ 94Don-389
❑ 94Fle-4
❑ 94Pac-30
❑ 94PawRedSF-943
❑ 94Sco-226
❑ 94ScoGolR-226
❑ 94StaClu-248
❑ 94StaCluFDI-248
❑ 94StaCluGR-248
❑ 94StaCluMOP-248
❑ 94Top-242
❑ 94TopGol-242
❑ 94TopSpa-242
Frolin, Darrel
❑ 75AndRanT-67
Fromme, Art
❑ 09AmeCarE90-1-41
❑ 09ColChiE-112
❑ 09RamT20-48
❑ 09T206-136
❑ 10CouT21-136
❑ 10DomDisP-46
❑ 10PeoT21-24
❑ 10RedCroT-26
❑ 10RedCroT-113
❑ 10RedCroT-194
❑ 10SweCapPP-98
❑ 11HelSta-113
❑ 11PinT-5-417
❑ 11S74Sil-74
❑ 11SpoLifCW-132
❑ 11SpoLifM-193
❑ 11T205-61
❑ 11TurRedT-93
❑ 12ColRedB-112
❑ 12ColTinT-112
❑ 12HasTriFT-73A
❑ 12T207-63
❑ 14PieStaT-45
❑ 15AmeCarE106-18
❑ 15VicT21-11
❑ 15Zee-138
❑ 16Zee-128
❑ 17Zee-105
❑ 18Zee-99
❑ 19Zee-136
❑ 20Zee-141
❑ 21Zee-157
❑ 72ClaCar-63
Froning, Tom
❑ 93BelBreCB-8
❑ 93BelBreFI-1704
Fronio, Jason
❑ 91WatIndC-5
❑ 91WatIndP-3360
❑ 92WatIndC-3
❑ 92WatIndF-3226
❑ 93CarLeaAGF-30
❑ 93KinIndC-10
❑ 93KinIndF-2241
❑ 93KinIndTI-9
❑ 94CanIndF-3114
❑ 94ExcFS7-43
❑ 94KinIndC-5
❑ 94KinIndF-2635
Frontera, Chad
❑ 94EveGiaC-8
❑ 94EveGiaF-3644
❑ 95Bow-51
❑ 97ShrCap-9
❑ 97ShrCapB-9
❑ 98ShrCapM-13
❑ 98ShrCapWS-13
Froschaner, Trevor
❑ 93AubAstC-10
❑ 93AubAstF-3447
Frost, Brady
❑ 94VerExpC-11
❑ 94VerExpF-3906
Frost, C. David
❑ 76VenLeaS-189
❑ 78AngFamF-11
❑ 78SalLakCGC-25
❑ 79Top-703
❑ 80Top-423
❑ 81Don-52
❑ 81Fle-275
❑ 81SalLakCGT-6
❑ 81Top-286
❑ 82Don-290
❑ 82Fle-460A
❑ 82Fle-460B
❑ 82Roy-7
❑ 82Top-24
❑ 82TopTra-37T
❑ 83Fle-111
❑ 83Top-656
Frost, Jerald
❑ 87SumBraP-1
❑ 88BurBraP-8
❑ 89DurBullS-12
❑ 89DurBullS-12
❑ 89DurBulTI-12
Frostad, Mike
❑ 96StCatSB-3
Fruge, Chris
❑ 90UtiBluSP-17
Fruge, Jeff
❑ 82QuaCitCT-8
❑ 83QuaCitCT-10
Frush, James
❑ 97BatCliTI-7
Fry, Brian
❑ 89BilMusP-2051
❑ 90BilMusP-3215
Fry, Dave
❑ 84ModA'sC-27
Fry, Jeff

❑ 97DanBraB-17
Fry, Jerry
❑ 75WesPalBES-13
❑ 79Top-720
Fry, Ryan
❑ 98SpoIndG-11
Fry, W.J.
❑ 87OldJudN-180
Frye, Dan
❑ 92PriRedC-23
❑ 92PriRedF-3093
❑ 93Bow-698
❑ 93ClaGolF-212
❑ 93ClaMVPF-8
❑ 93ExcFS7-20
❑ 93WesVirWC-7
❑ 93WesVirWF-2870
❑ 94WinSpiC-9
❑ 94WinSpiF-277
Frye, Jeff
❑ 88ButCopKSP-14
❑ 89GasRanP-1023
❑ 89GasRanS-7
❑ 89SouAtlLAGS-27
❑ 89Sta-137
❑ 90ChaRanS-7
❑ 91LinDriAA-579
❑ 91TulDriLD-579
❑ 91TulDriP-2778
❑ 91TulDriTI-7
❑ 92DonRoo-40
❑ 92FleUpd-60
❑ 92OklCit8F-1920
❑ 92OklCit8S-310
❑ 92SkyAAAF-142
❑ 93Don-724
❑ 93Fle-321
❑ 93LinVenB-195
❑ 93Pin-496
❑ 93RanKee-406
❑ 93Sco-274
❑ 93StaClu-133
❑ 93StaCluFDI-133
❑ 93StaCluMOP-133
❑ 93Top-197
❑ 93TopGol-197
❑ 93TopInaM-197
❑ 93TopInaR-197
❑ 93TopMic-197
❑ 93Ult-278
❑ 93UppDec-371
❑ 93UppDecGold-371
❑ 93USPlaCR-7C
❑ 94FleUpd-91
❑ 94StaCluT-261
❑ 94StaCluTFDI-261
❑ 94VenLinU-164
❑ 95ColCho-401
❑ 95ColChoGS-401
❑ 95ColChoSS-401
❑ 95Don-297
❑ 95DonPreP-297
❑ 95DonTopotO-158
❑ 95Fla-87
❑ 95Fle-284
❑ 95Lea-147
❑ 95Pac-425
❑ 95Pin-92
❑ 95PinArtP-92
❑ 95PinMusC-92
❑ 95RanCra-9
❑ 95Sco-269
❑ 95ScoGolR-269
❑ 95ScoPlaTS-269
❑ 95Sel-4
❑ 95SelArtP-4
❑ 95StaClu-230
❑ 95StaCluFDI-230
❑ 95StaCluMOP-230
❑ 95StaCluSTWS-230
❑ 95Top-591
❑ 95TopCyb-363
❑ 95TopD3-31
❑ 95Ult-334
❑ 95UltGolM-334
❑ 95UppDec-393
❑ 95UppDecED-393
❑ 95UppDecEDG-393
❑ 96ColCho-321
❑ 96ColChoGS-321
❑ 96ColChoSS-321
❑ 96Don-473
❑ 96DonPreP-473
❑ 96Fle-248
❑ 96FleTif-248
❑ 96Pin-13
❑ 96Sco-405
❑ 96StaClu-361
❑ 96StaCluMOP-361
❑ 96Ult-133
❑ 96UltGolM-133
❑ 97Don-241
❑ 97DonGolPP-241
❑ 97DonSilPP-241
❑ 97DonTea-53
❑ 97DonTeaSPE-53
❑ 97Fle-21
❑ 97FleTif-21
❑ 97Pac-38
❑ 97PacLigB-38
❑ 97PacSil-38
❑ 97Pin-7
❑ 97PinArtP-PP7
❑ 97PinMusC-7
❑ 97PinPrePla-7
❑ 97RedSoxS-10
❑ 97RedSoxSPl-10
❑ 97RedSoxSPr-10
❑ 97Sco-200
❑ 97ScoArtPWB-200
❑ 97ScoPreS-200
❑ 97ScoShoS-200
❑ 97ScoShoSAP-200
❑ 97Ult-484
❑ 97UltGolME-484
❑ 97UltPlaME-484
❑ 98ColCho-49
❑ 98Fle-296
❑ 98Pac-38
❑ 98PacPlaB-38
❑ 98PacRedT-38
❑ 98PacSil-38
❑ 98RedSoxS-11
❑ 98RedSoxSP-11
❑ 98Sco-191
❑ 98StaCluFDI-281
❑ 98StaCluI-281
❑ 98StaCluOneK-281
❑ 98StaCluPP-281
❑ 98Top-193
❑ 98TopChr-193
❑ 98TopChrR-193
❑ 98TopDevR-193
❑ 98TopDia-193
❑ 98TopMiniC-193
❑ 98UppDec-316
❑ 99Fle-404
❑ 99FleSta9-404
❑ 99FleWarT-404
Frye, Paul
❑ 86JamExpP-8
❑ 87WesPalBEP-654
❑ 88RocExpLC-14
Frye, Walter
❑ 94CarLeaA-DJ21
Fryer, Paul
❑ 82ReaPhiT-14
Fryhoff, John
❑ 83TriTriT-10
Fryman, Travis
❑ 88FayGenP-1094
❑ 89BasAmeAPB-AA2
❑ 89EasLeaAP-4
❑ 89LonTigP-1366
❑ 90Bow-360
❑ 90BowTif-360
❑ 90CMC-395
❑ 90FleUpd-96
❑ 90ProAAAF-385
❑ 90TigTeal-10
❑ 90TolMudHC-18
❑ 90TolMudHP-155
❑ 90TopTra-33T
❑ 90TopTraT-33T
❑ 90TriAllGP-AAA30
❑ 91Bow-145
❑ 91Cla1-T40
❑ 91ClaGam-124
❑ 91Don-768
❑ 91Fle-336
❑ 91Lea-149
❑ 91MajLeaCP-34
❑ 91OPC-128
❑ 91RedFolS-106
❑ 91Sco-570
❑ 91Sco100RS-68
❑ 91SevCoi-M5
❑ 91StaClu-355
❑ 91Stu-54
❑ 91TigCok-24
❑ 91TigPol-4
❑ 91Top-128
❑ 91TopDeb90-49
❑ 91TopDesS-128
❑ 91TopMic-128
❑ 91TopRoo-9
❑ 91TopTif-128
❑ 91ToyRoo-8
❑ 91Ult-122
❑ 91UppDec-225
❑ 92Bow-37
❑ 92ClaGam-88
❑ 92Don-349
❑ 92DonCraJ1-11
❑ 92Fle-134
❑ 92Hig5-47
❑ 92Lea-304
❑ 92LeaBlaG-304
❑ 92OPC-750
❑ 92OPCPre-56
❑ 92PanSti-107
❑ 92Pin-110
❑ 92PinTea2-4
❑ 92RedFolS-37
❑ 92Sco-65
❑ 92ScoImpP-47
❑ 92ScoProP-19
❑ 92StaClu-59
❑ 92Stu-174
❑ 92TigKro-9
❑ 92TigTeal-11
❑ 92Top-750
❑ 92TopGol-750
❑ 92TopGolW-750
❑ 92TopKid-78
❑ 92TopMic-750
❑ 92TriPla-86
❑ 92Ult-60
❑ 92UppDec-466
❑ 92UppDec-643
❑ 93Bow-67
❑ 93ClaGam-35
❑ 93Don-127
❑ 93Fin-135
❑ 93FinRef-135
❑ 93Fla-202
❑ 93Fle-228
❑ 93FleFruotL-20
❑ 93FunPac-187
❑ 93Lea-16
❑ 93LeaFas-19
❑ 93OPC-76
❑ 93OPCPre-102
❑ 93PacSpa-108
❑ 93PanSti-117
❑ 93Pin-79
❑ 93PinHomRC-48
❑ 93PinSlu-30
❑ 93PinTea2-10
❑ 93Sco-11
❑ 93Sel-44
❑ 93SP-237
❑ 93StaClu-298
❑ 93StaClu-448
❑ 93StaCluFDI-298
❑ 93StaCluFDI-448
❑ 93StaCluM-168
❑ 93StaCluMO-9
❑ 93StaCluMOP-298
❑ 93StaCluMOP-448
❑ 93StaCluMP-16
❑ 93Stu-108
❑ 93StuSil-5
❑ 93TigGat-8
❑ 93Top-392
❑ 93Top-404
❑ 93TOPBLAG-31
❑ 93TopGol-392
❑ 93TopGol-404
❑ 93TopInaM-392
❑ 93TopInaM-404
❑ 93TopInaR-392
❑ 93TopInaR-404
❑ 93TopMic-392
❑ 93TopMic-404
❑ 93Toy-87
❑ 93TriPla-59
❑ 93Ult-197
❑ 93UppDec-364
❑ 93UppDec-455
❑ 93UppDec-836
❑ 93UppDecDG-25
❑ 93UppDecGold-364
❑ 93UppDecGold-455
❑ 93UppDecGold-836
❑ 94Bow-621
❑ 94BowBes-R61
❑ 94BowBes-X108
❑ 94BowBesR-R61
❑ 94BowBesR-X108
❑ 94ChuHomS-15
❑ 94ChuHomSG-15
❑ 94ColC-375
❑ 94ColChoGS-375
❑ 94ColChoSS-375
❑ 94Don-378
❑ 94DonSpeE-378
❑ 94Fin-228
❑ 94FinJum-228
❑ 94FinRef-228
❑ 94Fla-292
❑ 94Fle-129
❑ 94FleAllS-8
❑ 94FleExtB-74
❑ 94FUnPac-80
❑ 94FUnPac-179
❑ 94KinDis-10
❑ 94Lea-405
❑ 94LeaL-32
❑ 94OPC-209
❑ 94Pac-216
❑ 94PanSti-64
❑ 94Pin-183
❑ 94PinArtP-183
❑ 94PinMusC-183
❑ 94PinPowS-PS14
❑ 94PinRunC-RC9
❑ 94PinTheN-21
❑ 94ProMag-50
❑ 94Sco-11
❑ 94ScoGolR-11
❑ 94ScoGolS-48
❑ 94Sel-295
❑ 94SelSki-SK10
❑ 94SP-177
❑ 94SPDieC-177
❑ 94SPHol-9
❑ 94SPHolDC-9
❑ 94Spo-16
❑ 94Spo-178
❑ 94SpoFanA-AS3
❑ 94StaClu-309
❑ 94StaCluFDI-309
❑ 94StaCluGR-309
❑ 94StaCluMOP-309
❑ 94Stu-191
❑ 94Top-285
❑ 94TopBlaG-6
❑ 94TopGol-285
❑ 94TopSpa-285
❑ 94TriPla-244
❑ 94TriPlaM-9
❑ 94Ult-53
❑ 94UltRisS-5
❑ 94UppDec-37
❑ 94UppDec-51
❑ 94UppDec-345
❑ 94UppDecAJ-23
❑ 94UppDecAJG-23
❑ 94UppDecED-37
❑ 94UppDecED-51
❑ 94UppDecED-345
❑ 95Baz-59
❑ 95Bow-302
❑ 95BowBes-R70
❑ 95BowBes-X7
❑ 95BowBesR-R70
❑ 95BowBesR-X7
❑ 95ClaPhoC-27
❑ 95ColCho-465
❑ 95ColChoGS-465
❑ 95ColChoSE-222
❑ 95ColChoSEGS-222
❑ 95ColChoSESS-222
❑ 95ColChoSS-465
❑ 95Don-82
❑ 95DonDiaK-DK21
❑ 95DonDom-5
❑ 95DonPreP-82
❑ 95DonTopotO-75
❑ 95Emo-43
❑ 95Fin-42
❑ 95FinRef-42
❑ 95Fla-39
❑ 95Fle-51
❑ 95FleAllS-14
❑ 95Lea-207
❑ 95LeaCor-2
❑ 95LeaLim-52
❑ 95Pac-152
❑ 95PacPri-49
❑ 95PanSti-59
❑ 95Pin-124
❑ 95PinArtP-124
❑ 95PinMusC-124
❑ 95PinPin-12
❑ 95PinPinR-12
❑ 95PinTeaP-TP6
❑ 95RedFol-18
❑ 95Sco-341
❑ 95ScoGolR-341
❑ 95ScoHaloG-HG79
❑ 95ScoPlaTS-341
❑ 95Sel-132
❑ 95SelArtP-132
❑ 95SelCer-40
❑ 95SelCerMG-40
❑ 95Spo-90
❑ 95SpoArtP-90
❑ 95StaClu-6
❑ 95StaCluCT-18
❑ 95StaCluFDI-6
❑ 95StaCluMO-17
❑ 95StaCluMOP-6
❑ 95StaCluSTWS-6
❑ 95StaCluVR-2
❑ 95StaCluVRMO-2
❑ 95Stu-27
❑ 95StuGolS-27
❑ 95Sum-91
❑ 95SumNthD-91
❑ 95Top-40
❑ 95TopCyb-32
❑ 95TopD3-51
❑ 95TopEmb-50
❑ 95TopEmbGI-50
❑ 95TopPre-PP5
❑ 95TopPreS-PP5
❑ 95UC3-40
❑ 95UC3ArtP-40
❑ 95Ult-285
❑ 95UltGolM-285
❑ 95UppDec-185
❑ 95UppDecED-185
❑ 95UppDecEDG-185
❑ 95UppDecSE-232
❑ 95UppDecSEG-232
❑ 95Zen-105
❑ 96Baz-19
❑ 96Bow-106
❑ 96BowBes-69
❑ 96BowBesAR-69
❑ 96BowBesR-69
❑ 96BowFoi-106
❑ 96Cir-39
❑ 96CirRav-39
❑ 96ColCho-550
❑ 96ColChoGS-550
❑ 96ColChoSS-550
❑ 96Don-176
❑ 96DonPreP-176
❑ 96EmoXL-60
❑ 96Fin-B152
❑ 96FinRef-B152
❑ 96Fla-80
❑ 96Fle-111
❑ 96FleTeaL-6
❑ 96FleTif-111
❑ 96Lea-68
❑ 96LeaLim-26
❑ 96LeaLimG-26
❑ 96LeaPre-14
❑ 96LeaPreP-14
❑ 96LeaPrePB-68
❑ 96LeaPrePG-68
❑ 96LeaPrePS-68
❑ 96LeaPreSG-4
❑ 96LeaPreSte-4
❑ 96LeaSigA-74
❑ 96LeaSigAG-74
❑ 96LeaSigAS-74
❑ 96LibSpo-4
❑ 96MetUni-59
❑ 96MetUniP-59
❑ 96Pac-315
❑ 96PanSti-143
❑ 96Pin-14
❑ 96PinAfi-86
❑ 96PinAfiAP-86
❑ 96PinAfiFPP-86
❑ 96PinArtP-9
❑ 96PinSta-9
❑ 96ProSta-123
❑ 96Sco-309
❑ 96ScoDugC-B34
❑ 96ScoDugCAP-B34
❑ 96Sel-13
❑ 96SelArtP-13
❑ 96SelCer-40
❑ 96SelCerAP-40
❑ 96SelCerCB-40
❑ 96SelCerCR-40
❑ 96SelCerMB-40
❑ 96SelCerMG-40
❑ 96SelCerMR-40
❑ 96SelTeaN-13
❑ 96SP-83
❑ 96Spo-68
❑ 96SpoArtP-68
❑ 96StaClu-431
❑ 96StaCluEPB-431
❑ 96StaCluEPG-431
❑ 96StaCluEPS-431
❑ 96StaCluMOP-431
❑ 96Stu-113
❑ 96StuPrePB-113
❑ 96StuPrePG-113
❑ 96StuPrePS-113
❑ 96Sum-26
❑ 96SumAbo&B-26
❑ 96SumArtP-26
❑ 96SumFoi-26
❑ 96TeaOut-26
❑ 96Top-190
❑ 96TopChr-60
❑ 96TopChrR-60
❑ 96TopGal-32
❑ 96TopGalPPI-32
❑ 96TopLas-81
❑ 96Ult-60
❑ 96UltGolM-60
❑ 96UppDec-328
❑ 96Zen-9
❑ 96ZenArtP-9
❑ 97Bow-259
❑ 97BowBes-81
❑ 97BowBesAR-81
❑ 97BowBesR-81
❑ 97BowChr-81
❑ 97BowChrI-81
❑ 97BowChrIR-81
❑ 97BowChrR-81
❑ 97BowInt-259
❑ 97Cir-187
❑ 97CirRav-187
❑ 97ColCho-110
❑ 97DenHol-6
❑ 97Don-8
❑ 97DonEli-96
❑ 97DonEliGS-96
❑ 97DonGolPP-8
❑ 97DonLim-31
❑ 97DonLimE-31
❑ 97DonLimENG-31
❑ 97DonPre-55
❑ 97DonPreCttC-55
❑ 97DonSilPP-8
❑ 97E-X2-21
❑ 97E-X2Cred-21
❑ 97E-X2EssCre-21
❑ 97Fin-18
❑ 97FinRef-18
❑ 97FlaShoLC-124
❑ 97FlaShoLeg0-124
❑ 97FlaShoLeg1-124
❑ 97FlaShoM-A124
❑ 97FlaShoM-B124
❑ 97FlaShoM-C124
❑ 97FlaShoR0-124
❑ 97FlaShoR1-124
❑ 97FlaShoR2-124
❑ 97Fle-98
❑ 97FleTif-98
❑ 97KinB-3
❑ 97Lea-222
❑ 97LeaFraM-222
❑ 97LeaFraMDC-222
❑ 97MetUni-109
❑ 97NewPin-112
❑ 97NewPinAP-112
❑ 97NewPinMC-112
❑ 97NewPinPP-112
❑ 97Pac-87
❑ 97PacLigB-87
❑ 97PacPri-31
❑ 97PacPriGotD-GD42
❑ 97PacPriLB-31
❑ 97PacPriP-31
❑ 97PacSil-87
❑ 97PinIns-22
❑ 97PinInsCE-22
❑ 97PinInsDE-22
❑ 97PinX-P-77
❑ 97PinX-PMoS-77
❑ 97Sco-195
❑ 97ScoArtPWB-195

❑ 97ScoPreS-195
❑ 97ScoShoS-195
❑ 97ScoShoSAP-195
❑ 97Sel-62
❑ 97SelArtP-62
❑ 97SelCom-62
❑ 97SelRegG-62
❑ 97SP-70
❑ 97SpoIll-138
❑ 97SpoIllEE-138
❑ 97StaClu-245
❑ 97StaCluMat-245
❑ 97StaCluMOP-245
❑ 97Stu-12
❑ 97StuPrePG-12
❑ 97StuPrePS-12
❑ 97Top-120
❑ 97TopChr-46
❑ 97TopChrR-46
❑ 97TopGal-62
❑ 97TopGalPPI-62
❑ 97TopIntF-ILM14
❑ 97TopIntFR-ILM14
❑ 97TopSta-67
❑ 97TopStaAM-67
❑ 97Ult-59
❑ 97UltGolME-59
❑ 97UltPlaME-59
❑ 97UppDec-63
❑ 98Bow-259
❑ 98BowBes-46
❑ 98BowBesAR-46
❑ 98BowBesR-46
❑ 98BowChr-259
❑ 98BowChrGA-259
❑ 98BowChrGAR-259
❑ 98BowChrI-259
❑ 98BowChrIR-259
❑ 98BowChrR-259
❑ 98BowGolA-259
❑ 98BowInt-259
❑ 98CirThu-53
❑ 98CirThuRav-53
❑ 98CirThuSupRav-53
❑ 98ColCho-353
❑ 98ColChoER-ER10
❑ 98Don-233
❑ 98DonColL-310
❑ 98DonGolPP-233
❑ 98DonPriCL-310
❑ 98DonSilPP-233
❑ 98E-X2-68
❑ 98E-X2ECFut-68
❑ 98E-X2ECNow-68
❑ 98Fin-266
❑ 98FinNo--266
❑ 98FinNo-R-266
❑ 98FinRef-266
❑ 98FlaShoLeg0-67
❑ 98FlaShoLeg1-67
❑ 98FlaShoLeg2-67
❑ 98FlaShoLeg3-67
❑ 98FlaShoLegM-67
❑ 98FlaShoR0-67
❑ 98FlaShoR1-67
❑ 98FlaShoR2-67
❑ 98FlaShoR3-67
❑ 98Fle-128
❑ 98Fle-491
❑ 98FleVin'-87
❑ 98FleVin'C-87
❑ 98KinDis-5
❑ 98Lea-111
❑ 98LeaFraDA-111
❑ 98LeaFraF-111
❑ 98LeaFraM-111
❑ 98LeaFraM-111
❑ 98LeaFraMDC-111
❑ 98LeaFraMDC-111
❑ 98LeaFraMZ2-111
❑ 98LeaRS-77
❑ 98LeaRSLHolo-77
❑ 98LeaRSLong-77
❑ 98LeaRTrue-77
❑ 98MetUni-8
❑ 98MetUniPMG-8
❑ 98Pac-88
❑ 98PacAur-28
❑ 98PacOme-70
❑ 98PacOmeR-70
❑ 98PacOnl-218
❑ 98PacOnlR-218
❑ 98PacOnlWC-218
❑ 98PacPar-36
❑ 98PacParC-36
❑ 98PacParG-36
❑ 98PacParHS-36
❑ 98PacParPB-36
❑ 98PacParR-36
❑ 98PacPlaB-88
❑ 98PacRedT-88
❑ 98PacSil-88
❑ 98Pin-47
❑ 98PinArtP-PP44
❑ 98PinMusC-PP44
❑ 98PinPerSftF-9
❑ 98PinPlu-32
❑ 98PinPreP-47
❑ 98PinSna-Cl2
❑ 98Sco-182
❑ 98ScoAllST-10
❑ 98ScoRT-166
❑ 98ScoRTSS-PP95
❑ 98ScoRTSSAP-PP95
❑ 98ScoRTSSAP1-PP95
❑ 98ScoSS-PP82
❑ 98ScoSSAP-PP82
❑ 98SP Aut-81
❑ 98SpoIll-40
❑ 98SpoIllEE-40
❑ 98SpoIllFE-40
❑ 98SpoIllTaN-81
❑ 98SpoIllTaNEE-81
❑ 98SpoIllWSF-64
❑ 98SpoIllWSFEE-64
❑ 98SpoIllWSFFE-64
❑ 98SPxFin-266
❑ 98SPxFin-337
❑ 98SPxFinR-266
❑ 98SPxFinR-337
❑ 98SPxFinS-266
❑ 98SPxFinS-337
❑ 98StaCluFDI-376
❑ 98StaCluI-376
❑ 98StaCluOneK-376
❑ 98StaCluPP-376
❑ 98Stu-86
❑ 98StuGPP-86
❑ 98StuSPP-86
❑ 98Top-390
❑ 98TopChr-390
❑ 98TopChrR-390
❑ 98TopDevR-390
❑ 98TopDia-390
❑ 98TopGal-17
❑ 98TopGalGP-17
❑ 98TopGalOPP-17
❑ 98TopGalPPI-17
❑ 98TopGalPPIA-17
❑ 98TopGolLabC1-23
❑ 98TopGolLabC1B-23
❑ 98TopGolLabC1One-23
❑ 98TopGolLabC1R-23
❑ 98TopGolLabC2-23
❑ 98TopGolLabC2B-23
❑ 98TopGolLabC2One-23
❑ 98TopGolLabC2R-23
❑ 98TopGolLabC3-23
❑ 98TopGolLabC3B-23
❑ 98TopGolLabC3One-23
❑ 98TopGolLabC3R-23
❑ 98TopMiniC-390
❑ 98TopSta-146
❑ 98TopStaB-146
❑ 98TopStaG-146
❑ 98TopStaGR-146
❑ 98TopStaS-146
❑ 98Ult-173
❑ 98Ult-359
❑ 98UltGolM-173
❑ 98UltGolM-359
❑ 98UltMas-173
❑ 98UltMas-359
❑ 98UltPlaM-173
❑ 98UltPlaM-359
❑ 98UppDec-670
❑ 99199Fin-47
❑ 99FinGolRef-47
❑ 99FinRef-47
❑ 99Fle-90
❑ 99FleSta9-90
❑ 99FleWarT-90
❑ 99MetUni-3
❑ 99MetUniGM-3
❑ 99MetUniPMG-3
❑ 99PacOme-72
❑ 99PacOmeC-72
❑ 99PacOmeG-72
❑ 99PacOmePB-72
❑ 99PacPar-72
❑ 99PacParC-72
❑ 99PacParG-72
❑ 99PacParHoloGold-72
❑ 99PacParHS-72
❑ 99PacParOD-72
❑ 99PacParPB-72
❑ 99PacParRed-72
❑ 99SkyMolM-52
❑ 99SkyMolMX-52
❑ 99SkyPre-195
❑ 99SkyPreR-195
❑ 99SkyThu-130
❑ 99SkyThuRant-130
❑ 99SkyThuRave-130
❑ 99SP SigAutoG-TF
❑ 99SpoIll-136
❑ 99SPSig-50
❑ 99StaClu-92
❑ 99StaCluFDI-92
❑ 99StaCluOoaK-92
❑ 99StaCluPP-92
❑ 99ThuSkySupR-130
❑ 99Top-353
❑ 99TopChr-353
❑ 99TopChrR-353
❑ 99TopMVPP-353
❑ 99UD Cho-78
❑ 99UD ChoP-78
❑ 99UD ChoPCR-78
❑ 99Ult-122
❑ 99UltGolM-122
❑ 99UltMas-122
❑ 99UltPlaM-122
❑ 99UppDec-79
❑ 99UppDecCLM-C26
❑ 99UppDecE-25
❑ 99UppDecEFXG-25
❑ 99UppDecEL1-79
❑ 99UppDecEL2-79
❑ 99UppDecM-64
❑ 99UppDecMGS-64
❑ 99UppDecMHFS-64
❑ 99UppDecMP-64
❑ 99UppDecMSS-64
❑ 99Vic-124

Fryman, Troy
❑ 91UtiBluSC-27
❑ 91UtiBluSP-3247
❑ 92SouBenWSC-21
❑ 92SouBenWSF-185
❑ 93MidLeaAGF-22
❑ 93SarWhiSF-1377
❑ 93SouBenWSC-1
❑ 93SouBenWSF-1439
❑ 94BirBarC-8
❑ 94BirBarF-629
❑ 94ClaGolF-155
❑ 96BirBarB-3

Fryman, Woodie
❑ 66PirEasH-22
❑ 66Top-498
❑ 67CokCapPi-15
❑ 67DexPre-77
❑ 67PirTeal-7
❑ 67Top-221
❑ 67TopPirS-9
❑ 68OPC-112
❑ 68Top-112
❑ 68TopVen-112
❑ 69MilBra-88
❑ 69MLBOffS-175
❑ 69OPC-51
❑ 69PhiTeal-3
❑ 69Top-51
❑ 69TopSta-75
❑ 69TopTeaP-8
❑ 70MLBOffS-88
❑ 70Top-677
❑ 71MLBOffS-177
❑ 71OPC-414
❑ 71Top-414
❑ 72MilBra-110
❑ 72OPC-357
❑ 72Top-357
❑ 72TopCloT-15
❑ 73OPC-146
❑ 73Top-146
❑ 74OPC-555
❑ 74Top-555
❑ 75ExpPos-15
❑ 75OPC-166
❑ 75Top-166
❑ 75TopMin-166
❑ 76ExpRed-11
❑ 76MonExpP-12
❑ 76OPC-467
❑ 76SSP-345
❑ 76Top-467
❑ 77OPC-126
❑ 77Top-28
❑ 78SSP270-249
❑ 78TigDeaCS-8
❑ 78Top-585
❑ 79ExpPos-9
❑ 79OPC-135
❑ 79Top-269
❑ 80ExpPos-9
❑ 80OPC-316
❑ 80Top-607
❑ 81Don-331
❑ 81Fle-159
❑ 81OPC-170
❑ 81OPCPos-10
❑ 81Top-394
❑ 82Don-68
❑ 82ExpHygM-8
❑ 82ExpPos-13
❑ 82ExpZel-12
❑ 82Fle-189
❑ 82OPC-181
❑ 82Top-788
❑ 83Don-162
❑ 83ExpPos-11
❑ 83ExpStu-2
❑ 83Fle-283
❑ 83FleSti-258
❑ 83OPC-137
❑ 83Top-137
❑ 86ExpGreT-10
❑ 93ExpDonM-22

Fu, Kuo-Lee Chien
❑ 90IBAWorA-9

Fucci, Dom
❑ 80GleFalWSBT-19
❑ 80GleFalWSCT-14
❑ 81GleFalWST-11
❑ 82EdmTraT-18
❑ 82GleFalWST-5

Fuccillo, Joe
❑ 93PriRedC-12
❑ 93PriRedF-4172

Fuchs, Charlie
❑ 43PhiTeal-9
❑ 90DodTar-261

Fudger, Fred
❑ 87OldJudN-181

Fuduric, Tony
❑ 93BriTigF-3641
❑ 94BriTigC-12
❑ 94BriTigF-3496
❑ 94ExcFS7-54
❑ 94Top-757
❑ 94TopGol-757
❑ 94TopSpa-757

Fuentes, Brian
❑ 96EveAquB-9
❑ 97WisTimR-10
❑ 98Bow-368
❑ 98BowChr-368
❑ 98BowChrGA-368
❑ 98BowChrGAR-368
❑ 98BowChrI-368
❑ 98BowChrIR-368
❑ 98BowChrR-368
❑ 98BowGolA-368
❑ 98BowInt-368
❑ 98Top-264
❑ 98TopChr-264
❑ 98TopChrR-264
❑ 98TopDevR-264
❑ 98TopDia-264
❑ 98TopMiniC-264

Fuentes, Javier
❑ 96LowSpiB-8
❑ 97MicBatC-10

Fuentes, Mickey (Miguel)
❑ 70OPC-88
❑ 70Top-88
❑ 83Pil69G-11

Fuentes, Mike
❑ 83WicAerDS-7
❑ 84Don-40
❑ 84ExpPos-10
❑ 84ExpStu-32
❑ 84IndIndTI-12
❑ 84IndIndTI-15
❑ 85IndIndTI-7
❑ 87MemChiB-25
❑ 87MemChiP-1

Fuentes, Roberto
❑ 85ElmPioT-6
❑ 86WinHavRSP-8

Fuentes, Tito
❑ 66Top-511
❑ 67CokCapG-4
❑ 67DexPre-78
❑ 67OPC-177
❑ 67Top-177
❑ 70OPC-42
❑ 70Top-42
❑ 71GiaTic-4
❑ 71MLBOffS-247
❑ 71OPC-378
❑ 71Top-378
❑ 72OPC-427
❑ 72OPC-428
❑ 72Top-427
❑ 72Top-428
❑ 73OPC-236
❑ 73Top-236
❑ 74OPC-305
❑ 74Top-305
❑ 74TopSta-104
❑ 75Hos-108
❑ 75OPC-425
❑ 75PadDea-6
❑ 75Top-425
❑ 75TopMin-425
❑ 76BlaDis-15
❑ 76BucDis-15
❑ 76CarDis-15
❑ 76CraDis-15
❑ 76DaiIsID-15
❑ 76IsaDis-15
❑ 76OPC-8
❑ 76OrbDis-15
❑ 76RedBarD-15
❑ 76SafDis-15
❑ 76SSP-124
❑ 76Top-8
❑ 76TowCluD-15
❑ 77Top-63
❑ 78Top-385
❑ 86PadGreT-2
❑ 97PhoFirDTTI-2

Fuhriman, Rick
❑ 97BakBlaB-29
❑ 97BakBlaTI-29

Fuhrman, Ollie (Alfred)
❑ 22E120-78
❑ 22W573-45

Fujimoto, Kenji
❑ 89VisOakCLC-116
❑ 89VisOakP-1432

Fujiwara, Mitsuru
❑ 79TCMJapPB-71

Fukushima, Akihiro
❑ 89SalLakTTI-12

Fulcar, Manuel
❑ 93LimRocDWB-101

Fulcher, John
❑ 96OgdRapTI-33
❑ 97BelSnaB-12

Fulgencio, Elvin
❑ 85CedRapRT-22

Fulgham, John
❑ 77St.PetCT-6
❑ 78ArkTraT-10
❑ 79Car5-9
❑ 80Top-152
❑ 81Don-70
❑ 81Top-523
❑ 82LouRedE-9
❑ 83LouRedR-20

Fuller, Aaron
❑ 94SarRedSC-9
❑ 94SarRedSF-1965
❑ 96SarRedSB-15
❑ 97TreThuB-17

Fuller, Brian
❑ 96FayGenB-16
❑ 97LakTigB-15

Fuller, Harry
❑ 88AubAstP-1956
❑ 89AshTouP-957

Fuller, Jim (James H.)
❑ 73BalOriP-14
❑ 74OPC-606
❑ 74Top-606
❑ 75OPC-594
❑ 75Top-594
❑ 75TopMin-594
❑ 78ColCliT-7
❑ 87AstShoSPT-7
❑ 91OriCro-147

Fuller, Jody
❑ 98LetBlaDG-11

Fuller, Jon
❑ 90ChaWheP-2244
❑ 91CedRapRC-14
❑ 91CedRapRP-2721
❑ 92CedRapRC-12
❑ 92CedRapRF-1074
❑ 92MidLeaATI-11
❑ 93ChaLooF-2364
❑ 94ChaLooF-1361

Fuller, Mark
❑ 92PitMetC-14
❑ 92PitMetF-3287
❑ 93St.LucMC-9
❑ 93St.LuMF-2916
❑ 94BinMetF-699
❑ 94St.LucMC-9
❑ 95BinMetTI-29
❑ 96BinMetB-7

Fuller, Nig (Charles F.)
❑ 90DodTar-954

Fuller, Paul
❑ 88UtiBluSP-5
❑ 89SarWhiSS-6
❑ 89Sta-58

Fuller, Scott
❑ 88UtiBluSP-19

Fuller, Steve
❑ 95AubAstTI-24
❑ 96AubDouB-5

Fuller, Tom
❑ 80AndBraT-4

Fuller, Vern
❑ 68OPC-71
❑ 68Top-71
❑ 68TopVen-71
❑ 69Top-291
❑ 69TopTeaP-13
❑ 70MLBOffS-197
❑ 70Top-558
❑ 72MilBra-111

Fuller, Wayne
❑ 88BatCliP-1669
❑ 96BatCliTI-30

Fuller, William B.
❑ 87OldJudN-182
❑ 87OldJudN-183
❑ 95NewN566-179

Fullerton, Charles
❑ 09ObaT21-290
❑ 11Zee-46
❑ 12ObaPreT-39

Fullerton, Curtis
❑ 27Zee-3
❑ 28Zee-5
❑ 31Zee-87

Fullerton, Darren
❑ 91SydWavF-9

Fullerton, Hugh
❑ 88PacEigMO-29
❑ 88PacEigMO-35
❑ 88PacEigMO-42
❑ 88PacEigMO-64

Fullis, Chick (Charles)
❑ 33ButCanV-17
❑ 33DouDisP-19
❑ 33TatOrbSDR-166
❑ 34BatR31-74
❑ 34DiaMatCSB-62
❑ 74Car193T-11
❑ 83ConMar-36
❑ 88ConNatA-9
❑ 92ConTSN-514

Fullmer, Brad
❑ 94Bow-76
❑ 94BowBes-B55
❑ 94BowBesR-B55
❑ 94ColC-643
❑ 94ColChoGS-643
❑ 94ColChoSS-643
❑ 94SP-4
❑ 94SPDieC-4
❑ 94UppDec-532
❑ 94UppDecAHNIL-5
❑ 94UppDecED-532
❑ 95Bes-81
❑ 95SigRoo-21
❑ 95SigRooSig-21
❑ 95SPML-92
❑ 95UppDecML-90
❑ 95UppDecMLFS-90
❑ 96Bow-369
❑ 96BowBes-143
❑ 96BowBesAR-143
❑ 96BowBesR-143
❑ 96BowFoi-369
❑ 96Exc-186

❑ 96HonShaHWB-20
❑ 96WesPalBEB-29
❑ 97Bes-46
❑ 97Bes-98
❑ 97BesAutSBPP-20
❑ 97BesAutSC-6
❑ 97BesLum-4
❑ 97Bow-171
❑ 97BowBes-175
❑ 97BowBesAR-175
❑ 97BowBesR-175
❑ 97BowCerBlaIA-CA27
❑ 97BowCerBluIA-CA27
❑ 97BowCerGolIA-CA27
❑ 97BowChr-166
❑ 97BowChrI-166
❑ 97BowChrIR-166
❑ 97BowChrR-166
❑ 97BowInt-171
❑ 97EasLeaTPB-11
❑ 97HarSen-13
❑ 97TopSta-102
❑ 97TopStaAM-102
❑ 98Bow-115
❑ 98BowBes-112
❑ 98BowBesAR-112
❑ 98BowBesP-BP5
❑ 98BowBesPAR-BP5
❑ 98BowBesPR-BP5
❑ 98BowBesR-112
❑ 98BowCerBlueAU-2
❑ 98BowCerGA-2
❑ 98BowCerSA-2
❑ 98BowChr-115
❑ 98BowChrGA-115
❑ 98BowChrGAR-115
❑ 98BowChrI-115
❑ 98BowChrIR-115
❑ 98BowChrR-115
❑ 98BowChrR-39
❑ 98BowChrRR-39
❑ 98BowGolA-115
❑ 98BowInt-115
❑ 98BowScoC-SC7
❑ 98CirThu-109
❑ 98CirThuFT-3
❑ 98CirThuRav-109
❑ 98CirThuSupRav-109
❑ 98ColCho-124
❑ 98CroRoy-82
❑ 98Don-284
❑ 98DonColL-377
❑ 98DonColP-702
❑ 98DonGolPP-284
❑ 98DonPre-152
❑ 98DonPreGES-12
❑ 98DonPreGX-12
❑ 98DonPreGXDC-12
❑ 98DonPreSeat-152
❑ 98DonPriCL-377
❑ 98DonPriCP-702
❑ 98DonRooDK-12
❑ 98DonRooDKC-12
❑ 98DonSig-88
❑ 98DonSigA-33
❑ 98DonSigAC-42
❑ 98DonSigAM-43
❑ 98DonSigP-88
❑ 98DonSigSP-6
❑ 98DonSilPP-284
❑ 98E-X2SD2001-11
❑ 98E-X2Sig2001-5
❑ 98Fin-241
❑ 98FinNo--241
❑ 98FinNo-R-241
❑ 98FinRef-241
❑ 98FlaShoWotF-5
❑ 98Fle-267
❑ 98FleProF-PF3
❑ 98Lea-178
❑ 98LeaFraDA-178
❑ 98LeaFraF-178
❑ 98LeaFraM-178
❑ 98LeaFraM-178
❑ 98LeaFraMDC-178
❑ 98LeaFraMDC-178
❑ 98LeaFraMZ2-178
❑ 98LeaRCMLHDSamp-19
❑ 98LeaRCrusUP-117
❑ 98LeaRS-142
❑ 98LeaRS-194
❑ 98LeaRSCrusUG-117
❑ 98LeaRSCrusUR-117
❑ 98LeaRSFOSamp-7
❑ 98LeaRSFresh-7
❑ 98LeaRSLHolo-142
❑ 98LeaRSLHolo-194
❑ 98LeaRSLong-142
❑ 98LeaRSLong-194
❑ 98LeaRSMLHD-19
❑ 98LeaRSTicMas-10
❑ 98LeaRSTicMasDC-10
❑ 98LeaRTrue-142
❑ 98LeaRTrue-194
❑ 98PacOme-148
❑ 98PacOmeR-148
❑ 98PacOmeRS-25
❑ 98PacOmeRST1-25
❑ 98PacOnl-447
❑ 98PacOnlR-447
❑ 98PacOnlWC-447
❑ 98PinIns-130
❑ 98PinInsCE-130
❑ 98PinInsDE-130
❑ 98PinPer-127
❑ 98PinPerPP-127
❑ 98PinPlu-58
❑ 98PinPluAP-PP25
❑ 98PinPluGAP-PP25
❑ 98PinPluMAP-PP25
❑ 98Revo-88
❑ 98RevoRooHH-11
❑ 98RevoRooHHG-11
❑ 98RevoSS-88
❑ 98ScoRT-249
❑ 98ScoRTSS-PP142
❑ 98ScoRTSSAP-PP142
❑ 98ScoRTSSAP1-PP142
❑ 98SkyDugA-113
❑ 98SkyDugAIA-113
❑ 98SP Aut-23
❑ 98SP MinPE-80
❑ 98SPMin-80
❑ 98SpoIll-165
❑ 98SpoIllEE-165
❑ 98SpoIllFE-165
❑ 98SpoIllTaN-144
❑ 98SpoIllTaNEE-144
❑ 98SpoIllWSF-142
❑ 98SpoIllWSFEE-142
❑ 98SpoIllWSFFE-142
❑ 98SPxFin-17
❑ 98SPxFinR-17
❑ 98SPxFinS-17
❑ 98StaCluBPP-BP2
❑ 98StaCluFDI-338
❑ 98StaCluI-338
❑ 98StaCluITW-W2
❑ 98StaCluOneK-338
❑ 98StaCluPP-338
❑ 98Stu-100
❑ 98StuFF-27
❑ 98StuFFDC-27
❑ 98StuGPP-100
❑ 98StuSPP-100
❑ 98TopGolLabC1-96
❑ 98TopGolLabC1B-96
❑ 98TopGolLabC1One-96
❑ 98TopGolLabC1R-96
❑ 98TopGolLabC2-96
❑ 98TopGolLabC2B-96
❑ 98TopGolLabC2One-96
❑ 98TopGolLabC2R-96
❑ 98TopGolLabC3-96
❑ 98TopGolLabC3B-96
❑ 98TopGolLabC3One-96
❑ 98TopGolLabC3R-96
❑ 98TopSta-97
❑ 98TopStaB-97
❑ 98TopStaG-97
❑ 98TopStaGR-97
❑ 98TopStaS-97
❑ 98TopStaSB-S7
❑ 98TopStaSG-S7
❑ 98TopStaSGR-S7
❑ 98TopStaSS-S7
❑ 98TopTek-77
❑ 98TopTekD-77
❑ 98UD3-5
❑ 98UD3-95
❑ 98UD3-185
❑ 98UD3DieCut-5
❑ 98UD3DieCut-95
❑ 98UD3DieCut-185
❑ 98Ult-283
❑ 98UltGolM-283
❑ 98UltMas-283
❑ 98UltPlaM-283
❑ 98UltRoctS-6
❑ 98UppDec-281
❑ 98UppDecBCP-BC5
❑ 98UppDecDS-DS40
❑ 98UppDecR-59
❑ 98UppDecR-121
❑ 98UppDecREP-7
❑ 98UppDecRNF-NF21
❑ 99199Fin-127
❑ 99199Fin-153
❑ 99Bow-67
❑ 99BowBes-39
❑ 99BowBesAR-39
❑ 99BowBesR-39
❑ 99BowChr-67
❑ 99BowChrG-67
❑ 99BowChrGR-67
❑ 99BowChrI-67
❑ 99BowChrIR-67
❑ 99BowChrR-67
❑ 99BowGol-67
❑ 99BowInt-67
❑ 99CroRoyB-86
❑ 99CroRoyL-86
❑ 99CroRoyOD-86
❑ 99E-X Cen-41
❑ 99E-X CenECFut-41
❑ 99E-X CenECNow-41
❑ 99FinGolRef-127
❑ 99FinGolRef-153
❑ 99FinMil-M40
❑ 99FinRef-127
❑ 99FinRef-153
❑ 99Fle-131
❑ 99FleRooFla-8
❑ 99FleSta9-131
❑ 99FleWarT-131
❑ 99MetUni-130
❑ 99MetUniGM-130
❑ 99MetUniPMG-130
❑ 99Pac-262
❑ 99PacAur-111
❑ 99PacAurOD-111
❑ 99PacInv-90
❑ 99PacInvOD-90
❑ 99PacInvPB-90
❑ 99PacPar-141
❑ 99PacParC-141
❑ 99PacParG-141
❑ 99PacParHoloGold-141
❑ 99PacParHS-141
❑ 99PacParOD-141
❑ 99PacParPB-141
❑ 99PacParRed-141
❑ 99PacPlaB-262
❑ 99PacRed-262
❑ 99SkyMolM-64
❑ 99SkyMolMX-64
❑ 99SkyPre-166
❑ 99SkyPreR-166
❑ 99SkyThu-228
❑ 99SkyThuRant-228
❑ 99SkyThuRave-228
❑ 99SP Aut-53
❑ 99SP AutC-BF
❑ 99SP AutCG-BF
❑ 99SP SigAuto-BF
❑ 99SPSig-127
❑ 99StaClu-26
❑ 99StaCluFDI-26
❑ 99StaCluOoaK-26
❑ 99StaCluPP-26
❑ 99ThuSkySupR-228
❑ 99Top-134
❑ 99TopBlaLC1-53
❑ 99TopBlaLC2-53
❑ 99TopBlaLC3-53
❑ 99TopChr-134
❑ 99TopChrNB-NB2
❑ 99TopChrNBR-NB2
❑ 99TopChrR-134
❑ 99TopGal-64
❑ 99TopGal-116
❑ 99TopGalP-PP3
❑ 99TopGalPP-64
❑ 99TopGalPP-116
❑ 99TopGalPPI-64
❑ 99TopGalPPI-116
❑ 99TopGolL-53
❑ 99TopGolLC1-53
❑ 99TopGolLC2-53
❑ 99TopGolLOtO-53
❑ 99TopMVPP-134
❑ 99TopNewB-NB2
❑ 99TopOpeD-80
❑ 99TopRedLC1-53
❑ 99TopRedLC2-53
❑ 99TopRedLC3-53
❑ 99TopSta-32
❑ 99TopSta1Foil-32
❑ 99TopSta2Foil-32
❑ 99TopStaFoil-32
❑ 99TopStaOS-32
❑ 99TopStaTS-32
❑ 99UD Cho-108
❑ 99UD ChoP-108
❑ 99UD ChoPCR-108
❑ 99Ult-204
❑ 99UltGolM-204
❑ 99UltMas-204
❑ 99UltPlaM-204
❑ 99UppDec-141
❑ 99UppDecBD-51
❑ 99UppDecBDD-51
❑ 99UppDecBDQ-51
❑ 99UppDecBDT-51
❑ 99UppDecE-54
❑ 99UppDecEFXG-54
❑ 99UppDecEL1-141
❑ 99UppDecEL2-141
❑ 99UppDecGJ-BF
❑ 99UppDecM-125
❑ 99UppDecMGS-125
❑ 99UppDecMHFS-125
❑ 99UppDecMP-125
❑ 99UppDecMP-BF
❑ 99UppDecMSS-125
❑ 99Vic-239

Fully, Edward
❑ 90KinMetB-11
❑ 90KinMetS-9
❑ 91ColMetPI-11
❑ 91ColMetPPI-3
❑ 91SouAtlLAGP-SAL15
❑ 92St.LucMCB-20
❑ 92St.LucMF-1761
❑ 93St.LucMC-10
❑ 93St.LuMF-2933
❑ 94BinMetF-716
❑ 95BinMetTI-28

Fulmer, Chris
❑ 87BucN28-2
❑ 87OldJudN-184
❑ 87OldJudN-185

Fulmer, Mike
❑ 84MadMusP-20
❑ 85ModA'sC-10
❑ 86StoPorP-9

Fulton, Bill
❑ 84GreHorT-12
❑ 86AlbYanT-26
❑ 87ColCliP-10
❑ 87ColCliP-27
❑ 87ColCliT-4
❑ 88ColCliC-4
❑ 88ColCliP-2
❑ 88ColCliP-312
❑ 89BlaYNPRWLU-14
❑ 89ColCliC-1
❑ 89ColCliP-3
❑ 89ColCliP-746
❑ 92YanWIZ8-64

Fulton, Ed
❑ 88SprCarB-24
❑ 89St.PetCS-13
❑ 90ArkTraGS-14
❑ 90LouRedBLBC-17
❑ 90TopTVCa-49
❑ 91LinDriAAA-235
❑ 91LouRedLD-235
❑ 91LouRedP-2916
❑ 91LouRedTI-28
❑ 92LouRedF-1889
❑ 93LouRedF-217
❑ 94TolMudHF-1029

Fulton, Greg
❑ 87ChaLooB-18
❑ 88VerMarP-942
❑ 89CalCanP-524
❑ 89WilBilP-648
❑ 90CalCanC-9
❑ 90CalCanP-656
❑ 90CMC-436
❑ 90ProAAAF-121
❑ 91HarSenLD-254
❑ 91HarSenP-629
❑ 91LinDriAA-254
❑ 92HarSenS-281
❑ 92IndIndF-1866
❑ 93HarSenF-283

Fults, Nathan
❑ 90IdaFalBP-3260

Fultz, Aaron
❑ 93ClaGolF-169
❑ 93CliGiaC-10
❑ 93CliGiaF-2483
❑ 93MidLeaAGF-39
❑ 94ExcFS7-291
❑ 94ForMyeMF-1161
❑ 95ForMyeMTI-7
❑ 95SigRooOJ-13
❑ 95SigRooOJP-13
❑ 95SigRooOJPS-13
❑ 95SigRooOJS-13
❑ 96SanJosGB-18
❑ 96WesOahCHWB-18
❑ 98ShrCapM-14
❑ 98ShrCapWS-14

Fultz, Bill
❑ 82LynMetT-20
❑ 83LynMetT-5
❑ 84JacMetT-7

Fultz, David
❑ 03BreE10-54
❑ 11SpoLifCW-133

Fultz, Vince
❑ 92AlbPolCB-16
❑ 92RocExpF-2107

Fultzer, Aaron
❑ 97ShrCap-10
❑ 97ShrCapB-10

Funaro, Joe
❑ 95ElmPioTI-6
❑ 95ElmPioUTI-6
❑ 96KanCouCTI-8
❑ 97BreCouMB-1
❑ 98PorSeaDQ-17

Funderburk, Mark
❑ 78WisRapTT-5
❑ 80OrlTwiT-19
❑ 82OrlTwiT-7
❑ 83OmaRoyT-15
❑ 85OrlTwiT-5
❑ 86Don-630
❑ 86Fle-652
❑ 86Spo-178
❑ 86TolMudHP-11
❑ 87OrlTwiP-25
❑ 88OrlTwiB-5
❑ 89OrlTwiB-3
❑ 89OrlTwiP-1344
❑ 90OrlSunRB-29
❑ 90OrlSunRP-1099
❑ 90OrlSunRS-25
❑ 91LinDriAA-500
❑ 91OrlSunRLD-500
❑ 91OrlSunRP-1866
❑ 92OrlSunRF-2863
❑ 92OrlSunRS-526
❑ 93NasXprF-419
❑ 94NasXprF-403

Funk, Art
❑ 36GouWidPPR-D9

Funk, Brian
❑ 83WatRedT-2
❑ 84CedRapRT-6

Funk, E.
❑ 31Exh-24
❑ 33Zee-114

Funk, Frank
❑ 60MapLeaSF-7
❑ 61Top-362
❑ 62Top-587
❑ 63Top-476
❑ 64Top-289
❑ 64TopVen-289
❑ 77Gia-7
❑ 80PenPilBT-26
❑ 81MarPos-17
❑ 84MarMot-27
❑ 86OmaRoyP-7
❑ 86OmaRoyT-24
❑ 87OmaRoyP-1
❑ 88RoySmo-2
❑ 88RoyTeal-10
❑ 90RoyPos-10
❑ 91CedRapRC-26
❑ 91CedRapRP-2735
❑ 92NasSouF-1849
❑ 92NasSouS-300
❑ 93ColSprSSF-3102
❑ 94ColSprSSF-749

Funk, Tom
❑ 86ColAstP-14
❑ 87TucTorP-25
❑ 88ColAstB-18

Fuqua, David
❑ 75LafDriT-22

Furcal, Lorenzo
❑ 89MadMusS-9
❑ 89MedAthB-17

Furcal, Manuel
❑ 90SanBerSB-11
❑ 90SanBerSCLC-98
❑ 90SanBerSP-2628
❑ 91PenPilC-4
❑ 91PenPilP-370

Furcal, Rafael
❑ 98DanBraQ-22
❑ 99Bow-364
❑ 99BowGol-364
❑ 99BowInt-364
❑ 99JustheS-20
❑ 99JustheSJB-20

Furch, John
❑ 88UtiBluSP-7

Furillo, Carl
❑ 46DodTeal-6
❑ 46SpoExcW-3-9
❑ 47DodTeal-7
❑ 47Exh-78
❑ 47HomBon-16
❑ 47PM1StaP1-62
❑ 47PM1StaP1-63
❑ 47PM1StaP1-64
❑ 47PM1StaP1-65
❑ 48DodTeal-10
❑ 48SweSpoT-20
❑ 49Bow-70
❑ 49EurSta-35
❑ 50Bow-58
❑ 50Dra-18
❑ 51Bow-81
❑ 52Bow-24
❑ 52CokTip-2
❑ 52TipTop-9
❑ 53BowC-78
❑ 53Dor-128
❑ 54Bow-122
❑ 54NewYorJA-5
❑ 55Bow-169
❑ 55DodGolS-18
❑ 55DodGolS-30
❑ 56Dod-10
❑ 56Top-190
❑ 57Top-45
❑ 57Top-400
❑ 58DodJayP-5
❑ 58DodTeal-8
❑ 58DodVol-5
❑ 58Top-417
❑ 59DodMor-2
❑ 59DodPos-4
❑ 59DodTeal-8
❑ 59DodVol-5
❑ 59Top-206
❑ 60DodBelB-8
❑ 60DodMor-4
❑ 60DodPos-4
❑ 60NuHi-32
❑ 60Top-387
❑ 60Top-408
❑ 61NuSco-432
❑ 72TopTes5-3
❑ 74dod195T-10
❑ 77GalGloG-11
❑ 78ReaRem-5
❑ 79TCM50-43
❑ 82GSGalAG-5
❑ 84FifNatCT-5
❑ 84OCoandSI-146
❑ 84TCMPla1-29
❑ 87Dod195T-4
❑ 88DodRinP1-2B
❑ 89DodSmoG-58
❑ 90DodTar-262
❑ 91TopArc1-305
❑ 92BazQua5A-2
❑ 95TopArcBD-35
❑ 95TopArcBD-60
❑ 95TopArcBD-87
❑ 95TopArcBD-132
❑ 95TopArcBD-155

Furman, Jon
❑ 83BirBarT-20

Furmanik, Dan
❑ 89ColMetB-6
❑ 89ColMetGS-8
❑ 90St.LucMS-7
❑ 91SalLakTP-3203
❑ 91SalLakTSP-2

Furniss, Eddy
❑ 99BasAmeTPA-16
❑ 99TeaBesR-29
❑ 99TeaBesRFS-17
❑ 99TeaBesRG-29
❑ 99TeaBesRS-29

Fursato, Yasutara

❑ 93BriTigF-3642
Furtado, Tim
❑ 93RivPilCLC-7
Furtak, Mark
❑ 87HawRai-16
Furuta, Atsuya
❑ 93GolCar-3
Furuya, Hideo
❑ 87JapPlaB-32
Fusco, Thomas
❑ 90HamRedB-5
❑ 90HamRedS-13
❑ 91SavCarP-1645
❑ 92SavCarC-20
❑ 92SavCarF-656
Fuson, Grady
❑ 82IdaFalAT-31
❑ 83IdaFalAT-31
❑ 89MedAthB-18
❑ 90SouOreAB-30
❑ 90SouOreAP-3449
❑ 91SouOreAP-3866
Fuson, Robin
❑ 78WatIndT-10
❑ 82ChaLooT-18
❑ 83BufBisT-1
❑ 84BufBisT-24
❑ 85PawRedST-13
Fussell, Chris
❑ 96Bow-263
❑ 96BowBes-163
❑ 96BowBesAR-163
❑ 96BowBesR-163
❑ 96BowFoi-263
❑ 96CarLeaA1B-1
❑ 96CarLeaA2B-1
❑ 96FreKeyB-9
❑ 96MauStiHWB-28
❑ 97Bow-95
❑ 97BowBay-17
❑ 97BowCerBlaIA-CA28
❑ 97BowCerBluIA-CA28
❑ 97BowCerGolIA-CA28
❑ 97BowInt-95
❑ 97EasLeaTPB-7
❑ 98Bow-364
❑ 98BowBayM-14
❑ 98BowChr-364
❑ 98BowChrGA-364
❑ 98BowChrGAR-364
❑ 98BowChrI-364
❑ 98BowChrIR-364
❑ 98BowChrR-364
❑ 98BowGolA-364
❑ 98BowInt-364
❑ 99Bow-382
❑ 99BowGol-382
❑ 99BowInt-382
❑ 99Fle-361
❑ 99FleSta9-361
❑ 99FleWarT-361
Fussell, Denny
❑ 92PriRedC-15
❑ 92PriRedF-3082
❑ 93BilMusF-3937
❑ 93BilMusSP-10
❑ 94BilMusF-3677
❑ 94BilMusSP-6
Fussell, Fred
❑ 25Zee-140
Fusselman, Les
❑ 52Top-378
❑ 53CarHunW-7
❑ 53Top-218
❑ 83TopRep5-378
❑ 91TopArc1-218
Futrell, Mark
❑ 90WelPirP-21
❑ 91AugPirC-6
❑ 91AugPirP-799
Fye, Chris
❑ 89CliGiaP-885
❑ 90Bes-159
❑ 90SanJosGB-16
❑ 90SanJosGCLC-43
❑ 90SanJosGP-2002
❑ 90SanJosGP-2172
❑ 90SanJosGS-10
Fyhrie, Mike
❑ 92BasCitRC-21
❑ 92BasCitRF-3838
❑ 93WilBluRC-10
❑ 94OmaRoyF-1218
❑ 95WicWraTI-25
❑ 96NorTidB-14
❑ 98NorTidP-10
❑ 98NorTidQ-11
Fynan, Kevin
❑ 88ClePhiS-11
❑ 89ClePhiS-9
❑ 90ClePhiS-7
Fyock, Wade
❑ 90HigSchPLS-23
❑ 91AppFoxCB-3
❑ 91AppFoxP-1709
❑ 91Cla/Bes-249
Fzelykovskyi, Andrei
❑ 89EasLcaDDP-DD13
Gabbani, Mike
❑ 90HunCubP-3284
❑ 91SydWavF-18
❑ 91WinSpiC-13
❑ 91WinSpiP-2831
❑ 92WinSpiC-20
❑ 92WinSpiF-1211
Gabbard, John
❑ 43ParSpo-77
Gabella, Jim
❑ 90WatIndS-24
❑ 91ColSprSSP-2202
❑ 91LinDriAAA-100
❑ 92CanIndF-707
❑ 93BurIndC-30
❑ 93BurIndF-3316
❑ 94BurIndC-29
Gabler, Frank
❑ 34BatR31-91
❑ 92ConTSN-606
Gabler, Glen
❑ 28Zee-30
❑ 29Zee-19
❑ 30Zee-27
❑ 31Zee-15
Gabler, John
❑ 60Lea-62
❑ 92YanWIZ6-44
Gables, Kenneth
❑ 48SomandK-5
❑ 49AngTeal-10
❑ 49SomandK-3
Gabriel, Denio
❑ 96FreKeyB-28
Gabriele, Dan
❑ 85ElmPioT-7
❑ 86GreHorP-6
❑ 87WinHavRSP-10
❑ 88NewBriRSP-898
❑ 89EasLeaAP-13
❑ 89NewBriRSP-604
❑ 89NewBriRSS-6
Gabriele, Mike
❑ 90SumBraB-3
❑ 90SumBraP-2426
Gabrielson, Len
❑ 47PM1StaP1-66
❑ 63Top-253
❑ 64Top-198
❑ 64TopVen-198
❑ 65OPC-14
❑ 65Top-14
❑ 66Top-395
❑ 67CokCapDA-19
❑ 67Top-469
❑ 68Top-357
❑ 68TopVen-357
❑ 69MilBra-89
❑ 69MLBOffS-147
❑ 69Top-615
❑ 69TopSta-44
❑ 70MLBOffS-50
❑ 70OPC-204
❑ 70Top-204
❑ 90DodTar-263
Gabrielson, Leonard
❑ 37Zee-33
❑ 37Zee-96
❑ 43CenFlo-9
Gabrielson, Paul
❑ 98PieBolWM-3
Gaddie, Mike
❑ 90JohCitCS-30
❑ 92JohCitCC-28
Gaddy, George
❑ 12HomRunKE-47
❑ 12Zee-80
Gaddy, John Wilson
❑ 90DodTar-955
Gaddy, Robert
❑ 89BatCliP-1928
❑ 90ProAaA-95
❑ 90SouAtlLAS-7
❑ 90SpaPhiB-3
❑ 90SpaPhiP-2484
❑ 90SpaPhiS-8
❑ 91ClePhiC-3
❑ 91ClePhiP-1614
❑ 92ClePhiC-4
❑ 92ClePhiF-2050
❑ 93ReaPhiF-291
❑ 94ScrRedBF-919
❑ 95ScrRedBTI-9
Gades, Rene
❑ 96HudValRB-28
Gaeckle, Chris
❑ 86GreHorP-7
❑ 87GreHorP-25
Gaedel, Eddie
❑ 60NuHi-26
❑ 61NuSco-426
❑ 73FleWilD-4
❑ 77FriOneYW-1
❑ 87SpoCubG-2
❑ 87SpoRea-3
❑ 91FouBal-34
Gaeta, Chris
❑ 85NewOriT-19
Gaeta, Frank
❑ 52LavPro-25
Gaetti, Gary
❑ 80WisRapTT-17
❑ 82OrlTwi8SCT-7
❑ 82TwiPos-12
❑ 83AllGamPl-32
❑ 83Don-53
❑ 83Fle-613
❑ 83Top-431
❑ 83TopSti-87
❑ 83TwiTeal-5
❑ 83TwiTeal-33
❑ 84Don-314
❑ 84Fle-565
❑ 84FunFooP-131
❑ 84MinTwiP-13
❑ 84Nes792-157
❑ 84OPC-157
❑ 84Top-157
❑ 84TopRubD-20
❑ 84TopSti-306
❑ 84TopTif-157
❑ 84TwiTeal-5
❑ 85AllGamPl-33
❑ 85Don-242
❑ 85Fle-278
❑ 85Lea-145
❑ 85OPC-304
❑ 85Top-304
❑ 85TopRubD-20
❑ 85TopSti-302
❑ 85TopTif-304
❑ 85Twi7-9
❑ 85TwiPos-9
❑ 85TwiTeal-5
❑ 85TwiTeal-7
❑ 86Don-314
❑ 86Fle-394
❑ 86OPC-97
❑ 86Top-97
❑ 86TopSti-283
❑ 86TopTif-97
❑ 86TwiTeal-5
❑ 87ClaGam-54
❑ 87Don-122
❑ 87DonOpeD-219
❑ 87Fle-540
❑ 87FleGamW-15
❑ 87FleGlo-540
❑ 87FleMin-40
❑ 87FleRecS-9
❑ 87FleStiC-43
❑ 87Lea-245
❑ 87OPC-179
❑ 87Spo-64
❑ 87Spo-114
❑ 87SpoTeaP-17
❑ 87Top-710
❑ 87TopGloS-3
❑ 87TopMinL-62
❑ 87TopSti-279
❑ 87TopTif-710
❑ 87TwiPos-8
❑ 87TwiTeal-5
❑ 88ClaBlu-233
❑ 88Don-19
❑ 88Don-194
❑ 88DonBasB-46
❑ 88DonSupD-19
❑ 88Fle-10
❑ 88FleGlo-10
❑ 88FleHotS-12
❑ 88FleLeaL-13
❑ 88FleMin-34
❑ 88FleStiC-43
❑ 88GreBasS-24
❑ 88KayB-11
❑ 88Lea-19
❑ 88Lea-200
❑ 88Nes-4
❑ 88OPC-257
❑ 88PanSti-140
❑ 88PanSti-445
❑ 88RedFolSB-26
❑ 88Sco-62
❑ 88ScoGlo-62
❑ 88Spo-154
❑ 88StaLinTw-7
❑ 88Top-578
❑ 88Top-609
❑ 88TopBig-127
❑ 88TopClo-49
❑ 88TopCoi-13
❑ 88TopRitTM-31
❑ 88TopSti-17
❑ 88TopSti-277
❑ 88TopTif-578
❑ 88TopTif-609
❑ 88TopUKM-25
❑ 88TopUKMT-25
❑ 88TwiMasBD-9
❑ 88TwiSmoC-2
❑ 88Woo-18
❑ 88Woo-22
❑ 89Bow-158
❑ 89BowTif-158
❑ 89CadElID-21
❑ 89ClaLigB-41
❑ 89Don-64
❑ 89DonAll-13
❑ 89DonBasB-102
❑ 89Fle-110
❑ 89FleGlo-110
❑ 89FleHeroB-15
❑ 89MasBreD-3
❑ 89OPC-220
❑ 89PanSti-389
❑ 89RedFolSB-46
❑ 89Sco-8
❑ 89ScoHot1S-21
❑ 89Scomast-16
❑ 89Spo-48
❑ 89Top-220
❑ 89TopBasT-91
❑ 89TopBig-264
❑ 89TopGloS-33
❑ 89TopMinL-61
❑ 89TopSti-289
❑ 89TopStiB-8
❑ 89TopTif-220
❑ 89TVSpoM-104
❑ 89UppDec-203
❑ 89UppDecS-3
❑ 90Bow-417
❑ 90BowTif-417
❑ 90Don-151
❑ 90DonBesA-10
❑ 90Fle-373
❑ 90FleBasA-10
❑ 90FleBasAC-10
❑ 90FleCan-373
❑ 90Hot50PS-14
❑ 90Lea-97
❑ 90LeaPre-11
❑ 90M.Vpin-55
❑ 90MLBBasB-100
❑ 90OPC-630
❑ 90PanSti-106
❑ 90PubIntS-286
❑ 90PubIntS-326
❑ 90Sco-145
❑ 90Sco100S-22
❑ 90Spo-51
❑ 90Top-630
❑ 90TopBig-254
❑ 90TopCoi-14
❑ 90TopDou-25
❑ 90TopGloS-28
❑ 90TopSti-288
❑ 90TopStiB-41
❑ 90TopTif-630
❑ 90UppDec-454
❑ 91AngSmo-13
❑ 91Bow-207
❑ 91CadElID-22
❑ 91ClaGam-49
❑ 91Don-547
❑ 91Fle-609
❑ 91FleUpd-9
❑ 91Lea-303
❑ 91OPC-430
❑ 91OPCPre-47
❑ 91PanFreS-302
❑ 91PanSti-250
❑ 91Sco-325
❑ 91ScoRoo-39T
❑ 91StaClu-353
❑ 91Stu-25
❑ 91Top-430
❑ 91TopDesS-430
❑ 91TopMic-430
❑ 91TopTif-430
❑ 91TopTra-44T
❑ 91TopTraT-44T
❑ 91UltUpd-8
❑ 91UppDec-34
❑ 91UppDec-233
❑ 91UppDec-731
❑ 92AngPol-10
❑ 92Bow-564
❑ 92Don-96
❑ 92Fle-58
❑ 92Lea-107
❑ 92LeaBlaG-107
❑ 92OPC-70
❑ 92PanSti-7
❑ 92Pin-81
❑ 92Sco-39
❑ 92ScoProP-8
❑ 92ScoProP-23
❑ 92StaClu-436
❑ 92Top-70
❑ 92TopGol-70
❑ 92TopGolW-70
❑ 92TopMic-70
❑ 92TriPla-223
❑ 92Ult-26
❑ 92UppDec-321
❑ 93AngMot-5
❑ 93CadDis-21
❑ 93Don-157
❑ 93DonSpiotG-SG15
❑ 93Fle-574
❑ 93Lea-514
❑ 93PacSpa-46
❑ 93PanSti-4
❑ 93Pin-112
❑ 93Sco-644
❑ 93Sel-262
❑ 93SelRoo-95T
❑ 93StaClu-512
❑ 93StaCluFDI-512
❑ 93StaCluMOP-512
❑ 93Top-139
❑ 93TopGol-139
❑ 93TopInaM-139
❑ 93TopInaR-139
❑ 93TopMic-139
❑ 93Ult-520
❑ 93UppDec-370
❑ 93UppDecGold-370
❑ 93UppDecHRH-HR28
❑ 94ColC-566
❑ 94ColChoGS-566
❑ 94ColChoSS-566
❑ 94Don-502
❑ 94Fin-394
❑ 94FinRef-394
❑ 94Fla-298
❑ 94Fle-153
❑ 94FleExtB-86
❑ 94Lea-427
❑ 94LeaL-37
❑ 94Sco-300
❑ 94ScoGolR-300
❑ 94StaClu-485
❑ 94StaCluFDI-485
❑ 94StaCluGR-485
❑ 94StaCluMOP-485
❑ 94Stu-183
❑ 94Top-403
❑ 94TopGol-403
❑ 94TopSpa-403
❑ 94Ult-363
❑ 94UppDec-466
❑ 94UppDecED-466
❑ 95ColCho-456
❑ 95ColChoGS-456
❑ 95ColChoSS-456
❑ 95DonTopotO-85
❑ 95Emo-49
❑ 95Fin-245
❑ 95FinRef-245
❑ 95Fla-44
❑ 95Fle-156
❑ 95Lea-315
❑ 95LeaLim-177
❑ 95Pac-200
❑ 95Pin-380
❑ 95PinArtP-380
❑ 95PinMusC-380
❑ 95Sco-343
❑ 95ScoGolR-343
❑ 95ScoPlaTS-343
❑ 95SPCha-161
❑ 95SPChaDC-161
❑ 95StaClu-9
❑ 95StaCluFDI-9
❑ 95StaCluMOP-9
❑ 95StaCluSTWS-9
❑ 95StaCluVR-4
❑ 95StaCluVRMO-4
❑ 95Top-353
❑ 95TopCyb-190
❑ 95Ult-288
❑ 95UltGolM-288
❑ 95UppDec-420
❑ 95UppDecED-420
❑ 95UppDecEDG-420
❑ 95Zen-36
❑ 96Baz-99
❑ 96CarPol-9
❑ 96ColCho-173
❑ 96ColCho-785
❑ 96ColChoGS-173
❑ 96ColChoSS-173
❑ 96Don-117
❑ 96DonPreP-117
❑ 96EmoXL-265
❑ 96Fin-B278
❑ 96FinRef-B278
❑ 96Fla-358
❑ 96Fle-125
❑ 96FleTeaL-7
❑ 96FleTif-125
❑ 96FleUpd-U188
❑ 96FleUpdTC-U188
❑ 96LeaSigA-75
❑ 96LeaSigAG-75
❑ 96LeaSigAS-75
❑ 96MetUni-223
❑ 96MetUniP-223
❑ 96MLBPin-10
❑ 96Pac-332
❑ 96PacPri-P106
❑ 96PacPriG-P106
❑ 96PanSti-183
❑ 96Pin-110
❑ 96PinArtP-43
❑ 96PinSta-43
❑ 96Sco-346
❑ 96ScoDugC-B71
❑ 96ScoDugCAP-B71
❑ 96SP-154
❑ 96Spo-40
❑ 96SpoArtP-40
❑ 96StaClu-109
❑ 96StaCluMOP-109
❑ 96StaCluMOP-PS12
❑ 96StaCluPS-PS12
❑ 96Sum-151
❑ 96SumAbo&B-151
❑ 96SumArtP-151
❑ 96SumFoi-151
❑ 96Top-204
❑ 96TopRoaW-RW7
❑ 96Ult-68
❑ 96Ult-546
❑ 96UltGolM-68
❑ 96UltGolM-546
❑ 96UppDec-153
❑ 96UppDec-506U
❑ 97CarPol-8
❑ 97Cir-93
❑ 97CirRav-93
❑ 97ColCho-442
❑ 97Don-248
❑ 97DonGolPP-248
❑ 97DonSilPP-248
❑ 97DonTea-161
❑ 97DonTeaSPE-161
❑ 97Fle-442
❑ 97FleTif-442
❑ 97Lea-277
❑ 97LeaFraM-277
❑ 97LeaFraMDC-277
❑ 97Pac-408
❑ 97PacLigB-408
❑ 97PacSil-408

❑ 97Pin-136
❑ 97PinArtP-PP136
❑ 97PinMusC-136
❑ 97PinPrePla-136
❑ 97Sco-295
❑ 97ScoArtPWB-295
❑ 97ScoPreS-295
❑ 97ScoShoS-295
❑ 97ScoShoSAP-295
❑ 97SP-149
❑ 97StaClu-144
❑ 97StaCluMOP-144
❑ 97Top-222
❑ 97TopGal-15
❑ 97TopGalPPI-15
❑ 97Ult-316
❑ 97UltGolME-316
❑ 97UltPlaME-316
❑ 97UppDec-256
❑ 97UppDec-373
❑ 97UppDec-468
❑ 98CarScoP-14
❑ 98ColCho-215
❑ 98Fin-197
❑ 98FinNo--197
❑ 98FinNo-R-197
❑ 98FinRef-197
❑ 98FleUpd-U54
❑ 98MetUni-31
❑ 98MetUniPMG-31
❑ 98Pac-411
❑ 98PacAur-182
❑ 98PacInv-133
❑ 98PacInvPBlue-133
❑ 98PacInvSilv-133
❑ 98PacOme-196
❑ 98PacOmeR-196
❑ 98PacOnl-610
❑ 98PacOnlR-610
❑ 98PacOnlWC-610
❑ 98PacPar-228
❑ 98PacParC-228
❑ 98PacParG-228
❑ 98PacParHS-228
❑ 98PacParPB-228
❑ 98PacParR-228
❑ 98PacPlaB-411
❑ 98PacRedT-411
❑ 98PacSil-411
❑ 98Revo-118
❑ 98RevoSS-118
❑ 98Sco-202
❑ 98ScoCar-14
❑ 98StaCluFDI-232
❑ 98StaCluI-232
❑ 98StaCluOneK-232
❑ 98StaCluPP-232
❑ 98Top-72
❑ 98TopChr-72
❑ 98TopChrR-72
❑ 98TopDevR-72
❑ 98TopDia-72
❑ 98TopMiniC-72
❑ 98Ult-15
❑ 98UltGolM-15
❑ 98UltMas-15
❑ 98UltPlaM-15
❑ 98UppDec-199
❑ 98UppDecSF-107
❑ 99Fle-407
❑ 99FleSta9-407
❑ 99FleWarT-407
❑ 99Pac-83
❑ 99PacCroC-55
❑ 99PacCroCPB-55
❑ 99PacPar-47
❑ 99PacParC-47
❑ 99PacParG-47
❑ 99PacParHoloGold-47
❑ 99PacParHS-47
❑ 99PacParOD-47
❑ 99PacParPB-47
❑ 99PacParRed-47
❑ 99PacPlaB-83
❑ 99PacRed-83
❑ 99SpoIll-9
❑ 99UppDec-333
❑ 99UppDecEL1-333
❑ 99UppDecEL2-333
❑ 99Vic-83

Gaff, Brent
❑ 78WauMetT-10
❑ 79WauTimT-1
❑ 81TidTidT-17
❑ 82TidTidT-20
❑ 83Don-553
❑ 83TidTidT-16
❑ 84TidTidT-8
❑ 85Fle-80
❑ 85MetColP-9
❑ 85MetTCM-10
❑ 85Top-546
❑ 85TopTif-546
❑ 86Top-18
❑ 86TopTif-18
❑ 91MetWIZ-130

Gaffke, Fabian
❑ 33WorCig(-25
❑ 78HalHalR-4
❑ 79DiaGre-235
❑ 94ConTSN-1306
❑ 94ConTSNB-1306

Gaffney, Bill
❑ 80SanJosMJitB-8

Gaffney, John H.
❑ 87OldJudN-186

Gafney, Jim
❑ 80BraTCM1-33

Gagliano, Manny
❑ 91OklStaC-9
❑ 92OklStaC-8
❑ 92SpoIndC-17
❑ 92SpoIndF-1302
❑ 94SanBerSC-3
❑ 94SanBerSF-2766

Gagliano, Phil
❑ 61UniOil-P7
❑ 62KahAtl-7
❑ 64Top-568
❑ 65CarTeal-11
❑ 65Top-503
❑ 66CarTeal-4
❑ 66Top-418
❑ 67Top-304
❑ 68Top-479
❑ 69Top-609
❑ 70OPC-143
❑ 70Top-143
❑ 71OPC-302
❑ 71Top-302
❑ 72MilBra-112
❑ 72OPC-472
❑ 72RedSoxTI-7
❑ 72Top-472
❑ 73OPC-69
❑ 73Top-69
❑ 74OPC-622
❑ 74Top-622

Gagliano, Ralph
❑ 65Top-501

Gagliano, Steve
❑ 98KanCouC-11
❑ 98KanCouCCP-11

Gagliardi, Joe
❑ 88CalLeaACLC-25
❑ 89CalLeaA-56
❑ 90CalLeaACLC-27
❑ 91CalLeLA-26

Gagne, Eric
❑ 96SavSanB-12
❑ 98VerBeaDM-11

Gagne, Greg
❑ 82OrlTwiT-8
❑ 83TolMudHT-14
❑ 84Don-39
❑ 85FleUpd-43
❑ 85TopTifT-36T
❑ 85TopTra-36T
❑ 85TwiPos-10
❑ 85TwiTeal-8
❑ 85TwiTeal-21
❑ 86Don-558
❑ 86Fle-395
❑ 86Top-162
❑ 86TopTif-162
❑ 86TwiTeal-22
❑ 87Don-395
❑ 87DonOpeD-223
❑ 87Fle-541
❑ 87FleGlo-541
❑ 87SpoTeaP-17
❑ 87Top-558
❑ 87TopSti-283
❑ 87TopTif-558
❑ 87TwiPos-9
❑ 87TwiTeal-4
❑ 88Don-441
❑ 88DonBasB-74
❑ 88Fle-11
❑ 88FleGlo-11
❑ 88OPC-343
❑ 88PanSti-141
❑ 88Sco-214
❑ 88ScoGlo-214
❑ 88StaLinTw-8
❑ 88Top-343
❑ 88TopBig-58
❑ 88TopTif-343
❑ 88TwiMasBD-11
❑ 88TwiSmoC-8
❑ 88Woo-32
❑ 89Bow-161
❑ 89BowTif-161
❑ 89Don-318
❑ 89DonBasB-158
❑ 89Fle-111
❑ 89FleGlo-111
❑ 89OPC-19
❑ 89PanSti-390
❑ 89Sco-159
❑ 89Top-19
❑ 89Top-429
❑ 89TopBig-186
❑ 89TopSti-288
❑ 89TopTif-19
❑ 89TopTif-429
❑ 89UppDec-166
❑ 90Bow-414
❑ 90BowTif-414
❑ 90Don-237
❑ 90DonBesA-135
❑ 90Fle-374
❑ 90FleCan-374
❑ 90Lea-302
❑ 90MLBBasB-99
❑ 90OPC-448
❑ 90PanSti-115
❑ 90PubIntS-327
❑ 90Sco-102
❑ 90Top-448
❑ 90TopBig-78
❑ 90TopSti-295
❑ 90TopTif-448
❑ 90UppDec-217
❑ 91Bow-338
❑ 91DodPho-16
❑ 91Don-284
❑ 91Fle-610
❑ 91Lea-426
❑ 91OPC-216
❑ 91PanFreS-303
❑ 91PanSti-245
❑ 91RedFolS-37
❑ 91Sco-211
❑ 91StaClu-277
❑ 91Stu-84
❑ 91Top-216
❑ 91TopDesS-216
❑ 91TopMic-216
❑ 91TopTif-216
❑ 91Ult-186
❑ 91UppDec-415
❑ 92Bow-660
❑ 92Don-204
❑ 92Fle-202
❑ 92Lea-146
❑ 92LeaBlaG-146
❑ 92OPC-663
❑ 92PanSti-118
❑ 92Pin-262
❑ 92RedFolS-38
❑ 92Sco-182
❑ 92ScoFacI-B1
❑ 92StaClu-376
❑ 92StaCluD-53
❑ 92Stu-203
❑ 92Top-663
❑ 92TopGol-663
❑ 92TopGolW-663
❑ 92TopMic-663
❑ 92TriPla-230
❑ 92Ult-395
❑ 92UppDec-168
❑ 93Bow-449
❑ 93CadDis-22
❑ 93Don-633
❑ 93DonSpiotG-SG13
❑ 93Fle-264
❑ 93FleFinE-217
❑ 93Lea-282
❑ 93OPC-101
❑ 93OPCPre-117
❑ 93PacSpa-487
❑ 93PanSti-105
❑ 93Pin-510
❑ 93RoyPol-7
❑ 93RoyStaC-16
❑ 93Sco-555
❑ 93Sel-178
❑ 93SelRoo-28T
❑ 93StaClu-631
❑ 93StaCluFDI-631
❑ 93StaCluMOP-631
❑ 93Stu-39
❑ 93Top-715
❑ 93TopGol-715
❑ 93TopInaM-715
❑ 93TopInaR-715
❑ 93TopMic-715
❑ 93Ult-559
❑ 93UppDec-708
❑ 93UppDecGold-708
❑ 94Bow-283
❑ 94ColC-406
❑ 94ColChoGS-406
❑ 94ColChoSS-406
❑ 94Don-595
❑ 94Fin-276
❑ 94FinRef-276
❑ 94Fla-57
❑ 94Fle-154
❑ 94FleExtB-87
❑ 94Lea-122
❑ 94LeaL-38
❑ 94OPC-141
❑ 94Pac-282
❑ 94PanSti-72
❑ 94Pin-354
❑ 94PinArtP-354
❑ 94PinMusC-354
❑ 94Sco-91
❑ 94ScoGolR-91
❑ 94Sel-270
❑ 94StaClu-159
❑ 94StaCluFDI-159
❑ 94StaCluGR-159
❑ 94StaCluMOP-159
❑ 94Stu-184
❑ 94Top-151
❑ 94TopGol-151
❑ 94TopSpa-151
❑ 94TriPla-233
❑ 94Ult-62
❑ 94UppDec-79
❑ 94UppDecED-79
❑ 95ColCho-457
❑ 95ColChoGS-457
❑ 95ColChoSS-457
❑ 95Don-195
❑ 95DonPreP-195
❑ 95DonTopotO-86
❑ 95Fin-174
❑ 95FinRef-174
❑ 95Fle-157
❑ 95Lea-144
❑ 95LeaLim-129
❑ 95Pac-201
❑ 95Pin-217
❑ 95PinArtP-217
❑ 95PinMusC-217
❑ 95Sco-47
❑ 95ScoGolR-47
❑ 95ScoPlaTS-47
❑ 95SP-162
❑ 95SPCha-162
❑ 95SPChaDC-162
❑ 95SPSil-162
❑ 95StaClu-294
❑ 95StaCluMOP-294
❑ 95StaCluSTWS-294
❑ 95StaCluVR-152
❑ 95StaCluVRMO-152
❑ 95Stu-110
❑ 95Top-494
❑ 95TopCyb-284
❑ 95TopD3-PB1
❑ 95Ult-56
❑ 95UltGolM-56
❑ 95UppDec-179
❑ 95UppDecED-179
❑ 95UppDecEDG-179
❑ 96ColCho-172
❑ 96ColCho-579
❑ 96ColChoGS-172
❑ 96ColChoGS-579
❑ 96ColChoSS-172
❑ 96ColChoSS-579
❑ 96DodFle-7
❑ 96DodMot-7
❑ 96DodPol-13
❑ 96Don-447
❑ 96DonPreP-447
❑ 96EmoXL-207
❑ 96Fin-B209
❑ 96FinRef-B209
❑ 96Fla-291
❑ 96Fle-434
❑ 96FleTif-434
❑ 96FleUpd-U143
❑ 96FleUpdTC-U143
❑ 96Pac-337
❑ 96Pin-362
❑ 96PinAfi-20
❑ 96PinAfiAP-20
❑ 96PinAfiFPP-20
❑ 96PinFoil-362
❑ 96Sco-159
❑ 96ScoDugC-A93
❑ 96ScoDugCAP-A93
❑ 96Sel-123
❑ 96SelArtP-123
❑ 96Top-56
❑ 96Ult-496
❑ 96UltGolM-496
❑ 96UppDec-97
❑ 97Cir-40
❑ 97CirRav-40
❑ 97ColCho-366
❑ 97ColChoT-LA9
❑ 97DodMot-7
❑ 97DodPol-8
❑ 97DodSco-10
❑ 97DodScoPl-10
❑ 97DodScoPr-10
❑ 97DonTea-119
❑ 97DonTeaSPE-119
❑ 97Fin-48
❑ 97FinRef-48
❑ 97Fle-361
❑ 97FleTif-361
❑ 97PacPriGotD-GD158
❑ 97Sco-220
❑ 97ScoArtPWB-220
❑ 97ScoPreS-220
❑ 97ScoShoS-220
❑ 97ScoShoSAP-220
❑ 97StaClu-311
❑ 97StaCluMOP-311
❑ 97Top-236
❑ 97Ult-215
❑ 97UltGolME-215
❑ 97UltPlaME-215
❑ 97UppDec-396
❑ 98ColCho-144
❑ 98DodSco-4
❑ 98DodScoP-4
❑ 98Pac-328
❑ 98PacPlaB-328
❑ 98PacRedT-328
❑ 98PacSil-328
❑ 98Sco-72
❑ 98Top-73
❑ 98TopChr-73
❑ 98TopChrR-73
❑ 98TopDevR-73
❑ 98TopDia-73
❑ 98TopMiniC-73
❑ 98UppDec-117

Gagnon, Clint
❑ 93IdaFalBF-4025
❑ 93IdaFalBSP-22

Gagus, Charles
❑ 88SFHesCreN32-10

Gahbrielson, Rick
❑ 86BakDodP-9

Gaiko, Rob
❑ 92OklStaC-9
❑ 95BatCliTI-13

Gaillard, Eddy
❑ 93NiaFalRF-3378
❑ 94LakTigC-8
❑ 94LakTigF-3029
❑ 95Bes-21
❑ 96JacSunB-13
❑ 97TolMudHB-13
❑ 98DurBulTI-10

Gainer, Chris
❑ 93DavLipB-9
❑ 94DavLipB-11
❑ 95DavLipB-13

Gainer, Delos C.
❑ 09SpoNewSM-75
❑ 11PloCanE-29
❑ 12T207-64
❑ 14B18B-17A
❑ 14B18B-17B
❑ 15SpoNewM-64
❑ 16BF2FP-3
❑ 16SpoNewM-63
❑ 17ColE13-53
❑ 22WilPatV-3

Gainer, Jay
❑ 90SpoIndSP-12
❑ 91CalLeLA-7
❑ 91Cla/Bes-230
❑ 91HigDesMC-19
❑ 91HigDesMP-2402
❑ 92ClaFS7-312
❑ 92ProFS7-336
❑ 92SkyAA F-279
❑ 92WicWraF-3661
❑ 92WicWraS-630
❑ 93Bow-444
❑ 93ColSprSSF-3093
❑ 93ExcFS7-109
❑ 93FleFinE-29
❑ 93TopTra-10T
❑ 94ColSprSSF-741
❑ 96ColSprSSTI-14
❑ 97ColSprSATTI-23

Gainer, Keith
❑ 79NewCoPT-18

Gaines, A. Joe
❑ 62RedEnq-9
❑ 62Top-414
❑ 63BalOriP-11
❑ 63Top-319
❑ 64BalOriP-14
❑ 64Top-364
❑ 64TopVen-364
❑ 65Top-594
❑ 66OPC-122
❑ 66Top-122
❑ 66TopVen-122
❑ 67AstTeal2-11
❑ 67VanMouSO-11
❑ 80Red196T-19
❑ 91OriCro-148

Gaines, Jerry
❑ 76AshTouT-14
❑ 77AshTouT-6

Gainey, Bryon
❑ 94SigRooDP-54
❑ 94SigRooDPS-54
❑ 96Bow-154
❑ 96BowFoi-154
❑ 97St.LucM-7
❑ 98St.LucMM-13

Gainey, Ty
❑ 82DayBeaAT-13
❑ 83ColAstT-10
❑ 85TucTorC-69
❑ 86Don-31
❑ 86TucTorP-5
❑ 87Don-533
❑ 87Spo-118
❑ 87SpoTeaP-8
❑ 87TucTorP-23
❑ 88Don-578
❑ 88Fle-448
❑ 88FleGlo-448
❑ 89ColSprSSC-22
❑ 89ColSprSSP-258
❑ 90CMC-463
❑ 90ColSprSSC-11
❑ 90ColSprSSP-50
❑ 90ProAAAF-231

Gainous, Trey
❑ 87EugEmeP-2662
❑ 88AppFoxP-151

Gaither, Horace
❑ 90SarWhiSS-8
❑ 91SouBenWSC-2
❑ 91SouBenWSP-2862

Gajkowski, Steve
❑ 90BurIndP-3005
❑ 91ColIndC-13
❑ 91ColIndP-1480
❑ 91WatIndC-6
❑ 91WatIndP-3361
❑ 92UtiBluSC-22
❑ 93SarWhiSC-10
❑ 93SarWhiSF-1363
❑ 94BirBarC-9
❑ 94BirBarF-615
❑ 96NasSouB-14
❑ 97TacRai-13
❑ 98TacRaiQ-12

Gakeler, Dan
❑ 85GreHorT-20
❑ 86GreHorP-8
❑ 87NewBriRSP-19
❑ 88NewBriRSP-904
❑ 89JacExpB-24
❑ 89JacExpP-157
❑ 90CMC-56

❑ 90IndIndC-6
❑ 90IndIndP-294
❑ 90ProAAAF-577
❑ 90WesPalBES-9
❑ 91Bow-144
❑ 91LinDriAAA-584
❑ 91TolMudHLD-584
❑ 91TolMudHP-1924
❑ 92Fle-135
❑ 92OPC-621
❑ 92Sco-831
❑ 92StaClu-276
❑ 92Top-621
❑ 92TopDeb91-59
❑ 92TopGol-621
❑ 92TopGolW-621
❑ 92TopMic-621
❑ 94NewBriRSF-646
❑ 96LowSpiB-2
❑ 97MicBatC-2
❑ 98SavSanGM-2

Galan, Augie

❑ 33Zee-40
❑ 34BatR31-135
❑ 34DiaMatCSB-63
❑ 35DiaMatCS3T1-56
❑ 36CubTeal-9
❑ 36DiaMatCS3T2-10
❑ 36ExhFou-3
❑ 36GouWidPPR-A36
❑ 36GouWidPPR-C12
❑ 36R31PasP-31
❑ 36R31PasP-45
❑ 36SandSW-22
❑ 36WorWidGV-106
❑ 37ExhFou-3
❑ 38ExhFou-3
❑ 39CubTeal-6
❑ 41CubTeal-5
❑ 41DouPlaR-101
❑ 42DodTeal-8
❑ 43DodTeal-10
❑ 46DodTeal-7
❑ 46SpoExcW-4-9
❑ 47Exh-79
❑ 48Bow-39
❑ 49Bow-230
❑ 49EurSta-103
❑ 49GiaTeal-6
❑ 50RemBre-6
❑ 53MotCoo-7
❑ 54Top-233
❑ 70SpoCarfCOP-28
❑ 73Dod194T-10
❑ 76TayBow4-58
❑ 78DodTCM4-30
❑ 83TCMPla1944-42
❑ 84CubBriPC-2C
❑ 89DodSmoG-48
❑ 90DodTar-264
❑ 91DodRinP2-9
❑ 94TopArc1-233
❑ 94TopArc1G-233
❑ 95ConTSN-1416

Galante, Joe

❑ 79BufBisT-4

Galante, Matt

❑ 75BurBeeT-7
❑ 76BurBeeT-13
❑ 77HolMilT-11
❑ 80ColAstT-10
❑ 83TucTorT-23
❑ 84TucTorC-50
❑ 85AstMot-27
❑ 86AstPol-26
❑ 87AstMot-27
❑ 87AstPol-26
❑ 88AstMot-27
❑ 89AstLenH-14
❑ 89AstMot-27
❑ 89AstSmo-15
❑ 90AstMot-27
❑ 91AstMot-28
❑ 92AstMot-27
❑ 93AstMot-28
❑ 94AstMot-27
❑ 95AstMot-28
❑ 96AstMot-28

Galarraga, Andres

❑ 80VenLeaS-107
❑ 85IndIndTI-3
❑ 86Don-33
❑ 86Don-33B
❑ 86DonRoo-7
❑ 86ExpPos-4
❑ 86ExpProPa-10
❑ 86Fle-647
❑ 86FleUpd-44
❑ 86Lea-27
❑ 86SpoRoo-27
❑ 86TopTra-40T
❑ 86TopTraT-40T
❑ 87ClaGam-71
❑ 87Don-303
❑ 87DonOpeD-90
❑ 87ExpPos-8
❑ 87Fle-319
❑ 87FleBasA-18
❑ 87FleGlo-319
❑ 87FleMin-41
❑ 87GenMilB-4C
❑ 87Lea-221
❑ 87OPC-272
❑ 87SpoTeaP-20
❑ 87Top-272
❑ 87TopSti-84
❑ 87TopTif-272
❑ 88Don-282
❑ 88DonBasB-90
❑ 88ExpPos-10
❑ 88Fle-184
❑ 88FleGlo-184
❑ 88FleLeaL-14
❑ 88FleMin-88
❑ 88FleSlu-14
❑ 88FleStiC-96
❑ 88FleTeaL-9
❑ 88FleWaxBC-C3
❑ 88Lea-121
❑ 88MSAHosD-8
❑ 88OPC-25
❑ 88PanSti-323
❑ 88Sco-19
❑ 88ScoGlo-19
❑ 88ScoYouS2-8
❑ 88Spo-182
❑ 88StaLinE-6
❑ 88Top-25
❑ 88TopBig-55
❑ 88TopGloS-58
❑ 88TopMinL-56
❑ 88TopSti-79
❑ 88TopStiB-2
❑ 88TopTif-25
❑ 89Bow-365
❑ 89BowTif-365
❑ 89CadEllD-22
❑ 89ClaLigB-46
❑ 89Don-14
❑ 89Don-130
❑ 89DonAll-45
❑ 89DonBasB-12
❑ 89DonBonM-BC16
❑ 89DonSupD-14
❑ 89ExpPos-8
❑ 89Fle-376
❑ 89Fle-638
❑ 89FleBasA-13
❑ 89FleBasM-12
❑ 89FleExcS-13
❑ 89FleForTR-3
❑ 89FleGlo-376
❑ 89FleGlo-638
❑ 89FleHeroB-16
❑ 89FleLeaL-14
❑ 89FleSup-15
❑ 89FleWaxBC-C8
❑ 89KayB-12
❑ 89OPC-93
❑ 89PanSti-119
❑ 89PanSti-224
❑ 89RedFolSB-47
❑ 89Sco-144
❑ 89ScoHot1S-74
❑ 89Scomast-33
❑ 89Spo-139
❑ 89SpollIFKI-63
❑ 89Top-386
❑ 89Top-590
❑ 89TopBasT-122
❑ 89TopBig-173
❑ 89TopCoi-13
❑ 89TopGloS-44
❑ 89TopHilTM-13
❑ 89TopMinL-22
❑ 89TopSti-76
❑ 89TopStiB-36
❑ 89TopTif-386
❑ 89TopTif-590
❑ 89TopUKM-28
❑ 89TVSpoM-14
❑ 89UppDec-115
❑ 89UppDec-677
❑ 89UppDecS-3
❑ 90Bow-113
❑ 90BowTif-113
❑ 90ClaBlu-115
❑ 90Don-97
❑ 90DonBesN-67
❑ 90ExpPos-10
❑ 90Fle-345
❑ 90FleCan-345
❑ 90Hot50PS-15
❑ 90Lea-450
❑ 90M.Vpin-59
❑ 90MSAHolD-4
❑ 90OPC-720
❑ 90PanSti-284
❑ 90PublntS-173
❑ 90PublntS-611
❑ 90RedFolSB-35
❑ 90Sco-25
❑ 90Sco100S-14
❑ 90Spo-148
❑ 90Top-720
❑ 90TopBig-108
❑ 90TopHilHM-31
❑ 90TopSti-75
❑ 90TopTif-720
❑ 90TopTVA-62
❑ 90UppDec-356
❑ 91Bow-446
❑ 91ClaGam-75
❑ 91Don-68
❑ 91DonGraS-9
❑ 91ExpPos-7
❑ 91Fle-232
❑ 91Lea-110
❑ 91OPC-610
❑ 91OPCPre-48
❑ 91PanCanT1-100
❑ 91PanFreS-139
❑ 91PosCan-3
❑ 91Sco-443
❑ 91StaClu-69
❑ 91Stu-197
❑ 91Top-610
❑ 91TopDesS-610
❑ 91TopMic-610
❑ 91TopTif-610
❑ 91Ult-203
❑ 91UppDec-456
❑ 92Bow-320
❑ 92CarPol-4
❑ 92Don-355
❑ 92Fle-480
❑ 92Lea-449
❑ 92LeaBlaG-449
❑ 92Mr.TurS-10
❑ 92OPC-240
❑ 92OPCPre-191
❑ 92PanSti-202
❑ 92Pin-381
❑ 92Sco-35
❑ 92ScoProP-9
❑ 92ScoRoo-60T
❑ 92SpollIFK1-274
❑ 92SpollIFK1-598
❑ 92StaClu-652
❑ 92StaCluNC-652
❑ 92Top-240
❑ 92TopGol-240
❑ 92TopGolW-240
❑ 92TopMic-240
❑ 92TopTra-36T
❑ 92TopTraG-36T
❑ 92UppDec-474
❑ 92UppDec-758
❑ 93Bow-204
❑ 93DiaMar-36
❑ 93Don-764
❑ 93ExpDonM-4
❑ 93Fin-130
❑ 93FinRef-130
❑ 93Fla-39
❑ 93FlaPro-3
❑ 93Fle-409
❑ 93FleFinE-30
❑ 93FunPac-173
❑ 93FunPac-176
❑ 93Hos-18
❑ 93Lea-322
❑ 93LinVenB-276
❑ 93LinVenB-280
❑ 93LinVenB-344
❑ 93MetBak-27
❑ 93OPCPre-58
❑ 93PacBeiA-22
❑ 93PacJugC-26
❑ 93PacSpa-427
❑ 93Pin-434
❑ 93PinExpOD-3
❑ 93RocStaC-11
❑ 93RocUSPC-1D
❑ 93RocUSPC-2S
❑ 93Sco-649
❑ 93SelRoo-102T
❑ 93SP-220
❑ 93StaClu-454
❑ 93StaCluFDI-454
❑ 93StaCluMOP-454
❑ 93Stu-163
❑ 93StuSupoC-9
❑ 93Top-173
❑ 93TopFulS-20
❑ 93TopGol-173
❑ 93ToplnaM-173
❑ 93ToplnaR-173
❑ 93TopMic-173
❑ 93TopTra-31T
❑ 93Ult-347
❑ 93UppDec-478
❑ 93UppDec-593
❑ 93UppDecGold-478
❑ 93UppDecGold-593
❑ 94Bow-526
❑ 94BowBes-R43
❑ 94BowBesR-R43
❑ 94ColC-312
❑ 94ColC-350
❑ 94ColC-360
❑ 94ColChoGS-312
❑ 94ColChoGS-350
❑ 94ColChoGS-360
❑ 94ColChoSS-312
❑ 94ColChoSS-350
❑ 94ColChoSS-360
❑ 94ColChoT-5
❑ 94DenHol-11
❑ 94Don-346
❑ 94DonDiaK-DK7
❑ 94DonDiaKJ-DK7
❑ 94DonEli-48
❑ 94DonLonBL-3
❑ 94DonMVP-4
❑ 94DonSpeE-346
❑ 94Fin-35
❑ 94FinPre-35P
❑ 94FinRef-35
❑ 94Fla-373
❑ 94Fle-440
❑ 94FleAllS-35
❑ 94FleExtB-244
❑ 94FleLeaL-7
❑ 94FleTeaL-18
❑ 94FUnPac-14
❑ 94KinDis-16
❑ 94Kra-21
❑ 94Lea-156
❑ 94LeaCleC-2
❑ 94LeaGolS-7
❑ 94LeaL-102
❑ 94LeaMVPC-N5
❑ 94LeaMVPCG-N5
❑ 94OPC-69
❑ 94OscMayR-21
❑ 94Pac-195
❑ 94PacAll-3
❑ 94PacSilP-20
❑ 94PacSilPC-20
❑ 94PanSti-11
❑ 94PanSti-174
❑ 94Pin-446
❑ 94PinArtP-446
❑ 94PinMusC-446
❑ 94PinRunC-RC30
❑ 94Pos-23
❑ 94ProMag-43
❑ 94RedFolMI-12
❑ 94RocPol-8
❑ 94RocPol-9
❑ 94Sco-8
❑ 94ScoGolR-8
❑ 94ScoGolS-11
❑ 94ScoSam-8
❑ 94ScoSam-8GR
❑ 94Sel-63
❑ 94SP-166
❑ 94SPDieC-166
❑ 94SPHol-10
❑ 94SPHolDC-10
❑ 94Spo-55
❑ 94SpoMov-MM6
❑ 94StaClu-454
❑ 94StaCluFDI-454
❑ 94StaCluGR-454
❑ 94StaCluMO-15
❑ 94StaCluMOP-454
❑ 94StaCluT-91
❑ 94StaCluTF-4
❑ 94StaCluTFDI-91
❑ 94Stu-177
❑ 94StuEdiC-4
❑ 94TomPiz-5
❑ 94Top-525
❑ 94TopBlaG-30
❑ 94TopGol-525
❑ 94TopSpa-525
❑ 94TopSupS-15
❑ 94TriPla-223
❑ 94Ult-480
❑ 94UltHitM-4
❑ 94UltLeaL-6
❑ 94UltOnBL-4
❑ 94UppDec-270
❑ 94UppDec-315
❑ 94UppDecAJ-39
❑ 94UppDecAJG-39
❑ 94UppDecDC-W2
❑ 94UppDecED-270
❑ 94UppDecED-315
❑ 94USPlaCA-1D
❑ 94VenLinU-41
❑ 95Baz-83
❑ 95Bow-355
❑ 95BowBes-R71
❑ 95BowBesR-R71
❑ 95ClaPhoC-23
❑ 95ColCho-440
❑ 95ColChoGS-440
❑ 95ColChoSE-205
❑ 95ColChoSEGS-205
❑ 95ColChoSESS-205
❑ 95ColChoSS-440
❑ 95DenHol-9
❑ 95Don-342
❑ 95DonBomS-5
❑ 95DonPreP-342
❑ 95DonTopotO-227
❑ 95Emo-125
❑ 95Fin-69
❑ 95FinRef-69
❑ 95Fla-130
❑ 95FlaInfP-4
❑ 95Fle-518
❑ 95KinDis-8
❑ 95Kra-21
❑ 95Lea-276
❑ 95LeaGreG-5
❑ 95LeaLim-141
❑ 95LinVen-14
❑ 95LinVen-274
❑ 95LinVen-275
❑ 95Pac-136
❑ 95PacGolCDC-9
❑ 95PacGolP-35
❑ 95PacLatD-13
❑ 95PacPri-45
❑ 95PanSti-34
❑ 95Pin-240
❑ 95PinArtP-240
❑ 95PinMusC-240
❑ 95PinPer-PP5
❑ 95RedFol-17
❑ 95RocPol-6
❑ 95Sco-338
❑ 95ScoGolR-338
❑ 95ScoHaloG-HG62
❑ 95ScoPlaTS-338
❑ 95Sel-85
❑ 95SelArtP-85
❑ 95SelCer-20
❑ 95SelCerMG-20
❑ 95SP-48
❑ 95SPCha-40
❑ 95SPChaDC-40
❑ 95Spo-96
❑ 95SpoArtP-96
❑ 95SPSil-48
❑ 95SPSpeF-35
❑ 95StaClu-32
❑ 95StaClu-313
❑ 95StaClu-499
❑ 95StaCluCC-CC23
❑ 95StaCluFDI-32
❑ 95StaCluMO-18
❑ 95StaCluMOP-32
❑ 95StaCluMOP-313
❑ 95StaCluMOP-499
❑ 95StaCluMOP-CC23
❑ 95StaCluMOP-PZ6
❑ 95StaCluMOP-RL40
❑ 95StaCluPZ-PZ6
❑ 95StaCluRL-RL40
❑ 95StaCluSTWS-32
❑ 95StaCluSTWS-313
❑ 95StaCluSTWS-499
❑ 95Stu-42
❑ 95StuGolS-42
❑ 95Sum-42
❑ 95SumNthD-42
❑ 95TomPiz-23
❑ 95Top-446
❑ 95TopD3-14
❑ 95TopEmb-90
❑ 95TopEmbGI-90
❑ 95TopFinIns-9
❑ 95TopLeaL-LL6
❑ 95UC3-19
❑ 95UC3ArtP-19
❑ 95Ult-374
❑ 95UltGolM-374
❑ 95UltHomRK-10
❑ 95UltHomRKGM-10
❑ 95UppDec-410
❑ 95UppDecED-410
❑ 95UppDecEDG-410
❑ 95UppDecPAW-H29
❑ 95UppDecPAWE-H29
❑ 95UppDecPLL-R38
❑ 95UppDecPLLE-R38
❑ 95UppDecSE-105
❑ 95UppDecSEG-105
❑ 95USPlaCMLA-6C
❑ 96-97LinVen-149
❑ 96Baz-89
❑ 96Bow-12
❑ 96BowBes-36
❑ 96BowBesAR-36
❑ 96BowBesR-36
❑ 96BowFoi-12
❑ 96Cir-123
❑ 96CirBos-34
❑ 96CirRav-123
❑ 96ColCho-131
❑ 96ColCho-341
❑ 96ColCho-753
❑ 96ColCho-758
❑ 96ColChoGS-131
❑ 96ColChoGS-341
❑ 96ColChoGS-753
❑ 96ColChoGS-758
❑ 96ColChoSS-131
❑ 96ColChoSS-341
❑ 96ColChoSS-753
❑ 96ColChoSS-758
❑ 96Don-332
❑ 96DonPreP-332
❑ 96EmoXL-175
❑ 96Fin-B139
❑ 96Fin-B254
❑ 96Fin-S345
❑ 96FinRef-B139
❑ 96FinRef-B254
❑ 96FinRef-S345
❑ 96Fla-246
❑ 96Fle-363
❑ 96FleTif-363
❑ 96FleUpd-U220
❑ 96FleUpdTC-U220
❑ 96Kin-13
❑ 96Lea-135
❑ 96LeaLim-18
❑ 96LeaLimG-18
❑ 96LeaPre-29
❑ 96LeaPreP-29
❑ 96LeaPrePB-135
❑ 96LeaPrePG-135
❑ 96LeaPrePS-135
❑ 96LeaPreSG-64
❑ 96LeaPreSte-64
❑ 96LeaSig-18
❑ 96LeaSigPPG-18
❑ 96LeaSigPPP-18
❑ 96MetUni-156
❑ 96MetUniP-156
❑ 96Pac-64
❑ 96PacEstL-EL11
❑ 96PacGolCD-DC11
❑ 96PacHom-HP8
❑ 96PacPri-P21
❑ 96PacPriG-P21
❑ 96PanSti-84
❑ 96Pin-93
❑ 96Pin-153
❑ 96PinAfi-14

❑ 96PinAfiAP-14
❑ 96PinAfiFPP-14
❑ 96PinArtP-35
❑ 96PinArtP-80
❑ 96PinSta-35
❑ 96PinSta-80
❑ 96ProMagDM-13
❑ 96ProSta-113
❑ 96RocFle-5
❑ 96RocPol-8
❑ 96Sco-329
❑ 96ScoDugC-B54
❑ 96ScoDugCAP-B54
❑ 96Sel-3
❑ 96SelArtP-3
❑ 96SelCer-14
❑ 96SelCerAP-14
❑ 96SelCerCB-14
❑ 96SelCerCR-14
❑ 96SelCerMB-14
❑ 96SelCerMG-14
❑ 96SelCerMR-14
❑ 96SelTeaN-4
❑ 96SP-77
❑ 96Spo-66
❑ 96SpoArtP-66
❑ 96SPx-25
❑ 96SPxGol-25
❑ 96StaClu-150
❑ 96StaCluEPB-150
❑ 96StaCluEPG-150
❑ 96StaCluEPS-150
❑ 96StaCluEWB-EW3
❑ 96StaCluEWG-EW3
❑ 96StaCluEWS-EW3
❑ 96StaCluMeg-MH7
❑ 96StaCluMO-13
❑ 96StaCluMOP-150
❑ 96StaCluMOP-MH7
❑ 96StaCluMOP-PP12
❑ 96StaCluPP-PP12
❑ 96Stu-124
❑ 96StuPrePB-124
❑ 96StuPrePG-124
❑ 96StuPrePS-124
❑ 96Sum-115
❑ 96SumAbo&B-115
❑ 96SumArtP-115
❑ 96SumFoi-115
❑ 96Top-249
❑ 96TopChr-96
❑ 96TopChrR-96
❑ 96TopClaC-CC8
❑ 96TopGal-44
❑ 96TopGalE-18
❑ 96TopGalPPI-44
❑ 96TopLas-106
❑ 96TopLasSS-3
❑ 96TopPro-NL12
❑ 96Ult-189
❑ 96UltGolM-189
❑ 96UltThu-9
❑ 96UltThuGM-9
❑ 96UppDec-65
❑ 96UppDecPRE-R45
❑ 96UppDecPreR-R45
❑ 96Zen-87
❑ 96ZenArtP-87
❑ 96ZenMoz-12
❑ 97Bow-59
❑ 97BowBes-88
❑ 97BowBesAR-88
❑ 97BowBesR-88
❑ 97BowChr-45
❑ 97BowChrI-45
❑ 97BowChrIR-45
❑ 97BowChrR-45
❑ 97BowInt-59
❑ 97Cir-307
❑ 97CirRav-307
❑ 97ColCho-57
❑ 97ColCho-58
❑ 97ColCho-320
❑ 97ColChoAC-28
❑ 97ColChoCtG-16A
❑ 97ColChoCtG-16B
❑ 97ColChoCtG-16C
❑ 97ColChoCtGE-CG16
❑ 97ColChoCtGIW-CG16
❑ 97ColChoNF-NF12
❑ 97ColChoPP-PP6
❑ 97ColChoPPG-PP6
❑ 97ColChoPPJ-PP6
❑ 97ColChoS-14
❑ 97ColChoSR-8
❑ 97ColChoT-CR10
❑ 97CraJac-13
❑ 97Don-4
❑ 97Don-439
❑ 97DonEli-98
❑ 97DonEliGS-98
❑ 97DonGolPP-4
❑ 97DonGolPP-439
❑ 97DonLim-64
❑ 97DonLim-140
❑ 97DonLimE-64
❑ 97DonLimE-140
❑ 97DonLimENG-64
❑ 97DonLimFotG-32
❑ 97DonPre-17
❑ 97DonPreCttC-17
❑ 97DonSig-10
❑ 97DonSigA-35
❑ 97DonSigAC-42
❑ 97DonSigAM-42
❑ 97DonSigPPP-10
❑ 97DonSilPP-4
❑ 97DonSilPP-439
❑ 97DonTea-91
❑ 97DonTeaSPE-91
❑ 97E-X2-69
❑ 97E-X2Cred-69
❑ 97E-X2EssCre-69
❑ 97Fin-170
❑ 97Fin-223
❑ 97Fin-321
❑ 97FinEmb-170
❑ 97FinEmb-321
❑ 97FinEmbR-170
❑ 97FinEmbR-321
❑ 97FinRef-170
❑ 97FinRef-223
❑ 97FinRef-321
❑ 97FlaShoLC-114
❑ 97FlaShoLeg0-114
❑ 97FlaShoLeg1-114
❑ 97FlaShoM-A114
❑ 97FlaShoM-B114
❑ 97FlaShoM-C114
❑ 97FlaShoR0-114
❑ 97FlaShoR1-114
❑ 97FlaShoR2-114
❑ 97Fle-310
❑ 97Fle-729
❑ 97FleLumC-7
❑ 97FleTif-310
❑ 97FleTif-729
❑ 97FleZon-5
❑ 97Lea-241
❑ 97LeaFraM-241
❑ 97LeaFraMDC-241
❑ 97MetUni-74
❑ 97MetUniBF-4
❑ 97NewPin-18
❑ 97NewPin-181
❑ 97NewPinAP-18
❑ 97NewPinAP-181
❑ 97NewPinMC-18
❑ 97NewPinMC-181
❑ 97NewPinPP-18
❑ 97NewPinPP-181
❑ 97Pac-282
❑ 97PacCar-26
❑ 97PacCarM-26
❑ 97PacGolCD-26
❑ 97PacLatotML-27
❑ 97PacLigB-282
❑ 97PacPri-98
❑ 97PacPriGA-GA22
❑ 97PacPriGotD-GD133
❑ 97PacPriLB-98
❑ 97PacPriP-98
❑ 97PacPriSL-SL9B
❑ 97PacSil-282
❑ 97PacTriCD-16
❑ 97Pin-187
❑ 97PinArtP-PP187
❑ 97PinCer-48
❑ 97PinCerMBla-48
❑ 97PinCerMBlu-48
❑ 97PinCerMG-48
❑ 97PinCerMR-48
❑ 97PinCerR-48
❑ 97PinIns-30
❑ 97PinInsCE-30
❑ 97PinInsDE-30
❑ 97PinInsFS-14
❑ 97PinMusC-187
❑ 97PinPrePla-187
❑ 97PinTotCPB-48
❑ 97PinTotCPG-48
❑ 97PinTotCPR-48
❑ 97PinX-P-8
❑ 97PinX-PMoS-8
❑ 97PinX-PSfF-22
❑ 97PinX-PSfFU-22
❑ 97RocPol-6
❑ 97RocSco-6
❑ 97RocScoPl-6
❑ 97RocScoPr-6
❑ 97Sco-155
❑ 97ScoArtPWB-155
❑ 97ScoPreS-155
❑ 97ScoShoS-155
❑ 97ScoShoSAP-155
❑ 97Sel-56
❑ 97SelArtP-56
❑ 97SelCom-56
❑ 97SelRegG-56
❑ 97SP-65
❑ 97SPMarM-MM2
❑ 97SpoIll-42
❑ 97SpoIllEE-42
❑ 97SpoIllGS-13
❑ 97SPSpxF-1
❑ 97SPSPxFA-1
❑ 97SPx-24
❑ 97SPxBro-24
❑ 97SPxGol-24
❑ 97SPxGraF-24
❑ 97SPxSil-24
❑ 97SPxSte-24
❑ 97StaClu-59
❑ 97StaClu-380
❑ 97StaCluFR-F4
❑ 97StaCluFW-F4
❑ 97StaCluMat-59
❑ 97StaCluMOP-59
❑ 97StaCluMOP-380
❑ 97StaCluMOP-FB4
❑ 97StaCluMOP-PG20
❑ 97StaCluMOP-PL7
❑ 97StaCluPG-PG20
❑ 97StaCluPL-PL7
❑ 97StrAll-21
❑ 97Stu-15
❑ 97StuPrePG-15
❑ 97StuPrePS-15
❑ 97Top-10
❑ 97TopAll-AS4
❑ 97TopChr-5
❑ 97TopChrAS-AS4
❑ 97TopChrDD-DD9
❑ 97TopChrDDR-DD9
❑ 97TopChrR-5
❑ 97TopChrSAR-AS4
❑ 97TopChrSB-10
❑ 97TopChrSBR-10
❑ 97TopChrSBR-11
❑ 97TopGal-3
❑ 97TopGalPG-PG13
❑ 97TopGalPPI-3
❑ 97TopHobM-HM20
❑ 97TopMemO5-16
❑ 97TopScr-4
❑ 97TopScrT-4
❑ 97TopSeaB-SB10
❑ 97TopSeaB-SB11
❑ 97TopSta-26
❑ 97TopStaAM-26
❑ 97TopTeaT-TT6
❑ 97UD3-5
❑ 97Ult-185
❑ 97UltDouT-13
❑ 97UltGolME-185
❑ 97UltPlaME-185
❑ 97UppDec-205
❑ 97UppDec-350
❑ 97UppDecAWJ-4
❑ 97UppDecAWJ-6
❑ 97UppDecHTH-HT8
❑ 97UppDecLDC-LD6
❑ 97UppDecP-15
❑ 97UppDecPE-15
❑ 97UppDecRP-RP8
❑ 98Bow-276
❑ 98BowBes-100
❑ 98BowBesAR-100
❑ 98BowBesR-100
❑ 98BowChr-276
❑ 98BowChrGA-276
❑ 98BowChrGAR-276
❑ 98BowChrI-276
❑ 98BowChrIR-276
❑ 98BowChrR-276
❑ 98BowGolA-276
❑ 98BowInt-276
❑ 98BowMinLM-MVP2
❑ 98CirThu-135
❑ 98CirThuRav-135
❑ 98CirThuSupRav-135
❑ 98CirThuTB-4
❑ 98ColCho-255
❑ 98ColCho-308
❑ 98ColChoRJ-SQ67
❑ 98ColChoSQ-SQ67
❑ 98CroRoy-10
❑ 98CroRoyDK-1
❑ 98CroRoyHRF-1
❑ 98Don-32
❑ 98Don-197
❑ 98DonCol-32
❑ 98DonColE-444
❑ 98DonColL-368
❑ 98DonColP-593
❑ 98DonColS-32
❑ 98DonCruG-66
❑ 98DonCruP-66
❑ 98DonCruR-66
❑ 98DonDom-24
❑ 98DonEli-44
❑ 98DonEliA-44
❑ 98DonEliS-44
❑ 98DonGolPP-32
❑ 98DonGolPP-197
❑ 98DonLonL-24
❑ 98DonPre-43
❑ 98DonPreSeat-43
❑ 98DonPreTW-18
❑ 98DonPriCD-32
❑ 98DonPriCE-444
❑ 98DonPriCL-368
❑ 98DonPriCP-593
❑ 98DonProLS-3
❑ 98DonSig-75
❑ 98DonSigAC-43
❑ 98DonSigAM-44
❑ 98DonSigP-75
❑ 98DonSilPP-32
❑ 98DonSilPP-197
❑ 98DonSonM9-19
❑ 98E-X2-31
❑ 98E-X2Cheap-11
❑ 98E-X2ECFut-31
❑ 98E-X2ECNow-31
❑ 98Fin-198
❑ 98FinMysF1-M32
❑ 98FinMysF1-M35
❑ 98FinMysF1-M38
❑ 98FinMysF1-M39
❑ 98FinMysFR-M32
❑ 98FinMysFR-M35
❑ 98FinMysFR-M38
❑ 98FinMysFR-M39
❑ 98FinNo--198
❑ 98FinNo-R-198
❑ 98FinPowZ-P9
❑ 98FinRef-198
❑ 98FinStaS-SS24
❑ 98FlaShoLeg0-90
❑ 98FlaShoLeg1-90
❑ 98FlaShoLeg2-90
❑ 98FlaShoLeg3-90
❑ 98FlaShoLegM-90
❑ 98FlaShoR0-90
❑ 98FlaShoR1-90
❑ 98FlaShoR2-90
❑ 98FlaShoR3-90
❑ 98Fle-14
❑ 98Fle-327
❑ 98Fle-352
❑ 98FleDecERT-5
❑ 98FleDecoE-5
❑ 98FleDiaS-5
❑ 98FlePowG-7
❑ 98FleVin'-20
❑ 98FleVin'-71
❑ 98FleVin'C-20
❑ 98FleVin'C-71
❑ 98Lea-169
❑ 98LeaCruG-66
❑ 98LeaCruP-66
❑ 98LeaCruR-66
❑ 98LeaFraDA-169
❑ 98LeaFraF-169
❑ 98LeaFraM-169
❑ 98LeaFraM-169
❑ 98LeaFraMDC-169
❑ 98LeaFraMDC-169
❑ 98LeaFraMZ2-169
❑ 98LeaRS-15
❑ 98LeaRS-173
❑ 98LeaRSGAHSamp-20
❑ 98LeaRSGreAH-20
❑ 98LeaRSLHolo-15
❑ 98LeaRSLHolo-173
❑ 98LeaRSLong-15
❑ 98LeaRSLong-173
❑ 98LeaRSTicMas-11
❑ 98LeaRSTicMasDC-11
❑ 98LeaRTrue-15
❑ 98LeaRTrue-173
❑ 98MetUni-139
❑ 98MetUniPMG-139
❑ 98Pac-283
❑ 98PacAur-102
❑ 98PacAurPF-32
❑ 98PacAurPFC-32
❑ 98PacAurPFPB-32
❑ 98PacAurPFR-32
❑ 98PacAurPFS-32
❑ 98PacGolCDC-13
❑ 98PacHomRH-10
❑ 98PacInv-92
❑ 98PacInvGems-144
❑ 98PacInvInt-4N
❑ 98PacInvMiT-5
❑ 98PacInvPBlue-92
❑ 98PacInvSilv-92
❑ 98PacInvTeam-9
❑ 98PacLatotML-13
❑ 98PacNes-5A
❑ 98PacOme-17
❑ 98PacOmeOnIns-22
❑ 98PacOmeR-17
❑ 98PacOnl-59
❑ 98PacOnlR-59
❑ 98PacOnlWC-59
❑ 98PacPar-127
❑ 98PacParC-127
❑ 98PacParG-127
❑ 98PacParHS-127
❑ 98PacParPB-127
❑ 98PacParR-127
❑ 98PacPlaB-283
❑ 98PacRedT-283
❑ 98PacSil-283
❑ 98PacTeaC-18
❑ 98Pin-25
❑ 98PinArtP-PP25
❑ 98PinIns-20
❑ 98PinInsCE-20
❑ 98PinInsDE-20
❑ 98PinMusC-PP25
❑ 98PinPer-44
❑ 98PinPerPP-44
❑ 98PinPerSftF-33
❑ 98PinPlu-39
❑ 98PinPluAP-PP20
❑ 98PinPluGAP-PP20
❑ 98PinPluMAP-PP20
❑ 98PinPluTP-11
❑ 98PinPluTPG-11
❑ 98PinPluTPM-11
❑ 98PinPreP-25
❑ 98PinSna-AB11
❑ 98PinSna-AB12
❑ 98Revo-10
❑ 98RevoShow-22
❑ 98RevoSS-10
❑ 98Sco-19
❑ 98ScoRT-214
❑ 98ScoRTSS-PP118
❑ 98ScoRTSSAP-PP118
❑ 98ScoRTSSAP1-PP118
❑ 98ScoSS-PP119
❑ 98ScoSSAP-PP119
❑ 98SkyDugA-148
❑ 98SkyDugAIA-148
❑ 98SkyDugAS-SH2
❑ 98SP Aut-50
❑ 98SpoIll-41
❑ 98SpoIllEE-41
❑ 98SpoIllFE-41
❑ 98SpoIllTaN-82
❑ 98SpoIllTaNEE-82
❑ 98SpoIllWSF-36
❑ 98SpoIllWSFEE-36
❑ 98SpoIllWSFFE-36
❑ 98SPxFin-227
❑ 98SPxFin-248
❑ 98SPxFin-332
❑ 98SPxFinHRH-HR7
❑ 98SPxFinR-227
❑ 98SPxFinR-248
❑ 98SPxFinR-332
❑ 98SPxFinS-227
❑ 98SPxFinS-248
❑ 98SPxFinS-332
❑ 98StaCluC-CS15
❑ 98StaCluC-CS17
❑ 98StaCluC-CS18
❑ 98StaCluFDI-388
❑ 98StaCluI-388
❑ 98StaCluOneK-388
❑ 98StaCluPP-388
❑ 98StaCluTIll-T7B
❑ 98StaCluTLme-T7B
❑ 98StaCluTLmo-T7B
❑ 98Stu-99
❑ 98StuGPP-99
❑ 98StuSony99-19
❑ 98StuSPP-99
❑ 98Top-274
❑ 98Top-295
❑ 98TopChr-274
❑ 98TopChr-295
❑ 98TopChrR-274
❑ 98TopChrR-295
❑ 98TopDevR-274
❑ 98TopDevR-295
❑ 98TopDia-274
❑ 98TopDia-295
❑ 98TopGal-14
❑ 98TopGalGP-14
❑ 98TopGalOPP-14
❑ 98TopGalPPI-14
❑ 98TopGalPPIA-14
❑ 98TopGolLabC1-4
❑ 98TopGolLabC1B-4
❑ 98TopGolLabC1One-4
❑ 98TopGolLabC1R-4
❑ 98TopGolLabC2-4
❑ 98TopGolLabC2B-4
❑ 98TopGolLabC2One-4
❑ 98TopGolLabC2R-4
❑ 98TopGolLabC3-4
❑ 98TopGolLabC3B-4
❑ 98TopGolLabC3One-4
❑ 98TopGolLabC3R-4
❑ 98TopMiniC-274
❑ 98TopMiniC-295
❑ 98TopMysF-ILM11
❑ 98TopMysFR-ILM11
❑ 98TopOpeD-122
❑ 98TopSta-16
❑ 98TopSta'S-11
❑ 98TopSta'SGH-11
❑ 98TopStaB-16
❑ 98TopStaG-16
❑ 98TopStaGR-16
❑ 98TopStaS-16
❑ 98TopStaSteG-11
❑ 98TopTek-85
❑ 98TopTekD-85
❑ 98UD3-52
❑ 98UD3-142
❑ 98UD3-232
❑ 98UD3DieCut-52
❑ 98UD3DieCut-142
❑ 98UD3DieCut-232
❑ 98Ult-57
❑ 98Ult-434
❑ 98UltGolM-57
❑ 98UltGolM-434
❑ 98UltMas-57
❑ 98UltMas-434
❑ 98UltPlaM-57
❑ 98UltPlaM-434
❑ 98UppDec-650
❑ 98UppDec10AP-23
❑ 98UppDec1APR-23
❑ 98UppDecAG-AG14
❑ 98UppDecAGDC-AG14
❑ 98UppDecCD-CD14
❑ 98UppDecNP-NP40
❑ 98UppDecR-6
❑ 98UppDecRBBop-BB21
❑ 98UppDecRGKoG-G15
❑ 98UppDecRTC-TC30
❑ 98UppDecTMT-2
❑ 98UppDecTMTG-2
❑ 98Zen-15
❑ 98Zen5 xx7-2
❑ 98Zen5x7GoldImp-2
❑ 98Zen5x7Imp-2
❑ 98ZenZ-G-15
❑ 98ZenZ-S-15
❑ 99199Fin-244
❑ 99AllMysFR-M2
❑ 99Bow-27
❑ 99BowBes-16
❑ 99BowBesAR-16
❑ 99BowBesR-16
❑ 99BowChr-27

❑ 99BowChrG-27
❑ 99BowChrGR-27
❑ 99BowChrI-27
❑ 99BowChrIR-27
❑ 99BowChrR-27
❑ 99BowGol-27
❑ 99BowInt-27
❑ 99BowPreProd-PP1
❑ 99E-X Cen-30
❑ 99E-X CenECFut-30
❑ 99E-X CenECNow-30
❑ 99FinGolRef-244
❑ 99FinLeaI-L7
❑ 99FinPeelHyp-8
❑ 99FinPeelSpark-8
❑ 99FinPeeSS-8
❑ 99FinProF-PF10
❑ 99FinProF-PF18
❑ 99FinProF-PF40
❑ 99FinRef-244
❑ 99FinSplS-SS7
❑ 99FinSplSDR-SS7
❑ 99FlaShoLeg1-79
❑ 99FlaShoLeg2-79
❑ 99FlaShoLeg3-79
❑ 99FlaShoLegM1-79
❑ 99FlaShoLegM2-79
❑ 99FlaShoLegM3-79
❑ 99FlaShoR1-79
❑ 99FlaShoR2-79
❑ 99FlaShoR3-79
❑ 99Fle-11
❑ 99FleBri-6
❑ 99FleBri2G-6
❑ 99FleBriBlu-6
❑ 99FleBriGol-6
❑ 99FleGolYar-5
❑ 99FleSta9-11
❑ 99FleVin'-11
❑ 99FleWarT-11
❑ 99MetUni-184
❑ 99MetUniGM-184
❑ 99MetUniPMG-184
❑ 99Pac-28
❑ 99Pac-28A
❑ 99PacAur-14
❑ 99PacAurOD-14
❑ 99PacCroC-21
❑ 99PacCroC-24
❑ 99PacCroCPB-21
❑ 99PacCroCTM-1
❑ 99PacPar-21
❑ 99PacParC-21
❑ 99PacParG-21
❑ 99PacParHoloGold-21
❑ 99PacParHS-21
❑ 99PacParOD-21
❑ 99PacParPB-21
❑ 99PacParRed-21
❑ 99PacPlaB-28
❑ 99PacPlaB-28A
❑ 99PacPri-10
❑ 99PacPriHB-10
❑ 99PacPriHG-10
❑ 99PacPriHM-10
❑ 99PacPriHP-10
❑ 99PacPriRed-10
❑ 99PacPriS-30
❑ 99PacPriS206-30
❑ 99PacPriS206R-30
❑ 99PacPriSP-30
❑ 99PacPriSV-30
❑ 99PacRed-28
❑ 99PacRed-28A
❑ 99PacTim-12
❑ 99SkyMolMOA-30
❑ 99SkyThu-194
❑ 99SkyThuRant-194
❑ 99SkyThuRave-194
❑ 99SP Aut-10
❑ 99SP AutEF-E3
❑ 99SP AutHRC-HR22
❑ 99SP AutR-R3
❑ 99SPAutHRCDC-HR22
❑ 99SpoIll-107
❑ 99SpoIllF4-10
❑ 99SpoIllF4E-10
❑ 99SPx-19
❑ 99SPxFinR-19
❑ 99SPxFinS-19
❑ 99SPxPowE-PE5
❑ 99StaClu-16
❑ 99StaCluFDI-16
❑ 99StaCluNC-NC14
❑ 99StaCluOoaK-16
❑ 99StaCluPP-16
❑ 99StaCluTI-T2C
❑ 99StaCluTI-T16B
❑ 99StaCluTL-T2C
❑ 99StaCluTL-T16B
❑ 99StaCluTL-T2C
❑ 99StaCluTL-T16B
❑ 99ThuSkySupR-194
❑ 99Top-2
❑ 99Top-450
❑ 99TopAll-AM10
❑ 99TopAllMF-M2
❑ 99TopAut-A5
❑ 99TopBlaLC1-2
❑ 99TopBlaLC2-2
❑ 99TopBlaLC3-2
❑ 99TopChr-2
❑ 99TopChr-450
❑ 99TopChrA-AE10
❑ 99TopChrAR-AE10
❑ 99TopChrLotD-LD13
❑ 99TopChrLotDR-LD13
❑ 99TopChrR-2
❑ 99TopChrR-450
❑ 99TopGal-26
❑ 99TopGalE-E20
❑ 99TopGalP-PP2
❑ 99TopGalPP-26
❑ 99TopGalPPI-26
❑ 99TopGolL-2
❑ 99TopGolLC1-2
❑ 99TopGolLC2-2
❑ 99TopGolLOtO-2
❑ 99TopLorotD-LD13
❑ 99TopMVPP-2
❑ 99TopMVPP-450
❑ 99TopOpeD-3
❑ 99TopPowB-PB2
❑ 99TopPowBR-PB2
❑ 99TopRedLC1-2
❑ 99TopRedLC2-2
❑ 99TopRedLC3-2
❑ 99TopSta-105
❑ 99TopSta'S-22
❑ 99TopSta'SG-22
❑ 99TopSta'SGDH-22
❑ 99TopStaFoil-105
❑ 99TopSupC-2
❑ 99TopSupCR-2
❑ 99TopTek-2A
❑ 99TopTek-2B
❑ 99TopTekG-2A
❑ 99TopTekG-2B
❑ 99UD Cho-54
❑ 99UD ChoP-54
❑ 99UD ChoPCR-54
❑ 99UD ChoYW-Y1
❑ 99UD Ion-8
❑ 99UD Ion-62
❑ 99UD IonR-8
❑ 99UD IonR-62
❑ 99Ult-48
❑ 99UltGolM-48
❑ 99UltMas-48
❑ 99UltPlaM-48
❑ 99UltRBIK-27
❑ 99UppDec-33
❑ 99UppDecBD-7
❑ 99UppDecBDD-7
❑ 99UppDecBDMN-M29
❑ 99UppDecBDMNE-M29
❑ 99UppDecBDQ-7
❑ 99UppDecBDT-7
❑ 99UppDecCf7-53
❑ 99UppDecCf7LL-L23
❑ 99UppDecCL-77
❑ 99UppDecCLCC-77
❑ 99UppDecCo7CE-53
❑ 99UppDecEL1-33
❑ 99UppDecEL2-33
❑ 99UppDecF-F5
❑ 99UppDecFD-F5
❑ 99UppDecFQ-F5
❑ 99UppDecFT-F5
❑ 99UppDecO-42
❑ 99UppDecOSO-42
❑ 99UppDecWY-W7
❑ 99UppDecWYD-W7
❑ 99UppDecWYHR-W7
❑ 99UppDecWYT-W7
❑ 99Vic-40

Galarza, Edgar
❑ 87WytCubP-14

Galarza, Joel
❑ 96SanJosGB-12

Galasso, Bob
❑ 76VenLeaS-164
❑ 78SpoIndC-21
❑ 80Top-711
❑ 80VanCanT-20
❑ 81SpoIndT-9
❑ 82Top-598
❑ 84RicBraT-16
❑ 89PacSenL-200
❑ 89TopSenL-100
❑ 90EliSenL-56
❑ 91PacSenL-114
❑ 94BreMilB-28

Galatzer, Milt
❑ 33MrsShePP-4
❑ 34DiaMatCSB-64
❑ 35DiaMatCS3T1-57
❑ 36NatChiFPR-28
❑ 77CinRedT-17

Galbato, Chan
❑ 86JamExpP-9

Galbraith, Moe
❑ 89TenTecGE-9

Galbreath, John W.
❑ 82OhiHaloF-56

Gale, Bill
❑ 91St.PetCP-2287

Gale, Rich
❑ 76WatRoyT-8
❑ 77JacSunT-5
❑ 78Roy-5
❑ 78SSP270-235
❑ 79OPC-149
❑ 79Top-298
❑ 80Top-433
❑ 81Don-462
❑ 81Fle-40
❑ 81OPC-363
❑ 81RoyPol-3
❑ 81RoyProPS-5
❑ 81Top-544
❑ 82Don-138
❑ 82Fle-408
❑ 82Gia25tATI-10
❑ 82OPC-67
❑ 82Top-67
❑ 82TopTra-38T
❑ 83Don-172
❑ 83Fle-260
❑ 83OPC-243
❑ 83RedYea-32
❑ 83Top-719
❑ 83TopTra-35T
❑ 84Don-140
❑ 84Fle-469
❑ 84FleUpd-41
❑ 84Nes792-142
❑ 84PawRedST-23
❑ 84Top-142
❑ 84TopTif-142
❑ 84TopTra-40T
❑ 84TopTraT-40T
❑ 85Top-606
❑ 85TopTif-606
❑ 89EasLeaDDP-DD43
❑ 89NewBriRSP-602
❑ 89NewBriRSS-24
❑ 89PacSenL-95
❑ 90NewBriRSB-26
❑ 90NewBriRSP-1335
❑ 90NewBriRSS-26
❑ 91LinDriAAA-375
❑ 91PacSenL-19
❑ 91PawRedSDD-5
❑ 91PawRedSLD-375
❑ 91PawRedSP-55
❑ 92RedSoxDD-12
❑ 93RedSoxP-15
❑ 95PorSeaDTI-6

Galehouse, Dennis
❑ 33WorCig(-26
❑ 34DiaMatCSB-65
❑ 35DiaMatCS3T1-58
❑ 40PlaBal-198
❑ 41BroW75-11
❑ 46SeaSLP-21
❑ 47TipTop-63
❑ 48RedSoxTI-7
❑ 61Fle-107
❑ 79DiaGre-190
❑ 83TCMPla1942-9
❑ 96Bro194F-16

Galinas, Mark
❑ 79BufBisT-10

Galindez, Luis
❑ 89BlaYNPRWL-114
❑ 89WatDiaP-1789
❑ 89WatDiaS-8
❑ 90Bes-171
❑ 90MidLeaASGS-32
❑ 90WatDiaB-5
❑ 90WatDiaP-2372
❑ 91Cla/Bes-179
❑ 91HigDesMC-4
❑ 91HigDesMP-2387
❑ 92ClaFS7-129
❑ 92HigDesMC-16
❑ 93RanCucQC-11
❑ 93RanCucQF-824
❑ 94RanCucQC-12
❑ 94RanCucQF-1629

Galindo, Luis
❑ 88LakTigS-5
❑ 89LakTigS-6
❑ 90LonTigP-1277
❑ 91LinDriAA-384
❑ 91LonTigLD-384
❑ 91LonTigP-1884
❑ 95LinVen-148

Gallagher, Alan
❑ 71OPC-224
❑ 71Top-224
❑ 72GiaTeal-6
❑ 72Top-693
❑ 72Top-694
❑ 78GreBraT-10
❑ 81DurBulT-14
❑ 82ChaLooT-23
❑ 83BufBisT-24
❑ 98MadBlaW-21

Gallagher, Allen
❑ 92BurIndC-17
❑ 92BurIndF-1648

Gallagher, Bob
❑ 74OPC-21
❑ 74Top-21
❑ 75OPC-406
❑ 75Top-406
❑ 75TopMin-406
❑ 76PheGiaCr-18
❑ 76PhoGiaCa-13
❑ 76PhoGiaCC-9
❑ 76PhoGiaVNB-7
❑ 76SSP-608
❑ 91MetWIZ-131

Gallagher, Dave
❑ 80BatTroT-25
❑ 81WatIndT-26
❑ 82ChaLooT-17
❑ 82WatIndF-11
❑ 83BufBisT-19
❑ 84MaiGuiT-7
❑ 85IntLeaAT-35
❑ 85MaiGuiT-27
❑ 86MaiGuiP-9
❑ 87CalCanP-2330
❑ 88DonRoo-7
❑ 88FleUpd-16
❑ 88FleUpdG-16
❑ 88ScoRoo-89T
❑ 88ScoRooG-89T
❑ 88VanCanC-24
❑ 88VanCanP-771
❑ 89Baz-8
❑ 89Bow-71
❑ 89BowTif-71
❑ 89ChaLooLITI-10
❑ 89Don-384
❑ 89DonBasB-67
❑ 89Fle-496
❑ 89FleGlo-496
❑ 89K-M-7
❑ 89PanSti-299
❑ 89Sco-455
❑ 89ScoHot1R-96
❑ 89ScoYouSI-4
❑ 89Spo-88
❑ 89Top-156
❑ 89TopBig-310
❑ 89TopGloS-49
❑ 89TopRoo-8
❑ 89TopSti-295
❑ 89TopSti-321
❑ 89TopTif-156
❑ 89ToyRoo-9
❑ 89UppDec-164
❑ 89WhiSoxC-9
❑ 90BalOriP-6
❑ 90ClaBlu-49
❑ 90Don-219
❑ 90Fle-532
❑ 90FleCan-532
❑ 90OPC-612
❑ 90PanSti-46
❑ 90PubIntS-387
❑ 90Sco-115
❑ 90Sco100S-56
❑ 90Spo-105
❑ 90Top-612
❑ 90TopSti-305
❑ 90TopTif-612
❑ 90UppDec-328
❑ 90WhiSoxC-5
❑ 91Fle-471
❑ 91OPC-349
❑ 91OriCro-498
❑ 91StaClu-563
❑ 91Top-349
❑ 91TopDesS-349
❑ 91TopMic-349
❑ 91TopTif-349
❑ 91UltUpd-9
❑ 91UppDec-508
❑ 92Don-377
❑ 92Fle-59
❑ 92Lea-224
❑ 92LeaBlaG-224
❑ 92MetColP-23
❑ 92MetKah-8
❑ 92OPC-552
❑ 92OPCPre-128
❑ 92Sco-239
❑ 92ScoRoo-55T
❑ 92StaClu-841
❑ 92StaCluECN-841
❑ 92Top-552
❑ 92TopGol-552
❑ 92TopGolW-552
❑ 92TopMic-552
❑ 92TopTra-37T
❑ 92TopTraG-37T
❑ 92Ult-530
❑ 92UppDec-289
❑ 93Don-170
❑ 93Fle-472
❑ 93Lea-479
❑ 93MetColP-33
❑ 93MetKah-8
❑ 93StaClu-476
❑ 93StaCluFDI-476
❑ 93StaCluMOP-476
❑ 93Top-471
❑ 93TopGol-471
❑ 93TopInaM-471
❑ 93TopInaR-471
❑ 93TopMic-471
❑ 93Ult-74
❑ 94BraLykP-8
❑ 94BraLykS-9
❑ 94BraUSPC-9C
❑ 94Don-626
❑ 94Fle-562
❑ 94Pac-401
❑ 94Sco-235
❑ 94ScoGolR-235
❑ 94StaCluT-37
❑ 94StaCluTFDI-37
❑ 94Top-274
❑ 94TopGol-274
❑ 94TopSpa-274
❑ 94TopTra-8T
❑ 95Fle-303
❑ 95Phi-12
❑ 95PhiMel-9
❑ 95Sco-390
❑ 95ScoGolR-390
❑ 95ScoPlaTS-390
❑ 95TopTra-90T
❑ 97TexAIIM-3
❑ 97TreThuB-2
❑ 98TreThuM-3

Gallagher, Doug
❑ 77FriOneYW-52

Gallagher, Joe
❑ 40DodTeal-9
❑ 78DodTCM4-33
❑ 90DodTar-265

Gallagher, Keith
❑ 96NewJerCB-11
❑ 97PeoChi-10

Gallagher, Sean
❑ 85CloHSS-16

Gallagher, Shawn
❑ 96Bow-150
❑ 96BowFoi-150
❑ 96ChaRivTI-9613
❑ 97AppLeaTPB-7
❑ 98Cha-14
❑ 99BasAmeTPLM-3
❑ 99JustheS-21
❑ 99JustheSJB-21
❑ 99SP TopP-48
❑ 99SP TopPPE-48

Gallagher, William
❑ 90KalBatN-4

Gallaher, Kevin
❑ 92BurAstF-537
❑ 93OscAstC-11
❑ 93OscAstF-620
❑ 94Bow-202
❑ 94Cla-16
❑ 94ExcFS7-200
❑ 94JacGenF-209
❑ 95Bow-142
❑ 95Exc-202
❑ 96TusTorB-8
❑ 97TolMudHB-14
❑ 98RocRedWQ-13

Gallardo, Luis
❑ 87QuaCitAP-31
❑ 87SalAngP-25
❑ 90OneYanP-3366
❑ 91GreHorP-3065
❑ 92ForLauYC-11
❑ 92ForLauYTI-12
❑ 92Ft.LauYF-2619
❑ 94VenLinU-131
❑ 94VenLinU-183
❑ 94VenLinU-263

Gallardo, Stalin
❑ 98MarPhiG-11

Galle, Mike
❑ 89GreFalDSP-28
❑ 90YakBeaTI-26
❑ 91BakDodCLC-16

Gallego, Mike
❑ 82TacTigT-30
❑ 82WesHavAT-12
❑ 84TacTigC-81
❑ 85A'sMot-24
❑ 86Don-156
❑ 86TacTigP-7
❑ 86Top-304
❑ 86TopTif-304
❑ 88A'sMot-22
❑ 88Don-379
❑ 88DonTeaBA-379
❑ 88ModA'sTI-33
❑ 88Sco-428
❑ 88ScoGlo-428
❑ 88StaLinAs-5
❑ 88Top-702
❑ 88TopBig-103
❑ 88TopTif-702
❑ 89A'sMot-23
❑ 89Don-422
❑ 89Fle-8
❑ 89FleGlo-8
❑ 89Sco-537
❑ 89Top-102
❑ 89TopTif-102
❑ 89UppDec-583A
❑ 89UppDec-583B
❑ 90A'sMot-25
❑ 90Bow-459
❑ 90BowTif-459
❑ 90Don-361
❑ 90Fle-7
❑ 90FleCan-7
❑ 90Lea-121
❑ 90OPC-293
❑ 90PubIntS-304
❑ 90Sco-323
❑ 90Top-293
❑ 90TopBig-73
❑ 90TopTif-293
❑ 90UppDec-230
❑ 91A'sMot-25
❑ 91A'sSFE-4
❑ 91Bow-219
❑ 91Don-158
❑ 91Fle-7
❑ 91Lea-78
❑ 91OPC-686
❑ 91Sco-476
❑ 91StaClu-151
❑ 91Top-686
❑ 91TopDesS-686
❑ 91TopMic-686
❑ 91TopTif-686
❑ 91Ult-246
❑ 91UppDec-151
❑ 92Bow-273
❑ 92Don-314
❑ 92Fle-256
❑ 92Lea-236

❑ 92LeaBlaG-236
❑ 92OPC-76
❑ 92OPCPre-131
❑ 92PanSti-16
❑ 92Pin-387
❑ 92Sco-43
❑ 92ScoProP-12
❑ 92ScoRoo-30T
❑ 92StaClu-106
❑ 92StaClu-627
❑ 92StaCluNC-627
❑ 92Stu-211
❑ 92Top-76
❑ 92TopGol-76
❑ 92TopGolW-76
❑ 92TopMic-76
❑ 92TopTra-38T
❑ 92TopTraG-38T
❑ 92Ult-112
❑ 92Ult-406
❑ 92UppDec-193
❑ 92UppDec-750
❑ 93CadDis-23
❑ 93Don-81
❑ 93Fle-648
❑ 93Lea-96
❑ 93Pin-388
❑ 93Sel-220
❑ 93StaClu-126
❑ 93StaCluFDI-126
❑ 93StaCluMOP-126
❑ 93Top-287
❑ 93TopGol-287
❑ 93TopInaM-287
❑ 93TopInaR-287
❑ 93TopMic-287
❑ 93TriPla-226
❑ 93Ult-240
❑ 93UppDec-600
❑ 93UppDecGold-600
❑ 93YanStaC-11
❑ 94ColC-104
❑ 94ColChoGS-104
❑ 94ColChoSS-104
❑ 94Don-495
❑ 94Fin-75
❑ 94FinRef-75
❑ 94Fla-80
❑ 94Fle-229
❑ 94FleExtB-129
❑ 94Lea-136
❑ 94Pac-422
❑ 94PanSti-100
❑ 94Pin-451
❑ 94PinArtP-451
❑ 94PinMusC-451
❑ 94Sco-244
❑ 94ScoGolR-244
❑ 94Sel-53
❑ 94StaClu-388
❑ 94StaCluFDI-388
❑ 94StaCluGR-388
❑ 94StaCluMOP-388
❑ 94StaCluT-183
❑ 94StaCluTFDI-183
❑ 94Top-432
❑ 94TopGol-432
❑ 94TopSpa-432
❑ 94TriPla-273
❑ 94Ult-398
❑ 94UppDec-412
❑ 94UppDecED-412
❑ 95AthMot-19
❑ 95ColCho-533T
❑ 95Don-277
❑ 95DonPreP-277
❑ 95Fle-68
❑ 95Pac-295
❑ 95Sco-180
❑ 95ScoGolR-180
❑ 95ScoPlaTS-180
❑ 95StaClu-179
❑ 95StaCluFDI-179
❑ 95StaCluMOP-179
❑ 95StaCluSTWS-179
❑ 95Top-531
❑ 95TopCyb-316
❑ 96CarPol-10
❑ 96ColCho-242
❑ 96ColChoGS-242
❑ 96ColChoSS-242
❑ 96LeaSigEA-56
❑ 96Pac-399
❑ 97Pac-409
❑ 97PacLigB-409
❑ 97PacSil-409

Gallegos, Matt
❑ 83NasSouTI-6
Gallia, Bert (Melvin)
❑ 17ColE13-54
❑ 19W514-76
Galligani, Marcel
❑ 92FroRowDP-67
❑ 92FroRowDPG-67
❑ 92FroRowDPS-67
❑ 92SouOreAC-3
❑ 92SouOreAF-3424
❑ 93SouOreAC-8
❑ 93SouOreAF-4071
❑ 94WesMicWC-9
❑ 94WesMicWF-2309
Galliher, Marve
❑ 75HawIsIC-9
Gallivan, Phil
❑ 90DodTar-266
Gallo, Ben
❑ 81CliGiaT-6
❑ 90RenSilSCLC-287
Gallo, Ismael
❑ 97GreFalDTI-12
Gallo, Raymond
❑ 81BurBeeT-6
❑ 83ElPasDT-14
Gallone, Santy
❑ 94SpaPhiF-1729
❑ 94SparPhiC-11
❑ 95ClePhiF-223
Galloway, Chick (Clarence E.)
❑ 21Exh-54
❑ 22E120-79
❑ 22W572-30
❑ 22W573-46
❑ 23WilChoV-46
❑ 27AmeCarE126-15
❑ 27YorCarE-58A
❑ 61Fle-108
❑ 93ConTSN-967
Galloway, Gill
❑ 89BilMusP-2065
Galloway, Ike
❑ 87UtiBluSP-31
❑ 88BatCliP-1680
Galloway, James
❑ 16Zee-6
❑ 17Zee-106
Galloway, Joseph
❑ 26Exh-106
Galloway, Paul
❑ 96BelGiaTI-15
Galloway, Troy
❑ 85VisOakT-24
❑ 86OrlTwiP-6
❑ 87VisOakP-9
Galvan, Mike
❑ 88UtiBluSP-20
❑ 89UtiBluSP-8
❑ 90SarWhiSS-9
❑ 90StaFS7-58
❑ 91SarWhiSC-4
❑ 91SarWhiSP-1107
Galvez, Balvino
❑ 85DomLeaS-30
❑ 86AlbDukP-8
❑ 86StaoftFT-19
❑ 89ColCliC-10
❑ 89ColCliP-4
❑ 89ColCliP-748
❑ 90DodTar-267
❑ 90IndIndP-296
❑ 90ProAAAF-579
❑ 92SanAntMF-3969
❑ 92SanAntMS-564
❑ 93LimRocDWB-61
Galvez, Ricardo
❑ 94OrlCubF-1388
Galvez, Roberto
❑ 78DunBluJT-8
Galvin, Pud (James)
❑ 75FlePio-11
❑ 76MotOldT-8
❑ 76ShaPiz-102
❑ 78DexHaloFP-16
❑ 80PerHaloFP-102
❑ 80SSPHOF-102
❑ 87OldJudN-187
❑ 88AugBecN-15
❑ 88SpoTimM-12
❑ 88WG1CarG-59
❑ 89EdgR.WG-10
❑ 89HOFStiB-80
❑ 94OriofB-30

Gama, Ricky
❑ 95IdaFalBTI-1
❑ 96RanCucQB-15
❑ 97MobBayBB-12
❑ 97RanCucQUG-2
Gamba, Tom J.
❑ 87WatIndP-8
❑ 88WatIndP-673
Gambee, Brad
❑ 86EveGiaC-4
❑ 86EveGiaPC-6
❑ 87EveGiaC-29
Gambeski, Mike
❑ 83SprCarF-23
Gambill, Chad
❑ 94BenRocC-7
❑ 94BenRocF-3606
❑ 95AshTouTI-24
❑ 96SalAvaB-9
❑ 97SalAva-16
❑ 98NewHavRM-6
❑ 98NewHavRMA-6
Gamble, Billy
❑ 88WytCubP-2000
Gamble, Freddie
❑ 89BriTigS-8
❑ 92EriSaiC-4
❑ 92EriSaiF-1630
❑ 93KanCouCC-8
❑ 93KanCouCF-922
❑ 93KanCouCTI-8
Gamble, John
❑ 74OPC-597
❑ 74Top-597
Gamble, Lee
❑ 38RedOraW-10
❑ 39OrcPhoAP-9
❑ 39RedTeal-8
❑ 40PlaBal-208
❑ 77CinRedT-22
Gamble, Oscar
❑ 70Top-654
❑ 71MLBOffS-178
❑ 71OPC-23
❑ 71Top-23
❑ 72OPC-423
❑ 72Top-423
❑ 73IndTeal-12
❑ 73OPC-372
❑ 73Top-372
❑ 74OPC-152
❑ 74Top-152
❑ 74TopSta-166
❑ 75CleIndP-12
❑ 75Hos-147
❑ 75IndJB R-5
❑ 75OPC-213
❑ 75Top-213
❑ 75TopMin-213
❑ 76OPC-74
❑ 76SSP-526
❑ 76Top-74
❑ 76TopTra-74T
❑ 77Top-505
❑ 77WhiSoxJT-4
❑ 77WhiSoxT-8
❑ 78Hos-100
❑ 78PadFamF-13
❑ 78Top-390
❑ 79OPC-132
❑ 79Top-263
❑ 80Top-698
❑ 80YanPhoA-7
❑ 81Don-229
❑ 81Fle-98
❑ 81OPC-139
❑ 81Top-139
❑ 81YanPhoA-6
❑ 82Don-360
❑ 82Fle-36
❑ 82OPC-229
❑ 82Top-472
❑ 82YanPhoA-7
❑ 83Don-461
❑ 83Fle-380
❑ 83OPC-19
❑ 83Top-19
❑ 83YanPhoA-7
❑ 84Fle-124
❑ 84Nes792-512
❑ 84OPC-13
❑ 84Top-512
❑ 84TopTif-512
❑ 85FleUpd-44
❑ 85OPC-93
❑ 85Top-724

❑ 85TopTif-724
❑ 85TopTifT-37T
❑ 85TopTra-37T
❑ 85WhiSoxC-0
❑ 89PacSenL-116
❑ 89T/MSenL-37
❑ 92YanWIZ7-51
❑ 92YanWIZ8-65
❑ 93RanKee-156
Gamble, Robert
❑ 87OldJudN-188
Gamboa, Javier
❑ 94EugEmeC-10
❑ 94EugEmeF-3704
❑ 95MidLeaA-18
❑ 95SprSulTI-10
❑ 96WilBluRB-7
❑ 97WicWra-3
Gamboa, Tom
❑ 88BlaYNPRWL-65
❑ 90CMC-691
❑ 90ProAAAF-394
❑ 90TolMudHC-22
❑ 90TolMudHP-164
Gambrell, Glen
❑ 91MelBusF-19
Gambs, Chris
❑ 92ClaFS7-320
❑ 92CliGiaC-13
❑ 92CliGiaF-3590
❑ 92StaCluD-54
❑ 93Bow-280
❑ 93CliGiaC-11
❑ 93CliGiaF-2484
❑ 94CliLumC-10
❑ 94CliLumF-1974
❑ 95BatCliTI-14
❑ 96DayCubB-12
Gamby, Steve
❑ 75CliPilT-6
Gamez, Bobby
❑ 91QuaCitAC-4
❑ 91QuaCitAP-2621
❑ 92PalSprAC-8
❑ 92PalSprAF-830
❑ 93MidAngF-317
❑ 94PhoFirF-1515
❑ 95PhoFirTI-22
❑ 97MidAngOHP-12
Gamez, Francisco
❑ 91BelBreCB-3
❑ 91BelBreP-2096
❑ 92ClaFS7-283
❑ 92StoPorC-16
❑ 92StoPorF-30
❑ 93Bow-267
❑ 93El PasDF-2943
❑ 94ElPasDF-3139
❑ 95ElPasDTI-8
Gamez, Rene
❑ 95OdgRapTI-7
Gammage, Mark
❑ 82BurRanF-17
❑ 82BurRanT-19
Gammill, Jimmy
❑ 88MisStaB-6
❑ 89MisStaB-13
❑ 90MisStaB-12
❑ 91MisStaB-17
Gammon, James
❑ 89MajLeaM-3
Gancasz, Michael
❑ 97LowSpiB-8
Ganch, Tim
❑ 78ChaPirT-7
Ganci, Lou
❑ 79WatIndT-2B
Gandarillas, Gus
❑ 92ClaDraP-118
❑ 92EliTwiF-3674
❑ 93ForWayWC-8
❑ 93ForWayWF-1961
❑ 93MidLeaAGF-6
❑ 93StaCluM-138
❑ 93Top-786
❑ 93TopGol-786
❑ 93TopInaM-786
❑ 93TopInaR-786
❑ 93TopMic-786
❑ 94ExcFS7-94
❑ 94FloStaLAF-FSL8
❑ 94ForMyeMC-7
❑ 94ForMyeMF-1162
❑ 95Bow-198
❑ 95Exc-84
❑ 95HarCitRCTI-6

❑ 95UppDecML-143
❑ 95UppDecMLFS-143
❑ 97NewBriRC-11
❑ 98SalLakBO-14
Gandil, Chick (Charles)
❑ 09ObaT21-40
❑ 09T206-137
❑ 10ChiE-14
❑ 10CouT21-137
❑ 10CouT21-138
❑ 10CouT21-284
❑ 11PinT-5-758
❑ 12ImpTobC-65
❑ 14B18B-40
❑ 14CraJacE-39
❑ 15CraJacE-39
❑ 16BF2FP-23
❑ 16SpoNewM-64
❑ 17ColE13-55
❑ 18WhiSoxTI-9
❑ 19W514-31
❑ 74CapPub-104
❑ 75WhiSox1T-8
❑ 88LitSunBS-2
❑ 88PacEigMO-9
❑ 88PacEigMO-22
❑ 88PacEigMO-25
❑ 88PacEigMO-46
❑ 88PacEigMO-48
❑ 88PacEigMO-106
❑ 92Man191BSR-9
❑ 94ConTSN-1031
❑ 94ConTSNB-1031
Gandolph, David
❑ 91GulCoaRSP-4
❑ 92GasRanC-16
❑ 92GasRanF-2246
❑ 93ChaRanC-10
❑ 93ChaRanF-1933
❑ 94JacGenF-210
Gandy, Chris
❑ 79CliDodT-13
Gandy, Josh
❑ 97AppLeaTPB-29
❑ 98ForWayW!-17
Gangemi, Joe
❑ 98LakElsSG-11
Gangerni, Joseph
❑ 97BoiHawG-11
Ganley, Robert
❑ 08AmeCarE91-47
❑ 08RosComP-78
❑ 09RamT20-49
❑ 09SenBarP-3
❑ 09T206-138
❑ 11SpoLifCW-134
❑ 72ClaCar-3
Gann, Chuck
❑ 94IdaFalBF-3578
❑ 94IdaFalBSP-11
Gann, Jamie
❑ 96AriBlaDB-18
❑ 97HigDesMG-8
❑ 98HigDesMG-10
Gann, Steve
❑ 93BilMusF-3953
❑ 93BilMusSP-18
❑ 94ChaWheC-1
❑ 94ChaWheF-2711
❑ 94SouAtlLAF-SAL41
Gannon, James
❑ 89MajLeaM-11
Ganote, Joe
❑ 90St.CatBJP-3461
❑ 91MyrBeaHC-5
❑ 91MyrBeaHP-2939
❑ 91SouAtlLAGP-SAL38
❑ 92DunBluJF-1993
❑ 93KnoSmoF-1247
❑ 94KnoSmoF-1297
Gant, Ron (Ronald Edwin)
❑ 86DurBulP-12
❑ 87GreBraB-13
❑ 87SouLeaAJ-13
❑ 88BlaYNPRWL-57
❑ 88Don-654
❑ 88DonBasB-2
❑ 88DonRoo-47
❑ 88Fle-538
❑ 88FleGlo-538
❑ 88RicBraC-12
❑ 88RicBraP-3
❑ 88Sco-647
❑ 88ScoGlo-647

❑ 88StaLinBra-5
❑ 88TopBig-249
❑ 88TopTra-39T
❑ 88TopTraT-39T
❑ 89Baz-9
❑ 89Bow-274
❑ 89BowTif-274
❑ 89BraDub-11
❑ 89ClaLigB-35
❑ 89Don-50
❑ 89Fle-590
❑ 89FleGlo-590
❑ 89K-M-2
❑ 89OPC-196
❑ 89PanSti-42
❑ 89Sco-372
❑ 89ScoHot1R-87
❑ 89ScoYouSI-16
❑ 89Spo-28
❑ 89SpoIllFKI-251
❑ 89Top-296
❑ 89TopBig-43
❑ 89TopGloS-10
❑ 89TopRoo-9
❑ 89TopSti-34
❑ 89TopSti-322
❑ 89TopTif-296
❑ 89TopUKM-29
❑ 89ToyRoo-10
❑ 89TVSpoM-59
❑ 89UppDec-378
❑ 90BraDubP-7
❑ 90BraDubS-8
❑ 90Don-475
❑ 90DonBesN-111
❑ 90Fle-582
❑ 90FleCan-582
❑ 90Lea-376
❑ 90OPC-567
❑ 90PublntS-113
❑ 90PublntS-612
❑ 90SupActM-11
❑ 90Top-567
❑ 90TopBig-66
❑ 90TopTif-567
❑ 90UppDec-232
❑ 91Bow-583
❑ 91BraDubP-10
❑ 91BraSubS-14
❑ 91Cla1-T5
❑ 91Cla3-T23
❑ 91Cla3-T24
❑ 91ClaGam-123
❑ 91Don-10
❑ 91Don-507
❑ 91DonSupD-10
❑ 91Fle-688
❑ 91Lea-129
❑ 91MajLeaCP-47
❑ 91OPC-725
❑ 91OPCPre-49
❑ 91PanCanT1-36
❑ 91PanCanT1-52
❑ 91PanFreS-23
❑ 91PanSti-27
❑ 91RedFolS-38
❑ 91Sco-448
❑ 91Sco100S-14
❑ 91StaClu-454
❑ 91StaPinB-19
❑ 91Stu-144
❑ 91Top-725
❑ 91TopCraJ2-19
❑ 91TopDesS-725
❑ 91TopMic-725
❑ 91TopTif-725
❑ 91TopTriH-N1
❑ 91Ult-4
❑ 91UppDec-82
❑ 91UppDec-361
❑ 92Bow-534
❑ 92BraLykP-12
❑ 92BraLykS-13
❑ 92Cla2-T19
❑ 92ClaGam-15
❑ 92Don-284
❑ 92Fle-357
❑ 92FleLumC-L9
❑ 92Hig5-22
❑ 92Hig5S-16
❑ 92Lea-15
❑ 92LeaBlaG-15
❑ 92OPC-25
❑ 92OPCPre-4
❑ 92PanSti-167
❑ 92Pin-128

❑ 92PinSlu-8
❑ 92Sco-25
❑ 92Sco100S-76
❑ 92ScoCokD-9
❑ 92ScoImpP-65
❑ 92ScoProP-9
❑ 92StaClu-730
❑ 92StaCluD-55
❑ 92StaCluNC-730
❑ 92StaGan-1
❑ 92StaGan-2
❑ 92StaGan-3
❑ 92StaGan-4
❑ 92StaGan-5
❑ 92StaGan-6
❑ 92StaGan-7
❑ 92StaGan-8
❑ 92StaGan-9
❑ 92StaGan-10
❑ 92StaGan-11
❑ 92Stu-3
❑ 92Top-25
❑ 92Top-391
❑ 92TopGol-25
❑ 92TopGol-391
❑ 92TopGolW-25
❑ 92TopGolW-391
❑ 92TopKid-32
❑ 92TopMcD-14
❑ 92TopMic-25
❑ 92TopMic-391
❑ 92TriPla-126
❑ 92Ult-161
❑ 92UppDec-345
❑ 92UppDecHRH-HR7
❑ 93Bow-382
❑ 93BraLykP-10
❑ 93BraLykS-12
❑ 93BraStaC-6
❑ 93DiaMar-37
❑ 93Don-210
❑ 93DonEliD-4
❑ 93Fin-68
❑ 93FinRef-68
❑ 93Fla-3
❑ 93Fle-3
❑ 93Lea-225
❑ 93OPC-108
❑ 93PacSpa-5
❑ 93PanSti-185
❑ 93Pin-445
❑ 93PinHomRC-20
❑ 93Sco-220
❑ 93Sel-133
❑ 93SP-57
❑ 93SPPlaP-PP7
❑ 93StaClu-28
❑ 93StaCluFDI-28
❑ 93StaCluM-98
❑ 93StaCluMOP-28
❑ 93Stu-88
❑ 93Top-393
❑ 93TopGol-393
❑ 93TopInaM-393
❑ 93TopInaR-393
❑ 93TopMic-393
❑ 93TriPla-199
❑ 93Ult-5
❑ 93UppDec-264
❑ 93UppDecGold-264
❑ 94BraUSPC-1C
❑ 94BraUSPC-2D
❑ 94BraUSPC-8D
❑ 94CarLeaA-DJ6
❑ 94Don-34
❑ 94DonDom-A8
❑ 94DonDomJ-A8
❑ 94DonSpeE-34
❑ 94Fin-165
❑ 94FinRef-165
❑ 94Fle-358
❑ 94Fle-706
❑ 94FleLumC-3
❑ 94Pac-8
❑ 94PacGolP-15
❑ 94PanSti-144
❑ 94RedKah-12
❑ 94Sco-332
❑ 94ScoGolR-332
❑ 94ScoGolS-14
❑ 94Spo-90
❑ 94StaClu-111
❑ 94StaClu-123
❑ 94StaClu-260
❑ 94StaCluFDI-111
❑ 94StaCluFDI-123
❑ 94StaCluFDI-260
❑ 94StaCluGR-111
❑ 94StaCluGR-123
❑ 94StaCluGR-260
❑ 94StaCluMO-26
❑ 94StaCluMOP-111
❑ 94StaCluMOP-123
❑ 94StaCluMOP-260
❑ 94StaCluP-123
❑ 94StaCluT-41
❑ 94StaCluTFDI-41
❑ 94Top-166
❑ 94TopBlaG-31
❑ 94TopGol-166
❑ 94TopSpa-166
❑ 94TopTra-55T
❑ 94TriPla-43
❑ 94TriPlaBS-7
❑ 94UltHomRK-11
❑ 94UltRBIK-9
❑ 94USPlaCA-5C
❑ 95BowBes-R62
❑ 95BowBesR-R62
❑ 95ClaPhoC-17
❑ 95ColCho-429
❑ 95ColChoGS-429
❑ 95ColChoSE-196
❑ 95ColChoSEGS-196
❑ 95ColChoSESS-196
❑ 95ColChoSS-429
❑ 95DonTopotO-212
❑ 95Emo-116
❑ 95EmoN-5
❑ 95Fin-230
❑ 95FinRef-230
❑ 95Fla-338
❑ 95FleUpd-132
❑ 95Lea-324
❑ 95LeaLim-182
❑ 95Pin-228
❑ 95PinArtP-228
❑ 95PinMusC-228
❑ 95RedKah-7
❑ 95Sel-141
❑ 95SelArtP-141
❑ 95SP-42
❑ 95SPCha-33
❑ 95SPCha-35
❑ 95SPChaDC-33
❑ 95SPChaDC-35
❑ 95SPPlaP-PP3
❑ 95SPSil-42
❑ 95StaClu-528
❑ 95StaCluMOP-528
❑ 95StaCluSTDW-RE528
❑ 95StaCluSTWS-528
❑ 95Top-627
❑ 95Ult-365
❑ 95UltGolM-365
❑ 95UppDec-489
❑ 95UppDecSE-166
❑ 95UppDecSEG-166
❑ 95Zen-92
❑ 96Baz-72
❑ 96Bow-31
❑ 96BowBes-12
❑ 96BowBesAR-12
❑ 96BowBesR-12
❑ 96BowFoi-31
❑ 96CarPol-8
❑ 96ColCho-110
❑ 96ColCho-711
❑ 96ColCho-784
❑ 96ColChoCtG-CG27
❑ 96ColChoCtG-CG27B
❑ 96ColChoCtG-CG27C
❑ 96ColChoCtGE-CR27
❑ 96ColChoCtGG-CG27
❑ 96ColChoCtGG-CG27B
❑ 96ColChoCtGG-CG27C
❑ 96ColChoCtGGE-CR27
❑ 96ColChoGS-110
❑ 96ColChoGS-711
❑ 96ColChoSS-110
❑ 96ColChoSS-711
❑ 96ColChoYMtP-14
❑ 96ColChoYMtP-14A
❑ 96ColChoYMtPGS-14
❑ 96ColChoYMtPGS-14A
❑ 96Don-415
❑ 96DonPreP-415
❑ 96EmoXL-266
❑ 96Fin-B244
❑ 96Fin-G308
❑ 96FinRef-B244
❑ 96FinRef-G308
❑ 96Fla-359
❑ 96Fle-340
❑ 96FleTif-340
❑ 96FleUpd-U189
❑ 96FleUpdTC-U189
❑ 96LeaPreSG-45
❑ 96LeaPreSte-45
❑ 96LeaSig-108
❑ 96LeaSigPPG-108
❑ 96LeaSigPPP-108
❑ 96MetUni-224
❑ 96MetUniP-224
❑ 96MLBPin-11
❑ 96Pac-48
❑ 96PacPri-P15
❑ 96PacPriG-P15
❑ 96PanSti-55
❑ 96Pin-152
❑ 96Pin-333
❑ 96PinAfi-27
❑ 96PinAfiAP-27
❑ 96PinAfiFPP-27
❑ 96PinArtP-79
❑ 96PinFoil-333
❑ 96PinSta-79
❑ 96Sco-337
❑ 96ScoDugC-B62
❑ 96ScoDugCAP-B62
❑ 96SP-156
❑ 96SPSpeFX-17
❑ 96SPSpeFXDC-17
❑ 96SPx-47
❑ 96SPxGol-47
❑ 96StaClu-203
❑ 96StaClu-364
❑ 96StaCluB&B-BB6
❑ 96StaCluEPB-364
❑ 96StaCluEPG-364
❑ 96StaCluEPS-364
❑ 96StaCluMM-MM10
❑ 96StaCluMOP-203
❑ 96StaCluMOP-364
❑ 96StaCluMOP-BB6
❑ 96StaCluMOP-MM10
❑ 96StaCluMOP-PP5
❑ 96StaCluPP-PP5
❑ 96Stu-89
❑ 96StuPrePB-89
❑ 96StuPrePG-89
❑ 96StuPrePS-89
❑ 96Sum-8
❑ 96SumAbo&B-8
❑ 96SumArtP-8
❑ 96SumFoi-8
❑ 96Top-70
❑ 96TopChr-25
❑ 96TopChrR-25
❑ 96TopChrWC-WC7
❑ 96TopChrWCR-WC7
❑ 96TopGal-68
❑ 96TopGalPPI-68
❑ 96TopLas-7
❑ 96TopPro-NL13
❑ 96TopRoaW-RW8
❑ 96TopWreC-WC7
❑ 96Ult-178
❑ 96Ult-547
❑ 96UltGolM-178
❑ 96UltGolM-547
❑ 96UppDec-152
❑ 96UppDec-443
❑ 96UppDecPRE-R33
❑ 96UppDecPreR-R33
❑ 97Bow-252
❑ 97BowBes-12
❑ 97BowBesAR-12
❑ 97BowBesR-12
❑ 97BowChr-75
❑ 97BowChrI-75
❑ 97BowChrIR-75
❑ 97BowChrR-75
❑ 97BowInt-252
❑ 97CarPol-9
❑ 97Cir-310
❑ 97CirRav-310
❑ 97ColCho-205
❑ 97Don-174
❑ 97DonEli-135
❑ 97DonEliGS-135
❑ 97DonGolPP-174
❑ 97DonLim-24
❑ 97DonLimE-24
❑ 97DonLimENG-24
❑ 97DonPre-73
❑ 97DonPreCttC-73
❑ 97DonSilPP-174
❑ 97DonTea-156
❑ 97DonTeaSPE-156
❑ 97E-X2-98
❑ 97E-X2Cred-98
❑ 97E-X2EssCre-98
❑ 97Fin-130
❑ 97Fin-333
❑ 97FinEmb-130
❑ 97FinEmb-333
❑ 97FinEmbR-130
❑ 97FinEmbR-333
❑ 97FinRef-130
❑ 97FinRef-333
❑ 97FlaShoLC-28
❑ 97FlaShoLeg0-28
❑ 97FlaShoLeg1-28
❑ 97FlaShoM-A28
❑ 97FlaShoM-B28
❑ 97FlaShoM-C28
❑ 97FlaShoR0-28
❑ 97FlaShoR1-28
❑ 97FlaShoR2-28
❑ 97Fle-443
❑ 97FleTif-443
❑ 97Lea-226
❑ 97LeaFraM-226
❑ 97LeaFraMDC-226
❑ 97MetUni-230
❑ 97NewPin-69
❑ 97NewPinAP-69
❑ 97NewPinMC-69
❑ 97NewPinPP-69
❑ 97Pac-410
❑ 97PacLigB-410
❑ 97PacPri-138
❑ 97PacPriLB-138
❑ 97PacPriP-138
❑ 97PacSil-410
❑ 97Pin-81
❑ 97PinArtP-PP81
❑ 97PinCer-65
❑ 97PinCerMBla-65
❑ 97PinCerMBlu-65
❑ 97PinCerMG-65
❑ 97PinCerMR-65
❑ 97PinCerR-65
❑ 97PinIns-108
❑ 97PinInsCE-108
❑ 97PinInsDE-108
❑ 97PinMusC-81
❑ 97PinPrePla-81
❑ 97PinTotCPB-65
❑ 97PinTotCPG-65
❑ 97PinTotCPR-65
❑ 97PinX-P-110
❑ 97PinX-PMoS-110
❑ 97PinX-PSfF-23
❑ 97PinX-PSfFU-23
❑ 97Sco-268
❑ 97ScoArtPWB-268
❑ 97ScoHeaotO-29
❑ 97ScoPreS-268
❑ 97ScoShoS-268
❑ 97ScoShoSAP-268
❑ 97Sel-80
❑ 97SelArtP-80
❑ 97SelCom-80
❑ 97SelRegG-80
❑ 97SP-150
❑ 97SpoIll-105
❑ 97SpoIllEE-105
❑ 97SPx-40
❑ 97SPxBro-40
❑ 97SPxGol-40
❑ 97SPxGraF-40
❑ 97SPxSil-40
❑ 97SPxSte-40
❑ 97StaClu-242
❑ 97StaCluMat-242
❑ 97StaCluMOP-242
❑ 97Stu-4
❑ 97StuPrePG-4
❑ 97StuPrePS-4
❑ 97Top-127
❑ 97TopChr-48
❑ 97TopChrR-48
❑ 97TopGal-59
❑ 97TopGalPPI-59
❑ 97TopMemO5-17
❑ 97TopSta-9
❑ 97TopStaAM-9
❑ 97UD3-24
❑ 97Ult-270
❑ 97UltDouT-18
❑ 97UltGolME-270
❑ 97UltPlaME-270
❑ 97UppDec-160
❑ 97UppDec-257
❑ 97UppDec-371
❑ 98BowBes-31
❑ 98BowBesAR-31
❑ 98BowBesR-31
❑ 98CarScoP-6
❑ 98CirThu-58
❑ 98CirThuRav-58
❑ 98CirThuSupRav-58
❑ 98ColCho-477
❑ 98Don-174
❑ 98DonGolPP-174
❑ 98DonSilPP-174
❑ 98Fin-126
❑ 98FinNo--126
❑ 98FinNo-R-126
❑ 98FinRef-126
❑ 98Fle-380
❑ 98FleVin'-116
❑ 98FleVin'C-116
❑ 98MetUni-168
❑ 98MetUniPMG-168
❑ 98Pac-412
❑ 98PacAur-183
❑ 98PacOme-197
❑ 98PacOmeR-197
❑ 98PacOnl-611
❑ 98PacOnlR-611
❑ 98PacOnlWC-611
❑ 98PacPar-229
❑ 98PacParC-229
❑ 98PacParG-229
❑ 98PacParHS-229
❑ 98PacParPB-229
❑ 98PacParR-229
❑ 98PacPlaB-412
❑ 98PacRedT-412
❑ 98PacSil-412
❑ 98PinPlu-160
❑ 98PinSna-SLC2
❑ 98PinSna-SLC17
❑ 98Sco-77
❑ 98ScoCar-6
❑ 98ScoRT-203
❑ 98ScoSS-PP33
❑ 98ScoSSAP-PP33
❑ 98SkyDugA-40
❑ 98SkyDugAIA-40
❑ 98SP Aut-163
❑ 98SpoIll-42
❑ 98SpoIllEE-42
❑ 98SpoIllFE-42
❑ 98SpoIllWSF-34
❑ 98SpoIllWSFEE-34
❑ 98SpoIllWSFFE-34
❑ 98SPxFin-312
❑ 98SPxFinR-312
❑ 98SPxFinS-312
❑ 98StaCluFDI-185
❑ 98StaCluI-185
❑ 98StaCluOneK-185
❑ 98StaCluPP-185
❑ 98Top-298
❑ 98TopChr-298
❑ 98TopChrR-298
❑ 98TopDevR-298
❑ 98TopDia-298
❑ 98TopGal-98
❑ 98TopGalGP-98
❑ 98TopGalOPP-98
❑ 98TopGalPPI-98
❑ 98TopGalPPIA-98
❑ 98TopMiniC-298
❑ 98TopOpeD-125
❑ 98TopSta-138
❑ 98TopStaB-138
❑ 98TopStaG-138
❑ 98TopStaGR-138
❑ 98TopStaS-138
❑ 98Ult-187
❑ 98UltGolM-187
❑ 98UltMas-187
❑ 98UltPlaM-187
❑ 98UppDec-203
❑ 98UppDecSF-111
❑ 99199Fin-161
❑ 99E-X Cen-79
❑ 99E-X CenECFut-79
❑ 99E-X CenECNow-79
❑ 99FinGolRef-161
❑ 99FinRef-161
❑ 99Fle-76
❑ 99FleSta9-76
❑ 99FleWarT-76
❑ 99Pac-353
❑ 99PacCroC-228
❑ 99PacCroCPB-228
❑ 99PacOme-178
❑ 99PacOmeC-178
❑ 99PacOmeG-178
❑ 99PacOmePB-178
❑ 99PacPar-178
❑ 99PacParC-178
❑ 99PacParG-178
❑ 99PacParHoloGold-178
❑ 99PacParHS-178
❑ 99PacParOD-178
❑ 99PacParPB-178
❑ 99PacParRed-178
❑ 99PacPlaB-353
❑ 99PacPri-118
❑ 99PacPriHB-118
❑ 99PacPriHG-118
❑ 99PacPriHM-118
❑ 99PacPriHP-118
❑ 99PacPriRed-118
❑ 99PacRed-353
❑ 99SkyMolMOA-11
❑ 99SkyPre-50
❑ 99SkyPreR-50
❑ 99SkyThu-145
❑ 99SkyThuRant-145
❑ 99SkyThuRave-145
❑ 99SP SigAuto-RGA
❑ 99SPSig-117
❑ 99StaClu-5
❑ 99StaCluFDI-5
❑ 99StaCluOoaK-5
❑ 99StaCluPP-5
❑ 99ThuSkySupR-145
❑ 99Top-131
❑ 99TopChr-131
❑ 99TopChrR-131
❑ 99TopMVPP-131
❑ 99TopOpeD-77
❑ 99UppDec-455
❑ 99UppDecEL1-455
❑ 99UppDecEL2-455
❑ 99UppDecM-161
❑ 99UppDecMGS-161
❑ 99UppDecMHFS-161
❑ 99UppDecMSS-161
❑ 99Vic-297

Gantner, Jim

❑ 76VenLeaS-216
❑ 77SpoIndC-4
❑ 77Top-494
❑ 79BrePlaPH-1
❑ 79Top-154
❑ 80BreTeal-8
❑ 80Top-374
❑ 81Don-204
❑ 81Fle-522
❑ 81OPC-122
❑ 81Top-482
❑ 82BrePol-17
❑ 82Don-406
❑ 82Fle-142
❑ 82FleSta-133
❑ 82OPC-207
❑ 82Top-613
❑ 83AllGamPI-11
❑ 83BreGar-8
❑ 83BrePol-17
❑ 83Don-232
❑ 83Fle-34
❑ 83FleSti-12
❑ 83OPC-88
❑ 83Top-88
❑ 84AllGamPI-102
❑ 84BreGar-7
❑ 84BrePol-17
❑ 84Don-115
❑ 84Fle-200
❑ 84Nes792-298
❑ 84OPC-298
❑ 84Top-298
❑ 84TopSti-298
❑ 84TopTif-298
❑ 85AllGamPI-12
❑ 85BreGar-7
❑ 85BrePol-17
❑ 85Don-229
❑ 85DonActA-2
❑ 85Fle-582
❑ 85Lea-217
❑ 85OPC-216
❑ 85Top-781
❑ 85TopSti-295
❑ 85TopTif-781
❑ 86BrePol-17

❑ 86Don-115
❑ 86Fle-487
❑ 86Lea-43
❑ 86MSAJayPCD-8
❑ 86OPC-51
❑ 86Top-582
❑ 86TopSti-202
❑ 86TopTat-9
❑ 86TopTif-582
❑ 87BrePol-17
❑ 87BreTeal-6
❑ 87Don-172
❑ 87DonOpeD-53
❑ 87Fle-345
❑ 87FleGlo-345
❑ 87OPC-108
❑ 87SmoAmeL-15
❑ 87Top-108
❑ 87TopSti-197
❑ 87TopTif-108
❑ 88BrePol-17
❑ 88BreTeal-14
❑ 88Don-214
❑ 88DonBasB-53
❑ 88Fle-165
❑ 88FleGlo-165
❑ 88Lea-161
❑ 88OPC-337
❑ 88PanSti-123
❑ 88PanSti-124
❑ 88Sco-197
❑ 88ScoGlo-197
❑ 88Spo-130
❑ 88StaLinBre-8
❑ 88Top-337
❑ 88TopSti-195
❑ 88TopTif-337
❑ 89Bow-141
❑ 89BowTif-141
❑ 89BreGar-3
❑ 89BrePol-17
❑ 89BreYea-17
❑ 89Don-264
❑ 89DonBasB-295
❑ 89Fle-186
❑ 89FleGlo-186
❑ 89OPC-134
❑ 89PanSti-372
❑ 89Sco-313
❑ 89Top-671
❑ 89TopBig-184
❑ 89TopSti-203
❑ 89TopTif-671
❑ 89TVSpoM-76
❑ 89UppDec-274
❑ 90Bow-400
❑ 90BowTif-400
❑ 90BreMilB-9
❑ 90BrePol-17
❑ 90Don-291
❑ 90Fle-324
❑ 90FleCan-324
❑ 90MLBBasB-81
❑ 90OPC-417
❑ 90PanSti-94
❑ 90PubIntS-496
❑ 90Sco-382
❑ 90Top-417
❑ 90TopBig-124
❑ 90TopSti-207
❑ 90TopTif-417
❑ 90UppDec-218
❑ 91Bow-48
❑ 91BreMilB-8
❑ 91BrePol-8
❑ 91Don-703
❑ 91Fle-584
❑ 91Lea-145
❑ 91OPC-23
❑ 91Sco-532
❑ 91StaClu-183
❑ 91Top-23
❑ 91TopDesS-23
❑ 91TopMic-23
❑ 91TopTif-23
❑ 91Ult-174
❑ 91UppDec-618
❑ 92Bow-301
❑ 92BreCarT-8
❑ 92BrePol-8
❑ 92Don-574
❑ 92Fle-176
❑ 92OPC-248
❑ 92PanSti-37
❑ 92Pin-71
❑ 92Sco-246
❑ 92ScoProP-20
❑ 92StaClu-502
❑ 92Top-248
❑ 92TopGol-248
❑ 92TopGolW-248
❑ 92TopMic-248
❑ 92Ult-382
❑ 92UppDec-360
❑ 93Fle-630
❑ 93PacSpa-156
❑ 93Pin-207
❑ 94BreMilB-29
❑ 94BreMilB-313

Ganzel, Babe (Foster Pirie)
❑ 28StaPlaCE-23
❑ 33WorCig(-27
❑ 33WorCig(-28
❑ 33WorCig(-29

Ganzel, Charles
❑ 87OldJudN-189
❑ 89N526N7C-5
❑ 95May-10
❑ 98CamPepP-28

Ganzel, John Henry
❑ 08RosComP-116
❑ 09T206-424
❑ 11SpoLifCW-135
❑ 12ImpTobC-26

Gapski, Mark
❑ 94WatIndC-10
❑ 94WatIndF-3929

Garabito, Eddy
❑ 98DelShoM-14

Garagiola, Joe
❑ 46SeaSLP-22
❑ 47TipTop-156
❑ 49EurSta-182
❑ 51Bow-122
❑ 52Bow-27
❑ 52Top-227
❑ 53BowC-21
❑ 54Bow-141
❑ 64TopRooAB-7
❑ 76TopGar-1
❑ 79DiaGre-162
❑ 79TCM50-262
❑ 80PacLeg-76
❑ 82DiaCla-34
❑ 83Car194T-33
❑ 83TopRep5-227
❑ 85TCMPhoC-26
❑ 85TCMPla1-24
❑ 90PacLeg-24
❑ 90SweBasG-14
❑ 91SweBasG-31
❑ 91TopArc1-314
❑ 92ActPacA-43
❑ 92BazQua5A-21
❑ 93TedWil-89
❑ 94UppDecAH-19
❑ 94UppDecAH1-19

Garagozzo, Keith
❑ 91OneYanP-4148
❑ 92ClaFS7-290
❑ 92GreHorC-2
❑ 92GreHorF-772
❑ 93PriWilCC-12
❑ 93PriWilCF-651
❑ 94Bow-656
❑ 94ColCliF-2947
❑ 94Fla-74
❑ 94Ult-388
❑ 98PriWilCASM-22

Garavito, Eddy
❑ 97AppLeaTPB-21

Garbark, Bob
❑ 36DiaMatCS3T2-11
❑ 39CubTeal-7
❑ 93ConTSN-946

Garbark, Mike
❑ 45A'sTeal-13
❑ 83TCMPla1944-8

Garber, Gene
❑ 74OPC-431
❑ 74Top-431
❑ 75OPC-444
❑ 75PhiPhiP-13
❑ 75PhiProPS-7
❑ 75Top-444
❑ 75TopMin-444
❑ 76OPC-14
❑ 76PhiPhiP-10
❑ 76SSP-458
❑ 76Top-14
❑ 77Top-289
❑ 78BraCok-4
❑ 78SSP270-38
❑ 78Top-177
❑ 79OPC-331
❑ 79Top-629
❑ 80OPC-263
❑ 80Top-504
❑ 81BraPol-26
❑ 81Don-77
❑ 81Fle-249
❑ 81OPC-307
❑ 81Top-307
❑ 82BraBurKL-8
❑ 82BraPol-26
❑ 82Don-123
❑ 82Fle-434
❑ 82Top-32
❑ 83BraPol-26
❑ 83Don-223
❑ 83Fle-136
❑ 83FleSta-66
❑ 83FleSti-87
❑ 83OPC-255
❑ 83OPC-256
❑ 83Top-255
❑ 83Top-256
❑ 83TopFol-4
❑ 83TopSti-213
❑ 84BraPol-26
❑ 84Don-287
❑ 84Fle-179
❑ 84Nes792-466
❑ 84Nes792-709
❑ 84OPC-167
❑ 84raPho-10
❑ 84Top-466
❑ 84Top-709
❑ 84TopSti-35
❑ 84TopTif-466
❑ 84TopTif-709
❑ 85BraHos-9
❑ 85BraPol-26
❑ 85Fle-325
❑ 85Top-129
❑ 85TopTif-129
❑ 86BraPol-26
❑ 86Fle-515
❑ 86Top-776
❑ 86TopTif-776
❑ 87BraSmo-9
❑ 87Don-414
❑ 87Fle-515
❑ 87FleExcS-17
❑ 87FleGlo-515
❑ 87FleRecS-10
❑ 87FleStiC-44
❑ 87Lea-172
❑ 87SpoTeaP-24
❑ 87Top-351
❑ 87TopSti-40
❑ 87TopTif-351
❑ 88Don-618
❑ 88DonBasB-63
❑ 88Fle-257
❑ 88FleGlo-257
❑ 88OPC-289
❑ 88RoySmo-11
❑ 88RoyTeal-11
❑ 88Sco-565
❑ 88ScoGlo-565
❑ 88Spo-88
❑ 88StaLinRo-4
❑ 88Top-597
❑ 88TopTif-597

Garber, Jeff
❑ 88EugEmeB-16
❑ 89AppFoxP-863
❑ 90BasCitRS-8
❑ 91LinDriAA-406
❑ 91MemChiLD-406
❑ 91MemChiP-660
❑ 92MemChiF-2425
❑ 92MemChiS-435
❑ 93MemChiF-380
❑ 94MemChiF-365
❑ 96SpoIndB-2
❑ 97SpoIndG-9
❑ 98SpoIndG-12

Garber, Joel
❑ 96HicCraB-7
❑ 96SouBenSHS-13

Garbey, Barbaro
❑ 81BirBarT-22
❑ 82BirBarT-2
❑ 83EvaTriT-18
❑ 84FleUpd-42
❑ 84TigFarJ-3
❑ 84TigTeal-14
❑ 84TigWavP-15
❑ 84TopTra-41T
❑ 84TopTraT-41T
❑ 85Don-456
❑ 85Fle-7
❑ 85FleStaS-121
❑ 85Lea-121
❑ 85OPC-243
❑ 85TigCaiD-7
❑ 85TigWen-8
❑ 85Top-243
❑ 85TopSti-263
❑ 85TopTif-243
❑ 86Don-349
❑ 86Fle-225
❑ 86OPC-88
❑ 86Top-609
❑ 86TopTif-609
❑ 88OklCit8C-16
❑ 88OklCit8P-45
❑ 89BirBarADB-13
❑ 90BirBarADB-13
❑ 93RanKee-157

Garbould, Bob
❑ 44CenFlo-8

Garbozo, Toribio
❑ 76VenLeaS-81
❑ 80VenLeaS-244

Garces, Jesus
❑ 90PriPatD-7
❑ 91BatCliCB-9
❑ 91BatCliP-3491
❑ 92SpaPhiC-5
❑ 92SpaPhiF-1268
❑ 93LinVenB-97
❑ 94VenLinU-178
❑ 95LinVen-110
❑ 96-97LinVen-74

Garces, Maduro
❑ 89HagSunB-6

Garces, Rich (Richard)
❑ 89KenTwiP-1076
❑ 89KenTwiS-6
❑ 89Sta-51
❑ 90CalLeaACLC-18
❑ 90ProAaA-140
❑ 90VisOakCLC-62
❑ 90VisOakP-2148
❑ 91Bow-324
❑ 91Cla1-T59
❑ 91Don-420
❑ 91LinDriAAA-408
❑ 91OPC-594
❑ 91PorBeaLD-408
❑ 91PorBeaP-1562
❑ 91StaClu-370
❑ 91Top-594
❑ 91TopDeb90-50
❑ 91TopDesS-594
❑ 91TopMic-594
❑ 91TopTif-594
❑ 91Ult-378
❑ 91UppDec-741
❑ 92Don-516
❑ 92OrlSunRF-2840
❑ 92OrlSunRS-505
❑ 92SkyAA F-217
❑ 93LinVenB-214
❑ 93PorBeaF-2379
❑ 94NasXprF-378
❑ 94VenLinU-196
❑ 95LinVen-120
❑ 95LinVen-283
❑ 95LinVen-287
❑ 96-97LinVen-81
❑ 96Pac-73
❑ 97PacPriGotD-GD20
❑ 98PacInvGems-20
❑ 98PacOnl-112
❑ 98PacOnlR-112
❑ 98PacOnlWC-112
❑ 98PawRedSQ-14

Garces, Robinson
❑ 87LakTigP-21
❑ 88FayGenP-1087
❑ 89HagSunP-281
❑ 89HagSunS-8
❑ 90ElPasDGS-13
❑ 93LinVenB-31
❑ 94VenLinU-208
❑ 95LinVen-66
❑ 96-97LinVen-191

Garcia, Adrian
❑ 92PulBraC-11
❑ 92PulBraF-3180
❑ 93MacBraC-9
❑ 93MacBraF-1402
❑ 94DurBulC-7
❑ 94DurBulF-330
❑ 94DurBulTI-6

Garcia, Alfredo
❑ 94HunCubC-10
❑ 94HunCubF-3546
❑ 95RocCubTI-21
❑ 96DayCubB-13
❑ 97OrlRayB-12
❑ 98WesTenDJM-9

Garcia, Amadeo
❑ 89EliTwiS-26

Garcia, Amaury
❑ 95ElmPioTI-7
❑ 95ElmPioUTI-7
❑ 96KanCouCTI-9
❑ 96KanCouCUTI-5
❑ 96MidLeaAB-32
❑ 97BreCouMB-13
❑ 98EasLeaTPM-9
❑ 98PorSeaDQ-18
❑ 99Bow-198
❑ 99BowChr-198
❑ 99BowChrG-198
❑ 99BowChrGR-198
❑ 99BowChrI-198
❑ 99BowChrIR-198
❑ 99BowChrR-198
❑ 99BowGol-198
❑ 99BowInt-198

Garcia, Anastacio
❑ 90MedHatBJB-13
❑ 91DunBluJC-13
❑ 91DunBluJP-209
❑ 92MyrBeaHC-5
❑ 92MyrBeaHF-2199
❑ 93KnoSmoF-1253

Garcia, Anthony
❑ 89SalDodTI-3
❑ 90BakDodCLC-245

Garcia, Antonio
❑ 76VenLeaS-208
❑ 80VenLeaS-234

Garcia, Apolinar
❑ 89MadMusS-10
❑ 90ModA'sC-10
❑ 90ModA'sP-2206
❑ 91HunStaTI-10
❑ 91LinDriAAA-534
❑ 91TacTigLD-534
❑ 91TacTigP-2298
❑ 92Ft.MyeMCB-5
❑ 92Ft.MyeMF-2738
❑ 93CanIndF-2833
❑ 93LimRocDWB-98
❑ 94CanIndF-3115

Garcia, Apostol
❑ 94BriTigC-13
❑ 94BriTigF-3510
❑ 96FayGenB-17
❑ 97WesMicW-14
❑ 98LakTigM-4

Garcia, Ariel
❑ 93SouBenWSC-10
❑ 93SouBenWSF-1424
❑ 95MidLeaA-19
❑ 96SouBenSHS-14
❑ 97HicCraRB-14
❑ 98HicCraM-15

Garcia, Bryan
❑ 98SouOreTG-10

Garcia, Butch
❑ 90ChaKniTI-10

Garcia, Butch (Victor)
❑ 86IndTeal-22
❑ 87ColMetP-16
❑ 87PeoChiP-2
❑ 87PeoChiPW-1
❑ 88CarLeaAS-27
❑ 88PriWilYS-11
❑ 88WinSpiS-3
❑ 89BlaYNPRWL-175
❑ 89ChaKniTI-7
❑ 89Ft.LauYS-5
❑ 89GreHorP-407
❑ 89IowCubC-11
❑ 89IowCubP-1693
❑ 90CedRapRB-16
❑ 90CedRapRP-2315
❑ 90Ft.LauYS-8
❑ 90MidLeaASGS-33
❑ 90ProAaA-122
❑ 91AlbYanLD-5
❑ 91AlbYanP-1001
❑ 91ChaLooLD-159
❑ 91ChaLooP-1954
❑ 91LinDriAA-5
❑ 91LinDriAA-159
❑ 92CanIndF-684
❑ 92CanIndS-107
❑ 93ChaLooF-2357
❑ 93LimRocDWB-102
❑ 94AshTouC-1

Garcia, Cano (Efrain)
❑ 90IBAWorA-6

Garcia, Carlos Jesus
❑ 88AugPirP-365
❑ 89SalBucS-9
❑ 90CMC-761
❑ 90EasLeaAP-EL25
❑ 90HarSenP-1199
❑ 90HarSenS-7
❑ 90ProAaA-28
❑ 91Bow-531
❑ 91BufBisLD-29
❑ 91BufBisP-546
❑ 91Fle-37
❑ 91LinDriAAA-29
❑ 91TopDeb90-51
❑ 91Ult-278
❑ 92Bow-576
❑ 92BufBisBS-9
❑ 92BufBisF-327
❑ 92BufBisS-33
❑ 92Cla1-T37
❑ 92Don-14
❑ 92Pin-264
❑ 92ProFS7-305
❑ 92Sco-821
❑ 92SkyAAAF-14
❑ 92TriA AAS-33
❑ 92UppDec-665
❑ 93Bow-626
❑ 93Don-598
❑ 93Fin-4
❑ 93FinRef-4
❑ 93Fla-112
❑ 93Fle-501
❑ 93Lea-277
❑ 93LinVenB-200
❑ 93OPCPre-111
❑ 93PacSpa-244
❑ 93Pin-558
❑ 93PirNatI-12
❑ 93Sco-246
❑ 93ScoBoyoS-14
❑ 93Sel-403
❑ 93SelRoo-40T
❑ 93SP-184
❑ 93StaClu-545
❑ 93StaCluFDI-545
❑ 93StaCluMOP-545
❑ 93Stu-49
❑ 93Top-27
❑ 93TopGol-27
❑ 93TopInaM-27
❑ 93TopInaR-27
❑ 93TopMic-27
❑ 93Toy-70
❑ 93TriPla-65
❑ 93Ult-450
❑ 93UppDec-334
❑ 93UppDecGold-334
❑ 94Bow-218
❑ 94ColC-105
❑ 94ColChoGS-105
❑ 94ColChoSS-105
❑ 94Don-161
❑ 94Fin-57
❑ 94FinRef-57
❑ 94Fla-420
❑ 94Fle-609
❑ 94FleExtB-345
❑ 94FleExtBSYS-7
❑ 94FUnPac-168
❑ 94Lea-248
❑ 94OPC-112
❑ 94OPCDiaD-18
❑ 94Pac-498
❑ 94PanSti-235
❑ 94Pin-108
❑ 94PinArtP-108
❑ 94PinMusC-108
❑ 94PirQui-7
❑ 94ProMag-106
❑ 94Sco-520
❑ 94ScoGolR-520
❑ 94Sel-119

❑ 94SP-141
❑ 94SPDieC-141
❑ 94StaClu-206
❑ 94StaCluFDI-206
❑ 94StaCluGR-206
❑ 94StaCluMOP-206
❑ 94Stu-145
❑ 94Top-309
❑ 94TopGol-309
❑ 94TopSpa-309
❑ 94TriPla-183
❑ 94Ult-555
❑ 94UppDec-198
❑ 94UppDecED-198
❑ 94USPlaCR-3H
❑ 94USPlaCR-6C
❑ 94USPlaCR-10D
❑ 94VenLinU-1
❑ 95Bow-373
❑ 95ColCho-376
❑ 95ColChoGS-376
❑ 95ColChoSE-178
❑ 95ColChoSEGS-178
❑ 95ColChoSESS-178
❑ 95ColChoSS-376
❑ 95Don-91
❑ 95DonPreP-91
❑ 95DonTopotO-315
❑ 95Fin-110
❑ 95FinRef-110
❑ 95Fla-399
❑ 95Fle-479
❑ 95FleAllS-12
❑ 95ForWayWTI-16
❑ 95Lea-2
❑ 95LeaLim-146
❑ 95LinVen-80
❑ 95LinVen-266
❑ 95Pac-343
❑ 95PacLatD-14
❑ 95PacPri-112
❑ 95PanSti-43
❑ 95Pin-116
❑ 95PinArtP-116
❑ 95PinMusC-116
❑ 95PirFil-10
❑ 95Sco-236
❑ 95ScoGolR-236
❑ 95ScoHaloG-HG51
❑ 95ScoPlaTS-236
❑ 95Sel-114
❑ 95SelArtP-114
❑ 95SP-93
❑ 95Spo-59
❑ 95SpoArtP-59
❑ 95SPSil-93
❑ 95StaClu-11
❑ 95StaCluFDI-11
❑ 95StaCluMOP-11
❑ 95StaCluSTWS-11
❑ 95StaCluVR-6
❑ 95StaCluVRMO-6
❑ 95Stu-54
❑ 95Top-515
❑ 95TopCyb-303
❑ 95TopD3-17
❑ 95TopEmb-74
❑ 95TopEmbGI-74
❑ 95Ult-215
❑ 95UltGolM-215
❑ 95UppDec-151
❑ 95UppDecED-151
❑ 95UppDecEDG-151
❑ 95UppDecSE-221
❑ 95UppDecSEG-221
❑ 96-97LinVen-13
❑ 96ColCho-685
❑ 96ColChoGS-685
❑ 96ColChoSS-685
❑ 96Don-457
❑ 96DonPreP-457
❑ 96EmoXL-253
❑ 96Fin-B187
❑ 96FinRef-B187
❑ 96Fla-345
❑ 96Fle-521
❑ 96FleTif-521
❑ 96ForWayWB-8
❑ 96Lea-81
❑ 96LeaPrePB-81
❑ 96LeaPrePG-81
❑ 96LeaPrePS-81
❑ 96LeaSigA-76
❑ 96LeaSigAG-76
❑ 96LeaSigAS-76
❑ 96MetUni-215
❑ 96MetUniP-215
❑ 96Pac-177
❑ 96PacPri-P57
❑ 96PacPriG-P57
❑ 96PanSti-69
❑ 96Pin-285
❑ 96PinFoil-285
❑ 96ProSta-92
❑ 96Sco-14
❑ 96SP-149
❑ 96StaClu-153
❑ 96StaCluMOP-153
❑ 96Top-415
❑ 96TopGal-80
❑ 96TopGalPPI-80
❑ 96Ult-531
❑ 96UltGolM-531
❑ 96UppDec-179
❑ 97BluJayOH-9
❑ 97BluJayS-7
❑ 97Cir-371
❑ 97CirRav-371
❑ 97ColCho-497
❑ 97Don-243
❑ 97DonGolPP-243
❑ 97DonSilPP-243
❑ 97Fin-217
❑ 97FinRef-217
❑ 97Fle-427
❑ 97Fle-553
❑ 97FleTif-427
❑ 97FleTif-553
❑ 97ForMyeM-11
❑ 97Lea-275
❑ 97LeaFraM-275
❑ 97LeaFraMDC-275
❑ 97NewPin-153
❑ 97NewPinAP-153
❑ 97NewPinMC-153
❑ 97NewPinPP-153
❑ 97PacPri-134
❑ 97PacPriGotD-GD192
❑ 97PacPriLB-134
❑ 97PacPriP-134
❑ 97Pin-34
❑ 97PinArtP-PP34
❑ 97PinMusC-34
❑ 97PinPrePla-34
❑ 97Sco-297
❑ 97Sco-353
❑ 97ScoArtPWB-297
❑ 97ScoArtPWB-353
❑ 97ScoPreS-297
❑ 97ScoResC-353
❑ 97ScoShoS-297
❑ 97ScoShoS-353
❑ 97ScoShoSAP-297
❑ 97ScoShoSAP-353
❑ 97StaClu-156
❑ 97StaCluMOP-156
❑ 97Stu-115
❑ 97StuPrePG-115
❑ 97StuPrePS-115
❑ 97Top-34
❑ 97Ult-260
❑ 97Ult-418
❑ 97UltGolME-260
❑ 97UltGolME-418
❑ 97UltPlaME-260
❑ 97UltPlaME-418
❑ 98Pac-220
❑ 98PacOnl-9
❑ 98PacOnlR-9
❑ 98PacOnlWC-9
❑ 98PacPlaB-220
❑ 98PacRedT-220
❑ 98PacSil-220
❑ 98ScoRT-84
❑ 98Top-54
❑ 98TopChr-54
❑ 98TopChrR-54
❑ 98TopDevR-54
❑ 98TopDia-54
❑ 98TopMiniC-54
❑ 98VanCanG-12

Garcia, Cheo
❑ 89KenTwiP-1083
❑ 89KenTwiS-7
❑ 91LinDriAA-480
❑ 91OrlSunRLD-480
❑ 91OrlSunRP-1855
❑ 92OrlSunRF-2853
❑ 92OrlSunRS-501
❑ 92ProFS7-94
❑ 93PawRedSDD-12
❑ 93PawRedSF-2413
❑ 93PawRedSTI-12

Garcia, Chico (Vinicio U.)
❑ 54OriEss-13
❑ 91OriCro-149
❑ 97BalOriP-19

Garcia, Chidez (Cornelio)
❑ 86AppFoxP-9
❑ 88FloStaLAS-37
❑ 88TamTarS-7
❑ 89BirBarB-9
❑ 89BirBarP-102
❑ 90BirBarB-9
❑ 90BirBarP-1117

Garcia, Damaso
❑ 76ForLauYS-15
❑ 77WesHavYT-10
❑ 78TacYanC-42
❑ 79ColCliT-4
❑ 81AllGamPI-12
❑ 81Don-269
❑ 81Fle-415
❑ 81OPC-233
❑ 81OPCPos-14
❑ 81Top-488
❑ 81TopScr-42
❑ 81TopSti-137
❑ 82BluJayS-4
❑ 82Don-479
❑ 82Fle-613
❑ 82FleSta-234
❑ 82OPC-293
❑ 82OPCPos-2
❑ 82Top-596
❑ 82TopSti-245
❑ 83AllGamPI-12
❑ 83Don-54
❑ 83DonActA-17
❑ 83Fle-427
❑ 83FleSta-67
❑ 83FleSti-105
❑ 83OPC-202
❑ 83OPC-222
❑ 83PerCreC-24
❑ 83PerCreCG-24
❑ 83Top-202
❑ 83Top-222
❑ 83TopSti-134
❑ 84AllGamPI-103
❑ 84BluJayFS-12
❑ 84Don-241
❑ 84Fle-153
❑ 84Nes792-124
❑ 84OPC-124
❑ 84Top-124
❑ 84TopRubD-14
❑ 84TopSti-364
❑ 84TopTif-124
❑ 85AllGamPI-13
❑ 85BluJayCC-3
❑ 85BluJayFS-11
❑ 85Don-315
❑ 85DonActA-6
❑ 85Fle-104
❑ 85Lea-65
❑ 85OPC-353
❑ 85OPCPos-15
❑ 85Top-645
❑ 85Top-702
❑ 85TopRubD-12
❑ 85TopSti-357
❑ 85TopTif-645
❑ 85TopTif-702
❑ 86BluJayAF-10
❑ 86BluJayFS-12
❑ 86Don-241
❑ 86DonAll-40
❑ 86Fle-59
❑ 86FleLimE-17
❑ 86FleMin-15
❑ 86FleStiC-41
❑ 86GenMilB-3E
❑ 86Lea-116
❑ 86OPC-45
❑ 86Spo-34
❑ 86Top-45
❑ 86Top-713
❑ 86TopSti-190
❑ 86TopTat-24
❑ 86TopTif-45
❑ 86TopTif-713
❑ 87BraSmo-22
❑ 87Don-614
❑ 87Fle-226
❑ 87FleGlo-226
❑ 87Lea-92
❑ 87OPC-395
❑ 87Spo-183
❑ 87Top-395
❑ 87TopSti-188
❑ 87TopTif-395
❑ 88Don-414
❑ 88Top-241
❑ 88TopTif-241
❑ 89ExpPos-9
❑ 89TopBig-275
❑ 90BluJayHS-1
❑ 90Fle-346
❑ 90FleCan-346
❑ 90OPC-432
❑ 90Top-432
❑ 90TopTif-432
❑ 90UppDec-649
❑ 92Nab-20
❑ 92YanWIZ7-52
❑ 97BluJayS-44

Garcia, Danny
❑ 76WatRoyT-9
❑ 80OmaRoyP-12
❑ 80VenLeaS-225
❑ 91SpoIndC-28
❑ 91SpoIndP-3966
❑ 92WicWraF-3670

Garcia, Dave
❑ 73OPC-12
❑ 73PadDea-7
❑ 73Top-12A
❑ 73Top-12B
❑ 78AngFamF-12
❑ 78SSP270-193
❑ 78Top-656
❑ 80IndTeal-10
❑ 80Top-451
❑ 81Don-442
❑ 81Top-665
❑ 82Don-337
❑ 82Ind-13
❑ 82IndBurK-1
❑ 82IndBurK-2
❑ 82IndWhe-4
❑ 83BrePol-NNO
❑ 83Top-546
❑ 84BrePol-NNO

Garcia, Eddy
❑ 97BurBeeB-9

Garcia, Eduardo
❑ 92GulCoaDF-3579
❑ 94HunCubC-11
❑ 94HunCubF-3565
❑ 94PriRedC-9
❑ 94PriRedF-3256
❑ 95BilMusTI-20

Garcia, Fermin
❑ 91PriRedC-27
❑ 91PriRedP-3506
❑ 92BilMusF-3347
❑ 92BilMusSP-23
❑ 92ChaWheF-2
❑ 92ChaWVWC-4
❑ 93WesVirWC-8
❑ 93WesVirWF-2860

Garcia, Francisco
❑ 90AppFoxBS-8
❑ 90AppFoxP-2107

Garcia, Frank
❑ 80AshTouT-23
❑ 80TulDriT-12
❑ 83St.PetCT-17
❑ 96StPetCB-8
❑ 97ArkTraB-3

Garcia, Freddy Adrian
❑ 93MedHatBJF-3744
❑ 93MedHatBJSP-14
❑ 94St.CatBJC-9
❑ 94St.CatBJF-3651
❑ 95Bow-213
❑ 95Exc-136
❑ 95FleUpd-147
❑ 95PirFil-11
❑ 95SP-18
❑ 95SPSil-18
❑ 95UppDec-261
❑ 95UppDecED-261
❑ 95UppDecEDG-261
❑ 95UppDecSE-222
❑ 95UppDecSEG-222
❑ 96-97LinVen-33
❑ 96Bow-129
❑ 96BowFoi-129
❑ 96ColCho-261
❑ 96ColChoGS-261
❑ 96ColChoSS-261
❑ 96LynHilB-10
❑ 97Bow-135
❑ 97BowChr-144
❑ 97BowChrI-144
❑ 97BowChrIR-144
❑ 97BowChrR-144
❑ 97BowInt-135
❑ 98Fle-565
❑ 98PacOnl-583
❑ 98PacOnlR-583
❑ 98PacOnlWC-583
❑ 98PinPlu-46
❑ 98Ult-261
❑ 98UltGolM-261
❑ 98UltMas-261
❑ 98UltPlaM-261
❑ 99Bow-126
❑ 99BowChr-126
❑ 99BowChrG-126
❑ 99BowChrGR-126
❑ 99BowChrI-126
❑ 99BowChrIR-126
❑ 99BowChrR-126
❑ 99BowGol-126
❑ 99BowInt-126
❑ 99Fle-104
❑ 99FleSta9-104
❑ 99FleWarT-104
❑ 99Pac-339
❑ 99PacCroC-219
❑ 99PacCroCPB-219
❑ 99PacPlaB-339
❑ 99PacRed-339
❑ 99Ult-21
❑ 99UltGolM-21
❑ 99UltMas-21
❑ 99UltPlaM-21
❑ 99UppDec-463
❑ 99UppDecEL1-463
❑ 99UppDecEL2-463
❑ 99Vic-315

Garcia, Freddy Antonio
❑ 96QuaCitRB-14
❑ 97KisCob-9
❑ 98JacGenM-6
❑ 98TexLeaTPG-11
❑ 99Bow-404
❑ 99BowAut-BA18
❑ 99BowGol-404
❑ 99BowInt-404
❑ 99CroRoyB-127
❑ 99CroRoyL-127
❑ 99CroRoyOD-127
❑ 99DumSet-132
❑ 99FleBri-141
❑ 99FleBri2G-141
❑ 99FleBriBlu-141
❑ 99FleBriGol-141
❑ 99FleMys-132
❑ 99FleMysM-132
❑ 99PacInv-132
❑ 99PacInvOD-132
❑ 99PacInvPB-132
❑ 99PacOme-218
❑ 99PacOmeC-218
❑ 99PacOmeG-218
❑ 99PacOmePB-218
❑ 99Rev-129
❑ 99RevPremDate-129
❑ 99RevRet-129
❑ 99RevShaSS-129
❑ 99SkyMolM-124
❑ 99SkyMolMF-24
❑ 99SkyMolMFS-24
❑ 99SkyMolMFT-24
❑ 99SkyMolMX-124
❑ 99SkyPre-226
❑ 99SkyPre-226
❑ 99SkyPreR-226
❑ 99SkyPreR-226

Garcia, G.G.
❑ 97SouLeaTP-7

Garcia, Gabe
❑ 97QuaCitRBB-10
❑ 98KisCobQ-15

Garcia, George
❑ 98BurBeeM-29

Garcia, Guillermo
❑ 91KinMetC-14
❑ 91KinMetP-3821
❑ 92PitMetC-6
❑ 92PitMetF-3299
❑ 93CapCitBC-6
❑ 93CapCitBF-462
❑ 93SouAtlLAGF-35
❑ 94FloStaLAF-FSL38
❑ 94St.LucMC-10
❑ 94St.LucMF-1198
❑ 97IndInd-8
❑ 98IndIndQ-20
❑ 99PacCroC-74
❑ 99PacCroCPB-74
❑ 99SkyPre-245
❑ 99SkyPre-245
❑ 99SkyPreR-245
❑ 99SkyPreR-245
❑ 99SkyThu-218
❑ 99SkyThuRant-218
❑ 99SkyThuRave-218
❑ 99SpoIll-64
❑ 99ThuSkySupR-218

Garcia, Ismael
❑ 98YakBeaG-13

Garcia, Jaime
❑ 92SouBenWSC-26
❑ 92SouBenWSF-194
❑ 93SouBenWSC-28
❑ 93SouBenWSF-1447
❑ 94SouBenSHC-26
❑ 94SouBenSHF-611
❑ 95PriWilCTI-30
❑ 96DelShoB-18
❑ 96PriWilCB-2
❑ 97BelSnaB-3

Garcia, Jason
❑ 94DanBraC-11
❑ 94DanBraF-3540
❑ 97GreBatB-4
❑ 98GreBatM-29

Garcia, Jesse
❑ 94OriPro-36
❑ 96HigDesMB-11
❑ 97BowBay-18
❑ 98BowBayM-15
❑ 99SkyMolM-110
❑ 99SkyMolMF-10
❑ 99SkyMolMFS-10
❑ 99SkyMolMFT-10
❑ 99SkyMolMX-110
❑ 99SkyPre-240
❑ 99SkyPre-240
❑ 99SkyPreR-240
❑ 99SkyPreR-240

Garcia, Joe
❑ 75SanAntBT-6

Garcia, Jose Antonio
❑ 97BelSnaB-13
❑ 97MidLeaTP-1
❑ 98StoPorG-9
❑ 99Bow-379
❑ 99BowGol-379
❑ 99BowInt-379

Garcia, Jose Cheo
❑ 94VenLinU-260
❑ 95LinVen-106
❑ 96-97LinVen-63

Garcia, Jose Luis
❑ 90CalLeaACLC-4
❑ 90CMC-714
❑ 90VisOakCLC-78
❑ 90VisOakP-2161
❑ 93BakDodCLC-8
❑ 93LimRocDWB-55
❑ 93LinVenB-56
❑ 93YakBeaC-9
❑ 93YakBeaF-3879
❑ 94VerBeaDF-64
❑ 95EugEmeTI-11
❑ 95SanAntMTI-26
❑ 96HelBreTI-5
❑ 96MacBraB-7

Garcia, Julio
❑ 89PriPirS-26
❑ 89SalBucS-NNO
❑ 91AugPirC-1
❑ 91AugPirP-823
❑ 92AugPirC-26
❑ 92WelPirC-29
❑ 92WelPirF-1342
❑ 93WelPirC-30
❑ 94BufBisF-1854
❑ 94OneYanF-3799
❑ 96FreKeyB-24
❑ 97HudValRB-27
❑ 98ChaRivDG-12

Garcia, Karim
❑ 93BakDodCLC-9
❑ 94Cla-167
❑ 94FloStaLAF-FSL46
❑ 94UppDecML-103

❑ 94VerBeaDC-7
❑ 94VerBeaDF-86
❑ 95Bow-92
❑ 95BowBes-B56
❑ 95BowBes-X13
❑ 95BowBesR-B56
❑ 95BowBesR-X13
❑ 95ColCho-39
❑ 95ColChoGS-39
❑ 95ColChoSS-39
❑ 95Exc-212
❑ 95SigRooOJ-14
❑ 95SigRooOJP-14
❑ 95SigRooOJPS-14
❑ 95SigRooOJS-14
❑ 95SigRooP'P-P3
❑ 95Top-237
❑ 95UppDec-9
❑ 95UppDecED-9
❑ 95UppDecEDG-9
❑ 95UppDecML-14
❑ 95UppDecMLFS-14
❑ 95UppDecSE-33
❑ 95UppDecSEG-33
❑ 96BesAutSA-21
❑ 96Bow-340
❑ 96BowBes-101
❑ 96BowBesAR-101
❑ 96BowBesMI-5
❑ 96BowBesMIAR-5
❑ 96BowBesMIR-5
❑ 96BowBesP-BBP29
❑ 96BowBesPAR-BBP29
❑ 96BowBesPR-BBP29
❑ 96BowBesR-101
❑ 96BowFoi-340
❑ 96BowMinLP-7
❑ 96ColCho-35
❑ 96ColChoGS-35
❑ 96ColChoSS-35
❑ 96DodFle-8
❑ 96DodPol-14
❑ 96Don-474
❑ 96DonPreP-474
❑ 96EmoXL-208
❑ 96Fin-G20
❑ 96FinRef-G20
❑ 96Fla-292
❑ 96FlaWavotF-10
❑ 96FlePro-5
❑ 96FleUpd-U144
❑ 96FleUpdTC-U144
❑ 96Lea-220
❑ 96LeaPrePB-220
❑ 96LeaPrePG-220
❑ 96LeaPrePS-220
❑ 96LeaSig-149
❑ 96LeaSigEA-57
❑ 96LeaSigEACM-6
❑ 96LeaSigPPG-149
❑ 96LeaSigPPP-149
❑ 96PacPri-P33
❑ 96PacPriG-P33
❑ 96Pin-368
❑ 96PinAfi-154
❑ 96PinAfi-173
❑ 96PinAfiAP-154
❑ 96PinAfiAP-173
❑ 96PinFoil-368
❑ 96PinProS-3
❑ 96PinTeaT-10
❑ 96SanAntMB-5
❑ 96Sco-220
❑ 96Sco-383
❑ 96ScoDugC-A102
❑ 96ScoDugC-B108
❑ 96ScoDugCAP-A102
❑ 96ScoDugCAP-B108
❑ 96ScoFutF-9
❑ 96Sel-192
❑ 96SelArtP-192
❑ 96SelCer-102
❑ 96SelCerAP-102
❑ 96SelCerCB-102
❑ 96SelCerCR-102
❑ 96SelCerMB-102
❑ 96SelCerMG-102
❑ 96SelCerMR-102
❑ 96SigRooOJMR-M3
❑ 96SP-15
❑ 96StaClu-255
❑ 96StaCluMOP-255
❑ 96Sum-159
❑ 96Sum-196
❑ 96SumAbo&B-159
❑ 96SumAbo&B-196
❑ 96SumArtP-159
❑ 96SumArtP-196
❑ 96SumFoi-159
❑ 96SumFoi-196
❑ 96Top-217
❑ 96TopChr-79
❑ 96TopChrR-79
❑ 96TopGal-131
❑ 96TopGalPPI-131
❑ 96Ult-497
❑ 96UltGolM-497
❑ 96UppDec-223
❑ 96UppDecBCP-BC8
❑ 96Zen-101
❑ 96ZenArtP-101
❑ 96ZenDiaC-19
❑ 96ZenDiaCP-19
❑ 97AlbDukGS-11
❑ 97Bow-136
❑ 97Bow98ROY-ROY2
❑ 97BowBes-147
❑ 97BowBesAR-147
❑ 97BowBesR-147
❑ 97BowCerBlaIA-CA29
❑ 97BowCerBluIA-CA29
❑ 97BowCerGolIA-CA29
❑ 97BowChr-145
❑ 97BowChr1RFR-ROY2
❑ 97BowChr98RF-ROY2
❑ 97BowChrI-145
❑ 97BowChrIR-145
❑ 97BowChrR-145
❑ 97BowInt-136
❑ 97BowIntB-BBI17
❑ 97BowIntBAR-BBI17
❑ 97BowIntBR-BBI17
❑ 97ColCho-138
❑ 97DodPol-9
❑ 97Don-360
❑ 97DonEli-64
❑ 97DonEliGS-64
❑ 97DonGolPP-360
❑ 97DonLim-111
❑ 97DonLimE-111
❑ 97DonPre-149
❑ 97DonPreCttC-149
❑ 97DonRatR-15
❑ 97DonSigA-36
❑ 97DonSigAC-43
❑ 97DonSigAM-43
❑ 97DonSilPP-360
❑ 97DonTea-118
❑ 97DonTeaSPE-118
❑ 97Fin-309
❑ 97FinEmb-309
❑ 97FinEmbR-309
❑ 97FinRef-309
❑ 97Fle-362
❑ 97FleTif-362
❑ 97Lea-337
❑ 97LeaFraM-337
❑ 97LeaFraMDC-337
❑ 97Pac-330
❑ 97PacLigB-330
❑ 97PacPri-110
❑ 97PacPriLB-110
❑ 97PacPriP-110
❑ 97PacPriSL-SL11C
❑ 97PacSil-330
❑ 97PinIns-134
❑ 97PinInsCE-134
❑ 97PinInsDD-20
❑ 97PinInsDE-134
❑ 97Sco-316
❑ 97ScoPreS-316
❑ 97ScoShoS-316
❑ 97Sel-108
❑ 97SelArtP-108
❑ 97SelCom-108
❑ 97SelRegG-108
❑ 97SelRooR-20
❑ 97SelToootT-5
❑ 97SelToootTMB-5
❑ 97StaClu-237
❑ 97StaCluC-CO10
❑ 97StaCluM-M18
❑ 97StaCluMat-237
❑ 97StaCluMOP-237
❑ 97StaCluMOP-M18
❑ 97Stu-150
❑ 97StuHarH-21
❑ 97StuPrePG-150
❑ 97StuPrePS-150
❑ 97Top-363
❑ 97TopChr-124
❑ 97TopChrR-124
❑ 97Ult-216
❑ 97UltGolME-216
❑ 97UltGolP-4
❑ 97UltPlaME-216
❑ 97UppDec-398
❑ 97UppDecBCP-BC13
❑ 97UppDecTTS-TS13
❑ 98BowBes-143
❑ 98BowBesAR-143
❑ 98BowBesR-143
❑ 98CirThu-94
❑ 98CirThuRav-94
❑ 98CirThuSupRav-94
❑ 98ColCho-297
❑ 98DiaBacP-23
❑ 98DiaMcD-13
❑ 98Don-72
❑ 98Don-326
❑ 98DonCol-72
❑ 98DonCol-205
❑ 98DonColP-669
❑ 98DonColS-72
❑ 98DonColS-200
❑ 98DonGolPP-72
❑ 98DonGolPP-326
❑ 98DonPre-119
❑ 98DonPreSeat-119
❑ 98DonPriCD-72
❑ 98DonPriCD-205
❑ 98DonPriCP-669
❑ 98DonRatR-30
❑ 98DonRatRM-30
❑ 98DonSilPP-72
❑ 98DonSilPP-326
❑ 98E-X2-89
❑ 98E-X2ECFut-89
❑ 98E-X2ECNow-89
❑ 98Fle-405
❑ 98FleProF-PF4
❑ 98FleVin'-68
❑ 98FleVin'C-68
❑ 98LeaRCrusUP-118
❑ 98LeaRS-248
❑ 98LeaRSCrusUG-118
❑ 98LeaRSCrusUR-118
❑ 98LeaRSLHolo-248
❑ 98LeaRSLong-248
❑ 98LeaRTrue-248
❑ 98Pac-329
❑ 98PacAur-98
❑ 98PacOmeRS-29
❑ 98PacOmeRST4-29
❑ 98PacOnl-40
❑ 98PacOnlR-40
❑ 98PacOnlWC-40
❑ 98PacPlaB-329
❑ 98PacRedT-329
❑ 98PacSil-329
❑ 98Pin-179
❑ 98PinArtP-PP82
❑ 98PinMusC-PP82
❑ 98PinPer-101
❑ 98PinPerPP-101
❑ 98PinPlu-112
❑ 98PinPluAP-PP35
❑ 98PinPluGAP-PP35
❑ 98PinPluMAP-PP35
❑ 98PinPreP-179
❑ 98PinSna-AD11
❑ 98ScoRT-227
❑ 98ScoRTSS-PP124
❑ 98ScoRTSSAP-PP124
❑ 98ScoRTSSAP1-PP124
❑ 98SkyDugA-111
❑ 98SkyDugAIA-111
❑ 98SP Aut-42
❑ 98Stu-23
❑ 98StuGPP-23
❑ 98StuSPP-23
❑ 98Top-463
❑ 98TopChr-463
❑ 98TopChrR-463
❑ 98TopDevR-463
❑ 98TopDia-463
❑ 98TopMiniC-463
❑ 98Ult-461
❑ 98UltGolM-461
❑ 98UltMas-461
❑ 98UltPlaM-461
❑ 98UltRoctS-9
❑ 98UppDec-643
❑ 98UppDecNP-NP24
❑ 99Fle-372
❑ 99FleSta9-372
❑ 99FleWarT-372
❑ 99Pac-20
❑ 99PacCroC-16
❑ 99PacCroCPB-16
❑ 99PacPlaB-20
❑ 99PacRed-20
❑ 99Ult-209
❑ 99UltGolM-209
❑ 99UltMas-209
❑ 99UltPlaM-209
❑ 99UltWorP-9
❑ 99UppDec-31
❑ 99UppDec-373
❑ 99UppDecEL1-31
❑ 99UppDecEL1-373
❑ 99UppDecEL2-31
❑ 99UppDecEL2-373
❑ 99Vic-149

Garcia, Ken
❑ 86AncGlaPTI-10

Garcia, Kiko (Alfonso)
❑ 77BalOriP-6
❑ 77Top-474
❑ 78BalOriP-10
❑ 78Top-287
❑ 79Top-543
❑ 80BalOriP-7
❑ 80Top-37
❑ 81AstPos-4
❑ 81Don-514
❑ 81Fle-191
❑ 81OPC-192
❑ 81Top-688
❑ 81TopTra-765
❑ 82AstAstI-9
❑ 82AstPos-3
❑ 82Don-470
❑ 82Fle-215
❑ 82Top-377
❑ 83Don-569
❑ 83Fle-447
❑ 83PorBeaT-25
❑ 83Top-198
❑ 83TopTra-36T
❑ 84Don-545
❑ 84Fle-30
❑ 84Nes792-458
❑ 84PhiTas-30
❑ 84Top-458
❑ 84TopTif-458
❑ 85PhiTas-29
❑ 85Top-763
❑ 85TopTif-763
❑ 87AstShoSPT-8
❑ 91OriCro-150

Garcia, Leo
❑ 81AppFoxT-15
❑ 82AppFoxFr-3
❑ 83WatRedT-17
❑ 84WicAerRD-4
❑ 87NasSouTI-5
❑ 89TolMudHC-16
❑ 89TolMudHP-767
❑ 90CMC-140
❑ 90NasSouC-15
❑ 90NasSouP-245
❑ 90ProAAAF-557
❑ 91LinDriAAA-256
❑ 91NasSouLD-256
❑ 91NasSouP-2169
❑ 92OmaRoyF-2974
❑ 92OmaRoyS-330

Garcia, Leonard
❑ 77SalLakCGC-NNO
❑ 78SalLakCGC-NNO
❑ 79SalLakCGT-23A
❑ 80SalLakCGT-19
❑ 81SalLakCGT-1
❑ 82SpoIndT-26
❑ 86EdmTraP-12

Garcia, Librado
❑ 89BelBre2S-11
❑ 89BelBreIS-6
❑ 90MiaMirIS-8

Garcia, Longo
❑ 87PanAmTUBI-21
❑ 87PanAmTURB-14
❑ 89MiaMirIS-7
❑ 89MiaMirIS-5

Garcia, Luis
❑ 90LSUTigP-13
❑ 92GulCoaRSP-15
❑ 92KenTwiC-16
❑ 92KenTwiF-596
❑ 93BriTigC-9
❑ 93BriTigF-3652
❑ 93ForMyeMC-8
❑ 93ForMyeMF-2649
❑ 93IdaFalBSP-18
❑ 94JamJamC-10
❑ 94JamJamF-3972
❑ 96Bow-138
❑ 96BowFoi-138
❑ 96JacSunB-14
❑ 97JacSun-11
❑ 98TolMudHQ-17
❑ 98WinWar-13

Garcia, Manny
❑ 89ButCopKSP-19
❑ 91KanCouCC-16
❑ 91KanCouCP-2663
❑ 91KanCouCTI-7

Garcia, Marcelino
❑ 92SpoIndC-11
❑ 92SpoIndF-1296

Garcia, Marcos
❑ 90PenPilS-8
❑ 91CalLeLA-22
❑ 91SanBerSC-4
❑ 91SanBerSP-1980
❑ 92JacSunS-356

Garcia, Mario
❑ 90PriPatD-8
❑ 91HunCubC-9
❑ 91HunCubP-3327
❑ 92HunCubF-3139

Garcia, Michael
❑ 89BriTigS-9
❑ 89BufBisC-7
❑ 89BufBisP-1686
❑ 90FayGenP-2398
❑ 90ProAaA-84
❑ 91LakTigP-261
❑ 92LonTigF-627
❑ 92LonTigS-408
❑ 93LonTigF-2300

Garcia, Miguel
❑ 75BurBeeT-8
❑ 76CliPilT-16

Garcia, Miguel Angel
❑ 86PalSprAP-14
❑ 86PalSprAS-8
❑ 87MidAngP-1
❑ 89Don-622
❑ 89Fle-647
❑ 89FleGlo-647
❑ 90HarSenP-1188
❑ 90HarSenS-8
❑ 90UppDec-538
❑ 93LimRocDWB-92
❑ 93LinVenB-34
❑ 94VenLinU-186
❑ 94WatIndC-11
❑ 95LinVen-121
❑ 96-97LinVen-88

Garcia, Miguel Antonio
❑ 94WatIndF-3952
❑ 95GreFalDTI-37
❑ 96GreFalDB-14
❑ 96GreFalDTI-10
❑ 97VerBeaD-10
❑ 98SanAntMG-10

Garcia, Mike (Edward M.)
❑ 49IndTeal-10
❑ 50Bow-147
❑ 50IndNumN-10
❑ 50IndTeal-11
❑ 51Bow-150
❑ 51TopRedB-40
❑ 52Bow-7
❑ 52IndNumN-7
❑ 52Top-272
❑ 53BowC-43
❑ 53IndPenCBP-12
❑ 53Top-75
❑ 54Bow-100
❑ 54DanDee-8
❑ 55Bow-128
❑ 55Ind-2
❑ 55IndCarBL-2
❑ 55IndGolS-4
❑ 56Top-210
❑ 57IndSoh-5
❑ 57IndTeal-7
❑ 57Top-300
❑ 58IndTeal-7
❑ 58Top-196
❑ 59Ind-3
❑ 59Top-516
❑ 60Top-532
❑ 70SpoCarfCOP-3
❑ 75TCM195Cl-8
❑ 75TCM195Cl-39
❑ 77BobParMBC-6
❑ 83TopRep5-272
❑ 91TopArc1-75
❑ 94TedWil-26

Garcia, Mike 80's
❑ 80AndBraT-22
❑ 81DurBulT-2
❑ 82DurBulT-1
❑ 89AncBucTI-22
❑ 90SouAtlLAS-8
❑ 91LakTigC-5

Garcia, Neil
❑ 94JamJamF-3968
❑ 95FayGenTI-11
❑ 97St.PetDR-17
❑ 97St.PetDRUB-17
❑ 98St.PetDRM-15

Garcia, Nelson Jose
❑ 75OklCit8TI-19
❑ 76VenLeaS-62
❑ 78ArkTraT-11
❑ 80ArkTraT-17
❑ 80VenLeaS-82

Garcia, Omar
❑ 90KinMetB-13
❑ 90KinMetS-10
❑ 91ColMetPI-9
❑ 91ColMetPI-30
❑ 91ColMetPPI-6
❑ 92ClaFS7-337
❑ 92ColMetC-21
❑ 92ColMetF-303
❑ 92ColMetPI-7
❑ 92ColMetPIISPI-8
❑ 93ClaFS7-188
❑ 93ClaGolF-157
❑ 93SouAtlLAPI-11
❑ 93St.LucMC-11
❑ 93St.LuMF-2927
❑ 94BinMetF-709
❑ 94ExcFS7-234
❑ 95NorTidTI-12
❑ 96RicBraB-12
❑ 96RicBraRC-10

Garcia, Orlando
❑ 93PocPosF-4215
❑ 93PocPosSP-12

Garcia, Oscar
❑ 89St.CatBJP-2075

Garcia, Ossie
❑ 93GleFalRC-13
❑ 93GleFalRF-4018
❑ 94NewJerCC-8
❑ 94NewJerCF-3430
❑ 96PeoChiB-11
❑ 97PriWilC-12
❑ 98ArkTraM-9

Garcia, Pedro
❑ 73LinPor-100
❑ 73OPC-609
❑ 73Top-609
❑ 74OPC-142
❑ 74Top-142
❑ 74TopSta-195
❑ 75OPC-147
❑ 75Top-147
❑ 75TopMin-147
❑ 76DetTigP-6
❑ 76OPC-187
❑ 76SSP-234
❑ 76Top-187
❑ 77OPC-166
❑ 77Top-453
❑ 77WatIndT-9
❑ 86BreGreT-2
❑ 94BreMilB-30

Garcia, Ralph
❑ 73OPC-602
❑ 73Top-602

Garcia, Ramon
❑ 90SarWhiSS-10
❑ 91BirBarLD-59
❑ 91BirBarP-1449
❑ 91DonRoo-13
❑ 91LinDriAA-59
❑ 92ClaGam-97
❑ 92Don-658
❑ 92DonRoo-41
❑ 92OPC-176
❑ 92ProFS7-42
❑ 92Sco-745
❑ 92SkyAAAF-282
❑ 92StaClu-866
❑ 92Top-176
❑ 92TopDeb91-60

❑ 92TopGol-176
❑ 92TopGolW-176
❑ 92TopMic-176
❑ 92VanCanF-2716
❑ 92VanCanS-635
❑ 93LinVenB-30
❑ 93NasSouF-567
❑ 94WelPirC-10
❑ 94WelPirF-3489
❑ 95LinVen-95
❑ 96-97LinVen-25
❑ 96BrePol-7
❑ 97AstMot-27
❑ 97PacPriGotD-GD55
❑ 98ColCho-386
❑ 98Pac-316
❑ 98PacPlaB-316
❑ 98PacRedT-316
❑ 98PacSil-316
❑ 98UppDec-683

Garcia, Raphael
❑ 90MedHatBJB-25
❑ 91MyrBeaHC-6
❑ 91MyrBeaHP-2940
❑ 92DunBluJC-14
❑ 92MyrBeaHF-2189

Garcia, Ray
❑ 85UtiBluST-19

Garcia, Reggie
❑ 88MarPhiS-15
❑ 89SpaPhiP-1039
❑ 89SpaPhiS-9

Garcia, Rene
❑ 86BakDodP-10
❑ 87VerBeaDP-27

Garcia, Rich
❑ 88T/MUmp-22
❑ 89T/MUmp-20
❑ 90T/MUmp-19

Garcia, Ricky
❑ 95ElmPioTI-8
❑ 95ElmPioUTI-8
❑ 96KanCouCTI-10

Garcia, Sandro
❑ 98ChaAllCM-18

Garcia, Sandy
❑ 97PriDevR-6

Garcia, Santiago
❑ 88VanCanC-13
❑ 88VanCanP-764

Garcia, Sonny
❑ 98BluOriQ-17

Garcia, Steve
❑ 83BeaGolGT-12
❑ 84BeaGolGT-18
❑ 85LasVegSC-115
❑ 86LasVegSP-4
❑ 87LasVegSP-20
❑ 88AlbDukCm-24
❑ 88AlbDukP-249

Garcia, Vincente
❑ 94AshTouF-1790
❑ 95LinVen-206
❑ 95SalAvaTI-18
❑ 96-97LinVen-170
❑ 97NewHavRB-7
❑ 97SalAva-33
❑ 98NewHavRM-7
❑ 98NewHavRMA-7

Garcia, Wilson
❑ 97JohCitCTI-12
❑ 98NewJerCM-9

Garcia-Luna, Frank
❑ 92WelPirC-8
❑ 92WelPirF-1316
❑ 94AugGreC-4

Garciaparra, Nomar
❑ 92SpoIllFK1-725
❑ 92TopTra-39T
❑ 92TopTraG-39T
❑ 93StaCluM-93
❑ 94ClaUpdCotC-CC11
❑ 94SigRooDP-12
❑ 94SigRooDPS-12
❑ 94StaCluDP-69
❑ 94StaCluDPFDI-69
❑ 95ActPacF-60
❑ 95Bes-3
❑ 95BesFra-F2
❑ 95Bow-249
❑ 95BowBes-B29
❑ 95BowBesR-B29
❑ 95BowGolF-249
❑ 95ColCho-29
❑ 95ColChoGS-29
❑ 95ColChoSS-29
❑ 95Exc-10
❑ 95SPML-3
❑ 95SPML-20
❑ 95SPMLA-9
❑ 95SPMLDtS-DS15
❑ 95StaClu-97
❑ 95StaCluFDI-97
❑ 95StaCluMOP-97
❑ 95StaCluSTWS-97
❑ 95Top-587
❑ 95TreThuTI-19
❑ 95UppDec-10
❑ 95UppDecED-10
❑ 95UppDecEDG-10
❑ 95UppDecML-205
❑ 95UppDecMLFS-205
❑ 95UppDecMLOP-OP3
❑ 95UppDecSE-78
❑ 95UppDecSEG-78
❑ 96Bow-181
❑ 96BowBes-92
❑ 96BowBesAR-92
❑ 96BowBesP-BBP27
❑ 96BowBesPAR-BBP27
❑ 96BowBesPR-BBP27
❑ 96BowBesR-92
❑ 96BowFoi-181
❑ 96Exc-12
❑ 96Top-211
❑ 96TopChr-73
❑ 96TopChrR-73
❑ 97Bow-328
❑ 97BowBes-177
❑ 97BowBesAR-177
❑ 97BowBesBC-BC20
❑ 97BowBesBCAR-BC20
❑ 97BowBesBCR-BC20
❑ 97BowBesJ-177
❑ 97BowBesJAR-177
❑ 97BowBesJR-177
❑ 97BowBesMI-MI1
❑ 97BowBesMIAR-MI1
❑ 97BowBesMIARI-MI1
❑ 97BowBesMII-MI1
❑ 97BowBesMIR-MI1
❑ 97BowBesMIRI-MI1
❑ 97BowBesP-16
❑ 97BowBesPAR-16
❑ 97BowBesPR-16
❑ 97BowBesR-177
❑ 97BowChr-224
❑ 97BowChrI-224
❑ 97BowChrIR-224
❑ 97BowChrR-224
❑ 97BowChrSHR-SHR15
❑ 97BowChrSHRR-SHR15
❑ 97BowInt-328
❑ 97BowIntB-BBI11
❑ 97BowIntBAR-BBI11
❑ 97BowIntBR-BBI11
❑ 97BowScoHR-15
❑ 97Cir-148
❑ 97CirRav-148
❑ 97ColCho-25
❑ 97ColChoBS-2
❑ 97ColChoBSGS-2
❑ 97Don-362
❑ 97DonFraFea-3
❑ 97DonGolPP-362
❑ 97DonLim-40
❑ 97DonLim-69
❑ 97DonLimE-40
❑ 97DonLimE-69
❑ 97DonLimENG-40
❑ 97DonLimFotG-18
❑ 97DonPre-147
❑ 97DonPre-200
❑ 97DonPreCttC-147
❑ 97DonPreCttC-200
❑ 97DonRooDK-7
❑ 97DonRooDKC-7
❑ 97DonSig-72
❑ 97DonSigAC-44
❑ 97DonSigAM-44
❑ 97DonSigPPP-72
❑ 97DonSilPP-362
❑ 97DonTea-60
❑ 97DonTeaSPE-60
❑ 97DonVxP1-31
❑ 97E-X2-10
❑ 97E-X2Cred-10
❑ 97E-X2EssCre-10
❑ 97Fin-41
❑ 97FinRef-41
❑ 97FlaShoLC-26
❑ 97FlaShoLeg0-26
❑ 97FlaShoLeg1-26
❑ 97FlaShoM-A26
❑ 97FlaShoM-B26
❑ 97FlaShoM-C26
❑ 97FlaShoR0-26
❑ 97FlaShoR1-26
❑ 97FlaShoR2-26
❑ 97Fle-22
❑ 97FleNewH-4
❑ 97FleRooS-13
❑ 97FleTif-22
❑ 97Lea-185
❑ 97Lea-400
❑ 97LeaFraM-185
❑ 97LeaFraM-400
❑ 97LeaFraMDC-185
❑ 97LeaFraMDC-400
❑ 97LeaGolS-30
❑ 97MetUni-21
❑ 97MetUniMfG-3
❑ 97NewPin-170
❑ 97NewPinAP-170
❑ 97NewPinMC-170
❑ 97NewPinPP-170
❑ 97Pac-39
❑ 97PacLigB-39
❑ 97PacPri-15
❑ 97PacPriLB-15
❑ 97PacPriP-15
❑ 97PacSil-39
❑ 97Pin-172
❑ 97PinArtP-PP172
❑ 97PinCer-114
❑ 97PinCerMBla-114
❑ 97PinCerMBlu-114
❑ 97PinCerMG-114
❑ 97PinCerMR-114
❑ 97PinCerR-114
❑ 97PinEpixGO-E5
❑ 97PinEpixPE-E5
❑ 97PinIns-146
❑ 97PinInsCE-146
❑ 97PinInsDE-146
❑ 97PinMusC-172
❑ 97PinPrePla-172
❑ 97PinTotCPB-114
❑ 97PinTotCPG-114
❑ 97PinTotCPR-114
❑ 97PinX-P-117
❑ 97PinX-PMoS-117
❑ 97PinX-PMP-14
❑ 97PinX-PMW-15
❑ 97PinX-PMWG-15
❑ 97PinX-PMWS-15
❑ 97PinX-PreMPS-14
❑ 97PreCon-24
❑ 97SarRedS-11
❑ 97Sco-473
❑ 97ScoArtPWB-473
❑ 97ScoResC-473
❑ 97ScoShoS-473
❑ 97ScoShoSAP-473
❑ 97Sel-106
❑ 97SelArtP-106
❑ 97SelCom-106
❑ 97SelRegG-106
❑ 97SelRooR-14
❑ 97SelToootT-25
❑ 97SelToootTMB-25
❑ 97SP-3
❑ 97SpoIll-6
❑ 97SpoIllEE-6
❑ 97SPx-13
❑ 97SPxBro-13
❑ 97SPxGol-13
❑ 97SPxGraF-13
❑ 97SPxSil-13
❑ 97SPxSte-13
❑ 97StaClu-157
❑ 97StaClu-188
❑ 97StaCluC-CO8
❑ 97StaCluM-M37
❑ 97StaCluMOP-157
❑ 97StaCluMOP-188
❑ 97StaCluMOP-M37
❑ 97StrAll-22
❑ 97Stu-160
❑ 97StuPrePG-160
❑ 97StuPrePS-160
❑ 97Top-293
❑ 97TopAweI-AI4
❑ 97TopChr-99
❑ 97TopChrR-99
❑ 97TopGal-151
❑ 97TopGalPPI-151
❑ 97TopScr-5
❑ 97TopScrT-5
❑ 97TopSta-93
❑ 97TopStaAM-93
❑ 97UD3-46
❑ 97UD3GenNex-GN18
❑ 97Ult-327
❑ 97UltGolME-327
❑ 97UltPlaME-327
❑ 97UppDec-234
❑ 97UppDecBCP-BC7
❑ 97UppDecSA-4
❑ 97UppDecSAG-4
❑ 97Zen-44
❑ 97Zen0x10-22
❑ 97Zen8x1D-22
❑ 98Bow-1
❑ 98BowBes-73
❑ 98BowBesAR-73
❑ 98BowBesMIF-MI3
❑ 98BowBesMIFAR-MI3
❑ 98BowBesMIFR-MI3
❑ 98BowBesR-73
❑ 98BowCerBlueAU-42
❑ 98BowCerGA-42
❑ 98BowCerSA-42
❑ 98BowChr-1
❑ 98BowChrGA-1
❑ 98BowChrGAR-1
❑ 98BowChrI-1
❑ 98BowChrIR-1
❑ 98BowChrR-1
❑ 98BowChrR-44
❑ 98BowChrRR-44
❑ 98BowGolA-1
❑ 98BowInt-1
❑ 98CirThu-5
❑ 98CirThuB-5
❑ 98CirThuFT-4
❑ 98CirThuLA-4
❑ 98CirThuQS-4
❑ 98CirThuRav-5
❑ 98CirThuRR-5
❑ 98CirThuSupRav-5
❑ 98ColCho-1
❑ 98ColCho-20
❑ 98ColCho-261
❑ 98ColCho-267
❑ 98ColCho-274
❑ 98ColCho-321
❑ 98ColChoB5-321
❑ 98ColChoCG-1
❑ 98ColChoCtG-CG15A
❑ 98ColChoCtG-CG15B
❑ 98ColChoCtG-CG15C
❑ 98ColChoCtGExch-CG15
❑ 98ColChoCtGIW-CG15
❑ 98ColChoGJ5-274
❑ 98ColChoMBH-7
❑ 98ColChoRJ-1
❑ 98ColChoS'-4
❑ 98ColChoSQ-SQ1
❑ 98ColChoSQ-SQ46
❑ 98ColChoSQDouble-25
❑ 98ColChoSQHR-25
❑ 98ColChoSQSingle-25
❑ 98ColChoSQTriple-25
❑ 98CroRoy-24
❑ 98CroRoyDK-5
❑ 98CroRoyFoB-5
❑ 98CroRoyFoBA-5
❑ 98CroRoyPotG-6
❑ 98Don-57
❑ 98Don-170
❑ 98Don-374
❑ 98Don-412
❑ 98DonCol-57
❑ 98DonCol-170
❑ 98DonCol-195
❑ 98DonColE-482
❑ 98DonColE-547
❑ 98DonColE-548
❑ 98DonColL-262
❑ 98DonColL-397
❑ 98DonColP-562
❑ 98DonColP-729
❑ 98DonColS-57
❑ 98DonColS-170
❑ 98DonColS-190
❑ 98DonCruG-13
❑ 98DonCruP-13
❑ 98DonCruR-13
❑ 98DonDay-5
❑ 98DonDom-27
❑ 98DonEli-82
❑ 98DonEli-147
❑ 98DonEli-148
❑ 98DonEliA-82
❑ 98DonEliA-147
❑ 98DonEliA-148
❑ 98DonEliBttF-8
❑ 98DonEliBttFA-8
❑ 98DonEliC-10
❑ 98DonEliI-12
❑ 98DonEliMC-10
❑ 98DonEliS-82
❑ 98DonEliS-147
❑ 98DonEliS-148
❑ 98DonFANT-14
❑ 98DonFANTDC-14
❑ 98DonGolPP-57
❑ 98DonGolPP-170
❑ 98DonGolPP-374
❑ 98DonGolPP-412
❑ 98DonLonL-20
❑ 98DonPre-12
❑ 98DonPre-179
❑ 98DonPreGB-19
❑ 98DonPreGES-21
❑ 98DonPreGoB-19
❑ 98DonPreGX-21
❑ 98DonPreGXDC-21
❑ 98DonPrePM-12
❑ 98DonPreSeat-12
❑ 98DonPreSeat-179
❑ 98DonPreTP-19
❑ 98DonPreTPD-10
❑ 98DonPreTPG-19
❑ 98DonPreTPS-19
❑ 98DonPreTW-1
❑ 98DonPriCD-57
❑ 98DonPriCD-170
❑ 98DonPriCD-195
❑ 98DonPriCE-482
❑ 98DonPriCE-547
❑ 98DonPriCE-548
❑ 98DonPriCL-262
❑ 98DonPriCL-397
❑ 98DonPriCP-562
❑ 98DonPriCP-729
❑ 98DonProLS-17
❑ 98DonRatR-20
❑ 98DonRatRM-20
❑ 98DonSig-3
❑ 98DonSigAC-44
❑ 98DonSigAM-45
❑ 98DonSigP-3
❑ 98DonSilPP-57
❑ 98DonSilPP-170
❑ 98DonSilPP-374
❑ 98DonSilPP-412
❑ 98DonSonM9-2
❑ 98E-X2-95
❑ 98E-X2ECFut-95
❑ 98E-X2ECNow-95
❑ 98Fin-140
❑ 98FinCen-C3
❑ 98FinCenR-C3
❑ 98FinMysF1-M11
❑ 98FinMysF1-M12
❑ 98FinMysF1-M13
❑ 98FinMysF1-M14
❑ 98FinMysF2-M1
❑ 98FinMysF2-M2
❑ 98FinMysF2-M3
❑ 98FinMysF2R-M1
❑ 98FinMysF2R-M2
❑ 98FinMysF2R-M3
❑ 98FinMysFR-M11
❑ 98FinMysFR-M12
❑ 98FinMysFR-M13
❑ 98FinMysFR-M14
❑ 98FinNo--140
❑ 98FinNo-R-140
❑ 98FinOve-A3
❑ 98FinOveR-A3
❑ 98FinPowZ-P10
❑ 98FinRef-140
❑ 98FinStaS-SS4
❑ 98FinStaSJ-3
❑ 98FinTheM-TM6
❑ 98FinTheMR-TM6
❑ 98FlaShoLeg0-5
❑ 98FlaShoLeg1-5
❑ 98FlaShoLeg2-5
❑ 98FlaShoLeg3-5
❑ 98FlaShoLegM-5
❑ 98FlaShoP1-6
❑ 98FlaShoR0-5
❑ 98FlaShoR1-5
❑ 98FlaShoR2-5
❑ 98FlaShoR3-5
❑ 98Fle-5
❑ 98Fle-313
❑ 98Fle-581
❑ 98FleDiamInk-4
❑ 98FleDiaS-6
❑ 98FleDiaT-DT3
❑ 98FleIn TC-IC5
❑ 98FleLumC-4
❑ 98FlePowG-8
❑ 98FleRooS-5
❑ 98FleVin'-9
❑ 98FleVin'C-9
❑ 98FleZon-5
❑ 98Lea-63
❑ 98Lea-198
❑ 98LeaFraDA-63
❑ 98LeaFraDA-198
❑ 98LeaFraF-63
❑ 98LeaFraF-198
❑ 98LeaFraM-63
❑ 98LeaFraM-198
❑ 98LeaFraM-63
❑ 98LeaFraM-198
❑ 98LeaFraMDC-63
❑ 98LeaFraMDC-198
❑ 98LeaFraMDC-63
❑ 98LeaFraMDC-198
❑ 98LeaFraMZ2-63
❑ 98LeaFraMZ2-198
❑ 98LeaRCMLHDSamp-3
❑ 98LeaRS-37
❑ 98LeaRS-155
❑ 98LeaRS-186
❑ 98LeaRSCross-9
❑ 98LeaRSExtM-10
❑ 98LeaRSExtMDC-10
❑ 98LeaRSGreHit-13
❑ 98LeaRSHRDerby-13
❑ 98LeaRSLHolo-37
❑ 98LeaRSLHolo-155
❑ 98LeaRSLHolo-186
❑ 98LeaRSLong-37
❑ 98LeaRSLong-155
❑ 98LeaRSLong-186
❑ 98LeaRSMLHD-3
❑ 98LeaRSTicMas-9
❑ 98LeaRSTicMasDC-9
❑ 98LeaRTrue-37
❑ 98LeaRTrue-155
❑ 98LeaRTrue-186
❑ 98LeaStaRep-8
❑ 98LeaStaS-13
❑ 98LeaStaSDC-13
❑ 98MetUni-16
❑ 98MetUniAT-10
❑ 98MetUniPMG-16
❑ 98MetUniT-10
❑ 98MetUniUL-10
❑ 98Pac-39
❑ 98PacAur-17
❑ 98PacAurCube-5
❑ 98PacAurHC-5
❑ 98PacAurKotML-4
❑ 98PacAurODLC-5
❑ 98PacAurPF-5
❑ 98PacAurPFC-5
❑ 98PacAurPFPB-5
❑ 98PacAurPFR-5
❑ 98PacAurPFS-5
❑ 98PacCraCh-4
❑ 98PacGolCDC-7
❑ 98PacInCage-4
❑ 98PacInv-14
❑ 98PacInv-147
❑ 98PacInvCCDB-4
❑ 98PacInvCCG-4
❑ 98PacInvCCG-4
❑ 98PacInvCCLB-4
❑ 98PacInvCCP-4
❑ 98PacInvCCR-4
❑ 98PacInvGems-21
❑ 98PacInvInt-3A
❑ 98PacInvPBlue-14
❑ 98PacInvPBlue-147
❑ 98PacInvPhoto-3
❑ 98PacInvSilv-14
❑ 98PacInvSilv-147
❑ 98PacInvTeam-4
❑ 98PacLatotML-6
❑ 98PacNes-11
❑ 98PacOme-37
❑ 98PacOmeEP-2
❑ 98PacOmeEP1o1-2
❑ 98PacOmeFTF-1
❑ 98PacOmeOnIns-2
❑ 98PacOmeP-2
❑ 98PacOmeR-37

❑ 98PacOnl-113A
❑ 98PacOnl-113B
❑ 98PacOnl-133
❑ 98PacOnlR-113A
❑ 98PacOnlR-113B
❑ 98PacOnlR-133
❑ 98PacOnlWC-113A
❑ 98PacOnlWC-113B
❑ 98PacOnlWC-133
❑ 98PacPar-20
❑ 98PacParC-20
❑ 98PacParFC-4
❑ 98PacParG-20
❑ 98PacParHS-20
❑ 98PacParI-35
❑ 98PacParPB-20
❑ 98PacParR-20
❑ 98PacParSD-4
❑ 98PacParTC-3
❑ 98PacPlaB-39
❑ 98PacRedT-39
❑ 98PacSil-39
❑ 98PacTeaC-3
❑ 98Pin-197
❑ 98Pin-198
❑ 98PinArtP-PP100
❑ 98PinEpixGE-E5
❑ 98PinEpixGP-E5
❑ 98PinEpixPO-E5
❑ 98PinEpixPP-E5
❑ 98PinEpixSE-E5
❑ 98PinEpixSO-E5
❑ 98PinEpixSP-E5
❑ 98PinIns-5
❑ 98PinIns-135
❑ 98PinInsBtN-6
❑ 98PinInsC-3
❑ 98PinInsCE-5
❑ 98PinInsCE-135
❑ 98PinInsCG-3
❑ 98PinInsDE-5
❑ 98PinInsDE-135
❑ 98PinInsSG-2AB
❑ 98PinInsSG-2CD
❑ 98PinInsSG-6AB
❑ 98PinInsSG-6CD
❑ 98PinInsSGS-2AB
❑ 98PinInsSGS-2CD
❑ 98PinInsSGS-6AB
❑ 98PinInsSGS-6CD
❑ 98PinMinB-26
❑ 98PinMinCB-26
❑ 98PinMinCBAP-26
❑ 98PinMinCGP-26
❑ 98PinMinCGPAP-26
❑ 98PinMinCN-26
❑ 98PinMinCNAP-26
❑ 98PinMinCSGR-26
❑ 98PinMinDC-26
❑ 98PinMinG-26
❑ 98PinMinMCSS-26
❑ 98PinMinMG-5
❑ 98PinMinMGC-5
❑ 98PinMinS-26
❑ 98PinMusC-PP100
❑ 98PinPer-12
❑ 98PinPerBB-6
❑ 98PinPerBBSamp-6
❑ 98PinPerBBSO-6
❑ 98PinPerLP-15
❑ 98PinPerPP-12
❑ 98PinPerPT-3
❑ 98PinPerSftF-10
❑ 98PinPerSftFShop-3
❑ 98PinPlu-8
❑ 98PinPlu-189
❑ 98PinPluAE-5
❑ 98PinPluAEE-5
❑ 98PinPluAEP-5
❑ 98PinPluAP-PP4
❑ 98PinPluGAP-PP4
❑ 98PinPluLM-1
❑ 98PinPluMAP-PP4
❑ 98PinPluPieGame-9
❑ 98PinPluSamp-8
❑ 98PinPluTP-14
❑ 98PinPluTPG-14
❑ 98PinPluTPM-14
❑ 98PinPluY-4
❑ 98PinPowPJ-16
❑ 98PinPowPJS-16
❑ 98PinPreP-197
❑ 98PinPreP-198
❑ 98PinPreP-E5
❑ 98PinPreP-S39
❑ 98PinPreP-S40
❑ 98PinPreP-S41
❑ 98PinPreP-S42
❑ 98PinPreP-S43
❑ 98PinSna-BRS9
❑ 98PinSna-BRS13
❑ 98PinSpe-39
❑ 98PinSpe-40
❑ 98PinSpe-41
❑ 98PinSpe-42
❑ 98PinSpe-43
❑ 98PreCon-3
❑ 98RedSoxS-7
❑ 98RedSoxSP-7
❑ 98Revo-24
❑ 98RevoFP-2
❑ 98RevoMLI-2
❑ 98RevoPTP-2
❑ 98RevoRooHH-24
❑ 98RevoShow-2
❑ 98RevoSS-24
❑ 98Sco-91
❑ 98ScoComP-9A
❑ 98ScoComP-9B
❑ 98ScoComP-9C
❑ 98ScoComPG-9A
❑ 98ScoComPG-9B
❑ 98ScoComPG-9C
❑ 98ScoEpix-E5
❑ 98ScoFirP-10
❑ 98ScoLoaL-LL9
❑ 98ScoNewS-NS2
❑ 98ScoRT-35
❑ 98ScoRT-260
❑ 98ScoRTASEpix-5
❑ 98ScoRTSS-PP35
❑ 98ScoRTSS-PP153
❑ 98ScoRTSSAP-PP35
❑ 98ScoRTSSAP-PP153
❑ 98ScoRTSSAP1-PP35
❑ 98ScoRTSSAP1-PP153
❑ 98ScoRTStarGaz-7
❑ 98ScoSS-PP139
❑ 98ScoSSAP-PP139
❑ 98SelSelSamp-2
❑ 98SkyDugA-57
❑ 98SkyDugA-121
❑ 98SkyDugAAR-5
❑ 98SkyDugADH-DH6
❑ 98SkyDugAIA-57
❑ 98SkyDugAIA-121
❑ 98SP Aut-60
❑ 98SP Aut-SD15
❑ 98SP AutC-NG
❑ 98SP AutSD-SD15
❑ 98SP AutSDT-SD15
❑ 98SpoIll-43
❑ 98SpoIll-195
❑ 98SpoIllEC-EC8
❑ 98SpoIllEE-43
❑ 98SpoIllEE-195
❑ 98SpoIllFE-43
❑ 98SpoIllFE-195
❑ 98SpoIllODMP-OD5
❑ 98SpoIllTaN-83
❑ 98SpoIllTaNEE-83
❑ 98SpoIllTaNGS-13
❑ 98SpoIllWSF-42
❑ 98SpoIllWSFEE-42
❑ 98SpoIllWSFFE-42
❑ 98SPxFin-1
❑ 98SPxFin-46
❑ 98SPxFin-146
❑ 98SPxFin-231
❑ 98SPxFin-255
❑ 98SPxFin-352
❑ 98SPxFinR-1
❑ 98SPxFinR-46
❑ 98SPxFinR-146
❑ 98SPxFinR-231
❑ 98SPxFinR-255
❑ 98SPxFinR-352
❑ 98SPxFinS-1
❑ 98SPxFinS-46
❑ 98SPxFinS-146
❑ 98SPxFinS-231
❑ 98SPxFinS-255
❑ 98SPxFinS-352
❑ 98StaCluBP-BP1
❑ 98StaCluC-CS1
❑ 98StaCluC-CS2
❑ 98StaCluC-CS3
❑ 98StaCluFDI-171
❑ 98StaCluI-171
❑ 98StaCluOneK-171
❑ 98StaCluPP-171
❑ 98StaCluTIll-T14B
❑ 98StaCluTLme-T14B
❑ 98StaCluTLmo-T14B
❑ 98Stu-60
❑ 98StuFF-12
❑ 98StuFFDC-12
❑ 98StuGPP-60
❑ 98StuMast-9
❑ 98StuPor8x10-13
❑ 98StuPor8x10GP-13
❑ 98StuSony99-2
❑ 98StuSPP-60
❑ 98Top-268
❑ 98Top-335
❑ 98Top-481
❑ 98TopBabB-BB3
❑ 98TopChr-268
❑ 98TopChr-335
❑ 98TopChr-481
❑ 98TopChrBB-BB3
❑ 98TopChrBBR-BB3
❑ 98TopChrR-268
❑ 98TopChrR-335
❑ 98TopChrR-481
❑ 98TopDevR-268
❑ 98TopDevR-335
❑ 98TopDevR-481
❑ 98TopDia-268
❑ 98TopDia-335
❑ 98TopDia-481
❑ 98TopFocP-FP2
❑ 98TopGal-140
❑ 98TopGalAG-AG5
❑ 98TopGalGoH-GH6
❑ 98TopGalGoHJ-GH6
❑ 98TopGalGP-140
❑ 98TopGalOPP-140
❑ 98TopGalPG-PG7
❑ 98TopGalPPI-140
❑ 98TopGalPPIA-140
❑ 98TopGolLabC1-78
❑ 98TopGolLabC1B-78
❑ 98TopGolLabC1One-78
❑ 98TopGolLabC1R-78
❑ 98TopGolLabC2-78
❑ 98TopGolLabC2B-78
❑ 98TopGolLabC2One-78
❑ 98TopGolLabC2R-78
❑ 98TopGolLabC3-78
❑ 98TopGolLabC3B-78
❑ 98TopGolLabC3One-78
❑ 98TopGolLabC3R-78
❑ 98TopMiniC-268
❑ 98TopMiniC-335
❑ 98TopMiniC-481
❑ 98TopMysFB-M1
❑ 98TopMysFB-M1
❑ 98TopMysFBR-M1
❑ 98TopMysFBR-M1
❑ 98TopOpeD-162
❑ 98TopSta-125
❑ 98TopSta'S-12
❑ 98TopSta'SGH-12
❑ 98TopStaB-125
❑ 98TopStaG-G3
❑ 98TopStaG-125
❑ 98TopStaGG-G3
❑ 98TopStaGGR-G3
❑ 98TopStaGR-125
❑ 98TopStaGS-G3
❑ 98TopStaLB-L14
❑ 98TopStaLG-L14
❑ 98TopStaLGR-L14
❑ 98TopStaLS-L14
❑ 98TopStaS-125
❑ 98TopStaSteG-12
❑ 98TopSup-34
❑ 98TopSup-34
❑ 98TopTek-15
❑ 98TopTekD-15
❑ 98UD3-35
❑ 98UD3-125
❑ 98UD3-215
❑ 98UD3DieCut-35
❑ 98UD3DieCut-125
❑ 98UD3DieCut-215
❑ 98UD3PCBlowup-35
❑ 98Ult-33
❑ 98Ult-214
❑ 98Ult-480
❑ 98UltBacttF-7
❑ 98UltDouT-16
❑ 98UltGolM-33
❑ 98UltGolM-214
❑ 98UltGolM-480
❑ 98UltKidG-8
❑ 98UltMas-33
❑ 98UltMas-214
❑ 98UltMas-480
❑ 98UltMilM-9
❑ 98UltNot-17
❑ 98UltPlaM-33
❑ 98UltPlaM-214
❑ 98UltPlaM-480
❑ 98UltTicS-4
❑ 98UltTop3-19
❑ 98UltWinN-17
❑ 98UppDec-320
❑ 98UppDec-452
❑ 98UppDec-533
❑ 98UppDec-616
❑ 98UppDec5x7-320
❑ 98UppDec5x7-616
❑ 98UppDecAC-AS25
❑ 98UppDecAG-AG17
❑ 98UppDecAGDC-AG17
❑ 98UppDecBCP-BC1
❑ 98UppDecCD-CD15
❑ 98UppDecDS-DS2
❑ 98UppDecR-13
❑ 98UppDecRBBop-BB4
❑ 98UppDecREP-1
❑ 98UppDecRGKoG-G3
❑ 98UppDecRL-1
❑ 98UppDecRQL-Q3
❑ 98UppDecRTC-TC4
❑ 98UppDecSFPD-PZ9
❑ 98UppDecSFPZSX-PZ9
❑ 98UppDecTMT-7
❑ 98UppDecTMTG-7
❑ 98UppDecU-5
❑ 98Zen-18
❑ 98Zen5 xx7-1
❑ 98Zen5x7GoldImp-1
❑ 98Zen5x7Imp-1
❑ 98ZenEpi-E5
❑ 98ZenRaitB-15
❑ 98ZenSampL-Z1
❑ 98ZenSamS-18
❑ 98ZenZ-G-18
❑ 98ZenZ-S-18
❑ 98ZenZ-T-13
❑ 98ZenZ-TG-13
❑ 99199Fin-50
❑ 99199Fin-103
❑ 99199Fin-251
❑ 99AllMysFR-M8
❑ 99AurComP-2A
❑ 99AurComP-2B
❑ 99AurKinotML-2
❑ 99AurOn DL-3
❑ 99AurPenF-4
❑ 99AurPenF-4
❑ 99AurPenFB-4
❑ 99AurPenFS-4
❑ 99AurSty-4
❑ 99Bow-263
❑ 99BowBes-35
❑ 99BowBes-89
❑ 99BowBesAR-35
❑ 99BowBesAR-89
❑ 99BowBesFBMI-FB4
❑ 99BowBesFBMII-FB4
❑ 99BowBesFBMIII-FB4
❑ 99BowBesMI-M9
❑ 99BowBesMIAR-M9
❑ 99BowBesMIR-M9
❑ 99BowBesR-35
❑ 99BowBesR-89
❑ 99BowChrDA-DA15
❑ 99BowChrDAR-DA15
❑ 99BowEarR-ER7
❑ 99BowGol-263
❑ 99BowInt-263
❑ 99CroRoyB-23
❑ 99CroRoyC2-2
❑ 99CroRoyCCDB-2
❑ 99CroRoyCCG-2
❑ 99CroRoyCCG-2
❑ 99CroRoyCCLB-2
❑ 99CroRoyCCP-2
❑ 99CroRoyCCP-2
❑ 99CroRoyCCR-2
❑ 99CroRoyL-23
❑ 99CroRoyLL-3
❑ 99CroRoyMP-4
❑ 99CroRoyOD-23
❑ 99CroRoyPotG-6
❑ 99CroRoyPP-6
❑ 99CroRoyPPN-6
❑ 99DumSet-156
❑ 99DumSet-ER7
❑ 99E-X Cen-2
❑ 99E-X CenECFut-2
❑ 99E-X CenECNow-2
❑ 99E-XCenFoF'-2
❑ 99FinAarAwC-HA3
❑ 99FinAarAwCR-HA3
❑ 99FinCom-C5
❑ 99FinComDualR-C5
❑ 99FinFraR-FR5
❑ 99FinFraRR-FR5
❑ 99FinGolRef-50
❑ 99FinGolRef-103
❑ 99FinGolRef-251
❑ 99FinMil-M29
❑ 99FinMil-M36
❑ 99FinPeelHyp-5
❑ 99FinPeelSpark-5
❑ 99FinPeeSS-5
❑ 99FinRef-50
❑ 99FinRef-103
❑ 99FinRef-251
❑ 99FinSplS-SS3
❑ 99FinSplSDR-SS3
❑ 99FinTeaFB-TF15
❑ 99FinTeaFBR-TF15
❑ 99FinTeaFG-TF15
❑ 99FinTeaFGR-TF15
❑ 99FinTeaFR-TF15
❑ 99FinTeaFRR-TF15
❑ 99FlaShoLeg1-10
❑ 99FlaShoLeg2-10
❑ 99FlaShoLeg3-10
❑ 99FlaShoLegM1-10
❑ 99FlaShoLegM2-10
❑ 99FlaShoLegM3-10
❑ 99FlaShoMoG-2
❑ 99FlaShoR1-10
❑ 99FlaShoR2-10
❑ 99FlaShoR3-10
❑ 99Fle-12
❑ 99Fle-580
❑ 99Fle-597
❑ 99FleBri-3
❑ 99FleBri2G-3
❑ 99FleBriBlu-3
❑ 99FleBriGol-3
❑ 99FleBriSS-5
❑ 99FleBriSSP-5
❑ 99FleDiaM-3
❑ 99FleDiaSkiSheet-NNO
❑ 99FleGolM-4
❑ 99FleMys-11
❑ 99FleMys-156
❑ 99FleMysD-4
❑ 99FleMysG-11
❑ 99FleMysM-11
❑ 99FleMysM-156
❑ 99FleSta9-12
❑ 99FleSta9-580
❑ 99FleSta9-597
❑ 99FleVin'-12
❑ 99FleWarT-12
❑ 99FleWarT-580
❑ 99FleWarT-597
❑ 99HomHer-4
❑ 99MetUni-179
❑ 99MetUni-288
❑ 99MetUniBWTW-11
❑ 99MetUniDS-12
❑ 99MetUniGM-179
❑ 99MetUniGM-288
❑ 99MetUniPM-10
❑ 99MetUniPMG-179
❑ 99MetUniPMG-288
❑ 99Pac-65
❑ 99Pac-65A
❑ 99PacAur-27
❑ 99PacAurOD-27
❑ 99PacCraCho-2
❑ 99PacCroC-45
❑ 99PacCroC-3
❑ 99PacCroCITC-3
❑ 99PacCroCPB-45
❑ 99PacCroCPC-2
❑ 99PacCroCTC-5
❑ 99PacCroCTM-3
❑ 99PacDynaD-2
❑ 99PacDynaDT-2
❑ 99PacGolCDC-3
❑ 99PacInv-23
❑ 99PacInvDM-2
❑ 99PacInvFP-5
❑ 99PacInvGotG-2
❑ 99PacInvOD-23
❑ 99PacInvPB-23
❑ 99PacInvSF-5
❑ 99PacInvSF-5B
❑ 99PacInvSH-5
❑ 99PacInvSH-5B
❑ 99PacInvTA-4
❑ 99PacOme-40
❑ 99PacOme5T-18
❑ 99PacOme5TT-18
❑ 99PacOmeC-40
❑ 99PacOmeDD-1
❑ 99PacOmeDM-8
❑ 99PacOmeEP-5
❑ 99PacOmeEP1o1-5
❑ 99PacOmeG-40
❑ 99PacOmeH'-5
❑ 99PacOmePB-40
❑ 99PacPar-38
❑ 99PacParC-38
❑ 99PacParCB-3
❑ 99PacParCBPP-3
❑ 99PacParFC-4
❑ 99PacParG-38
❑ 99PacParHoloGold-38
❑ 99PacParHS-38
❑ 99PacParOD-38
❑ 99PacParPB-8
❑ 99PacParPB-38
❑ 99PacParRed-38
❑ 99PacParTC-5
❑ 99PacPlaB-65
❑ 99PacPlaB-65A
❑ 99PacPri-22
❑ 99PacPriAotG-5
❑ 99PacPriBL-2
❑ 99PacPriDG-6
❑ 99PacPriEP-5
❑ 99PacPriHB-22
❑ 99PacPriHG-22
❑ 99PacPriHM-22
❑ 99PacPriHP-22
❑ 99PacPriRed-22
❑ 99PacPriS-4
❑ 99PacPriS206-4
❑ 99PacPriS206R-4
❑ 99PacPriSE-4
❑ 99PacPriSP-4
❑ 99PacPriSP-4
❑ 99PacPriSV-4
❑ 99PacRed-65
❑ 99PacRed-65A
❑ 99PacTeaC-3
❑ 99Pin-7
❑ 99Rev-24
❑ 99RevDiaL-9
❑ 99RevFouP-4
❑ 99RevMLBIcon-2
❑ 99RevPremDate-24
❑ 99RevRet-24
❑ 99RevShaSS-24
❑ 99RevThoitS-5
❑ 99RevTri-3
❑ 99RevTri-3
❑ 99SkyMolM-135
❑ 99SkyMolMF-35
❑ 99SkyMolMFS-35
❑ 99SkyMolMFT-35
❑ 99SkyMolMX-135
❑ 99SkyPre-29
❑ 99SkyPre-280
❑ 99SkyPre-298
❑ 99SkyPreIN-3
❑ 99SkyPreLB-6
❑ 99SkyPreR-29
❑ 99SkyPreR-280
❑ 99SkyPreR-298
❑ 99SkyPreSB-3
❑ 99SkyPreSotG-14
❑ 99SkyThu-294
❑ 99SkyThuDial1-D1
❑ 99SkyThuHip-H2
❑ 99SkyThuRant-294
❑ 99SkyThuRave-294
❑ 99SkyThuwww-WB2
❑ 99SP Aut-15
❑ 99SP AutC-NG
❑ 99SP AutCG-NG
❑ 99SP AutEF-E8
❑ 99SP AutHRC-HR13
❑ 99SP AutR-R8
❑ 99SP SigAuto-NG
❑ 99SP SigAutoG-NG
❑ 99SPAutHRCDC-HR13
❑ 99SpoIll-139
❑ 99SpoIllDD-8
❑ 99SpoIllH-17
❑ 99SPSig-1
❑ 99SPx-23
❑ 99SPxDom-FB4

❑ 99SPxFinR-23
❑ 99SPxFinS-23
❑ 99SPxPowE-PE8
❑ 99SPxPreS-PS16
❑ 99SPxStaF-SF4
❑ 99StaClu-225
❑ 99StaCluC-SCC1
❑ 99StaCluCR-SCC1
❑ 99StaCluFDI-225
❑ 99StaCluNC-NC9
❑ 99StaCluOoaK-225
❑ 99StaCluPP-225
❑ 99StaCluTI-T7A
❑ 99StaCluTI-T9B
❑ 99StaCluTL-T7A
❑ 99StaCluTL-T9B
❑ 99StaCluTL-T7A
❑ 99StaCluTL-T9B
❑ 99ThuSkySupR-294
❑ 99Top-265
❑ 99Top-452
❑ 99TopActF-2
❑ 99TopActFAU-2
❑ 99TopActFCU-2
❑ 99TopAllMF-M8
❑ 99TopBlaLC1-86
❑ 99TopBlaLC2-86
❑ 99TopBlaLC3-86
❑ 99TopChr-265
❑ 99TopChr-452
❑ 99TopChrERttH-ER1
❑ 99TopChrERttH-ER1
❑ 99TopChrF1-FF2
❑ 99TopChrF1R-FF2
❑ 99TopChrLotD-LD10
❑ 99TopChrLotDR-LD10
❑ 99TopChrNB-NB4
❑ 99TopChrNBR-NB4
❑ 99TopChrR-265
❑ 99TopChrR-452
❑ 99TopChrRN-RN6
❑ 99TopChrRNR-RN6
❑ 99TopGal-13
❑ 99TopGal-107
❑ 99TopGalE-E14
❑ 99TopGalGoH-GH6
❑ 99TopGalHer-TH3
❑ 99TopGalHerP-TH3
❑ 99TopGalPP-13
❑ 99TopGalPP-107
❑ 99TopGalPPI-13
❑ 99TopGalPPI-107
❑ 99TopGolL-86
❑ 99TopGolLC1-86
❑ 99TopGolLC2-86
❑ 99TopGolLOtO-86
❑ 99TopGolLRtA-RA6
❑ 99TopGolLRtAB-RA6
❑ 99TopGolLRtAOtO-RA6
❑ 99TopGolLRtAR-RA6
❑ 99TopLorotD-LD10
❑ 99TopMVPP-265
❑ 99TopMVPP-452
❑ 99TopNewB-NB4
❑ 99TopOpeD-138
❑ 99TopOver-B1
❑ 99TopPowB-PB17
❑ 99TopPowBR-PB17
❑ 99TopRecN-RN6
❑ 99TopRecNG-RN6
❑ 99TopRedLC1-86
❑ 99TopRedLC2-86
❑ 99TopRedLC3-86
❑ 99TopSta-4
❑ 99TopSta-171
❑ 99TopSta'S-41
❑ 99TopSta'SG-41
❑ 99TopSta'SGDH-41
❑ 99TopSta1Foil-4
❑ 99TopSta2Foil-4
❑ 99TopSta3Foil-4
❑ 99TopSta4Foil-4
❑ 99TopStaFoil-4
❑ 99TopStaFoil-171
❑ 99TopStaFS-4
❑ 99TopStaG-G3
❑ 99TopStaGFoil-G3
❑ 99TopStaOS-4
❑ 99TopStaTS-4
❑ 99TopStaTS-4
❑ 99TopSupC-23
❑ 99TopSupCR-23
❑ 99TopTek-38A
❑ 99TopTek-38B
❑ 99TopTekG-38A
❑ 99TopTekG-38B
❑ 99TopTekT-T9
❑ 99UD Cho-44
❑ 99UD Cho-62
❑ 99UD ChoBU-9
❑ 99UD ChoBUCG-9
❑ 99UD ChoMBH-B5
❑ 99UD ChoP-62
❑ 99UD ChoPCR-44
❑ 99UD ChoPCR-62
❑ 99UD ChoS-15
❑ 99UD ChoSD-15
❑ 99UD ChoSHR-15
❑ 99UD ChoST-15
❑ 99UD ChoYW-Y4
❑ 99UD Ion-12
❑ 99UD Ion-67
❑ 99UD IonC-C14
❑ 99UD IonH-H14
❑ 99UD IonR-12
❑ 99UD IonR-67
❑ 99UD IonWZ-WZ14
❑ 99UDHolo-12
❑ 99UDHoloAUsome-12
❑ 99UDHoloLau-L10
❑ 99UDHoloLauG-L10
❑ 99UDHoloStar-S4
❑ 99UDHoloStarG-S4
❑ 99Ult-69
❑ 99UltDamI-12
❑ 99UltGolM-69
❑ 99UltMas-69
❑ 99UltPlaM-69
❑ 99UltPromo-NNO
❑ 99UltRBIK-19
❑ 99UltTheBook-17
❑ 99UltThu-14
❑ 99UppDec-52
❑ 99UppDec-526
❑ 99UppDecBD-15
❑ 99UppDecBDD-15
❑ 99UppDecBDDom-D15
❑ 99UppDecBDDomE-D15
❑ 99UppDecBDMN-M7
❑ 99UppDecBDMNE-M7
❑ 99UppDecBDQ-15
❑ 99UppDecBDT-15
❑ 99UppDecCf7-13
❑ 99UppDecCf7-59
❑ 99UppDecCf7-C12
❑ 99UppDecCf7Cf7P-C12
❑ 99UppDecCf7LL-L19
❑ 99UppDecCf7SftF-S5
❑ 99UppDecCL-66
❑ 99UppDecCL-103
❑ 99UppDecCLCC-66
❑ 99UppDecCLCC-103
❑ 99UppDecCLM-C13
❑ 99UppDecCo7CE-13
❑ 99UppDecCo7CE-59
❑ 99UppDecE-14
❑ 99UppDecE-152
❑ 99UppDecE2C-2K8
❑ 99UppDecEFXG-14
❑ 99UppDecEFXG-152
❑ 99UppDecEL1-52
❑ 99UppDecEL1-526
❑ 99UppDecEL2-52
❑ 99UppDecEL2-526
❑ 99UppDecEPE-P8
❑ 99UppDecEUA-NG
❑ 99UppDecEUR-U15
❑ 99UppDecF-F9
❑ 99UppDecFD-F9
❑ 99UppDecFQ-F9
❑ 99UppDecFT-F9
❑ 99UppDecIP-I6
❑ 99UppDecIPD-I6
❑ 99UppDecIPHR-I6
❑ 99UppDecIPT-I6
❑ 99UppDecM-31
❑ 99UppDecM-P6
❑ 99UppDecMD-D3
❑ 99UppDecMGS-31
❑ 99UppDecMHFS-31
❑ 99UppDecMP-31
❑ 99UppDecMP-NG
❑ 99UppDecMSS-31
❑ 99UppDecMST-T11
❑ 99UppDecMST-S6
❑ 99UppDecO-33
❑ 99UppDecO-86
❑ 99UppDecOAPoH-NG
❑ 99UppDecOSO-33
❑ 99UppDecOSO-86
❑ 99UppDecOWP-R9
❑ 99UppDecR-15
❑ 99UppDecRDR-D5
❑ 99UppDecRDRL2-D5
❑ 99UppDecRG-15
❑ 99UppDecROSS-S26
❑ 99UppDecROSS-S26
❑ 99UppDecRP-15
❑ 99UppDecRTA-T13
❑ 99UppDecRTAL2-T13
❑ 99UppDecTE-T8
❑ 99UppDecTED-T8
❑ 99UppDecTEQ-T8
❑ 99UppDecTET-T8
❑ 99UppDecVtaT-V8
❑ 99UppDecVtaTD-V8
❑ 99UppDecVtaTQ-V8
❑ 99UppDecVtaTT-V8
❑ 99UppDecWY-W8
❑ 99UppDecWYD-W8
❑ 99UppDecWYHR-W8
❑ 99UppDecWYT-W8
❑ 99Vic-60
❑ 99Vic-61
❑ 99Vic-63

Garczyk, Eddie (Ed)
❑ 89SalLakTTI-9
❑ 90MiaMirIS-6

Gardella, Danny
❑ 83TCMPla1945-36

Gardella, Mike
❑ 88CapCodPPaLP-69
❑ 89OneYanP-2103
❑ 90CarLeaA-15
❑ 90PriWilCTI-10
❑ 91AlbYanLD-6
❑ 91AlbYanP-1002
❑ 91Cla/Bes-46
❑ 91LinDriAA-6
❑ 92AlbYanSk-7
❑ 92Bow-52
❑ 92CanIndF-685
❑ 92ClaFS7-4
❑ 93CanIndF-2834
❑ 94ShrCapF-1597

Gardenhire, Ron
❑ 81TidTidT-5
❑ 82Don-649
❑ 82MetPhoA-8
❑ 82Top-623
❑ 82TopTra-39T
❑ 83Don-175
❑ 83Fle-543
❑ 83TidTidT-20
❑ 83Top-469
❑ 85Don-360
❑ 85Fle-81
❑ 85MetColP-8
❑ 85MetTCM-23
❑ 85Top-144
❑ 85TopTif-144
❑ 86MetTCM-17
❑ 86TidTidP-10
❑ 86Top-274
❑ 86TopTif-274
❑ 87PorBeaP-25
❑ 88KenTwiP-1402
❑ 88MidLeaAGS-36
❑ 89OrlTwiB-5
❑ 89OrlTwiP-1355
❑ 90OrlSunRB-28
❑ 90OrlSunRP-1098
❑ 90OrlSunRS-24
❑ 91DodPho-4
❑ 91MetWIZ-132
❑ 92TexLon-14

Gardey, Rudy
❑ 88IdaFalBP-1855
❑ 90SalSpuCLC-123

Gardiner, Michelle
❑ 91FreStaLBS-2

Gardiner, Mike
❑ 89WauTimGS-28
❑ 90Bes-262
❑ 90EasLeaAP-EL17
❑ 90ProAaA-16
❑ 90StaFS7-49
❑ 90WilBilB-6
❑ 90WilBilP-1052
❑ 90WilBilS-7
❑ 91Cla3-T25
❑ 91Don-417
❑ 91DonRoo-46
❑ 91LinDriAAA-355
❑ 91PawRedSDD-6
❑ 91PawRedSLD-355
❑ 91PawRedSP-31
❑ 91RedSoxP-11
❑ 91Sco-721
❑ 91TopDeb90-52
❑ 91UppDec-14
❑ 92Don-290
❑ 92Lea-482
❑ 92LeaBlaG-482
❑ 92OPC-694
❑ 92Pin-505
❑ 92ProFS7-17
❑ 92RedSoxDD-13
❑ 92Sco-694
❑ 92StaClu-732
❑ 92StaCluNC-732
❑ 92Top-694
❑ 92TopGol-694
❑ 92TopGolW-694
❑ 92TopMic-694
❑ 92UppDec-588
❑ 93Don-515
❑ 93Fle-558
❑ 93FleFinE-94
❑ 93Top-241
❑ 93TopGol-241
❑ 93TopInaM-241
❑ 93TopInaR-241
❑ 93TopMic-241
❑ 93Ult-414
❑ 93UppDec-640
❑ 93UppDecGold-640
❑ 94FleUpd-44
❑ 94StaClu-474
❑ 94StaCluFDI-474
❑ 94StaCluGR-474
❑ 94StaCluMOP-474
❑ 95Fle-52
❑ 95Top-97
❑ 96NorTidB-15
❑ 98ChaKniQ-11

Gardiver, Jimmie
❑ 87ChaWheP-20

Gardner, Art
❑ 73CedRapAT-7
❑ 75IowOakT-8
❑ 78PhoGiaC-8
❑ 86TulDriTI-5
❑ 87GasRanP-24

Gardner, Billy
❑ 88EugEmeB-19
❑ 90PitMetP-27
❑ 94HigDesMC-29
❑ 94HigDesMF-2806
❑ 95ButCopKtI-22
❑ 96LowSpiB-1
❑ 97MicBatC-1
❑ 98MicBatCM-1

Gardner, Billy F.
❑ 55Bow-249
❑ 55GiaGolS-26
❑ 55Top-27
❑ 55TopDouH-61
❑ 56BalOriP-23
❑ 57Top-17
❑ 58Hir-37
❑ 58OriJayP-3
❑ 58Top-105
❑ 59OriJayP-3
❑ 59Top-89
❑ 59TopVen-89
❑ 60SenJayP-6
❑ 60Top-106
❑ 60TopVen-106
❑ 61Pos-96A
❑ 61Pos-96B
❑ 61Top-123
❑ 61TopStaI-179
❑ 61TwiCloD-5
❑ 61TwiPetM-14
❑ 61TwiUniMC-4
❑ 61Yan61RL-15
❑ 62SalPlaC-211
❑ 62ShiPlaC-211
❑ 62Top-163
❑ 62Top-338
❑ 62TopVen-163
❑ 63Top-408
❑ 64SeaPop-2
❑ 77ExpPos-15
❑ 77OPC-198
❑ 79MemChiT-21
❑ 81TwiPos-10
❑ 82Don-591
❑ 82TwiPos-13
❑ 83Top-11
❑ 83TwiTeal-27
❑ 83TwiTeal-34
❑ 83Yan196-15
❑ 84MinTwiP-14
❑ 84Nes792-771
❑ 84Top-771
❑ 84TopTif-771
❑ 84TwiTeal-28
❑ 85Top-213
❑ 85TopTif-213
❑ 85TwiPos-11
❑ 85TwiTeal-31
❑ 87TopTra-36T
❑ 87TopTraT-36T
❑ 91OriCro-151
❑ 91PitMetC-27
❑ 91PitMetP-3439
❑ 91YanRinP12-5
❑ 92St.LucMCB-27
❑ 92St.LucMF-1764
❑ 92YanWIZ6-45
❑ 93ButCopKSP-23

Gardner, Bob
❑ 52Par-88

Gardner, Chris
❑ 90AshTouP-2741
❑ 91JacGenP-919
❑ 92Bow-457
❑ 92Don-413
❑ 92Lea-8
❑ 92LeaBlaG-8
❑ 92Pin-599
❑ 92ProFS7-227
❑ 92SkyAAAF-271
❑ 92TopDeb91-61
❑ 92TucTorF-481
❑ 92TucTorS-607
❑ 94JacGenF-211
❑ 95TucTotTI-5

Gardner, Chuck
❑ 77CliDodT-8

Gardner, Damon
❑ 90MisStaB-13
❑ 91MisStaB-18

Gardner, Earl M.
❑ 11HelSta-44
❑ 11PinT-5-816
❑ 11SpoLifM-79
❑ 11T205-62

Gardner, Franklin W.
❑ 87OldJudN-190
❑ 87OldJudN-191

Gardner, Glen
❑ 88PulBraP-1756
❑ 89SouAtlLAGS-42
❑ 89SumBraP-1097
❑ 90Bes-217
❑ 90BurBraB-3
❑ 90BurBraP-2355
❑ 90BurBraS-11

Gardner, Harry R.
❑ 09ObaT21-243
❑ 16FleBreD-29
❑ 18Zee-45
❑ 20Zee-124
❑ 21Zee-142
❑ 22E120-33
❑ 22Zee-126

Gardner, Jeff
❑ 86LynMetP-10
❑ 87JacMetF-9
❑ 87TexLeaAF-7
❑ 88JacMetGS-10
❑ 89TidTidC-20
❑ 89TidTidP-1966
❑ 90CMC-367
❑ 90ProAAAF-282
❑ 90TidTidC-16
❑ 90TidTidP-551
❑ 90TopTVM-42
❑ 91LinDriAAA-555
❑ 91TidTidLD-555
❑ 91TidTidP-2517
❑ 91TriA AAGP-AAA48
❑ 92Fle-675A
❑ 92Fle-675B
❑ 92LasVegSF-2800
❑ 92LasVegSS-231
❑ 92ProFS7-279
❑ 92Sco-869
❑ 92SkyAAAF-114
❑ 92TopDeb91-62
❑ 93Don-470
❑ 93FleFinE-138
❑ 93Lea-238
❑ 93PadMot-22
❑ 93SelRoo-140T
❑ 93Top-663
❑ 93TopGol-663
❑ 93TopInaM-663
❑ 93TopInaR-663
❑ 93TopMic-663
❑ 93UppDec-639
❑ 93UppDecGold-639
❑ 94ColC-106
❑ 94ColChoGS-106
❑ 94ColChoSS-106
❑ 94Don-406
❑ 94Fin-196
❑ 94FinRef-196
❑ 94Fle-662
❑ 94Pac-522
❑ 94PanSti-255
❑ 94Pin-296
❑ 94PinArtP-296
❑ 94PinMusC-296
❑ 94Sco-478
❑ 94ScoGolR-478
❑ 94StaClu-58
❑ 94StaCluFDI-58
❑ 94StaCluGR-58
❑ 94StaCluMOP-58
❑ 94Top-544
❑ 94TopGol-544
❑ 94TopSpa-544
❑ 94Ult-278

Gardner, Jelly (Floyd)
❑ 74LauOldTBS-7

Gardner, Jimmie
❑ 86GenCubP-6

Gardner, John
❑ 86PeoChiP-7
❑ 87WytCubP-13
❑ 88ChaWheB-15
❑ 89ChaWheB-19
❑ 89ChaWheP-1769
❑ 90WinSpiTI-6
❑ 91ChaKniLD-132
❑ 91ChaKniP-1683
❑ 91LinDriAA-132
❑ 92IowCubF-4047
❑ 92IowCubS-208
❑ 92SkyAAAF-101

Gardner, L.
❑ 18Zee-21

Gardner, Larry (William L.)
❑ 09ColChiE-113A
❑ 09ColChiE-113B
❑ 11MecDFT-22
❑ 11PinT-5-666
❑ 11SpoLifM-8
❑ 12ColRedB-113A
❑ 12ColRedB-113B
❑ 12ColTinT-113A
❑ 12ColTinT-113B
❑ 12T207-65
❑ 15SpoNewM-65
❑ 16SpoNewM-65
❑ 17ColE13-56
❑ 17HolBreD-33
❑ 20GasAmeMBD-6
❑ 20NatCarE-31
❑ 21E121So1-27
❑ 21E121So8-25
❑ 21Exh-55
❑ 22AmeCarE122-21
❑ 22W575-38
❑ 23W501-24
❑ 23WilChoV-47
❑ 56BalOriP-15
❑ 56BalOriP-16
❑ 58BalOriP-8
❑ 77Ind192T-7
❑ 91ConTSN-147
❑ 95ConTSN-1355

Gardner, Mark
❑ 86JacExpT-15
❑ 87IndIndTI-19
❑ 88JacExpB-7
❑ 88JacExpP-987
❑ 89IndIndC-8
❑ 89IndIndP-1224
❑ 89TriAAAP-AAA10
❑ 90Bow-106
❑ 90BowTif-106
❑ 90ClaYel-T4
❑ 90Don-40
❑ 90DonRoo-20
❑ 90ExpPos-11
❑ 90Fle-646
❑ 90FleCan-646
❑ 90FleUpd-29
❑ 90Hot50RS-16
❑ 90Lea-371

❑ 90OPC-284
❑ 90Sco-639
❑ 90Sco100RS-66
❑ 90Top-284
❑ 90TopDeb89-41
❑ 90TopTif-284
❑ 90ToyRoo-10
❑ 90TriAAAC-10
❑ 90UppDec-743
❑ 91Don-443
❑ 91ExpPos-8
❑ 91Fle-233
❑ 91OPC-757
❑ 91PanCanT1-91
❑ 91PanSti-67
❑ 91Sco-518
❑ 91Sco100RS-71
❑ 91StaClu-592
❑ 91Top-757
❑ 91TopDesS-757
❑ 91TopMic-757
❑ 91TopTif-757
❑ 91UppDec-663
❑ 92Bow-562
❑ 92Don-238
❑ 92ExpDonD-9
❑ 92ExpPos-14
❑ 92Fle-481
❑ 92Lea-512
❑ 92LeaBlaG-512
❑ 92OPC-119
❑ 92Pin-215
❑ 92Sco-586
❑ 92Sco-785
❑ 92StaClu-42
❑ 92Top-119
❑ 92TopGol-119
❑ 92TopGolW-119
❑ 92TopMic-119
❑ 92UppDec-557
❑ 93Bow-421
❑ 93Don-64
❑ 93ExpPosN-12
❑ 93Fle-75
❑ 93FleFinE-218
❑ 93Lea-313
❑ 93OPCPre-21
❑ 93RoyPol-8
❑ 93RoyStaC-24
❑ 93Sco-390
❑ 93Sel-185
❑ 93StaClu-159
❑ 93StaClu-663
❑ 93StaCluFDI-159
❑ 93StaCluFDI-663
❑ 93StaCluMOP-159
❑ 93StaCluMOP-663
❑ 93Top-314
❑ 93TopGol-314
❑ 93TopInaM-314
❑ 93TopInaR-314
❑ 93TopMic-314
❑ 93Ult-560
❑ 93UppDec-348
❑ 93UppDec-641
❑ 93UppDecGold-348
❑ 93UppDecGold-641
❑ 94StaClu-546
❑ 94StaCluFDI-546
❑ 94StaCluGR-546
❑ 94StaCluMOP-546
❑ 94StaCluT-83
❑ 94StaCluTFDI-83
❑ 95Fle-332
❑ 96FleUpd-U206
❑ 96FleUpdTC-U206
❑ 96GiaMot-20
❑ 97Cir-66
❑ 97CirRav-66
❑ 97ColCho-457
❑ 97Fle-481
❑ 97FleTif-481
❑ 97MetUni-244
❑ 97Top-52
❑ 97Ult-295
❑ 97UltGolME-295
❑ 97UltPlaME-295
❑ 98ColCho-489
❑ 98GiaMot-12
❑ 98PacOnl-658
❑ 98PacOnlR-658
❑ 98PacOnlWC-658
❑ 98Sco-230
❑ 98Sco-256
❑ 98StaCluFDI-329
❑ 98StaCluI-329
❑ 98StaCluOneK-329
❑ 98StaCluPP-329
❑ 98Top-51
❑ 98TopChr-51
❑ 98TopChrR-51
❑ 98TopDevR-51
❑ 98TopDia-51
❑ 98TopMiniC-51
❑ 98UppDec-4
❑ 98UppDec-217
❑ 98UppDecSF-118
❑ 99Fle-412
❑ 99FleSta9-412
❑ 99FleWarT-412

Gardner, Mike
❑ 88WauTimGS-25

Gardner, Myron
❑ 86WatIndP-8
❑ 88SalLakCTTI-20

Gardner, Nathan
❑ 98ChaAllCM-5

Gardner, Rob
❑ 66MetVolC-4
❑ 66Top-534
❑ 67Top-217
❑ 68Top-219
❑ 68TopVen-219
❑ 71OPC-734
❑ 71Top-734
❑ 72OPC-22
❑ 72Top-22
❑ 73OPC-222
❑ 73Top-222
❑ 91MetWIZ-133
❑ 92YanWIZ7-53
❑ 94BreMilB-31

Gardner, Scott
❑ 82DayBeaAT-4
❑ 83MiaMarT-3
❑ 90HunCubP-3274
❑ 91HunCubC-10
❑ 91HunCubP-3328
❑ 92GenCubC-16
❑ 92GenCubF-1555
❑ 93PeoChiF-1077
❑ 93PeoChiTI-5
❑ 95FayGenTI-12
❑ 96StoPorB-16
❑ 97El PasDB-15

Gardner, Vassie
❑ 81ChaChaT-20
❑ 82KnoBluJT-19

Gardner, Wes
❑ 83LynMetT-23
❑ 84TidTidT-3
❑ 85IntLeaAT-21
❑ 85MetTCM-11
❑ 85TidTidT-9
❑ 87RedSoxP-9
❑ 88Don-634
❑ 88DonTeaBRS-634
❑ 88Fle-352
❑ 88FleGlo-352
❑ 88StaLinRS-8
❑ 88Top-189
❑ 88TopTif-189
❑ 89Bow-23
❑ 89BowTif-23
❑ 89Don-541
❑ 89Fle-88
❑ 89FleGlo-88
❑ 89Sco-412
❑ 89Top-526
❑ 89TopTif-526
❑ 90Bow-266
❑ 90BowTif-266
❑ 90Don-541
❑ 90Fle-275
❑ 90FleCan-275
❑ 90Lea-407
❑ 90OPC-38
❑ 90PubIntS-455
❑ 90RedSoxP-9
❑ 90Sco-348
❑ 90Top-38
❑ 90TopTif-38
❑ 90TopTVRS-10
❑ 91Bow-653
❑ 91Fle-94
❑ 91MetWIZ-134
❑ 91OPC-629
❑ 91PadMag-19A
❑ 91Sco-592
❑ 91Top-629
❑ 91TopDesS-629
❑ 91TopMic-629
❑ 91TopTif-629
❑ 91UppDec-214

Gardner, Willie
❑ 90HunCubP-3299
❑ 91GenCubC-7
❑ 91GenCubP-4229
❑ 91PeoChiC-20
❑ 91PeoChiP-1357
❑ 92ClaFS7-220
❑ 92PeoChiTI-7

Garey, Dan
❑ 98EveAquG-7

Garff, Jeff
❑ 97BurIndG-9

Gargano, Michael
❑ 98JohCCTI-12

Gargiulo, Jimmy
❑ 96JohCitCTI-13
❑ 97PeoChi-11

Gargiulo, Mike
❑ 94BluOriC-9
❑ 94BluOriF-3566
❑ 96FreKeyB-11
❑ 97St.LucM-8

Garguilo, Mike
❑ 94OriPro-37

Garham, John
❑ 91AubAstC-29

Garia, Mike
❑ 92BazQua5A-14

Garibaldi, Art
❑ 32Zee-100
❑ 33Zee-115
❑ 37Zee-54
❑ 40SolHug-7

Garibaldi, Bob
❑ 70Top-681
❑ 71OPC-701
❑ 71Top-701
❑ 81Gia196T-24
❑ 97PhoFirDTTI-21

Garibaldo, Chris
❑ 90BasCitRS-9

Gariglio, Robert
❑ 80WatIndT-32
❑ 81ChaLooT-1

Garland, Chaon
❑ 90SouOreAB-14
❑ 90SouOreAP-3428
❑ 91ModA'sC-5
❑ 91ModA'sP-3080
❑ 92ModA'sC-11
❑ 92ModA'sF-3893

Garland, Jon
❑ 97Bow-427
❑ 97BowChr-287
❑ 97BowChrI-287
❑ 97BowChrIR-287
❑ 97BowChrR-287
❑ 97BowInt-427
❑ 98Bow-175
❑ 98BowChr-175
❑ 98BowChrGA-175
❑ 98BowChrGAR-175
❑ 98BowChrI-175
❑ 98BowChrIR-175
❑ 98BowChrR-175
❑ 98BowGolA-175
❑ 98BowInt-175
❑ 98HicCraUO-19
❑ 98RocCubM-9
❑ 98RocCubTI-9
❑ 98StaCluFDI-397
❑ 98StaCluI-397
❑ 98StaCluOneK-397
❑ 98StaCluPP-397
❑ 98Top-245
❑ 98TopChr-245
❑ 98TopChrR-245
❑ 98TopDevR-245
❑ 98TopDia-245
❑ 98TopMiniC-245

Garland, Lou
❑ 33WorCig(-30

Garland, Mike
❑ 92BenRocF-1481

Garland, Tim
❑ 90GreHorB-21
❑ 90GreHorP-2673
❑ 90GreHorS-2
❑ 91Ft.LauYC-26
❑ 91Ft.LauYP-2440
❑ 92ClaFS7-222
❑ 92PriWilCC-15
❑ 92PriWilCF-160
❑ 96SanJosGB-8
❑ 97CalLeaATI-7
❑ 97SanJosG-11
❑ 98ShrCapM-15
❑ 98ShrCapWS-15

Garland, Wayne
❑ 73BalOriP-15
❑ 74OPC-596
❑ 74Top-596
❑ 75BalOriP-12
❑ 76BalOriP-14
❑ 76OPC-414
❑ 76SSP-376
❑ 76Top-414
❑ 77BurCheD-59
❑ 77ChiWilD-23
❑ 77DailsID-23
❑ 77DetCaeD-23
❑ 77HolInnD-23
❑ 77Hos-144
❑ 77Kel-21A
❑ 77Kel-21B
❑ 77MSADis-23
❑ 77OPC-138
❑ 77PepGloD-14
❑ 77RCColC-23
❑ 77SagDis-23
❑ 77sDis-23
❑ 77Top-33
❑ 77TopCloS-17
❑ 77WenDis-23
❑ 77ZipDis-23
❑ 78Hos-137
❑ 78IndTeal-11
❑ 78OPC-15
❑ 78RCColC-37
❑ 78Top-174
❑ 78WifBalD-25
❑ 79Top-636
❑ 80IndTeal-11
❑ 80Top-361
❑ 81Don-440
❑ 81Fle-394
❑ 81OPC-272
❑ 81Top-511
❑ 82Don-489
❑ 82Fle-367
❑ 82Top-446
❑ 87NasSouTI-6
❑ 88NasSouC-24
❑ 88NasSouP-494
❑ 89MetColP-30
❑ 89PacSenL-100
❑ 89T/MSenL-38
❑ 90EliSenL-68
❑ 91OriCro-152
❑ 93AugPirC-27
❑ 93AugPirF-1561
❑ 94CarMudF-1595

Garlick, Gene
❑ 85CloHSS-17

Garman, Mike
❑ 71OPC-512
❑ 71Top-512
❑ 72OPC-79
❑ 72Top-79
❑ 73OPC-616
❑ 73Top-616
❑ 75OPC-584
❑ 75St.LouCP-11
❑ 75Top-584
❑ 75TopMin-584
❑ 76OPC-34
❑ 76SSP-293
❑ 76Top-34
❑ 77Top-302
❑ 78SSP270-70
❑ 78Top-417
❑ 79ExpPos-10
❑ 79OPC-88
❑ 79PorBeaT-15
❑ 79Top-181
❑ 90DodTar-268

Garman, Pat
❑ 88GasRanP-1014
❑ 89ChaRanS-8
❑ 90CMC-162
❑ 90OklCit8C-12
❑ 90OklCit8P-438
❑ 90ProAAAF-684
❑ 91LinDriAA-580
❑ 91TulDriLD-580
❑ 91TulDriP-2779

Garman, Sean
❑ 94NewJerCC-9
❑ 94NewJerCF-3424
❑ 95NewJerCTI-10

Garmong, Aaron
❑ 98EugEme-13

Garms, Debs
❑ 34TarThoBD-11
❑ 35DiaMatCS3T1-59
❑ 38CloFotW-28
❑ 39PlaBal-72
❑ 40PlaBal-161
❑ 41DouPlaR-149
❑ 41Gou-29
❑ 41PlaBal-11
❑ 72TCMthe1-204
❑ 79DiaGre-176
❑ 83Car194T-22
❑ 91ConTSN-296

Garner, Darrin
❑ 86DayBeaIP-8
❑ 87GasRanP-22
❑ 88ChaRanS-7
❑ 88FloStaLAS-38
❑ 89TulDriGS-9
❑ 89TulDriTI-7
❑ 90TulDriP-1162
❑ 90TulDriTI-8
❑ 91LinDriAAA-309
❑ 91OklCit8LD-309
❑ 91OklCit8P-185
❑ 92GulCoaRSP-28
❑ 93ChaRanC-27
❑ 93ChaRanF-1956
❑ 94ChaRanF-2513
❑ 95PorCitRTI-9

Garner, Kevin
❑ 88RivRedWCLC-220
❑ 88RivRedWP-1431
❑ 89WicStaR-17
❑ 89WicWraR-33
❑ 91BirBarLD-60
❑ 91BirBarP-1462
❑ 91BriBanF-19
❑ 91LinDriAA-60
❑ 92BirBarF-2592
❑ 92ChaLooF-3825

Garner, Mike
❑ 87VerBeaDP-13
❑ 88RenSilSCLC-277

Garner, Phil
❑ 75OPC-623
❑ 75Top-623
❑ 75TopMin-623
❑ 76OPC-57
❑ 76SSP-495
❑ 76Top-57
❑ 77A'sPos-92
❑ 77BurCheD-109
❑ 77Hos-11
❑ 77OPC-34
❑ 77PirPosP-7
❑ 77Top-261
❑ 78Hos-52
❑ 78OPC-203
❑ 78Top-53
❑ 79Hos-75
❑ 79OPC-200
❑ 79Top-383
❑ 80OPC-65
❑ 80Top-118
❑ 81AllGamPI-101
❑ 81CokTeaS-113
❑ 81Don-372
❑ 81Fle-364
❑ 81FleStiC-71
❑ 81Kel-44
❑ 81OPC-99
❑ 81Top-573
❑ 81TopScr-102
❑ 81TopSti-209
❑ 81TopSti-253
❑ 82AstAstI-4
❑ 82AstPos-4
❑ 82Don-544A
❑ 82Don-544B
❑ 82Fle-216
❑ 82Squ-13
❑ 82Top-683
❑ 83AllGamPI-120
❑ 83AstPos-8
❑ 83Don-270
❑ 83Fle-448
❑ 83FleSta-68
❑ 83FleSti-205
❑ 83OPC-128
❑ 83Top-478
❑ 83TopSti-170
❑ 83TopSti-237
❑ 84AllGamPI-29
❑ 84AstMot-5
❑ 84AstPos-10
❑ 84Don-354
❑ 84Fle-226
❑ 84Nes792-752
❑ 84OPC-119
❑ 84Top-752
❑ 84TopRubD-11
❑ 84TopSti-63
❑ 84TopTif-752
❑ 85AllGamPI-119
❑ 85AstHouP-10
❑ 85AstMot-3
❑ 85Don-161
❑ 85Fle-351
❑ 85OPC-206
❑ 85Top-206
❑ 85TopRubD-11
❑ 85TopSti-64
❑ 85TopTif-206
❑ 86AstMilL-9
❑ 86AstPol-9
❑ 86AstTeal-6
❑ 86BasStaB-44
❑ 86Don-527
❑ 86Fle-301
❑ 86FleMin-64
❑ 86OPC-83
❑ 86Top-83
❑ 86TopSti-32
❑ 86TopTif-83
❑ 87A'sMot-16
❑ 87AstMot-6
❑ 87AstPol-24
❑ 87AstShoSPT-5
❑ 87Don-358
❑ 87DonOpeD-12
❑ 87Fle-58
❑ 87FleGlo-58
❑ 87OPC-304
❑ 87Top-304
❑ 87TopSti-30
❑ 87TopTif-304
❑ 88GiaMot-25
❑ 88Sco-431
❑ 88ScoGlo-431
❑ 88Top-174
❑ 88TopTif-174
❑ 89AstLenH-14
❑ 89AstMot-27
❑ 89AstSmo-16
❑ 90AstMot-27
❑ 90DodTar-269
❑ 91AstMot-28
❑ 91SweBasG-113
❑ 92BrePol-9
❑ 92OPC-291
❑ 92Top-291
❑ 92TopGol-291
❑ 92TopGolW-291
❑ 92TopMic-291
❑ 93BrePol-8
❑ 93Top-508
❑ 93TopGol-508
❑ 93TopInaM-508
❑ 93TopInaR-508
❑ 93TopMic-508
❑ 93UppDecAH-56
❑ 94BrePol-8
❑ 94BreTeal-7
❑ 94TedWil-78
❑ 96BrePol-8
❑ 97BrePol-9

Garner, Willie
❑ 92PeoChiC-14

Garnett, Brad
❑ 82AleDukT-11

Garr, Ralph
❑ 69AtlBraBPPS-8
❑ 70OPC-172
❑ 70Top-172
❑ 71MLBOffS-9
❑ 71OPC-494
❑ 71Top-494
❑ 72Kel-21
❑ 72OPC-85
❑ 72OPC-260
❑ 72SevTraC-16
❑ 72Top-85
❑ 72Top-260
❑ 73Kel2D-37
❑ 73LinPor-3
❑ 73OPC-15
❑ 73SevTraC-22
❑ 73Top-15
❑ 74OPC-570

❑ 74Top-570
❑ 74TopSta-4
❑ 75AtlBraP-11
❑ 75Hos-87
❑ 75Kel-35
❑ 75OPC-306
❑ 75OPC-550
❑ 75Top-306
❑ 75Top-550
❑ 75TopMin-306
❑ 75TopMin-550
❑ 76OPC-410
❑ 76SSP-17
❑ 76Top-410
❑ 76TopTra-410T
❑ 77BurCheD-80
❑ 77ChiWilD-24
❑ 77DailsID-24
❑ 77DetCaeD-24
❑ 77HolInnD-24
❑ 77Hos-108
❑ 77Kel-13
❑ 77MSADis-24
❑ 77OPC-77
❑ 77PepGloD-26
❑ 77RCColC-24
❑ 77SagDis-24
❑ 77sDis-24
❑ 77Top-133
❑ 77TopCloS-18
❑ 77WenDis-24
❑ 77WhiSoxJT-5
❑ 77WhiSoxT-9
❑ 77ZipDis-24
❑ 78Kel-37
❑ 78OPC-195
❑ 78PapGinD-37
❑ 78RCColC-21
❑ 78SagDis-21
❑ 78SSP270-155
❑ 78TasDis-21
❑ 78Top-628
❑ 78WifBalD-26
❑ 79OPC-156
❑ 79Top-309
❑ 80OPC-142
❑ 80Top-272
❑ 90PacLeg-25
❑ 90RicBra2ATI-9
❑ 90SweBasG-46
❑ 92IdaFalGF-3526
❑ 92IdaFalGSP-15
❑ 93UppDecAH-57
❑ 93UppDecS-2
❑ 94TedWil-42
❑ 94UppDecAH-184
❑ 94UppDecAH1-184

Garrelts, Scott

❑ 80CliGiaT-10
❑ 81ShrCapT-20
❑ 83PhoGiaBHN-3
❑ 84Don-646
❑ 84PhoGiaC-5
❑ 85GiaMot-23
❑ 85GiaPos-9
❑ 85TopTifT-38T
❑ 85TopTra-38T
❑ 86Don-309
❑ 86DonAll-35
❑ 86Fle-540
❑ 86FleLeaL-14
❑ 86FleMin-110
❑ 86FleStiC-42
❑ 86GiaMot-19
❑ 86GiaPos-11
❑ 86Lea-180
❑ 86OPC-395
❑ 86Spo-157
❑ 86Top-395
❑ 86TopSti-86
❑ 86TopTat-16
❑ 86TopTif-395
❑ 87Don-116
❑ 87Fle-273
❑ 87FleGlo-273
❑ 87FleHotS-17
❑ 87FleMin-42
❑ 87FleStiC-45
❑ 87GiaMot-11
❑ 87GiaPos-12
❑ 87Lea-75
❑ 87OPC-37
❑ 87RedFolSB-24
❑ 87Spo-68
❑ 87SpoTeaP-10
❑ 87Top-475
❑ 87TopSti-89
❑ 87TopTif-475
❑ 88Don-80
❑ 88DonBasB-162
❑ 88Fle-82
❑ 88FleGlo-82
❑ 88GiaMot-11
❑ 88GiaPos-11
❑ 88OPC-97
❑ 88PanSti-416
❑ 88Sco-533
❑ 88ScoGlo-533
❑ 88Spo-44
❑ 88StaLinG-7
❑ 88Top-97
❑ 88TopBig-240
❑ 88TopSti-90
❑ 88TopTif-97
❑ 89Bow-467
❑ 89BowTif-467
❑ 89Don-295
❑ 89DonBasB-218
❑ 89Fle-328
❑ 89FleGlo-328
❑ 89GiaMot-11
❑ 89OPC-214
❑ 89RedFolSB-48
❑ 89Sco-258
❑ 89Top-703
❑ 89TopTif-703
❑ 89UppDec-50
❑ 90Bow-228
❑ 90BowTif-228
❑ 90Don-217A
❑ 90Don-217B
❑ 90DonBesN-110
❑ 90Fle-56
❑ 90FleAwaW-14
❑ 90FleBasA-11
❑ 90FleBasAC-11
❑ 90FleCan-56
❑ 90GiaMot-16
❑ 90GiaSmo-8
❑ 90Lea-41
❑ 90OPC-602
❑ 90PanSti-367
❑ 90PubIntS-67
❑ 90Sco-246
❑ 90Spo-39
❑ 90Top-602
❑ 90TopBig-51
❑ 90TopMinL-85
❑ 90TopSti-82
❑ 90TopTif-602
❑ 90UppDec-478A
❑ 90UppDec-478B
❑ 91Bow-626
❑ 91Don-311
❑ 91Fle-262
❑ 91GiaMot-16
❑ 91GiaPacGaE-29
❑ 91GiaSFE-8
❑ 91Lea-5
❑ 91OPC-361
❑ 91Sco-541
❑ 91StaClu-182
❑ 91Stu-255
❑ 91Top-361
❑ 91TopDesS-361
❑ 91TopMic-361
❑ 91TopTif-361
❑ 91Ult-320
❑ 91UppDec-443
❑ 92Fle-636
❑ 92GiaPacGaE-17
❑ 92OPC-558
❑ 92Sco-117
❑ 92StaClu-832
❑ 92StaCluECN-832
❑ 92Top-558
❑ 92TopGol-558
❑ 92TopGolW-558
❑ 92TopMic-558

Garrett, Bobby

❑ 81WesHavAT-9

Garrett, Bryan

❑ 93WatIndC-9
❑ 93WatIndF-3575
❑ 94ColRedC-10
❑ 94ColRedF-454

Garrett, Clifton

❑ 90BoiHawP-3330
❑ 91Cla/Bes-248
❑ 91MidLeaAP-MWL26
❑ 91QuaCitAC-24
❑ 91QuaCitAP-2643
❑ 92Bow-51
❑ 92ClaFS7-210
❑ 92PalSprAC-25
❑ 92PalSprAF-854
❑ 92UppDecML-314
❑ 93CedRapKC-1
❑ 93ClaGolF-131

Garrett, Eric

❑ 83IdaFalAT-15
❑ 84MadMusP-19
❑ 84ModA'sC-12
❑ 85ModA'sC-6

Garrett, Greg

❑ 70Top-642
❑ 71MLBOffS-58
❑ 71OPC-377
❑ 71Top-377

Garrett, Hal

❑ 94SprSulC-11
❑ 94SprSulF-2031
❑ 96CliLumKTI-12
❑ 97LynHil-7
❑ 98VerBeaDM-12

Garrett, Jason

❑ 95ElmPioTI-9
❑ 95ElmPioUTI-9

Garrett, Jeff

❑ 94OgdRapF-3730
❑ 94OgdRapSP-6

Garrett, Jess

❑ 09ObaT21-26
❑ 09ObaT21-117

Garrett, Josh

❑ 96BesAutS1RP-FR12
❑ 97Bow-405
❑ 97BowChr-268
❑ 97BowChrI-268
❑ 97BowChrIR-268
❑ 97BowChrR-268
❑ 97BowInt-405
❑ 97MicBatC-11
❑ 97Top-273

Garrett, Lee

❑ 80WatRedT-9
❑ 81WatRedT-23
❑ 82IndIndTI-31
❑ 83IndIndTI-32
❑ 85IndIndTI-26
❑ 86IndIndTI-36

Garrett, Lynn

❑ 79WatIndT-1A
❑ 81WesHavAT-11
❑ 82WesHavAT-21
❑ 83TacTigT-15

Garrett, Neil

❑ 93Top-579
❑ 93TopGol-579
❑ 93TopInaM-579
❑ 93TopInaR-579
❑ 93TopMic-579
❑ 94AshTouC-8
❑ 94AshTouF-1773
❑ 96AshTouB-18
❑ 98SalAvaC-10

Garrett, Pat (H. Adrian)

❑ 66Top-553
❑ 71OPC-576
❑ 71Top-576
❑ 74OPC-656
❑ 74Top-656
❑ 76OPC-562
❑ 76Top-562
❑ 76VenLeaS-106
❑ 79TCMJapPB-31
❑ 82AppFoxFr-31
❑ 83GleFalWST-22
❑ 87OmaRoyP-16
❑ 88RoySmo-2
❑ 88RoyTeal-12
❑ 90RoyPos-11
❑ 91RoyPol-25
❑ 92RoyPol-27
❑ 93EdmTraF-1154
❑ 94EdmTraF-2892
❑ 97ChaKni-4
❑ 98ChaKniQ-3

Garrett, R. Wayne

❑ 69MetNewYDN-5
❑ 70OPC-198
❑ 70Top-198
❑ 70Top-628
❑ 71MLBOffS-152
❑ 71OPC-228
❑ 71Top-228
❑ 72Dia-19
❑ 72MetTeal-8
❑ 72OPC-518
❑ 72Top-518
❑ 73LinPor-111
❑ 73OPC-562
❑ 73Top-562
❑ 74MetDaiPA-18
❑ 74MetJapEB-2
❑ 74MetTeal-4
❑ 74OPC-510
❑ 74Top-510
❑ 74TopSta-61
❑ 75MetSSP-5
❑ 75OPC-111
❑ 75Top-111
❑ 75TopMin-111
❑ 76ExpRed-12
❑ 76OPC-222
❑ 76SSP-539
❑ 76Top-222
❑ 77ExpPos-16
❑ 77OPC-117
❑ 77Top-417
❑ 78OPC-198
❑ 78Top-679
❑ 79TCMJapPB-77
❑ 79Top-319
❑ 86MetGreT-4
❑ 89Met196C-3
❑ 89MetRinP69-10
❑ 89PacSenL-156
❑ 89T/MSenL-39
❑ 91MetWIZ-135
❑ 93UppDecS-10
❑ 94Met69CCPP-14
❑ 94Met69CS-13
❑ 94Met69T-23

Garrett, Scott

❑ 96BilMusTI-9
❑ 98ChaAllCM-13

Garrett, Smokey

❑ 95ChaKniTI-2

Garrett, Steve

❑ 80ElmPioRST-6

Garrick, Darren

❑ 86SanJosBP-8
❑ 88SalLakCTTI-3
❑ 89SalLakTTI-3

Garrick, Matt

❑ 98CedRapKTI-11

Garrido, Gil

❑ 61TacBan-7
❑ 61UniOil-T17
❑ 64Top-452
❑ 69AtlBraBPPS-9
❑ 69Top-331
❑ 70OPC-48
❑ 70Top-48
❑ 71MLBOffS-10
❑ 71OPC-173
❑ 71Top-173
❑ 72Top-758
❑ 88BurBraP-26
❑ 89SumBraP-1094
❑ 90BurBraP-2366
❑ 90BurBraS-28
❑ 91DurBulP-1677

Garrigan, Pat

❑ 92SanBerC-3
❑ 92SanBerSF-965

Garriott, Cece

❑ 47SigOil-25
❑ 48AngTeal-9
❑ 49AngTeal-11
❑ 49W725AngTI-9

Garrison, Ford

❑ 43RedSoxTI-8
❑ 83TCMPla1944-14

Garrison, Jim

❑ 87WatPirP-18
❑ 88AugPirP-369

Garrison, Marv

❑ 77LodDodT-3
❑ 78LodDodT-5

Garrison, Venoy

❑ 75CliPilT-29

Garrison, Webster

❑ 85KinBluJT-16
❑ 87DunBluJP-937
❑ 88SouLeaAJ-23
❑ 89KnoBluJB-6
❑ 89KnoBluJP-1131
❑ 89KnoBluJS-4
❑ 90CMC-342
❑ 90ProAAAF-358
❑ 90SyrChiC-16
❑ 90SyrChiMB-9
❑ 90SyrChiP-578
❑ 91LinDriAAA-535
❑ 91TacTigLD-535
❑ 91TacTigP-2313
❑ 92HunStaF-3956
❑ 92TacTigS-533
❑ 93TacTigF-3039
❑ 94ClaGolF-178
❑ 94ColSprSSF-742
❑ 97ColSprSATTI-17
❑ 98HunStaTI-24

Garrity, Pat

❑ 90LSUTigP-3
❑ 91LSUTigP-4

Garrow, David

❑ 92KenTwiC-17
❑ 92KenTwiF-612
❑ 93ForMyeMC-9
❑ 93ForMyeMF-2662
❑ 94ForMyeMC-8
❑ 94ForMyeMF-1179

Garside, Russ

❑ 90Bes-35
❑ 90ChaRaiB-1
❑ 90ChaRaiP-2038
❑ 90SpoIndSP-7

Garsky, Brian

❑ 96VerExpB-14

Garver, Ned

❑ 47PM1StaP1-67
❑ 49Bow-15
❑ 50Bow-51
❑ 51Bow-172
❑ 51FisBakL-7
❑ 51TopBluB-18
❑ 52BerRos-21
❑ 52Bow-29
❑ 52StaCalL-75A
❑ 52StaCalS-89A
❑ 52TipTop-10
❑ 52Top-212
❑ 53BowC-47
❑ 53TigGle-9
❑ 53Top-112
❑ 54Bow-39
❑ 54Top-44
❑ 55Bow-188
❑ 56A'sPos-18
❑ 56Top-189
❑ 57Top-285
❑ 58A'sJayP-3
❑ 58Top-292
❑ 59Top-245
❑ 60A'sJayP-4
❑ 60Top-471
❑ 61AngJayP-6
❑ 61Top-331
❑ 61TopStal-171
❑ 83TopRep5-212
❑ 89PacLegI-183
❑ 91TopArc1-112
❑ 94TopArc1-44
❑ 94TopArc1G-44

Garver, Steve

❑ 98ReaPhiM-20

Garvey, Don

❑ 91WelPirC-4
❑ 91WelPirP-3577
❑ 92AugPirF-245
❑ 93SalBucC-11
❑ 93SalBucF-440

Garvey, Steve

❑ 71DodTic-6
❑ 71MLBOffS-103
❑ 71OPC-341
❑ 71Top-341
❑ 72Top-686
❑ 73OPC-213
❑ 73Top-213
❑ 74OPC-575
❑ 74Top-575
❑ 75Hos-49
❑ 75HosTwi-49
❑ 75Kel-17
❑ 75OPC-140
❑ 75OPC-212
❑ 75OPC-460
❑ 75SSPPuzB-10
❑ 75Top-140
❑ 75Top-212
❑ 75Top-460
❑ 75TopMin-140
❑ 75TopMin-212
❑ 75TopMin-460
❑ 76BlaDis-16
❑ 76BucDis-16
❑ 76CarDis-16
❑ 76CraDis-16
❑ 76DailsID-16
❑ 76DodPos-5
❑ 76Hos-19
❑ 76HosTwi-19
❑ 76IsaDis-16
❑ 76Kel-54
❑ 76LinSup-115
❑ 76OPC-150
❑ 76OrbDis-16
❑ 76RedBarD-16
❑ 76SafDis-16
❑ 76SSP-77
❑ 76Top-150
❑ 76TowCluD-16
❑ 77BobParMBC-7
❑ 77BurCheD-150
❑ 77ChiWilD-25
❑ 77DailsID-25
❑ 77DetCaeD-25
❑ 77DodPho-2
❑ 77HolInnD-25
❑ 77Hos-35
❑ 77Kel-14
❑ 77MSADis-25
❑ 77OPC-255
❑ 77PepGloD-61
❑ 77RCColC-25
❑ 77SagDis-25
❑ 77sDis-25
❑ 77Spo-3419
❑ 77Spo-6701
❑ 77Top-400
❑ 77TopCloS-19
❑ 77WenDis-25
❑ 77ZipDis-25
❑ 78OPC-190
❑ 78Pep-31
❑ 78SagDis-3
❑ 78SSP270-71
❑ 78TasDis-3
❑ 78Top-350
❑ 78WifBalD-27
❑ 79BasPat-32
❑ 79DodBlu-4
❑ 79Hos-8
❑ 79OPC-21
❑ 79PosGarT-1
❑ 79PosGarT-2
❑ 79PosGarT-3
❑ 79PosGarT-4
❑ 79PosGarT-5
❑ 79PosGarT-6
❑ 79PosGarT-7
❑ 79PosGarT-8
❑ 79PosGarT-9
❑ 79PosGarT-10
❑ 79PosGarT-11
❑ 79PosGarT-12
❑ 79Top-50
❑ 79TopCom-24
❑ 80DodPol-6
❑ 80Kel-31
❑ 80OPC-152
❑ 80Top-290
❑ 80TopSup-13
❑ 81AllGamPI-95
❑ 81Dod-4
❑ 81Dod-10
❑ 81DodPol-6
❑ 81DodPos-2
❑ 81Don-56A
❑ 81Don-56B
❑ 81Don-176
❑ 81Dra-11
❑ 81Fle-110
❑ 81Fle-606
❑ 81FleStiC-1
❑ 81GafGar-1
❑ 81Kel-10
❑ 81LonBeaPT-1
❑ 81MSAMinD-13
❑ 81OPC-251
❑ 81PerCreC-12
❑ 81Squ-4
❑ 81Top-530
❑ 81TopScr-56
❑ 81TopSti-176
❑ 81TopSti-252
❑ 81TopSupHT-45
❑ 81TopSupN-6
❑ 82DodPol-6
❑ 82DodPos-2
❑ 82DodUniOV-5

- ❑ 82DogBuiE-3
- ❑ 82Don-3
- ❑ 82Don-84
- ❑ 82Dra-14
- ❑ 82FBIDis-9
- ❑ 82Fle-5
- ❑ 82FleSta-9
- ❑ 82K-M-26
- ❑ 82Kel-47
- ❑ 82LouSlu-1
- ❑ 82MonNew-6
- ❑ 82OnDecD-13
- ❑ 82OPC-179
- ❑ 82OPC-180
- ❑ 82PerCreC-11
- ❑ 82PerCreCG-11
- ❑ 82Top-179
- ❑ 82Top-180
- ❑ 82TopSti-54
- ❑ 82TopSti-258
- ❑ 83AllGamPl-94
- ❑ 83Don-488
- ❑ 83Fle-206
- ❑ 83FleSta-69
- ❑ 83FleSti-113
- ❑ 83OPC-198
- ❑ 83PadTeal-8
- ❑ 83Top-610
- ❑ 83TopFol-3
- ❑ 83TopSti-243
- ❑ 83TopTra-37T
- ❑ 84AllGamPl-4
- ❑ 84DodUniO-8
- ❑ 84Don-63
- ❑ 84DonActAS-38
- ❑ 84DonCha-56
- ❑ 84Dra-10
- ❑ 84Fle-300
- ❑ 84Fle-628
- ❑ 84FunFooP-9
- ❑ 84McGCloT-1
- ❑ 84MilBra-10
- ❑ 84MLBPen-18
- ❑ 84Nes792-380
- ❑ 84NesDreT-12
- ❑ 84OCoandSI-43
- ❑ 84OPC-380
- ❑ 84PadMot-7
- ❑ 84PadSmo-10
- ❑ 84RalPur-18
- ❑ 84SevCoi-W7
- ❑ 84StaGar-1
- ❑ 84StaGar-2
- ❑ 84StaGar-3
- ❑ 84StaGar-4
- ❑ 84StaGar-5
- ❑ 84StaGar-6
- ❑ 84StaGar-7
- ❑ 84StaGar-8
- ❑ 84StaGar-9
- ❑ 84StaGar-10
- ❑ 84StaGar-11
- ❑ 84StaGar-12
- ❑ 84StaGar-13
- ❑ 84StaGar-14
- ❑ 84StaGar-15
- ❑ 84StaGar-16
- ❑ 84StaGar-17
- ❑ 84StaGar-18
- ❑ 84StaGar-19
- ❑ 84StaGar-20
- ❑ 84StaGar-21
- ❑ 84StaGar-22
- ❑ 84StaGar-23
- ❑ 84StaGar-24
- ❑ 84StaGar-25
- ❑ 84StaGar-26
- ❑ 84StaGar-27
- ❑ 84StaGar-28
- ❑ 84StaGar-29
- ❑ 84StaGar-30
- ❑ 84StaGar-31
- ❑ 84StaGar-32
- ❑ 84StaGar-33
- ❑ 84StaGar-34
- ❑ 84StaGar-35
- ❑ 84StaGar-36
- ❑ 84Top-380
- ❑ 84TopCer-18
- ❑ 84TopGaloC-5
- ❑ 84TopRubD-21
- ❑ 84TopSti-156
- ❑ 84TopSup-22
- ❑ 84TopTif-380
- ❑ 85AllGamPl-95
- ❑ 85Don-307
- ❑ 85Dra-11
- ❑ 85Fle-32
- ❑ 85Fle-631
- ❑ 85Fle-633
- ❑ 85FleLimE-9
- ❑ 85GenMilS-3
- ❑ 85Lea-94
- ❑ 85OPC-177
- ❑ 85PadMot-6
- ❑ 85SevCoi-W8
- ❑ 85SpoIndGC-7
- ❑ 85Top-2
- ❑ 85Top-450
- ❑ 85TopGloA-2
- ❑ 85TopMin-450
- ❑ 85TopRubD-21
- ❑ 85TopSti-1
- ❑ 85TopSti-2
- ❑ 85TopSti-13
- ❑ 85TopSti-14
- ❑ 85TopSti-149
- ❑ 85TopSti-176
- ❑ 85TopSup-26
- ❑ 85TopTif-2
- ❑ 85TopTif-450
- ❑ 86BasStaB-45
- ❑ 86BurKinA-18
- ❑ 86Don-63
- ❑ 86DonAll-3
- ❑ 86DonPop-3
- ❑ 86Fle-321
- ❑ 86Fle-640
- ❑ 86FleLeaL-15
- ❑ 86FleMin-67
- ❑ 86FleStiC-43
- ❑ 86FleStiWBC-S3
- ❑ 86Lea-56
- ❑ 86MeaGolBB-4
- ❑ 86MeaGolSB-15
- ❑ 86MSAJifPD-18
- ❑ 86OPC-4
- ❑ 86QuaGra-6
- ❑ 86SevCoi-W14
- ❑ 86Spo-35
- ❑ 86Spo-51
- ❑ 86Spo-137
- ❑ 86SpoDecG-61
- ❑ 86Top-660
- ❑ 86TopGloA-13
- ❑ 86TopGloS-38
- ❑ 86TopSti-104
- ❑ 86TopSti-148
- ❑ 86TopSup-24
- ❑ 86TopTat-5
- ❑ 86TopTif-660
- ❑ 86TruVal-2
- ❑ 87BoaandB-18
- ❑ 87BurKinA-5
- ❑ 87ClaGam-27
- ❑ 87DodSmoA-8
- ❑ 87Don-81
- ❑ 87DonOpeD-143
- ❑ 87Fle-414
- ❑ 87FleExcS-18
- ❑ 87FleGamW-16
- ❑ 87FleGlo-414
- ❑ 87FleLimE-16
- ❑ 87FleMin-43
- ❑ 87FleStiC-46
- ❑ 87KraFoo-20
- ❑ 87Lea-114
- ❑ 87MandMSL-20
- ❑ 87nsBasASD-3
- ❑ 87OPC-100
- ❑ 87PadBohHB-6
- ❑ 87RalPur-2
- ❑ 87RedFolSB-61
- ❑ 87SmoNatL-10
- ❑ 87Spo-40
- ❑ 87SpoTeaP-16
- ❑ 87StuPan-12
- ❑ 87Top-100
- ❑ 87TopCoi-32
- ❑ 87TopSti-115
- ❑ 87TopTif-100
- ❑ 88DodSmo-15
- ❑ 88DodSmo-17
- ❑ 88DodSmo-21
- ❑ 88Sco-225
- ❑ 88ScoGlo-225
- ❑ 89DodSmoG-83
- ❑ 89PadMag-20
- ❑ 90BasWit-26
- ❑ 90DodTar-270
- ❑ 90PacLeg-27
- ❑ 90SweBasG-103
- ❑ 91DodUno7P-1
- ❑ 91DodUno7P-5
- ❑ 91LinDri-8
- ❑ 91SweBasG-32
- ❑ 92ActPacA-64
- ❑ 92DodStaTA-16
- ❑ 92MCIAmb-2
- ❑ 92UppDecS-15
- ❑ 92UppDecS-17
- ❑ 92UppDecS-18
- ❑ 93TedWil-14
- ❑ 93UppDecS-13
- ❑ 93UppDecS-20
- ❑ 93Yoo-7
- ❑ 94UppDecAH-185
- ❑ 94UppDecAH-213
- ❑ 94UppDecAH1-185
- ❑ 94UppDecAH1-213
- ❑ 94UppDecS-5
- ❑ 95MCIAmb-8
- ❑ 95SonGre-3
- ❑ 95SPCha-106
- ❑ 95SPChaCP-CP10
- ❑ 95SPChaCPDC-CP10
- ❑ 95SPChaDC-106
- ❑ 99SpoIllGotG-66
- ❑ 99SpoIllGotGA-26
- ❑ 99SpoIllGotGC-28
- ❑ 99SpoIllGotGC-46
- ❑ 99UppDecR-94
- ❑ 99UppDecRG-94
- ❑ 99UppDecRI-SG
- ❑ 99UppDecRIL2-SG
- ❑ 99UppDecRP-94

Garvin, Jerry (Theodore)
- ❑ 78BluJayP-6
- ❑ 78OPC-49
- ❑ 78Top-419
- ❑ 79OPC-145
- ❑ 79SyrChiTI-25
- ❑ 79Top-293
- ❑ 80OPC-320
- ❑ 80Top-611
- ❑ 81Don-150
- ❑ 81Fle-429
- ❑ 81OPC-124
- ❑ 81Top-124
- ❑ 82BluJayS-5
- ❑ 82Don-430
- ❑ 82Fle-614
- ❑ 82OPC-264
- ❑ 82Top-768
- ❑ 83Don-227
- ❑ 83Fle-428
- ❑ 83Top-358
- ❑ 92Nab-14

Garvin, Ned
- ❑ 03BreE10-55
- ❑ 11SpoLifCW-136
- ❑ 90DodTar-271

Garza, Alberto
- ❑ 96BurIndB-4
- ❑ 98CarLeaAC-24
- ❑ 98CarLeaTPQ-25
- ❑ 98KinIndQ-10

Garza, Alejandro
- ❑ 93CarMudF-2046
- ❑ 93CarMudTI-7

Garza, Armando
- ❑ 90NebCor-12

Garza, Chris
- ❑ 97ForWayW-12
- ❑ 98ForMyeMTI-13

Garza, Lonnie
- ❑ 83RedPioT-10

Garza, Mark
- ❑ 85CloHSS-18

Garza, Roberto
- ❑ 92BurIndC-16
- ❑ 92BurIndF-1649
- ❑ 93WatIndC-10
- ❑ 93WatIndF-3556

Garza, Willie
- ❑ 88WatIndP-670

Gash, Darius
- ❑ 90SpoIndSP-24
- ❑ 91WatDiaC-20
- ❑ 91WatDiaP-1267
- ❑ 92ClaFS7-2
- ❑ 92HigDesMC-27
- ❑ 93WicWraF-2988

Gaskill, Derek
- ❑ 94HelBreF-3607
- ❑ 94HelBreSP-20
- ❑ 96StCatSB-9
- ❑ 97PitMet-13
- ❑ 98CapCitBF5-7
- ❑ 98CapCitBM-7

Gaspar, Cade
- ❑ 94ClaUpdCotC-CC16
- ❑ 94SigRooDP-18
- ❑ 94SigRooDPS-18
- ❑ 94StaCluDP-13
- ❑ 94StaCluDPFDI-13
- ❑ 95Bow-78
- ❑ 95Exc-48
- ❑ 95SPML-54
- ❑ 95StaClu-105
- ❑ 95StaCluFDI-105
- ❑ 95StaCluMOP-105
- ❑ 95StaCluSTWS-105
- ❑ 95Top-492
- ❑ 95UppDecML-154
- ❑ 95UppDecMLFS-154
- ❑ 96RanCucQB-16

Gaspar, Harry
- ❑ 09ColChiE-114
- ❑ 09T206-139
- ❑ 10DomDisP-47
- ❑ 10SweCapPP-99
- ❑ 11HelSta-114
- ❑ 11MecDFT-10
- ❑ 11PinT-5-421
- ❑ 11SpoLifCW-137
- ❑ 11SpoLifM-194
- ❑ 11T205-63
- ❑ 12ColRedB-114
- ❑ 12ColTinT-114
- ❑ 12HasTriFT-10A
- ❑ 12HasTriFT-73B

Gaspar, Rod
- ❑ 70OPC-371
- ❑ 70Top-371
- ❑ 71MLBOffS-227
- ❑ 71OPC-383
- ❑ 71Top-383
- ❑ 75HawIsIC-6
- ❑ 76HawIsIC-18
- ❑ 89MetRinP69-12
- ❑ 91MetWIZ-136
- ❑ 94Met69CCPP-15
- ❑ 94Met69CS-14
- ❑ 94Met69T-25

Gass, Jeff
- ❑ 83EriCarT-16

Gassaway, Charles
- ❑ 45A'sTeal-14
- ❑ 46RemBre-7
- ❑ 47RemBre-4
- ❑ 47SigOil-45
- ❑ 47SmiClo-8
- ❑ 48SigOil-8
- ❑ 48SmiClo-10
- ❑ 49BowPCL-10
- ❑ 49RemBre-8
- ❑ 50RemBre-7

Gasser, Steve
- ❑ 86KenTwiP-10
- ❑ 87OrlTwiP-11
- ❑ 87SouLeaAJ-18
- ❑ 88OrlTwiB-23
- ❑ 89PitMetS-5

Gast, Joe
- ❑ 87NewOriP-14
- ❑ 89PenPilS-6

Gast, John
- ❑ 91PriRedC-4
- ❑ 91PriRedP-3521

Gastall, Tommy
- ❑ 56BalOriP-12
- ❑ 91OriCro-153

Gastelum, Macario
- ❑ 87BakDodP-3
- ❑ 89BakDodCLC-185

Gaston, Alex
- ❑ 21E121So1-28
- ❑ 21E121So8-26
- ❑ 21KoBreWSI-11
- ❑ 22W575-39
- ❑ 23W501-112
- ❑ 30Zee-142
- ❑ 32Zee-115
- ❑ 34TarThoBD-12
- ❑ 81ConTSN-69

Gaston, Cito (Clarence)
- ❑ 69MilBra-90
- ❑ 69PadVol-4
- ❑ 69Top-304
- ❑ 70DayDaiNM-73
- ❑ 70Top-604
- ❑ 71BazNumT-12
- ❑ 71BazUnn-30
- ❑ 71Kel-41
- ❑ 71MLBOffS-228
- ❑ 71OPC-25
- ❑ 71Top-25
- ❑ 71TopCoi-1
- ❑ 71TopSup-52
- ❑ 71TopTat-27
- ❑ 72MilBra-113
- ❑ 72OPC-431
- ❑ 72OPC-432
- ❑ 72PadPos-10
- ❑ 72Top-431
- ❑ 72Top-432
- ❑ 73OPC-159
- ❑ 73PadDea-1
- ❑ 73PadDea-8
- ❑ 73Top-159
- ❑ 74OPC-364
- ❑ 74PadDea-9
- ❑ 74Top-364A
- ❑ 74Top-364B
- ❑ 75AtlBraP-12
- ❑ 75OPC-427
- ❑ 75Top-427
- ❑ 75TopMin-427
- ❑ 76AtlBraP-12
- ❑ 76OPC-558
- ❑ 76SSP-18
- ❑ 76Top-558
- ❑ 76VenLeaS-122
- ❑ 77PadSchC-23A
- ❑ 77PadSchC-23B
- ❑ 77Top-192
- ❑ 78Top-716
- ❑ 79Top-208
- ❑ 84BluJayFS-13
- ❑ 85BluJayFS-12
- ❑ 86BluJayFS-13
- ❑ 86PadGreT-7
- ❑ 87BluJayFS-10
- ❑ 88BluJayFS-13
- ❑ 89BluJayFS-11
- ❑ 89TopTra-36T
- ❑ 89TopTraT-36T
- ❑ 90BluJayFS-9
- ❑ 90OPC-201
- ❑ 90Top-201
- ❑ 90TopTif-201
- ❑ 90TopTVA-33
- ❑ 91BluJayFS-9
- ❑ 91BluJayFS-9
- ❑ 91BluJayS-36
- ❑ 91OPC-81
- ❑ 91Top-81
- ❑ 91TopDesS-81
- ❑ 91TopMic-81
- ❑ 91TopTif-81
- ❑ 92OPC-699
- ❑ 92Top-699
- ❑ 92TopGol-699
- ❑ 92TopGolW-699
- ❑ 92TopMic-699
- ❑ 93BluJayD-13
- ❑ 93BluJayD4-28
- ❑ 93BluJayDM-15
- ❑ 93BluJayDM-24
- ❑ 93BluJayFS-10
- ❑ 93OPCWorC-18
- ❑ 93Top-514
- ❑ 93TopGol-514
- ❑ 93TopInaM-514
- ❑ 93TopInaR-514
- ❑ 93TopMic-514
- ❑ 95BluJayOH-13
- ❑ 96BluJayOH-9
- ❑ 97BluJayB-4
- ❑ 97BluJayOH-10
- ❑ 97BluJayS-24

Gaston, John
- ❑ 77TCMTheWY-4
- ❑ 83GreHorT-6

Gaston, Milt
- ❑ 27MidBre-28
- ❑ 33Gou-65
- ❑ 33GouCanV-65
- ❑ 34DiaMatCSB-66
- ❑ 72TCMthe3-28
- ❑ 72TCMthe3-117
- ❑ 79DiaGre-128
- ❑ 81ConTSN-70

Gaston, Russell
- ❑ 90SavCarP-2065
- ❑ 91JohCitCC-19
- ❑ 91SavCarC-5
- ❑ 91SavCarP-1646

Gaston, Welcome
- ❑ 90DodTar-956

Gastreich, Henry
- ❑ 87OldJudN-192

Gastright, Hank
- ❑ 90DodTar-272

Gate, Bill
- ❑ 91St.PetCC-24

Gateman, Wareham
- ❑ 88CapCodPB-25

Gates, Brent
- ❑ 91Cla/Bes-414
- ❑ 91ClaDraP-22
- ❑ 91FroRowDP-22
- ❑ 91FroRowDPG-22
- ❑ 91FroRowDPS-22
- ❑ 91SouOreAC-24
- ❑ 91SouOreAP-3855
- ❑ 92CalLeaACL-1
- ❑ 92ClaFS7-187
- ❑ 92DonRoo-42
- ❑ 92LeaGolR-BC2
- ❑ 92ModA'sC-15
- ❑ 92ModA'sF-3905
- ❑ 92OPC-216
- ❑ 92ProFS7-133
- ❑ 92Sco-805
- ❑ 92StaCluD-56
- ❑ 92Top-216
- ❑ 92TopGol-216
- ❑ 92TopGolW-216
- ❑ 92TopMic-216
- ❑ 92UppDecML-145
- ❑ 93AthMot-17
- ❑ 93AthStaC-19
- ❑ 93Bow-457
- ❑ 93ClaFisN-9
- ❑ 93ClaFS7-189
- ❑ 93ClaGolF-74
- ❑ 93ExcAllF-8
- ❑ 93ExcFS7-216
- ❑ 93Fla-258
- ❑ 93FleFinE-254
- ❑ 93FunPac-2
- ❑ 93JimDeaR-4
- ❑ 93Lea-536
- ❑ 93SelRoo-61T
- ❑ 93SelRooAR-2
- ❑ 93SP-39
- ❑ 93TacTigF-3040
- ❑ 93Top-451
- ❑ 93TopGol-451
- ❑ 93TopInaM-451
- ❑ 93TopInaR-451
- ❑ 93TopMic-451
- ❑ 93TopTra-91T
- ❑ 93UppDec-500
- ❑ 93UppDec-504
- ❑ 93UppDecGold-500
- ❑ 93UppDecGold-504
- ❑ 94A'sMot-21
- ❑ 94Bow-304
- ❑ 94ColC-107
- ❑ 94ColChoGS-107
- ❑ 94ColChoSS-107
- ❑ 94Don-111
- ❑ 94Fin-7
- ❑ 94FinJum-7
- ❑ 94FinRef-7
- ❑ 94Fla-330
- ❑ 94Fle-261
- ❑ 94FleExtB-149
- ❑ 94FleExtBSYS-8
- ❑ 94FUnPac-13
- ❑ 94FUnPac-221
- ❑ 94Lea-161
- ❑ 94OPC-231
- ❑ 94OPCDiaD-15
- ❑ 94Pac-449
- ❑ 94Pin-299
- ❑ 94PinArtP-299
- ❑ 94PinMusC-299
- ❑ 94Sco-187
- ❑ 94ScoBoyoS-19
- ❑ 94ScoGolR-187
- ❑ 94Sel-281
- ❑ 94SP-33
- ❑ 94SPDieC-33
- ❑ 94StaClu-65
- ❑ 94StaCluFDI-65
- ❑ 94StaCluGR-65
- ❑ 94StaCluMOP-65
- ❑ 94StaCluMOP-ST25
- ❑ 94StaCluST-ST25
- ❑ 94Stu-2

❑ 94Top-586
❑ 94TopGol-586
❑ 94TopSpa-586
❑ 94TriPla-3
❑ 94Ult-107
❑ 94UltSecYS-2
❑ 94UppDec-110
❑ 94UppDecED-110
❑ 94USPlaCR-5D
❑ 94USPlaCR-9H
❑ 95A'sCHP-1
❑ 95AthMot-21
❑ 95ColCho-124
❑ 95ColChoGS-124
❑ 95ColChoSE-46
❑ 95ColChoSEGS-46
❑ 95ColChoSESS-46
❑ 95ColChoSS-124
❑ 95Don-329
❑ 95DonPreP-329
❑ 95DonTopotO-136
❑ 95Fla-73
❑ 95Fle-245
❑ 95Lea-290
❑ 95Pin-191
❑ 95PinArtP-191
❑ 95PinMusC-191
❑ 95PinUps-US7
❑ 95Sco-241
❑ 95ScoGolR-241
❑ 95ScoPlaTS-241
❑ 95Sel-133
❑ 95SelArtP-133
❑ 95Spo-101
❑ 95SpoArtP-101
❑ 95StaClu-323
❑ 95StaCluMOP-323
❑ 95StaCluSTWS-323
❑ 95StaCluVR-166
❑ 95StaCluVRMO-166
❑ 95Sum-53
❑ 95Sum-163
❑ 95SumNthD-53
❑ 95Top-129
❑ 95TopCyb-80
❑ 95TopEmb-17
❑ 95TopEmbGI-17
❑ 95Ult-317
❑ 95UltGolM-317
❑ 95UppDec-283
❑ 95UppDecED-283
❑ 95UppDecEDG-283
❑ 95UppDecSE-108
❑ 95UppDecSEG-108
❑ 96A'sMot-6
❑ 96ColCho-645
❑ 96ColChoGS-645
❑ 96ColChoSS-645
❑ 96Don-76
❑ 96DonPreP-76
❑ 96EmoXL-102
❑ 96Fla-147
❑ 96Fle-207
❑ 96FleTif-207
❑ 96MetUni-100
❑ 96MetUniP-100
❑ 96Pac-389
❑ 96PanSti-220
❑ 96Sco-394
❑ 96StaClu-39
❑ 96StaCluMOP-39
❑ 96Top-31
❑ 96Ult-113
❑ 96UltGolM-113
❑ 96UppDec-424
❑ 97Fle-189
❑ 97FleTif-189
❑ 97Pac-168
❑ 97PacLigB-168
❑ 97PacSil-168
❑ 97Top-296
❑ 97Ult-111
❑ 97Ult-488
❑ 97UltGolME-111
❑ 97UltGolME-488
❑ 97UltPlaME-111
❑ 97UltPlaME-488
❑ 97UppDec-448
❑ 97UppDecMP-P18
❑ 98PacOnl-420
❑ 98PacOnlR-420
❑ 98PacOnlWC-420
❑ 98UppDec-697

Gates, Bryan
❑ 86AncGlaPTI-38
❑ 87AncGlaP-34

Gates, Eddie
❑ 81EvaTriT-20
❑ 82EvaTriT-20

Gates, Joe
❑ 75WatRoyT-13
❑ 77JacSunT-6
❑ 78KnoKnoST-7
❑ 80IowOakP-6
❑ 81EdmTraRR-16

Gates, Mathew
❑ 91BriBanF-6

Gates, Michael
❑ 80MemChiT-9
❑ 82WicAerTI-4
❑ 83Don-114
❑ 83OPC-195
❑ 83Top-657
❑ 83WicAerDS-8
❑ 84IndIndTI-29

Gates, Todd
❑ 91ButCopKSP-13
❑ 92ButCopKSP-7

Gatewood, Aubrey
❑ 64Top-127
❑ 64TopVen-127
❑ 65Top-422
❑ 66OPC-42
❑ 66Top-42
❑ 66TopVen-42

Gatewood, Henry
❑ 85VerBeaDT-11
❑ 86VisOakP-10
❑ 87OrlTwiP-5
❑ 88WinSpiS-4

Gatewood, Kenneth
❑ 98SpollITaNAotG-AG1

Gatins, Frank
❑ 90DodTar-957

Gatlin, Mike
❑ 77OrlTwiT-11
❑ 82OneYanT-16

Gaton, Frank
❑ 75BurBeeT-9
❑ 76BurBeeT-14

Gatti, Dom
❑ 93ButCopKSP-1
❑ 94HudValRC-5
❑ 94HudValRF-3398
❑ 95ChaRivTI-23

Gattis, Jim
❑ 89MiaMirIS-25
❑ 89MiaMirIS-6

Gaube, Gerry
❑ 77ForLauYS-9

Gaudet, Jim
❑ 77JacSunT-7
❑ 79Top-707
❑ 80EvaTriT-3
❑ 80OmaRoyP-13
❑ 81OmaRoyT-13
❑ 82SyrChiT-11
❑ 91JesHSA-7

Gaughan, Hank
❑ 82ChaLooT-25

Gault, Raymond
❑ 76BatTroTI-9
❑ 77WatIndT-10

Gause, Ernie
❑ 80CarMudF-10

Gausepohl, Dan
❑ 82HawIsIT-8

Gautreau, Doc
❑ 92ConTSN-545

Gautreau, Mike
❑ 94NewJerCC-10
❑ 94NewJerCF-3409
❑ 95PeoChiTI-31

Gautreau, Walter
❑ 28LaPre-9

Gautreaux, Sid
❑ 72TCMthe3-29
❑ 90DodTar-273

Gavaghan, Sean
❑ 92KenTwiF-597
❑ 93ForWayWC-9
❑ 93ForWayWF-1962
❑ 94NasXprF-379
❑ 96HarCitRCB-13

Gavello, Tim
❑ 94OgdRapF-3747
❑ 94OgdRapSP-16

Gavin, Dave
❑ 87ModA'sC-4
❑ 88MadMusP-11
❑ 89ModA'sC-28
❑ 89WatDiaP-1776
❑ 89WatDiaS-9

Gavin, Tom
❑ 90EliTwiS-10
❑ 91VisOakC-22
❑ 91VisOakP-1754

Gavlick, Daryle
❑ 92HunCubC-26
❑ 92HunCubF-3140
❑ 93PeoChiC-6
❑ 93PeoChiF-1078
❑ 93PeoChiTI-7
❑ 94DayCubC-7
❑ 94DayCubF-2345

Gay, Brad
❑ 93BelBreCB-9
❑ 93BelBreFI-1712
❑ 93HelBreF-4099
❑ 94StoPorC-8
❑ 94StoPorF-1696

Gay, Chris
❑ 93HicCraC-9

Gay, Frank
❑ 16Zee-111

Gay, Jeff
❑ 86SalAngC-78
❑ 87QuaCitAP-26
❑ 89PalSprACLC-34
❑ 89PalSprAP-466
❑ 90QuaCitAGS-16
❑ 91BirBarLD-61
❑ 91BirBarP-1457
❑ 91LinDriAA-61

Gay, Scott
❑ 87Ft.LauYP-17
❑ 88Ft.LauYS-9
❑ 89SalSpuP-1823

Gay, Steve
❑ 86LynMetP-11
❑ 94OgdRapF-3731
❑ 94OgdRapSP-7

Gaylor, Bobby
❑ 86JamExpP-10
❑ 87BurExpP-1084
❑ 88WesPalBES-11

Gaynor, John
❑ 91ParPatF-10
❑ 93AusFut-39

Gaynor, Richard Kent
❑ 83ReaPhiT-5
❑ 84PorBeaC-212
❑ 87BirBarB-11
❑ 88BirBarB-17

Gazarek, Marty
❑ 94WilCubC-8
❑ 94WilCubF-3778
❑ 95RocCubTI-33
❑ 96DayCubB-14
❑ 96WesOahCHWB-15
❑ 97OrlRayB-13
❑ 98IowCubQ-10
❑ 98WesTenDJM-10

Gazella, Mike
❑ 30Zee-5
❑ 31Zee-4
❑ 32Zee-6
❑ 75Yan192T-7
❑ 79Yan192T-10
❑ 84Yan192G-28
❑ 91ConTSN-121

Gazzilli, Dan
❑ 85UtiBluST-26

Gbur, Paul
❑ 79AppFoxT-25

Geary, Bob
❑ 21Zee-143
❑ 22Zee-99
❑ 23Zee-130
❑ 23Zee-131
❑ 24Zee-90
❑ 25Zee-108
❑ 26Zee-136
❑ 27Zee-111

Geary, Geoff
❑ 98BatMucTI-10

Gebhard, Bob
❑ 72OPC-28
❑ 72Top-28
❑ 72TwiPos-5
❑ 72TwiTeal-4
❑ 73TacTwiC-8
❑ 75IntLeaAT-29
❑ 82ExpPos-14

Geck, Joseph
❑ 93HicCraC-30
❑ 94HicCraC-30
❑ 94SouAtlLAF-SAL22
❑ 97HicCraRB-4
❑ 98HicCraM-4

Geddes, Jim
❑ 73OPC-561
❑ 73Top-561

Gedeon, Elmer Joe
❑ 12Zee-110
❑ 14Zee-11
❑ 15SpoNewM-66
❑ 15Zee-77
❑ 16BF2FP-35
❑ 16FleBreD-30
❑ 16SpoNewM-66
❑ 17ColE13-57
❑ 17HolBreD-34
❑ 19W514-39

Gedman, Rich
❑ 81PawRedST-24
❑ 82Don-512
❑ 82Fle-294
❑ 82RedSoxC-7
❑ 82Top-59
❑ 83Don-156
❑ 83Fle-184
❑ 83Top-602
❑ 84Don-579
❑ 84Fle-398
❑ 84Nes792-498
❑ 84OPC-296
❑ 84Top-498
❑ 84TopSti-222
❑ 84TopTif-498
❑ 85AllGamPI-40
❑ 85Don-457
❑ 85Fle-159
❑ 85OPC-18
❑ 85Top-529
❑ 85TopSti-217
❑ 85TopTif-529
❑ 86Don-273
❑ 86DonAll-56
❑ 86Fle-349
❑ 86Fle-643
❑ 86FleLimE-18
❑ 86FleMin-75
❑ 86FleStiC-44
❑ 86Lea-145
❑ 86OPC-375
❑ 86Spo-84
❑ 86Top-375
❑ 86TopSti-248
❑ 86TopTat-17
❑ 86TopTif-375
❑ 87ClaGam-49
❑ 87Don-153
❑ 87DonAll-39
❑ 87Fle-35
❑ 87FleGlo-35
❑ 87FleGlo-WS9
❑ 87FleRecS-11
❑ 87FleWorS-9
❑ 87Lea-254
❑ 87OPC-137
❑ 87RedSoxP-10
❑ 87Spo-149
❑ 87Spo-154
❑ 87Top-306
❑ 87Top-740
❑ 87TopSti-247
❑ 87TopTif-306
❑ 87TopTif-740
❑ 88Don-129
❑ 88DonBasB-140
❑ 88DonTeaBRS-129
❑ 88Fle-353
❑ 88FleGlo-353
❑ 88OPC-245
❑ 88PanSti-24
❑ 88Sco-241
❑ 88ScoGlo-241
❑ 88StaLinRS-9
❑ 88Top-245
❑ 88TopBig-152
❑ 88TopSti-252
❑ 88TopTif-245
❑ 89Bow-27
❑ 89BowTif-27
❑ 89Don-162
❑ 89Fle-89
❑ 89FleGlo-89
❑ 89OPC-178
❑ 89Sco-345
❑ 89Top-652
❑ 89TopBig-72
❑ 89TopSti-253
❑ 89TopTif-652
❑ 89UppDec-368
❑ 90Don-346
❑ 90Fle-276
❑ 90FleCan-276
❑ 90Lea-478
❑ 90MLBBasB-72
❑ 90OPC-123
❑ 90PubIntS-456
❑ 90RedSoxP-10
❑ 90Sco-173
❑ 90Top-123
❑ 90TopTif-123
❑ 90TopTVRS-18
❑ 90UppDec-402
❑ 91CarPol-29
❑ 91Lea-418
❑ 91UppDec-588
❑ 92CarPol-5
❑ 92Don-553
❑ 92Fle-577
❑ 92Sco-689
❑ 92StaClu-58
❑ 92Ult-566
❑ 94OriPro-38

Geeve, Dave
❑ 93ChaRanC-11
❑ 93ChaRanF-1934
❑ 94ExcFS7-133
❑ 94TulDriF-237
❑ 94TulDriTI-7
❑ 96TulDriTI-11

Geffner, Glenn
❑ 95RocRedWTI-45

Gegan, Fred
❑ 87VerBeaDP-9

Gehret, Scott
❑ 98PorRocG-15

Gehrig, Lou (Henry Louis)
❑ 25Exh-97
❑ 26Exh-99
❑ 27Exh-49
❑ 28Exh-50
❑ 28PorandAR-A10
❑ 28PorandAR-B10
❑ 28StaPlaCE-24
❑ 28W502-26
❑ 28W56PlaC-C3
❑ 28Yue-26
❑ 29ExhFou-26
❑ 29PorandAR-28
❑ 30SchR33-20
❑ 30W554-4
❑ 31Exh-26
❑ 31W517-35
❑ 32USCar*-26
❑ 33ButCanV-18
❑ 33CraJacP-7
❑ 33DelR33-7
❑ 33Gou-92
❑ 33Gou-160
❑ 33GouCanV-55
❑ 33WorCig-45
❑ 34BabRutG-25
❑ 34ButPreR-24
❑ 34ExhFou-13
❑ 34Gou-37
❑ 34Gou-61
❑ 34GouCanV-92
❑ 35AlDemDCR3-9
❑ 35ExhFou-13
❑ 35WheBB1-13
❑ 36ExhFou-13
❑ 36Halof FP-11
❑ 36OveCanR-15
❑ 36WheBB3-4
❑ 36WheBB4-2
❑ 36WorWidGV-96
❑ 37ExhFou-13
❑ 38BasTabP-11
❑ 38ExhFou-13
❑ 38OurNatGPP-11
❑ 39ExhSal-18
❑ 39PC7AlbHoF-22
❑ 46SpoExcW-3-4
❑ 47PM1StaP1-68
❑ 47PM1StaP1-69
❑ 48BluTin-29
❑ 48ExhHoF-12
❑ 48SweSpoT-14
❑ 49LeaPre-3
❑ 50CalHOFW-33
❑ 51R42SmaS-35
❑ 51TopConMA-5
❑ 53ArtHaloFP-37
❑ 58JayPubAG-3
❑ 60ExhWriH-11
❑ 60Fle-28
❑ 60KeyChal-18
❑ 60NuHi-24
❑ 60RawGloT-8
❑ 61Fle-31
❑ 61GolPre-16
❑ 61NuSco-424
❑ 61Top-405
❑ 62Top-140
❑ 62TopVen-140
❑ 63BasMagM-29
❑ 63BazA-15
❑ 63GadFunC-5
❑ 63GadFunC-43
❑ 63HalofFB-8
❑ 67TopVen-141
❑ 68LauWorS-25
❑ 68SpoMemAG-12
❑ 69Baz-4
❑ 69Baz-5
❑ 69Baz-7
❑ 69EquSpoHoF-BB5
❑ 70FleWorS-25
❑ 70FleWorS-29
❑ 70FleWorS-35
❑ 70Houof J-8
❑ 70MetMusoAB-2
❑ 70SpoCarfCOP-1
❑ 70SpoCarfCOP-9
❑ 71FleWorS-26
❑ 72FleFamF-5
❑ 72KelATG-13
❑ 72LauGreF-8
❑ 73HalofFPP-8
❑ 73OPC-472
❑ 73SevTraC-23
❑ 73SyrChiTI-8
❑ 73Top-472
❑ 74CapPub-2
❑ 74FleBasF-5
❑ 74NewYorNTDiS-20
❑ 74SyrChiTI-8
❑ 75SpoHobBG-5
❑ 75TCMHouoJ-8
❑ 75Yan192T-8
❑ 75YanAllTT-4
❑ 75YanDyn1T-16
❑ 75YanDyn1T-51
❑ 75YanDyn1T-52
❑ 75YanDyn1T-53
❑ 75YanDyn1T-54
❑ 76GalBasGHoF-11
❑ 76LauDiaJ-28
❑ 76OPC-341
❑ 76RowExh-4
❑ 76ShaPiz-18
❑ 76Top-341
❑ 77BobParHoF-22
❑ 77BobParMBC-8
❑ 77BobParMBC-17
❑ 77GalGloG-46
❑ 77GalGloG-181
❑ 77GalGloG-236
❑ 77SerSta-10
❑ 77ShaPiz-10
❑ 78DexHaloFP-17
❑ 79Pew-3
❑ 79Yan192T-11
❑ 80Lau300-29
❑ 80LauFamF-10
❑ 80MarExh-9
❑ 80PacLeg-13
❑ 80PerHaloFP-22
❑ 80SSPHOF-22
❑ 80YanGreT-1
❑ 81ConTSN-5
❑ 81SanDieSC-17
❑ 81SanDieSC-18
❑ 81SanDieSC-19
❑ 81SpoHaloF-6
❑ 81TigDetN-50
❑ 82BHCRSpoL-3
❑ 82DavHaloFB-9
❑ 82DiaCla-35
❑ 82TCMGreH-23
❑ 82TCMGreS-19
❑ 83BigLeaCOA-9
❑ 83ConMar-3
❑ 83TCMRut-2
❑ 83YanASFY-15
❑ 84GalHaloFRL-18
❑ 84OCoandSI-98
❑ 84OCoandSI-174
❑ 84SpoDesPW-25
❑ 84Yan192G-1

❑ 85BigLeaC3-49
❑ 85CirK-14
❑ 85Don-635
❑ 85DonHOFS-3
❑ 85DonWaxBC-PUZ
❑ 85FegMurCG-7
❑ 85GeoSteM-2
❑ 85Lea-635
❑ 85TCMPhoC-5
❑ 85TCMPhoC-16
❑ 85UltBasC-4
❑ 85Woo-14
❑ 86ConSer1-1
❑ 86ConSer1-17
❑ 86ConSer1-52
❑ 86ConSer1-57
❑ 86SpoDecG-10
❑ 86TCM-17
❑ 86TCMSupS-9
❑ 86TCMSupS-28
❑ 87ConSer2-1
❑ 87HygAllG-20
❑ 87NesDreT-1
❑ 87SpoCubG-2
❑ 87SpoRea-28
❑ 87Yan192T-8
❑ 88ConAmeA-10
❑ 88ConHar-3
❑ 88ConSer5-12
❑ 88GreBasS-30
❑ 89CMCBasG-3
❑ 89HOFStiB-1
❑ 89PacLegI-174
❑ 89RinPosG-1
❑ 89RinPosG-2
❑ 89RinPosG-3
❑ 89RinPosG-4
❑ 89RinPosG-5
❑ 89RinPosG-6
❑ 89RinPosG-7
❑ 89RinPosG-8
❑ 89RinPosG-9
❑ 89RinPosG-10
❑ 89SweBasG-25
❑ 89TopBasT-21
❑ 89USPLegSC-2
❑ 89YanCitAG-2
❑ 90BasWit-73
❑ 90Col-34
❑ 90HOFStiB-38
❑ 90PerGreM-4
❑ 90SweBasG-25
❑ 90YanMomPRP-1
❑ 91CadEllD-23
❑ 91ConTSN-111
❑ 91ConTSN-310
❑ 91ConTSNP-111
❑ 91DenBal-4
❑ 91HomCooC-9
❑ 91SweBasG-125
❑ 91USGamSBL-3C
❑ 91USGamSBL-3D
❑ 91USGamSBL-3H
❑ 91USGamSBL-3S
❑ 92ConTSN-529
❑ 92ConTSNCI-3
❑ 92ConTSNCI-8
❑ 92MegRut-81
❑ 92MegRut-122
❑ 92MegRutP-154
❑ 92OPC-40
❑ 92Pin-286
❑ 92Sco-881
❑ 92SpoIllFK1-108
❑ 92St.VinHHS-5
❑ 92Top-40
❑ 92TopGol-40
❑ 92TopGolPS-40
❑ 92TopGolW-40
❑ 92TopMic-40
❑ 92WhiLegtL-2
❑ 92WhiPro-2
❑ 92YanWIZA-22
❑ 92YanWIZH-11
❑ 93ActPacA-97
❑ 93ActPacA2-31G
❑ 93Ble-32
❑ 93Ble-33
❑ 93CadDis-24
❑ 93ConMasB-3
❑ 93ConTSN-673
❑ 93DiaStaES-130
❑ 93Hoy-3
❑ 93LegFoi-3
❑ 93SpeHOF2-1
❑ 93TedWil-63
❑ 93TedWil-122
❑ 93TedWilPC-23
❑ 93TedWilPC-24
❑ 93UppDecAH-58
❑ 93UppDecAH-131
❑ 93UppDecAH-133
❑ 94ConTSN-1082
❑ 94ConTSN-1249
❑ 94ConTSNB-1082
❑ 94ConTSNB-1249
❑ 94ConTSNCI-31
❑ 94MegRutS-3
❑ 94TedWil-147
❑ 94TedWilLC-LC13
❑ 94TedWilTfB-T5
❑ 94UppDecAH-4
❑ 94UppDecAH-40
❑ 94UppDecAH-112
❑ 94UppDecAH-160
❑ 94UppDecAH1-4
❑ 94UppDecAH1-40
❑ 94UppDecAH1-112
❑ 94UppDecAH1-160
❑ 94UppDecTAE-37
❑ 95ConTSN-1421
❑ 95ConTSNGJ-2
❑ 95ConTSNP-1421
❑ 95MegRut-3
❑ 95MegRut-6
❑ 95MegRut-12
❑ 95MegRut-13
❑ 95UppDecSHoB-4
❑ 96MetImpG-1
❑ 96MetImpG-2
❑ 96MetImpG-3
❑ 96MetImpG-4
❑ 96MetImpG-5
❑ 97HigMinMM-19
❑ 97HigMinMM-21
❑ 97HigMinMM-23
❑ 99SpoIllGotG-4
❑ 99SpoIllGotGRB-8
❑ 99SpoIllGotGRBG-8
❑ 99UppDecCL-6
❑ 99UppDecCL-124
❑ 99UppDecCLCC-6
❑ 99UppDecCLCC-124
❑ 99UppDecCLJotC-AC4

Gehringer, Charlie (Charles)
❑ 26Exh-95
❑ 27Exh-47
❑ 28StaPlaCE-25
❑ 29ExhFou-23
❑ 29PorandAR-29
❑ 31Exh-23
❑ 33ButCanV-19
❑ 33DelR33-5
❑ 33DouDisP-20
❑ 33ExhFou-12
❑ 33GeoCMil-14
❑ 33Gou-222
❑ 33TatOrbSDR-183
❑ 34BabRutG-26
❑ 34BatR31-42
❑ 34BatR31-130
❑ 34ButPreR-25
❑ 34DiaMatCSB-67
❑ 34DiaStaR-77
❑ 34ExhFou-12
❑ 34Gou-23
❑ 34GouCanV-57
❑ 34TigTeal-7
❑ 34WarBakSP-5
❑ 35ExhFou-12
❑ 35GouPuzR-1D
❑ 35GouPuzR-2D
❑ 35GouPuzR-16D
❑ 35GouPuzR-17D
❑ 36ExhFou-12
❑ 36GouWidPPR-A37
❑ 36GouWidPPR-C13
❑ 36NatChiFPR-29
❑ 36OveCanR-16
❑ 36R31Pre-L4
❑ 36SandSW-23
❑ 36WheBB4-3
❑ 36WheBB5-6
❑ 36WorWidGV-42
❑ 37DixLid-2
❑ 37DixPre-2
❑ 37ExhFou-12
❑ 37OPCBatUV-112
❑ 37WheBB6-4
❑ 37WheBB8-5
❑ 38CloFotW-29
❑ 38ExhFou-12
❑ 38GouHeaU-241
❑ 38GouHeaU-265
❑ 38OurNatGPP-10
❑ 38WheBB10-14
❑ 38WheBB11-3
❑ 38WheBB15-3A
❑ 38WheBB15-3B
❑ 39ExhSal-19
❑ 39GouPreR303A-16
❑ 39PC7AlbHoF-57
❑ 39PlaBal-50
❑ 39WorWidGTP-16
❑ 39WorWidGV-13
❑ 40PlaBal-41
❑ 41DouPlaR-53
❑ 41PlaBal-19
❑ 50CalHOFW-34
❑ 53ArtHaloFP-38
❑ 60Fle-58
❑ 61Fle-32
❑ 61GolPre-10
❑ 63HalofFB-28
❑ 70FleWorS-32
❑ 72TCMthe3-30
❑ 73SevTraC-24
❑ 74TigTCM1AC-11
❑ 76GalBasGHoF-12
❑ 76RowExh-7
❑ 76ShaPiz-56
❑ 76TigOldTS-9
❑ 77BobParHoF-88
❑ 77GalGloG-200
❑ 78TigDeaCS-17
❑ 79DiaGre-378
❑ 80PerHaloFP-57
❑ 80PerHaloFPS-2
❑ 80SSPHOF-57
❑ 80TigGreT-6
❑ 81ConTSN-78
❑ 81TigDetN-14
❑ 81TigSecNP-14
❑ 82DiaCla-5
❑ 82TCMGreH-34
❑ 83BigLeaCOA-7
❑ 83ConMar-5
❑ 83DonHOFH-28
❑ 83TigAlKS-33
❑ 83TigAlKS-39
❑ 84OCoandSI-96
❑ 84SpoDesPW-16
❑ 85FegMurCG-8
❑ 86ConSer1-43
❑ 86SpoDecG-12
❑ 86TigSpoD-4
❑ 87HygAllG-21
❑ 88ConAmeA-11
❑ 88ConSer5-13
❑ 89PerCelP-15
❑ 90PacLeg-81
❑ 90PerGreM-31
❑ 90PerMasW-1
❑ 90PerMasW-2
❑ 90PerMasW-3
❑ 90PerMasW-4
❑ 90PerMasW-5
❑ 92ConTSN-461
❑ 92ConTSN-553
❑ 92ConTSNGI-667
❑ 93ConTSN-667
❑ 94ConTSN-1076
❑ 94ConTSN-1122
❑ 94ConTSNB-1076
❑ 94ConTSNB-1122
❑ 94ConTSNCI-34
❑ 99UppDecCL-46
❑ 99UppDecCLCC-46

Gehrke, Jay
❑ 99Bow-438
❑ 99BowGol-438
❑ 99BowInt-438

Geier, Phil
❑ 11SpoLifCW-138

Geiger, Burt
❑ 82AlbDukTc-3
❑ 83AlbDukTc-2

Geiger, Gary
❑ 87EveGiaC-24
❑ 88FreSunCLC-23
❑ 88FreSunP-1229

Geiger, Gary Merle
❑ 58IndTeal-8
❑ 58Top-462
❑ 59Top-521
❑ 60Top-184
❑ 60TopVen-184
❑ 61Top-33
❑ 61TopStal-111
❑ 62Jel-60
❑ 62Pos-60
❑ 62PosCan-60
❑ 62RedSoxJP-3
❑ 62SalPlaC-38A
❑ 62SalPlaC-38B
❑ 62ShiPlaC-38
❑ 62Top-117
❑ 62TopStal-13
❑ 62TopVen-117
❑ 63Jel-81
❑ 63Pos-81
❑ 63Top-513
❑ 64Top-93
❑ 64TopVen-93
❑ 65Top-452
❑ 66BraPos-11
❑ 66Top-286
❑ 66TopVen-286
❑ 67BraPho-11
❑ 67CokCapB-1
❑ 67Top-566
❑ 69Top-278
❑ 72CedRapCT-17
❑ 77EvaTriT-10
❑ 81RedSoxBG2S-21

Geis, Jason
❑ 92SouOreAC-13
❑ 92SouOreAF-3433

Geis, John
❑ 97JohCitCTI-13
❑ 98PeoChiM-8

Geisel, Harry
❑ 94ConTSN-1205
❑ 94ConTSNB-1205

Geisel, J. Dave
❑ 79Top-716
❑ 80Top-676
❑ 82Don-633
❑ 82SyrChiTI-13
❑ 84Don-645
❑ 84Fle-154
❑ 84Nes792-256
❑ 84OPC-256
❑ 84SalLakCGC-175
❑ 84Top-256
❑ 84TopTif-256
❑ 85MarMot-22
❑ 86OklCit8P-6

Geisel, Mark
❑ 82SyrChiT-4

Geishert, Vern
❑ 67SeaPop-6
❑ 70Top-683

Geiske, Mark
❑ 90RivRedWCLC-10

Geisler, Phil
❑ 91MarPhiC-11
❑ 91MarPhiP-3460
❑ 92ClePhiC-18
❑ 92ClePhiF-2062
❑ 93ClePhiC-9
❑ 93ClePhiF-2695
❑ 94Bow-336
❑ 94Cla-19
❑ 94ExcFS7-245
❑ 94ScrRedBF-932
❑ 94Ult-546
❑ 94UppDecML-239
❑ 95ScrRedBTI-10
❑ 95UppDecML-132
❑ 95UppDecMLFS-132
❑ 96BinMetB-8
❑ 97NorTid-13
❑ 97NorTidB-13

Geiss, Emil
❑ 87OldJudN-193

Geist, Pete
❑ 86FloStaLAP-17
❑ 86VerBeaDP-6
❑ 87VerBeaDP-6
❑ 88DunBluJS-7

Geivett, Billy
❑ 86PalSprAP-15
❑ 86PalSprAS-23
❑ 87MidAngP-3

Gelatt, Dave
❑ 85LitFalMT-18
❑ 86ColMetP-10
❑ 87LynMetP-18
❑ 88St.LucMS-8

Gelb, Jac
❑ 89WytCubS-11
❑ 90PeoChiTI-22

Gelbert, Charlie (Charles M.)
❑ 31CarMet-10
❑ 31Exh-16
❑ 33ButCre-10
❑ 33ExhFou-8
❑ 36GouWidPPR-A38
❑ 36NatChiFPR-30
❑ 36NatChiFPR-100
❑ 36WorWidGV-49
❑ 39PlaBal-93
❑ 40PlaBal-18
❑ 72TCMthe3-31
❑ 91ConTSN-70
❑ 95ConTSN-1428

Gelfarb, Steve
❑ 81WesHavAT-12
❑ 82WesHavAT-13

Gelinas, Marc
❑ 78SalPirT-5

Gellinger, Mike
❑ 87DayBeaAP-25
❑ 89UtiBluSP-30
❑ 90BirBarB-24
❑ 90BirBarP-1400
❑ 91UtiBluSC-23
❑ 91UtiBluSP-3257
❑ 94SouBenSHC-25
❑ 94SouBenSHF-610

Gelnar, John
❑ 65OPC-143
❑ 65Top-143
❑ 67Top-472
❑ 70BreMcD-7
❑ 70OPC-393
❑ 70Top-393
❑ 71MLBOffS-436
❑ 71OPC-604
❑ 71Top-604
❑ 83Pil69G-18
❑ 94BreMilB-32

Genao, Huascar
❑ 92BurIndC-23
❑ 92BurIndF-1663

Gendron, Bob
❑ 84ShrCapFB-8

Gendron, Jonnie
❑ 92ClaDraP-104
❑ 94WelPirC-11
❑ 94WelPirF-3490

Generals, Fayetteville
❑ 90FayGenP-2422

Genewich, Joe (Joseph)
❑ 21Exh-56
❑ 25Exh-5
❑ 26Exh-5
❑ 27Exh-2
❑ 92ConTSN-573

Genins, C. Frank
❑ 87OldJudN-194

Genke, Todd
❑ 93MarPhiC-11
❑ 93MarPhiF-3465
❑ 94SpaPhiF-1717
❑ 94SparPhiC-12
❑ 95BatCliTI-15
❑ 96SalAvaB-10

Gennaro, Brad
❑ 93RanCucQC-12
❑ 93RanCucQF-843
❑ 94WicWraF-201
❑ 95MemChiTI-8

Gennin, Walt
❑ 21Zee-48

Genovese, George
❑ 49W72HolS-4
❑ 91HigSchPLS-35

Gentile, Gene
❑ 78ChaPirT-8
❑ 81BriRedST-4
❑ 83PawRedST-21
❑ 84AlbA'sT-3
❑ 86KinEagP-8
❑ 87HarSenP-21
❑ 88HarSenP-856

Gentile, Jim
❑ 47Exh-80
❑ 55DonWin-20
❑ 60BalOriP-6
❑ 60Top-448
❑ 61BalOriP-10
❑ 61NuSco-401
❑ 61Pos-68A
❑ 61Pos-68B
❑ 61Top-559
❑ 61TopStal-101
❑ 62AurRec-7
❑ 62BalOriP-9
❑ 62Baz-17
❑ 62ExhStaB-14
❑ 62Jel-27
❑ 62Pos-27A
❑ 62Pos-27B
❑ 62PosCan-27
❑ 62SalPlaC-1
❑ 62ShiPlaC-1
❑ 62Top-53
❑ 62Top-290
❑ 62TopBuc-30
❑ 62TopStal-5
❑ 62TopVen-53
❑ 63BalOriP-12
❑ 63BasMagM-30
❑ 63Baz-11
❑ 63ExhStaB-25
❑ 63Jel-57
❑ 63Pos-57
❑ 63SalMetC-47
❑ 63Top-4
❑ 63Top-260
❑ 63TopStil-16
❑ 64A's-6
❑ 64AthJayP-5
❑ 64Baz-11
❑ 64Top-196
❑ 64TopGia-15
❑ 64TopRooAB-9
❑ 64TopSta-75
❑ 64TopStaU-27
❑ 64TopVen-196
❑ 65AthJayP-5
❑ 65ChaTheY-28
❑ 65Top-365
❑ 66OPC-45
❑ 66Top-45
❑ 66TopVen-45
❑ 76UPIS-4
❑ 78TCM60I-4
❑ 82TCMGreS-37
❑ 83FraBroR-7
❑ 83FraBroR-12
❑ 85TCMPhoC-24
❑ 85TCMPhoC-27
❑ 85Woo-15
❑ 87AstShowSTh-8
❑ 90DodTar-274
❑ 91OriCro-154

Gentile, Randy
❑ 89EliTwiS-9
❑ 90KenTwiB-3
❑ 90KenTwiP-2300
❑ 90KenTwiS-4

Gentile, Scott
❑ 92ClaDraP-74
❑ 92FroRowDP-43
❑ 92FroRowDPG-43
❑ 92FroRowDPS-43
❑ 92JamExpC-17
❑ 92JamExpF-1495
❑ 93ClaGolF-122
❑ 93StaCluM-52
❑ 93WesPalBEC-5
❑ 93WesPalBEF-1332
❑ 94HarSenF-2084
❑ 95Bow-170
❑ 95Exc-221
❑ 95HarSenTI-18
❑ 95Top-369
❑ 97JacSun-12

Gentle, Mike
❑ 83VerBeaDT-4

Gentleman, Jean (J.P.)
❑ 88HamRedP-1743
❑ 88SavCarP-356

Gentry, Aaron
❑ 97NewJerCB-7
❑ 98PeoChiM-9

Gentry, Andry
❑ 90GeoColC-5

Gentry, Gary
❑ 69MetCit-3
❑ 69MetNewYDN-6
❑ 69OPC-31
❑ 69Top-31
❑ 70DayDaiNM-60
❑ 70MetTra-23B
❑ 70OPC-153
❑ 70Top-153
❑ 71MetTeal-6
❑ 71MetTealA-3

- 71MLBOffS-153
- 71OPC-725
- 71Top-725
- 72MetTeal-9
- 72OPC-105
- 72Top-105
- 73OPC-288
- 73Top-288
- 74OPC-415
- 74Top-415
- 75AtlBraP-13
- 75OPC-393
- 75Top-393
- 75TopMin-393
- 86MetGreT-9
- 87Met196T-5
- 89MetRinP69-13
- 91MetWIZ-137
- 94Met69CCPP-16
- 94Met69CS-15
- 94Met69T-16
- 97AriStaBG-9

Genzale, Henry
- 88MarMot-28
- 89MarMot-28
- 90MarMot-28

George, Andre
- 88PocGiaP-2075

George, Bill
- 58MonRoyF-8
- 59O'KAleMR-7

George, Chris
- 90MisStaB-14
- 91MisStaB-19
- 91PitMetC-23
- 91PitMetP-3416
- 92PitMetC-16
- 92PitMetF-3288
- 92St.LucMCB-25

George, Chris C.
- 99Bow-195
- 99BowBes-184
- 99BowBesAR-184
- 99BowBesR-184
- 99BowChr-195
- 99BowChrG-195
- 99BowChrGR-195
- 99BowChrI-195
- 99BowChrIR-195
- 99BowChrR-195
- 99BowGol-195
- 99BowInt-195
- 99StaClu-337
- 99StaCluFDI-337
- 99StaCluOoaK-337
- 99StaCluPP-337
- 99Top-439
- 99TopChr-439
- 99TopChrR-439
- 99TopMVPP-439

George, Chris Sean
- 89CalLeaA-38
- 89MisStaB-14
- 89StoPorB-2
- 89StoPorCLC-153
- 89StoPorP-391
- 89StoPorS-8
- 90El PasDAGTI-21
- 90ElPasDGS-14
- 90TexLeaAGS-17
- 91Bow-35
- 91Cla2-T50
- 91DenZepLD-138
- 91DenZepP-119
- 91LinDriAAA-138
- 92Bow-213
- 92ClaGam-20
- 92DenZepF-2632
- 92DenZepS-128
- 92Don-746
- 92Sco-835
- 92ScoRoo-9
- 92SkyAAAF-62
- 92StaClu-354
- 92TopDeb91-63
- 92UppDec-9
- 93Top-744
- 93TopGol-744
- 93TopInaM-744
- 93TopInaR-744
- 93TopMic-744
- 94BreMilB-125
- 94ElPasDF-3140

George, Curtis
- 92WatIndC-22
- 92WatIndF-3242

George, Frankie
- 74SalLakCAC-93
- 75SalLakCC-7
- 76SalLakCGC-4
- 77SalLakCGC-14

George, Greek
- 41CubTeal-6
- 90DodTar-275

George, Lefty (Thomas)
- 12T207-66

George, Leo
- 82QuaCitCT-14

George, Louis
- 88KimN18-14

George, Nattie
- 84GreHorT-7

George, Phil
- 83ButCopKT-5
- 85Ft.MyeRT-11
- 86Ft.MyeRP-11
- 86MemChiSTOS-7
- 86MemChiTOS-7
- 87MemChiB-11
- 87MemChiP-2

George, Steve
- 83GreHorT-7
- 84GreHorT-18
- 86AlbYanT-29
- 88Top-18A

George, W.G.
- 88KimN18-15

George, Will
- 80ChaO'sP-8
- 80ChaO'sW-8
- 82MiaMarT-1
- 83MiaMarT-1
- 87HagSunP-3
- 89KinIndS-27
- 90CanIndB-2
- 90CanIndP-1363
- 91CanIndP-996

George, William
- 87OldJudN-195
- 89SFHaCN-6

Georger, Joe
- 80LynSaiT-17
- 81LynSaiT-4
- 82LynSaiT-4
- 86WauTimP-10
- 87BelMarTI-12
- 89QuaCitAB-3
- 89QuaCitAGS-3
- 90QuaCitAGS-2
- 91QuaCitAC-28
- 91QuaCitAP-2646
- 92QuaCitRBC-29
- 92QuaCitRBF-827
- 93CedRapKC-28
- 93CedRapKF-1755
- 94CedRapKC-24
- 94CedRapKF-1125
- 97LakTigB-2
- 98LakTigM-28

Gerace, Joanne
- 88UtiBluSP-29
- 89UtiBluSP-32

Geraghty, Ben
- 90DodTar-276

Gerald, Dwayne
- 91HigSchPLS-23
- 92StaCluD-57
- 93EugEmeC-15
- 93EugEmeF-3862

Gerald, Ed (Edward)
- 89HigSchPLS-19
- 91AppFoxCB-24
- 91AppFoxP-1729
- 92AppFoxCB-25
- 92AppFoxFI-996
- 93St.PetCC-13
- 93St.PetCF-2640
- 94NasXprF-398

Gerard, Alfonzo
- 52LavPro-88

Gerber, Craig
- 82RedPioT-3
- 83NasAngT-13
- 84EdmTraC-105
- 86Don-545
- 86EdmTraP-13
- 86Fle-156
- 86Top-222
- 86TopTif-222
- 88EdmTraP-583
- 88MidAngGS-24

Gerber, Wally (Walter)
- 20NatCarE-32
- 21Exh-57
- 21Nei-49
- 22E120-96
- 22W573-47
- 22W575-40
- 25Exh-113
- 26Exh-117
- 27MidBre-29
- 92ConTSN-501

Gerberman, George
- 77FriOneYW-91

Gerdes, Rob
- 90LSUTigA-13

Geren, Bob
- 83SprCarF-13
- 84ArkTraT-11
- 87AlbYanP-5
- 88BlaYNPRWL-25
- 88ColCliC-11
- 88ColCliP-12
- 88ColCliP-303
- 88TriAAAP-9
- 88TriAAC-16
- 89ColCliC-11
- 89ColCliP-13
- 89ColCliP-758
- 89DonRoo-11
- 89FleUpd-48
- 89ScoHot1R-66
- 89ScoRoo-93T
- 89TopTra-37T
- 89TopTraT-37T
- 89YanScoNW-25
- 90AlbDecGB-4
- 90Baz-20
- 90Bow-438
- 90BowTif-438
- 90ClaBlu-25
- 90Don-395
- 90Fle-442
- 90FleCan-442
- 90Lea-182
- 90OPC-536
- 90PanSti-128
- 90Sco-464
- 90Sco100RS-50
- 90Spo-205
- 90SprCarDGB-28
- 90Top-536
- 90TopBig-209
- 90TopGloS-40
- 90TopRoo-9
- 90TopSti-316
- 90TopSti-321
- 90TopTif-536
- 90TopTVY-21
- 90ToyRoo-11
- 90UppDec-608
- 90YanScoNW-9
- 91Don-114
- 91Fle-663
- 91OPC-716
- 91PanFreS-323
- 91PanSti-265
- 91Sco-435
- 91StaClu-171
- 91StaCluP-16
- 91Top-716
- 91TopDesS-716
- 91TopMic-716
- 91TopTif-716
- 91Ult-231
- 91UppDec-202
- 92Fle-226
- 92OPC-341
- 92PawRedSF-925
- 92Sco-170
- 92Top-341
- 92TopGol-341
- 92TopGolW-341
- 92TopMic-341
- 92YanWIZ8-66
- 93PadMot-13
- 97DunDonPPS-9

Gergen, Bob
- 83BurRanF-13
- 83BurRanT-16
- 84TulDriTI-26
- 85TulDriTI-25
- 86TulDriTI-14

Gerhardt, Allen
- 83BeaGolGT-22
- 87GasRanP-10

Gerhardt, Bill
- 83MiaMarT-7

Gerhardt, Joe
- 86OldJudN-7
- 87BucN28-59
- 87OldJudN-196
- 89SFHaCN-7

Gerhardt, Rusty
- 84OklCit8T-5
- 85OklCit8T-24
- 86OklCit8P-7
- 89ChaRanS-27

Gerhart, Bert
- 91GulCoaRSP-21
- 92GasRanC-4
- 93EriSaiC-8
- 93EriSaiF-3107
- 94ChaRivC-7
- 94ChaRivF-2666
- 94SouAtlLAF-SAL4

Gerhart, Ken
- 84ChaO'sT-22
- 85ChaO'sT-1
- 86RocRedWP-3
- 87BalOriP-12
- 87Don-30
- 87DonOpeD-141
- 87DonRoo-24
- 87FleUpd-34
- 87FleUpdG-34
- 87Lea-30
- 87OriFreB-38
- 87SpoRool-7
- 87TopTra-37T
- 87TopTraT-37T
- 88BlaYNPRWL-84
- 88Don-213
- 88Fle-559
- 88FleGlo-559
- 88OPC-271
- 88OriFreB-38
- 88OriPos-11
- 88PanSti-14
- 88RedFolSB-27
- 88Sco-58
- 88ScoGlo-58
- 88StaLinO-4
- 88Top-271
- 88TopTif-271
- 88ToyRoo-11
- 89Fle-609
- 89FleGlo-609
- 89OPC-192
- 89PhoFirC-20
- 89PhoFirP-1499
- 89Sco-506
- 89Top-598
- 89TopTif-598
- 89UppDec-426
- 90HagSunDGB-11
- 91OriCro-155

Gerheauser, Al
- 43PhiTeal-10

Gering, Scott
- 79ElmPioRST-13

Gerken, George
- 28StaPlaCE-26

Gerkin, Steve
- 45A'sTeal-15

Gerlach, Jim
- 81QuaCitCT-27
- 83MidCubT-21

Gerland, Greg
- 95EugEmeTI-23

German, Rene
- 83QuaCitCT-11

Germann, Mark
- 86CedRapRT-16
- 87VerRedP-20
- 88ChaLooB-10
- 89NasSouC-15
- 89NasSouP-1275

Germer, Glen
- 81DurBulT-18

Germosen, Julio
- 97EriSeaWB-14

Gernentz, Keith
- 85RedWinA-19
- 86RedWinA-6

Gerner, Ed
- 20RedWorCP-7

Gernert, Dick
- 52StaCalL-71G
- 52Top-343
- 53BowBW-11
- 53RedSoxTI-9
- 54Bow-146
- 57Top-202
- 58RedSoxJP-3
- 58Top-38
- 59RedSoxJP-2
- 59Top-13
- 59Top-519
- 59TopVen-13
- 60Top-86
- 60TopVen-86
- 61TigJayP-8
- 61Top-284
- 61TopStal-151
- 62Col45'HC-6
- 62Top-536
- 62TopBuc-31
- 78ReaRem-6
- 79DiaGre-249
- 80Red196T-16
- 83TopRep5-343
- 89AstCol4S-18
- 93RanKee-158

Geronimo, Cesar
- 71OPC-447
- 71Top-447
- 72Top-719
- 73LinPor-55
- 73OPC-156
- 73Top-156
- 74OPC-181
- 74Top-181
- 74TopSta-26
- 75Hos-121
- 75Kel-50
- 75OPC-41
- 75Top-41
- 75TopMin-41
- 76Hos-150
- 76LinSup-99
- 76OPC-24
- 76RedIceL-5
- 76RedKro-9
- 76SSP-45
- 76Top-24
- 77BurCheD-202
- 77ChiWilD-26
- 77DailsID-26
- 77DetCaeD-26
- 77HolInnD-26
- 77Hos-76
- 77Kel-40
- 77MSADis-26
- 77OPC-160
- 77PepGloD-49
- 77SagDis-26
- 77sDis-26
- 77Top-535
- 77WenDis-26
- 77ZipDis-26
- 78OPC-32
- 78Pep-11
- 78SSP270-115
- 78Top-354
- 79OPC-111
- 79Top-220
- 80OPC-247
- 80RedEnq-20
- 80Top-475
- 81Don-305
- 81RoyProPS-6
- 81Top-390
- 81TopTra-766
- 82Don-322
- 82Fle-409
- 82Roy-8
- 82Top-693
- 83Don-448
- 83Fle-112
- 83RoyPos-11
- 83Top-194
- 84Don-252
- 84Nes792-544
- 84Top-544
- 84TopTif-544
- 85DomLeaS-21
- 87AstShoSTw-7
- 96Red76K-6
- 97BoiHawG-12
- 98LakElsSG-12

Gershberg, Howie
- 88BenBucL-28
- 89BenBucL-27
- 90BoiHawP-3333
- 91BoiHawP-3902
- 92BoiHawF-3647
- 93PalSprAC-28
- 93PalSprAF-87
- 94LakElsSC-27
- 94LakElsSF-1681
- 96HilStaHWB-13
- 96LakElsSB-29
- 97VanCanB-3

Gerstein, Ron
- 91SumFlyC-5
- 91SumFlyP-2328
- 92RocExpC-8
- 92RocExpF-2108
- 93StoPorF-739
- 94ElPasDF-3141
- 95ElPasDTI-9

Gerteisen, Aaron
- 93JohCitCC-11
- 93JohCitCF-3695
- 94MadHatC-11
- 94MadHatF-145
- 94NewJerCC-11
- 94NewJerCF-3431

Gertz, Mike
- 82WatIndF-14
- 82WatIndT-16
- 83WatIndF-22

Gessler, Doc (Harry)
- 09RamT20-50
- 11PinT-5-551
- 11SpoLifCW-139
- 11SpoLifM-124
- 14CraJacE-59
- 15CraJacE-59

Gettel, Allen
- 47IndTeal-10
- 47IndVanPP-9
- 50RemBre-8
- 51Bow-304
- 52MotCoo-3
- 75Gia195T-5
- 75OakOak2A-15

Getter, Kerry
- 75AndRanT-23
- 76CliPilT-17

Gettler, Chris
- 88BakDodCLC-253

Gettman, Jake
- 12ImpTobC-40

Getz, Gus (Gustave)
- 09ColChiE-115A
- 09ColChiE-115B
- 12ColRedB-115A
- 12ColRedB-115B
- 12ColTinT-115A
- 12ColTinT-115B
- 15SpoNewM-67
- 16SpoNewM-67
- 17ColE13-58
- 90DodTar-277

Getz, Rod
- 96KanCouCTI-11
- 97BreCouMB-14
- 98BurBeeM-8

Getzein, Charles
- 76SSP188WS-4
- 87BucN28-30
- 87OldJudN-197
- 87ScrDC-13
- 88AllandGN-3
- 88AllandGN-3
- 88GandBCGCE-17
- 88WG1CarG-21
- 89SFHaCN-8

Gewecke, Steve
- 90SprCarB-21

Geyer, Rube (Jacob)
- 09PC7HHB-14
- 09T206-140
- 10CouT21-139
- 14Zee-34
- 15VicT21-12

Gharrity, Patsy (Edward P.)
- 19W514-109
- 20WalMaiW-18
- 21E121So1-29
- 21Nei-50
- 22E120-107
- 22W572-31
- 22W573-48
- 22W575-41
- 23W501-12
- 23WilChoV-48
- 31SenTealPW-10
- 34DiaMatCSB-68

Ghelfi, Tony (Andrew)
- 84PhiTas-19

❑ 85PhiTas-17
❑ 85PorBeaC-40
❑ 86WatIndP-9
❑ 87KinIndP-16
❑ 88WilBilP-1308
❑ 88WilBilP-1314
❑ 89LasVegSC-5
❑ 89LasVegSP-1
Gholston, Rico
❑ 92WelPirC-9
❑ 92WelPirF-1330
❑ 93AugPirC-8
❑ 93AugPirF-1551
Ghostlaw, Derek
❑ 91HelBreSP-2
Giallella, Brian
❑ 95ButCopKtl-29
Giallombardo, Bob
❑ 59DarFar-7
❑ 59Top-321A
❑ 59Top-321B
❑ 60DarFar-9
❑ 61UniOil-SP3
❑ 90DodTar-278
Giamatti, A.Bartlett
❑ 89WicChaR-6
❑ 90Don-716
❑ 90OPC-396
❑ 90ScoRooDT-B1
❑ 90T/MUmp-65
❑ 90Top-396
❑ 90TopTif-396
Giambalvo, Paul
❑ 98LetBlaDG-12
Giambi, Jason
❑ 91TopTra-45T
❑ 91TopTraT-45T
❑ 92ClaDraP-42
❑ 92FroRowDP-40
❑ 92FroRowDPG-40
❑ 92FroRowDPPS-40
❑ 92FroRowDPS-40
❑ 92StaCluD-58
❑ 92TopDaiQTU-31
❑ 92TopTra-40T
❑ 92TopTraG-40T
❑ 92UppDecML-20
❑ 93ClaFS7-190
❑ 93ModA'sC-11
❑ 93ModA'sF-808
❑ 93StaCluM-156
❑ 93StaCluM-200
❑ 94ClaGolF-125
❑ 94ColC-657
❑ 94ColChoGS-657
❑ 94ColChoSS-657
❑ 94ExcFS7-120
❑ 94HunStaF-1336
❑ 94TedWil-123
❑ 94Top-369
❑ 94TopGol-369
❑ 94TopSpa-369
❑ 94UppDec-525
❑ 94UppDecED-525
❑ 94UppDecML-145
❑ 95A'sCHP-4
❑ 95Bow-13
❑ 95EdmTraTI-8
❑ 95Sum-163
❑ 95SumNthD-163
❑ 95UppDec-222
❑ 95UppDecED-222
❑ 95UppDecEDG-222
❑ 95UppDecML-9
❑ 95UppDecMLFS-9
❑ 95UppDecMLMLA-4
❑ 95UppDecSE-109
❑ 95UppDecSEG-109
❑ 96A'sMot-3
❑ 96Bow-97
❑ 96BowBes-29
❑ 96BowBesAR-29
❑ 96BowBesR-29
❑ 96BowFoi-97
❑ 96Cir-72
❑ 96CirRav-72
❑ 96ColCho-243
❑ 96ColChoGS-243
❑ 96ColChoSS-243
❑ 96Don-47
❑ 96DonPreP-47
❑ 96Fin-B159
❑ 96Fin-G330
❑ 96FinRef-B159
❑ 96FinRef-G330
❑ 96Fla-148
❑ 96Fle-208
❑ 96FleTif-208
❑ 96LeaLim-56
❑ 96LeaLimG-56
❑ 96LeaPre-87
❑ 96LeaPreP-87
❑ 96LeaSig-39
❑ 96LeaSigA-77
❑ 96LeaSigAG-77
❑ 96LeaSigAS-77
❑ 96LeaSigEA-58
❑ 96LeaSigEACM-7
❑ 96LeaSigPPG-39
❑ 96LeaSigPPP-39
❑ 96Pin-126
❑ 96Sco-44
❑ 96ScoDugC-A39
❑ 96ScoDugCAP-A39
❑ 96StaClu-61
❑ 96StaCluMOP-61
❑ 96Stu-13
❑ 96StuPrePB-13
❑ 96StuPrePG-13
❑ 96StuPrePS-13
❑ 96TeaOut-27
❑ 96Top-210
❑ 96TopChr-72
❑ 96TopChrR-72
❑ 96Ult-400
❑ 96UltGolM-400
❑ 96UltGolP-6
❑ 96UltGolPGM-6
❑ 96UppDec-412
❑ 97A'sMot-4
❑ 97Bow-6
❑ 97BowBes-87
❑ 97BowBesAR-87
❑ 97BowBesR-87
❑ 97BowInt-6
❑ 97Cir-368
❑ 97CirRav-368
❑ 97ColCho-184
❑ 97Don-47
❑ 97Don-446
❑ 97DonEli-39
❑ 97DonEliGS-39
❑ 97DonEliTotC-11
❑ 97DonEliTotCDC-11
❑ 97DonGolPP-47
❑ 97DonGolPP-446
❑ 97DonLim-168
❑ 97DonLimE-168
❑ 97DonPre-86
❑ 97DonPreCttC-86
❑ 97DonRocL-14
❑ 97DonSig-83
❑ 97DonSigPPP-83
❑ 97DonSilPP-47
❑ 97DonSilPP-446
❑ 97Fin-118
❑ 97FinEmb-118
❑ 97FinEmbR-118
❑ 97FinRef-118
❑ 97FlaShoLC-171
❑ 97FlaShoLeg0-171
❑ 97FlaShoLeg1-171
❑ 97FlaShoM-A171
❑ 97FlaShoM-B171
❑ 97FlaShoM-C171
❑ 97FlaShoR0-171
❑ 97FlaShoR1-171
❑ 97FlaShoR2-171
❑ 97Fle-190
❑ 97FleTif-190
❑ 97Lea-137
❑ 97LeaFraM-137
❑ 97LeaFraMDC-137
❑ 97MetUni-129
❑ 97NewPin-74
❑ 97NewPinAP-74
❑ 97NewPinMC-74
❑ 97NewPinPP-74
❑ 97Pac-169
❑ 97PacLigB-169
❑ 97PacPri-58
❑ 97PacPriLB-58
❑ 97PacPriP-58
❑ 97PacPriSL-SL5B
❑ 97PacSil-169
❑ 97PinCer-101
❑ 97PinCerMBla-101
❑ 97PinCerMBlu-101
❑ 97PinCerMG-101
❑ 97PinCerMR-101
❑ 97PinCerR-101
❑ 97PinIns-32
❑ 97PinInsCE-32
❑ 97PinInsDE-32
❑ 97PinTotCPB-101
❑ 97PinTotCPG-101
❑ 97PinTotCPR-101
❑ 97PinX-P-87
❑ 97PinX-PMoS-87
❑ 97Sco-241
❑ 97Sco-544
❑ 97ScoArtPWB-241
❑ 97ScoArtPWB-544
❑ 97ScoPreS-241
❑ 97ScoResC-544
❑ 97ScoShoS-241
❑ 97ScoShoS-544
❑ 97ScoShoSAP-241
❑ 97ScoShoSAP-544
❑ 97Sel-72
❑ 97SelArtP-72
❑ 97SelCom-72
❑ 97SelRegG-72
❑ 97SelToootT-10
❑ 97SelToootTMB-10
❑ 97SP-133
❑ 97SpoIll-167
❑ 97SpoIllEE-167
❑ 97StaClu-336
❑ 97StaCluMOP-336
❑ 97Stu-89
❑ 97StuHarH-15
❑ 97StuPrePG-89
❑ 97StuPrePS-89
❑ 97Top-209
❑ 97TopChr-77
❑ 97TopChrR-77
❑ 97TopGal-177
❑ 97TopGalPPI-177
❑ 97Ult-112
❑ 97UltDouT-8
❑ 97UltGolME-112
❑ 97UltPlaME-112
❑ 97UppDec-131
❑ 98A'sMot-3
❑ 98Bow-46
❑ 98BowBes-93
❑ 98BowBesAR-93
❑ 98BowBesR-93
❑ 98BowChr-46
❑ 98BowChrGA-46
❑ 98BowChrGAR-46
❑ 98BowChrI-46
❑ 98BowChrIR-46
❑ 98BowChrR-46
❑ 98BowGolA-46
❑ 98BowInt-46
❑ 98CirThu-157
❑ 98CirThuRav-157
❑ 98CirThuSupRav-157
❑ 98ColCho-456
❑ 98CroRoy-100
❑ 98Don-87
❑ 98DonCol-87
❑ 98DonColE-451
❑ 98DonColL-204
❑ 98DonColP-618
❑ 98DonColS-87
❑ 98DonCruG-38
❑ 98DonCruP-38
❑ 98DonCruR-38
❑ 98DonEli-51
❑ 98DonEliA-51
❑ 98DonEliS-51
❑ 98DonGolPP-87
❑ 98DonPre-68
❑ 98DonPreSeat-68
❑ 98DonPriCD-87
❑ 98DonPriCE-451
❑ 98DonPriCL-204
❑ 98DonPriCP-618
❑ 98DonSig-81
❑ 98DonSigA-34
❑ 98DonSigAC-45
❑ 98DonSigAM-46
❑ 98DonSigP-81
❑ 98DonSilPP-87
❑ 98E-X2-44
❑ 98E-X2ECFut-44
❑ 98E-X2ECNow-44
❑ 98Fin-172
❑ 98FinNo--172
❑ 98FinNo-R-172
❑ 98FinRef-172
❑ 98FlaShoLeg0-109
❑ 98FlaShoLeg1-109
❑ 98FlaShoLeg2-109
❑ 98FlaShoLeg3-109
❑ 98FlaShoLegM-109
❑ 98FlaShoR0-109
❑ 98FlaShoR1-109
❑ 98FlaShoR2-109
❑ 98FlaShoR3-109
❑ 98Fle-145
❑ 98KinDis-6
❑ 98Lea-4
❑ 98LeaFraDA-4
❑ 98LeaFraF-4
❑ 98LeaFraM-4
❑ 98LeaFraM-4
❑ 98LeaFraMDC-4
❑ 98LeaFraMDC-4
❑ 98LeaFraMZ2-4
❑ 98LeaRS-67
❑ 98LeaRSLHolo-67
❑ 98LeaRSLong-67
❑ 98LeaRSTicMas-20
❑ 98LeaRSTicMasDC-20
❑ 98LeaRTrue-67
❑ 98MetUni-88
❑ 98MetUniPMG-88
❑ 98Pac-165
❑ 98PacAur-65
❑ 98PacInv-58
❑ 98PacInvPBlue-58
❑ 98PacInvSilv-58
❑ 98PacInvTeam-20
❑ 98PacOme-175
❑ 98PacOmeR-175
❑ 98PacOnl-529
❑ 98PacOnlR-529
❑ 98PacOnlWC-529
❑ 98PacPar-78
❑ 98PacParC-78
❑ 98PacParG-78
❑ 98PacParHS-78
❑ 98PacParPB-78
❑ 98PacParR-78
❑ 98PacPlaB-165
❑ 98PacRedT-165
❑ 98PacSil-165
❑ 98Pin-38
❑ 98PinIns-75
❑ 98PinInsCE-75
❑ 98PinInsDE-75
❑ 98PinPer-69
❑ 98PinPerPP-69
❑ 98PinPreP-38
❑ 98Revo-105
❑ 98RevoSS-105
❑ 98Sco-61
❑ 98ScoRT-135
❑ 98ScoRTSS-PP84
❑ 98ScoRTSSAP-PP84
❑ 98ScoRTSSAP1-PP84
❑ 98ScoSS-PP24
❑ 98ScoSSAP-PP24
❑ 98SkyDugA-78
❑ 98SkyDugAIA-78
❑ 98SP Aut-148
❑ 98SpoIll-44
❑ 98SpoIllEE-44
❑ 98SpoIllFE-44
❑ 98SpoIllWSF-144
❑ 98SpoIllWSFEE-144
❑ 98SpoIllWSFFE-144
❑ 98SPxFin-111
❑ 98SPxFinR-111
❑ 98SPxFinS-111
❑ 98StaCluFDI-180
❑ 98StaCluI-180
❑ 98StaCluOneK-180
❑ 98StaCluPP-180
❑ 98Stu-155
❑ 98StuGPP-155
❑ 98StuSPP-155
❑ 98Top-176
❑ 98TopChr-176
❑ 98TopChrR-176
❑ 98TopDevR-176
❑ 98TopDia-176
❑ 98TopGal-97
❑ 98TopGalGP-97
❑ 98TopGalOPP-97
❑ 98TopGalPPI-97
❑ 98TopGalPPIA-97
❑ 98TopGolLabC1-38
❑ 98TopGolLabC1B-38
❑ 98TopGolLabC1One-38
❑ 98TopGolLabC1R-38
❑ 98TopGolLabC2-38
❑ 98TopGolLabC2B-38
❑ 98TopGolLabC2One-38
❑ 98TopGolLabC2R-38
❑ 98TopGolLabC3-38
❑ 98TopGolLabC3B-38
❑ 98TopGolLabC3One-38
❑ 98TopGolLabC3R-38
❑ 98TopMiniC-176
❑ 98TopOpeD-95
❑ 98TopSta-94
❑ 98TopStaB-94
❑ 98TopStaG-94
❑ 98TopStaGR-94
❑ 98TopStaS-94
❑ 98Ult-110
❑ 98UltGolM-110
❑ 98UltMas-110
❑ 98UltPlaM-110
❑ 98UppDec-183
❑ 98UppDecSF-95
❑ 98Zen-46
❑ 98Zen5 xx7-48
❑ 98Zen5x7GoldImp-48
❑ 98Zen5x7Imp-48
❑ 98ZenZ-G-46
❑ 98ZenZ-S-46
❑ 99199Fin-156
❑ 99Bow-267
❑ 99BowBes-24
❑ 99BowBesAR-24
❑ 99BowBesR-24
❑ 99BowGol-267
❑ 99BowInt-267
❑ 99CroRoyB-102
❑ 99CroRoyL-102
❑ 99CroRoyOD-102
❑ 99E-X Cen-53
❑ 99E-X CenECFut-53
❑ 99E-X CenECNow-53
❑ 99FinGolRef-156
❑ 99FinRef-156
❑ 99Fle-102
❑ 99FleBri-16
❑ 99FleBri2G-16
❑ 99FleBriBlu-16
❑ 99FleBriGol-16
❑ 99FleMys-55
❑ 99FleMysG-55
❑ 99FleMysM-55
❑ 99FleSta9-102
❑ 99FleWarT-102
❑ 99MetUni-138
❑ 99MetUniGM-138
❑ 99MetUniPMG-138
❑ 99Pac-310
❑ 99PacAur-135
❑ 99PacAurOD-135
❑ 99PacCroC-202
❑ 99PacCroCPB-202
❑ 99PacInv-107
❑ 99PacInvOD-107
❑ 99PacInvPB-107
❑ 99PacOme-168
❑ 99PacOmeC-168
❑ 99PacOmeG-168
❑ 99PacOmePB-168
❑ 99PacPar-170
❑ 99PacParC-170
❑ 99PacParG-170
❑ 99PacParHoloGold-170
❑ 99PacParHS-170
❑ 99PacParOD-170
❑ 99PacParPB-170
❑ 99PacParRed-170
❑ 99PacPlaB-310
❑ 99PacPri-104
❑ 99PacPriHB-104
❑ 99PacPriHG-104
❑ 99PacPriHM-104
❑ 99PacPriHP-104
❑ 99PacPriRed-104
❑ 99PacPriS-87
❑ 99PacPriS206-87
❑ 99PacPriS206R-87
❑ 99PacRed-310
❑ 99Rev-101
❑ 99RevPremDate-101
❑ 99RevRet-101
❑ 99RevShaSS-101
❑ 99SkyMolM-61
❑ 99SkyMolMX-61
❑ 99SkyPre-80
❑ 99SkyPreR-80
❑ 99SkyThu-84
❑ 99SkyThuRant-84
❑ 99SkyThuRave-84
❑ 99SP SigAuto-JAG
❑ 99SP SigAutoG-JAG
❑ 99SpoIll-82
❑ 99SPSig-66
❑ 99StaClu-242
❑ 99StaCluFDI-242
❑ 99StaCluOoaK-242
❑ 99StaCluPP-242
❑ 99ThuSkySupR-84
❑ 99Top-324
❑ 99TopBlaLC1-23
❑ 99TopBlaLC2-23
❑ 99TopBlaLC3-23
❑ 99TopChr-324
❑ 99TopChrR-324
❑ 99TopGal-60
❑ 99TopGalPP-60
❑ 99TopGalPPI-60
❑ 99TopGolL-23
❑ 99TopGolLC1-23
❑ 99TopGolLC2-23
❑ 99TopGolLOtO-23
❑ 99TopMVPP-324
❑ 99TopOpeD-112
❑ 99TopRedLC1-23
❑ 99TopRedLC2-23
❑ 99TopRedLC3-23
❑ 99TopSta-102
❑ 99TopStaFoil-102
❑ 99UD Cho-121
❑ 99UD ChoPCR-121
❑ 99Ult-162
❑ 99UltGolM-162
❑ 99UltMas-162
❑ 99UltPlaM-162
❑ 99UppDec-443
❑ 99UppDecBD-62
❑ 99UppDecBDD-62
❑ 99UppDecBDQ-62
❑ 99UppDecBDT-62
❑ 99UppDecCLM-C70
❑ 99UppDecE-65
❑ 99UppDecEFXG-65
❑ 99UppDecEL1-443
❑ 99UppDecEL2-443
❑ 99UppDecM-154
❑ 99UppDecMGS-154
❑ 99UppDecMHFS-154
❑ 99UppDecMP-154
❑ 99UppDecMSS-154
❑ 99UppDecO-22
❑ 99UppDecOSO-22
❑ 99UppDecR-63
❑ 99UppDecRG-63
❑ 99UppDecRP-63
❑ 99Vic-280
Giambi, Jeremy
❑ 96SpoIndB-12
❑ 97Bes-99
❑ 97LanLugTS-7
❑ 97MidLeaTP-13
❑ 98Bow-406
❑ 98BowBes-193
❑ 98BowBesAR-193
❑ 98BowBesR-193
❑ 98BowChr-406
❑ 98BowChrGA-406
❑ 98BowChrGAR-406
❑ 98BowChrI-406
❑ 98BowChrIR-406
❑ 98BowChrR-406
❑ 98BowGolA-406
❑ 98BowInt-406
❑ 98DonSig-123
❑ 98DonSigP-123
❑ 98FleUpd-U98
❑ 98LeaRS-322
❑ 98LeaRSLHolo-322
❑ 98LeaRSLong-322
❑ 98LeaRTrue-322
❑ 98OmaRoyM-8
❑ 98SP MinPE-64
❑ 98SPMin-64
❑ 99199Fin-146
❑ 99Bow-168
❑ 99BowAut-BA46
❑ 99BowBes-132
❑ 99BowBesAR-132
❑ 99BowBesR-132
❑ 99BowChr-168
❑ 99BowChrG-168
❑ 99BowChrGR-168
❑ 99BowChrI-168
❑ 99BowChrIR-168
❑ 99BowChrR-168
❑ 99BowChrSC-SC17
❑ 99BowChrSCR-SC17
❑ 99BowGol-168
❑ 99BowInt-168

- ❑ 99BowScoC-SC17
- ❑ 99DumSet-111
- ❑ 99E-X Cen-92
- ❑ 99E-X CenECFut-92
- ❑ 99E-X CenECNow-92
- ❑ 99E-X CenEQ-13
- ❑ 99E-XCenA-9
- ❑ 99FinGolRef-146
- ❑ 99FinRef-146
- ❑ 99FlaShoLeg1-38
- ❑ 99FlaShoLeg2-38
- ❑ 99FlaShoLeg3-38
- ❑ 99FlaShoLegM1-38
- ❑ 99FlaShoLegM2-38
- ❑ 99FlaShoLegM3-38
- ❑ 99FlaShoR1-38
- ❑ 99FlaShoR2-38
- ❑ 99FlaShoR3-38
- ❑ 99FlaShoWotF-12
- ❑ 99Fle-95
- ❑ 99FleBri-129
- ❑ 99FleBri2G-129
- ❑ 99FleBriBlu-129
- ❑ 99FleBriGol-129
- ❑ 99FleBriI-12
- ❑ 99FleMys-111
- ❑ 99FleMysM-111
- ❑ 99FleSta9-95
- ❑ 99FleWarT-95
- ❑ 99MetUni-268
- ❑ 99MetUniGM-268
- ❑ 99MetUniPMG-268
- ❑ 99Pac-204
- ❑ 99Pac-204A
- ❑ 99PacInv-73
- ❑ 99PacInvOD-73
- ❑ 99PacInvPB-73
- ❑ 99PacOme-115
- ❑ 99PacOmeC-115
- ❑ 99PacOmeG-115
- ❑ 99PacOmePB-115
- ❑ 99PacPar-111
- ❑ 99PacParC-111
- ❑ 99PacParG-111
- ❑ 99PacParHoloGold-111
- ❑ 99PacParHS-111
- ❑ 99PacParOD-111
- ❑ 99PacParPB-111
- ❑ 99PacParRed-111
- ❑ 99PacParTC-14
- ❑ 99PacPlaB-204
- ❑ 99PacPlaB-204A
- ❑ 99PacRed-204
- ❑ 99PacRed-204A
- ❑ 99SkyMolM-126
- ❑ 99SkyMolMF-26
- ❑ 99SkyMolMFS-26
- ❑ 99SkyMolMFT-26
- ❑ 99SkyMolMX-126
- ❑ 99SkyPre-253
- ❑ 99SkyPre-253
- ❑ 99SkyPreDD-4
- ❑ 99SkyPreR-253
- ❑ 99SkyPreR-253
- ❑ 99SkyThu-257
- ❑ 99SkyThuRant-257
- ❑ 99SkyThuRave-257
- ❑ 99SkyThuUnl-U6
- ❑ 00CP Aut 101
- ❑ 99SP AutC-JG
- ❑ 99SP AutCG-JG
- ❑ 99SP SigAuto-JEG
- ❑ 99SP SigAutoG-JEG
- ❑ 99SpoIll-67
- ❑ 99SpoIllOTW-15
- ❑ 99SPSig-32
- ❑ 99SPx-97
- ❑ 99SPxFinR-97
- ❑ 99SPxFinS-97
- ❑ 99StaClu-353
- ❑ 99StaCluFDI-353
- ❑ 99StaCluOoaK-353
- ❑ 99StaCluPP-353
- ❑ 99ThuSkySupR-257
- ❑ 99Top-207
- ❑ 99TopAll-AM19
- ❑ 99TopChr-207
- ❑ 99TopChrA-AE19
- ❑ 99TopChrAR-AE19
- ❑ 99TopChrR-207
- ❑ 99TopGal-148
- ❑ 99TopGalPP-148
- ❑ 99TopGalPPI-148
- ❑ 99UD Cho-26
- ❑ 99UD ChoPCR-26
- ❑ 99UDHolo-29
- ❑ 99UDHoloAUsome-29
- ❑ 99Ult-234
- ❑ 99UltGolM-234
- ❑ 99UltMas-234
- ❑ 99UltPlaM-234
- ❑ 99UppDec-18
- ❑ 99UppDecBD-98
- ❑ 99UppDecBDD-98
- ❑ 99UppDecBDQ-98
- ❑ 99UppDecBDT-98
- ❑ 99UppDecCf7-88
- ❑ 99UppDecCLM-C45
- ❑ 99UppDecCo7CE-88
- ❑ 99UppDecE-108
- ❑ 99UppDecEFXG-108
- ❑ 99UppDecEL1-18
- ❑ 99UppDecEL2-18
- ❑ 99UppDecM-99
- ❑ 99UppDecMGS-99
- ❑ 99UppDecMHFS-99
- ❑ 99UppDecMP-JG
- ❑ 99UppDecMSS-99
- ❑ 99UppDecO-71
- ❑ 99UppDecOSO-71
- ❑ 99UppDecR-42
- ❑ 99UppDecRG-42
- ❑ 99UppDecRP-42
- ❑ 99Vic-183

Gianini, Joseph
- ❑ 14Zee-80

Giannelli, Ray
- ❑ 89MyrBeaBJP-1470
- ❑ 89SouAtlLAGS-35
- ❑ 90DunBluJS-9
- ❑ 90StaFS7-64
- ❑ 91BluJayS-33
- ❑ 91Cla/Bes-26
- ❑ 91KnoBluJLD-357
- ❑ 91KnoBluJP-1774
- ❑ 91LinDriAA-357
- ❑ 92SkyAAAF-225
- ❑ 92SyrChiF-1974
- ❑ 92SyrChiMB-6
- ❑ 92SyrChiS-506
- ❑ 92TopDeb91-64
- ❑ 93SyrChiF-1003
- ❑ 94SyrChiF-978
- ❑ 94SyrChiTI-13
- ❑ 95LouRedF-288
- ❑ 96ColSprSSTI-15

Giannotta, Go
- ❑ 80EvaTriT-13

Giansanti, Ralph
- ❑ 83AndBraT-21

Giants, Bismarck
- ❑ 93NegLeaRL2-98

Giants, Cedar Rapids
- ❑ 76CedRapGT-37

Giants, Clinton
- ❑ 86CliGiaP-29
- ❑ 87CliGiaP-29
- ❑ 92CliGiaF-3615

Giants, New York
- ❑ 09MaxPubP-25
- ❑ 09SpoNewSM-83
- ❑ 13FatT20-13
- ❑ 38BasTabP-37
- ❑ 48ExhTea-7
- ❑ 48ExhTea-11
- ❑ 51TopTea-5
- ❑ 55GiaGolS-1
- ❑ 56Top-226
- ❑ 57Top-317
- ❑ 58Top-19
- ❑ 60NuHi-56
- ❑ 61NuSco-456
- ❑ 68LauWorS-9
- ❑ 68LauWorS-10
- ❑ 68LauWorS-14
- ❑ 68LauWorS-21
- ❑ 68LauWorS-33
- ❑ 68LauWorS-48
- ❑ 70FleWorS-9
- ❑ 70FleWorS-10
- ❑ 70FleWorS-14
- ❑ 70FleWorS-19
- ❑ 70FleWorS-33
- ❑ 70FleWorS-48
- ❑ 70FleWorS-59
- ❑ 71FleWorS-10
- ❑ 71FleWorS-20
- ❑ 71FleWorS-52
- ❑ 73FleWilD-29
- ❑ 74NewYorNTDiS-37
- ❑ 86JosHalC-11
- ❑ 93TedWilPC-17

Giants, Phoenix
- ❑ 82PhoGiaVNB-1
- ❑ 83PhoGiaBHN-27

Giants, San Francisco
- ❑ 58GiaFalBTP-1
- ❑ 58GiaFalBTP-2
- ❑ 58GiaFalBTP-3
- ❑ 58GiaFalBTP-4
- ❑ 59Top-69
- ❑ 59TopVen-69
- ❑ 60Top-151
- ❑ 60TopTat-63
- ❑ 60TopVen-151
- ❑ 61Top-167
- ❑ 61TopMagR-12
- ❑ 62GuyPotCP-17
- ❑ 62Top-226
- ❑ 63Top-417
- ❑ 64Top-257
- ❑ 64TopTatI-19
- ❑ 64TopVen-257
- ❑ 65GiaTeaI-10
- ❑ 65Top-379
- ❑ 66OPC-19
- ❑ 66Top-19
- ❑ 66TopRubI-118
- ❑ 66TopVen-19
- ❑ 67Top-516
- ❑ 68LauWorS-59
- ❑ 69FleCloS-21
- ❑ 69FleCloS-32
- ❑ 69TopStaA-22
- ❑ 70FleWorS-59
- ❑ 70Top-696
- ❑ 71FleWorS-60
- ❑ 71OPC-563
- ❑ 71Top-563
- ❑ 71TopTat-9
- ❑ 72Top-771
- ❑ 73OPC-434
- ❑ 73OPCBTC-22
- ❑ 73Top-434
- ❑ 73TopBluTC-22
- ❑ 74OPC-281
- ❑ 74OPCTC-22
- ❑ 74Top-281
- ❑ 74TopStaA-22
- ❑ 74TopTeaC-22
- ❑ 76OPC-443
- ❑ 76Top-443
- ❑ 78Top-82
- ❑ 83FleSta-247
- ❑ 83FleSti-NNO
- ❑ 87SpoTeaL-10
- ❑ 88FleStiWBC-S7
- ❑ 88FleWaxBC-C9
- ❑ 88PanSti-480
- ❑ 88RedFolSB-108
- ❑ 88Top-261
- ❑ 88TopTif-261
- ❑ 90FleWaxBC-C1
- ❑ 90PubIntS-626
- ❑ 90RedFolSB-125
- ❑ 92GiaATaTTP-1
- ❑ 92GiaATaTTP-2
- ❑ 92GiaATaTTP-3
- ❑ 92GiaATaTTP-4
- ❑ 92GiaATaTTP-5
- ❑ 92GiaATaTTP-6
- ❑ 92GiaATaTTP-7
- ❑ 92GiaATaTTP-8
- ❑ 92GiaATaTTP-9
- ❑ 92GiaATaTTP-10
- ❑ 92GiaATaTTP-11
- ❑ 92GiaATaTTP-12
- ❑ 92GiaATaTTP-13
- ❑ 92GiaATaTTP-14
- ❑ 92GiaATaTTP-15
- ❑ 92GiaATaTTP-16
- ❑ 92GiaATaTTP-17
- ❑ 92GiaATaTTP-18
- ❑ 92GiaATaTTP-19
- ❑ 92GiaATaTTP-20
- ❑ 92GiaATaTTP-21
- ❑ 92GiaATaTTP-22
- ❑ 92GiaATaTTP-23
- ❑ 92GiaATaTTP-24
- ❑ 92GiaATaTTP-25
- ❑ 92GiaATaTTP-26
- ❑ 92GiaATaTTP-27
- ❑ 92GiaATaTTP-28
- ❑ 92GiaATaTTP-29
- ❑ 92GiaATaTTP-30
- ❑ 92GiaATaTTP-31
- ❑ 92GiaATaTTP-32
- ❑ 92GiaATaTTP-33
- ❑ 92GiaATaTTP-34
- ❑ 92GiaATaTTP-35
- ❑ 93GiaPos-35
- ❑ 94ImpProP-28
- ❑ 94Sco-660
- ❑ 94ScoGolR-660
- ❑ 95PacPriTL-28
- ❑ 95PanSti-129
- ❑ 96PanSti-109
- ❑ 99Vic-349

Gianukakis, John
- ❑ 86BenPhiC-146

Giard, Joe
- ❑ 75Yan192T-9
- ❑ 79Yan192T-12
- ❑ 84Yan192G-30
- ❑ 91ConTSN-119

Giard, Ken
- ❑ 92IdaFalGF-3506
- ❑ 92IdaFalGSP-5
- ❑ 93MacBraC-10
- ❑ 93MacBraF-1395
- ❑ 94DurBulC-8
- ❑ 94DurBulF-324
- ❑ 94DurBulTI-7
- ❑ 95EugEmeTI-3
- ❑ 96DurBulBlB-3
- ❑ 96DurBulBrB-4
- ❑ 97DurBulTI-9
- ❑ 98CarMudM-3

Giardi, Mike
- ❑ 94EveGiaC-9
- ❑ 94EveGiaF-3658
- ❑ 95GreBatTI-12
- ❑ 96GreBatB-11
- ❑ 96WesPalBEB-26

Giaudrone, Charlie
- ❑ 90WicStaSGD-12

Gibbon, Joe
- ❑ 58JetPos-7
- ❑ 60KeyChal-19
- ❑ 60Top-512
- ❑ 61Top-523
- ❑ 62Kah-13
- ❑ 62Top-448
- ❑ 63Kah-12
- ❑ 63PirIDL-9
- ❑ 63Top-101
- ❑ 64PirKDK-12
- ❑ 64Top-307
- ❑ 64TopVen-307
- ❑ 65OPC-54
- ❑ 65Top-54
- ❑ 66Top-457
- ❑ 67Top-541
- ❑ 68OPC-32
- ❑ 68Top-32
- ❑ 68TopVen-32
- ❑ 69OPC-158
- ❑ 69Top-158
- ❑ 69TopFou-2
- ❑ 70OPC-517
- ❑ 70Top-517
- ❑ 72OPC-382
- ❑ 72Top-382
- ❑ 77PirTCM1WC-23
- ❑ 78TCM60I-219

Gibbons, Bill
- ❑ 89CliGiaP-907

Gibbons, Jay
- ❑ 99BasAmeTPLM-4

Gibbons, John
- ❑ 82BelBreFr-8
- ❑ 85Don-116
- ❑ 85IntLeaAT-15
- ❑ 85MetTCM-19
- ❑ 85TidTidT-15
- ❑ 86ElPasDP-12
- ❑ 86MetTCM-14
- ❑ 86StaoftFT-33
- ❑ 86TidTidP-11
- ❑ 87ChaLooB-22
- ❑ 87Don-626
- ❑ 87MetColP-32
- ❑ 87TidTidP-6
- ❑ 87TidTidT-10
- ❑ 88AlbDukCm-20
- ❑ 88AlbDukP-260
- ❑ 88VerMarP-950
- ❑ 89OklCit8C-12
- ❑ 89OklCit8P-1531
- ❑ 90CMC-236
- ❑ 90ProAAAF-304
- ❑ 90ScrRedBC-10
- ❑ 90ScrRedBP-602
- ❑ 91MetWIZ-138
- ❑ 94CapCitBC-28
- ❑ 94CapCitBF-1768
- ❑ 96HilStaHWB-26
- ❑ 96StLucMTI-1
- ❑ 97St.LucM-9
- ❑ 98BinMetQ-1

Gibbons, Michael
- ❑ 88SalLakCTTI-15
- ❑ 89RocExpLC-10

Gibbs, Jake
- ❑ 62Top-281
- ❑ 64ChatheY-9
- ❑ 64Top-281
- ❑ 64TopVen-281
- ❑ 65ChaTheY-7
- ❑ 65OPC-226
- ❑ 65Top-226
- ❑ 66OPC-117
- ❑ 66Top-117
- ❑ 66TopVen-117
- ❑ 67CokCapYM-V3
- ❑ 67Top-375
- ❑ 68OPC-89
- ❑ 68Top-89
- ❑ 68TopVen-89
- ❑ 68YanPhoS-66
- ❑ 69MilBra-91
- ❑ 69MLBOffS-74
- ❑ 69Top-401
- ❑ 69TopSta-203
- ❑ 69TopTeaP-19
- ❑ 69YanMal-2
- ❑ 70MLBOffS-245
- ❑ 70Top-594
- ❑ 70YanPhoS-11
- ❑ 71MLBOffS-488
- ❑ 71OPC-382
- ❑ 71Top-382
- ❑ 71YanCliDP-6
- ❑ 72MilBra-114
- ❑ 92YanWIZ6-46
- ❑ 92YanWIZ7-54
- ❑ 94TamYanF-2402
- ❑ 95TamYanYI-7

Gibbs, Jim (James)
- ❑ 88SprCarB-9
- ❑ 89MedAthB-4
- ❑ 90BenBucL-30
- ❑ 90MadMusB-15

Gibbs, Kevin
- ❑ 95YakBeaTI-10
- ❑ 96VerBeaDB-13
- ❑ 97SanAntMB-24
- ❑ 98AlbDukG-7
- ❑ 98Bow-365
- ❑ 98BowChr-365
- ❑ 98BowChrGA-365
- ❑ 98BowChrGAR-365
- ❑ 98BowChrI-365
- ❑ 98BowChrIR-365
- ❑ 98BowChrR-365
- ❑ 98BowGolA-365
- ❑ 98BowInt-365
- ❑ 98SanAntMM-24

Gibbs, Paul
- ❑ 92WatIndC-2
- ❑ 92WatIndF-3227
- ❑ 93ColRedC-10
- ❑ 93ColRedF-591

Gilbert, Dave
- ❑ 91ButCopKSP-8
- ❑ 92Ft.MyeMCB-15
- ❑ 92Ft.MyeMF-2739
- ❑ 93ChaRanC-12
- ❑ 93ChaRanF-1935
- ❑ 94ClaGolF-33
- ❑ 94TulDriF-238
- ❑ 94TulDriTI-8

Gibralter, David
- ❑ 94SarRedSC-10
- ❑ 94SarRedSF-1956
- ❑ 94UtiBluSC-12
- ❑ 94UtiBluSF-3827
- ❑ 95MicBatCTI-13
- ❑ 96SarRedSB-16
- ❑ 97EasLeaTPB-29
- ❑ 97TexAllM-16
- ❑ 97TreThuB-18

Gibralter, Steve
- ❑ 91ChaWheC-22
- ❑ 91ChaWheP-2899
- ❑ 91SouAtlLAGP-SAL7
- ❑ 92CedRapRC-17
- ❑ 92CedRapRF-1083
- ❑ 92ClaFS7-47
- ❑ 92MidLeaATI-12
- ❑ 92UppDecML-69
- ❑ 92UppDecML-284
- ❑ 92UppDecMLPotY-PY21
- ❑ 93Bow-694
- ❑ 93ChaLooF-2370
- ❑ 93ClaFisN-2
- ❑ 93ClaGolF-214
- ❑ 93ClaMVPF-5
- ❑ 93ExcFS7-21
- ❑ 93ExcLeaLF-14
- ❑ 94ChaLooF-1369
- ❑ 94Cla-112
- ❑ 94UppDecML-190
- ❑ 95Bes-62
- ❑ 95Bow-161
- ❑ 95IndIndF-107
- ❑ 96Bow-128
- ❑ 96BowBes-167
- ❑ 96BowBesAR-167
- ❑ 96BowBesR-167
- ❑ 96BowFoi-128
- ❑ 96Cir-116
- ❑ 96CirRav-116
- ❑ 96ColCho-514
- ❑ 96ColChoGS-514
- ❑ 96ColChoSS-514
- ❑ 96EmoXL-164
- ❑ 96Fin-B303
- ❑ 96FinRef-B303
- ❑ 96Fla-232
- ❑ 96FlaWavotF-11
- ❑ 96FleUpd-U119
- ❑ 96FleUpdTC-U119
- ❑ 96IndIndB-9
- ❑ 96LeaPre-122
- ❑ 96LeaPreP-122
- ❑ 96LeaSig-133
- ❑ 96LeaSigPPG-133
- ❑ 96LeaSigPPP-133
- ❑ 96Pin-374
- ❑ 96PinAfi-177
- ❑ 96PinAfiAP-177
- ❑ 96PinFoil-374
- ❑ 96Sel-167
- ❑ 96SelArtP-167
- ❑ 96SelCer-106
- ❑ 96SelCerAP-106
- ❑ 96SelCerCB-106
- ❑ 96SelCerCR-106
- ❑ 96SelCerMB-106
- ❑ 96SelCerMG-106
- ❑ 96SelCerMR-106
- ❑ 96Sum-165
- ❑ 96SumAbo&B-165
- ❑ 96SumArtP-165
- ❑ 96SumFoi-165
- ❑ 96Top-101
- ❑ 96Ult-460
- ❑ 96UltGolM-460
- ❑ 96UppDec-228
- ❑ 97DonRatR-11
- ❑ 97Lea-18
- ❑ 97LeaFraM-18
- ❑ 97LeaFraMDC-18
- ❑ 97Pin-164
- ❑ 97PinArtP-PP164
- ❑ 97PinIns-139
- ❑ 97PinInsCE-139
- ❑ 97PinInsDE-139
- ❑ 97PinMusC-164
- ❑ 97PinPrePla-164
- ❑ 97Sco-112
- ❑ 97ScoArtPWB-112
- ❑ 97ScoPreS-112
- ❑ 97ScoShoS-112
- ❑ 97ScoShoSAP-112
- ❑ 98IndIndQ-30

Gibree, Bob
- ❑ 86WauTimP-11
- ❑ 87SalSpuS-20

Gibson, Bob (Robert L.)
- ❑ 79BurBeeT-14
- ❑ 82ElPasDT-21
- ❑ 83BrePol-40
- ❑ 84Don-246
- ❑ 84Fle-201
- ❑ 84Nes792-349
- ❑ 84Top-349
- ❑ 84TopTif-349
- ❑ 84VanCanC-40
- ❑ 85BrePol-40
- ❑ 85Don-393
- ❑ 85TopTifT-39T
- ❑ 85TopTra-39T
- ❑ 86Don-271

❑ 86Fle-488
❑ 86Top-499
❑ 86TopTif-499
❑ 86VanCanP-12
❑ 87TidTidP-33
❑ 87TidTidT-3
❑ 88RocRedWC-5
❑ 88RocRedWP-196
❑ 88RocRedWTI-8
❑ 91MetWIZ-139
❑ 94BreMilB-126

Gibson, Bob (Robert)
❑ 59Top-514
❑ 60Top-73
❑ 60TopVen-73
❑ 61Top-211
❑ 62CarJayP-4
❑ 62Top-530
❑ 63CarJayP-7
❑ 63CarJayP-8
❑ 63Fle-61
❑ 63Jel-166
❑ 63Pos-166
❑ 63SalMetC-3
❑ 63Top-5
❑ 63Top-9
❑ 63Top-415
❑ 64Top-460
❑ 64TopCoi-59
❑ 64TopGia-41
❑ 65Baz-23
❑ 65CarJayP-3
❑ 65CarTeal-9
❑ 65OPC-12
❑ 65OPC-138
❑ 65Top-12
❑ 65Top-138
❑ 65Top-320
❑ 65TopEmbl-69
❑ 65TopTral-14
❑ 66Baz-21
❑ 66CarTeal-5
❑ 66Top-225
❑ 66Top-320
❑ 66TopRubl-35
❑ 66TopVen-225
❑ 66TopVen-320
❑ 67Baz-21
❑ 67Top-210
❑ 67Top-236
❑ 67TopVen-267
❑ 68AtlOilPBCC-20
❑ 68Baz-9
❑ 68LauWorS-64
❑ 68OPC-100
❑ 68OPC-154
❑ 68Top-100
❑ 68Top-154
❑ 68Top-378
❑ 68TopActS-10C
❑ 68TopVen-100
❑ 68TopVen-154
❑ 69KelPin-6
❑ 69MLBOffS-211
❑ 69MLBPin-44
❑ 69NabTeaF-9
❑ 69OPC-8
❑ 69OPC-10
❑ 69OPC-12
❑ 69OPC-107
❑ 69OPC-162
❑ 69OPC-168
❑ 69OPC-200
❑ 69OPCDec-7
❑ 69Top-8
❑ 69Top-10
❑ 69Top-12
❑ 69Top-107A
❑ 69Top-107B
❑ 69Top-162
❑ 69Top-168
❑ 69Top-200
❑ 69Top-432
❑ 69TopDec-29
❑ 69TopDecI-12
❑ 69TopFou-7
❑ 69TopFou-14
❑ 69TopFou-18
❑ 69TopSta-115
❑ 69TopSup-60
❑ 69TopTeaP-18
❑ 69TraSta-33
❑ 70CarTeal-12
❑ 70DayDaiNM-16
❑ 70Kel-71A
❑ 70Kel-71B
❑ 70MLBOffS-139
❑ 70OPC-67
❑ 70OPC-71
❑ 70OPC-530
❑ 70Top-67
❑ 70Top-68
❑ 70Top-71
❑ 70Top-530
❑ 70TopBoo-22
❑ 70TopSup-33
❑ 70TraSta-5A
❑ 71AllBasA-7
❑ 71BazNumT-41
❑ 71BazUnn-35
❑ 71CarTeal-11
❑ 71CarTeal-17
❑ 71CarTeal-18
❑ 71Kel-51
❑ 71MilDud-43
❑ 71MLBOffS-273
❑ 71MLBOffS-559
❑ 71OPC-70
❑ 71OPC-72
❑ 71OPC-450
❑ 71Top-70
❑ 71Top-72
❑ 71Top-450
❑ 71TopCoi-63
❑ 71TopGreM-24
❑ 71TopSup-48
❑ 71TopTat-120
❑ 71TopTat-121
❑ 72CarTeal-9
❑ 72Dia-59
❑ 72Kel-26A
❑ 72Kel-26B
❑ 72OPC-130
❑ 72SevTraC-17
❑ 72Top-130
❑ 73Kel2D-14
❑ 73LinPor-167
❑ 73OPC-190
❑ 73SevTraC-25
❑ 73Top-190
❑ 73TopCanL-19
❑ 74Kel-1
❑ 74OPC-350
❑ 74Top-350
❑ 74TopDecE-3
❑ 74TopPuz-5
❑ 74TopSta-114
❑ 75Hos-119
❑ 75OPC-3
❑ 75OPC-150
❑ 75OPC-206
❑ 75St.LouCP-12
❑ 75Top-3
❑ 75Top-150
❑ 75Top-206
❑ 75TopMin-3
❑ 75TopMin-150
❑ 75TopMin-206
❑ 76GrePlaG-40
❑ 77Spo-4705
❑ 78TCM60I-60
❑ 80PerHaloFP-175
❑ 80PerHaloFPS-40
❑ 80SSPHOF-174
❑ 82BraPol-45
❑ 82DavHaloFB-10
❑ 82K-M-14
❑ 82TCMGreP-15
❑ 83BraPol-45
❑ 83CarGreT-8
❑ 83KelCerB-10
❑ 83Oco& SSBG-8
❑ 84BraPol-45
❑ 84OCoandSI-16
❑ 84raPho-11
❑ 85DalNatCC-3
❑ 86SpoDecG-42
❑ 86TCMSupS-15
❑ 87K-M-3
❑ 87NesDreT-31
❑ 87SpoRea-9
❑ 88Top-664
❑ 88TopTif-664
❑ 89KahCoo-5
❑ 89TopBasT-23
❑ 90BasWit-31
❑ 90HOFStiB-74
❑ 90PacLeg-28
❑ 90SweBasG-120
❑ 91Col-23
❑ 91Kel3D-5
❑ 91KelStaU-6
❑ 91LinDri-3
❑ 91SweBasG-33
❑ 91UppDecS-11
❑ 91UppDecS-14
❑ 91UppDecS-19
❑ 92ActPacA-3
❑ 92ActPacA2-3G
❑ 92ActPacAP-2
❑ 92CarMcD-46
❑ 92UppDecF-52
❑ 92UppDecFG-52
❑ 92UppDecHH-HI4
❑ 92UppDecS-11
❑ 92UppDecS-29
❑ 92UppDecS-35
❑ 92Zip-2
❑ 93ActPacAC-3
❑ 93MetIma-10
❑ 93TedWil-90
❑ 93TedWil-142
❑ 94NabAllA-1
❑ 94UppDecAH-119
❑ 94UppDecAH-130
❑ 94UppDecAH-156
❑ 94UppDecAH-219
❑ 94UppDecAH1-119
❑ 94UppDecAH1-130
❑ 94UppDecAH1-156
❑ 94UppDecAH1-219
❑ 94UppDecS-2
❑ 94UppDecTAE-69
❑ 94UppDecTAELD-LD13
❑ 94Yoo-6
❑ 95EagBalL-9
❑ 95PirCocP-14
❑ 95TomPiz-AU3
❑ 95TopLegot6M-3
❑ 95UppDecSHoB-11
❑ 97DonSigSS-10
❑ 97FleMilDM-31
❑ 97FleMilDMR-31
❑ 97St.VinHHS-7
❑ 98SpollITaN-11
❑ 98SpollITaNA-2
❑ 98SpollITaNAR-2
❑ 98SpollITaNEE-11
❑ 98SpollITaNGS-18
❑ 98SpollIWSFAE-9
❑ 98SpollIWSFAEG-9
❑ 98UppDecR-79
❑ 98UppDecRSotT-BGI
❑ 99SpollIGotG-45
❑ 99SpollIGotGA-27
❑ 99TopStaRR-4
❑ 99TopStaRRA-4
❑ 99UppDecCL-31
❑ 99UppDecCL-127
❑ 99UppDecCLA-1960
❑ 99UppDecCLCC-31
❑ 99UppDecCLCC-127
❑ 99UppDecCLES-BG
❑ 99UppDecCLESC-BG

Gibson, Dave
❑ 80KnoBluJT-19

Gibson, Derrick
❑ 94BenRocC-8
❑ 94BenRocF-3607
❑ 95AshTouTI-34
❑ 95AshTouUTI-34
❑ 95Bes-67
❑ 95Bes-108
❑ 95BesFra-F8
❑ 95Bow-157
❑ 95Exc-186
❑ 95SPML-50
❑ 95SPMLDtS-DS19
❑ 96Bow-285
❑ 96BowBes-94
❑ 96BowBesAR-94
❑ 96BowBesP-BBP23
❑ 96BowBesPAR-BBP23
❑ 96BowBesPR-BBP23
❑ 96BowBesR-94
❑ 96BowFoi-285
❑ 96BowMinLP-2
❑ 96Exc-153
❑ 96ExcSeaC-4
❑ 96MauStiHWB-34
❑ 96NewHavRB-10
❑ 96NewHavRUSTI-34
❑ 96Top-436
❑ 97Bes-40
❑ 97BesAutSBPP-21
❑ 97Bow-191
❑ 97BowBes-165
❑ 97BowBesAR-165
❑ 97BowBesR-165
❑ 97BowChr-179
❑ 97BowChrI-179
❑ 97BowChrIR-179
❑ 97BowChrR-179
❑ 97BowInt-191
❑ 97ColCho-470
❑ 97Don-391
❑ 97DonGolPP-391
❑ 97DonSigA-37
❑ 97DonSigAC-45
❑ 97DonSigAM-45
❑ 97DonSilPP-391
❑ 97EasLeaTPB-17
❑ 97NewHavRB-8
❑ 97SP-6
❑ 97StaCluM-M30
❑ 97StaCluMOP-M30
❑ 97Top-290
❑ 98AriFalLTP-24
❑ 98Bes-67
❑ 98BesCon-1
❑ 98BesDiaB-3
❑ 98BesYouG-1
❑ 98Bow-144
❑ 98BowBes-174
❑ 98BowBesAR-174
❑ 98BowBesR-174
❑ 98BowChr-144
❑ 98BowChrGA-144
❑ 98BowChrGAR-144
❑ 98BowChrI-144
❑ 98BowChrIR-144
❑ 98BowChrR-144
❑ 98BowGolA-144
❑ 98BowInt-144
❑ 98ColSprSS-34
❑ 98Don-307
❑ 98DonColP-706
❑ 98DonGolPP-307
❑ 98DonPre-156
❑ 98DonPreSeat-156
❑ 98DonPriCP-706
❑ 98DonSigA-35
❑ 98DonSigAC-46
❑ 98DonSigAM-47
❑ 98DonSilPP-307
❑ 98E-X2Sig2001-2
❑ 98FleUpd-U63
❑ 98LeaRS-276
❑ 98LeaRSLHolo-276
❑ 98LeaRSLong-276
❑ 98LeaRTrue-276
❑ 98PinSna-CR10
❑ 98PinSna-CR17
❑ 98SP MinDTSPE-DS26
❑ 98SP MinPE-50
❑ 98SP MinSTHPE-H15
❑ 98SP SPTSC-DK
❑ 98SPMin-50
❑ 98SPMinDTS-DS26
❑ 98SPMinSTH-H15
❑ 98Stu-125
❑ 98StuGPP-125
❑ 98StuSPP-125
❑ 98Top-484
❑ 98TopChr-484
❑ 98TopChrR-484
❑ 98TopDevR-484
❑ 98TopDia-484
❑ 98TopMiniC-484
❑ 98Ult-402
❑ 98UltGolM-402
❑ 98UltMas-402
❑ 98UltPlaM-402
❑ 98UppDec-268
❑ 99Bow-75
❑ 99BowAut-BA48
❑ 99BowBes-137
❑ 99BowBesAR-137
❑ 99BowBesFFMI-FF9
❑ 99BowBesFFMI-FF9
❑ 99BowBesFFMII-FF9
❑ 99BowBesR-137
❑ 99BowChr-75
❑ 99BowChrG-75
❑ 99BowChrGR-75
❑ 99BowChrI-75
❑ 99BowChrIR-75
❑ 99BowChrR-75
❑ 99BowGol-75
❑ 99BowInt-75
❑ 99E-X Cen-99
❑ 99E-X CenECFut-99
❑ 99E-X CenECNow-99
❑ 99Fle-57
❑ 99FleSta9-57
❑ 99FleWarT-57
❑ 99Pac-144
❑ 99Pac-144A
❑ 99PacAur-61
❑ 99PacAurOD-61
❑ 99PacPlaB-144
❑ 99PacPlaB-144A
❑ 99PacRed-144
❑ 99PacRed-144A
❑ 99SkyMolM-35
❑ 99SkyMolMX-35
❑ 99SkyThu-162
❑ 99SkyThuRant-162
❑ 99SkyThuRave-162
❑ 99SP Aut-97
❑ 99SP SigAuto-DG
❑ 99SP SigAutoG-DG
❑ 99SpoIll-66
❑ 99SPSig-90
❑ 99SPx-89
❑ 99SPxFinR-89
❑ 99SPxFinS-89
❑ 99ThuSkySupR-162
❑ 99Top-392
❑ 99TopChr-392
❑ 99TopChrR-392
❑ 99TopMVPP-392
❑ 99Ult-235
❑ 99UltGolM-235
❑ 99UltMas-235
❑ 99UltPlaM-235
❑ 99UppDec-281
❑ 99UppDecE-124
❑ 99UppDecEFXG-124
❑ 99UppDecEL1-281
❑ 99UppDecEL2-281
❑ 99UppDecM-74
❑ 99UppDecMGS-74
❑ 99UppDecMHFS-74
❑ 99UppDecMP-DG
❑ 99UppDecMSS-74
❑ 99Vic-128

Gibson, Frank
❑ 25Exh-6

Gibson, Harry
❑ 98JohCCTI-13

Gibson, Hoot
❑ 81DurBulT-19

Gibson, J. Russ
❑ 64SeaPop-3
❑ 67Top-547
❑ 68Top-297
❑ 68TopVen-297
❑ 69MilBra-92
❑ 69OPC-89
❑ 69RedSoxAO-4
❑ 69RedSoxTI-3
❑ 69RedSoxTI-4
❑ 69Top-89
❑ 69TopSta-133
❑ 69TopTeaP-3
❑ 70OPC-237
❑ 70Top-237
❑ 71MLBOffS-248
❑ 71OPC-738
❑ 71Top-738
❑ 72GiaTeal-7
❑ 72MilBra-115
❑ 72Top-643
❑ 81RedSoxBG2S-81

Gibson, Joel
❑ 65Top-368
❑ 78TCM60I-208

Gibson, Josh
❑ 91NegLeaRL-24
❑ 95NegLeaL2-3
❑ 95NegLeaLI-24

Gibson, Josh Sr.
❑ 74LauOldTBS-8
❑ 76CooPapB-13
❑ 76ShaPiz-128
❑ 80PerHaloFP-128
❑ 80SSPHOF-128
❑ 83ConMar-51
❑ 83DonHOFH-4
❑ 85UltBasC-11
❑ 86NegLeaF-4
❑ 86NegLeaF-9
❑ 86NegLeaF-23
❑ 86NegLeaF-30
❑ 86NegLeaF-31
❑ 86NegLeaFS-30
❑ 87NegLeaPD-6
❑ 87SpoCubG-2
❑ 88ConNegA-5
❑ 88NegLeaD-12
❑ 89NegLeaRP-8
❑ 90NegLeaS-2
❑ 90PomBlaBNLP-2544
❑ 91PomBlaBPB-5
❑ 91PomBlaBPB-6
❑ 91PomBlaBPB-22
❑ 91PomBlaBPB-30
❑ 92NegLeaK-17
❑ 92NegLeaPL-3
❑ 93DiaStaES-N2
❑ 93TedWil-105
❑ 94PomNegLB-5
❑ 94TedWilLC-LC14
❑ 94UppDecTAE-44
❑ 95NegLeaL2-3
❑ 95S.FExaNLT-3
❑ 96NoiSatP-1
❑ 97NegLeaPC-1C
❑ 99UppDecCL-18
❑ 99UppDecCLCC-18

Gibson, Kirk
❑ 81CokTeaS-59
❑ 81Fle-481
❑ 81OPC-315
❑ 81TigDetN-20
❑ 81Top-315
❑ 81TopSti-78
❑ 82Don-407
❑ 82Dra-15
❑ 82Fle-267
❑ 82FleSta-161
❑ 82Kel-40
❑ 82OPC-105
❑ 82PerCreC-24
❑ 82PerCreCG-24
❑ 82Squ-6
❑ 82Top-105
❑ 82TopSti-184
❑ 83AllGamPI-53
❑ 83Don-459
❑ 83Fle-329
❑ 83OPC-321
❑ 83TigPos-11
❑ 83Top-430
❑ 83TopSti-67
❑ 84Don-593
❑ 84Fle-80
❑ 84FunFooP-21
❑ 84Nes792-65
❑ 84OPC-65
❑ 84TigFarJ-4
❑ 84TigFliJ-10
❑ 84TigTeal-15
❑ 84TigWavP-16
❑ 84Top-65
❑ 84TopSti-272
❑ 84TopTif-65
❑ 85AllGamPI-57
❑ 85Don-471
❑ 85Dra-12
❑ 85Fle-8
❑ 85FleStaS-22
❑ 85Lea-103
❑ 85OPC-372
❑ 85SevCoi-D13
❑ 85SevCoi-S8
❑ 85TigCaiD-8
❑ 85TigWen-9
❑ 85Top-565
❑ 85TopRubD-22
❑ 85TopSti-11
❑ 85TopSti-19
❑ 85TopSti-267
❑ 85TopSup-27
❑ 85TopTif-565
❑ 86BasStaB-46
❑ 86BurKinA-13
❑ 86Don-1
❑ 86Don-125
❑ 86DonSupD-1
❑ 86DonWaxBC-PC4
❑ 86Dra-28
❑ 86Fle-226
❑ 86FleLimE-19
❑ 86FleMin-47
❑ 86FleSlu-10
❑ 86FleStiC-45
❑ 86GenMilB-1B
❑ 86Lea-1
❑ 86OPC-295
❑ 86SevCoi-C16
❑ 86Spo-21
❑ 86TigCaiD-6
❑ 86Top-295
❑ 86TopGloS-29

❑ 86TopSti-266
❑ 86TopSup-25
❑ 86TopTat-22
❑ 86TopTif-295
❑ 86TruVal-8
❑ 86WilGloT-1
❑ 87BoaandB-29
❑ 87ClaGam-9
❑ 87Don-50
❑ 87Fle-151
❑ 87FleGamW-17
❑ 87FleGlo-151
❑ 87FleLimE-17
❑ 87FleMin-44
❑ 87FleStiC-47
❑ 87GenMilB-2C
❑ 87KraFoo-19
❑ 87Lea-104
❑ 87OPC-386
❑ 87RedFolSB-10
❑ 87SevCoi-D3
❑ 87Spo-48
❑ 87SpoTeaP-15
❑ 87StuPan-19
❑ 87TigCaiD-9
❑ 87TigCok-1
❑ 87TolMudHP-28
❑ 87Top-765
❑ 87TopCoi-11
❑ 87TopMinL-53
❑ 87TopSti-273
❑ 87TopTif-765
❑ 88DodMot-8
❑ 88DodPol-23
❑ 88Don-275
❑ 88DonBasB-66
❑ 88Fle-55
❑ 88FleGlo-55
❑ 88FleMin-82
❑ 88FleStiC-24
❑ 88FleUpd-93
❑ 88FleUpdG-93
❑ 88Lea-136
❑ 88OPC-201
❑ 88PanSti-95
❑ 88Sco-525
❑ 88ScoGlo-525
❑ 88ScoRoo-10T
❑ 88ScoRooG-10T
❑ 88Spo-111
❑ 88StaLinD-4
❑ 88StaLinTi-5
❑ 88TarPla-15
❑ 88Top-429
❑ 88Top-605
❑ 88TopBig-191
❑ 88TopSti-267
❑ 88TopTif-429
❑ 88TopTif-605
❑ 88TopTra-40T
❑ 88TopTraT-40T
❑ 88TopUKM-26
❑ 88TopUKMT-26
❑ 89Baz-10
❑ 89Bow-351
❑ 89BowTif-351
❑ 89CadEllD-23
❑ 89ClaTraO-120
❑ 89DodMot-8
❑ 89DodPol-14
❑ 89DodStaSV-5
❑ 89Don-15
❑ 89Don-132
❑ 89DonBasB-10
❑ 89DonSupD-15
❑ 89Fle-57
❑ 89FleBasA-14
❑ 89FleBasM-13
❑ 89FleExcS-14
❑ 89FleForTR-4
❑ 89FleGlo-57
❑ 89FleGlo-WS5
❑ 89FleHeroB-17
❑ 89FleLeaL-15
❑ 89FleSup-16
❑ 89FleWaxBC-C10
❑ 89FleWorS-5
❑ 89KayB-13
❑ 89KinDis-1
❑ 89MSAHolD-20
❑ 89OPC-340
❑ 89OPC-382
❑ 89PanSti-16
❑ 89PanSti-17
❑ 89PanSti-107
❑ 89PanSti-479
❑ 89RedFolSB-49
❑ 89Sco-210
❑ 89Sco-582
❑ 89ScoHot1S-30
❑ 89Spo-65
❑ 89Top-340
❑ 89Top-396
❑ 89TopAme2C-14
❑ 89TopBasT-67
❑ 89TopBig-299
❑ 89TopCapC-2
❑ 89TopCoi-1
❑ 89TopDouA-24
❑ 89TopGaloC-6
❑ 89TopGloS-55
❑ 89TopHilTM-14
❑ 89TopMinL-17
❑ 89TopSti-66
❑ 89TopStiB-49
❑ 89TopTif-340
❑ 89TopTif-396
❑ 89TopUKM-30
❑ 89TVSpoM-33
❑ 89TVSpoM-136
❑ 89UppDec-633
❑ 89UppDec-662
❑ 89UppDec-666
❑ 89UppDec-676
❑ 89Woo-2
❑ 89Woo-24
❑ 90Bow-97
❑ 90BowTif-97
❑ 90ClaUpd-T20
❑ 90DodMot-13
❑ 90DodPol-23
❑ 90DodTar-279
❑ 90Don-368
❑ 90DonBesN-41
❑ 90Fle-393
❑ 90FleCan-393
❑ 90GooHumICBLS-9
❑ 90KinDis-5
❑ 90Lea-173
❑ 90M.Vpin-47
❑ 90MLBBasB-6
❑ 90OPC-150
❑ 90PanSti-271
❑ 90PublntS-5
❑ 90PublntS-259
❑ 90Sco-487
❑ 90Top-150
❑ 90TopAmeA-20
❑ 90TopBig-326
❑ 90TopHilHM-25
❑ 90TopSti-60
❑ 90TopTif-150
❑ 90UppDec-264
❑ 91Bow-302
❑ 91CadEllD-24
❑ 91ClaGam-57
❑ 91Don-445
❑ 91Fle-199
❑ 91FleUpd-26
❑ 91Lea-249
❑ 91OPC-490
❑ 91OPCPre-50
❑ 91RoyPol-9
❑ 91Sco-800
❑ 91ScoRoo-10T
❑ 91StaClu-344
❑ 91Stu-66
❑ 91Top-490
❑ 91TopDesS-490
❑ 91TopMic-490
❑ 91TopTif-490
❑ 91TopTra-46T
❑ 91TopTraT-46T
❑ 91UltUpd-27
❑ 91UppDec-634
❑ 91UppDec-737
❑ 92Don-39
❑ 92Fle-157
❑ 92OPC-720
❑ 92PanSti-100
❑ 92Pin-481
❑ 92RoyPol-7
❑ 92Sco-520
❑ 92SpollIFK1-185
❑ 92StaClu-495
❑ 92StaClu-784
❑ 92StaCluECN-784
❑ 92Top-720
❑ 92TopGol-720
❑ 92TopGolW-720
❑ 92TopMic-720
❑ 92UppDec-180
❑ 93CadDis-25
❑ 93Fla-203
❑ 93FleFinE-209
❑ 93Lea-314
❑ 93MetBak-28
❑ 93PacJugC-5
❑ 93PacSpa-443
❑ 93StaClu-673
❑ 93StaCluFDI-673
❑ 93StaCluMOP-673
❑ 93Stu-165
❑ 93TigGat-9
❑ 93TopTra-8T
❑ 93Ult-549
❑ 93UppDec-766
❑ 93UppDecGold-766
❑ 94ColC-403
❑ 94ColChoGS-403
❑ 94ColChoSS-403
❑ 94Don-108
❑ 94Fla-50
❑ 94Fle-130
❑ 94FleExtB-75
❑ 94Lea-342
❑ 94Pac-217
❑ 94Pin-453
❑ 94PinArtP-453
❑ 94PinMusC-453
❑ 94ProMag-47
❑ 94Sco-421
❑ 94ScoGolR-421
❑ 94Sel-266
❑ 94Top-228
❑ 94TopGol-228
❑ 94TopSpa-228
❑ 94Ult-355
❑ 95ColCho-472
❑ 95ColChoGS-472
❑ 95ColChoSE-217
❑ 95ColChoSEGS-217
❑ 95ColChoSESS-217
❑ 95ColChoSS-472
❑ 95Don-257
❑ 95DonPreP-257
❑ 95DonTopotO-76
❑ 95Emo-44
❑ 95Fla-256
❑ 95Fle-53
❑ 95Lea-78
❑ 95Pac-153
❑ 95PanSti-94
❑ 95Pin-349
❑ 95PinArtP-349
❑ 95PinMusC-349
❑ 95Sco-94
❑ 95ScoGolR-94
❑ 95ScoPlaTS-94
❑ 95Sel-25
❑ 95SelArtP-25
❑ 95SelCer-45
❑ 95SelCerMG-45
❑ 95SP-156
❑ 95SPCha-107
❑ 95SPCha-154
❑ 95SPChaCP-CP3
❑ 95SPChaCPDC-CP3
❑ 95SPChaDC-107
❑ 95SPChaDC-154
❑ 95Spo-71
❑ 95SpoArtP-34
❑ 95SPSil-156
❑ 95Sum-109
❑ 95SumNthD-109
❑ 95Top-519
❑ 95TopCyb-306
❑ 95UC3-45
❑ 95UC3ArtP-45
❑ 95Ult-286
❑ 95UltGolM-286
❑ 95UppDec-186
❑ 95UppDecED-186
❑ 95UppDecEDG-186
❑ 95UppDecSE-231
❑ 95UppDecSEG-231
❑ 95Zen-66
❑ 96ColCho-142
❑ 96ColChoGS-142
❑ 96ColChoSS-142
❑ 98SpollIWSF-29
❑ 98SpollIWSFEE-29
❑ 98SpollIWSFFE-29
❑ 99UppDecCLMS-HR3
❑ 99UppDecR-101
❑ 99UppDecRG-101
❑ 99UppDecRI-KG
❑ 99UppDecRIL2-KG
❑ 99UppDecRP-101

Gibson, Leighton
❑ 87OldJudN-198
❑ 90KalBatN-22

Gibson, Michael
❑ 93GenCubC-12
❑ 93GenCubF-3190

Gibson, Monty
❑ 91PocPioP-3776
❑ 91PocPioSP-18

Gibson, Moon (George)
❑ 03WilCarE-15
❑ 08AmeCarE91-76
❑ 08RosComP-151
❑ 09AmeCarE90-1-42
❑ 09AmeCarE90-1-43
❑ 09ColChiE-116
❑ 09SpoNewSM-35
❑ 09T206-141
❑ 10DomDisP-48
❑ 10E-UOraBSC-11
❑ 10E101-21
❑ 10E12AmeCDCE125-17
❑ 10JHDABE-7
❑ 10MelMinE-21
❑ 10NadCarE-24
❑ 10NadE1-18
❑ 10PeoT21-25A
❑ 10PeoT21-25B
❑ 10PeoT21-25C
❑ 10PeoT21-25D
❑ 10PirAmeCE-3
❑ 10PirHerICP-6
❑ 10PirTipTD-6
❑ 10SepAnoP-14
❑ 10StaCarE-14
❑ 10SweCapPP-137
❑ 10W555-31
❑ 11HelSta-160
❑ 11MecDFT-23
❑ 11PinT-5-857
❑ 11S74Sil-110
❑ 11SpoLifCW-140
❑ 11SpoLifM-250
❑ 11T205-64
❑ 11TurRedT-94
❑ 12ColRedB-116
❑ 12ColTinT-116
❑ 12HasTriFT-14B
❑ 12HasTriFT-14C
❑ 12HasTriFT-16B
❑ 12HasTriFT-16C
❑ 12HasTriFT-30A
❑ 12HasTriFT-30E
❑ 12PhiCarE-11
❑ 14B18B-76A
❑ 14B18B-76B
❑ 14PieStaT-46
❑ 15AmeCarE106-19A
❑ 15AmeCarE106-19B
❑ 15SpoNewM-68
❑ 16SpoNewM-68
❑ 19W514-63
❑ 19Zee-94
❑ 21E121So1-30
❑ 22Zee-60
❑ 23W501-89
❑ 23WilChoV-49
❑ 33WorCig-46
❑ 34DiaMatCSB-69
❑ 68SCFOldT-11
❑ 72ClaCar-50
❑ 92ConTSN-516
❑ 93ConTSN-825

Gibson, Norwood
❑ 04RedSoxUP-8
❑ 11SpoLifCW-141

Gibson, Paul
❑ 80CedRapRT-18
❑ 82BirBarT-23
❑ 83OrlTwiT-20
❑ 86GleFalTP-6
❑ 86NasSouTI-9
❑ 87TolMudHP-10
❑ 87TolMudHT-17
❑ 88DonRoo-19
❑ 88FleUpd-26
❑ 88FleUpdG-26
❑ 88TigPep-48
❑ 89Baz-11
❑ 89BirBarADB-14
❑ 89Bow-99
❑ 89BowTif-99
❑ 89ClaTraO-140
❑ 89Don-445
❑ 89Fle-131
❑ 89FleGlo-131
❑ 89K-M-10
❑ 89PanSti-331
❑ 89Sco-595A
❑ 89Sco-595B
❑ 89TigMar-48
❑ 89Top-583
❑ 89TopBig-230
❑ 89TopGloS-20
❑ 89TopRoo-10
❑ 89TopSti-323
❑ 89TopTif-583
❑ 89ToyRoo-11
❑ 89UppDec-47
❑ 90BirBarADB-14
❑ 90Don-657
❑ 90Fle-602
❑ 90FleCan-602
❑ 90Lea-298
❑ 90OPC-11
❑ 90PublntS-470
❑ 90Sco-261
❑ 90TigCok-5
❑ 90TigTeal-12
❑ 90Top-11
❑ 90TopTif-11
❑ 90UppDec-496
❑ 91Don-353
❑ 91Fle-337
❑ 91Lea-55
❑ 91OPC-431
❑ 91Sco-152
❑ 91TigCok-48
❑ 91TigPol-5
❑ 91Top-431
❑ 91TopDesS-431
❑ 91TopMic-431
❑ 91TopTif-431
❑ 91UltUpd-23
❑ 91UppDec-579
❑ 92Don-375
❑ 92Fle-136
❑ 92Lea-461
❑ 92LeaBlaG-461
❑ 92MetColP-24
❑ 92MetKah-45
❑ 92OPC-143
❑ 92OPCPre-174
❑ 92Sco-261
❑ 92StaClu-223
❑ 92StaClu-694
❑ 92Top-143
❑ 92TopGol-143
❑ 92TopGolW-143
❑ 92TopMic-143
❑ 92Ult-531
❑ 92UppDec-489
❑ 93Fle-473
❑ 93MetColP-34
❑ 93NorTidF-2563
❑ 93StaClu-29
❑ 93StaCluFDI-29
❑ 93StaCluMOP-29
❑ 94Fle-230
❑ 94StaCluT-185
❑ 94StaCluTFDI-185
❑ 96ColCliB-14

Gibson, Sam
❑ 33Zee-110
❑ 33Zee-117
❑ 37Zee-71
❑ 93ConTSN-962

Gibson, Scott
❑ 82AppFoxFr-22
❑ 84VisOakT-22

Gibson, Steve
❑ 78NewWayCT-15
❑ 79BurBeeT-13
❑ 80BurBeeT-1
❑ 81BurBeeT-11

Gibson, Thomas
❑ 91NiaFalRC-4

Gick, Brady
❑ 97NewJerCB-8

Giddens, Ron
❑ 84CedRapRT-20
❑ 86MacPirP-10

Giddings, Wayne
❑ 83IdaFalAT-4
❑ 84MadMusP-18
❑ 85HunStaJ-42

Gideon, Brett
❑ 86PriWilPP-11
❑ 87HarSenP-18
❑ 88BufBisC-3
❑ 88BufBisP-1492
❑ 88Fle-330
❑ 88FleGlo-330
❑ 89ExpPos-10
❑ 89IndIndC-5
❑ 89IndIndP-1230
❑ 90Bow-105
❑ 90BowTif-105
❑ 90ExpPos-12
❑ 92CanIndF-686

Gideon, Jim
❑ 76SacSolC-15
❑ 76TacTwiDQ-7
❑ 77TacTwiDQ-20
❑ 77Top-478
❑ 82TulDriT-9
❑ 89PacSenL-81
❑ 89TopSenL-26
❑ 92TexLon-15
❑ 93RanKee-159

Gideon, Ron
❑ 86LynMetP-12
❑ 87LynMetP-8
❑ 88JacMetGS-1
❑ 89St.LucMS-7
❑ 90JacMetGS-23
❑ 91St.LucMC-27
❑ 91St.LucMP-728
❑ 92BinMetF-533
❑ 93KinMetC-25
❑ 93KinMetF-3811
❑ 94KinMetC-25
❑ 94KinMetF-3839
❑ 95PitMetTI-13
❑ 96PorRocB-1
❑ 97AshTou-27
❑ 98AshTouM-26

Giebell, Floyd
❑ 81TigDetN-88

Giegling, Matt
❑ 91CedRapRC-15
❑ 91CedRapRP-2722
❑ 92CedRapRC-6
❑ 92CedRapRF-1075

Giel, Paul
❑ 55Bow-125
❑ 55GiaGolS-9
❑ 58GiaJayP-3
❑ 58GiaSFCB-8
❑ 58Top-308
❑ 59Top-9
❑ 59TopVen-9
❑ 60Top-526
❑ 61Top-374
❑ 61TwiCloD-6
❑ 61TwiPetM-19
❑ 77PirTCM1WC-25

Gienger, Craig
❑ 92SouOreAC-14
❑ 92SouOreAF-3409
❑ 93SouOreAC-9
❑ 93SouOreAF-4056

Gierhan, Sam
❑ 78NewWayCT-16
❑ 79BurBeeT-5

Gies, Chris
❑ 90ButCopKSP-22
❑ 91Cla/Bes-191
❑ 91GasRanC-6
❑ 91GasRanP-2683
❑ 92ChaRanC-10
❑ 92ClaFS7-66
❑ 93TulDriF-2728
❑ 93TulDriTI-9

Giesdal, Brent
❑ 82OneYanT-3

Giesecke, Doc (Rob)
❑ 79CliDodT-21
❑ 82VerBeaDT-27
❑ 83VerBeaDT-27
❑ 85VerBeaDT-24
❑ 86VerBeaDP-7
❑ 87VerBeaDP-18
❑ 90SanAntMGS-4
❑ 90TexLeaAGS-19
❑ 94VerBeaDC-30
❑ 95VerBeaDTI-8
❑ 96VerBeaDB-4
❑ 98VerBeaDM-3

Gieseke, Mark
❑ 89WatDiaS-29
❑ 90RivRedWP-2614
❑ 91CalLeLA-20
❑ 91HigDesMC-20
❑ 91HigDesMP-2403
❑ 92WicWraF-3662

❑ 93WicWraF-2982
Giesen, Dan
❑ 87ReaPhiP-6
❑ 88ReaPhiP-874
Gietzen, Peter
❑ 92GreHorC-16
❑ 92GreHorF-773
Giggie, Bob
❑ 60BraJayP-5
❑ 60BraLaktL-11
Gigon, Norm
❑ 67Top-576
Gil, Benji
❑ 91ClaDraP-15
❑ 91FroRowDP-50
❑ 91FroRowDPG-50
❑ 91FroRowDPS-50
❑ 91HigSchPLS-27
❑ 92Bow-339
❑ 92ClaFS7-309
❑ 92GasRanC-1
❑ 92GasRanF-2260
❑ 92OPC-534
❑ 92Pin-302
❑ 92Sco-808
❑ 92StaCluD-59
❑ 92Top-534
❑ 92TopGol-534
❑ 92TopGolW-534
❑ 92TopMic-534
❑ 92UppDecML-174
❑ 93Bow-629
❑ 93ClaGolF-50
❑ 93ExcFS7-234
❑ 93FleFinE-278
❑ 93FunPac-3
❑ 93LeaGolR-R18
❑ 93LeaGolRJ-R18
❑ 93OPCPre-27
❑ 93PacBeiA-16
❑ 93PacSpa-639
❑ 93Pin-597
❑ 93RanKee-407
❑ 93RanStaC-9
❑ 93SelRoo-42T
❑ 93SouAtlLAIPI-5
❑ 93SouAtlLAPI-12
❑ 93SP-193
❑ 93StaClu-697
❑ 93StaCluFDI-697
❑ 93StaCluMOP-697
❑ 93Top-529
❑ 93TopGol-529
❑ 93TopInaM-529
❑ 93TopInaR-529
❑ 93TopMic-529
❑ 93TopTra-60T
❑ 93TulDriF-2740
❑ 93TulDriTI-29
❑ 93Ult-628
❑ 93UppDec-441
❑ 93UppDecGold-441
❑ 94ActPac-48
❑ 94Bow-185
❑ 94Bow-379
❑ 94Cla-126
❑ 94ClaTriF-T79
❑ 94ColC-108
❑ 94ColChoGS-108
❑ 94ColChoSS-108
❑ 94Don-103
❑ 94OklCit8F-1498
❑ 94Pac-616
❑ 94Pin-194
❑ 94PinArtP-194
❑ 94PinMusC-194
❑ 94Sco-606
❑ 94ScoGolR-606
❑ 94StaCluT-246
❑ 94StaCluTFDI-246
❑ 94Top-231
❑ 94TopGol-231
❑ 94TopSpa-231
❑ 94UppDec-135
❑ 94UppDecED-135
❑ 95Bow-33
❑ 95BowBes-R88
❑ 95BowBesR-R88
❑ 95ColCho-568T
❑ 95DonTopotO-159
❑ 95Emo-84
❑ 95Fin-222
❑ 95FinRef-222
❑ 95Fla-305
❑ 95Lea-253
❑ 95LeaLim-47
❑ 95RanCra-10
❑ 95SelCer-76
❑ 95SelCerMG-76
❑ 95SigRooMR-MR2
❑ 95SigRooMRS-MR2
❑ 95SigRooOJSS-6
❑ 95SigRooOJSSS-6
❑ 95SP-196
❑ 95SPCha-191
❑ 95SPChaDC-191
❑ 95SPSil-196
❑ 95StaClu-573
❑ 95StaCluCB-CB8
❑ 95StaCluMOP-573
❑ 95StaCluMOP-CB8
❑ 95StaCluSTWS-573
❑ 95Sum-112
❑ 95SumNewA-NA10
❑ 95SumNthD-112
❑ 95Top-336
❑ 95UppDec-392
❑ 95UppDecED-392
❑ 95UppDecEDG-392
❑ 95Zen-144
❑ 95ZenRooRC-18
❑ 96ColCho-322
❑ 96ColCho-333
❑ 96ColChoGS-322
❑ 96ColChoGS-333
❑ 96ColChoSS-322
❑ 96ColChoSS-333
❑ 96Don-223
❑ 96DonPreP-223
❑ 96Fin-B82
❑ 96FinRef-B82
❑ 96Fla-168
❑ 96Fle-249
❑ 96FleTif-249
❑ 96Lea-95
❑ 96LeaPrePB-95
❑ 96LeaPrePG-95
❑ 96LeaPrePS-95
❑ 96LeaSigA-78
❑ 96LeaSigAG-78
❑ 96LeaSigAS-78
❑ 96Pac-429
❑ 96Pin-288
❑ 96PinAfi-113
❑ 96PinAfiAP-113
❑ 96PinFoil-288
❑ 96ProSta-96
❑ 96RanDr P-9
❑ 96RanFle-5
❑ 96RanMot-26
❑ 96Sco-158
❑ 96ScoDugC-A92
❑ 96ScoDugCAP-A92
❑ 96Sel-82
❑ 96SelArtP-82
❑ 96SelCer-73
❑ 96SelCerAP-73
❑ 96SelCerCB-73
❑ 96SelCerCR-73
❑ 96SelCerMB-73
❑ 96SelCerMG-73
❑ 96SelCerMR-73
❑ 96StaClu-81
❑ 96StaCluMOP-81
❑ 96Sum-59
❑ 96SumAbo&B-59
❑ 96SumArtP-59
❑ 96SumFoi-59
❑ 96Top-152
❑ 96Ult-134
❑ 96UltGolM-134
❑ 96UppDec-464
❑ 96Zen-78
❑ 96ZenArtP-78
❑ 97ColCho-492
❑ 97ColChoT-TR11
❑ 97Don-317
❑ 97DonGolPP-317
❑ 97DonSilPP-317
❑ 97Fle-565
❑ 97FleTif-565
❑ 97Lea-287
❑ 97LeaFraM-287
❑ 97LeaFraMDC-287
❑ 97PacPriGotD-GD94
❑ 97RanDr P-8
❑ 97RanMot-11
❑ 97Sco-384
❑ 97ScoArtPWB-384
❑ 97ScoResC-384
❑ 97ScoShoS-384
❑ 97ScoShoSAP-384
❑ 97Ult-428
❑ 97UltGolME-428
❑ 97UltPlaME-428
❑ 98ColCho-337
❑ 98PacInvGems-102
❑ 98PacPar-29
❑ 98PacParC-29
❑ 98PacParG-29
❑ 98PacParHS-29
❑ 98PacParPB-29
❑ 98PacParR-29
❑ 98UppDec-231
Gil, Carlos
❑ 80QuaCitCT-8
❑ 80VenLeaS-152
❑ 83MidCubT-7
Gil, Danny
❑ 90BoiHawP-3336
❑ 91PalSprAP-2020
❑ 94HunCubC-12
❑ 94HunCubF-3566
❑ 94PeoChiC-9
❑ 94PeoChiF-2279
Gil, Geronimo
❑ 96SavSanB-10
❑ 97VerBeaD-11
❑ 98SanAntMG-11
Gil, Jose
❑ 82WisRapTF-15
❑ 93LinVenB-163
❑ 94VenLinU-214
❑ 94VenLinU-262
❑ 95LinVen-53
❑ 96-97LinVen-100
❑ 96-97LinVen-159
Gil, T. Gus
❑ 67Top-253
❑ 68SeaPop-6
❑ 69PilPos-31
❑ 69Top-651
❑ 75HawIsIC-1
❑ 76VenLeaS-157
❑ 76VenLeaS-225
❑ 77ForLauYS-27
❑ 77PilPosR-31
❑ 80VenLeaS-226
❑ 82DanSunF-2
❑ 94BreMilB-127
Gilbert, Andy (Andrew)
❑ 73OPC-252
❑ 73Top-252A
❑ 73Top-252B
❑ 74OPC-78
❑ 74Top-78
❑ 75RedSox1T-15
Gilbert, Angelo
❑ 80BatTroT-1
❑ 82IdaFalAT-8
Gilbert, Billy (William O.)
❑ 03BreE10-56
❑ 06GiaUIIAFS-5
❑ 08RosComP-164
❑ 09PC7HHB-15
❑ 09T206-142
❑ 11SpoLifCW-142
Gilbert, Brent
❑ 90TamYanD-9
❑ 91PriWilCC-1
❑ 91PriWilCP-1417
Gilbert, Buddy (Drew E.)
❑ 58RedEnq-14
❑ 59RedEnq-8
❑ 60HenHouW-16
❑ 60SeaPop-4
❑ 60Top-359
❑ 60UniOil-6
Gilbert, Charlie (Charles M.)
❑ 29ExhFou-16
❑ 40DodTeal-10
❑ 41CubTeal-7
❑ 42CubTeal-6
❑ 90DodTar-280
❑ 91JesHSA-2
Gilbert, Dennis
❑ 80ElPasDT-2
❑ 81HolMilT-10
❑ 82HolMilT-21
❑ 83RedPioT-11
Gilbert, Donald
❑ 92KanCouCC-4
❑ 92KanCouCF-97
❑ 92KanCouCTI-10
Gilbert, Greg
❑ 84EveGiaC-6A
❑ 85FreGiaSB-10
❑ 86FreGiaSB-7
❑ 87AncGlaP-13
❑ 87IdaFalBP-15
❑ 88SumBraP-405
Gilbert, Jeff
❑ 83SanJosBC-21
❑ 84ChaO'sT-18
❑ 85ChaO'sT-20
Gilbert, Larry (Lawrence W.)
❑ 16FleBreD-31
❑ 80BraTCM1-6
Gilbert, Mark
❑ 79QuaCitCT-12
❑ 80WatRedT-14
❑ 81WatRedT-19
❑ 82WatRedT-18
❑ 83IndIndTI-22
❑ 84WicAerRD-12
❑ 85BufBisT-13
Gilbert, Pat
❑ 86MedA'sC-59
❑ 87MadMusP-7
❑ 87MadMusP-7
❑ 88ModA'sCLC-79
❑ 88ModA'sTI-26
❑ 89HunStaB-21
Gilbert, Pete
❑ 90DodTar-958
Gilbert, Robbie
❑ 86MedA'sC-62
Gilbert, Roy
❑ 89FreKeyS-7
❑ 90FreKeyTI-14
❑ 91FreKeyP-2379
❑ 91LinDriAA-230
Gilbert, Shawn
❑ 86AncGlaPTI-11
❑ 88MidLeaAGS-32
❑ 88VisOakCLC-151
❑ 88VisOakP-91
❑ 89VisOakCLC-104
❑ 89VisOakP-1439
❑ 90Bes-88
❑ 90CMC-750
❑ 90OrlSunRB-4
❑ 90OrlSunRP-1089
❑ 90OrlSunRS-6
❑ 91LinDriAA-481
❑ 91OrlSunRLD-481
❑ 91OrlSunRP-1856
❑ 92PorBeaF-2672
❑ 92PorBeaS-406
❑ 92SkyAAAF-186
❑ 93NasSouF-577
❑ 93WhiSoxSC-30
❑ 94ScrRedBF-924
❑ 95ScrRedBTI-11
❑ 96NorTidB-16
❑ 97NorTid-14
❑ 97NorTidB-14
❑ 98NorTidP-11
❑ 98NorTidQ-12
❑ 98PacInvGems-182
Gilbert, Tookie (Harold)
❑ 50Bow-235
❑ 52MotCoo-31
❑ 52Top-61
❑ 83TopRep5-61
❑ 91JesHSA-5
Gilbert, Wally (Walter John)
❑ 90DodTar-959
❑ 92ConTSN-404
Gilbreath, Rod
❑ 74OPC-93
❑ 74Top-93
❑ 75AtlBraP-14
❑ 75OPC-431
❑ 75Top-431
❑ 75TopMin-431
❑ 76AtlBraP-13
❑ 76OPC-306
❑ 76SSP-10
❑ 76Top-306
❑ 77Top-126
❑ 78BraCok-5
❑ 78Top-217
❑ 79OPC-296
❑ 79PorBeaT-24
❑ 79Top-572
❑ 80PorBeaT-22
❑ 87IdaFalBP-9
Gilchrist, John
❑ 88EugEmeB-24
❑ 89EugEmeB-22
❑ 90AppFoxBS-9
❑ 90AppFoxP-2108
❑ 91BasCitRC-24
❑ 91BasCitRP-1410
Gilcrease, Doug
❑ 84MemChiT-19
❑ 85Ft.MyeRT-17
❑ 86MemChiSTOS-8
❑ 86MemChiTOS-8
Gilday, Bill (William)
❑ 52LavPro-75
Gilder, Ray
❑ 22Zee-150
❑ 23Zee-184
Gile, Don
❑ 61Top-236
❑ 62Top-244
❑ 63SeaPop-1
❑ 81RedSoxBG2S-22
Gile, Mark
❑ 83TriTriT-16
❑ 85TulDriTI-10
Giles, Brian Jeffrey
❑ 81TidTidT-4
❑ 82MetPhoA-27
❑ 82TidTidT-8
❑ 83Fle-544
❑ 83Top-548
❑ 83TopSti-322
❑ 84Don-563
❑ 84Fle-585
❑ 84JacMetF-5
❑ 84Nes792-676
❑ 84OPC-324
❑ 84TidTidT-24
❑ 84Top-676
❑ 84TopSti-111
❑ 84TopTif-676
❑ 85BrePol-26
❑ 87HawIsIP-8
❑ 88CalCanC-15
❑ 88CalCanP-784
❑ 89BlaYNPRWL-190
❑ 89ColSprSSC-13
❑ 89ColSprSSP-253
❑ 91MetWIZ-140
❑ 94BreMilB-223
Giles, Brian Stephen
❑ 90WatIndS-9
❑ 91CarLeaAP-CAR15
❑ 91Cla/Bes-16
❑ 91KinIndC-26
❑ 91KinIndP-338
❑ 92CanIndF-701
❑ 92CanIndS-108
❑ 92ClaFS7-38
❑ 92ProFS7-56
❑ 92SkyAA F-50
❑ 93CanIndF-2848
❑ 94ChaKniF-907
❑ 94UppDecML-27
❑ 95UppDecML-120
❑ 95UppDecMLFS-120
❑ 96BufBisB-8
❑ 96SigRooOJ-11
❑ 96SigRooOJS-11
❑ 97Cir-173
❑ 97CirRav-173
❑ 97ColCho-27
❑ 97ColChoT-CI1
❑ 97Don-166
❑ 97DonGolPP-166
❑ 97DonLim-174
❑ 97DonLimE-174
❑ 97DonLimENG-174
❑ 97DonPre-156
❑ 97DonPreCttC-156
❑ 97DonSigA-38
❑ 97DonSigAC-46
❑ 97DonSigAM-46
❑ 97DonSilPP-166
❑ 97DonTea-80
❑ 97DonTeaSPE-80
❑ 97Fin-206
❑ 97FinRef-206
❑ 97FlaShoLC-65
❑ 97FlaShoLeg0-65
❑ 97FlaShoLeg1-65
❑ 97FlaShoM-A65
❑ 97FlaShoM-B65
❑ 97FlaShoM-C65
❑ 97FlaShoR0-65
❑ 97FlaShoR1-65
❑ 97FlaShoR2-65
❑ 97Fle-78
❑ 97FleTif-78
❑ 97IndSco-15
❑ 97IndScoPl-15
❑ 97IndScoPr-15
❑ 97IndScoU-15
❑ 97IndScoUTC-15
❑ 97Lea-173
❑ 97LeaFraM-173
❑ 97LeaFraMDC-173
❑ 97NewPin-176
❑ 97NewPinAP-176
❑ 97NewPinMC-176
❑ 97NewPinPP-176
❑ 97Pac-69
❑ 97PacLigB-69
❑ 97PacSil-69
❑ 97PinCer-109
❑ 97PinCerMBla-109
❑ 97PinCerMBlu-109
❑ 97PinCerMG-109
❑ 97PinCerMR-109
❑ 97PinCerR-109
❑ 97PinTotCPB-109
❑ 97PinTotCPG-109
❑ 97PinTotCPR-109
❑ 97PinX-P-129
❑ 97PinX-PMoS-129
❑ 97Sco-309
❑ 97ScoArtPWB-309
❑ 97ScoPreS-309
❑ 97ScoShoS-309
❑ 97ScoShoSAP-309
❑ 97StaClu-139
❑ 97StaCluMOP-139
❑ 97Stu-145
❑ 97StuPrePG-145
❑ 97StuPrePS-145
❑ 97Ult-354
❑ 97UltGolME-354
❑ 97UltGolP-6
❑ 97UltPlaME-354
❑ 97UppDec-236
❑ 98Bow-273
❑ 98BowChr-273
❑ 98BowChrGA-273
❑ 98BowChrGAR-273
❑ 98BowChrI-273
❑ 98BowChrIR-273
❑ 98BowChrR-273
❑ 98BowGolA-273
❑ 98BowInt-273
❑ 98CirThu-177
❑ 98CirThuRav-177
❑ 98CirThuSupRav-177
❑ 98ColCho-77
❑ 98Don-92
❑ 98DonCol-92
❑ 98DonColL-253
❑ 98DonColP-683
❑ 98DonColS-92
❑ 98DonGolPP-92
❑ 98DonPre-133
❑ 98DonPreSeat-133
❑ 98DonPriCD-92
❑ 98DonPriCL-253
❑ 98DonPriCP-683
❑ 98DonSilPP-92
❑ 98Fin-44
❑ 98FinNo--44
❑ 98FinNo-R-44
❑ 98FinRef-44
❑ 98Fle-202
❑ 98IndSco-6
❑ 98IndScoP-6
❑ 98Lea-54
❑ 98LeaFraDA-54
❑ 98LeaFraF-54
❑ 98LeaFraM-54
❑ 98LeaFraM-54
❑ 98LeaFraMDC-54
❑ 98LeaFraMDC-54
❑ 98LeaFraMZ2-54
❑ 98LeaRS-117
❑ 98LeaRSLHolo-117
❑ 98LeaRSLong-117
❑ 98LeaRTrue-117
❑ 98Pac-69
❑ 98PacOmeP-6
❑ 98PacOnl-219
❑ 98PacOnlR-219
❑ 98PacOnlWC-219
❑ 98PacPlaB-69
❑ 98PacRedT-69

- ❑ 98PacSil-69
- ❑ 98PinSna-Cl4
- ❑ 98PinSna-Cl8
- ❑ 98Sco-54
- ❑ 98ScoRT-116
- ❑ 98ScoSS-PP18
- ❑ 98ScoSSAP-PP18
- ❑ 98SkyDugA-102
- ❑ 98SkyDugAIA-102
- ❑ 98SPxFin-18
- ❑ 98SPxFinR-18
- ❑ 98SPxFinS-18
- ❑ 98StaCluFDI-147
- ❑ 98StaClul-147
- ❑ 98StaCluOneK-147
- ❑ 98StaCluPP-147
- ❑ 98Top-190
- ❑ 98TopChr-190
- ❑ 98TopChrR-190
- ❑ 98TopDevR-190
- ❑ 98TopDia-190
- ❑ 98TopMiniC-190
- ❑ 98UppDec-73
- ❑ 98UppDecBCP-BC26
- ❑ 98UppDecSF-44
- ❑ 99Bow-237
- ❑ 99BowGol-237
- ❑ 99BowInt-237
- ❑ 99CroRoyB-109
- ❑ 99CroRoyL-109
- ❑ 99CroRoyOD-109
- ❑ 99E-X Cen-75
- ❑ 99E-X CenECFut-75
- ❑ 99E-X CenECNow-75
- ❑ 99FlaShoLeg1-101
- ❑ 99FlaShoLeg2-101
- ❑ 99FlaShoLeg3-101
- ❑ 99FlaShoLegM1-101
- ❑ 99FlaShoLegM2-101
- ❑ 99FlaShoLegM3-101
- ❑ 99FlaShoR1-101
- ❑ 99FlaShoR2-101
- ❑ 99FlaShoR3-101
- ❑ 99Fle-122
- ❑ 99FleBri-123
- ❑ 99FleBri2G-123
- ❑ 99FleBriBlu-123
- ❑ 99FleBriGol-123
- ❑ 99FleMys-19
- ❑ 99FleMysG-19
- ❑ 99FleMysM-19
- ❑ 99FleSta9-122
- ❑ 99FleWarT-122
- ❑ 99Pac-127
- ❑ 99PacAur-146
- ❑ 99PacAurOD-146
- ❑ 99PacInv-114
- ❑ 99PacInvOD-114
- ❑ 99PacInvPB-114
- ❑ 99PacOme-186
- ❑ 99PacOmeC-186
- ❑ 99PacOmeG-186
- ❑ 99PacOmePB-186
- ❑ 99PacPar-184
- ❑ 99PacParC-184
- ❑ 99PacParG-184
- ❑ 99PacParHoloGold-184
- ❑ 99PacParHS-184
- ❑ 99PacParOD-184
- ❑ 99PacParPB-184
- ❑ 99PacParRed-184
- ❑ 99PacPlaB-127
- ❑ 99PacRed-127
- ❑ 99Rev-110
- ❑ 99RevPremDate-110
- ❑ 99RevRet-110
- ❑ 99RevShaSS-110
- ❑ 99SkyPre-35
- ❑ 99SkyPreR-35
- ❑ 99SkyThu-54
- ❑ 99SkyThuRant-54
- ❑ 99SkyThuRave-54
- ❑ 99ThuSkySupR-54
- ❑ 99Top-161
- ❑ 99TopChr-161
- ❑ 99TopChrR-161
- ❑ 99TopMVPP-161
- ❑ 99UppDec-80
- ❑ 99UppDec-461
- ❑ 99UppDecE-72
- ❑ 99UppDecEFXG-72
- ❑ 99UppDecEL1-80
- ❑ 99UppDecEL1-461
- ❑ 99UppDecEL2-80
- ❑ 99UppDecEL2-461
- ❑ 99UppDecM-168
- ❑ 99UppDecMGS-168
- ❑ 99UppDecMHFS-168
- ❑ 99UppDecMSS-168
- ❑ 99Vic-306

Giles, George

- ❑ 86NegLeaF-51
- ❑ 87NegLeaPD-44
- ❑ 89NegLeaRP-5
- ❑ 91NegLeaRL-1
- ❑ 92NegLeaRLI-22
- ❑ 95NegLeaLI-1

Giles, Marcus

- ❑ 97DanBraB-18
- ❑ 98MacBraM-9
- ❑ 99BasAmeTPLM-5
- ❑ 99Bow-365
- ❑ 99BowGol-365
- ❑ 99BowInt-365
- ❑ 99JustheS-22
- ❑ 99JustheSJB-22
- ❑ 99JustheSJN-2
- ❑ 99JustheSJP-5
- ❑ 99SP TopP-50
- ❑ 99SP TopPPE-50
- ❑ 99TeaBesR-4

Giles, Tim

- ❑ 96MedHatBJTI-8
- ❑ 97HagSunB-14
- ❑ 98DunBluJSB-3
- ❑ 98DunBluJTI-9

Giles, Troy

- ❑ 87QuaCitAP-2
- ❑ 87SalAngP-4
- ❑ 88QuaCitAGS-15
- ❑ 89PalSprACLC-32
- ❑ 89PalSprAP-473

Giles, Warren

- ❑ 56Top-2
- ❑ 57Top-100
- ❑ 58Top-300
- ❑ 59Top-200
- ❑ 60Fle-73
- ❑ 61Fle-33
- ❑ 78DexHaloFP-18
- ❑ 80PerHaloFP-167
- ❑ 80SSPHOF-167
- ❑ 82OhiHaloF-17
- ❑ 84WilMay-27
- ❑ 89HOFStiB-92

Gilevich, Darryl

- ❑ 90LSUTigA-12

Gilfillan, Jason

- ❑ 97SpoIndG-10

Gilhooley, Frank

- ❑ 16FleBreD-32
- ❑ 17ColE13-59
- ❑ 22KolMotBPP-11

Gilkey, Bernard (Otis Bernard)

- ❑ 87SprCarB-25
- ❑ 88SprCarB-13
- ❑ 89ArkTraGS-6
- ❑ 90CMC-109
- ❑ 90Lea-353
- ❑ 90LouRedBC-9
- ❑ 90LouRedBLBC-2
- ❑ 90LouRedBLBC-18
- ❑ 90LouRedBP-415
- ❑ 90ProAAAF-529
- ❑ 90ScoRoo-106T
- ❑ 90TopTVCa-50
- ❑ 90TriAllGP-AAA19
- ❑ 91Bow-408
- ❑ 91CarPol-23
- ❑ 91Cla1-T93
- ❑ 91ClaGam-165
- ❑ 91Don-30
- ❑ 91Fle-633
- ❑ 91Lea-286
- ❑ 91LouRedTI-23
- ❑ 91OPC-126
- ❑ 91OPCPre-51
- ❑ 91Sco-709
- ❑ 91ScoRoo-11
- ❑ 91StaClu-402
- ❑ 91Stu-231
- ❑ 91Top-126
- ❑ 91TopDeb90-53
- ❑ 91TopDesS-126
- ❑ 91TopMic-126
- ❑ 91TopTif-126
- ❑ 91UppDec-16
- ❑ 92Bow-403
- ❑ 92CarPol-6
- ❑ 92Don-376
- ❑ 92Fle-578
- ❑ 92Lea-502
- ❑ 92LeaBlaG-502
- ❑ 92OPC-746
- ❑ 92Pin-88
- ❑ 92Sco-544
- ❑ 92Sco100RS-24
- ❑ 92ScoProP-22
- ❑ 92StaClu-234
- ❑ 92Top-746
- ❑ 92TopGol-746
- ❑ 92TopGolW-746
- ❑ 92TopMic-746
- ❑ 92Ult-567
- ❑ 92UppDec-552
- ❑ 93Bow-684
- ❑ 93CarPol-6
- ❑ 93CarStaC-3
- ❑ 93Don-284
- ❑ 93Fla-120
- ❑ 93Fle-125
- ❑ 93Lea-99
- ❑ 93OPC-61
- ❑ 93PacSpa-294
- ❑ 93PanSti-197
- ❑ 93Pin-88
- ❑ 93Pin-304
- ❑ 93Sco-81
- ❑ 93Sel-173
- ❑ 93SP-74
- ❑ 93StaClu-230
- ❑ 93StaCluFDI-230
- ❑ 93StaCluMOP-230
- ❑ 93Stu-7
- ❑ 93Top-203
- ❑ 93TopGol-203
- ❑ 93TopInaM-203
- ❑ 93TopInaR-203
- ❑ 93TopMic-203
- ❑ 93Toy-81
- ❑ 93TriPla-208
- ❑ 93Ult-106
- ❑ 93UppDec-394
- ❑ 93UppDec-482
- ❑ 93UppDecGold-394
- ❑ 93UppDecGold-482
- ❑ 94Bow-592
- ❑ 94CarPol-5
- ❑ 94ColC-109
- ❑ 94ColChoGS-109
- ❑ 94ColChoSS-109
- ❑ 94Don-90
- ❑ 94Fin-111
- ❑ 94FinRef-111
- ❑ 94Fla-428
- ❑ 94Fle-631
- ❑ 94FleExtB-358
- ❑ 94Lea-152
- ❑ 94LeaL-144
- ❑ 94Pac-590
- ❑ 94PanSti-242
- ❑ 94Pin-79
- ❑ 94PinArtP-79
- ❑ 94PinMusC-79
- ❑ 94PinRunC-RC42
- ❑ 94Sco-420
- ❑ 94ScoGolR-420
- ❑ 94Sel-20
- ❑ 94SP-62
- ❑ 94SPDieC-62
- ❑ 94Spo-140
- ❑ 94StaClu-231
- ❑ 94StaCluFDI-231
- ❑ 94StaCluGR-231
- ❑ 94StaCluMOP-231
- ❑ 94StaCluT-316
- ❑ 94StaCluTFDI-316
- ❑ 94Stu-50
- ❑ 94Top-377
- ❑ 94TopGol-377
- ❑ 94TopSpa-377
- ❑ 94TriPla-61
- ❑ 94Ult-565
- ❑ 94UppDec-406
- ❑ 94UppDecED-406
- ❑ 95ColCho-191
- ❑ 95ColChoGS-191
- ❑ 95ColChoSE-76
- ❑ 95ColChoSEGS-76
- ❑ 95ColChoSESS-76
- ❑ 95ColChoSS-191
- ❑ 95Don-379
- ❑ 95DonPreP-379
- ❑ 95DonTopotO-326
- ❑ 95Emo-179
- ❑ 95Fin-318
- ❑ 95FinRef-318
- ❑ 95Fla-192
- ❑ 95Fle-497
- ❑ 95Lea-239
- ❑ 95LeaLim-187
- ❑ 95Pac-406
- ❑ 95Pin-62
- ❑ 95PinArtP-62
- ❑ 95PinMusC-62
- ❑ 95Sco-485
- ❑ 95ScoGolR-485
- ❑ 95ScoPlaTS-485
- ❑ 95Sel-13
- ❑ 95SelArtP-13
- ❑ 95SelCer-15
- ❑ 95SelCerMG-15
- ❑ 95SP-98
- ❑ 95SPCha-86
- ❑ 95SPChaDC-86
- ❑ 95Spo-12
- ❑ 95SpoArtP-12
- ❑ 95SPSil-98
- ❑ 95StaClu-190
- ❑ 95StaCluFDI-190
- ❑ 95StaCluMOP-190
- ❑ 95StaCluSTWS-190
- ❑ 95Stu-68
- ❑ 95Sum-81
- ❑ 95SumNthD-81
- ❑ 95Top-547
- ❑ 95TopCyb-328
- ❑ 95Ult-222
- ❑ 95UltGolM-222
- ❑ 95UppDec-303
- ❑ 95UppDecED-303
- ❑ 95UppDecEDG-303
- ❑ 95UppDecSE-89
- ❑ 95UppDecSEG-89
- ❑ 95Zen-7
- ❑ 96Cir-156
- ❑ 96CirRav-156
- ❑ 96ColCho-288
- ❑ 96ColCho-620
- ❑ 96ColChoGS-288
- ❑ 96ColChoGS-620
- ❑ 96ColChoSS-288
- ❑ 96ColChoSS-620
- ❑ 96Don-49
- ❑ 96DonPreP-49
- ❑ 96EmoXL-231
- ❑ 96Fin-S231
- ❑ 96FinRef-S231
- ❑ 96Fla-319
- ❑ 96Fle-543
- ❑ 96FleTif-543
- ❑ 96FleUpd-U156
- ❑ 96FleUpdTC-U156
- ❑ 96LeaPre-108
- ❑ 96LeaPreP-108
- ❑ 96MetKah-10
- ❑ 96MetUni-225
- ❑ 96MetUniP-225
- ❑ 96Pac-216
- ❑ 96PacPri-P69
- ❑ 96PacPriG-P69
- ❑ 96PanSti-75
- ❑ 96Pin-346
- ❑ 96PinAfi-76
- ❑ 96PinAfiAP-76
- ❑ 96PinAfiFPP-76
- ❑ 96PinFoil-346
- ❑ 96ProSta-34
- ❑ 96Sco-32
- ❑ 96ScoDugC-A31
- ❑ 96ScoDugCAP-A31
- ❑ 96Sel-143
- ❑ 96SelArtP-143
- ❑ 96SP-127
- ❑ 96StaClu-32
- ❑ 96StaCluEPB-32
- ❑ 96StaCluEPG-32
- ❑ 96StaCluEPS-32
- ❑ 96StaCluMOP-32
- ❑ 96Stu-19
- ❑ 96StuPrePB-19
- ❑ 96StuPrePG-19
- ❑ 96StuPrePS-19
- ❑ 96Sum-132
- ❑ 96SumAbo&B-132
- ❑ 96SumArtP-132
- ❑ 96SumFoi-132
- ❑ 96TeaOut-28
- ❑ 96Top-256
- ❑ 96TopChr-101
- ❑ 96TopChrR-101
- ❑ 96Ult-273
- ❑ 96Ult-512
- ❑ 96UltGolM-273
- ❑ 96UltGolM-512
- ❑ 96UppDec-183
- ❑ 96UppDec-402
- ❑ 97Bow-11
- ❑ 97BowBes-47
- ❑ 97BowBesAR-47
- ❑ 97BowBesR-47
- ❑ 97BowInt-11
- ❑ 97Cir-317
- ❑ 97CirRav-317
- ❑ 97ColCho-170
- ❑ 97ColChoAC-43
- ❑ 97Don-96
- ❑ 97DonGolPP-96
- ❑ 97DonLim-42
- ❑ 97DonLimE-42
- ❑ 97DonLimENG-42
- ❑ 97DonPre-16
- ❑ 97DonPreCttC-16
- ❑ 97DonSilPP-96
- ❑ 97Fin-226
- ❑ 97FinRef-226
- ❑ 97FlaShoLC-83
- ❑ 97FlaShoLeg0-83
- ❑ 97FlaShoLeg1-83
- ❑ 97FlaShoM-A83
- ❑ 97FlaShoM-B83
- ❑ 97FlaShoM-C83
- ❑ 97FlaShoR0-83
- ❑ 97FlaShoR1-83
- ❑ 97FlaShoR2-83
- ❑ 97Fle-395
- ❑ 97FleTif-395
- ❑ 97Lea-113
- ❑ 97LeaFraM-113
- ❑ 97LeaFraMDC-113
- ❑ 97MetUni-193
- ❑ 97NewPin-17
- ❑ 97NewPinAP-17
- ❑ 97NewPinMC-17
- ❑ 97NewPinPP-17
- ❑ 97Pac-364
- ❑ 97PacLigB-364
- ❑ 97PacPri-123
- ❑ 97PacPriLB-123
- ❑ 97PacPriP-123
- ❑ 97PacSil-364
- ❑ 97PinCer-20
- ❑ 97PinCerMBla-20
- ❑ 97PinCerMBlu-20
- ❑ 97PinCerMG-20
- ❑ 97PinCerMR-20
- ❑ 97PinCerR-20
- ❑ 97PinTotCPB-20
- ❑ 97PinTotCPG-20
- ❑ 97PinTotCPR-20
- ❑ 97PinX-P-67
- ❑ 97PinX-PMoS-67
- ❑ 97PinX-PSfF-24
- ❑ 97PinX-PSfFU-24
- ❑ 97Sco-109
- ❑ 97ScoArtPWB-109
- ❑ 97ScoPreS-109
- ❑ 97ScoShoS-109
- ❑ 97ScoShoSAP-109
- ❑ 97SP-119
- ❑ 97SpoIll-89
- ❑ 97SpoIllEE-89
- ❑ 97StaClu-26
- ❑ 97StaCluMat-26
- ❑ 97StaCluMOP-26
- ❑ 97Top-160
- ❑ 97TopChr-63
- ❑ 97TopChrR-63
- ❑ 97TopGal-66
- ❑ 97TopGalPPI-66
- ❑ 97Ult-238
- ❑ 97UltGolME-238
- ❑ 97UltPlaME-238
- ❑ 97UppDec-115
- ❑ 97UppDecHTH-HT3
- ❑ 98CirThu-79
- ❑ 98CirThuRav-79
- ❑ 98CirThuSupRav-79
- ❑ 98ColCho-442
- ❑ 98Don-187
- ❑ 98DonGolPP-187
- ❑ 98DonSilPP-187
- ❑ 98Fin-208
- ❑ 98FinNo--208
- ❑ 98FinNo-R-208
- ❑ 98FinRef-208
- ❑ 98FlaShoLeg0-111
- ❑ 98FlaShoLeg1-111
- ❑ 98FlaShoLeg2-111
- ❑ 98FlaShoLeg3-111
- ❑ 98FlaShoLegM-111
- ❑ 98FlaShoR0-111
- ❑ 98FlaShoR1-111
- ❑ 98FlaShoR2-111
- ❑ 98FlaShoR3-111
- ❑ 98Fle-537
- ❑ 98FleVin'-105
- ❑ 98FleVin'C-105
- ❑ 98Pac-365
- ❑ 98PacOme-155
- ❑ 98PacOmeR-155
- ❑ 98PacOnl-477
- ❑ 98PacOnlR-477
- ❑ 98PacOnlWC-477
- ❑ 98PacPar-203
- ❑ 98PacParC-203
- ❑ 98PacParG-203
- ❑ 98PacParHS-203
- ❑ 98PacParPB-203
- ❑ 98PacParR-203
- ❑ 98PacPlaB-365
- ❑ 98PacRedT-365
- ❑ 98PacSil-365
- ❑ 98PinIns-107
- ❑ 98PinInsCE-107
- ❑ 98PinInsDE-107
- ❑ 98PinPlu-45
- ❑ 98PinSna-NYM5
- ❑ 98Revo-92
- ❑ 98RevoSS-92
- ❑ 98ScoRT-155
- ❑ 98SkyDugA-33
- ❑ 98SkyDugAIA-33
- ❑ 98SPxFin-302
- ❑ 98SPxFinR-302
- ❑ 98SPxFinS-302
- ❑ 98StaCluFDI-293
- ❑ 98StaClul-293
- ❑ 98StaCluOneK-293
- ❑ 98StaCluPP-293
- ❑ 98Top-153
- ❑ 98TopChr-153
- ❑ 98TopChrR-153
- ❑ 98TopDevR-153
- ❑ 98TopDia-153
- ❑ 98TopGal-32
- ❑ 98TopGalGP-32
- ❑ 98TopGalOPP-32
- ❑ 98TopGalPPI-32
- ❑ 98TopGalPPIA-32
- ❑ 98TopMiniC-153
- ❑ 98TopOpeD-80
- ❑ 98TopSta-23
- ❑ 98TopStaB-23
- ❑ 98TopStaG-23
- ❑ 98TopStaGR-23
- ❑ 98TopStaS-23
- ❑ 98Ult-284
- ❑ 98UltGolM-284
- ❑ 98UltMas-284
- ❑ 98UltPlaM-284
- ❑ 98UppDec-445
- ❑ 98Zen-52
- ❑ 98Zen5 xx7-57
- ❑ 98Zen5x7GoldImp-57
- ❑ 98Zen5x7Imp-57
- ❑ 98ZenZ-G-52
- ❑ 98ZenZ-S-52
- ❑ 99FlaShoLeg1-93
- ❑ 99FlaShoLeg2-93
- ❑ 99FlaShoLeg3-93
- ❑ 99FlaShoLegM1-93
- ❑ 99FlaShoLegM2-93
- ❑ 99FlaShoLegM3-93
- ❑ 99FlaShoR1-93
- ❑ 99FlaShoR2-93
- ❑ 99FlaShoR3-93
- ❑ 99Fle-402
- ❑ 99FleSta9-402
- ❑ 99FleWarT-402
- ❑ 99Pac-21
- ❑ 99PacAur-10
- ❑ 99PacAurOD-10
- ❑ 99PacPlaB-21
- ❑ 99PacRed-21
- ❑ 99StaClu-188
- ❑ 99StaCluFDI-188
- ❑ 99StaCluOoaK-188
- ❑ 99StaCluPP-188
- ❑ 99Top-323
- ❑ 99TopChr-323
- ❑ 99TopChrR-323
- ❑ 99TopMVPP-323
- ❑ 99Vic-22

Gilks, Robert

❑ 87OldJudN-199
Gill, Chris
❑ 89BilMusP-2046
❑ 90Bes-141
❑ 90ChaWheB-15
❑ 90ChaWheP-2246
❑ 91ChaWheC-17
❑ 91ChaWheP-2894
Gill, John
❑ 36CubTeal-10
❑ 36SandSW-24
❑ 37Zee-72
❑ 45CenFlo-10
Gill, Ken
❑ 73TacTwiC-9
Gill, Ron
❑ 77LynMetT-13
Gill, Shawn
❑ 82IdaFalAT-14
❑ 83MadMusF-11
❑ 84MadMusP-17
Gill, Sheldon
❑ 75ForLauYS-20
Gill, Steve
❑ 90AriWilP-6
❑ 91WatDiaC-21
❑ 91WatDiaP-1268
❑ 92HigDesMC-2
❑ 93El PasDF-2963
❑ 94WesPalBEC-10
❑ 94WesPalBEF-54
Gill, Turner
❑ 87WilBilP-25
❑ 88WilBilP-1312
Gill, Warren
❑ 13Zee-8
Gillaspie, Mark
❑ 83BeaGolGT-15
❑ 84BeaGolGT-5
❑ 85IowCubT-22
❑ 88MemChiB-13
Gilleaudeau, Joseph
❑ 94ConTSN-1112
❑ 94ConTSNB-1112
Gilleaudeau, Mrs. (Joseph)
❑ 94ConTSN-1112
❑ 94ConTSNB-1112
Gillen, Kevin
❑ 76WatRoyT-10
❑ 77JacSunT-8
Gillenwater, Carden
❑ 50WorWidGV-32
❑ 90DodTar-960
Gilles, Bob
❑ 83VerBeaDT-15
Gilles, Mark
❑ 87KinIndP-3
❑ 88KinIndS-7
❑ 89CanIndB-13
❑ 89CanIndP-1323
❑ 89CanIndS-7
Gilles, Tom
❑ 87AppFoxP-16
❑ 88KenTwiP-1387
❑ 89KnoBluJB-7
❑ 89KnoBluJP-1143
❑ 90CMC-330
❑ 90ProAAAF-344
❑ 90SyrChiC-4
❑ 90SyrChiMB-10
❑ 90SyrChiP-564
❑ 91RenSilSCLC-16
❑ 91TopDeb90-54
Gilles, Wayne
❑ 87AriWilP-3
Gillespie, Don
❑ 89WytCubS-12
Gillespie, Eric
❑ 96BoiHawB-13
❑ 97CedRapK-8
❑ 98LakElsSG-13
❑ 99BasAmeTP-45
❑ 99BasAmeTPG-45
Gillespie, John
❑ 22E120-172
Gillespie, Mark
❑ 84IdaFalATI-9
Gillespie, Paul
❑ 47SmiClo-20
❑ 48AngTeal-10
Gillespie, Pete
❑ 86OldJudN-8
❑ 87BucN28-68A
❑ 87BucN28-68B
❑ 87FouBasHN-4
❑ 87OldJudN-200
❑ 88AugBecN-16
❑ 90KalBatN-23
Gillespie, Robert
❑ 26Zee-48
❑ 27Zee-26
❑ 48WhiSoxTI-6
❑ 49SolSunP-5
❑ 52MotCoo-21
Gillette, Mike
❑ 90FayGenP-2409
❑ 91LakTigC-15
❑ 91LakTigP-269
❑ 92LonTigF-636
❑ 92LonTigS-409
Gilliam, Bo
❑ 86DavLipB-13
❑ 92ForLauYC-18
❑ 92ForLauYTI-13
❑ 92Ft.LauYF-2627
❑ 93SanBerSC-10
Gilliam, Darryl
❑ 86BakDodP-11
❑ 86TriTriC-199
Gilliam, Ed
❑ 78BurBeeT-14
Gilliam, Junior (James)
❑ 47PM1StaP1-70
❑ 47PM1StaP1-71
❑ 47StaPinP2-15
❑ 52LaPat-5
❑ 52Par-68
❑ 53Top-258
❑ 54Bow-74
❑ 54NewYorJA-6
❑ 54RedHeaF-10
❑ 54RedMan-NL14
❑ 54Top-35
❑ 55ArmCoi-7
❑ 55BigLeaIS-7
❑ 55Bow-98
❑ 55DaiQueS-7
❑ 55DodGolS-14
❑ 55Top-5
❑ 55TopDouH-129
❑ 56Dod-11
❑ 56Top-280
❑ 57SwiFra-10
❑ 57Top-115
❑ 58DodBelB-4
❑ 58DodTeal-9
❑ 58DodVol-6
❑ 58PacBel-3
❑ 58Top-215
❑ 59DodMor-3
❑ 59DodPos-7
❑ 59DodTeal-9
❑ 59DodVol-6
❑ 59Top-306
❑ 60DodBelB-4
❑ 60DodJayP-5
❑ 60DodTeal-7
❑ 60DodUniO-7
❑ 60KeyChal-20
❑ 60Lea-18
❑ 60MacSta-9
❑ 60Top-255
❑ 60TopTat-19
❑ 61DodBelB-19
❑ 61DodJayP-3
❑ 61DodUniO-8
❑ 61Pos-158A
❑ 61Pos-158B
❑ 61Top-238
❑ 62DodBelB-19
❑ 62DodJayP-4
❑ 62DodVol-4
❑ 62Jel-112
❑ 62Pos-112
❑ 62PosCan-112
❑ 62SalPlaC-201
❑ 62ShiPlaC-201
❑ 62Top-486
❑ 63DodJayP-6
❑ 63Jel-114
❑ 63Pos-114
❑ 63Top-80
❑ 64Top-310
❑ 64TopVen-310
❑ 64WheSta-18
❑ 73OPC-569
❑ 73Top-569
❑ 74OPC-144
❑ 74Top-144
❑ 75DodTCMA-5
❑ 78TCM60I-45
❑ 79TCM50-290
❑ 80DodGreT-2
❑ 84OCoandSI-118
❑ 86NegLeaF-76
❑ 87Dod195T-6
❑ 88PacLegI-44
❑ 88WilMulP-14
❑ 90DodTar-281
❑ 91DodRinP3-10
❑ 91TopArc1-258
❑ 92BazQua5A-8
❑ 93TedWil-135
❑ 93TedWil-149
❑ 93TedWilM-2
❑ 94TopArc1-35
❑ 94TopArc1G-35
❑ 95DodROY-4
❑ 95TopArcBD-55
❑ 95TopArcBD-69
❑ 95TopArcBD-91
❑ 95TopArcBD-128
❑ 95TopArcBD-161
❑ 97NegLeaPC-11C
Gilliam, Keith
❑ 83KinBluJTI-6
❑ 85SyrChiT-7
❑ 86KnoBluJP-8
❑ 87KnoBluJP-1506
Gilliam, Melvin
❑ 80AshTouT-4
Gilliam, Sean
❑ 90CMC-705
❑ 90GreHorB-22
❑ 90GreHorP-2674
❑ 90GreHorS-3
❑ 91GreHorP-3073
❑ 93SanBerSF-784
Gillian, Charles
❑ 97ForWayW-13
Gillick, Lawrence
❑ 32Zee-86
Gilliford, Paul
❑ 77FriOneYW-40
❑ 91OriCro-156
Gilligan, Barney
❑ 87BucN28-113
❑ 87OldJudN-201
Gilligan, Jim
❑ 87SalLakTTT-11
Gilligan, John
❑ 12Zee-57
❑ 90MedHatBJB-19
❑ 91SalLakTP-3204
❑ 91SalLakTSP-12
❑ 92SalLakTSP-7
Gilligan, Larry
❑ 91JohCitCC-7
❑ 91JohCitCP-3984
❑ 92HamRedC-18
❑ 92HamRedF-1599
Gillis, Grant
❑ 28StaPlaCE-27
Gillis, Jack
❑ 91OneYanP-4168
❑ 92OneYanC-27
Gillis, Louis
❑ 92NegLeaRLI-23
Gillis, Tim
❑ 90Bes-134
❑ 90BurBraB-13
❑ 90BurBraP-2356
❑ 90BurBraS-12
❑ 91CarLeaAP-CAR1
❑ 91DurBulC-17
❑ 91DurBulP-1553
❑ 92DurBulC-11
❑ 92DurBulF-1107
❑ 92DurBulTI-18
❑ 93GreBraF-356
❑ 94GreBraF-418
❑ 94GreBraTI-10
Gills, Amy
❑ 85AncGlaPTI-35
❑ 86AncGlaPTI-12
❑ 87AncGlaP-14
Gills, Jack
❑ 87OneYanP-32
Gillum, Kenneth (K.C.)
❑ 89BilMusP-2042
❑ 90BilMusP-3237
❑ 90ChaWheP-2251
❑ 90ProAaA-196
❑ 91CedRapRC-25
❑ 91CedRapRP-2731
❑ 91Cla/Bes-369
❑ 92ChaWheF-19
❑ 92ChaWVWC-15
❑ 92ClaFS7-58
❑ 93ChaLooF-2371
❑ 93ClaFS7-191
❑ 93SouAtlLAIPI-17
❑ 93SouAtlLAPI-13
Gilmartin, Dan
❑ 78NewWayCT-17
❑ 79BurBeeT-10
❑ 82BelBreFr-18
Gilmartin, Kevin
❑ 76SeaRaiC-5
Gilmartin, Paul
❑ 76SeaRaiC-6
Gilmore, Bill
❑ 87AppFoxP-2
Gilmore, Frank T.
❑ 87OldJudN-202
Gilmore, Joel
❑ 91MarPhiP-3448
❑ 92ClaFS7-264
❑ 92ClePhiF-2051
❑ 93ClePhiC-10
❑ 93ClePhiF-2679
❑ 95ReaPhiTI-38
Gilmore, Kale
❑ 94ButCopKSP-16
Gilmore, Lenny
❑ 88BurIndP-1774
Gilmore, Matt
❑ 90BurIndP-3014
Gilmore, Quincy Jordan
❑ 87NegLeaPD-23
Gilmore, Terry
❑ 87SpoIndP-19
❑ 88TexLeaAGS-29
❑ 88WicPilRD-20
❑ 89LasVegSC-4
❑ 89LasVegSP-16
❑ 90CMC-506
❑ 90LasVegSC-4
❑ 90LasVegSP-113
❑ 90ProAAAF-1
❑ 90TriAllGP-AAA18
❑ 91LasVegSLD-282
❑ 91LasVegSP-229
❑ 91LinDriAAA-282
Gilmore, Tony
❑ 80UtiBluJT-16
Gilmore, Tony R.
❑ 90ArkRaz-13
❑ 90AubAstP-3397
❑ 91BurAstC-25
❑ 91BurAstP-2805
❑ 91Cla/Bes-325
❑ 91MidLeaAP-MWL15
❑ 92OscAstC-2
❑ 92OscAstF-2533
❑ 93JacGenF-2110
❑ 94JacGenF-220
❑ 95JacGenTI-14
Gilson, Bob
❑ 89LonTigP-1358
Gilson, Hal
❑ 68OPC-162
❑ 68Top-162
❑ 68TopVen-162
❑ 69OPC-156
❑ 69Top-156
❑ 69TopFou-2
Giminez, Issac
❑ 75CliPilT-9
Giminez, Ray
❑ 75CliPilT-10
Ging, Adam
❑ 85SpoIndC-5
❑ 87ColMetP-8
❑ 88St.LucMS-9
Ginglardi, Henry
❑ 20Zee-21
Gingrich, Gary
❑ 75WesPalBES-2
❑ 76BurBeeT-15
❑ 77BurBeeT-10
Gingrich, Jeff
❑ 79MemChiT-18
Ginsberg, Joe (Myron)
❑ 52Top-192
❑ 53BowC-6
❑ 53TigGle-10
❑ 54Bow-52
❑ 55SeaPop-7
❑ 56A'sPos-19
❑ 56BalOriP-17
❑ 56BalOriP-18
❑ 57Top-236
❑ 58Top-67
❑ 59Top-66
❑ 59TopVen-66
❑ 60Top-304
❑ 61Top-79
❑ 75TCM195CI-9
❑ 79TCM50-52
❑ 81RedSoxBG2S-23
❑ 83TopRep5-192
❑ 91MetWIZ-141
❑ 91OriCro-157
Ginter, Keith
❑ 98AubDouTI-12
❑ 99TeaBesR-30
❑ 99TeaBesRG-30
❑ 99TeaBesRS-30
Gioia, Joe
❑ 86TriTriC-194
Gionfriddo, Al
❑ 48SweSpoT-9
❑ 50WorWidGV-24
❑ 68LauWorS-44
❑ 70FleWorS-44
❑ 90DodTar-282
❑ 91DodRinP4-9
Giordano, Marc
❑ 89PriPirS-7
❑ 90MiaMirIS-9
❑ 90MiaMirIS-7
❑ 91MiaMirC-20
❑ 91MiaMirP-414
Giordano, Mike
❑ 83OrlTwiT-21
Giovanola, Ed
❑ 89AncBucTI-13
❑ 90IdaFalBP-3269
❑ 91DurBulC-14
❑ 91DurBulP-1554
❑ 92GreBraF-1159
❑ 92GreBraS-233
❑ 93GreBraF-357
❑ 94GreBraF-419
❑ 95ARuFalLS-7
❑ 95RicBraRC-3
❑ 95RicBraTI-3
❑ 96LeaSigEA-59
❑ 96RicBraB-13
❑ 96RicBraRC-12
❑ 96RicBraUB-8
❑ 97PacPriGotD-GD111
❑ 97RicBra-10
❑ 98PacOnl-635
❑ 98PacOnlR-635
❑ 98PacOnlWC-635
❑ 98PadMot-25
Gipe, Alva
❑ 11PacCoaBD-22
Gipner, Marcus
❑ 92GulCoaYF-3793
❑ 92StaCluD-60
❑ 94GreBatF-478
❑ 94OneYanC-9
❑ 94OneYanF-3793
❑ 97GreBatC-8
Gipson, Charles
❑ 93AppFoxCB-8
❑ 93AppFoxFI-2468
❑ 94RivPilCLC-10
❑ 95PorCitRTI-10
❑ 96PorCitRB-12
❑ 98TacRaiQ-13
Girardi, Joe
❑ 87WinSpiP-17
❑ 88BasAmeAAB-8
❑ 88EasLeaAP-25
❑ 88PitCubP-1359
❑ 89CubMar-7
❑ 89DonRoo-23
❑ 89Fle-644
❑ 89FleGlo-644
❑ 89ScoRoo-84T
❑ 89UppDec-776
❑ 90CubMar-8
❑ 90Don-404
❑ 90DonBesN-87
❑ 90Fle-31
❑ 90FleCan-31
❑ 90Lea-289
❑ 90OPC-12
❑ 90Sco-535
❑ 90Sco100RS-33
❑ 90ScoYouS2-29
❑ 90Top-12
❑ 90TopDeb89-42
❑ 90TopTif-12
❑ 90TopTVCu-20
❑ 90UppDec-304
❑ 91Bow-415
❑ 91CubMar-7
❑ 91CubVinL-11
❑ 91Don-184
❑ 91Fle-421
❑ 91Lea-258
❑ 91OPC-214
❑ 91PanFreS-42
❑ 91PanSti-49
❑ 91Sco-585
❑ 91StaClu-247
❑ 91Stu-156
❑ 91Top-214
❑ 91TopDesS-214
❑ 91TopMic-214
❑ 91TopTif-214
❑ 91Ult-60
❑ 91UppDec-113
❑ 92Bow-636
❑ 92CubMar-7
❑ 92Don-175
❑ 92Lea-72
❑ 92LeaBlaG-72
❑ 92OPC-529
❑ 92Pin-498
❑ 92Sco-701
❑ 92StaClu-132
❑ 92Stu-13
❑ 92Top-529
❑ 92TopGol-529
❑ 92TopGolW-529
❑ 92TopMic-529
❑ 92TriPla-151
❑ 92Ult-469
❑ 92UppDec-351
❑ 93Bow-668
❑ 93Don-736
❑ 93Fla-40
❑ 93Fle-410
❑ 93FleFinE-31
❑ 93Lea-332
❑ 93MilBonSS-18
❑ 93PacSpa-428
❑ 93Pin-236
❑ 93PinExpOD-2
❑ 93RocStaC-10
❑ 93RocUSPC-4D
❑ 93RocUSPC-13S
❑ 93Sco-419
❑ 93Sel-53
❑ 93SP-221
❑ 93StaClu-620
❑ 93StaCluFDI-620
❑ 93StaCluMOP-620
❑ 93Stu-188
❑ 93Top-425
❑ 93TopGol-425
❑ 93TopInaM-425
❑ 93TopInaR-425
❑ 93TopMic-425
❑ 93TriPla-237
❑ 93Ult-348
❑ 93UppDec-571
❑ 93UppDecGold-571
❑ 94Bow-30
❑ 94ColC-396
❑ 94ColChoGS-396
❑ 94ColChoSS-396
❑ 94Don-165
❑ 94Fin-72
❑ 94FinRef-72
❑ 94Fla-153
❑ 94Fle-441
❑ 94FleExtB-245
❑ 94Lea-3
❑ 94LeaL-103
❑ 94Pac-196
❑ 94Pin-74
❑ 94PinArtP-74
❑ 94PinMusC-74
❑ 94RocPol-10
❑ 94Sco-76
❑ 94ScoGolR-76
❑ 94Sel-70
❑ 94StaClu-323
❑ 94StaCluFDI-323
❑ 94StaCluGR-323
❑ 94StaCluMOP-323
❑ 94StaCluT-107
❑ 94StaCluTFDI-107
❑ 94Stu-178
❑ 94Top-372

❑ 94TopGol-372
❑ 94TopSpa-372
❑ 94TriPla-224
❑ 94Ult-185
❑ 94UppDec-76
❑ 94UppDecED-76
❑ 95ColCho-448
❑ 95ColChoGS-448
❑ 95ColChoSS-448
❑ 95Don-367
❑ 95DonPreP-367
❑ 95DonTopotO-228
❑ 95Fin-193
❑ 95FinRef-193
❑ 95Fla-345
❑ 95Fle-519
❑ 95Lea-159
❑ 95LeaLim-50
❑ 95Pac-137
❑ 95Pin-357
❑ 95PinArtP-357
❑ 95PinMusC-357
❑ 95RocPol-7
❑ 95Sco-95
❑ 95ScoGolR-95
❑ 95ScoPlaTS-95
❑ 95StaClu-184
❑ 95StaCluFDI-184
❑ 95StaCluMOP-184
❑ 95StaCluSTWS-184
❑ 95StaCluVR-94
❑ 95StaCluVRMO-94
❑ 95Stu-149
❑ 95Top-539
❑ 95TopCyb-321
❑ 95Ult-153
❑ 95UltGolM-153
❑ 95UppDec-409
❑ 95UppDecED-409
❑ 95UppDecEDG-409
❑ 96ColCho-132
❑ 96ColCho-632
❑ 96ColChoGS-132
❑ 96ColChoGS-632
❑ 96ColChoSS-132
❑ 96ColChoSS-632
❑ 96Don-12
❑ 96DonPreP-12
❑ 96Fin-B311
❑ 96FinRef-B311
❑ 96Fla-127
❑ 96Fle-183
❑ 96FleTif-183
❑ 96FleUpd-U60
❑ 96FleUpdTC-U60
❑ 96MetUni-86
❑ 96MetUniP-86
❑ 96MLBPin-12
❑ 96Pac-66
❑ 96Sco-104
❑ 96StaClu-83
❑ 96StaCluEPB-83
❑ 96StaCluEPG-83
❑ 96StaCluEPS-83
❑ 96StaCluMOP-83
❑ 96Top-36
❑ 96Ult-384
❑ 96UltGolM-384
❑ 96UppDec-157
❑ 97Cir-78
❑ 97CirRav-78
❑ 97ColCho-402
❑ 97ColChoT-NY8
❑ 97Don-334
❑ 97DonGolPP-334
❑ 97DonSilPP-334
❑ 97DonTea-133
❑ 97DonTeaSPE-133
❑ 97Fin-86
❑ 97FinRef-86
❑ 97Fle-165
❑ 97FleTif-165
❑ 97PacPriGotD-GD72
❑ 97Sco-464
❑ 97ScoArtPWB-464
❑ 97ScoResC-464
❑ 97ScoShoS-464
❑ 97ScoShoSAP-464
❑ 97StaClu-298
❑ 97StaCluMOP-298
❑ 97Top-291
❑ 97Ult-97
❑ 97UltGolME-97
❑ 97UltPlaME-97
❑ 97UppDec-441
❑ 98ColCho-449
❑ 98Fin-48
❑ 98FinNo--48
❑ 98FinNo-R-48
❑ 98FinRef-48
❑ 98Fle-509
❑ 98Pac-148
❑ 98PacOnl-502
❑ 98PacOnlR-502
❑ 98PacOnlWC-502
❑ 98PacPlaB-148
❑ 98PacRedT-148
❑ 98PacSil-148
❑ 98PinSna-NYY3
❑ 98ScoRT-60
❑ 98StaCluFDI-279
❑ 98StaClul-279
❑ 98StaCluOneK-279
❑ 98StaCluPP-279
❑ 98Top-122
❑ 98TopChr-122
❑ 98TopChrR-122
❑ 98TopDevR-122
❑ 98TopDia-122
❑ 98TopMiniC-122
❑ 98UppDec-463
❑ 99Fle-388
❑ 99FleSta9-388
❑ 99FleWarT-388
❑ 99Pac-291
❑ 99PacPlaB-291
❑ 99PacRed-291
❑ 99UppDec-439
❑ 99UppDecEL1-439
❑ 99UppDecEL2-439
❑ 99YanFle-7

Girdley, Josh
❑ 99Bow-432
❑ 99BowGol-432
❑ 99BowInt-432

Giron, Alejandro
❑ 98PieBolWM-15

Giron, Emiliano
❑ 94PriRedC-10
❑ 94PriRedF-3257
❑ 95Exc-176

Giron, Isabel
❑ 98HagSunM-13

Giron, Tomas
❑ 85DomLeaS-137

Giron, Ysidro
❑ 86Ft.LauYP-7
❑ 87PriWilYP-17

Girot, Leo
❑ 12Zee-58

Girouard, Mike
❑ 88SouBenWSGS-19

Girt, Bob
❑ 89AncBucTI-29

Gislason, Garde
❑ 17Zee-67

Gissell, Chris
❑ 97Bow-162
❑ 97BowInt-162
❑ 97MidLeaTP-23
❑ 97RocCub-15
❑ 98Bow-305
❑ 98BowChr-305
❑ 98BowChrGA-305
❑ 98BowChrGAR-305
❑ 98BowChrI-305
❑ 98BowChrIR-305
❑ 98BowChrR-305
❑ 98BowGolA-305
❑ 98BowInt-305
❑ 98RocCubM-10
❑ 98RocCubTI-10
❑ 99Bow-199
❑ 99BowChr-199
❑ 99BowChrG-199
❑ 99BowChrGR-199
❑ 99BowChrI-199
❑ 99BowChrIR-199
❑ 99BowChrR-199
❑ 99BowGol-199
❑ 99BowInt-199

Gisselman, Bob
❑ 82WauTimF-31

Githens, John
❑ 86WatIndP-10
❑ 87WatIndP-13
❑ 88KinIndS-8
❑ 89HagSunB-2
❑ 89HagSunP-262
❑ 89HagSunS-9

Giudice, John
❑ 93BenRocCB-8
❑ 93BenRocF-3280
❑ 94AshTouC-9
❑ 94AshTouF-1795
❑ 94SouAtlLAF-SAL29
❑ 95SalAvaTI-6
❑ 96SalAvaB-11
❑ 97NewHavRB-9
❑ 98NewHavRM-10
❑ 98NewHavRMA-10

Giuliani, Tony
❑ 35DiaMatCS3T1-60
❑ 73Dod194T-11
❑ 78DodTCM4-21
❑ 90DodTar-283

Giuliano, Joe
❑ 94SigRooDP-70
❑ 94SigRooDPS-70
❑ 94StaCluDP-34
❑ 94StaCluDPFDI-34
❑ 95DanBraTI-12
❑ 96EugEmeB-9
❑ 97BurBeeB-10
❑ 98BurBeeM-9

Giusti, Dave
❑ 62Col.45B-7
❑ 62Top-509
❑ 63Top-189
❑ 64Top-354
❑ 64TopVen-354
❑ 65Top-524
❑ 66Top-258
❑ 66TopVen-258
❑ 67Ast-10
❑ 67AstTeal1-5
❑ 67AstTeal2-12
❑ 67CokCapAs-1
❑ 67DexPre-79
❑ 67Top-318
❑ 68CokCapA-1
❑ 68DexPre-36
❑ 68OPC-182
❑ 68Top-182
❑ 68TopVen-182
❑ 69MilBra-93
❑ 69OPC-98
❑ 69PirJacitB-4
❑ 69Top-98
❑ 69TopSta-95
❑ 70OPC-372
❑ 70Top-372
❑ 71MLBOffS-202
❑ 71OPC-562
❑ 71PirActP-16
❑ 71PirArc-4
❑ 71Top-562
❑ 72MilBra-116
❑ 72OPC-190
❑ 72Top-190
❑ 73LinPor-149
❑ 73OPC-465
❑ 73Top-465
❑ 74OPC-82
❑ 74Top-82
❑ 74TopSta-83
❑ 75OPC-53
❑ 75PitPirP-6
❑ 75Top-53
❑ 75TopMin-53
❑ 76OPC-352
❑ 76PirPos-3
❑ 76SSP-565
❑ 76Top-352
❑ 77Top-154
❑ 87AstSer1-11
❑ 87AstShoSO-8
❑ 89AstCol4S-3
❑ 89SweBasG-58

Giustino, Gerard
❑ 89SalLakTTI-26

Givens, Brian
❑ 85LitFalMT-5
❑ 86ColMetP-11A
❑ 86ColMetP-11B
❑ 87LynMetP-28
❑ 87MetColP-33
❑ 88JacMetGS-14
❑ 89JacMetGS-27
❑ 89MetColP-31
❑ 90CMC-355
❑ 90ProAAAF-268
❑ 90TidTidC-4
❑ 90TidTidP-537
❑ 93MemChiF-369
❑ 94BirBarC-10
❑ 94BirBarF-616
❑ 96Top-102

Givens, James
❑ 91BriTigC-1
❑ 91BriTigP-3613
❑ 92ClaFS7-165
❑ 92LakTigC-22
❑ 92LakTigF-2285
❑ 93ClaGolF-162
❑ 93LonTigF-2314
❑ 94TolMudHF-1031
❑ 95TolMudHTI-13

Givins, Steve
❑ 93IdaFalBF-4051

Givler, Doug
❑ 87ChaLooB-9
❑ 88ColAstB-7
❑ 89ColMudB-11
❑ 89ColMudP-124
❑ 89ColMudS-11

Gjesdal, Brent
❑ 86BeaGolGP-12

Glabman, Barry
❑ 76DubPacT-12

Gladd, Jim
❑ 52MotCoo-54
❑ 53MotCoo-29

Gladden, Danny (Dan)
❑ 81ShrCapT-9
❑ 82PhoGiaVNB-22
❑ 83PhoGiaBHN-8
❑ 84PhoGiaC-17
❑ 85Don-567
❑ 85Fle-607
❑ 85FleStaS-118
❑ 85GiaMot-3
❑ 85GiaPos-10
❑ 85Lea-30
❑ 85Top-386
❑ 85TopSti-166
❑ 85TopSti-374
❑ 85TopTif-386
❑ 86BasStaB-47
❑ 86Don-187
❑ 86Fle-541
❑ 86GiaMot-3
❑ 86GiaPos-12
❑ 86OPC-336
❑ 86Top-678
❑ 86TopSti-90
❑ 86TopTif-678
❑ 87Don-189
❑ 87DonOpeD-224
❑ 87Fle-274
❑ 87FleGlo-274
❑ 87FleUpd-36
❑ 87FleUpdG-36
❑ 87OPC-46
❑ 87Top-46
❑ 87TopSti-93
❑ 87TopTif-46
❑ 87TopTra-38T
❑ 87TopTraT-38T
❑ 87TwiPos-10
❑ 87TwiTeal-21
❑ 88Don-491
❑ 88DonBasB-130
❑ 88Fle-12
❑ 88FleGlo-12
❑ 88FleGlo-WS1
❑ 88FleWorS-1
❑ 88OPC-200
❑ 88PanSti-143
❑ 88Sco-324
❑ 88ScoGlo-324
❑ 88StaLinTw-9
❑ 88Top-502
❑ 88TopSti-19
❑ 88TopSti-281
❑ 88TopTif-502
❑ 88TwiSmoC-10
❑ 88Woo-20
❑ 89Bow-163
❑ 89BowTif-163
❑ 89Don-391
❑ 89DonBasB-298
❑ 89Fle-112
❑ 89FleGlo-112
❑ 89OPC-387
❑ 89PanSti-392
❑ 89RedFolSB-50
❑ 89Sco-62
❑ 89Top-426
❑ 89TopSti-286
❑ 89TopTif-426
❑ 89UppDec-400
❑ 90Bow-420
❑ 90BowTif-420
❑ 90ClaBlu-148
❑ 90Don-22
❑ 90Don-182
❑ 90DonBesA-108
❑ 90DonSupD-22
❑ 90Fle-375
❑ 90FleCan-375
❑ 90Lea-254
❑ 90M.Vpin-56
❑ 90OPC-298
❑ 90PanSti-111
❑ 90PubIntS-328
❑ 90Sco-61
❑ 90Spo-190
❑ 90Top-298
❑ 90TopBig-147
❑ 90TopSti-292
❑ 90TopTif-298
❑ 90UppDec-238
❑ 91Bow-318
❑ 91DodPho-14
❑ 91Don-228
❑ 91Fle-611
❑ 91Lea-76
❑ 91OPC-778
❑ 91PanFreS-304
❑ 91Sco-163
❑ 91StaClu-54
❑ 91Stu-85
❑ 91Top-778
❑ 91TopDesS-778
❑ 91TopMic-778
❑ 91TopTif-778
❑ 91Ult-187
❑ 91UppDec-659
❑ 92Don-585
❑ 92Fle-203
❑ 92FleUpd-21
❑ 92Lea-239
❑ 92LeaBlaG-239
❑ 92OPC-177
❑ 92OPCPre-11
❑ 92PanSti-121
❑ 92Pin-318
❑ 92Sco-28
❑ 92ScoRoo-28T
❑ 92StaClu-801
❑ 92StaCluD-61
❑ 92StaCluNC-801
❑ 92TigKro-10
❑ 92TigTeal-12
❑ 92Top-177
❑ 92TopGol-177
❑ 92TopGolW-177
❑ 92TopMic-177
❑ 92TopTra-41T
❑ 92TopTraG-41T
❑ 92Ult-361
❑ 92UppDec-332
❑ 92UppDec-737
❑ 93Don-467
❑ 93Fle-605
❑ 93Lea-60
❑ 93OPC-100
❑ 93PacSpa-109
❑ 93PanSti-118
❑ 93Pin-333
❑ 93Sco-207
❑ 93Sel-244
❑ 93StaClu-191
❑ 93StaCluFDI-191
❑ 93StaCluMOP-191
❑ 93TigGat-10
❑ 93Top-626
❑ 93TopGol-626
❑ 93TopInaM-626
❑ 93TopInaR-626
❑ 93TopMic-626
❑ 93Ult-198
❑ 93UppDec-251
❑ 93UppDecGold-251
❑ 94Don-138
❑ 94Fle-131
❑ 94Pac-218
❑ 94Sco-215
❑ 94ScoGolR-215
❑ 94Top-342
❑ 94TopGol-342
❑ 94TopSpa-342
❑ 97PhoFirDTTI-19

Gladden, Jeff
❑ 81ChaRoyT-17
❑ 82ForMyeRT-13
❑ 83CliGiaF-28

Gladding, Fred
❑ 64Top-312
❑ 64TopVen-312
❑ 65OPC-37
❑ 65Top-37
❑ 66Top-337
❑ 66TopVen-337
❑ 67Ast-11
❑ 67CokCapTi-7
❑ 67OPC-192
❑ 67Top-192
❑ 68CokCapA-5
❑ 68Top-423
❑ 69OPC-58
❑ 69Top-58
❑ 70AstPho-9
❑ 70AstTeal-4
❑ 70MLBOffS-41
❑ 70OPC-208
❑ 70Top-208
❑ 71AstTeal-8
❑ 71MLBOffS-80
❑ 71OPC-381
❑ 71Top-381
❑ 72AstTeal-9
❑ 72MilBra-117
❑ 72OPC-507
❑ 72Top-507
❑ 73OPC-17
❑ 73Top-17
❑ 76DetTigP-7
❑ 78TCM60I-158
❑ 78TigTeal-10
❑ 79TacTugT-25
❑ 86AshTouP-12
❑ 86AstGreT-11
❑ 87AstShoSO-9
❑ 87ColAstP-3
❑ 88ColAstB-20
❑ 89ColMudB-10
❑ 89ColMudP-139
❑ 90KinIndTI-27
❑ 91KinIndC-17
❑ 91KinIndP-341
❑ 92ColRedF-2408
❑ 93ColRedC-29
❑ 93ColRedF-615
❑ 94ColRedC-27
❑ 94ColRedF-461

Glade, Fred
❑ 04FanCraAL-21
❑ 08RosComP-47
❑ 11SpoLifCW-143

Gladu, Mike
❑ 88WytCubP-1993

Gladu, Roland
❑ 43ParSpo-78

Glaister, Henry
❑ 33Zee-56

Glanville, Doug
❑ 91Cla/Bes-402
❑ 91ClaDraP-9
❑ 91GenCubC-24
❑ 91GenCubP-4230
❑ 92ClaDraP-92
❑ 92ProFS7-210
❑ 92UppDecML-173
❑ 92WinSpiC-1
❑ 92WinSpiF-1219
❑ 93ClaFS7-5
❑ 93ClaGolF-39
❑ 93DayCubC-8
❑ 93DayCubF-868
❑ 93ExcFS7-8
❑ 94Bow-177
❑ 94Cla-116
❑ 94OrlCubF-1396
❑ 94UppDecML-85
❑ 95Bow-86
❑ 95IowCubTI-13
❑ 95Top-646
❑ 95UppDecML-129
❑ 95UppDecMLFS-129
❑ 96IowCubB-14
❑ 97Fle-594
❑ 97FleTif-594
❑ 97PacPriGotD-GD118
❑ 97Sco-470
❑ 97ScoArtPWB-470
❑ 97ScoResC-470
❑ 97ScoShoS-470
❑ 97ScoShoSAP-470
❑ 97StaClu-92
❑ 97StaCluMOP-92
❑ 97Ult-534
❑ 97UltGolME-534
❑ 97UltPlaME-534
❑ 98CirThu-52

❑ 98CirThuRav-52
❑ 98CirThuSupRav-52
❑ 98ColCho-56
❑ 98ColCho-458
❑ 98CroRoy-105
❑ 98Don-215
❑ 98DonGolPP-215
❑ 98DonSilPP-215
❑ 98Fin-227
❑ 98FinNo--227
❑ 98FinNo-R-227
❑ 98FinRef-227
❑ 98Fle-83
❑ 98Fle-384
❑ 98FleVin'-112
❑ 98FleVin'C-112
❑ 98LeaRS-124
❑ 98LeaRSLHolo-124
❑ 98LeaRSLong-124
❑ 98LeaRTrue-124
❑ 98Pac-249
❑ 98PacAur-170
❑ 98PacOme-182
❑ 98PacOmeR-182
❑ 98PacOnl-558
❑ 98PacOnlR-558
❑ 98PacOnlWC-558
❑ 98PacPar-212
❑ 98PacParC-212
❑ 98PacParG-212
❑ 98PacParHS-212
❑ 98PacParPB-212
❑ 98PacParR-212
❑ 98PacPlaB-249
❑ 98PacRedT-249
❑ 98PacSil-249
❑ 98PhiTeal-12
❑ 98Pin-132
❑ 98PinPlu-174
❑ 98PinPreP-132
❑ 98Revo-109
❑ 98RevoSS-109
❑ 98StaCluFDI-93
❑ 98StaClul-93
❑ 98StaCluOneK-93
❑ 98StaCluPP-93
❑ 98Top-37
❑ 98TopChr-37
❑ 98TopChrR-37
❑ 98TopDevR-37
❑ 98TopDia-37
❑ 98TopMiniC-37
❑ 98Ult-321
❑ 98UltGolM-321
❑ 98UltMas-321
❑ 98UltPlaM-321
❑ 98UppDec-49
❑ 98UppDec-713
❑ 99199Fin-86
❑ 99CroRoyB-106
❑ 99CroRoyL-106
❑ 99CroRoyOD-106
❑ 99FinGolRef-86
❑ 99FinRef-86
❑ 99FlaShoLeg1-125
❑ 99FlaShoLeg2-125
❑ 99FlaShoLeg3-125
❑ 99FlaShoLegM1-125
❑ 99FlaShoLegM2-125
❑ 99FlaShoLegM3-125
❑ 99FlaShoR1-125
❑ 99FlaShoR2-125
❑ 99FlaShoR3-125
❑ 99Fle-167
❑ 99FleSta9-167
❑ 99FleWarT-167
❑ 99MetUni-161
❑ 99MetUniGM-161
❑ 99MetUniPMG-161
❑ 99Pac-326
❑ 99PacCroC-213
❑ 99PacCroCPB-213
❑ 99PacInv-111
❑ 99PacInvOD-111
❑ 99PacInvPB-111
❑ 99PacOme-179
❑ 99PacOmeC-179
❑ 99PacOmeG-179
❑ 99PacOmePB-179
❑ 99PacPar-179
❑ 99PacParC-179
❑ 99PacParG-179
❑ 99PacParHoloGold-179
❑ 99PacParHS-179
❑ 99PacParOD-179
❑ 99PacParPB-179
❑ 99PacParRed-179
❑ 99PacPlaB-326
❑ 99PacPri-108
❑ 99PacPriHB-108
❑ 99PacPriHG-108
❑ 99PacPriHM-108
❑ 99PacPriHP-108
❑ 99PacPriRed-108
❑ 99PacPriS-88
❑ 99PacPriS206-88
❑ 99PacPriS206R-88
❑ 99PacRed-326
❑ 99Rev-106
❑ 99RevPrernDate-106
❑ 99RevRet-106
❑ 99RevShaSS-106
❑ 99SkyPre-52
❑ 99SkyPreR-52
❑ 99SkyThu-113
❑ 99SkyThuRant-113
❑ 99SkyThuRave-113
❑ 99SP Aut-66
❑ 99SP SigAuto-DGI
❑ 99SPSig-165
❑ 99SPx-61
❑ 99SPxFinR-61
❑ 99SPxFinS-61
❑ 99StaClu-198
❑ 99StaCluFDI-198
❑ 99StaCluOoaK-198
❑ 99StaCluPP-198
❑ 99ThuSkySupR-113
❑ 99Top-33
❑ 99TopChr-33
❑ 99TopChrR-33
❑ 99TopMVPP-33
❑ 99Ult-88
❑ 99UltGolM-88
❑ 99UltMas-88
❑ 99UltPlaM-88
❑ 99UppDec-172
❑ 99UppDecBD-64
❑ 99UppDecBDD-64
❑ 99UppDecBDQ-64
❑ 99UppDecBDT-64
❑ 99UppDecEL1-172
❑ 99UppDecEL2-172
❑ 99UppDecM-158
❑ 99UppDecMGS-158
❑ 99UppDecMHFS-158
❑ 99UppDecMP-158
❑ 99UppDecMSS-158
❑ 99Vic-295

Glanz, Scott
❑ 83PeoSunF-4

Glaser, Gordy
❑ 81ChaChaT-3
❑ 82ChaChaT-3
❑ 82Ind-14
❑ 83BufBisT-4

Glaser, Kris
❑ 91EugEmeC-28
❑ 91EugEmeP-3719

Glasker, Stephen
❑ 86SalRedBP-10
❑ 87PorChaRP-15
❑ 89ChaRanS-9

Glass, Bobby
❑ 77JacSunT-9

Glass, Chip
❑ 94WatIndC-12
❑ 94WatIndF-3953
❑ 96CarLeaA1B-21
❑ 96CarLeaA2B-21
❑ 96KenIndB-8
❑ 97AkrAer-9
❑ 97EasLeaTPB-2
❑ 98NorNavQ-12

Glass, Steve
❑ 87IdaFalBP-22
❑ 88BurBraP-9
❑ 89BurBraP-1607
❑ 89BurBraS-10
❑ 90SumBraB-29
❑ 90SumBraP-2452

Glass, Tim
❑ 76BatTroTI-10
❑ 78WatIndT-11
❑ 79WatIndT-2A
❑ 80WatIndT-5
❑ 81ChaLooT-11
❑ 82ChaLooT-6
❑ 83BufBisT-11
❑ 84BufBisT-3
❑ 85WatIndT-18

Glassco, Craig
❑ 74SacSolC-55

Glasscock, Jack (John)
❑ 75FlePio-21
❑ 86IndIndTI-5
❑ 87AllandGN-6
❑ 87BucN28-41A
❑ 87BucN28-41B
❑ 87OldJudN-203
❑ 87TobLit-5
❑ 88AugBecN-17
❑ 88GooN16-6
❑ 88SpoTimM-13
❑ 88WG1CarG-32
❑ 89EdgR.WG-11
❑ 94OriofB-67
❑ 95May-11A
❑ 95May-11B

Glasscock, Larry
❑ 83MemChiT-18

Glasser, Scott
❑ 97HigDesMG-9

Glassey, Josh
❑ 96YakBeaTI-45
❑ 98VerBeaDM-18

Glauber, Keith
❑ 94NewJerCC-12
❑ 94NewJerCF-3410
❑ 96PeoChiB-12
❑ 97ArkTraB-4
❑ 99SpolII-64

Glaus, Troy
❑ 97UCLBruTI-4
❑ 98Bes-15
❑ 98Bes-68
❑ 98BesAutSS-21
❑ 98BesBet-7
❑ 98BesCor-7
❑ 98BesDiaB-16
❑ 98BesNumOP-23
❑ 98BesPro-4
❑ 98Bow-134
❑ 98Bow99ROYF-ROY2
❑ 98BowBes-153
❑ 98BowBesAR-153
❑ 98BowBesR-153
❑ 98BowChr-134
❑ 98BowChrGA-134
❑ 98BowChrGAR-134
❑ 98BowChrI-134
❑ 98BowChrIR-134
❑ 98BowChrR-134
❑ 98BowGolA-134
❑ 98BowInt-134
❑ 98DonSig-122
❑ 98DonSigP-122
❑ 98FleUpd-U87
❑ 98LeaRS-314
❑ 98LeaRSLHolo-314
❑ 98LeaRSLong-314
❑ 98LeaRTrue-314
❑ 98MidAngG-15
❑ 98MidAngO-14
❑ 98TexLeaTPG-12
❑ 98Top-492
❑ 98TopChr-492
❑ 98TopChrR-492
❑ 98TopDevR-492
❑ 98TopDia-492
❑ 98TopMiniC-492
❑ 98TopTek-61
❑ 98TopTekD-61
❑ 98UppDecR-104
❑ 98UppDecRNF-NF4
❑ 98VanCanG-13
❑ 99199Fin-30
❑ 99199Fin-121
❑ 99BasAmeTPA-17
❑ 99Bow-341
❑ 99BowAut-BA2
❑ 99BowBes-121
❑ 99BowBesAR-121
❑ 99BowBesFFMI-FF2
❑ 99BowBesFFMI-FF2
❑ 99BowBesFFMII-FF2
❑ 99BowBesR-121
❑ 99BowBesRLRA-RA3
❑ 99BowBesRLRGUB-RB3
❑ 99BowBesRLRGWJ-RJ3
❑ 99BowChrDA-DA1
❑ 99BowChrDAR-DA1
❑ 99BowChrSC-SC4
❑ 99BowChrSCR-SC4
❑ 99BowGol-341
❑ 99BowInt-341
❑ 99BowScoC-SC4
❑ 99CroRoyB-3
❑ 99CroRoyL-3
❑ 99CroRoyOD-3
❑ 99E-X Cen-101
❑ 99E-X CenECFut-101
❑ 99E-X CenECNow-101
❑ 99E-X CenEQ-1
❑ 99E-XCenA-5
❑ 99FinFutF-FF2
❑ 99FinGolRef-30
❑ 99FinGolRef-121
❑ 99FinRef-30
❑ 99FinRef-121
❑ 99FinSplS-SS12
❑ 99FinSplSDR-SS12
❑ 99FlaShoLeg1-12
❑ 99FlaShoLeg2-12
❑ 99FlaShoLeg3-12
❑ 99FlaShoLegM1-12
❑ 99FlaShoLegM2-12
❑ 99FlaShoLegM3-12
❑ 99FlaShoR1-12
❑ 99FlaShoR2-12
❑ 99FlaShoR3-12
❑ 99FlaShoWotF-7
❑ 99Fle-50
❑ 99Fle-581
❑ 99FleBri-72
❑ 99FleBri2G-72
❑ 99FleBriBlu-72
❑ 99FleBriGol-72
❑ 99FleBriI-7
❑ 99FleMys-71
❑ 99FleMysFI-14
❑ 99FleMysG-71
❑ 99FleMysM-71
❑ 99FleMysP-7
❑ 99FleRooFla-9
❑ 99FleSta9-50
❑ 99FleSta9-581
❑ 99FleVin'-50
❑ 99FleWarT-50
❑ 99FleWarT-581
❑ 99MetUni-253
❑ 99MetUniGM-253
❑ 99MetUniN-1
❑ 99MetUniPMG-253
❑ 99PacInv-3
❑ 99PacInvOD-3
❑ 99PacInvPB-3
❑ 99PacOme-5
❑ 99PacOmeC-5
❑ 99PacOmeG-5
❑ 99PacOmePB-5
❑ 99PacPar-6
❑ 99PacParC-6
❑ 99PacParG-6
❑ 99PacParHoloGold-6
❑ 99PacParHS-6
❑ 99PacParOD-6
❑ 99PacParPB-6
❑ 99PacParRed-6
❑ 99Rev-3
❑ 99RevDiaL-1
❑ 99RevPremDate-3
❑ 99RevRet-3
❑ 99RevShaSS-3
❑ 99RevTri-21
❑ 99RevTri-21
❑ 99SkyMolM-113
❑ 99SkyMolMF-13
❑ 99SkyMolMFS-13
❑ 99SkyMolMFT-13
❑ 99SkyMolMX-113
❑ 99SkyPre-14
❑ 99SkyPreA-19
❑ 99SkyPreABlue-19
❑ 99SkyPreR-14
❑ 99SkyThu-245
❑ 99SkyThuRant-245
❑ 99SkyThuRave-245
❑ 99SkyThuUnl-U7
❑ 99SP Aut-91
❑ 99SP AutC-TGI
❑ 99SP AutCG-TGI
❑ 99SP AutHRC-HR38
❑ 99SP SigAuto-TGL
❑ 99SP SigAutoG-TGL
❑ 99SPAutHRCDC-HR38
❑ 99SpolII-42
❑ 99SpolIIOTW-7
❑ 99SPSig-21
❑ 99SPx-81
❑ 99SPxFinR-81
❑ 99SPxFinS-81
❑ 99SPxPowE-PE1
❑ 99StaClu-161
❑ 99StaClu-255
❑ 99StaCluC-SCC31
❑ 99StaCluC-CS2
❑ 99StaCluC-CS7
❑ 99StaCluC-CS14
❑ 99StaCluC-CS19
❑ 99StaCluCR-SCC31
❑ 99StaCluFDI-161
❑ 99StaCluFDI-255
❑ 99StaCluNC-NC20
❑ 99StaCluOoaK-161
❑ 99StaCluOoaK-255
❑ 99StaCluPP-161
❑ 99StaCluPP-255
❑ 99TeaBesR-5
❑ 99TeaBesRA-11
❑ 99TeaBesRFS-3
❑ 99ThuSkySupR-245
❑ 99Top-326
❑ 99TopAut-A8
❑ 99TopBlaLC1-35
❑ 99TopBlaLC2-35
❑ 99TopBlaLC3-35
❑ 99TopChr-326
❑ 99TopChrF1-FF4
❑ 99TopChrF1R-FF4
❑ 99TopChrR-326
❑ 99TopGal-98
❑ 99TopGal-124
❑ 99TopGalAuto-GA1
❑ 99TopGalPP-98
❑ 99TopGalPP-124
❑ 99TopGalPPI-98
❑ 99TopGalPPI-124
❑ 99TopGolL-35
❑ 99TopGolLC1-35
❑ 99TopGolLC2-35
❑ 99TopGolLOtO-35
❑ 99TopMVPP-326
❑ 99TopOpeD-106
❑ 99TopRedLC1-35
❑ 99TopRedLC2-35
❑ 99TopRedLC3-35
❑ 99TopSta-11
❑ 99TopSta-156
❑ 99TopSta1Foil-11
❑ 99TopSta2Foil-11
❑ 99TopSta3Foil-11
❑ 99TopStaBF-BF1
❑ 99TopStaBFFoil-BF1
❑ 99TopStaFoil-11
❑ 99TopStaFoil-156
❑ 99TopStaOS-11
❑ 99TopStaTS-11
❑ 99TopStaTS-11
❑ 99TopSupC-30
❑ 99TopSupCR-30
❑ 99TopTek-10A
❑ 99TopTek-10B
❑ 99TopTekFP-F2
❑ 99TopTekG-10A
❑ 99TopTekG-10B
❑ 99UD Cho-15
❑ 99UD Cho-39
❑ 99UD ChoMBH-B2
❑ 99UD ChoPCR-15
❑ 99UD ChoPCR-39
❑ 99UD ChoS-5
❑ 99UD ChoSD-5
❑ 99UD ChoSHR-5
❑ 99UD ChoST-5
❑ 99UD Ion-1
❑ 99UD IonR-1
❑ 99UDHolo-2
❑ 99UDHoloAUsome-2
❑ 99Ult-232
❑ 99UltGolM-232
❑ 99UltMas-232
❑ 99UltPlaM-232
❑ 99UppDec-1
❑ 99UppDec-21
❑ 99UppDecBD-91
❑ 99UppDecBDD-91
❑ 99UppDecBDMN-M15
❑ 99UppDecBDMNE-M15
❑ 99UppDecBDQ-91
❑ 99UppDecBDT-91
❑ 99UppDecCf7-42
❑ 99UppDecCf7-89
❑ 99UppDecCL-102
❑ 99UppDecCLCC-102
❑ 99UppDecCLM-C2
❑ 99UppDecCo7CE-42
❑ 99UppDecCo7CE-89
❑ 99UppDecE-91
❑ 99UppDecE-157
❑ 99UppDecEFXG-91
❑ 99UppDecEFXG-157
❑ 99UppDecEL1-1
❑ 99UppDecEL1-21
❑ 99UppDecEL2-1
❑ 99UppDecEL2-21
❑ 99UppDecERE-R6
❑ 99UppDecEREFXG-R6
❑ 99UppDecEUA-TG
❑ 99UppDecF-F2
❑ 99UppDecFD-F2
❑ 99UppDecFQ-F2
❑ 99UppDecFT-F2
❑ 99UppDecM-4
❑ 99UppDecMGS-4
❑ 99UppDecMHFS-4
❑ 99UppDecMP-4
❑ 99UppDecMSC-SC3
❑ 99UppDecMSS-4
❑ 99UppDecO-67
❑ 99UppDecOSO-67
❑ 99UppDecR-2
❑ 99UppDecRG-2
❑ 99UppDecROSS-S21
❑ 99UppDecROSS-S21
❑ 99UppDecRP-2
❑ 99Vic-5

Glaviano, Tommy (Thomas)
❑ 49EurSta-183
❑ 51Bow-301
❑ 51TopRedB-47
❑ 52Top-56
❑ 53Top-140
❑ 83TopRep5-56
❑ 91TopArc1-140

Glavine, Mike
❑ 96Exc-43
❑ 97SouAtlTPB-13
❑ 98CarLeaAC-30
❑ 98CarLeaTPQ-26
❑ 98KinIndQ-11
❑ 98SP MinPE-47
❑ 98SPMin-47
❑ 99BasAmeTP-46
❑ 99BasAmeTPG-46

Glavine, Tom
❑ 86GreBraTI-9
❑ 86SouLeaAJ-23
❑ 87IntLeaAT-32
❑ 87RicBraBC-8
❑ 87RicBraC-14
❑ 87RicBraT-5
❑ 87SpoTeaP-24
❑ 88Don-644
❑ 88Fle-539
❑ 88FleGlo-539
❑ 88Sco-638
❑ 88ScoGlo-638
❑ 88StaLinBra-6
❑ 88Top-779
❑ 88TopClo-39
❑ 88TopSti-44
❑ 88TopTif-779
❑ 89Bow-267
❑ 89BowTif-267
❑ 89BraDub-12
❑ 89ClaTraP-159
❑ 89Don-381
❑ 89DonBasB-2
❑ 89Fle-591
❑ 89FleGlo-591
❑ 89PanSti-34
❑ 89Sco-442
❑ 89ScoYouS2-23
❑ 89Top-157
❑ 89TopTif-157
❑ 89UppDec-360
❑ 90Bow-2
❑ 90BowTif-2
❑ 90BraDubP-8
❑ 90BraDubS-9
❑ 90ClaBlu-36
❑ 90Don-145
❑ 90DonBesN-2
❑ 90DOnBonM-BC12A
❑ 90DonLeaS-53
❑ 90Fle-583
❑ 90FleCan-583
❑ 90Lea-13
❑ 90M.Vpin-1
❑ 90OPC-506
❑ 90PanSti-219
❑ 90RedFolSB-36
❑ 90Sco-481

❑ 90Spo-34
❑ 90Top-506
❑ 90TopBig-99
❑ 90TopMag-74
❑ 90TopSti-26
❑ 90TopTif-506
❑ 90UppDec-571
❑ 91Bow-576
❑ 91BraDubP-11
❑ 91BraSubS-15
❑ 91Cla3-T26
❑ 91ClaGam-17
❑ 91Don-132
❑ 91Fle-689
❑ 91Lea-172
❑ 91OPC-82
❑ 91RedFolS-39
❑ 91Sco-206
❑ 91StaClu-558
❑ 91StaCluMO-16
❑ 91Stu-145
❑ 91Top-82
❑ 91TopDesS-82
❑ 91TopMic-82
❑ 91TopTif-82
❑ 91TopTriH-N1
❑ 91Ult-5
❑ 91UppDec-480
❑ 91UppDecFE-90F
❑ 91USPlaCA-1S
❑ 92Bow-699
❑ 92BraLykP-13
❑ 92BraLykS-14
❑ 92Cla1-T38
❑ 92Cla2-T17
❑ 92ClaGam-124
❑ 92Don-426
❑ 92Don-629
❑ 92DonBonC-BC4
❑ 92DonCraJ2-2
❑ 92Fle-358
❑ 92Fle-694
❑ 92FleAll-6
❑ 92FleCitTP-20
❑ 92FleSmo'nH-S7
❑ 92FleTeaL-11
❑ 92Fre-2
❑ 92Hig5-23
❑ 92Hig5S-13
❑ 92Lea-279
❑ 92LeaBlaG-279
❑ 92MooSna-22
❑ 92MVPPin-31
❑ 92OPC-305
❑ 92OPCPre-49
❑ 92PanSti-288
❑ 92PepDieM-5
❑ 92Pin-75
❑ 92Pin-594
❑ 92RedFolS-114
❑ 92Sco-450
❑ 92Sco-791
❑ 92Sco-890
❑ 92Sco100S-15
❑ 92ScoCokD-10
❑ 92ScoImpP-49
❑ 92ScoProaG-18
❑ 92SpoIllFK1-40
❑ 92SpoIllFK1-451
❑ 92SpoIllFK1-796
❑ 92StaClu-395
❑ 92StaCluD-62
❑ 92Stu-4
❑ 92SunSee-19
❑ 92Top-305
❑ 92Top-395
❑ 92TopGol-305
❑ 92TopGol-395
❑ 92TopGolW-305
❑ 92TopGolW-395
❑ 92TopKid-34
❑ 92TopMic-305
❑ 92TopMic-395
❑ 92TriPla-7
❑ 92Ult-162
❑ 92UltAllS-20
❑ 92UltAwaW-7
❑ 92UppDec-342
❑ 92UppDec-713
❑ 93Bow-410
❑ 93BraFloA-5
❑ 93BraLykP-11
❑ 93BraLykS-13
❑ 93BraStaC-1
❑ 93CadDis-26
❑ 93ClaGam-36
❑ 93ColAllG-14
❑ 93DiaMar-38
❑ 93Don-554
❑ 93DonDiaK-DK19
❑ 93DonEliD-14
❑ 93DonPre-1
❑ 93DurPowP1-21
❑ 93Fin-87
❑ 93FinJum-87
❑ 93FinRef-87
❑ 93Fla-4
❑ 93Fle-4
❑ 93FleAll-NL11
❑ 93FleAtl-9
❑ 93FleFruotL-21
❑ 93FleGla-1
❑ 93FleGla-1B
❑ 93FleGla-2
❑ 93FleGla-2B
❑ 93FleGla-3
❑ 93FleGla-3B
❑ 93FleGla-4
❑ 93FleGla-4B
❑ 93FleGla-5
❑ 93FleGla-6
❑ 93FleGla-7
❑ 93FleGla-7B
❑ 93FleGla-8
❑ 93FleGla-8B
❑ 93FleGla-9
❑ 93FleGla-9B
❑ 93FleGla-10
❑ 93FleGla-10B
❑ 93FleGla-11
❑ 93FleGla-12
❑ 93FleGla-13
❑ 93FleGla-14
❑ 93FleGla-15
❑ 93FleGla-AU0
❑ 93FlePro-B2
❑ 93FunPac-61
❑ 93FunPac-63
❑ 93Hos-22
❑ 93JimDea-14
❑ 93KinDis-19
❑ 93Kra-22
❑ 93Lea-295
❑ 93LeaGolA-R18
❑ 93MilBonSS-2
❑ 93MSABenSPD-6
❑ 93OPC-132
❑ 93OPCPreSP-21
❑ 93OPCPreSPF-21
❑ 93PacSpa-6
❑ 93PanSti-159
❑ 93PanSti-179
❑ 93Pin-90
❑ 93PinTeaP-2
❑ 93Pos-21
❑ 93RedFolS-31
❑ 93RedFolS-114
❑ 93Sco-15
❑ 93Sco-539
❑ 93ScoGolDT-8
❑ 93Sel-7
❑ 93SelAce-2
❑ 93SelChaS-10
❑ 93SelDufIP-6
❑ 93SelStaL-88
❑ 93SP-58
❑ 93StaClu-296
❑ 93StaClu-650
❑ 93StaCluFDI-296
❑ 93StaCluFDI-650
❑ 93StaCluM-106
❑ 93StaCluMMP-2
❑ 93StaCluMOP-296
❑ 93StaCluMOP-650
❑ 93Stu-145
❑ 93Top-280
❑ 93Top-410
❑ 93TOPBLAG-6
❑ 93TopComotH-18
❑ 93TopFulS-19
❑ 93TopGol-280
❑ 93TopGol-410
❑ 93TopInaM-280
❑ 93TopInaM-410
❑ 93TopInaR-280
❑ 93TopInaR-410
❑ 93TopMic-280
❑ 93TopMic-410
❑ 93TriPla-117
❑ 93TriPla-209
❑ 93Ult-6
❑ 93UppDec-75
❑ 93UppDec-472
❑ 93UppDecGold-75
❑ 93UppDecGold-472
❑ 93USPlaCA-2S
❑ 94Bow-21
❑ 94BowBes-R12
❑ 94BowBesR-R12
❑ 94BraLykP-9
❑ 94BraLykS-10
❑ 94BraUSPC-6H
❑ 94BraUSPC-13S
❑ 94ColC-306
❑ 94ColC-430
❑ 94ColChoGS-306
❑ 94ColChoGS-430
❑ 94ColChoSS-306
❑ 94ColChoSS-430
❑ 94Don-364
❑ 94DonSpeE-364
❑ 94Fin-267
❑ 94FinRef-267
❑ 94Fla-125
❑ 94Fle-359
❑ 94FleAllS-36
❑ 94FleExtB-201
❑ 94FleExtBGB-11
❑ 94FleExtBPD-9
❑ 94FleLeaL-11
❑ 94FleSun-11
❑ 94FUnPac-47
❑ 94Kra-22
❑ 94Lea-235
❑ 94LeaL-82
❑ 94OPC-250
❑ 94Pac-9
❑ 94PanSti-14
❑ 94PanSti-145
❑ 94Pin-284
❑ 94PinArtP-284
❑ 94PinMusC-284
❑ 94Pos-16
❑ 94RedFolMI-16
❑ 94Sco-30
❑ 94ScoDreT-2
❑ 94ScoGolR-30
❑ 94ScoGolS-16
❑ 94Sel-250
❑ 94SP-49
❑ 94SPDieC-49
❑ 94Spo-80
❑ 94StaClu-538
❑ 94StaClu-574
❑ 94StaCluFDI-538
❑ 94StaCluFDI-574
❑ 94StaCluGR-538
❑ 94StaCluGR-574
❑ 94StaCluMO-23
❑ 94StaCluMOP-538
❑ 94StaCluMOP-574
❑ 94StaCluT-56
❑ 94StaCluTFDI-56
❑ 94Stu-34
❑ 94Top-393
❑ 94Top-475
❑ 94TopBlaG-32
❑ 94TopGol-393
❑ 94TopGol-475
❑ 94TopSpa-393
❑ 94TopSpa-475
❑ 94TopSupS-16
❑ 94TriPla-44
❑ 94Ult-151
❑ 94UltAllS-19
❑ 94UltLeaL-9
❑ 94UppDec-144
❑ 94UppDecAJ-11
❑ 94UppDecAJG-11
❑ 94UppDecED-144
❑ 94USPlaCA-6S
❑ 95Baz-97
❑ 95Bow-286
❑ 95BraAtlC-2
❑ 95ColCho-165
❑ 95ColChoGS-165
❑ 95ColChoSE-59
❑ 95ColChoSEGS-59
❑ 95ColChoSESS-59
❑ 95ColChoSS-165
❑ 95Don-248
❑ 95DonPreP-248
❑ 95DonTopotO-183
❑ 95Emo-100
❑ 95Fin-64
❑ 95FinRef-64
❑ 95Fla-323
❑ 95Fle-304
❑ 95Lea-250
❑ 95LeaLim-32
❑ 95Pac-4
❑ 95PanSti-1
❑ 95Pin-264
❑ 95PinArtP-264
❑ 95PinMusC-264
❑ 95Sco-434
❑ 95ScoGolR-434
❑ 95ScoHaloG-HG65
❑ 95ScoPlaTS-434
❑ 95Sel-55
❑ 95SelArtP-55
❑ 95SP-32
❑ 95SPCha-24
❑ 95SPChaDC-24
❑ 95Spo-114
❑ 95SpoArtP-114
❑ 95SPSil-32
❑ 95StaClu-183
❑ 95StaCluFDI-183
❑ 95StaCluMOP-183
❑ 95StaCluSTDW-B183
❑ 95StaCluSTMP-2
❑ 95StaCluSTWS-183
❑ 95StaCluVR-93
❑ 95StaCluVRMO-93
❑ 95Stu-182
❑ 95Sum-23
❑ 95SumNthD-23
❑ 95Top-175
❑ 95TopCyb-101
❑ 95TopD3-28
❑ 95TopEmb-111
❑ 95TopEmbGI-111
❑ 95UC3-81
❑ 95UC3ArtP-81
❑ 95Ult-125
❑ 95UltGolM-125
❑ 95UppDec-46
❑ 95UppDecED-46
❑ 95UppDecEDG-46
❑ 95UppDecSE-147
❑ 95UppDecSEG-147
❑ 96Baz-44
❑ 96Bow-86
❑ 96BowBesMI-10
❑ 96BowBesMIAR-10
❑ 96BowBesMIR-10
❑ 96BowFoi-86
❑ 96BraFle-4
❑ 96Cir-99
❑ 96CirBos-25
❑ 96CirRav-99
❑ 96ColCho-395T
❑ 96ColCho-455
❑ 96ColChoGS-455
❑ 96ColChoSS-455
❑ 96Don-292
❑ 96DonPreP-292
❑ 96EmoXL-140
❑ 96Fin-S72
❑ 96FinRef-S72
❑ 96Fla-198
❑ 96Fle-291
❑ 96FlePosG-1
❑ 96FleTif-291
❑ 96Kin-11
❑ 96Lea-87
❑ 96LeaLim-57
❑ 96LeaLimG-57
❑ 96LeaPre-74
❑ 96LeaPreP-74
❑ 96LeaPrePB-87
❑ 96LeaPrePG-87
❑ 96LeaPrePS-87
❑ 96LeaSig-134
❑ 96LeaSigEA-60
❑ 96LeaSigEACM-8
❑ 96LeaSigPPG-134
❑ 96LeaSigPPP-134
❑ 96MetUni-127
❑ 96MetUniP-127
❑ 96Pac-13
❑ 96PacOctM-OM5
❑ 96PacPri-P1
❑ 96PacPriFT-FT4
❑ 96PacPriG-P1
❑ 96PanSti-2
❑ 96Pin-230
❑ 96PinAfi-35
❑ 96PinAfiAP-35
❑ 96PinAfiFPP-35
❑ 96PinArtP-130
❑ 96PinChrBC-4
❑ 96PinFoil-230
❑ 96PinSta-130
❑ 96ProSta-25
❑ 96Sco-327
❑ 96Sco-517
❑ 96ScoDugC-B52
❑ 96ScoDugCAP-B52
❑ 96Sel-94
❑ 96SelArtP-94
❑ 96SelCer-42
❑ 96SelCerAP-42
❑ 96SelCerCB-42
❑ 96SelCerCR-42
❑ 96SelCerIP-14
❑ 96SelCerMB-42
❑ 96SelCerMG-42
❑ 96SelCerMR-42
❑ 96SP-23
❑ 96Spo-25
❑ 96SpoArtP-25
❑ 96SPSpeFX-36
❑ 96SPSpeFXDC-36
❑ 96SPx-4
❑ 96SPxGol-4
❑ 96StaClu-49
❑ 96StaClu-237
❑ 96StaCluEPB-49
❑ 96StaCluEPG-49
❑ 96StaCluEPS-49
❑ 96StaCluMOP-49
❑ 96StaCluMOP-237
❑ 96StaCluMOP-TSCA3
❑ 96StaCluTA-3
❑ 96Stu-12
❑ 96StuPrePB-12
❑ 96StuPrePG-12
❑ 96StuPrePS-12
❑ 96Sum-106
❑ 96SumAbo&B-106
❑ 96SumArtP-106
❑ 96SumFoi-106
❑ 96TeaOut-29
❑ 96Top-8
❑ 96Top-262
❑ 96TopChr-8
❑ 96TopChr-105
❑ 96TopChrR-8
❑ 96TopChrR-105
❑ 96TopClaC-CC14
❑ 96TopGal-1
❑ 96TopGalPPI-1
❑ 96TopLas-55
❑ 96TopPowB-8
❑ 96TopPro-NL14
❑ 96Ult-154
❑ 96UltGolM-154
❑ 96UppDec-9
❑ 96UppDec-222
❑ 96UppDecPHE-H42
❑ 96UppDecPreH-H42
❑ 96Zen-98
❑ 96ZenArtP-98
❑ 97Bow-236
❑ 97BowBes-50
❑ 97BowBesAR-50
❑ 97BowBesR-50
❑ 97BowChr-63
❑ 97BowChrI-63
❑ 97BowChrIR-63
❑ 97BowChrR-63
❑ 97BowInt-236
❑ 97BraSco-4
❑ 97BraScoPl-4
❑ 97BraScoPr-4
❑ 97Cir-69
❑ 97CirRav-69
❑ 97ColCho-35
❑ 97ColChoT-AB8
❑ 97CraJac-17
❑ 97Don-86
❑ 97Don-429
❑ 97DonEli-46
❑ 97DonEliGS-46
❑ 97DonGolPP-86
❑ 97DonGolPP-429
❑ 97DonLim-67
❑ 97DonLim-115
❑ 97DonLim-189
❑ 97DonLimE-67
❑ 97DonLimE-115
❑ 97DonLimE-189
❑ 97DonLimENG-67
❑ 97DonPre-59
❑ 97DonPreCttC-59
❑ 97DonSig-38
❑ 97DonSigA-39
❑ 97DonSigAC-47
❑ 97DonSigAM-47
❑ 97DonSigPPP-38
❑ 97DonSilPP-86
❑ 97DonSilPP-429
❑ 97DonTea-19
❑ 97DonTeaSPE-19
❑ 97E-X2-52
❑ 97E-X2Cred-52
❑ 97E-X2EssCre-52
❑ 97Fin-317
❑ 97FinEmb-317
❑ 97FinEmbR-317
❑ 97FinRef-317
❑ 97FlaShoLC-74
❑ 97FlaShoLeg0-74
❑ 97FlaShoLeg1-74
❑ 97FlaShoM-A74
❑ 97FlaShoM-B74
❑ 97FlaShoM-C74
❑ 97FlaShoR0-74
❑ 97FlaShoR1-74
❑ 97FlaShoR2-74
❑ 97Fle-255
❑ 97FleTif-255
❑ 97KinB-19
❑ 97Lea-40
❑ 97Lea-382
❑ 97LeaFraM-40
❑ 97LeaFraM-382
❑ 97LeaFraMDC-40
❑ 97LeaFraMDC-382
❑ 97LeaGet-5
❑ 97MetUni-28
❑ 97NewPin-154
❑ 97NewPinAP-154
❑ 97NewPinMC-154
❑ 97NewPinPP-154
❑ 97Pac-232
❑ 97PacLigB-232
❑ 97PacSil-232
❑ 97Pin-61
❑ 97PinArtP-PP61
❑ 97PinCar-2
❑ 97PinIns-57
❑ 97PinInsCE-57
❑ 97PinInsDE-57
❑ 97PinMusC-61
❑ 97PinPrePla-61
❑ 97PinX-P-109
❑ 97PinX-PMoS-109
❑ 97Sco-89
❑ 97Sco-528
❑ 97ScoArtPWB-89
❑ 97ScoArtPWB-528
❑ 97ScoPreS-89
❑ 97ScoResC-528
❑ 97ScoShoS-89
❑ 97ScoShoS-528
❑ 97ScoShoSAP-89
❑ 97ScoShoSAP-528
❑ 97Sel-99
❑ 97SelArtP-99
❑ 97SelCom-99
❑ 97SelRegG-99
❑ 97SpoIll-74
❑ 97SpoIllEE-74
❑ 97StaClu-54
❑ 97StaCluMat-54
❑ 97StaCluMOP-54
❑ 97StrAll-23
❑ 97Stu-130
❑ 97StuPrePG-130
❑ 97StuPrePS-130
❑ 97Top-50
❑ 97TopAll-AS18
❑ 97TopChr-19
❑ 97TopChrAS-AS18
❑ 97TopChrR-19
❑ 97TopChrSAR-AS18
❑ 97TopGal-19
❑ 97TopGalPPI-19
❑ 97TopSta-33
❑ 97TopStaAM-33
❑ 97Ult-152
❑ 97UltGolME-152
❑ 97UltPlaME-152
❑ 97UppDec-16
❑ 97UppDec-66
❑ 97UppDec-261
❑ 98Bow-57
❑ 98BowBes-67
❑ 98BowBesAR-67
❑ 98BowBesR-67
❑ 98BowChr-57
❑ 98BowChrGA-57
❑ 98BowChrGAR-57

❑ 98BowChrI-57
❑ 98BowChrIR-57
❑ 98BowChrR-57
❑ 98BowGolA-57
❑ 98BowInt-57
❑ 98BraSco-11
❑ 98BraScoP-11
❑ 98CirThu-47
❑ 98CirThuRav-47
❑ 98CirThuSupRav-47
❑ 98ColCho-303
❑ 98CroRoy-11
❑ 98CroRoyPotG-4
❑ 98Don-5
❑ 98DonCol-5
❑ 98DonColE-450
❑ 98DonColP-602
❑ 98DonColS-5
❑ 98DonCruG-57
❑ 98DonCruP-57
❑ 98DonCruR-57
❑ 98DonEli-50
❑ 98DonEliA-50
❑ 98DonEliS-50
❑ 98DonGolPP-5
❑ 98DonPre-52
❑ 98DonPreSeat-52
❑ 98DonPriCD-5
❑ 98DonPriCE-450
❑ 98DonPriCP-602
❑ 98DonSig-65
❑ 98DonSigAC-47
❑ 98DonSigAM-48
❑ 98DonSigP-65
❑ 98DonSilPP-5
❑ 98DonSonM9-13
❑ 98E-X2-77
❑ 98E-X2ECFut-77
❑ 98E-X2ECNow-77
❑ 98Fin-228
❑ 98FinNo--228
❑ 98FinNo-R-228
❑ 98FinRef-228
❑ 98FlaShoLeg0-81
❑ 98FlaShoLeg1-81
❑ 98FlaShoLeg2-81
❑ 98FlaShoLeg3-81
❑ 98FlaShoLegM-81
❑ 98FlaShoR0-81
❑ 98FlaShoR1-81
❑ 98FlaShoR2-81
❑ 98FlaShoR3-81
❑ 98Fle-566
❑ 98FleVin'-72
❑ 98FleVin'C-72
❑ 98KinDis-13
❑ 98LeaRS-75
❑ 98LeaRSLHolo-75
❑ 98LeaRSLong-75
❑ 98LeaRTrue-75
❑ 98MetUni-59
❑ 98MetUniPMG-59
❑ 98Pac-232
❑ 98PacAur-103
❑ 98PacOme-18
❑ 98PacOmeR-18
❑ 98PacOnl-60
❑ 98PacOnlR-60
❑ 98PacOnlWC-60
❑ 98PacPar-128
❑ 98PacParC-128
❑ 98PacParG-128
❑ 98PacParHS-128
❑ 98PacParI-48
❑ 98PacParPB-128
❑ 98PacParR-128
❑ 98PacPlaB-232
❑ 98PacRedT-232
❑ 98PacSil-232
❑ 98Pin-6
❑ 98PinArtP-PP6
❑ 98PinIns-65
❑ 98PinInsCE-65
❑ 98PinInsDE-65
❑ 98PinMusC-PP6
❑ 98PinPer-53
❑ 98PinPerPP-53
❑ 98PinPreP-6
❑ 98PinSna-AB3
❑ 98Revo-11
❑ 98RevoSS-11
❑ 98Sco-142
❑ 98ScoRT-198
❑ 98ScoRTSS-PP111
❑ 98ScoRTSSAP-PP111
❑ 98ScoRTSSAP1-PP111
❑ 98ScoSS-PP156
❑ 98ScoSSAP-PP156
❑ 98SP Aut-44
❑ 98SpoIll-45
❑ 98SpoIllEE-45
❑ 98SpoIllFE-45
❑ 98SpoIllTaN-84
❑ 98SpoIllTaNEE-84
❑ 98SpoIllWSF-44
❑ 98SpoIllWSFEE-44
❑ 98SpoIllWSFFE-44
❑ 98SpoIllWSFMC-8
❑ 98SPxFin-57
❑ 98SPxFinR-57
❑ 98SPxFinS-57
❑ 98StaCluFDI-127
❑ 98StaCluI-127
❑ 98StaCluOneK-127
❑ 98StaCluPP-127
❑ 98Stu-157
❑ 98StuGPP-157
❑ 98StuSony99-13
❑ 98StuSPP-157
❑ 98Top-130
❑ 98TopChr-130
❑ 98TopChrR-130
❑ 98TopDevR-130
❑ 98TopDia-130
❑ 98TopGal-44
❑ 98TopGalGP-44
❑ 98TopGalOPP-44
❑ 98TopGalPPI-44
❑ 98TopGalPPIA-44
❑ 98TopGolLabC1-12
❑ 98TopGolLabC1B-12
❑ 98TopGolLabC1One-12
❑ 98TopGolLabC1R-12
❑ 98TopGolLabC2-12
❑ 98TopGolLabC2B-12
❑ 98TopGolLabC2One-12
❑ 98TopGolLabC2R-12
❑ 98TopGolLabC3-12
❑ 98TopGolLabC3B-12
❑ 98TopGolLabC3One-12
❑ 98TopGolLabC3R-12
❑ 98TopMiniC-130
❑ 98TopOpeD-65
❑ 98TopSta-137
❑ 98TopStaB-137
❑ 98TopStaG-137
❑ 98TopStaGR-137
❑ 98TopStaS-137
❑ 98TopTek-10
❑ 98TopTekD-10
❑ 98Ult-40
❑ 98UltGolM-40
❑ 98UltMas-40
❑ 98UltPlaM-40
❑ 98UppDec-299
❑ 98UppDec-362
❑ 98UppDec10AP-6
❑ 98UppDec1APR-6
❑ 98UppDecSFPD-PZ20
❑ 98UppDecSFPZOB-PZ15
❑ 98Zen-39
❑ 98ZenZ-G-39
❑ 98ZenZ-S-39
❑ 99199Fin-72
❑ 99Bow-270
❑ 99BowBes-78
❑ 99BowBesAR-78
❑ 99BowBesR-78
❑ 99BowGol-270
❑ 99BowInt-270
❑ 99E-X Cen-33
❑ 99E-X CenECFut-33
❑ 99E-X CenECNow-33
❑ 99FinGolRef-72
❑ 99FinRef-72
❑ 99FinSplS-SS11
❑ 99FinSplSDR-SS11
❑ 99FlaShoLeg1-53
❑ 99FlaShoLeg2-53
❑ 99FlaShoLeg3-53
❑ 99FlaShoLegM1-53
❑ 99FlaShoLegM2-53
❑ 99FlaShoLegM3-53
❑ 99FlaShoR1-53
❑ 99FlaShoR2-53
❑ 99FlaShoR3-53
❑ 99Fle-115
❑ 99FleBri-46
❑ 99FleBri2G-46
❑ 99FleBriBlu-46
❑ 99FleBriGol-46
❑ 99FleMys-25
❑ 99FleMysG-25
❑ 99FleMysM-25
❑ 99FleSta9-115
❑ 99FleWarT-115
❑ 99KinDis-10
❑ 99MetUni-165
❑ 99MetUniGM-165
❑ 99MetUniPMG-165
❑ 99Pac-29
❑ 99PacAur-15
❑ 99PacAurOD-15
❑ 99PacCroC-22
❑ 99PacCroCPB-22
❑ 99PacOme-20
❑ 99PacOmeC-20
❑ 99PacOmeG-20
❑ 99PacOmePB-20
❑ 99PacPar-22
❑ 99PacParC-22
❑ 99PacParG-22
❑ 99PacParHoloGold-22
❑ 99PacParHS-22
❑ 99PacParOD-22
❑ 99PacParPB-22
❑ 99PacParRed-22
❑ 99PacPlaB-29
❑ 99PacPri-11
❑ 99PacPriHB-11
❑ 99PacPriHG-11
❑ 99PacPriHM-11
❑ 99PacPriHP-11
❑ 99PacPriRed-11
❑ 99PacPriS-31
❑ 99PacPriS206-31
❑ 99PacPriS206R-31
❑ 99PacPriSP-31
❑ 99PacPriSV-31
❑ 99PacRed-29
❑ 99SkyMolM-62
❑ 99SkyMolMOA-23
❑ 99SkyMolMX-62
❑ 99SkyPre-40
❑ 99SkyPreA-20
❑ 99SkyPreABlue-20
❑ 99SkyPreR-40
❑ 99SkyThu-62
❑ 99SkyThuRant-62
❑ 99SkyThuRave-62
❑ 99SP Aut-11
❑ 99SP Aut-132
❑ 99SpoIll-14
❑ 99SpoIll-19
❑ 99SpoIll-174
❑ 99StaClu-72
❑ 99StaCluFDI-72
❑ 99StaCluOoaK-72
❑ 99StaCluPP-72
❑ 99StaCluTI-T11C
❑ 99StaCluTL-T11C
❑ 99StaCluTL-T11C
❑ 99ThuSkySupR-62
❑ 99Top-243
❑ 99TopBlaLC1-50
❑ 99TopBlaLC2-50
❑ 99TopBlaLC3-50
❑ 99TopChr-243
❑ 99TopChrR-243
❑ 99TopGal-47
❑ 99TopGalAG-AG4
❑ 99TopGalPP-47
❑ 99TopGalPPI-47
❑ 99TopGolL-50
❑ 99TopGolLC1-50
❑ 99TopGolLC2-50
❑ 99TopGolLOtO-50
❑ 99TopMVPP-243
❑ 99TopOpeD-107
❑ 99TopRedLC1-50
❑ 99TopRedLC2-50
❑ 99TopRedLC3-50
❑ 99TopSta-67
❑ 99TopSta1Foil-67
❑ 99TopStaFoil-67
❑ 99TopStaOS-67
❑ 99TopTek-30A
❑ 99TopTek-30B
❑ 99TopTekG-30A
❑ 99TopTekG-30B
❑ 99UD Ion-9
❑ 99UD IonR-9
❑ 99UDHolo-9
❑ 99UDHoloAUsome-9
❑ 99UppDec-313
❑ 99UppDec10AT-X21
❑ 99UppDec10ATD-X21
❑ 99UppDec10ATHR-X21
❑ 99UppDec10ATT-X21
❑ 99UppDecCL-71
❑ 99UppDecCLCC-71
❑ 99UppDecCLM-C8
❑ 99UppDecE-9
❑ 99UppDecEFXG-9
❑ 99UppDecEL1-313
❑ 99UppDecEL2-313
❑ 99UppDecM-18
❑ 99UppDecMGS-18
❑ 99UppDecMHFS-18
❑ 99UppDecMP-18
❑ 99UppDecMSS-18
❑ 99UppDecR-10
❑ 99UppDecRG-10
❑ 99UppDecRP-10
❑ 99Vic-34

Glaze, Gettys
❑ 92ElmPioC-20
❑ 92ElmPioF-1377
❑ 93Bow-311
❑ 93LynRedSC-10
❑ 93LynRedSF-2512
❑ 94LynRedSC-11
❑ 94LynRedSF-1888

Glaze, Ralph
❑ 08RosComP-1

Glaze, Randy
❑ 96SouOreTI-14
❑ 97SouOreTB-20

Glazner, Whitey (Charles)
❑ 20NatCarE-33
❑ 21E121So1-31
❑ 22E120-216
❑ 22W572-32
❑ 22W573-49
❑ 22W575-42
❑ 23W501-87
❑ 26Zee-22

Gleason, Harry
❑ 03BreE10-57
❑ 11SpoLifCW-144

Gleason, Jackie
❑ 92Pin-590

Gleason, Kid (William J.)
❑ 03BreE10-58
❑ 03BreE10-59
❑ 17HolBreD-35
❑ 18WhiSoxTI-10
❑ 19W514-112
❑ 20GasAmeMBD-1
❑ 21E121So1-32
❑ 21E121So8-27
❑ 22AmeCarE122-22
❑ 22W575-43
❑ 23W501-39
❑ 23W503-31
❑ 23WilChoV-50
❑ 23WilChoV-51
❑ 75WhiSox1T-9
❑ 76SSP188WS-9
❑ 87OldJudN-204
❑ 88ConSer5-14
❑ 88GandBCGCE-18
❑ 88LitSunBS-11
❑ 88PacEigMO-23
❑ 88PacEigMO-35
❑ 88PacEigMO-59
❑ 88PacEigMO-73
❑ 88PacEigMO-102
❑ 92Man191BSR-10
❑ 94ConTSN-1038
❑ 94ConTSNB-1038
❑ 94OriTeal-5

Gleason, Roy
❑ 77FriOneYW-44
❑ 90DodTar-961

Gleason, William G.
❑ 87BucN28-98
❑ 87LonJacN-5
❑ 87OldJudN-205A
❑ 87OldJudN-205B
❑ 87OldJudN-524B
❑ 87ScrDC-5
❑ 94OriofB-36

Gleason, William P.
❑ 11Zee-27
❑ 17ColE13-60

Gleaton, Jerry Don
❑ 80Top-673
❑ 80TulDriT-1
❑ 81MarPos-14
❑ 81Top-41
❑ 82Top-371
❑ 83SalLakCGT-2
❑ 84SalLakCGC-186
❑ 85BufBisT-19
❑ 85Top-216
❑ 85TopTif-216
❑ 86BufBisP-12
❑ 86Top-447
❑ 86TopTif-447
❑ 88Don-547
❑ 88Fle-258
❑ 88FleGlo-258
❑ 88OmaRoyC-5
❑ 88OmaRoyP-1497
❑ 88RoySmo-7
❑ 88RoyTeal-13
❑ 88Sco-343
❑ 88ScoGlo-343
❑ 88StaLinRo-5
❑ 88Top-116
❑ 88TopTif-116
❑ 89Don-444
❑ 89Fle-282
❑ 89FleGlo-282
❑ 89Sco-423
❑ 89Top-724
❑ 89TopTif-724
❑ 90TigCok-6
❑ 90TigTeal-11
❑ 90TulDriDGB-17
❑ 91Don-661
❑ 91Fle-338
❑ 91Lea-135
❑ 91OPC-597
❑ 91Sco-316
❑ 91StaClu-574
❑ 91TigCok-19
❑ 91TigPol-6
❑ 91Top-597
❑ 91TopDesS-597
❑ 91TopMic-597
❑ 91TopTif-597
❑ 92Don-607
❑ 92OPC-272
❑ 92Sco-375
❑ 92TexLon-16
❑ 92Top-272
❑ 92TopGol-272
❑ 92TopGolW-272
❑ 92TopMic-272
❑ 92UppDec-601
❑ 93EdmTraF-1130
❑ 93MarlStaClu-14
❑ 93RanKee-160

Gleckel, Scott
❑ 82OrlTwi8SCT-14

Gledhill, Chance
❑ 91BoiHawC-4
❑ 91BoiHawP-3870
❑ 92QuaCitRBC-14
❑ 92QuaCitRBF-802
❑ 93MidAngF-318
❑ 97MidAngOHP-13

Gleeson, Jim
❑ 39CubTeal-8
❑ 94ConTSN-1291
❑ 94ConTSNB-1291

Gleischmann, Gustave
❑ 15Zee-125
❑ 16Zee-129

Gleissner, James
❑ 82ForMyeRT-17

Glendenning, Mike
❑ 96BelGiaTI-14
❑ 97BakBlaB-1
❑ 97BakBlaTI-1
❑ 97CalLeaTP-1
❑ 98ShrCapM-16
❑ 98ShrCapWS-16
❑ 98TexLeaTPG-13

Glenn, Darrin
❑ 95BurBeeTI-3
❑ 96SanJosGB-26

Glenn, Joe
❑ 33WorCig(-32
❑ 34BatR31-87
❑ 36NatChiFPR-108
❑ 72TCMthe3-80
❑ 75YanDyn1T-17
❑ 92ConTSN-510

Glenn, John
❑ 62KahAtl-8
❑ 77FriOneYW-62

Glenn, Leon
❑ 90BelBreB-17
❑ 90BelBreS-9
❑ 90Bes-271
❑ 91BelBreCB-24
❑ 91BelBreP-2110
❑ 91BenBucCB-25
❑ 91BenBucP-3700
❑ 91Cla/Bes-215
❑ 92ClaFS7-284
❑ 92StoPorC-12
❑ 92StoPorF-40
❑ 93AusFut-20
❑ 93StoPorC-12
❑ 93StoPorF-751
❑ 94ElPasDF-3157
❑ 94UppDecML-206
❑ 95AusFut-102
❑ 95MidAngOHP-12
❑ 95MidAngTI-10
❑ 96MidAngOHP-12

Glenn, Mouse
❑ 87OldJudN-206

Glenn, Simon
❑ 80ElmPioRST-28

Glenn, Stanley
❑ 92NegLeaRLI-24
❑ 95NegLeaL2-32

Gliatto, Sal
❑ 76DalCon-4

Glick, David
❑ 96OgdRapTI-20

Glick, Tom
❑ 90JamExpP-31

Glinatsis, George
❑ 92CalLeaACL-28
❑ 92ClaFS7-394
❑ 92SanBerC-15
❑ 92SanBerSF-946
❑ 93ClaGolF-143
❑ 93JacSunF-2706
❑ 94RivPilCLC-5
❑ 95PorCitRTI-11
❑ 97St.PauS-10
❑ 98NewHavRM-8
❑ 98NewHavRMA-8

Glinatsis, Mike
❑ 82MiaMarT-2

Glinton, James
❑ 91ChaRanC-16

Glisson, Robert
❑ 86EriCarP-8
❑ 87SprCarB-18
❑ 88SprCarB-1

Gload, Ross
❑ 98KanCouC-12
❑ 98KanCouCCP-12
❑ 99SP TopP-25
❑ 99SP TopPPE-25

Globetrotters, Harlem
❑ 92NegLeaRLI-94
❑ 93NegLeaRL2-56
❑ 93NegLeaRL2-57
❑ 93NegLeaRL2-95

Globig, Dave
❑ 76BurBeeT-16

Glossop, Al (Alban)
❑ 43DodTeal-11
❑ 47SigOil-26
❑ 48AngTeal-11
❑ 49AngTeal-13
❑ 49BowPCL-17
❑ 49W725AngTI-10
❑ 90DodTar-284

Glover, Gary
❑ 96MedHatBJTI-9
❑ 97HagSunB-6
❑ 98KnoSG-4

Glover, Jason
❑ 96OgdRapTI-26

Glover, Jeff
❑ 86MedA'sC-68
❑ 87MadMusP-8
❑ 87MadMusP-17
❑ 88ModA'sCLC-60
❑ 88ModA'sTI-10

Glover, Reggie
❑ 88RenSilSCLC-271

Glover, Terence
❑ 88SalLakCTTI-23

Glowzenski, Len
❑ 76AshTouT-22

Glynn, Bill (William V.)
❑ 50WorWidGV-42
❑ 52MotCoo-56
❑ 53Top-171
❑ 54Top-178
❑ 55Top-39
❑ 55TopDouH-59

❑ 56SeaPop-6
❑ 57HygMea-5
❑ 57SeaPop-9
❑ 75TCM195Cl-10
❑ 91TopArc1-171
❑ 94TopArc1-178
❑ 94TopArc1G-178
Glynn, Dennis
❑ 86JacMetT-14
Glynn, Ed
❑ 77EvaTriT-11
❑ 77Top-487
❑ 79Top-343
❑ 80Top-509
❑ 81ChaChaT-4
❑ 81Top-93
❑ 82ChaChaT-4
❑ 82Ind-15
❑ 83ChaChaT-19
❑ 83Don-537
❑ 83Fle-408
❑ 83IndPos-16
❑ 83IndWhe-14
❑ 83Top-614
❑ 84MaiGuiT-22
❑ 86TidTidP-12
❑ 87TidTidP-15
❑ 87TidTidT-4
❑ 89PacSenL-129
❑ 91MetWIZ-142
❑ 91PacSenL-82
Glynn, Gene
❑ 83WicAerDS-9
❑ 84IndIndTI-22
❑ 85IndIndTI-26
❑ 85UtiBluST-25
❑ 86WesPalBEP-18
❑ 87JamExpP-2553
❑ 88RocExpLC-15
❑ 89JacExpB-27
❑ 89JacExpP-174
❑ 90SpoIndSP-26
❑ 90WatDiaB-23
❑ 90WatDiaP-2395
❑ 91SpoIndC-29
❑ 91SpoIndP-3965
❑ 92BenRocCB-24
❑ 92BenRocF-1488
❑ 94RocPol-27
Glynn, Ryan
❑ 95HudValRTI-23
❑ 98TexLeaC-6
❑ 98TexLeaTPG-14
❑ 98TulDriTI-4
❑ 99Bow-182
❑ 99BowChr-182
❑ 99BowChrG-182
❑ 99BowChrGR-182
❑ 99BowChrI-182
❑ 99BowChrIR-182
❑ 99BowChrR-182
❑ 99BowGol-182
❑ 99BowInt-182
Glynn, Val
❑ 29Zee-130
Gmitter, Joe
❑ 91HelBreSP-10
Gnacinski, Paul
❑ 84PawRedST-8
❑ 86GreBraTI-10
Gnirk, Mike
❑ 97BelSnaB-14
Goar, Jot
❑ 98CamPepP-29
Gobbo, Michael
❑ 85BelBreT-8
❑ 86StoPorP-10
❑ 87ElPasDP-26
Gobel, Donnie
❑ 91AugPirC-7
❑ 91AugPirP-800
Gobert, Chris
❑ 94DanBraC-12
❑ 94DanBraF-3525
❑ 95DanBraTI-13
Gochnaur, John
❑ 03BreE10-60
❑ 90DodTar-285
Goddard, Dick
❑ 97PinFan-PC3
Godfrey, Tim
❑ 98BilMusTI-11
Godfrey, Tyson
❑ 90HunCubP-3275
❑ 91Cla/Bes-432
❑ 91PeoChiC-12
❑ 91PeoChiP-1337
❑ 91PeoChiTI-8
❑ 92PeoChiC-17
❑ 92PeoChiTI-8
Godin, Steve
❑ 91KanCouCC-22
❑ 91KanCouCP-2669
❑ 91KanCouCTI-8
❑ 92FreKeyC-13
❑ 92FreKeyF-1819
Godwin, Glenn
❑ 83MadMusF-25
Goebel, Ed
❑ 24Zee-26
Goedde, Mike
❑ 85CedRapRT-8
❑ 89BilMusP-2049
Goedde, Roger
❑ 94SigRooDP-40
❑ 94SigRooDPS-40
Goedhart, Darrell
❑ 89MarPhiS-12
❑ 90SpaPhiB-4
❑ 90SpaPhiP-2485
❑ 90SpaPhiS-9
❑ 91ClePhiC-4
❑ 91ClePhiP-1615
❑ 92ClePhiC-3
❑ 92ReaPhiF-568
❑ 93ReaPhiF-292
Goelz, Jim
❑ 98YakBeaG-14
Goergen, Todd
❑ 89BatCliP-1927
❑ 90SpaPhiB-5
❑ 90SpaPhiP-2486
❑ 90SpaPhiS-10
❑ 91SpaPhiC-4
❑ 91SpaPhiP-889
❑ 92ClePhiF-2052
❑ 93ReaPhiF-293
Goettsch, Jeff
❑ 87SalAngP-30
Goetz, Barry
❑ 91ChaRanC-6
❑ 91ChaRanP-1310
❑ 92ChaRanC-20
❑ 92ChaRanF-2222
❑ 93TulDriF-2729
❑ 93TulDriTI-10
❑ 94OklCit8F-1492
Goetz, Geoff
❑ 97Bow-429
❑ 97BowChr-289
❑ 97BowChrI-289
❑ 97BowChrIR-289
❑ 97BowChrR-289
❑ 97BowInt-429
❑ 97TopSta-112
❑ 97TopStaAM-112
❑ 98BesAutSS-22
❑ 98BesNumOP-24
❑ 98Bow-122
❑ 98BowChr-122
❑ 98BowChrGA-122
❑ 98BowChrGAR-122
❑ 98BowChrI-122
❑ 98BowChrIR-122
❑ 98BowChrR-122
❑ 98BowGolA-122
❑ 98BowInt-122
❑ 98CapCitBF5-8
❑ 98CapCitBM-8
❑ 98SouAtlLPM-11
❑ 98Top-245
❑ 98TopChr-245
❑ 98TopChrR-245
❑ 98TopDevR-245
❑ 98TopDia-245
❑ 98TopMiniC-245
❑ 99JustheS-23
❑ 99JustheSAC-11
❑ 99JustheSAD-8
❑ 99JustheSJB-23
Goetz, Jack
❑ 75DubPacT-31
Goetz, John
❑ 61TacBan-8
Goetz, Lawrence
❑ 55Bow-311
Goff, Jerry L.
❑ 86BelMarCr-110
❑ 87WauTimP-17
❑ 88SanBerSB-12
❑ 88SanBerSCLC-33
❑ 89WilBilP-631
❑ 89WilBilS-7
❑ 90Bow-112
❑ 90BowTif-112
❑ 90CMC-63
❑ 90IndIndC-13
❑ 90IndIndP-291
❑ 90Lea-476
❑ 90ProAAAF-574
❑ 91Don-499
❑ 91IndIndLD-184
❑ 91IndIndP-467
❑ 91LinDriAAA-184
❑ 91PanFreS-153
❑ 91Sco-834
❑ 91TopDeb90-55
❑ 92IndIndF-1867
❑ 92IndIndS-182
❑ 92SkyAAAF-89
❑ 93BufBisF-520
❑ 94Top-463
❑ 94TopGol-463
❑ 94TopSpa-463
❑ 95TucTotTI-6
❑ 96TusTorB-9
Goff, Mike
❑ 86GreHorP-9
❑ 87BelMarTI-18
❑ 88MidLeaAGS-57
❑ 88WauTimGS-27
❑ 89CalLeaA-14
❑ 89SanBerSB-24
❑ 89SanBerSCLC-72
❑ 90WilBilB-7
❑ 90WilBilP-1053
❑ 90WilBilS-8
❑ 94BelMarF-3233
❑ 96WisTimRB-1
Goff, Tim
❑ 86EugEmeC-32
❑ 87Ft.MyeRP-17
Goff, Wally
❑ 79WauTimT-8
❑ 80PenPilBT-7
❑ 80PenPilCT-14
❑ 81ReaPhiT-10
Gogas, Keith
❑ 91MelBusF-3
❑ 93AusFut-60
Goggin, Chuck
❑ 74OPC-457
❑ 74Top-457
Gogolewski, Bill
❑ 71MLBOffS-539
❑ 71OPC-559
❑ 71SenTealW-10
❑ 71Top-559
❑ 72OPC-424
❑ 72RanTeal-9
❑ 72Top-424
❑ 73OPC-27
❑ 73RanTeal-10
❑ 73Top-27
❑ 74OPC-242
❑ 74Top-242
❑ 76SSP-134
❑ 93RanKee-12
Gogolewski, Chris
❑ 95ChaRivTI-10
Gogolewski, Gogo (Doug)
❑ 87OneYanP-10
❑ 88Ft.LauYS-10
❑ 89Ft.LauYS-6
❑ 90AlbYanP-1032
❑ 90AlbYanSt-5
❑ 90CMC-730
❑ 92ForLauYC-3
❑ 92ForLauYTI-14
❑ 92Ft.LauYF-2605
❑ 93AlbYanF-2156
❑ 94ShrCapF-1598
Gogolin, Elton
❑ 96SouOreTI-19
Gogos, Keith
❑ 95AusFut-49
Goguen, Phil
❑ 88NebCor-21
Gohl, Lefty
❑ 52Par-78
Gohmann, Ken
❑ 86LakTigP-6
❑ 87LakTigP-26
❑ 88GleFalTP-930
❑ 89SarWhiSS-7
Gohr, Greg
❑ 90Bow-347
❑ 90BowTif-347
❑ 90LakTigS-11
❑ 90Sco-679
❑ 91Bow-142
❑ 91LinDriAA-385
❑ 91LonTigLD-385
❑ 91LonTigP-1871
❑ 91TolMudHP-1925
❑ 92Bow-453
❑ 92ProFS7-65
❑ 92SkyAAAF-261
❑ 92TolMudHF-1036
❑ 92TolMudHS-584
❑ 92UppDecML-195
❑ 93Bow-671
❑ 93Don-605
❑ 93FleFinE-210
❑ 93LeaGolR-R6
❑ 93LeaGolRJ-R6
❑ 93OPCPre-17
❑ 93Pin-615
❑ 93StaClu-685
❑ 93StaCluFDI-685
❑ 93StaCluMOP-685
❑ 93Ult-550
❑ 93UppDec-685
❑ 93UppDecGold-685
❑ 94Don-167
❑ 94Fla-293
❑ 94Fle-132
❑ 94SpoRoo-42
❑ 94SpoRooAP-42
❑ 94TolMudHF-1021
❑ 94Top-711
❑ 94TopGol-711
❑ 94TopSpa-711
❑ 95ColCho-478
❑ 95ColChoGS-478
❑ 95ColChoSS-478
❑ 95Lea-139
❑ 95UppDec-421
❑ 95UppDecED-421
❑ 95UppDecEDG-421
❑ 96LeaSigA-79
❑ 96LeaSigAG-79
❑ 96LeaSigAS-79
Goike, Bryan
❑ 92FayGenC-27
❑ 93LakTigC-29
❑ 94LakTigC-30
❑ 95JacSunTI-11
Goins, Scott
❑ 87EveGiaC-3
❑ 89SanJosGB-27
❑ 89SanJosGCLC-233
❑ 89SanJosGP-438
❑ 89SanJosGS-10
Goins, Tim
❑ 92WatDiaC-15
❑ 92WatDiaF-2143
Gokey, Steve
❑ 87ModA'sP-8
❑ 88ModA'sTI-30
❑ 89ModA'sC-6
❑ 89ModA'sCLC-289
Gold, Bret
❑ 81MiaOriT-20
Gold, J.M.
❑ 99199Fin-278
❑ 99Bow-209
❑ 99BowBes-175
❑ 99BowBesAR-175
❑ 99BowBesR-175
❑ 99BowChr-209
❑ 99BowChrG-209
❑ 99BowChrGR-209
❑ 99BowChrI-209
❑ 99BowChrIR-209
❑ 99BowChrR-209
❑ 99BowGol-209
❑ 99BowInt-209
❑ 99FinGolRef-278
❑ 99FinRef-278
❑ 99StaClu-342
❑ 99StaCluFDI-342
❑ 99StaCluOoaK-342
❑ 99StaCluPP-342
❑ 99Top-218
❑ 99TopChr-218
❑ 99TopChrR-218
Gold, Mark
❑ 87WauTimP-23
Gold, Steve
❑ 94HelBreF-3608
❑ 94HelBreSP-5
Goldberg, Lonnie
❑ 93EriSaiC-9
❑ 93EriSaiF-3124
❑ 95ChaRivTI-5
Goldberg, Marc
❑ 90St.LucMS-31
❑ 91St.LucMC-29
❑ 92WesPalBEC-27
Golden Eagles, Tennessee Tech
❑ 89TenTecGE-36
Golden, Brian
❑ 89HamRedS-16
❑ 90EriSaiS-7
Golden, Ike
❑ 81AppFoxT-16
Golden, Jim
❑ 61Top-298
❑ 62Col.45B-8
❑ 62Col45'HC-7
❑ 62Top-568
❑ 63Top-297
❑ 64WhiSoxI-10
❑ 64WhiSoxTS-9
❑ 89AstCol4S-4
❑ 90DodTar-286
Golden, Matt
❑ 94NewJerCC-13
❑ 94NewJerCF-3411
❑ 96StPetCB-9
Golden, Roy
❑ 12T207-67
Goldetsky, Larry
❑ 78MemChiBC-4
❑ 79MemChiT-6
❑ 80MemChiT-7
❑ 83MemChiT-6
Goldgrabe, Curt
❑ 85FreGiaSB-30
Goldie, Jack
❑ 18Zee-79
Goldman, J.
❑ 31Exh-21
Goldpanners, Alaska
❑ 89AlaGol-1
Goldsberry, Gordon
❑ 49AngTeal-12
❑ 52Top-46
❑ 53Top-200
❑ 83TopRep5-46
❑ 91TopArc1-200
Goldsmith, Gary
❑ 93NiaFalRF-3379
❑ 94LakTigC-9
❑ 94LakTigF-3030
❑ 95JacSunTI-12
❑ 97JacSun-13
❑ 98TolMudHQ-18
Goldstein, David R.
❑ 80WesHavWCT-20B
Goldstein, Ike
❑ 87VisOakP-12
Goldstein, Isidore
❑ 34DiaMatCSB-70
Goldthorn, Burk
❑ 82AleDukT-15
❑ 83LynPirT-12
❑ 85PriWilPT-30
❑ 86HawIslP-10
Goldy, Purnal
❑ 62TigPosCF-8
❑ 63Top-516
Golenbock, Peter
❑ 90LitSunW-21
Goliat, Mike
❑ 50Bow-205
❑ 50PhiPhil-8
❑ 51BerRos-B10
❑ 51Bow-77
❑ 58MonRoyF-9
❑ 59O'KAleMR-8
❑ 61UniOil-SP4
❑ 75Phi195T-10
❑ 80Phi195T-10
Goligoski, Jason
❑ 94HicCraC-11
❑ 94HicCraF-2184
❑ 94SouAtlLAF-SAL23
❑ 95PriWilCTI-7
❑ 96NewHavRB-11
❑ 97HigDesMG-10
❑ 98TexLeaC-7
❑ 98TulDriTI-6
Gollehon, Chris
❑ 88BriTigP-1875
❑ 89SpoIndSP-20
Golmont, Van
❑ 89MadMusS-29
❑ 90EriSaiS-8
Golston, Toriano
❑ 94ButCopKSP-15
Goltz, Dave
❑ 73OPC-148
❑ 73Top-148
❑ 74OPC-636
❑ 74Top-636
❑ 75OPC-419
❑ 75Top-419
❑ 75TopMin-419
❑ 75TwiPos-12
❑ 75TwiTeal-14
❑ 76MinTwiP-8
❑ 76OPC-136
❑ 76SSP-218
❑ 76Top-136
❑ 77BurCheD-47
❑ 77Hos-48
❑ 77OPC-73
❑ 77Top-321
❑ 78Hos-96
❑ 78Kel-35
❑ 78OPC-5
❑ 78OPC-142
❑ 78Top-205
❑ 78Top-249
❑ 78TwiFriP-8
❑ 79Hos-16
❑ 79OPC-10
❑ 79Top-27
❑ 79TwiFriP-7
❑ 80DodPol-38
❑ 80OPC-108
❑ 80Top-193
❑ 81Dod-11
❑ 81DodPol-38
❑ 81Fle-127
❑ 81LonBeaPT-23
❑ 81OPC-289
❑ 81Top-548
❑ 82DodPol-38
❑ 82Don-604
❑ 82Fle-6
❑ 82Top-674
❑ 83Fle-90
❑ 83Top-468
❑ 90DodTar-287
Golvin, Walter
❑ 23Zee-6
❑ 24Zee-7
Gomera, Rafael
❑ 97GreFalDTI-13
❑ 98VerBeaDM-26
Gomes, Eugene
❑ 28Zee-50
Gomes, Tony
❑ 98YakBeaG-15
Gomes, Wayne
❑ 94ActPac-6
❑ 94Bow-608
❑ 94BowBes-B66
❑ 94BowBesR-B66
❑ 94Cla-175
❑ 94ClaGolF-36
❑ 94ClaGolN1PLF-LP4
❑ 94ClaGolREF-RE4
❑ 94ClaTriF-T61
❑ 94ClePhiC-15
❑ 94ClePhiF-2522
❑ 94ColC-22
❑ 94ColChoGS-22
❑ 94ColChoSS-22
❑ 94Pin-434
❑ 94PinArtP-434
❑ 94PinMusC-434
❑ 94Sco-494
❑ 94ScoGolR-494
❑ 94SigRoo-28
❑ 94SigRooS-28
❑ 94Top-742
❑ 94TopGol-742
❑ 94TopSpa-742
❑ 94Ult-547
❑ 94UppDec-540
❑ 94UppDecAHNIL-17
❑ 94UppDecED-540
❑ 94UppDecML-63
❑ 95Bes-87
❑ 95Bow-149
❑ 95Exc-242
❑ 95ReaPhiELC-14
❑ 95ReaPhiTI-21
❑ 95SPML-128
❑ 95Top-654

❑ 96Bow-193
❑ 96BowFoi-193
❑ 96ReaPhiB-5
❑ 97PhiCopQ-8
❑ 97ScrRedB-8
❑ 98Pac-380
❑ 98PacOnl-559
❑ 98PacOnlR-559
❑ 98PacOnlWC-559
❑ 98PacPlaB-380
❑ 98PacRedT-380
❑ 98PacSil-380
❑ 98PhiTeal-13
❑ 98UppDec-187
❑ 99Fle-457
❑ 99FleSta9-457
❑ 99FleWarT-457
❑ 99StaClu-257
❑ 99StaCluFDI-257
❑ 99StaCluOoaK-257
❑ 99StaCluPP-257

Gomez, Angel Ponco
❑ 96-97LinVen-95

Gomez, Art
❑ 81CliGiaT-8

Gomez, Augustine
❑ 94HicCraC-12
❑ 94HicCraF-2172
❑ 94VenLinU-140
❑ 95LinVen-135
❑ 96-97LinVen-221

Gomez, Chris
❑ 92ClaDraP-62
❑ 92FroRowDP-34
❑ 92FroRowDPG-34
❑ 92FroRowDPS-34
❑ 93Bow-39
❑ 93ClaFS7-192
❑ 93SelRoo-80T
❑ 93StaCluM-133
❑ 93TolMudHF-1659
❑ 94Bow-321
❑ 94ColC-110
❑ 94ColChoGS-110
❑ 94ColChoSS-110
❑ 94Don-628
❑ 94Fla-294
❑ 94FlaWavotF-B2
❑ 94Fle-133
❑ 94LeaLimR-35
❑ 94OPCDiaD-5
❑ 94Pac-220
❑ 94Pin-414
❑ 94PinArtP-414
❑ 94PinMusC-414
❑ 94Sco-309
❑ 94ScoGolR-309
❑ 94ScoRoo-RT95
❑ 94ScoRooGR-RT95
❑ 94Sel-194
❑ 94SpoRoo-103
❑ 94SpoRooAP-103
❑ 94StaClu-73
❑ 94StaCluFDI-73
❑ 94StaCluGR-73
❑ 94StaCluMOP-73
❑ 94Top-626
❑ 94TopGol-626
❑ 94TopSpa-626
❑ 94Ult-54
❑ 94UppDec-93
❑ 94UppDecED-93
❑ 95Bow-375
❑ 95ColCho-476
❑ 95ColChoGS-476
❑ 95ColChoSE-219
❑ 95ColChoSEGS-219
❑ 95ColChoSESS-219
❑ 95ColChoSS-476
❑ 95Don-172
❑ 95DonPreP-172
❑ 95DonTopotO-77
❑ 95Fin-3
❑ 95FinRef-3
❑ 95Fla-40
❑ 95Fle-54
❑ 95FleRooS-5
❑ 95Lea-35
❑ 95Pac-154
❑ 95PacLatD-15
❑ 95PanSti-66
❑ 95PanSti-108
❑ 95Pin-69
❑ 95PinArtP-69
❑ 95PinMusC-69
❑ 95Sco-116
❑ 95ScoGolR-116
❑ 95ScoPlaTS-116
❑ 95StaClu-383
❑ 95StaCluMOP-383
❑ 95StaCluSTWS-383
❑ 95StaCluVR-202
❑ 95StaCluVRMO-202
❑ 95Stu-53
❑ 95Top-277
❑ 95TopCyb-150
❑ 95TopD3-59
❑ 95TopEmb-42
❑ 95TopEmbGI-42
❑ 95Ult-47
❑ 95UltAllR-2
❑ 95UltAllRGM-2
❑ 95UltGolM-47
❑ 95UltSecYS-2
❑ 95UltSecYSGM-2
❑ 95UppDec-184
❑ 95UppDecED-184
❑ 95UppDecEDG-184
❑ 96ColCho-549
❑ 96ColChoGS-549
❑ 96ColChoSS-549
❑ 96Don-362
❑ 96DonPreP-362
❑ 96EmoXL-61
❑ 96Fla-81
❑ 96Fle-112
❑ 96FleTif-112
❑ 96LeaSigA-80
❑ 96LeaSigAG-80
❑ 96LeaSigAS-80
❑ 96MetUni-60
❑ 96MetUniP-60
❑ 96Pac-309
❑ 96PanSti-149
❑ 96Sco-142
❑ 96StaClu-145
❑ 96StaCluEPB-145
❑ 96StaCluEPG-145
❑ 96StaCluEPS-145
❑ 96StaCluMOP-145
❑ 96Top-134
❑ 96TopGal-123
❑ 96TopGalPPI-123
❑ 96Ult-61
❑ 96UltGolM-61
❑ 96UppDec-72
❑ 97Cir-378
❑ 97CirRav-378
❑ 97ColCho-447
❑ 97Fle-461
❑ 97FleTif-461
❑ 97Pac-423
❑ 97PacLigB-423
❑ 97PacSil-423
❑ 97PadMot-14
❑ 97StaClu-84
❑ 97StaCluMOP-84
❑ 97Top-301
❑ 97Ult-282
❑ 97UltGolME-282
❑ 97UltPlaME-282
❑ 97UppDec-489
❑ 98Fle-505
❑ 98Pac-426
❑ 98PacOnl-636
❑ 98PacOnlR-636
❑ 98PacOnlWC-636
❑ 98PacPlaB-426
❑ 98PacRedT-426
❑ 98PacSil-426
❑ 98PadMot-13
❑ 98StaCluFDI-25
❑ 98StaCluI-25
❑ 98StaCluOneK-25
❑ 98StaCluPP-25
❑ 98Top-117
❑ 98TopChr-117
❑ 98TopChrR-117
❑ 98TopDevR-117
❑ 98TopDia-117
❑ 98TopMiniC-117
❑ 98UppDec-496
❑ 99Fle-328
❑ 99FleSta9-328
❑ 99FleWarT-328
❑ 99Pac-367
❑ 99PacCroC-241
❑ 99PacCroCPB-241
❑ 99PacPlaB-367
❑ 99PacRed-367
❑ 99Top-54
❑ 99TopChr-54
❑ 99TopChrR-54
❑ 99TopMVPP-54
❑ 99UppDec-476
❑ 99UppDecEL1-476
❑ 99UppDecEL2-476
❑ 99UppDecMP-CG
❑ 99Vic-347

Gomez, Dana
❑ 87WinHavRSP-30

Gomez, Dennys
❑ 94EveGiaC-10
❑ 94EveGiaF-3645
❑ 96SanJosGB-15
❑ 97BakBlaB-20
❑ 97BakBlaTI-20

Gomez, Ernesto
❑ 80VenLeaS-156
❑ 93LinVenB-187
❑ 94VenLinU-184

Gomez, Fabio
❑ 88BurlndP-1788
❑ 89Sta-180
❑ 89WatIndS-8
❑ 90KinIndTI-7
❑ 91ColIndC-27
❑ 91KinIndP-329
❑ 92CalLeaACL-2
❑ 92RenSilSCLC-40
❑ 93HunStaF-2088
❑ 94NewHavRF-1556

Gomez, Henry
❑ 87GenCubP-17
❑ 88ChaWheB-14
❑ 90PeoChiTI-23
❑ 91ChaKniLD-133
❑ 91ChaKniP-1684
❑ 91LinDriAA-133
❑ 93LinVenB-49
❑ 93LonTigF-2301
❑ 94VenLinU-205

Gomez, Javier
❑ 96AriBlaDB-19

Gomez, Jorge
❑ 80AshTouT-3
❑ 82BurRanF-12
❑ 82BurRanT-20
❑ 83TulDriT-1
❑ 84TulDriTI-4

Gomez, Jose
❑ 83MiaMarT-14
❑ 85DomLeaS-196

Gomez, Jose Luis
❑ 36NatChiFPR-31
❑ 36OveCanR-17
❑ 77Top-13
❑ 78BluJayP-7
❑ 78Top-573
❑ 79Top-254
❑ 80OPC-95
❑ 80Top-169
❑ 81BraPol-9
❑ 81Don-88
❑ 81Fle-253
❑ 81Top-477
❑ 82Top-372
❑ 89PacSenL-17
❑ 89TopSenL-16
❑ 91PacSenL-143

Gomez, Juan A.
❑ 75TucTorC-12
❑ 75TucTorTI-3
❑ 76TusTorCr-33
❑ 77ModA'sC-22

Gomez, Lefty (Vernon)
❑ 29Zee-131
❑ 32OrbPinNP-120
❑ 32USCar*-31
❑ 33ButCanV-20
❑ 33CraJacP-8
❑ 33DelR33-14
❑ 33Gou-216
❑ 33TatOrbSDR-151
❑ 33WorCig-47
❑ 34BabRutG-27
❑ 34BatR31-23
❑ 34BatR31-86
❑ 34ButPreR-26
❑ 34ExhFou-13
❑ 35ExhFou-13
❑ 35GouPreR-11
❑ 36ExhFou-13
❑ 36GouBWR-14
❑ 36GouWidPPR-A39
❑ 36NatChiFPR-32
❑ 36NatChiFPR-92
❑ 36OveCanR-18
❑ 36R31PasP-34
❑ 36WheBB5-1
❑ 36WorWidGV-56
❑ 37ExhFou-13
❑ 38BasTabP-12
❑ 38CloFotW-30
❑ 38ExhFou-13
❑ 38OurNatGPP-12
❑ 39ExhSal-20
❑ 39GouPreR303A-17
❑ 39GouPreR303B-9
❑ 39PlaBal-48
❑ 39WheBB12-3
❑ 39WorWidGTP-17
❑ 40PlaBal-6
❑ 41DouPlaR-61
❑ 41PlaBal-72
❑ 42GilRazL-1
❑ 47PM1StaP1-72
❑ 48BabRutS-24
❑ 60Fle-54
❑ 61Fle-34
❑ 72LauGreF-18
❑ 72TCMthe3-32
❑ 72TCMthe3-81
❑ 75ShaPiz-3
❑ 75YanDyn1T-18
❑ 76RowExh-4
❑ 76ShaPiz-129
❑ 77BobParHoF-89
❑ 77GalGloG-76
❑ 77GalGloG-185
❑ 77GalGloG-265
❑ 79DiaGre-11
❑ 80MarExhH-13
❑ 80PacLeg-117
❑ 80PerHaloFP-129
❑ 80PerHaloFPS-17
❑ 80SSPHOF-129
❑ 81ConTSN-44
❑ 81DiaStaCD-118
❑ 82TCMGreP-20
❑ 83BigLeaCOA-4
❑ 83ConMar-22
❑ 83YanASFY-16
❑ 86ConSer1-45
❑ 86SpoDecG-9
❑ 87ConSer2-2
❑ 88ConAmeA-12
❑ 88ConSer5-15
❑ 89HOFStiB-76
❑ 89PerCelP-16
❑ 89YanCitAG-3
❑ 90PerGreM-44
❑ 90SweBasG-84
❑ 90YanMomPRP-8
❑ 91ConTSN-67
❑ 91ConTSNP-662
❑ 91HomCooC-3
❑ 91SweBasG-129
❑ 92ConTSN-536
❑ 92ConTSNAP-662G
❑ 92YanWIZA-23
❑ 92YanWIZH-12
❑ 93ActPacA-105
❑ 93ActPacA2-39G
❑ 93ConTSN-662
❑ 94ConTSN-1063
❑ 94ConTSN-1088
❑ 94ConTSNB-1063
❑ 94ConTSNB-1088
❑ 96NoiSatP-12

Gomez, Leo
❑ 87HagSunP-5
❑ 89BlaYNPRWL-76
❑ 89EasLeaAP-3
❑ 89HagSunB-1
❑ 89HagSunP-280
❑ 89HagSunS-10
❑ 90Bow-262
❑ 90BowTif-262
❑ 90CMC-311
❑ 90HagSunDGB-12
❑ 90ProAAAF-466
❑ 90RocRedWC-10
❑ 90RocRedWGC-6
❑ 90RocRedWP-709
❑ 90TriAllGP-AAA10
❑ 91BalOriP-9
❑ 91Bow-88
❑ 91Cla1-T12
❑ 91Cla3-T31
❑ 91ClaGam-164
❑ 91Don-35
❑ 91Fle-472
❑ 91Lea-35
❑ 91LeaPre-13
❑ 91OPCPre-52
❑ 91OriCro-158
❑ 91Sco-725
❑ 91ScoRoo-20
❑ 91SevCoi-A3
❑ 91Stu-3
❑ 91TopDeb90-56
❑ 91TopTra-47T
❑ 91TopTraT-47T
❑ 91Ult-16
❑ 91UppDec-6
❑ 92BalOriP-11
❑ 92Bow-344
❑ 92Cla2-T58
❑ 92ClaGam-58
❑ 92Don-199
❑ 92Fle-8
❑ 92Lea-87
❑ 92LeaBlaG-87
❑ 92OPC-84
❑ 92OPCPre-161
❑ 92PanSti-67
❑ 92Pin-356
❑ 92PinTea2-52
❑ 92Sco-240
❑ 92Sco100RS-66
❑ 92ScoImpP-16
❑ 92StaClu-664
❑ 92Top-84
❑ 92TopGol-84
❑ 92TopGolW-84
❑ 92TopMic-84
❑ 92TriPla-131
❑ 92Ult-4
❑ 92UppDec-161
❑ 93BalOriP-10
❑ 93Bow-381
❑ 93Don-31
❑ 93Fle-167
❑ 93Lea-155
❑ 93OPC-117
❑ 93PacSpa-17
❑ 93PanSti-74
❑ 93Pin-351
❑ 93Sco-104
❑ 93Sel-66
❑ 93StaClu-536
❑ 93StaCluFDI-536
❑ 93StaCluMOP-536
❑ 93Stu-99
❑ 93Top-164
❑ 93TopGol-164
❑ 93TopInaM-164
❑ 93TopInaR-164
❑ 93TopMic-164
❑ 93Ult-140
❑ 93UppDec-132
❑ 93UppDecGold-132
❑ 94BalOriP-11
❑ 94ColC-615
❑ 94ColChoGS-615
❑ 94ColChoSS-615
❑ 94Don-576
❑ 94Fla-254
❑ 94FleUpd-3
❑ 94OriPro-39
❑ 94OriUSPC-5S
❑ 94OriUSPC-10D
❑ 94Pac-31
❑ 94Pin-180
❑ 94PinArtP-180
❑ 94PinMusC-180
❑ 94Sco-55
❑ 94ScoGolR-55
❑ 94Sel-338
❑ 94Top-506
❑ 94TopGol-506
❑ 94TopSpa-506
❑ 95BalOriP-20
❑ 95ColCho-332
❑ 95ColChoGS-332
❑ 95ColChoSS-332
❑ 95Don-41
❑ 95DonPreP-41
❑ 95DonTopotO-7
❑ 95Fla-3
❑ 95Fle-7
❑ 95Lea-19
❑ 95Pac-21
❑ 95Pin-103
❑ 95PinArtP-103
❑ 95PinMusC-103
❑ 95Sco-31
❑ 95ScoGolR-31
❑ 95ScoPlaTS-31
❑ 95StaClu-373
❑ 95StaCluMOP-373
❑ 95StaCluSTWS-373
❑ 95StaCluVR-196
❑ 95StaCluVRMO-196
❑ 95Top-408
❑ 95TopCyb-208
❑ 95Ult-255
❑ 95UltGolM-255
❑ 95UppDec-367
❑ 95UppDecED-367
❑ 95UppDecEDG-367
❑ 96CubFle-5
❑ 96FleUpd-U109
❑ 96FleUpdTC-U109
❑ 96LeaSigA-81
❑ 96LeaSigAG-81
❑ 96LeaSigAS-81
❑ 97Fle-274
❑ 97FleTif-274
❑ 97Pac-248
❑ 97PacLigB-248
❑ 97PacSil-248
❑ 97Sco-137
❑ 97ScoArtPWB-137
❑ 97ScoPreS-137
❑ 97ScoShoS-137
❑ 97ScoShoSAP-137

Gomez, Luis
❑ 75TwiPos-13
❑ 75TwiTeal-15
❑ 77TacTwiDQ-2B
❑ 78OPC-121
❑ 79BluJayBY-9
❑ 79OPC-128
❑ 86BluJayGT-3

Gomez, Marcos
❑ 82BelBreFr-10

Gomez, Miguel
❑ 78DunBluJT-9

Gomez, Miguel Angel
❑ 96DunBluJUTI-2
❑ 97DunBluJTI-10

Gomez, Mike
❑ 92BatCliCB-18
❑ 92BatCliF-3272
❑ 93ClePhiC-11
❑ 93ClePhiF-2689
❑ 94ReaPhiF-2068

Gomez, Orlando
❑ 82TulDriT-23
❑ 83BurRanF-27
❑ 83BurRanT-26
❑ 84TulDriTI-23
❑ 85TulDriTI-23
❑ 86WatIndP-11
❑ 87BufBisP-25
❑ 88GasRanP-1009
❑ 89GasRanP-1017
❑ 89GasRanS-NNO
❑ 89SouAtlLAGS-2
❑ 90GasRanB-25
❑ 90GasRanP-2536
❑ 90GasRanS-26
❑ 90SouAtlLAS-24
❑ 91RanMot-28
❑ 92RanMot-28
❑ 93AppFoxCB-27
❑ 93AppFoxFI-2477
❑ 93RanKee-161
❑ 95EveAqaTI-7
❑ 96PorCitRB-1

Gomez, Pat
❑ 87PeoChiP-13
❑ 87PeoChiPW-2
❑ 88ChaWheB-13
❑ 89BlaYNPRWL-60
❑ 89WinSpiS-8
❑ 90Bes-49
❑ 90GreBraB-4
❑ 91GreBraC-1
❑ 91GreBraLD-207
❑ 91GreBraP-2995
❑ 91HunStaC-26
❑ 91LinDriAA-207
❑ 91RicBraBC-34
❑ 92RicBraBB-15
❑ 92RicBraF-371
❑ 92RicBraRC-6
❑ 92RicBraS-429
❑ 92SkyAAAF-196
❑ 93Bow-82
❑ 93Don-266
❑ 93FleFinE-139
❑ 93PacSpa-595
❑ 93Pin-610

- 93Sco-310
- 93Ult-471
- 94Fle-663
- 94FleUpd-193
- 94GiaMot-24
- 94Pac-523
- 95GiaMot-22
- 95Pac-377
- 97RicBraBC-9

Gomez, Paul
- 96StLucMTI-2

Gomez, Phil
- 93ElmPioC-8
- 93ElmPioF-3817

Gomez, Pierre
- 90MiaMirIS-8

Gomez, Preston (Pedro)
- 60DarFar-10
- 61UniOil-SP5
- 69OPC-74
- 69PadVol-5
- 69Top-74
- 70OPC-513
- 70Top-513
- 71OPC-737
- 71Top-737
- 72Top-637
- 73OPC-624
- 73Top-624
- 74AstFouTIP-1
- 74OPC-31
- 74Top-31
- 75AstPos-10
- 75OPC-487
- 75SSP18-6
- 75Top-487
- 75TopMin-487
- 76St.LouCP-12
- 80Top-381
- 86PadGreT-12
- 87AstShowSTh-9

Gomez, Ramon
- 96HicCraB-8

Gomez, Randy
- 84PhoGiaC-20
- 85DomLeaS-81
- 85PhoGiaC-179
- 86PhoFirP-6
- 87HawIsIP-24

Gomez, Ruben
- 47PM1StaP1-73
- 47StaPinP2-16
- 54NewYorJA-23
- 54Top-220
- 55GiaGolS-5
- 55Top-71
- 55TopDouH-89
- 56GiaJayP-3
- 56Top-9
- 56TopPin-39
- 57GiaJayP-4
- 57Top-58
- 58GiaJayP-4
- 58GiaSFCB-9
- 58Top-335
- 59Top-535
- 60Top-82
- 60TopVen-82
- 61Top-377
- 67Top-427A
- 67Top-427B
- 79TCM50-98
- 94TopArc1-220
- 94TopArc1G-220

Gomez, Rudy
- 91GenCubC-8
- 91GenCubP-4223
- 92WinSpiC-18
- 92WinSpiF-1213
- 93DayCubC-9
- 94OrlCubF-1391
- 95OrlCubF-18
- 97NorNavTI-10
- 97TexAllM-17
- 98ColCliD-9
- 98ColCliM-13

Gomez, Steve
- 86OrlTwiP-7
- 87OrlTwiP-13

Gonder, Jesse
- 59RedEnq-9
- 61Yan61RL-40
- 62RedEnq-10
- 62RedJayP-4
- 63RedEnq-10
- 63RedFreBC-6
- 63Top-29A
- 63Top-29B
- 64MetJayP-4
- 64MetTeal-3
- 64Top-457
- 64TopCoi-43
- 64TopSta-30
- 64TopStaU-28
- 65Top-423
- 66PirEasH-20
- 66Top-528
- 67CokCapPi-10
- 67PirTeal-8
- 67Top-301
- 67TopPirS-10
- 69Top-617
- 76Met63 S-6
- 78TCM60I-122
- 78TCM60I-238
- 91MetWIZ-143
- 91YanRinP12-2
- 92YanWIZ6-47

Gongora, Christopher
- 94DanBraC-13
- 94DanBraF-3526

Gonring, Doug
- 87AshTouP-8

Gonsalves, Dennis
- 83MadMusF-7
- 84MadMusP-16

Gontkosky, Rob
- 93KinMetC-12
- 93KinMetF-3791
- 94CapCitBC-7
- 94CapCitBF-1745

Gonzales, Ben (Benjamin)
- 89AubAstP-2171
- 90AshTouP-2740
- 91BurAstC-3
- 91BurAstP-2794
- 92ClaFS7-437
- 92OscAstC-16
- 92OscAstF-2523
- 93JacGenF-2103

Gonzales, Dan
- 77EvaTriT-12
- 80EvaTriT-20

Gonzales, Eddie
- 87SanJosBP-25

Gonzales, Javier
- 96HelBreTI-32

Gonzales, John
- 90AshTouC-21
- 91AshTouP-579

Gonzales, Johnny
- 95AshTouTI-12

Gonzales, Jose
- 80ChaO'sP-9
- 80ChaO'sW-9
- 82ArkTraT-13
- 87SpoTeaP-14
- 88AlbDukP-258
- 89AlbDukCm-17
- 89DodStaSV-10
- 98AshTouM-5

Gonzales, Larry
- 87HawRai-7
- 87PanAmTUBI-18
- 87PanAmTURB-10
- 89QuaCitAB-21
- 89QuaCitAGS-28
- 89SalDodTI-12
- 90QuaCitAGS-17
- 91MelBusF-4
- 91MidAngLD-435
- 91MidAngOHP-12
- 91MidAngP-436
- 92EdmTraS-159
- 92SkyAAAF-79
- 93VanCanF-2601
- 94MidAngOHP-5

Gonzales, Luis
- 72CedRapCT-14

Gonzales, Rene C.
- 83MemChiT-3
- 84IndIndTI-25
- 84IndIndTI-26
- 85IndIndTI-11
- 86IndIndTI-10
- 87BalOriP-13
- 88Don-582
- 88Fle-560
- 88FleGlo-560
- 88OriFreB-88
- 88OriPos-12
- 88StaLinO-5
- 88Top-98
- 88TopBig-209
- 88TopTif-98
- 89BalOriP-8
- 89Don-377
- 89OPC-213
- 89OriFreB-88
- 89Sco-585
- 89Top-213
- 89TopBig-87
- 89TopSti-234
- 89TopTif-213
- 90BalOriP-7
- 90Don-401
- 90OPC-787
- 90Sco-118
- 90Top-787
- 90TopTif-787
- 91BluJayFS-10
- 91BluJayS-14
- 91Bow-25
- 91Fle-473
- 91Lea-490
- 91OPC-377
- 91OPCPre-53
- 91OriCro-159
- 91Sco-638
- 91StaClu-406
- 91Top-377
- 91TopDesS-377
- 91TopMic-377
- 91TopTif-377
- 92AngPol-11
- 92Don-274
- 92OPC-681
- 92Sco-582
- 92ScoRoo-75T
- 92StaClu-704
- 92StaCluECN-704
- 92Top-681
- 92TopGol-681
- 92TopGolW-681
- 92TopMic-681
- 92TopTra-42T
- 92TopTraG-42T
- 92UppDec-729
- 93AngMot-14
- 93AngPol-11
- 93AngStaCl-15
- 93Don-785
- 93FleFinE-182
- 93Lea-345
- 93OPC-184
- 93PacSpa-47
- 93PanSti-11
- 93Pin-55
- 93Sco-604
- 93Sel-379
- 93StaClu-121
- 93StaCluFDI-121
- 93StaCluMOP-121
- 93Top-266
- 93TopGol-266
- 93TopInaM-266
- 93TopInaR-266
- 93TopMic-266
- 93Ult-164
- 93UppDec-188
- 93UppDecGold-188
- 94ChaKniF-902
- 94Don-640
- 94Fle-57
- 94OriPro-40
- 94Pin-364
- 94PinArtP-364
- 94PinMusC-364
- 94Sco-455
- 94ScoGolR-455
- 94Top-141
- 94TopGol-141
- 94TopSpa-141
- 95Pac-120
- 97ColSprSTI-7
- 97Pac-199
- 97PacLigB-199
- 97PacSil-199

Gonzales, Todd
- 87WatIndP-11
- 88KinIndS-9
- 89CanIndB-16
- 89CanIndP-1320
- 89CanIndS-8

Gonzales, Tommy
- 80PhoGiaVNB-25
- 81PhoGiaVNB-26

Gonzalez, Alex
- 96KanCouCUTI-6
- 97Bes-66
- 97BesAutSBPP-16
- 97BesAutSC-7
- 97Bow-298
- 97BowBes-104
- 97BowBesAR-104
- 97BowBesR-104
- 97BowChr-206
- 97BowChrI-206
- 97BowChrIR-206
- 97BowChrR-206
- 97BowInt-298
- 97EasLeaTPB-23
- 97PorSeaD-11
- 98BesDiaB-17
- 98Bow99ROYF-ROY10
- 98BowBes-165
- 98BowBesAR-165
- 98BowBesMIF-MI14
- 98BowBesMIFAR-MI14
- 98BowBesMIFR-MI14
- 98BowBesR-165
- 98BowChr-73
- 98BowChrGA-73
- 98BowChrGAR-73
- 98BowChrI-73
- 98BowChrIR-73
- 98BowChrR-73
- 98BowGolA-73
- 98BowInt-73
- 98ChaKniQ-12
- 98ColCho-423
- 98ColChoPCR-423
- 98E-X2Sig2001-14
- 98FleUpd-U35
- 98PorSeaD5AQ-10
- 98SP Aut-27
- 98SP MinDTSPE-DS30
- 98SP MinPE-60
- 98SP MinSTHPE-H24
- 98SPMin-60
- 98SPMinDTS-DS30
- 98SPMinSTH-H24
- 98SPxFin-187
- 98SPxFinR-187
- 98SPxFinS-187
- 98StaCluFDI-365
- 98StaCluI-365
- 98StaCluOneK-365
- 98StaCluPP-365
- 98Top-488
- 98TopChr-488
- 98TopChrR-488
- 98TopDevR-488
- 98TopDia-488
- 98TopMiniC-488
- 98UppDec-527
- 98UppDec-580
- 98UppDecDS-DS3
- 98UppDecR-114
- 98UppDecRNF-NF14
- 99199Fin-139
- 99Bow-201
- 99BowBes-116
- 99BowBesAR-116
- 99BowBesMI-M1
- 99BowBesMIAR-M1
- 99BowBesMIR-M1
- 99BowBesR-116
- 99BowChr-201
- 99BowChrG-201
- 99BowChrGR-201
- 99BowChrIR-201
- 99BowChrR-201
- 99BowChrSC-SC9
- 99BowChrSCR-SC9
- 99BowGol-201
- 99BowInt-201
- 99BowScoC-SC9
- 99CroRoyB-58
- 99CroRoyL-58
- 99CroRoyOD-58
- 99DumSet-AG
- 99DumSet-AG
- 99E-X Cen-72
- 99E-X CenECFut-72
- 99E-X CenECNow-72
- 99FinFutF-FF7
- 99FinGolRef-139
- 99FinRef-139
- 99FlaShoLeg1-97
- 99FlaShoLeg2-97
- 99FlaShoLeg3-97
- 99FlaShoLegM1-97
- 99FlaShoLegM2-97
- 99FlaShoLegM3-97
- 99FlaShoR1-97
- 99FlaShoR2-97
- 99FlaShoR3-97
- 99Fle-309
- 99FleBri-169
- 99FleBri2G-169
- 99FleBriBlu-169
- 99FleBriGol-169
- 99FleMys-21
- 99FleMysG-21
- 99FleMysM-21
- 99FleSta9-309
- 99FleWarT-125
- 99MetUni-259
- 99MetUniGM-259
- 99MetUniPMG-259
- 99Pac-176
- 99PacAur-74
- 99PacAurOD-74
- 99PacCroC-114
- 99PacCroC-29
- 99PacCroCPB-114
- 99PacInv-60
- 99PacInvOD-60
- 99PacInvPB-60
- 99PacOme-99
- 99PacOmeC-99
- 99PacOmeG-99
- 99PacOmePB-99
- 99PacPar-95
- 99PacParC-95
- 99PacParG-95
- 99PacParHoloGold-95
- 99PacParHS-95
- 99PacParOD-95
- 99PacParPB-95
- 99PacParRed-95
- 99PacPlaB-176
- 99PacPri-61
- 99PacPriHB-61
- 99PacPriHG-61
- 99PacPriHM-61
- 99PacPriHP-61
- 99PacPriRed-61
- 99PacPriS-89
- 99PacPriS206-89
- 99PacPriS206R-89
- 99PacRed-176
- 99Rev-57
- 99RevPremDate-57
- 99RevRet-57
- 99RevShaSS-57
- 99SkyPre-272
- 99SkyPre-272
- 99SkyPreDD-10
- 99SkyPreR-272
- 99SkyPreR-272
- 99SkyThu-164
- 99SkyThuRant-164
- 99SkyThuRave-164
- 99SP Aut-101
- 99SP AutC-AG
- 99SP AutCG-AG
- 99SP SigAuto-AG
- 99SP SigAutoG-AG
- 99SP TopP-3
- 99SP TopP-52
- 99SP TopPDtS-D6
- 99SP TopPPE-3
- 99SP TopPPE-52
- 99SpoIll-57
- 99SPSig-44
- 99SPx-95
- 99SPxFinR-95
- 99SPxFinS-95
- 99StaClu-164
- 99StaCluC-SCC34
- 99StaCluCR-SCC34
- 99StaCluFDI-164
- 99StaCluOoaK-164
- 99StaCluPP-164
- 99ThuSkySupR-164
- 99Top-247
- 99TopAll-AM20
- 99TopChr-247
- 99TopChrA-AE20
- 99TopChrAR-AE20
- 99TopChrR-247
- 99TopGal-137
- 99TopGalPP-137
- 99TopGalPPI-137
- 99TopMVPP-247
- 99TopSta-41
- 99TopSta1Foil-41
- 99TopSta2Foil-41
- 99TopStaBFFoil-BF6
- 99TopStaFoil-41
- 99TopStaOS-41
- 99TopStaTS-41
- 99TopTekFP-F4
- 99UD Cho-6
- 99UD ChoPCR-6
- 99UDHoloUDA-AG
- 99Ult-239
- 99UltGolM-239
- 99UltMas-239
- 99UltPlaM-239
- 99UppDec-374
- 99UppDecBD-116
- 99UppDecBDD-116
- 99UppDecBDQ-116
- 99UppDecBDT-116
- 99UppDecCL-114
- 99UppDecCLCC-114
- 99UppDecCLM-C37
- 99UppDecE-39
- 99UppDecEFXG-39
- 99UppDecEL1-374
- 99UppDecEL2-374
- 99UppDecM-83
- 99UppDecMGS-83
- 99UppDecMHFS-83
- 99UppDecMP-83
- 99UppDecMP-AG
- 99UppDecMSS-83
- 99UppDecO-69
- 99UppDecOSO-69
- 99UppDecR-35
- 99UppDecRG-35
- 99UppDecROSS-S28
- 99UppDecROSS-S28
- 99UppDecRP-35
- 99Vic-155

Gonzalez, Alex Scott
- 92Bow-596
- 92MyrBeaHC-11
- 92MyrBeaHF-2203
- 92UppDecML-60
- 92UppDecML-317
- 93Bow-374
- 93Bow-603
- 93ClaFS7-51
- 93ClaFS7-72
- 93ClaGolF-128
- 93ExcFS7-243
- 93KnoSmoF-1257
- 93SP-278
- 93UppDec-456
- 93UppDecGold-456
- 94ActPacP-2
- 94Bow-380
- 94Bow-469
- 94BowPre-6
- 94ColC-8
- 94ColChoGS-8
- 94ColChoSS-8
- 94ExcAllF-5
- 94ExcFS7-143
- 94Fin-433
- 94FinJum-433
- 94FinRef-433
- 94FleUpd-97
- 94FUnPac-139
- 94LeaLimR-46
- 94OPC-258
- 94OPCHotP-8
- 94Pin-505
- 94PinArtP-505
- 94PinMusC-505
- 94ScoRoo-RT145
- 94ScoRooGR-RT145
- 94Sel-178
- 94SelRooS-RS16
- 94SP-42
- 94SPDieC-42
- 94SpoRoo-76
- 94SpoRooAP-76
- 94SpoRooRS-TR6
- 94StaClu-695
- 94StaCluFDI-695
- 94StaCluGR-695
- 94StaCluMOP-695
- 94SyrChiTI-14
- 94TedWil-121
- 94Top-67
- 94TopGol-67
- 94TopSpa-67
- 94TriAAF-AAA18
- 94UppDec-13

❑ 94UppDecED-13
❑ 94UppDecML-1
❑ 94UppDecML-97
❑ 94UppDecML-150
❑ 94UppDecMLPotYF-PY4
❑ 94UppDecMLT1PJF-TP3
❑ 94UppDecMLT1PMF-3
❑ 94UppDecNG-4
❑ 94UppDecNGED-4
❑ 94VenLinU-119
❑ 95ActPac2G-5G
❑ 95ActPacF-11
❑ 95ActPacF-66
❑ 95Baz-126
❑ 95BluJayOH-14
❑ 95Bow-430
❑ 95BowBes-R85
❑ 95BowBesR-R85
❑ 95ColCho-138
❑ 95ColChoGS-138
❑ 95ColChoSE-53
❑ 95ColChoSEGS-53
❑ 95ColChoSESS-53
❑ 95ColChoSS-138
❑ 95Don-69
❑ 95DonPreP-69
❑ 95DonTopotO-173
❑ 95Emo-93
❑ 95EmoRoo-5
❑ 95Fin-251
❑ 95FinRef-251
❑ 95Fla-315
❑ 95Fle-93
❑ 95Lea-206
❑ 95LeaGolR-15
❑ 95LeaLim-71
❑ 95Pac-444
❑ 95PacLatD-16
❑ 95PacPri-141
❑ 95Pin-193
❑ 95PinArtP-193
❑ 95PinMusC-193
❑ 95Sco-597
❑ 95ScoGolR-597
❑ 95ScoHaloG-HG73
❑ 95ScoPlaTS-597
❑ 95ScoRooDT-RDT2
❑ 95Sel-95
❑ 95SelArtP-95
❑ 95SelCanM-CM7
❑ 95SelCer-112
❑ 95SelCerMG-112
❑ 95SelCerPU-6
❑ 95SelCerPU9-6
❑ 95SP-206
❑ 95Spo-161
❑ 95SpoArtP-161
❑ 95SPSil-206
❑ 95SPSpeF-25
❑ 95StaClu-526
❑ 95StaCluMOP-526
❑ 95StaCluSTWS-526
❑ 95Sum-125
❑ 95SumNewA-NA6
❑ 95SumNthD-125
❑ 95SumSam-125
❑ 95Top-267
❑ 95UC3-116
❑ 95UC3ArtP-116
❑ 95UC3CleS-CS10
❑ 95UC3CleS-PCS10
❑ 95Ult-119
❑ 95UltGolM-119
❑ 95UppDec-212
❑ 95UppDecED-212
❑ 95UppDecEDG-212
❑ 95UppDecPAW-H12
❑ 95UppDecPAWE-H12
❑ 95UppDecSE-67
❑ 95UppDecSEG-67
❑ 95Zen-148
❑ 96-97LinVen-140
❑ 96BesAutS-32
❑ 96BluJayOH-10
❑ 96Bow-19
❑ 96BowFoi-19
❑ 96ColCho-353
❑ 96ColChoGS-353
❑ 96ColChoSS-353
❑ 96Don-52
❑ 96DonPreP-52
❑ 96EmoXL-131
❑ 96Fin-B128
❑ 96FinRef-B128
❑ 96Fla-183
❑ 96Fle-273
❑ 96FleTif-273
❑ 96Lea-141
❑ 96LeaPrePB-141
❑ 96LeaPrePG-141
❑ 96LeaPrePS-141
❑ 96MetUni-119
❑ 96MetUniP-119
❑ 96Pac-449
❑ 96PacPri-P143
❑ 96PacPriG-P143
❑ 96PanSti-164
❑ 96Pin-204
❑ 96PinAfi-142
❑ 96PinAfiAP-142
❑ 96PinArtP-104
❑ 96PinFoil-204
❑ 96PinSta-104
❑ 96Sco-156
❑ 96ScoDugC-A91
❑ 96ScoDugCAP-A91
❑ 96Sel-112
❑ 96SelArtP-112
❑ 96SelTeaN-7
❑ 96SP-182
❑ 96StaClu-233
❑ 96StaCluMOP-233
❑ 96Stu-2
❑ 96StuPrePB-2
❑ 96StuPrePG-2
❑ 96StuPrePS-2
❑ 96Sum-67
❑ 96SumAbo&B-67
❑ 96SumArtP-67
❑ 96SumFoi-67
❑ 96Top-404
❑ 96TopChr-162
❑ 96TopChrR-162
❑ 96TopGal-114
❑ 96TopGalPPI-114
❑ 96Ult-145
❑ 96UltGolM-145
❑ 96UppDec-214
❑ 96ZenMoz-15
❑ 97BluJayB-5
❑ 97BluJayOH-11
❑ 97BluJayS-1
❑ 97BluJayS-51
❑ 97BluJayS-5
❑ 97Cir-89
❑ 97CirRav-89
❑ 97ColCho-506
❑ 97Don-202
❑ 97DonEli-90
❑ 97DonEliGS-90
❑ 97DonGolPP-202
❑ 97DonSilPP-202
❑ 97Fle-239
❑ 97FleTif-239
❑ 97Lea-89
❑ 97LeaFraM-89
❑ 97LeaFraMDC-89
❑ 97MetUni-183
❑ 97NewPin-49
❑ 97NewPinAP-49
❑ 97NewPinMC-49
❑ 97NewPinPP-49
❑ 97Pac-219
❑ 97PacLigB-219
❑ 97PacSil-219
❑ 97Pin-114
❑ 97PinArtP-PP114
❑ 97PinMusC-114
❑ 97PinPrePla-114
❑ 97Sco-40
❑ 97ScoArtPWB-40
❑ 97ScoPreS-40
❑ 97ScoShoS-40
❑ 97ScoShoSAP-40
❑ 97StaClu-122
❑ 97StaCluMOP-122
❑ 97Stu-135
❑ 97StuPrePG-135
❑ 97StuPrePS-135
❑ 97Top-155
❑ 97TopGal-99
❑ 97TopGalPPI-99
❑ 97Ult-143
❑ 97UltGolME-143
❑ 97UltPlaME-143
❑ 97UppDec-513
❑ 98Bow-73
❑ 98CirThu-76
❑ 98CirThuRav-76
❑ 98CirThuSupRav-76
❑ 98ColCho-528
❑ 98Fin-199
❑ 98FinNo--199
❑ 98FinNo-R-199
❑ 98FinRef-199
❑ 98Fle-281
❑ 98Pac-221
❑ 98PacOme-248
❑ 98PacOmeR-248
❑ 98PacOnl-763
❑ 98PacOnlR-763
❑ 98PacOnlWC-763
❑ 98PacPar-114
❑ 98PacParC-114
❑ 98PacParG-114
❑ 98PacParHS-114
❑ 98PacParPB-114
❑ 98PacParR-114
❑ 98PacPlaB-221
❑ 98PacRedT-221
❑ 98PacSil-221
❑ 98Pin-137
❑ 98PinPreP-137
❑ 98ScoRT-65
❑ 98StaCluFDI-357
❑ 98StaCluI-357
❑ 98StaCluOneK-357
❑ 98StaCluPP-357
❑ 98Top-109
❑ 98TopChr-109
❑ 98TopChrR-109
❑ 98TopDevR-109
❑ 98TopDia-109
❑ 98TopMiniC-109
❑ 98TopOpeD-56
❑ 99199Fin-71
❑ 99Bow-63
❑ 99BowChr-63
❑ 99BowChrG-63
❑ 99BowChrGR-63
❑ 99BowChrI-63
❑ 99BowChrI-201
❑ 99BowChrIR-63
❑ 99BowChrR-63
❑ 99BowGol-63
❑ 99BowInt-63
❑ 99FinGolRef-71
❑ 99FinRef-71
❑ 99Fle-125
❑ 99FleSta9-125
❑ 99FleWarT-309
❑ 99MetUni-58
❑ 99MetUniGM-58
❑ 99MetUniPMG-58
❑ 99Pac-443
❑ 99PacAur-198
❑ 99PacAurOD-198
❑ 99PacCroC-298
❑ 99PacCroCPB-298
❑ 99PacPar-246
❑ 99PacParC-246
❑ 99PacParG-246
❑ 99PacParHoloGold-246
❑ 99PacParHS-246
❑ 99PacParOD-246
❑ 99PacParPB-246
❑ 99PacParRed-246
❑ 99PacPlaB-443
❑ 99PacPri-150
❑ 99PacPriHB-150
❑ 99PacPriHG-150
❑ 99PacPriHM-150
❑ 99PacPriHP-150
❑ 99PacPriRed-150
❑ 99PacRed-443
❑ 99SkyPre-9
❑ 99SkyPreR-9
❑ 99StaClu-89
❑ 99StaCluFDI-89
❑ 99StaCluOoaK-89
❑ 99StaCluPP-89
❑ 99Top-305
❑ 99TopChr-305
❑ 99TopChrR-305
❑ 99TopMVPP-305
❑ 99TopStaBF-BF6
❑ 99UppDec-226
❑ 99UppDecEL1-226
❑ 99UppDecEL2-226
❑ 99Vic-420

Gonzalez, Angel
❑ 86WinHavRSP-9
❑ 87NewBriRSP-4
❑ 88NewBriRSP-910
❑ 88PawRedSC-17
❑ 88PawRedSP-462
❑ 89PawRedSC-22
❑ 89PawRedSP-684
❑ 89PawRedSTI-9
❑ 90CMC-266
❑ 90PawRedSC-15
❑ 90PawRedSDD-7
❑ 90PawRedSP-468
❑ 90ProAAAF-440
❑ 90TopTVRS-44
❑ 91LinDriAAA-257
❑ 91NasSouLD-257
❑ 91NasSouP-2162

Gonzalez, Arturo
❑ 73CedRapAT-1
❑ 74CedRapAT-4
❑ 85PorBeaC-33
❑ 86PhiTas-NNO
❑ 86PorBeaP-6

Gonzalez, Carlos
❑ 86Ft.MyeRP-12
❑ 87AppFoxP-14
❑ 88BasCitRS-12
❑ 89BasCitRS-7

Gonzalez, Cecilio
❑ 90JohCitCS-13
❑ 91JohCitCC-26
❑ 91JohCitCP-3972

Gonzalez, Chris
❑ 85CloHSS-19
❑ 90FreStaS-5

Gonzalez, Cliff
❑ 85LitFalMT-23
❑ 86LitFalMP-12
❑ 87ColMetP-4
❑ 89SarWhiSS-8
❑ 90SarWhiSS-11
❑ 91CalLeLA-46
❑ 91RenSilSCLC-12
❑ 92SalSpuC-20
❑ 92SalSpuF-3767

Gonzalez, David
❑ 91LinDriAA-407
❑ 91MemChiLD-407
❑ 91MemChiP-661

Gonzalez, Denny (Denio)
❑ 82PorBeaT-13
❑ 84HawIslC-130
❑ 85Don-600
❑ 85HawIslC-229
❑ 86Don-410
❑ 86Fle-608
❑ 86Top-746
❑ 86TopTif-746
❑ 88BufBisC-15
❑ 88BufBisP-1473
❑ 89ColSprSSC-14
❑ 89ColSprSSP-248
❑ 90CMC-368
❑ 90ProAAAF-283
❑ 90TidTidC-17
❑ 90TidTidP-552
❑ 90TopTVM-43
❑ 91LinDriAAA-258
❑ 91NasSouLD-258
❑ 91NasSouP-2163
❑ 93LimRocDP-P2
❑ 93LimRocDWB-137

Gonzalez, Dicky
❑ 97CapCitB-3
❑ 98CapCitBF5-9
❑ 98CapCitBM-9

Gonzalez, Eddie
❑ 90WesPalBES-10

Gonzalez, Edwin
❑ 98LanLugQ-6

Gonzalez, Efrain
❑ 92ButCopKSP-28

Gonzalez, Ender
❑ 97BriWhiSB-17
❑ 98BriWhiSQ-11

Gonzalez, Enrique
❑ 76VenLeaS-40
❑ 80VenLeaS-48

Gonzalez, Felipe
❑ 86FreGiaSB-5
❑ 87CliGiaP-7

Gonzalez, Ferdi
❑ 83GreHorT-14
❑ 84GreHorT-6
❑ 86AlbYanT-6
❑ 87AlbYanP-20
❑ 90MiaMirIS-28
❑ 91MiaMirC-1
❑ 91MiaMirP-423
❑ 92EriSaiC-30
❑ 92EriSaiF-1640
❑ 93HigDesMC-26
❑ 93HigDesMF-57
❑ 94BreCouMF-29
❑ 95BreCouMF-261
❑ 96BreCouMB-1
❑ 97PorSeaD-1
❑ 98ChaKniQ-2
❑ 98ChaKniQ-30

Gonzalez, Fernando (Jose Fern.)
❑ 74OPC-649
❑ 74Top-649
❑ 74TopTra-649T
❑ 77PirPosP-8
❑ 78ColCliT-8
❑ 78PadFamF-14
❑ 78Top-433
❑ 79PadFamF-13
❑ 79Top-531
❑ 80SalLakCGT-25
❑ 80Top-171
❑ 81SalLakCGT-18
❑ 82AleDukT-7
❑ 83LynPirT-3
❑ 89BlaYNPRWL-169
❑ 92YanWIZ7-55

Gonzalez, Frank
❑ 90FayGenP-2399
❑ 91LakTigC-6
❑ 91LakTigP-262
❑ 92ClaFS7-172
❑ 92LonTigF-628
❑ 92LonTigS-410
❑ 92SkyAA F-174
❑ 93TolMudHF-1647
❑ 94TolMudHF-1022
❑ 94VenLinU-207
❑ 95LinVen-60
❑ 95LinVen-305
❑ 95TolMudHTI-14
❑ 97CalCanB-12

Gonzalez, Freddy (Fred)
❑ 86Ft.LauYP-8
❑ 90VerBeaDS-14
❑ 91LinDriAA-535
❑ 91SanAntMLD-535
❑ 92SanAntMS-565
❑ 92VerBeaDF-2889
❑ 93LimRocDWB-75
❑ 93LinVenB-185
❑ 94BreCouMC-24
❑ 96-97LinVen-212

Gonzalez, Gabe
❑ 96BreCouMB-16
❑ 97PorSeaD-12
❑ 98Bow-343
❑ 98BowChr-343
❑ 98BowChrGA-343
❑ 98BowChrGAR-343
❑ 98BowChrI-343
❑ 98BowChrIR-343
❑ 98BowChrR-343
❑ 98BowGolA-343
❑ 98BowInt-343
❑ 98ChaKniQ-13

Gonzalez, Generoso
❑ 94BriTigC-14
❑ 94BriTigF-3497
❑ 96FayGenB-18

Gonzalez, German
❑ 87KenTwiP-26
❑ 88BasAmeAAB-18
❑ 88OrlTwiB-17
❑ 88SouLeaAJ-30
❑ 89Don-590
❑ 89DonRoo-24
❑ 89Fle-113
❑ 89FleGlo-113
❑ 89PanSti-379
❑ 89ScoHot1R-49
❑ 89Top-746
❑ 89TopTif-746
❑ 90Fle-376
❑ 90FleCan-376
❑ 90Hot50RS-17
❑ 90OPC-266
❑ 90Sco-133
❑ 90Sco100RS-81
❑ 90Top-266
❑ 90TopTif-266
❑ 90UppDec-352
❑ 91KisDodP-4193
❑ 92GreFalDSP-26
❑ 94VenLinU-188

Gonzalez, Gilberto
❑ 80ElmPioRST-32

Gonzalez, Henry
❑ 84NewOriT-18
❑ 85NewOriT-10

Gonzalez, Ignacio
❑ 97HudValRB-8
❑ 98ChaRivDG-13

Gonzalez, Jamie
❑ 91Cla/Bes-449

Gonzalez, Javier
❑ 87LitFalMP-2395
❑ 88ColMetGS-12
❑ 89BlaYNPRWL-176
❑ 90JacMetGS-13
❑ 91LinDriAA-632
❑ 91WilBilLD-632
❑ 91WilBilP-296
❑ 92TidTidF-899
❑ 92TidTidS-560
❑ 93BinMetF-2337
❑ 94NewBriRSF-652
❑ 97HelBreB-3

Gonzalez, Jeremi
❑ 93HunCubC-9
❑ 93HunCubF-3230
❑ 94PeoChiC-10
❑ 94PeoChiF-2259
❑ 94VenLinU-213
❑ 94WilCubC-9
❑ 94WilCubF-3757
❑ 95LinVen-58
❑ 95LinVen-305
❑ 95RocCubTI-20
❑ 96-97LinVen-120
❑ 96OrlCubB-9
❑ 97Bow-309
❑ 97BowChr-213
❑ 97BowChrI-213
❑ 97BowChrIR-213
❑ 97BowChrR-213
❑ 97BowInt-309
❑ 97Fle-752
❑ 97FleTif-752
❑ 97IowCub-13
❑ 97Sel-156
❑ 97SelCom-156
❑ 97TopStaFAS-FAS14
❑ 98CirThu-288
❑ 98CirThuRav-288
❑ 98CirThuSupRav-288
❑ 98ColCho-117
❑ 98Don-291
❑ 98DonGolPP-291
❑ 98DonSilPP-291
❑ 98Fin-13
❑ 98FinNo--13
❑ 98FinNo-R-13
❑ 98FinRef-13
❑ 98Fle-268
❑ 98LeaRS-283
❑ 98LeaRSLHolo-283
❑ 98LeaRSLong-283
❑ 98LeaRTrue-283
❑ 98MetUni-95
❑ 98MetUniPMG-95
❑ 98Pac-250
❑ 98PacInv-82
❑ 98PacInvPBlue-82
❑ 98PacInvSilv-82
❑ 98PacInvTeam-5
❑ 98PacOme-46
❑ 98PacOmeR-46
❑ 98PacOnl-140
❑ 98PacOnlR-140
❑ 98PacOnlWC-140
❑ 98PacPlaB-250
❑ 98PacRedT-250
❑ 98PacSil-250
❑ 98Pin-168
❑ 98PinArtP-PP71
❑ 98PinIns-131
❑ 98PinInsCE-131
❑ 98PinInsDE-131
❑ 98PinMusC-PP71
❑ 98PinPreP-168
❑ 98PinSna-CC3
❑ 98SPxFin-14
❑ 98SPxFinR-14
❑ 98SPxFinS-14
❑ 98StaCluFDI-46
❑ 98StaCluI-46
❑ 98StaCluOneK-46
❑ 98StaCluPP-46
❑ 98Stu-214
❑ 98StuGPP-214
❑ 98StuSPP-214
❑ 98Top-393

❑ 98TopChr-393
❑ 98TopChrR-393
❑ 98TopDevR-393
❑ 98TopDia-393
❑ 98TopGal-42
❑ 98TopGalGP-42
❑ 98TopGalOPP-42
❑ 98TopGalPPI-42
❑ 98TopGalPPIA-42
❑ 98TopMiniC-393
❑ 98Ult-52
❑ 98UltGolM-52
❑ 98UltMas-52
❑ 98UltPlaM-52
❑ 98UppDec-263
❑ 98UppDecSF-143
❑ 98WilCubJGTI-1
❑ 99Fle-440
❑ 99FleSta9-440
❑ 99FleWarT-440
❑ 99SpoIII-49
❑ 99StaClu-48
❑ 99StaCluFDI-48
❑ 99StaCluOoaK-48
❑ 99StaCluPP-48
❑ 99Top-341
❑ 99TopChr-341
❑ 99TopChrR-341
❑ 99TopMVPP-341

Gonzalez, Jess
❑ 94LetMouF-3873
❑ 94LetMouSP-11

Gonzalez, Jesus
❑ 91BurIndP-3295
❑ 93LinVenB-127
❑ 94VenLinU-132
❑ 95LinVen-176
❑ 96-97LinVen-42

Gonzalez, Jim
❑ 92BurAstC-22
❑ 92BurAstF-549

Gonzalez, Jimmy
❑ 91ClaDraP-36
❑ 91FroRowDP-32
❑ 91FroRowDPG-32
❑ 91FroRowDPS-32
❑ 92OPC-564
❑ 92StaCluD-63
❑ 92Top-564
❑ 92TopGol-564
❑ 92TopGolW-564
❑ 92TopMic-564
❑ 93Bow-292
❑ 93QuaCitRBC-9
❑ 93QuaCitRBF-102
❑ 94OscAstC-10
❑ 94OscAstF-1141
❑ 95QuaCitRBTI-7
❑ 96KisCobB-9
❑ 97KisCob-10
❑ 98GreFalDG-12
❑ 98MobBayBTI-11

Gonzalez, John
❑ 84IdaFalATI-10

Gonzalez, Johnny
❑ 80VenLeaS-154
❑ 94VenLinU-246
❑ 95LinVen-217
❑ 96-97LinVen-193

Gonzalez, Jose
❑ 83LouRedR-13
❑ 84Car5x7-7
❑ 84LouRedR-13

Gonzalez, Jose G.
❑ 97EveAquG-10
❑ 98WisTimRM-5

Gonzalez, Jose Rafael
❑ 86AlbDukP-9
❑ 87AlbDukD-26
❑ 87DodPol-25
❑ 87Don-525
❑ 87Fle-649
❑ 87FleGlo-649
❑ 88AlbDukCm-19
❑ 88Don-341
❑ 88Sco-364
❑ 88ScoGlo-364
❑ 89AlbDukP-80
❑ 89DonBasB-260
❑ 89DonBasB-275
❑ 89ScoHot1R-29
❑ 89UppDec-626
❑ 90ClaBlu-96
❑ 90DodMot-11
❑ 90DodPol-38
❑ 90DodTar-288
❑ 90Don-314
❑ 90Fle-394
❑ 90FleCan-394
❑ 90OPC-98
❑ 90Sco-368
❑ 90ScoYouSI-16
❑ 90Top-98
❑ 90TopTif-98
❑ 90UppDec-666
❑ 91DodMot-11
❑ 91DodPol-38
❑ 91Don-543
❑ 91OPC-279
❑ 91Sco-614
❑ 91StaClu-208
❑ 91Top-279B
❑ 91TopDesS-279
❑ 91TopMic-279
❑ 91TopTif-279
❑ 92EdmTraS-160
❑ 92Sco-733
❑ 92StaClu-774
❑ 92StaCluECN-774
❑ 93LimRocDWB-83
❑ 95LinVen-218
❑ 96-97LinVen-192
❑ 97PorRocG-8

Gonzalez, Juan
❑ 76CliPilT-18
❑ 76VenLeaS-99

Gonzalez, Juan A.
❑ 87GasRanP-4
❑ 88BlaYNPRWL-105
❑ 88ChaRanS-8
❑ 89BasAmeAPB-AA26
❑ 89BlaYNPRWL-42
❑ 89BlaYNPRWLU-52
❑ 89TexLeaAGS-34
❑ 89TulDriGS-10
❑ 89TulDriTI-8
❑ 90Bow-492
❑ 90BowTif-492
❑ 90ClaUpd-T21
❑ 90CMC-167
❑ 90Don-33A
❑ 90Don-33B
❑ 90Fle-297
❑ 90FleCan-297
❑ 90OklCit8C-17
❑ 90OklCit8P-444
❑ 90OPC-331
❑ 90ProAAAF-690
❑ 90Sco-637
❑ 90Top-331
❑ 90TopDeb89-43
❑ 90TopMag-84
❑ 90TopTif-331
❑ 90TriAllGP-AAA12
❑ 90TulDriDGB-25
❑ 90UppDec-72
❑ 91Bow-180
❑ 91Cla1-T70
❑ 91Cla2-T74
❑ 91ClaGam-122
❑ 91Don-371
❑ 91Fle-286
❑ 91Lea-119
❑ 91MajLeaCP-36
❑ 91OPC-224
❑ 91OPCPre-54
❑ 91RanMot-4
❑ 91RedFolS-107
❑ 91Sco-805
❑ 91Sco100RS-41
❑ 91ScoHotR-9
❑ 91SevCoi-T7
❑ 91StaClu-237
❑ 91StaGonRG-1
❑ 91StaGonRG-2
❑ 91StaGonRG-3
❑ 91StaGonRG-4
❑ 91StaGonRG-5
❑ 91StaGonRG-6
❑ 91StaGonRG-7
❑ 91StaGonRG-8
❑ 91StaGonRG-9
❑ 91StaGonRG-10
❑ 91StaGonRG-11
❑ 91Stu-124
❑ 91Top-224
❑ 91TopDesS-224
❑ 91TopMic-224
❑ 91TopTif-224
❑ 91TopTriH-A13
❑ 91TulDriTI-30
❑ 91UltUpd-55
❑ 91UppDec-646
❑ 92Bow-84
❑ 92ClaGam-158
❑ 92Don-393
❑ 92Fle-304
❑ 92Hig5-112
❑ 92Hig5S-14
❑ 92JimDea-14
❑ 92Lea-62
❑ 92LeaBlaG-62
❑ 92MVPPin-23
❑ 92OPC-27
❑ 92PanSti-81
❑ 92Pin-127
❑ 92PinTea2-26
❑ 92RanMot-4
❑ 92RanTeal-8
❑ 92RedFolS-39
❑ 92Sco-11
❑ 92Sco100S-69
❑ 92ScoImpP-27
❑ 92SpoIllFK1-121
❑ 92SpoIllFK1-596
❑ 92SpoStaCC-16
❑ 92StaClu-240
❑ 92Stu-242
❑ 92Top-27
❑ 92TopGol-27
❑ 92TopGolW-27
❑ 92TopKid-131
❑ 92TopMic-27
❑ 92TriPla-112
❑ 92Ult-132
❑ 92UppDec-243
❑ 92UppDecF-9
❑ 92UppDecFG-9
❑ 92UppDecHRH-HR19
❑ 92UppDecWB-T14
❑ 93Bow-305
❑ 93ClaGam-37
❑ 93ColAllG-15
❑ 93DenHol-20
❑ 93DiaMar-40
❑ 93DiaMarP-4
❑ 93Don-555
❑ 93DonDiaK-DK7
❑ 93DonEli-36
❑ 93DonEliD-11
❑ 93DonEliD-AU11
❑ 93DonEliS-18
❑ 93DonLonBL-LL14
❑ 93DonMasotG-11
❑ 93DonMVP-21
❑ 93DonSpiotG-SG5
❑ 93Fin-116
❑ 93FinJum-116
❑ 93FinRef-116
❑ 93Fla-280
❑ 93Fle-322
❑ 93Fle-709
❑ 93FleAll-AL6
❑ 93FleAtl-10
❑ 93FleFruotL-22
❑ 93FleGolM-B3
❑ 93FleTeaL-AL8
❑ 93FunPac-15
❑ 93FunPac-153
❑ 93FunPac-156
❑ 93FunPac-223
❑ 93FunPacA-AS7
❑ 93JimDea-8
❑ 93Lea-170
❑ 93LeaFas-5
❑ 93LeaGolA-R16
❑ 93OPC-97
❑ 93OPCPreSP-7
❑ 93OPCPreSPF-7
❑ 93PacBeiA-12
❑ 93PacBeiA-15
❑ 93PacJugC-6
❑ 93PacSpa-311A
❑ 93PacSpa-311B
❑ 93PacSpaGE-14
❑ 93PacSpaPI-14
❑ 93PanSti-86
❑ 93Pin-191
❑ 93PinCoo-25
❑ 93PinCooD-25
❑ 93PinHomRC-1
❑ 93PinSlu-1
❑ 93PinTea2-13
❑ 93PinTeaP-8
❑ 93Pos-23
❑ 93RanKee-408
❑ 93RanStaC-21
❑ 93Sco-51
❑ 93ScoFra-13
❑ 93Sel-40
❑ 93SelStaL-25
❑ 93SP-194
❑ 93SPPlaP-PP8
❑ 93StaClu-297
❑ 93StaClu-540
❑ 93StaCluFDI-297
❑ 93StaCluFDI-540
❑ 93StaCluMOP-297
❑ 93StaCluMOP-540
❑ 93Stu-160
❑ 93StuHer-2
❑ 93StuSil-4
❑ 93TedWil-151
❑ 93TedWil-152
❑ 93TedWil-153
❑ 93TedWil-154
❑ 93TedWil-AU151
❑ 93TedWil-AU152
❑ 93TedWil-AU153
❑ 93TedWil-AU154
❑ 93TedWilP-160
❑ 93Top-34
❑ 93TOPBLAG-32
❑ 93TopFulS-4
❑ 93TopGol-34
❑ 93TopInaM-34
❑ 93TopInaR-34
❑ 93TopMic-34
❑ 93Toy-85
❑ 93TriPla-221
❑ 93TriPlaA-22
❑ 93TriPlaLL-L4
❑ 93Ult-279
❑ 93UltAllS-16
❑ 93UltHomRK-1
❑ 93UltPer-2
❑ 93UppDec-52
❑ 93UppDec-497
❑ 93UppDec-755
❑ 93UppDec-831
❑ 93UppDecCP-R10
❑ 93UppDecDG-20
❑ 93UppDecFA-A6
❑ 93UppDecFAJ-A6
❑ 93UppDecFH-58
❑ 93UppDecGold-52
❑ 93UppDecGold-497
❑ 93UppDecGold-755
❑ 93UppDecGold-831
❑ 93UppDecHRH-HR1
❑ 93UppDecOD-D12
❑ 93UppDecS-19
❑ 93USPlaCA-1C
❑ 94Bow-45
❑ 94BowBes-R19
❑ 94BowBesR-R19
❑ 94ChuShoS-1
❑ 94ColC-313
❑ 94ColC-323
❑ 94ColC-347
❑ 94ColC-630
❑ 94ColC-633
❑ 94ColChoGS-313
❑ 94ColChoGS-323
❑ 94ColChoGS-347
❑ 94ColChoGS-630
❑ 94ColChoGS-633
❑ 94ColChoHRA-HA1
❑ 94ColChoSS-313
❑ 94ColChoSS-323
❑ 94ColChoSS-347
❑ 94ColChoSS-630
❑ 94ColChoSS-633
❑ 94ColChoT-7
❑ 94DenHol-13
❑ 94Don-49
❑ 94DonAwaWJ-9
❑ 94DonDom-A6
❑ 94DonDomJ-A6
❑ 94DonEli-42
❑ 94DonLonBL-10
❑ 94DonMVP-27
❑ 94DonSpeE-49
❑ 94DonSpiotG-5
❑ 94DonSpiotGJ-5
❑ 94Fin-211
❑ 94FinJum-211
❑ 94FinRef-211
❑ 94Fla-109
❑ 94FlaOutP-5
❑ 94Fle-307
❑ 94Fle-710
❑ 94FleAllS-9
❑ 94FleExtB-178
❑ 94FleExtBGB-12
❑ 94FleLumC-4
❑ 94FlePro-6
❑ 94FleSun-12
❑ 94FleTeaL-13
❑ 94FUnPac-19
❑ 94FUnPac-181
❑ 94FUnPac-196
❑ 94FUnPac-199
❑ 94FUnPac-215
❑ 94FUnPac-240
❑ 94Kra-4
❑ 94Lea-418
❑ 94LeaCleC-7
❑ 94LeaGam-3
❑ 94LeaGolS-13
❑ 94LeaL-72
❑ 94LeaMVPC-A7
❑ 94LeaMVPCG-A7
❑ 94LeaPowB-4
❑ 94LeaSli-7
❑ 94LeaStaS-3
❑ 94O-PJumAF-4
❑ 94OPC-28
❑ 94OPCAllR-4
❑ 94OPCJumA-4
❑ 94OscMayR-5
❑ 94Pac-617
❑ 94PacAll-14
❑ 94PacGolP-1
❑ 94PacPro-P3
❑ 94PacSilP-2
❑ 94PacSilPC-2
❑ 94PanSti-6
❑ 94PanSti-127
❑ 94Pin-350
❑ 94PinArtP-350
❑ 94PinMusC-350
❑ 94PinPowS-PS24
❑ 94PinRunC-RC7
❑ 94PinTeaP-7
❑ 94PinTheN-4
❑ 94PinTri-TR15
❑ 94Pos-3
❑ 94PosCan-15
❑ 94ProMag-133
❑ 94RanAllP-21
❑ 94RedFolMI-32
❑ 94Sco-27
❑ 94ScoCyc-TC16
❑ 94ScoDreT-7
❑ 94ScoGolR-27
❑ 94ScoGolS-33
❑ 94Sel-212
❑ 94SelCroC-CC7
❑ 94SelSki-SK5
❑ 94SP-148
❑ 94SPDieC-148
❑ 94SPHol-11
❑ 94SPHolDC-11
❑ 94Spo-35
❑ 94Spo-182
❑ 94SpoFanA-AS6
❑ 94SpoRooGGG-GG3
❑ 94SPPre-WR2
❑ 94StaClu-112
❑ 94StaClu-261
❑ 94StaClu-568
❑ 94StaCluF-F4
❑ 94StaCluFDI-112
❑ 94StaCluFDI-261
❑ 94StaCluFDI-568
❑ 94StaCluFJ-F4
❑ 94StaCluGR-112
❑ 94StaCluGR-261
❑ 94StaCluGR-568
❑ 94StaCluMO-1
❑ 94StaCluMOP-112
❑ 94StaCluMOP-261
❑ 94StaCluMOP-568
❑ 94StaCluMOP-F4
❑ 94StaCluMOP-ST27
❑ 94StaCluST-ST27
❑ 94StaCluT-241
❑ 94StaCluTF-5
❑ 94StaCluTFDI-241
❑ 94Stu-154
❑ 94StuEdiC-5
❑ 94StuPro-154
❑ 94StuSerS-9
❑ 94StuSerSG-9
❑ 94TomPiz-19
❑ 94Top-389
❑ 94Top-685
❑ 94TopBlaG-7
❑ 94TopGol-389
❑ 94TopGol-685
❑ 94TopPre-34
❑ 94TopSpa-389
❑ 94TopSpa-685
❑ 94TopSupS-17
❑ 94TriPla-194
❑ 94TriPlaBS-3
❑ 94TriPlaP-1
❑ 94Ult-127
❑ 94UltAllS-7
❑ 94UltHitM-5
❑ 94UltHomRK-1
❑ 94UltRBIK-4
❑ 94UppDec-52
❑ 94UppDec-155
❑ 94UppDec-293
❑ 94UppDecAJ-25
❑ 94UppDecAJG-25
❑ 94UppDecDC-W3
❑ 94UppDecED-52
❑ 94UppDecED-155
❑ 94UppDecED-293
❑ 94UppDecMLS-MM9
❑ 94UppDecMLSED-MM9
❑ 94UppDecNG-5
❑ 94UppDecNGED-5
❑ 94USPlaCA-13C
❑ 95Baz-68
❑ 95Bow-323
❑ 95BowBes-R30
❑ 95BowBes-X5
❑ 95BowBesR-R30
❑ 95BowBesR-X5
❑ 95ClaFanFPCP-3
❑ 95ClaPhoC-53
❑ 95ColCho-84
❑ 95ColCho-90
❑ 95ColChoCtG-CG7
❑ 95ColChoCtG-CG7B
❑ 95ColChoCtG-CG7C
❑ 95ColChoCtGE-7
❑ 95ColChoCtGG-CG7
❑ 95ColChoCtGG-CG7B
❑ 95ColChoCtGG-CG7C
❑ 95ColChoCtGGE-7
❑ 95ColChoGS-84
❑ 95ColChoGS-90
❑ 95ColChoSE-186
❑ 95ColChoSEGS-186
❑ 95ColChoSESS-186
❑ 95ColChoSS-84
❑ 95ColChoSS-90
❑ 95DenHol-10
❑ 95Don-42
❑ 95DonPreP-42
❑ 95DonTopotO-160
❑ 95Emo-85
❑ 95EmoMas-2
❑ 95Fin-158
❑ 95FinRef-158
❑ 95Fla-88
❑ 95FlaOutP-6
❑ 95Fle-285
❑ 95FleUpdH-10
❑ 95Kra-4
❑ 95Lea-202
❑ 95LeaLim-176
❑ 95LeaLimL-3
❑ 95LinVen-311
❑ 95NatPac-3
❑ 95Pac-426
❑ 95PacGolCDC-18
❑ 95PacGolP-11
❑ 95PacLatD-17
❑ 95PacPri-136
❑ 95PanSti-83
❑ 95Pin-227
❑ 95Pin-278
❑ 95PinArtP-227
❑ 95PinArtP-278
❑ 95PinFan-9
❑ 95PinMusC-227
❑ 95PinMusC-278
❑ 95PinPer-PP4
❑ 95PinUps-US10
❑ 95RanCra-11
❑ 95RedFol-4
❑ 95Sco-439
❑ 95ScoGolR-439
❑ 95ScoHaloG-HG58
❑ 95ScoPlaTS-439
❑ 95ScoRul-SR16
❑ 95ScoRulJ-SR16
❑ 95Sel-86
❑ 95SelArtP-86
❑ 95SP-195

❑ 95SPCha-190
❑ 95SPChaDC-190
❑ 95Spo-73
❑ 95SpoArtP-73
❑ 95SpoDet-DE9
❑ 95SpoHamT-HT15
❑ 95SPPlaP-PP11
❑ 95SPSil-195
❑ 95SPSpeF-22
❑ 95StaClu-145
❑ 95StaClu-406
❑ 95StaCluFDI-145
❑ 95StaCluMOP-145
❑ 95StaCluMOP-406
❑ 95StaCluMOP-RL23
❑ 95StaCluRL-RL23
❑ 95StaCluSTWS-145
❑ 95StaCluSTWS-406
❑ 95StaCluVR-74
❑ 95StaCluVRMO-74
❑ 95Stu-21
❑ 95StuGolS-21
❑ 95StuPlaS-21
❑ 95Sum-90
❑ 95SumNthD-90
❑ 95Top-70
❑ 95TopCyb-50
❑ 95TopCybSiR-3
❑ 95TopEmb-30
❑ 95TopEmbGI-30
❑ 95UC3-74
❑ 95UC3ArtP-74
❑ 95Ult-109
❑ 95UltGolM-109
❑ 95UltRisS-4
❑ 95UltRisSGM-4
❑ 95UppDec-104
❑ 95UppDec-395
❑ 95UppDecED-104
❑ 95UppDecED-395
❑ 95UppDecEDG-104
❑ 95UppDecEDG-395
❑ 95UppDecPAW-H2
❑ 95UppDecPAWE-H2
❑ 95UppDecPLL-R3
❑ 95UppDecPLL-R41
❑ 95UppDecPLLE-R3
❑ 95UppDecPLLE-R41
❑ 95UppDecSE-40
❑ 95UppDecSEG-40
❑ 95Zen-59
❑ 96Baz-73
❑ 96Bow-95
❑ 96BowBes-58
❑ 96BowBesAR-58
❑ 96BowBesR-58
❑ 96BowFoi-95
❑ 96Cir-86
❑ 96CirBos-23
❑ 96CirRav-86
❑ 96ColCho-338
❑ 96ColCho-417
❑ 96ColCho-740
❑ 96ColChoCtG-CG28
❑ 96ColChoCtG-CG28B
❑ 96ColChoCtG-CG28C
❑ 96ColChoCtGE-CR28
❑ 96ColChoCtGG-CG28
❑ 96ColChoCtGG-CG28B
❑ 96ColChoCtGG-CG28C
❑ 96ColChoCtGGE-CR28
❑ 96ColChoGS-338
❑ 96ColChoGS-417
❑ 96ColChoGS-740
❑ 96ColChoSS-338
❑ 96ColChoSS-417
❑ 96ColChoSS-740
❑ 96ColChoYMtP-15
❑ 96ColChoYMtP-15A
❑ 96ColChoYMtPGS-15
❑ 96ColChoYMtPGS-15A
❑ 96Don-375
❑ 96DonDiaK-5
❑ 96DonPreP-375
❑ 96EmoLegoB-3
❑ 96EmoXL-121
❑ 96Fin-B253
❑ 96Fin-G354
❑ 96Fin-S115
❑ 96FinRef-B253
❑ 96FinRef-G354
❑ 96FinRef-S115
❑ 96Fla-169
❑ 96FlaDiaC-4
❑ 96FlaPow-3
❑ 96Fle-250
❑ 96FleTeaL-13
❑ 96FleTif-250
❑ 96FleUpd-U221
❑ 96FleUpdH-6
❑ 96FleUpdSS-3
❑ 96FleUpdTC-U221
❑ 96Lea-107
❑ 96LeaLim-34
❑ 96LeaLimG-34
❑ 96LeaLimPC-1
❑ 96LeaPre-43
❑ 96LeaPreP-43
❑ 96LeaPrePB-107
❑ 96LeaPrePG-107
❑ 96LeaPrePS-107
❑ 96LeaPreSG-20
❑ 96LeaPreSte-20
❑ 96LeaSig-2
❑ 96LeaSigEA-61
❑ 96LeaSigEACM-9
❑ 96LeaSigPPG-2
❑ 96LeaSigPPP-2
❑ 96LeaTotB-11
❑ 96MetUni-113
❑ 96MetUniHM-3
❑ 96MetUniP-113
❑ 96Pac-423
❑ 96PacEstL-EL12
❑ 96PacPri-P136
❑ 96PacPriG-P136
❑ 96PanSti-232
❑ 96Pin-38
❑ 96Pin-163
❑ 96PinAfi-99
❑ 96PinAfiAP-99
❑ 96PinAfiFPP-99
❑ 96PinAfiSP-27
❑ 96PinArtP-57
❑ 96PinArtP-90
❑ 96PinPow-20
❑ 96PinSlu-15
❑ 96PinSta-57
❑ 96PinSta-90
❑ 96ProMagDM-24
❑ 96ProSta-98
❑ 96RanDr P-10
❑ 96RanFle-6
❑ 96RanMot-3
❑ 96Sco-348
❑ 96ScoDugC-B73
❑ 96ScoDugCAP-B73
❑ 96ScoNumG-21
❑ 96Sel-56
❑ 96SelArtP-56
❑ 96SelCer-56
❑ 96SelCerAP-56
❑ 96SelCerCB-56
❑ 96SelCerCR-56
❑ 96SelCerMB-56
❑ 96SelCerMG-56
❑ 96SelCerMR-56
❑ 96SelTeaN-14
❑ 96SP-175
❑ 96SPMarM-MM14
❑ 96SPMarMDC-14
❑ 96Spo-95
❑ 96SpoArtP-95
❑ 96SPSpeFX-29
❑ 96SPSpeFXDC-29
❑ 96SPx-58
❑ 96SPxGol-58
❑ 96StaClu-9
❑ 96StaCluEPB-9
❑ 96StaCluEPG-9
❑ 96StaCluEPS-9
❑ 96StaCluMOP-9
❑ 96StaCluMOP-PP11
❑ 96StaCluPP-PP11
❑ 96Stu-105
❑ 96StuPrePB-105
❑ 96StuPrePG-105
❑ 96StuPrePS-105
❑ 96Sum-60
❑ 96SumAbo&B-60
❑ 96SumArtP-60
❑ 96SumBal-7
❑ 96SumFoi-60
❑ 96TeaOut-30
❑ 96Top-325
❑ 96TopBigC-2
❑ 96TopChr-129
❑ 96TopChrR-129
❑ 96TopChrWC-WC8
❑ 96TopChrWCR-WC8
❑ 96TopGal-163
❑ 96TopGalPPI-163
❑ 96TopLas-8
❑ 96TopLasPC-13
❑ 96TopPro-AL14
❑ 96TopWreC-WC8
❑ 96Ult-135
❑ 96Ult-578
❑ 96UltChe-A3
❑ 96UltCheGM-A3
❑ 96UltGolM-135
❑ 96UltGolM-578
❑ 96UltHitM-3
❑ 96UltHitMGM-3
❑ 96UltHomRK-5
❑ 96UltHomRKGM-5
❑ 96UltHomRKR-5
❑ 96UltHomRKRGM-5
❑ 96UltThu-10
❑ 96UltThuGM-10
❑ 96UppDec-206
❑ 96UppDecDD-DD39
❑ 96UppDecDDG-DD39
❑ 96UppDecDDS-DD39
❑ 96UppDecPD-PD6
❑ 96UppDecPRE-R3
❑ 96UppDecPreR-R3
❑ 96UppDecRunP-RP6
❑ 96Zen-61
❑ 96ZenArtP-61
❑ 96ZenMoz-2
❑ 97BesLimA-12
❑ 97Bow-29
❑ 97BowBes-74
❑ 97BowBesAR-74
❑ 97BowBesJ-74
❑ 97BowBesJAR-74
❑ 97BowBesJR-74
❑ 97BowBesMI-MI6
❑ 97BowBesMIAR-MI6
❑ 97BowBesMIARI-MI6
❑ 97BowBesMII-MI6
❑ 97BowBesMIR-MI6
❑ 97BowBesMIRI-MI6
❑ 97BowBesR-74
❑ 97BowChr-25
❑ 97BowChrI-25
❑ 97BowChrIR-25
❑ 97BowChrR-25
❑ 97BowInt-29
❑ 97BowIntB-BBI3
❑ 97BowIntBAR-BBI3
❑ 97BowIntBR-BBI3
❑ 97Cir-373
❑ 97CirBos-5
❑ 97CirIco-1
❑ 97CirLimA-4
❑ 97CirRav-373
❑ 97CirRavR-3
❑ 97CirSupB-5
❑ 97ColCho-218
❑ 97ColCho-240
❑ 97ColChoAC-14
❑ 97ColChoCtG-30A
❑ 97ColChoCtG-30B
❑ 97ColChoCtG-30C
❑ 97ColChoCtGE-CG30
❑ 97ColChoCtGIW-CG30
❑ 97ColChoNF-NF7
❑ 97ColChoPP-PP5
❑ 97ColChoPPG-PP5
❑ 97ColChoPPJ-PP5
❑ 97ColChoS-22
❑ 97ColChoSR-9
❑ 97ColChoT-TR4
❑ 97ColChoTBS-45
❑ 97ColChoTBSWH-45
❑ 97ColChoTotT-T29
❑ 97DenHol-12
❑ 97Don-1
❑ 97Don-406
❑ 97DonDom-8
❑ 97DonEli-1
❑ 97DonEli-12
❑ 97DonEliGS-1
❑ 97DonFraFea-5
❑ 97DonGolPP-1
❑ 97DonGolPP-406
❑ 97DonLim-77
❑ 97DonLim-88
❑ 97DonLim-118
❑ 97DonLimE-77
❑ 97DonLimE-88
❑ 97DonLimE-118
❑ 97DonLimENG-118
❑ 97DonLimFotG-17
❑ 97DonLonL-8
❑ 97DonPowA-11
❑ 97DonPowADC-11
❑ 97DonPre-22
❑ 97DonPre-173
❑ 97DonPreCttC-22
❑ 97DonPreCttC-173
❑ 97DonPrePM-5
❑ 97DonPreS-6
❑ 97DonPreSS-6
❑ 97DonPreTB-5
❑ 97DonPreTBG-5
❑ 97DonPreTF-5
❑ 97DonPreTP-5
❑ 97DonPreTPG-5
❑ 97DonPreXP-3B
❑ 97DonRocL-6
❑ 97DonSig-43
❑ 97DonSigAC-48
❑ 97DonSigAM-48
❑ 97DonSigPPP-43
❑ 97DonSilPP-1
❑ 97DonSilPP-406
❑ 97DonTeaSMVP-15
❑ 97DonVxP1-18
❑ 97E-X2-46
❑ 97E-X2ACA-5
❑ 97E-X2Cred-46
❑ 97E-X2EssCre-46
❑ 97E-X2Hall-13
❑ 97Fin-150
❑ 97Fin-212
❑ 97Fin-332
❑ 97FinEmb-150
❑ 97FinEmb-332
❑ 97FinEmbR-150
❑ 97FinEmbR-332
❑ 97FinRef-150
❑ 97FinRef-212
❑ 97FinRef-332
❑ 97FlaShoDC-4
❑ 97FlaShoHG-3
❑ 97FlaShoLC-19
❑ 97FlaShoLeg0-19
❑ 97FlaShoLeg1-19
❑ 97FlaShoM-A19
❑ 97FlaShoM-B19
❑ 97FlaShoM-C19
❑ 97FlaShoR0-19
❑ 97FlaShoR1-19
❑ 97FlaShoR2-19
❑ 97Fle-221
❑ 97Fle-700
❑ 97Fle-747
❑ 97FleBleB-3
❑ 97FleDiaT-3
❑ 97FleHea-5
❑ 97FleLumC-8
❑ 97FleMilDM-38
❑ 97FleMilDMR-38
❑ 97FleNig&D-3
❑ 97FleSoaS-3
❑ 97FleSoaSG-3
❑ 97FleTeaL-13
❑ 97FleTif-221
❑ 97FleTif-700
❑ 97FleTif-747
❑ 97FleZon-6
❑ 97HigMinMCT-15
❑ 97HigMinMCT-16
❑ 97KinB-9
❑ 97Lea-101
❑ 97Lea-353
❑ 97LeaBanS-3
❑ 97LeaDrefS-13
❑ 97LeaFraM-101
❑ 97LeaFraM-353
❑ 97LeaFraMDC-101
❑ 97LeaFraMDC-353
❑ 97LeaGet-7
❑ 97LeaGolS-10
❑ 97LeaLeaotN-1
❑ 97LeaStaS-2
❑ 97LeaWarT-11
❑ 97MetUni-162
❑ 97MetUniBF-5
❑ 97NewPin-68
❑ 97NewPin-195
❑ 97NewPinAP-68
❑ 97NewPinAP-195
❑ 97NewPinIE-9
❑ 97NewPinKtP-1
❑ 97NewPinMC-68
❑ 97NewPinMC-195
❑ 97NewPinPP-68
❑ 97NewPinPP-195
❑ 97NewPinPP-I9A
❑ 97NewPinPP-K1
❑ 97Pac-200
❑ 97PacCar-19
❑ 97PacCarM-19
❑ 97PacCerCGT-11
❑ 97PacFirD-13
❑ 97PacGolCD-19
❑ 97PacLatotML-21
❑ 97PacLigB-200
❑ 97PacPri-68
❑ 97PacPriGA-GA16
❑ 97PacPriGotD-GD95
❑ 97PacPriLB-68
❑ 97PacPriP-68
❑ 97PacPriSL-SL7A
❑ 97PacSil-200
❑ 97PacTriCD-11
❑ 97Pin-18
❑ 97PinArtP-PP18
❑ 97PinCar-5
❑ 97PinCer-69
❑ 97PinCer-142
❑ 97PinCerCMGT-11
❑ 97PinCerCT-11
❑ 97PinCerMBla-69
❑ 97PinCerMBla-142
❑ 97PinCerMBlu-69
❑ 97PinCerMBlu-142
❑ 97PinCerMG-69
❑ 97PinCerMG-142
❑ 97PinCerMR-69
❑ 97PinCerMR-142
❑ 97PinCerR-69
❑ 97PinCerR-142
❑ 97PinEpixGO-E2
❑ 97PinEpixPE-E2
❑ 97PinFan-FF9
❑ 97PinIns-4
❑ 97PinIns-150
❑ 97PinInsC-11
❑ 97PinInsCE-4
❑ 97PinInsCE-150
❑ 97PinInsDD-13
❑ 97PinInsDE-4
❑ 97PinInsDE-150
❑ 97PinInsFS-1
❑ 97PinMin-6
❑ 97PinMinB-6
❑ 97PinMinCB-6
❑ 97PinMinCG-6
❑ 97PinMinCGR-6
❑ 97PinMinCN-6
❑ 97PinMinCSS-6
❑ 97PinMinG-6
❑ 97PinMinS-6
❑ 97PinMusC-18
❑ 97PinPastM-13
❑ 97PinPrePla-18
❑ 97PinPrePla-S2
❑ 97PinSha-2
❑ 97PinTeaP-8
❑ 97PinTeaP-10
❑ 97PinTotCPB-69
❑ 97PinTotCPB-142
❑ 97PinTotCPG-69
❑ 97PinTotCPG-142
❑ 97PinTotCPR-69
❑ 97PinTotCPR-142
❑ 97PinX-P-4
❑ 97PinX-PF&A-6
❑ 97PinX-PMoS-4
❑ 97PinX-PMP-9
❑ 97PinX-PMW-9
❑ 97PinX-PMWG-9
❑ 97PinX-PMWS-9
❑ 97PinX-PreMPS-9
❑ 97PinX-PSfF-25
❑ 97PinX-PSfFU-25
❑ 97PreCon-16
❑ 97RanDr P-9
❑ 97RanMot-3
❑ 97RanSco-11
❑ 97RanScoPl-11
❑ 97RanScoPr-11
❑ 97Sco-198
❑ 97Sco-498
❑ 97ScoAllF-13
❑ 97ScoArtPWB-198
❑ 97ScoArtPWB-498
❑ 97ScoBla-3
❑ 97ScoHeaotO-3
❑ 97ScoPreS-198
❑ 97ScoResC-498
❑ 97ScoShoS-198
❑ 97ScoShoS-498
❑ 97ScoShoSAP-198
❑ 97ScoShoSAP-498
❑ 97ScoStaaD-21
❑ 97ScoSteS-1
❑ 97ScoTitT-4
❑ 97Sel-1
❑ 97Sel-142
❑ 97SelArtP-1
❑ 97SelArtP-142
❑ 97SelCom-1
❑ 97SelCom-142
❑ 97SelRegG-1
❑ 97SelRegG-142
❑ 97SelToootT-7
❑ 97SelToootTMB-7
❑ 97SP-175
❑ 97SPInsI-23
❑ 97SpoIll-160
❑ 97SpoIllEE-160
❑ 97SpoIllGS-24
❑ 97SPSpeF-13
❑ 97SPSpxF-8
❑ 97SPSPxFA-8
❑ 97SPx-48
❑ 97SPxBoufG-20
❑ 97SPxBro-48
❑ 97SPxGol-48
❑ 97SPxGraF-48
❑ 97SPxSil-48
❑ 97SPxSte-48
❑ 97StaClu-20
❑ 97StaClu-387
❑ 97StaCluFR-F12
❑ 97StaCluFW-F12
❑ 97StaCluI-I12
❑ 97StaCluMat-20
❑ 97StaCluMOP-20
❑ 97StaCluMOP-387
❑ 97StaCluMOP-I12
❑ 97StaCluMOP-FB12
❑ 97StaCluMOP-PG11
❑ 97StaCluPG-PG11
❑ 97Stu-55
❑ 97StuHarH-20
❑ 97StuMasS-23
❑ 97StuMasS8-23
❑ 97StuPor8-11
❑ 97StuPrePG-55
❑ 97StuPrePS-55
❑ 97Top-124
❑ 97TopAll-AS15
❑ 97TopChr-47
❑ 97TopChrAS-AS15
❑ 97TopChrDD-DD6
❑ 97TopChrDDR-DD6
❑ 97TopChrR-47
❑ 97TopChrSAR-AS15
❑ 97TopChrSB-13
❑ 97TopChrSBR-13
❑ 97TopGal-73
❑ 97TopGalPPI-73
❑ 97TopHobM-HM9
❑ 97TopIntF-ILM4
❑ 97TopIntFR-ILM4
❑ 97TopMem05-18
❑ 97TopScr-6
❑ 97TopScrT-6
❑ 97TopSeaB-SB13
❑ 97TopSta-37
❑ 97TopStaAM-37
❑ 97TopTeaT-TT10
❑ 97UD3-6
❑ 97UD3Marq-MA3
❑ 97Ult-132
❑ 97UltChe-B10
❑ 97UltDouT-10
❑ 97UltFamGam-9
❑ 97UltGolME-132
❑ 97UltHRK-3
❑ 97UltLeaS-5
❑ 97UltPlaME-132
❑ 97UltPowP-A3
❑ 97UltPowP-B8
❑ 97UltRBIK-6
❑ 97UltStaR-10
❑ 97UltThu-5
❑ 97UltTop3-10
❑ 97UltTop3GM-10
❑ 97UppDec-200
❑ 97UppDec-219
❑ 97UppDec-247
❑ 97UppDec-423
❑ 97UppDec-510
❑ 97UppDecAWJ-20
❑ 97UppDecHC-HC7
❑ 97UppDecHTH-HT9
❑ 97UppDecLDC-LD5
❑ 97UppDecMM-B7

❑ 97UppDecP-28
❑ 97UppDecPE-28
❑ 97UppDecPP-PP19
❑ 97UppDecPPJ-PP19
❑ 97UppDecRP-RP6
❑ 97UppDecSA-17
❑ 97UppDecSAG-17
❑ 97Zen-13
❑ 97Zen8x10-15
❑ 97Zen8x1D-15
❑ 98Bow-66
❑ 98BowBes-8
❑ 98BowBesAR-8
❑ 98BowBesMIF-MI7
❑ 98BowBesMIFAR-MI7
❑ 98BowBesMIFR-MI7
❑ 98BowBesR-8
❑ 98BowChr-66
❑ 98BowChrGA-66
❑ 98BowChrGAR-66
❑ 98BowChrI-66
❑ 98BowChrIR-66
❑ 98BowChrR-66
❑ 98BowChrR-23
❑ 98BowChrRR-23
❑ 98BowGolA-66
❑ 98BowInt-66
❑ 98BowMinLM-MVP3
❑ 98CirThu-19
❑ 98CirThuB-6
❑ 98CirThuLA-5
❑ 98CirThuRav-19
❑ 98CirThuRR-6
❑ 98CirThuSupRav-19
❑ 98CirThuTB-5
❑ 98ColCho-245
❑ 98ColCho-273
❑ 98ColChoCtG-CG28A
❑ 98ColChoCtG-CG28B
❑ 98ColChoCtG-CG28C
❑ 98ColChoCtGExch-CG28
❑ 98ColChoCtGIW-CG28
❑ 98ColChoER-ER27
❑ 98ColChoGJ5-273
❑ 98ColChoMBH-28
❑ 98ColChoRJ-245
❑ 98ColChoS'-27
❑ 98ColChoSQ-SQ38
❑ 98ColChoSQ-SQ83
❑ 98ColChoSQDouble-18
❑ 98ColChoSQHR-18
❑ 98ColChoSQSingle-18
❑ 98ColChoSQTriple-18
❑ 98CroRoy-136
❑ 98CroRoyAS-9
❑ 98CroRoyCCPA-4
❑ 98CroRoyCCPrem-4
❑ 98CroRoyDK-23
❑ 98CroRoyFoB-23
❑ 98CroRoyFoBA-23
❑ 98CroRoyHRF-9
❑ 98CroRoyPotG-24
❑ 98Don-2
❑ 98Don-162
❑ 98Don-366
❑ 98Don-403
❑ 98DonCol-2
❑ 98DonCol-162
❑ 98DonColE-411
❑ 98DonColE-528
❑ 98DonColL-372
❑ 98DonColP-561
❑ 98DonColP-728
❑ 98DonColS-2
❑ 98DonColS-162
❑ 98DonCruG-44
❑ 98DonCruP-44
❑ 98DonCruR-44
❑ 98DonDom-7
❑ 98DonEli-11
❑ 98DonEli-128
❑ 98DonEliA-11
❑ 98DonEliA-128
❑ 98DonEliBttF-4
❑ 98DonEliBttFA-4
❑ 98DonEliC-20
❑ 98DonEliI-5
❑ 98DonEliMC-20
❑ 98DonEliPN-10A
❑ 98DonEliPN-10B
❑ 98DonEliPN-10C
❑ 98DonEliPNDC-10A
❑ 98DonEliPNDC-10B
❑ 98DonEliPNDC-10C
❑ 98DonEliPNS-10A
❑ 98DonEliPNS-10B
❑ 98DonEliPNS-10C
❑ 98DonEliS-11
❑ 98DonEliS-128
❑ 98DonGolPP-2
❑ 98DonGolPP-162
❑ 98DonGolPP-366
❑ 98DonGolPP-403
❑ 98DonLonL-21
❑ 98DonPre-11
❑ 98DonPre-178
❑ 98DonPreGB-11
❑ 98DonPreGES-23
❑ 98DonPreGoB-11
❑ 98DonPreGX-23
❑ 98DonPreGXDC-23
❑ 98DonPrePM-11
❑ 98DonPreSeat-11
❑ 98DonPreSeat-178
❑ 98DonPreTP-11
❑ 98DonPreTPD-6
❑ 98DonPreTPG-11
❑ 98DonPreTPS-11
❑ 98DonPreTW-11
❑ 98DonPriCD-2
❑ 98DonPriCD-162
❑ 98DonPriCE-411
❑ 98DonPriCE-528
❑ 98DonPriCL-372
❑ 98DonPriCP-561
❑ 98DonPriCP-728
❑ 98DonProLS-5
❑ 98DonSig-19
❑ 98DonSigAC-48
❑ 98DonSigAM-49
❑ 98DonSigP-19
❑ 98DonSigSP-7
❑ 98DonSilPP-2
❑ 98DonSilPP-162
❑ 98DonSilPP-366
❑ 98DonSilPP-403
❑ 98DonSonM9-16
❑ 98E-X2-5
❑ 98E-X2Cheap-6
❑ 98E-X2ECFut-5
❑ 98E-X2ECNow-5
❑ 98Fin-260
❑ 98FinCen-C9
❑ 98FinCenR-C9
❑ 98FinMysF1-M31
❑ 98FinMysF1-M32
❑ 98FinMysF1-M33
❑ 98FinMysF1-M34
❑ 98FinMysF2-M25
❑ 98FinMysF2-M26
❑ 98FinMysF2-M27
❑ 98FinMysF2R-M25
❑ 98FinMysF2R-M26
❑ 98FinMysF2R-M27
❑ 98FinMysFR-M31
❑ 98FinMysFR-M32
❑ 98FinMysFR-M33
❑ 98FinMysFR-M34
❑ 98FinNo--260
❑ 98FinNo-R-260
❑ 98FinOve-B7
❑ 98FinOveR-B7
❑ 98FinPowZ-P19
❑ 98FinRef-260
❑ 98FinStaS-SS12
❑ 98FinTheM-TM16
❑ 98FinTheMR-TM16
❑ 98FlaShoLeg0-44
❑ 98FlaShoLeg1-44
❑ 98FlaShoLeg2-44
❑ 98FlaShoLeg3-44
❑ 98FlaShoLegM-44
❑ 98FlaShoR0-44
❑ 98FlaShoR1-44
❑ 98FlaShoR2-44
❑ 98FlaShoR3-44
❑ 98Fle-19
❑ 98Fle-328
❑ 98Fle-582
❑ 98FleDiaS-7
❑ 98FleDiaT-DT4
❑ 98FleIn TC-IC6
❑ 98FleLumC-5
❑ 98FlePowG-9
❑ 98FleVin'-59
❑ 98FleVin'C-59
❑ 98FleZon-6
❑ 98HamHel-6
❑ 98KinDis-9
❑ 98Lea-173
❑ 98LeaFraDA-173
❑ 98LeaFraF-173
❑ 98LeaFraM-173
❑ 98LeaFraM-173
❑ 98LeaFraMDC-173
❑ 98LeaFraMDC-173
❑ 98LeaFraMZ2-173
❑ 98LeaHeaftH-7
❑ 98LeaHeaftHS-7
❑ 98LeaRCMLHDSamp-2
❑ 98LeaRS-36
❑ 98LeaRS-154
❑ 98LeaRSGAHSamp-10
❑ 98LeaRSGroAH-10
❑ 98LeaRSGreHit-12
❑ 98LeaRSHRDerby-14
❑ 98LeaRSLHolo-36
❑ 98LeaRSLHolo-154
❑ 98LeaRSLMVP-8
❑ 98LeaRSLMVPPE-8
❑ 98LeaRSLong-36
❑ 98LeaRSLong-154
❑ 98LeaRSMLHD-2
❑ 98LeaRSTicMas-8
❑ 98LeaRSTicMasDC-8
❑ 98LeaRTrue-36
❑ 98LeaRTrue-154
❑ 98LeaStaRep-19
❑ 98LeaStaS-8
❑ 98LeaStaSDC-8
❑ 98MetUni-32
❑ 98MetUniAT-5
❑ 98MetUniPMG-32
❑ 98MetUniT-5
❑ 98MetUniUL-5
❑ 98Pac-202
❑ 98PacAur-86
❑ 98PacAurCube-19
❑ 98PacAurODLC-19
❑ 98PacAurPF-19
❑ 98PacAurPFC-19
❑ 98PacAurPFPB-19
❑ 98PacAurPFR-19
❑ 98PacAurPFS-19
❑ 98PacGolCDC-33
❑ 98PacHomRH-20
❑ 98PacInCage-19
❑ 98PacInv-69
❑ 98PacInvGems-103
❑ 98PacInvMiT-19
❑ 98PacInvPBlue-69
❑ 98PacInvSilv-69
❑ 98PacInvTeam-27
❑ 98PacLatotML-34
❑ 98PacNes-2B
❑ 98PacOme-237
❑ 98PacOmeEP-9
❑ 98PacOmeEP1o1-9
❑ 98PacOmeFTF-10
❑ 98PacOmeOnIns-17
❑ 98PacOmeP-11
❑ 98PacOmeR-237
❑ 98PacOnl-732A
❑ 98PacOnl-732B
❑ 98PacOnl-750
❑ 98PacOnlR-732A
❑ 98PacOnlR-732B
❑ 98PacOnlR-750
❑ 98PacOnlWC-732A
❑ 98PacOnlWC-732B
❑ 98PacOnlWC-750
❑ 98PacPar-104
❑ 98PacParC-104
❑ 98PacParG-104
❑ 98PacParHS-104
❑ 98PacParI-26
❑ 98PacParPB-104
❑ 98PacParR-104
❑ 98PacPlaB-202
❑ 98PacRedT-202
❑ 98PacSil-202
❑ 98PacTeaC-13
❑ 98Pin-70
❑ 98PinArtP-PP63
❑ 98PinEpixGE-E2
❑ 98PinEpixGP-E2
❑ 98PinEpixPO-E2
❑ 98PinEpixPP-E2
❑ 98PinEpixSE-E2
❑ 98PinEpixSO-E2
❑ 98PinEpixSP-E2
❑ 98PinHitIH-9
❑ 98PinHitIHS-9
❑ 98PinIns-41
❑ 98PinInsC-4
❑ 98PinInsCE-41
❑ 98PinInsCG-4
❑ 98PinInsDE-41
❑ 98PinInsSG-11AB
❑ 98PinInsSG-11CD
❑ 98PinInsSG-18AB
❑ 98PinInsSG-18CD
❑ 98PinInsSGS-11AB
❑ 98PinInsSGS-11CD
❑ 98PinInsSGS-18AB
❑ 98PinInsSGS-18CD
❑ 98PinMinB-6
❑ 98PinMinCB-6
❑ 98PinMinCBAP-6
❑ 98PinMinCGP-6
❑ 98PinMinCGPAP-6
❑ 98PinMinCN-6
❑ 98PinMinCNAP-6
❑ 98PinMinCSGR-6
❑ 98PinMinDC-6
❑ 98PinMinG-6
❑ 98PinMinMCSS-6
❑ 98PinMinS-6
❑ 98PinMusC-PP63
❑ 98PinPer-11
❑ 98PinPerBB-11
❑ 98PinPerBBSamp-11
❑ 98PinPerBBSO-11
❑ 98PinPerPP-11
❑ 98PinPerPT-10
❑ 98PinPerSftF-11
❑ 98PinPerSftF-NNO
❑ 98PinPerSftFShop-4
❑ 98PinPlu-116
❑ 98PinPluAE-2
❑ 98PinPluAEE-2
❑ 98PinPluAEP-2
❑ 98PinPluAP-PP37
❑ 98PinPluGAP-PP37
❑ 98PinPluLM-19
❑ 98PinPluMAP-PP37
❑ 98PinPluPieGame-8
❑ 98PinPluTP-7
❑ 98PinPluTPG-7
❑ 98PinPluTPM-7
❑ 98PinPluY-8
❑ 98PinPreP-70
❑ 98PinPreP-E2
❑ 98PinPreP-H9
❑ 98PinSna-TR17
❑ 98PreCon-15
❑ 98RanPinM-2
❑ 98Revo-142
❑ 98RevoFP-10
❑ 98RevoPTP-10
❑ 98RevoRooHH-30
❑ 98RevoShow-17
❑ 98RevoSS-142
❑ 98ScoAllST-14
❑ 98ScoEpix-E2
❑ 98ScoFirP-6
❑ 98ScoRT-2
❑ 98ScoRTASEpix-2
❑ 98ScoRTSS-PP2
❑ 98ScoRTSSAP-PP2
❑ 98ScoRTSSAP1-PP2
❑ 98ScoRTStarGaz-9
❑ 98SkyDugA-85
❑ 98SkyDugA-135
❑ 98SkyDugADH-DH7
❑ 98SkyDugAG-G3
❑ 98SkyDugAIA-85
❑ 98SkyDugAIA-135
❑ 98SP Aut-190
❑ 98SP Aut-SD42
❑ 98SP AutSD-SD42
❑ 98SP AutSDT-SD42
❑ 98SpoIll-46
❑ 98SpoIllEE-46
❑ 98SpoIllFE-46
❑ 98SpoIllODMP-OD29
❑ 98SpoIllTaN-85
❑ 98SpoIllTaNEE-85
❑ 98SpoIllWSF-43
❑ 98SpoIllWSFEE-43
❑ 98SpoIllWSFFE-43
❑ 98SpoIllWSFRJP-4
❑ 98SPxFin-35
❑ 98SPxFin-135
❑ 98SPxFin-168
❑ 98SPxFin-235
❑ 98SPxFinHRH-HR9
❑ 98SPxFinR-35
❑ 98SPxFinR-135
❑ 98SPxFinR-168
❑ 98SPxFinR-235
❑ 98SPxFinS-35
❑ 98SPxFinS-135
❑ 98SPxFinS-168
❑ 98SPxFinS-235
❑ 98StaCluFDI-200
❑ 98StaCluI-200
❑ 98StaCluOneK-200
❑ 98StaCluPP-200
❑ 98StaCluPWP-P6
❑ 98StaCluRC-RC9
❑ 98StaCluTIII-T18C
❑ 98StaCluTLme-T18C
❑ 98StaCluTLmo-T18C
❑ 98Stu-160
❑ 98StuFF-23
❑ 98StuFFDC-23
❑ 98StuGPP-160
❑ 98StuHitPar-11
❑ 98StuMast-10
❑ 98StuPor8x10-14
❑ 98StuPor8x10GP-14
❑ 98StuSony99-16
❑ 98StuSPP-160
❑ 98Top-30
❑ 98Top-273
❑ 98Top-482
❑ 98TopChr-30
❑ 98TopChr-273
❑ 98TopChr-482
❑ 98TopChrHB-HB14
❑ 98TopChrHBR-HB14
❑ 98TopChrM-MS4
❑ 98TopChrMR-MS4
❑ 98TopChrR-30
❑ 98TopChrR-273
❑ 98TopChrR-482
❑ 98TopDevR-30
❑ 98TopDevR-273
❑ 98TopDevR-482
❑ 98TopDia-30
❑ 98TopDia-273
❑ 98TopDia-482
❑ 98TopFocP-FP1
❑ 98TopGal-41
❑ 98TopGalGoH-GH13
❑ 98TopGalGoHJ-GH13
❑ 98TopGalGP-41
❑ 98TopGalOPP-41
❑ 98TopGalPPI-41
❑ 98TopGalPPIA-41
❑ 98TopGolLabC1-50
❑ 98TopGolLabC1B-50
❑ 98TopGolLabC1One-50
❑ 98TopGolLabC1R-50
❑ 98TopGolLabC2-50
❑ 98TopGolLabC2B-50
❑ 98TopGolLabC2One-50
❑ 98TopGolLabC2R-50
❑ 98TopGolLabC3-50
❑ 98TopGolLabC3B-50
❑ 98TopGolLabC3One-50
❑ 98TopGolLabC3R-50
❑ 98TopHal-HB14
❑ 98TopMil-MS4
❑ 98TopMiniC-30
❑ 98TopMiniC-273
❑ 98TopMiniC-482
❑ 98TopMysFB-M13
❑ 98TopMysFB-M13
❑ 98TopMysFBR-M13
❑ 98TopMysFBR-M13
❑ 98TopOpeD-19
❑ 98TopSta-90
❑ 98TopSta'S-13
❑ 98TopSta'SGH-13
❑ 98TopStaB-90
❑ 98TopStaG-90
❑ 98TopStaGR-90
❑ 98TopStaLB-L3
❑ 98TopStaLG-L3
❑ 98TopStaLGR-L3
❑ 98TopStaLS-L3
❑ 98TopStaS-90
❑ 98TopStaSteG-13
❑ 98TopSup-8
❑ 98TopSup-8
❑ 98TopTek-60
❑ 98TopTekD-60
❑ 98UD3-59
❑ 98UD3-149
❑ 98UD3-239
❑ 98UD3DieCut-59
❑ 98UD3DieCut-149
❑ 98UD3DieCut-239
❑ 98UD3PCBlowup-59
❑ 98Ult-100
❑ 98Ult-486
❑ 98UltArtT-12
❑ 98UltBigS-5
❑ 98UltDial-12
❑ 98UltDiaP-10
❑ 98UltDouT-10
❑ 98UltFalC-11
❑ 98UltGolM-100
❑ 98UltGolM-486
❑ 98UltMas-100
❑ 98UltMas-486
❑ 98UltMilM-13
❑ 98UltNot-5
❑ 98UltPlaM-100
❑ 98UltPlaM-486
❑ 98UltPowP-7
❑ 98UltPriL-12
❑ 98UltTicS-8
❑ 98UltTop3-13
❑ 98UltWinN-12
❑ 98UppDec-520
❑ 98UppDec-622
❑ 98UppDec10AP-49
❑ 98UppDec1APR-49
❑ 98UppDecAC-AS26
❑ 98UppDecAG-AG9
❑ 98UppDecAGDC-AG9
❑ 98UppDecCD-CD23
❑ 98UppDecNP-NP27
❑ 98UppDecPN-PN36
❑ 98UppDecPN-PN37
❑ 98UppDecPN-PN38
❑ 98UppDecPN-PN39
❑ 98UppDecPN-PN40
❑ 98UppDecPN-PN41
❑ 98UppDecPN-PN42
❑ 98UppDecR-95
❑ 98UppDecR-21
❑ 98UppDecRBBop-BB16
❑ 98UppDecRQL-Q9
❑ 98UppDecRTC-TC22
❑ 98UppDecSFPD-PZ3
❑ 98UppDecSFPZOB-PZ2
❑ 98UppDecSFPZPD-PZ2
❑ 98UppDecSFPZSX-PZ3
❑ 98UppDecTMT-14
❑ 98UppDecTMTG-14
❑ 98UppDecU-18
❑ 98Zen-11
❑ 98Zen5 xx7-23
❑ 98Zen5x7GoldImp-23
❑ 98Zen5x7Imp-23
❑ 98ZenEpi-E2
❑ 98ZenRaitB-11
❑ 98ZenZ-G-11
❑ 98ZenZ-S-11
❑ 99199Fin-75
❑ 99199Fin-107
❑ 99199Fin-254
❑ 99AllMysFR-M15
❑ 99AurOn DL-19
❑ 99AurPenF-19
❑ 99AurPenF-19
❑ 99AurPenFB-19
❑ 99AurPenFS-19
❑ 99AurSty-19
❑ 99Bow-285
❑ 99BowBes-71
❑ 99BowBes-99
❑ 99BowBesAR-71
❑ 99BowBesAR-99
❑ 99BowBesFBMI-FB10
❑ 99BowBesFBMII-FB10
❑ 99BowBesFBMIII-FB10
❑ 99BowBesR-71
❑ 99BowBesR-99
❑ 99BowChrDA-DA17
❑ 99BowChrDAR-DA17
❑ 99BowGol-285
❑ 99BowInt-285
❑ 99CroRoyB-137
❑ 99CroRoyL-137
❑ 99CroRoyMP-19
❑ 99CroRoyOD-137
❑ 99CroRoyPotG-24
❑ 99CroRoyPP-24
❑ 99CroRoyPPN-24
❑ 99DumSet-160
❑ 99E-X Cen-11
❑ 99E-X CenECFut-11
❑ 99E-X CenECNow-11
❑ 99E-XCenFoF'-8
❑ 99FinAarAwC-HA1
❑ 99FinAarAwCR-HA1
❑ 99FinCom-C4
❑ 99FinComDualR-C4
❑ 99FinFraR-FR4
❑ 99FinFraRR-FR4
❑ 99FinGolRef-75

❑ 99FinGolRef-107
❑ 99FinGolRef-254
❑ 99FinLeaL-L6
❑ 99FinMil-M25
❑ 99FinPeelHyp-12
❑ 99FinPeelSpark-12
❑ 99FinPeeSS-12
❑ 99FinProF-PF5
❑ 99FinProF-PF13
❑ 99FinProF-PF31
❑ 99FinProF-PF46
❑ 99FinRef-75
❑ 99FinRef-107
❑ 99FinRef-254
❑ 99FinSplS-SS6
❑ 99FinSplSDR-SS6
❑ 99FinTeaFB-TF4
❑ 99FinTeaFBR-TF4
❑ 99FinTeaFG-TF4
❑ 99FinTeaFGR-TF4
❑ 99FinTeaFR-TF4
❑ 99FinTeaFRR-TF4
❑ 99FlaShoLeg1-19
❑ 99FlaShoLeg2-19
❑ 99FlaShoLeg3-19
❑ 99FlaShoLegM1-19
❑ 99FlaShoLegM2-19
❑ 99FlaShoLegM3-19
❑ 99FlaShoMoG-3
❑ 99FlaShoR1-19
❑ 99FlaShoR2-19
❑ 99FlaShoR3-19
❑ 99Fle-29
❑ 99FleBri-44
❑ 99FleBri2G-44
❑ 99FleBriBlu-44
❑ 99FleBriGol-44
❑ 99FleBriSS-8
❑ 99FleBriSSP-8
❑ 99FleGoiYar-6
❑ 99FleGolM-5
❑ 99FleMys-31
❑ 99FleMys-160
❑ 99FleMysD-2
❑ 99FleMysFl-15
❑ 99FleMysFtG-3
❑ 99FleMysG-31
❑ 99FleMysM-31
❑ 99FleMysM-160
❑ 99FleSta9-29
❑ 99FleVin'-29
❑ 99FleWarT-29
❑ 99HomHer-15
❑ 99KinDis-8
❑ 99MetUni-9
❑ 99MetUni-237
❑ 99MetUni-278
❑ 99MetUniBWTW-4
❑ 99MetUniDS-7
❑ 99MetUniGM-9
❑ 99MetUniGM-237
❑ 99MetUniGM-278
❑ 99MetUniPM-14
❑ 99MetUniPMG-9
❑ 99MetUniPMG-237
❑ 99MetUniPMG-278
❑ 99Pac-423
❑ 99Pac-423A
❑ 99PacAur-189
❑ 99PacAurOD-189
❑ 99PacCroC-282
❑ 99PacCroC-20
❑ 99PacCroCITC-19
❑ 99PacCroCPB-282
❑ 99PacCroCTC-29
❑ 99PacCroCTM-18
❑ 99PacDynaD-8
❑ 99PacDynaDT-8
❑ 99PacGolCDC-16
❑ 99PacInv-143
❑ 99PacInvFP-20
❑ 99PacInvOD-143
❑ 99PacInvPB-143
❑ 99PacInvSF-19
❑ 99PacInvSF-19B
❑ 99PacInvSH-20
❑ 99PacInvSH-20B
❑ 99PacInvTA-19
❑ 99PacOme-235
❑ 99PacOme5T-24
❑ 99PacOme5TT-24
❑ 99PacOmeC-235
❑ 99PacOmeDM-33
❑ 99PacOmeEP-20
❑ 99PacOmeEP1o1-20
❑ 99PacOmeG-235
❑ 99PacOmeH'-20
❑ 99PacOmePB-235
❑ 99PacPar-233
❑ 99PacParC-233
❑ 99PacParFC-19
❑ 99PacParG-233
❑ 99PacParHoloGold-233
❑ 99PacParHS-233
❑ 99PacParOD-233
❑ 99PacParPB-35
❑ 99PacParPB-233
❑ 99PacParRed-233
❑ 99PacParTC-29
❑ 99PacPlaB-423
❑ 99PacPlaB-423A
❑ 99PacPri-142
❑ 99PacPriDG-20
❑ 99PacPriHB-142
❑ 99PacPriHG-142
❑ 99PacPriHM-142
❑ 99PacPriHP-142
❑ 99PacPriRed-142
❑ 99PacPriS-5
❑ 99PacPriS206-5
❑ 99PacPriS206R-5
❑ 99PacPriSE-5
❑ 99PacPriSP-5
❑ 99PacPriSP-5
❑ 99PacPriSV-5
❑ 99PacRed-423
❑ 99PacRed-423A
❑ 99PacTeaC-13
❑ 99Pin-8
❑ 99Rev-140
❑ 99RevDiaL-34
❑ 99RevFouP-20
❑ 99RevPremDate-140
❑ 99RevRet-140
❑ 99RevShaSS-140
❑ 99RevThoitS-19
❑ 99RevTri-20
❑ 99RevTri-20
❑ 99SkyMolM-140
❑ 99SkyMolMF-40
❑ 99SkyMolMFS-40
❑ 99SkyMolMFT-40
❑ 99SkyMolMX-140
❑ 99SkyPre-106
❑ 99SkyPre-286
❑ 99SkyPreA-21
❑ 99SkyPreABlue-21
❑ 99SkyPreIN-11
❑ 99SkyPreLB-1
❑ 99SkyPreR-106
❑ 99SkyPreR-286
❑ 99SkyPreSB-4
❑ 99SkyPreSotG-7
❑ 99SkyThu-256
❑ 99SkyThuDial1-D2
❑ 99SkyThuHip-H3
❑ 99SkyThuInD-ID4
❑ 99SkyThuRant-256
❑ 99SkyThuRave-256
❑ 99SkyThuTur-TC2
❑ 99SP Aut-86
❑ 99SP Aut-126
❑ 99SP AutEF-E29
❑ 99SP AutHRC-HR8
❑ 99SP AutR-R29
❑ 99SP SigAutoG-JUG
❑ 99SPAutHRCDC-HR8
❑ 99SpoIll-11
❑ 99SpoIll-20
❑ 99SpoIll-75
❑ 99SpoIllF4-8
❑ 99SpoIllF4E-8
❑ 99SpoIllH-6
❑ 99SPSig-5
❑ 99SPx-77
❑ 99SPxDom-FB20
❑ 99SPxFinR-77
❑ 99SPxFinS-77
❑ 99SPxPowE-PE29
❑ 99SPxPreS-PS24
❑ 99SPxStaF-SF28
❑ 99StaClu-135
❑ 99StaCluA-SCA6
❑ 99StaCluC-SCC30
❑ 99StaCluC-CS24
❑ 99StaCluC-CS30
❑ 99StaCluC-CS36
❑ 99StaCluC-CS41
❑ 99StaCluCR-SCC30
❑ 99StaCluFDI-135
❑ 99StaCluOoaK-135
❑ 99StaCluPP-135
❑ 99StaCluTI-T13A
❑ 99StaCluTL-T13A
❑ 99StaCluTL-T13A
❑ 99ThuSkySupR-256
❑ 99Top-50
❑ 99Top-226
❑ 99Top-454
❑ 99TopActF-3
❑ 99TopActFAU-3
❑ 99TopActFCU-3
❑ 99TopAll-AM8
❑ 99TopAllMF-M15
❑ 99TopBlaLC1-65
❑ 99TopBlaLC2-65
❑ 99TopBlaLC3-65
❑ 99TopChr-50
❑ 99TopChr-226
❑ 99TopChr-454
❑ 99TopChrA-AE8
❑ 99TopChrAR-AE8
❑ 99TopChrERttH-ER4
❑ 99TopChrERttH-ER4
❑ 99TopChrLotD-LD8
❑ 99TopChrLotDR-LD8
❑ 99TopChrR-50
❑ 99TopChrR-226
❑ 99TopChrR-454
❑ 99TopGal-5
❑ 99TopGal-108
❑ 99TopGalAG-AG5
❑ 99TopGalHer-TH16
❑ 99TopGalHerP-TH16
❑ 99TopGalPP-5
❑ 99TopGalPP-108
❑ 99TopGalPPI-5
❑ 99TopGalPPI-108
❑ 99TopGolL-65
❑ 99TopGolLC1-65
❑ 99TopGolLC2-65
❑ 99TopGolLOtO-65
❑ 99TopGolLRtA-RA9
❑ 99TopGolLRtAB-RA9
❑ 99TopGolLRtAOtO-RA9
❑ 99TopGolLRtAR-RA9
❑ 99TopLorotD-LD8
❑ 99TopMVPP-50
❑ 99TopMVPP-454
❑ 99TopOpeD-27
❑ 99TopOver-A4
❑ 99TopPicP-P8
❑ 99TopPowB-PB5
❑ 99TopPowBR-PB5
❑ 99TopRedLC1-65
❑ 99TopRedLC2-65
❑ 99TopRedLC3-65
❑ 99TopSta-168
❑ 99TopSta'S-7
❑ 99TopSta'SG-7
❑ 99TopSta'SGDH-7
❑ 99TopSta1Foil-17
❑ 99TopSta2Foil-17
❑ 99TopSta3Foil-17
❑ 99TopStaFoil-168
❑ 99TopStaOS-17
❑ 99TopStaTS-17
❑ 99TopStaTS-17
❑ 99TopSupC-8
❑ 99TopSupCR-8
❑ 99TopTek-41A
❑ 99TopTek-41B
❑ 99TopTekG-41A
❑ 99TopTekG-41B
❑ 99UD Cho-31
❑ 99UD Cho-152
❑ 99UD ChoBUCG-3
❑ 99UD ChoMBH-B30
❑ 99UD ChoP-152
❑ 99UD ChoPCR-31
❑ 99UD ChoPCR-152
❑ 99UD ChoS-9
❑ 99UD ChoSD-9
❑ 99UD ChoSHR-9
❑ 99UD ChoST-9
❑ 99UD ChoYW-Y28
❑ 99UD Ion-58
❑ 99UD Ion-88
❑ 99UD IonC-C10
❑ 99UD IonH-HG10
❑ 99UD IonH-H10
❑ 99UD IonR-58
❑ 99UD IonR-88
❑ 99UD IonWZ-WZ10
❑ 99UDHolo-56
❑ 99UDHoloAUsome-56
❑ 99UDHoloLau-L6
❑ 99UDHoloLauG-L6
❑ 99Ult-191
❑ 99Ult-218
❑ 99UltDamI-7
❑ 99UltGolM-191
❑ 99UltGolM-218
❑ 99UltMas-191
❑ 99UltMas-218
❑ 99UltPlaM-191
❑ 99UltPlaM-218
❑ 99UltRBIK-14
❑ 99UltTheBook-5
❑ 99UltThu-9
❑ 99UppDec-242
❑ 99UppDec-502
❑ 99UppDec-521
❑ 99UppDec10AT-X18
❑ 99UppDec10ATD-X18
❑ 99UppDec10ATHR-X18
❑ 99UppDec10ATT-X18
❑ 99UppDecBD-85
❑ 99UppDecBDAPH-JG
❑ 99UppDecBDD-85
❑ 99UppDecBDDom-D18
❑ 99UppDecBDDomE-D18
❑ 99UppDecBDMN-M18
❑ 99UppDecBDMNE-M18
❑ 99UppDecBDQ-85
❑ 99UppDecBDT-85
❑ 99UppDecCf7-9
❑ 99UppDecCf7-55
❑ 99UppDecCf7-C9
❑ 99UppDecCf7Cf7P-C9
❑ 99UppDecCf7LL-L10
❑ 99UppDecCf7SftF-S13
❑ 99UppDecCL-62
❑ 99UppDecCLCC-62
❑ 99UppDecCLES-JG
❑ 99UppDecCLESC-JG
❑ 99UppDecCLM-C94
❑ 99UppDecCo7CE-9
❑ 99UppDecCo7CE-55
❑ 99UppDecE-87
❑ 99UppDecE-144
❑ 99UppDecE-171
❑ 99UppDecEDF-D7
❑ 99UppDecEDFFXG-D7
❑ 99UppDecEFXG-87
❑ 99UppDecEFXG-144
❑ 99UppDecEFXG-171
❑ 99UppDecEL1-242
❑ 99UppDecEL1-502
❑ 99UppDecEL1-521
❑ 99UppDecEL2-242
❑ 99UppDecEL2-502
❑ 99UppDecEL2-521
❑ 99UppDecEPE-P29
❑ 99UppDecEUR-U6
❑ 99UppDecF-F28
❑ 99UppDecFD-F28
❑ 99UppDecFQ-F28
❑ 99UppDecFT-F28
❑ 99UppDecGJ-JG
❑ 99UppDecM-204
❑ 99UppDecM-P5
❑ 99UppDecMD-D14
❑ 99UppDecMGS-204
❑ 99UppDecMHFS-204
❑ 99UppDecMP-204
❑ 99UppDecMSS-204
❑ 99UppDecO-44
❑ 99UppDecO-88
❑ 99UppDecOAPoH-JG
❑ 99UppDecOMP-S13
❑ 99UppDecOSO-44
❑ 99UppDecOSO-88
❑ 99UppDecOWP-R11
❑ 99UppDecR-82
❑ 99UppDecRDR-D11
❑ 99UppDecRDRL2-D11
❑ 99UppDecRG-82
❑ 99UppDecROSS-S9
❑ 99UppDecROSS-S9
❑ 99UppDecRP-82
❑ 99UppDecRTA-T9
❑ 99UppDecRTAL2-T9
❑ 99UppDecTE-T28
❑ 99UppDecTED-T28
❑ 99UppDecTEQ-T28
❑ 99UppDecTET-T28
❑ 99UppDecVtaT-V29
❑ 99UppDecVtaTD-V29
❑ 99UppDecVtaTQ-V29
❑ 99UppDecVtaTT-V29
❑ 99UppDecWY-W9
❑ 99UppDecWYD-W9
❑ 99UppDecWYHR-W9
❑ 99UppDecWYT-W9
❑ 99Vic-396
❑ 99Vic-397
❑ 99Vic-399
❑ 99Vic-468
❑ 99PacOmeDD-7
❑ 99TopSta-17
❑ 99TopStaFoil-17

Gonzalez, Juan Elias

❑ 94HelBreF-3609
❑ 94HelBreSP-23
❑ 95BelBreTI-18
❑ 96BreCouMB-17
❑ 97BreCouMB-15
❑ 98BesPreA-12

Gonzalez, Julian

❑ 83PeoSunF-23
❑ 85DomLeaS-40
❑ 85MidAngT-25
❑ 87SanJosBP-24
❑ 88SouBenWSGS-20

Gonzalez, Julio C.

❑ 77AstPho-7
❑ 78AstBurK-13
❑ 78AstPos-10
❑ 78Top-389
❑ 79AstPos-10
❑ 79Top-268
❑ 80Top-696
❑ 81Car5x7-5
❑ 81Fle-73
❑ 82Don-645
❑ 82Top-503
❑ 83EvaTriT-14
❑ 83Top-74
❑ 87AstShoSPT-9

Gonzalez, Lariel

❑ 98Bow-370
❑ 98BowChr-370
❑ 98BowChrGA-370
❑ 98BowChrGAR-370
❑ 98BowChrI-370
❑ 98BowChrIR-370
❑ 98BowChrR-370
❑ 98BowGolA-370
❑ 98BowInt-370
❑ 98EasLeaTPM-10
❑ 98NewHavRM-9
❑ 98NewHavRMA-9
❑ 99Bow-124
❑ 99BowAut-BA24
❑ 99BowChr-124
❑ 99BowChrG-124
❑ 99BowChrGR-124
❑ 99BowChrI-124
❑ 99BowChrIR-124
❑ 99BowChrR-124
❑ 99BowGol-124
❑ 99BowInt-124
❑ 99Fle-446
❑ 99FleSta9-446
❑ 99FleWarT-446

Gonzalez, Laril

❑ 91LinDriAA-435
❑ 92EdmTraF-3542
❑ 96AshTouB-19
❑ 97SalAva-17

Gonzalez, Luis

❑ 75WatRoyT-14
❑ 78AshTouT-7
❑ 79AshTouT-1
❑ 80TulDriT-14
❑ 96EriSeaB-11
❑ 98ColRedSM-15

Gonzalez, Luis E.

❑ 88AubAstP-1973
❑ 89OscAstS-6
❑ 89Sta-15
❑ 90Bes-95
❑ 90CMC-760
❑ 90ColMudB-4
❑ 90ColMudP-1352
❑ 90ColMudS-11
❑ 90ProAaA-59
❑ 90StaFS7-16
❑ 91AstMot-13
❑ 91Bow-550
❑ 91Cla2-T91
❑ 91Don-690
❑ 91DonRoo-17
❑ 91Fle-507
❑ 91LeaGolR-BC2
❑ 91LeaGolRNV-266
❑ 91ScoRoo-99T
❑ 91StaClu-576
❑ 91TopDeb90-57
❑ 91TopTra-48T
❑ 91TopTraT-48T
❑ 91UltUpd-82
❑ 91UppDec-567
❑ 91UppDec-702
❑ 92Bow-145
❑ 92ClaGam-3
❑ 92Don-270
❑ 92Fle-434
❑ 92Hig5-39
❑ 92Lea-160
❑ 92LeaBlaG-160
❑ 92OPC-12
❑ 92OPCPre-103
❑ 92PanSti-158
❑ 92Pin-163
❑ 92PinTea2-68
❑ 92Sco-210
❑ 92Sco100RS-6
❑ 92StaClu-227
❑ 92Top-12
❑ 92TopGol-12
❑ 92TopGolW-12
❑ 92TopMic-12
❑ 92TriPla-210
❑ 92Ult-203
❑ 92UppDec-372
❑ 93AstMot-15
❑ 93AstStaC-26
❑ 93Bow-40
❑ 93DiaMar-39
❑ 93Don-404
❑ 93Fin-195
❑ 93FinRef-195
❑ 93Fla-63
❑ 93Fle-51
❑ 93Lea-90
❑ 93LinVenB-43
❑ 93LinVenB-210
❑ 93OPC-178
❑ 93PacBeiA-24
❑ 93PacSpa-123
❑ 93PanSti-175
❑ 93Pin-312
❑ 93Sco-151
❑ 93Sel-205
❑ 93SP-34
❑ 93StaClu-302
❑ 93StaCluFDI-302
❑ 93StaCluMOP-302
❑ 93Stu-171
❑ 93Top-362
❑ 93TopGol-362
❑ 93TopInaM-362
❑ 93TopInaR-362
❑ 93TopMic-362
❑ 93Ult-40
❑ 93UppDec-572
❑ 93UppDecGold-572
❑ 94AstMot-4
❑ 94Bow-62
❑ 94ColC-111
❑ 94ColChoGS-111
❑ 94ColChoSS-111
❑ 94Don-83
❑ 94Fin-290
❑ 94FinRef-290
❑ 94Fla-170
❑ 94Fle-491
❑ 94FleExtB-274
❑ 94Lea-292
❑ 94LeaL-115
❑ 94OPC-263
❑ 94Pac-266
❑ 94PacAll-4
❑ 94Pin-323
❑ 94PinArtP-323
❑ 94PinMusC-323
❑ 94ProMag-57
❑ 94Sco-474
❑ 94ScoGolR-474
❑ 94Sel-348
❑ 94StaClu-35
❑ 94StaCluFDI-35
❑ 94StaCluGR-35
❑ 94StaCluMOP-35
❑ 94Stu-22
❑ 94Top-484
❑ 94TopGol-484
❑ 94TopSpa-484
❑ 94TriPla-27
❑ 94Ult-205
❑ 94UppDec-396
❑ 94UppDecED-396
❑ 94VenLinU-68
❑ 95AstMot-3

❑ 95ColCho-110
❑ 95ColChoGS-110
❑ 95ColChoSS-110
❑ 95Don-145
❑ 95DonPreP-145
❑ 95DonTopotO-198
❑ 95Fin-150
❑ 95FinRef-150
❑ 95Fla-146
❑ 95Fle-460
❑ 95Lea-216
❑ 95LeaLim-77
❑ 95LinVen-90
❑ 95Pac-187
❑ 95PacLatD-18
❑ 95PacPri-62
❑ 95Pin-33
❑ 95PinArtP-33
❑ 95PinMusC-33
❑ 95Sco-79
❑ 95ScoGolR-79
❑ 95ScoPlaTS-79
❑ 95StaClu-257
❑ 95StaCluFDI-257
❑ 95StaCluMOP-257
❑ 95StaCluSTWS-257
❑ 95StaCluVR-126
❑ 95StaCluVRMO-126
❑ 95Stu-95
❑ 95Top-162
❑ 95TopCyb-97
❑ 95TopEmb-58
❑ 95TopEmbGI-58
❑ 95Ult-386
❑ 95UltGolM-386
❑ 95UppDec-276
❑ 95UppDec-458
❑ 95UppDecED-276
❑ 95UppDecEDG-276
❑ 95UppDecSE-44
❑ 95UppDecSEG-44
❑ 96ColCho-87
❑ 96ColChoGS-87
❑ 96ColChoSS-87
❑ 96CubFle-6
❑ 96Don-358
❑ 96DonPreP-358
❑ 96EmoXL-154
❑ 96Fla-215
❑ 96Fle-318
❑ 96FleTif-318
❑ 96Lea-128
❑ 96LeaPrePB-128
❑ 96LeaPrePG-128
❑ 96LeaPrePS-128
❑ 96MetUni-140
❑ 96MetUniP-140
❑ 96Pac-33
❑ 96PacPri-P9
❑ 96PacPriG-P9
❑ 96PanSti-42
❑ 96Sco-146
❑ 96StaClu-101
❑ 96StaCluEPB-101
❑ 96StaCluEPG-101
❑ 96StaCluEPS-101
❑ 96StaCluMOP-101
❑ 96Top-278
❑ 96Ult-167
❑ 96UltGolM-167
❑ 96UppDec-38
❑ 97AstMot-5
❑ 97Cir-68
❑ 97CirRav-68
❑ 97ColCho-352
❑ 97Don-237
❑ 97DonGolPP-237
❑ 97DonSilPP-237
❑ 97Fle-275
❑ 97Fle-531
❑ 97FleTif-275
❑ 97FleTif-531
❑ 97Pac-249
❑ 97PacLigB-249
❑ 97PacPri-85
❑ 97PacPriLB-85
❑ 97PacPriP-85
❑ 97PacSil-249
❑ 97StaClu-331
❑ 97StaCluMOP-331
❑ 97Top-142
❑ 97Ult-504
❑ 97UltGolME-504
❑ 97UltPlaME-504
❑ 97UppDec-364
❑ 98CirThu-39
❑ 98CirThuRav-39
❑ 98CirThuSupRav-39
❑ 98ColCho-366
❑ 98Fle-26
❑ 98Fle-373
❑ 98Pac-317
❑ 98PacInv-104
❑ 98PacInvPBlue-104
❑ 98PacInvSilv-104
❑ 98PacOme-89
❑ 98PacOmeR-89
❑ 98PacOnl-273
❑ 98PacOnlR-273
❑ 98PacOnlWC-273
❑ 98PacPlaB-317
❑ 98PacRedT-317
❑ 98PacSil-317
❑ 98SPxFin-274
❑ 98SPxFinR-274
❑ 98SPxFinS-274
❑ 98StaCluFDI-231
❑ 98StaCluI-231
❑ 98StaCluOneK-231
❑ 98StaCluPP-231
❑ 98Top-210
❑ 98TopChr-210
❑ 98TopChrR-210
❑ 98TopDevR-210
❑ 98TopDia-210
❑ 98TopMiniC-210
❑ 98TopOpeD-103
❑ 98Ult-450
❑ 98UltGolM-450
❑ 98UltMas-450
❑ 98UltPlaM-450
❑ 98UppDec-103
❑ 98UppDec-676
❑ 99FlaShoLeg1-122
❑ 99FlaShoLeg2-122
❑ 99FlaShoLeg3-122
❑ 99FlaShoLegM1-122
❑ 99FlaShoLegM2-122
❑ 99FlaShoLegM3-122
❑ 99FlaShoR1-122
❑ 99FlaShoR2-122
❑ 99FlaShoR3-122
❑ 99Fle-156
❑ 99FleSta9-156
❑ 99FleWarT-156
❑ 99Pac-164
❑ 99PacCroC-108
❑ 99PacCroCPB-108
❑ 99PacOme-12
❑ 99PacOmeC-12
❑ 99PacOmeG-12
❑ 99PacOmePB-12
❑ 99PacPar-14
❑ 99PacParC-14
❑ 99PacParG-14
❑ 99PacParHoloGold-14
❑ 99PacParHS-14
❑ 99PacParOD-14
❑ 99PacParPB-14
❑ 99PacParRed-14
❑ 99PacPlaB-164
❑ 99PacPri-57
❑ 99PacPriHB-57
❑ 99PacPriHG-57
❑ 99PacPriHM-57
❑ 99PacPriHP-57
❑ 99PacPriRed-57
❑ 99PacRed-164
❑ 99Rev-7
❑ 99RevPremDate-7
❑ 99RevRet-7
❑ 99RevShaSS-7
❑ 99SkyThu-163
❑ 99SkyThuRant-163
❑ 99SkyThuRave-163
❑ 99StaClu-329
❑ 99StaCluFDI-329
❑ 99StaCluOoaK-329
❑ 99StaCluPP-329
❑ 99ThuSkySupR-163
❑ 99Top-361
❑ 99TopChr-361
❑ 99TopChrR-361
❑ 99TopMVPP-361
❑ 99Ult-197
❑ 99UltGolM-197
❑ 99UltMas-197
❑ 99UltPlaM-197

Gonzalez, Manny
❑ 95GreFalDTI-23
❑ 96SanBerSB-10
❑ 98BirBarG-11

Gonzalez, Manuel
❑ 80VenLeaS-94
❑ 93LinVenB-272
❑ 96-97LinVen-164
❑ 96SavSanB-4
❑ 97HicCraB-13
❑ 97HicCraRB-15

Gonzalez, Marcos
❑ 82MiaMarT-3
❑ 87FayGenP-20

Gonzalez, Mario
❑ 92GulCoaRSP-17
❑ 93LinVenB-135
❑ 94ChaRivC-8
❑ 94ChaRivF-2682
❑ 94VenLinU-91
❑ 95LinVen-247
❑ 96-97LinVen-234

Gonzalez, Maurico
❑ 93CenValRC-11
❑ 93CenValRF-2898
❑ 94CenValRC-8
❑ 94CenValRF-3210
❑ 95NewHavRTI-4

Gonzalez, Melvin
❑ 91ElmPioC-21
❑ 91ElmPioP-3266
❑ 93ForLauRSC-12
❑ 93ForLauRSFP-1589

Gonzalez, Miguel
❑ 17ColE13-61
❑ 21Exh-58
❑ 22W575-44
❑ 27YorCarE-34
❑ 28StaPlaCE-28
❑ 28W502-34
❑ 28Yue-34
❑ 31CarMet-11
❑ 46SeaSLP-23
❑ 92ConTSN-655

Gonzalez, Mike
❑ 20W52-7
❑ 20W52-19
❑ 21E121So8-28
❑ 21KoBreWSI-12
❑ 40PlaBal-115
❑ 41CarW75-8
❑ 74Car193T-12
❑ 75ShrCapT-3
❑ 76ShrCapT-6
❑ 83Car194T-29
❑ 86ConSer1-14
❑ 89BurIndS-11
❑ 90WatIndS-10
❑ 95ConTSN-1380
❑ 98AugGreM-1
❑ 98SouAtlLPM-12

Gonzalez, Orlando
❑ 75OklCit8TI-13
❑ 76VenLeaS-47
❑ 77Top-477
❑ 80BurBeeT-7
❑ 81Fle-585
❑ 83TamTarT-13
❑ 87NasSouTI-7
❑ 88MiaMarS-8
❑ 89PacSenL-82
❑ 89TopSenL-83
❑ 91PacSenL-35

Gonzalez, Otto
❑ 82BurRanF-27
❑ 82BurRanT-21
❑ 83BurRanF-17
❑ 83BurRanT-17
❑ 85TulDriTI-35
❑ 86DayBeaIP-9
❑ 86FloStaLAP-18
❑ 88BlaYNPRWL-40
❑ 88OklCit8C-12
❑ 88OklCit8P-47
❑ 89BlaYNPRWL-115
❑ 89MidAngGS-15

Gonzalez, Paul
❑ 91Cla/Bes-82
❑ 91HigDesMC-21
❑ 91HigDesMP-2404
❑ 92SkyAA F-280
❑ 92WicWraF-3663
❑ 92WicWraS-632
❑ 93WicWraF-2983
❑ 94WicWraF-196
❑ 95PriWilCTI-8

Gonzalez, Pedro
❑ 63Top-537
❑ 64ChatheY-10
❑ 64Top-581
❑ 64TopRooAB-3
❑ 65ChaTheY-8
❑ 65OPC-97
❑ 65Top-97
❑ 66Kah-13
❑ 66Top-266
❑ 66TopVen-266
❑ 67CokCapI-6
❑ 67DexPre-80
❑ 67Top-424
❑ 70WicAerM-8
❑ 91VerBeaDC-15
❑ 91VerBeaDP-776
❑ 92FayGenC-20
❑ 92LakTigF-2281
❑ 92TolMudHF-1045
❑ 92YanWIZ6-48
❑ 93LakTigC-8
❑ 96ColSprSSTI-16

Gonzalez, Pete (Pedro)
❑ 90VerBeaDS-15
❑ 93LakTigF-1313

Gonzalez, Pitcher (Mike)
❑ 76VenLeaS-147

Gonzalez, Raul
❑ 92AppFoxCB-19
❑ 92AppFoxFI-997
❑ 93CarLeaAGF-11
❑ 93WilBluRC-11
❑ 93WilBluRF-2010
❑ 94UppDecML-127
❑ 94WilBluRC-10
❑ 94WilBluRF-312
❑ 95WilBluRTI-14
❑ 96WicWraB-26
❑ 97WicWra-22
❑ 98WicWraM-14

Gonzalez, Rene
❑ 97LasVegS1A-15

Gonzalez, Rich
❑ 91St.PetCC-25
❑ 91St.PetCP-2288
❑ 94ChaWheC-11
❑ 95WatIndTI-13

Gonzalez, Ricky
❑ 97KinIndB-8

Gonzalez, Ruben
❑ 87BelMarTI-23
❑ 88WauTimGS-6
❑ 89CalLeaA-12
❑ 89SanBerSB-23
❑ 89SanBerSCLC-82
❑ 90Bes-198
❑ 90CMC-797
❑ 90WilBilB-8
❑ 90WilBilP-1062
❑ 91Cla/Bes-28
❑ 91JacSunLD-337
❑ 91JacSunP-157
❑ 91LinDriAA-337

Gonzalez, Santos
❑ 97IdaFalBTI-4
❑ 98CliLumG-5

Gonzalez, Tommy
❑ 83PhoGiaBHN-28

Gonzalez, Tony
❑ 47Exh-81
❑ 58PhiTeaI-8
❑ 60Top-518
❑ 61Top-93
❑ 61TopStaI-55
❑ 62Top-534
❑ 62TopStaI-168
❑ 63ExhStaB-26
❑ 63Jel-181
❑ 63Pos-181
❑ 63Top-32
❑ 64PhiPhiB-13
❑ 64PhiTeaS-4
❑ 64Top-379
❑ 64TopCoi-58
❑ 64TopGia-14
❑ 64TopSta-58
❑ 64TopStaU-29
❑ 65OPC-72
❑ 65Top-72
❑ 66PhiTeaI-7
❑ 66Top-478
❑ 67CokCapPh-17
❑ 67PhiPol-7
❑ 67Top-548
❑ 67TopVen-265
❑ 68Baz-8
❑ 68OPC-1
❑ 68Top-1
❑ 68Top-245
❑ 68TopActS-7C
❑ 68TopGamI-20
❑ 68TopVen-1
❑ 68TopVen-245
❑ 69AtlBraBPPS-10
❑ 69MilBra-94
❑ 69MLBOffS-192
❑ 69Top-501A
❑ 69Top-501B
❑ 69TopDecI-13
❑ 69TopSta-94
❑ 69TopTeaP-12
❑ 70MLBOffS-6
❑ 70OPC-105
❑ 70Top-105
❑ 71MLBOffS-345
❑ 71OPC-256
❑ 71Top-256
❑ 72MilBra-118
❑ 75PhoGiaC-19
❑ 75PhoGiaCK-5
❑ 77SpaPhiT-15
❑ 82DanSunF-13
❑ 83PhiPosGPaM-12

Gonzalez, Wallace
❑ 89BlaYNPRWL-177
❑ 90PulBraB-13
❑ 90PulBraP-3093
❑ 91MacBraC-15
❑ 91MacBraP-868

Gonzalez, Wiklenman
❑ 95LinVen-5
❑ 96-97LinVen-144
❑ 96AugGreB-12
❑ 97RanCucQUG-3
❑ 98RanCucQG-12
❑ 98RanCucQG-12

Gooch, Arnold
❑ 95AshTouTI-15
❑ 96Bow-254
❑ 96BowFoi-254
❑ 96StLucMTI-3
❑ 97BinMetB-11
❑ 97Bow-334
❑ 97BowInt-334
❑ 97EasLeaTPB-4
❑ 98BinMetQ-13
❑ 98Bow-90
❑ 98BowChr-90
❑ 98BowChrGA-90
❑ 98BowChrGAR-90
❑ 98BowChrI-90
❑ 98BowChrIR-90
❑ 98BowChrR-90
❑ 98BowGolA-90
❑ 98BowInt-90

Gooch, Charles
❑ 27Zee-4
❑ 28Zee-6

Gooch, Johnny (John B.)
❑ 22E120-217
❑ 27AmeCarE126-1
❑ 31Exh-8
❑ 79RedSoxEF-5
❑ 90DodTar-289
❑ 91ConTSN-244

Gooch, Ron
❑ 79TucTorT-7
❑ 79TulDriT-11
❑ 80TulDriT-17
❑ 81TulDriT-28

Good, Eric
❑ 99TeaBesR-31
❑ 99TeaBesRG-31
❑ 99TeaBesRS-31

Good, Thomathon
❑ 92LetMouSP-8
❑ 93EugEmeF-3868

Good, Wilbur
❑ 09MaxPubP-21
❑ 09T206-143
❑ 11PinT-5-717
❑ 11T205-65
❑ 15SpoNewM-69
❑ 16SpoNewM-69

Gooda, David
❑ 95HelBreTI-22

Goodale, Jeff
❑ 89NiaFalRP-9
❑ 90LakTigS-12
❑ 91LakTigC-24
❑ 91LakTigP-278

Goodale, Wes
❑ 75AndRanT-28

Goodbred, Richard
❑ 17Zee-25

Goodchild, Chris
❑ 80CliGiaT-6

Goode, William
❑ 14PieStaT-47

Goodell, Steve
❑ 95ElmPioTI-10
❑ 95ElmPioUTI-10
❑ 96KanCouCTI-12
❑ 97BreCouMB-16
❑ 98PorSeaDQ-19

Gooden, Carl
❑ 97JohCitCTI-14
❑ 98JohCCTI-14

Gooden, Derek
❑ 97JohCitCTI-15
❑ 98NewJerCM-10

Gooden, Doc (Dwight)
❑ 83LynMetT-10
❑ 84AllGamPI-77
❑ 84FleUpd-43
❑ 84FunFooP-27
❑ 84OCoandSI-107
❑ 84OCoandSI-239
❑ 84TopPewB-2
❑ 84TopTra-42T
❑ 84TopTraT-42T
❑ 85AllGamPI-169
❑ 85Don-190
❑ 85DonActA-47
❑ 85DonHig-32
❑ 85DonHig-33
❑ 85DonHig-48
❑ 85DonWaxBC-PC1
❑ 85Dra-36
❑ 85Fle-82
❑ 85Fle-634
❑ 85FleStaS-87
❑ 85FleStaS-95
❑ 85FleStaS-113
❑ 85Lea-234
❑ 85MetColP-19
❑ 85MetFanC-5
❑ 85MetTCM-12
❑ 85OPC-41
❑ 85PolMet-M3
❑ 85SevCoi-E9
❑ 85Top-3
❑ 85Top-620
❑ 85Top3-D-19
❑ 85TopGaloC-3
❑ 85TopGloS-38
❑ 85TopRubD-19
❑ 85TopSti-3
❑ 85TopSti-4
❑ 85TopSti-107
❑ 85TopSti-280
❑ 85TopSti-371
❑ 85TopSup-7
❑ 85TopTif-3
❑ 85TopTif-620
❑ 85Woo-16
❑ 86BurKinA-17
❑ 86Don-26
❑ 86Don-75
❑ 86DonAll-28
❑ 86DonHig-8
❑ 86DonSupD-26
❑ 86DorChe-5
❑ 86Dra-35
❑ 86Fle-81
❑ 86Fle-626
❑ 86Fle-638
❑ 86Fle-641
❑ 86FleAll-10
❑ 86FleLeaL-16
❑ 86FleLimE-20
❑ 86FleMin-19A
❑ 86FleMin-19B
❑ 86FleSlu-11
❑ 86FleStiC-46
❑ 86FleStiC-132
❑ 86GenMilB-4D
❑ 86KayB-15
❑ 86Lea-26
❑ 86MeaGolBB-5
❑ 86MeaGolM-4
❑ 86MeaGolSB-3
❑ 86MetColP-2
❑ 86MetFanC-4
❑ 86MetTCM-5
❑ 86MetWorSC-12
❑ 86MSAJifPD-20
❑ 86OPC-250

❑ 86OPCBoxB-F
❑ 86QuaGra-2
❑ 86SevCoi-C1
❑ 86SevCoi-E1
❑ 86SevCoi-S1
❑ 86SevCoi-W1
❑ 86Spo-100
❑ 86Spo-136
❑ 86Spo-143
❑ 86Spo-176
❑ 86Spo-184
❑ 86Spo-185
❑ 86SpoDecG-75
❑ 86SpoDecGS-1
❑ 86SpoRoo-47
❑ 86Top-202
❑ 86Top-250
❑ 86Top-709
❑ 86Top3-D-4
❑ 86TopGaloC-4
❑ 86TopGloS-41
❑ 86TopMinL-52
❑ 86TopSti-6
❑ 86TopSti-94
❑ 86TopSup-4
❑ 86TopTat-20
❑ 86TopTif-202
❑ 86TopTif-250
❑ 86TopTif-709
❑ 86TopWaxBC-F
❑ 87ClaGam-72
❑ 87Don-199
❑ 87DonAll-18
❑ 87DonP-18
❑ 87Dra-26
❑ 87Fle-9
❑ 87Fle-629
❑ 87Fle-640
❑ 87FleAwaW-15
❑ 87FleBasA-19
❑ 87FleExcS-19
❑ 87FleGamW-18
❑ 87FleGlo-9
❑ 87FleGlo-629
❑ 87FleGlo-640
❑ 87FleGlo-WS7
❑ 87FleHea-3
❑ 87FleHotS-18
❑ 87FleLeaL-20
❑ 87FleLimE-18
❑ 87FleMin-45
❑ 87FleRecS-12
❑ 87FleSlu-15
❑ 87FleStiC-48
❑ 87FleWaxBC-C4
❑ 87FleWorS-7
❑ 87GenMilB-5B
❑ 87K-M-26
❑ 87KayB-13
❑ 87Lea-84
❑ 87MetColP-4
❑ 87MSAJifPD-9
❑ 87OPC-130
❑ 87RedFolSB-6
❑ 87SevCoi-E7
❑ 87SevCoi-M9
❑ 87Spo-100
❑ 87Spo-120
❑ 87Spo-159
❑ 87SpoDeaP-4
❑ 87SpoIllS-6
❑ 87SpoRea-13
❑ 87SpoTeaP-2
❑ 87TidTidP-31
❑ 87TidTidT-30
❑ 87Top-130
❑ 87Top-603A
❑ 87Top-603B
❑ 87TopCoi-33
❑ 87TopGloA-10
❑ 87TopGloS-51
❑ 87TopMinL-23
❑ 87TopSti-5
❑ 87TopSti-6
❑ 87TopSti-96
❑ 87TopSti-163
❑ 87TopTif-130
❑ 87TopTif-603A
❑ 87TopTif-603B
❑ 88ActPacT-3
❑ 88Baz-8
❑ 88ClaRed-171
❑ 88Don-69
❑ 88DonBasB-96
❑ 88DonTeaBM-69
❑ 88Dra-28
❑ 88Fle-135
❑ 88FleAwaW-14
❑ 88FleBasA-12
❑ 88FleBasM-16
❑ 88FleExcS-15
❑ 88FleGlo-135
❑ 88FleHea-5
❑ 88FleHotS-13
❑ 88FleLeaL-15
❑ 88FleMin-92
❑ 88FleRecS-14
❑ 88FleSlu-15
❑ 88FleStiC-102
❑ 88FleSup-14
❑ 88FleTeaL-10
❑ 88GreBasS-20
❑ 88K-M-10
❑ 88KeyFooD-19
❑ 88Lea-48
❑ 88MetColP-4
❑ 88MetFanC-16
❑ 88MetKah-16
❑ 88MSAIceTD-18
❑ 88Nes-21
❑ 88OPC-287
❑ 88OurOwnTD-19
❑ 88PanSti-337
❑ 88Sco-350
❑ 88ScoGlo-350
❑ 88ScoYouS2-3
❑ 88Spo-200
❑ 88SpoGam-9
❑ 88StaCle-1
❑ 88StaCle-3
❑ 88StaCle-5
❑ 88StaCle-7
❑ 88StaCle-9
❑ 88StaCle-11
❑ 88StaGoo-1
❑ 88StaGoo-2
❑ 88StaGoo-3
❑ 88StaGoo-4
❑ 88StaGoo-5
❑ 88StaGoo-6
❑ 88StaGoo-7
❑ 88StaGoo-8
❑ 88StaGoo-9
❑ 88StaGoo-10
❑ 88StaGoo-11
❑ 88StaGooB-1
❑ 88StaGooB-2
❑ 88StaGooB-3
❑ 88StaGooB-4
❑ 88StaGooB-5
❑ 88StaGooB-6
❑ 88StaGooB-7
❑ 88StaGooB-8
❑ 88StaGooB-9
❑ 88StaGooB-10
❑ 88StaGooB-11
❑ 88StaGooB-12
❑ 88StaLinAl-12
❑ 88StaLinMe-8
❑ 88TarPla-16
❑ 88TetTeaD-19
❑ 88Top-405
❑ 88Top-480
❑ 88TopBig-11
❑ 88TopGloS-54
❑ 88TopMinL-60
❑ 88TopSti-101
❑ 88TopStiB-25
❑ 88TopTif-405
❑ 88TopTif-480
❑ 88TopUKM-27
❑ 88TopUKMT-27
❑ 88WeiMarD-19
❑ 89Bow-376
❑ 89BowTif-376
❑ 89ClaLigB-7
❑ 89ClaTraO-107
❑ 89ClaTraP-189
❑ 89Don-270
❑ 89DonAll-40
❑ 89DonBasB-14
❑ 89DonPop-40
❑ 89Fle-36
❑ 89Fle-635
❑ 89FleBasA-15
❑ 89FleBasM-14
❑ 89FleExcS-15
❑ 89FleGlo-36
❑ 89FleGlo-635
❑ 89FleHeroB-18
❑ 89FleLeaL-16
❑ 89FleSup-17
❑ 89K-M-31
❑ 89KayB-14
❑ 89KeyFooD-6
❑ 89MetCol8-31
❑ 89MetCol8-83
❑ 89MetColP-8
❑ 89MetFanC-16
❑ 89MetKah-9
❑ 89MSAIceTD-6
❑ 89OPC-30
❑ 89OurOwnTD-6
❑ 89PanSti-131
❑ 89PanSti-227
❑ 89RedFolSB-51
❑ 89Sco-200
❑ 89ScoHot1S-15
❑ 89Scomast-26
❑ 89Spo-140
❑ 89SpoIllFKI-151
❑ 89TetTeaD-6
❑ 89Top-30
❑ 89Top-661
❑ 89TopBasT-63
❑ 89TopBig-304
❑ 89TopCapC-17
❑ 89TopCoi-14
❑ 89TopDouM-5
❑ 89TopGloA-21
❑ 89TopGloS-37
❑ 89TopHeaUT-3
❑ 89TopMinL-26
❑ 89TopSti-99
❑ 89TopSti-162
❑ 89TopStiB-59
❑ 89TopTif-30
❑ 89TopTif-661
❑ 89TopUKM-31
❑ 89TVSpoM-3
❑ 89UppDec-565
❑ 89UppDecS-1
❑ 89WeiMarD-6
❑ 90AllBasT-6
❑ 90BasWit-35
❑ 90Bow-126
❑ 90BowIns-3
❑ 90BowInsL-3
❑ 90BowInsT-3
❑ 90BowTif-126
❑ 90BowTif-A3
❑ 90ClaBlu-58
❑ 90Col-2
❑ 90Don-171
❑ 90DonBesN-7
❑ 90DonLeaS-10
❑ 90Fle-204
❑ 90FleBasM-12
❑ 90FleBasMC-12
❑ 90FleCan-204
❑ 90GooHumICBLS-10
❑ 90HOFStiB-98
❑ 90Hot50PS-16
❑ 90K-M-10
❑ 90Lea-139
❑ 90M.Vpin-64
❑ 90MetColP-3
❑ 90MetColP-4
❑ 90MetFanC-16
❑ 90MetKah-16
❑ 90MLBBasB-9
❑ 90MSAIceTD-10
❑ 90OPC-510
❑ 90OPCBoxB-E
❑ 90PanSti-297
❑ 90Pos-29
❑ 90PubIntS-134
❑ 90PubIntS-260
❑ 90RedFolSB-37
❑ 90Sco-313
❑ 90Sco100S-99
❑ 90Spo-145
❑ 90Top-510
❑ 90TopBig-174
❑ 90TopDou-26
❑ 90TopGloS-23
❑ 90TopHeaU-3
❑ 90TopMag-51
❑ 90TopSti-96
❑ 90TopStiB-25
❑ 90TopTif-510
❑ 90TopTVA-58
❑ 90TopTVM-12
❑ 90TopWaxBC-E
❑ 90UppDec-62
❑ 90UppDec-114
❑ 91BasBesAotM-8
❑ 91Bow-472
❑ 91Cla1-T99
❑ 91Cla2-T39
❑ 91ClaGam-121
❑ 91Col-17
❑ 91ColGoo-1
❑ 91ColGoo-2
❑ 91ColGoo-3
❑ 91ColGoo-4
❑ 91ColGoo-5
❑ 91ColGoo-6
❑ 91ColGoo-7
❑ 91ColGoo-8
❑ 91ColGoo-9
❑ 91ColGoo-10
❑ 91ColGoo-11
❑ 91ColGoo-12
❑ 91ColGoo-xx
❑ 91DoctheV-1
❑ 91Don-266
❑ 91DonPre-8
❑ 91Fle-148
❑ 91FlePro-7
❑ 91JimDea-25
❑ 91KinDis-8
❑ 91Lea-165
❑ 91LeaPre-7
❑ 91MajLeaCP-74
❑ 91MetCol8-1
❑ 91MetColP-4
❑ 91MetKah-16
❑ 91MetPerPA-17
❑ 91MetTro-3
❑ 91MetWIZ-144
❑ 91OPC-330
❑ 91OPCPre-55
❑ 91PanCanT1-60
❑ 91PanCanT1-74
❑ 91PanFreS-86
❑ 91PanSti-89
❑ 91PepSup-1
❑ 91PetSta-12
❑ 91RedFolS-40
❑ 91Sco-540
❑ 91Sco-685
❑ 91Sco-866
❑ 91Sco100S-65
❑ 91Sev3DCN-5
❑ 91SevCoi-F8
❑ 91SevCoi-NE5
❑ 91SimandSMLBL-16
❑ 91StaClu-100
❑ 91StaPinB-20
❑ 91Stu-204
❑ 91StuPre-14
❑ 91SunSee-10
❑ 91Top-330
❑ 91TopCraJI-28
❑ 91TopDesS-330
❑ 91TopMic-330
❑ 91TopSta-15
❑ 91TopTif-330
❑ 91TopTriH-N7
❑ 91Ult-218
❑ 91UppDec-224
❑ 92Bow-480
❑ 92Cla2-T43
❑ 92ClaGam-53
❑ 92ColPro-7
❑ 92Don-446
❑ 92DonCraJ1-23
❑ 92DonDiaK-DK15
❑ 92DonEli-12
❑ 92DonSupD-DK15
❑ 92Fle-505
❑ 92FleSmo'nH-S8
❑ 92Hig5-72
❑ 92Hig5S-15
❑ 92LaKdec-13
❑ 92Lea-112
❑ 92LeaBlaG-112
❑ 92MetColP-3
❑ 92MetKah-16
❑ 92MooSna-18
❑ 92Mr.TurS-11
❑ 92MVPPin-45
❑ 92OPC-725
❑ 92OPCPre-47
❑ 92PepDieM-2
❑ 92Pin-111
❑ 92PinRool-6
❑ 92Pos-5
❑ 92Sco-10
❑ 92Sco100S-25
❑ 92ScoImpP-54
❑ 92SevCoi-1
❑ 92SpoStaCC-17
❑ 92StaClu-455
❑ 92StaClu-602
❑ 92StaCluECN-602
❑ 92StaCluMP-6
❑ 92Stu-65
❑ 92StuPre-7
❑ 92Top-725
❑ 92TopGol-725
❑ 92TopGolW-725
❑ 92TopKid-11
❑ 92TopMcD-32
❑ 92TopMic-725
❑ 92TopMic-G725
❑ 92TriPla-167
❑ 92Ult-232
❑ 92UppDec-84
❑ 92UppDec-135
❑ 92UppDecF-23
❑ 92UppDecFG-23
❑ 93Bow-242
❑ 93DiaMar-41
❑ 93Don-462
❑ 93DurPowP1-13
❑ 93Fin-113
❑ 93FinJum-113
❑ 93FinRef-113
❑ 93Fla-91
❑ 93Fle-474
❑ 93FleFruotL-23
❑ 93FunPac-123
❑ 93FunPac-126
❑ 93KinDis-14
❑ 93Lea-203
❑ 93MetBak-8
❑ 93MetColP-23
❑ 93MetKah-16
❑ 93OPC-92
❑ 93PacSpa-198
❑ 93PanSti-245
❑ 93Pin-96
❑ 93PinCoo-19
❑ 93PinCooD-19
❑ 93RedFolS-32
❑ 93Sco-53
❑ 93Sel-57
❑ 93SelAce-8
❑ 93SP-149
❑ 93StaClu-514
❑ 93StaCluFDI-514
❑ 93StaCluI-B2
❑ 93StaCluMOP-514
❑ 93StaCluMOP-MB2
❑ 93StaCluMP-17
❑ 93Stu-155
❑ 93Top-640
❑ 93TopGol-640
❑ 93TopInaM-640
❑ 93TopInaR-640
❑ 93TopMic-640
❑ 93TriPla-146
❑ 93TriPlaN-6
❑ 93Ult-427
❑ 93UppDec-665
❑ 93UppDecDG-15
❑ 93UppDecGold-665
❑ 94Bow-400
❑ 94CarLeaA-DJ27
❑ 94ChuHomS-2
❑ 94ChuHomSG-2
❑ 94ColC-342
❑ 94ColC-519
❑ 94ColChoGS-342
❑ 94ColChoGS-519
❑ 94ColChoSS-342
❑ 94ColChoSS-519
❑ 94ColChoT-6
❑ 94Don-17
❑ 94DonSpeE-17
❑ 94Fin-82
❑ 94FinPre-82P
❑ 94FinRef-82
❑ 94Fla-197
❑ 94Fle-563
❑ 94FleExtB-317
❑ 94FUnPac-16
❑ 94Lea-10
❑ 94MetColP-9
❑ 94MetShuST-1
❑ 94OPC-24
❑ 94Pac-402
❑ 94PanSti-217
❑ 94Pin-62
❑ 94PinArtP-62
❑ 94PinMusC-62
❑ 94ProMag-93
❑ 94RedFolMI-6
❑ 94Sco-22
❑ 94ScoGolR-22
❑ 94Sel-54
❑ 94SP-116
❑ 94SPDieC-116
❑ 94Spo-94
❑ 94StaClu-220
❑ 94StaCluFDI-220
❑ 94StaCluGR-220
❑ 94StaCluMOP-220
❑ 94Stu-114
❑ 94Top-150
❑ 94TopGol-150
❑ 94TopSpa-150
❑ 94TriPla-143
❑ 94Ult-236
❑ 94UppDec-205
❑ 94UppDecAJ-38
❑ 94UppDecAJG-38
❑ 94UppDecDC-E6
❑ 94UppDecED-205
❑ 95Fle-369
❑ 96Cir-64
❑ 96CirBos-16
❑ 96CirRav-64
❑ 96EmoXL-89
❑ 96Fin-S291
❑ 96FinRef-S291
❑ 96Fla-128
❑ 96FleUpd-U61
❑ 96FleUpdTC-U61
❑ 96LeaPre-92
❑ 96LeaPreP-92
❑ 96LeaSig-130
❑ 96LeaSigPPG-130
❑ 96LeaSigPPP-130
❑ 96MetMod-4
❑ 96MetTeal-2
❑ 96Ult-385
❑ 96UltGolM-385
❑ 97Cir-270
❑ 97CirRav-270
❑ 97ColCho-175
❑ 97ColCho-176
❑ 97ColChoT-NY2
❑ 97Don-154
❑ 97DonEli-122
❑ 97DonEli-148
❑ 97DonEliGS-122
❑ 97DonEliGS-148
❑ 97DonGolPP-154
❑ 97DonLim-139
❑ 97DonLimE-139
❑ 97DonLimENG-139
❑ 97DonPre-74
❑ 97DonPreCttC-74
❑ 97DonSilPP-154
❑ 97DonTea-129
❑ 97DonTeaSPE-129
❑ 97Fin-51
❑ 97FinRef-51
❑ 97FlaShoLC-111
❑ 97FlaShoLeg0-111
❑ 97FlaShoLeg1-111
❑ 97FlaShoM-A111
❑ 97FlaShoM-B111
❑ 97FlaShoM-C111
❑ 97FlaShoR0-111
❑ 97FlaShoR1-111
❑ 97FlaShoR2-111
❑ 97Fle-166
❑ 97FleGolM-2
❑ 97FleTif-166
❑ 97Lea-98
❑ 97LeaFraM-98
❑ 97LeaFraMDC-98
❑ 97MetUni-117
❑ 97NorNavTI-11
❑ 97Pac-151
❑ 97PacLigB-151
❑ 97PacSil-151
❑ 97Pin-82
❑ 97PinArtP-PP82
❑ 97PinCar-15
❑ 97PinCer-94
❑ 97PinCerMBla-94
❑ 97PinCerMBlu-94
❑ 97PinCerMG-94
❑ 97PinCerMR-94
❑ 97PinCerR-94
❑ 97PinIns-89
❑ 97PinInsCE-89
❑ 97PinInsDE-89
❑ 97PinMusC-82
❑ 97PinPrePla-82
❑ 97PinTotCPB-94

❑ 97PinTotCPG-94
❑ 97PinTotCPR-94
❑ 97Sco-171
❑ 97ScoArtPWB-171
❑ 97ScoPreS-171
❑ 97ScoShoS-171
❑ 97ScoShoSAP-171
❑ 97StaClu-105
❑ 97StaCluMOP-105
❑ 97Stu-76
❑ 97StuPrePG-76
❑ 97StuPrePS-76
❑ 97Top-100
❑ 97Top-175
❑ 97Ult-98
❑ 97UltGolME-98
❑ 97UltPlaME-98
❑ 97UppDec-120
❑ 97YanMcDP-1
❑ 97YanSco-11
❑ 97YanScoPl-11
❑ 97YanScoPr-11
❑ 98ColCho-178
❑ 98ColCho-354
❑ 98Pac-149
❑ 98PacAur-29
❑ 98PacOnl-220
❑ 98PacOnlR-220
❑ 98PacOnlWC-220
❑ 98PacPlaB-149
❑ 98PacRedT-149
❑ 98PacSil-149
❑ 98PinPlu-63
❑ 98Ult-334
❑ 98UltGolM-334
❑ 98UltMas-334
❑ 98UltPlaM-334
❑ 98UppDec-671
❑ 99Fle-461
❑ 99FleSta9-461
❑ 99FleWarT-461
❑ 99Pac-128
❑ 99PacPlaB-128
❑ 99PacRed-128
❑ 99StaClu-300
❑ 99StaCluFDI-300
❑ 99StaCluOoaK-300
❑ 99StaCluPP-300
❑ 99Top-254
❑ 99TopChr-254
❑ 99TopChrR-254
❑ 99TopMVPP-254
❑ 99UppDec-353
❑ 99UppDecEL1-353
❑ 99UppDecEL2-353

Gooden, Maury
❑ 85LitFalMT-24

Goodenough, Randy
❑ 86EugEmeC-39
❑ 87Ft.MyeRP-23

Goodfarm, Scott
❑ 77LynMetT-14

Goodfellow, Michael
❑ 87OldJudN-207

Goodhart, Steve
❑ 95BilMusTI-17
❑ 96Exc-147
❑ 97BurBeeB-11

Goodin, Craig
❑ 83ChaRoyT-6

Goodin, Rich (Rick)
❑ 83ChaRoyT-20
❑ 86MemChiSTOS-9
❑ 86MemChiTOS-9

Gooding, Jason
❑ 97SpoIndG-11
❑ 98Bow-310
❑ 98BowChr-310
❑ 98BowChrGA-310
❑ 98BowChrGAR-310
❑ 98BowChrI-310
❑ 98BowChrIR-310
❑ 98BowChrR-310
❑ 98BowGolA-310
❑ 98BowInt-310
❑ 98WicWraM-4

Goodlow, Sebastian
❑ 89SalDodTI-13

Goodman, Billy
❑ 47Exh-82A
❑ 47Exh-82B
❑ 47PM1StaP1-74
❑ 48RedSoxTI-8
❑ 49Bow-39
❑ 49Lea-30
❑ 49RedSoxTI-7
❑ 50Bow-99
❑ 50RedSoxTI-7
❑ 51BerRos-C2
❑ 51Bow-237
❑ 51FisBakL-8
❑ 51R42SmaS-33
❑ 51TopRedB-46
❑ 52Bow-81
❑ 52StaCalL-71E
❑ 52StaCalS-85C
❑ 52Top-23
❑ 53BowC-148
❑ 53ExhCan-63
❑ 53RedSoxFNSMS-1
❑ 53RedSoxTI-10
❑ 54Bow-82
❑ 55Bow-126
❑ 56BalOriP-19
❑ 56Top-245
❑ 57Top-303
❑ 58Top-225
❑ 58WhiSoxJP-5
❑ 59Top-103
❑ 59TopVen-103
❑ 60Top-69
❑ 60TopVen-69
❑ 60WhiSoxTS-7
❑ 61Top-247
❑ 68BraPos-12
❑ 77GalGloG-21
❑ 79TCM50-96
❑ 80AshTouT-1
❑ 81RedSoxBG2S-24
❑ 81WhiSox1T-9
❑ 83TopRep5-23
❑ 85TCMPla1-23
❑ 91OriCro-160
❑ 91TopArc1-334

Goodman, Douglas
❑ 92JohCitCC-3
❑ 92JohCitCF-3108
❑ 93SavCarC-15
❑ 93SavCarF-683

Goodman, Herbert
❑ 95BilMusTI-9

Goodman, Ival
❑ 34BatR31-127
❑ 35GouPuzR-8D
❑ 35GouPuzR-9D
❑ 38CloFotW-31
❑ 38ExhFou-4
❑ 38RedOraW-11
❑ 39GouPreR303A-18
❑ 39GouPreR303B-10
❑ 39OrcPhoAP-10
❑ 39RedTeal-9
❑ 39WorWidGTP-18
❑ 41DouPlaR-115
❑ 41HarHarW-7
❑ 44CubTeal-10
❑ 76RedParC-12
❑ 77CinRedT-5
❑ 79DiaGre-266
❑ 93ConTSN-854

Goodman, John
❑ 90TopMag-77

Goodrich, Jon
❑ 93BenRocCB-9
❑ 93BenRocF-3260
❑ 93Top-704
❑ 93TopGol-704
❑ 93TopInaM-704
❑ 93TopInaR-704
❑ 93TopMic-704

Goodrich, Randy
❑ 98SalVol-9

Goodson, J. Ed
❑ 72GiaTeal-8
❑ 73OPC-197
❑ 73Top-197
❑ 74Kel-18
❑ 74OPC-494
❑ 74Top-494
❑ 74TopSta-105
❑ 75AtlBraP-15
❑ 75OPC-322
❑ 75Top-322
❑ 75TopMin-322
❑ 76OPC-386
❑ 76SSP-588
❑ 76Top-386
❑ 77Top-584
❑ 78SSP270-65
❑ 78Top-586
❑ 90DodTar-290

Goodson, Kirk
❑ 91HunCubC-11
❑ 91HunCubP-3329

Goodson, Steven
❑ 98HudValR-7

Goodwin, Claire
❑ 13Zee-9

Goodwin, Curtis
❑ 92KanCouCC-5
❑ 92KanCouCF-104
❑ 92KanCouCTI-11
❑ 93AusFut-67
❑ 93CarLeaAGF-2
❑ 93FreKeyC-8
❑ 93FreKeyF-1039
❑ 94ActPac-10
❑ 94Bow-487
❑ 94BowBayF-2423
❑ 94BowBes-B38
❑ 94BowBesR-B38
❑ 94Cla-37
❑ 94ExcFS7-6
❑ 94OriPro-41
❑ 94UppDecML-32
❑ 94UppDecML-253
❑ 95ActPacF-25
❑ 95AusFut-105
❑ 95BalOriP-21
❑ 95Bow-66
❑ 95BowBes-B34
❑ 95BowBes-X10
❑ 95BowBesR-B34
❑ 95BowBesR-X10
❑ 95ColCho-37
❑ 95ColChoGS-37
❑ 95ColChoSS-37
❑ 95DonTopotO-8
❑ 95Emo-3
❑ 95Exc-5
❑ 95Fin-273
❑ 95FinRef-273
❑ 95LeaLim-116
❑ 95LinVen-2
❑ 95RocRedWTI-16
❑ 95SelCer-124
❑ 95SelCerF-2
❑ 95SelCerMG-124
❑ 95SelCerPU-12
❑ 95SelCerPU9-12
❑ 95SP-11
❑ 95SPCha-3
❑ 95SPChaDC-3
❑ 95SPSil-11
❑ 95Sum-123
❑ 95SumNthD-123
❑ 95Top-599
❑ 95TopTra-109T
❑ 95UltGolMR-M13
❑ 95UppDec-4
❑ 95UppDecED-4
❑ 95UppDecEDG-4
❑ 95UppDecML-58
❑ 95UppDecMLFS-58
❑ 95UppDecSE-51
❑ 95UppDecSEG-51
❑ 95Zen-113
❑ 95ZenRooRC-9
❑ 95ZenSam-113
❑ 96Bow-144
❑ 96BowFoi-144
❑ 96ColCho-50
❑ 96ColCho-769
❑ 96ColChoGS-50
❑ 96ColChoSS-50
❑ 96Don-42
❑ 96DonPreP-42
❑ 96Fle-8
❑ 96FleTif-8
❑ 96FleUpd-U120
❑ 96FleUpdTC-U120
❑ 96IndIndB-10
❑ 96MetUni-148
❑ 96MetUniP-148
❑ 96Pac-241
❑ 96Pin-111
❑ 96Sco-26
❑ 96ScoDugC-A25
❑ 96ScoDugCAP-A25
❑ 96StaClu-174
❑ 96StaCluMOP-174
❑ 96Top-121
❑ 96Ult-5
❑ 96UltGolM-5
❑ 96UppDec-12
❑ 96UppDecFSP-FS11
❑ 97DonLim-158
❑ 97DonLimE-158
❑ 97DonLimENG-158
❑ 97Lea-343
❑ 97LeaFraM-343
❑ 97LeaFraMDC-343
❑ 97PacPriGotD-GD125
❑ 98PacOnl-245
❑ 98PacOnlR-245
❑ 98PacOnlWC-245
❑ 98Sco-44
❑ 98ScoRT-121
❑ 98Ult-436
❑ 98UltGolM-436
❑ 98UltMas-436
❑ 98UltPlaM-436
❑ 99Pac-145
❑ 99PacPlaB-145
❑ 99PacRed-145

Goodwin, Danny
❑ 77SalLakCGC-7
❑ 78SSP270-204
❑ 79OgdA'sT-15
❑ 79Top-322
❑ 80Top-362
❑ 80TwiPos-9
❑ 81Don-494
❑ 81Top-527
❑ 81TwiPos-11
❑ 82Don-305
❑ 82Fle-554
❑ 82TacTigT-14
❑ 82Top-123
❑ 83TacTigT-25A
❑ 84TacTigC-91
❑ 85TacTigC-134

Goodwin, David
❑ 88GenCubP-1641
❑ 89ChaWheB-18
❑ 89ChaWheP-1768

Goodwin, Jim
❑ 48WhiSoxTI-7

Goodwin, Joey
❑ 95HudValRTI-9
❑ 96ChaRivTI-9614
❑ 98TexLeaC-8

Goodwin, Keith
❑ 96MicBatCB-11
❑ 97LowSpiB-9

Goodwin, Mike
❑ 86PriWilPP-12

Goodwin, Tom
❑ 89FreStaBS-9
❑ 89FreStaBS-10
❑ 89GreFalDSP-1
❑ 90BakDodCLC-261
❑ 90Bow-96
❑ 90BowTif-96
❑ 90SanAntMGS-13
❑ 90Sco-668
❑ 91AlbDukLD-6
❑ 91AlbDukP-1155
❑ 91Bow-608
❑ 91Cla3-T32
❑ 91LinDriAAA-6
❑ 91UppDecFE-9F
❑ 92AlbDukF-734
❑ 92AlbDukS-8
❑ 92Cla1-T39
❑ 92DonRoo-43
❑ 92Fle-652
❑ 92ProFS7-243
❑ 92Sco-830
❑ 92ScoRoo-34
❑ 92SkyAAAF-3
❑ 92StaClu-322
❑ 92TopDeb91-65
❑ 92UppDec-20
❑ 93DodPol-5
❑ 93Don-640
❑ 93Fle-446
❑ 93PacSpa-498
❑ 93Sel-349
❑ 93StaClu-446
❑ 93StaCluFDI-446
❑ 93StaCluMOP-446
❑ 93Top-228
❑ 93TopGol-228
❑ 93TopInaM-228
❑ 93TopInaR-228
❑ 93TopMic-228
❑ 93Ult-398
❑ 94OmaRoyF-1234
❑ 95DonTopotO-87
❑ 95Fin-307
❑ 95FinRef-307
❑ 95FleUpd-46
❑ 95Lea-383
❑ 95TopTra-86T
❑ 96ColCho-171
❑ 96ColChoGS-171
❑ 96ColChoSS-171
❑ 96Don-109
❑ 96DonPreP-109
❑ 96EmoXL-66
❑ 96Fin-B118
❑ 96FinRef-B118
❑ 96Fla-88
❑ 96Fle-126
❑ 96FleTif-126
❑ 96LeaSigA-82
❑ 96LeaSigAG-82
❑ 96LeaSigAS-82
❑ 96MetUni-64
❑ 96MetUniP-64
❑ 96Pac-325
❑ 96PanSti-184
❑ 96ProSta-116
❑ 96RoyPol-8
❑ 96Sco-140
❑ 96StaClu-133
❑ 96StaCluMOP-133
❑ 96Top-39
❑ 96TopGal-118
❑ 96TopGalPPI-118
❑ 96Ult-69
❑ 96UltGolM-69
❑ 96UppDec-351
❑ 97Cir-295
❑ 97CirRav-295
❑ 97ColCho-356
❑ 97Don-122
❑ 97DonEli-134
❑ 97DonEliGS-134
❑ 97DonGolPP-122
❑ 97DonSilPP-122
❑ 97Fin-98
❑ 97FinRef-98
❑ 97Fle-113
❑ 97FleTif-113
❑ 97Lea-295
❑ 97LeaFraM-295
❑ 97LeaFraMDC-295
❑ 97MetUni-93
❑ 97NewPin-41
❑ 97NewPinAP-41
❑ 97NewPinMC-41
❑ 97NewPinPP-41
❑ 97Pac-100
❑ 97PacLigB-100
❑ 97PacPri-36
❑ 97PacPriLB-36
❑ 97PacPriP-36
❑ 97PacSil-100
❑ 97PinIns-107
❑ 97PinInsCE-107
❑ 97PinInsDE-107
❑ 97RoyPol-8
❑ 97Sco-222
❑ 97ScoArtPWB-222
❑ 97ScoPreS-222
❑ 97ScoShoS-222
❑ 97ScoShoSAP-222
❑ 97Sel-93
❑ 97SelArtP-93
❑ 97SelCom-93
❑ 97SelRegG-93
❑ 97StaClu-176
❑ 97StaCluMOP-176
❑ 97Top-122
❑ 97TopChrSB-22
❑ 97TopChrSBR-22
❑ 97TopSeaB-SB22
❑ 97Ult-395
❑ 97UltGolME-395
❑ 97UltPlaME-395
❑ 97UppDec-86
❑ 98CirThu-204
❑ 98CirThuRav-204
❑ 98CirThuSupRav-204
❑ 98ColCho-517
❑ 98Fin-8
❑ 98FinNo--8
❑ 98FinNo-R-8
❑ 98FinRef-8
❑ 98Fle-158
❑ 98Pac-203
❑ 98PacAur-87
❑ 98PacOnl-733
❑ 98PacOnlR-733
❑ 98PacOnlWC-733
❑ 98PacPlaB-203
❑ 98PacRedT-203
❑ 98PacSil-203
❑ 98PinSna-TR9
❑ 98Revo-143
❑ 98RevoSS-143
❑ 98Sco-209
❑ 98ScoSS-PP101
❑ 98ScoSSAP-PP101
❑ 98SkyDugAFF-FF8
❑ 98StaCluFDI-208
❑ 98StaCluI-208
❑ 98StaCluOneK-208
❑ 98StaCluPP-208
❑ 98Top-376
❑ 98TopChr-376
❑ 98TopChrR-376
❑ 98TopDevR-376
❑ 98TopDia-376
❑ 98TopMiniC-376
❑ 98Ult-48
❑ 98UltGolM-48
❑ 98UltMas-48
❑ 98UltPlaM-48
❑ 99199Fin-171
❑ 99FinGolRef-171
❑ 99FinRef-171
❑ 99Fle-111
❑ 99FleSta9-111
❑ 99FleWarT-111
❑ 99MetUni-227
❑ 99MetUniGM-227
❑ 99MetUniPMG-227
❑ 99Pac-424
❑ 99PacAur-190
❑ 99PacAurOD-190
❑ 99PacInv-144
❑ 99PacInvOD-144
❑ 99PacInvPB-144
❑ 99PacPar-234
❑ 99PacParC-234
❑ 99PacParG-234
❑ 99PacParHoloGold-234
❑ 99PacParHS-234
❑ 99PacParOD-234
❑ 99PacParPB-234
❑ 99PacParRed-234
❑ 99PacPlaB-424
❑ 99PacRed-424
❑ 99SkyPre-196
❑ 99SkyPreR-196
❑ 99SkyThu-122
❑ 99SkyThuRant-122
❑ 99SkyThuRave-122
❑ 99StaClu-211
❑ 99StaCluFDI-211
❑ 99StaCluOoaK-211
❑ 99StaCluPP-211
❑ 99ThuSkySupR-122
❑ 99Top-111
❑ 99TopChr-111
❑ 99TopChrR-111
❑ 99TopMVPP-111
❑ 99TopOpeD-65
❑ 99UppDec-507
❑ 99UppDecEL1-507
❑ 99UppDecEL2-507
❑ 99Vic-407

Goossen, Greg
❑ 67Top-287
❑ 68Top-386
❑ 70BreMcD-8
❑ 70BreMil-5
❑ 70OPC-271
❑ 70Top-271
❑ 83Pil69G-33
❑ 91MetWIZ-145
❑ 94BreMilB-314

Gorbans, Glen
❑ 63GadFunC-9

Gorbould, Bob
❑ 45CenFlo-11

Gorbous, Glen
❑ 56Top-174

Gordnier, Aaron
❑ 98WatIndTI-12

Gordon, Adrian
❑ 94EliTwiC-9
❑ 94EliTwiF-3742
❑ 95Exc-85
❑ 95ForWayWTI-22
❑ 96ForWayWB-9
❑ 96MidLeaAB-30

Gordon, Alan
❑ 94LakElsSC-30

Gordon, Andrew
❑ 96NewJerCB-12

Gordon, Anthony
❑ 89BelMarL-5

❑ 90PenPilS-9
❑ 92BasCitRC-16
❑ 92SarWhiSCB-24
Gordon, Beebop (Harold)
❑ 93NegLeaRL2-10
Gordon, Brian
❑ 98SouBenSHM-10
Gordon, Don
❑ 83BirBarT-2
❑ 85SyrChiT-13
❑ 86BluJayAF-11
❑ 86BluJayFS-14
❑ 87IntLeaAT-10
❑ 87RocRedWT-29
❑ 87SyrChiP-1932
❑ 87SyrChiT-4
❑ 87SyrChiT-26
❑ 88ColSprSSC-3
❑ 88ColSprSSP-1538
❑ 88IndTeal-15
❑ 88ScoRoo-92T
❑ 88ScoRooG-92T
❑ 88Top-144
❑ 88TopTif-144
❑ 89ColSprSSC-2
❑ 89ColSprSSP-260
❑ 89Fle-405
❑ 89FleGlo-405
❑ 89Sco-547
❑ 90CMC-43
❑ 90DenZepC-18
❑ 90DenZepP-621
❑ 90ProAAAF-646
❑ 91ElPasDLD-183
❑ 91ElPasDP-2742
❑ 91LinDriAA-183
Gordon, Gary
❑ 97AshTou-10
Gordon, Herman
❑ 96DunBluJB-10
❑ 96DunBluJTI-12
❑ 96HagSunB-6
Gordon, Joe
❑ 36OveCanR-19
❑ 39ExhSal-21A
❑ 39ExhSal-21B
❑ 39GouPreR303A-19
❑ 39GouPreR303B-11
❑ 39WorWidGTP-19
❑ 41DouPlaR-67
❑ 41DouPlaR-83
❑ 41WheM5-21
❑ 43YanSta-12
❑ 46SpoExcW-4-10
❑ 47HomBon-17
❑ 47IndTeal-11
❑ 47IndVanPP-10
❑ 47PM1StaP1-75
❑ 48IndTeal-10
❑ 49Bow-210
❑ 49IndTeal-11
❑ 49IndVisEI-7
❑ 49IndVisEI-15
❑ 49Lea-117
❑ 50AmeNut&CCP-7
❑ 50Bow-129
❑ 50IndNumN-11
❑ 50IndTeal-12
❑ 50RoyDes-13
❑ 51R42SmaS-36
❑ 52MotCoo-19
❑ 53IndPenCBP-13
❑ 59Ind-4
❑ 59Kah-10
❑ 60Top-216
❑ 61A'sTeal-6
❑ 61AthJayP-8
❑ 61Top-224
❑ 61TopMagR-30
❑ 69RoySol-6
❑ 69RoyTeal-6
❑ 69Top-484
❑ 74TCMNic-24
❑ 75TCMGua-9
❑ 75YanDyn1T-19
❑ 77TCMTheWY-55
❑ 83TCMPla1942-1
❑ 86SpoDecG-24
❑ 92YanWIZA-24
❑ 93ActPacA-133
Gordon, Keith
❑ 90BilMusP-3228
❑ 91ChaWheC-23
❑ 92CedRapRC-1
❑ 92CedRapRF-1084
❑ 92UppDecML-204
❑ 93Bow-174
❑ 93ChaLooF-2372
❑ 95IndIndF-108
Gordon, Kevin
❑ 85PriWilPT-21
❑ 86NasPirP-8
Gordon, Mike
❑ 92GulCoaYF-3785
❑ 94GreBatF-466
❑ 95TamYanYI-8
❑ 96DunBluJB-11
❑ 96DunBluJTI-13
❑ 97AkrAer-10
❑ 98KnoSG-5
Gordon, Mike W.
❑ 78SSP270-251
Gordon, Oliver
❑ 96AubDouB-29
Gordon, Sid
❑ 47HomBon-18
❑ 47TipTop-123
❑ 48Bow-27
❑ 48GiaTeal-4
❑ 49Bow-101
❑ 49EurSta-104
❑ 49GiaTeal-7
❑ 49Lea-131
❑ 50Bow-109
❑ 50Dra-16
❑ 51Bow-19
❑ 51TopRedB-2
❑ 52Bow-60
❑ 52NatTeaL-11
❑ 52RedMan-NL6
❑ 52TipTop-11
❑ 52Top-267
❑ 53BowC-5
❑ 53BraJohC-23
❑ 53BraMer-8
❑ 53BraSpiaS3-12
❑ 53DixLid-6A
❑ 53DixLid-6B
❑ 53DixPre-6
❑ 53NorBreL-9
❑ 53Top-117
❑ 54Bow-11
❑ 54DanDee-9
❑ 54DixLid-3
❑ 55Bow-163
❑ 55RobGouS-24
❑ 55RobGouW-24
❑ 75JohMiz-1
❑ 76TayBow4-12
❑ 76TayBow4-112
❑ 79TCM50-67
❑ 83Bra53F-4
❑ 83TCMPla1943-45
❑ 83TopRep5-267
❑ 91TopArc1-117
Gordon, Tommy (Tom)
❑ 87EugEmeP-2673
❑ 87Ft.MyeRP-25
❑ 88AppFoxP-149
❑ 88MidLeaAGS-40
❑ 89Bow-115
❑ 89BowTif-115
❑ 89ClaTraP-182
❑ 89Don-45
❑ 89DonBasB-287
❑ 89DonRoo-4
❑ 89Fle-284
❑ 89FleGlo-284
❑ 89Sco-634
❑ 89ScoHot1R-68
❑ 89Scomast-7
❑ 89ScoYouS2-2
❑ 89StaGor-1
❑ 89StaGor-2
❑ 89StaGor-3
❑ 89StaGor-4
❑ 89StaGor-5
❑ 89StaGor-6
❑ 89StaGor-7
❑ 89StaGor-8
❑ 89StaGor-9
❑ 89StaGor-10
❑ 89StaGor-11
❑ 89TopTra-38T
❑ 89TopTraT-38T
❑ 89UppDec-736
❑ 90Baz-21
❑ 90Bow-365
❑ 90BowTif-365
❑ 90ClaBlu-4
❑ 90Don-297
❑ 90Fle-108
❑ 90FleAwaW-15
❑ 90FleCan-108
❑ 90FleSoaS-7
❑ 90Hot50RS-18
❑ 90Lea-14
❑ 90M.Vpin-44
❑ 90OPC-752
❑ 90PanSti-89
❑ 90PubIntS-348
❑ 90RoyPos-12
❑ 90Sco-472
❑ 90Sco100RS-1
❑ 90Spo-30
❑ 90Top-752
❑ 90TopBig-252
❑ 90TopCoi-15
❑ 90TopGloS-30
❑ 90TopHeaU-21
❑ 90TopMinL-15
❑ 90TopRoo-10
❑ 90TopSti-268
❑ 90TopSti-322
❑ 90TopTif-752
❑ 90ToyRoo-12
❑ 90UppDec-365
❑ 90UppDecS-5
❑ 91Bow-311
❑ 91Don-242
❑ 91Fle-559
❑ 91Lea-132
❑ 91OPC-248
❑ 91PanFreS-284
❑ 91PanSti-231
❑ 91RoyPol-10
❑ 91Sco-197
❑ 91SimandSMLBL-17
❑ 91StaClu-254
❑ 91Top-248
❑ 91TopDesS-248
❑ 91TopMic-248
❑ 91TopTif-248
❑ 91Ult-147
❑ 91UppDec-431
❑ 92Bow-477
❑ 92ClaGam-82
❑ 92Don-250
❑ 92Fle-158
❑ 92Lea-68
❑ 92LeaBlaG-68
❑ 92OPC-431
❑ 92Pin-238
❑ 92PinTea2-58
❑ 92RoyPol-8
❑ 92Sco-130
❑ 92ScoImpP-69
❑ 92StaClu-388
❑ 92Stu-182
❑ 92Top-431
❑ 92TopGol-431
❑ 92TopGolW-431
❑ 92TopMic-431
❑ 92Ult-370
❑ 92UppDec-476
❑ 93Don-497
❑ 93Fla-215
❑ 93Fle-237
❑ 93Lea-211
❑ 93OPC-75
❑ 93PacSpa-134
❑ 93Pin-105
❑ 93RoyPol-9
❑ 93RoyStaC-3
❑ 93Sco-184
❑ 93StaClu-523
❑ 93StaCluFDI-523
❑ 93StaCluMOP-523
❑ 93Top-611
❑ 93TopGol-611
❑ 93TopInaM-611
❑ 93TopInaR-611
❑ 93TopMic-611
❑ 93Ult-207
❑ 93UppDec-221
❑ 93UppDecGold-221
❑ 94ColC-112
❑ 94ColChoGS-112
❑ 94ColChoSS-112
❑ 94Don-450
❑ 94Fin-397
❑ 94FinRef-397
❑ 94Fla-299
❑ 94Fle-155
❑ 94FleExtB-88
❑ 94Lea-389
❑ 94Pac-283
❑ 94PanSti-73
❑ 94Pin-317
❑ 94PinArtP-317
❑ 94PinMusC-317
❑ 94ProMag-61
❑ 94Sco-234
❑ 94ScoGolR-234
❑ 94Sel-118
❑ 94Top-66
❑ 94TopGol-66
❑ 94TopSpa-66
❑ 94TriPla-234
❑ 94Ult-364
❑ 94UppDec-474
❑ 94UppDecED-474
❑ 95ColCho-461
❑ 95ColChoGS-461
❑ 95ColChoSS-461
❑ 95Don-494
❑ 95DonPreP-494
❑ 95DonTopotO-88
❑ 95Fla-264
❑ 95Fle-158
❑ 95Lea-249
❑ 95Pin-411
❑ 95PinArtP-411
❑ 95PinMusC-411
❑ 95Sco-464
❑ 95ScoGolR-464
❑ 95ScoPlaTS-464
❑ 95StaClu-455
❑ 95StaCluMOP-455
❑ 95StaCluSTWS-455
❑ 95StaCluVR-245
❑ 95StaCluVRMO-245
❑ 95Top-475
❑ 95TopCyb-268
❑ 95Ult-289
❑ 95UltGolM-289
❑ 95UppDec-418
❑ 95UppDecED-418
❑ 95UppDecEDG-418
❑ 95UppDecSE-53
❑ 95UppDecSEG-53
❑ 96ColCho-169
❑ 96ColCho-763
❑ 96ColChoGS-169
❑ 96ColChoSS-169
❑ 96Don-494
❑ 96DonPreP-494
❑ 96Fla-18
❑ 96Fle-127
❑ 96FleRedS-6
❑ 96FleTif-127
❑ 96FleUpd-U12
❑ 96FleUpdTC-U12
❑ 96MetUni-15
❑ 96MetUniP-15
❑ 96Pac-335
❑ 96Pin-9
❑ 96Pin-330
❑ 96PinFoil-330
❑ 96Sco-453
❑ 96Ult-70
❑ 96Ult-314
❑ 96UltGolM-70
❑ 96UltGolM-314
❑ 96UppDec-286
❑ 97Cir-361
❑ 97CirRav-361
❑ 97ColCho-48
❑ 97Fle-23
❑ 97FleTif-23
❑ 97MetUni-22
❑ 97Pac-40
❑ 97PacLigB-40
❑ 97PacSil-40
❑ 97RedSoxS-5
❑ 97RedSoxSPl-5
❑ 97RedSoxSPr-5
❑ 97Sco-119
❑ 97ScoArtPWB-119
❑ 97ScoPreS-119
❑ 97ScoShoS-119
❑ 97ScoShoSAP-119
❑ 97SP-37
❑ 97Ult-14
❑ 97UltGolME-14
❑ 97UltPlaME-14
❑ 97UppDec-311
❑ 98ColCho-52
❑ 98Fin-251
❑ 98FinNo--251
❑ 98FinNo-R-251
❑ 98FinRef-251
❑ 98Fle-413
❑ 98MetUni-160
❑ 98MetUniPMG-160
❑ 98Pac-40
❑ 98PacOnl-114
❑ 98PacOnlR-114
❑ 98PacOnlWC-114
❑ 98PacPlaB-40
❑ 98PacRedT-40
❑ 98PacSil-40
❑ 98PinSna-BRS11
❑ 98Top-64
❑ 98TopChr-64
❑ 98TopChrR-64
❑ 98TopDevR-64
❑ 98TopDia-64
❑ 98TopMiniC-64
❑ 98Ult-172
❑ 98UltGolM-172
❑ 98UltMas-172
❑ 98UltPlaM-172
❑ 98UppDec-43
❑ 99199Fin-62
❑ 99FinGolRef-62
❑ 99FinRef-62
❑ 99Fle-85
❑ 99FleSta9-85
❑ 99FleWarT-85
❑ 99MetUni-4
❑ 99MetUniGM-4
❑ 99MetUniPMG-4
❑ 99Pac-67
❑ 99PacPlaB-67
❑ 99PacRed-67
❑ 99SkyPre-180
❑ 99SkyPreR-180
❑ 99SkyThu-50
❑ 99SkyThuRant-50
❑ 99SkyThuRave-50
❑ 99SpoIll-17
❑ 99StaClu-28
❑ 99StaCluFDI-28
❑ 99StaCluOoaK-28
❑ 99StaCluPP-28
❑ 99ThuSkySupR-50
❑ 99Top-390
❑ 99TopChr-390
❑ 99TopChrR-390
❑ 99TopMVPP-390
❑ 99Ult-60
❑ 99UltGolM-60
❑ 99UltMas-60
❑ 99UltPlaM-60
Gordon, Tony
❑ 92SarWhiSF-200
❑ 93SarWhiSC-11
❑ 94ElPasDF-3142
Gore, Arthur
❑ 55Bow-289
Gore, Brad
❑ 91OklStaC-10
❑ 92OklStaC-10
Gore, Bryan
❑ 90ChaRanS-8
❑ 91LinDriAA-581
❑ 91TulDriLD-581
❑ 91TulDriP-2767
❑ 91TulDriTI-8
❑ 92TulDriF-2690
❑ 92TulDriS-606
Gore, George
❑ 87BucN28-69
❑ 87OldJudN-208
❑ 88WG1CarG-40
❑ 89SFHaCN-9
❑ 90HOFStiB-6
Gore, Kevin
❑ 89GenCubP-1865
Gore, Ricky
❑ 89IdaFalBP-2017
Gorecki, Rick
❑ 91GreFalDSP-24
❑ 91HigSchPLS-20
❑ 92BakDodCLC-12
❑ 92UppDecML-109
❑ 93Bow-266
❑ 93ClaFS7-136
❑ 93SanAntMF-2999
❑ 94AlbDukF-837
❑ 94Bow-482
❑ 94BowBes-B40
❑ 94BowBesR-B40
❑ 94Cla-145
❑ 94ExcFS7-213
❑ 94UppDecML-163
❑ 95Bow-80
❑ 97DonSigA-40
❑ 97DonSigAC-49
❑ 97DonSigAM-49
❑ 97SanBerS-7
❑ 98DevRayP-4
❑ 98Fle-237
❑ 98LeaRS-297
❑ 98LeaRSLHolo-297
❑ 98LeaRSLong-297
❑ 98LeaRTrue-297
Gorecki, Ryan
❑ 95HudValRTI-7
Gorey, Steve
❑ 86ModA'sP-9
Gorham, Bobby
❑ 92EveGiaC-25
❑ 92EveGiaF-1678
Gorin, Charles
❑ 54BraJohC-15
❑ 55BraGolS-13
❑ 55BraJohC-15
❑ 92TexLon-17
Gorinski, Bob
❑ 75TacTwiK-9
❑ 76TacTwiDQ-8
❑ 78Top-386
❑ 79TidTidT-24
Gorman, Bill
❑ 82OmaRoyT-24
❑ 83OmaRoyT-23
❑ 84OmaRoyT-14
❑ 85OmaRoyT-1
❑ 95OmaRoyTI-10
❑ 96OmaRoyB-7
❑ 97OmaRoyB-6
❑ 98OmaRoyM-26
Gorman, Charles
❑ 21Zee-158
❑ 23Zee-185
❑ 24Zee-128
Gorman, Dave
❑ 89UtiBluSP-9
❑ 90UtiBluSP-18
Gorman, Dirk
❑ 90KisDodD-12
Gorman, E. M.
❑ 25Zee-64
Gorman, Hubert
❑ 49W72HolS-5
❑ 50W720HolS-10
Gorman, Mike
❑ 84ModA'sC-13
❑ 86GleFalTP-7
Gorman, Patrick
❑ 98CapCitBF5-10
❑ 98CapCitBM-10
Gorman, Paul
❑ 91DaiDolF-14
❑ 93AusFut-49
❑ 95AusFut-8
❑ 95AusFut-92
Gorman, Tom (Thomas A.)
❑ 53BowBW-61
❑ 53Dor-134
❑ 54Bow-17
❑ 55A'sRodM-16
❑ 55A'sTeal-9
❑ 56A'sPos-20
❑ 56A'sPos-21
❑ 56Top-246
❑ 57Top-87
❑ 58Top-235
❑ 59Top-449
❑ 76A'sRodMC-11
Gorman, Tom (Thomas D.)
❑ 55Bow-293
❑ 84FifNatC-1
Gorman, Tom (Thomas P.)
❑ 80MemChiT-4
❑ 82WicAerTI-5
❑ 83TidTidT-11
❑ 84Nes792-774
❑ 84TidTidT-14
❑ 84Top-774
❑ 84TopTif-774
❑ 85Fle-83
❑ 85MetColP-31
❑ 85MetTCM-13
❑ 85Top-53
❑ 85TopTif-53
❑ 86Fle-82
❑ 86MetTCM-6
❑ 86PorBeaP-7
❑ 86Top-414

❑ 86TopTif-414
❑ 91MetWIZ-146
Gorr, Robb
❑ 98YakBeaG-16
Gorrell, Chris
❑ 97SouOreTB-21
❑ 98VisOakG-11
Gorrie, Brad
❑ 97SouOreTB-6
❑ 98SouOreTG-11
Gorsica, John
❑ 47TipTop-32
❑ 79DiaGre-384
Gorski, Gary
❑ 86SalAngC-82
❑ 88ModA'sCLC-62
❑ 88ModA'sTI-11
❑ 89ModA'sC-12
Gorton, Chris
❑ 89HamRedS-15
❑ 90Bes-181
❑ 90SprCarB-20
❑ 91St.PetCC-7
❑ 91St.PetCP-2270
Goryl, John
❑ 58Top-384
❑ 59Top-77
❑ 59TopVen-77
❑ 61TwiCloD-7
❑ 62Top-558
❑ 63Top-314
❑ 63TwiVol-6
❑ 64Top-194
❑ 64TopVen-194
❑ 77OrlTwiT-12
❑ 78OrlTwiT-7
❑ 78TwiFri-30
❑ 79TwiFriP-8
❑ 80TwiPos-10
❑ 81Don-527
❑ 81Top-669
❑ 81TwiPos-12
❑ 82Ind-16
❑ 82IndBurK-3
❑ 82IndBurK-4
❑ 82IndWhe-16
❑ 83IndWhe-15
❑ 84Ind-15
❑ 84IndWhe-NNO
❑ 85Ind-15
❑ 85IndPol-NNO
❑ 86IndOhH-NNO
❑ 86IndTeal-23
❑ 87IndGat-NNO
❑ 88IndGat-45
❑ 88IndTeal-16
Goselin, Scott
❑ 88PulBraP-1751
❑ 89SumBraP-1107
Gosger, Jim
❑ 63Top-553
❑ 66OPC-114
❑ 66RedSoxTI-4
❑ 66Top-114
❑ 66TopVen-114
❑ 67CokCapAt-18
❑ 67OPC-17
❑ 67Top-17
❑ 68Top-343
❑ 68TopVen-343
❑ 69MilBra-95
❑ 69PilPos-16
❑ 69Top-482A
❑ 69Top-482B
❑ 69TopTeaP-9
❑ 70ExpPin-6
❑ 70Top-651
❑ 71ExpLaPR-4
❑ 71ExpPS-8
❑ 71MLBOffS-128
❑ 71OPC-284
❑ 71Top-284
❑ 72MilBra-119
❑ 74MetDaiPA-6
❑ 77PilPosR-16
❑ 81RedSoxBG2S-82
❑ 83Pil69G-7
❑ 91MetWIZ-147
Goshay, Henry Lee
❑ 88VerBeaDS-8
❑ 89DunBluJS-5
Goshgarian, Dee Marge
❑ 91SalSpuC-28
Goslin, Goose (Leon)
❑ 21Nei-8
❑ 22E120-108
❑ 22W573-50
❑ 25Exh-123
❑ 26Exh-123
❑ 26SpoComoA-16
❑ 27Exh-61
❑ 27YorCarE-49
❑ 28Exh-61
❑ 28PorandAR-A11
❑ 28PorandAR-B11
❑ 28W502-49
❑ 28W56PlaC-C10
❑ 28Yue-49
❑ 29ExhFou-31
❑ 29PorandAR-30
❑ 30SchR33-27
❑ 31Exh-29
❑ 31W517-47
❑ 33CraJacP-9
❑ 33DelR33-24
❑ 33DouDisP-21
❑ 33ExhFou-15
❑ 33GeoCMil-15
❑ 33Gou-110
❑ 33Gou-168
❑ 33TatOrbSDR-173
❑ 33WorCig-44
❑ 33WorCig-48
❑ 34BatR31-85
❑ 34ExhFou-12
❑ 34TigTeal-8
❑ 35ExhFou-12
❑ 35GolMedFR-6
❑ 35GouPreR-10
❑ 35GouPuzR-5F
❑ 35GouPuzR-6F
❑ 35GouPuzR-11H
❑ 35GouPuzR-13F
❑ 35WheBB1-14
❑ 36ExhFou-12
❑ 36GouWidPPR-A40
❑ 36NatChiFPR-33
❑ 36NatChiFPR-120
❑ 36R31PasP-30
❑ 36WorWidGV-43
❑ 37ExhFou-12
❑ 37OPCBatUV-111
❑ 40PlaBal-232
❑ 48SweSpoT-13
❑ 60SenUniMC-5
❑ 61Fle-35
❑ 74TCMNic-6
❑ 74TigTCM1AC-12
❑ 74TigTCM1AC-36
❑ 75SenTCM1-7
❑ 76RowExh-7
❑ 76ShaPiz-110
❑ 76TigOldTS-10
❑ 77BobParHoF-23
❑ 77GalGloG-60
❑ 78TigDeaCS-5
❑ 80PacLeg-104
❑ 80PerHaloFP-109
❑ 80SSPHOF-109
❑ 81DiaStaCD-112
❑ 81TigDetN-124
❑ 81TigSecNP-18
❑ 84OCoandSI-217
❑ 85BigLeaC3-41
❑ 87ConSer2-38
❑ 90PerGreM-78
❑ 91ConTSN-62
❑ 91ConTSNP-520
❑ 92ConTSN-437
❑ 93ConTSN-907
❑ 95ConTSN-1385
Gosnell, Mark
❑ 93Sou-4
Goss, Howie
❑ 57JetPos-6
❑ 58JetPos-8
❑ 62Top-598
❑ 63Top-364
Gossage, Goose (Rich)
❑ 73OPC-174
❑ 73Top-174
❑ 74OPC-542
❑ 74Top-542
❑ 75OPC-554
❑ 75Top-554
❑ 75TopMin-554
❑ 76Hos-77
❑ 76OPC-180
❑ 76OPC-205
❑ 76SSP-156
❑ 76Top-180
❑ 76Top-205
❑ 77Hos-128
❑ 77PirPosP-9
❑ 77Spo-7524
❑ 77Top-319
❑ 78Kel-8
❑ 78RCColC-50
❑ 78Top-70
❑ 78YanBurK-10
❑ 78YanPhoA-8
❑ 79BasPat-33
❑ 79Hos-48
❑ 79OPC-114
❑ 79Top-8
❑ 79Top-225
❑ 79YanBurK-10
❑ 79YanPicA-14
❑ 80OPC-77
❑ 80Top-140
❑ 80YanPhoA-8
❑ 81AllGamPI-81
❑ 81Don-347
❑ 81Fle-89
❑ 81FleStiC-118
❑ 81Kel-41
❑ 81MSAMinD-14
❑ 81OPC-48
❑ 81Top-460
❑ 81TopSti-8
❑ 81TopSti-113
❑ 81TopSti-251
❑ 81TopSupHT-63
❑ 81TopSupN-7
❑ 81YanPhoA-7
❑ 82Don-283
❑ 82FBIDis-10
❑ 82Fle-37
❑ 82FleSta-116
❑ 82Kel-32
❑ 82OnDecD-14
❑ 82OPC-117
❑ 82OPC-286
❑ 82OPC-396
❑ 82Top-557
❑ 82Top-770
❑ 82Top-771
❑ 82TopSti-140
❑ 82TopSti-217
❑ 82YanPhoA-8
❑ 83Don-157
❑ 83Fle-381
❑ 83FleSta-70
❑ 83FleSti-36
❑ 83Kel-10
❑ 83OPC-240
❑ 83OPC-241
❑ 83Top-240
❑ 83Top-241
❑ 83TopFol-4
❑ 83TopGloS-11
❑ 83TopSti-100
❑ 83YanPhoA-8
❑ 83YanRoyRD-2
❑ 84AllGamPI-78
❑ 84Don-396
❑ 84Fle-125
❑ 84FleUpd-44
❑ 84FunFooP-85
❑ 84MLBPen-15
❑ 84Nes792-670
❑ 84Nes792-718
❑ 84OPC-121
❑ 84PadMot-2
❑ 84SevCoi-E22
❑ 84Top-670
❑ 84Top-718
❑ 84TopRubD-8
❑ 84TopSti-316
❑ 84TopTif-670
❑ 84TopTif-718
❑ 84TopTra-43T
❑ 84TopTraT-43T
❑ 85AllGamPI-170
❑ 85Don-185
❑ 85DonActA-14
❑ 85Fle-33
❑ 85Fle-633
❑ 85FleLimE-10
❑ 85FleStaS-108
❑ 85KASDis-3
❑ 85KitCloD-3
❑ 85Lea-204
❑ 85OPC-90
❑ 85PadMot-5
❑ 85SevCoi-W9
❑ 85SubDis-30
❑ 85ThoMcAD-30
❑ 85Top-90
❑ 85Top3-D-27
❑ 85TopGloS-19
❑ 85TopRubD-22
❑ 85TopSti-147
❑ 85TopSup-49
❑ 85TopTif-90
❑ 86BasStaB-48
❑ 86Don-2
❑ 86Don-185
❑ 86DonAll-31
❑ 86DonSupD-2
❑ 86Fle-322
❑ 86FleMin-68
❑ 86FleSlu-12
❑ 86Lea-2
❑ 86MeaGolSB-20
❑ 86OPC-104
❑ 86SevCoi-C7
❑ 86SevCoi-E7
❑ 86SevCoi-S7
❑ 86SevCoi-W7
❑ 86Spo-55
❑ 86Spo-190
❑ 86Top-530
❑ 86Top3-D-6
❑ 86TopGloS-56
❑ 86TopSti-107
❑ 86TopSup-26
❑ 86TopTat-1
❑ 86TopTif-530
❑ 87ClaGam-96
❑ 87Don-483
❑ 87Fle-415
❑ 87FleGlo-415
❑ 87FleLeaL-21
❑ 87OPC-380
❑ 87PadBohHB-54
❑ 87RedFolSB-9
❑ 87Top-380
❑ 87TopSti-109
❑ 87TopTif-380
❑ 88CubDavB-54
❑ 88Don-434
❑ 88DonBasB-26
❑ 88DonTeaBC-NEW
❑ 88Fle-583
❑ 88FleGlo-583
❑ 88FleUpd-76
❑ 88FleUpdG-76
❑ 88OPC-170
❑ 88Sco-331
❑ 88ScoGlo-331
❑ 88ScoRoo-14T
❑ 88ScoRooG-14T
❑ 88StaLinPa-3
❑ 88Top-170
❑ 88TopTif-170
❑ 88TopTra-41T
❑ 88TopTraT-41T
❑ 89Don-158
❑ 89Fle-425
❑ 89FleGlo-425
❑ 89GiaMot-27
❑ 89OPC-162
❑ 89OPCBoxB-D
❑ 89Sco-223
❑ 89Top-590
❑ 89TopBasT-101
❑ 89TopTif-415
❑ 89TopWaxBC-D
❑ 89UppDec-452
❑ 90Don-678
❑ 90PubIntS-68
❑ 91Bow-271
❑ 91Cla3-T98
❑ 91FleUpd-59
❑ 91Lea-236
❑ 91RanMot-16
❑ 91Stu-125
❑ 92AthMot-12
❑ 92Don-555
❑ 92Fle-305
❑ 92Lea-474
❑ 92LeaBlaG-474
❑ 92OPC-215
❑ 92PacRyaTEI-198
❑ 92Sco-538
❑ 92StaClu-719
❑ 92Top-215
❑ 92TopGol-215
❑ 92TopGolW-215
❑ 92TopMic-215
❑ 92YanWIZ7-56
❑ 92YanWIZ8-67
❑ 92YanWIZA-25
❑ 93AthMot-16
❑ 93Fla-259
❑ 93FleFinE-255
❑ 93PacSpa-567
❑ 93RanKee-162
❑ 93StaClu-17
❑ 93StaCluFDI-17
❑ 93StaCluMOP-17
❑ 93Ult-606
❑ 94Fle-262
❑ 94MarMot-12
❑ 94Pac-450
❑ 94Sco-260
❑ 94ScoGolR-260
❑ 94StaClu-191
❑ 94StaCluFDI-191
❑ 94StaCluGR-191
❑ 94StaCluMOP-191
❑ 95ColCho-285
❑ 95ColChoGS-285
❑ 95ColChoSE-126
❑ 95ColChoSE-262
❑ 95ColChoSEGS-126
❑ 95ColChoSEGS-262
❑ 95ColChoSESS-126
❑ 95ColChoSESS-262
❑ 95ColChoSS-285
❑ 95Fle-268
❑ 95Pac-397
❑ 95Sco-74
❑ 95ScoGolR-74
❑ 95ScoPlaTS-74
❑ 95UppDec-98
❑ 95UppDecED-98
❑ 95UppDecEDG-98
❑ 99SpoIllGotG-54
❑ 99SpoIllGotGA-28
Gosse, John
❑ 80WesHavWCT-19A
Gosselin, Pat
❑ 93WelPirF-3363
Gotay, Julio
❑ 62CarJayP-4
❑ 62Top-489
❑ 63Jel-161
❑ 63PirIDL-10
❑ 63Pos-161
❑ 63Top-122
❑ 64PirKDK-13
❑ 65Top-552
❑ 67Ast-12
❑ 68CokCapA-4
❑ 68DexPre-35
❑ 68OPC-41
❑ 68Top-41
❑ 68TopVen-41
❑ 69MilBra-96
❑ 87AstShoSTw-8
Gotay, Ruben
❑ 83ArkTraT-2
Gott, Jim (James)
❑ 81ArkTraT-17
❑ 82BluJayS-6
❑ 83Don-353
❑ 83OPC-62
❑ 83Top-506
❑ 84BluJayFS-14
❑ 84Don-268
❑ 84Fle-155
❑ 84Nes792-9
❑ 84OPC-9
❑ 84Top-9
❑ 84TopTif-9
❑ 85Don-632
❑ 85Fle-105
❑ 85FleUpd-45
❑ 85GiaMot-21
❑ 85GiaPos-11
❑ 85Lea-136
❑ 85OPC-311
❑ 85Top-311
❑ 85TopTif-311
❑ 85TopTifT-40T
❑ 85TopTra-40T
❑ 86Don-358
❑ 86Fle-542
❑ 86GiaMot-21
❑ 86GiaPos-13
❑ 86OPC-106
❑ 86Top-463
❑ 86TopTif-463
❑ 87FleUpd-35
❑ 87FleUpdG-35
❑ 87GiaMot-19
❑ 87GiaPos-13
❑ 87Top-231
❑ 87TopTif-231
❑ 87TopTra-39T
❑ 87TopTraT-39T
❑ 88Don-606
❑ 88DonBasB-213
❑ 88FleUpd-112
❑ 88FleUpdG-112
❑ 88Lea-253
❑ 88PirTeal-14
❑ 88Sco-320
❑ 88ScoGlo-320
❑ 88StaLinPi-12
❑ 88Top-127
❑ 88TopTif-127
❑ 89Bow-411
❑ 89BowTif-411
❑ 89Don-362
❑ 89Fle-210
❑ 89FleExcS-16
❑ 89FleGlo-210
❑ 89FleSup-18
❑ 89OPC-172
❑ 89PanSti-163
❑ 89PirVerFJ-35
❑ 89Sco-257
❑ 89ScoHot1S-98
❑ 89Spo-83
❑ 89Top-752
❑ 89TopMinL-32
❑ 89TopTif-752
❑ 89UppDec-539
❑ 90DodMot-24
❑ 90DodPol-35
❑ 90Don-605
❑ 90Fle-466
❑ 90FleCan-466
❑ 90OPC-292
❑ 90PubIntS-155
❑ 90Sco-515
❑ 90Top-292
❑ 90TopTif-292
❑ 90UppDec-89A
❑ 90UppDec-89B
❑ 90UppDec-701
❑ 91DodMot-24
❑ 91DodPol-35
❑ 91Don-601
❑ 91Fle-200
❑ 91Lea-229
❑ 91OPC-606
❑ 91Sco-621
❑ 91Top-606
❑ 91TopDesS-606
❑ 91TopMic-606
❑ 91TopTif-606
❑ 91UppDec-690
❑ 92DodMot-15
❑ 92DodPol-35
❑ 92DodSmo-4892
❑ 92Don-601
❑ 92Fle-454
❑ 92OPC-517
❑ 92Pin-228
❑ 92Pin-596
❑ 92Sco-172
❑ 92StaClu-483
❑ 92Top-517
❑ 92TopGol-517
❑ 92TopGolW-517
❑ 92TopMic-517
❑ 92Ult-504
❑ 93DodMot-17
❑ 93DodPol-6
❑ 93DodStaC-7
❑ 93Don-670
❑ 93Fla-69
❑ 93Fle-447
❑ 93Lea-511
❑ 93PacSpa-499
❑ 93Pin-435
❑ 93Sco-422
❑ 93StaClu-487
❑ 93StaCluFDI-487
❑ 93StaCluMOP-487
❑ 93Top-418
❑ 93TopGol-418
❑ 93TopInaM-418
❑ 93TopInaR-418
❑ 93TopMic-418
❑ 93UppDec-666
❑ 93UppDecGold-666
❑ 94ColC-113
❑ 94ColChoGS-113
❑ 94ColChoSS-113

❑ 94DodDaiN-17
❑ 94DodMot-18
❑ 94DodPol-8
❑ 94Don-92
❑ 94Fin-49
❑ 94FinRef-49
❑ 94Fle-509
❑ 94Lea-205
❑ 94Pac-307
❑ 94Pin-307
❑ 94PinArtP-307
❑ 94PinMusC-307
❑ 94Sco-402
❑ 94ScoGolR-402
❑ 94Top-87
❑ 94TopGol-87
❑ 94TopSpa-87
❑ 94Ult-215
❑ 94UppDec-336
❑ 94UppDecED-336
❑ 95FleUpd-148
❑ 95PirFil-12
❑ 95Sco-268
❑ 95ScoGolR-268
❑ 95ScoPlaTS-268
❑ 95Top-332
Gottsch, J.J.
❑ 94ButCopKSP-20
Goucher, Steve
❑ 89SanDieSAS-10
❑ 91BenBucCB-6
❑ 91BenBucP-3691
Goudie, Jamie
❑ 97YakBeaG-7
❑ 98SanBerS-11
❑ 98SanBerSTIS-11
❑ 98YakBeaG-17
Goughan, Bob
❑ 88RocRedWGCP-32
Gould, A. F.
❑ 21Zee-94
❑ 22Zee-79
❑ 23Zee-105
❑ 24Zee-78
❑ 26Zee-73
❑ 27Zee-53
❑ 28Zee-77
❑ 29Zee-111
❑ 30Zee-122
Gould, B.G.
❑ 98SouOreTG-12
Gould, Bob
❑ 85MadMusP-11
❑ 85MadMusT-14
❑ 86MadMusP-9
❑ 86MadMusP-9
❑ 87ModA'sC-5
❑ 87ModA'sP-11
Gould, Clint
❑ 96LanJetB-14
Gould, Frank
❑ 90EveGiaB-5
❑ 90EveGiaP-3121
Goulding, Rich
❑ 77CliDodT-9
❑ 78LodDodT-6
Gouldrup, Gary
❑ 85ElmPioT-8
Gourdin, Tom
❑ 94ForWayWC-9
❑ 94ForWayWF-2004
❑ 95ForWayWTI-6
❑ 96FtMyeMB-21
❑ 97NewBriRC-12
❑ 98NewBriRCM-10
Goure, Samuel
❑ 96MedHatBJTI-10
Gourlay, Matthew
❑ 96MedHatBJTI-11
❑ 98St.CatSM-12
Gousha, Sean
❑ 92EriSaiC-18
❑ 92EriSaiF-1626
❑ 93AusFut-56
❑ 93HigDesMC-5
❑ 93HigDesMF-44
❑ 94PorSeaDF-680
❑ 94PorSeaDTI-14
Gouthro, Laurie
❑ 95ColSilB-9
Governor, Tony
❑ 26Zee-74
❑ 27Zee-54
❑ 28ExhPCL-8
❑ 28Zee-78
❑ 29Zee-72
❑ 30Zee-81
Gowdy, Hank
❑ 11HelSta-78
❑ 12T207-68
❑ 14B18B-48A
❑ 14B18B-48B
❑ 14B18B-48C
❑ 14CraJacE-138
❑ 15CraJacE-138
❑ 15SpoNewM-70
❑ 16BF2FP-53
❑ 16FleBreD-33
❑ 16SpoNewM-70
❑ 17ColE13-62
❑ 17HolBreD-36
❑ 19W514-67
❑ 20NatCarE-34
❑ 20W516-22
❑ 21E121So1-33
❑ 21E121So8-29
❑ 21Exh-59
❑ 21Exh-60
❑ 22AmeCarE122-23
❑ 22E120-126
❑ 22W572-33
❑ 22W573-51
❑ 22W575-45
❑ 23W501-91
❑ 23W503-62
❑ 23WilChoV-52
❑ 34DiaMatCSB-71
❑ 36NatChiFPR-34
❑ 38RedOraW-12
❑ 39OrcPhoAP-11
❑ 39RedTeal-10
❑ 40PlaBal-82
❑ 41HarHarW-8
❑ 72FleFamF-33
❑ 80BraTCM1-4
❑ 81ConTSN-26
❑ 87ConSer2-39
❑ 88ConSer3-12
❑ 91ConTSN-209
❑ 95ConTSN-1325
Gowell, Larry
❑ 73SyrChiTI-9
❑ 92YanWIZ7-57
Gozzo, Goose (Mauro)
❑ 84LitFalMT-21
❑ 86LynMetP-13
❑ 87MemChiB-20
❑ 87MemChiP-3
❑ 88MemChiB-16
❑ 89KnoBluJB-8
❑ 89KnoBluJP-1145
❑ 89KnoBluJS-6
❑ 89Sta-121
❑ 90CMC-328
❑ 90Don-655
❑ 90Fle-82
❑ 90FleCan-82
❑ 90OPC-274
❑ 90ProAAAF-345
❑ 90Sco-610
❑ 90Sco100RS-48
❑ 90Spo-168
❑ 90SyrChiC-2
❑ 90SyrChiMB-11
❑ 90SyrChiP-565
❑ 90Top-274
❑ 90TopDeb89-44
❑ 90TopTif-274
❑ 91ColSprSSLD-82
❑ 91ColSprSSP-2179
❑ 91LinDriAAA-82
❑ 91MajLeaCP-19
❑ 91Sco-843
❑ 92PorBeaF-2661
❑ 92PorBeaS-407
❑ 93NorTidF-2564
❑ 94NorTidF-2913
Grabarkewitz, Bill
❑ 70DayDaiNM-57
❑ 70OPC-446
❑ 70Top-446
❑ 71Dod-5
❑ 71DodTic-7
❑ 71Kel-56
❑ 71MilDud-44
❑ 71MLBOffS-104
❑ 71OPC-85
❑ 71Top-85
❑ 71TopCoi-21
❑ 71TopTat-35
❑ 72Top-578
❑ 73OPC-301
❑ 73Top-301
❑ 74OPC-214
❑ 74Top-214
❑ 74TopSta-74
❑ 75OPC-233
❑ 75Top-233
❑ 75TopMin-233
❑ 75TucTorC-1
❑ 75TucTorTI-4
❑ 87DodSmoA-9
❑ 89DodSmoG-76
❑ 90DodTar-291
❑ 92DodStaTA-9
Graber, Red
❑ 61UniOil-SP6
Grable, Rob
❑ 91NiaFalRC-14
❑ 91NiaFalRP-3641
❑ 92FayGenC-18
❑ 92ProFS7-69
❑ 93ClePhiC-12
❑ 93ClePhiF-2690
❑ 93FloStaLAF-26
❑ 94ClaGolF-37
❑ 94ReaPhiF-2069
❑ 95ReaPhiELC-15
❑ 95ReaPhiTI-34
❑ 95TopTra-107T
❑ 96Exc-202
Grabowski, Jason
❑ 97AppLeaTPB-8
❑ 98SavSanGM-12
Grabowski, Johnny
❑ 28LaPre-20
❑ 75Yan192T-10
❑ 79Yan192T-13
❑ 84Yan192G-9
❑ 91ConTSN-124
Grabowski, Mike
❑ 75WesPalBES-19
Grabowski, Ray
❑ 34ButPreR-27
Grabowski, Reggie J.
❑ 34BabRutG-28
Grace, Earl
❑ 34BatR31-69
❑ 34DiaMatCSB-72
❑ 34DiaStaR-69
❑ 34Gou-58
❑ 35AlDemDCR3-142
❑ 35DiaMatCS3T1-61
❑ 36GouWidPPR-A41
❑ 36WorWidGV-103
❑ 93ConTSN-938
Grace, Joe
❑ 41BroW75-12
❑ 46SeaSLP-24
❑ 49SolSunP-4
❑ 52MotCoo-5
Grace, Mark
❑ 86PeoChiP-8
❑ 87PitCubP-10
❑ 88CubDavB-17
❑ 88Don-40
❑ 88DonBasB-4
❑ 88DonRoo-1
❑ 88DonTeaBC-40
❑ 88Fle-641
❑ 88FleGlo-641
❑ 88FleMin-68
❑ 88FleUpd-77
❑ 88FleUpdG-77
❑ 88IowCubC-14
❑ 88IowCubP-539
❑ 88Lea-40
❑ 88PeoChiTI-11
❑ 88PeoChiTI-34
❑ 88SanDieSAAG-6
❑ 88ScoRoo-80T
❑ 88ScoRooG-80T
❑ 88TopTra-42T
❑ 88TopTraT-42T
❑ 89Baz-12
❑ 89Bow-291
❑ 89BowTif-291
❑ 89ClaLigB-13
❑ 89ClaTraP-155
❑ 89CubMar-17
❑ 89Don-17
❑ 89Don-255
❑ 89DonSupD-17
❑ 89Fle-426
❑ 89FleBasM-15
❑ 89FleExcS-17
❑ 89FleGlo-426
❑ 89FleLeaL-17
❑ 89FleSup-19
❑ 89K-M-1
❑ 89MSAHolD-12
❑ 89Nis-12A
❑ 89Nis-12B
❑ 89OPC-297
❑ 89PanSti-55
❑ 89Sco-362
❑ 89ScoHot1R-78
❑ 89Scomast-22
❑ 89ScoYouSI-3
❑ 89Spo-15
❑ 89SpoIllFKI-283
❑ 89Top-465
❑ 89TopBig-189
❑ 89TopCoi-15
❑ 89TopGloS-29
❑ 89TopHeaUT-15
❑ 89TopRoo-11
❑ 89TopSti-50
❑ 89TopSti-324
❑ 89TopTif-465
❑ 89ToyRoo-12
❑ 89TVSpoM-17
❑ 89UppDec-140
❑ 89UppDecS-1
❑ 90Bow-29
❑ 90BowTif-29
❑ 90ClaBlu-8
❑ 90Col-31
❑ 90ColPosG-1
❑ 90ColPosG-2
❑ 90ColPosG-3
❑ 90ColPosG-4
❑ 90ColPosG-5
❑ 90ColPosG-6
❑ 90ColPosG-7
❑ 90ColPosG-8
❑ 90CubMar-9
❑ 90Don-577
❑ 90DonBesN-51
❑ 90Fle-32
❑ 90FleBasA-12
❑ 90FleBasAC-12
❑ 90FleCan-32
❑ 90FleLeaL-12
❑ 90FleLeaLC-12
❑ 90FleLeaS-6
❑ 90Hot50PS-17
❑ 90Lea-137
❑ 90M.Vpin-19
❑ 90MLBBasB-51
❑ 90NikMin-1
❑ 90OPC-240
❑ 90PanSti-241
❑ 90Pos-19
❑ 90PubIntS-194
❑ 90PubIntS-613
❑ 90RedFolSB-38
❑ 90Sco-150
❑ 90Sco100S-60
❑ 90Spo-15
❑ 90StaCla-3
❑ 90StaCla-5
❑ 90StaCla-7
❑ 90StaCla-9
❑ 90StaCla-11
❑ 90StaLonJS-2
❑ 90StaLonJS-16
❑ 90StaLonJS-40
❑ 90Top-240
❑ 90TopBig-19
❑ 90TopDou-27
❑ 90TopGloS-12
❑ 90TopMinL-49
❑ 90TopSti-56
❑ 90TopTif-240
❑ 90TopTVA-63
❑ 90TopTVCu-23
❑ 90UppDec-128
❑ 90W/RMarG-1
❑ 90W/RMarG-2
❑ 90W/RMarG-3
❑ 90W/RMarG-4
❑ 90W/RMarG-5
❑ 90W/RMarG-6
❑ 90W/RMarG-7
❑ 90W/RMarG-8
❑ 90W/RMarG-9
❑ 91Bow-433
❑ 91CadEllD-25
❑ 91Cla1-T27
❑ 91ClaGam-105
❑ 91Col-20
❑ 91CubMar-17
❑ 91CubVinL-12
❑ 91Don-199
❑ 91Fle-422
❑ 91Lea-170
❑ 91MajLeaCP-66
❑ 91OPC-520
❑ 91PanFreS-43
❑ 91PanSti-48
❑ 91Pos-22
❑ 91Sco-175
❑ 91Sco100S-91
❑ 91SevCoi-M6
❑ 91StaClu-290
❑ 91Stu-157
❑ 91Top-520
❑ 91TopCraJI-24
❑ 91TopDesS-520
❑ 91TopMic-520
❑ 91TopSta-16
❑ 91TopTif-520
❑ 91TopTriH-N2
❑ 91Ult-61
❑ 91UppDec-99
❑ 91UppDec-134
❑ 92Bow-580
❑ 92ClaGam-29
❑ 92CubMar-17
❑ 92Don-281
❑ 92DonCraJ2-5
❑ 92Fle-381
❑ 92Hig5-28
❑ 92Lea-26
❑ 92LeaBlaG-26
❑ 92OPC-140
❑ 92PanSti-182
❑ 92Pin-136
❑ 92Sco-445
❑ 92Sco100S-20
❑ 92SpoIllFK1-430
❑ 92SpoStaCC-18
❑ 92StaClu-174
❑ 92Stu-14
❑ 92Top-140
❑ 92TopGol-140
❑ 92TopGolW-140
❑ 92TopKid-4
❑ 92TopMic-140
❑ 92TriPla-114
❑ 92Ult-175
❑ 92UppDec-143
❑ 93Bow-440
❑ 93CadDis-27
❑ 93CubMar-7
❑ 93CubStaC-8
❑ 93DiaMar-42
❑ 93Don-532
❑ 93Fin-73
❑ 93FinRef-73
❑ 93Fla-14
❑ 93Fle-20
❑ 93FleFruotL-24
❑ 93FunPac-81
❑ 93HumDumC-28
❑ 93Lea-198
❑ 93LeaGolA-R12
❑ 93LeaGolA-U10
❑ 93MetBak-29
❑ 93OPC-86
❑ 93PacJugC-27
❑ 93PacSpa-58
❑ 93PanSti-203
❑ 93Pin-34
❑ 93RedFolS-33
❑ 93Sco-50
❑ 93Sel-73
❑ 93SelStaL-12
❑ 93SP-83
❑ 93StaClu-419
❑ 93StaCluFDI-419
❑ 93StaCluMO-10
❑ 93StaCluMOP-419
❑ 93StaCluMP-18
❑ 93Stu-42
❑ 93StuHer-5
❑ 93StuSupoC-8
❑ 93Top-630
❑ 93TopGol-630
❑ 93TopInaM-630
❑ 93TopInaR-630
❑ 93TopMic-630
❑ 93TriPla-11
❑ 93TriPla-211
❑ 93TriPlaP-11
❑ 93Ult-18
❑ 93UltAwaW-3
❑ 93UppDec-483
❑ 93UppDec-573
❑ 93UppDecGold-483
❑ 93UppDecGold-573
❑ 93UppDecIC-WI8
❑ 93UppDecICJ-WI8
❑ 94Bow-410
❑ 94BowBes-R9
❑ 94BowBesR-R9
❑ 94ColC-114
❑ 94ColChoGS-114
❑ 94ColChoSS-114
❑ 94Don-358
❑ 94DonMVP-2
❑ 94DonSpeE-358
❑ 94Fin-390
❑ 94FinRef-390
❑ 94Fla-360
❑ 94Fle-383
❑ 94FleAllS-37
❑ 94FleExtB-218
❑ 94FleExtBGB-13
❑ 94FUnPac-17
❑ 94Kra-23
❑ 94Lea-43
❑ 94LeaGam-6
❑ 94LeaL-90
❑ 94OPC-146
❑ 94Pac-98
❑ 94PacSilP-25
❑ 94PacSilPC-25
❑ 94PanSti-153
❑ 94Pin-336
❑ 94PinArtP-336
❑ 94PinMusC-336
❑ 94PinRunC-RC34
❑ 94Pos-14
❑ 94ProMag-22
❑ 94RedFolMI-11
❑ 94Sco-42
❑ 94ScoGolR-42
❑ 94ScoGolS-3
❑ 94Sel-230
❑ 94SP-69
❑ 94SPDieC-69
❑ 94Spo-120
❑ 94StaClu-403
❑ 94StaCluFDI-403
❑ 94StaCluGR-403
❑ 94StaCluMO-10
❑ 94StaCluMOP-403
❑ 94StaCluT-339
❑ 94StaCluTFDI-339
❑ 94Stu-60
❑ 94TomPiz-6
❑ 94Top-360
❑ 94TopBlaG-33
❑ 94TopGol-360
❑ 94TopSpa-360
❑ 94TopSupS-18
❑ 94TriPla-72
❑ 94TriPlaM-4
❑ 94Ult-455
❑ 94UltAwaW-11
❑ 94UltOnBL-5
❑ 94UppDec-440
❑ 94UppDecAJ-30
❑ 94UppDecAJG-30
❑ 94UppDecED-440
❑ 94USPlaCA-7D
❑ 95Baz-71
❑ 95BowBes-R19
❑ 95BowBesR-R19
❑ 95ClaPhoC-11
❑ 95ColCho-205
❑ 95ColChoGS-205
❑ 95ColChoSE-83
❑ 95ColChoSEGS-83
❑ 95ColChoSESS-83
❑ 95ColChoSS-205
❑ 95Don-519
❑ 95DonPreP-519
❑ 95DonTopotO-199
❑ 95Emo-110
❑ 95Fin-65
❑ 95FinRef-65
❑ 95Fla-332
❑ 95Fle-415
❑ 95Lea-277
❑ 95Lea300C-16
❑ 95LeaLim-8
❑ 95LeaLimIBP-8
❑ 95Pac-70
❑ 95PacPri-22
❑ 95PanSti-32
❑ 95Pin-371
❑ 95PinArtP-371
❑ 95PinMusC-371

❑ 95RedFol-13
❑ 95Sco-364
❑ 95ScoGolR-364
❑ 95ScoHaloG-HG86
❑ 95ScoPlaTS-364
❑ 95Sel-221
❑ 95SelArtP-221
❑ 95SelCer-90
❑ 95SelCerMG-90
❑ 95SP-38
❑ 95SPCha-29
❑ 95SPChaDC-29
❑ 95Spo-135
❑ 95SpoArtP-135
❑ 95SPSil-38
❑ 95StaClu-213
❑ 95StaClu-393
❑ 95StaCluFDI-213
❑ 95StaCluMOP-213
❑ 95StaCluMOP-393
❑ 95StaCluSTWS-213
❑ 95StaCluSTWS-393
❑ 95StaCluVR-206
❑ 95StaCluVRMO-206
❑ 95Stu-177
❑ 95Sum-26
❑ 95SumNthD-26
❑ 95Top-90
❑ 95TopCyb-61
❑ 95TopD3-35
❑ 95UC3-87
❑ 95UC3ArtP-87
❑ 95Ult-359
❑ 95UltGolM-359
❑ 95UppDec-65
❑ 95UppDecED-65
❑ 95UppDecEDG-65
❑ 95UppDecSE-257
❑ 95UppDecSEG-257
❑ 95Zen-70
❑ 95ZenSam-70
❑ 96Baz-48
❑ 96Bow-35
❑ 96BowBes-89
❑ 96BowBesAR-89
❑ 96BowBesR-89
❑ 96BowFoi-35
❑ 96Cir-109
❑ 96CirRav-109
❑ 96ColCho-80
❑ 96ColChoGS-80
❑ 96ColChoSS-80
❑ 96CubFle-7
❑ 96Don-189
❑ 96DonDiaK-14
❑ 96DonHitL-7
❑ 96DonPreP-189
❑ 96EmoXL-155
❑ 96EmoXLD-3
❑ 96Fin-B267
❑ 96Fin-S189
❑ 96Fin-S341
❑ 96FinRef-B267
❑ 96FinRef-S189
❑ 96FinRef-S341
❑ 96Fla-216
❑ 96Fle-319
❑ 96FleTif-319
❑ 96FleUpd-U222
❑ 96FleUpdTC-U222
❑ 96Lea-126
❑ 96LeaLim-54
❑ 96LeaLimG-54
❑ 96LeaPre-51
❑ 96LeaPreP-51
❑ 96LeaPrePB-126
❑ 96LeaPrePG-126
❑ 96LeaPrePS-126
❑ 96LeaPreSG-54
❑ 96LeaPreSte-54
❑ 96LeaSig-49
❑ 96LeaSigPPG-49
❑ 96LeaSigPPP-49
❑ 96MetUni-141
❑ 96MetUniP-141
❑ 96Pac-31
❑ 96PacPri-P10
❑ 96PacPriG-P10
❑ 96PanSti-47
❑ 96Pin-243
❑ 96Pin-306
❑ 96PinAfi-52
❑ 96PinAfiAP-52
❑ 96PinAfiFPP-52
❑ 96PinArtP-143
❑ 96PinArtP-191
❑ 96PinFoil-243
❑ 96PinFoil-306
❑ 96PinSta-143
❑ 96PinSta-191
❑ 96ProSta-36
❑ 96Sco-19
❑ 96ScoDugC-A18
❑ 96ScoDugCAP-A18
❑ 96Sel-81
❑ 96SelArtP-81
❑ 96SelCer-94
❑ 96SelCerAP-94
❑ 96SelCerCB-94
❑ 96SelCerCR-94
❑ 96SelCerMB-94
❑ 96SelCerMG-94
❑ 96SelCerMR-94
❑ 96SelTeaN-15
❑ 96SP-54
❑ 96Spo-82
❑ 96SpoArtP-82
❑ 96SPx-15
❑ 96SPxGol-15
❑ 96StaClu-160
❑ 96StaCluEPB-160
❑ 96StaCluEPG-160
❑ 96StaCluEPS-160
❑ 96StaCluMO-14
❑ 96StaCluMOP-160
❑ 96Stu-140
❑ 96StuPrePB-140
❑ 96StuPrePG-140
❑ 96StuPrePS-140
❑ 96Sum-145
❑ 96SumAbo&B-145
❑ 96SumArtP-145
❑ 96SumFoi-145
❑ 96TeaOut-31
❑ 96Top-55
❑ 96TopChr-20
❑ 96TopChrR-20
❑ 96TopGal-180
❑ 96TopGalPPI-180
❑ 96TopLas-23
❑ 96Ult-168
❑ 96UltGolM-168
❑ 96UltPriL-11
❑ 96UltPriLGM-11
❑ 96UltRaw-3
❑ 96UltRawGM-3
❑ 96UppDec-295
❑ 96Zen-73
❑ 96ZenArtP-73
❑ 96ZenMoz-6
❑ 97Bow-237
❑ 97BowBes-16
❑ 97BowBesAR-16
❑ 97BowBesR-16
❑ 97BowChr-64
❑ 97BowChrI-64
❑ 97BowChrIR-64
❑ 97BowChrR-64
❑ 97BowInt-237
❑ 97Cir-316
❑ 97CirRav-316
❑ 97ColCho-290
❑ 97Don-120
❑ 97DonEli-86
❑ 97DonEliGS-86
❑ 97DonGolPP-120
❑ 97DonLim-71
❑ 97DonLim-156
❑ 97DonLimE-71
❑ 97DonLimE-156
❑ 97DonLimENG-71
❑ 97DonLimFotG-66
❑ 97DonPre-84
❑ 97DonPreCttC-84
❑ 97DonSig-42
❑ 97DonSigPPP-42
❑ 97DonSilPP-120
❑ 97E-X2-61
❑ 97E-X2Cred-61
❑ 97E-X2EssCre-61
❑ 97Fin-141
❑ 97Fin-262
❑ 97FinEmb-141
❑ 97FinEmbR-141
❑ 97FinRef-141
❑ 97FinRef-262
❑ 97FlaShoLC-172
❑ 97FlaShoLeg0-172
❑ 97FlaShoLeg1-172
❑ 97FlaShoM-A172
❑ 97FlaShoM-B172
❑ 97FlaShoM-C172
❑ 97FlaShoR0-172
❑ 97FlaShoR1-172
❑ 97FlaShoR2-172
❑ 97Fle-276
❑ 97FleTeaL-16
❑ 97FleTif-276
❑ 97Lea-13
❑ 97Lea-395
❑ 97LeaFraM-13
❑ 97LeaFraM-395
❑ 97LeaFraMDC-13
❑ 97LeaFraMDC-395
❑ 97MetUni-11
❑ 97NewPin-39
❑ 97NewPinAP-39
❑ 97NewPinMC-39
❑ 97NewPinPP-39
❑ 97Pac-250
❑ 97PacLigB-250
❑ 97PacPri-84
❑ 97PacPriLB-84
❑ 97PacPriP-84
❑ 97PacSil-250
❑ 97Pin-106
❑ 97PinArtP-PP106
❑ 97PinIns-96
❑ 97PinInsCE-96
❑ 97PinInsDE-96
❑ 97PinMusC-106
❑ 97PinPrePla-106
❑ 97PinX-P-71
❑ 97PinX-PMoS-71
❑ 97Sco-179
❑ 97ScoArtPWB-179
❑ 97ScoPreS-179
❑ 97ScoShoS-179
❑ 97ScoShoSAP-179
❑ 97Sel-37
❑ 97SelArtP-37
❑ 97SelCom-37
❑ 97SelRegG-37
❑ 97SP-44
❑ 97SpoIll-96
❑ 97SpoIllEE-96
❑ 97StaClu-53
❑ 97StaCluMat-53
❑ 97StaCluMOP-53
❑ 97StaCluMOP-PL10
❑ 97StaCluPL-PL10
❑ 97StrAll-24
❑ 97Stu-66
❑ 97StuPrePG-66
❑ 97StuPrePS-66
❑ 97Top-37
❑ 97TopChr-13
❑ 97TopChrR-13
❑ 97TopGal-48
❑ 97TopGalPPI-48
❑ 97TopMem05-19
❑ 97TopSta-49
❑ 97TopStaAM-49
❑ 97TopSweS-SS5
❑ 97Ult-164
❑ 97UltDouT-12
❑ 97UltFieC-5
❑ 97UltGolME-164
❑ 97UltPlaME-164
❑ 97UppDec-35
❑ 97UppDec-141
❑ 98Bow-39
❑ 98BowBes-30
❑ 98BowBesAR-30
❑ 98BowBesR-30
❑ 98BowChr-39
❑ 98BowChrGA-39
❑ 98BowChrGAR-39
❑ 98BowChrI-39
❑ 98BowChrIR-39
❑ 98BowChrR-39
❑ 98BowGolA-39
❑ 98BowInt-39
❑ 98CirThu-22
❑ 98CirThuRav-22
❑ 98CirThuSupRav-22
❑ 98ColCho-59
❑ 98ColChoSQ-SQ54
❑ 98CroRoy-29
❑ 98Don-70
❑ 98Don-362
❑ 98DonCol-70
❑ 98DonColE-466
❑ 98DonColL-296
❑ 98DonColP-608
❑ 98DonColS-70
❑ 98DonCruG-60
❑ 98DonCruP-60
❑ 98DonCruR-60
❑ 98DonEli-66
❑ 98DonEliA-66
❑ 98DonEliS-66
❑ 98DonGolPP-70
❑ 98DonGolPP-362
❑ 98DonPre-58
❑ 98DonPreSeat-58
❑ 98DonPriCD-70
❑ 98DonPriCE-466
❑ 98DonPriCL-296
❑ 98DonPriCP-608
❑ 98DonSig-67
❑ 98DonSigP-67
❑ 98DonSilPP-70
❑ 98DonSilPP-362
❑ 98E-X2-64
❑ 98E-X2ECFut-64
❑ 98E-X2ECNow-64
❑ 98Fin-160
❑ 98FinNo--160
❑ 98FinNo-R-160
❑ 98FinRef-160
❑ 98FlaShoLeg0-113
❑ 98FlaShoLeg1-113
❑ 98FlaShoLeg2-113
❑ 98FlaShoLeg3-113
❑ 98FlaShoLegM-113
❑ 98FlaShoR0-113
❑ 98FlaShoR1-113
❑ 98FlaShoR2-113
❑ 98FlaShoR3-113
❑ 98Fle-44
❑ 98FleDecERT-6
❑ 98FleDecoE-6
❑ 98FleVin'-10
❑ 98FleVin'C-10
❑ 98Lea-97
❑ 98LeaFraDA-97
❑ 98LeaFraF-97
❑ 98LeaFraM-97
❑ 98LeaFraM-97
❑ 98LeaFraMDC-97
❑ 98LeaFraMDC-97
❑ 98LeaFraMS-97
❑ 98LeaFraMZ2-97
❑ 98LeaRS-53
❑ 98LeaRSLHolo-53
❑ 98LeaRSLong-53
❑ 98LeaRTrue-53
❑ 98MetUni-89
❑ 98MetUniPMG-89
❑ 98Pac-251
❑ 98PacAur-112
❑ 98PacInv-83
❑ 98PacInvGems-130
❑ 98PacInvPBlue-83
❑ 98PacInvSilv-83
❑ 98PacInvTeam-5
❑ 98PacOme-47
❑ 98PacOmeR-47
❑ 98PacOnl-141
❑ 98PacOnlR-141
❑ 98PacOnlWC-141
❑ 98PacPar-138
❑ 98PacParC-138
❑ 98PacParG-138
❑ 98PacParHS-138
❑ 98PacParI-31
❑ 98PacParPB-138
❑ 98PacParR-138
❑ 98PacPlaB-251
❑ 98PacRedT-251
❑ 98PacSil-251
❑ 98PacTeaC-16
❑ 98Pin-15
❑ 98PinArtP-PP15
❑ 98PinIns-45
❑ 98PinInsCE-45
❑ 98PinInsDE-45
❑ 98PinMusC-PP15
❑ 98PinPer-59
❑ 98PinPerPP-59
❑ 98PinPreP-15
❑ 98PinSna-CC1
❑ 98PinSna-CC5
❑ 98Revo-29
❑ 98RevoSS-29
❑ 98ScoRT-215
❑ 98ScoRTSS-PP119
❑ 98ScoRTSSAP-PP119
❑ 98ScoRTSSAP1-PP119
❑ 98SkyDugA-9
❑ 98SkyDugAIA-9
❑ 98SP Aut-65
❑ 98SpoIll-47
❑ 98SpoIllEE-47
❑ 98SpoIllFE-47
❑ 98SpoIllTaN-86
❑ 98SpoIllTaNEE-86
❑ 98SpoIllWSF-41
❑ 98SpoIllWSFEE-41
❑ 98SpoIllWSFFE-41
❑ 98SPxFin-68
❑ 98SPxFinR-68
❑ 98SPxFinS-68
❑ 98StaCluFDI-253
❑ 98StaCluI-253
❑ 98StaCluOneK-253
❑ 98StaCluPP-253
❑ 98Stu-40
❑ 98StuGPP-40
❑ 98StuSPP-40
❑ 98Top-168
❑ 98TopChr-168
❑ 98TopChrR-168
❑ 98TopDevR-168
❑ 98TopDia-168
❑ 98TopGal-58
❑ 98TopGalGP-58
❑ 98TopGalOPP-58
❑ 98TopGalPPI-58
❑ 98TopGalPPIA-58
❑ 98TopGolLabC1-92
❑ 98TopGolLabC1B-92
❑ 98TopGolLabC1One-92
❑ 98TopGolLabC1R-92
❑ 98TopGolLabC2-92
❑ 98TopGolLabC2B-92
❑ 98TopGolLabC2One-92
❑ 98TopGolLabC2R-92
❑ 98TopGolLabC3-92
❑ 98TopGolLabC3B-92
❑ 98TopGolLabC3One-92
❑ 98TopGolLabC3R-92
❑ 98TopMiniC-168
❑ 98TopMysF-ILM19
❑ 98TopMysFR-ILM19
❑ 98TopOpeD-89
❑ 98TopSta-114
❑ 98TopSta'S-14
❑ 98TopSta'SGH-14
❑ 98TopStaB-114
❑ 98TopStaG-114
❑ 98TopStaGR-114
❑ 98TopStaS-114
❑ 98TopStaSteG-14
❑ 98TopTek-78
❑ 98TopTekD-78
❑ 98UD3-84
❑ 98UD3-174
❑ 98UD3-264
❑ 98UD3DieCut-84
❑ 98UD3DieCut-174
❑ 98UD3DieCut-264
❑ 98Ult-68
❑ 98UltGolM-68
❑ 98UltMas-68
❑ 98UltPlaM-68
❑ 98UppDec-52
❑ 98UppDec10AP-24
❑ 98UppDec1APR-24
❑ 98UppDecR-17
❑ 98UppDecRGKoG-G18
❑ 98UppDecSF-31
❑ 98Zen-36
❑ 98Zen5 xx7-32
❑ 98Zen5x7GoldImp-32
❑ 98Zen5x7Imp-32
❑ 98ZenZ-G-36
❑ 98ZenZ-S-36
❑ 99199Fin-6
❑ 99199Fin-264
❑ 99Bow-64
❑ 99BowBes-61
❑ 99BowBesAR-61
❑ 99BowBesR-61
❑ 99BowChr-64
❑ 99BowChrG-64
❑ 99BowChrGR-64
❑ 99BowChrI-64
❑ 99BowChrIR-64
❑ 99BowChrR-64
❑ 99BowGol-64
❑ 99BowInt-64
❑ 99BowLatB-LB9
❑ 99CroRoyB-27
❑ 99CroRoyL-27
❑ 99CroRoyOD-27
❑ 99DumSet-MG
❑ 99DumSet-MG
❑ 99E-X Cen-47
❑ 99E-X CenECFut-47
❑ 99E-X CenECNow-47
❑ 99FinGolRef-6
❑ 99FinGolRef-264
❑ 99FinPre-PP6
❑ 99FinRef-6
❑ 99FinRef-264
❑ 99Fle-117
❑ 99FleBri-41
❑ 99FleBri2G-41
❑ 99FleBriBlu-41
❑ 99FleBriGol-41
❑ 99FleMys-77
❑ 99FleMysG-77
❑ 99FleMysM-77
❑ 99FleSta9-117
❑ 99FleWarT-117
❑ 99MetUni-144
❑ 99MetUniGM-144
❑ 99MetUniPMG-144
❑ 99Pac-84
❑ 99PacAur-33
❑ 99PacAurOD-33
❑ 99PacCroC-56
❑ 99PacCroCPB-56
❑ 99PacInv-29
❑ 99PacInvOD-29
❑ 99PacInvPB-29
❑ 99PacOme-47
❑ 99PacOmeC-47
❑ 99PacOmeG-47
❑ 99PacOmePB-47
❑ 99PacPar-48
❑ 99PacParC-48
❑ 99PacParG-48
❑ 99PacParHoloGold-48
❑ 99PacParHS-48
❑ 99PacParOD-48
❑ 99PacParPB-48
❑ 99PacParRed-48
❑ 99PacPlaB-84
❑ 99PacPri-28
❑ 99PacPriHB-28
❑ 99PacPriHG-28
❑ 99PacPriHM-28
❑ 99PacPriHP-28
❑ 99PacPriRed-28
❑ 99PacPriS-90
❑ 99PacPriS206-90
❑ 99PacPriS206R-90
❑ 99PacRed-84
❑ 99Rev-28
❑ 99RevPremDate-28
❑ 99RevRet-28
❑ 99RevShaSS-28
❑ 99SkyMolM-36
❑ 99SkyMolMX-36
❑ 99SkyPre-71
❑ 99SkyPreR-71
❑ 99SkyThu-186
❑ 99SkyThuRant-186
❑ 99SkyThuRave-186
❑ 99SP Aut-20
❑ 99SpoIll-99
❑ 99SPx-28
❑ 99SPxFinR-28
❑ 99SPxFinS-28
❑ 99StaClu-272
❑ 99StaCluFDI-272
❑ 99StaCluOoaK-272
❑ 99StaCluPP-272
❑ 99StaCluTI-T8B
❑ 99StaCluTL-T8B
❑ 99StaCluTL-T8B
❑ 99ThuSkySupR-186
❑ 99Top-280
❑ 99TopBlaLC1-3
❑ 99TopBlaLC2-3
❑ 99TopBlaLC3-3
❑ 99TopChr-280
❑ 99TopChrR-280
❑ 99TopGal-61
❑ 99TopGalPP-61
❑ 99TopGalPPI-61
❑ 99TopGolL-3
❑ 99TopGolLC1-3
❑ 99TopGolLC2-3
❑ 99TopGolLOtO-3
❑ 99TopMVPP-280
❑ 99TopOpeD-121
❑ 99TopRedLC1-3
❑ 99TopRedLC2-3
❑ 99TopRedLC3-3
❑ 99TopSta-53
❑ 99TopSta1Foil-53
❑ 99TopStaFoil-53

❑ 99TopStaOS-53
❑ 99TopTek-26A
❑ 99TopTek-26B
❑ 99TopTekG-26A
❑ 99TopTekG-26B
❑ 99UD Cho-68
❑ 99UD ChoPCR-68
❑ 99Ult-161
❑ 99UltGolM-161
❑ 99UltMas-161
❑ 99UltPlaM-161
❑ 99UppDec-61
❑ 99UppDecCL-91
❑ 99UppDecCLCC-91
❑ 99UppDecCLM-C17
❑ 99UppDecEL1-61
❑ 99UppDecEL2-61
❑ 99UppDecM-40
❑ 99UppDecMGS-40
❑ 99UppDecMHFS-40
❑ 99UppDecMP-40
❑ 99UppDecMSS-40
❑ 99UppDecO-7
❑ 99UppDecOSO-7
❑ 99UppDecR-18
❑ 99UppDecRG-18
❑ 99UppDecRP-18
❑ 99Vic-79
Grace, Michael
❑ 87AncGlaP-15
❑ 89SalLakTTI-14
❑ 90RocExpLC-9
❑ 90RocExpP-2702
❑ 91WinSpiC-20
❑ 91WinSpiP-2837
❑ 92ChaKniF-2780
❑ 92ChaKniS-156
❑ 92SkyAA F-72
Grace, Mike James
❑ 91BatCliCB-22
❑ 91BatCliP-3478
❑ 91Cla/Bes-431
❑ 92UppDecML-217
❑ 93OrlCubF-2792
❑ 95ReaPhiELC-16
❑ 95ReaPhiTI-35
❑ 96Bow-341
❑ 96BowBes-43
❑ 96BowBesAR-43
❑ 96BowBesR-43
❑ 96BowFoi-341
❑ 96Fin-S317
❑ 96FinRef-S317
❑ 96FleUpd-U164
❑ 96FleUpdNH-7
❑ 96FleUpdTC-U164
❑ 96LeaLimR-7
❑ 96LeaLimRG-7
❑ 96LeaPre-125
❑ 96LeaPreP-125
❑ 96LeaSigA-83
❑ 96LeaSigAG-83
❑ 96LeaSigAS-83
❑ 96PhiTeal-14
❑ 96PinAfi-172
❑ 96PinAfiAP-172
❑ 96Sel-178
❑ 96SelArtP-178
❑ 96SelCer-109
❑ 96SelCerAP-109
❑ 96SelCerCB-109
❑ 96SelCerCR-109
❑ 96SelCerMB-109
❑ 96SelCerMG-109
❑ 96SelCerMR-109
❑ 96SP-13
❑ 96Sum-186
❑ 96SumAbo&B-186
❑ 96SumArtP-186
❑ 96SumFoi-186
❑ 96Ult-521
❑ 96UltGolM-521
❑ 96UppDec-246
❑ 96Zen-114
❑ 96ZenArtP-114
❑ 97Fle-412
❑ 97FleTif-412
❑ 97Lea-69
❑ 97LeaFraM-69
❑ 97LeaFraMDC-69
❑ 97PhiCopQ-9
❑ 97Sco-292
❑ 97ScoArtPWB-292
❑ 97ScoPreS-292
❑ 97ScoShoS-292
❑ 97ScoShoSAP-292
❑ 97StaClu-137
❑ 97StaCluMOP-137
❑ 97Top-242
❑ 97Ult-250
❑ 97UltGolME-250
❑ 97UltPlaME-250
❑ 98ColCho-205
❑ 98PacOnl-560
❑ 98PacOnlR-560
❑ 98PacOnlWC-560
❑ 98PhiTeal-14
❑ 98UppDec-366
❑ 98UppDec-476
❑ 99UppDec-173
❑ 99UppDecEL1-173
❑ 99UppDecEL2-173
Grace, Mike Lee
❑ 77IndIndTI-12
❑ 78IndIndTI-16
❑ 79IndIndTI-18
❑ 80IndIndTI-4
❑ 80VenLeaS-173
❑ 83ColAstT-4
Grace, Willie
❑ 92NegLeaRLI-25
❑ 95NegLeaL2-29
Gracesqui, Franklin
❑ 98St.CatSM-13
Grachen, Tim
❑ 83QuaCitCT-12
Grady, Pat
❑ 80BatTroT-26
Graff, Milt
❑ 57Top-369
❑ 58Top-192
❑ 59Top-182
❑ 59TopVen-182
Graff, Stephen
❑ 86EriCarP-9
Graffanino, Tony (Anthony)
❑ 91IdaFalBP-4335
❑ 91IdaFalBSP-5
❑ 92ClaFS7-372
❑ 92MacBraC-1
❑ 92MacBraF-273
❑ 92ProFS7-195
❑ 93CarLeaAGF-37
❑ 93DurBulC-8
❑ 93DurBulF-490
❑ 93DurBulTI-22
❑ 94Bow-601
❑ 94ExcFS7-153
❑ 94GreBraF-420
❑ 94GreBraTI-11
❑ 94UppDecML-166
❑ 95Exc-150
❑ 95RicBraTI-4
❑ 95Top-645
❑ 95UppDec-251
❑ 95UppDecED-251
❑ 95UppDecEDG-251
❑ 95UppDecML-46
❑ 95UppDecMLFS-46
❑ 96MLBPin-13
❑ 96RicBraB-14
❑ 96RicBraRC-4
❑ 96RicBraUB-9
❑ 97Bow-388
❑ 97BowInt-388
❑ 97Don-382
❑ 97DonGolPP-382
❑ 97DonSilPP-382
❑ 97DonTea-29
❑ 97DonTeaSPE-29
❑ 97FlaShoLC-130
❑ 97FlaShoLeg0-130
❑ 97FlaShoLeg1-130
❑ 97FlaShoM-A130
❑ 97FlaShoM-B130
❑ 97FlaShoM-C130
❑ 97FlaShoR0-130
❑ 97FlaShoR1-130
❑ 97FlaShoR2-130
❑ 97Fle-617
❑ 97FleTif-617
❑ 97ScoPreS-311
❑ 97Ult-489
❑ 97UltGolME-489
❑ 97UltPlaME-489
❑ 98BraSco-12
❑ 98BraScoP-12
❑ 98Pac-233
❑ 98PacOnl-61
❑ 98PacOnlR-61
❑ 98PacOnlWC-61
❑ 98PacPlaB-233
❑ 98PacRedT-233
❑ 98PacSil-233
❑ 98Sco-144
❑ 98Ult-399
❑ 98UltGolM-399
❑ 98UltMas-399
❑ 98UltPlaM-399
❑ 99Ult-71
❑ 99UltGolM-71
❑ 99UltMas-71
❑ 99UltPlaM-71
Graham, Bert
❑ 09PC7HHB-16
❑ 11SpoLifM-108
Graham, Bill
❑ 09T206-144
❑ 72ClaCar-116
❑ 77FriOneYW-46
❑ 91MetWIZ-148
Graham, Brian
❑ 83MadMusF-28
❑ 84AlbA'sT-6
❑ 85HunStaJ-14
❑ 87KinIndP-11
❑ 88EasLeaAP-51
❑ 88WilBilP-1313
❑ 89WatIndS-11
❑ 90CarLeaA-32
❑ 90KinIndTI-28
❑ 91CarLeaAP-CAR16
❑ 91KinIndC-28
❑ 91KinIndP-340
❑ 92CanIndF-706
❑ 92CanIndS-124
❑ 93CanIndF-2852
❑ 94ChaKniF-909
❑ 96BufBisB-1
❑ 97BufBis-1
Graham, Bruce
❑ 85EveGiaIC-3
❑ 86EveGiaPC-7
❑ 87EveGiaC-33
❑ 89PhoFirP-1488
Graham, Charlie
❑ 09ObaT21-41
Graham, Dan
❑ 77TacTwiDQ-25
❑ 79TolMudHT-6
❑ 80BalOriP-8
❑ 80Top-669
❑ 80VenLeaS-188
❑ 81Don-233
❑ 81Fle-189
❑ 81OPC-161
❑ 81Top-161
❑ 82Don-455
❑ 82Fle-167
❑ 82RocRedWT-10
❑ 82Top-37
❑ 91OriCro-161
Graham, Derrick
❑ 91BilMusP-3766
❑ 91BilMusSP-9
❑ 92BilMusF-3362
❑ 92BilMusSP-20
Graham, Everett
❑ 82CliGiaF-10
❑ 86PhoFirP-7
❑ 87ShrCapP-1
❑ 88PhoFirC-20
❑ 88PhoFirP-60
❑ 89MidAngGS-16
Graham, Gordie
❑ 91BluOriC-2
❑ 91BluOriP-4134
Graham, Greg
❑ 91WinHavRSC-18
❑ 91WinHavRSP-497
❑ 92NewBriRSF-441
❑ 92NewBriRSS-486
❑ 93St.LuMF-2928
❑ 94BinMetF-710
❑ 95NorTidTI-13
Graham, Jack
❑ 50Bow-145
❑ 85TCMPpl1-41
❑ 90DodTar-292
Graham, Jason
❑ 98MicBatCM-13
Graham, Jeffrey L.
❑ 87SprCarB-9
Graham, Jeremy
❑ 93DavLipB-10
Graham, Johnny (John)
❑ 88AubAstP-1971
❑ 89AubAstP-2177
❑ 90AubAstB-20
Graham, Kyle
❑ 28Zee-152
❑ 28Zee-153
❑ 29Zee-157
❑ 97YakBeaG-8
Graham, Lee
❑ 81PawRedST-19
❑ 83PawRedST-22
❑ 84PawRedST-2
❑ 85RicBraT-19
❑ 86RicBraP-7
Graham, Lew
❑ 84LitFalMT-23
Graham, Lindsey
❑ 74GasRanT-11
Graham, Mark
❑ 93PocPosF-4204
❑ 93PocPosSP-6
Graham, Moonlight (Archibald)
❑ 93MooGra-1
❑ 93MooGra-2
❑ 93MooGra-3
❑ 93MooGra-4
Graham, Nancy
❑ 92WesPalBEC-28
Graham, Otto
❑ 52Whe-13A
❑ 52Whe-13B
❑ 74NewYorNTDiS-40
Graham, Peaches (George)
❑ 09AmeCarE90-1-44
❑ 09RamT20-51
❑ 09T206-145
❑ 11HelSta-95
❑ 11MecDFT-24
❑ 11S74Sil-43
❑ 11S74Sil-62
❑ 11SpoLifM-140
❑ 11T205-66A
❑ 11T205-66B
❑ 11TurRedT-95
❑ 12ColRedB-117
❑ 12HasTriFT-70B
❑ 12T207-69
Graham, Randy
❑ 83GreHorT-8
❑ 84NasSouTI-8
❑ 85AlbYanT-8
❑ 86ColCliP-9
❑ 86ColCliP-10
❑ 87ColCliP-11
❑ 87ColCliP-19
❑ 87ColCliT-5
Graham, Richard
❑ 92BelMarCB-5
❑ 92BelMarF-1436
❑ 93AppFoxCB-9
❑ 93AppFoxFI-2456
❑ 96SarRedSB-17
Graham, Steve
❑ 88HamRedP-1745
❑ 89HamRedS-13
❑ 90St.PetCS-9
❑ 94DanBraC-14
Graham, Tim
❑ 90ElmPioP-1
❑ 91ElmPioC-6
❑ 91ElmPioP-3283
❑ 92LynRedSC-12
❑ 92LynRedSF-2919
❑ 94HigDesMC-12
❑ 94HigDesMF-2799
Graham, Wayne
❑ 77FriOneYW-107
❑ 91MetWIZ-149
❑ 92TexLon-18
Graham, William
❑ 12ColTinT-117
Grahe, Joe
❑ 90MidAngGS-12
❑ 91Cla3-T27
❑ 91ClaGam-50
❑ 91Don-737
❑ 91EdmTraLD-164
❑ 91EdmTraP-1513
❑ 91LinDriAAA-164
❑ 91OPC-426
❑ 91Sco-367
❑ 91Top-426
❑ 91TopDeb90-58
❑ 91TopDesS-426
❑ 91TopMic-426
❑ 91TopTif-426
❑ 91UppDec-657
❑ 92ClaGam-68
❑ 92Don-445
❑ 92Lea-137
❑ 92LeaBlaG-137
❑ 92OPC-496
❑ 92OPCPre-158
❑ 92Pin-371
❑ 92Sco-674
❑ 92Sco100RS-97
❑ 92StaClu-579
❑ 92Top-496
❑ 92TopGol-496
❑ 92TopGolW-496
❑ 92TopMic-496
❑ 92UppDec-542
❑ 93AngMot-27
❑ 93AngStaCl-18
❑ 93Bow-201
❑ 93Don-401
❑ 93Fle-192
❑ 93Lea-372
❑ 93OPC-199
❑ 93PacSpa-369
❑ 93Pin-412
❑ 93Sco-188
❑ 93Sel-374
❑ 93StaClu-262
❑ 93StaCluFDI-262
❑ 93StaCluMOP-262
❑ 93Top-129
❑ 93TopGol-129
❑ 93TopInaM-129
❑ 93TopInaR-129
❑ 93TopMic-129
❑ 93TriPla-256
❑ 93Ult-165
❑ 93UppDec-290
❑ 93UppDecGold-290
❑ 94AngLAT-6
❑ 94AngMot-25
❑ 94ColC-467
❑ 94ColChoGS-467
❑ 94ColChoSS-467
❑ 94Don-454
❑ 94Fin-193
❑ 94FinRef-193
❑ 94Fle-58
❑ 94Lea-69
❑ 94Pac-79
❑ 94Sco-202
❑ 94ScoGolR-202
❑ 94Top-691
❑ 94TopGol-691
❑ 94TopSpa-691
❑ 94TriPla-16
❑ 94Ult-329
❑ 94UppDec-401
❑ 94UppDecED-401
❑ 95Fle-225
❑ 95Top-278
Grahek, Larry
❑ 81ChaRoyT-22
Grahovac, Mike
❑ 89EveGiaS-8
❑ 90CliGiaUTI-U5
❑ 91CliGiaP-837
Grain, Gregg
❑ 90ChaLooGS-3
Grajeda, Billy
❑ 92AriWilP-4
Gralewski, Bob
❑ 88CapCodPB-5
❑ 88CapCodPPaLP-154
Gramly, Tom
❑ 77FriOneYW-56
Grammas, Alex
❑ 54CarHunW-6
❑ 54Top-151
❑ 55Bow-186
❑ 55CarHunW-6
❑ 55Top-21
❑ 55TopDouH-107
❑ 55TopTesS-2
❑ 56Top-37
❑ 57RedSoh-6
❑ 57Top-222
❑ 58Top-254
❑ 59Top-6
❑ 59TopVen-6
❑ 60Top-168
❑ 60TopVen-168
❑ 61Pos-177A
❑ 61Pos-177B
❑ 61Top-64
❑ 61TopStal-87
❑ 62Jel-168
❑ 62Pos-168
❑ 62PosCan-168
❑ 62SalPlaC-197
❑ 62ShiPlaC-197
❑ 62Top-223
❑ 63Top-416
❑ 73OPC-296
❑ 73Top-296
❑ 74OPC-326
❑ 74Top-326
❑ 76OPC-606
❑ 76SSP-620
❑ 76Top-606
❑ 77Top-51
❑ 79DiaGre-174
❑ 83TigPos-12
❑ 84TigTeal-16
❑ 84TigWavP-17
❑ 88TigPep-NNO
❑ 89TigMar-NNO
❑ 90TigCok-28
❑ 90TigTeal-13
❑ 91TigCok-NNO
❑ 94TopArc1-151
❑ 94TopArc1G-151
Granadillo, Adel
❑ 97BurIndG-10
Granata, Chris
❑ 94WatIndC-13
❑ 94WatIndF-3930
❑ 96KenIndB-9
Granco, Julio
❑ 86SalAngC-79
Grandas, Bob
❑ 79OgdA'sT-25
❑ 79WatA'sT-20
❑ 80OgdA'sT-11
❑ 81TacTigT-27
❑ 82TacTigT-35
❑ 83EvaTriT-19
Grande, Marc
❑ 93EveGiaC-11
❑ 93EveGiaF-3764
Grandizio, Steve
❑ 95PeoChiTI-36
Grandquist, Ken
❑ 82IowCubT-27
❑ 83IowCubT-29
❑ 84IowCubT-5
❑ 85IowCubT-26
Grandy, Jack
❑ 92WatDiaC-29
Graney, Jack
❑ 09ObaT21-27
❑ 11PinT-5-618
❑ 12T207-70
❑ 14B18B-3A
❑ 14B18B-3B
❑ 15SpoNewM-71
❑ 16SpoNewM-71
❑ 17ColE13-63
❑ 17HolBreD-37
❑ 20NatCarE-35
❑ 21E121So1-34
❑ 21E121So8-30
❑ 22AmeCarE122-24
❑ 22E120-34
❑ 22W573-52
❑ 22W575-46
❑ 23W501-113
❑ 77Ind192T-8
❑ 92ConTSN-481
❑ 94ConTSN-1247
❑ 94ConTSNB-1247
❑ 95ConTSN-1366
Granger, George
❑ 36GouWidPPR-D10
Granger, Greg
❑ 93BriTigF-3643
❑ 94FayGenC-13
❑ 94FayGenF-2139
Granger, Jeff
❑ 91TopTra-49T
❑ 91TopTraT-49T
❑ 92StaCluD-64
❑ 92TopDaiQTU-18
❑ 92TopTra-43T
❑ 92TopTraG-43T
❑ 93StaCluM-22
❑ 94ActPac-16
❑ 94Bow-527
❑ 94BowBes-R90
❑ 94BowBesR-R90

□ 94ColC-23
□ 94ColChoGS-23
□ 94ColChoSS-23
□ 94FleExtB-89
□ 94FleMajLP-12
□ 94MemChiF-352
□ 94OPC-51
□ 94Pin-269
□ 94PinArtP-269
□ 94PinMusC-269
□ 94PinSam-269
□ 94PinSam-NNO
□ 94Sco-574
□ 94ScoBoyoS-59
□ 94ScoGolR-574
□ 94Sel-399
□ 94SP-172
□ 94SPDieC-172
□ 94Top-204
□ 94TopGol-204
□ 94TopSpa-204
□ 94UppDec-14
□ 94UppDecED-14
□ 95ActPacF-20
□ 95Bow-424
□ 95ColCho-452
□ 95ColChoGS-452
□ 95ColChoSS-452
□ 95Pin-443
□ 95PinArtP-443
□ 95PinMusC-443
□ 95Sco-577
□ 95ScoGolR-577
□ 95ScoPlaTS-577
□ 95Sel-143
□ 95SelArtP-143
□ 95Top-241
□ 95WicWraTI-34
□ 96OmaRoyB-12
□ 97CalCanB-13
□ 97Fle-625
□ 97FleTif-625
□ 97PacPriGotD-GD47
□ 97PirPos-14
□ 98OklRedM-21

Granger, Lee
□ 82MiaMarT-19
□ 83SanJosBC-4
□ 84RocRedWT-7
□ 85ChaO'sT-2
□ 86ChaOriW-12

Granger, Wayne
□ 69Top-551
□ 70DayDaiNM-42
□ 70MLBOffS-27
□ 70OPC-73
□ 70Top-73
□ 71MLBOffS-59
□ 71OPC-379
□ 71Top-379
□ 72Top-545
□ 72TwiPos-6
□ 73OPC-523
□ 73Top-523
□ 74OPC-644
□ 74Top-644
□ 75AstPos-11
□ 76ExpRed-13
□ 76MonExpP-13
□ 76OPC-516
□ 76Top-516
□ 76VenLeaS-148
□ 89PacSenL-202
□ 92YanWIZ7-58

Grant, Bob
□ 77LynMetT-15
□ 77WauMetT-8

Grant, Brian
□ 93MedHatBJF-3730
□ 93MedHatBJSP-5
□ 94St.CatBJC-10
□ 94St.CatBJF-3636

Grant, Charles
□ 52Par-10

Grant, Charlie
□ 74LauOldTBS-23
□ 86NegLeaF-70

Grant, Ed
□ 08RosComP-141
□ 09AmeCarE90-1-45
□ 09ColChiE-118A
□ 09ColChiE-118B
□ 10DomDisP-49
□ 10LuxCigPP-10
□ 10NadE1-19
□ 10SweCapPP-100
□ 11E94-15
□ 11HelSta-115
□ 11MecDFT-33
□ 11PinT-5-404
□ 11S74Sil-75
□ 11SpoLifCW-145
□ 11SpoLifM-230
□ 11T205-67
□ 12ColRedB-118A
□ 12ColRedB-118B
□ 12ColTinT-118A
□ 12ColTinT-118B
□ 12HasTriFT-40
□ 14B18B-68
□ 72ClaCar-26
□ 95ConTSN-1323

Grant, Frank
□ 74LauOldTBS-17

Grant, George
□ 93ConTSN-957

Grant, Ken
□ 86QuaCitAP-12
□ 87PalSprP-7
□ 88QuaCitAGS-21
□ 88VisOakCLC-152
□ 88VisOakP-86

Grant, Larry
□ 90ElmPioP-6
□ 91WinHavRSC-19
□ 91WinHavRSP-498

Grant, Mark
□ 82CliGiaF-23
□ 84PhoGiaC-3
□ 85DomLeaS-89
□ 85Don-601
□ 85PhoGiaC-199
□ 86PhoFirP-8
□ 86StaoftFT-40
□ 87Don-644
□ 87GiaMot-26
□ 87SpoTeaP-10
□ 88Don-511
□ 88DonBasB-133
□ 88Fle-584
□ 88FleGlo-584
□ 88PadCok-55
□ 88PadSmo-9
□ 88StaLinPa-4
□ 88Top-752
□ 88TopClo-40
□ 88TopTif-752
□ 89Fle-304
□ 89FleGlo-304
□ 89PadCok-5
□ 89PadPos-11
□ 89Sco-349
□ 89ScoYouSI-12
□ 89Top-178
□ 89TopBig-154
□ 89TopTif-178
□ 89UppDec-622
□ 90BraDubS-10
□ 90Don-441
□ 90Fle-156
□ 90FleCan-156
□ 90OPC-537
□ 90PadCok-5
□ 90PadMag-20
□ 90PubIntS-49
□ 90Sco-466
□ 90Top-537
□ 90TopTif-537
□ 90UppDec-412
□ 91BraDubP-12
□ 91BraSubS-16
□ 91Don-361
□ 91Fle-690
□ 91OPC-287
□ 91Sco-824
□ 91Top-287
□ 91TopDesS-287
□ 91TopMic-287
□ 91TopTif-287
□ 91UppDec-301
□ 92CalCanF-3727
□ 92OPC-392
□ 93AstMot-26
□ 93Fle-675
□ 95IowCubTI-14

Grant, Mudcat (Jim)
□ 58IndTeal-9
□ 58Top-394
□ 59Ind-5
□ 59Kah-11
□ 59Top-186
□ 59TopVen-186
□ 60IndJayP-2
□ 60Kah-10
□ 60Lea-25A
□ 60Lea-25B
□ 60Top-14
□ 60TopVen-14
□ 61Kah-15
□ 61Pos-60A
□ 61Pos-60B
□ 61Top-18
□ 61TopStal-135
□ 62IndJayP-4
□ 62Kah-14
□ 62SalPlaC-26
□ 62ShiPlaC-26
□ 62Top-307
□ 63IndJayP-7
□ 63Top-227
□ 64IndJayP-6
□ 64Kah-10
□ 64Top-133
□ 64TopCoi-99
□ 64TopSta-37
□ 64TopVen-133
□ 64TwiJayP-3
□ 64WheSta-19
□ 65Top-432
□ 66Baz-37
□ 66OPC-40
□ 66Top-40
□ 66Top-224
□ 66TopRubl-36
□ 66TopVen-40
□ 66TopVen-224
□ 66TwiFaiG-4
□ 67CokCapTw-15
□ 67DexPre-81
□ 67Top-545
□ 67TopVen-251
□ 68Top-398
□ 69ExpFudP-4
□ 69MLBOffS-158
□ 69Top-306
□ 69TopSta-55
□ 69TopTeaP-10
□ 71MLBOffS-201
□ 71OPC-509
□ 71PirActP-6
□ 71Top-509
□ 72MilBra-120
□ 72OPC-111
□ 72Top-111
□ 78TCM60I-200
□ 78TwiFri-5
□ 85DurBulT-15
□ 89PacLegI-186
□ 89SweBasG-84
□ 90DodTar-293
□ 91SweBasG-34
□ 92UppDecS-29
□ 93MCIAmb-3
□ 93TedWil-34
□ 94UppDecAH-31
□ 94UppDecAH1-31

Grant, Sam
□ 95AusFut-63

Grant, Tom
□ 82IowCubT-3
□ 83IowCubT-22
□ 84IowCubT-30
□ 85IowCubT-9

Grantham, George
□ 25Exh-52
□ 26Exh-52
□ 28W513-76
□ 29PorandAR-31
□ 31Exh-14
□ 33CraJacP-10
□ 33ExhFou-4
□ 33Gou-66
□ 33GouCanV-66
□ 33WorCig-43
□ 85BigLeaC3-18
□ 91ConTSN-292

Granzow, Judd
□ 95YakBeaTI-11

Grapenthien, Dan
□ 92StaCluD-65
□ 93AshTouF-2283
□ 93AubAstC-11
□ 93AubAstF-3453

Grapenthin, Dick
□ 83WicAerDS-10
□ 84IndIndTI-16
□ 84IndIndTI-21
□ 86LasVegSP-5
□ 87LouRedTI-14
□ 88LouRedBC-2
□ 88LouRedBP-426
□ 88LouRedBTI-20
□ 88TriAAAP-24
□ 89ColCliC-23
□ 89ColCliP-5
□ 89ColCliP-747

Graser, Rick
□ 80SanJosMJitB-9
□ 80WauTimT-18

Grass, Darren
□ 93BazTeaU-13
□ 93TopTra-101T
□ 94SpoIndC-10
□ 94SpoIndF-3325
□ 95RanCucQT-35

Grasser, Craig
□ 93GleFalRC-14
□ 93GleFalRF-3997
□ 94SavCarC-13
□ 94SavCarF-502
□ 94SouAtlLAF-SAL49
□ 95Exc-266

Grasso, Mickey (Newton M.)
□ 49BowPCL-6
□ 51Bow-205
□ 52Bow-174
□ 52Top-90
□ 53BowC-77
□ 53Bri-6
□ 53Top-148
□ 54Bow-184
□ 75TCM195Cl-11
□ 83TopRep5-90
□ 91TopArc1-148

Grate, Don
□ 88ChaLooLTI-13

Grater, Mark
□ 87SavCarP-11
□ 88SprCarB-2
□ 89St.PetCS-14
□ 90ArkTraGS-15
□ 90CMC-121
□ 90LouRedBC-21
□ 90LouRedBP-397
□ 90ProAAAF-511
□ 91LinDriAAA-236
□ 91LouRedLD-236
□ 91LouRedP-2909
□ 91LouRedTI-7
□ 92LouRedF-1882
□ 92LouRedS-263
□ 92TopDeb91-66
□ 93TolMudHF-1648
□ 98PriWilCQ-29

Graterol, Beiker
□ 96StCatSB-10
□ 98KnoSG-6

Graterol, Jose
□ 94VenLinU-256
□ 95LinVen-201

Graupmann, Tim
□ 83WisRapTF-9
□ 84VisOakT-16

Graus, Mike
□ 96MacBraB-29
□ 97MacBra-27
□ 98MacBraM-29

Graven, Tim
□ 79SavBraT-7

Graves, Bryan
□ 95BoiHawTI-18
□ 96CedRapKTI-9
□ 97CedRapK-9
□ 98MidAngO-15

Graves, Chris
□ 87QuaCitAP-22
□ 88QuaCitAGS-27
□ 89PalSprACLC-40
□ 89PalSprAP-483

Graves, Danny
□ 93BazTeaU-9
□ 93TopTra-97T
□ 95KinIndTI-11
□ 96Bow-153
□ 96BowBes-120
□ 96BowBesAR-120
□ 96BowBesR-120
□ 96BowFoi-153
□ 96BufBisB-9
□ 97BufBis-17
□ 97Cir-238
□ 97CirRav-238
□ 97Don-164
□ 97DonGolPP-164
□ 97DonSilPP-164
□ 97IndSco-14
□ 97IndScoPl-14
□ 97IndScoPr-14
□ 97Pac-70
□ 97PacLigB-70
□ 97PacSil-70
□ 97Sco-255
□ 97ScoArtPWB-255
□ 97ScoPreS-255
□ 97ScoShoS-255
□ 97ScoShoSAP-255
□ 97StaClu-275
□ 97StaCluMOP-275
□ 97Top-286
□ 97UppDec-276
□ 98IndIndQ-8
□ 99Fle-317
□ 99FleSta9-317
□ 99FleWarT-317

Graves, Frank M.
□ 87OldJudN-209

Graves, Joe
□ 83LynMetT-20
□ 84JacMetT-8
□ 86JacExpT-11

Graves, John
□ 89ButCopKSP-21
□ 90GasRanB-23
□ 90GasRanP-2517
□ 90GasRanS-10
□ 90ProAaA-82
□ 90SouAtlLAS-9
□ 92YakBeaC-2
□ 92YakBeaF-3441

Graves, Kenley
□ 85BenPhiC-7

Graves, Kenny
□ 90St.LucMS-8
□ 90TopTVM-44

Graves, Pamela
□ 96BelSnaTI-15

Graves, R. J.
□ 33Zee-119

Graves, Randy
□ 90KisDodD-13
□ 91GreFalDSP-16

Gray, Dan
□ 90GreFalDSP-2
□ 91YakBeaC-10
□ 91YakBeaP-4250
□ 92VerBeaDC-20
□ 92YakBeaC-4
□ 92YakBeaF-3453

Gray, Dave
□ 64Top-572

Gray, David
□ 88LynRedSS-7
□ 89LynRedSS-9

Gray, Dennis
□ 89AlaGol-16
□ 91St.CatBJC-16
□ 91St.CatBJP-3388
□ 92MyrBeaHC-7
□ 92MyrBeaHF-2190
□ 92StaCluD-66
□ 93DunBluJC-7
□ 93DunBluJF-1788
□ 93DunBluJFFN-7
□ 94KnoSmoF-1298
□ 96HarSenB-13
□ 98IowCubQ-11

Gray, Dick
□ 58Top-146
□ 60Top-24
□ 60TopVen-24
□ 90DodTar-294

Gray, Dolly (William)
□ 09AmeCarE90-1-46
□ 09SenBarP-4
□ 09T206-146
□ 10SweCapPP-58
□ 11HelSta-68
□ 11PinT-5-562
□ 11T205-68
□ 12HasTriFT-44
□ 12Zee-145
□ 13Zee-33

Gray, Elliott
□ 89MarPhiS-13
□ 90BatCliP-3057
□ 91Cla/Bes-141
□ 91ClePhiC-1
□ 91ClePhiP-1616
□ 92ClePhiC-12
□ 92ClePhiF-2053
□ 92ProFS7-301

Gray, Gary
□ 75AndRanT-15
□ 76SanAntBTI-11
□ 77TucTorC-19
□ 78TucTorC-27
□ 79TucTorT-1
□ 80TacTigT-17
□ 81Fle-402
□ 81MarPos-18
□ 81TopTra-767
□ 82Fle-511
□ 82MarPos-18
□ 82OPC-78
□ 82SalLakCGT-9
□ 82Top-523
□ 82TopSti-233
□ 83Don-637
□ 83Fle-480
□ 83Top-313
□ 93RanKee-163

Gray, Jason
□ 97BriWhiSB-3

Gray, Jeff
□ 86VerRedP-8
□ 87NasSouTI-8
□ 88BlaYNPRWLU-25
□ 88NasSouC-5
□ 88NasSouP-478
□ 88NasSouTI-10
□ 89BlaYNPRWL-91
□ 89NasSouC-3
□ 89NasSouP-1288
□ 89NasSouTI-5
□ 90CMC-276
□ 90PawRedSC-25
□ 90PawRedSDD-8
□ 90PawRedSP-456
□ 90ProAAAF-428
□ 91Don-721
□ 91Fle-95
□ 91Lea-356
□ 91OPC-731
□ 91RedSoxP-7
□ 91RedSoxP-12
□ 91Sco-586
□ 91StaClu-271
□ 91Top-731
□ 91TopDesS-731
□ 91TopMic-731
□ 91TopTif-731
□ 91UppDec-685
□ 92Don-122
□ 92Sco-187
□ 92StaClu-222
□ 96SarRedSB-2
□ 97SarRedS-28

Gray, John L.
□ 54A'STEAI-10
□ 55A'sRodM-17
□ 55Top-101
□ 55TopDouH-47
□ 58MonRoyF-10
□ 59O'KAleMR-9

Gray, Lorenzo
□ 77AppFoxT-6
□ 78AppFoxT-10
□ 79AppFoxT-9
□ 80GleFalWSBT-22
□ 80GleFalWSCT-26
□ 82EdmTraT-10
□ 84MaiGuiT-12
□ 84Nes792-163
□ 84Top-163
□ 84TopTif-163
□ 86SanJosBP-9

Gray, Mike
□ 98DanBraQ-25
□ 98EriSeaWM-12

Gray, Pete
□ 77FriOneYW-6
□ 77GalGloG-229
□ 87SpoRea-6

Gray, Samuel
□ 25Exh-107
□ 28StaPlaCE-29
□ 28W56PlaC-H10
□ 29ExhFou-29
□ 31Exh-30
□ 33ExhFou-15
□ 91ConTSN-75

Gray, Scott
□ 86AubAstP-10

Gray, Stanley
□ 43CenFlo-10

❑ 44CenFlo-9
Gray, Steve
❑ 89CliGiaP-899
❑ 89SalSpuP-1802
Gray, Ted
❑ 49Bow-10
❑ 50Bow-210
❑ 51Bow-178
❑ 52Bow-199
❑ 52Top-86
❑ 53BowC-72
❑ 53TigGle-11
❑ 53Top-52
❑ 54Bow-71
❑ 55Bow-86
❑ 59Top-244
❑ 81TigDetN-131
❑ 83TopRep5-86
❑ 91OriCro-162
❑ 91TopArc1-52
❑ 97BalOriP-20
Gray, Terry
❑ 77St.PetCT-10
Graybill, Dave
❑ 87JacExpP-443
❑ 89PalSprACLC-59
Grayner, Paul
❑ 82NasSouTI-13
❑ 83NasSouTI-7
Grays, Homestead
❑ 88NegLeaD-2
❑ 91PomBlaBPB-10
❑ 92NegLeaRLI-68
❑ 92NegLeaRLI-74
❑ 92NegLeaRLI-82
❑ 92NegLeaRLI-83
❑ 93NegLeaRL2-44
❑ 93NegLeaRL2-64
❑ 93NegLeaRL2-65
❑ 93NegLeaRL2-66
❑ 93NegLeaRL2-67
❑ 93NegLeaRL2-68
❑ 93TedWilPC-16
Grayson, Mike
❑ 89BelBrelS-7
Grayston, Joe
❑ 85BurRanT-1
Grayum, Richie
❑ 88MisStaB-7
❑ 89GenCubP-1871
❑ 89MisStaB-15
❑ 90ChaKniTI-23
❑ 91WinSpiC-24
❑ 91WinSpiP-2841
❑ 92ChaKniF-2783
❑ 92ChaKniS-157
❑ 93OrlCubF-2797
❑ 94OrlCubF-1397
Graziano, Andy
❑ 92GasRanC-27
❑ 93ChaRaiC-30
Grba, Eli
❑ 60Top-183
❑ 60TopVen-183
❑ 61Top-121
❑ 62AngJayP-4
❑ 62Top-96
❑ 62TopVen-96
❑ 63Top-231
❑ 82VanCanT-23
❑ 88VanCanP-769
❑ 89RenSilSCLC-265
❑ 90PriPatD-28
❑ 91MarPhiP-3471
❑ 92YanWIZ6-49
Greason, Bill
❑ 93NegLeaRL2-11
Grebe, Brett
❑ 90PulBraB-5
❑ 90PulBraP-3103
Grebeck, Brian
❑ 90BoiHawP-3321
❑ 90SanDieSA3-5
❑ 91QuaCitAC-17
❑ 91QuaCitAP-2636
❑ 92PalSprAC-11
❑ 92PalSprAF-847
❑ 93Bow-33
❑ 93ExcFS7-143
❑ 93MidAngF-329
❑ 94MidAngF-2444
❑ 94MidAngOHP-6
❑ 96VanCanB-14
❑ 97MidAngOHP-14
Grebeck, Craig
❑ 87PenWhiSP-10
❑ 88BirBarB-24
❑ 89BirBarADB-15
❑ 89BirBarB-17
❑ 89BirBarP-111
❑ 90BirBarADB-15
❑ 90Bow-318
❑ 90BowTif-318
❑ 90DonRoo-9
❑ 90FleUpd-85
❑ 90ScoRoo-105T
❑ 90UppDec-721
❑ 90WhiSoxC-6
❑ 90WhiSoxC-28
❑ 91Don-378
❑ 91Fle-120
❑ 91OPC-446
❑ 91Sco-69
❑ 91Sco100RS-35
❑ 91StaClu-559
❑ 91Top-446
❑ 91TopDeb90-59
❑ 91TopDesS-446
❑ 91TopMic-446
❑ 91TopTif-446
❑ 91UltUpd-15
❑ 91WhiSoxK-14
❑ 92Don-546
❑ 92Fle-81
❑ 92Lea-344
❑ 92LeaBlaG-344
❑ 92OPC-273
❑ 92Pin-334
❑ 92Sco-561
❑ 92StaClu-145
❑ 92Top-273
❑ 92TopGol-273
❑ 92TopGolW-273
❑ 92TopMic-273
❑ 92Ult-34
❑ 92UppDec-603
❑ 92WhiSoxK-14
❑ 93Don-199
❑ 93Fle-202
❑ 93PacSpa-71
❑ 93Pin-362
❑ 93Sco-126
❑ 93Sel-389
❑ 93StaClu-136
❑ 93StaCluFDI-136
❑ 93StaCluMOP-136
❑ 93Top-259
❑ 93TopGol-259
❑ 93TopInaM-259
❑ 93TopInaR-259
❑ 93TopMic-259
❑ 93Ult-531
❑ 93UppDec-738
❑ 93UppDecGold-738
❑ 93WhiSoxK-9
❑ 93WhiSoxSC-14
❑ 94Fle-81
❑ 94Pac-126
❑ 94StaClu-225
❑ 94StaCluFDI-225
❑ 94StaCluGR-225
❑ 94StaCluMOP-225
❑ 94StaCluT-133
❑ 94StaCluTFDI-133
❑ 94Top-176
❑ 94TopGol-176
❑ 94TopSpa-176
❑ 94Ult-336
❑ 94WhiSoxK-9
❑ 95Don-535
❑ 95DonPreP-535
❑ 95Fle-117
❑ 95Sco-136
❑ 95ScoGolR-136
❑ 95ScoPlaTS-136
❑ 95Top-343
❑ 95WhiSoxK-11
❑ 96LeaSigEA-62
❑ 97AngMot-16
❑ 97PacPriGotD-GD141
❑ 97Ult-468
❑ 97UltGolME-468
❑ 97UltPlaME-468
❑ 98PacOnl-764
❑ 98PacOnlR-764
❑ 98PacOnlWC-764
❑ 99Fle-431
❑ 99FleSta9-431
❑ 99FleWarT-431
Greco, George
❑ 80ElmPioRST-7
Greeley, Jerry
❑ 98BluOriQ-4
Greely, Jim
❑ 93LSUTigM-3
❑ 94BoiHawC-11
❑ 94BoiHawF-3367
❑ 94LSUTigMP-6
Green, Bert
❑ 94JohCitCC-11
❑ 94JohCitCF-3708
Green, Bob
❑ 86Ft.LauYP-9
❑ 87Ft.LauYP-6
❑ 88AlbYanP-1331
❑ 89AlbYanB-10
❑ 89ColCliC-20
❑ 89ColCliP-21
❑ 89ColCliP-734
Green, Chad
❑ 96BesAutS1RP-FR1
❑ 97Bes-73
❑ 97BesLimA-13
❑ 97BesWhe-4
❑ 97Bow-80
❑ 97BowChr-107
❑ 97BowChrI-107
❑ 97BowChrIR-107
❑ 97BowChrR-107
❑ 97BowInt-80
❑ 97CalLeaATI-8
❑ 97CalLeaTP-26
❑ 97StoPor-1
❑ 98BesAutPOY-4
❑ 98BesFulCA-4
❑ 98BesPreA-13
❑ 98Bow-113
❑ 98BowCerBlueAU-23
❑ 98BowCerGA-23
❑ 98BowCerSA-23
❑ 98BowChr-113
❑ 98BowChrGA-113
❑ 98BowChrGAR-113
❑ 98BowChrI-113
❑ 98BowChrIR-113
❑ 98BowChrR-113
❑ 98BowGolA-113
❑ 98BowInt-113
❑ 98SP MinPE-73
❑ 98SPMin-73
❑ 99Bow-297
❑ 99BowGol-297
❑ 99BowInt-297
❑ 99SP TopP-53
❑ 99SP TopPPE-53
Green, Charlie
❑ 87WatPirP-29
Green, Chris
❑ 94BelMarC-14
❑ 94BelMarF-3228
Green, Christopher
❑ 82AleDukT-6
❑ 85HawIslC-240
❑ 86EdmTraP-14
❑ 87RocRedWT-22
Green, Danny (Edward)
❑ 03BreE10-61
❑ 11SpoLifCW-146
Green, Daryl
❑ 86SalAngC-88
❑ 87QuaCitAP-10
❑ 88QuaCitAGS-13
❑ 89ModA'sC-11
❑ 89ModA'sCLC-271
❑ 90HunStaB-6
❑ 91St.PetCC-8
❑ 91St.PetCP-2271
Green, David A.
❑ 80HolMilT-14
❑ 82LouRedE-10
❑ 83Car-6
❑ 83Don-166
❑ 83Fle-6
❑ 83Top-578
❑ 83TopSti-323
❑ 84AllGamPI-5
❑ 84Car-8
❑ 84Car5x7-8
❑ 84Don-425
❑ 84Don-625
❑ 84Fle-323
❑ 84Nes792-362
❑ 84OPC-362
❑ 84Top-362
❑ 84TopSti-149
❑ 84TopTif-362
❑ 85AllGamPI-96
❑ 85Don-303
❑ 85Fle-224
❑ 85FleUpd-46
❑ 85GiaMot-17
❑ 85GiaPos-12
❑ 85Lea-191
❑ 85OPC-87
❑ 85Top-87
❑ 85TopSti-145
❑ 85TopTif-87
❑ 85TopTifT-41T
❑ 85TopTra-41T
❑ 86Don-114
❑ 86Fle-543
❑ 86OPC-122
❑ 86Top-727
❑ 86TopTif-727
❑ 87LouRedTI-15
❑ 88Fle-34
❑ 88FleGlo-34
❑ 88LouRedBC-14
❑ 88LouRedBP-421
❑ 88LouRedBTI-21
❑ 91LinDriAA-582
❑ 91TulDriLD-582
❑ 91TulDriP-2784
❑ 91TulDriTI-9
Green, Dick (Richard)
❑ 64A's-7
❑ 64Top-466
❑ 65AthJayP-6
❑ 65OPC-168
❑ 65Top-168
❑ 66Top-545
❑ 67CokCapAt-8
❑ 67DexPre-82
❑ 67OPC-54
❑ 67Top-54
❑ 67TopVen-215
❑ 68Top-303
❑ 68TopVen-303
❑ 69A'sJacitB-7
❑ 69MilBra-97
❑ 69Top-515
❑ 69TopSta-215
❑ 69TopTeaP-21
❑ 70MLBOffS-258
❑ 70OPC-311
❑ 70Top-311
❑ 71MLBOffS-514
❑ 71OPC-258
❑ 71Top-258
❑ 72MilBra-121
❑ 72Top-780
❑ 73OPC-456
❑ 73Top-456
❑ 74OPC-392
❑ 74Top-392
❑ 75OPC-91
❑ 75Top-91
❑ 75TopMin-91
❑ 86A'sGreT-2
Green, Don (Donald)
❑ 89HamRedS-18
❑ 90SavCarP-2066
Green, Fred
❑ 60KeyChal-21
❑ 60Top-272
❑ 61Top-181
❑ 77PirTCM1WC-22
Green, G. Dallas
❑ 60Lea-52
❑ 60Top-366
❑ 61Top-359
❑ 62SalPlaC-219
❑ 62ShiPlaC-219
❑ 62Top-111
❑ 62TopVen-111
❑ 63Top-91
❑ 64PhiJayP-6
❑ 64Top-464
❑ 65OPC-203
❑ 65PhiJayP-6
❑ 65Top-203
❑ 78TCM60I-187
❑ 80PhiBul-39
❑ 80PhiBurK-1
❑ 80Top-526
❑ 81Don-415
❑ 81Top-682
❑ 83PhiPosGPaM-11
❑ 84CubBriPC-10S
❑ 84CubUno-12
❑ 87CubCan-12
❑ 89Top-104
❑ 89TopTif-104
❑ 89YanScoNW-31
❑ 91MetWIZ-150
❑ 93MetColP-110
❑ 93TopTra-36T
❑ 94MetColP-3
❑ 94MetShuST-5
❑ 95MetColP-32
❑ 96MetKah-10
❑ 96MetKah-11
Green, Gary
❑ 85BeaGolGT-18
❑ 85Top-396
❑ 85TopTif-396
❑ 86LasVegSP-6
❑ 87LasVegSP-22
❑ 88LasVegSC-17
❑ 88LasVegSP-232
❑ 89PadPos-12
❑ 89UppDec-722
❑ 90CMC-163
❑ 90OklCit8C-13
❑ 90OklCit8P-439
❑ 90ProAAAF-685
❑ 91OPC-184
❑ 91StaClu-323
❑ 91Top-184
❑ 91TopDesS-184
❑ 91TopMic-184
❑ 91TopTif-184
❑ 92NasSouF-1837
❑ 93IndIndF-1494
❑ 93RanKee-164
❑ 95OmaRoyTI-11
❑ 98LakTigM-29
Green, Gene
❑ 55DonWin-21
❑ 58Top-366
❑ 59Top-37
❑ 59TopVen-37
❑ 60Lea-82
❑ 60Top-269
❑ 61Top-206
❑ 62Jel-72
❑ 62Pos-72
❑ 62PosCan-72
❑ 62SalPlaC-70
❑ 62ShiPlaC-70
❑ 62Top-78
❑ 62TopVen-78
❑ 63Top-506
❑ 91OriCro-163
Green, Harvey
❑ 90DodTar-962
Green, Jason
❑ 94Bow-545
❑ 94DanBraC-15
❑ 94DanBraF-3527
❑ 95AubAstTI-20
❑ 95DurBulTI-10
❑ 96AubDouB-2
❑ 97KisCob-11
❑ 97QuaCitRBB-11
❑ 97UCLBruTI-5
❑ 98KisCobQ-16
Green, Jeff
❑ 83BufBisT-8
Green, Joe
❑ 87NegLeaPD-8
Green, Joey
❑ 90OklSoo-5
Green, John
❑ 86GenCubP-7
❑ 86PeoChiP-9
❑ 87PeoChiP-3
❑ 87PeoChiPW-3
❑ 89Ft.LauYS-7
❑ 93HolLeg-7
Green, Larry
❑ 76DubPacT-13
Green, Lenny
❑ 56BalOriP-20
❑ 58Top-471
❑ 59Top-209
❑ 60Top-99
❑ 60TopVen-99
❑ 61Top-4
❑ 61TwiCloD-8
❑ 61TwiJayP-3
❑ 61TwiPetM-15
❑ 61TwiUniMC-5
❑ 62Jel-87
❑ 62Pos-87
❑ 62PosCan-87
❑ 62SalPlaC-69A
❑ 62SalPlaC-69B
❑ 62ShiPlaC-69
❑ 62Top-84
❑ 62TopBuc-32
❑ 62TopStal-75
❑ 62TopVen-84
❑ 63Jel-6
❑ 63Pos-6
❑ 63Top-198
❑ 63TwiVol-7
❑ 64Top-386
❑ 65Top-588
❑ 66Top-502
❑ 81RedSoxBG2S-83
❑ 91OriCro-164
Green, Marcie
❑ 91FreStaLBS-3
Green, Nat
❑ 85BenPhiC-8
Green, Otis
❑ 86SyrChiP-11
❑ 87SyrChiP-1942
❑ 87SyrChiT-14
❑ 88SyrChiC-19
❑ 88SyrChiP-831
❑ 89SyrChiC-12
❑ 89SyrChiMB-11
❑ 89SyrChiP-793
❑ 90CMC-68
❑ 90IndIndC-18
❑ 90IndIndP-293
❑ 90ProAAAF-576
❑ 91StoPorC-2
❑ 91StoPorP-3028
❑ 92DenZepF-2633
❑ 92DenZepS-129
❑ 92ProFS7-88
❑ 92SkyAAAF-63
❑ 93VanCanF-2589
Green, Pumpsie (Elijah)
❑ 60KeyChal-22
❑ 60RedSoxJP-5
❑ 60Top-317
❑ 61Top-454
❑ 62SalPlaC-187
❑ 62ShiPlaC-187
❑ 62Top-153
❑ 62TopVen-153
❑ 63Top-292
❑ 64Top-442
❑ 64TopRooAB-8
❑ 75OakOak2A-16
❑ 76Met63 S-7
❑ 81RedSoxBG2S-25
❑ 81TCM60I-297
❑ 91MetWIZ-151
Green, Randy
❑ 77ModA'sC-10
❑ 79WatA'sT-12
❑ 80OgdA'sT-5
Green, Rick
❑ 77VisOakT-6
❑ 92SalSpuF-3749
Green, Scarborough
❑ 96StPetCB-10
❑ 97ArkTraB-21
Green, Shawn
❑ 92ClaFS7-348
❑ 92DunBluJC-8
❑ 92DunBluJF-2011
❑ 92OPC-276
❑ 92StaCluD-67
❑ 92Top-276
❑ 92TopGol-276
❑ 92TopGolW-276
❑ 92TopMic-276
❑ 92UppDec-55
❑ 92UppDecML-225
❑ 93Bow-27
❑ 93ClaFS7-72
❑ 93KnoSmoF-1262
❑ 94Bow-253
❑ 94BowBes-B46
❑ 94BowBes-X110
❑ 94BowBesR-B46
❑ 94BowBesR-X110
❑ 94Cla-190
❑ 94ClaCreotC-C25
❑ 94ColC-9
❑ 94ColChoGS-9
❑ 94ColChoSS-9
❑ 94Don-607
❑ 94FleUpd-98
❑ 94LeaLimR-52
❑ 94ScoRoo-RT91
❑ 94ScoRooGR-RT91
❑ 94SpoRoo-48

❑ 94SpoRooAP-48
❑ 94SpoRooRS-TR16
❑ 94StaClu-66
❑ 94StaCluFDI-66
❑ 94StaCluGR-66
❑ 94StaCluMOP-66
❑ 94StaCluT-159
❑ 94StaCluTFDI-159
❑ 94SyrChiF-984
❑ 94SyrChiTI-15
❑ 94Top-237
❑ 94TopGol-237
❑ 94TopSpa-237
❑ 94UppDec-15
❑ 94UppDec-297
❑ 94UppDec-493
❑ 94UppDecED-15
❑ 94UppDecED-297
❑ 94UppDecED-493
❑ 95BluJayOH-15
❑ 95Bow-261
❑ 95BowBes-R75
❑ 95BowBes-X4
❑ 95BowBesR-R75
❑ 95BowBesR-X4
❑ 95BowGolF-261
❑ 95ColCho-144
❑ 95ColChoGS-144
❑ 95ColChoSE-58
❑ 95ColChoSEGS-58
❑ 95ColChoSESS-58
❑ 95ColChoSS-144
❑ 95Don-464
❑ 95DonPreP-464
❑ 95Emo-94
❑ 95EmoRoo-6
❑ 95Fin-327
❑ 95FinRef-327
❑ 95Fla-316
❑ 95FlaWavotF-7
❑ 95Fle-94
❑ 95FleUpdRU-3
❑ 95Lea-285
❑ 95LeaGolR-3
❑ 95LeaLim-82
❑ 95LinVen-167
❑ 95Pin-135
❑ 95Pin-279
❑ 95PinArtP-135
❑ 95PinArtP-279
❑ 95PinMusC-135
❑ 95PinMusC-279
❑ 95PinNewB-NB2
❑ 95PinPer-PP15
❑ 95PinUps-US16
❑ 95Sco-304
❑ 95ScoGolR-304
❑ 95ScoPlaTS-304
❑ 95ScoRooDT-RDT6
❑ 95Sel-202
❑ 95Sel-240
❑ 95SelArtP-202
❑ 95SelArtP-240
❑ 95SelCanM-CM12
❑ 95SelCer-105
❑ 95SelCerF-4
❑ 95SelCerMG-105
❑ 95SelCerPU-14
❑ 95SelCerPU9-14
❑ 95SP-204
❑ 95SPCha-199
❑ 95SPChaDC-199
❑ 95Spo-143
❑ 95SpoArtP-143
❑ 95SPSil-204
❑ 95StaClu-233
❑ 95StaCluCB-CB6
❑ 95StaCluFDI-233
❑ 95StaCluMOP-233
❑ 95StaCluMOP-CB6
❑ 95StaCluSTWS-233
❑ 95StaCluVR-118
❑ 95StaCluVRMO-118
❑ 95Stu-28
❑ 95StuGolS-28
❑ 95SumNewA-NA14
❑ 95Top-514
❑ 95TopCyb-302
❑ 95TopTra-13T
❑ 95UC3-106
❑ 95UC3ArtP-106
❑ 95UC3CleS-CS2
❑ 95Ult-338
❑ 95UltGolM-338
❑ 95UppDec-289
❑ 95UppDecED-289
❑ 95UppDecEDG-289
❑ 95UppDecPAW-H13
❑ 95UppDecPAWE-H13
❑ 95UppDecSE-68
❑ 95UppDecSEG-68
❑ 95Zen-150
❑ 95ZenRooRC-4
❑ 96Baz-105
❑ 96BluJayOH-11
❑ 96Bow-10
❑ 96BowFoi-10
❑ 96ColCho-751
❑ 96ColChoGS-751
❑ 96ColChoSS-751
❑ 96Don-229
❑ 96DonPreP-229
❑ 96EmoXL-132
❑ 96Fin-S41
❑ 96FinRef-S41
❑ 96Fla-184
❑ 96Fle-274
❑ 96FleRooS-6
❑ 96FleTif-274
❑ 96Lea-66
❑ 96LeaPre-6
❑ 96LeaPreP-6
❑ 96LeaPrePB-66
❑ 96LeaPrePG-66
❑ 96LeaPrePS-66
❑ 96LeaPreSG-62
❑ 96LeaPreSte-62
❑ 96MetUni-120
❑ 96MetUniMFG-3
❑ 96MetUniP-120
❑ 96Pac-443
❑ 96PanSti-161
❑ 96Pin-125
❑ 96PinAfi-104
❑ 96PinAfiAP-104
❑ 96PinArtP-33
❑ 96PinFirR-16
❑ 96PinSta-33
❑ 96Sco-24
❑ 96ScoDugC-A23
❑ 96ScoDugCAP-A23
❑ 96Sel-2
❑ 96SelArtP-2
❑ 96SelCer-44
❑ 96SelCerAP-44
❑ 96SelCerCB-44
❑ 96SelCerCR-44
❑ 96SelCerMB-44
❑ 96SelCerMG-44
❑ 96SelCerMR-44
❑ 96SelTeaN-7
❑ 96SP-183
❑ 96StaClu-34
❑ 96StaClu-231
❑ 96StaCluEPB-34
❑ 96StaCluEPG-34
❑ 96StaCluEPS-34
❑ 96StaCluMOP-34
❑ 96StaCluMOP-231
❑ 96Stu-108
❑ 96StuPrePB-108
❑ 96StuPrePG-108
❑ 96StuPrePS-108
❑ 96Sum-16
❑ 96SumAbo&B-16
❑ 96SumArtP-16
❑ 96SumFoi-16
❑ 96Top-417
❑ 96TopChr-163
❑ 96TopChrR-163
❑ 96TopGal-120
❑ 96TopGalPPI-120
❑ 96TopLas-65
❑ 96Ult-146
❑ 96UltGolM-146
❑ 96UppDec-216
❑ 96Zen-11
❑ 96ZenArtP-11
❑ 97BluJayB-6
❑ 97BluJayOH-12
❑ 97BluJayS-13
❑ 97Cir-301
❑ 97CirRav-301
❑ 97ColCho-503
❑ 97Don-315
❑ 97DonEli-75
❑ 97DonEliGS-75
❑ 97DonGolPP-315
❑ 97DonLim-51
❑ 97DonLimE-51
❑ 97DonLimENG-51
❑ 97DonPre-90
❑ 97DonPreCttC-90
❑ 97DonSigA-41
❑ 97DonSigAC-50
❑ 97DonSigAM-50
❑ 97DonSilPP-315
❑ 97FlaShoLC-131
❑ 97FlaShoLeg0-131
❑ 97FlaShoLeg1-131
❑ 97FlaShoM-A131
❑ 97FlaShoM-B131
❑ 97FlaShoM-C131
❑ 97FlaShoR0-131
❑ 97FlaShoR1-131
❑ 97FlaShoR2-131
❑ 97Fle-240
❑ 97FleTif-240
❑ 97Lea-140
❑ 97LeaFraM-140
❑ 97LeaFraMDC-140
❑ 97MetUni-184
❑ 97NewPin-135
❑ 97NewPinAP-135
❑ 97NewPinMC-135
❑ 97NewPinPP-135
❑ 97Pac-220
❑ 97PacLigB-220
❑ 97PacSil-220
❑ 97PinIns-54
❑ 97PinInsCE-54
❑ 97PinInsDE-54
❑ 97Sco-281
❑ 97ScoArtPWB-281
❑ 97ScoPreS-281
❑ 97ScoShoS-281
❑ 97ScoShoSAP-281
❑ 97Sel-74
❑ 97SelArtP-74
❑ 97SelCom-74
❑ 97SelRegG-74
❑ 97StaClu-147
❑ 97StaCluMOP-147
❑ 97Stu-106
❑ 97StuPrePG-106
❑ 97StuPrePS-106
❑ 97Top-214
❑ 97Ult-396
❑ 97UltGolME-396
❑ 97UltPlaME-396
❑ 97UppDec-514
❑ 98CirThu-210
❑ 98CirThuRav-210
❑ 98CirThuSupRav-210
❑ 98ColCho-526
❑ 98CroRoy-144
❑ 98Don-153
❑ 98DonCol-153
❑ 98DonColE-516
❑ 98DonColL-297
❑ 98DonColP-657
❑ 98DonColS-153
❑ 98DonCruG-50
❑ 98DonCruP-50
❑ 98DonCruR-50
❑ 98DonEli-116
❑ 98DonEliA-116
❑ 98DonEliS-116
❑ 98DonGolPP-153
❑ 98DonPre-107
❑ 98DonPreSeat-107
❑ 98DonPriCD-153
❑ 98DonPriCE-516
❑ 98DonPriCL-297
❑ 98DonPriCP-657
❑ 98DonSilPP-153
❑ 98Fin-88
❑ 98FinNo--88
❑ 98FinNo-R-88
❑ 98FinRef-88
❑ 98Fle-30
❑ 98Lea-98
❑ 98LeaFraDA-98
❑ 98LeaFraF-98
❑ 98LeaFraM-98
❑ 98LeaFraM-98
❑ 98LeaFraMDC-98
❑ 98LeaFraMDC-98
❑ 98LeaFraMS-98
❑ 98LeaFraMZ2-98
❑ 98LeaRS-100
❑ 98LeaRSLHolo-100
❑ 98LeaRSLong-100
❑ 98LeaRTrue-100
❑ 98MetUni-96
❑ 98MetUniPMG-96
❑ 98PacInvGems-112
❑ 98PacOnl-765
❑ 98PacOnlR-765
❑ 98PacOnlWC-765
❑ 98PinIns-92
❑ 98PinInsCE-92
❑ 98PinInsDE-92
❑ 98ScoRT-52
❑ 98ScoRTSS-PP52
❑ 98ScoRTSSAP-PP52
❑ 98ScoRTSSAP1-PP52
❑ 98SkyDugA-90
❑ 98SkyDugAIA-90
❑ 98StaCluFDI-234
❑ 98StaCluI-234
❑ 98StaCluOneK-234
❑ 98StaCluPP-234
❑ 98Stu-108
❑ 98StuGPP-108
❑ 98StuSPP-108
❑ 98Top-76
❑ 98TopChr-76
❑ 98TopChrR-76
❑ 98TopDevR-76
❑ 98TopDia-76
❑ 98TopMiniC-76
❑ 98Ult-101
❑ 98UltGolM-101
❑ 98UltMas-101
❑ 98UltPlaM-101
❑ 98UppDec-531
❑ 99199Fin-7
❑ 99Bow-243
❑ 99BowBes-76
❑ 99BowBesAR-76
❑ 99BowBesR-76
❑ 99BowGol-243
❑ 99BowInt-243
❑ 99CroRoyB-143
❑ 99CroRoyL-143
❑ 99CroRoyOD-143
❑ 99E-X Cen-68
❑ 99E-X CenECFut-68
❑ 99E-X CenECNow-68
❑ 99FinGolRef-7
❑ 99FinRef-7
❑ 99FlaShoLeg1-63
❑ 99FlaShoLeg2-63
❑ 99FlaShoLeg3-63
❑ 99FlaShoLegM1-63
❑ 99FlaShoLegM2-63
❑ 99FlaShoLegM3-63
❑ 99FlaShoR1-63
❑ 99FlaShoR2-63
❑ 99FlaShoR3-63
❑ 99Fle-233
❑ 99FleBri-29
❑ 99FleBri2G-29
❑ 99FleBriBlu-29
❑ 99FleBriGol-29
❑ 99FleMys-59
❑ 99FleMysFI-16
❑ 99FleMysG-59
❑ 99FleMysM-59
❑ 99FleSta9-233
❑ 99FleWarT-233
❑ 99MetUni-71
❑ 99MetUniGM-71
❑ 99MetUniPMG-71
❑ 99Pac-444
❑ 99PacInv-149
❑ 99PacInvOD-149
❑ 99PacInvPB-149
❑ 99PacOme-247
❑ 99PacOmeC-247
❑ 99PacOmeDM-36
❑ 99PacOmeG-247
❑ 99PacOmePB-247
❑ 99PacPar-247
❑ 99PacParC-247
❑ 99PacParG-247
❑ 99PacParHoloGold-247
❑ 99PacParHS-247
❑ 99PacParOD-247
❑ 99PacParPB-247
❑ 99PacParRed-247
❑ 99PacPlaB-444
❑ 99PacRed-444
❑ 99Rev-147
❑ 99RevDiaL-36
❑ 99RevPremDate-147
❑ 99RevRet-147
❑ 99RevShaSS-147
❑ 99SkyPre-3
❑ 99SkyPreA-22
❑ 99SkyPreABlue-22
❑ 99SkyPreR-3
❑ 99SkyThu-120
❑ 99SkyThuRant-120
❑ 99SkyThuRave-120
❑ 99SP Aut-88
❑ 99SpoIll-73
❑ 99StaClu-15
❑ 99StaCluFDI-15
❑ 99StaCluOoaK-15
❑ 99StaCluPP-15
❑ 99ThuSkySupR-120
❑ 99Top-109
❑ 99TopAut-A14
❑ 99TopBlaLC1-91
❑ 99TopBlaLC2-91
❑ 99TopBlaLC3-91
❑ 99TopChr-109
❑ 99TopChrR-109
❑ 99TopGal-80
❑ 99TopGalPP-80
❑ 99TopGalPPI-80
❑ 99TopGolL-91
❑ 99TopGolLC1-91
❑ 99TopGolLC2-91
❑ 99TopGolLOtO-91
❑ 99TopMVPP-109
❑ 99TopOpeD-63
❑ 99TopRedLC1-91
❑ 99TopRedLC2-91
❑ 99TopRedLC3-91
❑ 99TopSta-66
❑ 99TopSta1Foil-66
❑ 99TopStaFoil-66
❑ 99TopStaOS-66
❑ 99Ult-176
❑ 99UltGolM-176
❑ 99UltMas-176
❑ 99UltPlaM-176
❑ 99UppDec-513
❑ 99UppDecEL1-513
❑ 99UppDecEL2-513
❑ 99UppDecM-215
❑ 99UppDecMGS-215
❑ 99UppDecMHFS-215
❑ 99UppDecMSS-215
❑ 99Vic-414

Green, Stephen W.
❑ 88BakDodCLC-248
❑ 89VerBeaDS-9
❑ 90LonTigP-1279
❑ 93VerBeaDC-6
❑ 93VerBeaDF-2230

Green, Steve R.
❑ 78HolMilT-9
❑ 80OrlTwiT-4
❑ 82OrlTwi8SCT-15

Green, Terry
❑ 86OscAstP-9
❑ 87OscAstP-25
❑ 88ColAstB-22

Green, Tom (Tom)
❑ 86SumBraP-7
❑ 90WelPirP-13
❑ 91AugPirC-20
❑ 91AugPirP-819
❑ 92BufBisBS-10
❑ 92CarMudF-1193
❑ 92ClaFS7-241
❑ 92SalBucC-17
❑ 93CarMudF-2068
❑ 93CarMudTI-14

Green, Trent
❑ 92DavLipB-12

Green, Tyler
❑ 90WicStaSGD-13
❑ 91BatCliCB-20
❑ 91BatCliP-3479
❑ 91Cla/Bes-416
❑ 91ClaDraP-7
❑ 91ClaDraPP-1
❑ 91ClaGolB-BC19
❑ 91FroRowDP-34
❑ 91FroRowDPG-34
❑ 91FroRowDPS-34
❑ 92ClaFS7-230
❑ 92DonRooP-BC5
❑ 92FroRowTG-1
❑ 92FroRowTG-2
❑ 92FroRowTG-3
❑ 92FroRowTG-4
❑ 92FroRowTG-5
❑ 92FroRowTG-6
❑ 92FroRowTG-7
❑ 92OPC-764
❑ 92Pin-303
❑ 92ProFS7-303
❑ 92ReaPhiF-569
❑ 92ReaPhiS-531
❑ 92Sco-810
❑ 92SkyAA F-229
❑ 92StaCluD-68
❑ 92Top-764
❑ 92TopGol-764
❑ 92TopGolW-764
❑ 92TopMic-764
❑ 92UppDec-68
❑ 92UppDecML-40
❑ 92UppDecML-68
❑ 92UppDecML-167
❑ 93Bow-400
❑ 93ClaGolF-36
❑ 93ExcFS7-85
❑ 93PhiMed-15
❑ 93Pin-581
❑ 93ScrRedBF-2542
❑ 93ScrRedBTI-10
❑ 93TopTra-37T
❑ 93UppDec-505
❑ 93UppDecGold-505
❑ 94Bow-362
❑ 94Bow-422
❑ 94Don-433
❑ 94Fin-256
❑ 94FinRef-256
❑ 94PhiMed-11
❑ 94PhiUSPC-12S
❑ 94Pin-503
❑ 94PinArtP-503
❑ 94PinMusC-503
❑ 94ScrRedBF-920
❑ 94StaCluT-239
❑ 94StaCluTFDI-239
❑ 94Top-294
❑ 94TopGol-294
❑ 94TopSpa-294
❑ 94UppDec-72
❑ 94UppDecED-72
❑ 95BowBes-R73
❑ 95BowBesR-R73
❑ 95DonTopotO-304
❑ 95Fla-389
❑ 95FleUpd-119
❑ 95Phi-13
❑ 95PhiMel-10
❑ 95SPCha-76
❑ 95SPChaDC-76
❑ 95TopTra-131T
❑ 95TopTra-152T
❑ 95UltGolMR-M14
❑ 95UppDec-476
❑ 96ColCho-253
❑ 96ColChoGS-253
❑ 96ColChoSS-253
❑ 96Don-188
❑ 96DonPreP-188
❑ 96Fle-498
❑ 96FleTif-498
❑ 96Pac-163
❑ 96PacPri-P53
❑ 96PacPriG-P53
❑ 96PhiTeal-15
❑ 96Sco-42
❑ 96ScoDugC-A37
❑ 96ScoDugCAP-A37
❑ 96StaClu-175
❑ 96StaCluMOP-175
❑ 96Top-418
❑ 96Ult-252
❑ 96UltGolM-252
❑ 96UppDec-167
❑ 97PhiCopQ-10
❑ 97Sco-398
❑ 97ScoArtPWB-398
❑ 97ScoResC-398
❑ 97ScoShoS-398
❑ 97ScoShoSAP-398
❑ 97ScrRedB-2
❑ 98Fle-454
❑ 98Pac-381
❑ 98PacOnl-561
❑ 98PacOnlR-561
❑ 98PacOnlWC-561
❑ 98PacPlaB-381
❑ 98PacRedT-381
❑ 98PacSil-381
❑ 98PhiTeal-15
❑ 99Fle-263
❑ 99FleSta9-263
❑ 99FleWarT-263

Greenberg, Hank
❑ 34BatR31-57
❑ 34DiaStaR-54A
❑ 34DiaStaR-54B
❑ 34Gou-62

❑ 34TigTeal-9
❑ 35GouPreR-12
❑ 35GouPuzR-8F
❑ 35GouPuzR-9F
❑ 36GouBWR-15
❑ 36GouWidPPR-A42
❑ 36GouWidPPR-B11
❑ 36GouWidPPR-C14
❑ 36NatChiFPR-35
❑ 36NatChiFPR-109
❑ 36OveCanR-20
❑ 36R31PasP-12
❑ 36R31Pre-G9
❑ 36WheBB3-5
❑ 36WorWidGV-41
❑ 37OPCBatUV-107
❑ 38BasTabP-13
❑ 38ExhFou-12
❑ 38GouHeaU-253
❑ 38GouHeaU-277
❑ 38OurNatGPP-13
❑ 38WheBB11-5
❑ 38WheBB15-4
❑ 39ExhSal-22A
❑ 39ExhSal-22B
❑ 39GouPreR303A-20
❑ 39GouPreR303B-12
❑ 39PlaBal-56
❑ 39WheBB12-7
❑ 39WorWidGTP-20
❑ 40PlaBal-40
❑ 40WheM4-2A
❑ 40WheM4-7B
❑ 41DouPlaR-51
❑ 41DouPlaR-85
❑ 41PlaBal-18
❑ 41WheM5-16
❑ 43MPR302-1-12
❑ 46SpoExcW-4-1B
❑ 48BluTin-35
❑ 48IndTeal-11
❑ 48IndTeal-12
❑ 49IndTeal-12
❑ 50IndTeal-13
❑ 51R42SmaS-38
❑ 53ArtHaloFP-39
❑ 55IndGolS-27
❑ 58JayPubAG-6
❑ 60NuHi-42
❑ 61GolPre-4
❑ 61NuSco-442
❑ 63BasMagM-31
❑ 63BazA-19
❑ 63HalofFB-10
❑ 64TopRooAB-4
❑ 68LauWorS-42
❑ 70FleWorS-42
❑ 71FleWorS-43
❑ 73BooProC-6
❑ 73SevTraC-26
❑ 73TCMAllG-5
❑ 74TigTCM1AC-13
❑ 76GalBasGHoF-13
❑ 76RowExh-7
❑ 76ShaPiz-81
❑ 76TayBow4-36
❑ 76TigOldTS-11
❑ 77GalGloG-82
❑ 80MarExhH-14
❑ 80PacLeg-30
❑ 80PerHaloFP-81
❑ 80PerHaloFPS-7
❑ 80SSPHOF-81
❑ 80TigGreT-4
❑ 81ConTSN-79
❑ 81TigDetN-54
❑ 81TigDetN-133
❑ 81TigSecNP-17
❑ 82DavHaloFB-11
❑ 82DiaCla-49
❑ 82TCMGreS-27
❑ 83DonHOFH-16
❑ 83TigAlKS-39
❑ 83YanYealT-11
❑ 84OCoandSI-120
❑ 84SpoDesPW-33
❑ 84TCMPla1-4
❑ 85TCMPla1-42
❑ 85TopGloA-22
❑ 86SpoDecG-4
❑ 86TigSpoD-6
❑ 87HygAllG-22
❑ 87SpoRea-39
❑ 88WilMulP-5
❑ 89PacLegI-195
❑ 90PerGreM-88
❑ 91ConTSN-14
❑ 92ConTSN-430
❑ 92ConTSN-590
❑ 93ActPacA-107
❑ 93ActPacA2-41G
❑ 93ConTSN-733
❑ 94ConTSN-1005
❑ 94ConTSNB-1005
❑ 94TedWil-32
❑ 94UppDecTAE-54
❑ 94UppDecTAEGM-4
❑ 95ConTSN-1335
❑ 99UppDecCL-37
❑ 99UppDecCLCC-37

Greenberg, Steve
❑ 74SpoIndC-40

Greene, Al (Altar)
❑ 80EvaTriT-8
❑ 80Top-666

Greene, Allen
❑ 98OneYanG-11

Greene, Bart
❑ 92BriTigC-23
❑ 92BriTigF-1424

Greene, Charlie
❑ 92ChaRaiC-12
❑ 92ChaRaiF-122
❑ 93SpoIndC-30
❑ 93WatDiaC-16
❑ 93WatDiaF-1771
❑ 94St.LucMF-1199
❑ 95BinMetTI-21
❑ 96BinMetB-9
❑ 97NorTid-15
❑ 97NorTidB-15
❑ 97WilCubB-29
❑ 98RocRedWQ-14
❑ 98WilCubM-29

Greene, Clay
❑ 97SalVolG-14

Greene, Danny
❑ 97CedRapK-10
❑ 98MidAngO-16

Greene, Ed
❑ 86BelBreP-8

Greene, Grant
❑ 76LauIndC-8

Greene, Henry
❑ 77DayBealT-7

Greene, Jeff
❑ 86SumBraP-6
❑ 87DurBulP-22
❑ 87PenWhiSP-20
❑ 88BurBraP-14
❑ 88TamTarS-8

Greene, Joe (James)
❑ 78LauLonABS-13
❑ 97NegLeaPC-2S

Greene, Keith
❑ 86BenPhiC-137
❑ 87SpaPhiP-8

Greene, Nelson
❑ 90DodTar-963

Greene, Rick
❑ 92Bow-563
❑ 92ClaDraP-12
❑ 92LSUTigM-5
❑ 92TopTra-44T
❑ 92TopTraG-44T
❑ 92UppDecML-9
❑ 93Bow-263
❑ 93ClaFS7-193
❑ 93LakTigC-9
❑ 93LakTigF-1302
❑ 93StaCluM-188
❑ 93Top-233
❑ 93TopGol-233
❑ 93TopInaM-233
❑ 93TopInaR-233
❑ 93TopMic-233
❑ 93UppDec-446
❑ 93UppDecGold-446
❑ 94Bow-425
❑ 94Cla-146
❑ 94ClaGolF-110
❑ 94ExcFS7-55
❑ 94SigRoo-27
❑ 94SigRooS-27
❑ 94TreThuF-2116
❑ 94Ult-356
❑ 94UppDecML-49
❑ 95JacSunTI-13
❑ 96DouAllB-29
❑ 96JacSunB-15
❑ 97TolMudHB-15
❑ 98LouRedQ-2

Greene, Ryan
❑ 97EugEmeB-7
❑ 98MacBraM-8

Greene, Steve
❑ 77BurBeeT-11

Greene, Todd
❑ 91TopTra-50T
❑ 91TopTraT-50T
❑ 92StaCluD-69
❑ 92TopDaiQTU-20
❑ 93BoiHawC-1
❑ 93BoiHawF-3928
❑ 94ExcFirYPF-7
❑ 94ExcFS7-27
❑ 94LakElsSC-1
❑ 94LakElsSF-1666
❑ 95ARuFalLS-8
❑ 95Bes-9
❑ 95Bes-AU1
❑ 95Bow-227
❑ 95BowBes-B18
❑ 95BowBes-X12
❑ 95BowBesR-B18
❑ 95BowBesR-X12
❑ 95BowGolF-227
❑ 95ColCho-34
❑ 95ColChoGS-34
❑ 95ColChoSS-34
❑ 95Exc-20
❑ 95ExcAll-9
❑ 95MidAngOHP-13
❑ 95MidAngTI-11
❑ 95SPMLA-26
❑ 95Top-633
❑ 95UppDec-6
❑ 95UppDecED-6
❑ 95UppDecEDG-6
❑ 95UppDecML-25
❑ 95UppDecMLFS-25
❑ 95UppDecMLOP-OP4
❑ 95UppDecSE-127
❑ 95UppDecSEG-127
❑ 96BesAutSA-22
❑ 96Bow-178
❑ 96BowBes-128
❑ 96BowBesAR-128
❑ 96BowBesP-BBP18
❑ 96BowBesPAR-BBP18
❑ 96BowBesPR-BBP18
❑ 96BowBesR-128
❑ 96BowFoi-178
❑ 96ColCho-440
❑ 96ColCho-664
❑ 96ColChoGS-440
❑ 96ColChoGS-664
❑ 96ColChoSS-440
❑ 96ColChoSS-664
❑ 96EmoXL-27
❑ 96Fla-38
❑ 96FlaWavotF-12
❑ 96Fle-48
❑ 96FlePro-6
❑ 96FleTif-48
❑ 96FleUpdNH-8
❑ 96LeaSig-138
❑ 96LeaSigPPG-138
❑ 96LeaSigPPP-138
❑ 96MetUni-28
❑ 96MetUniMFG-4
❑ 96MetUniP-28
❑ 96MetUniProS-28
❑ 96MetUniProS-XX
❑ 96SP-14
❑ 96Top-213
❑ 96TopChr-75
❑ 96TopChrR-75
❑ 96TopGal-130
❑ 96TopGalPPI-130
❑ 96Ult-325
❑ 96UltGolM-325
❑ 96UppDec-240
❑ 96UppDecFSP-FS12
❑ 96UppDecPHE-H24
❑ 96UppDecPreH-H24
❑ 96VanCanB-15
❑ 97Bow-208
❑ 97BowBes-137
❑ 97BowBesAR-137
❑ 97BowBesR-137
❑ 97BowCerBlaIA-CA31
❑ 97BowCerBluIA-CA31
❑ 97BowCerGolIA-CA31
❑ 97BowChr-191
❑ 97BowChrI-191
❑ 97BowChrIR-191
❑ 97BowChrR-191
❑ 97BowInt-208
❑ 97Cir-63
❑ 97CirRav-63
❑ 97ColCho-259
❑ 97Don-374
❑ 97DonEli-84
❑ 97DonEliGS-84
❑ 97DonEliTotC-10
❑ 97DonEliTotCDC-10
❑ 97DonGolPP-374
❑ 97DonLim-41
❑ 97DonLim-82
❑ 97DonLimE-41
❑ 97DonLimE-82
❑ 97DonLimENG-41
❑ 97DonPre-151
❑ 97DonPreCttC-151
❑ 97DonRatR-26
❑ 97DonSig-89
❑ 97DonSigA-42
❑ 97DonSigAC-51
❑ 97DonSigAM-51
❑ 97DonSigPPP-89
❑ 97DonSilPP-374
❑ 97FlaShoLC-11
❑ 97FlaShoLeg0-11
❑ 97FlaShoLeg1-11
❑ 97FlaShoM-A11
❑ 97FlaShoM-B11
❑ 97FlaShoM-C11
❑ 97FlaShoR0-11
❑ 97FlaShoR1-11
❑ 97FlaShoR2-11
❑ 97FlaShoWotF-1
❑ 97Fle-44
❑ 97FleTif-44
❑ 97Lea-331
❑ 97LeaFraM-331
❑ 97LeaFraMDC-331
❑ 97PacPriGotD-GD5
❑ 97Pin-179
❑ 97PinArtP-PP179
❑ 97PinCer-120
❑ 97PinCerMBla-120
❑ 97PinCerMBlu-120
❑ 97PinCerMG-120
❑ 97PinCerMR-120
❑ 97PinCerR-120
❑ 97PinIns-136
❑ 97PinInsCE-136
❑ 97PinInsDE-136
❑ 97PinMusC-179
❑ 97PinPrePla-179
❑ 97PinTotCPB-120
❑ 97PinTotCPG-120
❑ 97PinTotCPR-120
❑ 97Sco-277
❑ 97ScoArtPWB-277
❑ 97ScoPreS-277
❑ 97ScoShoS-277
❑ 97ScoShoSAP-277
❑ 97Sel-109
❑ 97SelArtP-109
❑ 97SelCom-109
❑ 97SelRegG-109
❑ 97SelRooR-17
❑ 97SpoIll-7
❑ 97SpoIllEE-7
❑ 97StaClu-112
❑ 97StaCluM-M19
❑ 97StaCluMOP-112
❑ 97StaCluMOP-M19
❑ 97Stu-156
❑ 97StuPrePG-156
❑ 97StuPrePS-156
❑ 97Top-288
❑ 97TopSta-107
❑ 97TopStaAM-107
❑ 97UD3-47
❑ 97UD3GenNex-GN13
❑ 97Ult-28
❑ 97UltGolME-28
❑ 97UltPlaME-28
❑ 97UppDec-296
❑ 97VanCanB-16
❑ 98AngSco-2
❑ 98AngScoP-2
❑ 98Bow-58
❑ 98BowChr-58
❑ 98BowChrGA-58
❑ 98BowChrGAR-58
❑ 98BowChrI-58
❑ 98BowChrIR-58
❑ 98BowChrR-58
❑ 98BowGolA-58
❑ 98BowInt-58
❑ 98CirThu-117
❑ 98CirThuRav-117
❑ 98CirThuSupRav-117
❑ 98ColCho-26
❑ 98Don-84
❑ 98DonCol-84
❑ 98DonColE-505
❑ 98DonColL-237
❑ 98DonColP-663
❑ 98DonColS-84
❑ 98DonCruG-6
❑ 98DonCruP-6
❑ 98DonCruR-6
❑ 98DonEli-105
❑ 98DonEliA-105
❑ 98DonEliS-105
❑ 98DonGolPP-84
❑ 98DonPre-113
❑ 98DonPreGES-15
❑ 98DonPreGX-15
❑ 98DonPreGXDC-15
❑ 98DonPreSeat-113
❑ 98DonPriCD-84
❑ 98DonPriCE-505
❑ 98DonPriCL-237
❑ 98DonPriCP-663
❑ 98DonRooDK-11
❑ 98DonRooDKC-11
❑ 98DonSig-71
❑ 98DonSigA-36
❑ 98DonSigAC-49
❑ 98DonSigAM-50
❑ 98DonSigP-71
❑ 98DonSilPP-84
❑ 98Fin-17
❑ 98FinNo--17
❑ 98FinNo-R-17
❑ 98FinRef-17
❑ 98Fle-53
❑ 98Lea-37
❑ 98LeaFraDA-37
❑ 98LeaFraF-37
❑ 98LeaFraM-37
❑ 98LeaFraM-37
❑ 98LeaFraMDC-37
❑ 98LeaFraMDC-37
❑ 98LeaFraMZ2-37
❑ 98LeaRS-104
❑ 98LeaRSLHolo-104
❑ 98LeaRSLong-104
❑ 98LeaRTrue-104
❑ 98MetUni-97
❑ 98MetUniPMG-97
❑ 98PacAur-6
❑ 98PacInvGems-2
❑ 98PacPar-7
❑ 98PacParC-7
❑ 98PacParG-7
❑ 98PacParHS-7
❑ 98PacParPB-7
❑ 98PacParR-7
❑ 98PinIns-80
❑ 98PinInsCE-80
❑ 98PinInsDE-80
❑ 98PinPer-114
❑ 98PinPerPP-114
❑ 98PinSna-AA6
❑ 98PinSna-AA11
❑ 98Sco-71
❑ 98ScoRT-193
❑ 98ScoRTSS-PP108
❑ 98ScoRTSSAP-PP108
❑ 98ScoRTSSAP1-PP108
❑ 98ScoSS-PP30
❑ 98ScoSSAP-PP30
❑ 98SP Aut-37
❑ 98SpoIll-146
❑ 98SpoIllEE-146
❑ 98SpoIllFE-146
❑ 98StaCluFDI-217
❑ 98StaCluI-217
❑ 98StaCluOneK-217
❑ 98StaCluPP-217
❑ 98Stu-135
❑ 98StuGPP-135
❑ 98StuSPP-135
❑ 98Top-382
❑ 98TopBabB-BB12
❑ 98TopChr-382
❑ 98TopChrBB-BB12
❑ 98TopChrBBR-BB12
❑ 98TopChrR-382
❑ 98TopDevR-382
❑ 98TopDia-382
❑ 98TopMiniC-382
❑ 98Ult-133
❑ 98UltGolM-133
❑ 98UltMas-133
❑ 98UltPlaM-133
❑ 98UppDec-292
❑ 98VanCanG-14
❑ 99Fle-179
❑ 99FleSta9-179
❑ 99FleWarT-179
❑ 99SkyThu-153
❑ 99SkyThuRant-153
❑ 99SkyThuRave-153
❑ 99SpoIll-42
❑ 99ThuSkySupR-153
❑ 99Vic-10

Greene, Tommy (Ira Thomas)
❑ 88BobCamRB-15
❑ 88RicBraC-1
❑ 88RicBraP-2
❑ 89RicBraBC-7
❑ 89RicBraC-3
❑ 89RicBraP-831
❑ 89RicBraTI-8
❑ 89TriAAAP-AAA54
❑ 90Bow-1
❑ 90BowTif-1
❑ 90ClaUpd-T22
❑ 90CMC-296
❑ 90Don-576
❑ 90Fle-584
❑ 90FleCan-584
❑ 90ProAAAF-398
❑ 90RicBraBC-9
❑ 90RicBraC-20
❑ 90RicBraP-253
❑ 90RicBraTI-10
❑ 90Sco-640
❑ 90ScoYouS2-24
❑ 90Spo-224
❑ 90TopDeb89-45
❑ 90UppDec-49
❑ 91ClaGam-66
❑ 91Don-635
❑ 91FleUpd-108
❑ 91Lea-524
❑ 91OPC-486
❑ 91PhiMed-15
❑ 91Sco-808
❑ 91StaClu-549
❑ 91StaCluMO-3
❑ 91Top-486
❑ 91TopDesS-486
❑ 91TopMic-486
❑ 91TopTif-486
❑ 91UltUpd-99
❑ 91UppDecFE-62F
❑ 92Bow-227
❑ 92ClaGam-64
❑ 92Don-94
❑ 92Don-109
❑ 92Fle-531
❑ 92Lea-292
❑ 92LeaBlaG-292
❑ 92OPC-83
❑ 92PhiMed-14
❑ 92Pin-155
❑ 92PinTea2-53
❑ 92RedFolS-40
❑ 92Sco-336
❑ 92Sco-426
❑ 92StaClu-27
❑ 92Top-83
❑ 92TopGol-83
❑ 92TopGolW-83
❑ 92TopMic-83
❑ 92Ult-242
❑ 92UppDec-567
❑ 93Don-568
❑ 93Fin-149
❑ 93FinRef-149
❑ 93Fla-101
❑ 93Fle-489
❑ 93Lea-132
❑ 93OPC-144
❑ 93PhiMed-16
❑ 93PhiStaC-27
❑ 93Pin-313
❑ 93Sco-464
❑ 93SP-174
❑ 93StaClu-559
❑ 93StaCluFDI-559
❑ 93StaCluMOP-559
❑ 93Top-291
❑ 93TopGol-291
❑ 93TopInaM-291
❑ 93TopInaR-291

- ❑ 93TopMic-291
- ❑ 93Ult-441
- ❑ 93UppDec-549
- ❑ 93UppDecGold-549
- ❑ 94Bow-580
- ❑ 94ColC-115
- ❑ 94ColChoGS-115
- ❑ 94ColChoSS-115
- ❑ 94Don-482
- ❑ 94Fin-152
- ❑ 94FinRef-152
- ❑ 94Fla-412
- ❑ 94Fle-589
- ❑ 94FleExtB-333
- ❑ 94Lea-133
- ❑ 94OPC-137
- ❑ 94Pac-475
- ❑ 94PhiMed-12
- ❑ 94PhiMel-8
- ❑ 94PhiUSPC-7S
- ❑ 94PhiUSPC-13D
- ❑ 94Pin-78
- ❑ 94PinArtP-78
- ❑ 94PinMusC-78
- ❑ 94RedFolMI-13
- ❑ 94Sco-380
- ❑ 94ScoGolR-380
- ❑ 94Sel-155
- ❑ 94StaClu-705
- ❑ 94StaCluFDI-705
- ❑ 94StaCluGR-705
- ❑ 94StaCluMOP-705
- ❑ 94StaCluT-222
- ❑ 94StaCluTFDI-222
- ❑ 94Top-570
- ❑ 94TopGol-570
- ❑ 94TopSpa-570
- ❑ 94TriPla-174
- ❑ 94Ult-244
- ❑ 94UppDec-203
- ❑ 94UppDecED-203
- ❑ 95Don-518
- ❑ 95DonPreP-518
- ❑ 95Fin-41
- ❑ 95FinRef-41
- ❑ 95Fla-180
- ❑ 95Fle-392
- ❑ 95Sco-36
- ❑ 95ScoGolR-36
- ❑ 95ScoPlaTS-36
- ❑ 95StaClu-356
- ❑ 95StaCluMOP-356
- ❑ 95StaCluSTWS-356
- ❑ 95StaCluVR-186
- ❑ 95StaCluVRMO-186
- ❑ 95Top-144
- ❑ 95TopCyb-88
- ❑ 95TopEmb-55
- ❑ 95TopEmbGI-55
- ❑ 95Ult-419
- ❑ 95UltGolM-419
- ❑ 95UppDec-379
- ❑ 95UppDecED-379
- ❑ 95UppDecEDG-379
- ❑ 96StaClu-399
- ❑ 96StaCluMOP-399

Greene, Willie

- ❑ 90AugPirP-2470
- ❑ 90Bow-173
- ❑ 90BowTif-173
- ❑ 90CMC-849
- ❑ 90ProAaA-96
- ❑ 90Sco-682
- ❑ 91Bow-448
- ❑ 91Cla/Bes-350
- ❑ 91WesPalBEC-20
- ❑ 91WesPalBEP-1236
- ❑ 92Bow-429
- ❑ 92CedRapRC-20
- ❑ 92ChaLooF-3826
- ❑ 92ClaFS7-48
- ❑ 92FleUpd-81
- ❑ 92ProFS7-263
- ❑ 93Bow-349
- ❑ 93Bow-638
- ❑ 93ClaFS7-194
- ❑ 93Don-143
- ❑ 93Fin-148
- ❑ 93FinRef-148
- ❑ 93Fle-34
- ❑ 93IndIndF-1495
- ❑ 93Lea-456
- ❑ 93Pin-285
- ❑ 93Sco-250
- ❑ 93ScoBoyoS-12
- ❑ 93ScoProaG-8
- ❑ 93Sel-348
- ❑ 93StaClu-704
- ❑ 93StaCluFDI-704
- ❑ 93StaCluMOP-704
- ❑ 93Top-764
- ❑ 93TopGol-764
- ❑ 93TopInaM-764
- ❑ 93TopInaR-764
- ❑ 93TopMic-764
- ❑ 93Toy-46
- ❑ 93ToyMasP-4
- ❑ 93UppDec-4
- ❑ 93UppDecGold-4
- ❑ 94Bow-430
- ❑ 94BowBes-B69
- ❑ 94BowBesR-B69
- ❑ 94ColC-116
- ❑ 94ColChoGS-116
- ❑ 94ColChoSS-116
- ❑ 94Don-539
- ❑ 94Fle-410
- ❑ 94FUnPac-169
- ❑ 94Lea-326
- ❑ 94Pin-522
- ❑ 94PinArtP-522
- ❑ 94PinMusC-522
- ❑ 94ScoBoyoS-34
- ❑ 94Sel-102
- ❑ 94Top-428
- ❑ 94TopGol-428
- ❑ 94TopSpa-428
- ❑ 94TriPla-212
- ❑ 94Ult-170
- ❑ 94UppDec-230
- ❑ 94UppDecED-230
- ❑ 95ActPac2G-12G
- ❑ 95ActPacF-17
- ❑ 95ActPacF-73
- ❑ 95ColCho-428
- ❑ 95ColChoGS-428
- ❑ 95ColChoSS-428
- ❑ 95Don-210
- ❑ 95DonPreP-210
- ❑ 95IndIndF-101
- ❑ 95Lea-72
- ❑ 95Pac-105
- ❑ 95Pin-331
- ❑ 95PinArtP-331
- ❑ 95PinMusC-331
- ❑ 95PinUps-US28
- ❑ 95RedKah-8
- ❑ 95Sel-190
- ❑ 95SelArtP-190
- ❑ 95SigRoo-22
- ❑ 95SigRooSig-22
- ❑ 95Spo-110
- ❑ 95SpoArtP-110
- ❑ 95StaClu-308
- ❑ 95StaCluMOP-308
- ❑ 95StaCluSTWS-308
- ❑ 95Stu-83
- ❑ 95Sum-39
- ❑ 95SumNthD-39
- ❑ 95Top-467
- ❑ 95UppDec-168
- ❑ 95UppDecED-168
- ❑ 95UppDecEDG-168
- ❑ 96FleUpd-U121
- ❑ 96FleUpdTC-U121
- ❑ 96Pin-295
- ❑ 96PinAfi-144
- ❑ 96PinAfiAP-144
- ❑ 96PinFoil-295
- ❑ 97Cir-177
- ❑ 97CirRav-177
- ❑ 97ColCho-303
- ❑ 97Fle-294
- ❑ 97FleTif-294
- ❑ 97Lea-122
- ❑ 97LeaFraM-122
- ❑ 97LeaFraMDC-122
- ❑ 97NewPin-137
- ❑ 97NewPinAP-137
- ❑ 97NewPinMC-137
- ❑ 97NewPinPP-137
- ❑ 97Pac-268
- ❑ 97PacLigB-268
- ❑ 97PacSil-268
- ❑ 97Sco-425
- ❑ 97ScoArtPWB-425
- ❑ 97ScoResC-425
- ❑ 97ScoShoS-425
- ❑ 97ScoShoSAP-425
- ❑ 97Top-371
- ❑ 97Ult-328
- ❑ 97UltGolME-328
- ❑ 97UltPlaME-328
- ❑ 97UppDec-335
- ❑ 98CirThu-282
- ❑ 98CirThuRav-282
- ❑ 98CirThuSupRav-282
- ❑ 98ColCho-344
- ❑ 98E-X2-61
- ❑ 98E-X2ECFut-61
- ❑ 98E-X2ECNow-61
- ❑ 98Fin-138
- ❑ 98FinNo--138
- ❑ 98FinNo-R-138
- ❑ 98FinRef-138
- ❑ 98FlaShoLeg0-92
- ❑ 98FlaShoLeg1-92
- ❑ 98FlaShoLeg2-92
- ❑ 98FlaShoLeg3-92
- ❑ 98FlaShoLegM-92
- ❑ 98FlaShoR0-92
- ❑ 98FlaShoR1-92
- ❑ 98FlaShoR2-92
- ❑ 98FlaShoR3-92
- ❑ 98Fle-262
- ❑ 98MetUni-140
- ❑ 98MetUniPMG-140
- ❑ 98Pac-264
- ❑ 98PacOme-63
- ❑ 98PacOmeR-63
- ❑ 98PacOnl-189
- ❑ 98PacOnlR-189
- ❑ 98PacOnlWC-189
- ❑ 98PacPlaB-264
- ❑ 98PacRedT-264
- ❑ 98PacSil-264
- ❑ 98Pin-80
- ❑ 98PinPreP-80
- ❑ 98SP Aut-72
- ❑ 98SpoIll-48
- ❑ 98SpoIllEE-48
- ❑ 98SpoIllFE-48
- ❑ 98SpoIllTaN-87
- ❑ 98SpoIllTaNEE-87
- ❑ 98SPxFin-262
- ❑ 98SPxFinR-262
- ❑ 98SPxFinS-262
- ❑ 98StaCluFDI-27
- ❑ 98StaCluI-27
- ❑ 98StaCluOneK-27
- ❑ 98StaCluPP-27
- ❑ 98Top-104
- ❑ 98TopChr-104
- ❑ 98TopChrR-104
- ❑ 98TopDevR-104
- ❑ 98TopDia-104
- ❑ 98TopMiniC-104
- ❑ 98Ult-27
- ❑ 98UltGolM-27
- ❑ 98UltMas-27
- ❑ 98UltPlaM-27
- ❑ 98UppDec-66
- ❑ 98UppDecSF-41
- ❑ 99UppDec-512
- ❑ 99UppDecEL1-512
- ❑ 99UppDecEL2-512
- ❑ 99Vic-413

Greenfield, Kent

- ❑ 90DodTar-295
- ❑ 92ConTSN-617

Greenfield, Monroe

- ❑ 77PhoGiaVNB-6

Greengrass, Jim

- ❑ 47Exh-83
- ❑ 53Top-209
- ❑ 54Bow-28
- ❑ 54Top-22
- ❑ 55Bow-49
- ❑ 56Top-275
- ❑ 56YelBasP-12
- ❑ 58UniOil-3
- ❑ 79DiaGre-321
- ❑ 91TopArc1-209
- ❑ 94TopArc1-22
- ❑ 94TopArc1G-22

Greenhalgh, Dan

- ❑ 77ReaPhiT-11

Greenhalgh, Ted

- ❑ 46SunBre-7

Greenlee, Darren

- ❑ 93PocPosSP-18

Greenlee, Gus

- ❑ 88NegLeaD-5

Greenlee, Robert

- ❑ 87SanBerSP-19

Greenstein, Stu

- ❑ 77LynMetT-16A
- ❑ 77LynMetT-16B

Greenwell, Mike

- ❑ 85IntLeaAT-44
- ❑ 85PawRedST-4
- ❑ 86PawRedSP-10
- ❑ 86Spo-178
- ❑ 87Don-585
- ❑ 87DonRoo-4
- ❑ 87FleUpd-37
- ❑ 87FleUpdG-37
- ❑ 87RedSoxP-11
- ❑ 87SpoRool-8
- ❑ 87SpoTeaP-9
- ❑ 87Top-259
- ❑ 87TopTif-259
- ❑ 88ClaBlu-227
- ❑ 88Don-339
- ❑ 88DonBasB-177
- ❑ 88DonTeaBRS-339
- ❑ 88Fle-354
- ❑ 88Fle-630
- ❑ 88FleExcS-16
- ❑ 88FleGlo-354
- ❑ 88FleGlo-630
- ❑ 88FleHotS-14
- ❑ 88FleMin-7
- ❑ 88FleStiC-9
- ❑ 88Lea-153
- ❑ 88OPC-274
- ❑ 88PanSti-32
- ❑ 88Sco-175
- ❑ 88ScoGlo-175
- ❑ 88ScoYouSI-24
- ❑ 88Spo-118
- ❑ 88StaGre-1
- ❑ 88StaGre-2
- ❑ 88StaGre-3
- ❑ 88StaGre-4
- ❑ 88StaGre-5
- ❑ 88StaGre-6
- ❑ 88StaGre-7
- ❑ 88StaGre-8
- ❑ 88StaGre-9
- ❑ 88StaGre-10
- ❑ 88StaGre-11
- ❑ 88StaGreP-1
- ❑ 88StaGreP-2
- ❑ 88StaGreP-3
- ❑ 88StaGreP-4
- ❑ 88StaGreP-5
- ❑ 88StaGreP-6
- ❑ 88StaGreP-7
- ❑ 88StaGreP-8
- ❑ 88StaGreP-9
- ❑ 88StaGreP-10
- ❑ 88StaGreP-11
- ❑ 88StaLinRS-10
- ❑ 88TarPla-17
- ❑ 88Top-493
- ❑ 88TopBig-233
- ❑ 88TopCoi-14
- ❑ 88TopGloS-20
- ❑ 88TopRoo-3
- ❑ 88TopSti-249
- ❑ 88TopSti-312
- ❑ 88TopTif-493
- ❑ 88ToyRoo-12
- ❑ 89Bow-34
- ❑ 89BowTif-34
- ❑ 89CadEllD-24
- ❑ 89ClaTraO-149
- ❑ 89ColPosG-1
- ❑ 89ColPosG-2
- ❑ 89ColPosG-3
- ❑ 89ColPosG-4
- ❑ 89ColPosG-5
- ❑ 89ColPosG-6
- ❑ 89ColPosG-7
- ❑ 89ColPosG-8
- ❑ 89Don-1
- ❑ 89Don-186
- ❑ 89DonAll-15
- ❑ 89DonBasB-28
- ❑ 89DonBonM-BC13
- ❑ 89DonGraS-5
- ❑ 89DonSupD-1
- ❑ 89Fle-90
- ❑ 89FleAll-6
- ❑ 89FleBasA-16
- ❑ 89FleBasM-16
- ❑ 89FleExcS-18
- ❑ 89FleGlo-90
- ❑ 89FleHeroB-19
- ❑ 89FleLeaL-18
- ❑ 89FleSup-20
- ❑ 89FleWaxBC-C11
- ❑ 89KayB-15
- ❑ 89Nis-6
- ❑ 89OPC-374
- ❑ 89PanSti-280
- ❑ 89Sco-66
- ❑ 89Sco-659
- ❑ 89ScoHot1S-70
- ❑ 89Scomast-36
- ❑ 89Spo-143
- ❑ 89Spo-221
- ❑ 89SpoIllFKI-31
- ❑ 89TarPla-1
- ❑ 89Top-402
- ❑ 89Top-630
- ❑ 89TopBasT-119
- ❑ 89TopBig-211
- ❑ 89TopCoi-41
- ❑ 89TopDouA-6
- ❑ 89TopGloS-31
- ❑ 89TopHeaUT-22
- ❑ 89TopHilTM-15
- ❑ 89TopMinL-48
- ❑ 89TopSti-255
- ❑ 89TopStiB-16
- ❑ 89TopTif-402
- ❑ 89TopTif-630
- ❑ 89TopUKM-32
- ❑ 89TVSpoM-61
- ❑ 89TVSpoM-128
- ❑ 89UppDec-432
- ❑ 90Bow-274
- ❑ 90BowTif-274
- ❑ 90ClaBlu-47
- ❑ 90Don-66
- ❑ 90DonBesA-115
- ❑ 90DOnBonM-BC17
- ❑ 90DonLeaS-32
- ❑ 90Fle-277
- ❑ 90Fle-632
- ❑ 90FleBasA-13
- ❑ 90FleBasAC-13
- ❑ 90FleBasM-13
- ❑ 90FleBasMC-13
- ❑ 90FleCan-277
- ❑ 90FleCan-632
- ❑ 90FleLeaL-13
- ❑ 90FleLeaLC-13
- ❑ 90FleWaxBC-C8
- ❑ 90Lea-143
- ❑ 90M.Vpin-11
- ❑ 90MLBBasB-71
- ❑ 90MSAIceTD-18
- ❑ 90OPC-70
- ❑ 90PanSti-16
- ❑ 90PubIntS-287
- ❑ 90PubIntS-457
- ❑ 90RedFolSB-39
- ❑ 90RedSoxP-11
- ❑ 90Sco-345
- ❑ 90Sco100S-67
- ❑ 90Spo-50
- ❑ 90Top-70
- ❑ 90TopBig-61
- ❑ 90TopDou-28
- ❑ 90TopSti-254
- ❑ 90TopTif-70
- ❑ 90TopTVA-22
- ❑ 90TopTVRS-30
- ❑ 90UppDec-354
- ❑ 91Bow-116
- ❑ 91Cla3-T29
- ❑ 91ClaGam-18
- ❑ 91Don-553
- ❑ 91DonGraS-14
- ❑ 91Fle-96
- ❑ 91FlePro-8
- ❑ 91Lea-19
- ❑ 91OPC-792
- ❑ 91PanCanT1-32
- ❑ 91PanFreS-268
- ❑ 91RedSoxP-8
- ❑ 91RedSoxP-13
- ❑ 91Sco-130
- ❑ 91Sco100S-82
- ❑ 91StaClu-253
- ❑ 91Stu-15
- ❑ 91Top-792
- ❑ 91TopCraJ2-34
- ❑ 91TopDesS-792
- ❑ 91TopMic-792
- ❑ 91TopTif-792
- ❑ 91TopTriH-A2
- ❑ 91Ult-32
- ❑ 91UppDec-43
- ❑ 91UppDec-165
- ❑ 92Bow-615
- ❑ 92ClaGam-72
- ❑ 92Don-523
- ❑ 92Fle-39
- ❑ 92Lea-89
- ❑ 92LeaBlaG-89
- ❑ 92OPC-113
- ❑ 92PanSti-91
- ❑ 92Pin-131
- ❑ 92RedSoxDD-14
- ❑ 92Sco-545
- ❑ 92Sco100S-10
- ❑ 92SpoStaCC-19
- ❑ 92StaClu-446
- ❑ 92Top-113
- ❑ 92TopGol-113
- ❑ 92TopGolW-113
- ❑ 92TopKid-69
- ❑ 92TopMic-113
- ❑ 92TriPla-252
- ❑ 92Ult-16
- ❑ 92UppDec-275
- ❑ 93Bow-607
- ❑ 93DiaMar-43
- ❑ 93Don-223
- ❑ 93Fin-197
- ❑ 93FinRef-197
- ❑ 93Fla-164
- ❑ 93Fle-559
- ❑ 93FunPac-164
- ❑ 93Lea-197
- ❑ 93OPC-285
- ❑ 93PacSpa-33
- ❑ 93PanSti-96
- ❑ 93Pin-102
- ❑ 93RedSoxP-16
- ❑ 93RedSoxWHP-12
- ❑ 93Sco-385
- ❑ 93Sel-228
- ❑ 93SP-202
- ❑ 93StaClu-86
- ❑ 93StaCluFDI-86
- ❑ 93StaCluMOP-86
- ❑ 93Stu-161
- ❑ 93Top-323
- ❑ 93TopGol-323
- ❑ 93TopInaM-323
- ❑ 93TopInaR-323
- ❑ 93TopMic-323
- ❑ 93TriPla-46
- ❑ 93Ult-152
- ❑ 93UppDec-154
- ❑ 93UppDecGold-154
- ❑ 94Bow-259
- ❑ 94ColC-440
- ❑ 94ColChoGS-440
- ❑ 94ColChoSS-440
- ❑ 94Don-163
- ❑ 94Fin-322
- ❑ 94FinRef-322
- ❑ 94Fla-263
- ❑ 94Fle-33
- ❑ 94FleExtB-20
- ❑ 94FUnPac-39
- ❑ 94FUnPac-228
- ❑ 94Lea-182
- ❑ 94LeaL-10
- ❑ 94OPC-49
- ❑ 94Pac-56
- ❑ 94PanSti-30
- ❑ 94Pin-285
- ❑ 94PinArtP-285
- ❑ 94PinMusC-285
- ❑ 94ProMag-13
- ❑ 94Sco-83
- ❑ 94ScoGolR-83
- ❑ 94Sel-10
- ❑ 94SP-155
- ❑ 94SPDieC-155
- ❑ 94Spo-110
- ❑ 94StaClu-386
- ❑ 94StaCluFDI-386
- ❑ 94StaCluGR-386
- ❑ 94StaCluMOP-386
- ❑ 94Stu-162
- ❑ 94TomPiz-20
- ❑ 94Top-502
- ❑ 94TopGol-502
- ❑ 94TopSpa-502
- ❑ 94TriPla-204
- ❑ 94Ult-314
- ❑ 94UppDec-187
- ❑ 94UppDecED-187
- ❑ 95Bow-388
- ❑ 95ColCho-411
- ❑ 95ColChoGS-411
- ❑ 95ColChoSE-193
- ❑ 95ColChoSEGS-193

❑ 95ColChoSESS-193
❑ 95ColChoSS-411
❑ 95Don-547
❑ 95DonPreP-547
❑ 95DonTopotO-20
❑ 95Emo-12
❑ 95Fin-152
❑ 95FinRef-152
❑ 95Fla-12
❑ 95Fle-31
❑ 95Lea-298
❑ 95Lea300C-5
❑ 95LeaLim-74
❑ 95Pac-38
❑ 95PacPri-14
❑ 95Pin-40
❑ 95PinArtP-40
❑ 95PinMusC-40
❑ 95Sco-33
❑ 95ScoGolR-33
❑ 95ScoPlaTS-33
❑ 95Sel-110
❑ 95SelArtP-110
❑ 95Spo-106
❑ 95SpoArtP-106
❑ 95StaClu-121
❑ 95StaClu-311
❑ 95StaCluFDI-121
❑ 95StaCluMOP-121
❑ 95StaCluMOP-311
❑ 95StaCluSTDW-RS121
❑ 95StaCluSTWS-121
❑ 95StaCluSTWS-311
❑ 95Stu-121
❑ 95Top-215
❑ 95TopD3-34
❑ 95TopEmb-64
❑ 95TopEmbGI-64
❑ 95Ult-263
❑ 95UltGolM-263
❑ 95UppDec-400
❑ 95UppDecED-400
❑ 95UppDecEDG-400
❑ 95UppDecSE-80
❑ 95UppDecSEG-80
❑ 96Cir-11
❑ 96CirRav-11
❑ 96ColCho-472
❑ 96ColChoGS-472
❑ 96ColChoSS-472
❑ 96Don-307
❑ 96DonPreP-307
❑ 96EmoXL-14
❑ 96Fin-B178
❑ 96FinRef-B178
❑ 96Fla-19
❑ 96Fle-27
❑ 96FleRedS-7
❑ 96FleTif-27
❑ 96Lea-170
❑ 96LeaPrePB-170
❑ 96LeaPrePG-170
❑ 96LeaPrePS-170
❑ 96LeaSigA-84
❑ 96LeaSigAG-84
❑ 96LeaSigAS-84
❑ 96MetUni-16
❑ 96MetUniP-16
❑ 96Pac-251
❑ 96PanSti-138
❑ 96Pin-28
❑ 96Pin-303
❑ 96PinArtP-187
❑ 96PinFoil-303
❑ 96PinSta-187
❑ 96ProSta-108
❑ 96Sco-335
❑ 96ScoDugC-B60
❑ 96ScoDugCAP-B60
❑ 96StaClu-162
❑ 96StaCluEPB-162
❑ 96StaCluEPG-162
❑ 96StaCluEPS-162
❑ 96StaCluMOP-162
❑ 96Top-143
❑ 96TopGal-54
❑ 96TopGalPPI-54
❑ 96Ult-17
❑ 96UltGolM-17
❑ 96UppDec-23
❑ 97Fle-24
❑ 97FleTif-24
❑ 97Pac-41
❑ 97PacLigB-41
❑ 97PacSil-41
❑ 97RedSoxS-12
❑ 97RedSoxSPl-12
❑ 97RedSoxSPr-12
❑ 97Sco-226
❑ 97ScoArtPWB-226
❑ 97ScoPreS-226
❑ 97ScoShoS-226
❑ 97ScoShoSAP-226
❑ 97StaClu-63
❑ 97StaCluMOP-63
❑ 97Top-123

Greenwell, Richard
❑ 89HigSchPLS-12

Greenwood, Bob
❑ 55Bow-42

Greenwood, John
❑ 88PulBraP-1753

Greenwood, Mike
❑ 87PocGiaTB-9

Greenwood, William
❑ 87OldJudN-210

Greeny, Burdette
❑ 98HelBreM-16

Greer, Brian K.
❑ 80Top-685
❑ 82AmaGolST-2

Greer, Edward C.
❑ 88AugBecN-18

Greer, Ken
❑ 88OneYanP-2047
❑ 89PriWilCS-8
❑ 90Ft.LauYS-9
❑ 91Ft.LauYC-4
❑ 91Ft.LauYP-2418
❑ 92AlbYanF-2219
❑ 93ColCliF-1105
❑ 93ColCliP-4
❑ 94NorTidF-2914
❑ 95PhoFirTI-44

Greer, Matt
❑ 98YakBeaG-18

Greer, Michael
❑ 87OldJudN-211

Greer, Randy
❑ 80PenPilBT-14
❑ 80PenPilCT-20

Greer, Rusty
❑ 90ButCopKSP-4
❑ 91ChaRanC-21
❑ 91ChaRanP-1325
❑ 91Cla/Bes-172
❑ 91FloStaLAP-FSL4
❑ 92ProFS7-156
❑ 92SkyAA F-267
❑ 92TulDriF-2701
❑ 92TulDriS-607
❑ 93TulDriF-2741
❑ 93TulDriTI-11
❑ 94BowBes-B90
❑ 94BowBesR-B90
❑ 94LeaLimR-66
❑ 94OklCit8F-1504
❑ 94TopTra-29T
❑ 95ColCho-405
❑ 95ColChoGS-405
❑ 95ColChoSE-182
❑ 95ColChoSEGS-182
❑ 95ColChoSESS-182
❑ 95ColChoSS-405
❑ 95Don-513
❑ 95DonPreP-513
❑ 95DonTopotO-161
❑ 95Emo-86
❑ 95Fin-15
❑ 95FinRef-15
❑ 95Fla-89
❑ 95Lea-61
❑ 95LeaLim-73
❑ 95Pac-427
❑ 95PanSti-107
❑ 95Pin-253
❑ 95PinArtP-253
❑ 95PinMusC-253
❑ 95RanCra-12
❑ 95Sco-540
❑ 95ScoAi-AM18
❑ 95ScoGolR-540
❑ 95ScoPlaTS-540
❑ 95Sel-215
❑ 95SelArtP-215
❑ 95Spo-109
❑ 95SpoArtP-109
❑ 95StaClu-486
❑ 95StaCluMOP-486
❑ 95StaCluSTWS-486
❑ 95StaCluVR-266
❑ 95StaCluVRMO-266
❑ 95Stu-89
❑ 95Top-279
❑ 95TopCyb-151
❑ 95Ult-110
❑ 95UltAllR-3
❑ 95UltAllRGM-3
❑ 95UltGolM-110
❑ 95UltSecYS-3
❑ 95UltSecYSGM-3
❑ 95UppDec-156
❑ 95UppDecED-156
❑ 95UppDecEDG-156
❑ 95UppDecSE-173
❑ 95UppDecSEG-173
❑ 95Zen-96
❑ 96Cir-87
❑ 96CirRav-87
❑ 96ColCho-741
❑ 96ColChoGS-741
❑ 96ColChoSS-741
❑ 96Don-183
❑ 96DonPreP-183
❑ 96EmoXL-122
❑ 96Fla-170
❑ 96Fle-251
❑ 96FleTif-251
❑ 96Lea-71
❑ 96LeaLim-46
❑ 96LeaLimG-46
❑ 96LeaPrePB-71
❑ 96LeaPrePG-71
❑ 96LeaPrePS-71
❑ 96LeaSig-104
❑ 96LeaSigA-85
❑ 96LeaSigAG-85
❑ 96LeaSigAS-85
❑ 96LeaSigPPG-104
❑ 96LeaSigPPP-104
❑ 96MetUni-114
❑ 96MetUniP-114
❑ 96Pac-431
❑ 96RanDr P-11
❑ 96RanFle-7
❑ 96RanMot-9
❑ 96Sco-30
❑ 96ScoDugC-A29
❑ 96ScoDugCAP-A29
❑ 96StaClu-315
❑ 96StaCluMOP-315
❑ 96Stu-97
❑ 96StuPrePB-97
❑ 96StuPrePG-97
❑ 96StuPrePS-97
❑ 96Top-87
❑ 96Ult-136
❑ 96UltGolM-136
❑ 96UppDec-211
❑ 97Bow-284
❑ 97BowChr-95
❑ 97BowChrI-95
❑ 97BowChrIR-95
❑ 97BowChrR-95
❑ 97BowInt-284
❑ 97Cir-43
❑ 97CirRav-43
❑ 97ColCho-239
❑ 97ColChoT-TR3
❑ 97Don-226
❑ 97Don-422
❑ 97DonEli-127
❑ 97DonEliGS-127
❑ 97DonGolPP-226
❑ 97DonGolPP-422
❑ 97DonLim-44
❑ 97DonLim-133
❑ 97DonLimE-44
❑ 97DonLimE-133
❑ 97DonLimENG-133
❑ 97DonLimFotG-48
❑ 97DonPre-76
❑ 97DonPreCttC-76
❑ 97DonSig-80
❑ 97DonSigA-43
❑ 97DonSigAC-52
❑ 97DonSigAM-52
❑ 97DonSigPPP-80
❑ 97DonSilPP-226
❑ 97DonSilPP-422
❑ 97DonVxP1-23
❑ 97Fin-193
❑ 97FinRef-193
❑ 97FlaShoLC-156
❑ 97FlaShoLeg0-156
❑ 97FlaShoLeg1-156
❑ 97FlaShoM-A156
❑ 97FlaShoM-B156
❑ 97FlaShoM-C156
❑ 97FlaShoR0-156
❑ 97FlaShoR1-156
❑ 97FlaShoR2-156
❑ 97Fle-222
❑ 97FleTif-222
❑ 97Lea-28
❑ 97Lea-387
❑ 97LeaFraM-28
❑ 97LeaFraM-387
❑ 97LeaFraMDC-28
❑ 97LeaFraMDC-387
❑ 97LeaKnoG-7
❑ 97LeaWarT-8
❑ 97MetUni-163
❑ 97NewPin-63
❑ 97NewPinAP-63
❑ 97NewPinMC-63
❑ 97NewPinPP-63
❑ 97Pac-201
❑ 97PacLigB-201
❑ 97PacPri-69
❑ 97PacPriLB-69
❑ 97PacPriP-69
❑ 97PacSil-201
❑ 97PinCer-56
❑ 97PinCerMBla-56
❑ 97PinCerMBlu-56
❑ 97PinCerMG-56
❑ 97PinCerMR-56
❑ 97PinCerR-56
❑ 97PinIns-95
❑ 97PinInsCE-95
❑ 97PinInsDE-95
❑ 97PinTotCPB-56
❑ 97PinTotCPG-56
❑ 97PinTotCPR-56
❑ 97PinX-P-22
❑ 97PinX-PMoS-22
❑ 97RanCup-2
❑ 97RanDr P-10
❑ 97RanMinM-3
❑ 97RanMot-8
❑ 97RanSco-4
❑ 97RanScoPl-4
❑ 97RanScoPr-4
❑ 97Sco-43
❑ 97Sco-534
❑ 97ScoArtPWB-43
❑ 97ScoArtPWB-534
❑ 97ScoPreS-43
❑ 97ScoResC-534
❑ 97ScoShoS-43
❑ 97ScoShoS-534
❑ 97ScoShoSAP-43
❑ 97ScoShoSAP-534
❑ 97Sel-30
❑ 97SelArtP-30
❑ 97SelCom-30
❑ 97SelRegG-30
❑ 97SelToootT-21
❑ 97SelToootTMB-21
❑ 97SP-174
❑ 97SpoIll-43
❑ 97SpoIllEE-43
❑ 97StaClu-52
❑ 97StaCluMat-52
❑ 97StaCluMOP-52
❑ 97Stu-48
❑ 97StuPrePG-48
❑ 97StuPrePS-48
❑ 97Top-12
❑ 97TopChr-6
❑ 97TopChrR-6
❑ 97TopGal-94
❑ 97TopGalPPI-94
❑ 97Ult-133
❑ 97UltGolME-133
❑ 97UltPlaME-133
❑ 97UppDec-180
❑ 97UppDec-387
❑ 98BowBes-41
❑ 98BowBesAR-41
❑ 98BowBesR-41
❑ 98CirThu-137
❑ 98CirThuRav-137
❑ 98CirThuSupRav-137
❑ 98ColCho-520
❑ 98ColChoSQ-SQ49
❑ 98CroRoy-137
❑ 98Don-124
❑ 98DonCol-124
❑ 98DonColE-436
❑ 98DonColL-201
❑ 98DonColP-647
❑ 98DonColS-124
❑ 98DonCruG-47
❑ 98DonCruP-47
❑ 98DonCruR-47
❑ 98DonEli-36
❑ 98DonEliA-36
❑ 98DonEliS-36
❑ 98DonGolPP-124
❑ 98DonPre-97
❑ 98DonPreSeat-97
❑ 98DonPriCD-124
❑ 98DonPriCE-436
❑ 98DonPriCL-201
❑ 98DonPriCP-647
❑ 98DonProLO-10
❑ 98DonSig-76
❑ 98DonSigP-76
❑ 98DonSilPP-124
❑ 98Fin-6
❑ 98FinNo--6
❑ 98FinNo-R-6
❑ 98FinRef-6
❑ 98FlaShoLeg0-105
❑ 98FlaShoLeg1-105
❑ 98FlaShoLeg2-105
❑ 98FlaShoLeg3-105
❑ 98FlaShoLegM-105
❑ 98FlaShoR0-105
❑ 98FlaShoR1-105
❑ 98FlaShoR2-105
❑ 98FlaShoR3-105
❑ 98Fle-231
❑ 98FleVin'-60
❑ 98FleVin'C-60
❑ 98Lea-1
❑ 98LeaFraDA-1
❑ 98LeaFraF-1
❑ 98LeaFraM-1
❑ 98LeaFraM-1
❑ 98LeaFraMDC-1
❑ 98LeaFraMDC-1
❑ 98LeaFraMZ2-1
❑ 98LeaRS-76
❑ 98LeaRS-167
❑ 98LeaRSLHolo-76
❑ 98LeaRSLHolo-167
❑ 98LeaRSLong-76
❑ 98LeaRSLong-167
❑ 98LeaRTrue-76
❑ 98LeaRTrue-167
❑ 98LeaStaRep-30
❑ 98MetUni-131
❑ 98MetUniPMG-131
❑ 98Pac-204
❑ 98PacAur-88
❑ 98PacInv-70
❑ 98PacInvPBlue-70
❑ 98PacInvSilv-70
❑ 98PacInvTeam-27
❑ 98PacOme-238
❑ 98PacOmeR-238
❑ 98PacOnl-734
❑ 98PacOnlR-734
❑ 98PacOnlWC-734
❑ 98PacPar-105
❑ 98PacParC-105
❑ 98PacParG-105
❑ 98PacParHS-105
❑ 98PacParPB-105
❑ 98PacParR-105
❑ 98PacPlaB-204
❑ 98PacRedT-204
❑ 98PacSil-204
❑ 98Pin-72
❑ 98PinIns-63
❑ 98PinInsCE-63
❑ 98PinInsDE-63
❑ 98PinInsSG-18AB
❑ 98PinInsSG-18CD
❑ 98PinInsSGS-18AB
❑ 98PinInsSGS-18CD
❑ 98PinPer-86
❑ 98PinPerPP-86
❑ 98PinPlu-124
❑ 98PinPluAP-PP40
❑ 98PinPluGAP-PP40
❑ 98PinPluMAP-PP40
❑ 98PinPreP-72
❑ 98PinSna-TR6
❑ 98RanPinM-3
❑ 98ScoRT-218
❑ 98ScoRTSS-PP120
❑ 98ScoRTSSAP-PP120
❑ 98ScoRTSSAP1-PP120
❑ 98SP Aut-191
❑ 98SpoIll-49
❑ 98SpoIllEE-49
❑ 98SpoIllFE-49
❑ 98SpoIllWSF-63
❑ 98SpoIllWSFEE-63
❑ 98SpoIllWSFFE-63
❑ 98SPxFin-134
❑ 98SPxFinR-134
❑ 98SPxFinS-134
❑ 98StaCluFDI-7
❑ 98StaCluI-7
❑ 98StaCluOneK-7
❑ 98StaCluPP-7
❑ 98Stu-85
❑ 98StuGPP-85
❑ 98StuSPP-85
❑ 98Top-220
❑ 98TopChr-220
❑ 98TopChrR-220
❑ 98TopDevR-220
❑ 98TopDia-220
❑ 98TopGal-59
❑ 98TopGalGP-59
❑ 98TopGalOPP-59
❑ 98TopGalPPI-59
❑ 98TopGalPPIA-59
❑ 98TopGolLabC1-28
❑ 98TopGolLabC1B-28
❑ 98TopGolLabC1One-28
❑ 98TopGolLabC1R-28
❑ 98TopGolLabC2-28
❑ 98TopGolLabC2B-28
❑ 98TopGolLabC2One-28
❑ 98TopGolLabC2R-28
❑ 98TopGolLabC3-28
❑ 98TopGolLabC3B-28
❑ 98TopGolLabC3One-28
❑ 98TopGolLabC3R-28
❑ 98TopMiniC-220
❑ 98TopOpeD-107
❑ 98TopSta-12
❑ 98TopStaB-12
❑ 98TopStaG-12
❑ 98TopStaGR-12
❑ 98TopStaS-12
❑ 98Ult-151
❑ 98UltGolM-151
❑ 98UltMas-151
❑ 98UltPlaM-151
❑ 98UppDec-152
❑ 98UppDec-235
❑ 98UppDec-365
❑ 98UppDecSF-131
❑ 98Zen-33
❑ 98Zen5 xx7-10
❑ 98Zen5x7GoldImp-10
❑ 98Zen5x7Imp-10
❑ 98ZenZ-G-33
❑ 98ZenZ-S-33
❑ 99199Fin-92
❑ 99Bow-15
❑ 99BowChr-15
❑ 99BowChrG-15
❑ 99BowChrGR-15
❑ 99BowChrI-15
❑ 99BowChrIR-15
❑ 99BowChrR-15
❑ 99BowGol-15
❑ 99BowInt-15
❑ 99CroRoyB-138
❑ 99CroRoyL-138
❑ 99CroRoyOD-138
❑ 99FinGolRef-92
❑ 99FinRef-92
❑ 99FlaShoLeg1-121
❑ 99FlaShoLeg2-121
❑ 99FlaShoLeg3-121
❑ 99FlaShoLegM1-121
❑ 99FlaShoLegM2-121
❑ 99FlaShoLegM3-121
❑ 99FlaShoR1-121
❑ 99FlaShoR2-121
❑ 99FlaShoR3-121
❑ 99Fle-142
❑ 99FleBri-11
❑ 99FleBri2G-11
❑ 99FleBriBlu-11
❑ 99FleBriGol-11
❑ 99FleSta9-142
❑ 99FleWarT-142
❑ 99MetUni-214
❑ 99MetUniGM-214
❑ 99MetUniPMG-214
❑ 99Pac-425
❑ 99PacAur-191
❑ 99PacAurOD-191
❑ 99PacCroC-283
❑ 99PacCroCPB-283

❑ 99PacInv-145
❑ 99PacInvOD-145
❑ 99PacInvPB-145
❑ 99PacOme-236
❑ 99PacOmeC-236
❑ 99PacOmeG-236
❑ 99PacOmePB-236
❑ 99PacPar-235
❑ 99PacParC-235
❑ 99PacParG-235
❑ 99PacParHoloGold-235
❑ 99PacParHS-235
❑ 99PacParOD-235
❑ 99PacParPB-235
❑ 99PacParRed-235
❑ 99PacPlaB-425
❑ 99PacPri-143
❑ 99PacPriHB-143
❑ 99PacPriHG-143
❑ 99PacPriHM-143
❑ 99PacPriHP-143
❑ 99PacPriRed-143
❑ 99PacPriS-91
❑ 99PacPriS206-91
❑ 99PacPriS206R-91
❑ 99PacRed-425
❑ 99Rev-141
❑ 99RevPremDate-141
❑ 99RevRet-141
❑ 99RevShaSS-141
❑ 99SkyMolM-81
❑ 99SkyMolMX-81
❑ 99SkyPre-197
❑ 99SkyPreR-197
❑ 99SkyThu-151
❑ 99SkyThuRant-151
❑ 99SkyThuRave-151
❑ 99SP SigAuto-RGR
❑ 99SPSig-143
❑ 99StaClu-3
❑ 99StaCluFDI-3
❑ 99StaCluOoaK-3
❑ 99StaCluPP-3
❑ 99ThuSkySupR-151
❑ 99Top-128
❑ 99TopBlaLC1-92
❑ 99TopBlaLC2-92
❑ 99TopBlaLC3-92
❑ 99TopChr-128
❑ 99TopChrR-128
❑ 99TopGal-58
❑ 99TopGalPP-58
❑ 99TopGalPPI-58
❑ 99TopGolL-92
❑ 99TopGolLC1-92
❑ 99TopGolLC2-92
❑ 99TopGolLOtO-92
❑ 99TopMVPP-128
❑ 99TopOpeD-75
❑ 99TopRedLC1-92
❑ 99TopRedLC2-92
❑ 99TopRedLC3-92
❑ 99TopSta-106
❑ 99TopStaFoil-106
❑ 99Ult-40
❑ 99UltGolM-40
❑ 99UltMas-40
❑ 99UltPlaM-40
❑ 99UppDec-217
❑ 99UppDecEL1-217
❑ 99UppDecEL2-217
❑ 99UppDecM-210
❑ 99UppDecMGS-210
❑ 99UppDecMHFS-210
❑ 99UppDecMSS-210
❑ 99UppDecRI-RG
❑ 99UppDecRIL2-RG
❑ 99Vic-404

Gregg, David
❑ 12HomRunKE-37
❑ 12Zee-59

Gregg, Eric
❑ 88T/MUmp-34
❑ 89T/MUmp-32
❑ 90T/MUmp-31

Gregg, Hal
❑ 46DodTeal-8
❑ 47DodTeal-8
❑ 47TipTop-95
❑ 49EurSta-161
❑ 52Top-318
❑ 76TayBow4-73
❑ 83TopRep5-318
❑ 90DodTar-296

Gregg, Kevin
❑ 97VisOakG-12
❑ 98ModA'sG-11

Gregg, Neal
❑ 98OneYanG-12

Gregg, Sylvanus
❑ 09ObaT21-118
❑ 16FleBreD-34

Gregg, Tommy
❑ 86NasPirP-9
❑ 87HarSenP-19
❑ 88BufBisC-12
❑ 88BufBisP-1474
❑ 88Don-203
❑ 88FleUpd-113
❑ 88FleUpdG-113
❑ 88ScoRoo-69T
❑ 88ScoRooG-69T
❑ 89BraDub-13
❑ 89ClaTraP-192
❑ 89Don-121
❑ 89DonBasB-170
❑ 89Fle-592
❑ 89FleGlo-592
❑ 89PanSti-32
❑ 89TopTra-39T
❑ 89TopTraT-39T
❑ 89UppDec-751
❑ 90BraDubP-9
❑ 90BraDubS-11
❑ 90Don-239
❑ 90Fle-585
❑ 90FleCan-585
❑ 90Lea-86
❑ 90OPC-223
❑ 90PanSti-224
❑ 90PubIntS-114
❑ 90Sco-78
❑ 90ScoYouSI-39
❑ 90Top-223
❑ 90TopTif-223
❑ 90UppDec-121
❑ 91BraDubP-13
❑ 91BraSubS-17
❑ 91Don-244
❑ 91Fle-691
❑ 91Lea-144
❑ 91OPC-742
❑ 91PanFreS-19
❑ 91Sco-606
❑ 91StaClu-571
❑ 91Top-742
❑ 91TopDesS-742
❑ 91TopMic-742
❑ 91TopTif-742
❑ 91Ult-6
❑ 92BraLykP-14
❑ 92BraLykS-15
❑ 92Don-485
❑ 92OPC-53
❑ 92Sco-623
❑ 92StaClu-244
❑ 92Top-53
❑ 92TopGol-53
❑ 92TopGolW-53
❑ 92TopMic-53
❑ 93IndIndF-1496
❑ 96ChaKniB-12
❑ 97RicBra-11
❑ 97RicBraBC-22

Gregg, Vean
❑ 09SpoNewSM-71
❑ 11PloCanE-30
❑ 12T207-71
❑ 13NatGamW-17
❑ 13TomBarW-16
❑ 14CraJacE-29
❑ 14TexTomE-21
❑ 14TexTomE-53
❑ 15CraJacE-29
❑ 15SpoNewP-4
❑ 19W514-33
❑ 22Zee-127

Gregory, B.
❑ 09PC7HHB-17

Gregory, Brad
❑ 90MiaMirIS-10

Gregory, Howie
❑ 09PC7HHB-17
❑ 11Zee-28
❑ 12HomRunKE-21
❑ 12PCLPin-7
❑ 12Zee-31
❑ 13Zee-32
❑ 14Zee-81
❑ 15Zee-78

Gregory, Jim
❑ 72CedRapCT-7

Gregory, John
❑ 83VerBeaDT-17

Gregory, Lee (Grover)
❑ 62KahAtl-9
❑ 77FriOneYW-74

Gregory, Paul
❑ 47SigOil-7

Gregory, Scott
❑ 78DunBluJT-10

Gregson, Goose (Glenn)
❑ 77ReaPhiT-12
❑ 83MidCubT-3
❑ 84MidCubT-14
❑ 87WinSpiP-12
❑ 88GreFalDTI-27
❑ 89GreFalDSP-33
❑ 90BakDodCLC-246
❑ 91BakDodCLC-29
❑ 91CalLeLA-24
❑ 93AlbDukF-1480
❑ 94AlbDukF-859
❑ 98DodPol-30

Greif, Bill
❑ 72OPC-101
❑ 72PadPos-11
❑ 72Top-101
❑ 73OPC-583
❑ 73PadDea-9
❑ 73Top-583
❑ 74OPC-102
❑ 74PadDea-10
❑ 74PadMcDD-4
❑ 74PadTeal-5
❑ 74Top-102A
❑ 74Top-102B
❑ 74TopSta-92
❑ 75OPC-168
❑ 75PadDea-8
❑ 75Top-168
❑ 75TopMin-168
❑ 76OPC-184
❑ 76St.LouCP-13
❑ 76Top-184
❑ 77OPC-243
❑ 77Top-112

Greiner, Dan
❑ 19W514-80

Greisinger, Seth
❑ 97Bes-39
❑ 97BesAll-1
❑ 97BesLimA-14
❑ 97Bow-99
❑ 97BowBes-108
❑ 97BowBesAR-108
❑ 97BowBesR-108
❑ 97BowChr-121
❑ 97BowChrI-121
❑ 97BowChrIR-121
❑ 97BowChrR-121
❑ 97BowInt-99
❑ 97JacSun-2
❑ 97SouLeaTP-17
❑ 98BesAutPOY-5
❑ 98BesCasT-4
❑ 98BesPreA-14
❑ 98Bow-380
❑ 98BowChr-380
❑ 98BowChrGA-380
❑ 98BowChrGAR-380
❑ 98BowChrI-380
❑ 98BowChrIR-380
❑ 98BowChrR-380
❑ 98BowGolA-380
❑ 98BowInt-380
❑ 98FleUpd-U34
❑ 98SP MinPE-53
❑ 98SPMin-53
❑ 98TolMudHQ-1
❑ 99Fle-438
❑ 99FleSta9-438
❑ 99FleWarT-438
❑ 99Pac-165
❑ 99PacPlaB-165
❑ 99PacRed-165
❑ 99StaClu-282
❑ 99StaCluFDI-282
❑ 99StaCluOoaK-282
❑ 99StaCluPP-282
❑ 99Top-147
❑ 99TopChr-147
❑ 99TopChrR-147
❑ 99TopMVPP-147
❑ 99UppDec-9
❑ 99UppDecBD-100
❑ 99UppDecBDD-100
❑ 99UppDecBDQ-100
❑ 99UppDecBDT-100
❑ 99UppDecEL1-9
❑ 99UppDecEL2-9

Grejtak, Bryan
❑ 90OklSoo-1
❑ 91BluOriC-13
❑ 91BluOriP-4130

Greminger, Edward
❑ 09T206-486
❑ 10CouT21-25
❑ 11SpoLifCW-147

Grenert, Geoff
❑ 93BoiHawC-12
❑ 93BoiHawF-3909
❑ 94CedRapKC-11
❑ 94CedRapKF-1105
❑ 95CedRapKTI-21
❑ 96CedRapKTI-10

Grennan, Steve
❑ 91PocPioP-3777
❑ 91PocPioSP-19
❑ 92KinMetC-7
❑ 92KinMetF-1525
❑ 93PitMetC-7
❑ 93PitMetF-3701
❑ 94CapCitBC-8
❑ 94CapCitBF-1746
❑ 95StLucMTI-14

Grensky, Herb
❑ 80PenPilCT-15

Gresham, Kris
❑ 91BluOriC-1
❑ 91BluOriP-4131
❑ 92KanCouCC-9
❑ 92KanCouCF-93
❑ 92KanCouCTI-12
❑ 93FreKeyC-9
❑ 93FreKeyF-1029
❑ 94BowBayF-2416
❑ 94OriPro-42
❑ 95RocRedWTI-17
❑ 96BowBayB-15
❑ 97RocRedW-12
❑ 98JupHamQ-27

Gresko, Michael
❑ 97EriSeaWB-15

Gress, Loren
❑ 90IdaFalBP-3270
❑ 91IdaFalBP-4336
❑ 91MacBraP-871

Gressett, Leroy
❑ 22Zee-44
❑ 23Zee-66
❑ 24Zee-45

Grewal, Ranbir
❑ 90FreStaS-6
❑ 90JamExpP-17
❑ 91MidLeaAP-MWL45
❑ 91RocExpC-5
❑ 91RocExpP-2040
❑ 92ClaFS7-304
❑ 92WesPalBEC-12
❑ 92WesPalBEF-2084

Grice, Dan
❑ 98MadBlaW-8

Grich, Bob
❑ 69BalOriPC-1
❑ 71OPC-193
❑ 71Top-193
❑ 72OPC-338
❑ 72OriPos-14
❑ 72Top-338
❑ 73BalOriP-20
❑ 73Kel2D-39
❑ 73LinPor-10
❑ 73OPC-418
❑ 73OriJohP-3A
❑ 73OriJohP-3B
❑ 73OriTeal-17
❑ 73SevTraC-27
❑ 73Top-418
❑ 74OPC-109
❑ 74Top-109
❑ 74TopDecE-8
❑ 74TopSta-125
❑ 75BalOriP-13
❑ 75Hos-72
❑ 75Kel-4A
❑ 75Kel-4B
❑ 75OPC-225
❑ 75Top-225
❑ 75TopMin-225
❑ 76BalOriP-15
❑ 76Hos-13
❑ 76HosTwi-13
❑ 76OPC-335
❑ 76SSP-388
❑ 76Top-335
❑ 77BurCheD-126
❑ 77ChiWilD-27
❑ 77DailsID-27
❑ 77DetCaeD-27
❑ 77HolInnD-27
❑ 77Hos-131
❑ 77Kel-39
❑ 77MSADis-27
❑ 77OPC-28
❑ 77PepGloD-25
❑ 77RCColC-26
❑ 77SagDis-27
❑ 77sDis-27
❑ 77Spo-3502
❑ 77Top-521
❑ 77WenDis-27
❑ 77ZipDis-27
❑ 78AngFamF-13
❑ 78Hos-62
❑ 78OPC-133
❑ 78RCColC-57
❑ 78SSP270-194
❑ 78Top-18
❑ 79BasPat-34
❑ 79Hos-112
❑ 79OPC-248
❑ 79Top-477
❑ 80OPC-326
❑ 80Top-621
❑ 81AllGamPI-13
❑ 81Don-289
❑ 81Fle-269
❑ 81FleStiC-50
❑ 81LonBeaPT-2
❑ 81OPC-182
❑ 81Top-182
❑ 81TopSti-53
❑ 81TopSupHT-58
❑ 82Don-90
❑ 82Fle-461
❑ 82FleSta-218
❑ 82Kel-38
❑ 82OPC-284
❑ 82PerAll-5
❑ 82PerAllG-5
❑ 82SevSluC-12
❑ 82Top-162
❑ 82Top-284
❑ 82TopSti-4
❑ 82TopSti-162
❑ 83AllGamPI-13
❑ 83Don-468
❑ 83Fle-91
❑ 83Kel-60
❑ 83OPC-381
❑ 83OPC-387
❑ 83SevCoi-11
❑ 83Top-387
❑ 83Top-790
❑ 83TopSti-43
❑ 84AllGamPI-104
❑ 84AngSmo-10
❑ 84Don-179
❑ 84Fle-518
❑ 84Nes792-315
❑ 84OPC-315
❑ 84Top-315
❑ 84TopRubD-20
❑ 84TopSti-228
❑ 84TopTif-315
❑ 85AllGamPI-14
❑ 85AngSmo-12
❑ 85AngStrH-7
❑ 85Don-280
❑ 85Fle-302
❑ 85Lea-88
❑ 85OPC-155
❑ 85Top-465
❑ 85TopRubD-20
❑ 85TopSti-230
❑ 85TopTif-465
❑ 86AngSmo-12
❑ 86Don-207
❑ 86Fle-157
❑ 86OPC-155
❑ 86Top-155
❑ 86Top-486
❑ 86TopSti-181
❑ 86TopTat-23
❑ 86TopTif-155
❑ 86TopTif-486
❑ 86Woo-12
❑ 87AngGriS-1
❑ 87AngGriS-2
❑ 87AngGriS-3
❑ 87AngGriS-4
❑ 87AngGriS-5
❑ 87AngGriS-6
❑ 87AngGriS-7
❑ 87AngGriS-8
❑ 87AngGriS-9
❑ 87AngGriS-10
❑ 87AngGriS-11
❑ 87AngGriS-12
❑ 87AngGriS-13
❑ 87AngGriS-14
❑ 87AngGriS-15
❑ 87AngGriS-16
❑ 87AngGriS-17
❑ 87Don-456
❑ 87Fle-81
❑ 87FleGlo-81
❑ 87OPC-4
❑ 87RedFolSB-30
❑ 87Spo-184
❑ 87Top-677
❑ 87TopTif-677
❑ 89AngSmo-11
❑ 90PacLeg-31
❑ 90SweBasG-58
❑ 91OriCro-165
❑ 91UppDecS-12
❑ 92ActPacA-71
❑ 93OriCroASU-5
❑ 93TedWil-19
❑ 93UppDecAH-59
❑ 94UppDecAH-132
❑ 94UppDecAH1-132

Grier, Antron
❑ 87EriCarP-12
❑ 88HamRedP-1723
❑ 88SavCarP-355
❑ 89SprCarB-3
❑ 90St.PetCS-10

Grier, Dave
❑ 80BurBeeT-5
❑ 82ElPasDT-17

Grier, Mark
❑ 79NewCoPT-14

Griesser, Grant
❑ 90AppFoxBS-10
❑ 90AppFoxP-2097

Grieve, Ben
❑ 94Cla#1DPMF-DD2
❑ 94ClaUpdCotC-CC2
❑ 94SigRooDP-3
❑ 94SigRooDPS-3
❑ 94SouOreAC-7
❑ 94SouOreAF-3636
❑ 94StaCluDP-84
❑ 94StaCluDPFDI-84
❑ 94TopTra-44T
❑ 94UppDecAHNIL-18
❑ 95ActPac2G-18G
❑ 95ActPacF-53
❑ 95ActPacF-79
❑ 95Bes-37
❑ 95BesFra-F5
❑ 95Bow-258
❑ 95BowBes-B25
❑ 95BowBesR-B25
❑ 95BowGolF-258
❑ 95ColCho-40
❑ 95ColChoGS-40
❑ 95ColChoSS-40
❑ 95Exc-108
❑ 95ExcFirYP-7
❑ 95ModA'sTI-8
❑ 95Pin-175
❑ 95PinArtP-175
❑ 95PinETA-1
❑ 95PinMusC-175
❑ 95ScoDraP-DP12
❑ 95SelSurS-SS1
❑ 95SigRooFD-FD2
❑ 95SigRooFDS-FD2
❑ 95SPML-8
❑ 95SPML-125
❑ 95SPMLA-10
❑ 95SPMLDtS-DS5
❑ 95StaClu-103
❑ 95StaCluFDI-103
❑ 95StaCluMOP-103
❑ 95StaCluSTWS-103
❑ 95Top-212
❑ 95UppDec-3
❑ 95UppDecED-3
❑ 95UppDecEDG-3
❑ 95UppDecML-150

❑ 95UppDecML-216
❑ 95UppDecMLFS-150
❑ 95UppDecMLFS-216
❑ 95UppDecSE-107
❑ 95UppDecSEG-107
❑ 95WesMicWTI-22
❑ 96BesAutSA-23
❑ 96Bow-187
❑ 96BowBes-118
❑ 96BowBesAR-118
❑ 96BowBesMI-7
❑ 96BowBesMIR-7
❑ 96BowBesR-118
❑ 96BowFoi-187
❑ 96Exc-98
❑ 96HunStaTI-8
❑ 96ModA'sB-4
❑ 96SigRooOJRS-R2
❑ 96SigRooOJRSS-R2
❑ 96Top-436
❑ 97Bes-11
❑ 97BesAutAS-14
❑ 97BesAutP-H1
❑ 97BesAutSBPP-7
❑ 97BesAutSC-3
❑ 97BesCarCSP-3
❑ 97BesLimA-15
❑ 97BesLum-5
❑ 97Bow-386
❑ 97BowBes-169
❑ 97BowBesAR-169
❑ 97BowBesR-169
❑ 97BowCerBlaIA-CA32
❑ 97BowCerBluIA-CA32
❑ 97BowCerGolIA-CA32
❑ 97BowChr-255
❑ 97BowChrI-255
❑ 97BowChrIR-255
❑ 97BowChrR-255
❑ 97BowChrSHR-SHR7
❑ 97BowChrSHRR-SHR7
❑ 97BowInt-386
❑ 97BowScoHR-7
❑ 97DonSigA-44
❑ 97DonSigAC-53
❑ 97DonSigAM-53
❑ 97HunStaTI-9
❑ 97SouLeaTP-13
❑ 97Top-488
❑ 98A'sMot-8
❑ 98BesAutPOY-6
❑ 98BesCasT-5
❑ 98BesCon-2
❑ 98BesCon-3
❑ 98BesFulCA-5
❑ 98BesPreA-15
❑ 98BesYouG-2
❑ 98BesYouG-3
❑ 98Bow-97
❑ 98BowBes-105
❑ 98BowBesA-105
❑ 98BowBesAAR-105
❑ 98BowBesAR-105
❑ 98BowBesAR-105
❑ 98BowBesMIF-MI6
❑ 98BowBesMIFAR-MI6
❑ 98BowBesMIFR-MI6
❑ 98BowBesP-BP1
❑ 98BowBesPAR-BP1
❑ 98BowBesPR-BP1
❑ 98BowBesR-105
❑ 98BowCerBlueAU-27
❑ 98BowCerGA-27
❑ 98BowCerSA-27
❑ 98BowChr-97
❑ 98BowChrGA-97
❑ 98BowChrGAR-97
❑ 98BowChrI-97
❑ 98BowChrIR-97
❑ 98BowChrR-97
❑ 98BowChrR-46
❑ 98BowChrRR-46
❑ 98BowGolA-97
❑ 98BowInt-97
❑ 98BowScoC-SC4
❑ 98CirThu-1
❑ 98CirThuRav-1
❑ 98CirThuSupRav-1
❑ 98ColCho-21
❑ 98ColCho-110
❑ 98ColChoCtG-CG18A
❑ 98ColChoCtG-CG18B
❑ 98ColChoCtG-CG18C
❑ 98ColChoCtGExch-CG18
❑ 98ColChoCtGIW-CG18
❑ 98ColChoMBH-20
❑ 98ColChoSQ-SQ15
❑ 98ColChoSQDouble-23
❑ 98ColChoSQHR-23
❑ 98ColChoSQSingle-23
❑ 98ColChoSQTriple-23
❑ 98CroRoy-101
❑ 98CroRoyFoB-15
❑ 98CroRoyFoBA-15
❑ 98CroRoyPotG-18
❑ 98Don-144
❑ 98Don-415
❑ 98DonCol-144
❑ 98DonCol-203
❑ 98DonColE-497
❑ 98DonColL-380
❑ 98DonColP-693
❑ 98DonColP-749
❑ 98DonColS-144
❑ 98DonColS-198
❑ 98DonCruG-76
❑ 98DonCruP-76
❑ 98DonCruR-76
❑ 98DonEli-97
❑ 98DonEliA-97
❑ 98DonEliBttF-4
❑ 98DonEliBttFA-4
❑ 98DonEliC-16
❑ 98DonEliMC-16
❑ 98DonEliS-97
❑ 98DonGolPP-144
❑ 98DonGolPP-415
❑ 98DonPre-143
❑ 98DonPre-199
❑ 98DonPreGB-2
❑ 98DonPreGES-3
❑ 98DonPreGoB-2
❑ 98DonPreGX-3
❑ 98DonPreGXDC-3
❑ 98DonPrePM-28
❑ 98DonPreSeat-143
❑ 98DonPreSeat-199
❑ 98DonPreTP-2
❑ 98DonPreTPD-1
❑ 98DonPreTPG-2
❑ 98DonPreTPS-2
❑ 98DonPriCD-144
❑ 98DonPriCD-203
❑ 98DonPriCE-497
❑ 98DonPriCL-380
❑ 98DonPriCP-693
❑ 98DonPriCP-749
❑ 98DonRatR-28
❑ 98DonRatRM-28
❑ 98DonRooDK-7
❑ 98DonRooDKC-7
❑ 98DonSig-89
❑ 98DonSigA-37
❑ 98DonSigAC-50
❑ 98DonSigAM-51
❑ 98DonSigP-89
❑ 98DonSigSB-11
❑ 98DonSigSP-8
❑ 98DonSilPP-144
❑ 98DonSilPP-415
❑ 98DonSonM9-14
❑ 98E-X2-98
❑ 98E-X2ECFut-98
❑ 98E-X2ECNow-98
❑ 98E-X2SD2001-12
❑ 98E-X2Sig2001-7
❑ 98Fin-50
❑ 98FinMysF2-M26
❑ 98FinMysF2-M28
❑ 98FinMysF2-M30
❑ 98FinMysF2-M40
❑ 98FinMysF2R-M26
❑ 98FinMysF2R-M28
❑ 98FinMysF2R-M30
❑ 98FinMysF2R-M40
❑ 98FinNo--50
❑ 98FinNo-R-50
❑ 98FinRef-50
❑ 98FlaShoLeg0-4
❑ 98FlaShoLeg1-4
❑ 98FlaShoLeg2-4
❑ 98FlaShoLeg3-4
❑ 98FlaShoLegM-4
❑ 98FlaShoR0-4
❑ 98FlaShoR1-4
❑ 98FlaShoR2-4
❑ 98FlaShoR3-4
❑ 98FlaShoWotF-3
❑ 98Fle-20
❑ 98Fle-583
❑ 98FleProF-PF5
❑ 98FleRooS-6
❑ 98FleVin'-44
❑ 98FleVin'C-44
❑ 98Lea-181
❑ 98LeaCruG-76
❑ 98LeaCruP-76
❑ 98LeaCruR-76
❑ 98LeaFraDA-181
❑ 98LeaFraF-181
❑ 98LeaFraM-181
❑ 98LeaFraM-181
❑ 98LeaFraMDC-181
❑ 98LeaFraMDC-181
❑ 98LeaFraMZ2-181
❑ 98LeaRCMLHDSamp-13
❑ 98LeaRS-141
❑ 98LeaRS-162
❑ 98LeaRS-201
❑ 98LeaRSFOSamp-2
❑ 98LeaRSFresh-2
❑ 98LeaRSGreHit-5
❑ 98LeaRSLHolo-141
❑ 98LeaRSLHolo-162
❑ 98LeaRSLHolo-201
❑ 98LeaRSLong-141
❑ 98LeaRSLong-162
❑ 98LeaRSLong-201
❑ 98LeaRSMLHD-13
❑ 98LeaRSTicMas-20
❑ 98LeaRSTicMasDC-20
❑ 98LeaRTrue-141
❑ 98LeaRTrue-162
❑ 98LeaRTrue-201
❑ 98MetUni-50
❑ 98MetUniPMG-50
❑ 98Pac-166
❑ 98PacAur-66
❑ 98PacAurCube-12
❑ 98PacAurHC-12
❑ 98PacAurODLC-12
❑ 98PacAurPF-14
❑ 98PacAurPFC-14
❑ 98PacAurPFPB-14
❑ 98PacAurPFR-14
❑ 98PacAurPFS-14
❑ 98PacGolCDC-25
❑ 98PacInv-59
❑ 98PacInvGems-84
❑ 98PacInvMiT-13
❑ 98PacInvPBlue-59
❑ 98PacInvSilv-59
❑ 98PacInvTeam-20
❑ 98PacOme-176
❑ 98PacOmeEP-6
❑ 98PacOmeEP1o1-6
❑ 98PacOmeFTF-8
❑ 98PacOmeOnIns-12
❑ 98PacOmeP-8
❑ 98PacOmeR-176
❑ 98PacOmeRS-28
❑ 98PacOmeRST3-28
❑ 98PacOnl-530A
❑ 98PacOnl-530B
❑ 98PacOnl-550
❑ 98PacOnlR-530A
❑ 98PacOnlR-530B
❑ 98PacOnlR-550
❑ 98PacOnlWC-530A
❑ 98PacOnlWC-530B
❑ 98PacOnlWC-550
❑ 98PacPar-79
❑ 98PacParC-79
❑ 98PacParFC-12
❑ 98PacParG-79
❑ 98PacParHS-79
❑ 98PacParI-4
❑ 98PacParPB-79
❑ 98PacParR-79
❑ 98PacParSD-14
❑ 98PacParTC-10
❑ 98PacPlaB-166
❑ 98PacRedT-166
❑ 98PacSil-166
❑ 98PacTeaC-11
❑ 98Pin-160
❑ 98PinIns-113
❑ 98PinInsBtN-16
❑ 98PinInsC-5
❑ 98PinInsCE-113
❑ 98PinInsCG-5
❑ 98PinInsDE-113
❑ 98PinInsSG-13AB
❑ 98PinInsSG-13CD
❑ 98PinInsSGS-13AB
❑ 98PinInsSGS-13CD
❑ 98PinPer-121
❑ 98PinPerLP-1
❑ 98PinPerPP-121
❑ 98PinPlu-131
❑ 98PinPluAP-PP42
❑ 98PinPluGAP-PP42
❑ 98PinPluLM-5
❑ 98PinPluMAP-PP42
❑ 98PinPluTP-15
❑ 98PinPluTPG-15
❑ 98PinPluTPM-15
❑ 98PinPreP-160
❑ 98Revo-106
❑ 98RevoFP-7
❑ 98RevoPTP-7
❑ 98RevoRooHH-15
❑ 98RevoRooHHG-15
❑ 98RevoShow-13
❑ 98RevoSS-106
❑ 98Sco-244
❑ 98ScoNewS-NS9
❑ 98ScoRT-242
❑ 98ScoRTSS-PP135
❑ 98ScoRTSSAP-PP135
❑ 98ScoRTSSAP1-PP135
❑ 98ScoRTStarGaz-20
❑ 98SelSelSamp-3
❑ 98SkyDugA-77
❑ 98SkyDugA-94
❑ 98SkyDugAIA-77
❑ 98SkyDugAIA-94
❑ 98SP Aut-10
❑ 98SP Aut-SD21
❑ 98SP AutC-BG
❑ 98SP AutSD-SD21
❑ 98SP AutSDT-SD21
❑ 98SP MinDTSPE-DS6
❑ 98SP MinPE-3
❑ 98SP MinPE-90
❑ 98SP SPTSC-BG
❑ 98SPMin-3
❑ 98SPMin-90
❑ 98SPMinDTS-DS6
❑ 98SpoIll-50
❑ 98SpoIll-167
❑ 98SpoIllAuto-4
❑ 98SpoIllEE-50
❑ 98SpoIllEE-167
❑ 98SpoIllFE-50
❑ 98SpoIllFE-167
❑ 98SpoIllTaN-145
❑ 98SpoIllTaNEE-145
❑ 98SpoIllWSF-49
❑ 98SpoIllWSFEE-49
❑ 98SpoIllWSFFE-49
❑ 98SPxFin-20
❑ 98SPxFinR-20
❑ 98SPxFinS-20
❑ 98StaCluBPP-BP1
❑ 98StaCluFDI-330
❑ 98StaCluI-330
❑ 98StaCluITW-W3
❑ 98StaCluOneK-330
❑ 98StaCluPP-330
❑ 98StaCluRC-RC14
❑ 98Stu-27
❑ 98Stu8x10S-3
❑ 98StuAuto8X10-3
❑ 98StuFF-3
❑ 98StuFFDC-3
❑ 98StuGPP-27
❑ 98StuPor8x10-3
❑ 98StuPor8x10GP-3
❑ 98StuSony99-14
❑ 98StuSPP-27
❑ 98Top-255
❑ 98TopChr-255
❑ 98TopChrR-255
❑ 98TopChrRC-R10
❑ 98TopChrRCRef-R10
❑ 98TopDevR-255
❑ 98TopDia-255
❑ 98TopGal-55
❑ 98TopGalGP-55
❑ 98TopGalOPP-55
❑ 98TopGalPPI-55
❑ 98TopGalPPIA-55
❑ 98TopGolLabC1-79
❑ 98TopGolLabC1B-79
❑ 98TopGolLabC1One-79
❑ 98TopGolLabC1R-79
❑ 98TopGolLabC2-79
❑ 98TopGolLabC2B-79
❑ 98TopGolLabC2One-79
❑ 98TopGolLabC2R-79
❑ 98TopGolLabC3-79
❑ 98TopGolLabC3B-79
❑ 98TopGolLabC3One-79
❑ 98TopGolLabC3R-79
❑ 98TopMiniC-255
❑ 98TopRooCla-R10
❑ 98TopSta-25
❑ 98TopStaB-25
❑ 98TopStaG-25
❑ 98TopStaGR-25
❑ 98TopStaS-25
❑ 98TopStaSB-S1
❑ 98TopStaSG-S1
❑ 98TopStaSGR-S1
❑ 98TopStaSS-S1
❑ 98TopTek-1
❑ 98TopTekD-1
❑ 98UD3-10
❑ 98UD3-100
❑ 98UD3-190
❑ 98UD3DieCut-10
❑ 98UD3DieCut-100
❑ 98UD3DieCut-190
❑ 98Ult-239
❑ 98Ult-499
❑ 98UltGolM-239
❑ 98UltGolM-499
❑ 98UltMas-239
❑ 98UltMas-499
❑ 98UltMilM-14
❑ 98UltPlaM-239
❑ 98UltPlaM-499
❑ 98UltRoctS-1
❑ 98UltTop3-30
❑ 98UppDec-280
❑ 98UppDec-368
❑ 98UppDec-626
❑ 98UppDecAC-AS3
❑ 98UppDecAPA3-BG
❑ 98UppDecBCP-BC30
❑ 98UppDecDS-DS20
❑ 98UppDecR-125
❑ 98UppDecRBBop-BB12
❑ 98UppDecREP-10
❑ 98UppDecRGKoG-G8
❑ 98UppDecRNF-NF25
❑ 98UppDecRQL-Q6
❑ 98UppDecRSotT-BGR
❑ 98UppDecRTC-TC15
❑ 98UppDecU-3
❑ 98Zen-91
❑ 98Zen5 xx7-70
❑ 98Zen5x7GoldImp-70
❑ 98Zen5x7Imp-70
❑ 98ZenRooT-10
❑ 98ZenZ-G-91
❑ 98ZenZ-S-91
❑ 98ZenZ-T-10
❑ 98ZenZ-TG-10
❑ 99199Fin-45
❑ 99199Fin-122
❑ 99AllMysFR-M24
❑ 99Bow-1
❑ 99BowAut-BA68
❑ 99BowBes-83
❑ 99BowBes-97
❑ 99BowBesAR-83
❑ 99BowBesAR-97
❑ 99BowBesR-83
❑ 99BowBesR-97
❑ 99BowBesROY-ROY1
❑ 99BowBesROY-ROY1A
❑ 99BowChr-1
❑ 99BowChrG-1
❑ 99BowChrGR-1
❑ 99BowChrI-1
❑ 99BowChrIR-1
❑ 99BowChrR-1
❑ 99BowEarR-ER4
❑ 99BowGol-1
❑ 99BowInt-1
❑ 99CroRoyB-103
❑ 99CroRoyL-103
❑ 99CroRoyOD-103
❑ 99CroRoyPotG-17
❑ 99CroRoyPP-17
❑ 99CroRoyPPN-17
❑ 99DumSet-ER4
❑ 99E-X Cen-81
❑ 99E-X Cen-P81
❑ 99E-X CenECFut-81
❑ 99E-X CenECNow-81
❑ 99E-X CenEQ-7
❑ 99FinDouF-DF5
❑ 99FinDouFDualR-DF5
❑ 99FinGolRef-45
❑ 99FinGolRef-122
❑ 99FinMil-M33
❑ 99FinPeelHyp-13
❑ 99FinPeelSpark-13
❑ 99FinPeeSS-13
❑ 99FinRef-45
❑ 99FinRef-122
❑ 99FinSplS-SS13
❑ 99FinSplSDR-SS13
❑ 99FinTeaFB-TF20
❑ 99FinTeaFBR-TF20
❑ 99FinTeaFG-TF20
❑ 99FinTeaFGR-TF20
❑ 99FinTeaFR-TF20
❑ 99FinTeaFRR-TF20
❑ 99FlaShoLeg1-5
❑ 99FlaShoLeg2-5
❑ 99FlaShoLeg3-5
❑ 99FlaShoLegM1-5
❑ 99FlaShoLegM2-5
❑ 99FlaShoLegM3-5
❑ 99FlaShoR1-5
❑ 99FlaShoR2-5
❑ 99FlaShoR3-5
❑ 99FlaShoWotF-2
❑ 99Fle-23
❑ 99Fle-582
❑ 99FleBri-62
❑ 99FleBri2G-62
❑ 99FleBriBlu-62
❑ 99FleBriGol-62
❑ 99FleBriI-2
❑ 99FleDiaSkiSheet-NNO
❑ 99FleMys-89
❑ 99FleMysG-89
❑ 99FleMysM-89
❑ 99FleMysP-4
❑ 99FleRooFla-10
❑ 99FleSta9-23
❑ 99FleSta9-582
❑ 99FleVin'-23
❑ 99FleWarT-23
❑ 99FleWarT-582
❑ 99KinDis-28
❑ 99MetUni-131
❑ 99MetUni-247
❑ 99MetUni-293
❑ 99MetUniGM-131
❑ 99MetUniGM-247
❑ 99MetUniGM-293
❑ 99MetUniPMG-131
❑ 99MetUniPMG-247
❑ 99MetUniPMG-293
❑ 99Pac-311
❑ 99Pac-311A
❑ 99PacAur-136
❑ 99PacAurOD-136
❑ 99PacCroC-203
❑ 99PacCroCITC-12
❑ 99PacCroCPB-203
❑ 99PacCroCTC-21
❑ 99PacDynaD-5
❑ 99PacDynaDT-5
❑ 99PacGolCDC-12
❑ 99PacInv-108
❑ 99PacInvFP-13
❑ 99PacInvOD-108
❑ 99PacInvPB-108
❑ 99PacInvSF-13
❑ 99PacInvSF-13B
❑ 99PacInvSH-14
❑ 99PacInvSH-14B
❑ 99PacInvTA-12
❑ 99PacOme-169
❑ 99PacOmeC-169
❑ 99PacOmeG-169
❑ 99PacOmePB-169
❑ 99PacPar-171
❑ 99PacParC-171
❑ 99PacParG-171
❑ 99PacParHoloGold-171
❑ 99PacParHS-171
❑ 99PacParOD-171
❑ 99PacParPB-26
❑ 99PacParPB-171
❑ 99PacParRed-171
❑ 99PacParTC-21
❑ 99PacPlaB-311
❑ 99PacPlaB-311A
❑ 99PacPri-105
❑ 99PacPriHB-105
❑ 99PacPriHG-105
❑ 99PacPriHM-105
❑ 99PacPriHP-105
❑ 99PacPriRed-105
❑ 99PacPriS-32
❑ 99PacPriS206-32
❑ 99PacPriS206R-32
❑ 99PacPriSP-32

❑ 99PacPriSV-32
❑ 99PacRed-311
❑ 99PacRed-311A
❑ 99PacTeaC-10
❑ 99Pin-9
❑ 99Rev-102
❑ 99RevDiaL-24
❑ 99RevPremDate-102
❑ 99RevRet-102
❑ 99RevShaSS-102
❑ 99SkyMolM-150
❑ 99SkyMolMF-50
❑ 99SkyMolMFS-50
❑ 99SkyMolMFT-50
❑ 99SkyMolMX-150
❑ 99SkyPre-78
❑ 99SkyPre-289
❑ 99SkyPre-S83
❑ 99SkyPreLB-12
❑ 99SkyPreR-78
❑ 99SkyPreR-289
❑ 99SkyThu-247
❑ 99SkyThu-S247
❑ 99SkyThuRant-247
❑ 99SkyThuRave-247
❑ 99SkyThuUnl-U8
❑ 99SP Aut-61
❑ 99SP Aut-131
❑ 99SP AutC-BG
❑ 99SP AutCG-BG
❑ 99SP AutEF-E21
❑ 99SP AutR-R21
❑ 99SpoIll-18
❑ 99SpoIll-72
❑ 99SpoIllOTW-4
❑ 99SPx-58
❑ 99SPxFinR-58
❑ 99SPxFinS-58
❑ 99SPxPowE-PE21
❑ 99SPxPreS-PS23
❑ 99SPxStaF-SF30
❑ 99StaClu-14
❑ 99StaCluA-SCA5
❑ 99StaCluC-SCC23
❑ 99StaCluC-CS1
❑ 99StaCluC-CS7
❑ 99StaCluC-CS13
❑ 99StaCluC-CS19
❑ 99StaCluCR-SCC23
❑ 99StaCluFDI-14
❑ 99StaCluOoaK-14
❑ 99StaCluPP-14
❑ 99StaCluTI-T13C
❑ 99StaCluTL-T13C
❑ 99StaCluTL-T13C
❑ 99ThuSkySupR-247
❑ 99Top-110
❑ 99Top-457
❑ 99TopAllMF-M24
❑ 99TopAut-A7
❑ 99TopBlaLC1-75
❑ 99TopBlaLC2-75
❑ 99TopBlaLC3-75
❑ 99TopChr-110
❑ 99TopChr-457
❑ 99TopChrF1-FF13
❑ 99TopChrF1R-FF13
❑ 99TopChrNB-NB11
❑ 99TopChrNBR-NB11
❑ 99TopChrR-110
❑ 99TopChrR-457
❑ 99TopGal-36
❑ 99TopGal-118
❑ 99TopGalAG-AG2
❑ 99TopGalE-E5
❑ 99TopGalGoH-GH8
❑ 99TopGalHer-TH2
❑ 99TopGalHerP-TH2
❑ 99TopGalPP-36
❑ 99TopGalPP-118
❑ 99TopGalPPI-36
❑ 99TopGalPPI-118
❑ 99TopGolL-75
❑ 99TopGolLC1-75
❑ 99TopGolLC2-75
❑ 99TopGolLOtO-75
❑ 99TopMVPP-110
❑ 99TopMVPP-457
❑ 99TopNewB-NB11
❑ 99TopOpeD-64
❑ 99TopOver-A8
❑ 99TopRedLC1-75
❑ 99TopRedLC2-75
❑ 99TopRedLC3-75
❑ 99TopSta-7
❑ 99TopSta-174
❑ 99TopSta'S-2
❑ 99TopSta'SG-2
❑ 99TopSta'SGDH-2
❑ 99TopSta1Foil-7
❑ 99TopSta2Foil-7
❑ 99TopSta3Foil-7
❑ 99TopSta4Foil-7
❑ 99TopStaFoil-7
❑ 99TopStaFoil-174
❑ 99TopStaFS-7
❑ 99TopStaG-G6
❑ 99TopStaGFoil-G6
❑ 99TopStaOS-7
❑ 99TopStaTS-7
❑ 99TopStaTS-7
❑ 99TopSupC-19
❑ 99TopSupCR-19
❑ 99TopTek-1A
❑ 99TopTek-1B
❑ 99TopTekG-1A
❑ 99TopTekG-1B
❑ 99TopTekT-T4
❑ 99UD Cho-40
❑ 99UD Cho-123
❑ 99UD ChoMBH-B19
❑ 99UD ChoPCR-40
❑ 99UD ChoPCR-123
❑ 99UD ChoS-14
❑ 99UD ChoSD-14
❑ 99UD ChoSHR-14
❑ 99UD ChoST-14
❑ 99UD ChoYW-Y21
❑ 99UD Ion-44
❑ 99UD Ion-81
❑ 99UD IonC-C18
❑ 99UD IonH-H18
❑ 99UD IonR-44
❑ 99UD IonR-81
❑ 99UDHolo-42
❑ 99UDHoloAUsome-42
❑ 99Ult-196
❑ 99UltGolM-196
❑ 99UltMas-196
❑ 99UltPlaM-196
❑ 99UltRBIK-30
❑ 99UppDec-167
❑ 99UppDecBD-61
❑ 99UppDecBDD-61
❑ 99UppDecBDDom-D14
❑ 99UppDecBDDomE-D14
❑ 99UppDecBDMN-M14
❑ 99UppDecBDMNE-M14
❑ 99UppDecBDQ-61
❑ 99UppDecBDT-61
❑ 99UppDecCf7-40
❑ 99UppDecCf7-C29
❑ 99UppDecCf7Cf7P-C29
❑ 99UppDecCf7SftF-S8
❑ 99UppDecCL-112
❑ 99UppDecCLCC-112
❑ 99UppDecCLM-C68
❑ 99UppDecCo7CE-40
❑ 99UppDecE-40
❑ 99UppDecE-163
❑ 99UppDecEFXG-64
❑ 99UppDecEFXG-163
❑ 99UppDecEL1-167
❑ 99UppDecEL2-167
❑ 99UppDecEPE-P20
❑ 99UppDecF-F18
❑ 99UppDecFD-F18
❑ 99UppDecFQ-F18
❑ 99UppDecFT-F18
❑ 99UppDecGJ-BG
❑ 99UppDecIP-I8
❑ 99UppDecIPD-I8
❑ 99UppDecIPHR-I8
❑ 99UppDecIPT-I8
❑ 99UppDecM-149
❑ 99UppDecMGS-149
❑ 99UppDecMHFS-149
❑ 99UppDecMP-149
❑ 99UppDecMP-BG
❑ 99UppDecMSC-SC2
❑ 99UppDecMSS-149
❑ 99UppDecMST-T6
❑ 99UppDecO-17
❑ 99UppDecOAPoH-BG
❑ 99UppDecOAPoH-BGAU
❑ 99UppDecOSO-17
❑ 99UppDecR-62
❑ 99UppDecRG-62
❑ 99UppDecRP-62
❑ 99UppDecTE-T18
❑ 99UppDecTED-T18
❑ 99UppDecTEQ-T18
❑ 99UppDecTET-T18
❑ 99UppDecVtaT-V20
❑ 99UppDecVtaTD-V20
❑ 99UppDecVtaTQ-V20
❑ 99UppDecVtaTT-V20
❑ 99UppDecWY-W30
❑ 99UppDecWYD-W30
❑ 99UppDecWYHR-W30
❑ 99UppDecWYT-W30
❑ 99Vic-279
❑ 99Vic-283
❑ 99WesMicWAM-11

Grieve, Tim

❑ 94EugEmeC-11
❑ 94EugEmeF-3705
❑ 94StaCluDP-90
❑ 94StaCluDPFDI-90
❑ 94TopTra-66T
❑ 95Exc-60
❑ 97WilBluR-19
❑ 98HigDesMG-11

Grieve, Tom

❑ 71MLBOffS-540
❑ 71OPC-167
❑ 71Top-167
❑ 72RanTeal-10
❑ 72Top-609
❑ 73OPC-579
❑ 73Top-579
❑ 74OPC-268
❑ 74Top-268
❑ 75Hos-38
❑ 75OPC-234
❑ 75RanPos-12
❑ 75Top-234
❑ 75TopMin-234
❑ 76Hos-130
❑ 76OPC-106
❑ 76SSP-270
❑ 76Top-106
❑ 77BurCheD-25
❑ 77Hos-93
❑ 77Top-403
❑ 78MetDaiPA-8
❑ 78Top-337
❑ 79OPC-138
❑ 79Top-277
❑ 79TucTorT-14
❑ 91MetWIZ-152
❑ 93RanKee-13
❑ 96BowBesMIAR-7

Grieve, William

❑ 55Bow-275

Griffen, Leonard

❑ 91CedRapRC-5
❑ 91CedRapRP-2713
❑ 92CedRapRC-3
❑ 92CedRapRF-1067

Griffey, Craig

❑ 92BelMarCB-25
❑ 92BelMarF-1456
❑ 92LimRocGH-3
❑ 92UppDec-85
❑ 93AppFoxCB-10
❑ 93AppFoxFI-2471
❑ 93RivPilCLC-27
❑ 94JacSunF-1424
❑ 94SigRooFCD-1
❑ 94SigRooFCD-2
❑ 94SigRooFCS-AU1
❑ 94SigRooFCS-AU2
❑ 94SigRooFCS-AU3
❑ 94SigRooFCS-AU5
❑ 95PorCitRTI-12
❑ 95UppDecML-59
❑ 95UppDecMLFS-59
❑ 96PorCitRB-13
❑ 97TacRai-14

Griffey, Ken Jr.

❑ 83KelCerB-14
❑ 84OCoandSI-237
❑ 87BelMarTI-15
❑ 88CalLeaACLC-26
❑ 88SanBerSB-1
❑ 88SanBerSCLC-34
❑ 88VerMarP-NNO
❑ 89Bow-220
❑ 89Bow-259
❑ 89BowTif-220
❑ 89BowTif-259
❑ 89ClaTraO-131
❑ 89ClaTraP-193
❑ 89Don-33
❑ 89DonBasB-192
❑ 89DonRoo-3
❑ 89Fle-548
❑ 89FleGlo-548
❑ 89MarMot-3
❑ 89MotGriJ-1
❑ 89MotGriJ-2
❑ 89MotGriJ-3
❑ 89MotGriJ-4
❑ 89PacGriCB-1A
❑ 89PacGriCB-1B
❑ 89PacGriCB-1C
❑ 89Scomast-30
❑ 89ScoRoo-100T
❑ 89ScoYouS2-18
❑ 89SpoIllFKI-158
❑ 89TopHeaUT-5
❑ 89TopTra-41T
❑ 89TopTraT-41T
❑ 89UppDec-1
❑ 89UppDecS-2
❑ 89UppDecS-3
❑ 90AllBasT-17
❑ 90Baz-18
❑ 90Bow-481
❑ 90BowTif-481
❑ 90ClaBlu-20
❑ 90ClaYel-T1
❑ 90Col-3
❑ 90Don-4
❑ 90Don-365
❑ 90DonBesA-1
❑ 90DonLeaS-8
❑ 90DonSupD-4
❑ 90Fle-513
❑ 90FleAwaW-16
❑ 90FleBasA-14
❑ 90FleBasAC-14
❑ 90FleBasM-14
❑ 90FleBasMC-14
❑ 90FleCan-513
❑ 90FleLeaL-14
❑ 90FleLeaLC-14
❑ 90FleSoaS-6
❑ 90FleWaxBC-C10
❑ 90GooHumICBLS-11
❑ 90Hot50RS-19
❑ 90KinDis-16
❑ 90Lea-245
❑ 90LeaPre-4
❑ 90M.Vpin-28
❑ 90M.Vpin-94
❑ 90MarMot-3
❑ 90MLBBasB-117
❑ 90MSAIceTD-8
❑ 90OPC-336
❑ 90PanSti-155
❑ 90PlaPri-2
❑ 90Pos-23
❑ 90PubIntS-30
❑ 90PubIntS-433
❑ 90PubIntS-595
❑ 90RedFolSB-40
❑ 90Sco-560
❑ 90Sco100RS-3
❑ 90Spo-7
❑ 90StaGriJ-1
❑ 90StaGriJ-2
❑ 90StaGriJ-3
❑ 90StaGriJ-4
❑ 90StaGriJ-5
❑ 90StaGriJ-6
❑ 90StaGriJ-7
❑ 90StaGriJ-8
❑ 90StaGriJ-9
❑ 90StaGriJ-10
❑ 90StaGriJ-11
❑ 90SunSee-2
❑ 90SupActM-3
❑ 90Top-336
❑ 90TopBig-250
❑ 90TopCoi-16
❑ 90TopDeb89-46
❑ 90TopDou-29
❑ 90TopGloS-20
❑ 90TopHeaU-5
❑ 90TopMag-3
❑ 90TopMag-27
❑ 90TopRoo-11
❑ 90TopSti-225
❑ 90TopSti-323
❑ 90TopStiB-49
❑ 90TopTif-336
❑ 90ToyRoo-13
❑ 90UppDec-24
❑ 90UppDec-156
❑ 90UppDecS-3
❑ 90USPlaCA-11S
❑ 90WinDis-7
❑ 90WonBreS-18
❑ 91AlrGriG-1
❑ 91AlrGriG-2
❑ 91AlrGriG-3
❑ 91AlrGriG-4
❑ 91AlrGriP-1
❑ 91AreHol-2
❑ 91BasBesHM-7
❑ 91Ble23KGJ-1
❑ 91Ble23KGJ-2
❑ 91Ble23KGJ-3
❑ 91BlePro-1
❑ 91Bow-246
❑ 91CadEllD-26
❑ 91CarGuaPG-1
❑ 91Cla1-T3
❑ 91Cla2-T1
❑ 91Cla3-T30
❑ 91ClaGam-120
❑ 91Col-4
❑ 91ColGriJ-1
❑ 91ColGriJ-2
❑ 91ColGriJ-3
❑ 91ColGriJ-4
❑ 91ColGriJ-5
❑ 91ColGriJ-6
❑ 91ColGriJ-7
❑ 91ColGriJ-8
❑ 91ColGriJ-9
❑ 91ColGriJ-10
❑ 91ColGriJ-11
❑ 91ColGriJ-12
❑ 91Don-49
❑ 91Don-77
❑ 91Don-392
❑ 91DonPre-4
❑ 91Fle-450
❑ 91Fle-450A
❑ 91Fle-710
❑ 91FleAll-7
❑ 91FroRowKGJ-1
❑ 91FroRowKGJ-1P
❑ 91FroRowKGJ-2
❑ 91FroRowKGJ-2P
❑ 91FroRowKGJ-3
❑ 91FroRowKGJ-3P
❑ 91FroRowKGJ-4
❑ 91FroRowKGJ-4P
❑ 91FroRowKGJ-5
❑ 91FroRowKGJ-5P
❑ 91FroRowKGJ-6
❑ 91FroRowKGJ-7
❑ 91FroRowKGJ-8
❑ 91FroRowKGJ-9
❑ 91FroRowKGJ-10
❑ 91JimDea-2
❑ 91KinDis-6
❑ 91Lea-372
❑ 91MajLeaCP-4
❑ 91MarCouH-15
❑ 91MarCouH-28
❑ 91MooSna-4
❑ 91MotGri-1
❑ 91MotGri-3
❑ 91MotGri-4
❑ 91MSAHolD-9
❑ 91OPC-392
❑ 91OPC-790
❑ 91OPCPre-56
❑ 91PanCanT1-116
❑ 91PanFreS-172
❑ 91PanFreS-233
❑ 91PanSti-189
❑ 91PepGri-1
❑ 91PepGri-2
❑ 91PepGri-3
❑ 91PepGri-4
❑ 91PepGri-5
❑ 91PepGri-6
❑ 91PetSta-23
❑ 91PlaGriJ-1
❑ 91PlaGriJ-32
❑ 91PlaGriJ-33
❑ 91PlaGriJ-34
❑ 91PlaGriJ-35
❑ 91PlaGriJ-36
❑ 91PlaGriJ-37
❑ 91PlaGriJ-38
❑ 91PlaGriJ-49
❑ 91PlaGriJ-50
❑ 91PlaGriJ-61
❑ 91PlaGriJ-62
❑ 91PlaGriJ-63
❑ 91PlaGriJ-64
❑ 91PlaGriJ-65
❑ 91PlaGriJ-66
❑ 91PlaGriJ-xx
❑ 91Pos-11
❑ 91PosCan-26
❑ 91RedFolS-41
❑ 91RedFolS-120
❑ 91Sco-2
❑ 91Sco-396
❑ 91Sco-697
❑ 91Sco-841
❑ 91Sco-858
❑ 91Sco-892
❑ 91Sco100S-5
❑ 91ScoCoo-B3
❑ 91Sev3DCN-6
❑ 91SevCoi-A4
❑ 91SevCoi-F7
❑ 91SevCoi-M7
❑ 91SevCoi-NW4
❑ 91SevCoi-T8
❑ 91SevCoi-NC6
❑ 91SevCoi-NE6
❑ 91SevCoi-NW5
❑ 91SevCoi-SC3
❑ 91SimandSMLBL-18
❑ 91StaClu-270
❑ 91StaCluCM-10
❑ 91StaGri-1
❑ 91StaGri-2
❑ 91StaGri-4
❑ 91StaGri-6
❑ 91StaGri-8
❑ 91StaGri-10
❑ 91StaPinB-21
❑ 91Stu-112
❑ 91SunSee-11
❑ 91Top-392
❑ 91Top-790
❑ 91TopCraJI-36
❑ 91TopDesS-392
❑ 91TopDesS-790
❑ 91TopGloA-7
❑ 91TopMic-392
❑ 91TopMic-790
❑ 91TopSta-17
❑ 91TopTif-392
❑ 91TopTif-790
❑ 91TopTriH-A12
❑ 91Ult-336
❑ 91UltGol-4
❑ 91UppDec-555
❑ 91UppDec-572
❑ 91UppDecFE-79F
❑ 91UppDecFE-87F
❑ 91USPlaCA-1D
❑ 92AlrGriAAS-1
❑ 92AlrGriAAS-2
❑ 92AlrGriAAS-3
❑ 92AlrGriAAS-4
❑ 92AlrGriAAS-5
❑ 92AlrGriAAS-6
❑ 92AlrGriAAS-7
❑ 92AlrGriAAS-8
❑ 92AlrGriAAS-9
❑ 92AlrGriAAS-10
❑ 92AlrGriGM-1
❑ 92AlrGriGM-2
❑ 92AlrGriGM-3
❑ 92AlrGriGM-4
❑ 92AlrGriGM-5
❑ 92AlrGriGM-6
❑ 92AlrGriGM-7
❑ 92AlrGriGM-8
❑ 92AlrGriGM-9
❑ 92AlrGriGM-10
❑ 92AlrGriGMS-1
❑ 92AlrGriMc-1
❑ 92AlrGriMc-2
❑ 92AlrGriMc-3
❑ 92AreKidGCH-1
❑ 92AreKidGCH-2
❑ 92AreKidGCH-3
❑ 92AreKidGCH-4
❑ 92AreKidGCH-5
❑ 92Bow-100
❑ 92Cla1-T40
❑ 92Cla2-T44
❑ 92ClaBluBF-BC12
❑ 92ClaFS7-200
❑ 92ClaGam-186
❑ 92ClaRedB-BC12
❑ 92ColAllG-11
❑ 92ColAllP-11
❑ 92ColPro-8
❑ 92DEL-AU1
❑ 92Don-24
❑ 92Don-165

❑ 92DonCraJ1-12
❑ 92DonEli-13
❑ 92DonMcD-22
❑ 92DonPre-7
❑ 92Fle-279
❑ 92Fle-709
❑ 92FleAll-23
❑ 92FleCitTP-4
❑ 92FleTeaL-15
❑ 92FleUpdH-1
❑ 92Fre-15
❑ 92FroRowGCH-1
❑ 92FroRowGCH-2
❑ 92FroRowGCH-3
❑ 92FroRowGCH-4
❑ 92FroRowGCH-5
❑ 92FroRowGCH-6
❑ 92FroRowGCH-7
❑ 92FroRowGCH-8
❑ 92FroRowGCH-9
❑ 92FroRowGCH-10
❑ 92FroRowGG-1
❑ 92FroRowGG-2
❑ 92FroRowGG-3
❑ 92FroRowGH-1
❑ 92FroRowGH-2
❑ 92FroRowGH-3
❑ 92FroRowGJOC-NNO
❑ 92Hig5-107
❑ 92Hig5S-17
❑ 92Hig5S-32
❑ 92JimDea-11
❑ 92KinDis-8
❑ 92LaKdec-14
❑ 92Lea-392
❑ 92LeaBlaG-392
❑ 92LeaGolP-24
❑ 92LeaPre-24
❑ 92LimRocGH-2
❑ 92MarMot-2
❑ 92MooSna-7
❑ 92Mr.TurS-12
❑ 92MSABenSHD-10
❑ 92MTVRocnJ-3
❑ 92MVPPin-3
❑ 92New-9
❑ 92OPC-50
❑ 92OPCPre-167
❑ 92PanSti-60
❑ 92PanSti-277
❑ 92PepDieM-26
❑ 92PerGamGJ-1
❑ 92PerGamGJ-2
❑ 92PerGamGJ-3
❑ 92PerGamGJ-4
❑ 92PerGamGJ-5
❑ 92PerGamGJ-6
❑ 92PerGamGJ-7
❑ 92PerGamGJ-8
❑ 92PerGamGJ-9
❑ 92Pin-283
❑ 92Pin-549
❑ 92PinSlu-7
❑ 92PinTea2-47
❑ 92PinTeaP-9
❑ 92PlaGriJ-1
❑ 92PlaGriJ-2
❑ 92PlaGriJ-3
❑ 92PlaGriJ-4
❑ 92Pos-20
❑ 92RedFolS-41
❑ 92RedFolS-115
❑ 92Sco-1
❑ 92Sco-436
❑ 92Sco100S-1
❑ 92ScoImpP-28
❑ 92ScoProaG-7
❑ 92ScoSam-1
❑ 92SevCoi-26
❑ 92SpollIFK1-173
❑ 92SpollIFK1-734
❑ 92SpoStaCC-20
❑ 92StaClu-400
❑ 92StaClu-603
❑ 92StaCluD-70
❑ 92StaCluECN-603
❑ 92StaCluMP-7
❑ 92StaGriJ-1
❑ 92StaGriJ-2
❑ 92StaGriJ-3
❑ 92StaGriJ-4
❑ 92StaGriJ-5
❑ 92StaGriJ-6
❑ 92StaGriJ-7
❑ 92StaGriJ-8
❑ 92StaGriJ-9
❑ 92StaGriJ-10
❑ 92StaGriJ-11
❑ 92Stu-232
❑ 92SunSee-14
❑ 92Top-50
❑ 92TopGol-50
❑ 92TopGolW-50
❑ 92TopKid-122
❑ 92TopMcD-8
❑ 92TopMic-50
❑ 92TopMic-G50
❑ 92TriPla-152
❑ 92TriPlaG-GS8
❑ 92TriPlaP-1
❑ 92Ult-123
❑ 92UltAllS-6
❑ 92UltAwaW-22
❑ 92UppDec-85
❑ 92UppDec-424
❑ 92UppDec-650
❑ 92UppDecF-24
❑ 92UppDecFG-24
❑ 92UppDecTMH-22
❑ 92UppDecWB-T15
❑ 93AlrGri2TT-1
❑ 93AlrGri2TT-2
❑ 93AlrGri2TT-3
❑ 93AlrGri2TT-4
❑ 93AlrGri2TT-5
❑ 93AlrGri2TT-6
❑ 93AlrGrifMVO-1
❑ 93AlrGrifMVO-2
❑ 93AlrGrifMVO-3
❑ 93AlrGriT-1
❑ 93AlrGriTP-1
❑ 93Ble-10
❑ 93Ble-11
❑ 93Ble-12
❑ 93Ble-13
❑ 93Ble-14
❑ 93Ble-15
❑ 93Ble-16
❑ 93Ble-17
❑ 93Bow-375
❑ 93Bow-703
❑ 93CadDis-28
❑ 93ClaGam-38
❑ 93ColAllG-3
❑ 93DiaMar-44
❑ 93DiaMarA-3
❑ 93DiaMarP-5
❑ 93Don-553
❑ 93DonDiaK-DK1
❑ 93DonEliD-12
❑ 93DonLonBL-LL9
❑ 93DonMasotG-8
❑ 93DonMVP-20
❑ 93DonPre-20
❑ 93DurPowP2-15
❑ 93Fin-110
❑ 93FinJum-110
❑ 93FinRef-110
❑ 93Fla-270
❑ 93Fle-307
❑ 93FleAll-AL7
❑ 93FleAtl-11
❑ 93FleFruotL-25
❑ 93FleTeaL-AL10
❑ 93FroRowGJGC-1
❑ 93FroRowGJGC-2
❑ 93FroRowGJGC-3
❑ 93FroRowGJGC-4
❑ 93FroRowGJGC-5
❑ 93FroRowGJGC-6
❑ 93FroRowGJGC-7
❑ 93FroRowGJGC-8
❑ 93FroRowGJGC-9
❑ 93FroRowGJGC-10
❑ 93FunPac-16
❑ 93FunPac-24
❑ 93FunPac-30
❑ 93FunPac-111
❑ 93FunPac-114
❑ 93FunPac-224
❑ 93FunPacA-AS8
❑ 93Hos-25
❑ 93HumDumC-15
❑ 93JimDea-11
❑ 93KinDis-2
❑ 93Kra-8
❑ 93Lea-319
❑ 93LeaGolA-R7
❑ 93LeaGolA-U8
❑ 93MarDaiQ-4
❑ 93MariStaClu-1
❑ 93MarMot-4
❑ 93MetBak-9
❑ 93OPC-91
❑ 93OPCPreSP-9
❑ 93OPCPreSPF-9
❑ 93PacJugC-7
❑ 93PacSpa-286
❑ 93PanSti-63
❑ 93Pin-110
❑ 93PinCoo-22
❑ 93PinCooD-22
❑ 93PinHomRC-13
❑ 93PinSlu-28
❑ 93Pos-7
❑ 93PosCan-9
❑ 93RedFolS-34
❑ 93RedFolS-115
❑ 93Sco-1
❑ 93Sco-504
❑ 93Sco-536
❑ 93ScoFra-12
❑ 93ScoGolDT-5
❑ 93Sel-2
❑ 93SelChaS-19
❑ 93SelDufIP-7
❑ 93SelStaL-15
❑ 93SP-4
❑ 93SpeGolSGJ-1
❑ 93SPPlaP-PP9
❑ 93StaClu-591
❑ 93StaClu-707
❑ 93StaCluFDI-591
❑ 93StaCluFDI-707
❑ 93StaCluI-B4
❑ 93StaCluM-56
❑ 93StaCluMMP-3
❑ 93StaCluMO-11
❑ 93StaCluMOP-591
❑ 93StaCluMOP-707
❑ 93StaCluMOP-MB4
❑ 93StaCluMP-26
❑ 93Stu-96
❑ 93StuSupoC-1
❑ 93Top-179
❑ 93Top-405
❑ 93TOPBLAG-33
❑ 93TopFulS-2
❑ 93TopGol-179
❑ 93TopGol-405
❑ 93TopInaM-179
❑ 93TopInaM-405
❑ 93TopInaR-179
❑ 93TopInaR-405
❑ 93TopMic-179
❑ 93TopMic-405
❑ 93TopMic-P179
❑ 93TopPre-179
❑ 93TopPreS-6
❑ 93Toy-1
❑ 93ToyMasP-5
❑ 93TriPla-1
❑ 93TriPlaA-24
❑ 93TriPlaN-5
❑ 93TriPlaP-1
❑ 93Ult-619
❑ 93UltAllS-17
❑ 93UltAwaW-16
❑ 93UltPer-3
❑ 93UppDec-55
❑ 93UppDec-355
❑ 93UppDec-525
❑ 93UppDecCP-R11
❑ 93UppDecDG-13
❑ 93UppDecFA-A1
❑ 93UppDecFAJ-A1
❑ 93UppDecFH-59
❑ 93UppDecGold-55
❑ 93UppDecGold-355
❑ 93UppDecGold-525
❑ 93UppDecHRH-HR9
❑ 93UppDecIC-WI13
❑ 93UppDecICJ-WI13
❑ 93UppDecOD-D13
❑ 93UppDecS-19
❑ 93UppDecSH-HI9
❑ 93UppDecTriCro-TC4
❑ 93USPlaCA-4C
❑ 94AlrTacGJ-1
❑ 94AlrTacGJ-2
❑ 94AlrTacGJ-3
❑ 94AlrTacGJ-4
❑ 94AlrTacGJ-5
❑ 94AlrTacGJ-6
❑ 94AlrTacGJ-SP1
❑ 94AlrTacGJ-SP2
❑ 94AlrTacGJ-SP3
❑ 94AlrTacGJ-SP4
❑ 94AlrTacGJ-SP5
❑ 94Bow-5
❑ 94BowBes-R40
❑ 94BowBes-X96
❑ 94BowBesR-R40
❑ 94BowBesR-X96
❑ 94ChuShoS-3
❑ 94ColC-117
❑ 94ColC-317
❑ 94ColC-324
❑ 94ColC-340
❑ 94ColC-634
❑ 94ColC-P50
❑ 94ColChoGS-117
❑ 94ColChoGS-317
❑ 94ColChoGS-324
❑ 94ColChoGS-340
❑ 94ColChoGS-634
❑ 94ColChoHRA-HA2
❑ 94ColChoSS-117
❑ 94ColChoSS-317
❑ 94ColChoSS-324
❑ 94ColChoSS-340
❑ 94ColChoSS-634
❑ 94ColChoT-2
❑ 94ColChoT-7
❑ 94DaiQueKGJ-1
❑ 94DaiQueKGJ-2
❑ 94DaiQueKGJ-3
❑ 94DaiQueKGJ-4
❑ 94DaiQueKGJ-5
❑ 94DaiQueKGJ-6
❑ 94DaiQueKGJ-7
❑ 94DaiQueKGJ-8
❑ 94DaiQueKGJ-9
❑ 94DaiQueKGJ-10
❑ 94DenHol-12
❑ 94Don-4
❑ 94DonDiaK-DK14
❑ 94DonDiaKJ-DK14
❑ 94DonDom-A9
❑ 94DonDom-B6
❑ 94DonDomJ-A9
❑ 94DonDomJ-B6
❑ 94DonEli-45
❑ 94DonLonBL-5
❑ 94DonMVP-26
❑ 94DonPro-7
❑ 94DonSpeE-4
❑ 94DonSpiotG-3
❑ 94DonSpiotGJ-3
❑ 94Fin-232
❑ 94FinJum-232
❑ 94FinRef-232
❑ 94Fla-103
❑ 94FlaHotG-3
❑ 94FlaOutP-6
❑ 94Fle-286
❑ 94FleAllS-10
❑ 94FleExtB-166
❑ 94FleExtBGB-14
❑ 94FleGolM-4
❑ 94FleGolMJ-4
❑ 94FleLumC-5
❑ 94FleSun-13
❑ 94FleTeaL-12
❑ 94FUnPac-24
❑ 94FUnPac-182
❑ 94FUnPac-193
❑ 94FUnPac-200
❑ 94FUnPac-216
❑ 94FUnPac-224
❑ 94FUnPac-229
❑ 94FUnPac-235
❑ 94FUnPac-P172
❑ 94KinDis-6
❑ 94Kra-5
❑ 94Lea-368
❑ 94LeaGam-1
❑ 94LeaGolS-4
❑ 94LeaL-66
❑ 94LeaLimGA-11
❑ 94LeaMVPC-A8
❑ 94LeaMVPCG-A8
❑ 94LeaPowB-5
❑ 94LeaPro-3
❑ 94LeaSli-9
❑ 94LeaStaS-6
❑ 94MarMot-4
❑ 94NinGriJ-1
❑ 94O-PJumAF-8
❑ 94OPC-22
❑ 94OPCAllR-8
❑ 94OPCJumA-8
❑ 94OscMayR-6
❑ 94Pac-570
❑ 94PacGolP-2
❑ 94PacPro-P4
❑ 94PacSilP-8
❑ 94PacSilPC-8
❑ 94PanSti-118
❑ 94Pin-100
❑ 94PinArtP-100
❑ 94PinMusC-100
❑ 94PinPowS-PS23
❑ 94PinRunC-RC3
❑ 94PinTeaP-6
❑ 94PinTheN-3
❑ 94PinTri-TR17
❑ 94Pos-15
❑ 94PosCan-10
❑ 94ProMag-127
❑ 94ProMagP-1
❑ 94RedFolMI-33
❑ 94Sco-3
❑ 94Sco-628
❑ 94ScoCyc-TC17
❑ 94ScoGolR-3
❑ 94ScoGolR-628
❑ 94ScoGolS-32
❑ 94ScoSam-3
❑ 94ScoSam-3GR
❑ 94Sel-1
❑ 94SelCroC-CC10
❑ 94SigBatP-1
❑ 94SigRooFCD-3
❑ 94SigRooFCS-AU2
❑ 94SigRooFCS-AU4
❑ 94SigRooFCS-AU5
❑ 94SigRooFCS-AU6
❑ 94SigRooG-1
❑ 94SP-105
❑ 94SP-P24
❑ 94SPDieC-105
❑ 94SPHol-12
❑ 94SPHolDC-12
❑ 94Spo-143
❑ 94Spo-181
❑ 94SpoFanA-AS7
❑ 94SpoRooGGG-GG4
❑ 94SPPre-WR3
❑ 94StaClu-85
❑ 94StaClu-262
❑ 94StaClu-529
❑ 94StaCluDD-DD7
❑ 94StaCluF-F5
❑ 94StaCluFDI-85
❑ 94StaCluFDI-262
❑ 94StaCluFDI-529
❑ 94StaCluFJ-F5
❑ 94StaCluGR-85
❑ 94StaCluGR-262
❑ 94StaCluGR-529
❑ 94StaCluMO-17
❑ 94StaCluMOF-2
❑ 94StaCluMOP-85
❑ 94StaCluMOP-262
❑ 94StaCluMOP-529
❑ 94StaCluMOP-F5
❑ 94StaCluMOP-DD7
❑ 94Stu-101
❑ 94StuEdiC-3
❑ 94StuSerS-4
❑ 94StuSerSG-4
❑ 94TomPiz-21
❑ 94Top-388
❑ 94Top-400
❑ 94Top-606
❑ 94TopBlaG-8
❑ 94TopGol-388
❑ 94TopGol-400
❑ 94TopGol-606
❑ 94TopSpa-388
❑ 94TopSpa-400
❑ 94TopSpa-606
❑ 94TopSupS-19
❑ 94TopTraFI-5
❑ 94TriPla-127
❑ 94TriPlaBS-8
❑ 94TriPlaM-11
❑ 94TriPlaP-4
❑ 94Ult-120
❑ 94UltAllS-8
❑ 94UltAwaW-6
❑ 94UltHomRK-2
❑ 94UltOnBL-6
❑ 94UppDec-53
❑ 94UppDec-224
❑ 94UppDec-292
❑ 94UppDec-P224
❑ 94UppDec-GM1
❑ 94UppDec-KG1
❑ 94UppDecAJ-1
❑ 94UppDecAJ-48
❑ 94UppDecAJ-P48
❑ 94UppDecAJG-1
❑ 94UppDecAJG-48
❑ 94UppDecDC-W4
❑ 94UppDecED-53
❑ 94UppDecED-224
❑ 94UppDecED-292
❑ 94UppDecGJ-CL1
❑ 94UppDecGJ-CL2
❑ 94UppDecGJ-CL3
❑ 94UppDecGJ-CL4
❑ 94UppDecMLS-MM10
❑ 94UppDecMLSED-MM10
❑ 94UppDecNG-6
❑ 94UppDecNGED-6
❑ 94UppDecTTP-P6
❑ 94USPlaCA-12C
❑ 95Baz-31
❑ 95BazRedH-RH7
❑ 95Bow-321
❑ 95BowBes-R49
❑ 95BowBes-X12
❑ 95BowBesJR-2
❑ 95BowBesR-R49
❑ 95BowBesR-X12
❑ 95ClaFanFPCP-4
❑ 95ClaPhoC-50
❑ 95ColCho-62
❑ 95ColCho-70
❑ 95ColCho-88
❑ 95ColCho-P172
❑ 95ColChoCtG-CG8
❑ 95ColChoCtG-CG8B
❑ 95ColChoCtG-CG8C
❑ 95ColChoCtGE-8
❑ 95ColChoCtGG-CG8
❑ 95ColChoCtGG-CG8B
❑ 95ColChoCtGG-CG8C
❑ 95ColChoCtGGE-8
❑ 95ColChoGS-62
❑ 95ColChoGS-70
❑ 95ColChoGS-88
❑ 95ColChoSE-26
❑ 95ColChoSE-125
❑ 95ColChoSE-261
❑ 95ColChoSE-P125
❑ 95ColChoSEGS-26
❑ 95ColChoSEGS-125
❑ 95ColChoSEGS-261
❑ 95ColChoSESS-26
❑ 95ColChoSESS-125
❑ 95ColChoSESS-261
❑ 95ColChoSS-62
❑ 95ColChoSS-70
❑ 95ColChoSS-88
❑ 95ConTSNGJ-1
❑ 95ConTSNGJ-2
❑ 95ConTSNGJ-3
❑ 95ConTSNGJ-4
❑ 95ConTSNGJ-5
❑ 95ConTSNGJ-6
❑ 95ConTSNGJ-7
❑ 95ConTSNGJ-8
❑ 95DenHol-11
❑ 95Don-340
❑ 95DonAll-AL8
❑ 95DonBomS-1
❑ 95DonDiaK-DK27
❑ 95DonDom-8
❑ 95DonEli-54
❑ 95DonLonBL-3
❑ 95DonPreP-340
❑ 95DonTopotO-150
❑ 95Emo-77
❑ 95EmoMas-3
❑ 95EmoN-6
❑ 95Fin-118
❑ 95FinPowK-PK10
❑ 95FinRef-118
❑ 95Fla-81
❑ 95FlaHotG-3
❑ 95FlaHotN-4
❑ 95FlaOutP-7
❑ 95Fle-269
❑ 95FleAllF-7
❑ 95FleAllS-7
❑ 95FleLeaL-2
❑ 95FleLumC-6
❑ 95FleTeaL-12
❑ 95FleUpdDT-6
❑ 95FleUpdH-11
❑ 95FleUpdSL-3
❑ 95KinDis-11

- ❑ 95Kra-5
- ❑ 95Lea-211
- ❑ 95Lea300C-10
- ❑ 95LeaGolS-4
- ❑ 95LeaGreG-6
- ❑ 95LeaHeaftH-2
- ❑ 95LeaLim-118
- ❑ 95LeaLimG-6
- ❑ 95LeaLimIBP-5
- ❑ 95LeaLimL-4
- ❑ 95LeaOpeD-4
- ❑ 95LeaSli-8A
- ❑ 95LeaSli-8B
- ❑ 95LeaStaS-2
- ❑ 95MarMot-4
- ❑ 95MarPac-1
- ❑ 95MarPac-6
- ❑ 95MarPac-9
- ❑ 95MarPac-32
- ❑ 95MegGriJWL-2
- ❑ 95MegGriJWL-3
- ❑ 95MegGriJWL-4
- ❑ 95MegGriJWL-5
- ❑ 95MegGriJWL-6
- ❑ 95MegGriJWL-7
- ❑ 95MegGriJWL-8
- ❑ 95MegGriJWL-9
- ❑ 95MegGriJWL-10
- ❑ 95MegGriJWL-11
- ❑ 95MegGriJWL-12
- ❑ 95MegGriJWL-13
- ❑ 95MegGriJWL-14
- ❑ 95MegGriJWL-15
- ❑ 95MegGriJWL-16
- ❑ 95MegGriJWL-17
- ❑ 95MegGriJWL-18
- ❑ 95MegGriJWL-19
- ❑ 95MegGriJWL-20
- ❑ 95MegGriJWL-21
- ❑ 95MegGriJWL-22
- ❑ 95MegGriJWL-23
- ❑ 95MegGriJWL-24
- ❑ 95MegGriJWL-25
- ❑ 95MegGriJWL-XX
- ❑ 95MegRut-14
- ❑ 95MegRut-21
- ❑ 95NatPac-6
- ❑ 95Pac-398
- ❑ 95PacGolCDC-16
- ❑ 95PacGolP-21
- ❑ 95PacPri-126
- ❑ 95PanSti-86
- ❑ 95PanSti-123
- ❑ 95Pin-128
- ❑ 95Pin-304
- ❑ 95Pin-447
- ❑ 95Pin-450
- ❑ 95PinArtP-128
- ❑ 95PinArtP-304
- ❑ 95PinArtP-447
- ❑ 95PinArtP-450
- ❑ 95PinFan-11
- ❑ 95PinGatA-GA1
- ❑ 95PinMusC-128
- ❑ 95PinMusC-304
- ❑ 95PinMusC-447
- ❑ 95PinMusC-450
- ❑ 95PinPin-14
- ❑ 95PinPinR-14
- ❑ 95PinRedH-RH2
- ❑ 95PinTeaP-TP7
- ❑ 95PinWhiH-WH2
- ❑ 95PKKGriNP-1
- ❑ 95Pos-4
- ❑ 95PosCan-1
- ❑ 95RedFol-5
- ❑ 95Sco-437
- ❑ 95Sco-551
- ❑ 95ScoDouGC-GC2
- ❑ 95ScoDreT-DG7
- ❑ 95ScoGolR-1
- ❑ 95ScoGolR-437
- ❑ 95ScoGolR-551
- ❑ 95ScoHaloG-HG1
- ❑ 95ScoPlaTS-1
- ❑ 95ScoPlaTS-437
- ❑ 95ScoPlaTS-551
- ❑ 95ScoRul-SR1
- ❑ 95ScoRulJ-SR1
- ❑ 95Sel-89
- ❑ 95Sel-243
- ❑ 95Sel-250
- ❑ 95SelArtP-89
- ❑ 95SelArtP-243
- ❑ 95SelArtP-250
- ❑ 95SelBigS-BS2
- ❑ 95SelCer-70
- ❑ 95SelCerC-1
- ❑ 95SelCerGT-1
- ❑ 95SelCerMG-70
- ❑ 95SP-190
- ❑ 95SP-P100
- ❑ 95SP-AU190
- ❑ 95SPCha-183
- ❑ 95SPCha-185
- ❑ 95SPChaDC-183
- ❑ 95SPChaDC-185
- ❑ 95SPChaDFC-1
- ❑ 95SPChaFCDC-1
- ❑ 95Spo-1
- ❑ 95Spo-168
- ❑ 95SpoArtP-1
- ❑ 95SpoArtP-168
- ❑ 95SpoDet-DE3
- ❑ 95SpoDouT-9
- ❑ 95SpoHamT-HT1
- ❑ 95SpoPro-PM1
- ❑ 95SPPlaP-PP12
- ❑ 95SPSil-190
- ❑ 95SPSpeF-18
- ❑ 95StaClu-241
- ❑ 95StaClu-521
- ❑ 95StaCluCC-CC18
- ❑ 95StaCluCT-9
- ❑ 95StaCluFDI-241
- ❑ 95StaCluMO-19
- ❑ 95StaCluMOP-241
- ❑ 95StaCluMOP-521
- ❑ 95StaCluMOP-CC18
- ❑ 95StaCluMOP-PZ7
- ❑ 95StaCluMOP-RL14
- ❑ 95StaCluMOP-SS11
- ❑ 95StaCluMOP-VRE2
- ❑ 95StaCluPZ-PZ7
- ❑ 95StaCluRL-RL14
- ❑ 95StaCluSS-SS11
- ❑ 95StaCluSTDW-M241
- ❑ 95StaCluSTWS-241
- ❑ 95StaCluSTWS-521
- ❑ 95StaCluVE-VRE2
- ❑ 95StaCluVR-120
- ❑ 95StaCluVRMO-120
- ❑ 95Stu-5
- ❑ 95StuGolS-5
- ❑ 95StuPlaS-5
- ❑ 95Sum-1
- ❑ 95Sum-174
- ❑ 95Sum-195
- ❑ 95SumBigB-BB1
- ❑ 95SumNthD-1
- ❑ 95SumNthD-174
- ❑ 95SumNthD-195
- ❑ 95TomPiz-9
- ❑ 95Top-388
- ❑ 95Top-397
- ❑ 95TopCyb-199
- ❑ 95TopD3-43
- ❑ 95TopEmb-51
- ❑ 95TopEmbGI-51
- ❑ 95TopFinIns-3
- ❑ 95TopLeaL-LL31
- ❑ 95TopPre-PP6
- ❑ 95TopPreS-PP6
- ❑ 95TopTra-2T
- ❑ 95TopTra-160T
- ❑ 95TopTraPB-2
- ❑ 95UC3-73
- ❑ 95UC3-124
- ❑ 95UC3ArtP-73
- ❑ 95UC3ArtP-124
- ❑ 95UC3CycS-CS2
- ❑ 95UC3InM-IM2
- ❑ 95UDAUnsBC-NH1
- ❑ 95UDAUnsBC-NNO
- ❑ 95UDAUnsBC-NNO
- ❑ 95Ult-101
- ❑ 95UltAllS-7
- ❑ 95UltAllSGM-7
- ❑ 95UltAwaW-6
- ❑ 95UltAwaWGM-6
- ❑ 95UltGolM-101
- ❑ 95UltHitM-6
- ❑ 95UltHitMGM-6
- ❑ 95UltHomRK-1
- ❑ 95UltHomRKGM-1
- ❑ 95UltPowP-2
- ❑ 95UltPowPGM-2
- ❑ 95UppDec-100
- ❑ 95UppDec-110
- ❑ 95UppDec-P100
- ❑ 95UppDecED-100
- ❑ 95UppDecED-110
- ❑ 95UppDecEDG-100
- ❑ 95UppDecEDG-110
- ❑ 95UppDecPAW-H3
- ❑ 95UppDecPAWE-H3
- ❑ 95UppDecPC-MLB4
- ❑ 95UppDecPLL-R4
- ❑ 95UppDecPLL-R45
- ❑ 95UppDecPLL-R52
- ❑ 95UppDecPLLE-R4
- ❑ 95UppDecPLLE-R45
- ❑ 95UppDecPLLE-R52
- ❑ 95UppDecSE-255
- ❑ 95UppDecSEG-255
- ❑ 95USPlaCMLA-13C
- ❑ 95Zen-61
- ❑ 95ZenAllS-15
- ❑ 95ZenZ-2
- ❑ 96Baz-1
- ❑ 96Bow-79
- ❑ 96BowBes-71
- ❑ 96BowBesAR-71
- ❑ 96BowBesC-1
- ❑ 96BowBesCAR-1
- ❑ 96BowBesCR-1
- ❑ 96BowBesMI-7
- ❑ 96BowBesMIAR-7
- ❑ 96BowBesMIR-7
- ❑ 96BowBesP-BBP30
- ❑ 96BowBesPAR-BBP30
- ❑ 96BowBesPR-BBP30
- ❑ 96BowBesR-71
- ❑ 96BowFoi-79
- ❑ 96Cir-78
- ❑ 96Cir-198
- ❑ 96CirAcc-12
- ❑ 96CirBos-20
- ❑ 96CirRav-78
- ❑ 96CirRav-198
- ❑ 96Cla7/1PC-5
- ❑ 96ColCho-310
- ❑ 96ColCho-370T
- ❑ 96ColCho-415
- ❑ 96ColCho-P100
- ❑ 96ColChoCtG-CG26
- ❑ 96ColChoCtG-CG26B
- ❑ 96ColChoCtG-CG26C
- ❑ 96ColChoCtGE-CR26
- ❑ 96ColChoCtGG-CG26
- ❑ 96ColChoCtGG-CG26B
- ❑ 96ColChoCtGG-CG26C
- ❑ 96ColChoCtGGE-CR26
- ❑ 96ColChoGACA-CA1
- ❑ 96ColChoGACA-CA2
- ❑ 96ColChoGACA-CA3
- ❑ 96ColChoGACA-CA4
- ❑ 96ColChoGACA-CA5
- ❑ 96ColChoGACA-CA6
- ❑ 96ColChoGACA-CA7
- ❑ 96ColChoGACA-CA8
- ❑ 96ColChoGACA-CA9
- ❑ 96ColChoGACA-CA10
- ❑ 96ColChoGS-310
- ❑ 96ColChoGS-415
- ❑ 96ColChoSS-310
- ❑ 96ColChoSS-415
- ❑ 96ColChoYMtP-16
- ❑ 96ColChoYMtP-16A
- ❑ 96ColChoYMtPGS-16
- ❑ 96ColChoYMtPGS-16A
- ❑ 96CUIMCG-1
- ❑ 96CUIMCG-2
- ❑ 96CUIMCG-3
- ❑ 96CUIMCG-4
- ❑ 96CUIMCG-NNO
- ❑ 96Don-338
- ❑ 96Don-490
- ❑ 96DonEli-70
- ❑ 96DonFreF-2
- ❑ 96DonHitL-2
- ❑ 96DonLonBL-6
- ❑ 96DonPowA-10
- ❑ 96DonPowADC-10
- ❑ 96DonPreP-338
- ❑ 96DonPreP-490
- ❑ 96DonRouT-6
- ❑ 96DonSam-4
- ❑ 96DonSho-3
- ❑ 96EmoLegoB-4
- ❑ 96EmoN-4
- ❑ 96EmoXL-113
- ❑ 96EmoXLD-4
- ❑ 96Fin-B24
- ❑ 96Fin-G135
- ❑ 96Fin-S305
- ❑ 96FinBro-4
- ❑ 96FinRef-B24
- ❑ 96FinRef-G135
- ❑ 96FinRef-S305
- ❑ 96Fla-160
- ❑ 96FlaDiaC-5
- ❑ 96FlaHotG-4
- ❑ 96FlaPow-4
- ❑ 96Fle-238
- ❑ 96FleChe-2
- ❑ 96FleLumC-4
- ❑ 96FlePosG-2
- ❑ 96FleTeaL-12
- ❑ 96FleTif-238
- ❑ 96FleUpd-U223
- ❑ 96FleUpd-U247
- ❑ 96FleUpd-3
- ❑ 96FleUpdH-7
- ❑ 96FleUpdSL-4
- ❑ 96FleUpdSS-4
- ❑ 96FleUpdTC-U223
- ❑ 96FleUpdTC-U247
- ❑ 96FleZon-3
- ❑ 96GriNik-1
- ❑ 96Kin-6
- ❑ 96Lea-41
- ❑ 96LeaAllGMC-18
- ❑ 96LeaAllGMCG-18
- ❑ 96LeaGolS-4
- ❑ 96LeaHatO-5
- ❑ 96LeaLim-11
- ❑ 96LeaLimG-11
- ❑ 96LeaLimL-1
- ❑ 96LeaLimLB-1
- ❑ 96LeaLimPC-4
- ❑ 96LeaPicP-7
- ❑ 96LeaPre-1
- ❑ 96LeaPre-149
- ❑ 96LeaPreP-1
- ❑ 96LeaPreP-149
- ❑ 96LeaPrePB-41
- ❑ 96LeaPrePG-41
- ❑ 96LeaPrePS-41
- ❑ 96LeaPreSG-52
- ❑ 96LeaPreSP-3
- ❑ 96LeaPreSta-6
- ❑ 96LeaPreSte-52
- ❑ 96LeaSig-10
- ❑ 96LeaSigPPG-10
- ❑ 96LeaSigPPP-10
- ❑ 96LeaStaS-4
- ❑ 96LeaTotB-9
- ❑ 96LibSpo-6
- ❑ 96MarMot-4
- ❑ 96MetImpG-1
- ❑ 96MetImpG-2
- ❑ 96MetImpG-3
- ❑ 96MetImpG-4
- ❑ 96MetImpG-5
- ❑ 96MetImpG-6
- ❑ 96MetImpG-7
- ❑ 96MetImpG-8
- ❑ 96MetImpG-9
- ❑ 96MetImpG-10
- ❑ 96MetUni-107
- ❑ 96MetUniHM-4
- ❑ 96MetUniML-3
- ❑ 96MetUniP-107
- ❑ 96MetUniT-3
- ❑ 96Pac-410
- ❑ 96PacCraC-CC8
- ❑ 96PacGolCD-DC13
- ❑ 96PacHom-HP11
- ❑ 96PacMil-M9
- ❑ 96PacOctM-OM6
- ❑ 96PacPri-P131
- ❑ 96PacPriFB-FB6
- ❑ 96PacPriG-P131
- ❑ 96PacPriRHS-RH7
- ❑ 96PanSti-223
- ❑ 96Pin-122
- ❑ 96Pin-134
- ❑ 96Pin-195
- ❑ 96Pin-255
- ❑ 96Pin-301
- ❑ 96Pin-394
- ❑ 96Pin-399
- ❑ 96PinAfi-75
- ❑ 96PinAfi-196
- ❑ 96PinAfiAP-75
- ❑ 96PinAfiAP-196
- ❑ 96PinAfiFPP-75
- ❑ 96PinAfiMN-1
- ❑ 96PinAfiR-1
- ❑ 96PinAfiR-4
- ❑ 96PinAfiR-5
- ❑ 96PinAfiR-7
- ❑ 96PinAfiR-9
- ❑ 96PinAfiR-10
- ❑ 96PinAfiSP-3
- ❑ 96PinArtP-41
- ❑ 96PinArtP-61
- ❑ 96PinArtP-155
- ❑ 96PinArtP-185
- ❑ 96PinEssotG-7
- ❑ 96PinFan-3
- ❑ 96PinFirR-1
- ❑ 96PinFoil-255
- ❑ 96PinFoil-301
- ❑ 96PinFoil-394
- ❑ 96PinFoil-399
- ❑ 96PinPow-3
- ❑ 96PinSky-1
- ❑ 96PinSlu-2
- ❑ 96PinSta-41
- ❑ 96PinSta-61
- ❑ 96PinSta-155
- ❑ 96PinSta-185
- ❑ 96PinTeaP-6
- ❑ 96PinTeaS-2
- ❑ 96Pro-6
- ❑ 96ProMagA-3
- ❑ 96ProMagDM-21
- ❑ 96ProSta-61
- ❑ 96RedF-10
- ❑ 96SchDis-16
- ❑ 96Sco-273
- ❑ 96Sco-282
- ❑ 96ScoAll-3
- ❑ 96ScoBigB-2
- ❑ 96ScoDiaA-14
- ❑ 96ScoDreT-7
- ❑ 96ScoDugC-B7
- ❑ 96ScoDugCAP-B7
- ❑ 96ScoGolS-1
- ❑ 96ScoNumG-3
- ❑ 96ScoPowP-12
- ❑ 96ScoRef-2
- ❑ 96ScoTitT-4
- ❑ 96Sel-6
- ❑ 96Sel-151
- ❑ 96Sel-197
- ❑ 96SelArtP-6
- ❑ 96SelArtP-151
- ❑ 96SelArtP-197
- ❑ 96SelCer-47
- ❑ 96SelCer-136
- ❑ 96SelCerAP-47
- ❑ 96SelCerAP-136
- ❑ 96SelCerCB-47
- ❑ 96SelCerCB-136
- ❑ 96SelCerCR-47
- ❑ 96SelCerCR-136
- ❑ 96SelCerIP-1
- ❑ 96SelCerMB-47
- ❑ 96SelCerMB-136
- ❑ 96SelCerMG-47
- ❑ 96SelCerMG-136
- ❑ 96SelCerMR-47
- ❑ 96SelCerMR-136
- ❑ 96SelCerSF-3
- ❑ 96SelClaTF-3
- ❑ 96SelEnF-1
- ❑ 96SelTeaN-9
- ❑ 96SigRooOHKG-J1
- ❑ 96SigRooOHKG-J2
- ❑ 96SigRooOHKG-J3
- ❑ 96SigRooOHKG-J4
- ❑ 96SigRooOHKG-J5
- ❑ 96SigRooOJKGJA-J1
- ❑ 96SigRooOJKGJA-J2
- ❑ 96SigRooOJKGJA-J3
- ❑ 96SigRooOJKGJA-J4
- ❑ 96SigRooOJKGJA-J5
- ❑ 96SP-170
- ❑ 96SP-188
- ❑ 96SPBasH-90
- ❑ 96SPBasH-NNO
- ❑ 96SPMarM-MM1
- ❑ 96SPMarMDC-1
- ❑ 96Spo-18
- ❑ 96Spo-98
- ❑ 96Spo-142
- ❑ 96SpoArtP-18
- ❑ 96SpoArtP-98
- ❑ 96SpoArtP-142
- ❑ 96SpoDouT-4
- ❑ 96SpoHitP-1
- ❑ 96SpoPowS-2
- ❑ 96SpoPro-6
- ❑ 96SPPreF-1
- ❑ 96SPSpeFX-10
- ❑ 96SPSpeFXDC-10
- ❑ 96SPx-55
- ❑ 96SPx-KG1
- ❑ 96SPx-KGAU
- ❑ 96SPxBoufG-1
- ❑ 96SPxGol-55
- ❑ 96StaClu-105
- ❑ 96StaCluEPB-105
- ❑ 96StaCluEPG-105
- ❑ 96StaCluEPS-105
- ❑ 96StaCluEWB-EW8
- ❑ 96StaCluEWG-EW8
- ❑ 96StaCluEWS-EW8
- ❑ 96StaCluMeg-MH2
- ❑ 96StaCluMOP-105
- ❑ 96StaCluMOP-MH2
- ❑ 96StaCluMOP-PC3
- ❑ 96StaCluMOP-PP6
- ❑ 96StaCluMOP-TSCA5
- ❑ 96StaCluPC-PC3
- ❑ 96StaCluPP-PP6
- ❑ 96StaCluTA-5
- ❑ 96Stu-116
- ❑ 96StuHitP-2
- ❑ 96StuMas-7
- ❑ 96StuPrePB-116
- ❑ 96StuPrePG-116
- ❑ 96StuPrePS-116
- ❑ 96StuStaGS-2
- ❑ 96Sum-86
- ❑ 96Sum-158
- ❑ 96Sum-197
- ❑ 96SumAbo&B-86
- ❑ 96SumAbo&B-158
- ❑ 96SumAbo&B-197
- ❑ 96SumArtP-86
- ❑ 96SumArtP-158
- ❑ 96SumArtP-197
- ❑ 96SumBal-5
- ❑ 96SumBigB-2
- ❑ 96SumBigBM-2
- ❑ 96SumFoi-86
- ❑ 96SumFoi-158
- ❑ 96SumFoi-197
- ❑ 96SumHitI-4
- ❑ 96SumPos-8
- ❑ 96TeaOut-32
- ❑ 96TeaOut-C95
- ❑ 96Top-205
- ❑ 96Top-230
- ❑ 96TopBigC-3
- ❑ 96TopChr-70
- ❑ 96TopChr-90
- ❑ 96TopChrR-70
- ❑ 96TopChrR-90
- ❑ 96TopChrWC-WC9
- ❑ 96TopChrWCR-WC9
- ❑ 96TopClaC-CC1
- ❑ 96TopGal-146
- ❑ 96TopGalE-3
- ❑ 96TopGalPG-PG10
- ❑ 96TopGalPPI-146
- ❑ 96TopLas-42
- ❑ 96TopLasPC-14
- ❑ 96TopLasSS-4
- ❑ 96TopMysF-M16
- ❑ 96TopMysF-M25
- ❑ 96TopMysFR-M16
- ❑ 96TopMysFR-M25
- ❑ 96TopPro-AL5
- ❑ 96TopWreC-WC9
- ❑ 96Ult-126
- ❑ 96Ult-579
- ❑ 96UltCalttH-2
- ❑ 96UltCalttHGM-2
- ❑ 96UltChe-A4
- ❑ 96UltChe-B3
- ❑ 96UltCheGM-A4
- ❑ 96UltCheGM-B3
- ❑ 96UltDiaP-3
- ❑ 96UltDiaPGM-3
- ❑ 96UltGolM-126
- ❑ 96UltGolM-579
- ❑ 96UltHitM-4
- ❑ 96UltHitMGM-4
- ❑ 96UltHomRK-6
- ❑ 96UltHomRKGM-6
- ❑ 96UltHomRKR-6
- ❑ 96UltHomRKRGM-6
- ❑ 96UltPowP-3
- ❑ 96UltPowPGM-3
- ❑ 96UltPriL-6
- ❑ 96UltPriLGM-6
- ❑ 96UltPro-NNO
- ❑ 96UltRaw-4
- ❑ 96UltRawGM-4
- ❑ 96UltRes-2
- ❑ 96UltResGM-2

❑ 96UltThu-11
❑ 96UltThuGM-11
❑ 96UppDec-200
❑ 96UppDec-376
❑ 96UppDecA-9
❑ 96UppDecDD-DD35
❑ 96UppDecDDG-DD35
❑ 96UppDecDDS-DD35
❑ 96UppDecG-GF1
❑ 96UppDecHC-HC1
❑ 96UppDecMtSGR-1
❑ 96UppDecPD-PD7
❑ 96UppDecPHE-H4
❑ 96UppDecPRE-R4
❑ 96UppDecPRE-R15
❑ 96UppDecPRE-R24
❑ 96UppDecPreH-H4
❑ 96UppDecPreR-R4
❑ 96UppDecPreR-R15
❑ 96UppDecPreR-R24
❑ 96UppDecRunP-RP7
❑ 96UppDecVJLS-VJ10
❑ 96Zen-1
❑ 96Zen-135
❑ 96ZenArtP-1
❑ 96ZenArtP-135
❑ 96ZenDiaC-3
❑ 96ZenDiaCP-3
❑ 96ZenMoz-5
❑ 96ZenZ-1
❑ 97Bow-16
❑ 97BowBes-1
❑ 97BowBesAR-1
❑ 97BowBesBC-BC6
❑ 97BowBesBCAR-BC6
❑ 97BowBesBCR-BC6
❑ 97BowBesJ-1
❑ 97BowBesJAR-1
❑ 97BowBesJR-1
❑ 97BowBesMI-MI5
❑ 97BowBesMIAR-MI5
❑ 97BowBesMIARI-MI5
❑ 97BowBesMII-MI5
❑ 97BowBesMIR-MI5
❑ 97BowBesMIRI-MI5
❑ 97BowBesP-2
❑ 97BowBesPAR-2
❑ 97BowBesPR-2
❑ 97BowBesR-1
❑ 97BowChr-12
❑ 97BowChrI-12
❑ 97BowChrIR-12
❑ 97BowChrR-12
❑ 97BowInt-16
❑ 97BowIntB-BBI2
❑ 97BowIntBAR-BBI2
❑ 97BowIntBR-BBI2
❑ 97Cir-24
❑ 97Cir-395
❑ 97CirBos-6
❑ 97CirIco-2
❑ 97CirLimA-5
❑ 97CirRav-24
❑ 97CirRav-395
❑ 97CirRavR-4
❑ 97CirSupB-6
❑ 97ColCho-230
❑ 97ColCho-244
❑ 97ColCho-245
❑ 97ColCho-246
❑ 97ColCho-247
❑ 97ColCho-248
❑ 97ColCho-249
❑ 97ColCho-334
❑ 97ColChoAC-5
❑ 97ColChoBS-1
❑ 97ColChoBSGS-1
❑ 97ColChoCtG-28A
❑ 97ColChoCtG-28B
❑ 97ColChoCtG-28C
❑ 97ColChoCtGE-CG28
❑ 97ColChoCtGIW-CG28
❑ 97ColChoGriCD-CD1
❑ 97ColChoGriCD-CD2
❑ 97ColChoGriCD-CD3
❑ 97ColChoGriCD-CD4
❑ 97ColChoGriCD-CD5
❑ 97ColChoNF-NF11
❑ 97ColChoPP-PP3
❑ 97ColChoPPG-PP3
❑ 97ColChoPPJ-PP3
❑ 97ColChoS-24
❑ 97ColChoSR-10
❑ 97ColChoT-SM2
❑ 97ColChoTBS-43
❑ 97ColChoTBSWH-43
❑ 97ColChoTotT-T27
❑ 97Don-21
❑ 97Don-399
❑ 97Don-439
❑ 97Don-450
❑ 97DonArmaD-1
❑ 97DonDiaK-1
❑ 97DonDiaKC-1
❑ 97DonDom-2
❑ 97DonEli-5
❑ 97DonEli-7
❑ 97DonEliGS-5
❑ 97DonEliLaL-1
❑ 97DonFraFea-1
❑ 97DonGolPP-21
❑ 97DonGolPP-399
❑ 97DonGolPP-439
❑ 97DonGolPP-450
❑ 97DonLim-1
❑ 97DonLim-18
❑ 97DonLim-19
❑ 97DonLimE-1
❑ 97DonLimE-18
❑ 97DonLimE-19
❑ 97DonLimENG-1
❑ 97DonLimFotG-5
❑ 97DonLimFotG-45
❑ 97DonLonL-6
❑ 97DonPowA-2
❑ 97DonPowADC-2
❑ 97DonPre-2
❑ 97DonPre-175
❑ 97DonPreCttC-2
❑ 97DonPreCttC-175
❑ 97DonPrePM-2
❑ 97DonPreS-9
❑ 97DonPreSS-9
❑ 97DonPreTB-6
❑ 97DonPreTBG-6
❑ 97DonPreTF-6
❑ 97DonPreTP-6
❑ 97DonPreTPG-6
❑ 97DonPreXP-7A
❑ 97DonSig-6
❑ 97DonSig-99
❑ 97DonSigPPP-6
❑ 97DonSigPPP-99
❑ 97DonSilPP-21
❑ 97DonSilPP-399
❑ 97DonSilPP-439
❑ 97DonSilPP-450
❑ 97DonTea-136
❑ 97DonTeaSMVP-13
❑ 97DonTeaSPE-136
❑ 97DonVxP1-47
❑ 97DonVxP1CD-1
❑ 97E-X2-40
❑ 97E-X2ACA-2
❑ 97E-X2Cred-40
❑ 97E-X2EssCre-40
❑ 97E-X2Hall-2
❑ 97Fin-139
❑ 97Fin-238
❑ 97Fin-342
❑ 97FinEmb-139
❑ 97FinEmb-342
❑ 97FinEmbR-139
❑ 97FinEmbR-342
❑ 97FinRef-139
❑ 97FinRef-238
❑ 97FinRef-342
❑ 97FlaShoDC-5
❑ 97FlaShoHG-4
❑ 97FlaShoLC-24
❑ 97FlaShoLeg0-24
❑ 97FlaShoLeg1-24
❑ 97FlaShoM-A24
❑ 97FlaShoM-B24
❑ 97FlaShoM-C24
❑ 97FlaShoR0-24
❑ 97FlaShoR1-24
❑ 97FlaShoR2-24
❑ 97Fle-206
❑ 97Fle-492
❑ 97Fle-701
❑ 97Fle-745
❑ 97FleBleB-4
❑ 97FleDiaT-4
❑ 97FleGouG-2
❑ 97FleGouGF-2
❑ 97FleHea-6
❑ 97FleLumC-9
❑ 97FleNig&D-4
❑ 97FleSoaS-4
❑ 97FleSoaSG-4
❑ 97FleTeaL-12
❑ 97FleTif-206
❑ 97FleTif-492
❑ 97FleTif-701
❑ 97FleTif-745
❑ 97FleZon-7
❑ 97HigMinESC-1
❑ 97HigMinESC-2
❑ 97HigMinESC-3
❑ 97HigMinM-40
❑ 97HigMinM-41
❑ 97HigMinM-42
❑ 97HigMinMCT-17
❑ 97HigMinMCT-18
❑ 97HigMinMCT-19
❑ 97HigMinMM-1
❑ 97HigMinMM-2
❑ 97HigMinMM-3
❑ 97HigMinMSM-1
❑ 97HigMinMSM-2
❑ 97HigMinMSM-3
❑ 97Lea-193
❑ 97Lea-204
❑ 97Lea-371
❑ 97LeaBanS-2
❑ 97LeaDrefS-12
❑ 97LeaFraM-193
❑ 97LeaFraM-204
❑ 97LeaFraM-371
❑ 97LeaFraMDC-193
❑ 97LeaFraMDC-204
❑ 97LeaFraMDC-371
❑ 97LeaGet-1
❑ 97LeaGolS-3
❑ 97LeaKnoG-2
❑ 97LeaLeaotN-6
❑ 97LeaStaS-3
❑ 97LeaWarT-1
❑ 97MarSco-6
❑ 97MarScoPl-6
❑ 97MarScoPr-6
❑ 97MetUni-145
❑ 97MetUniBF-6
❑ 97MetUniMF-4
❑ 97MetUniML-4
❑ 97MetUniT-3
❑ 97NewPin-1
❑ 97NewPinAP-1
❑ 97NewPinIE-3
❑ 97NewPinKtP-4
❑ 97NewPinMC-1
❑ 97NewPinPP-1
❑ 97NewPinPP-I3A
❑ 97NewPinPP-K4
❑ 97NewPinPP-KG1
❑ 97NewPinPP-KG2
❑ 97NewPinPP-KG3
❑ 97NewPinPP-KG4
❑ 97NewPinPP-KG5
❑ 97NewPinPP-KG6
❑ 97NewPinS-KG1
❑ 97NewPinS-KG2
❑ 97NewPinS-KG3
❑ 97NewPinS-KG4
❑ 97NewPinS-KG5
❑ 97NewPinS-KG6
❑ 97Pac-186
❑ 97PacCar-17
❑ 97PacCarM-17
❑ 97PacCerCGT-13
❑ 97PacCraC-5
❑ 97PacFirD-11
❑ 97PacGolCD-16
❑ 97PacLigB-186
❑ 97PacPri-63
❑ 97PacPriGA-GA14
❑ 97PacPriGotD-GD86
❑ 97PacPriLB-63
❑ 97PacPriP-63
❑ 97PacPriSH-SH6A
❑ 97PacPriSL-SL6A
❑ 97PacSil-186
❑ 97PacTriCD-9
❑ 97Pin-193
❑ 97PinArtP-PP193
❑ 97PinCar-14
❑ 97PinCer-53
❑ 97PinCer-136
❑ 97PinCerCMGT-13
❑ 97PinCerCT-13
❑ 97PinCerLI-2
❑ 97PinCerMBla-53
❑ 97PinCerMBla-136
❑ 97PinCerMBlu-53
❑ 97PinCerMBlu-136
❑ 97PinCerMG-53
❑ 97PinCerMG-136
❑ 97PinCerMR-53
❑ 97PinCerMR-136
❑ 97PinCerR-53
❑ 97PinCerR-136
❑ 97PinEpixGO-E1
❑ 97PinEpixPE-E1
❑ 97PinFan-FF11
❑ 97PinHom-3
❑ 97PinHom-4
❑ 97PinIns-19
❑ 97PinInsC-8
❑ 97PinInsCE-19
❑ 97PinInsDD-6
❑ 97PinInsDE-19
❑ 97PinInsFS-12
❑ 97PinMin-1
❑ 97PinMinB-1
❑ 97PinMinCB-1
❑ 97PinMinCG-1
❑ 97PinMinCGR-1
❑ 97PinMinCN-1
❑ 97PinMinCSS-1
❑ 97PinMinG-1
❑ 97PinMinS-1
❑ 97PinMusC-193
❑ 97PinPasttM-2
❑ 97PinPrePla-193
❑ 97PinPrePla-S1
❑ 97PinSha-1
❑ 97PinTeaP-7
❑ 97PinTeaP-10
❑ 97PinTotCPB-53
❑ 97PinTotCPB-136
❑ 97PinTotCPG-53
❑ 97PinTotCPG-136
❑ 97PinTotCPR-53
❑ 97PinTotCPR-136
❑ 97PinTotCS-53
❑ 97PinX-P-7
❑ 97PinX-P-139
❑ 97PinX-PF&A-14
❑ 97PinX-PMoS-7
❑ 97PinX-PMoS-139
❑ 97PinX-PMP-6
❑ 97PinX-PMW-1
❑ 97PinX-PMWG-1
❑ 97PinX-PMWS-1
❑ 97PinX-PreMPS-6
❑ 97PinX-PSfF-26
❑ 97PinX-PSfF-U26
❑ 97PinX-PSfFU-26
❑ 97PreCon-17
❑ 97Sco-156
❑ 97Sco-499
❑ 97Sco-548
❑ 97ScoAllF-11
❑ 97ScoArtPWB-156
❑ 97ScoArtPWB-499
❑ 97ScoArtPWB-548
❑ 97ScoBla-6
❑ 97ScoFra-1
❑ 97ScoFraG-1
❑ 97ScoHeaot0-9
❑ 97ScoHigZ-2
❑ 97ScoPitP-14
❑ 97ScoPreS-156
❑ 97ScoResC-499
❑ 97ScoResC-548
❑ 97ScoShoS-156
❑ 97ScoShoS-499
❑ 97ScoShoS-548
❑ 97ScoShoSAP-156
❑ 97ScoShoSAP-499
❑ 97ScoShoSAP-548
❑ 97ScoStaaD-5
❑ 97ScoSteS-6
❑ 97ScoTitT-3
❑ 97Sel-47
❑ 97Sel-145
❑ 97Sel-150
❑ 97Sel-P47
❑ 97SelArtP-47
❑ 97SelArtP-145
❑ 97SelArtP-150
❑ 97SelCom-47
❑ 97SelCom-145
❑ 97SelCom-150
❑ 97SelRegG-47
❑ 97SelRegG-145
❑ 97SelRegG-150
❑ 97SelSam-P47
❑ 97SelTooотT-1
❑ 97SelToootTMB-1
❑ 97SP-165
❑ 97SP-183
❑ 97SPGamF-GF10
❑ 97SPGriH-91
❑ 97SPGriH-92
❑ 97SPGriH-93
❑ 97SPGriH-94
❑ 97SPGriH-95
❑ 97SPGriH-96
❑ 97SPGriH-97
❑ 97SPGriH-98
❑ 97SPGriH-99
❑ 97SPGriH-100
❑ 97SPInsI-1
❑ 97SPMarM-MM1
❑ 97SpoIll-28
❑ 97SpoIll-157
❑ 97SpoIll-172
❑ 97SpoIll-178
❑ 97SpoIllEE-28
❑ 97SpoIllEE-157
❑ 97SpoIllEE-172
❑ 97SpoIllEE-178
❑ 97SpoIllGS-25
❑ 97SPSpeF-1
❑ 97SPSpxF-1
❑ 97SPSPxFA-1
❑ 97SPVinAu-8
❑ 97SPVinAu-9
❑ 97SPVinAu-10
❑ 97SPVinAu-11
❑ 97SPVinAu-12
❑ 97SPx-45
❑ 97SPx-S45
❑ 97SPxBoufG-19
❑ 97SPxBoufGSS-2
❑ 97SPxBro-45
❑ 97SPxCorotG-1
❑ 97SPxGol-45
❑ 97SPxGraF-45
❑ 97SPxSil-45
❑ 97SPxSte-45
❑ 97StaClu-50
❑ 97StaClu-385
❑ 97StaCluFR-F5
❑ 97StaCluFW-F5
❑ 97StaCluMat-50
❑ 97StaCluMOP-50
❑ 97StaCluMOP-385
❑ 97StaCluMOP-FB5
❑ 97StaCluMOP-PG15
❑ 97StaCluMOP-PL4
❑ 97StaCluPG-PG15
❑ 97StaCluPL-PL4
❑ 97StrAll-25
❑ 97Stu-16
❑ 97Stu-163
❑ 97StuHarH-3
❑ 97StuMasS-3
❑ 97StuMasS8-3
❑ 97StuPor8-1
❑ 97StuPrePG-16
❑ 97StuPrePG-163
❑ 97StuPrePS-16
❑ 97StuPrePS-163
❑ 97Top-300
❑ 97Top22kG-1
❑ 97TopAll-AS13
❑ 97TopChr-101
❑ 97TopChrAS-AS13
❑ 97TopChrDD-DD3
❑ 97TopChrDDR-DD3
❑ 97TopChrJ-101
❑ 97TopChrR-101
❑ 97TopChrSAR-AS13
❑ 97TopChrSB-8
❑ 97TopChrSBR-8
❑ 97TopGal-79
❑ 97TopGalGoH-GH4
❑ 97TopGalPG-PG4
❑ 97TopGalPMS-5
❑ 97TopGalPMSSS-5
❑ 97TopGalPPI-79
❑ 97TopHobM-HM1
❑ 97TopIntF-ILM3
❑ 97TopIntFR-ILM3
❑ 97TopMem05-20
❑ 97TopScr-7
❑ 97TopScrPS-1
❑ 97TopScrPST-1
❑ 97TopScrT-7
❑ 97TopSeaB-SB8
❑ 97TopSta-4
❑ 97TopSta97AS-AS16
❑ 97TopStaAM-4
❑ 97TopStaASM-ASM5
❑ 97TopSweS-SS6
❑ 97TopTeaT-TT1
❑ 97UD3-3
❑ 97UD3Marq-MA1
❑ 97UD3SupSign-2
❑ 97Ult-121
❑ 97UltBasR-2
❑ 97UltChe-A3
❑ 97UltChe-B2
❑ 97UltDiaP-3
❑ 97UltDouT-9
❑ 97UltFamGam-1
❑ 97UltFieC-6
❑ 97UltGolME-121
❑ 97UltHitM-2
❑ 97UltHRK-4
❑ 97UltLeaS-1
❑ 97UltPlaME-121
❑ 97UltPowP-A4
❑ 97UltPowP-B1
❑ 97UltRBIK-7
❑ 97UltStaR-2
❑ 97UltThu-8
❑ 97UltTop3-2
❑ 97UltTop3GM-2
❑ 97UppDec-150
❑ 97UppDec-175
❑ 97UppDec-385
❑ 97UppDec-424
❑ 97UppDecAG-AG1
❑ 97UppDecGJ-GJ1
❑ 97UppDecHC-HC5
❑ 97UppDecKGJHR-1
❑ 97UppDecKGJHR-2
❑ 97UppDecKGJHR-3
❑ 97UppDecKGJHR-4
❑ 97UppDecKGJHR-5
❑ 97UppDecLDC-LD3
❑ 97UppDecMM-A9
❑ 97UppDecMM-B1
❑ 97UppDecMP-P2
❑ 97UppDecP-26
❑ 97UppDecPE-26
❑ 97UppDecPP-PP1
❑ 97UppDecPPJ-PP1
❑ 97UppDecRP-RP1
❑ 97UppDecSA-1
❑ 97UppDecSAG-1
❑ 97Zen-20
❑ 97Zen Z-Z-1
❑ 97Zen8x10-4
❑ 97Zen8x1D-4
❑ 97ZentheBP-4
❑ 97ZenV-2-1
❑ 98Bow-33
❑ 98BowBes-27
❑ 98BowBesAR-27
❑ 98BowBesMIF-MI6
❑ 98BowBesMIFAR-MI6
❑ 98BowBesMIFR-MI6
❑ 98BowBesR-27
❑ 98BowChr-33
❑ 98BowChrGA-33
❑ 98BowChrGAR-33
❑ 98BowChrI-33
❑ 98BowChrIR-33
❑ 98BowChrR-33
❑ 98BowChrR-13
❑ 98BowChrRR-13
❑ 98BowGolA-33
❑ 98BowInt-33
❑ 98CirThu-100
❑ 98CirThu-299
❑ 98CirThuB-7
❑ 98CirThuLA-6
❑ 98CirThuQS-5
❑ 98CirThuRav-100
❑ 98CirThuRR-7
❑ 98CirThuSupRav-100
❑ 98CirThuTB-6
❑ 98ColCho-10
❑ 98ColCho-19
❑ 98ColCho-240
❑ 98ColCho-254
❑ 98ColCho-255
❑ 98ColCho-269
❑ 98ColCho-275
❑ 98ColChoCG-10
❑ 98ColChoCtG-CG1A
❑ 98ColChoCtG-CG1B
❑ 98ColChoCtG-CG1C
❑ 98ColChoCtGExch-CG1
❑ 98ColChoCtGIW-CG1
❑ 98ColChoER-ER26
❑ 98ColChoGJ5-275
❑ 98ColChoMBH-25
❑ 98ColChoRJ-240
❑ 98ColChoS-25
❑ 98ColChoSQ-SQ30

❑ 98ColChoSQ-SQ90
❑ 98ColChoSQDouble-1
❑ 98ColChoSQHR-1
❑ 98ColChoSQSingle-1
❑ 98ColChoSQTriple-1
❑ 98CroRoy-125
❑ 98CroRoyAS-7
❑ 98CroRoyCCPA-2
❑ 98CroRoyCCPrem-2
❑ 98CroRoyDK-20
❑ 98CroRoyFoB-19
❑ 98CroRoyFoBA-19
❑ 98CroRoyHRF-7
❑ 98CroRoyPotG-22
❑ 98Don-28
❑ 98Don-156
❑ 98Don-375
❑ 98Don-386
❑ 98Don-420
❑ 98DonCol-28
❑ 98DonCol-156
❑ 98DonColE-401
❑ 98DonColE-518
❑ 98DonColL-299
❑ 98DonColL-355
❑ 98DonColP-551
❑ 98DonColP-718
❑ 98DonColS-28
❑ 98DonColS-156
❑ 98DonCruG-39
❑ 98DonCruP-39
❑ 98DonCruR-39
❑ 98DonDay-11
❑ 98DonDiaK-20
❑ 98DonDiaKC-20
❑ 98DonDom-5
❑ 98DonEli-1
❑ 98DonEli-118
❑ 98DonEliA-1
❑ 98DonEliA-118
❑ 98DonEliC-1
❑ 98DonElil-3
❑ 98DonEliMC-1
❑ 98DonEliPN-1A
❑ 98DonEliPN-1B
❑ 98DonEliPN-1C
❑ 98DonEliPNDC-1A
❑ 98DonEliPNDC-1B
❑ 98DonEliPNDC-1C
❑ 98DonEliPNS-1A
❑ 98DonEliPNS-1B
❑ 98DonEliPNS-1C
❑ 98DonEliS-1
❑ 98DonEliS-118
❑ 98DonFANT-2
❑ 98DonFANTDC-2
❑ 98DonGolPP-28
❑ 98DonGolPP-156
❑ 98DonGolPP-375
❑ 98DonGolPP-386
❑ 98DonGolPP-420
❑ 98DonLonL-1
❑ 98DonPre-1
❑ 98DonPre-168
❑ 98DonPreGB-21
❑ 98DonPreGES-2
❑ 98DonPreGoB-21
❑ 98DonPreGX-2
❑ 98DonPreGXDC-2
❑ 98DonPrePM-1
❑ 98DonPreSeat-1
❑ 98DonPreSeat-168
❑ 98DonPreTP-21
❑ 98DonPreTPD-11
❑ 98DonPreTPG-21
❑ 98DonPreTPS-21
❑ 98DonPreTW-8
❑ 98DonPriCD-28
❑ 98DonPriCD-156
❑ 98DonPriCE-401
❑ 98DonPriCE-518
❑ 98DonPriCL-299
❑ 98DonPriCL-355
❑ 98DonPriCP-551
❑ 98DonPriCP-718
❑ 98DonProLO-18
❑ 98DonProLPI-5
❑ 98DonProLS-2
❑ 98DonSig-24
❑ 98DonSig-107
❑ 98DonSigP-24
❑ 98DonSigP-107
❑ 98DonSilPP-28
❑ 98DonSilPP-156
❑ 98DonSilPP-375
❑ 98DonSilPP-386
❑ 98DonSilPP-420
❑ 98E-X2-10
❑ 98E-X2Cheap-2
❑ 98E-X2DesCoop-7
❑ 98E-X2ECFut-10
❑ 98E-X2ECNow-10
❑ 98Fin-100
❑ 98FinCen-C5
❑ 98FinCenR-C5
❑ 98FinMysF1-M1
❑ 98FinMysF1-M5
❑ 98FinMysF1-M6
❑ 98FinMysF1-M7
❑ 98FinMysF2-M7
❑ 98FinMysF2-M8
❑ 98FinMysF2-M9
❑ 98FinMysF2R-M7
❑ 98FinMysF2R-M8
❑ 98FinMysF2R-M9
❑ 98FinMysFO-1
❑ 98FinMysFOR-1
❑ 98FinMysFR-M1
❑ 98FinMysFR-M5
❑ 98FinMysFR-M6
❑ 98FinMysFR-M7
❑ 98FinNo--100
❑ 98FinNo-R-100
❑ 98FinOve-A8
❑ 98FinOveR-A8
❑ 98FinPowZ-P1
❑ 98FinRef-100
❑ 98FinStaS-SS1
❑ 98FinStaSJ-1
❑ 98FinTheM-TM1
❑ 98FinTheMR-TM1
❑ 98FlaShoLeg0-1
❑ 98FlaShoLeg1-1
❑ 98FlaShoLeg2-1
❑ 98FlaShoLeg3-1
❑ 98FlaShoLegM-1
❑ 98FlaShoP1-1
❑ 98FlaShoR0-1
❑ 98FlaShoR1-1
❑ 98FlaShoR2-1
❑ 98FlaShoR3-1
❑ 98Fle-1
❑ 98Fle-314
❑ 98Fle-329
❑ 98Fle-342
❑ 98Fle-572
❑ 98Fle-584
❑ 98FleDiaS-8
❑ 98FleDiaT-DT5
❑ 98FleIn TC-IC7
❑ 98FleLumC-6
❑ 98FlePowG-10
❑ 98FleUpd-U7
❑ 98FleVin'-55
❑ 98FleVin'C-55
❑ 98FleZon-7
❑ 98Lea-100
❑ 98Lea-156
❑ 98LeaFraDA-100
❑ 98LeaFraDA-156
❑ 98LeaFraF-100
❑ 98LeaFraF-156
❑ 98LeaFraM-100
❑ 98LeaFraM-156
❑ 98LeaFraM-100
❑ 98LeaFraM-156
❑ 98LeaFraMDC-100
❑ 98LeaFraMDC-156
❑ 98LeaFraMDC-100
❑ 98LeaFraMDC-156
❑ 98LeaFraMZ2-100
❑ 98LeaFraMZ2-156
❑ 98LeaHeaftH-8
❑ 98LeaHeaftHS-8
❑ 98LeaRCMLHDSamp-4
❑ 98LeaRS-26
❑ 98LeaRS-131
❑ 98LeaRS-170
❑ 98LeaRSCross-2
❑ 98LeaRSExtM-1
❑ 98LeaRSExtMDC-1
❑ 98LeaRSGAHSamp-3
❑ 98LeaRSGreAH-3
❑ 98LeaRSGreHit-1
❑ 98LeaRSHRDerby-19
❑ 98LeaRSLHolo-26
❑ 98LeaRSLHolo-131
❑ 98LeaRSLHolo-170
❑ 98LeaRSLMVP-7
❑ 98LeaRSLMVPPE-7
❑ 98LeaRSLong-26
❑ 98LeaRSLong-131
❑ 98LeaRSLong-170
❑ 98LeaRSMLHD-4
❑ 98LeaRSSOSamp-3
❑ 98LeaRSStaOva-3
❑ 98LeaRSTicMas-1
❑ 98LeaRSTicMasDC-1
❑ 98LeaRTrue-26
❑ 98LeaRTrue-131
❑ 98LeaRTrue-170
❑ 98LeaStaRep-1
❑ 98LeaStaS-2
❑ 98LeaStaSDC-2
❑ 98MarSco-4
❑ 98MarScoP-4
❑ 98MetUni-161
❑ 98MetUni-206
❑ 98MetUni-218
❑ 98MetUniAT-1
❑ 98MetUniDH-1
❑ 98MetUniPMG-161
❑ 98MetUniPMG-206
❑ 98MetUniPP-1
❑ 98MetUniT-1
❑ 98MetUniUL-1
❑ 98Pac-186
❑ 98PacAur-72
❑ 98PacAurCube-16
❑ 98PacAurHC-16
❑ 98PacAurKotML-9
❑ 98PacAurODLC-16
❑ 98PacAurPF-24
❑ 98PacAurPFC-24
❑ 98PacAurPFPB-24
❑ 98PacAurPFR-24
❑ 98PacAurPFS-24
❑ 98PacCraCh-9
❑ 98PacGolCDC-29
❑ 98PacHomRH-3
❑ 98PacHomRH-18
❑ 98PacInCage-16
❑ 98PacInv-64
❑ 98PacInv-149
❑ 98PacInvCCDB-9
❑ 98PacInvCCG-9
❑ 98PacInvCCG-9
❑ 98PacInvCCLB-9
❑ 98PacInvCCP-9
❑ 98PacInvCCR-9
❑ 98PacInvGems-91
❑ 98PacInvInt-11A
❑ 98PacInvMiT-17
❑ 98PacInvPBlue-64
❑ 98PacInvPBlue-149
❑ 98PacInvPhoto-14
❑ 98PacInvSilv-64
❑ 98PacInvSilv-149
❑ 98PacInvTeam-26
❑ 98PacOme-220
❑ 98PacOmeEP-7
❑ 98PacOmeEP1o1-7
❑ 98PacOmeFTF-2
❑ 98PacOmeOnIns-13
❑ 98PacOmeP-9
❑ 98PacOmeR-220
❑ 98PacOnl-686A
❑ 98PacOnl-686B
❑ 98PacOnl-701
❑ 98PacOnlR-686A
❑ 98PacOnlR-686B
❑ 98PacOnlR-701
❑ 98PacOnlWC-686A
❑ 98PacOnlWC-686B
❑ 98PacOnlWC-701
❑ 98PacPar-87
❑ 98PacParC-87
❑ 98PacParCB-9
❑ 98PacParCBPP-9
❑ 98PacParFC-16
❑ 98PacParG-87
❑ 98PacParHS-87
❑ 98PacParl-28
❑ 98PacParPB-87
❑ 98PacParR-87
❑ 98PacParSD-18
❑ 98PacParTC-11
❑ 98PacPlaB-186
❑ 98PacRedT-186
❑ 98PacSil-186
❑ 98PacTeaC-12
❑ 98Pin-187
❑ 98Pin-193
❑ 98Pin-198
❑ 98PinArtP-PP90
❑ 98PinArtP-PP96
❑ 98PinEpixGE-E1
❑ 98PinEpixGP-E1
❑ 98PinEpixPO-E1
❑ 98PinEpixPP-E1
❑ 98PinEpixSE-E1
❑ 98PinEpixSO-E1
❑ 98PinEpixSP-E1
❑ 98PinHitIH-2
❑ 98PinHitiHS-2
❑ 98PinIns-24
❑ 98PinIns-140
❑ 98PinIns-148
❑ 98PinInsBtN-1
❑ 98PinInsC-6
❑ 98PinInsCE-24
❑ 98PinInsCE-140
❑ 98PinInsCE-148
❑ 98PinInsCG-6
❑ 98PinInsDE-24
❑ 98PinInsDE-140
❑ 98PinInsDE-148
❑ 98PinInsSG-1AB
❑ 98PinInsSG-1CD
❑ 98PinInsSG-4AB
❑ 98PinInsSG-4CD
❑ 98PinInsSG-20AB
❑ 98PinInsSG-20CD
❑ 98PinInsSG-25AB
❑ 98PinInsSG-25CD
❑ 98PinInsSGS-1AB
❑ 98PinInsSGS-1CD
❑ 98PinInsSGS-4AB
❑ 98PinInsSGS-4CD
❑ 98PinInsSGS-20AB
❑ 98PinInsSGS-20CD
❑ 98PinInsSGS-25AB
❑ 98PinInsSGS-25CD
❑ 98PinMinB-7
❑ 98PinMinCB-7
❑ 98PinMinCBAP-7
❑ 98PinMinCGP-7
❑ 98PinMinCGPAP-7
❑ 98PinMinCN-7
❑ 98PinMinCNAP-7
❑ 98PinMinCSGR-7
❑ 98PinMinDC-7
❑ 98PinMinG-7
❑ 98PinMinMCSS-7
❑ 98PinMinMG-1
❑ 98PinMinMGC-1
❑ 98PinMinS-7
❑ 98PinMusC-PP90
❑ 98PinMusC-PP96
❑ 98PinPer-1
❑ 98PinPer-138
❑ 98PinPerBB-1
❑ 98PinPerBBSamp-1
❑ 98PinPerBBSO-1
❑ 98PinPerLP-2
❑ 98PinPerPP-1
❑ 98PinPerPP-138
❑ 98PinPerPT-8
❑ 98PinPerSftF-12
❑ 98PinPerSftFShop-5
❑ 98PinPlu-9
❑ 98PinPlu-183
❑ 98PinPluAE-1
❑ 98PinPluAEE-1
❑ 98PinPluAEP-1
❑ 98PinPluAP-PP5
❑ 98PinPluGAP-PP5
❑ 98PinPluLM-2
❑ 98PinPluMAP-PP5
❑ 98PinPluPieGame-1
❑ 98PinPluSamp-9
❑ 98PinPluTP-6
❑ 98PinPluTPG-6
❑ 98PinPluTPM-6
❑ 98PinPluY-7
❑ 98PinPowPJ-6
❑ 98PinPowPJ-12
❑ 98PinPowPJS-6
❑ 98PinPowPJS-12
❑ 98PinPreP-187
❑ 98PinPreP-193
❑ 98PinPreP-198
❑ 98PinPreP-E1
❑ 98PinPreP-H2
❑ 98PinPreP-S26
❑ 98PinPreP-S27
❑ 98PinPreP-S28
❑ 98PinPreP-S29
❑ 98PinPreP-S30
❑ 98PinPreP-S31
❑ 98PinPreP-S32
❑ 98PinSna-SM7
❑ 98PinSpe-26
❑ 98PinSpe-27
❑ 98PinSpe-28
❑ 98PinSpe-29
❑ 98PinSpe-30
❑ 98PinSpe-31
❑ 98PinSpe-32
❑ 98PinUnc-187
❑ 98PreCon-4
❑ 98PreCon-5
❑ 98Revo-132
❑ 98RevoFP-8
❑ 98RevoMLI-4
❑ 98RevoPTP-8
❑ 98RevoRooHH-28
❑ 98RevoShow-14
❑ 98RevoSS-132
❑ 98Sco-34
❑ 98Sco-269
❑ 98ScoAllST-13
❑ 98ScoComP-1A
❑ 98ScoComP-1B
❑ 98ScoComP-1C
❑ 98ScoComPG-1A
❑ 98ScoComPG-1B
❑ 98ScoComPG-1C
❑ 98ScoEpix-E1
❑ 98ScoFirP-1
❑ 98ScoLoaL-LL4
❑ 98ScoNewS-NS8
❑ 98ScoRT-13
❑ 98ScoRT-253
❑ 98ScoRTASEpix-1
❑ 98ScoRTComPla-1A
❑ 98ScoRTComPla-1B
❑ 98ScoRTComPla-1C
❑ 98ScoRTCPSamp-1A
❑ 98ScoRTCPSamp-1B
❑ 98ScoRTCPSamp-1C
❑ 98ScoRTSS-PP13
❑ 98ScoRTSS-PP146
❑ 98ScoRTSSAP-PP13
❑ 98ScoRTSSAP-PP146
❑ 98ScoRTSSAP1-PP13
❑ 98ScoRTSSAP1-PP146
❑ 98ScoRTStarGaz-1
❑ 98ScoSam-34
❑ 98ScoSS-PP123
❑ 98ScoSSAP-PP123
❑ 98SkyDugA-80
❑ 98SkyDugA-139
❑ 98SkyDugADH-DH8
❑ 98SkyDugAG-G4
❑ 98SkyDugAIA-80
❑ 98SkyDugAIA-139
❑ 98SkyDugAS-SH3
❑ 98SP Aut-180
❑ 98SP Aut-198
❑ 98SP Aut-S123
❑ 98SP Aut-SD1
❑ 98SP AutC-KG
❑ 98SP AutG3HR-300
❑ 98SP AutSD-SD1
❑ 98SP AutSDT-SD1
❑ 98SP AutTrade-4
❑ 98SP AutTrade-5
❑ 98SP AutTrade-6
❑ 98SP AutTrade-7
❑ 98SP AutTrade-8
❑ 98SPAutGJ5x7-1
❑ 98SpoIll-51
❑ 98SpoIll-144
❑ 98SpoIll-184
❑ 98SpoIll-191
❑ 98SpoIllC-C1
❑ 98SpoIllC-C3
❑ 98SpoIllEC-EC1
❑ 98SpoIllEE-51
❑ 98SpoIllEE-144
❑ 98SpoIllEE-184
❑ 98SpoIllEE-191
❑ 98SpoIllFE-51
❑ 98SpoIllFE-144
❑ 98SpoIllFE-184
❑ 98SpoIllFE-191
❑ 98SpoIllODMP-OD27
❑ 98SpoIllTaN-50
❑ 98SpoIllTaN-88
❑ 98SpoIllTaNC-C9
❑ 98SpoIllTaNEE-50
❑ 98SpoIllTaNEE-88
❑ 98SpoIllTaNGS-1
❑ 98SpoIllTaNRtC-RC3
❑ 98SpoIllWSF-50
❑ 98SpoIllWSFEE-50
❑ 98SpoIllWSFFE-50
❑ 98SpoIllWSFRJP-3
❑ 98SPxFin-50
❑ 98SPxFin-130
❑ 98SPxFin-165
❑ 98SPxFin-178
❑ 98SPxFin-240
❑ 98SPxFin-360
❑ 98SPxFinHRH-HR1
❑ 98SPxFinR-50
❑ 98SPxFinR-130
❑ 98SPxFinR-165
❑ 98SPxFinR-178
❑ 98SPxFinR-240
❑ 98SPxFinR-360
❑ 98SPxFinS-NNO
❑ 98SPxFinS-50
❑ 98SPxFinS-130
❑ 98SPxFinS-165
❑ 98SPxFinS-178
❑ 98SPxFinS-240
❑ 98SPxFinS-360
❑ 98StaCluBP-BP3
❑ 98StaCluFDI-199
❑ 98StaCluI-199
❑ 98StaCluNC-NC3
❑ 98StaCluOneK-199
❑ 98StaCluPP-199
❑ 98StaCluPWP-P10
❑ 98StaCluRC-RC1
❑ 98StaCluTIII-T3C
❑ 98StaCluTIII-T16B
❑ 98StaCluTLme-T3C
❑ 98StaCluTLme-T16B
❑ 98StaCluTLmo-T3C
❑ 98StaCluTLmo-T16B
❑ 98Stu-112
❑ 98Stu-CL6
❑ 98StuFF-1
❑ 98StuFFDC-1
❑ 98StuGPP-112
❑ 98StuGPP-CL6
❑ 98StuHitPar-6
❑ 98StuMast-20
❑ 98StuPor8x10-19
❑ 98StuPor8x10GP-19
❑ 98StuSPP-112
❑ 98StuSPP-CL6
❑ 98Top-321
❑ 98Top-479
❑ 98TopChr-321
❑ 98TopChr-479
❑ 98TopChrC9-C8
❑ 98TopChrC9R-C8
❑ 98TopChrF-FB2
❑ 98TopChrFR-FB2
❑ 98TopChrHB-HB9
❑ 98TopChrHBR-HB9
❑ 98TopChrM-MS5
❑ 98TopChrMR-MS5
❑ 98TopChrR-321
❑ 98TopChrR-479
❑ 98TopClo9-C8
❑ 98TopDevR-321
❑ 98TopDevR-479
❑ 98TopDia-321
❑ 98TopDia-479
❑ 98TopEtc-ES3
❑ 98TopFla-FB2
❑ 98TopFocP-FP5
❑ 98TopGal-120
❑ 98TopGalAG-AG1
❑ 98TopGalGoH-GH1
❑ 98TopGalGoHJ-GH1
❑ 98TopGalGP-120
❑ 98TopGalOPP-120
❑ 98TopGalPG-PG5
❑ 98TopGalPPI-120
❑ 98TopGalPPIA-120
❑ 98TopGolLabC1-100
❑ 98TopGolLabC1B-100
❑ 98TopGolLabC1One-100
❑ 98TopGolLabC1R-100
❑ 98TopGolLabC2-100
❑ 98TopGolLabC2B-100
❑ 98TopGolLabC2One-100
❑ 98TopGolLabC2R-100
❑ 98TopGolLabC3-100
❑ 98TopGolLabC3B-100
❑ 98TopGolLabC3One-100
❑ 98TopGolLabC3R-100
❑ 98TopGolLHRR-HR3
❑ 98TopGolLHRRB-HR3
❑ 98TopGolLHRRR-HR3
❑ 98TopGolLP-PP2
❑ 98TopHal-HB9
❑ 98TopMil-MS5
❑ 98TopMiniC-321
❑ 98TopMiniC-479

- ❑ 98TopMysF-ILM10
- ❑ 98TopMysFB-M20
- ❑ 98TopMysFB-M20
- ❑ 98TopMysFBR-M20
- ❑ 98TopMysFBR-M20
- ❑ 98TopMysFR-ILM10
- ❑ 98TopOpeD-147
- ❑ 98TopSta-100
- ❑ 98TopSta'S-15
- ❑ 98TopSta'SGH-15
- ❑ 98TopStaB-100
- ❑ 98TopStaG-G5
- ❑ 98TopStaG-100
- ❑ 98TopStaGG-G5
- ❑ 98TopStaGGR-G5
- ❑ 98TopStaGR-100
- ❑ 98TopStaGS-G5
- ❑ 98TopStaLB-L1
- ❑ 98TopStaLG-L1
- ❑ 98TopStaLGR-L1
- ❑ 98TopStaLS-L1
- ❑ 98TopStaS-100
- ❑ 98TopStaSteG-15
- ❑ 98TopSup-28
- ❑ 98TopSup-28
- ❑ 98TopTek-30
- ❑ 98TopTekD-30
- ❑ 98UD3-60
- ❑ 98UD3-150
- ❑ 98UD3-240
- ❑ 98UD3-S1
- ❑ 98UD3DieCut-60
- ❑ 98UD3DieCut-150
- ❑ 98UD3DieCut-240
- ❑ 98UD3PCBlowup-60
- ❑ 98Ult-1
- ❑ 98Ult-215
- ❑ 98Ult-246
- ❑ 98Ult-473
- ❑ 98Ult-476
- ❑ 98UltArtT-1
- ❑ 98UltBigS-1
- ❑ 98UltDial-1
- ❑ 98UltDiaP-1
- ❑ 98UltDouT-1
- ❑ 98UltFalC-1
- ❑ 98UltGolM-1
- ❑ 98UltGolM-215
- ❑ 98UltGolM-246
- ❑ 98UltGolM-473
- ❑ 98UltGolM-476
- ❑ 98UltMas-1
- ❑ 98UltMas-215
- ❑ 98UltMas-246
- ❑ 98UltMas-473
- ❑ 98UltMas-476
- ❑ 98UltMilM-2
- ❑ 98UltNot-2
- ❑ 98UltPlaM-1
- ❑ 98UltPlaM-215
- ❑ 98UltPlaM-246
- ❑ 98UltPlaM-473
- ❑ 98UltPlaM-476
- ❑ 98UltPowP-1
- ❑ 98UltPriL-1
- ❑ 98UltTicS-7
- ❑ 98UltTop3-23
- ❑ 98UltWinN-13
- ❑ 98UppDec-10
- ❑ 98UppDec-140
- ❑ 98UppDec-225
- ❑ 98UppDec-245
- ❑ 98UppDec-455
- ❑ 98UppDec-540
- ❑ 98UppDec-620
- ❑ 98UppDec10AP-48
- ❑ 98UppDec1APR-48
- ❑ 98UppDec5x7-225
- ❑ 98UppDec5x7-620
- ❑ 98UppDecAC-AS1
- ❑ 98UppDecAG-AG1
- ❑ 98UppDecAGDC-AG1
- ❑ 98UppDecAPA3-KG
- ❑ 98UppDecAPA3-KGS
- ❑ 98UppDecCD-CD30
- ❑ 98UppDecGHRC-1
- ❑ 98UppDecGHRC-2
- ❑ 98UppDecGHRC-3
- ❑ 98UppDecGHRC-4
- ❑ 98UppDecGHRC-5
- ❑ 98UppDecGHRC-6
- ❑ 98UppDecGHRC-7
- ❑ 98UppDecGHRC-8
- ❑ 98UppDecGHRC-9
- ❑ 98UppDecGHRC-10
- ❑ 98UppDecGHRC-11
- ❑ 98UppDecGHRC-12
- ❑ 98UppDecGHRC-13
- ❑ 98UppDecGHRC-14
- ❑ 98UppDecGHRC-15
- ❑ 98UppDecGHRC-16
- ❑ 98UppDecGHRC-17
- ❑ 98UppDecGHRC-18
- ❑ 98UppDecGHRC-19
- ❑ 98UppDecGHRC-20
- ❑ 98UppDecGHRC-21
- ❑ 98UppDecGHRC-22
- ❑ 98UppDecGHRC-23
- ❑ 98UppDecGHRC-24
- ❑ 98UppDecGHRC-25
- ❑ 98UppDecGHRC-26
- ❑ 98UppDecGHRC-27
- ❑ 98UppDecGHRC-28
- ❑ 98UppDecGHRC-29
- ❑ 98UppDecGHRC-30
- ❑ 98UppDecGHRC-31
- ❑ 98UppDecGHRC-32
- ❑ 98UppDecGHRC-33
- ❑ 98UppDecGHRC-34
- ❑ 98UppDecGHRC-35
- ❑ 98UppDecGHRC-36
- ❑ 98UppDecGHRC-37
- ❑ 98UppDecGHRC-38
- ❑ 98UppDecGHRC-39
- ❑ 98UppDecGHRC-40
- ❑ 98UppDecGHRC-41
- ❑ 98UppDecGHRC-42
- ❑ 98UppDecGHRC-43
- ❑ 98UppDecGHRC-44
- ❑ 98UppDecGHRC-45
- ❑ 98UppDecGHRC-46
- ❑ 98UppDecGHRC-47
- ❑ 98UppDecGHRC-48
- ❑ 98UppDecGHRC-49
- ❑ 98UppDecGHRC-50
- ❑ 98UppDecGHRC-51
- ❑ 98UppDecGHRC-52
- ❑ 98UppDecGHRC-53
- ❑ 98UppDecGHRC-54
- ❑ 98UppDecGHRC-55
- ❑ 98UppDecGHRC-56
- ❑ 98UppDecGMMHR-1
- ❑ 98UppDecGMMHR-2
- ❑ 98UppDecGMMHR-3
- ❑ 98UppDecGMMHR-4
- ❑ 98UppDecGMMHR-5
- ❑ 98UppDecGMMHR-6
- ❑ 98UppDecGMMHR-7
- ❑ 98UppDecGMMHR-8
- ❑ 98UppDecGMMHR-9
- ❑ 98UppDecGMMHR-10
- ❑ 98UppDecNP-NP39
- ❑ 98UppDecPN-PN1
- ❑ 98UppDecPN-PN2
- ❑ 98UppDecPN-PN3
- ❑ 98UppDecPN-PN4
- ❑ 98UppDecPN-PN5
- ❑ 98UppDecPN-PN6
- ❑ 98UppDecPN-PN7
- ❑ 98UppDecR-90
- ❑ 98UppDecR-20
- ❑ 98UppDecRBBop-BB13
- ❑ 98UppDecRGKoG-G10
- ❑ 98UppDecRL-2
- ❑ 98UppDecRQL-Q7
- ❑ 98UppDecRSotT-KGJ
- ❑ 98UppDecRTC-TC17
- ❑ 98UppDecSF-1
- ❑ 98UppDecSF-125
- ❑ 98UppDecSFPD-PZ10
- ❑ 98UppDecSFPZOB-PZ7
- ❑ 98UppDecSFPZPD-PZ10
- ❑ 98UppDecSFPZSX-PZ10
- ❑ 98UppDecTMT-10
- ❑ 98UppDecTMTG-10
- ❑ 98UppDecU-1
- ❑ 98UppDPDAG-1
- ❑ 98UppDPDAG-2
- ❑ 98UppDPDAG-3
- ❑ 98Zen-2
- ❑ 98Zen5 xx7-40
- ❑ 98Zen5x7GoldImp-40
- ❑ 98Zen5x7Imp-40
- ❑ 98ZenEpi-E1
- ❑ 98ZenRaitB-1
- ❑ 98ZenSampL-Z40
- ❑ 98ZenSamS-2
- ❑ 98ZenZ-G-2
- ❑ 98ZenZ-S-2
- ❑ 98ZenZ-T-2
- ❑ 98ZenZ-T5x7-2
- ❑ 98ZenZ-TG-2
- ❑ 99199Fin-101
- ❑ 99199Fin-200
- ❑ 99199Fin-256
- ❑ 99AllMysFR-M14
- ❑ 99AurComP-9A
- ❑ 99AurComP-9B
- ❑ 99AurKinotML-9
- ❑ 99AurOn DL-17
- ❑ 99AurPenF-17
- ❑ 99AurPenF-17
- ❑ 99AurPenFB-17
- ❑ 99AurPenFS-17
- ❑ 99AurSty-17
- ❑ 99Bow-52
- ❑ 99BowBes-80
- ❑ 99BowBes-86
- ❑ 99BowBesAR-80
- ❑ 99BowBesAR-86
- ❑ 99BowBesFBMI-FB2
- ❑ 99BowBesFBMII-FB2
- ❑ 99BowBesFBMIII-FB2
- ❑ 99BowBesMI-M2
- ❑ 99BowBesMIAR-M2
- ❑ 99BowBesMIR-M2
- ❑ 99BowBesR-80
- ❑ 99BowBesR-86
- ❑ 99BowChr-52
- ❑ 99BowChrDA-DA11
- ❑ 99BowChrDAR-DA11
- ❑ 99BowChrG-52
- ❑ 99BowChrGR-52
- ❑ 99BowChrI-52
- ❑ 99BowChrIR-52
- ❑ 99BowChrR-52
- ❑ 99BowGol-52
- ❑ 99BowInt-52
- ❑ 99CroRoyB-128
- ❑ 99CroRoyC2-9
- ❑ 99CroRoyCCDB-10
- ❑ 99CroRoyCCG-10
- ❑ 99CroRoyCCG-10
- ❑ 99CroRoyCCLB-10
- ❑ 99CroRoyCCP-10
- ❑ 99CroRoyCCP-10
- ❑ 99CroRoyCCR-10
- ❑ 99CroRoyL-128
- ❑ 99CroRoyLL-9
- ❑ 99CroRoyMP-17
- ❑ 99CroRoyOD-128
- ❑ 99CroRoyPotG-22
- ❑ 99CroRoyPP-22
- ❑ 99CroRoyPPN-22
- ❑ 99DumSet-151
- ❑ 99E-X Cen-17
- ❑ 99E-X CenECFut-17
- ❑ 99E-X CenECNow-17
- ❑ 99E-XCenFoF-4
- ❑ 99E-XCenMotC-4
- ❑ 99FinAarAwC-HA8
- ❑ 99FinAarAwCR-HA8
- ❑ 99FinDouF-DF1
- ❑ 99FinDouFDualR-DF1
- ❑ 99FinFraR-FR2
- ❑ 99FinFraRR-FR2
- ❑ 99FinGolRef-101
- ❑ 99FinGolRef-200
- ❑ 99FinGolRef-256
- ❑ 99FinLeaI-L3
- ❑ 99FinMil-M4
- ❑ 99FinMil-M12
- ❑ 99FinMil-M23
- ❑ 99FinMil-M39
- ❑ 99FinPeelHyp-4
- ❑ 99FinPeelSpark-4
- ❑ 99FinPeeSS-4
- ❑ 99FinProF-PF3
- ❑ 99FinProF-PF14
- ❑ 99FinProF-PF35
- ❑ 99FinProF-PF44
- ❑ 99FinRef-101
- ❑ 99FinRef-200
- ❑ 99FinRef-256
- ❑ 99FinSplS-SS2
- ❑ 99FinSplSDR-SS2
- ❑ 99FinTeaFB-TF12
- ❑ 99FinTeaFBR-TF12
- ❑ 99FinTeaFG-TF12
- ❑ 99FinTeaFGR-TF12
- ❑ 99FinTeaFR-TF12
- ❑ 99FinTeaFRR-TF12
- ❑ 99FlaShoLeg1-3
- ❑ 99FlaShoLeg2-3
- ❑ 99FlaShoLeg3-3
- ❑ 99FlaShoLegM1-3
- ❑ 99FlaShoLegM2-3
- ❑ 99FlaShoLegM3-3
- ❑ 99FlaShoMoG-4
- ❑ 99FlaShoR1-3
- ❑ 99FlaShoR2-3
- ❑ 99FlaShoR3-3
- ❑ 99Fle-3
- ❑ 99Fle-591
- ❑ 99FleBri-24
- ❑ 99FleBri2G-24
- ❑ 99FleBriBlu-24
- ❑ 99FleBriGol-24
- ❑ 99FleBriSS-1
- ❑ 99FleBriSSP-1
- ❑ 99FleDatWD-3
- ❑ 99FleDiaM-4
- ❑ 99FleGoiYar-7
- ❑ 99FleGolM-6
- ❑ 99FleMys-1
- ❑ 99FleMys-151
- ❑ 99FleMysE-1
- ❑ 99FleMysG-1
- ❑ 99FleMysM-1
- ❑ 99FleMysM-151
- ❑ 99FleSta9-3
- ❑ 99FleSta9-591
- ❑ 99FleVin'-3
- ❑ 99FleWarT-3
- ❑ 99FleWarT-591
- ❑ 99HomHer-7
- ❑ 99MetUni-95
- ❑ 99MetUni-233
- ❑ 99MetUni-273
- ❑ 99MetUni-298
- ❑ 99MetUniBWTW-1
- ❑ 99MetUniDS-8
- ❑ 99MetUniGM-95
- ❑ 99MetUniGM-233
- ❑ 99MetUniGM-273
- ❑ 99MetUniGM-298
- ❑ 99MetUniL-4
- ❑ 99MetUniPM-13
- ❑ 99MetUniPMG-95
- ❑ 99MetUniPMG-233
- ❑ 99MetUniPMG-273
- ❑ 99MetUniPMG-298
- ❑ 99Pac-396
- ❑ 99Pac-396A
- ❑ 99PacAur-176
- ❑ 99PacAurOD-176
- ❑ 99PacCraCho-4
- ❑ 99PacCroC-261
- ❑ 99PacCroCITC-16
- ❑ 99PacCroCPB-261
- ❑ 99PacCroCPC-4
- ❑ 99PacCroCTC-27
- ❑ 99PacCroCTM-16
- ❑ 99PacDynaD-6
- ❑ 99PacDynaDT-6
- ❑ 99PacGolCDC-13
- ❑ 99PacInv-133
- ❑ 99PacInvDM-9
- ❑ 99PacInvFP-18
- ❑ 99PacInvGotG-9
- ❑ 99PacInvOD-133
- ❑ 99PacInvPB-133
- ❑ 99PacInvSF-17
- ❑ 99PacInvSF-17B
- ❑ 99PacInvSH-18
- ❑ 99PacInvSH-18B
- ❑ 99PacInvTA-17
- ❑ 99PacOme-219
- ❑ 99PacOme5T-16
- ❑ 99PacOme5TT-16
- ❑ 99PacOmeC-219
- ❑ 99PacOmeDD-7
- ❑ 99PacOmeDM-30
- ❑ 99PacOmeEP-17
- ❑ 99PacOmeEP1o1-17
- ❑ 99PacOmeG-219
- ❑ 99PacOmeH'-17
- ❑ 99PacOmePB-219
- ❑ 99PacPar-216
- ❑ 99PacParC-216
- ❑ 99PacParCB-9
- ❑ 99PacParCBPP-9
- ❑ 99PacParFC-17
- ❑ 99PacParG-216
- ❑ 99PacParHoloGold-216
- ❑ 99PacParHS-216
- ❑ 99PacParOD-216
- ❑ 99PacParPB-32
- ❑ 99PacParPB-216
- ❑ 99PacParRed-216
- ❑ 99PacParTC-27
- ❑ 99PacPlaB-396
- ❑ 99PacPlaB-396A
- ❑ 99PacPri-133
- ❑ 99PacPriAotG-18
- ❑ 99PacPriBL-4
- ❑ 99PacPriDG-18
- ❑ 99PacPriEP-2
- ❑ 99PacPriHB-133
- ❑ 99PacPriHG-133
- ❑ 99PacPriHM-133
- ❑ 99PacPriHP-133
- ❑ 99PacPriRed-133
- ❑ 99PacPriS-6
- ❑ 99PacPriS206-6
- ❑ 99PacPriS206R-6
- ❑ 99PacPriSE-6
- ❑ 99PacPriSP-6
- ❑ 99PacPriSP-6
- ❑ 99PacPriSV-6
- ❑ 99PacRed-396
- ❑ 99PacRed-396A
- ❑ 99PacTeaC-11
- ❑ 99PacTim-7
- ❑ 99Pin-10
- ❑ 99Rev-130
- ❑ 99RevDiaL-31
- ❑ 99RevFouP-18
- ❑ 99RevMLBIcon-9
- ❑ 99RevPremDate-130
- ❑ 99RevRet-130
- ❑ 99RevShaSS-130
- ❑ 99RevThoitS-17
- ❑ 99RevTri-9
- ❑ 99RevTri-9
- ❑ 99SkyMolM-133
- ❑ 99SkyMolMF-33
- ❑ 99SkyMolMFS-33
- ❑ 99SkyMolMFT-33
- ❑ 99SkyMolMX-133
- ❑ 99SkyPre-137
- ❑ 99SkyPre-287
- ❑ 99SkyPre-299
- ❑ 99SkyPreIN-10
- ❑ 99SkyPreLB-14
- ❑ 99SkyPreR-137
- ❑ 99SkyPreR-287
- ❑ 99SkyPreR-299
- ❑ 99SkyPreSB-13
- ❑ 99SkyPreSotG-9
- ❑ 99SkyThu-292
- ❑ 99SkyThuDial1-D3
- ❑ 99SkyThuHip-H4
- ❑ 99SkyThuInD-ID5
- ❑ 99SkyThuRant-292
- ❑ 99SkyThuRave-292
- ❑ 99SkyThuTur-TC3
- ❑ 99SkyThuwww-WB3
- ❑ 99SP Aut-76
- ❑ 99SP Aut-124
- ❑ 99SP AutC-JR
- ❑ 99SP AutCG-JR
- ❑ 99SP AutEF-E26
- ❑ 99SP AutHRC-HR3
- ❑ 99SP AutHRC-HR41
- ❑ 99SP AutHRC-HR56
- ❑ 99SP AutR-R26
- ❑ 99SP AutRC-1
- ❑ 99SP AutRC-2
- ❑ 99SP AutRC-3
- ❑ 99SP AutRC-4
- ❑ 99SP AutRC-7
- ❑ 99SP AutRC-8
- ❑ 99SP AutRC-9
- ❑ 99SP AutRC-10
- ❑ 99SP SigAuto-JR
- ❑ 99SP SigAutoG-JR
- ❑ 99SP TopPR-R1
- ❑ 99SP TopPR-R2
- ❑ 99SP TopPR-R3
- ❑ 99SP TopPR-R4
- ❑ 99SP TopPR-R5
- ❑ 99SP TopPRAG-KG
- ❑ 99SPAutHRCDC-HR3
- ❑ 99SPAutHRCDC-HR41
- ❑ 99SPAutHRCDC-HR56
- ❑ 99SpoIll-10
- ❑ 99SpoIll-35
- ❑ 99SpoIll-97
- ❑ 99SpoIllDD-6
- ❑ 99SpoIllF4-3
- ❑ 99SpoIllF4E-3
- ❑ 99SpoIllH-11
- ❑ 99SPSig-2
- ❑ 99SPSig-S1
- ❑ 99SPx-70
- ❑ 99SPx-24EAST
- ❑ 99SPxDom-FB16
- ❑ 99SPxFinR-70
- ❑ 99SPxFinS-70
- ❑ 99SPxPowE-PE25
- ❑ 99SPxPreS-PS21
- ❑ 99SPxStaF-SF24
- ❑ 99SPxWinM-JR
- ❑ 99StaClu-200
- ❑ 99StaCluC-SCC20
- ❑ 99StaCluCR-SCC20
- ❑ 99StaCluFDI-200
- ❑ 99StaCluNC-NC3
- ❑ 99StaCluOoaK-200
- ❑ 99StaCluPP-200
- ❑ 99StaCluTI-T3B
- ❑ 99StaCluTI-T13B
- ❑ 99StaCluTL-T3B
- ❑ 99StaCluTL-T13B
- ❑ 99StaCluTL-T3B
- ❑ 99StaCluTL-T13B
- ❑ 99StaCluVR-VR3
- ❑ 99ThuSkySupR-292
- ❑ 99Top-100
- ❑ 99Top-224
- ❑ 99Top-454
- ❑ 99TopActF-4
- ❑ 99TopActFAU-4
- ❑ 99TopActFCU-4
- ❑ 99TopAll-AM3
- ❑ 99TopAllMF-M14
- ❑ 99TopBlaLC1-100
- ❑ 99TopBlaLC2-100
- ❑ 99TopBlaLC3-100
- ❑ 99TopChr-100
- ❑ 99TopChr-224
- ❑ 99TopChr-454
- ❑ 99TopChrA-AE3
- ❑ 99TopChrAR-AE3
- ❑ 99TopChrERttH-ER5
- ❑ 99TopChrERttH-ER5
- ❑ 99TopChrF1-FF5
- ❑ 99TopChrF1R-FF5
- ❑ 99TopChrLotD-LD1
- ❑ 99TopChrLotDR-LD1
- ❑ 99TopChrR-100
- ❑ 99TopChrR-224
- ❑ 99TopChrR-454
- ❑ 99TopChrRN-RN4
- ❑ 99TopChrRNR-RN4
- ❑ 99TopGal-6
- ❑ 99TopGal-101
- ❑ 99TopGalAG-AG7
- ❑ 99TopGalE-E7
- ❑ 99TopGalGoH-GH3
- ❑ 99TopGalHer-TH8
- ❑ 99TopGalHerP-TH8
- ❑ 99TopGalPP-6
- ❑ 99TopGalPP-101
- ❑ 99TopGalPPI-6
- ❑ 99TopGalPPI-101
- ❑ 99TopGolL-100
- ❑ 99TopGolLC1-100
- ❑ 99TopGolLC2-100
- ❑ 99TopGolLOtO-100
- ❑ 99TopGolLRtA-RA2
- ❑ 99TopGolLRtA-RA7
- ❑ 99TopGolLRtAB-RA2
- ❑ 99TopGolLRtAB-RA7
- ❑ 99TopGolLRtAOtO-RA2
- ❑ 99TopGolLRtAOtO-RA7
- ❑ 99TopGolLRtAR-RA2
- ❑ 99TopGolLRtAR-RA7
- ❑ 99TopLorotD-LD1
- ❑ 99TopMVPP-100
- ❑ 99TopMVPP-454
- ❑ 99TopOpeD-58
- ❑ 99TopOpeDO-3
- ❑ 99TopOver-A7
- ❑ 99TopPicP-P1
- ❑ 99TopPowB-PB3
- ❑ 99TopPowBR-PB3
- ❑ 99TopRecN-RN4
- ❑ 99TopRecNG-RN4
- ❑ 99TopRedLC1-100
- ❑ 99TopRedLC2-100
- ❑ 99TopRedLC3-100
- ❑ 99TopSta-1
- ❑ 99TopSta-178
- ❑ 99TopSta'S-26
- ❑ 99TopSta'SG-26
- ❑ 99TopSta'SGDH-26
- ❑ 99TopSta1Foil-1
- ❑ 99TopSta2Foil-1
- ❑ 99TopSta3Foil-1
- ❑ 99TopSta4Foil-1
- ❑ 99TopStaFoil-1
- ❑ 99TopStaFoil-178
- ❑ 99TopStaFS-1
- ❑ 99TopStaG-G9

❑ 99TopStaGFoil-G9
❑ 99TopStaOS-1
❑ 99TopStaTS-1
❑ 99TopStaTS-1
❑ 99TopSupC-18
❑ 99TopSupCR-18
❑ 99TopTek-5A
❑ 99TopTek-5B
❑ 99TopTekG-5A
❑ 99TopTekG-5B
❑ 99TopTekT-T1
❑ 99UD Cho-37
❑ 99UD Cho-142
❑ 99UD ChoBU-1
❑ 99UD ChoBUCG-7
❑ 99UD ChoMBH-B27
❑ 99UD ChoP-142
❑ 99UD ChoPCR-37
❑ 99UD ChoPCR-142
❑ 99UD ChoS-1
❑ 99UD ChoSD-1
❑ 99UD ChoSHR-1
❑ 99UD ChoST-1
❑ 99UD ChoYW-Y25
❑ 99UD Ion-52
❑ 99UD Ion-86
❑ 99UD Ion-S100
❑ 99UD IonC-C1
❑ 99UD IonH-HG1
❑ 99UD IonH-H1
❑ 99UD IonN-N1
❑ 99UD IonR-52
❑ 99UD IonR-86
❑ 99UD IonWZ-WZ1
❑ 99UDHolo-53
❑ 99UDHolo-S60
❑ 99UDHoloAUsome-53
❑ 99UDHoloFF-F4
❑ 99UDHoloFFG-F4
❑ 99UDHoloLau-L2
❑ 99UDHoloLauG-L2
❑ 99UDHoloStar-S2
❑ 99UDHoloStarG-S2
❑ 99UDHoloUDA-JR
❑ 99Ult-72
❑ 99Ult-215
❑ 99Ult-219
❑ 99UltDamI-8
❑ 99UltDiaP-1
❑ 99UltGolM-72
❑ 99UltGolM-215
❑ 99UltGolM-219
❑ 99UltMas-72
❑ 99UltMas-215
❑ 99UltMas-219
❑ 99UltPlaM-72
❑ 99UltPlaM-215
❑ 99UltPlaM-219
❑ 99UltRBIK-23
❑ 99UltTheBook-2
❑ 99UltThu-10
❑ 99UppDec-205
❑ 99UppDec-251
❑ 99UppDec-519
❑ 99UppDec-533
❑ 99UppDec-NNO
❑ 99UppDec10AT-X6
❑ 99UppDec10ATD-X6
❑ 99UppDec10ATHR-X6
❑ 99UppDec10ATT-X6
❑ 99UppDecBD-76
❑ 99UppDecBDD-76
❑ 99UppDecBDDom-D24
❑ 99UppDecBDDomE-D24
❑ 99UppDecBDMN-M2
❑ 99UppDecBDMNE-M2
❑ 99UppDecBDQ-76
❑ 99UppDecBDT-76
❑ 99UppDecCf7-3
❑ 99UppDecCf7-56
❑ 99UppDecCf7-80
❑ 99UppDecCf7-84
❑ 99UppDecCf7-C3
❑ 99UppDecCf7Cf7P-C3
❑ 99UppDecCf7LL-L1
❑ 99UppDecCf7SftF-S1
❑ 99UppDecCG-CG3
❑ 99UppDecCGD-CG3
❑ 99UppDecCGHR-CG3
❑ 99UppDecCGT-CG3
❑ 99UppDecCL-51
❑ 99UppDecCLA-1980
❑ 99UppDecCLA-1990
❑ 99UppDecCLCC-51
❑ 99UppDecCLES-JR
❑ 99UppDecCLES-SR
❑ 99UppDecCLESC-JR
❑ 99UppDecCLESC-SR
❑ 99UppDecCLM-C86
❑ 99UppDecCo7CE-3
❑ 99UppDecCo7CE-56
❑ 99UppDecCo7CE-80
❑ 99UppDecCo7CE-84
❑ 99UppDecCo7SftFA-JR
❑ 99UppDecE-81
❑ 99UppDecE-136
❑ 99UppDecE-166
❑ 99UppDecE2C-2K1
❑ 99UppDecEDF-D1
❑ 99UppDecEDFFXG-D1
❑ 99UppDecEFXG-81
❑ 99UppDecEFXG-136
❑ 99UppDecEFXG-166
❑ 99UppDecEL1-205
❑ 99UppDecEL1-251
❑ 99UppDecEL1-519
❑ 99UppDecEL1-533
❑ 99UppDecEL2-205
❑ 99UppDecEL2-251
❑ 99UppDecEL2-519
❑ 99UppDecEL2-533
❑ 99UppDecEPE-P26
❑ 99UppDecEUA-JR
❑ 99UppDecEUR-U1
❑ 99UppDecF-F26
❑ 99UppDecFD-F26
❑ 99UppDecFQ-F26
❑ 99UppDecFT-F26
❑ 99UppDecGJ-JR
❑ 99UppDecGJ-KG
❑ 99UppDecGJ-JRS
❑ 99UppDecGJ-KGAU
❑ 99UppDecIP-I9
❑ 99UppDecIPD-I9
❑ 99UppDecIPHR-I9
❑ 99UppDecIPT-I9
❑ 99UppDecKGJBB-1
❑ 99UppDecKGJBB-2
❑ 99UppDecKGJBB-3
❑ 99UppDecKGJBB-4
❑ 99UppDecKGJBB-5
❑ 99UppDecKGJBB-6
❑ 99UppDecKGJBB-7
❑ 99UppDecKGJBB-8
❑ 99UppDecKGJBB-9
❑ 99UppDecKGJBB-10
❑ 99UppDecKGJBBA-KG1989
❑ 99UppDecKGJBBA-KG1990
❑ 99UppDecKGJBBA-KG1991
❑ 99UppDecKGJBBA-KG1992
❑ 99UppDecKGJBBA-KG1993
❑ 99UppDecKGJBBA-KG1994
❑ 99UppDecKGJBBA-KG1995
❑ 99UppDecKGJBBA-KG1996
❑ 99UppDecKGJBBA-KG1997
❑ 99UppDecKGJBBA-KG1998
❑ 99UppDecKGJBBA-KG1999
❑ 99UppDecM-190
❑ 99UppDecM-218
❑ 99UppDecM-S3
❑ 99UppDecM-P3
❑ 99UppDecMD-D1
❑ 99UppDecMGS-190
❑ 99UppDecMGS-218
❑ 99UppDecMGUS-GUKG
❑ 99UppDecMGUS-GAKG
❑ 99UppDecMHFS-190
❑ 99UppDecMHFS-218
❑ 99UppDecMP-190
❑ 99UppDecMP-JR
❑ 99UppDecMSS-190
❑ 99UppDecMSS-218
❑ 99UppDecMSS-S3
❑ 99UppDecMST-T1
❑ 99UppDecMST-S1
❑ 99UppDecO-1
❑ 99UppDecO-81
❑ 99UppDecOAPoH-KGJ
❑ 99UppDecOMP-S5
❑ 99UppDecOSO-1
❑ 99UppDecOSO-81
❑ 99UppDecOWP-R3
❑ 99UppDecR-76
❑ 99UppDecRDR-D1
❑ 99UppDecRDRL2-D1
❑ 99UppDecRG-76
❑ 99UppDecRI-JR
❑ 99UppDecRIL2-JR
❑ 99UppDecRL-2
❑ 99UppDecRL-10
❑ 99UppDecRL-11
❑ 99UppDecRL-12
❑ 99UppDecRL-13
❑ 99UppDecROSS-S1
❑ 99UppDecROSS-S1
❑ 99UppDecRP-76
❑ 99UppDecRTA-T1
❑ 99UppDecRTAL2-T1
❑ 99UppDecTE-T27
❑ 99UppDecTED-T27
❑ 99UppDecTEQ-T27
❑ 99UppDecTET-T27
❑ 99UppDecVtaT-V26
❑ 99UppDecVtaTD-V26
❑ 99UppDecVtaTQ-V26
❑ 99UppDecVtaTT-V26
❑ 99UppDecWY-W10
❑ 99UppDecWYD-W10
❑ 99UppDecWYHR-W10
❑ 99UppDecWYT-W10
❑ 99Vic-366
❑ 99Vic-368
❑ 99Vic-370
❑ 99Vic-372
❑ 99Vic-465

Griffey, Ken Sr.

❑ 74OPC-598
❑ 74Top-598
❑ 75OPC-284
❑ 75Top-284
❑ 75TopMin-284
❑ 76BlaDis-17
❑ 76BucDis-17
❑ 76CarDis-17
❑ 76CraDis-17
❑ 76DailsID-17
❑ 76IsaDis-17
❑ 76Kel-44
❑ 76LinSup-94
❑ 76OPC-128
❑ 76OrbDis-17
❑ 76RedBarD-17
❑ 76RedIceL-6
❑ 76RedKro-10
❑ 76SafDis-17
❑ 76SSP-40
❑ 76Top-128
❑ 76TowCluD-17
❑ 77BurCheD-206
❑ 77ChiWilD-28
❑ 77DailsID-28
❑ 77DetCaeD-28
❑ 77HolInnD-28
❑ 77Hos-59
❑ 77Kel-49
❑ 77MSADis-28
❑ 77OPC-11
❑ 77PepGloD-50
❑ 77RCColC-27
❑ 77RedCarP-20
❑ 77SagDis-28
❑ 77sDis-28
❑ 77Top-320
❑ 77WenDis-28
❑ 77ZipDis-28
❑ 78Kel-4
❑ 78OPC-140
❑ 78Pep-12
❑ 78RCColC-11
❑ 78SSP270-118
❑ 78Top-80
❑ 79Hos-45
❑ 79Kel-39
❑ 79OPC-216
❑ 79Top-420
❑ 80OPC-285
❑ 80RedEnq-30
❑ 80Top-550
❑ 81AllGamPI-145
❑ 81CokTeaS-42
❑ 81Don-184
❑ 81Fle-199
❑ 81FleStiC-60
❑ 81OPC-280
❑ 81Top-280
❑ 81TopScr-91
❑ 81TopSti-163
❑ 81TopSupHT-36
❑ 82Don-634
❑ 82Fle-67
❑ 82FleSta-16
❑ 82OPC-171
❑ 82OPC-330
❑ 82Top-620
❑ 82Top-621
❑ 82Top-756
❑ 82TopTra-40T
❑ 82YanPhoA-9
❑ 83Don-486
❑ 83Fle-382
❑ 83FleSta-71
❑ 83FleSti-46
❑ 83OPC-110
❑ 83Top-110
❑ 83TopFol-3
❑ 83TopSti-98
❑ 83YanPhoA-9
❑ 83YanRoyRD-3
❑ 84AllGamPI-94
❑ 84Don-613
❑ 84DonActAS-21
❑ 84DonCha-25
❑ 84Fle-126
❑ 84Nes792-770
❑ 84OPC-306
❑ 84Top-770
❑ 84TopSti-317
❑ 84TopTif-770
❑ 85Don-347
❑ 85Fle-128
❑ 85Lea-193
❑ 85OPC-380
❑ 85Top-380
❑ 85TopTif-380
❑ 85YanTCMP-34
❑ 86Don-126
❑ 86Fle-105
❑ 86Lea-48
❑ 86OPC-40
❑ 86Top-40
❑ 86TopTif-40
❑ 86TopTra-41T
❑ 86TopTraT-41T
❑ 86YanTCM-32
❑ 87BraSmo-19
❑ 87Don-513
❑ 87DonOpeD-42
❑ 87Fle-516
❑ 87FleGlo-516
❑ 87FleMin-46
❑ 87FleStiC-49
❑ 87OPC-114
❑ 87SpoTeaP-24
❑ 87StuPan-2
❑ 87Top-711
❑ 87TopTif-711
❑ 88Don-202
❑ 88DonBasB-141
❑ 88Fle-540
❑ 88FleGlo-540
❑ 88Lea-165
❑ 88OPC-255
❑ 88PanSti-248
❑ 88RedFolSB-28
❑ 88Sco-390
❑ 88ScoGlo-390
❑ 88Spo-178
❑ 88StaLinBra-7
❑ 88Top-443
❑ 88Top-549
❑ 88TopBig-110
❑ 88TopSti-38
❑ 88TopTif-443
❑ 88TopTif-549
❑ 89Bow-259
❑ 89BowTif-259
❑ 89FleUpd-84
❑ 89RedKah-30
❑ 89Sco-609
❑ 89TopTra-40T
❑ 89TopTraT-40T
❑ 90Bow-60
❑ 90BowTif-60
❑ 90Don-469
❑ 90Fle-420
❑ 90FleCan-420
❑ 90KayB-13
❑ 90OPC-581
❑ 90RedKah-10
❑ 90Sco-338A
❑ 90Sco-338B
❑ 90StaGriJ-9
❑ 90Top-581
❑ 90TopBig-100
❑ 90TopMag-27
❑ 90TopTif-581
❑ 90UppDec-682
❑ 91AlrGriG-4
❑ 91Bow-255
❑ 91Cla2-T21
❑ 91ClaGam-141
❑ 91Don-452
❑ 91Lea-503
❑ 91MajLeaCP-5
❑ 91MarCouH-19
❑ 91MarCouH-28
❑ 91MotGri-2
❑ 91MotGri-3
❑ 91MotGri-4
❑ 91MSAHolD-11
❑ 91OPC-465
❑ 91PepGri-5
❑ 91PepGri-6
❑ 91PepGri-7
❑ 91PepGri-8
❑ 91Sco-835
❑ 91Sco-841
❑ 91SevCoi-NW4
❑ 91StaClu-342
❑ 91StaCluCM-10
❑ 91StaGri-1
❑ 91StaGri-3
❑ 91StaGri-5
❑ 91StaGri-7
❑ 91StaGri-9
❑ 91StaGri-11
❑ 91Stu-113
❑ 91Top-465
❑ 91TopDesS-465
❑ 91TopMic-465
❑ 91TopTif-465
❑ 91TopTriH-A12
❑ 91Ult-335
❑ 91UppDec-572
❑ 92AlrGriAAS-5
❑ 92AlrGriAAS-10
❑ 92AlrGriGM-5
❑ 92AlrGriGM-10
❑ 92LaKdec-15
❑ 92LimRocGH-1
❑ 92OPC-250
❑ 92PerGamGJ-8
❑ 92Top-250
❑ 92TopGol-250
❑ 92TopGolW-250
❑ 92TopMic-250
❑ 92UppDec-85
❑ 92UppDec-335
❑ 92YanWIZ8-69
❑ 93Bow-703
❑ 93MarMot-28
❑ 94SigRooFCD-3
❑ 94SigRooFCS-AU3
❑ 94SigRooFCS-AU4
❑ 94SigRooFCS-AU6
❑ 96Red76K-7
❑ 98UppDecR-23
❑ 98UppDecRSotT-KGS
❑ 99SP SigAuto-SR
❑ 99SPSig-179

Griffin, Alan

❑ 75TucTorC-18
❑ 75TucTorTI-5
❑ 76TucTorCa-13
❑ 76TusTorCr-34
❑ 78SanJosMMC-9

Griffin, Alfredo

❑ 79BluJayBY-10
❑ 79Top-705
❑ 80OPC-290
❑ 80Top-558
❑ 81AllGamPI-22
❑ 81Don-149
❑ 81Fle-430
❑ 81OPC-277
❑ 81OPCPos-15
❑ 81Top-277
❑ 81TopSti-140
❑ 82BluJayS-7
❑ 82Don-101
❑ 82Fle-615
❑ 82FleSta-236
❑ 82OPC-148
❑ 82Top-677
❑ 82TopSti-252
❑ 83AllGamPI-21
❑ 83Don-180
❑ 83Fle-429
❑ 83OPC-294
❑ 83Top-488
❑ 83TopSti-129
❑ 84AllGamPI-111
❑ 84BluJayFS-15
❑ 84Don-605
❑ 84Fle-156
❑ 84Nes792-76
❑ 84OPC-76
❑ 84Top-76
❑ 84TopSti-369
❑ 84TopTif-76
❑ 85A'sMot-5
❑ 85AllGamPI-22
❑ 85Don-73
❑ 85Fle-106
❑ 85FleUpd-47
❑ 85Lea-230
❑ 85OPC-361
❑ 85Top-361
❑ 85TopSti-366
❑ 85TopTif-361
❑ 85TopTifT-42T
❑ 85TopTra-42T
❑ 86A'sMot-5
❑ 86Don-101
❑ 86Fle-417
❑ 86Lea-34
❑ 86OPC-121
❑ 86Spo-136
❑ 86Top-566
❑ 86TopSti-168
❑ 86TopTat-16
❑ 86TopTif-566
❑ 87A'sSmoC-4
❑ 87Don-256
❑ 87DonOpeD-28
❑ 87Fle-392
❑ 87FleGlo-392
❑ 87Lea-198
❑ 87OPC-111
❑ 87Spo-164A
❑ 87Spo-164B
❑ 87SpoTeaP-23
❑ 87StuPan-24
❑ 87Top-111
❑ 87TopSti-166
❑ 87TopTif-111
❑ 88DodMot-7
❑ 88DodPol-7
❑ 88Don-226
❑ 88DonBasB-92
❑ 88Fle-280
❑ 88FleGlo-280
❑ 88FleUpd-94
❑ 88FleUpdG-94
❑ 88OPC-42
❑ 88PanSti-172
❑ 88Sco-88
❑ 88ScoGlo-88
❑ 88ScoRoo-37T
❑ 88ScoRooG-37T
❑ 88Spo-156
❑ 88StaLinAs-6
❑ 88StaLinD-5
❑ 88Top-726
❑ 88TopBig-247
❑ 88TopSti-169
❑ 88TopTif-726
❑ 88TopTra-43T
❑ 88TopTraT-43T
❑ 89Bow-345
❑ 89BowTif-345
❑ 89DodMot-7
❑ 89DodPol-5
❑ 89DodStaSV-1
❑ 89Don-79
❑ 89DonBasB-178
❑ 89Fle-58
❑ 89FleGlo-58
❑ 89OPC-62
❑ 89Sco-167
❑ 89Top-62
❑ 89TopSti-59
❑ 89TopTif-62
❑ 89UppDec-631
❑ 90Bow-95
❑ 90BowTif-95
❑ 90DodMot-8
❑ 90DodPol-7
❑ 90DodTar-297
❑ 90Don-195
❑ 90DonBesN-103
❑ 90Fle-395
❑ 90FleCan-395
❑ 90Lea-95
❑ 90OPC-643

❑ 90PanSti-270
❑ 90PubIntS-6
❑ 90Sco-156
❑ 90Top-643
❑ 90TopBig-18
❑ 90TopSti-58
❑ 90TopTif-643
❑ 90UppDec-338
❑ 91BluJayFS-10
❑ 91Bow-592
❑ 91DodMot-8
❑ 91DodPol-7
❑ 91Don-488
❑ 91Fle-201
❑ 91Lea-344
❑ 91OPC-226
❑ 91OPCBoxB-G
❑ 91PanFreS-58
❑ 91Sco-442
❑ 91StaClu-524
❑ 91Top-226
❑ 91TopDesS-226
❑ 91TopMic-226
❑ 91TopTif-226
❑ 91TopWaxBC-G
❑ 91Ult-161
❑ 91UppDec-119
❑ 92Don-692
❑ 92Fle-455
❑ 92OPC-418
❑ 92PanSti-195
❑ 92Sco-254
❑ 92Top-418
❑ 92TopGol-418
❑ 92TopGolW-418
❑ 92TopMic-418
❑ 92UppDec-282
❑ 93BluJayD-12
❑ 93BluJayD4-6
❑ 93BluJayFS-11
❑ 93Fle-692
❑ 93StaClu-561
❑ 93StaCluFDI-561
❑ 93StaCluMOP-561
❑ 94Fle-332
❑ 94Pac-641
❑ 96BluJayB-1
❑ 96BluJayOH-12
❑ 97BluJayOH-13
❑ 97BluJayS-25
Griffin, Barry
❑ 88BoiHawP-1614
Griffin, Bob
❑ 88MisStaB-8
Griffin, Chad
❑ 95EveAqaTI-8
Griffin, Dave
❑ 83AndBraT-20
❑ 84DurBulT-8
❑ 85DurBulT-24
❑ 86GreBraTI-11
❑ 87IntLeaAT-35
❑ 87RicBraBC-9
❑ 87RicBraC-24
❑ 87RicBraT-13
❑ 88BobCamRB-14
❑ 88RicBraC-19
❑ 88RicBraP-20
❑ 88TriAAC-17
❑ 89ColCliC-27
❑ 89TolMudHC-12
❑ 89TolMudHP-785
Griffin, Doug
❑ 71OPC-176
❑ 71RedSoxA-5
❑ 71Top-176
❑ 72RedSoxTI-8
❑ 72Top-703
❑ 72Top-704
❑ 73LinPor-21
❑ 73OPC-96
❑ 73Top-96
❑ 74OPC-219
❑ 74Top-219
❑ 75OPC-454
❑ 75Top-454
❑ 75TopMin-454
❑ 76OPC-654
❑ 76SSP-412
❑ 76Top-654
❑ 77Top-191
❑ 89PacSenL-53
Griffin, Edward
❑ 09ObaT21-51
❑ 09ObaT21-158A
❑ 09ObaT21-158B
Griffin, Francis
❑ 30Zee-82
Griffin, Frankie
❑ 83ReaPhiT-6
Griffin, Greg
❑ 83KnoBluJT-17
Griffin, Ivy M.
❑ 23WilChoV-53
Griffin, Kirk
❑ 98NewJerCM-11
Griffin, Mark
❑ 89Sta-29
❑ 89VerBeaDS-10
❑ 90VerBeaDS-16
❑ 91Cla/Bes-236
❑ 91FloStaLAP-FSL38
❑ 91VerBeaDC-27
❑ 91VerBeaDP-787
❑ 93WesPalBEC-6
❑ 93WesPalBEF-1353
❑ 94HarSenF-2104
Griffin, Martin
❑ 24Zee-91
❑ 25Zee-109
❑ 26Zee-137
Griffin, Matt
❑ 98WilCubM-11
Griffin, Michael
❑ 87OldJudN-212
❑ 89EdgR.WG-12
❑ 95May-12
❑ 98CamPepP-30
Griffin, Mike Leroy
❑ 77AshTouT-7
❑ 79WesHavYT-17
❑ 81ColCliP-36
❑ 81ColCliT-10
❑ 81Fle-107
❑ 81Top-483
❑ 82Don-533
❑ 82Top-146
❑ 83OklCit8T-8
❑ 84OklCit8T-7
❑ 85OmaRoyT-13
❑ 86OmaRoyP-8
❑ 86OmaRoyT-15
❑ 87BalOriP-14
❑ 87OriFreB-42
❑ 87RocRedWP-9
❑ 87RocRedWT-3
❑ 88Don-494
❑ 88Fle-561
❑ 88FleGlo-561
❑ 88RocRedWC-7
❑ 88RocRedWGCP-8
❑ 88RocRedWP-210
❑ 88RocRedWTI-9
❑ 89NasSouC-4
❑ 89NasSouP-1274
❑ 89NasSouTI-6
❑ 90ChaWheB-27
❑ 90ChaWheP-2258
❑ 90DodTar-298
❑ 91ChaLooLD-175
❑ 91ChaLooP-1975
❑ 91LinDriAA-175
❑ 92ChaLooF-3834
❑ 92YanWIZ7-59
❑ 92YanWIZ8-68
❑ 93IndIndF-1504
❑ 94IndIndF-1825
❑ 95IndIndF-112
Griffin, Nuje
❑ 91OriCro-166
Griffin, Rick
❑ 88MarMot-28
❑ 89MarMot-28
❑ 90MarMot-28
Griffin, Ryan
❑ 94AlbPolC-13
❑ 94AlbPolF-2231
❑ 94BluOriC-10
❑ 94BluOriF-3557
Griffin, Steve
❑ 91FreStaBS-5
❑ 92SouOreAC-15
❑ 92SouOreAF-3410
Griffin, Terry
❑ 87LitFalMP-2384
❑ 88LitFalMP-16
❑ 89St.LucMS-8
Griffin, Tim
❑ 90GreFalDSP-25
❑ 91VerBeaDC-20
❑ 91VerBeaDP-781
❑ 91YakBeaC-11
❑ 91YakBeaP-4253
❑ 92VerBeaDC-6
Griffin, Tom
❑ 69Top-614
❑ 70AstTeal-5
❑ 70RelPam-6
❑ 70Top-578
❑ 71AstTeal-9
❑ 71MLBOffS-81
❑ 71OPC-471
❑ 71Top-471
❑ 72AstTeal-10
❑ 72MilBra-122
❑ 73OPC-468
❑ 73Top-468
❑ 74AstFouTIP-3
❑ 74OPC-256
❑ 74Top-256
❑ 75AstPos-12
❑ 75OPC-188
❑ 75Top-188
❑ 75TopMin-188
❑ 76HouAstP-11
❑ 76OPC-454
❑ 76Top-454
❑ 77PadSchC-24
❑ 77Top-39
❑ 78AngFamF-14
❑ 78Top-318
❑ 79GiaPol-43
❑ 79Top-291
❑ 80GiaPol-43
❑ 80GiaTeal-6
❑ 80Top-649
❑ 81Don-75
❑ 81Fle-456
❑ 81GiaTeal-6
❑ 81Top-538
❑ 82Don-474
❑ 82Fle-389
❑ 82Top-777
❑ 87AstShoSO-10
❑ 87AstShoSPO-7
❑ 87AstShowSTh-26
❑ 87AstShowSTh-28
Griffin, Ty
❑ 87PanAmTUBI-14
❑ 87PanAmTURB-2
❑ 88TopTra-44T
❑ 88TopTraT-44T
❑ 89Bow-289
❑ 89BowTif-289
❑ 89ChaKniTI-14
❑ 89PeoChiTI-1
❑ 89PeoChiTI-21
❑ 89Top-713
❑ 89TopBig-170
❑ 89TopTif-713
❑ 90Bow-37
❑ 90BowTif-37
❑ 90ChaKniTI-14
❑ 90TopTVCu-45
❑ 91ChaKniLD-134
❑ 91ChaKniP-1700
❑ 91LinDriAA-134
❑ 92ChaLooF-3827
❑ 92ChaLooS-183
❑ 92SkyAA F-81
❑ 95ArkTraTI-13
Griffin, Wes
❑ 24Zee-129
❑ 25Zee-155
❑ 26Zee-49
❑ 33WorCig(-33
Griffith, Bart
❑ 75SenTCM1-8
Griffith, Calvin
❑ 78TwiFri-6
Griffith, Clark C.
❑ 04FanCraAL-22
❑ 05RotCP-6
❑ 05RotCP-7
❑ 09RamT20-52
❑ 09SpoNewSM-88
❑ 09T206-147
❑ 09T206-148
❑ 10CouT21-140
❑ 10CouT21-285
❑ 10DomDisP-50
❑ 10NotCov-5
❑ 10RedCroT-27
❑ 10RedCroT-114
❑ 10RedCroT-195
❑ 10StaCarE-15
❑ 10SweCapPP-101A
❑ 10SweCapPP-101B
❑ 10W555-32
❑ 11HelSta-69
❑ 11JonKeyaAC-326
❑ 11PinT-5-419
❑ 11S74Sil-76
❑ 11SpoLifCW-148
❑ 11SpoLifM-195
❑ 11T205-69
❑ 11TurRedT-17
❑ 12HasTriFT-59
❑ 13NatGamW-18
❑ 13TomBarW-17
❑ 14PieStaT-48
❑ 15CraJacE-167
❑ 15VicT21-13
❑ 16SpoNewM-72
❑ 19W514-41
❑ 31SenTealPW-11
❑ 39PC7AlbHoF-43
❑ 48ExhHoF-13
❑ 50CalHOFW-35
❑ 53ArtHaloFP-40
❑ 60ExhWriH-12
❑ 60Fle-15
❑ 60SenUniMC-6
❑ 61Fle-36
❑ 63BazA-37
❑ 72ClaCar-1
❑ 74CapPub-7
❑ 76ShaPiz-43
❑ 77GalGloG-150
❑ 80PacLeg-37
❑ 80PerHaloFP-43
❑ 80SSPHOF-43
❑ 87OldJudN-213
❑ 92ConTSN-464
❑ 92YanWIZH-13
❑ 93ConTSN-840
❑ 94OriofB-77
❑ 95ConTSN-1374
Griffith, David
❑ 16Zee-32
Griffith, Derrell (Robert D.)
❑ 65DodTeal-7
❑ 65OPC-112
❑ 65Top-112
❑ 66Top-573
❑ 67Top-502
❑ 90DodTar-299
Griffith, Jeff
❑ 87WatPirP-22
❑ 88AugPirP-363
Griffith, Kerry
❑ 86EriCarP-10
Griffith, Lynn
❑ 93DavLipB-23
❑ 94DavLipB-12
Griffith, Tommy
❑ 89BoiHawP-1984
❑ 91SalSpuC-6
❑ 91SalSpuP-2255
Griffith, Tommy (Thomas H.)
❑ 14B18B-49A
❑ 14B18B-49B
❑ 14B18B-49C
❑ 15SpoNewM-72
❑ 16FleBreD-35
❑ 16SpoNewM-73
❑ 17ColE13-64
❑ 20NatCarE-36
❑ 21E121So1-35
❑ 21E121So8-31
❑ 21Nei-58
❑ 22AmeCarE122-25
❑ 22E120-139
❑ 22W572-34
❑ 22W575-47
❑ 23W501-107
❑ 23W515-35
❑ 23WilChoV-54
❑ 80BraTCM1-11
❑ 90DodTar-300
Griffiths, Brian
❑ 89AshTouP-955
❑ 90OscAstS-8
❑ 91OscAstC-3
❑ 91OscAstP-675
❑ 92ClaFS7-324
❑ 92JacGenF-3994
❑ 92JacGenS-332
❑ 92SkyAA F-141
❑ 93ShrCapF-2752
❑ 93Top-483
❑ 93TopGol-483
❑ 93TopInaM-483
❑ 93TopInaR-483
❑ 93TopMic-483
Griffiths, Cade
❑ 97SpoIndG-12
Griffiths, Everard
❑ 96ButCopKB-13
❑ 97ChaRivDG-14
❑ 98St.PauSTI-9
Grifol, Pedro
❑ 91EliTwiP-4303
❑ 92ClaFS7-12
❑ 92Ft.MyeMCB-6
❑ 92Ft.MyeMF-2749
❑ 92ProFS7-101
❑ 93Bow-185
❑ 93NasXprF-406
❑ 94NasXprF-389
❑ 95HarCitRCTI-7
❑ 96BinMetB-10
❑ 97BinMetB-12
❑ 98BinMetQ-14
Griggs, Art
❑ 09PC7HHB-18
❑ 11PinT-5-112
❑ 16Zee-130
❑ 17Zee-107
❑ 18Zee-46
❑ 19Zee-52
❑ 20Zee-10
❑ 21Zee-10
❑ 22Zee-7
❑ 23Zee-7
Griggs, Hal
❑ 58SeaTeal-11
❑ 58Top-455
❑ 59SenTealW-8
❑ 59Top-434
❑ 60Lea-34
❑ 60Top-244
Griggs, Rod
❑ 96BilMusTI-10
Griggs, Skeet (Acie)
❑ 93NegLeaRL2-12
Griggs, Wiley
❑ 92NegLeaRLI-26
Grigsby, Benji
❑ 92ClaDraP-15
❑ 92ClaDraPFB-BC14
❑ 92UppDecML-11
❑ 93ClaFS7-195
❑ 93ModA'sC-1
❑ 93ModA'sF-794
❑ 93Pin-463
❑ 93Sco-495
❑ 93Sel-354
❑ 93StaCluM-151
❑ 93Top-518
❑ 93TopGol-518
❑ 93TopInaM-518
❑ 93TopInaR-518
❑ 93TopMic-518
❑ 94ModA'sC-12
❑ 94ModA'sF-3060
❑ 95HunStaTI-10
❑ 95UppDecML-153
❑ 95UppDecMLFS-153
❑ 98WesTenDJM-11
Grijak, Kevin
❑ 91IdaFalBP-4337
❑ 91IdaFalBSP-17
❑ 92ProFS7-197
❑ 92PulBraC-17
❑ 92PulBraF-3191
❑ 93MacBraC-11
❑ 93MacBraF-1406
❑ 94DurBulC-9
❑ 94DurBulF-339
❑ 94DurBulTI-8
❑ 94GreBraTI-12
❑ 95Exc-151
❑ 95RicBraRC-4
❑ 95RicBraTI-5
❑ 95SigRooOJ-15
❑ 95SigRooOJP-15
❑ 95SigRooOJPS-15
❑ 95SigRooOJS-15
❑ 96BesAutS-33
❑ 96RicBraUB-10
❑ 97GreBraG-10
❑ 98CarMudM-14
Grilione, Dave
❑ 86SalAngC-94
❑ 87QuaCitAP-29
Grilk, Jim
❑ 40SolHug-8
Grilli, Guido
❑ 64SeaPop-4
❑ 66Top-558
Grilli, Jason
❑ 98BesAutSS-23
❑ 98BesNumOP-25
❑ 98Bow-359
❑ 98BowBes-156
❑ 98BowBesAR-156
❑ 98BowBesR-156
❑ 98BowChr-359
❑ 98BowChrGA-359
❑ 98BowChrGAR-359
❑ 98BowChrI-359
❑ 98BowChrIR-359
❑ 98BowChrR-359
❑ 98BowGolA-359
❑ 98BowInt-359
❑ 98ShrCapM-1
❑ 98ShrCapWS-1
❑ 98TexLeaTPG-15
❑ 99Bow-117
❑ 99BowAut-BA30
❑ 99BowChr-117
❑ 99BowChrG-117
❑ 99BowChrGR-117
❑ 99BowChrI-117
❑ 99BowChrIR-117
❑ 99BowChrR-117
❑ 99BowGol-117
❑ 99BowInt-117
❑ 99JustheS-24
❑ 99JustheSAC-12
❑ 99JustheSAD-9
❑ 99JustheSJB-24
❑ 99SP TopP-54
❑ 99SP TopPPE-54
Grilli, Steve
❑ 76DetTigP-8
❑ 76OPC-591
❑ 76Top-591
❑ 77Top-506
❑ 78SyrChiT-11
❑ 79SyrChiT-17
❑ 79SyrChiTI-21
❑ 80SyrChiTI-9
❑ 81SyrChiT-4
Grilone, Dave
❑ 88BurBraP-18
Grim, Bob
❑ 55Bow-167
❑ 55RedMan-AL5
❑ 55Top-80
❑ 55TopDouH-57
❑ 56A'sPos-22
❑ 56Top-52
❑ 56YanTeal-9
❑ 57Top-36
❑ 58Top-224
❑ 59Top-423
❑ 60Lea-10
❑ 60Top-78
❑ 60TopVen-78
❑ 62Top-564
❑ 83YanASFY-17
❑ 84FifNatCT-7
❑ 92YanWIZA-26
❑ 94TopArc1-252
❑ 94TopArc1G-252
Grim, John
❑ 90DodTar-964
Grimes, Bob
❑ 88ChaWheB-27
❑ 89PeoChiTI-32
❑ 90ChaKniTI-24
❑ 96IowCubB-5
❑ 97IowCub-4
❑ 98IowCubQ-5
Grimes, Burleigh A.
❑ 21Exh-61
❑ 21Nei-89
❑ 21OxfConE-7
❑ 22E120-140
❑ 22W572-35
❑ 22W573-53
❑ 22WilPatV-31
❑ 23W515-16
❑ 23WilChoV-55
❑ 25Exh-12
❑ 26Exh-11
❑ 27Exh-7
❑ 27YorCarE-1
❑ 28PorandAR-A12
❑ 28PorandAR-B12
❑ 28W502-1
❑ 28W513-72

❑ 28Yue-1
❑ 29PorandAR-32
❑ 30UncJac-12
❑ 30W554-5
❑ 31CarMet-12
❑ 32CubTeal-8
❑ 32OrbPinNP-26
❑ 32OrbPinUP-21
❑ 33Gou-64
❑ 33GouCanV-64
❑ 33TatOrb-21
❑ 33TatOrbSDR-191
❑ 33WorCig(-34
❑ 35GouPuzR-1F
❑ 35GouPuzR-3D
❑ 35GouPuzR-14D
❑ 35GouPuzR-15D
❑ 60Fle-59
❑ 61Fle-37
❑ 70SpoCarfCOP-6
❑ 72TCMthe3-104
❑ 73TCMAllG-6
❑ 75TCMAllG-12
❑ 76GrePlaG-6
❑ 76RowExh-11
❑ 76ShaPiz-97
❑ 77BobParHoF-24
❑ 77DanBurG-1
❑ 77DanBurG-2
❑ 77DanBurG-3
❑ 77DanBurG-4
❑ 77DanBurG-5
❑ 77DanBurG-6
❑ 77DanBurG-7
❑ 77DanBurG-8
❑ 77DanBurG-9
❑ 77DanBurG-10
❑ 77DanBurG-11
❑ 77DanBurG-13
❑ 77DanBurG-14
❑ 77DanBurG-15
❑ 77DanBurG-16
❑ 77GalGloG-97
❑ 79DiaGre-76
❑ 80PacLeg-51
❑ 80PerHaloFP-97
❑ 80PerHaloFPS-11
❑ 80SSPHOF-97
❑ 82DiaCla-36
❑ 82TCMGreP-44
❑ 83DonHOFH-21
❑ 89DodSmoG-8
❑ 90DodTar-301
❑ 91ConTSN-25
❑ 92CarMcD-20
❑ 92ConTSN-433
❑ 92YanWIZH-14
❑ 93ConTSN-706
❑ 94ConTSN-997
❑ 94ConTSNB-997
❑ 95ConTSN-1382

Grimes, Dave (David)
❑ 89SprCarB-2
❑ 90St.PetCS-11
❑ 91ArkTraLD-35
❑ 91ArkTraP-1278
❑ 91LinDriAA-35

Grimes, John
❑ 84EveGiaC-25
❑ 85FreGiaSB-14
❑ 86ShrCapP-9
❑ 87ShrCapP-22

Grimes, Lee
❑ 87WinSpiP-14
❑ 88ChaWheB-6

Grimes, Mike (Michael)
❑ 88CapCodPPaLP-122
❑ 89MedAthB-6
❑ 91MadMusC-4
❑ 92ClaFS7-36
❑ 92ModA'sC-20
❑ 92ModA'sF-3894
❑ 93CenValRC-12
❑ 93CenValRF-2888

Grimes, Oscar Ray
❑ 21Exh-62
❑ 21Nei-105
❑ 22E120-157
❑ 22W572-36
❑ 25Zee-4
❑ 43YanSta-13
❑ 79DiaGre-282
❑ 95ConTSN-1419

Grimes, Steve
❑ 76CedRapGT-11A
❑ 76CedRapGT-11B
❑ 78HolMilT-10

Grimm, Charlie
❑ 20NatCarE-37
❑ 21E121So1-36
❑ 21Exh-63
❑ 22E120-218
❑ 22W575-48
❑ 22WilPatV-43
❑ 23W501-82
❑ 23WilChoV-56
❑ 25Exh-21
❑ 26Exh-21
❑ 26SpoComoA-17
❑ 27AmeCarE126-19
❑ 27Exh-10
❑ 28StaPlaCE-30
❑ 29ExhFou-6
❑ 30ChiEveAP-4
❑ 30SchR33-15
❑ 31CubTeal-8
❑ 31Exh-6
❑ 32CubTeal-6
❑ 32OrbPinNP-37
❑ 32OrbPinUP-22
❑ 32R33So2-423
❑ 33CraJacP-11
❑ 33ExhFou-3
❑ 33GeoCMil-16
❑ 33Gou-51
❑ 33GouCanV-51
❑ 33TatOrb-22
❑ 33WorCig-49
❑ 34DiaMatCSB-73
❑ 34DiaMatCSB-74
❑ 34ExhFou-3
❑ 34Gou-3
❑ 34GouCanV-61
❑ 34WarBakSP-6
❑ 35AlDemDCR3-160
❑ 35DiaMatCS2-7
❑ 35DiaMatCS3T1-62
❑ 35ExhFou-3
❑ 36CubTeal-10
❑ 36DiaMatCS4-5
❑ 36SandSW-25
❑ 36WorWidGV-89
❑ 40PlaBal-228
❑ 41CubTeal-25
❑ 46SpoExcW-2-5
❑ 48BabRutS-23
❑ 50CubGreB-6
❑ 53BowC-69
❑ 53BraJohC-1
❑ 53BraMer-9
❑ 54BraJohC-40
❑ 54BraMer-4
❑ 55Bow-298
❑ 55BraGolS-2
❑ 55BraJohC-40
❑ 56BraBilaBP-10
❑ 60Top-217
❑ 76ChiGre-8
❑ 77CubAllT-4
❑ 77CubAllT-5
❑ 77GalGloG-115
❑ 79DiaGre-101
❑ 80CubGreT-7
❑ 80PacLeg-75
❑ 82DiaCla-100
❑ 84CubBriPC-8C
❑ 84CubUno-8
❑ 85TCMPpl1-7
❑ 87ConSer2-40
❑ 88ConSer4-12
❑ 91ConTSN-95
❑ 91TopArc1-321
❑ 92CubOldS-9
❑ 93ConTSN-821

Grimm, John
❑ 92BriTigC-12
❑ 92BriTigF-1402
❑ 94LakTigC-10
❑ 94LakTigF-3031
❑ 95Exc-49

Grimmett, Ryan
❑ 98WesMicWM-6

Grimshaw, Moose (Myron)
❑ 09ColChiE-120A
❑ 09ColChiE-120B
❑ 09T206-425
❑ 11SpoLifCW-149
❑ 12ColRedB-120A
❑ 12ColRedB-120B
❑ 12ColTinT-120A
❑ 12ColTinT-120B

Grimsley, Jason
❑ 85BenPhiC-9
❑ 88ClePhiS-12
❑ 89BasAmeAPB-AA4
❑ 89EasLeaAP-16
❑ 89ReaPhiB-10
❑ 89ReaPhiP-670
❑ 89ReaPhiS-12
❑ 90Bow-151
❑ 90BowTif-151
❑ 90CMC-229
❑ 90Fle-653
❑ 90FleCan-653
❑ 90OPC-493
❑ 90PhiTas-10
❑ 90ProAAAF-297
❑ 90Sco-649
❑ 90ScrRedBC-3
❑ 90ScrRedBP-595
❑ 90Top-493
❑ 90TopDeb89-47
❑ 90TopTif-493
❑ 90UppDec-27
❑ 91Don-653
❑ 91Fle-396
❑ 91Lea-288
❑ 91OPC-173
❑ 91PhiMed-16
❑ 91Sco-818
❑ 91StaClu-294
❑ 91Top-173
❑ 91TopDesS-173
❑ 91TopMic-173
❑ 91TopTif-173
❑ 92Don-599
❑ 92Fle-532
❑ 92Sco-711
❑ 92StaClu-418
❑ 92TucTorF-482
❑ 92TucTorS-608
❑ 92UppDec-406
❑ 93ChaKniF-537
❑ 93LinVenB-220
❑ 94ChaKniF-887
❑ 94FleUpd-31
❑ 94VenLinU-25
❑ 95Don-164
❑ 95DonPreP-164
❑ 95Fla-31
❑ 95Fle-135
❑ 95Ult-279
❑ 95UltGolM-279
❑ 96AngMot-20
❑ 97TucTorB-3
❑ 98BufBisG-12

Grimsley, Ross
❑ 72OPC-99
❑ 72Top-99
❑ 73BalOriP-21
❑ 73OPC-357
❑ 73Top-357
❑ 74OPC-59
❑ 74Top-59
❑ 74TopTra-59T
❑ 75BalOriP-14
❑ 75Kel-2
❑ 75OPC-458
❑ 75Top-458
❑ 75TopMin-458
❑ 76BalOriP-16
❑ 76OPC-257
❑ 76SSP-377
❑ 76Top-257
❑ 77BalOriP-7
❑ 77BurCheD-40
❑ 77FriOneYW-4
❑ 77OPC-47
❑ 77Top-572
❑ 78ExpPos-5
❑ 78Top-691
❑ 79BasPat-35
❑ 79Hos-5
❑ 79Kel-3
❑ 79OPC-4
❑ 79Top-15
❑ 79TopCom-26
❑ 80ExpPos-10
❑ 80Kel-1
❑ 80OPC-195
❑ 80Top-375
❑ 81Fle-406
❑ 81Top-170
❑ 82BalOriP-3
❑ 84ChaLooT-7
❑ 86CalCanP-10
❑ 87CalCanP-2313
❑ 89BurBraP-1614
❑ 89BurBraS-28
❑ 89PacSenL-117
❑ 89T/MSenL-40
❑ 90EliSenL-81
❑ 90PenPilS-26
❑ 91CalCanLD-75
❑ 91CalCanP-531
❑ 91LinDriAAA-75
❑ 91OriCro-167
❑ 92CalCanF-3746
❑ 92CalCanS-75
❑ 93CalCanF-1183
❑ 96RocRedWB-3
❑ 97ReaPhi-2
❑ 98ReaPhiM-17
❑ 98ReaPhiUM-29

Grindle, Muriel
❑ 09ObaT21-261
❑ 12ObaPreT-10

Griner, Craig
❑ 90GeoColC-6

Griner, Dan
❑ 90DodTar-965

Grinstead, Carl
❑ 94ButCopKSP-11

Grisham, Wes
❑ 90LSUTigA-2
❑ 90LSUTigP-2
❑ 90WelPirP-15

Grissom, Antonio
❑ 90MarPhiP-3195
❑ 91BatCliCB-13
❑ 91BatCliP-3496
❑ 91SpaPhiC-24
❑ 91SpaPhiP-909
❑ 92AlbPolCB-26
❑ 92AlbPolF-2316
❑ 93BurBeeC-9
❑ 93BurBeeF-170
❑ 93ExcFS7-59
❑ 94WesPalBEC-11
❑ 94WesPalBEF-55
❑ 95HarSenTI-38

Grissom, Lee
❑ 38CloFotW-32
❑ 38RedOraW-13
❑ 39OrcPhoAP-12
❑ 39PlaBal-2
❑ 77CinRedT-23
❑ 78DodTCM4-15
❑ 79DiaGre-262
❑ 90DodTar-302

Grissom, Marquis
❑ 88JamExpP-1910
❑ 89BasAmeAPB-AA14
❑ 89JacExpB-1
❑ 89JacExpP-175
❑ 90Bow-115
❑ 90BowTif-115
❑ 90ClaBlu-65
❑ 90Don-36
❑ 90DonBesN-128
❑ 90DonRoo-45
❑ 90ExpPos-13
❑ 90Fle-347
❑ 90FleCan-347
❑ 90Hot50RS-20
❑ 90Lea-107
❑ 90OPC-714
❑ 90Sco-591
❑ 90Sco100RS-99
❑ 90ScoRooDT-B9
❑ 90ScoYouS2-6
❑ 90Spo-134
❑ 90Top-714
❑ 90TopBig-138
❑ 90TopDeb89-48
❑ 90TopTif-714
❑ 90UppDec-9
❑ 90UppDec-702
❑ 90UppDecS-2
❑ 91Bow-435
❑ 91Cla2-T38
❑ 91ClaGam-119
❑ 91Don-307
❑ 91Fle-234
❑ 91Lea-22
❑ 91OPC-283
❑ 91PanFreS-151
❑ 91Sco-234
❑ 91Sco100RS-38
❑ 91StaClu-8
❑ 91Stu-198
❑ 91Top-283
❑ 91TopDesS-283
❑ 91TopMic-283
❑ 91TopRoo-10
❑ 91TopTif-283
❑ 91ToyRoo-9
❑ 91Ult-204
❑ 91UppDec-477
❑ 92Bow-14
❑ 92ClaGam-39
❑ 92DenHol-1
❑ 92Don-137
❑ 92DonCraJ1-21
❑ 92ExpDonD-10
❑ 92ExpPos-15
❑ 92Fle-482
❑ 92Hig5-58
❑ 92Lea-273
❑ 92LeaBlaG-273
❑ 92OPC-647
❑ 92OPCPre-176
❑ 92PanSti-207
❑ 92Pin-129
❑ 92PinTea2-11
❑ 92RedFolS-42
❑ 92Sco-66
❑ 92ScoImpP-63
❑ 92SpoIllFK1-144
❑ 92StaClu-120
❑ 92Stu-55
❑ 92Top-647
❑ 92TopGol-647
❑ 92TopGolW-647
❑ 92TopKid-8
❑ 92TopMic-647
❑ 92TriPla-47
❑ 92Ult-518
❑ 92UppDec-455
❑ 92UppDec-719
❑ 93Bow-268
❑ 93ClaGam-39
❑ 93DenHol-10
❑ 93DiaMar-45
❑ 93Don-300
❑ 93ExpDonM-5
❑ 93Fin-40
❑ 93FinRef-40
❑ 93Fla-83
❑ 93Fle-461
❑ 93Fle-706
❑ 93FleFruotL-26
❑ 93FleTeaL-NL7
❑ 93FunPac-93
❑ 93FunPac-95
❑ 93FunPac-216
❑ 93FunPacA-AS8
❑ 93HumDumC-37
❑ 93Lea-129
❑ 93LeaFas-20
❑ 93LeaGolA-R17
❑ 93LeaGolA-U8
❑ 93OPC-209
❑ 93PacSpa-185
❑ 93PanSti-230
❑ 93Pin-346
❑ 93PinTea2-17
❑ 93RedFolS-35
❑ 93Sco-28
❑ 93Sel-99
❑ 93SelStaL-18
❑ 93SelStaL-58
❑ 93SP-12
❑ 93StaClu-529
❑ 93StaClu-598
❑ 93StaCluFDI-529
❑ 93StaCluFDI-598
❑ 93StaCluMOP-529
❑ 93StaCluMOP-598
❑ 93Stu-178
❑ 93Top-15
❑ 93TOPBLAG-7
❑ 93TopGol-15
❑ 93TopInaM-15
❑ 93TopInaR-15
❑ 93TopMic-15
❑ 93Toy-30
❑ 93ToyMasP-6
❑ 93TriPla-159
❑ 93Ult-415
❑ 93UppDec-356
❑ 93UppDec-481
❑ 93UppDecDG-10
❑ 93UppDecGold-356
❑ 93UppDecGold-481
❑ 93USPlaCA-1H
❑ 94Bow-284
❑ 94BowBes-R69
❑ 94BowBesR-R69
❑ 94ChuHomS-24
❑ 94ChuHomSG-24
❑ 94ColC-465
❑ 94ColChoGS-465
❑ 94ColChoSS-465
❑ 94Don-37
❑ 94DonSpeE-37
❑ 94Fin-229
❑ 94FinJum-229
❑ 94FinRef-229
❑ 94Fla-190
❑ 94Fle-540
❑ 94FleAllS-38
❑ 94FleExtB-306
❑ 94FleTeaL-22
❑ 94FUnPac-159
❑ 94Lea-174
❑ 94LeaL-125
❑ 94O-PJumAF-11
❑ 94OPC-18
❑ 94OPCAllR-11
❑ 94OPCJumA-11
❑ 94OscMayR-22
❑ 94Pac-382
❑ 94PanSti-210
❑ 94Pin-358
❑ 94PinArtP-358
❑ 94PinMusC-358
❑ 94PinRunC-RC38
❑ 94ProMag-83
❑ 94Sco-352
❑ 94ScoGolR-352
❑ 94ScoGolS-25
❑ 94Sel-242
❑ 94SelSki-SK7
❑ 94SP-84
❑ 94SPDieC-84
❑ 94Spo-48
❑ 94StaClu-706
❑ 94StaCluF-F6
❑ 94StaCluFDI-706
❑ 94StaCluFJ-F6
❑ 94StaCluGR-706
❑ 94StaCluMO-35
❑ 94StaCluMOP-706
❑ 94StaCluMOP-F6
❑ 94StaCluMOP-ST8
❑ 94StaCluST-ST8
❑ 94Stu-78
❑ 94TomPiz-7
❑ 94Top-590
❑ 94TopBlaG-34
❑ 94TopGol-590
❑ 94TopSpa-590
❑ 94TopSupS-20
❑ 94TriPla-95
❑ 94Ult-228
❑ 94UltAwaW-16
❑ 94UltRisS-6
❑ 94UppDec-39
❑ 94UppDec-390
❑ 94UppDecAJ-28
❑ 94UppDecAJG-28
❑ 94UppDecED-39
❑ 94UppDecED-390
❑ 94USPlaCA-10H
❑ 95Baz-37
❑ 95Bow-320
❑ 95BowBes-R68
❑ 95BowBesR-R68
❑ 95BraAtlC-3
❑ 95ColCho-237
❑ 95ColCho-537T
❑ 95ColCho-TC3
❑ 95ColChoGS-237
❑ 95ColChoSE-98
❑ 95ColChoSEGS-98
❑ 95ColChoSESS-98
❑ 95ColChoSS-237
❑ 95Don-251
❑ 95DonDom-8
❑ 95DonPreP-251
❑ 95DonTopotO-184
❑ 95Emo-101
❑ 95Fin-95
❑ 95Fin-237
❑ 95FinRef-95
❑ 95FinRef-237
❑ 95Fla-324
❑ 95FlaHotG-4
❑ 95Fle-351
❑ 95FleAllS-17
❑ 95FleUpd-90
❑ 95FleUpdSL-4
❑ 95Lea-335

❑ 95LeaGreG-7
❑ 95LeaLim-60
❑ 95Pac-268
❑ 95PacPri-87
❑ 95Pin-34
❑ 95PinArtP-34
❑ 95PinMusC-34
❑ 95Sco-246
❑ 95ScoGolR-246
❑ 95ScoHaloG-HG35
❑ 95ScoPlaTS-246
❑ 95Sel-39
❑ 95SelArtP-39
❑ 95SP-29
❑ 95SPCha-22
❑ 95SPChaDC-22
❑ 95Spo-28
❑ 95SpoArtP-28
❑ 95SPSil-29
❑ 95StaClu-440
❑ 95StaClu-617
❑ 95StaCluMO-20
❑ 95StaCluMOP-440
❑ 95StaCluMOP-617
❑ 95StaCluMOP-SS12
❑ 95StaCluSS-SS12
❑ 95StaCluSTWS-440
❑ 95StaCluSTWS-617
❑ 95StaCluVR-231
❑ 95StaCluVRMO-231
❑ 95Stu-34
❑ 95StuGolS-34
❑ 95Top-315
❑ 95TopCyb-171
❑ 95TopLeaL-LL43
❑ 95TopTra-65T
❑ 95UC3-49
❑ 95UC3ArtP-49
❑ 95Ult-403
❑ 95UltAwaW-16
❑ 95UltAwaWGM-16
❑ 95UltGolM-403
❑ 95UppDec-81
❑ 95UppDec-290
❑ 95UppDecED-81
❑ 95UppDecED-290
❑ 95UppDecEDG-81
❑ 95UppDecEDG-290
❑ 95UppDecSE-148
❑ 95UppDecSEG-148
❑ 95USPlaCMLA-9H
❑ 95Zen-72
❑ 96Baz-57
❑ 96Bow-102
❑ 96BowBes-50
❑ 96BowBesAR-50
❑ 96BowBesR-50
❑ 96BowFoi-102
❑ 96BraFle-5
❑ 96Cir-100
❑ 96CirRav-100
❑ 96ColCho-41
❑ 96ColChoGS-41
❑ 96ColChoSS-41
❑ 96Don-19
❑ 96DonPreP-19
❑ 96EmoXL-141
❑ 96Fin-B190
❑ 96FinRef-B190
❑ 96Fla-199
❑ 96Fle-292
❑ 96FleTif-292
❑ 96Lea-47
❑ 96LeaPrePB-47
❑ 96LeaPrePG-47
❑ 96LeaPrePS-47
❑ 96LeaSig-148
❑ 96LeaSigPPG-148
❑ 96LeaSigPPP-148
❑ 96MetUni-128
❑ 96MetUniP-128
❑ 96MLBPin-14
❑ 96Pac-17
❑ 96PanSti-5
❑ 96Pin-96
❑ 96PinAfi-63
❑ 96PinAfiAP-63
❑ 96PinAfiFPP-63
❑ 96PinChrBC-8
❑ 96Sco-334
❑ 96ScoDugC-B59
❑ 96ScoDugCAP-B59
❑ 96Sel-113
❑ 96SelArtP-113
❑ 96SelCerIP-25
❑ 96StaClu-422
❑ 96StaCluEPB-422
❑ 96StaCluEPG-422
❑ 96StaCluEPS-422
❑ 96StaCluMOP-422
❑ 96Stu-20
❑ 96StuPrePB-20
❑ 96StuPrePG-20
❑ 96StuPrePS-20
❑ 96Sum-83
❑ 96SumAbo&B-83
❑ 96SumArtP-83
❑ 96SumFoi-83
❑ 96TeaOut-33
❑ 96Top-297
❑ 96TopChr-117
❑ 96TopChrR-117
❑ 96TopGal-7
❑ 96TopGalPPI-7
❑ 96TopLas-66
❑ 96Ult-155
❑ 96UltGolM-155
❑ 96UppDec-8
❑ 97Bow-230
❑ 97BowBes-25
❑ 97BowBesAR-25
❑ 97BowBesR-25
❑ 97BowChr-57
❑ 97BowChrI-57
❑ 97BowChrIR-57
❑ 97BowChrR-57
❑ 97BowInt-230
❑ 97BraSco-14
❑ 97BraScoPI-14
❑ 97BraScoPr-14
❑ 97Cir-146
❑ 97CirRav-146
❑ 97ColCho-31
❑ 97ColChoT-CI11
❑ 97ColChoU-U9
❑ 97Don-64
❑ 97Don-278
❑ 97DonEli-143
❑ 97DonEliGS-143
❑ 97DonGolPP-64
❑ 97DonGolPP-278
❑ 97DonLim-8
❑ 97DonLimE-8
❑ 97DonPre-8
❑ 97DonPreCttC-8
❑ 97DonSilPP-64
❑ 97DonSilPP-278
❑ 97DonTea-85
❑ 97DonTeaSPE-85
❑ 97Fin-219
❑ 97FinRef-219
❑ 97FlaShoHG-5
❑ 97FlaShoLC-154
❑ 97FlaShoLeg0-154
❑ 97FlaShoLeg1-154
❑ 97FlaShoM-A154
❑ 97FlaShoM-B154
❑ 97FlaShoM-C154
❑ 97FlaShoR0-154
❑ 97FlaShoR1-154
❑ 97FlaShoR2-154
❑ 97Fle-256
❑ 97Fle-640
❑ 97FleTif-256
❑ 97FleTif-640
❑ 97Lea-292
❑ 97LeaFraM-292
❑ 97LeaFraMDC-292
❑ 97MetUni-29
❑ 97Pac-233
❑ 97PacLigB-233
❑ 97PacSil-233
❑ 97Pin-8
❑ 97PinArtP-PP8
❑ 97PinCer-89
❑ 97PinCerMBla-89
❑ 97PinCerMBlu-89
❑ 97PinCerMG-89
❑ 97PinCerMR-89
❑ 97PinCerR-89
❑ 97PinMusC-8
❑ 97PinPrePla-8
❑ 97PinTotCPB-89
❑ 97PinTotCPG-89
❑ 97PinTotCPR-89
❑ 97PinX-P-33
❑ 97PinX-PMoS-33
❑ 97Sco-246
❑ 97Sco-334
❑ 97ScoArtPWB-246
❑ 97ScoArtPWB-334
❑ 97ScoPreS-246
❑ 97ScoResC-334
❑ 97ScoShoS-246
❑ 97ScoShoS-334
❑ 97ScoShoSAP-246
❑ 97ScoShoSAP-334
❑ 97SP-57
❑ 97SpollI-44
❑ 97SpollIEE-44
❑ 97StaClu-201
❑ 97StaCluMat-201
❑ 97StaCluMOP-201
❑ 97Stu-69
❑ 97StuPrePG-69
❑ 97StuPrePS-69
❑ 97Top-184
❑ 97TopChr-71
❑ 97TopChrR-71
❑ 97TopGal-87
❑ 97TopGalPPI-87
❑ 97TopSta-48
❑ 97TopStaAM-48
❑ 97Ult-386
❑ 97UltFieC-7
❑ 97UltGolME-386
❑ 97UltPlaME-386
❑ 97UppDec-11
❑ 97UppDec-531
❑ 98BowBes-69
❑ 98BowBesAR-69
❑ 98BowBesR-69
❑ 98CirThu-280
❑ 98CirThuRav-280
❑ 98CirThuSupRav-280
❑ 98ColCho-405
❑ 98CroRoy-75
❑ 98Don-43
❑ 98Don-225
❑ 98DonCol-43
❑ 98DonColL-327
❑ 98DonColS-43
❑ 98DonGolPP-43
❑ 98DonGolPP-225
❑ 98DonPriCD-43
❑ 98DonPriCL-327
❑ 98DonSilPP-43
❑ 98DonSilPP-225
❑ 98E-X2-55
❑ 98E-X2ECFut-55
❑ 98E-X2ECNow-55
❑ 98Fin-226
❑ 98FinNo--226
❑ 98FinNo-R-226
❑ 98FinRef-226
❑ 98Fle-365
❑ 98FleVin'-101
❑ 98FleVin'C-101
❑ 98IndSco-12
❑ 98IndScoP-12
❑ 98Lea-128
❑ 98LeaFraDA-128
❑ 98LeaFraF-128
❑ 98LeaFraM-128
❑ 98LeaFraM-128
❑ 98LeaFraMDC-128
❑ 98LeaFraMDC-128
❑ 98LeaFraMZ2-128
❑ 98LeaRS-94
❑ 98LeaRS-166
❑ 98LeaRSLHolo-94
❑ 98LeaRSLHolo-166
❑ 98LeaRSLong-94
❑ 98LeaRSLong-166
❑ 98LeaRTrue-94
❑ 98LeaRTrue-166
❑ 98Pac-70
❑ 98PacAur-152
❑ 98PacOme-133
❑ 98PacOmeR-133
❑ 98PacOnl-394
❑ 98PacOnl-416
❑ 98PacOnlR-394
❑ 98PacOnlR-416
❑ 98PacOnlWC-394
❑ 98PacOnlWC-416
❑ 98PacPar-186
❑ 98PacParC-186
❑ 98PacParG-186
❑ 98PacParHS-186
❑ 98PacParPB-186
❑ 98PacParR-186
❑ 98PacPlaB-70
❑ 98PacRedT-70
❑ 98PacSil-70
❑ 98Pin-69
❑ 98PinArtP-PP62
❑ 98PinMusC-PP62
❑ 98PinPlu-73
❑ 98PinPreP-69
❑ 98Revo-79
❑ 98RevoSS-79
❑ 98Sco-188
❑ 98ScoRT-223
❑ 98ScoSS-PP87
❑ 98ScoSSAP-PP87
❑ 98SkyDugAFF-FF5
❑ 98SP Aut-120
❑ 98SpollIWSF-133
❑ 98SpollIWSFEE-133
❑ 98SpollIWSFFE-133
❑ 98SPxFin-295
❑ 98SPxFinR-295
❑ 98SPxFinS-295
❑ 98StaCluFDI-384
❑ 98StaCluI-384
❑ 98StaCluOneK-384
❑ 98StaCluPP-384
❑ 98Stu-178
❑ 98StuGPP-178
❑ 98StuSPP-178
❑ 98Top-70
❑ 98TopChr-70
❑ 98TopChrR-70
❑ 98TopDevR-70
❑ 98TopDia-70
❑ 98TopGal-9
❑ 98TopGalGP-9
❑ 98TopGalOPP-9
❑ 98TopGalPPI-9
❑ 98TopGalPPIA-9
❑ 98TopGolLabC1-37
❑ 98TopGolLabC1B-37
❑ 98TopGolLabC1One-37
❑ 98TopGolLabC1R-37
❑ 98TopGolLabC2-37
❑ 98TopGolLabC2B-37
❑ 98TopGolLabC2One-37
❑ 98TopGolLabC2R-37
❑ 98TopGolLabC3-37
❑ 98TopGolLabC3B-37
❑ 98TopGolLabC3One-37
❑ 98TopGolLabC3R-37
❑ 98TopMiniC-70
❑ 98TopOpeD-37
❑ 98TopPre-PP3
❑ 98TopSta-7
❑ 98TopStaB-7
❑ 98TopStaG-7
❑ 98TopStaGR-7
❑ 98TopStaS-7
❑ 98Ult-345
❑ 98UltGolM-345
❑ 98UltMas-345
❑ 98UltPlaM-345
❑ 98UppDec-422
❑ 98UppDec-692
❑ 98UppDec-748
❑ 98UppDecR-53
❑ 98UppDecRTC-TC43
❑ 99199Fin-229
❑ 99CroRoyB-78
❑ 99CroRoyL-78
❑ 99CroRoyOD-78
❑ 99FinGolRef-229
❑ 99FinRef-229
❑ 99FlaShoLeg1-106
❑ 99FlaShoLeg2-106
❑ 99FlaShoLeg3-106
❑ 99FlaShoLegM1-106
❑ 99FlaShoLegM2-106
❑ 99FlaShoLegM3-106
❑ 99FlaShoR1-106
❑ 99FlaShoR2-106
❑ 99FlaShoR3-106
❑ 99Fle-97
❑ 99FleSta9-97
❑ 99FleWarT-97
❑ 99Pac-232
❑ 99PacAur-99
❑ 99PacAurOD-99
❑ 99PacCroC-150
❑ 99PacCroCPB-150
❑ 99PacCroCTC-16
❑ 99PacInv-81
❑ 99PacInvOD-81
❑ 99PacInvPB-81
❑ 99PacOme-131
❑ 99PacOmeC-131
❑ 99PacOmeG-131
❑ 99PacOmePB-131
❑ 99PacPar-126
❑ 99PacParC-126
❑ 99PacParG-126
❑ 99PacParHoloGold-126
❑ 99PacParHS-126
❑ 99PacParOD-126
❑ 99PacParPB-126
❑ 99PacParRed-126
❑ 99PacParTC-16
❑ 99PacPlaB-232
❑ 99PacPri-80
❑ 99PacPriHB-80
❑ 99PacPriHG-80
❑ 99PacPriHM-80
❑ 99PacPriHP-80
❑ 99PacPriRed-80
❑ 99PacRed-232
❑ 99Rev-76
❑ 99RevPremDate-76
❑ 99RevRet-76
❑ 99RevShaSS-76
❑ 99SkyMolM-65
❑ 99SkyMolMOA-16
❑ 99SkyMolMX-65
❑ 99SkyThu-137
❑ 99SkyThuRant-137
❑ 99SkyThuRave-137
❑ 99StaClu-110
❑ 99StaCluFDI-110
❑ 99StaCluOoaK-110
❑ 99StaCluPP-110
❑ 99ThuSkySupR-137
❑ 99Top-383
❑ 99TopChr-383
❑ 99TopChrR-383
❑ 99TopMVPP-383
❑ 99TopSta-141
❑ 99TopStaFoil-141
❑ 99Ult-76
❑ 99UltGolM-76
❑ 99UltMas-76
❑ 99UltPlaM-76
❑ 99UppDec-128
❑ 99UppDecBD-46
❑ 99UppDecBDD-46
❑ 99UppDecBDQ-46
❑ 99UppDecBDT-46
❑ 99UppDecEL1-128
❑ 99UppDecEL2-128
❑ 99UppDecM-112
❑ 99UppDecMGS-112
❑ 99UppDecMHFS-112
❑ 99UppDecMP-112
❑ 99UppDecMSS-112
❑ 99Vic-215

Grissom, Marv
❑ 53RedSoxTI-11
❑ 54NewYorJA-22
❑ 55Bow-123
❑ 55GiaGolS-7
❑ 55RedMan-NL25
❑ 56Top-301
❑ 57Top-216
❑ 58GiaSFCB-10
❑ 58Hir-64
❑ 58Top-399
❑ 59Top-243
❑ 70TwiTeal-4
❑ 78AngFamF-15
❑ 79DiaGre-46

Grissom, Scott
❑ 94DavLipB-13

Groat, Dick
❑ 47Exh-84
❑ 52Top-369
❑ 53Top-154
❑ 54Top-43
❑ 55Top-26
❑ 55TopDouH-99
❑ 56PirTeal-9
❑ 56Top-24
❑ 56TopHocF-A1
❑ 56TopHocF-B3
❑ 56TopPin-42
❑ 57Kah-10
❑ 57Kah-11
❑ 57PirTeal-2
❑ 57Top-12
❑ 58HarSta-17
❑ 58Hir-21
❑ 58Kah-11
❑ 58PirTeal-4
❑ 58PirTeal-13
❑ 58Top-45
❑ 59Kah-12
❑ 59Top-160
❑ 59TopVen-160
❑ 60Kah-11
❑ 60PirJayP-6
❑ 60PirTag-24
❑ 60Top-258
❑ 60TopTat-20
❑ 61Baz-8
❑ 61ChePat-4
❑ 61Kah-16
❑ 61NuSco-413
❑ 61PirJayP-5
❑ 61PirRigF-3
❑ 61Pos-129A
❑ 61Pos-129B
❑ 61Top-1
❑ 61Top-41
❑ 61Top-486
❑ 61TopDicG-5
❑ 61TopStal-64
❑ 62ExhStaB-15
❑ 62Jel-172
❑ 62Kah-15
❑ 62Pos-172
❑ 62PosCan-172
❑ 62SalPlaC-138
❑ 62ShiPlaC-138
❑ 62Top-270
❑ 62TopBuc-33
❑ 62TopStal-177
❑ 63BasMagM-32
❑ 63CarJayP-9
❑ 63ExhStaB-27
❑ 63Jel-139
❑ 63Kah-13
❑ 63Pos-139
❑ 63SalMetC-16
❑ 63Top-130
❑ 64Baz-2
❑ 64CarTeal-3
❑ 64ChatheY-30
❑ 64Raw-4
❑ 64Top-7
❑ 64Top-40
❑ 64TopCoi-5
❑ 64TopCoi-147
❑ 64TopGia-19
❑ 64TopSta-81
❑ 64TopStaU-30
❑ 64TopTatI-40
❑ 64TopVen-7
❑ 64TopVen-40
❑ 64WheSta-20
❑ 65CarJayP-4
❑ 65ChaTheY-29
❑ 65OldLonC-11
❑ 65OPC-275
❑ 65Top-275
❑ 65TopTral-15
❑ 66OPC-103
❑ 66PhiTeal-8
❑ 66Top-103A
❑ 66Top-103B
❑ 66TopVen-103
❑ 67CokCapPh-6
❑ 67DexPre-83
❑ 67PhiPol-8
❑ 67Top-205
❑ 67TopVen-338
❑ 75OPC-198
❑ 75Top-198
❑ 75TopMin-198
❑ 77PirTCM1WC-4
❑ 78TCM60I-150
❑ 79DiaGre-372
❑ 81TCM60I-414
❑ 83TopRep5-369
❑ 84SpoDesPW-40
❑ 87Pir196T-3
❑ 88PacLegI-108
❑ 89SweBasG-91
❑ 90PacLeg-26
❑ 90SweBasG-49
❑ 91SweBasG-35
❑ 91TopArc1-154
❑ 92ActPacA-28
❑ 92BazQua5A-15
❑ 92CarMcD-28
❑ 92MDAMVP-2
❑ 94TopArc1-43
❑ 94TopArc1G-43
❑ 94UppDecS-2

Grob, Connie
❑ 59DarFar-8

Groch, Dick
❑ 89EasLeaDDP-DD47

Grodzicki, Johnny
❑ 81TCM60I-362
❑ 83Car194T-61

Groebner, Mark

❑ 98VerExpO-28
Groehing, Frank
❑ 17Zee-8
Groennert, John
❑ 87SalLakTTT-8
❑ 88BilMusP-1815
Groeschner, David
❑ 96BelGiaTI-36
❑ 97SanJosG-28
❑ 98SanJosGQ-29
Groh, Don
❑ 83PeoSunF-5
❑ 85EdmTraC-4
Groh, Heinie
❑ 15CraJacE-159
❑ 15SpoNewM-73
❑ 16FleBreD-36
❑ 16SpoNewM-74
❑ 17ColE13-65
❑ 19W514-46
❑ 20NatCarE-38
❑ 20RedWorCP-8
❑ 20W516-2
❑ 20WalMaiW-19
❑ 21E121So1-37
❑ 21E121So8-32
❑ 21Exh-64
❑ 21Exh-65
❑ 21Nei-88
❑ 22E120-186
❑ 22W572-37
❑ 22W573-54
❑ 22W575-49
❑ 22W575-50
❑ 22WilPatV-23
❑ 23W501-67
❑ 23W503-34
❑ 23W515-52
❑ 25Exh-34
❑ 68LauWorS-19
❑ 68SCFOldT-32
❑ 76RedParC-13
❑ 77GalGloG-139
❑ 81ConTSN-90
❑ 82DiaCla-80
❑ 86RedGreT-8
❑ 88PacEigMO-81
❑ 91ConTSN-163
❑ 94ConTSN-1270
❑ 94ConTSNB-1270
Grohs, Michael
❑ 91SpoIndC-4
❑ 91SpoIndP-3943
❑ 92ChaRaiF-117
Gromek, Steve
❑ 46SpoExcW-3-12
❑ 47Exh-85
❑ 47IndTeal-12
❑ 47IndVanPP-11
❑ 48IndTeal-13
❑ 49Bow-198
❑ 49IndTeal-13
❑ 50Bow-131
❑ 50IndNumN-12
❑ 50IndTeal-14
❑ 51Bow-115
❑ 52Bow-203
❑ 52IndNumN-8
❑ 52Top-258
❑ 53BowBW-63
❑ 53IndPenCBP-14
❑ 54Bow-199
❑ 55Bow-203
❑ 56Top-310
❑ 56YelBasP-13
❑ 57Top-258
❑ 79DiaGre-293
❑ 79TCM50-133
❑ 83TopRep5-258
❑ 85TCMPla1-39
Groninger, Gerry
❑ 88BilMusP-1803
❑ 89CedRapRB-23
❑ 89CedRapRP-930
❑ 89CedRapRS-23
❑ 90BilMusP-3238
❑ 91FayGenC-14
❑ 91FayGenP-1186
❑ 92FayGenC-24
❑ 92FayGenF-2184
❑ 93LakTigC-26
❑ 93LakTigF-1326
Groom, Bob
❑ 08AmeCarE91-77
❑ 09AmeCarE90-1-47
❑ 09ColChiE-121
❑ 09SenBarP-5
❑ 09T206-149
❑ 10CouT21-141
❑ 10DomDisP-51
❑ 10RedCroT-115
❑ 10RedCroT-196
❑ 10SweCapPP-59
❑ 11HelSta-70
❑ 11PinT-5-556
❑ 11T205-70
❑ 11TurRedT-96
❑ 12ColRedB-121
❑ 12ColTinT-121
❑ 12HasTriFT-44
❑ 14CraJacE-46
❑ 14PieStaT-49
❑ 15CraJacE-46
❑ 15VicT21-14
❑ 17ColE13-66
❑ 92ConTSN-350
Groom, Buddy
❑ 88TamTarS-9
❑ 89BirBarB-24
❑ 89BirBarP-109
❑ 89SouLeaAJ-17
❑ 90BirBarB-16
❑ 90BirBarP-1104
❑ 91LinDriAA-386
❑ 91LonTigLD-386
❑ 91LonTigP-1872
❑ 92DonRoo-44
❑ 92FleUpd-22
❑ 92TigTeal-13
❑ 92TolMudHF-1037
❑ 92TolMudHS-585
❑ 93Don-569
❑ 93TigGat-11
❑ 93TolMudHF-1649
❑ 93Top-353
❑ 93TopGol-353
❑ 93TopInaM-353
❑ 93TopInaR-353
❑ 93TopMic-353
❑ 94Don-637
❑ 94FleUpd-45
❑ 94TolMudHF-1023
❑ 95Fle-55
❑ 95Pac-155
❑ 96A'sMot-22
❑ 96LeaSigEA-63
❑ 97A'sMot-15
❑ 98A'sMot-15
❑ 98PacOnl-531
❑ 98PacOnlR-531
❑ 98PacOnlWC-531
Groot, Franz
❑ 92GreFalDSP-14
❑ 93YakBeaC-10
❑ 93YakBeaF-3880
❑ 95VerBeaDTI-9
Groover, Larry
❑ 79WatA'sT-17
Groppuso, Mike
❑ 91ClaDraP-39
❑ 91FroRowDP-39
❑ 91FroRowDPG-39
❑ 91FroRowDPS-39
❑ 92OscAstC-13
❑ 92OscAstF-2537
❑ 92Pin-543
❑ 93ClaFS7-196
❑ 93JacGenF-2112
❑ 94JacGenF-224
❑ 95JacGenTI-22
❑ 98El PasDG-13
Groseclose, David
❑ 96AshTouB-20
Groski, Gary
❑ 87ModA'sC-27
Gross, Bob
❑ 87GasRanP-5
Gross, Deryk
❑ 89KenTwiP-1064
❑ 89KenTwiS-8
❑ 90KenTwiB-4
❑ 90KenTwiP-2306
❑ 90KenTwiS-5
Gross, Don
❑ 57Kah-12
❑ 57RedSoh-7
❑ 57Top-341
❑ 58Top-172
❑ 59Top-228
❑ 60Top-284
❑ 77PirTCM1WC-31
Gross, George
❑ 78DayBeaAT-8
❑ 80TucTorT-10
❑ 81TucTorT-22
Gross, Greg
❑ 73LinPor-81
❑ 74AstFouTIP-1
❑ 75AstPos-13
❑ 75Hos-101
❑ 75Kel-5
❑ 75OPC-334
❑ 75Top-334
❑ 75TopMin-334
❑ 76CubTri-10
❑ 76Hos-90
❑ 76HouAstP-12
❑ 76Kel-56A
❑ 76Kel-56B
❑ 76OPC-171
❑ 76SSP-64
❑ 76Top-171
❑ 77Top-614
❑ 78SSP270-257
❑ 78Top-397
❑ 79OPC-302
❑ 79PhiBurK-22
❑ 79Top-579
❑ 80OPC-364
❑ 80PhiBurK-12
❑ 80Top-718
❑ 81Don-598
❑ 81Fle-18
❑ 81Top-459
❑ 82Don-371
❑ 82Fle-246
❑ 82Top-53
❑ 83Don-441
❑ 83Fle-162
❑ 83PhiTas-12
❑ 83Top-279
❑ 84Don-285
❑ 84Fle-31
❑ 84Nes792-613
❑ 84OCoandSI-236
❑ 84PhiTas-35
❑ 84Top-613
❑ 84TopTif-613
❑ 85Don-407
❑ 85Fle-251
❑ 85FleStaS-53
❑ 85OPC-117
❑ 85PhiCIG-5
❑ 85PhiTas-12
❑ 85PhiTas-35
❑ 85Top-117
❑ 85TopMin-117
❑ 85TopTif-117
❑ 86Don-163
❑ 86Fle-441
❑ 86OPC-302
❑ 86PhiCIG-5
❑ 86PhiTas-21
❑ 86Top-302
❑ 86TopTif-302
❑ 87AstShoSPO-8
❑ 87AstShoSTw-9
❑ 87Don-385
❑ 87Fle-173
❑ 87FleGlo-173
❑ 87OPC-338
❑ 87PhiTas-21
❑ 87RedFolSB-20
❑ 87Top-702
❑ 87TopTif-702
❑ 88Don-412
❑ 88Fle-302
❑ 88FleGlo-302
❑ 88PhiTas-11
❑ 88Sco-386
❑ 88ScoGlo-386
❑ 88StaLinPh-8
❑ 88Top-518
❑ 88TopTif-518
❑ 89AstLenH-2
❑ 89AstMot-12
❑ 89AstSmo-17
❑ 89Fle-568
❑ 89FleGlo-568
❑ 89OPCBoxB-E
❑ 89Sco-125
❑ 89Top-438
❑ 89TopTif-438
❑ 89TopWaxBC-E
❑ 89UppDec-534
❑ 91PadMag-12
❑ 95NewHavRTI-6
❑ 96NewHavRB-2
Gross, Jeremy
❑ 98OneYanG-13
Gross, John
❑ 90AppFoxBS-11
❑ 91BasCitRC-4
❑ 91BasCitRP-1391
❑ 91Cla/Bes-35
❑ 92BasCitRC-9
❑ 92BasCitRF-3839
❑ 93WilBluRC-12
❑ 93WilBluRF-1992
Gross, Kevin
❑ 83PorBeaT-5
❑ 84Don-381
❑ 84Fle-32
❑ 84Nes792-332
❑ 84PhiTas-20
❑ 84Top-332
❑ 84TopTif-332
❑ 85Don-477
❑ 85Fle-252
❑ 85PhiCIG-14
❑ 85PhiTas-9
❑ 85PhiTas-18
❑ 85Top-584
❑ 85TopTif-584
❑ 86BasStaB-49
❑ 86Don-529
❑ 86Fle-442
❑ 86PhiCIG-8
❑ 86PhiTas-46
❑ 86Top-764
❑ 86TopSti-119
❑ 86TopTif-764
❑ 87Don-236
❑ 87Fle-174
❑ 87FleGlo-174
❑ 87OPC-163
❑ 87PhiTas-46
❑ 87SpoTeaP-6
❑ 87Top-163
❑ 87TopTif-163
❑ 88Don-113
❑ 88DonBasB-103
❑ 88Fle-303
❑ 88FleGlo-303
❑ 88OPC-20
❑ 88PhiTas-12
❑ 88Sco-468
❑ 88ScoGlo-468
❑ 88Top-20
❑ 88TopSti-118
❑ 88TopTif-20
❑ 89Bow-355
❑ 89BowTif-355
❑ 89Don-194
❑ 89DonAll-48
❑ 89DonBasB-202
❑ 89DonBonM-BC12
❑ 89DonTra-3
❑ 89ExpPos-11
❑ 89Fle-569
❑ 89FleGlo-569
❑ 89FleUpd-96
❑ 89OPC-215
❑ 89PanSti-147
❑ 89Sco-227
❑ 89ScoRoo-39T
❑ 89Spo-213
❑ 89Top-215
❑ 89TopSti-116
❑ 89TopTif-215
❑ 89TopTra-42T
❑ 89TopTraT-42T
❑ 89UppDec-31
❑ 89UppDec-719
❑ 90Bow-109
❑ 90BowTif-109
❑ 90Don-248
❑ 90DonBesN-18
❑ 90ExpPos-14
❑ 90Fle-348
❑ 90FleCan-348
❑ 90Lea-61
❑ 90OPC-465
❑ 90PubIntS-174
❑ 90Sco-251
❑ 90Top-465
❑ 90TopBig-3
❑ 90TopSti-76
❑ 90TopTif-465
❑ 90UppDec-468
❑ 91Bow-611
❑ 91DodMot-17
❑ 91DodPol-45
❑ 91Don-569
❑ 91Fle-235
❑ 91FleUpd-94
❑ 91Lea-279
❑ 91OPC-674
❑ 91Sco-22
❑ 91ScoRoo-51T
❑ 91SimandSMLBL-19
❑ 91Top-674A
❑ 91Top-674B
❑ 91TopDesS-674
❑ 91TopMic-674
❑ 91TopTif-674
❑ 91UppDec-380
❑ 91UppDec-713
❑ 92DodMot-16
❑ 92DodPol-46
❑ 92DodSmo-5892
❑ 92Don-279
❑ 92Fle-456
❑ 92Lea-33
❑ 92LeaBlaG-33
❑ 92OPC-334
❑ 92Pin-344
❑ 92Sco-34
❑ 92ScoProP-10
❑ 92StaClu-72
❑ 92Top-334
❑ 92TopGol-334
❑ 92TopGolW-334
❑ 92TopMic-334
❑ 92UppDec-515
❑ 93DodMot-19
❑ 93DodPol-7
❑ 93DodStaC-5
❑ 93Don-458
❑ 93DonSpiotG-SG19
❑ 93Fle-448
❑ 93Lea-181
❑ 93OPC-111
❑ 93PacSpa-145
❑ 93Pin-177
❑ 93Sco-519
❑ 93StaClu-473
❑ 93StaCluFDI-473
❑ 93StaCluMOP-473
❑ 93Top-714
❑ 93TopGol-714
❑ 93TopInaM-714
❑ 93TopInaR-714
❑ 93TopMic-714
❑ 93Ult-399
❑ 93UppDec-198
❑ 93UppDecGold-198
❑ 94ColC-394
❑ 94ColChoGS-394
❑ 94ColChoSS-394
❑ 94DodDaiN-9
❑ 94DodMot-21
❑ 94DodPol-9
❑ 94Don-587
❑ 94Fla-396
❑ 94Fle-510
❑ 94FleExtB-287
❑ 94Lea-153
❑ 94Pac-308
❑ 94Sco-530
❑ 94ScoGolR-530
❑ 94Sel-157
❑ 94StaClu-281
❑ 94StaCluFDI-281
❑ 94StaCluGR-281
❑ 94StaCluMOP-281
❑ 94Top-516
❑ 94TopGol-516
❑ 94TopSpa-516
❑ 94Ult-516
❑ 94UppDec-166
❑ 94UppDecED-166
❑ 95ColCho-402
❑ 95ColChoGS-402
❑ 95ColChoSS-402
❑ 95Don-424
❑ 95DonPreP-424
❑ 95Fle-540
❑ 95FleUpd-82
❑ 95Lea-371
❑ 95RanCra-13
❑ 95StaClu-187
❑ 95StaCluFDI-187
❑ 95StaCluMOP-187
❑ 95StaCluSTWS-187
❑ 95StaCluVR-97
❑ 95StaCluVRMO-97
❑ 95Top-123
❑ 95TopCyb-78
❑ 95TopTra-14T
❑ 95Ult-335
❑ 95UltGolM-335
❑ 95UppDec-389
❑ 95UppDecED-389
❑ 95UppDecEDG-389
❑ 96ColCho-733
❑ 96ColChoGS-733
❑ 96ColChoSS-733
❑ 96Don-93
❑ 96DonPreP-93
❑ 96EmoXL-123
❑ 96Fla-171
❑ 96Fle-252
❑ 96FleTif-252
❑ 96LeaSigEA-64
❑ 96Pac-425
❑ 96RanDr P-12
❑ 96RanFle-8
❑ 96RanMot-10
❑ 96Ult-419
❑ 96UltGolM-419
❑ 96UppDec-208
❑ 97Fle-223
❑ 97FleTif-223
❑ 97PacPriGotD-GD96
❑ 97Top-328
Gross, Kip
❑ 86AncGlaPTI-13
❑ 87LynMetP-5
❑ 88FloStaLAS-6
❑ 88St.LucMS-10
❑ 89JacMetGS-22
❑ 91LinDriAAA-259
❑ 91NasSouLD-259
❑ 91NasSouP-2150
❑ 91TopDeb90-60
❑ 92DodPol-57
❑ 92DodSmo-5992
❑ 92Fle-407
❑ 92OPC-372
❑ 92Sco-740
❑ 92Sco100RS-92
❑ 92StaClu-247
❑ 92Top-372
❑ 92TopGol-372
❑ 92TopGolW-372
❑ 92TopMic-372
❑ 93DodPol-8
❑ 93Don-194
❑ 93StaClu-7
❑ 93StaCluFDI-7
❑ 93StaCluMOP-7
❑ 94VenLinU-36
Gross, Rafael
❑ 94GreFalDSP-15
❑ 95YakBeaTI-12
❑ 96SanBerSB-11
❑ 97AkrAer-11
❑ 98AkrAerM-27
Gross, Wayne
❑ 76TucTorCa-10
❑ 76TusTorCr-25
❑ 77Top-479
❑ 78Hos-141
❑ 78OPC-106
❑ 78Top-139
❑ 79Top-528
❑ 80OPC-189
❑ 80Top-363
❑ 81A'sGraG-10
❑ 81AllGamPI-32
❑ 81Don-237
❑ 81Fle-587
❑ 81OPC-86
❑ 81Top-86
❑ 81TopSti-118
❑ 82A'sGraG-2
❑ 82Don-139
❑ 82Fle-90
❑ 82FleSta-124
❑ 82OPC-303
❑ 82Top-692
❑ 83A'sGraG-10
❑ 83Don-591
❑ 83Fle-517
❑ 83Top-233
❑ 84BalOriP-15
❑ 84Don-375
❑ 84Fle-444
❑ 84FleUpd-45
❑ 84Nes792-741
❑ 84OPC-263
❑ 84Top-741
❑ 84TopSti-333
❑ 84TopTif-741
❑ 84TopTra-44T

❑ 84TopTraT-44T
❑ 85Don-228
❑ 85Fle-179
❑ 85OPC-233
❑ 85Top-416
❑ 85TopTif-416
❑ 86Don-535
❑ 86Fle-276
❑ 86OPC-173
❑ 86Top-173
❑ 86TopTif-173
❑ 87A'sMot-17
❑ 91OriCro-168

Grossman, Bob
❑ 75OklCit8Tl-1
❑ 75SanAntBT-7
❑ 76WilTomT-6

Grossman, Dave
❑ 82EdmTraT-24
❑ 86IowCubP-12
❑ 88IowCubP-531
❑ 89IowCubP-1703

Grossman, Jim
❑ 87KinIndP-8

Grote, Bob
❑ 79JacMetT-8

Grote, Jason
❑ 95ButCopKtl-9
❑ 96BurBeeTI-4
❑ 97BakBlaB-19
❑ 97BakBlaTI-19
❑ 97CalLeaATI-9
❑ 98SanJosGQ-1
❑ 99BasAmeTP-47
❑ 99BasAmeTPG-47

Grote, Jerry (Gerald)
❑ 64Top-226
❑ 64TopVen-226
❑ 65AstJayP-7
❑ 65Top-504
❑ 66MetTeal-6
❑ 66Top-328
❑ 66TopVen-328
❑ 67CokCapYM-V34
❑ 67DexPre-84
❑ 67MetTeal-6
❑ 67Top-413
❑ 68Top-582
❑ 69MetCit-4
❑ 69MetNewYDN-7
❑ 69MilBra-98
❑ 69MLBOffS-165
❑ 69OPC-55
❑ 69Top-55
❑ 69TopSta-63
❑ 69TopTeaP-24
❑ 70MetTeal-5
❑ 70MetTra-22C
❑ 70MLBOffS-76
❑ 70OPC-183
❑ 70Top-183
❑ 71MetTeal-7
❑ 71MetTealC-5
❑ 71MLBOffS-154
❑ 71OPC-278
❑ 71Top-278
❑ 71TopGreM-54
❑ 72MetTeal-3
❑ 72MilBra-123
❑ 72Top-655
❑ 73MetTeal-3
❑ 73NewYorSNM-13
❑ 73OPC-113
❑ 73Top-113
❑ 74MetDaiPA-16
❑ 74MetTeal-5
❑ 74OPC-311
❑ 74Top-311
❑ 74TopSta-62
❑ 75OPC-158
❑ 75Top-158
❑ 75TopMin-158
❑ 76Hos-78
❑ 76MetMSAP-1
❑ 76OPC-143
❑ 76Spo-9
❑ 76Top-143
❑ 77MetDaiPA-6
❑ 78SSP270-60
❑ 78Top-464
❑ 79Top-279
❑ 81RoyProPS-7
❑ 81TCM60I-438
❑ 84OCoandSI-186
❑ 86MetGreT-8
❑ 87Met196T-8
❑ 89Met196C-4
❑ 89MetRinP69-11
❑ 89PacSenL-120
❑ 89PacSenL-125
❑ 89T/MSenL-41
❑ 89TopSenL-34
❑ 90DodTar-303
❑ 91LinDri-17
❑ 91MetWIZ-153
❑ 91SweBasG-36
❑ 93UppDecAH-60
❑ 93UppDecS-10
❑ 94Met69CCPP-17
❑ 94Met69CS-16
❑ 94Met69T-8
❑ 94UppDecAH-181
❑ 94UppDecAH1-181
❑ 96Met69Y-3

Grotewold, Jeff
❑ 87SpaPhiP-21
❑ 88ClePhiS-13
❑ 89ClePhiS-10
❑ 90ReaPhiB-17
❑ 90ReaPhiP-1227
❑ 90ReaPhiS-10
❑ 91LinDriAAA-484
❑ 91ScrRedBLD-484
❑ 91ScrRedBP-2544
❑ 92DonRoo-45
❑ 92FleUpd-110
❑ 92PhiMed-40
❑ 92Ult-545
❑ 93Fle-490
❑ 93LinVenB-155
❑ 93LinVenB-296
❑ 93Sco-305
❑ 93StaClu-63
❑ 93StaCluFDI-63
❑ 93StaCluMOP-63
❑ 93Top-72
❑ 93TopGol-72
❑ 93TopInaM-72
❑ 93TopInaR-72
❑ 93TopMic-72
❑ 94SanBerSC-4
❑ 96OmaRoyB-13

Groth, Ernest
❑ 50RemBre-9

Groth, Johnny (John)
❑ 47Exh-86
❑ 50Bow-243
❑ 51Bow-249
❑ 51TopBluB-11
❑ 52Bow-67
❑ 52NatTeaL-12
❑ 52RedMan-AL10
❑ 52StaCalL-72F
❑ 52StaCalS-86C
❑ 52TipTop-12
❑ 52Top-25
❑ 53Top-36
❑ 54Bow-165
❑ 54Wil-7
❑ 55Bow-117
❑ 56A'sPos-23
❑ 56Top-279
❑ 56YelBasP-14
❑ 57Top-360
❑ 58Top-262
❑ 59Top-164
❑ 59TopVen-164
❑ 60Lea-133
❑ 60Top-171
❑ 60TopVen-171
❑ 79DiaGre-392
❑ 79TCM50-38
❑ 81TigDetN-33
❑ 83TopRep5-25
❑ 85TCMPpl1-28
❑ 91TopArc1-36

Grott, Matt
❑ 90MadMusP-2261
❑ 90MidLeaASGS-54
❑ 90ModA'sC-11
❑ 90ProAaA-115
❑ 91HunStaC-11
❑ 91HunStaLD-285
❑ 91HunStaP-1789
❑ 91HunStaTI-11
❑ 91LinDriAA-285
❑ 92ChaLooF-3812
❑ 92ChaLooS-184
❑ 93IndIndF-1482
❑ 94IndIndF-1804
❑ 96ScrRedBB-15
❑ 97TucTorB-4

Grout, Ron
❑ 79WisRapTT-7

Grove, George M.
❑ 20WalMaiW-20

Grove, Lefty (Robert M.)
❑ 28PorandAR-A13
❑ 28PorandAR-B13
❑ 28StaPlaCE-31
❑ 28W56PlaC-C13
❑ 29ExhFou-27
❑ 29PorandAR-33
❑ 30SchR33-49
❑ 30UncJac-13
❑ 30W554-6
❑ 31Exh-28
❑ 31W517-39
❑ 32OrbPinUP-23
❑ 32R33So2-408
❑ 32USCar*-27
❑ 33ButCanV-21
❑ 33ButCre-11
❑ 33CraJacP-12
❑ 33DelR33-23
❑ 33ExhFou-14
❑ 33GeoCMil-17
❑ 33Gou-220
❑ 33RitCE-8D
❑ 33TatOrb-23
❑ 33TatOrbSDR-182
❑ 33WorCig-50
❑ 34BabRutG-29
❑ 34BatR31-31
❑ 34BatR31-153
❑ 34ButPreR-28
❑ 34DiaStaR-1
❑ 34ExhFou-9
❑ 34ExhFou-14
❑ 34Gou-19
❑ 34GouCanV-54
❑ 35AlDemDCR3-79
❑ 35ExhFou-9
❑ 35WheBB1-15
❑ 36ExhFou-9
❑ 36NatChiFPR-36
❑ 36OveCanR-21
❑ 36R31PasP-36
❑ 36WheBB4-4
❑ 36WheBB5-10
❑ 36WorWidGV-88
❑ 37ExhFou-9
❑ 37OPCBatUV-137
❑ 37WheBB6-9
❑ 37WheBB8-6
❑ 37WheBB9-7
❑ 38BasTabP-14
❑ 38ExhFou-9
❑ 38WheBB10-9
❑ 38WheBB11-4
❑ 38WheBB15-5
❑ 39ExhSal-23
❑ 39PC7AlbHoF-52
❑ 41DouPlaR-105
❑ 46SpoExcW-4-4
❑ 48ExhHoF-14
❑ 50CalHOFW-36
❑ 51R42SmaS-39
❑ 53ArtHaloFP-41
❑ 60Fle-60
❑ 60Fle-80B
❑ 61Fle-38
❑ 61GolPre-17
❑ 63BasMagM-33
❑ 67TopVen-168
❑ 68SpoMemAG-6
❑ 69EquSpoHoF-BB6
❑ 72KelATG-7
❑ 72LauGreF-16
❑ 72TCMthe3-33
❑ 73SevTraC-28
❑ 74A's192T-13
❑ 75TCMAllG-13
❑ 76OPC-350
❑ 76RowExh-13
❑ 76ShaPiz-52
❑ 76Top-350
❑ 77GalGloG-55
❑ 77GalGloG-195
❑ 77PhiFav-4
❑ 77ShaPiz-7
❑ 79RedSoxEF-4
❑ 79RedSoxEF-12
❑ 79RedSoxEF-13
❑ 80Lau300-19
❑ 80LauFamF-8
❑ 80PacLeg-27
❑ 80PerHaloFP-52
❑ 80SSPHOF-52
❑ 81ConTSN-38
❑ 82DiaCla-43
❑ 82OhiHaloF-25
❑ 82TCMGreP-29
❑ 83A'sGreT-10
❑ 83BigLeaCOA-8
❑ 83ConMar-20
❑ 84OCoandSI-83
❑ 85FegMurCG-9
❑ 86ConSer1-47
❑ 86RedSoxGT-2
❑ 86SpoDecG-3
❑ 87HygAllG-23
❑ 87SpoRea-26
❑ 88ConAmeA-13
❑ 88ConSer4-13
❑ 88GreBasS-69
❑ 89HOFStiB-74
❑ 89PacLegI-185
❑ 89SweBasG-15
❑ 90BasWit-94
❑ 90HOFStiB-31
❑ 90SweBasG-70
❑ 91ConTSN-23
❑ 91ConTSN-255
❑ 91SweBasG-139
❑ 92ConTSN-431
❑ 92ConTSN-533
❑ 92ConTSNCI-2
❑ 93ActPacA-99
❑ 93ActPacA2-33G
❑ 93ConTSN-669
❑ 93ConTSN-930
❑ 93ConTSNP-1140
❑ 94ConTSN-999
❑ 94ConTSN-1140
❑ 94ConTSNB-999
❑ 94ConTSNB-1140
❑ 94TedWil-67
❑ 94UppDecTAE-41
❑ 99SP SigLC-LG
❑ 99UppDecCL-23
❑ 99UppDecCLCC-23
❑ 99UppDecCLLC-CY

Grove, LeRoy Orval
❑ 47Exh-87
❑ 48KelPep*-BB2
❑ 48WhiSoxTI-8
❑ 49Lea-66
❑ 79DiaGre-131
❑ 83TCMPla1943-11

Grove, Scott
❑ 88PulBraP-1752
❑ 89SumBraP-1114
❑ 90BurBraB-18
❑ 90BurBraP-2344
❑ 90BurBraS-13
❑ 92DunBluJC-13
❑ 92DunBluJF-1994
❑ 93DunBluJC-8
❑ 93DunBluJF-1789
❑ 93DunBluJFFN-8
❑ 93KnoSmoF-1248

Grove, Wayne
❑ 85DalNatCC-12

Groves, Jeff
❑ 86GreBraTI-12

Groves, Larry
❑ 86IndIndTI-27

Grovom, Carl
❑ 86AubAstP-11
❑ 87ChaWheP-15
❑ 88OscAstS-11
❑ 91JacGenP-920

Grow, Lorin
❑ 76IndIndTI-14

Grubb, Cary
❑ 87SalAngP-26
❑ 88RenSilSCLC-281

Grubb, Christopher
❑ 93JamExpC-7
❑ 93JamExpF-3333
❑ 97WilCubB-7
❑ 98RocCubM-11
❑ 98RocCubTI-11

Grubb, Dennis
❑ 95AusFut-45

Grubb, Johnny (John)
❑ 73LinPor-155
❑ 73PadDea-10
❑ 74OPC-32
❑ 74PadDea-11
❑ 74PadMcDD-5
❑ 74Top-32A
❑ 74Top-32B
❑ 74TopSta-93
❑ 75Hos-109
❑ 75Kel-43
❑ 75OPC-298
❑ 75PadDea-2
❑ 75PadDea-9
❑ 75SSPPuzB-11
❑ 75Top-298
❑ 75TopMin-298
❑ 76OPC-422
❑ 76SSP-130
❑ 76Top-422
❑ 77OPC-165
❑ 77PadSchC-25
❑ 77PepGloD-10
❑ 77Top-286
❑ 78IndTeal-12
❑ 78Top-608
❑ 79OPC-99
❑ 79Top-198
❑ 80OPC-165
❑ 80Top-313
❑ 81Don-148
❑ 81Fle-631
❑ 81Top-545
❑ 82Don-467
❑ 82Fle-317
❑ 82OPC-193
❑ 82Top-496
❑ 83Don-341
❑ 83Fle-567
❑ 83FleSta-72
❑ 83FleSti-167
❑ 83TigPos-13
❑ 83Top-724
❑ 83TopSti-123
❑ 83TopTra-38T
❑ 84Don-90
❑ 84Fle-81
❑ 84Nes792-42
❑ 84TigFarJ-5
❑ 84TigTeal-17
❑ 84TigWavP-18
❑ 84Top-42
❑ 84TopTif-42
❑ 85Don-578
❑ 85Fle-9
❑ 85TigCaiD-9
❑ 85TigWen-10
❑ 85Top-643
❑ 85TopTif-643
❑ 86Don-615
❑ 86Fle-227
❑ 86TigCaiD-7
❑ 86Top-243
❑ 86TopTif-243
❑ 87Don-476
❑ 87Fle-152
❑ 87FleGlo-152
❑ 87TigCaiD-12
❑ 87TigCok-18
❑ 87Top-384
❑ 87TopSti-265
❑ 87TopTif-384
❑ 88BobCamRB-23
❑ 88Sco-199
❑ 88ScoGlo-199
❑ 88Top-128
❑ 88TopTif-128
❑ 89PacSenL-191
❑ 89RicBraBC-8
❑ 89RicBraC-24
❑ 89RicBraP-821
❑ 89RicBraTI-25
❑ 89T/MSenL-42
❑ 90CMC-278
❑ 90EliSenL-57
❑ 90ProAAAF-420
❑ 90RicBraC-2
❑ 90RicBraP-275
❑ 90RicBraTI-11
❑ 91RicBraBC-41
❑ 91RicBraP-2586
❑ 93RanKee-165
❑ 95ColSilB-10
❑ 96ColSilB-12

Grubb, Sean
❑ 89HamRedS-17

Grube, Frank
❑ 32OrbPinNP-5
❑ 32OrbPinUP-24
❑ 33TatOrb-24
❑ 34DiaMatCSB-75
❑ 34Gou-64
❑ 35DiaMatCS3T1-63
❑ 35GouPuzR-8C
❑ 35GouPuzR-9C
❑ 41BroW75-13
❑ 92ConTSN-399
❑ 94ConTSN-1162
❑ 94ConTSNB-1162

Gruber, Henry
❑ 87OldJudN-214

Gruber, Kelly
❑ 80BatTroT-21
❑ 81WatIndT-22
❑ 82ChaLooT-16
❑ 83BufBisT-16
❑ 84BluJayFS-16
❑ 84SyrChiT-27
❑ 85BluJayFS-13
❑ 85Fle-645
❑ 85IntLeaAT-37
❑ 85SyrChiT-22
❑ 86BluJayAF-12
❑ 86BluJayFS-15
❑ 86DonRoo-16
❑ 87BluJayFS-11
❑ 87Don-444
❑ 87Fle-227
❑ 87FleGlo-227
❑ 87GenMilB-1D
❑ 87OPC-191
❑ 87Top-458
❑ 87TopTif-458
❑ 88BluJayFS-14
❑ 88Don-244
❑ 88DonBasB-255
❑ 88Fle-111
❑ 88FleGlo-111
❑ 88OPC-113
❑ 88PanSti-221
❑ 88Sco-422
❑ 88ScoGlo-422
❑ 88Top-113
❑ 88TopBig-134
❑ 88TopTif-113
❑ 89BluJayFS-12
❑ 89Bow-251
❑ 89BowTif-251
❑ 89Don-113
❑ 89DonBasB-31
❑ 89Fle-234
❑ 89FleGlo-234
❑ 89OPC-29
❑ 89PanSti-469
❑ 89Sco-194
❑ 89ScoYouS2-12
❑ 89Spo-163
❑ 89SpoIllFKI-189
❑ 89Top-29
❑ 89Top-201
❑ 89TopBig-95
❑ 89TopSti-187
❑ 89TopTif-29
❑ 89TopTif-201
❑ 89UppDec-575
❑ 90BluJayFS-10
❑ 90BluJayHS-1
❑ 90BluJayHS-5
❑ 90Bow-519
❑ 90BowTif-519
❑ 90ClaYel-T70
❑ 90Don-12
❑ 90Don-113A
❑ 90Don-113B
❑ 90DonBesA-84
❑ 90DonLeaS-30
❑ 90DonSupD-12
❑ 90Fle-83
❑ 90FleCan-83
❑ 90Lea-106
❑ 90OPC-505
❑ 90PanSti-171
❑ 90PubIntS-515
❑ 90RedFolSB-41
❑ 90Sco-425
❑ 90ScoMcD-9
❑ 90Spo-57
❑ 90Top-505
❑ 90TopBig-17
❑ 90TopSti-193
❑ 90TopTif-505
❑ 90UppDec-111
❑ 90USPlaCA-5S
❑ 90WinDis-5
❑ 91BasBesHRK-8
❑ 91BluJayFS-11
❑ 91BluJayFS-11
❑ 91BluJayS-15
❑ 91Bow-18

❑ 91Bow-369
❑ 91CadEllD-27
❑ 91ClaGam-19
❑ 91DenHol-6
❑ 91Don-149
❑ 91Fle-175
❑ 91Lea-9
❑ 91MSAHolD-15
❑ 91OPC-370
❑ 91OPC-388
❑ 91OPCPre-57
❑ 91PanCanT1-22
❑ 91PanCanT1-112
❑ 91PanFreS-338
❑ 91PanSti-161
❑ 91PetSta-26
❑ 91PosCan-15
❑ 91RedFolS-42
❑ 91Sco-595
❑ 91Sco100S-64
❑ 91SimandSMLBL-20
❑ 91StaClu-331
❑ 91StaPinB-22
❑ 91Stu-135
❑ 91SunSee-12
❑ 91Top-370
❑ 91Top-388
❑ 91TopCraJ2-4
❑ 91TopDesS-370
❑ 91TopDesS-388
❑ 91TopMic-370
❑ 91TopMic-388
❑ 91TopTif-370
❑ 91TopTif-388
❑ 91TopTriH-A14
❑ 91Ult-361
❑ 91UppDec-44
❑ 91UppDec-374
❑ 91UppDecSS-SS7
❑ 92BluJayP-4
❑ 92Bow-510
❑ 92Cla2-T20
❑ 92ClaGam-122
❑ 92Don-65
❑ 92DonCraJ1-5
❑ 92DonMcD-G3
❑ 92DonPre-8
❑ 92Fle-329
❑ 92Hig5-118
❑ 92Lea-27
❑ 92LeaBlaG-27
❑ 92MSABenSHD-5
❑ 92MVPPin-17
❑ 92OPC-298
❑ 92OPCPre-116
❑ 92PanSti-27
❑ 92PepDieM-20
❑ 92Pin-134
❑ 92PosCan-14
❑ 92RedFolS-43
❑ 92Sco-495
❑ 92Sco100S-64
❑ 92ScoCokD-11
❑ 92StaClu-570
❑ 92StaCluD-71
❑ 92Stu-255
❑ 92Top-298
❑ 92TopGol-298
❑ 92TopGolW-298
❑ 92TopKid-92
❑ 92TopMic-298
❑ 92TriPla-242
❑ 92Ult-146
❑ 92UppDec-324
❑ 93AngMot-13
❑ 93AngPol-5
❑ 93BluJayD4-7
❑ 93BluJayDM-5
❑ 93BluJayDM-17
❑ 93BluJayDM-18A
❑ 93BluJayDM-18B
❑ 93BluJayDM-19
❑ 93Don-453
❑ 93Fle-334
❑ 93Lea-532
❑ 93OPC-156
❑ 93OPCWorC-5
❑ 93PacSpa-323
❑ 93PanSti-5
❑ 93Pin-198
❑ 93RedFolS-36
❑ 93Sco-156
❑ 93Sel-200
❑ 93StaCluM-31
❑ 93Top-628
❑ 93TopGol-628
❑ 93TopInaM-628
❑ 93TopInaR-628
❑ 93TopMic-628
❑ 93UppDec-406
❑ 93UppDec-807
❑ 93UppDecGold-406
❑ 93UppDecGold-807
❑ 96BluJayB-4
❑ 96BluJayOH-13
❑ 97BluJayS-50
❑ 97RocRedW-13

Grudzielanek, Mark
❑ 91JamExpC-4
❑ 91JamExpP-3553
❑ 92RocExpC-20
❑ 92RocExpF-2123
❑ 93WesPalBEC-7
❑ 93WesPalBEF-1346
❑ 94AriFalLS-6
❑ 94HarSenF-2097
❑ 95Bow-224
❑ 95BowBes-R86
❑ 95BowBesR-R86
❑ 95BowGolF-224
❑ 95ColCho-549T
❑ 95Exc-222
❑ 95Fin-250
❑ 95FinRef-250
❑ 95Fla-376
❑ 95FleUpd-106
❑ 95SelCer-115
❑ 95SelCerMG-115
❑ 95SP-7
❑ 95SPSil-7
❑ 95StaClu-571
❑ 95StaCluCB-CB11
❑ 95StaCluMOP-571
❑ 95StaCluMOP-CB11
❑ 95StaCluSTWS-571
❑ 95Sum-124
❑ 95SumNthD-124
❑ 95TopTra-73T
❑ 95UC3-112
❑ 95UC3ArtP-112
❑ 95UppDec-234
❑ 95UppDecED-234
❑ 95UppDecEDG-234
❑ 95UppDecML-131
❑ 95UppDecMLFS-131
❑ 95UppDecPAW-H32
❑ 95UppDecPAWE-H32
❑ 95UppDecSE-136
❑ 95UppDecSEG-136
❑ 95Zen-122
❑ 96Bow-47
❑ 96BowBes-84
❑ 96BowBesAR-84
❑ 96BowBesR-84
❑ 96BowFoi-47
❑ 96Cir-149
❑ 96CirRav-149
❑ 96ColCho-213
❑ 96ColChoGS-213
❑ 96ColChoSS-213
❑ 96Don-13
❑ 96DonPreP-13
❑ 96ExpBoo-3
❑ 96ExpDis-9
❑ 96ExpDis-10
❑ 96Fin-B348
❑ 96FinRef-B348
❑ 96Fla-307
❑ 96Fle-458
❑ 96FleTif-458
❑ 96Lea-50
❑ 96LeaPre-73
❑ 96LeaPreP-73
❑ 96LeaPrePB-50
❑ 96LeaPrePG-50
❑ 96LeaPrePS-50
❑ 96LeaSig-76
❑ 96LeaSigA-86
❑ 96LeaSigAG-86
❑ 96LeaSigAS-86
❑ 96LeaSigPPG-76
❑ 96LeaSigPPP-76
❑ 96Sco-253
❑ 96SP-122
❑ 96StaClu-449
❑ 96StaCluMOP-449
❑ 96Stu-106
❑ 96StuPrePB-106
❑ 96StuPrePG-106
❑ 96StuPrePS-106
❑ 96TeaOut-34
❑ 96Ult-504
❑ 96UltGolM-504
❑ 96UppDec-132
❑ 97Bow-267
❑ 97BowInt-267
❑ 97Cir-6
❑ 97CirRav-6
❑ 97ColCho-163
❑ 97ColChoAC-31
❑ 97Don-112
❑ 97DonEli-82
❑ 97DonEliGS-82
❑ 97DonGolPP-112
❑ 97DonLim-40
❑ 97DonLimE-40
❑ 97DonLimENG-40
❑ 97DonPre-21
❑ 97DonPreCttC-21
❑ 97DonSigA-45
❑ 97DonSigAC-54
❑ 97DonSigAM-54
❑ 97DonSilPP-112
❑ 97Fin-70
❑ 97FinRef-70
❑ 97FlaShoLC-147
❑ 97FlaShoLeg0-147
❑ 97FlaShoLeg1-147
❑ 97FlaShoM-A147
❑ 97FlaShoM-B147
❑ 97FlaShoM-C147
❑ 97FlaShoR0-147
❑ 97FlaShoR1-147
❑ 97FlaShoR2-147
❑ 97Fle-380
❑ 97FleTif-380
❑ 97Lea-94
❑ 97LeaFraM-94
❑ 97LeaFraMDC-94
❑ 97MetUni-155
❑ 97NewPin-104
❑ 97NewPinAP-104
❑ 97NewPinMC-104
❑ 97NewPinPP-104
❑ 97Pac-345
❑ 97PacLigB-345
❑ 97PacPri-118
❑ 97PacPriLB-118
❑ 97PacPriP-118
❑ 97PacSil-345
❑ 97Pin-16
❑ 97PinArtP-PP16
❑ 97PinCer-93
❑ 97PinCerMBla-93
❑ 97PinCerMBlu-93
❑ 97PinCerMG-93
❑ 97PinCerMR-93
❑ 97PinCerR-93
❑ 97PinIns-80
❑ 97PinInsCE-80
❑ 97PinInsDE-80
❑ 97PinMusC-16
❑ 97PinPrePla-16
❑ 97PinTotCPB-93
❑ 97PinTotCPG-93
❑ 97PinTotCPR-93
❑ 97PinX-P-83
❑ 97PinX-PMoS-83
❑ 97Sco-133
❑ 97ScoArtPWB-133
❑ 97ScoPreS-133
❑ 97ScoShoS-133
❑ 97ScoShoSAP-133
❑ 97Sel-13
❑ 97SelArtP-13
❑ 97SelCom-13
❑ 97SelRegG-13
❑ 97SP-111
❑ 97SpoIll-86
❑ 97SpoIllEE-86
❑ 97StaClu-44
❑ 97StaCluM-M2
❑ 97StaCluMat-44
❑ 97StaCluMOP-44
❑ 97StaCluMOP-M2
❑ 97Stu-38
❑ 97StuPrePG-38
❑ 97StuPrePS-38
❑ 97Top-260
❑ 97TopChr-91
❑ 97TopChrR-91
❑ 97TopGal-173
❑ 97TopGalPPI-173
❑ 97Ult-230
❑ 97UltGolME-230
❑ 97UltPlaME-230
❑ 97UppDec-110
❑ 98Bow-49
❑ 98BowBes-29
❑ 98BowBesAR-29
❑ 98BowBesMIF-MI14
❑ 98BowBesMIFAR-MI14
❑ 98BowBesMIFR-MI14
❑ 98BowBesR-29
❑ 98BowChr-49
❑ 98BowChrGA-49
❑ 98BowChrGAR-49
❑ 98BowChrI-49
❑ 98BowChrIR-49
❑ 98BowChrR-49
❑ 98BowGolA-49
❑ 98BowInt-49
❑ 98CirThu-260
❑ 98CirThuRav-260
❑ 98CirThuSupRav-260
❑ 98ColCho-164
❑ 98Don-154
❑ 98DonCol-154
❑ 98DonColL-258
❑ 98DonColP-661
❑ 98DonColS-154
❑ 98DonGolPP-154
❑ 98DonPre-111
❑ 98DonPreSeat-111
❑ 98DonPriCD-154
❑ 98DonPriCL-258
❑ 98DonPriCP-661
❑ 98DonSigA-38
❑ 98DonSigAC-51
❑ 98DonSigAM-52
❑ 98DonSigSB-12
❑ 98DonSilPP-154
❑ 98Fin-98
❑ 98FinNo--98
❑ 98FinNo-R-98
❑ 98FinRef-98
❑ 98FlaShoLeg0-97
❑ 98FlaShoLeg1-97
❑ 98FlaShoLeg2-97
❑ 98FlaShoLeg3-97
❑ 98FlaShoLegM-97
❑ 98FlaShoR0-97
❑ 98FlaShoR1-97
❑ 98FlaShoR2-97
❑ 98FlaShoR3-97
❑ 98Fle-12
❑ 98FleUpd-U89
❑ 98Lea-59
❑ 98LeaFraDA-59
❑ 98LeaFraF-59
❑ 98LeaFraM-59
❑ 98LeaFraM-59
❑ 98LeaFraMDC-59
❑ 98LeaFraMDC-59
❑ 98LeaFraMZ2-59
❑ 98MetUni-70
❑ 98MetUniPMG-70
❑ 98Pac-345
❑ 98PacAur-156
❑ 98PacInv-113
❑ 98PacInvPBlue-113
❑ 98PacInvSilv-113
❑ 98PacInvTeam-17
❑ 98PacOme-149
❑ 98PacOmeR-149
❑ 98PacOnl-448
❑ 98PacOnlR-448
❑ 98PacOnlWC-448
❑ 98PacPar-194
❑ 98PacParC-194
❑ 98PacParG-194
❑ 98PacParHS-194
❑ 98PacParPB-194
❑ 98PacParR-194
❑ 98PacPlaB-345
❑ 98PacRedT-345
❑ 98PacSil-345
❑ 98Pin-157
❑ 98PinPer-93
❑ 98PinPerPP-93
❑ 98PinPlu-153
❑ 98PinPreP-157
❑ 98ScoRT-222
❑ 98SkyDugA-28
❑ 98SkyDugAIA-28
❑ 98SP Aut-128
❑ 98SpoIll-52
❑ 98SpoIllEE-52
❑ 98SpoIllFE-52
❑ 98SpoIllWSF-39
❑ 98SpoIllWSFEE-39
❑ 98SpoIllWSFFE-39
❑ 98SPxFin-98
❑ 98SPxFinR-98
❑ 98SPxFinS-98
❑ 98StaCluC-CS14
❑ 98StaCluC-CS16
❑ 98StaCluC-CS18
❑ 98StaCluFDI-112
❑ 98StaCluI-112
❑ 98StaCluOneK-112
❑ 98StaCluPP-112
❑ 98Top-69
❑ 98TopChr-69
❑ 98TopChrR-69
❑ 98TopDevR-69
❑ 98TopDia-69
❑ 98TopGal-43
❑ 98TopGalGP-43
❑ 98TopGalOPP-43
❑ 98TopGalPPI-43
❑ 98TopGalPPIA-43
❑ 98TopMiniC-69
❑ 98TopOpeD-36
❑ 98TopSta-113
❑ 98TopStaB-113
❑ 98TopStaG-113
❑ 98TopStaGR-113
❑ 98TopStaS-113
❑ 98Ult-178
❑ 98UltGolM-178
❑ 98UltMas-178
❑ 98UltPlaM-178
❑ 98UppDec10AP-44
❑ 98UppDec1APR-44
❑ 99199Fin-33
❑ 99DodPol-8
❑ 99FinGolRef-33
❑ 99FinRef-33
❑ 99Fle-419
❑ 99FleSta9-419
❑ 99FleWarT-419
❑ 99MetUni-207
❑ 99MetUniGM-207
❑ 99MetUniPMG-207
❑ 99Pac-218
❑ 99PacAur-92
❑ 99PacAurOD-92
❑ 99PacPar-116
❑ 99PacParC-116
❑ 99PacParG-116
❑ 99PacParHoloGold-116
❑ 99PacParHS-116
❑ 99PacParOD-116
❑ 99PacParPB-116
❑ 99PacParRed-116
❑ 99PacPlaB-218
❑ 99PacRed-218
❑ 99SkyPre-101
❑ 99SkyPreR-101
❑ 99StaClu-283
❑ 99StaCluFDI-283
❑ 99StaCluOoaK-283
❑ 99StaCluPP-283
❑ 99Top-308
❑ 99TopChr-308
❑ 99TopChrR-308
❑ 99TopMVPP-308
❑ 99UD Cho-100
❑ 99UD ChoP-100
❑ 99UD ChoPCR-100
❑ 99Ult-189
❑ 99UltGolM-189
❑ 99UltMas-189
❑ 99UltPlaM-189
❑ 99UppDec-401
❑ 99UppDecEL1-401
❑ 99UppDecEL2-401
❑ 99Vic-202

Grudzinski, Gary
❑ 85PriWilPT-19

Gruesbeck, Mark
❑ 94BriTigC-30
❑ 96WesOahCHWB-NNO
❑ 97LakTigB-3
❑ 98LakTigM-30

Grump, Mascot
❑ 96ScrRedBB-30
❑ 97ScrRedB-23
❑ 98ScrRedBQ-14

Grundler, Frank
❑ 75ShrCapT-4
❑ 76ShrCapT-17

Grundt, Ken
❑ 91EveGiaC-18
❑ 91EveGiaP-3906
❑ 92CliGiaC-23
❑ 92CliGiaF-3591
❑ 92MidLeaATI-13
❑ 92ProFS7-358
❑ 93ExcFS7-117
❑ 95AshTouTI-26
❑ 95NewHavRTI-25
❑ 96PawRedSDD-10
❑ 96TreThuB-11
❑ 97PawRedS-11
❑ 98ChaKniQ-14

Grundy, Phil
❑ 93EugEmeC-1
❑ 93EugEmeF-3851
❑ 94MidLeaAF-MDW23
❑ 94RocRoyC-11
❑ 94RocRoyF-559
❑ 95WilBluRTI-32
❑ 96WilBluRB-6
❑ 97WicWra-4
❑ 98WicWraM-19

Grunewald, Keith
❑ 94AshTouC-10
❑ 94AshTouF-1791
❑ 95SalAvaTI-16
❑ 96NewHavRB-12
❑ 97NewHavRB-10

Grunhard, Danny (Dan)
❑ 85AncGlaPTI-12
❑ 86QuaCitAP-13
❑ 87PalSprP-8
❑ 88MidAngGS-16
❑ 89MidAngGS-17
❑ 90CMC-493
❑ 90EdmTraC-16
❑ 90EdmTraP-528
❑ 90ProAAAF-104
❑ 91EdmTraLD-165
❑ 91EdmTraP-1528
❑ 91LinDriAAA-165
❑ 92TacTigF-2514
❑ 92TacTigS-534

Grunsky, Gary
❑ 76BatRouCT-11

Grunwald, Al
❑ 57JetPos-7
❑ 60Top-427

Gryboski, Kevin
❑ 95EveAqaTI-9
❑ 96WisTimRB-10
❑ 97CalLeaTP-10
❑ 97LanJet-12
❑ 98LanJetG-11

Grygiel, Joe
❑ 91SpoIndC-16
❑ 91SpoIndP-3944

Gryskevich, Larry
❑ 89HamRedS-14
❑ 90SavCarP-2073

Grzanich, Mike
❑ 93AubAstC-12
❑ 93AubAstF-3436
❑ 94QuaCitRBC-11
❑ 94QuaCitRBF-529
❑ 95JacGenTI-3
❑ 96JacGenB-9
❑ 96TexLeaAB-7
❑ 97JacGen-9
❑ 97JacGenS-6
❑ 98NewOrlZM-4
❑ 99SpoIll-43

Grzelaczyk, Kenneth
❑ 92SpoIndC-2
❑ 92SpoIndF-1286
❑ 93RanCucQC-13
❑ 93RanCucQF-825
❑ 94RanCucQC-13
❑ 94RanCucQF-1630

Grzenda, Joe
❑ 69OPC-121
❑ 69Top-121
❑ 69TopFou-20
❑ 70Top-691
❑ 71CarTeal-19
❑ 71MLBOffS-541
❑ 71OPC-518
❑ 71SenTealW-11
❑ 71Top-518
❑ 72CarTeal-10
❑ 72OPC-13
❑ 72Top-13
❑ 91MetWIZ-154

Grzybeck, Ben
❑ 77DayBealT-8

Gsellman, Bob
❑ 87ChaWheP-8

Guanchez, Harry
❑ 90EugEmeGS-9
❑ 91AppFoxCB-18

❑ 91AppFoxP-1724
❑ 93LinVenB-143
❑ 94VenLinU-85
❑ 95LinVen-233

Guante, Cecilio
❑ 81PorBeaT-10
❑ 82PorBeaT-3
❑ 83Don-423
❑ 84Don-78
❑ 84Fle-250
❑ 84Nes792-122
❑ 84Pir-6
❑ 84Top-122
❑ 84TopTif-122
❑ 85Don-357
❑ 85Fle-465
❑ 85Top-457
❑ 85TopTif-457
❑ 86Don-142
❑ 86Fle-609
❑ 86Top-668
❑ 86TopTat-8
❑ 86TopTif-668
❑ 87Don-238
❑ 87Fle-610
❑ 87FleGlo-610
❑ 87FleUpd-38
❑ 87FleUpdG-38
❑ 87OPC-219
❑ 87Top-219
❑ 87TopSti-127
❑ 87TopTif-219
❑ 87TopTra-40T
❑ 87TopTraT-40T
❑ 88DonBasB-276
❑ 88DonReaBY-NEW
❑ 88Top-84
❑ 88TopTif-84
❑ 89Don-260
❑ 89Fle-519
❑ 89FleGlo-519
❑ 89RanMot-23
❑ 89RanSmo-10
❑ 89Sco-439
❑ 89Top-766
❑ 89TopTif-766
❑ 89UppDec-576
❑ 90Don-403
❑ 90Fle-298
❑ 90FleCan-298
❑ 90IndTeal-14
❑ 90Lea-365
❑ 90OPC-532
❑ 90PubIntS-410
❑ 90Sco-438
❑ 90Top-532
❑ 90TopTif-532
❑ 92YanWIZ8-70
❑ 93LimRocDWB-117
❑ 93RanKee-166

Guarache, Jose
❑ 88St.CatBJP-2011
❑ 93LinVenB-108

Guardado, Eddie
❑ 91EliTwiP-4296
❑ 92KenTwiC-3
❑ 92KenTwiF-598
❑ 92ProFS7-102
❑ 93FleFinE-235
❑ 93NasXprF-395
❑ 94Don-139
❑ 94Fle-203
❑ 94SalLakBF-812
❑ 94Top-677
❑ 94TopGol-677
❑ 94TopSpa-677
❑ 94Ult-86
❑ 95FleUpd-59
❑ 96LeaSigEA-65
❑ 96Pac-355
❑ 97Pac-136
❑ 97PacLigB-136
❑ 97PacSil-136
❑ 98Pac-132
❑ 98PacOnl-421
❑ 98PacOnlR-421
❑ 98PacOnlWC-421
❑ 98PacPlaB-132
❑ 98PacRedT-132
❑ 98PacSil-132
❑ 98Top-28
❑ 98TopChr-28
❑ 98TopChrR-28
❑ 98TopDevR-28
❑ 98TopDia-28
❑ 98TopMiniC-28
❑ 99PacCroC-160
❑ 99PacCroCPB-160

Guarnaccia, John
❑ 77ReaPhiT-13

Guarnera, Rick
❑ 75SpoIndC-5

Guay, Larry
❑ 37Zee-74

Gubanich, Creighton
❑ 91SouOreAP-3850
❑ 92ClaFS7-177
❑ 92MadMusC-1
❑ 92MadMusF-1238
❑ 93MadMusC-12
❑ 93MadMusF-1824
❑ 94ModA'sC-13
❑ 94ModA'sF-3065
❑ 95HunStaTI-11
❑ 97TucTorB-13
❑ 98Las-9
❑ 99DumSet-107
❑ 99FleMys-107
❑ 99FleMysM-107

Gubicza, Mark
❑ 84FleUpd-46
❑ 84RoyPos-11
❑ 84TopTra-45T
❑ 84TopTraT-45T
❑ 85Don-344
❑ 85Fle-201
❑ 85OPC-127
❑ 85RoyTeal-9
❑ 85Top-127
❑ 85TopTif-127
❑ 86Don-583
❑ 86Fle-8
❑ 86Lea-226
❑ 86RoyKitCD-19
❑ 86RoyNatP-23
❑ 86RoyTeal-8
❑ 86Top-644
❑ 86TopTif-644
❑ 87Don-466
❑ 87Fle-368
❑ 87FleExcS-20
❑ 87FleGlo-368
❑ 87FleMin-47
❑ 87Lea-238
❑ 87OPC-326
❑ 87SpoTeaP-13
❑ 87Top-326
❑ 87TopTif-326
❑ 88Don-54
❑ 88DonBasB-95
❑ 88Fle-259
❑ 88FleGlo-259
❑ 88FleRecS-15
❑ 88OPC-378
❑ 88RoySmo-12
❑ 88RoyTeal-14
❑ 88Sco-516
❑ 88ScoGlo-516
❑ 88StaLinRo-6
❑ 88Top-507
❑ 88TopBig-199
❑ 88TopSti-262
❑ 88TopTif-507
❑ 89Bow-117
❑ 89BowTif-117
❑ 89CadEllD-25
❑ 89ClaTraO-138
❑ 89Don-179
❑ 89DonAll-18
❑ 89DonBasB-119
❑ 89Fle-283
❑ 89FleBasA-17
❑ 89FleExcS-19
❑ 89FleGlo-283
❑ 89OPC-379
❑ 89PanSti-350
❑ 89RoyTasD-9
❑ 89Sco-291
❑ 89ScoHot1S-69
❑ 89ScoYouS2-14
❑ 89Spo-102
❑ 89Top-430
❑ 89TopBig-26
❑ 89TopMinL-55
❑ 89TopSti-271
❑ 89TopStiB-26
❑ 89TopTif-430
❑ 89TopUKM-33
❑ 89UppDec-202
❑ 90Bow-363
❑ 90BowTif-363
❑ 90Don-204
❑ 90DonBesA-77
❑ 90Fle-109
❑ 90Fle-633
❑ 90FleBasA-15
❑ 90FleBasAC-15
❑ 90FleCan-109
❑ 90FleCan-633
❑ 90FleLeaL-15
❑ 90FleLeaLC-15
❑ 90Lea-145
❑ 90MLBBasB-105
❑ 90OPC-20
❑ 90PanSti-82
❑ 90PubIntS-349
❑ 90Sco-121
❑ 90Top-20
❑ 90TopBig-201
❑ 90TopSti-272
❑ 90TopTif-20
❑ 90UppDec-676
❑ 91ClaGam-20
❑ 91Don-145
❑ 91Fle-560
❑ 91OPC-265
❑ 91PanSti-228
❑ 91RoyPol-11
❑ 91Sco-212
❑ 91StaClu-240
❑ 91Stu-67
❑ 91Top-265
❑ 91TopDesS-265
❑ 91TopMic-265
❑ 91TopTif-265
❑ 91Ult-148
❑ 91UppDec-541
❑ 92Bow-215
❑ 92ClaGam-83
❑ 92Don-282
❑ 92Fle-159
❑ 92Lea-332
❑ 92LeaBlaG-332
❑ 92OPC-741
❑ 92Pin-102
❑ 92RoyPol-9
❑ 92Sco-459
❑ 92StaClu-542
❑ 92Stu-183
❑ 92Top-741
❑ 92TopGol-741
❑ 92TopGolW-741
❑ 92TopMic-741
❑ 92TriPla-233
❑ 92Ult-70
❑ 92UppDec-459
❑ 93Don-703
❑ 93Fle-618
❑ 93OPC-99
❑ 93PacSpa-135
❑ 93Pin-81
❑ 93RedFolS-37
❑ 93RoyPol-10
❑ 93RoyStaC-11
❑ 93Sco-581
❑ 93Sel-227
❑ 93StaClu-555
❑ 93StaCluFDI-555
❑ 93StaCluMOP-555
❑ 93Top-674
❑ 93TopGol-674
❑ 93TopInaM-674
❑ 93TopInaR-674
❑ 93TopMic-674
❑ 93TriPla-168
❑ 93Ult-208
❑ 93UppDec-85
❑ 93UppDecGold-85
❑ 94Fle-156
❑ 94StaClu-197
❑ 94StaCluFDI-197
❑ 94StaCluGR-197
❑ 94StaCluMOP-197
❑ 94Top-357
❑ 94TopGol-357
❑ 94TopSpa-357
❑ 95ColCho-464
❑ 95ColChoGS-464
❑ 95ColChoSS-464
❑ 95Don-80
❑ 95DonPreP-80
❑ 95DonTopotO-89
❑ 95Fla-45
❑ 95Fle-159
❑ 95Lea-157
❑ 95Pac-202
❑ 95Pin-427
❑ 95PinArtP-427
❑ 95PinMusC-427
❑ 95Sco-20
❑ 95ScoGolR-20
❑ 95ScoPlaTS-20
❑ 95TopTra-94T
❑ 95Ult-290
❑ 95UltGolM-290
❑ 96ColCho-572
❑ 96ColChoGS-572
❑ 96ColChoSS-572
❑ 96Don-56
❑ 96DonPreP-56
❑ 96EmoXL-67
❑ 96Fla-89
❑ 96Fle-128
❑ 96FleTif-128
❑ 96LeaSigA-87
❑ 96LeaSigAG-87
❑ 96LeaSigAS-87
❑ 96MetUni-65
❑ 96MetUniP-65
❑ 96Pac-330
❑ 96Pin-115
❑ 96ProSta-118
❑ 96RoyPol-9
❑ 96Sco-82
❑ 96StaClu-72
❑ 96StaCluMOP-72
❑ 96Top-157
❑ 96Ult-354
❑ 96UltGolM-354
❑ 96UppDec-352
❑ 97AngMot-24
❑ 97Cir-262
❑ 97CirRav-262
❑ 97Fle-579
❑ 97FleTif-579
❑ 97Ult-350
❑ 97UltGolME-350
❑ 97UltPlaME-350

Gudat, Marv
❑ 32CubTeal-7
❑ 37Zee-8

Guenther, Bob
❑ 87MyrBeaBJP-1460

Guercio, Maurice
❑ 86FloStaLAP-19
❑ 86Ft.LauYP-10
❑ 87AlbYanP-6

Guerra, Esmili
❑ 92PeoChiC-16
❑ 93LinVenB-68
❑ 93PeoChiTI-6
❑ 94VenLinU-210
❑ 95LinVen-65
❑ 96-97LinVen-122

Guerra, Fernando
❑ 80VenLeaS-145

Guerra, Mark
❑ 94PitMetC-9
❑ 94PitMetF-3517
❑ 95StLucMTI-15
❑ 96BinMetB-11
❑ 97BinMetB-13
❑ 98NorTidP-12

Guerra, Mike (Fermin)
❑ 47A'sTeal-13
❑ 48A'sTeal-10
❑ 49A'sTeal-15
❑ 49Bow-155
❑ 49PhiBul-21
❑ 50A'sTeal-11
❑ 50Bow-157
❑ 51Bow-202
❑ 85TCMPpl1-45

Guerra, Pete
❑ 91BurIndP-3303

Guerra, Rich
❑ 75SanAntBT-8
❑ 76WilTomT-7

Guerra, Robert
❑ 94VenLinU-97
❑ 95LinVen-237

Guerrero, Alex
❑ 75QuaCitAT-11

Guerrero, Ino (Inocencio)
❑ 83DurBulT-4
❑ 85DomLeaS-85
❑ 85GreBraTI-6
❑ 86GreBraTI-13
❑ 87GreBraB-17
❑ 87RicBraBC-10
❑ 88GreBraB-4
❑ 89DurBulIS-28
❑ 89DurBulIS-28
❑ 89DurBulTI-26
❑ 98LowSpiM-3

Guerrero, Juan
❑ 87PocGiaTB-27
❑ 88CliGiaP-701
❑ 89SanJosGB-21
❑ 89SanJosGCLC-219
❑ 89SanJosGP-451
❑ 89SanJosGS-11
❑ 89Sta-86
❑ 90ShrCapP-1450
❑ 90ShrCapS-8
❑ 91LinDriAA-305
❑ 91ShrCapLD-305
❑ 91ShrCapP-1828
❑ 92AstMot-15
❑ 92DonRoo-46
❑ 92FleUpd-85
❑ 92Lea-428
❑ 92LeaBlaG-428
❑ 92Pin-552
❑ 92ProFS7-348
❑ 92StaClu-775
❑ 92StaCluECN-775
❑ 92Ult-490
❑ 93Don-240
❑ 93Fle-435
❑ 93LimRocDWB-72
❑ 93Sco-259
❑ 93StaClu-16
❑ 93StaCluFDI-16
❑ 93StaCluMOP-16
❑ 93Top-414
❑ 93TopGol-414
❑ 93TopInaM-414
❑ 93TopInaR-414
❑ 93TopMic-414
❑ 93Ult-41
❑ 94TucTorF-766
❑ 95TucTotTI-7

Guerrero, Mario
❑ 73LinPor-22
❑ 73OPC-607
❑ 73Top-607
❑ 74OPC-192
❑ 74Top-192
❑ 75OPC-152
❑ 75St.LouCP-13
❑ 75Top-152
❑ 75TopMin-152
❑ 75TulOil7-23
❑ 76OPC-499
❑ 76SSP-285
❑ 76Top-499
❑ 77Top-628
❑ 78Top-339
❑ 79Hos-78
❑ 79Kel-43
❑ 79OPC-131
❑ 79Top-261
❑ 80Top-49
❑ 81Fle-591
❑ 81Top-547
❑ 85DomLeaS-151
❑ 89PacSenL-36
❑ 89T/MSenL-43

Guerrero, Mike
❑ 88BelBreGS-15
❑ 89BelBreIS-8
❑ 90StoPorB-8
❑ 90StoPorP-2193
❑ 91ElPasDP-2754
❑ 92ClaFS7-97
❑ 92ElPasDF-3930
❑ 92ElPasDS-211
❑ 93LimRocDWB-20
❑ 93MemChiF-381

Guerrero, Patrick
❑ 88St.CatBJP-2038

Guerrero, Pedro
❑ 79AlbDukTc-16
❑ 79Top-719
❑ 80DodPol-28
❑ 81Dod-5
❑ 81Dod-12
❑ 81DodPol-28
❑ 81DodPos-3
❑ 81LonBeaPT-7
❑ 81Top-651
❑ 82DodPol-28
❑ 82DodPos-3
❑ 82DodUniOV-6
❑ 82DogBuiE-4
❑ 82Don-136
❑ 82Fle-7
❑ 82FleSta-6
❑ 82LouSlu-2
❑ 82OPC-247
❑ 82Top-247
❑ 82TopSti-55
❑ 82TopSti-260
❑ 83AllGamPI-121
❑ 83DodPol-28
❑ 83DodPos-3
❑ 83Don-110
❑ 83Dra-9
❑ 83Fle-207
❑ 83FleSti-117
❑ 83Kel-20
❑ 83OPC-116
❑ 83PerCreC-5
❑ 83PerCreCG-5
❑ 83SevCoi-4
❑ 83Top-425
❑ 83Top-681
❑ 83TopFol-3
❑ 83TopSti-248
❑ 84AllGamPI-30
❑ 84DodPol-28
❑ 84Don-24
❑ 84Don-24A
❑ 84Don-174
❑ 84DonActAS-17
❑ 84Dra-11
❑ 84Fle-100
❑ 84FleSti-19
❑ 84FleSti-34
❑ 84FunFooP-26
❑ 84MilBra-11
❑ 84Nes792-90
❑ 84Nes792-306
❑ 84OPC-90
❑ 84RalPur-30
❑ 84SevCoi-W14
❑ 84Top-90
❑ 84Top-306
❑ 84TopCer-30
❑ 84TopGloS-25
❑ 84TopRubD-7
❑ 84TopSti-75
❑ 84TopSup-24
❑ 84TopTif-90
❑ 84TopTif-306
❑ 85AllGamPI-142
❑ 85DodCokP-11
❑ 85Don-174
❑ 85DonActA-34
❑ 85DonHig-19
❑ 85Dra-13
❑ 85Fle-370
❑ 85Lea-211
❑ 85OPC-34
❑ 85SevCoi-W10
❑ 85SubDis-31
❑ 85ThoMcAD-31
❑ 85Top-575
❑ 85TopMin-575
❑ 85TopRubD-8
❑ 85TopSti-70
❑ 85TopSup-44
❑ 85TopTif-575
❑ 86BasStaB-50
❑ 86DodCokP-10
❑ 86DodPol-28
❑ 86DodUniOP-6
❑ 86Don-174
❑ 86Dra-6
❑ 86Fle-130
❑ 86FleAll-8
❑ 86FleLimE-21
❑ 86FleMin-28
❑ 86FleSlu-13
❑ 86FleStiC-47
❑ 86GenMilB-5B
❑ 86Lea-105
❑ 86MeaGolBB-6
❑ 86MeaGolSB-18
❑ 86OPC-145
❑ 86OPCBoxB-G
❑ 86SevCoi-C4
❑ 86SevCoi-E4
❑ 86SevCoi-S4
❑ 86SevCoi-W4
❑ 86Spo-14
❑ 86Spo-148
❑ 86Spo-181
❑ 86SpoDecG-74
❑ 86Top-145
❑ 86Top-706
❑ 86Top3-D-8
❑ 86TopGloS-25
❑ 86TopMinL-44

❑ 86TopSti-65
❑ 86TopSup-27
❑ 86TopTat-23
❑ 86TopTif-145
❑ 86TopTif-706
❑ 86TopWaxBC-G
❑ 86TruVal-1
❑ 87BoaandB-27
❑ 87BurKinA-7
❑ 87ClaGam-39
❑ 87DodMot-2
❑ 87DodPho-3
❑ 87DodPol-14
❑ 87DodSmoA-10
❑ 87Don-53
❑ 87Fle-440
❑ 87FleGlo-440
❑ 87FleSlu-16
❑ 87GenMilB-6D
❑ 87KayB-14
❑ 87Lea-237
❑ 87MSAJifPD-10
❑ 87OPC-360
❑ 87RedFolSB-83
❑ 87SevCoi-W4
❑ 87Spo-27
❑ 87SpoTeaP-14
❑ 87StuPan-6
❑ 87Top-360
❑ 87TopSti-69
❑ 87TopTif-360
❑ 88DodMot-2
❑ 88DodPol-28
❑ 88DodSmo-28
❑ 88Don-278
❑ 88DonAll-48
❑ 88DonBasB-122
❑ 88DonBonM-BC16
❑ 88Dra-26
❑ 88Fle-514
❑ 88Fle-623
❑ 88FleAwaW-15
❑ 88FleGlo-514
❑ 88FleGlo-623
❑ 88FleMin-83
❑ 88FleSlu-16
❑ 88FleStiC-91
❑ 88K-M-11
❑ 88KayB-12
❑ 88Lea-101
❑ 88MSAFanSD-20
❑ 88Nes-24
❑ 88OPC-111
❑ 88PanSti-314
❑ 88RedFolSB-29
❑ 88Sco-9
❑ 88ScoGlo-9
❑ 88Spo-97
❑ 88StaLinD-6
❑ 88Top-489
❑ 88Top-550
❑ 88TopBig-171
❑ 88TopCoi-43
❑ 88TopGloS-24
❑ 88TopMinL-52
❑ 88TopRitTM-5
❑ 88TopSti-75
❑ 88TopStiB-15
❑ 88TopTif-489
❑ 88TopTif-550
❑ 88TopUKM-28
❑ 88TopUKMT-28
❑ 89Bow-440
❑ 89BowTif-440
❑ 89CadEllD-26
❑ 89CarSmo-7
❑ 89CarTeal-9
❑ 89ClaLigB-60
❑ 89DodSmoG-94
❑ 89Don-418
❑ 89DonBasB-75
❑ 89Fle-451
❑ 89FleGlo-451
❑ 89K-M-33
❑ 89KayB-16
❑ 89KinDis-20
❑ 89OPC-68
❑ 89PanSti-183
❑ 89RedFolSB-52
❑ 89Sco-564
❑ 89ScoHot1S-44
❑ 89Top-780
❑ 89TopAme2C-15
❑ 89TopBasT-74
❑ 89TopBatL-6
❑ 89TopBig-285
❑ 89TopCoi-16
❑ 89TopSti-40
❑ 89TopTif-780
❑ 89TopUKM-34
❑ 89TVSpoM-27
❑ 89UppDec-306
❑ 90Bow-201
❑ 90BowTif-201
❑ 90CarSmo-7
❑ 90ClaBlu-146
❑ 90DodTar-304
❑ 90Don-63
❑ 90Don-674A
❑ 90Don-674B
❑ 90DonBesN-95
❑ 90DOnBonM-BC6
❑ 90Fle-250
❑ 90FleBasA-16
❑ 90FleBasAC-16
❑ 90FleBasM-15
❑ 90FleBasMC-15
❑ 90FleCan-250
❑ 90FleLeaL-16
❑ 90FleLeaLC-16
❑ 90FleWaxBC-C11
❑ 90HOFStiB-85
❑ 90Hot50PS-18
❑ 90K-M-15
❑ 90Lea-44
❑ 90M.Vpin-98
❑ 90MLBBasB-32
❑ 90OPC-610
❑ 90PanSti-211
❑ 90PanSti-335
❑ 90Pos-22
❑ 90PubIntS-219
❑ 90RedFolSB-42
❑ 90Sco-13
❑ 90Sco100S-61
❑ 90Spo-66
❑ 90SunSee-10
❑ 90Top-610
❑ 90TopBatL-6
❑ 90TopBig-13
❑ 90TopCoi-47
❑ 90TopDou-30
❑ 90TopGloS-32
❑ 90TopHilHM-6
❑ 90TopMinL-75
❑ 90TopSti-35
❑ 90TopSti-151
❑ 90TopStiB-3
❑ 90TopTif-610
❑ 90TopTVA-50
❑ 90TopTVCa-25
❑ 90UppDec-244
❑ 90UppDecS-5
❑ 91BasBesHM-8
❑ 91Bow-403
❑ 91CarPol-28
❑ 91ClaGam-21
❑ 91DenHol-22
❑ 91Don-25
❑ 91Don-558
❑ 91DonSupD-25
❑ 91Fle-634A
❑ 91Fle-634B
❑ 91Lea-204
❑ 91LouRedTI-16
❑ 91OPC-20
❑ 91OPCPre-58
❑ 91PanFreS-31
❑ 91PanSti-37
❑ 91RedFolS-43
❑ 91Sco-140
❑ 91StaClu-314
❑ 91Stu-232
❑ 91Top-20
❑ 91TopCraJI-8
❑ 91TopDesS-20
❑ 91TopMic-20
❑ 91TopTif-20
❑ 91TopTriH-N12
❑ 91Ult-289
❑ 91UppDec-98
❑ 91UppDec-327
❑ 92Bow-377
❑ 92CarPol-7
❑ 92ClaGam-80
❑ 92DodStaTA-26
❑ 92Don-158
❑ 92Fle-579
❑ 92Lea-18
❑ 92LeaBlaG-18
❑ 92OPC-470
❑ 92PanSti-172
❑ 92Pin-392
❑ 92Sco-376
❑ 92StaClu-320
❑ 92Stu-91
❑ 92Top-470
❑ 92TopGol-470
❑ 92TopGolW-470
❑ 92TopKid-26
❑ 92TopMic-470
❑ 92TriPla-9
❑ 92Ult-263
❑ 92UppDec-357
❑ 93Don-600
❑ 93Fle-509
❑ 95MidAngOHP-14
❑ 95MidAngTI-12

Guerrero, Rafael

❑ 92GulCoaMF-3493
❑ 93KinMetC-13
❑ 93KinMetF-3809
❑ 94CapCitBC-9
❑ 94CapCitBF-1763
❑ 96StLucMTI-7
❑ 98St.PetDRM-24

Guerrero, Ramces

❑ 88IdaFalBP-1844
❑ 89IdaFalBP-2010

Guerrero, Ramon

❑ 93AusFut-50
❑ 93AusFut-106

Guerrero, Sandy (Epifano)

❑ 86VenGulP-8
❑ 87StoPorP-4
❑ 88CalLeaACLC-15
❑ 88StoPorCLC-196
❑ 88StoPorP-727
❑ 89ElPasDGS-22
❑ 90ElPasDGS-15
❑ 91DenZepLD-139
❑ 91DenZepP-130
❑ 91LinDriAAA-139
❑ 92DenZepF-2646
❑ 92ElPasDS-212
❑ 93LimRocDWB-119

Guerrero, Sergio

❑ 95HelBreTI-7
❑ 96HelBreTI-6
❑ 97StoPor-24
❑ 98BelSnaM-12
❑ 98StoPorG-10

Guerrero, Tony

❑ 81WisRapTT-4
❑ 83OrlTwiT-22
❑ 85VisOakT-21

Guerrero, Vladimir

❑ 95Bes-80
❑ 95Bow-90
❑ 95BowBes-B2
❑ 95BowBesR-B2
❑ 95SPML-7
❑ 95SPML-90
❑ 95SPMLA-11
❑ 95SPMLDtS-DS7
❑ 95UppDecML-127
❑ 95UppDecMLFS-127
❑ 96Bow-374
❑ 96BowBes-97
❑ 96BowBesAR-97
❑ 96BowBesMI-7
❑ 96BowBesMIAR-7
❑ 96BowBesMIR-7
❑ 96BowBesR-97
❑ 96BowFoi-374
❑ 96BowMinLP-14
❑ 96DouAllB-19
❑ 96Exc-187
❑ 96ExcAll-6
❑ 96ExcSeaC-5
❑ 96HarSenB-14
❑ 96LeaSig-110
❑ 96LeaSigPPG-110
❑ 96LeaSigPPP-110
❑ 96SigRooOJ-12
❑ 96Top-435
❑ 96WesPalBEB-1
❑ 96WesPalBEB-31
❑ 97Bow-416
❑ 97BowBes-101
❑ 97BowBesAR-101
❑ 97BowBesBC-BC18
❑ 97BowBesBCAR-BC18
❑ 97BowBesBCR-BC18
❑ 97BowBesJ-101
❑ 97BowBesJAR-101
❑ 97BowBesJR-101
❑ 97BowBesMI-MI10
❑ 97BowBesMIAR-MI10
❑ 97BowBesMIARI-MI10
❑ 97BowBesMII-MI10
❑ 97BowBesMIR-MI10
❑ 97BowBesMIRI-MI10
❑ 97BowBesP-17
❑ 97BowBesPAR-17
❑ 97BowBesPR-17
❑ 97BowBesR-101
❑ 97BowCerBlaIA-CA33
❑ 97BowCerBluIA-CA33
❑ 97BowCerGolIA-CA33
❑ 97BowChr-276
❑ 97BowChrI-276
❑ 97BowChrIR-276
❑ 97BowChrR-276
❑ 97BowChrSHR-SHR3
❑ 97BowChrSHRR-SHR3
❑ 97BowInt-416
❑ 97BowIntB-BBI14
❑ 97BowIntBAR-BBI14
❑ 97BowIntBR-BBI14
❑ 97BowScoHR-3
❑ 97Cir-313
❑ 97CirFasT-1
❑ 97CirRav-313
❑ 97ColCho-10
❑ 97ColChoCtG-21A
❑ 97ColChoCtG-21B
❑ 97ColChoCtG-21C
❑ 97ColChoCtGE-CG21
❑ 97ColChoCtGIW-CG21
❑ 97ColChoNF-NF34
❑ 97ColChoS-28
❑ 97ColChoSR-11
❑ 97ColChoTotT-T17
❑ 97DenHol-22
❑ 97Don-355
❑ 97DonEli-11
❑ 97DonEliGS-11
❑ 97DonFraFea-7
❑ 97DonGolPP-355
❑ 97DonLim-6
❑ 97DonLim-138
❑ 97DonLimE-6
❑ 97DonLimE-138
❑ 97DonLimENG-138
❑ 97DonLimFotG-23
❑ 97DonPowA-19
❑ 97DonPowADC-19
❑ 97DonPre-155
❑ 97DonPre-197
❑ 97DonPreCttC-155
❑ 97DonPreCttC-197
❑ 97DonPrePM-24
❑ 97DonRatR-27
❑ 97DonRooDK-2
❑ 97DonRooDKC-2
❑ 97DonSig-44
❑ 97DonSigA-46
❑ 97DonSigAC-55
❑ 97DonSigAM-55
❑ 97DonSigPPP-44
❑ 97DonSilPP-355
❑ 97DonVxP1-49
❑ 97E-X2-83
❑ 97E-X2Cred-83
❑ 97E-X2EssCre-83
❑ 97E-X2SD2000-15
❑ 97Fin-167
❑ 97Fin-315
❑ 97FinEmb-167
❑ 97FinEmb-315
❑ 97FinEmbR-167
❑ 97FinEmbR-315
❑ 97FinRef-167
❑ 97FinRef-315
❑ 97FlaShoLC-27
❑ 97FlaShoLeg0-27
❑ 97FlaShoLeg1-27
❑ 97FlaShoM-A27
❑ 97FlaShoM-B27
❑ 97FlaShoM-C27
❑ 97FlaShoR0-27
❑ 97FlaShoR1-27
❑ 97FlaShoR2-27
❑ 97FlaShoWotF-14
❑ 97FleNewH-5
❑ 97Lea-184
❑ 97Lea-398
❑ 97LeaFraM-184
❑ 97LeaFraM-398
❑ 97LeaFraMDC-184
❑ 97LeaFraMDC-398
❑ 97LeaGolS-27
❑ 97LeaLeaotN-15
❑ 97MetUni-156
❑ 97MetUniMfG-4
❑ 97NewPin-169
❑ 97NewPin-198
❑ 97NewPinAP-169
❑ 97NewPinAP-198
❑ 97NewPinIE-6
❑ 97NewPinMC-169
❑ 97NewPinMC-198
❑ 97NewPinPP-169
❑ 97NewPinPP-198
❑ 97NewPinPP-I6B
❑ 97PinCer-111
❑ 97PinCer-137
❑ 97PinCerMBla-111
❑ 97PinCerMBla-137
❑ 97PinCerMBlu-111
❑ 97PinCerMBlu-137
❑ 97PinCerMG-111
❑ 97PinCerMG-137
❑ 97PinCerMR-111
❑ 97PinCerMR-137
❑ 97PinCerR-111
❑ 97PinCerR-137
❑ 97PinIns-129
❑ 97PinInsCE-129
❑ 97PinInsDD-20
❑ 97PinInsDE-129
❑ 97PinTotCPB-111
❑ 97PinTotCPB-137
❑ 97PinTotCPG-111
❑ 97PinTotCPG-137
❑ 97PinTotCPR-111
❑ 97PinTotCPR-137
❑ 97PinX-P-123
❑ 97PinX-PMoS-123
❑ 97PinX-PMP-2
❑ 97PinX-PreMPS-2
❑ 97PinX-PSfF-27
❑ 97PinX-PSfFU-27
❑ 97PreCon-25
❑ 97Sco-489
❑ 97ScoArtPWB-489
❑ 97ScoBla-16
❑ 97ScoResC-489
❑ 97ScoShoS-489
❑ 97ScoShoSAP-489
❑ 97Sel-105
❑ 97SelArtP-105
❑ 97SelCom-105
❑ 97SelRegG-105
❑ 97SelRooR-10
❑ 97SelToootT-7
❑ 97SelToootTMB-7
❑ 97SP-10
❑ 97SPInsI-14
❑ 97SpoIll-8
❑ 97SpoIllEE-8
❑ 97SPSpeF-47
❑ 97SPSpxF-10
❑ 97SPSPxFA-10
❑ 97SPx-33
❑ 97SPxBro-33
❑ 97SPxCorotG-5
❑ 97SPxGol-33
❑ 97SPxGraF-33
❑ 97SPxSil-33
❑ 97SPxSte-33
❑ 97StaClu-185
❑ 97StaClu-210
❑ 97StaCluM-M36
❑ 97StaCluMat-210
❑ 97StaCluMOP-185
❑ 97StaCluMOP-210
❑ 97StaCluMOP-M36
❑ 97Stu-151
❑ 97StuAut-21
❑ 97StuMasS-15
❑ 97StuMasS8-15
❑ 97StuPor8-21
❑ 97StuPrePG-151
❑ 97StuPrePS-151
❑ 97Top-433
❑ 97TopAwel-AI5
❑ 97TopChr-153
❑ 97TopChrR-153
❑ 97TopGal-144
❑ 97TopGalPPI-144
❑ 97TopMemO5-52
❑ 97TopStaFAS-FAS3
❑ 97UD3-42
❑ 97UD3GenNex-GN2
❑ 97UD3SupSign-3
❑ 97Ult-509
❑ 97UltGolME-509
❑ 97UltGolP-2
❑ 97UltPlaME-509
❑ 97UppDec-271
❑ 97UppDecBCP-BC10
❑ 97UppDecHC-HC17
❑ 97Zen-48
❑ 97Zen8x10-23
❑ 97Zen8x1D-23
❑ 97ZenV-2-8
❑ 98Bow-30
❑ 98BowBes-80
❑ 98BowBesAR-80
❑ 98BowBesR-80
❑ 98BowChr-30
❑ 98BowChrGA-30
❑ 98BowChrGAR-30
❑ 98BowChrI-30
❑ 98BowChrIR-30
❑ 98BowChrR-30
❑ 98BowChrR-43
❑ 98BowChrRR-43
❑ 98BowGolA-30
❑ 98BowInt-30
❑ 98BowMinLM-MVP5
❑ 98CirThu-27
❑ 98CirThuRav-27
❑ 98CirThuSupRav-27
❑ 98ColCho-166
❑ 98ColChoCtG-CG13A
❑ 98ColChoCtG-CG13B
❑ 98ColChoCtG-CG13C
❑ 98ColChoCtGExch-CG13
❑ 98ColChoCtGIW-CG13
❑ 98ColChoER-ER17
❑ 98ColChoMBH-18
❑ 98ColChoSQDouble-9
❑ 98ColChoSQHR-9
❑ 98ColChoSQSingle-9
❑ 98ColChoSQTriple-9
❑ 98CroRoy-83
❑ 98Don-140
❑ 98Don-346
❑ 98DonCol-140
❑ 98DonColE-480
❑ 98DonColE-545
❑ 98DonColL-369
❑ 98DonColP-568
❑ 98DonColS-140
❑ 98DonCruG-84
❑ 98DonCruP-84
❑ 98DonCruR-84
❑ 98DonDom-25
❑ 98DonEli-80
❑ 98DonEli-145
❑ 98DonEliA-80
❑ 98DonEliA-145
❑ 98DonEliC-14
❑ 98DonEliMC-14
❑ 98DonEliS-80
❑ 98DonEliS-145
❑ 98DonGolPP-140
❑ 98DonGolPP-346
❑ 98DonLonL-9
❑ 98DonPre-18
❑ 98DonPreGB-17
❑ 98DonPreGES-24
❑ 98DonPreGoB-17
❑ 98DonPreGX-24
❑ 98DonPreGXDC-24
❑ 98DonPreSeat-18
❑ 98DonPreTP-17
❑ 98DonPreTPD-9
❑ 98DonPreTPG-17
❑ 98DonPreTPS-17
❑ 98DonPriCD-140
❑ 98DonPriCE-480
❑ 98DonPriCE-545
❑ 98DonPriCL-369
❑ 98DonPriCP-568
❑ 98DonProLPI-16
❑ 98DonSig-46
❑ 98DonSigA-39
❑ 98DonSigAC-52
❑ 98DonSigAM-53
❑ 98DonSigP-46
❑ 98DonSilPP-140
❑ 98DonSilPP-346
❑ 98E-X2-99
❑ 98E-X2Cheap-15
❑ 98E-X2ECFut-99
❑ 98E-X2ECNow-99
❑ 98Fin-273
❑ 98FinCen-C2
❑ 98FinCenR-C2
❑ 98FinNo--273
❑ 98FinNo-R-273

❑ 98FinRef-273
❑ 98FlaShoLeg0-37
❑ 98FlaShoLeg1-37
❑ 98FlaShoLeg2-37
❑ 98FlaShoLeg3-37
❑ 98FlaShoLegM-37
❑ 98FlaShoR0-37
❑ 98FlaShoR1-37
❑ 98FlaShoR2-37
❑ 98FlaShoR3-37
❑ 98Fle-244
❑ 98FleRooS-7
❑ 98FleVin'-35
❑ 98FleVin'C-35
❑ 98Lea-170
❑ 98LeaFraDA-170
❑ 98LeaFraF-170
❑ 98LeaFraM-170
❑ 98LeaFraM-170
❑ 98LeaFraMDC-170
❑ 98LeaFraMDC-170
❑ 98LeaFraMS-170
❑ 98LeaFraMZ2-170
❑ 98LeaRCMLHDSamp-15
❑ 98LeaRS-43
❑ 98LeaRS-150
❑ 98LeaRS-183
❑ 98LeaRSLHolo-43
❑ 98LeaRSLHolo-150
❑ 98LeaRSLHolo-183
❑ 98LeaRSLong-43
❑ 98LeaRSLong-150
❑ 98LeaRSLong-183
❑ 98LeaRSMLHD-15
❑ 98LeaRSTicMas-10
❑ 98LeaRSTicMasDC-10
❑ 98LeaRTrue-43
❑ 98LeaRTrue-150
❑ 98LeaRTrue-183
❑ 98LeaStaRep-12
❑ 98LeaStaS-15
❑ 98LeaStaSDC-15
❑ 98MetUni-75
❑ 98MetUniAT-15
❑ 98MetUniPMG-75
❑ 98MetUniPP-12
❑ 98MetUniT-15
❑ 98MetUniUL-15
❑ 98Pac-346
❑ 98PacAur-157
❑ 98PacAurPF-48
❑ 98PacAurPFC-48
❑ 98PacAurPFPB-48
❑ 98PacAurPFR-48
❑ 98PacAurPFS-48
❑ 98PacInv-114
❑ 98PacInvPBlue-114
❑ 98PacInvSilv-114
❑ 98PacInvTeam-17
❑ 98PacOme-150
❑ 98PacOmeR-150
❑ 98PacOnl-449
❑ 98PacOnl-468
❑ 98PacOnlR-449
❑ 98PacOnlR-468
❑ 98PacOnlWC-449
❑ 98PacOnlWC-468
❑ 98PacPar-195
❑ 98PacParC-195
❑ 98PacParG-195
❑ 98PacParHS-195
❑ 98PacParPB-195
❑ 98PacParR-195
❑ 98PacParSD-12
❑ 98PacParTC-24
❑ 98PacPlaB-346
❑ 98PacRedT-346
❑ 98PacSil-346
❑ 98Pin-62
❑ 98PinArtP-PP55
❑ 98PinIns-27
❑ 98PinInsC-7
❑ 98PinInsCE-27
❑ 98PinInsCG-7
❑ 98PinInsDE-27
❑ 98PinInsSG-9AB
❑ 98PinInsSG-9CD
❑ 98PinInsSG-11AB
❑ 98PinInsSG-11CD
❑ 98PinInsSGS-9AB
❑ 98PinInsSGS-9CD
❑ 98PinInsSGS-11AB
❑ 98PinInsSGS-11CD
❑ 98PinMinB-27
❑ 98PinMinCB-27
❑ 98PinMinCBAP-27
❑ 98PinMinCGP-27
❑ 98PinMinCGPAP-27
❑ 98PinMinCN-27
❑ 98PinMinCNAP-27
❑ 98PinMinCSGR-27
❑ 98PinMinDC-27
❑ 98PinMinG-27
❑ 98PinMinMCSS-27
❑ 98PinMinS-27
❑ 98PinMusC-PP55
❑ 98PinPer-18
❑ 98PinPerLP-6
❑ 98PinPerPP-18
❑ 98PinPerSftF-34
❑ 98PinPlu-182
❑ 98PinPluAP-PP60
❑ 98PinPluGAP-PP60
❑ 98PinPluMAP-PP60
❑ 98PinPreP-62
❑ 98Revo-89
❑ 98RevoSS-89
❑ 98Sco-267
❑ 98ScoNewS-NS7
❑ 98ScoRT-37
❑ 98ScoRTSS-PP37
❑ 98ScoRTSSAP-PP37
❑ 98ScoRTSSAP1-PP37
❑ 98ScoRTStarGaz-10
❑ 98SelSelSamp-1
❑ 98SkyDugA-29
❑ 98SkyDugAIA-29
❑ 98SP Aut-130
❑ 98SP Aut-SD16
❑ 98SP AutC-VG
❑ 98SP AutSD-SD16
❑ 98SP AutSDT-SD16
❑ 98SpoIll-53
❑ 98SpoIll-137
❑ 98SpoIllEE-53
❑ 98SpoIllEE-137
❑ 98SpoIllFE-53
❑ 98SpoIllFE-137
❑ 98SpoIllODMP-OD18
❑ 98SpoIllTaN-89
❑ 98SpoIllTaNEE-89
❑ 98SpoIllWSF-106
❑ 98SpoIllWSFEE-106
❑ 98SpoIllWSFFE-106
❑ 98SPxFin-16
❑ 98SPxFin-237
❑ 98SPxFin-299
❑ 98SPxFinR-16
❑ 98SPxFinR-237
❑ 98SPxFinR-299
❑ 98SPxFinS-16
❑ 98SPxFinS-237
❑ 98SPxFinS-299
❑ 98StaCluFDI-3
❑ 98StaCluI-3
❑ 98StaCluOneK-3
❑ 98StaCluPP-3
❑ 98Stu-162
❑ 98StuGPP-162
❑ 98StuHitPar-8
❑ 98StuPor8x10-27
❑ 98StuPor8x10GP-27
❑ 98StuSPP-162
❑ 98Top-5
❑ 98TopBabB-BB10
❑ 98TopChr-5
❑ 98TopChrBB-BB10
❑ 98TopChrBBR-BB10
❑ 98TopChrR-5
❑ 98TopDevR-5
❑ 98TopDia-5
❑ 98TopFocP-FP14
❑ 98TopGal-70
❑ 98TopGalGP-70
❑ 98TopGalOPP-70
❑ 98TopGalPPI-70
❑ 98TopGalPPIA-70
❑ 98TopGolLabC1-70
❑ 98TopGolLabC1B-70
❑ 98TopGolLabC1One-70
❑ 98TopGolLabC1R-70
❑ 98TopGolLabC2-70
❑ 98TopGolLabC2B-70
❑ 98TopGolLabC2One-70
❑ 98TopGolLabC2R-70
❑ 98TopGolLabC3-70
❑ 98TopGolLabC3B-70
❑ 98TopGolLabC3One-70
❑ 98TopGolLabC3R-70
❑ 98TopMiniC-5
❑ 98TopOpeD-5
❑ 98TopSta-21
❑ 98TopStaB-21
❑ 98TopStaG-21
❑ 98TopStaGR-21
❑ 98TopStaS-21
❑ 98TopSup-3
❑ 98TopSup-3
❑ 98TopTek-17
❑ 98TopTekD-17
❑ 98UD3-26
❑ 98UD3-116
❑ 98UD3-206
❑ 98UD3DieCut-26
❑ 98UD3DieCut-116
❑ 98UD3DieCut-206
❑ 98Ult-134
❑ 98UltBacttF-10
❑ 98UltDouT-2
❑ 98UltGolM-134
❑ 98UltKidG-12
❑ 98UltMas-134
❑ 98UltPlaM-134
❑ 98UppDec-135
❑ 98UppDec-440
❑ 98UppDec-628
❑ 98UppDec5x7-135
❑ 98UppDecBCP-BC18
❑ 98UppDecDS-DS31
❑ 98UppDecNP-NP14
❑ 98UppDecR-58
❑ 98UppDecR-122
❑ 98UppDecRNF-NF22
❑ 98UppDecRQL-Q29
❑ 98UppDecSF-82
❑ 98Zen-13
❑ 98Zen5 xx7-41
❑ 98Zen5x7GoldImp-41
❑ 98Zen5x7Imp-41
❑ 98ZenZ-G-13
❑ 98ZenZ-S-13
❑ 99199Fin-55
❑ 99199Fin-110
❑ 99199Fin-255
❑ 99AllMysFR-M25
❑ 99AurOn DL-10
❑ 99Bow-7
❑ 99BowBes-48
❑ 99BowBes-94
❑ 99BowBesAR-48
❑ 99BowBesAR-94
❑ 99BowBesMI-M7
❑ 99BowBesMIAR-M7
❑ 99BowBesMIR-M7
❑ 99BowBesR-48
❑ 99BowBesR-94
❑ 99BowChr-7
❑ 99BowChrG-7
❑ 99BowChrGR-7
❑ 99BowChrI-7
❑ 99BowChrIR-7
❑ 99BowChrR-7
❑ 99BowGol-7
❑ 99BowInt-7
❑ 99CroRoyB-87
❑ 99CroRoyL-87
❑ 99CroRoyMP-8
❑ 99CroRoyOD-87
❑ 99CroRoyPotG-12
❑ 99CroRoyPP-12
❑ 99CroRoyPPN-12
❑ 99E-X Cen-7
❑ 99E-X CenECFut-7
❑ 99E-X CenECNow-7
❑ 99E-XCenFoF'-14
❑ 99FinAarAwC-HA2
❑ 99FinAarAwCR-HA2
❑ 99FinCom-C7
❑ 99FinComDualR-C7
❑ 99FinGolRef-55
❑ 99FinGolRef-110
❑ 99FinGolRef-255
❑ 99FinMil-M10
❑ 99FinMil-M13
❑ 99FinMil-M35
❑ 99FinPeelHyp-19
❑ 99FinPeelSpark-19
❑ 99FinPeeSS-19
❑ 99FinProF-PF48
❑ 99FinRef-55
❑ 99FinRef-110
❑ 99FinRef-255
❑ 99FlaShoLeg1-27
❑ 99FlaShoLeg2-27
❑ 99FlaShoLeg3-27
❑ 99FlaShoLegM1-27
❑ 99FlaShoLegM2-27
❑ 99FlaShoLegM3-27
❑ 99FlaShoMoG-5
❑ 99FlaShoR1-27
❑ 99FlaShoR2-27
❑ 99FlaShoR3-27
❑ 99Fle-20
❑ 99Fle-583
❑ 99FleBri-9
❑ 99FleBri2G-9
❑ 99FleBriBlu-9
❑ 99FleBriGol-9
❑ 99FleBriSS-14
❑ 99FleBriSSP-14
❑ 99FleMys-9
❑ 99FleMysD-7
❑ 99FleMysG-9
❑ 99FleMysM-9
❑ 99FleSta9-20
❑ 99FleSta9-583
❑ 99FleVin'-20
❑ 99FleWarT-20
❑ 99FleWarT-583
❑ 99HomHer-12
❑ 99MetUni-120
❑ 99MetUniGM-120
❑ 99MetUniPMG-120
❑ 99Pac-263
❑ 99PacAur-112
❑ 99PacAurOD-112
❑ 99PacCroC-169
❑ 99PacCroC-34
❑ 99PacCroCITC-9
❑ 99PacCroCPB-169
❑ 99PacCroCTC-18
❑ 99PacCroCTM-11
❑ 99PacGolCDC-30
❑ 99PacInv-91
❑ 99PacInvFP-9
❑ 99PacInvOD-91
❑ 99PacInvPB-91
❑ 99PacInvSF-9
❑ 99PacInvSF-9B
❑ 99PacInvSH-9
❑ 99PacInvSH-9B
❑ 99PacInvTA-9
❑ 99PacOme-145
❑ 99PacOme5T-14
❑ 99PacOme5TT-14
❑ 99PacOmeC-145
❑ 99PacOmeDD-1
❑ 99PacOmeDM-19
❑ 99PacOmeG-145
❑ 99PacOmeH'-11
❑ 99PacOmePB-145
❑ 99PacPar-142
❑ 99PacParC-142
❑ 99PacParG-142
❑ 99PacParHoloGold-142
❑ 99PacParHS-142
❑ 99PacParOD-142
❑ 99PacParPB-19
❑ 99PacParPB-142
❑ 99PacParRed-142
❑ 99PacParTC-18
❑ 99PacPlaB-263
❑ 99PacPri-87
❑ 99PacPriHB-87
❑ 99PacPriHG-87
❑ 99PacPriHM-87
❑ 99PacPriHP-87
❑ 99PacPriRed-87
❑ 99PacPriS-33
❑ 99PacPriS206-33
❑ 99PacPriS206R-33
❑ 99PacPriSP-33
❑ 99PacPriSV-33
❑ 99PacRed-263
❑ 99PacTeaC-24
❑ 99Rev-84
❑ 99RevDiaL-19
❑ 99RevFouP-10
❑ 99RevPremDate-84
❑ 99RevRet-84
❑ 99RevShaSS-84
❑ 99RevTri-16
❑ 99RevTri-16
❑ 99SkyMolM-149
❑ 99SkyMolMF-49
❑ 99SkyMolMFS-49
❑ 99SkyMolMFT-49
❑ 99SkyMolMX-149
❑ 99SkyPre-213
❑ 99SkyPre-297
❑ 99SkyPreR-213
❑ 99SkyPreR-297
❑ 99SkyPreSotG-2
❑ 99SkyThu-277
❑ 99SkyThuRant-277
❑ 99SkyThuRave-277
❑ 99SkyThuTur-TC4
❑ 99SP Aut-51
❑ 99SP AutC-VG
❑ 99SP AutCG-VG
❑ 99SP AutEF-E17
❑ 99SP AutHRC-HR25
❑ 99SP AutR-R17
❑ 99SP SigAuto-VG
❑ 99SP SigAutoG-VG
❑ 99SPAutHRCDC-HR25
❑ 99SpoIll-173
❑ 99SpoIllH-1
❑ 99SPSig-10
❑ 99SPx-52
❑ 99SPxDom-FB11
❑ 99SPxFinR-52
❑ 99SPxFinS-52
❑ 99SPxPowE-PE18
❑ 99SPxPreS-PS19
❑ 99SPxStaF-SF16
❑ 99SPxWinM-VG
❑ 99StaClu-80
❑ 99StaCluA-SCA7
❑ 99StaCluC-SCC28
❑ 99StaCluCR-SCC28
❑ 99StaCluFDI-80
❑ 99StaCluOoaK-80
❑ 99StaCluPP-80
❑ 99ThuSkySupR-277
❑ 99Top-62
❑ 99Top-458
❑ 99TopAllMF-M25
❑ 99TopAut-A11
❑ 99TopBlaLC1-76
❑ 99TopBlaLC2-76
❑ 99TopBlaLC3-76
❑ 99TopChr-62
❑ 99TopChr-458
❑ 99TopChrERttH-ER7
❑ 99TopChrERttH-ER7
❑ 99TopChrF1-FF6
❑ 99TopChrF1R-FF6
❑ 99TopChrNB-NB8
❑ 99TopChrNBR-NB8
❑ 99TopChrR-62
❑ 99TopChrR-458
❑ 99TopGal-11
❑ 99TopGal-122
❑ 99TopGalE-E16
❑ 99TopGalPP-11
❑ 99TopGalPP-122
❑ 99TopGalPPI-11
❑ 99TopGalPPI-122
❑ 99TopGolL-76
❑ 99TopGolLC1-76
❑ 99TopGolLC2-76
❑ 99TopGolLOtO-76
❑ 99TopGolLRtA-RA4
❑ 99TopGolLRtAB-RA4
❑ 99TopGolLRtAOtO-RA4
❑ 99TopGolLRtAR-RA4
❑ 99TopMVPP-62
❑ 99TopMVPP-458
❑ 99TopNewB-NB8
❑ 99TopOpeD-34
❑ 99TopRedLC1-76
❑ 99TopRedLC2-76
❑ 99TopRedLC3-76
❑ 99TopSta-15
❑ 99TopSta-170
❑ 99TopSta'S-32
❑ 99TopSta'SG-32
❑ 99TopSta'SGDH-32
❑ 99TopSta1Foil-15
❑ 99TopSta2Foil-15
❑ 99TopSta3Foil-15
❑ 99TopStaFoil-15
❑ 99TopStaFoil-170
❑ 99TopStaG-G8
❑ 99TopStaGFoil-G8
❑ 99TopStaOS-15
❑ 99TopStaTS-15
❑ 99TopStaTS-15
❑ 99TopSupC-9
❑ 99TopSupCR-9
❑ 99TopTek-13A
❑ 99TopTek-13B
❑ 99TopTekG-13A
❑ 99TopTekG-13B
❑ 99TopTekT-T10
❑ 99UD Cho-110
❑ 99UD ChoP-110
❑ 99UD ChoPCR-110
❑ 99UD ChoS-18
❑ 99UD ChoSD-18
❑ 99UD ChoSHR-18
❑ 99UD ChoST-18
❑ 99UD ChoYW-Y18
❑ 99UD Ion-38
❑ 99UD IonC-C25
❑ 99UD IonR-38
❑ 99UDHolo-35
❑ 99UDHoloAUsome-35
❑ 99UDHoloLau-L11
❑ 99UDHoloLauG-L11
❑ 99Ult-20
❑ 99UltGolM-20
❑ 99UltMas-20
❑ 99UltPlaM-20
❑ 99UppDec-142
❑ 99UppDec-236
❑ 99UppDecBD-50
❑ 99UppDecBDD-50
❑ 99UppDecBDDom-D27
❑ 99UppDecBDDomE-D27
❑ 99UppDecBDMN-M21
❑ 99UppDecBDMNE-M21
❑ 99UppDecBDQ-50
❑ 99UppDecBDT-50
❑ 99UppDecCf7-16
❑ 99UppDecCf7-52
❑ 99UppDecCf7-C13
❑ 99UppDecCf7Cf7P-C13
❑ 99UppDecCf7LL-L15
❑ 99UppDecCf7SftF-S7
❑ 99UppDecCL-111
❑ 99UppDecCLCC-111
❑ 99UppDecCLES-VG
❑ 99UppDecCLESC-VG
❑ 99UppDecCLM-C56
❑ 99UppDecCo7CE-16
❑ 99UppDecCo7CE-52
❑ 99UppDecCo7SftFA-VG
❑ 99UppDecE-55
❑ 99UppDecE-145
❑ 99UppDecE2C-2K5
❑ 99UppDecEBPC-C-VG
❑ 99UppDecEDF-D12
❑ 99UppDecEDFFXG-D12
❑ 99UppDecEFXG-55
❑ 99UppDecEFXG-145
❑ 99UppDecEL1-142
❑ 99UppDecEL1-236
❑ 99UppDecEL2-142
❑ 99UppDecEL2-236
❑ 99UppDecEPE-P16
❑ 99UppDecEUR-U13
❑ 99UppDecF-F15
❑ 99UppDecFD-F15
❑ 99UppDecFQ-F15
❑ 99UppDecFT-F15
❑ 99UppDecM-123
❑ 99UppDecM-P7
❑ 99UppDecMD-D10
❑ 99UppDecMGS-123
❑ 99UppDecMHFS-123
❑ 99UppDecMP-123
❑ 99UppDecMSS-123
❑ 99UppDecMST-T5
❑ 99UppDecO-34
❑ 99UppDecOAPoH-VG
❑ 99UppDecOSO-34
❑ 99UppDecR-50
❑ 99UppDecRG-50
❑ 99UppDecROSS-S22
❑ 99UppDecROSS-S22
❑ 99UppDecRP-50
❑ 99UppDecRTA-T14
❑ 99UppDecRTAL2-T14
❑ 99UppDecTE-T14
❑ 99UppDecTED-T14
❑ 99UppDecTEQ-T14
❑ 99UppDecTET-T14
❑ 99UppDecVtaT-V16
❑ 99UppDecVtaTD-V16
❑ 99UppDecVtaTQ-V16
❑ 99UppDecVtaTT-V16
❑ 99Vic-237
❑ 99Vic-238

Guerrero, Wilton

❑ 93GreFalDSP-19
❑ 94VerBeaDC-8
❑ 94VerBeaDF-79
❑ 95Bes-77
❑ 95SanAntMTI-4
❑ 95SigRooOJ-16
❑ 95SigRooOJP-16
❑ 95SigRooOJPS-16
❑ 95SigRooOJS-16
❑ 95SPML-76

❑ 95UppDecML-152
❑ 95UppDecMLFS-152
❑ 96Bow-361
❑ 96BowBes-108
❑ 96BowBesAR-108
❑ 96BowBesR-108
❑ 96BowFoi-361
❑ 96ColCho-443
❑ 96ColChoGS-443
❑ 96ColChoSS-443
❑ 96Exc-175
❑ 96ExcAll-5
❑ 96ExcTL-3
❑ 96FleUpd-U145
❑ 96FleUpdNH-9
❑ 96FleUpdTC-U145
❑ 96Pin-383
❑ 96PinAfi-180
❑ 96PinAfiAP-180
❑ 96PinFoil-383
❑ 96Sel-182
❑ 96SelArtP-182
❑ 96SelCer-113
❑ 96SelCerAP-113
❑ 96SelCerCB-113
❑ 96SelCerCR-113
❑ 96SelCerMB-113
❑ 96SelCerMG-113
❑ 96SelCerMR-113
❑ 96Sum-180
❑ 96SumAbo&B-180
❑ 96SumArtP-180
❑ 96SumFoi-180
❑ 96Ult-498
❑ 96UltGolM-498
❑ 96UltGolP-7
❑ 96UltGolPHGM-7
❑ 96UppDec-254
❑ 96Zen-120
❑ 96ZenArtP-120
❑ 97AlbDukUG-3
❑ 97Bow-109
❑ 97BowBes-183
❑ 97BowBesA-183
❑ 97BowBesAAR-183
❑ 97BowBesAR-183
❑ 97BowBesAR-183
❑ 97BowBesBC-BC12
❑ 97BowBesBCAR-BC12
❑ 97BowBesBCR-BC12
❑ 97BowBesMI-MI8
❑ 97BowBesMIAR-MI8
❑ 97BowBesMIARI-MI8
❑ 97BowBesMII-MI8
❑ 97BowBesMIR-MI8
❑ 97BowBesMIRI-MI8
❑ 97BowBesP-11
❑ 97BowBesPAR-11
❑ 97BowBesPR-11
❑ 97BowBesR-183
❑ 97BowChr-129
❑ 97BowChrI-129
❑ 97BowChrIR-129
❑ 97BowChrR-129
❑ 97BowChrSHR-SHR14
❑ 97BowChrSHRR-SHR14
❑ 97BowInt-109
❑ 97BowScoHR-14
❑ 97Cir-113
❑ 97CirRav-113
❑ 97ColCho-368
❑ 97ColChoT-LA7
❑ 97DodMot-23
❑ 97DodPol-10
❑ 97Don-246
❑ 97DonFraFea-4
❑ 97DonGolPP-246
❑ 97DonLim-57
❑ 97DonLim-62
❑ 97DonLimE-57
❑ 97DonLimE-62
❑ 97DonLimENG-57
❑ 97DonLimFotG-53
❑ 97DonPre-152
❑ 97DonPreCttC-152
❑ 97DonRooDK-10
❑ 97DonRooDKC-10
❑ 97DonSig-56
❑ 97DonSigA-47
❑ 97DonSigAC-56
❑ 97DonSigAM-56
❑ 97DonSigPPP-56
❑ 97DonSilPP-246
❑ 97DonTea-116
❑ 97DonTeaSPE-116
❑ 97Fin-339
❑ 97FinEmb-339
❑ 97FinEmbR-339
❑ 97FinRef-339
❑ 97FlaShoLC-91
❑ 97FlaShoLeg0-91
❑ 97FlaShoLeg1-91
❑ 97FlaShoM-A91
❑ 97FlaShoM-B91
❑ 97FlaShoM-C91
❑ 97FlaShoR0-91
❑ 97FlaShoR1-91
❑ 97FlaShoR2-91
❑ 97Fle-363
❑ 97FleNewH-6
❑ 97FleRooS-14
❑ 97FleTif-363
❑ 97Lea-318
❑ 97LeaFraM-318
❑ 97LeaFraMDC-318
❑ 97LeaLeaotN-14
❑ 97MetUni-99
❑ 97MetUniMfG-5
❑ 97NewPin-168
❑ 97NewPinAP-168
❑ 97NewPinMC-168
❑ 97NewPinPP-168
❑ 97PacPriGotD-GD159
❑ 97Pin-181
❑ 97PinArtP-PP181
❑ 97PinCer-116
❑ 97PinCerMBla-116
❑ 97PinCerMBlu-116
❑ 97PinCerMG-116
❑ 97PinCerMR-116
❑ 97PinCerR-116
❑ 97PinMusC-181
❑ 97PinPrePla-181
❑ 97PinTotCPB-116
❑ 97PinTotCPG-116
❑ 97PinTotCPR-116
❑ 97PinX-P-121
❑ 97PinX-PMoS-121
❑ 97PinX-PMP-15
❑ 97PinX-PreMPS-15
❑ 97Sco-480
❑ 97ScoArtPWB-480
❑ 97ScoHeaotO-23
❑ 97ScoResC-480
❑ 97ScoShoS-480
❑ 97ScoShoSAP-480
❑ 97Sel-140
❑ 97SelArtP-140
❑ 97SelCom-140
❑ 97SelRegG-140
❑ 97SelRooA-2
❑ 97SP-11
❑ 97SpoIll-9
❑ 97SpoIllEE-9
❑ 97Ult-217
❑ 97UltGolME-217
❑ 97UltPlaME-217
❑ 97UppDec-399
❑ 97Zen-46
❑ 98DodPol-7
❑ 98DodSco-3
❑ 98DodScoP-3
❑ 98Don-90
❑ 98DonCol-90
❑ 98DonCol-191
❑ 98DonColE-479
❑ 98DonColL-288
❑ 98DonColP-662
❑ 98DonColS-90
❑ 98DonColS-186
❑ 98DonCruG-82
❑ 98DonCruP-82
❑ 98DonCruR-82
❑ 98DonEli-79
❑ 98DonEliA-79
❑ 98DonEliS-79
❑ 98DonGolPP-90
❑ 98DonPre-112
❑ 98DonPreSeat-112
❑ 98DonPriCD-90
❑ 98DonPriCD-191
❑ 98DonPriCE-479
❑ 98DonPriCL-288
❑ 98DonPriCP-662
❑ 98DonRatR-16
❑ 98DonRatRM-16
❑ 98DonSigA-40
❑ 98DonSigAC-53
❑ 98DonSigAM-54
❑ 98DonSilPP-90
❑ 98FleRooS-8
❑ 98FleUpd-U48
❑ 98Lea-89
❑ 98LeaFraDA-89
❑ 98LeaFraF-89
❑ 98LeaFraM-89
❑ 98LeaFraM-89
❑ 98LeaFraMDC-89
❑ 98LeaFraMDC-89
❑ 98LeaFraMS-89
❑ 98LeaFraMZ2-89
❑ 98Pac-330
❑ 98PacAur-142
❑ 98PacInv-106
❑ 98PacInvInt-15N
❑ 98PacInvMiT-8
❑ 98PacInvPBlue-106
❑ 98PacInvSilv-106
❑ 98PacInvTeam-14
❑ 98PacLatotML-18
❑ 98PacOme-120
❑ 98PacOmeR-120
❑ 98PacOnl-368
❑ 98PacOnlR-368
❑ 98PacOnlWC-368
❑ 98PacPar-174
❑ 98PacParC-174
❑ 98PacParG-174
❑ 98PacParHS-174
❑ 98PacParPB-174
❑ 98PacParR-174
❑ 98PacPlaB-330
❑ 98PacRedT-330
❑ 98PacSil-330
❑ 98Pin-46
❑ 98PinArtP-PP43
❑ 98PinIns-87
❑ 98PinInsCE-87
❑ 98PinInsDE-87
❑ 98PinMusC-PP43
❑ 98PinPreP-46
❑ 98PinSna-LAD4
❑ 98Sco-58
❑ 98ScoRT-147
❑ 98ScoRTSS-PP85
❑ 98ScoRTSSAP-PP85
❑ 98ScoRTSSAP1-PP85
❑ 98ScoSS-PP21
❑ 98ScoSSAP-PP21
❑ 98Stu-16
❑ 98StuGPP-16
❑ 98StuSPP-16
❑ 98Top-46
❑ 98TopChr-46
❑ 98TopChrR-46
❑ 98TopDevR-46
❑ 98TopDia-46
❑ 98TopMiniC-46
❑ 98TopOpeD-28
❑ 98UppDec-399
❑ 99CroRoyB-88
❑ 99CroRoyL-88
❑ 99CroRoyOD-88
❑ 99Fle-386
❑ 99FleSta9-386
❑ 99FleWarT-386
❑ 99MetUni-115
❑ 99MetUniGM-115
❑ 99MetUniPMG-115
❑ 99Pac-264
❑ 99PacAur-113
❑ 99PacAurOD-113
❑ 99PacCroC-170
❑ 99PacCroCPB-170
❑ 99PacOme-146
❑ 99PacOmeC-146
❑ 99PacOmeG-146
❑ 99PacOmePB-146
❑ 99PacPar-143
❑ 99PacParC-143
❑ 99PacParG-143
❑ 99PacParHoloGold-143
❑ 99PacParHS-143
❑ 99PacParOD-143
❑ 99PacParPB-143
❑ 99PacParRed-143
❑ 99PacPlaB-264
❑ 99PacPriS-34
❑ 99PacPriS206-34
❑ 99PacPriS206R-34
❑ 99PacPriSP-34
❑ 99PacPriSV-34
❑ 99PacRed-264
❑ 99Rev-85
❑ 99RevPremDate-85
❑ 99RevRet-85
❑ 99RevShaSS-85
❑ 99SkyPre-181
❑ 99SkyPreA-23
❑ 99SkyPreABlue-23
❑ 99SkyPreR-181
❑ 99SkyThu-198
❑ 99SkyThuRant-198
❑ 99SkyThuRave-198
❑ 99ThuSkySupR-198
❑ 99Top-246
❑ 99TopChr-246
❑ 99TopChrR-246
❑ 99TopMVPP-246
❑ 99UppDec-419
❑ 99UppDecEL1-419
❑ 99UppDecEL2-419
❑ 99Vic-244

Guerry, Kyle
❑ 93OscAstC-12
❑ 93OscAstF-621

Guess, Tom
❑ 77ForLauYS-16

Guest, Arthur
❑ 13Zee-34
❑ 14Zee-35
❑ 15Zee-33

Guetterman, Lee
❑ 84ChaLooT-15
❑ 85DomLeaS-171
❑ 86FleUpd-45
❑ 86MarPacNB-5
❑ 87Don-322
❑ 87Fle-585
❑ 87FleGlo-585
❑ 87Top-307
❑ 87TopTif-307
❑ 88Don-270
❑ 88DonReaBY-NEW
❑ 88Fle-374
❑ 88FleGlo-374
❑ 88OPC-382
❑ 88Sco-323
❑ 88ScoGlo-323
❑ 88Spo-45
❑ 88Top-656
❑ 88TopTif-656
❑ 89DonBasB-108
❑ 89TopTra-43T
❑ 89TopTraT-43T
❑ 89YanScoNW-24
❑ 90Don-127
❑ 90Fle-443
❑ 90FleCan-443
❑ 90Lea-333
❑ 90OPC-286
❑ 90PanSti-118
❑ 90PubIntS-534
❑ 90Sco-294
❑ 90Top-286
❑ 90TopTif-286
❑ 90TopTVY-9
❑ 90UppDec-318
❑ 90YanScoNW-17
❑ 91Don-124
❑ 91Fle-664
❑ 91Lea-52
❑ 91OPC-62
❑ 91Sco-34
❑ 91SimandSMLBL-21
❑ 91StaClu-361
❑ 91Top-62
❑ 91TopDesS-62
❑ 91TopMic-62
❑ 91TopTif-62
❑ 91Ult-232
❑ 91UppDec-481
❑ 92Don-507
❑ 92Fle-227
❑ 92Lea-320
❑ 92LeaBlaG-320
❑ 92OPC-578
❑ 92Sco-244
❑ 92ScoRoo-74T
❑ 92StaClu-346
❑ 92Top-578
❑ 92TopGol-578
❑ 92TopGolW-578
❑ 92TopMic-578
❑ 92UppDec-610
❑ 92YanWIZ8-71
❑ 93Don-542
❑ 93Fle-475
❑ 93StaClu-214
❑ 93StaCluFDI-214
❑ 93StaCluMOP-214
❑ 93Top-134
❑ 93TopGol-134
❑ 93TopInaM-134
❑ 93TopInaR-134
❑ 93TopMic-134
❑ 94Fle-632
❑ 94Pac-590
❑ 94StaClu-216
❑ 94StaCluFDI-216
❑ 94StaCluGR-216
❑ 94StaCluMOP-216
❑ 95MarPac-33
❑ 96TacRaiB-12

Guevara, Giomar
❑ 93BelMarCB-14
❑ 93BelMarF-3216
❑ 94AppFoxC-5
❑ 94AppFoxFl-1061
❑ 94MidLeaAF-MDW1
❑ 95Exc-116
❑ 95LinVen-17
❑ 95UppDecML-81
❑ 95UppDecMLFS-81
❑ 96-97LinVen-138
❑ 96PorCitRB-14
❑ 97TacRai-15
❑ 99Fle-426
❑ 99FleSta9-426
❑ 99FleWarT-426
❑ 99Pac-397
❑ 99PacCroC-262
❑ 99PacCroCPB-262
❑ 99PacPlaB-397
❑ 99PacRed-397
❑ 99SkyPre-257
❑ 99SkyPre-257
❑ 99SkyPreR-257
❑ 99SkyPreR-257
❑ 99SpoIll-56

Guggiana, Todd
❑ 90ButCopKSP-30
❑ 91Bow-697
❑ 91ChaRanC-18
❑ 91ChaRanP-1322
❑ 91Cla/Bes-204
❑ 93ChaRanC-13
❑ 93ChaRanF-1949
❑ 93FloStaLAF-2
❑ 94TulDriF-251
❑ 94TulDriTI-9

Gugino, Mark
❑ 94ElmPioC-6
❑ 94ElmPioF-3486

Guide, Sheldon
❑ 97ButCopKB-19
❑ 97ButCopKK-19

Guides, Maine
❑ 87IntLeaAT-45

Guidi, Jim
❑ 91SalLakTP-3205
❑ 91SalLakTSP-24
❑ 92SalLakTSP-26

Guidry, Ron
❑ 76OPC-599
❑ 76Top-599
❑ 77Spo-6102
❑ 77Top-656
❑ 77YanBurK-11
❑ 78Hos-25
❑ 78PapGinD-28
❑ 78SSP270-17
❑ 78Top-135
❑ 78YanBurK-4
❑ 78YanPhoA-9
❑ 78YanSSPD-17
❑ 79BasPat-36
❑ 79Hos-89
❑ 79Kel-11
❑ 79OPC-264
❑ 79Pew-4
❑ 79Top-5
❑ 79Top-7
❑ 79Top-202
❑ 79Top-500
❑ 79TopCom-13
❑ 79YanBurK-4
❑ 79YanPicA-15
❑ 80BurKinPHR-4
❑ 80Kel-4
❑ 80OPC-157
❑ 80Top-207
❑ 80Top-300
❑ 80TopSup-7
❑ 80YanPhoA-9
❑ 81AllGamPI-82
❑ 81Don-227
❑ 81Fle-88
❑ 81FleStiC-76
❑ 81Kel-45
❑ 81OPC-250
❑ 81Top-250
❑ 81TopSti-112
❑ 81TopSupHT-64
❑ 81YanPhoA-8
❑ 82Don-548
❑ 82Don-558
❑ 82Fle-38
❑ 82FleSta-120
❑ 82Kel-26
❑ 82OPC-9
❑ 82OPC-10
❑ 82Squ-9
❑ 82Top-9
❑ 82Top-10
❑ 82WilSpoG-3
❑ 82YanPhoA-10
❑ 83Don-17
❑ 83Don-31
❑ 83DonActA-15
❑ 83Fle-383
❑ 83FleSta-73
❑ 83FleSti-47
❑ 83OPC-104
❑ 83Top-440
❑ 83TopSti-102
❑ 83YanPhoA-10
❑ 83YanRoyRD-4
❑ 84Don-173
❑ 84DonActAS-51
❑ 84Fle-127
❑ 84FunFooP-96
❑ 84MilBra-12
❑ 84MLBPen-5
❑ 84Nes792-110
❑ 84Nes792-406
❑ 84Nes792-486
❑ 84Nes792-717
❑ 84NesDreT-10
❑ 84OCoandSI-45
❑ 84OPC-110
❑ 84OPC-204
❑ 84RalPur-31
❑ 84SevCoi-E16
❑ 84Top-110
❑ 84Top-406
❑ 84Top-486
❑ 84Top-717
❑ 84TopCer-31
❑ 84TopGloS-14
❑ 84TopRubD-11
❑ 84TopSti-194
❑ 84TopSti-318
❑ 84TopSup-17
❑ 84TopTif-110
❑ 84TopTif-406
❑ 84TopTif-486
❑ 84TopTif-717
❑ 85AllGamPI-77
❑ 85Don-214
❑ 85Fle-129
❑ 85Lea-237
❑ 85OPC-388
❑ 85PolMet-Y3
❑ 85SubDis-11
❑ 85ThoMcAD-11
❑ 85Top-790
❑ 85TopRubD-11
❑ 85TopSti-313
❑ 85TopTif-790
❑ 85YanTCMP-12
❑ 86BasStaB-51
❑ 86Don-103
❑ 86Dra-32
❑ 86Fle-106
❑ 86FleMin-22
❑ 86FleSlu-14
❑ 86FleStiC-48
❑ 86Lea-36
❑ 86OPC-109
❑ 86OPCBoxB-H
❑ 86SevCoi-C6
❑ 86SevCoi-E6
❑ 86SevCoi-S6
❑ 86SevCoi-W6
❑ 86Spo-18
❑ 86Spo-59
❑ 86Spo-149
❑ 86Spo-179
❑ 86Spo-185
❑ 86SpoDecG-71
❑ 86Top-610
❑ 86Top-721
❑ 86Top3-D-9
❑ 86TopGloS-12
❑ 86TopMinL-26

❑ 86TopSti-302
❑ 86TopSup-28
❑ 86TopTat-14
❑ 86TopTif-610
❑ 86TopTif-721
❑ 86TopWaxBC-H
❑ 86YanTCM-9
❑ 87ClaGam-68
❑ 87Don-93
❑ 87Fle-100
❑ 87FleAwaW-16
❑ 87FleGlo-100
❑ 87Lea-101
❑ 87OPC-375
❑ 87RedFolSB-54
❑ 87Spo-83
❑ 87Top-375
❑ 87TopSti-301
❑ 87TopTif-375
❑ 88Don-175
❑ 88DonReaBY-175
❑ 88Fle-207
❑ 88FleGlo-207
❑ 88FleStiWBC-S3
❑ 88Lea-180
❑ 88OPC-127
❑ 88Sco-310
❑ 88ScoGlo-310
❑ 88StaLinY-5
❑ 88Top-535
❑ 88TopBig-50
❑ 88TopSti-296
❑ 88TopStiB-61
❑ 88TopTif-535
❑ 89Sco-342
❑ 89Top-255
❑ 89TopBasT-110
❑ 89TopTif-255
❑ 89UppDec-307
❑ 89YanScoNW-28
❑ 90HOFStiB-97
❑ 91UppDecS-16
❑ 92YanWIZ7-60
❑ 92YanWIZ8-72
❑ 92YanWIZA-27
❑ 99SpoIllGotG-49
❑ 99SpoIllGotGA-29

Guiel, Aaron
❑ 94CedRapKC-12
❑ 94CedRapKF-1115
❑ 95LakElsSTI-15
❑ 96DouAllB-43
❑ 96Exc-27
❑ 96MidAngB-17
❑ 96MidAngOHP-13
❑ 96TexLeaAB-24
❑ 97MidAng-14
❑ 98Las-10

Guiel, Jeff
❑ 98LakElsSG-14

Guilfoyle, Mike
❑ 90BriTigP-3166
❑ 90BriTigS-7
❑ 91FayGenC-2
❑ 91FayGenP-1163
❑ 92LakTigC-13
❑ 92LakTigF-2272
❑ 93LakTigC-10
❑ 93LakTigF-1303
❑ 94TreThuF-2117
❑ 95JacSunTI-14
❑ 96TolMudHB-12
❑ 98BriBluM-14

Guiliano, Matt
❑ 94MarPhiC-7
❑ 94MarPhiF-3301
❑ 95PiePhiF-191
❑ 96ReaPhiB-18
❑ 97ReaPhi-16
❑ 98ReaPhiM-10
❑ 98ReaPhiUM-12

Guillen, Carlos
❑ 96-97LinVen-8
❑ 96Bow-353
❑ 96BowBes-162
❑ 96BowBesAR-162
❑ 96BowBesR-162
❑ 96BowFoi-353
❑ 97Bow-138
❑ 97BowBes-135
❑ 97BowBesAR-135
❑ 97BowBesR-135
❑ 97BowChr-146
❑ 97BowChrI-146
❑ 97BowChrIR-146
❑ 97BowChrR-146
❑ 97BowInt-138
❑ 97JacGen-10
❑ 97JacGenS-7
❑ 98FleUpd-U40
❑ 98NewOrlZM-5
❑ 98UppDec-559
❑ 99BowAut-BA11
❑ 99DumSet-105
❑ 99E-X Cen-98
❑ 99E-X CenECFut-98
❑ 99E-X CenECNow-98
❑ 99Fle-137
❑ 99FleBri-144
❑ 99FleBri2G-144
❑ 99FleBriBlu-144
❑ 99FleBriGol-144
❑ 99FleMys-105
❑ 99FleMysM-105
❑ 99FleSta9-137
❑ 99FleWarT-137
❑ 99MetUni-250
❑ 99MetUniGM-250
❑ 99MetUniPMG-250
❑ 99Pac-398
❑ 99PacAur-177
❑ 99PacAurOD-177
❑ 99PacCroC-263
❑ 99PacCroCPB-263
❑ 99PacPar-217
❑ 99PacParC-217
❑ 99PacParG-217
❑ 99PacParHoloGold-217
❑ 99PacParHS-217
❑ 99PacParOD-217
❑ 99PacParPB-217
❑ 99PacParRed-217
❑ 99PacPlaB-398
❑ 99PacPriS-93
❑ 99PacPriS206-93
❑ 99PacPriS206R-93
❑ 99PacRed-398
❑ 99SkyThu-280
❑ 99SkyThuRant-280
❑ 99SkyThuRave-280
❑ 99SP SigAutoG-CG
❑ 99SpoIll-56
❑ 99SPSig-56
❑ 99SPx-117
❑ 99SPxFinR-117
❑ 99SPxFinS-117
❑ 99ThuSkySupR-280
❑ 99Top-351
❑ 99TopChr-351
❑ 99TopChrR-351
❑ 99TopMVPP-351
❑ 99UD Cho-19
❑ 99UD ChoPCR-19
❑ 99Ult-238
❑ 99UltGolM-238
❑ 99UltMas-238
❑ 99UltPlaM-238
❑ 99UppDec-12
❑ 99UppDecCLM-C88
❑ 99UppDecE-102
❑ 99UppDecEFXG-102
❑ 99UppDecEL1-12
❑ 99UppDecEL2-12
❑ 99UppDecM-193
❑ 99UppDecMGS-193
❑ 99UppDecMHFS-193
❑ 99UppDecMSS-193
❑ 99UppDecO-75
❑ 99UppDecOSO-75
❑ 99UppDecR-79
❑ 99UppDecRG-79
❑ 99UppDecRP-79
❑ 99Vic-365

Guillen, Jose
❑ 93MadMusC-13
❑ 93MadMusF-1828
❑ 94WesMicWC-10
❑ 94WesMicWF-2305
❑ 95ModA'sTI-9
❑ 96BesAutS-34
❑ 96Bow-116
❑ 96BowBes-109
❑ 96BowBesAR-109
❑ 96BowBesR-109
❑ 96BowFoi-116
❑ 96CarLeaA1B-20
❑ 96CarLeaA2B-20
❑ 96CarLeaAIB-B9
❑ 96LynHilB-11
❑ 97Bow-106
❑ 97BowBes-189
❑ 97BowBesAR-189
❑ 97BowBesBC-BC16
❑ 97BowBesBCAR-BC16
❑ 97BowBesBCR-BC16
❑ 97BowBesMI-MI6
❑ 97BowBesMIAR-MI6
❑ 97BowBesMIARI-MI6
❑ 97BowBesMII-MI6
❑ 97BowBesMIR-MI6
❑ 97BowBesMIRI-MI6
❑ 97BowBesR-189
❑ 97BowCerBlaIA-CA34
❑ 97BowCerBluIA-CA34
❑ 97BowCerGolIA-CA34
❑ 97BowChr-126
❑ 97BowChrI-126
❑ 97BowChrIR-126
❑ 97BowChrR-126
❑ 97BowInt-106
❑ 97ColCho-465
❑ 97Don-367
❑ 97DonFraFea-11
❑ 97DonGolPP-367
❑ 97DonLim-136
❑ 97DonLim-146
❑ 97DonLimE-136
❑ 97DonLimE-146
❑ 97DonLimENG-146
❑ 97DonLimFotG-55
❑ 97DonPre-164
❑ 97DonPreCttC-164
❑ 97DonPrePM-25
❑ 97DonRooDK-6
❑ 97DonRooDKC-6
❑ 97DonSig-35
❑ 97DonSigA-48
❑ 97DonSigAC-57
❑ 97DonSigAM-57
❑ 97DonSigPPP-35
❑ 97DonSilPP-367
❑ 97DonVxP1-10
❑ 97Fin-182
❑ 97FinRef-182
❑ 97FlaShoLC-120
❑ 97FlaShoLeg0-120
❑ 97FlaShoLeg1-120
❑ 97FlaShoM-A120
❑ 97FlaShoM-B120
❑ 97FlaShoM-C120
❑ 97FlaShoR0-120
❑ 97FlaShoR1-120
❑ 97FlaShoR2-120
❑ 97FlaShoWotF-21
❑ 97Fle-554
❑ 97FleNewH-7
❑ 97FleTif-554
❑ 97HelBreB-11
❑ 97Lea-319
❑ 97LeaFraM-319
❑ 97LeaFraMDC-319
❑ 97LeaGolS-36
❑ 97NewPin-161
❑ 97NewPinAP-161
❑ 97NewPinMC-161
❑ 97NewPinPP-161
❑ 97PinCer-107
❑ 97PinCerMBla-107
❑ 97PinCerMBlu-107
❑ 97PinCerMG-107
❑ 97PinCerMR-107
❑ 97PinCerR-107
❑ 97PinTotCPB-107
❑ 97PinTotCPG-107
❑ 97PinTotCPR-107
❑ 97PinX-P-119
❑ 97PinX-PMoS-119
❑ 97PinX-PMP-1
❑ 97PinX-PreMPS-1
❑ 97PirPos-15
❑ 97Sco-484
❑ 97ScoArtPWB-484
❑ 97ScoResC-484
❑ 97ScoShoS-484
❑ 97ScoShoSAP-484
❑ 97Sel-134
❑ 97SelArtP-134
❑ 97SelCom-134
❑ 97SelRegG-134
❑ 97SelRooA-1
❑ 97SP-4
❑ 97SpoIll-10
❑ 97SpoIllEE-10
❑ 97TopStaFAS-FAS5
❑ 97Ult-495
❑ 97UltGolME-495
❑ 97UltGolP-8
❑ 97UltPlaME-495
❑ 97UppDec-542
❑ 97Zen-50
❑ 98Bow-55
❑ 98BowBes-72
❑ 98BowBesAR-72
❑ 98BowBesR-72
❑ 98BowChr-55
❑ 98BowChrGA-55
❑ 98BowChrGAR-55
❑ 98BowChrI-55
❑ 98BowChrIR-55
❑ 98BowChrR-55
❑ 98BowChrR-49
❑ 98BowChrRR-49
❑ 98BowGolA-55
❑ 98BowInt-55
❑ 98CirThu-138
❑ 98CirThuRav-138
❑ 98CirThuSupRav-138
❑ 98ColCho-211
❑ 98ColChoSQ-SQ6
❑ 98CroRoy-108
❑ 98Don-130
❑ 98Don-392
❑ 98DonCol-130
❑ 98DonCol-187
❑ 98DonColE-490
❑ 98DonColL-276
❑ 98DonColP-665
❑ 98DonColS-130
❑ 98DonColS-182
❑ 98DonCruG-90
❑ 98DonCruP-90
❑ 98DonCruR-90
❑ 98DonEli-90
❑ 98DonEliA-90
❑ 98DonEliS-90
❑ 98DonGolPP-130
❑ 98DonGolPP-392
❑ 98DonPre-115
❑ 98DonPreGES-20
❑ 98DonPreGX-20
❑ 98DonPreGXDC-20
❑ 98DonPreSeat-115
❑ 98DonPriCD-130
❑ 98DonPriCD-187
❑ 98DonPriCE-490
❑ 98DonPriCL-276
❑ 98DonPriCP-665
❑ 98DonRatR-12
❑ 98DonRatRM-12
❑ 98DonSig-12
❑ 98DonSigA-41
❑ 98DonSigAC-54
❑ 98DonSigAM-55
❑ 98DonSigP-12
❑ 98DonSigSB-13
❑ 98DonSilPP-130
❑ 98DonSilPP-392
❑ 98Fin-10
❑ 98FinNo--10
❑ 98FinNo-R-10
❑ 98FinRef-10
❑ 98FlaShoLeg0-56
❑ 98FlaShoLeg1-56
❑ 98FlaShoLeg2-56
❑ 98FlaShoLeg3-56
❑ 98FlaShoLegM-56
❑ 98FlaShoR0-56
❑ 98FlaShoR1-56
❑ 98FlaShoR2-56
❑ 98FlaShoR3-56
❑ 98Fle-283
❑ 98FleRooS-9
❑ 98Lea-77
❑ 98LeaFraDA-77
❑ 98LeaFraF-77
❑ 98LeaFraM-77
❑ 98LeaFraM-77
❑ 98LeaFraMDC-77
❑ 98LeaFraMDC-77
❑ 98LeaFraMZ2-77
❑ 98LeaRS-105
❑ 98LeaRS-163
❑ 98LeaRSLHolo-105
❑ 98LeaRSLHolo-163
❑ 98LeaRSLong-105
❑ 98LeaRSLong-163
❑ 98LeaRTrue-105
❑ 98LeaRTrue-163
❑ 98MetUni-24
❑ 98MetUniPMG-24
❑ 98Pac-395
❑ 98PacAur-175
❑ 98PacInv-128
❑ 98PacInvPBlue-128
❑ 98PacInvSilv-128
❑ 98PacInvTeam-22
❑ 98PacOme-189
❑ 98PacOmeR-189
❑ 98PacOnl-584
❑ 98PacOnlR-584
❑ 98PacOnlWC-584
❑ 98PacPar-221
❑ 98PacParC-221
❑ 98PacParG-221
❑ 98PacParHS-221
❑ 98PacParPB-221
❑ 98PacParR-221
❑ 98PacPlaB-395
❑ 98PacRedT-395
❑ 98PacSil-395
❑ 98Pin-57
❑ 98PinArtP-PP50
❑ 98PinIns-56
❑ 98PinInsCE-56
❑ 98PinInsDE-56
❑ 98PinInsSG-9AB
❑ 98PinInsSG-9CD
❑ 98PinInsSGS-9AB
❑ 98PinInsSGS-9CD
❑ 98PinMusC-PP50
❑ 98PinPer-94
❑ 98PinPerPP-94
❑ 98PinPreP-57
❑ 98ScoRT-48
❑ 98ScoRTSS-PP48
❑ 98ScoRTSSAP-PP48
❑ 98ScoRTSSAP1-PP48
❑ 98SP Aut-155
❑ 98SPxFin-8
❑ 98SPxFin-117
❑ 98SPxFinR-8
❑ 98SPxFinR-117
❑ 98SPxFinS-8
❑ 98SPxFinS-117
❑ 98StaCluFDI-246
❑ 98StaCluI-246
❑ 98StaCluOneK-246
❑ 98StaCluPP-246
❑ 98Stu-138
❑ 98StuGPP-138
❑ 98StuSPP-138
❑ 98Top-146
❑ 98TopBabB-BB8
❑ 98TopChr-146
❑ 98TopChrBB-BB8
❑ 98TopChrBBR-BB8
❑ 98TopChrR-146
❑ 98TopDevR-146
❑ 98TopDia-146
❑ 98TopGal-101
❑ 98TopGalGP-101
❑ 98TopGalOPP-101
❑ 98TopGalPPI-101
❑ 98TopGalPPIA-101
❑ 98TopMiniC-146
❑ 98TopOpeD-75
❑ 98TopSta-60
❑ 98TopStaB-60
❑ 98TopStaG-60
❑ 98TopStaGR-60
❑ 98TopStaS-60
❑ 98Ult-120
❑ 98UltBacttF-14
❑ 98UltGolM-120
❑ 98UltMas-120
❑ 98UltPlaM-120
❑ 98UppDec-255
❑ 98UppDec-485
❑ 98UppDecBCP-BC28
❑ 98UppDecDS-DS53
❑ 98UppDecR-76
❑ 98UppDecSF-137
❑ 98Zen-73
❑ 98Zen5 xx7-29
❑ 98Zen5x7GoldImp-29
❑ 98Zen5x7Imp-29
❑ 98ZenZ-G-73
❑ 98ZenZ-S-73
❑ 99199Fin-201
❑ 99Bow-50
❑ 99BowChr-50
❑ 99BowChrG-50
❑ 99BowChrGR-50
❑ 99BowChrI-50
❑ 99BowChrIR-50
❑ 99BowChrR-50
❑ 99BowGol-50
❑ 99BowInt-50
❑ 99CroRoyB-110
❑ 99CroRoyL-110
❑ 99CroRoyOD-110
❑ 99E-X Cen-65
❑ 99E-X CenECFut-65
❑ 99E-X CenECNow-65
❑ 99FinGolRef-201
❑ 99FinRef-201
❑ 99Fle-135
❑ 99FleSta9-135
❑ 99FleWarT-135
❑ 99MetUni-86
❑ 99MetUniGM-86
❑ 99MetUniPMG-86
❑ 99Pac-340
❑ 99PacAur-147
❑ 99PacAurOD-147
❑ 99PacCroC-220
❑ 99PacCroCPB-220
❑ 99PacPar-185
❑ 99PacParC-185
❑ 99PacParG-185
❑ 99PacParHoloGold-185
❑ 99PacParHS-185
❑ 99PacParOD-185
❑ 99PacParPB-185
❑ 99PacParRed-185
❑ 99PacPlaB-340
❑ 99PacPri-112
❑ 99PacPriHB-112
❑ 99PacPriHG-112
❑ 99PacPriHM-112
❑ 99PacPriHP-112
❑ 99PacPriRed-112
❑ 99PacPriS-92
❑ 99PacPriS206-92
❑ 99PacPriS206R-92
❑ 99PacRed-340
❑ 99SkyMolM-82
❑ 99SkyMolMX-82
❑ 99SkyPre-63
❑ 99SkyPreA-24
❑ 99SkyPreABlue-24
❑ 99SkyPreR-63
❑ 99SkyThu-86
❑ 99SkyThuRant-86
❑ 99SkyThuRave-86
❑ 99SP SigAuto-JG
❑ 99SPSig-116
❑ 99SPx-63
❑ 99SPxFinR-63
❑ 99SPxFinS-63
❑ 99StaClu-232
❑ 99StaCluC-CS22
❑ 99StaCluC-CS29
❑ 99StaCluC-CS35
❑ 99StaCluC-CS40
❑ 99StaCluFDI-232
❑ 99StaCluOoaK-232
❑ 99StaCluPP-232
❑ 99ThuSkySupR-86
❑ 99Top-11
❑ 99TopChr-11
❑ 99TopChrR-11
❑ 99TopGal-83
❑ 99TopGalPP-83
❑ 99TopGalPPI-83
❑ 99TopMVPP-11
❑ 99TopOpeD-8
❑ 99UD Cho-127
❑ 99UD ChoPCR-127
❑ 99Ult-14
❑ 99UltGolM-14
❑ 99UltMas-14
❑ 99UltPlaM-14
❑ 99UppDec-176
❑ 99UppDecBD-68
❑ 99UppDecBDD-68
❑ 99UppDecBDQ-68
❑ 99UppDecBDT-68
❑ 99UppDecEL1-176
❑ 99UppDecEL2-176
❑ 99UppDecM-164
❑ 99UppDecMGS-164
❑ 99UppDecMHFS-164
❑ 99UppDecMSS-164
❑ 99Vic-308

Guillen, Ozzie
❑ 83BeaGolGT-2
❑ 84LasVegSC-236
❑ 85DonHig-55
❑ 85FleUpd-48
❑ 85TopTifT-43T
❑ 85TopTra-43T
❑ 85WhiSoxC-13
❑ 86Don-208
❑ 86Fle-206
❑ 86FleLeaL-17

- 86FleMin-44
- 86FleStiC-49
- 86FleWaxBC-C3
- 86GenMilB-2E
- 86KayB-16
- 86Lea-140
- 86MSAJayPCD-9
- 86OPC-254
- 86QuaGra-20
- 86SevCoi-C13
- 86Spo-22
- 86Spo-176
- 86Top-254
- 86TopGaloC-5
- 86TopGloS-58
- 86TopSti-294
- 86TopSti-309
- 86TopSup-7
- 86TopTat-5
- 86TopTif-254
- 86WhiSoxC-13
- 87Don-87
- 87DonOpeD-235
- 87Fle-497
- 87FleAwaW-17
- 87FleGlo-497
- 87FleMin-48
- 87FleRecS-13
- 87FleStiC-50
- 87KraFoo-11
- 87Lea-117
- 87OPC-89
- 87RedFolSB-67
- 87SevCoi-C9
- 87Spo-186
- 87SpoTeaP-26
- 87StuPan-17
- 87Top-89
- 87TopSti-287
- 87TopTif-89
- 87WhiSoxC-12
- 88Don-137
- 88DonBasB-81
- 88Fle-398
- 88FleGlo-398
- 88FleMin-15
- 88FleRecS-16
- 88FleStiC-16
- 88Lea-59
- 88Nes-7
- 88OPC-296
- 88PanSti-61
- 88Sco-603
- 88ScoGlo-603
- 88ScoYouSI-21
- 88Spo-14
- 88StaLinWS-8
- 88Top-585
- 88TopBig-27
- 88TopSti-284
- 88TopTif-585
- 88WhiSoxC-9
- 88WhiSoxK-1
- 89Bow-64
- 89BowTif-64
- 89ClaTraP-175
- 89Don-176
- 89DonBasB-137
- 89DonBonM-BC23
- 89Fle-497
- 89FleBasA-18
- 89FleGlo-497
- 89KinDis-6
- 89OPC-195
- 89PanSti-309
- 89RedFolSB-53
- 89Sco-433
- 89ScoHot1S-51
- 89Spo-85
- 89Top-195
- 89TopBasT-149
- 89TopBig-148
- 89TopSti-303
- 89TopTif-195
- 89TopUKM-35
- 89TVSpoM-114
- 89UppDec-175
- 89UppDec-628A
- 89WhiSoxC-10
- 89WhiSoxK-6
- 90Bow-315
- 90BowTif-315
- 90ClaBlu-92
- 90Don-15
- 90Don-135
- 90DonBesA-74
- 90DonLeaS-13
- 90DonSupD-15
- 90Fle-533
- 90FleCan-533
- 90Lea-128
- 90M.Vpin-24
- 90OPC-365
- 90PanSti-41
- 90PubIntS-388
- 90Sco-6
- 90ScoMcD-21
- 90Spo-48
- 90Top-365
- 90TopBig-215
- 90TopSti-298
- 90TopTif-365
- 90TopTVA-3
- 90UppDec-79
- 90UppDec-267
- 90USPlaCA-6C
- 90WhiSoxC-7
- 90WhiSoxC-29
- 90WhiSoxK-3
- 90WinDis-9
- 91BasBesHM-9
- 91Bow-356
- 91ClaGam-53
- 91Don-577
- 91Fle-121
- 91Lea-331
- 91MooSna-12
- 91OPC-620
- 91PanCanT1-113
- 91PanFreS-315
- 91PanSti-261
- 91RedFolS-44
- 91Sco-11
- 91Sco-394
- 91Sco100S-15
- 91SevCoi-M8
- 91StaClu-70
- 91Top-620
- 91TopDesS-620
- 91TopMic-620
- 91TopTif-620
- 91Ult-74
- 91UppDec-325
- 91USPlaCA-2H
- 91WhiSoxK-13
- 91WhiSoxK-NNO0
- 92Bow-565
- 92ClaGam-98
- 92Don-229
- 92Fle-82
- 92Fle-706
- 92HitTheBB-15
- 92Lea-149
- 92LeaBlaG-149
- 92OPC-210
- 92PacSea-57
- 92PanSti-128
- 92Pin-79
- 92Sco-92
- 92Sco100S-13
- 92ScoCokD-12
- 92ScoImpP-84
- 92ScoProP-22
- 92StaClu-20
- 92StaCluD-72
- 92Top-210
- 92TopGol-210
- 92TopGolW-210
- 92TopKid-100
- 92TopMic-210
- 92Ult-35
- 92UppDec-436
- 92WhiSoxK-13
- 93Bow-287
- 93Don-255
- 93Fin-128
- 93FinRef-128
- 93Fla-184
- 93Fle-203
- 93Lea-85
- 93LinVenB-270
- 93OPC-102
- 93PacBeiA-4
- 93PacSpa-72
- 93PacSpaPl-15
- 93PanSti-138
- 93Pin-166
- 93Sco-94
- 93Sel-128
- 93SP-254
- 93StaClu-517
- 93StaCluFDI-517
- 93StaCluMOP-517
- 93Stu-167
- 93Top-474
- 93TopGol-474
- 93TopInaM-474
- 93TopInaR-474
- 93TopMic-474
- 93TriPla-115
- 93Ult-532
- 93UppDec-139
- 93UppDecGold-139
- 93WhiSoxK-10
- 93WhiSoxSC-12
- 94Bow-511
- 94ColC-435
- 94ColChoGS-435
- 94ColChoSS-435
- 94Don-359
- 94DonSpeE-359
- 94Fin-393
- 94FinRef-393
- 94Fla-31
- 94Fle-82
- 94FleExtB-47
- 94FUnPac-113
- 94Lea-107
- 94OPC-115
- 94Pac-125
- 94PanSti-47
- 94Pin-428
- 94PinArtP-428
- 94PinMusC-428
- 94Sco-93
- 94ScoGolR-93
- 94Sel-25
- 94Spo-33
- 94StaClu-389
- 94StaCluFDI-389
- 94StaCluGR-389
- 94StaCluMOP-389
- 94StaCluT-141
- 94StaCluTFDI-141
- 94Stu-206
- 94Top-5
- 94TopGol-5
- 94TopSpa-5
- 94TriPla-264
- 94Ult-337
- 94UppDec-156
- 94UppDecED-156
- 94VenLinU-90
- 94WhiSoxK-10
- 95Baz-8
- 95ColCho-494
- 95ColChoGS-494
- 95ColChoSE-236
- 95ColChoSEGS-236
- 95ColChoSESS-236
- 95ColChoSS-494
- 95Don-294
- 95DonPreP-294
- 95DonTopotO-49
- 95Emo-27
- 95Fla-25
- 95Fle-118
- 95Lea-117
- 95LeaLim-191
- 95LinVen-250
- 95Pac-88
- 95PacPri-29
- 95PanSti-67
- 95Pin-107
- 95PinArtP-107
- 95PinMusC-107
- 95Sco-428
- 95ScoGolR-428
- 95ScoPlaTS-428
- 95Sel-185
- 95SelArtP-185
- 95StaClu-206
- 95StaCluFDI-206
- 95StaCluMOP-206
- 95StaCluSTWS-206
- 95Stu-157
- 95Top-598
- 95TopCyb-370
- 95TopEmb-116
- 95TopEmbGI-116
- 95Ult-274
- 95UltGolM-274
- 95UppDec-196
- 95UppDecED-196
- 95UppDecEDG-196
- 95UppDecSE-21
- 95UppDecSEG-21
- 95WhiSoxK-12
- 96-97LinVen-245
- 96ColCho-94
- 96ColCho-340
- 96ColChoGS-94
- 96ColChoGS-340
- 96ColChoSS-94
- 96ColChoSS-340
- 96Don-509
- 96DonPreP-509
- 96EmoXL-37
- 96Fin-B80
- 96FinRef-B80
- 96Fla-51
- 96Fle-66
- 96FleTif-66
- 96Lea-193
- 96LeaPrePB-193
- 96LeaPrePG-193
- 96LeaPrePS-193
- 96MetUni-37
- 96MetUniP-37
- 96Pac-286
- 96PacEstL-EL13
- 96PacPri-P89
- 96PacPriG-P89
- 96PanSti-170
- 96Pin-310
- 96PinFoil-310
- 96ProSta-132
- 96Sco-404
- 96StaClu-117
- 96StaCluMOP-117
- 96TeaOut-35
- 96Top-129
- 96Ult-38
- 96UltGolM-38
- 96UppDec-41
- 96WhiSoxF-6
- 97Cir-182
- 97CirRav-182
- 97ColCho-296
- 97ColChoT-CW11
- 97DonTea-75
- 97DonTeaSPE-75
- 97Fin-224
- 97FinRef-224
- 97Fle-61
- 97FleTif-61
- 97Pac-53
- 97PacLigB-53
- 97PacSil-53
- 97Sco-160
- 97ScoArtPWB-160
- 97ScoPreS-160
- 97ScoShoS-160
- 97ScoShoSAP-160
- 97StaClu-67
- 97StaCluMOP-67
- 97Top-147
- 97Ult-39
- 97UltGolME-39
- 97UltPlaME-39
- 97UppDec-206
- 97UppDec-331
- 97WhiSoxTI-13
- 98Pac-57
- 98PacInv-18
- 98PacInvPBlue-18
- 98PacInvSilv-18
- 98PacInvTeam-6
- 98PacLatotML-8
- 98PacPar-14
- 98PacParC-14
- 98PacParG-14
- 98PacParHS-14
- 98PacParPB-14
- 98PacParR-14
- 98PacPlaB-57
- 98PacRedT-57
- 98PacSil-57
- 98Sco-62
- 98Top-164
- 98TopChr-164
- 98TopChrR-164
- 98TopDevR-164
- 98TopDia-164
- 98TopMiniC-164
- 98Ult-300
- 98UltGolM-300
- 98UltMas-300
- 98UltPlaM-300
- 98UppDec-652
- 98UppDecNP-NP42
- 98WhiSoxS-4
- 98WhiSoxSP-4
- 99Pac-30
- 99PacCroC-23
- 99PacCroCPB-23
- 99PacPlaB-30
- 99PacRed-30
- 99Top-301
- 99TopChr-301
- 99TopChrR-301
- 99TopMVPP-301
- 99UppDec-311
- 99UppDecEL1-311
- 99UppDecEL2-311

Guillot, Don
- 87PanAmTUBI-10
- 87PanAmTURB-9

Guin, Greg
- 82ArkTraT-14
- 83ArkTraT-17
- 84ArkTraT-10

Guindon, Bob
- 64SeaPop-5
- 65SeaPop-4
- 65Top-509

Guinn, Brian
- 84ModA'sC-15
- 85ModA'sC-7
- 86HunStaDJ-20
- 86SouLeaAJ-8
- 87PitCubP-11
- 88IowCubC-15
- 88IowCubP-526
- 89IowCubC-16
- 89IowCubP-1709
- 90CMC-87
- 90IowCubC-12
- 90IowCubP-324
- 90ProAAAF-631
- 90TopTVCu-46
- 91IowCubLD-206
- 91IowCubP-1066
- 91LinDriAAA-206
- 92VanCanS-629

Guinn, Skip (Drannon E.)
- 69Top-614
- 70OPC-316
- 70Top-316
- 71MLBOffS-82
- 71OPC-741
- 71Top-741

Guinn, Wayne
- 80CedRapRT-26

Guintini, Ben
- 48SomandK-14

Guise, Witt
- 41HarHarW-9

Guisto, Lou
- 16Zee-50
- 17ColE13-67
- 20Zee-22
- 23W503-58
- 24Zee-27
- 25Zee-27
- 26Zee-75
- 27Zee-55
- 28Zee-79

Gulan, Mike
- 92ClaDraP-38
- 92ClaFS7-426
- 92FroRowDP-11
- 92FroRowDPG-11
- 92FroRowDPS-11
- 92HamRedC-26
- 92HamRedF-1597
- 93Bow-656
- 93ExcFS7-98
- 93SprCarC-11
- 93SprCarF-1858
- 93StaCluM-90
- 94ExcFS7-266
- 94St.PetCC-10
- 94St.PetCF-2592
- 94UppDecML-136
- 94UppDecMLPotYF-PY7
- 95ArkTraTI-14
- 95Bes-95
- 96BesAutSA-24
- 96Bow-304
- 96BowFoi-304
- 96Exc-227
- 96LouRedB-19
- 97BesAutAS-15
- 97LouRedB-15
- 98SpoIll-150
- 98SpoIllEE-150
- 98SpoIllFE-150

Gulbit, German
- 89EasLeaDDP-DD3

Guldahl, Ralph
- 40WheM4-6A
- 40WheM4-6C

Gulden, Brad
- 77LodDodT-4
- 79ColCliT-1
- 80ColCliP-20
- 80ColCliT-6
- 80NasSouTI-10
- 80Top-670
- 81SpoIndT-30
- 83ColCliT-4
- 84RedEnq-15
- 85Don-365
- 85Fle-537
- 85OPC-251
- 85RedYea-7
- 85Top-251
- 85TopMin-251
- 85TopTif-251
- 86GiaMot-25
- 90DodTar-305
- 92YanWIZ7-61
- 92YanWIZ8-73

Gull, Sterling
- 80SalLakCGT-20

Gulledge, Derek
- 94BluOriF-3558

Gulledge, Hugh
- 90MadMusB-16
- 91MadMusC-8
- 91MadMusP-2125
- 92RenSilSCLC-41

Gullett, Don
- 70DayDaiNM-78
- 71MLBOffS-60
- 71OPC-124
- 71Top-124
- 72OPC-157
- 72Top-157
- 73LinPor-56
- 73OPC-595
- 73Top-595
- 74OPC-385
- 74Top-385
- 74TopSta-27
- 75Hos-107
- 75OPC-65
- 75Top-65
- 75TopMin-65
- 76BlaDis-18
- 76BucDis-18
- 76CarDis-18
- 76CraDis-18
- 76DailsID-18
- 76Hos-45
- 76HosTwi-45
- 76IsaDis-18
- 76Kel-3
- 76LinSup-90
- 76OPC-390
- 76OrbDis-18
- 76RedBarD-18
- 76RedIceL-7
- 76RedKro-11
- 76SafDis-18
- 76SSP-27
- 76Top-390
- 76TowCluD-18
- 77BurCheD-172
- 77ChiWilD-29
- 77DailsID-29
- 77DetCaeD-29
- 77HolInnD-29
- 77Hos-143
- 77MSADis-29
- 77OPC-250
- 77PepGloD-35
- 77RCColC-28
- 77RedCarP-5
- 77SagDis-29
- 77sDis-29
- 77Top-15
- 77WenDis-29
- 77YanBurK-6
- 77ZipDis-29
- 78OPC-30
- 78RCColC-28
- 78SSP270-18
- 78Top-225
- 78WifBalD-28
- 78YanBurK-8
- 78YanPhoA-10
- 78YanSSPD-18
- 79OPC-64

❑ 79Top-140
❑ 79YanPicA-16
❑ 80Top-435
❑ 80YanPhoA-10
❑ 90ChaLooGS-2
❑ 91LinDriAAA-275
❑ 91NasSouLD-275
❑ 91NasSouP-2173
❑ 92YanWIZ7-62
❑ 92YanWIZ8-74
❑ 93RedKah-8
❑ 94RedKah-33
❑ 95RedKah-34
❑ 96Red76K-8
Gulley, Napolean
❑ 93NegLeaRL2-13
❑ 95NegLeaL2-26
Gullickson, Bill
❑ 80ExpPos-11
❑ 81Don-91
❑ 81Fle-150
❑ 81OPC-41
❑ 81Top-203
❑ 81Top-578
❑ 82Don-162
❑ 82ExpHygM-9
❑ 82ExpPos-15
❑ 82ExpZel-15
❑ 82FBIDis-11
❑ 82Fle-190
❑ 82OPC-94
❑ 82OPC-172
❑ 82OPCPos-21
❑ 82Top-172
❑ 82Top-526
❑ 83Don-288
❑ 83ExpPos-12
❑ 83ExpStu-15
❑ 83Fle-284
❑ 83FleSti-263
❑ 83OPC-31
❑ 83Top-31
❑ 84Don-401
❑ 84ExpPos-11
❑ 84ExpStu-16
❑ 84Fle-276
❑ 84Nes792-318
❑ 84OPC-318
❑ 84Top-318
❑ 84TopSti-96
❑ 84TopTif-318
❑ 85Don-97
❑ 85Fle-399
❑ 85Lea-236
❑ 85OPC-143
❑ 85Top-687
❑ 85TopSti-91
❑ 85TopTif-687
❑ 86Don-331
❑ 86DonHig-40
❑ 86Fle-249
❑ 86FleUpd-46
❑ 86OPC-229
❑ 86RedTexG-34
❑ 86Top-229
❑ 86TopSti-78
❑ 86TopTif-229
❑ 86TopTra-42T
❑ 86TopTraT-42T
❑ 87Don-369
❑ 87Fle-203
❑ 87FleAwaW-18
❑ 87FleGlo-203
❑ 87FleMin-49
❑ 87FleRecS-14
❑ 87FleStiC-51
❑ 87RedKah-34
❑ 87SmoNatL-4
❑ 87SpoTeaP-4
❑ 87Top-281
❑ 87Top-489
❑ 87TopSti-140
❑ 87TopTif-489
❑ 88Don-586
❑ 88Fle-208
❑ 88FleGlo-208
❑ 88OPC-329
❑ 88Sco-585
❑ 88ScoGlo-585
❑ 88Top-711
❑ 88TopTif-711
❑ 90AstLenH-14
❑ 90AstMot-13
❑ 90Bow-65
❑ 90BowTif-65
❑ 90TigTeal-14
❑ 90TopTra-34T
❑ 90TopTraT-34T
❑ 90UppDec-799
❑ 91Bow-133
❑ 91Fle-508
❑ 91Lea-402
❑ 91Sco-177
❑ 91ScoRoo-56T
❑ 91Stu-55
❑ 91TigCok-36
❑ 91UppDec-590
❑ 92Bow-558
❑ 92Don-131
❑ 92Fle-137
❑ 92Lea-61
❑ 92LeaBlaG-61
❑ 92OPC-508
❑ 92PanSti-112
❑ 92Pin-87
❑ 92Sco-242
❑ 92ScoProP-21
❑ 92StaClu-119
❑ 92SunSee-2
❑ 92TigKro-11
❑ 92Top-508
❑ 92TopGol-508
❑ 92TopGolW-508
❑ 92TopMic-508
❑ 92TriPla-161
❑ 92Ult-362
❑ 92UppDec-317
❑ 92UppDecTMH-23
❑ 92YanWIZ8-75
❑ 93Don-523
❑ 93Fle-606
❑ 93Lea-103
❑ 93OPC-124
❑ 93PacSpa-110
❑ 93PanSti-112
❑ 93Pin-352
❑ 93Sco-643
❑ 93Sel-85
❑ 93StaClu-574
❑ 93StaCluFDI-574
❑ 93StaCluMOP-574
❑ 93TigGat-12
❑ 93Top-325
❑ 93TopComotH-7
❑ 93TopGol-325
❑ 93TopInaM-325
❑ 93TopInaR-325
❑ 93TopMic-325
❑ 93UppDec-398
❑ 93UppDecGold-398
❑ 94ColC-118
❑ 94ColChoGS-118
❑ 94ColChoSS-118
❑ 94Don-195
❑ 94Fin-398
❑ 94FinRef-398
❑ 94Fle-134
❑ 94Lea-147
❑ 94PanSti-65
❑ 94Sco-198
❑ 94ScoGolR-198
❑ 94StaClu-370
❑ 94StaCluFDI-370
❑ 94StaCluGR-370
❑ 94StaCluMOP-370
❑ 94Top-654
❑ 94TopGol-654
❑ 94TopSpa-654
❑ 94TriPla-245
❑ 94UppDec-458
❑ 94UppDecED-458
❑ 95ColCho-479
❑ 95ColChoGS-479
❑ 95ColChoSS-479
❑ 95Don-434
❑ 95DonPreP-434
❑ 95StaClu-250
❑ 95StaCluFDI-250
❑ 95StaCluMOP-250
❑ 95StaCluSTWS-250
❑ 95Top-249
❑ 95TopCyb-136
Gulliver, Glenn
❑ 77EvaTriT-13
❑ 80EvaTriT-21
❑ 81EvaTriT-15
❑ 82RocRedWT-12
❑ 83Don-131
❑ 83Fle-62
❑ 83RocRedWT-15
❑ 83Top-293
❑ 84RocRedWT-11
❑ 85RicBraT-13
❑ 86HagSunP-7
❑ 86RocRedWP-4
❑ 87HagSunP-11
❑ 91OriCro-169
❑ 91PacSenL-155
Gully, Scott
❑ 91OneYanP-4149
❑ 92GreHorC-13
❑ 92GreHorF-774
❑ 93PriWilCC-13
❑ 93PriWilCF-652
Gulseth, Mark
❑ 93EveGiaC-12
❑ 93EveGiaF-3773
❑ 95BurBeeTI-4
❑ 96BurBeeTI-17
❑ 97SanJosG-19
❑ 98SanJosGQ-8
Gumbert, Addison
❑ 87OldJudN-215
❑ 90DodTar-306
Gumbert, Harry
❑ 39PlaBal-54
❑ 40PlaBal-86
❑ 41CarW75-9
❑ 41DouPlaR-27
❑ 41DouPlaR-91
❑ 41PlaBal-26
❑ 49Bow-192
❑ 50Bow-171
❑ 79DiaGre-48
❑ 83Car194T-44
Gumbert, Rich
❑ 83GreHorT-9
Gumbs, Lincoln
❑ 90AubAstB-17
❑ 90AubAstP-3409
Gump, Chris
❑ 92AriWilP-5
❑ 93EveGiaC-13
❑ 93EveGiaF-3774
Gumpert, Dave
❑ 82BirBarT-5
❑ 83EvaTriT-3
❑ 84EvaTriT-8
❑ 84Nes792-371
❑ 84Top-371
❑ 84TopTif-371
❑ 85IowCubT-14
❑ 86IowCubP-13
❑ 86StaoftFT-9
❑ 87Fle-565
❑ 87FleGlo-565
❑ 87Top-487
❑ 87TopTif-487
❑ 89BirBarADB-16
❑ 90BirBarADB-16
Gumpert, Randy
❑ 47YanTeaT-10
❑ 48BluTin-23
❑ 48YanTeal-10
❑ 49Bow-87
❑ 50Bow-184
❑ 51Bow-59
❑ 52Bow-106
❑ 52Top-247
❑ 78ReaRem-7
❑ 83TopRep5-247
❑ 85TCMPpl1-38
Gumpf, John
❑ 90EliTwiS-11
❑ 91KenTwiC-9
❑ 91KenTwiP-2089
❑ 92Ft.MyeMCB-22
❑ 92Ft.MyeMF-2756
Gundelfinger, Matt
❑ 81RedPioT-14
❑ 83SprCarF-18
Gunderson, Eric
❑ 87EveGiaC-13
❑ 88CalLeaACLC-5
❑ 88SanJosGCLC-131
❑ 88SanJosGP-114
❑ 89ShrCapP-1833
❑ 90Bow-225
❑ 90BowTif-225
❑ 90CMC-534
❑ 90PhoFirC-7
❑ 90ScoRoo-99T
❑ 90UppDec-752
❑ 91Bow-628
❑ 91Don-416
❑ 91Sco-744
❑ 91Sco100RS-57
❑ 91TopDeb90-61
❑ 91UppDec-315
❑ 92ClaGam-41
❑ 92Fle-637
❑ 92JacSunS-357
❑ 92StaClu-397
❑ 93CalCanF-1160
❑ 95MetColP-13
❑ 96MetKah-11
❑ 97RanDr P-11
❑ 97RanMot-16
❑ 98PacInvGems-104
❑ 98PacOnl-735
❑ 98PacOnlR-735
❑ 98PacOnlWC-735
Gunderson, Greg
❑ 89BatCliP-1938
❑ 90SpaPhiB-6
❑ 90SpaPhiP-2487
❑ 90SpaPhiS-11
Gunderson, Matt
❑ 98WilCubM-12
Gunderson, Mike
❑ 94AubAstC-4
❑ 94AubAstF-3751
❑ 96QuaCitRB-15
Gunderson, Shane
❑ 96Exc-77
❑ 96FtMyeMB-22
❑ 97NewBriRC-13
❑ 98NewBriRCM-11
Gunn, Clay
❑ 86BelMarCr-126
❑ 87WauTimP-10
❑ 88SanBerSB-18
❑ 88SanBerSCLC-32
Gunn, Jeffrey
❑ 90PriPatD-9
Gunnarson, Bob
❑ 86ChaLooP-10
❑ 87ChaLooB-13
Gunner, Chie
❑ 97Top-471
Gunnett, Chris
❑ 94LetMouF-3874
❑ 94LetMouSP-12
Gunning, Thomas
❑ 87OldJudN-216
❑ 90KalBatN-24
Gunson, Joseph
❑ 87OldJudN-217
Gunter, Chet
❑ 76ShrCapT-19
❑ 77ShrCapT-6
Gunter, Reid
❑ 87PocGiaTB-8
Gunther, Fred
❑ 24Zee-8
Gunther, Kevin
❑ 96WesMicWB-10
❑ 97ModA'sG-10
❑ 98HunStaTI-23
Gura, Larry
❑ 71OPC-203
❑ 71Top-203
❑ 73OPC-501
❑ 73Top-501
❑ 74OPC-616
❑ 74Top-616
❑ 74TopTra-616T
❑ 75OPC-557
❑ 75Top-557
❑ 75TopMin-557
❑ 75YanSSP-7
❑ 76KanCitRP-9
❑ 76OPC-319
❑ 76Top-319
❑ 76VenLeaS-135
❑ 77Top-193
❑ 78Roy-6
❑ 78SSP270-237
❑ 78Top-441
❑ 79RoyTeal-3
❑ 79Top-19
❑ 80OPC-154
❑ 80Top-295
❑ 81AllGamPI-83
❑ 81CokTeaS-75
❑ 81Don-461
❑ 81Fle-38
❑ 81FleStiC-102
❑ 81Kel-59
❑ 81OPC-130
❑ 81RoyProPS-8
❑ 81Top-130
❑ 81TopScr-51
❑ 81TopSti-88
❑ 82Don-338
❑ 82Fle-410
❑ 82FleSta-205
❑ 82OPC-147
❑ 82Roy-9
❑ 82Top-96
❑ 82Top-790
❑ 82TopSti-195
❑ 83AllGamPI-79
❑ 83Don-160
❑ 83Fle-113
❑ 83FleSti-103
❑ 83Kel-42
❑ 83OPC-340
❑ 83OPC-395
❑ 83RoyPos-12
❑ 83Top-340
❑ 83Top-395
❑ 83TopSti-77
❑ 84AllGamPI-171
❑ 84Don-100
❑ 84Fle-347
❑ 84Nes792-96
❑ 84Nes792-625
❑ 84OPC-264
❑ 84RoyPos-12
❑ 84Top-96
❑ 84Top-625
❑ 84TopSti-285
❑ 84TopTif-96
❑ 84TopTif-625
❑ 85Don-217
❑ 85Fle-202
❑ 85RoyTeal-10
❑ 85Top-595
❑ 85TopSti-278
❑ 85TopTif-595
❑ 92UppDecS-20
❑ 92YanWIZ7-63
❑ 97AriStaBG-10
Gurchiek, Chris
❑ 88AppFoxP-156
❑ 88BoiHawP-1609
Gurtcheff, Jeff
❑ 86WatPirP-8
Guse, Bryan
❑ 97BakBlaB-22
❑ 97BakBlaTI-22
Gust, Chris
❑ 88MadMusP-12
Gustafson, Cliff
❑ 92TexLon-19
❑ 93Tex-1
Gustafson, Ed (Edward)
❑ 89EveGiaS-9
❑ 90Bes-85
❑ 90CliGiaB-6
❑ 90CliGiaP-2550
❑ 90ProAaA-118
❑ 91VisOakC-2
❑ 91VisOakP-1736
❑ 92OrlSunRF-2841
❑ 92OrlSunRS-506
Gustafson, Marc
❑ 94AshTouC-29
❑ 95NewHavRTI-NNO
❑ 96NewHavRB-4
❑ 97NewHavRB-26
Gustave, Michael
❑ 78WisRapTT-6
Gustavson, Dan
❑ 92HunCubC-13
❑ 92HunCubF-3141
Gustavson, Duane
❑ 82ForMyeRT-10
❑ 83ChaRoyT-25
❑ 85Ft.MyeRT-26
❑ 86Ft.MyeRP-13
❑ 87MemChiB-2
❑ 87MemChiP-21
❑ 88OrlTwiB-3
Gustine, Frank
❑ 47Exh-88A
❑ 47Exh-88B
❑ 47TipTop-140
❑ 49AngTeal-14
❑ 49Bow-99
❑ 49EurSta-57
❑ 49Lea-88
❑ 79DiaGre-369
❑ 83TCMPla1943-33
Guth, Bucky
❑ 73TacTwiC-10
Guthrie, David
❑ 96BilMusTI-11
❑ 98ChaLooG-12
Guthrie, Ken
❑ 98HelBreM-17
Guthrie, Mark
❑ 87LSUTigP-3
❑ 88VisOakCLC-167
❑ 89OrlTwiB-14
❑ 89OrlTwiP-1335
❑ 89SouLeaAJ-19
❑ 90Don-622
❑ 90LSUTigGM-9
❑ 90OPC-317
❑ 90PorBeaP-174
❑ 90ProAAAF-244
❑ 90Top-317
❑ 90TopDeb89-49
❑ 90TopTif-317
❑ 90UppDec-436
❑ 91Don-64
❑ 91Fle-612
❑ 91Lea-171
❑ 91OPC-698
❑ 91Sco-778
❑ 91StaClu-219
❑ 91Top-698
❑ 91TopDesS-698
❑ 91TopMic-698
❑ 91TopTif-698
❑ 91UppDec-505
❑ 92Don-691
❑ 92Lea-263
❑ 92LeaBlaG-263
❑ 92OPC-548
❑ 92Pin-511
❑ 92Sco-164
❑ 92StaClu-456
❑ 92Top-548
❑ 92TopGol-548
❑ 92TopGolW-548
❑ 92TopMic-548
❑ 92Ult-396
❑ 92UppDec-604
❑ 93Don-714
❑ 93Fle-265
❑ 93Lea-251
❑ 93PacSpa-170
❑ 93Pin-361
❑ 93StaClu-550
❑ 93StaCluFDI-550
❑ 93StaCluMOP-550
❑ 93Top-777
❑ 93TopGol-777
❑ 93TopInaM-777
❑ 93TopInaR-777
❑ 93TopMic-777
❑ 93Ult-581
❑ 93UppDec-399
❑ 93UppDecGold-399
❑ 94Don-530
❑ 94Fle-204
❑ 94Pac-352
❑ 95Fle-202
❑ 95Top-553
❑ 95TopCyb-332
❑ 96DodMot-26
❑ 96DodPol-15
❑ 96LeaSigEA-66
❑ 97DodMot-17
❑ 97DodPol-11
❑ 98DodMot-17
❑ 98DodPol-8
❑ 98PacOnl-369
❑ 98PacOnlR-369
❑ 98PacOnlWC-369
Gutierrez, Alfredo
❑ 96OgdRapTI-34
❑ 97BelSnaB-15
Gutierrez, Anthony
❑ 90AshTouP-2742
❑ 90CMC-677
❑ 91BurAstC-4
❑ 91BurAstP-2795
❑ 92OscAstC-18
❑ 92OscAstF-2524
❑ 93QuaCitRBC-10
❑ 93QuaCitRBF-93
Gutierrez, Bob (Robert)
❑ 84NewOriT-21
❑ 85NewOriT-15
Gutierrez, Cesar
❑ 69OPC-16
❑ 69Top-16
❑ 70OPC-269
❑ 70Top-269
❑ 71MLBOffS-392

❑ 71OPC-154
❑ 71Top-154
❑ 72Top-743
❑ 87SpoRea-4
❑ 93LinVenB-172
❑ 95LinVen-70
❑ 96-97LinVen-124
Gutierrez, Dimas
❑ 85PriWilPT-8
❑ 86NasPirP-10
❑ 87HarSenP-22
❑ 88EasLeaAP-15
❑ 88HarSenP-841
❑ 89MiaMirIS-8
Gutierrez, Felipe
❑ 85VerBeaDT-7
Gutierrez, Israel
❑ 78AshTouT-8
❑ 79WauTimT-7
Gutierrez, Jackie (Joaquin)
❑ 79ElmPioRST-7
❑ 84FleUpd-47
❑ 84TopTra-46T
❑ 84TopTraT-46T
❑ 85AllGamPl-23
❑ 85Don-335
❑ 85Fle-160
❑ 85Top-89
❑ 85TopSti-216
❑ 85TopSti-373
❑ 85TopTif-89
❑ 86Don-335
❑ 86Fle-350
❑ 86FleUpd-47
❑ 86OPC-73
❑ 86Top-633
❑ 86TopTif-633
❑ 87Don-601
❑ 87Fle-471
❑ 87FleGlo-471
❑ 87Top-276
❑ 87TopTif-276
❑ 88PhiTas-33
❑ 89PawRedSC-19
❑ 89PawRedSP-694
❑ 89PawRedSTI-10
❑ 89UppDec-430
❑ 90MiaMirIS-11
❑ 90MiaMirIS-9
❑ 91OriCro-170
Gutierrez, Javier
❑ 96EveAquB-10
❑ 97WisTimR-11
❑ 98StoPorG-11
Gutierrez, Jim
❑ 89BelMarL-6
❑ 90PenPilS-10
❑ 91SanBerSC-5
❑ 91SanBerSP-1981
❑ 93RivPilCLC-8
❑ 94JacSunF-1407
❑ 95JacSunTI-15
❑ 96JacSunB-16
❑ 97JacGen-11
❑ 97JacGenS-8
❑ 98NewOrlZM-6
Gutierrez, Julian
❑ 78St.PetCT-11
❑ 80ArkTraT-16
❑ 82ArkTraT-15
Gutierrez, Rafael
❑ 90EugEmeGS-10
❑ 92VerBeaDC-23
❑ 92YakBeaC-21
❑ 92YakBeaF-3442
Gutierrez, Ricky
❑ 89FreKeyS-8
❑ 90CarLeaA-4
❑ 90FreKeyTI-18
❑ 91Cla/Bes-55
❑ 91HagSunLD-231
❑ 91HagSunP-2462
❑ 91LinDriAA-231
❑ 92Bow-103
❑ 92RocRedWF-1945
❑ 92RocRedWS-453
❑ 92SkyAAAF-206
❑ 93Bow-462
❑ 93FleFinE-140
❑ 93Lea-493
❑ 93PacSpa-596
❑ 93PadMot-10
❑ 93Pin-577
❑ 93SelRoo-63T
❑ 93SP-166
❑ 93StaClu-676
❑ 93StaCluFDI-676
❑ 93StaCluMOP-676
❑ 93TopTra-21T
❑ 93UppDec-660
❑ 93UppDecGold-660
❑ 94Bow-560
❑ 94ColC-119
❑ 94ColChoGS-119
❑ 94ColChoSS-119
❑ 94Don-159
❑ 94Fin-53
❑ 94FinRef-53
❑ 94Fla-233
❑ 94Fle-664
❑ 94FUnPac-37
❑ 94Lea-196
❑ 94OPC-47
❑ 94Pac-524
❑ 94PadMot-9
❑ 94Pin-138
❑ 94PinArtP-138
❑ 94PinMusC-138
❑ 94Sco-271
❑ 94ScoBoyoS-13
❑ 94ScoGolR-271
❑ 94Sel-175
❑ 94StaClu-75
❑ 94StaCluFDI-75
❑ 94StaCluGR-75
❑ 94StaCluMOP-75
❑ 94StaCluMOP-ST13
❑ 94StaCluST-ST13
❑ 94Top-42
❑ 94TopGol-42
❑ 94TopSpa-42
❑ 94TriPla-166
❑ 94Ult-279
❑ 94UppDec-104
❑ 94UppDecED-104
❑ 94WatIndC-14
❑ 94WatIndF-3943
❑ 95Don-416
❑ 95DonPreP-416
❑ 95Fle-559
❑ 95FleUpd-140
❑ 95KinIndTI-12
❑ 95Pac-361
❑ 95Sco-65
❑ 95ScoGolR-65
❑ 95ScoPlaTS-65
❑ 95StaClu-119
❑ 95StaCluFDI-119
❑ 95StaCluMOP-119
❑ 95StaCluSTWS-119
❑ 95Top-524
❑ 95TopCyb-309
❑ 95TucTotTI-8
❑ 96AstMot-26
❑ 96CanIndB-13
❑ 96ColCho-358
❑ 96ColChoGS-358
❑ 96ColChoSS-358
❑ 96Exc-44
❑ 96Fle-407
❑ 96FleTif-407
❑ 96Pac-99
❑ 97AstMot-10
❑ 97Fle-345
❑ 97FleTif-345
❑ 97Pac-317
❑ 97PacLigB-317
❑ 97PacSil-317
❑ 98Pac-318
❑ 98PacOnl-321
❑ 98PacOnlR-321
❑ 98PacOnlWC-321
❑ 98PacPlaB-318
❑ 98PacRedT-318
❑ 98PacSil-318
❑ 98UppDec-387
❑ 99Fle-415
❑ 99FleSta9-415
❑ 99FleWarT-415
❑ 99MetUni-199
❑ 99MetUniGM-199
❑ 99MetUniPMG-199
❑ 99Pac-191
❑ 99PacCroC-125
❑ 99PacCroCPB-125
❑ 99PacPar-105
❑ 99PacParC-105
❑ 99PacParG-105
❑ 99PacParHoloGold-105
❑ 99PacParHS-105
❑ 99PacParOD-105
❑ 99PacParPB-105
❑ 99PacParRed-105
❑ 99PacPlaB-191
❑ 99PacRed-191
❑ 99StaClu-234
❑ 99StaCluFDI-234
❑ 99StaCluOoaK-234
❑ 99StaCluPP-234
❑ 99UppDec-109
❑ 99UppDec-385
❑ 99UppDecEL1-109
❑ 99UppDecEL1-385
❑ 99UppDecEL2-109
❑ 99UppDecEL2-385
Gutierrez, Victor
❑ 98AugGreM-19
Gutierrez, Willie
❑ 79KnoKnoST-13
Gutshall, Eric
❑ 98NewJerCM-12
Gutteridge, Don
❑ 47RedSoxTI-9
❑ 60Top-458
❑ 70OPC-123
❑ 70Top-123
❑ 70WhiSoxTI-4
❑ 75RedSox1T-16
❑ 79DiaGre-156
❑ 81WhiSox1T-42
❑ 83TCMPla1944-1
❑ 92ConTSN-636
❑ 96Bro194F-2
Guttormson, Ricky
❑ 98CliLumG-6
Guy, Bradley
❑ 97EriSeaWB-16
❑ 98AugGreM-10
Guy, Mark
❑ 91MelBusF-9
Guyn, Howard
❑ 09ObaT21-28
Guyton, Duffy
❑ 92JohCitCC-23
❑ 92JohCitCF-3109
Guzik, Brian
❑ 93CedRapKC-7
❑ 93CedRapKF-1746
Guzik, Robbi (Rob)
❑ 89KinMetS-11
❑ 90PitMetP-5
❑ 91ColMetPI-22
❑ 91ColMetPPI-2
❑ 92ColMetC-13
❑ 92ColMetF-289
❑ 92ColMetPI-15
❑ 93St.LucMC-12
❑ 93St.LuMF-2917
❑ 94St.LucMC-11
❑ 94St.LucMF-1188
Guzman, Antonio
❑ 98LetBlaDG-13
Guzman, Carlos
❑ 98PieBolWM-16
Guzman, Correa (Juan)
❑ 86VerBeaDP-8
❑ 87BakDodP-5
❑ 88KnoBluJB-18
❑ 89SyrChiC-9
❑ 89SyrChiMB-12
❑ 89SyrChiP-797
❑ 90Bes-79
❑ 90CMC-814
❑ 90KnoBluJB-8
❑ 90KnoBluJP-1242
❑ 91BluJayFS-12
❑ 91BluJayS-25
❑ 91LinDriAAA-504
❑ 91SyrChiLD-504
❑ 91SyrChiMB-6
❑ 91SyrChiP-2476
❑ 91UltUpd-60
❑ 92BluJayP-5
❑ 92Bow-294
❑ 92Cla2-T18
❑ 92ClaGam-12
❑ 92ColAllP-NNO
❑ 92Don-534
❑ 92Fle-330
❑ 92FleRooS-13
❑ 92Lea-35
❑ 92LeaBlaG-35
❑ 92MVPPin-16
❑ 92OPC-662
❑ 92OPCPre-168
❑ 92Pin-183
❑ 92PinTea2-27A
❑ 92PinTea2-27B
❑ 92ProFS7-161
❑ 92Sco-424
❑ 92Sco100RS-27
❑ 92ScoImpP-3
❑ 92StaClu-402
❑ 92Stu-256
❑ 92SyrChiTT-3
❑ 92Top-662
❑ 92TopDeb91-68
❑ 92TopGol-662
❑ 92TopGolW-662
❑ 92TopMic-662
❑ 92Ult-449
❑ 92UppDec-625
❑ 92UppDecTMH-24
❑ 93BluJayCP1-7
❑ 93BluJayCP1-12
❑ 93BluJayD-1
❑ 93BluJayD4-17
❑ 93BluJayFS-12
❑ 93Bow-55
❑ 93ClaGam-40
❑ 93DiaMar-46
❑ 93Don-189
❑ 93Fin-56
❑ 93FinRef-56
❑ 93Fla-290
❑ 93Fle-693
❑ 93FleFruotL-27
❑ 93FunPac-57
❑ 93HumDumC-25
❑ 93Lea-3
❑ 93LeaFas-9
❑ 93MSABenSPD-14
❑ 93OPC-187
❑ 93OPCPre-36
❑ 93OPCWorC-6
❑ 93PacSpa-324
❑ 93PacSpaGE-15
❑ 93PanSti-33
❑ 93Pin-364
❑ 93PosCan-2
❑ 93Sco-372
❑ 93Sel-180
❑ 93SelAce-11
❑ 93SP-48
❑ 93StaClu-244
❑ 93StaCluFDI-244
❑ 93StaCluM-2
❑ 93StaCluM-63
❑ 93StaCluMOP-244
❑ 93Stu-144
❑ 93Top-75
❑ 93TopComotH-15
❑ 93TopGol-75
❑ 93TopInaM-75
❑ 93TopInaR-75
❑ 93TopMic-75
❑ 93Toy-73
❑ 93TriPla-28
❑ 93TriPlaA-28
❑ 93Ult-640
❑ 93UltStrK-2
❑ 93UppDec-266
❑ 93UppDecGold-266
❑ 93USPlaCA-5S
❑ 94BluJayP-5
❑ 94BluJayUSPC-6S
❑ 94BluJayUSPC-13D
❑ 94Bow-553
❑ 94ColC-120
❑ 94ColChoGS-120
❑ 94ColChoSS-120
❑ 94Don-404
❑ 94Fin-132
❑ 94FinRef-132
❑ 94Fla-349
❑ 94Fle-333
❑ 94FleExtB-190
❑ 94FleSmo'nH-3
❑ 94FUnPac-66
❑ 94Lea-262
❑ 94OPC-177
❑ 94Pac-642
❑ 94PanSti-138
❑ 94Pin-172
❑ 94PinArtP-172
❑ 94PinMusC-172
❑ 94PosCan-6
❑ 94ProMag-138
❑ 94Sco-375
❑ 94ScoGolR-375
❑ 94Sel-253
❑ 94SP-43
❑ 94SPDieC-43
❑ 94Spo-116
❑ 94StaClu-149
❑ 94StaCluFDI-149
❑ 94StaCluGR-149
❑ 94StaCluMOP-149
❑ 94StaCluT-170
❑ 94StaCluTFDI-170
❑ 94Top-181
❑ 94TopGol-181
❑ 94TopSpa-181
❑ 94TriPla-33
❑ 94Ult-438
❑ 94UppDec-430
❑ 94UppDecED-430
❑ 95BluJayB-2
❑ 95BluJayOH-16
❑ 95BluJayP-3
❑ 95BluJayUSPC-3C
❑ 95BluJayUSPC-11D
❑ 95ColCho-148
❑ 95ColChoGS-148
❑ 95ColChoSE-56
❑ 95ColChoSEGS-56
❑ 95ColChoSESS-56
❑ 95ColChoSS-148
❑ 95Don-174
❑ 95DonPreP-174
❑ 95Fin-151
❑ 95FinFlaT-FT3
❑ 95FinRef-151
❑ 95Fla-97
❑ 95Fle-95
❑ 95Lea-85
❑ 95Pac-445
❑ 95PacPri-142
❑ 95Pin-261
❑ 95PinArtP-261
❑ 95PinMusC-261
❑ 95Sco-474
❑ 95ScoGolR-474
❑ 95ScoPlaTS-474
❑ 95StaClu-162
❑ 95StaCluFDI-162
❑ 95StaCluMOP-162
❑ 95StaCluSTWS-162
❑ 95StaCluVR-86
❑ 95StaCluVRMO-86
❑ 95Top-290
❑ 95TopCyb-157
❑ 95Ult-339
❑ 95UltGolM-339
❑ 95UppDec-287
❑ 95UppDecED-287
❑ 95UppDecEDG-287
❑ 95UppDecSE-66
❑ 95UppDecSEG-66
❑ 96BluJayOH-14
❑ 96Cir-95
❑ 96CirRav-95
❑ 96ColCho-745
❑ 96ColChoGS-745
❑ 96ColChoSS-745
❑ 96Don-374
❑ 96DonPreP-374
❑ 96Fla-185
❑ 96Fle-275
❑ 96FleTif-275
❑ 96LeaSigA-88
❑ 96LeaSigAG-88
❑ 96LeaSigAS-88
❑ 96Pac-438
❑ 96StaClu-324
❑ 96StaCluMOP-324
❑ 96Ult-430
❑ 96UltGolM-430
❑ 96UppDec-474
❑ 97BluJayB-7
❑ 97BluJayCC-1
❑ 97BluJayOH-14
❑ 97BluJayS-8
❑ 97Cir-167
❑ 97CirRav-167
❑ 97ColCho-62
❑ 97ColCho-499
❑ 97Don-94
❑ 97DonGolPP-94
❑ 97DonLim-119
❑ 97DonLimE-119
❑ 97DonLimENG-119
❑ 97DonPre-77
❑ 97DonPreCttC-77
❑ 97DonSilPP-94
❑ 97E-X2-50
❑ 97E-X2Cred-50
❑ 97E-X2EssCre-50
❑ 97Fin-72
❑ 97FinRef-72
❑ 97FlaShoLC-103
❑ 97FlaShoLeg0-103
❑ 97FlaShoLeg1-103
❑ 97FlaShoM-A103
❑ 97FlaShoM-B103
❑ 97FlaShoM-C103
❑ 97FlaShoR0-103
❑ 97FlaShoR1-103
❑ 97FlaShoR2-103
❑ 97Fle-241
❑ 97FleTif-241
❑ 97Lea-237
❑ 97LeaFraM-237
❑ 97LeaFraMDC-237
❑ 97MetUni-185
❑ 97NewPin-64
❑ 97NewPinAP-64
❑ 97NewPinMC-64
❑ 97NewPinPP-64
❑ 97Pac-221
❑ 97PacLigB-221
❑ 97PacPri-74
❑ 97PacPriLB-74
❑ 97PacPriP-74
❑ 97PacSil-221
❑ 97Sco-83
❑ 97ScoArtPWB-83
❑ 97ScoPreS-83
❑ 97ScoShoS-83
❑ 97ScoShoSAP-83
❑ 97SP-181
❑ 97SpoIll-135
❑ 97SpoIllEE-135
❑ 97StaClu-207
❑ 97StaCluMat-207
❑ 97StaCluMOP-207
❑ 97Top-458
❑ 97TopGal-124
❑ 97TopGalPPI-124
❑ 97Ult-144
❑ 97UltGolME-144
❑ 97UltPlaME-144
❑ 97UppDec-516
❑ 97UppDecAWJ-13
❑ 98BluOriQ-18
❑ 98Fin-254
❑ 98FinNo--254
❑ 98FinNo-R-254
❑ 98FinRef-254
❑ 98FleUpd-U18
❑ 98Pac-222
❑ 98PacOnl-766
❑ 98PacOnlR-766
❑ 98PacOnlWC-766
❑ 98PacPlaB-222
❑ 98PacRedT-222
❑ 98PacSil-222
❑ 98Sco-198
❑ 98ScoSS-PP93
❑ 98ScoSSAP-PP93
❑ 98SpoIll-54
❑ 98SpoIllEE-54
❑ 98SpoIllFE-54
❑ 98StaCluFDI-347
❑ 98StaCluI-347
❑ 98StaCluOneK-347
❑ 98StaCluPP-347
❑ 98Top-352
❑ 98TopChr-352
❑ 98TopChrR-352
❑ 98TopDevR-352
❑ 98TopDia-352
❑ 98TopMiniC-352
❑ 98UppDec-529
❑ 99199Fin-21
❑ 99Bow-47
❑ 99BowChr-47
❑ 99BowChrG-47
❑ 99BowChrGR-47
❑ 99BowChrI-47
❑ 99BowChrIR-47
❑ 99BowChrR-47
❑ 99BowGol-47
❑ 99BowInt-47
❑ 99FinGolRef-21
❑ 99FinRef-21
❑ 99Fle-403
❑ 99FleSta9-403
❑ 99FleWarT-403
❑ 99MetUni-96
❑ 99MetUniGM-96
❑ 99MetUniPMG-96
❑ 99PacCroC-36
❑ 99PacCroCPB-36

❑ 99SkyPre-53
❑ 99SkyPreR-53
❑ 99StaClu-82
❑ 99StaCluFDI-82
❑ 99StaCluOoaK-82
❑ 99StaCluPP-82
❑ 99Top-309
❑ 99TopChr-309
❑ 99TopChrR-309
❑ 99TopMVPP-309
❑ 99UppDec-322
❑ 99UppDecEL1-322
❑ 99UppDecEL2-322
Guzman, Cristian
❑ 97GreBatB-13
❑ 97SouAtlTPB-17
❑ 98Bow-349
❑ 98BowChr-349
❑ 98BowChrGA-349
❑ 98BowChrGAR-349
❑ 98BowChrI-349
❑ 98BowChrIR-349
❑ 98BowChrR-349
❑ 98BowGolA-349
❑ 98BowInt-349
❑ 98NewBriRCM-12
❑ 99Bow-143
❑ 99BowChr-143
❑ 99BowChrG-143
❑ 99BowChrGR-143
❑ 99BowChrI-143
❑ 99BowChrIR-143
❑ 99BowChrR-143
❑ 99BowGol-143
❑ 99BowInt-143
❑ 99DumSet-139
❑ 99FleMys-139
❑ 99FleMysM-139
❑ 99JustheS-25
❑ 99JustheSJB-25
❑ 99PacInv-86
❑ 99PacInvOD-86
❑ 99PacInvPB-86
❑ 99PacOme-142
❑ 99PacOmeC-142
❑ 99PacOmeG-142
❑ 99PacOmePB-142
❑ 99UppDecE-122
❑ 99UppDecEFXG-122
❑ 99Vic-222
Guzman, Doinini
❑ 89MedAthB-10
Guzman, Domingo
❑ 95IdaFalBTI-32
❑ 96IdaFalB-9
❑ 97CliLumG-8
❑ 97MidLeaTP-7
❑ 97RanCucQG-11
Guzman, Edwards
❑ 96SanJosGB-5
❑ 97ShrCap-11
❑ 97ShrCapB-11
❑ 98FreGriG-10
❑ 99DumSet-109
❑ 99FleMys-109
❑ 99FleMysM-109
❑ 99SkyPre-255
❑ 99SkyPre-255
❑ 99SkyPreDD-15
❑ 99SkyPreR-255
❑ 99SkyPreR-255
Guzman, Elpidio
❑ 97ButCopKB-8
❑ 97ButCopKK-8
❑ 98ButCopKG-13
Guzman, Hector
❑ 83VerBeaDT-18
Guzman, Ismael
❑ 93BriTigC-10
❑ 93BriTigF-3661
❑ 94JamJamC-11
❑ 94JamJamF-3978
Guzman, Johnny
❑ 90CMC-665
❑ 90ModA'sC-12
❑ 90ModA'sP-2207
❑ 90ProAaA-144
❑ 91LinDriAAA-536
❑ 91TacTigLD-536
❑ 91TacTigP-2299
❑ 92ClaFS7-136
❑ 92DonRoo-47
❑ 92HunStaF-3943
❑ 92HunStaS-310
❑ 92SkyAA F-131
❑ 92StaClu-498
❑ 92TopDeb91-67
❑ 93AthStaC-23
❑ 93ClaFS7-197
❑ 93LimRocDWB-100
❑ 93Pin-261
❑ 93Sco-270
❑ 93StaClu-284
❑ 93StaCluFDI-284
❑ 93StaCluMOP-284
❑ 93TacTigF-3026
Guzman, Jonathan
❑ 96HelBreTI-7
❑ 97HelBreB-12
Guzman, Jose Alberto
❑ 83BurRanF-7
❑ 83BurRanT-4
❑ 84TulDriTI-29
❑ 85OklCit8T-11
❑ 86Don-30
❑ 86DonRoo-24
❑ 86Fle-559
❑ 86RanLit-2
❑ 86RanPer-23
❑ 86TopTra-43T
❑ 86TopTraT-43T
❑ 87Don-101
❑ 87Fle-124
❑ 87FleGlo-124
❑ 87Lea-50
❑ 87RanMot-23
❑ 87RanSmo-3
❑ 87Top-363
❑ 87TopTif-363
❑ 88Don-136
❑ 88DonBasB-88
❑ 88Fle-467
❑ 88FleGlo-467
❑ 88Lea-55
❑ 88OPC-98
❑ 88RanMot-23
❑ 88RanSmo-20
❑ 88Sco-322
❑ 88ScoGlo-322
❑ 88StaLinRa-5
❑ 88Top-563
❑ 88TopTif-563
❑ 89BimBreD-11
❑ 89Don-284
❑ 89Fle-520
❑ 89FleGlo-520
❑ 89OPC-209
❑ 89PanSti-445
❑ 89RanMot-25
❑ 89RanSmo-11
❑ 89Sco-143
❑ 89ScoYouS2-11
❑ 89Top-462
❑ 89TopSti-241
❑ 89TopTif-462
❑ 89UppDec-73
❑ 90OPC-308
❑ 90PubIntS-411
❑ 90Top-308
❑ 90TopTif-308
❑ 90UppDec-617
❑ 91FleUpd-60
❑ 92Bow-668
❑ 92Don-271
❑ 92Fle-306
❑ 92Lea-222
❑ 92LeaBlaG-222
❑ 92OPC-188
❑ 92Pin-98
❑ 92RanMot-19
❑ 92RanTeal-9
❑ 92Sco-502
❑ 92ScoProP-21
❑ 92StaClu-153
❑ 92Stu-243
❑ 92Top-188
❑ 92TopGol-188
❑ 92TopGolW-188
❑ 92TopMic-188
❑ 92TriPla-215
❑ 92Ult-442
❑ 92UppDec-204
❑ 93Bow-412
❑ 93CubMar-8
❑ 93CubStaC-19
❑ 93Don-687
❑ 93Fin-145
❑ 93FinRef-145
❑ 93Fle-323
❑ 93FleFinE-7
❑ 93Lea-266
❑ 93OPC-121
❑ 93OPCPre-23
❑ 93PacBeiA-17
❑ 93PacSpa-377
❑ 93Pin-505
❑ 93RanKee-167
❑ 93Sco-256
❑ 93SelRoo-107T
❑ 93SP-84
❑ 93StaClu-648
❑ 93StaCluFDI-648
❑ 93StaCluMOP-648
❑ 93Stu-91
❑ 93Top-253
❑ 93TopGol-253
❑ 93TopInaM-253
❑ 93TopInaR-253
❑ 93TopMic-253
❑ 93TriPla-142
❑ 93Ult-313
❑ 93UppDec-323
❑ 93UppDec-515
❑ 93UppDecGold-323
❑ 93UppDecGold-515
❑ 94Bow-578
❑ 94ColC-463
❑ 94ColChoGS-463
❑ 94ColChoSS-463
❑ 94Don-507
❑ 94Fin-93
❑ 94FinPre-93P
❑ 94FinRef-93
❑ 94Fla-137
❑ 94Fle-384
❑ 94Lea-186
❑ 94OPC-180
❑ 94Pac-99
❑ 94Pin-55
❑ 94PinArtP-55
❑ 94PinMusC-55
❑ 94Sco-178
❑ 94ScoGolR-178
❑ 94Sel-90
❑ 94StaClu-615
❑ 94StaCluFDI-615
❑ 94StaCluGR-615
❑ 94StaCluMOP-615
❑ 94StaCluT-342
❑ 94StaCluTFDI-342
❑ 94Top-35
❑ 94TopGol-35
❑ 94TopSpa-35
❑ 94TriPla-73
❑ 94Ult-456
❑ 94UppDec-196
❑ 94UppDecED-196
❑ 95Pac-71
❑ 95PacPri-23
Guzman, Jose Antonio
❑ 89BriTigS-10
❑ 90FayGenP-2400
Guzman, Luis
❑ 79KnoKnoST-3
❑ 80UtiBluJT-17
Guzman, Pete (Pedro)
❑ 85DomLeaS-58
❑ 90ChaRaiB-10
❑ 90ChaRaiP-2037
Guzman, Ramon
❑ 92SouBenWSC-19
Guzman, Ruben
❑ 83WatRedT-18
❑ 86GleFalTP-8
❑ 87GleFalTP-1
Guzman, Santiago
❑ 70CarTeal-13
❑ 70Top-716
❑ 72OPC-316
❑ 72Top-316
Guzman, Toribio
❑ 96JohCitCTI-14
❑ 97JohCitCTI-16
❑ 98NewJerCM-13
❑ 98PeoChiM-10
Guzman, Wilson
❑ 98AugGreM-11
Gwaltney, Gary
❑ 85RedWinA-16
Gwaltney, Scott
❑ 85RedWinA-18
Gwinn, Tony
❑ 87PriWilYP-27
Gwosdz, Doug
❑ 81HawIsIT-5
❑ 82Top-731
❑ 84Don-383
❑ 84Nes792-753
❑ 84PadMot-16
❑ 84PadSmo-11
❑ 84Top-753
❑ 84TopTif-753
❑ 85GiaMot-22
❑ 85GiaPos-13
❑ 86JacMetT-11
❑ 87CalCanP-2331
❑ 88NasSouC-16
❑ 88NasSouP-480
❑ 88NasSouTI-11
❑ 89NasSouC-11
❑ 89NasSouP-1277
❑ 89NasSouTI-7
Gwynn, Chris
❑ 87AlbDukD-27
❑ 88AlbDukCm-12
❑ 88AlbDukP-259
❑ 88Fle-647
❑ 88FleGlo-647
❑ 88SanDieS-6
❑ 88SanDieS-7
❑ 88SanDieSAAG-7
❑ 88SanDieSAAG-8
❑ 88Sco-640
❑ 88ScoGlo-640
❑ 88TriAAAP-2
❑ 89AlbDukCm-15
❑ 89AlbDukP-64
❑ 89Fle-59
❑ 89FleGlo-59
❑ 89SanDieSAG-6
❑ 89SanDieSAG-7
❑ 89ScoHot1R-21
❑ 89UppDec-607
❑ 90ClaBlu-111
❑ 90DodMot-14
❑ 90DodPol-15
❑ 90DodTar-307
❑ 90Lea-411
❑ 90OPC-456
❑ 90ScoYouS2-39
❑ 90Top-456
❑ 90TopTif-456
❑ 90UppDec-526
❑ 91DodMot-14
❑ 91DodPho-12
❑ 91DodPol-15
❑ 91Don-598
❑ 91Fle-202
❑ 91OPC-99
❑ 91Sco-178
❑ 91StaClu-480
❑ 91Top-99
❑ 91TopDesS-99
❑ 91TopMic-99
❑ 91TopTif-99
❑ 91UppDec-560
❑ 92Don-648
❑ 92Fle-457
❑ 92Lea-518
❑ 92LeaBlaG-518
❑ 92OPC-604
❑ 92OPCPre-9
❑ 92RoyPol-10
❑ 92Sco-449
❑ 92ScoRoo-56T
❑ 92StaClu-815
❑ 92Top-604
❑ 92TopGol-604
❑ 92TopGolW-604
❑ 92TopMic-604
❑ 92Ult-371
❑ 92UppDec-83
❑ 92UppDec-689
❑ 93Don-657
❑ 93Lea-453
❑ 93RoyPol-11
❑ 93RoyStaC-9
❑ 93Top-472
❑ 93TopGol-472
❑ 93TopInaM-472
❑ 93TopInaR-472
❑ 93TopMic-472
❑ 93UppDec-632
❑ 93UppDecGold-632
❑ 94ColC-121
❑ 94ColChoGS-121
❑ 94ColChoSS-121
❑ 94DodDaiN-16
❑ 94DodMot-17
❑ 94DodPol-10
❑ 94Don-223
❑ 94Fle-157
❑ 94Lea-209
❑ 94Pac-284
❑ 94Pin-297
❑ 94PinArtP-297
❑ 94PinMusC-297
❑ 94Sco-381
❑ 94ScoGolR-381
❑ 94Top-731
❑ 94TopGol-731
❑ 94TopSpa-731
❑ 94Ult-63
❑ 95DodMot-15
❑ 95Sco-205
❑ 95ScoGolR-205
❑ 95ScoPlaTS-205
❑ 95Top-357
❑ 96PadMot-22
❑ 97PacPriGotD-GD206
Gwynn, Tony (Anthony)
❑ 82HawIsIT-10
❑ 83Don-598
❑ 83Fle-360
❑ 83OPC-143
❑ 83PadTeal-9
❑ 83Top-482
❑ 84AllGamPI-52
❑ 84Don-324
❑ 84Fle-301
❑ 84FunFooP-28
❑ 84MilLit-1
❑ 84Nes792-251
❑ 84OCoandSI-233
❑ 84PadMot-9
❑ 84PadSmo-12
❑ 84Top-251
❑ 84TopSti-160
❑ 84TopTif-251
❑ 85AllGamPI-143
❑ 85Don-25
❑ 85Don-63
❑ 85DonActA-19
❑ 85DonSupD-25
❑ 85Dra-14
❑ 85Fle-34
❑ 85FleLimE-11
❑ 85FleStaS-8
❑ 85KASDis-4
❑ 85KitCloD-4
❑ 85Lea-25
❑ 85OPC-383
❑ 85PadMot-2
❑ 85SevCoi-W11
❑ 85SubDis-32
❑ 85ThoMcAD-32
❑ 85Top-660
❑ 85Top-717
❑ 85Top3-D-13
❑ 85TopGaloC-4
❑ 85TopGloA-6
❑ 85TopGloS-29
❑ 85TopRubD-3
❑ 85TopSti-146
❑ 85TopSti-170
❑ 85TopSti-174
❑ 85TopSup-5
❑ 85TopTif-660
❑ 85TopTif-717
❑ 86BasStaB-52
❑ 86Don-112
❑ 86DonAll-1
❑ 86DonPop-1
❑ 86Fle-323
❑ 86FleLimE-22
❑ 86FleMin-69
❑ 86FleSlu-15
❑ 86FleStiC-50
❑ 86KayB-17
❑ 86Lea-41
❑ 86OPC-10
❑ 86PadFirPTB-3
❑ 86QuaGra-7
❑ 86SevCoi-W10
❑ 86Spo-13
❑ 86Spo-140
❑ 86Spo-181
❑ 86Top-10
❑ 86TopGloA-17
❑ 86TopGloS-57
❑ 86TopMinL-65
❑ 86TopSti-105
❑ 86TopSti-146
❑ 86TopSup-29
❑ 86TopTat-24
❑ 86TopTif-10
❑ 86Woo-13
❑ 87ClaGam-26
❑ 87Don-64
❑ 87DonAll-16
❑ 87DonHig-12
❑ 87DonOpeD-146
❑ 87DonP-16
❑ 87Dra-11
❑ 87Fle-416
❑ 87FleAwaW-19
❑ 87FleBasA-20
❑ 87FleGlo-416
❑ 87FleLimE-19
❑ 87FleMin-50
❑ 87FleSlu-17
❑ 87FleStiC-52
❑ 87GenMilB-6E
❑ 87HosSti-16
❑ 87KayB-15
❑ 87KeyFooD-16
❑ 87KraFoo-44
❑ 87Lea-235
❑ 87MandMSL-23
❑ 87MSAIceTD-16
❑ 87OPC-198
❑ 87OurOwnTD-16
❑ 87PadBohHB-19
❑ 87RedFolSB-113
❑ 87Spo-31
❑ 87Spo-117
❑ 87Spo-197
❑ 87SpoDeaP-3
❑ 87SpoSupD-7
❑ 87SpoTeaP-16
❑ 87StuPan-12
❑ 87Top-530
❑ 87Top-599
❑ 87TopCoi-34
❑ 87TopGaloC-6
❑ 87TopGloA-6
❑ 87TopGloS-2
❑ 87TopMinL-35
❑ 87TopSti-106
❑ 87TopSti-155
❑ 87TopTif-530
❑ 87TopTif-599
❑ 87WeiMarD-16
❑ 87Woo-16
❑ 88Baz-9
❑ 88CheBoy-6
❑ 88ClaBlu-220
❑ 88Don-164
❑ 88DonAll-51
❑ 88DonBasB-154
❑ 88DonBonM-BC6
❑ 88Dra-14
❑ 88Fle-585
❑ 88Fle-631
❑ 88Fle-634
❑ 88FleAwaW-16
❑ 88FleBasA-13
❑ 88FleBasM-17
❑ 88FleExcS-17
❑ 88FleGlo-585
❑ 88FleGlo-631
❑ 88FleGlo-634
❑ 88FleHotS-15
❑ 88FleLeaL-16
❑ 88FleMin-112
❑ 88FleRecS-17
❑ 88FleSlu-17
❑ 88FleStiC-123
❑ 88FleTeaL-11
❑ 88GreBasS-26
❑ 88K-M-12
❑ 88KayB-13
❑ 88KinDis-5
❑ 88Lea-90
❑ 88MSAFanSD-18
❑ 88Nes-40
❑ 88OPC-360
❑ 88OPCBoxB-F
❑ 88PadCok-19
❑ 88PadSmo-10
❑ 88PanSti-410
❑ 88PanSti-437
❑ 88SanDieS-8
❑ 88SanDieS-9
❑ 88SanDieSAAG-9
❑ 88Sco-385
❑ 88ScoGlo-385
❑ 88Spo-16
❑ 88StaBog/G-1
❑ 88StaBog/G-3
❑ 88StaBog/G-5
❑ 88StaBog/G-7
❑ 88StaBog/G-9
❑ 88StaBog/G-11
❑ 88StaGwy-1

❑ 88StaGwy-2
❑ 88StaGwy-3
❑ 88StaGwy-4
❑ 88StaGwy-5
❑ 88StaGwy-6
❑ 88StaGwy-7
❑ 88StaGwy-8
❑ 88StaGwy-9
❑ 88StaGwy-10
❑ 88StaGwy-11
❑ 88StaLinAl-13
❑ 88StaLinPa-5
❑ 88TarPla-18
❑ 88Top-360
❑ 88Top-402
❑ 88Top-699
❑ 88TopBig-161
❑ 88TopCoi-36
❑ 88TopGaloC-7
❑ 88TopGloS-38
❑ 88TopMinL-74
❑ 88TopRevLL-1
❑ 88TopRitTM-11
❑ 88TopSti-115
❑ 88TopStiB-16
❑ 88TopTif-360
❑ 88TopTif-402
❑ 88TopTif-699
❑ 88TopUKM-29
❑ 88TopUKMT-29
❑ 88TopWaxBC-F
❑ 88Woo-12
❑ 89Baz-13
❑ 89Bow-461
❑ 89BowTif-461
❑ 89CadEllD-27
❑ 89ClaLigB-30
❑ 89DodStaSV-7
❑ 89Don-6
❑ 89Don-128
❑ 89DonBasB-42
❑ 89DonBonM-BC20
❑ 89DonSupD-6
❑ 89Fle-305
❑ 89FleBasA-19
❑ 89FleBasM-17
❑ 89FleExcS-20
❑ 89FleGlo-305
❑ 89FleHeroB-20
❑ 89FleLeaL-19
❑ 89FleSup-21
❑ 89FleWaxBC-C12
❑ 89K-M-29
❑ 89KayB-17
❑ 89KinDis-21
❑ 89MSAHolD-6
❑ 89OPC-51
❑ 89PadCok-6
❑ 89PadMag-3
❑ 89PadPos-13
❑ 89PanSti-203
❑ 89PanSti-222
❑ 89RedFolSB-54
❑ 89SanDieSAG-8
❑ 89Sco-90
❑ 89ScoHot1S-40
❑ 89Scomast-37
❑ 89Spo-160
❑ 89SpoIllFKI-33
❑ 89Top-570
❑ 89Top-699
❑ 89TopBasT-62
❑ 89TopBatL-2
❑ 89TopBig-58
❑ 89TopCapC-5
❑ 89TopCoi-4
❑ 89TopGaloC-7
❑ 89TopGloS-58
❑ 89TopHeaUT-1
❑ 89TopHilTM-16
❑ 89TopMinL-39
❑ 89TopSti-109
❑ 89TopStiB-50
❑ 89TopTif-570
❑ 89TopUKM-36
❑ 89TVSpoM-45
❑ 89TVSpoM-130
❑ 89UppDec-384
❑ 89UppDec-683
❑ 90AllBasT-14
❑ 90BasWit-2
❑ 90Baz-6
❑ 90Bow-217
❑ 90BowTif-217
❑ 90ClaBlu-17
❑ 90ClaBlu-87A
❑ 90ClaBlu-87B
❑ 90Col-17
❑ 90Don-86
❑ 90Don-705
❑ 90Don-705A
❑ 90DonBesN-11
❑ 90DOnBonM-BC4
❑ 90DonLeaS-48
❑ 90DonPre-9
❑ 90Fle-157
❑ 90FleBasM-16
❑ 90FleBasMC-16
❑ 90FleCan-157
❑ 90FleLeaL-17
❑ 90FleLeaLC-17
❑ 90FleWaxBC-C12
❑ 90Hot50PS-19
❑ 90K-M-5
❑ 90KayB-14
❑ 90KinDis-3
❑ 90Lea-154
❑ 90M.Vpin-86
❑ 90MLBBasB-55
❑ 90MSAHolD-18
❑ 90OPC-403
❑ 90OPC-730
❑ 90PacGwyCB-1
❑ 90PadCok-6
❑ 90PadMag-1
❑ 90PadMag-15
❑ 90PanSti-207
❑ 90PanSti-351
❑ 90Pos-5
❑ 90PubIntS-50
❑ 90PubIntS-261
❑ 90RedFolSB-43
❑ 90Sco-255
❑ 90Sco-685
❑ 90Sco100S-3
❑ 90Spo-98
❑ 90StaLonJS-4
❑ 90StaLonJS-29
❑ 90SunSee-11
❑ 90Top-403
❑ 90Top-730
❑ 90TopBatL-2
❑ 90TopBig-93
❑ 90TopCoi-36
❑ 90TopDou-31
❑ 90TopGaloC-3
❑ 90TopGloA-8
❑ 90TopGloS-56
❑ 90TopHeaU-1
❑ 90TopMag-60
❑ 90TopMinL-80
❑ 90TopSti-101
❑ 90TopSti-146
❑ 90TopStiB-15
❑ 90TopTif-403
❑ 90TopTif-730
❑ 90TopTVA-39
❑ 90UppDec-344
❑ 90USPlaCA-11D
❑ 90WonBreS-12
❑ 91BasBesHM-10
❑ 91Bow-647
❑ 91CadEllD-28
❑ 91Cla2-T93
❑ 91Cla3-T33
❑ 91ClaGam-156
❑ 91Col-19
❑ 91Don-243
❑ 91Fle-529
❑ 91Lea-290
❑ 91LeaPre-11
❑ 91MajLeaCP-54
❑ 91MooSna-6
❑ 91MSAHolD-5
❑ 91OPC-180
❑ 91OPCPre-59
❑ 91PadMag-22
❑ 91PadSmo-11
❑ 91PanCanT1-104
❑ 91PanFreS-97
❑ 91PanSti-99
❑ 91PetSta-24
❑ 91Pos-10
❑ 91Sco-500
❑ 91Sco100S-94
❑ 91SevCoi-SC4
❑ 91StaClu-308
❑ 91StaPinB-23
❑ 91Stu-245
❑ 91Top-180
❑ 91TopCraJI-26
❑ 91TopDesS-180
❑ 91TopMic-180
❑ 91TopSta-18
❑ 91TopTif-180
❑ 91TopTriH-N10
❑ 91Ult-303
❑ 91UppDec-255
❑ 91UppDecFE-97F
❑ 91USPlaCA-1C
❑ 92Bow-50
❑ 92Cla2-T52
❑ 92ClaGam-61
❑ 92ColAllG-18
❑ 92ColAllP-18
❑ 92ColGwy-1
❑ 92ColGwy-2
❑ 92ColGwy-3
❑ 92ColGwy-4
❑ 92ColGwy-5
❑ 92ColGwy-6
❑ 92ColGwy-7
❑ 92ColGwy-8
❑ 92ColGwy-9
❑ 92ColGwy-10
❑ 92ColGwy-11
❑ 92ColGwy-12
❑ 92Don-425
❑ 92Don-441
❑ 92DonCraJ1-16
❑ 92DonEli-14
❑ 92Fle-605
❑ 92FleAll-2
❑ 92FleCitTP-10
❑ 92FleGwyCdA-1
❑ 92FleTeaL-7
❑ 92Fre-16
❑ 92Hig5-122
❑ 92Hig5S-18
❑ 92HitTheBB-16
❑ 92JimDea-13
❑ 92KinDis-10
❑ 92LaKdec-16
❑ 92Lea-206
❑ 92LeaBlaG-206
❑ 92Mr.TurS-13
❑ 92MSABenSHD-15
❑ 92MVPPin-36
❑ 92OPC-270
❑ 92OPCPre-106
❑ 92PadCarJ-7
❑ 92PadMot-7
❑ 92PadPolD-8
❑ 92PadSmo-9
❑ 92PanSti-236
❑ 92PanSti-286
❑ 92Pin-400
❑ 92Pin-591
❑ 92Pos-26
❑ 92RedFolS-44
❑ 92RedFolS-116
❑ 92Sco-625
❑ 92Sco-779
❑ 92Sco-887
❑ 92Sco100S-81
❑ 92ScoProaG-16
❑ 92SevCoi-23
❑ 92SpoIllFK1-288
❑ 92SpoIllFK1-695
❑ 92SpoStaCC-21
❑ 92StaClu-825
❑ 92StaCluD-73
❑ 92StaCluNC-825
❑ 92Stu-104
❑ 92StuPre-22
❑ 92Top-270
❑ 92TopGol-270
❑ 92TopGolW-270
❑ 92TopKid-53
❑ 92TopMic-270
❑ 92TopMic-G270
❑ 92TriPla-219
❑ 92Ult-277
❑ 92UltAwaW-12
❑ 92UltGwy-1
❑ 92UltGwy-2
❑ 92UltGwy-3
❑ 92UltGwy-4
❑ 92UltGwy-5
❑ 92UltGwy-6
❑ 92UltGwy-7
❑ 92UltGwy-8
❑ 92UltGwy-9
❑ 92UltGwy-10
❑ 92UltGwy-S1
❑ 92UltGwy-S2
❑ 92UltGwy-AU0
❑ 92UppDec-83
❑ 92UppDec-274
❑ 92UppDec-717
❑ 92UppDecF-25
❑ 92UppDecFG-25
❑ 92UppDecWB-T6
❑ 93Bow-630
❑ 93CadDis-29
❑ 93ClaGam-41
❑ 93ColAllG-18
❑ 93DiaMar-47
❑ 93Don-126
❑ 93DurPowP1-14
❑ 93Fin-77
❑ 93FinRef-77
❑ 93Fla-133
❑ 93Fle-138
❑ 93FleFruotL-28
❑ 93FunPac-138
❑ 93FunPac-211
❑ 93FunPacA-AS9
❑ 93HumDumC-47
❑ 93Kra-23
❑ 93Lea-28
❑ 93LeaGolA-R9
❑ 93LeaHeaftH-2
❑ 93MetBak-10
❑ 93OPC-94
❑ 93PacJugC-28
❑ 93PacSpa-257
❑ 93PadMot-3
❑ 93PanSti-262
❑ 93Pin-98
❑ 93Pin-289
❑ 93PinCoo-20
❑ 93PinCooD-20
❑ 93Pos-8
❑ 93RedFolS-38
❑ 93RedFolS-116
❑ 93Sco-24
❑ 93Sco-525
❑ 93Sel-5
❑ 93SelChaS-8
❑ 93SelDufIP-8
❑ 93SP-167
❑ 93StaClu-538
❑ 93StaCluFDI-538
❑ 93StaCluM-3
❑ 93StaCluMMP-4
❑ 93StaCluMOP-538
❑ 93Stu-100
❑ 93Top-5
❑ 93TOPBLAG-8
❑ 93TopFulS-7
❑ 93TopGol-5
❑ 93TopInaM-5
❑ 93TopInaR-5
❑ 93TopMic-5
❑ 93TriPla-51
❑ 93Ult-472
❑ 93UppDec-165
❑ 93UppDec-474
❑ 93UppDecDG-17
❑ 93UppDecGold-165
❑ 93UppDecGold-474
❑ 93UppDecOD-D14
❑ 93UppDecTAN-TN11
❑ 93USPlaCA-6D
❑ 94Bow-120
❑ 94BowBes-R78
❑ 94BowBesR-R78
❑ 94ColC-122
❑ 94ColC-344
❑ 94ColChoGS-122
❑ 94ColChoGS-344
❑ 94ColChoSS-122
❑ 94ColChoSS-344
❑ 94ColChoT-5
❑ 94DenHol-14
❑ 94Don-10
❑ 94Don-440
❑ 94DonAnn8-10
❑ 94DonDiaK-DK11
❑ 94DonDiaKJ-DK11
❑ 94DonDom-B1
❑ 94DonDomJ-B1
❑ 94DonEli-38
❑ 94DonMVP-13
❑ 94DonSpeE-10
❑ 94Fin-201
❑ 94FinJum-201
❑ 94FinRef-201
❑ 94Fla-436
❑ 94Fle-665
❑ 94Fle-711
❑ 94FleAllS-39
❑ 94FleExtB-372
❑ 94FlePro-9
❑ 94FleTeaL-27
❑ 94FleUpdDT-5
❑ 94FUnPac-119
❑ 94FUnPac-206
❑ 94Kra-24
❑ 94Lea-254
❑ 94LeaL-152
❑ 94LeaLimGA-12
❑ 94LeaStaS-9
❑ 94OPC-109
❑ 94OscMayR-23
❑ 94Pac-525
❑ 94PacSilP-35
❑ 94PacSilPC-35
❑ 94PadMot-2
❑ 94PanSti-256
❑ 94Pin-4
❑ 94PinArtP-4
❑ 94PinMusC-4
❑ 94PinRunC-RC35
❑ 94PinTheN-12
❑ 94Pos-13
❑ 94ProMag-119
❑ 94RedFolMI-5
❑ 94Sco-12
❑ 94ScoGolR-12
❑ 94ScoGolS-23
❑ 94Sel-77
❑ 94SP-130
❑ 94SPDieC-130
❑ 94SPHol-13
❑ 94SPHolDC-13
❑ 94Spo-25
❑ 94SpoMov-MM5
❑ 94StaClu-151
❑ 94StaClu-537
❑ 94StaCluFDI-151
❑ 94StaCluFDI-537
❑ 94StaCluGR-151
❑ 94StaCluGR-537
❑ 94StaCluMO-43
❑ 94StaCluMOP-151
❑ 94StaCluMOP-537
❑ 94Stu-132
❑ 94StuSerS-1
❑ 94StuSerSG-1
❑ 94SucSav-10
❑ 94TomPiz-8
❑ 94Top-620
❑ 94TopGol-620
❑ 94TopSpa-620
❑ 94TopSupS-21
❑ 94TriPla-167
❑ 94Ult-280
❑ 94UltHitM-6
❑ 94UppDec-219
❑ 94UppDec-279
❑ 94UppDecAJ-17
❑ 94UppDecAJG-17
❑ 94UppDecDC-W5
❑ 94UppDecED-219
❑ 94UppDecED-279
❑ 95Baz-30
❑ 95BazRedH-RH6
❑ 95Bow-304
❑ 95BowBes-R21
❑ 95BowBes-X11
❑ 95BowBesJR-3
❑ 95BowBesR-R21
❑ 95BowBesR-X11
❑ 95ClaPhoC-46
❑ 95ColCho-61
❑ 95ColCho-73
❑ 95ColChoGS-61
❑ 95ColChoGS-73
❑ 95ColChoSE-27
❑ 95ColChoSE-140
❑ 95ColChoSE-160
❑ 95ColChoSEGS-27
❑ 95ColChoSEGS-140
❑ 95ColChoSEGS-160
❑ 95ColChoSESS-27
❑ 95ColChoSESS-140
❑ 95ColChoSESS-160
❑ 95ColChoSS-61
❑ 95ColChoSS-73
❑ 95DenHol-12
❑ 95Don-224
❑ 95DonAll-NL8
❑ 95DonDiaK-DK24
❑ 95DonDom-9
❑ 95DonPreP-224
❑ 95DonTopotO-341
❑ 95Emo-187
❑ 95EmoMas-4
❑ 95Fin-196
❑ 95FinRef-196
❑ 95Fla-201
❑ 95Fle-560
❑ 95FleAllF-8
❑ 95FleAllS-7
❑ 95FleLeaL-6
❑ 95FleTeaL-27
❑ 95Kra-22
❑ 95Lea-299
❑ 95Lea300C-13
❑ 95LeaChe-7
❑ 95LeaGolS-3
❑ 95LeaHeaftH-7
❑ 95LeaLim-87
❑ 95LeaLimG-20
❑ 95LeaLimIBP-2
❑ 95NatPac-15
❑ 95Pac-362
❑ 95PacGolP-36
❑ 95PacPri-116
❑ 95PadCHP-1
❑ 95PadMot-2
❑ 95PanSti-79
❑ 95PanSti-115
❑ 95Pin-93
❑ 95Pin-291
❑ 95PinArtP-93
❑ 95PinArtP-291
❑ 95PinFan-20
❑ 95PinGatA-GA9
❑ 95PinMusC-93
❑ 95PinMusC-291
❑ 95PinPin-17
❑ 95PinPinR-17
❑ 95PinRedH-RH8
❑ 95PinTeaP-TP9
❑ 95PinWhiH-WH8
❑ 95Pos-7
❑ 95PosCan-13
❑ 95RedFol-32
❑ 95Sco-28
❑ 95Sco-561
❑ 95ScoDouGC-GC4
❑ 95ScoDreT-DG8
❑ 95ScoGolR-28
❑ 95ScoGolR-561
❑ 95ScoHaloG-HG14
❑ 95ScoPlaTS-28
❑ 95ScoPlaTS-561
❑ 95ScoRul-SR23
❑ 95ScoRulJ-SR23
❑ 95Sel-94
❑ 95SelArtP-94
❑ 95SelBigS-BS7
❑ 95SelCer-66
❑ 95SelCerGT-10
❑ 95SelCerMG-66
❑ 95SP-105
❑ 95SPCha-88
❑ 95SPCha-90
❑ 95SPChaDC-88
❑ 95SPChaDC-90
❑ 95Spo-16
❑ 95SpoArtP-16
❑ 95SpoDouT-11
❑ 95SpoHamT-HT10
❑ 95SPSil-105
❑ 95SPSpeF-46
❑ 95StaClu-475
❑ 95StaClu-508
❑ 95StaCluCC-CC3
❑ 95StaCluMO-21
❑ 95StaCluMOP-475
❑ 95StaCluMOP-508
❑ 95StaCluMOP-CC3
❑ 95StaCluMOP-RL7
❑ 95StaCluMOP-VRE6
❑ 95StaCluRL-RL7
❑ 95StaCluSTWS-475
❑ 95StaCluSTWS-508
❑ 95StaCluVE-VRE6
❑ 95StaCluVR-261
❑ 95StaCluVRMO-261
❑ 95Stu-25
❑ 95StuGolS-25
❑ 95StuPlaS-25
❑ 95Sum-6
❑ 95Sum-183
❑ 95SumBigB-BB10
❑ 95SumNthD-6
❑ 95SumNthD-183
❑ 95TomPiz-24
❑ 95Top-389
❑ 95Top-431
❑ 95TopCyb-228

❑ 95TopD3-42
❑ 95TopEmb-6
❑ 95TopEmbGI-6
❑ 95TopFinIns-12
❑ 95TopLeaL-LL4
❑ 95TopTra-7T
❑ 95TopTra-160T
❑ 95TopTraPB-7
❑ 95UC3-69
❑ 95UC3-133
❑ 95UC3ArtP-69
❑ 95UC3ArtP-133
❑ 95UC3CycS-CS13
❑ 95UDAUnsBC-NNO
❑ 95Ult-233
❑ 95UltAllS-8
❑ 95UltAllSGM-8
❑ 95UltGolM-233
❑ 95UltHitM-7
❑ 95UltHitMGM-7
❑ 95UltLeaL-6
❑ 95UltLeaLGM-6
❑ 95UltOnBL-7
❑ 95UltOnBLGM-7
❑ 95UppDec-135
❑ 95UppDecC-2B
❑ 95UppDecED-135
❑ 95UppDecEDG-135
❑ 95UppDecPC-MLB1
❑ 95UppDecPLL-R27
❑ 95UppDecPLLE-R27
❑ 95UppDecSE-270
❑ 95UppDecSEG-270
❑ 95USPlaCMLA-1D
❑ 95Zen-104
❑ 95ZenAllS-6
❑ 95ZenZ-12
❑ 96Baz-124
❑ 96Bow-71
❑ 96BowBes-38
❑ 96BowBesAR-38
❑ 96BowBesMI-7
❑ 96BowBesMIAR-7
❑ 96BowBesMIR-7
❑ 96BowBesP-BBP10
❑ 96BowBesPAR-BBP10
❑ 96BowBesPR-BBP10
❑ 96BowBesR-38
❑ 96BowFoi-71
❑ 96Cir-186
❑ 96CirAcc-27
❑ 96CirBos-47
❑ 96CirRav-186
❑ 96ColCho-2
❑ 96ColCho-290
❑ 96ColCho-408
❑ 96ColCho-760
❑ 96ColChoGS-2
❑ 96ColChoGS-290
❑ 96ColChoGS-408
❑ 96ColChoGS-760
❑ 96ColChoSS-2
❑ 96ColChoSS-290
❑ 96ColChoSS-408
❑ 96ColChoSS-760
❑ 96ColChoYMtP-17
❑ 96ColChoYMtP-17A
❑ 96ColChoYMtPGS-17
❑ 96ColChoYMtPGS-17A
❑ 96DenHol-15
❑ 96DenHolGS-4
❑ 96DenHolGSAP-4
❑ 96Don-525
❑ 96Don-550
❑ 96DonDiaK-9
❑ 96DonEli-72
❑ 96DonHitL-1
❑ 96DonPreP-525
❑ 96DonPreP-550
❑ 96DonSho-4
❑ 96EmoN-5
❑ 96EmoXL-277
❑ 96Fin-B61
❑ 96Fin-B320
❑ 96Fin-G6
❑ 96FinBro-2
❑ 96FinRef-B61
❑ 96FinRef-B320
❑ 96FinRef-G6
❑ 96Fla-374
❑ 96Fle-567
❑ 96FleRoaW-2
❑ 96FleTeaL-27
❑ 96FleTif-567
❑ 96FleUpd-U224
❑ 96FleUpd-4
❑ 96FleUpdH-8
❑ 96FleUpdTC-U224
❑ 96FleZon-4
❑ 96Kin-10
❑ 96Lea-99
❑ 96LeaAllGMC-8
❑ 96LeaAllGMCG-8
❑ 96LeaGolS-11
❑ 96LeaLim-53
❑ 96LeaLimG-53
❑ 96LeaPicP-6
❑ 96LeaPre-79
❑ 96LeaPreP-79
❑ 96LeaPrePB-99
❑ 96LeaPrePG-99
❑ 96LeaPrePS-99
❑ 96LeaPreSG-48
❑ 96LeaPreSta-4
❑ 96LeaPreSte-48
❑ 96LeaSig-98
❑ 96LeaSigEA-67
❑ 96LeaSigEACM-10
❑ 96LeaSigPPG-98
❑ 96LeaSigPPP-98
❑ 96LeaStaS-2
❑ 96MetUni-235
❑ 96MetUniP-235
❑ 96MetUniT-4
❑ 96Pac-184
❑ 96Pac-198
❑ 96PacCraC-CC6
❑ 96PacGolCD-DC35
❑ 96PacHom-HP3
❑ 96PacMil-M3
❑ 96PacPri-P61
❑ 96PacPriG-P61
❑ 96PacPriRHS-RH12
❑ 96PadMot-2
❑ 96PanSti-97
❑ 96PanSti-113
❑ 96Pin-205
❑ 96Pin-267
❑ 96Pin-336
❑ 96PinAfi-30
❑ 96PinAfiAP-30
❑ 96PinAfiFPP-30
❑ 96PinAfiR-16
❑ 96PinAfiR-18
❑ 96PinAfiR-20
❑ 96PinAfiR-21
❑ 96PinAfiR-23
❑ 96PinAfiR-24
❑ 96PinAfiSP-15
❑ 96PinArtP-105
❑ 96PinArtP-167
❑ 96PinArtP-200
❑ 96PinFan-7
❑ 96PinFoil-205
❑ 96PinFoil-267
❑ 96PinFoil-336
❑ 96PinSky-13
❑ 96PinSta-105
❑ 96PinSta-167
❑ 96PinSta-200
❑ 96Pro-7
❑ 96ProMagA-20
❑ 96ProMagDM-19
❑ 96ProSta-81
❑ 96RedF-8
❑ 96Sco-16
❑ 96Sco-378
❑ 96ScoAll-9
❑ 96ScoBigB-9
❑ 96ScoDiaA-23
❑ 96ScoDugC-A15
❑ 96ScoDugC-B103
❑ 96ScoDugCAP-A15
❑ 96ScoDugCAP-B103
❑ 96ScoGolS-6
❑ 96ScoNumG-9
❑ 96ScoRef-7
❑ 96Sel-59
❑ 96SelArtP-59
❑ 96SelCer-21
❑ 96SelCerAP-21
❑ 96SelCerCB-21
❑ 96SelCerCR-21
❑ 96SelCerIP-13
❑ 96SelCerMB-21
❑ 96SelCerMG-21
❑ 96SelCerMR-21
❑ 96SelClaTF-14
❑ 96SelEnF-13
❑ 96SelTeaN-22
❑ 96SP-160
❑ 96Spo-9
❑ 96SpoArtP-9
❑ 96SpoDouT-10
❑ 96SpoHitP-13
❑ 96SpoPro-11
❑ 96SPSpeFX-40
❑ 96SPSpeFXDC-40
❑ 96SPx-49
❑ 96SPxBoufG-9
❑ 96SPxGol-49
❑ 96StaClu-301
❑ 96StaCluEPB-301
❑ 96StaCluEPG-301
❑ 96StaCluEPS-301
❑ 96StaCluMM-MM9
❑ 96StaCluMO-15
❑ 96StaCluMOP-301
❑ 96StaCluMOP-MM9
❑ 96StaCluMOP-PC4
❑ 96StaCluPC-PC4
❑ 96Stu-145
❑ 96StuHitP-1
❑ 96StuMas-1
❑ 96StuPrePB-145
❑ 96StuPrePG-145
❑ 96StuPrePS-145
❑ 96Sum-134
❑ 96SumAbo&B-134
❑ 96SumArtP-134
❑ 96SumBal-18
❑ 96SumFoi-134
❑ 96SumHitI-1
❑ 96TeaOut-36
❑ 96Top-1
❑ 96Top-250
❑ 96TopChr-1
❑ 96TopChr-97
❑ 96TopChrMotG-12
❑ 96TopChrMotGR-12
❑ 96TopChrR-1
❑ 96TopChrR-97
❑ 96TopClaC-CC9
❑ 96TopGal-147
❑ 96TopGalE-15
❑ 96TopGalPPI-147
❑ 96TopLas-43
❑ 96TopLasSS-11
❑ 96TopMasotG-12
❑ 96TopMysF-M9
❑ 96TopMysFR-M9
❑ 96TopPowB-1
❑ 96Ult-284
❑ 96Ult-580
❑ 96UltCalttH-3
❑ 96UltCalttHGM-3
❑ 96UltChe-B4
❑ 96UltCheGM-B4
❑ 96UltDiaP-4
❑ 96UltDiaPGM-4
❑ 96UltGolM-284
❑ 96UltGolM-580
❑ 96UltOn-L-3
❑ 96UltOn-LGM-3
❑ 96UltPriL-16
❑ 96UltPriLGM-16
❑ 96UltPro-SC2
❑ 96UltRes-3
❑ 96UltResGM-3
❑ 96UltSeaC-2
❑ 96UltSeaCGM-2
❑ 96UppDec-116
❑ 96UppDec-377
❑ 96UppDec-450
❑ 96UppDecA-10
❑ 96UppDecDD-DD32
❑ 96UppDecDDG-DD32
❑ 96UppDecDDS-DD32
❑ 96UppDecHC-HC19
❑ 96UppDecPHE-H34
❑ 96UppDecPRE-R57
❑ 96UppDecPreH-H34
❑ 96UppDecPreR-R57
❑ 96UppDecRunP-RP8
❑ 96UppDecVJLS-VJ19
❑ 96Zen-91
❑ 96Zen-150
❑ 96ZenArtP-91
❑ 96ZenArtP-150
❑ 96ZenMoz-20
❑ 97Bow-274
❑ 97BowBes-29
❑ 97BowBesA-29
❑ 97BowBesAAR-29
❑ 97BowBesAR-29
❑ 97BowBesAR-29
❑ 97BowBesJ-29
❑ 97BowBesJAR-29
❑ 97BowBesJR-29
❑ 97BowBesR-29
❑ 97BowChr-91
❑ 97BowChrI-91
❑ 97BowChrIR-91
❑ 97BowChrR-91
❑ 97BowInt-274
❑ 97Cir-150
❑ 97CirBos-7
❑ 97CirIco-3
❑ 97CirLimA-6
❑ 97CirRav-150
❑ 97CirRavR-5
❑ 97CirSupB-7
❑ 97ColCho-56
❑ 97ColCho-210
❑ 97ColChoAC-23
❑ 97ColChoBS-19
❑ 97ColChoBSGS-19
❑ 97ColChoNF-NF2
❑ 97ColChoS-19
❑ 97ColChoSR-12
❑ 97ColChoTBS-39
❑ 97ColChoTBSWH-39
❑ 97ColChoTotT-T25
❑ 97Don-3
❑ 97Don-407
❑ 97DonEli-15
❑ 97DonEliGS-15
❑ 97DonFraFea-15
❑ 97DonGolPP-3
❑ 97DonGolPP-407
❑ 97DonLim-91
❑ 97DonLim-107
❑ 97DonLim-136
❑ 97DonLimE-91
❑ 97DonLimE-107
❑ 97DonLimE-136
❑ 97DonLimENG-91
❑ 97DonLimFotG-2
❑ 97DonLimFotG-25
❑ 97DonPowA-18
❑ 97DonPowADC-18
❑ 97DonPre-46
❑ 97DonPre-172
❑ 97DonPreCttC-46
❑ 97DonPreCttC-172
❑ 97DonPrePM-7
❑ 97DonPreS-10
❑ 97DonPreSS-10
❑ 97DonPreTB-7
❑ 97DonPreTBG-7
❑ 97DonPreTF-7
❑ 97DonPreTP-7
❑ 97DonPreTPG-7
❑ 97DonPreXP-10A
❑ 97DonSig-3
❑ 97DonSigAC-58
❑ 97DonSigAM-58
❑ 97DonSigPPP-3
❑ 97DonSilPP-3
❑ 97DonSilPP-407
❑ 97DonVxP1-20
❑ 97E-X2-93
❑ 97E-X2Cred-93
❑ 97E-X2EssCre-93
❑ 97E-X2Hall-8
❑ 97Fin-169
❑ 97Fin-298
❑ 97FinEmb-169
❑ 97FinEmb-298
❑ 97FinEmbR-169
❑ 97FinEmbR-298
❑ 97FinRef-169
❑ 97FinRef-298
❑ 97FlaShoDC-6
❑ 97FlaShoLC-37
❑ 97FlaShoLeg0-37
❑ 97FlaShoLeg1-37
❑ 97FlaShoM-A37
❑ 97FlaShoM-B37
❑ 97FlaShoM-C37
❑ 97FlaShoR0-37
❑ 97FlaShoR1-37
❑ 97FlaShoR2-37
❑ 97Fle-462
❑ 97Fle-702
❑ 97Fle-743
❑ 97FleDecoE-4
❑ 97FleDecoERT-4
❑ 97FleDiaT-5
❑ 97FleGouG-3
❑ 97FleGouGF-3
❑ 97FleHea-7
❑ 97FleMilDM-46
❑ 97FleMilDMR-46
❑ 97FleTeaL-27
❑ 97FleTif-462
❑ 97FleTif-702
❑ 97FleTif-743
❑ 97FleZon-8
❑ 97HigMinM-45
❑ 97Lea-17
❑ 97Lea-356
❑ 97LeaFraM-17
❑ 97LeaFraM-356
❑ 97LeaFraMDC-17
❑ 97LeaFraMDC-356
❑ 97LeaGolS-15
❑ 97LeaKnoG-4
❑ 97LeaLeaotN-12
❑ 97LeaWarT-6
❑ 97MetUni-219
❑ 97NewPin-71
❑ 97NewPinAP-71
❑ 97NewPinIE-3
❑ 97NewPinKtP-12
❑ 97NewPinMC-71
❑ 97NewPinPP-71
❑ 97NewPinPP-I3B
❑ 97NewPinPP-K12
❑ 97Pac-424
❑ 97PacCar-35
❑ 97PacCarM-35
❑ 97PacCraC-10
❑ 97PacFirD-19
❑ 97PacGolCD-35
❑ 97PacLigB-424
❑ 97PacPri-144
❑ 97PacPriGA-GA31
❑ 97PacPriGotD-GD207
❑ 97PacPriLB-144
❑ 97PacPriP-144
❑ 97PacPriSH-SH12A
❑ 97PacPriSL-SL12A
❑ 97PacSil-424
❑ 97PadMot-2
❑ 97Pin-42
❑ 97PinArtP-PP42
❑ 97PinCer-45
❑ 97PinCer-147
❑ 97PinCerLI-10
❑ 97PinCerMBla-45
❑ 97PinCerMBla-147
❑ 97PinCerMBlu-45
❑ 97PinCerMBlu-147
❑ 97PinCerMG-45
❑ 97PinCerMG-147
❑ 97PinCerMR-45
❑ 97PinCerMR-147
❑ 97PinCerR-45
❑ 97PinCerR-147
❑ 97PinEpixGO-E9
❑ 97PinFan-FF14
❑ 97PinIns-56
❑ 97PinInsC-24
❑ 97PinInsCE-56
❑ 97PinInsDD-10
❑ 97PinInsDE-56
❑ 97PinMin-21
❑ 97PinMinB-21
❑ 97PinMinCB-21
❑ 97PinMinCG-21
❑ 97PinMinCGR-21
❑ 97PinMinCN-21
❑ 97PinMinCSS-21
❑ 97PinMinG-21
❑ 97PinMinS-21
❑ 97PinMusC-42
❑ 97PinPrePla-42
❑ 97PinTotCPB-45
❑ 97PinTotCPB-147
❑ 97PinTotCPG-45
❑ 97PinTotCPG-147
❑ 97PinTotCPR-45
❑ 97PinTotCPR-147
❑ 97PinX-P-13
❑ 97PinX-PMoS-13
❑ 97PinX-PMW-11
❑ 97PinX-PMWG-11
❑ 97PinX-PMWS-11
❑ 97PreCon-18
❑ 97Sco-249
❑ 97Sco-535
❑ 97ScoAllF-10
❑ 97ScoArtPWB-249
❑ 97ScoArtPWB-535
❑ 97ScoHeaotO-25
❑ 97ScoPreS-249
❑ 97ScoResC-535
❑ 97ScoShoS-249
❑ 97ScoShoS-535
❑ 97ScoShoSAP-249
❑ 97ScoShoSAP-535
❑ 97Sel-3
❑ 97Sel-P3
❑ 97SelArtP-3
❑ 97SelCom-3
❑ 97SelRegG-3
❑ 97SelSam-P3
❑ 97SelTooottT-8
❑ 97SelTooottTMB-8
❑ 97SP-155
❑ 97SPInsI-19
❑ 97SPMarM-MM7
❑ 97SpoIll-119
❑ 97SpoIllEE-119
❑ 97SPSpeF-17
❑ 97SPSpxF-9
❑ 97SPSPxFA-9
❑ 97SPVinAu-13
❑ 97SPVinAu-14
❑ 97SPVinAu-15
❑ 97SPVinAu-16
❑ 97SPVinAu-17
❑ 97SPx-42
❑ 97SPxBoufG-15
❑ 97SPxBro-42
❑ 97SPxCorotG-4
❑ 97SPxGol-42
❑ 97SPxGraF-42
❑ 97SPxSil-42
❑ 97SPxSte-42
❑ 97StaClu-219
❑ 97StaCluC-CO10
❑ 97StaCluMat-219
❑ 97StaCluMOP-219
❑ 97StaCluMOP-PG6
❑ 97StaCluPG-PG6
❑ 97StrAll-26
❑ 97Stu-124
❑ 97StuMasS-20
❑ 97StuMasS8-20
❑ 97StuPor8-20
❑ 97StuPrePG-124
❑ 97StuPrePS-124
❑ 97Top-410
❑ 97TopChr-145
❑ 97TopChrR-145
❑ 97TopChrSB-1
❑ 97TopChrSBR-1
❑ 97TopGal-5
❑ 97TopGalGoH-GH9
❑ 97TopGalPPI-5
❑ 97TopHobM-HM5
❑ 97TopIntF-ILM4
❑ 97TopIntFR-ILM4
❑ 97TopMemO5-21
❑ 97TopScr-8
❑ 97TopScrT-8
❑ 97TopSeaB-SB1
❑ 97TopSta-11
❑ 97TopSta97AS-AS9
❑ 97TopStaAM-11
❑ 97TopSweS-SS7
❑ 97UD3-35
❑ 97Ult-283
❑ 97UltDouT-19
❑ 97UltFamGam-11
❑ 97UltGolME-283
❑ 97UltHitM-9
❑ 97UltLeaS-6
❑ 97UltPlaME-283
❑ 97UltStaR-12
❑ 97UltTop3-12
❑ 97UltTop3GM-12
❑ 97UppDec-378
❑ 97UppDec-492
❑ 97UppDecAG-AG19
❑ 97UppDecAWJ-2
❑ 97UppDecGJ-GJ2
❑ 97UppDecHC-HC16
❑ 97UppDecMM-B5
❑ 97UppDecP-23
❑ 97UppDecPE-23
❑ 97UppDecSA-5
❑ 97UppDecSAG-5
❑ 97Zen-2
❑ 97Zen8x10-2
❑ 97Zen8x1D-2
❑ 98Bow-22
❑ 98BowBes-23
❑ 98BowBesAR-23
❑ 98BowBesMIF-MI17
❑ 98BowBesMIFAR-MI17
❑ 98BowBesMIFR-MI17
❑ 98BowBesR-23
❑ 98BowChr-22

❑ 98BowChrGA-22
❑ 98BowChrGAR-22
❑ 98BowChrI-22
❑ 98BowChrIR-22
❑ 98BowChrR-22
❑ 98BowGolA-22
❑ 98BowInt-22
❑ 98BowMinLM-MVP4
❑ 98CirThu-250
❑ 98CirThuB-8
❑ 98CirThuLA-7
❑ 98CirThuRav-250
❑ 98CirThuRR-8
❑ 98CirThuSupRav-250
❑ 98ColCho-6
❑ 98ColCho-21
❑ 98ColCho-253
❑ 98ColCho-269
❑ 98ColCho-480
❑ 98ColChoB5-480
❑ 98ColChoCG-6
❑ 98ColChoER-ER24
❑ 98ColChoMBH-23
❑ 98ColChoRJ-6
❑ 98ColChoS'-23
❑ 98ColChoSQ-SQ43
❑ 98ColChoSQ-SQ65
❑ 98ColChoSQDouble-19
❑ 98ColChoSQHR-19
❑ 98ColChoSQSingle-19
❑ 98ColChoSQTriple-19
❑ 98CroRoy-116
❑ 98CroRoyAS-19
❑ 98CroRoyCCPA-10
❑ 98CroRoyCCPrem-10
❑ 98CroRoyDK-18
❑ 98CroRoyFoB-17
❑ 98CroRoyFoB-26
❑ 98CroRoyFoBA-17
❑ 98CroRoyFoBA-26
❑ 98CroRoyPotG-21
❑ 98Don-22
❑ 98Don-167
❑ 98Don-372
❑ 98Don-410
❑ 98DonCol-22
❑ 98DonCol-167
❑ 98DonColE-409
❑ 98DonColE-526
❑ 98DonColL-211
❑ 98DonColL-365
❑ 98DonColP-558
❑ 98DonColP-725
❑ 98DonColS-22
❑ 98DonColS-167
❑ 98DonCruG-97
❑ 98DonCruP-97
❑ 98DonCruR-97
❑ 98DonDiaK-4
❑ 98DonDiaKC-4
❑ 98DonDom-18
❑ 98DonEli-9
❑ 98DonEli-126
❑ 98DonEliA-9
❑ 98DonEliA-126
❑ 98DonEliC-9
❑ 98DonEliI-20
❑ 98DonEliMC-9
❑ 98DonEliPN-7A
❑ 98DonEliPN-7B
❑ 98DonEliPN-7C
❑ 98DonEliPNDC-7A
❑ 98DonEliPNDC-7B
❑ 98DonEliPNDC-7C
❑ 98DonEliPNS-7A
❑ 98DonEliPNS-7B
❑ 98DonEliPNS-7C
❑ 98DonEliS-9
❑ 98DonEliS-126
❑ 98DonFANT-12
❑ 98DonFANTDC-12
❑ 98DonGolPP-22
❑ 98DonGolPP-167
❑ 98DonGolPP-372
❑ 98DonGolPP-410
❑ 98DonPre-8
❑ 98DonPre-175
❑ 98DonPreGB-24
❑ 98DonPreGES-20
❑ 98DonPreGoB-24
❑ 98DonPreGX-20
❑ 98DonPreGXDC-20
❑ 98DonPrePM-8
❑ 98DonPreSeat-8
❑ 98DonPreSeat-175
❑ 98DonPreTP-24
❑ 98DonPreTPD-12
❑ 98DonPreTPG-24
❑ 98DonPreTPS-24
❑ 98DonPreTW-25
❑ 98DonPriCD-22
❑ 98DonPriCD-167
❑ 98DonPriCE-409
❑ 98DonPriCE-526
❑ 98DonPriCL-211
❑ 98DonPriCL-365
❑ 98DonPriCP-558
❑ 98DonPriCP-725
❑ 98DonProLO-14
❑ 98DonProLPI-20
❑ 98DonSig-68
❑ 98DonSigAC-55
❑ 98DonSigAM-56
❑ 98DonSigP-68
❑ 98DonSigSB-14
❑ 98DonSilPP-22
❑ 98DonSilPP-167
❑ 98DonSilPP-372
❑ 98DonSilPP-410
❑ 98E-X2-13
❑ 98E-X2DesCoop-9
❑ 98E-X2ECFut-13
❑ 98E-X2ECNow-13
❑ 98Fin-90
❑ 98FinMysF1-M21
❑ 98FinMysF1-M25
❑ 98FinMysF1-M26
❑ 98FinMysF1-M27
❑ 98FinMysFR-M21
❑ 98FinMysFR-M25
❑ 98FinMysFR-M26
❑ 98FinMysFR-M27
❑ 98FinNo--90
❑ 98FinNo-R-90
❑ 98FinRef-90
❑ 98FinStaS-SS18
❑ 98FinTheM-TM14
❑ 98FinTheMR-TM14
❑ 98FlaShoLeg0-19
❑ 98FlaShoLeg1-19
❑ 98FlaShoLeg2-19
❑ 98FlaShoLeg3-19
❑ 98FlaShoLegM-19
❑ 98FlaShoR0-19
❑ 98FlaShoR1-19
❑ 98FlaShoR2-19
❑ 98FlaShoR3-19
❑ 98Fle-250
❑ 98Fle-315
❑ 98Fle-585
❑ 98FleDecERT-7
❑ 98FleDecoE-7
❑ 98FleDiamInk-5
❑ 98FleIn TC-IC8
❑ 98FleLumC-7
❑ 98FleVin'-52
❑ 98FleVin'C-52
❑ 98FleZon-8
❑ 98Lea-11
❑ 98Lea-166
❑ 98LeaCruG-97
❑ 98LeaCruP-97
❑ 98LeaCruR-97
❑ 98LeaFraDA-11
❑ 98LeaFraDA-166
❑ 98LeaFraF-11
❑ 98LeaFraF-166
❑ 98LeaFraM-11
❑ 98LeaFraM-166
❑ 98LeaFraM-11
❑ 98LeaFraM-166
❑ 98LeaFraMDC-11
❑ 98LeaFraMDC-166
❑ 98LeaFraMDC-11
❑ 98LeaFraMDC-166
❑ 98LeaFraMZ2-11
❑ 98LeaFraMZ2-166
❑ 98LeaHeaftH-9
❑ 98LeaHeaftHS-9
❑ 98LeaRCMLHDSamp-10
❑ 98LeaRS-33
❑ 98LeaRS-151
❑ 98LeaRSExtM-3
❑ 98LeaRSExtMDC-3
❑ 98LeaRSGAHSamp-8
❑ 98LeaRSGreAH-8
❑ 98LeaRSGreHit-8
❑ 98LeaRSLHolo-33
❑ 98LeaRSLHolo-151
❑ 98LeaRSLMVP-18
❑ 98LeaRSLMVPPE-18
❑ 98LeaRSLong-33
❑ 98LeaRSLong-151
❑ 98LeaRSMLHD-10
❑ 98LeaRSSOSamp-5
❑ 98LeaRSStaOva-5
❑ 98LeaRSTicMas-5
❑ 98LeaRSTicMasDC-5
❑ 98LeaRTrue-33
❑ 98LeaRTrue-151
❑ 98LeaStaS-11
❑ 98LeaStaSDC-11
❑ 98MetUni-178
❑ 98MetUniPMG-178
❑ 98MetUniUL-19
❑ 98Pac-427
❑ 98PacAur-191
❑ 98PacAur-NNO
❑ 98PacAurCube-14
❑ 98PacAurHC-15
❑ 98PacAurKotML-8
❑ 98PacAurODLC-14
❑ 98PacAurPF-1
❑ 98PacAurPFC-1
❑ 98PacAurPFC-1AU
❑ 98PacAurPFPB-1
❑ 98PacAurPFPB-1AU
❑ 98PacAurPFR-1
❑ 98PacAurPFS-1
❑ 98PacAurPFS-1AU
❑ 98PacCraCh-8
❑ 98PacGolCDC-27
❑ 98PacInCage-14
❑ 98PacInv-139
❑ 98PacInvCCDB-8
❑ 98PacInvCCG-8
❑ 98PacInvCCG-8
❑ 98PacInvCCLB-8
❑ 98PacInvCCP-8
❑ 98PacInvCCR-8
❑ 98PacInvGems-209
❑ 98PacInvInt-5N
❑ 98PacInvMiT-16
❑ 98PacInvPBlue-139
❑ 98PacInvPhoto-12
❑ 98PacInvSilv-139
❑ 98PacInvTeam-24
❑ 98PacOme-205
❑ 98PacOme-NNO
❑ 98PacOmeEP-19
❑ 98PacOmeEP1o1-19
❑ 98PacOmeFTF-6
❑ 98PacOmeOnIns-35
❑ 98PacOmeP-20
❑ 98PacOmeR-205
❑ 98PacOmeR-NNO
❑ 98PacOnl-637A
❑ 98PacOnl-637B
❑ 98PacOnl-652
❑ 98PacOnl-SAMP
❑ 98PacOnlR-637A
❑ 98PacOnlR-637B
❑ 98PacOnlR-652
❑ 98PacOnlR-SAMP
❑ 98PacOnlWC-637A
❑ 98PacOnlWC-637B
❑ 98PacOnlWC-652
❑ 98PacPar-237
❑ 98PacParC-237
❑ 98PacParCB-7
❑ 98PacParCBPP-7
❑ 98PacParFC-14
❑ 98PacParG-237
❑ 98PacParHS-237
❑ 98PacParI-49
❑ 98PacParPB-237
❑ 98PacParR-237
❑ 98PacParSD-16
❑ 98PacParTC-29
❑ 98PacPlaB-427
❑ 98PacRedT-427
❑ 98PacSil-427
❑ 98PacTeaC-27
❑ 98PadMot-2
❑ 98Pin-1
❑ 98PinArtP-PP1
❑ 98PinEpixGE-E9
❑ 98PinEpixGP-E9
❑ 98PinEpixME-E9
❑ 98PinEpixMO-E9
❑ 98PinEpixMP-E9
❑ 98PinEpixSE-E9
❑ 98PinEpixSO-E9
❑ 98PinEpixSP-E9
❑ 98PinIns-37
❑ 98PinInsBtN-15
❑ 98PinInsC-8
❑ 98PinInsCE-37
❑ 98PinInsCG-8
❑ 98PinInsDE-37
❑ 98PinInsSG-1AB
❑ 98PinInsSG-1CD
❑ 98PinInsSGS-1AB
❑ 98PinInsSGS-1CD
❑ 98PinMinB-8
❑ 98PinMinCB-8
❑ 98PinMinCBAP-8
❑ 98PinMinCGP-8
❑ 98PinMinCGPAP-8
❑ 98PinMinCN-8
❑ 98PinMinCNAP-8
❑ 98PinMinCSGR-8
❑ 98PinMinDC-8
❑ 98PinMinG-8
❑ 98PinMinMCSS-8
❑ 98PinMinS-8
❑ 98PinMusC-PP1
❑ 98PinPer-8
❑ 98PinPer-145
❑ 98PinPerLP-7
❑ 98PinPerPP-8
❑ 98PinPerPP-145
❑ 98PinPlu-83
❑ 98PinPlu-192
❑ 98PinPluAE-9
❑ 98PinPluAEE-9
❑ 98PinPluAEP-9
❑ 98PinPluAP-PP31
❑ 98PinPluGAP-PP31
❑ 98PinPluLM-29
❑ 98PinPluMAP-PP31
❑ 98PinPowPJ-20
❑ 98PinPowPJS-20
❑ 98PinPreP-1
❑ 98PinPreP-E9
❑ 98PinPreP-S47
❑ 98PinPreP-S48
❑ 98PinPreP-S49
❑ 98PinPreP-S50
❑ 98PinSpe-47
❑ 98PinSpe-48
❑ 98PinSpe-49
❑ 98PinSpe-50
❑ 98PreCon-6
❑ 98Revo-124
❑ 98RevoMLI-10
❑ 98RevoPTP-20
❑ 98RevoRooHH-27
❑ 98RevoShow-35
❑ 98RevoSS-124
❑ 98Sco-50
❑ 98ScoAllST-12
❑ 98ScoEpix-E9
❑ 98ScoLoaL-LL2
❑ 98ScoRT-9
❑ 98ScoRT-264
❑ 98ScoRTASEpix-9
❑ 98ScoRTSS-PP9
❑ 98ScoRTSS-PP157
❑ 98ScoRTSSAP-PP9
❑ 98ScoRTSSAP-PP157
❑ 98ScoRTSSAP1-PP9
❑ 98ScoRTSSAP1-PP157
❑ 98ScoRTStarGaz-12
❑ 98ScoSS-PP132
❑ 98ScoSSAP-PP132
❑ 98SkyDugA-43
❑ 98SkyDugA-126
❑ 98SkyDugAAR-6
❑ 98SkyDugADH-DH18
❑ 98SkyDugAIA-43
❑ 98SkyDugAIA-126
❑ 98SP Aut-170
❑ 98SP Aut-SD19
❑ 98SP AutC-TG
❑ 98SP AutSD-SD19
❑ 98SP AutSDT-SD19
❑ 98SP AutTrade-9
❑ 98SPAutGJ5x7-5
❑ 98SpoIll-55
❑ 98SpoIll-131
❑ 98SpoIll-189
❑ 98SpoIllEE-55
❑ 98SpoIllEE-131
❑ 98SpoIllEE-189
❑ 98SpoIllFE-55
❑ 98SpoIllFE-131
❑ 98SpoIllFE-189
❑ 98SpoIllODMP-OD25
❑ 98SpoIllTaN-48
❑ 98SpoIllTaN-90
❑ 98SpoIllTaNA-3
❑ 98SpoIllTaNAR-3
❑ 98SpoIllTaNC-C11
❑ 98SpoIllTaNEE-48
❑ 98SpoIllTaNEE-90
❑ 98SpoIllTaNRtC-RC4
❑ 98SpoIllWSF-56
❑ 98SpoIllWSFEE-56
❑ 98SpoIllWSFFE-56
❑ 98SPxFin-123
❑ 98SPxFin-163
❑ 98SPxFin-359
❑ 98SPxFinR-123
❑ 98SPxFinR-163
❑ 98SPxFinR-359
❑ 98SPxFinS-123
❑ 98SPxFinS-163
❑ 98SPxFinS-359
❑ 98StaCluC-CS13
❑ 98StaCluC-CS14
❑ 98StaCluC-CS15
❑ 98StaCluFDI-113
❑ 98StaCluI-113
❑ 98StaCluNC-NC5
❑ 98StaCluOneK-113
❑ 98StaCluPP-113
❑ 98StaCluTIII-T17C
❑ 98StaCluTLme-T17C
❑ 98StaCluTLmo-T17C
❑ 98Stu-61
❑ 98StuFF-22
❑ 98StuFFDC-22
❑ 98StuGPP-61
❑ 98StuHitPar-1
❑ 98StuMast-13
❑ 98StuPor8x10-12
❑ 98StuPor8x10GP-12
❑ 98StuSPP-61
❑ 98Top-1
❑ 98TopChr-1
❑ 98TopChrF-FB6
❑ 98TopChrFR-FB6
❑ 98TopChrHB-HB2
❑ 98TopChrHBR-HB2
❑ 98TopChrM-MS6
❑ 98TopChrMR-MS6
❑ 98TopChrR-1
❑ 98TopDevR-1
❑ 98TopDia-1
❑ 98TopFla-FB6
❑ 98TopFruR-1
❑ 98TopGal-119
❑ 98TopGalAG-AG8
❑ 98TopGalGP-119
❑ 98TopGalOPP-119
❑ 98TopGalPPI-119
❑ 98TopGalPPIA-119
❑ 98TopGolLabC1-14
❑ 98TopGolLabC1B-14
❑ 98TopGolLabC1One-14
❑ 98TopGolLabC1R-14
❑ 98TopGolLabC2-14
❑ 98TopGolLabC2B-14
❑ 98TopGolLabC2One-14
❑ 98TopGolLabC2R-14
❑ 98TopGolLabC3-14
❑ 98TopGolLabC3B-14
❑ 98TopGolLabC3One-14
❑ 98TopGolLabC3R-14
❑ 98TopHal-HB2
❑ 98TopMil-MS6
❑ 98TopMiniC-1
❑ 98TopMysFB-M9
❑ 98TopMysFB-M9
❑ 98TopMysFBR-M9
❑ 98TopMysFBR-M9
❑ 98TopOpeD-1
❑ 98TopSta-75
❑ 98TopSta'S-16
❑ 98TopSta'SGH-16
❑ 98TopStaB-75
❑ 98TopStaG-75
❑ 98TopStaGR-75
❑ 98TopStaLB-L4
❑ 98TopStaLG-L4
❑ 98TopStaLGR-L4
❑ 98TopStaLS-L4
❑ 98TopStaS-75
❑ 98TopStaSteG-16
❑ 98TopSup-1
❑ 98TopSup-1
❑ 98TopTek-23
❑ 98TopTekD-23
❑ 98UD3-90
❑ 98UD3-180
❑ 98UD3-270
❑ 98UD3DieCut-90
❑ 98UD3DieCut-180
❑ 98UD3DieCut-270
❑ 98Ult-108
❑ 98Ult-216
❑ 98Ult-491
❑ 98UltArtT-14
❑ 98UltDiaI-11
❑ 98UltDiaP-12
❑ 98UltDouT-12
❑ 98UltFalC-13
❑ 98UltGolM-108
❑ 98UltGolM-216
❑ 98UltGolM-491
❑ 98UltMas-108
❑ 98UltMas-216
❑ 98UltMas-491
❑ 98UltPlaM-108
❑ 98UltPlaM-216
❑ 98UltPlaM-491
❑ 98UltPriL-14
❑ 98UltTicS-2
❑ 98UltTop3-10
❑ 98UltWinN-20
❑ 98UppDec-15
❑ 98UppDec-136
❑ 98UppDec-458
❑ 98UppDec-500
❑ 98UppDec-539
❑ 98UppDec-619
❑ 98UppDec10AP-55
❑ 98UppDec1APR-55
❑ 98UppDec5x7-500
❑ 98UppDec5x7-619
❑ 98UppDecAC-AS19
❑ 98UppDecAG-AG19
❑ 98UppDecAGDC-AG19
❑ 98UppDecAPA1-2
❑ 98UppDecAPA1-3
❑ 98UppDecCD-CD19
❑ 98UppDecPN-PN43
❑ 98UppDecPN-PN44
❑ 98UppDecPN-PN45
❑ 98UppDecPN-PN46
❑ 98UppDecPN-PN47
❑ 98UppDecPN-PN48
❑ 98UppDecPN-PN49
❑ 98UppDecR-85
❑ 98UppDecR-5
❑ 98UppDecRGKoG-G28
❑ 98UppDecRQL-Q20
❑ 98UppDecRSotT-TG
❑ 98UppDecRTC-TC49
❑ 98UppDecSF-9
❑ 98UppDecU-19
❑ 98Zen-7
❑ 98Zen5 xx7-22
❑ 98Zen5x7GoldImp-22
❑ 98Zen5x7Imp-22
❑ 98ZenEpi-E9
❑ 98ZenRaitB-4
❑ 98ZenSampL-Z22
❑ 98ZenZ-G-7
❑ 98ZenZ-S-7
❑ 99199Fin-20
❑ 99199Fin-106
❑ 99199Fin-275
❑ 99AurComP-8A
❑ 99AurComP-8B
❑ 99AurKinotML-8
❑ 99AurOn DL-16
❑ 99AurPenF-16
❑ 99AurPenF-S16
❑ 99AurPenF-16
❑ 99AurPenF-S16
❑ 99AurPenFB-16
❑ 99AurPenFB-S16
❑ 99AurPenFS-16
❑ 99AurPenFS-S16
❑ 99AurSty-16
❑ 99Bow-264
❑ 99BowBes-57
❑ 99BowBes-98
❑ 99BowBesAR-57
❑ 99BowBesAR-98
❑ 99BowBesR-57
❑ 99BowBesR-98
❑ 99BowGol-264
❑ 99BowInt-264
❑ 99CroRoyB-119
❑ 99CroRoyC2-8
❑ 99CroRoyCCDB-9
❑ 99CroRoyCCG-9
❑ 99CroRoyCCG-9
❑ 99CroRoyCCLB-9
❑ 99CroRoyCCP-9
❑ 99CroRoyCCP-9
❑ 99CroRoyCCR-9
❑ 99CroRoyL-119

❑ 99CroRoyLL-8
❑ 99CroRoyMP-15
❑ 99CroRoyOD-119
❑ 99CroRoyPotG-20
❑ 99CroRoyPP-21
❑ 99CroRoyPPN-21
❑ 99E-X Cen-4
❑ 99E-X CenECFut-4
❑ 99E-X CenECNow-4
❑ 99E-XCenFoF'-13
❑ 99FinCom-C2
❑ 99FinComDualR-C2
❑ 99FinFraR-FR10
❑ 99FinFraRR-FR10
❑ 99FinGolRef-20
❑ 99FinGolRef-106
❑ 99FinGolRef-275
❑ 99FinMil-M1
❑ 99FinProF-PF21
❑ 99FinRef-20
❑ 99FinRef-106
❑ 99FinRef-275
❑ 99FinSplS-SS5
❑ 99FinSplSDR-SS5
❑ 99FinTeaFB-TF19
❑ 99FinTeaFBR-TF19
❑ 99FinTeaFG-TF19
❑ 99FinTeaFGR-TF19
❑ 99FinTeaFR-TF19
❑ 99FinTeaFRR-TF19
❑ 99FlaShoLeg1-9
❑ 99FlaShoLeg2-9
❑ 99FlaShoLeg3-9
❑ 99FlaShoLegM1-9
❑ 99FlaShoLegM2-9
❑ 99FlaShoLegM3-9
❑ 99FlaShoMoG-6
❑ 99FlaShoR1-9
❑ 99FlaShoR2-9
❑ 99FlaShoR3-9
❑ 99Fle-43
❑ 99FleBri-79
❑ 99FleBri2G-79
❑ 99FleBriBlu-79
❑ 99FleBriGol-79
❑ 99FleDatWD-4
❑ 99FleDiaM-5
❑ 99FleMys-68
❑ 99FleMysD-1
❑ 99FleMysFl-17
❑ 99FleMysFtG-4
❑ 99FleMysG-68
❑ 99FleMysM-68
❑ 99FleSta9-43
❑ 99FleVin'-43
❑ 99FleWarT-43
❑ 99MetUni-47
❑ 99MetUni-239
❑ 99MetUni-283
❑ 99MetUniBWTW-8
❑ 99MetUniDS-14
❑ 99MetUniGM-47
❑ 99MetUniGM-239
❑ 99MetUniGM-283
❑ 99MetUniPMG-47
❑ 99MetUniPMG-239
❑ 99MetUniPMG-283
❑ 99Pac-368
❑ 99Pac-368A
❑ 99Pac-NNO
❑ 99PacAur-160
❑ 99PacAurOD-160
❑ 99PacCraCho-10
❑ 99PacCroC-242
❑ 99PacCroC-NNO
❑ 99PacCroCITC-15
❑ 99PacCroCPB-242
❑ 99PacCroCPC-10
❑ 99PacCroCTC-25
❑ 99PacDynaD-19
❑ 99PacDynaDT-19
❑ 99PacGolCDC-35
❑ 99PacInv-122
❑ 99PacInvDM-8
❑ 99PacInvFP-17
❑ 99PacInvGotG-8
❑ 99PacInvOD-122
❑ 99PacInvPB-122
❑ 99PacInvSF-16
❑ 99PacInvSF-16B
❑ 99PacInvSH-17
❑ 99PacInvSH-17B
❑ 99PacInvTA-16
❑ 99PacOme-202
❑ 99PacOme-1
❑ 99PacOme-2
❑ 99PacOme-3
❑ 99PacOme-4
❑ 99PacOme-5
❑ 99PacOme-6
❑ 99PacOme-7
❑ 99PacOme-8
❑ 99PacOme-9
❑ 99PacOme-10
❑ 99PacOme-11
❑ 99PacOme-12
❑ 99PacOme-13
❑ 99PacOme-14
❑ 99PacOme-15
❑ 99PacOme-16
❑ 99PacOme-17
❑ 99PacOme-18
❑ 99PacOme-19
❑ 99PacOme-20
❑ 99PacOme-21
❑ 99PacOme5T-23
❑ 99PacOme5TT-23
❑ 99PacOmeC-202
❑ 99PacOmeDD-10
❑ 99PacOmeDM-28
❑ 99PacOmeEP-15
❑ 99PacOmeEP1o1-15
❑ 99PacOmeG-202
❑ 99PacOmePB-202
❑ 99PacPar-198
❑ 99PacPar-NNO
❑ 99PacParC-198
❑ 99PacParCB-8
❑ 99PacParCBPP-8
❑ 99PacParFC-16
❑ 99PacParG-198
❑ 99PacParHoloGold-198
❑ 99PacParHS-198
❑ 99PacParOD-198
❑ 99PacParPB-30
❑ 99PacParPB-198
❑ 99PacParRed-198
❑ 99PacParTC-25
❑ 99PacPlaB-368
❑ 99PacPlaB-368A
❑ 99PacPri-123
❑ 99PacPri-SA
❑ 99PacPri-SAH
❑ 99PacPriAotG-17
❑ 99PacPriBL-10
❑ 99PacPriDG-17
❑ 99PacPriEP-4
❑ 99PacPriHB-123
❑ 99PacPriHG-123
❑ 99PacPriHM-123
❑ 99PacPriHP-123
❑ 99PacPriRed-123
❑ 99PacPriRed-SA
❑ 99PacPriRed-SAH
❑ 99PacPriS-7
❑ 99PacPriS206-7
❑ 99PacPriS206R-7
❑ 99PacPriSE-7
❑ 99PacPriSP-7
❑ 99PacPriSP-7
❑ 99PacPriSV-7
❑ 99PacRed-368
❑ 99PacRed-368A
❑ 99PacTeaC-29
❑ 99PacTim-20
❑ 99Pin-11
❑ 99Rev-120
❑ 99RevDiaL-29
❑ 99RevFouP-17
❑ 99RevMLBIcon-8
❑ 99RevPremDate-120
❑ 99RevRet-120
❑ 99RevShaSS-120
❑ 99RevThoitS-15
❑ 99RevTri-8
❑ 99RevTri-8
❑ 99SkyMolM-141
❑ 99SkyMolMF-41
❑ 99SkyMolMFS-41
❑ 99SkyMolMFT-41
❑ 99SkyMolMX-141
❑ 99SkyPre-119
❑ 99SkyPre-277
❑ 99SkyPreA-25
❑ 99SkyPreABlue-25
❑ 99SkyPreIN-2
❑ 99SkyPreLB-10
❑ 99SkyPreR-119
❑ 99SkyPreR-277
❑ 99SkyPreSB-2
❑ 99SkyPreSotG-5
❑ 99SkyThu-255
❑ 99SkyThuRant-255
❑ 99SkyThuRave-255
❑ 99SkyThuwww-WB4
❑ 99SP Aut-70
❑ 99SP AutC-TG
❑ 99SP AutCG-TG
❑ 99SP AutEF-E24
❑ 99SP AutR-R24
❑ 99SP SigAuto-TG
❑ 99SP SigAutoG-TG
❑ 99Spolll-84
❑ 99SPSig-13
❑ 99SPx-64
❑ 99SPxDom-FB14
❑ 99SPxFinR-64
❑ 99SPxFinS-64
❑ 99SPxPreS-PS27
❑ 99SPxStaF-SF22
❑ 99SPxWinM-TG
❑ 99StaClu-126
❑ 99StaCluFDI-126
❑ 99StaCluOoaK-126
❑ 99StaCluPP-126
❑ 99StaCluTI-T1C
❑ 99StaCluTL-T1C
❑ 99StaCluTL-T1C
❑ 99ThuSkySupR-255
❑ 99Top-75
❑ 99TopBlaLC1-6
❑ 99TopBlaLC2-6
❑ 99TopBlaLC3-6
❑ 99TopChr-75
❑ 99TopChrLotD-LD12
❑ 99TopChrLotDR-LD12
❑ 99TopChrR-75
❑ 99TopGal-78
❑ 99TopGal-112
❑ 99TopGalE-E8
❑ 99TopGalHer-TH6
❑ 99TopGalHerP-TH6
❑ 99TopGalPP-78
❑ 99TopGalPP-112
❑ 99TopGalPPI-78
❑ 99TopGalPPI-112
❑ 99TopGolL-6
❑ 99TopGolLC1-6
❑ 99TopGolLC2-6
❑ 99TopGolLOtO-6
❑ 99TopLorotD-LD12
❑ 99TopMVPP-75
❑ 99TopOpeD-43
❑ 99TopRedLC1-6
❑ 99TopRedLC2-6
❑ 99TopRedLC3-6
❑ 99TopSta-48
❑ 99TopSta-162
❑ 99TopSta'S-9
❑ 99TopSta'SG-9
❑ 99TopSta'SGDH-9
❑ 99TopSta1Foil-48
❑ 99TopSta2Foil-48
❑ 99TopStaFoil-48
❑ 99TopStaFoil-162
❑ 99TopStaOS-48
❑ 99TopStaTS-48
❑ 99TopSupC-13
❑ 99TopSupCR-13
❑ 99TopTek-37A
❑ 99TopTek-37B
❑ 99TopTekG-37A
❑ 99TopTekG-37B
❑ 99UD Cho-34
❑ 99UD Cho-137
❑ 99UD ChoBUCG-5
❑ 99UD ChoMBH-B24
❑ 99UD ChoP-137
❑ 99UD ChoPCR-34
❑ 99UD ChoPCR-137
❑ 99UD ChoS-8
❑ 99UD ChoSD-8
❑ 99UD ChoSHR-8
❑ 99UD ChoST-8
❑ 99UD Ion-49
❑ 99UD Ion-84
❑ 99UD IonC-C12
❑ 99UD IonH-H12
❑ 99UD IonR-49
❑ 99UD IonR-84
❑ 99UD IonWZ-WZ12
❑ 99UDHolo-50
❑ 99UDHoloAUsome-50
❑ 99UDHoloFF-F1
❑ 99UDHoloFFG-F1
❑ 99Ult-59
❑ 99UltDamI-14
❑ 99UltGolM-59
❑ 99UltMas-59
❑ 99UltPlaM-59
❑ 99UltRBIK-13
❑ 99UltTheBook-13
❑ 99UppDec-474
❑ 99UppDec10AT-X8
❑ 99UppDec10ATD-X8
❑ 99UppDec10ATHR-X8
❑ 99UppDec10ATT-X8
❑ 99UppDecBD-69
❑ 99UppDecBDAPH-TG
❑ 99UppDecBDD-69
❑ 99UppDecBDDom-D19
❑ 99UppDecBDDomE-D19
❑ 99UppDecBDMN-M28
❑ 99UppDecBDMNE-M28
❑ 99UppDecBDQ-69
❑ 99UppDecBDT-69
❑ 99UppDecCf7-73
❑ 99UppDecCL-49
❑ 99UppDecCL-54
❑ 99UppDecCLCC-49
❑ 99UppDecCLCC-54
❑ 99UppDecCLES-TG
❑ 99UppDecCLESC-TG
❑ 99UppDecCLJotC-TG
❑ 99UppDecCLM-C79
❑ 99UppDecCo7CE-73
❑ 99UppDecE-77
❑ 99UppDecE-167
❑ 99UppDecEBPC-C-TG
❑ 99UppDecEDF-D14
❑ 99UppDecEDFFXG-D14
❑ 99UppDecEFXG-77
❑ 99UppDecEFXG-167
❑ 99UppDecEL1-474
❑ 99UppDecEL2-474
❑ 99UppDecEPE-P24
❑ 99UppDecEUR-U4
❑ 99UppDecF-F23
❑ 99UppDecFD-F23
❑ 99UppDecFQ-F23
❑ 99UppDecFT-F23
❑ 99UppDecGJ-TGW
❑ 99UppDecIP-I10
❑ 99UppDecIPD-I10
❑ 99UppDecIPHR-I10
❑ 99UppDecIPT-I10
❑ 99UppDecM-176
❑ 99UppDecMD-D9
❑ 99UppDecMGS-176
❑ 99UppDecMHFS-176
❑ 99UppDecMP-176
❑ 99UppDecMSS-176
❑ 99UppDecMST-S4
❑ 99UppDecO-55
❑ 99UppDecOAPoH-TG
❑ 99UppDecOMP-S7
❑ 99UppDecOSO-55
❑ 99UppDecOWP-R16
❑ 99UppDecR-72
❑ 99UppDecRDR-D12
❑ 99UppDecRDRL2-D12
❑ 99UppDecRG-72
❑ 99UppDecRI-TG
❑ 99UppDecRIL2-TG
❑ 99UppDecROSS-S15
❑ 99UppDecROSS-S15
❑ 99UppDecRP-72
❑ 99UppDecRTA-T15
❑ 99UppDecRTAL2-T15
❑ 99UppDecTE-T24
❑ 99UppDecTED-T24
❑ 99UppDecTEQ-T24
❑ 99UppDecTET-T24
❑ 99UppDecVtaT-V24
❑ 99UppDecVtaTD-V24
❑ 99UppDecVtaTQ-V24
❑ 99UppDecVtaTT-V24
❑ 99UppDecWY-W11
❑ 99UppDecWYD-W11
❑ 99UppDecWYHR-W11
❑ 99UppDecWYT-W11
❑ 99Vic-337
❑ 99Vic-338
❑ 99Vic-339
❑ 99Vic-464

Gyarmati, Jeff
❑ 83BelBreFr-4
❑ 89BoiHawP-1985

Gyselman, Dick
❑ 34DiaMatCSB-76
❑ 43CenFlo-11
❑ 44CenFlo-10
❑ 47PadTeal-7

Gyselman, Jeff
❑ 93BatCliCB-10
❑ 93BatCliF-3147
❑ 94BatCliC-5
❑ 94BatCliF-3448
❑ 95ClePhiF-219
❑ 96ReaPhiB-14

Haad, Yamid
❑ 97EriSeaWB-17
❑ 98LynHilQ-13

Haag, Charlie
❑ 55JetPos-5

Haag, Jeff
❑ 93WatIndC-11
❑ 93WatIndF-3564
❑ 94WatIndC-15
❑ 94WatIndF-3940

Haag, Mike
❑ 93JamExpC-28

Haaland, Bill
❑ 85RedWinA-9
❑ 86RedWinA-20

Haar, Rich
❑ 93JamExpC-8
❑ 93JamExpF-3334
❑ 94WesPalBEC-12
❑ 94WesPalBEF-49

Haas, Bert (Berthold)
❑ 46SpoExcW-5-9
❑ 47Exh-89
❑ 49EurSta-105
❑ 49GiaTeal-8
❑ 84TCMPla1-38
❑ 90DodTar-308

Haas, Bill
❑ 63Top-544
❑ 64Top-398

Haas, Bruno
❑ 78HalHalR-3

Haas, Chris
❑ 96Exc-228
❑ 96HilStaHWB-20
❑ 96PeoChiB-13
❑ 96Top-434
❑ 97PeoChi-12
❑ 98ArkTraH-6
❑ 98ArkTraM-10
❑ 99Bow-90
❑ 99BowChr-90
❑ 99BowChrG-90
❑ 99BowChrGR-90
❑ 99BowChrI-90
❑ 99BowChrIR-90
❑ 99BowChrR-90
❑ 99BowGol-90
❑ 99BowInt-90
❑ 99SP SigAuto-CHA
❑ 99SP SigAutoG-CHA
❑ 99SPSig-81
❑ 99UppDec-283
❑ 99UppDecE-126
❑ 99UppDecEFXG-126
❑ 99UppDecEL1-283
❑ 99UppDecEL2-283

Haas, Danny
❑ 97LowSpiB-29
❑ 98MicBatCM-14

Haas, Dave
❑ 87AncGlaP-16
❑ 89LakTigS-7
❑ 90LonTigP-1263
❑ 91Bow-151
❑ 91LinDriAAA-585
❑ 91TolMudHLD-585
❑ 91TolMudHP-1926
❑ 92OPC-665
❑ 92Sco-825
❑ 92SkyAAAF-262
❑ 92StaClu-362
❑ 92TolMudHF-1038
❑ 92TolMudHS-586
❑ 92Top-665
❑ 92TopDeb91-69
❑ 92TopGol-665
❑ 92TopGolW-665
❑ 92TopMic-665
❑ 93Don-335
❑ 93Sco-215
❑ 93TigGat-13
❑ 93Top-536
❑ 93TopGol-536
❑ 93TopInaM-536
❑ 93TopInaR-536
❑ 93TopMic-536
❑ 93Ult-551
❑ 93USPlaCR-8S
❑ 94Pac-221

Haas, Eddie (G. Edwin)
❑ 55DesMoiHB-8
❑ 59Top-126
❑ 59TopVen-126
❑ 75AtlBraP-16
❑ 76AtlBraP-14
❑ 79SavBraT-16
❑ 79SavBraT-18
❑ 81RicBraT-21
❑ 82RicBraT-27
❑ 83RicBraT-23
❑ 84RicBraT-27
❑ 85BraHos-1
❑ 85BraPol-22
❑ 85TopTifT-44T
❑ 85TopTra-44T

Haas, Jeff
❑ 92EugEmeC-3
❑ 92EugEmeF-3025
❑ 93RocRoyC-14
❑ 93RocRoyF-713
❑ 93StaCluM-119

Haas, Matt
❑ 94VerExpC-12
❑ 94VerExpF-3912
❑ 96WesPalBEB-18

Haas, Moose (Bryan)
❑ 75BurBeeT-10
❑ 76SpoIndC-10
❑ 78Top-649
❑ 79Top-448
❑ 80BreTeal-9
❑ 80Top-181
❑ 81Don-85
❑ 81Fle-516
❑ 81OPC-327
❑ 81Top-327
❑ 81TopSti-98
❑ 82BrePol-30
❑ 82Don-206
❑ 82Fle-143
❑ 82FleSta-139
❑ 82OPC-12
❑ 82Top-12
❑ 83BreGar-9
❑ 83BrePol-30
❑ 83Don-204
❑ 83Fle-35
❑ 83OPC-317
❑ 83Top-503
❑ 84BreGar-8
❑ 84BrePol-30
❑ 84Don-368
❑ 84Fle-202
❑ 84FleSti-61
❑ 84Nes792-271
❑ 84Nes792-726
❑ 84OPC-271
❑ 84Top-271
❑ 84Top-726
❑ 84TopRubD-22
❑ 84TopSti-292
❑ 84TopTif-271
❑ 84TopTif-726
❑ 85BreGar-8
❑ 85BrePol-30
❑ 85Don-473
❑ 85Fle-583
❑ 85OPC-151
❑ 85Top-151
❑ 85TopMin-151
❑ 85TopRubD-23
❑ 85TopSti-293
❑ 85TopTif-151
❑ 86A'sMot-16
❑ 86Don-237
❑ 86Fle-489
❑ 86FleUpd-48
❑ 86OPC-9
❑ 86Top-759
❑ 86TopSti-201
❑ 86TopTat-2
❑ 86TopTif-759
❑ 86TopTra-44T
❑ 86TopTraT-44T
❑ 87A'sSmoC-5
❑ 87Don-528
❑ 87Fle-393
❑ 87FleGlo-393
❑ 87Lea-54
❑ 87OPC-369
❑ 87Top-413
❑ 87TopTif-413
❑ 88Sco-177
❑ 88ScoGlo-177

❑ 88Top-606
❑ 88TopTif-606
❑ 92BreCarT-9
❑ 94BreMilB-33
Haas, Mule (George W.)
❑ 28PorandAR-A14
❑ 28PorandAR-B14
❑ 29A'sVil-3
❑ 31Exh-28
❑ 31W517-32
❑ 32OrbPinNP-19
❑ 32OrbPinUP-25
❑ 33ButCanV-22
❑ 33Gou-219
❑ 33RitCE-1H
❑ 33TatOrb-25
❑ 34BabRutG-30
❑ 34BatR31-170
❑ 34ButPreR-29
❑ 35AlDemDCR3-11
❑ 35GouPuzR-8B
❑ 35GouPuzR-9B
❑ 36GouWidPPR-A43
❑ 36OveCanR-22
❑ 36R31PasP-38
❑ 36SandSW-26
❑ 36WorWidGV-68
❑ 38BasTabP-15
❑ 39WhiSoxTI-5
❑ 40PlaBal-184
❑ 40WhiSoxL-6
❑ 61Fle-109
❑ 74A's192T-14
❑ 74TCMNic-7
❑ 81ConTSN-60
❑ 83A'sGreT-6
❑ 84OCoandSI-176
❑ 85BigLeaC3-77
❑ 91ConTSN-323
❑ 94ConTSN-1138
❑ 94ConTSNB-1138
Haas, Randy
❑ 75CliPilT-8
Haase, Dean
❑ 91UtiBluSC-11
❑ 91UtiBluSP-3242
❑ 92SarWhiSCB-10
❑ 92SouBenWSF-179
Haber, Dave
❑ 90EugEmeGS-11
❑ 91EugEmeC-2
❑ 91EugEmeP-3732
Haberle, Dave
❑ 83CedRapRF-11
❑ 83CedRapRT-18
❑ 84CedRapRT-28
Habetz, Alyson
❑ 95ColSilB-11
❑ 96ColSilB-13
Habyan, John
❑ 85ChaO'sT-21
❑ 86Don-45
❑ 86RocRedWP-5
❑ 87BalOriP-14
❑ 87BalOriP-15
❑ 87ClaGam-95
❑ 87Don-494
❑ 87OriFreB-54
❑ 87RocRedWP-24
❑ 87RocRedWT-4
❑ 88Don-354
❑ 88Fle-562
❑ 88FleGlo-562
❑ 88OriPos-13
❑ 88RocRedWC-6
❑ 88RocRedWGCP-9
❑ 88RocRedWP-215
❑ 88RocRedWTI-10
❑ 88Sco-353
❑ 88ScoGlo-353
❑ 88Top-153
❑ 88TopTif-153
❑ 89BalOriP-9
❑ 90CMC-203
❑ 90ColCliC-3
❑ 90ColCliP-16
❑ 90ColCliP-671
❑ 90ProAAAF-321
❑ 90TopTVY-44
❑ 91Bow-167
❑ 91FleUpd-42
❑ 91Lea-480
❑ 91OriCro-171
❑ 91StaClu-590
❑ 91UltUpd-40
❑ 92Don-32
❑ 92Fle-228
❑ 92Lea-189
❑ 92LeaBlaG-189
❑ 92OPC-698
❑ 92Pin-433
❑ 92Sco-451
❑ 92StaClu-576
❑ 92Top-698
❑ 92TopGol-698
❑ 92TopGolW-698
❑ 92TopMic-698
❑ 92TriPla-228
❑ 93Don-107
❑ 93Fle-277
❑ 93Lea-162
❑ 93PacSpa-205
❑ 93Pin-409
❑ 93Sco-459
❑ 93StaClu-383
❑ 93StaCluFDI-383
❑ 93StaCluMOP-383
❑ 93Top-86
❑ 93TopGol-86
❑ 93TopInaM-86
❑ 93TopInaR-86
❑ 93TopMic-86
❑ 93Ult-241
❑ 93UppDec-719
❑ 93UppDecGold-719
❑ 93YanStaC-20
❑ 94Don-562
❑ 94Fle-158
❑ 94FleUpd-179
❑ 94Pac-285
❑ 94Sco-294
❑ 94ScoGolR-294
❑ 94StaClu-618
❑ 94StaCluFDI-618
❑ 94StaCluGR-618
❑ 94StaCluMOP-618
❑ 94StaCluT-325
❑ 94StaCluTFDI-325
❑ 94Top-614
❑ 94TopGol-614
❑ 94TopSpa-614
❑ 95Fle-498
❑ 95FleUpd-158
Hacen, Abraham
❑ 96BluOriB-14
❑ 97DelSho-18
❑ 98FreKeyM-9
Hack, Stan
❑ 32CubTeal-9
❑ 34BatR31-137
❑ 34DiaMatCSB-77
❑ 34DiaStaR-34
❑ 34DiaStaR-107
❑ 35DiaMatCS3T1-64
❑ 36CubTeal-12
❑ 36DiaMatCS3T2-12
❑ 36NatChiFPR-37
❑ 36R31PasP-29
❑ 36R31PasP-31
❑ 36SandSW-27
❑ 36WorWidGV-105
❑ 38CloFotW-33
❑ 39CubTeal-9
❑ 40WheM4-12
❑ 41CubTeal-8
❑ 41DouPlaR-3
❑ 41DouPlaR-97
❑ 41WheM5-21
❑ 42CubTeal-7
❑ 43CubTeal-9
❑ 43MPR302-1-13
❑ 47TipTop-107
❑ 50CubGreB-7
❑ 52MotCoo-60
❑ 53MotCoo-49
❑ 54Wil-8
❑ 55Top-6
❑ 55TopDouH-23
❑ 55TopTesS-3
❑ 61Fle-110
❑ 72TCMthe3-111
❑ 75ShaPiz-18
❑ 76TayBow4-90
❑ 77GalGloG-78
❑ 80PacLeg-83
❑ 83TCMPla1942-40
❑ 83TCMPla1945-24
❑ 84CubBriPC-10C
❑ 85BigLeaC3-4
❑ 91ConTSN-126
❑ 92CubOldS-10
Hacker, Rich
❑ 86CarTeal-14
❑ 87CarTeal-10
❑ 88CarTeal-9
❑ 89CarTeal-10
❑ 90TopTVCa-3
❑ 91BluJayFS-12
❑ 91BluJayFS-13
❑ 93BluJayFS-13
Hacker, Steve
❑ 96FugEmeB-10
❑ 97MacBra-14
❑ 98ForMyeMTI-14
Hacker, Warren
❑ 51Bow-318
❑ 52StaCalL-80G
❑ 52Top-324
❑ 53BowC-144
❑ 53DixLid-7
❑ 53DixPre-7
❑ 53NorBreL-10
❑ 53RedMan-NL23
❑ 54Bow-125
❑ 55Bow-8
❑ 56Top-282
❑ 57Kah-13
❑ 57RedSoh-8
❑ 57Top-370
❑ 58Top-251
❑ 83TopRep5-324
Hackett, Jason
❑ 96BluOriB-15
Hackett, John
❑ 86EriCarP-11
Hackett, Tom
❑ 52LaPat-6
❑ 52LavPro-108
Hackman, Luther
❑ 95AshTouTI-22
❑ 96MauStiHWB-25
❑ 96SalAvaB-12
❑ 97EasLeaTPB-18
❑ 97NewHavRB-19
❑ 97SalAva-U5
❑ 98NewHavRM-11
❑ 98NewHavRMA-11
Hacopian, Derek
❑ 92ClaDraP-96
❑ 92WatIndC-24
❑ 92WatIndF-3252
❑ 93ColRedC-1
❑ 93ColRedF-611
❑ 93SouAtlLAGF-13
❑ 94ClaGolF-44
❑ 94ExcFS7-44
❑ 94KinIndC-6
❑ 94KinIndF-2656
❑ 95BelBreTI-12
❑ 95Bes-22
❑ 95MidLeaA-20
❑ 96BesAutSA-25
Haddan, Russell
❑ 91SydWavF-17
Haddix, Harvey
❑ 53CarHunW-8
❑ 53Top-273
❑ 54CarHunW-7
❑ 54Top-9
❑ 55ArmCoi-8
❑ 55CarHunW-7
❑ 55Top-43
❑ 55TopDouH-41
❑ 55TopTesS-4
❑ 56Top-77
❑ 56TopHocF-A6
❑ 56TopHocF-B8
❑ 56TopPin-47
❑ 57Top-265
❑ 58Kah-12
❑ 58RedEnq-15
❑ 58RedJayP-6
❑ 58Top-118
❑ 59Kah-13
❑ 59Top-184
❑ 59TopVen-184
❑ 60Kah-12
❑ 60KeyChal-23
❑ 60NuHi-9
❑ 60PirJayP-7
❑ 60Top-340
❑ 61Kah-17
❑ 61NuSco-478
❑ 61Pos-134
❑ 61Top-100
❑ 61Top-410
❑ 61TopMagR-33
❑ 62Jel-180
❑ 62Kah-16
❑ 62Pos-180
❑ 62PosCan-180
❑ 62Top-67
❑ 62TopVen-67
❑ 63Kah-14
❑ 63PirIDL-11
❑ 63PirJayP-7
❑ 63Top-239
❑ 64BalOriP-15
❑ 64Top-439
❑ 65OPC-67
❑ 65Top-67
❑ 76LauDiaJ-31
❑ 76SSP-623
❑ 77GalGloG-241
❑ 77PirTCM1WC-20
❑ 78IndTeal-13
❑ 79DiaGre-171
❑ 79TCM50-39
❑ 82Don-651
❑ 82OhiHaloF-46
❑ 87SpoRea-33
❑ 88PacLegI-11
❑ 89SweBasG-13
❑ 90HOFStiB-57
❑ 90SweBasG-73
❑ 91OriCro-172
❑ 91TopArc1-273
❑ 92ActPacA-63
❑ 92BazQua5A-19
❑ 93TedWil-75
❑ 93UppDecAH-61
❑ 94TopArc1-9
❑ 94TopArc1G-9
❑ 94UppDecAH-12
❑ 94UppDecAH-81
❑ 94UppDecAH1-12
❑ 94UppDecAH1-81
Haddock, Darren
❑ 91BenBucCB-7
❑ 91BenBucP-3692
Haddock, George
❑ 87OldJudN-218
❑ 95May-13A
❑ 95May-13B
Haden, Paris
❑ 90HagSunB-11
Hadley, Bump (Irving)
❑ 29PorandAR-34
❑ 31SenTealPW-12
❑ 32OrbPinNP-24
❑ 32OrbPinUP-26
❑ 33Gou-140
❑ 33TatOrb-26
❑ 34DiaMatCSB-78
❑ 34ExhFou-15
❑ 34GouCanV-15
❑ 35DiaMatCS3T1-65
❑ 35GouPuzR-1C
❑ 35GouPuzR-2C
❑ 35GouPuzR-16C
❑ 35GouPuzR-17C
❑ 38CloFotW-34
❑ 38GouHeaU-251
❑ 38GouHeaU-275
❑ 38OurNatGPP-14
❑ 61Fle-111
❑ 74CapPub-57
❑ 75YanDyn1T-20
❑ 92ConTSN-508
❑ 93DiaStaES-131
Hadley, Kent
❑ 56A'sPos-24
❑ 59Top-127
❑ 59TopVen-127
❑ 60Lea-135
❑ 60Top-102
❑ 60TopVen-102
❑ 61UniOil-SD3
❑ 92YanWIZ6-50
Haeberle, Kevin
❑ 89IdaFalBP-2037
❑ 90SumBraB-27
❑ 90SumBraP-2427
Haefner, Mickey
❑ 47SenGunBP-4
❑ 49Bow-144
❑ 50Bow-183
❑ 83TCMPla1944-22
Haeger, Greg
❑ 90BriTigP-3159
❑ 90BriTigS-8
❑ 91FayGenC-3
❑ 91FayGenP-1164
❑ 92FayGenC-9
❑ 92FayGenF-2163
Haen, Dennis
❑ 98BriWhiSQ-4
Haeussinger, Jason
❑ 96CliLumKTI-13
❑ 97CliLumG-9
❑ 98MobBayBTI-12
Hafer, Jeff
❑ 97CapCitB-4
❑ 98St.LucMM-23
Hafey, Bud (Daniel A.)
❑ 32Zee-35
❑ 33Zee-25
❑ 33Zee-87
❑ 34BatR31-163
❑ 79DiaGre-366
Hafey, Chick (Charles J.)
❑ 27MidBre-9
❑ 28StaPlaCE-32
❑ 29ExhFou-16
❑ 29PorandAR-35
❑ 30SchR33-5
❑ 31CarMet-13
❑ 31Exh-16
❑ 31W517-29
❑ 32OrbPinUP-27
❑ 32USCar*-8
❑ 33ButCanV-23
❑ 33DelR33-19
❑ 33ExhFou-4
❑ 33GeoCMil-18
❑ 33NatLeaAC-10
❑ 33RitCE-2D
❑ 33TatOrb-27
❑ 33TatOrbSDR-207
❑ 33WorCig-6
❑ 34BabRutG-31
❑ 34BatR31-16
❑ 34ButPreR-30
❑ 34DiaMatCSB-79
❑ 34DiaStaR-18
❑ 34ExhFou-4
❑ 34Gou-34
❑ 34GouCanV-78
❑ 35DiaMatCS2-8
❑ 35ExhFou-4
❑ 36WorWidGV-94
❑ 61Fle-39
❑ 66CarCoi-6
❑ 72TCMthe3-34
❑ 74Bra193NLA-10
❑ 76RowExh-8
❑ 76ShaPiz-121
❑ 77BobParHoF-25
❑ 77GalGloG-217
❑ 80PacLeg-116
❑ 80PerHaloFP-121
❑ 80SSPHOF-121
❑ 82TCMGreH-35
❑ 83BigLeaCOA-32
❑ 83CarGreT-6
❑ 83ConMar-42
❑ 87ConSer2-14
❑ 88ConNatA-10
❑ 89HOFStiB-34
❑ 91ConTSN-33
❑ 91ConTSN-259
❑ 92CarMcD-11
❑ 92ConTSN-657
❑ 93ConTSN-677
❑ 93ConTSN-889
Hafey, Tom
❑ 46RemBre-12
❑ 47RemBre-11
❑ 47SigOil-46
❑ 47SmiClo-18
❑ 48AngTeal-12
❑ 48SmiClo-12
❑ 74TCMNic-28
❑ 96Bro194F-27
Hafey, Will
❑ 47RemBre-16
❑ 47SmiClo-19
❑ 48SigOil-9
❑ 48SmiClo-3
Haffley, Jay
❑ 90WicStaSGD-15
Haffner, Les
❑ 90QuaCitAGS-11
Hafner, Frank
❑ 87OldJudN-219
Hafner, Travis
❑ 98SavSanGM-13
Hagan, Danny
❑ 93PriRedC-13
❑ 93PriRedF-4173
❑ 94ChaWheC-12
❑ 94ChaWheF-2696
Hage, Tom
❑ 98BluOriQ-20
Hageman, Kurt
❑ 12T207-72
Hagemann, Tim
❑ 80CliGiaT-9
Hagen, Kevin
❑ 81ArkTraT-16
❑ 82ArkTraT-2
❑ 83LouRedR-6
❑ 84LouRedR-11
❑ 84Nes792-337
❑ 84Top-337
❑ 84TopTif-337
❑ 85LouRedR-7
❑ 86MaiGuiP-10
❑ 87PorBeaP-13
❑ 87TucTorP-17
❑ 88TucTorC-5
❑ 88TucTorJP-12
❑ 88TucTorP-180
Hagerman, Zeriah
❑ 13Zee-58
❑ 16Zee-51
Hagermann, Ken
❑ 79ElmPioRST-3
Haggas, Josh
❑ 92GulCoaMF-3490
❑ 93PitMetC-8
❑ 93PitMetF-3715
Hagge, Kirk
❑ 94BriTigF-3511
Haggerty, Roger
❑ 86ElmPioRSP-7
❑ 87WinHavRSP-26
❑ 88WinHavRSS-9
❑ 89LynRedSS-26
Haggins, Ray
❑ 93NegLeaRL2-14
Hagins, Steve
❑ 97ButCopKB-9
❑ 97ButCopKK-9
❑ 98LakElsSG-15
Haglund, Scott
❑ 97MicBatC-4
Hagman, Keith
❑ 81DurBulT-9
❑ 82DurBulT-2
Hague, Joe
❑ 69Top-559
❑ 70CarTeal-14
❑ 70OPC-362
❑ 70Top-362
❑ 71CarTeal-12
❑ 71CarTeal-20
❑ 71MLBOffS-274
❑ 71OPC-96
❑ 71Top-96
❑ 71TopCoi-139
❑ 72Top-546
❑ 73OPC-447
❑ 73Top-447
❑ 81TCM60I-427
Hagy, Gary
❑ 91BoiHawC-19
❑ 91BoiHawP-3886
❑ 92MidLeaATI-14
❑ 92QuaCitRBC-22
❑ 92QuaCitRBF-818
❑ 93PalSprAC-9
❑ 93PalSprAF-77
❑ 95KinIndTI-13
❑ 96KenIndB-10
Hahn, Brent
❑ 90SalSpuCLC-134
❑ 90SalSpuP-2725
Hahn, Don
❑ 71ExpPS-9
❑ 71MLBOffS-129
❑ 71OPC-94
❑ 71Top-94
❑ 72OPC-269
❑ 72Top-269
❑ 74OPC-291
❑ 74Top-291
❑ 75OPC-182
❑ 75Top-182
❑ 75TopMin-182
❑ 76PhoGiaVNB-8
❑ 77PhoGiaCC-7
❑ 77PhoGiaCP-6
❑ 77PhoGiaVNB-7

❑ 91MetWIZ-155
Hahn, Ed
❑ 09T206-150
❑ 10ChiE-15
❑ 11PinT-5-767
❑ 11SpoLifCW-151
❑ 11SpoLifM-24
❑ 12ColTinT-122
Hahn, Eric
❑ 87SavCarP-5
Hahn, Noodles (Frank)
❑ 03BreE10-62
❑ 09ColChiE-122
❑ 11SpoLifCW-152
❑ 12ColRedB-122
❑ 76RedParC-14
❑ 82OhiHaloF-47
Hahn, Willie
❑ 87OldJudN-220
Haid, Harold
❑ 33Zee-57
❑ 33Zee-156
❑ 34DiaMatCSB-80
❑ 37Zee-34
Haigler, Phil
❑ 97ForMyeM-12
Hailey, Freddie (Fred)
❑ 87OneYanP-15
❑ 88Ft.LauYS-11
❑ 89Ft.LauYS-8
❑ 90AlbYanB-20
❑ 90AlbYanP-1044
❑ 90AlbYanSt-6
Hailey, Roger
❑ 88PulBraP-1766
❑ 89PulBraP-1907
❑ 90Bes-160
❑ 90CMC-728
❑ 90ProAaA-93
❑ 90SouAtlLAS-31
❑ 90SumBraB-4
❑ 90SumBraP-2428
❑ 91DurBulP-1539
❑ 92DurBulF-1093
❑ 92DurBulTI-32
Hain, Bill
❑ 60HenHouW-6
❑ 60UniOil-7
❑ 61TacBan-9
Haines, Abner (Allan)
❑ 80GleFalWSBT-27
❑ 80GleFalWSCT-22
Haines, Dennis
❑ 77SanJosMC-11
❑ 79OgdA'sT-8
Haines, Jesse
❑ 21E121So1-38
❑ 21Exh-66
❑ 21Nei-103
❑ 22E120-230
❑ 22W573-55
❑ 22W575-51
❑ 23W501-76
❑ 23WilChoV-57
❑ 27MidBre-10
❑ 27YorCarE-30
❑ 28StaPlaCE-33
❑ 28W513-78
❑ 28W56PlaC-S10
❑ 29PorandAR-36
❑ 31CarMet-14
❑ 32OrbPinUP-28
❑ 33Gou-73
❑ 33TatOrb-28
❑ 34DiaMatCSB-81
❑ 34GouCanV-44
❑ 36WorWidGV-93
❑ 40PlaBal-227
❑ 61Fle-40
❑ 66CarCoi-8
❑ 72TCMthe3-35
❑ 74Car193T-13
❑ 76RowExh-3
❑ 76ShaPiz-118
❑ 77BobParHoF-90
❑ 77GalGloG-125
❑ 80PerHaloFP-118
❑ 80SSPHOF-118
❑ 82OhiHaloF-6
❑ 89PacLegI-208
❑ 91ConTSN-43
❑ 92CarMcD-17
❑ 92ConTSN-358
❑ 92ConTSN-647
❑ 93ConTSN-768
❑ 93DiaStaES-132
Haines, Michael
❑ 86JamExpP-11
Hainline, Jeff
❑ 88ButCopKSP-25
Hairston, Jason
❑ 97DanBraB-19
❑ 98MacBraM-11
Hairston, Jerry
❑ 74OPC-96
❑ 74Top-96
❑ 75OPC-327
❑ 75Top-327
❑ 75TopMin-327
❑ 76OPC-391
❑ 76SSP-153
❑ 76Top-391
❑ 83Don-616
❑ 83Fle-236
❑ 83Top-487
❑ 83WhiSoxTV-17
❑ 84Don-86
❑ 84Fle-60
❑ 84Nes792-177
❑ 84Top-177
❑ 84TopTif-177
❑ 84WhiSoxTV-15
❑ 85Don-135
❑ 85Fle-515
❑ 85Top-596
❑ 85TopTif-596
❑ 85WhiSoxC-17
❑ 86Don-424
❑ 86Fle-207
❑ 86Top-778
❑ 86TopTif-778
❑ 86WhiSoxC-17
❑ 87Don-285
❑ 87Fle-498
❑ 87FleGlo-498
❑ 87OPC-299
❑ 87Top-685
❑ 87TopTif-685
❑ 87WhiSoxC-13
❑ 88Don-285
❑ 88StaLinWS-9
❑ 88Top-281
❑ 88TopTif-281
Hairston, Jerry Jr.
❑ 98AriFalLTP-18
❑ 98CarLeaAC-12
❑ 98CarLeaTPQ-31
❑ 98FleUpd-U32
❑ 98FreKeyM-25
❑ 99BasAmeTP-48
❑ 99BasAmeTPG-48
❑ 99BowAut-BA5
❑ 99Fle-207
❑ 99FleSta9-207
❑ 99FleWarT-207
❑ 99PacOme-34
❑ 99PacOmeC-34
❑ 99PacOmeG-34
❑ 99PacOmePB-34
❑ 99SkyThu-184
❑ 99SkyThuRant-184
❑ 99SkyThuRave-184
❑ 99SP SigAuto-JHJ
❑ 99SP SigAutoG-JHJ
❑ 99StaClu-148
❑ 99StaCluFDI-148
❑ 99StaCluOoaK-148
❑ 99StaCluPP-148
❑ 99ThuSkySupR-184
❑ 99Top-426
❑ 99TopChr-426
❑ 99TopChrR-426
❑ 99TopMVPP-426
❑ 99UppDec-289
❑ 99UppDecEL1-289
❑ 99UppDecEL2-289
❑ 99UppDecM-30
❑ 99UppDecMGS-30
❑ 99UppDecMHFS-30
❑ 99UppDecMSS-30
❑ 99Vic-43
❑ 99Bow-299
❑ 99BowGol-299
❑ 99BowInt-299
❑ 99SPSig-55
❑ 99UppDecE-132
❑ 99UppDecEFXG-132
Hairston, John
❑ 90SouBenWSB-3
❑ 90SouBenWSGS-5
❑ 91SouBenWSC-8
❑ 91SouBenWSP-2863
Hairston, Rodd
❑ 91BurIndP-3308
Hairston, Sam Sr.
❑ 86BirBarTI-26
❑ 87BirBarB-2
❑ 87NegLeaPD-1
❑ 89BirBarB-29
❑ 89BirBarP-112
❑ 90BirBarB-26
❑ 90BirBarP-1398
❑ 91BirBarP-1470
❑ 91LinDriAA-75
❑ 94BirBarC-29
❑ 94BirBarF-640
❑ 97BirBarB-27
❑ 97NegLeaPC-2H
Hajeck, David
❑ 90AshTouP-2754
❑ 90CMC-675
❑ 90ProAaA-102
❑ 90SouAtlLAS-10
❑ 91OscAstC-18
❑ 91OscAstP-692
❑ 92JacGenF-4003
❑ 93JacGenF-2113
❑ 94TucTorF-767
❑ 95TucTotTI-9
❑ 96TusTorB-10
❑ 97TolMudHB-16
❑ 98Las-11
Haku, Jinten
❑ 79TCMJapPB-2
Halama, John
❑ 94AubAstC-5
❑ 94AubAstF-3752
❑ 95QuaCitRBTI-8
❑ 96JacGenB-10
❑ 98Bow-332
❑ 98BowChr-332
❑ 98BowChrGA-332
❑ 98BowChrGAR-332
❑ 98BowChrI-332
❑ 98BowChrIR-332
❑ 98BowChrR-332
❑ 98BowGolA-332
❑ 98BowInt-332
❑ 98Don-341
❑ 98DonGolPP-341
❑ 98DonSilPP-341
❑ 98Fle-480
❑ 98LeaRS-219
❑ 98LeaRSLHolo-219
❑ 98LeaRSLong-219
❑ 98LeaRTrue-219
❑ 98NewOrlZM-7
❑ 98PacAur-139
❑ 98PacOme-108
❑ 98PacOmeR-108
❑ 98PacOmeRS-17
❑ 98PacOmeRST3-17
❑ 98PacOnl-322
❑ 98PacOnlR-322
❑ 98PacOnlWC-322
❑ 98Ult-338
❑ 98UltGolM-338
❑ 98UltMas-338
❑ 98UltPlaM-338
❑ 99PacOme-221
❑ 99PacOmeC-221
❑ 99PacOmeG-221
❑ 99PacOmePB-221
Halama, Scott
❑ 87EriCarP-22
❑ 88HamRedP-1720
❑ 89JohCitCS-14
Halberg, Eric
❑ 83CliGiaF-2
Halcovich, Frank
❑ 87AriWilP-4
❑ 88AriWilP-4
Halderman, Gerlach
❑ 90IBAWorA-25
Hale, Bob
❑ 56BalOriP-17
❑ 56BalOriP-21
❑ 56Top-231
❑ 57Top-406
❑ 59Top-507
❑ 60Top-309
❑ 61Top-532
❑ 61Yan61RL-28
❑ 79TCM50-129
❑ 91OriCro-173
❑ 91YanRinP13-3
❑ 92YanWIZ6-51
❑ 97BalOriP-21
Hale, Chad
❑ 95MicBatCTI-14
❑ 96SarRedSB-18
❑ 97KisCob-12
Hale, Chip
❑ 84AriWilP-7
❑ 86AriWilP-3
❑ 87AriWilP-5
❑ 88OrlTwiB-18
❑ 89PorBeaC-24
❑ 89PorBeaP-208
❑ 90CMC-571
❑ 90Don-690
❑ 90OPC-704
❑ 90PorBeaC-19
❑ 90PorBeaP-183
❑ 90ProAAAF-253
❑ 90Sco-588
❑ 90Sco100RS-98
❑ 90Spo-223
❑ 90Top-704
❑ 90TopDeb89-50
❑ 90TopTif-704
❑ 90UppDec-475
❑ 91LinDriAAA-409
❑ 91PorBeaLD-409
❑ 91PorBeaP-1570
❑ 91Sco100RS-39
❑ 92PorBeaF-2673
❑ 92PorBeaS-408
❑ 93FleFinE-236
❑ 93PorBeaF-2387
❑ 93SelRoo-74T
❑ 94ColC-573
❑ 94ColChoGS-573
❑ 94ColChoSS-573
❑ 94Don-168
❑ 94Fle-205
❑ 94Lea-115
❑ 94Pac-353
❑ 94Sco-609
❑ 94ScoGolR-609
❑ 94Sel-162
❑ 94StaClu-501
❑ 94StaCluFDI-501
❑ 94StaCluGR-501
❑ 94StaCluMOP-501
❑ 94Top-583
❑ 94TopGol-583
❑ 94TopSpa-583
❑ 95Don-467
❑ 95DonPreP-467
❑ 95Fle-203
❑ 95LinVen-103
❑ 95Sco-490
❑ 95ScoGolR-490
❑ 95ScoPlaTS-490
❑ 96FleUpd-U52
❑ 96FleUpdTC-U52
❑ 96LeaSigEA-68
❑ 97DodMot-12
❑ 97DodPol-12
❑ 98MemRedG-6
Hale, Dad (Ray Luther)
❑ 08RosComP-2
Hale, Dan
❑ 86GreHorP-10
❑ 87GreHorP-20
Hale, DeMarlo
❑ 86NewBriRSP-12
❑ 88HunStaTI-5
❑ 88MadMusP-13
❑ 92NewBriRSS-500
❑ 93ForLauRSC-27
❑ 93ForLauRSFP-1613
❑ 94SarRedSC-29
❑ 94SarRedSF-1968
❑ 96HilStaHWB-34
❑ 96SarRedSB-1
❑ 97TexAllM-2
❑ 97TreThuB-1
❑ 98TreThuM-1
Hale, John
❑ 75AlbDukCa-5
❑ 76OPC-228
❑ 76Top-228
❑ 77MarPos-6
❑ 77Top-253
❑ 78Top-584
❑ 79OPC-23
❑ 79Top-56
❑ 80IndIndTI-6
❑ 80VenLeaS-178
❑ 81RocRedWT-6
❑ 81RocRedWW-18
❑ 90DodTar-309
Hale, Mark
❑ 72CedRapCT-2
Hale, Mark A.
❑ 96ButCopKB-14
❑ 97ChaRivDG-15
Hale, Odell (A. Odell)
❑ 34BatR31-112
❑ 34DiaMatCSB-82
❑ 35DiaMatCS3T1-66
❑ 36GouWidPPR-A44
❑ 36NatChiFPR-38
❑ 36WheBB5-8
❑ 37OPCBatUV-128
❑ 38ExhFou-11
❑ 40PlaBal-203
❑ 74TCMNic-14
❑ 81ConTSN-55
❑ 92ConTSN-415
❑ 93DiaStaES-133
Hale, Sammy (Samuel)
❑ 21Zee-49
❑ 25Exh-108
❑ 29ExhFou-28
❑ 31W517-44
❑ 31Zee-66
❑ 74A's192T-15
❑ 81ConTSN-56
❑ 91ConTSN-293
❑ 94ConTSN-1155
❑ 94ConTSNB-1155
Hale, Shane
❑ 91FreKeyC-3
❑ 91FreKeyP-2357
❑ 94AlbPolC-14
❑ 94AlbPolF-2232
❑ 94OriPro-43
❑ 96BowBayB-16
Halemanu, Josh
❑ 94AubAstC-6
❑ 94AubAstF-3765
❑ 95AubAstTI-7
Haley, Bart
❑ 86ElmPioRSP-8
❑ 87WinHavRSP-6
❑ 88LynRedSS-8
❑ 89LynRedSS-10
Haley, Bill
❑ 78GreBraT-11
Haley, Bo
❑ 94PitMetC-10
❑ 94PitMetF-3527
Haley, Mark
❑ 85AncGlaPTI-13
❑ 91SouBenWSC-23
❑ 91SouBenWSP-2875
❑ 92SouBenWSC-25
❑ 92SouBenWSF-195
❑ 93NasSouF-584
❑ 94HicCraC-28
❑ 94HicCraF-2194
❑ 96PriWilCB-3
❑ 98HicCraM-1
❑ 98HicCraUO-1
Haley, Rich
❑ 93YakBeaC-11
❑ 93YakBeaF-3895
Haley, Ryan
❑ 91NiaFalRC-5
❑ 91NiaFalRP-3635
Haley, Sam
❑ 83WauTimF-23
❑ 86WesPalBEP-19
Halicki, Ed
❑ 72GiaTeal-9
❑ 75OPC-467
❑ 75Top-467
❑ 75TopMin-467
❑ 76OPC-423
❑ 76SanFraGP-7
❑ 76Top-423
❑ 77Gia-8
❑ 77GiaTeal-10
❑ 77Top-343
❑ 78GiaTeal-8
❑ 78Hos-12
❑ 78Top-107
❑ 79GiaPol-28
❑ 79OPC-354
❑ 79Top-672
❑ 80GiaPol-28
❑ 80GiaTeal-7
❑ 80OPC-115
❑ 80Top-217
❑ 81Don-53
❑ 81Top-69
❑ 89PacSenL-74
Halicki, Kevin
❑ 82RedPioT-4
Hall, Albert
❑ 82RicBraT-19
❑ 82RicBraT-31
❑ 83RicBraT-18
❑ 85BraHos-10
❑ 85BraPol-2
❑ 85Fle-326
❑ 85Top-676
❑ 85TopTif-676
❑ 86RicBraP-8
❑ 87BraSmo-25
❑ 87FleUpd-39
❑ 87FleUpdG-39
❑ 87TopTra-41T
❑ 87TopTraT-41T
❑ 88Don-290
❑ 88DonBasB-253
❑ 88Fle-541
❑ 88FleGlo-541
❑ 88OPC-213
❑ 88PanSti-249
❑ 88Sco-148
❑ 88ScoGlo-148
❑ 88StaLinBra-8
❑ 88Top-213
❑ 88Top-549
❑ 88TopSti-39
❑ 88TopTif-213
❑ 88TopTif-549
❑ 89BlaYNPRWL-156
❑ 89BlaYNPRWLU-60
❑ 89BlaYNPRWLU-63
❑ 89Fle-593
❑ 89FleGlo-593
❑ 89OPC-153
❑ 89Sco-74
❑ 89Top-433
❑ 89TopBig-104
❑ 89TopSti-30
❑ 89TopTif-433
❑ 89UppDec-93
Hall, Andy
❑ 86MacPirP-11
❑ 86TriTriC-198
❑ 88CarLeaAS-8
❑ 88SalBucS-7
❑ 89BufBisC-10
❑ 89BufBisP-1672
❑ 89HarSenS-8
❑ 90MidAngGS-21
❑ 95NewJerCTI-11
❑ 96MidLeaAB-19
❑ 96PeoChiB-14
❑ 97PriWilC-13
Hall, Bert
❑ 09ObaT21-194
❑ 09ObaT21-227
Hall, Bill (William B.)
❑ 90DodTar-967
Hall, Bill (William Lemuel)
❑ 59Top-49
❑ 59TopVen-49
Hall, Billy
❑ 90WicStaSGD-16
❑ 92CalLeaACL-39
❑ 92HigDesMC-7
❑ 92UppDecML-285
❑ 93Bow-306
❑ 93ClaFS7-276
❑ 93ClaGolF-57
❑ 93WicWraF-2984
❑ 94ExcFS7-281
❑ 94UppDec-175
❑ 94UppDecED-175
❑ 94UppDecML-35
❑ 94WicWraF-197
❑ 95MidLeaA-21
❑ 95QuaCitRBTI-9
❑ 96ChaLooB-14
❑ 96KisCobB-10
❑ 97ChaLoo-11
❑ 97KisCob-13
Hall, Bob
❑ 49EurSta-10
❑ 54SeaPop-10
❑ 55Bow-113
❑ 90DodTar-1103
Hall, Carl
❑ 90WicStaSGD-17
❑ 94VerExpC-13
❑ 94VerExpF-3921

Hall, Charles Louis
❑ 09AmeCarE90-1-48
❑ 11SpoLifCW-153
❑ 11SpoLifM-9
❑ 12T207-73
❑ 17Zee-9
Hall, Chris
❑ 89BriTigS-11
❑ 90BriTigP-3155
❑ 90BriTigS-9
Hall, Darren
❑ 87MyrBeaBJP-1438
❑ 88DunBluJS-8
❑ 89DunBluJS-6
❑ 90KnoBluJB-21
❑ 90KnoBluJP-1244
❑ 90KnoBluJS-4
❑ 91KnoBluJLD-358
❑ 91KnoBluJP-1762
❑ 91LinDriAA-358
❑ 92ProFS7-165
❑ 92SyrChiF-1961
❑ 92SyrChiMB-7
❑ 92SyrChiS-507
❑ 93PriRedC-14
❑ 93PriRedF-4194
❑ 93SyrChiF-995
❑ 94Bow-85
❑ 94FleUpd-99
❑ 94LeaLimR-58
❑ 94PriRedC-11
❑ 94PriRedF-3276
❑ 94TopTra-26T
❑ 95BluJayOH-17
❑ 95ColCho-141
❑ 95ColChoGS-141
❑ 95ColChoSS-141
❑ 95Don-81
❑ 95DonPreP-81
❑ 95Fle-96
❑ 95FleRooS-6
❑ 95Lea-131
❑ 95Pac-446
❑ 95StaClu-466
❑ 95StaCluMOP-466
❑ 95StaCluSTWS-466
❑ 95Top-174
❑ 95Ult-120
❑ 95UltGolM-120
❑ 95UltSecYS-4
❑ 95UltSecYSGM-4
❑ 96ColCho-354
❑ 96ColChoGS-354
❑ 96ColChoSS-354
❑ 96DodMot-24
❑ 96DodPol-16
❑ 96LeaSigEA-69
❑ 97DodMot-24
❑ 97DodPol-13
❑ 98DodMot-24
❑ 98DodPol-9
❑ 98PacOnl-370
❑ 98PacOnlR-370
❑ 98PacOnlWC-370
Hall, Dave
❑ 62SeaPop-1
❑ 63MilSau-1
❑ 63SeaPop-2
❑ 81CedRapRT-26
❑ 82CedRapRT-19
❑ 83TamTarT-14
Hall, Dean
❑ 78NewWayCT-18
Hall, Doug
❑ 97RocCub-16
Hall, Drew
❑ 86PitCubP-8
❑ 87Don-594
❑ 87IowCubTI-2
❑ 88DonTeaBC-NEW
❑ 88Top-262
❑ 88TopTif-262
❑ 89Bow-221
❑ 89BowTif-221
❑ 89Don-522
❑ 89Fle-643
❑ 89FleGlo-643
❑ 89OklCit8P-1517
❑ 89RanSmo-12
❑ 89Top-593
❑ 89TopTif-593
❑ 89UppDec-324
❑ 90ExpPos-15
❑ 90Fle-299
❑ 90FleCan-299
❑ 90Lea-423
❑ 90OPC-463
❑ 90Sco-516
❑ 90Top-463
❑ 90TopTif-463
❑ 90UppDec-631
❑ 91Fle-236
❑ 91OPC-77
❑ 91Sco-581
❑ 91Top-77
❑ 91TopDesS-77
❑ 91TopMic-77
❑ 91TopTif-77
❑ 93RanKee-168
❑ 93ScrRedBTI-11
Hall, F. F.
❑ 17Zee-90
Hall, Gardner C. (Grady)
❑ 87BirBarB-14
❑ 88VanCanC-8
❑ 88VanCanP-761
❑ 89BirBarB-11
❑ 89BirBarP-108
❑ 89Fle-650
❑ 89FleGlo-650
❑ 90CMC-633
❑ 90ProAAAF-162
❑ 90VanCanC-6
❑ 90VanCanP-484
❑ 91LinDriAAA-632
❑ 91VanCanLD-632
❑ 91VanCanP-1589
❑ 92AlbDukF-713
Hall, Greg
❑ 85SpoIndC-6
❑ 87ChaRaiP-5
❑ 88RivRedWCLC-219
❑ 88RivRedWP-1415
❑ 89RivRedWB-26
❑ 89RivRedWCLC-6
❑ 89RivRedWP-1397
❑ 89SpoIndSP-8
Hall, Halsey
❑ 78HalHalR-1
Hall, Herbert
❑ 15Zee-79
❑ 16Zee-79
Hall, Irv
❑ 43A'STEAI-12
❑ 45A'sTeal-16
❑ 83TCMPla1944-15
Hall, Jeff
❑ 80ElmPioRST-11
Hall, Jimmie
❑ 63TwiVol-8
❑ 64Top-73
❑ 64TopCoi-16
❑ 64TopSta-3
❑ 64TopVen-73
❑ 64TwiJayP-4
❑ 65Top-580
❑ 65TwiPos-3
❑ 66OPC-190
❑ 66Top-190
❑ 66TopRubI-37
❑ 66TopVen-190
❑ 66TwiFaiG-5
❑ 67CokCapDA-23
❑ 67Top-432
❑ 68OPC-121
❑ 68Top-121
❑ 68TopVen-121
❑ 69MilBra-99
❑ 69OPC-61
❑ 69Top-61
❑ 69YanPhoS-40
❑ 70Top-649
❑ 78TwiFri-7
❑ 92YanWIZ6-52
Hall, Joe
❑ 88HamRedP-1747
❑ 89St.PetCS-15
❑ 90ArkTraGS-16
❑ 90TexLeaAGS-30
❑ 91LinDriAAA-633
❑ 91VanCanLD-633
❑ 91VanCanP-1600
❑ 92VanCanF-2730
❑ 92VanCanS-636
❑ 93LinVenB-178
❑ 93NasSouF-579
❑ 94Bow-651
❑ 94Fla-32
❑ 94FleUpd-26
❑ 94ScoRoo-RT143
❑ 94ScoRooGR-RT143
❑ 94Sel-404
❑ 94SpoRoo-114
❑ 94SpoRooAP-114
❑ 94TopTra-61T
❑ 94Ult-338
❑ 94VenLinU-257
❑ 94WhiSoxK-11
❑ 95LinVen-143
❑ 95Pac-89
❑ 95Sco-290
❑ 95ScoGolR-290
❑ 95ScoPlaTS-290
❑ 95TolMudHTI-15
❑ 96RocRedWB-15
❑ 97TolMudHB-17
Hall, Johnny
❑ 90DodTar-968
Hall, Josh
❑ 98BilMusTI-12
Hall, Justin
❑ 98SouOreTG-13
Hall, Kevin
❑ 88PocGiaP-2093
❑ 89EveGiaS-10
Hall, Lamar
❑ 88IdaFalBP-1840
❑ 89SumBraP-1106
Hall, Larry
❑ 80AppFoxT-27
Hall, Marty
❑ 86MadMusP-10
❑ 86MadMusP-10
❑ 87AshTouP-10
Hall, Matthew
❑ 86ChaLooP-11
❑ 87ChaLooB-21
Hall, Mel
❑ 82IowCubT-4
❑ 83CubThoAV-27
❑ 83Don-126
❑ 83TopTra-39T
❑ 84Don-411
❑ 84Fle-493
❑ 84FleSti-106
❑ 84IndWhe-34
❑ 84Nes792-508
❑ 84OPC-4
❑ 84Top-508
❑ 84TopSti-380
❑ 84TopTif-508
❑ 84TopTra-47T
❑ 84TopTraT-47T
❑ 85Don-338
❑ 85Fle-449
❑ 85Ind-16
❑ 85IndPol-27
❑ 85OPC-263
❑ 85Top-263
❑ 85TopMin-263
❑ 85TopSti-254
❑ 85TopTif-263
❑ 86Don-276
❑ 86Fle-587
❑ 86IndOhH-27
❑ 86IndTeal-24
❑ 86OPC-138
❑ 86Top-647
❑ 86TopTif-647
❑ 87Don-473
❑ 87Fle-252
❑ 87FleExcS-21
❑ 87FleGlo-252
❑ 87FleStiC-53
❑ 87IndGat-27
❑ 87OPC-51
❑ 87Spo-180
❑ 87SpoTeaP-3
❑ 87Top-51
❑ 87TopSti-206
❑ 87TopTif-51
❑ 88Don-342
❑ 88DonBasB-173
❑ 88Fle-610
❑ 88FleGlo-610
❑ 88IndGat-27
❑ 88IndTeal-17
❑ 88Lea-109
❑ 88OPC-318
❑ 88PanSti-79
❑ 88Sco-441
❑ 88ScoGlo-441
❑ 88Spo-189
❑ 88StaLinI-12
❑ 88Top-318
❑ 88TopBig-114
❑ 88TopSti-205
❑ 88TopTif-318
❑ 89Don-73
❑ 89DonTra-36
❑ 89Fle-406
❑ 89FleGlo-406
❑ 89FleUpd-49
❑ 89OPC-173
❑ 89PanSti-328
❑ 89RedFolSB-55
❑ 89Sco-17
❑ 89ScoRoo-54T
❑ 89Spo-144
❑ 89Top-173
❑ 89TopBig-13
❑ 89TopTif-173
❑ 89TopTra-44T
❑ 89TopTraT-44T
❑ 89TVSpoM-86
❑ 89UppDec-538
❑ 89UppDec-729
❑ 89YanScoNW-20
❑ 90Bow-437
❑ 90BowTif-437
❑ 90Don-598
❑ 90DonBesA-66
❑ 90Fle-444
❑ 90FleCan-444
❑ 90Lea-227
❑ 90MLBBasB-92
❑ 90OPC-436
❑ 90PanSti-122
❑ 90PubIntS-535
❑ 90Sco-383
❑ 90Top-436
❑ 90TopBig-123
❑ 90TopSti-313
❑ 90TopTif-436
❑ 90TopTVY-30
❑ 90UppDec-458
❑ 90YanScoNW-7
❑ 91Bow-179
❑ 91Cla3-T34
❑ 91Don-442
❑ 91Fle-665
❑ 91Lea-283
❑ 91OPC-738
❑ 91Sco-166
❑ 91StaClu-333
❑ 91Top-738
❑ 91TopDesS-738
❑ 91TopMic-738
❑ 91TopTif-738
❑ 91Ult-233
❑ 91UppDec-392
❑ 92Bow-425
❑ 92Cla2-T83
❑ 92Don-248
❑ 92Fle-229
❑ 92Hig5-86
❑ 92Lea-88
❑ 92LeaBlaG-88
❑ 92OPC-223
❑ 92PanSti-141
❑ 92Pin-144
❑ 92Sco-154
❑ 92StaClu-9
❑ 92Top-223
❑ 92TopGol-223
❑ 92TopGolW-223
❑ 92TopKid-87
❑ 92TopMic-223
❑ 92Ult-101
❑ 92UppDec-291
❑ 92UppDecS-1
❑ 92YanWIZ8-76
❑ 93Fle-278
❑ 93RedFolS-39
❑ 93Sel-89
❑ 93Top-114
❑ 93TopGol-114
❑ 93TopInaM-114
❑ 93TopInaR-114
❑ 93TopMic-114
❑ 93UppDec-291
❑ 93UppDecGold-291
❑ 96GiaMot-16
Hall, Noah
❑ 97VerExpB-15
❑ 98CapFeaCM-7
Hall, Richard W.
❑ 55Top-126
❑ 55TopDouH-57
❑ 56PirTeal-10
❑ 56Top-331
❑ 57Top-308
❑ 60Top-308
❑ 61Top-197
❑ 61TopStal-160
❑ 62BalOriP-10
❑ 62Top-189
❑ 62TopVen-189
❑ 63BalOriP-13
❑ 63Top-526
❑ 64BalOriP-16
❑ 65BalOriP-13
❑ 66BalOriP-15
❑ 67BalOriP-42
❑ 67Top-508
❑ 68OPC-17
❑ 68Top-17
❑ 68TopVen-17
❑ 70BalOriP-11
❑ 70OPC-182
❑ 70Top-182
❑ 71BalOriP-12
❑ 71MLBOffS-297
❑ 71OPC-417
❑ 71OriCha-5
❑ 71Top-417
❑ 78TCM60I-170
❑ 81Ori6F-15
❑ 90BalOriP-8
❑ 91OriCro-174
❑ 93BalOriP-11
❑ 95BalOriP-22
Hall, Robert P.
❑ 09T206-426
Hall, Rocky
❑ 78NewWayCT-19
❑ 79BurBeeT-6
❑ 79HolMilT-24
Hall, Ronnie
❑ 94BenRocF-3608
❑ 95AshTouTI-25
❑ 96SalAvaB-13
❑ 98WesTenDJM-12
Hall, Roy
❑ 85GreHorT-15
Hall, Ryan
❑ 94JohCitCC-12
❑ 94JohCitCF-3705
❑ 95PeoChiTI-16
❑ 96StPetCB-11
Hall, Sea Lion
❑ 24Zee-61
Hall, Tim
❑ 91SpoIndC-26
❑ 91SpoIndP-3950
❑ 92ChaRaiF-123
Hall, Toby
❑ 97HudValRB-7
❑ 98ChaRivDG-14
❑ 99BasAmeTP-49
❑ 99BasAmeTPG-49
❑ 99Bow-307
❑ 99BowGol-307
❑ 99BowInt-307
Hall, Todd
❑ 87PenWhiSP-24
❑ 88TamTarS-10A
❑ 89SarWhiSS-9
❑ 90BirBarB-17
❑ 90BirBarP-1105
❑ 90CMC-747
Hall, Tom E.
❑ 69Top-658
❑ 70OPC-169
❑ 70Top-169
❑ 71MLBOffS-462
❑ 71OPC-313
❑ 71Top-313
❑ 72MilBra-124
❑ 72OPC-417
❑ 72Top-417
❑ 73OPC-8
❑ 73Top-8
❑ 74MetTeal-6
❑ 74OPC-248
❑ 74Top-248
❑ 75MetSSP-3
❑ 75OPC-108
❑ 75Top-108
❑ 75TopMin-108
❑ 76KanCitRP-10
❑ 76OPC-621
❑ 76SSP-556
❑ 76Top-621
❑ 77TacTwiDQ-13
❑ 78TwiFri-31
❑ 91MetWIZ-156
Hall, Yates
❑ 94NewJerCC-14
❑ 94NewJerCF-3412
❑ 94SigRooDPBSDP-2
❑ 94StaCluDP-55
❑ 94StaCluDPFDI-55
❑ 95Exc-267
❑ 95SigRooMOP-P7
❑ 95SigRooMOPS-P7
❑ 96StPetCB-12
❑ 97PriWilC-14
❑ 98PriWilCQ-7
Halla, John
❑ 09ColChiE-123
❑ 11Zee-12
❑ 12ColRedB-123
❑ 12ColTinT-123
❑ 12Zee-10
❑ 13Zee-10
❑ 15Zee-80
Halla, Ryan
❑ 98LynHilQ-8
Halladay, Roy
❑ 95Bes-125
❑ 96DunBluJB-12
❑ 96DunBluJTI-14
❑ 96DunBluJUTI-3
❑ 97Bes-15
❑ 97BesAutSBPP-47
❑ 97BluJayS-59
❑ 97Bow-308
❑ 97BowBes-134
❑ 97BowBesAR-134
❑ 97BowBesR-134
❑ 97BowCerBlaIA-CA35
❑ 97BowCerBluIA-CA35
❑ 97BowCerGolIA-CA35
❑ 97BowChr-212
❑ 97BowChrI-212
❑ 97BowChrIR-212
❑ 97BowChrR-212
❑ 97BowInt-308
❑ 97KnoSmo-13
❑ 97SouLeaTP-19
❑ 97SyrSkyCB-11
❑ 98AriFalLTP-14
❑ 98Bow-75
❑ 98BowBes-128
❑ 98BowBesAR-128
❑ 98BowBesR-128
❑ 98BowCerBlueAU-54
❑ 98BowCerGA-54
❑ 98BowCerSA-54
❑ 98BowChr-75
❑ 98BowChrGA-75
❑ 98BowChrGAR-75
❑ 98BowChrI-75
❑ 98BowChrIR-75
❑ 98BowChrR-75
❑ 98BowGolA-75
❑ 98BowInt-75
❑ 98DonSig-134
❑ 98DonSigP-134
❑ 98LeaRS-328
❑ 98LeaRSLHolo-328
❑ 98LeaRSLong-328
❑ 98LeaRTrue-328
❑ 98SP MinPE-124
❑ 98SPMin-124
❑ 98SyrSkyG-14
❑ 98Top-264
❑ 98TopChr-264
❑ 98TopChrR-264
❑ 98TopDevR-264
❑ 98TopDia-264
❑ 98TopMiniC-264
❑ 99199Fin-140
❑ 99Bow-138
❑ 99BowAut-BA66
❑ 99BowBes-136
❑ 99BowBesAR-136
❑ 99BowBesR-136
❑ 99BowChr-138
❑ 99BowChrG-138
❑ 99BowChrGR-138
❑ 99BowChrI-138
❑ 99BowChrIR-138
❑ 99BowChrR-138
❑ 99BowChrSC-SC20
❑ 99BowChrSCR-SC20
❑ 99BowGol-138
❑ 99BowInt-138
❑ 99BowScoC-SC20
❑ 99CroRoyB-144
❑ 99CroRoyL-144
❑ 99CroRoyOD-144
❑ 99DumSet-114
❑ 99FinGolRef-140

❑ 99FinRef-140
❑ 99Fle-221
❑ 99FleBri-155
❑ 99FleBri2G-155
❑ 99FleBriBlu-155
❑ 99FleBriGol-155
❑ 99FleMys-114
❑ 99FleMysM-114
❑ 99FleSta9-221
❑ 99FleWarT-221
❑ 99Pac-445
❑ 99PacAur-199
❑ 99PacAurOD-199
❑ 99PacInv-150
❑ 99PacInvOD-150
❑ 99PacInvPB-150
❑ 99PacOme-250
❑ 99PacOmeC-250
❑ 99PacOmeG-250
❑ 99PacOmePB-250
❑ 99PacPar-248
❑ 99PacParC-248
❑ 99PacParG-248
❑ 99PacParHoloGold-248
❑ 99PacParHS-248
❑ 99PacParOD-248
❑ 99PacParPB-248
❑ 99PacParRed-248
❑ 99PacPlaB-445
❑ 99PacRed-445
❑ 99Rev-148
❑ 99RevPremDate-148
❑ 99RevRet-148
❑ 99RevShaSS-148
❑ 99SkyPre-269
❑ 99SkyPre-269
❑ 99SkyPreR-269
❑ 99SkyPreR-269
❑ 99SkyThu-253
❑ 99SkyThuRant-253
❑ 99SkyThuRave-253
❑ 99SP Aut-120
❑ 99SP SigAuto-RH
❑ 99SP SigAutoG-RH
❑ 99SP TopP-56
❑ 99SP TopPPE-56
❑ 99SpoIll-45
❑ 99SpoIllOTW-3
❑ 99SPSig-40
❑ 99ThuSkySupR-253
❑ 99Top-331
❑ 99TopAll-AM18
❑ 99TopChr-331
❑ 99TopChrA-AE18
❑ 99TopChrAR-AE18
❑ 99TopChrR-331
❑ 99TopMVPP-331
❑ 99TopSta-23
❑ 99TopSta1Foil-23
❑ 99TopSta2Foil-23
❑ 99TopStaFoil-23
❑ 99TopStaOS-23
❑ 99TopStaTS-23
❑ 99UppDec-269
❑ 99UppDecCL-107
❑ 99UppDecCLCC-107
❑ 99UppDecCLM-C98
❑ 99UppDecE-112
❑ 99UppDecEFXG-112
❑ 99UppDecEL1-269
❑ 99UppDecEL2-269
❑ 99UppDecERE-R7
❑ 99UppDecEREFXG-R7
❑ 99UppDecM-212
❑ 99UppDecMGS-212
❑ 99UppDecMHFS-212
❑ 99UppDecMSC-SC15
❑ 99UppDecMSS-212
❑ 99UppDecROSS-S19
❑ 99UppDecROSS-S19
❑ 99Vic-410

Hallahan, Bill
❑ 30UncJac-14
❑ 31CarMet-15
❑ 31Exh-16
❑ 32OrbPinNP-72
❑ 32OrbPinUP-29
❑ 33ExhFou-8
❑ 33Gou-200
❑ 33NatLeaAC-13
❑ 33TatOrb-29
❑ 34BatR31-40
❑ 34BatR31-121
❑ 34DiaMatCSB-83
❑ 34DiaStaR-23
❑ 34ExhFou-8
❑ 34Gou-82
❑ 34TarThoBD-13
❑ 35DiaMatCS3T1-67
❑ 35GolMedFR-7
❑ 36GouWidPPR-A45
❑ 36NatChiFPR-39
❑ 36SandSW-28
❑ 36WorWidGV-70
❑ 46SpoExcW-5-4
❑ 72TCMthe3-36
❑ 74Bra193NLA-13
❑ 74Car193T-14
❑ 74TCMNic-22
❑ 77GalGloG-211
❑ 83BigLeaCOA-34
❑ 87ConSer2-15
❑ 91ConTSN-214
❑ 92CarMcD-18
❑ 92ConTSN-639
❑ 93ConTSN-685

Halland, Jon
❑ 91BelMarCB-4
❑ 91BelMarP-3674
❑ 91PenPilP-385

Hallas, Bob
❑ 83MadMusF-16
❑ 84AlbA'sT-13

Hallberg, Lance
❑ 78WisRapTT-7
❑ 80OrlTwiT-8
❑ 82OrlTwi8SCT-11

Halle, Andrew
❑ 88BurIndP-1797

Hallead, John
❑ 96AshTouB-21
❑ 96PorRocB-14

Haller, Jim
❑ 75AlbDukCa-19
❑ 90GreHorB-7
❑ 90GreHorP-2653
❑ 90GreHorS-4
❑ 90ProAaA-87
❑ 91Cla/Bes-144
❑ 91PriWilCC-29
❑ 91PriWilCP-1418
❑ 92ForLauYTI-15
❑ 92Ft.LauYF-2606
❑ 93AlbYanF-2157

Haller, Tom
❑ 60TacBan-7
❑ 62GiaJayP-5
❑ 62Top-356
❑ 63GiaJayP-5
❑ 63Jel-108
❑ 63Pos-108
❑ 63Top-85
❑ 64GiaJayP-5
❑ 64Top-485
❑ 65GiaTeal-3
❑ 65Top-465
❑ 65TopTral-16
❑ 66Top-308
❑ 66TopVen-308
❑ 67CokCapG-9
❑ 67DexPre-85
❑ 67OPC-65
❑ 67Top-65
❑ 68OPC-185
❑ 68Top-185
❑ 68TopVen-185
❑ 69MilBra-100
❑ 69MLBOffS-148
❑ 69OPCDec-10
❑ 69Top-310
❑ 69TopDec-23
❑ 69TopDecl-14
❑ 69TopSta-45
❑ 69TopSup-47
❑ 69TopTeaP-22
❑ 69TraSta-43
❑ 70DayDaiNM-27
❑ 70Kel-25
❑ 70MilBra-9
❑ 70MLBOffS-51
❑ 70Top-685
❑ 71MLBOffS-105
❑ 71OPC-639
❑ 71Top-639
❑ 72MilBra-125
❑ 72OPC-175
❑ 72OPC-176
❑ 72Top-175
❑ 72Top-176
❑ 73OPC-454
❑ 73TigJew-8
❑ 73Top-454
❑ 77Gia-9
❑ 78TCM60I-188
❑ 79GiaPol-5
❑ 81Gia196T-6
❑ 84GiaMot-5
❑ 86BirBarTI-25
❑ 87DodSmoA-11
❑ 89DodSmoG-74
❑ 90DodTar-310
❑ 92DodStaTA-7
❑ 93UppDecS-7

Halley, Allen
❑ 96PriWilCB-13

Hallgren, Robert
❑ 76DubPacT-14
❑ 77CocAstT-7
❑ 78AshTouT-9

Hallgren, Tim
❑ 80SanJosMJitB-11
❑ 86SalRedBP-11

Halliday, Doc
❑ 90IdaFalBP-3264

Halliday, Troy
❑ 91ParPatF-6

Hallinan, Ed
❑ 12T207-74
❑ 13Zee-79
❑ 14Zee-82
❑ 15Zee-81
❑ 16Zee-80

Hallion, Tom
❑ 88T/MUmp-57
❑ 89T/MUmp-55
❑ 90T/MUmp-53

Hallman, Bill (William W.)
❑ 03BreE10-63
❑ 09T206-427
❑ 11PinT-5-1110
❑ 11SpoLifCW-154
❑ 87OldJudN-221
❑ 90DodTar-311
❑ 95May-34

Hallmark, Patrick
❑ 95SpoIndTI-6
❑ 96LanLugB-13
❑ 97LanLugTS-8
❑ 98CarLeaAC-4
❑ 98WilBluRC-14

Halloran, Matt
❑ 96BesAutS1RP-FR5
❑ 97BesLimA-16
❑ 97Bow-203
❑ 97BowChr-189
❑ 97BowChrl-189
❑ 97BowChrIR-189
❑ 97BowChrR-189
❑ 97BowInt-203
❑ 97CliLumG-10
❑ 97MidLeaTP-8
❑ 97Top-271
❑ 98BesPreA-16
❑ 98CliLumG-7

Halls, Gary
❑ 77BurBeeT-12

Hallstrom, Bill
❑ 79WatIndT-3A

Halper, Jason
❑ 98Bow-373
❑ 98BowChr-373
❑ 98BowChrGA-373
❑ 98BowChrGAR-373
❑ 98BowChrl-373
❑ 98BowChrIR-373
❑ 98BowChrR-373
❑ 98BowGolA-373
❑ 98BowInt-373

Halperin, Mike
❑ 94St.CatBJC-11
❑ 94St.CatBJF-3637
❑ 94StaCluDP-76
❑ 94StaCluDPFDI-76
❑ 95DunBluJTI-8
❑ 96KnoSmoB-14
❑ 98NasSouTI-13
❑ 98NasSouTISS-13

Halpin, Jeremy
❑ 98DelShoM-15

Halter, Shane
❑ 91EugEmeC-4
❑ 91EugEmeP-3733
❑ 92AppFoxCB-8
❑ 92AppFoxFI-991
❑ 92MidLeaATI-15
❑ 92StaCluD-74
❑ 93ExcFS7-173
❑ 93WilBluRC-13
❑ 93WilBluRF-2004
❑ 94Bow-31
❑ 94MemChiF-366
❑ 95OmaRoyTI-12
❑ 96ChaKniB-13
❑ 98Fle-48
❑ 98PacInvGems-53
❑ 98PacOnl-340
❑ 98PacOnlR-340
❑ 98PacOnlWC-340
❑ 98SpoIll-161
❑ 98SpoIllEE-161
❑ 98SpoIllFE-161
❑ 99UppDec-393
❑ 99UppDecEL1-393
❑ 99UppDecEL2-393

Haltiwanger, Garrick
❑ 96PitMetB-11
❑ 97CapCitB-25
❑ 98St.LucMM-10

Ham, Kevin
❑ 94BoiHawC-12
❑ 94BoiHawF-3368
❑ 95BoiHawTI-19
❑ 96CedRapKTI-11
❑ 97CedRapK-11
❑ 98LakElsSG-16

Ham, Mike (Michael)
❑ 87EveGiaC-17
❑ 88CliGiaP-709
❑ 89PhoFirP-1478
❑ 89SanJosGB-26
❑ 89SanJosGCLC-220
❑ 89SanJosGP-461
❑ 89SanJosGS-12
❑ 90ShrCapP-1447
❑ 90ShrCapS-9

Haman, Mack
❑ 97AppLeaTPB-20
❑ 98BluOriQ-27

Hambino, Great
❑ 98St.PauSTI-29

Hambright, Roger
❑ 72OPC-124
❑ 72Top-124
❑ 74SyrChiTI-9
❑ 92YanWIZ7-64

Hamburg, Leon
❑ 94SouOreAC-8
❑ 94SouOreAF-3637
❑ 95WesMicWTI-23

Hamel, Todd
❑ 85CloHSS-20

Hamelin, Bob
❑ 88EugEmeB-1
❑ 89BasAmeAPB-AA17
❑ 89MemChiB-1
❑ 89MemChiP-1201
❑ 89MemChiS-12
❑ 89SouLeaAJ-9
❑ 89Sta-42
❑ 89StaFutS-15
❑ 89StaFutS-16
❑ 90Bow-379
❑ 90BowTif-379
❑ 90CMC-199
❑ 90OmaRoyC-24
❑ 90OmaRoyP-71
❑ 90ProAAAF-606
❑ 90UppDec-45
❑ 91Bow-310
❑ 91LinDriAAA-336
❑ 91OmaRoyLD-336
❑ 91OmaRoyP-1042
❑ 92Fle-672
❑ 93Bow-617
❑ 93ClaFS7-198
❑ 93OmaRoyF-1684
❑ 94Bow-143
❑ 94ColC-393
❑ 94ColChoGS-393
❑ 94ColChoSS-393
❑ 94Don-435
❑ 94Fin-110
❑ 94FinRef-110
❑ 94Fla-58
❑ 94FleAllR-M5
❑ 94FleExtB-90
❑ 94FleExtBRS-7
❑ 94FleUpd-48
❑ 94Lea-363
❑ 94LeaGolR-11
❑ 94LeaL-39
❑ 94LeaLimRP-2
❑ 94Pin-404
❑ 94PinArtP-404
❑ 94PinMusC-404
❑ 94PinRooTP-2
❑ 94Sco-622
❑ 94ScoBoyoS-44
❑ 94ScoGolR-622
❑ 94ScoRoo-RT73
❑ 94ScoRooGR-RT73
❑ 94ScoRooSR-SU5
❑ 94Sel-191
❑ 94SelRooS-RS2
❑ 94Spo-152
❑ 94SpoRooRS-TR8
❑ 94StaClu-294
❑ 94StaClu-626
❑ 94StaCluFDI-294
❑ 94StaCluFDI-626
❑ 94StaCluGR-294
❑ 94StaCluGR-626
❑ 94StaCluMOP-294
❑ 94StaCluMOP-626
❑ 94Top-769
❑ 94TopGol-769
❑ 94TopSpa-769
❑ 94Ult-64
❑ 94UppDec-249
❑ 94UppDecED-249
❑ 95Baz-46
❑ 95Bow-381
❑ 95ColCho-78
❑ 95ColChoCtG-CG9
❑ 95ColChoCtG-CG9B
❑ 95ColChoCtG-CG9C
❑ 95ColChoCtGE-9
❑ 95ColChoCtGG-CG9
❑ 95ColChoCtGG-CG9B
❑ 95ColChoCtGG-CG9C
❑ 95ColChoCtGGE-9
❑ 95ColChoGS-78
❑ 95ColChoSE-215
❑ 95ColChoSEGS-215
❑ 95ColChoSESS-215
❑ 95ColChoSS-78
❑ 95Don-520
❑ 95DonPreP-520
❑ 95DonTopotO-90
❑ 95Fin-11
❑ 95FinPowK-PK1
❑ 95FinRef-11
❑ 95Fla-46
❑ 95Fle-160
❑ 95FleAwaW-5
❑ 95FleRooS-7
❑ 95FleTeaL-7
❑ 95Lea-198
❑ 95LeaChe-1
❑ 95LeaLim-51
❑ 95NatPac-4
❑ 95Pac-203
❑ 95PacGolP-8
❑ 95PacPri-64
❑ 95PanSti-97
❑ 95PanSti-106
❑ 95PanSti-114
❑ 95Pin-22
❑ 95PinArtP-22
❑ 95PinMusC-22
❑ 95Sco-433
❑ 95ScoAi-AM1
❑ 95ScoGolR-433
❑ 95ScoHaloG-HG107
❑ 95ScoPlaTS-433
❑ 95Sel-50
❑ 95SelArtP-50
❑ 95Spo-75
❑ 95SpoArtP-75
❑ 95StaClu-79
❑ 95StaCluCC-CC14
❑ 95StaCluFDI-79A
❑ 95StaCluFDI-79B
❑ 95StaCluMO-49
❑ 95StaCluMOP-79
❑ 95StaCluMOP-CC14
❑ 95StaCluSTWS-79
❑ 95StaCluVR-49
❑ 95StaCluVRMO-49
❑ 95Stu-30
❑ 95StuGolS-30
❑ 95Sum-72
❑ 95SumNthD-72
❑ 95TomPiz-3
❑ 95Top-143
❑ 95TopCyb-87
❑ 95TopD3-40
❑ 95TopEmb-117
❑ 95TopEmbGI-117
❑ 95UC3-93
❑ 95UC3ArtP-93
❑ 95Ult-57
❑ 95UltAllR-4
❑ 95UltAllRGM-4
❑ 95UltAwaW-23
❑ 95UltAwaWGM-23
❑ 95UltGolM-57
❑ 95UltSecYS-5
❑ 95UltSecYSGM-5
❑ 95UppDec-180
❑ 95UppDecED-180
❑ 95UppDecEDG-180
❑ 95UppDecSE-187
❑ 95UppDecSEG-187
❑ 96ColCho-571
❑ 96ColChoGS-571
❑ 96ColChoSS-571
❑ 96Don-190
❑ 96DonPreP-190
❑ 96Fla-90
❑ 96Fle-129
❑ 96FleTif-129
❑ 96Lea-53
❑ 96LeaPrePB-53
❑ 96LeaPrePG-53
❑ 96LeaPrePS-53
❑ 96Pac-324
❑ 96Pin-289
❑ 96PinFoil-289
❑ 96RoyPol-10
❑ 96StaCluMOF-1
❑ 96Ult-355
❑ 96UltGolM-355
❑ 97Pac-101
❑ 97PacLigB-101
❑ 97PacSil-101
❑ 97TolMudHB-18
❑ 98ColCho-89
❑ 98PacOnl-395
❑ 98PacOnlR-395
❑ 98PacOnlWC-395
❑ 98Top-195
❑ 98TopChr-195
❑ 98TopChrR-195
❑ 98TopDevR-195
❑ 98TopDia-195
❑ 98TopMiniC-195
❑ 98Ult-438
❑ 98UltGolM-438
❑ 98UltMas-438
❑ 98UltPlaM-438

Hamilton, Bill
❑ 52LavPro-55

Hamilton, Billy
❑ 53ArtHaloFP-42
❑ 61Fle-112
❑ 76ShaPiz-86
❑ 80PerHaloFP-86
❑ 80SSPHOF-86
❑ 87OldJudN-222
❑ 89HOFStiB-43
❑ 94OriofB-79
❑ 95May-35
❑ 98CamPepP-31

Hamilton, Bo (Paul)
❑ 93MarPhiF-3466
❑ 94MarPhiC-8
❑ 94MarPhiF-3284
❑ 95BatCliTI-16
❑ 95PiePhiF-182

Hamilton, Bob
❑ 47PadTeal-8
❑ 79NaSouTI-10
❑ 80WatRedT-13
❑ 85VerBeaDT-1
❑ 87SanAntDTI-18

Hamilton, Carl
❑ 86PitCubP-9
❑ 87IowCubTI-1
❑ 88PeoChiTI-13
❑ 90MidAngGS-17
❑ 91CarMudLD-108
❑ 91CarMudP-1081
❑ 91LinDriAA-108

Hamilton, Charlie
❑ 91KisDodP-4205

Hamilton, Clarence
❑ 31Zee-88

Hamilton, Darryl
❑ 85AncGlaPTI-14
❑ 87StoPorP-8
❑ 88BreTeal-15
❑ 88DenZepC-24
❑ 88DenZepP-1274
❑ 88FleUpd-38

- 88FleUpdG-38
- 88ScoRoo-72T
- 88ScoRooG-72T
- 89DenZepC-13
- 89DenZepP-39
- 89Fle-187
- 89FleGlo-187
- 89ScoHot1R-44
- 89Top-88
- 89TopTif-88
- 89UppDec-301
- 90Bow-397
- 90BowTif-397
- 90BreMilB-10
- 90BrePol-24
- 90Fle-325
- 90FleCan-325
- 90TopTra-35T
- 90TopTraT-35T
- 91BreMilB-9
- 91BrePol-9
- 91Don-517
- 91Fle-585
- 91OPC-781
- 91Sco-107
- 91StaClu-234
- 91Top-781
- 91TopDesS-781
- 91TopMic-781
- 91TopTif-781
- 91UltUpd-30
- 91UppDec-42
- 92Bow-74
- 92BrePol-10
- 92Don-593
- 92Fle-177
- 92Lea-12
- 92LeaBlaG-12
- 92OPC-278
- 92Pin-151
- 92Sco-497
- 92StaClu-253
- 92Top-278
- 92TopGol-278
- 92TopGolW-278
- 92TopMic-278
- 92TriPla-250
- 92Ult-383
- 92UppDec-460
- 93Bow-239
- 93BrePol-9
- 93BreSen5-5
- 93DiaMar-48
- 93Don-527
- 93Fin-45
- 93FinRef-45
- 93Fla-224
- 93Fle-250
- 93Lea-199
- 93OPC-158
- 93PacSpa-157
- 93PanSti-41
- 93Pin-144
- 93Sco-118
- 93Sel-168
- 93SP-65
- 93StaClu-303
- 93StaCluFDI-303
- 93StaCluMOP-303
- 93Stu-40
- 93Top-556
- 93TopGol-556
- 93TopInaM-556
- 93TopInaR-556
- 93TopMic-556
- 93Ult-219
- 93UppDec-192
- 93UppDecGold-192
- 94Bow-289
- 94BreMilB-34
- 94BrePol-9
- 94BreTeal-8
- 94ColC-386
- 94ColChoGS-386
- 94ColChoSS-386
- 94Don-398
- 94Fin-142
- 94FinRef-142
- 94Fla-67
- 94Fle-177
- 94FleExtB-102
- 94FUnPac-98
- 94Lea-281
- 94OPC-58
- 94Pac-329
- 94PanSti-80
- 94Pin-94
- 94PinArtP-94
- 94PinMusC-94
- 94ProMag-71
- 94Sco-395
- 94ScoGolR-395
- 94Sel-307
- 94Spo-57
- 94StaClu-188
- 94StaCluFDI-188
- 94StaCluGR-188
- 94StaCluMOP-188
- 94Stu-43
- 94Top-435
- 94TopGol-435
- 94TopSpa-435
- 94TriPla-53
- 94Ult-74
- 94UppDec-326
- 94UppDecED-326
- 95ColCho-178
- 95ColChoGS-178
- 95ColChoSS-178
- 95Don-443
- 95DonPreP-443
- 95DonTopotO-97
- 95Fla-270
- 95Fle-179
- 95Lea-247
- 95LeaLim-6
- 95Pin-207
- 95PinArtP-207
- 95PinMusC-207
- 95Sco-84
- 95ScoGolR-84
- 95ScoPlaTS-84
- 95StaClu-176
- 95StaCluFDI-176
- 95StaCluMOP-176
- 95StaCluSTWS-176
- 95Sum-49
- 95SumNthD-49
- 95Top-245
- 95Ult-64
- 95UltGolM-64
- 96ColCho-788
- 96Don-527
- 96DonPreP-527
- 96Fla-172
- 96Fle-145
- 96FleTif-145
- 96FleUpd-U89
- 96FleUpdTC-U89
- 96LeaPre-60
- 96LeaPreP-60
- 96LeaSigA-89
- 96LeaSigAG-89
- 96LeaSigAS-89
- 96Pac-348
- 96Pin-353
- 96PinFoil-353
- 96RanDr P-13
- 96RanFle-9
- 96RanMot-5
- 96Sco-85
- 96Top-365
- 96Ult-80
- 96Ult-420
- 96UltGolM-80
- 96UltGolM-420
- 96UppDec-467
- 97Cir-249
- 97CirRav-249
- 97ColCho-455
- 97Don-251
- 97Don-294
- 97DonGolPP-251
- 97DonGolPP-294
- 97DonLim-85
- 97DonLimE-85
- 97DonLimENG-85
- 97DonSilPP-251
- 97DonSilPP-294
- 97Fin-210
- 97FinRef-210
- 97Fle-224
- 97Fle-631
- 97FleTif-224
- 97FleTif-631
- 97Lea-210
- 97LeaFraM-210
- 97LeaFraMDC-210
- 97NewPin-157
- 97NewPinAP-157
- 97NewPinMC-157
- 97NewPinPP-157
- 97Pac-202
- 97PacLigB-202
- 97PacSil-202
- 97Pin-4
- 97PinArtP-PP4
- 97PinMusC-4
- 97PinPrePla-4
- 97RanSco-13
- 97RanScoPl-13
- 97RanScoPr-13
- 97Sco-231
- 97Sco-363
- 97ScoArtPWB-231
- 97ScoArtPWB-363
- 97ScoPreS-231
- 97ScoResC-363
- 97ScoShoS-231
- 97ScoShoS-363
- 97ScoShoSAP-231
- 97ScoShoSAP-363
- 97StaClu-126
- 97StaCluMOP-126
- 97Top-194
- 97Ult-134
- 97Ult-447
- 97UltGolME-134
- 97UltGolME-447
- 97UltPlaME-134
- 97UltPlaME-447
- 98ColCho-488
- 98Fin-38
- 98FinNo--38
- 98FinNo-R-38
- 98FinRef-38
- 98Fle-525
- 98FleUpd-U19
- 98GiaMot-10
- 98Pac-440
- 98PacOnl-659
- 98PacOnlR-659
- 98PacOnlWC-659
- 98PacPlaB-440
- 98PacRedT-440
- 98PacSil-440
- 98Pin-108
- 98PinPreP-108
- 98Sco-253
- 98ScoRT-200
- 98StaCluFDI-343
- 98StaCluI-343
- 98StaCluOneK-343
- 98StaCluPP-343
- 98Top-66
- 98TopChr-66
- 98TopChrR-66
- 98TopDevR-66
- 98TopDia-66
- 98TopMiniC-66
- 98Ult-268
- 98UltGolM-268
- 98UltMas-268
- 98UltPlaM-268
- 98UppDec-249
- 98UppDec-502
- 99Fle-300
- 99FleSta9-300
- 99FleWarT-300
- 99PacInv-50
- 99PacInvOD-50
- 99PacInvPB-50
- 99PacOme-83
- 99PacOmeC-83
- 99PacOmeG-83
- 99PacOmePB-83
- 99PacPar-81
- 99PacParC-81
- 99PacParG-81
- 99PacParHoloGold-81
- 99PacParHS-81
- 99PacParOD-81
- 99PacParPB-81
- 99PacParRed-81
- 99Rev-50
- 99RevPremDate-50
- 99RevRet-50
- 99RevShaSS-50
- 99StaClu-83
- 99StaCluFDI-83
- 99StaCluOoaK-83
- 99StaCluPP-83
- 99Top-289
- 99TopChr-289
- 99TopChrR-289
- 99TopMVPP-289
- 99UppDec-363
- 99UppDecEL1-363
- 99UppDecEL2-363
- 99Vic-137

Hamilton, Dave

- 74OPC-633
- 74Top-633
- 75OPC-428
- 75Top-428
- 75TopMin-428
- 76OPC-237
- 76Top-237
- 77OPC-224
- 77Top-367
- 77WhiSoxT-10
- 78CarTeal-9
- 78Top-288
- 79Top-147
- 80Top-86
- 81TacTigT-8

Hamilton, Don

- 12Zee-111

Hamilton, Earl

- 12T207-75
- 14B18B-31A
- 14B18B-31B
- 14FatPlaT-15
- 15CraJacE-171
- 15SpoNewM-74
- 16BF2FP-42
- 16SpoNewM-75
- 17ColE13-68
- 21Nei-68
- 22E120-219
- 22W573-58
- 26Zee-23
- 92ConTSN-339

Hamilton, George W.

- 88KimN18-16

Hamilton, Jack

- 62Top-593
- 63Top-132
- 65Top-288
- 66Top-262
- 66TopVen-262
- 67CokCapYM-V35
- 67DexPre-86
- 67OPC-2
- 67Top-2
- 68OPC-193
- 68Top-193
- 68TopVen-193
- 69Top-629
- 91MetWIZ-157

Hamilton, Jamie

- 80ElPasDT-23

Hamilton, Jason

- 93BriTigC-11
- 93BriTigF-3653

Hamilton, Jeff

- 86AlbDukP-10
- 86StaoftFT-18
- 87AlbDukD-19
- 87DodPol-16
- 87Don-464
- 87Top-266
- 87TopTif-266
- 88DodMot-19
- 88DodPol-33
- 88Don-525
- 88Fle-515
- 88FleGlo-515
- 88PanSti-312
- 88Top-62
- 88TopClo-42
- 88TopTif-62
- 89DodMot-19
- 89DodPol-3
- 89DodStaSV-6
- 89Don-550
- 89DonBasB-290
- 89Fle-60
- 89FleGlo-60
- 89Sco-570
- 89Top-736
- 89TopTif-736
- 89UppDec-615
- 90Bow-94
- 90BowTif-94
- 90DodMot-23
- 90DodPol-3
- 90DodTar-312
- 90Don-321
- 90Fle-396
- 90FleCan-396
- 90Lea-306
- 90OPC-426
- 90PubIntS-7
- 90Sco-132
- 90ScoYouS2-17
- 90Top-426
- 90TopBig-98
- 90TopSti-67
- 90TopTif-426
- 90UppDec-296
- 91DodMot-23
- 91DodPol-3
- 91DodSt.V-14
- 91Lea-509
- 91OPC-552
- 91StaClu-550
- 91Top-552
- 91TopDesS-552
- 91TopMic-552
- 91TopTif-552
- 91UppDec-779
- 92AlbDukF-726
- 92AlbDukS-10
- 92DodPol-3
- 92OPC-151
- 92Sco-684
- 92SkyAAAF-4
- 92StaClu-339
- 92Top-151
- 92TopGol-151
- 92TopGolW-151
- 92TopMic-151

Hamilton, Jimmy

- 96AppLeaAB-8
- 96BurIndB-5
- 98KinIndQ-12

Hamilton, Joe

- 94UtiBluSC-13
- 94UtiBluSF-3833
- 96MicBatCTI-15
- 96MicBatCB-12
- 98TreThuM-16

Hamilton, Joey

- 88MisStaB-9
- 89MisStaB-16
- 90MisStaB-15
- 91MisStaB-20
- 92CalLeaACL-42
- 92ChaRaiC-21
- 92ClaDraP-90
- 92ClaFS7-54
- 92FroRowDP-35
- 92FroRowDPG-35
- 92FroRowDPS-35
- 92UppDec-67
- 92UppDecML-39
- 92UppDecML-76
- 93ClaFS7-199
- 93RanCucQC-14
- 93RanCucQF-826
- 93StaCluM-49
- 94Bow-525
- 94BowBes-B8
- 94BowBesR-B8
- 94Cla-122
- 94Fla-437
- 94FlaWavotF-B3
- 94FleUpd-185
- 94LasVegSF-869
- 94LeaLimR-42
- 94ScoRoo-RT124
- 94ScoRooGR-RT124
- 94Sel-403
- 94SigRoo-26
- 94SigRooS-26
- 94SP-5
- 94SPDieC-5
- 94SpoRoo-139
- 94SpoRooAP-139
- 94TopTra-48T
- 94Ult-575
- 94UppDec-513
- 94UppDecED-513
- 94UppDecML-229
- 95Bow-283
- 95ColCho-346
- 95ColChoGS-346
- 95ColChoSE-161
- 95ColChoSEGS-161
- 95ColChoSESS-161
- 95ColChoSS-346
- 95Don-267
- 95DonPreP-267
- 95DonTopotO-342
- 95Emo-188
- 95Fin-10
- 95FinRef-10
- 95Fla-419
- 95Fle-561
- 95FleRooS-8
- 95Lea-114
- 95PadCHP-15
- 95PadMot-24
- 95PanSti-103
- 95Pin-344
- 95PinArtP-344
- 95PinMusC-344
- 95PinUps-US20
- 95Sco-482
- 95ScoGolR-482
- 95ScoPlaTS-482
- 95Sel-27
- 95SelArtP-27
- 95SelCer-83
- 95SelCerMG-83
- 95SP-109
- 95SPCha-91
- 95SPChaDC-91
- 95Spo-54
- 95SpoArtP-54
- 95SPSil-109
- 95StaClu-339
- 95StaCluMO-47
- 95StaCluMOP-339
- 95StaCluSTWS-339
- 95StaCluVR-178
- 95StaCluVRMO-178
- 95Stu-69
- 95Sum-68
- 95SumNthD-68
- 95Top-54
- 95TopCyb-39
- 95TopEmb-87
- 95TopEmbGI-87
- 95Ult-234
- 95UltAllR-5
- 95UltAllRGM-5
- 95UltGolM-234
- 95UltSecYS-6
- 95UltSecYSGM-6
- 95UppDec-137
- 95UppDecED-137
- 95UppDecEDG-137
- 95UppDecSE-266
- 95UppDecSEG-266
- 96ColCho-701
- 96ColChoGS-701
- 96ColChoSS-701
- 96Don-204
- 96DonPreP-204
- 96EmoXL-278
- 96Fla-375
- 96Fle-568
- 96FleTif-568
- 96Lea-73
- 96LeaPre-41
- 96LeaPreP-41
- 96LeaPrePB-73
- 96LeaPrePG-73
- 96LeaPrePS-73
- 96LeaSig-44
- 96LeaSigA-90
- 96LeaSigAG-90
- 96LeaSigAS-90
- 96LeaSigPPG-44
- 96LeaSigPPP-44
- 96MetUni-236
- 96MetUniP-236
- 96Pac-197
- 96PadMot-20
- 96PanSti-104
- 96Pin-23
- 96Sco-412
- 96StaClu-29
- 96StaClu-251
- 96StaCluMOP-29
- 96StaCluMOP-251
- 96Stu-136
- 96StuPrePB-136
- 96StuPrePG-136
- 96StuPrePS-136
- 96Top-403
- 96TopGal-112
- 96TopGalPPI-112
- 96TopLas-119
- 96Ult-285
- 96UltGolM-285
- 96UppDec-451
- 97Cir-20
- 97CirRav-20
- 97ColCho-444
- 97Don-45
- 97DonGolPP-45
- 97DonLim-74
- 97DonLimE-74

❑ 97DonLimENG-74
❑ 97DonPre-118
❑ 97DonPreCttC-118
❑ 97DonSilPP-45
❑ 97Fin-27
❑ 97FinRef-27
❑ 97FlaShoLC-150
❑ 97FlaShoLeg0-150
❑ 97FlaShoLeg1-150
❑ 97FlaShoM-A150
❑ 97FlaShoM-B150
❑ 97FlaShoM-C150
❑ 97FlaShoR0-150
❑ 97FlaShoR1-150
❑ 97FlaShoR2-150
❑ 97Fle-463
❑ 97FleTif-463
❑ 97Lea-125
❑ 97LeaFraM-125
❑ 97LeaFraMDC-125
❑ 97MetUni-220
❑ 97Pac-425
❑ 97PacLigB-425
❑ 97PacSil-425
❑ 97PadMot-16
❑ 97PinX-P-97
❑ 97PinX-PMoS-97
❑ 97Sco-261
❑ 97ScoArtPWB-261
❑ 97ScoPreS-261
❑ 97ScoShoS-261
❑ 97ScoShoSAP-261
❑ 97Sel-190
❑ 97SelCom-190
❑ 97SP-153
❑ 97SpoIll-45
❑ 97SpoIllEE-45
❑ 97StaClu-155
❑ 97StaCluMOP-155
❑ 97Stu-46
❑ 97StuPrePG-46
❑ 97StuPrePS-46
❑ 97Top-117
❑ 97TopChr-45
❑ 97TopChrR-45
❑ 97TopGal-95
❑ 97TopGalPPI-95
❑ 97Ult-284
❑ 97UltGolME-284
❑ 97UltPlaME-284
❑ 97UppDec-493
❑ 98CirThu-189
❑ 98CirThuRav-189
❑ 98CirThuSupRav-189
❑ 98ColCho-224
❑ 98Fle-465
❑ 98FleVin'-119
❑ 98FleVin'C-119
❑ 98MetUni-17
❑ 98MetUniPMG-17
❑ 98Pac-428
❑ 98PacOnl-638
❑ 98PacOnlR-638
❑ 98PacOnlWC-638
❑ 98PacPlaB-428
❑ 98PacRedT-428
❑ 98PacSil-428
❑ 98PadMot-9
❑ 98Sco-174
❑ 98ScoSS-PP76
❑ 98ScoSSAP-PP76
❑ 98SpoIll-56
❑ 98SpoIllEE-56
❑ 98SpoIllFE-56
❑ 98StaCluFDI-294
❑ 98StaCluI-294
❑ 98StaCluOneK-294
❑ 98StaCluPP-294
❑ 98Top-112
❑ 98TopChr-112
❑ 98TopChrR-112
❑ 98TopDevR-112
❑ 98TopDia-112
❑ 98TopMiniC-112
❑ 98TopOpeD-58
❑ 98Ult-104
❑ 98UltGolM-104
❑ 98UltMas-104
❑ 98UltPlaM-104
❑ 98UppDec-212
❑ 98UppDecSF-116
❑ 99Fle-152
❑ 99FleSta9-152
❑ 99FleWarT-152
❑ 99Pac-369
❑ 99PacPlaB-369
❑ 99PacRed-369
❑ 99SkyPre-85
❑ 99SkyPreR-85
❑ 99SkyThu-192
❑ 99SkyThuRant-192
❑ 99SkyThuRave-192
❑ 99StaClu-73
❑ 99StaCluFDI-73
❑ 99StaCluOoaK-73
❑ 99StaCluPP-73
❑ 99ThuSkySupR-192
❑ 99Top-381
❑ 99TopChr-381
❑ 99TopChrR-381
❑ 99TopMVPP-381
❑ 99UppDec-510
❑ 99UppDecEL1-510
❑ 99UppDecEL2-510
❑ 99Vic-419

Hamilton, Jonathan
❑ 97AppLeaTPB-6
❑ 97BurIndG-11
❑ 98ColRedSM-23

Hamilton, Joseph
❑ 12Zee-32

Hamilton, Josh
❑ 99Bow-431
❑ 99BowGol-431
❑ 99BowInt-431

Hamilton, Kenny
❑ 90GreFalDSP-19
❑ 91YakBeaC-17
❑ 91YakBeaP-4243
❑ 92VerBeaDC-5
❑ 92VerBeaDF-2869
❑ 93VerBeaDC-7
❑ 93VerBeaDF-2211

Hamilton, Mike
❑ 88ButCopKSP-1

Hamilton, Scott W.
❑ 86EriCarP-12
❑ 87SprCarB-17
❑ 88St.PetCS-8
❑ 90StoPorB-19
❑ 90StoPorCLC-180
❑ 90StoPorP-2180

Hamilton, Steve
❑ 55DonWin-22
❑ 63Top-171
❑ 64ChatheY-11
❑ 64Top-206
❑ 64TopVen-206
❑ 65ChaTheY-9
❑ 65Top-309
❑ 66Top-503
❑ 67CokCapYM-V15
❑ 67DexPre-87
❑ 67Top-567
❑ 67YanPhoS-91
❑ 68Top-496
❑ 68YanPhoS-67
❑ 69MilBra-101
❑ 69MLBOffS-75
❑ 69OPC-69
❑ 69Top-69
❑ 69YanMal-3
❑ 69YanPhoS-41
❑ 70MLBOffS-246
❑ 70OPC-349
❑ 70Top-349
❑ 70YanPhoS-12
❑ 71OPC-627
❑ 71Top-627
❑ 72MilBra-126
❑ 72Top-766
❑ 73OPC-214
❑ 73Top-214
❑ 75DetTigP-8
❑ 92YanWIZ6-53
❑ 92YanWIZ7-65

Hamilton, Tom
❑ 53A'sTeal-12

Hamilton, William
❑ 20Zee-23

Hamilton, Z.B.
❑ 89PriPirS-8

Hamlet, Macot
❑ 95LakElsSTI-28
❑ 96LakElsSB-30
❑ 97LakElsSG-15
❑ 97St.PauS-11
❑ 98LakElsSG-17

Hamlin, Jonas
❑ 91St.PetCC-21
❑ 91St.PetCP-2284
❑ 92SavCarC-12
❑ 92SavCarF-670
❑ 93SprCarC-12
❑ 93SprCarF-1859
❑ 94BelBreC-11
❑ 94BelBreFl-108
❑ 95Bes-27
❑ 96DouAllB-48
❑ 96El PasDB-11
❑ 96Exc-70
❑ 96TexLeaAB-25

Hamlin, Ken
❑ 55DonWin-23
❑ 60A'sTeal-6
❑ 60Top-542
❑ 61Pos-89A
❑ 61Pos-89B
❑ 61Top-263
❑ 62SalPlaC-34A
❑ 62SalPlaC-34B
❑ 62ShiPlaC-34
❑ 62Top-296
❑ 66OPC-69
❑ 66Top-69
❑ 66TopVen-69

Hamlin, Luke
❑ 34DiaMatCSB-84
❑ 34TigTeal-10
❑ 39PlaBal-13
❑ 40DodTeal-11
❑ 40PlaBal-70
❑ 41DodTeal-3
❑ 41PlaBal-53
❑ 73Dod194T-12
❑ 74TCMNic-26
❑ 74TigTCM1AC-14
❑ 76TigOldTS-12
❑ 78DodTCM4-31
❑ 90DodTar-313

Hamlin, Mark
❑ 96PorRocB-15
❑ 97AshTou-11
❑ 98CarLeaAC-37
❑ 98CarLeaTPQ-15
❑ 98SalAvaC-11

Hamm, Pete
❑ 71OPC-74
❑ 71Top-74
❑ 72OPC-501
❑ 72Top-501

Hamm, Stacy
❑ 91PocPioP-3796
❑ 91PocPioSP-26
❑ 92ChaRaiC-4
❑ 92ChaRaiF-132
❑ 92SpoIndC-23
❑ 92SpoIndF-1306

Hamm, Tim
❑ 82HawIsIT-18

Hamm, Willie
❑ 87OldJudN-223

Hammack, Brandon
❑ 96MidLeaAB-48
❑ 96RocCubTI-9
❑ 97OrlRayB-14
❑ 98WesTenDJM-13

Hammagren, Roy (Tucker)
❑ 88CapCodPPaLP-166
❑ 89AriStaB-10
❑ 90BilMusP-3225
❑ 91ChaWheC-12
❑ 91ChaWheP-2889
❑ 92ChaWheF-10
❑ 92ChaWVWC-7
❑ 93ClaGolF-186
❑ 93SouAtlLAPI-14

Hammaker, Atlee
❑ 81OmaRoyT-6
❑ 82Gia25tATI-11
❑ 82Top-471
❑ 83AllGamPI-166
❑ 83Don-298
❑ 83Fle-261
❑ 83FleSta-74
❑ 83FleSti-50
❑ 83GiaMot-13
❑ 83GiaPos-11
❑ 83Top-342
❑ 83TopSti-324
❑ 84Don-236
❑ 84Fle-373
❑ 84FleSti-65
❑ 84GiaMot-9
❑ 84GiaPos-7
❑ 84Nes792-85
❑ 84Nes792-137
❑ 84Nes792-576
❑ 84OPC-85
❑ 84SevCoi-W15
❑ 84Top-85
❑ 84Top-137
❑ 84Top-576
❑ 84TopGloS-7
❑ 84TopRubD-4
❑ 84TopSti-165
❑ 84TopSti-175
❑ 84TopTif-85
❑ 84TopTif-137
❑ 84TopTif-576
❑ 85Don-509
❑ 85Fle-608
❑ 85GiaMot-6
❑ 85GiaPos-14
❑ 85OPC-351
❑ 85Top-674
❑ 85TopMin-674
❑ 85TopRubD-4
❑ 85TopSti-165
❑ 85TopTif-674
❑ 86BasStaB-53
❑ 86Don-445
❑ 86Fle-544
❑ 86GiaMot-6
❑ 86GiaPos-14
❑ 86Lea-220
❑ 86Top-223
❑ 86TopTif-223
❑ 87FleUpd-40
❑ 87FleUpdG-40
❑ 87GiaPos-14
❑ 87OPC-358
❑ 87PhoFirP-24
❑ 87Top-781
❑ 87TopTif-781
❑ 88Don-450
❑ 88Fle-83
❑ 88FleGlo-83
❑ 88GiaMot-19
❑ 88GiaPos-12
❑ 88Sco-528
❑ 88ScoGlo-528
❑ 88StaLinG-8
❑ 88Top-157
❑ 88TopBig-259
❑ 88TopTif-157
❑ 89Don-414
❑ 89Fle-329
❑ 89FleGlo-329
❑ 89GiaMot-19
❑ 89OPC-2
❑ 89Sco-422
❑ 89Top-572
❑ 89TopBig-21
❑ 89TopTif-572
❑ 89UppDec-544
❑ 90Don-532
❑ 90Fle-57
❑ 90FleCan-57
❑ 90GiaMot-13
❑ 90GiaSmo-9
❑ 90OPC-447
❑ 90PubIntS-69
❑ 90Sco-231
❑ 90Top-447
❑ 90TopTif-447
❑ 90UppDec-620
❑ 91Don-707
❑ 91Fle-530
❑ 91OPC-34
❑ 91PadSmo-12
❑ 91StaClu-347
❑ 91Stu-246
❑ 91Top-34
❑ 91TopDesS-34
❑ 91TopMic-34
❑ 91TopTif-34
❑ 92Sco-233
❑ 94BirBarC-11

Hamman, Ed
❑ 76LauIndC-1
❑ 76LauIndC-12
❑ 76LauIndC-23
❑ 76LauIndC-32
❑ 76LauIndC-40

Hammell, Al
❑ 92GulCoaMF-3484
❑ 94CapCitBC-10
❑ 94CapCitBF-1754
❑ 94St.LucMC-12
❑ 95StLucMTI-16

Hammer, Ben
❑ 95AusFutGP-4

Hammer, M.C.
❑ 92MTVRocnJ-1

Hammer, Pete (James)
❑ 77WauMetT-9
❑ 79JacMetT-12

Hammerschmidt, Andy
❑ 96RanCucQB-17

Hammock, Robby
❑ 98LetBlaDG-14

Hammon, Randy
❑ 77PhoGiaVNB-8
❑ 78PhoGiaC-9
❑ 79PhoGiaVNB-13

Hammond, Allan
❑ 92SavCarC-19
❑ 92SavCarF-657

Hammond, Arthur S.
❑ 81VerBeaDT-6

Hammond, Chris
❑ 87TamTarP-15
❑ 88BasAmeAAB-17
❑ 88ChaLooB-2
❑ 88SouLeaAJ-36
❑ 89NasSouP-1279
❑ 89NasSouTI-8
❑ 90CMC-130
❑ 90Fle-421
❑ 90FleCan-421
❑ 90NasSouC-5
❑ 90NasSouP-225
❑ 90ProAAAF-537
❑ 90Sco-629
❑ 90TriAllGP-AAA51
❑ 90UppDec-52
❑ 91Bow-680
❑ 91Don-759
❑ 91DonRoo-19
❑ 91Fle-65
❑ 91Lea-373
❑ 91OPC-258
❑ 91OPCPre-60
❑ 91RedKah-45
❑ 91StaClu-575
❑ 91Stu-165
❑ 91Top-258
❑ 91TopDeb90-62
❑ 91TopDesS-258
❑ 91TopMic-258
❑ 91TopTif-258
❑ 91UltUpd-76
❑ 91UppDec-748
❑ 92Bow-328
❑ 92Don-172
❑ 92Fle-408
❑ 92Lea-178
❑ 92LeaBlaG-178
❑ 92OPC-744
❑ 92Pin-335
❑ 92RedKah-45
❑ 92Sco-513
❑ 92Sco100RS-89
❑ 92StaClu-751
❑ 92StaCluNC-751
❑ 92Top-744
❑ 92TopGol-744
❑ 92TopGolW-744
❑ 92TopMic-744
❑ 92Ult-189
❑ 92UppDec-105
❑ 93Don-346
❑ 93Fla-51
❑ 93Fle-35
❑ 93FleFinE-61
❑ 93Lea-475
❑ 93MarPub-11
❑ 93MarUppD-661
❑ 93MarUSPC-4H
❑ 93MarUSPC-12C
❑ 93Pin-449
❑ 93Sco-195
❑ 93SelRoo-104T
❑ 93SP-140
❑ 93StaClu-209
❑ 93StaCluFDI-209
❑ 93StaCluMOP-209
❑ 93Top-437
❑ 93TopGol-437
❑ 93TopInaM-437
❑ 93TopInaR-437
❑ 93TopMic-437
❑ 93TopTra-86T
❑ 93Ult-29
❑ 93Ult-376
❑ 93UppDec-216
❑ 93UppDec-661
❑ 93UppDecGold-216
❑ 93UppDecGold-661
❑ 94Bow-150
❑ 94ColC-362
❑ 94ColChoGS-362
❑ 94ColChoSS-362
❑ 94Don-315
❑ 94Fin-200
❑ 94FinRef-200
❑ 94Fla-163
❑ 94Fle-467
❑ 94FleExtB-260
❑ 94Lea-284
❑ 94MarTeal-5
❑ 94Pac-242
❑ 94Pin-59
❑ 94PinArtP-59
❑ 94PinMusC-59
❑ 94Sco-124
❑ 94ScoGolR-124
❑ 94SP-111
❑ 94SPDieC-111
❑ 94StaClu-367
❑ 94StaCluFDI-367
❑ 94StaCluGR-367
❑ 94StaCluMOP-367
❑ 94StaCluT-64
❑ 94StaCluTFDI-64
❑ 94Stu-109
❑ 94Top-189
❑ 94TopGol-189
❑ 94TopSpa-189
❑ 94TriPla-136
❑ 94Ult-492
❑ 94UppDec-209
❑ 94UppDecED-209
❑ 95ColCho-309
❑ 95ColChoGS-309
❑ 95ColChoSS-309
❑ 95Don-428
❑ 95DonPreP-428
❑ 95DonTopotO-243
❑ 95Emo-130
❑ 95Fin-315
❑ 95FinRef-315
❑ 95Fla-353
❑ 95Fle-333
❑ 95Lea-378
❑ 95Pin-96
❑ 95PinArtP-96
❑ 95PinMusC-96
❑ 95StaClu-360
❑ 95StaCluMOP-360
❑ 95StaCluSTWS-360
❑ 95Top-18
❑ 95Ult-162
❑ 95UltGolM-162
❑ 95UppDec-354
❑ 95UppDecED-354
❑ 95UppDecEDG-354
❑ 95UppDecSE-112
❑ 95UppDecSEG-112
❑ 96ColCho-153
❑ 96ColChoGS-153
❑ 96ColChoSS-153
❑ 96Don-98
❑ 96DonPreP-98
❑ 96EmoXL-186
❑ 96Fla-262
❑ 96Fle-387
❑ 96FleTif-387
❑ 96LeaSigA-91
❑ 96LeaSigAG-91
❑ 96LeaSigAS-91
❑ 96MetUni-165
❑ 96MetUniP-165
❑ 96PanSti-10
❑ 96ProSta-69
❑ 96Sco-107
❑ 96StaClu-314
❑ 96StaCluMOP-314
❑ 96Top-374
❑ 96Ult-200
❑ 96UltGolM-200
❑ 96UppDec-336
❑ 97Ult-479
❑ 97UltGolME-479
❑ 97UltPlaME-479
❑ 98ChaKniQ-15

Hammond, Chuck
❑ 75LynRanT-11

Hammond, David
❑ 90PriPatD-10

Hammond, Derry
❑ 98HelBreM-19

Hammond, Greg
❑ 91ChaWheC-13
❑ 91ChaWheP-2890
❑ 92ChaWheF-11
❑ 92ChaWVWC-17
❑ 93WinSpiC-7
❑ 93WinSpiF-1573
Hammond, Jamie
❑ 98VerExpO-22
Hammond, Joey
❑ 98BluOriQ-30
Hammond, Steve
❑ 78GreBraT-12
❑ 80RicBraT-6
❑ 81RicBraT-16
❑ 83Fle-114
❑ 83OmaRoyT-18
❑ 84OmaRoyT-10
❑ 86IowCubP-14
❑ 86StaoftFT-8
❑ 87JapPlaB-38
Hammonds, Jeffrey
❑ 91TopTra-51T
❑ 91TopTraT-51T
❑ 92Bow-617
❑ 92ClaDraP-4
❑ 92ClaDraPFB-BC4
❑ 92ClaDraPP-BB4
❑ 92ClaDraPP-1
❑ 92StaCluD-75
❑ 92TopDaiQTU-21
❑ 92TopTra-45T
❑ 92TopTraG-45T
❑ 92UppDecML-3
❑ 93BalOriP-12
❑ 93BowBayF-2200
❑ 93ClaGolF-166
❑ 93ClaInsC-3
❑ 93ClaYouG-YG4
❑ 93FlaWavotF-6
❑ 93FleFinE-159
❑ 93LeaGolR-U2
❑ 93LeaGolRJ-U2
❑ 93RocRedWF-252
❑ 93SelRoo-82T
❑ 93SelRooAR-6
❑ 93SP-156
❑ 93StaCluM-73
❑ 94BalOriP-12
❑ 94ColC-123
❑ 94ColChoGS-123
❑ 94ColChoSS-123
❑ 94Don-629
❑ 94Fla-2
❑ 94Fle-5
❑ 94FleExtB-5
❑ 94FleExtBRS-8
❑ 94FleRooS-8
❑ 94FUnPac-11
❑ 94Lea-403
❑ 94LeaL-1
❑ 94LeaLimRP-6
❑ 94OriPro-44
❑ 94OriUSPC-4D
❑ 94OriUSPC-12C
❑ 94Pac-32
❑ 94Pin-417
❑ 94PinArtP-417
❑ 94PinMusC-417
❑ 94PinNewG-NG4
❑ 94PinRooTP-7
❑ 94ProMag-10
❑ 94Sco-560
❑ 94ScoBoyoS-8
❑ 94ScoGolR-560
❑ 94ScoRoo-RT77
❑ 94ScoRooGR-RT77
❑ 94ScoRooSR-SU7
❑ 94Sel-180
❑ 94SelRooS-RS5
❑ 94SP-121
❑ 94SPDieC-121
❑ 94SPHol-14
❑ 94SPHolDC-14
❑ 94Spo-150
❑ 94SpoRooRS-TR3
❑ 94Stu-123
❑ 94TriPla-284
❑ 94Ult-1
❑ 94UltAllR-4
❑ 94UltAllRJ-4
❑ 94UltSecYS-3
❑ 94UppDec-210
❑ 94UppDecED-210
❑ 94UppDecNG-7
❑ 94UppDecNGED-7
❑ 95BalOriP-23
❑ 95ColCho-335
❑ 95ColChoGS-335
❑ 95ColChoSE-156
❑ 95ColChoSEGS-156
❑ 95ColChoSESS-156
❑ 95ColChoSS-335
❑ 95Don-231
❑ 95DonPreP-231
❑ 95DonTopotO-9
❑ 95Emo-4
❑ 95Fle-8
❑ 95Lea-385
❑ 95LeaLim-43
❑ 95Pac-22
❑ 95PacPri-7
❑ 95Pin-10
❑ 95PinArtP-10
❑ 95PinMusC-10
❑ 95Sco-450
❑ 95ScoGolR-450
❑ 95ScoHaloG-HG101
❑ 95ScoPlaTS-450
❑ 95Sel-18
❑ 95SelArtP-18
❑ 95SP-123
❑ 95Spo-2
❑ 95SpoArtP-2
❑ 95SPSil-123
❑ 95Stu-40
❑ 95StuGolS-40
❑ 95Sum-62
❑ 95SumNthD-62
❑ 95Ult-3
❑ 95UltGolM-3
❑ 95UltSecYS-7
❑ 95UltSecYSGM-7
❑ 95UppDec-129
❑ 95UppDecED-129
❑ 95UppDecEDG-129
❑ 95UppDecSE-184
❑ 95UppDecSEG-184
❑ 96BalOriP-12
❑ 96Bow-87
❑ 96BowBes-76
❑ 96BowBesAR-76
❑ 96BowBesR-76
❑ 96BowFoi-87
❑ 96ColCho-467
❑ 96ColChoGS-467
❑ 96ColChoSS-467
❑ 96Don-372
❑ 96DonPreP-372
❑ 96EmoXL-4
❑ 96Fla-5
❑ 96Fle-9
❑ 96FleTif-9
❑ 96Lea-208
❑ 96LeaPrePB-208
❑ 96LeaPrePG-208
❑ 96LeaPrePS-208
❑ 96OriFle-6
❑ 96Pac-235
❑ 96Sco-86
❑ 96SP-31
❑ 96Stu-117
❑ 96StuPrePB-117
❑ 96StuPrePG-117
❑ 96StuPrePS-117
❑ 96Ult-304
❑ 96UltGolM-304
❑ 96UppDec-277
❑ 97BalOriP-13
❑ 97ColCho-277
❑ 97Don-303
❑ 97DonGolPP-303
❑ 97DonLim-108
❑ 97DonLim-160
❑ 97DonLimE-108
❑ 97DonLimE-160
❑ 97DonLimENG-108
❑ 97DonSigA-49
❑ 97DonSigAC-59
❑ 97DonSigAM-59
❑ 97DonSilPP-303
❑ 97DonTea-41
❑ 97DonTeaSPE-41
❑ 97Fle-7
❑ 97FleTif-7
❑ 97OriSco-12
❑ 97OriScoPl-12
❑ 97OriScoPr-12
❑ 97Pac-23
❑ 97PacLigB-23
❑ 97PacSil-23
❑ 97Sco-205
❑ 97ScoArtPWB-205
❑ 97ScoPreS-205
❑ 97ScoShoS-205
❑ 97ScoShoSAP-205
❑ 97Top-438
❑ 97Ult-4
❑ 97UltGolME-4
❑ 97UltPlaME-4
❑ 98CirThu-121
❑ 98CirThuRav-121
❑ 98CirThuSupRav-121
❑ 98ColCho-313
❑ 98Don-42
❑ 98DonCol-42
❑ 98DonColL-285
❑ 98DonColS-42
❑ 98DonGolPP-42
❑ 98DonPriCD-42
❑ 98DonPriCL-285
❑ 98DonSilPP-42
❑ 98Fin-11
❑ 98FinNo--11
❑ 98FinNo-R-11
❑ 98FinRef-11
❑ 98Fle-82
❑ 98FleUpd-U69
❑ 98Lea-86
❑ 98LeaFraDA-86
❑ 98LeaFraF-86
❑ 98LeaFraM-86
❑ 98LeaFraM-86
❑ 98LeaFraMDC-86
❑ 98LeaFraMDC-86
❑ 98LeaFraMZ2-86
❑ 98MetUni-33
❑ 98MetUniPMG-33
❑ 98OriSco-14
❑ 98OriScoP-14
❑ 98PacInvGems-11
❑ 98PacOnl-89
❑ 98PacOnlR-89
❑ 98PacOnlWC-89
❑ 98Pin-115
❑ 98PinPreP-115
❑ 98PinSna-BO16
❑ 98Sco-208
❑ 98ScoRT-226
❑ 98ScoSS-PP100
❑ 98ScoSSAP-PP100
❑ 98StaCluFDI-159
❑ 98StaCluI-159
❑ 98StaCluOneK-159
❑ 98StaCluPP-159
❑ 98Stu-51
❑ 98StuGPP-51
❑ 98StuSPP-51
❑ 98Top-107
❑ 98TopChr-107
❑ 98TopChrR-107
❑ 98TopDevR-107
❑ 98TopDia-107
❑ 98TopMiniC-107
❑ 98TopOpeD-54
❑ 98Ult-132
❑ 98UltGolM-132
❑ 98UltMas-132
❑ 98UltPlaM-132
❑ 98UppDec-41
❑ 99Fle-350
❑ 99FleSta9-350
❑ 99FleWarT-350
❑ 99PacPriS-94
❑ 99PacPriS206-94
❑ 99PacPriS206R-94
Hammonds, Reggie
❑ 86NasPirP-11
Hammons, Matthew
❑ 96RocCubTI-10
Hamner, Granny
❑ 47PM1StaP1-76
❑ 49EurSta-135
❑ 49PhiBul-22
❑ 49PhiLumPB-4
❑ 50Bow-204
❑ 50PhiPhil-9
❑ 51BerRos-B7
❑ 51Bow-148
❑ 51TopBluB-29
❑ 52Bow-35
❑ 52NatTeaL-13
❑ 52RedMan-NL7
❑ 52TipTop-13
❑ 52Top-221
❑ 53BowC-60
❑ 53RedMan-NL18
❑ 53Top-146
❑ 54Bow-47
❑ 54Top-24
❑ 55Bow-112
❑ 55RedMan-NL15
❑ 55RobGouS-18
❑ 55RobGouW-18
❑ 56PhiPos-2
❑ 56Top-197
❑ 57Top-335
❑ 58Hir-20
❑ 58PhiJayP-6
❑ 58PhiTeal 9
❑ 58Top-268
❑ 59Top-436
❑ 60RawGloT-9
❑ 75Phi195T-11
❑ 75TCMHouoJ-9
❑ 77PhiFav-12
❑ 79TCM50-30
❑ 80Phi195T-11
❑ 83PhiPosGPaM-4
❑ 83TopRep5-221
❑ 85TCMPpl1-13
❑ 87Phi195T-5
❑ 91TopArc1-146
❑ 94TopArc1-24
❑ 94TopArc1G-24
Hamner, Ralph
❑ 49Bow-212
Hampton, Anthony
❑ 86OscAstP-10
Hampton, Henry
❑ 22Zee-63
Hampton, Ike (Isaac)
❑ 75SalLakCC-11
❑ 76SalLakCGC-12
❑ 76SSP-601
❑ 78AngFamF-16
❑ 78SSP270-196
❑ 78Top-503
❑ 91MetWIZ-158
Hampton, Lionel
❑ 95NegLeaL2-9
Hampton, Mark
❑ 90AubAstB-14
❑ 90AubAstP-3401
❑ 92GasRanC-5
❑ 92GasRanF-2247
❑ 93StoPorC-13
❑ 93StoPorF-740
Hampton, Mike
❑ 90HigSchPLS-20
❑ 91SanBerSC-6
❑ 91SanBerSP-1982
❑ 92Bow-638
❑ 92CalLeaACL-40
❑ 92ProFS7-145
❑ 92SanBerC-17
❑ 92SanBerSF-947
❑ 92UppDecML-252
❑ 93Bow-459
❑ 93ExcFS7-225
❑ 93FleFinE-270
❑ 93MariStaClu-22
❑ 93MarMot-24
❑ 93OPCPre-80
❑ 93StaClu-731
❑ 93StaCluFDI-731
❑ 93StaCluMOP-731
❑ 93TopTra-58T
❑ 93Ult-620
❑ 93UppDec-783
❑ 93UppDecGold-783
❑ 94AstMot-25
❑ 94BilMusF-3678
❑ 94BilMusSP-7
❑ 94Fin-407
❑ 94FinRef-407
❑ 94Pin-415
❑ 94PinArtP-415
❑ 94PinMusC-415
❑ 94StaClu-237
❑ 94StaClu-614
❑ 94StaCluDP-50
❑ 94StaCluDPFDI-50
❑ 94StaCluFDI-237
❑ 94StaCluFDI-614
❑ 94StaCluGR-237
❑ 94StaCluGR-614
❑ 94StaCluMOP-237
❑ 94StaCluMOP-614
❑ 95AstMot-22
❑ 95Bow-50
❑ 95Fle-461
❑ 95Top-133
❑ 96AstMot-10
❑ 96ColCho-158
❑ 96ColChoGS-158
❑ 96ColChoSS-158
❑ 96Don-202
❑ 96DonPreP-202
❑ 96EmoXL-199
❑ 96Fle-408
❑ 96FleTif-408
❑ 96Lea-83
❑ 96LeaPrePB-83
❑ 96LeaPrePG-83
❑ 96LeaPrePS-83
❑ 96LeaSigA-92
❑ 96LeaSigAG-92
❑ 96LeaSigAS-92
❑ 96StaClu-91
❑ 96StaClu-239
❑ 96StaCluMOP-91
❑ 96StaCluMOP-239
❑ 96Ult-209
❑ 96UltGolM-209
❑ 96UppDec-82
❑ 97AstMot-11
❑ 97BurBeeB-12
❑ 97Cir-387
❑ 97CirRav-387
❑ 97ColCho-121
❑ 97Don-244
❑ 97DonGolPP-244
❑ 97DonSilPP-244
❑ 97Fin-64
❑ 97FinRef-64
❑ 97Fle-346
❑ 97FleTif-346
❑ 97PacPriGotD-GD151
❑ 97StaClu-352
❑ 97StaCluMOP-352
❑ 97Top-366
❑ 97UppDec-362
❑ 98CirThu-261
❑ 98CirThuRav-261
❑ 98CirThuSupRav-261
❑ 98ColCho-133
❑ 98Fin-54
❑ 98FinNo--54
❑ 98FinNo-R-54
❑ 98FinRef-54
❑ 98Fle-393
❑ 98Pac-319
❑ 98PacAur-140
❑ 98PacOnl-323
❑ 98PacOnlR-323
❑ 98PacOnlWC-323
❑ 98PacPar-170
❑ 98PacParC-170
❑ 98PacParG-170
❑ 98PacParHS-170
❑ 98PacParPB-170
❑ 98PacParR-170
❑ 98PacPlaB-319
❑ 98PacRedT-319
❑ 98PacSil-319
❑ 98PinPlu-151
❑ 98ScoRT-123
❑ 98SP Aut-101
❑ 98SPxFin-86
❑ 98SPxFinR-86
❑ 98SPxFinS-86
❑ 98StaCluFDI-154
❑ 98StaCluI-154
❑ 98StaCluOneK-154
❑ 98StaCluPP-154
❑ 98Top-226
❑ 98TopChr-226
❑ 98TopChrR-226
❑ 98TopDevR-226
❑ 98TopDia-226
❑ 98TopMiniC-226
❑ 98Ult-344
❑ 98UltGolM-344
❑ 98UltMas-344
❑ 98UltPlaM-344
❑ 98UppDec-383
❑ 99Fle-448
❑ 99FleSta9-448
❑ 99FleWarT-448
❑ 99MetUni-12
❑ 99MetUniGM-12
❑ 99MetUniPMG-12
❑ 99Pac-192
❑ 99PacOme-106
❑ 99PacOmeC-106
❑ 99PacOmeG-106
❑ 99PacOmePB-106
❑ 99PacPlaB-192
❑ 99PacRed-192
❑ 99SkyPre-112
❑ 99SkyPreR-112
❑ 99StaClu-249
❑ 99StaCluFDI-249
❑ 99StaCluOoaK-249
❑ 99StaCluPP-249
❑ 99Top-338
❑ 99TopChr-338
❑ 99TopChrR-338
❑ 99TopMVPP-338
❑ 99Ult-175
❑ 99UltGolM-175
❑ 99UltMas-175
❑ 99UltPlaM-175
❑ 99UppDec-110
❑ 99UppDecEL1-110
❑ 99UppDecEL2-110
Hampton, Ray
❑ 82EvaTriT-21
Hampton, Robbie
❑ 96StCatSB-11
❑ 97HagSunB-22
Hampton, Scott
❑ 89TenTecGE-10
Hampton, Tony
❑ 85OscAstTI-23
Hamric, Bert (Odbert)
❑ 55Top-199
❑ 56BalOriP-22
❑ 58Top-336
❑ 91OriCro-175
❑ 95TopArcBD-107
Hamric, Rusty
❑ 80PenPilBT-18
❑ 80PenPilCT-24
❑ 81ReaPhiT-14
❑ 82OklCit8T-10
❑ 84PorBeaC-216
Hamrick, Ray
❑ 47RemBre-17
❑ 47SmiClo-5
❑ 48SigOil-10
❑ 48SmiClo-7
❑ 49RemBre-9
❑ 50RemBre-10
Hamrick, Stephen
❑ 78SanJosMMC-15
Hamulack, Tim
❑ 98QuaCitRBG-7
Hamza, Tony
❑ 86GenCubP-8
❑ 86PeoChiP-10
Han, Young Jun
❑ 97DunBluJTI-11
Hance, Bill
❑ 83TriTriT-13
❑ 84TulDriTI-28
Hancken, Buddy (Morris)
❑ 67Ast-13
❑ 71AstTeal-11
❑ 72AstTeal-11
Hancock, Andy
❑ 80AshTouT-5
Hancock, Brian
❑ 92UppDecML-188
❑ 93AusFut-14
❑ 93AusFut-105
❑ 93El PasDF-2944
❑ 94StoPorC-9
❑ 94StoPorF-1687
Hancock, Chris
❑ 89CliGiaP-890
❑ 89EveGiaS-11
❑ 90Bes-113
❑ 90CliGiaB-8
❑ 90CliGiaP-2543
❑ 90CliGiaUTI-U11
❑ 90MidLeaASGS-34
❑ 90ProAaA-119
❑ 92SanJosGC-19
❑ 93GiaStaC-16
❑ 93ShrCapF-2753
❑ 94ShrCapF-1599
Hancock, Garry
❑ 79RedSoxTI-3
❑ 79Top-702
❑ 81Fle-229
❑ 82Don-608
❑ 82Fle-295
❑ 82RedSoxC-8
❑ 82Top-322
❑ 84A'sMot-16
❑ 84Fle-445
❑ 84Nes792-197
❑ 84Top-197

❑ 84TopTif-197
Hancock, Jeff
❑ 89WatIndS-9
Hancock, Josh
❑ 99TeaBesR-32
❑ 99TeaBesR-32A
Hancock, Lee
❑ 87BelMarL-14
❑ 89SanBerSB-16
❑ 89SanBerSCLC-71
❑ 90Bes-32
❑ 90WilBilB-1
❑ 90WilBilP-1054
❑ 90WilBilS-9
❑ 91CarMudLD-109
❑ 91CarMudP-1082
❑ 91LinDriAA-109
❑ 92CarMudF-1176
❑ 92CarMudS-135
❑ 93CarMudF-2047
❑ 93CarMudTI-19
❑ 93ClaFS7-137
❑ 94BufBisF-1830
❑ 96LeaSigEA-70
❑ 97PhoFirTI-10
Hancock, Michael
❑ 92StoPorC-14
❑ 92StoPorF-31
Hancock, Ryan
❑ 94Bow-619
❑ 94LakElsSC-8
❑ 94LakElsSF-1657
❑ 94MidAngOHP-7
❑ 94Top-760
❑ 94TopGol-760
❑ 94TopSpa-760
❑ 94UppDec-523
❑ 94UppDecED-523
❑ 95Bow-82
❑ 95MidAngOHP-15
❑ 95MidAngTI-13
❑ 96VanCanB-16
❑ 97BesAutAS-16
❑ 97DonGolPP-158
❑ 97DonSilPP-158
❑ 97Lea-186
❑ 97LeaFraM-186
❑ 97LeaFraMDC-186
❑ 97Pin-158
❑ 97PinArtP-PP158
❑ 97PinMusC-158
❑ 97PinPrePla-158
❑ 97VanCanB-17
Hand, Harvey
❑ 29Zee-132
Hand, James
❑ 82TucTorT-23
Hand, Jon
❑ 98JohCCTI-15
Hand, Rich
❑ 71MLBOffS-369
❑ 71OPC-24
❑ 71Top-24
❑ 72OPC-317
❑ 72RanTeal-11
❑ 72Top-317
❑ 73OPC-398
❑ 73Top-398
❑ 74OPC-571
❑ 74Top-571
❑ 93RanKee-14
Handel, Peter
❑ 93AusFut-31
Handford, Charles
❑ 12ImpTobC-21
Handler, Marve
❑ 80ElmPioRST-34
Handley, Gene
❑ 40SolHug-9
❑ 47A'sTeal-14
❑ 49BowPCL-34
❑ 49W72HolS-6
❑ 50W720HolS-11
❑ 52MotCoo-7
❑ 53MotCoo-21
Handley, Jim
❑ 76AppFoxT-7
Handley, Lee E.
❑ 40PlaBal-221
❑ 41DouPlaR-33
❑ 49AngTeal-15
❑ 49BowPCL-28
❑ 49W725AngTI-11
❑ 84TCMPla1-42
❑ 93ConTSN-744
Handrahan, Bern
❑ 67VanMouSO-12
Hands, Bill (William Alfred)
❑ 66Top-392
❑ 67CubProPS-5
❑ 67OPC-16
❑ 67Top-16
❑ 68Top-279
❑ 68TopVen-279
❑ 69CubJewT-5
❑ 69MLBOffS-120
❑ 69OPC-115
❑ 69Top-115
❑ 69TopFou-10
❑ 69TopSta-13
❑ 69TopTeaP-4
❑ 70DayDaiNM-24
❑ 70MLBOffS-16
❑ 70OPC-405
❑ 70Top-405
❑ 71MLBOffS-31
❑ 71OPC-670
❑ 71Top-670
❑ 71TopTat-63
❑ 72CubTeal-3
❑ 72MilBra-127
❑ 72OPC-335
❑ 72Top-335
❑ 73OPC-555
❑ 73Top-555
❑ 74OPC-271
❑ 74Top-271
❑ 75OPC-412
❑ 75RanPos-13
❑ 75Top-412
❑ 75TopMin-412
❑ 76OPC-509
❑ 76SSP-253
❑ 76Top-509
❑ 78TwiFri-32
❑ 93RanKee-169
Handy, Russell
❑ 94BurBeeF-1076
❑ 94VerExpC-14
❑ 94VerExpF-3907
Hanebrink, Harry
❑ 58Top-454
❑ 59Top-322A
❑ 59Top-322B
❑ 80Bra195T-36
Hanel, Marcus
❑ 90WelPirP-17
❑ 91AugPirC-13
❑ 91AugPirP-807
❑ 92ClaFS7-242
❑ 92SalBucC-14
❑ 92SalBucF-67
❑ 93SalBucC-12
❑ 93SalBucF-435
❑ 94SalBucC-11
❑ 94SalBucF-2326
❑ 95CarMudF-160
❑ 96CarMudB-14
❑ 97CarMudC-11
❑ 98RicBraQ-15
Haney, Chris
❑ 90JamExpP-18
❑ 91Bow-443
❑ 91Cla/Bes-23
❑ 91DonRoo-44
❑ 91ExpPos-9
❑ 91HarSenLD-255
❑ 91HarSenP-618
❑ 91LinDriAA-255
❑ 91UppDecFE-23F
❑ 92Cla1-T41
❑ 92ClaGam-133
❑ 92Don-291
❑ 92ExpDonD-2A
❑ 92ExpPos-16
❑ 92Fle-483
❑ 92OPC-626
❑ 92OPCPre-186
❑ 92Pin-521
❑ 92ProFS7-258
❑ 92Sco-873
❑ 92Sco100RS-15
❑ 92StaClu-449
❑ 92Top-626
❑ 92TopDeb91-70
❑ 92TopGol-626
❑ 92TopGolW-626
❑ 92TopMic-626
❑ 92Ult-519
❑ 92UppDec-662
❑ 93ClaFS7-200
❑ 93Don-279
❑ 93FleFinE-219
❑ 93Lea-538
❑ 93OmaRoyF-1676
❑ 93Pin-194
❑ 93RoyPol-12
❑ 93Top-581
❑ 93TopGol-581
❑ 93TopInaM-581
❑ 93TopInaR-581
❑ 93TopMic-581
❑ 94ColC-398
❑ 94ColChoGS-398
❑ 94ColChoSS-398
❑ 94Don-251
❑ 94Fle-159
❑ 94Pac-286
❑ 94Sco-279
❑ 94ScoGolR-279
❑ 94StaClu-154
❑ 94StaCluFDI-154
❑ 94StaCluGR-154
❑ 94StaCluMOP-154
❑ 94Top-9
❑ 94TopGol-9
❑ 94TopSpa-9
❑ 94Ult-65
❑ 95Top-382
❑ 96ColCho-573
❑ 96ColChoGS-573
❑ 96ColChoSS-573
❑ 96Don-212
❑ 96DonPreP-212
❑ 96FleUpd-U40
❑ 96FleUpdTC-U40
❑ 96LeaSigA-93
❑ 96LeaSigAG-93
❑ 96LeaSigAS-93
❑ 96RoyPol-11
❑ 96Ult-356
❑ 96UltGolM-356
❑ 96UppDec-349
❑ 97ColCho-357
❑ 97Fle-114
❑ 97FleTif-114
❑ 97RoyPol-9
❑ 98PacOnl-341
❑ 98PacOnlR-341
❑ 98PacOnlWC-341
Haney, Fred G.
❑ 19Zee-8
❑ 20Zee-11
❑ 26Exh-66
❑ 27Exh-34
❑ 29ExhFou-16
❑ 30Zee-28
❑ 31Zee-16
❑ 32Zee-23
❑ 33Zee-3
❑ 47SigOil-8
❑ 49W72HolS-7
❑ 52MotCoo-13
❑ 54Top-75
❑ 56BraBilaBP-11
❑ 57BraSpiaS4-10
❑ 58JayPubA-8
❑ 58Top-475
❑ 59Top-551
❑ 78AtlCon-9
❑ 80Bra195T-38
❑ 83ASAWS-6
❑ 86BraGreT-12
❑ 87ConSer2-16
❑ 91TopArc1-316
❑ 93ConTSN-856
❑ 94TopArc1-75
❑ 94TopArc1G-75
Haney, Joe
❑ 86BelBreP-9
Haney, Larry (Wallace Larry)
❑ 64BalOriP-17
❑ 67BalOriP-43
❑ 67BalOriP-44
❑ 67CokCapO-17
❑ 67Top-507
❑ 68CokCapO-17
❑ 68OPC-42
❑ 68Top-42
❑ 68TopVen-42
❑ 69OPC-209
❑ 69PilPos-28
❑ 69Top-209
❑ 69TopFou-7
❑ 70Top-648
❑ 73OPC-563
❑ 73Top-563
❑ 75OPC-626
❑ 75Top-626
❑ 75TopMin-626
❑ 76OPC-446
❑ 76SSP-502
❑ 76Top-446
❑ 77PilPosR-28
❑ 77Top-12
❑ 78TCM60I-228
❑ 78Top-391
❑ 80BreTeal-10
❑ 81Ori6F-16
❑ 82BrePol-NNO
❑ 83BrePol-NNO
❑ 83Pil69G-39
❑ 85BrePol-NNO
❑ 86BrePol-12
❑ 87BrePol-NNO
❑ 88BrePol-NNO
❑ 88BreTeal-16
❑ 89BrePol-NNO
❑ 90BreMilB-32
❑ 90BrePol-NNO
❑ 91BreMilB-32
❑ 91BrePol-NNO
❑ 91OriCro-176
❑ 92BreCarT-xx
❑ 94BreMilB-35
Haney, Todd
❑ 87BelMarTI-11
❑ 88WauTimGS-14
❑ 89SanBerSB-25
❑ 89SanBerSCLC-81
❑ 89WilBilS-8
❑ 90CalCanC-18
❑ 90CalCanP-657
❑ 90CMC-445
❑ 90ProAAAF-122
❑ 90TriAllGP-AAA43
❑ 91IndIndLD-185
❑ 91IndIndP-468
❑ 91LinDriAAA-185
❑ 92ProFS7-257
❑ 93Don-342
❑ 93OttLynF-2442
❑ 93TriAAAGF-17
❑ 94ClaGolF-138
❑ 94IowCubF-1282
❑ 95IowCubTI-15
❑ 96LeaSigA-94
❑ 96LeaSigAG-94
❑ 96LeaSigAS-94
❑ 98NorTidP-13
❑ 98NorTidQ-13
Hanford, Charles
❑ 09ColChiE-125
❑ 11T205-190
❑ 12ColRedB-125
❑ 12ColTinT-125
Hanger, Charlie
❑ 96OklCit8B-27
Hanggie, Dan
❑ 81NasSouTI-5
❑ 84ChaLooT-3
❑ 85OrlTwiT-6
Hanifin, Pat
❑ 90DodTar-970
Hanisch, Ron
❑ 89BelBre2S-12
❑ 90AshTouC-29
❑ 90StoPorB-23
❑ 90StoPorCLC-202
❑ 93AshTouC-28
Hanker, Fred
❑ 88MadMusP-14
Hankins, Jay
❑ 77FriOneYW-25
Hankins, Mike
❑ 90OneYanP-3385
❑ 91CarLeaAP-CAR31
❑ 91Cla/Bes-143
❑ 91PriWilCC-5
❑ 91PriWilCP-1434
❑ 92Ft.LauYF-2620
❑ 92PriWilCC-4
❑ 93AlbYanF-2171
Hankins, Ryan
❑ 98BriWhiSQ-12
Hankinson, Frank
❑ 87BucN28-60
❑ 87FouBasHN-5
❑ 87OldJudN-224A
❑ 87OldJudN-224B
❑ 88GandBCGCE-19
Hanks, Chris
❑ 89ElmPioP-4
❑ 89WinHavRSS-9
❑ 90LynRedSTI-12
Hanlan, Ed
❑ 88KimN18-17
Hanley, George
❑ 88SFHesCreN32-11
Hanley, John
❑ 78AppFoxT-11
❑ 79KnoKnoST-15
❑ 81AppFoxT-17
Hanlin, Rich
❑ 89BelMarL-26
Hanlon, Dick
❑ 59SeaPop-19
Hanlon, Larry (Lawrence)
❑ 92ChaRanC-12
❑ 92ChaRanF-2232
❑ 92StaCluD-76
❑ 93OklCit8F-1632
❑ 94ChaRivC-9
❑ 94ChaRivF-2683
Hanlon, Ned (Edward J.)
❑ 03BreE10-64
❑ 06FanCraNL-20
❑ 11SpoLifCW-155
❑ 75FlePio-9
❑ 76SSP188WS-11
❑ 80PerHaloFP-227
❑ 87BucN28-31
❑ 87OldJudN-225
❑ 87ScrDC-14
❑ 88WG1CarG-22
❑ 90DodTar-314
❑ 94OriTeal-6
Hanna, Dave
❑ 83IdaFalAT-5
Hanna, Preston
❑ 76VenLeaS-7
❑ 79Top-296
❑ 80Top-489
❑ 81BraPol-49
❑ 81Don-523
❑ 81Fle-264
❑ 81Top-594
❑ 82BraBurKL-9
❑ 82BraPol-49
❑ 82Fle-435
❑ 83Top-127
Hannah, Harry
❑ 22Zee-151
❑ 23Zee-186
❑ 24Zee-130
❑ 25Zee-156
❑ 26Zee-24
❑ 27Zee-12
❑ 37Zee-9
Hannah, James
❑ 14Zee-83
❑ 15Zee-82
❑ 16Zee-81
❑ 17Zee-68
❑ 21Zee-159
❑ 28Zee-31
❑ 29Zee-20
❑ 32Zee-24
Hannah, Joe
❑ 61MapLeaBH-7
Hannah, Mike
❑ 75OklCit8TI-18
❑ 75SanAntBT-9
❑ 76WilTomT-8
Hannah, Neal
❑ 96YakBeaTI-27
❑ 97YakBeaG-9
Hannah, Roy
❑ 23Zee-8
❑ 30Zee-29
❑ 31Zee-17
Hannah, Truck
❑ 28ExhPCL-9
Hannahan, Buzz
❑ 98MarPhiG-12
Hannahs, Gerry (Gerald)
❑ 77ExpPos-17
❑ 79AlbDukTc-9
❑ 80AlbDukTc-25
❑ 81TolMudHT-5
❑ 90DodTar-315
Hannahs, Mitch
❑ 88CapCodPPaLP-45
❑ 89BelBre2S-13
❑ 90ElPasDGS-16
❑ 91ElPasDLD-184
❑ 91ElPasDP-2755
❑ 91LinDriAA-184
Hannan, Jim
❑ 63Top-121
❑ 64Top-261
❑ 64TopVen-261
❑ 65Top-394
❑ 66Top-479
❑ 67CokCapS-14
❑ 67Top-291
❑ 69OPC-106
❑ 69SenTeal-8
❑ 69Top-106
❑ 69TopSta-236
❑ 69TopTeaP-23
❑ 70Top-697
❑ 71OPC-229
❑ 71Top-229
❑ 72MilBra-128
❑ 94BreMilB-36
Hanneman, Blair
❑ 92EveGiaC-5
❑ 93EveGiaC-14
❑ 93EveGiaF-3765
Hannifan, John J.
❑ 09T206-428
Hannon, John
❑ 76BurBeeT-17
❑ 77HolMilT-12
Hannon, Phil
❑ 87GenCubP-22
❑ 87WinSpiP-6
❑ 88PeoChiTI-12
❑ 89WinSpiS-9
❑ 90ChaKniTI-2
❑ 90TopTVCu-47
❑ 91GenCubC-29
❑ 91GenCubP-4235
❑ 92HunCubC-28
❑ 93HunCubC-29
❑ 93HunCubF-3255
❑ 94HigDesMC-27
❑ 94HigDesMF-2804
Hanrahan, William
❑ 87OldJudN-226
Hanseen, Tye
❑ 98EugEme-14
Hansel, Damon
❑ 87MacPirP-18
Hansell, Greg
❑ 90WinHavRSS-10
❑ 91BakDodCLC-17
❑ 91CalLeLA-14
❑ 92AlbDukF-714
❑ 92Bow-314
❑ 92ClaFS7-344
❑ 92SanAntMS-566
❑ 92SkyAA F-246
❑ 92UppDecML-150
❑ 93AlbDukF-1454
❑ 93Bow-478
❑ 94AlbDukF-838
❑ 95Bow-72
❑ 95DodMot-26
❑ 95DodPol-8
❑ 95FleUpd-172
❑ 95SigRoo-23
❑ 95SigRooSig-23
❑ 95Top-429
❑ 95UppDec-317
❑ 95UppDecED-317
❑ 95UppDecEDG-317
❑ 97TucTorB-5
Hanselman, Carl
❑ 88PocGiaP-2099
❑ 89CliGiaP-903
❑ 89EveGiaS-12
❑ 90CliGiaB-14
❑ 90CliGiaP-2540
❑ 91CalLeLA-45
❑ 91SanJosGC-16
❑ 91SanJosGP-4
❑ 92SanJosGC-18
❑ 93Bow-84
❑ 93ShrCapF-2754
❑ 95ReaPhiTI-23
Hansen, Andy
❑ 48GiaTeal-5
❑ 49EurSta-106
❑ 49GiaTeal-9
❑ 52Top-74
❑ 53BowBW-64
❑ 83TopRep5-74
Hansen, Bob
❑ 75IntLeaASB-7

❑ 75OPC-508
❑ 75PacCoaLAB-7
❑ 75SacSolC-1
❑ 75Top-508
❑ 75TopMin-508
❑ 76SpolndC-17
❑ 82BrePol-NNO
❑ 94BreMilB-37

Hansen, Brent
❑ 93ForLauRSC-1
❑ 93ForLauRSFP-1590
❑ 94SarRedSC-11
❑ 94SarRedSF-1944
❑ 95TreThuTI-9

Hansen, Darel
❑ 83IdaFalAT-6
❑ 84MadMusP-15
❑ 85MadMusP-12
❑ 85MadMusT-15
❑ 86ModA'sC-8
❑ 86ModA'sP-10

Hansen, Dave
❑ 87BakDodP-21
❑ 88FloStaLAS-7
❑ 88VerBeaDS-9
❑ 89SanAntMB-17
❑ 90AlbDukCm-17
❑ 90AlbDukP-350
❑ 90AlbDukTr-9
❑ 90Bow-93
❑ 90BowTif-93
❑ 90CMC-419
❑ 90Fle-642
❑ 90FleCan-642
❑ 90FleUpd-21
❑ 90ProAAAF-71
❑ 90TriAllGP-AAA45
❑ 91AlbDukLD-7
❑ 91AlbDukP-1145
❑ 91Cla2-T35
❑ 91ClaGam-155
❑ 91Don-45
❑ 91Fle-203
❑ 91LinDriAAA-7
❑ 91TopDeb90-63
❑ 91UppDec-4
❑ 92Cla2-T23
❑ 92ClaGam-103
❑ 92DodMot-17
❑ 92DodPol-15
❑ 92DodSmo-9692
❑ 92Don-506
❑ 92Lea-389
❑ 92LeaBlaG-389
❑ 92ProFS7-238
❑ 92Sco-754
❑ 92StaClu-36
❑ 92Ult-505
❑ 93DodMot-24
❑ 93DodPol-9
❑ 93Don-244
❑ 93Fle-449
❑ 93PacSpa-146
❑ 93Pin-209
❑ 93RemUltK-5
❑ 93StaClu-263
❑ 93StaCluFDI-263
❑ 93StaCluMOP-263
❑ 93Top-469
❑ 93TopGol-469
❑ 93TopInaM-469
❑ 93TopInaR-469
❑ 93TopMic-469
❑ 93UppDec-537
❑ 93UppDecGold-537
❑ 94ColC-416
❑ 94ColChoGS-416
❑ 94ColChoSS-416
❑ 94DodMot-22
❑ 94DodPol-11
❑ 94Don-616
❑ 94Fle-511
❑ 94Pac-309
❑ 94PanSti-199
❑ 94Sco-259
❑ 94ScoGolR-259
❑ 94Sel-219
❑ 94StaClu-587
❑ 94StaCluFDI-587
❑ 94StaCluGR-587
❑ 94StaCluMOP-587
❑ 94Top-697
❑ 94TopGol-697
❑ 94TopSpa-697
❑ 95DodMot-10
❑ 95DodPol-9
❑ 95FleUpd-173
❑ 95Sco-169
❑ 95ScoGolR-169
❑ 95ScoPlaTS-169
❑ 95Top-218
❑ 96DodMot-15
❑ 96DodPol-17
❑ 96Fle-435
❑ 96FleTif-435
❑ 96LeaSigEA-71
❑ 99DodPol-9

Hansen, Elmer
❑ 21Zee-121

Hansen, Elston
❑ 92Bow-548
❑ 92ClaFS7-148
❑ 92ForLauYC-13
❑ 92ForLauYTI-16
❑ 92GreHorF-787
❑ 93GreHorC-9
❑ 93GreHorF-891
❑ 93OneYanC-8
❑ 93OneYanF-3509
❑ 94SanBerSC-5
❑ 94SanBerSF-2767
❑ 95TamYanYI-9

Hansen, Guy
❑ 83ButCopKT-31
❑ 89MemChiB-26
❑ 89MemChiP-1192
❑ 89MemChiS-24
❑ 90MemChiB-25
❑ 90MemChiP-1026
❑ 90MemChiS-26
❑ 91LinDriAAA-350
❑ 91OmaRoyP-1050
❑ 92RoyPol-27
❑ 93RoyPol-27

Hansen, Jed
❑ 94SigRooDPBSDP-3
❑ 95MidLeaA-22
❑ 95SigRooMOP-P6
❑ 95SigRooMOPS-P6
❑ 95SprSulTI-11
❑ 96Bow-300
❑ 96BowFoi-300
❑ 96DouAllB-46
❑ 96Exc-60
❑ 96TexLeaAB-26
❑ 96WicWraB-18
❑ 97OmaRoyB-16
❑ 97Top-203
❑ 98Fle-252
❑ 98OmaRoyM-9
❑ 98Pac-104
❑ 98PacInv-38
❑ 98PacInvPBlue-38
❑ 98PacInvSilv-38
❑ 98PacOnl-342
❑ 98PacOnlR-342
❑ 98PacOnlWC-342
❑ 98PacPlaB-104
❑ 98PacRedT-104
❑ 98PacSil-104
❑ 98StaCluFDI-333
❑ 98StaCluI-333
❑ 98StaCluOneK-333
❑ 98StaCluPP-333

Hansen, Jon
❑ 82ElPasDT-11

Hansen, Mike
❑ 87LakTigP-16
❑ 88FloStaLAS-39
❑ 88LakTigS-13
❑ 89LonTigP-1376

Hansen, Ray
❑ 86GreHorP-11
❑ 87GreHorP-17

Hansen, Roger
❑ 81ChaRoyT-6
❑ 82ChaRoyT-2
❑ 84MemChiT-18
❑ 86OmaRoyP-9
❑ 86OmaRoyT-5
❑ 87ChaLooB-14
❑ 88CalCanC-21
❑ 88CalCanP-790
❑ 89CalCanC-15
❑ 89CalCanP-530
❑ 92MarMot-27
❑ 96EveAquB-28

Hansen, Ron
❑ 83TriTriT-17

Hansen, Ron Lavern
❑ 47PM1StaP1-77
❑ 56BalOriP-23
❑ 58BalOriP-9
❑ 59Top-444
❑ 60OriJayP-4
❑ 60Top-127
❑ 60TopVen-127
❑ 60RivRedWB-6
❑ 61BalOriP-11
❑ 61Pos-72A
❑ 61Pos-72B
❑ 61SevElev-10
❑ 61Top-240
❑ 61TopStal-102
❑ 62BalOriP-11
❑ 62Jel-30
❑ 62Pos-30A
❑ 62Pos-30B
❑ 62PosCan-30
❑ 62SalPlaC-89
❑ 62ShiPlaC-89
❑ 62Top-245
❑ 62TopStal-6
❑ 63BasMagM-34
❑ 63Fle-2
❑ 63Jel-60
❑ 63Pos-60
❑ 63Top-88
❑ 63WhiSoxJP-3
❑ 63WhiSoxTS-8
❑ 64Top-384
❑ 64TopCoi-41
❑ 64TopRooAB-9
❑ 64WhiSoxI-11
❑ 64WhiSoxTS-10
❑ 65MacSta-4
❑ 65OPC-146
❑ 65Top-146
❑ 65WhiSoxJP-1
❑ 66Top-261
❑ 66TopVen-261
❑ 66WhiSoxTI-5
❑ 67CokCapWS-10
❑ 67DexPre-88
❑ 67OPC-9
❑ 67Top-9
❑ 67TopVen-233
❑ 68SenTeal-5
❑ 68Top-411
❑ 69MilBra-102
❑ 69Top-566
❑ 70MLBOffS-184
❑ 70OPC-217
❑ 70Top-217
❑ 70YanPhoS-13
❑ 71MLBOffS-489
❑ 71OPC-419
❑ 71Top-419
❑ 72MilBra-129
❑ 72Top-763
❑ 78TCM60I-142
❑ 80BreTeal-11
❑ 83BrePol-NNO
❑ 83FraBroR-7
❑ 85ExpPos-9
❑ 86ExpProPa-28
❑ 87ExpPos-9
❑ 87SpoRea-11
❑ 88ExpPos-11
❑ 89ExpPos-12
❑ 91OriCro-177
❑ 92BreCarT-xx
❑ 92YanWIZ7-66

Hansen, Snipe (Roy)
❑ 34DiaMatCSB-85
❑ 93ConTSN-953

Hansen, Sydney
❑ 26Zee-138
❑ 28Zee-131

Hansen, Terrel
❑ 87JamExpP-2547
❑ 89RocExpLC-11
❑ 90Bes-169
❑ 90CMC-690
❑ 90JacExpB-9
❑ 90JacExpP-1384
❑ 90ProAaA-54
❑ 91LinDriAAA-556
❑ 91TidTidLD-556
❑ 91TidTidP-2522
❑ 92SkyAAAF-251
❑ 92StaClu-878
❑ 92StaCluECN-878
❑ 92TidTidF-905
❑ 92TidTidS-557
❑ 93ClaFS7-277
❑ 93OttLynF-2445
❑ 94JacSunF-1425
❑ 95JacSunTI-16
❑ 96JacSunB-17

Hansen, Todd
❑ 86MacPirP-12
❑ 88ChaRaiP-1206
❑ 89RivRedWB-6
❑ 89RivRedWCLC-22
❑ 89RivRedWP-1413
❑ 90WicWraRD-7

Hanson, Craig
❑ 91SpolndC-15
❑ 91SpolndP-3945
❑ 92ChaRaiF-118
❑ 93WatDiaC-17
❑ 93WatDiaF-1762
❑ 94RanCucQC-14
❑ 94RanCucQF-1631
❑ 95MemChiTI-19
❑ 96PorCitRB-15

Hanson, Erik
❑ 87ChaLooB-10
❑ 88CalCanP-786
❑ 89BlaYNPRWL-191
❑ 89Bow-206
❑ 89BowTif-206
❑ 89ChaLooLITI-11
❑ 89ClaTraO-145
❑ 89Don-32
❑ 89DonBasB-320
❑ 89DonRoo-49
❑ 89Fle-549
❑ 89FleGlo-549
❑ 89MarMot-16
❑ 89TopTra-45T
❑ 89TopTraT-45T
❑ 89UppDec-766
❑ 90Bow-469
❑ 90BowTif-469
❑ 90ClaYel-T78
❑ 90Don-345
❑ 90DonBesA-68
❑ 90Fle-514
❑ 90FleCan-514
❑ 90Lea-430
❑ 90MarMot-8
❑ 90OPC-118
❑ 90PubIntS-434
❑ 90Sco-530
❑ 90Sco100RS-85
❑ 90ScoYouS2-18
❑ 90Top-118
❑ 90TopBig-289
❑ 90TopTif-118
❑ 90UppDec-235
❑ 91Bow-260
❑ 91Cla2-T22
❑ 91ClaGam-147
❑ 91Don-550
❑ 91Fle-451
❑ 91Lea-142
❑ 91MarCouH-24
❑ 91OPC-655
❑ 91PanCanT1-79
❑ 91PanFreS-235
❑ 91PanSti-186
❑ 91Sco-486
❑ 91Sco-688
❑ 91SevCoi-NW6
❑ 91StaClu-9
❑ 91Stu-114
❑ 91Top-655
❑ 91TopDesS-655
❑ 91TopMic-655
❑ 91TopTif-655
❑ 91Ult-337
❑ 91UppDec-551
❑ 92Bow-583
❑ 92Don-138
❑ 92Fle-280
❑ 92Lea-23
❑ 92LeaBlaG-23
❑ 92MarMot-7
❑ 92OPC-71
❑ 92Pin-188
❑ 92Sco-8
❑ 92StaClu-37
❑ 92Stu-233
❑ 92Top-71
❑ 92TopGol-71
❑ 92TopGolW-71
❑ 92TopKid-124
❑ 92TopMic-71
❑ 92TriPla-20
❑ 92Ult-124
❑ 92UppDec-572
❑ 93Don-317
❑ 93Fin-150
❑ 93FinRef-150
❑ 93Fla-271
❑ 93Fle-308
❑ 93Lea-354
❑ 93MariStaClu-17
❑ 93MarMot-12
❑ 93OPC-115
❑ 93PacSpa-287
❑ 93Pin-152
❑ 93Sco-136
❑ 93SP-131
❑ 93StaClu-423
❑ 93StaCluFDI-423
❑ 93StaCluMOP-423
❑ 93Top-342
❑ 93TopGol-342
❑ 93TopInaM-342
❑ 93TopInaR-342
❑ 93TopMic-342
❑ 93Ult-621
❑ 93UppDec-338
❑ 93UppDecGold-338
❑ 94ColC-124
❑ 94ColC-597
❑ 94ColChoGS-124
❑ 94ColChoGS-597
❑ 94ColChoSS-124
❑ 94ColChoSS-597
❑ 94Don-211
❑ 94Fin-395
❑ 94FinRef-395
❑ 94Fle-287
❑ 94FleExtB-232
❑ 94FleUpd-119
❑ 94Lea-426
❑ 94OPC-243
❑ 94Pin-472
❑ 94PinArtP-472
❑ 94PinMusC-472
❑ 94RedKah-13
❑ 94RedKah-30
❑ 94Sco-387
❑ 94ScoGolR-387
❑ 94ScoRoo-RT7
❑ 94ScoRooGR-RT7
❑ 94Sel-290
❑ 94StaClu-623
❑ 94StaCluFDI-623
❑ 94StaCluGR-623
❑ 94StaCluMOP-623
❑ 94Top-529
❑ 94TopGol-529
❑ 94TopSpa-529
❑ 94TopTra-73T
❑ 94Ult-472
❑ 94UppDec-508
❑ 94UppDecED-508
❑ 95DonTopotO-21
❑ 95Emo-13
❑ 95Fle-436
❑ 95Pac-106
❑ 95StaClu-95
❑ 95StaCluFDI-95
❑ 95StaCluMOP-95
❑ 95StaCluSTWS-95
❑ 95Top-322
❑ 95TopTra-78T
❑ 95UppDec-483
❑ 96BluJayOH-15
❑ 96ColCho-65
❑ 96ColCho-790
❑ 96ColChoGS-65
❑ 96ColChoSS-65
❑ 96Don-175
❑ 96DonPreP-175
❑ 96EmoXL-133
❑ 96Fla-186
❑ 96Fle-28
❑ 96FleTif-28
❑ 96FleUpd-U96
❑ 96FleUpdTC-U96
❑ 96LeaSigA-95
❑ 96LeaSigAG-95
❑ 96LeaSigAS-95
❑ 96MetUni-121
❑ 96MetUniP-121
❑ 96Pac-247
❑ 96Pin-311
❑ 96PinFoil-311
❑ 96Sco-318
❑ 96ScoDugC-B43
❑ 96ScoDugCAP-B43
❑ 96SP-184
❑ 96StaClu-394
❑ 96StaCluEPB-394
❑ 96StaCluEPG-394
❑ 96StaCluEPS-394
❑ 96StaCluMOP-394
❑ 96Top-383
❑ 96Ult-431
❑ 96UltGolM-431
❑ 96UppDec-510U
❑ 97BluJayOH-15
❑ 97BluJayS-14
❑ 97ColCho-501
❑ 97Sco-467
❑ 97ScoArtPWB-467
❑ 97ScoResC-467
❑ 97ScoShoS-467
❑ 97ScoShoSAP-467
❑ 97Top-38
❑ 98PacOnl-767
❑ 98PacOnlR-767
❑ 98PacOnlWC-767

Hanson, Kris
❑ 93WatIndC-12
❑ 93WatIndF-3557
❑ 94ColRedF-438
❑ 95KinIndTI-14
❑ 96KenIndB-11

Hanson, R.C.
❑ 40WheM4-9
❑ 41WheM5-14

Hanson, Roy
❑ 35DiaMatCS3T1-68

Hanyuda, Tad
❑ 88SanJosGCLC-119
❑ 88SanJosGP-128

Hanyzewski, Ed
❑ 42CubTeal-8
❑ 43CubTeal-10
❑ 44CubTeal-11

Hapeman, A.G.
❑ 87OldJudN-227

Hara, Hidefumi
❑ 92SalSpuC-18
❑ 92SalSpuF-3768

Hara, Shunsuke
❑ 96HonShaHWB-2

Haraguchi, Ted
❑ 87SanJosBP-10

Harber, Ryan
❑ 99TeaBesR-33
❑ 99TeaBesRG-33
❑ 99TeaBesRS-33

Harbor Seal, Polly the
❑ 98NewHavRM-22
❑ 98NewHavRMA-22

Hard, Shelby
❑ 90EveGiaB-23

Hardamon, Derrick
❑ 86GenCubP-9

Harden, Billie
❑ 97NegLeaPC-12S

Harden, Curry
❑ 88CapCodPPaLP-67

Harden, Jon
❑ 88MisStaB-10
❑ 89MisStaB-17
❑ 90MisStaB-16
❑ 91MisStaB-21
❑ 92MisStaB-16
❑ 92SalLakTSP-20

Harden, Nat
❑ 92MisStaB-17
❑ 93MisStaB-17
❑ 98DanBraQ-13

Harden, Ty
❑ 85BurRanT-21
❑ 86DayBealP-10

Harder, Mel
❑ 32OrbPinNP-29
❑ 32OrbPinUP-30
❑ 33TatOrb-30
❑ 33WorCig-52
❑ 34BatR31-134
❑ 34DiaMatCSB-86
❑ 34Gou-66
❑ 35DiaMatCS3T1-69
❑ 35ExhFou-11
❑ 35GouPuzR-8I
❑ 35GouPuzR-9I
❑ 36ExhFou-11
❑ 36GouWidPPR-A46
❑ 36GouWidPPR-C15
❑ 36NatChiFPR-40
❑ 36R31PasP-13
❑ 36R31Pre-G10
❑ 36R31Pre-L5
❑ 36SandSW-29
❑ 38CloFotW-35
❑ 41DouPlaR-133

❑ 47IndTeal-13
❑ 47IndVanPP-12
❑ 48IndTeal-14
❑ 49IndTeal-29
❑ 55IndGolS-28
❑ 57IndTeal-8
❑ 59Ind-6
❑ 60Top-460
❑ 75TCM195Cl-12
❑ 76GrePlaG-27
❑ 77GalGloG-81
❑ 79DiaGre-287
❑ 81DiaStaCD-113
❑ 82DiaCla-91
❑ 82OhiHaloF-37
❑ 83ConMar-23
❑ 88ConAmeA-14
❑ 89PacLegI-205
❑ 89SweBasG-41
❑ 93UppDecS-30
❑ 94ConTSN-1079
❑ 94ConTSNB-1079

Hardge, Michael
❑ 92RocExpC-6
❑ 92RocExpF-2124
❑ 93WesPalBEC-8
❑ 93WesPalBEF-1347
❑ 94HarSenF-2098
❑ 95PawRedSDD-11
❑ 95PawRedTI-10
❑ 95TreThuTI-29
❑ 98ArkTraM-11

Hardgrave, Eric
❑ 86BeaGolGP-13
❑ 87ElPasDP-7
❑ 88GleFalTP-915

Hardgrove, Tom
❑ 88CapCodPPaLP-132
❑ 89MarPhiS-14
❑ 89Sta-144
❑ 90Bes-38
❑ 90SpaPhiB-1
❑ 90SpaPhiP-2498
❑ 90SpaPhiS-12

Hardie, Pop
❑ 88SFHesCreN32-12A
❑ 88SFHesCreN32-12B

Hardin, Jim
❑ 67BalOriP-45
❑ 68Top-222
❑ 68TopVen-222
❑ 69MilBra-103
❑ 69Top-532
❑ 69Top-610
❑ 69TopSta-124
❑ 70BalOriP-12
❑ 70Top-656
❑ 71BalOriP-13
❑ 71MLBOffS-298
❑ 71OPC-491
❑ 71Top-491
❑ 72MilBra-130
❑ 72OPC-287
❑ 72Top-287
❑ 73OPC-124
❑ 73Top-124
❑ 91OriCro-178
❑ 92YanWIZ7-67

Harding, Greg
❑ 88St.CatBJP-2029
❑ 89MyrBeaBJP-1469

Harding, Todd
❑ 97BurIndG-12

Harding, Warren G.
❑ 94UppDecTAE-36

Hardtke, Jason
❑ 91Cla/Bes-7
❑ 91CollndC-25
❑ 91CollndP-1492
❑ 92MidLeaATI-16
❑ 92ProFS7-59
❑ 92UppDecML-98
❑ 92WatDiaC-21
❑ 92WatDiaF-2150
❑ 93RanCucQC-15
❑ 93RanCucQF-840
❑ 94ClaGolF-141
❑ 94ExcFS7-282
❑ 94Top-527
❑ 94TopGol-527
❑ 94TopSpa-527
❑ 94WicWraF-198
❑ 95BinMetTI-20
❑ 96BinMetB-12
❑ 96NorTidB-17
❑ 97NorTid-16
❑ 97NorTidB-16
❑ 98IowCubQ-12

Hardwick, Anthony
❑ 86BakDodP-12

Hardwick, Bill
❑ 94ClaGolF-175

Hardwick, Bubba
❑ 93StoPorC-14
❑ 93StoPorF-741
❑ 97StoPor-12
❑ 98El PasDG-16

Hardwick, Joe
❑ 92BoiHawC-3
❑ 92BoiHawF-3643
❑ 93CedRapKC-8
❑ 93CedRapKF-1751

Hardwick, Willie
❑ 82AmaGolST-19
❑ 83BeaGolGT-18
❑ 84ArkTraT-15

Hardy, Alex
❑ 12ImpTobC-78

Hardy, Bryan
❑ 96BurIndB-20

Hardy, Carlton
❑ 91MarPhiC-10
❑ 91MarPhiP-3461

Hardy, Carroll
❑ 58Top-446
❑ 59Ind-7
❑ 59SeaPop-20
❑ 59Top-168
❑ 59TopVen-168
❑ 60Top-341
❑ 61Top-257
❑ 62SalPlaC-220
❑ 62ShiPlaC-220
❑ 62Top-101
❑ 62TopVen-101
❑ 63Col45"P-7
❑ 63Top-468

Hardy, Hayland
❑ 93HelBreF-4109
❑ 93HelBreSP-16

Hardy, Jack
❑ 82GleFalWST-18
❑ 86BirBarTI-16
❑ 87BirBarB-18
❑ 87HawIsIP-3
❑ 88VanCanC-10
❑ 88VanCanP-755
❑ 89VanCanC-5
❑ 89VanCanP-586
❑ 90CMC-151
❑ 90OklCit8C-1
❑ 90OklCit8P-425
❑ 90ProAAAF-671
❑ 90TopDeb89-51

Hardy, Larry (Howard L.)
❑ 74PadDea-12
❑ 74PadTeal-6
❑ 75HawIsIC-15
❑ 75OPC-112
❑ 75Top-112
❑ 75TopMin-112
❑ 76HouAstP-13
❑ 76SSP-120
❑ 78ChaChaT-8
❑ 79ChaChaT-15
❑ 80KnoBluJT-18
❑ 80UtiBluJT-1
❑ 82KnoBluJT-21
❑ 84SyrChiT-2
❑ 86KnoBluJP-9
❑ 87AstShoSPT-10
❑ 87PhoFirP-11
❑ 90CMC-688
❑ 90PhoFirC-26
❑ 90PhoFirP-29
❑ 90ProAAAF-55
❑ 91LinDriAAA-400
❑ 91PhoFirP-85
❑ 92TexLon-20
❑ 95RanCra-14
❑ 96RanDr P-14
❑ 96RanMot-28
❑ 97RanDr P-13

Hardy, Mark
❑ 86JamExpP-12

Hare, Shawn
❑ 89LakTigS-8
❑ 89Sta-156
❑ 90CMC-391
❑ 90ProAAAF-392
❑ 90TolMudHC-14
❑ 90TolMudHP-162
❑ 91LinDriAAA-586
❑ 91TolMudHLD-586
❑ 91TolMudHP-1944
❑ 92DonRoo-48
❑ 92FleUpd-23
❑ 92Pin-598
❑ 92Sco-828
❑ 92SkyAAAF-263
❑ 92StaClu-465
❑ 92TolMudHS-587
❑ 92TopDeb91-71
❑ 92Ult-363
❑ 93Don-305
❑ 93TolMudHF-1663
❑ 93Top-491
❑ 93TopGol-491
❑ 93TopInaM-491
❑ 93TopInaR-491
❑ 93TopMic-491
❑ 94SpoRoo-47
❑ 94SpoRooAP-47
❑ 94TolMudHF-1037
❑ 95RanCra-15
❑ 96LouRedB-20
❑ 97TolMudHB-19

Harer, Wayne
❑ 80ColCliT-4
❑ 81ColCliP-22
❑ 81ColCliT-19
❑ 82ColCliP-22
❑ 82ColCliT-3

Harford, Bill
❑ 90PeoChiTI-34

Hargan, Steve
❑ 66Top-508
❑ 67Kah-14
❑ 67Top-233
❑ 67Top-440
❑ 67TopVen-262
❑ 68Kah-B13
❑ 68OPC-35
❑ 68Top-35
❑ 68TopActS-7A
❑ 68TopGamI-15
❑ 68TopVen-35
❑ 69Top-348
❑ 70Ind-5
❑ 70OPC-136
❑ 70Top-136
❑ 71Ind-5
❑ 71MLBOffS-370
❑ 71OPC-375
❑ 71Top-375
❑ 71TopCoi-110
❑ 72MilBra-131
❑ 72Top-615
❑ 75OPC-362
❑ 75RanPos-14
❑ 75Top-362
❑ 75TopMin-362
❑ 76Kel-1
❑ 76OPC-463
❑ 76SSP-254
❑ 76Top-463
❑ 77OPC-247
❑ 77Top-37
❑ 93RanKee-170

Hargesheimer, Al
❑ 81Fle-457
❑ 81PhoGiaVNB-13
❑ 81Top-502
❑ 82PhoGiaVNB-27
❑ 83IowCubT-4
❑ 84OmaRoyT-4
❑ 85OmaRoyT-26
❑ 86OmaRoyT-21
❑ 87OmaRoyP-13
❑ 88OmaRoyC-6
❑ 88OmaRoyP-1517

Hargis, Dan
❑ 89RocExpLC-12
❑ 90JamExpP-34
❑ 91RocExpP-2050

Hargis, Gary
❑ 76ShrCapT-1
❑ 77ColCliT-6
❑ 78ColCliT-9
❑ 79PorBeaT-13
❑ 80PorBeaT-15
❑ 81BufBisT-15

Hargis, Steve
❑ 91RocExpC-29

Hargrave, Bubbles (Eugene F.)
❑ 20WalMaiW-21
❑ 21Nei-60
❑ 22E120-173
❑ 22W573-56
❑ 28Exh-14
❑ 28W502-33
❑ 28Yue-33
❑ 76ISCHooHA-21
❑ 77RedCarP-4
❑ 81ConTSN-96
❑ 91ConTSN-245
❑ 94ConTSN-1179
❑ 94ConTSNB-1179

Hargrave, Pinky (William M.)
❑ 26Exh-113
❑ 27Exh-57
❑ 31SenTealPW-13
❑ 33Gou-172
❑ 33WorCig(-35
❑ 75SenTCM1-9
❑ 76ISCHooHA-21
❑ 81ConTSN-97
❑ 94ConTSN-1179
❑ 94ConTSNB-1179
❑ 94ConTSNB-1180

Hargraves, Charles R.
❑ 27YorCarE-33
❑ 28Exh-7
❑ 29ExhFou-14

Hargreaves, Brad
❑ 98WilCubM-13

Hargreaves, Charlie
❑ 79DiaGre-77
❑ 90DodTar-316

Hargrove, Harvey
❑ 97EveAquG-11
❑ 98WisTimRM-17

Hargrove, Mike (Dudley M.)
❑ 75Hos-106
❑ 75OPC-106
❑ 75RanPos-15
❑ 75Top-106
❑ 75TopMin-106
❑ 76Hos-88
❑ 76Kel-51A
❑ 76Kel-51B
❑ 76OPC-485
❑ 76SSP-263
❑ 76Top-485
❑ 77BurCheD-24
❑ 77ChiWilD-30
❑ 77DailsID-30
❑ 77DetCaeD-30
❑ 77HolInnD-30
❑ 77Hos-18
❑ 77Kel-30
❑ 77MSADis-30
❑ 77OPC-35
❑ 77PepGloD-5
❑ 77RCColC-29
❑ 77SagDis-30
❑ 77sDis-30
❑ 77Top-275
❑ 77TopCloS-20
❑ 77WenDis-30
❑ 77ZipDis-30
❑ 78Hos-41
❑ 78Kel-56
❑ 78OPC-176
❑ 78RanBurK-11
❑ 78RCColC-32
❑ 78SSP270-82
❑ 78Top-172
❑ 79BasPat-37
❑ 79Hos-148
❑ 79OPC-311
❑ 79PadFamF-12
❑ 79Top-591
❑ 80IndTeal-12
❑ 80OPC-162
❑ 80Top-308
❑ 81AllGamPI-5
❑ 81Don-78
❑ 81Fle-387
❑ 81Kel-66
❑ 81MSAMinD-15
❑ 81OPC-74
❑ 81Top-74
❑ 81TopScr-32
❑ 81TopSti-68
❑ 82Don-389
❑ 82Dra-16
❑ 82Fle-368
❑ 82FleSta-198
❑ 82Ind-17
❑ 82IndWhe-24
❑ 82OnDecD-15
❑ 82OPC-310
❑ 82Top-310
❑ 82Top-559
❑ 82TopSti-180
❑ 83Don-450
❑ 83Fle-409
❑ 83FleSta-75
❑ 83FleSti-242
❑ 83IndPos-17
❑ 83IndWhe-16
❑ 83OPC-37
❑ 83Top-660
❑ 83TopSti-56
❑ 84Don-495
❑ 84Fle-543
❑ 84FunFooP-101
❑ 84Ind-16
❑ 84IndWhe-21
❑ 84Nes792-546
❑ 84Nes792-764
❑ 84OPC-79
❑ 84SevCoi-C10
❑ 84Top-546
❑ 84Top-764
❑ 84TopSti-260
❑ 84TopTif-546
❑ 84TopTif-764
❑ 85Don-398
❑ 85Fle-450
❑ 85GenMilS-18
❑ 85Ind-17
❑ 85IndPol-21
❑ 85OPC-252
❑ 85SubDis-12
❑ 85ThoMcAD-12
❑ 85Top-425
❑ 85TopSti-248
❑ 85TopTif-425
❑ 86Don-590
❑ 86Fle-588
❑ 86Lea-228
❑ 86RanGreT-5
❑ 86Top-136
❑ 86TopTif-136
❑ 88EasLeaAP-52
❑ 88WilBilP-1306
❑ 89ColSprSSC-10
❑ 89ColSprSSP-246
❑ 90IndTeal-15
❑ 91IndFanC-30
❑ 91TopTra-52T
❑ 91TopTraT-52T
❑ 92IndFanC-10
❑ 92OPC-609
❑ 92Top-609
❑ 92TopGol-609
❑ 92TopGolW-609
❑ 92TopMic-609
❑ 93IndWUA-10
❑ 93RanKee-171
❑ 93Top-505
❑ 93TopGol-505
❑ 93TopInaM-505
❑ 93TopInaR-505
❑ 93TopMic-505
❑ 94RanAllP-3

Harigen, Charlie
❑ 81TacTigT-29

Harikkala, Tim
❑ 92BelMarCB-9
❑ 92BelMarF-1437
❑ 93BelMarF-3203
❑ 94AppFoxC-10
❑ 94AppFoxFl-1048
❑ 94MidLeaAF-MDW2
❑ 95Exc-117
❑ 95TacRaiTI-8
❑ 96TacRaiB-13
❑ 97TacRai-16
❑ 98OrlRayM-6

Harimoto, Isao
❑ 79TCMJapPB-61

Haring, Brett
❑ 98ChaAllCM-6

Harker, Paul
❑ 92PenPilC-30
❑ 95PorCitRTI-13
❑ 96PorCitRB-4
❑ 97St.PetDR-5
❑ 97St.PetDRUB-5

Harkey, Mike
❑ 88BasAmeAAB-2
❑ 88EasLeaAP-26
❑ 88PeoChiTI-35
❑ 88PitCubP-1377
❑ 88TriAAC-15
❑ 89Bow-286
❑ 89BowTif-286
❑ 89Don-43
❑ 89Fle-427
❑ 89FleGlo-427
❑ 89IowCubC-5
❑ 89IowCubP-1704
❑ 89PanSti-48
❑ 89Sco-624
❑ 89ScoHot1R-48
❑ 89ScoYouS2-31
❑ 89Spo-132
❑ 89Top-742
❑ 89TopTif-742
❑ 89UppDec-14
❑ 90Bow-28
❑ 90BowTif-28
❑ 90ClaYel-T47
❑ 90CubMar-10
❑ 90Don-522
❑ 90DonRoo-22
❑ 90Fle-33
❑ 90FleCan-33
❑ 90Lea-309
❑ 90PeoChiTI-20
❑ 90TopTra-36T
❑ 90TopTraT-36T
❑ 90TopTVCu-9
❑ 90UppDec-107
❑ 91Bow-417
❑ 91ClaGam-22
❑ 91CubMar-22
❑ 91CubVinL-13
❑ 91Don-447
❑ 91Fle-423
❑ 91Lea-90
❑ 91OPC-376
❑ 91PanFreS-51
❑ 91PanSti-46
❑ 91Sco-322
❑ 91Sco100RS-63
❑ 91StaClu-197
❑ 91Top-376
❑ 91TopDesS-376
❑ 91TopMic-376
❑ 91TopRoo-11
❑ 91TopTif-376
❑ 91ToyRoo-10
❑ 91Ult-62
❑ 91UppDec-475
❑ 92Don-241
❑ 92Fle-382
❑ 92OPC-98
❑ 92Pin-197
❑ 92Sco-67
❑ 92StaClu-501
❑ 92Top-98
❑ 92TopGol-98
❑ 92TopGolW-98
❑ 92TopMic-98
❑ 92UppDec-218
❑ 93CubMar-9
❑ 93CubStaC-14
❑ 93Don-450
❑ 93Fle-378
❑ 93Lea-533
❑ 93OPC-110
❑ 93Pin-395
❑ 93Sco-111
❑ 93Sel-397
❑ 93StaClu-656
❑ 93StaCluFDI-656
❑ 93StaCluMOP-656
❑ 93Top-657
❑ 93TopGol-657
❑ 93TopInaM-657
❑ 93TopInaR-657
❑ 93TopMic-657
❑ 93Ult-314
❑ 93UppDec-610
❑ 93UppDecGold-610
❑ 94ColC-417
❑ 94ColChoGS-417
❑ 94ColChoSS-417
❑ 94Don-121
❑ 94Fin-259
❑ 94FinRef-259
❑ 94Fla-154
❑ 94Fle-385
❑ 94FleUpd-124
❑ 94Lea-276
❑ 94Pac-100
❑ 94Pin-171
❑ 94PinArtP-171

❑ 94PinMusC-171
❑ 94RocPol-11
❑ 94Sco-96
❑ 94ScoGolR-96
❑ 94ScoRoo-RT68
❑ 94ScoRooGR-RT68
❑ 94SpoRoo-13
❑ 94SpoRooAP-13
❑ 94StaClu-41
❑ 94StaCluFDI-41
❑ 94StaCluGR-41
❑ 94StaCluMOP-41
❑ 94StaCluT-95
❑ 94StaCluTFDI-95
❑ 94Top-272
❑ 94TopGol-272
❑ 94TopSpa-272
❑ 94Ult-161
❑ 94UppDec-372
❑ 94UppDecED-372
❑ 95AthMot-23
❑ 95FleUpd-71
❑ 95Pin-343
❑ 95PinArtP-343
❑ 95PinMusC-343
❑ 96Fle-49
❑ 96FleTif-49
❑ 96Sco-434
❑ 97AlbDukGS-12

Harkins, John
❑ 87OldJudN-228

Harkins, W. E.
❑ 09ObaT21-101

Harkness, Don
❑ 77CocAstT-8
❑ 78DayBeaAT-9

Harkness, Specs (Frederick)
❑ 11PinT-5-614
❑ 11Zee-47
❑ 12HomRunKE-38
❑ 12Zee-60
❑ 14Zee-132

Harkness, Tim (Thomas W.)
❑ 61UniOil-SP7
❑ 62DodVol-24
❑ 62Top-404
❑ 63Top-436
❑ 64MetJayP-5
❑ 64MetTeal-4
❑ 64Top-57
❑ 64TopVen-57
❑ 90DodTar-317
❑ 91MetWIZ-159

Harkrider, Kip
❑ 98SanAntMG-12

Harkrider, Tim
❑ 93Tex-2
❑ 94Bow-201
❑ 94MidAngF-2445
❑ 94MidAngOHP-8
❑ 95MidAngOHP-16
❑ 95MidAngTI-14
❑ 96BesAutS-35
❑ 96Top-427
❑ 97MidAng-15

Harlan, Dan
❑ 88BasCitRS-13

Harley, Al
❑ 91AshTouP-575
❑ 91Cla/Bes-101
❑ 92BurAstC-23
❑ 92BurAstF-555
❑ 93OscAstC-13
❑ 93OscAstF-637

Harley, Quentin
❑ 95MemChiTI-3

Harley, Richard
❑ 03BreE10-65

Harlow, Larry
❑ 76SSP-397
❑ 77BalOriP-8
❑ 77RocRedWM-13
❑ 78BalOriP-11
❑ 78Top-543
❑ 79Top-314
❑ 80Top-68
❑ 81Fle-289
❑ 81LonBeaPT-25
❑ 81Top-121
❑ 82Fle-462
❑ 82Top-257
❑ 83LasVegSBHN-9
❑ 89TopSenL-103
❑ 91OriCro-179
❑ 91PacSenL-20

Harmes, Kris
❑ 90MedHatBJB-20
❑ 91DunBluJC-29
❑ 91DunBluJP-210
❑ 91St.CatBJC-4
❑ 91St.CatBJP-3397
❑ 92DunBluJC-9
❑ 92St.CatBJC-16
❑ 92St.CatBJF-3388
❑ 93HagSunC-12
❑ 93HagSunF-1881
❑ 93SouAtlLAGF-26
❑ 94ClaGolF-89
❑ 94DunBluJC-11
❑ 94DunBluJF-2559
❑ 95AusFut-32
❑ 95KnoSmoF-43
❑ 96KnoSmoB-15

Harmon, Brian
❑ 94GreFalDSP-9
❑ 95YakBeaTI-13
❑ 96SavSanB-5

Harmon, Chuck (Charles)
❑ 54Top-182
❑ 55Top-82
❑ 55TopDouH-55
❑ 56Top-308
❑ 57Top-299
❑ 58Top-48
❑ 94TopArc1-182
❑ 94TopArc1G-182

Harmon, Kevin
❑ 86SumBraP-8
❑ 87SumBraP-12
❑ 95RocRedWTI-48

Harmon, Larry
❑ 76BatTroTI-11

Harmon, Mark
❑ 92ColMetPI-38

Harmon, Merle
❑ 75BreBro-4

Harmon, Robert
❑ 09PC7HHB-19
❑ 09SpoNewSM-78
❑ 10DomDisP-52
❑ 10JuJuDE-20
❑ 10SweCapPP-147
❑ 11HelSta-170
❑ 11PinT-5-365
❑ 11PloCanE-31
❑ 11SpoLifCW-156
❑ 11SpoLifM-269
❑ 11T205-71A
❑ 11T205-71B
❑ 12HasTriFT-12
❑ 12T207-76
❑ 14PieStaT-50
❑ 14TexTomE-22
❑ 15SpoNewM-75
❑ 16FleBreD-37
❑ 16SpoNewM-76

Harmon, Terry
❑ 69Top-624
❑ 70OPC-486
❑ 70Top-486
❑ 71MLBOffS-179
❑ 71OPC-682
❑ 71PhiArcO-4
❑ 71Top-682
❑ 72OPC-377
❑ 72Top-377
❑ 72TopCloT-16
❑ 73OPC-166
❑ 73PhiTeal-8
❑ 73Top-166
❑ 74OPC-642
❑ 74Top-642
❑ 75OPC-399
❑ 75PhiPhiP-14
❑ 75Top-399
❑ 75TopMin-399
❑ 76OPC-247
❑ 76PhiPhiP-11
❑ 76Top-247
❑ 77Top-388
❑ 78SSP270-37
❑ 78Top-118

Harmon, Tommy
❑ 75TulOil7-22
❑ 76TulOilGP-3
❑ 82CubRedL-NNO
❑ 83MidCubT-2
❑ 92TexLon-21

Harmon, Wayne
❑ 83CedRapRF-6
❑ 83CedRapRT-28

Harms, Tom
❑ 87NewOriP-28
❑ 88HagSunS-8
❑ 89FreKeyS-9

Harnisch, Pete
❑ 88BasAmeAAB-11
❑ 88ChaKniTI-18
❑ 88RocRedWGCP-10
❑ 88SouLeaAJ-32
❑ 89BalOriP-10
❑ 89Bow-4
❑ 89BowTif-4
❑ 89Don-44
❑ 89OriFreB-42
❑ 89RocRedWP-1649
❑ 89ScoRoo-110T
❑ 89UppDec-744
❑ 90Bow-247
❑ 90BowTif-247
❑ 90ClaBlu-44
❑ 90Don-596
❑ 90DonBesA-101
❑ 90Fle-177
❑ 90FleCan-177
❑ 90Lea-39
❑ 90OPC-324
❑ 90Sco-355
❑ 90Sco100RS-76
❑ 90ScoYouS2-19
❑ 90Top-324
❑ 90TopRoo-12
❑ 90TopTif-324
❑ 90ToyRoo-14
❑ 90UppDec-623
❑ 91AstMot-3
❑ 91Bow-555
❑ 91Don-181
❑ 91Fle-474
❑ 91FleUpd-89
❑ 91Lea-245
❑ 91OPC-179
❑ 91OriCro-180
❑ 91RedFolS-45
❑ 91Sco-492
❑ 91ScoRoo-36T
❑ 91StaClu-343
❑ 91StaCluMO-17
❑ 91Stu-177
❑ 91Top-179
❑ 91TopDesS-179
❑ 91TopMic-179
❑ 91TopTif-179
❑ 91TopTra-53T
❑ 91TopTraT-53T
❑ 91UltUpd-83
❑ 91UppDec-302
❑ 91UppDec-772
❑ 91USPlaCA-3S
❑ 92AstMot-3
❑ 92Bow-514
❑ 92Cla2-T9
❑ 92ClaGam-4
❑ 92Don-235
❑ 92Fle-435
❑ 92Hig5-40
❑ 92Lea-77
❑ 92LeaBlaG-77
❑ 92OPC-765
❑ 92PanSti-159
❑ 92Pin-196
❑ 92PinTea2-67
❑ 92Sco-224
❑ 92Sco100S-12
❑ 92StaClu-391
❑ 92StaCluD-77
❑ 92Stu-36
❑ 92Top-765
❑ 92TopGol-765
❑ 92TopGolW-765
❑ 92TopMic-765
❑ 92TriPla-175
❑ 92Ult-204
❑ 92UppDec-635
❑ 92UppDecTMH-25
❑ 93AstMot-3
❑ 93AstStaC-19
❑ 93Bow-448
❑ 93Don-272
❑ 93Fin-62
❑ 93FinRef-62
❑ 93Fla-64
❑ 93Fle-52
❑ 93Lea-51
❑ 93OPC-185
❑ 93PacSpa-124
❑ 93PanSti-168
❑ 93Pin-113
❑ 93RedFolS-40
❑ 93Sco-395
❑ 93Sel-219
❑ 93SP-35
❑ 93StaClu-110
❑ 93StaCluFDI-110
❑ 93StaCluMOP-110
❑ 93Top-195
❑ 93TopComotH-21
❑ 93TopGol-195
❑ 93TopInaM-195
❑ 93TopInaR-195
❑ 93TopMic-195
❑ 93TriPla-241
❑ 93Ult-42
❑ 93UppDec-97
❑ 93UppDecGold-97
❑ 94AstMot-9
❑ 94Bow-286
❑ 94ColC-534
❑ 94ColChoGS-534
❑ 94ColChoSS-534
❑ 94Don-113
❑ 94Fin-120
❑ 94FinRef-120
❑ 94Fla-171
❑ 94Fle-492
❑ 94FleExtB-275
❑ 94FleSmo'nH-4
❑ 94Lea-398
❑ 94OPC-73
❑ 94Pac-267
❑ 94Pin-45
❑ 94PinArtP-45
❑ 94PinMusC-45
❑ 94Sco-78
❑ 94ScoGolR-78
❑ 94Sel-284
❑ 94Spo-113
❑ 94StaClu-190
❑ 94StaCluFDI-190
❑ 94StaCluGR-190
❑ 94StaCluMOP-190
❑ 94Top-456
❑ 94TopGol-456
❑ 94TopSpa-456
❑ 94TriPla-28
❑ 94Ult-504
❑ 94UppDec-379
❑ 94UppDecED-379
❑ 94USPlaCA-7S
❑ 95Bow-379
❑ 95ColCho-322
❑ 95ColChoGS-322
❑ 95ColChoSS-322
❑ 95Don-119
❑ 95DonPreP-119
❑ 95DonTopotO-292
❑ 95Fin-317
❑ 95FinRef-317
❑ 95Fla-384
❑ 95Fle-462
❑ 95FleUpd-112
❑ 95Lea-302
❑ 95MetColP-14
❑ 95Pac-188
❑ 95Pin-121
❑ 95PinArtP-121
❑ 95PinMusC-121
❑ 95Sco-509
❑ 95ScoGolR-509
❑ 95ScoPlaTS-509
❑ 95Sel-151
❑ 95SelArtP-151
❑ 95StaClu-535
❑ 95StaCluMOP-535
❑ 95StaCluSTWS-535
❑ 95Top-48
❑ 95TopCyb-36
❑ 95TopTra-141T
❑ 95UppDec-361
❑ 95UppDecED-361
❑ 95UppDecEDG-361
❑ 96ColCho-624
❑ 96ColChoGS-624
❑ 96ColChoSS-624
❑ 96Don-346
❑ 96DonPreP-346
❑ 96FleUpd-U157
❑ 96FleUpdTC-U157
❑ 96LeaSigA-96
❑ 96LeaSigAG-96
❑ 96LeaSigAS-96
❑ 96MetKah-12
❑ 96MetKah-12
❑ 96Sco-456
❑ 96StaClu-320
❑ 96StaCluMOP-320
❑ 96Top-333
❑ 96UppDec-403
❑ 97ColCho-172
❑ 97Fle-396
❑ 97FleTif-396
❑ 97StaClu-68
❑ 97StaCluMOP-68
❑ 97Top-125
❑ 97Ult-397
❑ 97UltGolME-397
❑ 97UltPlaME-397
❑ 97UppDec-432
❑ 98ColCho-347
❑ 98PacOnl-190
❑ 98PacOnlR-190
❑ 98PacOnlWC-190
❑ 98Ult-389
❑ 98UltGolM-389
❑ 98UltMas-389
❑ 98UltPlaM-389
❑ 98UppDec-663
❑ 99Fle-187
❑ 99FleSta9-187
❑ 99FleWarT-187
❑ 99Pac-112
❑ 99PacOme-64
❑ 99PacOmeC-64
❑ 99PacOmeG-64
❑ 99PacOmePB-64
❑ 99PacPlaB-112
❑ 99PacRed-112
❑ 99SkyPre-113
❑ 99SkyPreR-113
❑ 99SkyThu-188
❑ 99SkyThuRant-188
❑ 99SkyThuRave-188
❑ 99StaClu-104
❑ 99StaCluFDI-104
❑ 99StaCluOoaK-104
❑ 99StaCluPP-104
❑ 99ThuSkySupR-188
❑ 99Top-388
❑ 99TopChr-388
❑ 99TopChrR-388
❑ 99TopMVPP-388
❑ 99UD Cho-74
❑ 99UD ChoP-74
❑ 99UD ChoPCR-74
❑ 99Ult-157
❑ 99UltGolM-157
❑ 99UltMas-157
❑ 99UltPlaM-157
❑ 99UppDec-349
❑ 99UppDecEL1-349
❑ 99UppDecEL2-349
❑ 99UppDecM-53
❑ 99UppDecMGS-53
❑ 99UppDecMHFS-53
❑ 99UppDecMP-53
❑ 99UppDecMSS-53
❑ 99Vic-104

Harnisch, Ron
❑ 92AshTouC-30

Haro, Sam
❑ 84PriWilPT-22
❑ 85NasPirT-11
❑ 86HawIslP-11
❑ 87VanCanP-1607

Harp, Scott
❑ 96SpoIndB-13

Harper, Brandon
❑ 98KanCouC-13
❑ 98KanCouCCP-13

Harper, Brian
❑ 88MarPhiS-16

Harper, Brian David
❑ 78QuaCitAT-8
❑ 80ElPasDT-9
❑ 80VenLeaS-217
❑ 81SalLakCGT-15
❑ 84Don-142
❑ 84Nes792-144
❑ 84Pir-7
❑ 84Top-144
❑ 84TopTif-144
❑ 85CarTeal-11
❑ 85Don-566
❑ 85Fle-466
❑ 85Top-332
❑ 85TopTif-332
❑ 86CarKASD-8
❑ 86CarTeal-15
❑ 86Don-547
❑ 86Fle-36
❑ 86NasSouTI-10
❑ 86Top-656
❑ 86TopTif-656
❑ 88FleUpd-42
❑ 88FleUpdG-42
❑ 88PorBeaC-11
❑ 88PorBeaP-651
❑ 89Bow-155
❑ 89BowTif-155
❑ 89Don-641
❑ 89Fle-114
❑ 89FleGlo-114
❑ 89Sco-408
❑ 89Top-472
❑ 89TopTif-472
❑ 89UppDec-379
❑ 90Don-355
❑ 90DonBesA-37
❑ 90El PasDAGTI-35
❑ 90Fle-377
❑ 90FleCan-377
❑ 90Lea-479
❑ 90OPC-47
❑ 90PanSti-116
❑ 90PubIntS-329
❑ 90Sco-189
❑ 90Spo-121
❑ 90Top-47
❑ 90TopSti-290
❑ 90TopTif-47
❑ 90UppDec-391
❑ 91Bow-333
❑ 91Cla3-T35
❑ 91DodPho-15
❑ 91Don-22
❑ 91Don-398
❑ 91Don-582
❑ 91DonSupD-22
❑ 91Fle-613
❑ 91Lea-54
❑ 91OPC-554
❑ 91PanFreS-299
❑ 91PanSti-242
❑ 91Sco-312
❑ 91Sco100S-46
❑ 91StaClu-589
❑ 91Stu-86
❑ 91Top-554
❑ 91TopDesS-554
❑ 91TopMic-554
❑ 91TopTif-554
❑ 91Ult-188
❑ 91UppDec-212
❑ 92Bow-149
❑ 92Don-83
❑ 92Fle-204
❑ 92Lea-131
❑ 92LeaBlaG-131
❑ 92OPC-217
❑ 92PanSti-114
❑ 92Pin-73
❑ 92Sco-215
❑ 92ScoFacI-B4
❑ 92StaClu-296
❑ 92Stu-204
❑ 92Top-217
❑ 92TopGol-217
❑ 92TopGolW-217
❑ 92TopMic-217
❑ 92TriPla-76
❑ 92Ult-91
❑ 92UppDec-527
❑ 93Bow-537
❑ 93ColAllG-21
❑ 93Don-547
❑ 93Fin-51
❑ 93FinRef-51
❑ 93Fla-235
❑ 93Fle-266
❑ 93FleAll-AL10
❑ 93Lea-186
❑ 93OPC-125
❑ 93PacSpa-520
❑ 93PanSti-124
❑ 93Pin-54
❑ 93RedFolS-41
❑ 93Sco-72
❑ 93Sel-154
❑ 93SP-246
❑ 93StaClu-95
❑ 93StaCluFDI-95
❑ 93StaCluMOP-95
❑ 93Stu-27

❑ 93Top-389
❑ 93Top-408
❑ 93TOPBLAG-34
❑ 93TopGol-389
❑ 93TopGol-408
❑ 93TopInaM-389
❑ 93TopInaM-408
❑ 93TopInaR-389
❑ 93TopInaR-408
❑ 93TopMic-389
❑ 93TopMic-408
❑ 93TriPla-68
❑ 93TriPla-250
❑ 93Ult-582
❑ 93UppDec-110
❑ 93UppDecGold-110
❑ 94Bow-645
❑ 94BreMilB-315
❑ 94BrePol-10
❑ 94BreTeal-9
❑ 94ColC-492
❑ 94ColChoGS-492
❑ 94ColChoSS-492
❑ 94Don-196
❑ 94DonDiaK-DK6
❑ 94DonDiaKJ-DK6
❑ 94Fin-247
❑ 94FinRef-247
❑ 94Fla-304
❑ 94Fle-206
❑ 94FleExtB-103
❑ 94FleUpd-54
❑ 94Lea-290
❑ 94LeaL-43
❑ 94OPC-102
❑ 94Pac-354
❑ 94PanSti-90
❑ 94Pin-494
❑ 94PinArtP-494
❑ 94PinMusC-494
❑ 94Sco-37
❑ 94ScoGolR-37
❑ 94ScoGolS-55
❑ 94ScoRoo-RT32
❑ 94ScoRooGR-RT32
❑ 94Sel-225
❑ 94SP-58
❑ 94SPDieC-58
❑ 94SpoRoo-7
❑ 94SpoRooAP-7
❑ 94StaClu-707
❑ 94StaCluFDI-707
❑ 94StaCluGR-707
❑ 94StaCluMOP-707
❑ 94Stu-44
❑ 94Top-706
❑ 94TopGol-706
❑ 94TopSpa-706
❑ 94TopTra-21T
❑ 94TriPlaM-1
❑ 94Ult-371
❑ 94UppDec-441
❑ 94UppDecED-441
❑ 95ColCho-181
❑ 95ColChoGS-181
❑ 95ColChoSS-181
❑ 95Don-448
❑ 95DonPreP-448
❑ 95Fle-180
❑ 95Pac-232
❑ 95Sco-25
❑ 95ScoGolR-25
❑ 95ScoPlaTS-25
❑ 95UppDecSE-99
❑ 95UppDecSEG-99

Harper, David
❑ 77RocRedWM-21
❑ 77RocRedWM-22
❑ 77TucTorC-59
❑ 78TucTorC-59A

Harper, David Wayne
❑ 97LetBlaDB-22

Harper, Devallon
❑ 83KinBluJTI-7

Harper, George W.
❑ 21Exh-68
❑ 23W501-108
❑ 25Exh-41
❑ 26Exh-43
❑ 27Exh-18
❑ 28W513-85
❑ 29ExhFou-2
❑ 30Zee-30
❑ 31Zee-18
❑ 91ConTSN-246

Harper, Greg
❑ 88IdaFalBP-1847
❑ 88SumBraP-401
❑ 89SumBraP-1117
❑ 90BurBraB-22
❑ 90BurBraS-14

Harper, Harry C.
❑ 17ColE13-69
❑ 20GasAmeMBD-9
❑ 21E121So1-39
❑ 21E121So8-33
❑ 21KoBreWSI-33
❑ 22W575-52
❑ 90DodTar-318

Harper, Howard
❑ 15Zee-9
❑ 19Zee-95

Harper, Jack (Charles W.)
❑ 03BreE10-66
❑ 11SpoLifCW-157

Harper, Jon
❑ 77CedRapGT-18

Harper, Marshal
❑ 76AppFoxT-8
❑ 77AppFoxT-7

Harper, Milt
❑ 86WatIndP-12
❑ 87KinIndP-22
❑ 88WilBilP-1327
❑ 90RenSilSCLC-275

Harper, Terry
❑ 82RedPioT-22
❑ 83RedPioT-12

Harper, Terry (Terry Joe)
❑ 79RicBraT-14
❑ 80RicBraT-17
❑ 81BraPol-19
❑ 81Top-192
❑ 82BraBurKL-10
❑ 82RicBraT-24
❑ 82Top-507
❑ 83BraPol-19
❑ 83Don-607
❑ 83Fle-137
❑ 83Top-339
❑ 84BraPol-19
❑ 84Fle-180
❑ 84Nes792-624
❑ 84raPho-12
❑ 84Top-624
❑ 84TopTif-624
❑ 85BraPol-19
❑ 85Fle-327
❑ 85TopTifT-45T
❑ 85TopTra-45T
❑ 86BraPol-19
❑ 86Don-627
❑ 86Fle-516
❑ 86Lea-246
❑ 86OPC-247
❑ 86Top-247
❑ 86TopSti-41
❑ 86TopTif-247
❑ 87DonOpeD-217
❑ 87Fle-517
❑ 87FleExcS-22
❑ 87FleGlo-517
❑ 87Top-49
❑ 87TopTif-49
❑ 87TopTra-42T
❑ 87TopTraT-42T
❑ 88Fle-331
❑ 88FleGlo-331
❑ 90GreBraP-1145
❑ 91GreBraC-27
❑ 91GreBraLD-225
❑ 91GreBraP-3019
❑ 91LinDriAA-225

Harper, Tommy
❑ 62RedEnq-11
❑ 63RedEnq-11
❑ 63RedFreBC-7
❑ 63Top-158
❑ 64Kah-11
❑ 64RedJayP-3
❑ 64Top-330
❑ 64TopCoi-40
❑ 64TopSta-43
❑ 64TopVen-330
❑ 65Kah-15
❑ 65OPC-47
❑ 65RedEnq-10
❑ 65Top-47
❑ 66Kah-14
❑ 66RedVolC-5
❑ 66Top-214
❑ 66TopVen-214
❑ 67CokCapR-4
❑ 67DexPre-89
❑ 67Kah-15
❑ 67Top-392
❑ 67TopVen-294
❑ 68Top-590
❑ 69MilBra-104
❑ 69MLBOffS-95
❑ 69OPC-42
❑ 69PilPos-2
❑ 69PilWhe-2
❑ 69Top-42
❑ 69TopSta-225
❑ 69TopTeaP-9
❑ 70BreMcD-9
❑ 70BreMil-6
❑ 70BreTeal-3
❑ 70DayDaiNM-100
❑ 70Kel-74
❑ 70MLBOffS-270
❑ 70OPC-370
❑ 70SunPin-10
❑ 70Top-370
❑ 70TopBoo-11
❑ 70TopSup-9
❑ 71BazNumT-30
❑ 71BazUnn-9
❑ 71BreTeal-3
❑ 71Kel-47
❑ 71MilDud-8
❑ 71MLBOffS-437
❑ 71OPC-260
❑ 71Top-260
❑ 71TopCoi-140
❑ 71TopGreM-42
❑ 71TopSup-63
❑ 71TopTat-11
❑ 72MilBra-132
❑ 72OPC-455
❑ 72RedSoxTI-9
❑ 72Top-455
❑ 73LinPor-23
❑ 73OPC-620
❑ 73Top-620
❑ 74GreHeroBP-5
❑ 74OPC-204
❑ 74OPC-325
❑ 74Top-204
❑ 74Top-325
❑ 74TopSta-134
❑ 75CalAngP-17
❑ 75OPC-537
❑ 75Top-537
❑ 75TopMin-537
❑ 76BalOriP-17
❑ 76OPC-274
❑ 76Top-274
❑ 77PilPosR-2
❑ 77Top-414
❑ 81TCM60I-399
❑ 83Pil69G-37
❑ 90ExpPos-16
❑ 91OriCro-181
❑ 92ExpPos-17
❑ 94BreMilB-128

Harper, Travis
❑ 98HudValR-8
❑ 99Bow-372
❑ 99BowGol-372
❑ 99BowInt-372

Harrah, Doug
❑ 92SalBucC-6
❑ 92SalBucF-57
❑ 93CarMudF-2048
❑ 93CarMudTI-10
❑ 94OrlCubF-1380
❑ 95OrlCubF-3

Harrah, Toby
❑ 71SenPolP-5
❑ 71SenTealW-12
❑ 72OPC-104
❑ 72RanTeal-12
❑ 72Top-104
❑ 73LinPor-176
❑ 73OPC-216
❑ 73RanTeal-11
❑ 73SevTraC-29
❑ 73Top-216
❑ 74OPC-511
❑ 74Top-511
❑ 74TopSta-235
❑ 75Hos-14
❑ 75HosTwi-14
❑ 75OPC-131
❑ 75RanPos-16
❑ 75Top-131
❑ 75TopMin-131
❑ 76Hos-48
❑ 76HosTwi-48
❑ 76OPC-412
❑ 76SSP-264
❑ 76Top-412
❑ 77BurCheD-26
❑ 77Hos-37
❑ 77OPC-208
❑ 77Top-301
❑ 78Hos-123
❑ 78OPC-74
❑ 78RanBurK-13
❑ 78SSP270-89
❑ 78Top-44
❑ 79Hos-150
❑ 79OPC-119
❑ 79Top-234
❑ 80IndTeal-13
❑ 80OPC-333
❑ 80Top-636
❑ 81AllGamPI-33
❑ 81Don-318
❑ 81Fle-389
❑ 81OPC-67
❑ 81Top-721
❑ 81TopScr-46
❑ 81TopSti-65
❑ 82Don-72
❑ 82Fle-369
❑ 82FleSta-193
❑ 82Ind-18
❑ 82IndWhe-5
❑ 82OPC-16
❑ 82Top-532
❑ 82TopSti-177
❑ 83AllGamPI-33
❑ 83Don-13
❑ 83Don-337
❑ 83DonActA-39
❑ 83Fle-410
❑ 83Fle-635
❑ 83FleSta-76
❑ 83FleSti-247
❑ 83IndPos-18
❑ 83IndWhe-17
❑ 83Kel-44
❑ 83OPC-356
❑ 83PerCreC-25
❑ 83PerCreCG-25
❑ 83Top-141
❑ 83Top-480
❑ 83TopGloS-13
❑ 83TopSti-58
❑ 84AllGamPI-123
❑ 84Don-251
❑ 84Fle-544
❑ 84FleUpd-48
❑ 84Nes792-348
❑ 84OPC-348
❑ 84Top-348
❑ 84TopRubD-23
❑ 84TopSti-251
❑ 84TopTif-348
❑ 84TopTra-48T
❑ 84TopTraT-48T
❑ 85Fle-130
❑ 85FleUpd-49
❑ 85RanPer-11
❑ 85Top-94
❑ 85TopTif-94
❑ 85TopTifT-46T
❑ 85TopTra-46T
❑ 86Don-159
❑ 86Fle-560
❑ 86Lea-86
❑ 86OPC-72
❑ 86RanGreT-7
❑ 86RanPer-11
❑ 86Top-535
❑ 86TopMinL-32
❑ 86TopSti-238
❑ 86TopTat-19
❑ 86TopTif-535
❑ 87Don-408
❑ 87Fle-125
❑ 87FleGlo-125
❑ 87OklCit8P-12
❑ 87Top-152
❑ 87TopTif-152
❑ 88OklCit8C-25
❑ 88OklCit8P-46
❑ 88TriAAAP-51
❑ 89PacSenL-162
❑ 89RanMot-27
❑ 89RanSmo-13
❑ 89T/MSenL-44
❑ 89TopSenL-58
❑ 90EliSenL-22
❑ 90RanMot-27
❑ 91LinDri-10
❑ 91RanMot-28
❑ 91SweBasG-37
❑ 92RanMot-28
❑ 92UppDecS-12
❑ 92YanWIZ8-77
❑ 93RanKee-15
❑ 93RanKee-172
❑ 93UppDecAH-62
❑ 94RanAllP-3
❑ 94RanAllP-4
❑ 94UppDecAH-143
❑ 94UppDecAH1-143
❑ 95NorTidTI-1

Harrel, Donny
❑ 90EugEmeGS-12
❑ 91AppFoxCB-12
❑ 91AppFoxP-1718

Harrel, Greg
❑ 96OklCit8B-3
❑ 97OklCit8-4
❑ 98OklRedM-3

Harrell, Bill
❑ 58IndTeal-10
❑ 58Top-443
❑ 59Top-433
❑ 61Top-354
❑ 62SeaPop-2
❑ 63MilSau-2
❑ 63SeaPop-3
❑ 64SeaPop-6

Harrell, Greg
❑ 87PorChaRP-13
❑ 88TulDriTI-27
❑ 89TulDriGS-4
❑ 89TulDriTI-9
❑ 90TexLeaAGS-38
❑ 90TulDriTI-9
❑ 91TulDriTI-10

Harrell, John
❑ 70OPC-401
❑ 70Top-401

Harrell, Ken
❑ 98TamYanM-12

Harrell, Matt
❑ 93JamExpC-9
❑ 93JamExpF-3329

Harrell, Ray
❑ 74TCMNic-9
❑ 93ConTSN-960

Harrell, Scott
❑ 98BurBeeM-10

Harrell, Tim
❑ 98YakBeaG-19

Harrelson, Bill
❑ 68SeaPop-7
❑ 69Top-224

Harrelson, Bud (Derrel M.)
❑ 67Top-306
❑ 68OPC-132
❑ 68Top-132
❑ 68TopVen-132
❑ 69MetBoyS-2
❑ 69MetNewYDN-8
❑ 69MetTeal-6
❑ 69MetTealC-1
❑ 69MilBra-105
❑ 69MLBOffS-166
❑ 69MLBPin-45
❑ 69Top-456
❑ 69TopSta-64
❑ 69TopTeaP-24
❑ 70DayDaiNM-105
❑ 70MetTeal-6
❑ 70MetTealC-1
❑ 70MetTra-25B
❑ 70MLBOffS-77
❑ 70Top-634
❑ 71Kel-66A
❑ 71Kel-66B
❑ 71Kel-66C
❑ 71MetTeal-8
❑ 71MilDud-45
❑ 71MLBOffS-155
❑ 71OPC-355
❑ 71Top-355
❑ 71TopCoi-67
❑ 71TopGreM-55
❑ 71TopTat-104
❑ 72Kel-32A
❑ 72Kel-32B
❑ 72MetTeal-10
❑ 72MilBra-133
❑ 72OPC-53
❑ 72OPC-54
❑ 72OPC-496
❑ 72SevTraC-18
❑ 72Top-53
❑ 72Top-54
❑ 72Top-496
❑ 72TopPos-22
❑ 73LinPor-112
❑ 73MetAllEB-2
❑ 73MetTeal-4
❑ 73NewYorSNM-9
❑ 73OPC-223
❑ 73Top-223
❑ 73TopCanL-20
❑ 74MetDaiPA-9
❑ 74MetTeal-7
❑ 74OPC-380
❑ 74Top-380
❑ 74TopSta-63
❑ 75Hos-45
❑ 75OPC-395
❑ 75SSP42-16
❑ 75Top-395
❑ 75TopMin-395
❑ 76Hos-52
❑ 76HosTwi-52
❑ 76MetMSAP-1
❑ 76OPC-337
❑ 76SSP-545
❑ 76Top-337
❑ 77BurCheD-144
❑ 77MetDaiPA-7
❑ 77OPC-172
❑ 77Top-44
❑ 78Top-403
❑ 79Top-118
❑ 80OPC-294
❑ 80Top-566
❑ 81TCM60I-425
❑ 81Top-694
❑ 82MetPhoA-28
❑ 84FifNatC-2
❑ 84LitFalMT-13
❑ 84OCoandSI-79
❑ 86MetColP-17
❑ 86MetGreT-3
❑ 86MetTCM-38
❑ 86TopRos-70
❑ 87Met196T-2
❑ 87MetColP-34
❑ 88MetColP-25
❑ 88MetKah-3
❑ 89Met196C-5
❑ 89MetColP-32
❑ 89MetKah-10
❑ 89MetRinP69-14
❑ 90MetColP-8
❑ 90MetHaloF-2
❑ 90MetKah-3
❑ 90SweBasG-111
❑ 90TopTra-37T
❑ 90TopTraT-37T
❑ 90TopTVM-4
❑ 91MetColP-9
❑ 91MetKah-3
❑ 91MetPerPA-1
❑ 91MetWIZ-160
❑ 91OPC-261
❑ 91SweBasG-38
❑ 91Top-261
❑ 91TopDesS-261
❑ 91TopMic-261
❑ 91TopTif-261
❑ 92ActPacA-58
❑ 92UppDecS-10
❑ 93RanKee-173
❑ 93TedWil-56
❑ 93UppDecAH-63
❑ 94Met69CCPP-18
❑ 94Met69CS-17
❑ 94Met69T-6
❑ 94MetColP-10
❑ 94MetComR-1
❑ 94UppDecAH-69
❑ 94UppDecAH1-69
❑ 96Met69Y-4
❑ 96MetTeal-8
❑ 99SpollIGotG-81
❑ 99SpollIGotGA-30
❑ 99SpollIGotGC-21

Harrelson, Ken

❑ 64A's-8
❑ 64AthJayP-6
❑ 64Top-419
❑ 65AthJayP-7
❑ 65Top-479
❑ 66OPC-55
❑ 66Top-55
❑ 66TopRubI-38
❑ 66TopVen-55
❑ 67CokCapS-17
❑ 67DexPre-90
❑ 67OPC-188
❑ 67SenTeal-4
❑ 67Top-188
❑ 68RedSoxTI-4
❑ 68Top-566
❑ 68TopActS-10C
❑ 69MilBra-106
❑ 69MLBOffS-13
❑ 69MLBPin-8
❑ 69OPC-3
❑ 69OPC-5
❑ 69OPCDec-8
❑ 69Top-3
❑ 69Top-5
❑ 69Top-240
❑ 69Top-417
❑ 69TopDec-3
❑ 69TopDecI-15
❑ 69TopSta-134
❑ 69TopSup-4
❑ 69TopTeaP-3
❑ 69TraSta-23
❑ 70Ind-6
❑ 70Kel-68
❑ 70MLBOffS-198
❑ 70OPC-545
❑ 70Top-545
❑ 70TopPos-6
❑ 71BazNumT-15
❑ 71Ind-6
❑ 71MLBOffS-371
❑ 71OPC-510
❑ 71Top-510
❑ 71TopCoi-134
❑ 72MilBra-134
❑ 78TCM60I-247
❑ 81RedSoxBG2S-84
❑ 86WhiSoxC-NNO
❑ 88PacLegI-14

Harridge, Will
❑ 56Top-1
❑ 57Top-100
❑ 58Top-300
❑ 76ShaPiz-130
❑ 77BobParHoF-91
❑ 78DexHaloFP-19
❑ 80PerHaloFP-130
❑ 80SSPHOF-130

Harriger, Dennis
❑ 89PitMetS-6
❑ 90St.LucMS-9
❑ 91St.LucMC-21
❑ 92St.LucMCB-8
❑ 92St.LucMF-1741
❑ 93BinMetF-2329
❑ 94LasVegSF-870
❑ 96LasVegSB-13
❑ 97TolMudHB-20
❑ 98TolMudHQ-19

Harriger, Mark
❑ 96BoiHawB-14
❑ 97BoiHawG-13
❑ 97CedRapK-12
❑ 98CedRapKTI-12
❑ 99Bow-361
❑ 99BowGol-361
❑ 99BowInt-361
❑ 99JustheS-26
❑ 99JustheSAC-13
❑ 99JustheSAD-10
❑ 99JustheSJB-26
❑ 99JustheSJN-2
❑ 99SkyPreA-26
❑ 99SkyPreABlue-26
❑ 99Vic-2

Harring, Ken
❑ 89IdaFalBP-2014
❑ 90DurBulTI-5

Harrington, Jody
❑ 89EliTwiS-10
❑ 90KenTwiB-19
❑ 90KenTwiP-2288
❑ 90KenTwiS-6

Harrington, John
❑ 86MiaMarP-8
❑ 87MiaMarP-20

Harrington, Mark
❑ 94AubAstC-28
❑ 95AubAstTI-29
❑ 96AubDouB-30

Harris, Adoldo
❑ 90TamYanD-10

Harris, Andrew
❑ 28Zee-107
❑ 29Zee-112

Harris, B. Gail
❑ 56Top-91
❑ 57Top-281
❑ 58Top-309
❑ 59Top-378
❑ 60Top-152
❑ 60TopVen-152
❑ 79TCM50-275

Harris, Bill (William Milton)
❑ 23WilChoV-58

Harris, Bill (William Thomas)
❑ 58MonRoyF-11
❑ 60DarFar-18
❑ 60Top-128
❑ 60TopVen-128
❑ 90DodTar-971

Harris, Billy (James William)
❑ 59O'KAleMR-10
❑ 69Top-569
❑ 70OPC-512
❑ 70Top-512
❑ 77OrlTwiT-13

Harris, Bryan
❑ 93BoiHawC-13
❑ 93BoiHawF-3910
❑ 94LakElsSC-9
❑ 94LakElsSF-1658
❑ 95MidAngOHP-17
❑ 95MidAngTI-15
❑ 97BatCliTI-18
❑ 98ClePhiM-8
❑ 98ClePhiUM-8

Harris, Bubba (Charlie)
❑ 48A'sTeal-11
❑ 49A'sTeal-16
❑ 49PhiBul-23

Harris, Bucky (Stanley)
❑ 22E120-109
❑ 22W572-39
❑ 23MapCriV-21
❑ 23WilChoV-59
❑ 25Exh-124
❑ 26Exh-124
❑ 26SpoComoA-18
❑ 27YorCarE-41
❑ 28Exh-62
❑ 28W502-41
❑ 28Yue-41
❑ 31W517-9
❑ 33ButCanV-24
❑ 34BabRutG-32
❑ 34ButPreR-31
❑ 34DiaStaR-91
❑ 36GouBWR-16
❑ 36GouWidPPR-A47
❑ 36NatChiFPR-41
❑ 36R31PasP-32
❑ 36WorWidGV-130
❑ 40PlaBal-129
❑ 47YanTeaT-11
❑ 48BabRutS-24
❑ 48YanTeal-11
❑ 51Bow-275
❑ 52Bow-158
❑ 53BowBW-46
❑ 59FleWil-68
❑ 60SenUniMC-7
❑ 72TCMthe3-37
❑ 74TCMNic-15
❑ 75SenTCM1-10
❑ 75SenTCM1-38
❑ 75TCMAllG-14
❑ 76RowExh-10
❑ 76ShaPiz-148
❑ 77GalGloG-132
❑ 80PerHaloFP-148
❑ 80SSPHOF-148
❑ 81ConTSN-68
❑ 81TigDetN-105
❑ 86ConSer1-25
❑ 91ConTSN-61
❑ 91TopArc1-313
❑ 92ConTSN-593
❑ 92YanWIZH-15
❑ 93ConTSN-845

Harris, Buddy (Walter)
❑ 71AstTeal-10
❑ 71OPC-404
❑ 71Top-404

Harris, Candy (Alonzo)
❑ 67Top-564
❑ 68OPC-128
❑ 68Top-128
❑ 68TopVen-128

Harris, Carry
❑ 83KnoBluJT-10

Harris, Chalmer
❑ 42A'sTeal-15
❑ 56BalOriP-24

Harris, Craig
❑ 80WesHavWCT-11

Harris, D.J.
❑ 93PocPosF-4216
❑ 93PocPosSP-19
❑ 95DunBluJTI-9
❑ 96DunBluJB-13
❑ 96DunBluJTI-15
❑ 97DunBluJTI-12
❑ 98KnoSG-7

Harris, Dannie
❑ 90Bes-126
❑ 90HunStaB-7

Harris, David Stanley
❑ 25Exh-7
❑ 31SenTealPW-14
❑ 33Gou-9
❑ 33GouCanV-9

Harris, Donald
❑ 89ButCopKSP-4
❑ 90Bow-499
❑ 90BowTif-499
❑ 90CMC-793
❑ 90OPC-314
❑ 90Sco-661
❑ 90Top-314
❑ 90TopTif-314
❑ 90TulDriP-1167
❑ 90TulDriTI-10
❑ 91Bow-269
❑ 91Cla/Bes-12
❑ 91LinDriAA-583
❑ 91TulDriLD-583
❑ 91TulDriP-2785
❑ 91TulDriTI-11
❑ 92Bow-332
❑ 92ClaFS7-287
❑ 92Don-652
❑ 92Fle-660
❑ 92OPC-554
❑ 92Pin-597
❑ 92PinRool-16
❑ 92ProFS7-155
❑ 92SkyAA F-268
❑ 92StaClu-691
❑ 92StaCluNC-691
❑ 92Top-554
❑ 92TopDeb91-72
❑ 92TopGol-554
❑ 92TopGolW-554
❑ 92TopMic-554
❑ 92TulDriS-608
❑ 92Ult-443
❑ 92UppDec-11
❑ 93ClaFS7-201
❑ 93Don-291
❑ 93LinVenB-186
❑ 93OklCit8F-1637
❑ 93RanKee-174
❑ 93RanStaC-7
❑ 93Sco-254
❑ 93ScoBoyoS-21
❑ 93Sel-341
❑ 93StaClu-318
❑ 93StaCluFDI-318
❑ 93StaCluMOP-318
❑ 93Top-731
❑ 93TopGol-731
❑ 93TopInaM-731
❑ 93TopInaR-731
❑ 93TopMic-731
❑ 94Don-133
❑ 94OklCit8F-1505
❑ 94StaCluT-249
❑ 94StaCluTFDI-249
❑ 98MadBlaW-9

Harris, Doug
❑ 90EugEmeGS-13
❑ 91AppFoxCB-4
❑ 91AppFoxP-1710
❑ 92BasCitRF-3840
❑ 94MemChiF-353
❑ 96RocRedWB-16

Harris, Doyle
❑ 83LouRedR-29
❑ 84LouRedR-7
❑ 86LouRedTI-30

Harris, Eric
❑ 92KinMetC-8
❑ 92KinMetF-1534
❑ 93PitMetC-9
❑ 93PitMetF-3716
❑ 93SouOreAC-10
❑ 93SouOreAF-4077
❑ 94SouOreAC-9
❑ 94SouOreAF-3638

Harris, Frank
❑ 77EvaTriT-14
❑ 80OgdA'sT-12
❑ 82MadMusF-18
❑ 89ColMetB-26
❑ 89MedAthB-3

Harris, G.G.
❑ 93AugPirC-9
❑ 93AugPirF-1552
❑ 93WelPirC-6
❑ 93WelPirF-3364
❑ 94AugGreF-3015

Harris, Gary
❑ 90ArkRaz-14

Harris, Gene
❑ 86JamExpP-13
❑ 87WesPalBEP-677
❑ 88JacExpB-5
❑ 88JacExpP-980
❑ 89BlaYNPRWL-192
❑ 89DonBasB-325
❑ 89ExpPos-13
❑ 89FleUpd-58
❑ 89TopTra-46T
❑ 89TopTraT-46T
❑ 90Don-247
❑ 90Fle-515
❑ 90FleCan-515
❑ 90Lea-378
❑ 90MarMot-15
❑ 90OPC-738
❑ 90Sco-548
❑ 90Sco100RS-54
❑ 90Top-738
❑ 90TopDeb89-52
❑ 90TopTif-738
❑ 90UppDec-565
❑ 91Don-651
❑ 91Fle-452
❑ 91OPC-203
❑ 91Sco-627
❑ 91Top-203
❑ 91TopDesS-203
❑ 91TopMic-203
❑ 91TopTif-203
❑ 92OPC-390
❑ 92PadSmo-10
❑ 92StaClu-425
❑ 93Don-494
❑ 93Fla-134
❑ 93FleFinE-141
❑ 93Lea-517
❑ 93PacSpa-597
❑ 93PadMot-18
❑ 93SP-168
❑ 93TopTra-64T
❑ 93UppDec-657
❑ 93UppDecGold-657
❑ 94ColC-125
❑ 94ColChoGS-125
❑ 94ColChoSS-125
❑ 94Don-468
❑ 94Fin-340
❑ 94FinRef-340
❑ 94Fle-666
❑ 94FleExtB-76
❑ 94Lea-407
❑ 94Pac-526
❑ 94PadMot-16
❑ 94Pin-363
❑ 94PinArtP-363
❑ 94PinMusC-363
❑ 94Sco-138
❑ 94ScoGolR-138
❑ 94ScoRoo-RT33
❑ 94ScoRooGR-RT33
❑ 94Sel-125
❑ 94StaClu-325
❑ 94StaCluFDI-325
❑ 94StaCluGR-325
❑ 94StaCluMOP-325
❑ 94Top-514
❑ 94TopGol-514
❑ 94TopSpa-514
❑ 94TriPla-168
❑ 94Ult-576
❑ 95BalOriP-24
❑ 95FleUpd-120
❑ 95Phi-14
❑ 95PhiMel-11

Harris, Glenn
❑ 84SavCarT-18

Harris, Greg A.
❑ 79JacMetT-21
❑ 80TidTidT-11
❑ 81TidTidT-23
❑ 82IndIndTI-13
❑ 82RedCok-7
❑ 82Top-783
❑ 82TopTra-41T
❑ 83Don-295
❑ 83Fle-590
❑ 83IndIndTI-6
❑ 83Top-296
❑ 84ExpPos-12
❑ 84ExpStu-22
❑ 85Fle-35
❑ 85RanPer-27
❑ 85Top-242
❑ 85TopTif-242
❑ 85TopTifT-47T
❑ 85TopTra-47T
❑ 86Don-465
❑ 86Fle-561
❑ 86OPC-128
❑ 86RanPer-27
❑ 86Top-586
❑ 86TopSti-245
❑ 86TopTif-586
❑ 87Don-382
❑ 87Fle-126
❑ 87FleGlo-126
❑ 87FleStiC-54
❑ 87Lea-82
❑ 87OPC-44
❑ 87RanMot-11
❑ 87RanSmo-2
❑ 87Spo-126
❑ 87SpoTeaP-1
❑ 87Top-44
❑ 87TopSti-238
❑ 87TopTif-44
❑ 88AlaGolAA70TI-15
❑ 88Don-427
❑ 88Fle-468
❑ 88FleGlo-468
❑ 88FleUpd-109
❑ 88FleUpdG-109
❑ 88PhiTas-34
❑ 88Sco-179
❑ 88ScoGlo-179
❑ 88Top-369
❑ 88TopTif-369
❑ 89Don-548
❑ 89Fle-570
❑ 89FleGlo-570
❑ 89PhiTas-8
❑ 89Sco-476
❑ 89Top-627
❑ 89TopTif-627
❑ 90Don-582
❑ 90FleUpd-71
❑ 90Lea-499
❑ 90OPC-529
❑ 90PublntS-237
❑ 90Top-529
❑ 90TopTif-529
❑ 90TopTVRS-11
❑ 91Don-306
❑ 91Fle-97
❑ 91Lea-83
❑ 91MetWIZ-161
❑ 91OPC-123
❑ 91RedSoxP-9
❑ 91RedSoxP-14
❑ 91Sco-109
❑ 91StaClu-324
❑ 91Top-123
❑ 91TopDesS-123
❑ 91TopMic-123
❑ 91TopTif-123
❑ 91Ult-33
❑ 91UppDec-509
❑ 92Don-113
❑ 92Lea-154
❑ 92LeaBlaG-154
❑ 92OPC-468
❑ 92RedSoxDD-15
❑ 92Sco-156
❑ 92StaClu-49
❑ 92Stu-133
❑ 92Top-468
❑ 92TopGol-468
❑ 92TopGolW-468
❑ 92TopMic-468
❑ 92UppDec-658
❑ 93Don-663
❑ 93Fla-165
❑ 93Fle-560
❑ 93Lea-131
❑ 93PacSpa-359
❑ 93RanKee-175
❑ 93RedSoxP-17
❑ 93RedSoxWHP-13
❑ 93Sco-640
❑ 93StaClu-315
❑ 93StaCluFDI-315
❑ 93StaCluMOP-315
❑ 93Ult-511
❑ 93UppDec-414
❑ 93UppDecGold-414
❑ 94ColC-506
❑ 94ColChoGS-506
❑ 94ColChoSS-506
❑ 94Don-512
❑ 94Fin-303
❑ 94Fin-372
❑ 94FinRef-303
❑ 94Fle-34
❑ 94Pin-476
❑ 94PinArtP-476
❑ 94PinMusC-476
❑ 94Sco-272
❑ 94ScoGolR-272
❑ 94StaClu-407
❑ 94StaCluFDI-407
❑ 94StaCluGR-407
❑ 94StaCluMOP-407
❑ 94Top-738
❑ 94TopGol-738
❑ 94TopSpa-738
❑ 94Ult-15
❑ 96HudValRB-25
❑ 97HudValRB-28
❑ 97LasVegS1A-16
❑ 98St.PetDRM-29

Harris, Greg W.
❑ 85SpoIndC-7
❑ 86ChaRaiP-10
❑ 86SpoIndC-161
❑ 87ChaRaiP-3
❑ 87TexLeaAF-23
❑ 87WicPilRD-11
❑ 88BlaYNPRWLU-32
❑ 88LasVegSC-3
❑ 88LasVegSP-227
❑ 88TriAAAP-23
❑ 89BlaYNPRWLU-21
❑ 89Don-34
❑ 89DonRoo-46
❑ 89Fle-306
❑ 89FleGlo-306
❑ 89PadMag-18
❑ 89PadPos-14
❑ 89ScoRoo-87T
❑ 89Top-194
❑ 89TopTif-194
❑ 89UppDec-724
❑ 89WicWraR-19
❑ 90ClaYel-T13
❑ 90Don-65
❑ 90Fle-158
❑ 90FleCan-158
❑ 90Lea-452
❑ 90OPC-572
❑ 90PadCok-7
❑ 90PadMag-24
❑ 90PanSti-353
❑ 90Sco-257
❑ 90Sco100RS-24
❑ 90ScoYouSI-18
❑ 90Top-572
❑ 90TopRoo-13
❑ 90TopTif-572
❑ 90UppDec-622
❑ 91Bow-657
❑ 91Don-131
❑ 91Fle-531
❑ 91Lea-422
❑ 91OPC-749

❑ 91PadMag-13
❑ 91PadSmo-13
❑ 91Sco-251
❑ 91StaClu-205
❑ 91Top-749
❑ 91TopDesS-749
❑ 91TopMic-749
❑ 91TopTif-749
❑ 91Ult-304
❑ 91UppDec-489
❑ 92Bow-269
❑ 92Don-49
❑ 92Fle-606
❑ 92Lea-10
❑ 92LeaBlaG-10
❑ 92OPC-636
❑ 92PadCarJ-8
❑ 92PadMot-2
❑ 92PadPolD-9
❑ 92PadSmo-11
❑ 92Pin-169
❑ 92Sco-378
❑ 92StaClu-275
❑ 92Stu-105
❑ 92Top-636
❑ 92TopGol-636
❑ 92TopGolW-636
❑ 92TopMic-636
❑ 92TriPla-157
❑ 92Ult-278
❑ 92UppDec-306
❑ 93Don-154
❑ 93Fle-139
❑ 93Lea-82
❑ 93PacSpa-258
❑ 93PadMot-5
❑ 93Sco-599
❑ 93StaClu-312
❑ 93StaCluFDI-312
❑ 93StaCluMOP-312
❑ 93Top-78
❑ 93Top-436
❑ 93TopGol-78
❑ 93TopGol-436
❑ 93TopInaM-78
❑ 93TopInaM-436
❑ 93TopInaR-78
❑ 93TopInaR-436
❑ 93TopMic-78
❑ 93TopMic-436
❑ 93Ult-117
❑ 93UppDec-724
❑ 93UppDecGold-724
❑ 94ColC-126
❑ 94ColChoGS-126
❑ 94ColChoSS-126
❑ 94Don-193
❑ 94FinRef-372
❑ 94Fle-442
❑ 94FleExtB-246
❑ 94Lea-416
❑ 94Pin-470
❑ 94PinArtP-470
❑ 94PinMusC-470
❑ 94ProMag-44
❑ 94RocPol-12
❑ 94Sco-374
❑ 94ScoGolR-374
❑ 94StaClu-560
❑ 94StaCluFDI-560
❑ 94StaCluGR-560
❑ 94StaCluMOP-560
❑ 94StaCluT-99
❑ 94StaCluTFDI-99
❑ 94Top-18
❑ 94TopGol-18
❑ 94TopSpa-18
❑ 94Ult-481
❑ 94UppDec-194
❑ 94UppDecED-194
❑ 95Don-400
❑ 95DonPreP-400
❑ 95Fle-520
❑ 95Top-268
Harris, Gregg S.
❑ 88WicPilRD-19
Harris, J.T.
❑ 98ButCopKG-14
Harris, James
❑ 89KinMetS-12
❑ 89Sta-172
❑ 90ColMetGS-7
❑ 90ColMetPPI-5
❑ 90SouAtlLAS-32
❑ 90StaFS7-99
❑ 91St.LucMC-8
❑ 91St.LucMP-717
❑ 92St.LucMCB-6
❑ 92St.LucMF-1751
Harris, Jeff
❑ 96ForWayWB-10
❑ 97ForMyeM-13
❑ 98NewBriRCM-13
Harris, Joe
❑ 22E120-4
❑ 22W572-38
❑ 22W573-57
❑ 28W502-51
❑ 28W513-81
❑ 28Yue-51
❑ 75SenTCM1-11
❑ 90DodTar-319
❑ 94ConTSN-1241
❑ 94ConTSNB-1241
Harris, John
❑ 92GulCoaMF-3472
❑ 93YakBeaF-3896
Harris, John Thomas
❑ 77QuaCitAT-14
❑ 79SalLakCGT-16A
❑ 80SalLakCGT-12
❑ 81Top-214
❑ 82Don-444
❑ 82Fle-463
❑ 82SpoIndT-16
❑ 82Top-313
❑ 83IndIndTI-29
❑ 84EvaTriT-15
Harris, Josh
❑ 96BilMusTI-12
❑ 98BurBeeM-11
Harris, Julian
❑ 98ButCopKG-15
Harris, Keith
❑ 89UtiBluSP-10
Harris, Kevin
❑ 98SavSanGM-14
Harris, Kyle
❑ 86AncGlaPTI-39
Harris, Larry
❑ 81WisRapTT-5
Harris, Lenny
❑ 84CedRapRT-25
❑ 86VerRedP-9
❑ 87NasSouTI-9
❑ 88NasSouC-12
❑ 88NasSouP-489
❑ 88NasSouTI-12
❑ 89BlaYNPRWLU-2
❑ 89CedRapRAB-3
❑ 79DodStaSV-7
❑ 89Fle-645
❑ 89FleGlo-645
❑ 89RedKah-7
❑ 89UppDec-781
❑ 90CedRapRDGB-3
❑ 90DodMot-18
❑ 90DodPol-29
❑ 90DodTar-320
❑ 90Don-434
❑ 90Fle-397
❑ 90FleCan-397
❑ 90Lea-437
❑ 90OPC-277
❑ 90PubIntS-31
❑ 90Sco-23
❑ 90Sco100RS-83
❑ 90ScoYouSI-37
❑ 90Top-277
❑ 90TopTif-277
❑ 90UppDec-423
❑ 91Bow-607
❑ 91DodMot-18
❑ 91DodPol-29
❑ 91Don-224
❑ 91Fle-204
❑ 91OPC-453
❑ 91PanFreS-57
❑ 91PanSti-51
❑ 91Sco-144
❑ 91StaClu-65
❑ 91Top-453
❑ 91TopDesS-453
❑ 91TopMic-453
❑ 91TopTif-453
❑ 91Ult-162
❑ 91UppDec-239
❑ 92DodMot-5
❑ 92DodPol-29
❑ 92DodSmo-9792
❑ 92Don-226
❑ 92Fle-458
❑ 92Hig5-52
❑ 92Lea-213
❑ 92LeaBlaG-213
❑ 92OPC-92
❑ 92PanSti-194
❑ 92Pin-57
❑ 92Sco-291
❑ 92ScoProP-12
❑ 92StaClu-121
❑ 92Top-92
❑ 92TopGol-92
❑ 92TopGolW-92
❑ 92TopMic-92
❑ 92Ult-211
❑ 92UppDec-191
❑ 93DodMot-13
❑ 93DodPol-10
❑ 93DodStaC-13
❑ 93Don-590
❑ 93Fle-61
❑ 93Lea-127
❑ 93PacSpa-147
❑ 93PanSti-220
❑ 93Pin-119
❑ 93Sco-546
❑ 93Sel-384
❑ 93StaClu-98
❑ 93StaCluFDI-98
❑ 93StaCluMOP-98
❑ 93Top-177
❑ 93TopGol-177
❑ 93TopInaM-177
❑ 93TopInaR-177
❑ 93TopMic-177
❑ 93Ult-54
❑ 93UppDec-184
❑ 93UppDecGold-184
❑ 94RedKah-14
❑ 94Sco-152
❑ 94ScoGolR-152
❑ 95Don-500
❑ 95DonPreP-500
❑ 95DonTopotO-213
❑ 95RedKah-9
❑ 95Sco-359
❑ 95ScoGolR-359
❑ 95ScoPlaTS-359
❑ 95Top-401
❑ 95TopCyb-202
❑ 96Fle-341
❑ 96FleTif-341
❑ 97Pac-269
❑ 97PacLigB-269
❑ 97PacSil-269
❑ 98PacAur-118
❑ 98PacInvGems-136
❑ 98PacOnl-191
❑ 98PacOnlR-191
❑ 98PacOnlWC-191
❑ 98PacPar-146
❑ 98PacParC-146
❑ 98PacParG-146
❑ 98PacParHS-146
❑ 98PacParPB-146
❑ 98PacParR-146
Harris, Luman
❑ 43A'STEAI-13
❑ 46A'sTeal-7
❑ 60Top-455
❑ 65AstJayP-12
❑ 65OPC-274
❑ 65Top-274
❑ 66OPC-147
❑ 66Top-147
❑ 66TopVen-147
❑ 67AstTeal2-13
❑ 68BraPos-13
❑ 68Top-439
❑ 69AtlBraBPPS-11
❑ 69OPC-196
❑ 69Top-196
❑ 69TopFou-6
❑ 70AtlBraS-4
❑ 70OPC-86
❑ 70Top-86
❑ 71OPC-346
❑ 71Top-346
❑ 72OPC-484
❑ 72Top-484
❑ 83TCMPla1943-21
❑ 87AstSer1-30
Harris, Marc
❑ 93HicCraC-10
❑ 93HicCraF-1291
Harris, Mark AUTHOR
❑ 90LitSunW-19
Harris, Mark INF
❑ 79WesHavYT-26
Harris, Matt
❑ 96BelSnaTI-16
❑ 97BelSnaB-7
❑ 98BelSnaM-29
Harris, Michael
❑ 92StoPorF-48
❑ 93StoPorC-15
❑ 93StoPorF-757
Harris, Mickey (Maurice)
❑ 46RedSoxTI-11
❑ 47RedSoxTI-10
❑ 47TipTop-6
❑ 48RedSoxTI-9
❑ 49Bow-151
❑ 49Lea-27
❑ 49RedSoxTI-8
❑ 50Bow-160
❑ 51Bow-311
❑ 52Bow-135
❑ 52Top-207
❑ 75RedSox1T-17
❑ 83TopRep5-207
❑ 87RedSox1T-9
Harris, Mike
❑ 82SprCarF-19
❑ 83ArkTraT-13
❑ 84ArkTraT-26
❑ 86BirBarTI-10
❑ 93AusFut-108
❑ 93AusFut-116
❑ 93AusFut-125
❑ 94ElPasDF-3158
❑ 96El PasDB-12
Harris, Moon
❑ 81ConTSN-66
Harris, Pep
❑ 91BurIndP-3296
❑ 91HigSchPLS-26
❑ 92ColRedC-15
❑ 92ColRedF-2384
❑ 93ColRedC-11
❑ 93ColRedF-592
❑ 94KinIndC-7
❑ 94KinIndF-2636
❑ 96MidAngB-18
❑ 96VanCanB-17
❑ 97AngMot-25
❑ 98StaCluFDI-54
❑ 98StaCluI-54
❑ 98StaCluOneK-54
❑ 98StaCluPP-54
Harris, Rafael
❑ 80UtiBluJT-6
Harris, Ray
❑ 86AncGlaPTI-14
❑ 88SouOreAP-1713
❑ 89MadMusS-28
Harris, Reggie
❑ 87ElmPioRC-30
❑ 88ElmPio1C-1
❑ 88LynRedSS-9
❑ 89WinHavRSS-10
❑ 90Bow-446
❑ 90BowTif-446
❑ 91Cla1-T71
❑ 91Don-704
❑ 91OPC-177
❑ 91Sco-643
❑ 91Sco100RS-49
❑ 91TacTigP-2300
❑ 91Top-177
❑ 91TopDeb90-64
❑ 91TopDesS-177
❑ 91TopMic-177
❑ 91TopTif-177
❑ 91UppDec-672
❑ 92Don-781
❑ 92Sco100RS-48
❑ 92SkyAAAF-239
❑ 92StaClu-158
❑ 92TacTigF-2497
❑ 92TacTigS-535
❑ 93JacSunF-2707
❑ 97PhiTeal-40
❑ 98NewOrlZM-8
Harris, Robbie
❑ 85CloHSS-21
Harris, Robert
❑ 87WatPirP-3
❑ 88AugPirP-386
❑ 89SalBucS-NNO
❑ 90HarSenP-1205
❑ 90HarSenS-9
❑ 92BirBarF-2594
❑ 92BirBarS-83
Harris, Robert A.
❑ 41BroW75-14
❑ 42A'sTeal-14
❑ 79DiaGre-182
Harris, Rodger
❑ 96JohCitCTI-15
❑ 97PeoChi-13
Harris, Rusty
❑ 87AubAstP-2
❑ 88OscAstS-12
❑ 89OscAstS-7
❑ 90ColMudB-7
❑ 90ColMudP-1353
❑ 90ColMudS-12
❑ 91JacGenLD-559
❑ 91JacGenP-931
❑ 91LinDriAA-559
❑ 92JacGenF-4004
❑ 92JacGenS-333
❑ 94AubAstF-3777
❑ 96JacGenB-2
Harris, Sam
❑ 20NatCarE-40
❑ 21Exh-69
Harris, Sheriff
❑ 81ConTSN-67
Harris, Spence (Anthony S.)
❑ 33WorCig(-37
❑ 33WorCig(-38
Harris, Steve
❑ 85BenPhiC-10
Harris, Tony
❑ 91AdeGiaF-3
❑ 95AusFut-108
❑ 95VerBeaDTI-10
❑ 96VerBeaDB-2
❑ 97VerBeaD-2
❑ 98YakBeaG-20
Harris, Tracy
❑ 80SanJosMJitB-10
❑ 81LynSaiT-5
❑ 82SalLakCGT-10
❑ 83ChaLooT-17
Harris, Twayne
❑ 83IdaFalAT-21
❑ 85ModA'sC-4
❑ 86ModA'sC-9
❑ 86ModA'sP-11
Harris, Vic (Elander Victor)
❑ 87NegLeaPD-2
❑ 94TedWil-107
Harris, Vic Lanier
❑ 73LinPor-177
❑ 73OPC-594
❑ 73RanTeal-12
❑ 73Top-594
❑ 74OPC-157
❑ 74Top-157
❑ 74TopSta-13
❑ 75OPC-658
❑ 75Top-658
❑ 75TopMin-658
❑ 76SSP-321
❑ 76St.LouCP-14
❑ 77GiaTeal-11
❑ 77PhoGiaCC-8
❑ 77PhoGiaCP-7
❑ 78GiaTeal-9
❑ 78Top-436
❑ 79Top-338
❑ 79VanCanT-2
❑ 80VanCanT-21
❑ 84LouRedR-18
❑ 93RanKee-16
❑ 94BreMilB-129
Harris, Vince
❑ 88UtiBluSP-6
❑ 89ChaRaiP-976
❑ 90Bes-315
❑ 90CalLeaACLC-5
❑ 90CMC-718
❑ 90RivRedWB-9
❑ 90RivRedWCLC-12
❑ 90RivRedWP-2619
❑ 91LinDriAA-607
❑ 91WicWraLD-607
❑ 91WicWraP-2610
❑ 91WicWraRD-20
❑ 92SkyAA F-281
❑ 92WicWraF-3666
❑ 92WicWraS-633
❑ 93WicWraF-2989
Harris, Walt
❑ 88HagSunS-9
❑ 89RocRedWC-19
❑ 89RocRedWP-1651
❑ 90HagSunS-10
Harris, William
❑ 34DiaMatCSB-87
Harris, Wilmer
❑ 93NegLeaRL2-15
❑ 95NegLeaL2-25
Harrison, Adonis
❑ 97WisTimR-12
❑ 98LanJetG-12
❑ 99SP TopP-29
❑ 99SP TopPPE-29
Harrison, Bob (Robert Lee)
❑ 79TCM50-76
❑ 91OriCro-182
Harrison, Brett
❑ 87St.PetCP-7
❑ 88ArkTraGS-13
❑ 88TexLeaAGS-13
Harrison, Brian Lee
❑ 86SpoIndC-164
❑ 87ChaRaiP-8
❑ 88RivRedWCLC-210
❑ 88RivRedWP-1428
❑ 89RivRedWB-7
❑ 89RivRedWCLC-17
❑ 89RivRedWP-1410
❑ 90Bes-27
❑ 90ProAaA-133
❑ 90RivRedWB-10
❑ 90RivRedWCLC-17
❑ 90RivRedWP-2601
❑ 92AppFoxFI-979
❑ 93CarLeaAGF-12
❑ 93WilBluRC-14
❑ 93WilBluRF-1993
❑ 94MemChiF-354
❑ 94SanBerSC-6
❑ 95MemChiTI-13
❑ 96WicWraB-7
❑ 97OmaRoyB-9
❑ 98OmaRoyM-10
Harrison, Chuck (Charles)
❑ 66Top-244
❑ 66TopVen-244
❑ 67CokCapAs-6
❑ 67DexPre-91
❑ 67OPC-8
❑ 67Top-8
❑ 69OPC-116
❑ 69RoySol-7
❑ 69Top-116
❑ 69TopFou-10
❑ 71oySigST-8
❑ 87AstShoSO-11
❑ 87AstShoSTw-23
Harrison, Craig
❑ 89SanDieSAS-11
Harrison, Doug
❑ 78CliDodT-12
❑ 80AlbDukTc-9
Harrison, Jamal
❑ 98ForWayW!-3
Harrison, Keith
❑ 86ElmPioRSP-9
❑ 86SpoIndC-173
❑ 87ChaRaiP-22
❑ 88ChaRaiP-1207
Harrison, Mack
❑ 77ModA'sC-12
❑ 79OgdA'sT-7
Harrison, Matt (Mathew)
❑ 86FloStaLAP-20
❑ 86Ft.LauYP-11
❑ 87AlbYanP-13
❑ 88ColCliC-5
❑ 88ColCliP-3
❑ 88ColCliP-317
❑ 90AlbDecGB-8
Harrison, Mike
❑ 91BilMusP-3756
❑ 91BilMusSP-21
❑ 92ChaWheF-12
❑ 92ChaWVWC-8
❑ 92StaCluD-78
❑ 93WinSpiC-8
❑ 93WinSpiF-1574
❑ 94WinSpiC-10
❑ 94WinSpiF-275
Harrison, Pat

❑ 89AlaGol-7
Harrison, Phil
❑ 86GenCubP-10
❑ 87PeoChiP-23
❑ 88CarLeaAS-28
❑ 88WinSpiS-5
❑ 89ChaKniTI-21
❑ 90TopTVCu-48
Harrison, R.J.
❑ 78ArkTraT-12
❑ 80LynSaiT-19
❑ 81LynSaiT-6
❑ 82WauTimF-17
❑ 83WauTimF-30
❑ 86ChaLooP-12
Harrison, Robert
❑ 77St.PetCT-20
❑ 89JohCitCS-26
❑ 90HamRedS-28
Harrison, Ron
❑ 82MadMusF-21
❑ 83AlbA'sT-18
❑ 85TacTigC-137
❑ 87BelBreP-16
❑ 87DenZepP-8
Harrison, Roric E.
❑ 72OPC-474
❑ 72OriPos-15
❑ 72Top-474
❑ 73BalOriP-22
❑ 73OPC-229
❑ 73Top-229
❑ 74OPC-298
❑ 74Top-298
❑ 74TopSta-5
❑ 75AtlBraP-17
❑ 75OPC-287
❑ 75Top-287
❑ 75TopMin-287
❑ 76OPC-547
❑ 76SSP-507
❑ 76Top-547
❑ 77EvaTriT-15
❑ 78Top-536
❑ 91OriCro-183
Harrison, Scott
❑ 92JamExpC-20
❑ 92JamExpF-1496
❑ 93JamExpC-10
❑ 93JamExpF-3320
❑ 96BurIndB-6
❑ 97BurIndG-13
❑ 98ColRedSM-3
Harrison, Tommy
❑ 95DurBulTI-11
❑ 96GreBraB-13
❑ 96GreBraTI-36
❑ 96RicBraB-15
❑ 97RicBra-12
Harrison, Wayne
❑ 85DurBulT-25
❑ 86DurBulP-13
Harriss, Robin
❑ 94WatIndC-16
❑ 94WatIndF-3941
❑ 96KenIndB-12
❑ 97AkrAer-12
❑ 98AkrAerM-17
Harriss, Slim (Bryan)
❑ 20NatCarE-39
❑ 21Nei-38
❑ 22E120-80
❑ 27AmeCarE126-46
❑ 28Exh-34
❑ 33WorCig(-36
Harriss, Slim (William)
❑ 21Exh-70
Harrist, Earl
❑ 48WhiSoxTI-9
❑ 50RemBre-11
❑ 52Top-402
❑ 53Top-65
❑ 83TopRep5-402
❑ 91TopArc1-65
Harry, Whitney
❑ 82BurRanF-24
❑ 82BurRanT-22
❑ 83BurRanF-15
❑ 83BurRanT-18
❑ 84TulDriTI-20
Harryman, Jeff
❑ 77NewCoPT-16
❑ 78BurBeeT-15
Harsh, Nick
❑ 82ForMyeRT-7
Harshman, Jack
❑ 54Top-173
❑ 55RedMan-AL6
❑ 55Top-104
❑ 55TopDouH-65
❑ 56BalOriP-25
❑ 56Top-29
❑ 56TopPin-33
❑ 57Top-152
❑ 58Top-217
❑ 59Top-475
❑ 60Top-112
❑ 60TopVen-112
❑ 79DiaGre-146
❑ 79TCM50-33
❑ 91OriCro-184
❑ 94TopArc1-173
❑ 94TopArc1G-173
Harstadt, Oscar
❑ 16Zee-52
❑ 17Zee-47
Hart, Bob
❑ 94ConTSN-1195
❑ 94ConTSNB-1195
Hart, Brian
❑ 89BurIndS-12
Hart, Chris
❑ 85MiaHur-6
❑ 90SouOreAB-18
❑ 90SouOreAP-3431
❑ 91ModA'sP-3103
❑ 91SouOreAP-3861
❑ 92ModA'sC-5
❑ 93HunStaF-2094
❑ 94HunStaF-1343
❑ 95HunStaTI-12
Hart, Corey
❑ 98SpoIndG-13
Hart, Darrin
❑ 89WatDiaS-10
❑ 89WatDiaS-30
Hart, Hub (James Henry)
❑ 09T206-489
❑ 10CouT21-26
❑ 10CouT21-27
❑ 11SpoLifCW-158
Hart, James Aristotle
❑ 89N526N7C-6
Hart, James M.
❑ 81RocRedWW-17
❑ 83ColCliT-24
Hart, Jason
❑ 94PeoChiC-11
❑ 94PeoChiF-2260
❑ 96OrlCubB-10
❑ 98SouOreTG-14
❑ 99BasAmeTPLM-6
❑ 99TeaBesR-34
❑ 99TeaBesRFS-15
❑ 99TeaBesRG-34
❑ 99TeaBesRS-34
Hart, Jeff
❑ 89ChaRaiP-987
❑ 89WatDiaP-1781
❑ 90CMC-703
❑ 90WatDiaB-6
❑ 90WatDiaP-2373
Hart, Jim Ray
❑ 47PM1StaP1-78
❑ 64Top-452
❑ 65GiaTeal-4
❑ 65OPC-4
❑ 65Top-4
❑ 65Top-395
❑ 65TopEmbl-4
❑ 66Top-295
❑ 66TopRubl-39
❑ 66TopVen-295
❑ 67CokCapG-6
❑ 67DexPre-92
❑ 67Top-220
❑ 67TopVen-335
❑ 68AtlOilPBCC-21
❑ 68OPC-73
❑ 68Top-73
❑ 68TopVen-73
❑ 69MilBra-107
❑ 69MLBOffS-199
❑ 69MLBPin-46
❑ 69Top-555
❑ 69TopSta-104
❑ 69TopTeaP-14
❑ 70OPC-176
❑ 70Top-176
❑ 71OPC-461
❑ 71Top-461
❑ 72Top-733
❑ 73OPC-538
❑ 73Top-538
❑ 74OPC-159
❑ 74Top-159
❑ 78TCM60I-269
❑ 84GiaMot-20
❑ 92YanWIZ7-68
❑ 93UppDecS-7
Hart, John
❑ 75WatRoyT-15
❑ 85ChaO'sT-14
❑ 86RocRedWP-6
❑ 87RocRedWP-3
❑ 87RocRedWT-24
❑ 88OriFreB-47
❑ 88OriPos-14
❑ 90OPC-141
❑ 90Top-141
❑ 90TopTif-141
Hart, Keith
❑ 98LowSpiM-7
Hart, Kim
❑ 82IowCubT-31
❑ 83IowCubT-28
Hart, Len
❑ 97RocCub-17
Hart, Mike (Michael Lawrence)
❑ 79TucTorT-17
❑ 80ChaChaT-10
❑ 80LynSaiT-7
❑ 81RocRedWT-7
❑ 81SpoIndT-7
❑ 82SalLakCGT-11
❑ 83TolMudHT-20
❑ 85IntLeaAT-30
❑ 85TolMudHT-21
❑ 86RocRedWP-7
❑ 87BalOriP-16
❑ 87NewOriP-3
❑ 87RocRedWP-10
❑ 87RocRedWT-18
❑ 88CarLeaAS-2
❑ 88Top-69
❑ 88TopClo-43
❑ 88TopTif-69
❑ 89ReaPhiB-26
❑ 89ReaPhiP-658
❑ 89ReaPhiS-26a
❑ 90Ft.LauYS-23
❑ 91CarLeaAP-CAR32
❑ 91OriCro-185
❑ 91PriWilCC-24
❑ 91PriWilCP-1442
❑ 92PriWilCC-26
❑ 92PriWilCF-164
❑ 93AlbYanF-2177
❑ 93LinVenB-265
❑ 93RanKee-176
❑ 95BurBeeTI-32
❑ 97ShrCap-3
❑ 97ShrCapB-3
❑ 98ShrCapM-3
❑ 98ShrCapWS-3
Hart, Shelby
❑ 90EveGiaP-3139
❑ 91CliGiaC-17
❑ 91CliGiaP-846
❑ 92EveGiaC-11
❑ 92EveGiaF-1696
Hart, Tommy
❑ 80CarMudF-9
❑ 81ReaPhiT-3
Hart, William F.
❑ 09T206-488
❑ 87BucN28-53
❑ 87OldJudN-229
❑ 90DodTar-321
❑ 98CamPepP-32
Hart, William W.
❑ 46RemBre-6
❑ 47SmiClo-15
❑ 90DodTar-972
Hartas, Peter
❑ 91DaiDolF-13
❑ 93AusFut-46
Hartenstein, Chuck
❑ 68OPC-13
❑ 68Top-13
❑ 68TopVen-13
❑ 69PirTeal-8
❑ 69Top-596
❑ 70OPC-216
❑ 70PirTeal-7
❑ 70Top-216
❑ 75IntLeaASB-8
❑ 75PacCoaLAB-8
❑ 76HawIslC-1
❑ 77OPC-157
❑ 77Top-416
❑ 80HawIslT-11
❑ 81HawIslT-22
❑ 82HawIslT-24
❑ 84HawIslC-134
❑ 86PenWhiSP-11
❑ 87BrePol-NNO
❑ 88BrePol-NNO
❑ 88BreTeal-17
❑ 89BrePol-NNO
❑ 92TexLon-22
Harter, Andy
❑ 88AshTouP-1052
Hartford, Bruce
❑ 20Zee-125
Hartgraves, Dean
❑ 87AubAstP-24
❑ 88AshTouP-1072
❑ 89AshTouP-960
❑ 90ColMudB-6
❑ 90ColMudP-1343
❑ 90ColMudS-13
❑ 91JacGenLD-560
❑ 91JacGenP-921
❑ 91LinDriAA-560
❑ 92JacGenF-3995
❑ 92TucTorS-609
❑ 93LinVenB-48
❑ 93TucTorF-3054
❑ 94TucTorF-755
❑ 96Don-115
❑ 96DonPreP-115
❑ 96Fle-409
❑ 96FleTif-409
❑ 96RicBraUB-11
❑ 96TusTorB-11
❑ 97RicBra-13
❑ 98FreGriG-11
Hartgrove, Lyle
❑ 94UtiBluSF-3812
❑ 96SarRedSB-19
Hartje, Chris
❑ 90DodTar-973
Hartley, Grover
❑ 11HelSta-128
❑ 12T207-77
❑ 17ColE13-70
❑ 53ArtHaloFP-43
❑ 92ConTSN-520
Hartley, Mike (Michael)
❑ 83St.PetCT-7
❑ 85SprCarT-13
❑ 87BakDodP-1
❑ 88AlbDukCm-9
❑ 88AlbDukP-263
❑ 88BlaYNPRWL-182
❑ 89AlbDukCm-4
❑ 89AlbDukP-67
❑ 89BlaYNPRWL-24
❑ 90Bow-87
❑ 90BowTif-87
❑ 90ClaYel-T63
❑ 90DodPol-46
❑ 90DodTar-974
❑ 90DonRoo-34
❑ 90Fle-651
❑ 90FleCan-651
❑ 90FleUpd-22
❑ 90Sco-641
❑ 90SprCarDGB-15
❑ 90TopDeb89-53
❑ 91DodMot-19
❑ 91DodPol-46
❑ 91Don-545
❑ 91Fle-205
❑ 91OPC-199
❑ 91Sco-252
❑ 91Sco100RS-67
❑ 91Top-199
❑ 91TopDesS-199
❑ 91TopMic-199
❑ 91TopTif-199
❑ 91UppDec-686
❑ 92Don-726
❑ 92OPC-484
❑ 92PhiMed-41
❑ 92Sco-670
❑ 92ScrRedBS-485
❑ 92Top-484
❑ 92TopGol-484
❑ 92TopGolW-484
❑ 92TopMic-484
❑ 92UppDec-613
❑ 93Don-596
❑ 93Fle-102
❑ 93OPCPre-67
❑ 93StaClu-124
❑ 93StaCluFDI-124
❑ 93StaCluMOP-124
❑ 93Top-208
❑ 93TopGol-208
❑ 93TopInaM-208
❑ 93TopInaR-208
❑ 93TopMic-208
❑ 94Don-225
❑ 94Fle-207
❑ 95PawRedSDD-12
❑ 95PawRedTI-27
Hartley, Todd
❑ 86MedA'sC-63
Hartley, Tom
❑ 86AppFoxP-10
Hartley, Walter
❑ 12Zee-112
Hartline, Danny
❑ 87NewOriP-18
Hartman, Albert
❑ 82BurRanF-5
❑ 82BurRanT-23
Hartman, Doc (Ralph)
❑ 81RedPioT-26
❑ 82RedPioT-27
Hartman, Ed
❑ 87WatPirP-16
❑ 88AugPirP-366
❑ 89SalBucS-10
❑ 89Sta-94
Hartman, Harry
❑ 41HarHarW-34
Hartman, J.C.
❑ 61TopStal-161
❑ 62Col.45B-9
❑ 63Col45"P-8
❑ 63Top-442
Hartman, Jeff
❑ 86VerBeaDP-9
❑ 88VerBeaDS-10
Hartman, Kelly
❑ 92BelMarCB-10
❑ 92BelMarF-1438
Hartman, Red
❑ 77ColCliT-7
Hartman, Robert
❑ 59Top-128
❑ 59TopVen-128
❑ 60Top-129
❑ 60TopVen-129
Hartman, Ron
❑ 96AriBlaDB-20
❑ 97HigDesMUG-9
❑ 97SouBenSH-12
❑ 97Top-251
❑ 98TusSidM-21
Hartman, Trey
❑ 86DavLipB-14
Hartmann, Brian
❑ 92Min-7
Hartmann, Pete
❑ 93EriSaiC-10
❑ 93EriSaiF-3108
❑ 94ChaRanF-2492
Hartmann, Reid
❑ 89KinMetS-13
❑ 90ColMetGS-8
❑ 90ColMetPPI-4
Hartmann, Rich
❑ 94NewJerCC-15
❑ 94NewJerCF-3413
Hartnett, Bill
❑ 93AubAstC-13
❑ 93AubAstF-3437
❑ 94OscAstC-11
❑ 94OscAstF-1132
Hartnett, Dave
❑ 86BelMarCr-101
❑ 87WauTimP-22
Hartnett, Gabby (Charles)
❑ 21Exh-67
❑ 22E120-158
❑ 25Exh-22
❑ 26Exh-22
❑ 26SpoComoA-19
❑ 27Exh-11
❑ 27YorCarE-5
❑ 28Exh-10
❑ 28StaPlaCE-34
❑ 28W502-5
❑ 28Yue-5
❑ 29ExhFou-5
❑ 30ChiEveAP-5
❑ 30CubTeal-7
❑ 30SchR33-38
❑ 30UncJac-15
❑ 31CubTeal-9
❑ 31Exh-5
❑ 32CubTeal-10
❑ 32OrbPinUP-31
❑ 33ButCre-12
❑ 33CraJacP-13
❑ 33Gou-202
❑ 33NatLeaAC-7
❑ 33RitCE-13H
❑ 33TatOrb-31
❑ 33TatOrbSDR-200
❑ 33WorCig-53
❑ 34BatR31-136
❑ 34DiaMatCSB-88
❑ 35AlDemDCR3-152
❑ 35DiaMatCS3T1-70
❑ 35ExhFou-3
❑ 36CubTeal-13
❑ 36DiaMatCS3T2-13
❑ 36ExhFou-3
❑ 36GouWidPPR-A48
❑ 36GouWidPPR-C16
❑ 36NatChiFPR-91
❑ 36NatChiFPR-93
❑ 36NatChiFPR-102
❑ 36NatChiFPR-119
❑ 36R31PasP-31
❑ 36R31PasP-33
❑ 36R31PasP-48
❑ 36R31Pre-L6
❑ 36SandSW-30
❑ 36WheBB3-6
❑ 36WorWidGV-57
❑ 37DixLid-3
❑ 37DixPre-3
❑ 37ExhFou-3
❑ 37KelPepS-BB7
❑ 38BasTabP-16
❑ 38ExhFou-3
❑ 38OurNatGPP-15
❑ 39CubTeal-10
❑ 39ExhSal-24
❑ 40WheM4-6C
❑ 47PM1StaP1-79
❑ 50CalHOFW-37
❑ 50CubGreB-8
❑ 60Fle-29
❑ 61Fle-41
❑ 61GolPre-11
❑ 74Bra193NLA-7
❑ 76GalBasGHoF-14
❑ 76RowExh-9
❑ 76ShaPiz-75
❑ 77BobParHoF-59
❑ 77CubAllT-6
❑ 77GalGloG-62
❑ 77GalGloG-206
❑ 80CubGreT-5
❑ 80PacLeg-72
❑ 80PerHaloFP-76
❑ 80SSPHOF-76
❑ 81ConTSN-89
❑ 83BigLeaCOA-30
❑ 84CubBriPC-5C
❑ 84CubUno-3
❑ 84CubUno-6
❑ 85BigLeaC3-52
❑ 85FegMurCG-10
❑ 86SpoDecG-13
❑ 87ConSer2-17
❑ 87HygAllG-24
❑ 88ScoBoxC-T4
❑ 91ConTSN-59
❑ 91ConTSN-313
❑ 92ConTSN-586
❑ 92ConTSNGI-880
❑ 92CubOldS-11
❑ 93ConTSN-675
❑ 93ConTSN-880
❑ 93DiaStaES-134
❑ 94ConTSN-1052
❑ 94ConTSN-1103
❑ 94ConTSNB-1052
❑ 94ConTSNB-1103
❑ 94TedWil-16
❑ 95ConTSN-1404
❑ 95ConTSNP-1404
Harts, Greg

❑ 91MetWIZ-162
Hartsel, Topsy (Tully)
❑ 03BreE10-67
❑ 08AmeCarE91-11
❑ 08RosComP-60
❑ 09BriE97-12
❑ 09ColChiE-126A
❑ 09ColChiE-126B
❑ 09T206-151
❑ 10CouT21-28
❑ 10DomDisP-53
❑ 10E101-22
❑ 10E12AmeCDCE125-18
❑ 10MelMinE-22
❑ 10NadCarE-25
❑ 10NadE1-20
❑ 10PeoT21-26A
❑ 10PeoT21-26B
❑ 10RedCroT-28
❑ 10RedCroT-116
❑ 10RedCroT-197
❑ 10SweCapPP-45
❑ 10W555-33
❑ 11A'sFirT20-7
❑ 11D35RocB-7
❑ 11PinT-5-519
❑ 11S74Sil-31
❑ 11SpoLifCW-159
❑ 11SpoLifM-93
❑ 11T205-72
❑ 12ColRedB-126A
❑ 12ColRedB-126B
❑ 12ColTinT-126A
❑ 12ColTinT-126B
❑ 12ColTinT-127A
❑ 12ColTinT-127B
❑ 72ClaCar-36
Hartsfield, Bob
❑ 75CedRapGT-18
❑ 75CedRapGT-19
❑ 76CliPilT-19
❑ 82AubAstT-2
❑ 92JacSunF-3724
❑ 92JacSunS-374
Hartsfield, Roy
❑ 51Bow-277
❑ 52Bow-28
❑ 52Top-264
❑ 73OPC-237
❑ 73Top-237A
❑ 73Top-237B
❑ 74HawIslC-108
❑ 75IntLeaASB-9
❑ 75PacCoaLAB-9
❑ 76HawIslC-4
❑ 77OPC-238
❑ 77Top-113
❑ 78BluJayP-8
❑ 78OPC-218
❑ 78Top-444
❑ 79BluJayBY-11
❑ 79OPC-262
❑ 79TCM50-123
❑ 79Top-282
❑ 83IndIndTI-3
❑ 83TopRep5-264
Hartshorn, Kyle
❑ 85LynMetT-12
❑ 86JacMetT-5
❑ 87JacMetF-19
❑ 88JacMetGS-6
Hartshorn, Tyson
❑ 95HagSunF-62
❑ 95StCatSTI-3
❑ 96HagSunB-7
❑ 97DunBluJTI-13
❑ 98DunBluJSB-14
❑ 98DunBluJTI-10
❑ 99SP TopP-57
❑ 99SP TopPPE-57
Hartsock, Brian
❑ 82DanSunF-24
❑ 83PeoSunF-24
❑ 86MidAngP-9
❑ 87SanBerSP-13
❑ 89RenSilSCLC-249
Hartsock, Jeff
❑ 88GreFalDTI-21
❑ 89BakDodCLC-183
❑ 89CalLeaA-15
❑ 90SanAntMGS-14
❑ 91AlbDukLD-8
❑ 91AlbDukP-1135
❑ 91LinDriAAA-8
❑ 92IowCubF-4048
❑ 92IowCubS-209
❑ 92SkyAAAF-102
❑ 93Bow-648
❑ 93Don-160
❑ 94LouRedF-2978
Hartung, Andrew
❑ 90GenCubP-3044
❑ 90GenCubS-13
❑ 90ProAaA-180
❑ 91Cla/Bes-433
❑ 91PeoChiC-28
❑ 91PeoChiP-1349
❑ 91PeoChiTI-17
❑ 92ClaFS7-430
❑ 92WinSpiC-13
❑ 92WinSpiF-1214
❑ 93ClaFS7-202
❑ 93DayCubC-1
❑ 93DayCubF-864
❑ 93ExcFS7-9
❑ 94DayCubC-8
❑ 94DayCubF-2358
Hartung, Clinton
❑ 47TipTop-124
❑ 48BluTin-47
❑ 48Bow-37
❑ 48GiaTeal-6
❑ 49Bow-154
❑ 49EurSta-107
❑ 49GiaTeal-10
❑ 50Bow-118
❑ 50Dra-2
❑ 51Bow-234
❑ 52BerRos-22
❑ 52Top-141
❑ 75Gia195T-6
❑ 75OakOak2A-17
❑ 83TopRep5-141
❑ 85TCMPla1-21
Hartvigson, Chad
❑ 94EveGiaC-11
❑ 94EveGiaF-3646
❑ 96SanJosGB-19
❑ 96WesOahCHWB-42
Hartwell, Ed
❑ 94CliLumC-11
❑ 94CliLumF-1994
Hartwig, Dan
❑ 77CedRapGT-21
Hartwig, Rob
❑ 90BatCliP-3079
❑ 91SpaPhiC-25
❑ 91SpaPhiP-910
Hartwig, William
❑ 33Zee-88
❑ 33Zee-120
Hartzell, Paul
❑ 75QuaCitAT-25
❑ 77BurCheD-118
❑ 77Top-179
❑ 78AngFamF-17
❑ 78SSP270-191
❑ 78Top-529
❑ 79OPC-212
❑ 79Top-402
❑ 79TwiFriP-9
❑ 80OPC-366
❑ 80Top-721
❑ 80VenLeaS-187
❑ 84ElPasDT-20
❑ 91OriCro-186
❑ 94BreMilB-130
Hartzell, Roy A.
❑ 08AmeCarE91-48
❑ 09AmeCarE90-1-49
❑ 09AmeCarE90-1-50
❑ 09ColChiE-127A
❑ 09ColChiE-127B
❑ 09PC7HHB-20
❑ 09RamT20-53
❑ 10NadCarE-26A
❑ 10NadCarE-26B
❑ 10PeoT21-27A
❑ 10PeoT21-27B
❑ 11MecDFT-4
❑ 11PinT-5-108
❑ 11SpoLifCW-160
❑ 11SpoLifM-109
❑ 12ColRedB-127A
❑ 12ColRedB-127B
❑ 12HasTriFT-43
❑ 12HasTriFT-44
❑ 14B18B-23
❑ 15AmeCarE106-20
❑ 15SpoNewM-76
❑ 16FleBreD-38
❑ 16SpoNewM-77
❑ 92ConTSN-544
Hartzog, Cullen
❑ 90PriWilCTI-11
❑ 90TopTVY-45
❑ 91AlbYanLD-7
❑ 91AlbYanP-1003
❑ 91LinDriAA-7
❑ 95LynHilTI-9
Harvell, Pete
❑ 93BilMusF-3938
❑ 93BilMusSP-9
❑ 94ChaWheC-13
❑ 94ChaWheF-2697
❑ 97SouBenSH-13
Harvell, Rod
❑ 89GreFalDSP-26
Harvey, Aaron
❑ 93AusFut-87
❑ 95KanCouCTI-9
❑ 96BreCouMB-18
❑ 97BreCouMB-17
Harvey, Bob
❑ 91NegLeaRL-3
❑ 93NegLeaRL2-16
❑ 95NegLeaLI-3
Harvey, Bryan
❑ 86PalSprAP-16
❑ 86PalSprAS-12
❑ 87MidAngP-25
❑ 88AngSmo-21
❑ 88DonRoo-53
❑ 88EdmTraC-5
❑ 88FleUpd-14
❑ 88FleUpdG-14
❑ 88ScoRoo-87T
❑ 88ScoRooG-87T
❑ 88TopTra-45T
❑ 88TopTraT-45T
❑ 89Bow-40
❑ 89BowTif-40
❑ 89Don-525
❑ 89DonBasB-317
❑ 89Fle-479
❑ 89FleBasM-18
❑ 89FleGlo-479
❑ 89FleHeroB-21
❑ 89OPC-287
❑ 89PanSti-284
❑ 89Sco-185
❑ 89ScoHot1R-92
❑ 89ScoYouSI-30
❑ 89Spo-130
❑ 89Top-632
❑ 89TopSti-180
❑ 89TopTif-632
❑ 89ToyRoo-13
❑ 89UppDec-594
❑ 90AngSmo-7
❑ 90Don-372
❑ 90Fle-134
❑ 90FleCan-134
❑ 90Lea-116
❑ 90OPC-272
❑ 90RedFolSB-44
❑ 90Sco-8
❑ 90Spo-31
❑ 90Top-272
❑ 90TopSti-175
❑ 90TopTif-272
❑ 90UppDec-686
❑ 91AngSmo-17
❑ 91Bow-211
❑ 91Don-206
❑ 91Fle-315
❑ 91Lea-213
❑ 91OPC-153
❑ 91Sco-108
❑ 91StaClu-98
❑ 91Top-153
❑ 91TopDesS-153
❑ 91TopMic-153
❑ 91TopTif-153
❑ 91Ult-45
❑ 91UppDec-592
❑ 91USPlaCA-7D
❑ 92Bow-172
❑ 92Cla1-T42
❑ 92ClaGam-57
❑ 92Don-211
❑ 92Fle-61
❑ 92Fle-696
❑ 92Fre-6
❑ 92Hig5-13
❑ 92Lea-309
❑ 92LeaBlaG-309
❑ 92OPC-568
❑ 92PepDieM-9
❑ 92Pin-145
❑ 92Sco-322
❑ 92StaClu-410
❑ 92StaCluD-79
❑ 92Stu-146
❑ 92Top-407
❑ 92Top-568
❑ 92TopGol-407
❑ 92TopGol-568
❑ 92TopGolW-407
❑ 92TopGolW-568
❑ 92TopMic-407
❑ 92TopMic-568
❑ 92TriPla-37
❑ 92Ult-27
❑ 92UppDec-434
❑ 92UppDecF-26
❑ 92UppDecFG-26
❑ 93Bow-234
❑ 93Don-728
❑ 93Fin-3
❑ 93FinRef-3
❑ 93Fla-52
❑ 93FlaPro-4
❑ 93Fle-193
❑ 93FleFinE-62
❑ 93FunPac-120
❑ 93Lea-361
❑ 93MarlStaClu-2
❑ 93MarPub-12
❑ 93MarUppD-684
❑ 93MarUSPC-3D
❑ 93MarUSPC-10C
❑ 93OPC-14
❑ 93OPCPre-90
❑ 93PacSpa-463
❑ 93Pin-235
❑ 93RedFolS-42
❑ 93Sco-558
❑ 93ScoFra-27
❑ 93Sel-126
❑ 93SP-141
❑ 93StaClu-604
❑ 93StaCluFDI-604
❑ 93StaCluMOP-604
❑ 93Top-439
❑ 93TopGol-439
❑ 93TopInaM-439
❑ 93TopInaR-439
❑ 93TopMic-439
❑ 93TriPla-225
❑ 93Ult-377
❑ 93UppDec-684
❑ 93UppDecGold-684
❑ 94Bow-10
❑ 94ColC-127
❑ 94ColChoGS-127
❑ 94ColChoSS-127
❑ 94Don-374
❑ 94DonMVP-5
❑ 94DonSpeE-374
❑ 94Fin-164
❑ 94FinRef-164
❑ 94Fla-164
❑ 94Fle-468
❑ 94FleAllS-40
❑ 94FleExtB-261
❑ 94FUnPac-134
❑ 94Lea-140
❑ 94LeaL-107
❑ 94MarTeal-6
❑ 94OPC-239
❑ 94Pac-243
❑ 94PanSti-183
❑ 94Pin-344
❑ 94PinArtP-344
❑ 94PinMusC-344
❑ 94RedFolMI-24
❑ 94Sco-66
❑ 94ScoGolR-66
❑ 94Sel-103
❑ 94SP-112
❑ 94SPDieC-112
❑ 94Spo-47
❑ 94StaClu-452
❑ 94StaCluFDI-452
❑ 94StaCluGR-452
❑ 94StaCluMO-31
❑ 94StaCluMOP-452
❑ 94StaCluT-61
❑ 94StaCluTFDI-61
❑ 94Stu-110
❑ 94TomPiz-9
❑ 94Top-20
❑ 94TopGol-20
❑ 94TopSpa-20
❑ 94TriPla-137
❑ 94Ult-493
❑ 94UltFir-8
❑ 94UppDec-405
❑ 94UppDecAJ-3
❑ 94UppDecAJG-3
❑ 94UppDecED-405
❑ 95ColCho-310
❑ 95ColChoGS-310
❑ 95ColChoSS-310
❑ 95Don-345
❑ 95DonPreP-345
❑ 95Fin-97
❑ 95FinRef-97
❑ 95Fle-334
❑ 95Pin-239
❑ 95PinArtP-239
❑ 95PinMusC-239
❑ 95Sco-548
❑ 95ScoGolR-548
❑ 95ScoPlaTS-548
❑ 95Sel-139
❑ 95SelArtP-139
❑ 95StaClu-3
❑ 95StaCluFDI-3
❑ 95StaCluMOP-3
❑ 95StaCluSTWS-3
❑ 95Stu-103
❑ 95Top-311
❑ 95TopEmb-32
❑ 95TopEmbGI-32
❑ 95Ult-163
❑ 95UltGolM-163
❑ 96LeaSigEA-72
❑ 96Sco-450
❑ 96Ult-326
❑ 96UltGolM-326
Harvey, Craig
❑ 76BatTroTI-12
❑ 77WatIndT-11
Harvey, Don
❑ 88PacEigMO-16
Harvey, Doug (Harold)
❑ 84PadSmo-13
❑ 88T/MUmp-1
❑ 89T/MUmp-1
❑ 90T/MUmp-1
Harvey, Greg
❑ 88EugEmeB-3
❑ 89AppFoxP-853
❑ 90BasCitRS-10
❑ 90FloStaLAS-31
❑ 91BasCitRC-5
❑ 91BasCitRP-1392
❑ 92MemChiF-2413
Harvey, Ken
❑ 87SanAntDTI-23
Harvey, Randy
❑ 82BirBarT-12
❑ 85ModA'sC-11
❑ 86QuaCitAP-14
Harvey, Raymond
❑ 91CollndC-1
❑ 91CollndP-1498
❑ 92KinIndC-12
❑ 92KinIndF-2484
❑ 93KinIndC-11
❑ 93KinIndF-2260
❑ 93KinIndTI-10
❑ 94CanIndF-3130
Harvey, Robert
❑ 90SanBerSCLC-xxx
Harvey, Steve
❑ 82ReaPhiT-20
Harvey, Terry
❑ 93BazTeaU-1
❑ 93TopTra-41T
❑ 95WatIndTI-14
❑ 96KenIndB-13
❑ 96WesOahCHWB-20
❑ 97St.PetDR-18
❑ 97St.PetDRUB-18
Harvey, Wayne
❑ 91ParPatF-17
Harvick, Brad
❑ 87EriCarP-19
❑ 88SavCarP-345
❑ 89SavCarP-365
Harville, Chad
❑ 97VisOakG-13
❑ 98VisOakG-12
❑ 99BasAmeTP-50
❑ 99BasAmeTPG-50
❑ 99Bow-316
❑ 99BowGol-316
❑ 99BowInt-316
❑ 99PacOme-170
❑ 99PacOmeC-170
❑ 99PacOmeG-170
❑ 99PacOmePB-170
Harwell, David
❑ 88KinIndS-10
Harwell, Ernie
❑ 81TigDetN-62
❑ 83TigAlKS-26
❑ 88TigDom-6
❑ 89PacLegI-172
Harwell, Jim
❑ 61UniOil-SP8
Haryd, Mark
❑ 87BurExpP-1086
Hasbach, Dave
❑ 76OmaRoyTT-7
Hasegawa, Shigetoshi
❑ 97AngMot-12
❑ 97ColCho-258
❑ 97Don-379
❑ 97DonGolPP-379
❑ 97DonSilPP-379
❑ 97DonTea-13
❑ 97DonTeaSPE-13
❑ 97FlaShoLC-180
❑ 97FlaShoLeg0-180
❑ 97FlaShoLeg1-180
❑ 97FlaShoM-A180
❑ 97FlaShoM-B180
❑ 97FlaShoM-C180
❑ 97FlaShoR0-180
❑ 97FlaShoR1-180
❑ 97FlaShoR2-180
❑ 97Fle-690
❑ 97FleTif-690
❑ 97Ult-516
❑ 97UltGolME-516
❑ 97UltPlaME-516
❑ 98AngSco-3
❑ 98AngScoP-3
❑ 98Bow-NNO
❑ 98Fle-204
❑ 98Pac-8
❑ 98PacOme-7
❑ 98PacOmeR-7
❑ 98PacOnl-10
❑ 98PacOnlR-10
❑ 98PacOnlWC-10
❑ 98PacPar-8
❑ 98PacParC-8
❑ 98PacParG-8
❑ 98PacParHS-8
❑ 98PacParPB-8
❑ 98PacParR-8
❑ 98PacPlaB-8
❑ 98PacRedT-8
❑ 98PacSil-8
❑ 98PinSna-AA4
❑ 98Sco-73
❑ 98StaCluFDI-285
❑ 98StaCluI-285
❑ 98StaCluOneK-285
❑ 98StaCluPP-285
❑ 98Ult-116
❑ 98UltGolM-116
❑ 98UltMas-116
❑ 98UltPlaM-116
❑ 98UppDec-19
❑ 98UppDecNP-NP18
❑ 99Fle-401
❑ 99FleSta9-401
❑ 99FleWarT-401
❑ 99Pac-7
❑ 99PacCroC-5
❑ 99PacCroCPB-5
❑ 99PacPlaB-7
❑ 99PacRed-7
❑ 99UppDec-299
❑ 99UppDecEL1-299
❑ 99UppDecEL2-299
Haselman, Bill
❑ 88ChaRanS-9
❑ 89TexLeaAGS-33
❑ 89TulDriGS-11
❑ 89TulDriTI-10
❑ 90CMC-745
❑ 90ProAaA-68
❑ 90TexLeaAGS-25
❑ 90TulDriP-1158
❑ 90TulDriTI-11
❑ 91Don-679
❑ 91Fle-287
❑ 91LinDriAAA-310
❑ 91OklCit8LD-310

❑ 91OklCit8P-182
❑ 91Sco-377
❑ 91TopDeb90-65
❑ 92CalCanF-3734
❑ 92StaClu-574
❑ 93Bow-79
❑ 93FleFinE-271
❑ 93MariStaClu-7
❑ 93PacSpa-623
❑ 93RanKee-177
❑ 93Ult-622
❑ 94ColC-552
❑ 94ColChoGS-552
❑ 94ColChoSS-552
❑ 94Don-654
❑ 94Fle-288
❑ 94Lea-58
❑ 94MarMot-20
❑ 94Pac-571
❑ 94Sco-189
❑ 94ScoGolR-189
❑ 94StaClu-114
❑ 94StaCluFDI-114
❑ 94StaCluGR-114
❑ 94StaCluMOP-114
❑ 94Top-138
❑ 94TopGol-138
❑ 94TopSpa-138
❑ 95Sco-42
❑ 95ScoGolR-42
❑ 95ScoPlaTS-42
❑ 96LeaSigEA-73
❑ 97Cir-82
❑ 97CirRav-82
❑ 97Fle-681
❑ 97FleTif-681
❑ 97PacPriGotD-GD21
❑ 97Ult-473
❑ 97UltGolME-473
❑ 97UltPlaME-473
❑ 98Pac-41
❑ 98PacOnl-736
❑ 98PacOnlR-736
❑ 98PacOnlWC-736
❑ 98PacPlaB-41
❑ 98PacRedT-41
❑ 98PacSil-41

Haskins, Dean
❑ 89AncBucTI-18

Hasler, Curt
❑ 88SouBenWSGS-21
❑ 89SarWhiSS-10
❑ 91LinDriAAA-634
❑ 91VanCanLD-634
❑ 91VanCanP-1590
❑ 93HicCraC-28
❑ 93HicCraF-1296
❑ 94HicCraC-27
❑ 94HicCraF-2195
❑ 96SouBenSHS-2
❑ 98CarLeaAC-32
❑ 98CarLeaAC-42
❑ 98WinWar-2

Haslerig, Bill
❑ 78GreBraT-13
❑ 79SavBraT-4

Hasley, Mike
❑ 75DubPacT-30
❑ 76DubPacT-15

Haslin, Mickey
❑ 34BatR31-104

Haslock, Chris
❑ 88SpoIndP-1945
❑ 89ChaRaiP-981
❑ 90RivRedWB-11
❑ 90RivRedWCLC-18
❑ 90RivRedWP-2602
❑ 91HigDesMC-5
❑ 91HigDesMP-2388

Hassamaer, William L.
❑ 87OldJudN-230

Hassan, Theodore
❑ 92PulBraC-1
❑ 92PulBraF-3172

Hassel, Bob
❑ 84IdaFalATI-11

Hassel, Jay
❑ 92HunCubC-25
❑ 92HunCubF-3142
❑ 93ExcFS7-10
❑ 93PeoChiC-7
❑ 93PeoChiF-1079
❑ 93PeoChiTI-8

Hasselhoff, Derek
❑ 96MidLeaAB-51
❑ 96SouBenSHS-15

Hassett, Buddy (John)
❑ 36NatChiFPR-110
❑ 39ExhSal-25
❑ 39GouPreR303A-21
❑ 39PlaBal-57
❑ 39WorWidGTP-21
❑ 40PlaBal-62
❑ 41DouPlaR-121
❑ 72TCMthe3-100
❑ 90DodTar-322
❑ 93ConTSN-752
❑ 94ConTSN-1067
❑ 94ConTSNB-1067
❑ 95ConTSN-1333

Hassey, Ron
❑ 78IndTeal-14
❑ 79TacTugT-1
❑ 80IndTeal-14
❑ 80Top-222
❑ 81AllGamPI-41
❑ 81Don-80
❑ 81Fle-405
❑ 81OPC-187
❑ 81Top-564
❑ 81TopSti-71
❑ 82Don-463
❑ 82Fle-370
❑ 82Ind-19
❑ 82IndWhe-6
❑ 82OPC-54
❑ 82Top-54
❑ 83Don-159
❑ 83Fle-411
❑ 83Fle-642
❑ 83IndPos-19
❑ 83IndWhe-18
❑ 83Top-689
❑ 83TopSti-62
❑ 84CubChiT-14
❑ 84CubSev-15
❑ 84Don-460
❑ 84Fle-545
❑ 84FleUpd-49
❑ 84Ind-17
❑ 84Nes792-308
❑ 84OPC-308
❑ 84Top-308
❑ 84TopSti-262
❑ 84TopTif-308
❑ 84TopTra-49T
❑ 84TopTraT-49T
❑ 85FleUpd-50
❑ 85Top-742
❑ 85TopTif-742
❑ 85TopTifT-48T
❑ 85TopTra-48T
❑ 85YanTCMP-22
❑ 86Don-370
❑ 86Fle-107
❑ 86OPC-157
❑ 86Top-157
❑ 86TopTat-13
❑ 86TopTif-157
❑ 86YanTCM-20
❑ 87Don-532
❑ 87Fle-499
❑ 87FleGlo-499
❑ 87OPC-61
❑ 87SpoTeaP-26
❑ 87Top-667
❑ 87TopSti-285
❑ 87TopTif-667
❑ 87WhiSoxC-14
❑ 88A'sMot-16
❑ 88Don-580
❑ 88DonBasB-302
❑ 88DonTeaBA-NEW
❑ 88Fle-399
❑ 88FleGlo-399
❑ 88ScoRoo-33T
❑ 88ScoRooG-33T
❑ 88Top-458
❑ 88TopTif-458
❑ 88TopTra-46T
❑ 88TopTraT-46T
❑ 89A'sMot-15
❑ 89Bow-194
❑ 89BowTif-194
❑ 89Don-361
❑ 89Fle-9
❑ 89FleGlo-9
❑ 89OPC-272
❑ 89Sco-334
❑ 89Top-272
❑ 89TopBig-171
❑ 89TopSti-173
❑ 89TopTif-272
❑ 89UppDec-564
❑ 90A'sMot-12
❑ 90Bow-464
❑ 90BowTif-464
❑ 90Don-450
❑ 90Fle-8
❑ 90FleCan-8
❑ 90Lea-326
❑ 90OPC-527
❑ 90PubIntS-305
❑ 90Sco-168A
❑ 90Sco-168B
❑ 90Top-527
❑ 90TopBig-4
❑ 90TopTif-527
❑ 90UppDec-195
❑ 91Don-476
❑ 91ExpPos-10
❑ 91Fle-8
❑ 91FleUpd-98
❑ 91Lea-359
❑ 91OPC-327
❑ 91OPCPre-61
❑ 91Sco-806
❑ 91ScoRoo-43T
❑ 91StaClu-490
❑ 91Top-327
❑ 91TopDesS-327
❑ 91TopMic-327
❑ 91TopTif-327
❑ 91UppDec-401
❑ 92Sco-273
❑ 92YanWIZ8-78
❑ 94RocPol-27

Hassinger, Brad
❑ 90PriPatD-11
❑ 91Cla/Bes-140
❑ 91SpaPhiC-5
❑ 91SpaPhiP-890
❑ 92SpaPhiF-1259
❑ 94GreBraF-408
❑ 94GreBraTI-13

Hassler, Andy
❑ 75CalAngP-18
❑ 75OPC-261
❑ 75Top-261
❑ 75TopMin-261
❑ 76OPC-207
❑ 76SSP-186
❑ 76Top-207
❑ 77Top-602
❑ 78SSP270-225
❑ 78Top-73
❑ 79Top-696
❑ 80Top-353
❑ 81Don-581
❑ 81Fle-290
❑ 81LonBeaPT-14
❑ 81Top-454
❑ 81TopSti-55
❑ 82Don-519
❑ 82Fle-464
❑ 82Top-94
❑ 83Don-290
❑ 83Fle-92
❑ 83Top-573
❑ 84ArkTraT-25
❑ 84Don-255
❑ 84Fle-519
❑ 84Nes792-719
❑ 84Top-719
❑ 84TopTif-719
❑ 85CarTeal-12
❑ 85LouRedR-6
❑ 91MetWIZ-163

Hasson, Gene
❑ 39WorWidGV-14

Hastings, Charlie
❑ 93JusSo-6

Hastings, Lionel
❑ 94ElmPioC-7
❑ 94ElmPioF-3483
❑ 95BreCouMF-254
❑ 96PorSeaDB-14
❑ 97PorSeaD-13
❑ 98ChaKniQ-16

Hasty, Robert
❑ 10BisCoaLE99-10
❑ 22E120-81
❑ 23WilChoV-60
❑ 26Zee-165
❑ 27Zee-56
❑ 28Zee-80

Hatcher, Billy
❑ 83MidCubT-13
❑ 84IowCubT-24
❑ 85CubSev-22
❑ 85Don-41
❑ 85Fle-649
❑ 85IowCubT-10
❑ 86AstMilL-10
❑ 86AstPol-23
❑ 86AstTeal-7
❑ 86Don-433
❑ 86Fle-371
❑ 86FleUpd-49
❑ 86Top-46
❑ 86TopTif-46
❑ 86TopTra-45T
❑ 86TopTraT-45T
❑ 87AstMot-26
❑ 87AstPol-6
❑ 87Don-481
❑ 87DonOpeD-18
❑ 87Fle-59
❑ 87FleGlo-59
❑ 87FleRecS-15
❑ 87Top-578
❑ 87TopTif-578
❑ 88AstMot-6
❑ 88AstPol-11
❑ 88Don-23
❑ 88Don-261
❑ 88DonBasB-150
❑ 88DonSupD-23
❑ 88Fle-449
❑ 88FleGlo-449
❑ 88Lea-23
❑ 88Lea-110
❑ 88OPC-306
❑ 88PanSti-300
❑ 88RedFolSB-30
❑ 88Sco-505
❑ 88ScoGlo-505
❑ 88Spo-63
❑ 88StaLinAst-10
❑ 88Top-291
❑ 88Top-306
❑ 88TopBig-3
❑ 88TopMinL-49
❑ 88TopSti-28
❑ 88TopTif-291
❑ 88TopTif-306
❑ 88TopUKM-30
❑ 88TopUKMT-30
❑ 89AstLenH-1
❑ 89AstMot-5
❑ 89AstSmo-18
❑ 89Don-187
❑ 89DonBasB-150
❑ 89Fle-359
❑ 89FleGlo-359
❑ 89OPC-252
❑ 89PanSti-92
❑ 89Sco-61
❑ 89Spo-174
❑ 89Top-252
❑ 89TopBig-118
❑ 89TopSti-19
❑ 89TopTif-252
❑ 89TVSpoM-55
❑ 89UppDec-344
❑ 90Don-616
❑ 90DonBesN-125
❑ 90Fle-467
❑ 90FleCan-467
❑ 90FleUpd-13
❑ 90Lea-241
❑ 90OPC-119
❑ 90PirHomC-11
❑ 90PubIntS-96
❑ 90RedKah-11
❑ 90Sco-562
❑ 90ScoRoo-42T
❑ 90Top-119
❑ 90TopBig-222
❑ 90TopTif-119
❑ 90TopTra-38T
❑ 90TopTraT-38T
❑ 90UppDec-598
❑ 90UppDec-778
❑ 91Bow-670
❑ 91Don-196
❑ 91Don-763
❑ 91Fle-66
❑ 91FleWorS-2
❑ 91Lea-205
❑ 91OPC-604
❑ 91PanFreS-132
❑ 91RedFolS-46
❑ 91RedKah-22
❑ 91RedPep-10
❑ 91Sco-469
❑ 91StaClu-371
❑ 91StaCluCM-11
❑ 91Stu-166
❑ 91Top-604
❑ 91TopDesS-604
❑ 91TopMic-604
❑ 91TopTif-604
❑ 91Ult-94
❑ 91Ult-95
❑ 91UppDec-114
❑ 91Woo-27
❑ 92Don-537
❑ 92Fle-409
❑ 92OPC-432
❑ 92Pin-460
❑ 92Sco-447
❑ 92ScoRoo-72T
❑ 92StaClu-363
❑ 92Top-432
❑ 92TopGol-432
❑ 92TopGolW-432
❑ 92TopMic-432
❑ 92TriPla-222
❑ 92Ult-190
❑ 92UppDec-699
❑ 93Don-754
❑ 93Fla-166
❑ 93Fle-561
❑ 93Lea-109
❑ 93PacSpa-83
❑ 93RedSoxP-18
❑ 93RedSoxWHP-6
❑ 93Sco-657
❑ 93Sel-225
❑ 93Stu-186
❑ 93Top-725
❑ 93TopGol-725
❑ 93TopInaM-725
❑ 93TopInaR-725
❑ 93TopMic-725
❑ 93TriPla-157
❑ 93Ult-512
❑ 93UppDec-618
❑ 93UppDecGold-618
❑ 94ColC-128
❑ 94ColChoGS-128
❑ 94ColChoSS-128
❑ 94Don-434
❑ 94Fla-14
❑ 94Fla-413
❑ 94Fle-35
❑ 94FleExtB-334
❑ 94FleUpd-164
❑ 94Lea-34
❑ 94Pac-57
❑ 94PanSti-31
❑ 94PhiMel-19
❑ 94Pin-362
❑ 94PinArtP-362
❑ 94PinMusC-362
❑ 94Sco-443
❑ 94ScoGolR-443
❑ 94Sel-96
❑ 94Top-26
❑ 94TopGol-26
❑ 94TopSpa-26
❑ 94TriPla-205
❑ 94Ult-16
❑ 94UppDec-461
❑ 94UppDecED-461
❑ 95Don-470
❑ 95DonPreP-470
❑ 95Sco-515
❑ 95ScoGolR-515
❑ 95ScoPlaTS-515
❑ 95Top-383
❑ 97St.PetDR-3
❑ 97St.PetDRUB-3

Hatcher, Chris
❑ 90AubAstP-3395
❑ 91BurAstC-20
❑ 91BurAstP-2814
❑ 91Cla/Bes-312
❑ 91MidLeaAP-MWL16
❑ 92OscAstC-6
❑ 92OscAstF-2542
❑ 92ProFS7-230
❑ 93ClaFS7-203
❑ 93ClaGolF-167
❑ 93ExcFS7-43
❑ 93JacGenF-2119
❑ 94TucTorF-773
❑ 94VenLinU-3
❑ 95TucTotTI-10
❑ 96JacGenB-11
❑ 96TusTorB-12
❑ 97OmaRoyB-22
❑ 98OmaRoyM-11
❑ 99SpoIll-67

Hatcher, Hal
❑ 81ChaRoyT-5
❑ 82ForMyeRT-2
❑ 84MemChiT-20

Hatcher, Johnny
❑ 83DurBulT-5
❑ 84DurBulT-5
❑ 85DurBulT-26
❑ 87GreBraB-25

Hatcher, Ken
❑ 52LavPro-39

Hatcher, Mickey
❑ 79AlbDukTc-11
❑ 80DodPol-44
❑ 80Top-679
❑ 81DodPol-44A
❑ 81Don-526
❑ 81Fle-135
❑ 81Top-289
❑ 81TopTra-768
❑ 81TwiPos-13
❑ 82Don-480
❑ 82OPC-291
❑ 82Top-467
❑ 82TopSti-212
❑ 82TwiPos-14
❑ 83Don-615
❑ 83Fle-614
❑ 83Top-121
❑ 83TwiTeal-6
❑ 84Don-147
❑ 84Fle-566
❑ 84MinTwiP-15
❑ 84Nes792-746
❑ 84Top-746
❑ 84TopTif-746
❑ 84TwiTeal-6
❑ 85Don-194
❑ 85Fle-279
❑ 85Lea-224
❑ 85Top-18
❑ 85TopSti-304
❑ 85TopTif-18
❑ 85Twi7-3
❑ 85TwiPos-12
❑ 85TwiTeal-6
❑ 85TwiTeal-10
❑ 86Don-269
❑ 86Fle-396
❑ 86Lea-143
❑ 86OPC-356
❑ 86Top-356
❑ 86Top-786
❑ 86TopTif-356
❑ 86TopTif-786
❑ 86TwiTeal-6
❑ 87DodMot-25
❑ 87Don-491
❑ 87Fle-542
❑ 87FleGlo-542
❑ 87FleUpd-41
❑ 87FleUpdG-41
❑ 87OPC-341
❑ 87Top-504
❑ 87TopSti-276
❑ 87TopTif-504
❑ 87TopTra-43T
❑ 87TopTraT-43T
❑ 88DodMot-25
❑ 88DodPol-9
❑ 88Don-299
❑ 88Fle-516
❑ 88FleGlo-516
❑ 88Lea-122
❑ 88OPC-339
❑ 88Sco-298
❑ 88ScoGlo-298
❑ 88StaLinD-7
❑ 88Top-607
❑ 88TopSti-71
❑ 88TopTif-607
❑ 89Bow-347
❑ 89BowTif-347
❑ 89DodMot-25
❑ 89DodPol-6
❑ 89DodStaSV-14
❑ 89Don-346
❑ 89FleGlo-WS1
❑ 89FleWorS-1
❑ 89OPC-254

❑ 89OPC-390
❑ 89PanSti-23
❑ 89PanSti-105
❑ 89Sco-332
❑ 89Top-483
❑ 89TopBig-63
❑ 89TopTif-483
❑ 89UppDec-709
❑ 89Woo-31
❑ 90DodMot-6
❑ 90DodPol-8
❑ 90DodTar-323
❑ 90Don-439
❑ 90Fle-398
❑ 90FleCan-398
❑ 90Lea-332
❑ 90OPC-226
❑ 90PublntS-8
❑ 90Sco-359
❑ 90Top-226
❑ 90TopTif-226
❑ 90UppDec-283
❑ 91Fle-206
❑ 91OPC-152
❑ 91Sco-153
❑ 91Top-152
❑ 91TopDesS-152
❑ 91TopMic-152
❑ 91TopTif-152
❑ 91UppDec-666
❑ 92AlbDukF-738
❑ 93RanKee-436
❑ 94RanMagM-6
❑ 95GreFalDTI-32
❑ 96GreFalDB-1
❑ 96GreFalDTI-33
❑ 98DodMot-28
❑ 98SanBerS-12
❑ 98SanBerSTIS-12

Hatcher, Rick
❑ 82DurBulT-18

Hatfield, Fred
❑ 52Bow-153
❑ 52Top-354
❑ 53BowC-125
❑ 53TigGle-12
❑ 53Top-163
❑ 54Bow-119
❑ 55Bow-187
❑ 56Top-318
❑ 57Top-278
❑ 58Top-339
❑ 59DarFar-9
❑ 78TigTeal-11
❑ 80RicBraT-5
❑ 83TopRep5-354
❑ 86MiaMarP-9
❑ 91TopArc1-163

Hatfield, Gil (Gilbert)
❑ 87OldJudN-231
❑ 89SFHaCN-10
❑ 90DodTar-975

Hatfield, Rick
❑ 94AshTouC-11
❑ 94AshTouF-1784

Hatfield, Rob
❑ 86MacPirP-13
❑ 87SalBucP-4

Hathaway, Hilly
❑ 90BoiHawP-3311
❑ 90ProAaA-157
❑ 92MidAngOHP-7
❑ 92PalSprAF-831
❑ 93Bow-61
❑ 93ClaFS7-6
❑ 93Don-329
❑ 93FleFinE-183
❑ 93SelRoo-55T
❑ 93TopTra-87T
❑ 93VanCanF-2590
❑ 94ColC-129
❑ 94ColChoGS-129
❑ 94ColChoSS-129
❑ 94Don-170
❑ 94Fle-59
❑ 94LasVegSF-871
❑ 94Pin-127
❑ 94PinArtP-127
❑ 94PinMusC-127
❑ 94Sco-612
❑ 94ScoBoyoS-10
❑ 94ScoGolR-612
❑ 94StaClu-385
❑ 94StaCluFDI-385
❑ 94StaCluGR-385
❑ 94StaCluMOP-385
❑ 94Top-596
❑ 94TopGol-596
❑ 94TopSpa-596

Hathaway, Ray
❑ 43ParSpo-79

Hathaway, Shawn
❑ 88SprCarB-6
❑ 89St.PetCS-16
❑ 89Sta-50

Hattabaugh, Matt
❑ 91UtiBluSC-10
❑ 91UtiBluSP-3243

Hattaway, Wayne
❑ 85OrlTwiT-23
❑ 88OrlTwiB-26
❑ 89OrlTwiB-27
❑ 89OrlTwiP-1336
❑ 90OrlSunRB-26
❑ 90OrlSunRS-28

Hatteberg, Scott
❑ 91Cla/Bes-442
❑ 91ClaDraP-38
❑ 91FroRowDP-15
❑ 91FroRowDPG-15
❑ 91FroRowDPS-15
❑ 92Bow-83
❑ 92ClaFS7-196
❑ 92NewBriRSF-437
❑ 92NewBriRSS-487
❑ 92OPC-734
❑ 92Pin-569
❑ 92SkyAA F-207
❑ 92StaCluD-80
❑ 92Top-734
❑ 92TopGol-734
❑ 92TopGolW-734
❑ 92TopMic-734
❑ 92UppDecML-238
❑ 93Bow-87
❑ 93ClaFS7-7
❑ 93ClaGolF-28
❑ 93NewBriRSF-1225
❑ 94NewBriRSF-653
❑ 94PawRedSDD-8
❑ 94SigRoo-8
❑ 94SigRooS-8
❑ 94Top-764
❑ 94TopGol-764
❑ 94TopSpa-764
❑ 94UppDecML-246
❑ 95PawRedSDD-13
❑ 95PawRedTI-12
❑ 95Top-632
❑ 96PawRedSDD-11
❑ 96Sco-508
❑ 97DonLim-175
❑ 97DonLimE-175
❑ 97DonLimENG-175
❑ 98ColCho-51
❑ 98Fin-73
❑ 98FinNo--73
❑ 98FinNo-R-73
❑ 98FinRef-73
❑ 98MetUni-41
❑ 98MetUniPMG-41
❑ 98Pac-42
❑ 98PacOnl-115
❑ 98PacOnlR-115
❑ 98PacOnlWC-115
❑ 98PacPlaB-42
❑ 98PacRedT-42
❑ 98PacSil-42
❑ 98Pin-158
❑ 98PinPreP-158
❑ 98RedSoxS-5
❑ 98RedSoxSP-5
❑ 98Sco-80
❑ 98StaCluFDI-121
❑ 98StaClul-121
❑ 98StaCluOneK-121
❑ 98StaCluPP-121
❑ 98Top-228
❑ 98TopChr-228
❑ 98TopChrR-228
❑ 98TopDevR-228
❑ 98TopDia-228
❑ 98TopMiniC-228
❑ 98Ult-26
❑ 98UltGolM-26
❑ 98UltMas-26
❑ 98UltPlaM-26
❑ 98UppDec-317
❑ 99Fle-439
❑ 99FleSta9-439
❑ 99FleWarT-439
❑ 99Top-12
❑ 99TopChr-12
❑ 99TopChrR-12
❑ 99TopMVPP-12
❑ 99UppDec-53
❑ 99UppDecEL1-53
❑ 99UppDecEL2-53

Hatten, Joe
❑ 46DodTeal-9
❑ 47DodTeal-9
❑ 47HomBon-19
❑ 47TipTop-96
❑ 48DodTeal-11
❑ 49Bow-116
❑ 49EurSta-36
❑ 50Bow-166
❑ 51Bow-190
❑ 52Bow-144
❑ 52Top-194
❑ 79DiaGre-91
❑ 83TopRep5-194
❑ 85TCMPla1-4
❑ 90DodTar-324
❑ 91DodRinP4-7

Hatter, Clyde
❑ 35DiaMatCS3T1-71
❑ 74TigTCM1AC-15

Hattig, Keith
❑ 94BoiHawC-13
❑ 94BoiHawF-3362

Hatton, Grady
❑ 47Exh-90
❑ 47PM1StaP1-80
❑ 49Bow-62
❑ 49EurSta-85
❑ 50Bow-26
❑ 51Bow-47
❑ 51TopRedB-34
❑ 52Top-6
❑ 53Top-45
❑ 54Top-208
❑ 55Top-131
❑ 55TopDouH-71
❑ 56Top-26
❑ 56TopPin-23
❑ 66Top-504
❑ 67Ast-14
❑ 67AstTeal1-6
❑ 67Top-347
❑ 68Top-392
❑ 73OPC-624
❑ 73Top-624
❑ 74OPC-31
❑ 74Top-31
❑ 79DiaGre-268
❑ 81RedSoxBG2S-26
❑ 83TopRep5-6
❑ 84TCMPla1-39
❑ 91OriCro-187
❑ 91TopArc1-45
❑ 92TexLon-23
❑ 94TopArc1-208
❑ 94TopArc1G-208

Haugen, Troy
❑ 89HelBreSP-7
❑ 90BelBreB-24
❑ 90BelBreS-10
❑ 91StoPorC-12
❑ 91StoPorP-3039

Haughey, Chris
❑ 90DodTar-976

Haughney, Trevor
❑ 91GulCoaRSP-14

Haught, Gary
❑ 92SouOreAC-17
❑ 92SouOreAF-3411
❑ 93MadMusC-14
❑ 93MadMusF-1818
❑ 93MidLeaAGF-13
❑ 94ModA'sC-14
❑ 94ModA'sF-3061
❑ 95ModA'sTI-10
❑ 96HunStaTI-9

Haugstad, Phil
❑ 52Top-198
❑ 83TopRep5-198
❑ 90DodTar-325
❑ 95TopArcBD-11

Haurado, Yanko
❑ 87PriWilYP-2

Hause, Brendan
❑ 92HigSchPLS-8
❑ 94SouOreAC-10
❑ 94SouOreAF-3614
❑ 95MidLeaA-23
❑ 95WesMicWTI-16
❑ 96ModA'sB-15

Hauser, Arnold
❑ 09SpoNewSM-89
❑ 10DomDisP-54
❑ 10SweCapPP-148
❑ 11HelSta-171
❑ 11MecDFT-25
❑ 11PinT-5-355
❑ 11PloCanE-32
❑ 11S74Sil-119
❑ 11T205-73
❑ 12HasTriFT-70C
❑ 14PieStaT-51

Hauser, Jeff
❑ 88RocExpLC-16

Hauser, Joe
❑ 21Nei-53
❑ 22E120-82
❑ 22W572-40
❑ 26Exh-108
❑ 28Exh-55
❑ 28LaPre-15
❑ 33WorCig(-39
❑ 33WorCig(-40
❑ 33WorCig(-41
❑ 61Fle-113
❑ 78HalHalR-16
❑ 79DiaGre-328
❑ 92ConTSN-548
❑ 94ConTSN-1071
❑ 94ConTSNB-1071
❑ 95ConTSN-1386

Hausladen, Bob
❑ 83BurRanF-1
❑ 83BurRanT-19

Hausman, Tom (Thomas)
❑ 74SacSolC-52
❑ 76OPC-452
❑ 76Top-452
❑ 77SpoIndC-18
❑ 77Top-99
❑ 78TidTidT-10
❑ 79OPC-339
❑ 79Top-643
❑ 80Top-151
❑ 81Don-396
❑ 81Fle-333
❑ 81Top-359
❑ 82Don-301
❑ 82Fle-526
❑ 82MetPhoA-9
❑ 82Top-524
❑ 83Top-417
❑ 91MetWIZ-164
❑ 94BreMilB-131

Hausmann, Clem
❑ 50WorWidGV-13

Hausmann, George
❑ 49EurSta-109
❑ 83TCMPla1944-36

Hausmann, Jeff
❑ 88NebCor-4

Hausterman, David
❑ 86DayBealP-11

Hauswirth, Trentor
❑ 93RocRoyC-15
❑ 93RocRoyF-720

Havens, Brad
❑ 78QuaCitAT-9
❑ 82Don-382
❑ 82OrlTwi8SCT-16
❑ 82Top-92
❑ 82TwiPos-15
❑ 83Don-480
❑ 83Fle-615
❑ 83Top-751
❑ 83TwiTeal-19
❑ 84Nes792-509
❑ 84TolMudHT-8
❑ 84Top-509
❑ 84TopTif-509
❑ 85IntLeaAT-40
❑ 85RocRedWT-16
❑ 86BalOriP-9
❑ 86Don-599
❑ 87Fle-472
❑ 87FleGlo-472
❑ 87RocRedWP-17
❑ 87RocRedWT-5
❑ 87Top-398
❑ 87TopTif-398
❑ 87TopTra-44T
❑ 87TopTraT-44T
❑ 88DodMot-22
❑ 88DodPol-41
❑ 88Fle-517
❑ 88FleGlo-517
❑ 88IndTeal-18
❑ 88Top-698
❑ 88TopTif-698
❑ 89Fle-407
❑ 89FleGlo-407
❑ 89IndTeal-13
❑ 89Top-204
❑ 89TopTif-204
❑ 90DodTar-326
❑ 91OriCro-188

Havens, Jeff
❑ 94WilCubF-3758
❑ 96AugGreB-13

Havens, Tom
❑ 92MadMusC-8
❑ 92MadMusF-1242

Havens, Will
❑ 92PulBraC-15
❑ 92PulBraF-3173
❑ 93DanBraC-13
❑ 93DanBraF-3614

Haverbusch, Kevin
❑ 97EriSeaWB-18
❑ 98Bow-360
❑ 98BowChr-360
❑ 98BowChrGA-360
❑ 98BowChrGAR-360
❑ 98BowChrl-360
❑ 98BowChrIR-360
❑ 98BowChrR-360
❑ 98BowGolA-360
❑ 98BowInt-360
❑ 98CarLeaAC-19
❑ 98CarLeaTPQ-22
❑ 98LynHilQ-15
❑ 99Bow-314
❑ 99BowGol-314
❑ 99BowInt-314

Hawarny, Dave
❑ 82BirBarT-16
❑ 83BirBarT-6

Hawblitzel, Ryan
❑ 90HunCubP-3276
❑ 91CarLeaAP-CAR42
❑ 91WinSpiC-4
❑ 91WinSpiP-2823
❑ 92Bow-138
❑ 92ChaKniF-2765
❑ 92ChaKniS-158
❑ 92ClaFS7-61
❑ 92DonRoo-49
❑ 92ProFS7-205
❑ 92SkyAA F-73
❑ 92UppDec-59
❑ 92UppDecML-31
❑ 92UppDecML-298
❑ 93Bow-64
❑ 93ClaFS7-8
❑ 93ClaGolF-91
❑ 93ColSprSSF-3081
❑ 93ExcFS7-11
❑ 93FleFinE-32
❑ 93Top-648
❑ 93TopGol-648
❑ 93ToplnaM-648
❑ 93ToplnaR-648
❑ 93TopMic-648
❑ 93Ult-349
❑ 94ColSprSSF-727
❑ 96ColSprSSTI-17
❑ 97ColSprSATTI-25
❑ 97ScrRedB-30

Hawes, Roy Lee
❑ 55Bow-268
❑ 88ChaLooLTI-14

Hawk, Tom E.
❑ 98KinIndQ-30

Hawke, Bill
❑ 94OriTeal-7

Hawkes, Nelson
❑ 18Zee-22

Hawkeye, Mascot
❑ 98FarRedHM-9

Hawkins, Al
❑ 96OgdRapTI-50
❑ 98BelSnaM-4
❑ 98BesAutSS-24
❑ 98StoPorUG-1
❑ 99SP TopP-58
❑ 99SP TopPPE-58

Hawkins, Andy
❑ 82HawlsIT-14
❑ 84Fle-302
❑ 84Nes792-778
❑ 84PadMot-18
❑ 84Top-778
❑ 84TopTif-778
❑ 85Don-528
❑ 85DonHig-14
❑ 85DonHig-15
❑ 85Fle-36
❑ 85PadMot-13
❑ 85Top-299
❑ 85TopTif-299
❑ 86Don-284
❑ 86Fle-324
❑ 86FleMin-70
❑ 86FleStiC-51
❑ 86Lea-158
❑ 86OPC-5
❑ 86SevCoi-W12
❑ 86Spo-191
❑ 86Top-478
❑ 86TopSti-108
❑ 86TopTat-12
❑ 86TopTif-478
❑ 87Don-264
❑ 87Fle-417
❑ 87FleGlo-417
❑ 87PadBohHB-40
❑ 87SpoTeaP-16
❑ 87Top-81
❑ 87Top-183
❑ 87TopTif-81
❑ 87TopTif-183
❑ 88Fle-586
❑ 88FleGlo-586
❑ 88PadSmo-11
❑ 88Sco-347
❑ 88ScoGlo-347
❑ 88Top-9
❑ 88TopBig-257
❑ 88TopClo-44
❑ 88TopTif-9
❑ 89Bow-166
❑ 89BowTif-166
❑ 89Don-583
❑ 89DonBasB-52
❑ 89DonTra-52
❑ 89Fle-307
❑ 89FleGlo-307
❑ 89FleUpd-50
❑ 89PanSti-194
❑ 89Sco-118
❑ 89ScoRoo-14T
❑ 89Spo-84
❑ 89Top-533
❑ 89TopSti-111
❑ 89TopTif-533
❑ 89TopTra-47T
❑ 89TopTraT-47T
❑ 89UppDec-495
❑ 89UppDec-708
❑ 89YanScoNW-19
❑ 90ClaBlu-135
❑ 90Don-159
❑ 90Fle-445
❑ 90FleCan-445
❑ 90Lea-281
❑ 90OPC-335
❑ 90PanSti-130
❑ 90PublntS-536
❑ 90Top-335
❑ 90TopBig-36
❑ 90TopSti-317
❑ 90TopTif-335
❑ 90TopTVY-10
❑ 90UppDec-339
❑ 90YanScoNW-18
❑ 91Don-611
❑ 91DonBonC-BC12A
❑ 91DonBonC-BC12B
❑ 91Fle-666
❑ 91FleWaxBC-6
❑ 91OPC-635
❑ 91PanFreS-357
❑ 91PanSti-6
❑ 91Sco-47
❑ 91Sco-704
❑ 91StaClu-487
❑ 91StaCluCM-12
❑ 91Top-635
❑ 91TopDesS-635
❑ 91TopMic-635
❑ 91TopTif-635
❑ 91Ult-234
❑ 91UppDec-333
❑ 92CalCanS-59
❑ 92YanWIZ8-79

Hawkins, Burt
❑ 64TopRooAB-28

Hawkins, Cedric
❑ 86LitFalMP-13
Hawkins, Chris
❑ 87AubAstP-11
Hawkins, Craig
❑ 91EliTwiP-4306
❑ 92EliTwiC-14
❑ 92EliTwiF-3694
Hawkins, Frank
❑ 37Zee-75
Hawkins, Hersey
❑ 88PeoChiTI-14
Hawkins, J.R.
❑ 93YakBeaC-12
❑ 93YakBeaF-3897
Hawkins, Joe
❑ 90PitMetP-28
❑ 91St.LucMC-30
❑ 95NorTidTI-4
❑ 96NorTidB-4
❑ 97NorTid-4
❑ 97NorTidB-4
❑ 98NorTidP-14
❑ 98NorTidQ-35
Hawkins, John
❑ 84NasSouTI-9
❑ 85AlbYanT-32
❑ 86FloStaLAP-21
❑ 86Ft.LauYP-12
❑ 91SouBenWSC-28
Hawkins, Kraig
❑ 92OneYanC-25
❑ 93GreHorC-10
❑ 93GreHorF-898
❑ 94ExcFS7-104
❑ 94TamYanC-12
❑ 94TamYanF-2396
❑ 95AusFut-72
❑ 95NorNavTI-11
❑ 95TamYanYI-10
❑ 96TamYanY-12
❑ 97NorNav-17
Hawkins, Laig
❑ 97NorNavTI-12
Hawkins, LaTroy
❑ 93ForWayWC-10
❑ 93ForWayWF-1963
❑ 94BowBes-B65
❑ 94BowBesR-B65
❑ 94Cla-54
❑ 94ClaTriF-T46
❑ 94ExcFS7-95
❑ 94ExcLeaLF-9
❑ 94ForMyeMC-1
❑ 94ForMyeMF-1163
❑ 94SigRooTPD-T4
❑ 94SigRooTPS-T4
❑ 94SP-8
❑ 94SPDieC-8
❑ 94Ult-389
❑ 94UppDec-548
❑ 94UppDecAHNIL-6
❑ 94UppDecED-548
❑ 94UppDecML-248
❑ 94UppDecMLPotYF-PY26
❑ 95ActPac2G-15G
❑ 95ActPacF-28
❑ 95ActPacF-76
❑ 95ARuFalLS-9
❑ 95Bow-256
❑ 95BowBes-B53
❑ 95BowBesR-B53
❑ 95BowGolF-256
❑ 95ColChoSE-7
❑ 95ColChoSEGS-7
❑ 95ColChoSESS-7
❑ 95Exc-86
❑ 95ExcLeaL-8
❑ 95Fla-280
❑ 95Fle-204
❑ 95SelCer-103
❑ 95SelCerMG-103
❑ 95SigRooMOP-P2
❑ 95SigRooMOPS-P2
❑ 95SigRooOP-OP4
❑ 95SigRooOPS-OP4
❑ 95StaCluCB-CB15
❑ 95StaCluMOP-CB15
❑ 95Sum-172
❑ 95SumNthD-172
❑ 95Top-179
❑ 95UltGolP-5
❑ 95UltGolPGM-5
❑ 95UppDec-223
❑ 95UppDecED-223
❑ 95UppDecEDG-223
❑ 95UppDecML-7
❑ 95UppDecML-163
❑ 95UppDecMLFS-7
❑ 95UppDecMLFS-163
❑ 95UppDecMLMLA-5
❑ 95UppDecSE-81
❑ 95UppDecSEG-81
❑ 95Zen-136
❑ 95ZenRooRC-15
❑ 96ColCho-198
❑ 96ColCho-659
❑ 96ColChoGS-198
❑ 96ColChoGS-659
❑ 96ColChoSS-198
❑ 96ColChoSS-659
❑ 96Don-514
❑ 96DonPreP-514
❑ 96Fla-113
❑ 96FleUpd-U53
❑ 96FleUpdTC-U53
❑ 96Lea-56
❑ 96LeaPre-140
❑ 96LeaPreP-140
❑ 96LeaPrePB-56
❑ 96LeaPrePG-56
❑ 96LeaPrePS-56
❑ 96LeaSigA-97
❑ 96LeaSigAG-97
❑ 96LeaSigAS-97
❑ 96Pin-185
❑ 96PinAfi-170
❑ 96PinAfiAP-170
❑ 96Sco-224
❑ 96ScoDugC-A104
❑ 96ScoDugCAP-A104
❑ 96Sel-185
❑ 96SelArtP-185
❑ 96SelCer-125
❑ 96SelCerAP-125
❑ 96SelCerCB-125
❑ 96SelCerCR-125
❑ 96SelCerMB-125
❑ 96SelCerMG-125
❑ 96SelCerMR-125
❑ 96Stu-131
❑ 96StuPrePB-131
❑ 96StuPrePG-131
❑ 96StuPrePS-131
❑ 96Sum-183
❑ 96SumAbo&B-183
❑ 96SumArtP-183
❑ 96SumFoi-183
❑ 96Top-407
❑ 96Ult-373
❑ 96UltGolM-373
❑ 96UppDec-367
❑ 97DonEli-138
❑ 97DonEliGS-138
❑ 97DonRatR-2
❑ 97SalLakB-12
❑ 97Sco-260
❑ 97ScoArtPWB-260
❑ 97ScoPreS-260
❑ 97ScoShoS-260
❑ 97ScoShoSAP-260
❑ 98Fle-532
❑ 98Pac-133
❑ 98PacPlaB-133
❑ 98PacRedT-133
❑ 98PacSil-133
❑ 98Top-197
❑ 98TopChr-197
❑ 98TopChrR-197
❑ 98TopDevR-197
❑ 98TopDia-197
❑ 98TopMiniC-197
❑ 98Ult-327
❑ 98UltGolM-327
❑ 98UltMas-327
❑ 98UltPlaM-327
❑ 98UppDec-433
❑ 99Fle-389
❑ 99FleSta9-389
❑ 99FleWarT-389
❑ 99Top-169
❑ 99TopChr-169
❑ 99TopChrR-169
❑ 99TopMVPP-169
❑ 99UppDec-413
❑ 99UppDecEL1-413
❑ 99UppDecEL2-413
❑ 99Vic-233
Hawkins, Todd
❑ 87EveGiaC-18
❑ 88FreSunCLC-9
❑ 88FreSunP-1242
Hawkins, Ty
❑ 91SouBenWSP-2869
Hawkins, Walter
❑ 87IdaFalBP-11
Hawkins, Wes
❑ 93BluOriF-4139
❑ 94AlbPolF-2250
Hawkins, Wynn
❑ 60Top-536
❑ 61Top-34
❑ 63Top-334
Hawks, Boise
❑ 95BoiHawTI-35
Hawks, Larry
❑ 90SpoIndSP-5
❑ 91BenBucCB-24
❑ 91BenBucP-3696
❑ 91WatDiaC-28
❑ 91WatDiaP-1258
Hawks, Nelson
❑ 21KoBreWSI-34
❑ 22W575-53
❑ 22Zee-152
❑ 25Exh-42
Hawley, Billy
❑ 83CedRapRF-10
❑ 86VerRedP-10
❑ 87TamTarP-26
Hawley, Pink (Emerson P.)
❑ 98CamPepP-33
Haworth, Homer
❑ 14Zee-61
❑ 14Zee-62
❑ 16Zee-53
Haws, Scott
❑ 92MarPhiC-16
❑ 92MarPhiF-3060
❑ 93SpaPhiC-14
❑ 93SpaPhiF-1059
❑ 94ClePhiC-16
❑ 94ClePhiF-2331
❑ 97ClePhi-7
Haydel, Hal
❑ 71OPC-692
❑ 71Top-692
❑ 72OPC-28
❑ 72Top-28
Hayden, Alan
❑ 86ColMetP-12
❑ 87JacMetF-22
❑ 87LynMetP-11
❑ 88JacMetGS-25
❑ 89ChaLooB-25
❑ 89ChaLooGS-23
❑ 89JacMetGS-30
❑ 89NasSouTI-9
❑ 90ChaLooGS-15
Hayden, David
❑ 91BatCliCB-10
❑ 91BatCliP-3492
❑ 92SpaPhiC-18
❑ 92SpaPhiF-1269
❑ 93ClePhiC-13
❑ 93ClePhiF-2691
❑ 94ReaPhiF-2070
❑ 95ReaPhiTI-16
Hayden, John F.
❑ 08IndPos-11
❑ 09T206-429
Hayden, M.
❑ 11PinT-5-920
Hayden, Paris
❑ 89FreKeyS-10
❑ 90FreKeyTI-13
❑ 90HagSunP-1427
❑ 90HagSunS-11
❑ 91FloStaLAP-FSL22
❑ 91MiaMirC-28
❑ 91MiaMirP-421
Hayden, Richard
❑ 84ButCopKT-12
Hayes, Ben
❑ 82IndIndTI-21
❑ 83Fle-591
❑ 84Fle-470
❑ 84Nes792-448
❑ 84Top-448
❑ 84TopTif-448
❑ 85LouRedR-25
Hayes, Bill
❑ 80WicAerT-5
❑ 82IowCubT-5
❑ 83IowCubT-12
❑ 84IowCubT-15
❑ 85IowCubT-2
❑ 86OmaRoyP-10
❑ 86OmaRoyT-1
❑ 87IowCubTI-14
❑ 88GenCubP-1654
❑ 90GenCubP-3053
❑ 90GenCubS-26
❑ 91PeoChiC-22
❑ 91PeoChiP-1359
❑ 91PeoChiTI-1
❑ 92WinSpiC-26
❑ 92WinSpiF-1223
❑ 93DayCubC-24
❑ 93DayCubF-873
❑ 94CenValRC-26
❑ 94CenValRF-3218
❑ 95SalAvaTI-29
❑ 96NewHavRB-1
❑ 97NewHavRB-29
Hayes, Blimp (Frank)
❑ 39PlaBal-108
❑ 40PlaBal-24
❑ 41DouPlaR-47
❑ 41Gou-13
❑ 41PlaBal-41
❑ 42A'sTeal-16
❑ 45A'sTeal-17
❑ 47TipTop-7
❑ 92ConTSN-380
❑ 93ConTSN-864
Hayes, Brian
❑ 78LodDodT-7
❑ 79LodDodT-19
Hayes, Charlie
❑ 85FreGiaSB-11
❑ 86ShrCapP-11
❑ 87ShrCapP-17
❑ 87TexLeaAF-27
❑ 88BlaYNPRWL-151
❑ 88PhoFirC-15
❑ 88PhoFirP-57
❑ 89BlaYNPRWL-157
❑ 89Fle-330
❑ 89FleGlo-330
❑ 89FleUpd-106
❑ 89PhiTas-41
❑ 89PhoFirC-13
❑ 89PhoFirP-1487
❑ 89Sco-628
❑ 89ScoHot1R-39
❑ 89UppDec-707
❑ 90ClaBlu-98
❑ 90Don-548
❑ 90DonBesN-106
❑ 90Fle-558
❑ 90FleCan-558
❑ 90Hot50RS-21
❑ 90Lea-131
❑ 90OPC-577
❑ 90PhiTas-11
❑ 90Sco-507
❑ 90Sco100RS-12
❑ 90ScoYouSI-38
❑ 90Spo-36
❑ 90Top-577
❑ 90TopTif-577
❑ 90UppDec-437
❑ 91Bow-508
❑ 91Don-278
❑ 91Fle-397
❑ 91Lea-214
❑ 91OPC-312
❑ 91PanFreS-105
❑ 91PanSti-102
❑ 91PhiMed-17
❑ 91Sco-238
❑ 91Sco100S-19
❑ 91StaClu-163
❑ 91Stu-214
❑ 91Top-312
❑ 91TopDesS-312
❑ 91TopMic-312
❑ 91TopTif-312
❑ 91Ult-263
❑ 91UppDec-269
❑ 92Bow-147
❑ 92Don-547
❑ 92Fle-533
❑ 92FleUpd-42
❑ 92Lea-220
❑ 92LeaBlaG-220
❑ 92OPC-754
❑ 92OPCPre-6
❑ 92PanSti-244
❑ 92Pin-497
❑ 92Sco-301
❑ 92ScoRoo-16T
❑ 92StaClu-711
❑ 92StaCluNC-711
❑ 92Stu-212
❑ 92Top-754
❑ 92TopGol-754
❑ 92TopGolW-754
❑ 92TopMic-754
❑ 92TopTra-46T
❑ 92TopTraG-46T
❑ 92Ult-243
❑ 92Ult-407
❑ 92UppDec-208
❑ 92UppDec-768
❑ 93Bow-500
❑ 93CadDis-30
❑ 93DiaMar-49
❑ 93Don-181
❑ 93Don-776
❑ 93DurPowP2-4
❑ 93Fin-60
❑ 93FinRef-60
❑ 93Fla-41
❑ 93Fle-279
❑ 93FleFinE-33
❑ 93FunPac-177
❑ 93JimDea-26
❑ 93Lea-360
❑ 93OPC-54
❑ 93OPCPre-66
❑ 93PacSpa-429
❑ 93Pin-447
❑ 93PinExpOD-5
❑ 93PinHomRC-19
❑ 93RocStaC-3
❑ 93RocUSPC-1H
❑ 93RocUSPC-2C
❑ 93Sco-411
❑ 93Sel-194
❑ 93SP-222
❑ 93StaClu-743
❑ 93StaCluFDI-743
❑ 93StaCluMOP-743
❑ 93Stu-136
❑ 93Top-142
❑ 93Top-759
❑ 93TopGol-142
❑ 93TopGol-759
❑ 93TopInaM-142
❑ 93TopInaM-759
❑ 93TopInaR-142
❑ 93TopInaR-759
❑ 93TopMic-142
❑ 93TopMic-759
❑ 93TriPla-257
❑ 93Ult-350
❑ 93UppDec-647
❑ 93UppDecGold-647
❑ 94Bow-254
❑ 94ColC-130
❑ 94ColChoGS-130
❑ 94ColChoSS-130
❑ 94Don-46
❑ 94DonSpeE-46
❑ 94Fin-32
❑ 94FinRef-32
❑ 94Fla-374
❑ 94Fle-443
❑ 94FleExtB-247
❑ 94FUnPac-89
❑ 94Lea-134
❑ 94LeaL-104
❑ 94OPC-171
❑ 94Pac-197
❑ 94PacSilP-21
❑ 94PacSilPC-21
❑ 94PanSti-175
❑ 94Pin-14
❑ 94PinArtP-14
❑ 94PinMusC-14
❑ 94PinRunC-RC40
❑ 94RedFolMI-12
❑ 94RocPol-13
❑ 94Sco-50
❑ 94ScoCyc-TC7
❑ 94ScoGolR-50
❑ 94Sel-42
❑ 94SP-167
❑ 94SPDieC-167
❑ 94Spo-82
❑ 94StaClu-249
❑ 94StaCluFDI-249
❑ 94StaCluGR-249
❑ 94StaCluMOP-249
❑ 94StaCluT-114
❑ 94StaCluTFDI-114
❑ 94Stu-179
❑ 94Top-655
❑ 94TopGol-655
❑ 94TopSpa-655
❑ 94TriPla-225
❑ 94Ult-482
❑ 94UppDec-167
❑ 94UppDecAJ-39
❑ 94UppDecAJG-39
❑ 94UppDecED-167
❑ 95ColCho-445
❑ 95ColCho-567T
❑ 95ColChoGS-445
❑ 95ColChoSE-207
❑ 95ColChoSEGS-207
❑ 95ColChoSESS-207
❑ 95ColChoSS-445
❑ 95Don-252
❑ 95DonPreP-252
❑ 95DonTopotO-305
❑ 95Emo-166
❑ 95Fin-261
❑ 95FinRef-261
❑ 95Fla-390
❑ 95Fle-521
❑ 95FleUpd-121
❑ 95Lea-325
❑ 95LeaLim-18
❑ 95Pac-138
❑ 95Phi-15
❑ 95PhiMel-12
❑ 95Pin-79
❑ 95PinArtP-79
❑ 95PinMusC-79
❑ 95Sco-58
❑ 95ScoGolR-58
❑ 95ScoPlaTS-58
❑ 95SP-89
❑ 95Spo-9
❑ 95SpoArtP-9
❑ 95SPSil-89
❑ 95StaClu-123
❑ 95StaClu-559
❑ 95StaCluFDI-123
❑ 95StaCluMOP-123
❑ 95StaCluMOP-559
❑ 95StaCluSTWS-123
❑ 95StaCluSTWS-559
❑ 95StaCluVR-62
❑ 95StaCluVRMO-62
❑ 95Top-81
❑ 95TopCyb-57
❑ 95TopTra-140T
❑ 95Ult-154
❑ 95UltGolM-154
❑ 95UppDec-172
❑ 95UppDec-378
❑ 95UppDecED-172
❑ 95UppDecED-378
❑ 95UppDecEDG-172
❑ 95UppDecEDG-378
❑ 95UppDecSE-209
❑ 95UppDecSEG-209
❑ 96Cir-171
❑ 96CirRav-171
❑ 96ColCho-255
❑ 96ColCho-680
❑ 96ColChoGS-255
❑ 96ColChoGS-680
❑ 96ColChoSS-255
❑ 96ColChoSS-680
❑ 96Don-140
❑ 96DonPreP-140
❑ 96EmoXL-254
❑ 96Fin-B226
❑ 96FinRef-B226
❑ 96Fla-346
❑ 96Fle-499
❑ 96FleTif-499
❑ 96FleUpd-U176
❑ 96FleUpdTC-U176
❑ 96LeaSigA-98
❑ 96LeaSigAG-98
❑ 96LeaSigAS-98
❑ 96Pac-149
❑ 96PanSti-34
❑ 96Pin-124
❑ 96Pin-343
❑ 96PinAfi-44
❑ 96PinAfiAP-44
❑ 96PinAfiFPP-44
❑ 96PinFoil-343
❑ 96Sco-307
❑ 96ScoDugC-B32
❑ 96ScoDugCAP-B32
❑ 96Sel-131

❑ 96SelArtP-131
❑ 96SP-148
❑ 96StaClu-441
❑ 96StaCluEPB-441
❑ 96StaCluEPG-441
❑ 96StaCluEPS-441
❑ 96StaCluMOP-441
❑ 96Top-255
❑ 96Ult-253
❑ 96Ult-532
❑ 96UltGolM-253
❑ 96UltGolM-532
❑ 96UppDec-436
❑ 97ColCho-403
❑ 97ColChoT-NY9
❑ 97Don-99
❑ 97DonGolPP-99
❑ 97DonSilPP-99
❑ 97DonTea-127
❑ 97DonTeaSPE-127
❑ 97Fle-167
❑ 97FleTif-167
❑ 97PacPriGotD-GD73
❑ 97Sco-64
❑ 97ScoArtPWB-64
❑ 97ScoPreS-64
❑ 97ScoShoS-64
❑ 97ScoShoSAP-64
❑ 97Ult-323
❑ 97UltGolME-323
❑ 97UltPlaME-323
❑ 97UppDec-442
❑ 98ColCho-487
❑ 98GiaMot-20
❑ 98PacOnl-660
❑ 98PacOnlR-660
❑ 98PacOnlWC-660
❑ 98Sco-98
❑ 98Top-29
❑ 98TopChr-29
❑ 98TopChrR-29
❑ 98TopDevR-29
❑ 98TopDia-29
❑ 98TopMiniC-29
❑ 98Ult-270
❑ 98UltGolM-270
❑ 98UltMas-270
❑ 98UltPlaM-270
❑ 98UppDec-174
❑ 98UppDec-721
❑ 98YanSco-7
❑ 98YanScoP-7
❑ 99Fle-466
❑ 99FleSta9-466
❑ 99FleWarT-466
❑ 99MetUni-200
❑ 99MetUniGM-200
❑ 99MetUniPMG-200
❑ 99Top-48
❑ 99TopChr-48
❑ 99TopChrR-48
❑ 99TopMVPP-48

Hayes, Chris
❑ 87ModA'sC-19
❑ 87ModA'sP-13

Hayes, Chris Andrew
❑ 95StCatSTI-19
❑ 96DunBluJUTI-4
❑ 96HagSunB-8
❑ 97DunBluJTI-14
❑ 98HagSunM-14

Hayes, Damon
❑ 47RemBre-21
❑ 47SmiClo-21
❑ 48SmiClo-13

Hayes, Dan
❑ 84NewOriT-13

Hayes, Darren
❑ 96PriWilCB-14

Hayes, Emanuel
❑ 92MedHatBJF-3213
❑ 92MedHatBJSP-5
❑ 93St.CatBJC-9
❑ 93St.CatBJF-3980

Hayes, Heath
❑ 97KinIndB-9
❑ 98AkrAerM-18

Hayes, Jack
❑ 88SFHesCreN32-13

Hayes, Jackie (Minter)
❑ 29ExhFou-32
❑ 31SenTeaIPW-15
❑ 34Gou-63
❑ 35AlDemDCR3-15
❑ 35GouPuzR-8B
❑ 35GouPuzR-9B
❑ 37OPCBatUV-102
❑ 39WhiSoxTI-6
❑ 40WhiSoxL-7
❑ 81ConTSN-36
❑ 91ConTSN-71
❑ 95ConTSN-1429

Hayes, Jimmy (Jim)
❑ 88BriTigP-1874
❑ 90TamYanD-11

Hayes, Randy
❑ 84AriWilP-8

Hayes, Robbie
❑ 91MisStaB-22
❑ 92MisStaB-18
❑ 93MisStaB-18

Hayes, Terry
❑ 82WauTimF-29

Hayes, Todd
❑ 87SanBerSP-22
❑ 88SanBerSB-25
❑ 88SanBerSCLC-51

Hayes, Tom
❑ 81DurBulT-7
❑ 84RicBraT-6
❑ 85GreBraTI-7

Hayes, Von
❑ 80WatIndT-35
❑ 81ChaChaT-15
❑ 82Don-237
❑ 82Fle-371
❑ 82Ind-20
❑ 82IndWhe-25
❑ 82Top-141
❑ 82TopTra-42T
❑ 83AllGamPI-146
❑ 83Don-324
❑ 83Fle-412
❑ 83OPC-325
❑ 83PhiTas-13
❑ 83Top-325
❑ 83TopSti-311
❑ 83TopTra-40T
❑ 84Don-477
❑ 84Fle-33
❑ 84Nes792-587
❑ 84OPC-259
❑ 84PhiTas-36
❑ 84Top-587
❑ 84TopSti-124
❑ 84TopTif-587
❑ 85AllGamPI-144
❑ 85Don-326
❑ 85DonHig-16
❑ 85Fle-253
❑ 85Lea-93
❑ 85OPC-68
❑ 85PhiCIG-2
❑ 85PhiTas-12
❑ 85PhiTas-36
❑ 85Top-68
❑ 85TopMin-68
❑ 85TopSti-115
❑ 85TopTif-68
❑ 86BasStaB-54
❑ 86Don-305
❑ 86Fle-443
❑ 86FleMin-92
❑ 86FleStiC-52
❑ 86Lea-176
❑ 86OPC-146
❑ 86PhiCIG-3
❑ 86PhiKel-2
❑ 86PhiTas-9
❑ 86Top-420
❑ 86TopSti-120
❑ 86TopTat-10
❑ 86TopTif-420
❑ 87BurKinA-8
❑ 87ClaGam-63
❑ 87Don-12
❑ 87Don-113
❑ 87DonOpeD-152
❑ 87DonSupD-12
❑ 87Dra-3
❑ 87Fle-175
❑ 87FleExcS-23
❑ 87FleGamW-19
❑ 87FleGlo-175
❑ 87FleMin-51
❑ 87FleStiC-55
❑ 87KraFoo-24
❑ 87Lea-12
❑ 87Lea-130
❑ 87OPC-389
❑ 87PhiCha-1
❑ 87PhiTas-9
❑ 87RedFolSB-72
❑ 87Spo-193
❑ 87SpoTeaP-6
❑ 87Top-481
❑ 87Top-666
❑ 87TopCoi-35
❑ 87TopMinL-28
❑ 87TopSti-121
❑ 87TopTif-481
❑ 87TopTif-666
❑ 88Don-207
❑ 88DonBasB-128
❑ 88Dra-17
❑ 88Fle-304
❑ 88FleExcS-18
❑ 88FleGlo-304
❑ 88FleMin-99
❑ 88FleStiC-108
❑ 88Lea-197
❑ 88OPC-215
❑ 88PanSti-356
❑ 88PhiTas-13
❑ 88Sco-515
❑ 88ScoGlo-515
❑ 88Spo-62
❑ 88StaLinPh-9
❑ 88Top-215
❑ 88TopBig-139
❑ 88TopSti-117
❑ 88TopTif-215
❑ 89Bow-406
❑ 89BowTif-406
❑ 89Don-160
❑ 89DonBasB-47
❑ 89Fle-571
❑ 89FleGlo-571
❑ 89KinDis-18
❑ 89OPC-385
❑ 89PanSti-151
❑ 89PhiTas-9
❑ 89RedFolSB-56
❑ 89Sco-38
❑ 89Spo-181
❑ 89Top-385
❑ 89TopBig-302
❑ 89TopSti-115
❑ 89TopTif-385
❑ 89TVSpoM-30
❑ 89UppDec-246
❑ 90Bow-160
❑ 90BowTif-160
❑ 90ClaBlu-113
❑ 90Don-278
❑ 90DonBesN-140
❑ 90DOnBonM-BC25
❑ 90DonLeaS-18
❑ 90Fle-559
❑ 90FleAwaW-17
❑ 90FleBasA-17
❑ 90FleBasAC-17
❑ 90FleCan-559
❑ 90GooHumICBLS-12
❑ 90KinDis-7
❑ 90Lea-52
❑ 90M.Vpin-78
❑ 90MLBBasB-2
❑ 90OPC-710
❑ 90PanSti-319
❑ 90PhiTas-12
❑ 90Pos-27
❑ 90PubIntS-238
❑ 90RedFolSB-45
❑ 90Sco-36
❑ 90Sco100S-62
❑ 90Spo-147
❑ 90SunSee-12
❑ 90Top-710
❑ 90TopBig-69
❑ 90TopCoi-48
❑ 90TopDou-32
❑ 90TopMinL-69
❑ 90TopSti-114
❑ 90TopStiB-16
❑ 90TopTif-710
❑ 90TopTVA-54
❑ 90UppDec-7
❑ 90UppDec-453
❑ 91BasBesHRK-9
❑ 91Bow-487
❑ 91ClaGam-25
❑ 91Don-222
❑ 91Fle-398
❑ 91Lea-280
❑ 91OPC-15
❑ 91PanFreS-107
❑ 91PanSti-105
❑ 91PhiMed-18
❑ 91RedFolS-47
❑ 91Sco-426
❑ 91StaClu-127
❑ 91Top-15
❑ 91TopCraJ2-5
❑ 91TopDesS-15
❑ 91TopMic-15
❑ 91TopTif-15
❑ 91Ult-264
❑ 91Ult-398
❑ 91UppDec-368
❑ 92AngPol-12
❑ 92Bow-197
❑ 92Don-580
❑ 92Fle-534
❑ 92Lea-177
❑ 92LeaBlaG-177
❑ 92OPC-135
❑ 92OPCPre-127
❑ 92PanSti-248
❑ 92Pin-326
❑ 92Sco-207
❑ 92SpoStaCC-22
❑ 92StaClu-880
❑ 92Stu-147
❑ 92Top-135
❑ 92TopGol-135
❑ 92TopGolW-135
❑ 92TopKid-19
❑ 92TopMic-135
❑ 92TopTra-47T
❑ 92TopTraG-47T
❑ 92Ult-326
❑ 92UppDec-427
❑ 92UppDec-707

Hayford, Don
❑ 79ElmPioRST-10

Hayman, David
❑ 93MisStaB-19
❑ 96AriBlaDB-21
❑ 97Top-251

Haynes, Heath
❑ 91JamExpC-25
❑ 91JamExpP-3538
❑ 92MidLeaATI-17
❑ 92ProFS7-272
❑ 92RocExpC-21
❑ 92RocExpF-2109
❑ 93ClaGolF-37
❑ 93HarSenF-266
❑ 94ExcFS7-225
❑ 94OttLynF-2897
❑ 94VenLinU-212
❑ 94WatIndC-17
❑ 94WatIndF-3944
❑ 95EdmTraTI-9
❑ 95LinVen-59
❑ 96LakElsSB-5

Haynes, Jimmy
❑ 91HigSchPLS-6
❑ 92KanCouCC-18
❑ 92KanCouCF-85
❑ 92KanCouCTI-13
❑ 92UppDecML-168
❑ 93Bow-493
❑ 93ClaFS7-73
❑ 93FreKeyC-10
❑ 93FreKeyF-1021
❑ 94Bow-543
❑ 94BowBayF-2410
❑ 94BowBes-B15
❑ 94BowBesR-B15
❑ 94Cla-35
❑ 94ExcFS7-7
❑ 94OriPro-45
❑ 94UppDecML-194
❑ 95ActPacF-39
❑ 95Bow-130
❑ 95BowBes-B69
❑ 95BowBesR-B69
❑ 95Exc-6
❑ 95ExcLeaL-9
❑ 95LinVen-305
❑ 95RocRedWTI-18
❑ 95Sel-196
❑ 95SelArtP-196
❑ 95SigRooOJA-AS3
❑ 95SigRooOJAS-AS3
❑ 95UppDecML-61
❑ 95UppDecMLFS-61
❑ 96BalOriP-13
❑ 96Bow-184
❑ 96BowBes-159
❑ 96BowBesAR-159
❑ 96BowBesR-159
❑ 96BowFoi-184
❑ 96ColCho-22
❑ 96ColChoGS-22
❑ 96ColChoSS-22
❑ 96Don-475
❑ 96DonPreP-475
❑ 96Fin-B220
❑ 96FinRef-B220
❑ 96Fla-6
❑ 96Fle-10
❑ 96FleTif-10
❑ 96Lea-189
❑ 96LeaPrePB-189
❑ 96LeaPrePG-189
❑ 96LeaPrePS-189
❑ 96LeaSigA-99
❑ 96LeaSigAG-99
❑ 96LeaSigAS-99
❑ 96OriFle-7
❑ 96Pin-179
❑ 96PinAfi-186
❑ 96PinAfiAP-186
❑ 96Sco-509
❑ 96Sel-165
❑ 96SelArtP-165
❑ 96SelCer-132
❑ 96SelCerAP-132
❑ 96SelCerCB-132
❑ 96SelCerCR-132
❑ 96SelCerMB-132
❑ 96SelCerMG-132
❑ 96SelCerMR-132
❑ 96SP-8
❑ 96Spo-132
❑ 96SpoArtP-132
❑ 96Sum-195
❑ 96SumAbo&B-195
❑ 96SumArtP-195
❑ 96SumFoi-195
❑ 96Top-354
❑ 96TopChr-143
❑ 96TopChrR-143
❑ 96TopGal-132
❑ 96TopGalPPI-132
❑ 96TopLasBS-11
❑ 96Ult-305
❑ 96UltGolM-305
❑ 96UppDec-229
❑ 96UppDecFSP-FS13
❑ 97OriSco-14
❑ 97OriScoPl-14
❑ 97OriScoPr-14
❑ 97RocRedW-14
❑ 97Sco-234
❑ 97ScoArtPWB-234
❑ 97ScoPreS-234
❑ 97ScoShoS-234
❑ 97ScoShoSAP-234
❑ 98A'sMot-26
❑ 98Fle-395
❑ 98PacOnl-532
❑ 98PacOnlR-532
❑ 98PacOnlWC-532
❑ 98UppDec-472
❑ 99Fle-422
❑ 99FleSta9-422
❑ 99FleWarT-422
❑ 99Top-59
❑ 99TopChr-59
❑ 99TopChrR-59
❑ 99TopMVPP-59

Haynes, Joe
❑ 48WhiSoxTI-10
❑ 49Bow-191
❑ 51Bow-240
❑ 52Bow-103
❑ 52Top-145
❑ 54Top-223
❑ 83TopRep5-145
❑ 85TCMPpl1-33
❑ 94TopArc1-223
❑ 94TopArc1G-223
❑ 98EveAquG-8

Haynes, Marvin
❑ 87VerRedP-26

Haynes, Nathan
❑ 97Bow-428
❑ 97BowChr-288
❑ 97BowChrI-288
❑ 97BowChrIR-288
❑ 97BowChrR-288
❑ 97BowInt-428
❑ 98BesNumOP-26
❑ 98Bow-177
❑ 98BowChr-177
❑ 98BowChrGA-177
❑ 98BowChrGAR-177
❑ 98BowChrI-177
❑ 98BowChrIR-177
❑ 98BowChrR-177
❑ 98BowGolA-177
❑ 98BowInt-177
❑ 98ModA'sG-12
❑ 99BasAmeTPA-18
❑ 99Bow-137
❑ 99BowAut-BA67
❑ 99BowChr-137
❑ 99BowChrG-137
❑ 99BowChrGR-137
❑ 99BowChrI-137
❑ 99BowChrIR-137
❑ 99BowChrR-137
❑ 99BowGol-137
❑ 99BowInt-137
❑ 99TeaBesRA-12
❑ 99TeaBesRBW-4

Haynes, Rick
❑ 75DubPacT-14

Haynes, Sammy
❑ 97NegLeaPC-2D

Haynie, Jason
❑ 96EriSeaB-12
❑ 97AugGre-11
❑ 98CarMudM-4

Hays, Darrin
❑ 89ButCopKSP-23
❑ 90ChaRanS-9

Hays, David
❑ 89EasLeaDDP-DD50

Hays, Rob
❑ 90SpoIndSP-9
❑ 91WatDiaC-5
❑ 91WatDiaP-1252

Haysbert, Dennis
❑ 89MajLeaM-4
❑ 89MajLeaM-10

Hayward, Brent
❑ 92GulCoaMF-3473

Hayward, Jeff
❑ 86TamTarP-6

Hayward, Joe
❑ 94HigDesMC-13
❑ 94HigDesMF-2800

Hayward, Ray
❑ 83BeaGolGT-19
❑ 84LasVegSC-219
❑ 85LasVegSC-104
❑ 86LasVegSP-7
❑ 87Don-632
❑ 87LasVegSP-12
❑ 88FleUpd-63
❑ 88FleUpdG-63
❑ 88OklCit8C-7
❑ 88OklCit8P-49
❑ 88RanMot-16
❑ 88ScoRoo-67T
❑ 88ScoRooG-67T
❑ 88TopTra-47T
❑ 88TopTraT-47T
❑ 89Don-521
❑ 89Fle-521
❑ 89FleGlo-521
❑ 89Sco-514
❑ 90OklCit8P-426
❑ 90ProAAAF-672
❑ 93RanKee-178

Hayward, Steve
❑ 94LynRedSC-12
❑ 94LynRedSF-1889

Haywood, Buster (Albert)
❑ 78LauLonABS-20
❑ 86NegLeaF-42
❑ 87NegLeaPD-36
❑ 89NegLeaRP-4
❑ 92NegLeaK-8
❑ 92NegLeaRLI-27

Hayworth, Ray
❑ 33GeoCMil-19
❑ 34BatR31-165
❑ 34DiaStaR-90
❑ 34TigTeaI-11
❑ 35DiaMatCS3T1-72
❑ 36GouWidPPR-A49
❑ 36SandSW-31
❑ 36WorWidGV-50
❑ 39PlaBal-140
❑ 40PlaBal-155
❑ 72TCMthe3-112
❑ 74TigTCM1AC-16
❑ 76TigOldTS-13

❑ 79DiaGre-385
❑ 90DodTar-327
❑ 95MegRut-5
Hayworth, Red
❑ 96Bro194F-22
Hazelette, Moe
❑ 83KinBluJTI-8
Hazewood, Drungo L.
❑ 80ChaO'sP-10
❑ 80ChaO'sW-10
❑ 81RocRedWT-8
❑ 81RocRedWW-16
❑ 83RocRedWT-20
❑ 91OriCro-189
Hazle, Hurricane (Robert S.)
❑ 58BraJayP-6
❑ 58Top-83
❑ 80Bra195T-21
❑ 87Bra195T-3
Hazlett, Andy
❑ 97LowSpiB-19
Hazlett, Steve
❑ 91EliTwiP-4307
❑ 92KenTwiC-11
❑ 92KenTwiF-617
❑ 92MidLeaATI-18
❑ 93FloStaLAF-15
❑ 93ForMyeMC-10
❑ 93ForMyeMF-2668
❑ 94ClaGolF-66
❑ 94NasXprF-399
❑ 98MobBayBTI-13
Head, Ed
❑ 42DodTeal-9
❑ 43DodTeal-12
❑ 46DodTeal-10
❑ 90DodTar-328
❑ 91DodRinP2-5
Head, Hamilton R.
❑ 98JupHamQ-30
Headley, Kent
❑ 88VirGenS-9
Heakins, Craig
❑ 86WatPirP-9
❑ 87MacPirP-19
Healey, John
❑ 87OldJudN-232
Healy, Bob
❑ 77LynMetT-17
❑ 77QuaCitAT-15
Healy, Fran
❑ 72Top-663
❑ 73OPC-361
❑ 73Top-361
❑ 74OPC-238
❑ 74RoyPos-12
❑ 74Top-238
❑ 74TopSta-182
❑ 75OPC-120
❑ 75OPC-251
❑ 75RoyPos-12
❑ 75Top-120
❑ 75Top-251
❑ 75TopMin-120
❑ 75TopMin-251
❑ 76KanCitRP-11
❑ 76OPC-394
❑ 76SSP-184
❑ 76Top-394
❑ 77Top-148
❑ 77YanBurK-3
❑ 78SSP270-19
❑ 78Top-582
❑ 78YanSSPD-19
❑ 92YanWIZ7-69
Healy, Francis Xavier Paul
❑ 74Car193T-15
Healy, J.C.
❑ 87OldJudN-233
Healy, John
❑ 87BucN28-42
Heame, Shane
❑ 95EveAqaTI-10
Heap, James
❑ 52LavPro-79
Heaps, Chris
❑ 92GulCoaYF-3796
Heard, Jehosie
❑ 54OriEss-14
❑ 54Top-226
❑ 55SeaPop-8
❑ 91NegLeaRL-15
❑ 91OriCro-190
❑ 93NegLeaRL2-17
❑ 94TopArc1-226
❑ 94TopArc1G-226
❑ 95NegLeaLI-15
Hearn, Ed
❑ 83LynMetT-22
❑ 84JacMetT-NNO
❑ 85IntLeaAT-10
❑ 85TidTidT-21
❑ 86DonRoo-54
❑ 86MetTCM-32
❑ 86MetWorSC-8
❑ 86TidTidP-13
❑ 87Don-446
❑ 87DonOpeD-201
❑ 87Fle-10
❑ 87FleGlo-10
❑ 87Top-433
❑ 87TopTif-433
❑ 87ToyRoo-11
❑ 88RoyTeal-15
❑ 88Sco-569
❑ 88ScoGlo-569
❑ 88Top-56
❑ 88TopClo-45
❑ 88TopTif-56
❑ 89Don-297
❑ 89OmaRoyC-12
❑ 89OmaRoyP-1732
❑ 89Top-348
❑ 89TopTif-348
❑ 89TriAAAP-AAA4
❑ 89UppDec-42
❑ 91MetWIZ-165
Hearn, Jim
❑ 49Bow-190
❑ 49EurSta-184
❑ 50Bow-208
❑ 50JJKCopP-5
❑ 51Bow-61
❑ 51R42SmaS-44
❑ 52BerRos-23
❑ 52Bow-49
❑ 52RedMan-NL8
❑ 52TipTop-14
❑ 52Top-337
❑ 53BowC-76
❑ 53NorBreL-11
❑ 53Top-38
❑ 54NewYorJA-24
❑ 55Bow-220
❑ 55GiaGolS-8
❑ 56Top-202
❑ 57Top-348
❑ 58Top-298
❑ 59Top-63
❑ 59TopVen-63
❑ 75Gia195T-7
❑ 79TCM50-97
❑ 83TopRep5-337
❑ 91TopArc1-38
Hearn, Sean
❑ 92MedHatBJF-3219
❑ 92MedHatBJSP-3
❑ 93St.CatBJC-10
❑ 93St.CatBJF-3986
❑ 94DunBluJC-12
❑ 94DunBluJF-2569
Hearn, Tommy
❑ 86MiaMarP-10
Hearne, Hugh
❑ 90DodTar-977
Hearne, John
❑ 91PerHeaF-14
Hearron, Jeff
❑ 86BluJayFS-16
❑ 86StaoftFT-30
❑ 87BluJayFS-13
❑ 87Don-490
❑ 87KnoBluJP-1514
❑ 87OPC-274
❑ 87SyrChiT-3
❑ 87Top-274
❑ 87TopTif-274
❑ 89LasVegSC-17
❑ 89LasVegSP-11
❑ 90CMC-98
❑ 90IowCubC-23
❑ 90IowCubP-320
❑ 90ProAAAF-627
❑ 90TopTVCu-49
Heath, Al
❑ 82AppFoxFr-28
❑ 83AppFoxFr-29
❑ 84MadMusP-8
❑ 85ModA'sC-8
❑ 86KinEagP-9
❑ 87PalSprP-2
Heath, Bill (William)
❑ 66Top-539
❑ 67AstTeal1-7
❑ 67CokCapAs-7
❑ 67OPC-172
❑ 67Top-172
❑ 70OPC-541
❑ 70Top-541
❑ 87AstShowSTh-27
Heath, Dave
❑ 83PeoSunF-6
❑ 85MidAngT-6
❑ 86MidAngP-10
❑ 87EdmTraP-2063
Heath, Jason
❑ 92OklStaC-11
❑ 94BelMarC-15
❑ 94BelMarF-3240
Heath, Jeff (John Jeffrey)
❑ 39ExhSal-26A
❑ 39ExhSal-26B
❑ 39GouPreR303A-22
❑ 39GouPreR303B-13
❑ 39WorWidGTP-22
❑ 46SeaSLP-25
❑ 46SpoExcW-4-2
❑ 47TipTop-64
❑ 49Bow-169
❑ 49EurSta-11
❑ 73SpoScoHC-6
❑ 83TCMPla1945-15
❑ 85BigLeaC3-51
❑ 93ConTSN-939
Heath, Kelly
❑ 80OmaRoyP-14
❑ 81OmaRoyT-17
❑ 83OmaRoyT-16
❑ 84ColCliP-11
❑ 84ColCliT-2
❑ 85ColCliP-12
❑ 85ColCliT-16
❑ 85IntLeaAT-31
❑ 86RicBraP-9
❑ 87RicBraBC-11
❑ 87RicBraC-1
❑ 87RicBraT-18
❑ 88SyrChiC-20
❑ 88SyrChiP-811
❑ 89SyrChiC-17
❑ 89SyrChiMB-13
❑ 89SyrChiP-800
❑ 90CMC-239
❑ 90ProAAAF-307
❑ 90ScrRedBC-13
❑ 90ScrRedBP-605
❑ 92ReaPhiF-593
❑ 93ReaPhiF-312
❑ 96ReaPhiB-28
Heath, Lee
❑ 89PulBraP-1911
❑ 90SumBraB-5
❑ 90SumBraP-2445
❑ 91MacBraC-23
❑ 91MacBraP-876
❑ 92DurBulC-7
❑ 92DurBulF-1112
❑ 92DurBulTI-33
❑ 92UppDecML-88
❑ 93Bow-114
❑ 93GreBraF-360
❑ 94HigDesMC-14
❑ 94HigDesMF-2801
Heath, Mickey
❑ 28ExhPCL-10
❑ 28Zee-7
Heath, Mike
❑ 75ForLauYS-19
❑ 76ForLauYS-14
❑ 77WesHavYT-11
❑ 78YanPhoA-11
❑ 79Top-710
❑ 80Top-687
❑ 81A'sGraG-2
❑ 81Don-120
❑ 81Fle-583
❑ 81Top-437
❑ 82A'sGraG-3
❑ 82Don-413
❑ 82Fle-91
❑ 82OPC-318
❑ 82Top-318
❑ 83A'sGraG-2
❑ 83AllGamPI-41
❑ 83Don-517
❑ 83Fle-518
❑ 83Top-23
❑ 83TopSti-104
❑ 84A'sMot-9
❑ 84AllGamPI-130
❑ 84Don-223
❑ 84Fle-446
❑ 84Nes792-567
❑ 84Top-567
❑ 84TopSti-337
❑ 84TopTif-567
❑ 85A'sMot-4
❑ 85AllGamPI-41
❑ 85Don-298
❑ 85Fle-424
❑ 85OPC-396
❑ 85Top-662
❑ 85TopSti-326
❑ 85TopTif-662
❑ 86CarIGAS-5
❑ 86CarSchM-7
❑ 86CarTeal-16
❑ 86Don-253
❑ 86Fle-418
❑ 86FleUpd-50
❑ 86OPC-148
❑ 86Top-148
❑ 86TopSti-174
❑ 86TopTif-148
❑ 86TopTra-46T
❑ 86TopTraT-46T
❑ 87Don-496
❑ 87DonOpeD-214
❑ 87FleUpd-42
❑ 87FleUpdG-42
❑ 87TigCaiD-3
❑ 87TigCok-8
❑ 87Top-492
❑ 87TopTif-492
❑ 88Don-338
❑ 88DonBasB-69
❑ 88Fle-56
❑ 88FleGlo-56
❑ 88RedFolSB-31
❑ 88Sco-156
❑ 88ScoGlo-156
❑ 88StaLinTi-6
❑ 88TigPep-8
❑ 88Top-237
❑ 88TopTif-237
❑ 89Don-271
❑ 89DonBasB-147
❑ 89Fle-132A
❑ 89Fle-132B
❑ 89FleGlo-132
❑ 89Sco-131
❑ 89TigMar-8
❑ 89Top-609
❑ 89Top-743
❑ 89TopTif-609
❑ 89TopTif-743
❑ 89UppDec-654
❑ 90Bow-352
❑ 90BowTif-352
❑ 90ClaYel-T40
❑ 90Don-209
❑ 90DonBesA-90
❑ 90Fle-603
❑ 90FleCan-603
❑ 90Lea-60
❑ 90MLBBasB-91
❑ 90OPC-366
❑ 90PanSti-66
❑ 90PublntS-471
❑ 90Sco-172
❑ 90TigCok-7
❑ 90Top-366
❑ 90TopBig-166
❑ 90TopSti-280
❑ 90TopTif-366
❑ 90UppDec-306
❑ 91Bow-589
❑ 91BraDubP-14
❑ 91BraSubS-18
❑ 91Don-230
❑ 91Fle-339
❑ 91Lea-320
❑ 91OPC-16
❑ 91PanFreS-287
❑ 91PanSti-237
❑ 91Sco-112
❑ 91ScoPro-112
❑ 91ScoRoo-69T
❑ 91StaClu-393
❑ 91Top-16
❑ 91TopDesS-16
❑ 91TopMic-16
❑ 91TopTif-16
❑ 91UppDec-318
❑ 91UppDec-701
❑ 92OPC-512
❑ 92Sco-344
❑ 92StaClu-128
❑ 92TacTlgF-2506
❑ 92Top-512
❑ 92TopGol-512
❑ 92TopGolPS-512
❑ 92TopGolW-512
❑ 92TopMic-512
❑ 92TopPreS-16
❑ 92UppDec-304
❑ 92YanWIZ7-70
❑ 96BirBarB-22
Heath, Minor
❑ 29Zee-4
❑ 30Zee-7
Heath, Thomas
❑ 36GouWidPPR-D11
❑ 52MotCoo-46
❑ 53MotCoo-43
❑ 53SanFraSTI-7
Heath, Woody
❑ 97St.CatSB-15
Heathcock, Jeff
❑ 83ColAstT-14
❑ 84TucTorC-65
❑ 86Don-182
❑ 86Fle-302
❑ 86TucTorP-6
❑ 87TucTorP-18
❑ 88AstMot-18
❑ 88AstPol-12
❑ 88Fle-450
❑ 88FleGlo-450
❑ 89TucTorC-7
❑ 89TucTorJP-7
❑ 89TucTorP-196
❑ 90CMC-486
❑ 90EdmTraC-9
❑ 90EdmTraP-515
❑ 90ProAAAF-91
Heathcote, Clifton E.
❑ 21Exh-71
❑ 22E120-231
❑ 22W573-59
❑ 26Exh-23
❑ 27Exh-12
❑ 27YorCarE-35A
❑ 27YorCarE-35B
❑ 28StaPlaCE-35
❑ 30CubTeal-8
❑ 33Gou-115
❑ 34GouCanV-9
❑ 94ConTSN-1058
❑ 94ConTSNB-1058
❑ 95ConTSN-1409
Heathcott, Mike
❑ 91UtiBluSC-8
❑ 91UtiBluSP-3235
❑ 93SarWhiSC-12
❑ 93SarWhiSF-1365
❑ 94BirBarC-12
❑ 94BirBarF-617
❑ 95PriWilCTI-19
❑ 97BirBarB-16
Heatherly, Kyle
❑ 29Zee-158
Heaton, Mike
❑ 78QuaCitAT-10
Heaton, Neal
❑ 82ChaChaT-5
❑ 82Ind-21
❑ 83IndPos-20
❑ 83IndWhe-19
❑ 84Don-373
❑ 84Don-608
❑ 84Fle-546
❑ 84FleSti-113
❑ 84Ind-18
❑ 84IndWhe-44
❑ 85Don-373
❑ 85Fle-451
❑ 85Ind-18
❑ 85IndPol-44
❑ 86Don-338
❑ 86Fle-589
❑ 86IndOhH-44
❑ 86IndTeal-25
❑ 86Lea-203
❑ 87Don-615
❑ 87ExpPos-10
❑ 87Fle-543
❑ 87FleGlo-543
❑ 87FleUpd-43
❑ 87FleUpdG-43
❑ 87TopTra-45T
❑ 87TopTraT-45T
❑ 88Don-134
❑ 88DonBasB-124
❑ 88ExpPos-12
❑ 88Fle-185
❑ 88FleGlo-185
❑ 88FleMin-89
❑ 88MSAHosD-10
❑ 88OPC-354
❑ 88PanSti-319
❑ 88RedFolSB-32
❑ 88Sco-430
❑ 88ScoGlo-430
❑ 88Spo-81
❑ 88StaLinE-7
❑ 88Top-765
❑ 88TopBig-33
❑ 88TopSti-80
❑ 88TopStiB-29
❑ 88TopTif-765
❑ 89Don-224
❑ 89Fle-377
❑ 89FleGlo-377
❑ 89FleUpd-113
❑ 89OPC-197
❑ 89PirVerFJ-26
❑ 89Sco-253
❑ 89Top-197
❑ 89TopTif-197
❑ 89UppDec-99
❑ 90Don-658
❑ 90Fle-468
❑ 90FleCan-468
❑ 90Lea-460
❑ 90OPC-539
❑ 90PirHomC-12
❑ 90PublntS-156
❑ 90Top-539
❑ 90TopBig-255
❑ 90TopTif-539
❑ 90UppDec-86
❑ 90USPlaCA-7D
❑ 91BasBesAotM-9
❑ 91Don-475
❑ 91Fle-38
❑ 91OPC-451
❑ 91PanFreS-123
❑ 91PanSti-115
❑ 91Sco-233
❑ 91StaClu-53
❑ 91Top-451
❑ 91TopDesS-451
❑ 91TopMic-451
❑ 91TopTif-451
❑ 91Ult-279
❑ 91UppDec-36
❑ 92Don-522
❑ 92Fle-554
❑ 92OPC-89
❑ 92Sco-723
❑ 92StaClu-357
❑ 92StaClu-877
❑ 92StaCluNC-877
❑ 92Top-89
❑ 92TopGol-89
❑ 92TopGolW-89
❑ 92TopMic-89
❑ 92UppDec-417
❑ 93PacSpa-554
❑ 94BreMilB-132
Heaverlo, Dave
❑ 76OPC-213
❑ 76SanFraGP-8
❑ 76SSP-95
❑ 76Top-213
❑ 77GiaTeal-12
❑ 77PhoGiaCC-9
❑ 77PhoGiaCP-8
❑ 77Top-97
❑ 78Top-338
❑ 79Top-432
❑ 80MarPos-11
❑ 80Top-177
❑ 81Don-407
❑ 81Fle-594
❑ 81TacTigT-26
❑ 82TacTigT-3
❑ 83TacTigT-21
Hebb, Michael
❑ 91KanCouCC-6
❑ 91KanCouCP-2654
❑ 91KanCouCTI-9

Hebbert, Allan
❑ 94ElmPioC-8
❑ 94ElmPioF-3466
❑ 95KanCouCTI-32
Hebel, Jon
❑ 93BilMusF-3939
❑ 93BilMusSP-22
❑ 94ChaWheC-14
❑ 94ChaWheF-2698
Heberling, Keith
❑ 93OneYanF-3497
❑ 94BowBes-B89
❑ 94BowBesR-B89
❑ 94Cla-72
❑ 94ExcFS7-105
❑ 94FloStaLAF-FSL20
❑ 94TamYanC-13
❑ 94TamYanF-2377
❑ 95Exc-95
Hebert, Cedric
❑ 98GreFalDG-13
Hebert, Roger
❑ 52LavPro-65
Heble, Kurt
❑ 91St.CatBJC-11
❑ 91St.CatBJP-3403
❑ 92MyrBeaHC-26
❑ 92MyrBeaHF-2191
❑ 93DunBluJC-9
❑ 93DunBluJF-1790
❑ 93DunBluJFFN-9
❑ 94ExcFS7-144
❑ 94KnoSmoF-1299
❑ 95KnoSmoF-37
Hebner, Rich
❑ 69OPC-82
❑ 69PirTeal-9
❑ 69Top-82
❑ 69TopTeaP-16
❑ 70DayDaiNM-66
❑ 70DayDaiNM-95
❑ 70MLBOffS-101
❑ 70OPC-264
❑ 70PirTeal-8
❑ 70Top-264
❑ 71MLBOffS-203
❑ 71OPC-212
❑ 71Pir-4
❑ 71PirActP-17
❑ 71PirArc-5
❑ 71Top-212
❑ 72MilBra-136
❑ 72PirTeal-4
❑ 72Top-630
❑ 73OPC-2
❑ 73SevTraC-30
❑ 73Top-2
❑ 74OPC-450
❑ 74Top-450
❑ 74TopDecE-35
❑ 74TopSta-84
❑ 75Hos-57
❑ 75Kel-57
❑ 75OPC-492
❑ 75PitPirP-7
❑ 75Top-492
❑ 75TopMin-492
❑ 76OPC-376
❑ 76PirPos-4
❑ 76SSP-579
❑ 76Top-376
❑ 77OPC-168
❑ 77Top-167
❑ 78OPC-194
❑ 78RCColC-62
❑ 78SSP270-35
❑ 78Top-26
❑ 79OPC-293
❑ 79Top-567
❑ 80OPC-175
❑ 80Top-331
❑ 81CokTeaS-51
❑ 81Don-125
❑ 81Fle-474
❑ 81OPC-217
❑ 81Top-217
❑ 82Don-328
❑ 82Fle-268
❑ 82OPC-96
❑ 82Top-603
❑ 83Fle-307
❑ 83Top-778
❑ 84CubChiT-15
❑ 84CubSev-18
❑ 84Fle-251
❑ 84FleUpd-50
❑ 84Nes792-433
❑ 84Top-433
❑ 84TopTif-433
❑ 84TopTra-50T
❑ 84TopTraT-50T
❑ 85CubSev-18
❑ 85Don-564
❑ 85Fle-59
❑ 85Top-124
❑ 85TopTif-124
❑ 86Top-19
❑ 86TopTif-19
❑ 88MyrBeaBJP-1188
❑ 88SouAtlLAGS-1
❑ 90TopTVRS-5
❑ 91MetWIZ-166
❑ 91MetWIZ-172
❑ 91UppDecS-13
❑ 95SyrChiTI-14
❑ 96SyrChiTI-13
❑ 97LynHil-29
❑ 98NasSouTI-14
❑ 98NasSouTISS-14
Hebrard, Mike
❑ 82AmaGolST-24
Hebson, Bryan
❑ 98BesAutSS-25
❑ 98BesNumOP-27
❑ 98CapFeaCM-8
Hechinger, Mike
❑ 09MaxPubP-20
❑ 90DodTar-978
Hecht, Brian
❑ 97AubDouTI-26
❑ 98QuaCitRBG-8
Hecht, Steve
❑ 87PanAmTUBI-15
❑ 87PanAmTURB-7
❑ 89CalLeaA-35
❑ 89SanJosGB-24
❑ 89SanJosGCLC-221
❑ 89SanJosGP-457
❑ 89SanJosGS-13
❑ 90ShrCapP-1451
❑ 90ShrCapS-10
❑ 91IndIndLD-186
❑ 91IndIndP-474
❑ 91LinDriAAA-186
❑ 92HarSenF-470
❑ 92HarSenS-282
❑ 93ShrCapF-2768
❑ 94ShrCapF-1614
Heckel, Wally
❑ 90St.CatBJP-3477
Hecker, Doug
❑ 92ClaDraP-64
❑ 92FroRowDP-24
❑ 92FroRowDPG-24
❑ 92FroRowDPS-24
❑ 93Bow-411
❑ 93CarLeaAGF-7
❑ 93ClaGolF-151
❑ 93LynRedSC-11
❑ 93LynRedSF-2523
❑ 93StaCluM-64
❑ 94SarRedSC-12
❑ 94SarRedSF-1957
❑ 96SarRedSB-20
Hecker, Guy
❑ 87OldJudN-234
❑ 90HOFStiB-3
Heckman, Andy
❑ 92EveGiaC-29
❑ 92EveGiaF-1680
❑ 93CliGiaC-12
❑ 93CliGiaF-2485
❑ 94SanJosGC-9
❑ 94SanJosGF-2811
Heckman, Tom
❑ 82MadMusF-8
Hedfelt, Pancho
❑ 85UtiBluST-10
Hedge, Pat
❑ 89EriOriS-5
❑ 91FreKeyC-25
❑ 91FreKeyP-2380
Hedgearner, Pat
❑ 90FreKeyTI-28
Hedley, Brian
❑ 96HelBreTI-8
Hedley, Darren
❑ 90MarPhiP-3183
Hedlund, Mike
❑ 65Top-546
❑ 69RoySol-8
❑ 69Top-591
❑ 70OPC-187
❑ 70Top-187
❑ 71OPC-662
❑ 71oySigST-7
❑ 71Top-662
❑ 72MilBra-137
❑ 72OPC-81
❑ 72oyTeal-6
❑ 72Top-81
❑ 73OPC-591
❑ 73Top-591
Hedrick, Craig
❑ 79CedRapGT-23
Hedspeth, Dennis
❑ 94GreFalDSP-14
Hee, Dong
❑ 96WesOahCHWB-31
Heep, Danny
❑ 80TucTorT-1
❑ 81AstPos-5
❑ 81Fle-72
❑ 81Top-82
❑ 82AstAstI-5
❑ 82AstPos-5
❑ 82Fle-217
❑ 82Top-441
❑ 83Don-443
❑ 83Fle-449
❑ 83Top-538
❑ 83TopTra-41T
❑ 84Don-434
❑ 84Fle-586
❑ 84Nes792-29
❑ 84Top-29
❑ 84TopTif-29
❑ 85Don-556
❑ 85Fle-84
❑ 85MetColP-13
❑ 85MetTCM-34
❑ 85OPC-339
❑ 85Top-339
❑ 85TopTif-339
❑ 86Don-556
❑ 86Fle-83
❑ 86MetColP-18
❑ 86MetTCM-26
❑ 86MetWorSC-14
❑ 86Top-619
❑ 86TopTif-619
❑ 87AstShoSPT-11
❑ 87Don-649
❑ 87Fle-11
❑ 87FleGlo-11
❑ 87Top-241
❑ 87TopTif-241
❑ 88DodMot-20
❑ 88DodPol-12
❑ 88Sco-417
❑ 88ScoGlo-417
❑ 88Top-753
❑ 88TopTif-753
❑ 89Don-368
❑ 89Fle-61A
❑ 89Fle-61B
❑ 89FleGlo-61
❑ 89Sco-343
❑ 89ScoRoo-57T
❑ 89Top-198
❑ 89TopTif-198
❑ 90Bow-276
❑ 90BowTif-276
❑ 90DodTar-329
❑ 90Don-358
❑ 90Fle-278
❑ 90FleCan-278
❑ 90OPC-573
❑ 90Sco-113
❑ 90Top-573
❑ 90TopBig-90
❑ 90TopTif-573
❑ 90TopTVRS-24
❑ 91BraDubP-15
❑ 91LinDriAAA-635
❑ 91MetWIZ-167
❑ 91Sco-827
❑ 91VanCanLD-635
❑ 91VanCanP-1601
Heffernan, Bert
❑ 87PanAmTUBI-22
❑ 87PanAmTURB-18
❑ 89BelBre2S-14
❑ 89BelBreIS-9
❑ 89Sta-109
❑ 90ElPasDGS-17
❑ 90TexLeaAGS-5
❑ 91AlbDukLD-9
❑ 91AlbDukP-1143
❑ 91LinDriAAA-9
❑ 92CalCanS-60
❑ 92DonRoo-50
❑ 93CalCanF-1169
❑ 93ShrCapF-2762
❑ 98CapFeaCM-28
Heffernan, Greg
❑ 96NewJerCB-13
❑ 97NewJerCB-9
Heffner, Don
❑ 39PlaBal-44
❑ 40PlaBal-51
❑ 41BroW75-15
❑ 41DouPlaR-147
❑ 41Gou-11
❑ 60Top-462
❑ 66Top-269
❑ 66TopVen-269
❑ 75YanDyn1T-21
❑ 92ConTSN-521
Heffner, Robert
❑ 61SeaPop-6
❑ 61SeaPop-7
❑ 64Top-79
❑ 64TopVen-79
❑ 65OPC-199
❑ 65RedSoxTI-4
❑ 65Top-199
❑ 66Top-432
Heflin, Bailey
❑ 92DavLipB-13
❑ 93DavLipB-11
Heflin, Bronson
❑ 94BatCliC-6
❑ 94BatCliF-3438
❑ 95ClePhiF-212
❑ 95ReaPhiELC-17
❑ 95TenVolW-3
❑ 96Exc-203
❑ 96ReaPhiB-6
❑ 97ScrRedB-10
❑ 98ScrRedBQ-15
Heflin, Randy
❑ 46RedSoxTI-12
❑ 75RedSox1T-18
Hegan, J. Mike
❑ 66TolMudHTI-12
❑ 67Top-553
❑ 68Top-402
❑ 69PilPos-38
❑ 69PilWhe-3
❑ 69Top-577
❑ 70BreMcD-10
❑ 70BreMil-7
❑ 70BreTeal-4
❑ 70DayDaiNM-43
❑ 70MLBOffS-271
❑ 70OPC-111
❑ 70SunPin-11
❑ 70Top-111
❑ 70TopCanL-8
❑ 70TopScr-8
❑ 70YanPhoS-14
❑ 71BreTeal-4
❑ 71MLBOffS-438
❑ 71OPC-415
❑ 71Top-415
❑ 71TopCoi-116
❑ 72Top-632
❑ 73OPC-382
❑ 73Top-382
❑ 74OPC-517
❑ 74SyrChiTI-10
❑ 74Top-517
❑ 75OPC-99
❑ 75Top-99
❑ 75TopMin-99
❑ 76BreA&P-4
❑ 76LauDiaJ-21
❑ 76OPC-69
❑ 76OPC-377
❑ 76SSP-235
❑ 76Top-69
❑ 76Top-377
❑ 77PilPosR-38
❑ 77Top-507
❑ 83Pil69G-8
❑ 92YanWIZ6-54
❑ 92YanWIZ7-71
❑ 94BreMilB-133
❑ 97PinFan-PC5
Hegan, Jim
❑ 46SpoExcW-4-12
❑ 47Exh-91
❑ 47IndTeal-14
❑ 47IndVanPP-13
❑ 47PM1StaP1-81
❑ 48IndTeal-15
❑ 49IndTeal-14
❑ 49IndVisEI-10
❑ 49Lea-28
❑ 50Bow-7
❑ 50IndNumN-13
❑ 50IndTeal-15
❑ 51Bow-79
❑ 51TopRedB-12
❑ 52Bow-187
❑ 52IndNumN-2
❑ 52RedMan-AL11
❑ 52StaCalL-74D
❑ 52StaCalS-88A
❑ 52Top-17
❑ 53BowC-102
❑ 53IndPenCBP-15
❑ 53Top-80
❑ 54DanDee-10
❑ 54RedHeaF-11
❑ 54Top-29
❑ 55Ind-3
❑ 55IndCarBL-3
❑ 55IndGolS-10
❑ 55RedMan-AL7
❑ 55RobGouS-5
❑ 55RobGouW-5
❑ 55Top-7
❑ 55TopDouH-67
❑ 56Top-48
❑ 56TopPin-8
❑ 57IndSoh-6
❑ 57IndTeal-9
❑ 57Top-136
❑ 58Top-345
❑ 59TigGraASP-7
❑ 59Top-372
❑ 61Yan61RL-31
❑ 73OPC-116
❑ 73Top-116A
❑ 73Top-116B
❑ 75DetTigP-9
❑ 75TCM195CI-13
❑ 76DetTigP-9
❑ 76OPC-69
❑ 76TayBow4-105
❑ 76Top-69
❑ 78TigTeal-13
❑ 79DiaGre-286
❑ 79TCM50-139
❑ 79YanPicA-17
❑ 81TCM60I-481
❑ 83TigAIKS-15
❑ 83TopRep5-17
❑ 83Yan196-NNO
❑ 84TCMPla1-16
❑ 86IndGreT-8
❑ 91TopArc1-80
❑ 93UppDecAH-64
❑ 94TopArc1-29
❑ 94TopArc1G-29
Hegan, Steve
❑ 90MisStaB-17
❑ 91MisStaB-23
❑ 92MisStaB-19
❑ 93MisStaB-20
Hegman, Bob
❑ 81ChaRoyT-10
❑ 84MemChiT-13
❑ 85OmaRoyT-30
❑ 86OmaRoyP-11
❑ 86OmaRoyT-8
Hehl, Jake
❑ 90DodTar-979
Heib, Earl
❑ 92ButCopKSP-22
Heidelberg, Khary
❑ 91HigSchPLS-15
Heidemann, Jack
❑ 71MLBOffS-372
❑ 71OPC-87
❑ 71Top-87
❑ 72OPC-374
❑ 72Top-374
❑ 73OPC-644
❑ 73Top-644
❑ 75OPC-649
❑ 75Top-649
❑ 75TopMin-649
❑ 76SSP-544
❑ 77Top-553
❑ 78SpoIndC-9
❑ 79SpoIndT-15
❑ 91MetWIZ-168
❑ 94BreMilB-134
Heiden, Shawn
❑ 89BluOriS-11
❑ 90Bes-110
❑ 90WauTimB-13
❑ 90WauTimP-2126
❑ 90WauTimS-9
Heidenreich, Curt
❑ 82CedRapRT-3
❑ 83WatRedT-3
❑ 84WicAerRD-9
Heiderscheit, Pat
❑ 89JamExpP-2143
❑ 93JamExpC-27
❑ 93JamExpF-3343
❑ 94VerExpC-22
❑ 94VerExpF-3924
Heidrick, Emmet
❑ 03BreE10-68
Heifferon, Mike
❑ 86AlbYanT-11
❑ 87PriWilYP-14
❑ 88AlbYanP-1354
❑ 89ColCliP-24
❑ 89ColCliP-755
❑ 89TriAAAP-AAA3
❑ 90CMC-224
❑ 90ColCliP-693
❑ 92ColCliF-368
Height, Ron
❑ 87LitFalMP-2398
❑ 88LitFalMP-5
Heilgeist, Jim
❑ 90GatCitPP-3346
❑ 90GatCitPSP-11
Heilmann, Harry E.
❑ 13Zee-59
❑ 15Zee-107
❑ 17ColE13-71
❑ 17HolBreD-41
❑ 20NatCarE-41
❑ 21E121So1-40A
❑ 21E121So1-40B
❑ 21E121So8-34
❑ 21Exh-72
❑ 21Nei-27
❑ 22AmeCarE122-26
❑ 22E120-54
❑ 22W572-41
❑ 22W573-60
❑ 22W575-54
❑ 22WilPatV-22
❑ 23W501-6
❑ 23W515-18
❑ 23WilChoV-61
❑ 25Exh-92
❑ 26Exh-93
❑ 27Exh-48
❑ 27YorCarE-22
❑ 28StaPlaCE-36
❑ 28W502-22
❑ 28Yue-22
❑ 29ExhFou-24
❑ 31Exh-7
❑ 31W517-14
❑ 39PC7AlbHoF-61
❑ 40PlaBal-171
❑ 50CalHOFW-38
❑ 51R42SmaS-46
❑ 53ArtHaloFP-44
❑ 60Fle-65
❑ 61Fle-42
❑ 63BazA-2
❑ 73TCMAllG-7
❑ 74CapPub-6
❑ 76ShaPiz-61
❑ 77GalGloG-95
❑ 78DexHaloFP-20
❑ 80Lau300-28
❑ 80PerHaloFP-61
❑ 80SSPHOF-61
❑ 80TigGreT-7
❑ 81ConTSN-76
❑ 81TigDetN-4
❑ 81TigSecNP-8
❑ 82TCMGreH-20
❑ 86ConSer1-42
❑ 86TigSpoD-3
❑ 90PerGreM-47
❑ 91ConTSN-52
❑ 93ConTSN-915
Heimach, Fred
❑ 72TCMthe3-103
❑ 90DodTar-330
❑ 92ConTSN-480
Heimer, Todd

❑ 79TacTugT-8
❑ 80TacTigT-18
❑ 81ChaLooT-10
Heimueller, Gorman
❑ 81WesHavAT-20
❑ 82TacTigT-5
❑ 83TacTigT-4
❑ 84Don-131
❑ 84TacTigC-95
❑ 85OrlTwiT-25
❑ 86TolMudHP-12
❑ 87VisOakP-24
❑ 88VisOakCLC-174
❑ 88VisOakP-105
❑ 89VisOakCLC-119
❑ 89VisOakP-1420
❑ 90OrlSunRB-24
❑ 90OrlSunRP-1100
❑ 90OrlSunRS-26
❑ 91LinDriAAA-425
❑ 91PorBeaP-1583
❑ 92PorBeaF-2683
❑ 93PorBeaF-2397
❑ 94SalLakBF-832
❑ 95HarCitRCTI-8
❑ 96HarCitRCB-4
❑ 97NewBriRC-28
❑ 98SanAntMG-13
Heine, Kyle
❑ 98OneYanG-14
Heineman, Rick
❑ 96BriWhiSB-16
Heinen, Joe
❑ 75CedRapGT-4
Heinkel, Don
❑ 83BirBarT-9
❑ 84EvaTriT-19
❑ 86NasSouTI-11
❑ 87TolMudHP-7
❑ 87TolMudHT-2
❑ 88BlaYNPRWL-85
❑ 88FleUpd-27
❑ 88FleUpdG-27
❑ 88ScoRoo-79T
❑ 88ScoRooG-79T
❑ 89BirBarADB-17
❑ 89Bow-427
❑ 89BowTif-427
❑ 89Fle-133
❑ 89FleGlo-133
❑ 89LouRedBTI-21
❑ 89Sco-168
❑ 89Top-499
❑ 89TopTif-499
❑ 90BirBarADB-17
❑ 90WicStaSGD-14
❑ 93WicWraF-2974
Heinle, Dana
❑ 87KenTwiP-15
❑ 88VisOakCLC-168
❑ 88VisOakP-82
❑ 89VerBeaDS-11
Heinrichs, John
❑ 97UCLBruTI-6
Heins, C.H.
❑ 88KimN18-18
Heins, Jim
❑ 89NiaFalRP-10
Heintz, Chris
❑ 96BriWhiSB-17
❑ 97HicCraB-14
❑ 97HicCraRB-16
❑ 98CarLeaAC-6
❑ 98CarLeaAC-31
❑ 98WinWar-14
Heintzelman, Ken
❑ 49Bow-108
❑ 49EurSta-136
❑ 49PhiBul-24
❑ 50Bow-85
❑ 50PhiPhil-10
❑ 51BerRos-C10
❑ 51Bow-147
❑ 51R42SmaS-42
❑ 52Bow-148
❑ 52Top-362
❑ 53Top-136
❑ 75Phi195T-12
❑ 79DiaGre-367
❑ 79TCM50-78
❑ 80Phi195T-12
❑ 83TopRep5-362
❑ 91TopArc1-136
Heintzelman, Tom
❑ 74OPC-607
❑ 74Top-607
❑ 75PhoGiaC-13
❑ 75PhoGiaCK-17
❑ 76PheGiaCr-23
❑ 76PhoGiaCa-16
❑ 76PhoGiaCC-10
❑ 76PhoGiaVNB-9
❑ 77PhoGiaVNB-9
❑ 78GlaTeal-10
❑ 79PhoGiaVNB-12
Heise, Benjamin
❑ 75OklCit8TI-12
Heise, Larry Wayne
❑ 84NewOriT-19
❑ 87GreBraB-22
Heise, Robert
❑ 70OPC-478
❑ 70Top-478
❑ 71MLBOffS-250
❑ 71OPC-691
❑ 71Top-691
❑ 72OPC-402
❑ 72Top-402
❑ 73OPC-547
❑ 73Top-547
❑ 74OPC-51
❑ 74Top-51
❑ 74TopTra-51T
❑ 75OPC-441
❑ 75Top-441
❑ 75TopMin-441
❑ 91MetWIZ-169
❑ 94BreMilB-224
Heiser, Roy
❑ 77FriOneYW-57
Heiserman, Rick
❑ 94WatIndF-3931
❑ 95KinIndTI-15
❑ 95Top-398
❑ 96Exc-45
❑ 96StPetCB-13
❑ 97ArkTraB-5
❑ 98ArkTraM-12
❑ 98TexLeaTPG-16
Heisler, Laurence
❑ 92BatCliCB-16
❑ 92BatCliF-3257
❑ 94ClePhiC-17
❑ 94ClePhiF-2523
❑ 94SpaPhiF-1718
Heisler, Toni
❑ 95ColSilB-12
Heist, Al
❑ 58UniOil-4
❑ 61Top-302
❑ 62Col45'HC-8
❑ 62SalPlaC-195
❑ 62ShiPlaC-195
❑ 62Top-373
❑ 62TopStal-126
❑ 89AstCol4S-24
Heister, Elwood
❑ 11BigEatEU-7
❑ 11PacCoaBD-23
❑ 11Zee-68
❑ 12HomRunKE-48
❑ 12Zee-81
Heitmuller, Heinie (William)
❑ 09AmeCarE90-1-51
❑ 10LuxCigPP-11
❑ 11SpoLifM-94
❑ 11Zee-13
❑ 12HomRunKE-9
❑ 12Zee-11
Heitz, Chris
❑ 98RocCubM-12
❑ 98RocCubTI-12
Held, Dan
❑ 93BatCliCB-11
❑ 93BatCliF-3148
❑ 94SouAtlLAF-SAL54
❑ 94SpaPhiF-1727
❑ 94SparPhiC-13
❑ 95ClePhiF-224
❑ 95ReaPhiELC-18
❑ 96BesAutS-36
❑ 96Exc-204
❑ 96ExcTL-4
❑ 96ReaPhiB-19
❑ 97ReaPhi-17
❑ 98ScrRedBQ-16
Held, Matt
❑ 83IdaFalAT-16
Held, Mel
❑ 56BalOriP-25
❑ 64TopVen-105
❑ 91OriCro-191
Held, Travis
❑ 98NewJerCM-14
Held, Woodie
❑ 58A'sJayP-4
❑ 58IndTeal-27
❑ 58Top-202
❑ 59Ind-8
❑ 59Kah-14
❑ 59Top-266
❑ 60IndJayP-3
❑ 60Kah-13
❑ 60Lea-2
❑ 60Top-178
❑ 60TopVen-178
❑ 61Baz-33
❑ 61Kah-18
❑ 61NuSco-405
❑ 61Top-60
❑ 61TopStal-136
❑ 62Baz-8
❑ 62IndJayP-5
❑ 62Jel-44
❑ 62Kah-17
❑ 62Pos-44
❑ 62PosCan-44
❑ 62SalPlaC-5
❑ 62ShiPlaC-5
❑ 62Top-215
❑ 62TopBuc-34
❑ 62TopStal-35
❑ 63BasMagM-35
❑ 63IndJayP-8
❑ 63Jel-69
❑ 63Pos-69
❑ 63Top-435
❑ 64IndJayP-7
❑ 64Kah-12
❑ 64Top-105
❑ 64TopCoi-29
❑ 64TopSta-29
❑ 64TopStaU-31
❑ 64TopTatI-41
❑ 65Top-336
❑ 66BalOriP-16
❑ 66OPC-136
❑ 66SenTeal-6
❑ 66Top-136
❑ 66TopVen-136
❑ 67Top-251
❑ 68Top-289
❑ 68TopVen-289
❑ 69MilBra-108
❑ 69Top-636
❑ 78TCM60I-284
❑ 79TCM50-174
❑ 81Ori6F-17
❑ 91OriCro-192
Heldman, Carl
❑ 98BatMucTI-11
Helf, Henry
❑ 46SeaSLP-26
Helfand, Eric
❑ 88NebCor-5
❑ 89AlaGol-3
❑ 89AriStaB-11
❑ 90ProAaA-167
❑ 90SouOreAB-2
❑ 90SouOreAP-3426
❑ 91Cla/Bes-128
❑ 91ModA'sC-21
❑ 92CalLeaACL-3
❑ 92ClaFS7-188
❑ 92ModA'sC-3
❑ 92ModA'sF-3903
❑ 93ExcFS7-217
❑ 93HunStaF-2085
❑ 94A'sMot-23
❑ 94TacTigF-3178
❑ 94Top-363
❑ 94TopGol-363
❑ 94TopSpa-363
❑ 95AthMot-15
❑ 96BufBisB-10
❑ 97LasVegS1A-17
Helfrich, Allan
❑ 17Zee-48
Helfrich, Chris
❑ 94SouOreAC-11
❑ 94SouOreAF-3615
Heller, Brad
❑ 95ChaRivTI-16
❑ 98BirBarG-12
Heller, John
❑ 83LynMetT-17
Heller, Mark
❑ 86AlbDukP-11
Helling, Rick
❑ 91TopTra-54T
❑ 91TopTraT-54T
❑ 92Bow-641
❑ 92ClaDraP-17
❑ 92FroRowDP-81
❑ 92FroRowDPG-81
❑ 92FroRowDPPS-81
❑ 92FroRowDPS-81
❑ 92StaCluD-81
❑ 92TopTra-48T
❑ 92TopTraG-48T
❑ 92UppDecML-13
❑ 93Bow-165
❑ 93ClaFS7-204
❑ 93ClaPro-3
❑ 93Pin-459
❑ 93Sco-491
❑ 93Sel-358
❑ 93StaCluM-96
❑ 94Bow-297
❑ 94ClaGolF-181
❑ 94ExcFS7-134
❑ 94Fin-434
❑ 94FinJum-434
❑ 94FinRef-434
❑ 94Fla-110
❑ 94FleExtB-179
❑ 94FleExtBRS-9
❑ 94FleUpd-92
❑ 94LeaLimR-47
❑ 94Pin-525
❑ 94PinArtP-525
❑ 94PinMusC-525
❑ 94SigRooBS-P1
❑ 94SP-149
❑ 94SPDieC-149
❑ 94StaClu-632
❑ 94StaClu-697
❑ 94StaCluFDI-632
❑ 94StaCluFDI-697
❑ 94StaCluGR-632
❑ 94StaCluGR-697
❑ 94StaCluMOP-632
❑ 94StaCluMOP-697
❑ 94TopTra-58T
❑ 94Ult-431
❑ 94UppDecML-147
❑ 94UppDecML-240
❑ 94UppDecMLPotYF-PY20
❑ 95ColCho-397
❑ 95ColChoGS-397
❑ 95ColChoSE-181
❑ 95ColChoSEGS-181
❑ 95ColChoSESS-181
❑ 95ColChoSS-397
❑ 95Don-314
❑ 95DonPreP-314
❑ 95Fle-286
❑ 95Lea-123
❑ 95StaClu-387
❑ 95StaCluMOP-387
❑ 95StaCluSTWS-387
❑ 95UppDec-157
❑ 95UppDecED-157
❑ 95UppDecEDG-157
❑ 95UppDecSE-174
❑ 95UppDecSEG-174
❑ 96ColCho-323
❑ 96ColChoGS-323
❑ 96ColChoSS-323
❑ 96OklCit8B-11
❑ 96RanMot-11
❑ 97Fle-521
❑ 97FleTif-521
❑ 97MarPac-12
❑ 97Sco-380
❑ 97ScoArtPWB-380
❑ 97ScoResC-380
❑ 97ScoShoS-380
❑ 97ScoShoSAP-380
❑ 97Ult-472
❑ 97UltGolME-472
❑ 97UltPlaME-472
❑ 98Bow-285
❑ 98BowChr-285
❑ 98BowChrGA-285
❑ 98BowChrGAR-285
❑ 98BowChrI-285
❑ 98BowChrIR-285
❑ 98BowChrR-285
❑ 98BowGolA-285
❑ 98BowInt-285
❑ 98ColCho-246
❑ 98PacOme-239
❑ 98PacOmeR-239
❑ 98PacOnl-737
❑ 98PacOnlR-737
❑ 98PacOnlWC-737
❑ 98PinSna-TR12
❑ 99199Fin-23
❑ 99FinGolRef-23
❑ 99FinRef-23
❑ 99Fle-176
❑ 99FleSta9-176
❑ 99FleWarT-176
❑ 99MetUni-202
❑ 99MetUniGM-202
❑ 99MetUniPMG-202
❑ 99Pac-426
❑ 99PacCroC-284
❑ 99PacCroCPB-284
❑ 99PacPar-236
❑ 99PacParC-236
❑ 99PacParG-236
❑ 99PacParHoloGold-236
❑ 99PacParHS-236
❑ 99PacParOD-236
❑ 99PacParPB-236
❑ 99PacParRed-236
❑ 99PacPlaB-426
❑ 99PacPriS-95
❑ 99PacPriS206-95
❑ 99PacPriS206R-95
❑ 99PacRed-426
❑ 99SkyPre-30
❑ 99SkyPreR-30
❑ 99SkyThu-179
❑ 99SkyThuRant-179
❑ 99SkyThuRave-179
❑ 99SpoIll-14
❑ 99StaClu-209
❑ 99StaCluFDI-209
❑ 99StaCluOoaK-209
❑ 99StaCluPP-209
❑ 99ThuSkySupR-179
❑ 99Top-267
❑ 99TopChr-267
❑ 99TopChrR-267
❑ 99TopMVPP-267
❑ 99UppDec-218
❑ 99UppDecEL1-218
❑ 99UppDecEL2-218
❑ 99UppDecM-208
❑ 99UppDecMGS-208
❑ 99UppDecMHFS-208
❑ 99UppDecMSS-208
❑ 99UppDecR-85
❑ 99UppDecRG-85
❑ 99UppDecRP-85
❑ 99Vic-401
Hellman, Anthony
❑ 87OldJudN-235
Hellman, Jeff
❑ 87Ft.LauYP-25
Helm, J. Ross
❑ 09T206-490
Helm, Wayne
❑ 89BenBucL-4
❑ 90BoiHawP-3315
Helmer, Chad
❑ 97HelBreB-13
❑ 98StoPorG-12
Helmick, Tony
❑ 89GreFalDSP-6
❑ 90BakDodCLC-238
Helmquist, Doug
❑ 84BufBisT-25
Helms, Mike
❑ 90EveGiaB-18
❑ 90EveGiaP-3134
Helms, Ryan
❑ 94SigRooDPBSDP-4
❑ 96SigRooOJRS-R3
❑ 96SigRooOJRSS-R3
Helms, Tommy
❑ 65OPC-243
❑ 65RedEnq-11
❑ 65Top-243
❑ 66Top-311
❑ 66TopVen-311
❑ 67CokCapR-5
❑ 67DexPre-93
❑ 67Kah-16A
❑ 67Kah-16B
❑ 67Top-505
❑ 67TopVen-315
❑ 68Top-405
❑ 69MilBra-109
❑ 69MLBOffS-129
❑ 69MLBPin-47
❑ 69OPC-70
❑ 69OPCDec-9
❑ 69Top-70
❑ 69Top-418
❑ 69TopDec-20
❑ 69TopDecl-16
❑ 69TopSta-24
❑ 69TopSup-40
❑ 69TopTeaP-20
❑ 70AstPho-10
❑ 70DayDaiNM-33
❑ 70MLBOffS-28
❑ 70OPC-159
❑ 70Top-159
❑ 71MLBOffS-61
❑ 71OPC-272
❑ 71Top-272
❑ 72AstTeal-12
❑ 72MilBra-138
❑ 72OPC-204
❑ 72Top-204
❑ 73OPC-495
❑ 73Top-495
❑ 74AstFouTIP-3
❑ 74OPC-67
❑ 74Top-67
❑ 74TopSta-32
❑ 75AstPos-14
❑ 75OPC-119
❑ 75Top-119
❑ 75TopMin-119
❑ 76OPC-583
❑ 76PirPos-5
❑ 76SSP-56
❑ 76Top-583
❑ 76TopTra-583T
❑ 77Top-402
❑ 78Top-618
❑ 82AstAstI-2
❑ 84RedEnq-27
❑ 86RedTexG-NNO
❑ 87AstShoSO-12
❑ 87AstShowSTh-25
❑ 87RedKah-NNO
❑ 88RedKah-NNO
❑ 89RedKah-xx
❑ 90ChaKniTI-19
❑ 90OPC-110
❑ 90Top-110
❑ 90TopTif-110
❑ 91UtiBluSC-17
❑ 91UtiBluSP-3248
❑ 92SalSpuC-12
❑ 93RanKee-179
❑ 93UppDecS-8
Helms, Wes
❑ 94StaCluDP-77
❑ 94StaCluDPFDI-77
❑ 95MacBraTI-10
❑ 96BesAutS-37
❑ 96BesAutSA-26
❑ 96BowBes-152
❑ 96BowBesAR-152
❑ 96BowBesR-152
❑ 96BowMinLP-6
❑ 96CarLeaA1B-15
❑ 96CarLeaA2B-15
❑ 96CarLeaAIB-B1
❑ 96CarLeaAIB-B4
❑ 96DurBulBIB-30
❑ 96DurBulBrB-18
❑ 96Exc-126
❑ 96GreBraB-14
❑ 96GreBraTI-33
❑ 97Bes-50
❑ 97BesAutAS-17
❑ 97BesAutP-H2
❑ 97Bow-295
❑ 97BowBes-151
❑ 97BowBesAR-151
❑ 97BowBesR-151
❑ 97BowCerBlaIA-CA36
❑ 97BowCerBluIA-CA36
❑ 97BowCerGolIA-CA36
❑ 97BowChr-203
❑ 97BowChrI-203
❑ 97BowChrIR-203
❑ 97BowChrR-203
❑ 97BowInt-295
❑ 97GreBraG-11
❑ 97RicBra-14
❑ 97StaClu-183
❑ 97StaCluMOP-183
❑ 97Top-490
❑ 98Don-335

❑ 98DonColP-715
❑ 98DonGolPP-335
❑ 98DonPre-165
❑ 98DonPreSeat-165
❑ 98DonPriCP-715
❑ 98DonSilPP-335
❑ 98LeaRCrusUP-106
❑ 98LeaRS-203
❑ 98LeaRSCrusUG-106
❑ 98LeaRSCrusUR-106
❑ 98LeaRSLHolo-203
❑ 98LeaRSLong-203
❑ 98LeaRTrue-203
❑ 98PinSna-AB14
❑ 98RicBraQ-16
❑ 98SP MinPE-19
❑ 98SPMin-19
❑ 98Stu-205
❑ 98StuGPP-205
❑ 98StuSPP-205
❑ 98Ult-222
❑ 98UltGolM-222
❑ 98UltMas-222
❑ 98UltPlaM-222
❑ 98UppDec-582
❑ 98UppDecDS-DS27
❑ 99Bow-189
❑ 99BowChr-189
❑ 99BowChrG-189
❑ 99BowChrGR-189
❑ 99BowChrI-189
❑ 99BowChrIR-189
❑ 99BowChrR-189
❑ 99BowGol-189
❑ 99BowInt-189
❑ 99Fle-312
❑ 99FleSta9-312
❑ 99FleWarT-312

Helsel, Ronald

❑ 93DunBluJF-1808

Helsom, Bob

❑ 83St.PetCT-21
❑ 84ArkTraT-7

Helton, Keith

❑ 87BelMarTI-6
❑ 88CalLeaACLC-29
❑ 88SanBerSB-19
❑ 88SanBerSCLC-44
❑ 89Sta-123
❑ 89WilBilP-645
❑ 89WilBilS-9
❑ 90CalCanC-21
❑ 90CalCanP-646
❑ 90CMC-448
❑ 90ProAAAF-111
❑ 91CalCanLD-58
❑ 91CalCanP-510
❑ 91LinDriAAA-58
❑ 92JacGenF-3996

Helton, Todd

❑ 93BazTeaU-11
❑ 93TopTra-19T
❑ 95AshTouUTI-9
❑ 95Bes-126
❑ 95SPML-112
❑ 95TenVolW-4
❑ 95TenVolW-5
❑ 96Bow-378
❑ 96BowBes-171
❑ 96BowBesAR-171
❑ 96BowBesMI-1
❑ 96BowBesMIAR-1
❑ 96BowBesMIR-1
❑ 96BowBesR-171
❑ 96BowFoi-378
❑ 96DouAllB-17
❑ 96Exc-154
❑ 96ExcFirYP-5
❑ 96NewHavRB-13
❑ 96NewHavRUSTI-22
❑ 96SigRooOJPP-P4
❑ 96SigRooOJPPS-P4
❑ 96Top-13
❑ 96TopChr-13
❑ 96TopChrR-13
❑ 96TopPowB-13
❑ 97Bes-9
❑ 97BesAutSBPP-12
❑ 97BesCarCSP-4
❑ 97BesDiaB-10
❑ 97Bow-331
❑ 97Bow98ROY-ROY3
❑ 97BowBes-109
❑ 97BowBesAR-109
❑ 97BowBesMI-MI7
❑ 97BowBesMIAR-MI7
❑ 97BowBesMIARI-MI7
❑ 97BowBesMII-MI7
❑ 97BowBesMIR-MI7
❑ 97BowBesMIRI-MI7
❑ 97BowBesR-109
❑ 97BowChr-227
❑ 97BowChr1RFR-ROY3
❑ 97BowChr98RF-ROY3
❑ 97BowChrI-227
❑ 97BowChrIR-227
❑ 97BowChrR-227
❑ 97BowInt-331
❑ 97ColSprSTI-8
❑ 97DonSigA-50
❑ 97DonSigAC-60
❑ 97DonSigAM-60
❑ 97Fin-286
❑ 97FinEmb-286
❑ 97FinEmbR-286
❑ 97FinRef-286
❑ 97Sel-172
❑ 97SelCom-172
❑ 97StaClu-187
❑ 97StaCluMOP-187
❑ 97TopSta-104
❑ 97TopStaAM-104
❑ 98BesCon-4
❑ 98BesCon-5
❑ 98BesDiaBA-4
❑ 98BesFulCA-6
❑ 98BesPlaotYP-1
❑ 98BesPos-5
❑ 98BesYouG-4
❑ 98BesYouG-5
❑ 98Bow-119
❑ 98BowBes-115
❑ 98BowBesA-115
❑ 98BowBesAAR-115
❑ 98BowBesAR-115
❑ 98BowBesAR-115
❑ 98BowBesP-BP4
❑ 98BowBesPAR-BP4
❑ 98BowBesPR-BP4
❑ 98BowBesR-115
❑ 98BowCerBlueAU-22
❑ 98BowCerGA-22
❑ 98BowCerSA-22
❑ 98BowChr-119
❑ 98BowChrGA-119
❑ 98BowChrGAR-119
❑ 98BowChrI-119
❑ 98BowChrIR-119
❑ 98BowChrR-119
❑ 98BowGolA-119
❑ 98BowInt-119
❑ 98BowScoC-SC18
❑ 98CirThu-65
❑ 98CirThuFT-5
❑ 98CirThuRav-65
❑ 98CirThuSupRav-65
❑ 98ColCho-120
❑ 98ColChoSQ-SQ13
❑ 98ColChoSQDouble-29
❑ 98ColChoSQHR-29
❑ 98ColChoSQSingle-29
❑ 98ColChoSQTriple-29
❑ 98CroRoy-52
❑ 98Don-105
❑ 98Don-387
❑ 98DonCol-105
❑ 98DonCol-193
❑ 98DonColE-500
❑ 98DonColL-383
❑ 98DonColP-690
❑ 98DonColP-748
❑ 98DonColS-105
❑ 98DonColS-188
❑ 98DonCruG-71
❑ 98DonCruP-71
❑ 98DonCruR-71
❑ 98DonEli-100
❑ 98DonEliA-100
❑ 98DonEliBttF-2
❑ 98DonEliBttFA-2
❑ 98DonEliC-15
❑ 98DonEliMC-15
❑ 98DonEliS-100
❑ 98DonGolPP-105
❑ 98DonGolPP-387
❑ 98DonPre-140
❑ 98DonPre-198
❑ 98DonPreGB-1
❑ 98DonPreGES-4
❑ 98DonPreGoB-1
❑ 98DonPreGX-4
❑ 98DonPreGXDC-4
❑ 98DonPrePM-27
❑ 98DonPreSeat-140
❑ 98DonPreSeat-198
❑ 98DonPreTP-1
❑ 98DonPreTPD-1
❑ 98DonPreTPG-1
❑ 98DonPreTPS-1
❑ 98DonPriCD-105
❑ 98DonPriCD-193
❑ 98DonPriCE-500
❑ 98DonPriCL-383
❑ 98DonPriCP-690
❑ 98DonPriCP-748
❑ 98DonRatR-18
❑ 98DonRatRM-18
❑ 98DonRooDK-4
❑ 98DonRooDKC-4
❑ 98DonSig-91
❑ 98DonSigA-42
❑ 98DonSigAC-56
❑ 98DonSigAM-57
❑ 98DonSigP-91
❑ 98DonSigSP-9
❑ 98DonSilPP-105
❑ 98DonSilPP-387
❑ 98E-X2SD2001-10
❑ 98E-X2Sig2001-12
❑ 98Fin-111
❑ 98FinNo--111
❑ 98FinNo-R-111
❑ 98FinRef-111
❑ 98FlaShoLeg0-12
❑ 98FlaShoLeg1-12
❑ 98FlaShoLeg2-12
❑ 98FlaShoLeg3-12
❑ 98FlaShoLegM-12
❑ 98FlaShoR0-12
❑ 98FlaShoR1-12
❑ 98FlaShoR2-12
❑ 98FlaShoR3-12
❑ 98FlaShoWotF-2
❑ 98Fle-190
❑ 98FleProF-PF6
❑ 98FleRooS-10
❑ 98FleVin'-21
❑ 98FleVin'C-21
❑ 98Lea-184
❑ 98LeaFraDA-184
❑ 98LeaFraF-184
❑ 98LeaFraM-184
❑ 98LeaFraM-184
❑ 98LeaFraMDC-184
❑ 98LeaFraMDC-184
❑ 98LeaFraMZ2-184
❑ 98LeaRS-136
❑ 98LeaRS-192
❑ 98LeaRSFOSamp-1
❑ 98LeaRSFresh-1
❑ 98LeaRSHRDerby-10
❑ 98LeaRSLHolo-136
❑ 98LeaRSLHolo-192
❑ 98LeaRSLong-136
❑ 98LeaRSLong-192
❑ 98LeaRSTicMas-17
❑ 98LeaRSTicMasDC-17
❑ 98LeaRTrue-136
❑ 98LeaRTrue-192
❑ 98MetUni-186
❑ 98MetUniPMG-186
❑ 98PacAur-126
❑ 98PacOme-82
❑ 98PacOmeR-82
❑ 98PacOmeRS-21
❑ 98PacOmeRST4-21
❑ 98PacOnl-246
❑ 98PacOnlR-246
❑ 98PacOnlWC-246
❑ 98PacPar-154
❑ 98PacParC-154
❑ 98PacParG-154
❑ 98PacParHS-154
❑ 98PacParPB-154
❑ 98PacParR-154
❑ 98Pin-173
❑ 98PinArtP-PP76
❑ 98PinIns-126
❑ 98PinInsCE-126
❑ 98PinInsDE-126
❑ 98PinMusC-PP76
❑ 98PinPer-118
❑ 98PinPerLP-14
❑ 98PinPerPP-118
❑ 98PinPerSftF-35
❑ 98PinPlu-173
❑ 98PinPluAP-PP57
❑ 98PinPluGAP-PP57
❑ 98PinPluMAP-PP57
❑ 98PinPreP-173
❑ 98PinSna-CR6
❑ 98Revo-53
❑ 98RevoRooHH-6
❑ 98RevoRooHHG-6
❑ 98RevoSS-53
❑ 98Sco-251
❑ 98ScoNewS-NS3
❑ 98ScoRT-241
❑ 98ScoRTSS-PP134
❑ 98ScoRTSSAP-PP134
❑ 98ScoRTSSAP1-PP134
❑ 98SelSelSamp-7
❑ 98SkyDugA-120
❑ 98SkyDugAIA-120
❑ 98SP Aut-15
❑ 98SP Aut-SD27
❑ 98SP AutC-TH
❑ 98SP AutSD-SD27
❑ 98SP AutSDT-SD27
❑ 98SpoIll-156
❑ 98SpoIllEE-156
❑ 98SpoIllFE-156
❑ 98SpoIllTaN-146
❑ 98SpoIllTaNEE-146
❑ 98SpoIllWSF-54
❑ 98SpoIllWSFEE-54
❑ 98SpoIllWSFFE-54
❑ 98SPxFin-26
❑ 98SPxFinR-26
❑ 98SPxFinS-26
❑ 98StaCluBPP-BP7
❑ 98StaCluFDI-139
❑ 98StaCluI-139
❑ 98StaCluITW-W4
❑ 98StaCluOneK-139
❑ 98StaCluPP-139
❑ 98StaCluRC-RC13
❑ 98Stu-63
❑ 98Stu8x10S-2
❑ 98StuAuto8X10-2
❑ 98StuGPP-63
❑ 98StuHitPar-7
❑ 98StuPor8x10-2
❑ 98StuPor8x10GP-2
❑ 98StuSPP-63
❑ 98Top-323
❑ 98TopBabB-BB6
❑ 98TopChr-323
❑ 98TopChrBB-BB6
❑ 98TopChrBBR-BB6
❑ 98TopChrR-323
❑ 98TopChrRC-R3
❑ 98TopChrRCRef-R3
❑ 98TopDevR-323
❑ 98TopDia-323
❑ 98TopGal-66
❑ 98TopGalGP-66
❑ 98TopGalOPP-66
❑ 98TopGalPPI-66
❑ 98TopGalPPIA-66
❑ 98TopGolLabC1-81
❑ 98TopGolLabC1B-81
❑ 98TopGolLabC1One-81
❑ 98TopGolLabC1R-81
❑ 98TopGolLabC2-81
❑ 98TopGolLabC2B-81
❑ 98TopGolLabC2One-81
❑ 98TopGolLabC2R-81
❑ 98TopGolLabC3-81
❑ 98TopGolLabC3B-81
❑ 98TopGolLabC3One-81
❑ 98TopGolLabC3R-81
❑ 98TopMiniC-323
❑ 98TopOpeD-149
❑ 98TopRooCla-R3
❑ 98TopSta-131
❑ 98TopStaB-131
❑ 98TopStaG-131
❑ 98TopStaGR-131
❑ 98TopStaS-131
❑ 98TopStaSB-S3
❑ 98TopStaSG-S3
❑ 98TopStaSGR-S3
❑ 98TopStaSS-S3
❑ 98TopSup-29
❑ 98TopSup-29
❑ 98TopTek-69
❑ 98TopTekD-69
❑ 98UD3-14
❑ 98UD3-104
❑ 98UD3-194
❑ 98UD3DieCut-14
❑ 98UD3DieCut-104
❑ 98UD3DieCut-194
❑ 98Ult-224
❑ 98UltGolM-224
❑ 98UltMas-224
❑ 98UltPlaM-224
❑ 98UltRoctS-10
❑ 98UppDec-260
❑ 98UppDec-609
❑ 98UppDecAC-AS29
❑ 98UppDecBCP-BC11
❑ 98UppDecDS-DS10
❑ 98UppDecR-111
❑ 98UppDecREP-4
❑ 98UppDecRNF-NF11
❑ 98UppDecRQL-Q27
❑ 98UppDecSF-142
❑ 98Zen-89
❑ 98Zen5 xx7-66
❑ 98Zen5x7GoldImp-66
❑ 98Zen5x7Imp-66
❑ 98ZenRooT-6
❑ 98ZenZ-G-89
❑ 98ZenZ-S-89
❑ 98ZenZ-T-15
❑ 98ZenZ-TG-15
❑ 99199Fin-130
❑ 99199Fin-248
❑ 99AllMysFR-M23
❑ 99AurOn DL-7
❑ 99AurPenF-9
❑ 99AurPenF-9
❑ 99AurPenFB-9
❑ 99AurPenFS-9
❑ 99Bow-235
❑ 99BowBes-41
❑ 99BowBesAR-41
❑ 99BowBesR-41
❑ 99BowGol-235
❑ 99BowInt-235
❑ 99CroRoyB-49
❑ 99CroRoyL-49
❑ 99CroRoyOD-49
❑ 99E-X Cen-21
❑ 99E-X CenECFut-21
❑ 99E-X CenECNow-21
❑ 99E-X CenEQ-10
❑ 99E-XCenA-6
❑ 99FinGolRef-130
❑ 99FinGolRef-248
❑ 99FinPeelHyp-15
❑ 99FinPeelSpark-15
❑ 99FinPeeSS-15
❑ 99FinRef-130
❑ 99FinRef-248
❑ 99FinSplS-SS13
❑ 99FinSplSDR-SS13
❑ 99FinTeaFB-TF9
❑ 99FinTeaFBR-TF9
❑ 99FinTeaFG-TF9
❑ 99FinTeaFGR-TF9
❑ 99FinTeaFR-TF9
❑ 99FinTeaFRR-TF9
❑ 99FlaShoLeg1-81
❑ 99FlaShoLeg2-81
❑ 99FlaShoLeg3-81
❑ 99FlaShoLegM1-81
❑ 99FlaShoLegM2-81
❑ 99FlaShoLegM3-81
❑ 99FlaShoR1-81
❑ 99FlaShoR2-81
❑ 99FlaShoR3-81
❑ 99FlaShoWotF-6
❑ 99Fle-28
❑ 99Fle-584
❑ 99FleBri-54
❑ 99FleBri2G-54
❑ 99FleBriBlu-54
❑ 99FleBriGol-54
❑ 99FleBriI-6
❑ 99FleMys-30
❑ 99FleMysG-30
❑ 99FleMysM-30
❑ 99FleMysP-6
❑ 99FleRooFla-11
❑ 99FleSta9-28
❑ 99FleSta9-584
❑ 99FleVin'-28
❑ 99FleWarT-28
❑ 99FleWarT-584
❑ 99MetUni-91
❑ 99MetUniGM-91
❑ 99MetUniPMG-91
❑ 99Pac-146
❑ 99Pac-146A
❑ 99PacAur-62
❑ 99PacAurOD-62
❑ 99PacCroC-96
❑ 99PacCroCITC-7
❑ 99PacCroCPB-96
❑ 99PacGolCDC-25
❑ 99PacInv-51
❑ 99PacInvOD-51
❑ 99PacInvPB-51
❑ 99PacInvTA-8
❑ 99PacOme-82
❑ 99PacOmeC-82
❑ 99PacOmeG-82
❑ 99PacOmePB-82
❑ 99PacPar-82
❑ 99PacParC-82
❑ 99PacParFC-9
❑ 99PacParG-82
❑ 99PacParHoloGold-82
❑ 99PacParHS-82
❑ 99PacParOD-82
❑ 99PacParPB-14
❑ 99PacParPB-82
❑ 99PacParRed-82
❑ 99PacPlaB-146
❑ 99PacPlaB-146A
❑ 99PacPri-52
❑ 99PacPriAotG-10
❑ 99PacPriDG-10
❑ 99PacPriHB-52
❑ 99PacPriHG-52
❑ 99PacPriHM-52
❑ 99PacPriHP-52
❑ 99PacPriRed-52
❑ 99PacPriS-35
❑ 99PacPriS206-35
❑ 99PacPriS206R-35
❑ 99PacPriSP-35
❑ 99PacPriSV-35
❑ 99PacRed-146
❑ 99PacRed-146A
❑ 99PacTeaC-19
❑ 99Rev-51
❑ 99RevDiaL-13
❑ 99RevPremDate-51
❑ 99RevRet-51
❑ 99RevShaSS-51
❑ 99SkyMolM-128
❑ 99SkyMolMF-28
❑ 99SkyMolMFS-28
❑ 99SkyMolMFT-28
❑ 99SkyMolMX-128
❑ 99SkyPre-148
❑ 99SkyPreR-148
❑ 99SkyThu-243
❑ 99SkyThuRant-243
❑ 99SkyThuRave-243
❑ 99SkyThuUnl-U9
❑ 99SP Aut-32
❑ 99SP AutC-TH
❑ 99SP AutCG-TH
❑ 99SP SigAuto-THE
❑ 99SP SigAutoG-THE
❑ 99SpoIll-92
❑ 99SpoIllOTW-5
❑ 99SPSig-34
❑ 99SPx-37
❑ 99SPxFinR-37
❑ 99SPxFinS-37
❑ 99SPxWinM-TH
❑ 99StaClu-56
❑ 99StaCluA-SCA10
❑ 99StaCluC-CS2
❑ 99StaCluC-CS8
❑ 99StaCluC-CS13
❑ 99StaCluC-CS19
❑ 99StaCluFDI-56
❑ 99StaCluOoaK-56
❑ 99StaCluPP-56
❑ 99StaCluTI-T10A
❑ 99StaCluTL-T10A
❑ 99StaCluTL-T10A
❑ 99ThuSkySupR-243
❑ 99Top-52
❑ 99Top-457
❑ 99TopAllMF-M23
❑ 99TopBlaLC1-15
❑ 99TopBlaLC2-15
❑ 99TopBlaLC3-15
❑ 99TopChr-52
❑ 99TopChr-457
❑ 99TopChrNB-NB7
❑ 99TopChrNBR-NB7
❑ 99TopChrR-52
❑ 99TopChrR-457
❑ 99TopGal-29
❑ 99TopGal-119
❑ 99TopGalPP-29
❑ 99TopGalPP-119

❑ 99TopGalPPI-29
❑ 99TopGalPPI-119
❑ 99TopGolL-15
❑ 99TopGolLC1-15
❑ 99TopGolLC2-15
❑ 99TopGolLOtO-15
❑ 99TopMVPP-52
❑ 99TopMVPP-457
❑ 99TopNewB-NB7
❑ 99TopOpeD-29
❑ 99TopRedLC1-15
❑ 99TopRedLC2-15
❑ 99TopRedLC3-15
❑ 99TopSta-24
❑ 99TopSta-165
❑ 99TopSta1Foil-24
❑ 99TopSta2Foil-24
❑ 99TopStaFoil-24
❑ 99TopStaFoil-165
❑ 99TopStaOS-24
❑ 99TopStaTS-24
❑ 99TopTek-34A
❑ 99TopTek-34B
❑ 99TopTekG-34A
❑ 99TopTekG-34B
❑ 99UD Cho-81
❑ 99UD ChoPCR-81
❑ 99UDHolo-20
❑ 99UDHoloAUsome-20
❑ 99Ult-34
❑ 99UltGolM-34
❑ 99UltMas-34
❑ 99UltPlaM-34
❑ 99UppDec-87
❑ 99UppDecBD-30
❑ 99UppDecBDD-30
❑ 99UppDecBDQ-30
❑ 99UppDecBDT-30
❑ 99UppDecCf7-34
❑ 99UppDecCf7SftF-S12
❑ 99UppDecCLM-C30
❑ 99UppDecCo7CE-34
❑ 99UppDecCo7SftFA-TH
❑ 99UppDecE-31
❑ 99UppDecEBPC-C-TH
❑ 99UppDecEFXG-31
❑ 99UppDecEL1-87
❑ 99UppDecEL2-87
❑ 99UppDecGJ-TH
❑ 99UppDecM-71
❑ 99UppDecMGS-71
❑ 99UppDecMHFS-71
❑ 99UppDecMSC-SC10
❑ 99UppDecMSS-71
❑ 99UppDecR-29
❑ 99UppDecRG-29
❑ 99UppDecRP-29
❑ 99Vic-132

Helvey, Rob
❑ 94JohCitCC-13
❑ 94JohCitCF-3694
❑ 95NewJerCTI-12

Heman, Russell
❑ 59Top-283
❑ 60MapLeaSF-8

Hembree, Kirk
❑ 89CarNewE-24

Heming, Tom
❑ 92EugEmeC-15
❑ 92EugEmeF-3026

Hemingway, Ed
❑ 23Zee-86
❑ 25Zee-157
❑ 26Zee-25
❑ 27Zee-13

Hemm, Warren
❑ 78MemChiBC-5
❑ 79MemChiT-23

Hemmerich, Mike
❑ 89PitMetS-7

Hemmerly, John
❑ 89EriOriS-6
❑ 89SanDieSAS-12

Hemming, George
❑ 94OriTeal-8

Hemond, Scott
❑ 87HunStaTI-12
❑ 87MadMusP-9
❑ 87MadMusP-3
❑ 88HunStaTI-6
❑ 89HunStaB-1
❑ 90Bow-453
❑ 90BowTif-453
❑ 90CMC-593
❑ 90Fle-646
❑ 90FleCan-646
❑ 90ProAAAF-146
❑ 90Sco-598
❑ 90TacTigC-16
❑ 90TacTigP-99
❑ 90TopDeb89-54
❑ 90UppDec-727
❑ 91Bow-232
❑ 91Sco100RS-22
❑ 91TacTigP-2314
❑ 92AthMot-26
❑ 92Don-637
❑ 92Sco-617
❑ 92StaClu-62
❑ 92Ult-422
❑ 93AthMot-19
❑ 93AthStaC-21
❑ 93Don-623
❑ 93Ult-607
❑ 94A'sMot-17
❑ 94ColC-408
❑ 94ColChoGS-408
❑ 94ColChoSS-408
❑ 94Don-141
❑ 94Fle-263
❑ 94Pac-451
❑ 94StaClu-12
❑ 94StaCluFDI-12
❑ 94StaCluGR-12
❑ 94StaCluMOP-12
❑ 94Top-226
❑ 94TopGol-226
❑ 94TopSpa-226
❑ 95StaClu-167
❑ 95StaCluFDI-167
❑ 95StaCluMOP-167
❑ 95StaCluSTWS-167
❑ 96LouRedB-21

Hempen, Hal
❑ 88SavCarP-342

Hempfield, Keith
❑ 83ChaRoyT-7

Hemphill, Bret
❑ 94BoiHawC-1
❑ 94BoiHawF-3358
❑ 95CedRapKTI-31
❑ 95Exc-21
❑ 95Top-480
❑ 96LakElsSB-12
❑ 97MidAng-16
❑ 97TexAllM-18
❑ 97TexLeaTP-12
❑ 98VanCanG-15

Hemphill, Charles
❑ 03BreE10-69
❑ 08RosComP-48
❑ 09BriE97-13
❑ 09RamT20-54
❑ 09T206-152
❑ 10W555-35
❑ 11PinT-5-813
❑ 11S74Sil-22
❑ 11SpoLifCW-161
❑ 11T205-74
❑ 72ClaCar-22

Hemphill, James
❑ 96HelBreTI-9

Hemsley, Rollie (Ralston)
❑ 31CubTeal-10
❑ 32CubTeal-11
❑ 34BatR31-71
❑ 34ExhFou-15
❑ 35ExhFou-15
❑ 35GouPuzR-8C
❑ 35GouPuzR-9C
❑ 36ExhFou-15
❑ 36GouBWR-17
❑ 36GouWidPPR-A50
❑ 36OveCanR-23
❑ 36R31PasP-26
❑ 36SandSW-32
❑ 36WheBB4-5
❑ 37ExhFou-15
❑ 38BasTabP-17
❑ 38CloFotW-36
❑ 40PlaBal-205
❑ 41DouPlaR-133
❑ 41PlaBal-34
❑ 43YanSta-14
❑ 47CenFlo-8
❑ 54Top-143
❑ 91ConTSN-299
❑ 92YanWIZA-28
❑ 94TopArc1-143
❑ 94TopArc1G-143
❑ 95ConTSN-1420

Hemus, Solly
❑ 52Bow-212
❑ 52Top-196
❑ 53BowC-85
❑ 53CarHunW-9
❑ 53Top-231
❑ 54Bow-94
❑ 54CarHunW-8
❑ 54Top-117
❑ 55Bow-107
❑ 55CarHunW-8
❑ 57Top-231
❑ 58Top-207
❑ 59Top-527
❑ 60Top-218
❑ 61CarJayP-5
❑ 61Top-139
❑ 79DiaGre-172
❑ 79TCM50-93
❑ 81TCM60I-362
❑ 82MetGal62-28
❑ 91TopArc1-231
❑ 94TopArc1-117
❑ 94TopArc1G-117

Hence, Sam
❑ 90BurIndP-3020
❑ 91BurIndP-3315
❑ 92ColRedC-7
❑ 92ColRedF-2405
❑ 92WatIndF-3247
❑ 93ColRedC-12
❑ 93ColRedF-612
❑ 94KinIndC-8
❑ 94KinIndF-2657

Henderson, Ben
❑ 11PacCoaBD-24
❑ 14Zee-111

Henderson, Bill
❑ 33Zee-121
❑ 88FayGenP-1102
❑ 89LakTigS-9

Henderson, Brad
❑ 86FloStaLAP-22
❑ 86St.PetCP-10
❑ 87ArkTraP-24
❑ 88ArkTraGS-2

Henderson, Bruce
❑ 72CedRapCT-12

Henderson, Carl
❑ 90MisStaB-18
❑ 91MisStaB-24
❑ 92MisStaB-20
❑ 93MisStaB-21

Henderson, Chris
❑ 92BenRocCB-12
❑ 92BenRocF-1469
❑ 93BenRocCB-10
❑ 93BenRocF-3261
❑ 94CenValRC-9
❑ 94CenValRF-3196
❑ 95AshTouUTI-13

Henderson, Craig
❑ 82WisRapTF-26
❑ 83VisOakF-20
❑ 85OrlTwiT-26

Henderson, Daryl
❑ 91GulCoaRSP-22
❑ 92GasRanC-10
❑ 92GasRanF-2248
❑ 92UppDecML-243
❑ 93Bow-25
❑ 93ChaRanC-14
❑ 93ChaRanF-1936
❑ 93FloStaLAF-3
❑ 94ClaGolF-34

Henderson, Dave
❑ 80SpoIndT-16
❑ 81MarPos-19
❑ 82MarPos-19
❑ 82Top-711
❑ 83Fle-481
❑ 83Top-732
❑ 84Don-557
❑ 84Fle-611
❑ 84MarMot-3
❑ 84Nes792-154
❑ 84OPC-154
❑ 84Top-154
❑ 84TopSti-343
❑ 84TopTif-154
❑ 85Fle-489
❑ 85MarMot-4
❑ 85OPC-344
❑ 85Top-344
❑ 85TopSti-338
❑ 85TopTif-344
❑ 86Don-318
❑ 86Fle-465
❑ 86Lea-187
❑ 86MarMot-4
❑ 86OPC-221
❑ 86Top-221
❑ 86Top-546
❑ 86TopSti-222
❑ 86TopTif-221
❑ 86TopTif-546
❑ 87Don-622
❑ 87DonOpeD-189
❑ 87Fle-36
❑ 87FleGlo-36
❑ 87FleGlo-WS10
❑ 87FleHotS-19
❑ 87FleWorS-10
❑ 87Lea-103
❑ 87RedSoxP-12
❑ 87SpoTeaP-9
❑ 87Top-452
❑ 87TopSti-23
❑ 87TopTif-452
❑ 87Woo-22
❑ 88A'sMot-14
❑ 88DonTeaBA-NEW
❑ 88Fle-84
❑ 88FleGlo-84
❑ 88FleUpd-53
❑ 88FleUpdG-53
❑ 88Sco-228
❑ 88ScoGlo-228
❑ 88ScoRoo-49T
❑ 88ScoRooG-49T
❑ 88StaLinAs-7
❑ 88Top-628
❑ 88TopBig-131
❑ 88TopTif-628
❑ 88TopTra-48T
❑ 88TopTraT-48T
❑ 89A'sMot-13
❑ 89Bow-200
❑ 89BowTif-200
❑ 89Don-20
❑ 89Don-450
❑ 89DonBasB-190
❑ 89DonSupD-20
❑ 89Fle-10
❑ 89FleGlo-10
❑ 89OPC-327
❑ 89PanSti-423
❑ 89Sco-533
❑ 89Spo-127
❑ 89SpoIllFKI-289
❑ 89Top-527
❑ 89TopBig-326
❑ 89TopSti-164
❑ 89TopStiB-17
❑ 89TopTif-527
❑ 89TVSpoM-100
❑ 89UppDec-174
❑ 90A'sMot-18
❑ 90Bow-458
❑ 90BowTif-458
❑ 90Don-243
❑ 90DonBesA-39
❑ 90Fle-9
❑ 90FleCan-9
❑ 90OPC-68
❑ 90PanSti-133
❑ 90PublntS-306
❑ 90Sco-325
❑ 90Sco-702
❑ 90Top-68
❑ 90TopBig-309
❑ 90TopMag-59
❑ 90TopSti-184
❑ 90TopTif-68
❑ 90UppDec-206
❑ 90Woo-29
❑ 91A'sMot-18
❑ 91A'sSFE-5
❑ 91Bow-226
❑ 91Cla3-T36
❑ 91Don-320
❑ 91Fle-9
❑ 91Lea-232
❑ 91OPC-144
❑ 91PanFreS-197
❑ 91PanSti-150
❑ 91Sco-644
❑ 91StaClu-284
❑ 91Stu-103
❑ 91Top-144
❑ 91TopDesS-144
❑ 91TopMic-144
❑ 91TopTif-144
❑ 91TopTriH-A11
❑ 91Ult-247
❑ 91UppDec-108
❑ 91UppDecFE-88F
❑ 91USPlaCA-13H
❑ 92A'sUno7P-5
❑ 92AthMot-18
❑ 92Bow-488
❑ 92ClaGam-9
❑ 92Don-21
❑ 92Don-311
❑ 92Fle-257
❑ 92Hig5-104
❑ 92Lea-232
❑ 92LeaBlaG-232
❑ 92OPC-335
❑ 92PanSti-20
❑ 92PanSti-276
❑ 92Pin-16
❑ 92PinRool-8
❑ 92RedFolS-45
❑ 92RedFolS-117
❑ 92Sco-5
❑ 92Sco100S-92
❑ 92ScoCokD-13
❑ 92ScoProP-3
❑ 92ScoProP-4
❑ 92StaClu-218
❑ 92StaCluD-82
❑ 92Stu-224
❑ 92Top-335
❑ 92TopGol-335
❑ 92TopGolW-335
❑ 92TopKid-116
❑ 92TopMic-335
❑ 92TriPla-130
❑ 92TriPla-166
❑ 92Ult-113
❑ 92UppDec-172
❑ 93AthMot-9
❑ 93AthStaC-11
❑ 93Don-373
❑ 93Fle-664
❑ 93Lea-139
❑ 93OPC-155
❑ 93PacSpa-568
❑ 93PanSti-20
❑ 93Pin-170
❑ 93Sco-134
❑ 93StaClu-349
❑ 93StaCluFDI-349
❑ 93StaCluMOP-349
❑ 93Stu-30
❑ 93Top-473
❑ 93TopGol-473
❑ 93TopInaM-473
❑ 93TopInaR-473
❑ 93TopMic-473
❑ 93TriPla-119
❑ 93Ult-608
❑ 93UppDec-607
❑ 93UppDecGold-607
❑ 94ColC-431
❑ 94ColChoGS-431
❑ 94ColChoSS-431
❑ 94Don-513
❑ 94Fin-260
❑ 94FinRef-260
❑ 94Fla-59
❑ 94Fle-264
❑ 94FleExtB-91
❑ 94FleUpd-49
❑ 94Pac-452
❑ 94PanSti-109
❑ 94Pin-508
❑ 94PinArtP-508
❑ 94PinMusC-508
❑ 94Sco-463
❑ 94ScoGolR-463
❑ 94ScoRoo-RT18
❑ 94ScoRooGR-RT18
❑ 94Sel-298
❑ 94SpoRoo-15
❑ 94SpoRooAP-15
❑ 94StaClu-253
❑ 94StaClu-689
❑ 94StaCluFDI-253
❑ 94StaCluFDI-689
❑ 94StaCluGR-253
❑ 94StaCluGR-689
❑ 94StaCluMOP-253
❑ 94StaCluMOP-689
❑ 94Top-708
❑ 94TopGol-708
❑ 94TopSpa-708
❑ 94TopTra-23T
❑ 94Ult-365
❑ 94UppDec-507
❑ 94UppDecED-507
❑ 95Fle-161
❑ 95Pac-204
❑ 95StaClu-251
❑ 95StaCluFDI-251
❑ 95StaCluMOP-251
❑ 95StaCluSTWS-251
❑ 95Top-276
❑ 95TopCyb-149

Henderson, David
❑ 89AubAstP-2185
❑ 90OscAstS-9
❑ 91BurAstC-15
❑ 91BurAstP-2809
❑ 92SanBerSF-966

Henderson, Derek
❑ 89PitMetS-8
❑ 91St.LucMC-7
❑ 91St.LucMP-718
❑ 92KnoBluJF-2996
❑ 92KncBluJS-381
❑ 93KnoSmoF-1258
❑ 94KnoSmoF-1310

Henderson, Frank
❑ 88AppFoxP-154
❑ 88EugEmeB-23
❑ 89AppFoxP-857

Henderson, Hardie (James H.)
❑ 87OldJudN-236
❑ 87OldJudN-237
❑ 88KimN18-19

Henderson, Harry IV
❑ 89BilMusP-2059

Henderson, Jeff
❑ 91KinMetC-1
❑ 91KinMetP-3808

Henderson, Jim
❑ 89AriStaB-12
❑ 92JamExpC-2

Henderson, Joe
❑ 81CliGiaT-22
❑ 82BelBreFr-2
❑ 83ElPasDT-3
❑ 84MidCubT-1
❑ 96BatCliTI-31

Henderson, John
❑ 77QuaCitAT-16

Henderson, Joseph Lee
❑ 76IndIndTI-5
❑ 77IndIndTI-3
❑ 77Top-487

Henderson, Juan
❑ 94CedRapKC-13
❑ 94CedRapKF-1116
❑ 95CedRapKTI-11
❑ 96LakElsSB-17

Henderson, Kenneth J.
❑ 91EveGiaC-19
❑ 91EveGiaP-3929
❑ 92EveGiaC-6
❑ 92EveGiaF-1681

Henderson, Kenneth Jos.
❑ 65Top-497
❑ 66OPC-39
❑ 66Top-39
❑ 66TopVen-39
❑ 67Top-383
❑ 68Top-309
❑ 68TopVen-309
❑ 70DayDaiNM-89
❑ 70Gia-4
❑ 70OPC-298
❑ 70Top-298
❑ 71GiaTic-5
❑ 71MLBOffS-251
❑ 71OPC-155
❑ 71Top-155
❑ 71TopCoi-97
❑ 71TopTat-12
❑ 72OPC-443
❑ 72OPC-444
❑ 72Top-443
❑ 72Top-444
❑ 72WhiSox-4
❑ 73OPC-101
❑ 73SevTraC-31
❑ 73Top-101
❑ 74OPC-394
❑ 74Top-394

❑ 74TopSta-154
❑ 75Hos-136
❑ 75HosTwi-136
❑ 75OPC-59
❑ 75Top-59
❑ 75TopMin-59
❑ 76AtlBraP-15
❑ 76OPC-464
❑ 76SSP-147
❑ 76Top-464
❑ 76TopTra-464T
❑ 77Top-242
❑ 78MetDaiPA-9
❑ 78Pep-13
❑ 78Top-612
❑ 79Top-73
❑ 80Top-523
❑ 91MetWIZ-170
❑ 93RanKee-180

Henderson, Kenny
❑ 96CliLumKTI-14
❑ 97RanCucQG-12

Henderson, Lee
❑ 89GeoColC-10
❑ 90ChaRaiB-11
❑ 90ChaRaiP-2041
❑ 90GeoColC-7
❑ 91WatDiaC-12
❑ 91WatDiaP-1259
❑ 92HigDesMC-26
❑ 93RanCucQC-16
❑ 93RanCucQF-835
❑ 93WicWraF-2980
❑ 94SprSulC-12
❑ 94SprSulF-2039

Henderson, Lester
❑ 94MedHatBJF-3676
❑ 94MedHatBJSP-16

Henderson, Matt
❑ 79WisRapTT-8
❑ 80WisRapTT-22

Henderson, Mike
❑ 78HolMilT-11
❑ 79HolMilT-17
❑ 80VanCanT-17

Henderson, Pedro
❑ 90BurIndP-3021
❑ 91ColIndP-1499
❑ 91WatIndC-26
❑ 91WatIndP-3381

Henderson, Ramon
❑ 86ReaPhiP-9
❑ 87ReaPhiP-15
❑ 88MaiPhiC-19
❑ 88MaiPhiP-295
❑ 89ReaPhiB-13
❑ 89ReaPhiP-653
❑ 89ReaPhiS-13
❑ 90PriPatD-29
❑ 91ClePhiC-5
❑ 91ClePhiP-1639
❑ 92ClePhiC-24
❑ 92ClePhiF-2074
❑ 97ReaPhi-3
❑ 98PhiTeal-16

Henderson, Rats
❑ 86NegLeaF-34

Henderson, Rickey
❑ 77ModA'sC-5
❑ 79OgdA'sT-9
❑ 80Top-482
❑ 81A'sGraG-35
❑ 81AllGamPI-52
❑ 81Don-119
❑ 81Fle-351
❑ 81Fle-574
❑ 81FleStiC-54
❑ 81Kel-33
❑ 81OPC-261
❑ 81PerCreC-19
❑ 81Squ-28
❑ 81Top-4
❑ 81Top-261
❑ 81TopScr-39
❑ 81TopSti-15
❑ 81TopSti-115
❑ 82A'sGraG-4
❑ 82Don-113
❑ 82Fle-92
❑ 82Fle-643
❑ 82FleSta-123
❑ 82Kel-4
❑ 82OPC-268
❑ 82PerAll-6
❑ 82PerAllG-6
❑ 82PerCreC-23
❑ 82PerCreCG-23
❑ 82SevSluC-13
❑ 82Top-156
❑ 82Top-164
❑ 82Top-610
❑ 82TopSti-8
❑ 82TopSti-221
❑ 82TopStiV-221
❑ 83A'sGraG-35
❑ 83AllGamPI-54
❑ 83Don-11
❑ 83Don-35
❑ 83DonActA-22
❑ 83Fle-519
❑ 83Fle-639
❑ 83Fle-646
❑ 83FleSta-77
❑ 83FleSti-144
❑ 83FleSti-192
❑ 83Kel-8
❑ 83OPC-180
❑ 83OPC-391
❑ 83PerCreC-26
❑ 83PerCreCG-26
❑ 83Top-2
❑ 83Top-180
❑ 83Top-391
❑ 83Top-531
❑ 83Top-704
❑ 83TopFol-5
❑ 83TopGloS-33
❑ 83TopSti-21
❑ 83TopSti-103
❑ 83TopSti-159
❑ 83TopSti-197
❑ 83TopSti-198
❑ 83TopSti-199
❑ 83TopSti-200
❑ 83TopSti-201
❑ 83TopSti-202
❑ 83TopStiB-8
❑ 84A'sMot-2
❑ 84AllGamPI-143
❑ 84Don-54
❑ 84DonActAS-9
❑ 84Fle-447
❑ 84FleSti-53
❑ 84FleSti-92
❑ 84FunFooP-17
❑ 84MilBra-13
❑ 84MLBPen-7
❑ 84Nes792-2
❑ 84Nes792-134
❑ 84Nes792-156
❑ 84Nes792-230
❑ 84OCoandSI-27
❑ 84OPC-230
❑ 84RalPur-15
❑ 84SevCoi-W21
❑ 84Top-2
❑ 84Top-134
❑ 84Top-156
❑ 84Top-230
❑ 84TopCer-15
❑ 84TopGloS-6
❑ 84TopPewB-8
❑ 84TopRubD-24
❑ 84TopSti-3
❑ 84TopSti-4
❑ 84TopSti-202
❑ 84TopSti-327
❑ 84TopSup-19
❑ 84TopTif-2
❑ 84TopTif-134
❑ 84TopTif-156
❑ 84TopTif-230
❑ 85AllGamPI-58
❑ 85Don-176
❑ 85DonHig-17
❑ 85DonHig-42
❑ 85Fle-425
❑ 85Fle-629
❑ 85FleStaS-54
❑ 85FleUpd-51
❑ 85Lea-208
❑ 85OPC-115
❑ 85SevCoi-W12
❑ 85Top-115
❑ 85Top-706
❑ 85Top3-D-10
❑ 85TopRubD-24
❑ 85TopSti-283
❑ 85TopSti-321
❑ 85TopSup-14
❑ 85TopTif-115
❑ 85TopTif-706
❑ 85TopTifT-49T
❑ 85TopTra-49T
❑ 85Woo-17
❑ 85YanTCMP-35
❑ 86BasStaB-55
❑ 86Don-51
❑ 86DonAll-10
❑ 86DonPop-10
❑ 86DorChe-7
❑ 86Dra-5
❑ 86Fle-108
❑ 86FleAll-7
❑ 86FleLimE-23
❑ 86FleMin-23
❑ 86FleStiC-53
❑ 86GenMilB-1C
❑ 86Lea-37
❑ 86OPC-243
❑ 86QuaGra-25
❑ 86SevCoi-E12
❑ 86Spo-6
❑ 86Spo-184
❑ 86SpoDecG-69
❑ 86Top-500
❑ 86Top-716
❑ 86Top3-D-11
❑ 86TopGloA-7
❑ 86TopGloS-5
❑ 86TopMinL-27
❑ 86TopSti-155
❑ 86TopSti-297
❑ 86TopSup-30
❑ 86TopTat-24
❑ 86TopTif-500
❑ 86TopTif-716
❑ 86YanTCM-33
❑ 87A'sMot-20
❑ 87BoaandB-8
❑ 87BurKinA-9
❑ 87ClaGam-12
❑ 87Don-228
❑ 87DonAll-6
❑ 87DonOpeD-248
❑ 87DonP-6
❑ 87Dra-12
❑ 87Fle-101
❑ 87FleExcS-24
❑ 87FleGlo-101
❑ 87FleHea-4
❑ 87FleHotS-20
❑ 87FleMin-52
❑ 87FleSlu-18
❑ 87FleStiC-56
❑ 87GenMilB-2D
❑ 87K-M-27
❑ 87KayB-16
❑ 87KeyFooD-18
❑ 87KraFoo-31
❑ 87Lea-191
❑ 87MSAIceTD-18
❑ 87MSAJifPD-14
❑ 87OPC-7
❑ 87OPCBoxB-E
❑ 87OurOwnTD-18
❑ 87RedFolSB-80
❑ 87SevCoi-E3
❑ 87Spo-4
❑ 87Spo-157
❑ 87Spo-159
❑ 87Spo-198
❑ 87SpoDeaP-4
❑ 87SpoIllS-7
❑ 87SpoSupD-14
❑ 87SpoTeaP-7
❑ 87StuPan-23
❑ 87Top-311
❑ 87Top-406
❑ 87Top-735
❑ 87TopCoi-12
❑ 87TopGloA-18
❑ 87TopGloS-21
❑ 87TopMinL-64
❑ 87TopSti-147
❑ 87TopSti-296
❑ 87TopTif-311
❑ 87TopTif-406
❑ 87TopTif-735
❑ 87TopWaxBC-E
❑ 87WeiMarD-18
❑ 87Woo-3
❑ 88CheBoy-20
❑ 88ClaBlu-234
❑ 88Don-277
❑ 88DonAll-4
❑ 88DonBasB-76
❑ 88DonPop-4
❑ 88DonReaBY-277
❑ 88Dra-7
❑ 88Fle-209
❑ 88FleGlo-209
❑ 88FleHotS-16
❑ 88FleMin-40
❑ 88FleSluBC-C2
❑ 88FleStiWBC-S4
❑ 88FleSupBC-C2
❑ 88K-M-13
❑ 88Lea-145
❑ 88OPC-60
❑ 88OPCBoxB-M
❑ 88PanSti-158
❑ 88PanSti-231
❑ 88PanSti-434
❑ 88Sco-13
❑ 88ScoBoxC-7
❑ 88ScoGlo-13
❑ 88Spo-11
❑ 88SpoGam-8
❑ 88StaLinAl-14
❑ 88StaLinY-6
❑ 88TarPla-19
❑ 88Top-60
❑ 88TopBig-165
❑ 88TopGloA-7
❑ 88TopGloS-25
❑ 88TopMinL-26
❑ 88TopSti-155
❑ 88TopSti-297
❑ 88TopStiB-51
❑ 88TopTif-60
❑ 88TopUKM-31
❑ 88TopUKMT-31
❑ 88TopWaxBC-M
❑ 89Baz-14
❑ 89Bow-181
❑ 89BowTif-181
❑ 89CadEllD-28
❑ 89ClaLigB-50
❑ 89Don-245
❑ 89DonAll-4
❑ 89DonBasB-78
❑ 89DonPop-4
❑ 89Fle-254
❑ 89FleBasA-20
❑ 89FleExcS-21
❑ 89FleGlo-254
❑ 89FleSup-22
❑ 89FleUpd-54
❑ 89KayB-18
❑ 89ModA'sC-33
❑ 89OPC-282
❑ 89OPCBoxB-F
❑ 89PanSti-239
❑ 89PanSti-408
❑ 89Sco-70
❑ 89Sco-657
❑ 89ScoHot1S-45
❑ 89ScoRoo-50T
❑ 89Spo-145
❑ 89SpoIllFKI-46
❑ 89Top-380
❑ 89TopAme2C-16
❑ 89TopBasT-55
❑ 89TopBatL-15
❑ 89TopBig-271
❑ 89TopDouM-16
❑ 89TopGloA-7
❑ 89TopGloS-35
❑ 89TopMinL-66
❑ 89TopSti-145
❑ 89TopSti-312
❑ 89TopStiB-18
❑ 89TopTif-380
❑ 89TopTra-48T
❑ 89TopTraT-48T
❑ 89TopUKM-37
❑ 89TopWaxBC-F
❑ 89TVSpoM-83
❑ 89TVSpoM-127
❑ 89UppDec-210
❑ 90A'sMot-4
❑ 90AllBasT-5
❑ 90BasWit-37
❑ 90Baz-9
❑ 90Bow-457
❑ 90BowTif-457
❑ 90ClaBlu-37
❑ 90ClaYel-T27
❑ 90Col-8
❑ 90Don-304
❑ 90DonBesA-124
❑ 90DonLeaS-7
❑ 90Fle-10
❑ 90FleAwaW-18
❑ 90FleBasM-17
❑ 90FleBasMC-17
❑ 90FleCan-10
❑ 90FleLeaL-18
❑ 90FleLeaLC-18
❑ 90FleWorS-11
❑ 90HOFStiB-87
❑ 90Hot50PS-20
❑ 90K-M-23
❑ 90KayB-15
❑ 90KinDis-19
❑ 90Lea-84
❑ 90Lea-160
❑ 90M.Vpin-74
❑ 90MSAHolD-8
❑ 90OPC-7
❑ 90OPC-450
❑ 90OPCBoxB-F
❑ 90PanSti-138
❑ 90Pos-25
❑ 90PubIntS-288
❑ 90PubIntS-537
❑ 90Sco-360
❑ 90Sco-686
❑ 90Sco-698
❑ 90Sco-702
❑ 90Sco100S-90
❑ 90ScoMcD-5
❑ 90Spo-208
❑ 90StaHen-1
❑ 90StaHen-2
❑ 90StaHen-3
❑ 90StaHen-4
❑ 90StaHen-5
❑ 90StaHen-6
❑ 90StaHen-7
❑ 90StaHen-8
❑ 90StaHen-9
❑ 90StaHen-10
❑ 90StaHen-11
❑ 90SunSee-13
❑ 90Top-7
❑ 90Top-450
❑ 90TopAmeA-13
❑ 90TopBatL-21
❑ 90TopBig-292
❑ 90TopCoi-17
❑ 90TopDou-33
❑ 90TopGloS-37
❑ 90TopMag-30
❑ 90TopMinL-28
❑ 90TopSti-7
❑ 90TopSti-181
❑ 90TopStiB-50
❑ 90TopTif-7
❑ 90TopTif-450
❑ 90TopTVA-10
❑ 90TopWaxBC-F
❑ 90UppDec-334
❑ 90USPlaCA-13C
❑ 90WinDis-8
❑ 90Woo-14
❑ 90Woo-23
❑ 90Woo-31
❑ 91A'sMot-4
❑ 91A'sSFE-6
❑ 91BasBesRB-7
❑ 91Baz-2
❑ 91Bow-213
❑ 91Bow-371
❑ 91Bow-692
❑ 91CadEllD-29
❑ 91Cla1-T72
❑ 91Cla2-T75
❑ 91ClaGam-189
❑ 91Col-25
❑ 91Don-53
❑ 91Don-387
❑ 91Don-648
❑ 91Don-761
❑ 91DonEli-7
❑ 91Fle-10
❑ 91FleAll-6
❑ 91FlePro-F2
❑ 91FleWorS-4
❑ 91JimDea-17
❑ 91KinDis-5
❑ 91Lea-101
❑ 91LeaGolR-BC26
❑ 91LeaPre-23
❑ 91MajLeaCP-40
❑ 91MSAHolD-12
❑ 91OPC-391
❑ 91OPC-670
❑ 91OPCBoxB-H
❑ 91OPCPre-62
❑ 91PanCanT1-6
❑ 91PanCanT1-38
❑ 91PanCanT1-45
❑ 91PanCanT1-53
❑ 91PanFreS-171
❑ 91PanFreS-196
❑ 91PanSti-146
❑ 91PepRicH-1
❑ 91PepRicH-2
❑ 91PepRicH-3
❑ 91PepRicH-4
❑ 91PepRicH-5
❑ 91PepRicH-6
❑ 91PepRicH-7
❑ 91PepRicH-8
❑ 91PepRicH-9
❑ 91PepRicH-10
❑ 91PepRicHD-1
❑ 91PepRicHD-2
❑ 91PepRicHD-3
❑ 91PepRicHD-4
❑ 91PetSta-21
❑ 91Pos-27
❑ 91PosCan-24
❑ 91RedFolS-48
❑ 91RedFolS-121
❑ 91Sco-10
❑ 91Sco-397
❑ 91Sco-857
❑ 91Sco-875
❑ 91Sco-890
❑ 91Sco100S-10
❑ 91ScoCoo-B4
❑ 91Sev3DCN-7
❑ 91SevCoi-A5
❑ 91SevCoi-NC7
❑ 91SevCoi-NE7
❑ 91SevCoi-NW7
❑ 91SilHol-1
❑ 91StaClu-120
❑ 91StaCluCM-13
❑ 91StaCluCM-14
❑ 91StaCluMO-4
❑ 91StaCluMO-18
❑ 91StaHen-1
❑ 91StaHen-2
❑ 91StaHen-3
❑ 91StaHen-4
❑ 91StaHen-5
❑ 91StaHen-6
❑ 91StaHen-7
❑ 91StaHen-8
❑ 91StaHen-9
❑ 91StaHen-10
❑ 91StaHen-11
❑ 91StaPinB-24
❑ 91Stu-104
❑ 91Top-391
❑ 91Top-670
❑ 91TopCraJI-18
❑ 91TopDesS-391
❑ 91TopDesS-670
❑ 91TopGaloC-7
❑ 91TopGloA-6
❑ 91TopMic-391
❑ 91TopMic-670
❑ 91TopSta-19
❑ 91TopTif-391
❑ 91TopTif-670
❑ 91TopTriH-A11
❑ 91TopWaxBC-H
❑ 91Ult-248
❑ 91Ult-393
❑ 91UltGol-5
❑ 91UppDec-444
❑ 91UppDec-636
❑ 91UppDec-636A
❑ 91UppDec-SP2
❑ 91UppDecFE-86F
❑ 91UppDecSS-SS3
❑ 91USPlaCA-11H
❑ 91Woo-2
❑ 91Woo-26
❑ 92A'sUno7P-2
❑ 92AthMot-4
❑ 92Bow-166
❑ 92Cla1-T43
❑ 92ClaGam-118
❑ 92Don-30
❑ 92Don-193
❑ 92Don-215
❑ 92DonCraJ2-19
❑ 92DonEli-L2
❑ 92Fle-258
❑ 92Fle-681

❑ 92FleCitTP-17
❑ 92Fre-17
❑ 92Hig5-105
❑ 92Hig5S-19
❑ 92LaKdec-17
❑ 92Lea-116
❑ 92LeaDlaG 116
❑ 92MooSna-19
❑ 92Mr.TurS-14
❑ 92MVPPin-24
❑ 92New-10
❑ 92OPC-2
❑ 92OPC-560
❑ 92OPCPre-147
❑ 92PanSti-21
❑ 92PanSti-278
❑ 92PepDieM-28
❑ 92Pin-283
❑ 92Pin-401
❑ 92Pin-614
❑ 92PinRool-7
❑ 92PosCan-18
❑ 92RedFolS-46
❑ 92RedFolS-118
❑ 92Sco-430
❑ 92Sco-441
❑ 92Sco-480
❑ 92Sco100S-100
❑ 92SpoStaCC-23
❑ 92StaClu-750
❑ 92StaCluD-83
❑ 92StaCluMP-8
❑ 92StaPro-4
❑ 92Top-2
❑ 92Top-560
❑ 92TopGol-2
❑ 92TopGol-560
❑ 92TopGolW-2
❑ 92TopGolW-560
❑ 92TopKid-118
❑ 92TopMcD-3
❑ 92TopMic-2
❑ 92TopMic-560
❑ 92TopMic-G2
❑ 92TriPla-63
❑ 92Ult-114
❑ 92UppDec-90
❑ 92UppDec-155
❑ 92UppDec-640
❑ 92UppDec-648
❑ 92UppDec-782
❑ 92UppDecF-27
❑ 92UppDecFG-27
❑ 92UppDecWB-T7
❑ 92YanWIZ8-80
❑ 92YanWIZA-29
❑ 93AthMot-6
❑ 93AthStaC-8
❑ 93Bow-625
❑ 93CadDis-31
❑ 93ClaGam-42
❑ 93DenHol-3
❑ 93DiaMar-50
❑ 93Don-315
❑ 93Fin-86
❑ 93FinJum-86
❑ 93FinRef-86
❑ 93Fla-260
❑ 93Fle-294
❑ 93FleFruotL-29
❑ 93FunPac-50
❑ 93FunPac-212
❑ 93Hos-23
❑ 93HumDumC-14
❑ 93Lea-291
❑ 93MetBak-30
❑ 93OPC-130
❑ 93PacSpa-222
❑ 93PanSti-19
❑ 93Pin-29
❑ 93Pin-308
❑ 93PinCoo-7
❑ 93PinCooD-7
❑ 93PinHomRC 21
❑ 93RedFolS-43
❑ 93Sco-71
❑ 93Sel-106
❑ 93SelRoo-1T
❑ 93SP-40
❑ 93StaClu-558
❑ 93StaCluFDI-558
❑ 93StaCluMOP-558
❑ 93StaCluMP-19
❑ 93Stu-84
❑ 93Top-750
❑ 93TopGol-750
❑ 93TopInaM-750
❑ 93TopInaR-750
❑ 93TopMic-750
❑ 93TriPla-219
❑ 93Ult-258
❑ 93UppDec-136
❑ 93UppDecCP-R12
❑ 93UppDecDG-29
❑ 93UppDecGold-136
❑ 93UppDecSH-HI10
❑ 93UppDecTAN-TN3
❑ 93USPlaCA-8H
❑ 94A'sMot-6
❑ 94Bow-80
❑ 94BowBes-R4
❑ 94BowBesR-R4
❑ 94ColC-131
❑ 94ColC-510
❑ 94ColChoGS-131
❑ 94ColChoGS-510
❑ 94ColChoSS-131
❑ 94ColChoSS-510
❑ 94DenHol-15
❑ 94Don-19
❑ 94Don-290
❑ 94DonAnn8-4
❑ 94DonSpeE-19
❑ 94Fin-223
❑ 94FinJum-223
❑ 94FinRef-223
❑ 94Fla-331
❑ 94Fle-334
❑ 94FleExtB-150
❑ 94FleUpd-74
❑ 94FUnPac-124
❑ 94FUnPac-213
❑ 94Lea-259
❑ 94LeaL-60
❑ 94OPC-37
❑ 94OPCWorC-1
❑ 94Pac-643
❑ 94PanSti-139
❑ 94Pin-450
❑ 94PinArtP-450
❑ 94PinMusC-450
❑ 94PinRunC-RC10
❑ 94ProMag-100
❑ 94Sco-35
❑ 94ScoGolR-35
❑ 94ScoGolS-34
❑ 94ScoRoo-RT13
❑ 94ScoRooCP-CP6
❑ 94ScoRooGR-RT13
❑ 94Sel-254
❑ 94SP-34
❑ 94SPDieC-34
❑ 94SpoMov-MM8
❑ 94StaClu-107
❑ 94StaClu-654
❑ 94StaCluFDI-107
❑ 94StaCluFDI-654
❑ 94StaCluGR-107
❑ 94StaCluGR-654
❑ 94StaCluMO-38
❑ 94StaCluMOP-107
❑ 94StaCluMOP-654
❑ 94Stu-3
❑ 94SucSav-1
❑ 94Top-248
❑ 94TopGol-248
❑ 94TopSpa-248
❑ 94TopTra-65T
❑ 94TriPla-4
❑ 94Ult-408
❑ 94UppDec-60
❑ 94UppDecDC-W6
❑ 94UppDecED-60
❑ 94USPlaCA-9H
❑ 95AthMot-5
❑ 95Baz-62
❑ 95BluJayUSPC-3S
❑ 95BluJayUSPC-11H
❑ 95Bow-316
❑ 95ClaPhoC-42
❑ 95ColCho-53
❑ 95ColCho-125
❑ 95ColChoGS-53
❑ 95ColChoGS-125
❑ 95ColChoSE-48
❑ 95ColChoSEGS-48
❑ 95ColChoSESS-48
❑ 95ColChoSS-53
❑ 95ColChoSS-125
❑ 95Don-305
❑ 95DonPreP-305
❑ 95DonTopotO-137
❑ 95Emo-71
❑ 95Fin-47
❑ 95FinRef-47
❑ 95Fla-74
❑ 95Fle-246
❑ 95FleUpdDT-7
❑ 95Lea-22
❑ 95LeaLim-29
❑ 95Pac-312
❑ 95PacPri-102
❑ 95Pin-201
❑ 95PinArtP-201
❑ 95PinFan-15
❑ 95PinMusC-201
❑ 95Sco-441
❑ 95ScoGolR-441
❑ 95ScoHaloG-HG102
❑ 95ScoPlaTS-441
❑ 95Sel-134
❑ 95SelArtP-134
❑ 95SelCer-41
❑ 95SelCerMG-41
❑ 95SP-182
❑ 95SPCha-178
❑ 95SPChaDC-178
❑ 95Spo-4
❑ 95SpoArtP-4
❑ 95SPSil-182
❑ 95StaClu-415
❑ 95StaCluMOP-415
❑ 95StaCluMOP-RL35
❑ 95StaCluRL-RL35
❑ 95StaCluSTWS-415
❑ 95StaCluVR-213
❑ 95StaCluVRMO-213
❑ 95Stu-123
❑ 95Sum-54
❑ 95SumNthD-54
❑ 95Top-559
❑ 95TopCyb-335
❑ 95TopEmb-103
❑ 95TopEmbGI-103
❑ 95UC3-41
❑ 95UC3ArtP-41
❑ 95Ult-318
❑ 95UltGolM-318
❑ 95UppDec-30
❑ 95UppDecED-30
❑ 95UppDecEDG-30
❑ 95UppDecSE-245
❑ 95UppDecSEG-245
❑ 95Zen-87
❑ 96Baz-129
❑ 96Bow-38
❑ 96BowFoi-38
❑ 96Cir-187
❑ 96CirAcc-28
❑ 96CirBos-48
❑ 96CirRav-187
❑ 96ColCho-240
❑ 96ColCho-783
❑ 96ColChoGS-240
❑ 96ColChoSS-240
❑ 96Don-61
❑ 96DonPreP-61
❑ 96EmoXL-279
❑ 96Fin-S229
❑ 96FinRef-S229
❑ 96Fla-376
❑ 96Fle-209
❑ 96FleTif-209
❑ 96FleUpd-U197
❑ 96FleUpd-5
❑ 96FleUpdTC-U197
❑ 96LeaLim-78
❑ 96LeaLimG-78
❑ 96LeaPre-88
❑ 96LeaPreP-88
❑ 96LeaPreSG-57
❑ 96LeaPreSte-57
❑ 96LeaSig-142
❑ 96LeaSigPPG-142
❑ 96LeaSigPPP-142
❑ 96MetUni-237
❑ 96MetUniP-237
❑ 96Pac-396
❑ 96PacGolCD-DC9
❑ 96PacPri-P125
❑ 96PacPriG-P125
❑ 96PadMot-4
❑ 96PanSti-222
❑ 96Pin-338
❑ 96PinAfi-36
❑ 96PinAfiAP-36
❑ 96PinAfiFPP-36
❑ 96PinFoil-338
❑ 96RedF-16
❑ 96Sco-10
❑ 96ScoDugC-A10
❑ 96ScoDugCAP-A10
❑ 96Sel-108
❑ 96SelArtP-108
❑ 96SelCer-70
❑ 96SelCerAP-70
❑ 96SelCerCB-70
❑ 96SelCerCR-70
❑ 96SelCerMB-70
❑ 96SelCerMG-70
❑ 96SelCerMR-70
❑ 96SP-159
❑ 96Stu-149
❑ 96StuPrePB-149
❑ 96StuPrePG-149
❑ 96StuPrePS-149
❑ 96Sum-66
❑ 96SumAbo&B-66
❑ 96SumArtP-66
❑ 96SumFoi-66
❑ 96Top-397
❑ 96TopChr-159
❑ 96TopChrMotG-6
❑ 96TopChrMotGR-6
❑ 96TopChrR-159
❑ 96TopGal-79
❑ 96TopGalPPI-79
❑ 96TopLas-44
❑ 96TopMasotG-6
❑ 96Ult-114
❑ 96Ult-558
❑ 96UltCalttH-4
❑ 96UltCalttHGM-4
❑ 96UltGolM-114
❑ 96UltGolM-558
❑ 96UltOn-L-4
❑ 96UltOn-LGM-4
❑ 96UppDec-110
❑ 96UppDec-378
❑ 96UppDec-445
❑ 96Zen-42
❑ 96ZenArtP-42
❑ 96ZenMoz-20
❑ 97Cir-341
❑ 97CirRav-341
❑ 97ColCho-211
❑ 97Don-73
❑ 97DonEli-104
❑ 97DonEliGS-104
❑ 97DonGolPP-73
❑ 97DonLim-85
❑ 97DonLimE-85
❑ 97DonLimENG-85
❑ 97DonLimFotG-4
❑ 97DonSilPP-73
❑ 97E-X2-94
❑ 97E-X2Cred-94
❑ 97E-X2EssCre-94
❑ 97Fin-63
❑ 97FinRef-63
❑ 97Fle-464
❑ 97FleDecoE-5
❑ 97FleDecoERT-5
❑ 97FleMilDM-24
❑ 97FleMilDMR-24
❑ 97FleTif-464
❑ 97Lea-261
❑ 97LeaFraM-261
❑ 97LeaFraMDC-261
❑ 97MetUni-221
❑ 97Pac-426
❑ 97PacLigB-426
❑ 97PacPriGotD-GD208
❑ 97PacSil-426
❑ 97PadMot-5
❑ 97Pin-104
❑ 97PinArtP-PP104
❑ 97PinCer-76
❑ 97PinCerMBla-76
❑ 97PinCerMBlu-76
❑ 97PinCerMG-76
❑ 97PinCerMR-76
❑ 97PinCerR-76
❑ 97PinIns-51
❑ 97PinInsCE-51
❑ 97PinInsDE-51
❑ 97PinMusC-104
❑ 97PinPrePla-104
❑ 97PinTotCPB-76
❑ 97PinTotCPG-76
❑ 97PinTotCPR-76
❑ 97Sco-51
❑ 97ScoArtPWB-51
❑ 97ScoPreS-51
❑ 97ScoShoS-51
❑ 97ScoShoSAP-51
❑ 97Sel-50
❑ 97Sel-159
❑ 97SelArtP-50
❑ 97SelCom-50
❑ 97SelCom-159
❑ 97SelRegG-50
❑ 97SP-152
❑ 97StaClu-66
❑ 97StaCluMOP-66
❑ 97Stu-42
❑ 97StuPrePG-42
❑ 97StuPrePS-42
❑ 97Top-96
❑ 97TopChr-39
❑ 97TopChrR-39
❑ 97TopGal-11
❑ 97TopGalPPI-11
❑ 97TopSta-74
❑ 97TopStaAM-74
❑ 97Ult-285
❑ 97UltDouT-19
❑ 97UltGolME-285
❑ 97UltPlaME-285
❑ 97UppDec-494
❑ 98A'sMot-2
❑ 98AngSco-1
❑ 98AngScoP-1
❑ 98CirThu-87
❑ 98CirThuRav-87
❑ 98CirThuSupRav-87
❑ 98ColCho-30
❑ 98ColCho-455
❑ 98ColChoSQ-SQ60
❑ 98CroRoy-102
❑ 98Don-118
❑ 98Don-236
❑ 98DonCol-118
❑ 98DonColL-234
❑ 98DonColP-595
❑ 98DonColS-118
❑ 98DonGolPP-118
❑ 98DonGolPP-236
❑ 98DonPre-45
❑ 98DonPreSeat-45
❑ 98DonPriCD-118
❑ 98DonPriCL-234
❑ 98DonPriCP-595
❑ 98DonSig-18
❑ 98DonSigP-18
❑ 98DonSilPP-118
❑ 98DonSilPP-236
❑ 98Fle-430
❑ 98FleVin'-110
❑ 98FleVin'C-110
❑ 98Lea-34
❑ 98LeaFraDA-34
❑ 98LeaFraF-34
❑ 98LeaFraM-34
❑ 98LeaFraM-34
❑ 98LeaFraMDC-34
❑ 98LeaFraMDC-34
❑ 98LeaFraMZ2-34
❑ 98LeaRS-24
❑ 98LeaRSLHolo-24
❑ 98LeaRSLong-24
❑ 98LeaRTrue-24
❑ 98Pac-9
❑ 98PacAur-67
❑ 98PacInvTeam-1
❑ 98PacOme-177
❑ 98PacOmeR-177
❑ 98PacOnl-533
❑ 98PacOnlR-533
❑ 98PacOnlWC-533
❑ 98PacPar-80
❑ 98PacParC-80
❑ 98PacParG-80
❑ 98PacParHS-80
❑ 98PacParPB-80
❑ 98PacParR-80
❑ 98PacPlaB-9
❑ 98PacRedT-9
❑ 98PacSil-9
❑ 98PinInsSG-21AB
❑ 98PinInsSG-21CD
❑ 98PinInsSGS-21AB
❑ 98PinInsSGS-21CD
❑ 98PinPer-46
❑ 98PinPerPP-46
❑ 98Revo-107
❑ 98RevoSS-107
❑ 98Sco-18
❑ 98ScoRT-205
❑ 98SP Aut-147
❑ 98SP Aut-SD2
❑ 98SP AutSD-SD2
❑ 98SP AutSDT-SD2
❑ 98SpoIll-57
❑ 98SpoIllEE-57
❑ 98SpoIllFE-57
❑ 98SpoIllTaN-37
❑ 98SpoIllTaNEE-37
❑ 98SpoIllTaNRtC-RC5
❑ 98SpoIllWSF-14
❑ 98SpoIllWSFEE-14
❑ 98SpoIllWSFFE-14
❑ 98SPxFin-110
❑ 98SPxFin-344
❑ 98SPxFinR-110
❑ 98SPxFinR-344
❑ 98SPxFinS-110
❑ 98SPxFinS-344
❑ 98StaCluFDI-386
❑ 98StaCluI-386
❑ 98StaCluOneK-386
❑ 98StaCluPP-386
❑ 98Stu-187
❑ 98StuGPP-187
❑ 98StuSPP-187
❑ 98TopChrHB-HB8
❑ 98TopChrHBR-HB8
❑ 98TopHal-HB8
❑ 98Ult-431
❑ 98UltGolM-431
❑ 98UltMas-431
❑ 98UltPlaM-431
❑ 98UppDec-211
❑ 98UppDec-710
❑ 98UppDec10AP-54
❑ 98UppDec1APR-54
❑ 98UppDec5x7-211
❑ 98UppDecR-72
❑ 98UppDecR-2
❑ 98UppDecRTC-TC16
❑ 99199Fin-159
❑ 99Bow-223
❑ 99BowGol-223
❑ 99BowInt-223
❑ 99CroRoyB-91
❑ 99CroRoyL-91
❑ 99CroRoyOD-91
❑ 99E-X Cen-83
❑ 99E-X CenECFut-83
❑ 99E-X CenECNow-83
❑ 99FinGolRef-159
❑ 99FinRef-159
❑ 99Fle-133
❑ 99FleMys-52
❑ 99FleMysG-52
❑ 99FleMysM-52
❑ 99FleSta9-133
❑ 99FleWarT-133
❑ 99MetUni-122
❑ 99MetUniGM-122
❑ 99MetUniPMG-122
❑ 99Pac-312
❑ 99PacAur-119
❑ 99PacAurOD-119
❑ 99PacCroC-204
❑ 99PacCroCPB-204
❑ 99PacInv-95
❑ 99PacInvOD-95
❑ 99PacInvPB-95
❑ 99PacOme-153
❑ 99PacOmeC-153
❑ 99PacOmeG-153
❑ 99PacOmePB-153
❑ 99PacPar-150
❑ 99PacParC-150
❑ 99PacParG-150
❑ 99PacParHoloGold-150
❑ 99PacParHS-150
❑ 99PacParOD-150
❑ 99PacParPB-150
❑ 99PacParRed-150
❑ 99PacPlaB-312
❑ 99PacPri-106
❑ 99PacPriHB-106
❑ 99PacPriHG-106
❑ 99PacPriHM-106
❑ 99PacPriHP-106
❑ 99PacPriRed-106
❑ 99PacRed-312
❑ 99Rev-89
❑ 99RevPremDate-89
❑ 99RevRet-89
❑ 99RevShaSS-89
❑ 99SkyMolM-93
❑ 99SkyMolMX-93
❑ 99SkyPre-182

❑ 99SkyPreR-182
❑ 99SkyThu-143
❑ 99SkyThuRant-143
❑ 99SkyThuRave-143
❑ 99SP SigAutoG-RHE
❑ 99SpoIll-13
❑ 99SPSig-41
❑ 99StaClu-79
❑ 99StaCluFDI-79
❑ 99StaCluOoaK-79
❑ 99StaCluPP-79
❑ 99ThuSkySupR-143
❑ 99Top-277
❑ 99TopChr-277
❑ 99TopChrR-277
❑ 99TopMVPP-277
❑ 99TopSta-146
❑ 99TopStaFoil-146
❑ 99UD ChoMBH-B20
❑ 99UD Ion-45
❑ 99UD IonR-45
❑ 99Ult-170
❑ 99Ult-223
❑ 99UltGolM-170
❑ 99UltGolM-223
❑ 99UltMas-170
❑ 99UltMas-223
❑ 99UltPlaM-170
❑ 99UltPlaM-223
❑ 99UppDec-165
❑ 99UppDec-426
❑ 99UppDec10AT-X19
❑ 99UppDec10ATD-X19
❑ 99UppDec10ATHR-X19
❑ 99UppDec10ATT-X19
❑ 99UppDecCL-100
❑ 99UppDecCLCC-100
❑ 99UppDecCLEM-EM8
❑ 99UppDecCLM-C59
❑ 99UppDecE-58
❑ 99UppDecEFXG-58
❑ 99UppDecEL1-165
❑ 99UppDecEL1-426
❑ 99UppDecEL2-165
❑ 99UppDecEL2-426
❑ 99UppDecM-131
❑ 99UppDecMGS-131
❑ 99UppDecMHFS-131
❑ 99UppDecMSS-131
❑ 99Vic-253
❑ 99Vic-462

Henderson, Robbie
❑ 78CedRapGT-9
❑ 79CedRapGT-6

Henderson, Rod (Rodney)
❑ 92ClaDraP-76
❑ 92JamExpC-1
❑ 92JamExpF-1497
❑ 93ClaFS7-278
❑ 93FloStaLAF-49
❑ 93OPCPreTDP-3
❑ 93StaCluM-178
❑ 93WesPalBEC-9
❑ 93WesPalBEF-1333
❑ 94Bow-584
❑ 94BowBes-B37
❑ 94BowBesR-B37
❑ 94Cla-39
❑ 94ClaGolF-189
❑ 94ExcFS7-226
❑ 94Fla-191
❑ 94HarSenF-2085
❑ 94SigRoo-6
❑ 94SigRooS-6
❑ 94Ult-523
❑ 94UppDecML-81
❑ 94UppDecML-92
❑ 94UppDecML-267
❑ 94UppDecMLPotYF-PY10
❑ 95Bow-269
❑ 95BowGolF-269
❑ 95ColCho-12
❑ 95ColChoGS-12
❑ 95ColChoSEGS-10
❑ 95ColChoSESS-10
❑ 95ColChoSS-12
❑ 95Pin-418
❑ 95PinArtP-418
❑ 95PinMusC-418
❑ 98LouRedQ-27

Henderson, Ryan
❑ 92GreFalDSP-17
❑ 93VerBeaDC-8
❑ 93VerBeaDF-2212
❑ 94ExcFS7-214
❑ 95VerBeaDTI-11
❑ 96SanAntMB-6
❑ 97AlbDukGS-13
❑ 98BinMetQ-15

Henderson, Scott
❑ 98KanCouC-14
❑ 98KanCouCCP-14

Henderson, Steve
❑ 77IndIndTI-14
❑ 78Hos-126
❑ 78MetDaiPA-10
❑ 78OPC-53
❑ 78Top-134
❑ 79OPC-232
❑ 79Top-445
❑ 80OPC-156
❑ 80Top-299
❑ 81AllGamPI-146
❑ 81CokTeaS-17
❑ 81Don-157
❑ 81Fle-321
❑ 81Kel-25
❑ 81OPC-44
❑ 81Top-619
❑ 81TopScr-79
❑ 81TopSti-193
❑ 81TopTra-769
❑ 82CubRedL-28
❑ 82Don-183
❑ 82FBIDis-12
❑ 82Fle-597
❑ 82FleSta-98
❑ 82OPC-89
❑ 82Top-89
❑ 82TopSti-30
❑ 83Don-252
❑ 83Fle-496
❑ 83Top-335
❑ 83TopTra-42T
❑ 84Don-389
❑ 84Fle-612
❑ 84MarMot-21
❑ 84Nes792-501
❑ 84OPC-274
❑ 84Top-501
❑ 84TopRubD-25
❑ 84TopSti-341
❑ 84TopTif-501
❑ 85A'sMot-26
❑ 85Don-145
❑ 85Fle-490
❑ 85FleUpd-52
❑ 85OPC-38
❑ 85Top-640
❑ 85TopRubD-25
❑ 85TopTif-640
❑ 85TopTifT-50T
❑ 85TopTra-50T
❑ 86A'sMot-20
❑ 86Don-375
❑ 86Fle-419
❑ 86Top-748
❑ 86TopTif-748
❑ 87TacTigP-13
❑ 88AstMot-12
❑ 88AstPol-13
❑ 88Sco-547
❑ 88ScoGlo-547
❑ 88Top-527
❑ 88TopTif-527
❑ 89BufBisC-14
❑ 89BufBisP-1676
❑ 89PacSenL-5
❑ 89T/MSenL-45
❑ 89TopSenL-9
❑ 89TriAAAP-AAA22
❑ 90BufBisP-391
❑ 90BufBisTI-8
❑ 90EliSenL-17
❑ 90ProAAAF-506
❑ 90TriAAAC-9
❑ 91MetWIZ-171
❑ 91PacSenL-144
❑ 94AstMot-27
❑ 95AstMot-28
❑ 96AstMot-28

Henderson, Tim
❑ 89MisStaB-18
❑ 90MisStaB-19

Henderson, Todd
❑ 92HamRedC-27
❑ 92HamRedF-1606

Henderson, Valentine
❑ 89WelPirP-13

Henderson, Wendell
❑ 82QuaCitCT-15

Henderson, William
❑ 31Zee-106
❑ 32Zee-101

Hendley, Brett
❑ 90ModA'sC-13
❑ 91MadMusC-15
❑ 91MadMusP-2134
❑ 91MidLeaAP-MWL41
❑ 92ModA'sC-16
❑ 92ModA'sF-3906

Hendley, C. Bob
❑ 61Top-372
❑ 62Top-361
❑ 63BraJayP-5
❑ 63Top-62
❑ 64Top-189
❑ 64TopCoi-94
❑ 64TopVen-189
❑ 65Top-444
❑ 66OPC-82
❑ 66Top-82
❑ 66TopVen-82
❑ 67CokCapC-4
❑ 67Top-256
❑ 68Top-345
❑ 68TopVen-345
❑ 69OPC-144
❑ 69Top-144

Hendrick, George
❑ 71A'sPos-10
❑ 72OPC-406
❑ 72Top-406
❑ 73IndTeal-13
❑ 73LinPor-63
❑ 73OPC-13
❑ 73OPC-201
❑ 73Top-13
❑ 73Top-201
❑ 74OPC-303
❑ 74Top-303
❑ 74TopSta-167
❑ 75CleIndP-13
❑ 75Hos-140
❑ 75Kel-46
❑ 75OPC-109
❑ 75Top-109
❑ 75TopMin-109
❑ 76OPC-570
❑ 76SSP-527
❑ 76Top-570
❑ 77BurCheD-129
❑ 77Hos-123
❑ 77OPC-218
❑ 77PadSchC-26A
❑ 77PadSchC-26B
❑ 77PepGloD-40
❑ 77Top-330
❑ 78CarTeal-10
❑ 78Hos-82
❑ 78OPC-178
❑ 78Top-30
❑ 79Car5-8
❑ 79Hos-66
❑ 79OPC-82
❑ 79Top-175
❑ 80OPC-184
❑ 80Top-350
❑ 81AllGamPI-147
❑ 81Car5x7-6
❑ 81CokTeaS-122
❑ 81Don-430
❑ 81Dra-22
❑ 81Fle-542
❑ 81Kel-35
❑ 81OPC-230
❑ 81Top-230
❑ 81TopScr-85
❑ 81TopSti-22
❑ 81TopSti-220
❑ 81TopSti-256
❑ 82Don-9
❑ 82Don-40
❑ 82Dra-17
❑ 82Fle-113
❑ 82FleSta-25
❑ 82OPC-295
❑ 82Squ-16
❑ 82Top-420
❑ 82TopSti-91
❑ 83AllGamPI-147
❑ 83Car-7
❑ 83CarPanP-2
❑ 83Don-404
❑ 83Dra-10
❑ 83Fle-7
❑ 83FleSti-269
❑ 83Kel-25
❑ 83OPC-148
❑ 83PerCreC-6
❑ 83PerCreCG-6
❑ 83Top-650
❑ 83TopSti-153
❑ 83TopSti-285
❑ 84AllGamPI-53
❑ 84Car-9
❑ 84Car5x7-9
❑ 84Don-475
❑ 84DonActAS-32
❑ 84Dra-12
❑ 84Fle-324
❑ 84FleSti-9
❑ 84FunFooP-52
❑ 84Nes792-386
❑ 84Nes792-540
❑ 84OPC-163
❑ 84OPC-386
❑ 84Top-386
❑ 84Top-540
❑ 84TopGloS-23
❑ 84TopRubD-2
❑ 84TopSti-139
❑ 84TopSti-185
❑ 84TopStiB-11
❑ 84TopTif-386
❑ 84TopTif-540
❑ 85AllGamPI-145
❑ 85Don-181
❑ 85Fle-225
❑ 85FleStaS-27
❑ 85FleUpd-53
❑ 85Lea-259
❑ 85OPC-60
❑ 85Pir-7
❑ 85Top-60
❑ 85TopRubD-2
❑ 85TopSti-134
❑ 85TopTif-60
❑ 85TopTifT-51T
❑ 85TopTra-51T
❑ 86AngSmo-14
❑ 86Fle-158
❑ 86OPC-190
❑ 86Top-190
❑ 86TopTif-190
❑ 87AngSmo-22
❑ 87CalAngPPS-16
❑ 87DonOpeD-3
❑ 87Fle-82
❑ 87FleGlo-82
❑ 87OPC-248
❑ 87Top-725
❑ 87TopTif-725
❑ 88AngSmo-24
❑ 88Don-479
❑ 88Sco-308
❑ 88ScoGlo-308
❑ 88StaLinAn-8
❑ 88Top-304
❑ 88TopTif-304
❑ 89PacSenL-61
❑ 89T/MSenL-46
❑ 89TopSenL-12
❑ 90EliSenL-82
❑ 92CarMcD-45

Hendrick, Harvey
❑ 28PorandAR-C2
❑ 29ExhFou-3
❑ 29PorandAR-37
❑ 34DiaMatCSB-89
❑ 34DiaStaR-41
❑ 35AlDemDCR3-112
❑ 90DodTar-331
❑ 92ConTSN-522

Hendrick, Pete
❑ 86ElPasDP-14

Hendricks, Ellie (Elrod)
❑ 67BalOriP-46
❑ 67BalOriP-47
❑ 67BalOriP-48
❑ 69MilBra-110
❑ 69Top-277
❑ 70BalOriP-13
❑ 70BalOriP-14
❑ 70DayDaiNM-160
❑ 70OPC-528
❑ 70Top-528
❑ 71BalOriP-14
❑ 71MLBOffS-299
❑ 71OPC-219
❑ 71OriCha-6
❑ 71Top-219
❑ 72MilBra-139
❑ 72OPC-508
❑ 72OriPos-16
❑ 72Top-508
❑ 73BalOriP-23
❑ 73OriJohP-10
❑ 73OriTeal-18
❑ 75BalOriP-15
❑ 75OPC-609
❑ 75Top-609
❑ 75TopMin-609
❑ 76BalOriP-18
❑ 76OPC-371
❑ 76SSP-384
❑ 76Top-371
❑ 78BalOriP-12
❑ 80BalOriP-9
❑ 81BalOriP-7
❑ 83OriPos-13
❑ 84BalOriP-16
❑ 85BalOriP-10
❑ 85BalOriP-11
❑ 86BalOriP-10
❑ 87BalOriP-17
❑ 87BalOriP-18
❑ 87OriFreB-44
❑ 88OriFreB-44
❑ 88OriPos-15
❑ 89BalOriP-11
❑ 89OriFreB-44
❑ 89SweBasG-64
❑ 91BalOriP-10
❑ 91OriCro-193
❑ 92BalOriP-12
❑ 92YanWIZ7-72
❑ 93BalOriP-13
❑ 94BalOriP-13
❑ 96BalOriP-14

Hendricks, Jason
❑ 98VerExpO-33

Hendricks, Kacy
❑ 92GulCoaDF-3561
❑ 93ButCopKSP-10

Hendricks, Ryan
❑ 94BluOriC-11
❑ 94BluOriF-3567
❑ 96HigDesMB-12
❑ 97FreKey-9

Hendricks, Steve
❑ 87SpoIndP-22
❑ 88RivRedWCLC-221
❑ 88RivRedWP-1409
❑ 89WatDiaP-1772
❑ 89WatDiaS-11
❑ 89WicStaR-7
❑ 90CalLeaACLC-7
❑ 90RivRedWB-12
❑ 90RivRedWCLC-11
❑ 90RivRedWP-2615
❑ 91LinDriAA-462
❑ 91NewBriRSLD-462
❑ 91NewBriRSP-357

Hendrickson, Craig
❑ 77QuaCitAT-17
❑ 78CedRapGT-10

Hendrickson, Dan
❑ 89EveGiaS-13

Hendriksen, Claude
❑ 16FleBreD-39
❑ 16FleBreD-40

Hendrix, Claude
❑ 14CraJacE-76
❑ 14PolGroW-9
❑ 15CraJacE-76
❑ 15SpoNewM-77
❑ 16BF2FP-67
❑ 16SpoNewM-78
❑ 17ColE13-72
❑ 19W514-9
❑ 20NatCarE-42
❑ 92ConTSN-343

Hendrix, James
❑ 87ChaWheP-2
❑ 88VirGenS-10

Hendry, Keith
❑ 79WatIndT-4B

Hendry, Ted
❑ 88T/MUmp-35
❑ 89T/MUmp-33
❑ 90T/MUmp-32

Hendryx, Timothy
❑ 23Zee-132
❑ 24Zee-92
❑ 25Zee-111
❑ 26Zee-139

Hendy, Jim
❑ 94ElmPioC-24
❑ 94ElmPioF-3489

Hengel, Dave
❑ 86CalCanP-11
❑ 87CalCanP-2317
❑ 88CalCanC-18
❑ 88CalCanP-1550
❑ 88Don-629
❑ 88Fle-375
❑ 88FleGlo-375
❑ 89ChaLooLITI-12
❑ 89ColSprSSC-18
❑ 89ColSprSSP-243
❑ 89Top-531
❑ 89TopTif-531
❑ 92PhoFirS-382

Hengle, Emory
❑ 87OldJudN-238

Henika, Ron
❑ 84CedRapRT-27
❑ 86VerRedP-11
❑ 87NasSouTI-10
❑ 89CedRapRAB-17
❑ 90CedRapRDGB-17

Henion, Scott
❑ 87ColMetP-17
❑ 88SalBucS-8
❑ 89WesPalBES-12

Henke, Henry
❑ 22Zee-128

Henke, Rick
❑ 83WatIndF-26
❑ 86WatIndP-13
❑ 87WilBilP-15

Henke, Tom
❑ 82TulDriT-1
❑ 83OklCit8T-9
❑ 84Don-134
❑ 84OklCit8T-10
❑ 85BluJayFS-14
❑ 85Don-403
❑ 85IntLeaAT-41
❑ 85SyrChiT-8
❑ 86BluJayAF-13
❑ 86BluJayFS-17
❑ 86Don-437
❑ 86Fle-60
❑ 86FleStiC-54
❑ 86Lea-206
❑ 86OPC-333
❑ 86Top-333
❑ 86TopSti-189
❑ 86TopTif-333
❑ 87BluJayFS-12
❑ 87Don-197
❑ 87Fle-228
❑ 87FleExcS-25
❑ 87FleGlo-228
❑ 87FleSlu-19
❑ 87FleStiC-57
❑ 87GenMilB-1E
❑ 87Lea-73
❑ 87OPC-277
❑ 87SmoAmeL-14
❑ 87SpoTeaP-5
❑ 87SyrChi1A-6
❑ 87Top-510
❑ 87TopMinL-76
❑ 87TopSti-185
❑ 87TopTif-510
❑ 88BluJay5-6
❑ 88BluJayFS-15
❑ 88Don-490
❑ 88DonAll-28
❑ 88DonBasB-104
❑ 88Fle-112
❑ 88FleAll-2
❑ 88FleAwaW-18
❑ 88FleExcS-19
❑ 88FleGlo-112
❑ 88FleLeaL-17
❑ 88FleMin-62
❑ 88FleStiC-73
❑ 88FleTeaL-12
❑ 88MSAHosD-23
❑ 88OPC-220
❑ 88PanSti-213
❑ 88RedFolSB-33
❑ 88Sco-57
❑ 88ScoGlo-57
❑ 88Spo-65
❑ 88StaLinBJ-8
❑ 88Top-220
❑ 88Top-396
❑ 88TopBig-41

❑ 88TopClo-46
❑ 88TopGloS-35
❑ 88TopMinL-38
❑ 88TopRevLL-31
❑ 88TopSti-186
❑ 88TopStiB-64
❑ 88TopTif-220
❑ 88TopTif-396
❑ 88TopUKM-32
❑ 88TopUKMT-32
❑ 89BluJayFS-13
❑ 89Bow-246
❑ 89BowTif-246
❑ 89Don-385
❑ 89DonBasB-301
❑ 89Fle-235
❑ 89FleExcS-22
❑ 89FleGlo-235
❑ 89OPC-75
❑ 89PanSti-461
❑ 89Sco-318
❑ 89ScoHot1S-63
❑ 89Spo-126
❑ 89Top-75
❑ 89TopBasT-118
❑ 89TopSti-195
❑ 89TopTif-75
❑ 89UppDec-264
❑ 90BluJayFS-11
❑ 90BluJayHS-3
❑ 90BluJayHS-4
❑ 90Bow-506
❑ 90BowTif-506
❑ 90Don-349
❑ 90DonBesA-14
❑ 90Fle-84
❑ 90FleCan-84
❑ 90Lea-158
❑ 90MSAHolD-3
❑ 90OPC-695
❑ 90PubIntS-516
❑ 90Sco-157
❑ 90Spo-42
❑ 90Top-695
❑ 90TopBig-101
❑ 90TopSti-196
❑ 90TopTif-695
❑ 90TulDriDGB-19
❑ 90TulDriTI-28
❑ 90UppDec-282
❑ 91BluJayFS-13
❑ 91BluJayFS-14
❑ 91BluJayS-2
❑ 91Bow-16
❑ 91Don-205
❑ 91Fle-176
❑ 91Lea-517
❑ 91OPC-110
❑ 91OPCPre-63
❑ 91PanFreS-345
❑ 91Sco-579
❑ 91StaClu-24
❑ 91Top-110
❑ 91TopDesS-110
❑ 91TopMic-110
❑ 91TopTif-110
❑ 91Ult-362
❑ 91UppDec-149
❑ 92Don-141
❑ 92DonMcD-G5
❑ 92Fle-331
❑ 92Lea-159
❑ 92LeaBlaG-159
❑ 92OPC-451
❑ 92PepDieM-3
❑ 92Pin-417
❑ 92Sco-385
❑ 92Sco-439
❑ 92Sco100S-31
❑ 92StaClu-819
❑ 92StaCluECN-819
❑ 92SyrChiTT-4
❑ 92Top-451
❑ 92TopCol 451
❑ 92TopGolW-451
❑ 92TopKid-93
❑ 92TopMic-451
❑ 92Ult-450
❑ 92UppDec-395
❑ 93BluJayD4-18
❑ 93BluJayDM-7
❑ 93Bow-461
❑ 93Don-723
❑ 93Fin-164
❑ 93FinRef-164
❑ 93Fla-281
❑ 93Fle-335
❑ 93FleFinE-279
❑ 93KinDis-15
❑ 93Lea-278
❑ 93MSABenSPD-16
❑ 93OPC-202
❑ 93OPCPre-77
❑ 93OPCWorC-7
❑ 93PacSpa-640
❑ 93Pin-546
❑ 93RanKee-409
❑ 93RanStaC-17
❑ 93Sco-602
❑ 93Sel-211
❑ 93SelRoo-15T
❑ 93SP-195
❑ 93StaClu-637
❑ 93StaCluFDI-637
❑ 93StaCluMOP-637
❑ 93Top-376
❑ 93TopGol-376
❑ 93TopInaM-376
❑ 93TopInaR-376
❑ 93TopMic-376
❑ 93TopTra-14T
❑ 93Ult-629
❑ 93UppDec-557
❑ 93UppDecGold-557
❑ 94Bow-269
❑ 94ColC-628
❑ 94ColChoGS-628
❑ 94ColChoSS-628
❑ 94Don-162
❑ 94Fin-64
❑ 94FinRef-64
❑ 94Fla-111
❑ 94Fle-308
❑ 94FleExtB-180
❑ 94Lea-434
❑ 94OPC-242
❑ 94Pac-618
❑ 94PanSti-128
❑ 94Pin-42
❑ 94PinArtP-42
❑ 94PinMusC-42
❑ 94RanMagM-7
❑ 94Sco-542
❑ 94ScoGolR-542
❑ 94Sel-237
❑ 94Spo-104
❑ 94StaClu-19
❑ 94StaCluFDI-19
❑ 94StaCluGR-19
❑ 94StaCluMO-2
❑ 94StaCluMOP-19
❑ 94StaCluT-270
❑ 94StaCluTFDI-270
❑ 94Top-644
❑ 94TopGol-644
❑ 94TopSpa-644
❑ 94TriPla-195
❑ 94Ult-128
❑ 94UltFir-3
❑ 94UppDec-367
❑ 94UppDecED-367
❑ 95BluJayUSPC-4S
❑ 95BluJayUSPC-12H
❑ 95ColCho-196
❑ 95ColChoGS-196
❑ 95ColChoSS-196
❑ 95Don-473
❑ 95DonPreP-473
❑ 95DonTopotO-327
❑ 95Fin-238
❑ 95FinRef-238
❑ 95Fla-407
❑ 95Fle-287
❑ 95FleUpd-159
❑ 95Lea-351
❑ 95Pin-363
❑ 95PinArtP-363
❑ 95PinMusC-363
❑ 95Sco-150
❑ 95ScoGolR-150
❑ 95ScoPlaTS-150
❑ 95SP-101
❑ 95SPSil-101
❑ 95StaClu-261
❑ 95StaClu-545
❑ 95StaCluFDI-261
❑ 95StaCluMOP-261
❑ 95StaCluMOP-545
❑ 95StaCluSTWS-261
❑ 95StaCluSTWS-545
❑ 95StaCluVR-129
❑ 95StaCluVRMO-129
❑ 95TopTra-98T
❑ 95Ult-429
❑ 95UltGolM-429
❑ 95UppDec-455
❑ 96ColCho-285
❑ 96ColChoGS-285
❑ 96ColChoSS-285
❑ 96Don-320
❑ 96DonPreP-320
❑ 96Fle-544
❑ 96FleTif-544
❑ 96Pac-227
❑ 96PacPri-P70
❑ 96PacPriG-P70
❑ 96Sco-160
❑ 96StaClu-13
❑ 96StaClu-263
❑ 96StaCluEPB-13
❑ 96StaCluEPG-13
❑ 96StaCluEPS-13
❑ 96StaCluMOP-13
❑ 96StaCluMOP-263
❑ 96Top-90
❑ 96Ult-274
❑ 96UltGolM-274
❑ 96UppDec-185
❑ 97BluJayS-38

Henkel, Rob
❑ 91ElmPioC-20
❑ 91ElmPioP-3267
❑ 92ProFS7-26
❑ 92WinHavRSF-1770
❑ 93CarLeaAGF-8
❑ 93ClaFS7-9
❑ 93LynRedSC-12
❑ 93LynRedSF-2513
❑ 94SarRedSC-13
❑ 94UppDecML-176

Henkemeyer, Dick
❑ 82WisRapTF-17

Henkle, C. W.
❑ 19Zee-70

Henley, Bobby
❑ 93JamExpC-11
❑ 93JamExpF-3330
❑ 94BurBeeC-9
❑ 94BurBeeF-1083
❑ 94MidLeaAF-MDW32
❑ 95AusFut-74
❑ 96HarSenB-15
❑ 97HarSen-14
❑ 97Sel-121
❑ 97SelArtP-121
❑ 97SelCom-121
❑ 97SelCom-P121
❑ 97SelRegG-121
❑ 97TexAllM-39
❑ 98FleUpd-U17
❑ 99Fle-423
❑ 99FleSta9-423
❑ 99FleWarT-423
❑ 99PacPriS-96
❑ 99PacPriS206-96
❑ 99PacPriS206R-96
❑ 99SP SigAuto-BH
❑ 99SP SigAutoG-BH
❑ 99SPSig-82

Henley, Clarence
❑ 09ObaT21-52
❑ 09ObaT21-159
❑ 09ObaT21-323
❑ 11PacCoaBD-25
❑ 11Zee-87
❑ 12HomRunKE-64
❑ 12ObaPreT-72
❑ 12Zee-113
❑ 13Zee-108
❑ 14Zee-133
❑ 15Zee-126

Henley, Dan
❑ 85AncGlaPTI-15
❑ 88BakDodCLC-235
❑ 89SanAntMB-12
❑ 90AlbDukCm-18
❑ 90AlbDukP-351
❑ 90AlbDukTr-10
❑ 90CMC-420
❑ 90ProAAAF-72
❑ 91LinDriAAA-636
❑ 91VanCanLD-636
❑ 91VanCanP-1602

Henley, Gail
❑ 57JetPos-8

Henley, Mike
❑ 83AppFoxFr-11

Henley, Weldon
❑ 03BreE10-70
❑ 09ColChiE-128
❑ 11SpoLifCW-162
❑ 12ColRedB-128
❑ 12ColTinT-128
❑ 90DodTar-332

Henline, Butch (Walter)
❑ 20NatCarE-43
❑ 21Nei-59
❑ 22E120-198
❑ 22W572-42
❑ 23WilChoV-62
❑ 25Exh-43
❑ 26Exh-44
❑ 27AmeCarE126-31
❑ 27Exh-8
❑ 33MrsShePP-5
❑ 87ConSer2-18
❑ 90DodTar-333
❑ 92ConTSN-581

Henline, Noah
❑ 12ImpTobC-64

Henneman, Blair
❑ 92EveGiaF-1679

Henneman, Mike
❑ 86NasSouTI-12
❑ 87DonRoo-32
❑ 87FleUpd-44
❑ 87FleUpdG-44
❑ 87IntLeaAT-15
❑ 87SpoRoo2-29
❑ 87TolMudHP-16
❑ 87TolMudHT-13
❑ 87TopTra-46T
❑ 87TopTraT-46T
❑ 88ClaBlu-241
❑ 88Don-420
❑ 88DonBasB-91
❑ 88Fle-57
❑ 88FleGlo-57
❑ 88FleStiC-25
❑ 88OPC-3
❑ 88Sco-520
❑ 88ScoGlo-520
❑ 88ScoYouSI-15
❑ 88Spo-129
❑ 88StaLinTi-7
❑ 88TigPep-39
❑ 88Top-582
❑ 88TopBig-256
❑ 88TopGloS-10
❑ 88TopRoo-7
❑ 88TopTif-582
❑ 88ToyRoo-13
❑ 89BirBarADB-18
❑ 89Bow-98
❑ 89BowTif-98
❑ 89ClaLigB-94
❑ 89Don-327
❑ 89DonBasB-237
❑ 89Fle-134
❑ 89FleExcS-23
❑ 89FleGlo-134
❑ 89OPC-365
❑ 89PanSti-333
❑ 89Sco-293
❑ 89ScoHot1S-59
❑ 89Spo-56
❑ 89TigMar-39
❑ 89TigPol-39
❑ 89Top-365
❑ 89TopBig-252
❑ 89TopSti-273
❑ 89TopTif-365
❑ 89UppDec-373
❑ 90BirBarADB-18
❑ 90Bow-345
❑ 90BowTif-345
❑ 90Don-296
❑ 90DonBesA-105
❑ 90Fle-604
❑ 90FleCan-604
❑ 90Lea-2
❑ 90OPC-177
❑ 90PanSti-69
❑ 90PubIntS-472
❑ 90Sco-184
❑ 90Spo-144
❑ 90TigCok-8
❑ 90TigMilH-1
❑ 90TigMilH-2
❑ 90TigMilH-3
❑ 90TigMilH-4
❑ 90TigMilH-6
❑ 90Top-177
❑ 90TopBig-41
❑ 90TopSti-282
❑ 90TopTif-177
❑ 90UppDec-537
❑ 91Don-76
❑ 91Fle-340
❑ 91Lea-18
❑ 91OPC-641
❑ 91PanSti-236
❑ 91RedFolS-49
❑ 91Sco-142
❑ 91Sco100S-51
❑ 91StaClu-287
❑ 91TigCok-39
❑ 91Top-641
❑ 91TopDesS-641
❑ 91TopMic-641
❑ 91TopTif-641
❑ 91Ult-123
❑ 91UppDec-386
❑ 92Bow-441
❑ 92Don-253
❑ 92Fle-138
❑ 92Lea-325
❑ 92LeaBlaG-325
❑ 92OPC-293
❑ 92Pin-164
❑ 92Sco-217
❑ 92StaClu-34
❑ 92Stu-175
❑ 92TigKro-12
❑ 92TigTeal-15
❑ 92Top-293
❑ 92TopGol-293
❑ 92TopGolW-293
❑ 92TopMic-293
❑ 92Ult-364
❑ 92UppDec-339
❑ 93Bow-559
❑ 93Don-259
❑ 93Fla-204
❑ 93Fle-229
❑ 93Lea-81
❑ 93OPC-149
❑ 93Pin-385
❑ 93Sco-166
❑ 93Sel-138
❑ 93SP-238
❑ 93StaClu-480
❑ 93StaCluFDI-480
❑ 93StaCluMOP-480
❑ 93TigGat-14
❑ 93Top-756
❑ 93TopGol-756
❑ 93TopInaM-756
❑ 93TopInaR-756
❑ 93TopMic-756
❑ 93Ult-199
❑ 93UppDec-403
❑ 93UppDecGold-403
❑ 94Bow-181
❑ 94ColC-132
❑ 94ColChoGS-132
❑ 94ColChoSS-132
❑ 94Don-496
❑ 94Fin-34
❑ 94FinRef-34
❑ 94Fle-135
❑ 94FleExtB-77
❑ 94Lea-183
❑ 94OPC-52
❑ 94Pin-154
❑ 94PinArtP-154
❑ 94PinMusC-154
❑ 94RedFolMI-10
❑ 94Sco-117
❑ 94ScoGolR-117
❑ 94Sel-368
❑ 94SP-178
❑ 94SPDieC-178
❑ 94StaClu-401
❑ 94StaCluFDI-401
❑ 94StaCluGR-401
❑ 94StaCluMOP-401
❑ 94Top-430
❑ 94TopGol-438
❑ 94TopSpa-438
❑ 94TriPla-246
❑ 94Ult-55
❑ 94UppDec-321
❑ 94UppDecED-321
❑ 95ColCho-468
❑ 95ColChoGS-468
❑ 95ColChoSS-468
❑ 95DonTopotO-78
❑ 95Fin-153
❑ 95FinRef-153
❑ 95Fla-257
❑ 95Fle-56
❑ 95Sco-148
❑ 95ScoGolR-148
❑ 95ScoPlaTS-148
❑ 95StaClu-329
❑ 95StaCluMOP-329
❑ 95StaCluSTWS-329
❑ 95StaCluVR-170
❑ 95StaCluVRMO-170
❑ 95Top-307
❑ 95TopCyb-165
❑ 96ColCho-162
❑ 96ColChoGS-162
❑ 96ColChoSS-162
❑ 96Don-532
❑ 96DonPreP-532
❑ 96Fla-173
❑ 96LeaSigEA-74
❑ 96RanDr P-16
❑ 96RanMot-16
❑ 96StaClu-390
❑ 96StaCluMOP-390
❑ 96Top-390
❑ 96Ult-421
❑ 96UltGolM-421
❑ 97Fle-225
❑ 97FleTif-225
❑ 97Pac-203
❑ 97PacLigB-203
❑ 97PacSil-203
❑ 97Top-76
❑ 97Ult-135
❑ 97UltGolME-135
❑ 97UltPlaME-135

Hennessey, Scott
❑ 91BasCitRC-25
❑ 91BasCitRP-1411

Hennessey, Sean
❑ 93HunCubC-10
❑ 93HunCubF-3231

Hennessy, Brendan
❑ 83BurRanF-18
❑ 83BurRanT-20
❑ 83TriTriT-24

Hennessy, Mike
❑ 82CedRapRT-9
❑ 86SumBraP-9

Hennigan, Phil
❑ 71MLBOffS-373
❑ 71OPC-211
❑ 71Top-211
❑ 72Top-748
❑ 73OPC-107
❑ 73Top-107
❑ 91MetWIZ-173

Henning, Rich
❑ 85FreGiaSB-24
❑ 90BriTigP-3176
❑ 90BriTigS-28

Henninger, Rai
❑ 88IdaFalBP-1852

Henninger, Rich
❑ 74OPC-602
❑ 74SpoIndC-30
❑ 74Top-602
❑ 75OklCit8TI-4
❑ 93RanKee-181

Hennis, Randy (Randall)
❑ 87AubAstP-10
❑ 88FloStaLAS-8
❑ 88OscAstS-13
❑ 89ColMudB-9
❑ 89ColMudP-137
❑ 89ColMudS-12
❑ 90CMC-608
❑ 90TucTorC-6
❑ 90TucTorP-200
❑ 91Cla1-T45
❑ 91LinDriAAA-611
❑ 91Sco-752
❑ 91TopDeb90-66
❑ 91TucTorLD-611
❑ 91TucTorP-2209
❑ 96BreCouMB-3
❑ 98ChaKniQ-4

Hennisaire, Randy
❑ 90ProAAAF-190

Henrich, Bobby
❑ 58RedEnq-16
❑ 58Top-131
❑ 59RedEnq-10
❑ 59SeaPop-21

Henrich, Tommy

(Tom)
❑ 38CloFotW-37
❑ 39GouPreR303A-23
❑ 39PlaBal-52
❑ 39WorWidGTP-23
❑ 39WorWidGV-15
❑ 40PlaBal-4
❑ 41DouPlaR-111
❑ 41PlaBal-39
❑ 43MPR302-1-14
❑ 46SpoExcW-5-7
❑ 47Exh-92
❑ 47PM1StaP1-82
❑ 47PM1StaP1-83
❑ 47TipTop-51
❑ 47YanTeaT-12
❑ 48BluTin-42
❑ 48Bow-19
❑ 48YanTeal-12
❑ 49Bow-69
❑ 49Lea-55
❑ 49MPR302-2-xx
❑ 49YanTeal-9
❑ 50Bow-10
❑ 50Dra-23
❑ 50RoyDes-12
❑ 50YanTeal-10
❑ 51BerRos-B3
❑ 51Bow-291
❑ 51R42SmaS-47
❑ 53ExhCan-27
❑ 59TigGraASP-8
❑ 69EquSpoHoF-BB7
❑ 74NewYorNTDiS-23
❑ 74TCMNic-27
❑ 75YanDyn1T-22
❑ 76SSPYanOD-3
❑ 79TCM50-35
❑ 82OhiHaloF-38
❑ 83YanASFY-18
❑ 84TCMPla1-9
❑ 92ConTSNGI-770
❑ 92UppDecS-16
❑ 92YanWIZA-30
❑ 93ConTSN-770
❑ 94ConTSN-1061
❑ 94ConTSNB-1061
Henrichs, Shawn
❑ 91EveGiaC-16
❑ 91EveGiaP-3907
Henrickson, John
❑ 94LetMouF-3875
❑ 94LetMouSP-13
Henriksen, Olaf
❑ 12T207-78
❑ 15SpoNewM-78
❑ 16SpoNewM-79
❑ 17ColE13-73
Henrikson, Dan
❑ 90BenBucL-12
❑ 91CliGiaC-3
❑ 91CliGiaP-828
❑ 94CliLumC-12
❑ 94CliLumF-1975
Henriquez, Oscar
❑ 93AshTouC-8
❑ 93AshTouF-2270
❑ 93LinVenB-259
❑ 94Bow-418
❑ 96-97LinVen-21
❑ 96Bow-385
❑ 96BowFoi-385
❑ 96KisCobB-11
❑ 98Fle-297
❑ 98PacOnl-295
❑ 98PacOnlR-295
❑ 98PacOnlWC-295
❑ 98Ult-446
❑ 98UltGolM-446
❑ 98UltMas-446
❑ 98UltPlaM-446
Henriquez, Ralph
❑ 98DanBraQ-29
Henry Allen, Colt (Newton)
❑ 87NegLeaPD-41
Henry, Antoine
❑ 92JohCitCC-12
❑ 92JohCitCF-3130
❑ 93GleFalRC-15
❑ 93GleFalRF-4019
❑ 94SavCarC-14
❑ 94SavCarF-520
Henry, Bill F.
❑ 68Top-384
Henry, Bill R.
❑ 55Bow-264
❑ 59Top-46
❑ 59TopVen-46
❑ 60Kah-14
❑ 60Top-524
❑ 61Top-66
❑ 62Kah-18
❑ 62RedEnq-12
❑ 62Top-562
❑ 63RedEnq-12
❑ 63RedFreBC-8
❑ 63Top-378
❑ 64Top-49
❑ 64TopVen-49
❑ 65RedEnq-12
❑ 65Top-456
❑ 66OPC-115
❑ 66Top-115
❑ 66TopVen-115
❑ 67Top-579
❑ 68Top-239
❑ 68TopVen-239
❑ 80Red196T-34
❑ 82Bow195E-259
❑ 92YanWIZ6-55
Henry, Butch
❑ 88CedRapRP-1159
❑ 88MidLeaAGS-12
❑ 89CedRapRAB-23
❑ 89ChaLooB-9
❑ 89ChaLooGS-11
❑ 90CedRapRDGB-23
❑ 90ChaLooGS-16
❑ 91LinDriAAA-612
❑ 91TucTorLD-612
❑ 91TucTorP-2210
❑ 92AstMot-18
❑ 92Bow-502
❑ 92DonRoo-51
❑ 92FleUpd-86
❑ 92Lea-435
❑ 92LeaBlaG-435
❑ 92Pin-567
❑ 92StaClu-742
❑ 92StaCluECN-742
❑ 92Stu-37
❑ 92TopTra-49T
❑ 92TopTraG-49T
❑ 92UppDec-796
❑ 92UppDecSR-SR9
❑ 93Don-348
❑ 93Don-767
❑ 93Fle-411
❑ 93OPC-200
❑ 93OPCPre-30
❑ 93PacSpa-430
❑ 93Pin-511
❑ 93RocStaC-24
❑ 93RocUSPC-5S
❑ 93RocUSPC-11C
❑ 93Sco-569
❑ 93StaClu-311
❑ 93StaCluFDI-311
❑ 93StaCluMOP-311
❑ 93Top-281
❑ 93Top-719
❑ 93TopGol-281
❑ 93TopGol-719
❑ 93TopInaM-281
❑ 93TopInaM-719
❑ 93TopInaR-281
❑ 93TopInaR-719
❑ 93TopMic-281
❑ 93TopMic-719
❑ 93Ult-351
❑ 93UppDec-770
❑ 93UppDecGold-770
❑ 93USPlaCR-2S
❑ 94Fle-541
❑ 94TopTra-88T
❑ 95ColCho-247
❑ 95ColChoGS-247
❑ 95ColChoSS-247
❑ 95Don-455
❑ 95DonPreP-455
❑ 95Fle-352
❑ 95Sco-518
❑ 95ScoGolR-518
❑ 95ScoPlaTS-518
❑ 95StaClu-283
❑ 95StaCluMOP-283
❑ 95StaCluSTWS-283
❑ 95StaCluVR-146
❑ 95StaCluVRMO-146
❑ 95Top-498
❑ 95TopCyb-288
❑ 95Ult-191
❑ 95UltGolM-191
❑ 96ColCho-214
❑ 96ColChoGS-214
❑ 96ColChoSS-214
❑ 96Don-125
❑ 96DonPreP-125
❑ 98Pac-43
❑ 98PacOnl-116
❑ 98PacOnlR-116
❑ 98PacOnlWC-116
❑ 98PacPlaB-43
❑ 98PacRedT-43
❑ 98PacSil-43
Henry, Carlos
❑ 88AshTouP-1074
❑ 89AshTouP-965
Henry, Chris
❑ 80WauTimT-17
Henry, Dan
❑ 77CliDodT-10
❑ 77LodDodT-5
Henry, Doug
❑ 86BelBreP-10
❑ 87BelBreP-12
❑ 88StoPorCLC-177
❑ 88StoPorP-747
❑ 89ElPasDGS-8
❑ 90StoPorCLC-184
❑ 91DenZepLD-140
❑ 91DenZepP-120
❑ 91LinDriAAA-140
❑ 91TriA AAGP-AAA9
❑ 92BrePol-11
❑ 92ClaGam-78
❑ 92Don-663
❑ 92Lea-80
❑ 92LeaBlaG-80
❑ 92OPC-776
❑ 92ProFS7-82
❑ 92Sco-421
❑ 92ScoImpP-17
❑ 92StaClu-615
❑ 92Top-776
❑ 92TopDeb91-73
❑ 92TopGol-776
❑ 92TopGolW-776
❑ 92TopMic-776
❑ 92Ult-384
❑ 92UppDec-43
❑ 93BrePol-10
❑ 93Don-471
❑ 93Fle-251
❑ 93Lea-530
❑ 93OPC-181
❑ 93PacSpa-158
❑ 93Pin-415
❑ 93Sco-177
❑ 93Sel-399
❑ 93StaClu-521
❑ 93StaCluFDI-521
❑ 93StaCluMOP-521
❑ 93Top-343
❑ 93TopGol-343
❑ 93TopInaM-343
❑ 93TopInaR-343
❑ 93TopMic-343
❑ 93Ult-220
❑ 93UppDec-395
❑ 93UppDecGold-395
❑ 94BreMilB-225
❑ 94BrePol-11
❑ 94BreTeal-10
❑ 94ColC-413
❑ 94ColChoGS-413
❑ 94ColChoSS-413
❑ 94Don-119
❑ 94Fin-404
❑ 94FinRef-404
❑ 94Fle-178
❑ 94Lea-393
❑ 94Pac-330
❑ 94Pin-283
❑ 94PinArtP-283
❑ 94PinMusC-283
❑ 94Sco-119
❑ 94ScoGolR-119
❑ 94Top-16
❑ 94TopGol-16
❑ 94TopSpa-16
❑ 94Ult-75
❑ 95FleUpd-113
❑ 95MetColP-15
❑ 95Top-131
❑ 96ColCho-627
❑ 96ColChoGS-627
❑ 96ColChoSS-627
❑ 96LeaSigEA-75
❑ 96MetKah-13
❑ 96MetKah-13
❑ 98PacOnl-324
❑ 98PacOnlR-324
❑ 98PacOnlWC-324
❑ 99Pac-193
❑ 99PacPlaB-193
❑ 99PacRed-193
Henry, Dutch
❑ 30WhiSoxTI-12
❑ 90DodTar-334
❑ 93ConTSN-783
Henry, Dwayne
❑ 82BurRanF-4
❑ 82BurRanT-24
❑ 83TulDriT-11
❑ 84TulDriTI-36
❑ 85TulDriTI-29
❑ 86Don-603
❑ 86Fle-562
❑ 87Don-637
❑ 87OklCit8P-18
❑ 88BlaYNPRWL-183
❑ 88OklCit8C-2
❑ 88OklCit8P-33
❑ 88Top-178
❑ 88TopTif-178
❑ 89RicBraBC-9
❑ 89RicBraC-4
❑ 89RicBraP-844
❑ 89RicBraTI-9
❑ 89Top-496
❑ 89TopTif-496
❑ 89UppDec-51
❑ 90BraDubP-10
❑ 90BraDubS-12
❑ 91AstMot-24
❑ 91Fle-692
❑ 91Lea-329
❑ 91OPC-567
❑ 91Top-567
❑ 91TopDesS-567
❑ 91TopMic-567
❑ 91TopTif-567
❑ 92Don-114
❑ 92Fle-436
❑ 92Lea-433
❑ 92LeaBlaG-433
❑ 92OPC-668
❑ 92RedKah-48
❑ 92Sco-204
❑ 92StaClu-892
❑ 92StaCluECN-892
❑ 92Top-668
❑ 92TopGol-668
❑ 92TopGolW-668
❑ 92TopMic-668
❑ 92Ult-483
❑ 92UppDec-430
❑ 93Don-478
❑ 93Fle-391
❑ 93FleFinE-272
❑ 93MarMot-8
❑ 93RanKee-182
❑ 93Sco-474
❑ 93StaClu-577
❑ 93StaCluFDI-577
❑ 93StaCluMOP-577
❑ 93Top-29
❑ 93TopGol-29
❑ 93TopInaM-29
❑ 93TopInaR-29
❑ 93TopMic-29
❑ 94Pac-572
❑ 95TolMudHTI-16
Henry, Frank J.
❑ 33WorCig(-42
Henry, Harold
❑ 91UtiBluSC-18
❑ 91UtiBluSP-3253
❑ 92SouBenWSC-16
❑ 92SouBenWSF-189
❑ 93SarWhiSC-13
Henry, Jim (James Francis)
❑ 79RedSoxEF-6
Henry, Jimmy
❑ 90BriTigP-3171
❑ 90BriTigS-10
❑ 91NiaFalRP-3627
❑ 92LakTigC-17
❑ 92LonTigF-629
Henry, John M.
❑ 87OldJudN-239
Henry, John Park
❑ 11PinT-5-554
❑ 12T207-79
❑ 14FatPlaT-16
❑ 15SpoNewM-79
❑ 16SpoNewM-80
❑ 17ColE13-74
❑ 17HolBreD-42
Henry, Jon
❑ 90EliTwiS-12
❑ 91VisOakC-3
❑ 91VisOakP-1737
❑ 92OrlSunRF-2842
❑ 92OrlSunRS-507
❑ 93PorBeaF-2380
❑ 94NasXprF-380
Henry, Kevin
❑ 88IdaFalBP-1846
Henry, Mark
❑ 86PenWhiSP-12
❑ 87DayBeaAP-10
Henry, Michael
❑ 87SavCarP-10
❑ 88SprCarB-4
Henry, Paul
❑ 88NebCor-6
Henry, Prince Jo
❑ 76LauIndC-22
Henry, Ron
❑ 64TwiJayP-5
❑ 77FriOneYW-48
Henry, Ryan
❑ 89CarNewE-11
Henry, Santiago
❑ 92St.CatBJC-10
❑ 92St.CatBJF-3396
❑ 93HagSunC-13
❑ 93HagSunF-1889
❑ 94DunBluJC-13
❑ 94DunBluJF-2564
❑ 95KnoSmoF-48
❑ 96KnoSmoB-16
❑ 98SyrSkyG-15
Henry, Scott
❑ 90MadMusB-7
❑ 90SouOreAB-29
❑ 91MadMusC-17
❑ 91MadMusP-2135
❑ 92RenSilSCLC-42
Henry, Sugar (Jim)
❑ 91NiaFalRC-25
❑ 93LonTigF-2302
Henry, Tim
❑ 82BurRanF-14
❑ 82BurRanT-1
❑ 82TulDriT-6
❑ 83TulDriT-10
Henshaw, Roy
❑ 36CubTeal-14
❑ 90DodTar-335
Hensich, Phil
❑ 36GouWidPPR-D12
❑ 36WorWidGV-123
Hensiek, Phil
❑ 33WorCig(-43
❑ 33WorCig(-44
Hensley, Chuck
❑ 82WesHavAT-6
❑ 83TacTigT-5
❑ 84TacTigC-86
❑ 86PhoFirP-9
❑ 87RicBraBC-12
❑ 87RicBraC-37
❑ 87RicBraT-6
❑ 88AlbDukCm-10
❑ 88AlbDukP-273
❑ 89CalCanC-2
❑ 89CalCanP-531
❑ 90WilBilB-9
❑ 90WilBilP-1055
❑ 90WilBilS-10
Hensley, Mike
❑ 88OklSoo-2
❑ 89SavCarP-364
❑ 90Bes-235
❑ 90SprCarB-19
❑ 91St.PetCP-2272
Hensling, Arthur
❑ 09ObaT21-181
Henson, Drew
❑ 99SP TopP-93
❑ 99SP TopPPE-93
Henson, Hunter
❑ 94DavLipB-14
❑ 95DavLipB-14
Henson, Joey
❑ 92DavLipB-14
❑ 93DavLipB-12
❑ 93GleFalRC-16
❑ 93GleFalRF-4010
Henson, Mickey
❑ 91Cla/Bes-22
❑ 91GasRanC-7
❑ 91GasRanP-2684
Hentgen, Pat
❑ 87MyrBeaBJP-1444
❑ 88DunBluJS-9
❑ 89DunBluJS-7
❑ 90Bes-295
❑ 90KnoBluJB-4
❑ 90KnoBluJP-1240
❑ 90KnoBluJS-5
❑ 90ProAaA-45
❑ 91Bow-23
❑ 91LinDriAAA-505
❑ 91SyrChiK-2
❑ 91SyrChiLD-505
❑ 91SyrChiMB-7
❑ 91SyrChiP-2477
❑ 92Bow-696
❑ 92Cla2-T16
❑ 92Don-704
❑ 92FleUpd-64
❑ 92Pin-563
❑ 92ScoRoo-96T
❑ 92SpoIllFK1-611
❑ 92SyrChiF-1962
❑ 92SyrChiMB-8
❑ 92TopDeb91-74
❑ 93BluJayD-19
❑ 93BluJayD4-33
❑ 93BluJayFS-14
❑ 93Don-247
❑ 93Fla-291
❑ 93Fle-694
❑ 93Lea-540
❑ 93LinVenB-29
❑ 93OPC-245
❑ 93Sco-343
❑ 93Sel-309
❑ 93SP-49
❑ 93StaClu-26
❑ 93StaCluFDI-26
❑ 93StaCluMOP-26
❑ 93Top-752
❑ 93TopGol-752
❑ 93TopInaM-752
❑ 93TopInaR-752
❑ 93TopMic-752
❑ 93Ult-641
❑ 93UppDec-693
❑ 93UppDecGold-693
❑ 94BluJayUSPC-4S
❑ 94BluJayUSPC-9H
❑ 94BluJayUSPC-11D
❑ 94Bow-323
❑ 94ColC-133
❑ 94ColChoGS-133
❑ 94ColChoSS-133
❑ 94Don-200
❑ 94Fin-400
❑ 94FinRef-400
❑ 94Fla-118
❑ 94Fle-335
❑ 94FleAllS-11
❑ 94FleExtB-191
❑ 94Lea-185
❑ 94Pac-644
❑ 94Pin-316
❑ 94PinArtP-316
❑ 94PinMusC-316
❑ 94Sco-509
❑ 94ScoGolR-509
❑ 94Sel-48
❑ 94Spo-133
❑ 94StaClu-242
❑ 94StaCluFDI-242
❑ 94StaCluGR-242
❑ 94StaCluMOP-242
❑ 94StaCluT-158
❑ 94StaCluTFDI-158
❑ 94Stu-28
❑ 94Top-304
❑ 94TopGol-304
❑ 94TopSpa-304
❑ 94TriPla-34
❑ 94Ult-138
❑ 94UppDec-126
❑ 94UppDecED-126
❑ 95BluJayOH-18
❑ 95BluJayUSPC-2C
❑ 95BluJayUSPC-9D

❑ 95Bow-339
❑ 95ColCho-149
❑ 95ColChoGS-149
❑ 95ColChoSS-149
❑ 95Don-127
❑ 95DonPreP-127
❑ 95Emo-95
❑ 95Fin-78
❑ 95FinRef-78
❑ 95Fla-98
❑ 95Fle-97
❑ 95FleAllS-22
❑ 95FleTeaL-14
❑ 95FleUpdSS-5
❑ 95Lea-156
❑ 95PanSti-15
❑ 95Pin-27
❑ 95PinArtP-27
❑ 95PinMusC-27
❑ 95Sco-110
❑ 95ScoGolR-110
❑ 95ScoPlaTS-110
❑ 95Sel-26
❑ 95SelArtP-26
❑ 95SP-207
❑ 95Spo-102
❑ 95SpoArtP-102
❑ 95SPSil-207
❑ 95StaClu-454
❑ 95StaCluMOP-454
❑ 95StaCluSTWS-454
❑ 95StaCluVR-244
❑ 95StaCluVRMO-244
❑ 95Top-213
❑ 95TopCyb-121
❑ 95TopEmb-5
❑ 95TopEmbGI-5
❑ 95TopLeaL-LL21
❑ 95Ult-121
❑ 95UltGolM-121
❑ 95UppDec-37
❑ 95UppDecED-37
❑ 95UppDecEDG-37
❑ 95UppDecSE-196
❑ 95UppDecSEG-196
❑ 96BluJayB-2
❑ 96BluJayOH-16
❑ 96ColCho-743
❑ 96ColChoGS-743
❑ 96ColChoSS-743
❑ 96Don-433
❑ 96DonPreP-433
❑ 96EmoXL-134
❑ 96Fin-B87
❑ 96FinRef-B87
❑ 96Fla-187
❑ 96Fle-276
❑ 96FleTif-276
❑ 96MetUni-122
❑ 96MetUniP-122
❑ 96Pac-440
❑ 96ProSta-17
❑ 96Sco-451
❑ 96StaClu-149
❑ 96StaCluMOP-149
❑ 96Top-148
❑ 96Ult-147
❑ 96UltGolM-147
❑ 96UppDec-473
❑ 97BluJayB-8
❑ 97BluJayOH-16
❑ 97BluJayS-2
❑ 97BluJayS-30
❑ 97BluJayS-6
❑ 97Bow-245
❑ 97BowBes-14
❑ 97BowBesAR-14
❑ 97BowBesR-14
❑ 97BowChr-70
❑ 97BowChrI-70
❑ 97BowChrIR-70
❑ 97BowChrR-70
❑ 97BowInt-245
❑ 97Cir-355
❑ 97CirRav-355
❑ 97ColCho-495
❑ 97ColChoAC-9
❑ 97Don-177
❑ 97Don-430
❑ 97DonEli-128
❑ 97DonEliGS-128
❑ 97DonGolPP-177
❑ 97DonGolPP-430
❑ 97DonLim-183
❑ 97DonLimE-183
❑ 97DonPre-85
❑ 97DonPreCttC-85
❑ 97DonSig-95
❑ 97DonSigPPP-95
❑ 97DonSilPP-177
❑ 97DonSilPP-430
❑ 97E-X2-51
❑ 97E-X2Cred-51
❑ 97E-X2EssCre-51
❑ 97Fin-43
❑ 97FinRef-43
❑ 97FlaShoLC-87
❑ 97FlaShoLeg0-87
❑ 97FlaShoLeg1-87
❑ 97FlaShoM-A87
❑ 97FlaShoM-B87
❑ 97FlaShoM-C87
❑ 97FlaShoR0-87
❑ 97FlaShoR1-87
❑ 97FlaShoR2-87
❑ 97Fle-242
❑ 97FleTeaL-14
❑ 97FleTif-242
❑ 97Lea-59
❑ 97LeaBanS-13
❑ 97LeaFraM-59
❑ 97LeaFraMDC-59
❑ 97LeaGet-6
❑ 97MetUni-186
❑ 97NewPin-32
❑ 97NewPinAP-32
❑ 97NewPinMC-32
❑ 97NewPinPP-32
❑ 97Pac-222
❑ 97PacLigB-222
❑ 97PacPri-75
❑ 97PacPriLB-75
❑ 97PacPriP-75
❑ 97PacSil-222
❑ 97Pin-88
❑ 97PinArtP-PP88
❑ 97PinCar-6
❑ 97PinCer-55
❑ 97PinCerMBla-55
❑ 97PinCerMBlu-55
❑ 97PinCerMG-55
❑ 97PinCerMR-55
❑ 97PinCerR-55
❑ 97PinIns-97
❑ 97PinIns-149
❑ 97PinInsCE-97
❑ 97PinInsCE-149
❑ 97PinInsDE-97
❑ 97PinInsDE-149
❑ 97PinMusC-88
❑ 97PinPrePla-88
❑ 97PinTotCPB-55
❑ 97PinTotCPG-55
❑ 97PinTotCPR-55
❑ 97PinX-P-79
❑ 97PinX-PMoS-79
❑ 97Sco-264
❑ 97ScoArtPWB-264
❑ 97ScoPreS-264
❑ 97ScoShoS-264
❑ 97ScoShoSAP-264
❑ 97Sel-46
❑ 97SelArtP-46
❑ 97SelCom-46
❑ 97SelRegG-46
❑ 97SP-182
❑ 97SpoIll-134
❑ 97SpoIllEE-134
❑ 97StaClu-39
❑ 97StaCluMat-39
❑ 97StaCluMOP-39
❑ 97StrAll-27
❑ 97Stu-87
❑ 97StuPrePG-87
❑ 97StuPrePS-87
❑ 97Top-330
❑ 97TopAll-AS19
❑ 97TopChr-111
❑ 97TopChrAS-AS19
❑ 97TopChrR-111
❑ 97TopChrSAR-AS19
❑ 97TopChrSB-18
❑ 97TopChrSBR-18
❑ 97TopGal-123
❑ 97TopGalPPI-123
❑ 97TopMem05-22
❑ 97TopSeaB-SB18
❑ 97TopSta-68
❑ 97TopStaAM-68
❑ 97Ult-145
❑ 97UltGolME-145
❑ 97UltPlaME-145
❑ 97UltTop3-26
❑ 97UltTop3GM-26
❑ 97UppDec-213
❑ 97UppDecAWJ-22
❑ 98BowBes-59
❑ 98BowBesAR-59
❑ 98BowBesR-59
❑ 98CirThu-193
❑ 98CirThuRav-193
❑ 98CirThuSupRav-193
❑ 98ColCho-251
❑ 98Don-6
❑ 98DonCol-6
❑ 98DonColL-326
❑ 98DonColP-625
❑ 98DonColS-6
❑ 98DonGolPP-6
❑ 98DonPre-75
❑ 98DonPreSeat-75
❑ 98DonPriCD-6
❑ 98DonPriCL-326
❑ 98DonPriCP-625
❑ 98DonSilPP-6
❑ 98Fin-214
❑ 98FinNo--214
❑ 98FinNo-R-214
❑ 98FinRef-214
❑ 98FlaShoLeg0-106
❑ 98FlaShoLeg1-106
❑ 98FlaShoLeg2-106
❑ 98FlaShoLeg3-106
❑ 98FlaShoLegM-106
❑ 98FlaShoR0-106
❑ 98FlaShoR1-106
❑ 98FlaShoR2-106
❑ 98FlaShoR3-106
❑ 98Fle-101
❑ 98Lea-127
❑ 98LeaFraDA-127
❑ 98LeaFraF-127
❑ 98LeaFraM-127
❑ 98LeaFraM-127
❑ 98LeaFraMDC-127
❑ 98LeaFraMDC-127
❑ 98LeaFraMZ2-127
❑ 98LeaRS-72
❑ 98LeaRSLHolo-72
❑ 98LeaRSLong-72
❑ 98LeaRTrue-72
❑ 98MetUni-90
❑ 98MetUniPMG-90
❑ 98Pac-223
❑ 98PacAur-95
❑ 98PacInvTeam-28
❑ 98PacOnl-768
❑ 98PacOnlR-768
❑ 98PacOnlWC-768
❑ 98PacPar-115
❑ 98PacParC-115
❑ 98PacParG-115
❑ 98PacParHS-115
❑ 98PacParI-36
❑ 98PacParPB-115
❑ 98PacParR-115
❑ 98PacPlaB-223
❑ 98PacRedT-223
❑ 98PacSil-223
❑ 98PinPer-76
❑ 98PinPerPP-76
❑ 98PinPlu-19
❑ 98Sco-138
❑ 98ScoRT-87
❑ 98ScoRTSS-PP64
❑ 98ScoRTSSAP-PP64
❑ 98ScoRTSSAP1-PP64
❑ 98ScoSS-PP155
❑ 98ScoSSAP-PP155
❑ 98SP Aut-196
❑ 98SpoIll-58
❑ 98SpoIllEE-58
❑ 98SpoIllFE-58
❑ 98SpoIllWSF-53
❑ 98SpoIllWSFEE-53
❑ 98SpoIllWSFFE-53
❑ 98SPxFin-139
❑ 98SPxFinR-139
❑ 98SPxFinS-139
❑ 98StaCluFDI-78
❑ 98StaCluI-78
❑ 98StaCluOneK-78
❑ 98StaCluPP-78
❑ 98Stu-156
❑ 98StuGPP-156
❑ 98StuSPP-156
❑ 98Top-45
❑ 98TopChr-45
❑ 98TopChrR-45
❑ 98TopDevR-45
❑ 98TopDia-45
❑ 98TopGal-142
❑ 98TopGalGP-142
❑ 98TopGalOPP-142
❑ 98TopGalPPI-142
❑ 98TopGalPPIA-142
❑ 98TopMiniC-45
❑ 98TopOpeD-27
❑ 98TopSta-118
❑ 98TopStaB-118
❑ 98TopStaG-118
❑ 98TopStaGR-118
❑ 98TopStaS-118
❑ 98Ult-105
❑ 98UltGolM-105
❑ 98UltMas-105
❑ 98UltPlaM-105
❑ 98UppDec-238
❑ 98UppDecSF-133
❑ 99199Fin-243
❑ 99Bow-44
❑ 99BowChr-44
❑ 99BowChrG-44
❑ 99BowChrGR-44
❑ 99BowChrI-44
❑ 99BowChrIR-44
❑ 99BowChrR-44
❑ 99BowGol-44
❑ 99BowInt-44
❑ 99FinGolRef-243
❑ 99FinRef-243
❑ 99Fle-463
❑ 99FleSta9-463
❑ 99FleWarT-463
❑ 99Pac-446
❑ 99PacAur-200
❑ 99PacAurOD-200
❑ 99PacPlaB-446
❑ 99PacRed-446
❑ 99SkyMolM-94
❑ 99SkyMolMX-94
❑ 99StaClu-252
❑ 99StaCluFDI-252
❑ 99StaCluOoaK-252
❑ 99StaCluPP-252
❑ 99Top-298
❑ 99TopChr-298
❑ 99TopChrR-298
❑ 99TopMVPP-298
❑ 99UppDec-517
❑ 99UppDecEL1-517
❑ 99UppDecEL2-517

Henthorne, Kevin
❑ 96TamYanY-13
❑ 97NorNav-18
❑ 97NorNavTI-13

Hepler, William
❑ 66Top-574
❑ 67OPC-144
❑ 67Top-144
❑ 91MetWIZ-174

Hepting, Ernest
❑ 29Zee-88

Herbel, Ron
❑ 61TacBan-10
❑ 61UniOil-T28
❑ 63Top-208
❑ 64Top-47
❑ 64TopVen-47
❑ 65OPC-84
❑ 65Top-84
❑ 66Top-331
❑ 66TopVen-331
❑ 67OPC-156
❑ 67Top-156
❑ 68Top-333
❑ 68TopVen-333
❑ 69Top-251
❑ 70OPC-526
❑ 70Top-526
❑ 71MLBOffS-11
❑ 71OPC-387
❑ 71Top-387
❑ 72MilBra-140
❑ 72OPC-469
❑ 72Top-469
❑ 91MetWIZ-175

Herberholz, Craig
❑ 81BurBeeT-7

Herbert, Ray
❑ 47Exh-93
❑ 53TigGle-13
❑ 54Top-190
❑ 55A'sRodM-18
❑ 55A'sTeal-10
❑ 55Top-138
❑ 55TopDouH-105
❑ 56A'sPos-25
❑ 58Top-379
❑ 59Top-154
❑ 59TopVen-154
❑ 60A'sJayP-5
❑ 60A'sTeal-7
❑ 60Top-252
❑ 60TopTat-21
❑ 61A'sTeal-7
❑ 61AthJayP-9
❑ 61Pos-87A
❑ 61Pos-87B
❑ 61Top-498
❑ 61TopStal-162
❑ 62SalPlaC-6
❑ 62ShiPlaC-6
❑ 62Top-8
❑ 62TopStal-25
❑ 62TopVen-8
❑ 63Baz-29
❑ 63ExhStaB-28
❑ 63Fle-9
❑ 63Jel-45
❑ 63Pos-45
❑ 63SalMetC-42
❑ 63Top-8
❑ 63Top-560
❑ 63TopStil-17
❑ 63WhiSoxJP-4
❑ 63WhiSoxTS-9
❑ 64Top-215
❑ 64TopVen-215
❑ 64WhiSoxl-12
❑ 64WhiSoxTS-11
❑ 65Top-399
❑ 66OPC-121
❑ 66Top-121
❑ 66TopVen-121
❑ 67TopVen-183
❑ 76A'sRodMC-12
❑ 79DiaGre-396
❑ 94TopArc1-190
❑ 94TopArc1G-190

Herbert, Russ
❑ 96CarLeaA1B-8
❑ 96CarLeaA2B-8
❑ 96PriWilCB-15
❑ 97BirBarB-22
❑ 98PriWilCASM-8

Herbison, Brett
❑ 96AppLeaAB-22
❑ 96BesAutSA-27
❑ 97BesAutAS-18
❑ 97BesAutP-H3
❑ 97Bow-408
❑ 97BowInt-408
❑ 97CapCitB-5
❑ 97SouAtlTPB-7
❑ 98St.LucMM-21

Herbst, Michael
❑ 93CapCitBC-27
❑ 96BinMetB-13

Herde, Kevin
❑ 93JohCitCF-3681

Heredia, Cesar
❑ 95LinVen-220

Heredia, Felix
❑ 94KanCouCC-11
❑ 94KanCouCF-156
❑ 94KanCouCTI-11
❑ 95BreCouMF-240
❑ 96PorSeaDB-15
❑ 97Bow-72
❑ 97BowBes-124
❑ 97BowBesAR-124
❑ 97BowBesR-124
❑ 97BowInt-72
❑ 97Cir-55
❑ 97CirRav-55
❑ 97Fle-622
❑ 97FleTif-622
❑ 97MarPac-13
❑ 97Ult-514
❑ 97UltGolME-514
❑ 97UltPlaME-514
❑ 97UppDec-278
❑ 98ColCho-379
❑ 98Don-311
❑ 98DonGolPP-311
❑ 98DonSilPP-311
❑ 98LeaRS-290
❑ 98LeaRSLHolo-290
❑ 98LeaRSLong-290
❑ 98LeaRTrue-290
❑ 98Pac-302
❑ 98PacOnl-296
❑ 98PacOnlR-296
❑ 98PacOnlWC-296
❑ 98PacPlaB-302
❑ 98PacRedT-302
❑ 98PacSil-302
❑ 98PorSeaD5AQ-21
❑ 98StaCluFDI-286
❑ 98StaCluI-286
❑ 98StaCluOneK-286
❑ 98StaCluPP-286
❑ 98Ult-314
❑ 98UltGolM-314
❑ 98UltMas-314
❑ 98UltPlaM-314
❑ 98UppDec-380
❑ 99Fle-477
❑ 99FleSta9-477
❑ 99FleWarT-477
❑ 99PacCroC-57
❑ 99PacCroCPB-57

Heredia, Geysi
❑ 86OscAstP-11

Heredia, Gil (Gilbert)
❑ 86AriWilP-4
❑ 87AriWilP-6
❑ 87EveGiaC-2
❑ 88CalLeaACLC-2
❑ 88SanJosGCLC-132
❑ 88SanJosGP-130
❑ 90CMC-530
❑ 90PhoFirC-3
❑ 90PhoFirP-6
❑ 90ProAAAF-32
❑ 91LinDriAAA-383
❑ 91PhoFirLD-383
❑ 91PhoFirP-61
❑ 92Don-737
❑ 92Fle-665
❑ 92GiaPacGaE-18
❑ 92Sco-771
❑ 92SkyAAAF-294
❑ 92StaClu-895
❑ 92StaCluECN-895
❑ 92TopDeb91-75
❑ 93OttLynF-2430
❑ 94Pac-383
❑ 94StaClu-664
❑ 94StaCluFDI-664
❑ 94StaCluGR-664
❑ 94StaCluMOP-664
❑ 95Fla-162
❑ 95Fle-353
❑ 95Pac-269
❑ 95Top-509
❑ 95TopCyb-298
❑ 96Fle-459
❑ 96FleTif-459
❑ 96LeaSigEA-76
❑ 96RanDr P-15
❑ 96RanMot-18
❑ 97PacPriGotD-GD97

Heredia, Hector
❑ 87AlbDukD-10
❑ 88AlbDukCm-11
❑ 88AlbDukP-274
❑ 89AlbDukCm-5
❑ 89AlbDukP-66

Heredia, Julian
❑ 91BoiHawC-29
❑ 91BoiHawP-3871
❑ 91Cla/Bes-444
❑ 92ClaFS7-227
❑ 92ProFS7-40
❑ 92QuaCitRBC-1
❑ 92QuaCitRBF-803
❑ 93LimRocDWB-41
❑ 93MidAngF-319
❑ 94MidAngOHP-9
❑ 96PhoFirB-17
❑ 97MidAngOHP-15
❑ 98NasSouTI-15
❑ 98NasSouTISS-15

Heredia, Maximo
❑ 97DelSho-20

Heredia, Ubaldo
❑ 76VenLeaS-85
❑ 77LodDodT-6
❑ 78LodDodT-8
❑ 80VenLeaS-101
❑ 87IndIndTI-11

Heredia, Wilson
❑ 91GulCoaRSP-6
❑ 92GasRanC-7

❑ 92GasRanF-2249
❑ 93ChaRanC-15
❑ 93ChaRanF-1937
❑ 93FloStaLAF-4
❑ 93LimRocDWB-124
❑ 94TulDriF-239
❑ 94TulDriTI-10
❑ 95Fla-306
❑ 95FleUpd-83
❑ 95Sum-129
❑ 95SumNthD-129
❑ 98ColCliD-10
❑ 98ColCliM-14
❑ 98Pac-205
❑ 98PacPlaB-205
❑ 98PacRedT-205
❑ 98PacSil-205
Herges, Matt
❑ 92YakBeaC-15
❑ 92YakBeaF-3443
❑ 93BakDodCLC-10
❑ 94VerBeaDC-9
❑ 94VerBeaDF-65
❑ 95SanAntMTI-53
❑ 96SanAntMB-7
❑ 97AlbDukGS-14
❑ 98AlbDukG-8
Herling, Keith
❑ 94SigRoo-7
❑ 94SigRooS-7
Herman, Babe (Floyd C.)
❑ 25Zee-141
❑ 28PorandAR-A15
❑ 28PorandAR-B15
❑ 28W513-84
❑ 28W56PlaC-H7
❑ 29ExhFou-4
❑ 29PorandAR-38
❑ 30UncJac-16
❑ 31Exh-4
❑ 32OrbPinUP-32
❑ 32R33So2-418
❑ 33ButCre-13
❑ 33Gou-5
❑ 33GouCanV-5
❑ 33RitCE-1D
❑ 33TatOrb-32
❑ 33TatOrbSDR-195
❑ 34DiaMatCSB-90
❑ 35DiaMatCS3T1-73
❑ 36ExhFou-4
❑ 36GouWidPPR-A51
❑ 61Fle-114
❑ 70SpoCarfCOP-30
❑ 79DiaGre-78
❑ 82TCMGreS-28
❑ 85BigLeaC3-22
❑ 88ConSer5-16
❑ 90DodTar-336
❑ 91ConTSN-169
❑ 93DiaStaES-135
Herman, Billy
❑ 32CubTeal-12
❑ 32OrbPinNP-67
❑ 32OrbPinUP-33
❑ 33Gou-227
❑ 33RitCE-2S
❑ 33TatOrb-33
❑ 33WorCig-54
❑ 34BatR31-138
❑ 34DiaMatCSB-91
❑ 35AlDemDCR3-158
❑ 35GouPuzR-8K
❑ 35GouPuzR-9K
❑ 36CubTeal-15
❑ 36DiaMatCS3T2-14
❑ 36ExhFou-3
❑ 36R31PasP-29
❑ 36R31PasP-31
❑ 36SandSW-33
❑ 36WheBB4-6
❑ 36WheBB5-2
❑ 36WorWidGV-16
❑ 37ExhFou-3
❑ 37KelPepS-BB8
❑ 37WheBB14-6
❑ 37WheBB6-10
❑ 37WheBB9-8
❑ 38CloFotW-38
❑ 38ExhFou-3
❑ 39CubTeal-11
❑ 39GouPreR303A-24
❑ 39GouPreR303B-14
❑ 39WorWidGTP-24
❑ 40WheM4-10
❑ 41DouPlaR-3
❑ 42DodTeal-10
❑ 43DodTeal-13
❑ 46DodTeal-11
❑ 46SpoExcW-3-5
❑ 50CubGreB-9
❑ 50RemBre-12
❑ 52Top-394
❑ 54Top-86
❑ 55DodGolS-27
❑ 55Top-19
❑ 55TopDouH-53
❑ 56Dod-12
❑ 60Top-456
❑ 65OPC-251
❑ 65RedSoxTI-5
❑ 65Top-251
❑ 66OPC-37
❑ 66Top-37
❑ 66TopVen-37
❑ 73Dod194T-13
❑ 74dod195T-12
❑ 75TCMAllG-15
❑ 76ChiGre-9
❑ 76RowExh-9
❑ 76ShaPiz-149
❑ 76SSPYanOD-4
❑ 76TayBow4-98
❑ 77BobParHoF-60
❑ 77CubAllT-7
❑ 77GalGloG-84
❑ 78DodTCM4-16
❑ 78PadFamF-15
❑ 79DiaGre-105
❑ 79PadFamF-20
❑ 79TCM50-187
❑ 80CubGreT-9
❑ 80PacLeg-23
❑ 80PerHaloFP-149
❑ 80PerHaloFPS-27
❑ 80SSPHOF-149
❑ 82DiaCla-72
❑ 83TopRep5-394
❑ 84CubBriPC-6C
❑ 89DodSmoG-9
❑ 89KahCoo-6
❑ 89PerCelP-17
❑ 90DodTar-337
❑ 90PacLeg-30
❑ 90PerGreM-41
❑ 90SweBasG-59
❑ 91DodRinP4-1
❑ 91SweBasG-39
❑ 92ActPacA-9
❑ 92ActPacA2-9G
❑ 92ConTSN-421
❑ 92ConTSN-473
❑ 92CubOldS-12
❑ 93ConTSN-787
❑ 93DiaStaES-136
❑ 93SpeGolSH-1
❑ 93TedWil-21
❑ 94ConTSN-1092
❑ 94ConTSNB-1092
❑ 94TopArc1-86
❑ 94TopArc1G-86
❑ 95TopArcBD-31
❑ 95TopArcBD-70
❑ 95TopArcBD-92
Herman, Greg
❑ 77AppFoxT-8
Herman, Ty
❑ 80ElmPioRST-8
Hermann, Jeff
❑ 86GleFalTP-9
❑ 87GleFalTP-18
❑ 88WicPilRD-27
Hermann, LeRoy
❑ 36GouWidPPR-D13
Hermansen, Chad
❑ 95Bes-112
❑ 95SPML-106
❑ 96AugGreB-14
❑ 96BesAutSA-28
❑ 96Exc-217
❑ 96ExcFirYP-6
❑ 96HonShaHWB-17
❑ 96LynHilUB-1
❑ 97Bes-13
❑ 97BesAutAS-19
❑ 97BesAutP-H4
❑ 97BesAutSBPP-28
❑ 97BesLimA-17
❑ 97Bow-87
❑ 97BowBes-129
❑ 97BowBesAR-129
❑ 97BowBesR-129
❑ 97BowCerBlaIA-CA37
❑ 97BowCerBluIA-CA37
❑ 97BowCerGolIA-CA37
❑ 97BowChr-111
❑ 97BowChrI-111
❑ 97BowChrIR-111
❑ 97BowChrR-111
❑ 97BowInt-87
❑ 97CarMudC-16
❑ 97SouLeaTP-6
❑ 98AriFalLTP-23
❑ 98Bes-69
❑ 98BesAutPOY-7
❑ 98BesCasT-6
❑ 98BesFulCA-7
❑ 98BesPreA-17
❑ 98Bow-168
❑ 98Bow99ROYF-ROY3
❑ 98BowBes-162
❑ 98BowBesAR-162
❑ 98BowBesMIF-MI13
❑ 98BowBesMIFAR-MI13
❑ 98BowBesMIFR-MI13
❑ 98BowBesR-162
❑ 98BowCerBlueAU-53
❑ 98BowCerGA-53
❑ 98BowCerSA-53
❑ 98BowChr-168
❑ 98BowChrGA-168
❑ 98BowChrGAR-168
❑ 98BowChrI-168
❑ 98BowChrIR-168
❑ 98BowChrR-168
❑ 98BowGolA-168
❑ 98BowInt-168
❑ 98BowScoC-SC5
❑ 98NasSouTI-16
❑ 98NasSouTI-17
❑ 98NasSouTISS-16
❑ 98SP MinDTSPE-DS20
❑ 98SP MinPE-8
❑ 98SP MinPE-100
❑ 98SP MinSTHPE-H20
❑ 98SP SPTSC-CH
❑ 98SPMin-8
❑ 98SPMin-100
❑ 98SPMinDTS-DS20
❑ 98SPMinSTH-H20
❑ 98Top-260
❑ 98TopChr-260
❑ 98TopChrR-260
❑ 98TopDevR-260
❑ 98TopDia-260
❑ 98TopMiniC-260
❑ 99BasAmeTPA-19
❑ 99BasAmeTPBP-2
❑ 99Bow-163
❑ 99BowAut-BA29
❑ 99BowBes-108
❑ 99BowBesAR-108
❑ 99BowBesR-108
❑ 99BowChr-163
❑ 99BowChrG-163
❑ 99BowChrGR-163
❑ 99BowChrI-163
❑ 99BowChrIR-163
❑ 99BowChrR-163
❑ 99BowChrSC-SC15
❑ 99BowChrSCR-SC15
❑ 99BowGol-163
❑ 99BowInt-163
❑ 99BowScoC-SC15
❑ 99SP SigAuto-CH
❑ 99SP SigAutoG-CH
❑ 99SP TopP-59
❑ 99SP TopPC-CH
❑ 99SP TopPDtS-D14
❑ 99SP TopPGF-GF14
❑ 99SP TopPPE-59
❑ 99SPSig-62
❑ 99UppDec-462
❑ 99UppDecEL1-462
❑ 99UppDecEL2-462
Hermanski, Gene
❑ 46DodTeal-12
❑ 47DodTeal-10
❑ 47Exh-94
❑ 47TipTop-97
❑ 48DodTeal-12
❑ 49Bow-20
❑ 49EurSta-37
❑ 49Lea-102A
❑ 49Lea-102B
❑ 50Bow-113
❑ 51Bow-55
❑ 51TopRedB-11
❑ 52Bow-136
❑ 52TipTop-15
❑ 52Top-16
❑ 53Top-179
❑ 54Top-228
❑ 79DiaGre-92
❑ 79TCM50-165
❑ 83TopRep5-16
❑ 84FifNatC-3
❑ 85TCMPla1-6
❑ 88DodRinP1-12C
❑ 90DodTar-338
❑ 91TopArc1-179
❑ 94TopArc1-228
❑ 94TopArc1G-228
Hermanson, Dustin
❑ 93BazTeaU-7
❑ 93TopTra-22T
❑ 94Cla#1DPMF-DD3
❑ 94ClaUpdCotC-CC3
❑ 94SigRooDP-4
❑ 94SigRooDPS-4
❑ 94StaCluDP-87
❑ 94StaCluDPFDI-87
❑ 94TopTra-95T
❑ 94UppDecAHNIL-19
❑ 95ActPacF-54
❑ 95ARuFalLS-10
❑ 95Bow-274
❑ 95BowBes-B48
❑ 95BowBesR-B48
❑ 95BowGolF-274
❑ 95ColCho-25
❑ 95ColChoGS-25
❑ 95ColChoSE-3
❑ 95ColChoSEGS-3
❑ 95ColChoSESS-3
❑ 95ColChoSS-25
❑ 95Exc-284
❑ 95ExcFirYP-10
❑ 95Fin-302
❑ 95FinRef-302
❑ 95Fla-420
❑ 95FlaWavotF-8
❑ 95FleUpd-185
❑ 95ScoDraP-DP15
❑ 95SelSurS-SS5
❑ 95SP-5
❑ 95SPCha-7
❑ 95SPChaDC-7
❑ 95SPSil-5
❑ 95StaClu-107
❑ 95StaClu-572
❑ 95StaCluCB-CB2
❑ 95StaCluFDI-107
❑ 95StaCluMOP-107
❑ 95StaCluMOP-572
❑ 95StaCluMOP-CB2
❑ 95StaCluSTWS-107
❑ 95StaCluSTWS-572
❑ 95Sum-127
❑ 95SumNthD-127
❑ 95Top-231
❑ 95UppDec-219
❑ 95UppDecED-219
❑ 95UppDecEDG-219
❑ 95UppDecML-130
❑ 95UppDecML-164
❑ 95UppDecML-217
❑ 95UppDecMLFS-130
❑ 95UppDecMLFS-164
❑ 95UppDecMLFS-217
❑ 95UppDecSE-134
❑ 95UppDecSEG-134
❑ 95Zen-117
❑ 96Bow-303
❑ 96BowBes-114
❑ 96BowBesAR-114
❑ 96BowBesR-114
❑ 96BowFoi-303
❑ 96ColCho-651
❑ 96ColCho-702
❑ 96ColChoGS-651
❑ 96ColChoGS-702
❑ 96ColChoSS-651
❑ 96ColChoSS-702
❑ 96Don-393
❑ 96DonPreP-393
❑ 96Fle-569
❑ 96FleTif-569
❑ 96LasVegSB-14
❑ 96Pin-187
❑ 96PinArtP-100
❑ 96PinSta-100
❑ 96Sco-266
❑ 96Spo-133
❑ 96SpoArtP-133
❑ 96Top-218
❑ 97Fle-635
❑ 97FleTif-635
❑ 97Top-434
❑ 97Ult-511
❑ 97UltGolME-511
❑ 97UltPlaME-511
❑ 98ColCho-167
❑ 98Don-172
❑ 98DonGolPP-172
❑ 98DonSilPP-172
❑ 98Fin-24
❑ 98FinNo--24
❑ 98FinNo-R-24
❑ 98FinRef-24
❑ 98LeaRS-121
❑ 98LeaRSLHolo-121
❑ 98LeaRSLong-121
❑ 98LeaRTrue-121
❑ 98Pac-347
❑ 98PacOnl-450
❑ 98PacOnlR-450
❑ 98PacOnlWC-450
❑ 98PacPlaB-347
❑ 98PacRedT-347
❑ 98PacSil-347
❑ 98SP Aut-131
❑ 98StaCluFDI-248
❑ 98StaCluI-248
❑ 98StaCluOneK-248
❑ 98StaCluPP-248
❑ 98Top-421
❑ 98TopChr-421
❑ 98TopChrR-421
❑ 98TopDevR-421
❑ 98TopDia-421
❑ 98TopMiniC-421
❑ 98Ult-421
❑ 98UltGolM-421
❑ 98UltMas-421
❑ 98UltPlaM-421
❑ 98UppDec-437
❑ 99199Fin-8
❑ 99FinGolRef-8
❑ 99FinRef-8
❑ 99FlaShoLeg1-95
❑ 99FlaShoLeg2-95
❑ 99FlaShoLeg3-95
❑ 99FlaShoLegM1-95
❑ 99FlaShoLegM2-95
❑ 99FlaShoLegM3-95
❑ 99FlaShoR1-95
❑ 99FlaShoR2-95
❑ 99FlaShoR3-95
❑ 99Fle-163
❑ 99FleSta9-163
❑ 99FleWarT-163
❑ 99MetUni-72
❑ 99MetUniGM-72
❑ 99MetUniPMG-72
❑ 99Pac-265
❑ 99PacPlaB-265
❑ 99PacRed-265
❑ 99SkyPre-54
❑ 99SkyPreR-54
❑ 99SkyThu-139
❑ 99SkyThuRant-139
❑ 99SkyThuRave-139
❑ 99StaClu-97
❑ 99StaCluFDI-97
❑ 99StaCluOoaK-97
❑ 99StaCluPP-97
❑ 99ThuSkySupR-139
❑ 99Top-255
❑ 99TopChr-255
❑ 99TopChrR-255
❑ 99TopMVPP-255
❑ 99Ult-174
❑ 99UltGolM-174
❑ 99UltMas-174
❑ 99UltPlaM-174
❑ 99UppDec-143
❑ 99UppDecEL1-143
❑ 99UppDecEL2-143
❑ 99UppDecM-127
❑ 99UppDecMGS-127
❑ 99UppDecMHFS-127
❑ 99UppDecMP-127
❑ 99UppDecMSS-127
❑ 99Vic-242
Hermanson, Mike
❑ 92SpoIndC-9
❑ 92SpoIndF-1287
❑ 93WatDiaC-18
❑ 93WatDiaF-1763
❑ 94RanCucQC-15
❑ 94RanCucQF-1632
❑ 95RanCucQT-20
❑ 96LakElsSB-6
Hermoso, Angel
❑ 70OPC-147
❑ 70Top-147
❑ 76VenLeaS-225
Hermoso, Remigio
❑ 76VenLeaS-149
❑ 80VenLeaS-137
❑ 93LinVenB-32
❑ 96-97LinVen-256
Hern, Sam
❑ 14Zee-84
Hernaiz, Jesus R.
❑ 76OklCit8TI-11
❑ 77ReaPhiT-14
❑ 80CarMudF-23
❑ 83ColCliT-12
❑ 84IdaFalATI-12
❑ 88SouOreAP-1718
❑ 89BlaYNPRWL-31
❑ 91KinMetC-26
❑ 91KinMetP-3830
❑ 92KinMetC-24
❑ 92KinMetF-1549
❑ 93KinMetC-26
❑ 93KinMetF-3812
❑ 94KinMetC-26
❑ 94KinMetF-3840
Hernaiz, Juan
❑ 92GulCoaDF-3580
❑ 93GreFalDSP-2
❑ 95VerBeaDTI-12
❑ 95YakBeaTI-14
❑ 96SavSanB-19
❑ 97LakTigB-16
❑ 98JacSunM-12
Hernandez, Alex
❑ 95TopTra-69T
❑ 96EriSeaB-13
❑ 97LynHil-8
❑ 98Bes-16
❑ 98BesAutSS-26
❑ 98CarMudM-21
❑ 98SouLeaTPG-16
❑ 99BasAmeTP-51
❑ 99BasAmeTPG-51
❑ 99Bow-211
❑ 99BowChr-211
❑ 99BowChrG-211
❑ 99BowChrGR-211
❑ 99BowChrI-211
❑ 99BowChrIR-211
❑ 99BowChrR-211
❑ 99BowGol-211
❑ 99BowInt-211
Hernandez, Angel
❑ 76VenLeaS-15
❑ 80VenLeaS-11
❑ 95LinVen-162
Hernandez, Arned
❑ 90AppFoxBS-12
❑ 90AppFoxP-2110
Hernandez, Bobby (Roberto)
❑ 87ColMetP-15
Hernandez, Carlos Alberto
❑ 87BakDodP-25
❑ 88BakDodCLC-243
❑ 89SanAntMB-13
❑ 89TexLeaAGS-17
❑ 90AlbDukCm-16
❑ 90AlbDukP-349
❑ 90AlbDukTr-11
❑ 90CMC-418
❑ 90DonRoo-37
❑ 90ProAAAF-70
❑ 91AlbDukLD-10
❑ 91AlbDukP-1144
❑ 91DodPho-13
❑ 91Don-711
❑ 91Fle-207
❑ 91LinDriAAA-10
❑ 91MadMusC-24
❑ 91MadMusP-2138
❑ 91TopDeb90-67
❑ 91TriA AAGP-AAA2
❑ 92Bow-5
❑ 92Cla1-T44
❑ 92DodMot-18
❑ 92DodPol-41
❑ 92DodSmo-9892

❑ 92Don-778
❑ 92FleUpd-91
❑ 92Lea-54
❑ 92LeaBlaG-54
❑ 92Pin-456
❑ 92PinRoo-30
❑ 92ProFS7-239
❑ 92ScoRoo-91T
❑ 92TopTra-50T
❑ 92TopTraG-50T
❑ 92Ult-506
❑ 92UppDec-797
❑ 93DodMot-18
❑ 93DodPol-11
❑ 93DodStaC-4
❑ 93Don-406
❑ 93Fle-62
❑ 93Lea-442
❑ 93LinVenB-250
❑ 93PacSpa-148
❑ 93Pin-146
❑ 93Sco-348
❑ 93Sel-317
❑ 93StaClu-149
❑ 93StaCluFDI-149
❑ 93StaCluMOP-149
❑ 93Top-589
❑ 93TopGol-589
❑ 93TopInaM-589
❑ 93TopInaR-589
❑ 93TopMic-589
❑ 93Ult-400
❑ 93UppDec-148
❑ 93UppDecGold-148
❑ 94DodMot-26
❑ 94DodPol-12
❑ 94Don-122
❑ 94Fle-512
❑ 94Pac-310
❑ 94Sco-174
❑ 94ScoGolR-174
❑ 94StaClu-145
❑ 94StaCluFDI-145
❑ 94StaCluGR-145
❑ 94StaCluMOP-145
❑ 94Top-353
❑ 94TopGol-353
❑ 94TopSpa-353
❑ 94VenLinU-54
❑ 95DodMot-20
❑ 95DodPol-10
❑ 95FleUpd-174
❑ 95LinVen-26
❑ 95LinVen-258
❑ 95Pac-217
❑ 95Top-94
❑ 96-97LinVen-4
❑ 96-97LinVen-133
❑ 96DodMot-20
❑ 96DodPol-18
❑ 96Fle-436
❑ 96FleTif-436
❑ 96LeaSigEA-77
❑ 97PadMot-25
❑ 98ColCho-228
❑ 98Pac-429
❑ 98PacInv-140
❑ 98PacInvPBlue-140
❑ 98PacInvSilv-140
❑ 98PacOme-206
❑ 98PacOmeR-206
❑ 98PacOnl-639
❑ 98PacOnlR-639
❑ 98PacOnlWC-639
❑ 98PacPlaB-429
❑ 98PacRedT-429
❑ 98PacSil-429
❑ 98PadMot-10
❑ 99Fle-364
❑ 99FleSta9-364
❑ 99FleWarT-364
❑ 99Pac-370
❑ 99PacCroC-243
❑ 99PacCroCPB-243
❑ 99PacPar-199
❑ 99PacParC-199
❑ 99PacParG-199
❑ 99PacParHoloGold-199
❑ 99PacParHS-199
❑ 99PacParOD-199
❑ 99PacParPB-199
❑ 99PacParRed-199
❑ 99PacPlaB-370
❑ 99PacRed-370
❑ 99StaClu-307
❑ 99StaCluFDI-307
❑ 99StaCluOoaK-307
❑ 99StaCluPP-307
❑ 99UppDec-478
❑ 99UppDecEL1-478
❑ 99UppDecEL2-478
❑ 99UppDecM-182
❑ 99UppDecMGS-182
❑ 99UppDecMHFS-182
❑ 99UppDecMSS-182
❑ 99Vic-344

Hernandez, Carlos Eduardo
❑ 95QuaCitRBTI-10
❑ 96QuaCitRB-16
❑ 97JacGen-12
❑ 97JacGenS-9
❑ 98NewOrlZM-9
❑ 99Bow-313
❑ 99BowGol-313
❑ 99BowInt-313

Hernandez, Carlos Minors
❑ 80VenLeaS-143
❑ 85BurRanT-19

Hernandez, Cesar
❑ 86BurExpP-8
❑ 87WesPalBEP-665
❑ 88RocExpLC-17
❑ 90JacExpB-10
❑ 90JacExpP-1385
❑ 91HarSenLD-256
❑ 91HarSenP-639
❑ 91LinDriAA-256
❑ 92ChaLooS-185
❑ 92DonRoo-52
❑ 92OPC-618
❑ 92SkyAA F-82
❑ 92Top-618
❑ 92TopGol-618
❑ 92TopGolW-618
❑ 92TopMic-618
❑ 93Don-558
❑ 93Fle-392
❑ 93LimRocDWB-54
❑ 93PacSpa-400
❑ 93Pin-591
❑ 93Sco-302
❑ 93Top-301
❑ 93TopGol-301
❑ 93TopInaM-301
❑ 93TopInaR-301
❑ 93TopMic-301
❑ 94Pac-148

Hernandez, Chico
❑ 42CubTeal-9
❑ 43CubTeal-11

Hernandez, Chuck
❑ 86PalSprAP-17
❑ 86PalSprAS-3
❑ 87MidAngP-18
❑ 88EdmTraP-563
❑ 89EdmTraC-24
❑ 89EdmTraP-562
❑ 90CMC-485
❑ 90EdmTraC-8
❑ 90EdmTraP-532
❑ 90ProAAAF-108
❑ 93AngMot-28
❑ 94AngMot-28
❑ 95AngMot-28
❑ 96AngMot-28
❑ 97St.PetDR-4
❑ 97St.PetDRUB-4

Hernandez, Daniel
❑ 90HigSchPLS-8

Hernandez, Elvin
❑ 96AugGreB-15
❑ 97Bow-350
❑ 97BowInt-350
❑ 97CarMudC-5
❑ 98Bow-346
❑ 98BowChr-346
❑ 98BowChrGA-346
❑ 98BowChrGAR-346
❑ 98BowChrI-346
❑ 98BowChrIR-346
❑ 98BowChrR-346
❑ 98BowGolA-346
❑ 98BowInt-346
❑ 98CarMudM-5

Hernandez, Enzo
❑ 71MLBOffS-229
❑ 71OPC-529
❑ 71Top-529
❑ 72OPC-7
❑ 72PadPos-12
❑ 72Top-7
❑ 73OPC-438
❑ 73PadDea-11
❑ 73Top-438
❑ 74OPC-572
❑ 74PadDea-13
❑ 74PadMcDD-6
❑ 74Top-572
❑ 75OPC-84
❑ 75PadDea-10
❑ 75Top-84
❑ 75TopMin-84
❑ 76OPC-289
❑ 76SSP-125
❑ 76Top-289
❑ 76VenLeaS-113
❑ 77BurCheD-135
❑ 77PadSchC-27
❑ 77PadSchC-28
❑ 77Top-522
❑ 86PadGreT-3
❑ 90DodTar-339

Hernandez, Fernando
❑ 91BurIndP-3297
❑ 92ColRedC-16
❑ 92ColRedF-2385
❑ 93KinIndC-12
❑ 93KinIndF-2242
❑ 93KinIndTI-11
❑ 93LimRocDWB-103
❑ 96MemChiB-14
❑ 97Fle-633
❑ 97FleTif-633
❑ 97TolMudHB-21

Hernandez, Francis
❑ 96FreKeyB-26
❑ 97FreKey-10
❑ 98BowBayM-16

Hernandez, Francisco
❑ 97CalLeaATI-49

Hernandez, Guillermo (Willie)
❑ 76CubTri-11
❑ 76OklCit8TI-18
❑ 77CubJewT-7
❑ 78SSP270-255
❑ 78Top-99
❑ 79Top-614
❑ 80Top-472
❑ 81Don-589
❑ 81Fle-310
❑ 81Top-238
❑ 82CubRedL-38
❑ 82Top-23
❑ 83Don-174
❑ 83Fle-497
❑ 83Top-568
❑ 83TopTra-45T
❑ 84Don-163
❑ 84Fle-34
❑ 84FleUpd-51
❑ 84FunFooP-79
❑ 84Nes792-199
❑ 84OPC-199
❑ 84TigFarJ-6
❑ 84TigTeal-19
❑ 84TigWavP-19
❑ 84Top-199
❑ 84TopTif-199
❑ 84TopTra-51T
❑ 84TopTraT-51T
❑ 85AllGamPI-78
❑ 85Don-212
❑ 85Dra-37
❑ 85Fle-10
❑ 85FleStaS-101
❑ 85Lea-235
❑ 85OPC-333
❑ 85SevCoi-C7
❑ 85SevCoi-D10
❑ 85SevCoi-G1
❑ 85TigCaiD-10
❑ 85TigWen-11
❑ 85Top-333
❑ 85TopGaloC-5
❑ 85TopMin-333
❑ 85TopRubD-18
❑ 85TopSti-257
❑ 85TopSup-2
❑ 85TopTif-333
❑ 86Don-227
❑ 86DonAll-43
❑ 86DonWaxBC-PC5
❑ 86Fle-228
❑ 86FleLeaL-18
❑ 86FleStiC-56
❑ 86Lea-102
❑ 86OPC-341
❑ 86SevCoi-C9
❑ 86Spo-65
❑ 86Spo-85
❑ 86TigCaiD-8
❑ 86Top-670
❑ 86TopSti-275
❑ 86TopTat-8
❑ 86TopTif-670
❑ 87Don-522
❑ 87DonAll-43
❑ 87Fle-153
❑ 87FleExcS-26
❑ 87FleGamW-20
❑ 87FleGlo-153
❑ 87FleMin-54
❑ 87FleStiC-59
❑ 87OPC-339
❑ 87SevCoi-D4
❑ 87Spo-105
❑ 87SpoTeaP-15
❑ 87TigCaiD-13
❑ 87TigCok-15
❑ 87TolMudHP-27
❑ 87Top-515
❑ 87TopMinL-54
❑ 87TopSti-272
❑ 87TopTif-515
❑ 88Don-398
❑ 88DonBasB-125
❑ 88Fle-58
❑ 88FleGlo-58
❑ 88PanSti-84
❑ 88Sco-507
❑ 88ScoGlo-507
❑ 88StaLinTi-8
❑ 88TigPep-21
❑ 88Top-713
❑ 88TopBig-206
❑ 88TopTif-713
❑ 89BimBreD-9
❑ 89Don-62
❑ 89Fle-135
❑ 89FleGlo-135
❑ 89OPC-43
❑ 89Sco-275
❑ 89TigMar-21
❑ 89TigPol-21
❑ 89Top-43
❑ 89TopTif-43
❑ 89UppDec-279
❑ 90Don-610
❑ 90Fle-605
❑ 90FleCan-605
❑ 90PubIntS-473
❑ 90RedFolSB-46
❑ 90Sco-267
❑ 90UppDec-518

Hernandez, Henry
❑ 90St.PetCS-12

Hernandez, Jackie
❑ 65SeaPop-5
❑ 67CokCapDA-20
❑ 68Top-352
❑ 68TopVen-352
❑ 69RoySol-9
❑ 69Top-258
❑ 69TopSta-185
❑ 69TopTeaP-7
❑ 70MLBOffS-221
❑ 70RoyTeal-14
❑ 70Top-686
❑ 71MLBOffS-204
❑ 71OPC-144
❑ 71PirActP-18
❑ 71Top-144
❑ 72MilBra-141
❑ 72OPC-502
❑ 72Top-502
❑ 73OPC-363
❑ 73Top-363
❑ 74OPC-566
❑ 74Top-566
❑ 76VenLeaS-104

Hernandez, Javier
❑ 90AshTouC-5
❑ 91AshTouP-563
❑ 92OscAstF-2525

Hernandez, Jeremy
❑ 87EriCarP-26
❑ 88SprCarB-3
❑ 89St.PetCS-17
❑ 90TexLeaAGS-13
❑ 90WicWraRD-8
❑ 91LasVegSLD-283
❑ 91LasVegSP-230
❑ 91LinDriAAA-283
❑ 92Bow-73
❑ 92Don-756
❑ 92FleUpd-122
❑ 92LasVegSF-2792
❑ 92OPC-211
❑ 92PadMot-18
❑ 92PadSmo-12
❑ 92StaClu-734
❑ 92Top-211
❑ 92TopDeb91-76
❑ 92TopGol-211
❑ 92TopGolW-211
❑ 92TopMic-211
❑ 92Ult-576
❑ 92UppDec-42
❑ 93Don-180
❑ 93Fle-140
❑ 93Lea-502
❑ 93PacSpa-598
❑ 93StaClu-392
❑ 93StaCluFDI-392
❑ 93StaCluMOP-392
❑ 93Top-388
❑ 93TopGol-388
❑ 93TopInaM-388
❑ 93TopInaR-388
❑ 93TopMic-388
❑ 93Ult-473
❑ 93Ult-649
❑ 93UppDec-811
❑ 93UppDecGold-811
❑ 94Don-95
❑ 94Fle-105
❑ 94FleExtB-262
❑ 94FleUpd-135
❑ 94Sco-204
❑ 94ScoGolR-204
❑ 94StaClu-420
❑ 94StaCluFDI-420
❑ 94StaCluGR-420
❑ 94StaCluMOP-420
❑ 94Top-537
❑ 94TopGol-537
❑ 94TopSpa-537
❑ 95Don-366
❑ 95DonPreP-366
❑ 95Fla-138

Hernandez, Jesus
❑ 93LinVenB-46
❑ 95LinVen-28
❑ 96-97LinVen-151
❑ 96BurIndB-27
❑ 97AppLeaTPB-4
❑ 97BurIndG-14
❑ 98WatIndTI-13

Hernandez, John
❑ 97YakBeaG-10
❑ 98GreFalDG-14

Hernandez, Jose
❑ 89BlaYNPRWL-116
❑ 89GasRanP-1018
❑ 89GasRanS-8
❑ 90ChaRanS-10
❑ 91Cla/Bes-94
❑ 91LinDriAA-584
❑ 91TulDriLD-584
❑ 91TulDriP-2780
❑ 91TulDriTI-12
❑ 92CanIndF-698
❑ 92CanIndS-109
❑ 92Don-530
❑ 92Fle-307
❑ 92OPC-237
❑ 92Sco-866
❑ 92SkyAA F-51
❑ 92Top-237
❑ 92TopDeb91-77
❑ 92TopGol-237
❑ 92TopGolW-237
❑ 92TopMic-237
❑ 93OrlCubF-2793
❑ 93RanKee-183
❑ 94Ult-457
❑ 95Don-466
❑ 95DonPreP-466
❑ 95Fle-416
❑ 95Pac-72
❑ 96ColCho-498
❑ 96ColChoGS-498
❑ 96ColChoSS-498
❑ 96CubFle-8
❑ 96Don-136
❑ 96DonPreP-136
❑ 96Fle-320
❑ 96FleTif-320
❑ 96LeaSigEA-78
❑ 96Pac-23
❑ 97Pac-251
❑ 97PacLigB-251
❑ 97PacSil-251
❑ 98Pac-252
❑ 98PacOnl-142
❑ 98PacOnlR-142
❑ 98PacOnlWC-142
❑ 98PacPlaB-252
❑ 98PacRedT-252
❑ 98PacSil-252
❑ 98Top-234
❑ 98TopChr-234
❑ 98TopChrR-234
❑ 98TopDevR-234
❑ 98TopDia-234
❑ 98TopMiniC-234
❑ 99Fle-149
❑ 99FleSta9-149
❑ 99FleWarT-149
❑ 99MetUni-149
❑ 99MetUniGM-149
❑ 99MetUniPMG-149
❑ 99Pac-85
❑ 99PacCroC-58
❑ 99PacCroCPB-58
❑ 99PacPlaB-85
❑ 99PacRed-85
❑ 99SkyPre-55
❑ 99SkyPreR-55
❑ 99SkyThu-158
❑ 99SkyThuRant-158
❑ 99SkyThuRave-158
❑ 99StaClu-111
❑ 99StaCluFDI-111
❑ 99StaCluOoaK-111
❑ 99StaCluPP-111
❑ 99ThuSkySupR-158
❑ 99Top-90
❑ 99TopChr-90
❑ 99TopChrR-90
❑ 99TopMVPP-90

Hernandez, Keith
❑ 75OPC-623
❑ 75St.LouCP-14
❑ 75Top-623
❑ 75TopMin-623
❑ 76OPC-542
❑ 76SSP-590
❑ 76St.LouCP-15
❑ 76Top-542
❑ 77BurCheD-11
❑ 77Car5-11
❑ 77CarTeal-10
❑ 77Hos-115
❑ 77OPC-150
❑ 77Top-95
❑ 78CarTeal-11
❑ 78Hos-22
❑ 78OPC-109
❑ 78Top-143
❑ 79BasPat-38
❑ 79Car5-10
❑ 79Hos-108
❑ 79OPC-371
❑ 79Top-695
❑ 80BurKinPHR-16
❑ 80Kel-43
❑ 80OPC-170
❑ 80Top-201
❑ 80Top-321
❑ 80TopSup-26
❑ 81AllGamPI-96
❑ 81Car5x7-7
❑ 81CokTeaS-123
❑ 81Don-67
❑ 81Fle-545
❑ 81Kel-31
❑ 81MSAMinD-16
❑ 81OPC-195
❑ 81PerCreC-8
❑ 81Top-420
❑ 81TopScr-67
❑ 81TopSti-18
❑ 81TopSti-219
❑ 82Don-278
❑ 82FBIDis-13
❑ 82Fle-114
❑ 82FleSta-23
❑ 82K-M-36
❑ 82Kel-23
❑ 82OnDecD-16
❑ 82OPC-210
❑ 82PerCreC-8

❑ 82PerCreCG-8
❑ 82Top-186
❑ 82Top-210
❑ 82TopSti-92
❑ 83AllGamPI-95
❑ 83Car-8
❑ 83CarPanP-3
❑ 83Don-20
❑ 83Don-152
❑ 83DonActA-20
❑ 83Fle-8
❑ 83FleSta-78
❑ 83FleSti-6
❑ 83Kel-49
❑ 83OPC-262
❑ 83PerCreC-7
❑ 83PerCreCG-7
❑ 83Top-700
❑ 83TopFol-3
❑ 83TopGloS-4
❑ 83TopSti-188
❑ 83TopSti-290
❑ 83TopTra-43T
❑ 84AllGamPI-6
❑ 84Don-238
❑ 84DonActAS-23
❑ 84DonCha-46
❑ 84Dra-13
❑ 84Fle-587
❑ 84FleSti-49
❑ 84FunFooP-104
❑ 84MetFanC-4
❑ 84Nes792-120
❑ 84OPC-120
❑ 84RalPur-32
❑ 84RawGloT-1
❑ 84SevCoi-E24
❑ 84Top-120
❑ 84TopCer-32
❑ 84TopRubD-5
❑ 84TopSti-107
❑ 84TopStiB-6
❑ 84TopSup-26
❑ 84TopTif-120
❑ 85AllGamPI-97
❑ 85Don-68
❑ 85DonActA-41
❑ 85DonHig-21
❑ 85DonHig-27
❑ 85Dra-15
❑ 85Fle-85
❑ 85FleLimE-12
❑ 85FleStaS-25
❑ 85KASDis-5
❑ 85KitCloD-5
❑ 85Lea-62
❑ 85MetColP-25
❑ 85MetFanC-6
❑ 85MetTCM-24
❑ 85OPC-80
❑ 85PolMet-M5
❑ 85SevCoi-E10
❑ 85SubDis-33
❑ 85ThoMcAD-33
❑ 85Top-80
❑ 85Top-712
❑ 85Top3-D-11
❑ 85TopGloS-13
❑ 85TopRubD-6
❑ 85TopSti-98
❑ 85TopSup-36
❑ 85TopTif-80
❑ 85TopTif-712
❑ 86BasStaB-56
❑ 86Don-190
❑ 86DorChe-9
❑ 86Dra-10
❑ 86Fle-84
❑ 86FleMin-20
❑ 86FleStiC-55
❑ 86Lea-124
❑ 86MetColP-6
❑ 86MetFanC-5
❑ 86MetTCM-18
❑ 86MetWorSC-1
❑ 86OPC-252
❑ 86SevCoi-C3
❑ 86SevCoi-E3
❑ 86SevCoi-S3
❑ 86SevCoi-W3
❑ 86Spo-15
❑ 86Spo-62
❑ 86Spo-127
❑ 86Spo-179
❑ 86Spo-181
❑ 86Top-203
❑ 86Top-520
❑ 86Top-701
❑ 86Top3-D-10
❑ 86TopGloS-7
❑ 86TopMinL-53
❑ 86TopSti-99
❑ 86TopSup-31
❑ 86TopTat-1
❑ 86TopTif-203
❑ 86TopTif-520
❑ 86TopTif-701
❑ 86Woo-14
❑ 87BoaandB-12
❑ 87BurKinA-10
❑ 87ClaGam-4
❑ 87Don-76
❑ 87DonAll-11
❑ 87DonOpeD-124
❑ 87DonP-11
❑ 87Dra-10
❑ 87Fle-12
❑ 87Fle-629
❑ 87Fle-637
❑ 87FleGlo-12
❑ 87FleGlo-629
❑ 87FleGlo-637
❑ 87FleGlo-WS2
❑ 87FleHea-5
❑ 87FleHotS-21
❑ 87FleLimE-20
❑ 87FleMin-53
❑ 87FleStiC-58
❑ 87FleWaxBC-C6
❑ 87FleWorS-2
❑ 87GenMilB-5C
❑ 87KayB-17
❑ 87KeyFooD-4
❑ 87Lea-233
❑ 87MetColP-13
❑ 87MSAIceTD-4
❑ 87MSAJifPD-4
❑ 87OPC-350
❑ 87OurOwnTD-4
❑ 87RedFolSB-32
❑ 87SevCoi-E10
❑ 87SevCoi-M13
❑ 87Spo-133
❑ 87Spo-195
❑ 87SpoDeaP-3
❑ 87SpoSupD-13
❑ 87SpoTeaP-2
❑ 87StaHer-1
❑ 87StaHer-2
❑ 87StaHer-3
❑ 87StaHer-4
❑ 87StaHer-5
❑ 87StaHer-6
❑ 87StaHer-7
❑ 87StaHer-8
❑ 87StaHer-9
❑ 87StaHer-10
❑ 87StaHer-11
❑ 87StaHer-12
❑ 87StaHer-13
❑ 87StuPan-1
❑ 87Top-350
❑ 87Top-595
❑ 87TopCoi-36
❑ 87TopGloA-2
❑ 87TopGloS-26
❑ 87TopMinL-24
❑ 87TopSti-102
❑ 87TopSti-157
❑ 87TopTif-350
❑ 87TopTif-595
❑ 87WeiMarD-4
❑ 87Woo-31
❑ 88CheBoy-12
❑ 88Don-316
❑ 88DonAll-49
❑ 88DonBasB-152
❑ 88DonTeaBM-316
❑ 88Dra-5
❑ 88Fle-136
❑ 88Fle-639
❑ 88FleGlo-136
❑ 88FleGlo-639
❑ 88FleHotS-17
❑ 88FleLeaL-18
❑ 88FleMin-93
❑ 88FleStiC-103
❑ 88K-M-14
❑ 88Lea-117
❑ 88MetColP-5
❑ 88MetFanC-17
❑ 88MetKah-17
❑ 88MSAJifPD-9
❑ 88Nes-42
❑ 88OPC-68
❑ 88PanSti-339
❑ 88Sco-400
❑ 88ScoGlo-400
❑ 88Spo-31
❑ 88SpoGam-11
❑ 88StaLinAl-15
❑ 88StaLinMe-9
❑ 88TarPla-20
❑ 88Top-610
❑ 88TopBig-59
❑ 88TopGloS-32
❑ 88TopSti-97
❑ 88TopStiB-3
❑ 88TopTif-610
❑ 88TopUKM-33
❑ 88TopUKMT-33
❑ 89Bow-385
❑ 89BowTif-385
❑ 89ClaLigB-59
❑ 89Don-117
❑ 89DonBasB-208
❑ 89DonGraS-8
❑ 89Fle-37
❑ 89FleGlo-37
❑ 89MetCol8-57
❑ 89MetColP-9
❑ 89MetKah-11
❑ 89OPC-63
❑ 89OPCBoxB-G
❑ 89PanSti-137
❑ 89RedFolSB-57
❑ 89Sco-41
❑ 89ScoHot1S-23
❑ 89Spo-60
❑ 89Top-480
❑ 89TopBasT-48
❑ 89TopBatL-8
❑ 89TopBig-185
❑ 89TopDouM-8
❑ 89TopSti-93
❑ 89TopTif-291
❑ 89TopTif-480
❑ 89TopWaxBC-G
❑ 89TVSpoM-4
❑ 89UppDec-612
❑ 90BasWit-20
❑ 90Bow-342
❑ 90BowTif-342
❑ 90ClaYel-T36
❑ 90Don-388
❑ 90DonBesA-33
❑ 90Fle-205
❑ 90FleCan-205
❑ 90IndTeal-16
❑ 90KayB-16
❑ 90Lea-470
❑ 90MLBBasB-10
❑ 90OPC-230
❑ 90PubIntS-135
❑ 90PubIntS-262
❑ 90Sco-193
❑ 90Sco100S-29
❑ 90ScoRoo-57T
❑ 90Spo-106
❑ 90Top-230
❑ 90TopAmeA-8
❑ 90TopBatL-10
❑ 90TopBig-301
❑ 90TopTif-230
❑ 90TopTra-39T
❑ 90TopTraT-39T
❑ 90UppDec-222
❑ 90UppDec-777
❑ 91Fle-368
❑ 91MetWIZ-177
❑ 91Sco-89
❑ 92CarMcD-24
❑ 93ActPacA-148
❑ 94Yoo-7
❑ 97NewYorL-2

Hernandez, Kiki (Enrique)

❑ 89OneYanP-2100
❑ 90PriWilCTI-12
❑ 91GreHorP-3062
❑ 91SouAtlLAGP-SAL26
❑ 92AlbYanF-2228
❑ 92AlbYanSk-23
❑ 92Bow-637
❑ 92ClaFS7-102
❑ 92ForLauYTI-17
❑ 92ProFS7-125
❑ 92SkyAA F-3
❑ 92UppDecML-158
❑ 93ClaGolF-101
❑ 93ColCliF-1113
❑ 93ColCliP-11
❑ 94ColCliF-2954
❑ 94ColCliP-11
❑ 95ChaKniTI-11

Hernandez, Krandall

❑ 91HunCubC-12
❑ 91HunCubP-3337

Hernandez, Leo (Leonardo Jesus)

❑ 78CliDodT-13
❑ 79CliDodT-16
❑ 80VenLeaS-103
❑ 83TopTra-44T
❑ 84Nes792-71
❑ 84RocRedWT-15
❑ 84Top-71
❑ 84TopTif-71
❑ 85RocRedWT-5
❑ 86ColCliP-10
❑ 86ColCliP-11
❑ 91OriCro-194
❑ 92YanWIZ8-81
❑ 94VenLinU-182

Hernandez, Livan

❑ 96Bow-266
❑ 96BowFoi-266
❑ 96ChaKniB-14
❑ 96ColCho-432
❑ 96ColChoGS-432
❑ 96ColChoSS-432
❑ 96Fin-G294
❑ 96FinRef-G294
❑ 96Pin-372
❑ 96PinFoil-372
❑ 96PinProS-13
❑ 96Sel-174
❑ 96SelArtP-174
❑ 96Sum-172
❑ 96SumAbo&B-172
❑ 96SumArtP-172
❑ 96SumFoi-172
❑ 96UppDec-244
❑ 97Bow-153
❑ 97BowChr-153
❑ 97BowChrI-153
❑ 97BowChrIR-153
❑ 97BowChrR-153
❑ 97BowInt-153
❑ 97ChaKni-14
❑ 97Sel-181
❑ 97SelCom-181
❑ 97Top-382
❑ 98Bow-48
❑ 98BowBes-98
❑ 98BowBesAR-98
❑ 98BowBesR-98
❑ 98BowChr-48
❑ 98BowChrGA-48
❑ 98BowChrGAR-48
❑ 98BowChrI-48
❑ 98BowChrIR-48
❑ 98BowChrR-48
❑ 98BowChrR-50
❑ 98BowChrRR-50
❑ 98BowGolA-48
❑ 98BowInt-48
❑ 98CirThu-61
❑ 98CirThuFT-6
❑ 98CirThuRav-61
❑ 98CirThuSupRav-61
❑ 98ColCho-99
❑ 98CroRoy-58
❑ 98Don-106
❑ 98Don-376
❑ 98Don-419
❑ 98DonCol-106
❑ 98DonColE-495
❑ 98DonColL-394
❑ 98DonColP-700
❑ 98DonColS-106
❑ 98DonEli-95
❑ 98DonEliA-95
❑ 98DonEliS-95
❑ 98DonFANT-16
❑ 98DonFANTDC-16
❑ 98DonGolPP-106
❑ 98DonGolPP-376
❑ 98DonGolPP-419
❑ 98DonPre-150
❑ 98DonPreGES-7
❑ 98DonPreGX-7
❑ 98DonPreGXDC-7
❑ 98DonPreSeat-150
❑ 98DonPriCD-106
❑ 98DonPriCE-495
❑ 98DonPriCL-394
❑ 98DonPriCP-700
❑ 98DonRooDK-3
❑ 98DonRooDKC-3
❑ 98DonSig-73
❑ 98DonSigP-73
❑ 98DonSilPP-106
❑ 98DonSilPP-376
❑ 98DonSilPP-419
❑ 98E-X2-94
❑ 98E-X2ECFut-94
❑ 98E-X2ECNow-94
❑ 98E-X2SD2001-13
❑ 98Fin-131
❑ 98FinCen-C19
❑ 98FinCenR-C19
❑ 98FinNo--131
❑ 98FinNo-R-131
❑ 98FinRef-131
❑ 98FlaShoLeg0-16
❑ 98FlaShoLeg1-16
❑ 98FlaShoLeg2-16
❑ 98FlaShoLeg3-16
❑ 98FlaShoLegM-16
❑ 98FlaShoR0-16
❑ 98FlaShoR1-16
❑ 98FlaShoR2-16
❑ 98FlaShoR3-16
❑ 98Fle-366
❑ 98FleRooS-11
❑ 98FleVin'-93
❑ 98FleVin'C-93
❑ 98Lea-195
❑ 98LeaFraDA-195
❑ 98LeaFraF-195
❑ 98LeaFraM-195
❑ 98LeaFraM-195
❑ 98LeaFraMDC-195
❑ 98LeaFraMDC-195
❑ 98LeaFraMS-195
❑ 98LeaFraMZ2-195
❑ 98LeaRCrusUP-113
❑ 98LeaRS-238
❑ 98LeaRSCrusUG-113
❑ 98LeaRSCrusUR-113
❑ 98LeaRSFOSamp-6
❑ 98LeaRSFresh-6
❑ 98LeaRSLHolo-238
❑ 98LeaRSLong-238
❑ 98LeaRTrue-238
❑ 98MetUni-119
❑ 98MetUniPMG-119
❑ 98Pac-303
❑ 98PacAur-130
❑ 98PacGolCDC-16
❑ 98PacInv-99
❑ 98PacInvMiT-7
❑ 98PacInvPBlue-99
❑ 98PacInvSilv-99
❑ 98PacInvTeam-11
❑ 98PacLatotML-16
❑ 98PacNes-5B
❑ 98PacOme-96
❑ 98PacOmeR-96
❑ 98PacPar-160
❑ 98PacParC-160
❑ 98PacParG-160
❑ 98PacParHS-160
❑ 98PacParPB-160
❑ 98PacParR-160
❑ 98PacParTC-20
❑ 98PacPlaB-303
❑ 98PacRedT-303
❑ 98PacSil-303
❑ 98Pin-172
❑ 98PinArtP-PP75
❑ 98PinIns-61
❑ 98PinInsCE-61
❑ 98PinInsDE-61
❑ 98PinMinB-28
❑ 98PinMinCB-28
❑ 98PinMinCBAP-28
❑ 98PinMinCGP-28
❑ 98PinMinCGPAP-28
❑ 98PinMinCN-28
❑ 98PinMinCNAP-28
❑ 98PinMinCSGR-28
❑ 98PinMinDC-28
❑ 98PinMinG-28
❑ 98PinMinMCSS-28
❑ 98PinMinS-28
❑ 98PinMusC-PP75
❑ 98PinPer-111
❑ 98PinPerPP-111
❑ 98PinPlu-165
❑ 98PinPluAP-PP53
❑ 98PinPluGAP-PP53
❑ 98PinPluLM-3
❑ 98PinPluMAP-PP53
❑ 98PinPreP-172
❑ 98PorSeaD5AQ-20
❑ 98PreCon-16
❑ 98Revo-61
❑ 98RevoSS-61
❑ 98Sco-250
❑ 98ScoRT-197
❑ 98ScoRTSS-PP110
❑ 98ScoRTSSAP-PP110
❑ 98ScoRTSSAP1-PP110
❑ 98SkyDugA-142
❑ 98SkyDugAIA-142
❑ 98SP Aut-96
❑ 98SP AutC-LH
❑ 98SpoIll-59
❑ 98SpoIll-200
❑ 98SpoIllEE-59
❑ 98SpoIllEE-200
❑ 98SpoIllFE-59
❑ 98SpoIllFE-200
❑ 98SpoIllODMP-OD12
❑ 98SpoIllTaN-91
❑ 98SpoIllTaNEE-91
❑ 98SpoIllWSFMC-10
❑ 98SPxFin-278
❑ 98SPxFinR-278
❑ 98SPxFinS-278
❑ 98StaCluFDI-23
❑ 98StaCluFDI-40
❑ 98StaCluI-23
❑ 98StaCluI-40
❑ 98StaCluOneK-23
❑ 98StaCluOneK-40
❑ 98StaCluPP-23
❑ 98StaCluPP-40
❑ 98Stu-193
❑ 98StuGPP-193
❑ 98StuSPP-193
❑ 98Top-281
❑ 98Top-433
❑ 98TopChr-281
❑ 98TopChr-433
❑ 98TopChrR-281
❑ 98TopChrR-433
❑ 98TopDevR-281
❑ 98TopDevR-433
❑ 98TopDia-281
❑ 98TopDia-433
❑ 98TopGal-147
❑ 98TopGalAG-AG10
❑ 98TopGalGP-147
❑ 98TopGalOPP-147
❑ 98TopGalPPI-147
❑ 98TopGalPPIA-147
❑ 98TopMiniC-281
❑ 98TopMiniC-433
❑ 98TopSta-43
❑ 98TopStaB-43
❑ 98TopStaG-43
❑ 98TopStaGR-43
❑ 98TopStaS-43
❑ 98Ult-170
❑ 98UltGolM-170
❑ 98UltMas-170
❑ 98UltPlaM-170
❑ 98UppDec-91
❑ 98UppDec-420
❑ 98UppDec-430
❑ 98UppDecBCP-BC24
❑ 98UppDecNP-NP7
❑ 98UppDecR-38
❑ 98UppDecRTC-TC38
❑ 98UppDecSF-60
❑ 98Zen-75
❑ 98ZenZ-G-75
❑ 98ZenZ-S-75
❑ 99199Fin-42
❑ 99FinGolRef-42
❑ 99FinRef-42
❑ 99FlaShoLeg1-83
❑ 99FlaShoLeg2-83
❑ 99FlaShoLeg3-83
❑ 99FlaShoLegM1-83
❑ 99FlaShoLegM2-83
❑ 99FlaShoLegM3-83
❑ 99FlaShoR1-83
❑ 99FlaShoR2-83
❑ 99FlaShoR3-83
❑ 99Fle-157
❑ 99FleBri-48
❑ 99FleBri2G-48

❑ 99FleBriBlu-48
❑ 99FleBriGol-48
❑ 99FleMys-2
❑ 99FleMysG-2
❑ 99FleMysM-2
❑ 99FleSta9-157
❑ 99FleWarT-157
❑ 99MetUni-73
❑ 99MetUniGM-73
❑ 99MetUniPMG-73
❑ 99Pac-177
❑ 99PacAur-75
❑ 99PacAurOD-75
❑ 99PacCroC-115
❑ 99PacCroCPB-115
❑ 99PacCroCTC-12
❑ 99PacPar-96
❑ 99PacParC-96
❑ 99PacParG-96
❑ 99PacParHoloGold-96
❑ 99PacParHS-96
❑ 99PacParOD-96
❑ 99PacParPB-96
❑ 99PacParRed-96
❑ 99PacPlaB-177
❑ 99PacPri-62
❑ 99PacPriHB-62
❑ 99PacPriHG-62
❑ 99PacPriHM-62
❑ 99PacPriHP-62
❑ 99PacPriRed-62
❑ 99PacPriS-97
❑ 99PacPriS206-97
❑ 99PacPriS206R-97
❑ 99PacRed-177
❑ 99SkyMolM-78
❑ 99SkyMolMX-78
❑ 99SkyPre-86
❑ 99SkyPreR-86
❑ 99SkyThu-133
❑ 99SkyThuRant-133
❑ 99SkyThuRave-133
❑ 99SpoIll-125
❑ 99StaClu-78
❑ 99StaCluFDI-78
❑ 99StaCluOoaK-78
❑ 99StaCluPP-78
❑ 99ThuSkySupR-133
❑ 99Top-149
❑ 99TopChr-149
❑ 99TopChrR-149
❑ 99TopMVPP-149
❑ 99TopOpeD-85
❑ 99UD Cho-87
❑ 99UD ChoPCR-87
❑ 99UppDec-102
❑ 99UppDec-230
❑ 99UppDecEL1-102
❑ 99UppDecEL1-230
❑ 99UppDecEL2-102
❑ 99UppDecEL2-230
❑ 99UppDecEM-MC8
❑ 99UppDecEMFXG-MC8
❑ 99UppDecM-82
❑ 99UppDecMGS-82
❑ 99UppDecMHFS-82
❑ 99UppDecMP-82
❑ 99UppDecMSS-82
❑ 99Vic-157

Hernandez, Luis
❑ 90BriTigP-3153
❑ 90BriTigS-11
❑ 91BriTigC-5
❑ 91BriTigP-3614
❑ 92BriTigF-1418

Hernandez, Manny
❑ 82DayBeaAT-5
❑ 83DayBeaAT-6
❑ 84TucTorC-59
❑ 85DomLeaS-84
❑ 85TucTorC-56
❑ 86TucTorP-7
❑ 87TucTorP-7
❑ 88Don-481
❑ 88TucTorC-1
❑ 88TucTorJP-13
❑ 88TucTorP-169
❑ 89PorBeaC-2
❑ 89PorBeaP-221
❑ 90CMC-356
❑ 90ProAAAF-269
❑ 90TidTidC-5
❑ 90TidTidP-538
❑ 90TopTVM-45
❑ 91LinDriAAA-557
❑ 91MetWIZ-176
❑ 91TidTidLD-557
❑ 91TidTidP-2504

Hernandez, Marino
❑ 88PocGiaP-2085
❑ 89CliGiaP-884
❑ 90CliGiaB-16

Hernandez, Martin
❑ 86NasPirP-12
❑ 87SalBucP-11

Hernandez, Mike
❑ 94YakBeaF-3857
❑ 98OneYanG-15

Hernandez, Nick
❑ 78NewWayCT-20
❑ 79BurBeeT-8

Hernandez, Orlando
❑ 98Bow-221
❑ 98BowBes-183
❑ 98BowBesAR-183
❑ 98BowBesR-183
❑ 98BowChr-221
❑ 98BowChrGA-221
❑ 98BowChrGAR-221
❑ 98BowChrI-221
❑ 98BowChrIR-221
❑ 98BowChrR-221
❑ 98BowGolA-221
❑ 98BowInt-221
❑ 98ColCliD-11
❑ 98ColCliM-15
❑ 98CroRoy-92
❑ 98CroRoyDK-14
❑ 98DonSig-102
❑ 98DonSigP-102
❑ 98FleUpd-U14
❑ 98LeaRS-309
❑ 98LeaRSLHolo-309
❑ 98LeaRSLong-309
❑ 98LeaRTrue-309
❑ 98RevoRooHH-13
❑ 98RevoRooHHG-13
❑ 98RevoShow-10
❑ 98SpoIllWSF-127
❑ 98SpoIllWSFEE-127
❑ 98SpoIllWSFFE-127
❑ 98TopTek-73
❑ 98TopTekD-73
❑ 98UppDecR-124
❑ 98UppDecRNF-NF24
❑ 99199Fin-65
❑ 99Bow-30
❑ 99BowBes-21
❑ 99BowBesAR-21
❑ 99BowBesR-21
❑ 99BowChr-30
❑ 99BowChrG-30
❑ 99BowChrGR-30
❑ 99BowChrI-30
❑ 99BowChrIR-30
❑ 99BowChrR-30
❑ 99BowGol-30
❑ 99BowInt-30
❑ 99CroRoyB-96
❑ 99CroRoyL-96
❑ 99CroRoyOD-96
❑ 99E-X Cen-70
❑ 99E-X CenECFut-70
❑ 99E-X CenECNow-70
❑ 99FinGolRef-65
❑ 99FinRef-65
❑ 99Fle-100
❑ 99FleBri-61
❑ 99FleBri2G-61
❑ 99FleBriBlu-61
❑ 99FleBriGol-61
❑ 99FleDiaM-6
❑ 99FleMys-7
❑ 99FleMysD-5
❑ 99FleMysG-7
❑ 99FleMysM-7
❑ 99FleRooFla-12
❑ 99FleSta9-100
❑ 99FleWarT-100
❑ 99MetUni-265
❑ 99MetUniGM-265
❑ 99MetUniN-8
❑ 99MetUniPMG-265
❑ 99Pac-292
❑ 99PacAur-126
❑ 99PacAurOD-126
❑ 99PacCroC-188
❑ 99PacCroC-12
❑ 99PacCroCPB-188
❑ 99PacOme-162
❑ 99PacOmeC-162
❑ 99PacOmeG-162
❑ 99PacOmePB-162
❑ 99PacPar-160
❑ 99PacParC-160
❑ 99PacParG-160
❑ 99PacParHoloGold-160
❑ 99PacParHS-160
❑ 99PacParOD-160
❑ 99PacParPB-160
❑ 99PacParRed-160
❑ 99PacPlaB-292
❑ 99PacPri-98
❑ 99PacPriHB-98
❑ 99PacPriHG-98
❑ 99PacPriHM-98
❑ 99PacPriHP-98
❑ 99PacPriRed-98
❑ 99PacPriS-98
❑ 99PacPriS206-98
❑ 99PacPriS206R-98
❑ 99PacRed-292
❑ 99SkyMolM-103
❑ 99SkyMolMF-3
❑ 99SkyMolMFS-3
❑ 99SkyMolMFT-3
❑ 99SkyMolMX-103
❑ 99SkyPre-42
❑ 99SkyPreR-42
❑ 99SkyPreSB-9
❑ 99SkyThu-290
❑ 99SkyThuRant-290
❑ 99SkyThuRave-290
❑ 99SkyThuUnl-U10
❑ 99SP SigAuto-ED
❑ 99SP SigAutoG-ED
❑ 99SpoIll-41
❑ 99SPSig-14
❑ 99StaClu-35
❑ 99StaCluFDI-35
❑ 99StaCluNC-NC19
❑ 99StaCluOoaK-35
❑ 99StaCluPP-35
❑ 99ThuSkySupR-290
❑ 99Top-237
❑ 99Top-422
❑ 99TopAll-AM30
❑ 99TopBlaLC1-55
❑ 99TopBlaLC2-55
❑ 99TopBlaLC3-55
❑ 99TopChr-237
❑ 99TopChr-422
❑ 99TopChrA-AE30
❑ 99TopChrAR-AE30
❑ 99TopChrR-237
❑ 99TopChrR-422
❑ 99TopGal-95
❑ 99TopGalPP-95
❑ 99TopGalPPI-95
❑ 99TopGolL-55
❑ 99TopGolLC1-55
❑ 99TopGolLC2-55
❑ 99TopGolLOtO-55
❑ 99TopMVPP-422
❑ 99TopOpeD-128
❑ 99TopRedLC1-55
❑ 99TopRedLC2-55
❑ 99TopRedLC3-55
❑ 99TopSta-58
❑ 99TopSta1Foil-58
❑ 99TopStaFoil-58
❑ 99TopStaOS-58
❑ 99TopTek-40A
❑ 99TopTek-40B
❑ 99TopTekG-40A
❑ 99TopTekG-40B
❑ 99UD Cho-14
❑ 99UD ChoMBH-B15
❑ 99UD ChoPCR-14
❑ 99UD Ion-43
❑ 99UD IonR-43
❑ 99UDHolo-41
❑ 99UDHoloAUsome-41
❑ 99Ult-230
❑ 99UltGolM-230
❑ 99UltMas-230
❑ 99UltPlaM-230
❑ 99UltWorP-3
❑ 99UppDec-17
❑ 99UppDec-231
❑ 99UppDecBD-110
❑ 99UppDecBDD-110
❑ 99UppDecBDMN-M26
❑ 99UppDecBDMNE-M26
❑ 99UppDecBDQ-110
❑ 99UppDecBDT-110
❑ 99UppDecCLM-C67
❑ 99UppDecE-107
❑ 99UppDecEFXG-107
❑ 99UppDecEL1-17
❑ 99UppDecEL1-231
❑ 99UppDecEL2-17
❑ 99UppDecEL2-231
❑ 99UppDecM-145
❑ 99UppDecMGS-145
❑ 99UppDecMHFS-145
❑ 99UppDecMP-145
❑ 99UppDecMSS-145
❑ 99UppDecR-58
❑ 99UppDecRG-58
❑ 99UppDecRP-58
❑ 99Vic-269
❑ 99YanFle-8

Hernandez, Pedro
❑ 80KnoBluJT-17
❑ 81SyrChiT-15
❑ 81SyrChiTI-9
❑ 82SyrChiT-21
❑ 82SyrChiTI-14
❑ 85DomLeaS-78
❑ 85TucTorC-71
❑ 97GreFalDTI-14

Hernandez, Pete (Pedro Julio)
❑ 54SeaPop-11
❑ 78DayBeaAT-10

Hernandez, Rafael
❑ 91KinMetC-11
❑ 91KinMetP-3822
❑ 92PitMetC-8
❑ 92PitMetF-3304
❑ 93PitMetC-10
❑ 93PitMetF-3717

Hernandez, Ramon
❑ 91BilMusP-3760
❑ 91BilMusSP-17
❑ 92PriRedC-22
❑ 92PriRedF-3094
❑ 93BatCliCB-12
❑ 93BatCliF-3157
❑ 93SpaPhiC-15
❑ 93SpaPhiF-1061
❑ 96-97LinVen-179
❑ 96Bow-220
❑ 96BowFoi-220
❑ 96WesMicWB-11
❑ 97Bes-82
❑ 97BesAutSBPP-25
❑ 97BesDiaB-13
❑ 97Bow-418
❑ 97BowChr-278
❑ 97BowChrI-278
❑ 97BowChrIR-278
❑ 97BowChrR-278
❑ 97BowInt-418
❑ 97CalLeaATI-10
❑ 97CalLeaTP-30
❑ 97VisOakG-14
❑ 98Bes-70
❑ 98Bow-155
❑ 98BowBes-127
❑ 98BowBesAR-127
❑ 98BowBesR-127
❑ 98BowCerBlueAU-70
❑ 98BowCerGA-70
❑ 98BowCerSA-70
❑ 98BowChr-155
❑ 98BowChrGA-155
❑ 98BowChrGAR-155
❑ 98BowChrI-155
❑ 98BowChrIR-155
❑ 98BowChrR-155
❑ 98BowGolA-155
❑ 98BowInt-155
❑ 98ColCho-428
❑ 98ColChoPCR-428
❑ 98HunStaTI-10
❑ 98SouLeaTPG-12
❑ 98SP Aut-18
❑ 98SP MinDTSPE-DS3
❑ 98SP MinPE-93
❑ 98SP SPTSC-RH
❑ 98SPMin-93
❑ 98SPMinDTS-DS3
❑ 98Top-261
❑ 98TopChr-261
❑ 98TopChrR-261
❑ 98TopDevR-261
❑ 98TopDia-261
❑ 98TopMinC-261
❑ 98UppDec-565
❑ 98UppDecDS-DS47
❑ 99Bow-161
❑ 99BowBes-125
❑ 99BowBesAR-125
❑ 99BowBesR-125
❑ 99BowChr-161
❑ 99BowChrG-161
❑ 99BowChrGR-161
❑ 99BowChrI-161
❑ 99BowChrIR-161
❑ 99BowChrR-161
❑ 99BowGol-161
❑ 99BowInt-161
❑ 99SP TopP-60
❑ 99SP TopPC-RH
❑ 99SP TopPDtS-D15
❑ 99SP TopPGF-GF15
❑ 99SP TopPPE-60
❑ 99StaClu-352
❑ 99StaCluFDI-352
❑ 99StaCluOoaK-352
❑ 99StaCluPP-352
❑ 99Top-209
❑ 99TopChr-209
❑ 99TopChrR-209
❑ 99UppDec-446
❑ 99UppDecEL1-446
❑ 99UppDecEL2-446

Hernandez, Ramon Pitcher
❑ 67BraPho-12
❑ 67Top-576
❑ 68Top-382
❑ 73OPC-117
❑ 73Top-117
❑ 74OPC-222
❑ 74Top-222
❑ 75OPC-224
❑ 75PitPirP-8
❑ 75Top-224
❑ 75TopMin-224
❑ 76OPC-647
❑ 76PirPos-6
❑ 76SSP-567
❑ 76Top-647
❑ 77Top-468

Hernandez, Ray
❑ 66SeaPop-7

Hernandez, Rob
❑ 86LitFalMP-14
❑ 88St.LucMS-11
❑ 95ElmPioTI-11
❑ 95ElmPioUTI-11

Hernandez, Roberto M.
❑ 86SalAngC-100
❑ 87KenTwiP-2
❑ 87QuaCitAP-8
❑ 88BlaYNPRWL-70
❑ 88QuaCitAGS-20
❑ 89BlaYNPRWL-77
❑ 89MidAngGS-18
❑ 90Bes-216
❑ 90BirBarB-18
❑ 90BirBarP-1106
❑ 90CMC-820
❑ 91Bow-343
❑ 91LinDriAAA-637
❑ 91VanCanLD-637
❑ 91VanCanP-1591
❑ 92Bow-133
❑ 92Cla1-T45
❑ 92ClaGam-115
❑ 92Don-19
❑ 92Fle-677
❑ 92FleUpd-13
❑ 92OPC-667
❑ 92Pin-253
❑ 92PinRoo-9
❑ 92Sco-874
❑ 92SkyAAAF-284
❑ 92StaClu-356
❑ 92Top-667
❑ 92TopDeb91-78
❑ 92TopGol-667
❑ 92TopGolW-667
❑ 92TopMic-667
❑ 92Ult-336
❑ 92UppDec-7
❑ 92VanCanS-640
❑ 92WhiSoxK-39
❑ 93Don-403
❑ 93Fla-185
❑ 93Fle-583
❑ 93FleRooS-RSA4
❑ 93Lea-346
❑ 93OPC-126
❑ 93PacSpa-387
❑ 93Pin-129
❑ 93Sco-376
❑ 93Sel-311
❑ 93StaClu-21
❑ 93StaCluFDI-21
❑ 93StaCluMOP-21
❑ 93Top-70
❑ 93TopGol-70
❑ 93TopInaM-70
❑ 93TopInaR-70
❑ 93TopMic-70
❑ 93Toy-88
❑ 93Ult-533
❑ 93UppDec-352
❑ 93UppDecGold-352
❑ 93USPlaCR-9D
❑ 93WhiSoxK-11
❑ 93WhiSoxSC-8
❑ 94Bow-138
❑ 94ColC-134
❑ 94ColChoGS-134
❑ 94ColChoSS-134
❑ 94Don-116
❑ 94Fin-376
❑ 94FinRef-376
❑ 94Fla-277
❑ 94Fle-83
❑ 94FUnPac-77
❑ 94Lea-167
❑ 94OPC-94
❑ 94Pac-127
❑ 94PanSti-48
❑ 94Pin-164
❑ 94PinArtP-164
❑ 94PinMusC-164
❑ 94Sco-457
❑ 94ScoGolR-457
❑ 94Sel-277
❑ 94StaClu-182
❑ 94StaCluFDI-182
❑ 94StaCluGR-182
❑ 94StaCluMOP-182
❑ 94StaCluT-129
❑ 94StaCluTFDI-129
❑ 94Top-572
❑ 94TopGol-572
❑ 94TopSpa-572
❑ 94TriPla-265
❑ 94Ult-34
❑ 94UltFir-4
❑ 94UppDec-468
❑ 94UppDecED-468
❑ 94WhiSoxK-12
❑ 95ColCho-507
❑ 95ColChoGS-507
❑ 95ColChoSS-507
❑ 95Don-279
❑ 95DonPreP-279
❑ 95DonTopotO-50
❑ 95Fin-161
❑ 95FinRef-161
❑ 95Fla-245
❑ 95Fle-119
❑ 95Lea-164
❑ 95Pac-90
❑ 95Sco-449
❑ 95ScoGolR-449
❑ 95ScoPlaTS-449
❑ 95StaClu-420
❑ 95StaCluMOP-420
❑ 95StaCluSTWS-420
❑ 95StaCluVR-218
❑ 95StaCluVRMO-218
❑ 95Top-191
❑ 95TopCyb-109
❑ 95TopPre-PP8
❑ 95TopPreS-PP8
❑ 95Ult-29
❑ 95UltGolM-29
❑ 95UppDec-436
❑ 95UppDecED-436
❑ 95UppDecEDG-436
❑ 95UppDecSE-22
❑ 95UppDecSEG-22
❑ 95WhiSoxK-13
❑ 96Baz-87
❑ 96ColCho-96
❑ 96ColChoGS-96
❑ 96ColChoSS-96
❑ 96Don-205
❑ 96DonPreP-205
❑ 96Fin-B5
❑ 96FinRef-B5
❑ 96Fla-52
❑ 96Fle-67
❑ 96FleTif-67
❑ 96LeaSigA-100

❑ 96LeaSigAG-100
❑ 96LeaSigAS-100
❑ 96MetUni-38
❑ 96MetUniP-38
❑ 96Pac-288
❑ 96PacPri-P90
❑ 96PacPriG-P90
❑ 96Sco-192
❑ 96StaClu-22
❑ 96StaCluEPB-22
❑ 96StaCluEPG-22
❑ 96StaCluEPS-22
❑ 96StaCluMOP-22
❑ 96Top-405
❑ 96TopGal-86
❑ 96TopGalPPI-86
❑ 96Ult-39
❑ 96UltGolM-39
❑ 96UppDec-304
❑ 96WhiSoxF-7
❑ 97Bow-285
❑ 97BowChr-96
❑ 97BowChrI-96
❑ 97BowChrIR-96
❑ 97BowChrR-96
❑ 97BowInt-285
❑ 97Cir-229
❑ 97CirRav-229
❑ 97ColCho-297
❑ 97ColChoT-CW12
❑ 97Don-129
❑ 97DonGolPP-129
❑ 97DonSilPP-129
❑ 97DonTea-63
❑ 97DonTeaSPE-63
❑ 97Fin-19
❑ 97FinRef-19
❑ 97Fle-62
❑ 97FleTif-62
❑ 97Lea-10
❑ 97LeaFraM-10
❑ 97LeaFraMDC-10
❑ 97MetUni-59
❑ 97NewPin-46
❑ 97NewPinAP-46
❑ 97NewPinMC-46
❑ 97NewPinPP-46
❑ 97Pac-54
❑ 97PacLigB-54
❑ 97PacSil-54
❑ 97Sco-131
❑ 97ScoArtPWB-131
❑ 97ScoPreS-131
❑ 97ScoShoS-131
❑ 97ScoShoSAP-131
❑ 97SP-47
❑ 97StaCluMat-38
❑ 97Top-232
❑ 97TopAll-AS21
❑ 97TopChr-82
❑ 97TopChrAS-AS21
❑ 97TopChrR-82
❑ 97TopChrSAR-AS21
❑ 97TopGal-104
❑ 97TopGalPPI-104
❑ 97Ult-40
❑ 97UltGolME-40
❑ 97UltPlaME-40
❑ 97UppDec-332
❑ 97WhiSoxS-6
❑ 97WhiSoxSPI-6
❑ 97WhiSoxSPr-6
❑ 97WhiSoxTI-39
❑ 98CirThu-74
❑ 98CirThuRav-74
❑ 98CirThuSupRav-74
❑ 98ColCho-501
❑ 98DevRayP-5
❑ 98Fle-452
❑ 98FleDiamInk-6
❑ 98MetUni-34
❑ 98MetUniPMG-34
❑ 98Pac-441
❑ 98PacAur-80
❑ 98PacInvTeam-30
❑ 98PacOme-231
❑ 98PacOmeR-231
❑ 98PacOnl-709
❑ 98PacOnlR-709
❑ 98PacOnlWC-709
❑ 98PacPlaB-441
❑ 98PacRedT-441
❑ 98PacSil-441
❑ 98PacTeaC-30
❑ 98PinPlu-93
❑ 98PinSna-TBDR14
❑ 98SkyDugAAR-7
❑ 98SP Aut-186
❑ 98StaCluFDI-324
❑ 98StaCluI-324
❑ 98StaCluOneK-324
❑ 98StaCluPP-324
❑ 98Top-430
❑ 98TopChr-430
❑ 98TopChrR-430
❑ 98TopDevR-430
❑ 98TopDia-430
❑ 98TopMiniC-430
❑ 98Ult-5
❑ 98Ult-464
❑ 98UltGolM-5
❑ 98UltGolM-464
❑ 98UltMas-5
❑ 98UltMas-464
❑ 98UltPlaM-5
❑ 98UltPlaM-464
❑ 98UppDec-734
❑ 99Fle-365
❑ 99FleSta9-365
❑ 99FleWarT-365
❑ 99MetUni-108
❑ 99MetUniGM-108
❑ 99MetUniPMG-108
❑ 99Pac-410
❑ 99PacCroC-274
❑ 99PacCroCPB-274
❑ 99PacPar-226
❑ 99PacParC-226
❑ 99PacParG-226
❑ 99PacParHoloGold-226
❑ 99PacParHS-226
❑ 99PacParOD-226
❑ 99PacParPB-226
❑ 99PacParRed-226
❑ 99PacPlaB-410
❑ 99PacRed-410
❑ 99SkyPre-198
❑ 99SkyPreR-198
❑ 99StaClu-24
❑ 99StaCluFDI-24
❑ 99StaCluOoaK-24
❑ 99StaCluPP-24
❑ 99Top-81
❑ 99TopChr-81
❑ 99TopChrR-81
❑ 99TopMVPP-81
❑ 99Ult-125
❑ 99UltGolM-125
❑ 99UltMas-125
❑ 99UltPlaM-125
❑ 99UppDec-495
❑ 99UppDecEL1-495
❑ 99UppDecEL2-495
❑ 99Vic-383

Hernandez, Rudy (Rudolph Albert)
❑ 55DonWin-24
❑ 61Top-229

Hernandez, Rudy J.
❑ 89St.LucMS-9
❑ 90JacMetGS-21
❑ 90TexLeaAGS-21
❑ 91LinDriAA-633
❑ 91WilBilLD-633
❑ 91WilBilP-301
❑ 93LinVenB-168
❑ 94VenLinU-45
❑ 95LinVen-113

Hernandez, Santos
❑ 95BurBeeTI-5
❑ 96BurBeeTI-5
❑ 96MidLeaAB-14
❑ 97SanJosG-20
❑ 98DurBulTI-11

Hernandez, Toby
❑ 80UtiBluJT-18
❑ 80VenLeaS-56
❑ 83SyrChiT-14
❑ 84SyrChiT-15
❑ 85TolMudHT-13

Hernandez, Tom
❑ 91GasRanC-15
❑ 91GasRanP-2692

Hernandez, Victor
❑ 97SouOreTB-11

Hernandez, Wicho
❑ 94PitMetC-11
❑ 94PitMetF-3528

Hernandez, Xavier
❑ 88MyrBeaBJP-1178
❑ 88SouAtlLAGS-21
❑ 89KnoBluJB-9
❑ 89KnoBluJP-1144
❑ 89SyrChiMB-14
❑ 90AstLenH-15
❑ 90Don-682
❑ 90DonRoo-33
❑ 90Lea-517
❑ 90TopDeb89-55
❑ 90UppDec-26
❑ 91AstMot-26
❑ 91Bow-545
❑ 91Don-708
❑ 91Fle-509
❑ 91Lea-462
❑ 91OPC-194
❑ 91Sco-564
❑ 91StaClu-74
❑ 91Top-194
❑ 91TopDesS-194
❑ 91TopMic-194
❑ 91TopTif-194
❑ 92AstMot-26
❑ 92Don-782
❑ 92Fle-437
❑ 92OPC-640
❑ 92StaClu-736
❑ 92StaCluNC-736
❑ 92Top-640
❑ 92TopGol-640
❑ 92TopGolW-640
❑ 92TopMic-640
❑ 92Ult-205
❑ 93AstMot-23
❑ 93AstStaC-24
❑ 93Don-636
❑ 93Fle-53
❑ 93Lea-543
❑ 93OPC-233
❑ 93PacSpa-477
❑ 93Pin-453
❑ 93Sco-417
❑ 93StaClu-271
❑ 93StaCluFDI-271
❑ 93StaCluMOP-271
❑ 93Top-252
❑ 93TopGol-252
❑ 93TopInaM-252
❑ 93TopInaR-252
❑ 93TopMic-252
❑ 93Ult-43
❑ 93UppDec-319
❑ 93UppDecGold-319
❑ 94ColC-399
❑ 94ColChoGS-399
❑ 94ColChoSS-399
❑ 94Don-143
❑ 94Fin-373
❑ 94FinRef-373
❑ 94Fla-81
❑ 94Fle-493
❑ 94FleExtB-130
❑ 94FleUpd-67
❑ 94Lea-273
❑ 94Pac-268
❑ 94Pin-471
❑ 94PinArtP-471
❑ 94PinMusC-471
❑ 94ScoRoo-RT53
❑ 94ScoRooGR-RT53
❑ 94SpoRoo-18
❑ 94SpoRooAP-18
❑ 94StaClu-616
❑ 94StaCluFDI-616
❑ 94StaCluGR-616
❑ 94StaCluMOP-616
❑ 94StaCluT-201
❑ 94StaCluTFDI-201
❑ 94Top-512
❑ 94TopGol-512
❑ 94TopSpa-512
❑ 94TopTra-83T
❑ 94Ult-206
❑ 94Ult-399
❑ 94UppDec-342
❑ 94UppDecED-342
❑ 95Fle-69
❑ 95FleUpd-133
❑ 95Pac-296
❑ 95RedKah-10
❑ 96ColCho-518
❑ 96ColChoGS-518
❑ 96ColChoSS-518
❑ 96Don-170
❑ 96DonPreP-170
❑ 96Fle-342
❑ 96FleTif-342
❑ 96Pac-42
❑ 97Fle-641
❑ 97FleTif-641
❑ 97Pac-318
❑ 97PacLigB-318
❑ 97PacSil-318
❑ 97RanDr P-12
❑ 97RanMot-26
❑ 98OklRedM-22
❑ 99PacCroC-285
❑ 99PacCroCPB-285

Herndon, Eric
❑ 98DanBraQ-24

Herndon, Junior
❑ 98CliLumG-8
❑ 98MidLeaPM-8
❑ 99BasAmeTP-52
❑ 99BasAmeTPG-52
❑ 99Bow-362
❑ 99BowGol-362
❑ 99BowInt-362

Herndon, Larry
❑ 75PhoGiaC-9
❑ 75PhoGiaCK-20
❑ 75TulOil7-12
❑ 76PheGiaCr-11
❑ 76PhoGiaCC-11
❑ 76SanFraGP-9
❑ 77BurCheD-104
❑ 77Hos-47
❑ 77OPC-169
❑ 77Top-397
❑ 78GiaTeal-11
❑ 78Top-512
❑ 79GiaPol-31
❑ 79OPC-328
❑ 79Top-624
❑ 80GiaPol-31
❑ 80GiaTeal-8
❑ 80Top-257
❑ 81Don-196
❑ 81Fle-451
❑ 81OPC-108
❑ 81Top-409
❑ 81TopSti-236
❑ 82Don-172
❑ 82Fle-390
❑ 82OPC-182
❑ 82Top-182
❑ 82TopSti-109
❑ 82TopStiV-109
❑ 82TopTra-43T
❑ 83AllGamPI-55
❑ 83Don-585
❑ 83DonActA-5
❑ 83Fle-330
❑ 83FleSta-79
❑ 83FleSti-256
❑ 83OPC-13
❑ 83TigPos-14
❑ 83Top-13
❑ 83Top-261
❑ 83TopSti-68
❑ 84AllGamPI-144
❑ 84Don-349
❑ 84Fle-82
❑ 84Nes792-333
❑ 84OPC-333
❑ 84TigFarJ-7
❑ 84TigTeal-18
❑ 84TigWavP-20
❑ 84Top-333
❑ 84TopSti-264
❑ 84TopTif-333
❑ 85Don-150
❑ 85Fle-11
❑ 85Lea-249
❑ 85OPC-9
❑ 85SevCoi-D4
❑ 85TigCaiD-11
❑ 85TigWen-12
❑ 85Top-591
❑ 85TopSti-266
❑ 85TopTif-591
❑ 86Don-593
❑ 86Fle-229
❑ 86Lea-230
❑ 86OPC-61
❑ 86TigCaiD-9
❑ 86Top-688
❑ 86TopSti-271
❑ 86TopTif-688
❑ 87DonOpeD-211
❑ 87Fle-154
❑ 87FleGlo-154
❑ 87SevCoi-D5
❑ 87TigCaiD-11
❑ 87TigCok-2
❑ 87Top-298
❑ 87TopTif-298
❑ 88Don-353
❑ 88Fle-59
❑ 88FleGlo-59
❑ 88OPC-146
❑ 88RedFolSB-34
❑ 88Sco-138
❑ 88ScoGlo-138
❑ 88StaLinTi-9
❑ 88TigPep-31
❑ 88TigPol-6
❑ 88Top-743
❑ 88TopBig-56
❑ 88TopTif-743
❑ 89Sco-279
❑ 89UppDec-49
❑ 93TigGat-28

Herold, Bob
❑ 92OmaRoyF-2978
❑ 92OmaRoyS-350
❑ 96SpoIndB-1
❑ 97LanLugTS-9
❑ 98LanLugQ-28

Herr, Edward
❑ 19Zee-71
❑ 87OldJudN-240

Herr, Tommy (Thomas)
❑ 77St.PetCT-14
❑ 78ArkTraT-13
❑ 80Top-684
❑ 81Car5x7-8
❑ 81Car5x7-9
❑ 81CokTeaS-124
❑ 81Don-68
❑ 81Fle-550
❑ 81Top-266
❑ 82Don-530
❑ 82Fle-115
❑ 82FleSta-30
❑ 82Top-27
❑ 83AllGamPI-102
❑ 83Car-9
❑ 83CarPanP-3
❑ 83Don-217
❑ 83Fle-9
❑ 83FleSta-80
❑ 83OPC-97
❑ 83Top-489
❑ 83TopSti-286
❑ 84AllGamPI-11
❑ 84Car-10
❑ 84Car5x7-10
❑ 84Don-596
❑ 84Fle-325
❑ 84Nes792-649
❑ 84OPC-117
❑ 84Top-649
❑ 84TopSti-142
❑ 84TopTif-649
❑ 85AllGamPI-101
❑ 85CarTeal-13
❑ 85Don-425
❑ 85DonActA-43
❑ 85Fle-226
❑ 85OPC-113
❑ 85Top-113
❑ 85TopMin-113
❑ 85TopSti-142
❑ 85TopTif-113
❑ 86BasStaB-57
❑ 86CarIGAS-6
❑ 86CarKASD-15
❑ 86CarSchM-8
❑ 86CarTeal-17
❑ 86Don-83
❑ 86DonAll-2
❑ 86DonPop-2
❑ 86Dra-21
❑ 86Fle-37
❑ 86FleAll-2
❑ 86FleMin-8
❑ 86FleStiC-57
❑ 86Lea-79
❑ 86OPC-94
❑ 86SevCoi-S14
❑ 86Spo-113
❑ 86Top-550
❑ 86Top-702
❑ 86TopGloA-14
❑ 86TopGloS-32
❑ 86TopMinL-62
❑ 86TopSti-49
❑ 86TopSti-147
❑ 86TopSup-32
❑ 86TopTat-22
❑ 86TopTif-550
❑ 86TopTif-702
❑ 87CarSmo-20
❑ 87CarTeal-11
❑ 87Don-140
❑ 87DonOpeD-61
❑ 87Fle-296
❑ 87FleGlo-296
❑ 87FleLeaL-22
❑ 87Lea-121
❑ 87OPC-181
❑ 87RedFolSB-60
❑ 87SpoTeaP-12
❑ 87Top-721
❑ 87TopSti-49
❑ 87TopTif-721
❑ 88Don-208
❑ 88DonBasB-326
❑ 88Fle-35
❑ 88FleGlo-35
❑ 88FleGlo-WS7
❑ 88FleGlo-WS10
❑ 88FleHotS-18
❑ 88FleUpd-43
❑ 88FleUpdG-43
❑ 88FleWorS-7
❑ 88FleWorS-10
❑ 88Lea-201
❑ 88OPC-310
❑ 88PanSti-389
❑ 88PanSti-391
❑ 88Sco-84
❑ 88ScoGlo-84
❑ 88ScoRoo-8T
❑ 88ScoRooG-8T
❑ 88Spo-141
❑ 88StaLinCa-7
❑ 88Top-310
❑ 88TopBig-31
❑ 88TopSti-50
❑ 88TopStiB-4
❑ 88TopTif-310
❑ 88TopTra-49T
❑ 88TopTraT-49T
❑ 89Bow-403
❑ 89BowTif-403
❑ 89ClaTraP-166
❑ 89Don-301
❑ 89DonBasB-72
❑ 89DonTra-4
❑ 89Fle-115
❑ 89FleGlo-115
❑ 89FleUpd-107
❑ 89PhiTas-10
❑ 89Sco-191
❑ 89ScoRoo-9T
❑ 89Top-709
❑ 89TopBig-283
❑ 89TopTif-709
❑ 89TopTra-49T
❑ 89TopTraT-49T
❑ 89UppDec-558
❑ 89UppDec-720
❑ 90Bow-159
❑ 90BowTif-159
❑ 90Don-21
❑ 90Don-75
❑ 90DonBesN-32
❑ 90DonLeaS-16
❑ 90DonSupD-21
❑ 90Fle-560
❑ 90FleBasM-18
❑ 90FleBasMC-18
❑ 90FleCan-560
❑ 90Lea-184
❑ 90M.Vpin-79
❑ 90MLBBasB-1
❑ 90OPC-297
❑ 90PanSti-309
❑ 90PhiTas-13
❑ 90PubIntS-239
❑ 90RedFolSB-47
❑ 90Sco-171
❑ 90Sco100S-77
❑ 90Spo-63
❑ 90Top-297
❑ 90TopBig-206
❑ 90TopCoi-49
❑ 90TopSti-122
❑ 90TopTif-297
❑ 90UppDec-488
❑ 91Bow-480
❑ 91Don-610
❑ 91Fle-149

❑ 91Lea-48
❑ 91MetColP-17
❑ 91MetKah-28
❑ 91MetWIZ-178
❑ 91OPC-64
❑ 91Sco-820
❑ 91StaClu-532
❑ 91Stu-205
❑ 91Top-64
❑ 91TopDesS-64
❑ 91TopMic-64
❑ 91TopTif-64
❑ 91Ult-219
❑ 91UppDec-416
❑ 92CarMcD-37
Herrera, Desmond
❑ 96BilMusTI-13
Herrera, Edgar
❑ 89GeoColC-11
❑ 90GeoColC-8
❑ 93Bow-241
❑ 93ClaFS7-205
❑ 93EliTwiC-11
❑ 93EliTwiF-3428
❑ 93ForWayWC-11
❑ 93ForWayWF-1981
❑ 93LinVenB-51
❑ 94VenLinU-238
Herrera, Ezequiel
❑ 90Bes-41
❑ 90SprCarB-9
❑ 91St.PetCC-26
❑ 91St.PetCP-2289
❑ 92St.PetCC-22
❑ 92St.PetCF-2039
Herrera, Francisco
❑ 80VenLeaS-5
Herrera, Hector
❑ 87AubAstP-20
Herrera, Ivan
❑ 96BelGiaTI-27
Herrera, Jose C.
❑ 69Top-378
❑ 76VenLeaS-54
Herrera, Jose Ramon Catalina
❑ 91MedHatBJP-4115
❑ 91MedHatBJSP-9
❑ 92MedHatBJF-3220
❑ 92MedHatBJSP-9
❑ 93HagSunC-1
❑ 93HagSunF-1891
❑ 93SouAtlLAGF-27
❑ 94Bow-604
❑ 94Cla-8
❑ 94ClaTriF-T58
❑ 94ExcFS7-145
❑ 94ModA'sC-1
❑ 94ModA'sF-3075
❑ 94TedWil-122
❑ 94UppDecML-168
❑ 95Bow-177
❑ 95BowBes-B83
❑ 95BowBesR-B83
❑ 95Exc-109
❑ 95HunStaTI-13
❑ 95UppDecML-62
❑ 95UppDecML-108
❑ 95UppDecMLFS-62
❑ 95UppDecMLFS-108
❑ 96A'sMot-9
❑ 96ColChoGS-16
❑ 96ColChoSS-16
❑ 96Don-460
❑ 96DonPreP-460
❑ 96Fin-B352
❑ 96FinRef-B352
❑ 96Fle-210
❑ 96FleTif-210
❑ 96Lea-132
❑ 96LeaPre-144
❑ 96LeaPreP-144
❑ 96LeaPrePB-132
❑ 96LeaPrePG-132
❑ 96LeaPrePS-132
❑ 96Pin-190
❑ 96Sco-250
❑ 96Top-338
❑ 96UltGolP-7
❑ 96UltGolPGM-7
❑ 96UppDec-239
❑ 96UppDecPHE-H22
❑ 96UppDecPreH-H22
❑ 97Cir-22
❑ 97CirRav-22
❑ 97Fle-191
❑ 97FleTif-191
❑ 97Lea-283
❑ 97LeaFraM-283
❑ 97LeaFraMDC-283
❑ 97MetUni-130
❑ 97Pac-170
❑ 97PacLigB-170
❑ 97PacSil-170
❑ 97Sco-81
❑ 97ScoArtPWB-81
❑ 97ScoPreS-81
❑ 97ScoShoS-81
❑ 97ScoShoSAP-81
❑ 97StaClu-307
❑ 97StaCluMOP-307
❑ 97Top-48
❑ 98SyrSkyG-16
Herrera, Musulungo
❑ 95LinVen-259
Herrera, Pascuel
❑ 92MedHatBJSP-12
Herrera, Pedro
❑ 98SpoIndG-14
Herrera, Poncho (Juan)
❑ 58Top-433A
❑ 58Top-433B
❑ 59Top-129
❑ 59TopVen-129
❑ 60Lea-5
❑ 60PhiJayP-8
❑ 60Top-130
❑ 60TopVen-130
❑ 61Baz-27
❑ 61Pos-121A
❑ 61Pos-121B
❑ 61Top-569
❑ 61TopMagR-36
❑ 61TopStaI-56
❑ 62Jel-192
❑ 62Pos-192
❑ 62PosCan-192
❑ 62SalPlaC-122
❑ 62ShiPlaC-122
Herrera, Ramon
❑ 26Exh-67
❑ 86NegLeaF-84
Herrera, Raul
❑ 93ClaGolF-102
❑ 94VenLinU-254
Herrholtz, John
❑ 91UtiBluSC-3
❑ 91UtiBluSP-3236
❑ 92SouBenWSF-173
Herriage, Troy
❑ 56A'sPos-26
Herrick, Jason
❑ 94CedRapKC-14
❑ 94CedRapKF-1122
❑ 95CedRapKTI-14
❑ 96LakElsSB-24
❑ 97MidAng-17
❑ 98MidAngG-16
❑ 98MidAngO-18
Herrick, Neal
❑ 81MiaOriT-16
Herring, Art
❑ 46DodTeal-13
❑ 90DodTar-340
Herring, Jonathan
❑ 96MedHatBJTI-12
Herring, Paul
❑ 80WatRedT-5
❑ 81IndIndTI-27
❑ 82WatRedT-16
Herring, Vince
❑ 90SanJosGB-20
❑ 90SanJosGCLC-48
❑ 90SanJosGP-2010
❑ 90SanJosGS-11
❑ 91SanJosGC-17
❑ 91SanJosGP-5
❑ 92SanJosGC-22
Herrmann, August
❑ 09SpoNewSM-93
❑ 95ConTSN-1396
Herrmann, Ed
❑ 69Top-439
❑ 70OPC-368
❑ 70Top-368
❑ 71OPC-169
❑ 71Top-169
❑ 72OPC-452
❑ 72Top-452
❑ 72WhiSox-5
❑ 72WhiSoxC-2
❑ 72WhiSoxDS-2
❑ 72WhiSoxTI1-7
❑ 73LinPor-48
❑ 73OPC-73
❑ 73Top-73
❑ 74OPC-438
❑ 74Top-438
❑ 74TopSta-155
❑ 75Hos-86
❑ 75OPC-219
❑ 75Top-219
❑ 75TopMin-219
❑ 75YanSSP-8
❑ 76OPC-406
❑ 76SSP-440
❑ 76Top-406
❑ 77Top-143
❑ 78AstBurK-3
❑ 78Top-677
❑ 79ExpPos-11
❑ 79OPC-194
❑ 79Top-374
❑ 87AstShoSPT-12
❑ 92YanWIZ7-73
Herrmann, Gary
❑ 92BatCliCB-13
❑ 92BatCliF-3258
❑ 94ClePhiC-18
❑ 94ClePhiF-2524
❑ 95ClePhiF-213
❑ 96ReaPhiB-7
Herrmann, Leroy
❑ 31Zee-19
❑ 32CubTeal-13
❑ 32Zee-25
❑ 33Zee-122
❑ 37Zee-15
❑ 93ConTSN-973
Herrmann, Tim
❑ 89NiaFalRP-11
❑ 90FayGenP-2401
Herrnstein, John
❑ 63Top-553
❑ 64PhiPhiB-14
❑ 64Top-243
❑ 64TopVen-243
❑ 65Top-534
❑ 66BraPos-12
❑ 66Top-304
❑ 66TopVen-304
❑ 78TCM60I-124
Herrolz, John
❑ 92UtiBluSC-26
Herron, Tony
❑ 84PawRedST-11A
❑ 84PawRedST-11B
❑ 85PawRedST-16
Herrscher, Rick
❑ 76DalCon-5
❑ 77FriOneYW-69
❑ 91MetWIZ-179
Herry, David
❑ 92LSUTigM-15
Hersh, Dave
❑ 77BurBeeT-13
❑ 78AppFoxT-12
Hersh, Earl
❑ 60MapLeaSF-9
❑ 61MapLeaBH-8
Hershberger, N. Mike
❑ 61UniOil-SD4
❑ 62Top-341
❑ 63Top-254
❑ 63WhiSoxJP-5
❑ 63WhiSoxTS-10
❑ 64A's-9
❑ 64Top-465
❑ 64WhiSoxI-13
❑ 64WhiSoxTS-12
❑ 65AthJayP-8
❑ 65OPC-89
❑ 65Top-89
❑ 66Top-236
❑ 66TopVen-236
❑ 67CokCapAt-11
❑ 67DexPre-94
❑ 67Top-323
❑ 68OPC-18
❑ 68Top-18
❑ 68TopVen-18
❑ 69MilBra-111
❑ 69MLBOffS-86
❑ 69Top-655
❑ 69TopTeaP-21
❑ 70BreMcD-11
❑ 70BreMil-8
❑ 70BreTeal-5
❑ 70MLBOffS-272
❑ 70Top-596
❑ 71BreTeal-5
❑ 71OPC-149
❑ 71Top-149
❑ 72MilBra-142
❑ 78TCM60I-287
❑ 94BreMilB-226
Hershberger, Willard
❑ 38CloFotW-39
❑ 38RedOraW-14
❑ 39OrcPhoAP-13
❑ 39OrcPhoAP-29
❑ 39PlaBal-119
❑ 39RedTeal-11
❑ 40PlaBal-77
❑ 41HarHarW-10
❑ 77CinRedT-14
Hershiser, Gordon
❑ 88VerBeaDS-11
❑ 89SanAntMB-7
Hershiser, Orel
❑ 73BooProC-19
❑ 82AlbDukTc-4
❑ 83AlbDukTc-3
❑ 84DodPol-55
❑ 84FunFooP-83
❑ 84OCoandSI-225
❑ 85DodCokP-12
❑ 85Don-581
❑ 85Fle-371
❑ 85FleStaS-96
❑ 85Lea-38
❑ 85OPC-273
❑ 85Top-493
❑ 85TopSti-74
❑ 85TopTif-493
❑ 86BasStaB-58
❑ 86DodCokP-11
❑ 86DodPol-55
❑ 86DodUniOP-7
❑ 86Don-18
❑ 86Don-226
❑ 86DonSupD-18
❑ 86Dra-31
❑ 86Fle-131
❑ 86FleLimE-24
❑ 86FleSlu-16
❑ 86FleStiC-58
❑ 86Lea-18
❑ 86OPC-159
❑ 86SevCoi-W12
❑ 86Spo-9
❑ 86Top-159
❑ 86Top3-D-12
❑ 86TopGloS-24
❑ 86TopMinL-45
❑ 86TopSti-73
❑ 86TopSup-33
❑ 86TopTat-20
❑ 86TopTif-159
❑ 87ClaGam-92
❑ 87DodMot-6
❑ 87DodPho-4
❑ 87DodPol-28
❑ 87DodSmoA-12
❑ 87Don-106
❑ 87DonHig-13
❑ 87DonOpeD-79
❑ 87Fle-441
❑ 87FleGlo-441
❑ 87FleRecS-16
❑ 87Lea-246
❑ 87OPC-385
❑ 87RedFolSB-5
❑ 87SevCoi-W6
❑ 87Spo-43
❑ 87SpoTeaP-14
❑ 87Top-385
❑ 87TopMinL-14
❑ 87TopTif-385
❑ 88DodMot-6
❑ 88DodPol-55
❑ 88Don-94
❑ 88DonAll-56
❑ 88DonBasB-148
❑ 88Fle-518
❑ 88Fle-632
❑ 88FleAwaW-17
❑ 88FleBasA-14
❑ 88FleExcS-20
❑ 88FleGlo-518
❑ 88FleGlo-632
❑ 88FleHotS-19
❑ 88FleLeaL-19
❑ 88FleMin-84
❑ 88FleRecS-18
❑ 88FleSlu-18
❑ 88FleStiC-92
❑ 88FleSup-15
❑ 88FleTeaL-13
❑ 88Lea-62
❑ 88OPC-40
❑ 88PanSti-303
❑ 88Sco-470
❑ 88ScoGlo-470
❑ 88Spo-160
❑ 88StaHer-1
❑ 88StaHer-2
❑ 88StaHer-3
❑ 88StaHer-4
❑ 88StaHer-5
❑ 88StaHer-6
❑ 88StaHer-7
❑ 88StaHer-8
❑ 88StaHer-9
❑ 88StaHer-10
❑ 88StaHer-11
❑ 88StaLinD-8
❑ 88TarPla-21
❑ 88Top-40
❑ 88TopBig-91
❑ 88TopMinL-53
❑ 88TopRevLL-12
❑ 88TopSti-68
❑ 88TopTif-40
❑ 88TopUKM-34
❑ 88TopUKMT-34
❑ 89Baz-15
❑ 89Bow-341
❑ 89BowTif-341
❑ 89CadEllD-29
❑ 89CerSup-5
❑ 89ClaLigB-1
❑ 89ClaTraO-105
❑ 89ClaTraP-173
❑ 89DodMot-6
❑ 89DodPol-29
❑ 89DodSmoG-100
❑ 89DodStaSV-8
❑ 89Don-197
❑ 89Don-648
❑ 89DonAll-50
❑ 89DonBasB-225
❑ 89DonBonM-BC4
❑ 89Fle-62
❑ 89FleAll-7
❑ 89FleBasA-21
❑ 89FleBasM-19
❑ 89FleExcS-24
❑ 89FleGlo-62
❑ 89FleGlo-WS6
❑ 89FleGlo-WS11
❑ 89FleHeroB-22
❑ 89FleLeaL-20
❑ 89FleSup-23
❑ 89FleWaxBC-C14
❑ 89FleWorS-6
❑ 89FleWorS-11
❑ 89KayB-19
❑ 89KeyFooD-10
❑ 89KinDis-12
❑ 89MSAHolD-18
❑ 89MSAIceTD-10
❑ 89Nis-18
❑ 89OPC-41
❑ 89OPC-380
❑ 89OurOwnTD-10
❑ 89PanSti-9
❑ 89PanSti-13
❑ 89PanSti-18
❑ 89PanSti-19
❑ 89PanSti-25
❑ 89PanSti-97
❑ 89PanSti-225
❑ 89PanSti-474
❑ 89RedFolSB-58
❑ 89Sco-370
❑ 89Sco-582
❑ 89Sco-653
❑ 89ScoHot1S-35
❑ 89Scomast-21
❑ 89SocHer-1
❑ 89SocHer-2
❑ 89SocHer-3
❑ 89SocHer-4
❑ 89SocHer-5
❑ 89SocHer-6
❑ 89SocHer-7
❑ 89Spo-36
❑ 89Spo-222
❑ 89SpoIllFKI-5
❑ 89TetTeaD-10
❑ 89Top-5
❑ 89Top-394
❑ 89Top-550
❑ 89Top-669
❑ 89TopBasT-82
❑ 89TopBig-1
❑ 89TopCapC-3
❑ 89TopCoi-2
❑ 89TopDouA-21
❑ 89TopGaloC-8
❑ 89TopGloS-48
❑ 89TopHilTM-17
❑ 89TopMinL-18
❑ 89TopSti-12
❑ 89TopSti-65
❑ 89TopStiB-60
❑ 89TopTif-5
❑ 89TopTif-394
❑ 89TopTif-550
❑ 89TopTif-669
❑ 89TopUKM-38
❑ 89TVSpoM-34
❑ 89TVSpoM-135
❑ 89UppDec-130
❑ 89UppDec-661
❑ 89UppDec-665
❑ 89UppDec-667
❑ 89WeiMarD-10
❑ 89Woo-4
❑ 89Woo-21
❑ 89Woo-25
❑ 89Woo-33
❑ 90AllBasT-9
❑ 90BasWit-1
❑ 90Bow-84
❑ 90BowTif-84
❑ 90ClaBlu-81
❑ 90Col-6
❑ 90DodMot-12
❑ 90DodPol-55
❑ 90DodTar-341
❑ 90Don-197
❑ 90DonBesN-54
❑ 90DOnBonM-BC5
❑ 90Fle-399
❑ 90FleBasA-18
❑ 90FleBasAC-18
❑ 90FleBasM-19
❑ 90FleBasMC-19
❑ 90FleCan-399
❑ 90FleWaxBC-C14
❑ 90HOFStiB-99
❑ 90Hot50PS-21
❑ 90Lea-280
❑ 90M.Vpin-48
❑ 90MLBBasB-8
❑ 90MSAHolD-12
❑ 90OPC-780
❑ 90PanSti-275
❑ 90Pos-8
❑ 90PubIntS-9
❑ 90PubIntS-263
❑ 90RedFolSB-48
❑ 90Sco-50
❑ 90Sco100S-94
❑ 90Spo-197
❑ 90Top-780
❑ 90TopBig-82
❑ 90TopDou-34
❑ 90TopMinL-58
❑ 90TopSti-63
❑ 90TopTif-780
❑ 90TopTVA-46
❑ 90UppDec-10
❑ 90UppDec-256
❑ 90WonBreS-4
❑ 91Bow-595
❑ 91CadEllD-30
❑ 91Cla3-T38
❑ 91ClaGam-23
❑ 91DodMot-12
❑ 91DodPho-14
❑ 91DodPol-55
❑ 91DodUno7P-3
❑ 91Don-280
❑ 91Fle-208
❑ 91Lea-243
❑ 91OPC-690
❑ 91OPCPre-64
❑ 91PetSta-22
❑ 91SanAntMP-2968
❑ 91Sco-550
❑ 91SevCoi-SC5
❑ 91StaClu-244

❑ 91StaPinB-25
❑ 91Stu-183
❑ 91Top-690
❑ 91TopCraJ2-17
❑ 91TopDesS-690
❑ 91TopMic-690
❑ 91TopTif-690
❑ 91UltUpd-88
❑ 91UppDec-524
❑ 92Bow-517
❑ 92ClaGam-33
❑ 92DodMot-6
❑ 92DodPol-55
❑ 92DodSmo-4492
❑ 92DodStaTA-27
❑ 92Don-247
❑ 92Fle-459
❑ 92LaKdec-18
❑ 92Lea-81
❑ 92LeaBlaG-81
❑ 92OPC-175
❑ 92OPCPre-162
❑ 92PanSti-199
❑ 92Pin-21
❑ 92Pin-592
❑ 92RedFolS-47
❑ 92Sco-653
❑ 92ScoProP-8
❑ 92SpoStaCC-24
❑ 92StaClu-431
❑ 92Stu-44
❑ 92Top-175
❑ 92TopGol-175
❑ 92TopGolW-175
❑ 92TopKid-52
❑ 92TopMic-175
❑ 92TriPla-212
❑ 92Ult-507
❑ 92UppDec-261
❑ 93Bow-394
❑ 93CadDis-32
❑ 93DiaMar-51
❑ 93DodMot-10
❑ 93DodPol-12
❑ 93DodStaC-23
❑ 93Don-274
❑ 93DonDiaK-DK14
❑ 93DurPowP1-4
❑ 93Fin-184
❑ 93FinRef-184
❑ 93Fla-70
❑ 93Fle-63
❑ 93FunPac-88
❑ 93Kra-24
❑ 93Lea-53
❑ 93OPC-136
❑ 93PacSpa-149
❑ 93Pin-319
❑ 93RedFolS-44
❑ 93Sco-90
❑ 93Sel-49
❑ 93SP-93
❑ 93StaClu-544
❑ 93StaCluFDI-544
❑ 93StaCluMOP-544
❑ 93Top-255
❑ 93TopGol-255
❑ 93TopInaM-255
❑ 93TopInaR-255
❑ 93TopMic-255
❑ 93TriPla-121
❑ 93Ult-55
❑ 93UppDec-169
❑ 93UppDecGold-169
❑ 94Bow-566
❑ 94ColC-135
❑ 94ColChoGS-135
❑ 94ColChoSS-135
❑ 94DodDaiN-2
❑ 94DodMot-7
❑ 94DodPol-13
❑ 94Don-151
❑ 94Fin-98
❑ 94FinRef-98
❑ 94Fla-178
❑ 94Fle-513
❑ 94FleExtB-288
❑ 94FleExtBPD-10
❑ 94FUnPac-155
❑ 94Lea-16
❑ 94OPC-133
❑ 94Pac-311
❑ 94PanSti-200
❑ 94Pin-58
❑ 94PinArtP-58
❑ 94PinMusC-58
❑ 94ProMag-69
❑ 94RedFolMI-20
❑ 94Sco-102
❑ 94ScoGolR-102
❑ 94Sel-134
❑ 94SP-77
❑ 94SPDieC-77
❑ 94Spo-125
❑ 94StaClu-400
❑ 94StaCluFDI-400
❑ 94StaCluGR-400
❑ 94StaCluMOP-400
❑ 94Stu-68
❑ 94Top-460
❑ 94TopGol-460
❑ 94TopSpa-460
❑ 94TriPla-84
❑ 94Ult-517
❑ 94UppDec-355
❑ 94UppDecAJ-32
❑ 94UppDecAJG-32
❑ 94UppDecED-355
❑ 95ColCho-229
❑ 95ColCho-555T
❑ 95ColChoGS-229
❑ 95ColChoSE-89
❑ 95ColChoSEGS-89
❑ 95ColChoSESS-89
❑ 95ColChoSS-229
❑ 95Don-245
❑ 95DonPreP-245
❑ 95Emo-33
❑ 95Fin-304
❑ 95FinRef-304
❑ 95Fla-250
❑ 95Fle-541
❑ 95FleUpd-41
❑ 95Lea-370
❑ 95Pac-218
❑ 95Pin-378
❑ 95PinArtP-378
❑ 95PinMusC-378
❑ 95RedFol-22
❑ 95Sco-238
❑ 95ScoGolR-238
❑ 95ScoPlaTS-238
❑ 95SPCha-108
❑ 95SPChaDC-108
❑ 95StaClu-37
❑ 95StaClu-562
❑ 95StaCluFDI-37
❑ 95StaCluMOP-37
❑ 95StaCluMOP-562
❑ 95StaCluSTDW-I562
❑ 95StaCluSTMP-13
❑ 95StaCluSTWS-37
❑ 95StaCluSTWS-562
❑ 95StaCluVR-26
❑ 95StaCluVRMO-26
❑ 95Top-305
❑ 95TopCyb-164
❑ 95TopTra-61T
❑ 95Ult-396
❑ 95UltGolM-396
❑ 95UppDec-74
❑ 95UppDec-466
❑ 95UppDec-TC1
❑ 95UppDecED-74
❑ 95UppDecEDG-74
❑ 95UppDecT-TC1
❑ 96Baz-131
❑ 96ColCho-384T
❑ 96ColCho-393T
❑ 96ColCho-525
❑ 96ColChoGS-525
❑ 96ColChoSS-525
❑ 96Don-149
❑ 96DonPreP-149
❑ 96EmoXL-48
❑ 96Fin-B147
❑ 96FinRef-B147
❑ 96Fla-66
❑ 96Fle-87
❑ 96FlePosG-3
❑ 96FleTif-87
❑ 96IndFle-5
❑ 96Kin-8
❑ 96Lea-124
❑ 96LeaPrePB-124
❑ 96LeaPrePG-124
❑ 96LeaPrePS-124
❑ 96MetUni-45
❑ 96MetUniP-45
❑ 96Pac-296
❑ 96PanSti-178
❑ 96Pin-248
❑ 96PinArtP-148
❑ 96PinFoil-248
❑ 96PinSta-148
❑ 96SchDis-2
❑ 96Sco-96
❑ 96StaClu-350
❑ 96StaCluEPB-350
❑ 96StaCluEPG-350
❑ 96StaCluEPS-350
❑ 96StaCluMOP-350
❑ 96Stu-142
❑ 96StuPrePB-142
❑ 96StuPrePG-142
❑ 96StuPrePS-142
❑ 96Top-40
❑ 96TopGal-55
❑ 96TopGalPPI-55
❑ 96Ult-47
❑ 96UltGolM-47
❑ 96UppDec-59
❑ 96UppDec-220
❑ 97Cir-193
❑ 97CirRav-193
❑ 97ColCho-88
❑ 97ColChoT-CI4
❑ 97Don-266
❑ 97DonGolPP-266
❑ 97DonSilPP-266
❑ 97DonTea-83
❑ 97DonTeaSPE-83
❑ 97Fin-261
❑ 97FinRef-261
❑ 97Fle-79
❑ 97FleMilDM-18
❑ 97FleMilDMR-18
❑ 97FleTif-79
❑ 97IndScoU-12
❑ 97IndScoUTC-12
❑ 97Lea-76
❑ 97LeaFraM-76
❑ 97LeaFraMDC-76
❑ 97MetUni-81
❑ 97Pac-71
❑ 97PacLigB-71
❑ 97PacPriSH-SH4B
❑ 97PacSil-71
❑ 97Pin-121
❑ 97PinArtP-PP121
❑ 97PinMusC-121
❑ 97PinPrePla-121
❑ 97Sco-378
❑ 97ScoArtPWB-378
❑ 97ScoResC-378
❑ 97ScoShoS-378
❑ 97ScoShoSAP-378
❑ 97StaClu-357
❑ 97StaCluMOP-357
❑ 97Top-110
❑ 97TopGal-7
❑ 97TopGalPPI-7
❑ 97Ult-49
❑ 97UltGolME-49
❑ 97UltPlaME-49
❑ 97UppDec-53
❑ 98ColCho-79
❑ 98ColCho-486
❑ 98Fle-243
❑ 98Fle-359
❑ 98GiaMot-5
❑ 98Pac-71
❑ 98PacAur-197
❑ 98PacOme-211
❑ 98PacOmeR-211
❑ 98PacOnl-661
❑ 98PacOnlR-661
❑ 98PacOnlWC-661
❑ 98PacPar-245
❑ 98PacParC-245
❑ 98PacParG-245
❑ 98PacParHS-245
❑ 98PacParPB-245
❑ 98PacParR-245
❑ 98PacPlaB-71
❑ 98PacRedT-71
❑ 98PacSil-71
❑ 98Pin-131
❑ 98PinIns-95
❑ 98PinInsCE-95
❑ 98PinInsDE-95
❑ 98PinPlu-100
❑ 98PinPreP-131
❑ 98Revo-128
❑ 98RevoSS-128
❑ 98ScoRT-175
❑ 98SpoIllWSF-13
❑ 98SpoIllWSFEE-13
❑ 98SpoIllWSFFE-13
❑ 98SpoIllWSFMC-6
❑ 98SPxFin-318
❑ 98SPxFin-346
❑ 98SPxFinR-318
❑ 98SPxFinR-346
❑ 98SPxFinS-318
❑ 98SPxFinS-346
❑ 98StaCluFDI-63
❑ 98StaCluI-63
❑ 98StaCluOneK-63
❑ 98StaCluPP-63
❑ 98Top-179
❑ 98TopChr-179
❑ 98TopChrR-179
❑ 98TopDevR-179
❑ 98TopDia-179
❑ 98TopMiniC-179
❑ 98Ult-299
❑ 98UltGolM-299
❑ 98UltMas-299
❑ 98UltPlaM-299
❑ 98UppDec-71
❑ 98UppDec-720
❑ 98UppDecR-7
❑ 99Fle-138
❑ 99FleSta9-138
❑ 99FleWarT-138
❑ 99MetUni-13
❑ 99MetUniGM-13
❑ 99MetUniPMG-13
❑ 99Ult-144
❑ 99UltGolM-144
❑ 99UltMas-144
❑ 99UltPlaM-144
❑ 99UppDec-197
❑ 99UppDecCL-99
❑ 99UppDecCLCC-99
❑ 99UppDecEL1-197
❑ 99UppDecEL2-197
❑ 99Vic-260

Hershmann, William
❑ 86EriCarP-NNO
❑ 87St.PetCP-21
❑ 88SavCarP-340
❑ 89SavCarP-366

Hertel, Rick
❑ 78DunBluJT-11

Hertz, Steve
❑ 64Top-544

Hertzel, Patrick
❑ 98HudValR-9

Hertzler, Paul
❑ 85IndIndTI-18
❑ 86JacMetT-15

Herz, Steve
❑ 80TolMudHT-13
❑ 81TolMudHT-12
❑ 82SpoIndT-11
❑ 82VanCanT-11
❑ 84HawIslC-142
❑ 85HawIslC-244

Herzig, Spike (Lynn)
❑ 77HolMilT-13
❑ 78HolMilT-12

Herzog, Buck (Charles)
❑ 09SpoNewSM-90
❑ 09T206-153
❑ 09T206-154
❑ 10CouT21-142
❑ 10CouT21-143
❑ 10CouT21-286
❑ 10DarChoE-19
❑ 10RedCroT-117
❑ 10RedCroT-198
❑ 10SweCapPP-67
❑ 10SweCapPP-114
❑ 11HelSta-129
❑ 11MecDFT-26
❑ 11PinT-5-706
❑ 11S74Sil-44
❑ 11SpoLifM-141
❑ 11T205-75
❑ 11TurRedT-45
❑ 12PhiCarE-12
❑ 12T207-80
❑ 14CraJacE-85
❑ 14PieStaT-52
❑ 15CraJacE-85
❑ 15SpoNewM-80
❑ 16BF2FP-74
❑ 16FleBreD-41
❑ 16SpoNewM-81
❑ 17ColE13-75
❑ 17HolBreD-43
❑ 19W514-104
❑ 40PlaBal-229
❑ 72ClaCar-61
❑ 72ClaCar-101
❑ 75FlePio-27
❑ 92ConTSN-489

Herzog, Hans
❑ 84SavCarT-8
❑ 86St.PetCP-11
❑ 87St.PetCP-16

Herzog, Whitey
❑ 47Exh-95
❑ 56A'sPos-27
❑ 57Top-29
❑ 58Top-438
❑ 59Top-392
❑ 60A'sTeal-8
❑ 60Lea-71
❑ 60Top-92
❑ 60TopVen-92
❑ 61BalOriP-12
❑ 61Pos-88A
❑ 61Pos-88B
❑ 61SevElev-14
❑ 61Top-106
❑ 61TopStal-163
❑ 62BalOriP-12
❑ 62Top-513
❑ 63Top-302
❑ 73OPC-549
❑ 73RanTeal-13
❑ 73Top-549
❑ 75CalAngP-19
❑ 75RoyPos-13
❑ 75SSP18-13
❑ 76KanCitRP-12
❑ 76OPC-236
❑ 76SSP-185
❑ 76Top-236
❑ 77Top-371
❑ 78Roy-7
❑ 78SSP270-224
❑ 78Top-299
❑ 79Top-451
❑ 81Car5x7-10
❑ 81Top-684
❑ 82Don-190
❑ 83Car-10
❑ 83Don-530A
❑ 83Don-530B
❑ 83Top-186
❑ 84Car-11
❑ 84Car5x7-11
❑ 84Fle-660
❑ 84Nes792-561
❑ 84Top-561
❑ 84TopGloA-12
❑ 84TopTif-561
❑ 85CarTeal-14
❑ 85Top-683
❑ 85TopTif-683
❑ 86CarTeal-18
❑ 86Top-441
❑ 86TopTif-441
❑ 87CarSmo-25
❑ 87CarTeal-12
❑ 87DonAll-20
❑ 87DonP-20
❑ 87Top-243
❑ 87TopGloA-1
❑ 87TopTif-243
❑ 88CarSmo-1
❑ 88CarTeal-10
❑ 88Top-744
❑ 88TopClo-47
❑ 88TopTif-744
❑ 89CarSmo-8
❑ 89CarTeal-11
❑ 89DonAll-42
❑ 89DonPop-42
❑ 89Top-654
❑ 89TopGloA-12
❑ 89TopTif-654
❑ 90CarSmo-8
❑ 90OPC-261
❑ 90Top-261
❑ 90TopTif-261
❑ 90TopTVCa-1
❑ 91OriCro-195
❑ 92CarMcD-47
❑ 93RanKee-184

Hesketh, Joe
❑ 83MemChiT-19
❑ 84IndIndTI-6
❑ 85Don-157
❑ 85ExpPos-10
❑ 85Fle-652
❑ 85TopTifT-52T
❑ 85TopTra-52T
❑ 86Don-341
❑ 86ExpPos-5
❑ 86ExpProPa-21
❑ 86ExpProPo-6
❑ 86Fle-250
❑ 86Lea-150
❑ 86OPC-42
❑ 86SevCoi-S15
❑ 86Spo-177
❑ 86Top-472
❑ 86TopGloS-19
❑ 86TopTif-472
❑ 87Don-134
❑ 87ExpPos-11
❑ 87Fle-320
❑ 87FleGlo-320
❑ 87Lea-62
❑ 87OPC-189
❑ 87Top-189
❑ 87TopTif-189
❑ 88Don-504
❑ 88ExpPos-13
❑ 88IndIndP-512
❑ 88OPC-371
❑ 88Top-371
❑ 88TopTif-371
❑ 89Don-460
❑ 89ExpPos-14
❑ 89Fle-378
❑ 89FleGlo-378
❑ 89OPC-74
❑ 89Sco-498
❑ 89Top-614
❑ 89TopTif-614
❑ 89UppDec-60
❑ 90BraDubP-11
❑ 90Don-511
❑ 90Fle-349
❑ 90FleCan-349
❑ 90Lea-507
❑ 90OPC-24
❑ 90PubIntS-175
❑ 90Sco-483
❑ 90Top-24
❑ 90TopTif-24
❑ 90TopTra-40T
❑ 90TopTraT-40T
❑ 90UppDec-512
❑ 91OPC-269
❑ 91RedSoxP-15
❑ 91Top-269
❑ 91TopDesS-269
❑ 91TopMic-269
❑ 91TopTif-269
❑ 92Don-611
❑ 92Fle-40
❑ 92Lea-22
❑ 92LeaBlaG-22
❑ 92OPC-521
❑ 92Pin-415
❑ 92RedSoxDD-16
❑ 92Sco-359
❑ 92StaClu-636
❑ 92StaCluNC-636
❑ 92Top-521
❑ 92TopGol-521
❑ 92TopGolW-521
❑ 92TopMic-521
❑ 92Ult-17
❑ 92UppDec-570
❑ 93Fle-562
❑ 93PacSpa-360
❑ 93Pin-448
❑ 93RedSoxP-19
❑ 93RedSoxWHP-14
❑ 93Sco-467
❑ 93StaClu-107
❑ 93StaCluFDI-107
❑ 93StaCluMOP-107
❑ 93Top-162
❑ 93TopGol-162
❑ 93TopInaM-162
❑ 93TopInaR-162
❑ 93TopMic-162
❑ 93UppDec-620
❑ 93UppDecGold-620
❑ 94StaClu-455
❑ 94StaCluFDI-455
❑ 94StaCluGR-455
❑ 94StaCluMOP-455
❑ 95ColCho-416
❑ 95ColChoGS-416
❑ 95ColChoSS-416

❑ 95Don-229
❑ 95DonPreP-229
❑ 95Fle-32
Heslet, Harry
❑ 50WorWidGV-27
Hess, Mark
❑ 91DaiDolF-3
Hess, Otto
❑ 05IndSouPSoCP-9
❑ 11SpoLifCW-163
❑ 16Zee-131
❑ 17Zee-108
Hesse, A. J.
❑ 21Zee-95
Hessler, John
❑ 80ColAstT-13
Hessman, Michael
❑ 97MacBra-11
❑ 97SouAtlTPB-25
❑ 98CarLeaAC-40
❑ 98DanQ-C-4
Hestefer, Larry
❑ 08BufBisFJO-3
Hester, Marshall
❑ 80ChaO'sW-11
Hester, Steve
❑ 88GreHorP-1570
❑ 89CedRapRB-29
❑ 89CedRapRP-919
❑ 89CedRapRS-8
❑ 89CedRapRS-27
❑ 90CedRapRB-26
❑ 90CedRapRP-2323
Hetki, John
❑ 53Top-235
❑ 54Top-161
❑ 55TopDouH-61
❑ 91TopArc1-235
❑ 94TopArc1-161
❑ 94TopArc1G-161
Hetling, August
❑ 09ObaT21-119
❑ 09ObaT21-274
❑ 11Zee-29
❑ 12ObaPreT-23
❑ 12PCLPin-9
❑ 12Zee-33
❑ 12Zee-34
❑ 13Zee-35
❑ 14Zee-36
❑ 15Zee-127
Hetrick, B.
❑ 84JacMetT-11
Hetrick, Kent
❑ 87SalLakTTT-3
❑ 88BelBreGS-13
❑ 89StoPorB-9
❑ 89StoPorCLC-161
❑ 89StoPorP-376
❑ 89StoPorS-10
Hetzel, Eric
❑ 85GreHorT-18
❑ 87WinHavRSP-22
❑ 88PawRedSC-8
❑ 88PawRedSP-449
❑ 89Don-660
❑ 89PawRedSC-3
❑ 89PawRedSP-703
❑ 89PawRedSTI-11
❑ 90Don-539
❑ 90Fle-279
❑ 90FleCan-279
❑ 90LSUTigGM-5
❑ 90OPC-629
❑ 90PawRedSDD-9
❑ 90Sco-543
❑ 90Sco100RS-23
❑ 90Top-629
❑ 90TopDeb89-56
❑ 90TopTif-629
❑ 90TopTVRS-45
❑ 90UppDec-673
❑ 91LinDriAAA 356
❑ 91PawRedSDD-7
❑ 91PawRedSLD-356
❑ 91PawRedSP-32
Heuer, Mark
❑ 87SanAntDTI-24
Heusser, Ed
❑ 72TCMthe3-38
❑ 93ConTSN-970
Heving, Joe (Joseph W.)
❑ 34BatR31-43
❑ 39PlaBal-20
❑ 40PlaBal-35
❑ 41DouPlaR-135
❑ 72TCMthe1-174
❑ 81ConTSN-47
❑ 94ConTSN-1176
❑ 94ConTSNB-1176
Heving, Johnnie (John A.)
❑ 28StaPlaCE-37
❑ 29ExhFou-17
❑ 74A's192T-10
❑ 81ConTSN-48
❑ 92ConTSN-455
❑ 94ConTSN-1176
❑ 94ConTSNB-1176
Hewatt, B.
❑ 88PocGiaP-2090
Hewes, Pat
❑ 87SavCarP-9
❑ 88St.PetCS-9
❑ 89PenPilS-7
Heydeman, Greg
❑ 74AlbDukTI-6
Heydler, John
❑ 94ConTSN-1112
❑ 94ConTSNB-1112
Heydler, Mrs. (John)
❑ 94ConTSN-1112
❑ 94ConTSNB-1112
Heying, Scott
❑ 98St.CatSM-5
Hiatt, Jack
❑ 65Top-497
❑ 66Top-373
❑ 67Top-368
❑ 68DexPre-38
❑ 68Top-419
❑ 69MilBra-112
❑ 69OPC-204
❑ 69Top-204
❑ 69TopFou-11
❑ 70OPC-13
❑ 70Top-13
❑ 71AstTeal-12
❑ 71MLBOffS-83
❑ 71OPC-371
❑ 71Top-371
❑ 72AstTeal-13
❑ 72MilBra-143
❑ 72Top-633
❑ 73OPC-402
❑ 73Top-402
❑ 74WicAerODF-117
❑ 80WicAerT-8
❑ 82HolMilT-23
❑ 83ColAstT-22
❑ 88PocGiaP-2101
Hiatt, Phil
❑ 90EugEmeGS-14
❑ 91BasCitRC-17
❑ 91BasCitRP-1403
❑ 91Cla/Bes-151
❑ 91FloStaLAP-FSL1
❑ 92Bow-529
❑ 92ClaFS7-181
❑ 92MemChiF-2426
❑ 92MemChiS-436
❑ 92ProFS7-76
❑ 92SkyAA F-183
❑ 92UppDecML-45
❑ 92UppDecML-176
❑ 92UppDecMLPotY-PY22
❑ 93Bow-69
❑ 93ClaGolF-25
❑ 93Don-393
❑ 93ExcAllF-9
❑ 93ExcFS7-174
❑ 93Fla-216
❑ 93FleFinE-220
❑ 93FunPac-4
❑ 93LeaGolR-R14
❑ 93LeaGolRJ-R14
❑ 93PacSpa-488
❑ 93Pin-611
❑ 93RoyStaC-6
❑ 93SelRoo-66T
❑ 93SP-229
❑ 93StaClu-695
❑ 93StaCluFDI-695
❑ 93StaCluMOP-695
❑ 93Stu-107
❑ 93TopTra-29T
❑ 93Ult-561
❑ 93UltAllR-3
❑ 93UppDec-457
❑ 93UppDec-645
❑ 93UppDecDG-33
❑ 93UppDecGold-457
❑ 93UppDecGold-645
❑ 94ColC-136
❑ 94ColChoGS-136
❑ 94ColChoSS-136
❑ 94Don-279
❑ 94Fin-56
❑ 94FinRef-56
❑ 94Fle-160
❑ 94FUnPac-172
❑ 94Lea-90
❑ 94Pac-287
❑ 94Pin-327
❑ 94PinArtP-327
❑ 94PinMusC-327
❑ 94Sco-515
❑ 94ScoGolR-515-
❑ 94Top-94
❑ 94TopGol-94
❑ 94TopSpa-94
❑ 94Ult-66
❑ 94USPlaCR-4D
❑ 95DonTopotO-91
❑ 95SigRoo-24
❑ 95SigRooSig-24
❑ 96TolMudHB-13
❑ 98BufBisG-13
Hibbard, Billy
❑ 95HagSunF-63
❑ 97HagSunB-7
Hibbard, Greg
❑ 86EugEmeC-43
❑ 87AppFoxP-27
❑ 87Ft.MyeRP-6
❑ 88BlaYNPRWL-26
❑ 88VanCanC-11
❑ 88VanCanP-770
❑ 89VanCanC-3
❑ 89VanCanP-584
❑ 90Bow-303
❑ 90BowTif-303
❑ 90Don-384
❑ 90Fle-534
❑ 90FleCan-534
❑ 90Lea-523
❑ 90OPC-769
❑ 90Sco-369
❑ 90Sco100RS-77
❑ 90ScoYouS2-20
❑ 90Top-769
❑ 90TopDeb89-57
❑ 90TopRoo-14
❑ 90TopTif-769
❑ 90UppDec-543
❑ 90WhiSoxC-8
❑ 91Don-159
❑ 91Fle-122
❑ 91Lea-438
❑ 91OPC-256
❑ 91PanFreS-319
❑ 91PanSti-254
❑ 91Sco-128
❑ 91Stu-34
❑ 91Top-256
❑ 91TopDesS-256
❑ 91TopMic-256
❑ 91TopTif-256
❑ 91Ult-75
❑ 91UppDec-679
❑ 91WhiSoxK-27
❑ 92Bow-325
❑ 92Don-178
❑ 92Fle-83
❑ 92Lea-169
❑ 92LeaBlaG-169
❑ 92OPC-477
❑ 92Pin-364
❑ 92Sco-266
❑ 92StaClu-586
❑ 92Stu-153
❑ 92Top-477
❑ 92TopGol-477
❑ 92TopGolW-477
❑ 92TopMic-477
❑ 92TriPla-261
❑ 92Ult-36
❑ 92UppDec-420
❑ 92WhiSoxK-27
❑ 93Bow-88
❑ 93CubMar-10
❑ 93CubStaC-3
❑ 93Don-271
❑ 93Fla-15
❑ 93Fle-379
❑ 93FleFinE-8
❑ 93Lea-298
❑ 93PacSpa-378
❑ 93Pin-527
❑ 93Sco-622
❑ 93Sel-216
❑ 93SelRoo-103T
❑ 93StaClu-606
❑ 93StaCluFDI-606
❑ 93StaCluMOP-606
❑ 93Top-313
❑ 93TopGol-313
❑ 93TopInaM-313
❑ 93TopInaR-313
❑ 93TopMic-313
❑ 93Ult-315
❑ 93UppDec-539
❑ 93UppDecGold-539
❑ 94ColC-462
❑ 94ColChoGS-462
❑ 94ColChoSS-462
❑ 94Don-542
❑ 94Fin-389
❑ 94FinRef-389
❑ 94Fla-104
❑ 94Fle-386
❑ 94Lea-402
❑ 94MarMot-9
❑ 94Pac-101
❑ 94Pin-480
❑ 94PinArtP-480
❑ 94PinMusC-480
❑ 94Sco-432
❑ 94ScoGolR-432
❑ 94ScoRoo-RT15
❑ 94ScoRooGR-RT15
❑ 94Sel-294
❑ 94StaClu-704
❑ 94StaCluFDI-704
❑ 94StaCluGR-704
❑ 94StaCluMOP-704
❑ 94Top-148
❑ 94TopGol-148
❑ 94TopSpa-148
❑ 94TopTra-124T
❑ 94Ult-162
❑ 94UppDec-472
❑ 94UppDecED-472
❑ 95ColCho-296
❑ 95ColChoGS-296
❑ 95ColChoSS-296
Hibbett, Wendell
❑ 78ChaPirT-9
Hibbs, Al
❑ 85UtiBluST-11
❑ 86BenPhiC-132
Hibbs, Jim
❑ 73WicAerJPKB-4A
❑ 73WicAerJPKB-4B
❑ 77FriOneYW-39
Hibbs, Loren
❑ 84EveGiaC-15
❑ 90WicStaSGD-40
Hibner, Dave
❑ 78AshTouT-10
❑ 79AshTouT-25
❑ 80AshTouT-8
Hice, Bob
❑ 84ChaO'sT-1
❑ 85ChaO'sT-27
❑ 86ChaOriW-13
❑ 87ChaO'sW-NNO
Hickerson, Bryan
❑ 87CliGiaP-28
❑ 89SanJosGB-15
❑ 89SanJosGCLC-212
❑ 89SanJosGP-443
❑ 89SanJosGS-14
❑ 90ShrCapP-1438
❑ 90ShrCapS-11
❑ 91LinDriAA-306
❑ 91ShrCapLD-306
❑ 91ShrCapP-1815
❑ 92ClaGam-135
❑ 92Don-783
❑ 92Fle-638
❑ 92GiaMot-16
❑ 92GiaPacGaE-19
❑ 92Lea-280
❑ 92LeaBlaG-280
❑ 92OPC-8
❑ 92OPCPre-65
❑ 92ProFS7-349
❑ 92Sco-750
❑ 92StaClu-686
❑ 92StaCluECN-686
❑ 92Top-8
❑ 92TopDeb91-79
❑ 92TopGol-8
❑ 92TopGolW-8
❑ 92TopMic-8
❑ 92Ult-589
❑ 92UppDec-667
❑ 93Don-496
❑ 93Fle-530
❑ 93GiaMot-26
❑ 93GiaPos-17
❑ 93GiaStaC-29
❑ 93Lea-501
❑ 93OPC-162
❑ 93PacSpa-271
❑ 93StaClu-217
❑ 93StaCluFDI-217
❑ 93StaCluMOP-217
❑ 93Top-147
❑ 93TopGol-147
❑ 93TopInaM-147
❑ 93TopInaR-147
❑ 93TopMic-147
❑ 93Ult-485
❑ 93UppDec-778
❑ 93UppDecGold-778
❑ 94Don-181
❑ 94Fla-242
❑ 94Fle-691
❑ 94FleExtB-386
❑ 94GiaMot-26
❑ 94GiaTarBC-11
❑ 94GiaUSPC-5H
❑ 94GiaUSPC-12S
❑ 94Pac-546
❑ 94StaClu-711
❑ 94StaCluFDI-711
❑ 94StaCluGR-711
❑ 94StaCluMOP-711
❑ 94StaCluT-11
❑ 94StaCluTFDI-11
❑ 94Top-429
❑ 94TopGol-429
❑ 94TopSpa-429
❑ 94Ult-588
❑ 95Fle-580
❑ 97BakBlaB-28
❑ 97BakBlaTI-28
❑ 98SanJosGQ-28
Hickey, Bob
❑ 75SanAntBT-10
Hickey, Jim
❑ 85BufBisT-20
❑ 86BirBarTI-18
❑ 87BirBarB-16
❑ 89ColMudB-19
❑ 91BurAstC-26
❑ 91BurAstP-2818
❑ 92AshTouC-28
❑ 95QuaCitRBTI-11
❑ 96JacGenB-3
❑ 97JacGen-2
❑ 97JacGenS-10
Hickey, John
❑ 09ObaT21-212
Hickey, Kevin
❑ 79AppFoxT-6
❑ 80GleFalWSBT-10
❑ 80GleFalWSCT-7
❑ 82Don-631
❑ 82Fle-344
❑ 82OPC-362
❑ 82Top-778
❑ 83Don-445
❑ 83Fle-237
❑ 83Top-278
❑ 83WhiSoxTV-45
❑ 84Don-135
❑ 84Fle-61
❑ 84Nes792-459
❑ 84Top-459
❑ 84TopTif-459
❑ 86PorBeaP-8
❑ 87HawIslP-18
❑ 88RocRedWGCP-11
❑ 89BalOriP-12
❑ 89FleUpd-4
❑ 89OriFreB-23
❑ 90BalOriP-9
❑ 90Don-583A
❑ 90Don-583B
❑ 90Fle-178
❑ 90FleCan-178
❑ 90OPC-546
❑ 90PubIntS-577
❑ 90Sco-214
❑ 90Top-546
❑ 90TopTif-546
❑ 90UppDec-299
❑ 91BalOriP-11
❑ 91Fle-475
❑ 91HagSunLD-237
❑ 91HagSunP-2450
❑ 91LinDriAA-237
❑ 91OriCro-196
Hickey, Michael
❑ 90OklSoo-6
❑ 92BelMarCB-28
❑ 92BelMarF-1452
❑ 92ClaDraP-123
❑ 92FroRowDP-5
❑ 92FroRowDPG-5
❑ 92FroRowDPS-5
❑ 93AppFoxCB-11
❑ 93AppFoxFI-2469
❑ 94RivPilCLC-6
❑ 95PorCitRTI-14
❑ 96PorCitRB-16
Hickey, Thomas
❑ 19Zee-96
Hickman, Braxton
❑ 93EugEmeC-16
❑ 93EugEmeF-3863
❑ 93Tex-3
❑ 94RocRoyC-12
❑ 94RocRoyF-574
Hickman, Dave J.
❑ 90DodTar-342
Hickman, Gordon J.
❑ 09T206-491
Hickman, Jess
❑ 67SeaPop-7
❑ 77FriOneYW-36
Hickman, Jim
❑ 61UniOil-P8
❑ 62Top-598
❑ 63MetJayP-3
❑ 63Top-107
❑ 64MetJayP-6
❑ 64MetTeal-5
❑ 64Top-514
❑ 64TopCoi-92
❑ 65MetJayP-6
❑ 65OPC-114
❑ 65Top-114
❑ 66MetVolC-5
❑ 66Top-402
❑ 67Top-346
❑ 69CubJewT-6
❑ 69MilBra-113
❑ 69OPC-63
❑ 69Top-63
❑ 69TopTeaP-4
❑ 70DayDaiNM-72
❑ 70SunPin-3
❑ 70Top-612
❑ 71Kel-11
❑ 71MilDud-46
❑ 71MLBOffS-32
❑ 71OPC-175
❑ 71Top-175
❑ 71TopCoi-27
❑ 72CubTeal-4
❑ 72Top-534
❑ 73MetAllEB-3
❑ 73OPC-565
❑ 73Top-565
❑ 76Met63 S-8
❑ 82MetGal62-7
❑ 90DodTar-343
❑ 91MetWIZ-180
Hickman, Piano Legs (Charles)
❑ 03BreE10-71
❑ 04FanCraAL-23
❑ 08AmeLeaPC-8
❑ 10CouT21-29
❑ 11MecDFT-27
❑ 11PinT-5-1112
❑ 11SpoLifCW-164
Hickok, Rex
❑ 26Zee-76
Hickox, Tom
❑ 88CapCodPPaLP-86
❑ 91HelBreSP-21
Hicks, Aman
❑ 89EriOriS-7
❑ 90WauTimB-24
❑ 90WauTimP-2138
❑ 90WauTimS-10
❑ 91KanCouCC-23
❑ 91KanCouCP-2670
❑ 91KanCouCTI-10
Hicks, Charlie

❑ 92EveGiaC-27
❑ 92EveGiaF-1682
❑ 93SanJosGC-12
❑ 93SanJosGF-2
❑ 94SanJosGC-10

Hicks, Clarence Walter
❑ 50W720HolS-13

Hicks, Clay
❑ 77AppFoxT-9
❑ 78AppFoxT-13

Hicks, Ed
❑ 76WauMetT-13
❑ 89PacSenL-130

Hicks, Jamie
❑ 95DurBulTI-12
❑ 96MacBraB-14

Hicks, Jim
❑ 67Top-532
❑ 69Top-559
❑ 70OPC-173
❑ 70Top-173

Hicks, Joe (William J.)
❑ 60Lea-74
❑ 61Top-386
❑ 62Top-428
❑ 79QuaCitCT-11
❑ 81WhiSox1T-23
❑ 83IowCubT-14
❑ 84IowCubT-9
❑ 86IowCubP-15
❑ 86StaoftFT-11
❑ 87PriWilYP-26
❑ 89PacSenL-69
❑ 89TopSenL-105
❑ 91MetWIZ-181

Hicks, Mike
❑ 77AshTouT-8

Hicks, Rob
❑ 86PorBeaP-9
❑ 87ReaPhiP-26
❑ 88ElPasDB-27

Hicks, Robert
❑ 82SprCarF-7

Hidalgo, Richard
❑ 93AshTouC-1
❑ 93AshTouF-2288
❑ 93SouAtlLAGF-30
❑ 94Bow-586
❑ 94MidLeaAF-MDW52
❑ 94QuaCitRBC-12
❑ 94QuaCitRBF-547
❑ 94UppDecML-23
❑ 94VenLinU-20
❑ 95ActPacF-49
❑ 95Bow-62
❑ 95Exc-203
❑ 95ExcLeaL-10
❑ 95JacGenTI-15
❑ 95LinVen-81
❑ 95SPML-65
❑ 95SPMLA-12
❑ 95SPMLDtS-DS2
❑ 95UppDecML-38
❑ 95UppDecMLFS-38
❑ 96-97LinVen-15
❑ 96Bow-131
❑ 96BowBes-99
❑ 96BowBesAR-99
❑ 96BowBesP-BBP20
❑ 96BowBesPAR-BBP20
❑ 96BowBesPR-BBP20
❑ 96BowBesR-99
❑ 96BowFoi-131
❑ 96ColCho-439
❑ 96ColChoGS-439
❑ 96ColChoSS-439
❑ 96DouAllB-50
❑ 96Exc-171
❑ 96Fla-278
❑ 96FlaWavotF-13
❑ 96FleUpd-U139
❑ 96FleUpdNH-10
❑ 96FleUpdTC-U139
❑ 96JacGenB-12
❑ 96PinAfi-174
❑ 96PinAfiAP-174
❑ 96PinProS-10
❑ 96Sel-191
❑ 96SelArtP-191
❑ 96SelCer-122
❑ 96SelCerAP-122
❑ 96SelCerCB-122
❑ 96SelCerCR-122
❑ 96SelCerMB-122
❑ 96SelCerMG-122
❑ 96SelCerMR-122
❑ 96SP-6
❑ 96Sum-193
❑ 96SumAbo&B-193
❑ 96SumArtP-193
❑ 96SumFoi-193
❑ 96TexLeaAB-8
❑ 96Top-438
❑ 96Ult-487
❑ 96UltGolM-487
❑ 96UltGolP-8
❑ 96UltGolPHGM-8
❑ 96UppDec-257
❑ 97Bes-12
❑ 97Bow-84
❑ 97Bow98ROY-ROY4
❑ 97BowBes-102
❑ 97BowBesAR-102
❑ 97BowBesMI-MI6
❑ 97BowBesMIAR-MI6
❑ 97BowBesMIARI-MI6
❑ 97BowBesMII-MI6
❑ 97BowBesMIR-MI6
❑ 97BowBesMIRI-MI6
❑ 97BowBesR-102
❑ 97BowCerBlaIA-CA38
❑ 97BowCerBluIA-CA38
❑ 97BowCerGolIA-CA38
❑ 97BowChr-110
❑ 97BowChr1RFR-ROY4
❑ 97BowChr98RF-ROY4
❑ 97BowChrI-110
❑ 97BowChrIR-110
❑ 97BowChrR-110
❑ 97BowInt-84
❑ 97Top-488
❑ 97Ult-207
❑ 97UltGolME-207
❑ 97UltPlaME-207
❑ 97UppDecTTS-TS12
❑ 98Bow-303
❑ 98BowBes-150
❑ 98BowBesAR-150
❑ 98BowBesMIF-MI18
❑ 98BowBesMIFAR-MI18
❑ 98BowBesMIFR-MI18
❑ 98BowBesR-150
❑ 98BowCerBlueAU-12
❑ 98BowCerGA-12
❑ 98BowCerSA-12
❑ 98BowChr-303
❑ 98BowChrGA-303
❑ 98BowChrGAR-303
❑ 98BowChrI-303
❑ 98BowChrIR-303
❑ 98BowChrR-303
❑ 98BowChrR-40
❑ 98BowChrRR-40
❑ 98BowGolA-303
❑ 98BowInt-303
❑ 98BowScoC-SC2
❑ 98CirThu-186
❑ 98CirThuRav-186
❑ 98CirThuSupRav-186
❑ 98ColCho-135
❑ 98ColChoSQ-SQ21
❑ 98Don-266
❑ 98DonColE-512
❑ 98DonColL-390
❑ 98DonColP-688
❑ 98DonEli-112
❑ 98DonEliA-112
❑ 98DonEliS-112
❑ 98DonGolPP-266
❑ 98DonPre-138
❑ 98DonPreGES-16
❑ 98DonPreGX-16
❑ 98DonPreGXDC-16
❑ 98DonPreSeat-138
❑ 98DonPriCE-512
❑ 98DonPriCL-390
❑ 98DonPriCP-688
❑ 98DonSig-92
❑ 98DonSigA-43
❑ 98DonSigAC-57
❑ 98DonSigAM-58
❑ 98DonSigP-92
❑ 98DonSigSP-10
❑ 98DonSilPP-266
❑ 98E-X2SD2001-7
❑ 98Fin-159
❑ 98FinNo--159
❑ 98FinNo-R-159
❑ 98FinRef-159
❑ 98Fle-131
❑ 98FleProF-PF7
❑ 98Lea-191
❑ 98LeaFraDA-191
❑ 98LeaFraF-191
❑ 98LeaFraM-191
❑ 98LeaFraM-191
❑ 98LeaFraMDC-191
❑ 98LeaFraMDC-191
❑ 98LeaFraMZ2-191
❑ 98LeaRCrusUP-101
❑ 98LeaRS-231
❑ 98LeaRSCrusUG-101
❑ 98LeaRSCrusUR-101
❑ 98LeaRSFOSamp-9
❑ 98LeaRSFresh-9
❑ 98LeaRSLHolo-231
❑ 98LeaRSLong-231
❑ 98LeaRTrue-231
❑ 98MetUni-120
❑ 98MetUniPMG-120
❑ 98Pac-320
❑ 98PacAur-141
❑ 98PacInvTeam-12
❑ 98PacOme-109
❑ 98PacOmeR-109
❑ 98PacOmeRS-17
❑ 98PacOmeRST3-17
❑ 98PacOnl-325
❑ 98PacOnlR-325
❑ 98PacOnlWC-325
❑ 98PacPar-171
❑ 98PacParC-171
❑ 98PacParG-171
❑ 98PacParHS-171
❑ 98PacParPB-171
❑ 98PacParR-171
❑ 98PacPlaB-320
❑ 98PacRedT-320
❑ 98PacSil-320
❑ 98PinIns-128
❑ 98PinInsCE-128
❑ 98PinInsDE-128
❑ 98PinPer-65
❑ 98PinPerPP-65
❑ 98PinPlu-169
❑ 98PinPluAP-PP56
❑ 98PinPluGAP-PP56
❑ 98PinPluMAP-PP56
❑ 98Revo-68
❑ 98RevoRooHH-8
❑ 98RevoRooHHG-8
❑ 98RevoSS-68
❑ 98ScoRT-240
❑ 98ScoRTSS-PP133
❑ 98ScoRTSSAP-PP133
❑ 98ScoRTSSAP1-PP133
❑ 98SkyDugA-119
❑ 98SkyDugAIA-119
❑ 98SP Aut-98
❑ 98SP MinPE-61
❑ 98SPMin-61
❑ 98SPxFin-24
❑ 98SPxFinR-24
❑ 98SPxFinS-24
❑ 98StaCluBPP-BP10
❑ 98StaCluFDI-80
❑ 98StaCluI-80
❑ 98StaCluITW-W5
❑ 98StaCluOneK-80
❑ 98StaCluPP-80
❑ 98Stu-146
❑ 98StuGPP-146
❑ 98StuSPP-146
❑ 98Top-461
❑ 98TopChr-461
❑ 98TopChrR-461
❑ 98TopChrRC-R2
❑ 98TopChrRCRef-R2
❑ 98TopDevR-461
❑ 98TopDia-461
❑ 98TopGolLabC1-87
❑ 98TopGolLabC1B-87
❑ 98TopGolLabC1One-87
❑ 98TopGolLabC1R-87
❑ 98TopGolLabC2-87
❑ 98TopGolLabC2B-87
❑ 98TopGolLabC2One-87
❑ 98TopGolLabC2R-87
❑ 98TopGolLabC3-87
❑ 98TopGolLabC3B-87
❑ 98TopGolLabC3One-87
❑ 98TopGolLabC3R-87
❑ 98TopMiniC-461
❑ 98TopRooCla-R2
❑ 98TopSta-36
❑ 98TopStaB-36
❑ 98TopStaG-36
❑ 98TopStaGR-36
❑ 98TopStaS-36
❑ 98TopTek-84
❑ 98TopTekD-84
❑ 98Ult-230
❑ 98UltGolM-230
❑ 98UltMas-230
❑ 98UltPlaM-230
❑ 98UltRoctS-11
❑ 98UppDec-382
❑ 98UppDecDS-DS4
❑ 98UppDecR-117
❑ 98UppDecREP-9
❑ 98UppDecRNF-NF17
❑ 98Zen-93
❑ 98Zen5 xx7-75
❑ 98Zen5x7GoldImp-75
❑ 98Zen5x7Imp-75
❑ 98ZenRooT-12
❑ 98ZenZ-G-93
❑ 98ZenZ-S-93
❑ 99Fle-480
❑ 99FleSta9-480
❑ 99FleWarT-480
❑ 99MetUniN-5
❑ 99Pac-194
❑ 99PacAur-83
❑ 99PacAurOD-83
❑ 99PacCroC-126
❑ 99PacCroCPB-126
❑ 99PacOme-107
❑ 99PacOmeC-107
❑ 99PacOmeG-107
❑ 99PacOmePB-107
❑ 99PacPar-106
❑ 99PacParC-106
❑ 99PacParG-106
❑ 99PacParHoloGold-106
❑ 99PacParHS-106
❑ 99PacParOD-106
❑ 99PacParPB-106
❑ 99PacParRed-106
❑ 99PacPlaB-194
❑ 99PacRed-194
❑ 99SkyMolM-70
❑ 99SkyMolMX-70
❑ 99SkyThu-224
❑ 99SkyThuRant-224
❑ 99SkyThuRave-224
❑ 99SP AutC-RH
❑ 99SP AutCG-RH
❑ 99SPSig-154
❑ 99ThuSkySupR-224
❑ 99Top-407
❑ 99TopChr-407
❑ 99TopChrR-407
❑ 99TopMVPP-407
❑ 99UltWorP-11
❑ 99UppDec-386
❑ 99UppDecEL1-386
❑ 99UppDecEL2-386
❑ 99UppDecM-94
❑ 99UppDecMGS-94
❑ 99UppDecMHFS-94
❑ 99UppDecMP-RH
❑ 99UppDecMSS-94
❑ 99Vic-179

Hierholzer, David
❑ 90EugEmeGS-15
❑ 91AppFoxCB-5
❑ 91AppFoxP-1711

Hiester, Elwood
❑ 09ObaT21-141
❑ 09ObaT21-309
❑ 12ObaPreT-58

Higbe, Kirby
❑ 39ExhSal-27
❑ 40PhiTeal-7
❑ 41DouPlaR-23
❑ 41PhiTeal-7
❑ 41PlaBal-52
❑ 42DodTeal-11
❑ 43DodTeal-14
❑ 46DodTeal-14
❑ 46SpoExcW-5-2
❑ 47Exh-96
❑ 47TipTop-141
❑ 49Bow-215
❑ 49EurSta-108
❑ 49Lea-129
❑ 50Bow-200
❑ 73Dod194T-14
❑ 78DodTCM4-26
❑ 79DiaGre-83
❑ 89DodSmoG-50
❑ 90DodTar-344
❑ 91DodRinP4-5
❑ 93ConTSN-764
❑ 94ConTSN-1213
❑ 94ConTSNB-1213
❑ 95ConTSN-1344

Higginbotham, Irv
❑ 09PC7HHB-21
❑ 12Zee-61
❑ 13Zee-60
❑ 14Zee-63
❑ 15Zee-62
❑ 16Zee-33
❑ 72ClaCar-49

Higginbotham, Robin
❑ 91NiaFalRC-15
❑ 91NiaFalRP-3647
❑ 92NiaFalRF-3338

Higgins, Bill
❑ 90MarPhiP-3184

Higgins, Bob
❑ 12T207-81
❑ 90DodTar-980

Higgins, Dennis
❑ 66Top-529
❑ 67OPC-52
❑ 67Top-52
❑ 68Top-509
❑ 69Top-441A
❑ 69Top-441B
❑ 69TopSta-237
❑ 70Ind-7
❑ 70OPC-257
❑ 70Top-257
❑ 71MLBOffS-374
❑ 71OPC-479
❑ 71Top-479
❑ 72MilBra-144
❑ 72OPC-278
❑ 72Top-278

Higgins, Eddie
❑ 09ObaT21-399
❑ 12ObaPreT-148

Higgins, Frank
❑ 33ButCanV-25
❑ 34BatR31-171
❑ 36ExhFou-14
❑ 36GouWidPPR-A52
❑ 36NatChiFPR-42
❑ 36SandSW-34
❑ 39GouPreR303A-25
❑ 39GouPreR303B-15
❑ 39WorWidGTP-25

Higgins, Kevin
❑ 89AriStaB-13
❑ 89SpoIndSP-19
❑ 90Bes-102
❑ 90RivRedWB-13
❑ 90RivRedWCLC-6
❑ 90RivRedWP-2610
❑ 91LasVegSLD-284
❑ 91LasVegSP-239
❑ 91LinDriAAA-284
❑ 92LasVegSF-2801
❑ 92LasVegSS-232
❑ 93Bow-574
❑ 93FleFinE-142
❑ 93LasVegSF-951
❑ 93Lea-441
❑ 93SelRoo-136T
❑ 94Don-387
❑ 94Fle-667
❑ 94LasVegSF-874
❑ 94Pac-527
❑ 94Pin-215
❑ 94PinArtP-215
❑ 94PinMusC-215
❑ 94Sco-642
❑ 94ScoGolR-642
❑ 94StaClu-83
❑ 94StaCluFDI-83
❑ 94StaCluGR-83
❑ 94StaCluMOP-83
❑ 94Top-279
❑ 94TopGol-279
❑ 94TopSpa-279
❑ 94TriAAF-AAA34
❑ 96VerExpB-1
❑ 97VerExpB-2

Higgins, Mark
❑ 80BurBeeT-23
❑ 81BurBeeT-23

Higgins, Mark Douglas
❑ 86WatIndP-11
❑ 87WilBilP-9
❑ 88ColSprSSC-13
❑ 88ColSprSSP-1544
❑ 89ColSprSSC-15
❑ 89ColSprSSP-255
❑ 90CMC-41
❑ 90DenZepC-16
❑ 90DenZepP-631
❑ 90ProAAAF-656
❑ 90TopDeb89-58

Higgins, Mike
❑ 93BenRocCB-11
❑ 93BenRocF-3271
❑ 94AshTouC-12
❑ 94AshTouF-1785
❑ 95SalAvaTI-15
❑ 96NewHavRB-14
❑ 96SalAvaB-14

Higgins, Pinky (Mike)
❑ 33RitCE-11H
❑ 34Gou-78
❑ 35GouPuzR-1B
❑ 35GouPuzR-2B
❑ 35GouPuzR-16B
❑ 35GouPuzR-17B
❑ 36GouBWR-18
❑ 36GouWidPPR-C17
❑ 36OveCanR-24
❑ 38CloFotW-40
❑ 39TigSpo-4
❑ 40PlaBal-199
❑ 41DouPlaR-55
❑ 41PlaBal-35
❑ 47PM1StaP1-84
❑ 55Top-150
❑ 58RedSoxJP-4
❑ 59RedSoxJP-3
❑ 61Top-221
❑ 62RedSoxJP-4
❑ 62Top-559
❑ 72FleFamF-30
❑ 72LauGreF-11
❑ 74A's192T-16
❑ 75RedSox1T-19
❑ 81RedSoxBG2S-27
❑ 81TigDetN-89
❑ 83ConMar-10
❑ 83TCMPla1943-13
❑ 85BigLeaC3-89
❑ 88ConAmeA-15
❑ 90HOFStiB-37
❑ 91ConTSN-271
❑ 94ConTSN-1115
❑ 94ConTSNB-1115

Higgins, Rudy
❑ 93FreKeyC-29

Higgins, Ted
❑ 86FloStaLAP-23
❑ 86Ft.LauYP-13
❑ 87AlbYanP-8

Higginson, Bobby (Robert Leigh)
❑ 92NiaFalRC-14
❑ 92NiaFalRF-3339
❑ 93LakTigC-11
❑ 93LakTigF-1322
❑ 94AriFalLS-7
❑ 94ExcFS7-56
❑ 94TolMudHF-1038
❑ 95Bow-127
❑ 95ColCho-581T
❑ 95DonTopotO-79
❑ 95Emo-45
❑ 95Exc-50
❑ 95Fin-257
❑ 95FinRef-257
❑ 95Fla-258
❑ 95FleUpd-20
❑ 95LeaLim-106
❑ 95SelCer-102
❑ 95SelCerMG-102
❑ 95SPCha-156
❑ 95SPChaDC-156
❑ 95StaClu-611
❑ 95StaCluMOP-611
❑ 95StaCluSTWS-611
❑ 95Sum-134
❑ 95SumNthD-134
❑ 95TopTra-35T
❑ 95UltGolMR-M15
❑ 95UppDec-233
❑ 95UppDecED-233
❑ 95UppDecEDG-233
❑ 95Zen-131
❑ 96Cir-40
❑ 96CirRav-40
❑ 96ColCho-146

❑ 96ColChoGS-146
❑ 96ColChoSS-146
❑ 96Don-104
❑ 96DonPreP-104
❑ 96Fla-82
❑ 96Fle-113
❑ 96FleTif-113
❑ 96Lea-72
❑ 96LeaPrePB-72
❑ 96LeaPrePG-72
❑ 96LeaPrePS-72
❑ 96LeaSig-113
❑ 96LeaSigA-101
❑ 96LeaSigAG-101
❑ 96LeaSigAS-101
❑ 96LeaSigPPG-113
❑ 96LeaSigPPP-113
❑ 96Pac-319
❑ 96Pin-102
❑ 96PinAfi-146
❑ 96PinAfiAP-146
❑ 96Sco-278
❑ 96ScoDugC-B3
❑ 96ScoDugCAP-B3
❑ 96Sel-150
❑ 96SelArtP-150
❑ 96StaClu-170
❑ 96StaClu-234
❑ 96StaCluMOP-170
❑ 96StaCluMOP-234
❑ 96Sum-46
❑ 96SumAbo&B-46
❑ 96SumArtP-46
❑ 96SumFoi-46
❑ 96TeaOut-37
❑ 96TigHebN-7
❑ 96Top-98
❑ 96Ult-62
❑ 96UltGolM-62
❑ 96UppDec-68
❑ 97Bow-234
❑ 97BowChr-61
❑ 97BowChrI-61
❑ 97BowChrIR-61
❑ 97BowChrR-61
❑ 97BowInt-234
❑ 97Cir-52
❑ 97CirRav-52
❑ 97ColCho-108
❑ 97Don-61
❑ 97DonEli-81
❑ 97DonEliGS-81
❑ 97DonEliTotC-17
❑ 97DonEliTotCDC-17
❑ 97DonGolPP-61
❑ 97DonLim-200
❑ 97DonLimE-200
❑ 97DonPre-56
❑ 97DonPreCttC-56
❑ 97DonSilPP-61
❑ 97E-X2-22
❑ 97E-X2Cred-22
❑ 97E-X2EssCre-22
❑ 97Fin-76
❑ 97FinRef-76
❑ 97FlaShoLC-146
❑ 97FlaShoLeg0-146
❑ 97FlaShoLeg1-146
❑ 97FlaShoM-A146
❑ 97FlaShoM-B146
❑ 97FlaShoM-C146
❑ 97FlaShoR0-146
❑ 97FlaShoR1-146
❑ 97FlaShoR2-146
❑ 97Fle-99
❑ 97FleTeaL-6
❑ 97FleTif-99
❑ 97Lea-127
❑ 97LeaFraM-127
❑ 97LeaFraMDC-127
❑ 97MetUni-110
❑ 97NewPin-51
❑ 97NewPinAP-51
❑ 97NewPinMC-51
❑ 97NewPinPP-51
❑ 97Pac-88
❑ 97PacLigB-88
❑ 97PacPri-32
❑ 97PacPriLB-32
❑ 97PacPriP-32
❑ 97PacSil-88
❑ 97PinIns-76
❑ 97PinInsCE-76
❑ 97PinInsDE-76
❑ 97PinX-P-85
❑ 97PinX-PMoS-85
❑ 97Sco-307
❑ 97ScoArtPWB-307
❑ 97ScoPreS-307
❑ 97ScoShoS-307
❑ 97ScoShoSAP-307
❑ 97Sel-67
❑ 97SelArtP-67
❑ 97SelCom-67
❑ 97SelRegG-67
❑ 97SP-72
❑ 97SpoIll-136
❑ 97SpoIllEE-136
❑ 97StaClu-136
❑ 97StaCluMOP-136
❑ 97Stu-71
❑ 97StuPrePG-71
❑ 97StuPrePS-71
❑ 97Top-258
❑ 97TopChr-90
❑ 97TopChrR-90
❑ 97Ult-60
❑ 97UltGolME-60
❑ 97UltPlaME-60
❑ 97UppDec-355
❑ 98Bow-255
❑ 98BowBes-75
❑ 98BowBesAR-75
❑ 98BowBesR-75
❑ 98BowChr-255
❑ 98BowChrGA-255
❑ 98BowChrGAR-255
❑ 98BowChrI-255
❑ 98BowChrIR-255
❑ 98BowChrR-255
❑ 98BowGolA-255
❑ 98BowInt-255
❑ 98CirThu-196
❑ 98CirThuRav-196
❑ 98CirThuSupRav-196
❑ 98ColCho-371
❑ 98CroRoy-56
❑ 98Don-132
❑ 98DonCol-132
❑ 98DonColE-430
❑ 98DonColL-315
❑ 98DonColP-660
❑ 98DonColS-132
❑ 98DonCruG-26
❑ 98DonCruP-26
❑ 98DonCruR-26
❑ 98DonEli-30
❑ 98DonEliA-30
❑ 98DonEliS-30
❑ 98DonGolPP-132
❑ 98DonPre-110
❑ 98DonPreSeat-110
❑ 98DonPriCD-132
❑ 98DonPriCE-430
❑ 98DonPriCL-315
❑ 98DonPriCP-660
❑ 98DonSig-48
❑ 98DonSigP-48
❑ 98DonSilPP-132
❑ 98E-X2-45
❑ 98E-X2ECFut-45
❑ 98E-X2ECNow-45
❑ 98Fin-248
❑ 98FinNo--248
❑ 98FinNo-R-248
❑ 98FinRef-248
❑ 98FlaShoLeg0-34
❑ 98FlaShoLeg1-34
❑ 98FlaShoLeg2-34
❑ 98FlaShoLeg3-34
❑ 98FlaShoLegM-34
❑ 98FlaShoR0-34
❑ 98FlaShoR1-34
❑ 98FlaShoR2-34
❑ 98FlaShoR3-34
❑ 98Fle-234
❑ 98Lea-116
❑ 98LeaCruG-26
❑ 98LeaCruP-26
❑ 98LeaCruR-26
❑ 98LeaFraDA-116
❑ 98LeaFraF-116
❑ 98LeaFraM-116
❑ 98LeaFraM-116
❑ 98LeaFraMDC-116
❑ 98LeaFraMDC-116
❑ 98LeaFraMS-116
❑ 98LeaFraMZ2-116
❑ 98LeaRS-103
❑ 98LeaRSLHolo-103
❑ 98LeaRSLong-103
❑ 98LeaRTrue-103
❑ 98MetUni-121
❑ 98MetUniPMG-121
❑ 98Pac-89
❑ 98PacAur-38
❑ 98PacInv-33
❑ 98PacInvPBlue-33
❑ 98PacInvSilv-33
❑ 98PacInvTeam-10
❑ 98PacOme-90
❑ 98PacOmeR-90
❑ 98PacOnl-274
❑ 98PacOnlR-274
❑ 98PacOnlWC-274
❑ 98PacPar-47
❑ 98PacParC-47
❑ 98PacParG-47
❑ 98PacParHS-47
❑ 98PacParPB-47
❑ 98PacParR-47
❑ 98PacPlaB-89
❑ 98PacRedT-89
❑ 98PacSil-89
❑ 98Pin-114
❑ 98PinIns-4
❑ 98PinInsCE-4
❑ 98PinInsDE-4
❑ 98PinPer-92
❑ 98PinPerPP-92
❑ 98PinPlu-128
❑ 98PinPluAP-PP41
❑ 98PinPluGAP-PP41
❑ 98PinPluMAP-PP41
❑ 98PinPreP-114
❑ 98Revo-58
❑ 98RevoSS-58
❑ 98ScoRT-50
❑ 98ScoRTSS-PP50
❑ 98ScoRTSSAP-PP50
❑ 98ScoRTSSAP1-PP50
❑ 98SkyDugA-64
❑ 98SkyDugAIA-64
❑ 98SP Aut-91
❑ 98SpoIll-60
❑ 98SpoIllEE-60
❑ 98SpoIllFE-60
❑ 98SpoIllTaN-92
❑ 98SpoIllTaNEE-92
❑ 98SpoIllWSF-58
❑ 98SpoIllWSFEE-58
❑ 98SpoIllWSFFE-58
❑ 98SPxFin-83
❑ 98SPxFinR-83
❑ 98SPxFinS-83
❑ 98StaCluFDI-305
❑ 98StaCluI-305
❑ 98StaCluOneK-305
❑ 98StaCluPP-305
❑ 98Stu-37
❑ 98StuGPP-37
❑ 98StuSPP-37
❑ 98Top-436
❑ 98TopChr-436
❑ 98TopChrR-436
❑ 98TopDevR-436
❑ 98TopDia-436
❑ 98TopGal-47
❑ 98TopGalGP-47
❑ 98TopGalOPP-47
❑ 98TopGalPPI-47
❑ 98TopGalPPIA-47
❑ 98TopMiniC-436
❑ 98TopSta-148
❑ 98TopStaB-148
❑ 98TopStaG-148
❑ 98TopStaGR-148
❑ 98TopStaS-148
❑ 98Ult-21
❑ 98UltGolM-21
❑ 98UltMas-21
❑ 98UltPlaM-21
❑ 98UppDec-88
❑ 98UppDec-252
❑ 98UppDecSF-54
❑ 98Zen-56
❑ 98Zen5 xx7-34
❑ 98Zen5x7GoldImp-34
❑ 98Zen5x7Imp-34
❑ 98ZenZ-G-56
❑ 98ZenZ-S-56
❑ 99199Fin-76
❑ 99Bow-49
❑ 99BowChr-49
❑ 99BowChrG-49
❑ 99BowChrGR-49
❑ 99BowChrI-49
❑ 99BowChrIR-49
❑ 99BowChrR-49
❑ 99BowGol-49
❑ 99BowInt-49
❑ 99CroRoyB-53
❑ 99CroRoyL-53
❑ 99CroRoyOD-53
❑ 99FinGolRef-76
❑ 99FinRef-76
❑ 99FlaShoLeg1-54
❑ 99FlaShoLeg2-54
❑ 99FlaShoLeg3-54
❑ 99FlaShoLegM1-54
❑ 99FlaShoLegM2-54
❑ 99FlaShoLegM3-54
❑ 99FlaShoR1-54
❑ 99FlaShoR2-54
❑ 99FlaShoR3-54
❑ 99Fle-190
❑ 99FleBri-91
❑ 99FleBri2G-91
❑ 99FleBriBlu-91
❑ 99FleBriGol-91
❑ 99FleSta9-190
❑ 99FleWarT-190
❑ 99MetUni-87
❑ 99MetUniGM-87
❑ 99MetUniPMG-87
❑ 99Pac-166
❑ 99PacAur-67
❑ 99PacAurOD-67
❑ 99PacCroCTC-11
❑ 99PacInv-56
❑ 99PacInvOD-56
❑ 99PacInvPB-56
❑ 99PacOme-90
❑ 99PacOmeC-90
❑ 99PacOmeG-90
❑ 99PacOmePB-90
❑ 99PacPar-89
❑ 99PacParC-89
❑ 99PacParG-89
❑ 99PacParHoloGold-89
❑ 99PacParHS-89
❑ 99PacParOD-89
❑ 99PacParPB-89
❑ 99PacParRed-89
❑ 99PacPlaB-166
❑ 99PacPri-58
❑ 99PacPriHB-58
❑ 99PacPriHG-58
❑ 99PacPriHM-58
❑ 99PacPriHP-58
❑ 99PacPriRed-58
❑ 99PacPriS-99
❑ 99PacPriS206-99
❑ 99PacPriS206R-99
❑ 99PacRed-166
❑ 99Rev-55
❑ 99RevPremDate-55
❑ 99RevRet-55
❑ 99RevShaSS-55
❑ 99SkyMolM-17
❑ 99SkyMolMX-17
❑ 99SkyPre-56
❑ 99SkyPreA-27
❑ 99SkyPreABlue-27
❑ 99SkyPreR-56
❑ 99SkyThu-191
❑ 99SkyThuRant-191
❑ 99SkyThuRave-191
❑ 99SpoIll-113
❑ 99StaClu-195
❑ 99StaCluFDI-195
❑ 99StaCluOoaK-195
❑ 99StaCluPP-195
❑ 99ThuSkySupR-191
❑ 99Top-348
❑ 99TopChr-348
❑ 99TopChrR-348
❑ 99TopMVPP-348
❑ 99TopOpeD-153
❑ 99TopSta-144
❑ 99TopStaFoil-144
❑ 99UppDec-367
❑ 99UppDecEL1-367
❑ 99UppDecEL2-367
❑ 99UppDecM-78
❑ 99UppDecMGS-78
❑ 99UppDecMHFS-78
❑ 99UppDecMSS-78
❑ 99Vic-148

Higgs, Darrel
❑ 87OrlTwiP-24

High, Andy (Andrew)
❑ 21Exh-73
❑ 26Exh-2
❑ 27Exh-3
❑ 29PorandAR-39
❑ 31CarMet-16
❑ 33Gou-182
❑ 88ConSer3-13
❑ 90DodTar-345
❑ 92ConTSN-648
❑ 94ConTSN-1174
❑ 94ConTSNB-1174
❑ 95ConTSN-1336

High, Brent
❑ 94DavLipB-15

High, Charley
❑ 22Zee-45
❑ 23Zee-67
❑ 24Zee-46
❑ 25Zee-41

High, Hugh
❑ 15SpoNewM-81
❑ 16FleBreD-42
❑ 16SpoNewM-82
❑ 17ColE13-76A
❑ 17ColE13-76B
❑ 17ColE13-190A
❑ 19Zee-137
❑ 20Zee-142
❑ 21Zee-160
❑ 22Zee-153
❑ 23Zee-187
❑ 94ConTSN-1174
❑ 94ConTSNB-1174

Hightower, Barry
❑ 86ColMetP-13
❑ 87ColMetP-1
❑ 88SpoIndP-1942

Hightower, Mark
❑ 90GeoColC-9

Hightower, Vee
❑ 93PeoChiTI-9
❑ 96OrlCubB-11

Higson, Chuck
❑ 86EveGiaC-185
❑ 86EveGiaPC-8
❑ 88FreSunCLC-22
❑ 88FreSunP-1225

Higuchi, Alan
❑ 87HawRai-29

Higuchi, Roberta
❑ 96MedHatBJTI-13

Higuera, Teddy (Ted)
❑ 84ElPasDT-15
❑ 85BrePol-49
❑ 85FleUpd-54
❑ 85TopTifT-53T
❑ 85TopTra-53T
❑ 86BrePol-49
❑ 86Don-351
❑ 86Fle-490
❑ 86FleStiC-59
❑ 86Lea-157
❑ 86MSAJayPCD-10
❑ 86Spo-114
❑ 86Top-347
❑ 86TopTif-347
❑ 87BrePol-49
❑ 87BreTeal-7
❑ 87ClaUpdY-147
❑ 87Don-16
❑ 87Don-49
❑ 87DonAll-57
❑ 87DonOpeD-56
❑ 87DonSupD-16
❑ 87Fle-346
❑ 87FleExcS-27
❑ 87FleGamW-21
❑ 87FleGlo-346
❑ 87FleHotS-22
❑ 87FleLeaL-23
❑ 87FleLimE-21
❑ 87FleMin-55
❑ 87FleSlu-20
❑ 87FleStiC-60
❑ 87Lea-16
❑ 87Lea-95
❑ 87OPC-250
❑ 87RedFolSB-74
❑ 87Spo-11
❑ 87Spo-111
❑ 87SpoTeaP-19
❑ 87Top-250
❑ 87Top-615
❑ 87TopGloA-22
❑ 87TopMinL-60
❑ 87TopSti-199
❑ 87TopTif-250
❑ 87TopTif-615
❑ 88BrePol-49
❑ 88BreTeal-18
❑ 88Don-90
❑ 88DonBasB-127
❑ 88Fle-166
❑ 88FleAll-3
❑ 88FleAwaW-19
❑ 88FleBasA-15
❑ 88FleBasM-18
❑ 88FleExcS-21
❑ 88FleGlo-166
❑ 88FleHotS-20
❑ 88FleLeaL-20
❑ 88FleMin-30
❑ 88FleRecS-19
❑ 88FleSlu-19
❑ 88FleStiC-37
❑ 88FleSup-16
❑ 88FleTeaL-15
❑ 88GreBasS-60
❑ 88Lea-53
❑ 88OPC-110
❑ 88PanSti-116
❑ 88Sco-280
❑ 88ScoGlo-280
❑ 88Spo-20
❑ 88StaLinBre-9
❑ 88Top-110
❑ 88TopBig-87
❑ 88TopMinL-18
❑ 88TopSti-196
❑ 88TopTif-110
❑ 88TopUKM-35
❑ 88TopUKMT-35
❑ 89Bow-129
❑ 89BowTif-129
❑ 89BreGar-7
❑ 89BrePol-49
❑ 89BreYea-49
❑ 89ClaTraO-136
❑ 89Don-175
❑ 89DonBasB-183
❑ 89ElPasDGS-16
❑ 89Fle-188
❑ 89FleBasM-20
❑ 89FleGlo-188
❑ 89FleHeroB-23
❑ 89FleSup-24
❑ 89OPC-292
❑ 89PanSti-366
❑ 89RedFolSB-59
❑ 89Sco-132
❑ 89ScoHot1S-49
❑ 89Spo-47
❑ 89Top-595
❑ 89TopMinL-57
❑ 89TopSti-198
❑ 89TopStiB-28
❑ 89TopTif-595
❑ 89TopUKM-39
❑ 89TVSpoM-75
❑ 89UppDec-424
❑ 90Bow-384
❑ 90BowTif-384
❑ 90BreMilB-11
❑ 90BrePol-49
❑ 90ClaYel-T9
❑ 90Don-339
❑ 90DonBesA-92
❑ 90El PasDAGTI-6
❑ 90Fle-326
❑ 90FleCan-326
❑ 90Lea-506
❑ 90M.Vpin-51
❑ 90MLBBasB-83
❑ 90OPC-15
❑ 90PanSti-96
❑ 90PublntS-289
❑ 90PublntS-497
❑ 90Sco-305
❑ 90Spo-44
❑ 90Top-15
❑ 90TopBig-322
❑ 90TopSti-201
❑ 90TopTif-15
❑ 90UppDec-627
❑ 91BasBesAotM-10
❑ 91Bow-54
❑ 91BreMilB-10
❑ 91BrePol-10
❑ 91ClaGam-24
❑ 91Don-629
❑ 91Fle-586
❑ 91OPC-475
❑ 91Sco-260
❑ 91StaClu-46

❑ 91StuPre-6
❑ 91Top-475
❑ 91TopDesS-475
❑ 91TopMic-475
❑ 91TopTif-475
❑ 91Ult-175
❑ 91UppDec-341
❑ 92Bow-223
❑ 92BrePol-12
❑ 92Don-294
❑ 92Fle-178
❑ 92OPC-265
❑ 92Pin-439
❑ 92Sco-126
❑ 92StaClu-208
❑ 92Top-265
❑ 92TopGol-265
❑ 92TopGolW-265
❑ 92TopMic-265
❑ 92Ult-80
❑ 92UppDec-138
❑ 93BrePol-11
❑ 93PacSpa-511
❑ 93PacSpaPl-16
❑ 94BreMilB-227
❑ 94BrePol-12
❑ 94BreTeal-11
❑ 94ColC-451
❑ 94ColChoGS-451
❑ 94ColChoSS-451
❑ 94PanSti-81
❑ 94Sco-348
❑ 94ScoGolR-348
❑ 94StaClu-273
❑ 94StaCluFDI-273
❑ 94StaCluGR-273
❑ 94StaCluMOP-273
❑ 95Pac-233

Hijus, Erik
❑ 93CapCitBF-454

Hilbert, Adam
❑ 88PocGiaP-2081

Hilcher, Walter
❑ 33WorCig(-45

Hildebrand, George
❑ 21Exh-74
❑ 35AlDemDCR3-167
❑ 90DodTar-346
❑ 93ConTSN-708
❑ 94ConTSN-1208
❑ 94ConTSNB-1208

Hildebrand, Oral
❑ 33TatOrbSDR-163
❑ 33WorCig-55
❑ 34BatR31-123
❑ 34Gou-38
❑ 34GouCanV-95
❑ 35GouPuzR-1L
❑ 35GouPuzR-2E
❑ 35GouPuzR-16E
❑ 35GouPuzR-17E
❑ 36GouBWR-19
❑ 36GouWidPPR-A53
❑ 36GouWidPPR-B12
❑ 36NatChiFPR-43
❑ 36OveCanR-25
❑ 37ExhFou-15
❑ 38CloFotW-41
❑ 40PlaBal-123
❑ 75YanDyn1T-23
❑ 77GalGloG-186
❑ 83BigLeaCOA-13
❑ 91ConTSN-278

Hildebrand, Tom
❑ 86PenWhiSP-13

Hildreth, Brad
❑ 88MisStaB-11
❑ 89EriOriS-8
❑ 89MisStaB-19
❑ 90FreKeyTI-30
❑ 90WauTimS-11

Hiles, Cary
❑ 98BatMucTI-12

Hilgenberg, Scot
❑ 86CedRapRT-17
❑ 87TamTarP-24

Hilgendorf, Tom
❑ 70OPC-482
❑ 70Top-482
❑ 73IndTeal-14
❑ 74OPC-13
❑ 74Top-13
❑ 75OPC-377
❑ 75PhiPhiP-15
❑ 75Top-377
❑ 75TopMin-377
❑ 76OPC-168
❑ 76Top-168

Hiljus, Erik
❑ 92KinMetC-13
❑ 92KinMetF-1526
❑ 93CapCitBC-7
❑ 94St.LucMC-13
❑ 94St.LucMF-1189
❑ 95StLucMTI-17
❑ 96BesAutS-38
❑ 98JacSunM-13

Hill, A.J.
❑ 77AppFoxT-10
❑ 80AppFoxT-17
❑ 80GleFalWSBT-21
❑ 80GleFalWSCT-30
❑ 81AppFoxT-18
❑ 83MidCubT-26
❑ 84ChaLooT-20

Hill, Belden
❑ 98CamPepP-34

Hill, Bill
❑ 98HelBreM-18

Hill, Brad
❑ 85BurRanT-4
❑ 86SalRedBP-12

Hill, Carmen
❑ 93ConTSN-987

Hill, Chris
❑ 88LitFalMP-17
❑ 89ColMetB-13
❑ 89ColMetGS-9
❑ 89SouAtlLAGS-15
❑ 90St.LucMS-10
❑ 91LinDriAA-634
❑ 91WilBilLD-634
❑ 91WilBilP-286
❑ 92OscAstC-3
❑ 92OscAstF-2526
❑ 93ClaGolF-66
❑ 93ExcFS7-44
❑ 93JacGenF-2104
❑ 94JacGenF-212

Hill, Clay (Don)
❑ 83ChaLooT-15
❑ 84ChaLooT-27
❑ 85CalCanC-100
❑ 86CalCanP-12
❑ 88MiaMarS-9
❑ 93HelBreF-4110

Hill, Darryl
❑ 78DunBluJT-12

Hill, Donnie
❑ 82WesHavAT-14
❑ 83TacTigT-11
❑ 84A'sMot-13
❑ 84Don-96
❑ 84Fle-448
❑ 84Nes792-265
❑ 84Top-265
❑ 84TopTif-265
❑ 85A'sMot-12
❑ 85Don-375
❑ 85Fle-426
❑ 85TopTifT-54T
❑ 85TopTra-54T
❑ 86A'sMot-12
❑ 86Don-340
❑ 86Fle-420
❑ 86Lea-148
❑ 86OPC-310
❑ 86Top-484
❑ 86TopTif-484
❑ 87Don-405
❑ 87DonOpeD-237
❑ 87Fle-394
❑ 87FleGlo-394
❑ 87Top-339
❑ 87TopTif-339
❑ 87TopTra-47T
❑ 87TopTraT-47T
❑ 87WhiSoxC-15
❑ 88Don-87
❑ 88Fle-400
❑ 88FleGlo-400
❑ 88OPC-132
❑ 88Sco-572
❑ 88ScoGlo-572
❑ 88StaLinWS-10
❑ 88Top-132
❑ 88TopBig-137
❑ 88TopSti-286
❑ 88TopTif-132
❑ 88WhiSoxC-10
❑ 89Sco-583
❑ 89TacTigC-18
❑ 89TacTigP-1562
❑ 89Top-512
❑ 89TopTif-512
❑ 89UppDec-527
❑ 91AngSmo-12
❑ 91Don-376
❑ 91Fle-316
❑ 91Lea-177
❑ 91OPC-36
❑ 91Top-36
❑ 91TopDesS-36
❑ 91TopMic-36
❑ 91TopTif-36
❑ 91Ult-46
❑ 91UppDec-211
❑ 92Fle-60
❑ 92Lea-498
❑ 92LeaBlaG-498
❑ 92OPC-731
❑ 92Sco-183
❑ 92StaClu-702
❑ 92Top-731
❑ 92TopGol-731
❑ 92TopGolW-731
❑ 92TopMic-731
❑ 92UppDec-413
❑ 93HelBreSP-7

Hill, Elmer
❑ 20Zee-143

Hill, Eric
❑ 90BatCliP-3058
❑ 91SpaPhiC-6
❑ 91SpaPhiP-891
❑ 92ClePhiC-2
❑ 92ReaPhiF-570
❑ 93ReaPhiF-294
❑ 94ReaPhiF-2056
❑ 95ReaPhiTI-30
❑ 95ScrRedBTI-12

Hill, Fred
❑ 89WytCubS-13

Hill, Garry
❑ 70OPC-172
❑ 70Top-172

Hill, Glenallen
❑ 85KinBluJT-19
❑ 86KnoBluJP-10
❑ 86SouLeaAJ-16
❑ 87Don-561
❑ 87SpoTeaP-5
❑ 87SyrChiP-1950
❑ 87SyrChiT-20
❑ 88SyrChiC-15
❑ 88SyrChiP-812
❑ 89SyrChiC-15
❑ 89SyrChiMB-15
❑ 89SyrChiP-804
❑ 89TriAAAP-AAA31
❑ 90BluJayFS-12
❑ 90Bow-514
❑ 90BowTif-514
❑ 90ClaBlu-88
❑ 90Don-627
❑ 90DonRoo-24
❑ 90FleUpd-127
❑ 90Lea-317
❑ 90OPC-194
❑ 90Sco-601
❑ 90ScoYouS2-33
❑ 90Top-194
❑ 90TopDeb89-59
❑ 90TopTif-194
❑ 90TriAAAC-22
❑ 90UppDec-776
❑ 91BluJayFS-14
❑ 91Bow-24
❑ 91Don-380
❑ 91Fle-177
❑ 91FleUpd-17
❑ 91Lea-311
❑ 91OPC-509
❑ 91PanFreS-347
❑ 91Sco-514
❑ 91Sco100RS-60
❑ 91StaClu-425
❑ 91Stu-43
❑ 91Top-509
❑ 91TopDesS-509
❑ 91TopMic-509
❑ 91TopRoo-12
❑ 91TopTif-509
❑ 91TopTra-55T
❑ 91TopTraT-55T
❑ 91ToyRoo-11
❑ 91Ult-363
❑ 91UltUpd-19
❑ 91UppDec-276
❑ 91UppDecFE-52F
❑ 92Bow-659
❑ 92Don-643
❑ 92DonCraJ2-23
❑ 92Fle-110
❑ 92IndFanC-11
❑ 92Lea-70
❑ 92LeaBlaG-70
❑ 92OPC-364
❑ 92Pin-420
❑ 92Sco-448
❑ 92StaClu-413
❑ 92Stu-166
❑ 92Top-364
❑ 92TopGol-364
❑ 92TopGolW-364
❑ 92TopMic-364
❑ 92TriPla-181
❑ 92Ult-347
❑ 92UppDec-558
❑ 93Bow-65
❑ 93Don-201
❑ 93Fle-592
❑ 93IndWUA-11
❑ 93Lea-128
❑ 93OPC-114
❑ 93PacSpa-411
❑ 93Pin-123
❑ 93Sco-398
❑ 93StaClu-576
❑ 93StaCluFDI-576
❑ 93StaCluMOP-576
❑ 93Top-666
❑ 93TopGol-666
❑ 93TopInaM-666
❑ 93TopInaR-666
❑ 93TopMic-666
❑ 93TriPla-212
❑ 93Ult-540
❑ 93UppDec-584
❑ 93UppDecGold-584
❑ 94ColC-137
❑ 94ColChoGS-137
❑ 94ColChoSS-137
❑ 94Don-150
❑ 94Fla-138
❑ 94Fle-387
❑ 94Lea-18
❑ 94Sel-372
❑ 94StaCluT-351
❑ 94StaCluTFDI-351
❑ 94Top-63
❑ 94TopGol-63
❑ 94TopSpa-63
❑ 94Ult-458
❑ 94UppDec-149
❑ 94UppDecED-149
❑ 95ColCho-206
❑ 95ColCho-553T
❑ 95ColChoGS-206
❑ 95ColChoSS-206
❑ 95Don-90
❑ 95DonPreP-90
❑ 95DonTopotO-351
❑ 95Emo-194
❑ 95Fin-282
❑ 95FinRef-282
❑ 95Fla-424
❑ 95Fle-417
❑ 95FleUpd-193
❑ 95GiaMot-5
❑ 95Lea-375
❑ 95LeaLim-81
❑ 95Pin-249
❑ 95PinArtP-249
❑ 95PinMusC-249
❑ 95Sco-9
❑ 95ScoGolR-9
❑ 95ScoPlaTS-9
❑ 95SP-114
❑ 95SPCha-94
❑ 95SPChaDC-94
❑ 95SPSil-114
❑ 95StaClu-525
❑ 95StaCluMOP-525
❑ 95StaCluSTWS-525
❑ 95TopTra-84T
❑ 95Ult-137
❑ 95UltGolM-137
❑ 95UppDec-331
❑ 95UppDecED-331
❑ 95UppDecEDG-331
❑ 96ColCho-305
❑ 96ColChoGS-305
❑ 96ColChoSS-305
❑ 96Don-75
❑ 96DonPreP-75
❑ 96EmoXL-290
❑ 96Fin-B44
❑ 96FinRef-B44
❑ 96Fla-388
❑ 96Fle-588
❑ 96FleTif-588
❑ 96GiaMot-6
❑ 96Lea-183
❑ 96LeaPrePB-183
❑ 96LeaPrePG-183
❑ 96LeaPrePS-183
❑ 96LeaSigA-102
❑ 96LeaSigAG-102
❑ 96LeaSigAS-102
❑ 96MetUni-242
❑ 96MetUniP-242
❑ 96Pac-213
❑ 96PanSti-112
❑ 96Pin-63
❑ 96Pin-297
❑ 96PinFoil-297
❑ 96ProSta-55
❑ 96Sco-436
❑ 96SP-164
❑ 96StaClu-287
❑ 96StaCluB&B-BB8
❑ 96StaCluEPB-287
❑ 96StaCluEPG-287
❑ 96StaCluEPS-287
❑ 96StaCluMOP-287
❑ 96StaCluMOP-BB8
❑ 96Top-32
❑ 96TopChr-15
❑ 96TopChrR-15
❑ 96TopGal-76
❑ 96TopGalPPI-76
❑ 96Ult-294
❑ 96UltGolM-294
❑ 96UppDec-194
❑ 96UppDec-418
❑ 97Cir-194
❑ 97CirRav-194
❑ 97ColCho-215
❑ 97Don-332
❑ 97DonGolPP-332
❑ 97DonSilPP-332
❑ 97Fin-23
❑ 97FinRef-23
❑ 97Fle-482
❑ 97FleTif-482
❑ 97Lea-269
❑ 97LeaFraM-269
❑ 97LeaFraMDC-269
❑ 97MetUni-245
❑ 97PacPriGotD-GD217
❑ 97SP-161
❑ 97StaClu-146
❑ 97StaCluMOP-146
❑ 97Top-221
❑ 97TopGal-83
❑ 97TopGalPPI-83
❑ 97Ult-439
❑ 97UltGolME-439
❑ 97UltPlaME-439
❑ 97UppDec-495
❑ 98Fle-362
❑ 98FleUpd-U43
❑ 98Pac-442
❑ 98PacOme-221
❑ 98PacOmeR-221
❑ 98PacOnl-687
❑ 98PacOnlR-687
❑ 98PacOnlWC-687
❑ 98PacPlaB-442
❑ 98PacRedT-442
❑ 98PacSil-442
❑ 98Sco-255
❑ 98Top-189
❑ 98TopChr-189
❑ 98TopChrR-189
❑ 98TopDevR-189
❑ 98TopDia-189
❑ 98TopMiniC-189
❑ 98Ult-415
❑ 98UltGolM-415
❑ 98UltMas-415
❑ 98UltPlaM-415
❑ 98UppDec-723
❑ 99Fle-502
❑ 99FleSta9-502
❑ 99FleWarT-502
❑ 99PacOme-48
❑ 99PacOmeC-48
❑ 99PacOmeG-48
❑ 99PacOmePB-48
❑ 99UppDec-332
❑ 99UppDecEL1-332
❑ 99UppDecEL2-332
❑ 99Vic-85

Hill, H.A.
❑ 79KnoKnoST-22

Hill, Herman
❑ 70OPC-267
❑ 70Top-267

Hill, Hunter
❑ 08BufBisFJO-4
❑ 11SpoLifCW-165

Hill, Jason
❑ 94BoiHawC-14
❑ 94BoiHawF-3349
❑ 95CedRapKTI-19
❑ 96CedRapKTI-12
❑ 96LakElsSB-7
❑ 97LakElsSG-16
❑ 98MidAngG-17
❑ 98MidAngO-19
❑ 99TeaBesR-35
❑ 99TeaBesRG-35
❑ 99TeaBesRS-35

Hill, Jeremy
❑ 97SpoIndG-13
❑ 98LanLugQ-15

Hill, Jesse
❑ 33WorCig(-47
❑ 72TCMthe3-83

Hill, Jim
❑ 47CenFlo-9
❑ 92NegLeaRLI-28

Hill, Ken
❑ 87ArkTraP-19
❑ 89CarSmo-9
❑ 89CarTeal-12
❑ 89Don-536
❑ 89DonBasB-304
❑ 89DonRoo-31
❑ 89Fle-652
❑ 89FleGlo-652
❑ 89FleUpd-119
❑ 89LouRedBP-1268
❑ 89LouRedBTI-22
❑ 89ScoRoo-98T
❑ 89TopTra-50T
❑ 89TopTraT-50T
❑ 90Don-397
❑ 90Fle-251
❑ 90FleCan-251
❑ 90LouRedBLBC-19
❑ 90OPC-233
❑ 90Sco-233
❑ 90Sco100RS-34
❑ 90ScoYouSI-32
❑ 90Top-233
❑ 90TopRoo-15
❑ 90TopTif-233
❑ 90TopTVCa-13
❑ 90ToyRoo-15
❑ 90TriAllGP-AAA53
❑ 90UppDec-336
❑ 91Bow-390
❑ 91CarPol-43
❑ 91Don-670
❑ 91Fle-635
❑ 91Lea-376
❑ 91LouRedTI-4
❑ 91OPC-591
❑ 91Sco-567
❑ 91StaClu-435
❑ 91Top-591
❑ 91TopDesS-591
❑ 91TopMic-591
❑ 91TopTif-591
❑ 91UltUpd-106
❑ 91UppDec-647
❑ 92Bow-507
❑ 92ClaGam-168
❑ 92Don-31
❑ 92ExpDonD-11
❑ 92ExpPos-18
❑ 92Fle-580
❑ 92FleUpd-98
❑ 92Lea-468
❑ 92LeaBlaG-468
❑ 92OPC-664
❑ 92OPCPre-89
❑ 92Pin-486
❑ 92Sco-104
❑ 92ScoRoo-61T
❑ 92StaClu-138
❑ 92StaClu-735
❑ 92StaCluNC-735

❑ 92Stu-56
❑ 92Top-664
❑ 92TopGol-664
❑ 92TopGolW-664
❑ 92TopMic-664
❑ 92TopTra-51T
❑ 92TopTraG-51T
❑ 92Ult-520
❑ 92UppDec-628
❑ 92UppDec-790
❑ 93Bow-324
❑ 93Don-220
❑ 93ExpDonM-9
❑ 93Fin-35
❑ 93FinRef-35
❑ 93Fla-84
❑ 93Fle-76
❑ 93FunPac-96
❑ 93HumDumC-38
❑ 93Lea-201
❑ 93OPC-239
❑ 93PacSpa-186
❑ 93PanSti-223
❑ 93Pin-66
❑ 93Sco-48
❑ 93Sel-169
❑ 93SelAce-14
❑ 93SelStaL-89
❑ 93SP-104
❑ 93StaClu-227
❑ 93StaCluFDI-227
❑ 93StaCluMOP-227
❑ 93Top-495
❑ 93TopGol-495
❑ 93TopInaM-495
❑ 93TopInaR-495
❑ 93TopMic-495
❑ 93TriPla-174
❑ 93Ult-68
❑ 93UppDec-138
❑ 93UppDecGold-138
❑ 94Bow-444
❑ 94ColC-138
❑ 94ColChoGS-138
❑ 94ColChoSS-138
❑ 94Don-180
❑ 94Fin-25
❑ 94FinRef-25
❑ 94Fla-192
❑ 94Fle-542
❑ 94FleExtB-307
❑ 94FUnPac-44
❑ 94Lea-282
❑ 94LeaL-126
❑ 94OPC-140
❑ 94PanSti-211
❑ 94Pin-355
❑ 94PinArtP-355
❑ 94PinMusC-355
❑ 94Sco-64
❑ 94ScoGolR-64
❑ 94Sel-371
❑ 94StaClu-445
❑ 94StaCluFDI-445
❑ 94StaCluGR-445
❑ 94StaCluMOP-445
❑ 94Stu-79
❑ 94Top-315
❑ 94TopGol-315
❑ 94TopSpa-315
❑ 94TriPla-96
❑ 94Ult-229
❑ 94UppDec-173
❑ 94UppDecED-173
❑ 95Bow-349
❑ 95ColCho-236
❑ 95ColCho-541T
❑ 95ColChoGS-236
❑ 95ColChoSE-99
❑ 95ColChoSEGS-99
❑ 95ColChoSESS-99
❑ 95ColChoSS-236
❑ 95Don-227
❑ 95DonPreP-227
❑ 95DonTopotO-328
❑ 95Emo-180
❑ 95Fin-276
❑ 95FinRef-276
❑ 95Fla-408
❑ 95Fle-354
❑ 95FleAllS-19
❑ 95FleLeaL-9
❑ 95FleTeaL-22
❑ 95FleUpd-160
❑ 95Lea-395
❑ 95Pac-270
❑ 95PanSti-8
❑ 95Pin-115
❑ 95PinArtP-115
❑ 95PinMusC-115
❑ 95PosCan-6
❑ 95RedFol-25
❑ 95Sco-50
❑ 95ScoGolR-50
❑ 95ScoHaloG-HG44
❑ 95ScoPlaTS-50
❑ 95SP-102
❑ 95SPCha-84
❑ 95SPChaDC-84
❑ 95SPSil-102
❑ 95StaClu-22
❑ 95StaClu-408
❑ 95StaClu-616
❑ 95StaCluFDI-22
❑ 95StaCluMO-22
❑ 95StaCluMOP-22
❑ 95StaCluMOP-408
❑ 95StaCluMOP-616
❑ 95StaCluMOP-VRE9
❑ 95StaCluSTWS-22
❑ 95StaCluSTWS-408
❑ 95StaCluSTWS-616
❑ 95StaCluVE-VRE9
❑ 95StaCluVR-16
❑ 95StaCluVRMO-16
❑ 95Stu-120
❑ 95Sum-8
❑ 95SumNthD-8
❑ 95Top-46
❑ 95TopCyb-35
❑ 95TopTra-64T
❑ 95Ult-192
❑ 95UltGolM-192
❑ 95UppDec-77
❑ 95UppDec-309
❑ 95UppDec-467
❑ 95UppDecED-77
❑ 95UppDecED-309
❑ 95UppDecEDG-77
❑ 95UppDecEDG-309
❑ 95UppDecSE-227
❑ 95UppDecSEG-227
❑ 96Cir-88
❑ 96CirRav-88
❑ 96ColCho-789
❑ 96Don-454
❑ 96DonPreP-454
❑ 96EmoXL-124
❑ 96Fin-B310
❑ 96FinRef-B310
❑ 96Fla-174
❑ 96Fle-88
❑ 96FleTif-88
❑ 96FleUpd-U90
❑ 96FleUpdTC-U90
❑ 96LeaSigA-103
❑ 96LeaSigAG-103
❑ 96LeaSigAS-103
❑ 96Pin-348
❑ 96PinFoil-348
❑ 96RanDr P-17
❑ 96RanFle-10
❑ 96RanMot-17
❑ 96SP-178
❑ 96Sum-44
❑ 96SumAbo&B-44
❑ 96SumArtP-44
❑ 96SumFoi-44
❑ 96Top-414
❑ 96Ult-422
❑ 96UltGolM-422
❑ 96UppDec-468
❑ 97Cir-239
❑ 97CirRav-239
❑ 97ColCho-491
❑ 97ColChoT-TR12
❑ 97Don-181
❑ 97DonGolPP-181
❑ 97DonLim-155
❑ 97DonLimE-155
❑ 97DonLimENG-155
❑ 97DonPre-122
❑ 97DonPreCttC-122
❑ 97DonSilPP-181
❑ 97Fin-11
❑ 97FinRef-11
❑ 97FlaShoLC-144
❑ 97FlaShoLeg0-144
❑ 97FlaShoLeg1-144
❑ 97FlaShoM-A144
❑ 97FlaShoM-B144
❑ 97FlaShoM-C144
❑ 97FlaShoR0-144
❑ 97FlaShoR1-144
❑ 97FlaShoR2-144
❑ 97Fle-226
❑ 97FleTif-226
❑ 97Lea-148
❑ 97LeaFraM-148
❑ 97LeaFraMDC-148
❑ 97MetUni-164
❑ 97Pac-204
❑ 97PacLigB-204
❑ 97PacSil-204
❑ 97Pin-124
❑ 97PinArtP-PP124
❑ 97PinMusC-124
❑ 97PinPrePla-124
❑ 97PinX-P-17
❑ 97PinX-PMoS-17
❑ 97RanDr P-14
❑ 97RanMinM-4
❑ 97RanMot-17
❑ 97RanSco-3
❑ 97RanScoPl-3
❑ 97RanScoPr-3
❑ 97Sco-13
❑ 97ScoArtPWB-13
❑ 97ScoPreS-13
❑ 97ScoShoS-13
❑ 97ScoShoSAP-13
❑ 97StaClu-250
❑ 97StaCluMat-250
❑ 97StaCluMOP-250
❑ 97Top-235
❑ 97Ult-136
❑ 97UltGolME-136
❑ 97UltPlaME-136
❑ 97UppDec-508
❑ 98AngSco-7
❑ 98AngScoP-7
❑ 98ColCho-283
❑ 98Fin-219
❑ 98FinNo--219
❑ 98FinNo-R-219
❑ 98FinRef-219
❑ 98Fle-423
❑ 98PacAur-7
❑ 98PacInvGems-3
❑ 98PacOnl-11
❑ 98PacOnlR-11
❑ 98PacOnlWC-11
❑ 98PinSna-AA5
❑ 98Sco-125
❑ 98ScoSS-PP53
❑ 98ScoSSAP-PP53
❑ 98Top-446
❑ 98TopChr-446
❑ 98TopChrR-446
❑ 98TopDevR-446
❑ 98TopDia-446
❑ 98TopMiniC-446
❑ 98Ult-201
❑ 98UltGolM-201
❑ 98UltMas-201
❑ 98UltPlaM-201
❑ 98UppDec-293
❑ 99Fle-430
❑ 99FleSta9-430
❑ 99FleWarT-430
❑ 99Pac-8
❑ 99PacPlaB-8
❑ 99PacRed-8
❑ 99Top-26
❑ 99TopChr-26
❑ 99TopChrR-26
❑ 99TopMVPP-26
❑ 99UppDec-298
❑ 99UppDecEL1-298
❑ 99UppDecEL2-298

Hill, Lew
❑ 87OneYanP-1
❑ 89OneYanP-2111
❑ 90GreHorB-23
❑ 90GreHorP-2675
❑ 91GreHorP-3074
❑ 92ClaFS7-438
❑ 92GreHorC-20
❑ 92GreHorF-792
❑ 93AusFut-34
❑ 93ClaGolF-116
❑ 93ExcFS7-208
❑ 93PriWilCC-14
❑ 93PriWilCF-669
❑ 93SouAtlLAIPI-3
❑ 93SouAtlLAPI-15
❑ 94AlbYanF-1454
❑ 95ColCliP-12
❑ 95ColCliTI-12

Hill, Marc
❑ 75Gia-3
❑ 75GiaTeal-6
❑ 75OPC-620
❑ 75Top-620
❑ 75TopMin-620
❑ 76OPC-577
❑ 76SanFraGP-10
❑ 76SSP-100
❑ 76Top-577
❑ 77Gia-10
❑ 77GiaTeal-13
❑ 77Top-57
❑ 78GiaTeal-12
❑ 78Top-359
❑ 79GiaPol-2
❑ 79Top-11
❑ 80GiaPol-2
❑ 80GiaTeal-9
❑ 80MarPos-12
❑ 80OPC-125
❑ 80Top-236
❑ 81Top-486
❑ 81TopTra-770
❑ 82Top-748
❑ 83Don-230
❑ 83Top-124
❑ 83WhiSoxTV-7
❑ 84Don-330
❑ 84Fle-62
❑ 84Nes792-698
❑ 84Top-698
❑ 84TopTif-698
❑ 84WhiSoxTV-16
❑ 85Don-160
❑ 85Fle-516
❑ 85Top-312
❑ 85TopTif-312
❑ 85WhiSoxC-7
❑ 86Top-552
❑ 86TopTif-552
❑ 86WhiSoxC-7
❑ 88AstMot-27
❑ 92PenPilC-27
❑ 92PenPilF-2948
❑ 93ClaGolF-132
❑ 93ClaPla&MotYF-PM2
❑ 94JacSunF-1426
❑ 95LynHilTI-10
❑ 96CarMudB-26
❑ 97CarMudC-25

Hill, Mike
❑ 93EriSaiC-11
❑ 93EriSaiF-3128
❑ 94HudValRC-6
❑ 94HudValRF-3391

Hill, Milton
❑ 88CedRapRP-1163
❑ 89ChaLooB-6
❑ 89ChaLooGS-10
❑ 90CMC-126
❑ 90NasSouC-1
❑ 90NasSouP-226
❑ 90ProAAAF-538
❑ 91LinDriAAA-261
❑ 91NasSouLD-261
❑ 91NasSouP-2151
❑ 92Don-659
❑ 92NasSouF-1828
❑ 92NasSouS-282
❑ 92Sco-820
❑ 92StaClu-733
❑ 92StaCluECN-733
❑ 92TopDeb91-80
❑ 93Don-502
❑ 93Fle-36
❑ 93Top-642
❑ 93TopGol-642
❑ 93TopInaM-642
❑ 93TopInaR-642
❑ 93TopMic-642
❑ 94BraLykP-10
❑ 94BraLykS-11
❑ 94BraUSPC-7H
❑ 94StaCluT-33
❑ 94StaCluTFDI-33
❑ 95CarMudF-150
❑ 97PriDevR-2

Hill, Moe (Elmore)
❑ 78WisRapTT-8
❑ 97RocCub-3
❑ 97WilCubB-30

Hill, Nate
❑ 85SpoIndC-8

Hill, Orsino
❑ 83CedRapRF-23
❑ 83CedRapRT-23
❑ 88JacExpB-12
❑ 88JacExpP-965
❑ 89ChaKniTI-24
❑ 90CMC-644
❑ 90ProAAAF-177
❑ 90TriAllGP-AAA41
❑ 90VanCanC-17
❑ 90VanCanP-499
❑ 91LinDriAAA-638
❑ 91VanCanLD-638
❑ 91VanCanP-1606
❑ 92TacTigF-2515
❑ 92TacTigS-536

Hill, Perry W.
❑ 86DayBealP-12
❑ 90GasRanS-28
❑ 91GasRanP-2705
❑ 93RanKee-437
❑ 94RanMagM-14

Hill, Pete
❑ 74LauOldTBS-10

Hill, Quency
❑ 76OklCit8TI-23
❑ 78KnoKnoST-8
❑ 82QuaCitCT-27

Hill, Roger
❑ 88WatIndP-685

Hill, Ron
❑ 80ElmPioRST-9

Hill, Sandy
❑ 78SalPirT-6

Hill, Shane
❑ 94ButCopKSP-13

Hill, Shawn
❑ 93GenCubC-13
❑ 93GenCubF-3168
❑ 94MidLeaAF-MDW48
❑ 94PeoChiC-12
❑ 94PeoChiF-2261
❑ 95Exc-163

Hill, Steve (Stephen F.)
❑ 85AncGlaPTI-16
❑ 86St.PetCP-12
❑ 87PeoChiP-7
❑ 87PeoChiPW-4
❑ 87SprCarB-12
❑ 88St.PetCS-10
❑ 88WinSpiS-6
❑ 89ArkTraGS-7
❑ 89SanBerSB-15
❑ 89SanBerSCLC-84
❑ 89SalVol-10

Hill, Still (William C.)
❑ 90DodTar-981

Hill, T.J.
❑ 97ChaRivDG-16
❑ 97HudValRB-12

Hill, Terrance
❑ 98LowSpiM-22

Hill, Tony
❑ 86ElmPioRSP-10
❑ 87GreHorP-14

Hill, Tripp
❑ 90MisStaB-20
❑ 91MisStaB-25
❑ 92MisStaB-21
❑ 93MisStaB-22

Hill, Tyrone
❑ 91ClaDraP-12
❑ 91HelBreSP-8
❑ 91HigSchPLS-3
❑ 92BelBreCB-1
❑ 92BelBreFI-401
❑ 92ClaFS7-364
❑ 92MidLeaATI-19
❑ 92OPC-444
❑ 92Pin-301
❑ 92Sco-807
❑ 92StaCluD-84
❑ 92Top-444
❑ 92TopGol-444
❑ 92TopGolW-444
❑ 92TopMic-444
❑ 92UppDecML-29
❑ 92UppDecML-135
❑ 93Bow-368
❑ 93Bow-619
❑ 93ClaYouG-YG5
❑ 93ExcFS7-186
❑ 93StoPorC-1
❑ 93StoPorF-742
❑ 93UppDec-427
❑ 93UppDecGold-427
❑ 94ActPac-27
❑ 94FleMajLP-13
❑ 94SigRoo-15
❑ 94SigRooS-15
❑ 94StoPorC-10
❑ 94StoPorF-1688
❑ 94Ult-372
❑ 94UppDecML-233
❑ 96StoPorB-8
❑ 98MidAngG-18

Hilldales, Philadelphia
❑ 91PomBlaBPB-3
❑ 94PomNegLB-6

Hillebrand, Homer
❑ 11SpoLifCW-166

Hillegas, Shawn
❑ 87AlbDukD-11
❑ 87SpoRoo2-30
❑ 88AlbDukCm-1
❑ 88AlbDukP-265
❑ 88DodPol-49
❑ 88Don-35
❑ 88Fle-519
❑ 88FleGlo-519
❑ 88Lea-35
❑ 88Sco-612
❑ 88ScoGlo-612
❑ 88Top-455
❑ 88TopClo-48
❑ 88TopTif-455
❑ 89Bow-58
❑ 89BowTif-58
❑ 89Don-503
❑ 89Fle-498
❑ 89FleGlo-498
❑ 89PanSti-301
❑ 89Sco-488
❑ 89ScoYouS2-29
❑ 89Top-247
❑ 89TopTif-247
❑ 89UppDec-72A
❑ 89UppDec-478
❑ 89WhiSoxC-11
❑ 90CMC-635
❑ 90DodTar-982
❑ 90Don-619
❑ 90Fle-535
❑ 90FleCan-535
❑ 90OPC-93
❑ 90ProAAAF-163
❑ 90PublntS-389
❑ 90Sco-329
❑ 90Top-93
❑ 90TopTif-93
❑ 90UppDec-541
❑ 90VanCanC-7
❑ 90VanCanP-485
❑ 91Don-589
❑ 91FleUpd-18
❑ 91IndFanC-13
❑ 91Lea-513
❑ 91ScoRoo-65T
❑ 92ColCliF-346
❑ 92Don-72
❑ 92Fle-111
❑ 92OPC-523
❑ 92Sco-93
❑ 92ScoProP-21
❑ 92StaClu-76
❑ 92Top-523
❑ 92TopGol-523
❑ 92TopGolW-523
❑ 92TopMic-523
❑ 93AthMot-26
❑ 93AthStaC-20
❑ 93PacSpa-569
❑ 94Pac-453

Hillemann, Charlie (Charles)
❑ 87SpoIndP-9
❑ 88ChaRaiP-1197
❑ 89TexLeaAGS-9
❑ 89WicStaR-4
❑ 89WicUpdR-6
❑ 89WicWraR-18
❑ 90CMC-521
❑ 90LasVegSC-18
❑ 90LasVegSP-134
❑ 90ProAAAF-22
❑ 90WicWraRD-9
❑ 91Cla/Bes-50
❑ 91LinDriAA-608
❑ 91WicWraLD-608
❑ 91WicWraP-2611

Hillenbrand, Shea

❑ 96LowSpiB-9
❑ 97MicBatC-12
❑ 98MicBatCM-15
❑ 99BasAmeTPA-20
❑ 99Bow-304
❑ 99BowGol-304
❑ 99BowInt-304
❑ 99SP SigAuto-SHH
❑ 99SP SigAutoG-SHH
❑ 99SP TopP-41
❑ 99SP TopPPE-41
❑ 99SPSig-26
❑ 99TeaBesRA-13
❑ 99UppDec-267
❑ 99UppDecE-110
❑ 99UppDecEFXG-110
❑ 99UppDecEL1-267
❑ 99UppDecEL2-267
❑ 99UppDecMP-SH
❑ 99Vic-57
Hiller, Chuck
❑ 61Top-538
❑ 62GiaJayP-6
❑ 62SalPlaC-106
❑ 62ShiPlaC-106
❑ 62Top-188
❑ 62TopVen-188
❑ 63GiaJayP-6
❑ 63Jel-102
❑ 63Pos-102
❑ 63Top-145
❑ 63Top-185
❑ 64Top-313
❑ 64TopVen-313
❑ 65Top-531
❑ 66MetTeal-7
❑ 66OPC-154
❑ 66Top-154
❑ 66TopVen-154
❑ 67CokCapYM-V19
❑ 67MetTeal-7
❑ 67Top-198
❑ 68Top-461
❑ 73OPC-549
❑ 73Top-549
❑ 76KanCitRP-13
❑ 81Car5x7-11
❑ 81Gia196T-11
❑ 83Car-11
❑ 85GiaMot-27
❑ 85GiaPos-15
❑ 91MetWIZ-182
❑ 93RanKee-185
Hiller, Frank
❑ 48BluTin-37
❑ 48YanTeal-13
❑ 52Bow-114
❑ 52Top-156
❑ 83TopRep5-156
Hiller, John
❑ 66Top-209
❑ 66TopVen-209
❑ 68TigDetFPB-6
❑ 68Top-307
❑ 68TopVen-307
❑ 69MilBra-114
❑ 69TigTealC-5
❑ 69Top-642
❑ 70OPC-12
❑ 70Top-12
❑ 71MLBOffS-393
❑ 71OPC-629
❑ 71Top-629
❑ 72MilBra-146
❑ 73LinPor-70
❑ 73OPC-448
❑ 73Top-448
❑ 74OPC-24
❑ 74OPC-208
❑ 74Tig-5
❑ 74Top-24
❑ 74Top-208
❑ 74TopDecE-17
❑ 74TopSta-175
❑ 75DetTigP-10
❑ 75Kel-19
❑ 75OPC-415
❑ 75Top-415
❑ 75TopMin-415
❑ 76DetTigP-10
❑ 76OPC-37
❑ 76SSP-353
❑ 76Top-37
❑ 77BurCheD-95
❑ 77Hos-28
❑ 77OPC-257
❑ 77Top-595
❑ 78TigBurK-9
❑ 78TigTeal-14
❑ 78Top-258
❑ 79OPC-71
❑ 79Top-151
❑ 80OPC-229
❑ 80TigGreT-12
❑ 80Top-614
❑ 81TigDetN-12
❑ 83TigAlKS-52
❑ 86GleFalTP-10
❑ 86TigSpoD-22
❑ 87TolMudHP-25
❑ 88TigDom-7
Hillerman, Charlie
❑ 91WicWraRD-21
Hilliard, David
❑ 15Zee-63
Hilliker, T.J.
❑ 97GreFalDTI-15
Hillis, Jon
❑ 94HelBreF-3610
❑ 94HelBreSP-19
Hillis, Malcolm
❑ 26Zee-5
❑ 29Zee-89
❑ 30Zee-106
Hillman, Dave
❑ 57Top-351
❑ 58Top-41
❑ 59Top-319
❑ 60Top-68
❑ 60TopVen-68
❑ 61Top-326
❑ 62RedEnq-13
❑ 62Top-282
❑ 91MetWIZ-183
Hillman, Eric
❑ 87LitFalMP-2385
❑ 88ColMetGS-5
❑ 89ColMetB-11
❑ 89ColMetGS-10
❑ 91LinDriAAA-558
❑ 91MetColP-33
❑ 91TidTidLD-558
❑ 91TidTidP-2505
❑ 92Bow-326
❑ 92FleUpd-102
❑ 92SkyAAAF-252
❑ 92StaClu-847
❑ 92StaCluECN-847
❑ 92TidTidF-891
❑ 92TidTidS-558
❑ 93Fle-87
❑ 93MetColP-35
❑ 93NorTidF-2565
❑ 93Sco-280
❑ 93Sel-350
❑ 93Top-751
❑ 93TopGol-751
❑ 93TopInaM-751
❑ 93TopInaR-751
❑ 93TopMic-751
❑ 94ColC-139
❑ 94ColChoGS-139
❑ 94ColChoSS-139
❑ 94Don-514
❑ 94Fle-564
❑ 94MetColP-11
❑ 94Pac-403
❑ 94StaClu-480
❑ 94StaCluFDI-480
❑ 94StaCluGR-480
❑ 94StaCluMOP-480
❑ 94Top-453
❑ 94TopGol-453
❑ 94TopSpa-453
❑ 95Pac-281
Hillman, Greg
❑ 93GenCubC-14
❑ 93GenCubF-3169
❑ 94PeoChiC-13
❑ 94PeoChiF-2262
Hillman, Joe
❑ 88SouOreAP-1716
❑ 89ModA'sC-29
❑ 89ModA'sCLC-275
Hillman, Stewart
❑ 90CliGiaB-18
❑ 90CliGiaP-2542
Hillman, Trey
❑ 86WatIndP-12
❑ 87KinIndP-19
❑ 89PriWilCS-29
❑ 90CMC-224
❑ 90ColCliC-24
❑ 90ColCliP-693
❑ 90OneYanP-3389
❑ 91GreHorP-3075
❑ 91SouAtlLAGP-SAL27
❑ 92GreHorC-26
❑ 92GreHorF-796
❑ 93PriWilCC-26
❑ 93PriWilCF-672
❑ 94GreBatF-491
❑ 95GreBatTI-29
❑ 96TamYanY-1
❑ 97GreBatC-27
❑ 97NorNav-1
❑ 97NorNavTI-14
❑ 98NorNavQ-27
Hills, Mark
❑ 98SalVol-11
Hills, Rich
❑ 95IdaFalBTI-17
❑ 96CliLumKTI-15
❑ 97RanCucQUG-4
❑ 98OrlRayM-7
Hilo, Johnny
❑ 94GreFalDSP-10
❑ 95SanBerSTI-7
❑ 95YakBeaTI-15
Hilpert, Adam
❑ 86AncGlaPTI-15
❑ 89CliGiaP-883
Hilt, Scott
❑ 96HarCitRCB-14
Hilton, Howard
❑ 86St.PetCP-13
❑ 87SprCarB-13
❑ 88ArkTraGS-12
❑ 89LouRedBC-6
❑ 89LouRedBP-1251
❑ 89LouRedBTI-23
❑ 90Bow-189
❑ 90BowTif-189
❑ 90CMC-106
❑ 90LouRedBC-6
❑ 90LouRedBLBC-20
❑ 90LouRedBP-398
❑ 90ProAAAF-512
❑ 90TopTVCa-14
❑ 91TopDeb90-68
Hilton, John David
❑ 73OPC-615
❑ 73Top-615
❑ 74OPC-148
❑ 74PadDea-14
❑ 74Top-148A
❑ 74Top-148B
❑ 75OPC-509
❑ 75Top-509
❑ 75TopMin-509
❑ 76HawIslC-9
❑ 77OPC-139
❑ 77Top-163
❑ 79TCMJapPB-18
❑ 81PorBeaT-11
❑ 84VisOakT-10
❑ 85BrePol-NNO
❑ 88BrePol-NNO
❑ 88BreTeal-19
❑ 89PacSenL-216
❑ 89SanJosGCLC-30
❑ 90EliSenL-113
❑ 91PacSenL-124
❑ 91PacSenL-133
❑ 92IdaFalGF-3531
❑ 93GreBraF-365
❑ 94IdaFalBSP-28
❑ 94MacBraC-30
❑ 94MacBraF-2223
❑ 95MacBraTI-11
❑ 97FreKey-1
❑ 98DurBulTI-12
Hilton, Stan
❑ 84ModA'sC-16
❑ 85ModA'sC-22
❑ 86HunStaDJ-22
❑ 88WilBilP-1316
❑ 89BurIndS-28
❑ 89ColSprSSP-244
❑ 90BurIndP-3027
❑ 91BurIndP-3321
Hilton, Willy
❑ 96SouOreTI-27
Hina, Fred
❑ 88ColMetGS-18
❑ 89St.LucMS-27
❑ 90JacMetGS-6
Hinch, A.J.
❑ 93BazTeaU-14
❑ 93TopTra-12T
❑ 97Bes-83
❑ 97BesAutSBPP-22
❑ 97BesDiaB-16
❑ 97BesLum-7
❑ 97CalLeaATI-11
❑ 97ModA'sG-11
❑ 98A'sMot-10
❑ 98Bow-216
❑ 98BowBes-176
❑ 98BowBesAR-176
❑ 98BowBesMIF-MI10
❑ 98BowBesMIFAR-MI10
❑ 98BowBesMIFR-MI10
❑ 98BowBesR-176
❑ 98BowCerBlueAU-9
❑ 98BowCerGA-9
❑ 98BowCerSA-9
❑ 98BowChr-216
❑ 98BowChrGA-216
❑ 98BowChrGAR-216
❑ 98BowChrI-216
❑ 98BowChrIR-216
❑ 98BowChrR-216
❑ 98BowGolA-216
❑ 98BowInt-216
❑ 98CirThu-95
❑ 98CirThuRav-95
❑ 98CirThuSupRav-95
❑ 98ColCho-416
❑ 98ColChoPCR-416
❑ 98Don-272
❑ 98DonGolPP-272
❑ 98DonSig-85
❑ 98DonSigA-44
❑ 98DonSigAC-58
❑ 98DonSigAM-59
❑ 98DonSigP-85
❑ 98DonSigSP-11
❑ 98DonSilPP-272
❑ 98Fle-473
❑ 98FleProF-PF8
❑ 98LeaRCrusUP-123
❑ 98LeaRS-210
❑ 98LeaRSCrusUG-123
❑ 98LeaRSCrusUR-123
❑ 98LeaRSFOSamp-20
❑ 98LeaRSFresh-20
❑ 98LeaRSLHolo-210
❑ 98LeaRSLong-210
❑ 98LeaRTrue-210
❑ 98PacAur-68
❑ 98PacOme-178
❑ 98PacOmeR-178
❑ 98PacOmeRS-28
❑ 98PacOmeRST3-28
❑ 98PacOnl-534
❑ 98PacOnlR-534
❑ 98PacOnlWC-534
❑ 98PinPer-116
❑ 98PinPerPP-116
❑ 98SkyDugA-108
❑ 98SkyDugAIA-108
❑ 98SP Aut-8
❑ 98SP MinPE-92
❑ 98SP MinSTHPE-H26
❑ 98SPMin-92
❑ 98SPMinSTH-H26
❑ 98SpoIllWSF-125
❑ 98SpoIllWSFEE-125
❑ 98SpoIllWSFFE-125
❑ 98SPxFin-195
❑ 98SPxFinR-195
❑ 98SPxFinS-195
❑ 98StaCluBPP-BP9
❑ 98StaCluFDI-363
❑ 98StaCluI-363
❑ 98StaCluOneK-363
❑ 98StaCluPP-363
❑ 98Stu-194
❑ 98StuGPP-194
❑ 98StuSPP-194
❑ 98Top-487
❑ 98TopChr-487
❑ 98TopChrR-487
❑ 98TopDevR-487
❑ 98TopDia-487
❑ 98TopMiniC-487
❑ 98TopTek-83
❑ 98TopTekD-83
❑ 98UD3-2
❑ 98UD3-92
❑ 98UD3-182
❑ 98UD3DieCut-2
❑ 98UD3DieCut-92
❑ 98UD3DieCut-182
❑ 98Ult-383
❑ 98UltGolM-383
❑ 98UltMas-383
❑ 98UltPlaM-383
❑ 98UppDec-590
❑ 98UppDecDS-DS50
❑ 98UppDecR-126
❑ 98UppDecRNF-NF26
❑ 99Fle-166
❑ 99FleSta9-166
❑ 99FleWarT-166
❑ 99MetUni-109
❑ 99MetUniGM-109
❑ 99MetUniPMG-109
❑ 99Pac-313
❑ 99PacAur-137
❑ 99PacAurOD-137
❑ 99PacCroC-205
❑ 99PacCroCPB-205
❑ 99PacPlaB-313
❑ 99PacRed-313
❑ 99SkyMolM-79
❑ 99SkyMolMX-79
❑ 99SkyPre-57
❑ 99SkyPreR-57
❑ 99SkyThu-173
❑ 99SkyThuRant-173
❑ 99SkyThuRave-173
❑ 99SP Aut-63
❑ 99SPSig-129
❑ 99SPx-59
❑ 99SPxFinR-59
❑ 99SPxFinS-59
❑ 99StaClu-184
❑ 99StaCluFDI-184
❑ 99StaCluOoaK-184
❑ 99StaCluPP-184
❑ 99ThuSkySupR-173
❑ 99Top-132
❑ 99TopChr-132
❑ 99TopChrR-132
❑ 99TopMVPP-132
❑ 99TopOpeD-78
❑ 99UD Cho-120
❑ 99UD ChoP-120
❑ 99UD ChoPCR-120
❑ 99Ult-75
❑ 99UltGolM-75
❑ 99UltMas-75
❑ 99UltPlaM-75
❑ 99UppDec-166
❑ 99UppDecBD-111
❑ 99UppDecBDD-111
❑ 99UppDecBDQ-111
❑ 99UppDecBDT-111
❑ 99UppDecEL1-166
❑ 99UppDecEL2-166
❑ 99UppDecM-148
❑ 99UppDecMGS-148
❑ 99UppDecMHFS-148
❑ 99UppDecMP-148
❑ 99UppDecMSS-148
❑ 99Vic-286
Hinchliffe, Brett
❑ 94AppFoxC-11
❑ 94AppFoxFI-1049
❑ 95Exc-118
❑ 96LanJetB-15
❑ 98TacRaiQ-14
❑ 99DumSet-146
❑ 99FleMys-146
❑ 99FleMysM-146
❑ 99SkyPre-232
❑ 99SkyPre-232
❑ 99SkyPreR-232
❑ 99SkyPreR-232
Hinchman, Bill (William)
❑ 08AmeLeaPC-9
❑ 08RosComP-25
❑ 09BriE97-14
❑ 09T206-155
❑ 10W555-34
❑ 11PinT-5-1101
❑ 11SpoLifCW-168
❑ 72ClaCar-41
❑ 91ConTSN-155
❑ 94ConTSN-1113
❑ 94ConTSNB-1113
Hinchman, Harry
❑ 09ColChiE-129
❑ 09T206-430
❑ 11MecDFT-27
❑ 11PinT-5-1101
❑ 11PinT-5-1104
❑ 11SpoLifCW-167
❑ 12ColRedB-129
❑ 12ColTinT-129
Hinde, Michael
❑ 88CapCodPPaLP-62
❑ 89EliTwiS-11
Hindman, Randy
❑ 86CedRapRT-18
Hinds, Kevin
❑ 81CedRapRT-11
Hinds, Robert
❑ 92OneYanC-14
❑ 93GreHorC-11
❑ 93GreHorF-892
❑ 94FloStaLAF-FSL21
❑ 94TamYanC-14
❑ 94TamYanF-2392
❑ 95NorNagUTI-21
❑ 95NorNavTI-21
❑ 97NorNavTI-15
❑ 98NorNavQ-13
Hinds, Sam
❑ 77SpoIndC-17
❑ 78SpoIndC-19
❑ 78Top-303
❑ 79HolMilT-29
❑ 79VanCanT-19
❑ 94BreMilB-228
Hindy, Mark
❑ 95OdgRapTI-8
Hine, Frank
❑ 85CloHSS-22
Hine, Steve
❑ 96LowSpiB-10
❑ 98FarRedHM-10
Hines, Ben
❑ 84MarMot-27
❑ 86DodCokP-12
❑ 86DodPol-NNO
❑ 87AlbDukD-2
❑ 88DodMot-28
❑ 89DodMot-27
❑ 89DodPol-1
❑ 90DodMot-28
❑ 90DodPol-NNO
❑ 91DodMot-28
❑ 91DodPol-NNO
❑ 91DodSt.V-7
❑ 92DodMot-28
❑ 92DodPol-NNO
❑ 93DodMot-28
❑ 93DodPol-30
❑ 94AstMot-27
Hines, Bruce
❑ 94LakElsSC-28
❑ 94LakElsSF-1682
❑ 97VanCanB-1
Hines, Hunkey (Henry)
❑ 87OldJudN-241
❑ 90DodTar-347
Hines, Keith
❑ 90MedHatBJB-14
❑ 91St.CatBJC-12
❑ 91St.CatBJP-3408
❑ 92St.CatBJC-2
❑ 93HagSunC-14
❑ 93HagSunF-1892
Hines, Maurice
❑ 90MarPhiP-3187
Hines, Paul
❑ 87BucN28-114A
❑ 87BucN28-114B
❑ 87OldJudN-242
❑ 87TobLit-6
❑ 88WG1CarG-33
❑ 94OriofB-37
Hines, Pooh
❑ 95EugEmeTI-16
❑ 96EugEmeB-11
❑ 97EugEmeB-27
Hines, Rich
❑ 91GreHorP-3053
❑ 91SouAtlLAGP-SAL28
❑ 94ColCliP-12
❑ 95ColCliMCTI-5
❑ 95NorNavTI-39
❑ 96ColCliB-15
Hines, Richard
❑ 90TamYanD-12
❑ 92PriWilCC-6
❑ 92PriWilCF-141
❑ 93AlbYanF-2158
❑ 97GreBraG-12
Hines, Tim
❑ 89PitMetS-9
❑ 89St.LucMS-10

❑ 89Sta-158
❑ 90SalBucS-7
❑ 91CarMudLD-110
❑ 91CarMudP-1089
❑ 91LinDriAA-110
❑ 93WesPalBEF-1344

Hines, Todd
❑ 97BoiHawG-14

Hines, Zachary
❑ 97MacBra-22

Hingle, Larry
❑ 92BoiHawC-30
❑ 92BoiHawF-3620
❑ 92FroRowDP-73
❑ 92FroRowDPG-73
❑ 92FroRowDPS-73
❑ 93CedRapKC-9
❑ 93CedRapKF-1732
❑ 93MidLeaAGF-35
❑ 94LakElsSC-10
❑ 94LakElsSF-1659

Hinkel, John
❑ 78WauMetT-11

Hinkle, Gordon
❑ 35DiaMatCS3T1-74

Hinkle, Mike
❑ 87EriCarP-28
❑ 88SavCarP-331
❑ 89ArkTraGS-8
❑ 90CMC-105
❑ 90LouRedBC-5
❑ 90LouRedBLBC-21
❑ 90LouRedBP-399
❑ 90ProAAAF-513
❑ 90TopTVCa-52
❑ 91LouRedTI-10
❑ 92LouRedF-1883
❑ 92LouRedS-264

Hinnrichs, Dave
❑ 84EveGiaC-16
❑ 86FreGiaSB-13

Hinrichs, Phil
❑ 81PhoGiaVNB-17
❑ 83PhoGiaBHN-11

Hinshaw, George
❑ 82AmaGolST-1
❑ 83LasVegSBHN-10
❑ 84LasVegSC-234
❑ 85LasVegSC-113
❑ 87AlbDukD-28
❑ 88AlbDukCm-13
❑ 88AlbDukP-268
❑ 88TriAAC-40
❑ 90CMC-542
❑ 90PhoFirC-15
❑ 90PhoFirP-22
❑ 90ProAAAF-48

Hinske, Eric
❑ 98WilCubM-14

Hinsley, Jerry
❑ 64Top-576
❑ 65Top-449
❑ 70WicAerM-9
❑ 91MetWIZ-184

Hinson, Bo
❑ 82AubAstT-10

Hinson, Dean
❑ 91WelPirC-9
❑ 91WelPirP-3576
❑ 94HigDesMC-15
❑ 94HigDesMF-2783

Hinson, Gary
❑ 79WatIndT-8
❑ 80WatIndT-23
❑ 82BirBarT-14

Hinton, Chuck
❑ 47Exh-97
❑ 62Top-347
❑ 62TopStal-96
❑ 63Baz-25
❑ 63ExhStaB-29
❑ 63Jel-93
❑ 63Pos-93
❑ 63Top-2
❑ 63Top-330
❑ 63TopStil-18
❑ 64Baz-25
❑ 64Top-52
❑ 64TopCoi-38
❑ 64TopCoi-162A
❑ 64TopCoi-162B
❑ 64TopGia-20
❑ 64TopSta-47
❑ 64TopStaU-32
❑ 64TopVen-52
❑ 65Baz-3
❑ 65Kah-16
❑ 65OldLonC-26
❑ 65OPC-235
❑ 65Top-235
❑ 65TopEmbl-60
❑ 65TopTral-48
❑ 66IndTeal-5
❑ 66IndVolC-6
❑ 66Top-391
❑ 67CokCapl-18
❑ 67DexPre-95
❑ 67OPC-189
❑ 67Top-189
❑ 68Top-531
❑ 69MilBra-115
❑ 69MLBOffS-22
❑ 69Top-644
❑ 70MLBOffS-199
❑ 70OPC-27
❑ 70Top-27
❑ 71Ind-7
❑ 71MLBOffS-375
❑ 71OPC-429
❑ 71Top-429
❑ 72MilBra-147
❑ 78TCM60I-252
❑ 78TCM60I-265
❑ 89SweBasG-93

Hinton, Rich
❑ 72Top-724
❑ 73OPC-321
❑ 73Top-321
❑ 76IndIndTI-20
❑ 76OPC-607
❑ 76SSP-158
❑ 76Top-607
❑ 92YanWIZ7-74
❑ 93RanKee-17

Hinton, Steve
❑ 91EugEmeC-9
❑ 91EugEmeP-3734
❑ 92AppFoxCB-23
❑ 92AppFoxFI-992
❑ 92MidLeaATI-20
❑ 93AusFut-17
❑ 93WilBluRC-15
❑ 93WilBluRF-2005
❑ 95AusFut-3
❑ 95AusFut-87

Hinzo, Thomas
❑ 86AriWilP-5
❑ 87KinIndP-21
❑ 88ColSprSSC-14
❑ 88ColSprSSP-1527
❑ 88Don-526
❑ 88Fle-611
❑ 88FleGlo-611
❑ 88IndTeal-19
❑ 88OPC-294
❑ 88PanSti-73
❑ 88Sco-567
❑ 88ScoGlo-567
❑ 88StaLinI-13
❑ 88Top-576
❑ 88TopTif-576
❑ 89ColSprSSC-16
❑ 89ColSprSSP-256
❑ 89UppDec-34
❑ 93RocRedWF-249
❑ 93TriAAAGF-28
❑ 94CalCanF-795

Hipp, Mike
❑ 93Sou-10

Hippauf, Herb A.
❑ 66Top-518
❑ 87IdaFalBP-18
❑ 88IdaFalBP-1860

Hipps, Robert
❑ 32Zee-7

Hiraldo, Jerry
❑ 92GulCoaMF-3494
❑ 94KinMetC-4
❑ 94KinMetF-3834

Hird, Jeff
❑ 86AriWilP-6

Hirooka, Tatsuro
❑ 79TCMJapPB-25

Hirose, Sam
❑ 87SanJosBP-1
❑ 88SanJosGCLC-142
❑ 88SanJosGP-123

Hirsch, Chris
❑ 91SumFlyC-13
❑ 91SumFlyP-2336
❑ 93CedRapKF-1741

Hirsch, Jeff
❑ 86PeoChiP-11
❑ 87WinSpiP-23
❑ 88IowCubC-6
❑ 88IowCubP-532
❑ 89ChaKniTI-18
❑ 90PeoChiTI-20

Hirschbeck, John
❑ 88T/MUmp-50
❑ 89T/MUmp-48
❑ 90T/MUmp-46

Hirschbeck, Mark
❑ 89T/MUmp-59
❑ 90T/MUmp-57

Hirtensteiner, Rick
❑ 87PanAmTUBI-9
❑ 87PanAmTURB-17
❑ 88CapCodPPaLP-25
❑ 89BenBucL-20
❑ 90QuaCitAGS-27
❑ 91SalLakTP-3225
❑ 91SalLakTSP-6
❑ 92Bow-658
❑ 92HarSenF-471
❑ 92HarSenS-283
❑ 93AusFut-58
❑ 93OttLynF-2445
❑ 94PorSeaDF-690
❑ 94PorSeaDTI-15

Hiser, Gene
❑ 72OPC-61
❑ 72Top-61
❑ 74OPC-452
❑ 74Top-452
❑ 74WicAerODF-120
❑ 76SSP-314

Hisey, Jason
❑ 88AlaGolTI-9
❑ 90AriWilP-7
❑ 91HamRedC-11
❑ 91HamRedP-4034
❑ 92SavCarC-16
❑ 92SavCarF-658
❑ 93ClaFS7-243
❑ 93FloStaLAF-45
❑ 93St.PetCC-14
❑ 93St.PetCF-2623
❑ 94ClaGolF-171

Hisey, Steve
❑ 88SanBerSB-20
❑ 88SanBerSCLC-39

Hisle, Larry
❑ 68Top-579
❑ 69OPC-206
❑ 69PhiTeal-4
❑ 69Top-206
❑ 69TopFou-22
❑ 69TopTeaP-8
❑ 70DayDaiNM-49
❑ 70Kel-45
❑ 70MLBOffS-89
❑ 70OPC-288
❑ 70PhiTeal-4
❑ 70Top-288
❑ 71MLBOffS-180
❑ 71OPC-616
❑ 71PhiArcO-5
❑ 71Top-616
❑ 72MilBra-148
❑ 72OPC-398
❑ 72Top-398
❑ 73OPC-622
❑ 73Top-622
❑ 74OPC-366
❑ 74Top-366
❑ 75Hos-128
❑ 75OPC-526
❑ 75Top-526
❑ 75TopMin-526
❑ 75TwiPos-14
❑ 75TwiTeal-16
❑ 76Hos-73
❑ 76MinTwiP-9
❑ 76OPC-59
❑ 76SSP-220
❑ 76Top-59
❑ 77BurCheD-49
❑ 77OPC-33
❑ 77Top-375
❑ 78Hos-13
❑ 78OPC-3
❑ 78PapGinD-38
❑ 78RCColC-79
❑ 78SagDis-24
❑ 78TasDis-24
❑ 78Top-203
❑ 78Top-520
❑ 78WifBalD-29
❑ 79BasPat-39
❑ 79BrePlaPH-1
❑ 79Hos-95
❑ 79OPC-87
❑ 79Top-180
❑ 79TopCom-10
❑ 80BreTeal-12
❑ 80Kel-22
❑ 80OPC-222
❑ 80Top-430
❑ 81Don-87A
❑ 81Don-87B
❑ 81Fle-509
❑ 81FleStiC-94
❑ 81OPC-215
❑ 81Top-215
❑ 82BrePol-9
❑ 82Don-358
❑ 82Fle-144
❑ 82Top-93
❑ 83Top-773
❑ 86TwiGreT-6
❑ 91BluJayFS-15
❑ 93BluJayFS-15
❑ 94BreMilB-316
❑ 95BluJayOH-19

Hiss, William
❑ 75SanAntBT-11
❑ 77WatIndT-12

Hitchcock, Billy
❑ 48RedSoxTI-10
❑ 49RedSoxTI-9
❑ 50A'sTeal-12
❑ 51A'sTeal-11
❑ 51Bow-191
❑ 52A'sTeal-10
❑ 52Bow-89
❑ 52Top-182
❑ 53TigGle-14
❑ 53Top-17
❑ 60Top-461
❑ 62BalOriP-13
❑ 62Top-121
❑ 62TopVen-121
❑ 63BalOriP-14
❑ 63Top-213
❑ 66BraPos-13
❑ 67BraPho-13
❑ 67Top-199
❑ 79DiaGre-183
❑ 83TopRep5-182
❑ 91TopArc1-17

Hitchcock, Sterling
❑ 90CMC-822
❑ 90GreHorB-2
❑ 90GreHorP-2654
❑ 90GreHorS-5
❑ 90ProAaA-88
❑ 90TopTVY-46
❑ 91Cla/Bes-385
❑ 91PriWilCC-2
❑ 91PriWilCP-1419
❑ 92AlbYanF-2220
❑ 92AlbYanSk-8
❑ 92SkyAA F-4
❑ 93Bow-606
❑ 93ClaFS7-74
❑ 93ColCliF-1106
❑ 93ColCliP-5
❑ 93Don-345
❑ 93FleMajLP-A2
❑ 93Pin-579
❑ 93PinRooTP-2
❑ 93PinTea2-30
❑ 93Sco-311
❑ 93ScoBoyoS-22
❑ 93SelRoo-53T
❑ 93Top-530
❑ 93TopGol-530
❑ 93TopInaM-530
❑ 93TopInaR-530
❑ 93TopMic-530
❑ 93UppDec-10
❑ 93UppDecGold-16
❑ 93YanStaC-17
❑ 94Bow-333
❑ 94ColC-539
❑ 94ColChoGS-539
❑ 94ColChoSS-539
❑ 94ColCliF-2948
❑ 94ColCliP-13
❑ 94Don-638
❑ 94Fla-320
❑ 94FleUpd-68
❑ 94Pin-213
❑ 94PinArtP-213
❑ 94PinMusC-213
❑ 94Sco-565
❑ 94ScoGolR-565
❑ 94ScoRoo-RT83
❑ 94ScoRooGR-RT83
❑ 94Sel-397
❑ 94Spo-157
❑ 94StaClu-658
❑ 94StaCluFDI-658
❑ 94StaCluGR-658
❑ 94StaCluMOP-658
❑ 94StaCluT-203
❑ 94StaCluTFDI-203
❑ 94Top-103
❑ 94TopGol-103
❑ 94TopSpa-103
❑ 94UppDec-138
❑ 94UppDecED-138
❑ 95Don-51
❑ 95DonPreP-51
❑ 95Fla-284
❑ 95Fle-70
❑ 95Lea-59
❑ 95Pin-74
❑ 95PinArtP-74
❑ 95PinMusC-74
❑ 95Sco-546
❑ 95ScoGolR-546
❑ 95ScoPlaTS-546
❑ 95Sel-54
❑ 95SelArtP-54
❑ 95Top-266
❑ 95TopCyb-145
❑ 95Ult-309
❑ 95UltGolM-309
❑ 96ColCho-229
❑ 96ColChoGS-229
❑ 96ColChoSS-229
❑ 96Don-179
❑ 96DonPreP-179
❑ 96EmoXL-114
❑ 96Fin-S230
❑ 96FinRef-S230
❑ 96Fla-161
❑ 96Fle-239
❑ 96FleTif-239
❑ 96FleUpd-U79
❑ 96FleUpdTC-U79
❑ 96LeaLim-73
❑ 96LeaLimG-73
❑ 96LeaSigA-104
❑ 96LeaSigAG-104
❑ 96LeaSigAS-104
❑ 96MarMot-10
❑ 96Pac-373
❑ 96Pin-345
❑ 96PinAfi-108
❑ 96PinAfiAP-108
❑ 96PinFoil-345
❑ 96Sco-71
❑ 96Sel-105
❑ 96SelArtP-105
❑ 96SelCer-38
❑ 96SelCerAP-38
❑ 96SelCerCB-38
❑ 96SelCerCR-38
❑ 96SelCerMB-38
❑ 96SelCerMG-38
❑ 96SelCerMR-38
❑ 96StaClu-177
❑ 96StaCluMOP-177
❑ 96Sum-41
❑ 96SumAbo&B-41
❑ 96SumArtP-41
❑ 96SumFoi-41
❑ 96Ult-411
❑ 96UltGolM-411
❑ 96UppDec-463
❑ 96Zen-15
❑ 96ZenArtP-15
❑ 97Cir-227
❑ 97CirRav-227
❑ 07ColCho-231
❑ 97ColCho-448
❑ 97Don-168
❑ 97Don-290
❑ 97DonEli-101
❑ 97DonEliGS-101
❑ 97DonGolPP-168
❑ 97DonGolPP-290
❑ 97DonSilPP-168
❑ 97DonSilPP-290
❑ 97Fin-239
❑ 97FinRef-239
❑ 97Fle-207
❑ 97Fle-671
❑ 97FleTif-207
❑ 97FleTif-671
❑ 97MetUni-146
❑ 97Pac-187
❑ 97PacLigB-187
❑ 97PacSil-187
❑ 97PadMot-10
❑ 97Sco-66
❑ 97Sco-335
❑ 97ScoArtPWB-66
❑ 97ScoArtPWB-335
❑ 97ScoPreS-66
❑ 97ScoResC-335
❑ 97ScoShoS-66
❑ 97ScoShoS-335
❑ 97ScoShoSAP-66
❑ 97ScoShoSAP-335
❑ 97StaClu-106
❑ 97StaCluMOP-106
❑ 97Top-149
❑ 97Ult-122
❑ 97Ult-310
❑ 97UltGolME-122
❑ 97UltGolME-310
❑ 97UltPlaME-122
❑ 97UltPlaME-310
❑ 97UppDec-178
❑ 98ColCho-484
❑ 98Fle-434
❑ 98Pac-430
❑ 98PacOnl-640
❑ 98PacOnlR-640
❑ 98PacOnlWC-640
❑ 98PacPlaB-430
❑ 98PacRedT-430
❑ 98PacSil-430
❑ 98PadMot-6
❑ 98StaCluFDI-311
❑ 98StaClul-311
❑ 98StaCluOneK-311
❑ 98StaCluPP-311
❑ 98Top-402
❑ 98TopChr-402
❑ 98TopChrR-402
❑ 98TopDevR-402
❑ 98TopDia-402
❑ 98TopMiniC-402
❑ 98Ult-366
❑ 98UltGolM-366
❑ 98UltMas-366
❑ 98UltPlaM-366
❑ 98UppDec-497
❑ 99Fle-307
❑ 99FleSta9-307
❑ 99FleWarT-307
❑ 99SkyPre-183
❑ 99SkyPreR-183
❑ 99SP SigAuto-STH
❑ 99SpoIll-4
❑ 99SPSig-130
❑ 99UppDec-479
❑ 99UppDecCLM-C80
❑ 99UppDecEL1-479
❑ 99UppDecEL2-479
❑ 99UppDecM-177
❑ 99UppDecMGS-177
❑ 99UppDecMHFS-177
❑ 99UppDecMSS-177
❑ 99Vic-343

Hitchcox, Wally
❑ 93DavLipB-24

Hite, Kevin
❑ 97CliLumG-11

Hithe, Victor
❑ 87AshTouP-19
❑ 88OscAstS-14
❑ 89EasLeaAP-21
❑ 89HagSunB-5
❑ 89HagSunP-272
❑ 89HagSunS-11
❑ 90Bes-135
❑ 90CMC-323
❑ 90HagSunB-14
❑ 90HagSunP-1426
❑ 90ProAAAF-471
❑ 90RocRedWC-22
❑ 90RocRedWGC-24
❑ 90RocRedWP-714

Hitt, Danny (Daniel)
❑ 89SavCarP-369
❑ 90St.PetCS-13

Hitt, Roy
❑ 09ObaT21-71
❑ 09ObaT21-182
❑ 09ObaT21-347

❑ 10BisCoaLE99-11
❑ 11PacCoaBD-26
❑ 11Zee-114
❑ 12ObaPreT-96
❑ 12Zee-146
❑ 13Zee-136
❑ 14Zee-134
❑ 15Zee-128
❑ 15Zee-129
❑ 16Zee-132
❑ 17Zee-109
Hitta, Chief Powa
❑ 78RicBraT-20
❑ 79RicBraT-8
Hitting, Scott
❑ 90BatCliP-3084
Hittle, Red (Floyd)
❑ 48SmiClo-21
❑ 53MotCoo-42
Hivizda, Jim
❑ 88ButCopKSP-2
Hixon, Alan
❑ 86MiaMarP-11
Hiyama, Yasuhiro
❑ 87SalLakTTT-20
Hlodan, George
❑ 97AugGre-12
❑ 97EriSeaWB-19
❑ 98EriSeaWM-13
Hmielewski, Chris
❑ 92AlbPolCB-8
❑ 92AlbPolF-2317
❑ 93BurBeeC-10
❑ 93BurBeeF-166
❑ 93MidLeaAGF-30
❑ 94WesPalBEC-13
❑ 94WesPalBEF-34
Hoag, Myril
❑ 30Zee-123
❑ 34Gou-95
❑ 34TarThoBD-14
❑ 36GouWidPPR-A54
❑ 36NatChiFPR-44
❑ 36R31PasP-34
❑ 39PlaBal-109
❑ 40PlaBal-52
❑ 67SpoHobFC-23
❑ 72TCMthe3-79
❑ 75YanDyn1T-24
❑ 91ConTSN-233
❑ 93ConTSN-894
Hoak, Don
❑ 47Exh-98
❑ 52LaPat-7
❑ 52Par-57
❑ 53ExhCan-33
❑ 53Top-176
❑ 54Top-211
❑ 55Bow-21
❑ 55DodGolS-25
❑ 55Top-40
❑ 55TopDouH-25
❑ 56Top-335
❑ 57Kah-14
❑ 57RedSoh-9
❑ 57Top-274
❑ 58Kah-13
❑ 58RedEnq-17
❑ 58RedJayP-7
❑ 58Top-160
❑ 59Kah-15
❑ 59Top-25
❑ 59TopVen-25
❑ 60Kah-15
❑ 60KeyChal-24
❑ 60PirJayP-8
❑ 60PirTag-12
❑ 60Top-373
❑ 61Kah-19
❑ 61PirJayP-6
❑ 61PirRigF-4
❑ 61Pos-130A
❑ 61Pos-130B
❑ 61Top-230
❑ 61TopStal-65
❑ 61WilSpoGH828-1
❑ 61WilSpoGH828-1-2
❑ 62ExhStaB-16
❑ 62Jel-171
❑ 62Kah-19
❑ 62Pos-171
❑ 62PosCan-171
❑ 62SalPlaC-107
❑ 62ShiPlaC-107
❑ 62Top-95
❑ 62TopBuc-35
❑ 62TopStal-178
❑ 62TopVen-95
❑ 63ExhStaB-30
❑ 63Jel-140
❑ 63Pos-140
❑ 63Top-305
❑ 64Top-254
❑ 64TopVen-254
❑ 74CapPub-29
❑ 77PirTCM1WC-5
❑ 79TCM50-273
❑ 81TCM60I-388
❑ 90DodTar-348
❑ 91TopArc1-176
❑ 94TopArc1-211
❑ 94TopArc1G-211
❑ 95TopArcBD-50
❑ 95TopArcBD-81
❑ 95TopArcBD-94
❑ 95TopArcBD-121
Hoalton, Brandon
❑ 94IdaFalBF-3579
❑ 94IdaFalBSP-12
Hoban, John
❑ 80WatIndT-1
❑ 81WatIndT-9
❑ 82BelBreFr-7
Hobaugh, Brian
❑ 83WisRapTF-17
❑ 84VisOakT-12
Hobaugh, Ed
❑ 55DonWin-25
❑ 60Top-131
❑ 60TopVen-131
❑ 61Top-129
❑ 62Top-79
❑ 62TopVen-79
❑ 63Top-423
Hobbie, Glen
❑ 58Top-467
❑ 59Top-334
❑ 60Baz-32
❑ 60CubJayP-7
❑ 60Lea-20
❑ 60Top-182
❑ 60TopTat-22
❑ 60TopVen-182
❑ 61CubJayP-8
❑ 61Pos-197A
❑ 61Pos-197B
❑ 61Top-264
❑ 61Top-273A
❑ 61Top-393
❑ 62CubJayP-7
❑ 62SalPlaC-145
❑ 62ShiPlaC-145
❑ 62Top-585
❑ 62TopStal-108
❑ 63Fle-31
❑ 63Top-212
❑ 64CubJayP-6
❑ 64Top-578
Hobbie, Matt
❑ 93BurIndC-1
❑ 93BurIndF-3311
❑ 94BurIndC-7
❑ 94BurIndF-3807
❑ 96BoiHawB-15
Hobbs, Jack
❑ 82OrlTwi8SCT-17
❑ 82OrlTwiT-5
❑ 83OrlTwiT-16
Hobbs, John
❑ 80VenLeaS-106
Hobbs, Jon
❑ 88FreSunCLC-4
❑ 88FreSunP-1237
Hobbs, Rodney
❑ 80LynSaiT-3
❑ 81LynSaiT-22
❑ 82WesHavAT-22
❑ 84AlbA'sT-4
❑ 86NasSouTI-13
Hobbs, Shane
❑ 93MarPhiC-13
❑ 93MarPhiF-3478
Hobbs, Tyler
❑ 89KinMetS-29
Hoblitzell, Doc (Richard C.)
❑ 09ColChiE-130
❑ 09RamT20-55
❑ 09T206-156
❑ 10CouT21-144
❑ 10CouT21-145
❑ 10CouT21-146
❑ 10CouT21-287
❑ 10DomDisP-55
❑ 10JHDABE-8
❑ 10OrnOvaPP-6
❑ 10RedCroT-29
❑ 10RedCroT-118
❑ 10RedCroT-199
❑ 10SweCapPP-102
❑ 11HelSta-116
❑ 11PinT-5-420
❑ 11PloCanE-33
❑ 11S74Sil-77
❑ 11SpoLifCW-169
❑ 11SpoLifM-196
❑ 11T205-76A
❑ 11T205-76B
❑ 11TurRedT-97
❑ 12ColRedB-130
❑ 12ColTinT-130
❑ 12HasTriFT-40
❑ 12HasTriFT-71
❑ 13NatGamW-19
❑ 13TomBarW-18
❑ 14CraJacE-55
❑ 14PieStaT-53
❑ 15CraJacE-55
❑ 15SpoNewM-82
❑ 16FleBreD-43
❑ 16SpoNewM-83
❑ 17ColE13-77
❑ 72ClaCar-16
❑ 91ConTSN-148
Hobson, Butch
❑ 77Top-89
❑ 78Hos-1
❑ 78OPC-187
❑ 78PapGinD-4
❑ 78RCColC-59
❑ 78SSP270-172
❑ 78Top-155
❑ 79Hos-129
❑ 79OPC-136
❑ 79Top-270
❑ 80OPC-216
❑ 80Top-420
❑ 81AllGamPI-34
❑ 81Don-542
❑ 81Fle-227
❑ 81LonBeaPT-4
❑ 81OPC-7
❑ 81Top-595
❑ 81TopSti-54
❑ 81TopSupHT-59
❑ 81TopTra-771
❑ 82Don-577
❑ 82Fle-465
❑ 82FleSta-213
❑ 82OPC-357
❑ 82Top-357
❑ 82TopSti-164
❑ 82YanPhoA-11
❑ 83ColCliT-21
❑ 83Top-652
❑ 84ColCliP-12
❑ 84ColCliT-16
❑ 85ColCliP-13
❑ 85ColCliT-17
❑ 87ColMetP-10
❑ 88ColMetGS-1
❑ 89NewBriRSP-617
❑ 89NewBriRSS-23
❑ 89PacSenL-32
❑ 89T/MSenL-47
❑ 89TopSenL-49
❑ 90EasLeaAP-EL11
❑ 90NewBriRSB-23
❑ 90NewBriRSP-1334
❑ 90NewBriRSS-25
❑ 91LinDriAAA-374
❑ 91PawRedSDD-8
❑ 91PawRedSLD-374
❑ 91PawRedSP-54
❑ 92RedSoxDD-17
❑ 92TopTra-52T
❑ 92TopTraG-52T
❑ 92YanWIZ8-82
❑ 93RedSoxP-20
❑ 93Top-502
❑ 93TopGol-502
❑ 93TopInaM-502
❑ 93TopInaR-502
❑ 93TopMic-502
❑ 96ScrRedBB-1
Hobson, Daren
❑ 94SarRedSC-14
❑ 94SarRedSF-1945
Hobson, Todd
❑ 90ArkRaz-15
❑ 91AubAstC-18
❑ 91AubAstP-4286
❑ 92AshTouC-6
❑ 93AshTouC-9
❑ 93AshTouF-2289
Hockenberry, Charlie
❑ 75CalAngP-20
❑ 75SalLakCC-13
❑ 76SalLakCGC-13
Hockenbury, Bill
❑ 52Par-81
Hockett, Oris
❑ 83TCMPla1944-12
❑ 90DodTar-349
Hockette, George
❑ 35DiaMatCS3T1-75
Hockey, Gavin
❑ 95AusFut-47
Hocking, David
❑ 89EveGiaS-14
Hocking, Denny
❑ 91KenTwiC-4
❑ 91KenTwiP-2081
❑ 91MidLeaAP-MWL37
❑ 92ClaFS7-295
❑ 92VisOakC-20
❑ 92VisOakF-1020
❑ 93Bow-73
❑ 93ExcFS7-201
❑ 93ExcLeaLF-8
❑ 94Fla-313
❑ 94FleMajLP-14
❑ 94FleUpd-61
❑ 94LeaLimR-26
❑ 94Pin-421
❑ 94PinArtP-421
❑ 94PinMusC-421
❑ 94SalLakBF-823
❑ 94ScoRoo-RT106
❑ 94ScoRooGR-RT106
❑ 94Sel-379
❑ 94SpoRoo-34
❑ 94SpoRooAP-34
❑ 94StaClu-9
❑ 94StaCluFDI-9
❑ 94StaCluGR-9
❑ 94StaCluMOP-9
❑ 94Top-771
❑ 94TopGol-771
❑ 94TopSpa-771
❑ 94UppDec-114
❑ 94UppDecED-114
❑ 95ColCho-22
❑ 95Don-272
❑ 95DonPreP-272
❑ 95Fle-205
❑ 95Lea-52
❑ 95PacPri-79
❑ 95Sco-585
❑ 95ScoGolR-585
❑ 95ScoPlaTS-585
❑ 95StaClu-52
❑ 95StaCluFDI-52
❑ 95StaCluMOP-52
❑ 95StaCluSTWS-52
❑ 95Top-122
❑ 95Ult-302
❑ 95UltGolM-302
❑ 95UppDec-192
❑ 95UppDecED-192
❑ 95UppDecEDG-192
❑ 96StaClu-448
❑ 96StaCluMOP-448
❑ 97Pac-137
❑ 97PacLigB-137
❑ 97PacSil-137
❑ 98Pac-134
❑ 98PacOnl-422
❑ 98PacOnlR-422
❑ 98PacOnlWC-422
❑ 98PacPlaB-134
❑ 98PacRedT-134
❑ 98PacSil-134
❑ 99Pac-247
❑ 99PacPlaB-247
❑ 99PacRed-247
❑ 99UppDec-415
❑ 99UppDecEL1-415
❑ 99UppDecEL2-415
Hocutt, Mike
❑ 86IndIndTI-22
❑ 87JacMetF-10
❑ 88LouRedBTI-22
Hodapp, Johnny (Urban J.)
❑ 29PorandAR-40
❑ 33DouDisP-22
❑ 35AlDemDCR3-77
❑ 79DiaGre-132
❑ 83ConMar-13
❑ 88ConAmeA-16
❑ 92ConTSN-538
❑ 93ConTSN-810
Hodde, Rodney
❑ 82BurRanF-11
❑ 82BurRanT-2
Hoderlein, Mel
❑ 53Bri-7
❑ 54Bow-120
Hodge, Clarence
❑ 21E121So1-41
❑ 22E120-20
❑ 22W573-61
❑ 23W501-42
❑ 23Zee-133
❑ 24Zee-93
Hodge, Eddie
❑ 80OrlTwiT-5
❑ 82OrlTwiT-24
❑ 83TolMudHT-4
❑ 84FleUpd-52
❑ 85TolMudHT-8
❑ 85Top-639
❑ 85TopTif-639
Hodge, Gomer
❑ 81WatIndT-1
❑ 82WatIndF-2
❑ 82WatIndT-26
❑ 83WatIndF-28
❑ 86BelBreP-11
❑ 87BelBreP-18
❑ 88BelBreGS-1
❑ 89JacExpB-20
❑ 90IndIndP-308
❑ 90ProAAAF-591
❑ 91IndIndLD-200
❑ 91IndIndP-479
❑ 91LinDriAAA-200
❑ 92IndIndF-1877
❑ 92IndIndS-200
❑ 93HarSenF-285
❑ 96DouAllB-3
❑ 96TreThuB-2
Hodge, Hal
❑ 95SpoIndTI-7
Hodge, Jim
❑ 94BelBreC-12
❑ 94BelBreFI-115
❑ 94HelBreF-3624
❑ 94HelBreSP-15
Hodge, Kevin
❑ 88BufBisP-1482
Hodge, Nick
❑ 92IndIndF-NNO
Hodge, Pat
❑ 83DurBulT-6
❑ 84DurBulT-4
Hodge, Roy
❑ 92BluOriC-12
❑ 92BluOriF-2371
❑ 92KanCouCC-3
❑ 92KanCouCF-105
❑ 93AlbPolF-2038
❑ 94FreKeyC-11
❑ 94FreKeyF-2628
❑ 96HigDesMB-13
Hodge, Tim
❑ 88St.CatBJP-2016
❑ 89MyrBeaBJP-1457
❑ 90DunBluJS-10
❑ 91DunBluJC-20
❑ 91DunBluJP-218
❑ 92DunBluJC-15
❑ 92DunBluJF-2012
❑ 93KnoSmoF-1263
Hodges, Darren
❑ 90OneYanP-3377
❑ 90ProAaA-177
❑ 91CarLeaAP-CAR33
❑ 91PriWilCC-3
❑ 91PriWilCP-1420
❑ 92AlbYanF-2221
❑ 92AlbYanSk-9
❑ 92SkyAA F-5
❑ 93AlbYanF-2159
❑ 94AlbYanF-1436
❑ 98PriWilCASM-28
Hodges, Gil
❑ 47DodTeal-11
❑ 47Exh-99A
❑ 47Exh-99B
❑ 47HomBon-20
❑ 47PM1StaP1-85
❑ 47PM1StaP1-86
❑ 47PM1StaP1-87
❑ 47PM1StaP1-88
❑ 48DodTeal-13
❑ 49Bow-100
❑ 49EurSta-38
❑ 50Bow-112
❑ 50Dra-11
❑ 51Bow-7
❑ 51FisBakL-9
❑ 51TopRedB-31
❑ 52BerRos-24
❑ 52Bow-80
❑ 52CokTip-3
❑ 52StaCalL-79A
❑ 52StaCalS-91A
❑ 52TipTop-16
❑ 52Top-36
❑ 53BowC-92
❑ 53Bri-31
❑ 53Dor-129
❑ 53ExhCan-13
❑ 53StaMey-3
❑ 54Bow-138
❑ 54DanDee-11
❑ 54NewYorJA-7
❑ 54RedMan-NL22
❑ 54StaMey-3
❑ 54Top-102
❑ 54Wil-9
❑ 55BigLeaIS-8
❑ 55Bow-158
❑ 55DaiQueS-8
❑ 55DodGolS-13
❑ 55RedMan-NL3
❑ 55StaMey-3
❑ 55Top-187
❑ 56Dod-13
❑ 56Top-145
❑ 56TopPin-50
❑ 56YelBasP-15
❑ 57Top-80
❑ 57Top-400
❑ 58DodBelB-5
❑ 58DodJayP-6
❑ 58DodTeal-10
❑ 58DodVol-7
❑ 58PacBel-4
❑ 58Top-162
❑ 59DodMor-4
❑ 59DodPos-2
❑ 59DodTeal-10
❑ 59DodVol-7
❑ 59HomRunD-7
❑ 59Top-270
❑ 60Baz-23
❑ 60DodJayP-6
❑ 60DodMor-5
❑ 60DodPos-5
❑ 60DodTeal-8
❑ 60DodUniO-8
❑ 60NuHi-41
❑ 60Top-295
❑ 60Top-388
❑ 61DodBelB-14
❑ 61DodUniO-9
❑ 61NuSco-441
❑ 61Pos-168A
❑ 61Pos-168B
❑ 61SevElev-21
❑ 61Top-460
❑ 62Baz-27
❑ 62Jel-101
❑ 62MetJayP-4
❑ 62Pos-101
❑ 62PosCan-101
❑ 62SalPlaC-146A
❑ 62SalPlaC-146B
❑ 62ShiPlaC-146
❑ 62Top-85
❑ 62TopBuc-36
❑ 62TopStal-155
❑ 62TopVen-85
❑ 63BasMagM-36
❑ 63Jel-193
❑ 63MetJayP-4
❑ 63Pos-193
❑ 63Top-68
❑ 63Top-245
❑ 64Top-547
❑ 65OPC-99
❑ 65Top-99
❑ 66SenTeal-7

❑ 66Top-386
❑ 67SenTeal-5
❑ 67Top-228
❑ 68OPC-27
❑ 68Top-27
❑ 68TopVen-27
❑ 69MetNewYDN-9
❑ 69MetTeal-7
❑ 69Top-564
❑ 70MetTeal-7
❑ 70OPC-394
❑ 70Top-394
❑ 71MetTeal-9
❑ 71OPC-183
❑ 71Top-183
❑ 72OPC-465
❑ 72Top-465
❑ 73BooProC-20
❑ 74CapPub-27
❑ 74dod195T-14
❑ 74MetJapEB-3
❑ 74NewYorNTDiS-7
❑ 75DodTCMA-6
❑ 76TayBow4-7
❑ 77GalGloG-15
❑ 77GalGloG-233
❑ 77Spo-6318
❑ 79TCM50-43
❑ 79TCM50-71
❑ 80DodGreT-1
❑ 80MarExh-10
❑ 80PacLeg-63
❑ 81TCM60I-315
❑ 81TCM60I-407
❑ 81TCM60I-423
❑ 81TCM60I-482
❑ 82MetGal62-10
❑ 82TCMGreS-14
❑ 83TopRep5-36
❑ 84FifNatCT-8
❑ 84OCoandSI-113
❑ 84OCoandSI-151
❑ 84SpoDesPW-30
❑ 85CirK-29
❑ 85TCMPla1-5
❑ 86MetGreT-12
❑ 86SpoDecG-38
❑ 86SpoDesJM-19
❑ 86TCMSupS-5
❑ 87Dod195T-5
❑ 88DodRinP1-7C
❑ 88PacLegI-87
❑ 89BowInsT-4
❑ 89BowRepI-4
❑ 89BowTif-R4
❑ 89DodSmoG-54
❑ 89Met196C-6
❑ 89MetRinP69-15
❑ 89SweBasG-33
❑ 89Top-664
❑ 89TopTif-664
❑ 90DodTar-350
❑ 90MetHaloF-1
❑ 90SweBasG-132
❑ 91MetWIZ-185
❑ 91PacRyaTEI-11
❑ 91SweBasG-131
❑ 91TopArc1-296
❑ 92BazQua5A-16
❑ 93ActPacA-137
❑ 93TedWilM-3
❑ 93UppDecAH-65
❑ 94Met69CCPP-2
❑ 94Met69CS-1
❑ 94Met69T-29
❑ 94TedWil-11
❑ 94TedWil-148
❑ 94TopArc1-102
❑ 94TopArc1G-102
❑ 95TopArcBD-4
❑ 95TopArcBD-59
❑ 95TopArcBD-72
❑ 95TopArcBD-105
❑ 95TopArcBD-118
❑ 95TopArcBD-131
❑ 95TopArcBD-150
❑ 95UppDecSHoB-12
❑ 97NewYorL-3

Hodges, Guy
❑ 20Zee-64

Hodges, Kevin
❑ 94RocRoyC-13
❑ 94RocRoyF-560
❑ 95WilBluRTI-31
❑ 97WilBluR-20
❑ 98JacGenM-7

Hodges, Randy
❑ 95EugEmeTI-20
❑ 96MacBraB-18

Hodges, Reid
❑ 96BriWhiSB-18
❑ 97BriWhiSB-4

Hodges, Ron (Ronald W.)
❑ 74MetDaiPA-2
❑ 74MetOriEB-4
❑ 74MetTeal-8
❑ 74OPC-448
❑ 74Top-448
❑ 75CedRapGT-27
❑ 75OPC-134
❑ 75TidTidTI-13
❑ 75Top-134
❑ 75TopMin-134
❑ 76CedRapGT-12
❑ 77MetDaiPA-8
❑ 77Top-329
❑ 78MetDaiPA-11
❑ 78Top-653
❑ 79Top-46
❑ 80Top-172
❑ 81Top-537
❑ 82Fle-527
❑ 82MetPhoA-10
❑ 82Top-234
❑ 83Don-476
❑ 83Fle-545
❑ 83Top-713
❑ 84Don-603
❑ 84Fle-588
❑ 84Nes792-418
❑ 84Top-418
❑ 84TopTif-418
❑ 85Top-363
❑ 85TopTif-363
❑ 91MetWIZ-186

Hodges, Scott
❑ 97Bow-426
❑ 97BowChr-286
❑ 97BowChrI-286
❑ 97BowChrIR-286
❑ 97BowChrR-286
❑ 97BowInt-426
❑ 97TopSta-113
❑ 97TopStaAM-113
❑ 98VerExpO-23

Hodges, Steve
❑ 90IdaFalBP-3242

Hodgin, Elmer Ralph
❑ 47TipTop-20
❑ 48WhiSoxTI-11
❑ 49BowPCL-3
❑ 49SolSunP-6
❑ 79DiaGre-137
❑ 85TCMPla1-36

Hodgkins, Ellis
❑ 63GadFunC-71

Hodgson, Gordon
❑ 79QuaCitCT-18
❑ 80QuaCitCT-23

Hodgson, Paul
❑ 80KnoBluJT-5
❑ 82KnoBluJT-13
❑ 83KnoBluJT-18

Hodkinson, Chris
❑ 91ParPatF-7

Hodo, Doug
❑ 86BenPhiC-134

Hodson, Blair
❑ 94ColRedC-11
❑ 94ColRedF-449

Hodson, Steven
❑ 93WatIndC-13
❑ 93WatIndF-3568

Hoeft, Billy
❑ 52Top-370
❑ 53BowBW-18
❑ 53TigGle-15
❑ 53Top-165
❑ 54Bow-167
❑ 54DixLid-4
❑ 56Top-152
❑ 57Top-60
❑ 58Top-13A
❑ 58Top-13B
❑ 59TigGraASP-9
❑ 59Top-343
❑ 60Lea-90
❑ 60Top-369
❑ 61BalOriP-13
❑ 61Top-256
❑ 62BalOriP-14
❑ 62Top-134A
❑ 62Top-134B
❑ 62TopVen-134
❑ 63Top-346
❑ 64Top-551
❑ 65Top-471
❑ 66Top-409
❑ 79TCM50-37
❑ 81TigDetN-32
❑ 83TopRep5-370
❑ 91OriCro-197
❑ 91TopArc1-165

Hoeksema, Dave
❑ 83MemChiT-9
❑ 85IndIndTI-23

Hoelskoetter, Art
❑ 08RosComP-165
❑ 11SpoLifCW-173

Hoeme, Steve
❑ 88EugEmeB-2
❑ 89AppFoxP-852
❑ 90BasCitRS-11
❑ 92WatDiaC-9
❑ 92WicWraF-3654
❑ 93RanCucQF-827
❑ 93WicWraF-2975
❑ 94HarSenF-2086
❑ 95PawRedSDD-14
❑ 95PawRedTI-39
❑ 95TreThuTI-5

Hoenstine, Dave
❑ 80CedRapRT-3
❑ 81CedRapRT-12

Hoerner, Joe
❑ 64Top-544
❑ 66Top-544
❑ 67OPC-41
❑ 67Top-41
❑ 68Top-227
❑ 68TopVen-227
❑ 69Top-522
❑ 70MLBOffS-90
❑ 70OPC-511
❑ 70Top-511
❑ 71MLBOffS-181
❑ 71OPC-166
❑ 71PhiArcO-6
❑ 71Top-166
❑ 72OPC-482
❑ 72Top-482
❑ 73OPC-653
❑ 73Top-653
❑ 74OPC-493
❑ 74RoyPos-13
❑ 74Top-493
❑ 75OPC-629
❑ 75PhiPhiP-16
❑ 75Top-629
❑ 75TopMin-629
❑ 76SSP-456
❑ 77Top-256
❑ 93RanKee-186

Hoerner, Troy
❑ 90KenTwiB-5
❑ 90KenTwiP-2307
❑ 90KenTwiS-7

Hoerst, Frank
❑ 41PhiTeal-8

Hofer, John
❑ 89AppFoxP-878

Hofer, Ray
❑ 94IdaFalBF-3592
❑ 94IdaFalBSP-17

Hoff, Jim
❑ 83TamTarT-28
❑ 88BilMusP-1827

Hoff, Red (Chester)
❑ 12T207-82
❑ 17Zee-69

Hoff, Steve
❑ 97CliLumG-12
❑ 97RanCucQG-13

Hoffer, Bill
❑ 98CamPepP-27

Hoffert, Troy
❑ 93ClePhiC-29
❑ 94SparPhiC-28
❑ 96PieBolWB-3
❑ 97ReaPhi-4
❑ 98ReaPhiM-23

Hoffinger, Glenn
❑ 86MedA'sC-61

Hoffman, Artie
❑ 07CubA.CDPP-4
❑ 07CubGFGCP-4
❑ 08AmeCarE91-49
❑ 08CubPos-2
❑ 09PhiCarE-11
❑ 10ChiE-6
❑ 10SepAnoP-15
❑ 11PinT-5-216
❑ 11PloCanE-34
❑ 14CraJacE-9
❑ 15CraJacE-9

Hoffman, Clarence
❑ 25Zee-65
❑ 27Zee-89

Hoffman, Daniel
❑ 96BatCliTI-33

Hoffman, Danny
❑ 08RosComP-68
❑ 09PC7HHB-22
❑ 09T206-157
❑ 10CouT21-30
❑ 10CouT21-148
❑ 10DomDisP-56
❑ 10RedCroT-30
❑ 10SweCapPP-52
❑ 11PinT-5-109
❑ 11SpoLifCW-170
❑ 11SpoLifM-110
❑ 11T205-77

Hoffman, Dennis
❑ 88MarPhiS-17

Hoffman, Dutch
❑ 26Zee-113
❑ 28Zee-108

Hoffman, Edson
❑ 94OgdRapF-3732
❑ 94OgdRapSP-8

Hoffman, Frank J.
❑ 87OldJudN-243

Hoffman, Fred
❑ 22W575-55
❑ 28Exh-35
❑ 29Zee-43
❑ 30Zee-54
❑ 31Zee-31
❑ 46SeaSLP-27
❑ 92ConTSN-575

Hoffman, Glenn
❑ 81CokTeaS-5
❑ 81Don-95
❑ 81Fle-237
❑ 81OPC-349
❑ 81Top-349
❑ 81TopSupHT-5
❑ 82Don-460
❑ 82Fle-296
❑ 82FleSta-168
❑ 82RedSoxC-9
❑ 82Top-189
❑ 83AllGamPI-22
❑ 83Don-282
❑ 83Fle-185
❑ 83OPC-108
❑ 83Top-108
❑ 84AllGamPI-112
❑ 84Don-606
❑ 84Fle-399
❑ 84Nes792-523
❑ 84OPC-141
❑ 84Top-523
❑ 84TopSti-223
❑ 84TopTif-523
❑ 85Top-633
❑ 85TopTif-633
❑ 86Don-457
❑ 86Fle-351
❑ 86OPC-38
❑ 86Top-38
❑ 86TopTif-38
❑ 87PawRedSP-63
❑ 87Top-374
❑ 87TopTif-374
❑ 88PawRedSC-13
❑ 88PawRedSP-465
❑ 88StaLinD-9
❑ 88Top-202
❑ 88TopTif-202
❑ 90AlbDukCm-26
❑ 90AlbDukP-352
❑ 90AlbDukTr-12
❑ 90CMC-653
❑ 90DodTar-351
❑ 90Don-407
❑ 90ProAAAF-73
❑ 91BakDodCLC-30
❑ 92VerBeaDC-29
❑ 92VerBeaDF-2893
❑ 93SanAntMF-3020
❑ 97AlbDukGS-15
❑ 98AlbDukG-9
❑ 98DodMot-1
❑ 99DodPol-30

Hoffman, Guy
❑ 79IowOakP-8
❑ 80IowOakP-7
❑ 80Top-664
❑ 81EdmTraRR-6
❑ 82EdmTraT-6
❑ 86CubGat-50
❑ 86FleUpd-51
❑ 86IowCubP-16
❑ 87Fle-566
❑ 87FleGlo-566
❑ 87FleUpd-45
❑ 87FleUpdG-45
❑ 87RedKah-30
❑ 87TopTra-48T
❑ 87TopTraT-48T
❑ 88Don-452
❑ 88Fle-235
❑ 88FleGlo-235
❑ 88Sco-609
❑ 88ScoGlo-609
❑ 88Top-496
❑ 88TopTif-496
❑ 93RanKee-187

Hoffman, Harry C.
❑ 09T206-431
❑ 11PacCoaBD-27
❑ 11Zee-30
❑ 12HomRunKE-22
❑ 12Zee-35
❑ 13Zee-109

Hoffman, Hunter
❑ 89WauTimGS-18
❑ 90FayGenP-2410

Hoffman, Izzy
❑ 09ObaT21-275
❑ 12ObaPreT-24

Hoffman, Jeff
❑ 88OneYanP-2057
❑ 90Bes-230
❑ 90CMC-704
❑ 90GreHorB-3
❑ 90GreHorP-2655
❑ 90GreHorS-6
❑ 90SouAtlLAS-11
❑ 91PriWilCC-4
❑ 91PriWilCP-1421
❑ 92AlbYanF-2222
❑ 92AlbYanSk-10
❑ 92SkyAA F-6

Hoffman, John
❑ 87BelMarTI-7
❑ 88WauTimGS-9
❑ 89SanBerSCLC-77

Hoffman, John Edward
❑ 77FriOneYW-33

Hoffman, Rich
❑ 89St.PetCS-18
❑ 90ArkTraGS-17

Hoffman, Rob
❑ 90KisDodD-14

Hoffman, Trevor
❑ 88AriWilP-5
❑ 89BilMusP-2068
❑ 90ChaWheB-16
❑ 90ChaWheP-2247
❑ 91CedRapRC-6
❑ 91CedRapRP-2714
❑ 92Bow-11
❑ 92ChaLooS-186
❑ 92NasSouF-1829
❑ 92ProFS7-219
❑ 92SkyAA F-83
❑ 92UppDecML-105
❑ 93Bow-390
❑ 93Fla-135
❑ 93FlaWavotF-7
❑ 93FleFinE-143
❑ 93Lea-531
❑ 93MarlStaClu-20
❑ 93MarUppD-773
❑ 93MarUSPC-7D
❑ 93MarUSPC-12H
❑ 93OPCPre-113
❑ 93PacSpa-464
❑ 93Pin-602
❑ 93SP-169
❑ 93StaClu-451
❑ 93StaCluFDI-451
❑ 93StaCluMOP-451
❑ 93Top-572
❑ 93TopGol-572
❑ 93TopInaM-572
❑ 93TopInaR-572
❑ 93TopMic-572
❑ 93Ult-378
❑ 93UppDec-773
❑ 93UppDecGold-773
❑ 94ColC-494
❑ 94ColChoGS-494
❑ 94ColChoSS-494
❑ 94Don-187
❑ 94Fin-417
❑ 94FinRef-417
❑ 94Fla-234
❑ 94Fle-668
❑ 94FleExtB-373
❑ 94FleExtBSYS-9
❑ 94Lea-421
❑ 94Pac-528
❑ 94PadMot-23
❑ 94PanSti-257
❑ 94Pin-272
❑ 94PinArtP-272
❑ 94PinMusC-272
❑ 94SP-131
❑ 94SPDieC-131
❑ 94StaClu-312
❑ 94StaCluFDI-312
❑ 94StaCluGR-312
❑ 94StaCluMOP-312
❑ 94Stu-133
❑ 94Top-222
❑ 94TopGol-222
❑ 94TopSpa-222
❑ 94Ult-577
❑ 94UppDec-153
❑ 94UppDecED-153
❑ 94USPlaCR-4S
❑ 95ColCho-355
❑ 95ColChoGS-355
❑ 95ColChoSE-163
❑ 95ColChoSEGS-163
❑ 95ColChoSESS-163
❑ 95ColChoSS-355
❑ 95Don-318
❑ 95DonPreP-318
❑ 95DonTopotO-343
❑ 95Fin-269
❑ 95FinRef-269
❑ 95Fla-202
❑ 95Fle-562
❑ 95Lea-17
❑ 95Pac-363
❑ 95PadCHP-5
❑ 95PadMot-21
❑ 95Pin-85
❑ 95PinArtP-85
❑ 95PinMusC-85
❑ 95Sco-46
❑ 95ScoGolR-46
❑ 95ScoPlaTS-46
❑ 95StaClu-382
❑ 95StaCluMOP-382
❑ 95StaCluSTWS-382
❑ 95StaCluVR-201
❑ 95StaCluVRMO-201
❑ 95Stu-101
❑ 95Top-7
❑ 95TopCyb-5
❑ 95Ult-439
❑ 95UltGolM-439
❑ 95UppDec-374
❑ 95UppDecED-374
❑ 95UppDecEDG-374
❑ 95UppDecSE-135
❑ 95UppDecSEG-135
❑ 96ColCho-296
❑ 96ColChoGS-296
❑ 96ColChoSS-296
❑ 96Don-198
❑ 96DonPreP-198
❑ 96EmoXL-280
❑ 96Fin-B134
❑ 96FinRef-B134
❑ 96Fla-377
❑ 96Fle-570
❑ 96FleTif-570
❑ 96Lea-190
❑ 96LeaPrePB-190
❑ 96LeaPrePG-190
❑ 96LeaPrePS-190
❑ 96LeaSigA-105
❑ 96LeaSigAG-105
❑ 96LeaSigAS-105
❑ 96MetUni-238
❑ 96MetUniP-238
❑ 96Pac-193
❑ 96PadMot-17

❑ 96PanSti-99
❑ 96Pin-321
❑ 96PinAfi-117
❑ 96PinAfiAP-117
❑ 96PinFoil-321
❑ 96Sco-175
❑ 96Sel-80
❑ 96SelArtP-80
❑ 96StaClu-171
❑ 96StaCluMOP-171
❑ 96Sum-56
❑ 96SumAbo&B-56
❑ 96SumArtP-56
❑ 96SumFoi-56
❑ 96Top-313
❑ 96TopGal-90
❑ 96TopGalPPI-90
❑ 96Ult-286
❑ 96UltGolM-286
❑ 96UppDec-447
❑ 97Bow-39
❑ 97BowInt-39
❑ 97Cir-287
❑ 97CirRav-287
❑ 97ColCho-212
❑ 97Don-93
❑ 97DonGolPP-93
❑ 97DonSilPP-93
❑ 97Fin-149
❑ 97FinEmb-149
❑ 97FinEmbR-149
❑ 97FinRef-149
❑ 97FlaShoLC-151
❑ 97FlaShoLeg0-151
❑ 97FlaShoLeg1-151
❑ 97FlaShoM-A151
❑ 97FlaShoM-B151
❑ 97FlaShoM-C151
❑ 97FlaShoR0-151
❑ 97FlaShoR1-151
❑ 97FlaShoR2-151
❑ 97Fle-465
❑ 97FleTif-465
❑ 97Lea-75
❑ 97LeaFraM-75
❑ 97LeaFraMDC-75
❑ 97MetUni-222
❑ 97Pac-427
❑ 97PacLigB-427
❑ 97PacSil-427
❑ 97PadMot-18
❑ 97Pin-21
❑ 97PinArtP-PP21
❑ 97PinMusC-21
❑ 97PinPrePla-21
❑ 97Sco-36
❑ 97ScoArtPWB-36
❑ 97ScoPreS-36
❑ 97ScoShoS-36
❑ 97ScoShoSAP-36
❑ 97SP-157
❑ 97StaClu-202
❑ 97StaCluMat-202
❑ 97StaCluMOP-202
❑ 97Top-70
❑ 97TopChr-25
❑ 97TopChrR-25
❑ 97TopGal-130
❑ 97TopGalPPI-130
❑ 97Ult-286
❑ 97UltGolME-286
❑ 97UltPlaME-286
❑ 97UppDec-488
❑ 98CirThu-56
❑ 98CirThuRav-56
❑ 98CirThuSupRav-56
❑ 98ColCho-222
❑ 98Fin-232
❑ 98FinNo--232
❑ 98FinNo-R-232
❑ 98FinRef-232
❑ 98Fle-164
❑ 98MetUni-197
❑ 98MetUniPMG-197
❑ 98Pac-431
❑ 98PacOnl-641
❑ 98PacOnlR-641
❑ 98PacOnlWC-641
❑ 98PacPlaB-431
❑ 98PacRedT-431
❑ 98PacSil-431
❑ 98PadMot-12
❑ 98SP Aut-167
❑ 98SPxFin-124
❑ 98SPxFinR-124
❑ 98SPxFinS-124
❑ 98StaCluFDI-92
❑ 98StaCluI-92
❑ 98StaCluOneK-92
❑ 98StaCluPP-92
❑ 98Top-57
❑ 98TopChr-57
❑ 98TopChrR-57
❑ 98TopDevR-57
❑ 98TopDia-57
❑ 98TopMiniC-57
❑ 98TopOpeD-33
❑ 98TopSta-87
❑ 98TopStaB-87
❑ 98TopStaG-87
❑ 98TopStaGR-87
❑ 98TopStaS-87
❑ 98Ult-88
❑ 98UltGolM-88
❑ 98UltMas-88
❑ 98UltPlaM-88
❑ 98UppDec-495
❑ 99199Fin-163
❑ 99Bow-51
❑ 99BowChr-51
❑ 99BowChrG-51
❑ 99BowChrGR-51
❑ 99BowChrI-51
❑ 99BowChrIR-51
❑ 99BowChrR-51
❑ 99BowGol-51
❑ 99BowInt-51
❑ 99BowLatB-LB10
❑ 99CroRoyB-120
❑ 99CroRoyL-120
❑ 99CroRoyOD-120
❑ 99FinGolRef-163
❑ 99FinRef-163
❑ 99Fle-210
❑ 99FleBri-85
❑ 99FleBri2G-85
❑ 99FleBriBlu-85
❑ 99FleBriGol-85
❑ 99FleSta9-210
❑ 99FleWarT-210
❑ 99MetUni-30
❑ 99MetUniGM-30
❑ 99MetUniPMG-30
❑ 99Pac-371
❑ 99PacAur-161
❑ 99PacAurOD-161
❑ 99PacCroC-244
❑ 99PacCroCPB-244
❑ 99PacInv-123
❑ 99PacInvOD-123
❑ 99PacInvPB-123
❑ 99PacOme-203
❑ 99PacOmeC-203
❑ 99PacOmeG-203
❑ 99PacOmePB-203
❑ 99PacPar-200
❑ 99PacParC-200
❑ 99PacParG-200
❑ 99PacParHoloGold-200
❑ 99PacParHS-200
❑ 99PacParOD-200
❑ 99PacParPB-200
❑ 99PacParRed-200
❑ 99PacPlaB-371
❑ 99PacPri-124
❑ 99PacPriHB-124
❑ 99PacPriHG-124
❑ 99PacPriHM-124
❑ 99PacPriHP-124
❑ 99PacPriRed-124
❑ 99PacPriS-100
❑ 99PacPriS206-100
❑ 99PacPriS206R-100
❑ 99PacRed-371
❑ 99Rev-121
❑ 99RevPremDate-121
❑ 99RevRet-121
❑ 99RevShaSS-121
❑ 99SkyPre-37
❑ 99SkyPreR-37
❑ 99SkyThu-147
❑ 99SkyThuRant-147
❑ 99SkyThuRave-147
❑ 99SP Aut-128
❑ 99SP SigAuto-THO
❑ 99SP SigAutoG-THO
❑ 99SpoIll-17
❑ 99SpoIll-133
❑ 99SPSig-37
❑ 99StaClu-20
❑ 99StaCluFDI-20
❑ 99StaCluOoaK-20
❑ 99StaCluPP-20
❑ 99ThuSkySupR-147
❑ 99Top-105
❑ 99TopChr-105
❑ 99TopChrR-105
❑ 99TopGal-65
❑ 99TopGalPP-65
❑ 99TopGalPPI-65
❑ 99TopMVPP-105
❑ 99TopOpeD-61
❑ 99UD Cho-135
❑ 99UD ChoPCR-135
❑ 99UDHolo-51
❑ 99UDHoloAUsome-51
❑ 99Ult-47
❑ 99UltGolM-47
❑ 99UltMas-47
❑ 99UltPlaM-47
❑ 99UppDec-192
❑ 99UppDec-252
❑ 99UppDecCLM-C82
❑ 99UppDecE-76
❑ 99UppDecEFXG-76
❑ 99UppDecEL1-192
❑ 99UppDecEL1-252
❑ 99UppDecEL2-192
❑ 99UppDecEL2-252
❑ 99UppDecM-180
❑ 99UppDecMGS-180
❑ 99UppDecMHFS-180
❑ 99UppDecMSS-180
❑ 99UppDecR-73
❑ 99UppDecRG-73
❑ 99UppDecRP-73
❑ 99Vic-346

Hoffmann, Greg
❑ 85IowCubT-24

Hoffmeister, Paul
❑ 55DesMoiHB-9

Hoffner, Jamie
❑ 89PitMetS-27
❑ 91St.LucMC-6
❑ 91St.LucMP-719
❑ 92BinMetF-524
❑ 92BinMetS-58

Hofheinz, Roy
❑ 84WilMay-31

Hofman, Bobby (Robert G.)
❑ 49Bow-223
❑ 49GiaTeal-11
❑ 50RemBre-13
❑ 52Top-371
❑ 53Top-182
❑ 54NewYorJA-25
❑ 54Top-99
❑ 55GiaGolS-28
❑ 55Top-17
❑ 55TopDouH-95
❑ 55TopTesS-5
❑ 56Top-28
❑ 56TopPin-40
❑ 79TCM50-59
❑ 83TopRep5-371
❑ 91TopArc1-182
❑ 94TopArc1-99
❑ 94TopArc1G-99

Hofman, Rich
❑ 92HigSchPLS-29

Hofman, Solly (Arthur)
❑ 08RosComP-104
❑ 09ColChiE-131
❑ 09SpoNewSM-55
❑ 09T206-158
❑ 10CouT21-147
❑ 10RedCroT-119
❑ 10RedCroT-200
❑ 11BasBatEU-24
❑ 11HelSta-96
❑ 11MecDFT-28
❑ 11SpoLifCW-171
❑ 11SpoLifM-170
❑ 11TurRedT-98
❑ 12ColRedB-131
❑ 12ColTinT-131

Hofmann, Fred
❑ 21KoBreWSI-35
❑ 26SpoComoA-20
❑ 32Zee-36
❑ 33Zee-15
❑ 41BroW75-16

Hogan, Ben
❑ 52Whe-14A
❑ 52Whe-14B
❑ 74NewYorNTDiS-2

Hogan, David
❑ 91BriBanF-16

Hogan, Happy (William)
❑ 09ColChiE-132
❑ 09ObaT21-13
❑ 09ObaT21-72
❑ 09ObaT21-183
❑ 09ObaT21-348
❑ 12ColRedB-132
❑ 12ColTinT-132
❑ 12ObaPreT-97
❑ 12T207-83
❑ 13Zee-110

Hogan, Mike
❑ 82AubAstT-8
❑ 83DayBeaAT-8
❑ 86ModA'sP-12
❑ 88PhoFirC-6
❑ 88PhoFirP-73

Hogan, Rob
❑ 91WavRedF-6

Hogan, Robert
❑ 87OldJudN-244

Hogan, Sean
❑ 93AusFut-86
❑ 93GenCubC-15
❑ 93GenCubF-3170
❑ 94WilCubC-10
❑ 94WilCubF-3759

Hogan, Shanty (J. Francis)
❑ 28Exh-18
❑ 29ExhFou-10
❑ 29PorandAR-41
❑ 31Exh-9
❑ 33DouDisP-23
❑ 33Gou-30
❑ 33GouCanV-30
❑ 34BabRutG-33
❑ 34ButPreR-32
❑ 34DiaMatCSB-92
❑ 34DiaStaR-20
❑ 34ExhFou-1
❑ 34Gou-20
❑ 34GouCanV-66
❑ 35AlDemDCR3-132
❑ 35DiaMatCS2-9
❑ 35ExhFou-1
❑ 35GouPuzR-4E
❑ 35GouPuzR-7E
❑ 35GouPuzR-12E
❑ 87ConSer2-42
❑ 91ConTSN-294

Hogan, Shorty
❑ 33ButCanV-26

Hogan, Todd
❑ 96JohCitCTI-16
❑ 97PeoChi-14
❑ 98PriWilCQ-21

Hogan, Wallace
❑ 10BisCoaLE99-12
❑ 11PacCoaBD-28
❑ 11Zee-115
❑ 12HomRunKE-85
❑ 12Zee-147
❑ 13Zee-137
❑ 14Zee-135
❑ 15Zee-130

Hogdin, Ralph
❑ 83TCMPla1944-17

Hogestyn, Don
❑ 77ForLauYS-21

Hogg, Bill
❑ 11SpoLifCW-172

Hogg, Carter
❑ 16Zee-7

Hogg, David
❑ 82EdmTraT-16

Hogge, Shawn
❑ 96JohCitCTI-17
❑ 97JohCitCTI-17

Hogsett, Chief (Elon)
❑ 28LaPre-11
❑ 34DiaMatCSB-93
❑ 34TarThoBD-15
❑ 34TigTeal-12
❑ 74TigTCM1AC-17
❑ 76TigOldTS-14
❑ 79DiaGre-177
❑ 93ConTSN-969

Hogue, Bobby
❑ 49EurSta-12
❑ 52Top-9
❑ 83TopRep5-9

Hogue, Cal
❑ 53Top-238
❑ 54Top-134
❑ 91TopArc1-238
❑ 94TopArc1-134
❑ 94TopArc1G-134

Hohlmeyer, Lefty (Alice)
❑ 93TedWil-116

Hohn, Bill
❑ 90T/MUmp-60

Hohn, Eric
❑ 86EriCarP-13

Hohno, Takayuki
❑ 92SalSpuC-26

Hoiles, Chris
❑ 87GleFalTP-2
❑ 88BlaYNPRWL-86
❑ 88TolMudHC-19
❑ 88TolMudHP-597
❑ 89RocRedWP-1640
❑ 90Bow-259
❑ 90BowTif-259
❑ 90CMC-313
❑ 90FleUpd-65
❑ 90Lea-513
❑ 90ProAAAF-461
❑ 90RocRedWC-14
❑ 90RocRedWGC-4
❑ 90RocRedWP-704
❑ 90ScoRoo-96T
❑ 90TopDeb89-60
❑ 91BalOriP-12
❑ 91Bow-99
❑ 91Cla1-T13
❑ 91Don-358
❑ 91Fle-476
❑ 91Lea-131
❑ 91OPC-42
❑ 91OPCPre-65
❑ 91OriCro-198
❑ 91Sco-334
❑ 91Sco100RS-34
❑ 91StaClu-489
❑ 91StaCluMO-10
❑ 91Stu-4
❑ 91Top-42
❑ 91TopDesS-42
❑ 91TopMic-42
❑ 91TopTif-42
❑ 91Ult-17
❑ 91UppDec-306
❑ 92BalOriP-13
❑ 92Bow-472
❑ 92Don-156
❑ 92Fle-9
❑ 92Lea-211
❑ 92LeaBlaG-211
❑ 92LeaGolP-31
❑ 92OPC-125
❑ 92PanSti-64
❑ 92Pin-83
❑ 92Sco-641
❑ 92StaClu-161
❑ 92Stu-124
❑ 92Top-125
❑ 92TopGol-125
❑ 92TopGolW-125
❑ 92TopMic-125
❑ 92TriPla-256
❑ 92Ult-5
❑ 92UppDec-183
❑ 92UppDecWB-T16
❑ 93BalOriP-14
❑ 93Bow-549
❑ 93Don-323
❑ 93Fla-151
❑ 93Fle-168
❑ 93Lea-133
❑ 93OPC-142
❑ 93PacSpa-18
❑ 93PanSti-70
❑ 93Pin-186
❑ 93Sco-54
❑ 93Sel-144
❑ 93SP-157
❑ 93StaClu-345
❑ 93StaCluFDI-345
❑ 93StaCluMOP-345
❑ 93Stu-156
❑ 93Top-524
❑ 93TopGol-524
❑ 93TopInaM-524
❑ 93TopInaR-524
❑ 93TopMic-524
❑ 93TriPla-205
❑ 93Ult-495
❑ 93UppDec-402
❑ 93UppDecGold-402
❑ 94BalOriP-14
❑ 94Bow-131
❑ 94ColC-140
❑ 94ColChoGS-140
❑ 94ColChoSS-140
❑ 94Don-99
❑ 94Fin-141
❑ 94FinPre-141P
❑ 94FinRef-141
❑ 94Fla-3
❑ 94Fle-6
❑ 94FleExtB-6
❑ 94FUnPac-63
❑ 94KinDis-11
❑ 94Lea-195
❑ 94OPC-167
❑ 94OriPro-46
❑ 94OriUSPC-1C
❑ 94OriUSPC-8D
❑ 94Pac-33
❑ 94PanSti-20
❑ 94Pin-112
❑ 94PinArtP-112
❑ 94PinMusC-112
❑ 94PinPowS-PS2
❑ 94PinRunC-RC18
❑ 94Sco-357
❑ 94ScoGolR-357
❑ 94Sel-15
❑ 94SP-122
❑ 94SPDieC-122
❑ 94Spo-114
❑ 94Spo-180
❑ 94StaClu-451
❑ 94StaCluFDI-451
❑ 94StaCluGR-451
❑ 94StaCluMOP-451
❑ 94StaCluT-288
❑ 94StaCluTFDI-288
❑ 94Top-295
❑ 94TopBlaG-9
❑ 94TopGol-295
❑ 94TopSpa-295
❑ 94TriPla-154
❑ 94TriPlaM-1
❑ 94Ult-2
❑ 94UltAllS-1
❑ 94UppDec-77
❑ 94UppDecAJ-19
❑ 94UppDecAJG-19
❑ 94UppDecED-77
❑ 95BalOriP-25
❑ 95Baz-98
❑ 95Bow-288
❑ 95ColCho-331
❑ 95ColChoGS-331
❑ 95ColChoSE-158
❑ 95ColChoSEGS-158
❑ 95ColChoSESS-158
❑ 95ColChoSS-331
❑ 95Don-295
❑ 95DonPreP-295
❑ 95DonTopotO-10
❑ 95Fin-60
❑ 95FinRef-60
❑ 95Fla-221
❑ 95Fle-9
❑ 95Lea-54
❑ 95Pac-23
❑ 95PanSti-27
❑ 95Pin-38
❑ 95PinArtP-38
❑ 95PinMusC-38
❑ 95SP-121
❑ 95SPCha-119
❑ 95SPChaDC-119
❑ 95SPSil-121
❑ 95StaClu-135
❑ 95StaCluFDI-135
❑ 95StaCluMOP-135
❑ 95StaCluSTWS-135
❑ 95StaCluVR-70
❑ 95StaCluVRMO-70
❑ 95Top-546
❑ 95TopCyb-327
❑ 95TopEmb-34
❑ 95TopEmbGI-34
❑ 95Ult-4
❑ 95UltGolM-4
❑ 95UppDec-131
❑ 95UppDecED-131
❑ 95UppDecEDG-131
❑ 95UppDecSE-185
❑ 95UppDecSEG-185
❑ 96BalOriP-15

❑ 96ColCho-54
❑ 96ColChoGS-54
❑ 96ColChoSS-54
❑ 96Don-412
❑ 96DonPreP-412
❑ 96EmoXL-5
❑ 96Fin-B108
❑ 96FinRef-B108
❑ 96Fla-7
❑ 96Fle-11
❑ 96FleTif-11
❑ 96MetUni-4
❑ 96MetUniP-4
❑ 96MLBPin-15
❑ 96OriFle-8
❑ 96Pac-238
❑ 96PanSti-132
❑ 96Sco-136
❑ 96StaClu-219
❑ 96StaClu-279
❑ 96StaCluEPB-279
❑ 96StaCluEPG-279
❑ 96StaCluEPS-279
❑ 96StaCluMOP-219
❑ 96StaCluMOP-279
❑ 96Top-191
❑ 96TopGal-53
❑ 96TopGalPPI-53
❑ 96Ult-6
❑ 96UltGolM-6
❑ 96UppDec-14
❑ 97BalOriP-14
❑ 97Cir-46
❑ 97CirRav-46
❑ 97ColCho-38
❑ 97ColChoT-BO3
❑ 97Don-342
❑ 97DonGolPP-342
❑ 97DonSilPP-342
❑ 97DonTea-43
❑ 97DonTeaSPE-43
❑ 97Fin-195
❑ 97FinRef-195
❑ 97Fle-8
❑ 97FleTif-8
❑ 97MetUni-4
❑ 97OriSco-13
❑ 97OriScoPl-13
❑ 97OriScoPr-13
❑ 97Pac-24
❑ 97PacLigB-24
❑ 97PacSil-24
❑ 97Sco-223
❑ 97ScoArtPWB-223
❑ 97ScoPreS-223
❑ 97ScoShoS-223
❑ 97ScoShoSAP-223
❑ 97StaClu-330
❑ 97StaCluMOP-330
❑ 97Top-174
❑ 97Ult-5
❑ 97UltGolME-5
❑ 97UltPlaME-5
❑ 97UppDec-305
❑ 98ColCho-309
❑ 98Fle-438
❑ 98OriSco-6
❑ 98OriScoP-6
❑ 98Pac-25
❑ 98PacOnl-90
❑ 98PacOnlR-90
❑ 98PacOnlWC-90
❑ 98PacPlaB-25
❑ 98PacRedT-25
❑ 98PacSil-25
❑ 98PinSna-BO4
❑ 98Sco-90
❑ 98ScoRT-161
❑ 98StaCluFDI-164
❑ 98StaCluI-164
❑ 98StaCluOneK-164
❑ 98StaCluPP-164
❑ 98Top-142
❑ 98TopChr-142
❑ 98TopChrR-142
❑ 98TopDevR-142
❑ 98TopDia-142
❑ 98TopMiniC-142
❑ 98UppDec-308
❑ 99Fle-437
❑ 99FleSta9-437
❑ 99FleWarT-437
❑ 99Pac-52
❑ 99PacPlaB-52
❑ 99PacRed-52
❑ 99SpoIll-27

Hokanson, Mark
❑ 91KinMetC-21
❑ 91KinMetP-3809
❑ 92PitMetF-3289
❑ 93CapCitBC-8
❑ 93CapCitBF-455

Hoke, Leon
❑ 81MiaOriT-17
❑ 83SanJosBC-23

Hokuf, Ken
❑ 91ModA'sC-6
❑ 91ModA'sP-3081
❑ 92ModA'sC-22
❑ 92ModA'sF-3895

Holbert, Aaron
❑ 90ClaDraP-18
❑ 90HigSchPLS-4
❑ 90JohCitCS-14
❑ 91Bow-399
❑ 91Sco-676
❑ 92SavCarC-21
❑ 92SavCarF-671
❑ 92UppDecML-172
❑ 93Bow-304
❑ 93CarStaC-30
❑ 93ClaFS7-206
❑ 93SouAtlLAIPI-1
❑ 93SouAtlLAIPI-2
❑ 93SouAtlLAPI-16
❑ 93St.PetCC-15
❑ 93St.PetCF-2634
❑ 94ArkTraF-3096
❑ 94Bow-68
❑ 94ExcFS7-267
❑ 94UppDecML-221
❑ 95Bow-57
❑ 95LouRedF-282
❑ 95SPML-156
❑ 96BesAutS-39
❑ 96BesAutSA-29
❑ 96Bow-365
❑ 96BowFoi-365
❑ 96FleUpd-U190
❑ 96FleUpdTC-U190
❑ 96LouRedB-22
❑ 96Ult-548
❑ 96UltGolM-548
❑ 97Fle-444
❑ 97FleTif-444
❑ 97LouRedB-16
❑ 97Ult-271
❑ 97UltGolME-271
❑ 97UltPlaME-271
❑ 98OrlRayM-8

Holbert, Ray
❑ 89WatDiaP-1791
❑ 89WatDiaS-12
❑ 90Bes-9
❑ 90WatDiaB-1
❑ 90WatDiaP-2384
❑ 91HigDesMC-22
❑ 91HigDesMP-2405
❑ 92SkyAA F-282
❑ 92UppDecML-103
❑ 92WicWraF-3664
❑ 92WicWraS-634
❑ 93Bow-194
❑ 93ClaFS7-207
❑ 93WicWraF-2985
❑ 94Bow-532
❑ 94ColC-665
❑ 94ColChoGS-665
❑ 94ColChoSS-665
❑ 94ExcFS7-283
❑ 94LeaLimR-73
❑ 94SpoRoo-55
❑ 94SpoRooAP-55
❑ 94UppDecML-102
❑ 95FleUpd-186
❑ 95PadMot-16
❑ 95Pin-415
❑ 95PinArtP-415
❑ 95PinMusC-415
❑ 95Sel-179
❑ 95SelArtP-179
❑ 95StaClu-606
❑ 95StaCluMOP-606
❑ 95StaCluSTWS-606
❑ 95Sum-142
❑ 95SumNthD-142
❑ 95Top-571
❑ 97TolMudHB-22

Holbert, William
❑ 87OldJudN-245A
❑ 87OldJudN-245B

Holbrook, Sammy
(James)
❑ 35DiaMatCS3T1-76

Holcomb, Scott
❑ 87ModA'sC-6
❑ 87ModA'sP-24
❑ 88HunStaTI-7
❑ 89HunStaB-16
❑ 92AlbYanSk-11
❑ 93ChaLooF-2358

Holcomb, Shawn
❑ 92FroRowDP-65
❑ 92FroRowDPG-65
❑ 92FroRowDPS-65

Holcomb, Ted
❑ 86BakDodP-13
❑ 87BakDodP-18
❑ 88DurBulS-7

Holcombe, Ken
❑ 49BowPCL-19
❑ 51Bow-267
❑ 52Top-95
❑ 53RedSoxTI-12
❑ 83TopRep5-95

Holden, Bill
❑ 84IowCubT-10

Holden, Brian
❑ 98EugEme-15

Holden, Gary
❑ 81BatTroT-21

Holder, Brooks
❑ 33Zee-123
❑ 37Zee-76
❑ 46RemBre-23
❑ 47RemBre-3
❑ 47SigOil-47
❑ 47SmiClo-4
❑ 48SigOil-11
❑ 48SmiClo-2
❑ 49SomandK-16

Holding, Brook
❑ 95ButCopKtI-10

Holdren, Nate
❑ 93BenRocCB-12
❑ 93BenRocF-3277
❑ 94AshTouC-13
❑ 94AshTouF-1792
❑ 95SalAvaTI-14
❑ 95UppDecML-142
❑ 95UppDecMLFS-142
❑ 96SalAvaB-15
❑ 97NewHavRB-11

Holdridge, Dave
❑ 88QuaCitAGS-11
❑ 89ClePhiS-11
❑ 90Bes-17
❑ 90CMC-802
❑ 90ReaPhiB-1
❑ 90ReaPhiP-1216
❑ 90ReaPhiS-13
❑ 91Cla/Bes-155
❑ 91LinDriAA-510
❑ 91ReaPhiLD-510
❑ 91ReaPhiP-1368
❑ 92PalSprAC-9
❑ 92PalSprAF-832
❑ 93MidAngF-320
❑ 94MidAngF-2431
❑ 94MidAngOHP-10
❑ 94VanCanF-1860
❑ 95MidAngOHP-18
❑ 95MidAngTI-16
❑ 97MidAngOHP-16
❑ 98TacRaiQ-15
❑ 99SpoIll-56

Holdsworth, Fred
❑ 74OPC-596
❑ 74Top-596
❑ 75OPC-323
❑ 75Top-323
❑ 75TopMin-323
❑ 76BalOriP-19
❑ 77BalOriP-9
❑ 77Top-466
❑ 78ExpPos-6
❑ 80VanCanT-18
❑ 81TacTigT-21
❑ 91OriCro-199
❑ 94BreMilB-229

Holiday, Billie
❑ 96NoiSatP-10

Holifield, Rickey
(Rick)
❑ 89St.CatBJP-2096
❑ 90MyrBeaBJP-2787
❑ 91MyrBeaHC-24
❑ 91MyrBeaHP-2958
❑ 92MyrBeaHC-13
❑ 92MyrBeaHF-2211
❑ 93DunBluJC-10
❑ 93DunBluJF-1809
❑ 93DunBluJFFN-10
❑ 94KnoSmoF-1316
❑ 95Bow-200
❑ 95ReaPhiELC-19
❑ 95ScrRedBTI-13
❑ 96TreThuB-26
❑ 98RicBraQ-17

Holin, Andrew
❑ 94HunCubC-13
❑ 94HunCubF-3556

Holke, Walter
❑ 17ColE13-78
❑ 17HolBreD-44
❑ 20GasAmeMBD-21
❑ 21E121So1-42A
❑ 21E121So1-42B
❑ 21E121So8-35A
❑ 21E121So8-35B
❑ 21Exh-75
❑ 21Exh-76
❑ 21OxfConE-8
❑ 22AmeCarE122-27
❑ 22E120-127
❑ 22W575-56
❑ 23W501-92
❑ 23WilChoV-63
❑ 25Exh-44
❑ 91ConTSN-207
❑ 92ConTSN-491

Hollacher, Charlie
❑ 17Zee-49
❑ 20GasAmeMBD-25
❑ 21E121So8-36
❑ 22AmeCarE122-28

Holladay, Kolin
❑ 92DavLipB-15
❑ 94DavLipB-16
❑ 95DavLipB-15

Holland, Al
❑ 77ShrCapT-7
❑ 78ColCliT-10
❑ 79PorBeaT-1
❑ 80GiaEurFS-1
❑ 80GiaPol-19
❑ 80GiaTeal-10
❑ 81Fle-445
❑ 81GiaTeal-7
❑ 81Top-213
❑ 82Don-377
❑ 82Fle-391
❑ 82Gia25tATI-12
❑ 82Top-406
❑ 83Don-146
❑ 83Fle-262
❑ 83FleSta-81
❑ 83FleSti-56
❑ 83PhiTas-14
❑ 83Top-58
❑ 83TopSti-306
❑ 83TopTra-46T
❑ 84AllGamPI-79
❑ 84Don-204
❑ 84Fle-35
❑ 84FleSti-68
❑ 84FunFooP-87
❑ 84Nes792-138
❑ 84Nes792-564
❑ 84NesDreT-22
❑ 84OPC-206
❑ 84PhiTas-21
❑ 84Top-138
❑ 84Top-564
❑ 84TopSti-125
❑ 84TopSti-289
❑ 84TopSup-10
❑ 84TopTif-138
❑ 84TopTif-564
❑ 85Don-427
❑ 85Fle-254
❑ 85Fle-637
❑ 85FleStaS-107
❑ 85FleUpd-55
❑ 85Lea-151
❑ 85OPC-185
❑ 85PhiTas-9
❑ 85PhiTas-19
❑ 85Top-185
❑ 85TopMin-185
❑ 85TopSti-113
❑ 85TopTif-185
❑ 85TopTifT-55T
❑ 85TopTra-55T
❑ 86ColCliP-11
❑ 86ColCliP-12
❑ 86Don-573
❑ 86Fle-159
❑ 86OPC-369
❑ 86Top-369
❑ 86TopTif-369
❑ 86YanTCM-3
❑ 87ColCliP-12
❑ 87ColCliP-22
❑ 87ColCliT-6
❑ 89PacSenL-26
❑ 89PacSenL-113
❑ 90EliSenL-114
❑ 91PacSenL-139
❑ 92YanWIZ8-83
❑ 93UppDecS-12

Holland, Bill
❑ 78LauLonABS-21

Holland, Bob
❑ 30Zee-173
❑ 31Zee-118
❑ 32Zee-116
❑ 33WorCig(-48
❑ 33Zee-157

Holland, Donny
❑ 82WauTimF-20

Holland, Jay
❑ 92BenRocCB-13
❑ 92BenRocF-1470

Holland, Jim
❑ 94PriRedC-27

Holland, Joe
❑ 11PacCoaBD-29
❑ 11Zee-88

Holland, John
❑ 81BufBisT-2
❑ 82BufBisT-12

Holland, Mike
❑ 74CedRapAT-26
❑ 90EriSaiS-9

Holland, Monty
❑ 80BatTroT-9

Holland, Randy
❑ 86KnoBluJP-11
❑ 87KnoBluJP-1515
❑ 88SyrChiC-2
❑ 88SyrChiP-829
❑ 88TriAAAP-53
❑ 89SyrChiC-13
❑ 89SyrChiP-795
❑ 90SyrChiMB-12
❑ 91SyrChiMB-8

Holland, Rod
❑ 93ButCopKSP-15

Holland, Sid
❑ 91GasRanC-23
❑ 91GasRanP-2700
❑ 92ChaRanC-16
❑ 92ChaRanF-2237
❑ 97AubDouTI-6
❑ 97KisCob-30
❑ 98QuaCitRBG-9

Holland, Tim
❑ 89WatDiaP-1779
❑ 89WatDiaS-13
❑ 90CarLeaA-5
❑ 90FreKeyTI-15
❑ 91HagSunLD-232
❑ 91HagSunP-2463
❑ 91LinDriAA-232
❑ 91PerHeaF-8
❑ 92HagSunF-2562
❑ 92HagSunS-259
❑ 93AusFut-123
❑ 93BowBayF-2195
❑ 95AusFut-2

Hollander, William
❑ 18Zee-23

Hollandsworth, Todd
❑ 91FroRowDP-46
❑ 91FroRowDPG-46
❑ 91FroRowDPS-46
❑ 92BakDodCLC-1
❑ 92StaCluD-85
❑ 92UppDecML-160
❑ 92UppDecMLPotY-PY9
❑ 93Bow-98
❑ 93ClaFS7-138
❑ 93DodStaC-28
❑ 93SanAntMF-3017
❑ 94ActPac-50
❑ 94ActPac-66
❑ 94ActPac2G-12G
❑ 94ActPac2GD-12G
❑ 94AlbDukF-856
❑ 94Bow-359
❑ 94Bow-426
❑ 94BowBes-B45
❑ 94BowBesR-B45
❑ 94Cla-101
❑ 94ClaCreotC-C8
❑ 94ColC-658
❑ 94ColChoGS-658
❑ 94ColChoSS-658
❑ 94ExcFS7-215
❑ 94SigRoo-14
❑ 94SigRooHP-S3
❑ 94SigRooHPMP-S3
❑ 94SigRooHPMPS-S3
❑ 94SigRooHPS-S3
❑ 94SigRooS-14
❑ 94SP-6
❑ 94SPDieC-6
❑ 94UppDec-531
❑ 94UppDecED-531
❑ 94UppDecML-60
❑ 94UppDecML-266
❑ 95ActPacF-13
❑ 95Bow-268
❑ 95BowBes-B44
❑ 95BowBesR-B44
❑ 95BowGolF-268
❑ 95ColCho-231
❑ 95ColChoGS-231
❑ 95ColChoSE-91
❑ 95ColChoSEGS-91
❑ 95ColChoSESS-91
❑ 95ColChoSS-231
❑ 95DodMot-16
❑ 95DodPol-11
❑ 95Exc-213
❑ 95Fla-365
❑ 95FleAllR-M7
❑ 95Pin-420
❑ 95PinArtP-420
❑ 95PinMusC-420
❑ 95SelCer-120
❑ 95SelCerF-6
❑ 95SelCerMG-120
❑ 95SelCerPU-16
❑ 95SelCerPU9-16
❑ 95SigRoo-25
❑ 95SigRooOJSS-4
❑ 95SigRooOJSSS-4
❑ 95SigRooSig-25
❑ 95StaClu-590
❑ 95StaCluMOP-590
❑ 95StaCluSTWS-590
❑ 95Sum-159
❑ 95SumNewA-NA12
❑ 95SumNthD-159
❑ 95Top-247
❑ 95UC3-111
❑ 95UC3ArtP-111
❑ 95UppDec-224
❑ 95UppDecED-224
❑ 95UppDecEDG-224
❑ 95UppDecML-10
❑ 95UppDecMLFS-10
❑ 95UppDecMLMLA-6
❑ 95UppDecMLT1PF-10
❑ 95UppDecSE-34
❑ 95UppDecSEG-34
❑ 95Zen-147
❑ 95ZenRooRC-5
❑ 96Bow-40
❑ 96Bow-42
❑ 96BowBes-149
❑ 96BowBesAR-149
❑ 96BowBesR-149
❑ 96BowFoi-40
❑ 96ColCho-182
❑ 96ColChoGS-182
❑ 96ColChoSS-182
❑ 96DodFle-9
❑ 96DodMot-9
❑ 96DodPol-19
❑ 96Don-339
❑ 96DonPreP-339
❑ 96EmoXL-209
❑ 96Fin-B246
❑ 96FinRef-B246
❑ 96Fla-293
❑ 96Fle-437
❑ 96FleTif-437
❑ 96Lea-143
❑ 96LeaPre-133
❑ 96LeaPreP-133
❑ 96LeaPrePB-143
❑ 96LeaPrePG-143
❑ 96LeaPrePS-143

❑ 96LeaPreSG-13
❑ 96LeaPreSte-13
❑ 96LeaSig-93
❑ 96LeaSigPPG-93
❑ 96LeaSigPPP-93
❑ 96Pin-252
❑ 96PinAfi-165
❑ 96PinAfiAP-165
❑ 96PinArtP-152
❑ 96PinFoil-252
❑ 96PinProS-16
❑ 96PinSta-152
❑ 96Sco-112
❑ 96ScoDiaA-28
❑ 96ScoDugC-A76
❑ 96ScoDugCAP-A76
❑ 96Sel-181
❑ 96SelArtP-181
❑ 96SelCer-117
❑ 96SelCerAP-117
❑ 96SelCerCB-117
❑ 96SelCerCR-117
❑ 96SelCerMB-117
❑ 96SelCerMG-117
❑ 96SelCerMR-117
❑ 96Spo-122
❑ 96SpoArtP-122
❑ 96SpoRooJ-4
❑ 96Stu-4
❑ 96StuPrePB-4
❑ 96StuPrePG-4
❑ 96StuPrePS-4
❑ 96Sum-189
❑ 96SumAbo&B-189
❑ 96SumArtP-189
❑ 96SumFoi-189
❑ 96Top-48
❑ 96TopLasBS-12
❑ 96Ult-219
❑ 96UltGolM-219
❑ 96UppDec-118
❑ 96UppDecPHE-H55
❑ 96UppDecPreH-H55
❑ 97Bow-282
❑ 97BowBes-20
❑ 97BowBesAR-20
❑ 97BowBesR-20
❑ 97BowCerBlaIA-CA39
❑ 97BowCerBluIA-CA39
❑ 97BowCerGolIA-CA39
❑ 97BowInt-282
❑ 97Cir-251
❑ 97CirEmeA-251
❑ 97CirEmeAR-AU2
❑ 97CirFasT-2
❑ 97CirRav-251
❑ 97ColCho-139
❑ 97ColChoT-LA3
❑ 97ColChoTBS-25
❑ 97ColChoTBSWH-25
❑ 97DodDWPM-1
❑ 97DodMot-6
❑ 97DodPol-14
❑ 97DodSco-3
❑ 97DodScoPl-3
❑ 97DodScoPr-3
❑ 97Don-125
❑ 97DonEli-67
❑ 97DonEliGS-67
❑ 97DonGolPP-125
❑ 97DonLim-15
❑ 97DonLimE-15
❑ 97DonLimENG-15
❑ 97DonPre-119
❑ 97DonPreCttC-119
❑ 97DonSigA-51
❑ 97DonSigAC-61
❑ 97DonSigAM-62
❑ 97DonSilPP-125
❑ 97DonTea-110
❑ 97DonTeaSPE-110
❑ 97E-X2-78
❑ 97E-X2Cred-78
❑ 97E-X2EmeAuto-78
❑ 97E-X2EmeAutoR-AU2
❑ 97E-X2EssCre-78
❑ 97E-X2SD2000-12
❑ 97Fin-121
❑ 97FinEmb-121
❑ 97FinEmbR-121
❑ 97FinRef-121
❑ 97FlaShoLC-82
❑ 97FlaShoLeg0-82
❑ 97FlaShoLeg1-82
❑ 97FlaShoM-A82
❑ 97FlaShoM-B82
❑ 97FlaShoM-C82
❑ 97FlaShoR0-82
❑ 97FlaShoR1-82
❑ 97FlaShoR2-82
❑ 97Fle-364
❑ 97FleRooS-6
❑ 97FleTif-364
❑ 97Lea-58
❑ 97LeaBanS-15
❑ 97LeaFraM-58
❑ 97LeaFraMDC-58
❑ 97MetUni-100
❑ 97MetUniEA-AU2
❑ 97MetUniEAR-AU2
❑ 97MetUniPP-3
❑ 97NewPin-121
❑ 97NewPinAP-121
❑ 97NewPinMC-121
❑ 97NewPinPP-121
❑ 97Pac-331
❑ 97PacCar-29
❑ 97PacCarM-29
❑ 97PacGolCD-29
❑ 97PacLigB-331
❑ 97PacPri-111
❑ 97PacPriGA-GA24
❑ 97PacPriLB-111
❑ 97PacPriP-111
❑ 97PacSil-331
❑ 97Pin-118
❑ 97PinArtP-PP118
❑ 97PinCer-52
❑ 97PinCerMBla-52
❑ 97PinCerMBlu-52
❑ 97PinCerMG-52
❑ 97PinCerMR-52
❑ 97PinCerR-52
❑ 97PinIns-25
❑ 97PinIns-148
❑ 97PinInsCE-25
❑ 97PinInsCE-148
❑ 97PinInsDD-19
❑ 97PinInsDE-25
❑ 97PinInsDE-148
❑ 97PinMusC-118
❑ 97PinPrePla-118
❑ 97PinTotCPB-52
❑ 97PinTotCPG-52
❑ 97PinTotCPR-52
❑ 97PinX-P-105
❑ 97PinX-PMoS-105
❑ 97PreCon-26
❑ 97Sco-113
❑ 97ScoArtPWB-113
❑ 97ScoPreS-113
❑ 97ScoShoS-113
❑ 97ScoShoSAP-113
❑ 97ScoStaaD-16
❑ 97Sel-9
❑ 97SelArtP-9
❑ 97SelCom-9
❑ 97SelRegG-9
❑ 97SelRooR-3
❑ 97SelToootT-13
❑ 97SelToootTMB-13
❑ 97SP-93
❑ 97SpoIll-114
❑ 97SpoIllEE-114
❑ 97SPSpxF-7
❑ 97SPSPxFA-7
❑ 97SPVinAu-18
❑ 97StaClu-87
❑ 97StaCluC-CO5
❑ 97StaCluMOP-87
❑ 97Stu-6
❑ 97StuPrePG-6
❑ 97StuPrePS-6
❑ 97Top-177
❑ 97TopAwel-AI6
❑ 97TopChr-69
❑ 97TopChrR-69
❑ 97TopDodRotY-6
❑ 97TopGal-175
❑ 97TopGalPPI-175
❑ 97TopMemO5-23
❑ 97UD3-56
❑ 97UD3GenNex-GN14
❑ 97Ult-218
❑ 97UltAutE-6
❑ 97UltGolME-218
❑ 97UltPlaME-218
❑ 97UltRooR-4
❑ 97UltTop3-27
❑ 97UltTop3GM-27
❑ 97UppDec-92
❑ 97UppDecAWJ-19
❑ 97UppDecBCP-BC16
❑ 98ColCho-394
❑ 98DodPol-10
❑ 98DodSco-6
❑ 98DodScoP-6
❑ 98Don-175
❑ 98DonColL-260
❑ 98DonGolPP-175
❑ 98DonPriCL-260
❑ 98DonSilPP-175
❑ 98Fle-379
❑ 98Lea-61
❑ 98LeaFraDA-61
❑ 98LeaFraF-61
❑ 98LeaFraM-61
❑ 98LeaFraM-61
❑ 98LeaFraMDC-61
❑ 98LeaFraMDC-61
❑ 98LeaFraMZ2-61
❑ 98Pac-331
❑ 98PacAur-143
❑ 98PacOme-121
❑ 98PacOmeR-121
❑ 98PacOnl-371
❑ 98PacOnlR-371
❑ 98PacOnlWC-371
❑ 98PacPlaB-331
❑ 98PacRedT-331
❑ 98PacSil-331
❑ 98PinSna-LAD9
❑ 98Sco-83
❑ 98SkyDugAAR-8
❑ 98StaCluFDI-206
❑ 98StaCluI-206
❑ 98StaCluOneK-206
❑ 98StaCluPP-206
❑ 98Top-214
❑ 98TopChr-214
❑ 98TopChrR-214
❑ 98TopDevR-214
❑ 98TopDia-214
❑ 98TopMiniC-214
❑ 98TopOpeD-104
❑ 98Ult-206
❑ 98UltGolM-206
❑ 98UltMas-206
❑ 98UltPlaM-206
❑ 98UppDec-403
❑ 98UppDecAPA1-4
❑ 98UppDecAPA1-5
❑ 99DodPol-10
❑ 99Fle-449
❑ 99FleSta9-449
❑ 99FleWarT-449
❑ 99Pac-219
❑ 99PacPlaB-219
❑ 99PacRed-219
❑ 99SkyPreA-28
❑ 99SkyPreABlue-28
❑ 99UppDec-398
❑ 99UppDecEL1-398
❑ 99UppDecEL2-398

Holle, Gary
❑ 77HolMilT-14
❑ 78HolMilT-13
❑ 81EdmTraRR-1
❑ 93RanKee-188

Holleday, Juan
❑ 92AubAstC-25
❑ 92AubAstF-1349

Hollenback, Dave
❑ 88ModA'sCLC-83
❑ 88ModA'sTI-3
❑ 89ModA'sC-3
❑ 89ModA'sCLC-290
❑ 90ModA'sC-14
❑ 90ModA'sCLC-173
❑ 91ModA'sC-19
❑ 92CalLeaACL-23
❑ 92ModA'sC-27
❑ 95HunStaTI-14
❑ 96HunStaTI-10

Hollerson, George
❑ 26Zee-6
❑ 30Zee-8

Holley, Battle
❑ 94St.CatBJC-12
❑ 94St.CatBJF-3652
❑ 95HagSunF-74
❑ 95StCatSTI-18

Holley, Bobby
❑ 88EugEmeB-22
❑ 90BasCitRS-12
❑ 91CarLeaAP-CAR28
❑ 91PenPilC-21
❑ 91PenPilP-386
❑ 92JacSunF-3715
❑ 92JacSunS-359
❑ 92SkyAA F-151
❑ 93ClaFS7-279

Holley, Ed
❑ 33ButCanV-27
❑ 34BabRutG-34
❑ 34ButPreR-33
❑ 34Gou-55

Holley, Kenny
❑ 88WytCubP-1994

Holliday, Brian
❑ 92BurAstC-15
❑ 92BurAstF-538
❑ 92StaCluD-86
❑ 93OscAstC-14
❑ 93OscAstF-622

Holliday, Bug (James)
❑ 87OldJudN-246
❑ 98CamPepP-35

Holliday, Matt
❑ 99Bow-400
❑ 99BowBes-172
❑ 99BowBesAR-172
❑ 99BowBesR-172
❑ 99BowGol-400
❑ 99BowInt-400
❑ 99StaClu-341
❑ 99StaCluFDI-341
❑ 99StaCluOoaK-341
❑ 99StaCluPP-341
❑ 99Top-442
❑ 99TopChr-442
❑ 99TopChrR-442
❑ 99TopMVPP-442

Holliday, Tom
❑ 91OklStaC-11
❑ 92OklStaC-5

Hollifield, David
❑ 76QuaCitAT-16
❑ 77QuaCitAT-17

Hollimon, Ulysses
❑ 96NegLeaBMKC-1

Holling, Carl
❑ 19Zee-19
❑ 28Zee-51
❑ 29Zee-21
❑ 30Zee-31
❑ 31Zee-32

Hollinger, Adrian
❑ 92SpoIndC-19
❑ 92SpoIndF-1288
❑ 93WatDiaC-19
❑ 93WatDiaF-1764
❑ 94RanCucQC-16
❑ 94RanCucQF-1633
❑ 95BreCouMF-241

Hollingsworth, Al
❑ 79DiaGre-140
❑ 90DodTar-352
❑ 96Bro194F-4

Hollingsworth, Scot
❑ 91MisStaB-26

Hollins, Damon
❑ 92HigSchPLS-25
❑ 93Bow-170
❑ 93ClaGolF-149
❑ 93DanBraC-14
❑ 93DanBraF-3631
❑ 93StaCluM-185
❑ 94Bow-161
❑ 94CarLeaAF-CAR28
❑ 94Cla-75
❑ 94DurBulC-1
❑ 94DurBulF-340
❑ 94DurBulTI-9
❑ 94ExcFS7-154
❑ 95Bes-51
❑ 95Bow-10
❑ 95BreBtaTI-7
❑ 95Exc-152
❑ 95SigRoo-26
❑ 95SigRooSig-26
❑ 95SPML-12
❑ 95Top-645
❑ 95UppDec-5
❑ 95UppDecED-5
❑ 95UppDecEDG-5
❑ 95UppDecML-50
❑ 95UppDecMLFS-50
❑ 95UppDecSE-13
❑ 95UppDecSEG-13
❑ 96BesAutSA-30
❑ 96Bow-332
❑ 96BowFoi-332
❑ 96Exc-127
❑ 96RicBraB-16
❑ 96RicBraRC-13
❑ 96RicBraUB-12
❑ 97BesAutAS-20
❑ 97BesAutP-R6
❑ 97RicBra-15
❑ 98Fle-387
❑ 98LeaRS-126
❑ 98LeaRSLong-7
❑ 98LeaRTrue-126
❑ 98PacOmeRS-10
❑ 98PacOmeRST1-10
❑ 98RicBraQ-18

Hollins, Darontaye
❑ 97HicCraRB-17
❑ 98HicCraM-16

Hollins, Dave
❑ 87SpoIndP-8
❑ 88CalLeaACLC-44
❑ 88RivRedWCLC-222
❑ 88RivRedWP-1418
❑ 89WicChaR-11
❑ 89WicStaR-12
❑ 89WicWraR-7
❑ 90Bow-161
❑ 90BowTif-161
❑ 90ClaYel-T14
❑ 90DonRoo-47
❑ 90FleUpd-43
❑ 90PhiTas-14
❑ 90ScoRoo-75T
❑ 90ScoYouS2-35
❑ 90TopTra-41T
❑ 90TopTraT-41T
❑ 90UppDec-785
❑ 91Fle-399
❑ 91OPC-264
❑ 91PhiMed-19
❑ 91Sco-61
❑ 91Sco100RS-96
❑ 91ScrRedBP-2545
❑ 91Top-264
❑ 91TopDeb90-69
❑ 91TopDesS-264
❑ 91TopMic-264
❑ 91TopTif-264
❑ 91UppDec-518
❑ 92Bow-6
❑ 92Don-685
❑ 92Fle-535
❑ 92Lea-278
❑ 92LeaBlaG-278
❑ 92OPC-383
❑ 92PhiMed-15
❑ 92Pin-67
❑ 92PinTea2-16
❑ 92ProFS7-296
❑ 92Sco-553
❑ 92ScoProP-16
❑ 92StaClu-246
❑ 92Top-383
❑ 92TopGol-383
❑ 92TopGolW-383
❑ 92TopMic-383
❑ 92Ult-244
❑ 92UppDec-586
❑ 93Bow-216
❑ 93DenHol-18
❑ 93DiaMar-52
❑ 93Don-68
❑ 93Fin-23
❑ 93FinRef-23
❑ 93Fla-102
❑ 93Fle-353
❑ 93Fle-491
❑ 93FunPac-145
❑ 93Lea-239
❑ 93OPC-169
❑ 93PacSpa-236
❑ 93PanSti-273
❑ 93PhiMed-17
❑ 93PhiStaC-11
❑ 93Pin-127
❑ 93PinHomRC-11
❑ 93PinSlu-8
❑ 93Sco-99
❑ 93Sel-187
❑ 93SelStaL-41
❑ 93SP-175
❑ 93SPPlaP-PP10
❑ 93StaClu-339
❑ 93StaCluFDI-339
❑ 93StaCluMOP-339
❑ 93Stu-158
❑ 93Top-17
❑ 93TopGol-17
❑ 93TopInaM-17
❑ 93TopInaR-17
❑ 93TopMic-17
❑ 93Toy-18
❑ 93TriPla-38
❑ 93Ult-88
❑ 93UltHomRK-10
❑ 93UppDec-153
❑ 93UppDec-458
❑ 93UppDec-485
❑ 93UppDecDG-18
❑ 93UppDecGold-153
❑ 93UppDecGold-458
❑ 93UppDecGold-485
❑ 93UppDecHRH-HR10
❑ 93USPlaCA-2C
❑ 94Bow-524
❑ 94ColC-141
❑ 94ColChoGS-141
❑ 94ColChoSS-141
❑ 94Don-29
❑ 94DonSpeE-29
❑ 94Fin-47
❑ 94FinPre-47P
❑ 94FinRef-47
❑ 94Fla-207
❑ 94Fle-590
❑ 94FleAllS-41
❑ 94FleExtB-335
❑ 94FUnPac-115
❑ 94Lea-54
❑ 94LeaCleC-3
❑ 94OPC-186
❑ 94Pac-476
❑ 94PanSti-228
❑ 94PhiMed-13
❑ 94PhiMel-9
❑ 94PhiUSPC-1S
❑ 94PhiUSPC-7H
❑ 94Pin-121
❑ 94PinArtP-121
❑ 94PinMusC-121
❑ 94ProMag-103
❑ 94Sco-354
❑ 94ScoGolR-354
❑ 94Sel-28
❑ 94SP-136
❑ 94SPDieC-136
❑ 94Spo-145
❑ 94StaClu-96
❑ 94StaCluFDI-96
❑ 94StaCluGR-96
❑ 94StaCluMOP-96
❑ 94StaCluT-225
❑ 94StaCluTFDI-225
❑ 94Stu-139
❑ 94Top-476
❑ 94TopGol-476
❑ 94TopSpa-476
❑ 94TriPla-175
❑ 94TriPlaM-10
❑ 94Ult-245
❑ 94UppDec-432
❑ 94UppDecED-432
❑ 95Bow-281
❑ 95BowBes-R47
❑ 95BowBesR-R47
❑ 95ColCho-362
❑ 95ColChoGS-362
❑ 95ColChoSS-362
❑ 95Don-453
❑ 95DonPreP-453
❑ 95DonTopotO-306
❑ 95Emo-167
❑ 95Fin-159
❑ 95FinRef-159
❑ 95Fla-391
❑ 95Fle-393
❑ 95Lea-229
❑ 95LeaLim-45
❑ 95Phi-16
❑ 95PhiMel-13
❑ 95Pin-104
❑ 95PinArtP-104
❑ 95PinMusC-104
❑ 95Sco-77
❑ 95ScoGolR-77
❑ 95ScoHaloG-HG91
❑ 95ScoPlaTS-77
❑ 95SP-88
❑ 95Spo-71
❑ 95SpoArtP-71
❑ 95SPSil-88
❑ 95StaClu-144
❑ 95StaCluFDI-144
❑ 95StaCluMOP-144

❑ 95StaCluSTWS-144
❑ 95Stu-124
❑ 95Top-586
❑ 95TopCyb-359
❑ 95TopEmb-47
❑ 95TopEmbGI-47
❑ 95UC3-80
❑ 95UC3ArtP-80
❑ 95Ult-205
❑ 95UltGolM-205
❑ 95UppDec-377
❑ 95UppDecED-377
❑ 95UppDecEDG-377
❑ 95UppDecSE-207
❑ 95UppDecSEG-207
❑ 96ColCho-601
❑ 96ColChoGS-601
❑ 96ColChoSS-601
❑ 96Fin-B255
❑ 96FinRef-B255
❑ 96Fla-114
❑ 96FleUpd-U54
❑ 96FleUpdTC-U54
❑ 96LeaSigA-106
❑ 96LeaSigAG-106
❑ 96LeaSigAS-106
❑ 96TopLas-67
❑ 96Ult-374
❑ 96UltGolM-374
❑ 97AngMot-23
❑ 97Cir-141
❑ 97CirRav-141
❑ 97ColCho-262
❑ 97DonLim-58
❑ 97DonLimE-58
❑ 97DonLimENG-58
❑ 97DonTea-14
❑ 97DonTeaSPE-14
❑ 97Fle-506
❑ 97FleTif-506
❑ 97Pac-188
❑ 97PacLigB-188
❑ 97PacSil-188
❑ 97Pin-123
❑ 97PinArtP-PP123
❑ 97PinMusC-123
❑ 97Ult-311
❑ 97UltGolME-311
❑ 97UltPlaME-311
❑ 98AngSco-8
❑ 98AngScoP-8
❑ 98CirThu-197
❑ 98CirThuRav-197
❑ 98CirThuSupRav-197
❑ 98ColCho-29
❑ 98Don-245
❑ 98DonGolPP-245
❑ 98DonSilPP-245
❑ 98Fle-113
❑ 98Pac-10
❑ 98PacOnl-12
❑ 98PacOnlR-12
❑ 98PacOnlWC-12
❑ 98PacPlaB-10
❑ 98PacRedT-10
❑ 98PacSil-10
❑ 98PinSna-AA10
❑ 98Sco-137
❑ 98ScoRT-113
❑ 98StaCluFDI-250
❑ 98StaCluI-250
❑ 98StaCluOneK-250
❑ 98StaCluPP-250
❑ 98Top-53
❑ 98TopChr-53
❑ 98TopChrR-53
❑ 98TopDevR-53
❑ 98TopDia-53
❑ 98TopMiniC-53
❑ 98TopOpeD-32
❑ 98UppDec-24
❑ 98UppDecSF-14
❑ 99Fle-474
❑ 99FleSta9-474
❑ 99FleWarT-474
❑ 99Pac-9
❑ 99PacPlaB-9
❑ 99PacRed-9
❑ 99StaClu-304
❑ 99StaCluFDI-304
❑ 99StaCluOoaK-304
❑ 99StaCluPP-304
❑ 99Top-318
❑ 99TopChr-318
❑ 99TopChrR-318
❑ 99TopMVPP-318
❑ 99UppDec-23
❑ 99UppDecEL1-23
❑ 99UppDecEL2-23

Hollins, Jessie
❑ 89WytCubS-16
❑ 90GenCubP-3041
❑ 90GenCubS-14
❑ 90ProAaA-175
❑ 91Bow-423
❑ 91Cla/Bes-36
❑ 91WinSpiC-5
❑ 91WinSpiP-2824
❑ 92ChaKniF-2766
❑ 92ChaKniS-159
❑ 92SkyAA F-74
❑ 93Bow-348
❑ 93Bow-580
❑ 93CubStaC-27
❑ 93Don-368
❑ 93Top-487
❑ 93TopGol-487
❑ 93TopInaM-487
❑ 93TopInaR-487
❑ 93TopMic-487
❑ 93UppDec-18
❑ 93UppDecGold-18
❑ 94Bow-278

Hollins, Paul
❑ 86ChaLooP-13

Hollins, Stacy
❑ 93MadMusC-15
❑ 93MadMusF-1819
❑ 94AriFalLS-8
❑ 94ModA'sC-15
❑ 94ModA'sF-3062
❑ 95Bow-99
❑ 95HunStaTI-15
❑ 95SigRooOJ-17
❑ 95SigRooOJP-17
❑ 95SigRooOJPS-17
❑ 95SigRooOJS-17
❑ 96HunStaTI-11
❑ 97HunStaTI-10
❑ 98ShrCapM-17
❑ 98ShrCapWS-17

Hollins, Steve
❑ 90PriPatD-12

Hollinshed, Joe
❑ 86EriCarP-14

Hollis, Jack
❑ 52MotCoo-62
❑ 78DunBluJT-13
❑ 90ChaWheB-21
❑ 90ChaWheP-2252

Hollis, Ron
❑ 94YakBeaC-6
❑ 94YakBeaF-3841
❑ 95VerBeaDTI-13
❑ 96SanAntMB-8
❑ 96VerBeaDB-14

Hollmig, Stan
❑ 49EurSta-137
❑ 49PhiBul-25
❑ 50PhiPhil-11
❑ 75Phi195T-13
❑ 80Phi195T-13

Hollocher, Charles J.
❑ 16Zee-54
❑ 19W514-53
❑ 20NatCarE-44
❑ 21E121So1-43
❑ 21Exh-77
❑ 21Nei-110
❑ 22E120-159
❑ 22W572-43
❑ 22W573-62
❑ 22W575-57
❑ 23W501-57
❑ 23W515-59
❑ 23WilChoV-64
❑ 50CubGreB-10
❑ 93ConTSN-799

Holloman, Bobo
❑ 63GadFunC-38
❑ 77FriOneYW-11
❑ 90BasWit-69
❑ 90HOFStiB-47
❑ 91TopArc1-306

Holloway, Crush
❑ 78LauLonABS-24
❑ 86NegLeaF-22

Holloway, Ken
❑ 29ExhFou-22
❑ 93ConTSN-700

Holloway, Rick
❑ 81WesHavAT-13

Hollowell, Chuck
❑ 80BatTroT-12

Hollrah, Scot
❑ 93HicCraC-11
❑ 93HicCraF-1284

Holly, Chuck**
❑ 88MisStaB-12
❑ 89MisStaB-20
❑ 90MisStaB-21
❑ 91MisStaB-27

Holly, Jeff
❑ 77TacTwiDQ-24B
❑ 78OrlTwiT-8
❑ 79Top-371
❑ 79TwiFriP-10

Hollywood, Leonard
❑ 17Zee-91

Holm, Dave
❑ 75CliPilT-15

Holm, Jerry
❑ 86RedWinA-11

Holm, Mike
❑ 85NewOriT-8

Holm, Roscoe
❑ 33Gou-173

Holm, Vivian
❑ 94ColSilBC-3
❑ 95ColSilB9-9

Holm, Wattie
❑ 93ConTSN-691

Holm, William
❑ 44CubTeal-12

Holman, Brad
❑ 90EugEmeGS-16
❑ 91PenPilC-5
❑ 91PenPilP-371
❑ 92JacSunF-3704
❑ 92PenPilC-24
❑ 93CalCanF-1161
❑ 93LinVenB-35
❑ 94CalCanF-784
❑ 94Don-462
❑ 94Fle-289
❑ 94Lea-35
❑ 94Pac-573
❑ 94StaClu-76
❑ 94StaCluFDI-76
❑ 94StaCluGR-76
❑ 94StaCluMOP-76
❑ 94Top-631
❑ 94TopGol-631
❑ 94TopSpa-631
❑ 94VenLinU-39

Holman, Brian
❑ 86JacExpT-23
❑ 86SouLeaAJ-21
❑ 87JacExpP-452
❑ 88ExpPos-11
❑ 88FleUpd-100
❑ 88FleUpdG-100
❑ 88IndIndC-9
❑ 88IndIndP-504
❑ 89Bow-357
❑ 89BowTif-357
❑ 89Don-511
❑ 89Fle-379
❑ 89FleGlo-379
❑ 89TopTra-51T
❑ 89TopTraT-51T
❑ 89UppDec-356
❑ 90ClaBlu-66
❑ 90Don-143
❑ 90Fle-516
❑ 90FleCan-516
❑ 90Lea-273
❑ 90MarMot-20
❑ 90OPC-616
❑ 90PanSti-146
❑ 90PubIntS-176
❑ 90Sco-387
❑ 90ScoYouSI-7
❑ 90Top-616
❑ 90TopBig-282
❑ 90TopTif-616
❑ 90UppDec-362
❑ 91Bow-240
❑ 91Don-539
❑ 91Fle-453
❑ 91Lea-11
❑ 91MarCouH-21
❑ 91OPC-458
❑ 91Sco-285
❑ 91StaClu-106
❑ 91StaCluP-16
❑ 91Stu-115
❑ 91Top-458
❑ 91TopDesS-458
❑ 91TopMic-458
❑ 91TopTif-458
❑ 91Ult-338
❑ 91UppDec-252
❑ 92Don-43
❑ 92Fle-281
❑ 92MarMot-26
❑ 92OPC-239
❑ 92Pin-520
❑ 92Sco-228
❑ 92StaClu-295
❑ 92Top-239
❑ 92TopGol-239
❑ 92TopGolW-239
❑ 92TopMic-239
❑ 92UppDec-595
❑ 93Don-385
❑ 93MariStaClu-15
❑ 93UppDec-799
❑ 93UppDecGold-799

Holman, Craig
❑ 91BatCliCB-28
❑ 91BatCliP-3480
❑ 92SpaPhiC-1
❑ 92SpaPhiF-1260
❑ 93ClePhiC-14
❑ 94ReaPhiF-2057
❑ 95ReaPhiELC-20
❑ 95ReaPhiTI-18
❑ 96ScrRedBB-16
❑ 97ScrRedB-4
❑ 98ScrRedBQ-17

Holman, Dale
❑ 82AlbDukTc-20
❑ 84SyrChiT-28
❑ 85SyrChiT-5
❑ 86SyrChiP-12
❑ 87RicBraBC-13
❑ 87RicBraC-25
❑ 87RicBraT-23

Holman, Ed
❑ 75LynRanT-12
❑ 76SanAntBTI-12

Holman, Gary
❑ 69Top-361

Holman, Jeff
❑ 90StaFS7-92

Holman, R. Scott
❑ 77WauMetT-10
❑ 79TidTidT-17
❑ 82TidTidT-18
❑ 83Don-224
❑ 84Fle-589
❑ 84Nes792-13
❑ 84TidTidT-1
❑ 84Top-13
❑ 84TopTif-13
❑ 85IowCubT-15
❑ 91MetWIZ-187

Holman, Shawn
❑ 84PriWilPT-4
❑ 85PriWilPT-16
❑ 86NasPirP-13
❑ 87HarSenP-1
❑ 88BlaYNPRWL-87
❑ 88EasLeaAP-7
❑ 88GleFalTP-929
❑ 89BlaYNPRWLU-26
❑ 89TolMudHC-5
❑ 89TolMudHP-781
❑ 90CMC-381
❑ 90Fle-606
❑ 90FleCan-606
❑ 90ProAAAF-373
❑ 90Sco-620
❑ 90TolMudHC-4
❑ 90TolMudHP-143
❑ 90TopDeb89-61
❑ 93RicBraBB-14
❑ 93RicBraF-180
❑ 93RicBraP-23
❑ 93RicBraRC-9
❑ 93RicBraRC-10
❑ 94OttLynF-2898

Holman, Steve
❑ 78CedRapGT-11

Holmberg, Dennis
❑ 75BurBeeT-11
❑ 76BurBeeT-18
❑ 77NewCoPT-17
❑ 78DunBluJT-14
❑ 85SyrChiT-28
❑ 87DunBluJP-929
❑ 89DunBluJS-26
❑ 90DunBluJS-26
❑ 90FloStaLAS-48
❑ 91DunBluJC-25
❑ 91DunBluJP-223
❑ 92DunBluJC-26
❑ 92DunBluJF-2013
❑ 93DunBluJC-26
❑ 93DunBluJF-1811
❑ 93DunBluJFFN-11
❑ 95BluJayOH-20
❑ 96DunBluJB-27
❑ 96DunBluJTI-16
❑ 97DunBluJTI-15
❑ 98DunBluJSB-24
❑ 98DunBluJTI-11

Holmberg, Kenny
❑ 92DunBluJC-30
❑ 93DunBluJC-29

Holmes, Bill
❑ 89PriPirS-9
❑ 90AugPirP-2471

Holmes, Bob
❑ 12ImpTobC-79

Holmes, Carl
❑ 86SpoIndC-158

Holmes, Chris
❑ 88RenSilSCLC-282

Holmes, Craig
❑ 94OgdRapSP-27
❑ 95OdgRapTI-9

Holmes, Darren
❑ 86VerBeaDP-10
❑ 87VerBeaDP-5
❑ 89SanAntMB-4
❑ 90AlbDukCm-6
❑ 90AlbDukP-339
❑ 90AlbDukTr-13
❑ 90CMC-408
❑ 90ProAAAF-60
❑ 91BreMilB-11
❑ 91DenZepLD-141
❑ 91Don-669
❑ 91Lea-387
❑ 91LinDriAAA-141
❑ 91TopDeb90-70
❑ 92DenZepS-130
❑ 92Don-504
❑ 92Fle-179
❑ 92OPC-454
❑ 92Sco-753
❑ 92Sco100RS-39
❑ 92StaClu-155
❑ 92Top-454
❑ 92TopGol-454
❑ 92TopGolW-454
❑ 92TopMic-454
❑ 93Don-149
❑ 93Don-779
❑ 93Fle-412
❑ 93FleFinE-34
❑ 93Lea-383
❑ 93OPCPre-104
❑ 93PacSpa-431
❑ 93Pin-521
❑ 93RocStaC-17
❑ 93RocUSPC-6D
❑ 93RocUSPC-9S
❑ 93Sco-600
❑ 93StaClu-506
❑ 93StaCluFDI-506
❑ 93StaCluMOP-506
❑ 93Top-681
❑ 93TopGol-681
❑ 93TopInaM-681
❑ 93TopInaR-681
❑ 93TopMic-681
❑ 93TriPla-22
❑ 93Ult-352
❑ 93UppDec-668
❑ 93UppDecGold-668
❑ 94Bow-310
❑ 94BreMilB-230
❑ 94ColC-422
❑ 94ColChoGS-422
❑ 94ColChoSS-422
❑ 94Don-222
❑ 94Fin-307
❑ 94FinRef-307
❑ 94Fle-444
❑ 94Lea-119
❑ 94Pac-198
❑ 94Pin-375
❑ 94PinArtP-375
❑ 94PinMusC-375
❑ 94RocPol-14
❑ 94Sco-207
❑ 94ScoGolR-207
❑ 94StaClu-672
❑ 94StaCluFDI-672
❑ 94StaCluGR-672
❑ 94StaCluMOP-672
❑ 94StaCluT-117
❑ 94StaCluTFDI-117
❑ 94Top-562
❑ 94TopGol-562
❑ 94TopSpa-562
❑ 94TriPla-226
❑ 94Ult-483
❑ 94UppDec-128
❑ 94UppDecED-128
❑ 95FleUpd-167
❑ 95Top-26
❑ 96ColCho-533
❑ 96ColChoGS-533
❑ 96ColChoSS-533
❑ 96Don-476
❑ 96DonPreP-476
❑ 96Fla-247
❑ 96Fle-364
❑ 96FleTif-364
❑ 96LeaSigEA-79
❑ 96Pac-54
❑ 96RocFle-6
❑ 96RocPol-9
❑ 96Top-51
❑ 96Ult-190
❑ 96UltGolM-190
❑ 97Cir-164
❑ 97CirRav-164
❑ 97PacPriGotD-GD134
❑ 98Pac-284
❑ 98PacOnl-503
❑ 98PacOnlR-503
❑ 98PacOnlWC-503
❑ 98PacPlaB-284
❑ 98PacRedT-284
❑ 98PacSil-284
❑ 99YanFle-17

Holmes, Ducky
❑ 11SpoLifCW-174
❑ 12ImpTobC-60

Holmes, Fred
❑ 64SeaPop-7
❑ 65SeaPop-6

Holmes, Lester
❑ 26Zee-26

Holmes, Michael
❑ 95RocCubTI-NNO
❑ 96RocCubTI-11
❑ 97RocCub-5
❑ 97SouOreTB-22
❑ 97VisOakG-15
❑ 98VisOakG-13

Holmes, Stan
❑ 83VisOakF-10
❑ 85TolMudHT-22
❑ 86OrlTwiP-8
❑ 87MidAngP-17
❑ 88EdmTraC-14
❑ 88EdmTraP-571
❑ 89EdmTraC-11
❑ 89EdmTraP-555

Holmes, Tammy
❑ 96ColSilB-14

Holmes, Tim
❑ 88WatPirP-6

Holmes, Tommy
❑ 39ExhSal-28A
❑ 39ExhSal-28B
❑ 46SpoExcW-5-10
❑ 47HomBon-21
❑ 49Bow-72
❑ 49EurSta-13
❑ 49Lea-133
❑ 50AmeNut&CCP-8
❑ 50Bow-110
❑ 50JJKCopP-6
❑ 51TopRedB-52A
❑ 51TopRedB-52B
❑ 52Top-289
❑ 53ExhCan-18
❑ 74dod195T-15
❑ 76TayBow4-8
❑ 79DiaGre-215
❑ 83TCMPla1942-43
❑ 83TCMPla1945-39
❑ 85TCMPhoC-19
❑ 86BraGreT-7
❑ 90DodTar-353

Holmes, William
❑ 04FanCraAL-24

Holmquist, Doug
❑ 83NasSouTI-8

❑ 85ColCliT-25
Holobinko, Mike
❑ 97WilCubB-8
Holsclaw, Harry
❑ 33WorCig(-49
Holsman, Rich (Richard)
❑ 87SpolndP-6
❑ 88RivRedWCLC-211
❑ 88RivRedWP-1427
❑ 89TexLeaAGS-12
❑ 89WicChaR-4
❑ 89WicChaR-14
❑ 89WicStaR-20
❑ 89WicUpdR-20
❑ 89WicWraR-17
❑ 90WicWraRD-10
❑ 91HarSenLD-257
❑ 91HarSenP-619
❑ 91LinDriAA-257
Holt, Chris
❑ 92AubAstC-1
❑ 92AubAstF-1350
❑ 92ClaDraP-50
❑ 92FroRowDP-33
❑ 92FroRowDPG-33
❑ 92FroRowDPS-33
❑ 93Bow-264
❑ 93MidLeaAGF-47
❑ 93QuaCitRBC-1
❑ 93QuaCitRBF-94
❑ 93StaCluM-75
❑ 94ExcFS7-201
❑ 94JacGenF-213
❑ 95Exc-204
❑ 95JacGenTI-4
❑ 95TucTotTI-11
❑ 96Bow-315
❑ 96BowFoi-315
❑ 96TusTorB-13
❑ 97AstMot-21
❑ 97Bow-120
❑ 97BowInt-120
❑ 97Cir-263
❑ 97CirRav-263
❑ 97ColCho-351
❑ 97DonLim-104
❑ 97DonLimE-104
❑ 97DonLimENG-104
❑ 97Fle-628
❑ 97FleTif-628
❑ 97PinCer-132
❑ 97PinCerMBla-132
❑ 97PinCerMBlu-132
❑ 97PinCerMG-132
❑ 97PinCerMR-132
❑ 97PinCerR-132
❑ 97PinTotCPB-132
❑ 97PinTotCPG-132
❑ 97PinTotCPR-132
❑ 97Sco-487
❑ 97ScoArtPWB-487
❑ 97ScoResC-487
❑ 97ScoShoS-487
❑ 97ScoShoSAP-487
❑ 97Ult-457
❑ 97UltGolME-457
❑ 97UltPlaME-457
❑ 98ColCho-382
❑ 98Don-152
❑ 98DonCol-152
❑ 98DonColS-152
❑ 98DonGolPP-152
❑ 98DonPriCD-152
❑ 98DonSilPP-152
❑ 98PacInvGems-163
❑ 98PacPar-172
❑ 98PacParC-172
❑ 98PacParG-172
❑ 98PacParHS-172
❑ 98PacParPB-172
❑ 98PacParR-172
❑ 98Top-373
❑ 98TopChr-373
❑ 98TopChrR-373
❑ 98TopDevR-373
❑ 98TopDia-373
❑ 98TopMiniC-373
❑ 98Ult-162
❑ 98UltGolM-162
❑ 98UltMas-162
❑ 98UltPlaM-162
❑ 98UppDec-101
❑ 98UppDecSF-62
Holt, Darren
❑ 90VisOakCLC-86
Holt, Dave
❑ 79ElmPioRST-14
❑ 86FloStaLAP-24
❑ 86WinHavRSP-10
❑ 87NewBriRSP-18
❑ 89WinHavRSS-29
❑ 90WinHavRSS-26
❑ 91ElmPioC-27
❑ 91ElmPioP-3287
❑ 92ElmPioC-24
❑ 93UtiBluSC-25
❑ 93UtiBluSF-3548
❑ 94UtiBluSC-28
❑ 94UtiBluSF-3836
Holt, Gene
❑ 44CenFlo-11
Holt, Goldie
❑ 49EurSta-162
Holt, Jim
❑ 71MLBOffS-463
❑ 71OPC-7
❑ 71Top-7
❑ 72Top-588
❑ 73A'sPos-39
❑ 73OPC-259
❑ 73Top-259
❑ 74OPC-122
❑ 74Top-122
❑ 74TopSta-207
❑ 75OPC-607
❑ 75Top-607
❑ 75TopMin-607
❑ 76OPC-603
❑ 76SSP-498
❑ 76Top-603
❑ 76TucTorCa-11
❑ 76TusTorCr-37
❑ 77Top-349
❑ 78TwiFri-33
Holt, Kevin
❑ 94LetMouF-3886
❑ 94LetMouSP-25
Holt, Mike
❑ 78CliDodT-14
Holt, Norman
❑ 87HawRai-20
Holt, Red
❑ 28LaPre-7
Holt, Roger
❑ 77ForLauYS-13
❑ 79ColCliT-18
❑ 80ColCliP-11
❑ 80ColCliT-7
❑ 92YanWIZ8-84
Holter, Brian
❑ 92BurIndC-27
❑ 92BurIndF-1650
Holtgrave, Vern
❑ 77FriOneYW-30
Holton, Brian
❑ 81AlbDukTc-10
❑ 82AlbDukTc-5
❑ 83AlbDukTc-4
❑ 84AlbDukCr-168
❑ 85AlbDukCr-164
❑ 86AlbDukP-12
❑ 87DodMot-26
❑ 87DodPho-5
❑ 87DodPol-27
❑ 87Don-598
❑ 87DonRoo-54
❑ 87TopTra-49T
❑ 87TopTraT-49T
❑ 88DodMot-26
❑ 88DodPol-51
❑ 88Don-402
❑ 88RedFolSB-35
❑ 88Sco-208
❑ 88ScoGlo-208
❑ 88StaLinD-10
❑ 88Top-338
❑ 88TopTif-338
❑ 89BalOriP-13
❑ 89Bow-2
❑ 89BowTif-2
❑ 89Don-439
❑ 89DonTra-20
❑ 89Fle-63
❑ 89FleGlo-63
❑ 89FleUpd-5
❑ 89OriFreB-37
❑ 89Sco-507A
❑ 89Sco-507B
❑ 89ScoRoo-59T
❑ 89Top-368
❑ 89TopTif-368
❑ 89TopTra-52T
❑ 89TopTraT-52T
❑ 89UppDec-72A
❑ 89UppDec-72B
❑ 90DodTar-354
❑ 90Don-635
❑ 90Fle-179
❑ 90FleCan-179
❑ 90Lea-487
❑ 90OPC-179
❑ 90PubIntS-578
❑ 90RocRedWGC-32
❑ 90Sco-177
❑ 90Top-179
❑ 90TopTif-179
❑ 90UppDec-175
❑ 91OriCro-200
❑ 92AlbDukF-715
Holton, Mark
❑ 80UtiBluJT-19
Holtz, Ed
❑ 76AppFoxT-28
❑ 80KnoBluJT-28
❑ 84ChaLooT-5
❑ 88SumBraP-420
❑ 89SumBraP-1088
Holtz, Gerald
❑ 86ChaOriW-14
❑ 87ChaO'sW-17
❑ 88ChaKniTI-19
❑ 88RocRedWGCP-12
❑ 89ReaPhiS-14
Holtz, Mike
❑ 94BoiHawC-15
❑ 94BoiHawF-3350
❑ 95Exc-22
❑ 95LakElsSTI-16
❑ 96Exc-28
❑ 96MidAngB-19
❑ 96MidAngOHP-14
❑ 97AngMot-17
❑ 97Cir-335
❑ 97CirRav-335
❑ 97Fle-45
❑ 97FleTif-45
❑ 98PacInvGems-4
❑ 98PacOnl-13
❑ 98PacOnlR-13
❑ 98PacOnlWC-13
❑ 98Top-185
❑ 98TopChr-185
❑ 98TopChrR-185
❑ 98TopDevR-185
❑ 98TopDia-185
❑ 98TopMiniC-185
Holtzclaw, Shawn
❑ 90MyrBeaBJP-2788
❑ 90ProAaA-100
❑ 90SouAtlLAS-33
❑ 91DunBluJC-21
❑ 91DunBluJP-219
Holtzman, Ken
❑ 67CokCapC-14
❑ 67CubProPS-6
❑ 67DexPre-96
❑ 67OPC-185
❑ 67Top-185
❑ 68Baz-4
❑ 68OPC-60
❑ 68Top-60
❑ 68Top-356A
❑ 68Top-356B
❑ 68Top-380
❑ 68TopVen-60
❑ 68TopVen-356
❑ 69CubJewT-7
❑ 69CubPho-5
❑ 69CubTealC-3
❑ 69MilBra-116
❑ 69Top-288
❑ 69TopTeaP-4
❑ 70MLBOffS-18
❑ 70OPC-505
❑ 70Top-505
❑ 71MilDud-47
❑ 71MLBOffS-33
❑ 71OPC-410
❑ 71Top-410
❑ 72MilBra-149
❑ 72Top-670
❑ 73OPC-60
❑ 73Top-60
❑ 74Kel-31
❑ 74OPC-180
❑ 74Top-180
❑ 74TopSta-224
❑ 75Hos-16
❑ 75HosTwi-16
❑ 75OPC-145
❑ 75Top-145
❑ 75TopMin-145
❑ 76OPC-115
❑ 76OriEngCL-2
❑ 76SSP-482
❑ 76Top-115
❑ 77Top-625
❑ 77YanBurK-8
❑ 78SSP270-6
❑ 78Top-387
❑ 78YanSSPD-6
❑ 79Top-522
❑ 80Top-298
❑ 84CubBriPC-4D
❑ 86A'sGreT-10
❑ 87A'sMot-11
❑ 89PacLegI-138
❑ 89SweBasG-129
❑ 91LinDri-21
❑ 91OriCro-201
❑ 91SweBasG-40
❑ 92ActPacA-57
❑ 92YanWIZ7-75
❑ 93TedWil-45
❑ 93UppDecAH-66
❑ 93UppDecS-3
Holub, Edward
❑ 88BoiHawP-1612
Holub, Sean
❑ 92HelBreF-1720
❑ 92HelBreSP-12
Holum, Brett
❑ 90AshTouP-2755
Holway, John
❑ 90LitSunW-20
Holyfield, Vince
❑ 85BenPhiC-11
❑ 87SpaPhiP-20
❑ 88ReaPhiP-883
❑ 89ReaPhiB-14
❑ 89ReaPhiP-661
❑ 89ReaPhiS-15
❑ 90EasLeaAP-EL23
❑ 90ReaPhiB-21
❑ 90ReaPhiP-1231
❑ 90ReaPhiS-14
Holzbauer, Joe
❑ 98DanBraQ-21
Holzemer, Mark
❑ 88BenBucL-22
❑ 89QuaCitAB-9
❑ 89QuaCitAGS-21
❑ 90MidAngGS-16
❑ 92MidAngF-4021
❑ 92PalSprAC-27
❑ 93Bow-117
❑ 93VanCanF-2591
❑ 94Don-583
❑ 94Top-765
❑ 94TopGol-765
❑ 94TopSpa-765
❑ 94VanCanF-1861
❑ 96AngMot-26
❑ 96LeaSigEA-80
❑ 97TacRai-17
Homan, John
❑ 94OgdRapF-3733
❑ 94OgdRapSP-9
Hommel, Brian
❑ 95HelBreTI-27
❑ 97StoPor-6
❑ 98El PasDG-15
Hommel, Ken
❑ 58RedEnq-18
Homstedt, Vic
❑ 78WatIndT-12
Honeycutt, Heath
❑ 99JustheSAC-14
❑ 99TeaBesR-36
❑ 99TeaBesRG-36
❑ 99TeaBesRS-36
Honeycutt, Rick
❑ 77ShrCapT-8
❑ 79Top-612
❑ 80Top-307
❑ 81Don-46
❑ 81OPC-33
❑ 81Top-33
❑ 81TopTra-772
❑ 82Don-494
❑ 82Fle-318
❑ 82Top-751
❑ 83AllGamPI-80
❑ 83Don-415
❑ 83Fle-568
❑ 83RanAffF-40
❑ 83Top-557
❑ 84AllGamPI-80
❑ 84DodPol-40
❑ 84Don-494
❑ 84Fle-101
❑ 84FleSti-66
❑ 84Nes792-37
❑ 84Nes792-137
❑ 84Nes792-222
❑ 84OPC-222
❑ 84Top-37
❑ 84Top-137
❑ 84Top-222
❑ 84TopSti-84
❑ 84TopSti-176
❑ 84TopTif-37
❑ 84TopTif-137
❑ 84TopTif-222
❑ 85DodCokP-13
❑ 85Don-215
❑ 85Fle-372
❑ 85Lea-156
❑ 85OPC-174
❑ 85Top-174
❑ 85TopSti-78
❑ 85TopTif-174
❑ 86DodCokP-13
❑ 86DodPol-40
❑ 86DodUniOP-8
❑ 86Don-372
❑ 86Fle-132
❑ 86Top-439
❑ 86TopTif-439
❑ 87ClaGam-93
❑ 87DodMot-16
❑ 87DodPho-6
❑ 87DodPol-20
❑ 87Don-402
❑ 87Fle-442
❑ 87FleExcS-28
❑ 87FleGlo-442
❑ 87OPC-167
❑ 87Top-753
❑ 87TopSti-71
❑ 87TopTif-753
❑ 88A'sMot-23
❑ 88Don-590
❑ 88DonBasB-211
❑ 88DonTeaBA-590
❑ 88Fle-281
❑ 88FleGlo-281
❑ 88Sco-87
❑ 88ScoGlo-87
❑ 88Top-641
❑ 88TopTif-641
❑ 89A'sMot-25
❑ 89Bow-187
❑ 89BowTif-187
❑ 89Don-328
❑ 89DonBasB-313
❑ 89Fle-11
❑ 89FleGlo-11
❑ 89Sco-416
❑ 89Top-328
❑ 89TopTif-328
❑ 89UppDec-278
❑ 89Woo-28
❑ 90A'sMot-13
❑ 90Bow-450
❑ 90BowTif-450
❑ 90DodTar-355
❑ 90Don-386
❑ 90Fle-11
❑ 90FleCan-11
❑ 90Lea-372
❑ 90OPC-582
❑ 90PubIntS-307
❑ 90Sco-317
❑ 90Top-582
❑ 90TopBig-42
❑ 90TopTif-582
❑ 90UppDec-151
❑ 91A'sMot-13
❑ 91A'sSFE-7
❑ 91Don-373
❑ 91Fle-11
❑ 91Lea-210
❑ 91OPC-67
❑ 91Sco-539
❑ 91StaClu-415
❑ 91Stu-105
❑ 91Top-67
❑ 91TopDesS-67
❑ 91TopMic-67
❑ 91TopTif-67
❑ 91Ult-249
❑ 91UppDec-379
❑ 92AthMot-13
❑ 92Don-269
❑ 92Fle-259
❑ 92OPC-202
❑ 92Sco-456
❑ 92StaClu-581
❑ 92Top-202
❑ 92TopGol-202
❑ 92TopGolW-202
❑ 92TopMic-202
❑ 92UppDec-684
❑ 93AthMot-8
❑ 93AthStaC-13
❑ 93Fle-665
❑ 93PacSpa-223
❑ 93RanKee-189
❑ 94Don-169
❑ 94Fle-265
❑ 94Pac-454
❑ 94RanAllP-11
❑ 94RanMagM-8
❑ 94RanMagM-15
❑ 94Sco-208
❑ 94ScoGolR-208
❑ 94StaCluT-242
❑ 94StaCluTFDI-242
❑ 95AthMot-17
❑ 95Pac-428
❑ 96CarPol-11
❑ 96LeaSigEA-81
❑ 97CarPol-10
❑ 97PacPriGotD-GD199
Honeywell, Brent
❑ 90AugPirP-2457
Honig, Donald
❑ 92MegRut-155
Honma, Mitsuru
❑ 96MauStiHWB-3
Honochick, Jim
❑ 55Bow-267
Hood, Dennis
❑ 86SumBraP-10
❑ 87DurBulP-27
❑ 88GreBraB-5
❑ 89GreBraB-1
❑ 89GreBraP-1169
❑ 89GreBraS-8
❑ 90CMC-291
❑ 90ProAAAF-415
❑ 90RicBraBC-18
❑ 90RicBraC-13
❑ 90RicBraP-270
❑ 90RicBraTI-12
❑ 91CalCanLD-59
❑ 91CalCanP-527
❑ 91LinDriAAA-59
Hood, Don
❑ 73BalOriP-24
❑ 74OPC-436
❑ 74Top-436
❑ 75CleIndP-14
❑ 75OPC-516
❑ 75Top-516
❑ 75TopMin-516
❑ 76IndTeal-5
❑ 76OPC-132
❑ 76SSP-508
❑ 76Top-132
❑ 77Top-296
❑ 78IndTeal-15
❑ 78Top-398
❑ 79Top-667
❑ 79YanPicA-18
❑ 80Top-89
❑ 81Fle-547A
❑ 81Fle-547B
❑ 81OmaRoyT-8
❑ 82OmaRoyT-5
❑ 83Don-390
❑ 83Fle-115
❑ 83RoyPos-13
❑ 83Top-443
❑ 84Fle-348
❑ 84Nes792-743
❑ 84Top-743
❑ 84TopTif-743
❑ 89PacSenL-108
❑ 91OriCro-202
❑ 92YanWIZ7-76
Hood, Mike
❑ 80WauTimT-16
Hood, Randall

❑ 91HelBreSP-23
❑ 91StoPorC-16
❑ 91StoPorP-3045
❑ 92SarWhiSCB-16
❑ 92SarWhiSF-220
❑ 93SarWhiSC-14
❑ 93SarWhiSF-1383
❑ 94BirBarC-13
❑ 94BirBarF-632

Hood, Scott
❑ 82DurBulT-3
❑ 83DurBulT-7
❑ 84DurBulT-17

Hood, Shawn
❑ 98HicCraUO-4

Hood, Wally
❑ 23Zee-9
❑ 24Zee-9
❑ 25Zee-5
❑ 26Zee-27
❑ 27Zee-14
❑ 28ExhPCL-11
❑ 28Zee-32
❑ 29Zee-159
❑ 30Zee-124
❑ 90DodTar-983

Hoog, James
❑ 88CapCodPPaLP-178

Hoog, Michael
❑ 90IdaFalBP-3244

Hook, Chris
❑ 90ChaWheB-2
❑ 90ChaWheP-2234
❑ 91ChaWheC-4
❑ 91ChaWheP-2881
❑ 92CedRapRC-10
❑ 92CedRapRF-1068
❑ 93ChaLooF-2359
❑ 94ExcFS7-175
❑ 94PhoFirF-1516
❑ 95FleUpd-194
❑ 95GiaMot-18
❑ 95SigRoo-27
❑ 95SigRooSig-27
❑ 96Don-462
❑ 96DonPreP-462
❑ 96LeaSigEA-82
❑ 97LasVegS1A-18
❑ 98ShrCapM-18
❑ 98ShrCapWS-18

Hook, Ed
❑ 90HagSunDGB-13

Hook, Jay
❑ 58RedEnq-19
❑ 59RedShiBS-7
❑ 59SeaPop-22
❑ 60Kah-16
❑ 60RedJayP-3
❑ 60Top-187
❑ 60TopVen-187
❑ 61Kah-20
❑ 61Top-162
❑ 62MetJayP-5
❑ 62Top-94
❑ 62TopStal-156
❑ 62TopVen-94
❑ 63MetJayP-5
❑ 63Top-469
❑ 64MetTeal-6
❑ 64Top-361
❑ 64TopVen-361
❑ 80Red196T-39
❑ 82MetGal62-23
❑ 91MetWIZ-188

Hook, Kevin
❑ 98VerExpO-32

Hook, Mike
❑ 88AshTouP-1073
❑ 89Ft.LauYS-9
❑ 90MidLeaASGS-35
❑ 90QuaCitAGS-6
❑ 91FreKeyC-4
❑ 91FreKeyP-2358
❑ 92HagSunS-260

Hooker, Buck (W.E.)
❑ 09T206-492

Hooker, Kevin
❑ 95MarPhiTI-9
❑ 96Exc-205

Hooker, Len
❑ 91PomBlaBPB-22

Hooks, Alex
❑ 35DiaMatCS3T1-77
❑ 36GouWidPPR-B13

Hooper, Bob (Robert)
❑ 49OlmStu-4
❑ 50A'sTeal-13
❑ 51A'sTeal-12
❑ 51Bow-33
❑ 52A'sTeal-11
❑ 52Bow-10
❑ 52Top-340
❑ 53Top-84
❑ 54Bow-4
❑ 55Bow-271
❑ 75TCM195Cl-14
❑ 79DiaGre-344
❑ 83TopRep5-340
❑ 91TopArc1-84

Hooper, Daren
❑ 98DelShoM-16

Hooper, Ed
❑ 20W516-27

Hooper, Harry
❑ 08AmeCarE91-78
❑ 09ColChiE-133A
❑ 09ColChiE-133B
❑ 10E12AmeCDCE125-19
❑ 10SweCapPP-4
❑ 11PinT-5-667
❑ 11SpoLifM-10
❑ 12ColRedB-133A
❑ 12ColRedB-133B
❑ 12ColTinT-133A
❑ 12ColTinT-133B
❑ 12T207-84
❑ 14CraJacE-35
❑ 14TexTomE-54
❑ 15CraJacE-35
❑ 15SpoNewM-83
❑ 16BF2FP-4
❑ 16SpoNewM-84
❑ 17ColE13-79
❑ 19W514-64
❑ 20GasAmeMBD-2
❑ 20NatCarE-45
❑ 21E121So1-44
❑ 21E121So8-37
❑ 21Nei-13
❑ 22AmeCarE122-29
❑ 22E120-21
❑ 22W572-44
❑ 22W573-63
❑ 22W575-58
❑ 23W501-47
❑ 23WilChoV-65
❑ 25Exh-75
❑ 27Zee-27
❑ 40PlaBal-226
❑ 76ShaPiz-122
❑ 76WhiSoxTAG-3
❑ 77GalGloG-172
❑ 78DexHaloFP-21
❑ 80PerHaloFP-122
❑ 80SSPHOF-122
❑ 80WhiSoxGT-11
❑ 81ConTSN-15
❑ 87ConSer2-35
❑ 89HOFStiB-52
❑ 91ConTSN-135
❑ 92ConTSN-470
❑ 93ConTSN-802
❑ 93CraJac-14

Hooper, Jeff
❑ 87BelMarTI-1
❑ 88WauTimGS-16
❑ 89WilBilP-639
❑ 89WilBilS-10
❑ 90WilBilB-10
❑ 90WilBilP-1060
❑ 90WilBilS-11

Hooper, Jim
❑ 98SpoIndG-15

Hooper, Mike
❑ 90HelBreSP-2
❑ 91BelBreCB-25
❑ 91BelBreP-2097
❑ 92SalSpuF-3750
❑ 92SarWhiSCB-26

Hooper, Troy
❑ 92SalSpuF-3751

Hoosiers, Indianapolis
❑ 76ISCHooHA-25

Hooten, David
❑ 97ForWayW-14
❑ 98ForMyeMTI-15

Hooten, Leon
❑ 75IntLeaASB-10
❑ 75PacCoaLAB-10
❑ 75TucTorC-17
❑ 75TucTorTI-6
❑ 76TucTorCa-12
❑ 76TusTorCr-16
❑ 77OPC-67
❑ 77Top-478

Hooton, Burt
❑ 72OPC-61
❑ 72Top-61
❑ 73OPC-367
❑ 73Top-367
❑ 74OPC-378
❑ 74Top-378
❑ 74TopDecE-18
❑ 74TopSta-14
❑ 75Hos-11A
❑ 75Hos-11B
❑ 75HosTwi-11
❑ 75OPC-176
❑ 75Top-176
❑ 75TopMin-176
❑ 76DodPos-6
❑ 76OPC-280
❑ 76SSP-67
❑ 76Top-280
❑ 77DodPho-3
❑ 77Top-484
❑ 78Kel-42
❑ 78SSP270-55
❑ 78Top-41
❑ 79DodBlu-5
❑ 79Hos-49
❑ 79OPC-370
❑ 79Top-694
❑ 80DodPol-46
❑ 80OPC-96
❑ 80Top-170
❑ 81AllGamPI-169
❑ 81Dod-6
❑ 81Dod-13
❑ 81DodPol-46
❑ 81Don-541
❑ 81Fle-113
❑ 81FleStiC-61
❑ 81LonBeaPT-11
❑ 81LonBeaPT-22
❑ 81OPC-53
❑ 81Top-565
❑ 81TopSti-180
❑ 81TopSupHT-46
❑ 82DodPol-46
❑ 82DodUniOV-7
❑ 82Don-32
❑ 82Fle-8
❑ 82FleSta-5
❑ 82Kel-15
❑ 82OPC-315
❑ 82SevSluC-14
❑ 82Top-311
❑ 82Top-315
❑ 82TopSti-53
❑ 82TopStiV-53
❑ 83DodPol-46
❑ 83DodPos-4
❑ 83Don-32
❑ 83Fle-208
❑ 83FleSta-82
❑ 83FleSti-115
❑ 83OPC-82
❑ 83Top-775
❑ 84CubBriPC-1D
❑ 84DodPol-46
❑ 84Don-459
❑ 84Fle-102
❑ 84Nes792-15
❑ 84OPC-15
❑ 84Top-15
❑ 84TopTif-15
❑ 85Don-104
❑ 85Fle-373
❑ 85FleUpd-56
❑ 85OPC-201
❑ 85RanPer-46
❑ 85Top-201
❑ 85TopMin-201
❑ 85TopTif-201
❑ 85TopTifT-56T
❑ 85TopTra-56T
❑ 86Don-300
❑ 86Fle-563
❑ 86OPC-36
❑ 86Top-454
❑ 86TopSti-242
❑ 86TopTat-18
❑ 86TopTif-454
❑ 87DodSmoA-13
❑ 88DodSmo-19
❑ 89DodSmoG-95
❑ 89PacLegI-219
❑ 89SalDodTI-2
❑ 90DodTar-356
❑ 90SanAntMGS-2
❑ 91SanAntMP-2992
❑ 92DodStaTA-20
❑ 92TexLon-24
❑ 93RanKee-190
❑ 93SanAntMF-3021

Hootselle, Jeff
❑ 98PieBolWM-17

Hoover, Charles
❑ 87OldJudN-247
❑ 87OldJudN-248

Hoover, John
❑ 85ChaO'sT-22
❑ 85Top-397
❑ 85TopTif-397
❑ 86ChaOriW-15
❑ 87ChaO'sW-20
❑ 88JacExpB-4
❑ 88JacExpP-989
❑ 89TulDriTI-11
❑ 90CMC-153
❑ 90OklCit8C-3
❑ 90OklCit8P-427
❑ 90ProAAAF-673
❑ 91TopDeb90-71
❑ 93RanKee-191

Hoover, Paul
❑ 97PriDevR-15
❑ 98ChaRivDG-15
❑ 98HudValR-10
❑ 99Bow-158
❑ 99BowChr-158
❑ 99BowChrG-158
❑ 99BowChrGR-158
❑ 99BowChrI-158
❑ 99BowChrIR-158
❑ 99BowChrR-158
❑ 99BowGol-158
❑ 99BowInt-158

Hoover, Sgt. (Dick)
❑ 81ColCliP-NNO

Hoover, William
❑ 87OldJudN-9

Hope, John
❑ 89HigSchPLS-18
❑ 91WelPirC-26
❑ 91WelPirP-3567
❑ 92SalBucC-15
❑ 92SalBucF-58
❑ 93CarMudF-2049
❑ 93CarMudTI-11
❑ 94BufBisF-1831
❑ 94FleMajLP-15
❑ 94Top-491
❑ 94TopGol-491
❑ 94TopSpa-491
❑ 97ColSprSTI-9

Hopke, Fred
❑ 60Lea-91

Hopke, William
❑ 08IndPos-12

Hopkins, Dave
❑ 83BurRanF-23
❑ 83BurRanT-5

Hopkins, Don
❑ 75SSP18-12
❑ 76TucTorCa-2
❑ 76TusTorCr-11
❑ 77SanJosMC-13

Hopkins, Gail
❑ 70OPC-483
❑ 70Top-483
❑ 70WhiSoxTI-5
❑ 71MLBOffS-416
❑ 71OPC-269
❑ 71oySigST-9
❑ 71Top-269
❑ 72oyTeal-7
❑ 72Top-728
❑ 73OPC-441
❑ 73Top-441
❑ 74OPC-652
❑ 74Top-652
❑ 90DodTar-357

Hopkins, Hoppy (Gordon)
❑ 93NegLeaRL2-18

Hopkins, Meredith
❑ 33WorCig(-50

Hopkins, Randy
❑ 75ShrCapT-5
❑ 76ShrCapT-22
❑ 77ColCliT-8
❑ 78ColCliT-11

Hopkins, Rick
❑ 86WinSpiP-9
❑ 87PitCubP-20

Hopp, Dean
❑ 91MarPhiC-17
❑ 91MarPhiP-3455
❑ 92BatCliCB-24
❑ 92BatCliF-3269
❑ 93ClePhiC-15
❑ 93ClePhiF-2685

Hopp, Johnny (John)
❑ 41CarW75-10
❑ 46SpoExcW-6-9
❑ 47Exh-100
❑ 49Bow-207
❑ 49EurSta-163
❑ 49Lea-139
❑ 50Bow-122
❑ 50PirTeal-8
❑ 51Bow-146
❑ 52Top-214
❑ 54Top-193
❑ 76GrePlaG-26
❑ 79DiaGre-160
❑ 82Bow195E-265
❑ 83Car194T-19
❑ 83TCMPla1944-24
❑ 83TopRep5-214
❑ 84TCMPla1-33
❑ 89PacLegI-139
❑ 90DodTar-358
❑ 94TopArc1-193
❑ 94TopArc1G-193

Hoppe, Denny
❑ 91Cla/Bes-341
❑ 91KenTwiC-10
❑ 91KenTwiP-2068
❑ 92Ft.MyeMCB-21
❑ 92Ft.MyeMF-2740

Hoppe, Jim
❑ 73TacTwiC-11

Hoppel, Monty
❑ 90MidAngGS-NNO

Hopper, Brad
❑ 88EugEmeB-9
❑ 90BasCitRS-13
❑ 91BasCitRC-6
❑ 91BasCitRP-1393

Hopper, Clay
❑ 52MotCoo-55
❑ 53MotCoo-51

Hopper, Jim
❑ 47CenFlo-10

Hopper, Lefty
❑ 90DodTar-984

Hopson, Craig
❑ 97JohCitCTI-18
❑ 98JohCCTI-16

Horan, Dave
❑ 89SalSpuCLC-128
❑ 89SalSpuP-1800

Horan, Joe
❑ 25Zee-6

Horgan, Joe
❑ 96BurIndB-7
❑ 97WatIndTI-12

Horincewich, Thomas
❑ 92EliTwiC-6
❑ 92EliTwiF-3685
❑ 93ForMyeMC-11
❑ 93ForMyeMF-2663

Horlen, Joel
❑ 62Top-479
❑ 63Top-332
❑ 63WhiSoxJP-6
❑ 63WhiSoxTS-11
❑ 64Top-584
❑ 64WhiSoxl-14
❑ 64WhiSoxTS-13
❑ 65OPC-7
❑ 65Top-7
❑ 65Top-480
❑ 66Top-560
❑ 66TopRubI-40
❑ 66WhiSoxTI-6
❑ 67CokCapWS-14
❑ 67DexPre-97
❑ 67OPC-107
❑ 67ProPizC-8
❑ 67Top-107
❑ 67Top-233
❑ 67TopVen-228
❑ 68AtlOilPBCC-22
❑ 68Baz-11
❑ 68Kah-B14
❑ 68OPC-8
❑ 68OPC-125
❑ 68Top-8
❑ 68Top-125
❑ 68Top-377
❑ 68TopActS-1A
❑ 68TopActS-8B
❑ 68TopActS-14A
❑ 68TopVen-8
❑ 68TopVen-125
❑ 69Kah-B9
❑ 69KelPin-7
❑ 69MilBra-117
❑ 69MLBOffS-30
❑ 69MLBPin-9
❑ 69Top-328
❑ 69TopSta-154
❑ 69TopSup-12
❑ 69TopTeaP-11
❑ 69WhiSoxTI-5
❑ 70Kel-23
❑ 70MLBOffS-185
❑ 70OPC-35
❑ 70Top-35
❑ 70TopPos-1
❑ 70TopSup-20
❑ 70WhiSoxTI-6
❑ 71OPC-345
❑ 71Top-345
❑ 71TopCoi-120
❑ 72MilBra-150
❑ 72Top-685
❑ 81TCM60I-318
❑ 88ColMetGS-28
❑ 89PacLegI-217
❑ 89St.LucMS-26
❑ 90St.LucMS-29
❑ 91LinDriAA-638
❑ 91WilBilLD-638
❑ 91WilBilP-311
❑ 92OmaRoyF-2979
❑ 93PhoFirF-1534
❑ 94PhoFirF-1537
❑ 96PhoFirB-3
❑ 97PhoFirTI-11
❑ 98FreGriG-12

Horn, Beryln
❑ 30Zee-32
❑ 33Zee-89

Horn, Doc (Herman)
❑ 93NegLeaRL2-19
❑ 96NegLeaBMKC-2

Horn, Jeff
❑ 92EliTwiC-10
❑ 92EliTwiF-3682
❑ 93ForWayWC-12
❑ 93ForWayWF-1971
❑ 94ForMyeMC-9
❑ 94ForMyeMF-1170
❑ 95ForMyeMTI-10
❑ 97NewBriRC-14
❑ 98SalLakBO-15

Horn, Keith
❑ 95WatIndTI-15

Horn, Larry
❑ 75WesPalBES-25

Horn, Sam
❑ 86NewBriRSP-13
❑ 87IntLeaAT-7
❑ 87PawRedSP-52
❑ 87PawRedST-14
❑ 87SpoRoo2-38
❑ 88BlaYNPRWL-58
❑ 88ClaBlu-204
❑ 88Don-498
❑ 88DonTeaBRS-498
❑ 88Fle-355
❑ 88FleGlo-355
❑ 88FleMin-8
❑ 88Lea-237
❑ 88OPC-377
❑ 88Sco-201
❑ 88ScoGlo-201
❑ 88ScoYouSI-3
❑ 88Spo-114
❑ 88StaHor-1
❑ 88StaHor-2
❑ 88StaHor-3
❑ 88StaHor-4
❑ 88StaHor-5
❑ 88StaHor-6
❑ 88StaHor-7
❑ 88StaHor-8
❑ 88StaHor-9
❑ 88StaHor-10
❑ 88StaHor-11
❑ 88StaLinRS-11

❑ 88Top-377
❑ 88TopBig-252
❑ 88TopSti-246
❑ 88TopTif-377
❑ 88ToyRoo-14
❑ 90BalOriP-10
❑ 90ClaYel-T28
❑ 90PublntS-458
❑ 90RocRedWGC-11
❑ 90TopBig-307
❑ 90TopTra-42T
❑ 90TopTraT-42T
❑ 90UppDec-796
❑ 91BalOriP-13
❑ 91Don-733
❑ 91Fle-477
❑ 91Lea-332
❑ 91OPC-598
❑ 91OriCro-203
❑ 91Sco-605
❑ 91StaClu-316
❑ 91Stu-5
❑ 91Top-598
❑ 91TopDesS-598
❑ 91TopMic-598
❑ 91TopTif-598
❑ 91UppDec-530
❑ 92BalOriP-14
❑ 92Bow-177
❑ 92Don-278
❑ 92Fle-10
❑ 92Lea-219
❑ 92LeaBlaG-219
❑ 92OPC-422
❑ 92Pin-221
❑ 92Sco-290
❑ 92StaClu-269
❑ 92Stu-125
❑ 92Top-422
❑ 92TopGol-422
❑ 92TopGolW-422
❑ 92TopMic-422
❑ 92Ult-6
❑ 92UppDec-338
❑ 93ChaKniF-549
❑ 93Don-617
❑ 93Fle-542
❑ 93Pin-128
❑ 93Top-109
❑ 93TopGol-109
❑ 93TopInaM-109
❑ 93TopInaR-109
❑ 93TopMic-109
❑ 94ColCliF-2959
❑ 94ColCliP-14
❑ 94Pin-170
❑ 94PinArtP-170
❑ 94PinMusC-170
❑ 94Sco-543
❑ 94ScoGolR-543
❑ 94StaCluT-187
❑ 94StaCluTFDI-187

Horn, Terry
❑ 91ClaDraP-46
❑ 91FroRowDP-24
❑ 91FroRowDPG-24
❑ 91FroRowDPS-24
❑ 91HigSchPLS-24
❑ 92StaCluD-87

Horn, Tim
❑ 89TenTecGE-11

Horn, Walt
❑ 79WatA'sT-3
❑ 82WesHavAT-29
❑ 86TacTigP-8
❑ 89TacTigP-1543
❑ 93TriAAAGF-51
❑ 95EdmTraTI-10

Hornacek, Jay
❑ 86BakDodP-14
❑ 87VerBeaDP-20
❑ 88BakDodCLC-245
❑ 89SouBenWSGS-29
❑ 90SarWhiSS-12

Hornbeck, Ryan
❑ 94EveGiaC-12
❑ 94EveGiaF-3647

Horne, Geoff
❑ 91MedHatBJSP-25

Horne, Jeffrey
❑ 82AleDukT-5
❑ 84GreHorT-5

Horne, Lena
❑ 91PomBlaBPB-17

Horne, Tyrone
❑ 90GatCitPP-3348
❑ 90GatCitPSP-12
❑ 91SumFlyC-23
❑ 91SumFlyP-2348
❑ 92MidLeaATI-21
❑ 92RocExpC-24
❑ 92RocExpF-2127
❑ 93ExcFS7-60
❑ 93FloStaLAF-50
❑ 93WesPalBEC-10
❑ 93WesPalBEF-1354
❑ 94ClaGolF-190
❑ 94HarSenF-2105
❑ 95Bes-32
❑ 95HarSenTI-19
❑ 98ArkTraH-4
❑ 98ArkTraM-13
❑ 99BasAmeTPLM-7

Horner, Bob
❑ 78BraCok-6
❑ 79BasPat-40
❑ 79Hos-98
❑ 79Top-586
❑ 79TopCom-18
❑ 80OPC-59
❑ 80Top-108
❑ 80TopSup-27
❑ 81AllGamPI-120
❑ 81BraPol-5
❑ 81Don-99
❑ 81Dra-17
❑ 81Fle-244
❑ 81FleStiC-99
❑ 81Kel-61
❑ 81MSAMinD-17
❑ 81OPC-355
❑ 81PerCreC-6
❑ 81Top-355
❑ 81TopScr-61
❑ 81TopSti-20
❑ 81TopSti-145
❑ 82BraBurKL-11
❑ 82BraPol-5
❑ 82Don-173
❑ 82Dra-18
❑ 82Fle-436
❑ 82FleSta-69
❑ 82Kel-13
❑ 82OnDecD-17
❑ 82OPC-145
❑ 82Top-145
❑ 82TopSti-18
❑ 83AllGamPI-122
❑ 83BraPol-5
❑ 83Don-58
❑ 83DonActA-46
❑ 83Dra-11
❑ 83Fle-138
❑ 83FleSta-83
❑ 83FleSti-84
❑ 83Kel-54
❑ 83OPC-50
❑ 83Top-50
❑ 83TopGloS-12
❑ 83TopSti-214
❑ 84AllGamPI-31
❑ 84BraPol-5
❑ 84Don-14
❑ 84Don-14A
❑ 84Don-535
❑ 84DonActAS-10
❑ 84Dra-14
❑ 84Fle-181
❑ 84FunFooP-122
❑ 84Nes792-760
❑ 84OCoandSI-44
❑ 84OPC-239
❑ 84raPho-13
❑ 84SevCoi-W10
❑ 84Top-760
❑ 84TopGloS-13
❑ 84TopRubD-10
❑ 84TopSti-30
❑ 84TopTif-760
❑ 85AllGamPI-120
❑ 85BraHos-11
❑ 85BraPol-11
❑ 85Don-77
❑ 85Fle-328
❑ 85KASDis-6
❑ 85KitCloD-6
❑ 85Lea-240
❑ 85OPC-262
❑ 85SubDis-34
❑ 85ThoMcAD-34
❑ 85Top-276
❑ 85Top-410
❑ 85TopRubD-10
❑ 85TopSti-24
❑ 85TopTif-276
❑ 85TopTif-410
❑ 86BraPol-11
❑ 86Don-188
❑ 86DonHig-22
❑ 86Fle-517
❑ 86Fle-635
❑ 86FleLeaL-19
❑ 86FleMin-104
❑ 86FleStiC-60
❑ 86Lea-121
❑ 86OPC-220
❑ 86SevCoi-S13
❑ 86Spo-66
❑ 86Spo-115
❑ 86Top-220
❑ 86TopGloS-44
❑ 86TopSti-34
❑ 86TopTat-3
❑ 86TopTif-220
❑ 87BoaandB-23
❑ 87ClaGam-38
❑ 87Don-389
❑ 87Fle-518
❑ 87Fle-632
❑ 87FleGlo-518
❑ 87FleGlo-632
❑ 87FleHotS-23
❑ 87FleLeaL-24
❑ 87FleStiC-61
❑ 87FleStiWBC-S7
❑ 87JapPlaB-1
❑ 87Lea-136
❑ 87OPC-116
❑ 87RedFolSB-21
❑ 87Spo-73
❑ 87Spo-196
❑ 87Top-660
❑ 87TopMinL-1
❑ 87TopSti-41
❑ 87TopTif-660
❑ 88CarSmo-14
❑ 88CarTeal-11
❑ 88FleMin-107
❑ 88FleUpd-120
❑ 88FleUpdG-120
❑ 88StaLinCa-8
❑ 88TopBig-245
❑ 88TopTra-50T
❑ 88TopTraT-50T
❑ 89Fle-452
❑ 89FleGlo-452
❑ 89OPC-255
❑ 89Sco-68
❑ 89Top-510
❑ 89TopSti-35
❑ 89TopTif-510
❑ 89UppDec-125
❑ 90HOFStiB-89
❑ 90PacLeg-54
❑ 92ActPacA-30
❑ 93TedWil-47
❑ 93UppDecAH-67
❑ 94TedWil-149
❑ 94UppDecAH-194
❑ 94UppDecAH1-194
❑ 97AriStaBG-11
❑ 99SpoIllGotG-85
❑ 99SpoIllGotGA-31

Horner, Jim
❑ 97WisTimR-13
❑ 98OrlRayM-9

Horner, William F.
❑ 87OldJudN-249
❑ 87OldJudN-250

Hornsby, Dave
❑ 84EveGiaC-11
❑ 85EveGialC-4
❑ 86CliGiaP-10

Hornsby, Mascot
❑ 96TulDriTI-12
❑ 97TulDriTI-28

Hornsby, Rogers
❑ 17ColE13-80
❑ 17HolBreD-47
❑ 19W514-56
❑ 20NatCarE-46
❑ 20W516-7
❑ 21E121So1-45
❑ 21E121So8-38
❑ 21Exh-78
❑ 21Nei-81
❑ 21OxfConE-9
❑ 22AmeCarE122-30
❑ 22E120-232
❑ 22W572-45
❑ 22W573-64
❑ 22W575-59
❑ 22WilPatV-21
❑ 23Lec-3
❑ 23W501-115
❑ 23W503-42
❑ 23W515-55
❑ 23WilChoV-66
❑ 24MrsShePP-3
❑ 25Exh-61
❑ 26Exh-60
❑ 26SpoComoA-21
❑ 26SpoNewSM-3
❑ 27Exh-19
❑ 27YorCarE-13
❑ 28Exh-2
❑ 28PorandAR-A16
❑ 28PorandAR-B16
❑ 28W502-13
❑ 28W512-9
❑ 28W56PlaC-H4
❑ 28Yue-13
❑ 29CubCerICP-3
❑ 29ExhFou-5
❑ 29PorandAR-42
❑ 30ChiEveAP-6
❑ 30CubTeal-9
❑ 30SchR33-7
❑ 30UncJac-17
❑ 31CubTeal-11
❑ 31Exh-5
❑ 31W517-38
❑ 32OrbPinUP-34
❑ 32USCar*-11
❑ 33Gou-119
❑ 33Gou-188
❑ 33RitCE-6H
❑ 33TatOrb-34
❑ 33WorCig-56
❑ 34BabRutG-35
❑ 34BatR31-35
❑ 34ButPreR-34
❑ 34DiaStaR-44
❑ 34GouCanV-1
❑ 35AlDemDCR3-50
❑ 36Halof FP-12
❑ 36NatChiFPR-45
❑ 36R31PasP-14
❑ 36R31PasP-35
❑ 36R31Pre-L7
❑ 37OPCBatUV-140
❑ 39PC7AlbHoF-27
❑ 46SpoExcW-6-4
❑ 47PM1StaP1-89
❑ 48ExhHoF-15
❑ 50CalHOFW-39
❑ 51R42SmaS-48
❑ 53ArtHaloFP-45
❑ 58JayPubAG-4
❑ 61Fle-43
❑ 61GolPre-7
❑ 61Top-404
❑ 63BasMagM-37
❑ 63BazA-32
❑ 63GadFunC-22
❑ 63HalofFB-11
❑ 67TopVen-142
❑ 68SpoMemAG-13
❑ 69Baz-2
❑ 69Baz-12
❑ 71FleWorS-24
❑ 72FleFamF-2
❑ 72KelATG-2
❑ 72LauGreF-15
❑ 72TCMthe3-109
❑ 73HalofFPP-9
❑ 74MetOriEB-5
❑ 76JerJonPC-5
❑ 76OPC-342
❑ 76RowExh-2
❑ 76ShaPiz-27
❑ 76Top-342
❑ 77BobParHoF-26
❑ 77CubAllT-8
❑ 77GalGloG-92
❑ 77ShaPiz-14
❑ 79Pew-5
❑ 79Top-414
❑ 80CubGreT-11
❑ 80Lau300-17
❑ 80LauFamF-39
❑ 80PacLeg-20
❑ 80PerHaloFP-27
❑ 80SSPHOF-27
❑ 81ConTSN-19
❑ 81DiaStaCD-119
❑ 82DavHaloFB-12
❑ 82DiaCla-7
❑ 82MetGal62-29
❑ 82TCMGreH-15
❑ 82TCMGreS-21
❑ 83CarGreT-2
❑ 84CubBriPC-10H
❑ 84CubUno-3
❑ 84DonCha-20
❑ 84GalHaloFRL-27
❑ 85TCMPhoC-23
❑ 85Woo-18
❑ 86ConSer1-44
❑ 87HygAllG-25
❑ 87NesDreT-2
❑ 88ConSer3-14
❑ 89PacLegI-148
❑ 89SweBasG-20
❑ 90BasWit-97
❑ 90HOFStiB-27
❑ 90SweBasG-51
❑ 91ConTSN-1
❑ 91ConTSN-251
❑ 91SweBasG-137
❑ 91TopArc1-289
❑ 91USGamSBL-7C
❑ 91USGamSBL-7D
❑ 91USGamSBL-7H
❑ 91USGamSBL-7S
❑ 92BazQua5A-7
❑ 92CarMcD-4
❑ 92ConTSN-527
❑ 92ConTSN-622
❑ 92ConTSNCI-20
❑ 92CubOldS-13
❑ 92St.VinHHS-6
❑ 93ActPacA-95
❑ 93ActPacA2-29G
❑ 93ConMasB-8
❑ 93ConTSN-766
❑ 93ConTSN-842
❑ 93LegFoi-4
❑ 93SpeHOFI-4
❑ 93TedWil-91
❑ 93TedWil-124
❑ 93UppDecAH-68
❑ 93UppDecAH-132
❑ 93UppDecAH-139
❑ 93UppDecAH-160
❑ 93UppDecAH-162
❑ 94ConTSN-1253
❑ 94ConTSNB-1253
❑ 94UppDecAH-108
❑ 94UppDecAH-140
❑ 94UppDecAH-162
❑ 94UppDecAH1-108
❑ 94UppDecAH1-140
❑ 94UppDecAH1-162
❑ 94UppDecTAE-35
❑ 99UppDecCL-9
❑ 99UppDecCLA-1920
❑ 99UppDecCLCC-9

Hornung, Michael
❑ 87BucN28-7
❑ 87OldJudN-251
❑ 88WG1CarG-3

Horowitz, Ed
❑ 88CapCodPPaLP-140
❑ 89EriOriS-9
❑ 90FreKeyTI-21
❑ 91CarLeaAP-CAR8
❑ 91FreKeyC-13
❑ 91FreKeyP-2367
❑ 92HagSunS-261

Horowitz, Robert
❑ 90QuaCitAGS-4

Horsford, Jim
❑ 66TolMudHTI-13

Horsley, Clinton
❑ 88SavCarP-343

Horsman, Brent
❑ 97IdaFalBTI-5

Horsman, Vince
❑ 87MyrBeaBJP-1440
❑ 88DunBluJS-10
❑ 89DunBluJS-8
❑ 90DunBluJS-11
❑ 91KnoBluJP-1763
❑ 92AthMot-23
❑ 92DonRoo-53
❑ 92FleUpd-49
❑ 92Lea-487
❑ 92LeaBlaG-487
❑ 92Pin-524
❑ 92ProFS7-164
❑ 92ScoRoo-106T
❑ 92StaClu-637
❑ 92StaCluECN-637
❑ 92TopDeb91-81
❑ 92TopTra-53T
❑ 92TopTraG-53T
❑ 93Don-347
❑ 93Fle-295
❑ 93Sco-406
❑ 93Sel-316
❑ 93StaClu-256
❑ 93StaCluFDI-256
❑ 93StaCluMOP-256
❑ 93Top-263
❑ 93TopGol-263
❑ 93TopInaM-263
❑ 93TopInaR-263
❑ 93TopMic-263
❑ 93Ult-259
❑ 94A'sMot-24
❑ 94Fle-266
❑ 94Top-436
❑ 94TopGol-436
❑ 94TopSpa-436
❑ 96SyrChiTI-14

Horstman, Oscar
❑ 16Zee-8

Horstmann, Gary
❑ 75WesPalBES-22

Horta, Nedar
❑ 86AshTouP-13
❑ 87AshTouP-15
❑ 88AshTouP-1057
❑ 88AubAstP-1965

Horton, Aaron
❑ 96HudValRB-20

Horton, David
❑ 86EriCarP-15
❑ 87St.PetCP-12

Horton, Eric
❑ 94MedHatBJF-3677
❑ 94MedHatBJSP-17
❑ 95StCatSTI-9
❑ 96HagSunB-9

Horton, Ricky
❑ 82ArkTraT-3
❑ 82LouRedE-11
❑ 83LouRedR-23
❑ 84Car-12
❑ 84Car5x7-12
❑ 84FleUpd-53
❑ 84TopTra-52T
❑ 84TopTraT-52T
❑ 85CarTeal-15
❑ 85Don-83
❑ 85Fle-227
❑ 85Lea-253
❑ 85OPC-321
❑ 85Top-321
❑ 85TopTif-321
❑ 86CarSchM-9
❑ 86CarTeal-19
❑ 86Don-138
❑ 86Fle-38
❑ 86Top-783
❑ 86TopTif-783
❑ 87CarSmo-5
❑ 87CarTeal-13
❑ 87Don-234
❑ 87Fle-297
❑ 87FleGlo-297
❑ 87OPC-238
❑ 87Top-542
❑ 87TopTif-542
❑ 88Don-430
❑ 88Fle-36
❑ 88FleGlo-36
❑ 88FleUpd-17
❑ 88FleUpdG-17
❑ 88OPC-34
❑ 88Sco-412
❑ 88ScoGlo-412
❑ 88ScoRoo-24T
❑ 88ScoRooG-24T
❑ 88StaLinCa-9
❑ 88Top-34
❑ 88TopSti-48
❑ 88TopTif-34
❑ 88TopTra-51T
❑ 88TopTraT-51T
❑ 88WhiSoxC-11
❑ 88WhiSoxK-3
❑ 89Bow-338
❑ 89BowTif-338
❑ 89DodMot-20

❑ 89DodPol-18
❑ 89Don-582
❑ 89Sco-145
❑ 89Top-232
❑ 89TopTif-232
❑ 89UppDec-629
❑ 90CarSmo-9
❑ 90DodTar-985
❑ 90Don-666
❑ 90OPC-133
❑ 90PublntS-10
❑ 90Top-133
❑ 90TopTif-133
❑ 90TopTVCa-15
❑ 91ColSprSSLD-83
❑ 91LinDriAAA-83
❑ 92KinIndC-27
❑ 92KinIndF-2492

Horton, Tony
❑ 66RedSoxTI-5
❑ 68Kah-B15
❑ 69Kah-B10
❑ 69MilBra-118
❑ 69MLBOffS-41
❑ 69MLBPin-10
❑ 69NabTeaF-10
❑ 70DayDaiNM-21
❑ 70MLBOffS-200
❑ 71Kel-69
❑ 71MLBOffS-376
❑ 72MilBra-151
❑ 78TCM60I-128
❑ 81RedSoxBG2S-85

Horton, Vince
❑ 25Zee-66

Horton, Willie
❑ 64Top-512
❑ 65OPC-206
❑ 65Top-206
❑ 66Baz-2
❑ 66OPC-20
❑ 66TigVolC-5
❑ 66Top-20
❑ 66Top-218
❑ 66Top-220
❑ 66TopRubI-41
❑ 66TopVen-20
❑ 66TopVen-218
❑ 66TopVen-220
❑ 67CokCapA-32
❑ 67CokCapAAm-23
❑ 67CokCapTi-18
❑ 67DexPre-98
❑ 67TigDexP-3
❑ 67Top-465
❑ 67TopVen-195
❑ 68Baz-8
❑ 68CokCapT-18
❑ 68Kah-B16
❑ 68TigDetFPB-7
❑ 68Top-360
❑ 68TopActS-5C
❑ 68TopVen-360
❑ 69CitMetC-6
❑ 69MilBra-119
❑ 69MLBOffS-48
❑ 69MLBPin-11
❑ 69OPC-5
❑ 69OPC-163
❑ 69OPC-169
❑ 69OPC-180
❑ 69OPCDec-11
❑ 69TigTeal-3
❑ 69TigTealC-6
❑ 69Top-5
❑ 69Top-163
❑ 69Top-169
❑ 69Top-180
❑ 69Top-429
❑ 69TopDec-9
❑ 69TopDecI-17
❑ 69TopFou-15
❑ 69TopFou-16
❑ 69TopFou-23
❑ 69TopSta-173
❑ 69TopSup-16
❑ 69TopTeaP-1
❑ 69TraSta-2
❑ 70DayDaiNM-92
❑ 70Kel-69
❑ 70MLBOffS-207
❑ 70OPC-520
❑ 70Top-520
❑ 71AllBasA-8
❑ 71MLBOffS-394
❑ 71MLBOffS-560
❑ 71OPC-120
❑ 71Top-120
❑ 71TopCoi-130
❑ 72MilBra-152
❑ 72OPC-494
❑ 72Top-494
❑ 72Top-750
❑ 73LinPor-71
❑ 73OPC-433
❑ 73TigJew-9
❑ 73Top-433
❑ 74Kel-23
❑ 74OPC-115
❑ 74Top-115
❑ 74TopDecE-72
❑ 74TopSta-176
❑ 75DetTigP-12
❑ 75Hos-36
❑ 75HosTwi-36
❑ 75OPC-66
❑ 75Top-66
❑ 75TopMin-66
❑ 76BlaDis-19
❑ 76BucDis-19
❑ 76CarDis-19
❑ 76CraDis-19
❑ 76DailsID-19
❑ 76DetTigP-11
❑ 76Hos-26
❑ 76HosTwi-26
❑ 76IsaDis-19
❑ 76OPC-320
❑ 76OrbDis-19
❑ 76RedBarD-19
❑ 76SafDis-19
❑ 76SSP-360
❑ 76Top-320
❑ 76TowCluD-19
❑ 77BurCheD-97
❑ 77PepGloD-31
❑ 77Top-660
❑ 78IndTeal-16
❑ 78Top-290
❑ 79OPC-252
❑ 79Top-239
❑ 80MarPos-13
❑ 80OPC-277
❑ 80Top-532
❑ 81PorBeaT-12
❑ 81TigDetN-78
❑ 82PorBeaT-14
❑ 86TigSpoD-19
❑ 88TigDom-8
❑ 90PacLeg-83
❑ 91LinDri-29
❑ 91SweBasG-41
❑ 91UppDecS-22
❑ 92ActPacA-73
❑ 93RanKee-192
❑ 93UppDecS-15
❑ 93UppDecS-26

Hoscheidt, John
❑ 77DayBealT-9

Hoscheit, Vern
❑ 67BalOriP-49
❑ 73OPC-179
❑ 73Top-179A
❑ 73Top-179B
❑ 85MetTCM-2
❑ 86MetTCM-39
❑ 87MetColP-35
❑ 88MetColP-26
❑ 89MetColP-33
❑ 90MetColP-33

Hosey, Dwayne
❑ 88SouBenWSGS-7
❑ 89MadMusS-11
❑ 90CalLeaACLC-42
❑ 90ModA'sC-15
❑ 90ModA'sCLC-169
❑ 90ModA'sP-2225
❑ 91HunStaC-12
❑ 91HunStaLD-286
❑ 91HunStaP-1809
❑ 91LinDriAA-286
❑ 92SkyAA F-283
❑ 92WicWraF-3667
❑ 92WicWraS-635
❑ 93WicWraF-2990
❑ 94OmaRoyF-1235
❑ 94SigRooDP-93
❑ 94SigRooDPS-93
❑ 94TriAAF-AAA10
❑ 95Bow-221
❑ 95BowGolF-221
❑ 95OmaRoyTI-13
❑ 95Sel-209
❑ 95SelArtP-209
❑ 95StaClu-493
❑ 95StaCluMOP-493
❑ 95StaCluSTWS-493
❑ 96ColCho-473
❑ 96ColChoGS-473
❑ 96ColChoSS-473
❑ 96Don-344
❑ 96DonPreP-344
❑ 96EmoXL-15
❑ 96Fla-20
❑ 96Fle-29
❑ 96FleRedS-8
❑ 96FleTif-29
❑ 96Lea-32
❑ 96LeaPrePB-32
❑ 96LeaPrePG-32
❑ 96LeaPrePS-32
❑ 96LeaSigA-107
❑ 96LeaSigAG-107
❑ 96LeaSigAS-107
❑ 96Pac-254
❑ 96PawRedSDD-12
❑ 96Pin-290
❑ 96PinFoil-290
❑ 96Ult-315
❑ 96UltGolM-315
❑ 97PacPriGotD-GD22

Hosey, Steve
❑ 89EveGiaS-15
❑ 89FreStaBS-11
❑ 89Sta-193
❑ 90Bes-15
❑ 90Bow-242
❑ 90BowTif-242
❑ 90CMC-856
❑ 90SanJosGB-1
❑ 90SanJosGCLC-28
❑ 90SanJosGP-2025
❑ 90SanJosGS-12
❑ 90SanJosGS-26
❑ 90Sco-666
❑ 91Bow-629
❑ 91Cla/Bes-233
❑ 91LinDriAA-307
❑ 91ShrCapLD-307
❑ 91ShrCapP-1835
❑ 92Bow-544
❑ 92DonRoo-54
❑ 92FleUpd-127
❑ 92LeaGolR-BC23
❑ 92OPC-618
❑ 92PhoFirF-2832
❑ 92PhoFirS-383
❑ 92ProFS7-346
❑ 92SkyAAAF-176
❑ 92Top-618
❑ 92TopGol-618
❑ 92TopGolW-618
❑ 92TopMic-618
❑ 92UppDec-62
❑ 93Bow-360
❑ 93Bow-492
❑ 93ClaFS7-52
❑ 93Don-704
❑ 93FleMajLP-A11
❑ 93GiaStaC-15
❑ 93Lea-48
❑ 93PhoFirF-1527
❑ 93Pin-253
❑ 93PinRooTP-8
❑ 93PinTea2-21
❑ 93Sco-303
❑ 93Sel-346
❑ 93StaClu-333
❑ 93StaCluFDI-333
❑ 93StaCluMOP-333
❑ 93Top-653
❑ 93TopGol-653
❑ 93TopInaM-653
❑ 93TopInaR-653
❑ 93TopMic-653
❑ 93TriPla-54
❑ 93Ult-132
❑ 93UppDec-15
❑ 93UppDecGold-15
❑ 94ColC-613
❑ 94ColChoGS-613
❑ 94Don-265
❑ 94GiaUSPC-3C
❑ 94Spo-155
❑ 94StaCluT-7
❑ 94StaCluTFDI-7
❑ 94Top-547
❑ 94TopGol-547
❑ 94TopSpa-547
❑ 94VanCanF-1874
❑ 95MidAngOHP-19
❑ 95MidAngTI-17

Hoshino, Senichi
❑ 79TCMJapPB-72

Hoskins, Dave
❑ 54Top-81
❑ 55Top-133
❑ 55TopDouH-77
❑ 75TCM195Cl-15
❑ 86NegLeaF-81
❑ 94TopArc1-81
❑ 94TopArc1G-81

Hoskinson, Keith
❑ 86LakTigP-7

Hosley, Tim
❑ 72OPC-257
❑ 72Top-257
❑ 76OPC-482
❑ 76SSP-313
❑ 76Top-482
❑ 77SanJosMC-10
❑ 78Top-261
❑ 79OgdA'sT-2
❑ 80OgdA'sT-1
❑ 82TacTigT-12
❑ 89PacSenL-93

Hosp, Franz
❑ 09ObaT21-349
❑ 11PacCoaBD-30
❑ 11Zee-116
❑ 12HomRunKE-86
❑ 12ObaPreT-98
❑ 12Zee-148
❑ 13Zee-138
❑ 14Zee-136
❑ 15Zee-131
❑ 18Zee-100
❑ 19Zee-138

Hostetler, Brian
❑ 92HelBreF-1718
❑ 92HelBreSP-15
❑ 93BelBreFI-1713
❑ 93ExcFS7-187
❑ 93StoPorC-16
❑ 93StoPorF-747
❑ 94StoPorC-11
❑ 94StoPorF-1697

Hostetler, Dave
❑ 79MemChiT-9
❑ 83Don-89
❑ 83Fle-569
❑ 83OPC-339
❑ 83RanAffF-12
❑ 83Top-584
❑ 83TopSti-312
❑ 84Don-159
❑ 84Fle-418
❑ 84Nes792-62
❑ 84OPC-62
❑ 84Top-62
❑ 84TopTif-62
❑ 85IndIndTI-17
❑ 85IowCubT-23
❑ 87JapPlaB-39
❑ 93RanKee-193

Hostetler, Jeff
❑ 91FroRowDP-37
❑ 91FroRowDPG-37
❑ 91FroRowDPS-37
❑ 91JamExpC-20
❑ 91JamExpP-3539
❑ 92StaCluD-88
❑ 93BurBeeC-11
❑ 93BurBeeF-152
❑ 94HigDesMC-16
❑ 94HigDesMF-2784

Hostetler, Marcus
❑ 94MacBraC-8
❑ 94MacBraF-2197
❑ 95BreBtaTI-51
❑ 95Exc-153
❑ 96BowBayB-17

Hostetler, Mike
❑ 90IBAWorA-44
❑ 92DurBulC-17
❑ 92DurBulF-1094
❑ 92DurBulTI-24
❑ 92UppDecML-206
❑ 93Bow-30
❑ 93ClaGolF-89
❑ 93RicBraBB-7
❑ 93RicBraF-181
❑ 93RicBraRC-13
❑ 93RicBraRC-11
❑ 94ExcFS7-155
❑ 94RicBraF-2842
❑ 95BreBtaTI-33
❑ 96RicBraB-17
❑ 96RicBraRC-11
❑ 96RicBraUB-13

Hostetler, Tom
❑ 87EveGiaC-16
❑ 88CliGiaP-697
❑ 88MidLeaAGS-7
❑ 89SanJosGB-19
❑ 89SanJosGCLC-213
❑ 89SanJosGP-444
❑ 89SanJosGS-15
❑ 90ProAaA-66
❑ 90ShrCapP-1439
❑ 90ShrCapS-12
❑ 91LinDriAA-308
❑ 91ShrCapLD-308
❑ 91ShrCapP-1816

Hostetter, Geoff
❑ 98CedRapKTI-13

Hotaling, Pete
❑ 87OldJudN-252
❑ 88GandBCGCE-20

Hotchkiss, John
❑ 83TacTigT-12
❑ 84TacTigC-93
❑ 86MidAngP-11
❑ 87MidAngP-11

Hotchkiss, Thomas
❑ 90MedHatBJB-23
❑ 92DunBluJC-23
❑ 92DunBluJF-1995
❑ 93DunBluJC-11
❑ 93DunBluJF-1791
❑ 93DunBluJFFN-12

Hotz, Todd
❑ 90UtiBluSP-19

Houck, Byron Simon
❑ 14FatPlaT-17
❑ 16Zee-55
❑ 17Zee-50
❑ 19Zee-139
❑ 22Zee-154

Houck, Jeff
❑ 90ArkRaz-16

Hough, Charlie
❑ 72OPC-198
❑ 72Top-198
❑ 73OPC-610
❑ 73Top-610
❑ 74OPC-408
❑ 74Top-408
❑ 75OPC-71
❑ 75Top-71
❑ 75TopMin-71
❑ 76DodPos-7
❑ 76OPC-174
❑ 76SSP-68
❑ 76Top-174
❑ 77DodPho-4
❑ 77Kel-47
❑ 77Top-298
❑ 78SSP270-81
❑ 78Top-22
❑ 79DodBlu-6
❑ 79OPC-266
❑ 79Top-508
❑ 80DodPol-49
❑ 80Top-644
❑ 81Top-371
❑ 82Don-447
❑ 82Fle-319
❑ 82Top-718
❑ 83Don-69
❑ 83Fle-570
❑ 83FleSti-163
❑ 83OPC-343
❑ 83RanAffF-49
❑ 83Top-412
❑ 83Top-479
❑ 83TopSti-125
❑ 84Don-638
❑ 84Fle-419
❑ 84FunFooP-114
❑ 84Nes792-118
❑ 84OPC-118
❑ 84RanJarP-49
❑ 84Top-118
❑ 84TopSti-356
❑ 84TopTif-118
❑ 85Don-422
❑ 85Fle-558
❑ 85Lea-108
❑ 85OPC-276
❑ 85RanPer-49
❑ 85SpoIndGC-8
❑ 85Top-571
❑ 85TopSti-345
❑ 85TopTif-571
❑ 86Don-342
❑ 86Fle-564
❑ 86FleStiC-61
❑ 86Lea-152
❑ 86OPC-275
❑ 86RanPer-49
❑ 86Top-275
❑ 86Top-666
❑ 86TopMinL-33
❑ 86TopSti-241
❑ 86TopTat-9
❑ 86TopTif-275
❑ 86TopTif-666
❑ 87Don-7
❑ 87Don-470
❑ 87DonAll-49
❑ 87DonOpeD-178
❑ 87DonSupD-7
❑ 87Fle-127
❑ 87Fle-641
❑ 87FleBasA-21
❑ 87FleGlo-127
❑ 87FleGlo-641
❑ 87FleMin-56
❑ 87FleStiC-62
❑ 87Lea-7
❑ 87OPC-70
❑ 87RanMot-3
❑ 87RanSmo-1
❑ 87RedFolSB-26
❑ 87SmoAmeL-12
❑ 87SpoTeaP-1
❑ 87Top-70
❑ 87TopSti-240
❑ 87TopTif-70
❑ 88Don-99
❑ 88DonBasB-256
❑ 88Fle-469
❑ 88FleAwaW-20
❑ 88FleBasA-16
❑ 88FleBasM-19
❑ 88FleGlo-469
❑ 88FleMin-55
❑ 88FleStiC-64
❑ 88GreBasS-42
❑ 88Lea-89
❑ 88OPC-121
❑ 88PanSti-197
❑ 88RanMot-3
❑ 88RanSmo-13
❑ 88Sco-140
❑ 88ScoGlo-140
❑ 88Spo-87
❑ 88StaLinRa-6
❑ 88Top-680
❑ 88TopBig-47
❑ 88TopCoi-15
❑ 88TopMinL-36
❑ 88TopRevLL-32
❑ 88TopSti-236
❑ 88TopTif-680
❑ 88TopUKM-36
❑ 88TopUKMT-36
❑ 89Bow-224
❑ 89BowTif-224
❑ 89Don-165
❑ 89Fle-522
❑ 89FleGlo-522
❑ 89OPC-345
❑ 89PanSti-446
❑ 89RanMot-4
❑ 89RanSmo-14
❑ 89RedFolSB-60
❑ 89Sco-295
❑ 89Spo-92
❑ 89Top-345
❑ 89TopBasT-160
❑ 89TopSti-245
❑ 89TopTif-345
❑ 89TopUKM-40
❑ 89TVSpoM-119
❑ 89UppDec-437
❑ 90DodTar-359
❑ 90Don-411
❑ 90Fle-300
❑ 90FleCan-300
❑ 90KayB-17
❑ 90Lea-390
❑ 90OPC-735
❑ 90PublntS-412
❑ 90RanMot-5

- ❑ 90Sco-202
- ❑ 90Top-735
- ❑ 90TopBig-242
- ❑ 90TopTif-735
- ❑ 90UppDec-314
- ❑ 91Bow-355
- ❑ 91Don-146
- ❑ 91Fle-288
- ❑ 91FleUpd-12
- ❑ 91Lea-472
- ❑ 91OPC-495
- ❑ 91Sco-141
- ❑ 91StaClu-579
- ❑ 91Stu-35
- ❑ 91Top-495
- ❑ 91TopDesS-495
- ❑ 91TopMic-495
- ❑ 91TopTif-495
- ❑ 91TopTra-56T
- ❑ 91TopTraT-56T
- ❑ 91UppDec-313
- ❑ 91UppDec-792
- ❑ 91WhiSoxK-49
- ❑ 92Bow-153
- ❑ 92Don-69
- ❑ 92Fle-84
- ❑ 92Lea-39
- ❑ 92LeaBlaG-39
- ❑ 92OPC-191
- ❑ 92Pin-422
- ❑ 92Sco-302
- ❑ 92StaClu-894
- ❑ 92StaCluNC-894
- ❑ 92Top-191
- ❑ 92TopGol-191
- ❑ 92TopGolW-191
- ❑ 92TopMic-191
- ❑ 92Ult-37
- ❑ 92UppDec-418
- ❑ 92WhiSoxK-49
- ❑ 93Bow-530
- ❑ 93Fin-169
- ❑ 93FinRef-169
- ❑ 93Fle-584
- ❑ 93FleFinE-63
- ❑ 93Lea-384
- ❑ 93MarlStaClu-6
- ❑ 93MarPub-13
- ❑ 93MarUppD-518
- ❑ 93MarUSPC-8H
- ❑ 93MarUSPC-9S
- ❑ 93OPC-41
- ❑ 93PacSpa-465
- ❑ 93Pin-523
- ❑ 93PinExpOD-1
- ❑ 93RanKee-194
- ❑ 93Sco-223
- ❑ 93SelRoo-117T
- ❑ 93StaClu-610
- ❑ 93StaCluFDI-610
- ❑ 93StaClul-C2
- ❑ 93StaCluMOP-610
- ❑ 93StaCluMOP-MC2
- ❑ 93Stu-205
- ❑ 93Top-520
- ❑ 93TopGol-520
- ❑ 93TopInaM-520
- ❑ 93TopInaR-520
- ❑ 93TopMic-520
- ❑ 93Ult-379
- ❑ 93UppDec-207
- ❑ 93UppDec-518
- ❑ 93UppDecGold-207
- ❑ 93UppDecGold-518
- ❑ 94Bow-618
- ❑ 94ColC-359
- ❑ 94ColChoGS-359
- ❑ 94ColChoSS-359
- ❑ 94Don-269
- ❑ 94Fin-180
- ❑ 94FinRef-180
- ❑ 94Fla-382
- ❑ 94Fle-469
- ❑ 94FleExtB-263
- ❑ 94Lea-188
- ❑ 94MarTeal-7
- ❑ 94OPC-62
- ❑ 94Pac-244
- ❑ 94Pin-288
- ❑ 94PinArtP-288
- ❑ 94PinMusC-288
- ❑ 94ProMag-52
- ❑ 94RanAllP-14
- ❑ 94Sco-452
- ❑ 94ScoGolR-452
- ❑ 94StaClu-245
- ❑ 94StaCluFDI-245
- ❑ 94StaCluGR-245
- ❑ 94StaCluMOP-245
- ❑ 94StaCluT-69
- ❑ 94StaCluTFDI-69
- ❑ 94Top-625
- ❑ 94TopGol-625
- ❑ 94TopSpa-625
- ❑ 94Ult-494
- ❑ 94UppDec-449
- ❑ 94UppDecED-449
- ❑ 95ColCho-311
- ❑ 95ColChoGS-311
- ❑ 95ColChoSS-311
- ❑ 95UppDec-117
- ❑ 95UppDecED-117
- ❑ 95UppDecEDG-117
- ❑ 96SanBerSB-2
- ❑ 97SanBerS-2
- ❑ 98DodMot-28
- ❑ 98SanBerS-13

Hough, Stan

- ❑ 79JacMetT-22A
- ❑ 79TidTidT-16
- ❑ 83DayBeaAT-2
- ❑ 85TucTorC-62
- ❑ 86OscAstP-12
- ❑ 88TulDriTI-11
- ❑ 89OklCit8C-24
- ❑ 89OklCit8P-1521
- ❑ 90CMC-173
- ❑ 90OklCit8C-23
- ❑ 90OklCit8P-450
- ❑ 91LinDriAAA-325
- ❑ 91OklCit8LD-325
- ❑ 91OklCit8P-195

Houghs, Hughes

- ❑ 23Zee-87

Houk, Ralph

- ❑ 47YanTeaT-13
- ❑ 52Top-200
- ❑ 53Dor-106
- ❑ 60Top-465
- ❑ 61Top-133
- ❑ 61Yan61RL-26
- ❑ 61YanJayP-5
- ❑ 62Top-88
- ❑ 62TopVen-88
- ❑ 62YanJayP-7
- ❑ 63Top-382
- ❑ 63YanJayP-4
- ❑ 67Top-468
- ❑ 68OPC-47
- ❑ 68Top-47
- ❑ 68TopVen-47
- ❑ 69Top-447A
- ❑ 69Top-447B
- ❑ 69YanMal-4
- ❑ 70OPC-273
- ❑ 70Top-273
- ❑ 70YanPhoS-15
- ❑ 71OPC-146
- ❑ 71Top-146
- ❑ 71YanCliDP-7
- ❑ 72Top-533
- ❑ 73NewYorSNM-2
- ❑ 73OPC-116
- ❑ 73SyrChiTI-10
- ❑ 73Top-116A
- ❑ 73Top-116B
- ❑ 74OPC-578
- ❑ 74Top-578
- ❑ 75DetTigP-11
- ❑ 75OPC-18
- ❑ 75Top-18
- ❑ 75TopMin-18
- ❑ 76DetTigP-12
- ❑ 76OPC-361
- ❑ 76SSP-352
- ❑ 76Top-361
- ❑ 77Top-621
- ❑ 78TigBurK-1
- ❑ 78TigTeal-15
- ❑ 78Top-684
- ❑ 81TCM60I-455
- ❑ 81TCM60I-481
- ❑ 81Top-662
- ❑ 82Don-282
- ❑ 83Top-786
- ❑ 83TopRep5-200
- ❑ 83Yan196-26
- ❑ 84Nes792-381
- ❑ 84Top-381
- ❑ 84TopTif-381
- ❑ 85Top-11
- ❑ 85TopTif-11
- ❑ 87Yan196T-9
- ❑ 89SweBasG-42
- ❑ 90SweBasG-131
- ❑ 91LinDri-25
- ❑ 91SweBasG-42
- ❑ 91TopArc1-282
- ❑ 91YanRinP11-10

Houk, Tom

- ❑ 91Cla/Bes-351
- ❑ 91KenTwiC-26
- ❑ 91KenTwiP-2082
- ❑ 92VisOakC-12
- ❑ 92VisOakF-1021
- ❑ 93NasXprF-408
- ❑ 96OgdRapTI-5
- ❑ 98HelBreM-1

Houle, Rejean

- ❑ 82MonNew-7

Houp, Scott

- ❑ 85OscAstTI-24

House, Andy

- ❑ 28Zee-154
- ❑ 29Zee-160
- ❑ 30Zee-174
- ❑ 32Zee-55
- ❑ 33Zee-90

House, Brian

- ❑ 86WinSpiP-10
- ❑ 87PitCubP-7
- ❑ 88EasLeaAP-27
- ❑ 88PitCubP-1361
- ❑ 89IowCubC-17
- ❑ 89IowCubP-1700
- ❑ 90CMC-164
- ❑ 90OklCit8C-14
- ❑ 90OklCit8P-440
- ❑ 90ProAAAF-686

House, Gary

- ❑ 77NewCoPT-18

House, H. Frank

- ❑ 52Top-146
- ❑ 54Top-163
- ❑ 55Top-87
- ❑ 55TopDouH-13
- ❑ 56A'sPos-28
- ❑ 56Top-32
- ❑ 56TopPin-37
- ❑ 57Top-223
- ❑ 58A'sJayP-5
- ❑ 58Top-318
- ❑ 59TigGraASP-10
- ❑ 59Top-313
- ❑ 60Top-372
- ❑ 79TCM50-214
- ❑ 83TopRep5-146
- ❑ 94TopArc1-163
- ❑ 94TopArc1G-163

House, Howard

- ❑ 92Bow-581

House, John

- ❑ 09ObaT21-42

House, Mike

- ❑ 89EliTwiS-12
- ❑ 89Sta-149
- ❑ 90VisOakCLC-73
- ❑ 90VisOakP-2167

House, Mitch

- ❑ 91WelPirC-7
- ❑ 91WelPirP-3578
- ❑ 92LetMouSP-16
- ❑ 93WelPirC-1
- ❑ 93WelPirF-3365
- ❑ 94AugGreC-5
- ❑ 94AugGreF-3016
- ❑ 94Cla-181
- ❑ 94ClaTriF-T64

House, Pat

- ❑ 77FriOneYW-22

House, Thomas R.

- ❑ 69Top-331
- ❑ 72OPC-351
- ❑ 72Top-351
- ❑ 74OPC-164
- ❑ 74Top-164
- ❑ 75AtlBraP-18
- ❑ 75OPC-525
- ❑ 75Top-525
- ❑ 75TopMin-525
- ❑ 76OPC-231
- ❑ 76RedSoxSM-7
- ❑ 76SSP-2
- ❑ 76Top-231
- ❑ 76TopTra-231T
- ❑ 77MarPos-7
- ❑ 77Top-358
- ❑ 78Top-643
- ❑ 79Top-31
- ❑ 82AmaGolST-25
- ❑ 83LasVegSBHN-11
- ❑ 84LasVegSC-232
- ❑ 86RanPer-NNO
- ❑ 87RanMot-28
- ❑ 87RanSmo-20
- ❑ 88AlaGolAA60TI-8
- ❑ 88RanMot-27
- ❑ 89RanMot-27
- ❑ 89RanSmo-15
- ❑ 90RanMot-27
- ❑ 90RicBra2ATI-10
- ❑ 91RanMot-28
- ❑ 92PacRyaTEI-208
- ❑ 92RanMot-28
- ❑ 93RanKee-195

House, Trini

- ❑ 92BelBreCB-14
- ❑ 92BelBreFI-420

Householder, Brian

- ❑ 87ChaO'sW-21
- ❑ 88ChaKniTI-1
- ❑ 88SouLeaAJ-33

Householder, Ed

- ❑ 09ObaT21-419
- ❑ 12ObaPreT-168
- ❑ 90DodTar-986

Householder, Paul

- ❑ 79NaSouTI-11
- ❑ 80IndIndTI-15
- ❑ 81Don-303
- ❑ 81Fle-217
- ❑ 81IndIndTI-4
- ❑ 81Top-606
- ❑ 82Don-314
- ❑ 82Fle-68
- ❑ 82RedCok-8
- ❑ 82Top-351
- ❑ 83Don-566
- ❑ 83Fle-592
- ❑ 83RedYea-21
- ❑ 83Top-34
- ❑ 84Fle-471
- ❑ 84Nes792-214
- ❑ 84Top-214
- ❑ 84TopSti-61
- ❑ 84TopTif-214
- ❑ 85BrePol-7
- ❑ 86BrePol-7
- ❑ 86Don-414
- ❑ 86Fle-491
- ❑ 86Top-554
- ❑ 86TopTif-554
- ❑ 94BreMilB-231

Houser, Ben

- ❑ 12T207-85

Houser, Brett

- ❑ 78St.PetCT-12

Houser, Chris

- ❑ 87EriCarP-24
- ❑ 88HamRedP-1719

Houser, Kyle

- ❑ 94BenRocC-9
- ❑ 94BenRocF-3601
- ❑ 95AshTouTI-14
- ❑ 96CarLeaA1B-14
- ❑ 96CarLeaA2B-14
- ❑ 96SalAvaB-16
- ❑ 97SalAva-13
- ❑ 98NewHavRM-12
- ❑ 98NewHavRMA-12

Housey, Joe

- ❑ 81QuaCitCT-20
- ❑ 84MidCubT-7
- ❑ 86GenCubP-12
- ❑ 87PeoChiP-11
- ❑ 89WinSpiS-20
- ❑ 90GenCubP-3054
- ❑ 91GenCubC-28

Housie, Wayne

- ❑ 87LakTigP-1
- ❑ 88GleFalTP-913
- ❑ 89LonTigP-1382
- ❑ 90SalSpuP-2731
- ❑ 91LinDriAA-463
- ❑ 91NewBriRSLD-463
- ❑ 91NewBriRSP-365
- ❑ 92OPC-639
- ❑ 92PawRedSF-935
- ❑ 92PawRedSS-357
- ❑ 92Sco-836
- ❑ 92SkyAAAF-161
- ❑ 92StaClu-352
- ❑ 92Top-639
- ❑ 92TopDeb91-82
- ❑ 92TopGol-639
- ❑ 92TopGolW-639
- ❑ 92TopMic-639
- ❑ 92Ult-314
- ❑ 92UppDec-664
- ❑ 94NewBriRSF-662
- ❑ 97DunDonPPS-10

Housley, Adam

- ❑ 96BelSnaTI-17

Houston, Barry

- ❑ 82WisRapTF-16

Houston, Erv

- ❑ 87EugEmeP-2651

Houston, Ken (K.R.)

- ❑ 81EvaTriT-21
- ❑ 82EvaTriT-24
- ❑ 83WauTimF-1
- ❑ 86OscAstP-13
- ❑ 87OscAstP-24

Houston, Kevin

- ❑ 78DayBeaAT-11
- ❑ 82BufBisT-10

Houston, Maceo

- ❑ 91HigSchPLS-29
- ❑ 91HunCubC-13
- ❑ 91HunCubP-3347
- ❑ 92HunCubC-9
- ❑ 92HunCubF-3162

Houston, Mel

- ❑ 86WesPalBEP-20
- ❑ 87WesPalBEP-670
- ❑ 88IndIndC-23
- ❑ 88IndIndP-507
- ❑ 89JacExpB-3
- ❑ 89JacExpP-170
- ❑ 90CMC-70
- ❑ 90IndIndC-20
- ❑ 90IndIndP-295
- ❑ 90ProAAAF-578
- ❑ 91IndIndLD-196
- ❑ 91IndIndP-469
- ❑ 91LinDriAAA-196

Houston, Pete

- ❑ 88RenSilSCLC-289

Houston, Tyler

- ❑ 89HigSchPLS-5
- ❑ 89IdaFalBP-2021
- ❑ 90Bes-16
- ❑ 90Bes-324
- ❑ 90Bow-14
- ❑ 90BowTif-14
- ❑ 90CMC-827
- ❑ 90OPC-564
- ❑ 90ProAaA-104
- ❑ 90Sco-677
- ❑ 90SumBraB-1
- ❑ 90SumBraP-2436
- ❑ 90Top-564
- ❑ 90TopTif-564
- ❑ 91Bow-581
- ❑ 91Cla/Bes-267
- ❑ 91MacBraC-16
- ❑ 91MacBraP-869
- ❑ 91SouAtlLAGP-SAL32
- ❑ 92ClaFS7-91
- ❑ 92DurBulC-16
- ❑ 92DurBulF-1104
- ❑ 92DurBulTI-19
- ❑ 92UppDecML-151
- ❑ 93ClaFS7-208
- ❑ 93GreBraF-352
- ❑ 94ClaGolF-87
- ❑ 94RicBraF-2948
- ❑ 94StaCluT-45
- ❑ 94StaCluTFDI-45
- ❑ 94UppDecML-88
- ❑ 95RicBraRC-5
- ❑ 95RicBraTI-6
- ❑ 96PinAfi-192
- ❑ 96PinAfiAP-192
- ❑ 96Sum-194
- ❑ 96SumAbo&B-194
- ❑ 96SumArtP-194
- ❑ 96SumFoi-194
- ❑ 97DonRatR-12
- ❑ 97Fle-277
- ❑ 97FleTif-277
- ❑ 97Lea-312
- ❑ 97LeaFraM-312
- ❑ 97LeaFraMDC-312
- ❑ 97PacPriGotD-GD119
- ❑ 97Sco-259
- ❑ 97ScoArtPWB-259
- ❑ 97ScoPreS-259
- ❑ 97ScoShoS-259
- ❑ 97ScoShoSAP-259
- ❑ 97Ult-165
- ❑ 97UltGolME-165
- ❑ 97UltPlaME-165
- ❑ 98ColCho-57
- ❑ 98PacInvGems-131
- ❑ 98PacOnl-143
- ❑ 98PacOnlR-143
- ❑ 98PacOnlWC-143
- ❑ 98UppDec-322
- ❑ 99Fle-527
- ❑ 99FleSta9-527
- ❑ 99FleWarT-527
- ❑ 99PacOme-49
- ❑ 99PacOmeC-49
- ❑ 99PacOmeG-49
- ❑ 99PacOmePB-49

Houtteman, Art

- ❑ 50Bow-42
- ❑ 51Bow-45
- ❑ 52Top-238
- ❑ 53BowC-4
- ❑ 53TigGle-16
- ❑ 54Bow-20
- ❑ 54DanDee-12
- ❑ 55Bow-144
- ❑ 55IndCarBL-4
- ❑ 55IndGolS-6
- ❑ 56Top-281
- ❑ 57IndTeal-10
- ❑ 57Top-385
- ❑ 75TCM195CI-16
- ❑ 75TCM195CI-39
- ❑ 79TCM50-242
- ❑ 81TigDetN-46
- ❑ 83TopRep5-238
- ❑ 85TCMPpl1-29
- ❑ 91OriCro-204

Hovey, James

- ❑ 92BenRocCB-14
- ❑ 92BenRocF-1471
- ❑ 93CenValRC-13
- ❑ 93CenValRF-2889

Hovley, Steve

- ❑ 68SeaPop-8
- ❑ 69PilPos-20
- ❑ 70BreMcD-12
- ❑ 70BreMil-9
- ❑ 70MLBOffS-273
- ❑ 70OPC-514
- ❑ 70Top-514
- ❑ 71MLBOffS-515
- ❑ 71OPC-109
- ❑ 71Top-109
- ❑ 72oyTeal-8
- ❑ 72Top-683
- ❑ 73OPC-282
- ❑ 73Top-282
- ❑ 77PilPosR-20
- ❑ 83Pil69G-9
- ❑ 94BreMilB-317

Howard, Bob

- ❑ 63BasMagM-38

Howard, Brent

- ❑ 89CalLeaA-52
- ❑ 90CalLeaACLC-35

Howard, Bruce

- ❑ 64Top-107
- ❑ 64TopVen-107
- ❑ 65OPC-41
- ❑ 65Top-41
- ❑ 66Top-281
- ❑ 66TopVen-281
- ❑ 67BalOriP-50
- ❑ 67OPC-159
- ❑ 67Top-159
- ❑ 68Top-293
- ❑ 68TopVen-293
- ❑ 69Top-226
- ❑ 91OriCro-205

Howard, Chris (Christian)

- ❑ 87PriWilYP-11
- ❑ 88CarLeaAS-9
- ❑ 88PriWilYS-12
- ❑ 89Ft.LauYS-10
- ❑ 89Sta-78
- ❑ 90AlbYanP-1033
- ❑ 90Bes-239
- ❑ 90WilBilB-11
- ❑ 90WilBilP-1061
- ❑ 90WilBilS-12
- ❑ 91BirBarLD-62
- ❑ 91BirBarP-1450
- ❑ 91CalCanLD-60
- ❑ 91CalCanP-519
- ❑ 91LinDriAA-62

❑ 91LinDriAAA-60
❑ 92Bow-309
❑ 92CalCanF-3735
❑ 92CalCanS-61
❑ 92SkyAAAF-283
❑ 92TopDeb91-83
❑ 92VanCanF-2717
❑ 92VanCanS-638
❑ 93CalCanF-1170
❑ 93NasSouF-568
❑ 94BenRocC-10
❑ 94BenRocF-3587
❑ 94CalCanF-793
❑ 94FleUpd-12
❑ 94PawRedSDD-9
❑ 94PawRedSF-944
❑ 94Top-686
❑ 94TopGol-686
❑ 94TopSpa-686
❑ 94TopTra-68T
❑ 94TriAAF-AAA1
❑ 95Don-261
❑ 95DonPreP-261
❑ 95Fle-33
❑ 95Pac-39
❑ 95TacRaiTI-9
❑ 95Top-177
❑ 95Ult-11
❑ 95UltGolM-11
❑ 96LeaSigEA-83
❑ 96NorTidB-18

Howard, Christopher Hugh
❑ 89WauTimGS-27

Howard, Dave (David)
❑ 87Ft.MyeRP-32
❑ 88AppFoxP-145
❑ 89BasCitRS-9
❑ 89PriPirS-10
❑ 90MemChiB-5
❑ 90MemChiP-1015
❑ 90MemChiS-11
❑ 91Bow-295
❑ 91FleUpd-27
❑ 91Lea-325
❑ 91ScoRoo-83T
❑ 92Bow-307
❑ 92Don-567
❑ 92Fle-160
❑ 92Lea-4
❑ 92LeaBlaG-4
❑ 92OPC-641
❑ 92Pin-86
❑ 92RoyPol-11
❑ 92Sco-704
❑ 92Sco100RS-2
❑ 92ScoProP-25
❑ 92StaClu-245
❑ 92Top-641
❑ 92TopDeb91-84
❑ 92TopGol-641
❑ 92TopGolW-641
❑ 92TopMic-641
❑ 92TriPla-201
❑ 92Ult-71
❑ 92UppDec-216
❑ 93Fle-619
❑ 93PacSpa-136
❑ 93Sco-645
❑ 93Top-519
❑ 93TopGol-519
❑ 93TopInaM-519
❑ 93TopInaR-519
❑ 93TopMic-519
❑ 94Pac-288
❑ 94Sco-206
❑ 94ScoGolR-206
❑ 95Sco-206
❑ 95ScoGolR-206
❑ 95ScoPlaTS-206
❑ 95TamYanYI-30
❑ 96Fle-130
❑ 96FleTif-130
❑ 96RoyPol-12
❑ 96StaClu-353
❑ 96StaCluMOP-353
❑ 97Pac-102
❑ 97PacLigB-102
❑ 97PacSil-102
❑ 97RoyPol-10
❑ 97TamYan-2
❑ 98PacInvGems-54
❑ 98PacOnl-612
❑ 98PacOnlR-612
❑ 98PacOnlWC-612
❑ 98Ult-393
❑ 98UltGolM-393
❑ 98UltMas-393
❑ 98UltPlaM-393

Howard, Del (George Elmer)
❑ 06FanCraNL-21
❑ 09ColChiE-134
❑ 09RamT20-56
❑ 09T206-159
❑ 10RedCroT-31
❑ 10RedCroT-201
❑ 11SpoLifCW-175
❑ 12ColRedB-134
❑ 12ColTinT-134
❑ 13Zee-111
❑ 14Zee-112
❑ 15Zee-34
❑ 16Zee-34
❑ 17Zee-26
❑ 18Zee-24
❑ 19Zee-20
❑ 20Zee-24
❑ 23Zee-37

Howard, Dennis
❑ 80UtiBluJT-20
❑ 82KnoBluJT-4
❑ 83SyrChiT-8
❑ 84SyrChiT-4
❑ 85SyrChiT-9
❑ 86SyrChiP-13

Howard, Doug
❑ 88SalLakCTTI-19

Howard, Doug Lynn
❑ 74TacTwiC-18
❑ 75TulOil7-13
❑ 77OPC-112

Howard, Elston
❑ 47Exh-101
❑ 47PM1StaP1-90
❑ 47StaPinP2-17
❑ 53Dor-139
❑ 55Bow-68
❑ 55DonWin-26
❑ 56Top-208
❑ 56YanJayP-7
❑ 56YanTeal-10
❑ 57Top-82
❑ 57YanJayP-6
❑ 58Top-275
❑ 58YanJayP-5
❑ 59Top-395
❑ 60Top-65
❑ 60TopVen-65
❑ 60YanJayP-4
❑ 61Pos-2A
❑ 61Pos-2B
❑ 61Top-495
❑ 61TopStaI-194
❑ 61Yan61RL-4
❑ 61YanJayP-6
❑ 62Jel-8
❑ 62Pos-8
❑ 62PosCan-8
❑ 62SalPlaC-95
❑ 62ShiPlaC-95
❑ 62Top-51
❑ 62Top-400
❑ 62Top-473
❑ 62TopBuc-37
❑ 62TopStal-86
❑ 62TopVen-51
❑ 62YanJayP-8
❑ 63Jel-18
❑ 63Kah-15
❑ 63Pos-18
❑ 63ReqKP-8
❑ 63SalMetC-45
❑ 63Top-60
❑ 63Top-306
❑ 63YanJayP-5
❑ 64Baz-29
❑ 64ChatheY-12
❑ 64Top-100
❑ 64TopCoi-23
❑ 64TopCoi-135
❑ 64TopGia-21
❑ 64TopSta-72
❑ 64TopStaU-33
❑ 64TopVen-100
❑ 64WheSta-21
❑ 64YanJayP-5
❑ 65Baz-29
❑ 65ChaTheY-10
❑ 65OPC-1
❑ 65Top-1
❑ 65Top-450
❑ 66Top-405
❑ 66YanTeal-4
❑ 67AshOil-2
❑ 67CokCapA-25
❑ 67CokCapAAm-29
❑ 67CokCapYM-V9
❑ 67DexPre-99
❑ 67OPC-25
❑ 67Top-25
❑ 67TopVen-255
❑ 68CokCapRS-18
❑ 68OPC-167
❑ 68Top-167
❑ 68TopVen-167
❑ 70YanPhoS-16
❑ 73OPC-116
❑ 73Top-116A
❑ 73Top-116B
❑ 74SyrChiTI-11
❑ 75OPC-201
❑ 75SyrChiTI-6
❑ 75Top-201
❑ 75TopMin-201
❑ 76SSP-619
❑ 78TCM60I-236
❑ 79DiaGre-24
❑ 79ElsHowS-1
❑ 79TCM50-271
❑ 81RedSoxBG2S-86
❑ 81TCM60I-474
❑ 82ASAMicM-42
❑ 82K-M-3
❑ 83Yan196-4
❑ 84OCoandSI-109
❑ 85GeoSteM-4
❑ 86SpoDecG-49
❑ 87SpoCubG-3
❑ 87Yan196T-5
❑ 88PacLegI-19A
❑ 88PacLegI-19B
❑ 90YanMomPRP-4
❑ 91YanRinP12-12
❑ 92YanWIZ6-56
❑ 92YanWIZA-31
❑ 94TedWil-59
❑ 94TedWilM-M26
❑ 94TopArc1-253
❑ 94TopArc1G-253
❑ 98BowChrR-8
❑ 98BowChrRR-8

Howard, Ernest E.
❑ 09T206-493

Howard, Frank
❑ 47Exh-102
❑ 60DarFar-17
❑ 60DodJayP-7
❑ 60DodTeal-9
❑ 60DodUniO-9
❑ 60Top-132
❑ 60TopVen-132
❑ 61DodJayP-4
❑ 61DodMor-3
❑ 61DodUniO-10
❑ 61Top-280
❑ 61TopMagR-34
❑ 61TopStal-27
❑ 62Baz-15
❑ 62DodBelB-25
❑ 62DodJayP-5
❑ 62DodVol-17
❑ 62Top-175
❑ 62TopBuc-38
❑ 62TopStal-135
❑ 62TopVen-175
❑ 63DodJayP-7
❑ 63ExhStaB-31
❑ 63Top-123
❑ 64DodHea-5
❑ 64Top-139
❑ 64Top-371
❑ 64TopCoi-61
❑ 64TopGia-24
❑ 64TopSta-83
❑ 64TopStaU-34
❑ 64TopTatI-42
❑ 64TopVen-139
❑ 65OPC-40
❑ 65Top-40
❑ 65TopTral-49
❑ 66Baz-3
❑ 66SenTeal-8
❑ 66Top-515
❑ 66TopRubl-42
❑ 67Baz-3
❑ 67CokCapAAm-20
❑ 67CokCapS-6
❑ 67DexPre-100
❑ 67OPCPapl-7
❑ 67SenPos-11
❑ 67SenTeal-6
❑ 67Top-255
❑ 67TopGiaSU-15
❑ 67TopPos-7
❑ 67TopTesF-7
❑ 67TopVen-201
❑ 68Baz-7
❑ 68OPC-6
❑ 68SenTeal-6
❑ 68Top-6
❑ 68Top-320
❑ 68TopActS-11C
❑ 68TopGamI-21
❑ 68TopPla-4
❑ 68TopPos-3
❑ 68TopVen-320
❑ 69CitMetC-10
❑ 69MilBra-120
❑ 69MLBOffS-105
❑ 69MLBPin-12
❑ 69OPC-3
❑ 69OPC-5
❑ 69OPC-170
❑ 69OPCDec-12
❑ 69SenTeal-9
❑ 69SenTeal8-12
❑ 69Top-3
❑ 69Top-5
❑ 69Top-170
❑ 69TopDec-16
❑ 69TopDecl-18
❑ 69TopFou-20
❑ 69TopSta-238
❑ 69TopSup-30
❑ 69TopTeaP-23
❑ 69TraSta-29
❑ 70DayDaiNM-36
❑ 70Kel-6
❑ 70MilBra-10
❑ 70MLBOffS-283
❑ 70OPC-66
❑ 70SenPolY-5
❑ 70Top-66
❑ 70Top-550
❑ 70TopCanL-9
❑ 70TopPos-22
❑ 70TopSup-16
❑ 70TraSta-12B
❑ 71AllBasA-9
❑ 71BazNumT-20
❑ 71BazUnn-20
❑ 71Kel-14
❑ 71MilDud-9
❑ 71MLBOffS-542
❑ 71MLBOffS-561
❑ 71OPC-65
❑ 71OPC-620
❑ 71SenPolP-6
❑ 71SenTealW-13
❑ 71Top-63
❑ 71Top-65
❑ 71Top-620
❑ 71TopCoi-22
❑ 71TopGreM-48
❑ 71TopSup-17
❑ 71TopTat-64
❑ 71TopTat-65
❑ 72MilBra-153
❑ 72OPC-350
❑ 72RanTeal-13
❑ 72SevTraC-19
❑ 72Top-350
❑ 72TopCloT-17
❑ 73OPC-560
❑ 73Top-560
❑ 76SpoIndC-13
❑ 78TCM60I-220
❑ 78TigDeaCS-7
❑ 80BreTeal-13
❑ 81PadFamF-10
❑ 81Top-685
❑ 82MetPhoA-28
❑ 82TCMGreS-10
❑ 83MLBPin-9
❑ 83TopTra-47T
❑ 84Nes792-621
❑ 84OCoandSI-195
❑ 84Top-621
❑ 84TopTif-621
❑ 85BrePol-NNO
❑ 85CirK-23
❑ 85Woo-19
❑ 86BrePol-33
❑ 87MarMot-28
❑ 88DodSmo-3
❑ 88PacLegI-17
❑ 90DodTar-360
❑ 90HOFStiB-75
❑ 93RanKee-18
❑ 94TedWil-88
❑ 95DodROY-5
❑ 96MetKah-14
❑ 96MetKah-14

Howard, Fred
❑ 77AppFoxT-11
❑ 78KnoKnoST-9
❑ 80Top-72

Howard, Ivan Chester
❑ 09ObaT21-4
❑ 09ObaT21-86
❑ 09ObaT21-262
❑ 11PacCoaBD-31
❑ 11Zee-14
❑ 12ObaPreT-11
❑ 12Zee-12
❑ 13Zee-11
❑ 15SpoNewM-84
❑ 16SpoNewM-85
❑ 17ColE13-81
❑ 22Zee-27
❑ 23Zee-35
❑ 23Zee-36
❑ 24Zee-28
❑ 25Zee-28
❑ 26Zee-77
❑ 28Zee-81
❑ 29Zee-73

Howard, Jamie
❑ 94ClaGolF-47

Howard, Jim
❑ 86KnoBluJP-12
❑ 87AlbYanP-12

Howard, Larry
❑ 70AstPho-11
❑ 71AstTeal-13
❑ 71OPC-102
❑ 71Top-102
❑ 87AstShowSTh-29

Howard, Marcus
❑ 97LowSpiB-10
❑ 98MicBatCM-16

Howard, Matt (Mathew)
❑ 88CapCodPPaLP-120
❑ 89GreFalDSP-23
❑ 90BakDodCLC-253
❑ 90CalLeaACLC-14
❑ 91FloStaLAP-FSL39
❑ 91VerBeaDC-21
❑ 91VerBeaDP-782
❑ 92ClaFS7-244
❑ 92ProFS7-246
❑ 92SanAntMF-3983
❑ 92SanAntMS-567
❑ 92SkyAA F-247
❑ 93AlbDukF-1468
❑ 94AlbDukF-850
❑ 95BowBayTI-22
❑ 96ColCliB-16
❑ 97ColCliB-14
❑ 97ColCliD-10
❑ 98FreGriG-13

Howard, Mike
❑ 75QuaCitAT-14

Howard, Mike (Michael Frederick)
❑ 78CliDodT-15
❑ 79JacMetT-14
❑ 80VenLeaS-160
❑ 81TidTidT-12
❑ 82MetPhoA-11
❑ 82TidTidT-5
❑ 83TidTidT-18
❑ 84HawIsIC-135
❑ 91MetWIZ-189

Howard, Mike (Michael Stephen)
❑ 81PawRedST-2

Howard, Rich
❑ 94ButCopKSP-6

Howard, Rob
❑ 89AncBucTI-5

Howard, Ron
❑ 88BriTigP-1870
❑ 89FayGenP-1592
❑ 90FayGenP-2413
❑ 91LakTigC-19
❑ 91LakTigP-272
❑ 92LakTigC-6
❑ 92LakTigF-2286

Howard, Steve
❑ 83IdaFalAT-27
❑ 85ModA'sC-16
❑ 86ModA'sC-10
❑ 86ModA'sP-13
❑ 87HunStaTI-13
❑ 88HunStaTI-8
❑ 88SouLeaAJ-3
❑ 89TacTigC-21
❑ 89TacTigP-1552
❑ 90CMC-594
❑ 90ProAAAF-155
❑ 90TacTigC-17
❑ 90TacTigP-108
❑ 90TopTra-43T
❑ 90TopTraT-43T
❑ 91Sco-364
❑ 91SouOreAAP-SOA23
❑ 91TopDeb90-72
❑ 91UppDec-277
❑ 92RicBraS-426

Howard, Thomas
❑ 86SpoIndC-171
❑ 87TexLeaAF-18
❑ 87WicPilRD-13
❑ 88BlaYNPRWL-88
❑ 88LasVegSC-11
❑ 88LasVegSP-239
❑ 89BlaYNPRWL-126
❑ 89LasVegSC-15
❑ 89LasVegSP-8
❑ 89UppDec-726
❑ 90Bow-212
❑ 90BowTif-212
❑ 90FleUpd-56
❑ 90LasVegSP-135
❑ 90ProAAAF-23
❑ 91Bow-644
❑ 91Don-746
❑ 91Fle-532
❑ 91LasVegSP-248
❑ 91PadMag-3
❑ 91PadSmo-14
❑ 91Sco-335
❑ 91Sco100RS-9
❑ 91StaClu-403
❑ 91TopDeb90-73
❑ 91Ult-305
❑ 91UppDecFE-39F
❑ 92Don-266
❑ 92Fle-607
❑ 92FleUpd-15
❑ 92IndFanC-12
❑ 92Lea-84
❑ 92Lea-456
❑ 92LeaBlaG-84
❑ 92LeaBlaG-456
❑ 92OPC-539
❑ 92Sco-293
❑ 92StaClu-401
❑ 92Top-539
❑ 92TopGol-539
❑ 92TopGolW-539
❑ 92TopMic-539
❑ 92Ult-279
❑ 92Ult-348
❑ 92UppDec-416
❑ 93Don-257
❑ 93Fle-215
❑ 93IndWUA-12
❑ 93OPC-139
❑ 93Pin-399
❑ 93Sco-426
❑ 93StaClu-515
❑ 93StaCluFDI-515
❑ 93StaCluMOP-515
❑ 93Top-113
❑ 93TopGol-113
❑ 93TopInaM-113
❑ 93TopInaR-113
❑ 93TopMic-113
❑ 93Ult-185
❑ 93UppDec-299
❑ 93UppDecGold-299
❑ 94Don-164
❑ 94Fle-411
❑ 94RedKah-15
❑ 94Sco-501
❑ 94ScoGolR-501
❑ 94StaClu-496
❑ 94StaCluFDI-496
❑ 94StaCluGR-496
❑ 94StaCluMOP-496
❑ 94Top-246
❑ 94TopGol-246

❑ 94TopSpa-246
❑ 94Ult-473
❑ 95Don-100
❑ 95DonPreP-100
❑ 95ElmPioTI-12
❑ 95ElmPioUTI-12
❑ 95Fle-437
❑ 95RedKah-11
❑ 95Sco-391
❑ 95ScoGolR-391
❑ 95ScoPlaTS-391
❑ 95StaClu-280
❑ 95StaCluMOP-280
❑ 95StaCluSTDW-RE280
❑ 95StaCluSTWS-280
❑ 95Top-381
❑ 96ColCho-109
❑ 96ColChoGS-109
❑ 96ColChoSS-109
❑ 96Don-245
❑ 96DonPreP-245
❑ 96Fle-343
❑ 96FleTif-343
❑ 96LeaSigA-108
❑ 96LeaSigAG-108
❑ 96LeaSigAS-108
❑ 96Pac-36
❑ 96StaClu-330
❑ 96StaCluMOP-330
❑ 96Top-283
❑ 96Ult-461
❑ 96UltGolM-461
❑ 96UppDec-49
❑ 97AstMot-24
❑ 97Cir-157
❑ 97CirRav-157
❑ 97ColCho-84
❑ 97Fle-295
❑ 97Fle-596
❑ 97FleTif-295
❑ 97FleTif-596
❑ 97Pac-270
❑ 97PacLigB-270
❑ 97PacSil-270
❑ 97Top-231
❑ 98DodPol-11
❑ 98Pac-321
❑ 98PacOnl-372
❑ 98PacOnlR-372
❑ 98PacOnlWC-372
❑ 98PacPlaB-321
❑ 98PacRedT-321
❑ 98PacSil-321

Howard, Tim
❑ 89PitMetS-10
❑ 90ColMetGS-11
❑ 90ColMetPPI-6
❑ 90SouAtlLAS-34
❑ 91Bow-538
❑ 91Cla/Bes-232
❑ 91St.LucMC-23
❑ 91St.LucMP-720
❑ 92BinMetF-527
❑ 92BinMetS-59
❑ 92SkyAA F-25
❑ 92UppDecML-218
❑ 93NorTidF-2582
❑ 95NasSouTI-6
❑ 95PawRedSDD-15
❑ 95PawRedTI-11

Howard, Wilbur
❑ 74OPC-606
❑ 74Top-606
❑ 75AstPos-15
❑ 75OPC-563
❑ 75Top-563
❑ 75TopMin-563
❑ 76HouAstP-14
❑ 76OPC-97
❑ 76SSP-65
❑ 76Top-97
❑ 77Top-248
❑ 78AstBurK-20
❑ 78AstPos-11
❑ 78Top-534
❑ 79ChaChaT-17
❑ 79Top-642
❑ 87AstShoSPO-9
❑ 87AstShoSPT-13
❑ 94BreMilB-318

Howarth, Jim
❑ 72GiaTeal-10
❑ 73OPC-459
❑ 73Top-459
❑ 74OPC-404
❑ 74Top-404

Howatt, Jeff
❑ 95PitMetTI-46
❑ 97St.LucM-10

Howe, Art
❑ 75PitPirP-9
❑ 76HouAstP-15
❑ 76SSP-585
❑ 77AstPho-8
❑ 78AstBurK-16
❑ 78AstPos-12
❑ 78Top-13
❑ 79AstPos-11
❑ 79AstTeal-7
❑ 79OPC-165
❑ 79Top-327
❑ 80OPC-287
❑ 80Top-554
❑ 81AstPos-6
❑ 81CokTeaS-64
❑ 81Don-258
❑ 81Fle-51
❑ 81OPC-129
❑ 81Top-129
❑ 81TopScr-99
❑ 81TopSti-170
❑ 81TopSupHT-99
❑ 82AstAstI-4
❑ 82AstPos-6
❑ 82Don-92
❑ 82Fle-218
❑ 82FleSta-48
❑ 82Kel-34
❑ 82OPC-248
❑ 82SevSluC-15
❑ 82Top-66
❑ 82Top-453
❑ 82TopSti-43
❑ 83AstPos-9
❑ 83Don-396
❑ 83Fle-450
❑ 83FleSta-84
❑ 83FleSti-211
❑ 83OPC-372
❑ 83Top-639
❑ 83TopSti-236
❑ 84Car-13
❑ 84Car5x7-13
❑ 84Fle-227
❑ 84FleUpd-54
❑ 84Nes792-679
❑ 84Top-679
❑ 84TopTif-679
❑ 84TopTra-53T
❑ 84TopTraT-53T
❑ 85Fle-228
❑ 85RanPer-NNO
❑ 85Top-204
❑ 85TopTif-204
❑ 86RanLit-3
❑ 86RanPer-NNO
❑ 87AstShoSPO-10
❑ 87RanMot-28
❑ 87RanSmo-25
❑ 88RanMot-27
❑ 89AstLenH-25
❑ 89AstMot-1
❑ 89AstSmo-19
❑ 89TopTra-53T
❑ 89TopTraT-53T
❑ 90AstLenH-16
❑ 90AstMot-1
❑ 90OPC-579
❑ 90Top-579
❑ 90TopTif-579
❑ 91AstMot-1
❑ 91OPC-51
❑ 91Top-51
❑ 91TopDesS-51
❑ 91TopMic-51
❑ 91TopTif-51
❑ 92AstMot-1
❑ 92OPC-729
❑ 92Top-729
❑ 92TopGol-729
❑ 92TopGolW-729
❑ 92TopMic-729
❑ 93AstMot-1
❑ 93RanKee-196
❑ 93Top-506
❑ 93TopGol-506
❑ 93TopInaM-506
❑ 93TopInaR-506
❑ 93TopMic-506
❑ 95LinVen-304
❑ 96A'sMot-1
❑ 97A'sMot-1
❑ 98A'sMot-1

Howe, Gordie
❑ 83TigAlKS-13

Howe, Greg
❑ 83VisOakF-21
❑ 85TolMudHT-23

Howe, Matthew
❑ 98SouOreTG-15

Howe, Steve
❑ 81Dod-14
❑ 81DodPol-57
❑ 81DodPos-4
❑ 81Don-511
❑ 81Fle-136
❑ 81LonBeaPT-15
❑ 81OPC-159
❑ 81Top-693
❑ 81TopSupHT-47
❑ 82DodPol-57
❑ 82DodPos-4
❑ 82DodUniOV-8
❑ 82Don-158
❑ 82Fle-9
❑ 82OPC-14
❑ 82Top-14
❑ 83DodPol-57
❑ 83DodPos-5
❑ 83Don-630
❑ 83Fle-209
❑ 83FleSta-85
❑ 83FleSti-119
❑ 83OPC-170
❑ 83Top-170
❑ 84Fle-103
❑ 84Nes792-425
❑ 84OPC-196
❑ 84Top-425
❑ 84TopTif-425
❑ 85DodCokP-14
❑ 85DomLeaS-27
❑ 86SanJosBP-10
❑ 87DodSmoA-14
❑ 88Don-593
❑ 88Sco-543
❑ 88ScoGlo-543
❑ 89DodSmoG-98
❑ 89LonTigP-1357
❑ 90DodTar-361
❑ 90SalSpuCLC-117
❑ 91ColCliLD-105
❑ 91ColCliP-5
❑ 91ColCliP-592
❑ 91FleUpd-43
❑ 91Lea-440
❑ 91LinDriAAA-105
❑ 91StaClu-401
❑ 91Stu-93
❑ 91UppDecFE-31F
❑ 92DodStaTA-21
❑ 92Don-106
❑ 92Fle-230
❑ 92OPC-318
❑ 92Pin-507
❑ 92Sco-275
❑ 92StaClu-827
❑ 92StaCluNC-827
❑ 92Top-318
❑ 92TopGol-318
❑ 92TopGolW-318
❑ 92TopMic-318
❑ 92Ult-408
❑ 92UppDec-630
❑ 93Don-763
❑ 93PacSpa-555
❑ 93Pin-559
❑ 93RanKee-197
❑ 93StaClu-738
❑ 93StaCluFDI-738
❑ 93StaCluMOP-738
❑ 93Ult-594
❑ 93UppDec-707
❑ 93UppDecGold-707
❑ 94ColChoSS-613
❑ 94Fle-231
❑ 94StaClu-595
❑ 94StaCluFDI-595
❑ 94StaCluGR-595
❑ 94StaCluMOP-595
❑ 94StaCluT-193
❑ 94StaCluTFDI-193
❑ 94Top-637
❑ 94TopGol-637
❑ 94TopSpa-637
❑ 95Baz-91
❑ 95ColCho-522
❑ 95ColChoGS-522
❑ 95ColChoSS-522
❑ 95DodROY-9
❑ 95Don-381
❑ 95DonPreP-381
❑ 95Fle-71
❑ 95Pac-297
❑ 95Pin-435
❑ 95PinArtP-435
❑ 95PinMusC-435
❑ 95Sco-23
❑ 95ScoGolR-23
❑ 95ScoPlaTS-23
❑ 95StaClu-372
❑ 95StaCluMOP-372
❑ 95StaCluSTWS-372
❑ 95StaCluVR-195
❑ 95StaCluVRMO-195
❑ 95Top-294
❑ 95TopCyb-175
❑ 96LeaSigA-109
❑ 96LeaSigAG-109
❑ 96LeaSigAS-109

Howe, Tom
❑ 91MisStaB-28
❑ 92MisStaB-22

Howell, Dave (David)
❑ 89OneYanP-2113
❑ 90PriWilCTI-13
❑ 91Ft.LauYC-20
❑ 91Ft.LauYP-2433
❑ 92ArkTraF-1137
❑ 92St.PetCC-11

Howell, Dixie (Homer)
❑ 48SomandK-19
❑ 49EurSta-86
❑ 51Bow-252
❑ 52Bow-222
❑ 52Top-135
❑ 53Top-255
❑ 83TopRep5-135
❑ 90DodTar-362
❑ 91TopArc1-255
❑ 95TopArcBD-54
❑ 95TopArcBD-113

Howell, Dixie (Millard)
❑ 56Top-149
❑ 57Top-221
❑ 58Top-421

Howell, Harry
❑ 03BreE10-72
❑ 04FanCraAL-25
❑ 08RosComP-69
❑ 09AmeCarE90-1-52
❑ 09AmeCarE90-1-53
❑ 09PC7HHB-23
❑ 09RamT20-57
❑ 09T206-160
❑ 09T206-161
❑ 10CouT21-31
❑ 10NadCarE-27A
❑ 10NadCarE-27B
❑ 11PinT-5-115
❑ 11SpoLifCW-176
❑ 11SpoLifM-111
❑ 90DodTar-363

Howell, Jack
❑ 85EdmTraC-24
❑ 86Don-524
❑ 86EdmTraP-15
❑ 86OPC-127
❑ 86Top-127
❑ 86TopTif-127
❑ 87AngSmo-16
❑ 87CalAngPPS-17
❑ 87Don-305
❑ 87Fle-83
❑ 87FleGlo-83
❑ 87OPC-2
❑ 87Top-422
❑ 87TopTif-422
❑ 88AngSmo-3
❑ 88Don-333
❑ 88DonBasB-59
❑ 88Fle-491
❑ 88FleGlo-491
❑ 88OPC-114
❑ 88PanSti-44
❑ 88PanSti-187
❑ 88Sco-124
❑ 88ScoGlo-124
❑ 88StaLinAn-9
❑ 88Top-381
❑ 88Top-631
❑ 88TopBig-121
❑ 88TopSti-175
❑ 88TopTif-381
❑ 88TopTif-631
❑ 89Bow-48
❑ 89BowTif-48
❑ 89Don-288
❑ 89DonBasB-307
❑ 89Fle-480
❑ 89FleGlo-480
❑ 89OPC-216
❑ 89PanSti-293
❑ 89RedFolSB-61
❑ 89Sco-261
❑ 89Top-216
❑ 89TopBig-228
❑ 89TopSti-181
❑ 89TopTif-216
❑ 89UppDec-138
❑ 90AngSmo-8
❑ 90Bow-296
❑ 90BowTif-296
❑ 90Don-254
❑ 90DonBesA-45
❑ 90Fle-135
❑ 90FleCan-135
❑ 90Lea-327
❑ 90OPC-547
❑ 90PubIntS-371
❑ 90Sco-206
❑ 90Top-547
❑ 90TopBig-34
❑ 90TopTif-547
❑ 90UppDec-19
❑ 91AngSmo-11
❑ 91Don-247
❑ 91OPC-57
❑ 91PanFreS-182
❑ 91Sco-842
❑ 91StaClu-198
❑ 91Top-57
❑ 91TopDesS-57
❑ 91TopMic-57
❑ 91TopTif-57
❑ 91Ult-47
❑ 91UppDec-213
❑ 92Don-646
❑ 92OPC-769
❑ 92PanSti-234
❑ 92Sco-706
❑ 92Top-769
❑ 92TopGol-769
❑ 92TopGolW-769
❑ 92TopMic-769
❑ 92UppDec-419
❑ 93GolCar-1
❑ 96AngMot-19
❑ 96LeaSigEA-84
❑ 97AngMot-26
❑ 97PacPriGotD-GD6
❑ 98PacOnl-326
❑ 98PacOnlR-326
❑ 98PacOnlWC-326

Howell, Jay
❑ 79IndIndTI-24
❑ 80IndIndTI-11
❑ 82IowCubT-16
❑ 82Top-51
❑ 83Don-587
❑ 83YanPhoA-11
❑ 84Fle-128
❑ 84Nes792-239
❑ 84Top-239
❑ 84TopTif-239
❑ 85A'sMot-18
❑ 85Don-103
❑ 85DonHig-18
❑ 85Fle-131
❑ 85FleUpd-57
❑ 85Lea-244
❑ 85Top-559
❑ 85TopTif-559
❑ 85TopTifT-57T
❑ 85TopTra-57T
❑ 86A'sMot-18
❑ 86Don-223
❑ 86DonAll-57
❑ 86Fle-421
❑ 86FleMin-89
❑ 86FleStiC-62
❑ 86Lea-100
❑ 86OPC-115
❑ 86SevCoi-W15
❑ 86Spo-192
❑ 86Top-115
❑ 86TopSti-175
❑ 86TopSup-34
❑ 86TopTat-11
❑ 86TopTif-115
❑ 87A'sMot-25
❑ 87A'sSmoC-6
❑ 87Don-503
❑ 87Fle-395
❑ 87FleGlo-395
❑ 87FleStiC-63
❑ 87OPC-391
❑ 87RedFolSB-89
❑ 87Top-391
❑ 87TopTif-391
❑ 88DodMot-16
❑ 88DodPol-50
❑ 88Don-55
❑ 88DonAll-11
❑ 88Fle-282
❑ 88FleGlo-282
❑ 88FleUpd-95
❑ 88FleUpdG-95
❑ 88OPC-91
❑ 88Sco-522
❑ 88ScoGlo-522
❑ 88ScoRoo-35T
❑ 88ScoRooG-35T
❑ 88Spo-86
❑ 88Top-690
❑ 88TopSti-166
❑ 88TopTif-690
❑ 88TopTra-52T
❑ 88TopTraT-52T
❑ 89Bow-335
❑ 89BowTif-335
❑ 89CarNewE-8
❑ 89DodMot-16
❑ 89DodPol-26
❑ 89DodSmoG-89
❑ 89DodStaSV-9
❑ 89Don-610
❑ 89DonBasB-36
❑ 89Fle-64
❑ 89FleGlo-64
❑ 89OPC-212
❑ 89PanSti-22
❑ 89PanSti-98
❑ 89Sco-378
❑ 89Top-425
❑ 89TopBig-79
❑ 89TopSti-61
❑ 89TopTif-425
❑ 89UppDec-610
❑ 89Woo-30
❑ 90Bow-83
❑ 90BowTif-83
❑ 90DodMot-15
❑ 90DodPol-50
❑ 90DodTar-364
❑ 90Don-203
❑ 90DonBesN-66
❑ 90Fle-400
❑ 90FleCan-400
❑ 90K-M-13
❑ 90Lea-42
❑ 90OPC-40
❑ 90PanSti-274
❑ 90PubIntS-11
❑ 90RedFolSB-49
❑ 90Sco-227
❑ 90Spo-78
❑ 90Top-40
❑ 90TopMinL-59
❑ 90TopSti-65
❑ 90TopStiB-32
❑ 90TopTif-40
❑ 90TopTVA-47
❑ 90UppDec-508
❑ 91Bow-603
❑ 91DodMot-15
❑ 91DodPho-15
❑ 91DodPol-50
❑ 91DodSt.V-16
❑ 91Don-486
❑ 91Fle-209
❑ 91Lea-98
❑ 91OPC-770
❑ 91Sco-29
❑ 91StaClu-278
❑ 91StaCluP-17
❑ 91Top-770
❑ 91TopDesS-770
❑ 91TopMic-770
❑ 91TopTif-770
❑ 91Ult-163
❑ 91UppDec-558
❑ 92Bow-408
❑ 92DodMot-19
❑ 92DodPol-50

❑ 92DodSmo-9992
❑ 92DodStaTA-28
❑ 92Don-395
❑ 92Fle-460
❑ 92OPC-205
❑ 92Pin-444
❑ 92Sco-119
❑ 92StaClu-457
❑ 92Top-205
❑ 92TopGol-205
❑ 92TopGolW-205
❑ 92TopMic-205
❑ 92UppDec-511
❑ 92YanWIZ8-85
❑ 93BraLykP-12
❑ 93BraLykS-15
❑ 93BraStaC-19
❑ 93Don-538
❑ 93Fle-450
❑ 93FleFinE-2
❑ 93OPC-160
❑ 93PacSpa-150
❑ 93Top-311
❑ 93TopGol-311
❑ 93TopInaM-311
❑ 93TopInaR-311
❑ 93TopMic-311
❑ 93UppDec-731
❑ 93UppDecGold-731
❑ 94Fle-360
❑ 94Lea-322
❑ 94RanMagM-16
❑ 94StaCluT-262
❑ 94StaCluTFDI-262
❑ 94Top-592
❑ 94TopGol-592
❑ 94TopSpa-592
Howell, Ken
❑ 84AlbDukCr-165
❑ 85DodCokP-15
❑ 85DomLeaS-17
❑ 85Don-592
❑ 85Fle-374
❑ 85TopTifT-58T
❑ 85TopTra-58T
❑ 86DodCokP-14
❑ 86DodPol-43
❑ 86DodUniOP-9
❑ 86Don-275
❑ 86Fle-133
❑ 86OPC-349
❑ 86Top-654
❑ 86TopSti-69
❑ 86TopTif-654
❑ 87DodMot-19
❑ 87DodPho-7
❑ 87DodPol-22
❑ 87Don-229
❑ 87Fle-443
❑ 87FleGlo-443
❑ 87OPC-187
❑ 87PhiTas-37
❑ 87Top-477
❑ 87TopTif-477
❑ 88DodMot-24
❑ 88DodPol-43
❑ 88Don-130
❑ 88Fle-520
❑ 88FleGlo-520
❑ 88OPC-149
❑ 88Sco-406
❑ 88ScoGlo-406
❑ 88Top-149
❑ 88TopTif-149
❑ 89Bow-394
❑ 89BowTif-394
❑ 89DonBasB-184
❑ 89FleUpd-108
❑ 89PhiTas-11
❑ 89Top-93
❑ 89TopTif-93
❑ 89TopTra-54T
❑ 89TopTraT-54T
❑ 90Bow-147
❑ 90BowTif-147
❑ 90DodTar-365
❑ 90Don-430
❑ 90DonBesN-44
❑ 90Fle-561
❑ 90FleCan-561
❑ 90Lea-316
❑ 90OPC-756
❑ 90PanSti-314
❑ 90PhiTas-15
❑ 90PubIntS-240
❑ 90Top-756
❑ 90TopBig-269
❑ 90TopSti-116
❑ 90TopTif-756
❑ 90UppDec-559
❑ 91Don-204
❑ 91Fle-400
❑ 91OPC-209
❑ 91PanFreS-110
❑ 91PanSti-108
❑ 91PhiMed-20
❑ 91Sco-458
❑ 91StaClu-71
❑ 91Top-209
❑ 91TopDesS-209
❑ 91TopMic-209
❑ 91TopTif-209
❑ 91Ult-265
❑ 91UppDec-488
❑ 94SanBerSC-7
Howell, Pat
❑ 89PitMetS-11
❑ 89Sta-159
❑ 90ColMetGS-9
❑ 90ColMetPPI-3
❑ 90SouAtlLAS-35
❑ 91Cla/Bes-217
❑ 91FloStaLAP-FSL32
❑ 91St.LucMC-25
❑ 91St.LucMP-724
❑ 92DonRoo-55
❑ 92FleUpd-103
❑ 92ProFS7-284
❑ 92SkyAAAF-253
❑ 92TidTidF-910
❑ 92TidTidS-559
❑ 93Don-116
❑ 93PorBeaF-2393
❑ 93Top-215
❑ 93TopGol-215
❑ 93TopInaM-215
❑ 93TopInaR-215
❑ 93TopMic-215
❑ 93UppDec-161
❑ 93UppDecGold-161
❑ 94BinMetF-717
❑ 94NorTidF-2932
Howell, Peter
❑ 92KanCouCC-28
❑ 92KanCouCTI-14
❑ 93AlbPolCB-25
❑ 94AlbPolC-29
Howell, Roy Lee
❑ 74SpoIndC-41
❑ 75RanPos-17
❑ 76OPC-279
❑ 76SSP-265
❑ 76Top-279
❑ 77Top-608
❑ 78BluJayP-9
❑ 78Hos-84
❑ 78OPC-31
❑ 78Top-394
❑ 79BasPat-41
❑ 79BluJayBY-12
❑ 79Hos-137
❑ 79Kel-54
❑ 79OPC-45
❑ 79Top-101
❑ 80OPC-254
❑ 80Top-488
❑ 81Don-392
❑ 81Fle-417
❑ 81OPC-40
❑ 81Top-581
❑ 81TopTra-773
❑ 82BrePol-13
❑ 82Don-204
❑ 82Fle-145
❑ 82Top-68
❑ 83BrePol-13
❑ 83Don-358
❑ 83Fle-36
❑ 83Top-218
❑ 84BreGar-9
❑ 84BrePol-13
❑ 84Fle-203
❑ 84Nes792-687
❑ 84Top-687
❑ 84TopTif-687
❑ 85Don-577
❑ 85Top-372
❑ 85TopTif-372
❑ 86BluJayGT-4
❑ 89PacSenL-12
❑ 89T/MSenL-48
❑ 89TopSenL-88
❑ 90EliSenL-6
❑ 92BreCarT-10
❑ 93RanKee-198
❑ 94BreMilB-319
Hower, Dan
❑ 94HudValRC-7
❑ 94HudValRF-3377
❑ 94StaCluDP-57
❑ 94StaCluDPFDI-57
❑ 95ChaRivTI-20
Howerton, Bill
❑ 50Bow-239
❑ 51Bow-229
❑ 52Bow-119
❑ 52Top-167
❑ 53MotCoo-16
❑ 83TopRep5-167
Howerton, R.J.
❑ 96ButCopKB-15
Howerton, Rick
❑ 77WatIndT-13
Howerton, Troy
❑ 84NewOriT-3
Howes, Jeff
❑ 84LitFalMT-12
❑ 87HawRai-25
Howes, John
❑ 87BurExpP-1088
❑ 88WesPalBES-12
Howes, William
❑ 87OldJudN-253
Howey, Todd
❑ 87ClePhiP-26
❑ 88ClePhiS-14
Howie, Mark
❑ 85MadMusP-13
❑ 85MadMusT-16
❑ 86MadMusP-11
❑ 86MadMusP-11
❑ 87HunStaTI-14
❑ 88EasLeaAP-39
❑ 88WilBilP-1322
❑ 89MidAngGS-19
❑ 90LSUTigGM-2
❑ 90MidAngGS-7
❑ 91LinDriAA-436
❑ 91MidAngLD-436
❑ 91MidAngOHP-13
❑ 91MidAngP-442
❑ 92NasSouF-1838
❑ 92NasSouS-285
❑ 92ProFS7-31
❑ 92SkyAA F-292
❑ 92SkyAAAF-132
Howitt, Dann
❑ 86MedA'sC-67
❑ 87ModA'sC-7
❑ 87ModA'sP-20
❑ 88ModA'sCLC-67
❑ 88ModA'sTI-27
❑ 89HunStaB-7
❑ 90CMC-597
❑ 90Fle-644
❑ 90FleCan-644
❑ 90ProAAAF-147
❑ 90TacTigC-20
❑ 90TacTigP-100
❑ 90TopDeb89-62
❑ 90UppDec-747
❑ 91Bow-229
❑ 91LinDriAAA-538
❑ 91SouOreAAP-SOA17
❑ 91TacTigLD-538
❑ 91TacTigP-2315
❑ 91UppDec-442
❑ 92Bow-521
❑ 92Don-751
❑ 92Sco-861
❑ 92Sco100RS-68
❑ 92SkyAAAF-240
❑ 92TacTigS-537
❑ 93CalCanF-1177
❑ 93Don-349
❑ 94NasSouF-1261
❑ 94WhiSoxK-13
❑ 97ColSprSTI-10
Howley, Dan
❑ 08IndPos-13
❑ 11PinT-5-905
❑ 12HomRunKE-39
❑ 12Zee-62
❑ 33Gou-175
Howry, Bob
❑ 94EveGiaC-13
❑ 94EveGiaF-3648
❑ 94SigRooDP-89
❑ 94SigRooDPS-89
❑ 97ShrCap-12
❑ 97ShrCapB-12
❑ 97TexAllM-40
❑ 98FleUpd-U91
❑ 98LeaRS-327
❑ 98LeaRSLHolo-327
❑ 98LeaRSLong-327
❑ 98LeaRTrue-327
❑ 99Fle-434
❑ 99FleSta9-434
❑ 99FleWarT-434
❑ 99Top-364
❑ 99TopChr-364
❑ 99TopChrR-364
❑ 99TopMVPP-364
❑ 99Vic-99
Howser, Dick
❑ 61A'sTeal-8
❑ 61AthJayP-10
❑ 61Top-416
❑ 62Baz-10
❑ 62Jel-94
❑ 62Pos-94
❑ 62PosCan-94
❑ 62SalPlaC-31
❑ 62ShiPlaC-31
❑ 62Top-13
❑ 62TopBuc-39
❑ 62TopStal-53
❑ 62TopVen-13
❑ 63AthJayP-5
❑ 63BasMagM-39
❑ 63Fle-15
❑ 63Top-124
❑ 64Top-478
❑ 64TopRooAB-10
❑ 65Kah-17
❑ 65OPC-92
❑ 65Top-92
❑ 66IndTeal-6
❑ 66IndVolC-7
❑ 66Top-567
❑ 67Top-411
❑ 68Top-467
❑ 68YanPhoS-68
❑ 69MilBra-121
❑ 70YanPhoS-17
❑ 73OPC-116
❑ 73Top-116A
❑ 73Top-116B
❑ 78TCM60I-233
❑ 80Top-424
❑ 80YanPhoA-11
❑ 81Fle-84
❑ 82Roy-10
❑ 83Don-590
❑ 83RoyPos-14
❑ 83Top-96
❑ 84Nes792-471
❑ 84RoyPos-13
❑ 84Top-471
❑ 84TopTif-471
❑ 85RoyTeal-11
❑ 85Top-334
❑ 85TopTif-334
❑ 86RoyNatP-10
❑ 86RoyTeal-9
❑ 86Top-199
❑ 86TopTif-199
❑ 87DonAll-10
❑ 87DonP-10
❑ 87Top-18
❑ 87TopGloA-12
❑ 87TopTif-18
❑ 90OPC-661
❑ 90Top-661
❑ 90TopTif-661
❑ 92YanWIZ6-57
❑ 93RoySta2-4
Howze, Ben
❑ 89RocExpLC-13
❑ 90RocExpLC-10
❑ 91RocExpC-6
❑ 91RocExpP-2041
❑ 94DayCubC-9
❑ 94DayCubF-2346
Hoy, Dummy (William)
❑ 73FleWilD-8
❑ 87OldJudN-254
❑ 88WG1CarG-65
❑ 89EdgR.WG-13
❑ 94OriofB-44
❑ 98CamPepP-36
Hoy, Pete
❑ 89ElmPioP-5
❑ 90WinHavRSS-11
❑ 91LinDriAA-464
❑ 91NewBriRSLD-464
❑ 91NewBriRSP-349
❑ 92Bow-292
❑ 92Cla2-T92
❑ 92DonRoo-56
❑ 92Lea-515
❑ 92LeaBlaG-515
❑ 92PawRedSF-917
❑ 92Pin-526
❑ 92Ult-315
❑ 93ForLauRSC-13
❑ 93ForLauRSFP-1591
❑ 93NewBriRSF-1214
❑ 93RedSoxWHP-15
❑ 93Sco-230
❑ 97DunDonPPS-11
Hoy, Wayne
❑ 94St.CatBJC-13
❑ 94St.CatBJF-3638
❑ 95StCatSTI-7
Hoyer, Brad
❑ 88SpoIndP-1937
❑ 89WatDiaP-1794
❑ 89WatDiaS-14
❑ 90WatDiaB-8
❑ 90WatDiaP-2374
❑ 91LynRedSC-4
❑ 91LynRedSP-1193
Hoyt, Dave
❑ 82WisRapTF-5
❑ 83SprCarF-16
Hoyt, Dewey (LaMarr)
❑ 78AppFoxT-14
❑ 79IowOakP-9
❑ 80IowOakP-8
❑ 81Don-160
❑ 81Top-164
❑ 82Don-117
❑ 82Fle-345
❑ 82FleSta-190
❑ 82Top-428
❑ 83Don-632
❑ 83Fle-238
❑ 83FleSta-86
❑ 83FleSti-159
❑ 83OPC-226
❑ 83Top-591
❑ 83Top-618
❑ 83Top-705
❑ 83TopSti-16
❑ 83TopSti-53
❑ 83WhiSoxTV-31
❑ 84Don-488
❑ 84Fle-63
❑ 84FunFooP-91
❑ 84Nes792-97
❑ 84Nes792-135
❑ 84Nes792-405
❑ 84NesDreT-9
❑ 84OPC-97
❑ 84OPC-177
❑ 84SevCoi-C23
❑ 84Top-97
❑ 84Top-135
❑ 84Top-405
❑ 84TopGloS-32
❑ 84TopRubD-26
❑ 84TopSti-11
❑ 84TopSti-178
❑ 84TopSti-192
❑ 84TopSti-240
❑ 84TopSup-3
❑ 84TopTif-97
❑ 84TopTif-135
❑ 84TopTif-405
❑ 84WhiSoxTV-17
❑ 85Don-86
❑ 85DonHig-23
❑ 85Fle-517
❑ 85FleUpd-58
❑ 85Lea-37
❑ 85OPC-312
❑ 85PadMot-17
❑ 85Top-520
❑ 85TopMin-520
❑ 85TopRubD-26
❑ 85TopTif-520
❑ 85TopTifT-59T
❑ 85TopTra-59T
❑ 86Don-139
❑ 86DonAll-9
❑ 86DonPop-9
❑ 86Fle-325
❑ 86FleLimE-25
❑ 86FleStiC-63
❑ 86Lea-61
❑ 86OPC-380
❑ 86Spo-59
❑ 86Spo-193
❑ 86Top-380
❑ 86TopGloA-21
❑ 86TopSti-113
❑ 86TopSti-154
❑ 86TopTat-14
❑ 86TopTif-380
❑ 87Don-434
❑ 87Fle-418
❑ 87FleGlo-418
❑ 87Top-275
❑ 87TopTif-275
❑ 92PacSea-59
Hoyt, Todd
❑ 94AugGreC-30
Hoyt, Waite
❑ 20GasAmeMBD-10
❑ 20NatCarE-47
❑ 21E121So1-46
❑ 21E121So8-39
❑ 21KoBreWSI-36
❑ 21Nei-44
❑ 22E120-64
❑ 22W572-46
❑ 22W573-65
❑ 22W575-60
❑ 22WilPatV-32
❑ 23MapCriV-7
❑ 23W501-32
❑ 23W503-11
❑ 23W515-8
❑ 23WilChoV-67
❑ 26SpoComoA-22
❑ 28StaPlaCE-38
❑ 28W502-30
❑ 28W513-62
❑ 28W56PlaC-H11
❑ 28Yue-30
❑ 29ExhFou-25
❑ 29PorandAR-43
❑ 30W554-7
❑ 31Exh-24
❑ 33ButCanV-28
❑ 33Gou-60
❑ 33GouCanV-60
❑ 34BabRutG-36
❑ 34ButPreR-35
❑ 34DiaMatCSB-94
❑ 35DiaMatCS3T1-78
❑ 35GouPuzR-1E
❑ 35GouPuzR-3C
❑ 35GouPuzR-5C
❑ 35GouPuzR-14C
❑ 36GouWidPPR-A55
❑ 36NatChiFPR-46
❑ 36WorWidGV-39
❑ 40PlaBal-118
❑ 56RedBurB-7
❑ 59RedBurBP-5
❑ 60Fle-69
❑ 61Fle-44
❑ 68LauWorS-18
❑ 71FleWorS-19
❑ 73TCMAllG-8
❑ 74A's192T-12
❑ 75Yan192T-11
❑ 76ShaPiz-114
❑ 77BobParHoF-61
❑ 77GalGloG-117
❑ 78DexHaloFP-22
❑ 79DiaGre-32
❑ 79Yan192T-14
❑ 80PerHaloFP-113
❑ 80SSPHOF-113
❑ 82DiaCla-28
❑ 82OhiHaloF-7
❑ 84OCoandSI-111
❑ 84Yan192G-18
❑ 85FegMurCG-11
❑ 86ConSer1-26
❑ 87Yan192T-4
❑ 89DodSmoG-10
❑ 89HOFStiB-71
❑ 90DodTar-366
❑ 91ConTSN-115
❑ 92ConTSN-468
❑ 92MegRut-157
❑ 92YanWIZH-16
❑ 93ConTSN-757
❑ 93DiaStaES-137
Hrabar, Shaun

❑ 91KanCouCC-1
❑ 91KanCouCP-2671
❑ 91KanCouCTI-11
❑ 91PerHeaF-3
❑ 93AusFut-72
Hrabcsak, Edward
❑ 52Par-87
Hrabosky, Al
❑ 70CarTeal-16
❑ 71OPC-594
❑ 71Top-594
❑ 73OPC-153
❑ 73Top-153
❑ 74OPC-108
❑ 74Top-108
❑ 75OPC-122
❑ 75St.LouCP-15
❑ 75Top-122
❑ 75TopMin-122
❑ 76BlaDis-20
❑ 76BucDis-20
❑ 76CarDis-20
❑ 76CraDis-20
❑ 76DailsID-20
❑ 76Hos-50
❑ 76HosTwi-50
❑ 76IsaDis-20
❑ 76Kel-23
❑ 76OPC-205
❑ 76OPC-315
❑ 76OrbDis-20
❑ 76RedBarD-20
❑ 76SafDis-20
❑ 76SSP-291
❑ 76St.LouCP-16
❑ 76Top-205
❑ 76Top-315
❑ 76TowCluD-20
❑ 77BurCheD-10
❑ 77Car5-12
❑ 77CarTeal-11
❑ 77ChiWilD-31
❑ 77DailsID-31
❑ 77DetCaeD-31
❑ 77HolInnD-31
❑ 77MSADis-31
❑ 77PepGloD-37
❑ 77SagDis-31
❑ 77sDis-31
❑ 77Top-495
❑ 77WenDis-31
❑ 77ZipDis-31
❑ 78RCColC-80
❑ 78Roy-8
❑ 78SSP270-228
❑ 78Top-230
❑ 78WifBalD-30
❑ 79Hos-25
❑ 79OPC-19
❑ 79Top-45
❑ 80OPC-306
❑ 80Top-585
❑ 81BraPol-39
❑ 81Don-550
❑ 81Fle-262
❑ 81OPC-354
❑ 81Top-636
❑ 82BraBurKL-12
❑ 82BraPol-39
❑ 82Don-97
❑ 82Fle-438A
❑ 82Fle-438B
❑ 82Fle-438C
❑ 82OPC-393
❑ 82Top-393
❑ 83Don-475
❑ 89PacLegI-115
❑ 89PacSenL-179
❑ 89T/MSenL-49
❑ 89TopSenL-15
❑ 91SweBasG-43
❑ 91UppDecS-14
❑ 92CarMcD-55
❑ 99SpoIllGotG-71
❑ 99SpoIllGotGA-32
Hrbek, Kent
❑ 80WisRapTT-18
❑ 82Don-557
❑ 82Top-766
❑ 82TopTra-44T
❑ 82TwiPos-16
❑ 83AllGamPI-4
❑ 83Don-19
❑ 83Don-179
❑ 83DonActA-49
❑ 83Fle-616
❑ 83Fle-633
❑ 83FleSta-87
❑ 83FleSti-135
❑ 83Kel-53
❑ 83OPC-251
❑ 83Top-690
❑ 83Top-771
❑ 83TopGloS-35
❑ 83TopSti-88
❑ 83TopSti-313
❑ 83TwiTeal-9
❑ 83TwiTeal-31
❑ 83TwiTeal-33
❑ 84AllGamPI-95
❑ 84Don-70
❑ 84DonActAS-37
❑ 84Fle-567
❑ 84FunFooP-111
❑ 84MinTwiP-16
❑ 84Nes792-11
❑ 84Nes792-345
❑ 84OCoandSI-38
❑ 84OPC-345
❑ 84SevCoi-C11
❑ 84Top-11
❑ 84Top-345
❑ 84TopRubD-17
❑ 84TopSti-305
❑ 84TopTif-11
❑ 84TopTif-345
❑ 84TwiTeal-10
❑ 85AllGamPI-5
❑ 85Don-70
❑ 85DonActA-40
❑ 85Dra-16
❑ 85Fle-281
❑ 85FleLimE-13
❑ 85KASDis-7
❑ 85KitCloD-7
❑ 85Lea-200
❑ 85OPC-308
❑ 85SevCoi-C11
❑ 85SubDis-13
❑ 85ThoMcAD-13
❑ 85Top-510
❑ 85TopRubD-16
❑ 85TopSti-296
❑ 85TopSup-41
❑ 85TopTif-510
❑ 85Twi7-4
❑ 85TwiPos-13
❑ 85TwiTeal-10
❑ 86Don-70
❑ 86DonHig-19
❑ 86DorChe-6
❑ 86Fle-397
❑ 86FleLeaL-20
❑ 86FleMin-84
❑ 86FleSlu-17
❑ 86FleStiC-64
❑ 86GenMilB-2F
❑ 86Lea-67
❑ 86OPC-63
❑ 86Spo-36
❑ 86Top-430
❑ 86TopSti-277
❑ 86TopTat-17
❑ 86TopTif-430
❑ 86TruVal-24
❑ 86TwiTeal-9
❑ 87BoaandB-28
❑ 87ClaGam-53
❑ 87Don-73
❑ 87DonOpeD-228
❑ 87Fle-544
❑ 87FleExcS-29
❑ 87FleGlo-544
❑ 87FleLimE-22
❑ 87FleMin-57
❑ 87FleStiC-64
❑ 87KraFoo-25
❑ 87Lea-99
❑ 87OPC-161
❑ 87RedFolSB-49
❑ 87Spo-15
❑ 87SpoTeaP-17
❑ 87StuPan-22
❑ 87Top-679
❑ 87TopCoi-13
❑ 87TopGloS-25
❑ 87TopSti-281
❑ 87TopTif-679
❑ 87TwiPos-11
❑ 87TwiTeal-8
❑ 88ClaRed-192
❑ 88Don-320
❑ 88DonBasB-102
❑ 88Fle-13
❑ 88FleBasA-17
❑ 88FleGlo-13
❑ 88FleGlo-WS9
❑ 88FleLeaL-21
❑ 88FleMin-35
❑ 88FleStiC-44
❑ 88FleSup-17
❑ 88FleTeaL-14
❑ 88FleWorS-9
❑ 88Lea-139
❑ 88MSAJifPD-10
❑ 88OPC-45
❑ 88PanSti-136
❑ 88Sco-43
❑ 88ScoGlo-43
❑ 88Spo-95
❑ 88StaLinTw-10
❑ 88Top-45
❑ 88Top-609
❑ 88TopBig-84
❑ 88TopClo-49
❑ 88TopGloS-8
❑ 88TopMinL-22
❑ 88TopSti-24
❑ 88TopSti-274
❑ 88TopTif-45
❑ 88TopTif-609
❑ 88TopUKM-37
❑ 88TopUKMT-37
❑ 88TwiMasBD-10
❑ 88TwiSmoC-3
❑ 88Woo-30
❑ 89Bow-157
❑ 89BowTif-157
❑ 89CadEllD-30
❑ 89ClaLigB-55
❑ 89Don-199
❑ 89DonBasB-18
❑ 89Fle-116
❑ 89FleGlo-116
❑ 89OPC-265
❑ 89PanSti-387
❑ 89RedFolSB-62
❑ 89Sco-382
❑ 89ScoHot1S-14
❑ 89Spo-188
❑ 89Top-265
❑ 89TopBasT-157
❑ 89TopBatL-16
❑ 89TopBig-209
❑ 89TopCoi-42
❑ 89TopGloS-7
❑ 89TopSti-287
❑ 89TopTif-265
❑ 89TopUKM-41
❑ 89TVSpoM-101
❑ 89UppDec-213
❑ 90AllBasT-20
❑ 90Bow-418
❑ 90BowTif-418
❑ 90ClaUpd-T23
❑ 90Don-81
❑ 90DonBesA-65
❑ 90DonLeaS-36
❑ 90Fle-378
❑ 90FleBasM-20
❑ 90FleBasMC-20
❑ 90FleCan-378
❑ 90Lea-228
❑ 90M.Vpin-57
❑ 90MLBBasB-97
❑ 90OPC-125
❑ 90PanSti-112
❑ 90PublntS-290
❑ 90PublntS-330
❑ 90RedFolSB-50
❑ 90Sco-381
❑ 90Spo-203
❑ 90Top-125
❑ 90TopAmeA-19
❑ 90TopBatL-22
❑ 90TopBig-27
❑ 90TopCoi-18
❑ 90TopHilHM-11
❑ 90TopSti-287
❑ 90TopTif-125
❑ 90UppDec-452
❑ 91BasBesHRK-10
❑ 91Bow-321
❑ 91Cla2-T15
❑ 91ClaGam-118
❑ 91DenHol-7
❑ 91DodPho-20
❑ 91Don-95
❑ 91Fle-614
❑ 91Lea-313
❑ 91OPC-710
❑ 91PanFreS-300
❑ 91PanSti-251
❑ 91RedFolS-50
❑ 91Sco-292
❑ 91Sco100S-78
❑ 91StaClu-248
❑ 91Stu-87
❑ 91SunSee-13
❑ 91Top-710
❑ 91TopCraJ2-24
❑ 91TopDesS-710
❑ 91TopMic-710
❑ 91TopTif-710
❑ 91TopTriH-A9
❑ 91Ult-189
❑ 91UppDec-167
❑ 92Bow-445
❑ 92ClaGam-94
❑ 92DenHol-19
❑ 92Don-326
❑ 92DonCraJ1-29
❑ 92Fle-205
❑ 92Hig5-83
❑ 92Lea-362
❑ 92LeaBlaG-362
❑ 92New-11
❑ 92OPC-347
❑ 92OPCPre-46
❑ 92PanSti-115
❑ 92Pin-68
❑ 92RedFolS-48
❑ 92Sco-530
❑ 92Sco100S-98
❑ 92ScoProP-17
❑ 92StaClu-235
❑ 92StaCluD-89
❑ 92Stu-205
❑ 92Top-347
❑ 92TopGol-347
❑ 92TopGolW-347
❑ 92TopKid-111
❑ 92TopMic-347
❑ 92TriPla-135
❑ 92Ult-92
❑ 92UppDec-334
❑ 93Bow-677
❑ 93DiaMar-53
❑ 93Don-283
❑ 93DonLonBL-LL7
❑ 93Fin-117
❑ 93FinRef-117
❑ 93Fla-236
❑ 93Fle-267
❑ 93Lea-76
❑ 93MetBak-31
❑ 93OPC-150
❑ 93PacSpa-171
❑ 93PanSti-125
❑ 93Pin-27
❑ 93Pin-307
❑ 93PinHomRC-45
❑ 93Sco-98
❑ 93Sel-80
❑ 93SP-247
❑ 93StaClu-525
❑ 93StaCluFDI-525
❑ 93StaCluMOP-525
❑ 93Stu-35
❑ 93Top-9
❑ 93TopGol-9
❑ 93ToplnaM-9
❑ 93ToplnaR-9
❑ 93TopMic-9
❑ 93TriPla-128
❑ 93Ult-231
❑ 93UppDec-50
❑ 93UppDec-74
❑ 93UppDecGold-50
❑ 93UppDecGold-74
❑ 94ColC-486
❑ 94ColChoGS-486
❑ 94ColChoSS-486
❑ 94DenHol-16
❑ 94Don-443
❑ 94Fin-261
❑ 94FinRef-261
❑ 94Fla-75
❑ 94Fle-208
❑ 94FleExtB-117
❑ 94Lea-269
❑ 94LeaL-48
❑ 94OPC-261
❑ 94Pac-355
❑ 94PanSti-91
❑ 94Pin-206
❑ 94PinArtP-206
❑ 94PinMusC-206
❑ 94ProMag-76
❑ 94Sco-65
❑ 94ScoGolR-65
❑ 94Sel-261
❑ 94Spo-100
❑ 94StaClu-224
❑ 94StaCluFDI-224
❑ 94StaCluGR-224
❑ 94StaCluMOP-224
❑ 94StaCluMOP-ST23
❑ 94StaCluST-ST23
❑ 94Stu-196
❑ 94Top-490
❑ 94TopGol-490
❑ 94TopSpa-490
❑ 94TriPla-253
❑ 94Ult-87
❑ 94UppDec-98
❑ 94UppDecAJ-14
❑ 94UppDecAJG-14
❑ 94UppDecED-98
❑ 95ColChoSE-227
❑ 95ColChoSEGS-227
❑ 95ColChoSESS-227
❑ 95Pac-249
❑ 95UppDec-195
❑ 95UppDecED-195
❑ 95UppDecEDG-195
❑ 99SpoIllGotG-57
❑ 99SpoIllGotGA-33
❑ 99SpoIllGotGC-44
Hreha, Dan
❑ 90ArkRaz-17
Hriniak, Walt
❑ 69Top-611
❑ 70OPC-392
❑ 70Top-392
❑ 75ExpPos-16
❑ 90WhiSoxC-30
❑ 91WhiSoxK-NNO
❑ 92WhiSoxK-NNO
❑ 93WhiSoxK-30
❑ 94WhiSoxK-30
❑ 95WhiSoxK-27
❑ 95WhiSoxK-31
Hritz, Derrick
❑ 93BurIndC-12
❑ 93BurIndF-3291
❑ 95WatIndTI-16
Hrovat, Dale
❑ 75WatRoyT-16
❑ 76WatRoyT-11
❑ 77HolMilT-15
❑ 78SpoIndC-4
Hrusovsky, John
❑ 91PriRedC-8
❑ 91PriRedP-3507
❑ 92ChaWheF-3
❑ 92ChaWVWC-3
❑ 92ProFS7-221
❑ 93CarLeaAGF-41
❑ 93ClaGolF-187
❑ 93SouAtlLAPI-17
❑ 93WinSpiC-9
❑ 93WinSpiF-1564
❑ 94CanIndF-3116
❑ 94ChaLooF-1357
❑ 94ExcFS7-176
Hrynko, Larry
❑ 80WatIndT-11
❑ 81WatIndT-4
❑ 82ChaChaT-6
❑ 83ChaChaT-3
Hubbard, Cal
❑ 55Bow-315
❑ 76ShaPiz-154
❑ 80PerHaloFP-154
❑ 80PerHaloFPS-30
❑ 80SSPHOF-154
❑ 89HOFStiB-99
❑ 90BasWit-75
Hubbard, Don
❑ 78WatIndT-13
Hubbard, Glenn
❑ 78BraCok-7
❑ 78RicBraT-5
❑ 79Top-715
❑ 80RicBraT-15
❑ 81AllGamPI-102
❑ 81BraPol-17
❑ 81Don-459
❑ 81Fle-260
❑ 81OPC-247
❑ 81Top-247
❑ 81TopSti-149
❑ 82BraBurKL-13
❑ 82BraPol-17
❑ 82Don-436
❑ 82Fle-437
❑ 82Top-482
❑ 82TopSti-23
❑ 83AllGamPI-103
❑ 83BraPol-17
❑ 83Don-184
❑ 83Fle-139
❑ 83OPC-322
❑ 83Top-624
❑ 83TopSti-215
❑ 84AllGamPI-12
❑ 84BraPol-17
❑ 84Don-432
❑ 84Fle-182
❑ 84Nes792-25
❑ 84OPC-25
❑ 84raPho-14
❑ 84Top-25
❑ 84TopSti-29
❑ 84TopTif-25
❑ 85AllGamPI-102
❑ 85BraHos-12
❑ 85BraPol-17
❑ 85Don-199
❑ 85Fle-329
❑ 85Lea-242
❑ 85OPC-195
❑ 85Top-195
❑ 85TopSti-33
❑ 85TopTif-195
❑ 86BraPol-17
❑ 86Don-141
❑ 86Fle-518
❑ 86Lea-71
❑ 86OPC-112
❑ 86Top-539
❑ 86TopSti-36
❑ 86TopTat-4
❑ 86TopTif-539
❑ 87BraSmo-21
❑ 87Don-634
❑ 87DonOpeD-48
❑ 87Fle-519
❑ 87FleGlo-519
❑ 87OPC-68
❑ 87SpoTeaP-24
❑ 87Top-31
❑ 87Top-745
❑ 87TopTif-31
❑ 87TopTif-745
❑ 88A'sMot-18
❑ 88Don-22
❑ 88Don-314
❑ 88DonSupD-22
❑ 88DonTeaBA-NEW
❑ 88Fle-542
❑ 88FleGlo-542
❑ 88Lea-22
❑ 88OPC-325
❑ 88PanSti-243
❑ 88RedFolSB-36
❑ 88Sco-111
❑ 88ScoGlo-111
❑ 88ScoRoo-58T
❑ 88ScoRooG-58T
❑ 88StaLinBra-9
❑ 88Top-325
❑ 88TopBig-200
❑ 88TopTif-325
❑ 88TopTra-53T
❑ 88TopTraT-53T
❑ 89A'sMot-19
❑ 89Bow-199
❑ 89BowTif-199
❑ 89Don-568
❑ 89Fle-12
❑ 89FleGlo-12
❑ 89Sco-34
❑ 89Top-237
❑ 89TopBig-232
❑ 89TopTif-237
❑ 89UppDec-395
❑ 90RicBra2ATI-11
❑ 91MacBraC-10
❑ 91MacBraP-882
❑ 92MacBraC-27
❑ 92MacBraF-285
❑ 92UppDecS-4
❑ 93RicBraF-203
❑ 93RicBraRC-3

❑ 94MacBraC-29
❑ 94MacBraF-2224
❑ 95RicBraTI-28
❑ 96RicBraB-3
❑ 97MacBra-30
❑ 98MacBraM-27
Hubbard, Jack
❑ 89Ft.LauYS-28
Hubbard, Jeff
❑ 89ChaRanS-28
❑ 90ChaRanS-30
❑ 91LinDriAA-600
❑ 91TulDriP-2790
❑ 91TulDriTI-13
Hubbard, Jeremy
❑ 98WilCubM-15
Hubbard, Joe
❑ 90EliTwiS-26
Hubbard, Mark
❑ 91OneYanP-4165
❑ 92ClaFS7-306
❑ 92GreHorC-24
❑ 92GreHorF-793
❑ 92StaCluD-90
❑ 93PriWilCC-15
❑ 93PriWilCF-670
❑ 94GreBatF-467
❑ 95NorNagUTI-38
❑ 95TamYanYI-11
❑ 96SigRooOJTP-T3
❑ 97GreBatC-9
❑ 97NorNav-19
Hubbard, Mike
❑ 92GenCubC-15
❑ 92GenCubF-1563
❑ 93DayCubC-10
❑ 93DayCubF-862
❑ 93FloStaLAF-31
❑ 94Bow-606
❑ 94ClaGolF-50
❑ 94OrlCubF-1389
❑ 95Bow-34
❑ 95Exc-164
❑ 95IowCubTI-16
❑ 96Fle-321
❑ 96FleTif-321
❑ 96IowCubB-15
❑ 97IowCub-14
❑ 98PacInvGems-132
Hubbard, Trenidad
❑ 86AubAstP-12
❑ 87AshTouP-2
❑ 88OscAstS-15
❑ 89ColMudP-132
❑ 89ColMudS-13
❑ 91JacGenLD-561
❑ 91JacGenP-932
❑ 91LinDriAA-561
❑ 92TucTorF-496
❑ 92TucTorS-610
❑ 93ColSprSSF-3094
❑ 93ExcFS7-45
❑ 93LinVenB-89
❑ 94ColSprSSF-744
❑ 94TopTra-56T
❑ 94TriAAF-AAA28
❑ 96ColSprSSTI-18
❑ 96Don-64
❑ 96DonPreP-64
❑ 96FleUpd-U128
❑ 96FleUpdTC-U128
❑ 96RocPol-10
❑ 96StaClu-447
❑ 96StaCluMOP-447
❑ 96Top-103
❑ 96Ult-468
❑ 96UltGolM-468
❑ 97BufBis-18
❑ 97ColSprSATTI-22
❑ 97DonSigA-52
❑ 97DonSigAC-62
❑ 97DonSigAM-63
❑ 98DodMot-25
❑ 98DodPol-12
❑ 98PacOnl-373
❑ 98PacOnlR-373
❑ 98PacOnlWC-373
❑ 99Pac-220
❑ 99PacPlaB-220
❑ 99PacRed-220
Hubbard, Ty III
❑ 83TamTarT-15
Hubbel, Travis
❑ 98St.CatSM-6
Hubbell, Carl
❑ 28PorandAR-A17
❑ 28PorandAR-B17
❑ 30SchR33-22
❑ 32GiaSch-1
❑ 33Gou-230
❑ 33Gou-234
❑ 33NatLeaAC-12
❑ 33SpoKin-42
❑ 33WorCig-57
❑ 34BatR31-5
❑ 34DiaMatCSB-95
❑ 34DiaStaR-39
❑ 34ExhFou-5
❑ 34Gou-12
❑ 34GouCanV-71
❑ 34HOFStiB-32
❑ 35DiaMatCS2-10
❑ 35DiaMatCS3T1-79
❑ 35ExhFou-5
❑ 35WheBB1-16
❑ 36DiaMatCS4-6
❑ 36ExhFou-5
❑ 36GouWidPPR-C18
❑ 36SandSW-35
❑ 36WheBB3-7
❑ 36WheBB5-11
❑ 37DixLid-4
❑ 37DixPre-4
❑ 37ExhFou-5
❑ 37WheBB14-7
❑ 37WheBB6-6
❑ 37WheBB8-7
❑ 37WheBB9-9
❑ 38CloFotW-42
❑ 38DixLid-4
❑ 38DixLidP-4
❑ 38ExhFou-5
❑ 38OurNatGPP-16
❑ 38WheBB10-5
❑ 38WheBB15-6
❑ 39ExhSal-29
❑ 39PC7AlbHoF-53
❑ 39PlaBal-53
❑ 40PlaBal-87
❑ 41DouPlaR-139
❑ 41Gou-20
❑ 41PlaBal-6
❑ 43MPR302-1-15
❑ 46SpoExcW-7-4
❑ 47PM1StaP1-91
❑ 47PM1StaP1-92
❑ 48ExhHoF-16
❑ 48SweSpoT-8
❑ 50CalHOFW-40
❑ 51R42SmaS-49
❑ 53ArtHaloFP-46
❑ 58JayPubAG-5
❑ 59OklTodML-13
❑ 60Fle-4
❑ 60NuHi-11
❑ 61Fle-45
❑ 61GolPre-6
❑ 61NuSco-479
❑ 67TopVen-172
❑ 68LauWorS-34
❑ 69EquSpoHoF-BB8
❑ 70FleWorS-34
❑ 70MetMusoAB-3
❑ 71FleWorS-31
❑ 72LauGreF-36
❑ 72TCMthe3-39
❑ 72TCMthe3-40
❑ 73SevTraC-32
❑ 74Bra193NLA-12
❑ 74LauAllG-34
❑ 74NewYorNTDiS-10
❑ 75GiaAllT-3
❑ 76GalBasGHoF-15
❑ 76GrePlaG-2
❑ 76RowExh-12
❑ 76ShaPiz-53
❑ 77BobParHoF-27
❑ 77GalGloG-88
❑ 77GalGloG-208
❑ 77GalGloG-240
❑ 79DiaGre-35
❑ 80GiaGreT-3
❑ 80PacLeg-89
❑ 80PerHaloFP-53
❑ 80PerHaloFPS-1
❑ 80SSPHOF-53
❑ 82DiaCla-6
❑ 82TCMGreP-37
❑ 83BigLeaCOA-31
❑ 83ConMar-43
❑ 83DonHOFH-33
❑ 83TCMPla1942-34
❑ 84DonCha-55
❑ 84OCoandSI-130
❑ 84SpoDesPW-32
❑ 85FegMurCG-12
❑ 86ConSer1-15
❑ 86SpoDecG-6
❑ 86TCM-4
❑ 87HygAllG-26
❑ 87NesDreT-10
❑ 87SpoRea-31
❑ 88ConNatA-11
❑ 88ConSer3-15
❑ 89HOFStiB-75
❑ 90BasWit-95
❑ 90HOFStiB-32
❑ 90PerGreM-35
❑ 91ConTSN-10
❑ 91ConTSN-253
❑ 92ConTSN-360
❑ 92ConTSN-552
❑ 92ConTSNCI-12
❑ 92ConTSNGI-665
❑ 93ActPacA-103
❑ 93ActPacA2-37G
❑ 93ConTSN-665
❑ 93ConTSNP-1105
❑ 93LegFoi-5
❑ 93UppDecAH-69
❑ 93UppDecAH-136
❑ 94ConTSN-1105
❑ 94ConTSNB-1105
❑ 94UppDecTAE-46
❑ 99UppDecCL-45
❑ 99UppDecCLCC-45
Hubbell, Wilbert
❑ 20NatCarE-48
❑ 21Exh-79
❑ 21Nei-96
❑ 22E120-199
❑ 22W572-47
❑ 25Exh-45
❑ 29Zee-44
❑ 30Zee-175
❑ 31Zee-89
❑ 90DodTar-987
Hubbs, Dan
❑ 93GreFalDSP-21
❑ 94SanAntMF-2462
❑ 95SanAntMTI-34
❑ 97AlbDukGS-16
❑ 98AlbDukG-10
❑ 98YakBeaG-21
Hubbs, Ken
❑ 47Exh-103
❑ 62CubJayP-8
❑ 62Top-461
❑ 63Baz-27
❑ 63CubJayP-6
❑ 63ExhStaB-32
❑ 63Jel-174
❑ 63Pos-174
❑ 63Top-15
❑ 63TopStil-19
❑ 64Top-550
❑ 66Top-447
❑ 84CubBriPC-7D
❑ 84CubUno-2
❑ 92CubOldS-14
Huber, Aaron
❑ 94SouOreAC-12
❑ 94SouOreAF-3616
Huber, Clarence
❑ 22MrsShePP-4
❑ 26Exh-45
Huber, Jeff
❑ 91ChaRaiC-7
❑ 91ChaRaiP-93
❑ 92ChaRaiC-10
❑ 92ChaRaiF-119
❑ 93RanCucQC-17
❑ 93RanCucQF-828
❑ 94WicWraF-185
❑ 97El PasDB-16
❑ 97TucTorB-6
Huble, Ian
❑ 91WavRedF-5
Huckaby, Ken
❑ 91GreFalDSP-17
❑ 92ClaFS7-353
❑ 92VerBeaDC-27
❑ 92VerBeaDF-2878
❑ 93FloStaLAF-47
❑ 93VerBeaDC-9
❑ 93VerBeaDF-2223
❑ 94BakDodC-10
❑ 94ExcFS7-216
❑ 94SanAntMF-2472
❑ 97AlbDukGS-17
Hudak, Joe
❑ 88MisStaB-37
❑ 90MisStaB-41
❑ 91MisStaB-29
Hudek, John
❑ 88SouBenWSGS-22
❑ 89SarWhiSS-11
❑ 89Sta-59
❑ 90Bes-296
❑ 90BirBarB-19
❑ 90BirBarP-1107
❑ 90CMC-771
❑ 91BirBarLD-63
❑ 91BirBarP-1451
❑ 91LinDriAA-63
❑ 92BirBarS-84
❑ 92SkyAA F-40
❑ 92VanCanF-2718
❑ 92VanCanS-641
❑ 93TolMudHF-1650
❑ 94AstMot-17
❑ 94Bow-34
❑ 94Fla-390
❑ 94FlaWavotF-B4
❑ 94FleAllR-M6
❑ 94FleExtB-276
❑ 94FleUpd-143
❑ 94LeaLimR-57
❑ 94ScoRoo-RT104
❑ 94ScoRooGR-RT104
❑ 94Sel-405
❑ 94SP-31
❑ 94SPDieC-31
❑ 94SpoRooRS-TR1
❑ 94TopTra-45T
❑ 94UppDec-517
❑ 94UppDecED-517
❑ 94VenLinU-13
❑ 95AstMot-18
❑ 95Bow-400
❑ 95ColCho-108
❑ 95ColChoGS-108
❑ 95ColChoSE-42
❑ 95ColChoSEGS-42
❑ 95ColChoSESS-42
❑ 95ColChoSS-108
❑ 95Don-170
❑ 95DonPreP-170
❑ 95DonTopotO-254
❑ 95Emo-138
❑ 95Fin-9
❑ 95FinFlaT-FT4
❑ 95FinRef-9
❑ 95Fla-147
❑ 95Fle-463
❑ 95FleAllS-21
❑ 95FleRooS-9
❑ 95Lea-187
❑ 95Pac-189
❑ 95PanSti-104
❑ 95Pin-149
❑ 95PinArtP-149
❑ 95PinMusC-149
❑ 95Sco-543
❑ 95ScoGolR-543
❑ 95ScoPlaTS-543
❑ 95StaClu-279
❑ 95StaCluMOP-279
❑ 95StaCluSTWS-279
❑ 95StaCluVR-143
❑ 95StaCluVRMO-143
❑ 95Top-500
❑ 95TopCyb-290
❑ 95Ult-173
❑ 95UltAllR-6
❑ 95UltAllRGM-6
❑ 95UltGolM-173
❑ 95UltSecYS-8
❑ 95UltSecYSGM-8
❑ 95UppDec-277
❑ 95UppDecED-277
❑ 95UppDecEDG-277
❑ 95UppDecSE-43
❑ 95UppDecSEG-43
❑ 96AstMot-19
❑ 96Fle-410
❑ 96FleTif-410
❑ 96LeaSigA-110
❑ 96LeaSigAG-110
❑ 96LeaSigAS-110
❑ 96StaClu-406
❑ 96StaCluMOP-406
❑ 96UppDec-419
❑ 97AstMot-18
❑ 97Fle-694
❑ 97FleTif-694
❑ 97Ult-317
❑ 97UltGolME-317
❑ 97UltPlaME-317
❑ 98PacOnl-478
❑ 98PacOnlR-478
❑ 98PacOnlWC-478
❑ 99Pac-113
❑ 99PacPlaB-113
❑ 99PacRed-113
Hudgens, Dave
❑ 79WatIndT-29
❑ 83TacTigT-16
❑ 84TacTigC-74
❑ 93JacGenF-2124
Hudgens, James
❑ 27Zee-136
❑ 28Zee-155
Hudik, Matt
❑ 90St.CatBJP-3452
Hudler, Rex
❑ 82NasSouTI-14
❑ 84ColCliP-13
❑ 84ColCliT-8
❑ 85ColCliP-14
❑ 85ColCliT-18
❑ 85Don-469
❑ 85YanTCMP-26
❑ 86RocRedWP-8
❑ 87RocRedWT-28
❑ 88BlaYNPRWL-152
❑ 88ExpPos-15
❑ 88FleUpd-101
❑ 88FleUpdG-101
❑ 88IndIndC-10
❑ 88IndIndP-513
❑ 89Bow-364
❑ 89BowTif-364
❑ 89Don-452
❑ 89Fle-380
❑ 89FleGlo-380
❑ 89OPC-346
❑ 89Sco-470
❑ 89Top-346
❑ 89TopBig-248
❑ 89TopTif-346
❑ 89UppDec-405
❑ 90CarSmo-10
❑ 90Don-366
❑ 90ExpPos-17
❑ 90Lea-439
❑ 90OPC-647
❑ 90PubIntS-177
❑ 90Sco-287
❑ 90Top-647
❑ 90TopTif-647
❑ 90UppDec-411
❑ 91Bow-409
❑ 91CarPol-10
❑ 91Don-599
❑ 91FleUpd-116
❑ 91Lea-212
❑ 91OPC-228
❑ 91OriCro-206
❑ 91PanFreS-37
❑ 91Sco-589
❑ 91StaClu-280
❑ 91Stu-233
❑ 91Top-228
❑ 91TopDesS-228
❑ 91TopMic-228
❑ 91TopTif-228
❑ 91UppDec-482
❑ 92CarPol-8
❑ 92Don-438
❑ 92Fle-581
❑ 92Lea-25
❑ 92LeaBlaG-25
❑ 92OPC-47
❑ 92Pin-315
❑ 92Pin-589
❑ 92Sco-180
❑ 92StaClu-851
❑ 92StaCluNC-851
❑ 92Stu-92
❑ 92Top-47
❑ 92TopGol-47
❑ 92TopGolW-47
❑ 92TopMic-47
❑ 92TriPla-41
❑ 92TriPla-207
❑ 92Ult-568
❑ 92UppDec-670
❑ 92YanWIZ8-86
❑ 93Don-96
❑ 93Fle-510
❑ 93StaClu-113
❑ 93StaCluFDI-113
❑ 93StaCluMOP-113
❑ 94AngLAT-16
❑ 94AngMot-20
❑ 94FleUpd-17
❑ 94ScoRoo-RT56
❑ 94ScoRooGR-RT56
❑ 94Sel-367
❑ 94SpoRoo-141
❑ 94SpoRooAP-141
❑ 94StaClu-685
❑ 94StaCluFDI-685
❑ 94StaCluGR-685
❑ 94StaCluMOP-685
❑ 95AngCHP-10
❑ 95AngMot-26
❑ 95Fle-226
❑ 95Sco-66
❑ 95ScoGolR-66
❑ 95ScoPlaTS-66
❑ 95StaClu-51
❑ 95StaCluFDI-51
❑ 95StaCluMOP-51
❑ 95StaCluSTWS-51
❑ 95Ult-269
❑ 95UltGolM-269
❑ 96AngMot-21
❑ 96ColCho-484
❑ 96ColChoGS-484
❑ 96ColChoSS-484
❑ 96LeaSigA-111
❑ 96LeaSigAG-111
❑ 96LeaSigAS-111
❑ 97ColCho-422
❑ 97Fle-46
❑ 97Fle-557
❑ 97FleTif-46
❑ 97FleTif-557
❑ 97Pac-9
❑ 97PacLigB-9
❑ 97PacSil-9
❑ 97PhiCopQ-11
❑ 97PhiTeal-14
❑ 97Sco-415
❑ 97ScoArtPWB-415
❑ 97ScoResC-415
❑ 97ScoShoS-415
❑ 97ScoShoSAP-415
❑ 97StaClu-358
❑ 97StaCluMOP-358
❑ 97Top-254
❑ 97Ult-344
❑ 97UltGolME-344
❑ 97UltPlaME-344
❑ 97UppDec-454
❑ 98PacOnl-562
❑ 98PacOnlR-562
❑ 98PacOnlWC-562
❑ 98PhiTeal-17
Hudlin, Willis
❑ 29PorandAR-44
❑ 33Gou-96
❑ 33GouCanV-72
❑ 34BatR31-48
❑ 34BatR31-103
❑ 34DiaStaR-79
❑ 35GouPuzR-5B
❑ 35GouPuzR-6B
❑ 35GouPuzR-11K
❑ 35GouPuzR-13B
❑ 36GouWidPPR-B14
❑ 36NatChiFPR-47
❑ 38CloFotW-43
❑ 96Bro194F-5
Hudson, Bert
❑ 97LetBlaDB-14
❑ 97SouBenSH-14
❑ 98SouBenSHM-11
Hudson, Charles
❑ 84Don-448
❑ 84Fle-36
❑ 84Nes792-432
❑ 84PhiTas-22
❑ 84Top-432
❑ 84TopTif-432
❑ 85Don-355
❑ 85Fle-255
❑ 85OPC-379
❑ 85PhiTas-9
❑ 85PhiTas-20
❑ 85Top-379
❑ 85TopMin-379
❑ 85TopSti-120
❑ 85TopTif-379
❑ 86Don-622

❑ 86Fle-444
❑ 86PhiClG-13
❑ 86PhiTas-49
❑ 86Top-792
❑ 86TopTat-13
❑ 86TopTif-792
❑ 87Don-630
❑ 87Fle-176
❑ 87FleGlo-176
❑ 87FleUpd-46
❑ 87FleUpdG-46
❑ 87Top-191
❑ 87TopTif-191
❑ 87TopTra-50T
❑ 87TopTraT-50T
❑ 88Don-374
❑ 88DonReaBY-374
❑ 88Fle-210
❑ 88FleGlo-210
❑ 88Top-636
❑ 88TopBig-212
❑ 88TopClo-50
❑ 88TopTif-636
❑ 89Don-514
❑ 89DonTra-50
❑ 89OPC-236
❑ 89Sco-415
❑ 89TigMar-27
❑ 89Top-236
❑ 89TopBig-88
❑ 89TopTif-236
❑ 89UppDec-586
❑ 90PubIntS-474
❑ 90UppDec-520
❑ 92YanWIZ8-87
❑ 93RanKee-199

Hudson, Charlie
❑ 73RanTeal-14
❑ 75SalLakCC-18
❑ 76SalLakCGC-21
❑ 76TucTorCa-18
❑ 83PorBeaT-19
❑ 84TopSti-17
❑ 85PhiClG-16
❑ 86Lea-239

Hudson, Deryk
❑ 90RocExpLC-11
❑ 90RocExpP-2701

Hudson, Hap (David)
❑ 86LouRedTI-3
❑ 87LouRedTI-29
❑ 88LouRedBP-434
❑ 88LouRedBTI-51
❑ 89LouRedBC-5
❑ 89LouRedBP-1253
❑ 89LouRedBTI-38
❑ 89TriAAAP-AAA12

Hudson, Jack
❑ 76WatRoyT-12

Hudson, Jesse James
❑ 70OPC-348
❑ 70Top-348
❑ 91MetWIZ-190

Hudson, Jim
❑ 87EugEmeP-2671
❑ 89BasCitRS-10

Hudson, Joe
❑ 92ElmPioC-18
❑ 92ElmPioF-1378
❑ 93ClaFS7-102
❑ 93LynRedSC-13
❑ 93LynRedSF-2514
❑ 94SarRedSC-15
❑ 94SarRedSF-1946
❑ 95TreThuTI-10
❑ 96PawRedSDD-13
❑ 97PawRedS-12
❑ 98PawRedSQ-15

Hudson, John
❑ 39PlaBal-154
❑ 40DodTeal-12
❑ 40PlaBal-147
❑ 41CubTeal-9
❑ 90DodTar-367

Hudson, Kevin
❑ 89BilMusP-2039
❑ 91BilMusSP-26

Hudson, Lance
❑ 86MiaMarP-12
❑ 88LakTigS-14
❑ 90MiaMirIS-10

Hudson, Luke
❑ 98PorRocG-16
❑ 98TenKry-12

Hudson, Maryann
❑ 87SalSpuS-4

Hudson, Nathaniel
❑ 87LonJacN-6
❑ 87OldJudN-255A
❑ 87OldJudN-255B

Hudson, Rex
❑ 74AlbDukTI-7
❑ 75AlbDukCa-13

Hudson, Robert
❑ 79WatIndT-31
❑ 81WauTimT-3
❑ 83ChaLooT-14

Hudson, Sid
❑ 41PlaBal-46
❑ 47SenGunBP-5
❑ 49Lea-84
❑ 50Bow-17
❑ 51Bow-169
❑ 51TopRedB-44
❑ 52Bow-123
❑ 52Top-60
❑ 53BowBW-29
❑ 53RedSoxTI-13
❑ 53Top-251
❑ 54Bow-194
❑ 54Top-93
❑ 55Bow-318
❑ 68SenTeal81/2-2
❑ 76TayBow4-87
❑ 79DiaGre-66
❑ 83TopRep5-60
❑ 91TopArc1-251
❑ 93RanKee-42
❑ 94TopArc1-93
❑ 94TopArc1G-93

Hudson, Stan
❑ 75AlbDukCa-14

Hudson, Tim
❑ 97SouOreTB-23
❑ 98HunStaTI-13
❑ 98ModA'sG-13
❑ 99Bow-375
❑ 99BowGol-375
❑ 99BowInt-375
❑ 99PacOme-171
❑ 99PacOmeC-171
❑ 99PacOmeG-171
❑ 99PacOmePB-171

Hudson, Todd
❑ 92LetMouSP-1

Hudson, Tony
❑ 80TulDriT-3
❑ 81TulDriT-21
❑ 82BurRanF-21
❑ 82BurRanT-3
❑ 85TulDriTI-20
❑ 86KnoBluJP-13
❑ 87SyrChiP-1939

Huebner, John
❑ 88GreFalDTI-18
❑ 89BakDodCLC-196

Hueda, Alejandro
❑ 96StCatSB-12
❑ 98St.CatSM-14

Huelsmann, Mike
❑ 96WatIndTI-10
❑ 97KinIndB-10
❑ 98CarLeaAC-38
❑ 98CarLeaAC-41
❑ 98KinIndQ-13
❑ 99BasAmeTP-53
❑ 99BasAmeTPG-53

Huenneke, Derek
❑ 86AriWilP-7

Hueston, Steve
❑ 96SpoIndB-14
❑ 97LanLugTS-10

Huey, John
❑ 83MadMusF-26
❑ 84MidCubT-5

Huff, Aubrey
❑ 99BasAmeTP-54
❑ 99BasAmeTPG-54
❑ 99Bow-426
❑ 99BowGol-426
❑ 99BowInt-426
❑ 99TeaBesR-37
❑ 99TeaBesRG-37
❑ 99TeaBesRS-37

Huff, B.J.
❑ 96PitMetB-12
❑ 97CapCitB-26
❑ 98St.LucMM-9

Huff, Brad
❑ 88WytCubP-1979
❑ 89WytCubS-14
❑ 90GenCubP-3032
❑ 90GenCubS-15
❑ 91WinSpiC-14

Huff, Larry
❑ 94MarPhiC-1
❑ 94MarPhiF-3302
❑ 95PiePhiF-192
❑ 97ReaPhi-18
❑ 98ReaPhiM-26
❑ 98ReaPhiUM-13

Huff, Matt
❑ 87SalLakTTT-23
❑ 88MiaMarS-10
❑ 93ButCopKSP-8

Huff, Mike
❑ 86VerBeaDP-11
❑ 87SanAntDTI-16
❑ 88SanAntMB-19
❑ 88TexLeaAGS-33
❑ 89AlbDukCm-24
❑ 89AlbDukP-79
❑ 89TriAAAP-AAA48
❑ 90AlbDukCm-24
❑ 90AlbDukP-358
❑ 90AlbDukTr-14
❑ 90ClaUpd-T24
❑ 90CMC-426
❑ 90Fle-649
❑ 90FleCan-649
❑ 90ProAAAF-79
❑ 90Sco-597
❑ 90TopDeb89-63
❑ 90TriAAAC-38
❑ 90TriAllGP-AAA46
❑ 91Bow-73
❑ 91Fle-210
❑ 91IndFanC-14
❑ 91LeaGolR-BC22
❑ 91ScoRoo-52T
❑ 92Don-579
❑ 92Fle-85
❑ 92Lea-342
❑ 92LeaBlaG-342
❑ 92OPC-532
❑ 92OPCPre-21
❑ 92Pin-485
❑ 92Sco-664
❑ 92StaClu-329
❑ 92Top-532
❑ 92TopGol-532
❑ 92TopGolW-532
❑ 92TopMic-532
❑ 92Ult-337
❑ 92WhiSoxK-12
❑ 93Don-788
❑ 93PacSpa-388
❑ 93WhiSoxK-12
❑ 93WhiSoxSC-24
❑ 94FleUpd-100
❑ 94StaCluT-140
❑ 94StaCluTFDI-140
❑ 95BluJayOH-21
❑ 95Don-140
❑ 95DonPreP-140
❑ 95Fla-99
❑ 95Fle-98
❑ 95Pin-324
❑ 95PinArtP-324
❑ 95PinMusC-324
❑ 95Sco-549
❑ 95ScoGolR-549
❑ 95ScoPlaTS-549
❑ 95Ult-340
❑ 95UltGolM-340
❑ 96SyrChiTI-15

Huff, Tim
❑ 97St.CatSB-16
❑ 98HagSunM-15

Huffaker, Mike
❑ 97NewJerCB-10
❑ 98PriWilCQ-8

Huffman, Ben
❑ 75TCMGua-18

Huffman, Jason
❑ 94EugEmeC-27
❑ 94EugEmeF-3706
❑ 94RocRoyC-14
❑ 94RocRoyF-561

Huffman, Jeff
❑ 94UtiBluSC-14
❑ 94UtiBluSF-3813

Huffman, Kris
❑ 88SavCarP-351
❑ 89SprCarB-9

Huffman, Phil
❑ 79BluJayBY-13
❑ 80OPC-79
❑ 80SyrChiT-9
❑ 80SyrChiTI-10
❑ 80Top-142
❑ 81OPC-2
❑ 81SyrChiT-5
❑ 81SyrChiTI-10
❑ 81Top-506
❑ 82OmaRoyT-6
❑ 85RocRedWT-17
❑ 86RocRedWP-9
❑ 87RocRedWP-1
❑ 87RocRedWT-6
❑ 91OriCro-207

Huffman, Rod
❑ 91CliGiaC-5
❑ 91CliGiaP-829
❑ 91MidLeaAP-MWL4
❑ 92ProFS7-355
❑ 92SanJosGC-20

Huffman, Ryan
❑ 94LSUTig-10

Hufford, Scott
❑ 87SpaPhiP-26
❑ 88LakTigS-15

Huffstickler, Danny
❑ 79ElmPioRST-4

Hufft, Fuzzy
❑ 26Zee-166
❑ 27Zee-137
❑ 28ExhPCL-12
❑ 28Zee-156
❑ 29Zee-45
❑ 30Zee-55
❑ 31Zee-33
❑ 32Zee-56

Huggins, David
❑ 97St.CatSB-17
❑ 98HagSunM-16
❑ 98St.CatSM-15

Huggins, Miller
❑ 06FanCraNL-22
❑ 08RosComP-117
❑ 09ColChiE-135
❑ 09PC7HHB-24
❑ 09RamT20-58
❑ 09T206-162
❑ 09T206-163
❑ 10CouT21-32
❑ 10CouT21-33
❑ 10CouT21-149
❑ 10CouT21-150
❑ 10CouT21-288
❑ 10CouT21-289
❑ 10DomDisP-57
❑ 10RedCroT-32
❑ 10RedCroT-120
❑ 10RedCroT-121
❑ 10RedCroT-202
❑ 10RedCroT-203
❑ 10SweCapPP-149A
❑ 10SweCapPP-149B
❑ 11DiaGumP-15
❑ 11HelSta-172
❑ 11MecDFT-5
❑ 11PinT-5-354
❑ 11PloCanE-35
❑ 11S74Sil-120
❑ 11SpoLifCW-178
❑ 11SpoLifM-270
❑ 11T205-78
❑ 12ColRedB-135
❑ 12ColTinT-135
❑ 12HasTriFT-67A
❑ 13NatGamW-20
❑ 13TomBarW-19
❑ 14B18B-85A
❑ 14B18B-85B
❑ 14CraJacE-75
❑ 14FatPlaT-18
❑ 14PieStaT-54
❑ 15CraJacE-75
❑ 15SpoNewM-85
❑ 16BF2FP-96
❑ 16SpoNewM-86
❑ 19W514-34
❑ 20GasAmeMBD-11
❑ 21E121So1-47
❑ 21E121So8-40
❑ 21KoBreWSI-37
❑ 22W575-61
❑ 22WilPatV-10
❑ 23W501-26
❑ 23W515-36
❑ 23WilChoV-68
❑ 61Fle-46
❑ 62Top-137
❑ 62TopVen-137
❑ 75TCMAllG-16
❑ 75Yan192T-12
❑ 75Yan192T-29
❑ 76ShaPiz-98
❑ 77BobParHoF-28
❑ 77GalGloG-128
❑ 78DexHaloFP-23
❑ 79Yan192T-15
❑ 80PerHaloFP-98
❑ 80SSPHOF-98
❑ 81ConTSN-3
❑ 81SpoHaloF-2
❑ 82OhiHaloF-39
❑ 83TCMRut-3
❑ 84Yan192G-12
❑ 86ConSer1-16
❑ 87SpoCubG-3
❑ 87Yan192T-1
❑ 89CMCRut-17
❑ 91ConTSN-101
❑ 92CarMcD-5
❑ 92ConTSN-649
❑ 92MegRut-124
❑ 92YanWIZH-17
❑ 93ConTSN-830
❑ 93CraJac-22
❑ 94MegRutS-5
❑ 95MegRut-18

Hughes, Bobby E.
❑ 92ClaDraP-35
❑ 93BelBreCB-10
❑ 93BelBreFI-1714
❑ 93Bow-507
❑ 93ClaFS7-280
❑ 94BowBes-X104
❑ 94BowBesR-X104
❑ 94ExcFS7-81
❑ 94StoPorC-1
❑ 94StoPorF-1698
❑ 95SigRooOJ-18
❑ 95SigRooOJP-18
❑ 95SigRooOJPS-18
❑ 95SigRooOJS-18
❑ 96FleUpd-U46
❑ 96FleUpdTC-U46
❑ 96Ult-363
❑ 96UltGolM-363
❑ 97TucTorB-12
❑ 98Don-244
❑ 98DonGolPP-244
❑ 98DonSilPP-244
❑ 98LeaRS-228
❑ 98LeaRSLHolo-228
❑ 98LeaRSLong-228
❑ 98LeaRTrue-228
❑ 98PacOmeRS-18
❑ 98PacOmeRST2-18
❑ 98PacOnl-396
❑ 98PacOnlR-396
❑ 98PacOnlWC-396
❑ 99Fle-420
❑ 99FleSta9-420
❑ 99FleWarT-420
❑ 99Pac-233
❑ 99PacPlaB-233
❑ 99PacRed-233
❑ 99UppDec-410
❑ 99UppDecEL1-410
❑ 99UppDecEL2-410

Hughes, Butch
❑ 82ReaPhiT-3
❑ 83PhoGiaBHN-18
❑ 86ModA'sC-24
❑ 86ModA'sP-14
❑ 87ModA'sC-24
❑ 87ModA'sP-9
❑ 94WilCubC-27

Hughes, Danan
❑ 92HelBreF-1727
❑ 92HelBreSP-17
❑ 93ExcFS7-188

Hughes, Dick (Richard)
❑ 62KahAtl-10
❑ 66TolMudHTI-14
❑ 67Top-384
❑ 68Top-253
❑ 68TopVen-253
❑ 69OPC-39
❑ 69Top-39

Hughes, Doc (Leo)
❑ 48SomandK-29
❑ 49SomandK-23
❑ 53SanFraSTI-8

Hughes, Gregory
❑ 79NaSouTI-12
❑ 80WatRedT-22
❑ 81TulDriT-23

Hughes, Harry
❑ 13Zee-112
❑ 14Zee-113

Hughes, Jim (James Jay)
❑ 11SpoLifCW-179
❑ 90DodTar-368

Hughes, Jim (James Michael)
❑ 74TacTwiC-7
❑ 75TwiTeal-17
❑ 76Hos-53
❑ 76HosTwi-53
❑ 76OPC-11
❑ 76SSP-211
❑ 76Top-11
❑ 76VenLeaS-96
❑ 77TacTwiDQ-21
❑ 77Top-304
❑ 78Top-395
❑ 78TucTorC-59B

Hughes, Jim (James Robert)
❑ 49W72HolS-8
❑ 52Par-56
❑ 53Top-216
❑ 54NewYorJA-8
❑ 54Top-169
❑ 55Bow-156
❑ 55DodGolS-7
❑ 55Top-51
❑ 55TopDouH-19
❑ 74dod195T-11
❑ 79TCM50-268
❑ 90DodTar-369
❑ 91TopArc1-216
❑ 94TopArc1-169
❑ 94TopArc1G-169
❑ 95TopArcBD-51
❑ 95TopArcBD-78
❑ 95TopArcBD-96
❑ 95TopArcBD-130

Hughes, Jim PCL
❑ 67VanMouSO-13

Hughes, John
❑ 83CliGiaF-16

Hughes, Keith
❑ 85AlbYanT-35
❑ 86AlbYanT-7
❑ 87ColCliP-13
❑ 87ColCliP-17
❑ 87ColCliT-21
❑ 88BlaYNPRWLU-26
❑ 88Don-643
❑ 88Fle-305
❑ 88FleGlo-305
❑ 88OriPos-16
❑ 88RocRedWC-15
❑ 88RocRedWGCP-13
❑ 88RocRedWP-213
❑ 88RocRedWTI-11
❑ 88Sco-635
❑ 88ScoGlo-635
❑ 88Top-781
❑ 88TopTif-781
❑ 89RocRedWC-13
❑ 89RocRedWP-1659
❑ 89TriAAAP-AAA23
❑ 90AlbDecGB-32
❑ 90CMC-375
❑ 90MetColP-34
❑ 90ProAAAF-287
❑ 90TidTidC-24
❑ 90TidTidP-556
❑ 90TopTVM-46
❑ 90TriAllGP-AAA6
❑ 91ColCliLD-106
❑ 91ColCliP-6
❑ 91ColCliP-601
❑ 91LinDriAAA-106
❑ 91MetWIZ-191
❑ 91OriCro-208
❑ 92PorBeaF-2674
❑ 92PorBeaS-409
❑ 92YanWIZ8-88
❑ 93IndIndF-1501
❑ 95OmaRoyTI-14
❑ 96HonShaHWB-30
❑ 96WilBluRB-30
❑ 97WilBluR-29

Hughes, Kiley
❑ 93Sou-11

Hughes, Michael P.

❑ 97WatIndTI-13
❑ 98ColRedSM-4
Hughes, Michael Raymond
❑ 96BoiHawB-16
❑ 97BoiHawG-15
Hughes, Mickey (Michael)
❑ 74BroClu-9
❑ 87OldJudN-80
❑ 87OldJudN-256
❑ 90DodTar-370
Hughes, Nial
❑ 98GreFalDG-15
Hughes, Robert
❑ 94VerExpC-15
Hughes, Roy
❑ 47RoyMon-2
❑ 84TCMPla1-37
❑ 92ConTSN-566
❑ 94ConTSN-1069
❑ 94ConTSNB-1069
Hughes, Sammy T.
❑ 78LauLonABS-15
❑ 86NegLeaF-111
❑ 90NegLeaS-35
Hughes, Steve
❑ 80CedRapRT-8
Hughes, Terry W.
❑ 73OPC-603
❑ 73Top-603
❑ 74OPC-604
❑ 74Top-604
❑ 75OPC-612
❑ 75Top-612
❑ 75TopMin-612
Hughes, Tom
❑ 75CedRapGT-1
Hughes, Tom (Thomas)
❑ 08AmeCarE91-79
❑ 08RosComP-80
❑ 09ColChiE-136A
❑ 09ColChiE-136B
❑ 09ColChiE-136C
❑ 09ColChiE-137
❑ 11HelSta-71
❑ 11PinT-5-815
❑ 11SpoLifCW-180
❑ 12ColRedB-136A
❑ 12ColRedB-136B
❑ 12ColRedB-136C
❑ 12ColRedB-137
❑ 12ColTinT-136A
❑ 12ColTinT-136B
❑ 12ColTinT-136C
❑ 12ColTinT-137
❑ 12ImpTobC-66
❑ 14Zee-12
❑ 15Zee-10
❑ 16Zee-82
❑ 17Zee-70
❑ 21Zee-11
❑ 22Zee-8
❑ 24Zee-10
❑ 77FriOneYW-110
❑ 80BraTCM1-3
❑ 91ConTSN-161
Hughes, Troy
❑ 90PulBraB-20
❑ 90PulBraP-3088
❑ 91MacBraC-24
❑ 91MacBraP-877
❑ 92ClaFS7-92
❑ 92DurBulC-15
❑ 92DurBulF-1113
❑ 92DurBulTI-27
❑ 92ProFS7-191
❑ 93GreBraF-361
❑ 94RicBraF-2859
❑ 94UppDecML-18
❑ 95BreBtaTI-10
❑ 96OrlCubB-12
❑ 97HunStaTI-11
Hughes, William
❑ 24Zee-62
❑ 25Zee-67
❑ 26Zee-114
❑ 27Zee-69
❑ 28Zee-52
Hughey, Jim
❑ 98CamPepP-37
Hughs, Eric
❑ 89AlaGol-18
Hughson, Tex (Cecil)
❑ 42RedSoxTI-14
❑ 43RedSoxTI-9
❑ 46RedSoxTI-13
❑ 46SpoExcW-6-2
❑ 47Exh-104
❑ 47RedSoxTI-11
❑ 47TipTop-8
❑ 49Bow-199
❑ 49RedSoxTI-10
❑ 75RedSox1T-20
❑ 76TayBow4-63
❑ 83TCMPla1942-5
❑ 85TCMPpl1-25
❑ 87RedSox1T-8
❑ 92TexLon-25
Hugo, Sean
❑ 92OklStaC-12
❑ 95BowBayTI-24
Huisman, Rick
❑ 90CliGiaUTI-U6
❑ 91CalLeLA-31
❑ 91Cla/Bes-32
❑ 91SanJosGC-27
❑ 91SanJosGP-6
❑ 92Bow-217
❑ 92ClaFS7-255
❑ 92ProFS7-350
❑ 92ShrCapF-3865
❑ 92ShrCapS-585
❑ 92SkyAA F-258
❑ 92UppDecML-186
❑ 93ClaFS7-281
❑ 93ExcFS7-118
❑ 94JacGenF-214
❑ 95Bow-118
❑ 95BowBes-B43
❑ 95BowBesR-B43
❑ 95Exc-205
❑ 95Top-650
❑ 95TucTotTI-12
❑ 96OmaRoyB-14
❑ 96RoyPol-13
❑ 97RoyPol-11
❑ 98FreGriG-14
Huismann, Mark
❑ 81ChaRoyT-18
❑ 82ForMyeRT-16
❑ 84Don-339
❑ 84RoyPos-14
❑ 85DomLeaS-204
❑ 85Don-583
❑ 85Fle-203
❑ 85OmaRoyT-15
❑ 85Top-644
❑ 85TopTif-644
❑ 86MarPacNB-6
❑ 86RoyNatP-38
❑ 87Fle-586
❑ 87FleGlo-586
❑ 87MarMot-16
❑ 87Top-187
❑ 87TopTif-187
❑ 88TolMudHC-11
❑ 88TolMudHP-588
❑ 88TriAAAP-42
❑ 88TriAAC-26
❑ 89RocRedWC-10
❑ 89RocRedWP-1650
❑ 90BufBisC-4
❑ 90BufBisP-367
❑ 90BufBisTI-9
❑ 90CMC-4
❑ 90ProAAAF-482
❑ 91BufBisLD-30
❑ 91BufBisP-535
❑ 91LinDriAAA-30
❑ 91OriCro-209
❑ 92OmaRoyF-2956
❑ 92OmaRoyS-331
Huizenga, Ken
❑ 77BriRedST-8
Hulbert, William
❑ 80PerHaloFP-222
❑ 94OriofB-24
Hulett, Tim
❑ 81GleFalWST-12
❑ 82GleFalWST-6
❑ 84WhiSoxTV-18
❑ 85Don-645
❑ 85FleUpd-59
❑ 85TopTifT-60T
❑ 85TopTra-60T
❑ 85WhiSoxC-32
❑ 86Don-404
❑ 86Fle-208
❑ 86OPC-87
❑ 86Top-724
❑ 86TopSti-295
❑ 86TopTif-724
❑ 86WhiSoxC-32
❑ 87Don-260
❑ 87DonOpeD-231
❑ 87Fle-500
❑ 87FleGlo-500
❑ 87OPC-286
❑ 87Top-566
❑ 87TopSti-289
❑ 87TopTif-566
❑ 87WhiSoxC-16
❑ 88IndIndC-17
❑ 88IndIndP-522
❑ 88Top-158
❑ 88TopTif-158
❑ 89RocRedWC-16
❑ 89RocRedWP-1653
❑ 90BalOriP-11
❑ 90FleUpd-66
❑ 91Don-706
❑ 91Fle-478
❑ 91OPC-468
❑ 91OriCro-210
❑ 91Sco-632
❑ 91StaClu-517
❑ 91Top-468
❑ 91TopDesS-468
❑ 91TopMic-468
❑ 91TopTif-468
❑ 92BalOriP-15
❑ 92Fle-11
❑ 92OPC-396
❑ 92Sco-391
❑ 92StaClu-104
❑ 93Don-661
❑ 93Fle-543
❑ 93OPC-167
❑ 93PacSpa-343
❑ 93StaClu-14
❑ 93StaCluFDI-14
❑ 93StaCluMOP-14
❑ 93Top-327
❑ 93TopGol-327
❑ 93TopInaM-327
❑ 93TopInaR-327
❑ 93TopMic-327
❑ 94BalOriP-15
❑ 94Don-129
❑ 94Fle-7
❑ 94OriPro-47
❑ 94OriUSPC-6S
❑ 94OriUSPC-11D
❑ 94Pac-34
❑ 94Sco-165
❑ 94ScoGolR-165
❑ 94StaClu-430
❑ 94StaCluFDI-430
❑ 94StaCluGR-430
❑ 94StaCluMOP-430
❑ 94StaCluT-298
❑ 94StaCluTFDI-298
❑ 94Top-32
❑ 94TopGol-32
❑ 94TopSpa-32
Hull, Jeff
❑ 85Ft.MyeRT-8
❑ 86Ft.MyeRP-14
❑ 87SalSpuS-25
❑ 88BlaYNPRWLU-4
❑ 88EasLeaAP-35
❑ 88VerMarP-961
❑ 89CalCanC-8
❑ 89CalCanP-526
❑ 90OrlSunRB-8
❑ 90OrlSunRP-1085
Huller, Mike
❑ 98SalVol-12
Hulme, Pat
❑ 90UtiBluSP-20
Huls, Steve
❑ 97ForWayW-15
❑ 98ForMyeMTI-16
Hulse, David
❑ 90ButCopKSP-8
❑ 91ChaRanC-22
❑ 91ChaRanP-1326
❑ 91Cla/Bes-197
❑ 92SkyAA F-269
❑ 92TulDriF-2707
❑ 92TulDriS-609
❑ 93Bow-601
❑ 93Don-706
❑ 93Fla-282
❑ 93Fle-683
❑ 93Lea-355
❑ 93OPC-146
❑ 93OPCPre-40
❑ 93PacSpa-641
❑ 93Pin-269
❑ 93PinRooTP-10
❑ 93RanKee-410
❑ 93RanStaC-4
❑ 93Sco-293
❑ 93ScoBoyoS-26
❑ 93SelRoo-35T
❑ 93SelRooAR-7
❑ 93StaClu-705
❑ 93StaCluFDI-705
❑ 93StaCluMOP-705
❑ 93Top-118
❑ 93TopGol-118
❑ 93TopInaM-118
❑ 93TopInaR-118
❑ 93TopMic-118
❑ 93Toy-75
❑ 93Ult-630
❑ 93UppDec-374
❑ 93UppDecGold-374
❑ 94ColC-142
❑ 94ColChoGS-142
❑ 94ColChoSS-142
❑ 94Don-560
❑ 94Fin-148
❑ 94FinRef-148
❑ 94Fla-112
❑ 94Fle-309
❑ 94Lea-278
❑ 94Pac-620
❑ 94Pin-162
❑ 94PinArtP-162
❑ 94PinMusC-162
❑ 94RanMagM-9
❑ 94RanMagM-17
❑ 94Sco-523
❑ 94ScoBoyoS-22
❑ 94ScoCyc-TC14
❑ 94ScoGolR-523
❑ 94Sel-302
❑ 94StaClu-449
❑ 94StaCluFDI-449
❑ 94StaCluGR-449
❑ 94StaCluMOP-449
❑ 94StaCluT-251
❑ 94StaCluTFDI-251
❑ 94Stu-155
❑ 94Top-498
❑ 94TopGol-498
❑ 94TopSpa-498
❑ 94TriPla-196
❑ 94Ult-129
❑ 94UppDec-377
❑ 94UppDecED-377
❑ 94USPlaCR-10H
❑ 94USPlaCR-13D
❑ 95ColCho-392
❑ 95ColChoGS-392
❑ 95ColChoSS-392
❑ 95Don-228
❑ 95DonPreP-228
❑ 95Fin-323
❑ 95FinRef-323
❑ 95Fla-271
❑ 95Fle-288
❑ 95FleUpd-51
❑ 95Pac-429
❑ 95Sco-130
❑ 95ScoGolR-130
❑ 95ScoPlaTS-130
❑ 95StaClu-293
❑ 95StaCluMOP-293
❑ 95StaCluSTWS-293
❑ 95Ult-111
❑ 95UltGolM-111
❑ 96BrePol-9
❑ 96Don-410
❑ 96DonPreP-410
❑ 96Fle-146
❑ 96FleTif-146
❑ 96LeaSigEA-85
❑ 96Pac-346
❑ 96Ult-81
❑ 96UltGolM-81
❑ 97Pac-118
❑ 97PacLigB-118
❑ 97PacSil-118
Hulse, Jeff
❑ 88EugEmeB-14
❑ 89AppFoxP-866
❑ 90ClePhiS-8
Hulstrom, Bruce
❑ 87PenWhiSP-14
Hulswitt, Rudy
❑ 08RosComP-118
❑ 09ColChiE-138A
❑ 09ColChiE-138B
❑ 09ColChiE-138C
❑ 09PC7HHB-25
❑ 09T206-164
❑ 11SpoLifCW-181
❑ 11SpoLifM-271
❑ 12ColRedB-138A
❑ 12ColRedB-138B
❑ 12ColRedB-138C
❑ 12ColTinT-138A
❑ 12ColTinT-138B
❑ 12ColTinT-138C
Hulvey, Hensel
❑ 25Zee-90
❑ 26Zee-7
Hulvey, James
❑ 28Zee-8
Humber, Frank
❑ 89GreFalDSP-21
❑ 90BakDodCLC-239
Hume, Thomas H.
❑ 88KimN18-20
Hume, Tom (Thomas Hubert)
❑ 76IndIndTI-9
❑ 77IndIndTI-5
❑ 78Pep-14
❑ 78SSP270-120
❑ 78Top-701
❑ 79Top-301
❑ 80RedEnq-47
❑ 80Top-149
❑ 81CokTeaS-43
❑ 81Fle-211
❑ 81OPC-292
❑ 81Top-8
❑ 81Top-419
❑ 81TopSti-31
❑ 81TopSti-166
❑ 81TopSupHT-37
❑ 82Don-229
❑ 82Fle-69
❑ 82OPC-79
❑ 82RedCok-9
❑ 82Top-763
❑ 82TopSti-38
❑ 83Don-229
❑ 83Fle-593
❑ 83FleSta-88
❑ 83FleSti-146
❑ 83FleSti-213
❑ 83OPC-86
❑ 83RedYea-47
❑ 83Top-86
❑ 84Don-550
❑ 84Fle-472
❑ 84Nes792-607
❑ 84OPC-186
❑ 84RedEnq-19
❑ 84Top-607
❑ 84TopSti-59
❑ 84TopTif-607
❑ 85Don-408
❑ 85Fle-538
❑ 85OPC-223
❑ 85Top-223
❑ 85TopMin-223
❑ 85TopTif-223
❑ 86Don-365
❑ 86Fle-179
❑ 86FleUpd-52
❑ 86PhiTas-41
❑ 86Top-573
❑ 86TopTif-573
❑ 86TopTra-47T
❑ 86TopTraT-47T
❑ 87Fle-177
❑ 87FleGlo-177
❑ 87OPC-251
❑ 87PhiTas-41
❑ 87Top-719
❑ 87TopTif-719
❑ 88Fle-236
❑ 88FleGlo-236
❑ 88Sco-494
❑ 88ScoGlo-494
Hummel, Dan
❑ 98NewJerCM-15
Hummel, Dean
❑ 86ShrCapP-10
Hummel, John E.
❑ 08RosComP-95
❑ 09ColChiE-139
❑ 09RamT20-59
❑ 09T206-165
❑ 10CouT21-151
❑ 10CouT21-152
❑ 10CouT21-290
❑ 10DomDisP-58
❑ 10RedCroT-33
❑ 10RedCroT-122
❑ 10RedCroT-204
❑ 10SweCapPP-74
❑ 11HelSta-87
❑ 11PinT-5-451
❑ 11PloCanE-36
❑ 11S74Sil-53
❑ 11SpoLifCW-182
❑ 11SpoLifM-156
❑ 11T205-79
❑ 12ColRedB-139
❑ 12ColTinT-139
❑ 12HasTriFT-27
❑ 14B18B-58
❑ 14CraJacE-50
❑ 14PieStaT-55
❑ 15CraJacE-50
❑ 18Zee-80
❑ 72ClaCar-62
❑ 90DodTar-371
Humphrey, Al
❑ 90DodTar-988
Humphrey, Claude
❑ 80PhiBul-8
Humphrey, Daryl
❑ 83GreHorT-10
Humphrey, Rich
❑ 93AubAstC-14
❑ 93AubAstF-3438
❑ 96JacGenB-13
❑ 97JacGenS-11
Humphrey, Sly
❑ 83IdaFalAT-28
Humphrey, Terry
❑ 72Dia-20
❑ 72OPC-489
❑ 72Top-489
❑ 73OPC-106
❑ 73Top-106
❑ 75DetTigP-13
❑ 76OPC-552
❑ 76SSP-373
❑ 76Top-552
❑ 77Top-369
❑ 78AngFamF-18
❑ 78SSP270-210
❑ 78Top-71
❑ 79Top-503
Humphreys, Bob (Robert W.)
❑ 65OPC-154
❑ 65Top-154
❑ 66Top-342
❑ 66TopVen-342
❑ 67CokCapS-1
❑ 67SenPos-12
❑ 67Top-478
❑ 68Top-268
❑ 68TopVen-268
❑ 69OPC-84
❑ 69Top-84
❑ 70OPC-538
❑ 70Top-538
❑ 71MLBOffS-439
❑ 71OPC-236
❑ 71Top-236
❑ 72MilBra-154
❑ 80KnoBluJT-25
❑ 81SyrChiT-23
❑ 81SyrChiTI-11
❑ 83SyrChiT-26
❑ 94BreMilB-320
Humphreys, Kevin
❑ 96BoiHawB-17
❑ 97CedRapK-14
Humphreys, Mike
❑ 87SalLakTTT-16
❑ 88SpoIndP-1926
❑ 89CalLeaA-10
❑ 89RivRedWB-8
❑ 89RivRedWCLC-5
❑ 89RivRedWP-1400
❑ 90TexLeaAGS-7
❑ 90WicWraRD-11
❑ 91Bow-162
❑ 91ColCliLD-107
❑ 91ColCliP-7
❑ 91ColCliP-608
❑ 91LinDriAAA-107

❑ 91UppDecFE-35F
❑ 92ColCliF-363
❑ 92ColCliP-21
❑ 92ColCliS-105
❑ 92Don-769
❑ 92Fle-231
❑ 92Pin-277
❑ 92Sco-815
❑ 92ScoRoo-26
❑ 92SkyAAAF-47
❑ 92StaClu-319
❑ 92TopDeb91-85
❑ 92UppDec-432
❑ 93ColCliF-1121
❑ 93ColCliP-21
❑ 93FleFinE-246
❑ 93Ult-595
❑ 93YanStaC-10
❑ 94ColCliF-2963
❑ 94ColCliP-15

Humphries, Joe
❑ 87MyrBeaBJP-1459
❑ 88SanAntMB-20

Humphries, John
❑ 93ConTSN-951

Humphry, Brandt
❑ 80ElPasDT-1
❑ 81HolMilT-22

Humphry, Trevor
❑ 92ClaDraP-59
❑ 92MarPhiF-3051
❑ 93MarPhiC-14
❑ 93MarPhiF-3467
❑ 93PhiStaC-16
❑ 93SpaPhiC-16
❑ 93SpaPhiF-1051
❑ 93StaCluM-87
❑ 95PiePhiF-183

Hund, John
❑ 75QuaCitAT-18

Hundhammer, Paul
❑ 84PawRedST-10A
❑ 84PawRedST-10B
❑ 85PawRedST-5

Hundley, Randy
❑ 66Top-392
❑ 67CokCapC-10
❑ 67CubProPS-7
❑ 67DexPre-101
❑ 67OPC-106
❑ 67ProPizC-9
❑ 67Top-106
❑ 68OPC-136
❑ 68Top-136
❑ 68TopVen-136
❑ 69CubBumS-3
❑ 69CubJewT-8
❑ 69CubPho-6
❑ 69CubTealC-4
❑ 69MilBra-122
❑ 69MLBOffS-121
❑ 69Top-347
❑ 69TopSta-14
❑ 69TopTeaP-4
❑ 70CubDunD-3
❑ 70DayDaiNM-146
❑ 70Kel-31
❑ 70MLBOffS-17
❑ 70OPC-265
❑ 70SunPin-4
❑ 70Top-265
❑ 71BazNumT-46
❑ 71BazUnn-16
❑ 71MilDud-48
❑ 71MLBOffS-34
❑ 71OPC-592
❑ 71Top-592
❑ 71TopCoi-51
❑ 71TopTat-20
❑ 72CubTeal-5
❑ 72MilBra-155
❑ 72OPC-258
❑ 72Top-258
❑ 73OPC-21
❑ 73Top-21
❑ 74OPC-319
❑ 74Top-319
❑ 74TopSta-15
❑ 74TopTra-319T
❑ 75PadDea-3
❑ 75PadDea-11
❑ 76OPC-351
❑ 76SSP-121
❑ 76Top-351
❑ 77Top-502
❑ 78TwiFri-34
❑ 84CubUno-2
❑ 84CubUno-6
❑ 89PacLegI-207
❑ 92CubOldS-15
❑ 92UppDecS-28

Hundley, Todd
❑ 87LitFalMP-2396
❑ 88LitFalMP-6
❑ 89ColMetB-1
❑ 89ColMetGS-11
❑ 89SouAtlLAGS-17
❑ 90Bow-142
❑ 90BowTif-142
❑ 90ClaYel-T100
❑ 90FleUpd-36
❑ 90JacMetGS-1
❑ 90MetColP-35
❑ 90ScoRoo-76T
❑ 90TopTra-44T
❑ 90TopTraT-44T
❑ 90TopTVM-47
❑ 90UppDec-726
❑ 91Bow-467
❑ 91Don-641
❑ 91Fle-150
❑ 91LinDriAAA-559
❑ 91MajLeaCP-75
❑ 91MetColP-34
❑ 91MetWIZ-192
❑ 91OPC-457
❑ 91OPCPre-66
❑ 91RedFolS-108
❑ 91Sco-340
❑ 91Sco100RS-79
❑ 91ScoRoo-23
❑ 91StaClu-349
❑ 91TidTidLD-559
❑ 91TidTidP-2513
❑ 91Top-457
❑ 91TopDeb90-74
❑ 91TopDesS-457
❑ 91TopMic-457
❑ 91TopTif-457
❑ 91TriA AAGP-AAA49
❑ 91Ult-220
❑ 91UppDec-440
❑ 92Bow-101
❑ 92ClaGam-54
❑ 92Don-568
❑ 92Fle-506
❑ 92LeaGolR-BC7
❑ 92MetColP-16
❑ 92MetKah-9
❑ 92OPC-673
❑ 92Pin-571
❑ 92PinRoo-17
❑ 92PinRool-10
❑ 92PinTea2-78
❑ 92ProFS7-277
❑ 92Sco-602
❑ 92Sco100RS-80
❑ 92ScoHotR-6
❑ 92ScoImpP-31
❑ 92ScoRoo-6
❑ 92StaClu-290
❑ 92Stu-66
❑ 92Top-673
❑ 92TopGol-673
❑ 92TopGolW-673
❑ 92TopMcD-42
❑ 92TopMic-673
❑ 92TriPla-104
❑ 92Ult-233
❑ 92UppDec-260
❑ 92UppDecSR-SR10
❑ 93Bow-398
❑ 93Don-66
❑ 93Fla-92
❑ 93Fle-88
❑ 93Lea-75
❑ 93MetColP-36
❑ 93MetKah-9
❑ 93OPC-116
❑ 93PacSpa-542
❑ 93PanSti-246
❑ 93Pin-126
❑ 93Sco-167
❑ 93Sel-293
❑ 93SelChaR-19
❑ 93SP-150
❑ 93StaClu-72
❑ 93StaCluFDI-72
❑ 93StaCluMOP-72
❑ 93Stu-206
❑ 93Top-380
❑ 93TopGol-380
❑ 93TopInaM-380
❑ 93TopInaR-380
❑ 93TopMic-380
❑ 93Toy-12
❑ 93TriPla-218
❑ 93Ult-75
❑ 93UppDec-293
❑ 93UppDecGold-293
❑ 94Bow-456
❑ 94ColC-143
❑ 94ColChoGS-143
❑ 94ColChoSS-143
❑ 94Don-128
❑ 94Fin-319
❑ 94FinRef-319
❑ 94Fla-198
❑ 94Fle-565
❑ 94FleExtB-318
❑ 94Lea-323
❑ 94MetColP-12
❑ 94MetShuST-8
❑ 94Pac-404
❑ 94PanSti-218
❑ 94Pin-155
❑ 94PinArtP-155
❑ 94PinMusC-155
❑ 94ProMag-92
❑ 94Sco-458
❑ 94ScoGolR-458
❑ 94Sel-73
❑ 94SP-117
❑ 94SPDieC-117
❑ 94StaClu-82
❑ 94StaCluFDI-82
❑ 94StaCluGR-82
❑ 94StaCluMOP-82
❑ 94Stu-115
❑ 94Top-8
❑ 94TopGol-8
❑ 94TopSpa-8
❑ 94TriPla-144
❑ 94Ult-237
❑ 94UppDec-242
❑ 94UppDecED-242
❑ 95ColCho-324
❑ 95ColChoGS-324
❑ 95ColChoSS-324
❑ 95Don-65
❑ 95DonPreP-65
❑ 95DonTopotO-293
❑ 95Fin-138
❑ 95FinRef-138
❑ 95Fla-171
❑ 95Fle-370
❑ 95Lea-3
❑ 95LeaLim-124
❑ 95MetColP-16
❑ 95Pac-282
❑ 95Pin-32
❑ 95PinArtP-32
❑ 95PinMusC-32
❑ 95Sco-416
❑ 95ScoGolR-416
❑ 95ScoPlaTS-416
❑ 95Sel-154
❑ 95SelArtP-154
❑ 95StaClu-205
❑ 95StaCluFDI-205
❑ 95StaCluMOP-205
❑ 95StaCluSTWS-205
❑ 95StaCluVR-107
❑ 95StaCluVRMO-107
❑ 95Top-223
❑ 95TopCyb-125
❑ 95Ult-412
❑ 95UltGolM-412
❑ 95UppDec-123
❑ 95UppDecED-123
❑ 95UppDecEDG-123
❑ 95UppDecSE-194
❑ 95UppDecSEG-194
❑ 96Baz-86
❑ 96Bow-62
❑ 96BowFoi-62
❑ 96Cir-157
❑ 96CirRav-157
❑ 96ColCho-221
❑ 96ColChoGS-221
❑ 96ColChoSS-221
❑ 96Don-249
❑ 96DonPreP-249
❑ 96EmoXL-232
❑ 96Fin-B85
❑ 96FinRef-B85
❑ 96Fla-320
❑ 96Fle-479
❑ 96FleTif-479
❑ 96Lea-100
❑ 96LeaPrePB-100
❑ 96LeaPrePG-100
❑ 96LeaPrePS-100
❑ 96LeaSig-45
❑ 96LeaSigPPG-45
❑ 96LeaSigPPP-45
❑ 96MetKah-15
❑ 96MetKah-15
❑ 96MetMod-5
❑ 96MetUni-200
❑ 96MetUniP-200
❑ 96Pac-147
❑ 96PanSti-28
❑ 96ProSta-71
❑ 96Sco-73
❑ 96SP-128
❑ 96StaClu-70
❑ 96StaCluEPB-70
❑ 96StaCluEPG-70
❑ 96StaCluEPS-70
❑ 96StaCluMOP-70
❑ 96Stu-100
❑ 96StuPrePB-100
❑ 96StuPrePG-100
❑ 96StuPrePS-100
❑ 96Sum-28
❑ 96SumAbo&B-28
❑ 96SumArtP-28
❑ 96SumFoi-28
❑ 96TeaOut-38
❑ 96Top-409
❑ 96TopGal-10
❑ 96TopGalPPI-10
❑ 96TopLas-68
❑ 96Ult-242
❑ 96UltGolM-242
❑ 96UppDec-399
❑ 97Bow-288
❑ 97BowBes-4
❑ 97BowBesAR-4
❑ 97BowBesR-4
❑ 97BowChr-98
❑ 97BowChrI-98
❑ 97BowChrIR-98
❑ 97BowChrR-98
❑ 97BowInt-288
❑ 97Cir-366
❑ 97CirRav-366
❑ 97ColCho-395
❑ 97ColChoAC-35
❑ 97ColChoNF-NF38
❑ 97ColChoPP-PP11
❑ 97ColChoPPG-PP11
❑ 97ColChoPPJ-PP11
❑ 97ColChoTotT-T18
❑ 97DenHol-23
❑ 97Don-26
❑ 97Don-443
❑ 97DonEli-141
❑ 97DonEliGS-141
❑ 97DonGolPP-26
❑ 97DonGolPP-443
❑ 97DonLim-179
❑ 97DonLim-188
❑ 97DonLimE-179
❑ 97DonLimE-188
❑ 97DonLimENG-179
❑ 97DonPre-62
❑ 97DonPreCttC-62
❑ 97DonSig-85
❑ 97DonSigA-53
❑ 97DonSigAC-63
❑ 97DonSigAM-61
❑ 97DonSigPPP-85
❑ 97DonSilPP-26
❑ 97DonSilPP-443
❑ 97E-X2-85
❑ 97E-X2Cred-85
❑ 97E-X2EssCre-85
❑ 97Fin-171
❑ 97Fin-324
❑ 97FinEmb-171
❑ 97FinEmb-324
❑ 97FinEmbR-171
❑ 97FinEmbR-324
❑ 97FinRef-171
❑ 97FinRef-324
❑ 97FlaShoDC-7
❑ 97FlaShoLC-90
❑ 97FlaShoLeg0-90
❑ 97FlaShoLeg1-90
❑ 97FlaShoM-A90
❑ 97FlaShoM-B90
❑ 97FlaShoM-C90
❑ 97FlaShoR0-90
❑ 97FlaShoR1-90
❑ 97FlaShoR2-90
❑ 97Fle-397
❑ 97Fle-738
❑ 97FleGolM-3
❑ 97FleLumC-10
❑ 97FleMilDM-6
❑ 97FleMilDMR-6
❑ 97FleTeaL-23
❑ 97FleTif-397
❑ 97FleTif-738
❑ 97Lea-248
❑ 97LeaFraM-248
❑ 97LeaFraMDC-248
❑ 97MetUni-194
❑ 97MetUniBF-7
❑ 97NewPin-132
❑ 97NewPinAP-132
❑ 97NewPinMC-132
❑ 97NewPinPP-132
❑ 97Pac-365
❑ 97PacCar-32
❑ 97PacCarM-32
❑ 97PacGolCD-32
❑ 97PacLigB-365
❑ 97PacPri-124
❑ 97PacPriGA-GA27
❑ 97PacPriLB-124
❑ 97PacPriP-124
❑ 97PacSil-365
❑ 97Pin-73
❑ 97PinArtP-PP73
❑ 97PinCer-87
❑ 97PinCerMBla-87
❑ 97PinCerMBlu-87
❑ 97PinCerMG-87
❑ 97PinCerMR-87
❑ 97PinCerR-87
❑ 97PinIns-117
❑ 97PinInsCE-117
❑ 97PinInsDE-117
❑ 97PinInsFS-5
❑ 97PinMusC-73
❑ 97PinPrePla-73
❑ 97PinTotCPB-87
❑ 97PinTotCPG-87
❑ 97PinTotCPR-87
❑ 97PinX-P-29
❑ 97PinX-PMoS-29
❑ 97PinX-PSfF-28
❑ 97PinX-PSfFU-28
❑ 97Sco-219
❑ 97Sco-330
❑ 97Sco-493
❑ 97ScoArtPWB-219
❑ 97ScoArtPWB-330
❑ 97ScoArtPWB-493
❑ 97ScoPreS-219
❑ 97ScoPreS-330
❑ 97ScoResC-493
❑ 97ScoShoS-219
❑ 97ScoShoS-330
❑ 97ScoShoS-493
❑ 97ScoShoSAP-219
❑ 97ScoShoSAP-330
❑ 97ScoShoSAP-493
❑ 97ScoTitT-9
❑ 97Sel-83
❑ 97SelArtP-83
❑ 97SelCom-83
❑ 97SelRegG-83
❑ 97SP-120
❑ 97SpoIll-88
❑ 97SpoIllEE-88
❑ 97SPSpeF-29
❑ 97SPx-34
❑ 97SPxBro-34
❑ 97SPxGol-34
❑ 97SPxGraF-34
❑ 97SPxSil-34
❑ 97SPxSte-34
❑ 97StaClu-41
❑ 97StaCluC-CO2
❑ 97StaCluI-I3
❑ 97StaCluMat-41
❑ 97StaCluMOP-41
❑ 97StaCluMOP-I3
❑ 97StrAll-28
❑ 97Stu-141
❑ 97StuPrePG-141
❑ 97StuPrePS-141
❑ 97Top-145
❑ 97Top-466
❑ 97TopAll-AS2
❑ 97TopChr-55
❑ 97TopChrAS-AS2
❑ 97TopChrR-55
❑ 97TopChrSAR-AS2
❑ 97TopGal-64
❑ 97TopGalPPI-64
❑ 97TopIntF-ILM10
❑ 97TopIntFR-ILM10
❑ 97TopMem05-24
❑ 97TopSta-61
❑ 97TopStaAM-61
❑ 97UD3-11
❑ 97Ult-239
❑ 97UltGolME-239
❑ 97UltHRK-5
❑ 97UltPlaME-239
❑ 97UppDec-322
❑ 97UppDec-430
❑ 97UppDecLDC-LD11
❑ 98Bow-21
❑ 98BowBes-99
❑ 98BowBesAR-99
❑ 98BowBesR-99
❑ 98BowChr-21
❑ 98BowChrGA-21
❑ 98BowChrGAR-21
❑ 98BowChrI-21
❑ 98BowChrIR-21
❑ 98BowChrR-21
❑ 98BowChrR-17
❑ 98BowChrRR-17
❑ 98BowGolA-21
❑ 98BowInt-21
❑ 98CirThu-164
❑ 98CirThuRav-164
❑ 98CirThuSupRav-164
❑ 98ColCho-440
❑ 98ColChoER-ER18
❑ 98ColChoS'-18
❑ 98ColChoSQ-SQ78
❑ 98Don-11
❑ 98DonCol-11
❑ 98DonColE-465
❑ 98DonColL-316
❑ 98DonColP-626
❑ 98DonColS-11
❑ 98DonCruG-87
❑ 98DonCruP-87
❑ 98DonCruR-87
❑ 98DonEli-65
❑ 98DonEliA-65
❑ 98DonEliS-65
❑ 98DonGolPP-11
❑ 98DonPre-76
❑ 98DonPreSeat-76
❑ 98DonPriCD-11
❑ 98DonPriCE-465
❑ 98DonPriCL-316
❑ 98DonPriCP-626
❑ 98DonSig-30
❑ 98DonSigP-30
❑ 98DonSilPP-11
❑ 98E-X2-67
❑ 98E-X2ECFut-67
❑ 98E-X2ECNow-67
❑ 98Fin-109
❑ 98FinNo--109
❑ 98FinNo-R-109
❑ 98FinRef-109
❑ 98Fle-125
❑ 98FleVin'-37
❑ 98FleVin'C-37
❑ 98Lea-117
❑ 98LeaFraDA-117
❑ 98LeaFraF-117
❑ 98LeaFraM-117
❑ 98LeaFraM-117
❑ 98LeaFraMDC-117
❑ 98LeaFraMDC-117
❑ 98LeaFraMS-117
❑ 98LeaFraMZ2-117
❑ 98LeaRS-78
❑ 98LeaRSLHolo-78
❑ 98LeaRSLong-78
❑ 98LeaRTrue-78
❑ 98MetUni-187
❑ 98MetUniPMG-187
❑ 98Pac-366
❑ 98PacAur-164
❑ 98PacInvTeam-18
❑ 98PacOme-156
❑ 98PacOmeR-156
❑ 98PacPar-204
❑ 98PacParC-204
❑ 98PacParG-204
❑ 98PacParHS-204
❑ 98PacParPB-204

❑ 98PacParR-204
❑ 98PacParTC-25
❑ 98PacPlaB-366
❑ 98PacRedT-366
❑ 98PacSil-366
❑ 98Pin-27
❑ 98PinArtP-PP27
❑ 98PinIns-9
❑ 98PinIns-138
❑ 98PinInsCE-9
❑ 98PinInsCE-138
❑ 98PinInsDE-9
❑ 98PinInsDE-138
❑ 98PinMusC-PP27
❑ 98PinPer-77
❑ 98PinPerPP-77
❑ 98PinPerSftF-36
❑ 98PinPreP-27
❑ 98PinSna-NYM2
❑ 98PinSna-NYM16
❑ 98Sco-108
❑ 98Sco-261
❑ 98ScoRT-76
❑ 98ScoRTSS-PP60
❑ 98ScoRTSSAP-PP60
❑ 98ScoRTSSAP1-PP60
❑ 98ScoSS-PP145
❑ 98ScoSSAP-PP145
❑ 98SkyDugA-150
❑ 98SkyDugAIA-150
❑ 98SP Aut-135
❑ 98SpoIll-61
❑ 98SpoIllEE-61
❑ 98SpoIllFE-61
❑ 98SpoIllTaN-46
❑ 98SpoIllTaNEE-46
❑ 98SPxFin-101
❑ 98SPxFinR-101
❑ 98SPxFinS-101
❑ 98StaCluC-CS25
❑ 98StaCluC-CS28
❑ 98StaCluC-CS29
❑ 98StaCluFDI-8
❑ 98StaCluI-8
❑ 98StaCluOneK-8
❑ 98StaCluPP-8
❑ 98Stu-182
❑ 98StuGPP-182
❑ 98StuSPP-182
❑ 98Top-294
❑ 98TopChr-294
❑ 98TopChrR-294
❑ 98TopDevR-294
❑ 98TopDia-294
❑ 98TopGal-51
❑ 98TopGalGP-51
❑ 98TopGalOPP-51
❑ 98TopGalPPI-51
❑ 98TopGalPPIA-51
❑ 98TopMiniC-294
❑ 98TopMysF-ILM5
❑ 98TopMysFR-ILM5
❑ 98TopOpeD-121
❑ 98TopSta-91
❑ 98TopSta'S-17
❑ 98TopSta'SGH-17
❑ 98TopStaB-91
❑ 98TopStaG-91
❑ 98TopStaGR-91
❑ 98TopStaS-91
❑ 98TopStaSteG-17
❑ 98UD3-66
❑ 98UD3-156
❑ 98UD3-246
❑ 98UD3DieCut-66
❑ 98UD3DieCut-156
❑ 98UD3DieCut-246
❑ 98Ult-71
❑ 98UltGolM-71
❑ 98UltMas-71
❑ 98UltPlaM-71
❑ 98UppDec-165
❑ 98UppDec10AP-16
❑ 98UppDec1APR-16
❑ 98UppDecSF-90
❑ 98Zen-57
❑ 98Zen5 xx7-36
❑ 98Zen5x7GoldImp-36
❑ 98Zen5x7Imp-36
❑ 98ZenZ-G-57
❑ 98ZenZ-S-57
❑ 99199Fin-187
❑ 99Bow-246
❑ 99BowBes-9
❑ 99BowBesAR-9
❑ 99BowBesR-9
❑ 99BowGol-246
❑ 99BowInt-246
❑ 99CroRoyB-72
❑ 99CroRoyL-72
❑ 99CroRoyOD-72
❑ 99DodPol-11
❑ 99E-X Cen-74
❑ 99E-X CenECFut-74
❑ 99E-X CenECNow-74
❑ 99FinGolRef-187
❑ 99FinRef-187
❑ 99FlaShoLeg1-85
❑ 99FlaShoLeg2-85
❑ 99FlaShoLeg3-85
❑ 99FlaShoLegM1-85
❑ 99FlaShoLegM2-85
❑ 99FlaShoLegM3-85
❑ 99FlaShoR1-85
❑ 99FlaShoR2-85
❑ 99FlaShoR3-85
❑ 99Fle-305
❑ 99FleBri-114
❑ 99FleBri2G-114
❑ 99FleBriBlu-114
❑ 99FleBriGol-114
❑ 99FleMys-38
❑ 99FleMysG-38
❑ 99FleMysM-38
❑ 99FleSta9-305
❑ 99FleWarT-305
❑ 99MetUni-162
❑ 99MetUniGM-162
❑ 99MetUniPMG-162
❑ 99Pac-277
❑ 99PacInv-75
❑ 99PacInvOD-75
❑ 99PacInvPB-75
❑ 99PacOme-120
❑ 99PacOmeC-120
❑ 99PacOmeG-120
❑ 99PacOmePB-120
❑ 99PacPar-117
❑ 99PacParC-117
❑ 99PacParG-117
❑ 99PacParHoloGold-117
❑ 99PacParHS-117
❑ 99PacParOD-117
❑ 99PacParPB-117
❑ 99PacParRed-117
❑ 99PacPlaB-277
❑ 99PacRed-277
❑ 99Rev-70
❑ 99RevPremDate-70
❑ 99RevRet-70
❑ 99RevShaSS-70
❑ 99SkyMolM-88
❑ 99SkyMolMX-88
❑ 99SkyPre-170
❑ 99SkyPreR-170
❑ 99StaClu-318
❑ 99StaCluFDI-318
❑ 99StaCluOoaK-318
❑ 99StaCluPP-318
❑ 99Top-412
❑ 99TopBlaLC1-10
❑ 99TopBlaLC2-10
❑ 99TopBlaLC3-10
❑ 99TopChr-412
❑ 99TopChrR-412
❑ 99TopGal-81
❑ 99TopGalPP-81
❑ 99TopGalPPI-81
❑ 99TopGolL-10
❑ 99TopGolLC1-10
❑ 99TopGolLC2-10
❑ 99TopGolLOtO-10
❑ 99TopMVPP-412
❑ 99TopOpeD-141
❑ 99TopRedLC1-10
❑ 99TopRedLC2-10
❑ 99TopRedLC3-10
❑ 99TopSta-80
❑ 99TopSta1Foil-80
❑ 99TopStaFoil-80
❑ 99TopStaOS-80
❑ 99UppDec-399
❑ 99UppDecEL1-399
❑ 99UppDecEL2-399
❑ 99Vic-197

Hundrick, Gink
❑ 28W513-63

Hundt, Bo
❑ 97AugGre-20

Hunger, Chris
❑ 81WauTimT-9
❑ 83ChaLooT-3

Hungling, Bernie (Bernard)
❑ 22E120-141
❑ 90DodTar-989

Hunnefield, William
❑ 25Zee-42
❑ 26Exh-76
❑ 27Exh-38
❑ 30ChiEveAP-15
❑ 31Exh-21
❑ 93ConTSN-696

Hunsacker, Frank
❑ 77St.PetCT-8
❑ 80ArkTraT-15
❑ 81BirBarT-9

Hunsinger, Alan
❑ 82SprCarF-17
❑ 83ArkTraT-18
❑ 90SprCarDGB-7

Hunt, Art
❑ 32Zee-102
❑ 33Zee-124

Hunt, Ben
❑ 09ObaT21-143
❑ 11PinT-5-662
❑ 75CliPilT-19

Hunt, Benjamin
❑ 09ObaT21-310
❑ 12ObaPreT-59

Hunt, Chris
❑ 92BoiHawF-3630
❑ 93PocPosSP-9

Hunt, Joe
❑ 98EriSeaWM-14

Hunt, Jon
❑ 96HicCraB-9
❑ 97HicCraRB-18

Hunt, Ken L.
❑ 60Lea-33
❑ 60Top-522
❑ 61Top-156
❑ 62AngJayP-5
❑ 62Jel-79
❑ 62Pos-79
❑ 62PosCan-79
❑ 62Top-68
❑ 62TopBuc-40
❑ 62TopVen-68
❑ 63AngJayP-6
❑ 63Top-207
❑ 64Top-294
❑ 64TopCoi-89
❑ 64TopVen-294
❑ 92YanWIZ6-58

Hunt, Ken R.
❑ 61Top-556
❑ 62Jel-129
❑ 62Kah-20
❑ 62Pos-129
❑ 62PosCan-129
❑ 62RedEnq-14
❑ 62SalPlaC-76A
❑ 62SalPlaC-76B
❑ 62ShiPlaC-76
❑ 62Top-364
❑ 62TopStal-65
❑ 63RedEnq-13
❑ 80Red196T-31

Hunt, Kenya
❑ 94SpoIndC-11
❑ 94SpoIndF-3329
❑ 95IdaFalBTI-16

Hunt, Randy
❑ 82SprCarF-20
❑ 83ArkTraT-11
❑ 85LouRedR-11
❑ 86IndIndTI-6
❑ 86Top-218
❑ 86TopTif-218
❑ 87Don-625
❑ 88MemChiB-15
❑ 90SprCarDGB-33

Hunt, Riegal
❑ 92WelPirC-10
❑ 92WelPirF-1337
❑ 93WelPirC-7
❑ 93WelPirF-3372

Hunt, Ron (Ronald K.)
❑ 61TopStal-172
❑ 63Top-558
❑ 64Baz-26
❑ 64MetJayP-7
❑ 64MetTeal-7
❑ 64Top-235
❑ 64TopCoi-164
❑ 64TopGia-6
❑ 64TopSta-93
❑ 64TopStaU-35
❑ 64TopVen-235
❑ 65Baz-26
❑ 65MetJayP-7
❑ 65MetPos-4
❑ 65OldLonC-12
❑ 65Top-285
❑ 65TopEmbl-35
❑ 65TopTral-50
❑ 66MetPos-2
❑ 66MetVolC-6
❑ 66Top-360
❑ 66TopVen-360
❑ 67CokCapD-6
❑ 67CokCapDA-6
❑ 67DexPre-102
❑ 67OPCPapl-31
❑ 67Top-525
❑ 67TopPos-31
❑ 68DexPre-39
❑ 68OPC-15
❑ 68Top-15
❑ 68TopVen-15
❑ 69MilBra-123
❑ 69MLBOffS-200
❑ 69Top-664
❑ 69TopSta-105
❑ 69TopTeaP-14
❑ 70ExpPin-7
❑ 70Gia-5
❑ 70MLBOffS-125
❑ 70OPC-276
❑ 70Top-276
❑ 71ExpPS-10
❑ 71MLBOffS-130
❑ 71OPC-161
❑ 71Top-578
❑ 72Dia-21
❑ 72MilBra-156
❑ 72OPC-110
❑ 72ProStaP-6
❑ 72SevTraC-20
❑ 72Top-110
❑ 73OPC-149
❑ 73Top-149
❑ 74ExpWes-5
❑ 74Kel-25
❑ 74OPC-275
❑ 74Top-275
❑ 74TopSta-55
❑ 75OPC-610
❑ 75Top-610
❑ 75TopMin-610
❑ 78TCM60I-212
❑ 81RedPioT-15
❑ 81TCM60I-357
❑ 82HolMilT-15
❑ 86MetGreT-2
❑ 90DodTar-372
❑ 90PacLeg-84
❑ 91MetWIZ-193
❑ 92Nab-5
❑ 93UppDecAH-70
❑ 94UppDecAH-33
❑ 94UppDecAH1-33

Hunt, Ronald
❑ 82RedPioT-21

Hunt, Shannon
❑ 90BenBucL-28

Hunt, Tom
❑ 80LynSaiT-16
❑ 81WauTimT-28
❑ 82WauTimF-30
❑ 83ChaLooT-23
❑ 84ChaLooT-9
❑ 86ChaLooP-14
❑ 87ChaLooB-26

Hunt, Will
❑ 93BriTigF-3644
❑ 93LSUTigM-6
❑ 94FayGenC-14
❑ 94FayGenF-2140

Hunter, Andy
❑ 96IdaFalB-10

Hunter, Bert
❑ 86AshTouP-14
❑ 86AubAstP-13
❑ 87AshTouP-16
❑ 88OscAstS-16
❑ 89ColMudP-148
❑ 89ColMudS-14
❑ 90ColMudB-8
❑ 90ColMudP-1358
❑ 90ColMudS-14
❑ 91JacGenLD-562
❑ 91JacGenP-937
❑ 91LinDriAA-562
❑ 92BinMetF-528
❑ 92BinMetS-60
❑ 93NorTidF-2583
❑ 97JacGen-3
❑ 98SalVol-13

Hunter, Billy (Gordon)
❑ 53Top-166
❑ 54Bow-5
❑ 54OriTeal-10
❑ 54Top-48
❑ 55Bow-69
❑ 57Top-207
❑ 58BalOriP-10
❑ 58IndTeal-28
❑ 58Top-98A
❑ 58Top-98B
❑ 59Top-11
❑ 59TopVen-11
❑ 64BalOriP-18
❑ 65BalOriP-14
❑ 66BalOriP-17
❑ 67BalOriP-51
❑ 67BalOriP-52
❑ 67BalOriP-53
❑ 70BalOriP-15
❑ 71BalOriP-15
❑ 72OriPos-17
❑ 73BalOriP-25
❑ 73OPC-136
❑ 73OriTeal-19
❑ 73Top-136A
❑ 73Top-136B
❑ 74OPC-306
❑ 74Top-306
❑ 75BalOriP-16
❑ 76BalOriP-20
❑ 77BalOriP-10
❑ 78RanBurK-1
❑ 78SSP270-104
❑ 78Top-548
❑ 79TCM50-118
❑ 81Ori6F-18
❑ 86RanGreT-4
❑ 91OriCro-211
❑ 91TopArc1-166
❑ 93RanKee-200
❑ 94TopArc1-48
❑ 94TopArc1G-48
❑ 97BalOriP-22

Hunter, Bobby (Bob)
❑ 88OneYanP-2056
❑ 91AugPirC-8
❑ 92CarMudF-1177
❑ 92SalBucC-13
❑ 92SalBucF-59
❑ 93CarMudF-2050
❑ 93CarMudTI-20

Hunter, Brian L.
❑ 90AshTouP-2761
❑ 90CMC-848
❑ 91OscAstC-24
❑ 91OscAstP-698
❑ 92ClaFS7-206
❑ 92OscAstC-9
❑ 92OscAstF-2543
❑ 92UppDecML-324
❑ 93AstStaC-21
❑ 93Bow-12
❑ 93ClaFS7-209
❑ 93JacGenF-2120
❑ 94ActPac-52
❑ 94AriFalLS-9
❑ 94Bow-670
❑ 94BowBes-B31
❑ 94BowBesR-B31
❑ 94Cla-147
❑ 94ColC-659
❑ 94ColChoGS-659
❑ 94ColChoSS-659
❑ 94ExcAllF-8
❑ 94ExcFS7-202
❑ 94FleUpd-144
❑ 94LeaLimR-63
❑ 94ScoRoo-RT142
❑ 94ScoRooGR-RT142
❑ 94SP-7
❑ 94SPDieC-7
❑ 94SpoRoo-31
❑ 94SpoRooAP-31
❑ 94StaClu-651
❑ 94StaCluFDI-651
❑ 94StaCluGR-651
❑ 94StaCluMOP-651
❑ 94TedWilDGC-DG7
❑ 94TucTorF-774
❑ 94Ult-505
❑ 94UppDec-16
❑ 94UppDecED-16
❑ 94UppDecML-100
❑ 94UppDecML-135
❑ 94UppDecML-159
❑ 94VenLinU-7
❑ 95ActPac2G-9G
❑ 95ActPacF-7
❑ 95ActPacF-70
❑ 95AstMot-26
❑ 95Bow-267
❑ 95BowBes-B82
❑ 95BowBes-X11
❑ 95BowBesR-B82
❑ 95BowBesR-X11
❑ 95BowGolF-267
❑ 95ColCho-111
❑ 95ColChoGS-111
❑ 95ColChoSE-43
❑ 95ColChoSEGS-43
❑ 95ColChoSESS-43
❑ 95ColChoSS-111
❑ 95Don-184
❑ 95DonPreP-184
❑ 95DonTopotO-255
❑ 95Fin-300
❑ 95FinRef-300
❑ 95FleMajLP-6
❑ 95LeaGolR-10
❑ 95LeaLim-104
❑ 95Pin-164
❑ 95PinArtP-164
❑ 95PinMusC-164
❑ 95PinNewB-NB3
❑ 95Sco-297
❑ 95ScoGolR-297
❑ 95ScoPlaTS-297
❑ 95ScoPlaTS-403
❑ 95ScoRooDT-RDT7
❑ 95Sel-162
❑ 95Sel-238
❑ 95SelArtP-162
❑ 95SelArtP-238
❑ 95SelCer-116
❑ 95SelCerF-7
❑ 95SelCerMG-116
❑ 95SelCerPU-17
❑ 95SelCerPU9-17
❑ 95SP-59
❑ 95SPCha-53
❑ 95SPChaDC-53
❑ 95Spo-153
❑ 95SpoArtP-153
❑ 95SPSil-59
❑ 95StaClu-437
❑ 95StaCluMOP-322
❑ 95StaCluMOP-437
❑ 95StaCluSTWS-322
❑ 95StaCluSTWS-437
❑ 95Stu-172
❑ 95Top-237
❑ 95TopTra-39T
❑ 95TucTotTI-13
❑ 95Ult-387
❑ 95UltGolM-387
❑ 95UltGolP-6
❑ 95UltGolPGM-6
❑ 95UppDec-27
❑ 95UppDecED-27
❑ 95UppDecEDG-27
❑ 95UppDecPAW-H17
❑ 95UppDecPAWE-H17
❑ 95Zen-137
❑ 95ZenRooRC-10
❑ 96AstMot-12
❑ 96Baz-9
❑ 96Bow-15
❑ 96BowBes-60
❑ 96BowBesAR-60
❑ 96BowBesR-60
❑ 96BowFoi-15
❑ 96Cir-137
❑ 96CirRav-137
❑ 96ColCho-161
❑ 96ColChoGS-161
❑ 96ColChoSS-161
❑ 96Don-68
❑ 96DonPreP-68
❑ 96EmoRarB-3
❑ 96EmoXL-200
❑ 96Fin-B75
❑ 96FinRef-B75
❑ 96Fla-279
❑ 96Fle-411

❑ 96FleRooS-7
❑ 96FleTif-411
❑ 96FleTomL-3
❑ 96Lea-179
❑ 96LeaLim-33
❑ 96LeaLimG-33
❑ 96LeaPre-48
❑ 96LeaPreP-48
❑ 96LeaPrePB-179
❑ 96LeaPrePG-179
❑ 96LeaPrePS-179
❑ 96LeaSig-115
❑ 96LeaSigA-112
❑ 96LeaSigAG-112
❑ 96LeaSigAS-112
❑ 96LeaSigPPG-115
❑ 96LeaSigPPP-115
❑ 96MetUni-178
❑ 96MetUniMFG-5
❑ 96MetUniP-178
❑ 96Pac-84
❑ 96PanSti-58
❑ 96Pin-54
❑ 96PinAfi-105
❑ 96PinAfiAP-105
❑ 96PinArtP-21
❑ 96PinSta-21
❑ 96ScoDiaA-2
❑ 96ScoDugC-A28
❑ 96ScoDugCAP-A28
❑ 96ScoRef-4
❑ 96Sel-55
❑ 96SelArtP-55
❑ 96SelCer-83
❑ 96SelCerAP-83
❑ 96SelCerCB-83
❑ 96SelCerCR-83
❑ 96SelCerIP-20
❑ 96SelCerMB-83
❑ 96SelCerMG-83
❑ 96SelCerMR-83
❑ 96SP-92
❑ 96Spo-59
❑ 96SpoArtP-59
❑ 96StaClu-230
❑ 96StaCluMOP-230
❑ 96Stu-81
❑ 96StuPrePB-81
❑ 96StuPrePG-81
❑ 96StuPrePS-81
❑ 96Sum-50
❑ 96SumAbo&B-50
❑ 96SumArtP-50
❑ 96SumFoi-50
❑ 96TacRaiB-14
❑ 96Top-268
❑ 96TopChr-108
❑ 96TopChrR-108
❑ 96TopGal-107
❑ 96TopGalPPI-107
❑ 96TopLas-107
❑ 96TopLasBS-1
❑ 96Ult-210
❑ 96UltFreF-4
❑ 96UltFreFGM-4
❑ 96UltGolM-210
❑ 96UltRisS-5
❑ 96UltRisSGM-5
❑ 96UppDec-84
❑ 96UppDecBCP-BC18
❑ 96Zen-64
❑ 96ZenArtP-64
❑ 97Bow-62
❑ 97BowInt-62
❑ 97Cir-369
❑ 97CirRav-369
❑ 97ColCho-126
❑ 97ColCho-335
❑ 97Don-116
❑ 97Don-293
❑ 97DonEli-107
❑ 97DonEliGS-107
❑ 97DonGolPP-116
❑ 97DonGolPP-293
❑ 97DonPre-87
❑ 97DonPreCttC-87
❑ 97DonSilPP-116
❑ 97DonSilPP-293
❑ 97Fin-194
❑ 97FinRef-194
❑ 97Fle-347
❑ 97Fle-526
❑ 97FleTif-347
❑ 97FleTif-526
❑ 97Lea-280
❑ 97LeaFraM-280
❑ 97LeaFraMDC-280
❑ 97MetUni-137
❑ 97NewPin-75
❑ 97NewPinAP-75
❑ 97NewPinMC-75
❑ 97NewPinPP-75
❑ 97Pac-319
❑ 97PacLigB-319
❑ 97PacSil-319
❑ 97PinCer-11
❑ 97PinCerMBla-11
❑ 97PinCerMBlu-11
❑ 97PinCerMG-11
❑ 97PinCerMR-11
❑ 97PinCerR-11
❑ 97PinTotCPB-11
❑ 97PinTotCPG-11
❑ 97PinTotCPR-11
❑ 97PinX-P-95
❑ 97PinX-PMoS-95
❑ 97Sco-140
❑ 97Sco-424
❑ 97ScoArtPWB-140
❑ 97ScoArtPWB-424
❑ 97ScoPreS-140
❑ 97ScoResC-424
❑ 97ScoShoS-140
❑ 97ScoShoS-424
❑ 97ScoShoSAP-140
❑ 97ScoShoSAP-424
❑ 97Sel-185
❑ 97SelCom-185
❑ 97SP-69
❑ 97StaClu-73
❑ 97StaCluM-M15
❑ 97StaCluMOP-73
❑ 97StaCluMOP-M15
❑ 97Stu-111
❑ 97StuPrePG-111
❑ 97StuPrePS-111
❑ 97Top-208
❑ 97Ult-404
❑ 97UltGolME-404
❑ 97UltPlaME-404
❑ 98Bow-52
❑ 98BowBes-54
❑ 98BowBesAR-54
❑ 98BowBesR-54
❑ 98BowChr-52
❑ 98BowChrGA-52
❑ 98BowChrGAR-52
❑ 98BowChrI-52
❑ 98BowChrIR-52
❑ 98BowChrR-52
❑ 98BowGolA-52
❑ 98BowInt-52
❑ 98CirThu-148
❑ 98CirThuRav-148
❑ 98CirThuSupRav-148
❑ 98ColCho-256
❑ 98ColCho-370
❑ 98Don-224
❑ 98DonColL-324
❑ 98DonGolPP-224
❑ 98DonPriCL-324
❑ 98DonSilPP-224
❑ 98Fin-165
❑ 98FinNo--165
❑ 98FinNo-R-165
❑ 98FinRef-165
❑ 98Fle-49
❑ 98Lea-125
❑ 98LeaFraDA-125
❑ 98LeaFraF-125
❑ 98LeaFraM-125
❑ 98LeaFraM-125
❑ 98LeaFraMDC-125
❑ 98LeaFraMDC-125
❑ 98LeaFraMZ2-125
❑ 98LeaRS-95
❑ 98LeaRSLHolo-95
❑ 98LeaRSLong-95
❑ 98LeaRTrue-95
❑ 98Pac-90
❑ 98PacAur-39
❑ 98PacOme-91
❑ 98PacOmeR-91
❑ 98PacOnl-275
❑ 98PacOnlR-275
❑ 98PacOnlWC-275
❑ 98PacPar-48
❑ 98PacParC-48
❑ 98PacParG-48
❑ 98PacParHS-48
❑ 98PacParPB-48
❑ 98PacParR-48
❑ 98PacPlaB-90
❑ 98PacRedT-90
❑ 98PacSil-90
❑ 98PinPlu-64
❑ 98Revo-59
❑ 98RevoSS-59
❑ 98ScoRT-153
❑ 98SkyDugAFF-FF1
❑ 98SP Aut-92
❑ 98SpoIllWSF-69
❑ 98SpoIllWSFEE-69
❑ 98SpoIllWSFFE-69
❑ 98SPxFin-84
❑ 98SPxFinR-84
❑ 98SPxFinS-84
❑ 98StaCluFDI-79
❑ 98StaCluI-79
❑ 98StaCluOneK-79
❑ 98StaCluPP-79
❑ 98Stu-53
❑ 98StuGPP-53
❑ 98StuSPP-53
❑ 98Top-34
❑ 98TopChr-34
❑ 98TopChrR-34
❑ 98TopDevR-34
❑ 98TopDia-34
❑ 98TopGal-122
❑ 98TopGalGP-122
❑ 98TopGalOPP-122
❑ 98TopGalPPI-122
❑ 98TopGalPPIA-122
❑ 98TopGolLabC1-67
❑ 98TopGolLabC1B-67
❑ 98TopGolLabC1One-67
❑ 98TopGolLabC1R-67
❑ 98TopGolLabC2-67
❑ 98TopGolLabC2B-67
❑ 98TopGolLabC2One-67
❑ 98TopGolLabC2R-67
❑ 98TopGolLabC3-67
❑ 98TopGolLabC3B-67
❑ 98TopGolLabC3One-67
❑ 98TopGolLabC3R-67
❑ 98TopMiniC-34
❑ 98TopOpeD-23
❑ 98TopSta-39
❑ 98TopStaB-39
❑ 98TopStaG-39
❑ 98TopStaGR-39
❑ 98TopStaS-39
❑ 98Ult-274
❑ 98UltGolM-274
❑ 98UltMas-274
❑ 98UltPlaM-274
❑ 98UppDec-360
❑ 99199Fin-172
❑ 99Bow-39
❑ 99BowChr-39
❑ 99BowChrG-39
❑ 99BowChrGR-39
❑ 99BowChrI-39
❑ 99BowChrIR-39
❑ 99BowChrR-39
❑ 99BowGol-39
❑ 99BowInt-39
❑ 99CroRoyB-54
❑ 99CroRoyL-54
❑ 99CroRoyOD-54
❑ 99FinGolRef-172
❑ 99FinRef-172
❑ 99Fle-478
❑ 99FleSta9-478
❑ 99FleWarT-478
❑ 99Pac-167
❑ 99PacAur-68
❑ 99PacAurOD-68
❑ 99PacInv-57
❑ 99PacInvOD-57
❑ 99PacInvPB-57
❑ 99PacOme-220
❑ 99PacOmeC-220
❑ 99PacOmeG-220
❑ 99PacOmePB-220
❑ 99PacPar-90
❑ 99PacParC-90
❑ 99PacParG-90
❑ 99PacParHoloGold-90
❑ 99PacParHS-90
❑ 99PacParOD-90
❑ 99PacParPB-90
❑ 99PacParRed-90
❑ 99PacPlaB-167
❑ 99PacPri-59
❑ 99PacPriHB-59
❑ 99PacPriHG-59
❑ 99PacPriHM-59
❑ 99PacPriHP-59
❑ 99PacPriRed-59
❑ 99PacRed-167
❑ 99Rev-131
❑ 99RevPremDate-131
❑ 99RevRet-131
❑ 99RevShaSS-131
❑ 99StaClu-29
❑ 99StaCluFDI-29
❑ 99StaCluOoaK-29
❑ 99StaCluPP-29
❑ 99Top-274
❑ 99TopChr-274
❑ 99TopChrR-274
❑ 99TopMVPP-274
❑ 99Ult-169
❑ 99UltGolM-169
❑ 99UltMas-169
❑ 99UltPlaM-169
❑ 99UppDec-96
❑ 99UppDecEL1-96
❑ 99UppDecEL2-96
❑ 99Vic-153

Hunter, Brian R.

❑ 88BurBraP-25
❑ 88MidLeaAGS-18
❑ 89GreBraB-2
❑ 89GreBraP-1158
❑ 89GreBraS-9
❑ 89Sta-35
❑ 90CMC-295
❑ 90ProAAAF-416
❑ 90RicBraC-19
❑ 90RicBraP-271
❑ 90RicBraTI-13
❑ 91BraSubS-19
❑ 91Cla3-T39
❑ 91DonRoo-9
❑ 91LinDriAAA-431
❑ 91RicBraBC-25
❑ 91RicBraLD-431
❑ 91RicBraP-2581
❑ 91RicBraTI-18
❑ 91UltUpd-67
❑ 91UppDecFE-54F
❑ 92Bow-662
❑ 92BraLykP-15
❑ 92BraLykS-17
❑ 92ClaGam-16
❑ 92Don-163
❑ 92Fle-359
❑ 92Lea-374
❑ 92LeaBlaG-374
❑ 92OPC-611
❑ 92OPCPre-78
❑ 92Pin-412
❑ 92PinTea2-29
❑ 92ProFS7-177
❑ 92Sco-417
❑ 92Sco100RS-3
❑ 92ScoImpP-9
❑ 92StaClu-432
❑ 92Top-611
❑ 92TopDeb91-86
❑ 92TopGol-611
❑ 92TopGolW-611
❑ 92TopMic-611
❑ 92Ult-163
❑ 92UppDec-366
❑ 93BraLykP-13
❑ 93BraLykS-16
❑ 93BraStaC-23
❑ 93Don-290
❑ 93Fle-5
❑ 93OPC-157
❑ 93PacSpa-7
❑ 93Pin-414
❑ 93Sco-549
❑ 93Sel-189
❑ 93StaClu-491
❑ 93StaCluFDI-491
❑ 93StaCluMOP-491
❑ 93Top-102
❑ 93TopGol-102
❑ 93TopInaM-102
❑ 93TopInaR-102
❑ 93TopMic-102
❑ 93Ult-305
❑ 93UppDec-582
❑ 93UppDecGold-582
❑ 94ColC-586
❑ 94ColChoGS-586
❑ 94ColChoSS-586
❑ 94Fin-336
❑ 94FinRef-336
❑ 94Fla-421
❑ 94FleExtB-346
❑ 94FleUpd-173
❑ 94Lea-275
❑ 94Pin-502
❑ 94PinArtP-502
❑ 94PinMusC-502
❑ 94PirQui-8
❑ 94ScoRoo-RT42
❑ 94ScoRooGR-RT42
❑ 94Sel-91
❑ 94TopTra-39T
❑ 95ColCho-426
❑ 95ColChoGS-426
❑ 95ColChoSS-426
❑ 95FleUpd-134
❑ 95RedKah-12
❑ 95Sco-403
❑ 95ScoGolR-403
❑ 95StaClu-322
❑ 95Ult-366
❑ 95UltGolM-366
❑ 95UppDec-164
❑ 95UppDecED-164
❑ 95UppDecEDG-164
❑ 97Fle-208
❑ 97FleTif-208
❑ 97IndInd-9
❑ 98PacOnl-613
❑ 98PacOnlR-613
❑ 98PacOnlWC-613

Hunter, Catfish (Jim)

❑ 65Top-526
❑ 66OPC-36
❑ 66Top-36
❑ 66TopVen-36
❑ 67CokCapAt-15
❑ 67Top-369
❑ 67TopGiaSU-23
❑ 68Baz-2
❑ 68Top-385
❑ 68TopActS-10A
❑ 68TopPla-5
❑ 68TopPos-5
❑ 69A'sJacitB-8
❑ 69MilBra-124
❑ 69MLBOffS-87
❑ 69Top-235
❑ 69TopSta-216
❑ 69TopTeaP-21
❑ 70DayDaiNM-75
❑ 70MLBOffS-259
❑ 70Top-565
❑ 71BazNumT-48
❑ 71BazUnn-18
❑ 71MilDud-10
❑ 71MLBOffS-516
❑ 71OPC-45
❑ 71Top-45
❑ 71TopCoi-80
❑ 71TopTat-74
❑ 72Kel-22
❑ 72MilBra-157
❑ 72OPC-330
❑ 72Top-330
❑ 73A'sPos-29
❑ 73Kel2D-20
❑ 73LinPor-140
❑ 73OPC-235
❑ 73OPC-344
❑ 73SevTraC-33
❑ 73Top-235
❑ 73Top-344
❑ 73TopCanL-21
❑ 74Kel-44
❑ 74OPC-196
❑ 74OPC-339
❑ 74Top-7
❑ 74Top-339
❑ 74TopDecE-6
❑ 74TopSta-225
❑ 75BlaBacD-3
❑ 75Hos-148
❑ 75Kel-44A
❑ 75Kel-44B
❑ 75OPC-230
❑ 75OPC-310
❑ 75OPC-311
❑ 75SSPSam-2
❑ 75Top-230
❑ 75Top-310
❑ 75Top-311
❑ 75TopMin-230
❑ 75TopMin-310
❑ 75TopMin-311
❑ 75YanSSP-1
❑ 76BlaDis-21
❑ 76BucDis-21
❑ 76CarDis-21
❑ 76CraDis-21
❑ 76DailsID-21
❑ 76Hos-141
❑ 76IsaDis-21
❑ 76Kel-5
❑ 76LauDiaJ-7
❑ 76OPC-100
❑ 76OPC-200
❑ 76OPC-202
❑ 76OrbDis-21
❑ 76RedBarD-21
❑ 76SafDis-21
❑ 76SafSupLB-3
❑ 76SafSupLB-7
❑ 76SafSupLB-10
❑ 76SafSupLB-11
❑ 76SafSupLB-12
❑ 76SSP-425
❑ 76SSP-593A
❑ 76SSP-593B
❑ 76Top-100
❑ 76Top-200
❑ 76Top-202
❑ 76TowCluD-21
❑ 77BurCheD-178
❑ 77ChiWilD-32
❑ 77DailsID-32
❑ 77DetCaeD-32
❑ 77HolInnD-32
❑ 77Hos-79
❑ 77MSADis-32
❑ 77OPC-10
❑ 77RCColC-30
❑ 77SagDis-32
❑ 77sDis-32
❑ 77Spo-1409
❑ 77Spo-1410
❑ 77Top-280
❑ 77TopCloS-21
❑ 77WenDis-32
❑ 77YanBurK-4
❑ 77ZipDis-32
❑ 78OPC-69
❑ 78RCColC-58
❑ 78SSP270-23
❑ 78Top-460
❑ 78WifBalD-31
❑ 78YanBurK-7
❑ 78YanPhoA-12
❑ 78YanSSPD-23
❑ 79OPC-352
❑ 79Top-670
❑ 79YanBurK-6
❑ 79YanPicA-19
❑ 80PerHaloFP-198
❑ 80PerHaloFPS-61
❑ 80SSPHOF-198
❑ 82TCMGreP-25
❑ 83MLBPin-10
❑ 83YanASFY-20
❑ 86A'sGreT-9
❑ 86SpoDecG-63
❑ 87A'sMot-6
❑ 87DonHig-19
❑ 88PacLegI-16
❑ 88TopGloA-11
❑ 89HOFStiB-82
❑ 89PacLegI-193
❑ 89PerCelP-18
❑ 89SweBasG-10
❑ 90PacLeg-68
❑ 90PerGreM-62
❑ 91UppDecS-7
❑ 91UppDecS-16
❑ 92A'sUno7P-3
❑ 92A'sUno7P-4
❑ 92Pin-587
❑ 92UppDecS-27
❑ 92YanWIZ7-77
❑ 92YanWIZA-32
❑ 92YanWIZH-18
❑ 93ActPacA-126
❑ 93ActPacA2-60G
❑ 93MCIAmb-8
❑ 93NabAllA-3
❑ 94TedWil-68
❑ 95JimDeaAG-2
❑ 98DonSigSS-4

Hunter, George

❑ 09ColChiE-140
❑ 09T206-166
❑ 10CouT21-34
❑ 11SpoLifM-157

❑ 12ColRedB-140
❑ 12ColTinT 140
❑ 90DodTar-990
Hunter, Germaine
❑ 97MicBatC-13
❑ 98MicBatCM-17
Hunter, Greg
❑ 91Cla/Bes-178
❑ 91SanBerSC-15
❑ 91SanBerSP-1992
❑ 92PenPilC-19
❑ 92PenPilF-2938
Hunter, Herb H.
❑ 16FleBreD-44
❑ 18Zee-81
Hunter, Jeff
❑ 80ElmPioRST-21
Hunter, Jim (James McGregor)
❑ 86BurExpP-9
❑ 87StoPorP-19
❑ 88ElPasDB-28
❑ 89ElPasDGS-9
❑ 91BreMilB-12
❑ 92DenZepF-2634
❑ 92DenZepS-148
❑ 92ElPasDS-214
❑ 92Sco-741
❑ 92SkyAA F-94
❑ 92TopDeb91-87
❑ 93NewOrlZF-965
❑ 94BreMilB-321
Hunter, Jon
❑ 97IdaFalBTI-6
❑ 98CliLumG-9
Hunter, Marion
❑ 81RedPioT-16
Hunter, Mark
❑ 82MonNew-8
Hunter, Marty
❑ 90BenBucL-5
Hunter, Rich
❑ 93MarPhiC-15
❑ 93MarPhiF-3468
❑ 94MarPhiC-9
❑ 94MarPhiF-3285
❑ 95Bes-90
❑ 95PiePhiF-184
❑ 95ReaPhiELC-21
❑ 96Bow-283
❑ 96BowFoi-283
❑ 96Exc-206
❑ 96ExcCli-4
❑ 96Fin-B207
❑ 96FinRef-B207
❑ 96FleUpd-U165
❑ 96FleUpdTC-U165
❑ 96Top-430
❑ 96Ult-522
❑ 96UltGolM-522
❑ 96UppDec-262
❑ 97PacPriGotD-GD182
❑ 97ReaPhi-19
Hunter, Scott
❑ 94GreFalDSP-16
❑ 95SanBerSTI-8
❑ 96HilStaHWB-6
❑ 96StLucMTI-18
❑ 97BinMetB-14
❑ 98BinMetQ-16
❑ 98EasLeaTPM-29
❑ 99Bow-196
❑ 99BowChr-196
❑ 99BowChrG-196
❑ 99BowChrGR-196
❑ 99BowChrI-196
❑ 99BowChrIR-196
❑ 99BowChrR-196
❑ 99BowGol-196
❑ 99BowInt-196
❑ 99DumSet-118
❑ 99E-X Cen-97
❑ 99E-X CenECFut-97
❑ 99E-X CenECNow-97
❑ 99FlaShoLeg1-48
❑ 99FlaShoLeg2-48
❑ 99FlaShoLeg3-48
❑ 99FlaShoLegM1-48
❑ 99FlaShoLegM2-48
❑ 99FlaShoLegM3-48
❑ 99FlaShoR1-48
❑ 99FlaShoR2-48
❑ 99FlaShoR3-48
❑ 99FleBri-152
❑ 99FleBri2G-152
❑ 99FleBriBlu-152
❑ 99FleBriGol-152
❑ 99FleMys-118
❑ 99FleMysM-118
❑ 99SkyMolM-125
❑ 99SkyMolMF-25
❑ 99SkyMolMFS-25
❑ 99SkyMolMFT-25
❑ 99SkyMolMX-125
❑ 99SkyPreA-29
❑ 99SkyPreABlue-29
Hunter, Spike
❑ 33WorCig(-51
Hunter, Torii
❑ 94Bow-104
❑ 94Cla-182
❑ 94ClaGolF-80
❑ 94ClaGolN1PLF-LP5
❑ 94ClaGolREF-RE5
❑ 94Pin-267
❑ 94PinArtP-267
❑ 94PinMusC-267
❑ 94Sco-640
❑ 94ScoGolR-640
❑ 95Bow-143
❑ 95ForMyeMTI-11
❑ 95UppDecML-128
❑ 95UppDecMLFS-128
❑ 96Bow-111
❑ 96BowFoi-111
❑ 96HarCitRCB-15
❑ 97Bow-176
❑ 97BowChr-168
❑ 97BowChrI-168
❑ 97BowChrIR-168
❑ 97BowChrR-168
❑ 97BowInt-176
❑ 97EasLeaTPB-13
❑ 97NewBriRC-15
❑ 97Sel-116
❑ 97SelArtP-116
❑ 97SelCom-116
❑ 97SelRegG-116
❑ 98AriFalLTP-8
❑ 98ColCho-158
❑ 98EasLeaTPM-11
❑ 98LeaRS-311
❑ 98LeaRSLHolo-311
❑ 98LeaRSLong-311
❑ 98LeaRTrue-311
❑ 98NewBriRCM-14
❑ 98UppDec-412
❑ 99DumSet-126
❑ 99FleMys-126
❑ 99FleMysM-126
❑ 99PacInv-87
❑ 99PacInvOD-87
❑ 99PacInvPB-87
❑ 99PacOme-141
❑ 99PacOmeC-141
❑ 99PacOmeG-141
❑ 99PacOmePB-141
❑ 99SkyPre-270
❑ 99SkyPre-270
❑ 99SkyPreR-270
❑ 99SkyPreR-270
❑ 99Vic-231
Hunter, Traver
❑ 92OklStaC-13
Hunter, Travis
❑ 98KanCouC-15
❑ 98KanCouCCP-15
Hunter, Willard
❑ 82MetGal62-21
❑ 90DodTar-373
❑ 91MetWIZ-194
Huntley, James
❑ 94HunCubC-14
❑ 94HunCubF-3560
Hunts, Chris
❑ 93PocPosF-4210
Huntsman, Brandon
❑ 96BluOriB-16
❑ 96HigDesMB-14
❑ 98DelShoM-17
Huntsman, Scott
❑ 95BelBreTI-23
❑ 96StoPorB-6
❑ 97El PasDB-17
❑ 98El PasDG-14
Huntz, Steve
❑ 69OPC-136
❑ 69Top-136
❑ 69TopFou-25
❑ 70OPC-282
❑ 70Top-282
❑ 71MLBOffS-252
❑ 71OPC-486
❑ 71Top-486
❑ 72OPC-73
❑ 72Top-73
❑ 75HawIsIC-2
❑ 75IntLeaASB-11
❑ 75PacCoaLAB-11
❑ 76HawIsIC-20
❑ 76SSP-126
Hunziker, Kent
❑ 76CliPilT-20
❑ 77AppFoxT-12
Hupke, Doug
❑ 87EugEmeP-2650
Huppert, Dave (David B.)
❑ 80ChaO'sP-11
❑ 80ChaO'sW-12
❑ 81RocRedWT-9
❑ 81RocRedWW-15
❑ 83RocRedWT-11
❑ 84VanCanC-37
❑ 86ElPasDP-13
❑ 88CalLeaACLC-19
❑ 88StoPorCLC-202
❑ 88StoPorP-740
❑ 89StoPorB-29
❑ 89StoPorCLC-176
❑ 89StoPorP-386
❑ 89StoPorS-22
❑ 90ElPasDGS-1
❑ 90TexLeaAGS-18
❑ 91ElPasDLD-199
❑ 91ElPasDP-2762
❑ 91LinDriAA-199
❑ 91OriCro-212
❑ 92WhiSoxK-NNO
❑ 93SarWhiSC-28
❑ 93SarWhiSF-1386
❑ 94BreMilB-322
❑ 94PriWilCC-25
❑ 94PriWilCF-1936
❑ 95PriWilCTI-28
❑ 96PriWilCB-1
❑ 97BirBarB-30
❑ 98BirBarG-13
Hurd, Thomas
❑ 55Top-116
❑ 55TopDouH-119
❑ 56Top-256
Hurdle, Clint (Clinton)
❑ 76WatRoyT-13
❑ 78Roy-9
❑ 78SSP270-229
❑ 78Top-705
❑ 79Top-547
❑ 80OPC-273
❑ 80Top-525
❑ 81Don-224
❑ 81Fle-45
❑ 81OPC-98
❑ 81RoyPol-4
❑ 81Top-98
❑ 81TopSti-85
❑ 82Don-516
❑ 82Fle-411
❑ 82RedCok-10
❑ 82Top-297
❑ 83TidTidT-4
❑ 84TidTidT-28
❑ 85MetColP-14
❑ 85MetTCM-38
❑ 86CarSchM-10
❑ 86CarTeal-20
❑ 86Don-434
❑ 86Top-438
❑ 86TopTif-438
❑ 87Fle-298
❑ 87FleGlo-298
❑ 87MetColP-36
❑ 87OPC-317
❑ 87TidTidP-1
❑ 87TidTidT-22
❑ 87Top-317
❑ 87TopTif-317
❑ 89MetColP-34
❑ 89PacSenL-111
❑ 89St.LucMS-6
❑ 89T/MSenL-50
❑ 89TidTidC-12
❑ 89TopSenL-98
❑ 90EliSenL-115
❑ 90JacMetGS-5
❑ 90MetColP-15
❑ 91LinDriAA-649
❑ 91MetColP-35
❑ 91MetWIZ-195
❑ 91WilBilLD-649
❑ 91WilBilP-309
❑ 92MetColP-35
❑ 92TidTidF-912
❑ 92TidTidS-574
❑ 93NorTidF-2585
Hurdle, Mike
❑ 80UtiBluJT-29
Hurlbert, Gordon
❑ 90EasLeaAP-EL47
❑ 90NewBriRSB-15
❑ 90NewBriRSS-27
Hurlbutt, Robert
❑ 90AshTouC-18
❑ 90AubAstB-7
❑ 90AubAstP-3416
❑ 91AshTouP-570
Hurley, Edwin
❑ 55Bow-260
Hurley, Mike
❑ 89OklSoo-15
Hurley, Pat
❑ 90DodTar-991
Hurni, Rick
❑ 88SalLakCTTI-12
Hursey, Darren
❑ 87FayGenP-13
❑ 88LakTigS-16
❑ 89LonTigP-1370
❑ 90LakTigS-13
❑ 91LinDriAA-387
❑ 91LonTigLD-387
❑ 91LonTigP-1873
Hurst, Bill
❑ 91JohCitCP-3973
❑ 95BreCouMF-242
❑ 96PorSeaDB-16
❑ 97ChaKni-15
❑ 98PorSeaD5AQ-32
❑ 98TolMudHQ-20
Hurst, Bruce
❑ 81PawRedST-3
❑ 81Top-689
❑ 82Fle-297
❑ 82Top-381
❑ 83Don-134
❑ 83Fle-186
❑ 83Top-82
❑ 84AllGamPI-172
❑ 84Don-213
❑ 84Fle-400
❑ 84Nes792-213
❑ 84OPC-213
❑ 84Top-213
❑ 84TopSti-226
❑ 84TopTif-213
❑ 85Don-493
❑ 85Fle-161
❑ 85Lea-73
❑ 85OPC-134
❑ 85Top-451
❑ 85TopSti-211
❑ 85TopTif-451
❑ 86Don-517
❑ 86DonHig-47
❑ 86Fle-352
❑ 86OPC-193
❑ 86Top-581
❑ 86TopMinL-6
❑ 86TopTif-581
❑ 87ClaGam-83
❑ 87Don-174
❑ 87Fle-37
❑ 87FleBasA-22
❑ 87FleGlo-37
❑ 87FleGlo-WS1
❑ 87FleStiC-65
❑ 87FleWorS-1
❑ 87Lea-253
❑ 87OPC-31
❑ 87RedSoxP-13
❑ 87RedSoxSAP-8
❑ 87Spo-38
❑ 87SpoTeaP-9
❑ 87Top-705
❑ 87TopMinL-43
❑ 87TopSti-19
❑ 87TopTif-705
❑ 87Woo-19
❑ 87Woo-28
❑ 88Don-252
❑ 88DonAll-14
❑ 88DonBasB-233
❑ 88DonTeaBRS-252
❑ 88Fle-356
❑ 88FleBasA-18
❑ 88FleGlo-356
❑ 88FleStiC-10
❑ 88Lea-179
❑ 88OPC-125
❑ 88PanSti-22
❑ 88RedFolSB-37
❑ 88Sco-380
❑ 88ScoGlo-380
❑ 88Spo-197
❑ 88StaLinRS-12
❑ 88Top-125
❑ 88TopSti-253
❑ 88TopStiB-62
❑ 88TopTif-125
❑ 89Bow-451
❑ 89BowTif-451
❑ 89ClaTraP-194
❑ 89Don-423
❑ 89DonBasB-77
❑ 89DonTra-45
❑ 89Fle-91
❑ 89FleGlo-91
❑ 89FleUpd-124
❑ 89PadCok-7
❑ 89PadMag-21
❑ 89PadPos-15
❑ 89PanSti-271
❑ 89Sco-325
❑ 89ScoHot1S-79
❑ 89ScoRoo-19T
❑ 89Spo-175
❑ 89Top-675
❑ 89TopBasT-111
❑ 89TopGloS-28
❑ 89TopMinL-49
❑ 89TopStiB-29
❑ 89TopTif-675
❑ 89TopTra-55T
❑ 89TopTraT-55T
❑ 89TopUKM-42
❑ 89UppDec-387
❑ 89UppDec-792
❑ 90Bow-208
❑ 90BowTif-208
❑ 90ClaBlu-102
❑ 90Don-183
❑ 90DonBesN-84
❑ 90Fle-159
❑ 90FleBasA-19
❑ 90FleBasAC-19
❑ 90FleCan-159
❑ 90Lea-23
❑ 90MLBBasB-57
❑ 90OPC-315
❑ 90PadCok-8
❑ 90PadMag-23
❑ 90PanSti-357
❑ 90PubIntS-51
❑ 90Sco-270
❑ 90Sco100S-18
❑ 90Spo-47
❑ 90Top-315
❑ 90TopBig-324
❑ 90TopMinL-81
❑ 90TopSti-108
❑ 90TopTif-315
❑ 90TopTVA-48
❑ 90UppDec-433
❑ 91Bow-661
❑ 91ClaGam-84
❑ 91Don-83
❑ 91Fle-533
❑ 91Lea-469
❑ 91MajLeaCP-56
❑ 91OPC-65
❑ 91PadMag-5
❑ 91PadMag-19B
❑ 91PadSmo-15
❑ 91PanCanT1-90
❑ 91Sco-145
❑ 91StaClu-475
❑ 91Top-65
❑ 91TopDesS-65
❑ 91TopMic-65
❑ 91TopTif-65
❑ 91Ult-306
❑ 91UppDec-602
❑ 92Bow-187
❑ 92Don-123
❑ 92Fle-608
❑ 92Hig5-123
❑ 92Lea-216
❑ 92LeaBlaG-216
❑ 92OPC-595
❑ 92PadCarJ-9
❑ 92PadMot-20
❑ 92PadPolD-10
❑ 92PadSmo-13
❑ 92PanSti-238
❑ 92Pin-40
❑ 92Sco-111
❑ 92ScoProP-4
❑ 92ScoProP-9
❑ 92StaClu-312
❑ 92Top-595
❑ 92TopGol-595
❑ 92TopGolW-595
❑ 92TopMic-595
❑ 92TriPla-57
❑ 92Ult-280
❑ 92UppDec-437
❑ 93Don-576
❑ 93Fle-521
❑ 93Lea-341
❑ 93OPC-118
❑ 93PadMot-9
❑ 93PanSti-256
❑ 93Pin-327
❑ 93Sco-133
❑ 93Sel-141
❑ 93SelAce-19
❑ 93StaClu-347
❑ 93StaCluFDI-347
❑ 93StaCluMOP-347
❑ 93Top-111
❑ 93TopGol-111
❑ 93TopInaM-111
❑ 93TopInaR-111
❑ 93TopMic-111
❑ 93Ult-474
❑ 93UppDec-304
❑ 93UppDecGold-304
❑ 94Pin-504
❑ 94PinArtP-504
❑ 94PinMusC-504
❑ 94RanMagM-18
❑ 94StaCluT-243
❑ 94StaCluTFDI-243
Hurst, Charlie (Charles)
❑ 89MarPhiS-15
❑ 90BatCliP-3059
❑ 91SpaPhiC-7
❑ 91SpaPhiP-892
❑ 92SpaPhiC-13
❑ 92SpaPhiF-1261
Hurst, Don (Frank O.)
❑ 29ExhFou-11
❑ 29PorandAR-45
❑ 31Exh-12
❑ 33ExhFou-6
❑ 33RitCE-6S
❑ 33RitCE-11D
❑ 34ExhFou-6
❑ 34Gou-33
❑ 34GouCanV-80
❑ 35AlDemDCR3-115
❑ 85BigLeaC3-8
❑ 86PhiGreT-11
❑ 92ConTSN-519
Hurst, James Lavon
❑ 92ChaRanC-7
❑ 92ChaRanF-2223
❑ 93TulDriF-2730
❑ 93TulDriTI-13
❑ 94Bow-625
❑ 94OklCit8F-1493
❑ 94RanMagM-10
❑ 94RanMagM-19
❑ 94Sel-199
❑ 94SpoRoo-75
❑ 94SpoRooAP-75
❑ 94VenLinU-98
❑ 95LinVen-244
Hurst, Jimmy
❑ 92UtiBluSC-4
❑ 93SouBenWSC-11
❑ 93SouBenWSF-1444
❑ 94Bow-483
❑ 94BowBes-B58
❑ 94BowBes-X98
❑ 94BowBesR-B58
❑ 94BowBesR-X98
❑ 94CarLeaAF-CAR8
❑ 94PriWilCC-1
❑ 94PriWilCF-1934
❑ 95Bow-42
❑ 95BowBes-B70
❑ 95BowBesR-B70
❑ 95Exc-29
❑ 95SigRooOJ-19

❑ 95SigRooOJP-19
❑ 95SigRooOJPS-19
❑ 95SigRooOJS-19
❑ 95SP-12
❑ 95SPSil-12
❑ 95UppDec-254
❑ 95UppDecED-254
❑ 95UppDecEDG-254
❑ 95UppDecML-36
❑ 95UppDecMLFS-36
❑ 95UppDecSE-156
❑ 95UppDecSEG-156
❑ 96BirBarB-4
❑ 96Bow-142
❑ 96BowFoi-142
❑ 97TolMudHB-23
❑ 98PawRedSQ-16
❑ 98PriWilCASM-19

Hurst, Jody
❑ 88CapCodPPaLP-110
❑ 88MisStaB-13
❑ 89MisStaB-21
❑ 89NiaFalRP-12
❑ 90LakTigS-14
❑ 90StaFS7-35
❑ 92TolMudHF-1054
❑ 92TolMudHS-588
❑ 93TolMudHF-1664

Hurst, Jonathan
❑ 88ChaRanS-10
❑ 89ChaRanS-10
❑ 90Bes-105
❑ 90GasRanB-9
❑ 90GasRanP-2518
❑ 90GasRanS-11
❑ 90SouAtlLAS-12
❑ 91Cla/Bes-199
❑ 91FloStaLAP-FSL23
❑ 91MiaMirC-8
❑ 91MiaMirP-402
❑ 92Bow-388
❑ 92DonRoo-57
❑ 92IndIndS-184
❑ 92SkyAAAF-90
❑ 93OttLynF-2431
❑ 93Pin-242
❑ 93Sco-299
❑ 93StaClu-306
❑ 93StaCluFDI-306
❑ 93StaCluMOP-306
❑ 93Top-727
❑ 93TopGol-727
❑ 93TopInaM-727
❑ 93TopInaR-727
❑ 93TopMic-727
❑ 94MetColP-13
❑ 94Ult-529
❑ 95Sco-307
❑ 95ScoGolR-307
❑ 95ScoPlaTS-307
❑ 98TulDriTI-17

Hurst, Robert
❑ 26Zee-140
❑ 29Zee-74
❑ 30Zee-83
❑ 31Zee-47
❑ 32Zee-57

Hurst, Roy
❑ 94WilCubC-11
❑ 94WilCubF-3768

Hurta, Bob (Robert)
❑ 87UtiBluSP-28
❑ 88SpaPhiP-1026
❑ 88SpaPhiS-24
❑ 90AubAstB-2
❑ 90AubAstP-3399
❑ 91BurAstC-5
❑ 91BurAstP-2796
❑ 92JacGenF-3997
❑ 92JacGenS-334
❑ 92TucTorF-483
❑ 93JacGenF-2105
❑ 93TucTorF-3055

Hurtado, Edwin
❑ 93LinVenB-38
❑ 93St.CatBJC-11
❑ 93St.CatBJF-3969
❑ 94HagSunC-8
❑ 94HagSunF-2722
❑ 94VenLinU-121
❑ 95Bow-134
❑ 95LinVen-184
❑ 96-97LinVen-52
❑ 96ColCho-16
❑ 96Don-327
❑ 96DonPreP-327
❑ 96FleUpd-U80
❑ 96FleUpdTC-U80
❑ 96LeaSigEA-86
❑ 96MarMot-26
❑ 96Ult-412
❑ 96UltGolM-412
❑ 96UppDec-217
❑ 98ButCopKG-16

Hurtado, Jose
❑ 85BenPhiC-12

Hurtado, Victor
❑ 96KanCouCTI-13
❑ 96KanCouCUTI-7
❑ 96MidLeaAB-33
❑ 97BreCouMB-19

Husband, Perry
❑ 85VisOakT-3

Huseby, Ken
❑ 87TamTarP-4
❑ 88GreHorP-1564
❑ 89AugPirP-503

Huskey, Butch
❑ 90KinMetS-11
❑ 91ColMetPI-29
❑ 91ColMetPI-30
❑ 91ColMetPPI-5
❑ 91SouAtlLAGP-SAL16
❑ 92Bow-539
❑ 92ClaFS7-273
❑ 92ColMetPI-42
❑ 92ColMetPIISPI-2
❑ 92ColMetPIISPI-4
❑ 92St.LucMCB-1
❑ 92St.LucMF-1752
❑ 92UppDecML-37
❑ 92UppDecML-269
❑ 93BinMetF-2340
❑ 93Bow-46
❑ 93ClaGolF-70
❑ 93ClaYouG-YG6
❑ 93Don-506
❑ 93ExcFS7-74
❑ 93UppDec-436
❑ 93UppDecGold-436
❑ 94ActPac-37
❑ 94Bow-100
❑ 94Cla-40
❑ 94ColC-10
❑ 94ColChoGS-10
❑ 94ColChoSS-10
❑ 94Don-426
❑ 94FleMajLP-16
❑ 94LeaGolR-3
❑ 94NorTidF-2926
❑ 94Pac-405
❑ 94Pin-235
❑ 94PinArtP-235
❑ 94PinMusC-235
❑ 94PinNewG-NG12
❑ 94PinRooTP-4
❑ 94Sco-605
❑ 94ScoBoyoS-52
❑ 94ScoGolR-605
❑ 94Spo-149
❑ 94Top-179
❑ 94TopGol-179
❑ 94TopSpa-179
❑ 94TriPla-297
❑ 94UppDec-17
❑ 94UppDecED-17
❑ 95NorTidTI-14
❑ 95Sel-174
❑ 95SelArtP-174
❑ 96Bow-123
❑ 96BowFoi-123
❑ 96ColCho-227
❑ 96ColChoGS-227
❑ 96ColChoSS-227
❑ 96Don-351
❑ 96DonPreP-351
❑ 96Fin-B264
❑ 96FinRef-B264
❑ 96Fle-480
❑ 96FleTif-480
❑ 96Lea-83
❑ 96LeaPreP-83
❑ 96LeaSigA-113
❑ 96LeaSigAG-113
❑ 96LeaSigAS-113
❑ 96MetKah-16
❑ 96Pin-309
❑ 96PinAfi-118
❑ 96PinAfiAP-118
❑ 96PinFoil-309
❑ 96Sel-72
❑ 96SelArtP-72
❑ 96SelCer-78
❑ 96SelCerAP-78
❑ 96SelCerCB-78
❑ 96SelCerCR-78
❑ 96SelCerMB-78
❑ 96SelCerMG-78
❑ 96SelCerMR-78
❑ 96SigRooOJ-13
❑ 96SigRooOJS-13
❑ 96StaClu-86
❑ 96StaClu-257
❑ 96StaCluMOP-86
❑ 96StaCluMOP-257
❑ 96Stu-17
❑ 96StuPrePB-17
❑ 96StuPrePG-17
❑ 96StuPrePS-17
❑ 96Sum-93
❑ 96SumAbo&B-93
❑ 96SumArtP-93
❑ 96SumFoi-93
❑ 96Top-103
❑ 96Top-104
❑ 96Ult-243
❑ 96UltGolM-243
❑ 97ColCho-173
❑ 97Don-222
❑ 97DonEli-147
❑ 97DonEliGS-147
❑ 97DonGolPP-222
❑ 97DonLim-178
❑ 97DonLimE-178
❑ 97DonLimENG-178
❑ 97DonSilPP-222
❑ 97Fle-398
❑ 97FleTif-398
❑ 97Lea-266
❑ 97LeaFraM-266
❑ 97LeaFraMDC-266
❑ 97Pac-366
❑ 97PacLigB-366
❑ 97PacSil-366
❑ 97Sco-278
❑ 97ScoArtPWB-278
❑ 97ScoPreS-278
❑ 97ScoShoS-278
❑ 97ScoShoSAP-278
❑ 97StaClu-308
❑ 97StaCluMOP-308
❑ 97Top-73
❑ 97Ult-240
❑ 97UltGolME-240
❑ 97UltPlaME-240
❑ 97UppDec-116
❑ 98Bow-251
❑ 98BowChr-251
❑ 98BowChrGA-251
❑ 98BowChrGAR-251
❑ 98BowChrI-251
❑ 98BowChrIR-251
❑ 98BowChrR-251
❑ 98BowGolA-251
❑ 98BowInt-251
❑ 98CirThu-28
❑ 98CirThuRav-28
❑ 98CirThuSupRav-28
❑ 98ColCho-175
❑ 98Don-223
❑ 98DonColL-292
❑ 98DonColP-670
❑ 98DonGolPP-223
❑ 98DonPre-120
❑ 98DonPreSeat-120
❑ 98DonPriCL-292
❑ 98DonPriCP-670
❑ 98DonSigA-45
❑ 98DonSigAC-59
❑ 98DonSigAM-60
❑ 98DonSilPP-223
❑ 98Fin-122
❑ 98FinNo--122
❑ 98FinNo-R-122
❑ 98FinRef-122
❑ 98Fle-253
❑ 98Lea-93
❑ 98LeaFraDA-93
❑ 98LeaFraF-93
❑ 98LeaFraM-93
❑ 98LeaFraM-93
❑ 98LeaFraMDC-93
❑ 98LeaFraMDC-93
❑ 98LeaFraMS-93
❑ 98LeaFraMZ2-93
❑ 98Pac-367
❑ 98PacOme-157
❑ 98PacOmeR-157
❑ 98PacOnl-479
❑ 98PacOnlR-479
❑ 98PacOnlWC-479
❑ 98PacPar-205
❑ 98PacParC-205
❑ 98PacParG-205
❑ 98PacParHS-205
❑ 98PacParPB-205
❑ 98PacParR-205
❑ 98PacPlaB-367
❑ 98PacRedT-367
❑ 98PacSil-367
❑ 98Pin-84
❑ 98PinPreP-84
❑ 98PinSna-NYM7
❑ 98SP Aut-132
❑ 98SPxFin-301
❑ 98SPxFinR-301
❑ 98SPxFinS-301
❑ 98StaCluFDI-145
❑ 98StaCluI-145
❑ 98StaCluOneK-145
❑ 98StaCluPP-145
❑ 98Stu-175
❑ 98StuGPP-175
❑ 98StuSPP-175
❑ 98Top-68
❑ 98TopChr-68
❑ 98TopChrR-68
❑ 98TopDevR-68
❑ 98TopDia-68
❑ 98TopMiniC-68
❑ 98TopOpeD-35
❑ 98TopSta-53
❑ 98TopStaB-53
❑ 98TopStaG-53
❑ 98TopStaGR-53
❑ 98TopStaS-53
❑ 98Ult-374
❑ 98UltGolM-374
❑ 98UltMas-374
❑ 98UltPlaM-374
❑ 98UppDec-162
❑ 98UppDecSF-86
❑ 99Fle-455
❑ 99FleSta9-455
❑ 99FleWarT-455
❑ 99Pac-278
❑ 99PacPar-218
❑ 99PacParC-218
❑ 99PacParG-218
❑ 99PacParHoloGold-218
❑ 99PacParHS-218
❑ 99PacParOD-218
❑ 99PacParPB-218
❑ 99PacParRed-218
❑ 99PacPlaB-278
❑ 99PacRed-278
❑ 99Top-106
❑ 99TopChr-106
❑ 99TopChrR-106
❑ 99TopMVPP-106
❑ 99Ult-104
❑ 99UltGolM-104
❑ 99UltMas-104
❑ 99UltPlaM-104
❑ 99UppDec-147
❑ 99UppDec-492
❑ 99UppDecEL1-147
❑ 99UppDecEL1-492
❑ 99UppDecEL2-147
❑ 99UppDecEL2-492

Huslig, James
❑ 88OklSoo-1
❑ 89OklSoo-16
❑ 90CliGiaUTI-U7
❑ 90EveGiaB-6
❑ 90EveGiaP-3122
❑ 90OklSoo-14

Huson, Jeff
❑ 86BurExpP-10
❑ 87WesPalBEP-674
❑ 88JacExpB-18
❑ 88JacExpP-966
❑ 88SouLeaAJ-16
❑ 89IndIndC-18
❑ 89IndIndP-1233
❑ 89ScoHot1R-69
❑ 89TriAAAP-AAA11
❑ 90Don-693
❑ 90DonBesA-83
❑ 90DonRoo-11
❑ 90ExpPos-18
❑ 90Fle-350
❑ 90FleCan-350
❑ 90FleUpd-123
❑ 90Lea-285
❑ 90OPC-72
❑ 90RanMot-23
❑ 90Sco-615
❑ 90Sco100RS-14
❑ 90ScoRoo-41T
❑ 90ScoRooDT-B7
❑ 90ScoYouSI-41
❑ 90Spo-176
❑ 90Top-72
❑ 90TopTif-72
❑ 90TopTra-45T
❑ 90TopTraT-45T
❑ 90TriAAAC-4
❑ 90UppDec-434
❑ 90UppDec-788
❑ 91Baz-16
❑ 91Bow-273
❑ 91Don-305
❑ 91Fle-289
❑ 91Lea-134
❑ 91OPC-756
❑ 91PanFreS-255
❑ 91PanSti-206
❑ 91RanMot-23
❑ 91Sco-263
❑ 91Sco100RS-18
❑ 91StaClu-160
❑ 91Top-756
❑ 91TopDesS-756
❑ 91TopMic-756
❑ 91TopRoo-13
❑ 91TopTif-756
❑ 91ToyRoo-12
❑ 91Ult-349
❑ 91UppDec-195
❑ 92Don-456
❑ 92Fle-308
❑ 92Lea-251
❑ 92LeaBlaG-251
❑ 92OPC-314
❑ 92PanSti-78
❑ 92RanMot-23
❑ 92RanTeal-11
❑ 92Sco-466
❑ 92StaClu-341
❑ 92Top-314
❑ 92TopGol-314
❑ 92TopGolW-314
❑ 92TopMic-314
❑ 92Ult-133
❑ 92UppDec-196
❑ 93Don-583
❑ 93Fle-324
❑ 93Lea-137
❑ 93PacSpa-312
❑ 93PanSti-83
❑ 93RanKee-411
❑ 93RanStaC-12
❑ 93StaClu-281
❑ 93StaCluFDI-281
❑ 93StaCluMOP-281
❑ 93Top-143
❑ 93TopGol-143
❑ 93TopInaM-143
❑ 93TopInaR-143
❑ 93TopMic-143
❑ 93Ult-280
❑ 93UppDec-289
❑ 93UppDecGold-289
❑ 94Don-432
❑ 94Pac-619
❑ 94RanMagM-20
❑ 94StaCluT-253
❑ 94StaCluTFDI-253
❑ 95BalOriP-26
❑ 95RocRedWTI-19
❑ 96BalOriP-16
❑ 96LeaSigEA-87
❑ 97BrePol-10
❑ 98PacOnl-688
❑ 98PacOnlR-688
❑ 98PacOnlWC-688

Hussman, Darrell
❑ 98BilMusTI-13

Hust, Gary
❑ 90HigSchPLS-15
❑ 91SouOreAC-16
❑ 91SouOreAP-3862
❑ 92MadMusC-9
❑ 92MadMusF-1249
❑ 92ProFS7-134
❑ 93MadMusC-16
❑ 93MadMusF-1836
❑ 94ModA'sC-16
❑ 94ModA'sF-3076
❑ 95ModA'sTI-11
❑ 96HunStaTI-12

Husted, Brent
❑ 97YakBeaG-11
❑ 98SanBerS-14
❑ 98SanBerSTIS-13

Huston, Pat
❑ 91GenCubC-9
❑ 91GenCubP-4224

Hutcheon, Mike
❑ 88MisStaB-37
❑ 89MisStaB-44

Hutcheson, Dave
❑ 93PeoChiTI-10
❑ 94DayCubC-10
❑ 94DayCubF-2347
❑ 95Exc-165
❑ 95OrlCubF-4
❑ 96OrlCubB-13

Hutcheson, Joe
❑ 90DodTar-992

Hutcheson, Todd
❑ 83MiaMarT-28
❑ 84BeaGolGT-23
❑ 85BeaGolGT-23
❑ 86LasVegSP-8
❑ 87LasVegSP-13
❑ 88LasVegSP-226
❑ 89LasVegSP-28
❑ 90CMC-683
❑ 90LasVegSC-25

Hutchings, John R.
❑ 41HarHarW-11
❑ 77CinRedT-12

Hutchings, Mark
❑ 97SalVolG-15
❑ 98SalVol-14

Hutchingson, Chris
❑ 86OscAstP-14

Hutchins, Jason
❑ 92BenRocCB-15
❑ 92BenRocF-1472
❑ 93Bow-584
❑ 93CenValRC-14
❑ 93CenValRF-2890
❑ 93ClaFS7-103
❑ 93ExcFS7-34
❑ 93Top-537
❑ 93TopGol-537
❑ 93TopInaM-537
❑ 93TopInaR-537
❑ 93TopMic-537
❑ 94CenValRC-10
❑ 94CenValRF-3197

Hutchins, Lance
❑ 88SanJosGCLC-144
❑ 88SanJosGP-124

Hutchins, Norm
❑ 96Bow-314
❑ 96BowFoi-314
❑ 96CedRapKTI-13
❑ 97BesAll-5
❑ 97Bow-340
❑ 97BowInt-340
❑ 97CalLeaTP-8
❑ 97LakElsSG-17
❑ 98Bes-17
❑ 98Bow-156
❑ 98BowCerBlueAU-39
❑ 98BowCerGA-39
❑ 98BowCerSA-39
❑ 98BowChr-156
❑ 98BowChrGA-156
❑ 98BowChrGAR-156
❑ 98BowChrI-156
❑ 98BowChrIR-156
❑ 98BowChrR-156
❑ 98BowGolA-156
❑ 98BowInt-156
❑ 98MidAngG-19
❑ 98MidAngO-20
❑ 98SP MinPE-11
❑ 98SPMin-11
❑ 98TexLeaTPG-17
❑ 98Top-484
❑ 98TopChr-484
❑ 98TopChrR-484
❑ 98TopDevR-484
❑ 98TopDia-484
❑ 98TopMiniC-484
❑ 98UppDec-549

Hutchinson, Chad
❑ 98NewJerCM-1
❑ 99BasAmeTP-55
❑ 99BasAmeTPG-55
❑ 99SP SigAuto-CHU

❑ 99SP SigAutoG-CHU
❑ 99SP TopP-49
❑ 99SP TopPPE-49
❑ 99SPSig-68
❑ 99TeaBesR-38
❑ 99TeaBesRFS-19
❑ 99TeaBesRG-38
❑ 99TeaBesRS-38
❑ 99UppDec-292
❑ 99UppDecE-135
❑ 99UppDecEFXG-135
❑ 99UppDecEL1-292
❑ 99UppDecEL2-292
❑ 99Vic-318

Hutchinson, Don
❑ 88CapCodPPaLP-68

Hutchinson, Fred
❑ 39GouPreR303A-26
❑ 39WorWidGTP-26
❑ 39WorWidGV-16
❑ 47Exh-105
❑ 47TipTop-33
❑ 49Bow-196
❑ 49Lea-163
❑ 50Bow-151
❑ 51Bow-141
❑ 52Bow-3
❑ 52StaCalL-72E
❑ 52StaCalS-86C
❑ 52Top-126
❑ 53BowC-132
❑ 53NorBreL-12
❑ 53Top-72
❑ 55SeaPop-9
❑ 56RedBurB-8
❑ 59RedBurBP-6
❑ 59SeaPop-23
❑ 60RedJayP-4
❑ 60Top-219
❑ 61RedJayP-5
❑ 61Top-135
❑ 62RedEnq-15
❑ 62RedJayP-5
❑ 62Top-172
❑ 62TopVen-172
❑ 63RedEnq-14
❑ 63RedFreBC-9
❑ 63RedJayP-3
❑ 63Top-422
❑ 64RedJayP-4
❑ 64Top-207
❑ 64TopVen-207
❑ 75ShaPiz-11
❑ 76TayBow4-65
❑ 79TCM50-138
❑ 80PacLeg-25
❑ 80Red196T-9
❑ 81TigDetN-48
❑ 82OhiHaloF-40
❑ 83TopRep5-126
❑ 85TCMPla1-4
❑ 91TopArc1-72
❑ 95HutPop-1
❑ 95HutPop-2
❑ 95HutPop-3
❑ 95HutPop-4
❑ 96HutPop-1
❑ 96HutPop-2
❑ 96HutPop-3
❑ 96HutPop-4
❑ 97HutPop-1
❑ 97HutPop-2
❑ 97HutPop-3
❑ 97HutPop-4

Hutchinson, Harpo (Ray)
❑ 76DubPacT-16

Hutchinson, Ira
❑ 39PlaBal-142
❑ 41CarW75-11
❑ 90DodTar-374

Hutchinson, Sean
❑ 89PulBraP-1909

Hutchinson, Tom
❑ 94ButCopKSP-3

Hutchinson, William
❑ 87OldJudN-258

Hutchison, Bernard
❑ 96PorRocB-16
❑ 98SalAvaC-12

Huth, Ken
❑ 84SavCarT-7

Hutson, Jason
❑ 90MyrBeaBJP-2771

Hutson, Roy
❑ 90DodTar-993

Hutson, Scott
❑ 89St.CatBJP-2074

Hutter, Mitch
❑ 98BriWhiSQ-5

Hutto, Jim
❑ 75IntLeaAT-11
❑ 75IntLeaAT-17
❑ 76SSP-385
❑ 84NewOriT-23
❑ 84RocRedWT-4
❑ 91OriCro-213

Hutto, Paul
❑ 90GatCitPP-3351
❑ 90GatCitPSP-13

Hutton, Mark
❑ 89OneYanP-2118
❑ 90GreHorB-4
❑ 90GreHorP-2656
❑ 90GreHorS-7
❑ 91FloStaLAP-FSL13
❑ 91Ft.LauYC-5
❑ 91Ft.LauYP-2419
❑ 92AlbYanF-2223
❑ 92AlbYanSk-12
❑ 92Bow-598
❑ 92ClaBluBF-BC2
❑ 92ClaFS7-5
❑ 92ClaRedB-BC2
❑ 92DonRoo-58
❑ 92LeaGolR-BC6
❑ 92SkyAA F-7
❑ 92UppDecML-147
❑ 93Bow-651
❑ 93ClaFS7-75
❑ 93ClaGolF-2
❑ 93ColCliF-1107
❑ 93ColCliP-8
❑ 93Don-671
❑ 93ExcFS7-209
❑ 93Top-806
❑ 93TopGol-806
❑ 93TopInaM-806
❑ 93TopInaR-806
❑ 93TopMic-806
❑ 93YanStaC-24
❑ 94Bow-437
❑ 94Cla-117
❑ 94ColC-11
❑ 94ColChoGS-11
❑ 94ColChoSS-11
❑ 94ColCliF-2949
❑ 94ColCliP-16
❑ 94Don-87
❑ 94Pac-423
❑ 94Pin-412
❑ 94PinArtP-412
❑ 94PinMusC-412
❑ 94PinRooTP-9
❑ 94Sco-608
❑ 94ScoBoyoS-32
❑ 94ScoGolR-608
❑ 94ScoRoo-RT133
❑ 94ScoRooGR-RT133
❑ 94Spo-150
❑ 94StaClu-279
❑ 94StaCluFDI-279
❑ 94StaCluGR-279
❑ 94StaCluMOP-279
❑ 94StaCluT-182
❑ 94StaCluTFDI-182
❑ 94Top-269
❑ 94TopGol-269
❑ 94TopSpa-269
❑ 94UppDec-18
❑ 94UppDecED-18
❑ 95ColCliMCTI-14
❑ 95ColCliP-13
❑ 95ColCliTI-13
❑ 95Sco-600
❑ 95ScoGolR-600
❑ 95ScoPlaTS-600
❑ 96LeaSigA-114
❑ 96LeaSigAG-114
❑ 96LeaSigAS-114
❑ 97ColCho-343
❑ 97Fle-661
❑ 97FleTif-661
❑ 97MarPac-14
❑ 98PacOnl-192
❑ 98PacOnlR-192
❑ 98PacOnlWC-192

Hutton, Tom
❑ 67Top-428
❑ 69Top-266
❑ 72Dia-22
❑ 72Top-741
❑ 73OPC-271
❑ 73PhiTeal-9
❑ 73Top-271
❑ 74OPC-443
❑ 74Top-443
❑ 75OPC-477
❑ 75PhiPhiP-17
❑ 75Top-477
❑ 75TopMin-477
❑ 76OPC-91
❑ 76PhiPhiP-12
❑ 76SSP-472
❑ 76Top-91
❑ 77Top-264
❑ 78Hos-103
❑ 78Top-568
❑ 79ExpPos-12
❑ 79OPC-355
❑ 79Top-673
❑ 80ExpPos-12
❑ 80OPC-219
❑ 80Top-427
❑ 81Don-93
❑ 81Fle-164
❑ 81OPC-374
❑ 81Top-374
❑ 85SpoIndGC-9
❑ 90DodTar-375
❑ 90SweBasG-87

Hutzler, Jeff
❑ 96BurBeeTI-6
❑ 97BakBlaB-23
❑ 97BakBlaTI-23

Huyke, Woody
❑ 67VanMouSO-14
❑ 78ChaPirT-10

Huyler, Mike
❑ 88WatPirP-19
❑ 89AugPirP-509
❑ 90CarLeaA-22
❑ 90SalBucS-8
❑ 91CarMudLD-111
❑ 91CarMudP-1093
❑ 91Cla/Bes-300
❑ 91LinDriAA-111
❑ 92BelBreCB-26
❑ 92BelBreFI-411
❑ 93StoPorC-17
❑ 93StoPorF-752

Hvizda, Jim (James)
❑ 89BlaYNPRWLU-27
❑ 89GasRanP-1019
❑ 89GasRanS-9
❑ 89SouAtlLAGS-25
❑ 89Sta-140
❑ 90ChaRanS-11
❑ 90TulDriTI-12
❑ 91BelBreCB-28
❑ 91BelBreP-2098

Hyatt, Robert Ham
❑ 10JuJuDE-21
❑ 10NadE1-21
❑ 10PirAmeCE-4
❑ 10PirTipTD-20
❑ 11PinT-5-870
❑ 11SpoLifCW-183
❑ 11SpoLifM-251
❑ 12T207-86
❑ 14B18B-77A
❑ 14B18B-77B
❑ 20MrsShePP-6
❑ 21Zee-161
❑ 22Zee-155
❑ 72ClaCar-114

Hyde, Brandon
❑ 98BriWhiSQ-13

Hyde, Bubba
❑ 91NegLeaRL-29
❑ 91PomBlaBPB-5

Hyde, Cowan
❑ 92NegLeaRLI-29
❑ 93TedWil-106
❑ 95NegLeaLI-29

Hyde, Dick
❑ 57Top-403
❑ 58SeaTeal-12
❑ 58SenJayP-4
❑ 58Top-156
❑ 59Top-498
❑ 60Top-193
❑ 60TopVen-193
❑ 91OriCro-214

Hyde, Matt
❑ 91QuaCitAC-5
❑ 91QuaCitAP-2647
❑ 91QuaCitAP-2648
❑ 92QuaCitRBC-28
❑ 92QuaCitRBF-828
❑ 93CedRapKC-27
❑ 93CedRapKF-1756

Hyde, Mickey
❑ 89BatCliP-1931
❑ 90BenBucL-4
❑ 91ClePhiC-21
❑ 91ClePhiP-1632
❑ 92ClePhiC-6
❑ 92ReaPhiF-587
❑ 93ReaPhiF-307

Hyde, Rich
❑ 91EveGiaP-3908
❑ 92CliGiaC-2
❑ 93SanJosGC-13
❑ 93SanJosGF-3

Hyde, Scott
❑ 75TopPho-123

Hydes, Kyle
❑ 75PhoGiaC-20

Hyers, Matt
❑ 96AubDouB-14
❑ 97QuaCitRBB-12
❑ 98KisCobQ-17
❑ 98QuaCitRBG-10

Hyers, Tim
❑ 90MedHatBJB-3
❑ 91MyrBeaHC-20
❑ 91MyrBeaHP-2954
❑ 92DunBluJC-10
❑ 92DunBluJF-2007
❑ 93KnoSmoF-1259
❑ 94Bow-148
❑ 94ClaGolF-109
❑ 94ColC-612
❑ 94ColChoGS-612
❑ 94ColChoSS-612
❑ 94Fla-438
❑ 94FleAllR-M7
❑ 94FleExtB-374
❑ 94FleUpd-186
❑ 94PadMot-15
❑ 94Pin-530
❑ 94PinArtP-530
❑ 94PinMusC-530
❑ 94ScoRoo-RT100
❑ 94ScoRooGR-RT100
❑ 94Sel-416
❑ 94SpoRoo-90
❑ 94SpoRooAP-90
❑ 94Ult-578
❑ 94UppDec-516
❑ 94UppDecED-516
❑ 95Don-393
❑ 95DonPreP-393
❑ 95Pac-364
❑ 96TolMudHB-14
❑ 97TolMudHB-24
❑ 98TusSidM-22

Hyman, Don
❑ 81QuaCitCT-2
❑ 83MidCubT-17
❑ 84MidCubT-3

Hyman, Pat
❑ 89ColMetB-24

Hymel, Gary
❑ 90LSUTigP-7
❑ 91LSUTigP-7
❑ 91LSUTigP-12
❑ 92AlbPolCB-24
❑ 92AlbPolF-2309
❑ 92ClaFS7-9
❑ 93BurBeeC-12
❑ 93BurBeeF-160
❑ 93OttLynF-2438
❑ 94HarSenF-1096
❑ 95HarSenTI-6

Hypes, Kyle
❑ 75LafDriT-17
❑ 76PheGiaCr-36
❑ 76PhoGiaCa-3
❑ 76PhoGiaCC-12
❑ 76PhoGiaVNB-10
❑ 77PhoGiaCC-10
❑ 77PhoGiaCP-9
❑ 77PhoGiaVNB-10
❑ 78PhoGiaC-10
❑ 79PhoGiaVNB-2

Hyson, Cole
❑ 89AubAstP-2170
❑ 90OscAstS-10
❑ 91OscAstC-4
❑ 91OscAstP-676
❑ 92WatDiaC-25
❑ 93RanCucQC-18
❑ 93RanCucQF-829

Hyuk Lim, Soo
❑ 96HilStaHWB-31

Hyun Kim, Gong
❑ 96HilStaHWB-28

Hyzdu, Adam
❑ 90ClaDraP-15
❑ 90ClaYel-T90
❑ 90EveGiaB-1
❑ 90EveGiaP-3140
❑ 90ProAaA-169
❑ 91Bow-617
❑ 91Cla/Bes-321
❑ 91CliGiaC-20
❑ 91CliGiaP-847
❑ 91Sco-388
❑ 92CalLeaACL-5
❑ 92SanJosGC-8
❑ 92UppDecML-244
❑ 93SanJosGC-1
❑ 93SanJosGF-25
❑ 94ChaLooF-1363
❑ 95ChaLooTI-7
❑ 96TreThuB-27
❑ 97PawRedS-13

Iacona, Andy
❑ 88SalLakCTTI-6

Iannini, Steve
❑ 87ModA'sC-8
❑ 87ModA'sP-15

Iapoce, Anthony
❑ 96BelSnaTI-18
❑ 97StoPor-7
❑ 98El PasDG-17

Iasparro, Donnie
❑ 86VisOakP-11

Iatarola, Aaron
❑ 93BoiHawC-14
❑ 93BoiHawF-3929
❑ 94CedRapKF-1123
❑ 95CedRapKTI-16
❑ 95MidLeaA-24

Iavarone, Greg
❑ 87PeoChiP-9
❑ 90TulDriP-1159
❑ 90TulDriTI-13
❑ 91LinDriAA-585
❑ 91TulDriLD-585
❑ 91TulDriP-2775
❑ 91TulDriTI-14

Ibanez, Raul
❑ 93AppFoxCB-12
❑ 93AppFoxFI-2462
❑ 93BelMarCB-15
❑ 93BelMarF-3213
❑ 94AppFoxC-12
❑ 94AppFoxFI-1057
❑ 94MidLeaAF-MDW3
❑ 95SPML-150
❑ 96BesAutS-40
❑ 96Bow-267
❑ 96BowBes-172
❑ 96BowBesAR-172
❑ 96BowBesR-172
❑ 96BowFoi-267
❑ 96ColCho-431
❑ 96ColChoGS-431
❑ 96ColChoSS-431
❑ 96Exc-105
❑ 96ExcAll-9
❑ 96FleUpd-U81
❑ 96FleUpdNH-11
❑ 96FleUpdTC-U81
❑ 96TacRaiB-15
❑ 96Top-432
❑ 96Ult-413
❑ 96UltGolM-413
❑ 96UltGolP-9
❑ 96UltGolPHGM-9
❑ 97Fle-209
❑ 97FleTif-209
❑ 97MarSco-13
❑ 97MarScoPl-13
❑ 97MarScoPr-13
❑ 97PacPriGotD-GD87
❑ 97Sco-258
❑ 97ScoArtPWB-258
❑ 97ScoPreS-258
❑ 97ScoShoS-258
❑ 97ScoShoSAP-258
❑ 97Sel-120
❑ 97SelArtP-120
❑ 97SelCom-120
❑ 97SelRegG-120
❑ 97TacRai-18
❑ 97Top-201
❑ 97Ult-123
❑ 97UltGolME-123
❑ 97UltPlaME-123
❑ 97UppDec-233
❑ 98Bow-206
❑ 98BowChr-206
❑ 98BowChrGA-206
❑ 98BowChrGAR-206
❑ 98BowChrI-206
❑ 98BowChrIR-206
❑ 98BowChrR-206
❑ 98BowGolA-206
❑ 98BowInt-206
❑ 98DonCol-198
❑ 98DonColE-475
❑ 98DonColL-396
❑ 98DonColS-193
❑ 98DonEli-75
❑ 98DonEliA-75
❑ 98DonEliS-75
❑ 98DonPriCD-198
❑ 98DonPriCE-475
❑ 98DonPriCL-396
❑ 98DonRatR-23
❑ 98DonRatRM-23
❑ 98DonSigA-46
❑ 98DonSigAC-60
❑ 98DonSigAM-61
❑ 98Lea-197
❑ 98LeaFraDA-197
❑ 98LeaFraF-197
❑ 98LeaFraM-197
❑ 98LeaFraM-197
❑ 98LeaFraMDC-197
❑ 98LeaFraMDC-197
❑ 98LeaFraMZ2-197
❑ 98Pac-187
❑ 98PacPlaB-187
❑ 98PacRedT-187
❑ 98PacSil-187
❑ 98PinIns-119
❑ 98PinInsCE-119
❑ 98PinInsDE-119
❑ 98PinPlu-94
❑ 98PinSna-SM8
❑ 98TacRaiQ-16
❑ 98UppDec-513
❑ 98Zen-85
❑ 98ZenRooT-4
❑ 98ZenZ-G-85
❑ 98ZenZ-S-85
❑ 99Fle-468
❑ 99FleSta9-468
❑ 99FleWarT-468
❑ 99PacCroC-264
❑ 99PacCroCPB-264

Ibarguen, Ricky
❑ 89BriTigS-12

Ibarguen, Steve
❑ 82JacMetT-5

Ibarra, Carlos
❑ 82EdmTraT-1

Ibarra, Jesse
❑ 94EveGiaC-14
❑ 94EveGiaF-3659
❑ 94StaCluDP-71
❑ 94StaCluDPFDI-71
❑ 95BurBeeTI-6
❑ 95SPML-145
❑ 96BesAutS-41
❑ 96Bow-246
❑ 96BowFoi-246
❑ 96Exc-245
❑ 96Top-424
❑ 97JacSun-14
❑ 98SP MinPE-56
❑ 98SPMin-56
❑ 98TolMudHQ-21

Ibarra, Jesus
❑ 96SanJosGB-1

Ibarra, Luis
❑ 85MexCitTT-28

Ibarra, Miguel
❑ 80CarMudF-6
❑ 81ReaPhiT-12

Ickes, Mike
❑ 87WinHavRSP-25

Iddon, Brent
❑ 95EveAqaTI-11
❑ 96MidLeaAB-4
❑ 96WisTimRB-11
❑ 97SarRedS-12
❑ 98RanCucQG-13
❑ 98RanCucQG-13

Iglesias, Luis
❑ 87SpaPhiP-18

❑ 88ClePhiS-15
Iglesias, Mario
❑ 96BriWhiSB-19
❑ 96HicCraB-10
❑ 97HicCraB-15
❑ 97HicCraRB-19
❑ 98CarLeaAC-27
❑ 98WinWar-15
Iglesias, Michael
❑ 91KisDodP-4178
❑ 94VerBeaDC-10
❑ 98AlbDukG-11
Iglesias, Mike
❑ 93BakDodCLC-11
❑ 94VerBeaDF-66
❑ 95BakBlaTI-14
❑ 96MauStiHWB-35
❑ 96VerBeaDB-15
❑ 97SanAntMB-4
❑ 98SanAntMM-4
Ignash, Reggie
❑ 93ButCopKSP-19
❑ 94BurIndC-8
❑ 94BurIndF-3808
Ignasiak, Mike
❑ 89CalLeaA-39
❑ 89StoPorB-3
❑ 89StoPorCLC-157
❑ 89StoPorP-400
❑ 89StoPorS-5
❑ 90ElPasDGS-18
❑ 90StoPorB-16
❑ 90StoPorCLC-177
❑ 90StoPorP-2176
❑ 91DenZepLD-142
❑ 91DenZepP-121
❑ 91LinDriAAA-142
❑ 92Bow-15
❑ 92DenZepF-2635
❑ 92DenZepS-131
❑ 92Sco-837
❑ 92SkyAAAF-64
❑ 92TopDeb91-88
❑ 93FleFinE-224
❑ 93NewOrlZF-966
❑ 94BreMilB-38
❑ 94BrePol-13
❑ 94Fle-179
❑ 94NewOrlZF-1462
❑ 94StaClu-489
❑ 94StaCluFDI-489
❑ 94StaCluGR-489
❑ 94StaCluMOP-489
❑ 94Top-564
❑ 94TopGol-564
❑ 94TopSpa-564
❑ 94Ult-76
❑ 95StaClu-575
❑ 95StaCluMOP-575
❑ 95StaCluSTWS-575
Ihde, Alan Dale
❑ 49AngTeal-16
❑ 49W725AngTI-12
Ikebe, Iwao
❑ 79TCMJapPB-49
Ikegaya, Kojiro
❑ 79TCMJapPB-26
Ikesue, Kazutaka
❑ 91SalSpuC-21
❑ 91SalSpuP-2236
Ikeue, Kouichi
❑ 87SalLakTTT-15
Illig, Brett
❑ 95GreFalDTI-24
❑ 96GreFalDB-15
❑ 98SanBerS-17
❑ 98SanBerSTIS-14
Ilsley, Blaise
❑ 86AshTouP-15
❑ 87ColAstP-8
❑ 88ColAstB-17
❑ 89OscAstS-8
❑ 91LinDriAAA-613
❑ 91TucTorLD-613
❑ 91TucTorP-2211
❑ 92LouRedF-1884
❑ 92LouRedS-265
❑ 93IowCubF-2131
❑ 94Bow-188
❑ 94SpoRoo-95
❑ 94SpoRooAP-95
❑ 94Ult-459
❑ 95Pac-73
❑ 95Sco-289
❑ 95ScoGolR-289
❑ 95ScoPlaTS-289
❑ 95ScrRedBTI-14
❑ 98FarRedHM-11
Imes, Rod (Rodney)
❑ 87OneYanP-25
❑ 88Ft.LauYS-12
❑ 89AlbYanB-21
❑ 89AlbYanP-314
❑ 89AlbYanSt-8
❑ 89BasAmeAPB-AA8
❑ 89EasLeaAP-10
❑ 90AlbDecGB-16
❑ 90CMC-132
❑ 90NasSouC-7
❑ 90NasSouP-227
❑ 90ProAAAF-539
❑ 91LinDriAAA-262
❑ 91NasSouLD-262
❑ 91NasSouP-2152
❑ 92ChaLooF-3813
❑ 92ChaLooS-187
Impagliazzo, Joe
❑ 86AlbYanT-27
Imperial, Jason
❑ 92BelBreFI-412
❑ 93BelBreCB-11
❑ 93BelBreFI-1717
Imrisek, Jason
❑ 96TamYanY-15
Inaba, Atsunori
❑ 96WesOahCHWB-27
Inabata, Nelson
❑ 87HawRai-2
Inagaki, Shuji
❑ 87MiaMarP-13
❑ 88MiaMarS-12
Incantalupo, Todd
❑ 97HelBreB-14
❑ 98BelSnaM-13
Incaviglia, Pete
❑ 86DonRoo-23
❑ 86FleUpd-53
❑ 86RanPer-29
❑ 86SpoRoo-3
❑ 86TopTra-48T
❑ 86TopTraT-48T
❑ 87ClaGam-16
❑ 87ClaUpdY-131
❑ 87Don-224
❑ 87DonOpeD-175
❑ 87Fle-128
❑ 87Fle-625
❑ 87FleGlo-128
❑ 87FleGlo-625
❑ 87FleHotS-24
❑ 87FleLeaL-25
❑ 87FleMin-58
❑ 87FleSlu-21
❑ 87FleStiC-66
❑ 87KraFoo-39
❑ 87Lea-185
❑ 87OPC-384
❑ 87RanMot-2
❑ 87RanSmo-15
❑ 87RedFolSB-130
❑ 87Spo-37
❑ 87SpoTeaP-1
❑ 87StuPan-26
❑ 87Top-550
❑ 87TopCoi-14
❑ 87TopGloS-29
❑ 87TopRoo-6
❑ 87TopSti-236
❑ 87TopSti-308
❑ 87TopTif-550
❑ 87ToyRoo-12
❑ 88ClaRed-177
❑ 88Don-304
❑ 88DonBasB-55
❑ 88Fle-470
❑ 88FleGlo-470
❑ 88FleMin-56
❑ 88FleSlu-20
❑ 88FleStiC-65
❑ 88FleSupBC-C1
❑ 88GreBasS-33
❑ 88HouSho-20
❑ 88Lea-147
❑ 88Nes-20
❑ 88OPC-280
❑ 88PanSti-207
❑ 88RanMot-2
❑ 88RanSmo-4
❑ 88Sco-485
❑ 88ScoGlo-485
❑ 88ScoYouSI-32
❑ 88Spo-169
❑ 88StaLinRa-7
❑ 88TarPla-22
❑ 88Top-201
❑ 88Top-280
❑ 88TopBig-73
❑ 88TopSti-239
❑ 88TopTif-201
❑ 88TopTif-280
❑ 89Bow-238
❑ 89BowTif-238
❑ 89Don-3
❑ 89Don-56
❑ 89DonBasB-144
❑ 89DonSupD-3
❑ 89Fle-523
❑ 89FleGlo-523
❑ 89FleLeaL-21
❑ 89KinDis-24
❑ 89OPC-42
❑ 89PanSti-455
❑ 89RanMot-10
❑ 89RanSmo-16
❑ 89RedFolSB-63
❑ 89Sco-201
❑ 89Spo-112
❑ 89Top-706
❑ 89TopBasT-127
❑ 89TopBig-127
❑ 89TopSti-249
❑ 89TopTif-706
❑ 89TVSpoM-118
❑ 89UppDec-484
❑ 90Bow-491
❑ 90BowTif-491
❑ 90Don-48
❑ 90Fle-301
❑ 90FleCan-301
❑ 90Lea-231
❑ 90OPC-430
❑ 90PanSti-157
❑ 90PubIntS-413
❑ 90RanMot-4
❑ 90Sco-93
❑ 90Top-430
❑ 90TopBig-81
❑ 90TopSti-247
❑ 90TopTif-430
❑ 90UppDec-333
❑ 91Bow-131
❑ 91Don-464
❑ 91Fle-290
❑ 91Lea-366
❑ 91OPC-172
❑ 91OPCPre-67
❑ 91PanFreS-258
❑ 91RedFolS-51
❑ 91Sco-278
❑ 91ScoRoo-3T
❑ 91StaClu-78
❑ 91TigCok-29
❑ 91Top-172
❑ 91TopDesS-172
❑ 91TopMic-172
❑ 91TopTif-172
❑ 91TopTra-57T
❑ 91TopTraT-57T
❑ 91UppDec-453
❑ 91UppDec-747
❑ 92AstMot-4
❑ 92Bow-43
❑ 92Fle-139
❑ 92Lea-458
❑ 92LeaBlaG-458
❑ 92OPC-679
❑ 92OPCPre-126
❑ 92Pin-325
❑ 92Sco-306
❑ 92ScoRoo-17T
❑ 92StaClu-874
❑ 92StaCluNC-874
❑ 92Top-679
❑ 92TopGol-679
❑ 92TopGolW-679
❑ 92TopMic-679
❑ 92TopTra-54T
❑ 92TopTraG-54T
❑ 92Ult-491
❑ 92UppDec-271
❑ 92UppDec-759
❑ 93Don-480
❑ 93Fla-103
❑ 93Fle-436
❑ 93FleFinE-110
❑ 93Lea-276
❑ 93OPC-242
❑ 93OPCPre-95
❑ 93PacSpa-577
❑ 93PhiMed-18
❑ 93PhiStaC-22
❑ 93Pin-492
❑ 93RanKee-201
❑ 93Sco-568
❑ 93SelRoo-114T
❑ 93SP-176
❑ 93StaClu-47
❑ 93StaClu-636
❑ 93StaCluFDI-47
❑ 93StaCluFDI-636
❑ 93StaCluMOP-47
❑ 93StaCluMOP-636
❑ 93Top-7
❑ 93TopGol-7
❑ 93TopInaM-7
❑ 93TopInaR-7
❑ 93TopMic-7
❑ 93TopPreS-7
❑ 93TopTra-73T
❑ 93Ult-442
❑ 93UppDec-522
❑ 93UppDecGold-522
❑ 94Bow-84
❑ 94ColC-144
❑ 94ColChoGS-144
❑ 94ColChoSS-144
❑ 94Don-594
❑ 94Fin-140
❑ 94FinRef-140
❑ 94Fle-591
❑ 94FleExtB-336
❑ 94Lea-265
❑ 94Pac-477
❑ 94PhiMed-14
❑ 94PhiMel-10
❑ 94PhiUSPC-1C
❑ 94PhiUSPC-4H
❑ 94Pin-468
❑ 94PinArtP-468
❑ 94PinMusC-468
❑ 94Sco-416
❑ 94ScoGolR-416
❑ 94Sel-280
❑ 94StaClu-559
❑ 94StaCluFDI-559
❑ 94StaCluGR-559
❑ 94StaCluMOP-559
❑ 94StaCluT-215
❑ 94StaCluTFDI-215
❑ 94Stu-140
❑ 94Top-323
❑ 94TopGol-323
❑ 94TopSpa-323
❑ 94Ult-246
❑ 94UppDec-491
❑ 94UppDecED-491
❑ 95Don-98
❑ 95DonPreP-98
❑ 95Fle-394
❑ 95Sco-131
❑ 95ScoGolR-131
❑ 95ScoPlaTS-131
❑ 96Cir-166
❑ 96CirRav-166
❑ 96FleUpd-U166
❑ 96FleUpdTC-U166
❑ 96PhiTeal-16
❑ 97BalOriP-15
❑ 97BalOriP-16
❑ 97DonTea-45
❑ 97DonTeaSPE-45
❑ 97Sco-44
❑ 97ScoArtPWB-44
❑ 97ScoPreS-44
❑ 97ScoShoS-44
❑ 97ScoShoSAP-44
❑ 98NewOrlZM-10
Incaviglia, Tony
❑ 81BufBisT-20
Indians, Burlington
❑ 92BurIndF-1674
Indians, Cleveland
❑ 13FatT20-3
❑ 35GouPreR-2
❑ 48ExhTea-2
❑ 48ExhTea-12
❑ 56Top-85A
❑ 56Top-85B
❑ 56Top-85C
❑ 57Top-275
❑ 58Top-158
❑ 59Top-476
❑ 60Top-174
❑ 60TopTat-67
❑ 60TopVen-174
❑ 61Top-467
❑ 61TopMagR-10
❑ 62GuyPotCP-6
❑ 62Top-537
❑ 63GadFunC-65
❑ 63Top-451
❑ 64Top-172
❑ 64TopTatI-7
❑ 64TopVen-172
❑ 65Top-481
❑ 66Top-303
❑ 66TopRubI-107
❑ 66TopVen-303
❑ 67Top-544
❑ 69FleCloS-8
❑ 69FleCloS-33
❑ 69TopStaA-8
❑ 70FleWorS-45
❑ 70Top-637
❑ 71FleWorS-18
❑ 71FleWorS-46
❑ 71FleWorS-52
❑ 71OPC-584
❑ 71Top-584
❑ 71TopTat-60
❑ 72Top-547
❑ 73OPC-629
❑ 73OPCBTC-8
❑ 73Top-629
❑ 73TopBluTC-8
❑ 74OPC-541
❑ 74OPCTC-8
❑ 74Top-541
❑ 74TopStaA-8
❑ 74TopTeaC-8
❑ 78Top-689
❑ 80MarExh-31
❑ 83FleSta-232
❑ 83FleSti-NNO
❑ 83FleSti-NNO
❑ 87IndGat-NNO
❑ 87SpoTeaL-3
❑ 87Top-11
❑ 87TopTif-11
❑ 88IndGat-NNO
❑ 88PanSti-459
❑ 88RedFolSB-114
❑ 90PubIntS-647
❑ 90RedFolSB-105
❑ 93TedWilPC-9
❑ 94ImpProP-5
❑ 94Sco-321
❑ 94ScoGolR-321
❑ 95PacPriTL-5
❑ 95PanSti-143
❑ 95StaCluSTWS-R19L
❑ 96IndFle-19
❑ 96IndUppD-1
❑ 96PanSti-179
❑ 97ColChoT-CI
❑ 99Vic-113
Indians, Indianapolis
❑ 38BasTabP-38
❑ 77IndIndTI-1
❑ 78IndIndTI-1
❑ 79IndIndTI-1
❑ 80IndIndTI-1
❑ 81IndIndTI-1
❑ 82IndIndTI-1
❑ 83IndIndTI-1
❑ 84IndIndTI-1
❑ 85IndIndTI-1
❑ 86IndIndTI-14
❑ 87IndIndTI-1
❑ 96IndIndB-1
❑ 98IndIndQ-1
Indians, Kinston
❑ 95KinIndTI-30
Indriago, Juan
❑ 92AppFoxCB-24
❑ 92AppFoxFI-993
Infante, Alexis
❑ 85SyrChiT-14
❑ 86StaoftFT-27
❑ 86SyrChiP-14
❑ 87SyrChiP-1935
❑ 87SyrChiT-15
❑ 88SyrChiC-21
❑ 88SyrChiP-813
❑ 89DonRoo-30
❑ 90Bow-17
❑ 90BowTif-17
❑ 90BraDubP-12
❑ 90BraDubS-14
❑ 90PubIntS-517
❑ 93LinVenB-153
❑ 94VenLinU-109
❑ 94VenLinU-169
❑ 95LinVen-165
❑ 96-97LinVen-40
Infante, Ken (Kennedy)
❑ 86St.PetCP-14
❑ 87ArkTraP-5
❑ 88ArkTraGS-11
❑ 89CedRapRB-15
❑ 89CedRapRS-28
❑ 90ClePhiS-9
Infante, Tom
❑ 89HamRedS-19
❑ 90SprCarB-17
Ingalls, Rick
❑ 88BenBucL-29
❑ 89BenBucL-28
Inge, Adele
❑ 40WheM4-10
Inge, Brandon
❑ 99TeaBesR-39
❑ 99TeaBesRFS-9
❑ 99TeaBesRG-39
❑ 99TeaBesRS-39
Ingle, Mike
❑ 86KinEagP-10
Ingle, Randy
❑ 83AndBraT-4
❑ 84DurBulT-29
❑ 85GreBraTI-8
❑ 86GreBraTI-14
❑ 87GreBraB-4
❑ 89GreBraB-21
❑ 89GreBraP-1177
❑ 90GreBraP-1146
❑ 90GreBraS-24
❑ 90PulBraB-26
❑ 90PulBraP-3114
❑ 91GreBraC-28
❑ 91LinDriAA-225
❑ 91PulBraC-14
❑ 91PulBraP-4022
❑ 92GreBraS-250
❑ 92PulBraC-27
❑ 92PulBraF-3195
❑ 93MacBraC-27
❑ 93MacBraF-1417
❑ 93SouAtlLAGF-37
❑ 94GreBraF-430
❑ 94GreBraTI-4
❑ 95BreBtaTI-12
❑ 96DurBulBIB-13
❑ 97GreBraG-13
❑ 98GreBraG-9
Inglin, Jeff
❑ 96BriWhiSB-20
❑ 97HicCraB-16
❑ 97HicCraRB-20
❑ 98BirBarG-14
❑ 98SP MinPE-39
❑ 98SPMin-39
Ingram, Darron
❑ 94PriRedC-12
❑ 94PriRedF-3277
❑ 96BilMusTI-14
❑ 97BurBeeB-13
❑ 97MidLeaTP-4
❑ 98Bow-441
❑ 98BowChr-441
❑ 98BowChrGA-441
❑ 98BowChrGAR-441
❑ 98BowChrI-441
❑ 98BowChrIR-441
❑ 98BowChrR-441
❑ 98BowGolA-441
❑ 98BowInt-441
❑ 98ChaLooG-13
❑ 98ColCho-419
❑ 98ColChoPCR-419
❑ 98SP MinPE-40
❑ 98SPMin-40
❑ 98UppDec-574
❑ 98UppDecDS-DS44
Ingram, Garey (Gerald)
❑ 88EugEmeB-26
❑ 90GreFalDSP-18
❑ 91BakDodCLC-14
❑ 91CalLeLA-12
❑ 92SanAntMF-3986
❑ 93SanAntMF-3011
❑ 94BowBes-B82
❑ 94BowBesR-B82
❑ 94FleUpd-150

❑ 94LeaLimR-65
❑ 94SanAntMF-2177
❑ 94SpoRoo-32
❑ 94SpoRooAP-32
❑ 95ColChoGS-22
❑ 95ColChoSS-22
❑ 95Don-258
❑ 95DonPreP-258
❑ 95Fle-542
❑ 95Pac-219
❑ 95PacPri-69
❑ 95Pin-154
❑ 95PinArtP-154
❑ 95PinMusC-154
❑ 95Sco-287
❑ 95ScoGolR-287
❑ 95ScoPlaTS-287
❑ 95Ult-397
❑ 95UltGolM-397
❑ 96DodPol-20
❑ 97SanAntMB-16
❑ 98AlbDukG-12
❑ 98SanAntMM-16

Ingram, Jeff
❑ 89UtiBluSP-11
❑ 90SouBenWSB-5
❑ 90SouBenWSGS-6

Ingram, John
❑ 90BatCliP-3061
❑ 91MarPhiC-22
❑ 91MarPhiP-3449

Ingram, Linty
❑ 89FayGenP-1572
❑ 90FayGenP-2402
❑ 92HigDesMC-10
❑ 92LasVegSS-242

Ingram, Riccardo
❑ 89LakTigS-10
❑ 90LonTigP-1280
❑ 91LinDriAA-388
❑ 91LonTigLD-388
❑ 91LonTigP-1890
❑ 92Bow-164
❑ 92SkyAAAF-264
❑ 92TolMudHF-1055
❑ 92TolMudHS-589
❑ 92UppDecML-213
❑ 93TolMudHF-1665
❑ 94TolMudHF-1039
❑ 94TopTra-30T
❑ 96LasVegSB-15
❑ 98ForWayW!-27

Ingram, Todd
❑ 91SouOreAC-9
❑ 91SouOreAP-3835
❑ 92RenSilSCLC-43
❑ 93ModA'sC-12
❑ 93ModA'sF-795
❑ 94HunStaF-1325
❑ 95KnoSmoF-38
❑ 95TreThuTI-11

Inks, Bert
❑ 90DodTar-994

Inman, Bert
❑ 90OklSoo-16
❑ 91OneYanP-4150
❑ 92GreHorC-17
❑ 92GreHorF-775
❑ 92OneYanC-11
❑ 93GreHorC-12
❑ 93GreHorF-881
❑ 94SanBerSC-8
❑ 94SanBerSF-2751

Inman, Wade
❑ 88OklSoo-21
❑ 89OklSoo-17

Innis, Brian
❑ 83VerBeaDT-5

Innis, Jeff
❑ 84JacMetT-6
❑ 85LynMetT-4
❑ 86JacMetT-6
❑ 87TidTidP-8
❑ 87TidTidT-5
❑ 88DonTeaBM-NEW
❑ 88FleUpd-105
❑ 88FleUpdG-105
❑ 88TidTidCa-21
❑ 88TidTidCM-3
❑ 88TidTidP-1582
❑ 88TopTra-54T
❑ 88TopTraT-54T
❑ 89MetColP-35
❑ 89MetKah-U1
❑ 89TidTidC-3
❑ 89TidTidP-1950
❑ 90CMC-357
❑ 90Don-408
❑ 90Fle-206
❑ 90FleCan-206
❑ 90MetColP-36
❑ 90MetKah-40
❑ 90OPC-557
❑ 90ProAAAF-270
❑ 90TidTidC-6
❑ 90TidTidP-539
❑ 90Top-557
❑ 90TopTif-557
❑ 90TopTVM-13
❑ 90UppDec-562A
❑ 90UppDec-562B
❑ 91FleUpd-103
❑ 91MetColP-36
❑ 91MetKah-40
❑ 91MetPerPA-18
❑ 91MetWIZ-196
❑ 91OPC-443
❑ 91StaClu-547
❑ 91Top-443
❑ 91TopDesS-443
❑ 91TopMic-443
❑ 91TopTif-443
❑ 91UltUpd-97
❑ 92Don-587
❑ 92Fle-507
❑ 92MetColP-40
❑ 92MetKah-40
❑ 92OPC-139
❑ 92Sco-327
❑ 92StaClu-863
❑ 92Top-139
❑ 92TopGol-139
❑ 92TopGolW-139
❑ 92TopMic-139
❑ 92TriPla-64
❑ 92TriPlaP-8
❑ 92Ult-234
❑ 92UppDec-298
❑ 93Don-330
❑ 93Fle-476
❑ 93MetColP-37
❑ 93MetKah-40
❑ 93OPC-141
❑ 93PacSpa-543
❑ 93Pin-557
❑ 93Sco-409
❑ 93StaClu-433
❑ 93StaCluFDI-433
❑ 93StaCluMOP-433
❑ 93Top-297
❑ 93TopGol-297
❑ 93TopInaM-297
❑ 93TopInaR-297
❑ 93TopMic-297
❑ 93Ult-428
❑ 93UppDec-119
❑ 93UppDecGold-119
❑ 94Fle-566
❑ 94Pac-406
❑ 94Sco-291
❑ 94ScoGolR-291
❑ 94Top-37
❑ 94TopGol-37
❑ 94TopSpa-37

Inouye, Jay
❑ 98DunBluJSB-21
❑ 98DunBluJTI-12

Inouye, Kelly
❑ 94ColSilBC-4
❑ 95ColSilB9-7

Intorcia, Trent
❑ 87WauTimP-21
❑ 88MiaMarS-13

Inzunza, Miguel
❑ 95NewJerCTI-13
❑ 96PeoChiB-15

Iopoce, Anthony
❑ 95HelBreTI-2

Iorg, Dane
❑ 76OklCit8TI-8
❑ 78CarTeal-12
❑ 79Car5-11
❑ 80Top-139
❑ 81Car5x7-12
❑ 81Don-311
❑ 81Fle-543
❑ 81Top-334
❑ 82Don-166
❑ 82Fle-116
❑ 82FleSta-24
❑ 82Top-86
❑ 83Car-17
❑ 83Don-469
❑ 83Fle-10
❑ 83FleSti-5
❑ 83Top-788
❑ 83TopFol-3
❑ 83TopSti-189
❑ 83TopSti-190
❑ 84Don-571
❑ 84Fle-326
❑ 84FleUpd-55
❑ 84Nes792-416
❑ 84RoyPos-15
❑ 84Top-416
❑ 84TopTif-416
❑ 84TopTra-54T
❑ 84TopTraT-54T
❑ 85Don-252
❑ 85Fle-204
❑ 85RoyTeal-12
❑ 85Top-671
❑ 85TopTif-671
❑ 86Fle-9
❑ 86FleUpd-54
❑ 86RoyKitCD-9
❑ 86Spo-186
❑ 86Top-269
❑ 86TopSti-18
❑ 86TopTif-269
❑ 86TopTra-49T
❑ 86TopTraT-49T
❑ 87OPC-151
❑ 87Top-690
❑ 87TopTif-690

Iorg, Garth
❑ 75ForLauYS-26
❑ 76VenLeaS-72
❑ 78Top-704
❑ 79SyrChiT-12
❑ 79SyrChiTI-9
❑ 80SyrChiT-1
❑ 80SyrChiTI-11
❑ 80VenLeaS-72
❑ 81Fle-423
❑ 81OPC-78
❑ 81OPCPos-16
❑ 81Top-444
❑ 82BluJayS-8
❑ 82Don-353
❑ 82Fle-616
❑ 82OPC-83
❑ 82Top-518
❑ 83Don-306
❑ 83Fle-430
❑ 83FleSta-89
❑ 83FleSti-110
❑ 83OPC-326
❑ 83Top-326
❑ 84BluJayFS-17
❑ 84Don-561
❑ 84Fle-157
❑ 84Nes792-39
❑ 84OPC-39
❑ 84Top-39
❑ 84TopTif-39
❑ 85BluJayFS-15
❑ 85Don-363
❑ 85Fle-107
❑ 85OPC-168
❑ 85Top-168
❑ 85TopTif-168
❑ 86BasStaB-59
❑ 86BluJayAF-14
❑ 86BluJayFS-18
❑ 86Don-640
❑ 86Fle-61
❑ 86Lea-252
❑ 86OPC-277
❑ 86Top-694
❑ 86TopTif-694
❑ 87BluJayFS-14
❑ 87Don-394
❑ 87Fle-229
❑ 87FleGlo-229
❑ 87OPC-59
❑ 87SyrChi1A-4
❑ 87Top-751
❑ 87TopTif-751
❑ 88Don-444
❑ 88Fle-113A
❑ 88Fle-113B
❑ 88FleGlo-113
❑ 88OPC-273
❑ 88PanSti-220
❑ 88Sco-204
❑ 88ScoGlo-204
❑ 88StaLinBJ-9
❑ 88Top-273
❑ 88TopTif-273
❑ 89PacSenL-152
❑ 89T/MSenL-51
❑ 89TopSenL-86
❑ 90EliSenL-36
❑ 91MyrBeaHC-27
❑ 91MyrBeaHP-2961
❑ 91PacSenL-41
❑ 92KnoBluJF-3006
❑ 92KnoBluJS-399
❑ 92Nab-28
❑ 92UppDecS-3
❑ 93KnoSmoF-1265
❑ 93LinVenB-255
❑ 94KnoSmoF-1319
❑ 95KnoSmoF-55
❑ 97SyrSkyCB-27

Ippolito, Rob
❑ 92AriWilP-6
❑ 94BelMarC-16
❑ 94BelMarF-3229

Irabu, Hideki
❑ 97Bes-16
❑ 97BesAll-2
❑ 97BesAutSBPP-8
❑ 97BesBetP-3
❑ 97BesCarCSP-7
❑ 97BesDiaB-1
❑ 97BesFiv-4
❑ 97BesIntB-IB2
❑ 97Bow-221
❑ 97Bow-441
❑ 97BowBes-149
❑ 97BowBesAR-149
❑ 97BowBesR-149
❑ 97BowChr-198
❑ 97BowChrI-198
❑ 97BowChrIR-198
❑ 97BowChrR-198
❑ 97BowInt-221
❑ 97BowInt-441
❑ 97ColChoU-U20
❑ 97Don-361
❑ 97DonGolPP-361
❑ 97DonLim-121
❑ 97DonLim-135
❑ 97DonLimE-121
❑ 97DonLimE-135
❑ 97DonSilPP-361
❑ 97DonTea-135
❑ 97DonTeaSPE-135
❑ 97Fin-320
❑ 97FinEmb-320
❑ 97FinEmbR-320
❑ 97FinRef-320
❑ 97FlaShoWotF-WF1
❑ 97Fle-751
❑ 97FleNewH-8
❑ 97FleTif-751
❑ 97HigMinM-48
❑ 97Lea-324
❑ 97LeaFraM-324
❑ 97LeaFraMDC-324
❑ 97PinCer-129
❑ 97PinCerMBla-129
❑ 97PinCerMBlu-129
❑ 97PinCerMG-129
❑ 97PinCerMR-129
❑ 97PinCerR-129
❑ 97PinTotCPB-129
❑ 97PinTotCPG-129
❑ 97PinTotCPR-129
❑ 97PinX-P-137
❑ 97PinX-PMoS-137
❑ 97Sco-551A
❑ 97Sco-551B
❑ 97ScoArtPWB-551
❑ 97ScoResC-551
❑ 97ScoShoS-551
❑ 97ScoShoSAP-551
❑ 97Sel-153
❑ 97SelCom-153
❑ 97SP-184
❑ 97SpoIII-11
❑ 97SpoIII-31
❑ 97SpoIIIEE-11
❑ 97SpoIIIEE-31
❑ 97TamYan-33
❑ 97TopStaFAS-FAS15
❑ 97Ult-553
❑ 97UltGolME-553
❑ 97UltIrabuComm-C1
❑ 97UltIrabuComm-C2
❑ 97UltIrabuComm-C3
❑ 97UltIrabuComm-C4
❑ 97UltIrabuComm-C5
❑ 97UltIrabuComm-C6
❑ 97UltIrabuComm-C7
❑ 97UltPlaMF-553
❑ 97UppDec-550
❑ 97Zen-45
❑ 97Zen8x10-20
❑ 97Zen8x1D-20
❑ 98Bow-64
❑ 98Bow-NNO
❑ 98BowChr-64
❑ 98BowChrGA-64
❑ 98BowChrGAR-64
❑ 98BowChrI-64
❑ 98BowChrIR-64
❑ 98BowChrR-64
❑ 98BowGolA-64
❑ 98BowInt-64
❑ 98CirThu-168
❑ 98CirThuRav-168
❑ 98CirThuSupRav-168
❑ 98CroRoy-93
❑ 98CroRoyPotG-16
❑ 98Don-119
❑ 98DonCol-119
❑ 98DonCol-180
❑ 98DonColE-476
❑ 98DonColE-542
❑ 98DonColL-257
❑ 98DonColP-686
❑ 98DonColS-119
❑ 98DonColS-175
❑ 98DonCruG-36
❑ 98DonCruP-36
❑ 98DonCruR-36
❑ 98DonEli-76
❑ 98DonEli-142
❑ 98DonEliA-76
❑ 98DonEliA-142
❑ 98DonEliS-76
❑ 98DonEliS-142
❑ 98DonGolPP-119
❑ 98DonPre-136
❑ 98DonPreGES-14
❑ 98DonPreGX-14
❑ 98DonPreGXDC-14
❑ 98DonPreSeat-136
❑ 98DonPriCD-119
❑ 98DonPriCD-180
❑ 98DonPriCE-476
❑ 98DonPriCE-542
❑ 98DonPriCL-257
❑ 98DonPriCP-686
❑ 98DonRatR-5
❑ 98DonRatRM-5
❑ 98DonSig-116
❑ 98DonSigP-116
❑ 98DonSilPP-119
❑ 98E-X2-80
❑ 98E-X2ECFut-80
❑ 98E-X2ECNow-80
❑ 98Fin-52
❑ 98FinNo--52
❑ 98FinNo-R-52
❑ 98FinRef-52
❑ 98FlaShoLeg0-46
❑ 98FlaShoLeg1-46
❑ 98FlaShoLeg2-46
❑ 98FlaShoLeg3-46
❑ 98FlaShoLegM-46
❑ 98FlaShoR0-46
❑ 98FlaShoR1-46
❑ 98FlaShoR2-46
❑ 98FlaShoR3-46
❑ 98Fle-256
❑ 98Fle-303
❑ 98Fle-316
❑ 98FleRooS-12
❑ 98Lea-58
❑ 98LeaFraDA-58
❑ 98LeaFraF-58
❑ 98LeaFraM-58
❑ 98LeaFraM-58
❑ 98LeaFraMDC-58
❑ 98LeaFraMDC-58
❑ 98LeaFraMS-58
❑ 98LeaFraMZ2-58
❑ 98LeaRS-118
❑ 98LeaRSLHolo-118
❑ 98LeaRSLong-118
❑ 98LeaRTrue-118
❑ 98MetUni-132
❑ 98MetUniPMG-132
❑ 98Pac-150
❑ 98PacInv-51
❑ 98PacInvGems-72
❑ 98PacInvInt-7A
❑ 98PacInvPBlue-51
❑ 98PacInvSilv-51
❑ 98PacOme-164
❑ 98PacOmeFTF-9
❑ 98PacOmeR-164
❑ 98PacOnl-504
❑ 98PacOnlR-504
❑ 98PacOnlWC-504
❑ 98PacPar-68
❑ 98PacParC-68
❑ 98PacParG-68
❑ 98PacParHS-68
❑ 98PacParPB-68
❑ 98PacParR-68
❑ 98PacPlaB-150
❑ 98PacRedT-150
❑ 98PacSil-150
❑ 98Pin-54
❑ 98PinArtP-PP49
❑ 98PinMusC-PP49
❑ 98PinPreP-54
❑ 98PinSna-NYY10
❑ 98Revo-98
❑ 98RevoPTP-5
❑ 98RevoShow-32
❑ 98RevoSS-98
❑ 98Sco-14
❑ 98ScoRT-89
❑ 98SpoIll-62
❑ 98SpoIll-188
❑ 98SpoIllEE-62
❑ 98SpoIllEE-188
❑ 98SpoIllFE-62
❑ 98SpoIllFE-188
❑ 98StaCluFDI-252
❑ 98StaCluI-252
❑ 98StaCluOneK-252
❑ 98StaCluPP-252
❑ 98Stu-18
❑ 98StuGPP-18
❑ 98StuSPP-18
❑ 98Top-181
❑ 98TopChr-181
❑ 98TopChrR-181
❑ 98TopDevR-181
❑ 98TopDia-181
❑ 98TopGolLabC1-48
❑ 98TopGolLabC1B-48
❑ 98TopGolLabC1One-48
❑ 98TopGolLabC1R-48
❑ 98TopGolLabC2-48
❑ 98TopGolLabC2B-48
❑ 98TopGolLabC2One-48
❑ 98TopGolLabC2R-48
❑ 98TopGolLabC3-48
❑ 98TopGolLabC3B-48
❑ 98TopGolLabC3One-48
❑ 98TopGolLabC3R-48
❑ 98TopMiniC-181
❑ 98TopOpeD-97
❑ 98Ult-124
❑ 98UltBacttF-8
❑ 98UltDouT-18
❑ 98UltGolM-124
❑ 98UltMas-124
❑ 98UltPlaM-124
❑ 98UppDec-176
❑ 98UppDec5x7-176
❑ 98UppDecNP-NP17
❑ 98YanSco-1
❑ 98YanScoP-1
❑ 98YanUppD-176
❑ 99199Fin-168
❑ 99FinGolRef-168
❑ 99FinRef-168
❑ 99Fle-418
❑ 99FleSta9-418
❑ 99FleWarT-418
❑ 99MetUni-110
❑ 99MetUniGM-110
❑ 99MetUniPMG-110
❑ 99Pac-293
❑ 99Pac-293A
❑ 99PacAur-127
❑ 99PacAurOD-127
❑ 99PacCroC-189
❑ 99PacCroCPB-189
❑ 99PacPar-161
❑ 99PacParC-161
❑ 99PacParG-161
❑ 99PacParHoloGold-161
❑ 99PacParHS-161
❑ 99PacParOD-161
❑ 99PacParPB-161
❑ 99PacParRed-161

❑ 99PacPlaB-293
❑ 99PacPlaB-293A
❑ 99PacPri-99
❑ 99PacPriHB-99
❑ 99PacPriHG-99
❑ 99PacPriHM-99
❑ 99PacPriHP-99
❑ 99PacPriRed-99
❑ 99PacRed-293
❑ 99PacRed-293A
❑ 99StaClu-196
❑ 99StaCluFDI-196
❑ 99StaCluOoaK-196
❑ 99StaCluPP-196
❑ 99Top-115
❑ 99TopChr-115
❑ 99TopChrR-115
❑ 99TopMVPP-115
❑ 99TopOpeD-68
❑ 99TopSta-124
❑ 99TopStaFoil-124
❑ 99Ult-182
❑ 99UltGolM-182
❑ 99UltMas-182
❑ 99UltPlaM-182
❑ 99UppDec-442
❑ 99UppDecBD-57
❑ 99UppDecBDD-57
❑ 99UppDecBDQ-57
❑ 99UppDecBDT-57
❑ 99UppDecEL1-442
❑ 99UppDecEL2-442
❑ 99YanFle-13

Ireland, Billy
❑ 83MiaMarT-13

Ireland, Eric
❑ 97AubDouTI-24
❑ 98QuaCitRBG-11

Ireland, Harold
❑ 12HomRunKE-49
❑ 12Zee-82

Ireland, Rich
❑ 92ClaDraP-72
❑ 92FroRowDP-61
❑ 92FroRowDPG-61
❑ 92FroRowDPS-61
❑ 93ClaGolF-190
❑ 93StaCluM-192
❑ 93Top-767
❑ 93TopGol-767
❑ 93TopInaM-767
❑ 93TopInaR-767
❑ 93TopMic-767

Ireland, Tim
❑ 77JacSunT-10
❑ 80OmaRoyP-15
❑ 80VenLeaS-216
❑ 81OmaRoyT-18
❑ 81Top-66
❑ 89PacSenL-104
❑ 89SalSpuCLC-146
❑ 89SalSpuP-1822
❑ 89T/MSenL-52
❑ 89TopSenL-67
❑ 90CMC-552
❑ 90EliSenL-69
❑ 90PhoFirC-25
❑ 90PhoFirP-28
❑ 90ProAAAF-54
❑ 92StoPorC-23
❑ 92StoPorF-51
❑ 93El PasDF-2966
❑ 94ElPasDF-3161
❑ 95ElPasDTI-10

Irisawa, Jun
❑ 89VerBeaDS-29

Irish, Jeffrey
❑ 90DunBluJS-12
❑ 90St.CatBJP-3475

Irons, Alex
❑ 93DavLipB-13

Irvin, Kyle
❑ 88EugEmeB-7

Irvin, Monte
❑ 47Exh-106
❑ 47PM1StaP1-93
❑ 47PM1StaP1-94
❑ 47PM1StaP1-95
❑ 51Bow-198
❑ 51TopRedB-50
❑ 52BerRos-25
❑ 52Bow-162
❑ 52DixLid-10
❑ 52DixPre-10
❑ 52RedMan-NL9
❑ 52StaCalL-78F
❑ 52StaCalS-90A
❑ 52Top-26
❑ 53BowC-51
❑ 53Bri-32
❑ 53DixLid-8
❑ 53DixPre-8
❑ 53ExhCan-6
❑ 53NorBreL-13
❑ 53StaMey-4
❑ 53Top-62
❑ 54DanDee-13
❑ 54DixLid-5
❑ 54NewYorJA-26
❑ 54RedMan-NL5
❑ 54StaMey-4
❑ 54Top-3
❑ 55GiaGolS-20
❑ 55StaMey-4
❑ 55Top-100
❑ 55TopDouH-3
❑ 56GiaJayP-4
❑ 56Top-194
❑ 75Gia195T-8
❑ 75TCMAllG-17
❑ 76ShaPiz-137
❑ 76SSPYanOD-5
❑ 77BobParHoF-92
❑ 77GalGloG-26
❑ 79BasGre-65
❑ 79DiaGre-45
❑ 79TCM50-168
❑ 80PerHaloFP-137
❑ 80PerHaloFPS-21
❑ 80SSPHOF-137
❑ 83DonHOFH-15
❑ 83TopRep5-26
❑ 84WilMay-4
❑ 86NegLeaF-6
❑ 86NegLeaF-89
❑ 86NegLeaFS-89
❑ 88NegLeaD-20
❑ 88PacLegI-79
❑ 89HOFStiB-32
❑ 89NegLeaRP-1
❑ 89PerCelP-19
❑ 90NegLeaS-9
❑ 90PacLeg-32
❑ 90PerGreM-27
❑ 90SweBasG-85
❑ 91LinDri-42
❑ 91NegLeaRL-20
❑ 91SweBasG-44
❑ 91TopArc1-62
❑ 92ActPacA-10
❑ 92ActPacA2-10G
❑ 92BazQua5A-10
❑ 92FroRowI-1
❑ 92FroRowI-1AU
❑ 92FroRowI-2
❑ 92FroRowI-3
❑ 92FroRowI-4
❑ 92FroRowI-5
❑ 92NegLeaK-4
❑ 92NegLeaPL-1
❑ 92NegLeaRLI-30
❑ 93ActPacAC-10
❑ 93TedWil-54
❑ 93TedWil-136
❑ 93TedWil-146
❑ 93UppDecAH-71
❑ 93UppDecAH-154
❑ 93UppDecAH-163
❑ 94TedWilM-M21
❑ 94TopArc1-3
❑ 94TopArc1G-3
❑ 94UppDecAH-53
❑ 94UppDecAH1-53
❑ 95NegLeaL2-4
❑ 95NegLeaLI-20
❑ 95S.FExaNLT-8
❑ 95UppDecSHoB-13
❑ 97NegLeaPC-11D
❑ 97NewYorL-4
❑ 97St.VinHHS-8
❑ 97TopStaHRR-6
❑ 97TopStaRRAU-6

Irvine, Daryl
❑ 85GreHorT-17
❑ 86WinHavRSP-11
❑ 87NewBriRSP-14
❑ 88NewBriRSP-890
❑ 89EasLeaAP-12
❑ 89NewBriRSP-611
❑ 89NewBriRSS-7
❑ 89Sta-127
❑ 90CMC-256
❑ 90PawRedSC-5
❑ 90PawRedSDD-10
❑ 90PawRedSP-457
❑ 90ProAAAF-429
❑ 90TopTVRS-46
❑ 91Fle-98
❑ 91OPC-189
❑ 91PawRedSDD-9
❑ 91PawRedSP-33
❑ 91Sco-333
❑ 91StaClu-122
❑ 91Top-189
❑ 91TopDeb90-75
❑ 91TopDesS-189
❑ 91TopMic-189
❑ 91TopTif-189
❑ 91TriA AAGP-AAA30
❑ 91Ult-34
❑ 92Fle-41
❑ 92PawRedSF-918
❑ 92PawRedSS-358
❑ 92Sco-726
❑ 92SkyAAAF-162
❑ 93BufBisF-511
❑ 93RedSoxWHP-16
❑ 97DunDonPPS-12

Irvine, Ed
❑ 81ElPasDT-1
❑ 82VanCanT-8
❑ 84VanCanC-44

Irvine, Kirk
❑ 97HicCraB-17
❑ 97HicCraRB-21

Irvine, Michael
❑ 95IdaFalBTI-11

Irvis, Damon
❑ 96AppLeaAB-16

Irwin, Arthur
❑ 87BucN28-81
❑ 87OldJudN-260
❑ 88WG1CarG-52
❑ 89EdgR.WG-14
❑ 90KalBatN-25
❑ 90KalBatN-26

Irwin, Charles
❑ 90DodTar-376
❑ 98CamPepP-39

Irwin, Dennis
❑ 78TacYanC-14

Irwin, Jim
❑ 75BreBro-1

Irwin, John
❑ 87OldJudN-259
❑ 88WG1CarG-66

Irwin, Michael
❑ 90AubAstB-13
❑ 90AubAstP-3412

Irwin, Tom
❑ 92BatCliCB-27
❑ 92BatCliF-3259
❑ 93BatCliCB-13
❑ 93BatCliF-3141
❑ 93SpaPhiF-1052

Isa, Kelsey
❑ 87PenWhiSP-21

Isaac, Joe Keith
❑ 78WisRapTT-9

Isaac, Luis
❑ 70WicAerM-10
❑ 76WilTomT-12
❑ 81BatTroT-28
❑ 88IndGat-7
❑ 88IndTeal-20
❑ 89BlaYNPRWL-32
❑ 89IndTeal-28
❑ 90IndTeal-17
❑ 91IndFanC-30
❑ 92ColSprSSF-767
❑ 92ColSprSSS-100
❑ 93ChaKniF-560

Isaacson, Christopher
❑ 88KinIndS-11

Isales, Orlando
❑ 81OklCit8T-8
❑ 82IndIndTI-10
❑ 83IndIndTI-18

Isbell, Cecil
❑ 40WheM4-7A
❑ 40WheM4-7C

Isbell, Frank
❑ 03BreE10-73
❑ 04FanCraAL-26
❑ 07WhiSoxGWH-5
❑ 08RosComP-14
❑ 09AmeCarE90-1-55
❑ 09T206-167
❑ 11SpoLifCW-184

Isenia, Derrick
❑ 98GreFalDG-16

Ishee, Gabe
❑ 96OgdRapTI-3
❑ 97BelSnaB-16
❑ 97StoPor-15

Ishibashi, Keith
❑ 87HawRai-9

Ishige, Hiromichi
❑ 87JapPlaB-36

Ishimaru, Taisuke
❑ 96GreFalDB-16

Ishimine, Kazuhiko
❑ 87JapPlaB-28

Ishimoto, Yoshiaki
❑ 87JapPlaB-17

Ishiwata, Shigeru
❑ 79TCMJapPB-47

Ishmael, Mike (Michael)
❑ 87BurExpP-1085
❑ 87JamExpP-2540

Isom, Jeff
❑ 93WelPirC-8
❑ 93WelPirF-3350
❑ 94AugGreC-6

Isom, Johnny
❑ 96CarLeaA1B-19
❑ 96CarLeaA2B-19
❑ 96FreKeyB-20
❑ 97BowBay-19
❑ 98BowBayM-17
❑ 98RocRedWQ-15

Isringhausen, Jason
❑ 92GulCoaMF-3474
❑ 93PitMetC-11
❑ 93PitMetF-3702
❑ 94Bow-326
❑ 94Cla-68
❑ 94ExcFS7-235
❑ 94FloStaLAF-FSL39
❑ 94St.LucMC-14
❑ 94St.LucMF-1190
❑ 95BinMetTI-44
❑ 95Bow-180
❑ 95BowBes-B38
❑ 95BowBesR-B38
❑ 95ColChoSE-19
❑ 95ColChoSEGS-19
❑ 95ColChoSESS-19
❑ 95Exc-231
❑ 95NorTidTI-15
❑ 95SigRooOJ-20
❑ 95SigRooOJP-20
❑ 95SigRooOJPS-20
❑ 95SigRooOJS-20
❑ 95SPCha-19
❑ 95SPChaDC-19
❑ 95Top-653
❑ 95UltGolMR-M16
❑ 95UppDec-14
❑ 95UppDecED-14
❑ 95UppDecEDG-14
❑ 95UppDecML-65
❑ 95UppDecMLFS-65
❑ 95UppDecSE-63
❑ 95UppDecSEG-63
❑ 96Baz-69
❑ 96Bow-83
❑ 96BowBes-70
❑ 96BowBesAR-70
❑ 96BowBesC-2
❑ 96BowBesCAR-2
❑ 96BowBesCR-2
❑ 96BowBesR-70
❑ 96BowFoi-83
❑ 96Cir-158
❑ 96CirRav-158
❑ 96ColCho-30
❑ 96ColChoGS-30
❑ 96ColChoSS-30
❑ 96DenHol-17
❑ 96Don-101
❑ 96DonDiaK-19
❑ 96DonPreP-101
❑ 96EmoRarB-4
❑ 96EmoXL-233
❑ 96Fin-G51
❑ 96FinRef-G51
❑ 96Fla-321
❑ 96Fle-481
❑ 96FleRooS-8
❑ 96FleTif-481
❑ 96FleTomL-4
❑ 96FleUpd-U225
❑ 96FleUpdTC-U225
❑ 96Lea-26
❑ 96LeaPre-37
❑ 96LeaPreP-37
❑ 96LeaPrePB-26
❑ 96LeaPrePG-26
❑ 96LeaPrePS-26
❑ 96LeaPreSG-42
❑ 96LeaPreSte-42
❑ 96LeaSig-33
❑ 96LeaSigPPG-33
❑ 96LeaSigPPP-33
❑ 96MetKah-16
❑ 96MetKah-17
❑ 96MetUni-201
❑ 96MetUniP-201
❑ 96MetUniPP-4
❑ 96Pac-146
❑ 96PacPri-P48
❑ 96PacPriG-P48
❑ 96PanSti-25
❑ 96PanSti-241
❑ 96Pin-223
❑ 96PinAfi-101
❑ 96PinAfiAP-101
❑ 96PinArtP-123
❑ 96PinFan-28
❑ 96PinFoil-223
❑ 96PinSta-123
❑ 96Sco-131
❑ 96Sco-380
❑ 96ScoDugC-A82
❑ 96ScoDugC-B105
❑ 96ScoDugCAP-A82
❑ 96ScoDugCAP-B105
❑ 96ScoFutF-1
❑ 96ScoGolS-10
❑ 96Sel-61
❑ 96SelArtP-61
❑ 96SelCer-16
❑ 96SelCerAP-16
❑ 96SelCerCB-16
❑ 96SelCerCR-16
❑ 96SelCerIP-10
❑ 96SelCerMB-16
❑ 96SelCerMG-16
❑ 96SelCerMR-16
❑ 96SelTeaN-21
❑ 96SP-125
❑ 96Spo-42
❑ 96SpoArtP-42
❑ 96SPSpeFX-7
❑ 96SPSpeFXDC-7
❑ 96SPx-40
❑ 96SPxGol-40
❑ 96StaClu-286
❑ 96StaCluEPB-286
❑ 96StaCluEPG-286
❑ 96StaCluEPS-286
❑ 96StaCluMOP-286
❑ 96Stu-38
❑ 96StuPrePB-38
❑ 96StuPrePG-38
❑ 96StuPrePS-38
❑ 96Sum-99
❑ 96SumAbo&B-99
❑ 96SumArtP-99
❑ 96SumFoi-99
❑ 96Top-369
❑ 96TopChr-151
❑ 96TopChrR-151
❑ 96TopGal-106
❑ 96TopGalPPI-106
❑ 96TopLas-120
❑ 96Ult-244
❑ 96UltGolM-244
❑ 96UppDec-140
❑ 96UppDec-147
❑ 96UppDecBCP-BC3
❑ 96UppDecPHE-H43
❑ 96UppDecPreH-H43
❑ 96Zen-41
❑ 96ZenArtP-41
❑ 96ZenMoz-24
❑ 97Cir-38
❑ 97CirRav-38
❑ 97ColCho-394
❑ 97Don-33
❑ 97DonEli-63
❑ 97DonEliGS-63
❑ 97DonGolPP-33
❑ 97DonPre-9
❑ 97DonPreCttC-9
❑ 97DonSilPP-33
❑ 97Fle-399
❑ 97FleTif-399
❑ 97Lea-156
❑ 97LeaFraM-156
❑ 97LeaFraMDC-156
❑ 97NewPin-5
❑ 97NewPinAP-5
❑ 97NewPinMC-5
❑ 97NewPinPP-5
❑ 97NorTid-17
❑ 97NorTidB-17
❑ 97Pac-367
❑ 97PacLigB-367
❑ 97PacSil-367
❑ 97PinCer-105
❑ 97PinCerMBla-105
❑ 97PinCerMBlu-105
❑ 97PinCerMG-105
❑ 97PinCerMR-105
❑ 97PinCerR-105
❑ 97PinIns-11
❑ 97PinInsCE-11
❑ 97PinInsDE-11
❑ 97PinTotCPB-105
❑ 97PinTotCPG-105
❑ 97PinTotCPR-105
❑ 97Sco-306
❑ 97Sco-530
❑ 97ScoArtPWB-306
❑ 97ScoArtPWB-530
❑ 97ScoPreS-306
❑ 97ScoResC-530
❑ 97ScoShoS-306
❑ 97ScoShoS-530
❑ 97ScoShoSAP-306
❑ 97ScoShoSAP-530
❑ 97Sel-77
❑ 97SelArtP-77
❑ 97SelCom-77
❑ 97SelRegG-77
❑ 97StaClu-257
❑ 97StaCluMOP-257
❑ 97Stu-3
❑ 97StuPrePG-3
❑ 97StuPrePS-3
❑ 97Top-317
❑ 97TopGal-172
❑ 97TopGalPPI-172
❑ 97Ult-241
❑ 97UltGolME-241
❑ 97UltPlaME-241
❑ 97UppDec-433
❑ 98StaCluFDI-254
❑ 98StaCluI-254
❑ 98StaCluOneK-254
❑ 98StaCluPP-254

Issac, Richard
❑ 86AppFoxP-11

Ithier, Pete
❑ 76WilTomT-13
❑ 78SanJosMMC-10

Iverson, Tom
❑ 89GreHorP-430
❑ 90ChaWheB-28
❑ 91PriRedC-30
❑ 92CedRapRC-30
❑ 93WesVirWC-27
❑ 94ChaWheC-27

Ivie, Lonnie
❑ 81MiaOriT-15

Ivie, Mike
❑ 72OPC-457
❑ 72Top-457
❑ 73OPC-613
❑ 73Top-613
❑ 75PadDea-12
❑ 76Hos-103
❑ 76OPC-134
❑ 76SSP-127
❑ 76Top-134
❑ 77BurCheD-134
❑ 77OPC-241
❑ 77PadSchC-29A
❑ 77PadSchC-29B
❑ 77PadSchC-29C
❑ 77Top-325
❑ 78GiaTeal-13
❑ 78Top-445
❑ 79GiaPol-15
❑ 79Top-538
❑ 80GiaPol-15
❑ 80GiaTeal-11
❑ 80OPC-34
❑ 80Top-62
❑ 81AstPos-7
❑ 81Don-312
❑ 81Fle-435
❑ 81OPC-236

❑ 81Top-236
❑ 81TopTra-77T
❑ 82Don-396
❑ 82Top-734
❑ 82TopTra-45T
❑ 83Don-485
❑ 83Fle-331
❑ 83OPC-117
❑ 83TigPos-15
❑ 83Top-613
❑ 87AstShoSPT-14
Ivie, Ryan
❑ 92WatDiaC-7
❑ 92WatDiaF-2139
Ivie, Tamara
❑ 95ColSilB-13
❑ 96ColSilB-15
Ivie, Tom
❑ 91ChaRaiC-27
Ivory, Sap (James)
❑ 93NegLeaRL2-20
Iwasaki, Junichi
❑ 98BilMusTI-14
Iwema, Todd
❑ 91HelBreSP-17
Izquierdo, Hank
❑ 77FriOneYW-58
❑ 98HicCraM-17
❑ 98HicCraUO-21
Izturis, Cesar
❑ 97St.CatSB-18
❑ 98HagSunM-17
Jabalera, Francisco
❑ 83ColAstT-12
❑ 85DomLeaS-205
Jablonowski, Pete
❑ 33Gou-83
❑ 34GouCanV-34
Jablonski, Ray
❑ 53CarHunW-10
❑ 53Top-189
❑ 54CarHunW-9
❑ 54Top-26
❑ 54Wil-10
❑ 55RedMan-NL21
❑ 55Top-56
❑ 55TopDouH-51
❑ 56Kah-7
❑ 56Top-86
❑ 57Top-218
❑ 58GiaSFCB-11
❑ 58Hir-35
❑ 58Top-362
❑ 59Top-342
❑ 61UniOil-H1
❑ 79DiaGre-173
❑ 91TopArc1-189
❑ 94CarLeaA-DJ9
❑ 94TopArc1-26
❑ 94TopArc1G-26
Jacas, Andre
❑ 86MadMusP-12
❑ 86MadMusP-12
❑ 88St.LucMS-12
Jacas, Dave (David)
❑ 87KenTwiP-12
❑ 88KenTwiP-1389
❑ 89CalLeaA-8
❑ 89VisOakCLC-109
❑ 89VisOakP-1447
❑ 90CMC-572
❑ 90PorBeaC-20
❑ 90PorBeaP-192
❑ 90ProAAAF-262
❑ 91ElPasDLD-186
❑ 91ElPasDP-2760
❑ 91LinDriAA-186
❑ 92HunStaF-3962
❑ 92HunStaS-311
❑ 92SkyAA F-132
Jaccar, Mike
❑ 77AshTouT-9
Jacinto, Larry
❑ 91GreFalDSP-8
Jacklitsch, Fred
❑ 03BreE10-74
❑ 09T206-168
❑ 10E101-23
❑ 10MelMinE-23
❑ 10NadCarE-28
❑ 10NadE1-22
❑ 10PeoT21-28A
❑ 10PeoT21-28B
❑ 11SpoLifCW-185
❑ 11SpoLifM-231
❑ 11T205-80
❑ 12ImpTobC-62
❑ 15AmeCarE106-21
❑ 16TanBraE-13
❑ 90DodTar-377
Jackman, Bill
❑ 86NegLeaF-68
Jackowski, Bill
❑ 55Bow-284
Jackson, Alvin
❑ 62MetJayP-6
❑ 62Top-464
❑ 63Baz-19
❑ 63Fle-48
❑ 63MetJayP-6
❑ 63Top-111
❑ 63TopStil-20
❑ 64MetJayP-8
❑ 64MetTeal-8
❑ 64Top-494
❑ 64TopCoi-17
❑ 64TopSta-85
❑ 64TopStaU-36
❑ 64TopTatl-43
❑ 65MetJayP-8
❑ 65MetPos-5
❑ 65Top-381
❑ 65TopTral-17
❑ 66MetPos-1
❑ 66Top-206
❑ 66TopVen-206
❑ 67OPC-195
❑ 67Top-195
❑ 68Top-503
❑ 69MetTeal-8
❑ 69MilBra-125
❑ 69Top-649
❑ 70OPC-443
❑ 70Top-443
❑ 73MetAllEB-4
❑ 78TCM60I-193
❑ 82MetGal62-11
❑ 83TidTidT-24
❑ 84TidTidT-22
❑ 87LitFalMP-2410
❑ 88LitFalMP-27
❑ 89BalOriP-14
❑ 89OriFreB-31
❑ 91MetWIZ-197
Jackson, Andrew
❑ 92SalLakTSP-3
Jackson, Bo
❑ 84OCoandSI-204
❑ 86DonHig-43
❑ 86DonRoo-38
❑ 86MemChiSTOS-10
❑ 86MemChiTOS-10
❑ 86SouLeaAJ-13
❑ 86SpoRoo-40
❑ 86TopTra-50T
❑ 86TopTraT-50T
❑ 87ClaGam-15
❑ 87ClaUpdY-109
❑ 87Don-35
❑ 87DonOpeD-205
❑ 87DonRoo-14
❑ 87Fle-369
❑ 87FleGlo-369
❑ 87FleSluBC-M4
❑ 87FleStiC-132
❑ 87Lea-35
❑ 87Spo-190
❑ 87SpoSupD-16
❑ 87SpoTeaP-13
❑ 87Top-170
❑ 87TopTif-170
❑ 87ToyRoo-13
❑ 88ClaBlu-208
❑ 88Don-220
❑ 88DonBasB-119
❑ 88Fle-260
❑ 88FleGlo-260
❑ 88Lea-187
❑ 88OPC-8
❑ 88PanSti-110
❑ 88RedFolSB-38
❑ 88RoySmo-5
❑ 88RoyTeal-16
❑ 88Sco-180
❑ 88ScoGlo-180
❑ 88Spo-148
❑ 88StaLinRo-7
❑ 88Top-750
❑ 88TopBig-49
❑ 88TopSti-258
❑ 88TopTif-750
❑ 89Bow-126
❑ 89BowTif-126
❑ 89ClaTraO-122
❑ 89ClaTraP-167
❑ 89Don-208
❑ 89DonBasB-169
❑ 89Fle-285
❑ 89FleGlo-285
❑ 89KinDis-11
❑ 89OPC-84
❑ 89PanSti-358
❑ 89RedFolSB-64
❑ 89RoyTasD-6
❑ 89Sco-330
❑ 89Scomast-1
❑ 89ScoYouSI-5
❑ 89Spo-70
❑ 89SpoIllFKI-75
❑ 89Top-540
❑ 89Top-789
❑ 89TopAme2C-17
❑ 89TopBig-238
❑ 89TopHeaUT-8
❑ 89TopSti-265
❑ 89TopTif-540
❑ 89TopTif-789
❑ 89TopUKM-43
❑ 89TVSpoM-108
❑ 89UppDec-221
❑ 90AllBasT-7
❑ 90Bow-378
❑ 90BowIns-4
❑ 90BowInsL-4
❑ 90BowInsT-4
❑ 90BowTif-378
❑ 90BowTif-A4
❑ 90ClaBlu-2
❑ 90ClaBlu-59A
❑ 90ClaBlu-59B
❑ 90ClaUpd-T25
❑ 90ClaUpd-T26
❑ 90Col-1
❑ 90ColtheSBM-85
❑ 90Don-1
❑ 90Don-61
❑ 90Don-650A
❑ 90Don-650B
❑ 90DonBesA-63
❑ 90DOnBonM-BC1
❑ 90DonGraS-12
❑ 90DonLeaS-38
❑ 90DonPre-3
❑ 90DonSupD-1
❑ 90Fle-110
❑ 90Fle-635
❑ 90FleAwaW-19
❑ 90FleBasA-20
❑ 90FleBasAC-20
❑ 90FleBasM-21
❑ 90FleBasMC-21
❑ 90FleCan-110
❑ 90FleCan-635
❑ 90FleLeaL-19
❑ 90FleLeaLC-19
❑ 90FleWaxBC-C15
❑ 90FraGloT-1
❑ 90Hot50PS-22
❑ 90KinDis-17
❑ 90Lea-125
❑ 90M.Vpin-45
❑ 90MLBBasB-104
❑ 90MSAIceTD-5
❑ 90OPC-300
❑ 90PanSti-84
❑ 90PanSti-198
❑ 90PanSti-384
❑ 90Pos-14
❑ 90PubIntS-350
❑ 90PubIntS-596
❑ 90RedFolSB-51
❑ 90RoyPos-13
❑ 90Sco-280A
❑ 90Sco-280B
❑ 90Sco-566
❑ 90Sco-687
❑ 90Sco-697
❑ 90Sco100S-40
❑ 90ScoYouSI-1
❑ 90Spo-200
❑ 90SunSee-4
❑ 90Top-300
❑ 90TopBig-6
❑ 90TopCoi-19
❑ 90TopDou-35
❑ 90TopGloA-17
❑ 90TopGloS-44
❑ 90TopHeaU-8
❑ 90TopMag-9
❑ 90TopMag-52
❑ 90TopMinL-16
❑ 90TopSti-155
❑ 90TopSti-264
❑ 90TopStiB-51
❑ 90TopTif-300
❑ 90TopTVA-5
❑ 90UppDec-32
❑ 90UppDec-75
❑ 90UppDec-105
❑ 90UppDec-555
❑ 90WonBreS-1
❑ 91BasBesHRK-11
❑ 91CadEllD-32
❑ 91Cla1-T48
❑ 91ClaGam-186
❑ 91Don-632
❑ 91DonBonC-BC10
❑ 91Fle-561
❑ 91FlePro-5
❑ 91LeaPre-19
❑ 91MajLeaCP-20
❑ 91OPC-600
❑ 91PanFreS-281
❑ 91PanSti-226
❑ 91RoyPol-12
❑ 91Sco-5
❑ 91Sco-412
❑ 91Sco-420
❑ 91Sco-692
❑ 91Sco-773
❑ 91Sco100S-2
❑ 91ScoRoo-1T
❑ 91StaClu-224
❑ 91Top-600
❑ 91TopCraJI-25
❑ 91TopDesS-600
❑ 91TopMic-600
❑ 91TopSta-20
❑ 91TopTif-600
❑ 91TopTra-58T
❑ 91TopTraT-58T
❑ 91Ult-149
❑ 91UltGol-6
❑ 91UppDec-545
❑ 91UppDec-744
❑ 91WhiSoxK-8
❑ 92ClaGam-108
❑ 92Don-470
❑ 92Fle-86
❑ 92Fle-701
❑ 92MVPPin-9
❑ 92New-12
❑ 92OPC-290
❑ 92Sco-361
❑ 92ScoImpP-53
❑ 92SpoStaCC-25
❑ 92StaBoJ-1
❑ 92StaBoJ-2
❑ 92StaBoJ-3
❑ 92StaBoJ-4
❑ 92StaBoJ-5
❑ 92StaBoJ-6
❑ 92StaBoJ-7
❑ 92StaBoJ-8
❑ 92StaBoJ-9
❑ 92StaBoJ-10
❑ 92StaBoJ-11
❑ 92StaClu-654
❑ 92Top-290
❑ 92TopGol-290
❑ 92TopGolW-290
❑ 92TopKid-103
❑ 92TopMcD-33
❑ 92TopMic-290
❑ 92TriPla-164
❑ 92UppDec-555
❑ 93Bow-415
❑ 93CadDis-33
❑ 93DiaMar-54
❑ 93Fin-91
❑ 93FinJum-91
❑ 93FinRef-91
❑ 93Fla-186
❑ 93FleFinE-195
❑ 93FunPac-31
❑ 93FunPac-199
❑ 93Lea-316
❑ 93OPC-151
❑ 93PacJugC-8
❑ 93PacSpa-389
❑ 93Pin-524
❑ 93PinHomRC-43
❑ 93SP-255
❑ 93StaClu-495
❑ 93StaCluFDI-495
❑ 93StaCluMOP-495
❑ 93Stu-110
❑ 93Top-400
❑ 93TopGol-400
❑ 93TopInaM-400
❑ 93TopInaR-400
❑ 93TopMic-400
❑ 93Ult-534
❑ 93UppDec-775
❑ 93UppDecGold-775
❑ 93UppDecOD-D15
❑ 93WhiSoxK-13
❑ 93WhiSoxSC-2
❑ 94AngLAT-7
❑ 94AngMot-7
❑ 94Bow-535
❑ 94ColC-356
❑ 94ColChoGS-356
❑ 94ColChoSS-356
❑ 94Don-173
❑ 94DonLonBL-4
❑ 94Fin-241
❑ 94FinRef-241
❑ 94Fla-23
❑ 94Fle-84
❑ 94FleExtB-36
❑ 94FleGolM-5
❑ 94FleGolMJ-5
❑ 94FleUpd-18
❑ 94FUnPac-151
❑ 94Lea-307
❑ 94OPC-116
❑ 94Pac-128
❑ 94PanSti-49
❑ 94Pin-509
❑ 94PinArtP-509
❑ 94PinMusC-509
❑ 94PinTri-TR4
❑ 94Sco-513
❑ 94ScoGolR-513
❑ 94ScoGolS-35
❑ 94ScoRoo-RT3
❑ 94ScoRooCP-CP4
❑ 94ScoRooGR-RT3
❑ 94ScoRooS-RT3
❑ 94Sel-356
❑ 94SP-24
❑ 94SPDieC-24
❑ 94SPHol-15
❑ 94SPHolDC-15
❑ 94SpoRoo-150
❑ 94SpoRooAP-150
❑ 94StaClu-167
❑ 94StaClu-547
❑ 94StaCluFDI-167
❑ 94StaCluFDI-547
❑ 94StaCluGR-167
❑ 94StaCluGR-547
❑ 94StaCluMOP-167
❑ 94StaCluMOP-547
❑ 94Stu-12
❑ 94Top-500
❑ 94TopGol-500
❑ 94TopSpa-500
❑ 94TopTra-90T
❑ 94Ult-330
❑ 94UppDec-117
❑ 94UppDecDC-W7
❑ 94UppDecED-117
❑ 95ColCho-95
❑ 95ColChoGS-95
❑ 95ColChoSE-36
❑ 95ColChoSEGS-36
❑ 95ColChoSESS-36
❑ 95ColChoSS-95
❑ 95Don-507
❑ 95DonPreP-507
❑ 95Fle-227
❑ 95Pac-61
❑ 95PacPri-20
❑ 95Pin-208
❑ 95PinArtP-208
❑ 95PinMusC-208
❑ 95PinSam-208
❑ 95Sco-342
❑ 95ScoGolR-342
❑ 95ScoPlaTS-342
❑ 95Spo-140
❑ 95SpoArtP-140
❑ 95StaClu-2
❑ 95StaCluFDI-2
❑ 95StaCluMOP-2
❑ 95StaCluSTWS-2
❑ 95Top-592
❑ 95TopCyb-364
❑ 95UppDec-20
❑ 95UppDecED-20
❑ 95UppDecEDG-20
Jackson, Brandon
❑ 98St.CatSM-7
Jackson, Bubba
❑ 98TulDriTI-17
Jackson, Charles
❑ 13Zee-12
Jackson, Chief
❑ 92ColCliP-25
Jackson, Chris
❑ 98SalVol-15
Jackson, Chuck
❑ 85TucTorC-67
❑ 86TucTorP-8
❑ 87DonRoo-55
❑ 87FleUpd-47
❑ 87FleUpdG-47
❑ 88AstMot-25
❑ 88AstPol-14
❑ 88Sco-222
❑ 88ScoGlo-222
❑ 88Top-94
❑ 88TopTif-94
❑ 89AstSmo-20
❑ 89Sco-584
❑ 89TucTorC-20
❑ 89TucTorJP-8
❑ 89TucTorP-205
❑ 89UppDec-323
❑ 91CalCanLD-61
❑ 91CalCanP-521
❑ 91LinDriAAA-61
❑ 92OklCit8F-1921
❑ 92OklCit8S-311
❑ 92SkyAAAF-143
❑ 93EdmTraF-1143
❑ 94OklCit8F-1499
Jackson, Damian
❑ 92BurIndC-3
❑ 92BurIndF-1664
❑ 93ColRedC-13
❑ 93ColRedF-604
❑ 94CanIndF-3122
❑ 95Bes-14
❑ 95Bow-132
❑ 95Exc-40
❑ 95UppDecML-179
❑ 95UppDecMLFS-179
❑ 96Bow-163
❑ 96BowFoi-163
❑ 96BufBisB-11
❑ 97BesAutSBPP-2
❑ 97BesWhe-3
❑ 97Bow-78
❑ 97BowCerBlaIA-CA40
❑ 97BowCerBluIA-CA40
❑ 97BowCerGolIA-CA40
❑ 97BowInt-78
❑ 97BufBis-19
❑ 97ColCho-7
❑ 97Fle-626
❑ 97FleTif-626
❑ 97StaClu-337
❑ 97StaCluMOP-337
❑ 97UppDec-471
❑ 98Bow-398
❑ 98BowBes-186
❑ 98BowBesAR-186
❑ 98BowBesR-186
❑ 98BowChr-398
❑ 98BowChrGA-398
❑ 98BowChrGAR-398
❑ 98BowChrI-398
❑ 98BowChrIR-398
❑ 98BowChrR-398
❑ 98BowGolA-398
❑ 98BowInt-398
❑ 98Don-339
❑ 98DonColL-281
❑ 98DonGolPP-339
❑ 98DonPriCL-281
❑ 98DonSigA-47
❑ 98DonSigAC-61
❑ 98DonSigAM-62
❑ 98DonSigSP-12
❑ 98DonSilPP-339
❑ 98IndIndQ-24
❑ 98Lea-82
❑ 98LeaFraDA-82
❑ 98LeaFraF-82
❑ 98LeaFraM-82
❑ 98LeaFraM-82
❑ 98LeaFraMDC-82
❑ 98LeaFraMDC-82

❑ 98LeaFraMZ2-82
❑ 98LeaRS-233
❑ 98LeaRSLHolo-233
❑ 98LeaRSLong-233
❑ 98LeaRTrue-233
❑ 98PacAur-119
❑ 98PacOnl-193
❑ 98PacOnlR-193
❑ 98PacOnlWC-193
❑ 98ScoRT-72
❑ 98ScoRTSS-PP57
❑ 98ScoRTSSAP-PP57
❑ 98ScoRTSSAP1-PP57
❑ 98Stu-185
❑ 98StuGPP-185
❑ 98StuSPP-185
❑ 98Ult-429
❑ 98UltGolM-429
❑ 98UltMas-429
❑ 98UltPlaM-429
❑ 98UppDec-664

Jackson, Danny
❑ 82ChaRoyT-6
❑ 83OmaRoyT-6
❑ 84Don-461
❑ 84RoyPos-16
❑ 85Don-374
❑ 85Fle-205
❑ 85RoyTeal-13
❑ 86Don-95
❑ 86Fle-10
❑ 86Lea-30
❑ 86RoyKitCD-16
❑ 86RoyNatP-25
❑ 86RoyTeal-10
❑ 86Spo-186
❑ 87Don-157
❑ 87DonOpeD-203
❑ 87Fle-370
❑ 87FleGlo-370
❑ 87TopTra-51T
❑ 87TopTraT-51T
❑ 88Don-132
❑ 88DonBasB-166
❑ 88Fle-261
❑ 88FleGlo-261
❑ 88FleSlu-21
❑ 88FleUpd-84
❑ 88FleUpdG-84
❑ 88OPC-324
❑ 88RedKah-20
❑ 88Sco-398
❑ 88ScoGlo-398
❑ 88ScoRoo-2T
❑ 88ScoRooG-2T
❑ 88Top-324
❑ 88TopTif-324
❑ 88TopTra-55T
❑ 88TopTraT-55T
❑ 89Bow-304
❑ 89BowTif-304
❑ 89CadEllD-31
❑ 89ClaLigB-100
❑ 89ClaTraO-123
❑ 89Don-124
❑ 89DonAll-52
❑ 89DonBasB-54
❑ 89Fle-163
❑ 89Fle-636
❑ 89FleBasA-22
❑ 89FleBasM-21
❑ 89FleExcS-25
❑ 89FleGlo-163
❑ 89FleGlo-636
❑ 89FleHeroB-24
❑ 89FleLeaL-22
❑ 89FleWaxBC-C15
❑ 89KinDis-23
❑ 89OPC-319
❑ 89PanSti-67
❑ 89PanSti-225
❑ 89RedKah-20
❑ 89Sco-555
❑ 89ScoHot1S-75
❑ 89ScoYouS2-41
❑ 89Spo-80
❑ 89Top-395
❑ 89Top-730
❑ 89TopBasT-107
❑ 89TopDouA-22
❑ 89TopGloS-57
❑ 89TopHilTM-18
❑ 89TopMinL-10
❑ 89TopSti-143
❑ 89TopStiB-62
❑ 89TopTif-395
❑ 89TopTif-730
❑ 89TVSpoM-40
❑ 89UppDec-640
❑ 90Bow-44
❑ 90BowTif-44
❑ 90Don-80
❑ 90Fle-422
❑ 90FleCan-422
❑ 90Lea-279
❑ 90M.Vpin-29
❑ 90OPC-445
❑ 90PanSti-255
❑ 90PubIntS-32
❑ 90PubIntS-264
❑ 90RedKah-13
❑ 90Sco-289
❑ 90Spo-89
❑ 90Top-445
❑ 90TopSti-142
❑ 90TopTif-445
❑ 90UppDec-120
❑ 91Bow-412
❑ 91ClaGam-69
❑ 91CubMar-32
❑ 91CubVinL-14
❑ 91Don-96
❑ 91Don-678
❑ 91Fle-67
❑ 91FleUpd-78
❑ 91Lea-268
❑ 91OPC-92
❑ 91OPCPre-68
❑ 91Sco-601
❑ 91ScoRoo-17T
❑ 91StaClu-433
❑ 91Top-92
❑ 91TopDesS-92
❑ 91TopMic-92
❑ 91TopTif-92
❑ 91TopTra-59T
❑ 91TopTraT-59T
❑ 91UltUpd-70
❑ 91UppDec-414
❑ 91UppDec-723
❑ 92Bow-142
❑ 92ClaGam-86
❑ 92CubMar-32
❑ 92Don-91
❑ 92Fle-383
❑ 92Lea-381
❑ 92LeaBlaG-381
❑ 92OPC-619
❑ 92Pin-457
❑ 92Sco-120
❑ 92StaClu-406
❑ 92Top-619
❑ 92TopGol-619
❑ 92TopGolW-619
❑ 92TopMic-619
❑ 92Ult-176
❑ 92UppDec-104
❑ 93Don-202
❑ 93Fla-104
❑ 93Fle-492
❑ 93FleFinE-111
❑ 93Lea-308
❑ 93PacSpa-578
❑ 93PhiMed-19
❑ 93PhiStaC-5
❑ 93Pin-514
❑ 93Sco-421
❑ 93Sel-371
❑ 93SelRoo-94T
❑ 93Ult-443
❑ 93UppDec-753
❑ 93UppDecGold-753
❑ 94ColC-145
❑ 94ColChoGS-145
❑ 94ColChoSS-145
❑ 94Don-131
❑ 94Fin-320
❑ 94FinRef-320
❑ 94Fla-208
❑ 94Fle-592
❑ 94FleExtB-337
❑ 94Lea-83
❑ 94LeaL-137
❑ 94OPC-240
❑ 94Pac-478
❑ 94PhiMed-15
❑ 94PhiMel-11
❑ 94PhiUSPC-2S
❑ 94PhiUSPC-5D
❑ 94Pin-144
❑ 94PinArtP-144
❑ 94PinMusC-144
❑ 94Sco-209
❑ 94ScoGolR-209
❑ 94SP-137
❑ 94SPDieC-137
❑ 94StaClu-296
❑ 94StaCluFDI-296
❑ 94StaCluGR-296
❑ 94StaCluMOP-296
❑ 94StaCluT-235
❑ 94StaCluTFDI-235
❑ 94Stu-141
❑ 94Top-199
❑ 94TopGol-199
❑ 94TopSpa-199
❑ 94TriPla-176
❑ 94Ult-247
❑ 94UppDec-453
❑ 94UppDecED-453
❑ 95ColCho-189
❑ 95ColChoGS-189
❑ 95ColChoSE-172
❑ 95ColChoSEGS-172
❑ 95ColChoSESS-172
❑ 95ColChoSS-189
❑ 95Don-105
❑ 95DonPreP-105
❑ 95DonTopotO-329
❑ 95Fla-409
❑ 95Fle-395
❑ 95FleAllS-22
❑ 95FleTeaL-24
❑ 95FleUpd-161
❑ 95Lea-301
❑ 95Pac-330
❑ 95PanSti-5
❑ 95Pin-369
❑ 95PinArtP-369
❑ 95PinMusC-369
❑ 95Sco-107
❑ 95ScoGolR-107
❑ 95ScoPlaTS-107
❑ 95Spo-123
❑ 95SpoArtP-123
❑ 95Top-393
❑ 95Top-420
❑ 95TopCyb-220
❑ 95Ult-430
❑ 95UltGolM-430
❑ 95UppDec-308
❑ 95UppDecED-308
❑ 95UppDecEDG-308
❑ 95UppDecSE-224
❑ 95UppDecSEG-224
❑ 96CarPol-12
❑ 96ColCho-284
❑ 96ColChoGS-284
❑ 96ColChoSS-284
❑ 96Top-167
❑ 97CarPol-11

Jackson, Darrell
❑ 78OrlTwiT-9
❑ 79TolMudHT-18
❑ 79Top-246
❑ 80Top-386
❑ 80TwiPos-11
❑ 81Don-547
❑ 81Fle-567
❑ 81OPC-89
❑ 81Top-89
❑ 81TwiPos-14
❑ 82Don-179
❑ 82Fle-555A
❑ 82Fle-555B
❑ 82Fle-555C
❑ 82Top-193
❑ 82TwiPos-17

Jackson, Darrin
❑ 82QuaCitCT-22
❑ 84MidCubT-16
❑ 86PitCubP-10
❑ 87IowCubTI-25
❑ 88CubDavB-30
❑ 88DonRoo-45
❑ 88DonTeaBC-NEW
❑ 88Fle-641
❑ 88FleGlo-641
❑ 88FleUpd-78
❑ 88FleUpdG-78
❑ 88ScoRoo-109T
❑ 88ScoRooG-109T
❑ 88TopTra-56T
❑ 88TopTraT-56T
❑ 89Fle-428
❑ 89FleGlo-428
❑ 89Sco-360
❑ 89Top-286
❑ 89TopRoo-12
❑ 89TopTif-286
❑ 89ToyRoo-14
❑ 89UppDec-214
❑ 90Don-641
❑ 90Fle-160
❑ 90FleCan-160
❑ 90OPC-624
❑ 90PadMag-6
❑ 90PubIntS-195
❑ 90Sco-541
❑ 90Top-624
❑ 90TopTif-624
❑ 90UppDec-414
❑ 91FleUpd-124
❑ 91Lea-346
❑ 91OPC-373
❑ 91PadMag-6
❑ 91PadSmo-16
❑ 91Sco-169
❑ 91Top-373
❑ 91TopDesS-373
❑ 91TopMic-373
❑ 91TopTif-373
❑ 91UltUpd-112
❑ 92Bow-456
❑ 92Don-292
❑ 92Fle-609
❑ 92Lea-129
❑ 92LeaBlaG-129
❑ 92OPC-88
❑ 92PadCarJ-10
❑ 92PadMot-15
❑ 92PadPolD-11
❑ 92PadSmo-14
❑ 92PanSti-237
❑ 92Pin-207
❑ 92Sco-521
❑ 92StaClu-226
❑ 92Top-88
❑ 92TopGol-88
❑ 92TopGolW-88
❑ 92TopMic-88
❑ 92TriPla-189
❑ 92UppDec-328
❑ 93BluJayD-22
❑ 93BluJayDM-33
❑ 93BluJayFS-16
❑ 93Don-230
❑ 93Fle-141
❑ 93FleFinE-102
❑ 93Lea-140
❑ 93OPC-143
❑ 93PacSpa-259
❑ 93PanSti-264
❑ 93Pin-125
❑ 93Sco-155
❑ 93Sel-199
❑ 93SelRoo-133T
❑ 93StaClu-19
❑ 93StaCluFDI-19
❑ 93StaCluMOP-19
❑ 93Top-761
❑ 93TopGol-761
❑ 93TopInaM-761
❑ 93TopInaR-761
❑ 93TopMic-761
❑ 93TriPla-138
❑ 93Ult-118
❑ 93Ult-642
❑ 93UppDec-258
❑ 93UppDec-673
❑ 93UppDecGold-258
❑ 93UppDecGold-673
❑ 94ColC-370
❑ 94ColChoGS-370
❑ 94ColChoSS-370
❑ 94Fin-262
❑ 94FinRef-262
❑ 94Fla-33
❑ 94Fle-567
❑ 94FleExtB-48
❑ 94FleUpd-27
❑ 94Lea-300
❑ 94Pin-531
❑ 94PinArtP-531
❑ 94PinMusC-531
❑ 94ScoRoo-RT38
❑ 94ScoRooGR-RT38
❑ 94Sel-352
❑ 94SpoRoo-8
❑ 94SpoRooAP-8
❑ 94StaClu-157
❑ 94StaClu-659
❑ 94StaCluFDI-157
❑ 94StaCluFDI-659
❑ 94StaCluGR-157
❑ 94StaCluGR-659
❑ 94StaCluMOP-157
❑ 94StaCluMOP-659
❑ 94StaCluT-150
❑ 94StaCluTFDI-150
❑ 94Top-576
❑ 94TopGol-576
❑ 94TopSpa-576
❑ 94TopTra-108T
❑ 94Ult-339
❑ 94UppDec-411
❑ 94UppDecED-411
❑ 94WhiSoxK-14
❑ 95Don-384
❑ 95DonPreP-384
❑ 95Fle-120
❑ 95Pac-91
❑ 95Pin-66
❑ 95PinArtP-66
❑ 95PinMusC-66
❑ 95Sco-16
❑ 95ScoGolR-16
❑ 95ScoPlaTS-16
❑ 95StaClu-71
❑ 95StaCluFDI-71
❑ 95StaCluMOP-71
❑ 95StaCluSTWS-71
❑ 95StaCluVR-44
❑ 95StaCluVRMO-44
❑ 95Top-106
❑ 95TopCyb-69
❑ 95UppDec-203
❑ 95UppDecED-203
❑ 95UppDecEDG-203
❑ 98PacOnl-397
❑ 98PacOnlR-397
❑ 98PacOnlWC-397

Jackson, Doug
❑ 78DayBeaAT-12

Jackson, Evan
❑ 95DurBulTI-14
❑ 96DurBulBIB-18

Jackson, Gavin
❑ 94SarRedSC-16
❑ 94SarRedSF-1958
❑ 96HilStaHWB-9
❑ 96PawRedSDD-14
❑ 96SarRedSB-21
❑ 97TreThuB-19
❑ 98TreThuM-17

Jackson, Gayron
❑ 86AubAstP-14

Jackson, Grant
❑ 66Top-591
❑ 67Top-402A
❑ 67Top-402B
❑ 68Top-512
❑ 69OPC-174
❑ 69Top-174
❑ 69TopFou-21
❑ 70MLBOffS-91
❑ 70OPC-6
❑ 70PhiTeal-5
❑ 70Top-6
❑ 71BalOriP-16
❑ 71MLBOffS-300
❑ 71OPC-392
❑ 71Top-392
❑ 72MilBra-158
❑ 72OPC-212
❑ 72OriPos-18
❑ 72Top-212
❑ 73BalOriP-26
❑ 73OPC-396
❑ 73OriJohP-23
❑ 73OriTeal-20
❑ 73Top-396
❑ 74OPC-68
❑ 74Top-68
❑ 74TopSta-126
❑ 75BalOriP-17
❑ 75OPC-303
❑ 75Top-303
❑ 75TopMin-303
❑ 76BalOriP-21
❑ 76OPC-233
❑ 76SSP-378
❑ 76Top-233
❑ 77PirPosP-10
❑ 77Top-49
❑ 78Top-661
❑ 79Top-117
❑ 80OPC-218
❑ 80Top-426
❑ 81Don-15
❑ 81Fle-378
❑ 81OPC-232
❑ 81Top-518
❑ 82Don-518
❑ 82Fle-191
❑ 82OPC-104
❑ 82Top-779
❑ 82TopTra-46T
❑ 88EasLeaAP-48
❑ 89ChaKniTI-3
❑ 89ChaLooLITI-13
❑ 89PacSenL-66
❑ 89T/MSenL-53
❑ 91IowCubLD-225
❑ 91IowCubP-1077
❑ 91LinDriAAA-225
❑ 91OriCro-215
❑ 92YanWIZ7-78
❑ 93ChaLooF-2376
❑ 94RedKah-33
❑ 95RedKah-34
❑ 96IndIndB-4
❑ 97IndInd-2
❑ 98IndIndQ-3

Jackson, Greg
❑ 86SalAngC-85
❑ 87QuaCitAP-30
❑ 87SalAngP-9
❑ 87WytCubP-12

Jackson, Harold
❑ 80WisRapTT-8

Jackson, Harold FB
❑ 74NewYorNTDiS-31

Jackson, James
❑ 84IdaFalATI-13

Jackson, James B.
❑ 05IndSouPSoCP-10
❑ 09T206-432

Jackson, Jason
❑ 87BriYouC-8
❑ 88NewBriRSP-912
❑ 90CanIndS-7

Jackson, Jeff
❑ 89MarPhiS-16
❑ 90BatCliP-3080
❑ 90Bow-157
❑ 90BowTif-157
❑ 90OPC-74
❑ 90Sco-678
❑ 90Top-74
❑ 90TopTif-74
❑ 91Bow-491
❑ 91Cla/Bes-125
❑ 91SpaPhiC-26
❑ 91SpaPhiP-911
❑ 92Bow-72
❑ 92ClePhiC-1
❑ 92ClePhiF-2070
❑ 92UppDecML-301
❑ 93ClaGolF-99
❑ 93PhiStaC-24
❑ 93ReaPhiF-308
❑ 94ReaPhiF-2075
❑ 98FarRedHM-12

Jackson, Jelly
❑ 86NegLeaF-96

Jackson, Jeremy
❑ 97PorRocG-9
❑ 98AshTouM-6
❑ 98SpoIndG-16

Jackson, Joe
❑ 11PinT-5-616
❑ 14E&SP-3
❑ 16BF2FP-13
❑ 18WhiSoxTI-11
❑ 73SpoScoHC-7
❑ 74CapPub-88
❑ 76CliPilT-21
❑ 82TCMGreH-16
❑ 88LitSunBS-4
❑ 99UppDecCL-35
❑ 99UppDecCLCC-35

Jackson, John
❑ 90EveGiaB-25
❑ 90EveGiaP-3141
❑ 91Cla/Bes-255
❑ 91SanJosGC-26
❑ 91SanJosGP-23
❑ 91SanJosGP-26
❑ 92ClaFS7-186
❑ 92MidAngOHP-8
❑ 92MidAngS-459
❑ 92UppDecML-205
❑ 93MidAngF-332
❑ 94VanCanF-1875
❑ 97MidAngOHP-17

Jackson, Karun
❑ 93GenCubC-18
❑ 93GenCubF-3183
Jackson, Ken
(Kenneth)
❑ 85PhiTas-44
❑ 86ReaPhiP-10
❑ 87MaiGuiP-7
❑ 87MaiGuiT-11
❑ 87PhiTas-51
❑ 88MaiPhiP-287
❑ 89ScrRedBC-17
❑ 89ScrRedBP-729
❑ 90StoPorB-12
❑ 90StoPorCLC-197
❑ 92DenZepS-132
Jackson, Kenny
❑ 86EugEmeC-37
❑ 87AppFoxP-28
❑ 88BasCitRS-14
❑ 88MaiPhiC-17
❑ 89BelBre2S-15
❑ 90StoPorP-2197
❑ 91ElPasDLD-187
❑ 91ElPasDP-2761
❑ 91LinDriAA-187
❑ 92DenZepF-2653
❑ 92LSUTigM-13
❑ 93LSUTigM-7
❑ 94LSUTigMP-2
Jackson, Larry
❑ 81CedRapRT-1
Jackson, Larry
(Lawrence C.)
❑ 55CarHunW-9
❑ 56Top-119
❑ 57Top-196
❑ 58CarJayP-6
❑ 58Top-97A
❑ 58Top-97B
❑ 59Top-399
❑ 60CarJayP-4
❑ 60Lea-15
❑ 60Top-492
❑ 61CarJayP-6
❑ 61Pos-174A
❑ 61Pos-174B
❑ 61Top-535
❑ 61TopStal-88
❑ 62CarJayP-5
❑ 62Jel-165
❑ 62Pos-165
❑ 62PosCan-165
❑ 62Top-83
❑ 62Top-306
❑ 62TopBuc-41
❑ 62TopStal-184
❑ 62TopVen-83
❑ 63CubJayP-7
❑ 63Top-95
❑ 64CubJayP-7
❑ 64Top-444
❑ 64TopCoi-114
❑ 64TopSta-13
❑ 64TopTatl-44
❑ 64WheSta-22
❑ 65Baz-2
❑ 65CubJayP-8
❑ 65OPC-10
❑ 65Top-10
❑ 65Top-420
❑ 66CubTeal-8
❑ 66Top-595
❑ 67CokCapPh-14
❑ 67DexPre-103
❑ 67PhiPol-9
❑ 67Top-229
❑ 68OPC-81
❑ 68Top-81
❑ 68TopVen-81
❑ 69MilBra-126
❑ 78TCM60I-222
❑ 78TCM60I-286
❑ 84CubUno-2
Jackson, LaVerne
❑ 85GreHorT-26
❑ 86WinHavRSP-12
❑ 87WinHavRSP-8
❑ 89EasLeaDDP-DD31
❑ 89NewBriRSP-615
❑ 89NewBriRSS-2
❑ 90CanIndP-1303
Jackson, Lee
❑ 90CanIndB-13
Jackson, Lloyd
❑ 85EveGialC-5
❑ 86CliGiaP-11
Jackson, Lonnie
❑ 91KisDodP-4201
Jackson, Lou
❑ 59Top-130
❑ 59TopVen-130
❑ 61MapLeaBH-9
❑ 64BalOriP-19
❑ 64Top-511
❑ 78TCM60I-115
❑ 91OriCro-216
Jackson, Mark
❑ 86CedRapRT-20
❑ 87TamTarP-18
Jackson, Martinez
❑ 92NegLeaK-18
Jackson, Miccal
❑ 91SavCarC-17
❑ 91SavCarP-1658
Jackson, Mike
(Michael)
❑ 86ReaPhiP-11
❑ 87DonRoo-36
❑ 87FleUpd-48
❑ 87FleUpdG-48
❑ 87PhiTas-33
❑ 87SpoRoo2-33
❑ 88Don-139
❑ 88Fle-306
❑ 88FleGlo-306
❑ 88FleUpd-60
❑ 88FleUpdG-60
❑ 88MarMot-19
❑ 88RedFolSB-39
❑ 88Sco-144
❑ 88ScoGlo-144
❑ 88ScoRoo-62T
❑ 88ScoRooG-62T
❑ 88Top-651
❑ 88TopTif-651
❑ 89Bow-207
❑ 89BowTif-207
❑ 89Don-652
❑ 89Fle-550
❑ 89FleBasM-22
❑ 89FleGlo-550
❑ 89MarMot-19
❑ 89OPC-169
❑ 89Sco-398
❑ 89ScoYouSI-14
❑ 89Top-169
❑ 89TopTif-169
❑ 89UppDec-142
❑ 90Fle-517
❑ 90FleCan-517
❑ 90Lea-351
❑ 90MarMot-19
❑ 90OPC-761
❑ 90PublntS-435
❑ 90Sco-546
❑ 90Top-761
❑ 90TopTif-761
❑ 90UppDec-494
❑ 91Don-676
❑ 91Fle-454
❑ 91Lea-452
❑ 91MarCouH-23
❑ 91OPC-534
❑ 91Sco-91
❑ 91Top-534
❑ 91TopDesS-534
❑ 91TopMic-534
❑ 91TopTif-534
❑ 91UltUpd-51
❑ 91UppDec-496
❑ 92Bow-513
❑ 92Don-584
❑ 92Fle-282
❑ 92FleUpd-128
❑ 92GiaMot-12
❑ 92GiaPacGaE-20
❑ 92Lea-481
❑ 92LeaBlaG-481
❑ 92OPC-411
❑ 92Pin-437
❑ 92Sco-194
❑ 92ScoRoo-40T
❑ 92StaClu-653
❑ 92StaCluECN-653
❑ 92Stu-116
❑ 92Top-411
❑ 92TopGol-411
❑ 92TopGolW-411
❑ 92TopMic-411
❑ 92Ult-590
❑ 92UppDec-593
❑ 92UppDec-738
❑ 93Don-314
❑ 93Fla-142
❑ 93Fle-156
❑ 93GiaMot-20
❑ 93GiaPos-19
❑ 93GiaStaC-18
❑ 93Lea-84
❑ 93PacSpa-611
❑ 93StaClu-373
❑ 93StaCluFDI-373
❑ 93StaCluMOP-373
❑ 93Top-283
❑ 93TopGol-283
❑ 93TopInaM-283
❑ 93TopInaR-283
❑ 93TopMic-283
❑ 93Ult-133
❑ 93UppDec-170
❑ 93UppDecGold-170
❑ 94ColC-622
❑ 94ColChoGS-622
❑ 94ColChoSS-622
❑ 94Don-525
❑ 94Fin-311
❑ 94FinRef-311
❑ 94Fla-243
❑ 94Fle-692
❑ 94FleExtB-387
❑ 94GiaAMC-10
❑ 94GiaMot-23
❑ 94GiaTarBC-12
❑ 94GiaUSPC-5C
❑ 94GiaUSPC-11H
❑ 94Lea-301
❑ 94Pac-547
❑ 94Sco-243
❑ 94ScoGolR-243
❑ 94StaClu-565
❑ 94StaCluFDI-565
❑ 94StaCluGR-565
❑ 94StaCluMOP-565
❑ 94StaCluT-25
❑ 94StaCluTFDI-25
❑ 94Top-58
❑ 94TopGol-58
❑ 94TopSpa-58
❑ 94Ult-290
❑ 94UppDec-311
❑ 94UppDecED-311
❑ 95ColCho-261
❑ 95ColChoGS-261
❑ 95ColChoSS-261
❑ 95Don-459
❑ 95DonPreP-459
❑ 95Fle-581
❑ 95RedKah-13
❑ 95Sco-524
❑ 95ScoGolR-524
❑ 95ScoPlaTS-524
❑ 95Top-333
❑ 95TopCyb-181
❑ 95Ult-444
❑ 95UltGolM-444
❑ 96Don-523
❑ 96DonPreP-523
❑ 96Fle-344
❑ 96FleTif-344
❑ 96FleUpd-U82
❑ 96FleUpdTC-U82
❑ 96MarMot-18
❑ 96Ult-414
❑ 96UltGolM-414
❑ 97PacPriGotD-GD88
❑ 97Ult-524
❑ 97UltGolME-524
❑ 97UltPlaME-524
❑ 98IndSco-8
❑ 98IndScoP-8
❑ 98Pac-72
❑ 98PacOnl-221
❑ 98PacOnlR-221
❑ 98PacOnlWC-221
❑ 98PacPlaB-72
❑ 98PacRedT-72
❑ 98PacSil-72
❑ 98Sco-119
❑ 98ScoSS-PP49
❑ 98ScoSSAP-PP49
❑ 98StaCluFDI-224
❑ 98StaClul-224
❑ 98StaCluOneK-224
❑ 98StaCluPP-224
❑ 98UppDec-669
❑ 99Fle-505
❑ 99FleSta9-505
❑ 99FleWarT-505
❑ 99Pac-129
❑ 99PacPlaB-129
❑ 99PacRed-129
❑ 99Top-408
❑ 99TopChr-408
❑ 99TopChrR-408
❑ 99TopMVPP-408
❑ 99UppDec-355
❑ 99UppDecEL1-355
❑ 99UppDecEL2-355
Jackson, Mikki
❑ 83MadMusF-20
Jackson, Paige
❑ 88OklSoo-19
Jackson, Randy
(Ransom)
❑ 52Bow-175
❑ 52StaCalL-80C
❑ 52StaCalS-92B
❑ 52Top-322
❑ 53BowBW-12
❑ 54Bow-189
❑ 55Bow-87
❑ 56Dod-14
❑ 56Top-223
❑ 57Top-190
❑ 58DodTeal-11
❑ 58Top-301
❑ 59Top-394
❑ 79DiaGre-117
❑ 83TopRep5-322
❑ 90DodTar-378
❑ 92TexLon-26
❑ 95TopArcBD-156
Jackson, Ray
❑ 91EveGiaC-7
❑ 91EveGiaP-3930
❑ 92ClaFS7-78
❑ 92CliGiaC-9
❑ 92CliGiaF-3609
Jackson, Reggie
❑ 83LynMetT-1
❑ 84JacMetT-5
Jackson, Reggie
(Reginald M.)
❑ 69A'sJacitB-9
❑ 69MilBra-127
❑ 69Raw-1
❑ 69Top-260
❑ 69TopDecl-19
❑ 69TopSup-28
❑ 69TopTeaP-21
❑ 70DayDaiNM-31
❑ 70Kel-32
❑ 70MilBra-11
❑ 70MLBOffS-260
❑ 70OPC-64
❑ 70OPC-66
❑ 70OPC-140
❑ 70OPC-459
❑ 70Top-64
❑ 70Top-66
❑ 70Top-140
❑ 70Top-459
❑ 70TopBoo-10
❑ 70TopCanL-10
❑ 70TopSup-28
❑ 70TraSta-11B
❑ 71AllBasA-10
❑ 71BazNumT-18
❑ 71BazUnn-3
❑ 71MLBOffS-517
❑ 71MLBOffS-562
❑ 71OPC-20
❑ 71Top-20
❑ 71TopCoi-108
❑ 71TopGreM-47
❑ 71TopSup-38
❑ 71TopTat-21
❑ 72'sA'sPos-14
❑ 72Kel-20
❑ 72MilBra-159
❑ 72OPC-90
❑ 72OPC-435
❑ 72OPC-436
❑ 72ProStaP-26
❑ 72SevTraC-21
❑ 72Top-90
❑ 72Top-435
❑ 72Top-436
❑ 73Kel2D-22
❑ 73LinPor-141
❑ 73OPC-255
❑ 73SevTraC-34
❑ 73Top-255
❑ 73TopCanL-22
❑ 73TopCom-8
❑ 73TopPin-8
❑ 74A'sPos-52
❑ 74Kel-20
❑ 74LauAllG-71
❑ 74OPC-130
❑ 74OPC-202
❑ 74OPC-203
❑ 74OPC-338
❑ 74OPC-470
❑ 74OPC-477
❑ 74Top-130
❑ 74Top-202
❑ 74Top-203
❑ 74Top-338
❑ 74Top-470
❑ 74Top-477
❑ 74TopDecE-61
❑ 74TopPuz-6
❑ 74TopSta-226
❑ 75Hos-88
❑ 75Kel-54
❑ 75OPC-211
❑ 75OPC-300
❑ 75OPC-461
❑ 75SSP42-11
❑ 75SSPPuzB-12
❑ 75Top-211
❑ 75Top-300
❑ 75Top-461
❑ 75TopMin-211
❑ 75TopMin-300
❑ 75TopMin-461
❑ 76BalOriP-22
❑ 76BlaDis-22A
❑ 76BlaDis-22B
❑ 76BucDis-22A
❑ 76BucDis-22B
❑ 76CarDis-22A
❑ 76CarDis-22B
❑ 76CraDis-22A
❑ 76CraDis-22B
❑ 76DailsID-22A
❑ 76DailsID-22B
❑ 76Hos-146
❑ 76IsaDis-22A
❑ 76IsaDis-22B
❑ 76Kel-8
❑ 76OPC-194
❑ 76OPC-500
❑ 76OrbDis-22A
❑ 76OrbDis-22B
❑ 76RedBarD-22A
❑ 76RedBarD-22B
❑ 76SafDis-22A
❑ 76SafDis-22B
❑ 76SSP-494
❑ 76Top-194
❑ 76Top-500
❑ 76TowCluD-22A
❑ 76TowCluD-22B
❑ 77BurCheD-176
❑ 77ChiWilD-33
❑ 77DailsID-33
❑ 77DetCaeD-33
❑ 77HolInnD-33
❑ 77Hos-3
❑ 77MSADis-33
❑ 77OPC-200
❑ 77PepGloD-34
❑ 77SagDis-33
❑ 77sDis-33
❑ 77Spo-1409
❑ 77Top-10
❑ 77TopCloS-22
❑ 77WenDis-33
❑ 77YanBurK-17
❑ 77YanNedC-2
❑ 77ZipDis-33
❑ 78Hos-47
❑ 78Kel-40
❑ 78OPC-110
❑ 78OPC-242
❑ 78PapGinD-26
❑ 78Pep-32
❑ 78RCColC-81
❑ 78SSP270-26
❑ 78Top-7
❑ 78Top-200
❑ 78Top-413
❑ 78WifBalD-32
❑ 78YanBurK-21
❑ 78YanPhoA-13
❑ 78YanSSPD-26
❑ 79BasPat-42
❑ 79Hos-120
❑ 79Kel-46
❑ 79OPC-374
❑ 79Top-700
❑ 79TopCom-12
❑ 79YanBurK-21
❑ 79YanPicA-20
❑ 80BurKinPHR-17
❑ 80Kel-26
❑ 80OPC-314
❑ 80PerHaloFP-216
❑ 80PerHaloFPS-76
❑ 80Top-600
❑ 80TopSup-6
❑ 80YanPhoA-12
❑ 81AccRegJ-1
❑ 81AccRegJ-2
❑ 81AccRegJ-3
❑ 81AllGamPI-53
❑ 81Don-228
❑ 81Don-348
❑ 81Don-468
❑ 81Dra-10
❑ 81Fle-79
❑ 81Fle-650
❑ 81Fle-650B
❑ 81FleStiC-115
❑ 81FleStiC-126
❑ 81Kel-3
❑ 81MSAMinD-18
❑ 81OPC-370
❑ 81PerAll-14
❑ 81PerCreC-7
❑ 81Squ-5
❑ 81TigDetN-120
❑ 81Top-2
❑ 81Top-400
❑ 81TopScr-3
❑ 81TopSti-11
❑ 81TopSti-107
❑ 81TopSti-245
❑ 81TopSupHT-65
❑ 81TopSupN-8
❑ 81YanPhoA-9
❑ 82Don-535
❑ 82Don-575
❑ 82Dra-19
❑ 82Fle-39
❑ 82Fle-646
❑ 82Fle-646B
❑ 82FleSta-110
❑ 82FleSta-112
❑ 82K-M-23
❑ 82Kel-14
❑ 82OnDecD-18
❑ 82OPC-300
❑ 82OPC-301
❑ 82OPC-377
❑ 82PerAll-7
❑ 82PerAllG-7
❑ 82PerCreC-20
❑ 82PerCreCG-20
❑ 82Squ-5
❑ 82Top-300
❑ 82Top-301
❑ 82Top-551
❑ 82TopSti-216
❑ 82TopStiV-216
❑ 82TopTra-47T
❑ 83AllGamPI-56
❑ 83Don-3
❑ 83Don-115
❑ 83DonActA-3A
❑ 83DonActA-3B
❑ 83Dra-12
❑ 83Fle-93
❑ 83Fle-640
❑ 83Fle-645
❑ 83FleSta-90
❑ 83FleSti-32
❑ 83Kel-3
❑ 83KelCerB-15
❑ 83OPC-56
❑ 83OPC-219
❑ 83OPC-390
❑ 83PerCreC-27
❑ 83PerCreCG-27
❑ 83SevCoi-5
❑ 83Top-390
❑ 83Top-500
❑ 83Top-501
❑ 83Top-702
❑ 83TopFol-2
❑ 83TopGloS-39
❑ 83TopSti-5
❑ 83TopSti-17

❑ 83TopSti-41
❑ 83TopSti-163
❑ 83TopStiB-4
❑ 84AllGamPI-145
❑ 84AngSmo-11
❑ 84DodUniO-10
❑ 84Don-57
❑ 84DonActAS-36
❑ 84DonCha-9
❑ 84Dra-15
❑ 84Fle-520
❑ 84FunFooP-16
❑ 84GalRegJ-1
❑ 84GalRegJ-2
❑ 84GalRegJ-3
❑ 84GalRegJ-4
❑ 84GalRegJ-5
❑ 84GalRegJ-6
❑ 84GalRegJ-7
❑ 84GalRegJ-8
❑ 84GalRegJ-9
❑ 84GalRegJ-10
❑ 84GalRegJ-11
❑ 84GalRegJ-12
❑ 84GalRegJ-13
❑ 84GalRegJ-14
❑ 84GalRegJ-15
❑ 84GalRegJ-16
❑ 84GalRegJ-17
❑ 84GalRegJ-18
❑ 84GalRegJ-19
❑ 84GalRegJ-20
❑ 84GalRegJ-21
❑ 84GalRegJ-22
❑ 84GalRegJ-23
❑ 84GalRegJ-24
❑ 84GalRegJ-25
❑ 84GalRegJ-26
❑ 84GalRegJ-27
❑ 84GalRegJ-28
❑ 84GalRegJ-29
❑ 84GalRegJ-30
❑ 84MilBra-14
❑ 84MLBPen-3
❑ 84Nes792-100
❑ 84Nes792-711
❑ 84Nes792-712
❑ 84Nes792-713
❑ 84OCoandSI-21
❑ 84OCoandSI-95
❑ 84OPC-100
❑ 84RalPur-19
❑ 84SevCoi-W12
❑ 84Top-100
❑ 84Top-711
❑ 84Top-712
❑ 84Top-713
❑ 84TopCer-19
❑ 84TopGaloC-6
❑ 84TopRubD-27
❑ 84TopSti-102B
❑ 84TopSti-231
❑ 84TopSup-21
❑ 84TopTif-100
❑ 84TopTif-711
❑ 84TopTif-712
❑ 84TopTif-713
❑ 85AllGamPI-59
❑ 85AngSmo-2
❑ 85AngStrH-8
❑ 85CirK-13
❑ 85Don-57
❑ 85DonActA-39
❑ 85Dra-17
❑ 85Fle-303
❑ 85Fle-639
❑ 85FleLimE-14
❑ 85GenMilS-19
❑ 85Lea-170
❑ 85OPC-200
❑ 85SevCoi-C12
❑ 85SevCoi-W13
❑ 85StaRegJ-1
❑ 85StaRegJ-2
❑ 85StaRegJ-3
❑ 85StaRegJ-4
❑ 85StaRegJ-5
❑ 85StaRegJ-6
❑ 85StaRegJ-7
❑ 85StaRegJ-8
❑ 85StaRegJ-9
❑ 85StaRegJ-10
❑ 85StaRegJ-11
❑ 85StaRegJ-12
❑ 85StaRegJ-13
❑ 85StaRegJ-14
❑ 85StaRegJ-15
❑ 85StaRegJ-16
❑ 85StaRegJ-17
❑ 85StaRegJ-18
❑ 85StaRegJ-19
❑ 85StaRegJ-20
❑ 85StaRegJ-21
❑ 85StaRegJ-22
❑ 85StaRegJ-23
❑ 85StaRegJ-24
❑ 85Top-200
❑ 85Top3-D-14
❑ 85TopGloA-19
❑ 85TopGloS-15
❑ 85TopRubD-27
❑ 85TopSti-187
❑ 85TopSti-220
❑ 85TopSup-29
❑ 85TopTif-200
❑ 86AngSmo-2
❑ 86BurKinA-12
❑ 86Don-377
❑ 86DonHig-10
❑ 86DorChe-11
❑ 86Dra-3
❑ 86Fle-160
❑ 86FleFutHoF-6
❑ 86FleLimE-26
❑ 86FleMin-32
❑ 86FleSlu-18
❑ 86FleStiC-65
❑ 86GenMilB-2G
❑ 86Lea-173
❑ 86MeaGolBB-7
❑ 86MeaGolSB-6
❑ 86MSAJifPD-8
❑ 86OPC-394
❑ 86OPCBoxB-I
❑ 86QuaGra-26
❑ 86SevCoi-W9
❑ 86Spo-37
❑ 86Spo-57
❑ 86Spo-61
❑ 86Spo-71
❑ 86Spo-147
❑ 86Spo-150
❑ 86SpoDecG-53
❑ 86Top-700
❑ 86Top3-D-13
❑ 86TopGloS-2
❑ 86TopSti-177
❑ 86TopSup-35
❑ 86TopTat-17
❑ 86TopTif-700
❑ 86TopWaxBC-I
❑ 86TruVal-13
❑ 86Woo-15
❑ 87A'sMot-5
❑ 87A'sMot-27
❑ 87A'sSmoC-7
❑ 87ClaGam-24
❑ 87Don-210
❑ 87DonOpeD-22
❑ 87Fle-84
❑ 87FleGlo-84
❑ 87FleUpd-49
❑ 87FleUpdG-49
❑ 87GenMilB-3E
❑ 87K-M-16
❑ 87Lea-201
❑ 87OPC-300
❑ 87RedFolSB-108
❑ 87Spo-44
❑ 87SpoTeaP-23
❑ 87Top-300
❑ 87Top-312
❑ 87TopCoi-15
❑ 87TopGloS-54
❑ 87TopTif-300
❑ 87TopTif-312
❑ 87TopTra-52T
❑ 87TopTraT-52T
❑ 87Woo-4
❑ 88Fle-283
❑ 88FleGlo-283
❑ 88GreBasS-3
❑ 88PanSti-175
❑ 88Sco-500
❑ 88Sco-501
❑ 88Sco-502
❑ 88Sco-503
❑ 88Sco-504
❑ 88ScoGlo-500
❑ 88ScoGlo-501
❑ 88ScoGlo-502
❑ 88ScoGlo-503
❑ 88ScoGlo-504
❑ 88Spo-120
❑ 88StaLinAs-8
❑ 89AngSmo-15
❑ 89PacLegI-111
❑ 89TopBasT-9
❑ 90BasWit-42
❑ 90HOFStiB-88
❑ 90PerGreM-104
❑ 90UppDecJH-1
❑ 90UppDecJH-2
❑ 90UppDecJH-3
❑ 90UppDecJH-4
❑ 90UppDecJH-5
❑ 90UppDecJH-6
❑ 90UppDecJH-7
❑ 90UppDecJH-8
❑ 90UppDecJH-9
❑ 90UppDecJH-AU1
❑ 90UppDecJH-NNO0
❑ 90UppDecS-2
❑ 91A'sMot-28
❑ 91BasBesRB-8
❑ 91FouBal-32
❑ 91OriCro-217
❑ 91UppDecCBP-4
❑ 91UppDecHoB5-1
❑ 91UppDecS-1
❑ 91UppDecS-5
❑ 91UppDecS-11
❑ 91UppDecS-12
❑ 92A'sUno7P-2
❑ 92A'sUno7P-5
❑ 92TVSpoMF5HRC-4
❑ 92UppDecF-46
❑ 92UppDecFG-46
❑ 92UppDecHH-HI5
❑ 92UppDecS-4
❑ 92UppDecS-17
❑ 92UppDecS-27
❑ 92UppDecS-34
❑ 92YanWIZ7-79
❑ 92YanWIZ8-89
❑ 92YanWIZA-33
❑ 93FunPac-28
❑ 93UppDecAH-72
❑ 93UppDecAH-135
❑ 93UppDecAH-165
❑ 93UppDecAHP-2
❑ 93UppDecAHP-3
❑ 93UppDecAHP-4
❑ 93UppDecCRJ-C1
❑ 93UppDecCRJ-C2
❑ 93UppDecCRJ-C3
❑ 93UppDecFA-A9
❑ 93UppDecFAJ-A9
❑ 93UppDecJHJ-1
❑ 93UppDecJHJ-2
❑ 93UppDecJHJ-3
❑ 93UppDecJHJ-4
❑ 93UppDecJHJ-5
❑ 93UppDecJHJ-6
❑ 93UppDecJHJ-7
❑ 93UppDecJHJ-8
❑ 93UppDecJHJ-9
❑ 93UppDecS-1
❑ 93UppDecS-3
❑ 93UppDecS-18
❑ 93UppDecS-20
❑ 93UppDecS-23
❑ 93UppDecTAN-TN16
❑ 94TedWil5C-2
❑ 94UppDecAH-9
❑ 94UppDecAH-44
❑ 94UppDecAH-107
❑ 94UppDecAH-122
❑ 94UppDecAH-167
❑ 94UppDecAH-210
❑ 94UppDecAH-P44
❑ 94UppDecAH1-9
❑ 94UppDecAH1-44
❑ 94UppDecAH1-107
❑ 94UppDecAH1-122
❑ 94UppDecAH1-167
❑ 94UppDecAH1-210
❑ 94UppDecAHA-2
❑ 94UppDecS-5
❑ 94UppDecS-8
❑ 94UppDecTAE-75
❑ 94UppDecTAELD-LD15
❑ 95EagBalL-2
❑ 95SPCha-109
❑ 95SPChaCP-CP1
❑ 95SPChaCPDC-CP1
❑ 95SPChaDC-109
❑ 95UppDecA-2
❑ 95UppDecSDRJ-1
❑ 95UppDecSDRJ-2
❑ 95UppDecSDRJ-3
❑ 95UppDecSHoB-10
❑ 97AriStaBG-12
❑ 97DonSigNN-4
❑ 97DonSigSS-11A
❑ 97DonSigSS-11B
❑ 97St.VinHHS-9
❑ 98SpollIWSF-10
❑ 98SpollIWSFAE-4
❑ 98SpollIWSFAEG-4
❑ 98SpollIWSFEE-10
❑ 98SpollIWSFFE-10
❑ 99SpollIGotG-44
❑ 99SpollIGotGA-34A
❑ 99SpollIGotGA-34B
❑ 99SpollIGotGA-34C
❑ 99SpollIGotGC-18
❑ 99SpollIGotGC-31
❑ 99SpollIGotGC-33
❑ 99SpollIGotGC-39
❑ 99TopHaloFC-HOF6
❑ 99UppDecCL-48
❑ 99UppDecCLCC-48
❑ 99UppDecCLES-RJ
❑ 99UppDecCLESC-RJ
❑ 99UppDecR-106
❑ 99UppDecRG-106
❑ 99UppDecRP-106
❑ 99SP SigAuto-RJ
❑ 99SPSig-177

Jackson, Robert

❑ 85EveGialC-6

Jackson, Roderick

❑ 93NiaFalRF-3380
❑ 96IdaFalB-11

Jackson, Ron

❑ 85LouRedR-30
❑ 86BakDodP-15
❑ 87GasRanP-20

Jackson, Ron H.

❑ 55ArmCoi-9
❑ 55Top-66
❑ 55TopDouH-49
❑ 56Top-186
❑ 58Top-26
❑ 59Top-73
❑ 59TopVen-73
❑ 60Lea-29
❑ 60Top-426
❑ 81WhiSox1T-20

Jackson, Ronnie D.

❑ 75IntLeaASB-12
❑ 75PacCoaLAB-12
❑ 75SalLakCC-4
❑ 77BurCheD-120
❑ 77Top-153
❑ 78AngFamF-19
❑ 78SSP270-213
❑ 78Top-718
❑ 79Kel-59
❑ 79OPC-173
❑ 79Top-339
❑ 79TwiFriP-11
❑ 80OPC-5
❑ 80Top-18
❑ 80TwiPos-12
❑ 81Don-489
❑ 81Fle-557
❑ 81OPC-271
❑ 81Top-631
❑ 81TopSti-103
❑ 81TwiPos-15
❑ 82Don-602
❑ 82Fle-269
❑ 82OPC-359
❑ 82SpoIndT-21
❑ 82Top-488
❑ 82TopTra-48T
❑ 83Don-639A
❑ 83Don-639B
❑ 83Don-639C
❑ 83Fle-94
❑ 83Top-262
❑ 84AngSmo-12
❑ 84Don-133
❑ 84Fle-521
❑ 84Nes792-548
❑ 84Top-548
❑ 84TopTif-548
❑ 88VanCanP-768
❑ 89BirBarB-26
❑ 89BirBarP-113
❑ 89PacSenL-92
❑ 89T/MSenL-54
❑ 89TopSenL-117
❑ 90EliSenL-70
❑ 90SarWhiSS-28
❑ 91OriCro-218
❑ 91PacSenL-5
❑ 93NewOrlZF-988
❑ 94NewOrlZF-1485
❑ 95WhiSoxK-31

Jackson, Roy Lee

❑ 78TidTidT-11
❑ 79TidTidT-1
❑ 80TidTidT-19
❑ 81Don-36
❑ 81Top-223
❑ 81TopTra-775
❑ 82BluJayS-9
❑ 82Don-541
❑ 82OPC-71
❑ 82OPCPos-7
❑ 82Top-71
❑ 83Don-479
❑ 83Fle-431
❑ 83OPC-194
❑ 83Top-427
❑ 84BluJayFS-18
❑ 84Don-195
❑ 84Fle-158
❑ 84Nes792-339
❑ 84OPC-339
❑ 84Top-339
❑ 84TopTif-339
❑ 85Don-606
❑ 85Fle-108
❑ 85Lea-106
❑ 85OPC-37
❑ 85Top-516
❑ 85TopSti-364
❑ 85TopTif-516
❑ 86Fle-326
❑ 86Top-634
❑ 86TopTif-634
❑ 87Fle-545
❑ 87FleGlo-545
❑ 87Top-138
❑ 87TopTif-138
❑ 91MetWIZ-198

Jackson, Ryan

❑ 94ElmPioC-9
❑ 94ElmPioF-3487
❑ 95KanCouCLTI-6
❑ 95KanCouCTI-17
❑ 95MidLeaA-25
❑ 96Exc-162
❑ 97Bes-67
❑ 97PorSeaD-14
❑ 98Bow-101
❑ 98BowBes-121
❑ 98BowBesAR-121
❑ 98BowBesR-121
❑ 98BowChr-101
❑ 98BowChrGA-101
❑ 98BowChrGAR-101
❑ 98BowChrI-101
❑ 98BowChrIR-101
❑ 98BowChrR-101
❑ 98BowGolA-101
❑ 98BowInt-101
❑ 98Don-194
❑ 98DonGolPP-194
❑ 98DonSilPP-194
❑ 98Fle-554
❑ 98LeaRS-209
❑ 98LeaRSLHolo-209
❑ 98LeaRSLong-209
❑ 98LeaRTrue-209
❑ 98PacOme-97
❑ 98PacOmeR-97
❑ 98PacOmeRS-27
❑ 98PacOmeRST2-27
❑ 98PacOnl-297
❑ 98PacOnlR-297
❑ 98PacOnlWC-297
❑ 98PorSeaD5AQ-7
❑ 98SkyDugA-105
❑ 98SkyDugAIA-105
❑ 98Top-263
❑ 98TopChr-263
❑ 98TopChrR-263
❑ 98TopDevR-263
❑ 98TopDia-263
❑ 98TopMiniC-263
❑ 99Fle-447
❑ 99FleSta9-447
❑ 99FleWarT-447
❑ 99MetUni-105
❑ 99MetUniGM-105
❑ 99MetUniPMG-105
❑ 99Pac-178
❑ 99PacPlaB-178
❑ 99PacRed-178
❑ 99Top-31
❑ 99TopChr-31
❑ 99TopChrR-31
❑ 99TopMVPP-31
❑ 99UppDec-15
❑ 99UppDecEL1-15
❑ 99UppDecEL2-15

Jackson, Shoeless (Joe)

❑ 09AmeCarE90-1-56
❑ 09ColChiE-141
❑ 09SpoNewSM-69
❑ 11SpoLifCW-186
❑ 12ColRedB-141
❑ 12ColTinT-141
❑ 13NatGamW-21
❑ 13TomBarW-20
❑ 14B18B-4A
❑ 14B18B-4B
❑ 14CraJacE-103
❑ 14PolGroW-10
❑ 14TexTomE-23
❑ 15CraJacE-103
❑ 15SpoNewM-86
❑ 16SpoNewM-87
❑ 17ColE13-82
❑ 17HolBreD-48
❑ 19W514-15
❑ 40PlaBal-225
❑ 46SpoExcW-4-11
❑ 75WhiSox1T-10
❑ 77GalGloG-154
❑ 77GalGloG-259
❑ 77SerSta-11
❑ 77ShaPiz-21
❑ 80Lau300-13
❑ 80LauFamF-24
❑ 80PacLeg-107
❑ 82OhiHaloF-48
❑ 84OCoandSI-199
❑ 86IndGreT-5
❑ 88FriBasCM-4
❑ 88PacEigMO-13
❑ 88PacEigMO-31
❑ 88PacEigMO-32
❑ 88PacEigMO-36
❑ 88PacEigMO-37
❑ 88PacEigMO-55
❑ 88PacEigMO-62
❑ 88PacEigMO-69
❑ 88PacEigMO-77
❑ 88PacEigMO-110
❑ 89PacLegI-220
❑ 91ConTSNP-14
❑ 91ConTSNP-400
❑ 92ConTSN-444
❑ 92ConTSN1N-400
❑ 92ConTSNCI-21
❑ 92Man191BSR-11
❑ 92Man191BSR-12
❑ 93ActPacA-131
❑ 93ConTSNP-1030
❑ 93CraJac-2
❑ 94ConTSN-1030
❑ 94ConTSN-1042
❑ 94ConTSNB-1030
❑ 94ConTSNB-1042
❑ 94UppDecTAE-29
❑ 95ConTSNGJ-6
❑ 95UppDecSHoB-17

Jackson, Sonny (Roland)

❑ 65AstJayP-8
❑ 65OPC-16
❑ 65Top-16
❑ 66Top-244
❑ 66TopVen-244
❑ 67AstTeal1-8
❑ 67CokCapAs-8
❑ 67DexPre-104
❑ 67Top-415
❑ 68BraPos-14
❑ 68CokCapB-14
❑ 68DexPre-40
❑ 68OPC-187
❑ 68Top-187
❑ 68TopVen-187
❑ 69AtlBraBPPS-12
❑ 69MilBra-128
❑ 69OPC-53
❑ 69Top-53
❑ 69TopSta-5

❑ 69TopTeaP-2
❑ 70OPC-413
❑ 70Top-413
❑ 71MLBOffS-12
❑ 71OPC-587
❑ 71Top-587
❑ 72MilBra-160
❑ 72OPC-318
❑ 72Top-318
❑ 73OPC-403
❑ 73Top-403
❑ 74GreHeroBP-6
❑ 74OPC-591
❑ 74Top-591
❑ 75HawIslC-10
❑ 76LauIndC-37
❑ 79SavBraT-8
❑ 80AndBraT-8
❑ 83BraPol-36
❑ 84DurBulT-30
❑ 85RicBraT-25
❑ 87AstSer1-12
❑ 87AstShoSO-13
❑ 87GreBraB-3
❑ 89RicBraBC-10
❑ 89RicBraC-24
❑ 89RicBraP-832
❑ 90CMC-278
❑ 90ProAAAF-422
❑ 90RicBraC-2
❑ 90RicBraP-277
❑ 90RicBraTI-14
❑ 91LinDriAAA-450
❑ 91RicBraBC-39
❑ 91RicBraP-2587
❑ 92RicBraBB-23
❑ 92RicBraF-393
❑ 92RicBraRC-7
❑ 96SanJosGB-28
❑ 98GiaMot-28

Jackson, Stonewall (Travis C.)
❑ 22WilPatV-36
❑ 25Exh-35
❑ 28PorandAR-A18
❑ 28PorandAR-B18
❑ 29ExhFou-10
❑ 31Exh-9
❑ 31W517-12
❑ 33CraJacP-14
❑ 33Gou-102
❑ 33WorCig-58
❑ 33WorCig-59
❑ 34BatR31-180
❑ 34DiaStaR-63
❑ 34GouCanV-24
❑ 35AlDemDCR3-86
❑ 35GouPuzR-1K
❑ 35GouPuzR-3B
❑ 35GouPuzR-14B
❑ 35GouPuzR-15B
❑ 35WheBB1-17
❑ 40PlaBal-158
❑ 46SpoExcW-4-8
❑ 61Fle-115
❑ 79DiaGre-33
❑ 80PacLeg-87
❑ 80PerHaloFP-179
❑ 80PerHaloFPS-44
❑ 80SSPHOF-180
❑ 82DiaCla-102
❑ 91ConTSN-42
❑ 94ConTSN-1101
❑ 94ConTSNB-1101

Jackson, Vince
❑ 91HigSchPLS-9
❑ 91KisDodP-4202
❑ 92GreFalDSP-2
❑ 93YakBeaC-13
❑ 93YakBeaF-3898

Jackson, Wade
❑ 96BoiHawB-18

Jackson, William
❑ 52LavPro-34
❑ 96BurIndB-28

Jackson, William PCL
❑ 12Zee-114
❑ 21Zee-96

Jacob, Mark
❑ 83SanJosBC-12

Jacobo, Ed
❑ 85VerBeaDT-10
❑ 86VerBeaDP-12

Jacobs, Anthony R.
❑ 55CarHunW-10
❑ 55Top-183

Jacobs, Art
❑ 20Zee-9
❑ 33Zee-80
❑ 77CinRedT-19

Jacobs, Dwayne
❑ 96MacBraB-8
❑ 97DurBulTI-10
❑ 98DanQ-C-10

Jacobs, Elmer
❑ 20WalMaiW-22
❑ 21Zee-144
❑ 22Zee-129
❑ 23Zee-161
❑ 29Zee-133
❑ 30Zee-143
❑ 31Zee-107
❑ 32Zee-103

Jacobs, Frank
❑ 91Cla/Bes-398
❑ 91PitMetC-4
❑ 91PitMetP-3429
❑ 92ClaFS7-274
❑ 92St.LucMCB-24
❑ 92St.LucMF-1753
❑ 93BinMetF-2341
❑ 93ClaFS7-139
❑ 94BinMetF-711
❑ 95BinMetTI-47

Jacobs, Jack
❑ 30Zee-84

Jacobs, Jake
❑ 89EugEmeB-4
❑ 90AppFoxBS-13
❑ 90AppFoxP-2090
❑ 91BasCitRC-7
❑ 91BasCitRP-1394
❑ 98ForWayW!-18

Jacobs, Lamar
❑ 77FriOneYW-68

Jacobs, P. W.
❑ 21Zee-97

Jacobs, Ray
❑ 24Zee-11
❑ 25Zee-7
❑ 26Zee-28
❑ 29Zee-22
❑ 30Zee-33

Jacobs, Ron
❑ 76SpoIndC-5
❑ 77HolMilT-16
❑ 78HolMilT-14
❑ 79VanCanT-3

Jacobs, Russell
❑ 96HonShaHWB-31
❑ 96WisTimRB-12
❑ 97MidLeaTP-28
❑ 97WisTimR-14
❑ 98HigDesMG-12

Jacobs, Ryan
❑ 93DanBraC-16
❑ 93DanBraF-3615
❑ 94MacBraC-9
❑ 94MacBraF-2198
❑ 95DurBulTI-13
❑ 96Exc-128
❑ 96GreBraB-15
❑ 96GreBraTI-48
❑ 97GreBraG-14
❑ 98GreBraG-10

Jacobs, Spook (Forrest)
❑ 47PM1StaP1-96
❑ 52Par-54
❑ 53ExhCan-46
❑ 54A'STEAI-11
❑ 54Top-129
❑ 55A'sRodM-19
❑ 55JetPos-6
❑ 55Top-61
❑ 55TopDouH-47
❑ 56Top-151
❑ 56TopHocF-A17
❑ 58JetPos-9
❑ 88ChaLooLTI-15
❑ 94TopArc1-129
❑ 94TopArc1G-129

Jacobs, Terrell
❑ 40WheM4-9

Jacobsen, Bucky
❑ 98BelSnaM-1
❑ 98MidLeaPM-1
❑ 99Bow-324
❑ 99BowGol-324
❑ 99BowInt-324
❑ 99SP TopP-16
❑ 99SP TopPPE-16

Jacobsen, Joe
❑ 93YakBeaC-14
❑ 93YakBeaF-3881
❑ 94SanAntMF-2463
❑ 96Exc-176
❑ 96SanAntMB-9
❑ 97PorSeaD-15
❑ 98MidAngO-21

Jacobsen, Nels
❑ 87BurExpP-1069
❑ 88FloStaLAS-9
❑ 88WesPalBES-13

Jacobsen, Robert
❑ 85VerBeaDT-16
❑ 86VerBeaDP-13

Jacobson, Albert
❑ 04FanCraAL-27

Jacobson, Andy
❑ 97BriWhiSB-5
❑ 98BriWhiSQ-14

Jacobson, Baby Doll (William)
❑ 17HolBreD-49
❑ 19W514-61
❑ 20GasAmeMBD-19
❑ 20NatCarE-49
❑ 21E121So8-41
❑ 21Exh-80
❑ 22AmeCarE122-31
❑ 22E120-97
❑ 22W572-48
❑ 23MapCriV-18
❑ 23WilChoV-69
❑ 25Exh-114
❑ 26Exh-114
❑ 27AmeCarE126-45
❑ 87ConSer2-43
❑ 88ConSer4-14
❑ 93ConTSN-740

Jacobson, Brian
❑ 96GreFalDB-17
❑ 96GreFalDTI-11

Jacobson, Jeff
❑ 82AubAstT-3
❑ 85ChaO'sT-3

Jacobson, Kelton
❑ 95FayGenTI-13
❑ 96LakTigB-14

Jacobson, Kevin
❑ 82RedPioT-23

Jacobson, Merwin
❑ 22W575-62
❑ 90DodTar-379

Jacobson, Peter
❑ 93AusFut-55

Jacobucci, Steve
❑ 89PitMetS-26
❑ 90St.LucMS-30
❑ 91ElmPioC-30

Jacoby, Brook
❑ 80AndBraT-27
❑ 82RicBraT-13
❑ 83RicBraT-13
❑ 84Don-542
❑ 84FleUpd-56
❑ 84Ind-19
❑ 84IndWhe-26
❑ 84TopTra-55T
❑ 84TopTraT-55T
❑ 85Don-154
❑ 85Fle-452
❑ 85Ind-19
❑ 85IndPol-26
❑ 85OPC-327
❑ 85Top-327
❑ 85TopSti-251
❑ 85TopSti-370
❑ 85TopTif-327
❑ 86Don-154
❑ 86Fle-590
❑ 86FleMin-116
❑ 86IndOhH-26
❑ 86IndTeal-26
❑ 86Lea-82
❑ 86OPC-116
❑ 86Top-116
❑ 86TopSti-207
❑ 86TopTat-5
❑ 86TopTif-116
❑ 87ClaGam-40
❑ 87Don-8
❑ 87Don-104
❑ 87DonAll-37
❑ 87DonOpeD-112
❑ 87DonSupD-8
❑ 87Fle-253
❑ 87FleGlo-253
❑ 87HosSti-22
❑ 87IndGat-26
❑ 87Lea-8
❑ 87Lea-134
❑ 87OPC-98
❑ 87RedFolSB-53
❑ 87Spo-109
❑ 87SpoTeaP-3
❑ 87Top-405
❑ 87TopSti-212
❑ 87TopTif-405
❑ 88Don-131
❑ 88DonBasB-229
❑ 88Fle-612
❑ 88FleExcS-22
❑ 88FleGlo-612
❑ 88FleStiC-20
❑ 88IndGat-26
❑ 88IndTeal-21
❑ 88Lea-51
❑ 88OPC-248
❑ 88PanSti-76
❑ 88Sco-39
❑ 88ScoGlo-39
❑ 88Spo-72
❑ 88StaLinI-14
❑ 88Top-555
❑ 88TopBig-17
❑ 88TopSti-211
❑ 88TopTif-555
❑ 88TopUKM-38
❑ 88TopUKMT-38
❑ 89Bow-86
❑ 89BowTif-86
❑ 89Don-114
❑ 89DonBasB-61
❑ 89Fle-408
❑ 89FleGlo-408
❑ 89IndTeal-14
❑ 89OPC-1
❑ 89PanSti-326
❑ 89RedFolSB-65
❑ 89Sco-19
❑ 89Spo-192
❑ 89Top-141
❑ 89Top-739
❑ 89TopBig-195
❑ 89TopSti-212
❑ 89TopTif-141
❑ 89TopTif-739
❑ 89UppDec-198
❑ 90Bow-341
❑ 90BowTif-341
❑ 90Don-83
❑ 90DonBesA-75
❑ 90Fle-493
❑ 90FleCan-493
❑ 90IndTeal-18
❑ 90Lea-74
❑ 90M.Vpin-31
❑ 90OPC-208
❑ 90PanSti-58
❑ 90PubIntS-561
❑ 90RicBra2ATI-12
❑ 90Sco-56
❑ 90Spo-155
❑ 90Top-208
❑ 90TopBig-276
❑ 90TopSti-219
❑ 90TopTif-208
❑ 90UppDec-459
❑ 90USPlaCA-5C
❑ 91Bow-59
❑ 91DenHol-9
❑ 91Don-176
❑ 91Fle-369
❑ 91IndFanC-11
❑ 91Lea-421
❑ 91OPC-47
❑ 91PanFreS-216
❑ 91PanSti-178
❑ 91Sco-162
❑ 91Sco100S-92
❑ 91StaClu-286
❑ 91Stu-44
❑ 91Top-47
❑ 91TopDesS-47
❑ 91TopMic-47
❑ 91TopTif-47
❑ 91Ult-113
❑ 91UltUpd-46
❑ 91UppDec-137
❑ 91UppDecFE-78F
❑ 92Cla1-T46
❑ 92Don-670
❑ 92Fle-260
❑ 92IndFanC-13
❑ 92OPC-606
❑ 92Pin-376
❑ 92Sco-577
❑ 92StaClu-828
❑ 92StaCluNC-828
❑ 92Top-606
❑ 92TopGol-606
❑ 92TopGolW-606
❑ 92TopMic-606
❑ 92Ult-349
❑ 92UppDec-528
❑ 93Don-493
❑ 93Fle-593
❑ 93Sco-567
❑ 93Top-303
❑ 93TopGol-303
❑ 93TopInaM-303
❑ 93TopInaR-303
❑ 93TopMic-303
❑ 93UppDec-200
❑ 93UppDecGold-200

Jacoby, Don
❑ 91BurIndP-3322

Jacome, Jason
❑ 91KinMetC-23
❑ 91KinMetP-3810
❑ 92ColMetC-10
❑ 92ColMetPI-28
❑ 92ColMetPIISPI-9
❑ 92ProFS7-292
❑ 92St.LucMF-1742
❑ 93St.LucMC-13
❑ 93St.LuMF-2918
❑ 94Bow-210
❑ 94Cla-76
❑ 94LeaLimR-24
❑ 94NorTidF-2915
❑ 94SigRooDP-94
❑ 94SigRooDPS-94
❑ 95ColCho-327
❑ 95ColChoGS-327
❑ 95ColChoSE-146
❑ 95ColChoSEGS-146
❑ 95ColChoSESS-146
❑ 95ColChoSS-327
❑ 95Don-136
❑ 95DonPreP-136
❑ 95Fle-371
❑ 95Lea-307
❑ 95MetColP-17
❑ 95NorTidTI-16
❑ 95Pin-383
❑ 95PinArtP-383
❑ 95PinMusC-383
❑ 95Sel-147
❑ 95SelArtP-147
❑ 95StaClu-321
❑ 95StaCluMOP-321
❑ 95StaCluSTWS-321
❑ 95StaCluVR-167
❑ 95StaCluVRMO-167
❑ 95Top-337
❑ 95TopCyb-183
❑ 95UC3-120
❑ 95UC3ArtP-120
❑ 95Ult-413
❑ 95UltGolM-413
❑ 95UppDec-124
❑ 95UppDecED-124
❑ 95UppDecEDG-124
❑ 96Fle-131
❑ 96FleTif-131
❑ 96LeaSigA-115
❑ 96LeaSigAG-115
❑ 96LeaSigAS-115
❑ 96RoyPol-14
❑ 96StaClu-282
❑ 96StaCluMOP-282
❑ 96Ult-71
❑ 96UltGolM-71
❑ 96UppDec-92
❑ 97Pac-103
❑ 97PacLigB-103
❑ 97PacSil-103
❑ 97RoyPol-12
❑ 98BufBisG-14

Jacomino, Mandy
❑ 98WesMicWM-7

Jacques, Eric
❑ 89WytCubS-17
❑ 91WinSpiP-2825

Jacquez, Thomas
❑ 97BatCliTI-17
❑ 97UCLBruTI-7
❑ 98ClePhiM-9
❑ 98ClePhiUM-9

Jaeckel, Paul
❑ 65Top-386

Jagnow, Jim
❑ 85BurRanT-17

Jaha, John
❑ 86TriTriC-195
❑ 87BelBreP-3
❑ 88StoPorCLC-193
❑ 88StoPorP-743
❑ 89CalLeaA-45
❑ 89StoPorB-16
❑ 89StoPorCLC-165
❑ 89StoPorP-380
❑ 89StoPorS-3
❑ 91Cla/Bes-291
❑ 91DaiDolF-18
❑ 91ElPasDLD-188
❑ 91ElPasDP-2756
❑ 91LinDriAA-188
❑ 92Bow-399
❑ 92Bow-542
❑ 92DenZepF-2647
❑ 92DenZepS-133
❑ 92Don-398
❑ 92FleUpd-35
❑ 92OPC-126
❑ 92ProFS7-84
❑ 92SkyAA F-290
❑ 92SkyAAAF-65
❑ 92Top-126
❑ 92TopGol-126
❑ 92TopGolW-126
❑ 92TopMic-126
❑ 93Bow-183
❑ 93BrePol-12
❑ 93Don-207
❑ 93Fin-152
❑ 93FinRef-152
❑ 93Fla-225
❑ 93Fle-252
❑ 93Lea-350
❑ 93OPC-190
❑ 93PacSpa-159
❑ 93Pin-228
❑ 93Sco-236
❑ 93Sel-308
❑ 93SP-66
❑ 93StaClu-701
❑ 93StaCluFDI-701
❑ 93StaCluMOP-701
❑ 93Stu-89
❑ 93Top-181
❑ 93TopGol-181
❑ 93TopInaM-181
❑ 93TopInaR-181
❑ 93TopMic-181
❑ 93Toy-91
❑ 93Ult-221
❑ 93UppDec-177
❑ 93UppDecGold-177
❑ 94Bow-65
❑ 94BreMilB-39
❑ 94BrePol-14
❑ 94BreTeal-12
❑ 94ColC-146
❑ 94ColChoGS-146
❑ 94ColChoSS-146
❑ 94Don-569
❑ 94Fin-106
❑ 94FinRef-106
❑ 94Fla-68
❑ 94Fle-180
❑ 94FleExtB-104
❑ 94Lea-317
❑ 94LeaL-44
❑ 94OPC-131
❑ 94Pac-331
❑ 94PanSti-82
❑ 94Pin-312
❑ 94PinArtP-312
❑ 94PinMusC-312
❑ 94ProMag-74
❑ 94Sco-173
❑ 94ScoGolR-173
❑ 94Sel-216
❑ 94Spo-40
❑ 94StaClu-105
❑ 94StaCluFDI-105
❑ 94StaCluGR-105
❑ 94StaCluMOP-105
❑ 94StaCluMOP-ST22
❑ 94StaCluST-ST22
❑ 94Stu-45
❑ 94Top-283

❑ 94TopGol-283
❑ 94TopSpa-283
❑ 94TriPla-54
❑ 94Ult-77
❑ 94UppDec-476
❑ 94UppDecED-476
❑ 95ColCho-184
❑ 95ColChoGS-184
❑ 95ColChoSS-184
❑ 95Don-232
❑ 95DonPreP-232
❑ 95Fin-195
❑ 95FinRef-195
❑ 95Fle-181
❑ 95Lea-275
❑ 95LeaLim-117
❑ 95Pac-234
❑ 95Pin-356
❑ 95PinArtP-356
❑ 95PinMusC-356
❑ 95Sco-235
❑ 95ScoGolR-235
❑ 95ScoPlaTS-235
❑ 95StaClu-371
❑ 95StaCluMOP-371
❑ 95StaCluSTWS-371
❑ 95Stu-131
❑ 95Top-505
❑ 95TopCyb-295
❑ 95Ult-65
❑ 95UltGolM-65
❑ 95UppDec-299
❑ 95UppDecED-299
❑ 95UppDecEDG-299
❑ 96BrePol-10
❑ 96ColCho-595
❑ 96ColChoGS-595
❑ 96ColChoSS-595
❑ 96Don-84
❑ 96DonPreP-84
❑ 96EmoXL-73
❑ 96Fla-101
❑ 96Fle-147
❑ 96FleTif-147
❑ 96Lea-104
❑ 96LeaPrePB-104
❑ 96LeaPrePG-104
❑ 96LeaPrePS-104
❑ 96LeaSig-119
❑ 96LeaSigA-116
❑ 96LeaSigAG-116
❑ 96LeaSigAS-116
❑ 96LeaSigPPG-119
❑ 96LeaSigPPP-119
❑ 96MetUni-70
❑ 96MetUniP-70
❑ 96Pac-340
❑ 96PacPri-P109
❑ 96PacPriG-P109
❑ 96PanSti-193
❑ 96Pin-98
❑ 96ProSta-28
❑ 96Sco-315
❑ 96ScoDugC-B40
❑ 96ScoDugCAP-B40
❑ 96SelTeaN-28
❑ 96StaClu-102
❑ 96StaCluMOP-102
❑ 96Sum-74
❑ 96SumAbo&B-74
❑ 96SumArtP-74
❑ 96SumFoi-74
❑ 96Top-317
❑ 96Ult-364
❑ 96UltGolM-364
❑ 96UppDec-123
❑ 97Bow-250
❑ 97BowBes-39
❑ 97BowBesAR-39
❑ 97BowBesR-39
❑ 97BowInt-250
❑ 97BrePol-11
❑ 97Cir-379
❑ 97CirRav-379
❑ 97ColCho-370
❑ 97DenHol-8
❑ 97Don-252
❑ 97DonEli-116
❑ 97DonEliGS-116
❑ 97DonGolPP-252
❑ 97DonLim-176
❑ 97DonLimE-176
❑ 97DonPre-57
❑ 97DonPreCttC-57
❑ 97DonSilPP-252
❑ 97Fin-114
❑ 97FinEmb-114
❑ 97FinEmbR-114
❑ 97FinRef-114
❑ 97FlaShoLC-169
❑ 97FlaShoLeg0-169
❑ 97FlaShoLeg1-169
❑ 97FlaShoM-A169
❑ 97FlaShoM-B169
❑ 97FlaShoM-C169
❑ 97FlaShoR0-169
❑ 97FlaShoR1-169
❑ 97FlaShoR2-169
❑ 97Fle-129
❑ 97FleTeaL-8
❑ 97FleTif-129
❑ 97Lea-27
❑ 97LeaFraM-27
❑ 97LeaFraMDC-27
❑ 97MetUni-65
❑ 97NewPin-23
❑ 97NewPinAP-23
❑ 97NewPinMC-23
❑ 97NewPinPP-23
❑ 97Pac-119
❑ 97PacLigB-119
❑ 97PacPri-39
❑ 97PacPriLB-39
❑ 97PacPriP-39
❑ 97PacSil-119
❑ 97PinCer-57
❑ 97PinCerMBla-57
❑ 97PinCerMBlu-57
❑ 97PinCerMG-57
❑ 97PinCerMR-57
❑ 97PinCerR-57
❑ 97PinIns-98
❑ 97PinInsCE-98
❑ 97PinInsDE-98
❑ 97PinTotCPB-57
❑ 97PinTotCPG-57
❑ 97PinTotCPR-57
❑ 97PinX-P-93
❑ 97PinX-PMoS-93
❑ 97PinX-PSfF-29
❑ 97PinX-PSfFU-29
❑ 97Sco-68
❑ 97ScoArtPWB-68
❑ 97ScoPreS-68
❑ 97ScoShoS-68
❑ 97ScoShoSAP-68
❑ 97Sel-54
❑ 97SelArtP-54
❑ 97SelCom-54
❑ 97SelRegG-54
❑ 97SP-100
❑ 97SpoIll-151
❑ 97SpoIllEE-151
❑ 97StaClu-35
❑ 97StaCluMat-35
❑ 97StaCluMOP-35
❑ 97Stu-63
❑ 97StuPrePG-63
❑ 97StuPrePS-63
❑ 97Top-446
❑ 97TopChr-158
❑ 97TopChrR-158
❑ 97TopGal-98
❑ 97TopGalPPI-98
❑ 97TopIntF-ILM9
❑ 97TopIntFR-ILM9
❑ 97Ult-76
❑ 97UltGolME-76
❑ 97UltPlaME-76
❑ 97UppDec-100
❑ 98Bow-17
❑ 98BowChr-17
❑ 98BowChrGA-17
❑ 98BowChrGAR-17
❑ 98BowChrI-17
❑ 98BowChrIR-17
❑ 98BowChrR-17
❑ 98BowGolA-17
❑ 98BowInt-17
❑ 98CirThu-62
❑ 98CirThuRav-62
❑ 98CirThuSupRav-62
❑ 98ColCho-404
❑ 98Don-176
❑ 98DonGolPP-176
❑ 98DonSilPP-176
❑ 98FlaShoLeg0-116
❑ 98FlaShoLeg1-116
❑ 98FlaShoLeg2-116
❑ 98FlaShoLeg3-116
❑ 98FlaShoLegM-116
❑ 98FlaShoR0-116
❑ 98FlaShoR1-116
❑ 98FlaShoR2-116
❑ 98FlaShoR3-116
❑ 98Fle-468
❑ 98MetUni-141
❑ 98MetUniPMG-141
❑ 98Pac-116
❑ 98PacAur-153
❑ 98PacOme-134
❑ 98PacOmeR-134
❑ 98PacOnl-398
❑ 98PacOnlR-398
❑ 98PacOnlWC-398
❑ 98PacPar-187
❑ 98PacParC-187
❑ 98PacParG-187
❑ 98PacParHS-187
❑ 98PacParPB-187
❑ 98PacParR-187
❑ 98PacParTC-23
❑ 98PacPlaB-116
❑ 98PacRedT-116
❑ 98PacSil-116
❑ 98PinPlu-44
❑ 98Sco-215
❑ 98ScoSS-PP104
❑ 98ScoSSAP-PP104
❑ 98SkyDugA-25
❑ 98SkyDugAIA-25
❑ 98SpoIll-63
❑ 98SpoIllEE-63
❑ 98SpoIllFE-63
❑ 98StaCluFDI-142
❑ 98StaCluI-142
❑ 98StaCluOneK-142
❑ 98StaCluPP-142
❑ 98Top-32
❑ 98TopChr-32
❑ 98TopChrR-32
❑ 98TopDevR-32
❑ 98TopDia-32
❑ 98TopMiniC-32
❑ 98TopOpeD-15
❑ 98Ult-199
❑ 98UltGolM-199
❑ 98UltMas-199
❑ 98UltPlaM-199
❑ 98UppDec-410
❑ 99Fle-451
❑ 99FleSta9-451
❑ 99FleWarT-451
❑ 99Pac-234
❑ 99PacPlaB-234
❑ 99PacRed-234
❑ 99Rev-103
❑ 99RevPremDate-103
❑ 99RevRet-103
❑ 99RevShaSS-103
❑ 99Top-307
❑ 99TopChr-307
❑ 99TopChrR-307
❑ 99TopMVPP-307
❑ 99Ult-128
❑ 99UltGolM-128
❑ 99UltMas-128
❑ 99UltPlaM-128
❑ 99Vic-281

Jahn, Arthur
❑ 26Zee-29
❑ 27Zee-15
❑ 29Zee-90
❑ 30Zee-144

Jaime, Angel
❑ 92GreFalDSP-23
❑ 93BakDodCLC-12
❑ 93YakBeaC-15
❑ 94VerBeaDC-11
❑ 94VerBeaDF-87
❑ 95SanAntMTI-23
❑ 96StLucMTI-24
❑ 97St.LucM-11

Jaime, Ismael
❑ 85MexCitTT-16

Jaime, Jorge
❑ 89HigSchPLS-17

Jaime, Juan
❑ 90MyrBeaBJP-2780
❑ 91MyrBeaHC-13
❑ 91MyrBeaHP-2947

Jakubowski, John
❑ 81BatTroT-30

Jakubowski, Stan
❑ 77AshTouT-10
❑ 79TucTorT-6

Jakucki, Jack (Sigmund)
❑ 47CenFlo-11
❑ 47SigOil-77
❑ 96Bro194F-6

James, Artie (Arthur)
❑ 75DetTigP-14
❑ 77EvaTriT-16
❑ 79RocRedWT-6

James, Author (Bill)
❑ 92MegRut-143
❑ 92MegRut-144
❑ 92MegRut-145
❑ 95MegGriJWL-15

James, Bevan
❑ 91SydWavF-5

James, Bill (William)
❑ 13Zee-61
❑ 14B18B-50A
❑ 14B18B-50B
❑ 15CraJacE-153
❑ 15SpoNewM-87
❑ 16BF2FP-54
❑ 16SpoNewM-88
❑ 17ColE13-84
❑ 22Zee-156
❑ 23Zee-188
❑ 24Zee-63
❑ 75WhiSox1T-11
❑ 80BraTCM1-26
❑ 88ConSer5-17
❑ 88PacEigMO-61
❑ 94ConTSN-1035
❑ 94ConTSN-1041
❑ 94ConTSNB-1035
❑ 94ConTSNB-1041

James, Bob
❑ 82ExpHygM-10
❑ 82ExpPos-16
❑ 83ExpPos-13
❑ 83WicAerDS-11
❑ 84Don-87
❑ 84ExpPos-13
❑ 84ExpStu-10
❑ 84Fle-277
❑ 84Nes792-579
❑ 84OPC-336
❑ 84Top-579
❑ 84TopTif-579
❑ 85Don-279
❑ 85Fle-400
❑ 85FleUpd-60
❑ 85OPC-114
❑ 85Top-114
❑ 85TopMin-114
❑ 85TopTif-114
❑ 85TopTifT-61T
❑ 85TopTra-61T
❑ 85WhiSoxC-43
❑ 86BasStaB-60
❑ 86Don-379
❑ 86Fle-209
❑ 86FleStiC-66
❑ 86OPC-284
❑ 86SevCoi-C11
❑ 86Spo-158
❑ 86Top-467
❑ 86TopSti-290
❑ 86TopSup-36
❑ 86TopTat-3
❑ 86TopTif-467
❑ 86WhiSoxC-43
❑ 87Don-493
❑ 87Fle-501
❑ 87FleGlo-501
❑ 87FleStiC-67
❑ 87OPC-342
❑ 87RedFolSB-15
❑ 87SpoTeaP-26
❑ 87Top-342
❑ 87TopTif-342
❑ 87WhiSoxC-17
❑ 88Don-507
❑ 88Fle-401
❑ 88FleGlo-401
❑ 88OPC-232
❑ 88PanSti-54
❑ 88Top-232
❑ 88TopSti-289
❑ 88TopTif-232

James, Brandon
❑ 98BelSnaM-14

James, Calvin
❑ 85MiaHur-7
❑ 86OscAstP-15
❑ 87OscAstP-7
❑ 88ColAstB-26

James, Charlie (Charles)
❑ 60Top-517
❑ 61Top-561
❑ 62Top-412
❑ 63Jel-163
❑ 63Pos-163
❑ 63Top-83
❑ 64CarTeal-4
❑ 64Top-357
❑ 64TopVen-357
❑ 65OPC-141
❑ 65RedEnq-13
❑ 65Top-141
❑ 78TCM60I-292

James, Chris
❑ 85PhiTas-43
❑ 85PorBeaC-29
❑ 86FleUpd-55
❑ 86PhiTas-26
❑ 86PorBeaP-10
❑ 87Don-42
❑ 87FleUpd-50
❑ 87FleUpdG-50
❑ 87Lea-42
❑ 87PhiTas-18
❑ 87TopTra-53T
❑ 87TopTraT-53T
❑ 88Don-453
❑ 88DonBasB-159
❑ 88Fle-307
❑ 88FleGlo-307
❑ 88OPC-1
❑ 88PanSti-362
❑ 88PhiTas-14
❑ 88Sco-409
❑ 88ScoGlo-409
❑ 88ScoYouSI-14
❑ 88StaLinPh-10
❑ 88Top-572
❑ 88TopSti-122
❑ 88TopTif-572
❑ 89Bow-404
❑ 89BowTif-404
❑ 89Don-312
❑ 89DonBasB-266
❑ 89Fle-572
❑ 89FleGlo-572
❑ 89OPC-298
❑ 89PadCok-8
❑ 89PadMag-23
❑ 89PadPos-16
❑ 89PanSti-156
❑ 89PhiTas-12
❑ 89RedFolSB-66
❑ 89Sco-202
❑ 89ScoRoo-46T
❑ 89Top-298
❑ 89TopSti-119
❑ 89TopTif-298
❑ 89TopTra-56T
❑ 89TopTraT-56T
❑ 89UppDec-513
❑ 90Bow-340
❑ 90BowTif-340
❑ 90Don-323
❑ 90DonGraS-3
❑ 90Fle-161
❑ 90FleCan-161
❑ 90FleUpd-92
❑ 90IndTeal-20
❑ 90Lea-319
❑ 90OPC-178
❑ 90PanSti-350
❑ 90PubIntS-241
❑ 90Sco-498
❑ 90ScoRoo-60T
❑ 90Top-178
❑ 90TopSti-105
❑ 90TopTif-178
❑ 90TopTra-46T
❑ 90TopTraT-46T
❑ 90UppDec-435
❑ 90UppDec-798
❑ 91Bow-67
❑ 91Don-227
❑ 91Fle-370
❑ 91IndFanC-15
❑ 91Lea-175
❑ 91OPC-494
❑ 91PanSti-181
❑ 91Sco-491
❑ 91StaClu-422
❑ 91Stu-45
❑ 91Top-494
❑ 91TopDesS-494
❑ 91TopMic-494
❑ 91TopTif-494
❑ 91Ult-114
❑ 91UppDec-140
❑ 92Don-82
❑ 92Fle-112
❑ 92GiaMot-27
❑ 92GiaPacGaE-21
❑ 92Lea-497
❑ 92LeaBlaG-497
❑ 92OPC-709
❑ 92OPCPre-20
❑ 92Sco-262
❑ 92StaClu-23
❑ 92StaClu-747
❑ 92StaCluECN-747
❑ 92Top-709
❑ 92TopGol-709
❑ 92TopGolW-709
❑ 92TopMic-709
❑ 92UppDec-560
❑ 93AstMot-21
❑ 93AstStaC-5
❑ 93Don-604
❑ 93Fle-531
❑ 93FleFinE-79
❑ 93PacSpa-272
❑ 93Pin-120
❑ 93RanKee-412
❑ 93Top-38
❑ 93TopGol-38
❑ 93TopInaM-38
❑ 93TopInaR-38
❑ 93TopMic-38
❑ 94ColC-507
❑ 94ColChoGS-507
❑ 94ColChoSS-507
❑ 94Fin-385
❑ 94FinRef-385
❑ 94FleExtB-181
❑ 94FleUpd-93
❑ 94Lea-358
❑ 94RanMagM-21
❑ 94StaClu-621
❑ 94StaCluFDI-621
❑ 94StaCluGR-621
❑ 94StaCluMOP-621
❑ 94Ult-432
❑ 94UppDec-398
❑ 94UppDecED-398
❑ 95Fle-289
❑ 95Sco-108
❑ 95ScoGolR-108
❑ 95ScoPlaTS-108
❑ 95Top-150

James, Cleo
❑ 72OPC-117
❑ 72Top-117A
❑ 72Top-117B
❑ 74WicAerODF-113
❑ 90DodTar-380

James, Darin
❑ 84EveGiaC-6B
❑ 85EveGialC-7

James, Delvin
❑ 97PriDevR-22
❑ 98HudValR-11

James, Dewey
❑ 82BelBreFr-11
❑ 83BelBreFr-3

James, Dion
❑ 82ElPasDT-2
❑ 84BrePol-14
❑ 84Don-31
❑ 84FleUpd-57
❑ 85BreGar-9
❑ 85BrePol-14
❑ 85Don-211
❑ 85Fle-584
❑ 85Lea-162
❑ 85Top-228
❑ 85TopTif-228
❑ 86Don-89
❑ 86Top-76
❑ 86TopTif-76
❑ 86VanCanP-13
❑ 87BraSmo-24
❑ 87ClaUpdY-144
❑ 87DonOpeD-44
❑ 87FleUpd-51
❑ 87FleUpdG-51
❑ 87SpoTeaP-24
❑ 87TopTra-54T
❑ 87TopTraT-54T
❑ 88Don-190
❑ 88DonBasB-29
❑ 88Fle-543

❑ 88FleGlo-543
❑ 88FleMin-64
❑ 00TlcCtiC 76
❑ 88OPC-82
❑ 88PanSti-250
❑ 88Sco-395
❑ 88ScoGlo-395
❑ 88ScoYouSI-7
❑ 88Spo-36
❑ 88StaLinBra-10
❑ 88Top-408
❑ 88Top-549
❑ 88TopBig-220
❑ 88TopCoi-44
❑ 88TopMinL-40
❑ 88TopSti-42
❑ 88TopTif-408
❑ 88TopTif-549
❑ 88TopUKM-39
❑ 88TopUKMT-39
❑ 89Bow-277
❑ 89BowTif-277
❑ 89Don-340
❑ 89DonBasB-253
❑ 89Fle-594
❑ 89FleGlo-594
❑ 89PanSti-44
❑ 89Sco-163
❑ 89ScoRoo-51T
❑ 89Top-678
❑ 89TopBig-223
❑ 89TopSti-24
❑ 89TopTif-678
❑ 89UppDec-587
❑ 90Bow-331
❑ 90BowTif-331
❑ 90Don-428
❑ 90El PasDAGTI-14
❑ 90Fle-494
❑ 90FleCan-494
❑ 90IndTeal-19
❑ 90OPC-319
❑ 90PanSti-64
❑ 90PubIntS-115
❑ 90Sco-514
❑ 90Top-319
❑ 90TopBig-132
❑ 90TopTif-319
❑ 90UppDec-591
❑ 91Don-348
❑ 91Fle-371
❑ 91OPC-117
❑ 91Sco-131
❑ 91Top-117
❑ 91TopDesS-117
❑ 91TopMic-117
❑ 91TopTif-117
❑ 91UppDec-399
❑ 92Bow-494
❑ 92Lea-365
❑ 92LeaBlaG-365
❑ 92StaClu-884
❑ 92StaCluNC-884
❑ 92Ult-409
❑ 93Don-735
❑ 93Fle-649
❑ 93PacSpa-556
❑ 93StaClu-266
❑ 93StaCluFDI-266
❑ 93StaCluMOP-266
❑ 94BreMilB-40
❑ 94Don-446
❑ 94Fle-232
❑ 94Pac-424
❑ 94Sco-175
❑ 94ScoGolR-175
James, Drue
❑ 98DanBraQ-19
James, Duane
❑ 85TulDriTI-29
❑ 86SalRedBP-13
James, Howard
❑ 90CedRapRB-27
James, Jeff
❑ 69Top-477
❑ 70OPC-302
❑ 70Top-302
James, Joey
❑ 89WatIndS-10
❑ 90Bes-127
❑ 90CliGiaB-20
❑ 90CliGiaP-2554
❑ 90MidLeaASGS-36
❑ 90ProAaA-127
❑ 91CalLeLA-33
❑ 91Cla/Bes-378
❑ 91SanJosGC-29
❑ 91SanJosGP-18
James, John
❑ 60Top-499
❑ 61Top-457
❑ 61Yan61RL-27
❑ 91YanRinP12-11
❑ 92YanWIZ6-59
James, Keith
❑ 87PocGiaTB-22
James, Kenny
❑ 95TopTra-129T
❑ 97VerExpB-16
❑ 98CapFeaCM-9
James, Mike
❑ 88GreFalDTI-23
❑ 89BakDodCLC-186
❑ 90SanAntMGS-15
❑ 90TexLeaAGS-14
❑ 91LinDriAA-536
❑ 91SanAntMLD-536
❑ 91SanAntMP-2969
❑ 92AlbDukS-11
❑ 92SanAntMF-3970
❑ 93AlbDukF-1455
❑ 93Bow-674
❑ 93DodStaC-26
❑ 94VanCanF-1862
❑ 95AngMot-27
❑ 95FleUpd-66
❑ 96AngMot-23
❑ 96Don-257
❑ 96DonPreP-257
❑ 96Fle-50
❑ 96FleTif-50
❑ 96LeaSigEA-88
❑ 97AngMot-21
❑ 97Fle-47
❑ 97FleTif-47
❑ 97Sco-369
❑ 97ScoArtPWB-369
❑ 97ScoResC-369
❑ 97ScoShoS-369
❑ 97ScoShoSAP-369
❑ 97Top-431
❑ 98AngSco-10
❑ 98AngScoP-10
❑ 98PacInvGems-5
❑ 98PacOnl-14
❑ 98PacOnlR-14
❑ 98PacOnlWC-14
❑ 98Sco-171
❑ 98UppDec-633
James, Paul
❑ 86DayBealP-13
James, Richard
❑ 83St.PetCT-22
James, Robert Byrne
❑ 33Gou-208
James, Russell
❑ 20Zee-82
James, Skip
❑ 74PhoGiaC-80
❑ 75PhoGiaC-5
❑ 75PhoGiaCK-14
❑ 76PheGiaCr-15
❑ 76PhoGiaCa-5
❑ 76PhoGiaCC-13
❑ 76PhoGiaVNB-11
❑ 77Gia-11
❑ 77PhoGiaCC-11
❑ 77PhoGiaCP-10
❑ 77PhoGiaCP-11
❑ 77PhoGiaVNB-11
❑ 78GiaTeal-14
❑ 79VanCanT-1
❑ 97PhoFirDTTI-13
James, Sonny
❑ 84SavCarT-1
James, Todd
❑ 88BenBucL-23
❑ 89PalSprACLC-56
❑ 91LinDriAA-437
❑ 91MidAngLD-437
❑ 91MidAngP-431
❑ 92EdmTraS-161
❑ 92MidAngF-4022
❑ 92MidAngOHP-9
❑ 92SkyAAAF-80
James, Tony
❑ 11PinT-5-1001
❑ 98LowSpiM-8
James, Troy
❑ 86ColMetP-14
❑ 87LynMetP-23
❑ 88VisOakCLC-164
❑ 88VisOakP-88
James, W. J.
❑ 25Zee-68
Jameyson, Rick
❑ 92WatIndC-29
❑ 94ColRedC-29
❑ 98ColRedSM-29
Jamieson, Charles
❑ 17ColE13-85
❑ 21Exh-81
❑ 22E120-35
❑ 22W572-49
❑ 23Lec-4
❑ 23WilChoV-70
❑ 25Exh-82
❑ 27AmeCarE126-21
❑ 28Exh-41
❑ 28StaPlaCE-39
❑ 29PorandAR-46
❑ 33Gou-171
❑ 77Ind192T-9
❑ 93ConTSN-692
❑ 95ConTSN-1360
Jamison, Bob
❑ 81NasSouTI-14
❑ 87NasSouTI-25
❑ 89NasSouTI-26
Jamison, David
❑ 85CloHSS-23
Jamzy, Mascot
❑ 93FayGenC-29
Janeski, Gerry
❑ 71MLBOffS-543
❑ 71OPC-673
❑ 71Top-673
❑ 93RanKee-19
Janiak, Joseph
❑ 52LavPro-8
Janicki, Pete
❑ 92ClaDraP-119
❑ 93Bow-641
❑ 93PalSprAC-10
❑ 93Pin-468
❑ 93Sco-500
❑ 93UppDec-422
❑ 93UppDecGold-422
❑ 94MidAngF-2432
❑ 94MidAngOHP-11
❑ 95LakElsSTI-17
❑ 96Bow-363
❑ 96BowFoi-363
❑ 96VanCanB-18
❑ 97VanCanB-18
Janikowski, Randy
❑ 88BoiHawP-1619
Janke, Jared
❑ 95MarPhiTI-10
❑ 96PieBolWB-13
Janney, Barry
❑ 77SpaPhiT-22
Janowicz, Vic
❑ 53Top-222
❑ 54Bow-203
❑ 54Top-16
❑ 55Bow-114
❑ 72TopTes5-6
❑ 91TopArc1-222
❑ 94TopArc1-16
❑ 94TopArc1G-16
Jansen, Larry
❑ 46SpoExcW-5-11
❑ 47HomBon-22
❑ 48BluTin-6
❑ 48Bow-23
❑ 48GiaTeal-7
❑ 49Bow-202
❑ 49EurSta-110
❑ 49GiaTeal-12
❑ 49Lea-56
❑ 50Bow-66
❑ 50JJKCopP-7
❑ 51Bow-162
❑ 51FisBakL-10
❑ 51TopRedB-21
❑ 52BerRos-26
❑ 52Bow-90
❑ 52RedMan-NL10
❑ 52StaCalL-78D
❑ 52StaCalS-90B
❑ 52TipTop-17
❑ 52Top-5
❑ 53BowBW-40
❑ 54Bow-169
❑ 54NewYorJA-27
❑ 54Top-200
❑ 55SeaPop-10
❑ 56SeaPop-7
❑ 57HygMea-6
❑ 57SeaPop-10
❑ 73OPC-01
❑ 73Top-81A
❑ 73Top-81B
❑ 75Gia195T-9
❑ 76TayBow4-95
❑ 79TCM50-255
❑ 81Gia196T-3
❑ 83TopRep5-5
❑ 85TCMPpl1-21
❑ 93UppDecAH-73
❑ 94TopArc1-200
❑ 94TopArc1G-200
Jansing, Henry
❑ 09ObaT21-43
Jantzen, A.C.
❑ 87OldJudN-261
Janus, Ed
❑ 82MadMusF-33
❑ 83MadMusF-1
Janvrin, Harold
❑ 15CraJacE-149
❑ 15SpoNewM-88
❑ 16FleBreD-45
❑ 16SpoNewM-89
❑ 17ColE13-83
❑ 17HolBreD-50
❑ 90DodTar-381
❑ 91ConTSN-144
Janzen, Marty
❑ 92GulCoaYF-3786
❑ 95TamYanYI-12
❑ 96BesAutS-42
❑ 96BluJayOH-17
❑ 96Bow-265
❑ 96BowBes-170
❑ 96BowBesAR-170
❑ 96BowBesR-170
❑ 96BowFoi-265
❑ 96Exc-90
❑ 96Fin-G300
❑ 96FinRef-G300
❑ 96FleUpd-U97
❑ 96FleUpdTC-U97
❑ 96SyrChiTI-16
❑ 96Top-429
❑ 96Ult-432
❑ 96UltGolM-432
❑ 96UltGolP-10
❑ 96UltGolPHGM-10
❑ 97BluJayS-53
❑ 97ColCho-11
❑ 97Fle-243
❑ 97FleTif-243
❑ 97PacPriGotD-GD101
❑ 97StaClu-356
❑ 97StaCluMOP-356
❑ 97SyrSkyCB-12
❑ 97Top-225
❑ 97Ult-146
❑ 97UltGolME-146
❑ 97UltPlaME-146
❑ 97UppDec-231
❑ 98ColCho-252
❑ 98ColCliD-12
❑ 98ColCliM-16
Jaques, Eric
❑ 89Sta-164
❑ 90PeoChiTI-24
❑ 91WinSpiC-6
❑ 92ChaKniF-2767
❑ 92ChaKniS-160
Jaquette, Bryan
❑ 92BelBreCB-30
❑ 93BelBreCB-29
❑ 95ElPasDTI-11
❑ 96El PasDB-5
❑ 97SarRedS-30
❑ 98TreThuM-4
Jaramillo, Frankie
❑ 98SavSanGM-15
Jaramillo, Lee
❑ 98HelBreM-20
Jaramillo, Mike
❑ 97UCLBruTI-8
❑ 98GreFalDG-17
Jaramillo, Rudy
❑ 76SanAntBTI-13
❑ 90AstMot-27
❑ 91AstMot-28
❑ 92AstMot-27
❑ 93AstMot-28
❑ 94BenRocC-28
❑ 95RanCra-16
❑ 96RanDr P-18
❑ 96RanMot-28
❑ 97RanDr P-15
Jarlett, Al
❑ 46SunBre-8
Jarolimek, Jonathan
❑ 92GenCubC-14
❑ 92GenCubF-1556
Jaroncyk, Ryan
❑ 95Bes-115
❑ 95BowBes-X4
❑ 95BowBesR-X4
❑ 95SPML-114
❑ 95TopTra-30T
❑ 96AppLeaAB-23
❑ 96BesAutSA-31
❑ 96Top-19
❑ 96TopPowB-19
❑ 97BesAutAS-21
Jarquin, Skeeter (Gersan)
❑ 77RocRedWM-21
❑ 78RocRedWT-9
❑ 79HolMilT-13
Jarrell, Joe
❑ 86MemChiSTOS-11
❑ 86MemChiTOS-11
❑ 87ChaO'sW-13
❑ 88ChaKniTI-9
Jarrett, Link
❑ 94BenRocC-11
❑ 94BenRocF-3602
❑ 95AshTouTI-5
❑ 96NewHavRB-15
❑ 97SalAva-19
❑ 98NewHavRM-14
❑ 98NewHavRMA-14
Jarrett, Mark
❑ 82MadMusF-12
Jarvis, Jason
❑ 94OneYanC-10
❑ 94OneYanF-3786
❑ 95Exc-96
❑ 95GreBatTI-13
❑ 96DunBluJB-14
❑ 96DunBluJTI-17
❑ 97DunBluJTI-16
Jarvis, John
❑ 90GreHorB-14
❑ 90GreHorP-2666
❑ 90GreHorS-8
❑ 91PriWilCC-15
❑ 91PriWilCP-1431
Jarvis, Kevin
❑ 91PriRedC-23
❑ 91PriRedP-3508
❑ 92ChaWheF-4
❑ 92ChaWVWC-12
❑ 93WinSpiC-10
❑ 93WinSpiF-1565
❑ 94Bow-48
❑ 94IndIndF-1805
❑ 94SpoRoo-116
❑ 94SpoRooAP-116
❑ 95Bow-202
❑ 95Fle-438
❑ 95Pac-107
❑ 95RedKah-14
❑ 95TopTra-93T
❑ 95Ult-144
❑ 95UltGolM-144
❑ 96ColCho-517
❑ 96ColChoGS-517
❑ 96ColChoSS-517
❑ 96IndIndB-11
❑ 96UppDec-51
❑ 97ColCho-81
❑ 97UppDec-337
Jarvis, LeRoy
❑ 47TipTop-142
❑ 49SomandK-9
❑ 90DodTar-382
Jarvis, Matt
❑ 92KanCouCC-6
❑ 92KanCouCF-86
❑ 92KanCouCTI-15
❑ 93AlbPolCB-15
❑ 93AlbPolF-2023
❑ 93SouAtlLAGF-3
❑ 94Bow-599
❑ 94ClaGolF-6
❑ 94FreKeyC-12
❑ 94FreKeyF-2608
❑ 94OriPro-48
❑ 95BowBayTI-37
❑ 96BowBayB-18
❑ 97ArkTraB-6
❑ 98ArkTraM-14
Jarvis, Pat (Robert Pat)
❑ 67BraPho-14
❑ 67OPC-57
❑ 67Top-57
❑ 68BraPos-15
❑ 68CokCapB-4
❑ 68DexPre-41
❑ 68OPC-134
❑ 68Top-134
❑ 68TopVen-134
❑ 69AtlBraBPPS-13
❑ 69MilBra-129
❑ 69MLBOffS-114
❑ 69Top-282
❑ 69TopSta-6
❑ 69TopTeaP-2
❑ 70AtlBraS-5
❑ 70MLBOffS-7
❑ 70OPC-438
❑ 70Top-438
❑ 71MLBOffS-13
❑ 71OPC-623
❑ 71Top-623
❑ 71TopCoi-85
❑ 72MilBra-161
❑ 72Top-675
❑ 73OPC-192
❑ 73Top-192
❑ 78AtlCon-10
❑ 78TCM60I-264
Jarvis, Ray
❑ 70OPC-361
❑ 70Top-361
❑ 71OPC-526
❑ 71Top-526
Jasco, Elinton
❑ 94HunCubC-15
❑ 94HunCubF-3561
❑ 96RocCubTI-12
Jaster, Larry
❑ 65CarTeal-12
❑ 67Top-356
❑ 68OPC-117
❑ 68Top-117
❑ 68TopVen-117
❑ 69AtlBraBPPS-14
❑ 69Top-496
❑ 69TopSta-56
❑ 69TopTeaP-10
❑ 70ExpPos-13
❑ 70OPC-124
❑ 70Top-124
❑ 71MLBOffS-14
❑ 71RicBraTI-8
❑ 72MilBra-162
❑ 86DurBulP-14
❑ 87SumBraP-21
❑ 88SumBraP-415
❑ 89DurBullS-27
❑ 89DurBullS-27
❑ 89DurBulTI-27
❑ 90DurBulTI-28
❑ 91DurBulC-16
❑ 91DurBulP-1678
❑ 92MacBraC-28
❑ 92MacBraF-286
❑ 93MacBraC-29
❑ 93MacBraF-1418
❑ 94MacBraC-28
❑ 94MacBraF-2225
❑ 95MacBraTI-12
❑ 97DelSho-11
❑ 98FreKeyM-4
Jaster, Scott
❑ 86ColMetP-15
❑ 87LynMetP-21
❑ 88ColMetGS-25
❑ 88St.LucMS-13
❑ 89St.LucMS-11
❑ 90SalSpuP-2732
❑ 91BirBarLD-64
❑ 91BirBarP-1465
❑ 91LinDriAA-64
❑ 92BirBarF-2595
❑ 92BirBarS-85
❑ 92SkyAA F-41
❑ 93MemChiF-387
Jaszczak, Steve
❑ 93MisStaB-23
Jata, Paul
❑ 72OPC-257
❑ 72Top-257
Jauss, Dave

❑ 89WesPalBES-29
❑ 90WesPalBES-30
❑ 91WesPalBEC-27
❑ 91WesPalBEP-1245
❑ 92WesPalBEC-26
❑ 92WesPalBEF-2103
❑ 94HarSenF-2107
❑ 95LinVen-35
❑ 96-97LinVen-162

Javery, Al
❑ 77TCMTheWY-62
❑ 83TCMPla1943-39

Javier, Ignacio Alfredo
❑ 73CedRapAT-21
❑ 75IowOakT-9
❑ 80WicAerT-10
❑ 85DomLeaS-170

Javier, M. Julian
❑ 60Top-133
❑ 60TopVen-133
❑ 61CarJayP-7
❑ 61Top-148
❑ 61TopStal-89
❑ 62CarJayP-6
❑ 62Top-118
❑ 62TopStal-185
❑ 62TopVen-118
❑ 63CarJayP-10
❑ 63Jel-159
❑ 63Pos-159
❑ 63Top-226
❑ 64CarTeal-5
❑ 64Top-446
❑ 64TopRooAB-9
❑ 64WheSta-23
❑ 65CarJayP-5
❑ 65CarTeal-13
❑ 65Top-447
❑ 66CarTeal-6
❑ 66Top-436
❑ 67Top-226
❑ 67TopVen-320
❑ 68Baz-5
❑ 68OPC-25
❑ 68Top-25
❑ 68TopVen-25
❑ 69MilBra-130
❑ 69MLBOffS-212
❑ 69Top-497
❑ 69TopSta-116
❑ 69TopTeaP-18
❑ 70CarTeal-15
❑ 70MLBOffS-140
❑ 70OPC-415
❑ 70Top-415
❑ 71CarTeal-13
❑ 71CarTeal-21
❑ 71MLBOffS-275
❑ 71OPC-185
❑ 71Top-185
❑ 71TopCoi-39
❑ 72MilBra-163
❑ 72Top-745
❑ 78TCM60I-288
❑ 81TCM60I-414
❑ 92CarMcD-27

Javier, Stan
❑ 83GreHorT-24
❑ 84NasSouTI-10
❑ 85DomLeaS-45
❑ 85HunStaJ-20
❑ 86Don-584
❑ 86FleUpd-56
❑ 86TacTigP-9
❑ 87Don-590
❑ 87FleUpd-52
❑ 87FleUpdG-52
❑ 87Top-263
❑ 87TopTif-263
❑ 88A'sMot-15
❑ 88DonBasB-155
❑ 88DonTeaBA-NEW
❑ 88Sco-367
❑ 88ScoGlo-367
❑ 89A'sMot-21
❑ 89Don-185
❑ 89Fle-13
❑ 89FleGlo-13
❑ 89OPC-248
❑ 89Sco-322
❑ 89Top-622
❑ 89TopBig-277
❑ 89TopTif-622
❑ 89UppDec-581
❑ 90A'sMot-23
❑ 90Don-568
❑ 90Fle-12
❑ 90FleCan-12
❑ 90FleUpd-23
❑ 90Lea-445
❑ 90OPC-102
❑ 90PubIntS-308
❑ 90Sco-394
❑ 90ScoRoo-52T
❑ 90ScoYouS2-21
❑ 90Top-102
❑ 90TopTif-102
❑ 90TopTra-47T
❑ 90TopTraT-47T
❑ 90UppDec-209
❑ 91Bow-599
❑ 91DodMot-27
❑ 91DodPho-16
❑ 91DodPol-5
❑ 91DodSt.V-1
❑ 91Don-239
❑ 91Fle-211
❑ 91Lea-155
❑ 91OPC-61
❑ 91PanFreS-61
❑ 91Sco-281
❑ 91StaClu-39
❑ 91StaCluP-18
❑ 91Top-61
❑ 91TopDesS-61
❑ 91TopMic-61
❑ 91TopTif-61
❑ 91UppDec-688
❑ 92DodMot-20
❑ 92DodPol-5
❑ 92DodSmo-10092
❑ 92Don-322
❑ 92Fle-461
❑ 92OPC-581
❑ 92Sco-583
❑ 92StaClu-187
❑ 92Top-581
❑ 92TopGol-581
❑ 92TopGolW-581
❑ 92TopMic-581
❑ 92Ult-212
❑ 92YanWIZ8-90
❑ 93AngMot-23
❑ 93Don-280
❑ 93Fle-493
❑ 93PacBeiA-2
❑ 93PacSpa-237
❑ 93PanSti-276
❑ 93Top-712
❑ 93TopGol-712
❑ 93TopInaM-712
❑ 93TopInaR-712
❑ 93TopMic-712
❑ 93UppDec-249
❑ 93UppDec-730
❑ 93UppDecGold-249
❑ 93UppDecGold-730
❑ 94A'sMot-8
❑ 94ColC-598
❑ 94ColChoGS-598
❑ 94ColChoSS-598
❑ 94Fin-403
❑ 94FinRef-403
❑ 94Fla-92
❑ 94Fle-60
❑ 94FleExtB-151
❑ 94FleUpd-75
❑ 94Lea-325
❑ 94Pac-80
❑ 94Pin-313
❑ 94PinArtP-313
❑ 94PinMusC-313
❑ 94Sco-252
❑ 94ScoGolR-252
❑ 94ScoRoo-RT36
❑ 94ScoRooGR-RT36
❑ 94Sel-115
❑ 94SpoRoo-143
❑ 94SpoRooAP-143
❑ 94StaClu-613
❑ 94StaCluFDI-613
❑ 94StaCluGR-613
❑ 94StaCluMOP-613
❑ 94Top-446
❑ 94TopGol-446
❑ 94TopSpa-446
❑ 94TopTra-107T
❑ 94Ult-409
❑ 94UppDec-384
❑ 94UppDecED-384
❑ 95AthMot-9
❑ 95ColCho-129
❑ 95ColChoGS-129
❑ 95ColChoSS-129
❑ 95Don-485
❑ 95DonPreP-485
❑ 95DonTopotO-138
❑ 95Fla-75
❑ 95Fle-247
❑ 95Lea-323
❑ 95Pac-313
❑ 95Pin-109
❑ 95PinArtP-109
❑ 95PinMusC-109
❑ 95Sco-39
❑ 95ScoGolR-39
❑ 95ScoPlaTS-39
❑ 95StaClu-50
❑ 95StaCluFDI-50
❑ 95StaCluMOP-50
❑ 95StaCluSTWS-50
❑ 95StaCluVR-32
❑ 95StaCluVRMO-32
❑ 95Top-338
❑ 95TopCyb-184
❑ 95Ult-93
❑ 95UltGolM-93
❑ 96Don-155
❑ 96DonPreP-155
❑ 96EmoXL-291
❑ 96Fla-389
❑ 96Fle-211
❑ 96FleTif-211
❑ 96FleUpd-U207
❑ 96FleUpdTC-U207
❑ 96GiaMot-14
❑ 96MetUni-243
❑ 96MetUniP-243
❑ 96Pac-400
❑ 96Sco-420
❑ 96StaClu-207
❑ 96StaCluMOP-207
❑ 96Top-57
❑ 96Ult-568
❑ 96UltGolM-568
❑ 97Fle-483
❑ 97FleTif-483
❑ 97Pac-444
❑ 97PacLigB-444
❑ 97PacSil-444
❑ 97Top-308
❑ 98Fin-167
❑ 98FinNo--167
❑ 98FinNo-R-167
❑ 98FinRef-167
❑ 98Fle-75
❑ 98Fle-555
❑ 98GiaMot-13
❑ 98Pac-443
❑ 98PacInv-145
❑ 98PacInvPBlue-145
❑ 98PacInvSilv-145
❑ 98PacInvTeam-25
❑ 98PacOme-212
❑ 98PacOmeR-212
❑ 98PacOnl-662
❑ 98PacOnlR-662
❑ 98PacOnlWC-662
❑ 98PacPar-246
❑ 98PacParC-246
❑ 98PacParG-246
❑ 98PacParHS-246
❑ 98PacParPB-246
❑ 98PacParR-246
❑ 98PacPlaB-443
❑ 98PacRedT-443
❑ 98PacSil-443
❑ 98Sco-254
❑ 98StaCluFDI-86
❑ 98StaCluI-86
❑ 98StaCluOneK-86
❑ 98StaCluPP-86
❑ 98Top-116
❑ 98TopChr-116
❑ 98TopChrR-116
❑ 98TopDevR-116
❑ 98TopDia-116
❑ 98TopMiniC-116
❑ 98Ult-392
❑ 98UltGolM-392
❑ 98UltMas-392
❑ 98UltPlaM-392
❑ 98UppDec-507
❑ 99Fle-495
❑ 99FleSta9-495
❑ 99FleWarT-495
❑ 99Pac-381
❑ 99PacCroC-251
❑ 99PacCroCPB-251
❑ 99PacInv-129
❑ 99PacInvOD-129
❑ 99PacInvPB-129
❑ 99PacOme-212
❑ 99PacOmeC-212
❑ 99PacOmeG-212
❑ 99PacOmePB-212
❑ 99PacPlaB-381
❑ 99PacRed-381
❑ 99Ult-160
❑ 99UltGolM-160
❑ 99UltMas-160
❑ 99UltPlaM-160
❑ 99UppDec-485
❑ 99UppDecEL1-485
❑ 99UppDecEL2-485
❑ 99Vic-362

Javier, Vicente
❑ 88BilMusP-1824
❑ 89GreHorP-422
❑ 90CedRapRB-4
❑ 90CedRapRP-2327
❑ 91CedRapRC-18
❑ 91CedRapRP-2727

Jay, Joe
❑ 47Exh-107
❑ 54BraJohC-47
❑ 54Top-141
❑ 55BraGolS-11
❑ 55BraJohC-47
❑ 55Top-134
❑ 56RedBurB-9
❑ 58Top-472
❑ 59RedBurBP-7
❑ 59Top-273
❑ 60BraJayP-6
❑ 60BraLaktL-12
❑ 60BraSpiaS-9
❑ 60Lea-23
❑ 60Top-266
❑ 61Kah-21
❑ 61RedJayP-6
❑ 61SevElev-3
❑ 61Top-233
❑ 61TopStal-43
❑ 62Baz-13
❑ 62Jel-124
❑ 62Kah-21
❑ 62Pos-124A
❑ 62Pos-124B
❑ 62PosCan-124
❑ 62RedEnq-16
❑ 62RedJayP-6
❑ 62SalPlaC-126
❑ 62ShiPlaC-126
❑ 62Top-58
❑ 62Top-233
❑ 62Top-263
❑ 62Top-440
❑ 62TopBuc-42
❑ 62TopStal-116
❑ 62TopVen-58
❑ 63BasMagM-40
❑ 63ExhStaB-33
❑ 63Jel-133
❑ 63Kah-16
❑ 63Pos-133
❑ 63RedEnq-15
❑ 63RedFreBC-10
❑ 63RedJayP-4
❑ 63Top-7
❑ 63Top-225
❑ 64Kah-13
❑ 64RedJayP-5
❑ 64Top-346
❑ 64TopVen-346
❑ 65Kah-18
❑ 65OPC-174
❑ 65RedEnq-14
❑ 65Top-174
❑ 66Top-406
❑ 78TCM60I-216
❑ 80Bra195T-2
❑ 80Red196T-27
❑ 90BasWit-81
❑ 94TopArc1-141
❑ 94TopArc1G-141

Jaye, Jamie
❑ 95BakBlaTI-25

Jean, Domingo
❑ 91MidLeaAP-MWL10
❑ 91SouBenWSC-16
❑ 91SouBenWSP-2852
❑ 92Bow-130
❑ 92ForLauYTI-18
❑ 92Ft.LauYF-2607
❑ 92UppDecML-307
❑ 93AlbYanF-2160
❑ 93Bow-159
❑ 93ClaFS7-76
❑ 93FlaWavotF-8
❑ 93YanStaC-30
❑ 94Bow-90
❑ 94Cla-136
❑ 94ColC-147
❑ 94ColChoGS-147
❑ 94ColChoSS-147
❑ 94Don-117
❑ 94Fle-233
❑ 94Pac-425
❑ 94Pin-238
❑ 94PinArtP-238
❑ 94PinMusC-238
❑ 94Sco-256
❑ 94ScoBoyoS-14
❑ 94ScoGolR-256
❑ 94Top-212
❑ 94TopGol-212
❑ 94TopSpa-212
❑ 94TucTorF-756
❑ 94Ult-506
❑ 96ChaLooB-15
❑ 98NewHavRM-15
❑ 98NewHavRMA-15

Jeanes, Tex
❑ 75SenTCM1-12

Jeansonne, Kevin
❑ 76BatTroTI-13
❑ 77WatIndT-14

Jeckell, Matt
❑ 98FarRedHM-13

Jeffcoat, Charles
❑ 29Zee-75
❑ 30Zee-85

Jeffcoat, George
❑ 90DodTar-383

Jeffcoat, Hal
❑ 49EurSta-58
❑ 51Bow-211
❑ 52Bow-104
❑ 52Top-341
❑ 53BowBW-37
❑ 53Top-29
❑ 54Bow-205
❑ 55Bow-223
❑ 56RedBurB-10
❑ 56Top-289
❑ 57Kah-15
❑ 57RedSoh-10
❑ 57Top-93
❑ 58Kah-14
❑ 58RedEnq-20
❑ 58RedJayP-8
❑ 58Top-294
❑ 59RedEnq-11
❑ 59RedShiBS-8
❑ 59Top-81
❑ 59TopVen-81
❑ 60SeaPop-5
❑ 83TopRep5-341
❑ 85TCMPpl1-9
❑ 91TopArc1-29

Jeffcoat, Mike
❑ 81WatIndT-10
❑ 82WatIndT-4
❑ 83ChaChaT-2
❑ 84Don-43
❑ 84FleUpd-58
❑ 84Ind-20
❑ 84IndWhe-46
❑ 84TopTra-56T
❑ 84TopTraT-56T
❑ 85Don-251
❑ 85Fle-453
❑ 85Ind-20
❑ 85Top-303
❑ 85TopTif-303
❑ 86Fle-545
❑ 86PhoFirP-10
❑ 86Top-571
❑ 86TopTif-571
❑ 87OklCit8P-10
❑ 88BlaYNPRWLU-17
❑ 89Fle-524
❑ 89FleGlo-524
❑ 89OklCit8C-4
❑ 89OklCit8P-1520
❑ 90Don-521
❑ 90Fle-302
❑ 90FleCan-302
❑ 90Lea-416
❑ 90OPC-778
❑ 90RanMot-19
❑ 90Sco-158
❑ 90Top-778
❑ 90TopTif-778
❑ 91Bow-278
❑ 91Fle-291
❑ 91Lea-386
❑ 91OPC-244
❑ 91RanMot-19
❑ 91Sco-174
❑ 91StaClu-216
❑ 91Top-244
❑ 91TopDesS-244
❑ 91TopMic-244
❑ 91TopTif-244
❑ 92Don-351
❑ 92Fle-309
❑ 92OklCit8S-312
❑ 92OPC-464
❑ 92RanTeal-10
❑ 92Sco-174
❑ 92StaClu-265
❑ 92Top-464
❑ 92TopGol-464
❑ 92TopGolW-464
❑ 92TopMic-464
❑ 92Ult-134
❑ 92UppDec-597
❑ 93RanKee-202
❑ 94EdmTraF-2870

Jefferies, Daryl
❑ 97WilCubB-9

Jefferies, Gregg
❑ 86ColMetP-16
❑ 87JacMetF-24
❑ 87TexLeaAF-11
❑ 88ClaBlu-243
❑ 88Don-657
❑ 88DonTeaBM-657
❑ 88Fle-137
❑ 88FleGlo-137
❑ 88FleMin-94
❑ 88Lea-259
❑ 88MetColP-27
❑ 88Sco-645
❑ 88ScoGlo-645
❑ 88StaJef-1
❑ 88StaJef-2
❑ 88StaJef-3
❑ 88StaJef-4
❑ 88StaJef-5
❑ 88StaJef-6
❑ 88StaJef-7
❑ 88StaJef-8
❑ 88StaJef-9
❑ 88StaJef-10
❑ 88StaJef-11
❑ 88TidTidCa-9
❑ 88TidTidCM-15A
❑ 88TidTidCM-15B
❑ 88TidTidP-1600
❑ 88TriAAAP-40
❑ 88TriAAC-27
❑ 89Baz-16
❑ 89Bow-381
❑ 89BowTif-381
❑ 89ClaLigB-6
❑ 89ClaTraP-154
❑ 89Don-35
❑ 89DonBasB-152
❑ 89DonRoo-2
❑ 89Fle-38
❑ 89FleExcS-26
❑ 89FleGlo-38
❑ 89FleLeaL-23
❑ 89FleSup-25
❑ 89JefCarCC-1
❑ 89JefCarCC-2
❑ 89JefCarCC-3
❑ 89JefCarCC-4
❑ 89JefCarCC-5
❑ 89JefCarCC-6
❑ 89JefCarCC-7
❑ 89JefCarCC-8
❑ 89JefCarCC-9
❑ 89JefCarCC-10
❑ 89JefCarCC-11
❑ 89JefCarCC-12
❑ 89JefCarCC-13
❑ 89JefCarCC-14
❑ 89JefCarCC-15
❑ 89JefCarCC-16
❑ 89K-M-11
❑ 89MetCol8-9

❑ 89MetCol8-32
❑ 89MetColP-10
❑ 89MetFanC-0
❑ 89MetKah-12
❑ 89MSAHolD-11
❑ 89Nis-11
❑ 89OPC-233
❑ 89PanSti-128
❑ 89Sco-600
❑ 89ScoHot1R-1
❑ 89Scomast-39
❑ 89ScoYouSl-1
❑ 89Spo-90
❑ 89Spo-223
❑ 89Top-233
❑ 89TopBasT-87
❑ 89TopBig-253
❑ 89TopDouM-2
❑ 89TopHeaUT-10
❑ 89TopRoo-13
❑ 89TopTif-233
❑ 89TopUKM-44
❑ 89ToyRoo-15
❑ 89TVSpoM-8
❑ 89UppDec-9
❑ 89Woo-22
❑ 90Baz-14
❑ 90Bow-140
❑ 90BowTif-140
❑ 90ClaUpd-T1
❑ 90Don-270
❑ 90DonBesN-117
❑ 90Fle-207
❑ 90FleCan-207
❑ 90Hot50RS-22
❑ 90Lea-171
❑ 90MetCol8-17
❑ 90MetColP-5
❑ 90MetFanC-9
❑ 90MetKah-9
❑ 90MLBBasB-18
❑ 90OPC-457
❑ 90PanSti-298
❑ 90PublntS-136
❑ 90PublntS-614
❑ 90Sco-468
❑ 90Sco100RS-10
❑ 90Spo-14
❑ 90StaLonJS-12
❑ 90StaLonJS-32
❑ 90Top-457
❑ 90TopBig-57
❑ 90TopDou-36
❑ 90TopGloS-60
❑ 90TopRoo-16
❑ 90TopSti-324
❑ 90TopStiB-5
❑ 90TopTif-457
❑ 90TopTVM-24
❑ 90ToyRoo-16
❑ 90UppDec-166
❑ 90UppDecS-4
❑ 91BasBesHM-11
❑ 91Bow-481
❑ 91Cla2-T40
❑ 91ClaGam-117
❑ 91Don-79
❑ 91Fle-151
❑ 91Lea-465
❑ 91MajLeaCP-77
❑ 91MetColP-5
❑ 91MetKah-9
❑ 91MetPerPA-19
❑ 91MetTro-4
❑ 91MetWIZ-199
❑ 91OPC-30
❑ 91PanFreS-80
❑ 91PanSti-83
❑ 91Pos-9
❑ 91Sco-660
❑ 91Sco100S-80
❑ 91Sev3DCN-8
❑ 91SevCoi-NE8
❑ 91StaClu-257
❑ 91Stu-206
❑ 91Top-30
❑ 91TopDesS-30
❑ 91TopMic-30
❑ 91TopTif-30
❑ 91Ult-221
❑ 91Ult-397
❑ 91UppDec-95
❑ 91UppDec-156
❑ 92Bow-13
❑ 92ClaGam-171
❑ 92Don-372
❑ 92Fle-508
❑ 92FleUpd-26
❑ 92Hig5-73
❑ 92Lea-215
❑ 92LeaBlaG-215
❑ 92OPC-707
❑ 92OPCPre-95
❑ 92PanSti-223
❑ 92Pin-330
❑ 92PinTea2-45
❑ 92RoyPol-12
❑ 92Sco-192
❑ 92ScoRoo-39T
❑ 92SpollIFK1-292
❑ 92StaClu-737
❑ 92StaCluNC-737
❑ 92Stu-184
❑ 92Top-707
❑ 92TopGol-707
❑ 92TopGolW-707
❑ 92TopKid-14
❑ 92TopMic-707
❑ 92TopTra-55T
❑ 92TopTraG-55T
❑ 92Ult-372
❑ 92UppDec-133
❑ 92UppDec-725
❑ 93Bow-544
❑ 93CarPol-7
❑ 93CarStaC-12
❑ 93DiaMar-55
❑ 93Don-307
❑ 93Fin-83
❑ 93FinRef-83
❑ 93Fla-121
❑ 93Fle-238
❑ 93FleFinE-124
❑ 93FunPac-75
❑ 93Lea-265
❑ 93OPC-123
❑ 93OPCPre-98
❑ 93PacSpa-137
❑ 93PanSti-106
❑ 93Pin-24
❑ 93Pin-480
❑ 93RedFolS-45
❑ 93Sco-17
❑ 93ScoFra-7
❑ 93Sel-152
❑ 93SelRoo-12T
❑ 93SP-75
❑ 93StaClu-628
❑ 93StaCluFDI-628
❑ 93StaCluMOP-628
❑ 93Stu-90
❑ 93Top-105
❑ 93TopGol-105
❑ 93ToplnaM-105
❑ 93ToplnaR-105
❑ 93TopMic-105
❑ 93TopTra-122T
❑ 93TriPla-130
❑ 93Ult-209
❑ 93Ult-463
❑ 93UppDec-54
❑ 93UppDec-176
❑ 93UppDec-545
❑ 93UppDec-818
❑ 93UppDecGold-54
❑ 93UppDecGold-176
❑ 93UppDecGold-545
❑ 93UppDecGold-818
❑ 94Bow-536
❑ 94BowBes-R27
❑ 94BowBesR-R27
❑ 94CarLeaA-DJ32
❑ 94CarMagG-2
❑ 94CarPol-6
❑ 94ColC-148
❑ 94ColChoGS-148
❑ 94ColChoSS-148
❑ 94Don-9
❑ 94DonDiaK-DK21
❑ 94DonDiaKJ-DK21
❑ 94DonMVP-12
❑ 94DonSpeE-9
❑ 94Fin-92
❑ 94FinPre-92P
❑ 94FinRef-92
❑ 94Fla-429
❑ 94Fle-633
❑ 94FleExtB-359
❑ 94FleTeaL-26
❑ 94FUnPac-153
❑ 94Lea-56
❑ 94LeaL-145
❑ 94LeaLimGA-2
❑ 94LeaMVPC-N6
❑ 94LeaMVPCG-N6
❑ 94OPC-77
❑ 94OscMayR-24
❑ 94Pac-591
❑ 94PacSilP-27
❑ 94PacSilPC-27
❑ 94PanSti-243
❑ 94Pin-204
❑ 94PinArtP-204
❑ 94PinMusC-204
❑ 94PinRunC-RC27
❑ 94Pos-28
❑ 94ProMag-115
❑ 94Sco-29
❑ 94ScoCyc-TC5
❑ 94ScoGolR-29
❑ 94ScoGolS-9
❑ 94Sel-232
❑ 94SP-63
❑ 94SPDieC-63
❑ 94Spo-74
❑ 94SpoMov-MM1
❑ 94StaClu-109
❑ 94StaClu-531
❑ 94StaCluFDI-109
❑ 94StaCluFDI-531
❑ 94StaCluGR-109
❑ 94StaCluGR-531
❑ 94StaCluMO-19
❑ 94StaCluMOP-109
❑ 94StaCluMOP-531
❑ 94StaCluMOP-ST12
❑ 94StaCluST-ST12
❑ 94StaCluT-317
❑ 94StaCluTFDI-317
❑ 94Stu-51
❑ 94StuHer-7
❑ 94TomPiz-10
❑ 94Top-660
❑ 94TopBlaG-35
❑ 94TopGol-660
❑ 94TopSpa-660
❑ 94TopSupS-22
❑ 94TriPla-62
❑ 94TriPlaN-8
❑ 94Ult-266
❑ 94UltOnBL-7
❑ 94UppDec-265
❑ 94UppDecAJ-4
❑ 94UppDecAJG-4
❑ 94UppDecED-265
❑ 94USPlaCA-6H
❑ 94USPlaCA-12D
❑ 95Baz-25
❑ 95Bow-315
❑ 95ColCho-360
❑ 95ColChoGS-360
❑ 95ColChoSE-80
❑ 95ColChoSEGS-80
❑ 95ColChoSESS-80
❑ 95ColChoSS-360
❑ 95Don-417
❑ 95DonAll-NL3
❑ 95DonDiaK-DK28
❑ 95DonPreP-417
❑ 95DonTopotO-307
❑ 95Emo-168
❑ 95Fin-219
❑ 95FinRef-219
❑ 95Fla-392
❑ 95Fle-499
❑ 95FleAllS-2
❑ 95FleTeaL-26
❑ 95FleUpd-122
❑ 95KinDis-12
❑ 95Kra-23
❑ 95Lea-398
❑ 95LeaLim-72
❑ 95Pac-407
❑ 95PacGolP-2
❑ 95PacPri-131
❑ 95PanSti-33
❑ 95Phi-17
❑ 95PhiMel-14
❑ 95Pin-364
❑ 95PinArtP-364
❑ 95PinMusC-364
❑ 95PinPer-PP10
❑ 95RedFol-31
❑ 95Sco-354
❑ 95ScoGolR-354
❑ 95ScoPlaTS-354
❑ 95Sel-220
❑ 95SelArtP-220
❑ 95SP-86
❑ 95SPCha-75
❑ 95SPChaDC-75
❑ 95Spo-133
❑ 95SpoArtP-133
❑ 95SPSil-86
❑ 95StaClu-361
❑ 95StaClu-625
❑ 95StaCluMOP-361
❑ 95StaCluMOP-625
❑ 95StaCluSTWS-361
❑ 95StaCluSTWS-625
❑ 95Stu-47
❑ 95StuGolS-47
❑ 95Sum-56
❑ 95SumNthD-56
❑ 95Top-526
❑ 95TopCyb-311
❑ 95TopTra-77T
❑ 95UC3-44
❑ 95UC3ArtP-44
❑ 95Ult-420
❑ 95UltGolM-420
❑ 95UppDec-250
❑ 95UppDec-475
❑ 95UppDec-TC5
❑ 95UppDecED-59
❑ 95UppDecEDG-59
❑ 95UppDecPLL-R28
❑ 95UppDecPLLE-R28
❑ 95UppDecSE-76
❑ 95UppDecSEG-76
❑ 95UppDecT-TC5
❑ 95USPlaCMLA-2D
❑ 95Zen-38
❑ 96Baz-82
❑ 96Bow-44
❑ 96BowFoi-44
❑ 96ColCho-670
❑ 96ColChoGS-670
❑ 96ColChoSS-670
❑ 96Don-341
❑ 96DonDiaK-17
❑ 96DonPreP-341
❑ 96EmoXL-246
❑ 96Fin-S37
❑ 96FinRef-S37
❑ 96Fla-335
❑ 96Fle-500
❑ 96FleTif-500
❑ 96Lea-93
❑ 96LeaLim-25
❑ 96LeaLimG-25
❑ 96LeaPre-3
❑ 96LeaPreP-3
❑ 96LeaPrePB-93
❑ 96LeaPrePG-93
❑ 96LeaPrePS-93
❑ 96LeaPreSG-7
❑ 96LeaPreSte-7
❑ 96LeaSig-13
❑ 96LeaSigPPG-13
❑ 96LeaSigPPP-13
❑ 96MetUni-211
❑ 96MetUniP-211
❑ 96Pac-159
❑ 96PacPri-P54
❑ 96PacPriG-P54
❑ 96PanSti-39
❑ 96PhiTeal-17
❑ 96Pin-47
❑ 96PinAfi-89
❑ 96PinAfiAP-89
❑ 96PinAfiFPP-89
❑ 96PinArtP-19
❑ 96PinSta-19
❑ 96ProSta-87
❑ 96Sco-321
❑ 96ScoDugC-B46
❑ 96ScoDugCAP-B46
❑ 96Sel-23
❑ 96SelArtP-23
❑ 96SelCer-23
❑ 96SelCerAP-23
❑ 96SelCerCB-23
❑ 96SelCerCR-23
❑ 96SelCerMB-23
❑ 96SelCerMG-23
❑ 96SelCerMR-23
❑ 96SelTeaN-10
❑ 96SP-145
❑ 96Spo-78
❑ 96SpoArtP-78
❑ 96StaClu-425
❑ 96StaCluEPB-425
❑ 96StaCluEPG-425
❑ 96StaCluEPS-425
❑ 96StaCluMOP-425
❑ 96Stu-5
❑ 96StuPrePD-5
❑ 96StuPrePG-5
❑ 96StuPrePS-5
❑ 96Sum-17
❑ 96SumAbo&B-17
❑ 96SumArtP-17
❑ 96SumFoi-17
❑ 96Top-180
❑ 96TopChr-53
❑ 96TopChrR-53
❑ 96TopGal-63
❑ 96TopGalPPI-63
❑ 96TopLas-24
❑ 96Ult-254
❑ 96UltGolM-254
❑ 96UppDec-170
❑ 96Zen-23
❑ 96ZenArtP-23
❑ 97Bow-262
❑ 97BowBes-68
❑ 97BowBesAR-68
❑ 97BowBesR-68
❑ 97Bowlnt-262
❑ 97Cir-311
❑ 97CirRav-311
❑ 97ColCho-195
❑ 97Don-87
❑ 97DonGolPP-87
❑ 97DonPre-128
❑ 97DonPreCttC-128
❑ 97DonSilPP-87
❑ 97E-X2-88
❑ 97E-X2Cred-88
❑ 97E-X2EssCre-88
❑ 97Fin-38
❑ 97FinRef-38
❑ 97Fle-413
❑ 97FleTif-413
❑ 97Lea-12
❑ 97LeaFraM-12
❑ 97LeaFraMDC-12
❑ 97MetUni-201
❑ 97NewPin-6
❑ 97NewPinAP-6
❑ 97NewPinMC-6
❑ 97NewPinPP-6
❑ 97Pac-379
❑ 97PacLigB-379
❑ 97PacPri-129
❑ 97PacPriLB-129
❑ 97PacPriP-129
❑ 97PacSil-379
❑ 97PhiCopQ-12
❑ 97PhiTeal-25
❑ 97Sco-10
❑ 97ScoArtPWB-10
❑ 97ScoPreS-10
❑ 97ScoShoS-10
❑ 97ScoShoSAP-10
❑ 97SP-138
❑ 97StaClu-76
❑ 97StaCluC-CO4
❑ 97StaCluMOP-76
❑ 97Top-229
❑ 97TopChr-81
❑ 97TopChrR-81
❑ 97TopGal-23
❑ 97TopGalPPI-23
❑ 97ToplntF-ILM12
❑ 97ToplntFR-ILM12
❑ 97Ult-336
❑ 97UltGolME-336
❑ 97UltPlaME-336
❑ 97UppDec-155
❑ 98CirThu-106
❑ 98CirThuRav-106
❑ 98CirThuSupRav-106
❑ 98ColCho-462
❑ 98Fin-188
❑ 98FinNo--188
❑ 98FinNo-R-188
❑ 98FinRef-188
❑ 98Fle-470
❑ 98FleVin'-113
❑ 98FleVin'C-113
❑ 98Pac-382
❑ 98PacAur-171
❑ 98Paclnv-124
❑ 98PaclnvPBlue-124
❑ 98PaclnvSilv-124
❑ 98PaclnvTeam-21
❑ 98PacOme-183
❑ 98PacOmeR-183
❑ 98PacOnl-563
❑ 98PacOnlR-563
❑ 98PacOnlWC-563
❑ 98PacPar-213
❑ 98PacParC-213
❑ 98PacParG-213
❑ 98PacParHS-213
❑ 98PacParPB-213
❑ 98PacParR-213
❑ 98PacPlaB-382
❑ 98PacRedT-382
❑ 98PacSil-382
❑ 98PhiTeal-18
❑ 98Pin-151
❑ 98PinPreP-151
❑ 98Sco-226
❑ 98SPxFin-113
❑ 98SPxFinR-113
❑ 98SPxFinS-113
❑ 98StaCluFDI-28
❑ 98StaClul-28
❑ 98StaCluOneK-28
❑ 98StaCluPP-28
❑ 98Top-341
❑ 98TopChr-341
❑ 98TopChrR-341
❑ 98TopDevR-341
❑ 98TopDia-341
❑ 98TopMiniC-341
❑ 98Ult-355
❑ 98UltGolM-355
❑ 98UltMas-355
❑ 98UltPlaM-355
❑ 98UppDec-473
❑ 99199Fin-237
❑ 99FinGolRef-237
❑ 99FinRef-237
❑ 99Fle-497
❑ 99FleSta9-497
❑ 99FleWarT-497
❑ 99SkyPre-46
❑ 99SkyPreR-46
❑ 99StaClu-334
❑ 99StaCluFDI-334
❑ 99StaCluOoaK-334
❑ 99StaCluPP-334
❑ 99Top-258
❑ 99TopChr-258
❑ 99TopChrR-258
❑ 99TopMVPP-258

Jeffers, Steve

❑ 87EriCarP-6
❑ 88SprCarB-20

Jefferson, David

❑ 96RocCubTI-13

Jefferson, George

❑ 86NegLeaF-105
❑ 91PomBlaBPB-2

Jefferson, Jesse

❑ 73BalOriP-27
❑ 73OPC-604
❑ 73Top-604
❑ 74OPC-509
❑ 74Top-509
❑ 75BalOriP-18
❑ 75OPC-539
❑ 75Top-539
❑ 75TopMin-539
❑ 76OPC-47
❑ 76Top-47
❑ 76VenLeaS-30
❑ 77OPC-184
❑ 77Top-326
❑ 78BluJayP-10
❑ 78OPC-22
❑ 78Top-144
❑ 79BluJayBY-14
❑ 79OPC-112
❑ 79Top-221
❑ 80OPC-244
❑ 80Top-467
❑ 81Fle-419A
❑ 81Fle-419B
❑ 81Fle-419C
❑ 81LonBeaPT-10
❑ 82Fle-466
❑ 82Top-682
❑ 91OriCro-219
❑ 92Nab-32

Jefferson, Jim

❑ 86FloStaLAP-25
❑ 86TamTarP-7
❑ 87VerRedP-2
❑ 88ChaLooB-19
❑ 88NasSouTI-13

Jefferson, Reggie

- 87CedRapRP-14
- 88CedRapRP-1146
- 89CedRapRAB-9
- 89ChaLooB-1
- 89ChaLooGS-12
- 90Bow-51
- 90BowTif-51
- 90CedRapRDGB-9
- 90CMC-147
- 90NasSouC-22
- 90NasSouP-238
- 90ProAAAF-550
- 91Bow-678
- 91Cla1-T35
- 91DonRoo-55
- 91Lea-514
- 91LinDriAAA-263
- 91NasSouLD-263
- 91NasSouP-2164
- 91TopTra-60T
- 91TopTraT-60T
- 91Ult-379
- 91UppDec-746
- 91UppDecFE-73F
- 92Bow-25
- 92ClaGam-47
- 92Don-12
- 92Fle-113
- 92IndFanC-14
- 92Lea-86
- 92LeaBlaG-86
- 92OPC-93
- 92Pin-476
- 92PinTea2-79
- 92ProFS7-213
- 92Sco-409
- 92ScoHotR-10
- 92StaClu-335
- 92Top-93
- 92TopDeb91-89
- 92TopGol-93
- 92TopGolW-93
- 92TopMic-93
- 92TriPla-24
- 92Ult-50
- 92UppDec-656
- 93Bow-557
- 93Don-303
- 93Fin-139
- 93FinRef-139
- 93Fle-594
- 93IndWUA-13
- 93Lea-302
- 93OPC-163
- 93PacSpa-412
- 93PanSti-48
- 93Pin-550
- 93Sco-433
- 93Sel-330
- 93SP-121
- 93StaClu-425
- 93StaCluFDI-425
- 93StaCluMOP-425
- 93Stu-152
- 93Top-496
- 93TopGol-496
- 93TopInaM-496
- 93TopInaR-496
- 93TopMic-496
- 93Toy-83
- 93Ult-541
- 93UppDec-544
- 93UppDecGold-544
- 93USPlaCR-2D
- 94ColC-149
- 94ColC-428
- 94ColChoGS-149
- 94ColChoGS-428
- 94ColChoSS-149
- 94ColChoSS-428
- 94Don-653
- 94Fin-333
- 94FinRef-333
- 94Fla-105
- 94Fle-106
- 94FleExtB-167
- 94FleUpd-83
- 94Lea-298
- 94MarMot-8
- 94Pac-170
- 94Pin-161
- 94PinArtP-161
- 94PinMusC-161
- 94Sco-391
- 94ScoGolR-391
- 94ScoRoo-RT43
- 94ScoRooGR-RT43
- 94Sel-292
- 94SpoRoo-11
- 94SpoRooAP-11
- 94Top-121
- 94TopGol-121
- 94TopSpa-121
- 94UppDec-478
- 94UppDecED-478
- 95ColCho-295
- 95ColChoGS-295
- 95ColChoSE-128
- 95ColChoSEGS-128
- 95ColChoSESS-128
- 95ColChoSS-295
- 95Don-338
- 95DonPreP-338
- 95Fle-270
- 95Pin-48
- 95PinArtP-48
- 95PinMusC-48
- 95Sco-353
- 95ScoGolR-353
- 95ScoPlaTS-353
- 95Sel-106
- 95SelArtP-106
- 95Spo-44
- 95SpoArtP-44
- 95StaClu-284
- 95StaCluMOP-284
- 95StaCluSTWS-284
- 95Top-614
- 95TopCyb-382
- 95Ult-102
- 95UltGolM-102
- 95UppDec-111
- 95UppDecED-111
- 95UppDecEDG-111
- 96Don-359
- 96DonPreP-359
- 96FleUpd-U13
- 96FleUpdTC-U13
- 96LeaSigA-117
- 96LeaSigAG-117
- 96LeaSigAS-117
- 96Sco-425
- 97Cir-267
- 97CirRav-267
- 97ColCho-278
- 97Don-103
- 97DonGolPP-103
- 97DonLim-7
- 97DonLimE-7
- 97DonLimENG-7
- 97DonSilPP-103
- 97DonTea-47
- 97DonTeaSPE-47
- 97Fle-25
- 97FleTif-25
- 97Lea-91
- 97LeaFraM-91
- 97LeaFraMDC-91
- 97Pac-42
- 97PacLigB-42
- 97PacPri-16
- 97PacPriLB-16
- 97PacPriP-16
- 97PacSil-42
- 97Pin-72
- 97PinArtP-PP72
- 97PinMusC-72
- 97PinPrePla-72
- 97RedSoxS-4
- 97RedSoxSPl-4
- 97RedSoxSPr-4
- 97Sco-110
- 97ScoArtPWB-110
- 97ScoPreS-110
- 97ScoShoS-110
- 97ScoShoSAP-110
- 97StaClu-173
- 97StaCluMOP-173
- 97Top-29
- 97Ult-304
- 97UltGolME-304
- 97UltPlaME-304
- 97UppDec-313
- 98CirThu-201
- 98CirThuRav-201
- 98CirThuSupRav-201
- 98ColCho-322
- 98Don-52
- 98DonCol-52
- 98DonColL-207
- 98DonColP-648
- 98DonColS-52
- 98DonGolPP-52
- 98DonPre-98
- 98DonPreSeat-98
- 98DonPriCD-52
- 98DonPriCL-207
- 98DonPriCP-648
- 98DonSilPP-52
- 98Fin-205
- 98FinNo--205
- 98FinNo-R-205
- 98FinRef-205
- 98Fle-232
- 98Lea-7
- 98LeaFraDA-7
- 98LeaFraF-7
- 98LeaFraM-7
- 98LeaFraM-7
- 98LeaFraMDC-7
- 98LeaFraMDC-7
- 98LeaFraMZ2-7
- 98Pac-44
- 98PacOme-38
- 98PacOmeR-38
- 98PacOnl-117
- 98PacOnlR-117
- 98PacOnlWC-117
- 98PacPar-21
- 98PacParC-21
- 98PacParG-21
- 98PacParHS-21
- 98PacParPB-21
- 98PacParR-21
- 98PacPlaB-44
- 98PacRedT-44
- 98PacSil-44
- 98Pin-129
- 98PinPlu-127
- 98PinPreP-129
- 98RedSoxS-9
- 98RedSoxSP-9
- 98Revo-25
- 98RevoSS-25
- 98Sco-159
- 98ScoRT-70
- 98ScoSS-PP65
- 98ScoSSAP-PP65
- 98StaCluFDI-37
- 98StaClul-37
- 98StaCluOneK-37
- 98StaCluPP-37
- 98Stu-73
- 98StuGPP-73
- 98StuSPP-73
- 98Top-427
- 98TopChr-427
- 98TopChrR-427
- 98TopDevR-427
- 98TopDia-427
- 98TopMiniC-427
- 98Ult-343
- 98UltGolM-343
- 98UltMas-343
- 98UltPlaM-343
- 98UppDec-315
- 99Fle-529
- 99FleSta9-529
- 99FleWarT-529
- 99Pac-68
- 99PacAur-28
- 99PacAurOD-28
- 99PacPar-39
- 99PacParC-39
- 99PacParG-39
- 99PacParHoloGold-39
- 99PacParHS-39
- 99PacParOD-39
- 99PacParPB-39
- 99PacParRed-39
- 99PacPlaB-68
- 99PacRed-68
- 99Top-322
- 99TopChr-322
- 99TopChrR-322
- 99TopMVPP-322
- 99Ult-46
- 99UltGolM-46
- 99UltMas-46
- 99UltPlaM-46
- 99UppDec-323
- 99UppDecEL1-323
- 99UppDecEL2-323

Jefferson, Stan
- 86MetColP-23
- 86MetTCM-33
- 86StaoftFT-31
- 86TidTidP-14
- 87Don-642
- 87DonRoo-43
- 87FleUpd-53
- 87FleUpdG-53
- 87PadBohHB-22
- 87SpoRool-9
- 87TopTra-55T
- 87TopTraT-55T
- 88BlaYNPRWL-119
- 88Don-187
- 88Fle-587
- 88FleGlo-587
- 88OPC-223
- 88PadCok-22
- 88PadSmo-12
- 88PanSti-411
- 88Sco-114
- 88ScoGlo-114
- 88ScoYouSl-11
- 88StaLinPa-6
- 88Top-223
- 88TopBig-86
- 88TopSti-109
- 88TopTif-223
- 89Bow-180
- 89BowTif-180
- 89ColCliC-28
- 89Sco-519
- 89Top-689A
- 89Top-689B
- 89TopBig-165
- 89TopTif-689
- 91ColSprSSLD-84
- 91LinDriAAA-84
- 91MetWIZ-200
- 91OriCro-220
- 92YanWIZ8-91
- 94ButCopKSP-29
- 95PitMetTI-11

Jeffery, Scott
- 88GreHorP-1553
- 89CedRapRB-3
- 89CedRapRP-913
- 89CedRapRS-9
- 90CedRapRB-25
- 91ChaLooP-1955
- 93MedHatBJF-3734
- 93MedHatBJSP-17

Jeffries, James
- 82BurRanF-25
- 82BurRanT-4

Jefts, Chris
- 86PenWhiSP-14
- 87DayBeaAP-16

Jelic, Chris
- 86Ft.MyeRP-15
- 87LynMetP-4
- 88JacMetGS-8
- 88MetColP-28
- 89JacMetGS-5
- 89MetColP-36
- 90CMC-369
- 90ProAAAF-284
- 90TidTidC-18
- 90TidTidP-553
- 90TopTVM-48
- 91Cla1-T66
- 91LasVegSLD-285
- 91LasVegSP-249
- 91LinDriAAA-285
- 91MetWIZ-201
- 91TopDeb90-76
- 92LasVegSF-2802
- 92WicWraS-636
- 93LasVegSF-957

Jelinek, Joey
- 91MarPhiC-9
- 91MarPhiP-3462
- 92MarPhiC-8
- 92MarPhiF-3065

Jelks, Greg
- 86PorBeaP-11
- 87MaiGuiP-9
- 87MaiGuiT-12
- 87PhiTas-45
- 88Fle-648
- 88FleGlo-648
- 88MaiPhiC-18
- 88MaiPhiP-298
- 89LouRedBC-19
- 89LouRedBP-1258
- 89LouRedBTI-24
- 93AusFut-74
- 93AusFut-124
- 95AusFut-101

Jelks, Pat
- 85GreHorT-22
- 86NewBriRSP-14
- 88RivRedWCLC-228
- 88RivRedWP-1411
- 88WicPilRD-28

Jeltz, Steve
- 82ReaPhiT-15
- 83PorBeaT-6
- 84PorBeaC-205
- 85Don-44
- 85Fle-653
- 85PhiCIG-10
- 85PhiTas-11
- 85PhiTas-30
- 85TopTifT-62T
- 85TopTra-62T
- 86PhiCIG-9
- 86PhiTas-30
- 86Top-453
- 86TopTif-453
- 87Don-359
- 87DonOpeD-157
- 87Fle-178
- 87FleGlo-178
- 87PhiCha-2
- 87PhiTas-30
- 87Top-294
- 87TopTif-294
- 88Don-576
- 88Fle-308
- 88FleGlo-308
- 88OPC-126
- 88PanSti-361
- 88PhiTas-15
- 88Sco-435
- 88ScoGlo-435
- 88StaLinPh-11
- 88Top-126
- 88TopTif-126
- 89Don-431
- 89DonBasB-271
- 89Fle-573
- 89FleGlo-573
- 89PhiTas-13
- 89Sco-355
- 89Top-707
- 89TopBig-52
- 89TopSti-114
- 89TopTif-707
- 89UppDec-219
- 90Don-133
- 90Fle-562
- 90FleCan-562
- 90OPC-607
- 90PubIntS-242
- 90RedFolSB-52
- 90RoyPos-14
- 90Sco-421
- 90ScoRoo-59T
- 90Top-607
- 90TopSti-113
- 90TopTif-607
- 90UppDec-495
- 91LinDriAAA-457
- 91OPC-507
- 91RocRedWLD-457
- 91RocRedWP-1908
- 91Sco-272
- 91Top-507
- 91TopDesS-507
- 91TopMic-507
- 91TopTif-507

Jemison, Greg
- 77AshTouT-11
- 79WesHavYT-15
- 80NasSouTI-11
- 83BurRanF-26
- 83BurRanT-27
- 84TulDriTI-14

Jendra, Rick
- 80CedRapRT-11

Jenkins, Ab
- 40WheM4-5

Jenkins, Anthony
- 91SavCarC-25
- 91SavCarP-1666

Jenkins, Arthur
- 94SpoIndC-12
- 94SpoIndF-3318

Jenkins, Ben
- 96MarPhiB-10

Jenkins, Bernie
- 88AubAstP-1959
- 89OscAstS-9
- 90Bes-66
- 90ColMudB-10
- 90ColMudP-1359
- 90ColMudS-15
- 91JacGenLD-563
- 91JacGenP-938
- 91LinDriAA-563
- 92CedRapRF-1085
- 93ChaLooF-2373

Jenkins, Brett
- 92WesPalBEC-21
- 92WesPalBEF-2094
- 93SanJosGC-14
- 93SanJosGF-18

Jenkins, Buddy
- 91JamExpC-21
- 91JamExpP-3540

Jenkins, Corey
- 95Bes-113
- 95BowBes-X8
- 95BowBesR-X8
- 95TopTra-106T
- 96LowSpiB-11
- 96Top-20
- 96TopPowB-20
- 97MicBatC-14

Jenkins, Daniel
- 96BilMusTI-15

Jenkins, Dee
- 91PriRedC-14
- 91PriRedP-3522
- 92BilMusF-3363
- 92BilMusSP-12
- 93ExcFS7-22
- 93WesVirWC-9
- 93WesVirWF-2871
- 94UppDecML-109
- 94WinSpiC-11
- 94WinSpiF-278
- 98StoPorG-14
- 98VisOakG-14

Jenkins, Fats
- 74LauOldTBS-28
- 86NegLeaF-113

Jenkins, Fergie
- 66Top-254
- 66TopVen-254
- 67CokCapC-1
- 67CubProPS-8
- 67ProPizC-10
- 67Top-333
- 67TopVen-306
- 68Baz-10
- 68Kah-B17
- 68OPC-9
- 68OPC-11
- 68Top-9
- 68Top-11
- 68Top-410
- 68TopActS-11C
- 68TopVen-9
- 68TopVen-11
- 69CubJewT-9
- 69CubPho-7
- 69CubTealC-5
- 69MilBra-131
- 69MLBOffS-122
- 69OPC-10
- 69OPC-12
- 69Top-10
- 69Top-12
- 69Top-640
- 69TopDecl-20
- 69TopSta-15
- 69TopSup-37
- 69TopTeaP-4
- 70MLBOffS-19
- 70OPC-69
- 70OPC-71
- 70OPC-240
- 70SunPin-5
- 70Top-69
- 70Top-71
- 70Top-240
- 70TopCanL-11
- 71AllBasA-11
- 71BazNumT-13
- 71MilDud-49
- 71MLBOffS-35
- 71MLBOffS-563
- 71OPC-70
- 71OPC-72
- 71OPC-280
- 71Top-70
- 71Top-72
- 71Top-280
- 71TopCoi-7
- 71TopSup-42

❑ 71TopTat-81
❑ 71TopTat-82
❑ 72CubChi-3
❑ 72CubTeal-6
❑ 72Dia-60
❑ 72Kel-8
❑ 72MilBra-164
❑ 72OPC-93
❑ 72OPC-95
❑ 72OPC-410
❑ 72ProStaP-16
❑ 72SevTraC-22
❑ 72Top-93
❑ 72Top-95
❑ 72Top-410
❑ 72TopPos-10
❑ 73Kel2D-28
❑ 73LinPor-178
❑ 73OPC-180
❑ 73Top-180
❑ 73TopCanL-23
❑ 74LauAllG-67
❑ 74OPC-87
❑ 74Top-87
❑ 74TopDecE-59
❑ 74TopSta-236
❑ 75Hos-116
❑ 75Kel-22
❑ 75OPC-60
❑ 75OPC-310
❑ 75RanPos-18
❑ 75Top-60
❑ 75Top-310
❑ 75TopMin-60
❑ 75TopMin-310
❑ 76Hos-138
❑ 76LinSup-105
❑ 76OPC-250
❑ 76RedSoxSM-8
❑ 76SSP-255
❑ 76Top-250
❑ 76TopTra-250T
❑ 77BurCheD-31
❑ 77Kel-3
❑ 77OPC-187
❑ 77Spo-4702
❑ 77Top-430
❑ 78RanBurK-8
❑ 78SSP270-84
❑ 78Top-720
❑ 79Top-544
❑ 80Kel-47
❑ 80OPC-203
❑ 80PerHaloFP-208
❑ 80PerHaloFPS-71
❑ 80Top-390
❑ 81Don-146
❑ 81Fle-622
❑ 81FleStiC-84
❑ 81Top-158
❑ 82CubRedL-31
❑ 82Don-643
❑ 82Fle-320
❑ 82FleSta-173
❑ 82OPC-137
❑ 82Top-624
❑ 82TopTra-49T
❑ 83AllGamPI-167
❑ 83CubThoAV-31
❑ 83Don-300
❑ 83Fle-498
❑ 83FleSta-91
❑ 83FleSti-130
❑ 83OPC-230
❑ 83OPC-231
❑ 83Top-51
❑ 83Top-230
❑ 83Top-231
❑ 83TopFol-1
❑ 83TopSti-224
❑ 84CubBriPC-2D
❑ 84CubUno-5
❑ 84Don-189
❑ 84DonCha-33
❑ 84Fle-494
❑ 84Nes792-456
❑ 84Nes792-483
❑ 84Nes792-706
❑ 84OPC-343
❑ 84SevCoi-C20
❑ 84SpoDesPW-46
❑ 84Top-456
❑ 84Top-483
❑ 84Top-706
❑ 84TopSti-48
❑ 84TopTif-456
❑ 84TopTif-483
❑ 84TopTif-706
❑ 88HouSho-19
❑ 88OklCit8C-6
❑ 88OklCit8P-50
❑ 88PacLegI-43
❑ 89ChaLooLITI-14
❑ 89OklCit8C-25
❑ 89OklCit8P-1513
❑ 89PacSenL-29
❑ 89T/MSenL-55
❑ 89TopSenL-119
❑ 90EliSenL-97
❑ 90EliSenL-125
❑ 90PerGreM-93
❑ 91CubVinL-15
❑ 91PacSenL-108
❑ 91SweBasG-45
❑ 91UppDecHoB-H3
❑ 91UppDecHoB-AU3
❑ 91UppDecS-11
❑ 91UppDecS-18
❑ 91UppDecS-21
❑ 92ActPacA-4
❑ 92ActPacA2-4G
❑ 92CubOldS-16
❑ 92KodCelD-2
❑ 92MCIAmb-13
❑ 92MCIAmb-15
❑ 93RanKee-203
❑ 93TedWil-22
❑ 93UppDecAH-74
❑ 93UppDecAH-159
❑ 93UppDecS-1
❑ 93UppDecS-21
❑ 94MCIAmb-5
❑ 94UppDecAH-97
❑ 94UppDecAH-212
❑ 94UppDecAH1-97
❑ 94UppDecAH1-212
❑ 95SonGre-4
❑ 97St.VinHHS-10
❑ 98SpollITaN-12
❑ 98SpollITaNEE-12
❑ 98SpollITaNGS-16
❑ 99SpollIGotG-12
❑ 99SpollIGotGA-35
❑ 99SpollIGotGC-23

Jenkins, Garrett

❑ 89ElmPioP-6
❑ 90FloStaLAS-32
❑ 90WinHavRSS-12
❑ 91Cla/Bes-72
❑ 91WinHavRSC-22
❑ 91WinHavRSP-501

Jenkins, Geoff

❑ 95Bes-114
❑ 95SPML-107
❑ 96BesAutSA-32
❑ 96Bow-362
❑ 96BowBes-136
❑ 96BowBesAR-136
❑ 96BowBesR-136
❑ 96BowFoi-362
❑ 96El PasDB-1
❑ 96Exc-71
❑ 96ExcFirYP-7
❑ 96Top-24
❑ 96TopPowB-24
❑ 97BesAutAS-22
❑ 97BesAutP-H5
❑ 97Bow-188
❑ 97Bow98ROY-ROY5
❑ 97BowBes-133
❑ 97BowBesAR-133
❑ 97BowBesR-133
❑ 97BowChr-176
❑ 97BowChr1RFR-ROY5
❑ 97BowChr98RF-ROY5
❑ 97BowChrI-176
❑ 97BowChrIR-176
❑ 97BowChrR-176
❑ 97BowInt-188
❑ 97Top-201
❑ 98Bes-18
❑ 98BesNumOP-28
❑ 98Bow-192
❑ 98BowBes-172
❑ 98BowBesAR-172
❑ 98BowBesR-172
❑ 98BowCerBlueAU-13
❑ 98BowCerGA-13
❑ 98BowCerSA-13
❑ 98BowChr-192
❑ 98BowChrGA-192
❑ 98BowChrGAR-192
❑ 98BowChrI-192
❑ 98BowChrIR-192
❑ 98BowChrR-192
❑ 98BowGolA-192
❑ 98BowInt-192
❑ 98Don-278
❑ 98DonGolPP-278
❑ 98DonSigA-48
❑ 98DonSigAC-62
❑ 98DonSigAM-63
❑ 98DonSilPP-278
❑ 98Fle-394
❑ 98LeaRS-204
❑ 98LeaRSLHolo-204
❑ 98LeaRSLong-204
❑ 98LeaRTrue-204
❑ 98LouRedQ-11
❑ 98PacOmeRS-18
❑ 98PacOmeRST2-18
❑ 98PacOnl-399
❑ 98PacOnlR-399
❑ 98PacOnlWC-399
❑ 98SPxFin-205
❑ 98SPxFinR-205
❑ 98SPxFinS-205
❑ 98Stu-91
❑ 98StuGPP-91
❑ 98StuSPP-91
❑ 98UppDec-586
❑ 98UppDecR-119
❑ 98UppDecRNF-NF19
❑ 99Bow-360
❑ 99BowGol-360
❑ 99BowInt-360
❑ 99Fle-129
❑ 99FleSta9-129
❑ 99FleWarT-129
❑ 99MetUni-74
❑ 99MetUniGM-74
❑ 99MetUniPMG-74
❑ 99Pac-235
❑ 99PacAur-100
❑ 99PacAurOD-100
❑ 99PacInv-79
❑ 99PacInvOD-79
❑ 99PacInvPB-79
❑ 99PacOme-132
❑ 99PacOmeC-132
❑ 99PacOmeG-132
❑ 99PacOmePB-132
❑ 99PacPar-127
❑ 99PacParC-127
❑ 99PacParG-127
❑ 99PacParHoloGold-127
❑ 99PacParHS-127
❑ 99PacParOD-127
❑ 99PacParPB-127
❑ 99PacParRed-127
❑ 99PacPlaB-235
❑ 99PacRed-235
❑ 99SkyMolM-28
❑ 99SkyMolMX-28
❑ 99SkyPre-77
❑ 99SkyPreR-77
❑ 99SkyThu-101
❑ 99SkyThuRant-101
❑ 99SkyThuRave-101
❑ 99SP Aut-106
❑ 99SP SigAuto-GJ
❑ 99SPSig-107
❑ 99SPx-102
❑ 99SPxFinR-102
❑ 99SPxFinS-102
❑ 99ThuSkySupR-101
❑ 99Ult-131
❑ 99UltGolM-131
❑ 99UltMas-131
❑ 99UltPlaM-131
❑ 99UppDec-408
❑ 99UppDecBD-106
❑ 99UppDecBDD-106
❑ 99UppDecBDQ-106
❑ 99UppDecBDT-106
❑ 99UppDecEL1-408
❑ 99UppDecEL2-408
❑ 99UppDecM-115
❑ 99UppDecMGS-115
❑ 99UppDecMHFS-115
❑ 99UppDecMP-115
❑ 99UppDecMSS-115
❑ 99Vic-216

Jenkins, Jack

❑ 70OPC-286
❑ 70Top-286
❑ 90DodTar-384

Jenkins, Jake

❑ 59SeaPop-24

Jenkins, Jerry

❑ 77NewCoPT-19
❑ 78BurBeeT-16
❑ 82ElPasDT-13

Jenkins, Joe

❑ 18WhiSoxTI-12
❑ 20Zee-83
❑ 21Zee-98
❑ 22Zee-80
❑ 24Zee-79
❑ 26Zee-167
❑ 75WhiSox1T-24
❑ 92Man191BSR-13

Jenkins, Jon (Jonathan)

❑ 90UtiBluSP-21
❑ 91Cla/Bes-219
❑ 91SouBenWSC-17
❑ 91SouBenWSP-2853
❑ 92SouBenWSC-12
❑ 93SouBenWSC-12
❑ 93SouBenWSF-1425

Jenkins, Mack

❑ 88GreHorP-1566
❑ 90BilMusP-3239
❑ 91BilMusP-3771
❑ 91BilMusSP-27
❑ 91CedRapRC-28
❑ 91CedRapRP-2737
❑ 92CedRapRC-29
❑ 93WesVirWC-26
❑ 93WesVirWF-2881
❑ 94ChaWheC-26
❑ 94ChaWheF-2719
❑ 96ChaLooB-2
❑ 97ChaLoo-2
❑ 98ChaLooG-14

Jenkins, Pete

❑ 96OgdRapTI-48

Jenkins, Richie

❑ 98TenKry-13

Jennette, Les

❑ 92SalLakTSP-27

Jenney, Lloyd

❑ 54SeaPop-12

Jennings, Doug

❑ 86PalSprAP-18
❑ 86PalSprAS-26
❑ 87MidAngP-16
❑ 87TexLeaAF-4
❑ 88A'sMot-24
❑ 88DonRoo-13
❑ 88DonTeaBA-NEW
❑ 88FleSlu-22
❑ 88FleUpd-54
❑ 88FleUpdG-54
❑ 89Don-505
❑ 89Fle-14
❑ 89FleGlo-14
❑ 89Sco-459
❑ 89TacTigC-19
❑ 89TacTigP-1541
❑ 89Top-166
❑ 89TopTif-166
❑ 89UppDec-585
❑ 90CMC-595
❑ 90ProAAAF-148
❑ 90TacTigC-18
❑ 90TacTigP-101
❑ 91Fle-12
❑ 91LinDriAAA-539
❑ 91Sco-819
❑ 91TacTigLD-539
❑ 92RocRedWF-1950
❑ 92RocRedWS-454
❑ 93CubMar-11
❑ 93IowCubF-2139
❑ 93LinVenB-128
❑ 94IndIndF-1821
❑ 94Pac-102
❑ 94SigRooDP-95
❑ 94SigRooDPS-95
❑ 94TriAAF-AAA31

Jennings, Hugh

❑ 03WilCarE-16
❑ 07TigACDPP-6
❑ 07TigACDPP-21
❑ 09AmeCarE90-1-57
❑ 09ColChiE-142
❑ 09SpoNewSM-12
❑ 09T206-169
❑ 09T206-170
❑ 09T206-171
❑ 09TigHMTP-7
❑ 09TigHMTP-8
❑ 09TigHMTP-9
❑ 09TigMorBBBP-7
❑ 09TigMorPWBPP-5
❑ 09TigTaCP-7
❑ 09WolNewDTPP-8
❑ 10CouT21-153
❑ 10CouT21-154
❑ 10CouT21-291
❑ 10CouT21-292
❑ 10DomDisP-59
❑ 10E101-24
❑ 10E98-16
❑ 10MelMinE-24
❑ 10NadCarE-29
❑ 10NadE1-23
❑ 10PeoT21-29A
❑ 10PeoT21-29B
❑ 10RedCroT-34
❑ 10RedCroT-35
❑ 10RedCroT-123
❑ 10RedCroT-205
❑ 10RedCroT-206
❑ 10StaCarE-16
❑ 10SweCapPP-25A
❑ 10SweCapPP-25B
❑ 10W555-36
❑ 11DiaGumP-16
❑ 11E94-16
❑ 11HelSta-32
❑ 11L1L-128
❑ 11MecDFT-29
❑ 11PinT-5-153
❑ 11S81LarS-103
❑ 11SpoLifCW-188
❑ 11SpoLifM-59
❑ 11T205-81
❑ 11TurRedT-18
❑ 12ColRedB-142
❑ 12ColTinT-142
❑ 12HasTriFT-48G
❑ 12HasTriFT-75A
❑ 12PhiCarE-13
❑ 13NatGamW-22
❑ 13TomBarW-21
❑ 14CraJacE-77
❑ 14FatPlaT-19
❑ 14PieStaT-56
❑ 14PolGroW-11
❑ 15AmeCarE106-22
❑ 15CraJacE-77
❑ 15SpoNewM-89
❑ 16BF2FP-30
❑ 16FleBreD-46
❑ 16SpoNewM-90
❑ 16TanBraE-11
❑ 17ColE13-86
❑ 17HolBreD-51
❑ 19W514-106
❑ 20GasAmeMBD-29
❑ 21E121So8-42
❑ 21KoBreWSI-13
❑ 22W575-63
❑ 23W515-34
❑ 39PC7AlbHoF-35
❑ 40PlaBal-223
❑ 48ExhHoF-17
❑ 50CalHOFW-41
❑ 53ArtHaloFP-47
❑ 60Fle-67
❑ 61Fle-47
❑ 72ClaCar-12
❑ 72LauGreF-23
❑ 74CapPub-59
❑ 76ShaPiz-35
❑ 77GalGloG-176
❑ 80PerHaloFP-35
❑ 80SSPHOF-35
❑ 81ConTSN-2
❑ 81TigDetN-34
❑ 81TigSecNP-2
❑ 84GalHaloFRL-35
❑ 86TigSpoD-2
❑ 89DodSmoG-11
❑ 89HOFStiB-16
❑ 90DodTar-385
❑ 91ConTSN-16
❑ 91ConTSNP-450
❑ 92ConTSN-556
❑ 93ConMasC-9
❑ 93ConTSN-847
❑ 93UppDecTR-2
❑ 93UppDecTR-5
❑ 94ConTSNCI-25
❑ 94OriTeal-9

Jennings, Jason

❑ 99Bow-435
❑ 99BowGol-435
❑ 99BowInt-435

Jennings, Lance

❑ 91AppFoxCB-13
❑ 91AppFoxP-1719
❑ 92BasCitRC-5
❑ 92Bow-633
❑ 92ClaFS7-21
❑ 92MemChiF-2423
❑ 92UppDecML-107
❑ 93ExcFS7-175
❑ 93MemChiF-379
❑ 94CarLeaAF-CAR17
❑ 94WilBluRC-11
❑ 94WilBluRF-303

Jennings, Robin

❑ 92GenCubC-13
❑ 92GenCubF-1572
❑ 93PeoChiC-8
❑ 93PeoChiF-1095
❑ 93PeoChiTI-11
❑ 94DayCubC-11
❑ 94DayCubF-2365
❑ 95OrlCubF-21
❑ 96BesAutS-43
❑ 96BowBes-175
❑ 96BowBesAR-175
❑ 96BowBesR-175
❑ 96CubFle-9
❑ 96Exc-137
❑ 96Fla-217
❑ 96FlaWavotF-14
❑ 96FleUpd-U110
❑ 96FleUpdNH-12
❑ 96FleUpdTC-U110
❑ 96IowCubB-16
❑ 96LeaPre-119
❑ 96LeaPreP-119
❑ 96SelCer-103
❑ 96SelCerAP-103
❑ 96SelCerCB-103
❑ 96SelCerCR-103
❑ 96SelCerMB-103
❑ 96SelCerMG-103
❑ 96SelCerMR-103
❑ 96Ult-449
❑ 96UltGolM-449
❑ 96UltGolP-11
❑ 96UltGolPHGM-11
❑ 96Zen-104
❑ 96ZenArtP-104
❑ 97Cir-74
❑ 97CirRav-74
❑ 97ColCho-22
❑ 97DonRatR-10
❑ 97Fle-278
❑ 97FleTif-278
❑ 97IowCub-15
❑ 97Lea-180
❑ 97LeaFraM-180
❑ 97LeaFraMDC-180
❑ 97PacPriGotD-GD120
❑ 97Pin-165
❑ 97PinArtP-PP165
❑ 97PinIns-137
❑ 97PinInsCE-137
❑ 97PinInsDE-137
❑ 97PinMusC-165
❑ 97PinPrePla-165
❑ 97Sco-319
❑ 97ScoArtPWB-319
❑ 97ScoPreS-319
❑ 97ScoShoS-319
❑ 97ScoShoSAP-319
❑ 97Ult-166
❑ 97UltGolME-166
❑ 97UltPlaME-166
❑ 97UppDec-242
❑ 98PinSna-CC18
❑ 98ScoRT-99

Jennings, Ted

❑ 37Zee-77

Jennings, William

❑ 52Par-5

Jenny, Shane

❑ 88KenTwiP-1401

Jensen, Blair

❑ 94BurIndC-9

Jensen, Dave

❑ 85LynMetT-8

Jensen, Jackie

❑ 47Exh-108
❑ 47PM1StaP1-97
❑ 47PM1StaP1-98
❑ 47PM1StaP1-99
❑ 47PM1StaP1-100

❑ 49RemBre-10
❑ 50YanTeal-11
❑ 51Bow-254
❑ 52Bow-161
❑ 52Top-122
❑ 53BowC-24
❑ 53Bri-8
❑ 53DixLid-9
❑ 53DixPre-9
❑ 53NorBreL-14
❑ 53RedMan-AL6
❑ 53Top-265
❑ 54Bow-2
❑ 54DixLid-6
❑ 54Top-80
❑ 55ArmCoi-10
❑ 55RedMan-AL19
❑ 55Top-200
❑ 56Top-115
❑ 56TopPin-24
❑ 57SwiFra-15
❑ 57Top-220
❑ 58Hir-56
❑ 58JayPubA-9
❑ 58RedSoxJP-5
❑ 58Top-130
❑ 58Top-489
❑ 59ArmCoi-10
❑ 59Baz-12
❑ 59HomRunD-8
❑ 59RedSoxJP-4
❑ 59Top-400
❑ 60Baz-21
❑ 60KeyChal-25
❑ 60TopTat-23
❑ 60TopTat-90
❑ 61Top-173
❑ 61Top-476
❑ 61Top-540
❑ 61TopStal-112
❑ 62Jel-62
❑ 62Pos-62
❑ 62PosCan-62
❑ 62SalPlaC-73
❑ 62ShiPlaC-73
❑ 63BasMagM-41
❑ 75OPC-196
❑ 75Top-196
❑ 75TopMin-196
❑ 77GalGloG-18
❑ 79TCM50-229
❑ 80MarExh-11
❑ 81RedSoxBG2S-28
❑ 82DiaCla-65
❑ 83TopRep5-122
❑ 91TopArc1-265
❑ 92BazQua5A-11
❑ 94TopArc1-80
❑ 94TopArc1G-80
Jensen, Jared
❑ 97SouOreTB-24
❑ 98VisOakG-15
Jensen, Jason
❑ 97LetBlaDB-23
❑ 98SouBenSHM-17
Jensen, Jeff
❑ 94BatCliC-7
❑ 94BatCliF-3453
Jensen, John
❑ 89WinSpiS-10
❑ 90WinSpiTI-15
❑ 91CarLeaAP-CAR43
❑ 91WinSpiC-25
❑ 91WinSpiP-2842
❑ 92ChaKniF-2784
❑ 92ChaKniS-161
❑ 92ProFS7-206
❑ 93OrlCubF-2798
Jensen, Marcus
❑ 90EveGiaB-14
❑ 90EveGiaP-3130
❑ 90ProAaA-171
❑ 92CliGiaC-24
❑ 92CliGiaF-3602
❑ 93CliGiaC-13
❑ 93CliGiaF-2492
❑ 93MidLeaAGF-40
❑ 94Cla-5
❑ 94ExcFS7-292
❑ 94SanJosGC-11
❑ 94SanJosGF-2820
❑ 95Bow-30
❑ 95UppDecML-158
❑ 95UppDecMLFS-158
❑ 96Bow-242
❑ 96BowFoi-242
❑ 96FleUpd-U208
❑ 96FleUpdNH-13
❑ 96FleUpdTC-U208
❑ 96PhoFirB-18
❑ 96Ult-569
❑ 96UltGolM-569
❑ 96UppDec-252
❑ 97Don-238
❑ 97DonGolPP-238
❑ 97DonSilPP-238
❑ 97Fle-484
❑ 97FleTif-484
❑ 97Sco-327
❑ 97ScoArtPWB-327
❑ 97ScoPreS-327
❑ 97ScoShoS-327
❑ 97ScoShoSAP-327
❑ 97StaClu-324
❑ 97StaCluMOP-324
❑ 97Ult-296
❑ 97UltGolME-296
❑ 97UltPlaME-296
❑ 98LouRedQ-29
Jensen, Ryan
❑ 96BelGiaTI-26
❑ 97SalVolG-16
Jensen, Swede (John)
❑ 47PadTeal-9
❑ 49BowPCL-13
Jensen, Woody (Forrest)
❑ 36GouWidPPR-A56
❑ 36NatChiFPR-48
❑ 79DiaGre-362
Jenson, Curt
❑ 61SeaPop-8
❑ 61SeaPop-9
❑ 62SeaPop-3
Jenson, Jeff
❑ 91SouOreAP-3836
Jergenson, Brian
❑ 97IdaFalBTI-7
Jericho, Mascot
❑ 90MiaMirIS-30
❑ 90MiaMirIS-31
Jernigan, Pete
❑ 63MilSau-3
❑ 63SeaPop-4
❑ 63Top-253
Jersild, Aaron
❑ 92St.CatBJC-26
❑ 92St.CatBJF-3383
❑ 93HagSunC-15
❑ 93HagSunF-1875
❑ 94DunBluJC-14
❑ 94DunBluJF-2552
❑ 94FloStaLAF-FSL6
❑ 95Exc-137
❑ 95KnoSmoF-39
Jerue, Tristan
❑ 97NewJerCB-11
❑ 98PeoChiM-11
Jerzembeck, Mike
❑ 93OneYanC-9
❑ 94TamYanC-15
❑ 94TamYanF-2378
❑ 96NorNavB-12
❑ 97EasLeaTPB-20
❑ 97NorNav-20
❑ 97NorNavTI-16
❑ 98Bow-399
❑ 98BowChr-399
❑ 98BowChrGA-399
❑ 98BowChrGAR-399
❑ 98BowChrI-399
❑ 98BowChrIR-399
❑ 98BowChrR-399
❑ 98BowGolA-399
❑ 98BowInt-399
❑ 98ColCliD-13
❑ 98ColCliM-17
❑ 98FleUpd-U60
❑ 99Bow-427
❑ 99BowAut-BA23
❑ 99BowGol-427
❑ 99BowInt-427
❑ 99Fle-456
❑ 99FleSta9-456
❑ 99FleWarT-456
Jesperson, Bob
❑ 91BilMusP-3767
❑ 91BilMusSP-24
❑ 92ChaWheF-20
❑ 93WesVirWC-10
❑ 93WesVirWF-2877
❑ 94CarLeaAF-CAR48
❑ 94ChaWheC-15
Jessop, Kim
❑ 91BriBanF-15
❑ 95AusFutSFP-SFFP2
Jessup, Steve
❑ 88UtiBluSP-28
Jestadt, Garry
❑ 70OPC-109
❑ 70Top-109
❑ 71OPC-576
❑ 71Top-576
❑ 72OPC-143
❑ 72PadPos-13
❑ 72Top-143
❑ 74HawIslC-102
❑ 77PhoGiaCC-12
❑ 77PhoGiaCP-12
❑ 77PhoGiaVNB-12
Jester, Billy
❑ 86ClePhiP-10
Jester, Virgil
❑ 83Bra53F-22
Jeter, Derek
❑ 92ClaBluBF-BC22
❑ 92ClaDraP-6
❑ 92ClaDraPFB-BC6
❑ 92ClaFS7-402
❑ 92FroRowDP-55
❑ 92FroRowDPG-55
❑ 92FroRowDPPS-55
❑ 92FroRowDPS-55
❑ 92GulCoaYF-3797
❑ 92HigSchPLS-2
❑ 92HigSchPLS-NNO
❑ 92SpoIllFK1-589
❑ 92UppDecML-5
❑ 93Ble-18
❑ 93Bow-511
❑ 93ClaFS7-91
❑ 93ClaGolF-115
❑ 93ClaInsC-4
❑ 93ClaPro-1
❑ 93ExcFS7-210
❑ 93GreHorC-1
❑ 93GreHorF-893
❑ 93Pin-457
❑ 93Sco-489
❑ 93Sel-360
❑ 93SouAtlLAGF-21
❑ 93SP-279
❑ 93StaCluM-117
❑ 93Top-98
❑ 93TopGol-98
❑ 93TopInaM-98
❑ 93TopInaR-98
❑ 93TopMic-98
❑ 93UppDec-449
❑ 93UppDecGold-449
❑ 94ActPac-43
❑ 94AlbYanTI-2
❑ 94Bow-376
❑ 94Bow-633
❑ 94BowBes-B2
❑ 94BowBes-X95
❑ 94BowBesR-B2
❑ 94BowBesR-X95
❑ 94Cla-60
❑ 94ClaCreotC-C17
❑ 94ClaGolA-SH3
❑ 94ClaGolF-83
❑ 94ClaTriF-T55
❑ 94ColC-644
❑ 94ColChoGS-644
❑ 94ColChoSS-644
❑ 94ExcFS7-106
❑ 94ExcLeaLF-10
❑ 94FloStaLAF-FSL22
❑ 94SigRoo-35
❑ 94SigRooHP-S4
❑ 94SigRooHPMP-S4
❑ 94SigRooHPMPS-S4
❑ 94SigRooHPS-S4
❑ 94SigRooS-35
❑ 94TamYanC-1
❑ 94TamYanF-2393
❑ 94TedWil-124
❑ 94TedWilDGC-DG3
❑ 94Top-158
❑ 94TopGol-158
❑ 94TopSpa-158
❑ 94UppDec-550
❑ 94UppDecAHNIL-7
❑ 94UppDecED-550
❑ 94UppDecML-185
❑ 95ActPac2G-6G
❑ 95ActPac2G-AU1
❑ 95ActPac2G-AU2
❑ 95ActPacF-1
❑ 95ActPacF-10
❑ 95ActPacF-67
❑ 95Bow-229
❑ 95BowBes-B1
❑ 95BowBesR-B1
❑ 95BowGolF-229
❑ 95ColCho-15
❑ 95ColChoGS-15
❑ 95ColChoSE-2
❑ 95ColChoSEGS-2
❑ 95ColChoSESS-2
❑ 95ColChoSS-15
❑ 95ColCliMCTI-13
❑ 95ColCliP-14
❑ 95ColCliTI-14
❑ 95Emo-60
❑ 95Exc-97
❑ 95ExcAll-5
❑ 95Fin-279
❑ 95FinRef-279
❑ 95FleMajLP-7
❑ 95SelCer-122
❑ 95SelCerMG-122
❑ 95SigRooFD-FD3
❑ 95SigRooFDS-FD3
❑ 95SigRooOJSS-3
❑ 95SigRooOJSSS-3
❑ 95SP-181
❑ 95SPCha-20
❑ 95SPChaDC-20
❑ 95SPSil-181
❑ 95StaCluCB-CB14
❑ 95StaCluMOP-CB14
❑ 95Top-199
❑ 95UltGolP-7
❑ 95UltGolPGM-7
❑ 95UppDec-225
❑ 95UppDecED-225
❑ 95UppDecEDG-225
❑ 95UppDecML-1
❑ 95UppDecML-165
❑ 95UppDecMLFS-1
❑ 95UppDecMLFS-165
❑ 95UppDecMLMLA-7
❑ 95UppDecMLT1PF-1
❑ 95UppDecPAW-H14
❑ 95UppDecPAWE-H14
❑ 95UppDecSE-5
❑ 95UppDecSEG-5
❑ 95Zen-134
❑ 95ZenRooRC-2
❑ 96Baz-80
❑ 96Bow-112
❑ 96BowBes-79
❑ 96BowBesAR-79
❑ 96BowBesC-3
❑ 96BowBesCAR-3
❑ 96BowBesCR-3
❑ 96BowBesP-BBP15
❑ 96BowBesPAR-BBP15
❑ 96BowBesPR-BBP15
❑ 96BowBesR-79
❑ 96BowFoi-112
❑ 96Cir-65
❑ 96CirRav-65
❑ 96ColCho-231
❑ 96ColChoGS-231
❑ 96ColChoSS-231
❑ 96Don-491
❑ 96DonPreP-491
❑ 96EmoXL-90
❑ 96Fin-B92
❑ 96Fin-S350
❑ 96FinRef-B92
❑ 96FinRef-S350
❑ 96Fla-129
❑ 96Fle-184
❑ 96FleTif-184
❑ 96FleUpd-U226
❑ 96FleUpdTC-U226
❑ 96Lea-211
❑ 96LeaLimR-4
❑ 96LeaLimRG-4
❑ 96LeaPre-116
❑ 96LeaPreP-116
❑ 96LeaPrePB-211
❑ 96LeaPrePG-211
❑ 96LeaPrePS-211
❑ 96LeaPreSG-40
❑ 96LeaPreSta-3
❑ 96LeaPreSte-40
❑ 96LeaSig-67
❑ 96LeaSigA-118
❑ 96LeaSigAG-118
❑ 96LeaSigAS-118
❑ 96LeaSigEA-89
❑ 96LeaSigEACM-11
❑ 96LeaSigPPG-67
❑ 96LeaSigPPP-67
❑ 96MetUni-87
❑ 96MetUniMFG-6
❑ 96MetUniP-87
❑ 96MLBPin-16
❑ 96Pac-383
❑ 96Pin-171
❑ 96Pin-279
❑ 96PinAfi-163
❑ 96PinAfiAP-163
❑ 96PinAfiSP-18
❑ 96PinArtP-97
❑ 96PinArtP-179
❑ 96PinFirR-13
❑ 96PinFoil-279
❑ 96PinProS-2
❑ 96PinSta-97
❑ 96PinSta-179
❑ 96PinTeaS-3
❑ 96PinTeaT-9
❑ 96Sco-240
❑ 96Sco-384
❑ 96ScoDiaA-11
❑ 96ScoDugC-A106
❑ 96ScoDugC-B109
❑ 96ScoDugCAP-A106
❑ 96ScoDugCAP-B109
❑ 96ScoFutF-3
❑ 96ScoNumG-26
❑ 96ScoRef-10
❑ 96ScoSam-240
❑ 96Sel-161
❑ 96SelArtP-161
❑ 96SelCer-100
❑ 96SelCerAP-100
❑ 96SelCerCB-100
❑ 96SelCerCR-100
❑ 96SelCerIP-6
❑ 96SelCerMB-100
❑ 96SelCerMG-100
❑ 96SelCerMR-100
❑ 96SelCerSF-2
❑ 96SP-135
❑ 96SPMarM-MM3
❑ 96SPMarMDC-4
❑ 96Spo-139
❑ 96SpoArtP-139
❑ 96SpoDouT-9
❑ 96SpoRooJ-6
❑ 96SPSpeFX-48
❑ 96SPSpeFXDC-48
❑ 96SPx-43
❑ 96SPxGol-43
❑ 96StaClu-123
❑ 96StaClu-260
❑ 96StaCluEPB-123
❑ 96StaCluEPG-123
❑ 96StaCluEPS-123
❑ 96StaCluMOP-123
❑ 96StaCluMOP-260
❑ 96Stu-33
❑ 96StuPrePB-33
❑ 96StuPrePG-33
❑ 96StuPrePS-33
❑ 96Sum-154
❑ 96Sum-171
❑ 96SumAbo&B-154
❑ 96SumAbo&B-171
❑ 96SumArtP-154
❑ 96SumArtP-171
❑ 96SumBal-6
❑ 96SumFoi-154
❑ 96SumFoi-171
❑ 96TeaOut-39
❑ 96Top-219
❑ 96TopBigC-4
❑ 96TopChr-80
❑ 96TopChrR-80
❑ 96TopGal-143
❑ 96TopGalPPI-143
❑ 96TopLas-82
❑ 96TopLasBS-2
❑ 96TopLasBS-13
❑ 96Ult-386
❑ 96UltChe-B5
❑ 96UltCheGM-B5
❑ 96UltGolM-386
❑ 96UltGolP-8
❑ 96UltGolPGM-8
❑ 96UppDec-156
❑ 96UppDecBCP-BC17
❑ 96UppDecDD-DD28
❑ 96UppDecDDG-DD28
❑ 96UppDecDDS-DD28
❑ 96UppDecPHE-H25
❑ 96UppDecPreH-H25
❑ 96UppDecVJLS-VJ3
❑ 96Zen-93
❑ 96Zen-147
❑ 96ZenArtP-93
❑ 96ZenArtP-147
❑ 97Bow-1
❑ 97BowBes-82
❑ 97BowBesA-82
❑ 97BowBesAAR-82
❑ 97BowBesAR-82
❑ 97BowBesAR-82
❑ 97BowBesBC-BC1
❑ 97BowBesBCAR-BC1
❑ 97BowBesBCR-BC1
❑ 97BowBesJ-82
❑ 97BowBesJAR-82
❑ 97BowBesJR-82
❑ 97BowBesMI-MI1
❑ 97BowBesMIAR-MI1
❑ 97BowBesMIARI-MI1
❑ 97BowBesMII-MI1
❑ 97BowBesMIR-MI1
❑ 97BowBesMIRI-MI1
❑ 97BowBesP-4
❑ 97BowBesPAR-4
❑ 97BowBesPR-4
❑ 97BowBesR-82
❑ 97BowCerBlaIA-CA41
❑ 97BowCerBluIA-CA41
❑ 97BowCerBluIA-CA41B
❑ 97BowCerGolIA-CA41
❑ 97BowCerGreIJA-CA41
❑ 97BowChr-1
❑ 97BowChrI-1
❑ 97BowChrIR-1
❑ 97BowChrR-1
❑ 97BowInt-1
❑ 97Cir-200
❑ 97CirBos-8
❑ 97CirFasT-3
❑ 97CirIco-4
❑ 97CirLimA-7
❑ 97CirRav-200
❑ 97CirSupB-8
❑ 97ColCho-180
❑ 97ColCho-331
❑ 97ColChoAC-40
❑ 97ColChoBS-13
❑ 97ColChoBSGS-13
❑ 97ColChoNF-NF29
❑ 97ColChoT-NY5
❑ 97ColChoTBS-34
❑ 97ColChoTBSWH-34
❑ 97ColChoTotT-T19
❑ 97CraJac-5
❑ 97DenHol-14
❑ 97Don-49
❑ 97Don-415
❑ 97DonArmaD-11
❑ 97DonEli-24
❑ 97DonEliGS-24
❑ 97DonEliPtT-11
❑ 97DonEliPtT-12
❑ 97DonEliPtTA-11
❑ 97DonEliPtTA-12
❑ 97DonEliTotC-7
❑ 97DonEliTotC-P7
❑ 97DonEliTotCDC-7
❑ 97DonFraFea-14
❑ 97DonGolPP-49
❑ 97DonGolPP-415
❑ 97DonLim-22
❑ 97DonLim-83
❑ 97DonLim-116
❑ 97DonLimE-22
❑ 97DonLimE-83
❑ 97DonLimE-116
❑ 97DonLimENG-22
❑ 97DonLimFotG-61
❑ 97DonPowA-24
❑ 97DonPowADC-24
❑ 97DonPre-125
❑ 97DonPre-184
❑ 97DonPreCttC-125
❑ 97DonPreCttC-184
❑ 97DonPrePM-21
❑ 97DonPreS-7
❑ 97DonPreSS-7
❑ 97DonPreTB-8
❑ 97DonPreTBG-8
❑ 97DonPreTF-8
❑ 97DonPreTP-8

❑ 97DonPreTPG-8
❑ 97DonSig-51
❑ 97DonSigAC-64
❑ 97DonSigAM-64
❑ 97DonSigPPP-51
❑ 97DonSilPP-49
❑ 97DonSilPP-415
❑ 97DonTea-123
❑ 97DonTeaSPE-123
❑ 97DonVxP1-22
❑ 97E-X2-33
❑ 97E-X2Cred-33
❑ 97E-X2EssCre-33
❑ 97E-X2SD2000-7
❑ 97Fin-15
❑ 97Fin-166
❑ 97Fin-310
❑ 97FinEmb-166
❑ 97FinEmb-310
❑ 97FinEmbR-166
❑ 97FinEmbR-310
❑ 97FinPro-15
❑ 97FinRef-15
❑ 97FinRef-166
❑ 97FinRef-310
❑ 97FlaShoDC-13
❑ 97FlaShoHG-6
❑ 97FlaShoLC-2
❑ 97FlaShoLeg0-2
❑ 97FlaShoLeg1-2
❑ 97FlaShoM-A2
❑ 97FlaShoM-B2
❑ 97FlaShoM-C2
❑ 97FlaShoR0-2
❑ 97FlaShoR1-2
❑ 97FlaShoR2-2
❑ 97Fle-168
❑ 97Fle-703
❑ 97Fle-739
❑ 97FleGouG-4
❑ 97FleGouGF-4
❑ 97FleHea-8
❑ 97FleMilDM-2
❑ 97FleMilDMR-2
❑ 97FleRooS-7
❑ 97FleSoaS-5
❑ 97FleSoaSG-5
❑ 97FleTif-168
❑ 97FleTif-703
❑ 97FleTif-739
❑ 97HigMinM-50
❑ 97HigMinM-51
❑ 97HigMinM-52
❑ 97Lea-165
❑ 97Lea-200
❑ 97Lea-358
❑ 97LeaBanS-14
❑ 97LeaFraM-165
❑ 97LeaFraM-200
❑ 97LeaFraM-358
❑ 97LeaFraMDC-165
❑ 97LeaFraMDC-200
❑ 97LeaFraMDC-358
❑ 97LeaGet-14
❑ 97LeaGolS-7
❑ 97LeaLeaotN-4
❑ 97LeaStaS-12
❑ 97MetUni-118
❑ 97MetUniMF-5
❑ 97MetUniPP-4
❑ 97NewPin-53
❑ 97NewPinAP-53
❑ 97NewPinIE-6
❑ 97NewPinKtP-9
❑ 97NewPinMC-53
❑ 97NewPinPP-53
❑ 97NewPinPP-I6A
❑ 97NewPinPP-K9
❑ 97Pac-152
❑ 97PacBaeS-9
❑ 97PacCar-13
❑ 97PacCarM-13
❑ 97PacCerCGT-3
❑ 97PacFirD-7
❑ 97PacGolCD-11
❑ 97PacLigB-152
❑ 97PacPri-51
❑ 97PacPriGA-GA9
❑ 97PacPriLB-51
❑ 97PacPriP-51
❑ 97PacPriSH-SH5A
❑ 97PacPriSL-SL4A
❑ 97PacSil-152
❑ 97Pin-139
❑ 97PinArtP-PP139
❑ 97PinCer-51
❑ 97PinCer-141
❑ 97PinCerCMGT-3
❑ 97PinCerCT-3
❑ 97PinCerMBla-51
❑ 97PinCerMBla-141
❑ 97PinCerMBlu-51
❑ 97PinCerMBlu-141
❑ 97PinCerMG-51
❑ 97PinCerMG-141
❑ 97PinCerMR-51
❑ 97PinCerMR-141
❑ 97PinCerR-51
❑ 97PinCerR-141
❑ 97PinEpixGO-E8
❑ 97PinHom-17
❑ 97PinHom-18
❑ 97PinIns-87
❑ 97PinIns-148
❑ 97PinInsC-16
❑ 97PinInsCE-87
❑ 97PinInsCE-148
❑ 97PinInsDD-11
❑ 97PinInsDE-87
❑ 97PinInsDE-148
❑ 97PinMin-16
❑ 97PinMinB-16
❑ 97PinMinCB-16
❑ 97PinMinCG-16
❑ 97PinMinCGR-16
❑ 97PinMinCN-16
❑ 97PinMinCSS-16
❑ 97PinMinG-16
❑ 97PinMinS-16
❑ 97PinMusC-139
❑ 97PinPrePla-139
❑ 97PinTotCPB-51
❑ 97PinTotCPB-141
❑ 97PinTotCPG-51
❑ 97PinTotCPG-141
❑ 97PinTotCPR-51
❑ 97PinTotCPR-141
❑ 97PinX-P-32
❑ 97PinX-PMoS-32
❑ 97PinX-PMP-19
❑ 97PinX-PMW-5
❑ 97PinX-PMWG-5
❑ 97PinX-PMWS-5
❑ 97PinX-PreMPS-19
❑ 97PreCon-2
❑ 97Sco-35
❑ 97Sco-545
❑ 97ScoArtPWB-35
❑ 97ScoArtPWB-545
❑ 97ScoHeaotO-16
❑ 97ScoPreS-35
❑ 97ScoResC-545
❑ 97ScoShoS-35
❑ 97ScoShoS-545
❑ 97ScoShoSAP-35
❑ 97ScoShoSAP-545
❑ 97ScoStaaD-9
❑ 97Sel-60
❑ 97Sel-148
❑ 97SelArtP-60
❑ 97SelArtP-148
❑ 97SelCom-60
❑ 97SelCom-148
❑ 97SelRegG-60
❑ 97SelRegG-148
❑ 97SelRooR-2
❑ 97SelToootT-25
❑ 97SelToootTMB-25
❑ 97SP-125
❑ 97SPGamF-GF6
❑ 97SPInsI-17
❑ 97SPMarM-MM10
❑ 97SpollI-62
❑ 97SpollI-128
❑ 97SpollI-179
❑ 97SpollIEE-62
❑ 97SpollIEE-128
❑ 97SpollIEE-179
❑ 97SpollIGS-16
❑ 97SPSpeF-16
❑ 97SPSpxF-6
❑ 97SPSPxFA-6
❑ 97SPx-36
❑ 97SPxBoufG-13
❑ 97SPxBro-36
❑ 97SPxCorotG-10
❑ 97SPxGol-36
❑ 97SPxGraF-36
❑ 97SPxSil-36
❑ 97SPxSte-36
❑ 97StaClu-55
❑ 97StaCluC-CO1
❑ 97StaClul-I17
❑ 97StaCluM-M1
❑ 97StaCluMat-55
❑ 97StaCluMOP-55
❑ 97StaCluMOP-I17
❑ 97StaCluMOP-M1
❑ 97StaCluMOP-PG19
❑ 97StaCluMOP-PL13
❑ 97StaCluPG-PG19
❑ 97StaCluPL-PL13
❑ 97Stu-91
❑ 97StuHarH-13
❑ 97StuMasS-1
❑ 97StuMasS8-1
❑ 97StuPor8-10
❑ 97StuPrePG-91
❑ 97StuPrePS-91
❑ 97Top-13
❑ 97Top-NNO
❑ 97TopAweI-AI7
❑ 97TopChr-7
❑ 97TopChrDD-DD2
❑ 97TopChrDDR-DD2
❑ 97TopChrR-7
❑ 97TopGal-161
❑ 97TopGalGoH-GH1
❑ 97TopGalP-PP2
❑ 97TopGalPG-PG6
❑ 97TopGalPMS-1
❑ 97TopGalPMSSS-1
❑ 97TopGalPPI-161
❑ 97TopHobM-HM18
❑ 97TopMem05-25
❑ 97TopScr-9
❑ 97TopScrT-9
❑ 97TopStaFAS-FAS1
❑ 97UD3-55
❑ 97UD3GenNex-GN15
❑ 97UD3SupSign-4
❑ 97Ult-99
❑ 97UltBasR-3
❑ 97UltChe-B9
❑ 97UltDouT-7
❑ 97UltFamGam-7
❑ 97UltGolME-99
❑ 97UltHitM-7
❑ 97UltLeaS-4
❑ 97UltPlaME-99
❑ 97UltRooR-5
❑ 97UltStaR-9
❑ 97UltTop3-9
❑ 97UltTop3GM-9
❑ 97UppDec-421
❑ 97UppDec-440
❑ 97UppDecAWJ-18
❑ 97UppDecBCP-BC2
❑ 97UppDecHC-HC3
❑ 97UppDecHTH-HT2
❑ 97UppDecMM-B3
❑ 97UppDecP-19
❑ 97UppDecPE-19
❑ 97UppDecRSF-RS3
❑ 97UppDecTTS-TS5
❑ 97YanSco-3
❑ 97YanScoPl-3
❑ 97YanScoPr-3
❑ 97Zen-17
❑ 97Zen Z-Z-7
❑ 97Zen8x10-17
❑ 97Zen8x1D-17
❑ 97ZentheBP-17
❑ 97ZenV-2-7
❑ 98Bow-224
❑ 98BowBes-77
❑ 98BowBesAR-77
❑ 98BowBesR-77
❑ 98BowChr-224
❑ 98BowChrGA-224
❑ 98BowChrGAR-224
❑ 98BowChrI-224
❑ 98BowChrIR-224
❑ 98BowChrR-224
❑ 98BowChrR-38
❑ 98BowChrRR-38
❑ 98BowGolA-224
❑ 98BowInt-224
❑ 98BowMinLM-MVP6
❑ 98CirThu-2
❑ 98CirThuB-9
❑ 98CirThuLA-8
❑ 98CirThuRav-2
❑ 98CirThuRR-9
❑ 98CirThuSupRav-2
❑ 98ColCho-450
❑ 98ColChoB5-450
❑ 98ColChoMBH-19
❑ 98ColChoS'-19
❑ 98ColChoSQ-SQ53
❑ 98ColChoSQDouble-6
❑ 98ColChoSQHR-6
❑ 98ColChoSQSingle-6
❑ 98ColChoSQTriple-6
❑ 98CroRoy-94
❑ 98CroRoyAS-5
❑ 98CroRoyDK-15
❑ 98Don-100
❑ 98Don-165
❑ 98Don-367
❑ 98Don-404
❑ 98DonCol-100
❑ 98DonCol-165
❑ 98DonColE-408
❑ 98DonColE-525
❑ 98DonColL-363
❑ 98DonColP-559
❑ 98DonColP-726
❑ 98DonColS-100
❑ 98DonColS-165
❑ 98DonCruG-32
❑ 98DonCruP-32
❑ 98DonCruR-32
❑ 98DonDay-12
❑ 98DonDiaK-10
❑ 98DonDiaKC-10
❑ 98DonEli-8
❑ 98DonEli-125
❑ 98DonEliA-8
❑ 98DonEliA-125
❑ 98DonEliC-8
❑ 98DonEliI-4
❑ 98DonEliMC-8
❑ 98DonEliS-8
❑ 98DonEliS-125
❑ 98DonFANT-18
❑ 98DonFANTDC-18
❑ 98DonGolPP-100
❑ 98DonGolPP-165
❑ 98DonGolPP-367
❑ 98DonGolPP-404
❑ 98DonPre-9
❑ 98DonPre-176
❑ 98DonPreGB-9
❑ 98DonPreGES-21
❑ 98DonPreGoB-9
❑ 98DonPreGX-21
❑ 98DonPreGXDC-21
❑ 98DonPrePM-9
❑ 98DonPreSeat-9
❑ 98DonPreSeat-176
❑ 98DonPreTP-9
❑ 98DonPreTPD-5
❑ 98DonPreTPG-9
❑ 98DonPreTPS-9
❑ 98DonPreTW-10
❑ 98DonPriCD-100
❑ 98DonPriCD-165
❑ 98DonPriCE-408
❑ 98DonPriCE-525
❑ 98DonPriCL-363
❑ 98DonPriCP-559
❑ 98DonPriCP-726
❑ 98DonProLO-20
❑ 98DonSig-2
❑ 98DonSigAC-63
❑ 98DonSigAM-64
❑ 98DonSigP-2
❑ 98DonSilPP-100
❑ 98DonSilPP-165
❑ 98DonSilPP-367
❑ 98DonSilPP-404
❑ 98DonSonM9-6
❑ 98E-X2-7
❑ 98E-X2DesCoop-13
❑ 98E-X2ECFut-7
❑ 98E-X2ECNow-7
❑ 98Fin-92
❑ 98FinMysF1-M12
❑ 98FinMysF1-M15
❑ 98FinMysF1-M18
❑ 98FinMysF1-M19
❑ 98FinMysF2-M14
❑ 98FinMysF2-M16
❑ 98FinMysF2-M18
❑ 98FinMysF2R-M14
❑ 98FinMysF2R-M16
❑ 98FinMysF2R-M18
❑ 98FinMysFO-2
❑ 98FinMysFOR-2
❑ 98FinMysFR-M12
❑ 98FinMysFR-M15
❑ 98FinMysFR-M18
❑ 98FinMysFR-M19
❑ 98FinNo--92
❑ 98FinNo-R-92
❑ 98FinRef-92
❑ 98FinStaS-SS7
❑ 98FinTheM-TM9
❑ 98FinTheMR-TM9
❑ 98FlaShoLeg0-14
❑ 98FlaShoLeg1-14
❑ 98FlaShoLeg2-14
❑ 98FlaShoLeg3-14
❑ 98FlaShoLegM-14
❑ 98FlaShoR0-14
❑ 98FlaShoR1-14
❑ 98FlaShoR2-14
❑ 98FlaShoR3-14
❑ 98Fle-2
❑ 98Fle-343
❑ 98Fle-586
❑ 98FleDiaS-9
❑ 98FleDiaSCS-NNO
❑ 98FleIn TC-IC9
❑ 98FleVin'-38
❑ 98FleVin'C-38
❑ 98Lea-164
❑ 98LeaFraDA-164
❑ 98LeaFraF-164
❑ 98LeaFraM-164
❑ 98LeaFraM-164
❑ 98LeaFraMDC-164
❑ 98LeaFraMDC-164
❑ 98LeaFraMZ2-164
❑ 98LeaRCMLHDSamp-11
❑ 98LeaRS-34
❑ 98LeaRS-152
❑ 98LeaRSCross-10
❑ 98LeaRSGreHit-9
❑ 98LeaRSLHolo-34
❑ 98LeaRSLHolo-152
❑ 98LeaRSLong-34
❑ 98LeaRSLong-152
❑ 98LeaRSMLHD-11
❑ 98LeaRSTicMas-6
❑ 98LeaRSTicMasDC-6
❑ 98LeaRTrue-34
❑ 98LeaRTrue-152
❑ 98LeaStaRep-18
❑ 98LeaStaS-23
❑ 98LeaStaSDC-23
❑ 98MetUni-199
❑ 98MetUni-208
❑ 98MetUniAT-9
❑ 98MetUniPMG-199
❑ 98MetUniPMG-208
❑ 98MetUniPP-7
❑ 98MetUniT-9
❑ 98MetUniUL-9
❑ 98Pac-151
❑ 98PacAur-58
❑ 98PacAurCube-11
❑ 98PacAurHC-11
❑ 98PacAurODLC-11
❑ 98PacAurPF-2
❑ 98PacAurPFC-2
❑ 98PacAurPFPB-2
❑ 98PacAurPFR-2
❑ 98PacAurPFS-2
❑ 98PacGolCDC-22
❑ 98PacInv-52
❑ 98PacInvGems-73
❑ 98PacInvInt-8A
❑ 98PacInvPBlue-52
❑ 98PacInvPhoto-9
❑ 98PacInvSilv-52
❑ 98PacInvTeam-19
❑ 98PacOme-165
❑ 98PacOmeOnIns-10
❑ 98PacOmeP-7
❑ 98PacOmeR-165
❑ 98PacOnl-505A
❑ 98PacOnl-505B
❑ 98PacOnlR-505A
❑ 98PacOnlR-505B
❑ 98PacOnlWC-505A
❑ 98PacOnlWC-505B
❑ 98PacPar-69
❑ 98PacParC-69
❑ 98PacParFC-11
❑ 98PacParG-69
❑ 98PacParHS-69
❑ 98PacParI-13
❑ 98PacParPB-69
❑ 98PacParR-69
❑ 98PacParSD-13
❑ 98PacParTC-9
❑ 98PacPlaB-151
❑ 98PacRedT-151
❑ 98PacSil-151
❑ 98PacTeaC-10
❑ 98Pin-64
❑ 98Pin-185
❑ 98PinArtP-PP57
❑ 98PinArtP-PP88
❑ 98PinEpixGE-E8
❑ 98PinEpixGP-E8
❑ 98PinEpixME-E8
❑ 98PinEpixMO-E8
❑ 98PinEpixMP-E8
❑ 98PinEpixSE-E8
❑ 98PinEpixSO-E8
❑ 98PinEpixSP-E8
❑ 98PinIns-2
❑ 98PinIns-133
❑ 98PinInsBtN-14
❑ 98PinInsC-9
❑ 98PinInsCE-2
❑ 98PinInsCE-133
❑ 98PinInsCG-9
❑ 98PinInsDE-2
❑ 98PinInsDE-133
❑ 98PinInsSG-6AB
❑ 98PinInsSG-6CD
❑ 98PinInsSG-19AB
❑ 98PinInsSG-19CD
❑ 98PinInsSGS-6AB
❑ 98PinInsSGS-6CD
❑ 98PinInsSGS-19AB
❑ 98PinInsSGS-19CD
❑ 98PinMinB-9
❑ 98PinMinCB-9
❑ 98PinMinCBAP-9
❑ 98PinMinCGP-9
❑ 98PinMinCGPAP-9
❑ 98PinMinCN-9
❑ 98PinMinCNAP-9
❑ 98PinMinCSGR-9
❑ 98PinMinDC-9
❑ 98PinMinG-9
❑ 98PinMinMCSS-9
❑ 98PinMinS-9
❑ 98PinMusC-PP57
❑ 98PinMusC-PP88
❑ 98PinPer-9
❑ 98PinPer-146
❑ 98PinPerLP-3
❑ 98PinPerPP-9
❑ 98PinPerPP-146
❑ 98PinPluAE-8
❑ 98PinPluAEE-8
❑ 98PinPluAEP-8
❑ 98PinPluLM-24
❑ 98PinPowPJ-4
❑ 98PinPowPJS-4
❑ 98PinPreP-64
❑ 98PinPreP-185
❑ 98PinPreP-E8
❑ 98PinSna-NYY4
❑ 98PinSna-NYY9
❑ 98PinUnc-185
❑ 98PreCon-20
❑ 98Revo-99
❑ 98RevoPTP-6
❑ 98RevoShow-11
❑ 98RevoSS-99
❑ 98Sco-22
❑ 98ScoComP-3A
❑ 98ScoComP-3B
❑ 98ScoComP-3C
❑ 98ScoComPG-3A
❑ 98ScoComPG-3B
❑ 98ScoComPG-3C
❑ 98ScoEpix-E8
❑ 98ScoFirP-7
❑ 98ScoRT-6
❑ 98ScoRT-262
❑ 98ScoRTASEpix-8
❑ 98ScoRTSS-PP6
❑ 98ScoRTSS-PP155
❑ 98ScoRTSSAP-PP6
❑ 98ScoRTSSAP-PP155
❑ 98ScoRTSSAP1-PP6
❑ 98ScoRTSSAP1-PP155
❑ 98ScoRTStarGaz-8
❑ 98ScoSS-PP7
❑ 98ScoSSAP-PP7
❑ 98SelSelSamp-8
❑ 98SkyDugA-73
❑ 98SkyDugA-124
❑ 98SkyDugADH-DH4
❑ 98SkyDugAIA-73
❑ 98SkyDugAIA-124
❑ 98SP Aut-145
❑ 98SP Aut-SD41

❑ 98SP AutSD-SD41
❑ 98SP AutSDT-SD41
❑ 98SpoIll-64
❑ 98SpoIll-148
❑ 98SpoIllC-C2
❑ 98SpoIllEC-EC6
❑ 98SpoIllEE-64
❑ 98SpoIllEE-148
❑ 98SpoIllFE-64
❑ 98SpoIllFE-148
❑ 98SpoIllTaN-93
❑ 98SpoIllTaNEE-93
❑ 98SpoIllTaNGS-8
❑ 98SpoIllWSF-65
❑ 98SpoIllWSFEE-65
❑ 98SpoIllWSFFE-65
❑ 98SPxFin-30
❑ 98SPxFin-159
❑ 98SPxFin-305
❑ 98SPxFinR-30
❑ 98SPxFinR-159
❑ 98SPxFinR-305
❑ 98SPxFinS-30
❑ 98SPxFinS-159
❑ 98SPxFinS-305
❑ 98StaCluC-CS2
❑ 98StaCluC-CS4
❑ 98StaCluC-CS6
❑ 98StaCluFDI-241
❑ 98StaClul-241
❑ 98StaCluNC-NC10
❑ 98StaCluOneK-241
❑ 98StaCluPP-241
❑ 98StaCluTIII-T2A
❑ 98StaCluTIII-T14A
❑ 98StaCluTLme-T2A
❑ 98StaCluTLme-T14A
❑ 98StaCluTLmo-T2A
❑ 98StaCluTLmo-T14A
❑ 98Stu-163
❑ 98StuFF-2
❑ 98StuFFDC-2
❑ 98StuGPP-163
❑ 98StuMast-12
❑ 98StuPor8x10-6
❑ 98StuPor8x10GP-6
❑ 98StuSony99-6
❑ 98StuSPP-163
❑ 98Top-160
❑ 98TopBabB-BB1
❑ 98TopChr-160
❑ 98TopChrBB-BB1
❑ 98TopChrBBR-BB1
❑ 98TopChrR-160
❑ 98TopDevR-160
❑ 98TopDia-160
❑ 98TopFruR-2
❑ 98TopGal-115
❑ 98TopGalGoH-GH2
❑ 98TopGalGoHJ-GH2
❑ 98TopGalGP-115
❑ 98TopGalOPP-115
❑ 98TopGalPG-PG3
❑ 98TopGalPPI-115
❑ 98TopGalPPIA-115
❑ 98TopGolLabC1-7
❑ 98TopGolLabC1B-7
❑ 98TopGolLabC1One-7
❑ 98TopGolLabC1R-7
❑ 98TopGolLabC2-7
❑ 98TopGolLabC2B-7
❑ 98TopGolLabC2One-7
❑ 98TopGolLabC2R-7
❑ 98TopGolLabC3-7
❑ 98TopGolLabC3B-7
❑ 98TopGolLabC3One-7
❑ 98TopGolLabC3R-7
❑ 98TopMiniC-160
❑ 98TopMysF-ILM6
❑ 98TopMysFB-M8
❑ 98TopMysFB-M8
❑ 98TopMysFBR-M8
❑ 98TopMysFBR-M8
❑ 98TopMysFR-ILM6
❑ 98TopOpeD-83
❑ 98TopPre-PP4
❑ 98TopSta-33
❑ 98TopSta'S-18
❑ 98TopSta'SGH-18
❑ 98TopStaB-33
❑ 98TopStaG-33
❑ 98TopStaGR-33
❑ 98TopStaS-33
❑ 98TopStaSteG-18
❑ 98TopSup-13
❑ 98TopSup-13
❑ 98TopTek-14
❑ 98TopTekD-14
❑ 98UD3-79
❑ 98UD3-169
❑ 98UD3-259
❑ 98UD3DieCut-79
❑ 98UD3DieCut-169
❑ 98UD3DieCut-259
❑ 98Ult-150
❑ 98Ult-481
❑ 98UltArtT-6
❑ 98UltBacttF-3
❑ 98UltDial-10
❑ 98UltDiaP-6
❑ 98UltDouT-5
❑ 98UltFalC-6
❑ 98UltGolM-150
❑ 98UltGolM-481
❑ 98UltKidG-3
❑ 98UltMas-150
❑ 98UltMas-481
❑ 98UltMilM-4
❑ 98UltNot-20
❑ 98UltPlaM-150
❑ 98UltPlaM-481
❑ 98UltPriL-6
❑ 98UltTicS-11
❑ 98UltTop3-18
❑ 98UltWinN-6
❑ 98UppDec-141
❑ 98UppDec-450
❑ 98UppDec-618
❑ 98UppDec10AP-41
❑ 98UppDec1APR-41
❑ 98UppDec5x7-450
❑ 98UppDecAC-AS11
❑ 98UppDecAG-AG2
❑ 98UppDecAGDC-AG2
❑ 98UppDecBCP-BC15
❑ 98UppDecCD-CD2
❑ 98UppDecDS-DS28
❑ 98UppDecR-67
❑ 98UppDecRGKoG-G24
❑ 98UppDecRQL-Q22
❑ 98UppDecRTC-TC13
❑ 98YanSco-2
❑ 98YanScoP-2
❑ 98YanUppD-450
❑ 98YanUppDWSC-1
❑ 98Zen-17
❑ 98Zen5 xx7-15
❑ 98Zen5x7GoldImp-15
❑ 98Zen5x7Imp-15
❑ 98ZenEpi-E8
❑ 98ZenSampL-Z15
❑ 98ZenSamS-17
❑ 98ZenZ-G-17
❑ 98ZenZ-S-17
❑ 98ZenZ-T-7
❑ 98ZenZ-T5x7-7
❑ 98ZenZ-TG-7
❑ 99199Fin-90
❑ 99199Fin-115
❑ 99199Fin-258
❑ 99AllMysFR-M9
❑ 99AurOn DL-12
❑ 99AurPenF-12
❑ 99AurPenF-12
❑ 99AurPenFB-12
❑ 99AurPenFS-12
❑ 99AurSty-12
❑ 99Bow-290
❑ 99BowBes-73
❑ 99BowBes-88
❑ 99BowBesAR-73
❑ 99BowBesAR-88
❑ 99BowBesFBMI-FB6
❑ 99BowBesFBMII-FB6
❑ 99BowBesFBMIII-FB6
❑ 99BowBesFF-FR1A
❑ 99BowBesFF-FR1C
❑ 99BowBesFFA-FR1A
❑ 99BowBesFFA-FR1C
❑ 99BowBesMI-M3
❑ 99BowBesMIAR-M3
❑ 99BowBesMIR-M3
❑ 99BowBesR-73
❑ 99BowBesR-88
❑ 99BowChrDA-DA13
❑ 99BowChrDAR-DA13
❑ 99BowEarR-ER8
❑ 99BowGol-290
❑ 99BowInt-290
❑ 99CroRoyB-97
❑ 99CroRoyCCDB-6
❑ 99CroRoyCCG-6
❑ 99CroRoyCCG-6
❑ 99CroRoyCCLB-6
❑ 99CroRoyCCP-6
❑ 99CroRoyCCP-6
❑ 99CroRoyCCR-6
❑ 99CroRoyL-97
❑ 99CroRoyMP-11
❑ 99CroRoyOD-97
❑ 99CroRoyPotG-15
❑ 99CroRoyPP-15
❑ 99CroRoyPPN-15
❑ 99DumSet-159
❑ 99DumSet-ER8
❑ 99E-X Cen-9
❑ 99E-X CenECFut-9
❑ 99E-X CenECNow-9
❑ 99E-XCenFoF'-7
❑ 99FinCom-C5
❑ 99FinComDualR-C5
❑ 99FinGolRef-90
❑ 99FinGolRef-115
❑ 99FinGolRef-258
❑ 99FinMil-M9
❑ 99FinMil-M38
❑ 99FinPeelHyp-7
❑ 99FinPeelSpark-7
❑ 99FinPeeSS-7
❑ 99FinRef-90
❑ 99FinRef-115
❑ 99FinRef-258
❑ 99FinSplS-SS3
❑ 99FinSplSDR-SS3
❑ 99FinTeaFB-TF16
❑ 99FinTeaFBR-TF16
❑ 99FinTeaFG-TF16
❑ 99FinTeaFGR-TF16
❑ 99FinTeaFR-TF16
❑ 99FinTeaFRR-TF16
❑ 99FlaShoLeg1-22
❑ 99FlaShoLeg2-22
❑ 99FlaShoLeg3-22
❑ 99FlaShoLegM1-22
❑ 99FlaShoLegM2-22
❑ 99FlaShoLegM3-22
❑ 99FlaShoMoG-7
❑ 99FlaShoR1-22
❑ 99FlaShoR2-22
❑ 99FlaShoR3-22
❑ 99Fle-5
❑ 99Fle-585
❑ 99Fle-598
❑ 99FleBri-2
❑ 99FleBri2G-2
❑ 99FleBriBlu-2
❑ 99FleBriGol-2
❑ 99FleBriSS-4
❑ 99FleBriSSP-4
❑ 99FleDiaM-7
❑ 99FleDiaSkiSheet-NNO
❑ 99FleMys-26
❑ 99FleMys-159
❑ 99FleMysE-2
❑ 99FleMysG-26
❑ 99FleMysM-26
❑ 99FleMysM-159
❑ 99FleSta9-5
❑ 99FleSta9-585
❑ 99FleSta9-598
❑ 99FleVin'-5
❑ 99FleWarT-5
❑ 99FleWarT-585
❑ 99FleWarT-598
❑ 99KinDis-27
❑ 99MetUni-97
❑ 99MetUni-238
❑ 99MetUni-281
❑ 99MetUniBWTW-12
❑ 99MetUniDS-4
❑ 99MetUniGM-97
❑ 99MetUniGM-238
❑ 99MetUniGM-281
❑ 99MetUniL-7
❑ 99MetUniPM-6
❑ 99MetUniPMG-97
❑ 99MetUniPMG-238
❑ 99MetUniPMG-281
❑ 99MetUniSamp-NNOA
❑ 99MetUniSamp-NNO
❑ 99Pac-294
❑ 99Pac-294A
❑ 99PacAur-128
❑ 99PacAurOD-128
❑ 99PacCroC-190
❑ 99PacCroCITC-11
❑ 99PacCroCPB-190
❑ 99PacCroCTC-20
❑ 99PacDynaD-4
❑ 99PacDynaDT-4
❑ 99PacGolCDC-10
❑ 99PacInv-100
❑ 99PacInvFP-12
❑ 99PacInvOD-100
❑ 99PacInvPB-100
❑ 99PacInvSF-12
❑ 99PacInvSF-12B
❑ 99PacInvSH-12
❑ 99PacInvSH-12B
❑ 99PacInvTA-11
❑ 99PacOme-163
❑ 99PacOme5T-26
❑ 99PacOme5TT-26
❑ 99PacOmeC-163
❑ 99PacOmeDD-2
❑ 99PacOmeDM-22
❑ 99PacOmeEP-12
❑ 99PacOmeEP1o1-12
❑ 99PacOmeG-163
❑ 99PacOmeH'-13
❑ 99PacOmePB-163
❑ 99PacPar-162
❑ 99PacParC-162
❑ 99PacParFC-12
❑ 99PacParG-162
❑ 99PacParHoloGold-162
❑ 99PacParHS-162
❑ 99PacParOD-162
❑ 99PacParPB-23
❑ 99PacParPB-162
❑ 99PacParRed-162
❑ 99PacPlaB-294
❑ 99PacPlaB-294A
❑ 99PacPri-100
❑ 99PacPriAotG-13
❑ 99PacPriDG-13
❑ 99PacPriHB-100
❑ 99PacPriHG-100
❑ 99PacPriHM-100
❑ 99PacPriHP-100
❑ 99PacPriRed-100
❑ 99PacPriS-8
❑ 99PacPriS206-8
❑ 99PacPriS206R-8
❑ 99PacPriSE-8
❑ 99PacPriSP-8
❑ 99PacPriSP-8
❑ 99PacPriSV-8
❑ 99PacRed-294
❑ 99PacRed-294A
❑ 99PacTeaC-9
❑ 99PacTim-6
❑ 99Pin-12
❑ 99Rev-95
❑ 99RevDiaL-22
❑ 99RevFouP-12
❑ 99RevMLBIcon-6
❑ 99RevPremDate-95
❑ 99RevRet-95
❑ 99RevShaSS-95
❑ 99RevThoitS-11
❑ 99RevTri-17
❑ 99RevTri-17
❑ 99SkyMolM-142
❑ 99SkyMolMF-42
❑ 99SkyMolMFS-42
❑ 99SkyMolMFT-42
❑ 99SkyMolMX-142
❑ 99SkyPre-154
❑ 99SkyPre-276
❑ 99SkyPreIN-12
❑ 99SkyPreLB-11
❑ 99SkyPreR-154
❑ 99SkyPreR-276
❑ 99SkyPreSB-15
❑ 99SkyPreSotG-4
❑ 99SkyThu-273
❑ 99SkyThuHip-H5
❑ 99SkyThuRant-273
❑ 99SkyThuRave-273
❑ 99SkyThuwww-WB5
❑ 99SP Aut-57
❑ 99SP AutEF-E18
❑ 99SP AutR-R18
❑ 99SpoIll-152
❑ 99SpoIllH-21
❑ 99SPx-55
❑ 99SPxDom-FB13
❑ 99SPxFinR-55
❑ 99SPxFinS-55
❑ 99SPxPreS-PS12
❑ 99SPxStaF-SF18
❑ 99StaClu-65
❑ 99StaCluC-SCC25
❑ 99StaCluC-CS4
❑ 99StaCluC-CS10
❑ 99StaCluC-CS15
❑ 99StaCluC-CS20
❑ 99StaCluCR-SCC25
❑ 99StaCluFDI-65
❑ 99StaCluNC-NC10
❑ 99StaCluOoaK-65
❑ 99StaCluPP-65
❑ 99StaCluTI-T4A
❑ 99StaCluTI-T9C
❑ 99StaCluTL-T4A
❑ 99StaCluTL-T9C
❑ 99StaCluTL-T4A
❑ 99StaCluTL-T9C
❑ 99ThuSkySupR-273
❑ 99Top-85
❑ 99Top-230
❑ 99Top-452
❑ 99TopActF-5
❑ 99TopActFAU-5
❑ 99TopActFCU-5
❑ 99TopAllMF-M9
❑ 99TopBlaLC1-22
❑ 99TopBlaLC2-22
❑ 99TopBlaLC3-22
❑ 99TopChr-85
❑ 99TopChr-230
❑ 99TopChr-452
❑ 99TopChrERttH-ER2
❑ 99TopChrERttH-ER2
❑ 99TopChrF1-FF3
❑ 99TopChrF1R-FF3
❑ 99TopChrNB-NB9
❑ 99TopChrNBR-NB9
❑ 99TopChrR-85
❑ 99TopChrR-230
❑ 99TopChrR-452
❑ 99TopGal-20
❑ 99TopGal-109
❑ 99TopGalE-E12
❑ 99TopGalGoH-GH5
❑ 99TopGalHer-TH9
❑ 99TopGalHerP-TH9
❑ 99TopGalPP-20
❑ 99TopGalPP-109
❑ 99TopGalPPI-20
❑ 99TopGalPPI-109
❑ 99TopGolL-22
❑ 99TopGolLC1-22
❑ 99TopGolLC2-22
❑ 99TopGolLOtO-22
❑ 99TopMVPP-85
❑ 99TopMVPP-452
❑ 99TopNewB-NB9
❑ 99TopOpeD-48
❑ 99TopPicP-P10
❑ 99TopPre-PP3
❑ 99TopRedLC1-22
❑ 99TopRedLC2-22
❑ 99TopRedLC3-22
❑ 99TopSta-5
❑ 99TopSta-172
❑ 99TopSta'S-34
❑ 99TopSta'SG-34
❑ 99TopSta'SGDH-34
❑ 99TopSta1Foil-5
❑ 99TopSta2Foil-5
❑ 99TopSta3Foil-5
❑ 99TopSta4Foil-5
❑ 99TopStaFoil-5
❑ 99TopStaFoil-172
❑ 99TopStaFS-5
❑ 99TopStaG-G7
❑ 99TopStaGFoil-G7
❑ 99TopStaOS-5
❑ 99TopStaTS-5
❑ 99TopStaTS-5
❑ 99TopSupC-14
❑ 99TopSupCR-14
❑ 99TopTek-24A
❑ 99TopTek-24B
❑ 99TopTekG-24A
❑ 99TopTekG-24B
❑ 99TopTekP-PP1A
❑ 99TopTekT-T6
❑ 99UD Cho-33
❑ 99UD Cho-115
❑ 99UD ChoBU-6
❑ 99UD ChoBUCG-4
❑ 99UD ChoMBH-B16
❑ 99UD ChoP-115
❑ 99UD ChoPCR-33
❑ 99UD ChoPCR-115
❑ 99UD ChoS-4
❑ 99UD ChoSD-4
❑ 99UD ChoSHR-4
❑ 99UD ChoST-4
❑ 99UD Ion-41
❑ 99UD Ion-78
❑ 99UD IonC-C8
❑ 99UD IonH-HG8
❑ 99UD IonH-H8
❑ 99UD IonN-N8
❑ 99UD IonR-41
❑ 99UD IonR-78
❑ 99UD IonWZ-WZ8
❑ 99UDHolo-38
❑ 99UDHoloAUsome-38
❑ 99Ult-30
❑ 99UltDamI-5
❑ 99UltDiaP-10
❑ 99UltGolM-30
❑ 99UltMas-30
❑ 99UltPlaM-30
❑ 99UltRBIK-18
❑ 99UltTheBook-19
❑ 99UltThu-6
❑ 99UppDec-154
❑ 99UppDec10AT-X25
❑ 99UppDec10ATD-X25
❑ 99UppDec10ATHR-X25
❑ 99UppDec10ATT-X25
❑ 99UppDecBD-56
❑ 99UppDecBDD-56
❑ 99UppDecBDDom-D2
❑ 99UppDecBDDomE-D2
❑ 99UppDecBDMN-M8
❑ 99UppDecBDMNE-M8
❑ 99UppDecBDQ-56
❑ 99UppDecBDT-56
❑ 99UppDecCL-67
❑ 99UppDecCL-116
❑ 99UppDecCLCC-67
❑ 99UppDecCLCC-116
❑ 99UppDecCLM-C61
❑ 99UppDecE-59
❑ 99UppDecE-165
❑ 99UppDecE-173
❑ 99UppDecE2C-2K2
❑ 99UppDecEFXG-59
❑ 99UppDecEFXG-165
❑ 99UppDecEFXG-173
❑ 99UppDecEL1-154
❑ 99UppDecEL2-154
❑ 99UppDecEPE-P19
❑ 99UppDecEUR-U12
❑ 99UppDecF-F17
❑ 99UppDecFD-F17
❑ 99UppDecFQ-F17
❑ 99UppDecFT-F17
❑ 99UppDecIP-I27
❑ 99UppDecIPD-I27
❑ 99UppDecIPHR-I27
❑ 99UppDecIPT-I27
❑ 99UppDecM-139
❑ 99UppDecMD-D11
❑ 99UppDecMGS-139
❑ 99UppDecMHFS-139
❑ 99UppDecMP-139
❑ 99UppDecMSS-139
❑ 99UppDecMST-T4
❑ 99UppDecMST-S12
❑ 99UppDecO-13
❑ 99UppDecO-84
❑ 99UppDecOAPoH-DJ
❑ 99UppDecOMP-S16
❑ 99UppDecOSO-13
❑ 99UppDecOSO-84
❑ 99UppDecOWP-R10
❑ 99UppDecR-55
❑ 99UppDecRDR-D15
❑ 99UppDecRDRL2-D15
❑ 99UppDecRG-55
❑ 99UppDecROSS-S30
❑ 99UppDecROSS-S30
❑ 99UppDecRP-55
❑ 99UppDecTE-T17
❑ 99UppDecTED-T17
❑ 99UppDecTEQ-T17
❑ 99UppDecTET-T17
❑ 99UppDecVtaT-V19
❑ 99UppDecVtaTD-V19
❑ 99UppDecVtaTQ-V19
❑ 99UppDecVtaTT-V19
❑ 99UppDecWY-W12
❑ 99UppDecWYD-W12
❑ 99UppDecWYHR-W12
❑ 99UppDecWYT-W12
❑ 99Vic-265
❑ 99Vic-267
❑ 99YanFle-1

Jeter, John
❑ 70OPC-141
❑ 70Top-141
❑ 71MLBOffS-205
❑ 71OPC-47
❑ 71Top-47
❑ 72OPC-288
❑ 72PadPos-14
❑ 72Top-288
❑ 73OPC-423
❑ 73Top-423
❑ 74OPC-615
❑ 74Top-615
Jeter, Shawn
❑ 87DunBluJP-943
❑ 88DunBluJS-12
❑ 89KnoBluJB-10
❑ 89KnoBluJP-1130
❑ 89KnoBluJS-8
❑ 90KnoBluJB-6
❑ 90KnoBluJP-1257
❑ 90KnoBluJS-6
❑ 91LinDriAAA-506
❑ 91SyrChiLD-506
❑ 91SyrChiMB-9
❑ 91SyrChiP-2493
❑ 92DonRoo-59
❑ 92FleUpd-14
❑ 92VanCanS-639
❑ 93LinVenB-196
❑ 93NasSouF-580
❑ 93Pin-265
❑ 93StaClu-453
❑ 93StaCluFDI-453
❑ 93StaCluMOP-453
❑ 93Top-800
❑ 93TopGol-800
❑ 93TopInaM-800
❑ 93TopInaR-800
❑ 93TopMic-800
Jethroe, Sam
❑ 47Exh-109
❑ 50Bow-248
❑ 51BerRos-D10
❑ 51Bow-242
❑ 51TopBluB-12
❑ 52Bow-84
❑ 52Top-27
❑ 53BowC-3
❑ 53ExhCan-10
❑ 79TCM50-44
❑ 83TopRep5-27
❑ 84OCoandSI-133
❑ 86NegLeaF-38
❑ 89PacLegI-206
❑ 89SweBasG-62
❑ 91PomBlaBPB-2
❑ 92NegLeaK-10
❑ 92NegLeaRLI-31
❑ 93TedWil-137
❑ 95NegLeaL2-19
❑ 97NegLeaPC-9D
Jevne, Frederick
❑ 87OldJudN-262
Jevyak, Brian
❑ 89CarNewE-13
Jewell, Jim
❑ 43CenFlo-12
Jewell, Mike
❑ 91WatIndC-7
❑ 91WatIndP-3362
❑ 92WatIndC-6
❑ 92WatIndF-3228
Jewett, Earl
❑ 89PulBraP-1897
❑ 90SumBraB-7
❑ 90SumBraP-2429
❑ 91MacBraC-2
❑ 91MacBraP-856
Jewett, Trent
❑ 89SalBucS-11
❑ 90HarSenP-1197
❑ 90HarSenS-10
❑ 91CarMudLD-125
❑ 91LinDriAA-125
❑ 92WelPirC-28
❑ 92WelPirF-1340
❑ 94SalBucC-26
❑ 94SalBucF-2339
❑ 95CarMudF-173
❑ 97CalCanB-1
❑ 98NasSouTI-18
❑ 98NasSouTISS-17
Jim, Diamond
❑ 90ColMudS-27
Jimaki, Jim
❑ 88CapCodPPaLP-84
Jimenez, Alex
❑ 87LitFalMP-2399
❑ 88ColMetGS-15
❑ 89ColMetB-29
❑ 89ColMetGS-12
❑ 90JacMetGS-3
❑ 91LinDriAAA-560
❑ 91TidTidLD-560
❑ 91TidTidP-2518
Jimenez, Cesar
❑ 86DurBulP-15
❑ 87DurBulP-1
❑ 88DurBulS-8
❑ 88FleUpd-72
❑ 88FleUpdG-72
Jimenez, D'Angelo
❑ 96Bow-124
❑ 96BowFoi-124
❑ 96GreBatB-12
❑ 97TamYan-14
❑ 98ColCliD-14
❑ 98ColCliM-18
❑ 98EasLeaTPM-12
Jimenez, Elvio (Felix)
❑ 65OPC-226
❑ 65Top-226
❑ 66TolMudHTI-15
❑ 69Top-567
❑ 85DomLeaS-42
❑ 92YanWIZ6-62
Jimenez, Felipe
❑ 97WilCubB-10
❑ 98RocCubM-13
❑ 98RocCubTI-13
Jimenez, German
❑ 88FleUpd-72
❑ 88FleUpdG-72
❑ 89GreBraB-23
❑ 89GreBraP-1153
❑ 89GreBraS-10
❑ 89Top-569
❑ 89TopTif-569
❑ 89UppDec-113
Jimenez, Houston (Alfonso)
❑ 83TolMudHT-15
❑ 84MinTwiP-17
❑ 84Nes792-411
❑ 84Top-411
❑ 84TopTif-411
❑ 84TwiTeal-3
❑ 85Don-269
❑ 85Fle-282
❑ 85TolMudHT-16
❑ 85Top-562
❑ 85TopTif-562
❑ 87VanCanP-1609
Jimenez, Jason
❑ 97HudValRB-25
❑ 98HudValR-12
Jimenez, Jhonny
❑ 96EveAquB-11
Jimenez, Jose
❑ 96PeoChiB-16
❑ 97PriWilC-15
❑ 98ArkTraH-9
❑ 98ArkTraM-15
❑ 98FleUpd-U39
❑ 99Bow-381
❑ 99BowGol-381
❑ 99BowInt-381
❑ 99CroRoyB-114
❑ 99CroRoyL-114
❑ 99CroRoyOD-114
❑ 99DumSet-133
❑ 99Fle-427
❑ 99FleMys-133
❑ 99FleMysM-133
❑ 99FleSta9-427
❑ 99FleWarT-427
❑ 99PacCroC-229
❑ 99PacCroCPB-229
❑ 99UppDec-470
❑ 99UppDecEL1-470
❑ 99UppDecEL2-470
Jimenez, Juan
❑ 85DomLeaS-74
❑ 86BurExpP-11
Jimenez, Luis
❑ 78ChaPirT-11
❑ 80VenLeaS-141
Jimenez, Manny Collado
❑ 91PulBraC-7
❑ 91PulBraP-4013
❑ 92MacBraC-8
❑ 92MacBraF-274
❑ 92ProFS7-194
❑ 93DurBulC-9
❑ 93DurBulF-491
❑ 93DurBulTI-10
❑ 94GreBraF-421
❑ 94GreBraTI-14
❑ 95DurBulTI-15
❑ 96GreBraB-16
❑ 96GreBraTI-12
❑ 97GreBraG-15
❑ 97TexAllM-41
Jimenez, Manuel
❑ 75QuaCitAT-12
Jimenez, Manuel Emilio
❑ 61AthJayP-11
❑ 62Top-598
❑ 63AthJayP-6
❑ 63Jel-87
❑ 63Pos-87
❑ 63Top-195
❑ 64A's-10
❑ 64AthJayP-7
❑ 64Top-574
❑ 66Top-458
❑ 67Top-586
❑ 68Top-538
❑ 69MilBra-132
Jimenez, Miguel
❑ 91SouOreAC-14
❑ 91SouOreAP-3837
❑ 92MadMusC-7
❑ 92MadMusF-1228
❑ 93Bow-133
❑ 93ClaFS7-210
❑ 93HunStaF-2078
❑ 93LimRocDWB-86
❑ 94A'sMot-11
❑ 94Bow-108
❑ 94ColC-12
❑ 94ColChoGS-12
❑ 94ColChoSS-12
❑ 94FleMajLP-17
❑ 94LeaGolR-13
❑ 94LeaLimR-50
❑ 94ScoRoo-RT152
❑ 94ScoRooGR-RT152
❑ 94SpoRoo-86
❑ 94SpoRooAP-86
❑ 94StaClu-356
❑ 94StaCluFDI-356
❑ 94StaCluGR-356
❑ 94StaCluMOP-356
❑ 94Top-773
❑ 94TopGol-773
❑ 94TopSpa-773
❑ 94Ult-108
❑ 95Don-262
❑ 95DonPreP-262
❑ 95EdmTraTI-11
❑ 95Lea-46
❑ 95Pac-314
❑ 95StaClu-201
❑ 95StaCluFDI-201
❑ 95StaCluMOP-201
❑ 95StaCluSTWS-201
❑ 97HunStaTI-12
❑ 98IowCubQ-13
Jimenez, Oscar
❑ 93EugEmeC-17
❑ 93EugEmeF-3869
❑ 94Bow-583
❑ 94RocRoyC-15
❑ 94RocRoyF-576
❑ 95WilBluRTI-17
Jimenez, Ramon
❑ 90Bes-40
❑ 90CMC-697
❑ 90GreHorB-17
❑ 90GreHorP-2669
❑ 90GreHorS-9
❑ 90SouAtlLAS-13
❑ 90StaFS7-93
❑ 91PriWilCC-18
❑ 91PriWilCP-1435
❑ 92PriWilCC-11
❑ 92PriWilCF-156
Jimenez, Ray
❑ 83PeoSunF-1
Jimenez, Roberto
❑ 90BurIndP-3011
Jimenez, Ruben
❑ 94JohCitCC-14
❑ 94JohCitCF-3709
❑ 96NewJerCB-14
❑ 98KinIndQ-14
Jimenez, Steve
❑ 93Sou-12
Jimenez, Vincent
❑ 91IdaFalBSP-21
Jiminez, Alex
❑ 86LitFalMP-15
❑ 87ColMetP-28
Jiminez, D'Angelo
❑ 98NorNavQ-14
Jiminez, Vincent
❑ 90PulBraB-14
❑ 90PulBraP-3092
Jirschele, Mike
❑ 78AshTouT-11
❑ 79WauTimT-21
❑ 80AshTouT-28
❑ 80TulDriT-15
❑ 81TulDriT-29
❑ 82TulDriT-19
❑ 83OklCit8T-10
❑ 84OklCit8T-9
❑ 85OklCit8T-4
❑ 89OmaRoyC-17
❑ 90AppFoxBS-14
❑ 90AppFoxP-2112
❑ 90TulDriDGB-20
❑ 91AppFoxCB-27
❑ 91AppFoxP-1732
❑ 93RocRoyC-28
❑ 93RocRoyF-731
❑ 94CarLeaAF-CAR18
❑ 94WilBluRC-24
❑ 94WilBluRF-315
❑ 95OmaRoyTI-15
❑ 96OmaRoyB-1
❑ 97OmaRoyB-1
Job, Ryan
❑ 85OscAstTI-18
❑ 86ColAstP-15
Jobes, Tracy
❑ 88MisStaB-14
❑ 89MisStaB-22
❑ 90MisStaB-22
Jockish, Mike
❑ 88St.CatBJP-2031
❑ 89St.CatBJP-2078
❑ 90EriSaiS-10
Jodie, Brett
❑ 98OneYanG-16
❑ 99TeaBesR-40
❑ 99TeaBesRG-40
❑ 99TeaBesRS-40
Jodo, Daijiro
❑ 88SanJosGCLC-120
Joffrion, Jack
❑ 97HudValRB-10
Johdo, Joe
❑ 88SanJosGP-136
Johjima, Kenji
❑ 96MauStiHWB-8
John, Tommy
❑ 64Top-146
❑ 64TopVen-146
❑ 65OPC-208
❑ 65Top-208
❑ 66Top-486
❑ 66WhiSoxTI-7
❑ 67CokCapWS-15
❑ 67DexPre-105
❑ 67Top-609
❑ 68OPC-72
❑ 68Top-72
❑ 68TopVen-72
❑ 69MilBra-133
❑ 69MLBOffS-31
❑ 69NabTeaF-11
❑ 69Top-465
❑ 69TopSta-155
❑ 69TopTeaP-11
❑ 69TraSta-22
❑ 69WhiSoxTI-6
❑ 70MLBOffS-186
❑ 70OPC-180
❑ 70Top-180
❑ 70WhiSoxTI-7
❑ 71Kel-74
❑ 71MilDud-11
❑ 71OPC-520
❑ 71Top-520
❑ 71TopCoi-56
❑ 72MilBra-165
❑ 72OPC-264
❑ 72Top-264
❑ 73OPC-258
❑ 73Top-258
❑ 74OPC-451
❑ 74Top-451
❑ 75OPC-47
❑ 75Top-47
❑ 75TopMin-47
❑ 76DodPos-8
❑ 76OPC-416
❑ 76SSP-69
❑ 76Top-416
❑ 77DodPho-5
❑ 77Spo-3204
❑ 77Top-128
❑ 78Hos-7
❑ 78Kel-36
❑ 78RCColC-82
❑ 78SSP270-75
❑ 78Top-375
❑ 79BasPat-43
❑ 79OPC-129
❑ 79Top-255
❑ 79YanBurK-9
❑ 79YanPicA-21
❑ 80OPC-348
❑ 80Top-690
❑ 80TopSup-23
❑ 80WilGloT-3
❑ 80YanPhoA-13
❑ 81AllGamPI-84
❑ 81Don-107
❑ 81Fle-81
❑ 81FleStiC-121
❑ 81Kel-52
❑ 81OPC-96
❑ 81Top-550
❑ 81TopScr-52
❑ 81TopSti-2
❑ 81TopSti-114
❑ 81TopSti-250
❑ 81TopSupHT-66
❑ 81YanPhoA-10
❑ 82Don-409
❑ 82Don-558
❑ 82Fle-40
❑ 82FleSta-115
❑ 82OPC-75
❑ 82Top-75
❑ 82Top-486
❑ 82TopSti-214
❑ 82WilSpoG-4
❑ 82YanPhoA-12
❑ 83Don-570
❑ 83Fle-95
❑ 83FleSta-92
❑ 83FleSti-25
❑ 83OPC-144
❑ 83OPC-196
❑ 83SevCoi-9
❑ 83Top-735
❑ 83Top-736
❑ 83TopFol-1
❑ 84AngSmo-13
❑ 84Don-301
❑ 84DonCha-36
❑ 84Fle-522
❑ 84FunFooP-92
❑ 84Nes792-415
❑ 84Nes792-715
❑ 84OPC-284
❑ 84Top-415
❑ 84Top-715
❑ 84TopRubD-28
❑ 84TopSti-232
❑ 84TopTif-415
❑ 84TopTif-715
❑ 85AngSmo-23
❑ 85Don-423
❑ 85Fle-304
❑ 85OPC-179
❑ 85Top-179
❑ 85TopSti-229
❑ 85TopTif-179
❑ 86Fle-422
❑ 86FleUpd-57
❑ 86Top-240
❑ 86TopTif-240
❑ 86WilGloT-1
❑ 86YanTCM-1
❑ 87DodSmoA-15
❑ 87Fle-102
❑ 87FleGlo-102
❑ 87OPC-236
❑ 87Top-236
❑ 87TopTif-236
❑ 88Don-17
❑ 88Don-401
❑ 88DonBasB-220
❑ 88DonReaBY-401
❑ 88DonSupD-17
❑ 88Fle-211
❑ 88FleGlo-211
❑ 88Lea-17
❑ 88Lea-230
❑ 88PanSti-148
❑ 88Sco-240
❑ 88ScoGlo-240
❑ 88Spo-122
❑ 88StaLinY-7
❑ 88Top-611
❑ 88TopTif-611
❑ 89ClaLigB-40
❑ 89DodSmoG-91
❑ 89Fle-255
❑ 89FleGlo-255
❑ 89Sco-477
❑ 89Top-359
❑ 89TopBasT-139
❑ 89TopSti-310
❑ 89TopTif-359
❑ 89UppDec-230
❑ 90DodTar-386
❑ 92DodStaTA-17
❑ 92YanWIZ7-80
❑ 92YanWIZ8-92
❑ 92YanWIZA-34
❑ 93ActPacA-157
❑ 93UppDecAH-75
❑ 94TedWil-12
❑ 94UppDecAH-78
❑ 94UppDecAH1-78
❑ 95SonGre-5
❑ 99SpoIllGotG-87
❑ 99SpoIllGotGA-36
Johnigan, Steve
❑ 87WatIndP-4
❑ 92MisStaB-23
❑ 93MisStaB-24
Johns, Augustus
❑ 30Zee-9
❑ 32Zee-8
❑ 33Zee-4
Johns, Clarence
❑ 94JohCitCC-15
❑ 94JohCitCF-3695
Johns, Douglas
❑ 90SouOreAB-5
❑ 91MadMusC-9
❑ 91MadMusP-2126
❑ 92RenSilSCLC-44
❑ 93HunStaF-2079
❑ 94HunStaF-1326
❑ 94TacTigF-3168
❑ 95EdmTraTI-12
❑ 96A'sMot-8
❑ 96ColCho-31
❑ 96ColChoGS-31
❑ 96ColChoSS-31
❑ 96Don-377
❑ 96DonPreP-377
❑ 96EmoXL-103
❑ 96Fla-149
❑ 96Fle-212
❑ 96FleTif-212
❑ 96StaClu-154
❑ 96StaCluMOP-154
❑ 96Ult-401
❑ 96UltGolM-401
❑ 96UppDec-163
❑ 97UppDec-129
Johns, Jeffrey
❑ 80VenLeaS-34
Johns, Keith
❑ 92FroRowDP-52
❑ 92FroRowDPG-52
❑ 92FroRowDPS-52
❑ 92HamRedC-12
❑ 92HamRedF-1600
❑ 93ClaGolF-118
❑ 93ExcFS7-99
❑ 93MidLeaAGF-51
❑ 93SprCarC-13
❑ 93SprCarF-1860
❑ 94St.PetCC-11
❑ 94St.PetCF-2593
❑ 95ArkTraTI-15
❑ 96ArkTraB-15
❑ 97TucTorB-17
❑ 98PawRedSQ-17
Johns, Michael
❑ 97PorRocG-10
❑ 98AshTouM-7
Johns, Ronald M.

❑ 86FloStaLAP-26
❑ 86St.PetCP-15
❑ 87SprCarB-6
❑ 88HarSenP-849
Johnson, A.J.
❑ 92KenTwiC-9
❑ 98RanCucQG-14
❑ 98RanCucQG-14
Johnson, Abner
❑ 78WisRapTT-10
❑ 81ChaRoyT-19
Johnson, Adam
❑ 96EugEmeB-12
❑ 97Bow-369
❑ 97BowChr-247
❑ 97BowChrI-247
❑ 97BowChrIR-247
❑ 97BowChrR-247
❑ 97BowInt-369
❑ 97CalLeaATI-32
❑ 97CarLeaTP-24
❑ 97DurBulTI-30
❑ 98GreBraG-11
❑ 98SP MinPE-24
❑ 98SP MinSTHPE-H6
❑ 98SPMin-24
❑ 98SPMinSTH-H6
Johnson, Alan
❑ 98ForMyeMTI-17
Johnson, Alex
❑ 64PhiPhiB-15
❑ 65Top-352
❑ 66CarTeal-7
❑ 66OPC-104
❑ 66Top-104A
❑ 66Top-104B
❑ 66TopVen-104
❑ 67OPC-108
❑ 67Top-108
❑ 68Top-441
❑ 69Kah-B11
❑ 69Top-280
❑ 69TopSta-25
❑ 69TopTeaP-20
❑ 70DayDaiNM-13
❑ 70MLBOffS-173
❑ 70OPC-115
❑ 70Top-115
❑ 71AllBasA-12
❑ 71AngJacitB-5
❑ 71Kel-54A
❑ 71Kel-54B
❑ 71Kel-54C
❑ 71MilDud-12
❑ 71MLBOffS-346
❑ 71MLBOffS-564
❑ 71OPC-61
❑ 71OPC-590
❑ 71Top-61
❑ 71Top-590
❑ 71TopCoi-84
❑ 71TopGreM-17
❑ 71TopSup-8
❑ 71TopTat-122
❑ 72MilBra-166
❑ 72OPC-215
❑ 72SevTraC-23
❑ 72Top-215
❑ 73OPC-425
❑ 73RanTeal-15
❑ 73Top-425
❑ 74OPC-107
❑ 74Top-107
❑ 74TopSta-237
❑ 75OPC-534
❑ 75Top-534
❑ 75TopMin-534
❑ 75YanSSP-17
❑ 76DetTigP-13
❑ 77Top-637
❑ 85AngStrH-9
❑ 92YanWIZ7-81
❑ 93RanKee-204
Johnson, Andre
❑ 91PulBraC-12
❑ 91PulBraP-4018
❑ 92IdaFalGF-3527
❑ 92IdaFalGSP-7
Johnson, Andrew
❑ 94OriofB-14
Johnson, Angela
❑ 89GeoColC-12
Johnson, Anthony
❑ 89SanDieSAS-13
❑ 90PulBraB-21
❑ 90PulBraP-3086

Johnson, Anthony Clair
❑ 79MemChiT-10
❑ 80MemChiT-3
❑ 83Don-629
❑ 83SyrChiT-22
❑ 84SyrChiT-7
Johnson, Arthur
❑ 91NiaFalRC-3
❑ 92BriTigF-1419
Johnson, Artis
❑ 93HunCubC-11
❑ 93HunCubF-3250
❑ 94HunCubC-16
❑ 94HunCubF-3567
Johnson, Avery
❑ 89BurIndS-13
Johnson, B.J. (Brian Lloyd)
❑ 88BurIndP-1798
❑ 89KinIndS-10
❑ 90KinIndTI-6
Johnson, Ban
❑ 04FanCraAL-28
❑ 09SpoNewSM-14
❑ 36Halof FP-13
❑ 39PC7AlbHoF-7
❑ 50CalHOFW-42
❑ 53ArtHaloFP-48
❑ 61Fle-48
❑ 63BazA-16
❑ 69Baz-2
❑ 74CapPub-46
❑ 76ShaPiz-10
❑ 77GalGloG-170
❑ 80PerHaloFP-7
❑ 80SSPHOF-7
❑ 84GalHaloFRL-10
❑ 88PacEigMO-78
❑ 89HOFStiB-96
❑ 94OriofB-80
❑ 95ConTSN-1396
Johnson, Barry
❑ 90AriWilP-8
❑ 93SarWhiSC-15
❑ 94BirBarC-14
❑ 94BirBarF-618
❑ 96BirBarB-16
❑ 97CalCanB-14
❑ 98OklRedM-7
Johnson, Bart (C. Barth)
❑ 70Top-669
❑ 71OPC-156
❑ 71Top-156
❑ 72OPC-126
❑ 72Top-126
❑ 72WhiSoxDS-3
❑ 73OPC-506
❑ 73Top-506
❑ 74OPC-147
❑ 74Top-147
❑ 75OPC-446
❑ 75Top-446
❑ 75TopMin-446
❑ 76OPC-513
❑ 76Top-513
❑ 77BurCheD-77
❑ 77Top-177
❑ 77WhiSoxT-11
Johnson, Ben
❑ 88AlaGolTI-10
❑ 90WelPirP-6
Johnson, Ben (Benjamin F.)
❑ 54BraJohC-12
❑ 60Top-528
Johnson, Bert
❑ 82ChaRoyT-9
Johnson, Bill
❑ 47YanTeaT-15
❑ 49Bow-129
❑ 49YanTeal-10
❑ 50YanTeal-12
❑ 83ReaPhiT-7
❑ 84IowCubT-29
❑ 85IowCubT-16
❑ 89SpoIndSP-12
❑ 90ChaRaiB-12
❑ 90ChaRaiP-2040
❑ 91ChaRaiC-8
❑ 91ChaRaiP-94
Johnson, Billy
❑ 87LouRedTI-30
❑ 92WatDiaC-5
Johnson, Billy (William Russell)
❑ 43YanSta-15
❑ 46SpoExcW-6-10
❑ 47Exh-110
❑ 48BluTin-1
❑ 48Bow-33
❑ 48YanTeal-14
❑ 49Lea-14
❑ 50Bow-102
❑ 51BerRos-A5
❑ 51Bow-74
❑ 51TopBluB-21
❑ 52Bow-122
❑ 52Top-83
❑ 53CarHunW-11
❑ 53Top-21
❑ 75JohMiz-13
❑ 77TCMTheWY-55
❑ 79TCM50-230
❑ 83TopRep5-83
❑ 83YanASFY-21
❑ 85TCMPla1-9
❑ 91TopArc1-21
❑ 92YanWIZA-35
Johnson, Bo
❑ 94JohCitCC-16
❑ 94JohCitCF-3696
❑ 95PeoChiTI-26
Johnson, Bob
❑ 79WauTimT-12
Johnson, Bob (Robert Dale)
❑ 70RoyTeal-15
❑ 70Top-702
❑ 71OPC-71
❑ 71OPC-365
❑ 71PirActP-7
❑ 71Top-71
❑ 71Top-365
❑ 72MilBra-167
❑ 72OPC-27
❑ 72Top-27
❑ 73OPC-657
❑ 73Top-657
❑ 74OPC-269
❑ 74SpoIndC-29
❑ 74Top-269
❑ 74TopTra-269T
❑ 76OmaRoyTT-8
❑ 91MetWIZ-202
Johnson, Bob (Robert Wallace)
❑ 55DonWin-27
❑ 60A'sTeal-9
❑ 61SenJayP-4
❑ 62Top-519
❑ 62TopStal-97
❑ 63BalOriP-15
❑ 63Jel-96
❑ 63Pos-96
❑ 63Top-504
❑ 64BalOriP-20
❑ 64Top-304
❑ 64TopVen-304
❑ 65BalOriP-15
❑ 65Top-363
❑ 66BalOriP-18
❑ 66OPC-148
❑ 66Top-148
❑ 66TopVen-148
❑ 67BalOriP-54
❑ 67OPC-38
❑ 67Top-38
❑ 68BraPos-16
❑ 68Top-338
❑ 68TopVen-338
❑ 69MilBra-134
❑ 69Top-261
❑ 70Top-693
❑ 78TCM60I-279
❑ 81Ori6F-19
❑ 91MetWIZ-204
❑ 91OriCro-221
Johnson, Bobby E.
❑ 76VenLeaS-125
❑ 78AshTouT-12
❑ 80TulDriT-21
❑ 82Top-418
❑ 83Don-494
❑ 83RanAffF-8
❑ 83TopTra-48T
❑ 84Don-500
❑ 84Fle-420
❑ 84Nes792-608
❑ 84Top-608
❑ 84TopTif-608
❑ 87OPC-234
❑ 88OPC-228
❑ 93RanKee-205
Johnson, Boo (Curley)
❑ 90PeoChiTI-10
Johnson, Brian David
❑ 90Bes-214
❑ 90CarLeaA-40
❑ 90GreHorB-13
❑ 90GreHorP-2665
❑ 90GreHorS-10
❑ 90SouAtlLAS-14
❑ 90TopTVY-47
❑ 91Cla/Bes-9
❑ 91ColSprSSLD-85
❑ 91ColSprSSP-2186
❑ 91FloStaLAP-FSL14
❑ 91Ft.LauYC-16
❑ 91Ft.LauYP-2429
❑ 91LinDriAAA-85
❑ 92ColSprSSF-754
❑ 92WicWraF-3659
❑ 92WicWraS-637
❑ 93LasVegSF-948
❑ 94ExcFS7-284
❑ 94PadMot-12
❑ 94SpoRoo-115
❑ 94SpoRooAP-115
❑ 94StaClu-601
❑ 94StaCluFDI-601
❑ 94StaCluGR-601
❑ 94StaCluMOP-601
❑ 94Top-789
❑ 94TopGol-789
❑ 94TopSpa-789
❑ 94Ult-579
❑ 95Fin-321
❑ 95FinRef-321
❑ 95Fla-203
❑ 95HelBreTI-10
❑ 95PadCHP-4
❑ 95PadMot-10
❑ 95Sco-149
❑ 95ScoGolR-149
❑ 95ScoPlaTS-149
❑ 96ColCho-713
❑ 96ColChoGS-713
❑ 96ColChoSS-713
❑ 96Don-416
❑ 96DonPreP-416
❑ 96Fle-571
❑ 96FleTif-571
❑ 96LeaSigEA-90
❑ 96PadMot-9
❑ 97ColCho-336
❑ 97Fle-466
❑ 97Fle-688
❑ 97FleTif-466
❑ 97FleTif-688
❑ 97Pac-428
❑ 97PacLigB-428
❑ 97PacSil-428
❑ 97Ult-318
❑ 97UltGolME-318
❑ 97UltPlaME-318
❑ 97UppDec-357
❑ 98CirThu-143
❑ 98CirThuRav-143
❑ 98CirThuSupRav-143
❑ 98ColCho-189
❑ 98ColCho-229
❑ 98Fin-51
❑ 98FinNo--51
❑ 98FinNo-R-51
❑ 98FinRef-51
❑ 98Fle-495
❑ 98GiaMot-6
❑ 98Pac-444
❑ 98PacOnl-663
❑ 98PacOnlR-663
❑ 98PacOnlWC-663
❑ 98PacPar-247
❑ 98PacParC-247
❑ 98PacParG-247
❑ 98PacParHS-247
❑ 98PacParPB-247
❑ 98PacParR-247
❑ 98PacPlaB-444
❑ 98PacRedT-444
❑ 98PacSil-444
❑ 98StaCluFDI-256
❑ 98StaCluI-256
❑ 98StaCluOneK-256
❑ 98StaCluPP-256
❑ 98Top-407
❑ 98TopChr-407
❑ 98TopChrR-407
❑ 98TopDevR-407
❑ 98TopDia-407
❑ 98TopMiniC-407
❑ 98Ult-443
❑ 98UltGolM-443
❑ 98UltMas-443
❑ 98UltPlaM-443
❑ 98UppDec-503
❑ 99Fle-520
❑ 99FleSta9-520
❑ 99FleWarT-520
❑ 99Pac-382
❑ 99PacPlaB-382
❑ 99PacRed-382
❑ 99StaClu-119
❑ 99StaCluFDI-119
❑ 99StaCluOoaK-119
❑ 99StaCluPP-119
❑ 99Top-102
❑ 99TopChr-102
❑ 99TopChrR-102
❑ 99TopMVPP-102
Johnson, Carl
❑ 88VerBeaDS-12
❑ 89KenTwiP-1065
❑ 89KenTwiS-9
❑ 90BurIndP-3006
❑ 91KinIndC-3
❑ 91KinIndP-315
❑ 92KinIndC-13
❑ 94KinIndC-9
❑ 94KinIndF-2637
Johnson, Chad
❑ 98LowSpiM-9
Johnson, Charles Edward
❑ 91MiaHurBB-7
❑ 91TopTra-61T
❑ 91TopTraT-61T
❑ 92Bow-661
❑ 92StaCluD-91
❑ 92TopDaiQTU-27
❑ 92TopTra-56T
❑ 92TopTraG-56T
❑ 93ClaExp#PF-EP2
❑ 93ClaFS7-211
❑ 93KanCouCC-1
❑ 93KanCouCF-918
❑ 93KanCouCTI-9
❑ 93MarUppD-435
❑ 93MidLeaAGF-8
❑ 93StaCluM-76
❑ 93UppDec-435
❑ 93UppDecGold-435
❑ 93WorUniG-1
❑ 94ActPac-7
❑ 94ActPac-58
❑ 94ActPac2G-4G
❑ 94ActPac2GD-4G
❑ 94AriFalLS-10
❑ 94Cla-180
❑ 94ClaCreotC-C18
❑ 94ClaGolF-105
❑ 94ColC-660
❑ 94ColChoGS-660
❑ 94ColChoSS-660
❑ 94ExcAllF-1
❑ 94ExcFS7-191
❑ 94LeaLimR-1
❑ 94MarTeal-8
❑ 94PorSeaDF-681
❑ 94PorSeaDTI-16
❑ 94ScoRoo-RT120
❑ 94ScoRooGR-RT120
❑ 94Sel-407
❑ 94SigRooBS-P2
❑ 94SP-113
❑ 94SPDieC-113
❑ 94SpoRoo-35
❑ 94SpoRooAP-35
❑ 94SpoRooRS-TR18
❑ 94TedWil-125
❑ 94TedWilDGC-DG4
❑ 94UppDec-536
❑ 94UppDecED-536
❑ 94UppDecML-93
❑ 94UppDecML-110
❑ 94UppDecML-269
❑ 94UppDecMLPotYF-PY14
❑ 94UppDecMLT1PJF-TP4
❑ 94UppDecMLT1PMF-4
❑ 95ActPac2G-1G
❑ 95ActPacF-3
❑ 95ActPacF-62
❑ 95ColCho-1
❑ 95ColChoGS-1
❑ 95ColChoSE-135
❑ 95ColChoSEGS-135
❑ 95ColChoSESS-135
❑ 95ColChoSS-1
❑ 95Don-27
❑ 95DonPreP-27
❑ 95DonTopotO-244
❑ 95Emo-131
❑ 95EmoRoo-7
❑ 95Fla-139
❑ 95Fla-354
❑ 95FleMajLP-8
❑ 95FleUpd-97
❑ 95FleUpdRU-4
❑ 95KanCouCLTI-7
❑ 95Lea-345
❑ 95LeaGolR-9
❑ 95LeaLim-67
❑ 95PacPri-56
❑ 95Pin-158
❑ 95PinArtP-158
❑ 95PinMusC-158
❑ 95PinNewB-NB5
❑ 95Sco-575
❑ 95ScoAi-AM5
❑ 95ScoGolR-575
❑ 95ScoPlaTS-575
❑ 95ScoRooDT-RDT5
❑ 95Sel-102
❑ 95Sel-236
❑ 95SelArtP-102
❑ 95SelArtP-236
❑ 95SelCanM-CM3
❑ 95SelCer-117
❑ 95SelCerMG-117
❑ 95SelCerPU-8
❑ 95SelCerPU9-8
❑ 95SigRooMOP-P5
❑ 95SigRooMOPS-P5
❑ 95SigRooMR-MR3
❑ 95SigRooMRS-MR3
❑ 95SigRooOJSS-2
❑ 95SigRooOJSSS-2
❑ 95SP-58
❑ 95SPCha-46
❑ 95SPChaDC-46
❑ 95Spo-150
❑ 95SpoArtP-150
❑ 95SPSil-58
❑ 95SPSpeF-36
❑ 95Stu-140
❑ 95Sum-130
❑ 95SumNewA-NA8
❑ 95SumNthD-130
❑ 95SumSam-130
❑ 95UC3-122
❑ 95UC3ArtP-122
❑ 95UC3CleS-CS4
❑ 95Ult-380
❑ 95UltGolM-380
❑ 95UltGolP-8
❑ 95UltGolPGM-8
❑ 95UppDec-220
❑ 95UppDecED-220
❑ 95UppDecEDG-220
❑ 95UppDecPAW-H18
❑ 95UppDecPAWE-H18
❑ 95UppDecSE-113
❑ 95UppDecSEG-113
❑ 95Zen-133
❑ 95ZenRooRC-17
❑ 96Cir-129
❑ 96CirBos-35
❑ 96CirRav-129
❑ 96ColCho-155
❑ 96ColChoGS-155
❑ 96ColChoSS-155
❑ 96Don-313
❑ 96DonPreP-313
❑ 96EmoRarB-5
❑ 96EmoXL-187
❑ 96Fla-263
❑ 96Fle-388
❑ 96FleRooS-9
❑ 96FleTif-388
❑ 96FleTomL-5
❑ 96Lea-22
❑ 96LeaLim-60
❑ 96LeaLimG-60
❑ 96LeaPre-42
❑ 96LeaPreP-42
❑ 96LeaPrePB-22
❑ 96LeaPrePG-22
❑ 96LeaPrePS-22

❑ 96LeaPreSG-50
❑ 96LeaPreSte-50
❑ 96LeaSig-60
❑ 96LeaSigPPG-60
❑ 96LeaSigPPP-60
❑ 96MetUni-166
❑ 96MetUniMFG-7
❑ 96MetUniP-166
❑ 96Pac-80
❑ 96PacPri-P26
❑ 96PacPriG-P26
❑ 96PanSti-11
❑ 96PanSti-245
❑ 96Pin-52
❑ 96PinAfi-150
❑ 96PinAfiAP-150
❑ 96PinArtP-20
❑ 96PinProS-7
❑ 96PinSta-20
❑ 96Sco-289
❑ 96ScoDugC-B14
❑ 96ScoDugCAP-B14
❑ 96ScoFutF-15
❑ 96Sel-44
❑ 96SelArtP-44
❑ 96SelCer-39
❑ 96SelCerAP-39
❑ 96SelCerCB-39
❑ 96SelCerCR-39
❑ 96SelCerMB-39
❑ 96SelCerMG-39
❑ 96SelCerMR-39
❑ 96SelTeaN-16
❑ 96SP-87
❑ 96Spo-61
❑ 96SpoArtP-61
❑ 96Stu-51
❑ 96StuPrePB-51
❑ 96StuPrePG-51
❑ 96StuPrePS-51
❑ 96Sum-51
❑ 96SumAbo&B-51
❑ 96SumArtP-51
❑ 96SumFoi-51
❑ 96SumPos-5
❑ 96Ult-201
❑ 96UltGolM-201
❑ 96UppDec-73
❑ 96Zen-60
❑ 96ZenArtP-60
❑ 96ZenMoz-16
❑ 97Cir-176
❑ 97CirRav-176
❑ 97ColCho-114
❑ 97ColChoT-FM5
❑ 97Don-18
❑ 97DonArmaD-12
❑ 97DonEli-129
❑ 97DonEliGS-129
❑ 97DonGolPP-18
❑ 97DonLim-167
❑ 97DonLimE-167
❑ 97DonLimENG-167
❑ 97DonPre-37
❑ 97DonPreCttC-37
❑ 97DonSilPP-18
❑ 97FlaShoLC-78
❑ 97FlaShoLeg0-78
❑ 97FlaShoLeg1-78
❑ 97FlaShoM-A78
❑ 97FlaShoM-B78
❑ 97FlaShoM-C78
❑ 97FlaShoR0-78
❑ 97FlaShoR1-78
❑ 97FlaShoR2-78
❑ 97Fle-330
❑ 97FleTif-330
❑ 97Lea-131
❑ 97LeaFraM-131
❑ 97LeaFraMDC-131
❑ 97MarPac-15
❑ 97MetUni-175
❑ 97NewPin-38
❑ 97NewPinAP-38
❑ 97NewPinMC-38
❑ 97NewPinPP-38
❑ 97Pac-301
❑ 97PacLigB-301
❑ 97PacPri-102
❑ 97PacPriLB-102
❑ 97PacPriP-102
❑ 97PacSil-301
❑ 97PinCer-99
❑ 97PinCerMBla-99
❑ 97PinCerMBlu-99
❑ 97PinCerMG-99
❑ 97PinCerMR-99
❑ 97PinCerR-99
❑ 97PinIns-99
❑ 97PinInsCE-99
❑ 97PinInsDE-99
❑ 97PinTotCPB-99
❑ 97PinTotCPG-99
❑ 97PinTotCPR-99
❑ 97Sco-294
❑ 97ScoArtPWB-294
❑ 97ScoPreS-294
❑ 97ScoShoS-294
❑ 97ScoShoSAP-294
❑ 97Sel-61
❑ 97SelArtP-61
❑ 97SelCom-61
❑ 97SelRegG-61
❑ 97SelToootT-20
❑ 97SelToootTMB-20
❑ 97SP-79
❑ 97StrAll-29
❑ 97Stu-62
❑ 97StuPrePG-62
❑ 97StuPrePS-62
❑ 97Ult-197
❑ 97UltFieC-8
❑ 97UltGolME-197
❑ 97UltPlaME-197
❑ 97UppDec-79
❑ 97UppDec-139
❑ 97UppDecRSF-RS8
❑ 98Bow-238
❑ 98BowChr-238
❑ 98BowChrGA-238
❑ 98BowChrGAR-238
❑ 98BowChrI-238
❑ 98BowChrIR-238
❑ 98BowChrR-238
❑ 98BowGolA-238
❑ 98BowInt-238
❑ 98CirThu-187
❑ 98CirThuRav-187
❑ 98CirThuSupRav-187
❑ 98ColCho-97
❑ 98ColCho-187
❑ 98ColChoRJ-97
❑ 98DodMot-7
❑ 98Don-54
❑ 98DonCol-54
❑ 98DonColL-222
❑ 98DonColP-601
❑ 98DonColS-54
❑ 98DonGolPP-54
❑ 98DonPre-51
❑ 98DonPreSeat-51
❑ 98DonPriCD-54
❑ 98DonPriCL-222
❑ 98DonPriCP-601
❑ 98DonSilPP-54
❑ 98Fin-249
❑ 98FinNo--249
❑ 98FinNo-R-249
❑ 98FinRef-249
❑ 98FlaShoLeg0-42
❑ 98FlaShoLeg1-42
❑ 98FlaShoLeg2-42
❑ 98FlaShoLeg3-42
❑ 98FlaShoLegM-42
❑ 98FlaShoR0-42
❑ 98FlaShoR1-42
❑ 98FlaShoR2-42
❑ 98FlaShoR3-42
❑ 98Fle-238
❑ 98Fle-441
❑ 98FleVin'-26
❑ 98FleVin'-109
❑ 98FleVin'C-26
❑ 98FleVin'C-109
❑ 98Lea-22
❑ 98LeaFraDA-22
❑ 98LeaFraF-22
❑ 98LeaFraM-22
❑ 98LeaFraM-22
❑ 98LeaFraMDC-22
❑ 98LeaFraMDC-22
❑ 98LeaFraMS-22
❑ 98LeaFraMZ2-22
❑ 98LeaRS-74
❑ 98LeaRSLHolo-74
❑ 98LeaRSLong-74
❑ 98LeaRTrue-74
❑ 98MetUni-142
❑ 98MetUniPMG-142
❑ 98Pac-304
❑ 98PacAur-131
❑ 98PacInvTeam-11
❑ 98PacOme-122
❑ 98PacOmeR-122
❑ 98PacOnl-374
❑ 98PacOnlR-374
❑ 98PacOnlWC-374
❑ 98PacPar-161
❑ 98PacParC-161
❑ 98PacParG-161
❑ 98PacParHS-161
❑ 98PacParPB-161
❑ 98PacParR-161
❑ 98PacPlaB-304
❑ 98PacRedT-304
❑ 98PacSil-304
❑ 98PinIns-97
❑ 98PinIns-147
❑ 98PinInsCE-97
❑ 98PinInsCE-147
❑ 98PinInsDE-97
❑ 98PinInsDE-147
❑ 98PinInsSG-7AB
❑ 98PinInsSG-7CD
❑ 98PinInsSGS-7AB
❑ 98PinInsSGS-7CD
❑ 98PinPer-52
❑ 98PinPerPP-52
❑ 98PinPlu-96
❑ 98PorSeaD5AQ-1
❑ 98PreCon-16
❑ 98Revo-74
❑ 98RevoSS-74
❑ 98Sco-154
❑ 98ScoRT-189
❑ 98ScoRTSS-PP105
❑ 98ScoRTSSAP-PP105
❑ 98ScoRTSSAP1-PP105
❑ 98ScoSS-PP63
❑ 98ScoSSAP-PP63
❑ 98SkyDugA-16
❑ 98SkyDugAIA-16
❑ 98SP Aut-114
❑ 98SP AutC-CJ
❑ 98SpoIll-65
❑ 98SpoIll-134
❑ 98SpoIll-187
❑ 98SpoIllEE-65
❑ 98SpoIllEE-134
❑ 98SpoIllEE-187
❑ 98SpoIllFE-65
❑ 98SpoIllFE-134
❑ 98SpoIllFE-187
❑ 98SpoIllTaN-94
❑ 98SpoIllTaNEE-94
❑ 98SpoIllTaNGS-15
❑ 98SpoIllWSF-62
❑ 98SpoIllWSFEE-62
❑ 98SpoIllWSFFE-62
❑ 98SPxFin-291
❑ 98SPxFin-342
❑ 98SPxFinR-291
❑ 98SPxFinR-342
❑ 98SPxFinS-291
❑ 98SPxFinS-342
❑ 98Stu-84
❑ 98StuGPP-84
❑ 98StuSPP-84
❑ 98TopSta-69
❑ 98TopStaB-69
❑ 98TopStaG-69
❑ 98TopStaGR-69
❑ 98TopStaS-69
❑ 98UD3-83
❑ 98UD3-173
❑ 98UD3-263
❑ 98UD3DieCut-83
❑ 98UD3DieCut-173
❑ 98UD3DieCut-263
❑ 98Ult-60
❑ 98Ult-257
❑ 98UltGolM-60
❑ 98UltGolM-257
❑ 98UltKidG-10
❑ 98UltMas-60
❑ 98UltMas-257
❑ 98UltPlaM-60
❑ 98UltPlaM-257
❑ 98UppDec-92
❑ 98UppDec-690
❑ 98UppDecR-44
❑ 98UppDecRGKoG-G20
❑ 98UppDecRTC-TC41
❑ 98UppDecSF-56
❑ 98Zen-51
❑ 98ZenZ-G-51
❑ 98ZenZ-S-51
❑ 99199Fin-174
❑ 99FinGolRef-174
❑ 99FinRef-174
❑ 99FlaShoLeg1-136
❑ 99FlaShoLeg2-136
❑ 99FlaShoLeg3-136
❑ 99FlaShoLegM1-136
❑ 99FlaShoLegM2-136
❑ 99FlaShoLegM3-136
❑ 99FlaShoR1-136
❑ 99FlaShoR2-136
❑ 99FlaShoR3-136
❑ 99Fle-128
❑ 99FleSta9-128
❑ 99FleWarT-128
❑ 99MetUni-37
❑ 99MetUniGM-37
❑ 99MetUniPMG-37
❑ 99Pac-221
❑ 99PacOme-35
❑ 99PacOmeC-35
❑ 99PacOmeG-35
❑ 99PacOmePB-35
❑ 99PacPar-34
❑ 99PacParC-34
❑ 99PacParG-34
❑ 99PacParHoloGold-34
❑ 99PacParHS-34
❑ 99PacParOD-34
❑ 99PacParPB-34
❑ 99PacParRed-34
❑ 99PacPlaB-221
❑ 99PacRed-221
❑ 99SkyMolM-68
❑ 99SkyMolMX-68
❑ 99SkyPre-38
❑ 99SkyPreR-38
❑ 99SkyThu-79
❑ 99SkyThuRant-79
❑ 99SkyThuRave-79
❑ 99StaClu-102
❑ 99StaCluFDI-102
❑ 99StaCluOoaK-102
❑ 99StaCluPP-102
❑ 99ThuSkySupR-79
❑ 99Top-175
❑ 99TopChr-175
❑ 99TopChrR-175
❑ 99TopMVPP-175
❑ 99TopSta-132
❑ 99TopStaFoil-132
❑ 99UD Cho-97
❑ 99UD ChoPCR-97
❑ 99Ult-29
❑ 99UltGolM-29
❑ 99UltMas-29
❑ 99UltPlaM-29
❑ 99UppDec-126
❑ 99UppDec-316
❑ 99UppDecCLM-C11
❑ 99UppDecEL1-126
❑ 99UppDecEL1-316
❑ 99UppDecEL2-126
❑ 99UppDecEL2-316
❑ 99UppDecGJ-CJ
❑ 99UppDecM-24
❑ 99UppDecMGS-24
❑ 99UppDecMHFS-24
❑ 99UppDecMSS-24
❑ 99Vic-47

Johnson, Chet
❑ 45CenFlo-12

Johnson, Chip
❑ 91OklStaC-12

Johnson, Chris
❑ 88BelBreGS-25
❑ 89BelBre2S-16
❑ 89BelBreIS-10
❑ 90CalLeaACLC-56
❑ 90CMC-712
❑ 90ProAaA-137
❑ 90StoPorB-15
❑ 90StoPorCLC-176
❑ 90StoPorP-2174
❑ 91Bow-45
❑ 91Cla/Bes-282
❑ 91ElPasDLD-189
❑ 91ElPasDP-2743
❑ 91LinDriAA-189
❑ 91UppDec-76
❑ 92HarSenF-456
❑ 92HarSenS-284
❑ 92SkyAA F-120
❑ 93HarSenF-267
❑ 93OrlCubF-2779
❑ 94OrlCubF-1381
❑ 95OrlCubF-5

Johnson, Chuck
❑ 86AriWilP-8

Johnson, Chuck (Charles)
❑ 87SavCarP-2
❑ 88SprCarB-12
❑ 89St.PetCS-19

Johnson, Chuck (Chuck)
❑ 81GleFalWST-4
❑ 82GleFalWST-19

Johnson, Cliff
❑ 75AstPos-16
❑ 75OPC-143
❑ 75Top-143
❑ 75TopMin-143
❑ 76HouAstP-16
❑ 76OPC-249
❑ 76SSP-51
❑ 76Top-249
❑ 77Top-514
❑ 78SSP270-2
❑ 78Top-309
❑ 78YanBurK-3
❑ 78YanPhoA-14
❑ 78YanSSPD-2
❑ 79OPC-50
❑ 79Top-114
❑ 79YanBurK-3
❑ 80IndTeal-15
❑ 80OPC-321
❑ 80Top-612
❑ 81Don-484
❑ 81Fle-303
❑ 81OPC-17
❑ 81Top-17
❑ 81TopTra-776
❑ 82A'sGraG-5
❑ 82Don-339
❑ 82Fle-93
❑ 82OPC-333
❑ 82Top-422
❑ 82TopSti-226
❑ 82TopStiV-226
❑ 83Don-601
❑ 83Fle-520
❑ 83Top-762
❑ 83TopTra-49T
❑ 84BluJayFS-19
❑ 84Don-512
❑ 84Fle-159
❑ 84Nes792-221
❑ 84OPC-221
❑ 84Top-221
❑ 84TopSti-366
❑ 84TopTif-221
❑ 85Don-512
❑ 85Fle-109
❑ 85FleUpd-61
❑ 85Lea-115
❑ 85OPC-7
❑ 85RanPer-44
❑ 85Top-4
❑ 85Top-568
❑ 85TopMin-568
❑ 85TopSti-367
❑ 85TopTif-4
❑ 85TopTif-568
❑ 85TopTifT-63T
❑ 85TopTra-63T
❑ 85Woo-20
❑ 86BluJayAF-15
❑ 86BluJayFS-19
❑ 86Don-639
❑ 86Fle-62
❑ 86Lea-250
❑ 86OPC-348
❑ 86Top-348
❑ 86TopTif-348
❑ 87AstShoSPT-15
❑ 87AstShoSTw-10
❑ 87Don-645
❑ 87Fle-231
❑ 87FleGlo-231
❑ 87OPC-118
❑ 87Top-663
❑ 87TopTif-663
❑ 90EliSenL-83
❑ 92Nab-2
❑ 92YanWIZ7-82
❑ 93RanKee-206
❑ 93UppDecAH-76

Johnson, Clinton
❑ 81BriRedST-20

Johnson, Connie (Clifford)
❑ 56BalOriP-35
❑ 56BalOriP-26
❑ 56Top-326
❑ 57Top-43
❑ 58OriJayP-4
❑ 58Top-266
❑ 59Top-21
❑ 59TopVen-21
❑ 87NegLeaPD-43
❑ 91OriCro-222
❑ 92NegLeaRLI-32
❑ 96NegLeaBMKC-3
❑ 97NegLeaPC-NNO

Johnson, Craig
❑ 98WesMicWM-8

Johnson, Curtis
❑ 88St.CatBJP-2022
❑ 89MyrBeaBJP-1471

Johnson, Damon
❑ 94MedHatBJF-3693
❑ 94MedHatBJSP-6
❑ 95StCatSTI-22
❑ 96StCatSB-13
❑ 97HagSunB-23
❑ 98DunBluJSB-15
❑ 98DunBluJTI-13

Johnson, Dana
❑ 87DunBluJP-930

Johnson, Dane
❑ 93El PasDF-2945
❑ 94FleUpd-28
❑ 94NasSouF-1246
❑ 94WhiSoxK-15
❑ 95NasSouTI-7
❑ 96SyrChiTI-17

Johnson, Danny
❑ 98St.PauSTI-10

Johnson, Dante
❑ 88BilMusP-1812
❑ 89GreHorP-417

Johnson, Darrell
❑ 54OriEss-15
❑ 57Top-306
❑ 58Top-61A
❑ 58Top-61B
❑ 59Top-533
❑ 60Top-263
❑ 62RedEnq-17
❑ 62Top-16
❑ 62TopVen-16
❑ 63RocRedWSP-7
❑ 74OPC-403
❑ 74Top-403
❑ 75OPC-172
❑ 75Top-172
❑ 75TopMin-172
❑ 76OPC-118
❑ 76SSP-417
❑ 76Top-118
❑ 77MarPos-8
❑ 77Top-597
❑ 78Top-79
❑ 79Top-659
❑ 80Red196T-25
❑ 80Top-282
❑ 83Top-37
❑ 91OriCro-223
❑ 93RanKee-207

Johnson, Darron
❑ 90EugEmeGS-17

Johnson, Dave (David Allen)
❑ 65BalOriP-16
❑ 65Top-473
❑ 66BalOriP-19
❑ 66Top-579
❑ 67BalOriP-55
❑ 67BalOriP-56
❑ 67BalOriP-57
❑ 67CokCapO-8
❑ 67DexPre-106
❑ 67Top-363
❑ 67TopVen-256
❑ 68BalOriDPCP-7
❑ 68CokCapO-8
❑ 68DexPre-42
❑ 68Top-273
❑ 68TopVen-273
❑ 69BalOriPC-2
❑ 69MilBra-135
❑ 69MLBOffS-4
❑ 69OPC-203
❑ 69Top-203
❑ 69TopFou-11
❑ 69TopSta-125
❑ 69TopTeaP-5

❑ 70BalOriP-16
❑ 70DayDaiNM-107
❑ 70MLBOffS-150
❑ 70OPC-45
❑ 70Ori-6
❑ 70Top-45
❑ 71BalOriP-17
❑ 71MilDud-13
❑ 71MLBOffS-301
❑ 71OPC-595
❑ 71OriCha-7
❑ 71Top-595
❑ 71TopCoi-2
❑ 71TopTat-28
❑ 72Kel-43A
❑ 72Kel-43B
❑ 72MilBra-168
❑ 72OPC-224
❑ 72OriDMV-5
❑ 72OriPos-19
❑ 72Top-224
❑ 72Top-680
❑ 73LinPor-4
❑ 73OPC-550
❑ 73Top-550
❑ 74Kel-50
❑ 74OPC-45
❑ 74Top-45
❑ 74TopDecE-50
❑ 74TopSta-6
❑ 75AtlBraP-20
❑ 75BalOriP-19
❑ 75OPC-57
❑ 75Top-57
❑ 75TopMin-57
❑ 78Top-317
❑ 79Top-513
❑ 81Ori6F-20
❑ 83FraBroR-22
❑ 83FraBroR-26
❑ 83TidTidT-23
❑ 84JacMetF-6
❑ 84MetFanC-1
❑ 84TopTra-57T
❑ 84TopTraT-57T
❑ 85MetColP-1
❑ 85MetTCM-1
❑ 85PolMet-M2
❑ 85Top-492
❑ 85TopTif-492
❑ 86MetColP-5
❑ 86MetTCM-37
❑ 86MetWorSC-23
❑ 86OriGreT-12
❑ 86Top-501
❑ 86TopTif-501
❑ 87MetColP-15
❑ 87Top-543
❑ 87TopTif-543
❑ 88DonAll-42
❑ 88DonPop-20
❑ 88MetColP-29
❑ 88MetKah-5
❑ 88Top-164
❑ 88TopClo-51
❑ 88TopGloA-12
❑ 88TopTif-164
❑ 89MetColP-37
❑ 89MetKah-13
❑ 89Top-684
❑ 89TopTif-684
❑ 90BalOriP-13
❑ 90MetCol8-8
❑ 90MetColP-9
❑ 90MetKah-5
❑ 90OPC-291
❑ 90PacLeg-33
❑ 90SweBasG-61
❑ 90Top-291
❑ 90TopTif-291
❑ 90TopTVM-1
❑ 91BalOriP-14
❑ 91MDAA-13
❑ 91OriCro-225
❑ 91SweBasG-46
❑ 92ActPacA-75
❑ 92UppDecS-4
❑ 93RedKah-10
❑ 93TedWil-83
❑ 93TopTra-36T
❑ 93UppDecAH-77
❑ 94RedKah-16
❑ 95RedKah-15
❑ 96BalOriP-17
❑ 99DodPol-12

Johnson, Dave (David Wayne)
❑ 84PriWilPT-30
❑ 85NasPirT-12
❑ 86HawIslP-12
❑ 86QuaCitAP-15
❑ 87VanCanP-1606
❑ 88BufBisC-4
❑ 88BufBisP-1476
❑ 88BufBisTI-2
❑ 89BalOriP-15
❑ 89RocRedWC-11
❑ 89RocRedWP-1656
❑ 90BalOriP-12
❑ 90Don-702
❑ 90FleUpd-67
❑ 90Lea-434
❑ 90OPC-416
❑ 90Sco-528
❑ 90Sco100RS-43
❑ 90Top-416
❑ 90TopTif-416
❑ 90UppDec-425
❑ 91Don-126
❑ 91Fle-479
❑ 91Lea-248
❑ 91LinDri-34
❑ 91OPC-163
❑ 91OriCro-224
❑ 91PanSti-199
❑ 91Sco-506
❑ 91StaClu-117
❑ 91StaCluP-19
❑ 91Top-163
❑ 91TopDesS-163
❑ 91TopMic-163
❑ 91TopTif-163
❑ 91Ult-18
❑ 91UppDec-299
❑ 92EdmTraS-162
❑ 92Fle-12
❑ 92MVP-5
❑ 92MVP2H-20
❑ 92OPC-657
❑ 92Sco-604
❑ 92Top-657
❑ 92TopGol-657
❑ 92TopGolW-657
❑ 92TopMic-657
❑ 93BalOriP-15
❑ 93TolMudHF-1651

Johnson, David
❑ 83AleDukT-20
❑ 87PalSprP-3

Johnson, David C.
❑ 77Top-478
❑ 78Top-627
❑ 78TwiFriP-9
❑ 91OriCro-226

Johnson, David M.
❑ 77SanJosMC-24
❑ 78St.PetCT-13
❑ 79ArkTraT-21
❑ 80ArkTraT-14

Johnson, David M. Pitcher
❑ 97PorRocG-11
❑ 98AshTouM-8

Johnson, Dean
❑ 85LitFalMT-25

Johnson, Deron
❑ 86BelMarCr-105
❑ 87WauTimP-18

Johnson, Deron Andre
❑ 88WatPirP-20
❑ 89WelPirP-14
❑ 90AugPirP-2472

Johnson, Deron Roger
❑ 59Top-131
❑ 59TopVen-131
❑ 60Top-134
❑ 60TopVen-134
❑ 61Top-68
❑ 61Yan61RL-41
❑ 62Top-82
❑ 62TopVen-82
❑ 64Top-449
❑ 65Kah-19
❑ 65MacSta-5
❑ 65OPC-75
❑ 65RedEnq-15
❑ 65Top-75
❑ 66Kah-15
❑ 66RedVolC-6
❑ 66Top-219
❑ 66Top-440
❑ 66TopRubI-43
❑ 66TopVen-219
❑ 67CokCapR-6
❑ 67DexPre-107
❑ 67Kah-17
❑ 67OPC-135
❑ 67Top-135
❑ 67TopVen-331
❑ 68BraPos-17
❑ 68CokCapB-15
❑ 68Kah-B18
❑ 68Top-323
❑ 68TopVen-323
❑ 69MilBra-136
❑ 69PhiTeal-5
❑ 69Top-297
❑ 70OPC-125
❑ 70PhiTeal-6
❑ 70Top-125
❑ 70TopBoo-20
❑ 71MLBOffS-182
❑ 71OPC-490
❑ 71PhiArcO-7
❑ 71Top-490
❑ 71TopCoi-79
❑ 71TopSup-58
❑ 72MilBra-169
❑ 72OPC-167
❑ 72OPC-168
❑ 72SevTraC-24
❑ 72Top-167
❑ 72Top-168
❑ 73OPC-590
❑ 73Top-590
❑ 74OPC-312
❑ 74Top-312
❑ 74TopSta-227
❑ 75SSP18-18
❑ 76OPC-529
❑ 76Top-529
❑ 78SalLakCGC-7
❑ 78TCM60I-213
❑ 84PhiTas-11
❑ 85MarMot-27
❑ 86MarMot-28
❑ 88AlbYanP-1351
❑ 90SweBasG-34
❑ 91YanRinP13-2
❑ 92YanWIZ6-60
❑ 94BreMilB-41

Johnson, Dodd
❑ 86SumBraP-11
❑ 87DurBulP-28
❑ 88DurBulS-9A
❑ 89PenPilS-8
❑ 91RenSilSCLC-22
❑ 91SydWavF-14

Johnson, Dominick
❑ 87PocGiaTB-15
❑ 89CliGiaP-904
❑ 90SanJosGB-25
❑ 90SanJosGCLC-47
❑ 90SanJosGP-2011
❑ 90SanJosGS-13
❑ 91RenSilSCLC-6
❑ 92PalSprAF-833
❑ 93PalSprAC-11
❑ 93PalSprAF-63
❑ 94MidAngF-2433
❑ 94MidAngOHP-12

Johnson, Don Roy
❑ 47TipTop-108
❑ 47YanTeaT-14
❑ 48AngTeal-13
❑ 52Top-190
❑ 53BowBW-55
❑ 53Top-219
❑ 54Top-146
❑ 55Bow-101A
❑ 55Bow-101B
❑ 55Bow-157A
❑ 55OriEss-10
❑ 55Top-165
❑ 83TopRep5-190
❑ 91OriCro-227
❑ 91TopArc1-219
❑ 94TopArc1-146
❑ 94TopArc1G-146
❑ 97BalOriP-23

Johnson, Don Spore
❑ 33Zee-26
❑ 44CubTeal-13

Johnson, Doug
❑ 97AppLeaTPB-11
❑ 97PriDevR-16
❑ 98SP MinPE-118
❑ 98SP MinSTHPE-H19
❑ 98SPMin-118
❑ 98SPMinSTH-H19

Johnson, Drew
❑ 92KanCouCC-2
❑ 92KanCouCF-98
❑ 92KanCouCTI-16

Johnson, Duan
❑ 96EveAquB-12
❑ 97EveAquG-12
❑ 98WisTimRM-12

Johnson, Duane
❑ 98MarPhiG-14

Johnson, Earl Douglas
❑ 46RedSoxTI-14
❑ 47RedSoxTI-12
❑ 47TipTop-9
❑ 48RedSoxTI-11
❑ 49Bow-231
❑ 49RedSoxTI-11
❑ 50Bow-188
❑ 50RedSoxTI-8
❑ 51Bow-321
❑ 52MotCoo-14
❑ 75RedSox1T-21
❑ 77TCMTheWY-88

Johnson, Earl Ramon
❑ 93SpoIndC-9
❑ 93SpoIndF-3603
❑ 94SprSulC-13
❑ 94SprSulF-2050
❑ 95AusFut-20
❑ 95Exc-285
❑ 95ExcLeaL-11
❑ 95RanCucQT-3
❑ 96BesAutSA-33
❑ 96MemChiB-15
❑ 97BesAutAS-23
❑ 97MobBayBB-9
❑ 98TolMudHQ-22

Johnson, Earnie
❑ 90SouBenWSGS-7
❑ 91OriCro-228
❑ 91SarWhiSC-5
❑ 91SarWhiSP-1108
❑ 92BirBarF-2576
❑ 93OrlCubF-2780

Johnson, Eric
❑ 97SalVolG-17
❑ 98SalVol-16

Johnson, Erik
❑ 87PocGiaTB-29
❑ 88CliGiaP-708
❑ 88MidLeaAGS-3
❑ 89ShrCapP-1845
❑ 90PhoFirP-19
❑ 90ProAAAF-45
❑ 90ShrCapS-13
❑ 91LinDriAA-309
❑ 91ShrCapLD-309
❑ 91ShrCapP-1829
❑ 92PhoFirF-2827
❑ 92PhoFirS-384
❑ 93PhoFirF-1523
❑ 94PhoFirF-1526
❑ 95Pac-378
❑ 98PorRocG-17

Johnson, Ernest R.
❑ 13Zee-13
❑ 14Zee-13
❑ 20Zee-84
❑ 21Exh-82
❑ 22E120-22
❑ 22W573-66
❑ 23WilChoV-71
❑ 26Zee-94
❑ 27Zee-70
❑ 28Zee-92
❑ 29Zee-161
❑ 30Zee-176
❑ 32Zee-117

Johnson, Ernest T.
❑ 53BraJohC-7
❑ 53BraSpiaS3-13
❑ 54Bow-144
❑ 54BraJohC-32
❑ 54BraSpiaSP-10
❑ 55Bow-101A
❑ 55Bow-157A
❑ 55Bow-157B
❑ 55BraGolS-10
❑ 55BraJohC-32
❑ 55BraSpiaSD-9
❑ 56BalOriP-27
❑ 56Top-294
❑ 57BraSpiaS4-11
❑ 57Top-333
❑ 58Top-78A
❑ 58Top-78B
❑ 59Top-279
❑ 60Top-228
❑ 64TopRooAB-22
❑ 78AtlCon-11
❑ 80Bra195T-7
❑ 83Bra53F-32

Johnson, Frank
❑ 69Top-227
❑ 71MLBOffS-253
❑ 71OPC-128
❑ 71Top-128
❑ 74PhoGiaC-88
❑ 75PhoGiaCK-23

Johnson, Gabe
❑ 98JohCCTI-17
❑ 99TeaBesR-41
❑ 99TeaBesRG-41
❑ 99TeaBesRS-41

Johnson, Gary
❑ 92DavLipB-16
❑ 93DavLipB-14
❑ 94DavLipB-17
❑ 94DavLipB-18

Johnson, George
❑ 17Zee-110
❑ 18Zee-82
❑ 18Zee-83
❑ 78LauLonABS-25

Johnson, Greg
❑ 77QuaCitAT-19
❑ 79SavBraT-10
❑ 79WatIndT-30
❑ 81ChaRoyT-1
❑ 87AubAstP-18
❑ 88AshTouP-1051
❑ 89AshTouP-959
❑ 90OrlSunRB-15
❑ 90OrlSunRP-1078
❑ 90OrlSunRS-7
❑ 90ProAaA-42
❑ 91Cla/Bes-105
❑ 91LinDriAA-482
❑ 91OrlSunRLD-482
❑ 91OrlSunRP-1844
❑ 92KenTwiC-10
❑ 92KenTwiF-613
❑ 92PorBeaF-2662
❑ 92PorBeaS-410
❑ 92SkyAAAF-187

Johnson, Gregory S.
❑ 97LakElsSG-18
❑ 98LakElsSG-18
❑ 98MidAngO-22

Johnson, Hank
❑ 32R33So2-409
❑ 33Gou-14
❑ 33GouCanV-14
❑ 36GouWidPPR-D14
❑ 77CinRedT-9
❑ 92ConTSN-382

Johnson, Heath
❑ 97ForWayW-16

Johnson, Herman
❑ 92SouOreAC-23
❑ 92SouOreAF-3418

Johnson, Home Run (Grant)
❑ 74LauOldTBS-22
❑ 86NegLeaF-109

Johnson, Hook (Ken Wahdersee)
❑ 49EurSta-185
❑ 51Bow-293

Johnson, Howard
❑ 81BirBarT-12
❑ 83Don-328
❑ 83Fle-332
❑ 83TigPos-16
❑ 84TigFarJ-8
❑ 84TigTeal-20
❑ 84TigWavP-21
❑ 85Don-247
❑ 85Fle-12
❑ 85FleUpd-62
❑ 85MetColP-4
❑ 85MetTCM-25
❑ 85OPC-192
❑ 85Top-192
❑ 85TopSti-262
❑ 85TopTif-192
❑ 85TopTifT-64T
❑ 85TopTra-64T
❑ 86Don-312
❑ 86Fle-85
❑ 86MetColP-11
❑ 86MetFanC-6
❑ 86MetTCM-19
❑ 86MetWorSC-15
❑ 86OPC-304
❑ 86Top-751
❑ 86TopSti-101
❑ 86TopTif-751
❑ 87Don-646
❑ 87DonHig-43
❑ 87DonOpeD-132
❑ 87Fle-13
❑ 87FleGlo-13
❑ 87MetColP-5
❑ 87OPC-267
❑ 87Top-267
❑ 87TopTif-267
❑ 88Don-569
❑ 88DonBasB-97
❑ 88DonTeaBM-569
❑ 88Fle-138
❑ 88FleGlo-138
❑ 88FleMin-95
❑ 88FleRecS-20
❑ 88FleStiC-104
❑ 88KayB-14
❑ 88Lea-238
❑ 88MetColP-6
❑ 88MetFanC-20
❑ 88MetKah-20
❑ 88OPC-85
❑ 88OPCBoxB-K
❑ 88PanSti-343
❑ 88PanSti-439
❑ 88RedFolSB-40
❑ 88Sco-69
❑ 88ScoGlo-69
❑ 88Spo-138
❑ 88SpoGam-17
❑ 88StaLinMe-10
❑ 88Top-85
❑ 88TopBig-129
❑ 88TopGloS-52
❑ 88TopMinL-61
❑ 88TopSti-99
❑ 88TopTif-85
❑ 88TopWaxBC-K
❑ 89BirBarADB-2
❑ 89Don-235
❑ 89DonBasB-126
❑ 89Fle-39
❑ 89FleGlo-39
❑ 89MetColP-11
❑ 89MetKah-14
❑ 89OPC-383
❑ 89Sco-136
❑ 89Top-383
❑ 89TopAme2C-18
❑ 89TopBig-208
❑ 89TopDouM-10
❑ 89TopGloS-22
❑ 89TopSti-91
❑ 89TopStiB-41
❑ 89TopTif-383
❑ 89UppDec-582
❑ 90BirBarADB-2
❑ 90Bow-133
❑ 90BowTif-133
❑ 90ClaBlu-144
❑ 90Don-18
❑ 90Don-99
❑ 90Don-654A
❑ 90Don-654B
❑ 90DonBesN-19
❑ 90DOnBonM-BC2
❑ 90DonPre-8
❑ 90DonSupD-18
❑ 90Fle-208
❑ 90Fle-639
❑ 90FleAll-4
❑ 90FleAwaW-20
❑ 90FleBasA-21
❑ 90FleBasAC-21
❑ 90FleBasM-22
❑ 90FleBasMC-22
❑ 90FleCan-208
❑ 90FleCan-639
❑ 90FleWaxBC-C16
❑ 90K-M-3
❑ 90Lea-272
❑ 90M.Vpin-65
❑ 90MetColP-4
❑ 90MetFanC-20
❑ 90MetKah-20
❑ 90MLBBasB-16
❑ 90MSAHolD-10

❑ 90MSAlceTD-2
❑ 90OPC-399
❑ 90OPC-680
❑ 90PanSti-210
❑ 90PanSti-306
❑ 90PanSti-385
❑ 90PubIntS-137
❑ 90PubIntS-265
❑ 90Sco-124
❑ 90Sco100S-83
❑ 90Spo-109
❑ 90SunSee-3
❑ 90Top-399
❑ 90Top-680
❑ 90TopBig-216
❑ 90TopCoi-50
❑ 90TopDou-37
❑ 90TopGloA-4
❑ 90TopGloS-43
❑ 90TopHilHM-33
❑ 90TopMag-80
❑ 90TopMinL-67
❑ 90TopSti-90
❑ 90TopSti-150
❑ 90TopStiB-8
❑ 90TopTif-399
❑ 90TopTif-680
❑ 90TopTVA-53
❑ 90TopTVM-25
❑ 90UppDec-263
❑ 90UppDecS-1
❑ 90WonBreS-17
❑ 91BasBesHRK-12
❑ 91BasBesRB-9
❑ 91Bow-464
❑ 91CadEllD-33
❑ 91Cla3-T40
❑ 91ClaGam-76
❑ 91DenHol-11
❑ 91Don-454
❑ 91Fle-152
❑ 91Lea-34
❑ 91MetColP-18
❑ 91MetKah-20
❑ 91MetPerPA-20
❑ 91MetTro-5
❑ 91MetWIZ-203
❑ 91OPC-470
❑ 91PanFreS-81
❑ 91PanSti-86
❑ 91RedFolS-52
❑ 91Sco-185
❑ 91Sco100S-86
❑ 91SpoNSP-1
❑ 91StaClu-86
❑ 91StaCluMO-19
❑ 91StaCluP-20
❑ 91Stu-207
❑ 91Top-470
❑ 91TopCraJ2-33
❑ 91TopDesS-470
❑ 91TopMic-470
❑ 91TopTif-470
❑ 91TopTriH-N7
❑ 91Ult-222
❑ 91UppDec-124
❑ 91USPlaCA-4C
❑ 92Bow-10
❑ 92Cla1-T47
❑ 92Cla2-T41
❑ 92ClaGam-145
❑ 92DenHol-16
❑ 92Don-341
❑ 92DonCraJ2-17
❑ 92DonEli-15
❑ 92DonMcD-25
❑ 92Fle-509
❑ 92Fle-689
❑ 92FleTeaL-2
❑ 92Fre-4
❑ 92Hig5-74
❑ 92Hig5S-20
❑ 92HitTheBB-17
❑ 92KinDis-6
❑ 92LaKdec-19
❑ 92Lea-132
❑ 92LeaBlaG-132
❑ 92LeaGolP-7
❑ 92LeaPre-7
❑ 92MetColP-4
❑ 92MetKah-20
❑ 92MSABenSHD-16
❑ 92New-13
❑ 92OPC-590
❑ 92OPCPre-42
❑ 92PanSti-147
❑ 92PanSti-224
❑ 92PepDieM-23
❑ 92Pin-15
❑ 92Pos-28
❑ 92RedFolS-49
❑ 92Sco-550
❑ 92Sco-776
❑ 92Sco100S-68
❑ 92SpoStaCC-26
❑ 92StaClu-430
❑ 92StaClu-610
❑ 92StaCluD-92
❑ 92StaCluECN-610
❑ 92Stu-67
❑ 92SunSee-6
❑ 92Top-388
❑ 92Top-590
❑ 92TopGol-388
❑ 92TopGol-590
❑ 92TopGolW-388
❑ 92TopGolW-590
❑ 92TopKid-12
❑ 92TopMcD-23
❑ 92TopMic-388
❑ 92TopMic-590
❑ 92TriPla-236
❑ 92Ult-235
❑ 92UppDec-37
❑ 92UppDec-256
❑ 92UppDec-720
❑ 92UppDecF-28
❑ 92UppDecFG-28
❑ 92UppDecHRH-HR3
❑ 92UppDecTMH-26
❑ 93Bow-130
❑ 93CadDis-34
❑ 93DiaMar-56
❑ 93Don-434
❑ 93Fin-143
❑ 93FinRef-143
❑ 93Fla-93
❑ 93Fle-89
❑ 93FunPac-127
❑ 93Lea-39
❑ 93MetBak-11
❑ 93MetColP-24
❑ 93MetKah-20
❑ 93OPC-166
❑ 93PacSpa-199
❑ 93PanSti-251
❑ 93Pin-389
❑ 93PinHomRC-44
❑ 93PinSlu-18
❑ 93RedFolS-46
❑ 93Sco-62
❑ 93Sel-101
❑ 93SP-151
❑ 93StaClu-404
❑ 93StaCluFDI-404
❑ 93StaCluMOP-404
❑ 93Stu-128
❑ 93Top-106
❑ 93TopGol-106
❑ 93TopInaM-106
❑ 93TopInaR-106
❑ 93TopMic-106
❑ 93TriPla-86
❑ 93Ult-76
❑ 93UppDec-484
❑ 93UppDec-676
❑ 93UppDecGold-484
❑ 93UppDecGold-676
❑ 93UppDecIC-WI14
❑ 93UppDecICJ-WI14
❑ 93UppDecTAN-TN12
❑ 94Bow-142
❑ 94ColC-530
❑ 94ColChoGS-530
❑ 94ColChoSS-530
❑ 94Don-487
❑ 94Fin-374
❑ 94FinRef-374
❑ 94Fle-568
❑ 94FleExtB-248
❑ 94FleUpd-125
❑ 94FUnPac-86
❑ 94Lea-432
❑ 94OPC-31
❑ 94Pac-407
❑ 94PanSti-219
❑ 94Pin-518
❑ 94PinArtP-518
❑ 94PinMusC-518
❑ 94RocPol-15
❑ 94Sco-414
❑ 94ScoGolR-414
❑ 94ScoRoo-RT63
❑ 94ScoRooGR-RT63
❑ 94Sel-315
❑ 94SpoRoo-23
❑ 94SpoRooAP-23
❑ 94StaClu-640
❑ 94StaCluFDI-640
❑ 94StaCluGR-640
❑ 94StaCluMOP-640
❑ 94StaCluT-109
❑ 94StaCluTFDI-109
❑ 94Top-302
❑ 94TopGol-302
❑ 94TopSpa-302
❑ 94TopTra-82T
❑ 94TriPla-227
❑ 94Ult-484
❑ 94UppDec-462
❑ 94UppDecED-462
❑ 95ColCho-542T
❑ 95Sco-505
❑ 95ScoGolR-505
❑ 95ScoPlaTS-505
❑ 95StaCluMOP-RL9
❑ 95StaCluRL-RL9
❑ 95Top-206
❑ 95UppDec-316
❑ 95UppDecED-316
❑ 95UppDecEDG-316
❑ 95UppDecSE-260
❑ 95UppDecSEG-260
❑ 96ButCopKB-4
❑ 96ColCho-83
❑ 96ColChoGS-83
❑ 96ColChoSS-83
❑ 96MetMod-6

Johnson, Indian Bob (Robert Lee)
❑ 30Zee-107
❑ 32Zee-73
❑ 34BatR31-20
❑ 34Gou-68
❑ 35ExhFou-14
❑ 35GouPuzR-8J
❑ 35GouPuzR-9J
❑ 36ExhFou-14
❑ 36GouWidPPR-A57
❑ 36OveCanR-26
❑ 37ExhFou-14
❑ 37OPCBatUV-123
❑ 38ExhFou-14
❑ 38WheBB10-6
❑ 39ExhSal-30
❑ 39GouPreR303A-27
❑ 39PlaBal-97
❑ 39WorWidGTP-27
❑ 40PlaBal-25
❑ 41DouPlaR-49
❑ 41PlaBal-22
❑ 42A'sTeal-17
❑ 47CenFlo-12
❑ 47SigOil-78
❑ 74TCMNic-23
❑ 76GrePlaG-17
❑ 77ShaPiz-C
❑ 79DiaGre-326
❑ 81ConTSN-33
❑ 82DiaCla-53
❑ 83TCMPla1942-22
❑ 83TCMPla1944-10
❑ 85BigLeaC3-45
❑ 91ConTSN-96
❑ 92ConTSN-547
❑ 93ConTSN-776
❑ 93DiaStaES-138
❑ 94ConTSN-1173
❑ 94ConTSNB-1173

Johnson, J.J.
❑ 91ClaDraP-33
❑ 91FroRowDP-48
❑ 91FroRowDPG-48
❑ 91FroRowDPS-48
❑ 91YakBeaC-6
❑ 92Pin-577
❑ 93UtiBluSC-10
❑ 93UtiBluSF-3546
❑ 94Bow-7
❑ 94CenValRF-3198
❑ 94Cla-66
❑ 94LynRedSC-13
❑ 94LynRedSF-1905
❑ 96BowBes-141
❑ 96BowBesAR-141
❑ 96BowBesR-141
❑ 96HarCitRCB-16
❑ 97Bow-89
❑ 97BowCerBlaIA-CA69
❑ 97BowCerBluIA-CA69
❑ 97BowCerGolIA-CA69
❑ 97BowChr-113
❑ 97BowChrI-113
❑ 97BowChrIR-113
❑ 97BowChrR-113
❑ 97BowInt-89
❑ 97NewBriRC-16
❑ 97SalLakB-13
❑ 97Sel-124
❑ 97SelArtP-124
❑ 97SelCom-124
❑ 97SelRegG-124
❑ 98NewBriRCM-15

Johnson, Jace
❑ 96SouOreTI-25

Johnson, Jack
❑ 87SpoCubG-1

Johnson, Jack Eric
❑ 89AncGlaP-16
❑ 90AriWilP-9
❑ 92BakDodCLC-13
❑ 93ClaFS7-282
❑ 93OrlCubF-2788
❑ 93PeoChiC-9
❑ 93PeoChiF-1088
❑ 94PriWilCC-10
❑ 94PriWilCF-1923
❑ 95RocCubTI-29
❑ 97MidAng-18

Johnson, James
❑ 81CliGiaT-19
❑ 96CliLumKTI-16

Johnson, Jason
❑ 93BenRocCB-13
❑ 93BenRocF-3262
❑ 94AugGreC-7
❑ 94AugGreF-3001
❑ 94Bow-498
❑ 94CenValRC-11
❑ 95HudValRTI-20
❑ 95NewHavRTI-32
❑ 96ChaRivTI-9615
❑ 96LynHilB-12
❑ 96MarPhiB-11
❑ 97BatCliTI-21
❑ 97EriSeaWB-20
❑ 97LynHil-9
❑ 98LeaRS-310
❑ 98LeaRSLHolo-310
❑ 98LeaRSLong-310
❑ 98LeaRTrue-310
❑ 98PacOmeRS-15
❑ 98PacOmeRST3-15
❑ 98PieBolWM-18
❑ 98RocCubM-14
❑ 98RocCubTI-14
❑ 98SouAtlLPM-13

Johnson, Jay
❑ 87SumBraP-30
❑ 94SpoIndC-13
❑ 94SpoIndF-3336

Johnson, Jeff
❑ 88OneYanP-2069
❑ 89PriWilCS-9
❑ 90Ft.LauYS-10
❑ 91Bow-159
❑ 91ColCliLD-108
❑ 91ColCliP-8
❑ 91ColCliP-593
❑ 91DonRoo-47
❑ 91FleUpd-44
❑ 91LinDriAAA-108
❑ 91ScoRoo-110T
❑ 91TopTra-62T
❑ 91TopTraT-62T
❑ 92Bow-362
❑ 92ColCliP-11
❑ 92Don-275
❑ 92OPC-449
❑ 92Pin-464
❑ 92PinTea2-23
❑ 92ProFS7-109
❑ 92Sco-523
❑ 92Sco100RS-40
❑ 92StaClu-471
❑ 92Top-449
❑ 92TopDeb91-90
❑ 92TopGol-449
❑ 92TopGolW-449
❑ 92TopMic-449
❑ 92TriPla-93
❑ 92Ult-410
❑ 92UppDec-626
❑ 93ColCliF-1108
❑ 93Fle-650
❑ 93ForLauRSC-14
❑ 93ForLauRSFP-1592
❑ 93UtiBluSC-11
❑ 94ChaKniF-888

Johnson, Jeffrey
❑ 96SouBenSHS-16

Johnson, Jerome
❑ 75LynRanT-14

Johnson, Jerry
❑ 81ArkTraT-11
❑ 83ArkTraT-9
❑ 84BeaGolGT-19
❑ 84LouRedR-26
❑ 85RocRedWT-18

Johnson, Jerry Michael
❑ 69Top-253
❑ 70OPC-162
❑ 70Top-162
❑ 71MLBOffS-254
❑ 71OPC-412
❑ 71Top-412
❑ 72OPC-35
❑ 72OPC-36
❑ 72Top-35
❑ 72Top-36
❑ 73IndTeal-15
❑ 73OPC-248
❑ 73Top-248
❑ 75HawIslC-18
❑ 75IntLeaASB-13
❑ 75OPC-218
❑ 75PacCoaLAB-13
❑ 75PadDea-13
❑ 75Top-218
❑ 75TopMin-218
❑ 76HawIslC-19
❑ 76OPC-658
❑ 76Top-658
❑ 78OPC-184
❑ 78Top-169
❑ 81TCM60I-440
❑ 82HawIslT-5
❑ 83LasVegSBHN-12

Johnson, Jimmy (Jim)
❑ 80TucTorT-9
❑ 81TucTorT-12
❑ 82TucTorT-24
❑ 85TucTorC-53
❑ 95NorNagUTI-NNO
❑ 95NorNavTI-14
❑ 96ColCliB-1
❑ 96GreBatB-1

Johnson, Jody
❑ 89GeoColC-13

Johnson, Joe
❑ 84RicBraT-21
❑ 85GreBraTI-9
❑ 85IntLeaAT-17
❑ 86BraPol-38
❑ 86Don-624
❑ 86Fle-519
❑ 87BluJayFS-15
❑ 87Don-650
❑ 87Fle-230
❑ 87FleGlo-230
❑ 87Lea-91
❑ 87TopTra-56T
❑ 87TopTraT-56T
❑ 88EdmTraC-7
❑ 88EdmTraP-560
❑ 88OPC-347
❑ 88Top-347
❑ 88TopTif-347
❑ 90CMC-258
❑ 90PawRedSC-7
❑ 90PawRedSDD-11
❑ 90PawRedSP-458
❑ 90ProAAAF-430
❑ 90TopTVRS-47

Johnson, Joel
❑ 91EugEmeC-26
❑ 91EugEmeP-3720
❑ 92ColRedF-2386
❑ 92Ult-72

Johnson, John
❑ 86BirBarTI-9
❑ 87Ft.LauYP-23

Johnson, John Henry
❑ 75CedRapGT-14
❑ 75TulOil7-19
❑ 76CedRapGT-13
❑ 79Hos-39
❑ 79Kel-6
❑ 79OPC-361
❑ 79Top-681
❑ 80OPC-97
❑ 80Top-173
❑ 81Top-216
❑ 82Don-550
❑ 82Fle-321
❑ 82Top-527
❑ 84Don-91
❑ 84Fle-401
❑ 84Nes792-419
❑ 84Top-419
❑ 84TopTif-419
❑ 85Fle-162
❑ 85HawIslC-246
❑ 85Top-734
❑ 85TopTif-734
❑ 86VanCanP-14
❑ 87BrePol-38
❑ 87Fle-347
❑ 87FleGlo-347
❑ 87Top-377
❑ 87TopTif-377
❑ 93RanKee-208
❑ 94BreMilB-42

Johnson, John Ralph
❑ 87OldJudN-263

Johnson, Jonathan
❑ 95Bes-121
❑ 95SPML-102
❑ 96Bow-270
❑ 96BowFoi-270
❑ 96DouAllB-52
❑ 96Exc-111
❑ 96SigRooOJPP-P3
❑ 96SigRooOJPPS-P3
❑ 96TexLeaAB-9
❑ 96Top-242
❑ 96TulDriTI-13
❑ 97Bow-103
❑ 97BowInt-103
❑ 97OklCit8-17
❑ 98OklRedM-6
❑ 99Fle-429
❑ 99FleSta9-429
❑ 99FleWarT-429
❑ 99SpoIll-63

Johnson, Josh
❑ 86NegLeaF-13
❑ 86NegLeaF-63
❑ 91NegLeaRL-26
❑ 92NegLeaRLI-33
❑ 95NegLeaL2-8
❑ 95NegLeaLI-26

Johnson, Judd
❑ 89SumBraP-1102
❑ 90Bes-193
❑ 90GreBraB-13
❑ 90GreBraS-8
❑ 91GreBraC-2
❑ 91GreBraLD-208
❑ 91GreBraP-2996
❑ 91LinDriAA-208
❑ 92GreBraF-1151
❑ 92GreBraS-234
❑ 93RicBraBB-22
❑ 93RicBraF-182
❑ 93RicBraP-24
❑ 93RicBraRC-22
❑ 93RicBraRC-12
❑ 94RicBraF-2843

Johnson, Judy (William Julius)
❑ 74LauOldTBS-36
❑ 76ShaPiz-150
❑ 78DexHaloFP-24
❑ 78LauLonABS-29
❑ 80PerHaloFP-150
❑ 80PerHaloFPS-28
❑ 80SSPHOF-150
❑ 83ConMar-59
❑ 86NegLeaF-4
❑ 86NegLeaF-5
❑ 88ConNegA-6
❑ 88NegLeaD-9
❑ 89PerCelP-20
❑ 90NegLeaS-18
❑ 90PerGreM-46
❑ 90PomBlaBNLP-2547
❑ 91PomBlaBPB-11
❑ 93TedWil-107
❑ 94PomNegLB-4
❑ 95S.FExaNLT-4
❑ 97NegLeaPC-5S

Johnson, Karl
❑ 89EliTwiS-13

Johnson, Keith

❑ 92FroRowDP-21
❑ 92FroRowDPG-21
❑ 92FroRowDPS-21
❑ 92YakBeaC-6
❑ 92YakBeaF-3458
❑ 93StaCluM-110
❑ 93VerBeaDC-10
❑ 93VerBeaDF-2227
❑ 94BakDodC-11
❑ 95SanBerSTI-9
❑ 96MauStiHWB-15
❑ 96SanAntMB-10
❑ 97SanAntMB-17
❑ 98AlbDukG-13
❑ 98MicBatCM-4
❑ 98SanAntMM-17

Johnson, Ken (Kenneth Travis)
❑ 50PhiPhil-12
❑ 60A'sTeal-10
❑ 60Top-135
❑ 60TopVen-135
❑ 61A'sTeal-9
❑ 61MapLeaBH-10
❑ 61Top-24
❑ 62Col.45B-10
❑ 62Col45'HC-9
❑ 62Col45'JP-7
❑ 62Top-278
❑ 63Col45"P-9
❑ 63Top-352
❑ 64Col.45JP-5
❑ 64Top-158
❑ 64TopGia-2
❑ 64TopSta-70
❑ 64TopStaU-37
❑ 64TopTatI-45
❑ 64TopVen-158
❑ 65OldLonC-13
❑ 65Top-359
❑ 66BraPos-14
❑ 66Top-466
❑ 67BraPho-15
❑ 67CokCapB-10
❑ 67DexPre-108
❑ 67Kah-18
❑ 67OPC-101
❑ 67Top-101
❑ 68BraPos-18
❑ 68CokCapB-10
❑ 68DexPre-43
❑ 68Top-342
❑ 68TopVen-342
❑ 69Top-238
❑ 75Phi195T-14
❑ 78AtlCon-12
❑ 78TCM60I-232
❑ 80Phi195T-14
❑ 80Red196T-32
❑ 87AstSer1-13
❑ 89AstCol4S-5
❑ 92YanWIZ6-61

Johnson, Kent
❑ 79CliDodT-14

Johnson, Kevin
❑ 80CliGiaT-12
❑ 91SpoIndC-20
❑ 91SpoIndP-3951

Johnson, Kris
❑ 98WatIndTI-8

Johnson, Lamar
❑ 76OPC-596
❑ 76Top-596
❑ 76VenLeaS-204
❑ 77BurCheD-76
❑ 77Top-443
❑ 77WhiSoxJT-6
❑ 77WhiSoxT-12
❑ 78SSP270-137
❑ 78Top-693
❑ 79Hos-43
❑ 79OPC-192
❑ 79Top-372
❑ 80Top-242
❑ 81CokTeaS-30
❑ 81Don-38
❑ 81Fle-350
❑ 81OPC-366
❑ 81Top-589
❑ 81TopScr-26
❑ 81TopSti-58
❑ 81TopSupHT-16
❑ 82Don-269
❑ 82Fle-346
❑ 82Top-13
❑ 82TopTra-50T
❑ 83Don-142
❑ 83Fle-571
❑ 83FleSti-162
❑ 83Top-453
❑ 90EliSenL-7
❑ 91DenZepLD-150
❑ 91DenZepP-138
❑ 91LinDriAAA-150
❑ 92DenZepF-2657
❑ 92DenZepS-150
❑ 93RanKee-209
❑ 93StoPorC-27
❑ 93StoPorF-760
❑ 94StoPorC-27
❑ 94StoPorF-1708

Johnson, Lance
❑ 86ArkTraP-8
❑ 87LouRedTI-16
❑ 88Don-31
❑ 88Fle-37
❑ 88FleGlo-37
❑ 88Lea-31
❑ 88StaLinCa-10
❑ 88TopBig-251
❑ 88WhiSoxC-12
❑ 89Don-606
❑ 89Fle-499
❑ 89FleGlo-499
❑ 89PanSti-312
❑ 89RedFolSB-67
❑ 89ScoHot1R-33
❑ 89Top-122
❑ 89TopTif-122
❑ 89TriAAAP-AAA30
❑ 89VanCanC-18
❑ 89VanCanP-576
❑ 90Don-573
❑ 90Fle-536
❑ 90FleCan-536
❑ 90Lea-259
❑ 90OPC-587
❑ 90Sco-570
❑ 90ScoYouS2-38
❑ 90Top-587
❑ 90TopBig-274
❑ 90TopTif-587
❑ 90UppDec-90
❑ 90WhiSoxC-9
❑ 91Bow-349
❑ 91Don-259
❑ 91Fle-123
❑ 91Lea-403
❑ 91OPC-243
❑ 91PanFreS-317
❑ 91PanSti-253
❑ 91Sco-157
❑ 91StaClu-199
❑ 91Top-243
❑ 91TopDesS-243
❑ 91TopMic-243
❑ 91TopTif-243
❑ 91Ult-76
❑ 91UppDec-248
❑ 91WhiSoxK-1
❑ 92Bow-208
❑ 92Don-267
❑ 92Fle-87
❑ 92Lea-237
❑ 92LeaBlaG-237
❑ 92OPC-736
❑ 92PanSti-130
❑ 92Pin-373
❑ 92Sco-146
❑ 92StaClu-444
❑ 92StaCluMP-9
❑ 92Stu-154
❑ 92Top-736
❑ 92TopGol-736
❑ 92TopGolW-736
❑ 92TopMic-736
❑ 92TriPla-239
❑ 92Ult-38
❑ 92UppDec-188
❑ 92WhiSoxK-1
❑ 93Don-301
❑ 93Fin-64
❑ 93FinRef-64
❑ 93Fla-187
❑ 93Fle-204
❑ 93Lea-373
❑ 93OPC-176
❑ 93PacSpa-390
❑ 93PanSti-141
❑ 93Pin-137
❑ 93Sco-109
❑ 93Sel-266
❑ 93SelStaL-19
❑ 93SP-256
❑ 93StaClu-359
❑ 93StaCluFDI-359
❑ 93StaCluMOP-359
❑ 93Stu-192
❑ 93Top-94
❑ 93TopGol-94
❑ 93TopInaM-94
❑ 93TopInaR-94
❑ 93TopMic-94
❑ 93Ult-174
❑ 93UppDec-280
❑ 93UppDecGold-280
❑ 93WhiSoxK-14
❑ 93WhiSoxSC-15
❑ 94Bow-623
❑ 94BowBes-R10
❑ 94BowBesR-R10
❑ 94ColC-150
❑ 94ColChoGS-150
❑ 94ColChoSS-150
❑ 94Don-552
❑ 94Fin-54
❑ 94FinRef-54
❑ 94Fla-278
❑ 94Fle-85
❑ 94FleExtB-49
❑ 94Lea-13
❑ 94OPC-262
❑ 94Pac-129
❑ 94Pin-86
❑ 94PinArtP-86
❑ 94PinMusC-86
❑ 94Sco-69
❑ 94ScoCyc-TC11
❑ 94ScoGolR-69
❑ 94Sel-13
❑ 94Spo-123
❑ 94StaClu-194
❑ 94StaCluFDI-194
❑ 94StaCluGR-194
❑ 94StaCluMOP-194
❑ 94StaCluT-134
❑ 94StaCluTFDI-134
❑ 94Top-452
❑ 94TopGol-452
❑ 94TopSpa-452
❑ 94TriPla-266
❑ 94Ult-35
❑ 94UppDec-118
❑ 94UppDecED-118
❑ 94WhiSoxK-16
❑ 95ColCho-499
❑ 95ColChoGS-499
❑ 95ColChoSS-499
❑ 95Don-298
❑ 95DonPreP-298
❑ 95DonTopotO-51
❑ 95Fin-168
❑ 95FinRef-168
❑ 95Fla-246
❑ 95Fle-121
❑ 95Lea-200
❑ 95Pac-92
❑ 95Pin-41
❑ 95PinArtP-41
❑ 95PinMusC-41
❑ 95Sco-360
❑ 95ScoGolR-360
❑ 95ScoPlaTS-360
❑ 95StaClu-173
❑ 95StaCluFDI-173
❑ 95StaCluMO-24
❑ 95StaCluMOP-173
❑ 95StaCluSTWS-173
❑ 95StaCluVR-90
❑ 95StaCluVRMO-90
❑ 95Stu-97
❑ 95Top-314
❑ 95TopCyb-170
❑ 95TopEmb-78
❑ 95TopEmbGI-78
❑ 95Ult-30
❑ 95UltGolM-30
❑ 95UppDec-437
❑ 95UppDecED-437
❑ 95UppDecEDG-437
❑ 95WhiSoxK-14
❑ 96Baz-107
❑ 96Cir-159
❑ 96CirRav-159
❑ 96ColCho-97
❑ 96ColCho-625
❑ 96ColChoGS-97
❑ 96ColChoGS-625
❑ 96ColChoSS-97
❑ 96ColChoSS-625
❑ 96Don-48
❑ 96DonPreP-48
❑ 96EmoXL-234
❑ 96Fin-B200
❑ 96FinRef-B200
❑ 96Fla-322
❑ 96Fle-68
❑ 96FleTif-68
❑ 96FleUpd-U158
❑ 96FleUpdTC-U158
❑ 96MetKah-18
❑ 96MetUni-202
❑ 96MetUniP-202
❑ 96Pac-277
❑ 96PanSti-169
❑ 96Pin-352
❑ 96PinAfi-29
❑ 96PinAfiAP-29
❑ 96PinAfiFPP-29
❑ 96PinFoil-352
❑ 96Sco-148
❑ 96Sel-115
❑ 96SelArtP-115
❑ 96StaClu-152
❑ 96StaCluEPB-152
❑ 96StaCluEPG-152
❑ 96StaCluEPS-152
❑ 96StaCluMO-16
❑ 96StaCluMOP-152
❑ 96Sum-9
❑ 96SumAbo&B-9
❑ 96SumArtP-9
❑ 96SumFoi-9
❑ 96TeaOut-40
❑ 96Top-375
❑ 96TopGal-60
❑ 96TopGalPPI-60
❑ 96Ult-40
❑ 96Ult-513
❑ 96UltGolM-40
❑ 96UltGolM-513
❑ 96UppDec-502U
❑ 97Bow-258
❑ 97BowBes-69
❑ 97BowBesAR-69
❑ 97BowBesR-69
❑ 97BowChr-80
❑ 97BowChrI-80
❑ 97BowChrIR-80
❑ 97BowChrR-80
❑ 97BowInt-258
❑ 97Cir-207
❑ 97CirRav-207
❑ 97ColCho-396
❑ 97ColChoAC-41
❑ 97Don-249
❑ 97DonGolPP-249
❑ 97DonLim-73
❑ 97DonLimE-73
❑ 97DonLimENG-73
❑ 97DonPre-97
❑ 97DonPreCttC-97
❑ 97DonSilPP-249
❑ 97Fin-119
❑ 97FinEmb-119
❑ 97FinEmbR-119
❑ 97FinRef-119
❑ 97FlaShoLC-139
❑ 97FlaShoLeg0-139
❑ 97FlaShoLeg1-139
❑ 97FlaShoM-A139
❑ 97FlaShoM-B139
❑ 97FlaShoM-C139
❑ 97FlaShoR0-139
❑ 97FlaShoR1-139
❑ 97FlaShoR2-139
❑ 97Fle-400
❑ 97FleTif-400
❑ 97Lea-32
❑ 97LeaFraM-32
❑ 97LeaFraMDC-32
❑ 97MetUni-195
❑ 97Pac-369
❑ 97PacLigB-369
❑ 97PacPri-125
❑ 97PacPriGA-GA28
❑ 97PacPriLB-125
❑ 97PacPriP-125
❑ 97PacSil-369
❑ 97Pin-20
❑ 97PinArtP-PP20
❑ 97PinMusC-20
❑ 97PinPrePla-20
❑ 97PinX-P-51
❑ 97PinX-PMoS-51
❑ 97Sco-237
❑ 97ScoArtPWB-237
❑ 97ScoPreS-237
❑ 97ScoShoS-237
❑ 97ScoShoSAP-237
❑ 97SP-118
❑ 97StaClu-222
❑ 97StaCluMat-222
❑ 97StaCluMOP-222
❑ 97Top-261
❑ 97TopChr-92
❑ 97TopChrR-92
❑ 97TopChrSB-25
❑ 97TopChrSBR-25
❑ 97TopGal-22
❑ 97TopGalPPI-22
❑ 97TopSeaB-SB25
❑ 97TopSta-24
❑ 97TopStaAM-24
❑ 97Ult-242
❑ 97UltGolME-242
❑ 97UltPlaME-242
❑ 97UppDec-435
❑ 98CirThu-248
❑ 98CirThuRav-248
❑ 98CirThuSupRav-248
❑ 98ColCho-332
❑ 98Don-200
❑ 98DonColL-341
❑ 98DonColP-636
❑ 98DonGolPP-200
❑ 98DonPre-86
❑ 98DonPreSeat-86
❑ 98DonPriCL-341
❑ 98DonPriCP-636
❑ 98DonSilPP-200
❑ 98Fin-139
❑ 98FinNo--139
❑ 98FinNo-R-139
❑ 98FinRef-139
❑ 98Fle-239
❑ 98Lea-142
❑ 98LeaFraDA-142
❑ 98LeaFraF-142
❑ 98LeaFraM-142
❑ 98LeaFraM-142
❑ 98LeaFraMDC-142
❑ 98LeaFraMDC-142
❑ 98LeaFraMZ2-142
❑ 98Pac-253
❑ 98PacAur-113
❑ 98PacOme-48
❑ 98PacOmeR-48
❑ 98PacOnl-144
❑ 98PacOnlR-144
❑ 98PacOnlWC-144
❑ 98PacPar-139
❑ 98PacParC-139
❑ 98PacParG-139
❑ 98PacParHS-139
❑ 98PacParPB-139
❑ 98PacParR-139
❑ 98PacPlaB-253
❑ 98PacRedT-253
❑ 98PacSil-253
❑ 98PinSna-CC6
❑ 98PinSna-CC17
❑ 98Sco-173
❑ 98ScoRT-71
❑ 98ScoSS-PP75
❑ 98ScoSSAP-PP75
❑ 98StaCluFDI-176
❑ 98StaCluI-176
❑ 98StaCluOneK-176
❑ 98StaCluPP-176
❑ 98Stu-179
❑ 98StuGPP-179
❑ 98StuSPP-179
❑ 98Top-314
❑ 98TopChr-314
❑ 98TopChrR-314
❑ 98TopDevR-314
❑ 98TopDia-314
❑ 98TopGal-46
❑ 98TopGalGP-46
❑ 98TopGalOPP-46
❑ 98TopGalPPI-46
❑ 98TopGalPPIA-46
❑ 98TopMiniC-314
❑ 98TopOpeD-140
❑ 98TopSta-24
❑ 98TopStaB-24
❑ 98TopStaG-24
❑ 98TopStaGR-24
❑ 98TopStaS-24
❑ 98Ult-309
❑ 98UltGolM-309
❑ 98UltMas-309
❑ 98UltPlaM-309
❑ 98UppDec-321
❑ 99CroRoyB-28
❑ 99CroRoyL-28
❑ 99CroRoyOD-28
❑ 99Fle-550
❑ 99FleSta9-550
❑ 99FleWarT-550
❑ 99Pac-86
❑ 99PacAur-34
❑ 99PacAurOD-34
❑ 99PacInv-30
❑ 99PacInvOD-30
❑ 99PacInvPB-30
❑ 99PacPar-49
❑ 99PacParC-49
❑ 99PacParG-49
❑ 99PacParHoloGold-49
❑ 99PacParHS-49
❑ 99PacParOD-49
❑ 99PacParPB-49
❑ 99PacParRed-49
❑ 99PacPlaB-86
❑ 99PacPri-29
❑ 99PacPriHB-29
❑ 99PacPriHG-29
❑ 99PacPriHM-29
❑ 99PacPriHP-29
❑ 99PacPriRed-29
❑ 99PacRed-86
❑ 99Top-406
❑ 99TopChr-406
❑ 99TopChrR-406
❑ 99TopMVPP-406

Johnson, Larry D.
❑ 80RocRedWT-20
❑ 81EvaTriT-12

Johnson, Ledowick
❑ 95HelBreTI-13
❑ 96HelBreTI-1

Johnson, Lee
❑ 90DurBulUTI-1
❑ 90GreBraP-1124
❑ 90GreBraS-9
❑ 91OscAstC-5
❑ 91OscAstP-677

Johnson, Lefty (Arthur Henry)
❑ 77TCMTheWY-63
❑ 77TCMTheWY-77

Johnson, Lindsey
❑ 86KinEagP-11
❑ 89MiaMirIS-9
❑ 89MiaMirIS-7

Johnson, Lloyd
❑ 32Zee-37
❑ 33Zee-27
❑ 34Gou-86

Johnson, Lou
❑ 60Top-476
❑ 61MapLeaBH-11
❑ 63Top-238
❑ 65DodJayP-6
❑ 65DodTeal-8
❑ 66OPC-13
❑ 66Top-13
❑ 66TopVen-13
❑ 67CokCapD-8
❑ 67CokCapDA-8
❑ 67DexPre-109
❑ 67Top-410
❑ 67TopVen-290
❑ 68OPC-184
❑ 68Top-184
❑ 68TopVen-184
❑ 69AngJacitB-4
❑ 69MilBra-137
❑ 69Top-367
❑ 69TopTeaP-13
❑ 90DodTar-387

Johnson, Luther
❑ 88MarPhiS-18
❑ 89AubAstP-2176
❑ 90AshTouP-2762
❑ 91OscAstC-25
❑ 91OscAstP-699

Johnson, Marcel
❑ 88NebCor-22
❑ 90KinMetB-23
❑ 90KinMetS-12
❑ 92PulBraC-9
❑ 92PulBraF-3184
❑ 93IdaFalBF-4045

❑ 93IdaFalBSP-13
Johnson, Mark
❑ 86DavLipB-15
Johnson, Mark ARK
❑ 90ArkRaz-18
Johnson, Mark J.
❑ 97BesLimA-18
❑ 97Bow-323
❑ 97BowChr-222
❑ 97BowChrI-222
❑ 97BowChrIR-222
❑ 97BowChrR-222
❑ 97BowInt-323
❑ 97CarLeaTP-26
❑ 97KisCob-14
❑ 97Top-483
❑ 98BesPreA-18
❑ 98PorSeaDQ-6
Johnson, Mark L.
❑ 94SigRooDP-25
❑ 94SigRooDPS-25
❑ 94StaCluDP-12
❑ 94StaCluDPFDI-12
❑ 95Exc-254
❑ 95Pin-174
❑ 95PinArtP-174
❑ 95PinMusC-174
❑ 95ScoDraP-DP11
❑ 95SigRooOJA-AS4
❑ 95SigRooOJAS-AS4
❑ 95StaClu-104
❑ 95StaCluFDI-104
❑ 95Top-605
❑ 95UppDecML-193
❑ 95UppDecMLFS-193
❑ 96MidLeaAB-52
❑ 96SouBenSHS-17
❑ 98BirBarG-15
❑ 98ColCho-421
❑ 98ColChoPCR-421
❑ 98SouLeaTPG-5
❑ 98UppDec-564
❑ 98UppDecDS-DS57
❑ 99BasAmeTPA-21
❑ 99FleBri-153
❑ 99FleBri2G-153
❑ 99FleBriBlu-153
❑ 99FleBriGol-153
❑ 99FleSta9-150
❑ 99FleWarT-150
❑ 99PacOme-61
❑ 99PacOmeC-61
❑ 99PacOmeG-61
❑ 99PacOmePB-61
❑ 99SP TopP-61
❑ 99SP TopPPE-61
❑ 99SpoIll-70
❑ 99UppDec-342
❑ 99UppDecEL1-342
❑ 99UppDecEL2-342
❑ 99Vic-90
Johnson, Mark Patrick
❑ 88CapCodPB-2
❑ 88CapCodPPaLP-1
❑ 91AugPirC-15
❑ 91AugPirP-811
❑ 91EugEmeC-11
❑ 91EugEmeP-3738
❑ 92AppFoxCB-10
❑ 92AppFoxFI-994
❑ 92CarMudF-1187
❑ 92CarMudS-136
❑ 92MidLeaATI-22
❑ 92ProFS7-79
❑ 93CarMudF-2061
❑ 93CarMudTI-17
❑ 93ClaFS7-140
❑ 93ClaGolF-104
❑ 93MemChiF-388
❑ 94CarMudF-1585
❑ 95Bow-225
❑ 95BowGolF-225
❑ 95DonTopotO-316
❑ 95Emo-174
❑ 95Fin-236
❑ 95FinRef-236
❑ 95Fla-400
❑ 95FleUpd-149
❑ 95PirFil-13
❑ 95StaCluMOP-104
❑ 95StaCluSTWS-104
❑ 95UppDec-252
❑ 95UppDecED-252
❑ 95UppDecEDG-252
❑ 95UppDecML-209
❑ 95UppDecMLFS-209
❑ 96ColCho-260
❑ 96ColChoGS-260
❑ 96ColChoSS-260
❑ 96Don-286
❑ 96DonPreP-286
❑ 96Fle-522
❑ 96FleTif-522
❑ 96LeaSigEA-92
❑ 96Sco-40
❑ 96Ult-264
❑ 96UltGolM-264
❑ 96UppDec-176
❑ 97Cir-169
❑ 97CirRav-169
❑ 97ColCho-423
❑ 97Don-215
❑ 97DonGolPP-215
❑ 97DonSilPP-215
❑ 97Fin-9
❑ 97FinRef-9
❑ 97Fle-428
❑ 97FleTif-428
❑ 97Lea-119
❑ 97LeaFraM-119
❑ 97LeaFraMDC-119
❑ 97Pac-393
❑ 97PacLigB-393
❑ 97PacSil-393
❑ 97Pin-90
❑ 97PinArtP-PP90
❑ 97PinMusC-90
❑ 97PinPrePla-90
❑ 97PirPos-16
❑ 97Sco-265
❑ 97ScoArtPWB-265
❑ 97ScoPreS-265
❑ 97ScoShoS-265
❑ 97ScoShoSAP-265
❑ 97Top-99
❑ 97Ult-261
❑ 97UltGolME-261
❑ 97UltPlaME-261
❑ 97UppDec-459
❑ 98IndIndQ-25
Johnson, Mark S.
❑ 88T/MUmp-51
❑ 89T/MUmp-49
❑ 90T/MUmp-47
Johnson, Matt
❑ 92MedHatBJF-3214
❑ 92MedHatBJSP-1
❑ 93DunBluJC-12
❑ 93DunBluJF-1804
❑ 93DunBluJFFN-13
❑ 94DunBluJC-15
❑ 94DunBluJF-2565
❑ 95KnoSmoF-49
Johnson, Mike
❑ 79AppFoxT-10
❑ 82WauTimF-18
❑ 84ChaLooT-13
Johnson, Mike Keith
❑ 93KinMetC-14
❑ 93KinMetF-3802
❑ 94MedHatBJF-3678
❑ 94MedHatBJSP-18
❑ 96HagSunB-10
❑ 97BalOriP-17
❑ 97Bow-314
❑ 97BowInt-314
❑ 97ColChoU-U4
❑ 97Fle-532
❑ 97FleTif-532
❑ 98arSenW1-12
❑ 98HarSenM-12
Johnson, Mitch
❑ 80ElmPioRST-18
❑ 85PawRedST-19
❑ 86PawRedSP-11
❑ 87PawRedSP-58
❑ 87PawRedST-7
❑ 88PawRedSC-3
❑ 88PawRedSP-455
❑ 89TucTorC-2
❑ 89TucTorJP-9
❑ 89TucTorP-187
Johnson, Nick
❑ 97GreBatB-14
❑ 97SouAtlTPB-18
❑ 98TamYanM-13
❑ 99199Fin-287
❑ 99Bow-185
❑ 99Bow200RF-ROY10
❑ 99BowAut-BA41
❑ 99BowBes-168
❑ 99BowBesAR-168
❑ 99BowBesMI-M8
❑ 99BowBesMIAR-M8
❑ 99BowBesMIR-M8
❑ 99BowBesR-168
❑ 99BowChr-185
❑ 99BowChrG-185
❑ 99BowChrGR-185
❑ 99BowChrI-185
❑ 99BowChrIR-185
❑ 99BowChrR-185
❑ 99BowGol-185
❑ 99BowInt-185
❑ 99FinGolRef-287
❑ 99FinRef-287
❑ 99JustheS-27
❑ 99JustheSJB-27
❑ 99JustheSJD-5
❑ 99JustheSJN-5
❑ 99StaClu-144
❑ 99StaCluFDI-144
❑ 99StaCluOoaK-144
❑ 99StaCluPP-144
❑ 99TopBlaLC1-33
❑ 99TopBlaLC2-33
❑ 99TopBlaLC3-33
❑ 99TopGal-129
❑ 99TopGalPP-129
❑ 99TopGalPPI-129
❑ 99TopGolL-33
❑ 99TopGolLC1-33
❑ 99TopGolLC2-33
❑ 99TopGolLOtO-33
❑ 99TopRedLC1-33
❑ 99TopRedLC2-33
❑ 99TopRedLC3-33
❑ 99TopSta-83
❑ 99TopSta1Foil-83
❑ 99TopStaFoil-83
❑ 99TopStaOS-83
Johnson, North
❑ 91KinIndC-30
Johnson, Osborne
❑ 23Zee-38
❑ 24Zee-29
Johnson, Otis
❑ 11MecDFT-30
Johnson, Owen
❑ 66Top-356
❑ 66TopVen-356
Johnson, Patrick
❑ 97ButCopKB-10
❑ 97ButCopKK-10
Johnson, Paul
❑ 89PitMetS-12
❑ 89Sta-160
❑ 90St.LucMS-11
Johnson, Paul Oscar
❑ 22W573-69
Johnson, Perry
❑ 83IdaFalAT-7
Johnson, Randy (Randall David)
❑ 84raPho-15
❑ 86WesPalBEP-21
❑ 87JacExpP-451
❑ 87SouLeaAJ-16
❑ 88IndIndC-1
❑ 88IndIndP-510
❑ 88TriAAC-13
❑ 89ClaLigB-95
❑ 89Don-42
❑ 89DonBasB-80
❑ 89DonRoo-43
❑ 89ExpPos-15
❑ 89Fle-381
❑ 89FleGlo-381
❑ 89FleUpd-59
❑ 89OPC-186
❑ 89PanSti-111
❑ 89Sco-645
❑ 89ScoHot1R-63
❑ 89ScoRoo-77T
❑ 89ScoYouS2-32
❑ 89Spo-224
❑ 89Top-647
❑ 89TopBig-287
❑ 89TopTif-647
❑ 89TopTra-57T
❑ 89TopTraT-57T
❑ 89UppDec-25
❑ 89Woo-13
❑ 90Bow-468
❑ 90BowTif-468
❑ 90ClaYel-T22
❑ 90Don-379
❑ 90DonBesA-111
❑ 90Fle-518
❑ 90FleCan-518
❑ 90Hot50RS-23
❑ 90Lea-483
❑ 90MarMot-13
❑ 90OPC-431
❑ 90PanSti-154
❑ 90Sco-415
❑ 90Sco100RS-52
❑ 90Spo-64
❑ 90Top-431
❑ 90TopSti-230
❑ 90TopTif-431
❑ 90UppDec-563
❑ 90USPlaCA-3S
❑ 91Bow-253
❑ 91ClaGam-35
❑ 91Don-134
❑ 91DonBonC-BC2
❑ 91Fle-455
❑ 91FleWaxBC-2
❑ 91Lea-319
❑ 91MajLeaCP-6
❑ 91MarCouH-26
❑ 91OPC-225
❑ 91PanFreS-353
❑ 91PanSti-2
❑ 91PanSti-188
❑ 91RedFolS-53
❑ 91Sco-290
❑ 91Sco-700
❑ 91SevCoi-NW9
❑ 91StaClu-409
❑ 91StaCluCM-15
❑ 91Stu-116
❑ 91Top-225
❑ 91TopDesS-225
❑ 91TopMic-225
❑ 91TopTif-225
❑ 91Ult-339
❑ 91UppDec-376
❑ 92Bow-178
❑ 92Don-207
❑ 92DonDiaK-DK22
❑ 92DonSupD-DK22
❑ 92Fle-283
❑ 92FleSmo'nH-S11
❑ 92Hig5-108
❑ 92Lea-302
❑ 92LeaBlaG-302
❑ 92MarMot-13
❑ 92OPC-525
❑ 92OPCPre-173
❑ 92PanSti-62
❑ 92Pin-379
❑ 92Pin-595
❑ 92Sco-584
❑ 92SpoIllFK1-199
❑ 92StaClu-720
❑ 92Stu-234
❑ 92SunSee-15
❑ 92Top-525
❑ 92TopGol-525
❑ 92TopGolW-525
❑ 92TopKid-126
❑ 92TopMic-525
❑ 92TriPla-71
❑ 92Ult-125
❑ 92UppDec-164
❑ 92UppDecTMH-27
❑ 93Bow-413
❑ 93CadDis-35
❑ 93Don-581
❑ 93Fin-154
❑ 93FinRef-154
❑ 93Fla-272
❑ 93Fle-676
❑ 93FunPac-115
❑ 93Lea-380
❑ 93MarDaiQ-1
❑ 93MariStaClu-16
❑ 93MarMot-15
❑ 93OPC-140
❑ 93PacSpa-288
❑ 93PanSti-60
❑ 93Pin-41
❑ 93Sco-384
❑ 93Sel-118
❑ 93SelStaL-73
❑ 93SP-132
❑ 93StaClu-501
❑ 93StaCluFDI-501
❑ 93StaCluMOP-501
❑ 93Stu-153
❑ 93Top-460
❑ 93TopComotH-16
❑ 93TopGol-460
❑ 93TopInaM-460
❑ 93TopInaR-460
❑ 93TopMic-460
❑ 93TriPla-167
❑ 93Ult-269
❑ 93UltStrK-3
❑ 93UppDec-336
❑ 93UppDec-824
❑ 93UppDecGold-336
❑ 93UppDecGold-824
❑ 94Bow-285
❑ 94ColC-307
❑ 94ColC-357
❑ 94ColChoGS-307
❑ 94ColChoGS-357
❑ 94ColChoSS-307
❑ 94ColChoSS-357
❑ 94Don-352
❑ 94DonSpeE-352
❑ 94Fin-213
❑ 94FinJum-213
❑ 94FinRef-213
❑ 94Fla-337
❑ 94Fle-290
❑ 94FleAllS-12
❑ 94FleExtB-168
❑ 94FleExtBPD-2
❑ 94FleSmo'nH-5
❑ 94FUnPac-51
❑ 94FUnPac-175
❑ 94FUnPac-197
❑ 94Lea-164
❑ 94LeaL-67
❑ 94MarMot-2
❑ 94OPC-81
❑ 94Pac-574
❑ 94PacSilP-7
❑ 94PacSilPC-7
❑ 94PanSti-9
❑ 94PanSti-119
❑ 94Pin-278
❑ 94PinArtP-278
❑ 94PinMusC-278
❑ 94PinTheN-10
❑ 94PinTri-TR9
❑ 94ProMag-128
❑ 94RedFolMI-7
❑ 94Sco-33
❑ 94ScoGolR-33
❑ 94ScoGolS-43
❑ 94Sel-19
❑ 94SelCroC-CC4
❑ 94SelSam-19
❑ 94SelSki-SK1
❑ 94SP-106
❑ 94SPDieC-106
❑ 94Spo-30
❑ 94StaClu-438
❑ 94StaCluDD-DD11
❑ 94StaCluFDI-438
❑ 94StaCluGR-438
❑ 94StaCluMO-22
❑ 94StaCluMOP-438
❑ 94StaCluMOP-DD11
❑ 94Stu-102
❑ 94Top-290
❑ 94TopBlaG-10
❑ 94TopGol-290
❑ 94TopSpa-290
❑ 94TopSupS-23
❑ 94TriPla-128
❑ 94TriPlaM-13
❑ 94Ult-419
❑ 94UltLeaL-5
❑ 94UltStrK-1
❑ 94UppDec-31
❑ 94UppDec-330
❑ 94UppDecAJ-20
❑ 94UppDecAJG-20
❑ 94UppDecED-31
❑ 94UppDecED-330
❑ 95Baz-54
❑ 95BazRedH-RH11
❑ 95Bow-395
❑ 95BowBes-R1
❑ 95BowBes-X14
❑ 95BowBesR-R1
❑ 95BowBesR-X14
❑ 95ClaPhoC-51
❑ 95ColCho-74
❑ 95ColChoGS-74
❑ 95ColChoSE-123
❑ 95ColChoSE-143
❑ 95ColChoSE-250
❑ 95ColChoSEGS-123
❑ 95ColChoSEGS-143
❑ 95ColChoSEGS-250
❑ 95ColChoSESS-123
❑ 95ColChoSESS-143
❑ 95ColChoSESS-250
❑ 95ColChoSS-74
❑ 95Don-18
❑ 95DonMouM-7
❑ 95DonPreP-18
❑ 95DonTopotO-151
❑ 95Emo-78
❑ 95Fin-76
❑ 95FinFlaT-FT5
❑ 95FinRef-76
❑ 95Fla-82
❑ 95Fle-271
❑ 95FleAllS-21
❑ 95FleLeaL-5
❑ 95FleTeaL-12
❑ 95Lea-244
❑ 95LeaLim-40
❑ 95MarMot-2
❑ 95MarPac-5
❑ 95MarPac-14
❑ 95MarPac-34
❑ 95NatPac2-3
❑ 95Pac-399
❑ 95PacPri-127
❑ 95PanSti-16
❑ 95PanSti-126
❑ 95Pin-330
❑ 95PinArtP-330
❑ 95PinArtP-351
❑ 95PinMusC-330
❑ 95RedFol-34
❑ 95Sco-222
❑ 95ScoGolR-222
❑ 95ScoHaloG-HG7
❑ 95ScoPlaTS-222
❑ 95Sel-135
❑ 95SelArtP-135
❑ 95SelCer-61
❑ 95SelCerMG-61
❑ 95SP-189
❑ 95SPCha-186
❑ 95SPChaDC-186
❑ 95Spo-29
❑ 95SpoArtP-29
❑ 95SPSil-189
❑ 95SPSpeF-19
❑ 95StaClu-340
❑ 95StaCluMO-23
❑ 95StaCluMOP-340
❑ 95StaCluMOP-SS20
❑ 95StaCluSS-SS20
❑ 95StaCluSTDW-M340
❑ 95StaCluSTWS-340
❑ 95StaCluVR-179
❑ 95StaCluVRMO-179
❑ 95Stu-48
❑ 95StuGolS-48
❑ 95Sum-97
❑ 95Sum-193
❑ 95SumNthD-97
❑ 95SumNthD-193
❑ 95Top-203
❑ 95TopCyb-116
❑ 95TopEmb-69
❑ 95TopEmbGI-69
❑ 95TopLeaL-LL46
❑ 95TopTra-164T
❑ 95UC3-64
❑ 95UC3-130
❑ 95UC3ArtP-64
❑ 95UC3ArtP-130
❑ 95Ult-103
❑ 95UltGolM-103
❑ 95UltLeaL-4
❑ 95UltLeaLGM-4
❑ 95UltStrK-3
❑ 95UltStrKGM-3
❑ 95UppDec-102
❑ 95UppDec-112
❑ 95UppDecC-4B
❑ 95UppDecED-102
❑ 95UppDecED-112
❑ 95UppDecEDG-102
❑ 95UppDecEDG-112
❑ 95UppDecSE-118
❑ 95UppDecSEG-118
❑ 95USPlaCMLA-3S
❑ 95Zen-83
❑ 95ZenAllS-9
❑ 96Baz-95
❑ 96Bow-48
❑ 96BowBes-21

- ❑ 96BowBesAR-21
- ❑ 96BowBesMI-10
- ❑ 96BowBesMIAR-10
- ❑ 96BowBesMIR-10
- ❑ 96BowBesR-21
- ❑ 96BowFoi-48
- ❑ 96Cir-79
- ❑ 96CirAcc-13
- ❑ 96CirBos-21
- ❑ 96CirRav-79
- ❑ 96ColCho-7
- ❑ 96ColCho-8
- ❑ 96ColCho-269
- ❑ 96ColCho-315
- ❑ 96ColCho-365
- ❑ 96ColCho-708
- ❑ 96ColChoGS-7
- ❑ 96ColChoGS-8
- ❑ 96ColChoGS-269
- ❑ 96ColChoGS-315
- ❑ 96ColChoGS-365
- ❑ 96ColChoGS-708
- ❑ 96ColChoSS-7
- ❑ 96ColChoSS-8
- ❑ 96ColChoSS-269
- ❑ 96ColChoSS-315
- ❑ 96ColChoSS-365
- ❑ 96ColChoSS-708
- ❑ 96ColChoYMtP-18
- ❑ 96ColChoYMtP-18A
- ❑ 96ColChoYMtPGS-18
- ❑ 96ColChoYMtPGS-18A
- ❑ 96Don-478
- ❑ 96DonPreP-478
- ❑ 96DonSho-2
- ❑ 96EmoN-6
- ❑ 96EmoXL-115
- ❑ 96Fin-G270
- ❑ 96Fin-S77
- ❑ 96FinRef-G270
- ❑ 96FinRef-S77
- ❑ 96Fla-162
- ❑ 96Fle-240
- ❑ 96FlePosG-4
- ❑ 96FleSmo'H-5
- ❑ 96FleTif-240
- ❑ 96FleUpd-U227
- ❑ 96FleUpdH-9
- ❑ 96FleUpdTC-U227
- ❑ 96FleZon-5
- ❑ 96Kin-5
- ❑ 96Lea-165
- ❑ 96LeaLim-38
- ❑ 96LeaLimG-38
- ❑ 96LeaPre-52
- ❑ 96LeaPreP-52
- ❑ 96LeaPrePB-165
- ❑ 96LeaPrePG-165
- ❑ 96LeaPrePS-165
- ❑ 96LeaPreSG-60
- ❑ 96LeaPreSte-60
- ❑ 96LeaSig-37
- ❑ 96LeaSigEA-91
- ❑ 96LeaSigEACM-12
- ❑ 96LeaSigPPG-37
- ❑ 96LeaSigPPP-37
- ❑ 96MarMot-2
- ❑ 96MetUni-108
- ❑ 96MetUniP-108
- ❑ 96Pac-401
- ❑ 96Pac-418
- ❑ 96PacGolCD-DC33
- ❑ 96PacOctM-OM7
- ❑ 96PacPri-P132
- ❑ 96PacPriFT-FT1
- ❑ 96PacPriG-P132
- ❑ 96PacPriRHS-RH17
- ❑ 96PanSti-124
- ❑ 96PanSti-226
- ❑ 96Pin-236
- ❑ 96Pin-273
- ❑ 96PinAfi-10
- ❑ 96PinAfiAP-10
- ❑ 96PinAfiFPP-10
- ❑ 96PinAfiSP-25
- ❑ 96PinArtP-136
- ❑ 96PinArtP-173
- ❑ 96PinFan-25
- ❑ 96PinFoil-236
- ❑ 96PinFoil-273
- ❑ 96PinSta-136
- ❑ 96PinSta-173
- ❑ 96PinTeaP-9
- ❑ 96ProMagDM-22
- ❑ 96ProSta-62
- ❑ 96SchDis-15
- ❑ 96Sco-34
- ❑ 96Sco-193
- ❑ 96Sco-367
- ❑ 96Sco-512
- ❑ 96ScoAll-11
- ❑ 96ScoDugC-A33
- ❑ 96ScoDugC-B92
- ❑ 96ScoDugCAP-A33
- ❑ 96ScoDugCAP-B92
- ❑ 96ScoGolS-29
- ❑ 96ScoNumG-25
- ❑ 96ScoRef-18
- ❑ 96Sel-63
- ❑ 96SelArtP-63
- ❑ 96SelCer-17
- ❑ 96SelCerAP-17
- ❑ 96SelCerCB-17
- ❑ 96SelCerCR-17
- ❑ 96SelCerIP-13
- ❑ 96SelCerMB-17
- ❑ 96SelCerMG-17
- ❑ 96SelCerMR-17
- ❑ 96SelClaTF-19
- ❑ 96SelEnF-19
- ❑ 96SelTeaN-9
- ❑ 96SP-169
- ❑ 96Spo-51
- ❑ 96SpoArtP-51
- ❑ 96SPSpeFX-31
- ❑ 96SPSpeFXDC-31
- ❑ 96SPx-56
- ❑ 96SPxGol-56
- ❑ 96StaClu-16
- ❑ 96StaClu-235
- ❑ 96StaCluEPB-16
- ❑ 96StaCluEPG-16
- ❑ 96StaCluEPS-16
- ❑ 96StaCluMM-MM1
- ❑ 96StaCluMO-17
- ❑ 96StaCluMOP-16
- ❑ 96StaCluMOP-235
- ❑ 96StaCluMOP-MM1
- ❑ 96StaCluMOP-PS1
- ❑ 96StaCluMOP-TSCA9
- ❑ 96StaCluPS-PS1
- ❑ 96StaCluTA-9
- ❑ 96Stu-73
- ❑ 96StuPrePB-73
- ❑ 96StuPrePG-73
- ❑ 96StuPrePS-73
- ❑ 96Sum-110
- ❑ 96SumAbo&B-110
- ❑ 96SumArtP-110
- ❑ 96SumFoi-110
- ❑ 96SumPos-6
- ❑ 96TeaOut-41
- ❑ 96Top-150
- ❑ 96Top-224
- ❑ 96TopBroLL-5
- ❑ 96TopChr-43
- ❑ 96TopChr-84
- ❑ 96TopChrR-43
- ❑ 96TopChrR-84
- ❑ 96TopClaC-CC11
- ❑ 96TopGal-162
- ❑ 96TopGalE-10
- ❑ 96TopGalPG-PG2
- ❑ 96TopGalPPI-162
- ❑ 96TopLas-56
- ❑ 96TopLasSS-12
- ❑ 96TopMysF-M3
- ❑ 96TopMysFR-M3
- ❑ 96TopPro-AL6
- ❑ 96Ult-127
- ❑ 96Ult-581
- ❑ 96UltGolM-127
- ❑ 96UltGolM-581
- ❑ 96UltSeaC-3
- ❑ 96UltSeaCGM-3
- ❑ 96UppDec-460
- ❑ 96UppDecDD-DD37
- ❑ 96UppDecDDG-DD37
- ❑ 96UppDecDDS-DD37
- ❑ 96UppDecHC-HC9
- ❑ 96UppDecPHE-H14
- ❑ 96UppDecPreH-H14
- ❑ 96UppDecVJLS-VJ12
- ❑ 96Zen-75
- ❑ 96ZenArtP-75
- ❑ 96ZenDiaC-17
- ❑ 96ZenDiaCP-17
- ❑ 96ZenMoz-5
- ❑ 97Bow-225
- ❑ 97BowBes-93
- ❑ 97BowBesAR-93
- ❑ 97BowBesR-93
- ❑ 97BowChr-55
- ❑ 97BowChrI-55
- ❑ 97BowChrIR-55
- ❑ 97BowChrR-55
- ❑ 97BowInt-225
- ❑ 97Cir-276
- ❑ 97CirRav-276
- ❑ 97ColCho-485
- ❑ 97ColChoT-SM7
- ❑ 97ColChoTBS-44
- ❑ 97ColChoTBSWH-44
- ❑ 97Don-89
- ❑ 97Don-426
- ❑ 97DonArmaD-5
- ❑ 97DonEli-30
- ❑ 97DonEliGS-30
- ❑ 97DonGolPP-89
- ❑ 97DonGolPP-426
- ❑ 97DonLim-52
- ❑ 97DonLim-120
- ❑ 97DonLim-187
- ❑ 97DonLimE-52
- ❑ 97DonLimE-120
- ❑ 97DonLimE-187
- ❑ 97DonLimENG-52
- ❑ 97DonPre-104
- ❑ 97DonPreCttC-104
- ❑ 97DonSig-29
- ❑ 97DonSigNN-5
- ❑ 97DonSigPPP-29
- ❑ 97DonSilPP-89
- ❑ 97DonSilPP-426
- ❑ 97DonTea-139
- ❑ 97DonTeaSPE-139
- ❑ 97DonVxP1-8
- ❑ 97E-X2-41
- ❑ 97E-X2Cred-41
- ❑ 97E-X2EssCre-41
- ❑ 97Fin-110
- ❑ 97Fin-348
- ❑ 97FinEmb-110
- ❑ 97FinEmb-348
- ❑ 97FinEmbR-110
- ❑ 97FinEmbR-348
- ❑ 97FinRef-110
- ❑ 97FinRef-348
- ❑ 97FlaShoLC-20
- ❑ 97FlaShoLeg0-20
- ❑ 97FlaShoLeg1-20
- ❑ 97FlaShoM-A20
- ❑ 97FlaShoM-B20
- ❑ 97FlaShoM-C20
- ❑ 97FlaShoR0-20
- ❑ 97FlaShoR1-20
- ❑ 97FlaShoR2-20
- ❑ 97Fle-210
- ❑ 97FleTif-210
- ❑ 97HigMinMM-4
- ❑ 97HigMinMM-7
- ❑ 97Lea-132
- ❑ 97Lea-379
- ❑ 97LeaFraM-132
- ❑ 97LeaFraM-379
- ❑ 97LeaFraMDC-132
- ❑ 97LeaFraMDC-379
- ❑ 97LeaGet-4
- ❑ 97MarSco-9
- ❑ 97MarScoPl-9
- ❑ 97MarScoPr-9
- ❑ 97MetUni-147
- ❑ 97NewPin-100
- ❑ 97NewPinAP-100
- ❑ 97NewPinKtP-17
- ❑ 97NewPinMC-100
- ❑ 97NewPinPP-100
- ❑ 97NewPinPP-K17
- ❑ 97Pac-189
- ❑ 97PacLigB-189
- ❑ 97PacPriSH-SH6B
- ❑ 97PacSil-189
- ❑ 97PinCar-3
- ❑ 97PinCer-54
- ❑ 97PinCerLI-17
- ❑ 97PinCerMBla-54
- ❑ 97PinCerMBlu-54
- ❑ 97PinCerMG-54
- ❑ 97PinCerMR-54
- ❑ 97PinCerR-54
- ❑ 97PinIns-127
- ❑ 97PinInsCE-127
- ❑ 97PinInsDE-127
- ❑ 97PinTotCPB-54
- ❑ 97PinTotCPG-54
- ❑ 97PinTotCPR-54
- ❑ 97PinX-P-96
- ❑ 97PinX-P-142
- ❑ 97PinX-PMoS-96
- ❑ 97PinX-PMoS-142
- ❑ 97Sco-192
- ❑ 97Sco-529
- ❑ 97ScoArtPWB-192
- ❑ 97ScoArtPWB-529
- ❑ 97ScoHigZ-17
- ❑ 97ScoPitP-15
- ❑ 97ScoPreS-192
- ❑ 97ScoResC-529
- ❑ 97ScoShoS-192
- ❑ 97ScoShoS-529
- ❑ 97ScoShoSAP-192
- ❑ 97ScoShoSAP-529
- ❑ 97ScoStaaD-8
- ❑ 97Sel-78
- ❑ 97SelArtP-78
- ❑ 97SelCom-78
- ❑ 97SelRegG-78
- ❑ 97SP-167
- ❑ 97SpoIll-36
- ❑ 97SpoIll-159
- ❑ 97SpoIllEE-36
- ❑ 97SpoIllEE-159
- ❑ 97SpoIllGS-22
- ❑ 97SPSPxFA-5
- ❑ 97StaClu-247
- ❑ 97StaCluMat-247
- ❑ 97StaCluMOP-247
- ❑ 97StrAll-30
- ❑ 97Stu-113
- ❑ 97StuPrePG-113
- ❑ 97StuPrePS-113
- ❑ 97Top-325
- ❑ 97TopChr-110
- ❑ 97TopChrR-110
- ❑ 97TopGal-52
- ❑ 97TopGalPPI-52
- ❑ 97TopHobM-HM7
- ❑ 97TopMem05-26
- ❑ 97TopScr-10
- ❑ 97TopScrT-10
- ❑ 97TopSta-43
- ❑ 97TopSta97AS-AS2
- ❑ 97TopStaAM-43
- ❑ 97TopStaASM-ASM4
- ❑ 97Ult-124
- ❑ 97UltGolME-124
- ❑ 97UltPlaME-124
- ❑ 97UppDec-72
- ❑ 97UppDec-501
- ❑ 97UppDecMP-P8
- ❑ 97Zen-31
- ❑ 98Bow-257
- ❑ 98BowBes-70
- ❑ 98BowBesAR-70
- ❑ 98BowBesMIF-MI9
- ❑ 98BowBesMIFAR-MI9
- ❑ 98BowBesMIFR-MI9
- ❑ 98BowBesR-70
- ❑ 98BowChr-257
- ❑ 98BowChrGA-257
- ❑ 98BowChrGAR-257
- ❑ 98BowChrI-257
- ❑ 98BowChrIR-257
- ❑ 98BowChrR-257
- ❑ 98BowGolA-257
- ❑ 98BowInt-257
- ❑ 98CirThu-134
- ❑ 98CirThuRav-134
- ❑ 98CirThuSupRav-134
- ❑ 98ColCho-13
- ❑ 98ColCho-493
- ❑ 98ColChoSQ-SQ55
- ❑ 98CroRoyFoB-20
- ❑ 98CroRoyFoBA-20
- ❑ 98Don-4
- ❑ 98Don-383
- ❑ 98DonCol-4
- ❑ 98DonColE-426
- ❑ 98DonColL-230
- ❑ 98DonColP-580
- ❑ 98DonColP-741
- ❑ 98DonColS-4
- ❑ 98DonCruG-41
- ❑ 98DonCruP-41
- ❑ 98DonCruR-41
- ❑ 98DonDiaK-9
- ❑ 98DonDiaKC-9
- ❑ 98DonDom-9
- ❑ 98DonEli-26
- ❑ 98DonEliA-26
- ❑ 98DonEliS-26
- ❑ 98DonGolPP-4
- ❑ 98DonGolPP-383
- ❑ 98DonPre-30
- ❑ 98DonPre-191
- ❑ 98DonPrePM-23
- ❑ 98DonPreSeat-30
- ❑ 98DonPreSeat-191
- ❑ 98DonPreTW-21
- ❑ 98DonPriCD-4
- ❑ 98DonPriCE-426
- ❑ 98DonPriCL-230
- ❑ 98DonPriCP-580
- ❑ 98DonPriCP-741
- ❑ 98DonSig-51
- ❑ 98DonSigAC-64
- ❑ 98DonSigAM-65
- ❑ 98DonSigP-51
- ❑ 98DonSilPP-4
- ❑ 98DonSilPP-383
- ❑ 98E-X2-73
- ❑ 98E-X2ECFut-73
- ❑ 98E-X2ECNow-73
- ❑ 98Fin-237
- ❑ 98FinNo--237
- ❑ 98FinNo-R-237
- ❑ 98FinOve-B3
- ❑ 98FinOveR-B3
- ❑ 98FinRef-237
- ❑ 98FinTheM-TM18
- ❑ 98FinTheMR-TM18
- ❑ 98FlaShoLeg0-57
- ❑ 98FlaShoLeg1-57
- ❑ 98FlaShoLeg2-57
- ❑ 98FlaShoLeg3-57
- ❑ 98FlaShoLegM-57
- ❑ 98FlaShoR0-57
- ❑ 98FlaShoR1-57
- ❑ 98FlaShoR2-57
- ❑ 98FlaShoR3-57
- ❑ 98Fle-137
- ❑ 98Fle-304
- ❑ 98Fle-317
- ❑ 98Fle-587
- ❑ 98FleDecERT-8
- ❑ 98FleDecoE-8
- ❑ 98FleDiaS-10
- ❑ 98FlePowG-11
- ❑ 98FleUpd-U49
- ❑ 98FleVin'-56
- ❑ 98FleVin'C-56
- ❑ 98Lea-30
- ❑ 98LeaCruG-41
- ❑ 98LeaCruP-41
- ❑ 98LeaCruR-41
- ❑ 98LeaFraDA-30
- ❑ 98LeaFraF-30
- ❑ 98LeaFraM-30
- ❑ 98LeaFraM-30
- ❑ 98LeaFraMDC-30
- ❑ 98LeaFraMDC-30
- ❑ 98LeaFraMZ2-30
- ❑ 98LeaRS-3
- ❑ 98LeaRSLHolo-3
- ❑ 98LeaRSLong-3
- ❑ 98LeaRTrue-3
- ❑ 98LeaStaRep-27
- ❑ 98LeaStaS-18
- ❑ 98LeaStaSDC-18
- ❑ 98MarSco-9
- ❑ 98MarScoP-9
- ❑ 98MetUni-9
- ❑ 98MetUni-209
- ❑ 98MetUniPMG-9
- ❑ 98MetUniPMG-209
- ❑ 98Pac-188
- ❑ 98PacAur-73
- ❑ 98PacAurPF-50
- ❑ 98PacAurPFC-50
- ❑ 98PacAurPFPB-50
- ❑ 98PacAurPFR-50
- ❑ 98PacAurPFS-50
- ❑ 98PacGolCDC-30
- ❑ 98PacInv-65
- ❑ 98PacInvGems-92
- ❑ 98PacInvInt-12A
- ❑ 98PacInvPBlue-65
- ❑ 98PacInvSilv-65
- ❑ 98PacInvTeam-26
- ❑ 98PacOme-222
- ❑ 98PacOmeR-222
- ❑ 98PacOnl-689
- ❑ 98PacOnlR-689
- ❑ 98PacOnlWC-689
- ❑ 98PacPar-88
- ❑ 98PacParC-88
- ❑ 98PacParG-88
- ❑ 98PacParHS-88
- ❑ 98PacParPB-88
- ❑ 98PacParR-88
- ❑ 98PacPlaB-188
- ❑ 98PacRedT-188
- ❑ 98PacSil-188
- ❑ 98PinIns-39
- ❑ 98PinInsCE-39
- ❑ 98PinInsDE-39
- ❑ 98PinInsSG-4AB
- ❑ 98PinInsSG-4CD
- ❑ 98PinInsSG-12AB
- ❑ 98PinInsSG-12CD
- ❑ 98PinInsSGS-4AB
- ❑ 98PinInsSGS-4CD
- ❑ 98PinInsSGS-12AB
- ❑ 98PinInsSGS-12CD
- ❑ 98PinMinB-10
- ❑ 98PinMinCB-10
- ❑ 98PinMinCBAP-10
- ❑ 98PinMinCGP-10
- ❑ 98PinMinCGPAP-10
- ❑ 98PinMinCN-10
- ❑ 98PinMinCNAP-10
- ❑ 98PinMinCSGR-10
- ❑ 98PinMinDC-10
- ❑ 98PinMinG-10
- ❑ 98PinMinMCSS-10
- ❑ 98PinMinS-10
- ❑ 98PinPer-31
- ❑ 98PinPerPP-31
- ❑ 98PinPlu-13
- ❑ 98PinPluAP-PP7
- ❑ 98PinPluGAP-PP7
- ❑ 98PinPluLM-30
- ❑ 98PinPluMAP-PP7
- ❑ 98PinSna-SM14
- ❑ 98PinSna-SM15
- ❑ 98Revo-133
- ❑ 98RevoSS-133
- ❑ 98Sco-145
- ❑ 98ScoAllST-18
- ❑ 98ScoRT-7
- ❑ 98ScoRTSS-PP7
- ❑ 98ScoRTSSAP-PP7
- ❑ 98ScoRTSSAP1-PP7
- ❑ 98ScoSS-PP157
- ❑ 98ScoSSAP-PP157
- ❑ 98SkyDugA-79
- ❑ 98SkyDugA-131
- ❑ 98SkyDugAD-D4
- ❑ 98SkyDugAIA-79
- ❑ 98SkyDugAIA-131
- ❑ 98SP Aut-176
- ❑ 98SP Aut-SD32
- ❑ 98SP AutSD-SD32
- ❑ 98SP AutSDT-SD32
- ❑ 98SpoIll-66
- ❑ 98SpoIll-139
- ❑ 98SpoIlC-C8
- ❑ 98SpoIllEE-66
- ❑ 98SpoIllEE-139
- ❑ 98SpoIllFE-66
- ❑ 98SpoIllFE-139
- ❑ 98SpoIllTaN-51
- ❑ 98SpoIllTaN-95
- ❑ 98SpoIllTaNEE-51
- ❑ 98SpoIllTaNEE-95
- ❑ 98SpoIllWSF-78
- ❑ 98SpoIllWSFEE-78
- ❑ 98SpoIllWSFFE-78
- ❑ 98SpoIllWSFRJP-15
- ❑ 98SPxFin-166
- ❑ 98SPxFin-211
- ❑ 98SPxFin-320
- ❑ 98SPxFinR-166
- ❑ 98SPxFinR-211
- ❑ 98SPxFinR-320
- ❑ 98SPxFinS-166
- ❑ 98SPxFinS-211
- ❑ 98SPxFinS-320
- ❑ 98StaCluC-CS31
- ❑ 98StaCluC-CS34
- ❑ 98StaCluC-CS35
- ❑ 98StaCluFDI-88
- ❑ 98StaCluI-88
- ❑ 98StaCluNC-NC7
- ❑ 98StaCluOneK-88
- ❑ 98StaCluPP-88
- ❑ 98StaCluTIII-T9C
- ❑ 98StaCluTLme-T9C
- ❑ 98StaCluTLmo-T9C
- ❑ 98Stu-34
- ❑ 98StuFF-10
- ❑ 98StuFFDC-10
- ❑ 98StuGPP-34
- ❑ 98StuSPP-34
- ❑ 98Top-150
- ❑ 98Top-265

❑ 98TopChr-150
❑ 98TopChr-265
❑ 98TopChrF-FB4
❑ 98TopChrFR-FB4
❑ 98TopChrHB-HB15
❑ 98TopChrHBR-HB15
❑ 98TopChrR-150
❑ 98TopChrR-265
❑ 98TopDevR-150
❑ 98TopDevR-265
❑ 98TopDia-150
❑ 98TopDia-265
❑ 98TopFla-FB4
❑ 98TopGal-56
❑ 98TopGalGP-56
❑ 98TopGalOPP-56
❑ 98TopGalPPI-56
❑ 98TopGalPPIA-56
❑ 98TopGolLabC1-8
❑ 98TopGolLabC1B-8
❑ 98TopGolLabC1One-8
❑ 98TopGolLabC1R-8
❑ 98TopGolLabC2-8
❑ 98TopGolLabC2B-8
❑ 98TopGolLabC2One-8
❑ 98TopGolLabC2R-8
❑ 98TopGolLabC3-8
❑ 98TopGolLabC3B-8
❑ 98TopGolLabC3One-8
❑ 98TopGolLabC3R-8
❑ 98TopHal-HB15
❑ 98TopMiniC-150
❑ 98TopMiniC-265
❑ 98TopMysF-ILM12
❑ 98TopMysFR-ILM12
❑ 98TopOpeD-78
❑ 98TopPre-PP5
❑ 98TopSta-120
❑ 98TopSta'S-19
❑ 98TopSta'SGH-19
❑ 98TopStaB-120
❑ 98TopStaG-120
❑ 98TopStaGR-120
❑ 98TopStaS-120
❑ 98TopStaSteG-19
❑ 98TopSup-12
❑ 98TopSup-12
❑ 98TopTek-39
❑ 98TopTekD-39
❑ 98UD3-69
❑ 98UD3-159
❑ 98UD3-249
❑ 98UD3DieCut-69
❑ 98UD3DieCut-159
❑ 98UD3DieCut-249
❑ 98Ult-80
❑ 98Ult-217
❑ 98UltGolM-80
❑ 98UltGolM-217
❑ 98UltMas-80
❑ 98UltMas-217
❑ 98UltPlaM-80
❑ 98UltPlaM-217
❑ 98UppDec-250
❑ 98UppDec-515
❑ 98UppDec-601
❑ 98UppDec10AP-9
❑ 98UppDec1APR-9
❑ 98UppDecAC-AS28
❑ 98UppDecAG-AG26
❑ 98UppDecAGDC-AG26
❑ 98UppDecCD-CD16
❑ 98UppDecR-91
❑ 98UppDecR-17
❑ 98UppDecRTC-TC18
❑ 98UppDecU-14
❑ 98Zen-10
❑ 98Zen5 xx7-44
❑ 98Zen5x7GoldImp-44
❑ 98Zen5x7Imp-44
❑ 98ZenZ-G-10
❑ 98ZenZ-S-10
❑ 99199Fin-185
❑ 99199Fin-274
❑ 99Bow-248
❑ 99BowBes-74
❑ 99BowBesAR-74
❑ 99BowBesR-74
❑ 99BowGol-248
❑ 99BowInt-248
❑ 99CroRoyB-8
❑ 99CroRoyL-8
❑ 99CroRoyOD-8
❑ 99E-X Cen-32
❑ 99E-X CenECFut-32
❑ 99E-X CenECNow-32
❑ 99FinGolRef-185
❑ 99FinGolRef-274
❑ 99FinRef-185
❑ 99FinRef-274
❑ 99FlaShoLeg1-28
❑ 99FlaShoLeg2-28
❑ 99FlaShoLeg3-28
❑ 99FlaShoLegM1-28
❑ 99FlaShoLegM2-28
❑ 99FlaShoLegM3-28
❑ 99FlaShoR1-28
❑ 99FlaShoR2-28
❑ 99FlaShoR3-28
❑ 99Fle-36
❑ 99FleBri-117
❑ 99FleBri2G-117
❑ 99FleBriBlu-117
❑ 99FleBriGol-117
❑ 99FleDiaM-8
❑ 99FleGolM-7
❑ 99FleMys-22
❑ 99FleMysG-22
❑ 99FleMysM-22
❑ 99FleSta9-36
❑ 99FleVin'-36
❑ 99FleWarT-36
❑ 99MetUni-139
❑ 99MetUni-234
❑ 99MetUni-274
❑ 99MetUniGM-139
❑ 99MetUniGM-234
❑ 99MetUniGM-274
❑ 99MetUniPMG-139
❑ 99MetUniPMG-234
❑ 99MetUniPMG-274
❑ 99Pac-195
❑ 99PacAur-11
❑ 99PacAurOD-11
❑ 99PacCroC-127
❑ 99PacCroCPB-127
❑ 99PacInv-7
❑ 99PacInvOD-7
❑ 99PacInvPB-7
❑ 99PacOme-13
❑ 99PacOme5T-1
❑ 99PacOme5TT-1
❑ 99PacOmeC-13
❑ 99PacOmeG-13
❑ 99PacOmePB-13
❑ 99PacPar-15
❑ 99PacParC-15
❑ 99PacParG-15
❑ 99PacParHoloGold-15
❑ 99PacParHS-15
❑ 99PacParOD-15
❑ 99PacParPB-15
❑ 99PacParRed-15
❑ 99PacPlaB-195
❑ 99PacPri-69
❑ 99PacPriHB-69
❑ 99PacPriHG-69
❑ 99PacPriHM-69
❑ 99PacPriHP-69
❑ 99PacPriRed-69
❑ 99PacPriS-101
❑ 99PacPriS206-101
❑ 99PacPriS206R-101
❑ 99PacRed-195
❑ 99PacTim-17
❑ 99Pin-13
❑ 99Rev-8
❑ 99RevPremDate-8
❑ 99RevRet-8
❑ 99RevShaSS-8
❑ 99SkyMolM-22
❑ 99SkyMolMX-22
❑ 99SkyPre-58
❑ 99SkyPre-295
❑ 99SkyPreR-58
❑ 99SkyPreR-295
❑ 99SkyThu-250
❑ 99SkyThuHip-H6
❑ 99SkyThuRant-250
❑ 99SkyThuRave-250
❑ 99SP Aut-6
❑ 99SpoIll-112
❑ 99SpoIllDD-3
❑ 99SpoIllH-2
❑ 99SPx-14
❑ 99SPxFinR-14
❑ 99SPxFinS-14
❑ 99SPxPreS-PS28
❑ 99SPxStaF-SF15
❑ 99StaClu-136
❑ 99StaClu-328
❑ 99StaCluFDI-136
❑ 99StaCluFDI-328
❑ 99StaCluOoaK-136
❑ 99StaCluOoaK-328
❑ 99StaCluPP-136
❑ 99StaCluPP-328
❑ 99StaCluTI-T6C
❑ 99StaCluTL-T6C
❑ 99StaCluTL-T6C
❑ 99ThuSkySupR-250
❑ 99Top-418
❑ 99Top-448
❑ 99TopAll-AM28
❑ 99TopBlaLC1-43
❑ 99TopBlaLC2-43
❑ 99TopBlaLC3-43
❑ 99TopChr-418
❑ 99TopChr-448
❑ 99TopChrA-AE28
❑ 99TopChrAR-AE28
❑ 99TopChrR-418
❑ 99TopChrR-448
❑ 99TopGal-73
❑ 99TopGalPP-73
❑ 99TopGalPPI-73
❑ 99TopGolL-43
❑ 99TopGolLC1-43
❑ 99TopGolLC2-43
❑ 99TopGolLOtO-43
❑ 99TopMVPP-418
❑ 99TopMVPP-448
❑ 99TopOpeD-120
❑ 99TopRedLC1-43
❑ 99TopRedLC2-43
❑ 99TopRedLC3-43
❑ 99TopSta-30
❑ 99TopSta1Foil-30
❑ 99TopSta2Foil-30
❑ 99TopStaFoil-30
❑ 99TopStaOS-30
❑ 99TopStaTS-30
❑ 99TopTek-17A
❑ 99TopTek-17B
❑ 99TopTekG-17A
❑ 99TopTekG-17B
❑ 99UD Cho-32
❑ 99UD Cho-92
❑ 99UD ChoMBH-B1
❑ 99UD ChoPCR-32
❑ 99UD ChoPCR-92
❑ 99UD ChoS-12
❑ 99UD ChoSD-12
❑ 99UD ChoSHR-12
❑ 99UD ChoST-12
❑ 99UD Ion-29
❑ 99UD Ion-76
❑ 99UD IonR-29
❑ 99UD IonR-76
❑ 99UDHolo-4
❑ 99UDHoloAUsome-4
❑ 99Ult-166
❑ 99UltGolM-166
❑ 99UltMas-166
❑ 99UltPlaM-166
❑ 99UppDec-301
❑ 99UppDec10AT-X10
❑ 99UppDec10ATD-X10
❑ 99UppDec10ATHR-X10
❑ 99UppDec10ATT-X10
❑ 99UppDecBD-39
❑ 99UppDecBDD-39
❑ 99UppDecBDQ-39
❑ 99UppDecBDT-39
❑ 99UppDecCL-70
❑ 99UppDecCLCC-70
❑ 99UppDecCLM-C4
❑ 99UppDecE-4
❑ 99UppDecEFXG-4
❑ 99UppDecEL1-301
❑ 99UppDecEL2-301
❑ 99UppDecEUR-U10
❑ 99UppDecIP-I11
❑ 99UppDecIPD-I11
❑ 99UppDecIPHR-I11
❑ 99UppDecIPT-I11
❑ 99UppDecM-8
❑ 99UppDecMGS-8
❑ 99UppDecMHFS-8
❑ 99UppDecMSS-8
❑ 99UppDecO-52
❑ 99UppDecOMP-S8
❑ 99UppDecOSO-52
❑ 99UppDecOWP-R20
❑ 99UppDecR-4
❑ 99UppDecRG-4
❑ 99UppDecRP-4
❑ 99UppDecWY-W13
❑ 99UppDecWYD-W13
❑ 99UppDecWYHR-W13
❑ 99UppDecWYT-W13
❑ 99Vic-16
❑ 99Vic-459

Johnson, Randy (Randall Glenn)

❑ 81RicBraT-22
❑ 82BraBurKL-14
❑ 82BraPol-6
❑ 83BraPol-6
❑ 83Top-596
❑ 84BraPol-6
❑ 84Don-321
❑ 84Fle-183
❑ 84Nes792-289
❑ 84Top-289
❑ 84TopTif-289
❑ 85Don-531
❑ 85Fle-330
❑ 85RicBraT-14
❑ 85Top-458
❑ 85TopTif-458
❑ 86PhoFirP-11
❑ 89EveGiaS-16
❑ 90CliGiaB-15
❑ 90CliGiaP-2561

Johnson, Randy (Randall Stuart)

❑ 80GleFalWSBT-18
❑ 80GleFalWSCT-4
❑ 81GleFalWST-18
❑ 82TopTra-51T
❑ 82TwiPos-18
❑ 83Don-305
❑ 83Fle-617
❑ 83TolMudHT-21
❑ 83Top-354
❑ 85BufBisT-14
❑ 87JapPlaB-12
❑ 89PacSenL-181
❑ 90EliSenL-23
❑ 91BriBanF-17

Johnson, Reginald

❑ 92GreFalDSP-11
❑ 93VerBeaDC-11
❑ 93VerBeaDF-2228

Johnson, Ric

❑ 96QuaCitRB-17
❑ 97KisCob-15
❑ 98KisCobQ-18

Johnson, Rich

❑ 86AshTouP-16
❑ 87ColAstP-23
❑ 88ColAstB-14

Johnson, Rocky

❑ 88NebCor-12

Johnson, Roger

❑ 86KinEagP-12

Johnson, Ron (Rondin)

❑ 81OmaRoyT-19
❑ 82OmaRoyT-17A
❑ 82OmaRoyT-17B
❑ 83RoyPos-15
❑ 84IndIndTI-24
❑ 84OmaRoyT-25
❑ 85OmaRoyT-21
❑ 86OmaRoyP-12
❑ 86OmaRoyT-2
❑ 87Ft.MyeRP-34
❑ 87OmaRoyP-11
❑ 88OmaRoyC-10
❑ 88OmaRoyP-1515
❑ 89BasCitRS-27
❑ 90BasCitRS-30
❑ 91BasCitRC-29
❑ 91BasCitRP-1415
❑ 91DaiDolF-5
❑ 92BasCitRC-24
❑ 92BasCitRF-3860
❑ 93CarLeaAGF-13
❑ 93WilBluRC-27
❑ 93WilBluRF-2013
❑ 94MemChiF-373
❑ 95AusFut-6
❑ 95WicWraTI-21
❑ 96WicWraB-27
❑ 97WicWra-28
❑ 98OmaRoyM-1

Johnson, Rontrez

❑ 97MicBatC-15

Johnson, Roy Cleveland

❑ 27Zee-112
❑ 28Zee-132
❑ 29PorandAR-47
❑ 32OrbPinUP-35
❑ 32R33So2-xx
❑ 33Gou-8
❑ 33GouCanV-8
❑ 33TatOrb-35
❑ 34BatR31-63
❑ 34ExhFou-9
❑ 36CubTeal-16
❑ 38ExhFou-1
❑ 39CubTeal-12
❑ 44CenFlo-12
❑ 75YanDyn1T-25
❑ 81ConTSN-32
❑ 83ConMar-11
❑ 85BigLeaC3-87
❑ 88ConAmeA-17
❑ 91ConTSN-199
❑ 93ConTSN-777
❑ 94ConTSN-1173
❑ 94ConTSNB-1173

Johnson, Roy Edward

❑ 82ExpPos-17
❑ 82WicAerTI-6
❑ 82WicAerTI-7
❑ 83Don-492
❑ 83WicAerDS-12
❑ 83WicAerDS-24
❑ 84ExpPos-14
❑ 84IndIndTI-7
❑ 84IndIndTI-15
❑ 85IndIndTI-5
❑ 86HunStaDJ-45
❑ 87TacTigP-15
❑ 88TacTigC-15
❑ 88TacTigP-621

Johnson, Russ

❑ 92LSUTigM-14
❑ 93BazTeaU-12
❑ 93LSUTigM-13
❑ 93TopTra-115T
❑ 94LSUTig-3
❑ 94LSUTigMP-3
❑ 94SigRooDPBSDP-5
❑ 94StaCluDP-15
❑ 94StaCluDPFDI-15
❑ 95JacGenTI-23
❑ 95SigRooDDS-DD3
❑ 95SigRooDDSS-DD3
❑ 95SigRooMOP-P8
❑ 95SigRooMOPS-P8
❑ 95Top-423
❑ 96Bow-294
❑ 96BowFoi-294
❑ 96DouAllB-49
❑ 96JacGenB-14
❑ 96TexLeaAB-10
❑ 97Bow-148
❑ 97Bow98ROY-ROY6
❑ 97BowBes-152
❑ 97BowBesAR-152
❑ 97BowBesR-152
❑ 97BowChr-152
❑ 97BowChr1RFR-ROY6
❑ 97BowChr98RF-ROY6
❑ 97BowChrI-152
❑ 97BowChrIR-152
❑ 97BowChrR-152
❑ 97BowInt-148
❑ 97Fle-516
❑ 97FleTif-516
❑ 97SpoIll-12
❑ 97SpoIllEE-12
❑ 97Top-487
❑ 97Ult-480
❑ 97UltGolME-480
❑ 97UltPlaME-480
❑ 98Bow-96
❑ 98BowChr-96
❑ 98BowChrGA-96
❑ 98BowChrGAR-96
❑ 98BowChrI-96
❑ 98BowChrIR-96
❑ 98BowChrR-96
❑ 98BowGolA-96
❑ 98BowInt-96
❑ 98Fle-179
❑ 98MetUni-42
❑ 98MetUniPMG-42
❑ 98NewOrlZM-11
❑ 98StaCluFDI-342
❑ 98StaCluI-342
❑ 98StaCluITW-W6
❑ 98StaCluOneK-342
❑ 98StaCluPP-342
❑ 98Top-262
❑ 98TopChr-262
❑ 98TopChrR-262
❑ 98TopDevR-262
❑ 98TopDia-262
❑ 98TopMiniC-262
❑ 98Ult-231
❑ 98UltGolM-231
❑ 98UltMas-231
❑ 98UltPlaM-231
❑ 99Pac-196
❑ 99Pac-196A
❑ 99PacOme-110
❑ 99PacOmeC-110
❑ 99PacOmeG-110
❑ 99PacOmePB-110
❑ 99PacPlaB-196
❑ 99PacPlaB-196A
❑ 99PacRed-196
❑ 99PacRed-196A

Johnson, Scott

❑ 81MiaOriT-21
❑ 87WatIndP-9
❑ 88KinIndS-12
❑ 89SouBenWSGS-6
❑ 90SouBenWSB-25
❑ 90SouBenWSGS-8
❑ 92SarWhiSCB-30
❑ 94ElmPioC-10
❑ 94ElmPioF-3467
❑ 95ButCopKtl-6

Johnson, Sean

❑ 88SalLakCTTI-30

Johnson, Silas

❑ 30SchR33-34
❑ 33DouDisP-24
❑ 34DiaMatCSB-96
❑ 40PhiTeal-8
❑ 41PhiTeal-9
❑ 43PhiTeal-11
❑ 47TipTop-80
❑ 77TCMTheWY-57
❑ 85BigLeaC3-72

Johnson, Solomon

❑ 98BriWhiSQ-15

Johnson, Stan

❑ 61UniOil-SD5
❑ 63SeaPop-5
❑ 64SeaPop-8
❑ 77FriOneYW-63

Johnson, Steve

❑ 83BeaGolGT-3
❑ 84BeaGolGT-20
❑ 86WatIndP-13
❑ 92SavCarC-9
❑ 92SavCarF-659
❑ 93SprCarC-14
❑ 93SprCarF-1845
❑ 94St.PetCC-12
❑ 94St.PetCF-2579

Johnson, Swede (John Clifford)

❑ 77TCMTheWY-85

Johnson, Sylvester

❑ 20Zee-44
❑ 21Nei-24
❑ 21Zee-50
❑ 22E120-55
❑ 22W572-50
❑ 22W573-67
❑ 23MapCriV-13
❑ 31CarMet-17
❑ 34BatR31-54
❑ 34DiaMatCSB-97
❑ 35AlDemDCR3-107
❑ 39PlaBal-28
❑ 40PhiTeal-9
❑ 40PlaBal-99
❑ 41PhiTeal-10
❑ 43CenFlo-13
❑ 44CenFlo-13
❑ 45CenFlo-13
❑ 85BigLeaC3-88
❑ 92ConTSN-654
❑ 93ConTSN-901

Johnson, T.J. (Terence)

❑ 84LitFalMT-14
❑ 85LitFalMT-19

Johnson, Terry

❑ 83BurRanF-10
❑ 83BurRanT-6
❑ 83TulDriT-24
❑ 84TulDriTI-34
❑ 85TulDriTI-30

Johnson, Thomas

❑ 97PitMet-14

❑ 98CapCitBF5-28
❑ 98CapCitBM-28
Johnson, Tim
❑ 74OPC-554
❑ 74Top-554
❑ 75OPC-556
❑ 75Top-556
❑ 75TopMin-556
❑ 76BreA&P-6
❑ 76OPC-613
❑ 76Top-613
❑ 76VenLeaS-205
❑ 77Top-406
❑ 78BluJayP-11
❑ 78Top-542
❑ 79OPC-89
❑ 79Top-182
❑ 80OPC-155
❑ 80Top-297
❑ 86BreGreT-3
❑ 88GreFalDTI-26
❑ 89BakDodCLC-206
❑ 89CalLeaA-23
❑ 90CMC-75
❑ 90IndIndC-25
❑ 90IndIndP-307
❑ 90ProAAAF-590
❑ 93ExpPosN-13
❑ 94BreMilB-43
❑ 97IowCub-1
Johnson, Todd
❑ 90FreStaS-7
❑ 91FreStaBS-6
❑ 91TopTra-63T
❑ 91TopTraT-63T
❑ 92StaCluD-93
❑ 92TopDaiQTU-24
❑ 93BurIndC-13
❑ 93BurIndF-3301
❑ 94KinIndC-10
❑ 94KinIndF-2646
❑ 95KinIndTI-16
Johnson, Tom
❑ 81QuaCitCT-13
❑ 83MidCubT-23
❑ 86BurExpP-12
❑ 87Ft.MyeRP-19
❑ 88VirGenS-11
❑ 89BasCitRS-11
Johnson, Tom R.
❑ 75OPC-618
❑ 75TacTwiK-11
❑ 75Top-618
❑ 75TopMin-618
❑ 75TwiTeal-18
❑ 76OPC-448
❑ 76TacTwiDQ-9
❑ 76Top-448
❑ 77BurCheD-46
❑ 77Top-202
❑ 78Hos-59
❑ 78Kel-9
❑ 78Top-54
❑ 78TwiFriP-10
❑ 79OPC-77
❑ 79Top-162
❑ 80GleFalWSBT-3
❑ 80GleFalWSCT-28
Johnson, Tony
❑ 84IdaFalATI-14
Johnson, Tookie
❑ 90LSUTigA-5
❑ 90LSUTigP-16
❑ 91LSUTigP-5
Johnson, Travis
❑ 96ForWayWB-11
❑ 97ForMyeM-14
Johnson, Wade
❑ 85RedWinA-10
❑ 86RedWinA-19
Johnson, Wally (Wallace)
❑ 82ExpPos-18
❑ 82Fle-192
❑ 82WicAerTI-8
❑ 83Fle-285
❑ 85IndIndTI-21
❑ 86IndIndTI-19
❑ 87ExpPos-12
❑ 87Fle-321
❑ 87FleGlo-321
❑ 87Top-588
❑ 87TopTif-588
❑ 88ExpPos-16
❑ 88Fle-186
❑ 88FleGlo-186
❑ 88Sco-433
❑ 88ScoGlo-433
❑ 88StaLinE-8
❑ 88Top-228
❑ 88TopTif-228
❑ 89Don-484
❑ 89Fle-382
❑ 89FleGlo-382
❑ 89OPC-138
❑ 89PanSti-120
❑ 89Sco-196
❑ 89Top-138
❑ 89TopTif-138
❑ 89UppDec-124
❑ 90Don-570
❑ 90ExpPos-19
❑ 90Fle-351
❑ 90FleCan-351
❑ 90Lea-344
❑ 90OPC-318
❑ 90PubIntS-178
❑ 90Sco-479
❑ 90Top-318
❑ 90TopBig-46
❑ 90TopTif-318
❑ 95EugEmeTI-31
❑ 96MacBraB-27
❑ 97DurBulTI-3
Johnson, Walter P.
❑ 08AmeCarE91-80
❑ 08RosComP-81
❑ 09RamT20-60
❑ 09SenBarP-6
❑ 09SpoNewSM-40
❑ 09T206-172
❑ 09T206-173
❑ 10CouT21-155
❑ 10CouT21-293
❑ 10DarChoE-20
❑ 10DomDisP-60
❑ 10OrnOvaPP-7
❑ 10RedCroT-36
❑ 10RedCroT-124
❑ 10RedCroT-207
❑ 10SenWasT-2
❑ 10SepAnoP-16
❑ 10SweCapPP-60A
❑ 10SweCapPP-60B
❑ 11BasBatEU-25
❑ 11HelSta-72
❑ 11L1L-135
❑ 11MecDFT-44
❑ 11PinT-5-561
❑ 11PloCanE-37
❑ 11S74Sil-39
❑ 11S81LarS-110
❑ 11SpoLifM-125
❑ 11T205-82
❑ 11TurRedT-99
❑ 12HasTriFT-7
❑ 12HasTriFT-49
❑ 12SenNatPC-1
❑ 12T207-87
❑ 12VasSwe-3
❑ 13LawSemC-4
❑ 13NatGamW-23
❑ 13TomBarW-22
❑ 14B18B-41
❑ 14CraJacE-57
❑ 14FatPlaT-20
❑ 14TexTomE-24
❑ 14TexTomE-55
❑ 15CraJacE-57
❑ 15SpoNewM-90
❑ 15SpoNewP-5
❑ 15VicT21-15
❑ 16BF2FP-47
❑ 16SpoNewM-91
❑ 17ColE13-87
❑ 19W514-90
❑ 20NatCarE-50
❑ 20W516-8
❑ 20WalMaiW-23
❑ 21E121So1-48
❑ 21E121So8-43A
❑ 21E121So8-43B
❑ 21Exh-84
❑ 21Nei-47
❑ 21OxfConE-10
❑ 22AmeCarE122-32
❑ 22E120-110
❑ 22W572-51
❑ 22W573-68
❑ 22W575-64
❑ 22WilPatV-47
❑ 23MapCriV-30
❑ 23W501-17
❑ 23W503-23
❑ 23W515-38
❑ 23W551-5
❑ 23WilChoV-72
❑ 24MrsShePP-4
❑ 25Exh-125
❑ 25SenOakT-1
❑ 26Exh-125
❑ 26SpoComoA-23
❑ 27AmeCarE126-28
❑ 27Exh-62
❑ 27YorCarE-45
❑ 28W56PlaC-S2
❑ 31SenTealPW-16
❑ 34BabRutG-37
❑ 34ButPreR-36
❑ 36Halof FP-14
❑ 37KelPepS-BB9
❑ 39PC7AlbHoF-2
❑ 40PlaBal-120
❑ 47PM1StaP1-101
❑ 48ExhHoF-18
❑ 48SweSpoT-4
❑ 49LeaPre-4
❑ 50CalHOFW-43
❑ 51R42SmaS-54
❑ 51TopConMA-6
❑ 53ArtHaloFP-49
❑ 58SeaTeal-13
❑ 60ExhWriH-13
❑ 60Fle-6
❑ 60NuHi-40
❑ 60SenUniMC-8
❑ 61Fle-49
❑ 61GolPre-29
❑ 61NuSco-440
❑ 61Top-409
❑ 63BasMagM-42
❑ 63BazA-12
❑ 63GadFunC-39
❑ 63HalofFB-12
❑ 67TopVen-139
❑ 68LauWorS-22
❑ 68SpoMemAG-3
❑ 69Baz-2
❑ 69Baz-6
❑ 70FleWorS-22
❑ 71FleWorS-22
❑ 71FleWorS-23
❑ 72ClaCar-2
❑ 72FleFamF-8
❑ 72KelATG-1
❑ 72LauGreF-2
❑ 73BooProC-7
❑ 73OPC-476
❑ 73OPC-478
❑ 73SevTraC-35
❑ 73TCMAllG-9
❑ 73Top-476
❑ 73Top-478
❑ 74CapPub-91
❑ 74NewYorNTDiS-30
❑ 75McCCob-6
❑ 75SenTCM1-13
❑ 75SenTCM1-40
❑ 76GrePlaG-15
❑ 76OPC-349
❑ 76RowExh-10
❑ 76ShaPiz-3
❑ 76Top-349
❑ 77BobParHoF-62
❑ 77GalGloG-105
❑ 77GalGloG-144
❑ 77GalGloG-234
❑ 77ShaPiz-4
❑ 79Pew-6
❑ 79Top-417
❑ 79Top-418
❑ 80Lau300-3
❑ 80LauFamF-25
❑ 80PacLeg-45
❑ 80PerHaloFP-2
❑ 80SSPHOF-3
❑ 81ConTSN-37
❑ 81SpoHaloF-23
❑ 82DavHaloFB-13
❑ 82DiaCla-37
❑ 82TCMGreP-17
❑ 83DonHOFH-2
❑ 83TCMRut-4
❑ 84DonCha-37
❑ 84GalHaloFRL-3
❑ 84OCoandSI-81
❑ 85UltBasC-13
❑ 85Woo-21
❑ 86ConSer1-4
❑ 86TCM-14
❑ 86TCMSupS-8
❑ 87ConSer2-6
❑ 87HygAllG-27
❑ 87NesDreT-9
❑ 87SpoRea-36
❑ 89PacLegI-192
❑ 89SweBasG-3
❑ 90BasWit-62
❑ 90HOFStiB-28
❑ 90PerGreM-8
❑ 90SweBasG-75
❑ 91ConTSN-9
❑ 91ConTSN-258
❑ 91LinDri-45
❑ 91SweBasG-130
❑ 91USGamSBL-9C
❑ 91USGamSBL-9D
❑ 91USGamSBL-9H
❑ 91USGamSBL-9S
❑ 92ConTSN-353
❑ 92ConTSN-564
❑ 92ConTSNCI-7
❑ 92ConTSNGI-934G
❑ 92MegRut-9
❑ 92MegRut-73
❑ 92MegRut-95
❑ 92MegRut-126
❑ 93ActPacA-90
❑ 93ActPacA2-24G
❑ 93ConMasB-3
❑ 93ConMasC-3
❑ 93ConTSN-758
❑ 93ConTSN-804
❑ 93ConTSN-934
❑ 93ConTSNP-934
❑ 93CraJac-5
❑ 93Hoy-4
❑ 93LegFoi-6
❑ 93PacRyaFM-12
❑ 93UppDecAH-78
❑ 93UppDecAH-138
❑ 93UppDecAH-142
❑ 93UppDecAH-143
❑ 93UppDecTR-4
❑ 94ConTSN-1255
❑ 94ConTSNB-1255
❑ 94ConTSNCI-30
❑ 94TedWil-89
❑ 94TedWilLC-LC15
❑ 94UppDecAH-80
❑ 94UppDecAH-109
❑ 94UppDecAH-152
❑ 94UppDecAH1-80
❑ 94UppDecAH1-109
❑ 94UppDecAH1-152
❑ 94UppDecTAE-15
❑ 94UppDecTAELD-LD6
❑ 95UppDecSHoB-18
❑ 96BalHOF1C-2
❑ 96ColCho-502
❑ 96ColChoGS-502
❑ 96ColChoSS-502
❑ 99SP SigLC-W
❑ 99SpollIGotG-70
❑ 99SpollIGotGRB-10
❑ 99SpollIGotGRBG-10
❑ 99UppDecCL-4
❑ 99UppDecCL-129
❑ 99UppDecCLCC-4
❑ 99UppDecCLCC-129
❑ 99UppDecCLLC-RC
Johnson, Wayne
❑ 82WatIndF-25
❑ 82WatIndT-5
❑ 83BufBisT-2
❑ 85WatIndT-10
❑ 91MarPhiC-4
❑ 91MarPhiP-3467
❑ 92BatCliCB-9
❑ 92BatCliF-3277
Johnson, Wes
❑ 88MisStaB-15
Johnson, William PCL
❑ 12HomRunKE-65
❑ 12Zee-115
Johnson, Willy
❑ 75LynRanT-13
❑ 88SumBraP-417
❑ 89SumBraP-1092
❑ 90SumBraB-26
❑ 93MacBraC-30
❑ 93SouAtlLAGF-38
❑ 94SouAtlLAF-SAL44
❑ 95MacBraTI-13
❑ 96DurBulBIB-9
❑ 97DurBulTI-5
Johnson, Yoan
❑ 98MarPhiG-13
Johnston, Chris
❑ 83KnoBluJT-11
❑ 86StaoftFT-29
Johnston, Clint
❑ 99TeaBesR-42
❑ 99TeaBesRFS-17
❑ 99TeaBesRG-42
❑ 99TeaBesRS-42
Johnston, Craig
❑ 88MarPhiS-19
❑ 89KinMetS-14
❑ 91SydWavF-11
Johnston, Dan
❑ 88GenCubP-1644
❑ 90GreHorB-5
❑ 90GreHorP-2657
❑ 90GreHorS-11
❑ 91PriWilCC-6
❑ 91PriWilCP-1422
❑ 92ForLauYC-8
❑ 92ForLauYTI-19
❑ 92Ft.LauYF-2608
❑ 93UtiBluSF-3528
Johnston, Doc (Wheeler)
❑ 15CraJacE-150
❑ 22E120-83
❑ 23Zee-162
❑ 77Ind192T-10
Johnston, Doug
❑ 97HelBreB-15
❑ 98BelSnaM-3
❑ 98BesAutSS-27
❑ 98StoPorUG-2
❑ 99SP TopP-62
❑ 99SP TopPPE-62
Johnston, Ellis
❑ 16Zee-133
Johnston, Fred Ivy
❑ 90DodTar-388
Johnston, George
❑ 16Zee-134
Johnston, Greg
❑ 78PhoGiaC-11
❑ 79PhoGiaVNB-10
❑ 79Top-726
❑ 80Top-686
❑ 80VenLeaS-18
❑ 81Top-328
❑ 81TwiPos-16
❑ 91ParPatF-12
Johnston, James H.
❑ 09ObaT21-196
❑ 13Zee-113
❑ 15Zee-35
❑ 17ColE13-88
❑ 17HolBreD-54
❑ 20NatCarE-51
❑ 21E121So8-44
❑ 21Exh-83
❑ 22AmeCarE122-33
❑ 22E120-142
❑ 22W572-52
❑ 22W575-65
❑ 23W515-41
❑ 23WilChoV-73
❑ 25Exh-13
❑ 90DodTar-389
Johnston, Jody
❑ 82JacMetT-6
❑ 82LynMetT-22
Johnston, Joel
❑ 86SyrChiP-15
❑ 88EugEmeB-11
❑ 89BasCitRS-12
❑ 90MemChiB-17
❑ 90MemChiP-1010
❑ 91Bow-297
❑ 91LinDriAAA-337
❑ 91OmaRoyLD-337
❑ 91OmaRoyP-1031
❑ 92Bow-199
❑ 92DonRoo-60
❑ 92Fle-673
❑ 92OPC-328
❑ 92Pin-259
❑ 92PinRoo-10
❑ 92ProFS7-73
❑ 92RoyPol-13
❑ 92Sco-764
❑ 92ScoRoo-15
❑ 92StaClu-345
❑ 92Top-328
❑ 92TopDeb91-91
❑ 92TopGol-328
❑ 92TopGolW-328
❑ 92TopMic-328
❑ 93BufBisF-512
❑ 93Don-791
❑ 93SelRoo-137T
❑ 94Don-246
❑ 94Fle-610
❑ 94Sco-308
❑ 94ScoGolR-308
❑ 94Top-557
❑ 94TopGol-557
❑ 94TopSpa-557
❑ 94TriPla-184
Johnston, John
❑ 16FleBreD-47
Johnston, Len
❑ 77SerSta-12
❑ 92BluOriC-24
❑ 93BluOriC-25
❑ 94BluOriC-25
❑ 94BluOriF-3579
❑ 98BluOriQ-2
Johnston, Mark
❑ 79WesHavYT-1
❑ 82ElPasDT-10
❑ 83BelBreFr-10
❑ 94IowCubF-1292
Johnston, Rex
❑ 64PirKDK-14
❑ 77FriOneYW-59
Johnston, Richard
❑ 87BucN28-8
❑ 87OldJudN-264
❑ 88GandBCGCE-21
❑ 88WG1CarG-4
❑ 89N526N7C-7
Johnston, Ron
❑ 93AusFut-18
Johnston, Rusty
❑ 77ShrCapT-9
Johnston, Ryan
❑ 88SavCarP-352
Johnston, Sean
❑ 92UtiBluSC-21
❑ 93MidLeaAGF-23
❑ 93SouBenWSC-13
❑ 93SouBenWSF-1426
❑ 94CarLeaAF-CAR9
❑ 94ClaGolF-156
❑ 94PriWilCC-11
❑ 94PriWilCF-1915
❑ 94SigRooDP-33
❑ 94SigRooDPS-33
❑ 95SPML-115
❑ 96BesAutS-44
❑ 96StLucMTI-8
❑ 97St.LucM-12
Johnston, Stan
❑ 86BakDodP-16
❑ 87BakDodP-14
❑ 88BakDodCLC-264
❑ 89AlbDukP-74
❑ 93TriAAAGF-14
Johnston, Tom
❑ 93WelPirC-9
❑ 93WelPirF-3366
❑ 94OgdRapF-3741
❑ 94OgdRapSP-3
Johnstone, Jay
❑ 66SeaPop-8
❑ 67CokCapDA-34
❑ 67Top-213
❑ 68Top-389
❑ 69AngJacitB-5
❑ 69MilBra-138
❑ 69OPC-59
❑ 69Top-59
❑ 70DayDaiNM-115
❑ 70MLBOffS-174
❑ 70OPC-485
❑ 70Top-485
❑ 70TopBoo-3
❑ 71OPC-292
❑ 71Top-292
❑ 72MilBra-170
❑ 72OPC-233
❑ 72Top-233
❑ 72WhiSoxTI1-8
❑ 75OPC-242
❑ 75PhiPhiP-18
❑ 75Top-242
❑ 75TopMin-242
❑ 76OPC-114

❑ 76PhiPhiP-13
❑ 76SSP-463
❑ 76Top-114
❑ 77BurCheD-166
❑ 77Kel-33
❑ 77OPC-226
❑ 77PepGloD-71
❑ 77Top-415
❑ 78SSP270-43
❑ 78Top-675
❑ 78YanPhoA-15
❑ 79OPC-287
❑ 79PadFamF-34
❑ 79Top-558
❑ 79YanBurK-5
❑ 80DodPol-21
❑ 80OPC-15
❑ 80Top-31
❑ 81Dod-15
❑ 81DodPol-21
❑ 81Don-300
❑ 81Fle-128
❑ 81OPC-372
❑ 81Top-372
❑ 82CubRedL-21
❑ 82DodPol-21
❑ 82Don-262
❑ 82Fle-10
❑ 82Top-774
❑ 82TopTra-52T
❑ 83CubThoAV-21
❑ 83Don-561
❑ 83Fle-499
❑ 83OPC-152
❑ 83Top-152
❑ 83TopSti-220
❑ 84CubSev-21
❑ 84Don-540
❑ 84Fle-495
❑ 84Nes792-249
❑ 84Top-249
❑ 84TopSti-50
❑ 84TopTif-249
❑ 85DodCokP-16
❑ 86Top-496
❑ 86TopTif-496
❑ 90DodTar-390
❑ 92YanWIZ7-83

Johnstone, John

❑ 89PitMetS-13
❑ 89Sta-169
❑ 90FloStaLAS-7
❑ 90St.LucMS-12
❑ 91Cla/Bes-64
❑ 91LinDriAA-635
❑ 91MetColP-37
❑ 91WilBilLD-635
❑ 91WilBilP-287
❑ 92BinMetF-510
❑ 92BinMetS-61
❑ 92SkyAA F-26
❑ 92UppDecML-310
❑ 93Don-784
❑ 93EdmTraF-1131
❑ 93StaClu-734
❑ 93StaCluFDI-734
❑ 93StaCluMOP-734
❑ 93Top-454
❑ 93TopGol-454
❑ 93TopInaM-454
❑ 93TopInaR-454
❑ 93TopMic-454
❑ 94EdmTraF-2871
❑ 95Sco-311
❑ 95ScoGolR-311
❑ 95ScoPlaTS-311
❑ 97PhoFirTI-12
❑ 98GiaMot-26
❑ 98PacOnl-664
❑ 98PacOnlR-664
❑ 98PacOnlWC-664
❑ 99Fle-540
❑ 99FleSta9-540
❑ 99FleWarT-540

Joiner, Dave

❑ 87LitFalMP-2400
❑ 88ColMetGS-16
❑ 89ColMetB-8
❑ 89ColMetGS-13

Joiner, Pop (Roy)

❑ 30Zee-86
❑ 32Zee-58
❑ 33Zee-58
❑ 34DiaMatCSB-98
❑ 35DiaMatCS3T1-80
❑ 40PlaBal-211

Jok, Stan

❑ 52Par-93
❑ 54Top-196
❑ 55Bow-251
❑ 94TopArc1-196
❑ 94TopArc1G-196

Jolley, Mike

❑ 91SavCarC-6
❑ 91SavCarP-1647
❑ 92SavCarC-2
❑ 92SavCarF-660

Jolley, Smead

❑ 28ExhPCL-13
❑ 28PorandAR-C3
❑ 28PorandAR-D3
❑ 28Zee-133
❑ 29Zee-134
❑ 30ChiEveAP-16
❑ 30WhiSoxTI-13
❑ 31Exh-20
❑ 32OrbPinNP-25
❑ 32OrbPinUP-36
❑ 33TatOrb-36
❑ 33Zee-5
❑ 36WorWidGV-98
❑ 79DiaGre-136
❑ 79RedSoxEF-19
❑ 85BigLeaC3-39
❑ 87ConSer2-23
❑ 93ConTSN-858

Jolly, Dave

❑ 53BraJohC-8
❑ 53BraSpiaS3-14
❑ 54BraJohC-17
❑ 54BraSpiaSP-11
❑ 54Top-188
❑ 55Bow-71
❑ 55BraGolS-9
❑ 55BraJohC-16
❑ 55BraSpiaSD-10
❑ 55Top-35
❑ 55TopDouH-95
❑ 55TopTesS-6
❑ 57Top-389
❑ 58Top-183
❑ 62TigPosCF-10
❑ 80Bra195T-39
❑ 83Bra53F-16
❑ 94TopArc1-188
❑ 94TopArc1G-188

Jolly, James

❑ 23Zee-189
❑ 26Zee-141
❑ 27Zee-113

Jonas, John

❑ 90SalSpuCLC-144

Jonas, Pete

❑ 43CenFlo-14
❑ 47CenFlo-13
❑ 47SigOil-79

Jonckowski, Jeff

❑ 98FarRedHM-14

Jones, Aaron

❑ 98OneYanG-17
❑ 98TamYanM-14

Jones, Al

❑ 82AppFoxFr-7
❑ 83AppFoxFr-20
❑ 85Don-404
❑ 85Top-437
❑ 85TopTif-437
❑ 86BufBisP-13
❑ 86Top-227
❑ 86TopTif-227
❑ 87DenZepP-26

Jones, Allen

❑ 60MapLeaSF-10

Jones, Andruw

❑ 92SpoIlFK1-582
❑ 95Bes-50
❑ 95Bes-106
❑ 95Bes-AU2
❑ 95BesFra-F9
❑ 95Bow-23
❑ 95BowBes-B7
❑ 95BowBesR-B7
❑ 95MacBraTI-14
❑ 95MacBraUTI-3
❑ 95SPML-1
❑ 95SPML-15
❑ 95SPMLA-13
❑ 95SPMLDtS-DS1
❑ 96BesAutSA-34
❑ 96BesPlaotYAJ-1
❑ 96BesPlaotYAJ-2
❑ 96BesPlaotYAJ-3
❑ 96BesPlaotYAJ-4
❑ 96BesPlaotYAJ-5
❑ 96BesPlaotYAJA-2
❑ 96BesPlaotYAJA-3
❑ 96BesPlaotYAJA-4
❑ 96BesPlaotYAJA-5
❑ 96Bow-192
❑ 96BowBes-91
❑ 96BowBesAR-91
❑ 96BowBesC-4
❑ 96BowBesCAR-4
❑ 96BowBesCR-4
❑ 96BowBesMI-6
❑ 96BowBesMIAR-6
❑ 96BowBesMIR-6
❑ 96BowBesP-BBP9
❑ 96BowBesPAR-BBP9
❑ 96BowBesPR-BBP9
❑ 96BowBesR-91
❑ 96BowFoi-192
❑ 96BowMinLP-1
❑ 96CarLeaA1B-18
❑ 96CarLeaA2B-18
❑ 96CarLeaAIB-B5
❑ 96CarLeaAIB-B6
❑ 96CarLeaAIB-B7
❑ 96Cir-101
❑ 96CirRav-101
❑ 96DurBulBlB-1
❑ 96DurBulBrB-2
❑ 96Exc-129
❑ 96ExcAll-7
❑ 96ExcSeaC-6
❑ 96GreBraB-17
❑ 96GreBraTI-6
❑ 96LeaLimR-8
❑ 96LeaSig-101
❑ 96LeaSigEA-93
❑ 96LeaSigEACM-13
❑ 96LeaSigPPG-101
❑ 96LeaSigPPP-101
❑ 96RicBraRC-23
❑ 96RicBraUB-1
❑ 96RicBraUB-14
❑ 96RicBraUB-15
❑ 96Top-435
❑ 97BesLimA-AJ
❑ 97Bow-107
❑ 97BowBes-186
❑ 97BowBesAR-186
❑ 97BowBesBC-BC14
❑ 97BowBesBCAR-BC14
❑ 97BowBesBCR-BC14
❑ 97BowBesJ-186
❑ 97BowBesJAR-186
❑ 97BowBesJR-186
❑ 97BowBesMI-MI5
❑ 97BowBesMIAR-MI5
❑ 97BowBesMIARI-MI5
❑ 97BowBesMII-MI5
❑ 97BowBesMIR-MI5
❑ 97BowBesMIRI-MI5
❑ 97BowBesP-15
❑ 97BowBesPAR-15
❑ 97BowBesPR-15
❑ 97BowBesR-186
❑ 97BowCerBlaIA-CA42
❑ 97BowCerBluIA-CA42
❑ 97BowCerGolIA-CA42
❑ 97BowChr-127
❑ 97BowChrI-127
❑ 97BowChrIR-127
❑ 97BowChrR-127
❑ 97BowChrSHR-SHR13
❑ 97BowChrSHRR-SHR13
❑ 97BowInt-107
❑ 97BowIntB-BBI13
❑ 97BowIntBAR-BBI13
❑ 97BowIntBR-BBI13
❑ 97BowScoHR-13
❑ 97BraSco-15
❑ 97BraScoPl-15
❑ 97BraScoPr-15
❑ 97Cir-329
❑ 97Cir-394
❑ 97CirBos-9
❑ 97CirFasT-4
❑ 97CirRav-329
❑ 97CirRav-394
❑ 97CirSupB-9
❑ 97ColCho-1
❑ 97ColCho-325
❑ 97ColChoCtG-3A
❑ 97ColChoCtG-3B
❑ 97ColChoCtG-3C
❑ 97ColChoCtGE-CG3
❑ 97ColChoCtGIW-CG3
❑ 97ColChoNF-NF18
❑ 97ColChoS-2
❑ 97ColChoSR-13
❑ 97ColChoT-AB1
❑ 97ColChoTBS-3
❑ 97ColChoTBSWH-3
❑ 97ColChoTotT-T1
❑ 97DenHol-15
❑ 97Don-358
❑ 97DonEli-10
❑ 97DonEliGS-10
❑ 97DonEliPtT-5
❑ 97DonEliPtT-6
❑ 97DonEliPtTA-5
❑ 97DonEliPtTA-6
❑ 97DonEliTotC-2
❑ 97DonEliTotCDC-2
❑ 97DonFraFea-1
❑ 97DonGolPP-358
❑ 97DonLim-94
❑ 97DonLim-128
❑ 97DonLimE-94
❑ 97DonLimE-128
❑ 97DonLimENG-128
❑ 97DonLimFotG-51
❑ 97DonPowA-6
❑ 97DonPowADC-6
❑ 97DonPre-143
❑ 97DonPre-179
❑ 97DonPreCttC-143
❑ 97DonPreCttC-179
❑ 97DonPrePM-23
❑ 97DonPreS-18
❑ 97DonPreSS-18
❑ 97DonPreTB-9
❑ 97DonPreTBG-9
❑ 97DonPreTF-9
❑ 97DonPreTP-9
❑ 97DonPreTPG-9
❑ 97DonPreXP-8B
❑ 97DonRatR-20
❑ 97DonRooDK-1
❑ 97DonRooDKC-1
❑ 97DonSig-70
❑ 97DonSigAC-65
❑ 97DonSigAM-65
❑ 97DonSigPPP-70
❑ 97DonSilPP-358
❑ 97DonTea-28
❑ 97DonTeaSPE-28
❑ 97DonVxP1-38
❑ 97E-X2-53
❑ 97E-X2Cred-53
❑ 97E-X2EssCre-53
❑ 97E-X2SD2000-2
❑ 97Fin-100
❑ 97Fin-162
❑ 97Fin-306
❑ 97FinEmb-162
❑ 97FinEmb-306
❑ 97FinEmbR-162
❑ 97FinEmbR-306
❑ 97FinRef-100
❑ 97FinRef-162
❑ 97FinRef-306
❑ 97FlaShoDC-8
❑ 97FlaShoLC-1
❑ 97FlaShoLeg0-1
❑ 97FlaShoLeg1-1
❑ 97FlaShoM-A1
❑ 97FlaShoM-B1
❑ 97FlaShoM-C1
❑ 97FlaShoR0-1
❑ 97FlaShoR1-1
❑ 97FlaShoR2-1
❑ 97FlaShoWotF-2
❑ 97Fle-257
❑ 97Fle-493
❑ 97Fle-704
❑ 97Fle-NNO
❑ 97FleAndJA-1
❑ 97FleHea-9
❑ 97FleMilDM-26
❑ 97FleMilDMR-26
❑ 97FleNewH-9
❑ 97FleRooS-15
❑ 97FleSoaS-6
❑ 97FleSoaSG-6
❑ 97FleTif-257
❑ 97FleTif-493
❑ 97FleTif-704
❑ 97HigMinM-55
❑ 97Lea-168
❑ 97Lea-199
❑ 97Lea-349
❑ 97LeaDrefS-17
❑ 97LeaFraM-168
❑ 97LeaFraM-199
❑ 97LeaFraM-349
❑ 97LeaFraMDC-168
❑ 97LeaFraMDC-199
❑ 97LeaFraMDC-349
❑ 97LeaGet-10
❑ 97LeaGolS-4
❑ 97LeaWarT-4
❑ 97MetUni-30
❑ 97MetUniMfG-6
❑ 97MetUniML-5
❑ 97NewPin-175
❑ 97NewPinAP-175
❑ 97NewPinIE-2
❑ 97NewPinMC-175
❑ 97NewPinPP-175
❑ 97NewPinPP-I2A
❑ 97NewPinPP-AJ1
❑ 97NewPinPP-AJ2
❑ 97NewPinPP-AJ3
❑ 97NewPinPP-AJ4
❑ 97NewPinPP-AJ5
❑ 97NewPinPP-AJ6
❑ 97NewPinS-AJ1
❑ 97NewPinS-AJ2
❑ 97NewPinS-AJ3
❑ 97NewPinS-AJ4
❑ 97NewPinS-AJ5
❑ 97NewPinS-AJ6
❑ 97Pac-234
❑ 97PacCar-21
❑ 97PacCarM-21
❑ 97PacCerCGT-14
❑ 97PacFirD-14
❑ 97PacGolCD-21
❑ 97PacLatotML-23
❑ 97PacLigB-234
❑ 97PacPri-78
❑ 97PacPriGA-GA17
❑ 97PacPriLB-78
❑ 97PacPriP-78
❑ 97PacPriSH-SH8A
❑ 97PacPriSL-SL8C
❑ 97PacSil-234
❑ 97PacTriCD-12
❑ 97Pin-163
❑ 97Pin-198
❑ 97PinArtP-PP163
❑ 97PinArtP-PP198
❑ 97PinCer-106
❑ 97PinCer-150
❑ 97PinCerCMGT-14
❑ 97PinCerCT-14
❑ 97PinCerMBla-106
❑ 97PinCerMBla-150
❑ 97PinCerMBlu-106
❑ 97PinCerMBlu-150
❑ 97PinCerMG-106
❑ 97PinCerMG-150
❑ 97PinCerMR-106
❑ 97PinCerMR-150
❑ 97PinCerR-106
❑ 97PinCerR-150
❑ 97PinEpixGO-E20
❑ 97PinEpixPE-E20
❑ 97PinFan-FF12
❑ 97PinIns-128
❑ 97PinInsC-18
❑ 97PinInsCE-128
❑ 97PinInsDD-6
❑ 97PinInsDE-128
❑ 97PinMin-10
❑ 97PinMinB-10
❑ 97PinMinCB-10
❑ 97PinMinCG-10
❑ 97PinMinCGR-10
❑ 97PinMinCN-10
❑ 97PinMinCSS-10
❑ 97PinMinG-10
❑ 97PinMinS-10
❑ 97PinMusC-163
❑ 97PinMusC-198
❑ 97PinPrePla-163
❑ 97PinPrePla-198
❑ 97PinTotCPB-106
❑ 97PinTotCPB-150
❑ 97PinTotCPG-106
❑ 97PinTotCPG-150
❑ 97PinTotCPR-106
❑ 97PinTotCPR-150
❑ 97PinX-P-116
❑ 97PinX-PF&A-8
❑ 97PinX-PMoS-116
❑ 97PinX-PMP-3
❑ 97PinX-PMW-3
❑ 97PinX-PMWG-3
❑ 97PinX-PMWS-3
❑ 97PinX-PreMPS-3
❑ 97PinX-PSfF-30
❑ 97PinX-PSfF-NNO
❑ 97PinX-PSfFU-30
❑ 97PreCon-27
❑ 97PreCon-28
❑ 97Sco-310
❑ 97Sco-500
❑ 97ScoAllF-12
❑ 97ScoAndJBPS-1
❑ 97ScoArtPWB-310
❑ 97ScoArtPWB-500
❑ 97ScoBla-7
❑ 97ScoHeaotO-20
❑ 97ScoPreS-310
❑ 97ScoResC-500
❑ 97ScoShoS-310
❑ 97ScoShoS-500
❑ 97ScoShoSAP-310
❑ 97ScoShoSAP-500
❑ 97ScoStaaD-1
❑ 97Sel-101
❑ 97SelArtP-101
❑ 97SelCom-101
❑ 97SelRegG-101
❑ 97SelRooA-3
❑ 97SelRooR-1
❑ 97SelToootT-1
❑ 97SelToootTMB-1
❑ 97SP-1
❑ 97SPGamF-GF3
❑ 97SPInsI-25
❑ 97SpoIll-13
❑ 97SpoIllEE-13
❑ 97SPSpeF-45
❑ 97SPSpxF-10
❑ 97SPSPxFA-10
❑ 97SPx-4
❑ 97SPxBoufG-1
❑ 97SPxBoufGSS-3
❑ 97SPxBro-4
❑ 97SPxCorotG-5
❑ 97SPxGol-4
❑ 97SPxGraF-4
❑ 97SPxSil-4
❑ 97SPxSte-4
❑ 97StaClu-181
❑ 97StaClu-255
❑ 97StaCluI-I21
❑ 97StaCluM-M21
❑ 97StaCluMat-255
❑ 97StaCluMOP-181
❑ 97StaCluMOP-255
❑ 97StaCluMOP-I21
❑ 97StaCluMOP-M21
❑ 97Stu-149
❑ 97StuMasS-9
❑ 97StuMasS8-9
❑ 97StuPor8-4
❑ 97StuPrePG-149
❑ 97StuPrePS-149
❑ 97Top-455
❑ 97TopAwel-AI8
❑ 97TopChr-160
❑ 97TopChrDD-DD1
❑ 97TopChrDDR-DD1
❑ 97TopChrR-160
❑ 97TopGal-146
❑ 97TopGalP-PP1
❑ 97TopGalPPI-146
❑ 97TopMem05-53
❑ 97TopScr-11
❑ 97TopScrT-11
❑ 97TopStaFAS-FAS2
❑ 97UD3-41
❑ 97UD3GenNex-GN5
❑ 97Ult-153
❑ 97Ult-NNO
❑ 97UltChe-B1
❑ 97UltGolME-153
❑ 97UltGolP-1
❑ 97UltHitM-1
❑ 97UltPlaME-153
❑ 97UltStaR-1
❑ 97UltTop3-1
❑ 97UltTop3GM-1
❑ 97UppDec-196
❑ 97UppDec-240
❑ 97UppDec-262
❑ 97UppDec-324
❑ 97UppDec-415
❑ 97UppDecBCP-BC1
❑ 97UppDecHC-HC2

❑ 97UppDecHTH-HT5
❑ 97UppDecLDC-LD20
❑ 97UppDecMM-A1
❑ 97UppDecP-1
❑ 97UppDecPE-1
❑ 97UppDecTTS-TS14
❑ 97Zen-43
❑ 97Zen Z-Z-8
❑ 97Zen8x10-21
❑ 97Zen8x1D-21
❑ 97ZenV-2-2
❑ 98Bow-262
❑ 98BowBes-78
❑ 98BowBesAR-78
❑ 98BowBesR-78
❑ 98BowChr-262
❑ 98BowChrGA-262
❑ 98BowChrGAR-262
❑ 98BowChrI-262
❑ 98BowChrIR-262
❑ 98BowChrR-262
❑ 98BowChrR-42
❑ 98BowChrRR-42
❑ 98BowGolA-262
❑ 98BowInt-262
❑ 98BowMinLM-MVP7
❑ 98BraSco-1
❑ 98BraScoP-1
❑ 98CirThu-273
❑ 98CirThuRav-273
❑ 98CirThuSupRav-273
❑ 98ColCho-35
❑ 98ColCho-271
❑ 98ColChoCtG-CG14A
❑ 98ColChoCtG-CG14B
❑ 98ColChoCtG-CG14C
❑ 98ColChoCtGExch-CG14
❑ 98ColChoCtGIW-CG14
❑ 98ColChoGJ5-271
❑ 98ColChoRJ-35
❑ 98ColChoS'-1
❑ 98ColChoSQDouble-8
❑ 98ColChoSQHR-8
❑ 98ColChoSQSingle-8
❑ 98ColChoSQTriple-8
❑ 98CroRoy-12
❑ 98Don-104
❑ 98Don-402
❑ 98DonCol-104
❑ 98DonColE-410
❑ 98DonColE-527
❑ 98DonColL-373
❑ 98DonColP-563
❑ 98DonColP-730
❑ 98DonColS-104
❑ 98DonCruG-54
❑ 98DonCruP-54
❑ 98DonCruR-54
❑ 98DonDiaK-16
❑ 98DonDiaKC-16
❑ 98DonDom-6
❑ 98DonEli-10
❑ 98DonEli-127
❑ 98DonEliA-10
❑ 98DonEliA-127
❑ 98DonEliC-17
❑ 98DonEliI-2
❑ 98DonEliMC-17
❑ 98DonEliS-10
❑ 98DonEliS-127
❑ 98DonFANT-10
❑ 98DonFANTDC-10
❑ 98DonGolPP-104
❑ 98DonGolPP-402
❑ 98DonPre-13
❑ 98DonPre-180
❑ 98DonPreGB-15
❑ 98DonPreGES-23
❑ 98DonPreGoB-15
❑ 98DonPreGX-23
❑ 98DonPreGXDC-23
❑ 98DonPrePM-13
❑ 98DonPreSeat-13
❑ 98DonPreSeat-180
❑ 98DonPreTP-15
❑ 98DonPreTPD-8
❑ 98DonPreTPG-15
❑ 98DonPreTPS-15
❑ 98DonPreTW-13
❑ 98DonPriCD-104
❑ 98DonPriCE-410
❑ 98DonPriCE-527
❑ 98DonPriCL-373
❑ 98DonPriCP-563
❑ 98DonPriCP-730
❑ 98DonSig-25
❑ 98DonSigP-25
❑ 98DonSilPP-104
❑ 98DonSilPP-402
❑ 98DonSonM9-7
❑ 98E-X2-18
❑ 98E-X2Cheap-20
❑ 98E-X2ECFut-18
❑ 98E-X2ECNow-18
❑ 98Fin-2
❑ 98FinCen-C1
❑ 98FinCenR-C1
❑ 98FinMysF1-M13
❑ 98FinMysF1-M16
❑ 98FinMysF1-M18
❑ 98FinMysF1-M20
❑ 98FinMysFR-M13
❑ 98FinMysFR-M16
❑ 98FinMysFR-M18
❑ 98FinMysFR-M20
❑ 98FinNo--2
❑ 98FinNo-R-2
❑ 98FinRef-2
❑ 98FlaShoLeg0-25
❑ 98FlaShoLeg1-25
❑ 98FlaShoLeg2-25
❑ 98FlaShoLeg3-25
❑ 98FlaShoLegM-25
❑ 98FlaShoR0-25
❑ 98FlaShoR1-25
❑ 98FlaShoR2-25
❑ 98FlaShoR3-25
❑ 98Fle-271
❑ 98Fle-330
❑ 98Fle-344
❑ 98FleRooS-13
❑ 98FleVin'-3
❑ 98FleVin'C-3
❑ 98Lea-174
❑ 98LeaCruG-54
❑ 98LeaCruP-54
❑ 98LeaCruR-54
❑ 98LeaFraDA-174
❑ 98LeaFraF-174
❑ 98LeaFraM-174
❑ 98LeaFraM-174
❑ 98LeaFraMDC-174
❑ 98LeaFraMDC-174
❑ 98LeaFraMZ2-174
❑ 98LeaRS-38
❑ 98LeaRS-156
❑ 98LeaRSHRDerby-12
❑ 98LeaRSLHolo-38
❑ 98LeaRSLHolo-156
❑ 98LeaRSLMVP-17
❑ 98LeaRSLMVPPE-17
❑ 98LeaRSLong-38
❑ 98LeaRSLong-156
❑ 98LeaRSTicMas-11
❑ 98LeaRSTicMasDC-11
❑ 98LeaRTrue-38
❑ 98LeaRTrue-156
❑ 98LeaStaRep-6
❑ 98MetUni-150
❑ 98MetUniAT-7
❑ 98MetUniDH-3
❑ 98MetUniPMG-150
❑ 98MetUniPP-5
❑ 98MetUniT-7
❑ 98MetUniUL-7
❑ 98Pac-234
❑ 98PacAur-104
❑ 98PacInv-76
❑ 98PacInvPBlue-76
❑ 98PacInvSilv-76
❑ 98PacInvTeam-2
❑ 98PacLatotML-1
❑ 98PacOme-19
❑ 98PacOmeR-19
❑ 98PacOnl-62
❑ 98PacOnlR-62
❑ 98PacOnlWC-62
❑ 98PacPar-129
❑ 98PacParC-129
❑ 98PacParG-129
❑ 98PacParHS-129
❑ 98PacParPB-129
❑ 98PacParR-129
❑ 98PacPlaB-234
❑ 98PacRedT-234
❑ 98PacSil-234
❑ 98Pin-37
❑ 98PinArtP-PP36
❑ 98PinEpixGE-E20
❑ 98PinEpixGP-E20
❑ 98PinEpixME-E20
❑ 98PinEpixMO-E20
❑ 98PinEpixMP-E20
❑ 98PinEpixPO-E20
❑ 98PinEpixPP-E20
❑ 98PinIns-25
❑ 98PinInsBtN-8
❑ 98PinInsC-10
❑ 98PinInsCE-25
❑ 98PinInsCG-10
❑ 98PinInsDE-25
❑ 98PinInsSG-2AB
❑ 98PinInsSG-2CD
❑ 98PinInsSG-3AB
❑ 98PinInsSG-3CD
❑ 98PinInsSG-9AB
❑ 98PinInsSG-9CD
❑ 98PinInsSG-25AB
❑ 98PinInsSG-25CD
❑ 98PinInsSGS-2AB
❑ 98PinInsSGS-2CD
❑ 98PinInsSGS-3AB
❑ 98PinInsSGS-3CD
❑ 98PinInsSGS-9AB
❑ 98PinInsSGS-9CD
❑ 98PinInsSGS-25AB
❑ 98PinInsSGS-25CD
❑ 98PinMinB-29
❑ 98PinMinCB-29
❑ 98PinMinCBAP-29
❑ 98PinMinCGP-29
❑ 98PinMinCGPAP-29
❑ 98PinMinCN-29
❑ 98PinMinCNAP-29
❑ 98PinMinCSGR-29
❑ 98PinMinDC-29
❑ 98PinMinG-29
❑ 98PinMinMCSS-29
❑ 98PinMinS-29
❑ 98PinMusC-PP36
❑ 98PinPer-13
❑ 98PinPerBB-20
❑ 98PinPerBBSamp-20
❑ 98PinPerBBSO-20
❑ 98PinPerLP-12
❑ 98PinPerPP-13
❑ 98PinPerSftF-37
❑ 98PinPlu-148
❑ 98PinPluAE-20
❑ 98PinPluAEE-20
❑ 98PinPluAEP-20
❑ 98PinPluAP-PP49
❑ 98PinPluGAP-PP49
❑ 98PinPluLM-15
❑ 98PinPluMAP-PP49
❑ 98PinPluTP-9
❑ 98PinPluTPG-9
❑ 98PinPluTPM-9
❑ 98PinPowPJ-18
❑ 98PinPowPJS-18
❑ 98PinPreP-37
❑ 98PinPreP-E20
❑ 98PinSna-AB9
❑ 98Revo-12
❑ 98RevoSS-12
❑ 98Sco-1
❑ 98ScoAllST-16
❑ 98ScoAllSTGJAU-1
❑ 98ScoAndJIC-1
❑ 98ScoComP-8A
❑ 98ScoComP-8B
❑ 98ScoComP-8C
❑ 98ScoComPG-8A
❑ 98ScoComPG-8B
❑ 98ScoComPG-8C
❑ 98ScoEpix-E20
❑ 98ScoFirP-9
❑ 98ScoRT-18
❑ 98ScoRT-266
❑ 98ScoRTSS-PP18
❑ 98ScoRTSS-PP159
❑ 98ScoRTSSAP-PP18
❑ 98ScoRTSSAP-PP159
❑ 98ScoRTSSAP1-PP18
❑ 98ScoRTSSAP1-PP159
❑ 98ScoRTStarGaz-13
❑ 98ScoSS-PP1
❑ 98ScoSSAP-PP1
❑ 98SkyDugA-144
❑ 98SkyDugAIA-144
❑ 98SkyDugAS-SH5
❑ 98SP Aut-46
❑ 98SP Aut-SD17
❑ 98SP AutC-AJ
❑ 98SP AutSD-SD17
❑ 98SP AutSDT-SD17
❑ 98SpoIll-67
❑ 98SpoIllEE-67
❑ 98SpoIllFE-67
❑ 98SpoIllTaN-96
❑ 98SpoIllTaNEE-96
❑ 98SpoIllTaNGS-4
❑ 98SpoIllWSF-57
❑ 98SpoIllWSFEE-57
❑ 98SpoIllWSFFE-57
❑ 98SPxFin-25
❑ 98SPxFin-232
❑ 98SPxFin-249
❑ 98SPxFinR-25
❑ 98SPxFinR-232
❑ 98SPxFinR-249
❑ 98SPxFinS-25
❑ 98SPxFinS-232
❑ 98SPxFinS-249
❑ 98StaCluFDI-258
❑ 98StaCluI-258
❑ 98StaCluOneK-258
❑ 98StaCluPP-258
❑ 98StaCluTIII-T1B
❑ 98StaCluTLme-T1B
❑ 98StaCluTLmo-T1B
❑ 98Stu-201
❑ 98StuFF-13
❑ 98StuFFDC-13
❑ 98StuGPP-201
❑ 98StuMast-8
❑ 98StuPor8x10-24
❑ 98StuPor8x10GP-24
❑ 98StuSony99-7
❑ 98StuSPP-201
❑ 98Top-334
❑ 98TopBabB-BB9
❑ 98TopChr-334
❑ 98TopChrBB-BB9
❑ 98TopChrBBR-BB9
❑ 98TopChrR-334
❑ 98TopDevR-334
❑ 98TopDia-334
❑ 98TopFocP-FP15
❑ 98TopGal-1
❑ 98TopGalGP-1
❑ 98TopGalOPP-1
❑ 98TopGalPPI-1
❑ 98TopGalPPIA-1
❑ 98TopGolLabC1-17
❑ 98TopGolLabC1B-17
❑ 98TopGolLabC1One-17
❑ 98TopGolLabC1R-17
❑ 98TopGolLabC2-17
❑ 98TopGolLabC2B-17
❑ 98TopGolLabC2One-17
❑ 98TopGolLabC2R-17
❑ 98TopGolLabC3-17
❑ 98TopGolLabC3B-17
❑ 98TopGolLabC3One-17
❑ 98TopGolLabC3R-17
❑ 98TopMiniC-334
❑ 98TopMysFB-M18
❑ 98TopMysFB-M18
❑ 98TopMysFBR-M18
❑ 98TopMysFBR-M18
❑ 98TopOpeD-161
❑ 98TopSta-108
❑ 98TopSta'S-20
❑ 98TopSta'SGH-20
❑ 98TopStaB-108
❑ 98TopStaG-108
❑ 98TopStaGR-108
❑ 98TopStaS-108
❑ 98TopStaSteG-20
❑ 98TopSup-33
❑ 98TopSup-33
❑ 98TopTek-26
❑ 98TopTekD-26
❑ 98UD3-25
❑ 98UD3-115
❑ 98UD3-205
❑ 98UD3DieCut-25
❑ 98UD3DieCut-115
❑ 98UD3DieCut-205
❑ 98Ult-49
❑ 98Ult-482
❑ 98UltArtT-2
❑ 98UltBacttF-1
❑ 98UltDial-8
❑ 98UltDiaP-2
❑ 98UltDouT-3
❑ 98UltFalC-2
❑ 98UltGolM-49
❑ 98UltGolM-482
❑ 98UltKidG-1
❑ 98UltMas-49
❑ 98UltMas-482
❑ 98UltMilM-5
❑ 98UltNot-11
❑ 98UltPlaM-49
❑ 98UltPlaM-482
❑ 98UltPowP-2
❑ 98UltPriL-2
❑ 98UltTicS-14
❑ 98UltTop3-17
❑ 98UltWinN-2
❑ 98UppDec-151
❑ 98UppDec-305
❑ 98UppDec-627
❑ 98UppDecAC-AS5
❑ 98UppDecAG-AG29
❑ 98UppDecAGDC-AG29
❑ 98UppDecAPA2-AJ
❑ 98UppDecBCP-BC25
❑ 98UppDecCD-CD25
❑ 98UppDecNP-NP8
❑ 98UppDecR-7
❑ 98UppDecRBBop-BB22
❑ 98UppDecRGKoG-G16
❑ 98UppDecRTC-TC31
❑ 98UppDecSFPD-PZ12
❑ 98UppDecSFPZOB-PZ9
❑ 98UppDecTMT-22
❑ 98UppDecTMTG-22
❑ 98Zen-5
❑ 98Zen5 xx7-9
❑ 98Zen5x7GoldImp-9
❑ 98Zen5x7Imp-9
❑ 98ZenEpi-E20
❑ 98ZenRaitB-12
❑ 98ZenSampL-Z9
❑ 98ZenZ-G-5
❑ 98ZenZ-S-5
❑ 99199Fin-215
❑ 99Bow-32
❑ 99BowBes-72
❑ 99BowBesAR-72
❑ 99BowBesR-72
❑ 99BowChr-32
❑ 99BowChrG-32
❑ 99BowChrGR-32
❑ 99BowChrI-32
❑ 99BowChrIR-32
❑ 99BowChrR-32
❑ 99BowGol-32
❑ 99BowInt-32
❑ 99CroRoyB-11
❑ 99CroRoyL-11
❑ 99CroRoyOD-11
❑ 99E-X Cen-25
❑ 99E-X CenECFut-25
❑ 99E-X CenECNow-25
❑ 99FinCom-C7
❑ 99FinComDualR-C7
❑ 99FinDouF-DF2
❑ 99FinDouFDualR-DF2
❑ 99FinGolRef-215
❑ 99FinRef-215
❑ 99FlaShoLeg1-44
❑ 99FlaShoLeg2-44
❑ 99FlaShoLeg3-44
❑ 99FlaShoLegM1-44
❑ 99FlaShoLegM2-44
❑ 99FlaShoLegM3-44
❑ 99FlaShoR1-44
❑ 99FlaShoR2-44
❑ 99FlaShoR3-44
❑ 99Fle-31
❑ 99FleBri-86
❑ 99FleBri2G-86
❑ 99FleBriBlu-86
❑ 99FleBriGol-86
❑ 99FleMys-39
❑ 99FleMysD-6
❑ 99FleMysG-39
❑ 99FleMysM-39
❑ 99FleSta9-31
❑ 99FleVin'-31
❑ 99FleWarT-31
❑ 99MetUni-38
❑ 99MetUni-294
❑ 99MetUniBWTW-14
❑ 99MetUniGM-38
❑ 99MetUniGM-294
❑ 99MetUniPM-2
❑ 99MetUniPMG-38
❑ 99MetUniPMG-294
❑ 99Pac-31
❑ 99PacAur-16
❑ 99PacAurOD-16
❑ 99PacCroC-24
❑ 99PacCroC-25
❑ 99PacCroCPB-24
❑ 99PacInv-12
❑ 99PacInvOD-12
❑ 99PacInvPB-12
❑ 99PacOme-21
❑ 99PacOmeC-21
❑ 99PacOmeDM-4
❑ 99PacOmeG-21
❑ 99PacOmePB-21
❑ 99PacPar-23
❑ 99PacParC-23
❑ 99PacParG-23
❑ 99PacParHoloGold-23
❑ 99PacParHS-23
❑ 99PacParOD-23
❑ 99PacParPB-10
❑ 99PacParPB-23
❑ 99PacParRed-23
❑ 99PacPlaB-31
❑ 99PacPri-12
❑ 99PacPriHB-12
❑ 99PacPriHG-12
❑ 99PacPriHM-12
❑ 99PacPriHP-12
❑ 99PacPriRed-12
❑ 99PacPriS-36
❑ 99PacPriS206-36
❑ 99PacPriS206R-36
❑ 99PacPriSP-36
❑ 99PacPriSV-36
❑ 99PacRed-31
❑ 99Rev-11
❑ 99RevDiaL-5
❑ 99RevFouP-2
❑ 99RevPremDate-11
❑ 99RevRet-11
❑ 99RevShaSS-11
❑ 99RevTri-22
❑ 99RevTri-22
❑ 99SkyMolM-101
❑ 99SkyMolMF-1
❑ 99SkyMolMFS-1
❑ 99SkyMolMFT-1
❑ 99SkyMolMOA-12
❑ 99SkyMolMX-101
❑ 99SkyPre-149
❑ 99SkyPreR-149
❑ 99SkyThu-244
❑ 99SkyThuRant-244
❑ 99SkyThuRave-244
❑ 99SP Aut-9
❑ 99SP AutEF-E4
❑ 99SP AutHRC-HR30
❑ 99SP AutR-R4
❑ 99SP SigAuto-AJ
❑ 99SP SigAutoG-AJ
❑ 99SPAutHRCDC-HR30
❑ 99SpoIll-117
❑ 99SpoIllH-23
❑ 99SPSig-33
❑ 99SPx-18
❑ 99SPxFinR-18
❑ 99SPxFinS-18
❑ 99StaClu-190
❑ 99StaCluC-SCC7
❑ 99StaCluCR-SCC7
❑ 99StaCluFDI-190
❑ 99StaCluOoaK-190
❑ 99StaCluPP-190
❑ 99StaCluTI-T2A
❑ 99StaCluTL-T2A
❑ 99StaCluTL-T2A
❑ 99ThuSkySupR-244
❑ 99Top-195
❑ 99TopAut-A12
❑ 99TopBlaLC1-83
❑ 99TopBlaLC2-83
❑ 99TopBlaLC3-83
❑ 99TopChr-195
❑ 99TopChrNB-NB12
❑ 99TopChrNBR-NB12
❑ 99TopChrR-195
❑ 99TopGal-92
❑ 99TopGal-126
❑ 99TopGalPP-92
❑ 99TopGalPP-126
❑ 99TopGalPPI-92
❑ 99TopGalPPI-126
❑ 99TopGolL-83
❑ 99TopGolLC1-83
❑ 99TopGolLC2-83
❑ 99TopGolLOtO-83
❑ 99TopMVPP-195
❑ 99TopNewB-NB12
❑ 99TopOpeD-104
❑ 99TopRedLC1-83
❑ 99TopRedLC2-83
❑ 99TopRedLC3-83

❑ 99TopSta-29
❑ 99TopSta1Foil-29
❑ 99TopSta2Foil-29
❑ 99TopStaFoil-29
❑ 99TopStaOS-29
❑ 99TopStaTS-29
❑ 99UD Cho-53
❑ 99UD ChoPCR-53
❑ 99UD Ion-7
❑ 99UD Ion-63
❑ 99UD IonC-C24
❑ 99UD IonR-7
❑ 99UD IonR-63
❑ 99UDHolo-8
❑ 99UDHoloAUsome-8
❑ 99Ult-25
❑ 99UltGolM-25
❑ 99UltMas-25
❑ 99UltPlaM-25
❑ 99UltPromo-NNO
❑ 99UltRBIK-17
❑ 99UltTheBook-9
❑ 99UltThu-2
❑ 99UppDec-314
❑ 99UppDecBD-10
❑ 99UppDecBDD-10
❑ 99UppDecBDQ-10
❑ 99UppDecBDT-10
❑ 99UppDecCf7-35
❑ 99UppDecCf7-C26
❑ 99UppDecCf7Cf7P-C26
❑ 99UppDecCf7LL-L28
❑ 99UppDecCo7CE-35
❑ 99UppDecE-10
❑ 99UppDecEFXG-10
❑ 99UppDecEL1-314
❑ 99UppDecEL2-314
❑ 99UppDecF-F30
❑ 99UppDecFD-F30
❑ 99UppDecFQ-F30
❑ 99UppDecFT-F30
❑ 99UppDecM-16
❑ 99UppDecMGS-16
❑ 99UppDecMHFS-16
❑ 99UppDecMP-16
❑ 99UppDecMSS-16
❑ 99UppDecR-9
❑ 99UppDecRG-9
❑ 99UppDecRP-9
❑ 99UppDecTE-T4
❑ 99UppDecTED-T4
❑ 99UppDecTEQ-T4
❑ 99UppDecTET-T4
❑ 99UppDecWY-W14
❑ 99UppDecWYD-W14
❑ 99UppDecWYHR-W14
❑ 99UppDecWYT-W14
❑ 99Vic-36

Jones, Available (Sheldon)
❑ 47HomBon-23
❑ 48Bow-34
❑ 48GiaTeal-8
❑ 49Bow-68
❑ 49EurSta-111
❑ 49GiaTeal-13
❑ 50Bow-83
❑ 50Dra-7
❑ 51Bow-199
❑ 52BerRos-27
❑ 52Bow-215
❑ 52Top-130
❑ 75Gia195T-10
❑ 83TopRep5-130
❑ 85TCMPpl1-22

Jones, B.J. (Bobby)
❑ 94BriTigC-15
❑ 94BriTigF-3518

Jones, Barry
❑ 85PriWilPT-3
❑ 86HawIslP-13
❑ 86SumBraP-12
❑ 87Don-602
❑ 87DurBulP-2
❑ 87Fle-611
❑ 87FleGlo-611
❑ 87Top-494
❑ 87TopTif-494
❑ 88BobCamRB-24
❑ 88FleUpd-114
❑ 88FleUpdG-114
❑ 88GreBraB-8
❑ 88PirTeal-15
❑ 88SouLeaAJ-14
❑ 88Top-168
❑ 88TopTif-168
❑ 89BlaYNPRWL-25
❑ 89Don-647
❑ 89Fle-500
❑ 89FleGlo-500
❑ 89RicBraBC-11
❑ 89RicBraC-20
❑ 89RicBraP-846
❑ 89RicBraTI-10
❑ 89Sco-333
❑ 89Top-539
❑ 89TopTif-539
❑ 89UppDec-457
❑ 89WhiSoxC-12
❑ 90CMC-288
❑ 90Lea-431
❑ 90OPC-243
❑ 90ProAAAF-417
❑ 90PubIntS-390
❑ 90RicBraBC-11
❑ 90RicBraC-12
❑ 90RicBraP-272
❑ 90RicBraTI-15
❑ 90Sco-152
❑ 90Top-243
❑ 90TopTif-243
❑ 90WhiSoxC-10
❑ 91Bow-439
❑ 91ColSprSSLD-86
❑ 91ColSprSSP-2196
❑ 91Don-534
❑ 91ExpPos-11
❑ 91Fle-124
❑ 91Lea-406
❑ 91LinDriAAA-86
❑ 91OPC-33
❑ 91OPCPre-69
❑ 91PanSti-259
❑ 91Sco-115
❑ 91ScoPro-115
❑ 91ScoRoo-75T
❑ 91StaClu-551
❑ 91Top-33
❑ 91TopDesS-33
❑ 91TopMic-33
❑ 91TopTif-33
❑ 91TopTra-64T
❑ 91TopTraT-64T
❑ 91UltUpd-91
❑ 91UppDec-39
❑ 91UppDec-789
❑ 92Don-155
❑ 92Fle-484
❑ 92Lea-484
❑ 92LeaBlaG-484
❑ 92OPC-361
❑ 92PhiMed-16
❑ 92Sco-297
❑ 92StaClu-671
❑ 92StaCluECN-671
❑ 92Top-361
❑ 92TopGol-361
❑ 92TopGolW-361
❑ 92TopMic-361
❑ 92Ult-546
❑ 92UppDec-681
❑ 93NasSouF-569
❑ 93RicBraBB-17
❑ 93RicBraF-195
❑ 93RicBraRC-13
❑ 94NewOrlZF-1463

Jones, Ben
❑ 92ClaDraP-102
❑ 92FroRowDP-66
❑ 92FroRowDPG-66
❑ 92FroRowDPS-66
❑ 93EliTwiC-12
❑ 93EliTwiF-3429
❑ 94ForWayWC-10
❑ 94ForWayWF-2022
❑ 95ForMyeMTI-12
❑ 96FtMyeMB-23

Jones, Bill
❑ 86St.PetCP-16

Jones, Bobby
❑ 87BelBreP-8
❑ 87UtiBluSP-8
❑ 88CalLeaACLC-13
❑ 88StoPorCLC-190
❑ 88StoPorP-732
❑ 89BenBucL-21
❑ 89CalLeaA-32
❑ 89StoPorB-24
❑ 89StoPorCLC-166
❑ 89StoPorP-383
❑ 89StoPorS-15
❑ 90FloStaLAS-50
❑ 90QuaCitAGS-30
❑ 91MidAngAGS-438
❑ 91MidAngOHP-14
❑ 91MidAngP-445
❑ 92HelBreF-1710
❑ 92HelBreSP-7
❑ 92MidAngOHP-10
❑ 92MidAngS-460
❑ 93BelBreCB-12
❑ 93BelBreFI-1705
❑ 93BriTigC-12
❑ 93BriTigF-3662
❑ 94StoPorF-1689
❑ 95NewHavRTI-33
❑ 96ColSprSSTI-19

Jones, Bobby (Robert Joseph)
❑ 90FreStaS-8
❑ 91ClaDraP-32
❑ 91FreStaBS-7
❑ 91FroRowDP-11
❑ 91FroRowDPG-11
❑ 91FroRowDPS-11
❑ 91LinDriAA-438
❑ 92BinMetF-511
❑ 92BinMetS-62
❑ 92Bow-389
❑ 92ClaFS7-341
❑ 92ColMetPI-40
❑ 92ColMetPIISPI-5
❑ 92Pin-548
❑ 92SkyAA F-27
❑ 92StaCluD-94
❑ 92UppDecML-294
❑ 92UppDecMLPotY-PY14
❑ 93Bow-355
❑ 93Bow-650
❑ 93ClaFS7-104
❑ 93ClaGolF-61
❑ 93ExcAllF-5
❑ 93ExcFS7-75
❑ 93NorTidF-2566
❑ 93Top-817
❑ 93TopGol-817
❑ 93TopInaM-817
❑ 93TopInaR-817
❑ 93TopMic-817
❑ 93Ult-429
❑ 93UppDec-19
❑ 93UppDecGold-19
❑ 94Bow-652
❑ 94ColC-151
❑ 94ColChoGS-151
❑ 94ColChoSS-151
❑ 94Don-501
❑ 94Fin-109
❑ 94FinRef-109
❑ 94Fla-199
❑ 94Fle-569
❑ 94FleExtB-319
❑ 94FUnPac-46
❑ 94Lea-304
❑ 94MetColP-14
❑ 94MetShuST-7
❑ 94OPC-108
❑ 94OPCDiaD-6
❑ 94Pin-380
❑ 94PinArtP-380
❑ 94PinMusC-380
❑ 94PinNewG-NG14
❑ 94Sel-167
❑ 94SP-118
❑ 94SPDieC-118
❑ 94Spo-148
❑ 94StaClu-620
❑ 94StaCluFDI-620
❑ 94StaCluGR-620
❑ 94StaCluMOP-620
❑ 94StoPorC-12
❑ 94Stu-116
❑ 94Top-539
❑ 94TopGol-539
❑ 94TopSpa-539
❑ 94TriPla-145
❑ 94Ult-530
❑ 94UppDec-119
❑ 94UppDecED-119
❑ 95Bow-401
❑ 95ColCho-328
❑ 95ColChoGS-328
❑ 95ColChoSE-149
❑ 95ColChoSEGS-149
❑ 95ColChoSESS-149
❑ 95ColChoSS-328
❑ 95Don-6
❑ 95DonPreP-6
❑ 95DonTopotO-294
❑ 95Emo-160
❑ 95Fin-73
❑ 95FinRef-73
❑ 95Fla-385
❑ 95Fle-372
❑ 95LeaLim-69
❑ 95MetColP-18
❑ 95Pin-71
❑ 95PinArtP-71
❑ 95PinMusC-71
❑ 95Sco-232
❑ 95ScoGolR-232
❑ 95ScoPlaTS-232
❑ 95SP-83
❑ 95SPCha-69
❑ 95SPCha-71
❑ 95SPChaDC-69
❑ 95SPChaDC-71
❑ 95SPSil-83
❑ 95StaClu-342
❑ 95StaCluMOP-342
❑ 95StaCluSTWS-342
❑ 95StaCluVR-181
❑ 95StaCluVRMO-181
❑ 95Stu-188
❑ 95Top-252
❑ 95TopCyb-139
❑ 95TopEmb-27
❑ 95TopEmbGI-27
❑ 95Ult-197
❑ 95UltGolM-197
❑ 95UppDec-125
❑ 95UppDecED-125
❑ 95UppDecEDG-125
❑ 95UppDecSE-193
❑ 95UppDecSEG-193
❑ 95USPlaCMLA-4S
❑ 96ColCho-222
❑ 96ColChoGS-222
❑ 96ColChoSS-222
❑ 96Don-430
❑ 96DonPreP-430
❑ 96EmoXL-235
❑ 96Fla-323
❑ 96Fle-482
❑ 96FleTif-482
❑ 96LeaSigA-119
❑ 96LeaSigAG-119
❑ 96LeaSigAS-119
❑ 96MetKah-17
❑ 96MetKah-19
❑ 96MetUni-203
❑ 96MetUniP-203
❑ 96Pac-141
❑ 96ProSta-75
❑ 96Sco-433
❑ 96StaClu-273
❑ 96StaCluMOP-273
❑ 96Top-133
❑ 96TopGal-40
❑ 96TopGalPPI-40
❑ 96Ult-245
❑ 96UltGolM-245
❑ 96UppDec-398
❑ 97Cir-344
❑ 97CirRav-344
❑ 97ColCho-391
❑ 97DonLim-25
❑ 97DonLimE-25
❑ 97DonLimENG-25
❑ 97DonSigA-54
❑ 97DonSigAC-66
❑ 97DonSigAM-66
❑ 97Fin-137
❑ 97FinEmb-137
❑ 97FinEmbR-137
❑ 97FinRef-137
❑ 97Fle-401
❑ 97FleTif-401
❑ 97Lea-304
❑ 97LeaFraM-304
❑ 97LeaFraMDC-304
❑ 97MetUni-196
❑ 97Pac-368
❑ 97PacLigB-368
❑ 97PacSil-368
❑ 97Sco-401
❑ 97ScoArtPWB-401
❑ 97ScoResC-401
❑ 97ScoShoS-401
❑ 97ScoShoSAP-401
❑ 97Sel-192
❑ 97SelCom-192
❑ 97SpoIll-90
❑ 97SpoIllEE-90
❑ 97StaClu-95
❑ 97StaCluMOP-95
❑ 97StrAll-31
❑ 97Top-361
❑ 97TopSta-54
❑ 97TopStaAM-54
❑ 97Ult-243
❑ 97UltGolME-243
❑ 97UltPlaME-243
❑ 97UppDec-434
❑ 98CirThu-118
❑ 98CirThuRav-118
❑ 98CirThuSupRav-118
❑ 98ColCho-171
❑ 98DonColL-323
❑ 98DonPriCL-323
❑ 98Fin-211
❑ 98FinNo--211
❑ 98FinNo-R-211
❑ 98FinRef-211
❑ 98Fle-80
❑ 98Lea-124
❑ 98LeaFraDA-124
❑ 98LeaFraF-124
❑ 98LeaFraM-124
❑ 98LeaFraM-124
❑ 98LeaFraMDC-124
❑ 98LeaFraMDC-124
❑ 98LeaFraMZ2-124
❑ 98MetUni-148
❑ 98MetUniPMG-148
❑ 98Pac-368
❑ 98PacOme-158
❑ 98PacOmeR-158
❑ 98PacOnl-480
❑ 98PacOnlR-480
❑ 98PacOnlWC-480
❑ 98PacPar-206
❑ 98PacParC-206
❑ 98PacParG-206
❑ 98PacParHS-206
❑ 98PacParPB-206
❑ 98PacParR-206
❑ 98PacPlaB-368
❑ 98PacRedT-368
❑ 98PacSil-368
❑ 98Pin-17
❑ 98PinArtP-PP17
❑ 98PinMusC-PP17
❑ 98PinPreP-17
❑ 98PinSna-NYM14
❑ 98Sco-47
❑ 98ScoRT-57
❑ 98ScoSS-PP130
❑ 98ScoSSAP-PP130
❑ 98SP Aut-137
❑ 98SpoIll-68
❑ 98SpoIllEE-68
❑ 98SpoIllFE-68
❑ 98SpoIllWSF-59
❑ 98SpoIllWSFEE-59
❑ 98SpoIllWSFFE-59
❑ 98StaCluFDI-319
❑ 98StaCluI-319
❑ 98StaCluOneK-319
❑ 98StaCluPP-319
❑ 98Top-417
❑ 98TopChr-417
❑ 98TopChrR-417
❑ 98TopDevR-417
❑ 98TopDia-417
❑ 98TopGal-144
❑ 98TopGalGP-144
❑ 98TopGalOPP-144
❑ 98TopGalPPI-144
❑ 98TopGalPPIA-144
❑ 98TopMiniC-417
❑ 98TopSta-147
❑ 98TopStaB-147
❑ 98TopStaG-147
❑ 98TopStaGR-147
❑ 98TopStaS-147
❑ 98Ult-74
❑ 98UltGolM-74
❑ 98UltMas-74
❑ 98UltPlaM-74
❑ 98UppDec-444
❑ 98UppDecR-61
❑ 99199Fin-209
❑ 99FinGolRef-209
❑ 99FinRef-209
❑ 99Fle-481
❑ 99FleSta9-481
❑ 99FleWarT-481
❑ 99Pac-279
❑ 99PacPlaB-279
❑ 99PacRed-279
❑ 99StaClu-256
❑ 99StaCluFDI-256
❑ 99StaCluOoaK-256
❑ 99StaCluPP-256
❑ 99Top-176
❑ 99TopChr-176
❑ 99TopChrR-176
❑ 99TopMVPP-176
❑ 99TopOpeD-96
❑ 99UppDec-148
❑ 99UppDec-428
❑ 99UppDecEL1-148
❑ 99UppDecEL1-428
❑ 99UppDecEL2-148
❑ 99UppDecEL2-428

Jones, Bobby (Robert O.)
❑ 74SpoIndC-36
❑ 75IntLeaASB-14
❑ 75PacCoaLAB-14
❑ 75SpoIndC-9
❑ 76SacSolC-5
❑ 77Top-16
❑ 77Top-431
❑ 78SalLakCGC-15
❑ 79TCMJapPB-78
❑ 83OklCit8T-11
❑ 83RanAffF-6
❑ 84Nes792-451
❑ 84RanJarP-6
❑ 84Top-451
❑ 84TopTif-451
❑ 85Don-134
❑ 85Fle-559
❑ 85RanPer-6
❑ 85Top-648
❑ 85TopTif-648
❑ 86OklCit8P-8
❑ 86Top-142
❑ 86TopTif-142
❑ 88ChaRanS-14
❑ 89ChaRanS-26
❑ 89PacSenL-98
❑ 89TopSenL-3
❑ 90ChaRanS-29
❑ 90EliSenL-71
❑ 91LinDriAA-599
❑ 91PacSenL-59
❑ 91TulDriLD-599
❑ 91TulDriP-2788
❑ 91TulDriTI-15
❑ 92TulDriF-2709
❑ 92TulDriS-624
❑ 93OklCit8F-1639
❑ 93RanKee-210
❑ 94OklCit8F-1508
❑ 95TulDriTI-28
❑ 96TulDriTI-14
❑ 97TulDriTI-13
❑ 98TulDriTI-2

Jones, Bobby BK
❑ 80PhiBul-16

Jones, Bobby M.
❑ 97ColSprSTI-11
❑ 98PacOmeRS-21
❑ 98PacOmeRST4-21
❑ 98PacOnl-247
❑ 98PacOnlR-247
❑ 98PacOnlWC-247
❑ 99Fle-503
❑ 99FleSta9-503
❑ 99FleWarT-503
❑ 99Pac-147
❑ 99PacPlaB-147
❑ 99PacRed-147

Jones, Brian
❑ 85PriWilPT-31
❑ 86PriWilPP-13
❑ 87HarSenP-17
❑ 95Lea-16

Jones, Bryan
❑ 76WatRoyT-14

Jones, Butter
❑ 92EveGiaC-13
❑ 92EveGiaF-1703

Jones, Caldwell
❑ 80PhiBul-27

Jones, Calvin
❑ 87ChaLooB-6
❑ 88VerMarP-962
❑ 89SanBerSCLC-64
❑ 89WilBilS-11
❑ 90SanBerSB-3
❑ 90SanBerSCLC-96
❑ 90SanBerSP-2629

❑ 91CalCanLD-62
❑ 91CalCanP-511
❑ 91LinDriAAA-62
❑ 92Don-690
❑ 92Lea-71
❑ 92LeaBlaG-71
❑ 92MarMot-21
❑ 92ProFS7-139
❑ 92Sco-868
❑ 92StaClu-127
❑ 92TopDeb91-92
❑ 92Ult-433
❑ 92UppDec-731
❑ 93Don-749
❑ 93Fle-413
❑ 93StaClu-578
❑ 93StaCluFDI-578
❑ 93StaCluMOP-578
❑ 93Top-664
❑ 93TopGol-664
❑ 93TopInaM-664
❑ 93TopInaR-664
❑ 93TopMic-664
❑ 94ChaKniF-889
❑ 95LinVen-25
❑ 95PawRedSDD-16
❑ 95PawRedTI-36

Jones, Carl

❑ 87SumBraP-14

Jones, Carroll

❑ 20Zee-45
❑ 21Zee-71

Jones, Casey (Clinton)

❑ 92NegLeaK-2
❑ 92NegLeaRLI-34

Jones, Charlie

❑ 83VerBeaDT-6

Jones, Charlie (William Charles)

❑ 98SouBenSHM-18

Jones, Charlie C.

❑ 03BreE10-75
❑ 11SpoLifCW-189

Jones, Chipper

❑ 90ClaDraP-1
❑ 90ClaDraP-NNO
❑ 90ClaYel-T92
❑ 90ClaYel-NNO0
❑ 91Bow-569
❑ 91Cla/Bes-268
❑ 91MacBraC-19
❑ 91MacBraP-872
❑ 91OPC-333
❑ 91Sco-671
❑ 91SouAtlLAGP-SAL33
❑ 91Top-333
❑ 91TopDesS-333
❑ 91TopMic-333
❑ 91TopTif-333
❑ 91UppDec-55
❑ 92Bow-28
❑ 92ClaBluBF-BC7
❑ 92ClaFS7-93
❑ 92ClaRedB-BC7
❑ 92DurBulC-1
❑ 92DurBulF-1108
❑ 92DurBulTI-10
❑ 92OPC-551
❑ 92ProFS7-190
❑ 92SpolllFK1-447
❑ 92StaCluFDP-1
❑ 92Top-551
❑ 92TopGol-551
❑ 92TopGolW-551
❑ 92TopMic-551
❑ 92UppDecML-66
❑ 92UppDecML-165
❑ 92UppDecMLPotY-PY5
❑ 92UppDecMLTPHF-TP3
❑ 93Bow-86
❑ 93Bow-347
❑ 93BraStaC-9
❑ 93ClaFisN-5
❑ 93ClaGolF-172
❑ 93ClaYouG-YG7
❑ 93Don-721
❑ 93EliTwiC-27
❑ 93ExcAllF-2
❑ 93ExcFS7-2
❑ 93LeaGolR-R19
❑ 93LeaGolRJ-R19
❑ 93RicBraBB-13
❑ 93RicBraF-190
❑ 93RicBraP-6
❑ 93RicBraRC-15
❑ 93RicBraRC-14
❑ 93SanBerSC-27
❑ 93SP-280
❑ 93StaClu-638
❑ 93StaCluFDI-638
❑ 93StaCluMOP-638
❑ 93Top-529
❑ 93TopGol-529
❑ 93TopInaM-529
❑ 93TopInaR-529
❑ 93TopMic-529
❑ 93TriAAAGF-1
❑ 93UppDec-24
❑ 93UppDec-459
❑ 93UppDecFA-A11
❑ 93UppDecFAJ-A11
❑ 93UppDecGold-24
❑ 93UppDecGold-459
❑ 93UppDecOD-D16
❑ 93UtiBluSC-27
❑ 94Bow-353
❑ 94Bow-489
❑ 94BowBes-B1
❑ 94BowBes-X108
❑ 94BowBesR-B1
❑ 94BowBesR-X108
❑ 94BraLykP-11
❑ 94BraLykS-12
❑ 94BraUSPC-2C
❑ 94ColC-152
❑ 94ColChoGS-152
❑ 94ColChoSS-152
❑ 94Don-453
❑ 94FleMajLP-18
❑ 94FUnPac-5
❑ 94Lea-46
❑ 94OPC-57
❑ 94Pac-10
❑ 94Pin-236
❑ 94PinArtP-236
❑ 94PinMusC-236
❑ 94PinNewG-NG20
❑ 94PinRooTP-5
❑ 94Sco-572
❑ 94ScoBoyoS-58
❑ 94ScoGolR-572
❑ 94Spo-160
❑ 94StaClu-638
❑ 94StaCluFDI-638
❑ 94StaCluGR-638
❑ 94StaCluMOP-638
❑ 94StaCluT-50
❑ 94StaCluTFDI-50
❑ 94Top-777
❑ 94TopGol-777
❑ 94TopSpa-777
❑ 94TriPla-281
❑ 94Ult-152
❑ 94UppDec-185
❑ 94UppDecED-185
❑ 95Bow-262
❑ 95BowGolF-262
❑ 95ClaPhoC-1
❑ 95ColCho-154
❑ 95ColChoGS-154
❑ 95ColChoSS-154
❑ 95DonTopotO-185
❑ 95Emo-102
❑ 95EmoRoo-8
❑ 95Fin-221
❑ 95FinRef-221
❑ 95Fla-325
❑ 95FlaWavotF-9
❑ 95FleUpd-91
❑ 95FleUpdRU-5
❑ 95Lea-369
❑ 95LeaLim-78
❑ 95LeaLimG-22
❑ 95Pin-111
❑ 95Pin-303
❑ 95PinArtP-111
❑ 95PinArtP-303
❑ 95PinMusC-111
❑ 95PinMusC-303
❑ 95PinNewB-NB6
❑ 95Sel-173
❑ 95Sel-235
❑ 95SelArtP-173
❑ 95SelArtP-235
❑ 95SelCanM-CM11
❑ 95SelCer-107
❑ 95SelCerF-1
❑ 95SelCerMG-107
❑ 95SelCerPU-11
❑ 95SelCerPU9-11
❑ 95SP-34
❑ 95SPCha-26
❑ 95SPChaDC-26
❑ 95Spo-162
❑ 95SpoArtP-162
❑ 95SpoSam-162
❑ 95SPSil-34
❑ 95StaClu-543
❑ 95StaCluCB-CB1
❑ 95StaCluMOP-543
❑ 95StaCluMOP-CB1
❑ 95StaCluSTDW-B543
❑ 95StaCluSTMP-3
❑ 95StaCluSTWS-543
❑ 95Stu-160
❑ 95Sum-115
❑ 95SumNewA-NA11
❑ 95SumNthD-115
❑ 95Top-535
❑ 95TopTra-128T
❑ 95UC3-101
❑ 95UC3ArtP-101
❑ 95UC3CleS-CS9
❑ 95Ult-347
❑ 95UltGolM-347
❑ 95UppDec-293
❑ 95UppDecED-293
❑ 95UppDecEDG-293
❑ 95UppDecPAW-H39
❑ 95UppDecPAWE-H39
❑ 95UppDecSE-14
❑ 95UppDecSEG-14
❑ 95Zen-111
❑ 95ZenRooRC-3
❑ 95ZenSam-111
❑ 96Baz-96
❑ 96Bow-76
❑ 96BowBes-7
❑ 96BowBesAR-7
❑ 96BowBesC-5
❑ 96BowBesCAR-5
❑ 96BowBesCR-5
❑ 96BowBesMI-3
❑ 96BowBesMIAR-3
❑ 96BowBesMIR-3
❑ 96BowBesP-BBP1
❑ 96BowBesPAR-BBP1
❑ 96BowBesPR-BBP1
❑ 96BowBesR-7
❑ 96BowFoi-76
❑ 96BraFle-6
❑ 96Cir-102
❑ 96CirRav-102
❑ 96ColCho-42
❑ 96ColCho-374T
❑ 96ColChoCtG-CG1
❑ 96ColChoCtG-CG1B
❑ 96ColChoCtG-CG1C
❑ 96ColChoCtGE-CR1
❑ 96ColChoCtGG-CG1
❑ 96ColChoCtGG-CG1B
❑ 96ColChoCtGG-CG1C
❑ 96ColChoCtGGE-CR1
❑ 96ColChoGS-42
❑ 96ColChoSS-42
❑ 96ColChoYMtP-19
❑ 96ColChoYMtP-19A
❑ 96ColChoYMtPGS-19
❑ 96ColChoYMtPGS-19A
❑ 96Don-437
❑ 96DonEli-66
❑ 96DonFreF-7
❑ 96DonPreP-437
❑ 96EmoRarB-6
❑ 96EmoXL-142
❑ 96Fin-B16
❑ 96Fin-G141
❑ 96Fin-G192
❑ 96FinRef-B16
❑ 96FinRef-G141
❑ 96FinRef-G192
❑ 96Fla-200
❑ 96Fle-293
❑ 96FleChe-3
❑ 96FleRooS-10
❑ 96FleTif-293
❑ 96FleTomL-6
❑ 96FleUpd-U228
❑ 96FleUpdH-10
❑ 96FleUpdSS-5
❑ 96FleUpdTC-U228
❑ 96Lea-28
❑ 96LeaAllGMC-11
❑ 96LeaAllGMCG-11
❑ 96LeaGolS-9
❑ 96LeaLim-27
❑ 96LeaLimG-27
❑ 96LeaLimL-7
❑ 96LeaLimLB-7
❑ 96LeaLimPC-10
❑ 96LeaPicP-5
❑ 96LeaPre-40
❑ 96LeaPreP-40
❑ 96LeaPrePB-28
❑ 96LeaPrePG-28
❑ 96LeaPrePS-28
❑ 96LeaPreSG-33
❑ 96LeaPreSta-1
❑ 96LeaPreSte-33
❑ 96LeaSig-26
❑ 96LeaSigPPG-26
❑ 96LeaSigPPP-26
❑ 96LeaStaS-8
❑ 96MetUni-129
❑ 96MetUniMFG-8
❑ 96MetUniP-129
❑ 96MetUniPP-5
❑ 96MetUniProS-129
❑ 96Pac-4
❑ 96PacGolCD-DC31
❑ 96PacHom-HP7
❑ 96PacOctM-OM8
❑ 96PacPri-P2
❑ 96PacPriFB-FB7
❑ 96PacPriG-P2
❑ 96PacPriRHS-RH3
❑ 96PanSti-8
❑ 96PanSti-243
❑ 96Pin-114
❑ 96Pin-200
❑ 96Pin-266
❑ 96Pin-396
❑ 96Pin-399
❑ 96PinAfi-127
❑ 96PinAfiAP-127
❑ 96PinAfiMN-6
❑ 96PinAfiSP-30
❑ 96PinArtP-45
❑ 96PinArtP-166
❑ 96PinChrBC-5
❑ 96PinEssotG-5
❑ 96PinFan-21
❑ 96PinFirR-4
❑ 96PinFoil-266
❑ 96PinFoil-396
❑ 96PinFoil-399
❑ 96PinProS-6
❑ 96PinSky-15
❑ 96PinSta-45
❑ 96PinSta-166
❑ 96PinTeaS-10
❑ 96PinTeaT-6
❑ 96Sco-322
❑ 96ScoAll-18
❑ 96ScoBigB-20
❑ 96ScoDiaA-8
❑ 96ScoDugC-B47
❑ 96ScoDugCAP-B47
❑ 96ScoFutF-2
❑ 96ScoGolS-12
❑ 96ScoNumG-19
❑ 96ScoRef-1
❑ 96Sel-41
❑ 96SelArtP-41
❑ 96SelCer-7
❑ 96SelCer-142
❑ 96SelCerAP-7
❑ 96SelCerAP-142
❑ 96SelCerCB-7
❑ 96SelCerCB-142
❑ 96SelCerCR-7
❑ 96SelCerCR-142
❑ 96SelCerIP-11
❑ 96SelCerMB-7
❑ 96SelCerMB-142
❑ 96SelCerMG-7
❑ 96SelCerMG-142
❑ 96SelCerMR-7
❑ 96SelCerMR-142
❑ 96SelCerSF-9
❑ 96SelClaTF-11
❑ 96SelEnF-12
❑ 96SelTeaN-12
❑ 96SP-26
❑ 96SPBasH-85
❑ 96SPMarM-MM18
❑ 96SPMarMDC-18
❑ 96Spo-19
❑ 96Spo-97
❑ 96SpoArtP-19
❑ 96SpoArtP-97
❑ 96SpoDouT-3
❑ 96SpoHitP-15
❑ 96SpoPowS-1
❑ 96SpoPro-10
❑ 96SPSpeFX-15
❑ 96SPSpeFXDC-15
❑ 96SPx-2
❑ 96SPxBoufG-6
❑ 96SPxGol-2
❑ 96StaClu-10
❑ 96StaClu-226
❑ 96StaCluEPB-10
❑ 96StaCluEPG-10
❑ 96StaCluEPS-10
❑ 96StaCluMO-48
❑ 96StaCluMOP-10
❑ 96StaCluMOP-226
❑ 96StaCluMOP-TSCA8
❑ 96StaCluTA-8
❑ 96Stu-72
❑ 96StuPrePB-72
❑ 96StuPrePG-72
❑ 96StuPrePS-72
❑ 96StuStaGS-5
❑ 96Sum-126
❑ 96Sum-161
❑ 96SumAbo&B-126
❑ 96SumAbo&B-161
❑ 96SumArtP-126
❑ 96SumArtP-161
❑ 96SumBigB-15
❑ 96SumBigBM-15
❑ 96SumFoi-126
❑ 96SumFoi-161
❑ 96SumHitI-14
❑ 96SumPos-3
❑ 96TeaOut-42
❑ 96Top-177
❑ 96TopChr-52
❑ 96TopChrR-52
❑ 96TopGal-100
❑ 96TopGalE-6
❑ 96TopGalPPI-100
❑ 96TopLas-45
❑ 96TopLasBS-14
❑ 96TopMysF-M4
❑ 96TopMysFR-M4
❑ 96TopPro-NL15
❑ 96Ult-156
❑ 96Ult-582
❑ 96Ult-596
❑ 96UltChe-A5
❑ 96UltCheGM-A5
❑ 96UltFreF-5
❑ 96UltFreFGM-5
❑ 96UltGolM-156
❑ 96UltGolM-582
❑ 96UltGolM-596
❑ 96UltRisS-6
❑ 96UltRisSGM-6
❑ 96UppDec-5
❑ 96UppDec-149
❑ 96UppDec-219
❑ 96UppDecBCP-BC10
❑ 96UppDecDD-DD1
❑ 96UppDecDDG-DD1
❑ 96UppDecDDS-DD1
❑ 96UppDecG-GF7
❑ 96UppDecHC-HC11
❑ 96UppDecPHE-H35
❑ 96UppDecPRE-R34
❑ 96UppDecPreH-H35
❑ 96UppDecPreR-R34
❑ 96Zen-55
❑ 96Zen-137
❑ 96ZenArtP-55
❑ 96ZenArtP-137
❑ 96ZenDiaC-20
❑ 96ZenDiaCP-20
❑ 96ZenMoz-1
❑ 96ZenZ-7
❑ 97Bow-3
❑ 97BowBes-9
❑ 97BowBesAR-9
❑ 97BowBesBC-BC2
❑ 97BowBesBCAR-BC2
❑ 97BowBesBCR-BC2
❑ 97BowBesJ-9
❑ 97BowBesJAR-9
❑ 97BowBesJR-9
❑ 97BowBesMI-MI9
❑ 97BowBesMIAR-MI9
❑ 97BowBesMIARI-MI9
❑ 97BowBesMII-MI9
❑ 97BowBesMIR-MI9
❑ 97BowBesMIRI-MI9
❑ 97BowBesP-5
❑ 97BowBesPAR-5
❑ 97BowBesPR-5
❑ 97BowBesR-9
❑ 97BowChr-2
❑ 97BowChrI-2
❑ 97BowChrIR-2
❑ 97BowChrR-2
❑ 97BowInt-3
❑ 97BraSco-10
❑ 97BraScoPI-10
❑ 97BraScoPr-10
❑ 97ChiJonP-1
❑ 97Cir-381
❑ 97CirBos-10
❑ 97CirFasT-5
❑ 97CirIco-5
❑ 97CirLimA-8
❑ 97CirRav-381
❑ 97CirSupB-10
❑ 97ColCho-270
❑ 97ColCho-326
❑ 97ColChoAC-30
❑ 97ColChoBS-15
❑ 97ColChoBSGS-15
❑ 97ColChoCtG-2A
❑ 97ColChoCtG-2B
❑ 97ColChoCtG-2C
❑ 97ColChoCtGE-CG2
❑ 97ColChoCtGIW-CG2
❑ 97ColChoNF-NF30
❑ 97ColChoS-10
❑ 97ColChoSR-14
❑ 97ColChoT-AB10
❑ 97ColChoTBS-2
❑ 97ColChoTBSWH-2
❑ 97ColChoTotT-T2
❑ 97CraJac-4
❑ 97Don-34
❑ 97Don-401
❑ 97DonArmaD-3
❑ 97DonDiaK-10
❑ 97DonDiaKC-10
❑ 97DonDom-9
❑ 97DonEli-8
❑ 97DonEli-5
❑ 97DonEliGS-8
❑ 97DonEliLaL-4
❑ 97DonEliTotC-3
❑ 97DonEliTotCDC-3
❑ 97DonFraFea-6
❑ 97DonGolPP-34
❑ 97DonGolPP-401
❑ 97DonLim-23
❑ 97DonLim-45
❑ 97DonLim-55
❑ 97DonLimE-23
❑ 97DonLimE-45
❑ 97DonLimE-55
❑ 97DonLimENG-23
❑ 97DonLimFotG-6
❑ 97DonPowA-10
❑ 97DonPowADC-10
❑ 97DonPre-93
❑ 97DonPre-170
❑ 97DonPreCttC-93
❑ 97DonPreCttC-170
❑ 97DonPrePM-16
❑ 97DonPreS-3
❑ 97DonPreSS-3
❑ 97DonPreTB-10
❑ 97DonPreTBG-10
❑ 97DonPreTF-10
❑ 97DonPreTP-10
❑ 97DonPreTPG-10
❑ 97DonPreXP-8A
❑ 97DonRocL-3
❑ 97DonSig-18
❑ 97DonSigAC-67
❑ 97DonSigAM-67
❑ 97DonSigPPP-18
❑ 97DonSilPP-34
❑ 97DonSilPP-401
❑ 97DonTea-18
❑ 97DonTeaSMVP-10
❑ 97DonTeaSPE-18
❑ 97DonVxP1-43
❑ 97DurBulATI-5
❑ 97E-X2-54
❑ 97E-X2Cred-54
❑ 97E-X2EssCre-54
❑ 97E-X2SD2000-5
❑ 97Fin-108
❑ 97Fin-273
❑ 97Fin-330
❑ 97FinEmb-108
❑ 97FinEmb-330
❑ 97FinEmbR-108
❑ 97FinEmbR-330

❑ 97FinRef-108
❑ 97FinRef-273
❑ 97FinRef-330
❑ 97FlaShoDC-9
❑ 97FlaShoHG-7
❑ 97FlaShoLC-10
❑ 97FlaShoLeg0-10
❑ 97FlaShoLeg1-10
❑ 97FlaShoM-A10
❑ 97FlaShoM-B10
❑ 97FlaShoM-C10
❑ 97FlaShoR0-10
❑ 97FlaShoR1-10
❑ 97FlaShoR2-10
❑ 97Fle-258
❑ 97Fle-494
❑ 97Fle-705
❑ 97FleGouG-5
❑ 97FleGouGF-5
❑ 97FleHea-10
❑ 97FleMilDM-10
❑ 97FleMilDMR-10
❑ 97FleSoaS-7
❑ 97FleSoaSG-7
❑ 97FleTeaL-15
❑ 97FleTif-258
❑ 97FleTif-494
❑ 97FleTif-705
❑ 97FleZon-9
❑ 97HigMinESC-10
❑ 97HigMinESC-11
❑ 97HigMinESC-12
❑ 97HigMinM-60
❑ 97HigMinM-61
❑ 97HigMinM-62
❑ 97Lea-189
❑ 97Lea-201
❑ 97Lea-374
❑ 97LeaBanS-9
❑ 97LeaDrefS-18
❑ 97LeaFraM-189
❑ 97LeaFraM-201
❑ 97LeaFraM-374
❑ 97LeaFraMDC-189
❑ 97LeaFraMDC-201
❑ 97LeaFraMDC-374
❑ 97LeaGet-4
❑ 97LeaGolS-5
❑ 97LeaKnoG-9
❑ 97LeaLeaotN-2
❑ 97LeaStaS-6
❑ 97MetUni-31
❑ 97MetUniML-6
❑ 97MetUniPP-5
❑ 97MetUniT-4
❑ 97NewPin-123
❑ 97NewPin-194
❑ 97NewPinAP-123
❑ 97NewPinAP-194
❑ 97NewPinIE-4
❑ 97NewPinMC-123
❑ 97NewPinMC-194
❑ 97NewPinPP-123
❑ 97NewPinPP-194
❑ 97NewPinPP-I4B
❑ 97NewPinPP-CJ1
❑ 97NewPinPP-CJ2
❑ 97NewPinPP-CJ3
❑ 97NewPinPP-CJ4
❑ 97NewPinPP-CJ5
❑ 97NewPinPP-CJ6
❑ 97NewPinPP-CJ7
❑ 97NewPinS-CJ1
❑ 97NewPinS-CJ2
❑ 97NewPinS-CJ3
❑ 97NewPinS-CJ4
❑ 97NewPinS-CJ5
❑ 97NewPinS-CJ6
❑ 97NewPinS-CJ7
❑ 97Pac-235
❑ 97PacCar-22
❑ 97PacCarM-22
❑ 97PacCerCGT-4
❑ 97PacCraC-7
❑ 97PacFirD-15
❑ 97PacGolCD-22
❑ 97PacLigB-235
❑ 97PacPri-79
❑ 97PacPriGA-GA18
❑ 97PacPriGotD-GD112
❑ 97PacPriLB-79
❑ 97PacPriP-79
❑ 97PacPriSH-SH9A
❑ 97PacPriSL-SL8B
❑ 97PacSil-235
❑ 97PacTriCD-13
❑ 97Pin-96
❑ 97PinArtP-PP96
❑ 97PinCar-7
❑ 97PinCer-59
❑ 97PinCerCMGT-4
❑ 97PinCerCT-4
❑ 97PinCerMBla-59
❑ 97PinCerMBlu-59
❑ 97PinCerMG-59
❑ 97PinCerMR-59
❑ 97PinCerR-59
❑ 97PinEpixPE-E15
❑ 97PinFan-FF6
❑ 97PinHom-1
❑ 97PinHom-2
❑ 97PinIns-31
❑ 97PinInsC-15
❑ 97PinInsCE-31
❑ 97PinInsDD-7
❑ 97PinInsDE-31
❑ 97PinMin-9
❑ 97PinMinB-9
❑ 97PinMinCB-9
❑ 97PinMinCG-9
❑ 97PinMinCGR-9
❑ 97PinMinCN-9
❑ 97PinMinCSS-9
❑ 97PinMinG-9
❑ 97PinMinS-9
❑ 97PinMusC-96
❑ 97PinPasttM-8
❑ 97PinPrePla-96
❑ 97PinTeaP-4
❑ 97PinTeaP-10
❑ 97PinTotCPB-59
❑ 97PinTotCPG-59
❑ 97PinTotCPR-59
❑ 97PinX-P-23
❑ 97PinX-PF&A-9
❑ 97PinX-PMoS-23
❑ 97PinX-PMW-8
❑ 97PinX-PMWG-8
❑ 97PinX-PMWS-8
❑ 97PinX-PSfF-31
❑ 97PinX-PSfFU-31
❑ 97PreCon-3
❑ 97Sco-193
❑ 97Sco-509
❑ 97ScoAllF-6
❑ 97ScoArtPWB-193
❑ 97ScoArtPWB-509
❑ 97ScoBla-8
❑ 97ScoFra-4
❑ 97ScoFraG-4
❑ 97ScoHeaotO-19
❑ 97ScoHigZ-11
❑ 97ScoPreS-193
❑ 97ScoResC-509
❑ 97ScoShoS-193
❑ 97ScoShoS-509
❑ 97ScoShoSAP-193
❑ 97ScoShoSAP-509
❑ 97ScoStaaD-3
❑ 97ScoTitT-14
❑ 97Sel-63
❑ 97SelArtP-63
❑ 97SelCom-63
❑ 97SelRegG-63
❑ 97SelToootT-3
❑ 97SelToootTMB-3
❑ 97SP-25
❑ 97SPGamF-GF8
❑ 97SPInsI-22
❑ 97SPMarM-MM9
❑ 97SpoIll-33
❑ 97SpoIll-76
❑ 97SpoIllEE-33
❑ 97SpoIllEE-76
❑ 97SpoIllGS-1
❑ 97SPSpeF-7
❑ 97SPSpxF-6
❑ 97SPSPxFA-6
❑ 97SPVinAu-19
❑ 97SPVinAu-20
❑ 97SPVinAu-21
❑ 97SPx-5
❑ 97SPxBoufG-2
❑ 97SPxBro-5
❑ 97SPxCorotG-3
❑ 97SPxGol-5
❑ 97SPxGraF-5
❑ 97SPxSil-5
❑ 97SPxSte-5
❑ 97StaClu-1
❑ 97StaClu-376
❑ 97StaCluFR-F8
❑ 97StaCluFW-F8
❑ 97StaCluM-M6
❑ 97StaCluMat-1
❑ 97StaCluMOP-1
❑ 97StaCluMOP-376
❑ 97StaCluMOP-M6
❑ 97StaCluMOP-FB8
❑ 97StaCluMOP-PG7
❑ 97StaCluPG-PG7
❑ 97StaCluPP-PP1
❑ 97StrAll-32
❑ 97Stu-79
❑ 97StuHarH-12
❑ 97StuMasS-17
❑ 97StuMasS8-17
❑ 97StuPor8-8
❑ 97StuPrePG-79
❑ 97StuPrePS-79
❑ 97Top-277
❑ 97TopAll-AS8
❑ 97TopAwel-AI9
❑ 97TopChr-97
❑ 97TopChrAS-AS8
❑ 97TopChrDD-DD1
❑ 97TopChrDDR-DD1
❑ 97TopChrJ-97
❑ 97TopChrR-97
❑ 97TopChrSAR-AS8
❑ 97TopGal-137
❑ 97TopGalGoH-GH2
❑ 97TopGalPG-PG5
❑ 97TopGalPMS-4
❑ 97TopGalPMSSS-4
❑ 97TopGalPPI-137
❑ 97TopHobM-HM13
❑ 97TopIntF-ILM13
❑ 97TopIntFR-ILM13
❑ 97TopMemO5-27
❑ 97TopScr-12
❑ 97TopScrPS-2
❑ 97TopScrPST-2
❑ 97TopScrT-12
❑ 97TopSta-5
❑ 97TopStaAM-5
❑ 97TopSweS-SS8
❑ 97TopTeaT-TT15
❑ 97UD3-60
❑ 97UD3GenNex-GN10
❑ 97Ult-154
❑ 97UltBasR-4
❑ 97UltChe-B8
❑ 97UltDiaP-4
❑ 97UltDouT-11
❑ 97UltGolME-154
❑ 97UltPlaME-154
❑ 97UltPowP-A5
❑ 97UltPowP-B6
❑ 97UltStaR-8
❑ 97UltThu-7
❑ 97UltTop3-8
❑ 97UltTop3GM-8
❑ 97UppDec-10
❑ 97UppDec-246
❑ 97UppDec-416
❑ 97UppDecAG-AG5
❑ 97UppDecBCP-BC15
❑ 97UppDecHC-HC6
❑ 97UppDecLDC-LD18
❑ 97UppDecMM-A2
❑ 97UppDecP-2
❑ 97UppDecPE-2
❑ 97UppDecRP-RP20
❑ 97UppDecRSF-RS5
❑ 97UppDecSA-7
❑ 97UppDecSAG-7
❑ 97UppDecTTS-TS1
❑ 97Zen-12
❑ 97Zen8x10-14
❑ 97Zen8x1D-14
❑ 98Bow-70
❑ 98BowBes-5
❑ 98BowBesA-5
❑ 98BowBesAAR-5
❑ 98BowBesAR-5
❑ 98BowBesAR-5
❑ 98BowBesMIF-MI15
❑ 98BowBesMIFAR-MI15
❑ 98BowBesMIFR-MI15
❑ 98BowBesR-5
❑ 98BowChr-70
❑ 98BowChrGA-70
❑ 98BowChrGAR-70
❑ 98BowChrI-70
❑ 98BowChrIR-70
❑ 98BowChrR-70
❑ 98BowChrR-29
❑ 98BowChrRR-29
❑ 98BowGolA-70
❑ 98BowInt-70
❑ 98BraSco-7
❑ 98BraScoP-7
❑ 98CirThu-10
❑ 98CirThuB-10
❑ 98CirThuRav-10
❑ 98CirThuSupRav-10
❑ 98ColCho-306
❑ 98ColChoB5-306
❑ 98ColChoCtG-CG27A
❑ 98ColChoCtG-CG27B
❑ 98ColChoCtG-CG27C
❑ 98ColChoCtGExch-CG27
❑ 98ColChoCtGIW-CG27
❑ 98ColChoMBH-4
❑ 98ColChoRJ-SQ74
❑ 98ColChoS'-2
❑ 98ColChoSQ-SQ74
❑ 98ColChoSQDouble-16
❑ 98ColChoSQHR-16
❑ 98ColChoSQSingle-16
❑ 98ColChoSQTriple-16
❑ 98CroRoy-13
❑ 98CroRoyAS-12
❑ 98CroRoyCCPA-6
❑ 98CroRoyCCPrem-6
❑ 98CroRoyDK-2
❑ 98CroRoyFoB-2
❑ 98CroRoyFoBA-2
❑ 98CroRoyPotG-3
❑ 98Don-21
❑ 98Don-158
❑ 98Don-368
❑ 98Don-405
❑ 98DonCol-21
❑ 98DonCol-158
❑ 98DonColE-407
❑ 98DonColE-524
❑ 98DonColL-329
❑ 98DonColL-352
❑ 98DonColP-557
❑ 98DonColP-724
❑ 98DonColS-21
❑ 98DonColS-158
❑ 98DonCruG-53
❑ 98DonCruP-53
❑ 98DonCruR-53
❑ 98DonDom-17
❑ 98DonEli-7
❑ 98DonEli-124
❑ 98DonEliA-7
❑ 98DonEliA-124
❑ 98DonEliBttF-3
❑ 98DonEliBttFA-3
❑ 98DonEliC-7
❑ 98DonEliI-11
❑ 98DonEliMC-7
❑ 98DonEliPN-6A
❑ 98DonEliPN-6B
❑ 98DonEliPN-6C
❑ 98DonEliPNDC-6A
❑ 98DonEliPNDC-6B
❑ 98DonEliPNDC-6C
❑ 98DonEliPNS-6A
❑ 98DonEliPNS-6B
❑ 98DonEliPNS-6C
❑ 98DonEliS-7
❑ 98DonEliS-124
❑ 98DonFANT-9
❑ 98DonFANTDC-9
❑ 98DonGolPP-21
❑ 98DonGolPP-158
❑ 98DonGolPP-368
❑ 98DonGolPP-405
❑ 98DonLonL-8
❑ 98DonPre-7
❑ 98DonPre-174
❑ 98DonPreGB-7
❑ 98DonPreGES-22
❑ 98DonPreGoB-7
❑ 98DonPreGX-22
❑ 98DonPreGXDC-22
❑ 98DonPrePM-7
❑ 98DonPreSeat-7
❑ 98DonPreSeat-174
❑ 98DonPreTP-7
❑ 98DonPreTPD-4
❑ 98DonPreTPG-7
❑ 98DonPreTPS-7
❑ 98DonPreTW-22
❑ 98DonPriCD-21
❑ 98DonPriCD-158
❑ 98DonPriCE-407
❑ 98DonPriCE-524
❑ 98DonPriCL-329
❑ 98DonPriCL-352
❑ 98DonPriCP-557
❑ 98DonPriCP-724
❑ 98DonProLO-13
❑ 98DonProLPI-7
❑ 98DonSig-79
❑ 98DonSigAC-65
❑ 98DonSigAM-66
❑ 98DonSigP-79
❑ 98DonSigSP-13
❑ 98DonSilPP-21
❑ 98DonSilPP-158
❑ 98DonSilPP-368
❑ 98DonSilPP-405
❑ 98E-X2-6
❑ 98E-X2DesCoop-6
❑ 98E-X2ECFut-6
❑ 98E-X2ECNow-6
❑ 98Fin-242
❑ 98FinCen-C16
❑ 98FinCenR-C16
❑ 98FinMysF1-M33
❑ 98FinMysF1-M36
❑ 98FinMysF1-M38
❑ 98FinMysF1-M40
❑ 98FinMysFR-M33
❑ 98FinMysFR-M36
❑ 98FinMysFR-M38
❑ 98FinMysFR-M40
❑ 98FinNo--242
❑ 98FinNo-R-242
❑ 98FinOve-B4
❑ 98FinOveR-B4
❑ 98FinRef-242
❑ 98FinStaS-SS8
❑ 98FinTheM-TM4
❑ 98FinTheMR-TM4
❑ 98FlaShoLeg0-10
❑ 98FlaShoLeg1-10
❑ 98FlaShoLeg2-10
❑ 98FlaShoLeg3-10
❑ 98FlaShoLegM-10
❑ 98FlaShoR0-10
❑ 98FlaShoR1-10
❑ 98FlaShoR2-10
❑ 98FlaShoR3-10
❑ 98Fle-10
❑ 98Fle-345
❑ 98Fle-588
❑ 98FleDiaS-11
❑ 98FleIn TC-IC10
❑ 98FleLumC-8
❑ 98FleVin'-4
❑ 98FleVin'C-4
❑ 98FleZon-9
❑ 98Lea-130
❑ 98Lea-153
❑ 98LeaFraDA-130
❑ 98LeaFraDA-153
❑ 98LeaFraF-130
❑ 98LeaFraF-153
❑ 98LeaFraM-130
❑ 98LeaFraM-153
❑ 98LeaFraM-130
❑ 98LeaFraM-153
❑ 98LeaFraMDC-130
❑ 98LeaFraMDC-153
❑ 98LeaFraMDC-130
❑ 98LeaFraMDC-153
❑ 98LeaFraMZ2-130
❑ 98LeaFraMZ2-153
❑ 98LeaRCMLHDSamp-9
❑ 98LeaRS-32
❑ 98LeaRS-146
❑ 98LeaRSCross-7
❑ 98LeaRSGAHSamp-7
❑ 98LeaRSGreAH-7
❑ 98LeaRSGreHit-7
❑ 98LeaRSHRDerby-16
❑ 98LeaRSLHolo-32
❑ 98LeaRSLHolo-146
❑ 98LeaRSLMVP-13
❑ 98LeaRSLMVPPE-13
❑ 98LeaRSLong-32
❑ 98LeaRSLong-146
❑ 98LeaRSMLHD-9
❑ 98LeaRSTicMas-4
❑ 98LeaRSTicMasDC-4
❑ 98LeaRTrue-32
❑ 98LeaRTrue-146
❑ 98LeaStaRep-5
❑ 98LeaStaS-7
❑ 98LeaStaSDC-7
❑ 98MetUni-188
❑ 98MetUniAT-3
❑ 98MetUniPMG-188
❑ 98MetUniPP-3
❑ 98MetUniT-3
❑ 98MetUniUL-3
❑ 98Pac-235
❑ 98PacAur-105
❑ 98PacAurCube-2
❑ 98PacAurHC-2
❑ 98PacAurKotML-1
❑ 98PacAurODLC-2
❑ 98PacAurPF-10
❑ 98PacAurPFC-10
❑ 98PacAurPFPB-10
❑ 98PacAurPFR-10
❑ 98PacAurPFS-10
❑ 98PacGolCDC-1
❑ 98PacInCage-1
❑ 98PacInv-77
❑ 98PacInvGems-118
❑ 98PacInvInt-2N
❑ 98PacInvMiT-1
❑ 98PacInvPBlue-77
❑ 98PacInvSilv-77
❑ 98PacInvTeam-2
❑ 98PacOme-20
❑ 98PacOmeEP-13
❑ 98PacOmeEP1o1-13
❑ 98PacOmeFTF-7
❑ 98PacOmeOnIns-23
❑ 98PacOmeP-13
❑ 98PacOmeR-20
❑ 98PacOnl-63A
❑ 98PacOnl-63B
❑ 98PacOnl-78
❑ 98PacOnlR-63A
❑ 98PacOnlR-63B
❑ 98PacOnlR-78
❑ 98PacOnlWC-63A
❑ 98PacOnlWC-63B
❑ 98PacOnlWC-78
❑ 98PacPar-130
❑ 98PacParC-130
❑ 98PacParFC-1
❑ 98PacParG-130
❑ 98PacParHS-130
❑ 98PacParI-8
❑ 98PacParPB-130
❑ 98PacParR-130
❑ 98PacParSD-1
❑ 98PacParTC-16
❑ 98PacPlaB-235
❑ 98PacRedT-235
❑ 98PacSil-235
❑ 98PacTeaC-15
❑ 98Pin-18
❑ 98Pin-194
❑ 98Pin-198
❑ 98PinArtP-PP18
❑ 98PinArtP-PP97
❑ 98PinEpixME-E15
❑ 98PinEpixMO-E15
❑ 98PinEpixMP-E15
❑ 98PinEpixPO-E15
❑ 98PinEpixPP-E15
❑ 98PinEpixSE-E15
❑ 98PinEpixSO-E15
❑ 98PinEpixSP-E15
❑ 98PinIns-10
❑ 98PinIns-146
❑ 98PinInsBtN-18
❑ 98PinInsC-11
❑ 98PinInsCE-10
❑ 98PinInsCE-146
❑ 98PinInsCG-11
❑ 98PinInsDE-10
❑ 98PinInsDE-146
❑ 98PinInsSG-3AB
❑ 98PinInsSG-3CD
❑ 98PinInsSG-8AB
❑ 98PinInsSG-8CD
❑ 98PinInsSGS-3AB
❑ 98PinInsSGS-3CD
❑ 98PinInsSGS-8AB
❑ 98PinInsSGS-8CD
❑ 98PinMinB-11
❑ 98PinMinBM-1
❑ 98PinMinCB-11
❑ 98PinMinCBAP-11
❑ 98PinMinCGP-11
❑ 98PinMinCGPAP-11
❑ 98PinMinCN-11
❑ 98PinMinCNAP-11
❑ 98PinMinCSGR-11
❑ 98PinMinDC-11
❑ 98PinMinG-11
❑ 98PinMinMCSS-11

❑ 98PinMinS-11
❑ 98PinMusC-PP18
❑ 98PinMusC-PP97
❑ 98PinPer-7
❑ 98PinPer-143
❑ 98PinPerBB-4
❑ 98PinPerBBSamp-4
❑ 98PinPerBBSO-4
❑ 98PinPerLP-10
❑ 98PinPerPP-7
❑ 98PinPerPP-143
❑ 98PinPerPT-7
❑ 98PinPerSftF-38
❑ 98PinPerSftFShop-6
❑ 98PinPlu-56
❑ 98PinPlu-187
❑ 98PinPlu-197
❑ 98PinPluAE-15
❑ 98PinPluAEE-15
❑ 98PinPluAEP-15
❑ 98PinPluAP-PP23
❑ 98PinPluGAP-PP23
❑ 98PinPluLM-18
❑ 98PinPluMAP-PP23
❑ 98PinPluPieGame-4
❑ 98PinPluSamp-56
❑ 98PinPluTP-5
❑ 98PinPluTPG-5
❑ 98PinPluTPM-5
❑ 98PinPowPJ-13
❑ 98PinPowPJ-23
❑ 98PinPowPJS-13
❑ 98PinPowPJS-23
❑ 98PinPreP-18
❑ 98PinPreP-194
❑ 98PinPreP-198
❑ 98PinPreP-E15
❑ 98PinSna-AB6
❑ 98PreCon-7
❑ 98Revo-13
❑ 98RevoFP-13
❑ 98RevoMLI-6
❑ 98RevoPTP-13
❑ 98RevoRooHH-21
❑ 98RevoShow-23
❑ 98RevoSS-13
❑ 98Sco-51
❑ 98ScoEpix-E15
❑ 98ScoFirP-5
❑ 98ScoNewS-NS14
❑ 98ScoRT-27
❑ 98ScoRT-258
❑ 98ScoRTComPla-9A
❑ 98ScoRTComPla-9B
❑ 98ScoRTComPla-9C
❑ 98ScoRTCPSamp-9A
❑ 98ScoRTCPSamp-9B
❑ 98ScoRTCPSamp-9C
❑ 98ScoRTSS-PP27
❑ 98ScoRTSS-PP151
❑ 98ScoRTSSAP-PP27
❑ 98ScoRTSSAP-PP151
❑ 98ScoRTSSAP1-PP27
❑ 98ScoRTSSAP1-PP151
❑ 98ScoRTStarGaz-3
❑ 98ScoSam-51
❑ 98ScoSS-PP133
❑ 98ScoSSAP-PP133
❑ 98SkyDugA-4
❑ 98SkyDugA-134
❑ 98SkyDugADH-DH9
❑ 98SkyDugAIA-4
❑ 98SkyDugAIA-134
❑ 98SkyDugAS-SH4
❑ 98SP Aut-47
❑ 98SP Aut-SD25
❑ 98SP AutC-CP
❑ 98SP AutSD-SD25
❑ 98SP AutSDT-SD25
❑ 98SpoIll-69
❑ 98SpoIll-177
❑ 98SpoIllEE-69
❑ 98SpoIllEE-177
❑ 98SpoIllFE-69
❑ 98SpoIllFE-177
❑ 98SpoIllTaN-97
❑ 98SpoIllTaNEE-97
❑ 98SpoIllTaNGS-5
❑ 98SpoIllWSF-72
❑ 98SpoIllWSFEE-72
❑ 98SpoIllWSFFE-72
❑ 98SPxFin-48
❑ 98SPxFin-55
❑ 98SPxFin-141
❑ 98SPxFinHRH-HR10
❑ 98SPxFinR-48
❑ 98SPxFinR-55
❑ 98SPxFinR-141
❑ 98SPxFinS-48
❑ 98SPxFinS-55
❑ 98SPxFinS-141
❑ 98StaCluBP-BP7
❑ 98StaCluFDI-1
❑ 98StaCluI-1
❑ 98StaCluNC-NC11
❑ 98StaCluOneK-1
❑ 98StaCluPP-1
❑ 98StaCluPWP-P3
❑ 98StaCluRC-RC4
❑ 98StaCluTIII-T1A
❑ 98StaCluTIII-T13B
❑ 98StaCluTLme-T1A
❑ 98StaCluTLme-T13B
❑ 98StaCluTLmo-T1A
❑ 98StaCluTLmo-T13B
❑ 98Stu-159
❑ 98StuFF-9
❑ 98StuFFDC-9
❑ 98StuGPP-159
❑ 98StuMast-14
❑ 98StuPor8x10-10
❑ 98StuPor8x10GP-10
❑ 98StuSPP-159
❑ 98Top-305
❑ 98Top-481
❑ 98TopChr-305
❑ 98TopChr-481
❑ 98TopChrR-305
❑ 98TopChrR-481
❑ 98TopDevR-305
❑ 98TopDevR-481
❑ 98TopDia-305
❑ 98TopDia-481
❑ 98TopGal-95
❑ 98TopGalGoH-GH12
❑ 98TopGalGoHJ-GH12
❑ 98TopGalGP-95
❑ 98TopGalOPP-95
❑ 98TopGalPPI-95
❑ 98TopGalPPIA-95
❑ 98TopGolLabC1-27
❑ 98TopGolLabC1B-27
❑ 98TopGolLabC1One-27
❑ 98TopGolLabC1R-27
❑ 98TopGolLabC2-27
❑ 98TopGolLabC2B-27
❑ 98TopGolLabC2One-27
❑ 98TopGolLabC2R-27
❑ 98TopGolLabC3-27
❑ 98TopGolLabC3B-27
❑ 98TopGolLabC3One-27
❑ 98TopGolLabC3R-27
❑ 98TopMiniC-305
❑ 98TopMiniC-481
❑ 98TopMysF-ILM1
❑ 98TopMysFB-M2
❑ 98TopMysFB-M2
❑ 98TopMysFBR-M2
❑ 98TopMysFBR-M2
❑ 98TopMysFR-ILM1
❑ 98TopOpeD-132
❑ 98TopSta-95
❑ 98TopSta'S-21
❑ 98TopSta'SGH-21
❑ 98TopStaB-95
❑ 98TopStaG-G4
❑ 98TopStaG-95
❑ 98TopStaGG-G4
❑ 98TopStaGGR-G4
❑ 98TopStaGR-95
❑ 98TopStaGS-G4
❑ 98TopStaS-95
❑ 98TopStaSteG-21
❑ 98TopSup-22
❑ 98TopSup-22
❑ 98TopTek-19
❑ 98TopTekD-19
❑ 98UD3-58
❑ 98UD3-148
❑ 98UD3-238
❑ 98UD3DieCut-58
❑ 98UD3DieCut-148
❑ 98UD3DieCut-238
❑ 98UD3PCBlowup-58
❑ 98Ult-202
❑ 98Ult-483
❑ 98UltArtT-7
❑ 98UltBigS-3
❑ 98UltDial-9
❑ 98UltDiaP-7
❑ 98UltDouT-4
❑ 98UltFalC-7
❑ 98UltGolM-202
❑ 98UltGolM-483
❑ 98UltKidG-4
❑ 98UltMas-202
❑ 98UltMas-483
❑ 98UltMilM-7
❑ 98UltNot-12
❑ 98UltPlaM-202
❑ 98UltPlaM-483
❑ 98UltPriL-7
❑ 98UltTicS-12
❑ 98UltTop3-16
❑ 98UltWinN-4
❑ 98UppDec-300
❑ 98UppDec-615
❑ 98UppDec10AP-36
❑ 98UppDec1APR-36
❑ 98UppDecAC-AS16
❑ 98UppDecAG-AG10
❑ 98UppDecAGDC-AG10
❑ 98UppDecBCP-BC20
❑ 98UppDecCD-CD10
❑ 98UppDecNP-NP36
❑ 98UppDecR-8
❑ 98UppDecR-30
❑ 98UppDecRBBop-BB20
❑ 98UppDecRL-3
❑ 98UppDecRQL-Q13
❑ 98UppDecRTC-TC32
❑ 98UppDecSFPD-PZ15
❑ 98UppDecSFPZOB-PZ13
❑ 98UppDecTMT-23
❑ 98UppDecTMTG-23
❑ 98UppDecU-12
❑ 98Zen-20
❑ 98Zen5 xx7-19
❑ 98Zen5x7GoldImp-19
❑ 98Zen5x7Imp-19
❑ 98ZenEpi-E15
❑ 98ZenRaitB-14
❑ 98ZenZ-G-20
❑ 98ZenZ-S-20
❑ 98ZenZ-T-8
❑ 98ZenZ-T5x7-8
❑ 98ZenZ-TG-8
❑ 99199Fin-16
❑ 99199Fin-116
❑ 99199Fin-270
❑ 99AllMysFR-M11
❑ 99AurOn DL-1
❑ 99AurPenF-1
❑ 99AurPenF-1
❑ 99AurPenFB-1
❑ 99AurPenFS-1
❑ 99AurSty-1
❑ 99Bow-43
❑ 99BowBes-1
❑ 99BowBes-95
❑ 99BowBesAR-1
❑ 99BowBesAR-95
❑ 99BowBesFBMI-FB9
❑ 99BowBesFBMII-FB9
❑ 99BowBesFBMIII-FB9
❑ 99BowBesMI-M6
❑ 99BowBesMIAR-M6
❑ 99BowBesMIR-M6
❑ 99BowBesR-1
❑ 99BowBesR-95
❑ 99BowChr-43
❑ 99BowChrDA-DA12
❑ 99BowChrDAR-DA12
❑ 99BowChrG-43
❑ 99BowChrGR-43
❑ 99BowChrI-43
❑ 99BowChrIR-43
❑ 99BowChrR-43
❑ 99BowGol-43
❑ 99BowInt-43
❑ 99CroRoyB-12
❑ 99CroRoyL-12
❑ 99CroRoyMP-1
❑ 99CroRoyOD-12
❑ 99CroRoyPotG-2
❑ 99CroRoyPP-2
❑ 99CroRoyPPN-2
❑ 99E-X Cen-8
❑ 99E-X CenECFut-8
❑ 99E-X CenECNow-8
❑ 99E-XCenFoF'-15
❑ 99FinDouF-DF2
❑ 99FinDouFDualR-DF2
❑ 99FinGolRef-16
❑ 99FinGolRef-116
❑ 99FinGolRef-270
❑ 99FinPeelHyp-16
❑ 99FinPeelSpark-16
❑ 99FinPeeSS-16
❑ 99FinProF-PF28
❑ 99FinProF-PF37
❑ 99FinRef-16
❑ 99FinRef-116
❑ 99FinRef-270
❑ 99FinSplS-SS8
❑ 99FinSplSDR-SS8
❑ 99FinTeaFB-TF17
❑ 99FinTeaFBR-TF17
❑ 99FinTeaFG-TF17
❑ 99FinTeaFGR-TF17
❑ 99FinTeaFR-TF17
❑ 99FinTeaFRR-TF17
❑ 99FlaShoLeg1-4
❑ 99FlaShoLeg2-4
❑ 99FlaShoLeg3-4
❑ 99FlaShoLegM1-4
❑ 99FlaShoLegM2-4
❑ 99FlaShoLegM3-4
❑ 99FlaShoMoG-8
❑ 99FlaShoR1-4
❑ 99FlaShoR2-4
❑ 99FlaShoR3-4
❑ 99Fle-44
❑ 99Fle-592
❑ 99FleBri-10
❑ 99FleBri2G-10
❑ 99FleBriBlu-10
❑ 99FleBriGol-10
❑ 99FleBriSS-9
❑ 99FleBriSSP-9
❑ 99FleDiaM-9
❑ 99FleDiaSkiSheet-NNO
❑ 99FleGoiYar-8
❑ 99FleMys-45
❑ 99FleMysE-3
❑ 99FleMysFI-18
❑ 99FleMysG-45
❑ 99FleMysM-45
❑ 99FleSta9-44
❑ 99FleSta9-592
❑ 99FleVin'-44
❑ 99FleWarT-44
❑ 99FleWarT-592
❑ 99MetUni-208
❑ 99MetUni-245
❑ 99MetUni-292
❑ 99MetUniBWTW-10
❑ 99MetUniDS-3
❑ 99MetUniGM-208
❑ 99MetUniGM-245
❑ 99MetUniGM-292
❑ 99MetUniL-8
❑ 99MetUniPM-4
❑ 99MetUniPMG-208
❑ 99MetUniPMG-245
❑ 99MetUniPMG-292
❑ 99Pac-32
❑ 99Pac-32A
❑ 99PacAur-17
❑ 99PacAurOD-17
❑ 99PacCroC-25
❑ 99PacCroCITC-1
❑ 99PacCroCPB-25
❑ 99PacCroCTC-3
❑ 99PacCroCTM-2
❑ 99PacDynaD-10
❑ 99PacDynaDT-10
❑ 99PacGolCDC-21
❑ 99PacInv-13
❑ 99PacInvFP-2
❑ 99PacInvOD-13
❑ 99PacInvPB-13
❑ 99PacInvSF-2
❑ 99PacInvSF-2B
❑ 99PacInvSH-2
❑ 99PacInvSH-2B
❑ 99PacInvTA-2
❑ 99PacOme-22
❑ 99PacOme5T-11
❑ 99PacOme5TT-11
❑ 99PacOmeC-22
❑ 99PacOmeDD-4
❑ 99PacOmeDM-5
❑ 99PacOmeEP-2
❑ 99PacOmeEP1o1-2
❑ 99PacOmeG-22
❑ 99PacOmeH'-3
❑ 99PacOmePB-22
❑ 99PacPar-24
❑ 99PacParC-24
❑ 99PacParFC-1
❑ 99PacParG-24
❑ 99PacParHoloGold-24
❑ 99PacParHS-24
❑ 99PacParOD-24
❑ 99PacParPB-4
❑ 99PacParPB-24
❑ 99PacParRed-24
❑ 99PacParTC-3
❑ 99PacPlaB-32
❑ 99PacPlaB-32A
❑ 99PacPri-13
❑ 99PacPriAotG-3
❑ 99PacPriDG-13
❑ 99PacPriHB-13
❑ 99PacPriHG-13
❑ 99PacPriHM-13
❑ 99PacPriHP-13
❑ 99PacPriRed-13
❑ 99PacPriS-9
❑ 99PacPriS206-9
❑ 99PacPriS206R-9
❑ 99PacPriSE-9
❑ 99PacPriSP-9
❑ 99PacPriSP-9
❑ 99PacPriSV-9
❑ 99PacRed-32
❑ 99PacRed-32A
❑ 99PacTeaC-16
❑ 99PacTim-13
❑ 99Pin-14
❑ 99Rev-12
❑ 99RevDiaL-4
❑ 99RevFouP-1
❑ 99RevPremDate-12
❑ 99RevRet-12
❑ 99RevShaSS-12
❑ 99RevThoitS-2
❑ 99RevTri-12
❑ 99RevTri-12
❑ 99SkyMolM-143
❑ 99SkyMolMF-43
❑ 99SkyMolMFS-43
❑ 99SkyMolMFT-43
❑ 99SkyMolMOA-7
❑ 99SkyMolMX-143
❑ 99SkyPre-167
❑ 99SkyPre-296
❑ 99SkyPreIN-8
❑ 99SkyPreLB-13
❑ 99SkyPreR-167
❑ 99SkyPreR-296
❑ 99SkyPreSB-6
❑ 99SkyPreSotG-3
❑ 99SkyThu-263
❑ 99SkyThuDial1-D4
❑ 99SkyThuHip-H7
❑ 99SkyThuRant-263
❑ 99SkyThuRave-263
❑ 99SP Aut-7
❑ 99SP AutC-CJ
❑ 99SP AutCG-CJ
❑ 99SP AutEF-E5
❑ 99SP AutHRC-HR27
❑ 99SP AutR-R5
❑ 99SP SigAuto-CJ
❑ 99SP SigAutoG-CJ
❑ 99SPAutHRCDC-HR27
❑ 99SpoIll-98
❑ 99SpoIllH-4
❑ 99SPSig-8
❑ 99SPx-16
❑ 99SPxDom-FB1
❑ 99SPxFinR-16
❑ 99SPxFinS-16
❑ 99SPxPowE-PE4
❑ 99SPxPreS-PS15
❑ 99SPxStaF-SF1
❑ 99StaClu-2
❑ 99StaCluA-SCA2
❑ 99StaCluC-SCC22
❑ 99StaCluC-CS4
❑ 99StaCluC-CS9
❑ 99StaCluC-CS16
❑ 99StaCluC-CS20
❑ 99StaCluCR-SCC22
❑ 99StaCluFDI-2
❑ 99StaCluNC-NC17
❑ 99StaCluOoaK-2
❑ 99StaCluPP-2
❑ 99StaCluTI-T2B
❑ 99StaCluTI-T12A
❑ 99StaCluTL-T2B
❑ 99StaCluTL-T12A
❑ 99StaCluTL-T2B
❑ 99StaCluTL-T12A
❑ 99ThuSkySupR-263
❑ 99Top-355
❑ 99Top-453
❑ 99TopActF-6
❑ 99TopActFAU-6
❑ 99TopActFCU-6
❑ 99TopAllMF-M11
❑ 99TopAut-A2
❑ 99TopBlaLC1-16
❑ 99TopBlaLC2-16
❑ 99TopBlaLC3-16
❑ 99TopChr-355
❑ 99TopChr-453
❑ 99TopChrERttH-ER6
❑ 99TopChrERttH-ER6
❑ 99TopChrF1-FF14
❑ 99TopChrF1R-FF14
❑ 99TopChrLotD-LD2
❑ 99TopChrLotDR-LD2
❑ 99TopChrR-355
❑ 99TopChrR-453
❑ 99TopGal-86
❑ 99TopGal-105
❑ 99TopGalGoH-GH9
❑ 99TopGalHer-TH12
❑ 99TopGalHerP-TH12
❑ 99TopGalPP-86
❑ 99TopGalPP-105
❑ 99TopGalPPI-86
❑ 99TopGalPPI-105
❑ 99TopGolL-16
❑ 99TopGolLC1-16
❑ 99TopGolLC2-16
❑ 99TopGolLOtO-16
❑ 99TopLorotD-LD2
❑ 99TopMVPP-355
❑ 99TopMVPP-453
❑ 99TopOpeD-116
❑ 99TopOver-B6
❑ 99TopPowB-PB16
❑ 99TopPowBR-PB16
❑ 99TopRedLC1-16
❑ 99TopRedLC2-16
❑ 99TopRedLC3-16
❑ 99TopSta-2
❑ 99TopSta-176
❑ 99TopSta'S-3
❑ 99TopSta'SG-3
❑ 99TopSta'SGDH-3
❑ 99TopSta1Foil-2
❑ 99TopSta2Foil-2
❑ 99TopSta3Foil-2
❑ 99TopSta4Foil-2
❑ 99TopStaFoil-2
❑ 99TopStaFoil-176
❑ 99TopStaFS-2
❑ 99TopStaOS-2
❑ 99TopStaPre-PP5
❑ 99TopStaTS-2
❑ 99TopStaTS-2
❑ 99TopSupC-24
❑ 99TopSupCR-24
❑ 99TopTek-16A
❑ 99TopTek-16B
❑ 99TopTekG-16A
❑ 99TopTekG-16B
❑ 99UD Cho-42
❑ 99UD Cho-55
❑ 99UD ChoMBH-B3
❑ 99UD ChoPCR-42
❑ 99UD ChoPCR-55
❑ 99UD ChoS-10
❑ 99UD ChoSD-10
❑ 99UD ChoSHR-10
❑ 99UD ChoST-10
❑ 99UD ChoYW-Y2
❑ 99UD Ion-5
❑ 99UD Ion-64
❑ 99UD IonC-C7
❑ 99UD IonH-HG7
❑ 99UD IonH-H7
❑ 99UD IonN-N7
❑ 99UD IonR-5
❑ 99UD IonR-64
❑ 99UD IonWZ-WZ7
❑ 99UDHolo-6
❑ 99UDHoloAUsome-6
❑ 99UDHoloLau-L9
❑ 99UDHoloLauG-L9
❑ 99UDHoloStar-S9
❑ 99UDHoloStarG-S9
❑ 99UDHoloUDA-CJ
❑ 99Ult-156
❑ 99UltDamI-4
❑ 99UltDiaP-9
❑ 99UltGolM-156
❑ 99UltMas-156
❑ 99UltPlaM-156
❑ 99UltRBIK-10
❑ 99UltTheBook-16

❑ 99UltThu-4
❑ 99UppDec-309
❑ 99UppDec-523
❑ 99UppDec10AT-X4
❑ 99UppDec10ATD-X4
❑ 99UppDec10ATHR-X4
❑ 99UppDec10ATT-X4
❑ 99UppDecBD-8
❑ 99UppDecBDD-8
❑ 99UppDecBDDom-D10
❑ 99UppDecBDDomE-D10
❑ 99UppDecBDMN-M6
❑ 99UppDecBDMNE-M6
❑ 99UppDecBDQ-8
❑ 99UppDecBDT-8
❑ 99UppDecCf7-18
❑ 99UppDecCf7-74
❑ 99UppDecCf7-C15
❑ 99UppDecCf7Cf7P-C15
❑ 99UppDecCf7LL-L16
❑ 99UppDecCf7SftF-S9
❑ 99UppDecCL-81
❑ 99UppDecCL-119
❑ 99UppDecCLCC-81
❑ 99UppDecCLCC-119
❑ 99UppDecCLM-C6
❑ 99UppDecCo7CE-18
❑ 99UppDecCo7CE-74
❑ 99UppDecE-8
❑ 99UppDecE-179
❑ 99UppDecE2C-2K6
❑ 99UppDecEDF-D13
❑ 99UppDecEDFFXG-D13
❑ 99UppDecEFXG-8
❑ 99UppDecEFXG-179
❑ 99UppDecEL1-309
❑ 99UppDecEL1-523
❑ 99UppDecEL2-309
❑ 99UppDecEL2-523
❑ 99UppDecEPE-P4
❑ 99UppDecF-F6
❑ 99UppDecFD-F6
❑ 99UppDecFQ-F6
❑ 99UppDecFT-F6
❑ 99UppDecGJ-CJ
❑ 99UppDecIP-I12
❑ 99UppDecIPD-I12
❑ 99UppDecIPHR-I12
❑ 99UppDecIPT-I12
❑ 99UppDecM-15
❑ 99UppDecM-P8
❑ 99UppDecMD-D7
❑ 99UppDecMGS-15
❑ 99UppDecMGUS-GUCJ
❑ 99UppDecMGUS-GACJ
❑ 99UppDecMHFS-15
❑ 99UppDecMP-15
❑ 99UppDecMP-CJ
❑ 99UppDecMSS-15
❑ 99UppDecMST-T15
❑ 99UppDecMST-S9
❑ 99UppDecO-56
❑ 99UppDecO-85
❑ 99UppDecOAPoH-CJ
❑ 99UppDecOMP-S3
❑ 99UppDecOSO-56
❑ 99UppDecOSO-85
❑ 99UppDecR-8
❑ 99UppDecRDR-D10
❑ 99UppDecRDRL2-D10
❑ 99UppDecRG-8
❑ 99UppDecRI-CJ
❑ 99UppDecRIL2-CJ
❑ 99UppDecROSS-S5
❑ 99UppDecROSS-S5
❑ 99UppDecRP-8
❑ 99UppDecTE-T3
❑ 99UppDecTED-T3
❑ 99UppDecTEQ-T3
❑ 99UppDecTET-T3
❑ 99UppDecVtaT-V4
❑ 99UppDecVtaTD-V4
❑ 99UppDecVtaTQ-V4
❑ 99UppDecVtaTT-V4
❑ 99UppDecWY-W15
❑ 99UppDecWYD-W15
❑ 99UppDecWYHR-W15
❑ 99UppDecWYT-W15
❑ 99Vic-29
❑ 99Vic-30
❑ 99Vic-32
❑ 99Vic-451

Jones, Chris

❑ 78WauMetT-12
❑ 82TucTorT-2
❑ 83TucTorT-19
❑ 84TucTorC-52
❑ 85TucTorC-51
❑ 98SalVol-17
❑ 99Bow-177
❑ 99BowBes-199
❑ 99BowBesAR-199
❑ 99BowBesR-199
❑ 99BowChr-177
❑ 99BowChrG-177
❑ 99BowChrGR-177
❑ 99BowChrI-177
❑ 99BowChrIR-177
❑ 99BowChrR-177
❑ 99BowGol-177
❑ 99BowInt-177
❑ 99Top-213
❑ 99TopChr-213
❑ 99TopChrR-213

Jones, Chris C.

❑ 86CedRapRT-21
❑ 86PhoFirP-12
❑ 87DunBluJP-939
❑ 87PhoFirP-1
❑ 87VerRedP-22
❑ 88ChaLooB-6
❑ 88IdaFalBP-1843
❑ 88KnoBluJB-16
❑ 88SanDieSAAG-10
❑ 89KnoBluJB-11
❑ 89KnoBluJP-1134
❑ 89KnoBluJS-9
❑ 89NasSouC-20
❑ 89NasSouP-1290
❑ 89SanDieSAG-9
❑ 90CMC-141
❑ 90NasSouC-16
❑ 90NasSouP-246
❑ 90ProAAAF-558
❑ 91AlbDukLD-11
❑ 91AlbDukP-1136
❑ 91Bow-676
❑ 91DonRoo-50
❑ 91ScoRoo-92T
❑ 91TopTra-65T
❑ 91TopTraT-65T
❑ 92AstMot-22
❑ 92Don-464
❑ 92Fle-410
❑ 92Lea-444
❑ 92LeaBlaG-444
❑ 92OPC-332
❑ 92Sco-811
❑ 92Sco100RS-69
❑ 92StaClu-698
❑ 92Top-332
❑ 92TopDeb91-93
❑ 92TopGol-332
❑ 92TopGolW-332
❑ 92TopMic-332
❑ 93Fla-42
❑ 93FleFinE-35
❑ 93RocStaC-19
❑ 93TopTra-102T
❑ 94Don-510
❑ 94Fle-445
❑ 94Pac-199
❑ 94PanSti-176
❑ 94Sco-148
❑ 94ScoGolR-148
❑ 94Top-496
❑ 94TopGol-496
❑ 94TopSpa-496
❑ 96ColCho-226
❑ 96ColChoGS-226
❑ 96ColChoSS-226
❑ 96Fle-483
❑ 96FleTif-483
❑ 96LeaSigEA-94
❑ 96MetKah-18
❑ 96MetKah-20
❑ 97PadMot-20
❑ 98DiaBacP-24
❑ 98GiaMot-19
❑ 98PacInvGems-210

Jones, Chris L.

❑ 88CapCodPPaLP-164
❑ 90KnoBluJB-20
❑ 90KnoBluJP-1243
❑ 90KnoBluJS-7
❑ 91LinDriAAA-11

Jones, Clarence W.

❑ 68Top-506
❑ 86SumBraP-13
❑ 87SumBraP-6
❑ 88RicBraC-25
❑ 88RicBraP-17
❑ 89BraDub-14
❑ 90BraDubS-15
❑ 91BraSubS-20
❑ 92BraLykS-18
❑ 93BraLykS-17
❑ 94BraLykP-12
❑ 94BraLykS-13

Jones, Cleon Joseph

❑ 65Top-308
❑ 66MetPos-5
❑ 66MetTeal-8
❑ 66OPC-67
❑ 66Top-67
❑ 66TopVen-67
❑ 67CokCapA-31
❑ 67CokCapNLA-35
❑ 67CokCapYM-V24
❑ 67DexPre-110
❑ 67Kah-19
❑ 67MetTeal-8
❑ 67OPC-165
❑ 67OPCPapI-13
❑ 67Top-165
❑ 67TopPos-13
❑ 67TopTesF-8
❑ 68Top-254
❑ 68TopVen-254
❑ 69MetBoyS-6
❑ 69MetCit-7
❑ 69MetNewYDN-10
❑ 69MetTeal-9
❑ 69MilBra-139
❑ 69MLBOffS-167
❑ 69Top-512
❑ 69TopSta-65
❑ 69TopSup-50
❑ 70Kel-3
❑ 70MetTeal-8
❑ 70MetTra-24C
❑ 70MLBOffS-78
❑ 70OPC-61
❑ 70Top-61
❑ 70Top-575
❑ 70TopBoo-19
❑ 70TraSta-1C
❑ 71MetTeal-10
❑ 71MLBOffS-156
❑ 71OPC-527
❑ 71Top-527
❑ 71TopCoi-103
❑ 71TopTat-4
❑ 72MetTeal-4
❑ 72MilBra-171
❑ 72OPC-31
❑ 72OPC-32
❑ 72Top-31
❑ 72Top-32
❑ 73LinPor-113
❑ 73MetAllEB-5
❑ 73MetTeal-5
❑ 73NewYorSNM-15
❑ 73OPC-540
❑ 73Top-540
❑ 74MetDaiPA-15
❑ 74OPC-245
❑ 74OPC-476
❑ 74Top-245
❑ 74Top-476
❑ 74TopSta-64
❑ 75Hos-123
❑ 75Kel-21
❑ 75MetSSP-11
❑ 75OPC-43
❑ 75Top-43
❑ 75TopMin-43
❑ 81TCM60I-322
❑ 86MetGreT-5
❑ 87Met196T-3
❑ 89Met196C-7
❑ 89MetRinP69-16
❑ 91MetWIZ-207
❑ 92UppDecS-10
❑ 94Met69CCPP-19
❑ 94Met69CS-18
❑ 94Met69T-14
❑ 96Met69Y-5

Jones, Cliff

❑ 92PitMetC-17
❑ 92PitMetF-3290

Jones, Craig

❑ 84RicBraT-13

Jones, D.J.

❑ 87DurBulP-23

Jones, Dan

❑ 83MiaMarT-15
❑ 91Cla/Bes-423
❑ 91WelPirC-29
❑ 91WelPirP-3568
❑ 92SalBucC-21
❑ 92SalBucF-60
❑ 92StaCluD-95
❑ 93CarMudF-2051
❑ 93CarMudTI-9

Jones, Darryl

❑ 78TacYanC-15
❑ 79ColCliT-28
❑ 80Top-670
❑ 92YanWIZ7-84

Jones, David

❑ 85DurBulT-7
❑ 86SumBraP-14

Jones, Davy (David Jefferson)

❑ 03WilCarE-17
❑ 07TigACDPP-7
❑ 09ColChiE-144
❑ 09TigMorPWBPP-6
❑ 09TigTaCP-8
❑ 09WolNewDTPP-9
❑ 10NadE1-24
❑ 10StaCarE-17
❑ 10W555-37
❑ 11HelSta-33
❑ 11PinT-5-163
❑ 11S74Sil-15
❑ 11SpoLifCW-190
❑ 11SpoLifM-60
❑ 11T205-83
❑ 11TurRedT-100
❑ 12ColRedB-144
❑ 12ColTinT-144
❑ 12HasTriFT-47
❑ 14PieStaT-57
❑ 81TigDetN-19
❑ 93ConTSN-753

Jones, Dax

❑ 91Cla/Bes-421
❑ 91EveGiaC-8
❑ 91EveGiaP-3931
❑ 92ClaFS7-79
❑ 92CliGiaC-1
❑ 92CliGiaF-3610
❑ 93ShrCapF-2771
❑ 94PhoFirF-1532
❑ 95PhoFirTI-24
❑ 96PhoFirB-19
❑ 97PhoFirTI-13
❑ 97Sco-323
❑ 97ScoArtPWB-323
❑ 97ScoPreS-323
❑ 97ScoShoS-323
❑ 97ScoShoSAP-323

Jones, Deacon (Grover)

❑ 63Top-253
❑ 63WhiSoxTS-12
❑ 76HouAstP-17
❑ 78AstPos-13
❑ 81AstPos-8
❑ 82AstPos-7
❑ 84PadMot-27
❑ 85PadMot-27

Jones, Dennis

❑ 87MyrBeaBJP-1447
❑ 88BasAmeAAB-19
❑ 88KnoBluJB-16
❑ 89KnoBluJB-12
❑ 89KnoBluJP-1136
❑ 89KnoBluJS-10
❑ 90KnoBluJB-24
❑ 90KnoBluJS-8

Jones, DeWayne

❑ 88SouOreAP-1698

Jones, Donny

❑ 77QuaCitAT-20
❑ 78QuaCitAT-11
❑ 80ElPasDT-18

Jones, Donny 90's

❑ 93UtiBluSC-12
❑ 94HigDesMC-17
❑ 94HigDesMF-2803

Jones, Doug

❑ 78NewWayCT-21
❑ 79BurBeeT-12
❑ 81ElPasDT-11
❑ 82BrePol-45
❑ 82VanCanT-13
❑ 84ElPasDT-7
❑ 84VanCanC-39
❑ 85WatIndT-12
❑ 86MaiGuiP-11
❑ 87IndGat-46
❑ 88Don-588
❑ 88DonBasB-325
❑ 88Fle-613
❑ 88FleGlo-613
❑ 88IndGat-11
❑ 88IndTeal-22
❑ 88Sco-594
❑ 88ScoGlo-594
❑ 88StaLinI-15
❑ 88Top-293
❑ 88TopTif-293
❑ 89Bow-78
❑ 89BowTif-78
❑ 89ClaLigB-89
❑ 89Don-438
❑ 89DonAll-20
❑ 89DonBasB-173
❑ 89Fle-409
❑ 89FleBasA-23
❑ 89FleBasM-23
❑ 89FleGlo-409
❑ 89IndTeal-15
❑ 89OPC-312
❑ 89PanSti-5
❑ 89PanSti-319
❑ 89Sco-387
❑ 89Sco-656
❑ 89ScoHot1S-41
❑ 89Spo-38
❑ 89Top-6
❑ 89Top-690
❑ 89TopBasT-161
❑ 89TopMinL-51
❑ 89TopSti-3
❑ 89TopSti-215
❑ 89TopStiB-32
❑ 89TopTif-6
❑ 89TopTif-690
❑ 89UppDec-540
❑ 89Woo-14
❑ 90Bow-328
❑ 90BowTif-328
❑ 90ClaBlu-114
❑ 90Don-320
❑ 90DonBesA-61
❑ 90El PasDAGTI-15
❑ 90Fle-495
❑ 90FleBasA-22
❑ 90FleBasAC-22
❑ 90FleCan-495
❑ 90FleLeaL-20
❑ 90FleLeaLC-20
❑ 90GeoColC-10
❑ 90IndTeal-21
❑ 90Lea-153
❑ 90M.Vpin-32
❑ 90OPC-75
❑ 90PanSti-63
❑ 90PubIntS-562
❑ 90Sco-130
❑ 90Spo-96
❑ 90Top-75
❑ 90TopBig-316
❑ 90TopSti-215
❑ 90TopTif-75
❑ 90UppDec-632
❑ 90USPlaCA-7S
❑ 91Bow-77
❑ 91ClaGam-55
❑ 91Don-232
❑ 91Fle-372
❑ 91IndFanC-16
❑ 91Lea-57
❑ 91OPC-745
❑ 91PanCanT1-87
❑ 91PanFreS-224
❑ 91PanSti-173
❑ 91RedFolS-54
❑ 91Sco-45
❑ 91Sco-884
❑ 91Sco100S-54
❑ 91StaClu-145
❑ 91Stu-46
❑ 91Top-745
❑ 91TopDesS-745
❑ 91TopMic-745
❑ 91TopTif-745
❑ 91Ult-115
❑ 91UppDec-216
❑ 92AstMot-16
❑ 92Don-674
❑ 92Fle-114
❑ 92FleUpd-87
❑ 92Lea-253
❑ 92LeaBlaG-253
❑ 92OPC-461
❑ 92OPCPre-51
❑ 92Pin-499
❑ 92Sco-53
❑ 92ScoProP-11
❑ 92ScoRoo-38T
❑ 92StaClu-616
❑ 92StaCluNC-616
❑ 92Stu-38
❑ 92Top-461
❑ 92TopGol-461
❑ 92TopGolW-461
❑ 92TopMic-461
❑ 92TopTra-57T
❑ 92TopTraG-57T
❑ 92UppDec-798
❑ 93AstMot-14
❑ 93AstStaC-15
❑ 93Bow-532
❑ 93Don-296
❑ 93Fin-69
❑ 93FinRef-69
❑ 93Fla-65
❑ 93Fle-54
❑ 93Lea-161
❑ 93OPC-267
❑ 93PacSpa-478
❑ 93Pin-443
❑ 93Sco-197
❑ 93Sel-67
❑ 93StaClu-411
❑ 93StaCluFDI-411
❑ 93StaCluM-53
❑ 93StaCluMOP-411
❑ 93Stu-115
❑ 93Top-171
❑ 93TopGol-171
❑ 93TopInaM-171
❑ 93TopInaR-171
❑ 93TopMic-171
❑ 93TriPla-175
❑ 93Ult-44
❑ 93UppDec-171
❑ 93UppDecGold-171
❑ 94BreMilB-135
❑ 94ColC-513
❑ 94ColChoGS-513
❑ 94ColChoSS-513
❑ 94Don-533
❑ 94Fin-380
❑ 94FinRef-380
❑ 94Fla-209
❑ 94Fle-494
❑ 94FleExtB-338
❑ 94FleUpd-165
❑ 94Lea-377
❑ 94PanSti-195
❑ 94PhiMed-16
❑ 94PhiMel-12
❑ 94Pin-222
❑ 94PinArtP-222
❑ 94PinMusC-222
❑ 94Sco-544
❑ 94ScoGolR-544
❑ 94ScoRoo-RT69
❑ 94ScoRooGR-RT69
❑ 94StaClu-580
❑ 94StaCluFDI-580
❑ 94StaCluGR-580
❑ 94StaCluMOP-580
❑ 94StaCluT-216
❑ 94StaCluTFDI-216
❑ 94Top-334
❑ 94TopGol-334
❑ 94TopSpa-334
❑ 94TopTra-126T
❑ 94Ult-207
❑ 94Ult-548
❑ 94UppDec-374
❑ 94UppDecED-374
❑ 95BalOriP-27
❑ 95ColCho-368
❑ 95ColCho-563T
❑ 95ColChoGS-368
❑ 95ColChoSE-174
❑ 95ColChoSEGS-174
❑ 95ColChoSESS-174
❑ 95ColChoSS-368
❑ 95DonTopotO-11
❑ 95Fin-268
❑ 95FinRef-268
❑ 95Fla-222
❑ 95Fle-396
❑ 95FleAllS-25
❑ 95FleUpd-5
❑ 95Lea-394
❑ 95Sco-467

❑ 95ScoGolR-467
❑ 95ScoPlaTS-467
❑ 95StaClu-89
❑ 95StaClu-564
❑ 95StaCluFDI-89
❑ 95StaCluMOP-89
❑ 95StaCluMOP-564
❑ 95StaCluSTWS-89
❑ 95StaCluSTWS-564
❑ 95StaCluVR-55
❑ 95StaCluVRMO-55
❑ 95Top-495
❑ 95TopCyb-285
❑ 95TopTra-113T
❑ 95UppDecSE-74
❑ 95UppDecSEG-74
❑ 96ColCho-767
❑ 96CubFle-10
❑ 96Don-237
❑ 96DonPreP-237
❑ 96Fla-218
❑ 96Fle-12
❑ 96FleTif-12
❑ 96FleUpd-U111
❑ 96FleUpdTC-U111
❑ 96StaClu-38
❑ 96StaCluMOP-38
❑ 96Top-183
❑ 96Ult-7
❑ 96Ult-450
❑ 96UltGolM-7
❑ 96UltGolM-450
❑ 96UppDec-487U
❑ 97BrePol-12
❑ 98CirThu-113
❑ 98CirThuRav-113
❑ 98CirThuSupRav-113
❑ 98ColCho-402
❑ 98Fle-139
❑ 98Pac-117
❑ 98PacOnl-400
❑ 98PacOnlR-400
❑ 98PacOnlWC-400
❑ 98PacPar-188
❑ 98PacParC-188
❑ 98PacParG-188
❑ 98PacParHS-188
❑ 98PacParPB-188
❑ 98PacParR-188
❑ 98PacPlaB-117
❑ 98PacRedT-117
❑ 98PacSil-117
❑ 98Pin-85
❑ 98PinPreP-85
❑ 98StaCluFDI-259
❑ 98StaCluI-259
❑ 98StaCluOneK-259
❑ 98StaCluPP-259
❑ 98Top-138
❑ 98TopChr-138
❑ 98TopChrR-138
❑ 98TopDevR-138
❑ 98TopDia-138
❑ 98TopMiniC-138
❑ 98UppDec-124
❑ 98UppDecSF-76

Jones, Ducky (Bobby)
❑ 26Zee-50
❑ 27Zee-28
❑ 28ExhPCL-14
❑ 28Zee-33
❑ 28Zee-34
❑ 29Zee-23

Jones, Elijah
❑ 12ImpTobC-52

Jones, Eric
❑ 81BatTroT-22

Jones, Eugene
❑ 89GreHorP-416
❑ 90Bes-207
❑ 90ChaWheB-22
❑ 90ChaWheP-2253
❑ 90CMC-695
❑ 91CedRapRC-22
❑ 91CedRapRP-2732
❑ 92ChaWheF-21
❑ 93WinSpiF-1580

Jones, Fielder
❑ 03BreE10-76
❑ 04FanCraAL-29
❑ 07WhiSoxGWH-6
❑ 08RosComP-15
❑ 09T206-176
❑ 09T206-177
❑ 15SpoNewM-91
❑ 16BF2FP-43
❑ 16SpoNewM-92
❑ 17ColE13-89
❑ 19W514-50
❑ 87ConSer2-44
❑ 90DodTar-391
❑ 90HOFStiB-20

Jones, Fontella
❑ 98HelBreM-21

Jones, Gary
❑ 83QuaCitCT-21
❑ 86FreGiaSB-4
❑ 86HunStaDJ-11
❑ 87TacTigP-5
❑ 88SanJosGCLC-121
❑ 88SanJosGP-112
❑ 88TacTigC-23
❑ 88TacTigP-612
❑ 89HunStaB-17
❑ 91MadMusC-22
❑ 91MadMusP-2146
❑ 92RenSilSCLC-59
❑ 93MadMusC-27
❑ 93MadMusF-1838
❑ 94BenRocC-12
❑ 94BenRocF-3603
❑ 94HunStaF-1347
❑ 95EdmTraTI-13
❑ 98A'sMot-28

Jones, Gary (Gareth Howell)
❑ 71OPC-559
❑ 71Top-559
❑ 92YanWIZ7-85

Jones, Geary
❑ 86ColMetP-17
❑ 87LynMetP-17
❑ 88JacMetGS-3
❑ 88St.LucMS-14
❑ 92KinMetC-26
❑ 92KinMetF-1548

Jones, George
❑ 85EveGiaC-6A
❑ 85EveGiaC-6B

Jones, Glenn
❑ 82CliGiaF-21
❑ 91AdeGiaF-1

Jones, Golfer (Bobby)
❑ 32USCar*-3
❑ 87SpoCubG-1

Jones, Gordon
❑ 82RedPioT-5

Jones, Gordon Bassett
❑ 55CarHunW-11
❑ 55Top-78
❑ 55TopDouH-5
❑ 59Top-458
❑ 60BalOriP-7
❑ 60Lea-73
❑ 60Top-98
❑ 60TopVen-98
❑ 61Top-442
❑ 91OriCro-229

Jones, Gordon PCL
❑ 22Zee-28
❑ 23Zee-39
❑ 29Zee-135

Jones, Greg
❑ 95ArkTraTI-16
❑ 97BoiHawG-16

Jones, Grier
❑ 94ForWayWC-11
❑ 94ForWayWF-2012

Jones, Gus
❑ 86EugEmeC-47
❑ 87Ft.MyeRP-14

Jones, Guy
❑ 78QuaCitAT-12

Jones, Hank
❑ 77LodDodT-7
❑ 78LodDodT-9
❑ 79LodDodT-20

Jones, Harold
❑ 62Top-49
❑ 62TopVen-49

Jones, Ivory
❑ 96FtMyeMB-24

Jones, J. Dalton
❑ 63SeaPop-6
❑ 64Top-459
❑ 65OPC-178
❑ 65Top-178
❑ 66Top-317
❑ 66TopVen-317
❑ 67CokCapRS-8
❑ 67DexPre-111
❑ 67OPC-139
❑ 67Top-139
❑ 67TopRedSS-8
❑ 67TopVen-237
❑ 68CokCapRS-8
❑ 68DexPre-44
❑ 68OPC-106
❑ 68Top-106
❑ 68TopVen-106
❑ 69MilBra-140
❑ 69RedSoxAO-5
❑ 69RedSoxTI-4
❑ 69Top-457
❑ 70Top-682
❑ 71MLBOffS-395
❑ 71OPC-367
❑ 71Top-367
❑ 72MilBra-172
❑ 72OPC-83
❑ 72RanTeal-14
❑ 72Top-83
❑ 73OPC-512
❑ 73Top-512
❑ 81RedSoxBG2S-87
❑ 89PacSenL-55
❑ 93RanKee-20

Jones, Jack
❑ 97SanBerS-22

Jones, Jacque
❑ 97Bes-75
❑ 97Bow-329
❑ 97BowChr-225
❑ 97BowChrI-225
❑ 97BowChrIR-225
❑ 97BowChrR-225
❑ 97BowInt-329
❑ 97FloStaLTPB-11
❑ 97ForMyeM-15
❑ 98Bow-143
❑ 98BowCerBlueAU-28
❑ 98BowCerGA-28
❑ 98BowCerSA-28
❑ 98BowChr-143
❑ 98BowChrGA-143
❑ 98BowChrGAR-143
❑ 98BowChrI-143
❑ 98BowChrIR-143
❑ 98BowChrR-143
❑ 98BowGolA-143
❑ 98BowInt-143
❑ 98EasLeaTPM-13
❑ 98NewBriRCM-16
❑ 98SP MinDTSPE-DS18
❑ 98SP MinPE-76
❑ 98SP MinSTHPE-H9
❑ 98SP SPTSC-JJ
❑ 98SPMin-76
❑ 98SPMinDTS-DS18
❑ 98SPMinSTH-H9
❑ 99Bow-121
❑ 99BowAut-BA32
❑ 99BowChr-121
❑ 99BowChrG-121
❑ 99BowChrGR-121
❑ 99BowChrI-121
❑ 99BowChrIR-121
❑ 99BowChrR-121
❑ 99BowGol-121
❑ 99BowInt-121
❑ 99PacOme-142
❑ 99PacOmeC-142
❑ 99PacOmeG-142
❑ 99PacOmePB-142
❑ 99SP TopP-63
❑ 99SP TopPPE-63

Jones, Jaime
❑ 95Bes-122
❑ 95ElmPioUTI-NNO
❑ 95SPML-105
❑ 96KanCouCTI-15
❑ 96KanCouCUTI-8
❑ 96MauStiHWB-27
❑ 97BreCouMB-20
❑ 97FloStaLTPB-1
❑ 98Bow-120
❑ 98BowChr-120
❑ 98BowChrGA-120
❑ 98BowChrGAR-120
❑ 98BowChrI-120
❑ 98BowChrIR-120
❑ 98BowChrR-120
❑ 98BowGolA-120
❑ 98BowInt-120
❑ 98EasLeaTPM-14
❑ 98PorSeaDQ-24
❑ 98SP MinPE-58
❑ 98SPMin-58
❑ 99BasAmeTP-56
❑ 99BasAmeTPG-56

Jones, Jake
❑ 48RedSoxTI-12
❑ 85TCMPla1-2

Jones, James
❑ 07NewEveWS-4
❑ 86EveGiaC-25
❑ 86EveGiaPC-9
❑ 86ModA'sC-11
❑ 88CapCodPB-3
❑ 88CapCodPPaLP-70
❑ 89BenBucL-5

Jones, Jeffrey A.
❑ 79OgdA'sT-23
❑ 81Top-687
❑ 82Don-213
❑ 82Fle-94
❑ 82FleSta-130
❑ 82TacTigT-24
❑ 82Top-139
❑ 83Don-651
❑ 83TacTigT-28
❑ 83Top-259
❑ 84Nes792-464
❑ 84Top-464
❑ 84TopTif-464
❑ 85Top-319
❑ 85TopTif-319
❑ 91PacSenL-32

Jones, Jeffrey R.
❑ 80CedRapRT-19
❑ 81CedRapRT-16
❑ 82CedRapRT-24
❑ 84Don-262
❑ 84MidCubT-20
❑ 84TacTigC-82
❑ 87GleFalTP-4
❑ 88GleFalTP-936
❑ 89CedRapRAB-19
❑ 89FayGenP-1570
❑ 90CedRapRDGB-19
❑ 90CMC-399
❑ 90ProAAAF-395
❑ 90TolMudHC-26
❑ 90TolMudHP-165
❑ 91LinDriAA-400
❑ 91LonTigLD-400
❑ 91LonTigP-1893
❑ 92LonTigF-650
❑ 93TolMudHF-1669
❑ 94SpoIndC-14
❑ 94SpoIndF-3319
❑ 94TolMudHF-1042
❑ 96JacSunB-3
❑ 97TolMudHB-3
❑ 98TolMudHQ-4

Jones, Jim
❑ 84MadMusP-14
❑ 85ModA'sC-15
❑ 86ModA'sP-15
❑ 87PocGiaTB-7
❑ 87SpoTeaP-16
❑ 88TacTigP-618
❑ 89CalLeaA-30
❑ 89DenZepP-40
❑ 89SanJosGB-23
❑ 89SanJosGCLC-222
❑ 89SanJosGP-460
❑ 89SanJosGS-16
❑ 90SanJosGB-11
❑ 90SanJosGCLC-38
❑ 90SanJosGP-2016
❑ 90SanJosGS-14
❑ 91RenSilSCLC-5

Jones, Jimmy (James C.)
❑ 84BeaGolGT-1
❑ 85BeaGolGT-8
❑ 86LasVegSP-9
❑ 87Don-557
❑ 87Fle-650
❑ 87FleGlo-650
❑ 87FleUpd-54
❑ 87FleUpdG-54
❑ 87HunStaTI-15
❑ 87LasVegSP-17
❑ 87SouLeaAJ-12
❑ 87SpoRoo2-35
❑ 88Don-141
❑ 88DonBasB-189
❑ 88Fle-588
❑ 88FleGlo-588
❑ 88HunStaTI-9
❑ 88PadCok-45
❑ 88PadSmo-13
❑ 88Sco-246
❑ 88ScoGlo-246
❑ 88TacTigC-21
❑ 88Top-63
❑ 88TopTif-63
❑ 89Bow-169
❑ 89BowTif-169
❑ 89ColCliC-9
❑ 89ColCliP-6
❑ 89ColCliP-752
❑ 89DenZepC-17
❑ 89Don-247
❑ 89DonBasB-217
❑ 89Fle-308
❑ 89FleGlo-308
❑ 89Sco-294
❑ 89Top-748
❑ 89TopTif-748
❑ 89TopTra-58T
❑ 89TopTraT-58T
❑ 89UppDec-286
❑ 89YanScoNW-26
❑ 90CMC-223
❑ 90ColCliC-23
❑ 90ColCliP-19
❑ 90ColCliP-672
❑ 90OPC-359
❑ 90ProAAAF-322
❑ 90Top-359
❑ 90TopTif-359
❑ 90TopTVY-48
❑ 90YanScoNW-21
❑ 91AstMot-12
❑ 91Bow-553
❑ 91Fle-667
❑ 91Lea-371
❑ 91Sco-583
❑ 92AstMot-12
❑ 92Don-272
❑ 92Fle-438
❑ 92OPC-184
❑ 92Sco-33
❑ 92ScoProP-6
❑ 92StaClu-53
❑ 92Top-184
❑ 92TopGol-184
❑ 92TopGolW-184
❑ 92TopMic-184
❑ 92UppDec-392
❑ 92YanWIZ8-93
❑ 93Don-324
❑ 93ExpPosN-14
❑ 93Fle-437
❑ 93OPC-293
❑ 93PacSpa-125
❑ 93Sco-463
❑ 93Top-477
❑ 93TopGol-477
❑ 93TopInaM-477
❑ 93TopInaR-477
❑ 93TopMic-477
❑ 93UppDec-698
❑ 93UppDecGold-698

Jones, Joe
❑ 77SpaPhiT-9
❑ 80CarMudF-7
❑ 97PirPos-17

Jones, John
❑ 94SouOreAC-13
❑ 94SouOreAF-3629

Jones, John PCL
❑ 23Zee-68
❑ 24Zee-47

Jones, Keith
❑ 82BurRanF-10
❑ 82BurRanT-5
❑ 84TulDriTI-6
❑ 91JohCitCC-16
❑ 91JohCitCP-3989
❑ 92SprCarC-10
❑ 92SprCarF-882
❑ 93St.PetCC-16
❑ 93St.PetCF-2641
❑ 94MadHatC-12
❑ 94MadHatF-146

Jones, Keith R.
❑ 97LetBlaDB-8
❑ 98SouBenSHM-5

Jones, Ken
❑ 78WauMetT-13
❑ 81WatRedT-4
❑ 82WatRedT-4
❑ 83WatRedT-4
❑ 87MadMusP-14

Jones, Kenneth
❑ 93GenCubC-17
❑ 93GenCubF-3191

Jones, Kevin
❑ 85OscAstTI-28
❑ 89EveGiaS-17
❑ 90BilMusP-3229
❑ 90ChaWheB-17

Jones, Kiki (Keith Tyrone)
❑ 89GreFalDSP-18
❑ 90BakDodCLC-230
❑ 90Bow-86
❑ 90BowTif-86
❑ 90CalLeaACLC-20
❑ 90Sco-676
❑ 91Cla/Bes-212
❑ 91UppDec-59
❑ 91VerBeaDC-8
❑ 91VerBeaDP-769
❑ 92ClaFS7-292
❑ 92VerBeaDC-1
❑ 93VerBeaDC-12
❑ 93VerBeaDF-2213

Jones, Kirk
❑ 80BatTroT-6
❑ 80WatIndT-12
❑ 85OscAstTI-29

Jones, Lance
❑ 88CapCodPPaLP-133
❑ 89AncBucTI-20

Jones, Larry K.
❑ 80RocRedWT-7
❑ 81RocRedWT-19
❑ 81RocRedWW-10
❑ 82IowCubT-17
❑ 83IowCubT-5

Jones, Lee
❑ 83RedPioT-13

Jones, Lefty (Earl)
❑ 48SigOil-12
❑ 49RemBre-11

Jones, Lynn
❑ 78IndIndTI-20
❑ 80Top-123
❑ 81Top-337
❑ 82Don-542
❑ 82Fle-270
❑ 82Top-64
❑ 83Fle-333
❑ 83TigPos-17
❑ 83Top-483
❑ 84Nes792-731
❑ 84RoyPos-17
❑ 84Top-731
❑ 84TopTif-731
❑ 84TopTra-58T
❑ 84TopTraT-58T
❑ 85RoyTeal-14
❑ 85Top-513
❑ 85TopTif-513
❑ 86Don-466
❑ 86Fle-11
❑ 86RoyNatP-35
❑ 86RoyTeal-11
❑ 86Top-671
❑ 86TopTif-671
❑ 91RoyPol-26
❑ 92RoyPol-27
❑ 93ElmPioC-27
❑ 93ElmPioF-3839
❑ 94KanCouCC-27
❑ 94KanCouCF-178
❑ 94KanCouCTI-10
❑ 95KanCouCTI-10
❑ 96KanCouCTI-16
❑ 98PorSeaDQ-26

Jones, Mack
❑ 62Top-186
❑ 62TopVen-186
❑ 63Top-137
❑ 65BraTeal-6
❑ 65OPC-241
❑ 65Top-241
❑ 66BraPos-15
❑ 66Kah-16
❑ 66Top-446
❑ 67BraIrvD-2
❑ 67BraPho-16
❑ 67CokCapB-18
❑ 67Top-435
❑ 67TopVen-277
❑ 68CokCapB-18
❑ 68Kah-B19
❑ 68Top-353
❑ 68TopVen-353
❑ 69ExpFudP-5
❑ 69MLBOffS-159

❑ 69Top-625
❑ 69TopSta-57
❑ 69TopTeaP-10
❑ 70DayDaiNM-22
❑ 70ExpPin-8
❑ 70ExpPos-10
❑ 70MLBOffS-66
❑ 70OPC-38
❑ 70Top-38
❑ 70TopScr-9
❑ 71ExpPS-11
❑ 71MLBOffS-131
❑ 71OPC-142
❑ 71Top-142
❑ 71TopCoi-135
❑ 72MilBra-173
❑ 76LauDiaJ-20
❑ 78TCM60I-277
❑ 92Nab-27
❑ 93ExpDonM-15

Jones, Marcus
❑ 98VisOakG-16

Jones, Mark
❑ 88VisOakCLC-173

Jones, Marty
❑ 90AubAstB-15
❑ 90AubAstP-3403

Jones, Matt
❑ 92WelPirC-11
❑ 92WelPirF-1331
❑ 93LetMouF-4156
❑ 93LetMouSP-13
❑ 95ButCopKtl-11

Jones, Mike
❑ 74CedRapAT-8
❑ 88BriTigP-1889
❑ 88KnoBluJB-4
❑ 88NasSouC-6
❑ 88NasSouP-485
❑ 88NasSouTI-14
❑ 89LakTigS-11
❑ 89RocRedWC-1
❑ 89RocRedWP-1657
❑ 89Sta-31
❑ 90CMC-305
❑ 90RocRedWC-4
❑ 91BilMusP-3761
❑ 91BilMusSP-18
❑ 92CedRapRC-16
❑ 92CedRapRF-1077
❑ 96EugEmeB-13

Jones, Mike (Michael C.)
❑ 81OmaRoyT-9
❑ 81Top-66
❑ 82CliGiaF-7
❑ 82Fle-412
❑ 82Top-471
❑ 84OmaRoyT-20
❑ 84ShrCapFB-9
❑ 85Don-640A
❑ 85Don-640B
❑ 85FreGiaSB-6
❑ 85RoyTeal-15
❑ 85Top-244
❑ 85TopTif-244
❑ 86Don-419
❑ 86Fle-12
❑ 86RicBraP-10
❑ 86ShrCapP-12
❑ 86Top-514
❑ 86TopTif-514
❑ 86VenGulP-9
❑ 87DunBluJP-926
❑ 88BlaYNPRWL-184
❑ 90WicStaSGD-18

Jones, Motorboat
❑ 92ChaWVWC-10
❑ 93CarLeaAGF-42
❑ 93WinSpiC-11
❑ 94UppDecML-29

Jones, Neil
❑ 91MelBusF-2

Jones, Nippy (Vernal)
❑ 49EurSta-186
❑ 49MPR302-2-111
❑ 50Bow-238
❑ 51R42SmaS-51
❑ 51R42SmaS-53
❑ 52Top-213
❑ 58UniOil-5
❑ 79DiaGre-169
❑ 80Bra195T-14
❑ 83Car194T-37
❑ 83TopRep5-213
❑ 85TCMPla1-25

Jones, Norm
❑ 89DenZepP-56

Jones, Odell
❑ 77PirPosP-11
❑ 78ColCliT-12
❑ 78Top-407
❑ 80PorBeaT-17
❑ 80Top-342
❑ 80VenLeaS-191
❑ 81PorBeaT-13
❑ 82PorBeaT-4
❑ 83RanAffF-21
❑ 83TopTra-50T
❑ 84Don-256
❑ 84Fle-421
❑ 84Nes792-734
❑ 84OPC-382
❑ 84RanJarP-21
❑ 84Top-734
❑ 84TopTif-734
❑ 85Don-525
❑ 85Fle-560
❑ 85RocRedWT-19
❑ 85Top-29
❑ 85TopTif-29
❑ 86RocRedWP-10
❑ 87Don-582
❑ 87SyrChiT-5
❑ 88BrePol-28
❑ 88BreTeal-20
❑ 89Fle-189
❑ 89FleGlo-189
❑ 89PacSenL-171
❑ 89Sco-579
❑ 89T/MSenL-56
❑ 89UppDec-608
❑ 91OriCro-231
❑ 91PacSenL-27
❑ 93RanKee-211
❑ 94BreMilB-232

Jones, Oscar
❑ 11SpoLifCW-191
❑ 90DodTar-392

Jones, P.J.
❑ 93BluOriC-14

Jones, Parnelli
❑ 68AtlOil-6

Jones, Paul
❑ 92BluOriC-18
❑ 92BluOriF-2365

Jones, Percy
❑ 22E120-160
❑ 23Zee-10
❑ 27AmeCarE126-18
❑ 29PorandAR-48
❑ 92ConTSN-456

Jones, Pookie
❑ 94BenRocC-13
❑ 94BenRocF-3609
❑ 95Exc-187
❑ 96SalAvaB-17

Jones, Randy
❑ 73PadDea-12
❑ 74OPC-173
❑ 74PadDea-15
❑ 74PadMcDD-7
❑ 74PadTeal-7
❑ 74Top-173A
❑ 74Top-173B
❑ 74TopSta-94
❑ 75OPC-248
❑ 75PadDea-14
❑ 75Top-248
❑ 75TopMin-248
❑ 76BlaDis-23
❑ 76BucDis-23
❑ 76CarDis-23
❑ 76CraDis-23
❑ 76DailsID-23
❑ 76Hos-143
❑ 76IsaDis-23
❑ 76Kel-4
❑ 76OPC-199
❑ 76OPC-201
❑ 76OPC-310
❑ 76OrbDis-23
❑ 76RedBarD-23
❑ 76SafDis-23
❑ 76Spo-6
❑ 76SSP-118
❑ 76Top-199
❑ 76Top-201
❑ 76Top-310
❑ 76TowCluD-23
❑ 77BurCheD-132
❑ 77ChiWilD-34
❑ 77DailsID-34
❑ 77DetCaeD-34
❑ 77HolInnD-34
❑ 77Hos-26
❑ 77Kel-17
❑ 77MSADis-34
❑ 77OPC-5
❑ 77OPC-113
❑ 77PadFamF-3
❑ 77PadSchC-30A
❑ 77PadSchC-30B
❑ 77PadSchC-31
❑ 77RCColC-31
❑ 77SagDis-34
❑ 77sDis-34
❑ 77Spo-1704
❑ 77Top-5
❑ 77Top-550
❑ 77TopCloS-23
❑ 77WenDis-34
❑ 77ZipDis-34
❑ 78OPC-101
❑ 78PadFamF-16
❑ 78RCColC-61
❑ 78Top-56
❑ 78WifBalD-33
❑ 79OPC-95
❑ 79Top-194
❑ 80OPC-160
❑ 80Top-305
❑ 80TopSup-48
❑ 81CokTeaS-88
❑ 81Don-122
❑ 81Fle-487
❑ 81OPC-148
❑ 81Top-458
❑ 81TopTra-777
❑ 82Fle-528
❑ 82MetPhoA-12
❑ 82OPC-274
❑ 82Top-626
❑ 83Fle-546
❑ 83FleSti-222
❑ 83OPC-29
❑ 83Top-29
❑ 86PadGreT-10
❑ 88GreBasS-36
❑ 89PadMag-16
❑ 91MetWIZ-205
❑ 93UppDecS-13
❑ 93UppDecS-22
❑ 94TedWil-84
❑ 99SpollIGotG-35
❑ 99SpollIGotGA-37
❑ 99SpollIGotGC-30

Jones, Rex
❑ 80ColAstT-22
❑ 83ColAstT-24
❑ 84TucTorC-56
❑ 85TucTorC-74
❑ 86TucTorP-9
❑ 88TucTorP-192
❑ 94AstMot-28

Jones, Rick
❑ 89SpaPhiP-1032
❑ 89SpaPhiS-26
❑ 90SpaPhiB-27
❑ 90SpaPhiP-2509

Jones, Rick (Thomas F.)
❑ 77Top-118
❑ 79PorBeaT-23
❑ 80VenLeaS-164
❑ 82RocRedWT-13
❑ 83RocRedWT-16
❑ 86RocRedWP-11

Jones, Ricky
❑ 85ChaO'sT-23
❑ 85RocRedWT-6
❑ 87ChaO'sW-7
❑ 88PorBeaC-14
❑ 88PorBeaP-656
❑ 91OriCro-230

Jones, Robert Walter
❑ 15Zee-108
❑ 16Zee-112
❑ 22E120-56
❑ 23WilChoV-74

Jones, Ron
❑ 85BenPhiC-13
❑ 86ClePhiP-11
❑ 86FloStaLAP-27
❑ 87MaiGuiP-23
❑ 87MaiGuiT-17
❑ 88BlaYNPRWL-89
❑ 88MaiPhiC-14
❑ 88MaiPhiP-280
❑ 88PhiTas-27
❑ 89Bow-407
❑ 89BowTif-407
❑ 89ClaLigB-96
❑ 89Don-40
❑ 89DonRoo-42
❑ 89Fle-574
❑ 89FleGlo-574
❑ 89PanSti-143
❑ 89PhiTas-14
❑ 89Sco-639
❑ 89ScoHot1R-25
❑ 89ScoYouS2-3
❑ 89Spo-178
❑ 89Spo-225
❑ 89Top-349
❑ 89TopTif-349
❑ 89ToyRoo-16
❑ 89UppDec-11
❑ 90CMC-245
❑ 90Don-487
❑ 90Fle-563
❑ 90FleCan-563
❑ 90OPC-129
❑ 90PhiTas-16
❑ 90ProAAAF-312
❑ 90PublntS-243
❑ 90Sco-364
❑ 90Sco100RS-31
❑ 90ScrRedBC-19
❑ 90ScrRedBP-610
❑ 90Top-129
❑ 90TopTif-129
❑ 90UppDec-94
❑ 91Sco-653
❑ 92Don-738
❑ 92Sco-342
❑ 93RicBraBB-9
❑ 93RicBraF-196
❑ 93RicBraP-14
❑ 93RicBraRC-23
❑ 93RicBraRC-15

Jones, Ronnie
❑ 81BurBeeT-25

Jones, Ross
❑ 82AlbDukTc-17
❑ 83AlbDukTc-16
❑ 84TidTidT-18
❑ 85BurRanT-26
❑ 85TidTidT-22
❑ 85UtiBluST-2
❑ 86ChaLooP-15
❑ 86DayBealP-14
❑ 87GasRanP-17
❑ 88Fle-262
❑ 88FleGlo-262
❑ 88Sco-598
❑ 88ScoGlo-598
❑ 88Top-169
❑ 88TopTif-169
❑ 88WesPalBES-14
❑ 89WesPalBES-13
❑ 91MetWIZ-208
❑ 93AusFut-54
❑ 93AusFut-103
❑ 93AusFut-129
❑ 95AusFut-100
❑ 95AusFutSFP-SFFP6

Jones, Ruppert
❑ 75OmaRoyTI-7
❑ 76OmaRoyTT-9
❑ 76VenLeaS-118
❑ 77MarPos-9
❑ 77Top-488
❑ 78Hos-121
❑ 78OPC-20
❑ 78Top-141
❑ 79Hos-99
❑ 79OPC-218
❑ 79Top-422
❑ 80OPC-43
❑ 80Top-78
❑ 80YanPhoA-14
❑ 81Don-349
❑ 81Fle-101
❑ 81OPC-225
❑ 81Top-225
❑ 81TopSupHT-67
❑ 81TopTra-778
❑ 82Don-346
❑ 82Fle-573
❑ 82FleSta-102
❑ 82OPC-217
❑ 82Top-511
❑ 82TopSti-99
❑ 83AllGamPl-148
❑ 83Don-373
❑ 83Fle-361
❑ 83FleSta-93
❑ 83OPC-287
❑ 83PadTeal-10
❑ 83Top-695
❑ 83TopGloS-38
❑ 83TopSti-295
❑ 84Don-261
❑ 84Fle-303
❑ 84FleUpd-59
❑ 84Nes792-327
❑ 84OPC-327
❑ 84TigWavP-22
❑ 84Top-327
❑ 84TopSti-158
❑ 84TopTif-327
❑ 84TopTra-59T
❑ 84TopTraT-59T
❑ 85AngSmo-19
❑ 85Don-612
❑ 85Fle-13
❑ 85FleUpd-63
❑ 85Top-126
❑ 85TopTif-126
❑ 85TopTifT-65T
❑ 85TopTra-65T
❑ 86AngSmo-19
❑ 86Don-423
❑ 86Fle-161
❑ 86OPC-186
❑ 86Top-464
❑ 86TopSti-184
❑ 86TopTif-464
❑ 87AngSmo-21
❑ 87CalAngPPS-18
❑ 87Don-428
❑ 87Fle-85
❑ 87FleGlo-85
❑ 87SpoTeaP-11
❑ 87Top-53
❑ 87TopTif-53
❑ 88Fle-492
❑ 88FleGlo-492
❑ 88PanSti-47
❑ 88Sco-333
❑ 88ScoGlo-333
❑ 88StaLinAn-10
❑ 92YanWIZ8-94

Jones, Ryan
❑ 93MedHatBJF-3745
❑ 94ExcFS7-146
❑ 94HagSunC-9
❑ 94HagSunF-2739
❑ 95DunBluJTI-10
❑ 96Bow-355
❑ 96BowBes-134
❑ 96BowBesAR-134
❑ 96BowBesR-134
❑ 96BowFoi-355
❑ 96Exc-115
❑ 96KnoSmoB-17
❑ 97ColCho-472
❑ 97FlaShoWotF-25
❑ 97Fle-513
❑ 97FleTif-513
❑ 97Sel-132
❑ 97SelArtP-132
❑ 97SelCom-132
❑ 97SelRegG-132
❑ 97SyrSkyCB-13
❑ 97Ult-462
❑ 97UltGolME-462
❑ 97UltPlaME-462
❑ 98KnoSG-8

Jones, Sad Sam (Samuel)
❑ 52IndNumN-19
❑ 52NatTeaL-14
❑ 52Top-382
❑ 53Top-6
❑ 56Top-259
❑ 57Top-287
❑ 58CarJayP-7
❑ 58Top-287
❑ 59Top-75
❑ 59TopVen-75
❑ 60GiaJayP-6
❑ 60KeyChal-26
❑ 60Lea-14
❑ 60Top-410
❑ 60TopTat-24
❑ 61GiaJayP-6
❑ 61Pos-143A
❑ 61Pos-143B
❑ 61Top-49
❑ 61Top-555
❑ 61TopMagR-31
❑ 62Jel-138
❑ 62Pos-138
❑ 62PosCan-138
❑ 62SalPlaC-162
❑ 62ShiPlaC-162
❑ 62Top-92
❑ 62TopStal-127
❑ 62TopVen-92
❑ 83TopRep5-382
❑ 84CubBriPC-11D
❑ 84GiaMot-15
❑ 86NegLeaF-80
❑ 91OriCro-232
❑ 91TopArc1-6

Jones, Sam
❑ 75BurBeeT-12
❑ 76BurBeeT-19
❑ 77DayBealT-10

Jones, Sam P.
❑ 19W514-8
❑ 21Exh-85
❑ 21Nei-43
❑ 22E120-65
❑ 22W573-70
❑ 22WilPatV-17
❑ 23W515-43
❑ 23WilChoV-75
❑ 27MidBre-30
❑ 28Exh-63
❑ 28W502-38
❑ 28Yue-38
❑ 29ExhFou-32
❑ 29PorandAR-49
❑ 31SenTealPW-17
❑ 33Gou-81
❑ 34GouCanV-31
❑ 35DiaMatCS3T1-81
❑ 74CapPub-34
❑ 74TCMNic-13
❑ 77GalGloG-129
❑ 91ConTSN-140
❑ 91ConTSN-174
❑ 92ConTSN-356
❑ 93ConTSN-801
❑ 94ConTSN-1003
❑ 94ConTSNB-1003

Jones, Scott
❑ 83CedRapRF-18
❑ 83CedRapRT-2
❑ 93PitMetC-12
❑ 93PitMetF-3703
❑ 96MicBatCB-13
❑ 96MidLeaAB-44

Jones, Sean
❑ 91PerHeaF-9
❑ 95AusFut-31
❑ 98BluOriQ-28

Jones, Shane
❑ 94OgdRapF-3742
❑ 94OgdRapSP-4
❑ 95OdgRapTI-10

Jones, Shannon
❑ 89GenCubP-1881
❑ 90CarLeaA-46
❑ 90WinSpiTI-12
❑ 91ChaKniLD-135
❑ 91ChaKniP-1685
❑ 91LinDriAA-135
❑ 92SalLakTSP-10

Jones, Sherman
❑ 60TacBan-8
❑ 61Top-161
❑ 74MetOriEB-6
❑ 80Red196T-38
❑ 91MetWIZ-206

Jones, Slim
❑ 86NegLeaF-79

Jones, Stacy
❑ 89FreKeyS-11
❑ 90FreKeyTI-12
❑ 91HagSunLD-233
❑ 91HagSunP-2451
❑ 91LinDriAA-233
❑ 92Fle-701
❑ 92FreKeyC-25
❑ 92FreKeyF-1801
❑ 92ProFS7-7
❑ 92Sco-832
❑ 92TopDeb91-94
❑ 93FreKeyC-11
❑ 93FreKeyF-1022
❑ 94ShrCapF-1600
❑ 98ShrCapWS-30

Jones, Steve
❑ 91JohCitCC-25
❑ 91JohCitCP-3974
❑ 92HamRedC-10
❑ 92HamRedF-1587
❑ 92ProFS7-328
Jones, Steve H.
❑ 69OPC-49
❑ 69Top-49A
❑ 69Top-49B
Jones, Terry
❑ 87Ft.MyeRP-21
Jones, Terry Lee
❑ 93BenRocCB-14
❑ 93BenRocF-3281
❑ 94CenValRC-12
❑ 94CenValRF-3215
❑ 95Exc-188
❑ 95NewHavRTI-10
❑ 96ColSprSSTI-20
❑ 96Exc-155
❑ 97ColSprSTI-12
❑ 99Pac-266
❑ 99PacPlaB-266
❑ 99PacRed-266
Jones, Terry R.
❑ 76OklCit8TI-1
Jones, Thomas
❑ 07TigACDPP-22
❑ 08RosComP-70
❑ 09ColChiE-145
❑ 09PC7HHB-27
❑ 09RamT20-61
❑ 09T206-174
❑ 09T206-175
❑ 09TigMorBBBP-8
❑ 09TigTaCP-9
❑ 10NadE1-25
❑ 10SweCapPP-26
❑ 11PinT-5-165
❑ 11SpoLifCW-192
❑ 11SpoLifM-61
❑ 11T205-84
❑ 12ColRedB-145
❑ 12ColTinT-145
❑ 12HasTriFT-28
❑ 12HasTriFT-73A
❑ 12HasTriFT-73B
Jones, Tim
❑ 92BriTigC-13
❑ 92BriTigF-1403
❑ 94ChaKniF-903
Jones, Tim (William Timothy)
❑ 87ArkTraP-14
❑ 87LouRedTI-17
❑ 88LouRedBC-13
❑ 88LouRedBP-433
❑ 88LouRedBTI-23
❑ 89Bow-439
❑ 89BowTif-439
❑ 89CarSmo-10
❑ 89CarTeal-13
❑ 89Don-555
❑ 89DonRoo-28
❑ 89Fle-453
❑ 89FleGlo-453
❑ 89Sco-649
❑ 89ScoHot1R-28
❑ 89UppDec-348
❑ 90CarSmo-11
❑ 90Don-686
❑ 90OPC-533
❑ 90Sco-579
❑ 90Sco100RS-62
❑ 90Top-533
❑ 90TopTif-533
❑ 90TopTVCa-26
❑ 90UppDec-501
❑ 91Don-66
❑ 91FleUpd-117
❑ 91LouRedTI-19
❑ 91OPC-262
❑ 91StaClu-121
❑ 91Top-262
❑ 91TopDesS-262
❑ 91TopMic-262
❑ 91TopTif-262
❑ 92StaClu-206
❑ 92Ult-569
❑ 93Don-624
❑ 93LouRedF-222
❑ 93StaClu-280
❑ 93StaCluFDI-280
❑ 93StaCluMOP-280
❑ 94Pac-592
Jones, Tim S.
❑ 96SouOreTI-2
❑ 97ModA'sG-12
❑ 98ModA'sG-14
Jones, Timothy Byron
❑ 75ShrCapT-6
❑ 77CliDodT-11
❑ 77ColCliT-9
❑ 78CliDodT-16
❑ 78Top-703
Jones, Todd
❑ 90OscAstS-12
❑ 91Cla/Bes-333
❑ 91OscAstC-6
❑ 91OscAstP-678
❑ 92Bow-202
❑ 92JacGenF-3998
❑ 92JacGenS-335
❑ 92SkyAA F-142
❑ 92UppDecML-219
❑ 93AstStaC-25
❑ 93Bow-352
❑ 93Bow-392
❑ 93ExcFS7-46
❑ 93LinVenB-58
❑ 93TucTorF-3056
❑ 93UppDec-423
❑ 93UppDecGold-423
❑ 94AstMot-20
❑ 94Bow-22
❑ 94ColC-153
❑ 94ColChoGS-153
❑ 94ColChoSS-153
❑ 94Don-171
❑ 94Fin-265
❑ 94FinRef-265
❑ 94Fla-172
❑ 94Fle-495
❑ 94Lea-415
❑ 94Pac-269
❑ 94Sco-246
❑ 94ScoGolR-246
❑ 94StaClu-226
❑ 94StaCluFDI-226
❑ 94StaCluGR-226
❑ 94StaCluMOP-226
❑ 94Top-97
❑ 94TopGol-97
❑ 94TopSpa-97
❑ 94Ult-507
❑ 95AstMot-23
❑ 95ColCho-121
❑ 95ColChoGS-121
❑ 95ColChoSS-121
❑ 95Don-60
❑ 95DonPreP-60
❑ 95DonTopotO-256
❑ 95Fla-360
❑ 95Fle-464
❑ 95Lea-161
❑ 95Sco-516
❑ 95ScoGolR-516
❑ 95ScoPlaTS-516
❑ 95StaClu-129
❑ 95StaCluFDI-129
❑ 95StaCluMOP-129
❑ 95StaCluSTWS-129
❑ 95StaCluVR-65
❑ 95StaCluVRMO-65
❑ 95Top-560
❑ 95TopCyb-336
❑ 95Ult-174
❑ 95UltGolM-174
❑ 96AstMot-25
❑ 96ColCho-562
❑ 96ColChoGS-562
❑ 96ColChoSS-562
❑ 96Don-228
❑ 96DonPreP-228
❑ 96Fla-280
❑ 96Fle-412
❑ 96FleTif-412
❑ 96LeaSigA-120
❑ 96LeaSigAG-120
❑ 96LeaSigAS-120
❑ 96Pac-90
❑ 96Ult-211
❑ 96UltGolM-211
❑ 96UppDec-341
❑ 97Cir-274
❑ 97CirRav-274
❑ 97ColCho-122
❑ 97ColCho-324
❑ 97Fle-348
❑ 97Fle-576
❑ 97FleTif-348
❑ 97FleTif-576
❑ 97PacPriGotD-GD152
❑ 97Top-68
❑ 97Ult-208
❑ 97Ult-402
❑ 97UltGolME-208
❑ 97UltGolME-402
❑ 97UltPlaME-208
❑ 97UltPlaME-402
❑ 98ColCho-91
❑ 98Fin-61
❑ 98FinNo--61
❑ 98FinNo-R-61
❑ 98FinRef-61
❑ 98Fle-279
❑ 98Pac-91
❑ 98PacOnl-276
❑ 98PacOnlR-276
❑ 98PacOnlWC-276
❑ 98PacPar-49
❑ 98PacParC-49
❑ 98PacParG-49
❑ 98PacParHS-49
❑ 98PacParPB-49
❑ 98PacParR-49
❑ 98PacPlaB-91
❑ 98PacRedT-91
❑ 98PacSil-91
❑ 98StaCluFDI-66
❑ 98StaClul-66
❑ 98StaCluOneK-66
❑ 98StaCluPP-66
❑ 98Top-133
❑ 98TopChr-133
❑ 98TopChrR-133
❑ 98TopDevR-133
❑ 98TopDia-133
❑ 98TopMiniC-133
❑ 98TopOpeD-67
❑ 98UppDec-371
❑ 99Fle-509
❑ 99FleSta9-509
❑ 99FleWarT-509
❑ 99MetUni-150
❑ 99MetUniGM-150
❑ 99MetUniPMG-150
❑ 99Pac-168
❑ 99PacPlaB-168
❑ 99PacRed-168
❑ 99StaClu-229
❑ 99StaCluFDI-229
❑ 99StaCluOoaK-229
❑ 99StaCluPP-229
❑ 99Top-178
❑ 99TopChr-178
❑ 99TopChrR-178
❑ 99TopMVPP-178
❑ 99Ult-74
❑ 99UltGolM-74
❑ 99UltMas-74
❑ 99UltPlaM-74
❑ 99UppDec-97
❑ 99UppDecEL1-97
❑ 99UppDecEL2-97
Jones, Tommy
❑ 80CliGiaT-27
❑ 81PhoGiaVNB-16
❑ 83ButCopKT-30
❑ 86MemChiSTOS-12
❑ 86MemChiTOS-12
❑ 87AlbYanP-19
❑ 88AlbYanP-1352
❑ 89WauTimGS-2
❑ 90BatCliP-3060
❑ 90CalCanC-23
❑ 90CalCanP-664
❑ 90CMC-450
❑ 90ProAAAF-129
❑ 91SanBerSC-27
❑ 91SanBerSP-2003
❑ 93OrlCubF-2801
❑ 97LetBlaDB-1
Jones, Tracy
❑ 83TamTarT-26
❑ 86BasStaB-61
❑ 86DonRoo-2
❑ 86FleUpd-58
❑ 86RedTexG-29
❑ 87Don-413
❑ 87Fle-651
❑ 87FleGlo-651
❑ 87FleUpd-55
❑ 87FleUpdG-55
❑ 87RedKah-29
❑ 87SpoTeaP-4
❑ 87Top-146
❑ 87TopTif-146
❑ 88ClaRed-185
❑ 88Don-310
❑ 88DonBasB-174
❑ 88ExpPos-17
❑ 88Fle-237
❑ 88FleGlo-237
❑ 88Lea-107
❑ 88OPC-101
❑ 88PanSti-283
❑ 88RedKah-29
❑ 88Sco-326
❑ 88ScoGlo-326
❑ 88ScoYouSI-38
❑ 88Spo-38
❑ 88StaLinRe-11
❑ 88Top-553
❑ 88TopTif-553
❑ 89Bow-479
❑ 89BowTif-479
❑ 89Don-574
❑ 89Fle-383
❑ 89FleGlo-383
❑ 89FleUpd-31
❑ 89GiaMot-14
❑ 89OPC-373
❑ 89PanSti-124
❑ 89Sco-510
❑ 89ScoRoo-43T
❑ 89Top-373
❑ 89TopTif-373
❑ 89UppDec-96
❑ 89UppDec-798
❑ 90Don-636
❑ 90Fle-607
❑ 90FleCan-607
❑ 90OPC-767
❑ 90PubIntS-70
❑ 90Sco-291
❑ 90TigCok-9
❑ 90Top-767
❑ 90TopTif-767
❑ 90UppDec-309
❑ 91Don-594
❑ 91FleUpd-53
❑ 91MarCouH-16
❑ 91OPC-87
❑ 91Sco-87
❑ 91StaClu-446
❑ 91Top-87
❑ 91TopDesS-87
❑ 91TopMic-87
❑ 91TopTif-87
❑ 92Don-519
❑ 92Fle-284
❑ 92OPC-271
❑ 92Sco-206
❑ 92Top-271
❑ 92TopGol-271
❑ 92TopGolW-271
❑ 92TopMic-271
Jones, Victor
❑ 91ColIndC-2
❑ 91ColIndP-1500
Jones, Willie
❑ 47PM1StaP1-102
❑ 49Bow-92
❑ 49EurSta-138
❑ 49PhiBul-26
❑ 49PhiLumPB-5
❑ 50Bow-67
❑ 50PhiPhil-13
❑ 51BerRos-B8
❑ 51Bow-112
❑ 51FisBakL-11
❑ 51TopBluB-43
❑ 52Bow-20
❑ 52RedMan-NL11
❑ 52Top-47
❑ 53BowC-133
❑ 53Top-88
❑ 54Bow-143
❑ 54Top-41
❑ 55Bow-172
❑ 56PhiPos-3
❑ 56Top-127
❑ 57Top-174
❑ 58Hir-60
❑ 58PhiTeal-10
❑ 58Top-181
❑ 59Top-208
❑ 60Lea-98
❑ 60Top-289
❑ 61RedJayP-7
❑ 61Top-497
❑ 75Phi195T-15
❑ 77PhiFav-10
❑ 79TCM50-29
❑ 80Phi195T-15
❑ 80Red196T-18
❑ 83PhiPosGPaM-10
❑ 83TopRep5-47
❑ 85TCMPpl1-14
❑ 87SpoCubG-2
❑ 91TopArc1-88
❑ 94TopArc1-41
❑ 94TopArc1G-41
Jongewaard, Steve
❑ 87EriCarP-8
Jonnard, Clarence
❑ 23W503-24
❑ 35GouPuzR-6C
❑ 35GouPuzR-11E
❑ 35GouPuzR-13C
❑ 35GouPuzR-15C
Jonson, Greg
❑ 82ForMyeRT-6
Joost, Eddie (Edwin)
❑ 33Zee-28
❑ 38RedOraW-15
❑ 39OrcPhoAP-14
❑ 39PlaBal-67
❑ 39RedTeal-12
❑ 40PlaBal-151
❑ 41DouPlaR-117
❑ 41HarHarW-12
❑ 46SpoExcW-3-11
❑ 47A'sTeal-15
❑ 47HomBon-24
❑ 48A'sTeal-12
❑ 48Bow-15
❑ 49A'sTeal-17
❑ 49Bow-55
❑ 49Lea-62
❑ 49MPR302-2-115
❑ 49PhiBul-27
❑ 50A'sTeal-14
❑ 50Bow-103
❑ 51A'sTeal-13
❑ 51Bow-119
❑ 51FisBakL-12
❑ 51R42SmaS-50
❑ 51TopBluB-15
❑ 52A'sTeal-12
❑ 52Bow-26
❑ 52RedMan-AL12
❑ 52TipTop-18
❑ 52Top-45
❑ 53A'sTeal-13
❑ 53BowC-105
❑ 53RedMan-AL7
❑ 54A'STEAI-12
❑ 54Bow-35
❑ 55Bow-263
❑ 61Fle-116
❑ 76TayBow4-13
❑ 77CinRedT-24
❑ 79DiaGre-264
❑ 83TopRep5-45
❑ 85TCMPla1-21
Joppie, Dave
❑ 95HunStaTI-16
❑ 96HunStaTI-13
❑ 97ModA'sG-13
Jordan, Adrian
❑ 90BriTigP-3152
❑ 90BriTigS-12
❑ 93LinVenB-237
❑ 94VenLinU-261
❑ 95LinVen-208
❑ 96-97LinVen-181
Jordan, Brian
❑ 90ArkTraGS-18
❑ 91LinDriAAA-238
❑ 91LouRedLD-238
❑ 91LouRedP-2927
❑ 91LouRedTI-24
❑ 91LouRedTI-32
❑ 92Bow-464
❑ 92DonRooP-BC14
❑ 92DonUpd-U3
❑ 92JimDeaRS-3
❑ 92Lea-337
❑ 92LeaBlaG-337
❑ 92Pin-555
❑ 92PinTea2-39
❑ 92ScoRoo-83T
❑ 92SpollIFK1-588
❑ 92Stu-93
❑ 92TopTra-58T
❑ 92TopTraG-58T
❑ 92UppDec-3
❑ 92UppDec-702
❑ 92UppDecSR-SR11
❑ 93CarPol-8
❑ 93CarStaC-25
❑ 93Don-442
❑ 93Fle-511
❑ 93Lea-229
❑ 93OPC-134
❑ 93PacSpa-632
❑ 93Pin-540
❑ 93Sco-217
❑ 93Sel-280
❑ 93StaClu-435
❑ 93StaCluFDI-435
❑ 93StaCluMOP-435
❑ 93Top-754
❑ 93TopGol-754
❑ 93TopInaM-754
❑ 93TopInaR-754
❑ 93TopMic-754
❑ 93Toy-97
❑ 93TriPla-62
❑ 93Ult-107
❑ 93UppDec-596
❑ 93UppDecGold-596
❑ 93USPlaCR-6D
❑ 94Bow-676
❑ 94CarPol-7
❑ 94ColC-154
❑ 94ColChoGS-154
❑ 94ColChoSS-154
❑ 94Don-586
❑ 94Fin-360
❑ 94FinRef-360
❑ 94Fla-225
❑ 94Fle-634
❑ 94Lea-272
❑ 94PanSti-244
❑ 94Pin-124
❑ 94PinArtP-124
❑ 94PinMusC-124
❑ 94Sco-201
❑ 94ScoGolR-201
❑ 94Sel-62
❑ 94Spo-105
❑ 94StaClu-63
❑ 94StaCluFDI-63
❑ 94StaCluGR-63
❑ 94StaCluMOP-63
❑ 94StaCluT-308
❑ 94StaCluTFDI-308
❑ 94Top-632
❑ 94TopGol-632
❑ 94TopSpa-632
❑ 94TriPla-63
❑ 94Ult-267
❑ 94UppDec-223
❑ 94UppDecAJ-4
❑ 94UppDecAJG-4
❑ 94UppDecED-223
❑ 95BowBes-R54
❑ 95BowBesR-R54
❑ 95ColCho-192
❑ 95ColChoGS-192
❑ 95ColChoSS-192
❑ 95Don-221
❑ 95DonPreP-221
❑ 95DonTopotO-330
❑ 95Emo-181
❑ 95Fin-326
❑ 95FinRef-326
❑ 95Fla-410
❑ 95Fle-500
❑ 95Lea-64
❑ 95LeaLim-34
❑ 95Pin-271
❑ 95PinArtP-271
❑ 95PinMusC-271
❑ 95Sco-143
❑ 95ScoGolR-143
❑ 95ScoPlaTS-143
❑ 95Sel-90
❑ 95SelArtP-90
❑ 95SP-103
❑ 95Spo-55
❑ 95SpoArtP-55
❑ 95SPSil-103
❑ 95StaClu-355
❑ 95StaCluMOP-355
❑ 95StaCluSTWS-355
❑ 95Top-62
❑ 95TopCyb-44
❑ 95Ult-223
❑ 95UltGolM-223
❑ 95UppDec-58
❑ 95UppDecED-58

95UppDecEDG-58
95UppDecSE-226
95UppDecSEG-226
95Zen-11
96Baz-115
96Bow-33
96BowFoi-33
96CarPol-13
96Cir-177
96CirRav-177
96ColCho-289
96ColChoGS-289
96ColChoSS-289
96Don-87
96DonDiaK-25
96DonPreP-87
96EmoXL-267
96Fin-B28
96FinRef-B28
96Fla-360
96Fle-545
96FleTif-545
96Lea-142
96LeaLim-79
96LeaLimG-79
96LeaPre-81
96LeaPreP-81
96LeaPrePB-142
96LeaPrePG-142
96LeaPrePS-142
96LeaPreSG-61
96LeaPreSte-61
96LeaSig-126
96LeaSigA-121
96LeaSigAG-121
96LeaSigAS-121
96LeaSigPPG-126
96LeaSigPPP-126
96LibSpo-5
96MetUni-226
96MetUniP-226
96MLBPin-17
96Pac-229
96PacPri-P71
96PacPriG-P71
96PanSti-78
96Pin-233
96PinAfi-103
96PinAfiAP-103
96PinArtP-133
96PinFoil-233
96PinSta-133
96ProSta-31
96Sco-22
96ScoDugC-A21
96ScoDugCAP-A21
96Sel-90
96SelArtP-90
96SelCer-90
96SelCerAP-90
96SelCerCB-90
96SelCerCR-90
96SelCerMB-90
96SelCerMG-90
96SelCerMR-90
96SelTeaN-2
96SP-157
96StaClu-118
96StaCluEPB-118
96StaCluEPG-118
96StaCluEPS-118
96StaCluMOP-118
96Stu-147
96StuPrePB-147
96StuPrePG-147
96StuPrePS-147
96Sum-122
96SumAbo&B-122
96SumArtP-122
96SumFoi-122
96TeaOut-43
96Top-126
96TopChr-35
96TopChrR-35
96TopGal-75
96TopGalPPI-75
96TopLas-9
96Ult-275
96UltGolM-275
96UppDec-180
96Zen-56
96ZenArtP-56
96ZenMoz-11
97ArkTraB-30
97Bow-272
97BowBes-46
97BowBesAR-46
97BowBesR-46
97BowChr-89
97BowChrI-89
97BowChrIR-89
97BowChrR-89
97BowInt-272
97CarPol-12
97Cir-196
97CirRav-196
97ColCho-220
97ColCho-440
97ColChoBS-3
97ColChoBSGS-3
97ColChoNF-NF28
97Don-9
97Don-444
97DonEli-65
97DonEliGS-65
97DonGolPP-9
97DonGolPP-444
97DonLim-146
97DonLim-148
97DonLimE-146
97DonLimE-148
97DonLimENG-146
97DonPre-45
97DonPre-190
97DonPreCttC-45
97DonPreCttC-190
97DonSigA-55
97DonSigAC-68
97DonSigAM-68
97DonSilPP-9
97DonSilPP-444
97DonTea-151
97DonTeaSPE-151
97E-X2-99
97E-X2Cred-99
97E-X2EssCre-99
97Fin-3
97Fin-293
97FinEmb-293
97FinEmbR-293
97FinRef-3
97FinRef-293
97FlaShoLC-56
97FlaShoLeg0-56
97FlaShoLeg1-56
97FlaShoM-A56
97FlaShoM-B56
97FlaShoM-C56
97FlaShoR0-56
97FlaShoR1-56
97FlaShoR2-56
97Fle-445
97Fle-746
97FleTeaL-26
97FleTif-445
97FleTif-746
97Lea-116
97Lea-394
97LeaDrefS-14
97LeaFraM-116
97LeaFraM-394
97LeaFraMDC-116
97LeaFraMDC-394
97LeaGet-11
97MetUni-231
97NewPin-44
97NewPinAP-44
97NewPinIE-1
97NewPinMC-44
97NewPinPP-44
97NewPinPP-I1B
97Pac-411
97PacGolCD-33
97PacLigB-411
97PacPri-139
97PacPriLB-139
97PacPriP-139
97PacSil-411
97Pin-41
97PinArtP-PP41
97PinCar-17
97PinCer-80
97PinCerLI-4
97PinCerMBla-80
97PinCerMBlu-80
97PinCerMG-80
97PinCerMR-80
97PinCerR-80
97PinIns-18
97PinInsCE-18
97PinInsDD-10
97PinInsDE-18
97PinMin-29
97PinMinB-29
97PinMinCB-29
97PinMinCG-29
97PinMinCGR-29
97PinMinCN-29
97PinMinCSS-29
97PinMinG-29
97PinMinS-29
97PinMusC-41
97PinPrePla-41
97PinPrePla-S7
97PinSha-7
97PinTotCPB-80
97PinTotCPG-80
97PinTotCPR-80
97PinX-P-108
97PinX-PMoS-108
97PreCon-10
97Sco-55
97ScoAllF-14
97ScoArtPWB-55
97ScoBla-17
97ScoHeatoO-28
97ScoPreS-55
97ScoShoS-55
97ScoShoSAP-55
97Sel-38
97SelArtP-38
97SelCom-38
97SelRegG-38
97SelToootT-21
97SelToootTMB-21
97SP-146
97SpolII-103
97SpolIIEE-103
97StaClu-4
97StaCluI-I16
97StaCluMat-4
97StaCluMOP-4
97StaCluMOP-I16
97Stu-140
97StuHarH-24
97StuPrePG-140
97StuPrePS-140
97Top-415
97TopChr-147
97TopChrR-147
97TopGal-134
97TopGalPPI-134
97TopIntF-ILM7
97Ult-272
97UltGolME-272
97UltPlaME-272
97UppDec-162
97UppDec-245
97UppDec-258
98Bow-290
98BowChr-290
98BowChrGA-290
98BowChrGAR-290
98BowChrI-290
98BowChrIR-290
98BowChrR-290
98BowGolA-290
98BowInt-290
98CarScoP-13
98CirThu-294
98CirThuRav-294
98CirThuSupRav-294
98ColCho-473
98CroRoy-113
98Don-45
98DonCol-45
98DonColP-674
98DonColS-45
98DonCruG-96
98DonCruP-96
98DonCruR-96
98DonGolPP-45
98DonPre-124
98DonPreSeat-124
98DonPriCD-45
98DonPriCP-674
98DonSig-115
98DonSigP-115
98DonSilPP-45
98Fin-256
98FinNo--256
98FinNo-R-256
98FinRef-256
98Fle-466
98LeaRS-110
98LeaRSLHolo-110
98LeaRSLong-110
98LeaRSTicMas-15
98LeaRSTicMasDC-15
98LeaRTrue-110
98Pac-413
98PacAur-184
98PacOme-198
98PacOmeR-198
98PacOnl-614
98PacOnlR-614
98PacOnlWC-614
98PacPar-230
98PacParC-230
98PacParG-230
98PacParHS-230
98PacParPB-230
98PacParR-230
98PacPlaB-413
98PacRedT-413
98PacSil-413
98PinIns-103
98PinInsCE-103
98PinInsDE-103
98PinPer-102
98PinPerPP-102
98PinPlu-117
98PinSna-SLC11
98PinSna-SLC13
98PinSnaS-4
98Revo-119
98RevoSS-119
98Sco-184
98ScoCar-13
98ScoRT-210
98ScoRTSS-PP116
98ScoRTSSAP-PP116
98ScoRTSSAP1-PP116
98ScoSS-PP84
98ScoSSAP-PP84
98SP Aut-162
98SP AutTrade-10
98SpolII-70
98SpolIIEE-70
98SpolIIFE-70
98SPxFin-311
98SPxFinR-311
98SPxFinS-311
98StaCluFDI-17
98StaCluI-17
98StaCluOneK-17
98StaCluPP-17
98Stu-71
98StuGPP-71
98StuSPP-71
98Top-287
98TopChr-287
98TopChrR-287
98TopDevR-287
98TopDia-287
98TopGal-15
98TopGalGP-15
98TopGalOPP-15
98TopGalPPI-15
98TopGalPPIA-15
98TopGolLabC1-58
98TopGolLabC1B-58
98TopGolLabC1One-58
98TopGolLabC1R-58
98TopGolLabC2-58
98TopGolLabC2B-58
98TopGolLabC2One-58
98TopGolLabC2R-58
98TopGolLabC3-58
98TopGolLabC3B-58
98TopGolLabC3One-58
98TopGolLabC3R-58
98TopMiniC-287
98TopOpeD-114
98TopSta-56
98TopStaB-56
98TopStaG-56
98TopStaGR-56
98TopStaS-56
98TopTek-75
98TopTekD-75
98Ult-22
98UltGolM-22
98UltMas-22
98UltPlaM-22
98UppDec-489
98Zen-63
98Zen5 xx7-59
98Zen5x7GoldImp-59
98Zen5x7Imp-59
98ZenZ-G-63
98ZenZ-S-63
99199Fin-184
99Bow-253
99BowBes-2
99BowBesAR-2
99BowBesR-2
99BowGol-253
99BowInt-253
99CroRoyB-13
99CroRoyL-13
99CroRoyOD-13
99E-X Cen-82
99E-X CenECFut-82
99E-X CenECNow-82
99FinGolRef-184
99FinRef-184
99Fle-109
99FleBri-119
99FleBri2G-119
99FleBriBlu-119
99FleBriGol-119
99FleMys-4
99FleMysG-4
99FleMysM-4
99FleSta9-109
99FleWarT-109
99MetUni-163
99MetUniGM-163
99MetUniPMG-163
99Pac-354
99PacAur-18
99PacAurOD-18
99PacCroC-230
99PacCroCPB-230
99PacInv-14
99PacInvOD-14
99PacInvPB-14
99PacOme-23
99PacOmeC-23
99PacOmeG-23
99PacOmePB-23
99PacPar-25
99PacParC-25
99PacParG-25
99PacParHoloGold-25
99PacParHS-25
99PacParOD-25
99PacParPB-25
99PacParRed-25
99PacPlaB-354
99PacPri-119
99PacPriHB-119
99PacPriHG-119
99PacPriHM-119
99PacPriHP-119
99PacPriRed-119
99PacPriS-102
99PacPriS206-102
99PacPriS206R-102
99PacRed-354
99Rev-13
99RevPremDate-13
99RevRet-13
99RevShaSS-13
99SkyMolM-3
99SkyMolMOA-6
99SkyMolMX-3
99SkyPre-201
99SkyPreR-201
99SkyThu-183
99SkyThuRant-183
99SkyThuRave-183
99SP SigAutoG-BJ
99SPSig-43
99StaClu-322
99StaCluFDI-322
99StaCluOoaK-322
99StaCluPP-322
99StaCluTI-T5A
99StaCluTL-T5A
99StaCluTL-T5A
99ThuSkySupR-183
99Top-306
99TopBlaLC1-9
99TopBlaLC2-9
99TopBlaLC3-9
99TopChr-306
99TopChrR-306
99TopGal-75
99TopGalPP-75
99TopGalPPI-75
99TopGolL-9
99TopGolLC1-9
99TopGolLC2-9
99TopGolLOtO-9
99TopMVPP-306
99TopOpeD-126
99TopRedLC1-9
99TopRedLC2-9
99TopRedLC3-9
99TopSta-109
99TopStaFoil-109
99Ult-155
99UltGolM-155
99UltMas-155
99UltPlaM-155
99UppDec-307
99UppDecBD-82
99UppDecBDD-82
99UppDecBDQ-82
99UppDecBDT-82
99UppDecCf7-15
99UppDecCo7CE-15
99UppDecEL1-307
99UppDecEL2-307
99UppDecM-20
99UppDecMGS-20
99UppDecMHFS-20
99UppDecMSS-20
99Vic-37

Jordan, Buck (Baxter)
31SenTeaIPW-18
34DiaMatCSB-99
34DiaStaR-49
34Gou-31
34GouCanV-75
35DiaMatCS3T1-82
36DiaMatCS4-7
36GouWidPPR-A58
36OveCanR-27
37WheBB9-10
79DiaGre-203

Jordan, Dutch (Adolph)
09T206-494
10CouT21-35
11SpoLifCW-193
90DodTar-995

Jordan, Harry K.
75PhoGiaCK-24
76PheGiaCr-NNO
76PhoGiaCC-24
76PhoGiaVNB-12
77PhoGiaCC-13
77PhoGiaCP-13
77PhoGiaVNB-13
78PhoGiaC-12
79PhoGiaVNB-24
80PhoGiaVNB-26
81PhoGiaVNB-2
82PhoGiaVNB-9

Jordan, Jason
94JamJamC-12
94JamJamF-3959
95FayGenTI-14

Jordan, Jim
78BurBeeT-17

Jordan, Jim William
33ButCanV-29
34BabRutG-38
34ButPreR-37
72TCMthe3-41
74TCMNic-16

Jordan, Joe
85EveGialC-8
89OklSoo-4

Jordan, Kevin
90NebCor-13
90OneYanP-3386
90ProAaA-181
91Cla/Bes-96
91FloStaLAP-FSL15
91Ft.LauYC-21
91Ft.LauYP-2434
92ClaFS7-223
92PriWilCC-22
92PriWilCF-157
93AlbYanF-2172
93AusFut-97
93AusFut-102
93AusFut-117
93AusFut-122
93ClaFS7-77
93ClaGolF-35
93ExcFS7-211
94Bow-224
94ExcFS7-107
94ScrRedBF-925
94UppDecML-113
94VenLinU-181
95Bow-108
95ScrRedBTI-15
95Top-654
96ColCho-33
96ColChoGS-33

❑ 96ColChoSS-33
❑ 96Don-497
❑ 96DonPreP-497
❑ 96Fle-501
❑ 96FleTif-501
❑ 96LeaSigA-122
❑ 96LeaSigAG-122
❑ 96LeaSigAS-122
❑ 96PhiTeal-18
❑ 96Sco-230
❑ 96Top-426
❑ 96UltGolP-9
❑ 96UltGolPGM-9
❑ 97Pac-380
❑ 97PacLigB-380
❑ 97PacSil-380
❑ 97PhiCopQ-13
❑ 97PhiTeal-23
❑ 97ScrRedB-5
❑ 98AubDouTI-13
❑ 98PacInvGems-187
❑ 98PacOnl-564
❑ 98PacOnlR-564
❑ 98PacOnlWC-564
❑ 98PhiTeal-19
❑ 98PriWilCASM-29
❑ 99Pac-327
❑ 99PacPlaB-327
❑ 99PacRed-327
❑ 99UppDec-454
❑ 99UppDecEL1-454
❑ 99UppDecEL2-454
❑ 99Vic-302

Jordan, Michael

❑ 91UppDec-SP1
❑ 92SpollIFK1-270
❑ 94ActPac-23
❑ 94BirBarC-23
❑ 94BirBarF-633
❑ 94Cla-1
❑ 94ColC-635
❑ 94ColC-661
❑ 94ColChoGS-635
❑ 94ColChoGS-661
❑ 94ColChoSS-635
❑ 94ColChoSS-661
❑ 94FUnPac-170
❑ 94SPHol-16
❑ 94SPHolDC-16
❑ 94SPPre-CR2
❑ 94TedWilDGC-DG1
❑ 94UppDec-19
❑ 94UppDecDC-C2
❑ 94UppDecED-19
❑ 94UppDecML-MJ23
❑ 94UppDecML-MJ23
❑ 94UppDecNG-8
❑ 94UppDecNGED-8
❑ 94UppDecTAE-BC2
❑ 94WilJor-1
❑ 95ColCho-500
❑ 95ColChoGS-500
❑ 95ColChoSE-238
❑ 95ColChoSEGS-238
❑ 95ColChoSESS-238
❑ 95ColChoSS-500
❑ 95SPMLA-14
❑ 95SPMLMJC-TC1
❑ 95SPMLMJC-TC2
❑ 95SPMLMJC-TC3
❑ 95SPMLMJC-TC4
❑ 95UppDec-200
❑ 95UppDecED-200
❑ 95UppDecEDG-200
❑ 95UppDecML-45
❑ 95UppDecMLFS-45
❑ 95UppDecMLMJJ-MJ1
❑ 95UppDecMLMJJ-MJ2
❑ 95UppDecMLMJJ-MJ3
❑ 95UppDecMLMJJ-MJ4
❑ 95UppDecMLMJJ-MJ5
❑ 95UppDecMLMJOoO-1
❑ 95UppDecMLMJOoO-2
❑ 95UppDecMLMJOoO-3
❑ 95UppDecMLMJOoO-4
❑ 95UppDecMLMJOoO-5
❑ 95UppDecMLMJOoO-6
❑ 95UppDecMLMJOoO-7
❑ 95UppDecMLMJOoO-8
❑ 95UppDecMLMJOoO-9
❑ 95UppDecMLMJOoO-10
❑ 95UppDecMLMJS-MJ1
❑ 95UppDecMLMJS-MJ2
❑ 95UppDecMLMJS-MJ3
❑ 95UppDecMLMJS-MJ4
❑ 95UppDecMLMJS-MJ5
❑ 95UppDecMLMJS-MJ6
❑ 95UppDecMLMJS-MJ7
❑ 95UppDecMLMJS-MJ8
❑ 95UppDecMLMJS-MJ9
❑ 95UppDecMLMJS-MJ10
❑ 95UppDecMLOP-OP6
❑ 95UppDecSoaD-SD15
❑ 97HigMinMCP-3
❑ 97HigMinMCP-4
❑ 97HigMinMCP-5
❑ 99SP TopPR-R6
❑ 99SP TopPR-R7
❑ 99SP TopPR-R8
❑ 99SP TopPR-R9
❑ 99SP TopPR-R10
❑ 99SP TopPRAG-MJ

Jordan, Milton

❑ 53TigGle-17

Jordan, Ricardo

❑ 91MyrBeaHC-7
❑ 91MyrBeaHP-2941
❑ 92DunBluJC-11
❑ 92DunBluJF-1996
❑ 94KnoSmoF-1300
❑ 95Exc-138
❑ 96ScrRedBB-17
❑ 97NorTid-18
❑ 97NorTidB-18
❑ 97Pac-381
❑ 97PacLigB-381
❑ 97PacSil-381
❑ 98IndIndQ-9
❑ 98PacOnl-194
❑ 98PacOnlR-194
❑ 98PacOnlWC-194

Jordan, Ricky

❑ 86PhiTas-NNO
❑ 86ReaPhiP-12
❑ 87ReaPhiP-16
❑ 88BlaYNPRWL-90
❑ 88FleUpd-110
❑ 88FleUpdG-110
❑ 88MaiPhiC-11
❑ 88MaiPhiP-286
❑ 88PhiTas-35
❑ 88ScoRoo-68T
❑ 88ScoRooG-68T
❑ 88StaJor-1
❑ 88StaJor-2
❑ 88StaJor-3
❑ 88StaJor-4
❑ 88StaJor-5
❑ 88StaJor-6
❑ 88StaJor-7
❑ 88StaJor-8
❑ 88StaJor-9
❑ 88StaJor-10
❑ 88StaJor-11
❑ 88TriAAC-28
❑ 89Baz-17
❑ 89Bow-401
❑ 89BowTif-401
❑ 89ClaTraO-129
❑ 89Don-624
❑ 89DonBasB-103
❑ 89Fle-575
❑ 89FleBasA-24
❑ 89FleExcS-27
❑ 89FleGlo-575
❑ 89FleHeroB-25
❑ 89PanSti-144
❑ 89PhiTas-15
❑ 89Sco-548
❑ 89ScoHot1R-88
❑ 89ScoYouSI-15
❑ 89Spo-44
❑ 89Top-358
❑ 89TopBig-246
❑ 89TopCoi-17
❑ 89TopHeaUT-4
❑ 89TopRoo-14
❑ 89TopTif-358
❑ 89TopUKM-45
❑ 89ToyRoo-17
❑ 89TVSpoM-31
❑ 89UppDec-35
❑ 90Bow-156
❑ 90BowTif-156
❑ 90ClaBlu-32A
❑ 90ClaBlu-32B
❑ 90Don-76
❑ 90DonBesN-8
❑ 90Fle-564
❑ 90FleCan-564
❑ 90FleLeaL-21
❑ 90FleLeaLC-21
❑ 90FleSoaS-11
❑ 90Hot50PS-23
❑ 90Lea-236
❑ 90MLBBasB-3
❑ 90OPC-216
❑ 90PanSti-315
❑ 90PhiTas-17
❑ 90PubIntS-244
❑ 90PubIntS-615
❑ 90Sco-16
❑ 90Spo-153
❑ 90Top-216
❑ 90TopBig-172
❑ 90TopDou-38
❑ 90TopSti-112
❑ 90TopTif-216
❑ 90UppDec-576
❑ 91Bow-494
❑ 91DenHol-13
❑ 91Don-466
❑ 91Fle-401
❑ 91OPC-712
❑ 91PanFreS-103
❑ 91PhiMed-21
❑ 91RedFolS-55
❑ 91Sco-15
❑ 91StaClu-192
❑ 91Stu-215
❑ 91Top-712
❑ 91TopDesS-712
❑ 91TopMic-712
❑ 91TopTif-712
❑ 91UltUpd-100
❑ 91UppDec-160
❑ 92Don-458
❑ 92Fle-536
❑ 92OPC-103
❑ 92PhiMed-42
❑ 92Pin-530
❑ 92Sco-476
❑ 92StaClu-188
❑ 92Top-103
❑ 92TopGol-103
❑ 92TopGolW-103
❑ 92TopMic-103
❑ 92Ult-245
❑ 92UppDec-106
❑ 93CadDis-36
❑ 93Don-514
❑ 93Fle-103
❑ 93Lea-169
❑ 93PacSpa-579
❑ 93PhiMed-20
❑ 93Pin-187
❑ 93Sco-141
❑ 93StaClu-229
❑ 93StaCluFDI-229
❑ 93StaCluMOP-229
❑ 93Top-585
❑ 93TopGol-585
❑ 93TopInaM-585
❑ 93TopInaR-585
❑ 93TopMic-585
❑ 93Ult-89
❑ 93UppDec-561
❑ 93UppDecGold-561
❑ 94ColC-447
❑ 94ColChoGS-447
❑ 94ColChoSS-447
❑ 94Don-394
❑ 94Fin-297
❑ 94FinRef-297
❑ 94Fla-414
❑ 94Fle-593
❑ 94FleExtB-339
❑ 94PhiMed-17
❑ 94PhiMel-13
❑ 94PhiUSPC-6H
❑ 94PhiUSPC-10S
❑ 94Sco-116
❑ 94ScoGolR-116
❑ 94Sel-95
❑ 94StaClu-657
❑ 94StaCluFDI-657
❑ 94StaCluGR-657
❑ 94StaCluMOP-657
❑ 94StaCluT-228
❑ 94StaCluTFDI-228
❑ 94Top-86
❑ 94TopGol-86
❑ 94TopSpa-86
❑ 94Ult-248
❑ 95ColCho-369
❑ 95ColChoGS-369
❑ 95ColChoSS-369
❑ 95Don-395
❑ 95DonPreP-395
❑ 95Fle-397
❑ 95Sco-234
❑ 95ScoGolR-234
❑ 95ScoPlaTS-234
❑ 95Top-269
❑ 96FleUpd-U83
❑ 96FleUpdTC-U83
❑ 96LeaSigEA-95
❑ 96MarMot-5
❑ 97CarMudC-17

Jordan, Rocky

❑ 75SalLakCC-10

Jordan, Scott

❑ 86WatIndP-14
❑ 87KinIndP-12
❑ 88EasLeaAP-40
❑ 88WilBilP-1326
❑ 89Don-609

Jordan, Steve

❑ 81BurBeeT-16

Jordan, Tim

❑ 77NewCoPT-20
❑ 78NewWayCT-22
❑ 90JohCitCS-15
❑ 91SavCarC-26
❑ 91SavCarP-1667
❑ 92HamRedC-20
❑ 92HamRedF-1607
❑ 93SprCarC-15
❑ 93SprCarF-1863

Jordan, Tim Joseph

❑ 03WilCarE-18
❑ 09AmeCarE90-1-58
❑ 09T206-178
❑ 09T206-179
❑ 10CouT21-156
❑ 10CouT21-157
❑ 10CouT21-294
❑ 11SpoLifM-158
❑ 11TurRedT-20
❑ 11TurRedT-45
❑ 12ImpTobC-87
❑ 72ClaCar-78
❑ 90DodTar-393

Jordan, Tom (Thomas Jefferson)

❑ 77TCMTheWY-70

Jordan, Tony

❑ 80WauTimT-4

Jordon, J.H.

❑ 88KimN18-21

Jorgens, Arndt

❑ 34DiaMatCSB-100
❑ 34Gou-72
❑ 34TarThoBD-16
❑ 35DiaMatCS3T1-83
❑ 39PlaBal-42
❑ 40PlaBal-2
❑ 72TCMthe3-82
❑ 75YanDyn1T-26
❑ 91ConTSN-78

Jorgensen, Karl

❑ 33Zee-125

Jorgensen, Mike

❑ 70OPC-348
❑ 70Top-348
❑ 71OPC-596
❑ 71Top-596
❑ 72Dia-23
❑ 72Dia-65
❑ 72OPC-16
❑ 72ProStaP-7
❑ 72Top-16
❑ 73ExpPos-5
❑ 73OPC-281
❑ 73Top-281
❑ 74ExpWes-6
❑ 74OPC-549
❑ 74Top-549
❑ 74TopSta-56
❑ 75ExpPos-17
❑ 75Hos-105
❑ 75OPC-286
❑ 75Top-286
❑ 75TopMin-286
❑ 76ExpRed-14
❑ 76Hos-144
❑ 76MonExpP-14
❑ 76OPC-117
❑ 76SSP-327
❑ 76Top-117
❑ 77ExpPos-18
❑ 77OPC-9
❑ 77Top-368
❑ 78SSP270-107
❑ 78Top-406
❑ 79Top-22
❑ 80Top-213
❑ 81Don-274
❑ 81Fle-324
❑ 81Top-698
❑ 82Don-224
❑ 82Fle-529
❑ 82MetPhoA-13
❑ 82Top-566
❑ 83Fle-547
❑ 83Top-107
❑ 83TopTra-51T
❑ 84BraPol-11
❑ 84Car-14
❑ 84Nes792-313
❑ 84Top-313
❑ 84TopTif-313
❑ 84TopTra-60T
❑ 84TopTraT-60T
❑ 85CarTeal-16
❑ 85Fle-229
❑ 85Top-783
❑ 85TopTif-783
❑ 86CarTeal-21
❑ 86Top-422
❑ 86TopTif-422
❑ 87LouRedTI-1
❑ 88LouRedBC-25
❑ 88LouRedBP-441
❑ 88LouRedBTI-1
❑ 89LouRedBC-25
❑ 89LouRedBP-1256
❑ 89LouRedBTI-6
❑ 91MetWIZ-209
❑ 93RanKee-212

Jorgensen, Randy

❑ 93BelMarCB-16
❑ 93BelMarF-3217
❑ 94RivPilCLC-11
❑ 96BesAutS-45
❑ 96PorCitRB-17
❑ 98TacRaiQ-17

Jorgensen, Spider (John)

❑ 43ParSpo-80
❑ 47DodTeal-12
❑ 47TipTop-98
❑ 48DodTeal-14
❑ 49EurSta-39
❑ 53MotCoo-55
❑ 75Gia195T-11
❑ 75OakOak2A-18
❑ 85TCMPhoC-18
❑ 85TCMPla1-28
❑ 90DodTar-394

Jorgensen, Terry

❑ 86AncGlaPTI-16
❑ 88OrlTwiB-15
❑ 89OrlTwiB-15
❑ 89OrlTwiP-1352
❑ 89SouLeaAJ-12
❑ 90CMC-569
❑ 90PorBeaC-17
❑ 90PorBeaP-184
❑ 90ProAAAF-254
❑ 90Sco-655
❑ 90TopDeb89-64
❑ 91LinDriAAA-410
❑ 91PorBeaLD-410
❑ 91PorBeaP-1571
❑ 92PorBeaF-2675
❑ 92PorBeaS-411
❑ 92SkyAAAF-188
❑ 93Don-151
❑ 93Fle-268
❑ 93OPCPre-106
❑ 93PacSpa-521
❑ 93Pin-594
❑ 93Sco-458
❑ 93SelRoo-144T
❑ 93Top-805
❑ 93TopGol-805
❑ 93TopInaM-805
❑ 93TopInaR-805
❑ 93TopMic-805
❑ 93Ult-232
❑ 93UppDec-697
❑ 93UppDecGold-697
❑ 94Don-563
❑ 94Fle-209
❑ 94Pac-356
❑ 94PorSeaDF-685
❑ 94PorSeaDTI-17
❑ 94Ult-88
❑ 95ChaKniTI-12

Jorgensen, Tim

❑ 95WatIndTI-17
❑ 96KenIndB-14
❑ 97KinIndB-11

Jorn, David A.

❑ 78St.PetCT-14
❑ 80ArkTraT-25
❑ 81ArkTraT-12
❑ 89PriWilCS-28
❑ 90GreHorB-30
❑ 90GreHorP-2680
❑ 90GreHorS-26
❑ 91AlbYanLD-25
❑ 91AlbYanP-1024
❑ 91LinDriAA-25
❑ 92AlbYanF-2349
❑ 92AlbYanSk-25
❑ 93CapCitBC-26
❑ 94CapCitBC-27
❑ 94CapCitBF-1769
❑ 98LetBlaDG-15

Jose, Elio

❑ 88ChaWheB-23

Jose, Felix (Domingo Felix)

❑ 84IdaFalATI-15
❑ 85MadMusP-14
❑ 85MadMusT-17
❑ 86ModA'sC-12
❑ 86ModA'sP-16
❑ 87HunStaTI-16
❑ 88TacTigC-24
❑ 88TacTigP-614
❑ 89A'sMot-22
❑ 89Don-38
❑ 89Fle-15
❑ 89FleGlo-15
❑ 89Sco-629
❑ 89ScoHot1R-22
❑ 89TacTigC-14
❑ 89TacTigP-1542
❑ 89UppDec-22
❑ 90A'sMot-17
❑ 90Bow-455
❑ 90BowTif-455
❑ 90ClaYel-T33
❑ 90Don-564
❑ 90DonRoo-5
❑ 90Fle-13
❑ 90FleCan-13
❑ 90Hot50RS-24
❑ 90Lea-385
❑ 90OPC-238
❑ 90Sco-321
❑ 90Top-238
❑ 90TopTif-238
❑ 90UppDec-228
❑ 91Baz-17
❑ 91Bow-401
❑ 91CarPol-34
❑ 91Cla3-T41
❑ 91ClaGam-64
❑ 91Don-656
❑ 91Fle-636
❑ 91Lea-392
❑ 91OPC-368
❑ 91Sco-784
❑ 91Sco100RS-90
❑ 91StaClu-366
❑ 91Top-368
❑ 91TopDesS-368
❑ 91TopMic-368
❑ 91TopRoo-14
❑ 91TopTif-368
❑ 91ToyRoo-13
❑ 91UltUpd-107
❑ 91UppDec-387
❑ 91USPlaCA-9S
❑ 92Bow-176
❑ 92CarPol-9
❑ 92Cla2-T53
❑ 92DenHol-4
❑ 92Don-233
❑ 92DonDiaK-DK13
❑ 92DonSupD-DK13
❑ 92Fle-582
❑ 92FleAll-1
❑ 92Hig5-96
❑ 92Lea-63
❑ 92LeaBlaG-63
❑ 92LeaGolP-10
❑ 92LeaPre-10
❑ 92MooSna-9
❑ 92OPC-105
❑ 92PanSti-176
❑ 92Pin-159

- ❑ 92RedFolS-50
- ❑ 92RedFolS-119
- ❑ 92Sco-40
- ❑ 92Sco100S-99
- ❑ 92StaClu-407
- ❑ 92StaCluD-96
- ❑ 92Stu-94
- ❑ 92Top-105
- ❑ 92TopGol-105
- ❑ 92TopGolW-105
- ❑ 92TopKid-29
- ❑ 92TopMic-105
- ❑ 92TriPla-75
- ❑ 92Ult-264
- ❑ 92UppDec-264
- ❑ 93Bow-393
- ❑ 93ClaGam-43
- ❑ 93Don-574
- ❑ 93DonLonBL-LL12
- ❑ 93Fin-81
- ❑ 93FinRef-81
- ❑ 93Fla-217
- ❑ 93Fle-126
- ❑ 93FleAll-NL5
- ❑ 93FunPac-183
- ❑ 93Lea-349
- ❑ 93LeaFas-12
- ❑ 93LimRocDWB-82
- ❑ 93OPC-182
- ❑ 93OPCPre-128
- ❑ 93PacBeiA-8
- ❑ 93PacSpa-295
- ❑ 93PacSpaGE-4
- ❑ 93PanSti-198
- ❑ 93Pin-36
- ❑ 93RedFolS-47
- ❑ 93RoyPol-13
- ❑ 93RoyStaC-21
- ❑ 93Sco-110
- ❑ 93Sel-131
- ❑ 93SelRoo-110T
- ❑ 93SP-230
- ❑ 93StaClu-653
- ❑ 93StaCluFDI-653
- ❑ 93StaCluMOP-653
- ❑ 93Top-67
- ❑ 93TopGol-67
- ❑ 93TopInaM-67
- ❑ 93TopInaR-67
- ❑ 93TopMic-67
- ❑ 93TopTra-66T
- ❑ 93TriPla-114
- ❑ 93Ult-562
- ❑ 93UppDec-156
- ❑ 93UppDec-542
- ❑ 93UppDec-835
- ❑ 93UppDecGold-156
- ❑ 93UppDecGold-542
- ❑ 93UppDecGold-835
- ❑ 94Bow-667
- ❑ 94ColC-493
- ❑ 94ColChoGS-493
- ❑ 94ColChoSS-493
- ❑ 94Don-529
- ❑ 94Fin-306
- ❑ 94FinRef-306
- ❑ 94Fla-300
- ❑ 94Fle-161
- ❑ 94FleExtB-92
- ❑ 94Lea-168
- ❑ 94OPC-191
- ❑ 94Pac-289
- ❑ 94PanSti-74
- ❑ 94Pin-77
- ❑ 94PinArtP-77
- ❑ 94PinMusC-77
- ❑ 94Sco-433
- ❑ 94ScoGolR-433
- ❑ 94Sel-37
- ❑ 94SP-173
- ❑ 94SPDieC-173
- ❑ 94StaClu-298
- ❑ 94StaCluFDI-298
- ❑ 94StaCluGR-298
- ❑ 94StaCluMOP-298
- ❑ 94Stu-185
- ❑ 94Top-672
- ❑ 94TopGol-672
- ❑ 94TopSpa-672
- ❑ 94TriPla-235
- ❑ 94Ult-67
- ❑ 94UppDec-226
- ❑ 94UppDecED-226
- ❑ 95ColChoSE-212
- ❑ 95ColChoSEGS-212
- ❑ 95ColChoSESS-212
- ❑ 95Don-95
- ❑ 95DonPreP-95
- ❑ 95Fle-162
- ❑ 95Pac-205
- ❑ 95PacLatD-19
- ❑ 95PacPri-65
- ❑ 95Pin-43
- ❑ 95PinArtP-43
- ❑ 95PinMusC-43
- ❑ 95Sco-82
- ❑ 95ScoGolR-82
- ❑ 95ScoPlaTS-82
- ❑ 95Top-607
- ❑ 95TopCyb-377
- ❑ 96SyrChiTI-18

Jose, Manny

- ❑ 85GreHorT-4
- ❑ 86WinHavRSP-13
- ❑ 87WinHavRSP-17
- ❑ 88NewBriRSP-897
- ❑ 89LonTigP-1385
- ❑ 91LinDriAAA-265
- ❑ 91NasSouLD-265
- ❑ 91NasSouP-2170
- ❑ 93LimRocDWB-123

Joseph, Glen

- ❑ 98BilMusTI-15

Joseph, Kevin

- ❑ 97SalVolG-18
- ❑ 98SalVol-18

Joseph, Newt (Walter Lee)

- ❑ 87NegLeaPD-31

Joseph, Ricardo

- ❑ 68Top-434
- ❑ 69Top-329
- ❑ 70OPC-186
- ❑ 70PhiTeal-7
- ❑ 70Top-186
- ❑ 72MilBra-174

Joseph, Sam

- ❑ 86QuaCitAP-16

Joseph, Terry

- ❑ 96RocCubTI-14
- ❑ 97OrlRayB-15
- ❑ 97TexAllM-42
- ❑ 98WesTenDJM-14

Josepher, Rich

- ❑ 93OneYanC-10
- ❑ 93OneYanF-3510

Josephina, Michael

- ❑ 92MacBraC-16
- ❑ 92MacBraF-279

Josephson, Duane

- ❑ 66WhiSoxTI-8
- ❑ 67Top-373
- ❑ 68Top-329
- ❑ 68TopVen-329
- ❑ 69MilBra-141
- ❑ 69MLBOffS-32
- ❑ 69Top-222
- ❑ 69TopSta-156
- ❑ 69TopTeaP-11
- ❑ 69WhiSoxTI-7
- ❑ 70MLBOffS-187
- ❑ 70OPC-263
- ❑ 70Top-263
- ❑ 70WhiSoxTI-8
- ❑ 71OPC-56
- ❑ 71RedSoxTI-4
- ❑ 71Top-56
- ❑ 71TopCoi-92
- ❑ 72MilBra-175
- ❑ 72Top-543

Josephson, Paul

- ❑ 81BirBarT-24
- ❑ 83AlbA'sT-5
- ❑ 84DurBulT-21

Joshua, Joe

- ❑ 54SeaPop-13

Joshua, Von

- ❑ 71OPC-57
- ❑ 71Top-57
- ❑ 73OPC-544
- ❑ 73Top-544
- ❑ 74OPC-551
- ❑ 74Top-551
- ❑ 75GiaTeal-7
- ❑ 75OPC-547
- ❑ 75Top-547
- ❑ 75TopMin-547
- ❑ 76BreA&P-5
- ❑ 76Kel-39
- ❑ 76OPC-82
- ❑ 76SSP-109
- ❑ 76Top-82
- ❑ 77BurCheD-85
- ❑ 77Top-651
- ❑ 78Top-108
- ❑ 80Top-209
- ❑ 85SpoIndGC-10
- ❑ 88AlbDukP-254
- ❑ 89AlbDukP-73
- ❑ 90AlbDukCm-28
- ❑ 90AlbDukP-362
- ❑ 90AlbDukTr-15
- ❑ 90CMC-658
- ❑ 90DodTar-395
- ❑ 90ProAAAF-84
- ❑ 91AlbDukLD-25
- ❑ 91AlbDukP-1158
- ❑ 91LinDriAAA-25
- ❑ 92AlbDukF-739
- ❑ 92AlbDukS-25
- ❑ 93SouBenWSC-29
- ❑ 93SouBenWSF-1448
- ❑ 94BreMilB-323
- ❑ 94PriWilCC-27
- ❑ 94PriWilCF-1937

Joslin, Chris

- ❑ 83BurRanF-16
- ❑ 83BurRanT-7

Joslyn, John

- ❑ 88VirGenS-12

Joss, Addie (Adrian)

- ❑ 03BreE10-77
- ❑ 04FanCraAL-30
- ❑ 05IndSouPSoCP-11
- ❑ 08AmeLeaPC-10
- ❑ 08RosComP-26
- ❑ 09AmeCarE90-1-59
- ❑ 09AmeCarE90-1-60
- ❑ 09ColChiE-147
- ❑ 09SpoNewSM-29
- ❑ 09T206-180
- ❑ 09T206-181
- ❑ 10StaCarE-18
- ❑ 10W555-38
- ❑ 11PinT-5-601
- ❑ 11PinT-5-602
- ❑ 11SpoLifM-44
- ❑ 11T205-85
- ❑ 11TurRedT-19
- ❑ 12ColRedB-147
- ❑ 12ColTinT-147
- ❑ 61Fle-117
- ❑ 67SpoHobFC-12
- ❑ 77BobParHoF-93
- ❑ 77GalGloG-168
- ❑ 78DexHaloFP-25
- ❑ 80PacLeg-114
- ❑ 80PerHaloFP-164
- ❑ 80SSPHOF-164
- ❑ 82TCMGreP-43
- ❑ 91ConTSN-272
- ❑ 94ConTSN-1016
- ❑ 94ConTSNB-1016
- ❑ 94OriofB-97
- ❑ 94UppDecTAE-23

Jourdan, Ted

- ❑ 18WhiSoxTI-13
- ❑ 21Zee-99
- ❑ 92Man191BSR-14

Joyce, Bill (William)

- ❑ 90DodTar-396
- ❑ 95May-14

Joyce, Dick

- ❑ 77FriOneYW-27

Joyce, James

- ❑ 91PocPioP-3784

Joyce, Jesse

- ❑ 98AubDouTI-14
- ❑ 99TeaBesR-43
- ❑ 99TeaBesRG-43
- ❑ 99TeaBesRS-43

Joyce, Jim

- ❑ 90T/MUmp-59

Joyce, Kevin

- ❑ 78CliDodT-17
- ❑ 79CliDodT-24

Joyce, Michael

- ❑ 63Top-66
- ❑ 63WhiSoxTS-13
- ❑ 64Top-477
- ❑ 64WhiSoxl-15
- ❑ 88CarTeal-12

Joyce, Richard

- ❑ 91PocPioSP-4

Joyce, Robert Emmett

- ❑ 48SomandK-6

Joyce, Tom

- ❑ 76AppFoxT-9

Joyner, Wally

- ❑ 85EdmTraC-2
- ❑ 86AngSmo-22
- ❑ 86BasStaB-62
- ❑ 86DonHig-23
- ❑ 86DonRoo-1
- ❑ 86FleSlu-19
- ❑ 86FleUpd-59
- ❑ 86SpoRoo-7
- ❑ 86StaJoyR-1
- ❑ 86StaJoyR-2
- ❑ 86StaJoyR-3
- ❑ 86StaJoyR-4
- ❑ 86StaJoyR-5
- ❑ 86StaJoyR-6
- ❑ 86StaJoyR-7
- ❑ 86StaJoyR-8
- ❑ 86StaJoyR-9
- ❑ 86StaJoyR-10
- ❑ 86StaJoyR-11
- ❑ 86StaJoyR-12
- ❑ 86StaJoyR-13
- ❑ 86StaJoyR-14
- ❑ 86StaJoyR-15
- ❑ 86StaStiJ-1
- ❑ 86StaStiJ-2
- ❑ 86StaStiJ-3
- ❑ 86StaStiJ-4
- ❑ 86StaStiJ-5
- ❑ 86StaStiJ-6
- ❑ 86StaStiJ-7
- ❑ 86StaStiJ-8
- ❑ 86StaStiJ-9
- ❑ 86StaStiJ-10
- ❑ 86StaStiJ-11
- ❑ 86StaStiJ-12
- ❑ 86StaStiJ-13
- ❑ 86StaStiJ-14
- ❑ 86StaStiJ-15
- ❑ 86TopTra-51T
- ❑ 86TopTraT-51T
- ❑ 87AngSmo-12
- ❑ 87BurKinA-11
- ❑ 87CalAngPPS-19
- ❑ 87ClaGam-6
- ❑ 87ClaUpdY-108
- ❑ 87Don-1
- ❑ 87Don-135
- ❑ 87DonAll-1
- ❑ 87DonHig-35
- ❑ 87DonOpeD-7
- ❑ 87DonP-1
- ❑ 87DonSupD-1
- ❑ 87Dra-2
- ❑ 87Fle-86
- ❑ 87Fle-628
- ❑ 87FleBasA-23
- ❑ 87FleExcS-30
- ❑ 87FleGamW-22
- ❑ 87FleGlo-86
- ❑ 87FleGlo-628
- ❑ 87FleHotS-25
- ❑ 87FleLeaL-26
- ❑ 87FleLimE-23
- ❑ 87FleMin-59
- ❑ 87FleRecS-17
- ❑ 87FleSlu-22
- ❑ 87FleStiC-68
- ❑ 87FleWaxBC-C7
- ❑ 87GenMilB-3F
- ❑ 87HosSti-20
- ❑ 87KayB-18
- ❑ 87KeyFooD-10
- ❑ 87KraFoo-9
- ❑ 87Lea-1
- ❑ 87Lea-252
- ❑ 87MandMSL-1
- ❑ 87MSAIceTD-10
- ❑ 87OPC-80
- ❑ 87OurOwnTD-10
- ❑ 87RedFolSB-82
- ❑ 87SevCoi-W3
- ❑ 87Spo-26
- ❑ 87Spo-75
- ❑ 87SpoDeaP-2
- ❑ 87SpoTeaP-11
- ❑ 87StuPan-16
- ❑ 87Top-80
- ❑ 87TopCoi-16
- ❑ 87TopGloA-13
- ❑ 87TopGloS-39
- ❑ 87TopMinL-45
- ❑ 87TopRoo-7
- ❑ 87TopSti-150
- ❑ 87TopSti-174
- ❑ 87TopSti-313
- ❑ 87TopTif-80
- ❑ 87ToyRoo-14
- ❑ 87WeiMarD-10
- ❑ 88AngSmo-17
- ❑ 88Baz-10
- ❑ 88ClaBlu-206
- ❑ 88Don-110
- ❑ 88DonBasB-115
- ❑ 88DonBonM-BC13
- ❑ 88Fle-493
- ❑ 88Fle-622
- ❑ 88FleAwaW-21
- ❑ 88FleBasA-19
- ❑ 88FleBasM-20
- ❑ 88FleExcS-23
- ❑ 88FleGlo-493
- ❑ 88FleGlo-622
- ❑ 88FleHotS-21
- ❑ 88FleLeaL-22
- ❑ 88FleMin-11
- ❑ 88FleRecS-21
- ❑ 88FleStiC-12
- ❑ 88FleSup-18
- ❑ 88FleTeaL-16
- ❑ 88FleWaxBC-C4
- ❑ 88GreBasS-8
- ❑ 88KayB-15
- ❑ 88KinDis-9
- ❑ 88Lea-50
- ❑ 88MSAFanSD-4
- ❑ 88MSAJifPD-11
- ❑ 88Nes-44
- ❑ 88OPC-168
- ❑ 88PanSti-40
- ❑ 88RedFolSB-41
- ❑ 88Sco-7
- ❑ 88ScoGlo-7
- ❑ 88ScoYouSI-27
- ❑ 88Spo-75
- ❑ 88StaLinAn-11
- ❑ 88TarPla-23
- ❑ 88Top-381
- ❑ 88Top-420
- ❑ 88TopBig-52
- ❑ 88TopCoi-16
- ❑ 88TopGloS-48
- ❑ 88TopMinL-6
- ❑ 88TopRitTM-15
- ❑ 88TopSti-179
- ❑ 88TopStiB-34
- ❑ 88TopTif-381
- ❑ 88TopTif-420
- ❑ 88TopUKM-40
- ❑ 88TopUKMT-40
- ❑ 88UppDecP-A700
- ❑ 88UppDecP-B700
- ❑ 88UppDecP-C700
- ❑ 89AngSmo-18
- ❑ 89Bow-47
- ❑ 89BowTif-47
- ❑ 89ClaLigB-29
- ❑ 89Don-52
- ❑ 89DonBasB-139
- ❑ 89DonBonM-BC21
- ❑ 89Fle-481
- ❑ 89FleExcS-28
- ❑ 89FleGlo-481
- ❑ 89FleSup-26
- ❑ 89FleWaxBC-C16
- ❑ 89MasBreD-7
- ❑ 89MSAHolD-1
- ❑ 89Nis-1
- ❑ 89OPC-270
- ❑ 89PanSti-291
- ❑ 89RedFolSB-68
- ❑ 89Sco-65
- ❑ 89ScoHot1S-73
- ❑ 89Spo-2
- ❑ 89Top-270
- ❑ 89TopBasT-49
- ❑ 89TopBig-201
- ❑ 89TopSti-183
- ❑ 89TopTif-270
- ❑ 89TopUKM-46
- ❑ 89TVSpoM-109
- ❑ 89UppDec-573
- ❑ 89UppDec-668
- ❑ 90AngSmo-9
- ❑ 90Bow-299
- ❑ 90BowTif-299
- ❑ 90ClaUpd-T42
- ❑ 90Don-94
- ❑ 90DonBesA-31
- ❑ 90Fle-136
- ❑ 90FleCan-136
- ❑ 90Hot50PS-24
- ❑ 90Lea-24
- ❑ 90M.Vpin-16
- ❑ 90MLBBasB-93
- ❑ 90OPC-525
- ❑ 90PanSti-31
- ❑ 90PublntS-372
- ❑ 90Sco-120
- ❑ 90Sco100S-81
- ❑ 90Spo-49
- ❑ 90SunSee-19
- ❑ 90Top-525
- ❑ 90TopAmeA-30
- ❑ 90TopBig-168
- ❑ 90TopSti-166
- ❑ 90TopTif-525
- ❑ 90UppDec-693
- ❑ 91AngSmo-6
- ❑ 91Bow-195
- ❑ 91Cla3-T42
- ❑ 91DenHol-23
- ❑ 91Don-677
- ❑ 91Fle-317
- ❑ 91Lea-31
- ❑ 91OPC-195
- ❑ 91PanFreS-180
- ❑ 91PanSti-141
- ❑ 91RedFolS-56
- ❑ 91Sco-470
- ❑ 91Sco-873
- ❑ 91Sco100S-57
- ❑ 91SevCoi-SC7
- ❑ 91StaClu-2
- ❑ 91StaPinB-26
- ❑ 91Stu-26
- ❑ 91Top-195
- ❑ 91TopDesS-195
- ❑ 91TopMic-195
- ❑ 91TopTif-195
- ❑ 91TopTriH-A3
- ❑ 91Ult-48
- ❑ 91UppDec-575
- ❑ 92Bow-435
- ❑ 92ClaGam-164
- ❑ 92Don-333
- ❑ 92DonUpd-U14
- ❑ 92Fle-62
- ❑ 92FleUpd-27
- ❑ 92Lea-438
- ❑ 92LeaBlaG-438
- ❑ 92OPC-629
- ❑ 92OPCPre-61
- ❑ 92PanSti-5
- ❑ 92Pin-284
- ❑ 92Pin-537
- ❑ 92Pos-4
- ❑ 92RedFolS-51
- ❑ 92RoyPol-14
- ❑ 92Sco-535
- ❑ 92Sco100S-29
- ❑ 92ScoRoo-13T
- ❑ 92SpoStaCC-27
- ❑ 92StaClu-122
- ❑ 92StaClu-710
- ❑ 92StaCluNC-710
- ❑ 92Stu-185
- ❑ 92StuPre-10
- ❑ 92Top-629
- ❑ 92TopGol-629
- ❑ 92TopGolW-629
- ❑ 92TopKid-95
- ❑ 92TopMic-629
- ❑ 92TopTra-59T
- ❑ 92TopTraG-59T
- ❑ 92TriPlaG-GS2
- ❑ 92Ult-373
- ❑ 92UppDec-343
- ❑ 92UppDec-744
- ❑ 92UppDecF-29
- ❑ 92UppDecFG-29
- ❑ 93Bow-645
- ❑ 93ClaGam-44
- ❑ 93DenHol-24
- ❑ 93DiaMar-57
- ❑ 93Don-129
- ❑ 93DonDiaK-DK8
- ❑ 93Fin-59
- ❑ 93FinRef-59
- ❑ 93Fla-218
- ❑ 93Fle-239
- ❑ 93FunPac-184
- ❑ 93Hos-24
- ❑ 93Lea-376
- ❑ 93MetBak-12
- ❑ 93MilBonSS-11
- ❑ 93OPC-148
- ❑ 93PacSpa-138

❑ 93PanSti-103
❑ 93Pin-51
❑ 93RedFolS-48
❑ 93RoyPol-14
❑ 93RoyStaC-4
❑ 93Sco-43
❑ 93Sel-34
❑ 93SP-231
❑ 93StaClu-537
❑ 93StaCluFDI-537
❑ 93StaCluMOP-537
❑ 93Stu-164
❑ 93Top-375
❑ 93TopGol-375
❑ 93TopInaM-375
❑ 93TopInaR-375
❑ 93TopMic-375
❑ 93TriPla-153
❑ 93TriPlaA-25
❑ 93Ult-210
❑ 93UppDec-54
❑ 93UppDec-252
❑ 93UppDecGold-54
❑ 93UppDecGold-252
❑ 94Bow-443
❑ 94ColC-155
❑ 94ColChoGS-155
❑ 94ColChoSS-155
❑ 94Don-345
❑ 94DonMVP-21
❑ 94DonSpeE-345
❑ 94Fin-176
❑ 94FinRef-176
❑ 94Fla-60
❑ 94Fle-162
❑ 94FleExtB-93
❑ 94FUnPac-48
❑ 94Lea-141
❑ 94LeaL-40
❑ 94OPC-91
❑ 94Pac-290
❑ 94PanSti-75
❑ 94Pin-291
❑ 94PinArtP-291
❑ 94PinMusC-291
❑ 94ProMag-64
❑ 94Sco-67
❑ 94ScoGolR-67
❑ 94Sel-35
❑ 94SP-174
❑ 94SPDieC-174
❑ 94Spo-23
❑ 94StaClu-431
❑ 94StaCluFDI-431
❑ 94StaCluGR-431
❑ 94StaCluMOP-431
❑ 94Stu-186
❑ 94Top-275
❑ 94TopGol-275
❑ 94TopSpa-275
❑ 94TriPla-236
❑ 94Ult-366
❑ 94UppDec-169
❑ 94UppDec-287
❑ 94UppDecED-169
❑ 94UppDecED-287
❑ 95Bow-364
❑ 95BowBes-R43
❑ 95BowBesR-R43
❑ 95ColCho-453
❑ 95ColChoGS-453
❑ 95ColChoSE-214
❑ 95ColChoSEGS-214
❑ 95ColChoSESS-214
❑ 95ColChoSS-453
❑ 95Don-447
❑ 95DonPreP-447
❑ 95DonTopotO-92
❑ 95Fin-39
❑ 95FinRef-39
❑ 95Fla-47
❑ 95Fle-163
❑ 95Lea-194
❑ 95LeaLim-102
❑ 95Pac-206
❑ 95PacPri-66
❑ 95Pin-77
❑ 95PinArtP-77
❑ 95PinMusC-77
❑ 95Sco-256
❑ 95ScoGolR-256
❑ 95ScoPlaTS-256
❑ 95Sel-74
❑ 95SelArtP-74
❑ 95SelCer-29
❑ 95SelCerMG-29
❑ 95SP-159
❑ 95SPCha-158
❑ 95SPChaDC-158
❑ 95Spo-74
❑ 95SpoArtP-74
❑ 95SPSil-159
❑ 95StaClu-419
❑ 95StaCluMOP-419
❑ 95StaCluSTWS-419
❑ 95StaCluVR-217
❑ 95StaCluVRMO-217
❑ 95Stu-192
❑ 95Sum-61
❑ 95SumNthD-61
❑ 95Top-115
❑ 95TopCyb-74
❑ 95TopEmb-63
❑ 95TopEmbGI-63
❑ 95UC3-29
❑ 95UC3ArtP-29
❑ 95Ult-291
❑ 95UltGolM-291
❑ 95UppDec-181
❑ 95UppDecED-181
❑ 95UppDecEDG-181
❑ 95Zen-108
❑ 96Cir-188
❑ 96CirRav-188
❑ 96ColCho-700
❑ 96ColChoGS-700
❑ 96ColChoSS-700
❑ 96Don-520
❑ 96DonDiaK-24
❑ 96DonPreP-520
❑ 96EmoXL-281
❑ 96Fin-S263
❑ 96FinRef-S263
❑ 96Fla-378
❑ 96Fle-132
❑ 96FleTif-132
❑ 96FleUpd-U198
❑ 96FleUpdTC-U198
❑ 96LeaLim-36
❑ 96LeaLimG-36
❑ 96MetUni-239
❑ 96MetUniP-239
❑ 96Pac-336
❑ 96PacPri-P107
❑ 96PacPriG-P107
❑ 96PadMot-3
❑ 96PanSti-188
❑ 96Pin-367
❑ 96PinAfi-4
❑ 96PinAfiAP-4
❑ 96PinAfiFPP-4
❑ 96PinFoil-367
❑ 96RedF-29
❑ 96Sco-53
❑ 96ScoDugC-A46
❑ 96ScoDugCAP-A46
❑ 96Sel-124
❑ 96SelArtP-124
❑ 96SP-161
❑ 96StaClu-93
❑ 96StaCluMOP-93
❑ 96Stu-61
❑ 96StuPrePB-61
❑ 96StuPrePG-61
❑ 96StuPrePS-61
❑ 96Sum-21
❑ 96SumAbo&B-21
❑ 96SumArtP-21
❑ 96SumFoi-21
❑ 96TeaOut-44
❑ 96Top-386
❑ 96TopChr-155
❑ 96TopChrR-155
❑ 96Ult-72
❑ 96Ult-559
❑ 96UltGolM-72
❑ 96UltGolM-559
❑ 96UppDec-88
❑ 96UppDec-509U
❑ 96Zen-53
❑ 96ZenArtP-53
❑ 96ZenMoz-20
❑ 97Cir-30
❑ 97CirRav-30
❑ 97ColCho-445
❑ 97Don-152
❑ 97DonGolPP-152
❑ 97DonLim-185
❑ 97DonLimE-185
❑ 97DonLimENG-185
❑ 97DonSilPP-152
❑ 97Fin-201
❑ 97FinRef-201
❑ 97Fle-467
❑ 97FleTif-467
❑ 97Lea-279
❑ 97LeaFraM-279
❑ 97LeaFraMDC-279
❑ 97MetUni-223
❑ 97NewPin-105
❑ 97NewPinAP-105
❑ 97NewPinMC-105
❑ 97NewPinPP-105
❑ 97Pac-429
❑ 97PacLigB-429
❑ 97PacPri-145
❑ 97PacPriLB-145
❑ 97PacPriP-145
❑ 97PacSil-429
❑ 97PadMot-4
❑ 97PinCer-33
❑ 97PinCerMBla-33
❑ 97PinCerMBlu-33
❑ 97PinCerMG-33
❑ 97PinCerMR-33
❑ 97PinCerR-33
❑ 97PinTotCPB-33
❑ 97PinTotCPG-33
❑ 97PinTotCPR-33
❑ 97Sco-152
❑ 97ScoArtPWB-152
❑ 97ScoPreS-152
❑ 97ScoShoS-152
❑ 97ScoShoSAP-152
❑ 97StaClu-342
❑ 97StaCluMOP-342
❑ 97Stu-53
❑ 97StuPrePG-53
❑ 97StuPrePS-53
❑ 97Top-132
❑ 97TopChr-50
❑ 97TopChrR-50
❑ 97TopGal-30
❑ 97TopGalPPI-30
❑ 97Ult-337
❑ 97UltGolME-337
❑ 97UltPlaME-337
❑ 97UppDec-168
❑ 98CirThu-154
❑ 98CirThuRav-154
❑ 98CirThuSupRav-154
❑ 98ColCho-482
❑ 98CroRoy-117
❑ 98Don-128
❑ 98DonCol-128
❑ 98DonColL-271
❑ 98DonColS-128
❑ 98DonGolPP-128
❑ 98DonPriCD-128
❑ 98DonPriCL-271
❑ 98DonSilPP-128
❑ 98Fin-58
❑ 98FinNo--58
❑ 98FinNo-R-58
❑ 98FinRef-58
❑ 98Fle-291
❑ 98Lea-72
❑ 98LeaFraDA-72
❑ 98LeaFraF-72
❑ 98LeaFraM-72
❑ 98LeaFraM-72
❑ 98LeaFraMDC-72
❑ 98LeaFraMDC-72
❑ 98LeaFraMZ2-72
❑ 98Pac-432
❑ 98PacAur-192
❑ 98PacInv-141
❑ 98PacInvPBlue-141
❑ 98PacInvSilv-141
❑ 98PacInvTeam-24
❑ 98PacOme-207
❑ 98PacOmeR-207
❑ 98PacOnl-642
❑ 98PacOnlR-642
❑ 98PacOnlWC-642
❑ 98PacPar-238
❑ 98PacParC-238
❑ 98PacParG-238
❑ 98PacParHS-238
❑ 98PacParPB-238
❑ 98PacParR-238
❑ 98PacPlaB-432
❑ 98PacRedT-432
❑ 98PacSil-432
❑ 98PacTeaC-27
❑ 98PadMot-5
❑ 98Pin-143
❑ 98PinPreP-143
❑ 98Revo-125
❑ 98RevoSS-125
❑ 98ScoRT-232
❑ 98SP Aut-179
❑ 98SPxFin-316
❑ 98SPxFinR-316
❑ 98SPxFinS-316
❑ 98StaCluFDI-274
❑ 98StaCluI-274
❑ 98StaCluOneK-274
❑ 98StaCluPP-274
❑ 98Top-131
❑ 98TopChr-131
❑ 98TopChrR-131
❑ 98TopDevR-131
❑ 98TopDia-131
❑ 98TopMiniC-131
❑ 98TopOpeD-66
❑ 98Ult-254
❑ 98UltGolM-254
❑ 98UltMas-254
❑ 98UltPlaM-254
❑ 98UppDec-494
❑ 99199Fin-96
❑ 99CroRoyB-121
❑ 99CroRoyL-121
❑ 99CroRoyOD-121
❑ 99FinGolRef-96
❑ 99FinRef-96
❑ 99Fle-273
❑ 99FleSta9-273
❑ 99FleWarT-273
❑ 99KinDis-30
❑ 99Pac-372
❑ 99PacAur-162
❑ 99PacAurOD-162
❑ 99PacCroC-245
❑ 99PacCroCPB-245
❑ 99PacInv-124
❑ 99PacInvOD-124
❑ 99PacInvPB-124
❑ 99PacOme-204
❑ 99PacOmeC-204
❑ 99PacOmeG-204
❑ 99PacOmePB-204
❑ 99PacPar-201
❑ 99PacParC-201
❑ 99PacParG-201
❑ 99PacParHoloGold-201
❑ 99PacParHS-201
❑ 99PacParOD-201
❑ 99PacParPB-201
❑ 99PacParRed-201
❑ 99PacPlaB-372
❑ 99PacPri-125
❑ 99PacPriHB-125
❑ 99PacPriHG-125
❑ 99PacPriHM-125
❑ 99PacPriHP-125
❑ 99PacPriRed-125
❑ 99PacPriS-103
❑ 99PacPriS206-103
❑ 99PacPriS206R-103
❑ 99PacRed-372
❑ 99Rev-122
❑ 99RevPremDate-122
❑ 99RevRet-122
❑ 99RevShaSS-122
❑ 99SkyPre-155
❑ 99SkyPreR-155
❑ 99SkyThu-115
❑ 99SkyThuRant-115
❑ 99SkyThuRave-115
❑ 99SP Aut-71
❑ 99SP SigAuto-WJ
❑ 99SPSig-149
❑ 99StaClu-113
❑ 99StaCluFDI-113
❑ 99StaCluOoaK-113
❑ 99StaCluPP-113
❑ 99ThuSkySupR-115
❑ 99Top-295
❑ 99TopChr-295
❑ 99TopChrR-295
❑ 99TopMVPP-295
❑ 99TopOpeD-152
❑ 99UD Cho-133
❑ 99UD ChoPCR-133
❑ 99Ult-28
❑ 99UltGolM-28
❑ 99UltMas-28
❑ 99UltPlaM-28
❑ 99UppDec-193
❑ 99UppDecEL1-193
❑ 99UppDecEL2-193
❑ 99UppDecM-179
❑ 99UppDecMGS-179
❑ 99UppDecMHFS-179
❑ 99UppDecMSS-179
❑ 99Vic-342

Ju Cha, Myung
❑ 96HilStaHWB-7

Juarbe, Ken
❑ 88BlaYNPRWL-106
❑ 89BlaYNPRWL-117
❑ 89OneYanP-2114
❑ 90GreHorB-6
❑ 90GreHorP-2658
❑ 90GreHorS-12

Juarez, Raul
❑ 96ForWayWB-12

Jubyna, Chad
❑ 90GeoColC-11

Juday, Bob
❑ 92ClaDraP-105
❑ 92ElmPioC-23
❑ 92ElmPioF-1389
❑ 93CarLeaAGF-9
❑ 93LynRedSC-14
❑ 93LynRedSF-2524
❑ 94LynRedSC-14
❑ 94LynRedSF-1899

Juday, Richard
❑ 91EriSaiC-6
❑ 91EriSaiP-4076
❑ 92WinSpiC-5
❑ 92WinSpiF-1215
❑ 93SalBucF-441
❑ 95WesMicWTI-9

Judd, Mike
❑ 96GreBatB-13
❑ 96SavSanB-26
❑ 97VerBeaD-12
❑ 98AlbDukG-14
❑ 98Bow-381
❑ 98BowChr-381
❑ 98BowChrGA-381
❑ 98BowChrGAR-381
❑ 98BowChrI-381
❑ 98BowChrIR-381
❑ 98BowChrR-381
❑ 98BowGolA-381
❑ 98BowInt-381
❑ 98Don-210
❑ 98DonGolPP-210
❑ 98DonSilPP-210
❑ 98LeaRS-221
❑ 98LeaRSLHolo-221
❑ 98LeaRSLong-221
❑ 98LeaRTrue-221

Judd, Oscar
❑ 40SolHug-10
❑ 42RedSoxTI-15
❑ 43RedSoxTI-10
❑ 83TCMPla1943-19
❑ 85TCMPla1-36

Judd, Ralph
❑ 33WorCig(-52

Juden, Jeff
❑ 90Bes-243
❑ 90Bow-64
❑ 90BowTif-64
❑ 90FloStaLAS-8
❑ 90OPC-164
❑ 90OscAstS-11
❑ 90StaFS7-2
❑ 90Top-164
❑ 90TopTif-164
❑ 91Bow-547
❑ 91Cla/Bes-302
❑ 91Cla3-T43
❑ 91JacGenLD-564
❑ 91JacGenP-922
❑ 91UppDec-52
❑ 92Bow-188
❑ 92ClaGam-5
❑ 92Don-405
❑ 92OPC-34
❑ 92ProFS7-226
❑ 92SkyAAAF-272
❑ 92StaClu-479
❑ 92Top-34
❑ 92TopDeb91-95
❑ 92TopGol-34
❑ 92TopGolW-34
❑ 92TopMic-34
❑ 92TucTorF-484
❑ 92TucTorS-611
❑ 92Ult-492
❑ 92UppDec-6
❑ 93AstStaC-6
❑ 93Bow-180
❑ 93ExcFS7-47
❑ 93OPC-309
❑ 93StaClu-698
❑ 93StaCluFDI-698
❑ 93StaCluMOP-698
❑ 93Top-709
❑ 93TopGol-709
❑ 93TopInaM-709
❑ 93TopInaR-709
❑ 93TopMic-709
❑ 93Toy-94
❑ 93TucTorF-3057
❑ 94ColC-662
❑ 94ColChoGS-662
❑ 94ColChoSS-662
❑ 94Fla-210
❑ 94PhiMed-18
❑ 94ScoRoo-RT153
❑ 94ScoRooGR-RT153
❑ 94Sel-409
❑ 94SpoRoo-120
❑ 94SpoRooAP-120
❑ 94StaClu-609
❑ 94StaCluFDI-609
❑ 94StaCluGR-609
❑ 94StaCluMOP-609
❑ 94StaCluT-218
❑ 94StaCluTFDI-218
❑ 94Top-541
❑ 94TopGol-541
❑ 94TopSpa-541
❑ 94Ult-549
❑ 94UppDec-504
❑ 94UppDecED-504
❑ 95ScrRedBTI-16
❑ 96GiaMot-23
❑ 96LeaSigA-123
❑ 96LeaSigAG-123
❑ 96LeaSigAS-123
❑ 98IndSco-10
❑ 98IndScoP-10
❑ 98PacOnl-401
❑ 98PacOnlR-401
❑ 98PacOnlWC-401
❑ 98Sco-147
❑ 98ScoSS-PP61
❑ 98ScoSSAP-PP61
❑ 98Top-394
❑ 98TopChr-394
❑ 98TopChrR-394
❑ 98TopDevR-394
❑ 98TopDia-394
❑ 98TopMiniC-394
❑ 98Ult-85
❑ 98UltGolM-85
❑ 98UltMas-85
❑ 98UltPlaM-85

Judge, Joe
❑ 16BF2FP-48
❑ 16SpoNewM-93
❑ 17ColE13-90A
❑ 17ColE13-90B
❑ 17HolBreD-55
❑ 20NatCarE-52
❑ 21E121So1-49
❑ 21E121So8-45
❑ 21Exh-86
❑ 22AmeCarE122-34
❑ 22E120-111
❑ 22W572-53
❑ 22W575-66
❑ 22WilPatV-44
❑ 23W501-13
❑ 23WilChoV-76
❑ 25Exh-126
❑ 26Exh-126
❑ 26SpoComoA-24
❑ 27AmeCarE126-26
❑ 28StaPlaCE-40
❑ 28W502-35
❑ 28Yue-35
❑ 29ExhFou-31
❑ 29PorandAR-50
❑ 30W554-8
❑ 31Exh-32
❑ 31SenTealPW-19
❑ 31W517-53
❑ 33DouDisP-25
❑ 33ExhFou-16
❑ 33Gou-155
❑ 33GouCanV-88
❑ 60SenUniMC-9
❑ 61Fle-118
❑ 72TCMthe3-42
❑ 75SenTCM1-14
❑ 77GalGloG-130

□ 77GalGloG-171
□ 85BigLeaC3-69
□ 88ConSer3-16
□ 90DodTar-397
□ 91ConTSN-68
Judice, Bryan
□ 95SpoIndTI-8
Judnich, Walt
□ 37Zee-35
□ 41BroW75-17
□ 41PlaBal-67
□ 46SeaSLP-28
□ 47Exh-111
□ 47TipTop-65
□ 48IndTeal-16
□ 49SomandK-28
□ 52MotCoo-8
□ 53IndPenCBP-16
□ 74CapPub-49
□ 76TayBow4-84
□ 77TCMTheWY-60
□ 83TCMPla1942-7
□ 93ConTSN-816
Judson, Erik
□ 90BatCliP-3072
□ 91SpaPhiC-16
□ 91SpaPhiP-900
Judson, Howie (Howard)
□ 48WhiSoxTI-12
□ 50Bow-185
□ 51Bow-123
□ 52Bow-149
□ 52NatTeaL-15
□ 52Top-169
□ 53BowBW-42
□ 53Top-12
□ 55Bow-193
□ 56SeaPop-8
□ 57SeaPop-11
□ 83TopRep5-169
□ 91TopArc1-12
Juelsgaard, Jarod
□ 91EveGiaC-14
□ 91EveGiaP-3909
□ 92CliGiaC-15
□ 92CliGiaF-3592
□ 93AusFut-57
□ 93KanCouCC-9
□ 93KanCouCF-911
□ 93KanCouCTI-10
□ 94PorSeaDF-673
□ 94PorSeaDTI-18
□ 95PorSeaDTI-7
□ 96ChaKniB-15
□ 97ChaKni-16
□ 98TacRaiQ-18
Juenke, Dan
□ 86FloStaLAP-28
□ 86MiaMarP-13
Juhl, Mike
□ 92SpaPhiC-6
□ 92SpaPhiF-1262
□ 93ClePhiC-16
□ 93ClePhiF-2680
□ 93FloStaLAF-27
□ 94ClaGolF-38
□ 95ReaPhiELC-22
□ 95ReaPhiTI-15
Juice, (Mascot)
□ 97MidAng-26
Julio, Jorge
□ 98VerExpO-34
Jumonville, Joe
□ 93GleFalRC-1
□ 93GleFalRF-4011
□ 94SavCarC-15
□ 94SavCarF-515
□ 95PeoChiTI-22
□ 96StPetCB-14
Jundy, Lorin
□ 85LitFalMT-6
□ 86LitFalMP-16
□ 87LitFalMP-2386
□ 89BasCitRS-13
Juney, Frank
□ 20Zee-46
Junker, Lance
□ 81CliGiaT-27
□ 83RedPioT-14
Jurado, Pat
□ 91RocExpC-7
□ 91RocExpP-2042
Jurak, Ed
□ 77BriRedST-9
□ 81BriRedST-12
□ 84Don-127
□ 84Fle-402
□ 84Nes792-628
□ 84Top-628
□ 84TopTif-628
□ 85Don-579
□ 85Top-233
□ 85TopTif-233
□ 86Top-749
□ 86TopTif-749
□ 87TexLeaAF-9
□ 88DonTeaBA-NEW
□ 88TacTigC-13
□ 88TacTigP-615
□ 88TriAAAP-6
□ 89GiaMot-20
□ 90CalCanC-10
□ 90CalCanP-658
□ 90CMC-437
□ 90ProAAAF-123
□ 90TulDriDGB-21
□ 93HolLeg-12
Jurewicz, Mike
□ 77FriOneYW-49
□ 92YanWIZ6-63
Jurgena, Matt
□ 97AppLeaTPB-30
Jurgens, Scott
□ 89BoiHawP-1980
Jurges, Bill
□ 31CubTeal-12
□ 32CubTeal-14
□ 32OrbPinNP-33A
□ 32OrbPinNP-33B
□ 32OrbPinUP-37
□ 33Gou-225
□ 33TatOrb-37
□ 34BatR31-139
□ 34DiaMatCSB-101
□ 35DiaMatCS3T1-84
□ 36CubTeal-17
□ 36DiaMatCS3T2-15
□ 36NatChiFPR-101
□ 36R31PasP-31
□ 36SandSW-36
□ 36WorWidGV-97
□ 39PlaBal-35
□ 40PlaBal-89
□ 41PlaBal-59
□ 50CubGreB-11
□ 58SeaTeal-14
□ 60RedSoxJP-6
□ 60Top-220
□ 84TCMPla1-30
□ 95ConTSN-1376
Jurisch, Al
□ 83Car194T-57
Jury, Frank
□ 88BoiHawP-1630
Justice, Dave (David)
□ 86SumBraP-15
□ 87GreBraB-9
□ 88BobCamRB-13
□ 88RicBraC-17
□ 88RicBraP-24
□ 89RicBraBC-12
□ 89RicBraC-15
□ 89RicBraP-838
□ 89RicBraTI-11
□ 89ScoHot1R-26
□ 89SpoIllFKI-259
□ 90BraDubP-13
□ 90BraDubS-16
□ 90CarColJB-1
□ 90CarColJB-2
□ 90CarColJB-3
□ 90CarColJB-4
□ 90CarColJB-5
□ 90CarColJB-6
□ 90CarColJB-7
□ 90CarColJB-8
□ 90CarColJB-9
□ 90CarColJB-10
□ 90CarColJB-11
□ 90CarColJB-12
□ 90CarColJB-13
□ 90CarColJB-14
□ 90CarColJB-15
□ 90CarColJB-16
□ 90ClaYel-T97
□ 90CMC-285
□ 90Don-704
□ 90DonRoo-14
□ 90Fle-586
□ 90FleCan-586
□ 90Lea-297
□ 90ProAAAF-418
□ 90RicBraC-9
□ 90RicBraP-273
□ 90RicBraTI-16
□ 90Sco-650
□ 90StaJus-1
□ 90StaJus-2
□ 90StaJus-3
□ 90StaJus-4
□ 90StaJus-5
□ 90StaJus-6
□ 90StaJus-7
□ 90StaJus-8
□ 90StaJus-9
□ 90StaJus-10
□ 90StaJus-11
□ 90TopDeb89-65
□ 90TopMag-36
□ 90TopTra-48T
□ 90TopTraT-48T
□ 90UppDec-711
□ 91Baz-18
□ 91BlePro-2
□ 91Bow-574
□ 91BraDubP-16
□ 91BraSubS-21
□ 91CadEllD-31
□ 91Cla1-T11
□ 91Cla1-NNO
□ 91Cla2-T63
□ 91Cla3-T24
□ 91ClaGam-193
□ 91Col-33
□ 91ColJus-1
□ 91ColJus-2
□ 91ColJus-3
□ 91ColJus-4
□ 91ColJus-5
□ 91ColJus-6
□ 91ColJus-7
□ 91ColJus-8
□ 91ColJus-9
□ 91ColJus-10
□ 91ColJus-11
□ 91ColJus-12
□ 91ColJus-xx
□ 91DenHol-25
□ 91Don-402
□ 91Don-548
□ 91Don-683
□ 91DonPre-1
□ 91Fle-693
□ 91JimDea-14
□ 91KinDis-18
□ 91Lea-77
□ 91Lea-84
□ 91LeaPre-1
□ 91MajLeaCP-46
□ 91MooSna-9
□ 91OPC-329
□ 91OPCPre-70
□ 91PanFreS-25
□ 91PanSti-29
□ 91PepSup-9
□ 91Pos-1
□ 91PosCan-12
□ 91Sco-55
□ 91Sco-861
□ 91Sco-880
□ 91Sco100RS-45
□ 91ScoHotR-1
□ 91SevCoi-A7
□ 91SevCoi-F9
□ 91SevCoi-NW10
□ 91SilHol-3
□ 91StaClu-26
□ 91StaCluCM-16
□ 91StaPinB-27
□ 91Stu-146
□ 91StuPre-10
□ 91SunSee-15
□ 91Top-329
□ 91TopCraJI-14
□ 91TopDesS-329
□ 91TopGaloC-8
□ 91TopMic-329
□ 91TopRoo-15
□ 91TopSta-21
□ 91TopTif-329
□ 91TopTriH-N1
□ 91ToyRoo-14
□ 91Ult-7
□ 91Ult-394
□ 91UppDec-363
□ 91Woo-5
□ 92Ble23KJ-1
□ 92Ble23KJ-2
□ 92Ble23KJ-3
□ 92Bow-312
□ 92BraLykP-16
□ 92BraLykS-19
□ 92Cla2-T15
□ 92ClaGam-17
□ 92ColPro-9
□ 92Don-327
□ 92DonCraJ2-3
□ 92DonDiaK-DK6
□ 92DonMcD-23
□ 92DonSupD-DK6
□ 92Fle-360
□ 92Fle-713
□ 92FleCitTP-8
□ 92Fre-15
□ 92Hig5-24
□ 92Hig5S-21
□ 92Hig5S-33
□ 92HitTheBB-18
□ 92LaKdec-20
□ 92Lea-404
□ 92LeaBlaG-404
□ 92Mr.TurS-15
□ 92MVPPin-29
□ 92OPC-80
□ 92OPCPre-117
□ 92PanSti-166
□ 92Pin-100
□ 92Pin-588
□ 92Pin-604
□ 92Pin-620
□ 92PinSlu-5
□ 92PinTea2-9
□ 92PinTeaP-10
□ 92Pos-29
□ 92RedFolS-52
□ 92Sco-4
□ 92Sco100S-42
□ 92ScoFacI-B3
□ 92ScoFacI-B5
□ 92ScoImpP-44
□ 92ScoProP-3
□ 92ScoProP-24
□ 92ScoSam-2
□ 92SevCoi-10
□ 92SpoStaCC-28
□ 92StaClu-182
□ 92StaClu-592
□ 92StaCluD-97
□ 92StaJus-1
□ 92StaJus-2
□ 92StaJus-3
□ 92StaJus-4
□ 92StaJus-5
□ 92StaJus-6
□ 92StaJus-7
□ 92StaJus-8
□ 92StaJus-9
□ 92StaJus-10
□ 92StaJus-11
□ 92Stu-5
□ 92StuPre-8
□ 92Top-80
□ 92TopGol-80
□ 92TopGolW-80
□ 92TopKid-31
□ 92TopMcD-28
□ 92TopMic-80
□ 92TriPla-217
□ 92TriPlaG-GS9
□ 92Ult-164
□ 92UppDec-29
□ 92UppDec-546
□ 92UppDecWB-T17
□ 93Bow-578
□ 93BraLykP-14
□ 93BraLykS-18
□ 93BraStaC-3
□ 93CadDis-37
□ 93ClaGam-45
□ 93ColAllG-16
□ 93DiaMar-58
□ 93DiaMarA-4
□ 93Don-580
□ 93DonEliD-5
□ 93DonLonBL-LL5
□ 93DonMasotG-12
□ 93DonSpiotG-SG2
□ 93Fin-1
□ 93FinRef-1
□ 93Fla-5
□ 93FlaPro-5
□ 93Fle-367
□ 93FleFruotL-30
□ 93FunPac-64
□ 93Lea-50
□ 93LeaFas-18
□ 93LeaGolA-R8
□ 93LeaGolA-U9
□ 93MetBak-13
□ 93OPC-180
□ 93PacSpa-8
□ 93PanSti-187
□ 93Pin-344
□ 93PinHomRC-31
□ 93PinSlu-15
□ 93RedFolS-49
□ 93Sco-107
□ 93Sel-39
□ 93SP-13
□ 93SPPlaP-PP11
□ 93StaClu-660
□ 93StaCluFDI-660
□ 93StaCluMOP-660
□ 93Stu-173
□ 93Top-170
□ 93TopGol-170
□ 93TopInaM-170
□ 93TopInaR-170
□ 93TopMic-170
□ 93Toy-14
□ 93TriPla-249
□ 93TriPlaA-29
□ 93Ult-306
□ 93UppDec-366
□ 93UppDec-460
□ 93UppDecFA-A7
□ 93UppDecFAJ-A7
□ 93UppDecGold-366
□ 93UppDecGold-460
□ 93UppDecHRH-HR17
□ 93UppDecS-19
□ 94Bow-133
□ 94BowBes-R63
□ 94BowBesR-R63
□ 94BraLykP-13
□ 94BraLykS-14
□ 94BraUSPC-1H
□ 94BraUSPC-8C
□ 94ChuShoS-4
□ 94ClaGolF-AU1
□ 94ColC-156
□ 94ColC-325
□ 94ColC-332
□ 94ColC-636
□ 94ColChoGS-156
□ 94ColChoGS-325
□ 94ColChoGS-332
□ 94ColChoGS-636
□ 94ColChoHRA-HA7
□ 94ColChoSS-156
□ 94ColChoSS-325
□ 94ColChoSS-332
□ 94ColChoSS-636
□ 94ColChoT-4
□ 94ColEdgDJ-1
□ 94DenHol-17
□ 94Don-25
□ 94DonLonBL-6
□ 94DonMVP-1
□ 94DonSpeE-25
□ 94DonSpiotG-8
□ 94DonSpiotGJ-8
□ 94Fin-233
□ 94FinJum-233
□ 94FinRef-233
□ 94Fla-126
□ 94FlaOutP-7
□ 94Fle-361
□ 94Fle-706
□ 94FleAllS-42
□ 94FleExtB-202
□ 94FleExtBGB-15
□ 94FleLumC-6
□ 94FleSun-14
□ 94FleTeaL-15
□ 94FUnPac-23
□ 94FUnPac-192
□ 94Kra-25
□ 94Lea-263
□ 94LeaGam-5
□ 94LeaGolS-3
□ 94LeaL-83
□ 94LeaLimGA-14
□ 94LeaMVPC-N7
□ 94LeaMVPCG-N7
□ 94LeaPowB-2
□ 94LeaPro-4
□ 94LeaSli-10
□ 94O-PJumAF-24
□ 94OPC-233
□ 94OPCAllR-24
□ 94OPCJumA-24
□ 94Pac-11
□ 94PacGolP-12
□ 94PanSti-146
□ 94Pin-40
□ 94PinArtP-40
□ 94PinMusC-40
□ 94PinPowS-PS1
□ 94PinRunC-RC32
□ 94PinTeaP-8
□ 94PinTheN-5
□ 94PinTri-TR5
□ 94Pos-6
□ 94PosCan-17
□ 94ProMag-4
□ 94Sco-422
□ 94ScoCyc-TC19
□ 94ScoGolR-422
□ 94ScoGolS-24
□ 94Sel-236
□ 94SP-50
□ 94SPDieC-50
□ 94SPHol-17
□ 94SPHolDC-17
□ 94Spo-6
□ 94Spo-192
□ 94StaClu-94
□ 94StaClu-111
□ 94StaClu-263
□ 94StaClu-530
□ 94StaCluF-F7
□ 94StaCluFDI-94
□ 94StaCluFDI-111
□ 94StaCluFDI-263
□ 94StaCluFDI-530
□ 94StaCluFJ-F7
□ 94StaCluGR-94
□ 94StaCluGR-111
□ 94StaCluGR-263
□ 94StaCluGR-530
□ 94StaCluMO-5
□ 94StaCluMOP-94
□ 94StaCluMOP-111
□ 94StaCluMOP-263
□ 94StaCluMOP-530
□ 94StaCluMOP-F7
□ 94StaCluT-49
□ 94StaCluTF-6
□ 94StaCluTFDI-49
□ 94Stu-35
□ 94SucSav-13
□ 94TomPiz-11
□ 94Top-389
□ 94Top-630
□ 94TopBlaG-36
□ 94TopGol-389
□ 94TopGol-630
□ 94TopSpa-389
□ 94TopSpa-630
□ 94TopSupS-24
□ 94TriPla-45
□ 94TriPlaBS-5
□ 94Ult-442
□ 94UltAllS-18
□ 94UltHomRK-8
□ 94UltRBIK-8
□ 94UppDec-267
□ 94UppDec-375
□ 94UppDecAJ-33
□ 94UppDecAJG-33
□ 94UppDecDC-E7
□ 94UppDecED-267
□ 94UppDecED-375
□ 94UppDecMLS-MM11
□ 94UppDecMLSED-MM11
□ 94UppDecNG-9
□ 94UppDecNGED-9
□ 94USPlaCA-10C
□ 95Baz-6
□ 95Bow-386
□ 95BowBes-R34
□ 95BowBesR-R34
□ 95BraAtlC-4
□ 95ClaPhoC-2
□ 95ColCho-156
□ 95ColChoCtG-CG10
□ 95ColChoCtG-CG10B
□ 95ColChoCtG-CG10C
□ 95ColChoCtGE-10
□ 95ColChoCtGG-CG10
□ 95ColChoCtGG-CG10B
□ 95ColChoCtGG-CG10C
□ 95ColChoCtGGE-10

❑ 95ColChoGS-156
❑ 95ColChoSE-67
❑ 95ColChoSEGS-67
❑ 95ColChoSESS-67
❑ 95ColChoSS-156
❑ 95Don-1
❑ 95DonAll-NL9
❑ 95DonPreP-1
❑ 95DonTopotO-186
❑ 95Emo-103
❑ 95Fin-98
❑ 95FinRef-98
❑ 95Fla-326
❑ 95Fle-305
❑ 95FleAllS-8
❑ 95FleTeaL-15
❑ 95KinDis-15
❑ 95Lea-62
❑ 95LeaLim-95
❑ 95Pac-5
❑ 95PacGolP-27
❑ 95PacPri-1
❑ 95PanSti-77
❑ 95Pin-50
❑ 95Pin-285
❑ 95PinArtP-50
❑ 95PinArtP-285
❑ 95PinMusC-50
❑ 95PinMusC-285
❑ 95PinPin-15
❑ 95PinPinR-15
❑ 95PinRedH-RH20
❑ 95PinTeaP-TP8
❑ 95PinWhiH-WH20
❑ 95Pos-10
❑ 95RedFol-9
❑ 95Sco-271
❑ 95Sco-555
❑ 95ScoGolR-271
❑ 95ScoGolR-555
❑ 95ScoHaloG-HG5
❑ 95ScoPlaTS-271
❑ 95ScoPlaTS-555
❑ 95ScoRul-SR26
❑ 95ScoRulJ-SR26
❑ 95Sel-67
❑ 95SelArtP-67
❑ 95SelCer-64
❑ 95SelCerMG-64
❑ 95SP-28
❑ 95Spo-32
❑ 95SpoArtP-32
❑ 95SpoDouT-8
❑ 95SPSil-28
❑ 95StaClu-446
❑ 95StaCluMOP-446
❑ 95StaCluSTDW-B446
❑ 95StaCluSTMP-4
❑ 95StaCluSTWS-446
❑ 95StaCluVR-237
❑ 95StaCluVRMO-237
❑ 95Stu-31
❑ 95StuGolS-31
❑ 95Sum-111
❑ 95SumBigB-BB18
❑ 95SumNthD-111
❑ 95Top-620
❑ 95TopCyb-388
❑ 95TopD3-1
❑ 95TopEmb-101
❑ 95TopEmbGI-101
❑ 95UC3-67
❑ 95UC3ArtP-67
❑ 95Ult-126
❑ 95UltGolM-126
❑ 95UltOnBL-8
❑ 95UltOnBLGM-8
❑ 95UppDec-295
❑ 95UppDecED-295
❑ 95UppDecEDG-295
❑ 95UppDecPC-MLB10
❑ 95UppDecPLL-R39
❑ 95UppDecPLLE-R39
❑ 95UppDecSE-15
❑ 95UppDecSEG-15
❑ 95Zen-22
❑ 96Baz-116
❑ 96Bow-72
❑ 96BowBes-41
❑ 96BowBesAR-41
❑ 96BowBesR-41
❑ 96BowFoi-72
❑ 96BraFle-7
❑ 96Cir-103
❑ 96CirRav-103
❑ 96ColCho-43
❑ 96ColCho-394T
❑ 96ColChoGS-43
❑ 96ColChoSS-43
❑ 96Don-197
❑ 96DonPreP-197
❑ 96EmoXL-143
❑ 96Fin-B56
❑ 96Fin-B248
❑ 96FinRef-B56
❑ 96FinRef-B248
❑ 96Fla-201
❑ 96Fle-294
❑ 96FleTif-294
❑ 96Lea-60
❑ 96LeaPrePB-60
❑ 96LeaPrePG-60
❑ 96LeaPrePS-60
❑ 96LeaPreSG-10
❑ 96LeaPreSte-10
❑ 96LeaSig-120
❑ 96LeaSigPPG-120
❑ 96LeaSigPPP-120
❑ 96MetUni-130
❑ 96MetUniP-130
❑ 96Pac-16
❑ 96PacOctM-OM9
❑ 96PacPri-P3
❑ 96PacPriFB-FB8
❑ 96PacPriG-P3
❑ 96PanSti-1
❑ 96Pin-286
❑ 96PinAfi-91
❑ 96PinAfiAP-91
❑ 96PinAfiFPP-91
❑ 96PinChrBC-3
❑ 96PinFoil-286
❑ 96ProMagA-17
❑ 96ProMagDM-1
❑ 96ProSta-23
❑ 96Sco-58
❑ 96Sco-385
❑ 96ScoDugC-A51
❑ 96ScoDugC-B110
❑ 96ScoDugCAP-A51
❑ 96ScoDugCAP-B110
❑ 96ScoPowP-17
❑ 96Sel-53
❑ 96SelArtP-53
❑ 96SP-28
❑ 96Spo-62
❑ 96SpoArtP-62
❑ 96StaClu-159
❑ 96StaCluEPB-159
❑ 96StaCluEPG-159
❑ 96StaCluEPS-159
❑ 96StaCluMOP-159
❑ 96Stu-109
❑ 96StuPrePB-109
❑ 96StuPrePG-109
❑ 96StuPrePS-109
❑ 96Sum-96
❑ 96SumAbo&B-96
❑ 96SumArtP-96
❑ 96SumFoi-96
❑ 96Top-60
❑ 96TopChr-22
❑ 96TopChrR-22
❑ 96TopGal-59
❑ 96TopGalPG-PG12
❑ 96TopGalPPI-59
❑ 96TopLas-69
❑ 96TopPro-NL16
❑ 96Ult-157
❑ 96UltGolM-157
❑ 96UppDec-4
❑ 97Bow-273
❑ 97BowBes-79
❑ 97BowBesAR-79
❑ 97BowBesR-79
❑ 97BowChr-90
❑ 97BowChrI-90
❑ 97BowChrIR-90
❑ 97BowChrR-90
❑ 97BowInt-273
❑ 97BraSco-2
❑ 97BraScoPl-2
❑ 97BraScoPr-2
❑ 97Cir-137
❑ 97CirRav-137
❑ 97ColChoNF-NF21
❑ 97ColChoT-CI10
❑ 97ColChoU-U10
❑ 97DenHol-5
❑ 97Don-175
❑ 97Don-291
❑ 97DonGolPP-175
❑ 97DonGolPP-291
❑ 97DonLim-99
❑ 97DonLim-154
❑ 97DonLimE-99
❑ 97DonLimE-154
❑ 97DonLimENG-154
❑ 97DonLimFotG-20
❑ 97DonPre-34
❑ 97DonPreCttC-34
❑ 97DonSig-28
❑ 97DonSigA-56
❑ 97DonSigAC-69
❑ 97DonSigAM-69
❑ 97DonSigPPP-28
❑ 97DonSilPP-175
❑ 97DonSilPP-291
❑ 97DonTea-86
❑ 97DonTeaSPE-86
❑ 97DonVxP1-45
❑ 97DurBulATI-6
❑ 97Fin-271
❑ 97FinRef-271
❑ 97FlaShoLC-73
❑ 97FlaShoLeg0-73
❑ 97FlaShoLeg1-73
❑ 97FlaShoM-A73
❑ 97FlaShoM-B73
❑ 97FlaShoM-C73
❑ 97FlaShoR0-73
❑ 97FlaShoR1-73
❑ 97FlaShoR2-73
❑ 97Fle-259
❑ 97Fle-514
❑ 97FleTif-259
❑ 97FleTif-514
❑ 97HigMinMCT-20
❑ 97HigMinMCT-21
❑ 97Lea-299
❑ 97Lea-378
❑ 97LeaFraM-299
❑ 97LeaFraM-378
❑ 97LeaFraMDC-299
❑ 97LeaFraMDC-378
❑ 97LeaWarT-17
❑ 97NewPin-33
❑ 97NewPinAP-33
❑ 97NewPinMC-33
❑ 97NewPinPP-33
❑ 97Pac-236
❑ 97PacBaeS-10
❑ 97PacLigB-236
❑ 97PacSil-236
❑ 97PinX-P-34
❑ 97PinX-PMoS-34
❑ 97PinX-PSfF-32
❑ 97PinX-PSfFU-32
❑ 97Sco-33
❑ 97Sco-442
❑ 97ScoArtPWB-33
❑ 97ScoArtPWB-442
❑ 97ScoPreS-33
❑ 97ScoResC-442
❑ 97ScoShoS-33
❑ 97ScoShoS-442
❑ 97ScoShoSAP-33
❑ 97ScoShoSAP-442
❑ 97ScoStaaD-19
❑ 97Sel-164
❑ 97SelCom-164
❑ 97SP-58
❑ 97SpoIll-143
❑ 97SpoIllEE-143
❑ 97StaClu-223
❑ 97StaCluMat-223
❑ 97StaCluMOP-223
❑ 97StrAll-33
❑ 97Stu-19
❑ 97StuPrePG-19
❑ 97StuPrePS-19
❑ 97Top-244
❑ 97TopChr-86
❑ 97TopChrR-86
❑ 97TopGal-86
❑ 97TopGalPPI-86
❑ 97TopSta-6
❑ 97TopStaAM-6
❑ 97Ult-373
❑ 97UltGolME-373
❑ 97UltPlaME-373
❑ 97UppDec-298
❑ 97UppDec-532
❑ 97Zen-30
❑ 98Bow-20
❑ 98BowBes-57
❑ 98BowBesAR-57
❑ 98BowBesR-57
❑ 98BowChr-20
❑ 98BowChrGA-20
❑ 98BowChrGAR-20
❑ 98BowChrI-20
❑ 98BowChrIR-20
❑ 98BowChrR-20
❑ 98BowGolA-20
❑ 98BowInt-20
❑ 98CirThu-296
❑ 98CirThuRav-296
❑ 98CirThuSupRav-296
❑ 98ColCho-356
❑ 98ColChoSQ-SQ23
❑ 98CroRoy-43
❑ 98Don-7
❑ 98Don-360
❑ 98DonCol-7
❑ 98DonColE-453
❑ 98DonColL-250
❑ 98DonColP-616
❑ 98DonColS-7
❑ 98DonCruG-21
❑ 98DonCruP-21
❑ 98DonCruR-21
❑ 98DonDay-4
❑ 98DonDiaK-12
❑ 98DonDiaKC-12
❑ 98DonEli-53
❑ 98DonEliA-53
❑ 98DonEliS-53
❑ 98DonGolPP-7
❑ 98DonGolPP-360
❑ 98DonPre-66
❑ 98DonPreSeat-66
❑ 98DonPriCD-7
❑ 98DonPriCE-453
❑ 98DonPriCL-250
❑ 98DonPriCP-616
❑ 98DonProLPI-18
❑ 98DonSig-1
❑ 98DonSigP-1
❑ 98DonSilPP-7
❑ 98DonSilPP-360
❑ 98E-X2-47
❑ 98E-X2Cheap-18
❑ 98E-X2ECFut-47
❑ 98E-X2ECNow-47
❑ 98Fin-5
❑ 98FinNo--5
❑ 98FinNo-R-5
❑ 98FinRef-5
❑ 98FlaShoLeg0-53
❑ 98FlaShoLeg1-53
❑ 98FlaShoLeg2-53
❑ 98FlaShoLeg3-53
❑ 98FlaShoLegM-53
❑ 98FlaShoR0-53
❑ 98FlaShoR1-53
❑ 98FlaShoR2-53
❑ 98FlaShoR3-53
❑ 98Fle-81
❑ 98FleVin'-15
❑ 98FleVin'C-15
❑ 98IndSco-9
❑ 98IndScoP-9
❑ 98Lea-51
❑ 98LeaFraDA-51
❑ 98LeaFraF-51
❑ 98LeaFraM-51
❑ 98LeaFraM-51
❑ 98LeaFraMDC-51
❑ 98LeaFraMDC-51
❑ 98LeaFraMZ2-51
❑ 98LeaRCMLHDSamp-20
❑ 98LeaRS-17
❑ 98LeaRSGreHit-16
❑ 98LeaRSLHolo-17
❑ 98LeaRSLong-17
❑ 98LeaRSMLHD-20
❑ 98LeaRTrue-17
❑ 98LeaStaRep-23
❑ 98LeaStaS-22
❑ 98LeaStaSDC-22
❑ 98MetUni-82
❑ 98MetUniPMG-82
❑ 98Pac-73
❑ 98PacAur-30
❑ 98PacAurHC-7
❑ 98PacAurPF-37
❑ 98PacAurPFC-37
❑ 98PacAurPFPB-37
❑ 98PacAurPFR-37
❑ 98PacAurPFS-37
❑ 98PacGolCDC-11
❑ 98PacHomRH-6
❑ 98PacInCage-7
❑ 98PacInv-23
❑ 98PacInvGems-38
❑ 98PacInvMiT-4
❑ 98PacInvPBlue-23
❑ 98PacInvSilv-23
❑ 98PacInvTeam-8
❑ 98PacOme-71
❑ 98PacOmeR-71
❑ 98PacOnl-222
❑ 98PacOnlR-222
❑ 98PacOnlWC-222
❑ 98PacPar-37
❑ 98PacParC-37
❑ 98PacParFC-6
❑ 98PacParG-37
❑ 98PacParHS-37
❑ 98PacParI-12
❑ 98PacParPB-37
❑ 98PacParR-37
❑ 98PacParSD-7
❑ 98PacPlaB-73
❑ 98PacRedT-73
❑ 98PacSil-73
❑ 98PinIns-23
❑ 98PinInsCE-23
❑ 98PinInsDE-23
❑ 98PinInsSG-23AB
❑ 98PinInsSG-23CD
❑ 98PinInsSGS-23AB
❑ 98PinInsSGS-23CD
❑ 98PinPer-67
❑ 98PinPerPP-67
❑ 98PinPerSftF-13
❑ 98PinPlu-15
❑ 98PinPluAP-PP9
❑ 98PinPluGAP-PP9
❑ 98PinPluMAP-PP9
❑ 98PinSna-Cl7
❑ 98PreCon-17
❑ 98Revo-44
❑ 98RevoSS-44
❑ 98Sco-136
❑ 98ScoRT-16
❑ 98ScoRTSS-PP16
❑ 98ScoRTSSAP-PP16
❑ 98ScoRTSSAP1-PP16
❑ 98ScoSS-PP154
❑ 98ScoSSAP-PP154
❑ 98SP Aut-77
❑ 98SpoIll-71
❑ 98SpoIllEE-71
❑ 98SpoIllFE-71
❑ 98SpoIllODMP-OD9
❑ 98SpoIllTaN-98
❑ 98SpoIllTaNAotG-AG5
❑ 98SpoIllTaNEE-98
❑ 98SpoIllWSF-68
❑ 98SpoIllWSFEE-68
❑ 98SpoIllWSFFE-68
❑ 98SPxFin-74
❑ 98SPxFinR-74
❑ 98SPxFinS-74
❑ 98StaCluFDI-317
❑ 98StaCluI-317
❑ 98StaCluOneK-317
❑ 98StaCluPP-317
❑ 98StaCluTIII-T8C
❑ 98StaCluTIII-T15B
❑ 98StaCluTLme-T8C
❑ 98StaCluTLme-T15B
❑ 98StaCluTLmo-T8C
❑ 98StaCluTLmo-T15B
❑ 98Stu-188
❑ 98StuFF-7
❑ 98StuFFDC-7
❑ 98StuGPP-188
❑ 98StuSPP-188
❑ 98Top-336
❑ 98TopChr-336
❑ 98TopChrR-336
❑ 98TopDevR-336
❑ 98TopDia-336
❑ 98TopGal-94
❑ 98TopGalGP-94
❑ 98TopGalOPP-94
❑ 98TopGalPPI-94
❑ 98TopGalPPIA-94
❑ 98TopGolLabC1-63
❑ 98TopGolLabC1B-63
❑ 98TopGolLabC1One-63
❑ 98TopGolLabC1R-63
❑ 98TopGolLabC2-63
❑ 98TopGolLabC2B-63
❑ 98TopGolLabC2One-63
❑ 98TopGolLabC2R-63
❑ 98TopGolLabC3-63
❑ 98TopGolLabC3B-63
❑ 98TopGolLabC3One-63
❑ 98TopGolLabC3R-63
❑ 98TopMiniC-336
❑ 98TopOpeD-163
❑ 98TopSta-101
❑ 98TopSta'S-22
❑ 98TopSta'SGH-22
❑ 98TopStaB-101
❑ 98TopStaG-101
❑ 98TopStaGR-101
❑ 98TopStaS-101
❑ 98TopStaSteG-22
❑ 98TopTek-18
❑ 98TopTekD-18
❑ 98Ult-103
❑ 98UltDouT-20
❑ 98UltGolM-103
❑ 98UltMas-103
❑ 98UltPlaM-103
❑ 98UppDec-74
❑ 98UppDecRTC-TC9
❑ 98UppDecSF-46
❑ 98Zen-54
❑ 98Zen5 xx7-39
❑ 98Zen5x7GoldImp-39
❑ 98Zen5x7Imp-39
❑ 98ZenZ-G-54
❑ 98ZenZ-S-54
❑ 99199Fin-73
❑ 99AllMysFR-M21
❑ 99Bow-53
❑ 99BowBes-3
❑ 99BowBesAR-3
❑ 99BowBesR-3
❑ 99BowChr-53
❑ 99BowChrG-53
❑ 99BowChrGR-53
❑ 99BowChrI-53
❑ 99BowChrIR-53
❑ 99BowChrR-53
❑ 99BowGol-53
❑ 99BowInt-53
❑ 99CroRoyB-43
❑ 99CroRoyL-43
❑ 99CroRoyOD-43
❑ 99FinGolRef-73
❑ 99FinRef-73
❑ 99FlaShoLeg1-111
❑ 99FlaShoLeg2-111
❑ 99FlaShoLeg3-111
❑ 99FlaShoLegM1-111
❑ 99FlaShoLegM2-111
❑ 99FlaShoLegM3-111
❑ 99FlaShoR1-111
❑ 99FlaShoR2-111
❑ 99FlaShoR3-111
❑ 99Fle-153
❑ 99FleBri-96
❑ 99FleBri2G-96
❑ 99FleBriBlu-96
❑ 99FleBriGol-96
❑ 99FleSta9-153
❑ 99FleWarT-153
❑ 99MetUni-25
❑ 99MetUniGM-25
❑ 99MetUniPMG-25
❑ 99Pac-130
❑ 99PacAur-52
❑ 99PacAurOD-52
❑ 99PacCroC-86
❑ 99PacCroCPB-86
❑ 99PacInv-44
❑ 99PacInvOD-44
❑ 99PacInvPB-44
❑ 99PacOme-73
❑ 99PacOmeC-73
❑ 99PacOmeG-73
❑ 99PacOmePB-73
❑ 99PacPar-73
❑ 99PacParC-73
❑ 99PacParG-73
❑ 99PacParHoloGold-73
❑ 99PacParHS-73
❑ 99PacParOD-73
❑ 99PacParPB-73
❑ 99PacParRed-73
❑ 99PacPlaB-130
❑ 99PacPri-43
❑ 99PacPriHB-43
❑ 99PacPriHG-43
❑ 99PacPriHM-43
❑ 99PacPriHP-43
❑ 99PacPriRed-43
❑ 99PacRed-130
❑ 99Pin-15

❏ 99Rev-43
❏ 99RevPremDate-43
❏ 99RevRet-43
❏ 99RevShaSS-43
❏ 99SkyMolM-115
❏ 99SkyMolMF-15
❏ 99SkyMolMFS-15
❏ 99SkyMolMFT-15
❏ 99SkyMolMOA-8
❏ 99SkyMolMX-115
❏ 99SkyPre-31
❏ 99SkyPreR-31
❏ 99SkyThu-161
❏ 99SkyThuRant-161
❏ 99SkyThuRave-161
❏ 99SpoIll-5
❏ 99StaClu-264
❏ 99StaCluFDI-264
❏ 99StaCluOoaK-264
❏ 99StaCluPP-264
❏ 99ThuSkySupR-161
❏ 99Top-283
❏ 99Top-456
❏ 99TopAllMF-M21
❏ 99TopBlaLC1-38
❏ 99TopBlaLC2-38
❏ 99TopBlaLC3-38
❏ 99TopChr-283
❏ 99TopChr-456
❏ 99TopChrR-283
❏ 99TopChrR-456
❏ 99TopGal-18
❏ 99TopGalPP-18
❏ 99TopGalPPI-18
❏ 99TopGolL-38
❏ 99TopGolLC1-38
❏ 99TopGolLC2-38
❏ 99TopGolLOtO-38
❏ 99TopMVPP-283
❏ 99TopMVPP-456
❏ 99TopOpeD-130
❏ 99TopRedLC1-38
❏ 99TopRedLC2-38
❏ 99TopRedLC3-38
❏ 99TopSta-120
❏ 99TopStaFoil-120
❏ 99UppDec-81
❏ 99UppDecEL1-81
❏ 99UppDecEL2-81
❏ 99Vic-119

Justiniano, Rene
❏ 95ButCopKtl-12

Justis, Walter
❏ 12ImpTobC-42

Jutze, Skip (Alfred Henry)
❏ 73OPC-613
❏ 73Top-613
❏ 74OPC-328
❏ 74Top-328
❏ 75AstPos-17
❏ 76HouAstP-18
❏ 76OPC-489
❏ 76SSP-52
❏ 76Top-489
❏ 78Top-532
❏ 87AstShoSPT-16
❏ 87AstShowSTh-29

Ka'akimaka, Lehua
❏ 91HawWomS-4

Kaage, George
❏ 77CliDodT-12
❏ 78LodDodT-10

Kaaihue, Kala
❏ 76HawIslC-17
❏ 87HawIslP-20

Kaat, Jim
❏ 60Top-136
❏ 60TopVen-136
❏ 61Top-63
❏ 61TopStal-180
❏ 61TwiCloD-9
❏ 61TwiJayP-4
❏ 61TwiPetM-7
❏ 61TwiUniMC-6
❏ 62AmeTraS-XX
❏ 62Top-21
❏ 62TopVen-21
❏ 63Fle-22
❏ 63Jel-10
❏ 63Pos-10
❏ 63SalMetC-40
❏ 63Top-10
❏ 63Top-165
❏ 63TwiJayP-5
❏ 63TwiVol-9
❏ 64Top-567
❏ 64TwiJayP-6
❏ 65OPC-62
❏ 65Top-62
❏ 65TwiPos-4
❏ 66Top-224
❏ 66Top-445
❏ 66TopVen-224
❏ 66TwiFaiG-6
❏ 67Baz-18
❏ 67CokCapTw-16
❏ 67Top-235
❏ 67Top-237
❏ 67Top-278
❏ 67Top-300
❏ 67TopVen-236
❏ 68DexPre-45
❏ 68OPC-67
❏ 68Top-67
❏ 68Top-450
❏ 68TopVen-67
❏ 69MilBra-142
❏ 69MLBOffS-67
❏ 69Top-290
❏ 69TopSta-194
❏ 69TopTeaP-15
❏ 69TwiTealC-5
❏ 70DayDaiNM-145
❏ 70MLBOffS-233
❏ 70OPC-75
❏ 70Top-75
❏ 70TwiSupV-4
❏ 71MLBOffS-464
❏ 71OPC-245
❏ 71Top-245
❏ 71TopGreM-7
❏ 72MilBra-176
❏ 72Top-709
❏ 72Top-710
❏ 72TwiPos-7
❏ 73OPC-530
❏ 73Top-530
❏ 74OPC-440
❏ 74Top-440
❏ 75Hos-110
❏ 75HosTwi-110
❏ 75OPC-243
❏ 75SSPPuzB-13
❏ 75Top-243
❏ 75TopMin-243
❏ 76BlaDis-24
❏ 76BucDis-24
❏ 76CarDis-24
❏ 76CraDis-24
❏ 76DailsID-24
❏ 76IsaDis-24
❏ 76Kel-25A
❏ 76Kel-25B
❏ 76OPC-80
❏ 76OrbDis-24
❏ 76PhiPhiP-14
❏ 76RedBarD-24
❏ 76SafDis-24
❏ 76SSP-136
❏ 76Top-80
❏ 76TopTra-80T
❏ 76TowCluD-24
❏ 77BurCheD-169
❏ 77Top-638
❏ 78Top-715
❏ 79Top-136
❏ 79YanPicA-22
❏ 80Top-250
❏ 81Car5x7-13
❏ 81Don-536
❏ 81Fle-536
❏ 81Top-563
❏ 82Don-217
❏ 82Fle-117
❏ 82FleSta-240
❏ 82Top-367
❏ 83Car-12
❏ 83Don-343
❏ 83Fle-11
❏ 83OPC-211
❏ 83OPC-383
❏ 83Top-672
❏ 83Top-673
❏ 83TopSti-135
❏ 83TopSti-136
❏ 86TwiGreT-10
❏ 87HygAllG-28
❏ 88ChaLooLTI-16
❏ 88PacLegI-88
❏ 89SweBasG-88
❏ 92YanWIZ7-86
❏ 92YanWIZ8-95
❏ 93ActPacA-149
❏ 93TedWil-48
❏ 94Yoo-8

Kable, David
❏ 81ArkTraT-9
❏ 82LouRedE-12
❏ 83LouRedR-28
❏ 84LouRedR-29
❏ 85LouRedR-9
❏ 86ArkTraP-9

Kaboom, (Mascot)
❏ 97LanJet-30
❏ 98LanJetG-13

Kaczmarski, Randy
❏ 82AmaGolST-21
❏ 83BeaGolGT-4

Kading, John
❏ 09ObaT21-372
❏ 12ObaPreT-121

Kadota, Hiromitsu
❏ 87JapPlaB-41

Kaear, Luther
❏ 46A'sTeal-8

Kaelin, Kris
❏ 91PocPioP-3789
❏ 91PocPioSP-20

Kagawa, Nobuyuki
❏ 87JapPlaB-37

Kagawa, Ross
❏ 87HawRai-11

Kahl, Nick
❏ 05IndSouPSoCP-12

Kahler, George
❏ 11PinT-5-623
❏ 11PinT-5-1067
❏ 12T207-88
❏ 15Zee-64
❏ 16Zee-9

Kahlon, Bobby
❏ 95HudValRTI-11

Kahmann, Jim
❏ 86WesPalBEP-22
❏ 87JacExpP-456
❏ 88JacExpP-974
❏ 89OrlTwiB-6
❏ 89OrlTwiP-1349

Kahn, Roger
❏ 79HawIsIT-20
❏ 90LitSunW-13

Kahoe, Michael
❏ 03BreE10-78
❏ 09RamT20-62
❏ 11SpoLifCW-194

Kail, Joe
❏ 94HudValRC-8
❏ 94HudValRF-3392

Kain, Marty
❏ 82AmaGolST-20
❏ 84EdmTraC-100
❏ 85EdmTraC-11

Kainer, Don W.
❏ 79TucTorT-11
❏ 93RanKee-213

Kainer, Ronald
❏ 76WatRoyT-15

Kairis, Bob
❏ 88BurIndP-1794

Kaiser, Bart
❏ 86ClePhiP-12
❏ 87ClePhiP-25

Kaiser, C. Don
❏ 56Top-124
❏ 57Top-134

Kaiser, Jeff
❏ 85A'sMot-25
❏ 86TacTigP-10
❏ 87BufBisP-16
❏ 88ColSprSSC-4
❏ 88ColSprSSP-1531
❏ 88IndGat-47
❏ 89ColSprSSC-3
❏ 89Fle-410
❏ 89FleGlo-410
❏ 89SalSpuCLC-142
❏ 89SalSpuP-1805
❏ 90CMC-462
❏ 90ColSprSSC-10
❏ 90TopTra-49T
❏ 90TopTraT-49T
❏ 91DenZepLD-143
❏ 91DenZepP-122
❏ 91LinDriAAA-143
❏ 91OPC-576
❏ 91SouOreAAP-SOA32
❏ 91Top-576
❏ 91TopDesS-576
❏ 91TopMic-576
❏ 91TopTif-576
❏ 92StaClu-526
❏ 92TolMudHF-1039
❏ 92TolMudHS-590
❏ 92TriA AAS-590

Kaiser, Keith
❏ 88GreHorP-1573
❏ 89ChaLooB-2
❏ 89ChaLooGS-13
❏ 90ChaLooGS-17
❏ 91JacGenLD-565
❏ 91JacGenP-923
❏ 91LinDriAA-565

Kaiser, Ken
❏ 88T/MUmp-31
❏ 89T/MUmp-29
❏ 90T/MUmp-28

Kaiser, Nick
❏ 91EugEmeC-6
❏ 91EugEmeP-3735

Kaiserling, George
❏ 15CraJacE-157

Kajima, Ken
❏ 89SalSpuCLC-148

Kakefu, Masayuki
❏ 79TCMJapPB-83
❏ 87JapPlaB-22

Kalas, Harry
❏ 84PhiTas-7
❏ 88PhiTas-39
❏ 90PhiTas-35

Kalin, Frank
❏ 53MotCoo-44
❏ 53SanFraSTI-9

Kaline, Al
❏ 47Exh-112A
❏ 47Exh-112B
❏ 54Top-201
❏ 55Bow-23
❏ 55Top-4
❏ 55TopDouH-45
❏ 56Top-20
❏ 56TopPin-38
❏ 56YelBasP-16
❏ 57Top-125
❏ 58JayPubS-4
❏ 58Top-70A
❏ 58Top-70B
❏ 58Top-304
❏ 59HomRunD-9
❏ 59Top-34
❏ 59Top-360
❏ 59Top-463
❏ 59Top-562
❏ 59TopVen-34
❏ 60ArmCoi-12
❏ 60Baz-18
❏ 60KeyChal-27
❏ 60NuHi-65
❏ 60Pos-4
❏ 60RawGloT-10
❏ 60TigJayP-7
❏ 60Top-50
❏ 60Top-561
❏ 60TopTat-25
❏ 60TopVen-50
❏ 61Baz-20
❏ 61ChePat-5
❏ 61NuSco-465
❏ 61Pos-35A
❏ 61Pos-35B
❏ 61TigJayP-9
❏ 61Top-429
❏ 61Top-580
❏ 61TopDicG-6
❏ 61TopStal-152A
❏ 61TopStal-152B
❏ 62AurRec-8
❏ 62Baz-12
❏ 62ExhStaB-17
❏ 62Jel-20
❏ 62Pos-20
❏ 62PosCan-20
❏ 62SalPlaC-67
❏ 62ShiPlaC-67
❏ 62TigJayP-7
❏ 62Top-51
❏ 62Top-150
❏ 62Top-470
❏ 62TopBuc-43
❏ 62TopStal-47
❏ 62TopVen-51
❏ 62TopVen-150
❏ 63BasMagM-43
❏ 63Baz-34
❏ 63ExhStaB-34
❏ 63Jel-51
❏ 63Pos-51
❏ 63SalMetC-63
❏ 63TigJayP-8
❏ 63Top-25
❏ 63TopStil-21
❏ 64Baz-34
❏ 64ChatheY-31
❏ 64TigJayP-6
❏ 64TigLid-7
❏ 64Top-8
❏ 64Top-12
❏ 64Top-250
❏ 64Top-331
❏ 64TopCoi-100
❏ 64TopCoi-129
❏ 64TopGia-12
❏ 64TopSta-95
❏ 64TopStaU-38
❏ 64TopTatI-46
❏ 64TopVen-8
❏ 64TopVen-12
❏ 64TopVen-250
❏ 64TopVen-331
❏ 64WheSta-24
❏ 65Baz-34
❏ 65ChaTheY-30
❏ 65OldLonC-27
❏ 65OPC-130
❏ 65TigJayP-7
❏ 65Top-130
❏ 65TopEmbl-13
❏ 65TopTral-51
❏ 66Baz-46
❏ 66TigVolC-6
❏ 66Top-410
❏ 66TopRubl-44
❏ 67AshOil-3
❏ 67Baz-46
❏ 67CokCapA-22
❏ 67CokCapAAm-19
❏ 67CokCapTi-17
❏ 67DexPre-112
❏ 67DexPre-113
❏ 67OPC-30
❏ 67OPCPapI-21
❏ 67TigDexP-4
❏ 67Top-30
❏ 67Top-216
❏ 67Top-239
❏ 67TopGiaSU-10
❏ 67TopPos-21
❏ 67TopVen-210
❏ 68AtlOilPBCC-23
❏ 68Baz-1
❏ 68CokCapT-17
❏ 68OPC-2
❏ 68TigDetFPB-8
❏ 68Top-2
❏ 68Top-240
❏ 68TopActS-1C
❏ 68TopActS-6B
❏ 68TopActS-16C
❏ 68TopGamI-27
❏ 68TopPla-6
❏ 68TopPos-9
❏ 68TopVen-2
❏ 68TopVen-240
❏ 69EquSpoHoF-BB9
❏ 69KelPin-8
❏ 69MilBra-143
❏ 69MLBOffS-49
❏ 69MLBPin-13
❏ 69NabTeaF-12
❏ 69OPC-166
❏ 69TigTeal-4
❏ 69TigTealC-7
❏ 69Top-166
❏ 69Top-410
❏ 69TopFou-24
❏ 69TopSta-174
❏ 69TopTeaP-1
❏ 69TraSta-6
❏ 70DayDaiNM-15
❏ 70Houof J-10
❏ 70Kel-52
❏ 70MLBOffS-208
❏ 70Top-640
❏ 70TopScr-10
❏ 70TraSta-14A
❏ 71AllBasA-13
❏ 71BazNumT-14
❏ 71Kel-42
❏ 71MatMin-5
❏ 71MatMin-6
❏ 71MLBOffS-396
❏ 71MLBOffS-565
❏ 71OPC-180
❏ 71Top-180
❏ 71TopCoi-62
❏ 71TopGreM-19
❏ 71TopSup-54
❏ 71TopTat-36
❏ 71TopTat-37
❏ 72MilBra-177
❏ 72ProStaP-27
❏ 72SevTraC-25
❏ 72Top-600
❏ 73Kel2D-52
❏ 73LinPor-72
❏ 73OPC-280
❏ 73TigJew-10
❏ 73Top-280
❏ 73TopCanL-24
❏ 74LauAllG-57
❏ 74OPC-215
❏ 74SunPopK-1
❏ 74Tig-6
❏ 74Top-215
❏ 74TopSta-177
❏ 75OPC-4
❏ 75SSP42-34
❏ 75TCMHouoJ-10
❏ 75Top-4
❏ 75TopMin-4
❏ 76GalBasGHoF-16
❏ 76UPIS-5
❏ 77BobParHoF-94
❏ 77Spo-8720
❏ 78TCM60I-40
❏ 78TigDeaCS-12
❏ 79TCM50-184
❏ 80PacLeg-65
❏ 80PerHaloFP-170
❏ 80PerHaloFPS-38
❏ 80SSPHOF-171
❏ 80TigGreT-5
❏ 81SanDieSC-4
❏ 81TigDetN-100
❏ 81TigDetN-132
❏ 82CraJac-4
❏ 82TCMGreH-8
❏ 83DonHOFH-18
❏ 83FraBroR-13
❏ 83MLBPin-11
❏ 83Oco& SSBG-9
❏ 83TigAlKS-1A
❏ 83TigAlKS-1B
❏ 83TigAlKS-2
❏ 83TigAlKS-3
❏ 83TigAlKS-4
❏ 83TigAlKS-5
❏ 83TigAlKS-6
❏ 83TigAlKS-7
❏ 83TigAlKS-8
❏ 83TigAlKS-9
❏ 83TigAlKS-10
❏ 83TigAlKS-11
❏ 83TigAlKS-12
❏ 83TigAlKS-13
❏ 83TigAlKS-14
❏ 83TigAlKS-15
❏ 83TigAlKS-16
❏ 83TigAlKS-17
❏ 83TigAlKS-18
❏ 83TigAlKS-19
❏ 83TigAlKS-20
❏ 83TigAlKS-21
❏ 83TigAlKS-22
❏ 83TigAlKS-23
❏ 83TigAlKS-24
❏ 83TigAlKS-25
❏ 83TigAlKS-26
❏ 83TigAlKS-27
❏ 83TigAlKS-28
❏ 83TigAlKS-29
❏ 83TigAlKS-30
❏ 83TigAlKS-31
❏ 83TigAlKS-32
❏ 83TigAlKS-33
❏ 83TigAlKS-34
❏ 83TigAlKS-35
❏ 83TigAlKS-36
❏ 83TigAlKS-37
❏ 83TigAlKS-38
❏ 83TigAlKS-39
❏ 83TigAlKS-40
❏ 83TigAlKS-41
❏ 83TigAlKS-42
❏ 83TigAlKS-43

❑ 83TigAlKS-44
❑ 83TigAlKS-45
❑ 83TigAlKS-46
❑ 83TigAlKS-47
❑ 83TigAlKS-48
❑ 83TigAlKS-49
❑ 83TigAlKS-50
❑ 83TigAlKS-51
❑ 83TigAlKS-52
❑ 83TigAlKS-53
❑ 83TigAlKS-54
❑ 83TigAlKS-55
❑ 83TigAlKS-56
❑ 83TigAlKS-57
❑ 83TigAlKS-58
❑ 83TigAlKS-59
❑ 83TigAlKS-60
❑ 83TigAlKS-61
❑ 83TigAlKS-62
❑ 83TigAlKS-63
❑ 83TigAlKS-64
❑ 83TigAlKS-65
❑ 83TigAlKS-66
❑ 83TigAlKS-67
❑ 83TigAlKS-68
❑ 83TigAlKS-69
❑ 83TigAlKS-70
❑ 83TigAlKS-71
❑ 83TigAlKS-72
❑ 84OCoandSI-4
❑ 84OCoandSI-115
❑ 84SpoDesPW-12
❑ 85CirK-21
❑ 86SpoDecG-51
❑ 86TigSpoD-12
❑ 87LeaSpeO*-H10
❑ 88GreBasS-12
❑ 88PacLegI-104
❑ 88TigDom-9
❑ 89PerCelP-21
❑ 89SweBasG-40
❑ 89TopBasT-24
❑ 90AGFA-5
❑ 90HOFStiB-52
❑ 90PerGreM-2
❑ 91MDAA-18
❑ 91SweBasG-53
❑ 91UppDecS-22
❑ 92ActPacA-6
❑ 92ActPacA2-6G
❑ 93ActPacAC-6
❑ 93TedWil-38
❑ 93UppDecS-18
❑ 93Yoo-8
❑ 94TedWilM-M30
❑ 94TopArc1-201
❑ 94TopArc1G-201
❑ 94UppDecAH-98
❑ 94UppDecAH-173
❑ 94UppDecAH1-98
❑ 94UppDecAH1-173
❑ 95EagBalL-7
❑ 95JimDeaAG-3
❑ 95MrTurBG-2
❑ 95UppDecSHoB-16
❑ 97DonSigSS-12
❑ 97FleMilDM-21
❑ 97FleMilDMR-21
❑ 97SpoIllCC-6
❑ 97TopMan-36
❑ 97TopManF-36
❑ 97TopManFR-36
❑ 97TopStaHRR-7
❑ 97TopStaRRAU-7
❑ 98DonSigSB-15
❑ 98DonSigSS-5
❑ 98SpoIllTaN-13
❑ 98SpoIllTaNEE-13
❑ 98UppDecR-41
❑ 98UppDecRSotT-AK
❑ 99SpoIllGotG-60
❑ 99SpoIllGotGA-38
❑ 99SpoIllGotGC-10
Kaline, Louise
❑ 83TigAlKS-7
❑ 83TigAlKS-32
Kaline, Mark
❑ 83TigAlKS-28
❑ 83TigAlKS-32
Kaline, Michael
❑ 83TigAlKS-28
❑ 83TigAlKS-32
Kaline, Naomi
❑ 83TigAlKS-54
❑ 83TigAlKS-65
Kaline, Nicholas
❑ 83TigAlKS-54
❑ 83TigAlKS-65
Kalinowski, John
❑ 97PorRocG-12
❑ 98AshTouM-9
Kallevig, Dane
❑ 90WatIndS-11
Kallevig, Greg
❑ 86PeoChiP-12
❑ 87WinSpiP-2
❑ 88MidLeaAGS-28
❑ 88PeoChiTI-18
❑ 89ChaKniTI-16
❑ 90CMC-79
❑ 90IowCubC-4
❑ 90IowCubP-314
❑ 90ProAAAF-621
❑ 90TopTVCu-50
Kallio, Rudy
❑ 20Zee-47
❑ 21Zee-51
❑ 22Zee-81
❑ 23Zee-106
❑ 26Zee-115
❑ 27Zee-90
❑ 28ExhPCL-15
❑ 28Zee-109
❑ 29Zee-162
❑ 30Zee-177
❑ 31Zee-67
❑ 32Zee-118
❑ 33Zee-81
Kamanaka, Masaaki
❑ 89VerBeaDS-12
Kamei, Kat
❑ 87SanJosBP-8
Kamenshek, Dotty
❑ 93TedWil-117
Kamerschen, Robbie
❑ 90MarPhiP-3199
Kamieniecki, Scott
❑ 87PriWilYP-6
❑ 88Ft.LauYS-13
❑ 89AlbYanB-25
❑ 89AlbYanP-316
❑ 89EasLeaAP-15
❑ 90AlbYanB-5
❑ 90AlbYanP-1034
❑ 90AlbYanSt-7
❑ 90Bes-63
❑ 90TopTVY-49
❑ 91ColCliLD-109
❑ 91ColCliP-9
❑ 91ColCliP-594
❑ 91DonRoo-51
❑ 91FleUpd-45
❑ 91LinDriAAA-109
❑ 91StaClu-568
❑ 91TopTra-66T
❑ 91TopTraT-66T
❑ 91UppDecFE-33F
❑ 92Don-195
❑ 92Fle-232
❑ 92ForLauYC-14
❑ 92OPC-102
❑ 92OPCPre-110
❑ 92ProFS7-110
❑ 92Sco-415
❑ 92Sco100RS-23
❑ 92StaClu-649
❑ 92Top-102
❑ 92TopDeb91-96
❑ 92TopGol-102
❑ 92TopGolW-102
❑ 92TopMic-102
❑ 92UppDec-46
❑ 93Don-681
❑ 93Fle-651
❑ 93Lea-520
❑ 93PacSpa-557
❑ 93Pin-570
❑ 93Sco-377
❑ 93StaClu-410
❑ 93StaCluFDI-410
❑ 93StaCluMOP-410
❑ 93Top-749
❑ 93TopGol-749
❑ 93TopInaM-749
❑ 93TopInaR-749
❑ 93TopMic-749
❑ 93YanStaC-19
❑ 94ColC-487
❑ 94ColChoGS-487
❑ 94ColChoSS-487
❑ 94Don-553
❑ 94Fin-60
❑ 94FinRef-60
❑ 94Fle-234
❑ 94Pin-309
❑ 94PinArtP-309
❑ 94PinMusC-309
❑ 94Sco-350
❑ 94ScoGolR-350
❑ 94StaClu-101
❑ 94StaCluFDI-101
❑ 94StaCluGR-101
❑ 94StaCluMOP-101
❑ 94StaCluT-186
❑ 94StaCluTFDI-186
❑ 94Top-489
❑ 94TopGol-489
❑ 94TopSpa-489
❑ 94Ult-94
❑ 95ColCho-523
❑ 95ColChoGS-523
❑ 95ColChoSS-523
❑ 95Don-59
❑ 95DonPreP-59
❑ 95Fle-72
❑ 95Pin-438
❑ 95PinArtP-438
❑ 95PinMusC-438
❑ 95Sco-92
❑ 95ScoGolR-92
❑ 95ScoPlaTS-92
❑ 95StaClu-310
❑ 95StaCluMOP-310
❑ 95StaCluSTWS-310
❑ 95StaCluVR-165
❑ 95StaCluVRMO-165
❑ 95TamYanYI-13
❑ 95Top-352
❑ 95TopCyb-195
❑ 95Ult-81
❑ 95UltGolM-81
❑ 96ColCho-628
❑ 96ColChoGS-628
❑ 96ColChoSS-628
❑ 96Fle-185
❑ 96FleTif-185
❑ 96Sco-191
❑ 96UppDec-408
❑ 97BalOriP-18
❑ 97Ult-498
❑ 97UltGolME-498
❑ 97UltPlaME-498
❑ 98PacOnl-91
❑ 98PacOnlR-91
❑ 98PacOnlWC-91
Kamm, Willie
❑ 18Zee-38
❑ 19Zee-97
❑ 20Zee-110
❑ 21Exh-87
❑ 21Zee-122
❑ 22WilPatV-7
❑ 22Zee-100
❑ 23W503-29
❑ 23W515-42
❑ 25Exh-76
❑ 26Exh-77
❑ 26SpoComoA-25
❑ 27Exh-39
❑ 28StaPlaCE-41
❑ 28W502-40
❑ 28W56PlaC-H3A
❑ 28Yue-40
❑ 29ExhFou-19
❑ 29PorandAR-51
❑ 30ChiEveAP-17
❑ 30WhiSoxTI-14
❑ 31Exh-19
❑ 31W517-13
❑ 32OrbPinNP-10
❑ 32OrbPinUP-38
❑ 33Gou-75
❑ 33GouCanV-68
❑ 33TatOrb-38
❑ 33TatOrbSDR-164
❑ 33Zee-29
❑ 34BatR31-39
❑ 34ExhFou-11
❑ 34Gou-14
❑ 34GouCanV-60
❑ 34TarThoBD-17
❑ 35DiaMatCS3T1-85
❑ 35ExhFou-11
❑ 35GouPuzR-1L
❑ 35GouPuzR-2E
❑ 35GouPuzR-5A
❑ 35GouPuzR-6A
❑ 35GouPuzR-11J
❑ 35GouPuzR-13A
❑ 35GouPuzR-16E
❑ 35GouPuzR-17E
❑ 67SpoHobFC-24
❑ 76WhiSoxTAG-4
❑ 79DiaGre-134
❑ 80WhiSoxGT-6
❑ 85BigLeaC3-19
❑ 91ConTSN-166
❑ 93ConTSN-899
Kammerer, James
❑ 96AshTouB-22
❑ 97AshTou-12
❑ 97SalAva-U6
Kammeyer, Bob
❑ 78TacYanC-21
❑ 79ColCliT-23
❑ 80ColCliP-29
❑ 80ColCliT-10
❑ 92YanWIZ7-87
Kammeyer, Tim
❑ 82RedPioT-6
❑ 83RedPioT-15
Kampouris, Alex
❑ 33Zee-91
❑ 35GouPuzR-8D
❑ 35GouPuzR-9D
❑ 36ExhFou-4
❑ 36GouWidPPR-A59
❑ 41DouPlaR-13
❑ 42DodTeal-12
❑ 73Dod194T-15
❑ 78DodTCM4-25
❑ 90DodTar-398
Kampsen, Doug
❑ 85CedRapRT-9
Kane, Frank
❑ 90DodTar-997
Kane, Jim (James Joseph)
❑ 08RosComP-152
Kane, Joey
❑ 88AlaGolTI-11
❑ 89AlaGol-13
Kane, John Francis
❑ 09ObaT21-350
❑ 11SpoLifM-171
❑ 11Zee-117
❑ 12HomRunKE-87
❑ 12ObaPreT-99
❑ 12Zee-149
❑ 13Zee-139
❑ 14Zee-137
❑ 15Zee-132
❑ 16Zee-10
Kane, Johnny
❑ 88KimN18-22
Kane, Kevin
❑ 81BriRedST-3
❑ 85PawRedST-18
❑ 98OneYanG-18
Kane, Kyle
❑ 98BriWhiSQ-16
Kane, Mike
❑ 93BoiHawC-15
❑ 93BoiHawF-3911
Kane, Ryan
❑ 95BoiHawTI-20
❑ 96CedRapKTI-14
❑ 96Exc-29
❑ 97TamYan-15
Kane, Tom
❑ 86GreHorP-12
❑ 87GreHorP-1
❑ 91LinDriAA-465
❑ 91NewBriRSLD-465
❑ 91NewBriRSP-350
Kaneda, Tomehiro
❑ 79TCMJapPB-28
Kanehl, Rod
❑ 62Top-597
❑ 63Fle-49
❑ 63Jel-199
❑ 63MetJayP-7
❑ 63Pos-199
❑ 63Top-371
❑ 64MetJayP-9
❑ 64Top-582
❑ 74MetOriEB-7
❑ 76Met63 S-9
❑ 82MetGal62-8
❑ 90SweBasG-44
❑ 91MetWIZ-210
Kaney, Joe
❑ 47CenFlo-14
Kanikeberg, Ken
❑ 76SeaRaiC-7
Kannenberg, Scott
❑ 86QuaCitAP-17
❑ 87QuaCitAP-9
❑ 88PalSprACLC-88
❑ 88PalSprAP-1444
Kanovich, Jason
❑ 98VerExpO-13
Kanter, John
❑ 85MadMusP-15
❑ 85MadMusT-18
❑ 86ModA'sP-17
Kantlehner, Erving
❑ 16FleBreD-48
❑ 18Zee-84
Kantor, Brad
❑ 91WatIndC-18
❑ 91WatIndP-3373
❑ 92WatIndC-20
❑ 92WatIndF-3243
Kanwisher, Billy
❑ 91OklStaC-13
❑ 92OklStaC-14
Kanwisher, Gary
❑ 85BelBreT-20
❑ 86StoPorP-11
❑ 87StoPorP-25
Kapano, Corey
❑ 89BenBucL-17
❑ 90QuaCitAGS-19
❑ 91CalLeLA-16
❑ 91PalSprAP-2023
❑ 92MidAngOHP-11
❑ 92MidAngS-461
❑ 92SkyAA F-195
❑ 92WinSpiF-1220
❑ 93ClaFS7-212
❑ 93OrlCubF-2799
Kapler, Gabe
❑ 96FayGenB-19
❑ 96WesOahCHWB-19
❑ 97FloStaLTPB-16
❑ 97LakTigB-17
❑ 98AriFalLTP-6
❑ 98Bes-71
❑ 98Bow-125
❑ 98BowChr-125
❑ 98BowChrGA-125
❑ 98BowChrGAR-125
❑ 98BowChrI-125
❑ 98BowChrIR-125
❑ 98BowChrR-125
❑ 98BowGolA-125
❑ 98BowInt-125
❑ 98DonSig-130
❑ 98DonSigP-130
❑ 98FleUpd-U59
❑ 98JacSunM-14
❑ 98LeaRS-321
❑ 98LeaRSLHolo-321
❑ 98LeaRSLong-321
❑ 98LeaRTrue-321
❑ 98UppDec-543
❑ 99199Fin-150
❑ 99Bow-300
❑ 99BowBes-124
❑ 99BowBesAR-124
❑ 99BowBesR-124
❑ 99BowBesRLRA-RA4
❑ 99BowBesRLRGUB-RB4
❑ 99BowGol-300
❑ 99BowInt-300
❑ 99CroRoyB-55
❑ 99CroRoyL-55
❑ 99CroRoyOD-55
❑ 99DumSet-122
❑ 99E-X Cen-117
❑ 99E-X CenECFut-117
❑ 99E-X CenECNow-117
❑ 99E-X CenEQ-8
❑ 99FinFutF-FF6
❑ 99FinGolRef-150
❑ 99FinRef-150
❑ 99FlaShoLeg1-37
❑ 99FlaShoLeg2-37
❑ 99FlaShoLeg3-37
❑ 99FlaShoLegM1-37
❑ 99FlaShoLegM2-37
❑ 99FlaShoLegM3-37
❑ 99FlaShoR1-37
❑ 99FlaShoR2-37
❑ 99FlaShoR3-37
❑ 99Fle-215
❑ 99FleBri-128
❑ 99FleBri2G-128
❑ 99FleBriBlu-128
❑ 99FleBriGol-128
❑ 99FleMys-122
❑ 99FleMysFI-19
❑ 99FleMysM-122
❑ 99FleMysP-5
❑ 99FleSta9-215
❑ 99FleWarT-215
❑ 99JustheS-28
❑ 99JustheSAC-15
❑ 99JustheSAD-11
❑ 99JustheSJB-28
❑ 99JustheSJD-6
❑ 99JustheSJN-3
❑ 99JustheSJN-6
❑ 99JustheSJP-6
❑ 99MetUni-257
❑ 99MetUniGM-257
❑ 99MetUniPMG-257
❑ 99PacInv-58
❑ 99PacInvOD-58
❑ 99PacInvPB-58
❑ 99PacOme-91
❑ 99PacOme5T-7
❑ 99PacOme5TT-7
❑ 99PacOmeC-91
❑ 99PacOmeDM-15
❑ 99PacOmeG-91
❑ 99PacOmePB-91
❑ 99Rev-56
❑ 99RevDiaL-15
❑ 99RevPremDate-56
❑ 99RevRet-56
❑ 99RevShaSS-56
❑ 99SkyPre-260
❑ 99SkyPre-260
❑ 99SkyPreA-30
❑ 99SkyPreABlue-30
❑ 99SkyPreDD-13
❑ 99SkyPreR-260
❑ 99SkyPreR-260
❑ 99SkyThu-295
❑ 99SkyThuRant-295
❑ 99SkyThuRave-295
❑ 99SkyThuUnI-U11
❑ 99SP Aut-98
❑ 99SP AutC-GK
❑ 99SP AutCG-GK
❑ 99SP AutHRC-HR39
❑ 99SP SigAuto-GK
❑ 99SP SigAutoG-GK
❑ 99SP TopP-9
❑ 99SP TopP-106
❑ 99SP TopPDtS-D25
❑ 99SP TopPPE-9
❑ 99SP TopPPE-106
❑ 99SPAutHRCDC-HR39
❑ 99SpoIll-68
❑ 99SpoIllOTW-6
❑ 99SPSig-19
❑ 99SPx-90
❑ 99SPxFinR-90
❑ 99SPxFinS-90
❑ 99StaClu-169
❑ 99StaCluC-SCC39
❑ 99StaCluCR-SCC39
❑ 99StaCluFDI-169
❑ 99StaCluOoaK-169
❑ 99StaCluPP-169
❑ 99ThuSkySupR-295
❑ 99Top-205
❑ 99Top-432
❑ 99TopAll-AM15
❑ 99TopChr-205
❑ 99TopChr-432
❑ 99TopChrA-AE15
❑ 99TopChrAR-AE15
❑ 99TopChrR-205
❑ 99TopChrR-432
❑ 99TopGal-146
❑ 99TopGalPP-146
❑ 99TopGalPPI-146
❑ 99TopMVPP-432
❑ 99TopSta-46
❑ 99TopSta1Foil-46
❑ 99TopSta2Foil-46
❑ 99TopStaBF-BF5
❑ 99TopStaBFFoil-BF5
❑ 99TopStaFoil-46
❑ 99TopStaOS-46
❑ 99TopStaTS-46
❑ 99UD Cho-1
❑ 99UD ChoMBH-B13
❑ 99UD ChoPCR-1
❑ 99UD Ion-27
❑ 99UD IonR-27
❑ 99UDHoloUDA-GK

❑ 99Ult-233
❑ 99UltGolM-233
❑ 99UltMas-233
❑ 99UltPlaM-233
❑ 99UppDec-371
❑ 99UppDecCf7-44
❑ 99UppDecCf7SftF-S10
❑ 99UppDecCL-120
❑ 99UppDecCLCC-120
❑ 99UppDecCLM-C33
❑ 99UppDecCo7CE-44
❑ 99UppDecCo7SftFA-GK
❑ 99UppDecE-37
❑ 99UppDecEBPC-C-GK
❑ 99UppDecEFXG-37
❑ 99UppDecEL1-371
❑ 99UppDecEL2-371
❑ 99UppDecEPE-P6
❑ 99UppDecERE-R3
❑ 99UppDecEREFXG-R3
❑ 99UppDecM-75
❑ 99UppDecMGS-75
❑ 99UppDecMHFS-75
❑ 99UppDecMP-GK
❑ 99UppDecMSC-SC4
❑ 99UppDecMSS-75
❑ 99UppDecO-62
❑ 99UppDecOSO-62
❑ 99UppDecRI-GK
❑ 99UppDecRIL2-GK
❑ 99UppDecROSS-S16
❑ 99UppDecROSS-S16
❑ 99UppDecVtaT-V6
❑ 99UppDecVtaTD-V6
❑ 99UppDecVtaTQ-V6
❑ 99UppDecVtaTT-V6
❑ 99Vic-142

Kappell, Henry
❑ 87OldJudN-266

Kappesser, Bob
❑ 89HelBreSP-19
❑ 90CalLeaACLC-48
❑ 90StoPorB-4
❑ 90StoPorCLC-189
❑ 90StoPorP-2188
❑ 91VisOakC-25
❑ 91VisOakP-1745
❑ 92ElPasDF-3925
❑ 92ElPasDS-215
❑ 93El PasDF-2952
❑ 94ElPasDF-3149
❑ 95ElPasDTI-12

Karabinus, Chris
❑ 97YakBeaG-12

Karasinski, Dave
❑ 88BurBraP-16
❑ 89BurBraP-1611
❑ 89BurBraS-11
❑ 90DurBulTI-26
❑ 91SalSpuC-20
❑ 91SalSpuP-2237

Karcher, Carl
❑ 92AngPol-13
❑ 93AngPol-2

Karcher, Kevin
❑ 86EugEmeC-41

Karcher, Rick
❑ 90IdaFalBP-3255
❑ 91MacBraC-20
❑ 91MacBraP-873
❑ 92DurBulC-3
❑ 92DurBulF-1109
❑ 92DurBulTI-22

Karchner, Matt
❑ 89EugEmeB-6
❑ 90AppFoxBS-15
❑ 90AppFoxP-2091
❑ 91BasCitRC-8
❑ 91BasCitRP-1395
❑ 92MemChiF-2414
❑ 92MemChiS-437
❑ 93ClaGolF-126
❑ 93MemChiF-370
❑ 94BirBarC-15
❑ 94BirBarF-619
❑ 96ColCho-509
❑ 96ColChoGS-509
❑ 96ColChoSS-509
❑ 96Fle-69
❑ 96FleTif-69
❑ 96LeaSigEA-96
❑ 96StaClu-85
❑ 96StaCluMOP-85
❑ 96WhiSoxF-8
❑ 97WhiSoxTI-47
❑ 98ColCho-66
❑ 98Fin-83
❑ 98FinNo--83
❑ 98FinNo-R-83
❑ 98FinRef-83
❑ 98Pac-58
❑ 98PacOnl-172
❑ 98PacOnlR-172
❑ 98PacOnlWC-172
❑ 98PacPlaB-58
❑ 98PacRedT-58
❑ 98PacSil-58
❑ 98StaCluFDI-295
❑ 98StaCluI-295
❑ 98StaCluOneK-295
❑ 98StaCluPP-295
❑ 98Top-223
❑ 98TopChr-223
❑ 98TopChrR-223
❑ 98TopDevR-223
❑ 98TopDia-223
❑ 98TopMiniC-223
❑ 98Ult-428
❑ 98UltGolM-428
❑ 98UltMas-428
❑ 98UltPlaM-428
❑ 98UppDec-332
❑ 99SP SigAuto-MKA
❑ 99SPSig-99

Karcl, Darin
❑ 90ProAaA-114

Karczewski, Ray
❑ 88SalLakCTTI-7
❑ 89SalLakTTI-7

Kardamis, Mike
❑ 93AlbPolCB-28

Karger, Edwin
❑ 08RosComP-166
❑ 09AmeCarE90-1-61
❑ 09RamT20-63
❑ 09T206-182
❑ 10DomDisP-61
❑ 10SweCapPP-5
❑ 11PinT-5-660
❑ 11SpoLifCW-195
❑ 11SpoLifM-11
❑ 11T205-86
❑ 12PhiCarE-14

Karkovice, Ron
❑ 83AppFoxFr-22
❑ 86BirBarTI-8
❑ 86SouLeaAJ-5
❑ 87Don-334
❑ 87DonOpeD-234
❑ 87Fle-645
❑ 87FleGlo-645
❑ 87SevCoi-C11
❑ 87SpoTeaP-26
❑ 87Top-491
❑ 87TopTif-491
❑ 87WhiSoxC-18
❑ 88BlaYNPRWLU-33
❑ 88Sco-374
❑ 88ScoGlo-374
❑ 88Top-86
❑ 88TopClo-52
❑ 88TopTif-86
❑ 88VanCanC-15
❑ 88VanCanP-773
❑ 89BirBarADB-19
❑ 89Top-308
❑ 89TopTif-308
❑ 89UppDec-183
❑ 89WhiSoxC-13
❑ 90BirBarADB-19
❑ 90Don-413
❑ 90Lea-307
❑ 90OPC-717
❑ 90PubIntS-391
❑ 90Sco-22
❑ 90Top-717
❑ 90TopTif-717
❑ 90UppDec-69
❑ 90WhiSoxC-11
❑ 91Don-220
❑ 91DonGraS-12
❑ 91Fle-125
❑ 91Lea-515
❑ 91OPC-568
❑ 91Sco-833
❑ 91StaClu-102
❑ 91Top-568
❑ 91TopDesS-568
❑ 91TopMic-568
❑ 91TopTif-568
❑ 91UltUpd-16
❑ 91UppDec-209
❑ 91WhiSoxK-20
❑ 92Don-374
❑ 92Fle-88
❑ 92Lea-105
❑ 92LeaBlaG-105
❑ 92OPC-153
❑ 92Pin-413
❑ 92Sco-532
❑ 92StaClu-257
❑ 92Top-153
❑ 92TopGol-153
❑ 92TopGolW-153
❑ 92TopMic-153
❑ 92Ult-39
❑ 92UppDec-169
❑ 92WhiSoxK-20
❑ 93Don-331
❑ 93Fle-205
❑ 93Lea-63
❑ 93OPC-198
❑ 93PacSpa-391
❑ 93PanSti-142
❑ 93Pin-195
❑ 93Sco-152
❑ 93Sel-381
❑ 93SP-257
❑ 93StaClu-427
❑ 93StaCluFDI-427
❑ 93StaCluMOP-427
❑ 93Top-286
❑ 93TopGol-286
❑ 93TopInaM-286
❑ 93TopInaR-286
❑ 93TopMic-286
❑ 93TriPla-216
❑ 93Ult-175
❑ 93UppDec-199
❑ 93UppDecGold-199
❑ 93WhiSoxK-15
❑ 93WhiSoxSC-17
❑ 94Bow-71
❑ 94ColC-157
❑ 94ColChoGS-157
❑ 94ColChoSS-157
❑ 94Don-416
❑ 94Fin-71
❑ 94FinRef-71
❑ 94Fla-279
❑ 94Fle-86
❑ 94FleExtB-50
❑ 94Lea-184
❑ 94OPC-71
❑ 94Pac-130
❑ 94Pin-116
❑ 94PinArtP-116
❑ 94PinMusC-116
❑ 94Sco-403
❑ 94ScoGolR-403
❑ 94Sel-33
❑ 94StaClu-57
❑ 94StaCluFDI-57
❑ 94StaCluGR-57
❑ 94StaCluMOP-57
❑ 94StaCluT-123
❑ 94StaCluTFDI-123
❑ 94Top-684
❑ 94TopGol-684
❑ 94TopSpa-684
❑ 94Ult-36
❑ 94UppDec-121
❑ 94UppDecED-121
❑ 94WhiSoxK-17
❑ 95ColCho-502
❑ 95ColChoGS-502
❑ 95ColChoSS-502
❑ 95Don-198
❑ 95DonPreP-198
❑ 95DonTopotO-52
❑ 95Fla-247
❑ 95Fle-122
❑ 95Lea-44
❑ 95Pin-68
❑ 95PinArtP-68
❑ 95PinMusC-68
❑ 95Sco-481
❑ 95ScoGolR-481
❑ 95ScoPlaTS-481
❑ 95StaClu-88
❑ 95StaCluFDI-88
❑ 95StaCluMOP-88
❑ 95StaCluSTWS-88
❑ 95StaCluVR-54
❑ 95StaCluVRMO-54
❑ 95Top-372
❑ 95TopCyb-197
❑ 95Ult-31
❑ 95UltGolM-31
❑ 95WhiSoxK-15
❑ 96ColCho-508
❑ 96ColChoGS-508
❑ 96ColChoSS-508
❑ 96Don-88
❑ 96DonPreP-88
❑ 96Fla-53
❑ 96Fle-70
❑ 96FleTif-70
❑ 96LeaSigA-124
❑ 96LeaSigAG-124
❑ 96LeaSigAS-124
❑ 96Pac-291
❑ 96ProSta-134
❑ 96Sco-182
❑ 96StaClu-220
❑ 96StaClu-432
❑ 96StaCluMOP-220
❑ 96StaCluMOP-432
❑ 96Top-52
❑ 96Ult-41
❑ 96UltGolM-41
❑ 96WhiSoxF-9
❑ 97Cir-261
❑ 97CirRav-261
❑ 97ColCho-298
❑ 97Fle-63
❑ 97FleTif-63
❑ 97Pac-55
❑ 97PacLigB-55
❑ 97PacSil-55
❑ 97Sco-233
❑ 97ScoArtPWB-233
❑ 97ScoPreS-233
❑ 97ScoShoS-233
❑ 97ScoShoSAP-233
❑ 97StaClu-346
❑ 97StaCluMOP-346
❑ 97Top-81
❑ 97WhiSoxS-12
❑ 97WhiSoxSPl-12
❑ 97WhiSoxSPr-12
❑ 97WhiSoxTI-20

Karl, Andy
❑ 43RedSoxTI-11
❑ 83TCMPla1945-44

Karl, Scott
❑ 92HelBreF-1711
❑ 92HelBreSP-16
❑ 93El PasDF-2946
❑ 93ExcFS7-189
❑ 94AriFalLS-11
❑ 94Bow-477
❑ 94ExcFS7-82
❑ 94NewOrlZF-1464
❑ 95FleUpd-52
❑ 95TopTra-43T
❑ 96BrePol-11
❑ 96ColCho-596
❑ 96ColChoGS-596
❑ 96ColChoSS-596
❑ 96Don-414
❑ 96DonPreP-414
❑ 96Fle-148
❑ 96FleTif-148
❑ 96LeaSigEA-97
❑ 96Pac-347
❑ 96UppDec-124
❑ 97BrePol-13
❑ 97Cir-154
❑ 97CirRav-154
❑ 97ColCho-144
❑ 97Fle-130
❑ 97FleTif-130
❑ 97Lea-74
❑ 97LeaFraM-74
❑ 97LeaFraMDC-74
❑ 97MetUni-66
❑ 97Pac-120
❑ 97PacLigB-120
❑ 97PacSil-120
❑ 97Top-58
❑ 97Ult-77
❑ 97UltGolME-77
❑ 97UltPlaME-77
❑ 97UppDec-406
❑ 98ColCho-151
❑ 98Fle-426
❑ 98Pac-118
❑ 98PacOme-135
❑ 98PacOmeR-135
❑ 98PacOnl-402
❑ 98PacOnlR-402
❑ 98PacOnlWC-402
❑ 98PacPlaB-118
❑ 98PacRedT-118
❑ 98PacSil-118
❑ 98StaCluFDI-187
❑ 98StaCluI-187
❑ 98StaCluOneK-187
❑ 98StaCluPP-187
❑ 98UppDec-407
❑ 99Fle-303
❑ 99FleSta9-303
❑ 99FleWarT-303
❑ 99Pac-236
❑ 99PacCroC-151
❑ 99PacCroCPB-151
❑ 99PacPlaB-236
❑ 99PacRed-236
❑ 99SkyPreA-31
❑ 99SkyPreABlue-31
❑ 99UppDec-131
❑ 99UppDecEL1-131
❑ 99UppDecEL2-131
❑ 99UppDecMP-SK
❑ 99Vic-212

Karli, Todd
❑ 90RenSilSCLC-291

Karmeris, Joe
❑ 85VerBeaDT-14

Karnuth, Jason
❑ 97NewJerCB-12

Karp, Ryan
❑ 92OneYanC-7
❑ 93GreHorC-13
❑ 93GreHorF-882
❑ 93SouAtlLAGF-22
❑ 94Bow-552
❑ 94ClaGolF-84
❑ 94ExcFS7-108
❑ 94ExcLeaLF-11
❑ 94ReaPhiF-2058
❑ 94UppDecML-64
❑ 94UppDecMLPotYF-PY28
❑ 95ReaPhiELC-23
❑ 95ReaPhiTI-11
❑ 95ScrRedBTI-17
❑ 95SigRooOJ-21
❑ 95SigRooOJP-21
❑ 95SigRooOJPS-21
❑ 95SigRooOJS-21
❑ 96ScrRedBB-18
❑ 97ScrRedB-15
❑ 98DurBulTI-13

Karpoel, Herb
❑ 50W720HolS-14

Karpuk, Greg
❑ 86WatIndP-15
❑ 87WilBilP-26

Karr, Benjamin
❑ 15Zee-109
❑ 22E120-5
❑ 22W573-71
❑ 27AmeCarE126-20

Karr, Jeff
❑ 84LitFalMT-7

Karrmann, Jason
❑ 92Min-8

Karros, Eric
❑ 88GreFalDTI-2
❑ 89BakDodCLC-201
❑ 89CalLeaA-2
❑ 90SanAntMGS-16
❑ 90TexLeaAGS-1
❑ 90TopMag-100
❑ 91AlbDukLD-12
❑ 91AlbDukP-1146
❑ 91Bow-604
❑ 91Cla2-T36
❑ 91ClaGam-171
❑ 91DodPho-17
❑ 91LinDriAAA-12
❑ 91Ult-380
❑ 91UppDec-24
❑ 92Bow-288
❑ 92Cla2-T21
❑ 92ClaGam-34
❑ 92DodMot-21
❑ 92DodPol-23
❑ 92DodSmo-4992
❑ 92Don-16
❑ 92DonRooP-BC6
❑ 92Fle-462
❑ 92JimDeaRS-4
❑ 92Lea-293
❑ 92LeaBlaG-293
❑ 92OPC-194
❑ 92OPCPre-63
❑ 92Pin-256
❑ 92PinRoo-24
❑ 92PinTea2-76
❑ 92ProFS7-240
❑ 92Sco-827
❑ 92ScoRoo-31
❑ 92SpollIFK1-390
❑ 92StaClu-236
❑ 92StaPro-5
❑ 92Stu-45
❑ 92Top-194
❑ 92TopDeb91-97
❑ 92TopGol-194
❑ 92TopGolW-194
❑ 92TopMcD-43
❑ 92TopMic-194
❑ 92Ult-508
❑ 92UltAllR-1
❑ 92UppDec-534
❑ 92UppDecSR-SR12
❑ 93Bow-14
❑ 93ClaGam-46
❑ 93DiaMar-59
❑ 93DodMot-2
❑ 93DodPol-13
❑ 93DodStaC-8
❑ 93Don-430
❑ 93DonDiaK-DK30
❑ 93DonMVP-8
❑ 93DonPre-5
❑ 93Fin-32
❑ 93FinRef-32
❑ 93Fla-71
❑ 93Fle-64
❑ 93FleFruotL-31
❑ 93FleRooS-RSA6
❑ 93FleTeaL-NL4
❑ 93FunPac-86
❑ 93FunPac-89
❑ 93HumDumC-34
❑ 93JimDea-24
❑ 93Lea-234
❑ 93LeaFas-7
❑ 93OPC-208
❑ 93OPCPreSP-8
❑ 93OPCPreSPF-8
❑ 93PacSpa-151
❑ 93PanSti-166
❑ 93PanSti-214
❑ 93Pin-14
❑ 93PinTea2-26
❑ 93Pos-6
❑ 93RemUltK-1
❑ 93RemUltK-2
❑ 93RemUltK-3
❑ 93RemUltK-4
❑ 93RemUltK-5
❑ 93Sco-63
❑ 93Sco-486
❑ 93Sel-278
❑ 93SelChaR-5
❑ 93SP-94
❑ 93StaClu-292
❑ 93StaClu-528
❑ 93StaCluFDI-292
❑ 93StaCluFDI-528
❑ 93StaCluMOP-292
❑ 93StaCluMOP-528
❑ 93StaKarA-1
❑ 93Stu-92
❑ 93StuHer-10
❑ 93Top-11
❑ 93TOPBLAG-9
❑ 93TopGol-11
❑ 93TopInaM-11
❑ 93TopInaR-11
❑ 93TopMic-11
❑ 93TopPre-11
❑ 93Toy-63
❑ 93TriPla-4
❑ 93TriPlaA-7
❑ 93TriPlaLL-L3
❑ 93TriPlaP-4
❑ 93Ult-56
❑ 93UltAwaW-20
❑ 93UltPer-4
❑ 93UppDec-385
❑ 93UppDec-490
❑ 93UppDecFA-A10
❑ 93UppDecFAJ-A10
❑ 93UppDecGold-385
❑ 93UppDecGold-490
❑ 93UppDecHRH-HR19
❑ 93UppDecIC-WI9
❑ 93UppDecICJ-WI9
❑ 93UppDecOD-D17
❑ 93USPlaCR-1S

❑ 94Bow-14
❑ 94ColC-158
❑ 94ColChoGS-158
❑ 94ColChoSS-158
❑ 94DodDaiN-10
❑ 94DodMot-4
❑ 94DodPol-16
❑ 94Don-338
❑ 94DonSpeE-338
❑ 94Fin-356
❑ 94FinRef-356
❑ 94Fla-397
❑ 94Fle-514
❑ 94Fle-713
❑ 94FleExtB-289
❑ 94FUnPac-146
❑ 94Lea-171
❑ 94LeaL-118
❑ 94OPC-163
❑ 94Pac-312
❑ 94PanSti-201
❑ 94Pin-87
❑ 94PinArtP-87
❑ 94PinMusC-87
❑ 94PinPowS-PS18
❑ 94ProMag-66
❑ 94Sco-26
❑ 94ScoGolR-26
❑ 94Sel-44
❑ 94SP-78
❑ 94SPDieC-78
❑ 94Spo-5
❑ 94StaClu-240
❑ 94StaCluFDI-240
❑ 94StaCluGR-240
❑ 94StaCluMOP-240
❑ 94Stu-69
❑ 94Top-115
❑ 94TopGol-115
❑ 94TopSpa-115
❑ 94TriPla-85
❑ 94Ult-518
❑ 94UppDec-208
❑ 94UppDecED-208
❑ 95Baz-66
❑ 95Bow-402
❑ 95BowBes-R14
❑ 95BowBesR-R14
❑ 95ColCho-220
❑ 95ColChoGS-220
❑ 95ColChoSE-92
❑ 95ColChoSEGS-92
❑ 95ColChoSESS-92
❑ 95ColChoSS-220
❑ 95DodMot-5
❑ 95DodPol-12
❑ 95DodROY-12
❑ 95Don-488
❑ 95DonPreP-488
❑ 95DonTopotO-265
❑ 95Emo-141
❑ 95Fin-58
❑ 95FinRef-58
❑ 95Fla-366
❑ 95Fle-543
❑ 95Lea-252
❑ 95LeaLim-36
❑ 95Pac-220
❑ 95Pin-7
❑ 95PinArtP-7
❑ 95PinMusC-7
❑ 95Sco-399
❑ 95ScoGolR-399
❑ 95ScoPlaTS-399
❑ 95SelCer-80
❑ 95SelCerMG-80
❑ 95SP-66
❑ 95SPCha-59
❑ 95SPChaDC-59
❑ 95Spo-50
❑ 95SpoArtP-50
❑ 95SPSil-66
❑ 95SPSpeF-40
❑ 95StaClu-278
❑ 95StaCluMOP-278
❑ 95StaCluSTDW-D278
❑ 95StaCluSTWS-278
❑ 95StaCluVR-142
❑ 95StaCluVRMO-142
❑ 95Stu-147
❑ 95Top-487
❑ 95TopCyb-279
❑ 95TopEmb-119
❑ 95TopEmbGI-119
❑ 95Ult-181
❑ 95UltGolM-181
❑ 95UppDec-70
❑ 95UppDecED-70
❑ 95UppDecEDG-70
❑ 95UppDecSE-172
❑ 95UppDecSEG-172
❑ 95Zen-31
❑ 96Baz-36
❑ 96Bow-66
❑ 96BowBes-81
❑ 96BowBesAR-81
❑ 96BowBesR-81
❑ 96BowFoi-66
❑ 96Cir-141
❑ 96CirRav-141
❑ 96ColCho-183
❑ 96ColChoCtG-CG20
❑ 96ColChoCtG-CG20B
❑ 96ColChoCtG-CG20C
❑ 96ColChoCtGE-CR20
❑ 96ColChoCtGG-CG20
❑ 96ColChoCtGG-CG20B
❑ 96ColChoCtGG-CG20C
❑ 96ColChoCtGGE-CR20
❑ 96ColChoGS-183
❑ 96ColChoSS-183
❑ 96DodFle-10
❑ 96DodMot-5
❑ 96DodPol-21
❑ 96Don-158
❑ 96DonPreP-158
❑ 96EmoXL-210
❑ 96Fin-B163
❑ 96FinRef-B163
❑ 96Fla-294
❑ 96Fle-438
❑ 96FleTif-438
❑ 96Lea-23
❑ 96LeaPre-69
❑ 96LeaPreP-69
❑ 96LeaPrePB-23
❑ 96LeaPrePG-23
❑ 96LeaPrePS-23
❑ 96LeaSig-114
❑ 96LeaSigPPG-114
❑ 96LeaSigPPP-114
❑ 96MetUni-183
❑ 96MetUniP-183
❑ 96MetUniProS-183
❑ 96Pac-111
❑ 96PacPri-P34
❑ 96PacPriFB-FB9
❑ 96PacPriG-P34
❑ 96PanSti-96
❑ 96Pin-62
❑ 96Pin-132
❑ 96PinAfi-70
❑ 96PinAfiAP-70
❑ 96PinAfiFPP-70
❑ 96PinArtP-25
❑ 96PinSta-25
❑ 96ProSta-42
❑ 96Sco-355
❑ 96ScoDugC-B80
❑ 96ScoDugCAP-B80
❑ 96ScoPowP-18
❑ 96Sel-83
❑ 96SelArtP-83
❑ 96SP-101
❑ 96Spo-41
❑ 96SpoArtP-41
❑ 96SPSpeFX-2
❑ 96SPSpeFXDC-2
❑ 96SPx-32
❑ 96SPxGol-32
❑ 96StaClu-63
❑ 96StaCluEPB-63
❑ 96StaCluEPG-63
❑ 96StaCluEPS-63
❑ 96StaCluMO-18
❑ 96StaCluMOP-63
❑ 96Stu-7
❑ 96StuPrePB-7
❑ 96StuPrePG-7
❑ 96StuPrePS-7
❑ 96Sum-127
❑ 96SumAbo&B-127
❑ 96SumArtP-127
❑ 96SumFoi-127
❑ 96Top-196
❑ 96TopChr-64
❑ 96TopChrR-64
❑ 96TopGal-69
❑ 96TopGalPPI-69
❑ 96TopLas-70
❑ 96Ult-220
❑ 96UltGolM-220
❑ 96UppDec-355
❑ 96UppDecPD-PD8
❑ 96UppDecPHE-H36
❑ 96UppDecPreH-H36
❑ 97Bow-25
❑ 97BowBes-75
❑ 97BowBesAR-75
❑ 97BowBesR-75
❑ 97BowChr-21
❑ 97BowChrI-21
❑ 97BowChrIR-21
❑ 97BowChrR-21
❑ 97BowInt-25
❑ 97Cir-186
❑ 97CirRav-186
❑ 97ColCho-140
❑ 97ColChoCtG-19A
❑ 97ColChoCtG-19B
❑ 97ColChoCtG-19C
❑ 97ColChoCtGE-CG19
❑ 97ColChoCtGIW-CG19
❑ 97ColChoT-LA4
❑ 97DodDWPM-2
❑ 97DodMot-2
❑ 97DodPol-15
❑ 97DodSco-14
❑ 97DodScoPl-14
❑ 97DodScoPr-14
❑ 97Don-216
❑ 97DonEli-108
❑ 97DonEliGS-108
❑ 97DonGolPP-216
❑ 97DonLim-11
❑ 97DonLimE-11
❑ 97DonLimENG-11
❑ 97DonPre-124
❑ 97DonPreCttC-124
❑ 97DonSigA-57
❑ 97DonSigAC-70
❑ 97DonSigAM-70
❑ 97DonSilPP-216
❑ 97DonTea-115
❑ 97DonTeaSPE-115
❑ 97E-X2-79
❑ 97E-X2Cred-79
❑ 97E-X2EssCre-79
❑ 97Fin-255
❑ 97FinRef-255
❑ 97FlaShoLC-69
❑ 97FlaShoLeg0-69
❑ 97FlaShoLeg1-69
❑ 97FlaShoM-A69
❑ 97FlaShoM-B69
❑ 97FlaShoM-C69
❑ 97FlaShoR0-69
❑ 97FlaShoR1-69
❑ 97FlaShoR2-69
❑ 97Fle-365
❑ 97FleTif-365
❑ 97Lea-72
❑ 97LeaFraM-72
❑ 97LeaFraMDC-72
❑ 97MetUni-101
❑ 97Pac-332
❑ 97PacLigB-332
❑ 97PacSil-332
❑ 97Pin-116
❑ 97PinArtP-PP116
❑ 97PinCer-37
❑ 97PinCerMBla-37
❑ 97PinCerMBlu-37
❑ 97PinCerMG-37
❑ 97PinCerMR-37
❑ 97PinCerR-37
❑ 97PinIns-66
❑ 97PinInsCE-66
❑ 97PinInsDE-66
❑ 97PinMusC-116
❑ 97PinPrePla-116
❑ 97PinTotCPB-37
❑ 97PinTotCPG-37
❑ 97PinTotCPR-37
❑ 97Sco-103
❑ 97ScoArtPWB-103
❑ 97ScoPreS-103
❑ 97ScoShoS-103
❑ 97ScoShoSAP-103
❑ 97SP-94
❑ 97SpoIll-113
❑ 97SpoIllEE-113
❑ 97SpoIllGS-14
❑ 97SPSpeF-31
❑ 97StaClu-23
❑ 97StaCluC-CO7
❑ 97StaCluMat-23
❑ 97StaCluMOP-23
❑ 97Stu-83
❑ 97StuPrePG-83
❑ 97StuPrePS-83
❑ 97Top-321
❑ 97TopChr-108
❑ 97TopChrR-108
❑ 97TopDodRotY-2
❑ 97TopGal-119
❑ 97TopGalPPI-119
❑ 97Ult-355
❑ 97UltGolME-355
❑ 97UltPlaME-355
❑ 97UppDec-400
❑ 98Bow-228
❑ 98BowBes-58
❑ 98BowBesAR-58
❑ 98BowBesR-58
❑ 98BowChr-228
❑ 98BowChrGA-228
❑ 98BowChrGAR-228
❑ 98BowChrI-228
❑ 98BowChrIR-228
❑ 98BowChrR-228
❑ 98BowGolA-228
❑ 98BowInt-228
❑ 98CirThu-71
❑ 98CirThuRav-71
❑ 98CirThuSupRav-71
❑ 98ColCho-395
❑ 98CroRoy-70
❑ 98DodFanA-2
❑ 98DodMot-2
❑ 98DodPol-13
❑ 98DodSco-12
❑ 98DodScoP-12
❑ 98Don-65
❑ 98DonColL-338
❑ 98DonColP-623
❑ 98DonColS-65
❑ 98DonGolPP-65
❑ 98DonPre-73
❑ 98DonPreSeat-73
❑ 98DonPriCD-65
❑ 98DonPriCL-338
❑ 98DonPriCP-623
❑ 98DonSigA-49
❑ 98DonSigAC-66
❑ 98DonSigAM-67
❑ 98DonSilPP-65
❑ 98E-X2-54
❑ 98E-X2ECFut-54
❑ 98E-X2ECNow-54
❑ 98Fin-195
❑ 98FinNo--195
❑ 98FinNo-R-195
❑ 98FinRef-195
❑ 98FlaShoLeg0-69
❑ 98FlaShoLeg1-69
❑ 98FlaShoLeg2-69
❑ 98FlaShoLeg3-69
❑ 98FlaShoLegM-69
❑ 98FlaShoR0-69
❑ 98FlaShoR1-69
❑ 98FlaShoR2-69
❑ 98FlaShoR3-69
❑ 98Fle-483
❑ 98FleVin'-99
❑ 98FleVin'C-99
❑ 98Lea-139
❑ 98LeaFraDA-139
❑ 98LeaFraF-139
❑ 98LeaFraM-139
❑ 98LeaFraM-139
❑ 98LeaFraMDC-139
❑ 98LeaFraMDC-139
❑ 98LeaFraMZ2-139
❑ 98LeaRS-70
❑ 98LeaRSLHolo-70
❑ 98LeaRSLong-70
❑ 98LeaRTrue-70
❑ 98MetUni-71
❑ 98MetUniPMG-71
❑ 98Pac-332
❑ 98PacAur-144
❑ 98PacInv-107
❑ 98PacInvPBlue-107
❑ 98PacInvSilv-107
❑ 98PacOme-123
❑ 98PacOmeR-123
❑ 98PacOnl-375
❑ 98PacOnlR-375
❑ 98PacOnlWC-375
❑ 98PacPar-175
❑ 98PacParC-175
❑ 98PacParG-175
❑ 98PacParHS-175
❑ 98PacParPB-175
❑ 98PacParR-175
❑ 98PacPlaB-332
❑ 98PacRedT-332
❑ 98PacSil-332
❑ 98PinInsSG-17AB
❑ 98PinInsSG-17CD
❑ 98PinInsSGS-17AB
❑ 98PinInsSGS-17CD
❑ 98PinPer-74
❑ 98PinPerPP-74
❑ 98PinPerSftF-39
❑ 98PinSna-LAD2
❑ 98PinSna-LAD16
❑ 98Revo-75
❑ 98RevoSS-75
❑ 98SanBerS-15
❑ 98Sco-179
❑ 98Sco-262
❑ 98ScoRT-62
❑ 98ScoSS-PP80
❑ 98ScoSSAP-PP80
❑ 98SP Aut-115
❑ 98SpoIll-72
❑ 98SpoIllEE-72
❑ 98SpoIllFE-72
❑ 98SpoIllTaN-99
❑ 98SpoIllTaNEE-99
❑ 98SpoIllWSF-70
❑ 98SpoIllWSFEE-70
❑ 98SpoIllWSFFE-70
❑ 98SPxFin-94
❑ 98SPxFinR-94
❑ 98SPxFinS-94
❑ 98StaCluC-CS3
❑ 98StaCluC-CS5
❑ 98StaCluC-CS6
❑ 98StaCluFDI-10
❑ 98StaCluI-10
❑ 98StaCluOneK-10
❑ 98StaCluPP-10
❑ 98StaCluTIll-T6C
❑ 98StaCluTLme-T6C
❑ 98StaCluTLmo-T6C
❑ 98Stu-82
❑ 98StuGPP-82
❑ 98StuSPP-82
❑ 98Top-454
❑ 98TopChr-454
❑ 98TopChrR-454
❑ 98TopDevR-454
❑ 98TopDia-454
❑ 98TopGal-143
❑ 98TopGalGP-143
❑ 98TopGalOPP-143
❑ 98TopGalPPI-143
❑ 98TopGalPPIA-143
❑ 98TopGolLabC1-49
❑ 98TopGolLabC1B-49
❑ 98TopGolLabC1One-49
❑ 98TopGolLabC1R-49
❑ 98TopGolLabC2-49
❑ 98TopGolLabC2B-49
❑ 98TopGolLabC2One-49
❑ 98TopGolLabC2R-49
❑ 98TopGolLabC3-49
❑ 98TopGolLabC3B-49
❑ 98TopGolLabC3One-49
❑ 98TopGolLabC3R-49
❑ 98TopMiniC-454
❑ 98TopMysF-ILM15
❑ 98TopMysFR-ILM15
❑ 98TopOpeD-156
❑ 98TopSta-119
❑ 98TopStaB-119
❑ 98TopStaG-119
❑ 98TopStaGR-119
❑ 98TopStaS-119
❑ 98TopTek-11
❑ 98TopTekD-11
❑ 98UD3-71
❑ 98UD3-161
❑ 98UD3-251
❑ 98UD3DieCut-71
❑ 98UD3DieCut-161
❑ 98UD3DieCut-251
❑ 98Ult-198
❑ 98UltGolM-198
❑ 98UltMas-198
❑ 98UltPlaM-198
❑ 98UppDec-120
❑ 98UppDecR-45
❑ 98UppDecSF-73
❑ 99199Fin-194
❑ 99Bow-55
❑ 99BowBes-38
❑ 99BowBesAR-38
❑ 99BowBesR-38
❑ 99BowChr-55
❑ 99BowChrG-55
❑ 99BowChrGR-55
❑ 99BowChrI-55
❑ 99BowChrIR-55
❑ 99BowChrR-55
❑ 99BowGol-55
❑ 99BowInt-55
❑ 99CroRoyB-73
❑ 99CroRoyL-73
❑ 99CroRoyOD-73
❑ 99DodPol-13
❑ 99FinGolRef-194
❑ 99FinRef-194
❑ 99FlaShoLeg1-113
❑ 99FlaShoLeg2-113
❑ 99FlaShoLeg3-113
❑ 99FlaShoLegM1-113
❑ 99FlaShoLegM2-113
❑ 99FlaShoLegM3-113
❑ 99FlaShoR1-113
❑ 99FlaShoR2-113
❑ 99FlaShoR3-113
❑ 99Fle-160
❑ 99FleBri-60
❑ 99FleBri2G-60
❑ 99FleBriBlu-60
❑ 99FleBriGol-60
❑ 99FleMys-57
❑ 99FleMysG-57
❑ 99FleMysM-57
❑ 99FleSta9-160
❑ 99FleWarT-160
❑ 99Pac-222
❑ 99PacAur-93
❑ 99PacAurOD-93
❑ 99PacCroC-141
❑ 99PacCroCPB-141
❑ 99PacOme-121
❑ 99PacOmeC-121
❑ 99PacOmeG-121
❑ 99PacOmePB-121
❑ 99PacPar-118
❑ 99PacParC-118
❑ 99PacParG-118
❑ 99PacParHoloGold-118
❑ 99PacParHS-118
❑ 99PacParOD-118
❑ 99PacParPB-118
❑ 99PacParRed-118
❑ 99PacPlaB-222
❑ 99PacPri-74
❑ 99PacPriHB-74
❑ 99PacPriHG-74
❑ 99PacPriHM-74
❑ 99PacPriHP-74
❑ 99PacPriRed-74
❑ 99PacPriS-104
❑ 99PacPriS206-104
❑ 99PacPriS206R-104
❑ 99PacRed-222
❑ 99Rev-71
❑ 99RevPremDate-71
❑ 99RevRet-71
❑ 99RevShaSS-71
❑ 99SkyMolM-75
❑ 99SkyMolMX-75
❑ 99SkyThu-107
❑ 99SkyThuRant-107
❑ 99SkyThuRave-107
❑ 99SpoIll-169
❑ 99StaClu-130
❑ 99StaCluFDI-130
❑ 99StaCluOoaK-130
❑ 99StaCluPP-130
❑ 99ThuSkySupR-107
❑ 99Top-63
❑ 99TopBlaLC1-78
❑ 99TopBlaLC2-78
❑ 99TopBlaLC3-78
❑ 99TopChr-63
❑ 99TopChrR-63
❑ 99TopGal-35
❑ 99TopGalPP-35
❑ 99TopGalPPI-35
❑ 99TopGolL-78
❑ 99TopGolLC1-78
❑ 99TopGolLC2-78
❑ 99TopGolLOtO-78
❑ 99TopMVPP-63
❑ 99TopOpeD-35
❑ 99TopRedLC1-78
❑ 99TopRedLC2-78

❑ 99TopRedLC3-78
❑ 99TopSta-116
❑ 99TopStaFoil-116
❑ 99UppDec-121
❑ 99UppDecEL1-121
❑ 99UppDecEL2-121
❑ 99UppDecM-106
❑ 99UppDecMGS-106
❑ 99UppDecMHFS-106
❑ 99UppDecMP-106
❑ 99UppDecMSS-106
❑ 99Vic-205
Karsay, Steve
❑ 90ProAaA-179
❑ 90St.CatBJP-3472
❑ 91BluJayS-31
❑ 91Bow-12
❑ 91Cla/Bes-119
❑ 91Cla2-T60
❑ 91ClaGam-88
❑ 91MyrBeaHC-8
❑ 91MyrBeaHP-2942
❑ 91Sco-675
❑ 91UppDec-54
❑ 92Bow-158
❑ 92ClaFS7-193
❑ 92DunBluJC-1
❑ 92DunBluJF-1997
❑ 92ProFS7-171
❑ 92UppDecML-154
❑ 93Bow-83
❑ 93ClaFS7-78
❑ 93ExcFS7-244
❑ 93KnoSmoF-1249
❑ 94A'sMot-12
❑ 94Bow-220
❑ 94Bow-377
❑ 94ColC-13
❑ 94ColChoGS-13
❑ 94ColChoSS-13
❑ 94Don-197
❑ 94Fin-438
❑ 94FinJum-438
❑ 94FinRef-438
❑ 94Fla-93
❑ 94FlaWavotF-A3
❑ 94FleExtB-152
❑ 94FleExtBRS-10
❑ 94FleMajLP-19
❑ 94FleUpd-76
❑ 94FUnPac-8
❑ 94LeaGolR-9
❑ 94LeaLimR-32
❑ 94OPC-11
❑ 94Pin-247
❑ 94PinArtP-247
❑ 94PinMusC-247
❑ 94Sco-558
❑ 94ScoBoyoS-50
❑ 94ScoGolR-558
❑ 94ScoRoo-RT74
❑ 94ScoRooGR-RT74
❑ 94ScoRooSR-SU6
❑ 94Sel-179
❑ 94SelRooS-RS8
❑ 94SP-35
❑ 94SPDieC-35
❑ 94SPHol-18
❑ 94SPHolDC-18
❑ 94Spo-163
❑ 94SpoRooRS-TR14
❑ 94StaClu-631
❑ 94StaClu-708
❑ 94StaCluFDI-631
❑ 94StaCluFDI-708
❑ 94StaCluGR-631
❑ 94StaCluGR-708
❑ 94StaCluMOP-631
❑ 94StaCluMOP-708
❑ 94Top-131
❑ 94TopGol-131
❑ 94TopSpa-131
❑ 94TriPla-291
❑ 94Ult-109
❑ 94UppDec-20
❑ 94UppDecED-20
❑ 95ColCho-133
❑ 95ColChoGS-133
❑ 95ColChoSE-47
❑ 95ColChoSEGS-47
❑ 95ColChoSESS-47
❑ 95ColChoSS-133
❑ 95Don-203
❑ 95DonPreP-203
❑ 95Fin-21
❑ 95FinRef-21
❑ 95Fle-248
❑ 95Pin-358
❑ 95PinArtP-358
❑ 95PinMusC-358
❑ 95PinUps-US26
❑ 95Sco-194
❑ 95ScoGolR-194
❑ 95ScoPlaTS-194
❑ 95Sel-49
❑ 95SelArtP-49
❑ 95StaClu-345
❑ 95StaCluMOP-345
❑ 95StaCluSTWS-345
❑ 95Stu-184
❑ 95SumNthD-110
❑ 95Top-569
❑ 95Ult-319
❑ 95UltGolM-319
❑ 95UppDec-31
❑ 95UppDecED-31
❑ 95UppDecEDG-31
❑ 95UppDecSoaD-SD7
❑ 96ModA'sB-12
❑ 97A'sMot-12
❑ 97ColCho-412
❑ 97Don-351
❑ 97DonGolPP-351
❑ 97DonSilPP-351
❑ 97Fle-592
❑ 97FleTif-592
❑ 97Lea-281
❑ 97LeaFraM-281
❑ 97LeaFraMDC-281
❑ 97Sco-375
❑ 97ScoArtPWB-375
❑ 97ScoResC-375
❑ 97ScoShoS-375
❑ 97ScoShoSAP-375
❑ 98BufBisG-15
❑ 98Pin-109
❑ 98PinPreP-109
❑ 98ScoRT-55
❑ 98Top-84
❑ 98TopChr-84
❑ 98TopChrR-84
❑ 98TopDevR-84
❑ 98TopDia-84
❑ 98TopMiniC-84
❑ 98UppDec-178
Karvala, Kyle
❑ 94MarPhiC-10
❑ 94MarPhiF-3286
❑ 95BatCliTI-17
Kaseda, Yuki
❑ 89SalSpuCLC-130
❑ 89SalSpuP-1808
Kashiwabara, Junichi
❑ 79TCMJapPB-39
Kashiwada, Takashi
❑ 97ColChoU-U19
❑ 97NorTid-19
❑ 97NorTidB-19
❑ 98Fle-273
❑ 98Pac-369
❑ 98PacPlaB-369
❑ 98PacRedT-369
❑ 98PacSil-369
❑ 98Ult-192
❑ 98UltGolM-192
❑ 98UltMas-192
❑ 98UltPlaM-192
❑ 98UppDec-161
❑ 98UppDecNP-NP19
Kasich, Charles
❑ 29Zee-76
❑ 30Zee-87
❑ 32Zee-59
Kasko, Eddie
❑ 56RedBurB-11
❑ 57Top-363
❑ 58CarJayP-8
❑ 58Top-8A
❑ 58Top-8B
❑ 59RedBurBP-8
❑ 59RedShiBS-9
❑ 59Top-232
❑ 60Kah-17
❑ 60Lea-9
❑ 60Top-61
❑ 60TopVen-61
❑ 61Kah-22
❑ 61Pos-185A
❑ 61Pos-185B
❑ 61RedJayP-8
❑ 61Top-534
❑ 61TopStal-18
❑ 62Jel-119
❑ 62Kah-22
❑ 62Pos-119
❑ 62PosCan-119
❑ 62RedEnq-18
❑ 62RedJayP-7
❑ 62SalPlaC-147
❑ 62ShiPlaC-147
❑ 62Top-193
❑ 62TopStal-117
❑ 62TopVen-193
❑ 63Jel-128
❑ 63Kah-17
❑ 63Pos-128
❑ 63RedEnq-16
❑ 63RedFreBC-11
❑ 63RedJayP-5
❑ 63Top-498
❑ 65AstJayP-9
❑ 67AstTeal2-14
❑ 70OPC-489
❑ 70Top-489
❑ 71OPC-578
❑ 71Top-31
❑ 72OPC-218
❑ 72Top-218
❑ 73OPC-131
❑ 73Top-131A
❑ 73Top-131B
❑ 78TCM60I-249
❑ 80Red196T-1
❑ 81RedSoxBG2S-88
❑ 87AstSer1-14
❑ 87AstSer1-28
Kasper, Kevin
❑ 89EveGiaS-18
❑ 90CliGiaB-17
❑ 90CliGiaP-2556
❑ 91SanJosGC-7
❑ 91SanJosGP-19
❑ 92ShrCapF-3882
❑ 92ShrCapS-586
❑ 93ShrCapF-2769
Kaspryzak, Dennis
❑ 77JacSunT-11
Kast, Nick
❑ 95NewJerCTI-14
❑ 96PeoChiB-17
Kastelic, Bruce
❑ 82LynMetT-5
Kastelic, Matt
❑ 96ButCopKB-16
Kasunick, Joe
❑ 83ButCopKT-29
Katalinas, Ed
❑ 81TigDetN-127
Katcher, Sy
❑ 95BurBeeTI-35
Kath, Merlin
❑ 93LetMouF-4147
❑ 93LetMouSP-11
Kating, Jim
❑ 87BakDodP-11
❑ 88SanAntMB-9
❑ 89HunStaB-6
❑ 90HunStaB-17
Kato, Hideki
❑ 92SalSpuC-10
❑ 92SalSpuF-3764
Kato, Takaaki
❑ 98WilCubM-16
Kato, Toshio
❑ 79TCMJapPB-38
Kats, Bill
❑ 43CenFlo-15
❑ 45CenFlo-14
Katt, Ray
❑ 54Bow-121
❑ 54NewYorJA-28
❑ 55Bow-183
❑ 55GiaGolS-24
❑ 57Top-331
❑ 58Hir-57
❑ 58Top-284
❑ 60Top-468
❑ 61UniOil-P9
❑ 79TCM50-235
Katz, Bob
❑ 78ReaRem-8
Katz, Jason
❑ 96DanBraB-12
❑ 97MacBra-24
❑ 98DanQ-C-19
Katzaroff, Rob (Robert)
❑ 90JamExpP-8
❑ 91Cla/Bes-20
❑ 91HarSenLD-258
❑ 91HarSenP-640
❑ 91LinDriAA-258
❑ 92BinMetF-529
❑ 92BinMetS-63
❑ 92ClaFS7-26
❑ 92ProFS7-262
❑ 92SkyAA F-28
❑ 93PhoFirF-1528
❑ 93ShrCapF-2772
❑ 94MidAngOHP-13
❑ 95PorSeaDTI-8
Kaub, Keith
❑ 88JamExpP-1911
❑ 89MiaMirIS-21
❑ 89RocExpLC-14
❑ 90RocExpP-2704
Kauff, Bennie (Benjamin)
❑ 10OrnOvaPP-9
❑ 15CraJacE-160
❑ 15SpoNewM-92
❑ 16BF2FP-79
❑ 16FleBreD-49
❑ 16SpoNewM-94
❑ 17ColE13-92
❑ 17HolBreD-56
❑ 19W514-100
❑ 20W516-16
❑ 20W52-10
❑ 77SerSta-13
❑ 92ConTSN-484
❑ 94ConTSN-1269
❑ 94ConTSNB-1269
Kauffman, Ewing M.
❑ 93UppDecS-5
Kauflin, Dave
❑ 94BriTigF-3498
❑ 94StaCluDP-63
❑ 94StaCluDPFDI-63
Kaufman, Brad
❑ 93SpoIndC-10
❑ 93SpoIndF-3586
❑ 94SprSulC-14
❑ 94SprSulF-2032
❑ 95MemChiTI-14
❑ 96MemChiB-16
❑ 97LasVegS1A-19
❑ 98Las-12
❑ 98MobBayBTI-14
Kaufman, Curt
❑ 81NasSouTI-6
❑ 82ColCliP-24
❑ 82ColCliT-5
❑ 83ColCliT-11
❑ 84AngSmo-14
❑ 85Don-524
❑ 85EdmTraC-20
❑ 85Fle-305
❑ 85Top-61
❑ 85TopTif-61
❑ 92YanWIZ8-96
Kaufman, John
❑ 96ButCopKB-17
❑ 97St.PetDR-19
❑ 97St.PetDRUB-19
❑ 98St.PetDRM-8
Kaufman, Ron
❑ 82QuaCitCT-9
Kaufmann, Tony (Anthony)
❑ 21Exh-88
❑ 31CarMet-18
❑ 47TipTop-157
❑ 93ConTSN-927
Kaull, Kurt
❑ 83EriCarT-25
❑ 84SavCarT-5
Kausnicka, Jay
❑ 90VisOakCLC-72
Kautz, Scott
❑ 88HarSenP-862
Kautzer, Bill
❑ 75AppFoxT-8
❑ 76AppFoxT-10
Kavanagh, Mike
❑ 75ShrCapT-7
❑ 77ShrCapT-10
Kavanaugh, Marty
❑ 14B18B-18
Kavanaugh, Tim
❑ 83EriCarT-19
Kawabata, Kyle
❑ 95BatCliTI-18
❑ 96BatCliTI-4
❑ 97PieBolWB-15
❑ 98ClePhiM-10
❑ 98ClePhiUM-10
Kawabata, Yasuhiro
❑ 89VerBeaDS-13
Kawahara, Orin
❑ 96MauStiHWB-11
❑ 97EveAquG-13
❑ 98EveAquG-9
Kawakami, Mark
❑ 87HawRai-13
Kawano, Rye
❑ 91SalSpuC-11
❑ 91SalSpuP-2256
Kay, Belinda
❑ 90ColMudS-29
Kaye, Jeff
❑ 86ClePhiP-13
❑ 87ClePhiP-8
❑ 87PhiTas-xx
❑ 88ReaPhiP-872
Kaye, Justin
❑ 97WisTimR-15
❑ 98WisTimRM-6
Kaylor, Teddy
❑ 13Zee-36
❑ 14Zee-37
Kayser, Tom
❑ 77HolMilT-17
❑ 79HolMilT-30
❑ 80HolMilT-10
❑ 81HolMilT-3
Kaysner, Brent
❑ 95SpoIndTI-9
❑ 96LanLugB-14
Kazak, Eddie (Edward)
❑ 49EurSta-187
❑ 50Bow-36
❑ 51Bow-85
❑ 52Top-165
❑ 53Top-194
❑ 59SeaPop-5
❑ 79DiaGre-164
❑ 79TCM50-250
❑ 83TopRep5-165
❑ 91TopArc1-194
Kazama, Yuhito
❑ 95OdgRapTI-11
Kazanski, Ted
❑ 54Top-78
❑ 55Top-46
❑ 55TopDouH-5
❑ 57Top-27
❑ 58Top-36
❑ 59Top-99
❑ 59TopVen-99
❑ 94TopArc1-78
❑ 94TopArc1G-78
Kazmierczak, Bill (William)
❑ 87PeoChiP-28
❑ 88WinSpiS-7
❑ 90ChaKniTI-13
Kazmirski, Bob
❑ 96WesMicWB-12
Kea, Rusty
❑ 89GeoColC-14
❑ 90GeoColC-12
Keagle, Greg
❑ 93SpoIndC-11
❑ 93SpoIndF-3587
❑ 94RanCucQC-17
❑ 94RanCucQF-1634
❑ 94Top-753
❑ 94TopGol-753
❑ 94TopSpa-753
❑ 95MemChiTI-15
❑ 95UppDecML-63
❑ 95UppDecMLFS-63
❑ 96Bow-276
❑ 96BowFoi-276
❑ 96SigRooOJ-14
❑ 96SigRooOJS-14
❑ 96TigHebN-8
❑ 96Ult-346
❑ 96UltGolM-346
❑ 97TolMudHB-25
❑ 98PacOnl-277
❑ 98PacOnlR-277
❑ 98PacOnlWC-277
Kealey, Steve
❑ 69Top-224
❑ 71OPC-43
❑ 71Top-43
❑ 72OPC-146
❑ 72Top-146
❑ 73OPC-581
❑ 73Top-581
Keane, Johnny
❑ 29Zee-46
❑ 60Top-468
❑ 62CarJayP-7
❑ 62Top-198
❑ 63CarJayP-11
❑ 63CarJayP-12
❑ 63Top-166
❑ 64Top-413
❑ 65OPC-131
❑ 65Top-131
❑ 66Top-296
❑ 66TopVen-296
❑ 66YanTeal-5
❑ 81TCM60I-371
Kearney, Bob (Robert)
❑ 78CedRapGT-12
❑ 80PhoGiaVNB-15
❑ 81TacTigT-5
❑ 82TacTigT-27
❑ 83Don-539
❑ 83TopTra-52T
❑ 84Don-462
❑ 84Fle-449
❑ 84FleUpd-60
❑ 84MarMot-4
❑ 84Nes792-326
❑ 84Top-326
❑ 84TopSti-381
❑ 84TopTif-326
❑ 84TopTra-61T
❑ 84TopTraT-61T
❑ 85Don-362
❑ 85Fle-491
❑ 85MarMot-13
❑ 85OPC-386
❑ 85Top-679
❑ 85TopSti-335
❑ 85TopTif-679
❑ 86Don-74
❑ 86Fle-466
❑ 86MarMot-23
❑ 86OPC-13
❑ 86Top-13
❑ 86TopTif-13
❑ 87Don-445
❑ 87Fle-587
❑ 87FleGlo-587
❑ 87MarMot-12
❑ 87OPC-73
❑ 87Top-498
❑ 87TopTif-498
❑ 92TexLon-27
Kearney, Chad
❑ 94MarPhiF-3308
❑ 95MarPhiTI-11
Kearney, Ryan
❑ 98WatIndTI-14
Kearns, Austin
❑ 98BilMusTI-16
❑ 99199Fin-133
❑ 99Bow-200
❑ 99BowBes-160
❑ 99BowBesAR-160
❑ 99BowBesR-160
❑ 99BowChr-200
❑ 99BowChrG-200
❑ 99BowChrGR-200
❑ 99BowChrI-200
❑ 99BowChrIR-200
❑ 99BowChrR-200
❑ 99BowGol-200
❑ 99BowInt-200
❑ 99FinGolRef-133
❑ 99FinRef-133
❑ 99StaClu-338
❑ 99StaCluFDI-338
❑ 99StaCluOoaK-338
❑ 99StaCluPP-338
❑ 99Top-439
❑ 99TopChr-439
❑ 99TopChrR-439
❑ 99TopMVPP-439
Kearns, Bernard
❑ 21Zee-27
❑ 23Zee-107
Kearns, John
❑ 83WisRapTF-10
Kearse, Edward
❑ 46RemBre-14
❑ 47RemBre-7
❑ 47SmiClo-14
Keathley, Davan
❑ 96MedHatBJTI-14

Keathley, Don
❑ 91ModA'sP-3090
Keathley, Robin
❑ 83TriTriT-8
❑ 85BurRanT-22
Keating, Dave
❑ 89NiaFalRP-5a
❑ 90BriTigS-13
❑ 93SarWhiSC-16
❑ 93SarWhiSF-1366
❑ 94PriWilCC-12
❑ 94PriWilCF-1916
Keating, Dennis
❑ 79AppFoxT-2
❑ 80AppFoxT-24
Keating, Mike
❑ 90SavCarP-2074
Keating, Ray H.
❑ 14B18B-24
❑ 14CraJacE-95
❑ 14FatPlaT-21
❑ 15CraJacE-95
❑ 16FleBreD-50
❑ 20Zee-12
❑ 25Zee-69
❑ 26Zee-116
❑ 27Zee-91
❑ 28ExhPCL-32
❑ 28Zee-110
❑ 29Zee-113
❑ 30Zee-125
❑ 31Zee-68
Keatley, Greg
❑ 81OmaRoyT-14
❑ 82OmaRoyT-11
Keaveney, Jeff
❑ 96LowSpiB-12
❑ 97LowSpiB-11
❑ 98MicBatCM-18
Keck, Brian
❑ 96PorRocB-17
❑ 97AshTou-13
❑ 97SalAva-U7
❑ 98SalAvaC-14
Keck, Frank
❑ 24Zee-131
Keckler, Mike
❑ 85Ft.MyeRT-23
Keedy, Pat
❑ 81HolMilT-16
❑ 82HolMilT-16
❑ 84EdmTraC-118
❑ 85EdmTraC-1
❑ 86EdmTraP-16
❑ 87HawIslP-27
❑ 88Top-486
❑ 88TopClo-53
❑ 88TopTif-486
❑ 88TucTorC-22
❑ 88TucTorJP-14
❑ 88TucTorP-175
❑ 89IndTeal-16
Keefe, Bob
❑ 11SpoLifCW-196
Keefe, Dave
❑ 25Zee-43
❑ 27Zee-92
❑ 28Zee-111
❑ 45A'sTeal-18
❑ 46A'sTeal-9
❑ 47A'sTeal-16
❑ 48A'sTeal-13
❑ 49A'sTeal-18
❑ 93ConTSN-885
Keefe, George
❑ 87OldJudN-269
Keefe, Jamie (Jim)
❑ 92ClaDraP-69
❑ 92FroRowDP-42
❑ 92FroRowDPG-42
❑ 92FroRowDPS-42
❑ 93ClaGolF-199
❑ 94AugGreC-8
❑ 96MemChiB-17
Keefe, Kevin
❑ 79AlbDukTc-8
❑ 80AlbDukTc-17
❑ 81AlbDukTc-11
Keefe, Tim (Timothy)
❑ 67SpoHobFC-19
❑ 76ShaPiz-99
❑ 77BobParHoF-29
❑ 78DexHaloFP-26
❑ 80PerHaloFP-99
❑ 80SSPHOF-99
❑ 86OldJudN-9
❑ 87AllandGN-7
❑ 87BucN28-70A
❑ 87BucN28-70B
❑ 87OldJudN-267
❑ 87OldJudN-268
❑ 87TobLit-7
❑ 88AugBecN-19
❑ 88GandBCGCE-22
❑ 88GooN16-7
❑ 88SpoTimM-14
❑ 88WG1CarG-41
❑ 89EdgR.WG-7
❑ 90HOFStiB-4
❑ 90KalBatN-27
❑ 94OriofB-57
Keefer, Paul
❑ 89WelPirP-15
Keegan, Bob (Robert)
❑ 53Top-196
❑ 54Top-100
❑ 55Top-10
❑ 55TopDouH-51
❑ 56Top-54
❑ 57Top-99
❑ 58Top-200
❑ 59Top-86
❑ 59TopVen-86
❑ 60Top-291
❑ 77Top-436
❑ 91TopArc1-196
❑ 94TopArc1-100
❑ 94TopArc1G-100
Keegan, Ed
❑ 61Top-248
❑ 62Top-249
Keehn, Mike
❑ 83TriTriT-18
Keel, David
❑ 93SouOreAC-11
❑ 93SouOreAF-4078
❑ 94WesMicWC-11
❑ 94WesMicWF-2310
❑ 97TamYan-16
Keeler, Devo (Jay)
❑ 83WatIndF-9
Keeler, Willie
❑ 03BreE10-79
❑ 04FanCraAL-31
❑ 08RosComP-49
❑ 09AmeCarE90-1-62
❑ 09AmeCarE90-1-63
❑ 09AmeCarE90-1-64
❑ 09BriE97-15
❑ 09ColChiE-150
❑ 09RamT20-64
❑ 09T206-183
❑ 09T206-184
❑ 10W555-39
❑ 11SpoLifCW-197
❑ 11TurRedT-101
❑ 12ColRedB-150
❑ 12ColTinT-150
❑ 36Halof FP-15
❑ 39PC7AlbHoF-23
❑ 40PlaBal-237
❑ 48ExhHoF-19
❑ 50CalHOFW-44
❑ 53ArtHaloFP-50
❑ 63BazA-31
❑ 63HalofFB-25
❑ 72ClaCar-71
❑ 72FleFamF-40
❑ 72LauGreF-31
❑ 74CapPub-12
❑ 76ShaPiz-19
❑ 78DexHaloFP-27
❑ 80PacLeg-99
❑ 80PerHaloFP-23
❑ 80SSPHOF-23
❑ 82TCMGreH-17
❑ 84GalHaloFRL-19
❑ 89DodSmoG-12
❑ 89HOFStiB-51
❑ 90BasWit-74
❑ 90DodTar-399
❑ 90PerGreM-25
❑ 92YanWIZH-19
❑ 94ConTSN-1018
❑ 94ConTSNB-1018
❑ 94OriofB-81
❑ 96PitPosH-7
Keeline, Jason
❑ 91PulBraC-8
❑ 91PulBraP-4014
❑ 92MacBraC-19
❑ 92MacBraF-275
❑ 93MacBraC-12
❑ 93MacBraF-1407
❑ 94DurBulC-10
❑ 94DurBulF-333
❑ 94DurBulTI-10
Keely, Bob (Robert William)
❑ 54BraJohC-35
❑ 54Top-176
❑ 55BraJohC-35
❑ 56BraBilaBP-12
❑ 80Bra195T-33
❑ 94TopArc1-176
❑ 94TopArc1G-176
Keen, Vic
❑ 27MidBre-11
❑ 93ConTSN-976
Keenan, Brad
❑ 92BilMusF-3364
❑ 92BilMusSP-3
❑ 93PriRedC-15
❑ 93PriRedF-4174
❑ 93WesVirWC-11
❑ 93WesVirWF-2872
❑ 94ChaWheC-16
❑ 94ChaWheF-2699
Keenan, Chris
❑ 93BriTigC-13
❑ 93BriTigF-3663
Keenan, James
❑ 23WilChoV-77
❑ 87OldJudN-270
Keenan, Kerry
❑ 77AshTouT-12
❑ 79WauTimT-4
Keenan, Kevin
❑ 80ElmPioRST-10
Keene, Andre
❑ 92CliGiaC-10
❑ 92CliGiaF-3604
❑ 92MidLeaATI-23
❑ 92UppDecML-123
❑ 93ExcFS7-119
❑ 94SanJosGC-12
❑ 94SanJosGF-2824
Keene, Kurt
❑ 98TenKry-14
Keener, Jeff
❑ 82ArkTraT-4
❑ 83LouRedR-10
❑ 84LouRedR-22
❑ 85LouRedR-8
Keenum, Larry
❑ 76BatRouCT-12
Kees, Justin
❑ 98LetBlaDG-16
Keesey, James
❑ 28Zee-93
❑ 29Zee-91
❑ 31Zee-108
❑ 32Zee-104
Keeter, Lonnie
❑ 90WicWraRD-26
❑ 91HigDesMP-2413
Keeton, Buster (Rickey)
❑ 79VanCanT-10
❑ 82Don-618
❑ 82Fle-146
❑ 82Top-268
❑ 82TucTorT-13
❑ 83TucTorT-3
❑ 84OmaRoyT-6
❑ 85DomLeaS-203
❑ 85OmaRoyT-28
❑ 91AugPirC-27
❑ 91AugPirP-824
❑ 92SalBucC-27
❑ 92SalBucF-80
❑ 94BreMilB-44
❑ 96SpoIndB-2
❑ 97WilBluR-28
Keeton, Garry
❑ 83AppFoxFr-26
Keffer, Jamie
❑ 98AugGreM-30
Kehn, Chet
❑ 90DodTar-998
Kehoe, John
❑ 96HagSunB-11
Kehrli, Ed
❑ 93GleFalRC-17
❑ 93GleFalRF-3998
Keifer, Greg
❑ 94EveGiaC-15
❑ 94EveGiaF-3667
Keighley, Chris
❑ 95OdgRapTI-12
Keighley, Steve
❑ 91RocExpC-15
❑ 91RocExpP-2051
❑ 92WesPalBEC-6
❑ 92WesPalBEF-2092
Keim, Chris
❑ 89BilMusP-2062
❑ 90BilMusP-3216
Keiser, Earl
❑ 22Zee-29
❑ 23Zee-40
Keisler, Randy
❑ 99TeaBesR-44
❑ 99TeaBesRFS-13
❑ 99TeaBesRG-44
❑ 99TeaBesRS-44
Keister, Bill
❑ 11SpoLifCW-198
Keister, Tripp
❑ 92PitMetC-3
❑ 92PitMetF-3306
❑ 93St.LucMC-14
❑ 94St.LucMC-15
❑ 94St.LucMF-1207
❑ 95StLucMTI-18
Keiter, Bruce
❑ 98RocCubTI-15
Keitges, Jeff
❑ 89WauTimGS-24
❑ 90SanBerSB-6
❑ 90SanBerSCLC-110
❑ 90SanBerSP-2639
❑ 91SanBerSC-16
❑ 91SanBerSP-1993
Keith, Jeff
❑ 94EveGiaC-16
❑ 94EveGiaF-3649
❑ 95BurBeeTI-7
❑ 96BurBeeTI-7
❑ 97BakBlaB-18
❑ 97BakBlaTI-18
❑ 98SanJosGQ-23
Kekich, Mike
❑ 65Top-561
❑ 69Top-262
❑ 69YanPhoS-58
❑ 70OPC-536
❑ 70Top-536
❑ 70YanPhoS-18
❑ 71MLBOffS-490
❑ 71OPC-703
❑ 71Top-703
❑ 72OPC-138
❑ 72Top-138
❑ 73OPC-371
❑ 73SyrChiTI-11
❑ 73Top-371
❑ 74OPC-199
❑ 74Top-199
❑ 76OPC-582
❑ 76Top-582
❑ 76VenLeaS-131
❑ 78SanJosMMC-24
❑ 89PacSenL-73
❑ 89T/MSenL-57
❑ 90DodTar-400
❑ 90EliSenL-84
❑ 92YanWIZ6-64
❑ 92YanWIZ7-88
❑ 93RanKee-214
Kelbe, Frank
❑ 89WatIndS-27
Keliher, Paul
❑ 91PulBraC-2
Keliipuleole, Carl
❑ 88KinIndS-13
❑ 89CanIndB-18
❑ 89CanIndP-1300
❑ 89CanIndS-9
❑ 90Bes-137
❑ 90CanIndB-21
❑ 90CanIndP-1290
❑ 90CanIndS-8
❑ 90CMC-835
❑ 90IndTeal-22
❑ 91HarSenP-620
Keling, Korey
❑ 88OklSoo-14
❑ 89OklSoo-18
❑ 90OklSoo-23
❑ 91BoiHawC-25
❑ 91BoiHawP-3872
❑ 92CalLeaACL-31
❑ 92PalSprAC-10
❑ 92PalSprAF-834
❑ 92ProFS7-37
❑ 93PalSprAC-12
❑ 93PalSprAF-64
❑ 94MidAngF-2434
❑ 94MidAngOHP-14
❑ 95AusFut-15
❑ 95MidAngOHP-20
❑ 95MidAngTI-18
❑ 96LakElsSB-8
❑ 96MidAngB-20
❑ 96MidAngOHP-15
Kelipuleole, Carl
❑ 87BriYouC-4
Kell, George
❑ 45A'sTeal-19
❑ 47Exh-113
❑ 47TipTop-34
❑ 49Bow-26
❑ 49Lea-120
❑ 50Bow-8
❑ 50RoyDes-3
❑ 51Bow-46
❑ 51FisBakL-13
❑ 51R42SmaS-57
❑ 51TopCurA-5
❑ 52BerRos-28
❑ 52Bow-75
❑ 52RedMan-AL13
❑ 52RoyPre-6
❑ 52StaCalL-72A
❑ 52StaCalS-86A
❑ 52TipTop-19
❑ 52Top-246
❑ 52Whe-15A
❑ 52Whe-15B
❑ 53BowC-61
❑ 53RedMan-AL8
❑ 53RedSoxTI-14
❑ 53Top-138
❑ 54Bow-50
❑ 54RedHeaF-12
❑ 54RedMan-AL4A
❑ 54RedMan-AL4B
❑ 55Bow-213
❑ 56BalOriP-20
❑ 56BalOriP-31
❑ 56BalOriP-28
❑ 56Top-195
❑ 57Top-230
❑ 58Top-40
❑ 76TayBow4-31
❑ 77GalGloG-9
❑ 79TCM50-86
❑ 80MarExh-13
❑ 80PacLeg-118
❑ 80PerHaloFP-182
❑ 80PerHaloFPS-47
❑ 80SSPHOF-183
❑ 80TigGreT-1
❑ 81RedSoxBG2S-29
❑ 81TigDetN-10
❑ 82DiaCla-15
❑ 82GSGalAG-14
❑ 83TigAlKS-26
❑ 83TigAlKS-30
❑ 83TigAlKS-39
❑ 83TigAlKS-57
❑ 83TigAlKS-58
❑ 83TopRep5-246
❑ 84TCMPla1-5
❑ 86SpoDecG-24
❑ 86TigSpoD-10
❑ 88PacLegI-69
❑ 89HOFStiB-24
❑ 89PerCelP-22
❑ 90PacLeg-86
❑ 90PerGreM-59
❑ 91OriCro-233
❑ 91SweBasG-47
❑ 91TopArc1-138
❑ 92ActPacA-11
❑ 92ActPacA2-11G
❑ 92BazQua5A-11
❑ 93ActPacAC-11
❑ 93TedWil-39
❑ 93UppDecAH-79
❑ 93UppDecS-2
❑ 94UppDecAH-96
❑ 94UppDecAH1-96
❑ 98SpoIllTaN-14
❑ 98SpoIllTaNEE-14
Kell, Rob
❑ 93EriSaiC-12
❑ 93EriSaiF-3109
❑ 94ChaRivC-10
❑ 94ChaRivF-2667
❑ 95ChaRivUTIS-33
❑ 97TulDriTI-14
Kell, Skeeter (Everett)
❑ 52A'sTeal-13
❑ 52Bow-242
Kelleher, Frank
❑ 47SigOil-9
❑ 49BowPCL-27
❑ 49W72HolS-9
❑ 50W720HolS-15
❑ 53MotCoo-37
Kelleher, Hal
❑ 93ConTSN-968
Kelleher, John
❑ 21Nei-87
❑ 22E120-161
❑ 90DodTar-401
Kelleher, Mick
❑ 75TulOil7-7
❑ 76CubTri-12
❑ 76SSP-605
❑ 76VenLeaS-88
❑ 77Top-657
❑ 78SSP270-269
❑ 78Top-564
❑ 79Top-53
❑ 80Top-323
❑ 81Don-513
❑ 81Top-429
❑ 81TopTra-779
❑ 82Don-601
❑ 82Top-184
❑ 82TopTra-53T
❑ 83Top-79
❑ 93StoPorC-28
❑ 93StoPorF-761
Kelleher, Pat
❑ 97GreFalDTI-16
❑ 98VerBeaDM-27
Kellelmark, Joe
❑ 87VerBeaDP-19
Keller, Buzz (Carlton)
❑ 77ArkTraT-2A
❑ 77ArkTraT-2B
Keller, Charlie
❑ 39ExhSal-31A
❑ 39ExhSal-31B
❑ 39PlaBal-88
❑ 40PlaBal-9
❑ 41DouPlaR-83
❑ 41PlaBal-21
❑ 43YanSta-16
❑ 47Exh-114
❑ 47HomBon-25
❑ 47TipTop-52
❑ 47YanTeaT-16
❑ 48BluTin-48
❑ 48YanTeal-15
❑ 49Bow-209
❑ 49YanTeal-11
❑ 50AmeNut&CCP-9
❑ 50Bow-211
❑ 51Bow-177
❑ 75YanDyn1T-27
❑ 76TayBow4-34
❑ 77TCMTheWY-55
❑ 80MarExh-12
❑ 80RicBraT-12
❑ 83YanASFY-22
❑ 84OCoandSI-171
❑ 84TCMPla1-8
❑ 85TCMPhoC-29
❑ 89PacLegI-194
❑ 90SweBasG-22
❑ 91SweBasG-48
❑ 92YanWIZA-36
❑ 93TedWil-64
Keller, Clyde
❑ 87PanAmTUBI-4
❑ 87PanAmTURB-21
❑ 90Bes-82
❑ 90MidLeaASGS-37
❑ 90SprCarB-18
❑ 91MidLeaAP-MWL14
❑ 91SprCarC-18
❑ 91SprCarP-739
❑ 92ProFS7-318
❑ 92St.LucMCB-11
Keller, Dan
❑ 97UCLBruTI-9
Keller, Dave (David)
❑ 86TamTarP-8
❑ 88BilMusP-1802
❑ 89BilMusP-2048
❑ 90BurIndP-3026

❑ 91BurIndP-3320
❑ 91CanIndLD-100
❑ 91CanIndP-997
❑ 91LinDriAA-100
❑ 92KinIndC-26
❑ 92KinIndF-2491
❑ 93CarLeaAGF-31
❑ 93KinIndC-27
❑ 93KinIndF-2263
❑ 93KinIndTI-12
❑ 94KinIndC-23
❑ 94KinIndF-2660
❑ 96SouBenSHS-1
❑ 97BufBis-3
❑ 98BufBisG-16
Keller, Edward
❑ 94ConTSN-1113
Keller, Harold
❑ 47SenGunBP-3
Keller, Jeremy
❑ 96BilMusTI-16
Keller, Jerry
❑ 79RicBraT-19
❑ 81RicBraT-3
❑ 82RicBraT-10
❑ 83PorBeaT-7
❑ 84SyrChiT-10
❑ 85SyrChiT-18
❑ 90RicBra2ATI-13
Keller, Lloyd
❑ 23Zee-108
Keller, Phil
❑ 74AlbDukCa-70
❑ 74AlbDukTI-8
Keller, Rick
❑ 93HolLeg-13
Keller, Ron
❑ 77FriOneYW-51
Keller, Steve
❑ 89SpaPhiP-1055
❑ 89SpaPhiS-10
Kellert, Frank
❑ 55DodGolS-20
❑ 56Top-291
❑ 90DodTar-402
❑ 91OriCro-234
❑ 95TopArcBD-114
Kelley, Anthony
❑ 86ColAstP-16
❑ 86SouLeaAJ-22
❑ 87TucTorP-21
❑ 88TucTorC-2
❑ 88TucTorJP-15
❑ 88TucTorP-186
❑ 89TucTorC-3
❑ 89TucTorJP-10
❑ 89TucTorP-186
❑ 90FloStaLAS-9
❑ 90MiaMirIS-13
❑ 90MiaMirIS-11
❑ 90RocRedWGC-30
❑ 90StaFS7-73
Kelley, Brad
❑ 87PanAmTUBI-NNO
❑ 94PriRedC-28
❑ 94PriRedF-3280
Kelley, Chris
❑ 92ButCopKSP-23
❑ 93ButCopKSP-12
Kelley, Dean Alan
❑ 87OneYanP-29
❑ 88CarLeaAS-10
❑ 88PriWilYS-13
❑ 89Ft.LauYS-11
❑ 90WicWraRD-12
❑ 91LasVegSLD-286
❑ 91LasVegSP-242
❑ 91LinDriAAA-286
Kelley, Erskine
❑ 92WelPirC-12
❑ 92WelPirF-1338
❑ 93WelPirC-10
❑ 93WelPirF-3373
❑ 94AugGreC-9
❑ 94AugGreF-3020
❑ 96LynHilB-13
❑ 97LynHil-10
Kelley, Harry
❑ 37ExhFou-14
❑ 37OPCBatUV-121
❑ 38ExhFou-14
❑ 93ConTSN-721
Kelley, Jack
❑ 12ImpTobC-15
Kelley, Jason
❑ 94HunCubC-17
❑ 94HunCubF-3547
❑ 94SigRooDP-76
❑ 94SigRooDPS-76
❑ 94StaCluDP-70
❑ 94StaCluDPFDI-70
❑ 95Bow-7
❑ 97RocCub-18
❑ 97WilCubB-11
❑ 98RocCubM-15
❑ 98RocCubTI-16
Kelley, Joe
❑ 03BreE10-80
❑ 06FanCraNL-23
❑ 09BriE97-16
❑ 09T206-433
❑ 10CouT21-158
❑ 10CouT21-159
❑ 10CouT21-295
❑ 10RedCroT-125
❑ 10RedCroT-208
❑ 11SpoLifCW-199
❑ 12ImpTobC-27
❑ 14B18B-78A
❑ 14B18B-78B
❑ 24Zee-94
❑ 76ShaPiz-123
❑ 80PerHaloFP-123
❑ 80SSPHOF-123
❑ 89DodSmoG-13
❑ 89HOFStiB-35
❑ 90DodTar-403
❑ 94OriofB-96
❑ 94OriTeal-10
Kelley, M.
❑ 20W516-26
Kelley, Mike
❑ 80QuaCitCT-21
Kelley, Rich
❑ 91NiaFalRC-18
❑ 91NiaFalRP-3628
❑ 92FayGenF-2164
❑ 93FloStaLAF-18
❑ 93LakTigF-1304
❑ 94LakTigC-11
❑ 94LakTigF-3032
❑ 98RocRedWQ-16
Kelley, Richard
❑ 64Top-476
❑ 66OPC-84
❑ 66Top-84
❑ 66TopVen-84
❑ 67BraPho-17
❑ 67CokCapB-16
❑ 67OPC-138
❑ 67Top-138
❑ 67Top-214
❑ 68BraPos-19
❑ 68CokCapB-16
❑ 68Top-203
❑ 68TopVen-203
❑ 69MLBOffS-193
❑ 69Top-359
❑ 69TopTeaP-12
❑ 70MLBOffS-114
❑ 70OPC-474
❑ 70Top-474
❑ 72MilBra-178
❑ 72OPC-412
❑ 72Top-412
Kelley, Robert John
❑ 49AngTeal-17
Kelley, Rodd
❑ 94BoiHawC-16
❑ 94BoiHawF-3363
Kelley, Steve
❑ 75QuaCitAT-26
Kelley, Thomas
❑ 64Top-552
❑ 66OPC-44
❑ 66Top-44
❑ 66TopVen-44
❑ 71OPC-463
❑ 71Top-463
❑ 72OPC-97
❑ 72Top-97
Kelliher, Paul
❑ 91IdaFalBP-4332
❑ 91PulBraP-4008
Kellman, Howard
❑ 85IndIndTI-27
❑ 88IndIndP-525
❑ 89IndIndP-1216
Kellner, Alex
❑ 47Exh-115
❑ 49A'sTeal-19
❑ 49Bow-222
❑ 49PhiBul-28
❑ 50A'sTeal-15
❑ 50Bow-14
❑ 51A'sTeal-14
❑ 51Bow-57
❑ 51FisBakL-14
❑ 52A'sTeal-14
❑ 52Bow-226
❑ 52Top-201
❑ 53A'sTeal-14
❑ 53BowC-107
❑ 53ExhCan-64
❑ 54A'STEAI-13
❑ 54Bow-51
❑ 55A'sRodM-20
❑ 55A'sTeal-11
❑ 55Bow-53
❑ 56A'sPos-29
❑ 56Top-176
❑ 57Top-280
❑ 58Top-3
❑ 59Top-101
❑ 59TopVen-101
❑ 76A'sRodMC-13
❑ 79TCM50-55
❑ 80MarExh-14
❑ 83TopRep5-201
Kellner, Frank
❑ 90OscAstS-13
❑ 91OscAstC-19
❑ 91OscAstP-693
❑ 92JacGenF-4005
❑ 92JacGenS-336
❑ 93JacGenF-2114
❑ 94TucTorF-768
❑ 96TusTorB-14
❑ 97TucTorB-18
Kellner, Ryan
❑ 98YakBeaG-22
Kellogg, Geoff
❑ 90HelBreSP-17
❑ 91BelBreCB-4
❑ 91BelBreP-2099
❑ 92HigDesMC-18
❑ 93WicWraF-2976
Kelly, Bill
❑ 47SigOil-27
❑ 49W725AngTI-13
❑ 79NaSouTI-13
❑ 80IndIndTI-23
❑ 81IndIndTI-22
❑ 82OmaRoyT-7
Kelly, Brian
❑ 75CliPilT-4
Kelly, Bryan
❑ 83EvaTriT-4
❑ 85NasSouTI-7
❑ 86NasSouTI-14
❑ 87TolMudHP-29
❑ 98ChaRivDG-16
Kelly, Charles H.
❑ 87OldJudN-274
Kelly, Christopher
❑ 92IndIndF-NNO
❑ 98NewJerCM-16
Kelly, Eliqio
❑ 78NewWayCT-23
Kelly, Ernest
❑ 30Zee-6
❑ 30Zee-56
❑ 32Zee-38
❑ 33Zee-59
❑ 33Zee-158
Kelly, Gene
❑ 59RedBurBP-9
Kelly, George L.
❑ 20NatCarE-53
❑ 20W52-18
❑ 21E121So1-50
❑ 21E121So8-46
❑ 21Exh-89
❑ 21KoBreWSI-14
❑ 21Nei-119
❑ 22AmeCarE122-35
❑ 22E120-187
❑ 22W572-54
❑ 22W575-67
❑ 22WilPatV-15
❑ 23W501-72
❑ 23W503-6
❑ 23W515-32
❑ 23WilChoV-78
❑ 27AmeCarE126-60
❑ 27YorCarE-20
❑ 28StaPlaCE-42
❑ 28W502-20
❑ 28Yue-20
❑ 29ExhFou-7
❑ 30CubTeal-10
❑ 31W517-11
❑ 40PlaBal-142
❑ 49RemBre-12
❑ 50RemBre-11
❑ 68SCFOldT-23
❑ 73TCMAllG-10
❑ 76RowExh-8
❑ 76ShaPiz-138
❑ 77GalGloG-119
❑ 78DexHaloFP-28
❑ 80PacLeg-62
❑ 80PerHaloFP-138
❑ 80SSPHOF-138
❑ 82DiaCla-88
❑ 87ConSer2-45
❑ 89DodSmoG-14
❑ 89HOFStiB-8
❑ 90DodTar-404
❑ 91ConTSN-60
❑ 92ConTSN-561
❑ 93ConTSN-908
Kelly, Hal
❑ 79TulDriT-22
Kelly, Herbert
❑ 16Zee-56
Kelly, Jeff
❑ 96AugGreB-16
❑ 97CarMudC-6
Kelly, Jim
❑ 85RedWinA-17
❑ 86RedWinA-18
❑ 88KnoBluJB-5
❑ 89DunBluJS-9
❑ 90St.LucMS-13
Kelly, Joe (Joseph)
❑ 21Zee-123
❑ 23Zee-134
❑ 25Zee-112
❑ 88CapCodPPaLP-173
❑ 90YakBeaTI-17
Kelly, John
❑ 90JohCitCS-16
❑ 91Cla/Bes-166
❑ 91SavCarC-7
❑ 91SavCarP-1648
❑ 91SouAtlLAGP-SAL42
❑ 92ClaFS7-279
❑ 92ProFS7-319
❑ 92St.PetCC-20
❑ 92St.PetCF-2024
❑ 93ArkTraF-2810
❑ 93ExcFS7-100
❑ 93ExcLeaLF-11
❑ 94ArkTraF-3085
❑ 94ExcFS7-268
❑ 94PitMetC-12
❑ 94PitMetF-3518
❑ 95JacSunTI-17
❑ 96HonShaHWB-22
❑ 96StLucMTI-13
❑ 98OrlRayM-10
Kelly, John O.
❑ 87OldJudN-272
Kelly, Kenny
❑ 99BasAmeTP-57
❑ 99BasAmeTPG-57
❑ 99JustheS-29
❑ 99JustheSJB-29
Kelly, Kevin
❑ 89BurBraP-1623
❑ 89BurBraS-12
❑ 90BurBraB-21
❑ 90BurBraP-2345
❑ 90BurBraS-15
Kelly, King (Michael Joseph)
❑ 39PC7AlbHoF-36
❑ 50CalHOFW-45
❑ 53ArtHaloFP-51
❑ 74CapPub-15
❑ 75FlePio-8
❑ 76ShaPiz-36
❑ 77BobParHoF-30
❑ 80PerHaloFP-36
❑ 80SSPHOF-36
❑ 84GalHaloFRL-36
❑ 87AllandGN-8
❑ 87BucN28-9A
❑ 87BucN28-9B
❑ 87FouBasHN-6
❑ 87OldJudN-271
❑ 87TobLit-8
❑ 88AugBecN-20
❑ 88GandBCGCE-23
❑ 88GooN16-8
❑ 88SpoTimM-15
❑ 88WG1CarG-5
❑ 89EdgR.WG-9
❑ 89N526N7C-8
❑ 90PerGreM-61
❑ 94OriofB-48
❑ 94UppDecAH-23
❑ 94UppDecAH-102
❑ 94UppDecAH1-23
❑ 94UppDecAH1-102
❑ 94UppDecTAE-9
❑ 94UppDecTAELD-LD3
Kelly, Leonard
❑ 87BurExpP-1067
Kelly, Mike
❑ 87ElmPioBC-15
❑ 87ElmPioRC-15
❑ 88WinHavRSS-10
❑ 89LynRedSS-11
❑ 90Bes-191
❑ 90EasLeaAP-EL39
❑ 90NewBriRSB-11
❑ 90NewBriRSP-1330
❑ 90NewBriRSS-6
Kelly, Mike (Michael Raymond)
❑ 88CapCodPPaLP-10
❑ 89AlaGol-6
❑ 89AriStaB-14
❑ 91Cla/Bes-399
❑ 91ClaDraP-2
❑ 91ClaDraPP-2
❑ 91ClaGolB-BC16
❑ 91DurBulC-6
❑ 91DurBulUP-1
❑ 91TopGolS-2
❑ 92ClaBluBF-BC9
❑ 92ClaDraP-87
❑ 92ClaDraPFB-BC19
❑ 92ClaFS7-116
❑ 92ClaRedB-BC9
❑ 92GreBraF-1164
❑ 92GreBraS-235
❑ 92ProFS7-185
❑ 92SkyAA F-100
❑ 92UppDec-794
❑ 92UppDecCPH-CP2
❑ 92UppDecML-28
❑ 92UppDecML-275
❑ 92UppDecMLTPHF-TP4
❑ 93ClaFisN-6
❑ 93ClaFS7-10
❑ 93ClaGolF-18
❑ 93ClaGolLF-4
❑ 93ClaGolP-1
❑ 93ClaInsC-5
❑ 93ExcFS7-3
❑ 93RicBraBB-8
❑ 93RicBraF-197
❑ 93RicBraP-16
❑ 93RicBraRC-14
❑ 93RicBraRC-16
❑ 93UppDec-756
❑ 93UppDecGold-756
❑ 94Bow-261
❑ 94BowBes-B54
❑ 94BowBesR-B54
❑ 94BraLykP-14
❑ 94BraLykS-15
❑ 94BraUSPC-9D
❑ 94ClaGolF-144
❑ 94ColC-663
❑ 94ColChoGS-663
❑ 94ColChoSS-663
❑ 94ExcFS7-156
❑ 94Fin-329
❑ 94FinRef-329
❑ 94Fla-127
❑ 94FleExtB-203
❑ 94FleMajLP-20
❑ 94FleUpd-101
❑ 94LeaLimR-60
❑ 94Pin-534
❑ 94PinArtP-534
❑ 94PinMusC-534
❑ 94RicBraF-2860
❑ 94ScoRoo-RT159
❑ 94ScoRooGR-RT159
❑ 94Sel-386
❑ 94SigRoo-34
❑ 94SigRooHP-S5
❑ 94SigRooHPMP-S5
❑ 94SigRooHPMPS-S5
❑ 94SigRooHPS-S5
❑ 94SigRooS-34
❑ 94SpoRoo-101
❑ 94SpoRooAP-101
❑ 94TopTra-35T
❑ 94Ult-443
❑ 94UppDec-338
❑ 94UppDecED-338
❑ 94UppDecML-15
❑ 95ColCho-157
❑ 95ColChoGS-157
❑ 95ColChoSS-157
❑ 95Don-299
❑ 95DonPreP-299
❑ 95Fle-306
❑ 95LeaGolR-13
❑ 95Pac-6
❑ 95Pin-440
❑ 95PinArtP-440
❑ 95PinMusC-440
❑ 95PinUps-US21
❑ 95RicBraRC-6
❑ 95Sco-283
❑ 95ScoAi-AM16
❑ 95ScoGolR-283
❑ 95ScoPlaTS-283
❑ 95Sel-118
❑ 95SelArtP-118
❑ 95Spo-163
❑ 95SpoArtP-163
❑ 95StaClu-439
❑ 95StaCluMOP-439
❑ 95StaCluSTWS-439
❑ 95Top-61
❑ 95TopCyb-43
❑ 95Ult-348
❑ 95UltGolM-348
❑ 95UppDec-47
❑ 95UppDecED-47
❑ 95UppDecEDG-47
❑ 96Don-298
❑ 96DonPreP-298
❑ 96Fla-233
❑ 96Fle-295
❑ 96FleTif-295
❑ 96FleUpd-U122
❑ 96FleUpdTC-U122
❑ 96IndIndB-12
❑ 96Pin-363
❑ 96PinAfi-115
❑ 96PinAfiAP-115
❑ 96PinFoil-363
❑ 96Sco-180
❑ 96Sel-139
❑ 96SelArtP-139
❑ 96SelCer-60
❑ 96SelCerAP-60
❑ 96SelCerCB-60
❑ 96SelCerCR-60
❑ 96SelCerMB-60
❑ 96SelCerMG-60
❑ 96SelCerMR-60
❑ 96Sum-68
❑ 96SumAbo&B-68
❑ 96SumArtP-68
❑ 96SumFoi-68
❑ 96Ult-462
❑ 96UltGolM-462
❑ 97AriStaBG-13
❑ 97IndInd-10
❑ 97PacPriGotD-GD126
❑ 98ColCho-506
❑ 98DevRayP-22
❑ 98Fle-416
❑ 98PacOnl-710
❑ 98PacOnlR-710
❑ 98PacOnlWC-710
❑ 99Fle-396
❑ 99FleSta9-396
❑ 99FleWarT-396
❑ 99Pac-411
❑ 99PacPlaB-411
❑ 99PacRed-411
Kelly, Pat
❑ 95RicBraRC-7
Kelly, Pat (Dale Patrick)
❑ 75QuaCitAT-17
❑ 78SyrChiT-12
❑ 79SyrChiTI-6
❑ 79Top-714
❑ 80OPC-329
❑ 80SyrChiT-15
❑ 80SyrChiTI-12
❑ 80Top-674
❑ 83GleFalWST-11
❑ 86ChaRaiP-11

❑ 88WicPilRD-40
❑ 89WicChaR-15
❑ 89WicStaR-15
❑ 89WicUpdR-2
❑ 89WicWraR-6
❑ 90CMC-525
❑ 90CMC-787
❑ 90LasVegSC-22
❑ 90LasVegSP-136
❑ 90ProAAAF-25
❑ 90SumBraB-8
❑ 90SumBraP-2440
❑ 91DurBulP-1555
❑ 91RocExpC-27
❑ 91RocExpP-2062
❑ 92GreBraF-1160
❑ 92GreBraS-236
❑ 92IndIndF-1875
❑ 92IndIndS-199
❑ 93ChaLooF-2375
❑ 93DurBulC-10
❑ 93DurBulF-492
❑ 93DurBulTI-11
❑ 94ChaLooF-1373
❑ 94RicBraF-2852
❑ 95HarSenTI-30
❑ 96HarSenB-1

Kelly, Pat (Harold Patrick)

❑ 69RoySol-10
❑ 69RoyTeal-7
❑ 69Top-619
❑ 69TopTeaP-7
❑ 70MLBOffS-222
❑ 70OPC-57
❑ 70RoyTeal-16
❑ 70Top-57
❑ 71OPC-413
❑ 71oySigST-10
❑ 71Top-413
❑ 72MilBra-179
❑ 72OPC-326
❑ 72Top-326
❑ 72WhiSox-6
❑ 72WhiSoxC-3
❑ 72WhiSoxTI1-9
❑ 73OPC-261
❑ 73Top-261
❑ 74Kel-47
❑ 74OPC-46
❑ 74Top-46
❑ 74TopSta-156
❑ 75OPC-82
❑ 75Top-82
❑ 75TopMin-82
❑ 76OPC-212
❑ 76SSP-152
❑ 76Top-212
❑ 77BalOriP-11
❑ 77Top-469
❑ 78BalOriP-13
❑ 78Top-616
❑ 79Top-188
❑ 80BalOriP-10
❑ 80Top-543
❑ 81Don-600
❑ 82Fle-372
❑ 82Top-417
❑ 89PacSenL-134
❑ 91OriCro-235
❑ 91PacSenL-56

Kelly, Pat F.

❑ 88OneYanP-2043
❑ 89PriWilCS-10
❑ 89Sta-89
❑ 89TexLeaAGS-1
❑ 90AlbYanB-16
❑ 90AlbYanP-1041
❑ 90AlbYanSt-8
❑ 90EasLeaAP-EL21
❑ 90ProAaA-32
❑ 90TopMag-63
❑ 91AlbYanCB-1
❑ 91Bow-155
❑ 91Cla3-T44
❑ 91ColCliLD-110
❑ 91ColCliP-10
❑ 91ColCliP-602
❑ 91DonRoo-1
❑ 91FleUpd-46
❑ 91LeaGolR-BC17
❑ 91LinDriAAA-110
❑ 91ScoRoo-107T
❑ 91StaClu-381
❑ 91TopTra-67T
❑ 91TopTraT-67T
❑ 91Ult-381
❑ 91UltUpd-41
❑ 91UppDec-76
❑ 92Bow-535
❑ 92Cla1-T48
❑ 92Don-370
❑ 92Fle-233
❑ 92Lea-104
❑ 92LeaBlaG-104
❑ 92OPC-612
❑ 92OPCPre-71
❑ 92PanSti-137
❑ 92Pin-54
❑ 92PinTea2-7
❑ 92ProFS7-108
❑ 92Sco-185
❑ 92Sco100RS-5
❑ 92StaClu-89
❑ 92Stu-213
❑ 92Top-612
❑ 92TopDeb91-98
❑ 92TopGol-612
❑ 92TopGolW-612
❑ 92TopMic-612
❑ 92TriPla-46
❑ 92TriPla-193
❑ 92Ult-102
❑ 92UppDec-435
❑ 92UppDecS-1
❑ 93Bow-187
❑ 93Don-503
❑ 93Fla-246
❑ 93Fle-280
❑ 93Lea-447
❑ 93OPC-24
❑ 93PacSpa-206
❑ 93PanSti-150
❑ 93Pin-134
❑ 93Sco-370
❑ 93Sel-255
❑ 93StaClu-155
❑ 93StaCluFDI-155
❑ 93StaCluMOP-155
❑ 93Stu-111
❑ 93Top-196
❑ 93TopGol-196
❑ 93TopInaM-196
❑ 93TopInaR-196
❑ 93TopMic-196
❑ 93Ult-242
❑ 93UppDec-215
❑ 93UppDecGold-215
❑ 93YanStaC-16
❑ 94Bow-549
❑ 94ColC-483
❑ 94ColChoGS-483
❑ 94ColChoSS-483
❑ 94Don-483
❑ 94Fin-63
❑ 94FinRef-63
❑ 94Fla-321
❑ 94Fle-235
❑ 94FleExtB-131
❑ 94Lea-51
❑ 94OPC-156
❑ 94Pac-426
❑ 94PanSti-101
❑ 94Pin-197
❑ 94PinArtP-197
❑ 94PinMusC-197
❑ 94Sco-397
❑ 94ScoGolR-397
❑ 94Sel-142
❑ 94StaClu-52
❑ 94StaCluFDI-52
❑ 94StaCluGR-52
❑ 94StaCluMOP-52
❑ 94StaCluT-196
❑ 94StaCluTFDI-196
❑ 94Stu-213
❑ 94Top-88
❑ 94TopGol-88
❑ 94TopSpa-88
❑ 94TriPla-274
❑ 94Ult-95
❑ 94UppDec-264
❑ 94UppDecED-264
❑ 95ColCho-512
❑ 95ColChoGS-512
❑ 95ColChoSS-512
❑ 95Don-93
❑ 95DonPreP-93
❑ 95Fla-285
❑ 95Fle-73
❑ 95Lea-242
❑ 95Pin-9
❑ 95PinArtP-9
❑ 95PinMusC-9
❑ 95Sco-369
❑ 95ScoGolR-369
❑ 95ScoPlaTS-369
❑ 95StaClu-394
❑ 95StaCluMOP-394
❑ 95StaCluSTWS-394
❑ 95StaCluVR-207
❑ 95StaCluVRMO-207
❑ 95TamYanYI-14
❑ 95Top-468
❑ 95TopCyb-262
❑ 95Ult-82
❑ 95UltGolM-82
❑ 95UppDec-442
❑ 95UppDecED-442
❑ 95UppDecEDG-442
❑ 96ColCho-631
❑ 96ColChoGS-631
❑ 96ColChoSS-631
❑ 96DonPreP-71
❑ 96Fle-186
❑ 96FleTif-186
❑ 96MLBPin-18
❑ 96Sco-93
❑ 96StaClu-363
❑ 96StaCluMOP-363
❑ 96Ult-387
❑ 96UltGolM-387
❑ 96UppDec-404
❑ 97PacPriGotD-GD74
❑ 97Sco-440
❑ 97ScoArtPWB-440
❑ 97ScoResC-440
❑ 97ScoShoS-440
❑ 97ScoShoSAP-440
❑ 98PacInvGems-74
❑ 98Sco-102
❑ 98SyrSkyG-17
❑ 98Top-61
❑ 98TopChr-61
❑ 98TopChrR-61
❑ 98TopDevR-61
❑ 98TopDia-61
❑ 98TopMiniC-61
❑ 98YanSco-8
❑ 98YanScoP-8

Kelly, Rafael

❑ 75QuaCitAT-13
❑ 76QuaCitAT-17

Kelly, Reynolds

❑ 22Zee-130
❑ 23Zee-163

Kelly, Rich

❑ 92FayGenC-14
❑ 93ClaGolF-52
❑ 93SouAtlLAPI-18

Kelly, Robert Edward

❑ 49AngTeal-18
❑ 49W725AngTI-14
❑ 52Top-348
❑ 55SeaPop-11
❑ 58RedEnq-21
❑ 83TopRep5-348

Kelly, Roberto

❑ 83GreHorT-19
❑ 84GreHorT-4
❑ 86AlbYanT-2
❑ 87ColCliP-14
❑ 87ColCliP-14
❑ 87ColCliT-22
❑ 87IntLeaAT-4
❑ 88Don-635
❑ 88DonReaBY-635
❑ 88DonRoo-16
❑ 88Fle-212
❑ 88FleGlo-212
❑ 88Sco-634
❑ 88ScoGlo-634
❑ 88TopTra-57T
❑ 88TopTraT-57T
❑ 89Bow-183
❑ 89BowTif-183
❑ 89ClaTraP-167
❑ 89Don-433
❑ 89DonBasB-273
❑ 89Fle-256
❑ 89FleGlo-256
❑ 89PanSti-395
❑ 89Sco-487
❑ 89ScoHot1R-90
❑ 89ScoYouS2-25
❑ 89Top-691
❑ 89TopBig-152
❑ 89TopTif-691
❑ 89ToyRoo-18
❑ 89UppDec-590
❑ 89YanScoNW-18
❑ 90AlbDecGB-3
❑ 90Bow-444
❑ 90BowTif-444
❑ 90ClaUpd-T27
❑ 90Don-192
❑ 90DonBesA-94
❑ 90Fle-446
❑ 90FleCan-446
❑ 90Lea-17
❑ 90OPC-109
❑ 90PanSti-119
❑ 90PubIntS-538
❑ 90PubIntS-597
❑ 90Sco-100
❑ 90Sco100S-57
❑ 90Spo-184
❑ 90Top-109
❑ 90TopBig-247
❑ 90TopSti-312
❑ 90TopTif-109
❑ 90TopTVY-31
❑ 90UppDec-193
❑ 90YanScoNW-6
❑ 91Bow-166
❑ 91ClaGam-28
❑ 91Don-400
❑ 91Don-538
❑ 91Fle-668
❑ 91Lea-38
❑ 91OPC-11
❑ 91PanCanT1-31
❑ 91PanCanT1-47
❑ 91PanFreS-328
❑ 91PanSti-268
❑ 91RedFolS-57
❑ 91Sco-119
❑ 91Sco100S-96
❑ 91ScoPro-119
❑ 91Sev3DCN-9
❑ 91SevCoi-NE9
❑ 91StaClu-319
❑ 91Stu-94
❑ 91Top-11
❑ 91TopCraJ2-16
❑ 91TopDesS-11
❑ 91TopMic-11
❑ 91TopTif-11
❑ 91Ult-235
❑ 91UppDec-49
❑ 91UppDec-372
❑ 92Bow-12
❑ 92Cla2-T81
❑ 92ClaGam-51
❑ 92Don-73
❑ 92DonMcD-4
❑ 92Fle-234
❑ 92Hig5-87
❑ 92Lea-156
❑ 92LeaBlaG-156
❑ 92OPC-266
❑ 92OPCPre-83
❑ 92PanSti-140
❑ 92Pin-114
❑ 92RedFolS-53
❑ 92Sco-324
❑ 92Sco100S-96
❑ 92ScoImpP-80
❑ 92StaClu-393
❑ 92Stu-214
❑ 92Top-266
❑ 92TopGol-266
❑ 92TopGolW-266
❑ 92TopKid-88
❑ 92TopMic-266
❑ 92TriPla-72
❑ 92Ult-103
❑ 92UltAllS-7
❑ 92UppDec-577
❑ 92YanWIZ8-97
❑ 93Bow-610
❑ 93ClaGam-47
❑ 93DiaMar-60
❑ 93Don-313
❑ 93DonDiaK-DK12
❑ 93Fin-120
❑ 93FinRef-120
❑ 93Fla-26
❑ 93Fle-393
❑ 93FleFinE-15
❑ 93FunPac-169
❑ 93Lea-289
❑ 93OPC-79
❑ 93OPCPre-109
❑ 93PacJugC-29
❑ 93PacSpa-401
❑ 93PanSti-295
❑ 93Pin-520
❑ 93RedFolS-50
❑ 93RedKah-11
❑ 93Sco-438
❑ 93Sel-64
❑ 93SelRoo-20T
❑ 93SP-209
❑ 93StaClu-632
❑ 93StaCluFDI-632
❑ 93StaCluM-162
❑ 93StaCluMOP-632
❑ 93Stu-23
❑ 93Top-60
❑ 93TopGol-60
❑ 93TopInaM-60
❑ 93TopInaR-60
❑ 93TopMic-60
❑ 93TopTra-105T
❑ 93Ult-329
❑ 93UppDec-47
❑ 93UppDec-473
❑ 93UppDec-655
❑ 93UppDecGold-47
❑ 93UppDecGold-473
❑ 93UppDecGold-655
❑ 94Bow-626
❑ 94BraLykP-15
❑ 94ColC-484
❑ 94ColChoGS-484
❑ 94ColChoSS-484
❑ 94Don-344
❑ 94DonSpeE-344
❑ 94Fin-163
❑ 94FinPre-163P
❑ 94FinRef-163
❑ 94Fla-353
❑ 94Fle-412
❑ 94FleExtB-204
❑ 94FleUpd-102
❑ 94Lea-40
❑ 94LeaL-84
❑ 94OPC-139
❑ 94Pac-149
❑ 94PanSti-162
❑ 94Pin-286
❑ 94PinArtP-286
❑ 94PinMusC-286
❑ 94Sco-334
❑ 94ScoGolR-334
❑ 94ScoRoo-RT65
❑ 94ScoRooCP-CP3
❑ 94ScoRooGR-RT65
❑ 94Sel-312
❑ 94SP-51
❑ 94SPDieC-51
❑ 94SpoRoo-5
❑ 94SpoRooAP-5
❑ 94StaClu-372
❑ 94StaCluFDI-372
❑ 94StaCluGR-372
❑ 94StaCluMOP-372
❑ 94Stu-36
❑ 94Top-457
❑ 94TopGol-457
❑ 94TopSpa-457
❑ 94TopTra-103T
❑ 94TriPla-213
❑ 94Ult-171
❑ 94UppDec-387
❑ 94UppDecED-387
❑ 95Baz-52
❑ 95Bow-300
❑ 95ColCho-158
❑ 95ColCho-546T
❑ 95ColChoGS-158
❑ 95ColChoSE-61
❑ 95ColChoSEGS-61
❑ 95ColChoSESS-61
❑ 95ColChoSS-158
❑ 95DodMot-6
❑ 95Don-301
❑ 95DonPreP-301
❑ 95DonTopotO-266
❑ 95Fin-33
❑ 95Fin-297
❑ 95FinRef-33
❑ 95FinRef-297
❑ 95Fla-102
❑ 95Fle-307
❑ 95FleUpd-107
❑ 95Lea-377
❑ 95LeaLim-149
❑ 95Pac-7
❑ 95Pin-254
❑ 95PinArtP-254
❑ 95PinMusC-254
❑ 95PinUps-US24
❑ 95Sco-59
❑ 95ScoGolR-59
❑ 95ScoHaloG-HG45
❑ 95ScoPlaTS-59
❑ 95Sel-230
❑ 95SelArtP-230
❑ 95Spo-113
❑ 95SpoArtP-113
❑ 95StaClu-219
❑ 95StaClu-414
❑ 95StaCluFDI-219
❑ 95StaCluMOP-219
❑ 95StaCluMOP-414
❑ 95StaCluSTWS-219
❑ 95StaCluSTWS-414
❑ 95StaCluVR-212
❑ 95StaCluVRMO-212
❑ 95Stu-57
❑ 95Top-532
❑ 95TopCyb-317
❑ 95TopEmb-46
❑ 95TopEmbGI-46
❑ 95TopTra-139T
❑ 95Ult-127
❑ 95UltGolM-127
❑ 95UppDec-43
❑ 95UppDec-326
❑ 95UppDec-461
❑ 95UppDecED-43
❑ 95UppDecED-326
❑ 95UppDecEDG-43
❑ 95UppDecEDG-326
❑ 95UppDecSE-139
❑ 95UppDecSEG-139
❑ 96Cir-56
❑ 96CirRav-56
❑ 96ColCho-184
❑ 96ColCho-336
❑ 96ColCho-604
❑ 96ColChoGS-184
❑ 96ColChoGS-336
❑ 96ColChoGS-604
❑ 96ColChoSS-184
❑ 96ColChoSS-336
❑ 96ColChoSS-604
❑ 96Don-543
❑ 96DonPreP-543
❑ 96EmoXL-81
❑ 96Fla-115
❑ 96Fle-439
❑ 96FleTif-439
❑ 96FleUpd-U55
❑ 96FleUpdTC-U55
❑ 96LeaSigA-125
❑ 96LeaSigAG-125
❑ 96LeaSigAS-125
❑ 96Pac-114
❑ 96PacHom-HP15
❑ 96Sco-457
❑ 96Ult-375
❑ 96UltGolM-375
❑ 96UppDec-501U
❑ 97Cir-99
❑ 97CirRav-99
❑ 97ColCho-377
❑ 97Fle-146
❑ 97FleTif-146
❑ 97Lea-298
❑ 97LeaFraM-298
❑ 97LeaFraMDC-298
❑ 97Pac-138
❑ 97PacLatotML-12
❑ 97PacLigB-138
❑ 97PacPri-45
❑ 97PacPriLB-45
❑ 97PacPriP-45
❑ 97PacSil-138
❑ 97Sco-454
❑ 97ScoArtPWB-454
❑ 97ScoResC-454
❑ 97ScoShoS-454
❑ 97ScoShoSAP-454
❑ 98Fle-570
❑ 98Pac-189
❑ 98PacLatotML-31
❑ 98PacOme-240
❑ 98PacOmeR-240
❑ 98PacOnl-738
❑ 98PacOnlR-738
❑ 98PacOnlWC-738
❑ 98PacPar-106
❑ 98PacParC-106

❑ 98PacParG-106
❑ 98PacParHS-106
❑ 98PacParPB-106
❑ 98PacParR-106
❑ 98PacPlaB-189
❑ 98PacRedT-189
❑ 98PacSil-189
❑ 98PinSna-TR10
❑ 98Top-408
❑ 98TopChr-408
❑ 98TopChrR-408
❑ 98TopDevR-408
❑ 98TopDia-408
❑ 98TopMiniC-408
❑ 98Ult-424
❑ 98UltGolM-424
❑ 98UltMas-424
❑ 98UltPlaM-424
❑ 98UppDec-739
❑ 99Fle-472
❑ 99FleSta9-472
❑ 99FleWarT-472
❑ 99Pac-427
❑ 99PacAur-192
❑ 99PacAurOD-192
❑ 99PacCroC-286
❑ 99PacCroCPB-286
❑ 99PacPlaB-427
❑ 99PacRed-427
❑ 99Top-116
❑ 99TopChr-116
❑ 99TopChrR-116
❑ 99TopMVPP-116

Kelly, Tim
❑ 86BakDodP-17
❑ 87PalSprP-18
❑ 88MidAngGS-3

Kelly, Tom
❑ 73TacTwiC-12
❑ 74TacTwiC-25
❑ 75TacTwiK-19
❑ 77TacTwiDQ-10
❑ 82OrlTwi8SCT-12
❑ 82OrlTwiT-13
❑ 83TwiTeal-26
❑ 83TwiTeal-34
❑ 84MinTwiP-19
❑ 84TwiTeal-27
❑ 85TwiPos-14
❑ 85TwiTeal-12
❑ 85TwiTeal-30
❑ 86TwiTeal-28
❑ 87Top-618
❑ 87TopTif-618
❑ 87TwiPos-12
❑ 87TwiTeal-7
❑ 88Top-194
❑ 88TopTif-194
❑ 89DonAll-10
❑ 89DonPop-10
❑ 89Top-14
❑ 89TopGloA-1
❑ 89TopTif-14
❑ 90OPC-429
❑ 90Top-429
❑ 90TopTif-429
❑ 91DodPho-1
❑ 91OPC-201
❑ 91Top-201
❑ 91TopDesS-201
❑ 91TopMic-201
❑ 91TopTif-201
❑ 92OPC-459
❑ 92Top-459
❑ 92TopGol-459
❑ 92TopGolW-459
❑ 92TopMic-459
❑ 93RedFolS-117
❑ 93Top-509
❑ 93TopGol-509
❑ 93TopInaM-509
❑ 93TopInaR-509
❑ 93TopMic-509

Kelly, Van
❑ 71RicBraTI-9

Kelly, William J.
❑ 09SpoNewSM-70
❑ 12ColRedB-151A
❑ 12ColRedB-151B
❑ 12T207-89
❑ 48AngTeal-14
❑ 49AngTeal-19

Kelman, Paul
❑ 33Zee-16

Kelso, Bill
❑ 65OPC-194
❑ 65Top-194
❑ 66SeaPop-9
❑ 67SeaPop-8
❑ 67Top-367
❑ 68Top-511
❑ 92AubAstC-29
❑ 92AubAstF-1371

Kelso, Jeff
❑ 88BenBucL-9
❑ 89BenBucL-22
❑ 90PalSprACLC-214
❑ 90PalSprAP-2590

Keltner, Ken
❑ 36OveCanR-28
❑ 36R31Pre-G11
❑ 39ExhSal-32
❑ 39GouPreR303A-28
❑ 39GouPreR303B-16
❑ 39WorWidGTP-28
❑ 41DouPlaR-79
❑ 46SpoExcW-1-11
❑ 47Exh-116
❑ 47HomBon-26
❑ 47IndTeal-15
❑ 47IndVanPP-14
❑ 48IndTeal-17
❑ 49Bow-125
❑ 49IndTeal-15
❑ 49IndVisEl-8
❑ 49Lea-45
❑ 50AmeNut&CCP-10
❑ 50Bow-186
❑ 50RedSoxTI-9
❑ 53IndPenCBP-17
❑ 76GrePlaG-19
❑ 76TayBow4-35
❑ 79DiaGre-288
❑ 83TCMPla1942-11
❑ 89PacLegI-143
❑ 89SweBasG-87
❑ 91UppDecS-4
❑ 94ConTSN-1043
❑ 94ConTSNB-1043

Kelton, David
❑ 99Bow-368
❑ 99BowGol-368
❑ 99BowInt-368

Kemmerer, Russ
❑ 55Bow-222
❑ 55DonWin-28
❑ 55Top-18
❑ 55TopDouH-3
❑ 58SeaTeal-15
❑ 58Top-137
❑ 59SenTealW-9
❑ 59Top-191
❑ 59TopVen-191
❑ 60Top-362
❑ 61Top-56
❑ 61TopStal-121
❑ 62Top-576
❑ 62WhiSoxJP-4
❑ 63Top-338

Kemmler, Rudolph
❑ 87OldJudN-276A
❑ 87OldJudN-276B

Kemnitz, Brent
❑ 85AncGlaPTI-17
❑ 86AncGlaPTI-17
❑ 87AncGlaP-17
❑ 90WicStaSGD-41

Kemp, Bill
❑ 90GeoColC-13

Kemp, Hugh
❑ 84CedRapRT-7
❑ 87NasSouTI-11
❑ 88NasSouC-7
❑ 88NasSouP-479
❑ 88NasSouTI-15
❑ 88TriAAAP-27
❑ 89NasSouC-5
❑ 89NasSouP-1294
❑ 89NasSouTI-10
❑ 90BufBisC-5
❑ 90BufBisP-368
❑ 90BufBisTI-10
❑ 90CMC-5
❑ 90ProAAAF-483

Kemp, Joe
❑ 88SanBerSB-21
❑ 88SanBerSCLC-35
❑ 89ModA'sCLC-280

Kemp, Rick
❑ 75SpoIndC-15

Kemp, Rod
❑ 79LodDodT-1

Kemp, Steve
❑ 77Top-492
❑ 78Hos-55
❑ 78OPC-167
❑ 78TigBurK-18
❑ 78Top-21
❑ 79Hos-15
❑ 79OPC-97
❑ 79Top-196
❑ 80Kel-33
❑ 80OPC-166
❑ 80Top-315
❑ 80TopSup-29
❑ 81AllGamPI-54
❑ 81CokTeaS-52
❑ 81Don-249
❑ 81Dra-27
❑ 81Fle-459
❑ 81FleStiC-7
❑ 81MSAMinD-19
❑ 81OPC-152
❑ 81Squ-27
❑ 81TigDetN-86
❑ 81Top-593
❑ 81TopScr-11
❑ 81TopSti-74
❑ 82Don-594
❑ 82Fle-271
❑ 82FleSta-160
❑ 82Kel-39
❑ 82OnDecD-19
❑ 82OPC-296
❑ 82Top-666
❑ 82Top-670
❑ 82TopSti-185
❑ 82TopTra-54T
❑ 83AllGamPI-57
❑ 83Don-269
❑ 83Dra-13
❑ 83Fle-239
❑ 83FleSta-94
❑ 83FleSti-149
❑ 83OPC-260
❑ 83Top-260
❑ 83TopSti-50
❑ 83TopTra-53T
❑ 83YanPhoA-12
❑ 83YanRoyRD-5
❑ 84AllGamPI-146
❑ 84Don-469
❑ 84Dra-16
❑ 84Fle-129
❑ 84FunFooP-58
❑ 84Nes792-440
❑ 84OPC-301
❑ 84Top-440
❑ 84TopRubD-12
❑ 84TopTif-440
❑ 85AllGamPI-146
❑ 85Don-225
❑ 85Fle-132
❑ 85FleUpd-64
❑ 85Lea-100
❑ 85OPC-120
❑ 85Pir-8
❑ 85Top-120
❑ 85TopMin-120
❑ 85TopRubD-15
❑ 85TopTif-120
❑ 85TopTifT-66T
❑ 85TopTra-66T
❑ 86Don-200
❑ 86Fle-610
❑ 86LasVegSP-10
❑ 86Top-387
❑ 86TopTif-387
❑ 87OklCit8P-11
❑ 88AlaGolAA70TI-19
❑ 88RanMot-8
❑ 89PacSenL-10
❑ 89T/MSenL-58
❑ 89TopSenL-52
❑ 90EliSenL-8
❑ 90SouCalS-6
❑ 92YanWIZ8-98
❑ 93HolLeg-8
❑ 93RanKee-215

Kemper, Robbie
❑ 89CliGiaP-896
❑ 90EriSaiS-11

Kempfer, Jason
❑ 91IdaFalBSP-24
❑ 92PulBraC-16
❑ 92PulBraF-3174

Kenady, Jake
❑ 93BakDodCLC-13
❑ 93GreFalDSP-25
❑ 94YakBeaC-7
❑ 94YakBeaF-3842
❑ 95BakBlaTI-16
❑ 96SanBerSB-12
❑ 97St.PauS-12
❑ 98SalAvaC-13

Kenaga, Jeff
❑ 81BirBarT-13
❑ 82EvaTriT-22
❑ 83EvaTriT-20
❑ 84ChaO'sT-8

Kenan, Kerry
❑ 80AshTouT-15

Kendall, Fred
❑ 72PadPos-15
❑ 72Top-532
❑ 73OPC-221
❑ 73PadDea-13
❑ 73Top-221
❑ 74OPC-53
❑ 74PadDea-16
❑ 74PadMcDD-8
❑ 74Top-53A
❑ 74Top-53B
❑ 74TopSta-95
❑ 75OPC-332
❑ 75PadDea-15
❑ 75Top-332
❑ 75TopMin-332
❑ 76OPC-639
❑ 76SSP-122
❑ 76Top-639
❑ 77IndTeal-12
❑ 77OPC-213
❑ 77PadSchC-32A
❑ 77PadSchC-32B
❑ 77Top-576
❑ 78PapGinD-13
❑ 78SSP270-182
❑ 78Top-426
❑ 79PadFamF-23
❑ 79Top-83
❑ 80Top-598
❑ 86PadGreT-8
❑ 93HicCraC-26
❑ 93HicCraF-1295
❑ 94HicCraC-26
❑ 94HicCraF-2192
❑ 94SouAtlLAF-SAL24
❑ 94VenLinU-166

Kendall, Jason
❑ 2000TopPre-PP2
❑ 92ClaBluBF-BC26
❑ 92ClaDraP-18
❑ 92ClaFS7-408
❑ 92FroRowDP-89
❑ 92FroRowDPG-89
❑ 92FroRowDPS-89
❑ 92HigSchPLS-11
❑ 92HigSchPLS-NNO
❑ 92UppDecML-14
❑ 93AugPirC-1
❑ 93AugPirF-1547
❑ 93Bow-162
❑ 93ClaFS7-105
❑ 93ClaGolF-195
❑ 93Pin-458
❑ 93Sco-490
❑ 93Sel-359
❑ 93SouAtlLAGF-33
❑ 93StaCluM-148
❑ 93Top-334
❑ 93TopGol-334
❑ 93TopInaM-334
❑ 93TopInaR-334
❑ 93TopMic-334
❑ 94Bow-246
❑ 94CarLeaAF-CAR40
❑ 94ClaGolF-19
❑ 94ExcFS7-252
❑ 94SalBucC-12
❑ 94SalBucF-2327
❑ 94SigRoo-33
❑ 94SigRooS-33
❑ 94Top-686
❑ 94TopGol-686
❑ 94TopSpa-686
❑ 94UppDecML-124
❑ 95ARuFalLS-12
❑ 95Bes-91
❑ 95Bes-101
❑ 95BesFra-F11
❑ 95Bow-41
❑ 95CarMudF-161
❑ 95Exc-255
❑ 95SPML-137
❑ 95SPMLA-15
❑ 95SPMLDtS-DS16
❑ 95Top-480
❑ 95UppDecML-27
❑ 95UppDecMLFS-27
❑ 96BesAutSA-35
❑ 96Bow-293
❑ 96BowBes-15
❑ 96BowBesAR-15
❑ 96BowBesR-15
❑ 96BowFoi-293
❑ 96Cir-172
❑ 96CirRav-172
❑ 96ColCho-445
❑ 96ColChoGS-445
❑ 96ColChoSS-445
❑ 96EmoXL-255
❑ 96Exc-218
❑ 96ExcAll-1
❑ 96Fin-S241
❑ 96FinRef-S241
❑ 96Fla-347
❑ 96FlaWavotF-15
❑ 96FleUpd-U177
❑ 96FleUpdNH-14
❑ 96FleUpdTC-U177
❑ 96LeaLimR-6
❑ 96LeaLimRG-6
❑ 96LeaPre-124
❑ 96LeaPreP-124
❑ 96LeaSig-68
❑ 96LeaSigEA-98
❑ 96LeaSigEACM-14
❑ 96LeaSigPPG-68
❑ 96LeaSigPPP-68
❑ 96Pin-376
❑ 96PinAfi-190
❑ 96PinAfiAP-190
❑ 96PinFoil-376
❑ 96Sel-169
❑ 96SelArtP-169
❑ 96SelCer-108
❑ 96SelCerAP-108
❑ 96SelCerCB-108
❑ 96SelCerCR-108
❑ 96SelCerMB-108
❑ 96SelCerMG-108
❑ 96SelCerMR-108
❑ 96SP-17
❑ 96SPSpeFX-21
❑ 96SPSpeFXDC-21
❑ 96SPx-46
❑ 96SPxGol-46
❑ 96Stu-79
❑ 96StuPrePB-79
❑ 96StuPrePG-79
❑ 96StuPrePS-79
❑ 96Sum-156
❑ 96Sum-188
❑ 96SumAbo&B-156
❑ 96SumAbo&B-188
❑ 96SumArtP-156
❑ 96SumArtP-188
❑ 96SumFoi-156
❑ 96SumFoi-188
❑ 96TeaOut-45
❑ 96Top-342
❑ 96TopChr-135
❑ 96TopChrR-135
❑ 96TopLasBS-3
❑ 96Ult-533
❑ 96UltChe-B6
❑ 96UltCheGM-B6
❑ 96UltGolM-533
❑ 96UppDec-241
❑ 96UppDecPHE-H57
❑ 96UppDecPreH-H57
❑ 96Zen-113
❑ 96ZenArtP-113
❑ 96ZenMoz-23
❑ 97Bow-57
❑ 97BowInt-57
❑ 97Cir-226
❑ 97CirRav-226
❑ 97ColCho-430
❑ 97ColChoTBS-37
❑ 97ColChoTBSWH-37
❑ 97DenHol-24
❑ 97Don-43
❑ 97DonEli-77
❑ 97DonEliGS-77
❑ 97DonEliTotC-14
❑ 97DonEliTotCDC-14
❑ 97DonGolPP-43
❑ 97DonLim-167
❑ 97DonLim-192
❑ 97DonLimE-167
❑ 97DonLimE-192
❑ 97DonLimENG-167
❑ 97DonPre-91
❑ 97DonPreCttC-91
❑ 97DonSig-98
❑ 97DonSigA-58
❑ 97DonSigAC-71
❑ 97DonSigAM-71
❑ 97DonSigPPP-98
❑ 97DonSilPP-43
❑ 97E-X2-91
❑ 97E-X2Cred-91
❑ 97E-X2EssCre-91
❑ 97E-X2SD2000-8
❑ 97Fin-124
❑ 97FinEmb-124
❑ 97FinEmbR-124
❑ 97FinRef-124
❑ 97FlaShoLC-81
❑ 97FlaShoLeg0-81
❑ 97FlaShoLeg1-81
❑ 97FlaShoM-A81
❑ 97FlaShoM-B81
❑ 97FlaShoM-C81
❑ 97FlaShoR0-81
❑ 97FlaShoR1-81
❑ 97FlaShoR2-81
❑ 97Fle-429
❑ 97Fle-742
❑ 97FleRooS-8
❑ 97FleTif-429
❑ 97FleTif-742
❑ 97Lea-31
❑ 97LeaFraM-31
❑ 97LeaFraMDC-31
❑ 97MetUni-238
❑ 97MetUniPP-6
❑ 97NewPin-120
❑ 97NewPinAP-120
❑ 97NewPinMC-120
❑ 97NewPinPP-120
❑ 97Pac-394
❑ 97PacLigB-394
❑ 97PacPri-135
❑ 97PacPriLB-135
❑ 97PacPriP-135
❑ 97PacSil-394
❑ 97Pin-91
❑ 97PinArtP-PP91
❑ 97PinCer-46
❑ 97PinCerMBla-46
❑ 97PinCerMBlu-46
❑ 97PinCerMG-46
❑ 97PinCerMR-46
❑ 97PinCerR-46
❑ 97PinIns-62
❑ 97PinInsCE-62
❑ 97PinInsDE-62
❑ 97PinMusC-91
❑ 97PinPrePla-91
❑ 97PinTotCPB-46
❑ 97PinTotCPG-46
❑ 97PinTotCPR-46
❑ 97PinX-P-111
❑ 97PinX-PMoS-111
❑ 97PirPos-18
❑ 97PirPosG-1
❑ 97Sco-31
❑ 97ScoArtPWB-31
❑ 97ScoPreS-31
❑ 97ScoShoS-31
❑ 97ScoShoSAP-31
❑ 97Sel-42
❑ 97SelArtP-42
❑ 97SelCom-42
❑ 97SelRegG-42
❑ 97SelRooR-5
❑ 97SelToootT-4
❑ 97SelToootTMB-4
❑ 97SP-140
❑ 97SpoIll-63
❑ 97SpoIllEE-63
❑ 97StaClu-77
❑ 97StaCluC-CO5
❑ 97StaCluM-M10
❑ 97StaCluMOP-77
❑ 97StaCluMOP-M10
❑ 97Stu-60
❑ 97StuPrePG-60
❑ 97StuPrePS-60
❑ 97Top-195
❑ 97TopAwel-AI10
❑ 97TopChr-75
❑ 97TopChrR-75

❑ 97TopGal-152
❑ 97TopGalPPI-152
❑ 97UD3-48
❑ 97UD3GenNex-GN8
❑ 97Ult-262
❑ 97UltGolME-262
❑ 97UltPlaME-262
❑ 97UltRooR-6
❑ 97UppDec-157
❑ 97UppDecBCP-BC19
❑ 97UppDecRSF-RS12
❑ 97UppDecTTS-TS8
❑ 98Bow-10
❑ 98BowBes-51
❑ 98BowBesAR-51
❑ 98BowBesR-51
❑ 98BowChr-10
❑ 98BowChrGA-10
❑ 98BowChrGAR-10
❑ 98BowChrI-10
❑ 98BowChrIR-10
❑ 98BowChrR-10
❑ 98BowGolA-10
❑ 98BowInt-10
❑ 98CirThu-18
❑ 98CirThuRav-18
❑ 98CirThuSupRav-18
❑ 98ColCho-470
❑ 98CroRoy-109
❑ 98Don-136
❑ 98DonCol-136
❑ 98DonColL-279
❑ 98DonColP-654
❑ 98DonColS-136
❑ 98DonCruG-91
❑ 98DonCruP-91
❑ 98DonCruR-91
❑ 98DonGolPP-136
❑ 98DonPre-104
❑ 98DonPreSeat-104
❑ 98DonPriCD-136
❑ 98DonPriCL-279
❑ 98DonPriCP-654
❑ 98DonSig-114
❑ 98DonSigP-114
❑ 98DonSilPP-136
❑ 98Fin-81
❑ 98FinNo--81
❑ 98FinNo-R-81
❑ 98FinRef-81
❑ 98Fle-18
❑ 98FleVin'-47
❑ 98FleVin'C-47
❑ 98Lea-80
❑ 98LeaCruG-91
❑ 98LeaCruP-91
❑ 98LeaCruR-91
❑ 98LeaFraDA-80
❑ 98LeaFraF-80
❑ 98LeaFraM-80
❑ 98LeaFraM-80
❑ 98LeaFraMDC-80
❑ 98LeaFraMDC-80
❑ 98LeaFraMZ2-80
❑ 98LeaRS-99
❑ 98LeaRSLHolo-99
❑ 98LeaRSLong-99
❑ 98LeaRTrue-99
❑ 98MetUni-18
❑ 98MetUniPMG-18
❑ 98Pac-396
❑ 98PacAur-176
❑ 98PacOme-190
❑ 98PacOmeR-190
❑ 98PacOnl-585
❑ 98PacOnlR-585
❑ 98PacOnlWC-585
❑ 98PacPlaB-396
❑ 98PacRedT-396
❑ 98PacSil-396
❑ 98Pin-126
❑ 98PinIns-104
❑ 98PinInsCE-104
❑ 98PinInsDE-104
❑ 98PinPer-81
❑ 98PinPerPP-81
❑ 98PinPreP-126
❑ 98Revo-113
❑ 98RevoSS-113
❑ 98ScoRT-58
❑ 98ScoRTSS-PP54
❑ 98ScoRTSSAP-PP54
❑ 98ScoRTSSAP1-PP54
❑ 98SkyDugA-39
❑ 98SkyDugAIA-39
❑ 98SP Aut-157
❑ 98SpollITaN-100
❑ 98SpollITaNEE-100
❑ 98SPxFin-310
❑ 98SPxFinR-310
❑ 98SPxFinS-310
❑ 98StaCluFDI-245
❑ 98StaCluI-245
❑ 98StaCluOneK-245
❑ 98StaCluPP-245
❑ 98Stu-38
❑ 98StuGPP-38
❑ 98StuSPP-38
❑ 98Top-304
❑ 98TopChr-304
❑ 98TopChrR-304
❑ 98TopDevR-304
❑ 98TopDia-304
❑ 98TopGal-53
❑ 98TopGalGP-53
❑ 98TopGalOPP-53
❑ 98TopGalPPI-53
❑ 98TopGalPPIA-53
❑ 98TopGolLabC1-44
❑ 98TopGolLabC1B-44
❑ 98TopGolLabC1One-44
❑ 98TopGolLabC1R-44
❑ 98TopGolLabC2-44
❑ 98TopGolLabC2B-44
❑ 98TopGolLabC2One-44
❑ 98TopGolLabC2R-44
❑ 98TopGolLabC3-44
❑ 98TopGolLabC3B-44
❑ 98TopGolLabC3One-44
❑ 98TopGolLabC3R-44
❑ 98TopMiniC-304
❑ 98TopOpeD-131
❑ 98TopSta-81
❑ 98TopStaB-81
❑ 98TopStaG-81
❑ 98TopStaGR-81
❑ 98TopStaS-81
❑ 98TopTek-52
❑ 98TopTekD-52
❑ 98Ult-125
❑ 98UltGolM-125
❑ 98UltMas-125
❑ 98UltPlaM-125
❑ 98UppDec-480
❑ 98UppDecR-77
❑ 98Zen-64
❑ 98ZenZ-G-64
❑ 98ZenZ-S-64
❑ 99199Fin-87
❑ 99AllMysFR-M30
❑ 99Bow-25
❑ 99BowBes-4
❑ 99BowBesAR-4
❑ 99BowBesR-4
❑ 99BowChr-25
❑ 99BowChrG-25
❑ 99BowChrGR-25
❑ 99BowChrI-25
❑ 99BowChrIR-25
❑ 99BowChrR-25
❑ 99BowGol-25
❑ 99BowInt-25
❑ 99CroRoyB-111
❑ 99CroRoyL-111
❑ 99CroRoyOD-111
❑ 99FinGolRef-87
❑ 99FinRef-87
❑ 99FlaShoLeg1-66
❑ 99FlaShoLeg2-66
❑ 99FlaShoLeg3-66
❑ 99FlaShoLegM1-66
❑ 99FlaShoLegM2-66
❑ 99FlaShoLegM3-66
❑ 99FlaShoR1-66
❑ 99FlaShoR2-66
❑ 99FlaShoR3-66
❑ 99Fle-169
❑ 99FleBri-93
❑ 99FleBri2G-93
❑ 99FleBriBlu-93
❑ 99FleBriGol-93
❑ 99FleMys-56
❑ 99FleMysG-56
❑ 99FleMysM-56
❑ 99FleSta9-169
❑ 99FleWarT-169
❑ 99MetUni-145
❑ 99MetUniGM-145
❑ 99MetUniPMG-145
❑ 99Pac-341
❑ 99PacAur-148
❑ 99PacAurOD-148
❑ 99PacCroC-221
❑ 99PacCroCPB-221
❑ 99PacCroCTC-23
❑ 99PacInv-116
❑ 99PacInvOD-116
❑ 99PacInvPB-116
❑ 99PacOme-187
❑ 99PacOmeC-187
❑ 99PacOmeG-187
❑ 99PacOmePB-187
❑ 99PacPar-186
❑ 99PacParC-186
❑ 99PacParG-186
❑ 99PacParHoloGold-186
❑ 99PacParHS-186
❑ 99PacParOD-186
❑ 99PacParPB-186
❑ 99PacParRed-186
❑ 99PacParTC-23
❑ 99PacPlaB-341
❑ 99PacPri-113
❑ 99PacPriHB-113
❑ 99PacPriHG-113
❑ 99PacPriHM-113
❑ 99PacPriHP-113
❑ 99PacPriRed-113
❑ 99PacPriS-105
❑ 99PacPriS206-105
❑ 99PacPriS206R-105
❑ 99PacRed-341
❑ 99PacTeaC-27
❑ 99Rev-111
❑ 99RevPremDate-111
❑ 99RevRet-111
❑ 99RevShaSS-111
❑ 99SkyMolM-14
❑ 99SkyMolMX-14
❑ 99SkyPre-72
❑ 99SkyPreR-72
❑ 99SkyThu-114
❑ 99SkyThuRant-114
❑ 99SkyThuRave-114
❑ 99SP Aut-69
❑ 99SP SigAuto-JK
❑ 99SP SigAutoG-JK
❑ 99Spolll-126
❑ 99SPSig-36
❑ 99StaClu-174
❑ 99StaCluFDI-174
❑ 99StaCluOoaK-174
❑ 99StaCluPP-174
❑ 99ThuSkySupR-114
❑ 99Top-191
❑ 99Top-459
❑ 99TopAllMF-M30
❑ 99TopBlaLC1-32
❑ 99TopBlaLC2-32
❑ 99TopBlaLC3-32
❑ 99TopChr-191
❑ 99TopChr-459
❑ 99TopChrR-191
❑ 99TopChrR-459
❑ 99TopGal-28
❑ 99TopGalPP-28
❑ 99TopGalPPI-28
❑ 99TopGolL-32
❑ 99TopGolLC1-32
❑ 99TopGolLC2-32
❑ 99TopGolLOtO-32
❑ 99TopMVPP-191
❑ 99TopMVPP-459
❑ 99TopOpeD-101
❑ 99TopPre-PP6
❑ 99TopRedLC1-32
❑ 99TopRedLC2-32
❑ 99TopRedLC3-32
❑ 99TopSta-59
❑ 99TopSta1Foil-59
❑ 99TopStaFoil-59
❑ 99TopStaOS-59
❑ 99TopTek-35A
❑ 99TopTek-35B
❑ 99TopTekG-35A
❑ 99TopTekG-35B
❑ 99UD Cho-128
❑ 99UD ChoP-128
❑ 99UD ChoPCR-128
❑ 99UDHolo-47
❑ 99UDHoloAUsome-47
❑ 99UppDec-458
❑ 99UppDecBD-67
❑ 99UppDecBDD-67
❑ 99UppDecBDQ-67
❑ 99UppDecBDT-67
❑ 99UppDecCLM-C74
❑ 99UppDecE-71
❑ 99UppDecEBPC-C-JK
❑ 99UppDecEFXG-71
❑ 99UppDecEL1-458
❑ 99UppDecEL2-458
❑ 99UppDecM-162
❑ 99UppDecMGS-162
❑ 99UppDecMHFS-162
❑ 99UppDecMSS-162
❑ 99UppDecO-60
❑ 99UppDecOSO-60
❑ 99UppDecR-67
❑ 99UppDecRG-67
❑ 99UppDecRP-67
❑ 99Vic-307

Kendall, Jeremey
❑ 92MarPhiC-15
❑ 92MarPhiF-3071
❑ 93BatCliCB-14
❑ 93BatCliF-3158
❑ 94SouAtlLAF-SAL55
❑ 94SpaPhiF-1735
❑ 94SparPhiC-14
❑ 95Bow-116
❑ 95Exc-243
❑ 96ReaPhiB-22

Kendall, Phil
❑ 91BilMusP-3748
❑ 91BilMusSP-25
❑ 96HelBreTI-10
❑ 97HelBreB-16
❑ 98BelSnaM-15

Kendall, Scott
❑ 98WatIndTI-8

Kenders, Al
❑ 77FriOneYW-80

Kendrena, Ken
❑ 92EriSaiC-15
❑ 92EriSaiF-1614
❑ 93HigDesMC-6
❑ 93HigDesMF-33
❑ 93Top-726
❑ 93TopGol-726
❑ 93TopInaM-726
❑ 93TopInaR-726
❑ 93TopMic-726
❑ 94BreCouMC-6
❑ 94BreCouMF-4
❑ 95HarSenTI-32

Kendrick, Patrick
❑ 92HunCubC-22
❑ 92HunCubF-3143

Kendrick, Pete
❑ 83MadMusF-23
❑ 84AlbA'sT-14
❑ 85ModA'sC-14
❑ 87ElPasDP-4
❑ 88DenZepP-1269

Kenna, David
❑ 96BelGiaTI-13
❑ 97SalVolG-19

Kenna, Ed
❑ 23Zee-190
❑ 33Zee-126

Kennedy, Adam
❑ 97Bow-430
❑ 97BowChr-290
❑ 97BowChrI-290
❑ 97BowChrIR-290
❑ 97BowChrR-290
❑ 97BowInt-430
❑ 97NewJerCB-13
❑ 97NewJerCB-4
❑ 97TopSta-118
❑ 97TopStaAM-118
❑ 98ArkTraH-8
❑ 98ArkTraM-2
❑ 98Bes-19
❑ 98BesNumOP-29
❑ 98Bow-77
❑ 98BowChr-77
❑ 98BowChrGA-77
❑ 98BowChrGAR-77
❑ 98BowChrI-77
❑ 98BowChrIR-77
❑ 98BowChrR-77
❑ 98BowGolA-77
❑ 98BowInt-77
❑ 98PriWilCASM-4
❑ 98PriWilCQ-22
❑ 98SP MinPE-102
❑ 98SPMin-102
❑ 98StaCluFDI-393
❑ 98StaCluI-393
❑ 98StaCluOneK-393
❑ 98StaCluPP-393
❑ 98Top-248
❑ 98TopChr-248
❑ 98TopChrR-248
❑ 98TopDevR-248
❑ 98TopDia-248
❑ 98TopMiniC-248
❑ 99BasAmeTPA-22
❑ 99Bow-72
❑ 99BowChr-72
❑ 99BowChrG-72
❑ 99BowChrGR-72
❑ 99BowChrI-72
❑ 99BowChrIR-72
❑ 99BowChrR-72
❑ 99BowGol-72
❑ 99BowInt-72
❑ 99JustheS-30
❑ 99JustheSAC-16
❑ 99JustheSJB-30
❑ 99SP TopP-64
❑ 99SP TopPPE-64
❑ 99Top-433
❑ 99TopChr-433
❑ 99TopChrR-433

Kennedy, Bill (William G.)
❑ 49Bow-105
❑ 52Top-102
❑ 53RedSoxTI-15
❑ 53Top-94
❑ 55SeaPop-12
❑ 56SeaPop-9
❑ 57HygMea-7
❑ 57SeaPop-12
❑ 58SeaRaIT-10
❑ 59SeaPop-6
❑ 60HenHouW-25
❑ 83TopRep5-102
❑ 91TopArc1-94

Kennedy, Bo
❑ 87PenWhiSP-23
❑ 88SouBenWSGS-23
❑ 89SarWhiSS-12
❑ 90BirBarB-20
❑ 90BirBarP-1108
❑ 90CMC-770
❑ 91BirBarLD-65
❑ 91BirBarP-1452
❑ 91LinDriAA-65
❑ 92BirBarF-2577
❑ 92BirBarS-86
❑ 92SkyAA F-42
❑ 92VanCanF-2719
❑ 93IndIndF-1483

Kennedy, Brad
❑ 96NewJerCB-15

Kennedy, Brickyard (William V.)
❑ 03BreE10-81
❑ 11SpoLifCW-200
❑ 90DodTar-406
❑ 95May-15

Kennedy, Dan
❑ 89WinSpiS-11
❑ 89WytCubS-18

Kennedy, Darryl
❑ 92GasRanC-11
❑ 93ChaRanC-16
❑ 93ChaRanF-1944
❑ 93FloStaLAF-5
❑ 94ChaRanF-2500
❑ 94FloStaLAF-FSL2
❑ 95TulDriTI-9
❑ 97ShrCap-13
❑ 97ShrCapB-13

Kennedy, Dave
❑ 89ElmPioP-23

Kennedy, David
❑ 93BoiHawC-16
❑ 93BoiHawF-3923
❑ 95NewHavRTI-31
❑ 96ColSprSSTI-21
❑ 96Exc-156
❑ 97St.PauS-13
❑ 98St.PauSTI-11

Kennedy, Gregg
❑ 94LynRedSC-15
❑ 94LynRedSF-1890

Kennedy, Gus
❑ 94DanBraC-16
❑ 95MacBraTI-15
❑ 95MacBraUTI-4
❑ 96DurBulBIB-17
❑ 96DurBulBrB-17
❑ 96Exc-130
❑ 98RanCucQG-15
❑ 98RanCucQG-17

Kennedy, James
❑ 91GulCoaRSP-12

Kennedy, Jesse
❑ 94DanBraF-3545

Kennedy, John E.
❑ 64Top-203
❑ 64TopVen-203
❑ 65DodTeal-9
❑ 65OPC-119
❑ 65Top-119
❑ 66DodVolT-4
❑ 66Top-407
❑ 67CokCapD-11
❑ 67CokCapDA-11
❑ 67DexPre-114
❑ 67OPC-111
❑ 67Top-111
❑ 69PilPos-14
❑ 69Top-631
❑ 69YanPhoS-42
❑ 70BreMcD-13
❑ 70BreMil-10
❑ 70OPC-53
❑ 70Top-53
❑ 71MLBOffS-319
❑ 71OPC-498
❑ 71Top-498
❑ 72RedSoxTI-10
❑ 72Top-674
❑ 73LinPor-24
❑ 73OPC-437
❑ 73Top-437
❑ 77PilPosR-14
❑ 86AlbYanT-24
❑ 90DodTar-407
❑ 92YanWIZ6-65
❑ 94BreMilB-45

Kennedy, John Fitzgerald
❑ 94UppDecTAE-65

Kennedy, Junior
❑ 76IndIndTI-13
❑ 77PhoGiaCC-14
❑ 77PhoGiaCP-14
❑ 77PhoGiaVNB-14
❑ 78Pep-15
❑ 78SSP270-134
❑ 79Top-501
❑ 80RedEnq-26
❑ 80Top-377
❑ 81Don-424
❑ 81Fle-203
❑ 81Top-447
❑ 82CubRedL-15
❑ 82Don-188
❑ 82Fle-70
❑ 82Top-723
❑ 82TopTra-55T
❑ 83Don-529
❑ 83Fle-500
❑ 83Top-204

Kennedy, Justin
❑ 95MarPhiTI-12

Kennedy, Kevin
❑ 77RocRedWM-24
❑ 78RocRedWT-10
❑ 79RocRedWT-3
❑ 80RocRedWT-11
❑ 81RocRedWT-10
❑ 87BakDodP-15
❑ 88BlaYNPRWL-161
❑ 88SanAntMB-23
❑ 88TexLeaAGS-22
❑ 89AlbDukP-72
❑ 90AlbDukCm-27
❑ 90AlbDukP-361
❑ 90AlbDukTr-16
❑ 90CMC-667
❑ 90ProAAAF-82
❑ 90TriAllGP-AAA32
❑ 91AlbDukLD-24
❑ 91AlbDukP-1157
❑ 91LinDriAAA-24
❑ 93RanKee-393
❑ 93Top-513
❑ 93TopGol-513
❑ 93TopInaM-513
❑ 93TopInaR-513
❑ 93TopMic-513
❑ 94RanMagM-22

Kennedy, Kyle
❑ 92MisStaB-24
❑ 93MisStaB-25

Kennedy, Mike
❑ 90ModA'sC-16
❑ 91SouOreAC-21

❑ 91SouOreAP-3849
Kennedy, Monte
❑ 47TipTop-125
❑ 49Bow-237
❑ 49EurSta-112
❑ 49GiaTeal-14
❑ 50Bow-175
❑ 51Bow-163
❑ 52BerRos-29
❑ 52Bow-213
❑ 52Top-124
❑ 75Gia195T-12
❑ 83TopRep5-124
Kennedy, Robert D.
❑ 39WhiSoxTI-7
❑ 40WhiSoxL-8
❑ 47TipTop-21
❑ 48IndTeal-18
❑ 48WhiSoxTI-13
❑ 49IndTeal-16
❑ 50IndNumN-14
❑ 50IndTeal-16
❑ 51Bow-296
❑ 51TopRedB-29
❑ 52IndNumN-16
❑ 52Top-77
❑ 53IndPenCBP-18
❑ 53Top-33
❑ 54OriEss-16
❑ 54Top-155
❑ 55OriEss-11
❑ 55Top-48
❑ 55TopDouH-87
❑ 56Top-38
❑ 56TopPin-34
❑ 57Top-149
❑ 64CubJayP-8
❑ 64Top-486
❑ 65CubJayP-9
❑ 65Top-457
❑ 67BraPho-18
❑ 68OPC-183
❑ 68Top-183
❑ 68TopVen-183
❑ 75TCM195Cl-17
❑ 76TayBow4-85
❑ 82Bow195E-253
❑ 83TopRep5-77
❑ 85Top-135
❑ 85TopTif-135
❑ 90DodTar-405
❑ 91OriCro-236
❑ 91TopArc1-33
❑ 94TopArc1-155
❑ 94TopArc1G-155
❑ 97BalOriP-24
Kennedy, Ryan
❑ 97PorRocG-13
❑ 98PorRocG-18
Kennedy, Scott
❑ 93MedHatBJF-3731
❑ 93MedHatBJSP-6
Kennedy, Shawn
❑ 91ButCopKSP-12
Kennedy, Terry
❑ 78ArkTraT-14
❑ 79Car5-12
❑ 79Top-724
❑ 80Top-569
❑ 81AllGamPI-131
❑ 81Don-428
❑ 81Fle-541
❑ 81OPC-353
❑ 81Top-353
❑ 81TopTra-780
❑ 82Don-121
❑ 82Dra-20
❑ 82Fle-574
❑ 82FleSta-105
❑ 82OPC-65
❑ 82Top-65
❑ 82TopSti-100
❑ 83AllGamPI-132
❑ 83Don-26
❑ 83Don-220
❑ 83DonActA-11
❑ 83Fle-362
❑ 83FleSti-223
❑ 83OPC-274
❑ 83PadTeal-11
❑ 83Top-274
❑ 83Top-742
❑ 83TopGloS-6
❑ 83TopSti-293
❑ 84AllGamPI-42
❑ 84Don-112
❑ 84DonActAS-8
❑ 84Fle-304
❑ 84FunFooP-47
❑ 84Nes792-366
❑ 84Nes792-455
❑ 84OPC-166
❑ 84PadMot-5
❑ 84PadSmo-14
❑ 84SevCoi-W17
❑ 84Top-366
❑ 84Top-455
❑ 84TopRubD-28
❑ 84TopSti-154
❑ 84TopTif-366
❑ 84TopTif-455
❑ 85AllGamPI-131
❑ 85Don-429
❑ 85Fle-37
❑ 85Lea-33
❑ 85OPC-194
❑ 85PadMot-10
❑ 85Top-135
❑ 85Top-635
❑ 85TopRubD-28
❑ 85TopSti-148
❑ 85TopTif-135
❑ 85TopTif-635
❑ 86Don-356
❑ 86DonAll-7
❑ 86DonPop-7
❑ 86Fle-327
❑ 86GenMilB-5C
❑ 86OPC-230
❑ 86Top-230
❑ 86Top-306
❑ 86TopGloA-20
❑ 86TopSti-111
❑ 86TopSti-152
❑ 86TopTif-230
❑ 86TopTif-306
❑ 87BalOriP-19
❑ 87Don-205
❑ 87DonOpeD-142
❑ 87Fle-419
❑ 87FleGlo-419
❑ 87FleUpd-56
❑ 87FleUpdG-56
❑ 87OPC-303
❑ 87OriFreB-15
❑ 87SpoTeaP-21
❑ 87Top-81
❑ 87Top-540
❑ 87TopSti-108
❑ 87TopTif-81
❑ 87TopTif-540
❑ 87TopTra-57T
❑ 87TopTraT-57T
❑ 88Don-150
❑ 88DonAll-9
❑ 88DonBasB-30
❑ 88DonPop-9
❑ 88Fle-563
❑ 88FleGlo-563
❑ 88Lea-99
❑ 88OPC-180
❑ 88OriFreB-15
❑ 88OriPos-17
❑ 88PanSti-7
❑ 88PanSti-227
❑ 88Sco-123
❑ 88ScoBoxC-1
❑ 88ScoGlo-123
❑ 88Spo-94
❑ 88StaLinAl-16
❑ 88StaLinO-6
❑ 88Top-180
❑ 88TopGloA-9
❑ 88TopSti-161
❑ 88TopSti-225
❑ 88TopStiB-55
❑ 88TopTif-180
❑ 89Bow-470
❑ 89BowTif-470
❑ 89Don-141
❑ 89Fle-610
❑ 89FleGlo-610
❑ 89FleUpd-128
❑ 89GiaMot-8
❑ 89OPC-309
❑ 89PanSti-256
❑ 89Sco-123
❑ 89ScoRoo-30T
❑ 89Top-705
❑ 89TopBig-180
❑ 89TopSti-235
❑ 89TopTif-705
❑ 89TopTra-59T
❑ 89TopTraT-59T
❑ 89UppDec-469
❑ 90Bow-241
❑ 90BowTif-241
❑ 90Don-602
❑ 90DonBesN-132
❑ 90Fle-58
❑ 90FleCan-58
❑ 90GiaMot-12
❑ 90GiaSmo-10
❑ 90Lea-67
❑ 90OPC-372
❑ 90PubIntS-71
❑ 90Sco-7
❑ 90Top-372
❑ 90TopBig-16
❑ 90TopTif-372
❑ 90UppDec-397
❑ 91Bow-631
❑ 91Don-94
❑ 91Fle-263
❑ 91GiaMot-12
❑ 91GiaPacGaE-5
❑ 91GiaPos-1
❑ 91Lea-216
❑ 91OPC-66
❑ 91OriCro-237
❑ 91PanFreS-66
❑ 91Sco-548
❑ 91SimandSMLBL-22
❑ 91StaClu-91
❑ 91Top-66
❑ 91TopDesS-66
❑ 91TopMic-66
❑ 91TopTif-66
❑ 91Ult-321
❑ 91Ult-399
❑ 91UppDec-404
❑ 92OPC-253
❑ 92Sco-503
❑ 92Top-253
❑ 92TopGol-253
❑ 92TopGolW-253
❑ 92TopMic-253
❑ 92UppDec-192
❑ 93St.PetCC-29
❑ 93St.PetCF-2644
❑ 94VerExpC-21
❑ 94VerExpF-3923
❑ 95TacRaiTI-3
❑ 96TacRaiB-2
❑ 98IowCubQ-2
Kennedy, Theodore A.
❑ 87OldJudN-277
Kennedy, Vern
❑ 34DiaMatCSB-102
❑ 35DiaMatCS3T1-86
❑ 36SandSW-37
❑ 37ExhFou-10
❑ 37OPCBatUV-135
❑ 38GouHeaU-256
❑ 38GouHeaU-280
❑ 47PadTeal-10
❑ 79DiaGre-188
❑ 92ConTSN-365
❑ 94ConTSN-1123
❑ 94ConTSNB-1123
❑ 95ConTSN-1392
Kennedy, William
❑ 87BucN28-50
Kennelley, Steve
❑ 87ColMetP-11
Kennemur, Paul
❑ 76BatRouCT-13
Kenner, Jeff
❑ 86ArkTraP-10
Kenney, Jerry
❑ 69Top-519
❑ 69YanPhoS-43
❑ 70OPC-219
❑ 70Top-219
❑ 70YanCliDP-11
❑ 70YanPhoS-19
❑ 71MLBOffS-491
❑ 71OPC-572
❑ 71Top-572
❑ 71YanCliDP-8
❑ 72MilBra-180
❑ 72OPC-158
❑ 72Top-158
❑ 73OPC-514
❑ 73Top-514
❑ 75SyrChiTI-7
❑ 92YanWIZ6-66
❑ 92YanWIZ7-89
Kennison, Kyle
❑ 96EveAquB-13
❑ 97WisTimR-16
❑ 98LanJetG-14
Kenny, Brian
❑ 91GenCubC-10
❑ 91GenCubP-4210
❑ 92MidLeaATI-24
❑ 92PeoChiC-7
❑ 92PeoChiTI-9
❑ 92PeoChiTI-31
Kenny, Sean
❑ 93PitMetF-3704
❑ 94CapCitBC-11
❑ 94CapCitBF-1747
❑ 95StLucMTI-19
Kenny, Terry
❑ 75CedRapGT-31
Kent, Bernard
❑ 85BelBreT-12
Kent, Bo (John)
❑ 86MedA'sC-73
❑ 86ModA'sC-4
❑ 87ModA'sC-9
❑ 87ModA'sP-1
❑ 88HunStaTI-10
Kent, Dave
❑ 89OneYanP-2119
Kent, Jeff
❑ 88CapCodPPaLP-169
❑ 89St.CatBJP-2091
❑ 90DunBluJS-13
❑ 90FloStaLAS-33
❑ 90StaFS7-65
❑ 91Cla/Bes-108
❑ 91KnoBluJLD-360
❑ 91KnoBluJP-1775
❑ 91LinDriAA-360
❑ 92DonRoo-61
❑ 92FleUpd-104
❑ 92Lea-445
❑ 92LeaBlaG-445
❑ 92Pin-522
❑ 92ScoRoo-84T
❑ 93BluJayD4-41
❑ 93Bow-426
❑ 93Don-302
❑ 93Fle-90
❑ 93Lea-185
❑ 93LinVenB-160
❑ 93MetColP-38
❑ 93MetKah-12
❑ 93OPC-213
❑ 93Pin-155
❑ 93Sco-189
❑ 93Sel-318
❑ 93StaClu-269
❑ 93StaCluFDI-269
❑ 93StaCluMOP-269
❑ 93Top-703
❑ 93TopGol-703
❑ 93TopInaM-703
❑ 93TopInaR-703
❑ 93TopMic-703
❑ 93Toy-84
❑ 93Ult-77
❑ 93UppDec-401
❑ 93UppDecGold-401
❑ 93USPlaCR-7S
❑ 94Bow-296
❑ 94Bow-385
❑ 94ColC-159
❑ 94ColChoGS-159
❑ 94ColChoSS-159
❑ 94Don-185
❑ 94Fin-33
❑ 94FinRef-33
❑ 94Fla-200
❑ 94Fle-570
❑ 94FleExtB-320
❑ 94FUnPac-157
❑ 94Lea-112
❑ 94LeaL-131
❑ 94MetColP-4
❑ 94MetShuST-1
❑ 94OPC-166
❑ 94Pac-408
❑ 94PanSti-220
❑ 94Pin-122
❑ 94PinArtP-122
❑ 94PinMusC-122
❑ 94Sco-516
❑ 94ScoGolR-516
❑ 94Sel-85
❑ 94SP-119
❑ 94SPDieC-119
❑ 94SPHol-19
❑ 94SPHolDC-19
❑ 94StaClu-362
❑ 94StaCluDD-DD10
❑ 94StaCluFDI-362
❑ 94StaCluGR-362
❑ 94StaCluMOP-362
❑ 94StaCluMOP-DD10
❑ 94Stu-117
❑ 94Top-424
❑ 94TopGol-424
❑ 94TopSpa-424
❑ 94TriPla-146
❑ 94Ult-238
❑ 94UppDec-178
❑ 94UppDecAJ-38
❑ 94UppDecAJG-38
❑ 94UppDecED-178
❑ 95Baz-82
❑ 95Bow-342
❑ 95ClaPhoC-37
❑ 95ColCho-315
❑ 95ColChoGS-315
❑ 95ColChoSE-147
❑ 95ColChoSEGS-147
❑ 95ColChoSESS-147
❑ 95ColChoSS-315
❑ 95Don-97
❑ 95DonPreP-97
❑ 95DonTopotO-295
❑ 95Fin-121
❑ 95FinRef-121
❑ 95Fla-172
❑ 95Fle-373
❑ 95Lea-220
❑ 95LeaLim-107
❑ 95MetColP-4
❑ 95Pac-283
❑ 95PacPri-93
❑ 95Pin-242
❑ 95PinArtP-242
❑ 95PinMusC-242
❑ 95PinUps-US13
❑ 95Sco-48
❑ 95ScoGolR-48
❑ 95ScoPlaTS-48
❑ 95Sel-77
❑ 95SelArtP-77
❑ 95SP-81
❑ 95Spo-30
❑ 95SpoArtP-30
❑ 95SpoDouT-3
❑ 95SPSil-81
❑ 95StaClu-61
❑ 95StaCluFDI-61
❑ 95StaCluMOP-61
❑ 95StaCluSTWS-61
❑ 95StaCluVR-37
❑ 95StaCluVRMO-37
❑ 95Stu-64
❑ 95Sum-107
❑ 95SumNthD-107
❑ 95Top-185
❑ 95TopCyb-105
❑ 95TopEmb-9
❑ 95TopEmbGI-9
❑ 95Ult-198
❑ 95UltGolM-198
❑ 95UppDec-359
❑ 95UppDecED-359
❑ 95UppDecEDG-359
❑ 95UppDecSE-61
❑ 95UppDecSEG-61
❑ 95Zen-49
❑ 96ColCho-225
❑ 96ColChoGS-225
❑ 96ColChoSS-225
❑ 96Don-285
❑ 96DonPreP-285
❑ 96EmoXL-236
❑ 96Fla-324
❑ 96Fle-484
❑ 96FleTif-484
❑ 96Lea-20
❑ 96LeaPrePB-20
❑ 96LeaPrePG-20
❑ 96LeaPrePS-20
❑ 96MetKah-19
❑ 96MetTeal-4
❑ 96MetUni-204
❑ 96MetUniP-204
❑ 96Pac-144
❑ 96Pin-41
❑ 96ProSta-73
❑ 96Sco-316
❑ 96ScoDugC-B41
❑ 96ScoDugCAP-B41
❑ 96SP-126
❑ 96StaClu-99
❑ 96StaCluEPB-99
❑ 96StaCluEPG-99
❑ 96StaCluEPS-99
❑ 96StaCluMOP-99
❑ 96Top-207
❑ 96Ult-246
❑ 96UltGolM-246
❑ 96UppDec-143
❑ 97Bow-65
❑ 97BowInt-65
❑ 97Cir-36
❑ 97CirRav-36
❑ 97ColChoU-U24
❑ 97Don-338
❑ 97DonGolPP-338
❑ 97DonSilPP-338
❑ 97Fin-254
❑ 97FinRef-254
❑ 97Fle-509
❑ 97FleTif-509
❑ 97IndSco-13
❑ 97IndScoPI-13
❑ 97IndScoPr-13
❑ 97Lea-273
❑ 97LeaFraM-273
❑ 97LeaFraMDC-273
❑ 97Pac-72
❑ 97PacLigB-72
❑ 97PacSil-72
❑ 97PinX-PSfF-33
❑ 97PinX-PSfFU-33
❑ 97Sco-230
❑ 97Sco-352
❑ 97ScoArtPWB-230
❑ 97ScoArtPWB-352
❑ 97ScoPreS-230
❑ 97ScoResC-352
❑ 97ScoShoS-230
❑ 97ScoShoS-352
❑ 97ScoShoSAP-230
❑ 97ScoShoSAP-352
❑ 97Sel-184
❑ 97SelCom-184
❑ 97SP-163
❑ 97Top-346
❑ 97Ult-388
❑ 97UltGolME-388
❑ 97UltPlaME-388
❑ 97UppDec-546
❑ 98Bow-8
❑ 98BowChr-8
❑ 98BowChrGA-8
❑ 98BowChrGAR-8
❑ 98BowChrI-8
❑ 98BowChrIR-8
❑ 98BowChrR-8
❑ 98BowGolA-8
❑ 98BowInt-8
❑ 98CirThu-215
❑ 98CirThuRav-215
❑ 98CirThuSupRav-215
❑ 98ColCho-230
❑ 98ColChoSQ-SQ36
❑ 98Don-257
❑ 98DonGolPP-257
❑ 98DonSilPP-257
❑ 98Fin-87
❑ 98FinNo--87
❑ 98FinNo-R-87
❑ 98FinRef-87
❑ 98Fle-398
❑ 98FleVin'-120
❑ 98FleVin'C-120
❑ 98GiaMot-4
❑ 98MetUni-169
❑ 98MetUniPMG-169
❑ 98Pac-445
❑ 98PacAur-198
❑ 98PacOme-213
❑ 98PacOmeR-213
❑ 98PacOnl-665
❑ 98PacOnlR-665
❑ 98PacOnlWC-665
❑ 98PacPar-248
❑ 98PacParC-248
❑ 98PacParG-248
❑ 98PacParHS-248
❑ 98PacParPB-248
❑ 98PacParR-248
❑ 98PacPlaB-445
❑ 98PacRedT-445
❑ 98PacSil-445
❑ 98Pin-86

❑ 98PinIns-101
❑ 98PinInsCE-101
❑ 98PinInsDE-101
❑ 98PinPreP-86
❑ 98Revo-129
❑ 98RevoSS-129
❑ 98Sco-206
❑ 98ScoRT-141
❑ 98ScoSS-PP98
❑ 98ScoSSAP-PP98
❑ 98SP Aut-173
❑ 98SpoIll-73
❑ 98SpoIllEE-73
❑ 98SpoIllFE-73
❑ 98SPxFin-126
❑ 98SPxFinR-126
❑ 98SPxFinS-126
❑ 98StaCluFDI-89
❑ 98StaClul-89
❑ 98StaCluOneK-89
❑ 98StaCluPP-89
❑ 98Top-24
❑ 98TopChr-24
❑ 98TopChrR-24
❑ 98TopDevR-24
❑ 98TopDia-24
❑ 98TopGal-61
❑ 98TopGalGP-61
❑ 98TopGalOPP-61
❑ 98TopGalPPI-61
❑ 98TopGalPPIA-61
❑ 98TopMiniC-24
❑ 98TopOpeD-17
❑ 98TopSta-86
❑ 98TopStaB-86
❑ 98TopStaG-86
❑ 98TopStaGR-86
❑ 98TopStaS-86
❑ 98Ult-176
❑ 98UltDouT-14
❑ 98UltGolM-176
❑ 98UltMas-176
❑ 98UltPlaM-176
❑ 98UppDec-220
❑ 98UppDecSF-122
❑ 99199Fin-234
❑ 99Bow-261
❑ 99BowGol-261
❑ 99BowInt-261
❑ 99CroRoyB-125
❑ 99CroRoyL-125
❑ 99CroRoyOD-125
❑ 99FinGolRef-234
❑ 99FinRef-234
❑ 99FlaShoLeg1-124
❑ 99FlaShoLeg2-124
❑ 99FlaShoLeg3-124
❑ 99FlaShoLegM1-124
❑ 99FlaShoLegM2-124
❑ 99FlaShoLegM3-124
❑ 99FlaShoR1-124
❑ 99FlaShoR2-124
❑ 99FlaShoR3-124
❑ 99Fle-171
❑ 99FleBri-37
❑ 99FleBri2G-37
❑ 99FleBriBlu-37
❑ 99FleBriGol-37
❑ 99FleMys-3
❑ 99FleMysG-3
❑ 99FleMysM-3
❑ 99FleSta9-171
❑ 99FleWarT-171
❑ 99MetUni-140
❑ 99MetUniGM-140
❑ 99MetUniPMG-140
❑ 99Pac-383
❑ 99PacAur-171
❑ 99PacAurOD-171
❑ 99PacCroC-252
❑ 99PacCroCPB-252
❑ 99PacInv-128
❑ 99PacInvOD-128
❑ 99PacInvPB-128
❑ 99PacOme-213
❑ 99PacOmeC-213
❑ 99PacOmeG-213
❑ 99PacOmePB-213
❑ 99PacPar-210
❑ 99PacParC-210
❑ 99PacParG-210
❑ 99PacParHoloGold-210
❑ 99PacParHS-210
❑ 99PacParOD-210
❑ 99PacParPB-210
❑ 99PacParRed-210
❑ 99PacPlaB-383
❑ 99PacPri-129
❑ 99PacPriHB-129
❑ 99PacPriHG-129
❑ 99PacPriHM-129
❑ 99PacPriHP-129
❑ 99PacPriRed-129
❑ 99PacPriS-106
❑ 99PacPriS206-106
❑ 99PacPriS206R-106
❑ 99PacRed-383
❑ 99Rev-126
❑ 99RevPremDate-126
❑ 99RevRet-126
❑ 99RevShaSS-126
❑ 99SkyMolM-21
❑ 99SkyMolMX-21
❑ 99SkyPre-73
❑ 99SkyPreR-73
❑ 99SkyThu-116
❑ 99SkyThuRant-116
❑ 99SkyThuRave-116
❑ 99SP Aut-75
❑ 99SP AutHRC-HR32
❑ 99SPAutHRCDC-HR32
❑ 99SpoIll-131
❑ 99StaClu-192
❑ 99StaCluFDI-192
❑ 99StaCluOoaK-192
❑ 99StaCluPP-192
❑ 99ThuSkySupR-116
❑ 99Top-330
❑ 99TopBlaLC1-13
❑ 99TopBlaLC2-13
❑ 99TopBlaLC3-13
❑ 99TopChr-330
❑ 99TopChrR-330
❑ 99TopGal-24
❑ 99TopGalPP-24
❑ 99TopGalPPI-24
❑ 99TopGolL-13
❑ 99TopGolLC1-13
❑ 99TopGolLC2-13
❑ 99TopGolLOtO-13
❑ 99TopMVPP-330
❑ 99TopOpeD-142
❑ 99TopRedLC1-13
❑ 99TopRedLC2-13
❑ 99TopRedLC3-13
❑ 99UppDec-198
❑ 99UppDec-486
❑ 99UppDecBD-75
❑ 99UppDecBDD-75
❑ 99UppDecBDQ-75
❑ 99UppDecBDT-75
❑ 99UppDecEL1-198
❑ 99UppDecEL1-486
❑ 99UppDecEL2-198
❑ 99UppDecEL2-486
❑ 99UppDecM-188
❑ 99UppDecMGS-188
❑ 99UppDecMHFS-188
❑ 99UppDecMSS-188
❑ 99Vic-357

Kent, Lewis
❑ 87KinIndP-7
❑ 88KinIndS-14

Kent, Matt
❑ 86StoPorP-12

Kent, Maury
❑ 90DodTar-999

Kent, Robert
❑ 96IdaFalB-12
❑ 97RanCucQG-14
❑ 98RanCucQG-16
❑ 98RanCucQG-15

Kent, Troy
❑ 88MarPhiS-20
❑ 89SpaPhiP-1033
❑ 89SpaPhiS-11
❑ 91SanBerSC-7
❑ 91SanBerSP-1983
❑ 92JacSunF-3705
❑ 92JacSunS-360
❑ 92SkyAA F-152
❑ 93CalCanF-1162
❑ 96WatIndTI-11
❑ 98KinIndQ-15

Kent, Wes
❑ 81AppFoxT-26
❑ 82AppFoxFr-13
❑ 83GleFalWST-3

Kenworthy, Dick
❑ 68OPC-63
❑ 68Top-63
❑ 68TopVen-63
❑ 77SerSta-14
❑ 81TCM60I-332

Kenworthy, Duke (William)
❑ 13Zee-80
❑ 16Zee-35
❑ 19Zee-9
❑ 20WalMaiW-24
❑ 20Zee-126
❑ 24Zee-48

Kenworthy, Harry
❑ 22Zee-46

Kenyon, J.J.
❑ 87OldJudN-278

Kenyon, Robert
❑ 81VerBeaDT-7
❑ 82VerBeaDT-7

Keon, Kevin
❑ 90NiaFalRP-19

Keough, Joseph
❑ 69RoyTeal-8
❑ 69Top-603
❑ 70RoyTeal-17
❑ 70Top-589
❑ 71MLBOffS-417
❑ 71OPC-451
❑ 71Top-451
❑ 72OPC-133
❑ 72oyTeal-9
❑ 72Top-133
❑ 93UppDecS-4

Keough, Matt
❑ 78Top-709
❑ 79Hos-59
❑ 79OPC-284
❑ 79Top-554
❑ 80OPC-74
❑ 80Top-134
❑ 81A'sGraG-27
❑ 81AllGamPI-85
❑ 81Don-358
❑ 81Fle-588
❑ 81OPC-301
❑ 81Top-301
❑ 82A'sGraG-6
❑ 82Don-71
❑ 82Fle-95
❑ 82FleSta-129
❑ 82OPC-87
❑ 82Top-87
❑ 82TopSti-225
❑ 83A'sGraG-27
❑ 83Don-239
❑ 83Fle-521
❑ 83Top-413
❑ 83TopSti-109
❑ 83TopTra-54T
❑ 83YanPhoA-13
❑ 84Don-627
❑ 84Fle-130
❑ 84Nes792-203
❑ 84OPC-203
❑ 84Top-203
❑ 84TopTif-203
❑ 85LouRedR-16
❑ 87A'sMot-18
❑ 87JapPlaB-15
❑ 88ChaLooLTI-17
❑ 90SweBasG-127
❑ 92YanWIZ8-99

Keough, R. Marty
❑ 58Top-371
❑ 59Top-303
❑ 60Top-71
❑ 60TopVen-71
❑ 61Top-146
❑ 62Jel-69
❑ 62Pos-69
❑ 62PosCan-69
❑ 62RedEnq-19
❑ 62SalPlaC-79
❑ 62ShiPlaC-79
❑ 62Top-258
❑ 63Jel-135
❑ 63Pos-135
❑ 63RedEnq-17
❑ 63RedFreBC-12
❑ 63RedJayP-6
❑ 63Top-21
❑ 64Top-166
❑ 64TopVen-166
❑ 65OPC-263
❑ 65RedEnq-16
❑ 65Top-263
❑ 66Top-334
❑ 66TopVen-334
❑ 81RedSoxBG2S-30

Keppen, Jeff
❑ 95YakBeaTI-16
❑ 96SanBerSB-13
❑ 96SavSanB-20
❑ 97VerBeaD-13

Kepshire, Kurt
❑ 81CedRapRT-2
❑ 82CedRapRT-5
❑ 83ArkTraT-4
❑ 84LouRedR-17
❑ 85CarTeal-17
❑ 85Don-382
❑ 85Fle-230
❑ 85Top-474
❑ 85TopTif-474
❑ 86CarKASD-13
❑ 86CarSchM-11
❑ 86CarTeal-22
❑ 86Don-504
❑ 86Fle-39
❑ 86LouRedTI-14
❑ 86Top-256
❑ 86TopTif-256
❑ 88IndIndC-2
❑ 88IndIndP-506
❑ 89PorBeaC-3
❑ 89PorBeaP-215

Kerfeld, Charlie
❑ 85TucTorC-73
❑ 86AstMilL-11
❑ 86AstPol-10
❑ 86AstTeal-8
❑ 86BasStaB-63
❑ 86DonRoo-6
❑ 86Fle-303
❑ 86SpoRoo-23
❑ 86TopTra-52T
❑ 86TopTraT-52T
❑ 87AstMot-12
❑ 87Don-209
❑ 87Fle-60
❑ 87FleExcS-31
❑ 87FleGlo-60
❑ 87Lea-195
❑ 87OPC-145
❑ 87Spo-146
❑ 87SpoTeaP-8
❑ 87Top-145
❑ 87TopSti-28
❑ 87TopTif-145
❑ 87ToyRoo-15
❑ 88ColAstB-1
❑ 88OPC-392
❑ 88Sco-479
❑ 88ScoGlo-479
❑ 88Top-608
❑ 88TopTif-608
❑ 89AstSmo-21
❑ 89TucTorC-8
❑ 89TucTorJP-11
❑ 89TucTorP-188
❑ 90BraDubP-14
❑ 93HolLeg-9

Kerfut, George
❑ 90FloStaLAS-10
❑ 90MiaMirIS-14
❑ 90MiaMirIS-12
❑ 90StaFS7-74
❑ 91MiaMirC-15
❑ 91MiaMirP-403
❑ 92SalLakTSP-17
❑ 93HigDesMC-7
❑ 93HigDesMF-34

Keriazakos, Gus (Const.)
❑ 55Bow-14

Kerins, John
❑ 87OldJudN-279

Kerkes, Kevin
❑ 89WauTimGS-22

Kerley, Collin
❑ 92GenCubC-12
❑ 92GenCubF-1557
❑ 93PeoChiC-10
❑ 93PeoChiF-1080
❑ 93PeoChiTI-12
❑ 94DayCubC-12
❑ 94DayCubF-2348
❑ 95HarSenTI-45

Kermode, Al
❑ 92JamExpC-11
❑ 92JamExpF-1498
❑ 94BurBeeC-10
❑ 94BurBeeF-1077

Kern, Bill
❑ 77FriOneYW-65

Kern, Brian
❑ 97VisOakG-16

Kern, Jim (James)
❑ 75CleIndP-15
❑ 75OklCit8TI-8
❑ 75OPC-621
❑ 75Top-621
❑ 75TopMin-621
❑ 76SSP-509
❑ 77IndTeal-13
❑ 77PepGloD-7
❑ 77Top-41
❑ 78IndTeal-17
❑ 78OPC-165
❑ 78Top-253
❑ 79BasPat-44
❑ 79OPC-297
❑ 79Top-573
❑ 80OPC-192
❑ 80Top-369
❑ 81Don-27
❑ 81Fle-618
❑ 81FleStiC-18
❑ 81OPC-197
❑ 81Top-197
❑ 82Don-89
❑ 82Fle-322
❑ 82OPC-59
❑ 82RedCok-11
❑ 82Top-463
❑ 82TopTra-56T
❑ 83Don-355
❑ 83Fle-240
❑ 83Top-772
❑ 83TopFol-4
❑ 83WhiSoxTV-67
❑ 86IndOhH-46
❑ 86IndTeal-27
❑ 86RanGreT-3
❑ 92UppDecS-12
❑ 93RanKee-216
❑ 94BreMilB-46
❑ 94RanAllP-7

Kern, Lloyd D.
❑ 77WesHavYT-12
❑ 79WesHavYT-28
❑ 80LynSaiT-22
❑ 81LynSaiT-26

Kernan, Phil
❑ 95ButCopKtI-13

Kernek, George B.
❑ 65CarTeal-14
❑ 66Top-544

Kernels, Cedar Rapids
❑ 96CedRapKTI-31

Kernick, Craig
❑ 91WavRedF-7

Kerns, Henry
❑ 11BigEatEU-9
❑ 11Zee-69

Kerns, Mickey
❑ 92BoiHawC-13
❑ 92BoiHawF-3637
❑ 93CedRapKC-10
❑ 93CedRapKF-1752

Kerns, Russ
❑ 50WorWidGV-38

Kerr, Buddy (John J.)
❑ 46SpoExcW-7-9
❑ 47HomBon-27
❑ 48Bow-20
❑ 48GiaTeal-9
❑ 49Bow-186
❑ 49EurSta-113
❑ 49GiaTeal-15
❑ 49MPR302-2-102
❑ 50Bow-55
❑ 50Dra-15
❑ 51Bow-171
❑ 79DiaGre-127
❑ 79TCM50-113
❑ 83TCMPla1945-37

Kerr, Dickie (Richard)
❑ 19W514-23
❑ 20GasAmeMBD-3
❑ 20NatCarE-54
❑ 21E121So1-51
❑ 21E121So8-47
❑ 21Exh-90
❑ 22AmeCarE122-36
❑ 22W575-68
❑ 23W501-37
❑ 26Zee-142
❑ 68SCFOldT-18
❑ 75WhiSox1T-12
❑ 75WhiSox1T-24
❑ 88PacEigMO-47
❑ 88PacEigMO-56
❑ 88PacEigMO-97
❑ 94ConTSN-1037
❑ 94ConTSN-1041
❑ 94ConTSNB-1037
❑ 94ConTSNB-1041

Kerr, Frank
❑ 47PadTeal-11
❑ 49RemBre-13

Kerr, Jason
❑ 91YakBeaC-16
❑ 91YakBeaP-4244
❑ 92ProFS7-250
❑ 92VerBeaDC-9
❑ 92VerBeaDF-2870
❑ 93RanCucQC-19
❑ 93RanCucQF-830

Kerr, Jim
❑ 96ButCopKB-18

Kerr, John Francis
❑ 33Gou-214
❑ 34DiaMatCSB-103
❑ 35DiaMatCS3T1-87

Kerr, John L.
❑ 26Zee-8
❑ 28ExhPCL-16
❑ 28Zee-10
❑ 29ExhFou-19
❑ 30WhiSoxTI-16

Kerr, Paul S.
❑ 80PerHaloFP-C

Kerr, Zach (Zackary)
❑ 89EriOriS-10
❑ 90CarLeaA-1
❑ 90FreKeyTI-10
❑ 91FreKeyC-5

Kerrigan, Joe
❑ 75WesPalBES-9
❑ 76ExpRed-15
❑ 77ExpPos-19
❑ 77OPC-171
❑ 77Top-341
❑ 78BalOriP-14
❑ 78OPC-108
❑ 78Top-549
❑ 79BalOriP-8
❑ 79RocRedWT-2
❑ 79Top-37
❑ 81IndIndTI-24
❑ 82OklCit8T-13
❑ 83ExpPos-14
❑ 84ExpPos-15
❑ 84ExpStu-33
❑ 84ExpStu-38
❑ 86ExpProPa-14
❑ 87JacExpP-454
❑ 88IndIndC-25
❑ 88IndIndP-499
❑ 89IndIndC-24
❑ 89IndIndP-1227
❑ 90IndIndP-309
❑ 90ProAAAF-592
❑ 91HarSenLD-275
❑ 91HarSenP-644
❑ 91LinDriAA-275
❑ 91OriCro-238
❑ 92ExpPos-19

Kerrigan, Rob
❑ 47PadTeal-12
❑ 87JamExpP-2558
❑ 88JamExpP-1898
❑ 88RocExpLC-18
❑ 89RocExpLC-15
❑ 90WesPalBES-11

Kerry, William
❑ 98JohCCTI-18

Kersgeiter, Greg
❑ 93ChaRanC-30

Kershaw, Scott
❑ 86AppFoxP-12

Kershner, Jason
❑ 95MarPhiTI-13
❑ 96PieBolWB-14
❑ 97ClePhi-8
❑ 98ClePhiM-11
❑ 98ClePhiUM-11

Kersten, Eugene
❑ 21Zee-28

Kertis, John
❑ 98SavSanGM-16

Keshock, Christopher
❑ 87ChaWheP-22

Kesler, Mike
❑ 87QuaCitAP-13

Kessel, Kyle
- 96PitMetB-13
- 97CapCitB-6
- 98St.LucMM-6

Kesselmark, Joe
- 88SanAntMB-11
- 89SanAntMB-9
- 90CanIndB-10
- 90CanIndP-1304

Kessels, Steve
- 76WauMetT-14

Kesses, Steve
- 77LynMetT-18

Kessinger, Don
- 66OPC-24
- 66Top-24
- 66TopVen-24
- 67CubProPS-9
- 67ProPizC-11
- 67Top-419
- 68OPC-159
- 68Top-159
- 68TopVen-159
- 69CubBumS-4
- 69CubJewT-10
- 69CubPho-8
- 69CubTealC-6
- 69KelPin-9
- 69MilBra-144
- 69MLBOffS-123
- 69MLBPin-48
- 69Top-225
- 69Top-422
- 69TopDec-18
- 69TopSta-16
- 69TopTeaP-4
- 70CubDunD-4
- 70DayDaiNM-108
- 70MLBOffS-20
- 70OPC-80
- 70OPC-456
- 70SunPin-6
- 70Top-80
- 70Top-456
- 71Kel-9A
- 71Kel-9B
- 71Kel-9C
- 71MilDud-50
- 71MLBOffS-36
- 71OPC-455
- 71Top-455
- 71TopCoi-119
- 71TopTat-123
- 72CubChi-4
- 72CubTeal-7
- 72MilBra-181
- 72OPC-145
- 72Top-145
- 73LinPor-41
- 73OPC-285
- 73SevTraC-36
- 73Top-285
- 74OPC-38
- 74Top-38
- 74TopDecE-52
- 74TopSta-16
- 75Hos-77
- 75HosTwi-77
- 75OPC-315
- 75Top-315
- 75TopMin-315
- 76BlaDis-25
- 76BucDis-25
- 76CarDis-25
- 76CraDis-25
- 76DaiIsID-25
- 76Hos-134
- 76IsaDis-25
- 76OPC-574
- 76OrbDis-25
- 76RedBarD-25
- 76SafDis-25
- 76SSP-315
- 76St.LouCP-17
- 76Top-574
- 76TowCluD-25
- 77CarTeal-12
- 77Top-229
- 78SSP270-154
- 78Top-672
- 79Top-404
- 79Top-467
- 84CubUno-2
- 84CubUno-7
- 89SweBasG-112
- 90PacLeg-34
- 90SweBasG-69
- 91SweBasG-115
- 91UppDecS-21
- 92ActPacA-76
- 92UppDecS-28
- 93UppDecAH-80
- 94TedWil-17

Kessinger, Keith
- 89BluOriS-12
- 90WauTimB-18
- 90WauTimP-2131
- 90WauTimS-12
- 91FreKeyC-29
- 92CedRapRC-8
- 92CedRapRF-1078
- 93ChaLooF-2366
- 94IndIndF-1817
- 94Pin-251
- 94PinArtP-251
- 94PinMusC-251
- 94PinRooTP-3
- 94Sco-621
- 94ScoBoyoS-42
- 94ScoGolR-621
- 95IowCubTI-17
- 96IowCubB-17

Kessler, Dave
- 92BoiHawC-5
- 92BoiHawF-3631
- 93CedRapKC-11
- 93CedRapKF-1742
- 94CedRapKC-16
- 94CedRapKF-1112

Kessler, Greg
- 89WytCubS-19
- 90GenCubP-3037
- 90GenCubS-16

Kester, Rick
- 70Top-621
- 71OPC-494
- 71RicBraTI-10
- 71Top-494
- 72OPC-351
- 72Top-351

Kester, Tim
- 93AubAstC-15
- 93AubAstF-3439
- 94OscAstC-12
- 94OscAstF-1133
- 95MidLeaA-26
- 95QuaCitRBTI-12
- 96JacGenB-15
- 97JacGen-13
- 97JacGenS-12
- 98JacGenM-8

Kester, William H.
- 08BufBisFJO-5

Ketcham, Lee Anne
- 95ColSilB-14
- 96ColSilB-16

Ketchen, Douglas
- 90AshTouC-6
- 90AubAstB-8
- 91AshTouP-564
- 92OscAstC-10
- 92OscAstF-2527
- 93JacGenF-2106
- 94JacGenF-215

Ketchen, J.B.
- 90AubAstP-3415

Ketleers, Cotuit
- 88CapCodPB-24

Keusch, Joe
- 94HudValRC-9
- 94HudValRF-3378

Keuter, Greg
- 89WytCubS-30
- 92HunCubC-30
- 95RocCubTI-NNO
- 96RocCubTI-15

Key, Calvin
- 98PieBolWM-19

Key, Denny
- 91BurIndP-3298
- 92WatIndC-5
- 92WatIndF-3229

Key, Greg
- 83RedPioT-16
- 85MidAngT-3

Key, Jeffrey
- 93MarPhiC-16
- 93MarPhiF-3489
- 95PiePhiF-197
- 97ClePhi-9
- 98ReaPhiM-15

Key, Jimmy
- 84BluJayFS-20
- 84FleUpd-61
- 84TopTra-62T
- 84TopTraT-62T
- 85BluJayCC-4
- 85BluJayFS-16
- 85Don-559
- 85Fle-110
- 85OPC-193
- 85Top-193
- 85TopTif-193
- 86BluJayAF-16
- 86BluJayFS-20
- 86Don-561
- 86DonAll-53
- 86Fle-63
- 86Fle-642
- 86KayB-18
- 86Lea-219
- 86OPC-291
- 86Top-545
- 86TopMinL-35
- 86TopSti-191
- 86TopTif-545
- 87BluJayFS-16
- 87Don-244
- 87DonOpeD-37
- 87Fle-232
- 87FleGlo-232
- 87GenMilB-1F
- 87Lea-187
- 87OPC-29
- 87SpoTeaP-5
- 87SyrChi1A-8
- 87Top-29
- 87TopSti-192
- 87TopTif-29
- 88BluJay5-7
- 88BluJayFS-16
- 88ClaBlu-249
- 88Don-72
- 88DonBasB-143
- 88Fle-114
- 88FleAwaW-22
- 88FleExcS-24
- 88FleGlo-114
- 88FleHotS-22
- 88FleLeaL-23
- 88FleMin-63
- 88FleRecS-22
- 88FleStiC-74
- 88FleSup-19
- 88FleTeaL-17
- 88Lea-67
- 88MSAHosD-24
- 88OPC-47
- 88PanSti-214
- 88RedFolSB-42
- 88Sco-216
- 88ScoGlo-216
- 88Spo-116
- 88StaLinBJ-10
- 88Top-395
- 88Top-682
- 88TopClo-54
- 88TopCoi-17
- 88TopMinL-39
- 88TopRevLL-27
- 88TopSti-190
- 88TopTif-395
- 88TopTif-682
- 89BluJayFS-14
- 89Bow-243
- 89BowTif-243
- 89Don-188
- 89DonBasB-87
- 89Fle-236
- 89FleGlo-236
- 89OPC-229
- 89PanSti-462
- 89Sco-480
- 89Spo-167
- 89Top-229
- 89TopBasT-129
- 89TopSti-186
- 89TopTif-229
- 89UppDec-291
- 90BluJayFS-13
- 90BluJayHS-3
- 90Bow-509
- 90BowTif-509
- 90Don-231
- 90DonBesA-42
- 90Fle-85
- 90FleCan-85
- 90Lea-211
- 90OPC-371
- 90PanSti-181
- 90PubIntS-518
- 90RedFolSB-53
- 90Sco-407
- 90Top-371
- 90TopSti-191
- 90TopTif-371
- 90UppDec-462
- 90VicPos-2
- 91BluJayFS-15
- 91BluJayFS-16
- 91BluJayS-3
- 91BluJayS-38
- 91Bow-19
- 91Cla3-T45
- 91ClaGam-63
- 91Don-98
- 91Fle-178
- 91Lea-103
- 91OPC-741
- 91OPCPre-71
- 91PanFreS-351
- 91Sco-422
- 91StaClu-221
- 91Top-741
- 91TopDesS-741
- 91TopMic-741
- 91TopTif-741
- 91Ult-364
- 91UppDec-667
- 91USPlaCA-8D
- 92BluJayP-6
- 92Bow-588
- 92Don-219
- 92DonMcD-14
- 92Fle-332
- 92Lea-111
- 92LeaBlaG-111
- 92OPC-482
- 92Pin-193
- 92RedFolS-120
- 92Sco-96
- 92SpoIllFK1-305
- 92StaClu-24
- 92StaCluD-98
- 92Top-482
- 92TopGol-482
- 92TopGolW-482
- 92TopMic-482
- 92Ult-147
- 92UppDec-302
- 93BluJayD4-19
- 93BluJayDM-20
- 93BluJayDWS-5
- 93Bow-427
- 93Don-710
- 93Fin-174
- 93FinRef-174
- 93Fla-247
- 93Fle-336
- 93FleFinE-247
- 93FunPac-207
- 93Lea-317
- 93MSABenSPD-19
- 93OPC-269
- 93OPCPre-15
- 93OPCWorC-8
- 93OPCWorSH-2
- 93PacSpa-558
- 93Pin-9
- 93Sco-639
- 93Sel-376
- 93SelRoo-13T
- 93SP-264
- 93StaClu-639
- 93StaCluFDI-639
- 93StaCluM-24
- 93StaCluMOP-639
- 93Stu-168
- 93Top-596
- 93TopGol-596
- 93TopInaM-596
- 93TopInaR-596
- 93TopMic-596
- 93TopTra-68T
- 93Ult-596
- 93UppDec-358
- 93UppDec-543
- 93UppDecGold-358
- 93UppDecGold-543
- 93YanStaC-13
- 94Bow-465
- 94BowBes-R60
- 94BowBesR-R60
- 94ColC-160
- 94ColChoGS-160
- 94ColChoSS-160
- 94Don-30
- 94DonSpeE-30
- 94Fin-299
- 94FinRef-299
- 94Fla-82
- 94Fle-236
- 94FleAllS-13
- 94FleExtB-132
- 94FleExtBPD-3
- 94FUnPac-165
- 94Lea-412
- 94LeaL-55
- 94LeaLimGA-17
- 94OPC-174
- 94Pac-427
- 94Pin-52
- 94PinArtP-52
- 94PinMusC-52
- 94Sco-75
- 94ScoGolR-75
- 94Sel-43
- 94SP-197
- 94SPDieC-197
- 94Spo-34
- 94StaClu-469
- 94StaCluFDI-469
- 94StaCluGR-469
- 94StaCluMOP-469
- 94StaCluT-205
- 94StaCluTFDI-205
- 94Stu-214
- 94Top-120
- 94Top-393
- 94TopGol-120
- 94TopGol-393
- 94TopSpa-120
- 94TopSpa-393
- 94TriPla-275
- 94Ult-96
- 94UppDec-259
- 94UppDecED-259
- 94USPlaCA-3S
- 95Baz-85
- 95BazRedH-RH17
- 95BluJayUSPC-6H
- 95BluJayUSPC-13S
- 95Bow-383
- 95ColCho-68
- 95ColChoGS-68
- 95ColChoSE-141
- 95ColChoSE-248
- 95ColChoSEGS-141
- 95ColChoSEGS-248
- 95ColChoSESS-141
- 95ColChoSESS-248
- 95ColChoSS-68
- 95Don-78
- 95DonAll-AL1
- 95DonMouM-5
- 95DonPreP-78
- 95Emo-61
- 95Fin-160
- 95FinRef-160
- 95Fla-64
- 95Fle-74
- 95FleAllS-9
- 95FleLeaL-4
- 95FleTeaL-10
- 95KinDis-24
- 95Kra-6
- 95Lea-75
- 95LeaLim-28
- 95Pac-298
- 95PacGolP-34
- 95PacPri-96
- 95PanSti-12
- 95PanSti-127
- 95Pin-268
- 95PinArtP-268
- 95PinMusC-268
- 95PosCan-10
- 95RedFol-27
- 95Sco-76
- 95ScoDreT-DG10
- 95ScoGolR-76
- 95ScoHaloG-HG47
- 95ScoPlaTS-76
- 95Sel-73
- 95SelArtP-73
- 95SelCer-13
- 95SelCerMG-13
- 95SP-177
- 95Spo-66
- 95SpoArtP-66
- 95SpoDouT-12
- 95SPSil-177
- 95StaClu-418
- 95StaCluMO-25
- 95StaCluMOP-418
- 95StaCluMOP-VRE10
- 95StaCluSTWS-418
- 95StaCluVE-VRE10
- 95StaCluVR-216
- 95StaCluVRMO-216
- 95Stu-155
- 95Sum-98
- 95SumNthD-98
- 95TomPiz-10
- 95Top-393
- 95Top-549
- 95TopCyb-330
- 95TopEmb-128
- 95TopEmbGI-128
- 95UC3-9
- 95UC3ArtP-9
- 95Ult-83
- 95UltGolM-83
- 95UltLeaL-3
- 95UltLeaLGM-3
- 95UppDec-205
- 95UppDecED-205
- 95UppDecEDG-205
- 95UppDecSE-142
- 95UppDecSEG-142
- 95Zen-52
- 96Don-381
- 96DonPreP-381
- 96Fla-130
- 96FleUpd-U62
- 96FleUpdTC-U62
- 96ProSta-137
- 96Sco-444
- 96Top-273
- 96Ult-388
- 96UltGolM-388
- 97BalOriP-19
- 97Cir-333
- 97CirRav-333
- 97ColCho-273
- 97ColChoT-BO10
- 97Don-309
- 97DonGolPP-309
- 97DonLim-60
- 97DonLimE-60
- 97DonLimENG-60
- 97DonSigA-59
- 97DonSigAC-72
- 97DonSigAM-72
- 97DonSilPP-309
- 97DonTea-42
- 97DonTeaSPE-42
- 97Fin-211
- 97FinRef-211
- 97FlaShoLC-122
- 97FlaShoLeg0-122
- 97FlaShoLeg1-122
- 97FlaShoM-A122
- 97FlaShoM-B122
- 97FlaShoM-C122
- 97FlaShoR0-122
- 97FlaShoR1-122
- 97FlaShoR2-122
- 97Fle-169
- 97Fle-585
- 97FleTif-169
- 97FleTif-585
- 97Lea-249
- 97LeaFraM-249
- 97LeaFraMDC-249
- 97NewPin-89
- 97NewPinAP-89
- 97NewPinMC-89
- 97NewPinPP-89
- 97OriSun-1
- 97Sco-410
- 97ScoArtPWB-410
- 97ScoResC-410
- 97ScoShoS-410
- 97ScoShoSAP-410
- 97SpoIll-46
- 97SpoIllEE-46
- 97StaClu-343
- 97StaCluMOP-343
- 97StrAll-34
- 97Top-121
- 97Ult-356
- 97UltGolME-356
- 97UltPlaME-356
- 97UppDec-526
- 98CirThu-257

❑ 98CirThuRav-257
❑ 98CirThuSupRav-257
❑ 98ColCho-42
❑ 98Don-97
❑ 98DonCol-97
❑ 98DonColL-241
❑ 98DonColP-643
❑ 98DonColS-97
❑ 98DonGolPP-97
❑ 98DonPre-93
❑ 98DonPreSeat-93
❑ 98DonPriCD-97
❑ 98DonPriCL-241
❑ 98DonPriCP-643
❑ 98DonSilPP-97
❑ 98Fin-246
❑ 98FinNo--246
❑ 98FinNo-R-246
❑ 98FinRef-246
❑ 98Fle-230
❑ 98Lea-41
❑ 98LeaFraDA-41
❑ 98LeaFraF-41
❑ 98LeaFraM-41
❑ 98LeaFraM-41
❑ 98LeaFraMDC-41
❑ 98LeaFraMDC-41
❑ 98LeaFraMZ2-41
❑ 98OriSco-2
❑ 98OriScoP-2
❑ 98Pac-26
❑ 98PacOme-31
❑ 98PacOmeR-31
❑ 98PacOnl-92
❑ 98PacOnlR-92
❑ 98PacOnlWC-92
❑ 98PacPlaB-26
❑ 98PacRedT-26
❑ 98PacSil-26
❑ 98Pin-41
❑ 98PinArtP-PP39
❑ 98PinMusC-PP39
❑ 98PinPreP-41
❑ 98PinSna-B09
❑ 98Sco-37
❑ 98ScoRT-209
❑ 98ScoSS-PP12
❑ 98ScoSSAP-PP12
❑ 98SpoIll-74
❑ 98SpoIllEE-74
❑ 98SpoIllFE-74
❑ 98SpoIllTaN-101
❑ 98SpoIllTaNEE-101
❑ 98StaCluFDI-57
❑ 98StaClul-57
❑ 98StaCluOneK-57
❑ 98StaCluPP-57
❑ 98Top-450
❑ 98TopChr-450
❑ 98TopChrR-450
❑ 98TopDevR-450
❑ 98TopDia-450
❑ 98TopMiniC-450
❑ 98Ult-177
❑ 98UltGolM-177
❑ 98UltMas-177
❑ 98UltPlaM-177
❑ 98UppDec-2
❑ 98UppDec-35
❑ 98UppDec10AP-8
❑ 98UppDec1APR-8
❑ 98UppDecSF-22
❑ 99Pac-53
❑ 99PacPlaB-53
❑ 99PacRed-53
Key, Scott
❑ 96LanLugB-15
❑ 97SpoIndG-14
❑ 98LanLugQ-7
Keyes, Stewart
❑ 88CapCodPPaLP-148
Keyote, Mascot
❑ 93FreKeyC-30
❑ 96FreKeyB-29
❑ 97FreKey-30
❑ 98FreKeyM-2
Keys, Woody
❑ 77ForLauYS-2
Keyser, Brian
❑ 89UtiBluSP-12
❑ 90SarWhiSS-13
❑ 91SarWhiSC-6
❑ 91SarWhiSP-1109
❑ 92BirBarF-2578
❑ 93LinVenB-252
❑ 93NasSouF-570
❑ 94NasSouF-1247
❑ 94VenLinU-152
❑ 95LinVen-134
❑ 95NasSouTI-8
❑ 95WhiSoxK-16
❑ 96Don-187
❑ 96DonPreP-187
❑ 96LeaSigEA-99
❑ 96Pac-281
❑ 96UppDec-43
❑ 98IndIndQ-10
Khalifa, Sammy
❑ 83AleDukT-2
❑ 85HawIslC-227
❑ 86Don-308
❑ 86Fle-611
❑ 86Lea-178
❑ 86Top-316
❑ 86TopSti-127
❑ 86TopTat-6
❑ 86TopTif-316
❑ 87Top-164
❑ 87TopTif-164
❑ 87VanCanP-1608
❑ 89BufBisC-15
❑ 89BufBisP-1667
Khoury, Mike
❑ 86WatPirP-10
Khoury, Scott
❑ 86HagSunP-8
❑ 87HagSunP-26
❑ 88WatIndP-672
❑ 89CanIndB-19
❑ 89CanIndP-1310
❑ 89CanIndS-10
Khoury, Tony
❑ 93HunCubC-12
❑ 93HunCubF-3238
❑ 95RocCubTI-25
Kibbe, Jay
❑ 81RedPioT-4
❑ 84EdmTraC-119
Kibbee, Jim
❑ 77ForLauYS-15
Kibler, John
❑ 88T/MUmp-4
❑ 89T/MUmp-2
❑ 90T/MUmp-2
Kibler, Russell
❑ 85MadMusP-16
❑ 85MadMusT-19
❑ 86MadMusP-13
❑ 86MadMusP-13
❑ 87HunStaTI-17
Kibota, Richie
❑ 87HawRai-5
Kida, Masao
❑ 88MiaMarS-14
❑ 99199Fin-299
❑ 99BowBes-200
❑ 99BowBesAR-200
❑ 99BowBesR-200
❑ 99FinGolRef-299
❑ 99FinRef-299
❑ 99FleBri-170
❑ 99FleBri2G-170
❑ 99FleBriBlu-170
❑ 99FleBriGol-170
❑ 99PacOme-94
❑ 99PacOmeC-94
❑ 99PacOmeG-94
❑ 99PacOmePB-94
❑ 99SkyMolM-127
❑ 99SkyMolMF-27
❑ 99SkyMolMFS-27
❑ 99SkyMolMFT-27
❑ 99SkyMolMX-127
❑ 99SkyPre-244
❑ 99SkyPre-244
❑ 99SkyPreR-244
❑ 99SkyPreR-244
❑ 99TopGal-132
❑ 99TopGalPP-132
❑ 99TopGalPPI-132
Kidd, Dennis
❑ 90MiaMirIS-12
❑ 90MiaMirIS-13
❑ 91MiaMirC-29
❑ 91MiaMirP-422
Kidd, Jake
❑ 98PorRocG-19
Kidd, Pete
❑ 92SkyAA F-270
Kidd, Scott
❑ 98GreBatM-6
Kidder, Jim
❑ 77ShrCapT-11
Kidwell, Tommy
❑ 98NewJerCM-17
Kiecker, Dana
❑ 86NewBriRSP-15
❑ 87NewBriRSP-17
❑ 88PawRedSC-10
❑ 88PawRedSP-461
❑ 89PawRedSC-4
❑ 89PawRedSP-701
❑ 89PawRedSTI-12
❑ 90DonRoo-28
❑ 90FleUpd-72
❑ 90Lea-525
❑ 90ScoRoo-102T
❑ 90TopTra-50T
❑ 90TopTraT-50T
❑ 90TopTVRS-12
❑ 91Bow-108
❑ 91Don-347
❑ 91Fle-99
❑ 91Lea-341
❑ 91OPC-763
❑ 91RedSoxP-10
❑ 91RedSoxP-16
❑ 91Sco-77
❑ 91Sco100RS-92
❑ 91StaClu-140
❑ 91Top-763
❑ 91TopDeb90-77
❑ 91TopDesS-763
❑ 91TopMic-763
❑ 91TopTif-763
❑ 91ToyRoo-15
❑ 91UltUpd-6
❑ 91UppDec-507
❑ 92OPC-163
❑ 92Sco-732
❑ 92Top-163
❑ 92TopGol-163
❑ 92TopGolW-163
❑ 92TopMic-163
Kiefer, Dax
❑ 97WilCubB-12
Kiefer, Mark
❑ 89BelBre2S-17
❑ 89BelBreIS-11
❑ 91ElPasDLD-190
❑ 91ElPasDP-2744
❑ 91LinDriAA-190
❑ 92Bow-674
❑ 92DenZepF-2636
❑ 92DenZepS-134
❑ 92SkyAAAF-66
❑ 93Bow-155
❑ 93BrePol-13
❑ 93Don-263
❑ 93El PasDF-2947
❑ 93LeaGolR-R3
❑ 93LeaGolRJ-R3
❑ 93StaClu-417
❑ 93StaCluFDI-417
❑ 93StaCluMOP-417
❑ 94BreMilB-136
❑ 94BrePol-15
❑ 94BreTeal-13
❑ 94ColC-161
❑ 94ColChoGS-161
❑ 94ColChoSS-161
❑ 94Fla-69
❑ 94Pin-526
❑ 94PinArtP-526
❑ 94PinMusC-526
❑ 94ScoRoo-RT139
❑ 94ScoRooGR-RT139
❑ 94Sel-380
❑ 94SpoRoo-107
❑ 94SpoRooAP-107
❑ 94Top-770
❑ 94TopGol-770
❑ 94TopSpa-770
❑ 94Ult-373
❑ 95Fla-272
❑ 95FleUpd-53
❑ 95Lea-143
❑ 95Sco-294
❑ 95ScoGolR-294
❑ 95ScoPlaTS-294
❑ 95StaClu-581
❑ 95StaCluMOP-581
❑ 95StaCluSTWS-581
❑ 95TopTra-17T
❑ 96Don-448
❑ 96DonPreP-448
❑ 96Fle-149
❑ 96FleTif-149
❑ 96LeaSigA-126
❑ 96LeaSigAG-126
❑ 96LeaSigAS-126
Kiefer, Steve
❑ 82MadMusF-3
❑ 83AlbA'sT-12
❑ 84TacTigC-78
❑ 85Don-35
❑ 85Fle-647
❑ 85Lea-27
❑ 85TacTigC-139
❑ 86Don-420
❑ 86VanCanP-15
❑ 87DenZepP-18
❑ 88BrePol-30
❑ 88BreTeal-21
❑ 88Don-542
❑ 88Fle-167
❑ 88FleGlo-167
❑ 88Sco-630
❑ 88ScoGlo-630
❑ 88StaLinBre-10
❑ 88Top-187
❑ 88TopClo-55
❑ 88TopTif-187
❑ 89ColCliC-15
❑ 89ColCliP-15
❑ 89ColCliP-740
❑ 90BufBisC-17
❑ 90BufBisP-379
❑ 90BufBisTI-11
❑ 90CMC-17
❑ 90ProAAAF-494
❑ 92YanWIZ8-100
❑ 94BreMilB-137
Kiely, John
❑ 89LakTigS-12
❑ 90CMC-768
❑ 90LonTigP-1264
❑ 90ProAaA-18
❑ 91LinDriAAA-587
❑ 91TolMudHLD-587
❑ 91TolMudHP-1927
❑ 92FleUpd-24
❑ 92SkyAAAF-265
❑ 92StaClu-384
❑ 92TigKro-13
❑ 92TolMudHF-1040
❑ 92TolMudHS-591
❑ 92TopDeb91-99
❑ 93Don-203
❑ 93Fle-230
❑ 93StaClu-212
❑ 93StaCluFDI-212
❑ 93StaCluMOP-212
❑ 93Top-107
❑ 93TopGol-107
❑ 93TopInaM-107
❑ 93TopInaR-107
❑ 93TopMic-107
❑ 93Ult-200
❑ 93UppDec-378
❑ 93UppDecGold-378
❑ 94TolMudHF-1024
Kiely, Leo
❑ 52Top-54
❑ 54Top-171
❑ 55Top-36
❑ 55TopDouH-43
❑ 58Top-204
❑ 59Top-199
❑ 60Top-94
❑ 60TopVen-94
❑ 81RedSoxBG2S-31
❑ 83TopRep5-54
❑ 94TopArc1-171
❑ 94TopArc1G-171
Kieran, Jack
❑ 95ConTSN-1400
Kiernan, J.F.
❑ 09T206-495
Kierst, Kevin
❑ 87KnoBluJP-1517
Kies, Norman
❑ 36WorWidGV-120
Kieschnick, Brooks
❑ 93Tex-4
❑ 94ActPac-4
❑ 94ActPac-57
❑ 94ActPac2G-3G
❑ 94ActPac2GD-3G
❑ 94AriFalLS-12
❑ 94Bow-354
❑ 94Bow-438
❑ 94BowBes-B5
❑ 94BowBes-X92
❑ 94BowBesR-B5
❑ 94BowBesR-X92
❑ 94Cla-200
❑ 94ClaBonB-BB4
❑ 94ClaCreotC-C4
❑ 94ClaGolF-130
❑ 94ClaGolN1PLF-LP6
❑ 94ClaGolREF-RE6
❑ 94ClaGolREF-RE20
❑ 94ClaTriF-T13
❑ 94ColC-28
❑ 94ColChoGS-28
❑ 94ColChoSS-28
❑ 94ExcFS7-165
❑ 94FleExtB-219
❑ 94FleExtBMLH-5
❑ 94OrlCubF-1398
❑ 94Pin-262
❑ 94PinArtP-262
❑ 94PinMusC-262
❑ 94Sco-517
❑ 94ScoGolR-517
❑ 94SigRoo-32
❑ 94SigRooS-32
❑ 94SP-9
❑ 94SPDieC-9
❑ 94SPHol-20
❑ 94SPHolDC-20
❑ 94Top-205
❑ 94TopGol-205
❑ 94TopSpa-205
❑ 94Ult-460
❑ 94UppDec-530
❑ 94UppDecED-530
❑ 94UppDecML-2
❑ 95Bes-57
❑ 95Bow-263
❑ 95BowBes-B12
❑ 95BowBesR-B12
❑ 95BowGolF-263
❑ 95Exc-166
❑ 95Fle-418
❑ 95IowCubTI-18
❑ 95PinETA-6
❑ 95Sel-164
❑ 95SelArtP-164
❑ 95SPML-2
❑ 95SPML-30
❑ 95SPMLA-16
❑ 95SPMLDtS-DS4
❑ 95Top-246
❑ 95UppDecML-15
❑ 95UppDecMLFS-15
❑ 95UppDecMLOP-OP5
❑ 96BesAutSA-36
❑ 96Bow-196
❑ 96BowBes-113
❑ 96BowBesAR-113
❑ 96BowBesP-BBP3
❑ 96BowBesPAR-BBP3
❑ 96BowBesPR-BBP3
❑ 96BowBesR-113
❑ 96BowFoi-196
❑ 96ColCho-430
❑ 96ColChoGS-430
❑ 96ColChoSS-430
❑ 96CubFle-11
❑ 96Exc-138
❑ 96ExcTL-5
❑ 96Fin-B316
❑ 96FinRef-B316
❑ 96FleUpd-U112
❑ 96FleUpdNH-15
❑ 96FleUpdTC-U112
❑ 96IowCubB-1
❑ 96LeaPre-130
❑ 96LeaPreP-130
❑ 96LeaSig-95
❑ 96LeaSigA-127
❑ 96LeaSigAG-127
❑ 96LeaSigAS-127
❑ 96LeaSigPPG-95
❑ 96LeaSigPPP-95
❑ 96Pin-377
❑ 96PinAfi-181
❑ 96PinAfiAP-181
❑ 96PinFoil-377
❑ 96PinProS-11
❑ 96Sel-121
❑ 96SelArtP-121
❑ 96SelCer-114
❑ 96SelCerAP-114
❑ 96SelCerCB-114
❑ 96SelCerCR-114
❑ 96SelCerMB-114
❑ 96SelCerMG-114
❑ 96SelCerMR-114
❑ 96Stu-115
❑ 96StuPrePB-115
❑ 96StuPrePG-115
❑ 96StuPrePS-115
❑ 96Sum-164
❑ 96SumAbo&B-164
❑ 96SumArtP-164
❑ 96SumFoi-164
❑ 96Top-344
❑ 96TopChr-136
❑ 96TopChrR-136
❑ 96TopGal-135
❑ 96TopGalPPI-135
❑ 96TopLasBS-4
❑ 96Ult-451
❑ 96UltGolM-451
❑ 96UppDec-242
❑ 96UppDecBCP-BC12
❑ 96UppDecPHE-H58
❑ 96UppDecPreH-H58
❑ 96Zen-121
❑ 96ZenArtP-121
❑ 97Bow-141
❑ 97BowCerBlaIA-CA43
❑ 97BowCerBluIA-CA43
❑ 97BowCerGolIA-CA43
❑ 97BowChr-149
❑ 97BowChrI-149
❑ 97BowChrIR-149
❑ 97BowChrR-149
❑ 97BowInt-141
❑ 97ColCho-286
❑ 97Don-368
❑ 97DonEliTotC-16
❑ 97DonEliTotCDC-16
❑ 97DonGolPP-368
❑ 97DonLim-33
❑ 97DonLim-156
❑ 97DonLimE-33
❑ 97DonLimE-156
❑ 97DonLimENG-33
❑ 97DonPre-154
❑ 97DonPreCttC-154
❑ 97DonRatR-17
❑ 97DonSigA-60
❑ 97DonSigAC-73
❑ 97DonSigAM-73
❑ 97DonSilPP-368
❑ 97E-X2SD2000-4
❑ 97Fin-218
❑ 97FinRef-218
❑ 97Fle-279
❑ 97FleTif-279
❑ 97Lea-133
❑ 97Lea-344
❑ 97LeaFraM-133
❑ 97LeaFraM-344
❑ 97LeaFraMDC-133
❑ 97LeaFraMDC-344
❑ 97Pac-252
❑ 97PacLigB-252
❑ 97PacPri-86
❑ 97PacPriLB-86
❑ 97PacPriP-86
❑ 97PacSil-252
❑ 97PinCer-118
❑ 97PinCerMBla-118
❑ 97PinCerMBlu-118
❑ 97PinCerMG-118
❑ 97PinCerMR-118
❑ 97PinCerR-118
❑ 97PinTotCPB-118
❑ 97PinTotCPG-118
❑ 97PinTotCPR-118
❑ 97PinX-P-127
❑ 97PinX-PMoS-127
❑ 97Sco-71
❑ 97ScoArtPWB-71
❑ 97ScoPreS-71
❑ 97ScoShoS-71
❑ 97ScoShoSAP-71
❑ 97StaClu-94
❑ 97StaCluM-M29
❑ 97StaCluMOP-94
❑ 97StaCluMOP-M29
❑ 97Stu-153
❑ 97StuPrePG-153
❑ 97StuPrePS-153
❑ 97Top-389
❑ 97TopAwel-AI11
❑ 98DurBulTI-14
❑ 98Pac-254
❑ 98PacPlaB-254
❑ 98PacRedT-254
❑ 98PacSil-254

❑ 98PinPlu-121
❑ 98PinSna-TBDR9
❑ 98PinSna-TBDR17
❑ 98ScoRT-229
❑ 98Top-472
❑ 98TopChr-472
❑ 98TopChrR-472
❑ 98TopDevR-472
❑ 98TopDia-472
❑ 98TopMiniC-472
Kiess, Paul
❑ 80PenPilBT-17
❑ 80PenPilCT-23
Kifer, Jack
❑ 21Zee-100
Kiil, Skip
❑ 97PieBolWB-16
❑ 98ClePhiM-12
❑ 98ClePhiUM-12
Kiker, Ed
❑ 89GeoColC-15
Kilburg, Joe
❑ 97BurIndG-15
❑ 98ColRedSM-16
Kildoo, Don
❑ 57JetPos-9
Kilduff, Pete
❑ 17HolBreD-57
❑ 20GasAmeMBD-22
❑ 20NatCarE-55A
❑ 20NatCarE-55B
❑ 21E121So1-52
❑ 21E121So8-48
❑ 22AmeCarE122-37
❑ 22W575-69
❑ 22Zee-101
❑ 23W501-94
❑ 23WilChoV-79
❑ 23Zee-135
❑ 24Zee-95
❑ 25Zee-113
❑ 26Zee-143
Kile, Darryl
❑ 89BasAmeAPB-AA12
❑ 89ColMudB-4
❑ 89ColMudP-133
❑ 89ColMudS-15
❑ 89TucTorJP-12
❑ 90Bow-61
❑ 90BowTif-61
❑ 90CMC-606
❑ 90ProAAAF-191
❑ 90TucTorC-4
❑ 90TucTorP-201
❑ 91AstMot-27
❑ 91Bow-548
❑ 91DonRoo-5
❑ 91FleUpd-90
❑ 91ScoRoo-86T
❑ 91Stu-178
❑ 91TopTra-68T
❑ 91TopTraT-68T
❑ 91UltUpd-84
❑ 91UppDec-774
❑ 92AstMot-24
❑ 92Bow-601
❑ 92Cla1-T49
❑ 92ClaGam-116
❑ 92Don-309
❑ 92Fle-439
❑ 92Lea-198
❑ 92LeaBlaG-198
❑ 92OPC-134
❑ 92OPCPre-196
❑ 92Pin-225
❑ 92Sco-494
❑ 92Sco100RS-4
❑ 92StaClu-837
❑ 92StaCluNC-837
❑ 92Stu-39
❑ 92Top-134
❑ 92TopDeb91-100
❑ 92TopGol-134
❑ 92TopGolW-134
❑ 92TopMic-134
❑ 92Ult-206
❑ 92UppDec-374
❑ 93AstMot-19
❑ 93AstStaC-17
❑ 93Don-668
❑ 93Fla-66
❑ 93Fle-438
❑ 93Lea-143
❑ 93PacSpa-479
❑ 93Pin-430
❑ 93Sco-430
❑ 93SP-36
❑ 93StaClu-518
❑ 93StaCluFDI-518
❑ 93StaCluMO-12
❑ 93StaCluMOP-518
❑ 93Top-308
❑ 93TopGol-308
❑ 93TopInaM-308
❑ 93TopInaR-308
❑ 93TopMic-308
❑ 93Ult-393
❑ 93UppDec-314
❑ 93UppDecGold-314
❑ 94AstMot-6
❑ 94Bow-614
❑ 94ColC-162
❑ 94ColChoGS-162
❑ 94ColChoSS-162
❑ 94Don-32
❑ 94DonSpeE-32
❑ 94Fin-244
❑ 94FinRef-244
❑ 94Fla-173
❑ 94Fle-496
❑ 94FleAllS-43
❑ 94FleExtB-277
❑ 94FleGolM-10
❑ 94FleGolMJ-10
❑ 94FUnPac-52
❑ 94Lea-314
❑ 94OPC-176
❑ 94Pac-270
❑ 94PanSti-196
❑ 94Pin-321
❑ 94PinArtP-321
❑ 94PinMusC-321
❑ 94Sco-231
❑ 94Sco-630
❑ 94ScoGolR-231
❑ 94ScoGolR-630
❑ 94Sel-326
❑ 94Spo-72
❑ 94StaClu-327
❑ 94StaCluFDI-327
❑ 94StaCluGR-327
❑ 94StaCluMOP-327
❑ 94Stu-23
❑ 94Top-703
❑ 94TopGol-703
❑ 94TopSpa-703
❑ 94TriPla-29
❑ 94Ult-208
❑ 94UppDec-435
❑ 94UppDecED-435
❑ 95AstMot-4
❑ 95ColCho-118
❑ 95ColChoGS-118
❑ 95ColChoSE-41
❑ 95ColChoSEGS-41
❑ 95ColChoSESS-41
❑ 95ColChoSS-118
❑ 95Don-398
❑ 95DonPreP-398
❑ 95Fla-148
❑ 95Fle-465
❑ 95Lea-110
❑ 95Pin-238
❑ 95PinArtP-238
❑ 95PinMusC-238
❑ 95Sco-177
❑ 95ScoGolR-177
❑ 95ScoPlaTS-177
❑ 95Sel-20
❑ 95SelArtP-20
❑ 95StaClu-447
❑ 95StaCluMOP-447
❑ 95StaCluSTWS-447
❑ 95StaCluVR-238
❑ 95StaCluVRMO-238
❑ 95Top-228
❑ 95TopCyb-128
❑ 95Ult-388
❑ 95UltGolM-388
❑ 95UppDec-22
❑ 95UppDecED-22
❑ 95UppDecEDG-22
❑ 95UppDecSE-178
❑ 95UppDecSEG-178
❑ 96AstMot-5
❑ 96Cir-138
❑ 96CirRav-138
❑ 96ColCho-564
❑ 96ColChoGS-564
❑ 96ColChoSS-564
❑ 96Don-519
❑ 96DonPreP-519
❑ 96Fle-413
❑ 96FleTif-413
❑ 96Ult-488
❑ 96UltGolM-488
❑ 96UppDec-346
❑ 97AstMot-4
❑ 97Cir-199
❑ 97CirRav-199
❑ 97ColCho-349
❑ 97Don-337
❑ 97DonGolPP-337
❑ 97DonLim-114
❑ 97DonLimE-114
❑ 97DonLimENG-114
❑ 97DonSilPP-337
❑ 97FlaShoLC-157
❑ 97FlaShoLeg0-157
❑ 97FlaShoLeg1-157
❑ 97FlaShoM-A157
❑ 97FlaShoM-B157
❑ 97FlaShoM-C157
❑ 97FlaShoR0-157
❑ 97FlaShoR1-157
❑ 97FlaShoR2-157
❑ 97Fle-349
❑ 97FleTif-349
❑ 97Lea-293
❑ 97LeaFraM-293
❑ 97LeaFraMDC-293
❑ 97MetUni-138
❑ 97Pac-320
❑ 97PacLigB-320
❑ 97PacSil-320
❑ 97Pin-49
❑ 97PinArtP-PP49
❑ 97PinMusC-49
❑ 97PinPrePla-49
❑ 97Sco-371
❑ 97ScoArtPWB-371
❑ 97ScoShoS-371
❑ 97ScoShoSAP-371
❑ 97Sel-177
❑ 97SelCom-177
❑ 97SP-81
❑ 97StaClu-295
❑ 97StaCluMOP-295
❑ 97StrAll-35
❑ 97Top-315
❑ 97TopSta-99
❑ 97TopStaAM-99
❑ 97Ult-209
❑ 97UltGolME-209
❑ 97UltPlaME-209
❑ 97UppDec-368
❑ 98CirThu-295
❑ 98CirThuRav-295
❑ 98CirThuSupRav-295
❑ 98ColCho-365
❑ 98Don-3
❑ 98Don-201
❑ 98DonCol-3
❑ 98DonColL-325
❑ 98DonColS-3
❑ 98DonGolPP-3
❑ 98DonGolPP-201
❑ 98DonPriCD-3
❑ 98DonPriCL-325
❑ 98DonSilPP-3
❑ 98DonSilPP-201
❑ 98E-X2-57
❑ 98E-X2ECFut-57
❑ 98E-X2ECNow-57
❑ 98FlaShoLeg0-87
❑ 98FlaShoLeg1-87
❑ 98FlaShoLeg2-87
❑ 98FlaShoLeg3-87
❑ 98FlaShoLegM-87
❑ 98FlaShoR0-87
❑ 98FlaShoR1-87
❑ 98FlaShoR2-87
❑ 98FlaShoR3-87
❑ 98Fle-57
❑ 98Fle-357
❑ 98FleVin'-89
❑ 98FleVin'C-89
❑ 98Lea-126
❑ 98LeaFraDA-126
❑ 98LeaFraF-126
❑ 98LeaFraM-126
❑ 98LeaFraM-126
❑ 98LeaFraMDC-126
❑ 98LeaFraMDC-126
❑ 98LeaFraMZ2-126
❑ 98MetUni-19
❑ 98MetUniPMG-19
❑ 98Pac-322
❑ 98PacAur-127
❑ 98PacInv-105
❑ 98PacInvPBlue-105
❑ 98PacInvSilv-105
❑ 98PacInvTeam-12
❑ 98PacOme-83
❑ 98PacOmeR-83
❑ 98PacOnl-248
❑ 98PacOnlR-248
❑ 98PacOnlWC-248
❑ 98PacPar-155
❑ 98PacParC-155
❑ 98PacParG-155
❑ 98PacParHS-155
❑ 98PacParPB-155
❑ 98PacParR-155
❑ 98PacPlaB-322
❑ 98PacRedT-322
❑ 98PacSil-322
❑ 98Pin-22
❑ 98PinArtP-PP22
❑ 98PinMusC-PP22
❑ 98PinPlu-95
❑ 98PinPreP-22
❑ 98PinSna-CR4
❑ 98PinSna-CR12
❑ 98Sco-148
❑ 98ScoRT-173
❑ 98ScoSS-PP158
❑ 98ScoSSAP-PP158
❑ 98SkyDugA-15
❑ 98SkyDugAD-D7
❑ 98SkyDugAIA-15
❑ 98SP Aut-87
❑ 98SpoIll-75
❑ 98SpoIll-140
❑ 98SpoIllEE-75
❑ 98SpoIllEE-140
❑ 98SpoIllFE-75
❑ 98SpoIllFE-140
❑ 98SpoIllTaN-102
❑ 98SpoIllTaNEE-102
❑ 98SpoIllWSF-60
❑ 98SpoIllWSFEE-60
❑ 98SpoIllWSFFE-60
❑ 98SPxFin-269
❑ 98SPxFin-338
❑ 98SPxFinR-269
❑ 98SPxFinR-338
❑ 98SPxFinS-269
❑ 98SPxFinS-338
❑ 98StaCluFDI-368
❑ 98StaCluI-368
❑ 98StaCluOneK-368
❑ 98StaCluPP-368
❑ 98Stu-72
❑ 98StuGPP-72
❑ 98StuSPP-72
❑ 98Top-170
❑ 98TopChr-170
❑ 98TopChrR-170
❑ 98TopDevR-170
❑ 98TopDia-170
❑ 98TopGal-10
❑ 98TopGalGP-10
❑ 98TopGalOPP-10
❑ 98TopGalPPI-10
❑ 98TopGalPPIA-10
❑ 98TopMiniC-170
❑ 98TopOpeD-90
❑ 98TopSta-2
❑ 98TopStaB-2
❑ 98TopStaG-2
❑ 98TopStaGR-2
❑ 98TopStaS-2
❑ 98Ult-13
❑ 98Ult-303
❑ 98UltDouT-11
❑ 98UltGolM-13
❑ 98UltGolM-303
❑ 98UltMas-13
❑ 98UltMas-303
❑ 98UltPlaM-13
❑ 98UltPlaM-303
❑ 98UppDec-99
❑ 98UppDec-675
❑ 99FlaShoLeg1-133
❑ 99FlaShoLeg2-133
❑ 99FlaShoLeg3-133
❑ 99FlaShoLegM1-133
❑ 99FlaShoLegM2-133
❑ 99FlaShoLegM3-133
❑ 99FlaShoR1-133
❑ 99FlaShoR2-133
❑ 99FlaShoR3-133
❑ 99Fle-91
❑ 99FleSta9-91
❑ 99FleWarT-91
❑ 99MetUni-156
❑ 99MetUniGM-156
❑ 99MetUniPMG-156
❑ 99Pac-148
❑ 99PacAur-63
❑ 99PacAurOD-63
❑ 99PacCroC-97
❑ 99PacCroCPB-97
❑ 99PacOme-84
❑ 99PacOmeC-84
❑ 99PacOmeG-84
❑ 99PacOmePB-84
❑ 99PacPar-83
❑ 99PacParC-83
❑ 99PacParG-83
❑ 99PacParHoloGold-83
❑ 99PacParHS-83
❑ 99PacParOD-83
❑ 99PacParPB-83
❑ 99PacParRed-83
❑ 99PacPlaB-148
❑ 99PacRed-148
❑ 99SkyPre-44
❑ 99SkyPreR-44
❑ 99SkyThu-102
❑ 99SkyThuRant-102
❑ 99SkyThuRave-102
❑ 99StaClu-176
❑ 99StaCluFDI-176
❑ 99StaCluOoaK-176
❑ 99StaCluPP-176
❑ 99ThuSkySupR-102
❑ 99Top-192
❑ 99TopChr-192
❑ 99TopChrR-192
❑ 99TopMVPP-192
❑ 99Ult-154
❑ 99UltGolM-154
❑ 99UltMas-154
❑ 99UltPlaM-154
❑ 99UppDec-88
❑ 99UppDecEL1-88
❑ 99UppDecEL2-88
❑ 99UppDecM-68
❑ 99UppDecMGS-68
❑ 99UppDecMHFS-68
❑ 99UppDecMP-68
❑ 99UppDecMSS-68
❑ 99Vic-135
Kiley, Craig
❑ 84LitFalMT-15
Kilgo, Dub
❑ 89AriStaB-15
❑ 94HelBreF-3628
❑ 94HelBreSP-25
❑ 95BelBreTI-29
Kilgo, Rusty
❑ 89AriStaB-16
❑ 89AriStaB-17
❑ 89JamExpP-2156
❑ 90MidLeaASGS-11
❑ 90ProAaA-110
❑ 90RocExpLC-12
❑ 90RocExpP-2685
❑ 91FloStaLAP-FSL43
❑ 91WesPalBEC-6
❑ 91WesPalBEP-1222
❑ 92CedRapRC-15
❑ 92CedRapRF-1069
❑ 92ChaLooF-3814
❑ 92RocExpC-4
❑ 93ChaLooF-2360
❑ 94IndIndF-1806
❑ 95ChaLooTI-8
❑ 96MemChiB-18
Kilgus, Paul
❑ 86TulDriTI-20
❑ 87OklCit8P-1
❑ 88Don-469
❑ 88DonBasB-111
❑ 88Fle-471
❑ 88FleGlo-471
❑ 88RanMot-19
❑ 88Sco-536
❑ 88ScoGlo-536
❑ 88Top-427
❑ 88TopTif-427
❑ 89Bow-285
❑ 89BowTif-285
❑ 89CubMar-39
❑ 89Don-283
❑ 89DonBasB-149
❑ 89DonTra-42
❑ 89Fle-525
❑ 89FleGlo-525
❑ 89FleUpd-76
❑ 89OPC-276
❑ 89Sco-271
❑ 89Top-276
❑ 89TopTif-276
❑ 89TopTra-60T
❑ 89TopTraT-60T
❑ 89UppDec-335
❑ 89UppDec-797
❑ 90BluJayFS-14
❑ 90Bow-508
❑ 90BowTif-508
❑ 90CMC-335
❑ 90Don-276
❑ 90Fle-34
❑ 90FleCan-34
❑ 90OPC-86
❑ 90ProAAAF-346
❑ 90PubIntS-196
❑ 90Sco-196
❑ 90SyrChiC-9
❑ 90SyrChiMB-13
❑ 90SyrChiP-566
❑ 90Top-86
❑ 90TopTif-86
❑ 90UppDec-155
❑ 91BalOriP-15
❑ 91OriCro-499
❑ 92LouRedF-1885
❑ 92LouRedS-266
❑ 92Sco-268
❑ 92StaClu-722
❑ 93FleFinE-125
❑ 93LouRedF-209
❑ 93RanKee-217
❑ 94CarPol-8
❑ 94Pac-593
❑ 94StaCluT-324
❑ 94StaCluTFDI-324
❑ 94Top-737
❑ 94TopGol-737
❑ 94TopSpa-737
Kiihullen, Joseph
❑ 17Zee-27
❑ 22Zee-47
Kilkenny, Mike
❑ 69TigTeal-5
❑ 69Top-544
❑ 70MLBOffS-209
❑ 70OPC-424
❑ 70Top-424
❑ 71MLBOffS-397
❑ 71OPC-86
❑ 71Top-86
❑ 72OPC-337
❑ 72Top-337
❑ 73OPC-551
❑ 73Top-551
❑ 77PadSchC-33
Killebrew, Cameron
❑ 79WauTimT-22
Killebrew, Harmon
❑ 47Exh-117A
❑ 47Exh-117B
❑ 47Exh-117C
❑ 47PM1StaP1-103
❑ 55DonWin-29
❑ 55DonWin-43
❑ 55Top-124
❑ 55TopDouH-111
❑ 56Top-164
❑ 58HarSta-16
❑ 58Top-288
❑ 59HomRunD-10
❑ 59Top-515
❑ 59WilSpoG-4
❑ 60Baz-20
❑ 60KeyChal-28
❑ 60NuHi-49
❑ 60Pos-5
❑ 60RawGloT-11
❑ 60SenJayP-7
❑ 60SenUniMC-10
❑ 60Top-210
❑ 60TopTat-26
❑ 60TopTat-91
❑ 61ChePat-6
❑ 61NuSco-449
❑ 61Pos-92A
❑ 61Pos-92B
❑ 61Top-80
❑ 61TopStaI-181
❑ 61TwiCloD-10
❑ 61TwiJayP-5
❑ 61TwiPetM-18

❑ 61TwiUniMC-7
❑ 62BasPen-2
❑ 62Baz-44
❑ 62ExhStaB-18
❑ 62Jel-85
❑ 62Pos-85
❑ 62PosCan-85
❑ 62SalPlaC-36
❑ 62ShiPlaC-36
❑ 62Top-53
❑ 62Top-70
❑ 62Top-316
❑ 62TopBuc-44
❑ 62TopStal-76
❑ 62TopVen-53
❑ 62TopVen-70
❑ 63BasMagM-44
❑ 63Baz-7
❑ 63ExhStaB-35
❑ 63Jel-5
❑ 63Pos-5
❑ 63Top-4
❑ 63Top-500
❑ 63TopStil-22
❑ 63TwiJayP-6
❑ 63TwiVol-10
❑ 64Baz-7
❑ 64Top-10
❑ 64Top-12
❑ 64Top-81
❑ 64Top-177
❑ 64TopCoi-112
❑ 64TopCoi-133
❑ 64TopGia-38
❑ 64TopSta-34
❑ 64TopStaU-39
❑ 64TopTatl-47
❑ 64TopVen-10
❑ 64TopVen-12
❑ 64TopVen-81
❑ 64TopVen-177
❑ 64TwiJayP-7
❑ 64WheSta-25
❑ 65Baz-7
❑ 65OldLonC-28
❑ 65OPC-3
❑ 65OPC-5
❑ 65Top-3
❑ 65Top-5
❑ 65Top-400
❑ 65TopEmbl-56
❑ 65TopTral-52
❑ 65TwiPos-5
❑ 66Baz-11
❑ 66OPC-120
❑ 66Top-120
❑ 66TopRubl-45
❑ 66TopVen-120
❑ 66TwiFaiG-7
❑ 67AshOil-4
❑ 67Baz-11
❑ 67CokCapA-18
❑ 67CokCapAAm-26
❑ 67CokCapTw-6
❑ 67DexPre-115
❑ 67DexPre-116
❑ 67OPCPapl-23
❑ 67Top-241
❑ 67Top-243
❑ 67Top-334
❑ 67Top-460
❑ 67TopGiaSU-6
❑ 67TopPos-23
❑ 67TopVen-206
❑ 67TwiTeal-7
❑ 68Baz-8
❑ 68DexPre-46
❑ 68OPC-4
❑ 68OPC-6
❑ 68Top-4
❑ 68Top-6
❑ 68Top-220
❑ 68Top-361
❑ 68Top-490
❑ 68TopActS-2B
❑ 68TopActS-9A
❑ 68TopActS-14B
❑ 68TopGaml-5
❑ 68TopPla-7
❑ 68TopPos-10
❑ 68TopVen-4
❑ 68TopVen-6
❑ 68TopVen-220
❑ 68TopVen-361
❑ 69CitMetC-4
❑ 69MilBra-145
❑ 69MLBOffS-68
❑ 69MLBPin-14
❑ 69Top-375
❑ 69TopDecl-21
❑ 69TopSta-195
❑ 69TopSup-19
❑ 69TopTeaP-15
❑ 69TraSta-11
❑ 69TwiTealC-6
❑ 70DayDaiNM-4
❑ 70Houof J-11
❑ 70Kel-61
❑ 70MilBra-12
❑ 70MLBOffS-234
❑ 70OPC-64
❑ 70OPC-66
❑ 70OPC-150
❑ 70Top-64
❑ 70Top-66
❑ 70Top-150
❑ 70TopCanL-12
❑ 70TopScr-11
❑ 70TopSup-4
❑ 70TraSta-15B
❑ 70TwiSupV-5
❑ 71AllBasA-14
❑ 71BazNumT-17
❑ 71BazUnn-2
❑ 71Kel-55
❑ 71MilDud-14
❑ 71MLBOffS-465
❑ 71MLBOffS-566
❑ 71OPC-65
❑ 71OPC-550
❑ 71Top-65
❑ 71Top-550
❑ 71TopCoi-100
❑ 71TopGreM-8
❑ 71TopSup-60
❑ 71TopTat-49
❑ 71TopTat-50
❑ 72MilBra-182
❑ 72OPC-51
❑ 72OPC-52
❑ 72OPC-88
❑ 72ProStaP-28
❑ 72SevTraC-26
❑ 72Top-51
❑ 72Top-52
❑ 72Top-88
❑ 72TopPos-20
❑ 72TwiPos-8
❑ 73OPC-170
❑ 73Top-170
❑ 73TopCanL-25
❑ 73TopCom-9
❑ 73TopPin-9
❑ 74OPC-400
❑ 74Top-400
❑ 74TopSta-208
❑ 75OPC-207
❑ 75OPC-640
❑ 75RoyPos-14
❑ 75TCMHouoJ-11
❑ 75Top-207
❑ 75Top-640
❑ 75TopMin-207
❑ 75TopMin-640
❑ 76LauDiaJ-13
❑ 76SSP-168
❑ 77SerSta-15
❑ 78TCM60I-90
❑ 78TwiFri-8
❑ 80Lau300-14
❑ 80MarExh-15
❑ 80PacLeg-69
❑ 80PerHaloFP-188
❑ 80PerHaloFPS-53
❑ 80SSPHOF-185
❑ 80TwiPos-13
❑ 82CraJac-5
❑ 82DiaCla-89
❑ 82K-M-15
❑ 82TCMGreS-1
❑ 83FraBroR-28
❑ 83FraBroR-40
❑ 83YanYealT-7
❑ 84OCoandSI-19
❑ 84SpoDesPW-23
❑ 84TwiTeal-33
❑ 85CirK-5
❑ 86BigLeaC-5
❑ 86SpoDecG-48
❑ 86TCMSupS-12
❑ 86TwiGreT-1
❑ 87K-M-4
❑ 87NesDreT-22
❑ 88ChaLooLTI-18
❑ 88GreBasS-18
❑ 88PacLegl-86
❑ 89KahCoo-7
❑ 89PacLegl-163
❑ 89PerCelP-23
❑ 89SweBasG-70
❑ 89TopBasT-13
❑ 90AGFA-3
❑ 90PacLeg-35
❑ 90PerGreM-48
❑ 91Col-34
❑ 91Kel3D-6
❑ 91LinDri-41
❑ 91MDAA-16
❑ 91SweBasG-49
❑ 91UppDecHoB-H1
❑ 91UppDecHoB-AU1
❑ 91UppDecHoB5-1
❑ 92MDAMVP-6
❑ 92MDAMVP-20
❑ 92MVP-6
❑ 92MVP2H-8
❑ 92TVSpoMF5HRC-5
❑ 93ActPacA-118
❑ 93ActPacA2-52G
❑ 93MCIAmb-10
❑ 93Pin-481
❑ 93UppDecS-15
❑ 94TedWil-49
❑ 94TedWil5C-3
❑ 94TopArc1-254
❑ 94TopArc1G-254
❑ 95EagBalL-4
❑ 95EagBalL-S4
❑ 95MCIAmb-6
❑ 95SonGre-6
❑ 95TopLegot6M-11
❑ 97DonSigSS-13
❑ 98DonSigSS-6
❑ 98SpollITaN-15
❑ 98SpollITaNA-4
❑ 98SpollITaNAR-4
❑ 98SpollITaNC-C3
❑ 98SpollITaNEE-15
❑ 98SpollITaNGS-19
❑ 99SP SigAuto-HK
❑ 99SpollIGotG-33
❑ 99SpollIGotGA-39
❑ 99SPSig-175
❑ 99UppDecAP-HK
❑ 99UppDecAPH5AU-HKAU
❑ 99UppDecCLES-HK
❑ 99UppDecCLESC-HK
❑ 99UppDecR-99
❑ 99UppDecRG-99
❑ 99UppDecRI-HK
❑ 99UppDecRIL2-HK
❑ 99UppDecRP-99

Killeen, Evans
❑ 77FriOneYW-104

Killeen, Jack
❑ 20Zee-65

Killeen, Tim
❑ 92SouOreAC-12
❑ 92SouOreAF-3419
❑ 93MadMusC-17
❑ 93MadMusF-1825
❑ 94ModA'sC-17
❑ 94ModA'sF-3066
❑ 95MemChiTI-23
❑ 96MemChiB-19
❑ 97MobBayBB-15

Killefer, Bill
❑ 09ColChiE-152A
❑ 09ColChiE-152B
❑ 10JuJuDE-22
❑ 12ColRedB-152A
❑ 12ColRedB-152B
❑ 12ColTinT-152A
❑ 12ColTinT-152B
❑ 14CraJacE-135
❑ 15CraJacE-135
❑ 15SpoNewM-93
❑ 16BF2FP-89
❑ 16SpoNewM-95
❑ 17ColE13-93
❑ 17HolBreD-58
❑ 19W514-87
❑ 21E121So1-53A
❑ 21E121So1-53B
❑ 21E121So8-49A
❑ 21Exh-91
❑ 22AmeCarE122-38
❑ 23W501-56
❑ 23WilChoV-80
❑ 74CapPub-50
❑ 94ConTSN-1178
❑ 94ConTSN-1274
❑ 94ConTSNB-1178
❑ 94ConTSNB-1274

Killefer, Red (Wade H.)
❑ 09TigMorBBBP-9
❑ 16FleBreD-51
❑ 17Zee-10
❑ 18Zee-9
❑ 19Zee-10
❑ 20Zee-13
❑ 21Zee-12
❑ 22Zee-9
❑ 23Zee-11
❑ 24Zee-117
❑ 26Zee-168
❑ 27Zee-138
❑ 28Zee-53
❑ 29Zee-47
❑ 30Zee-57
❑ 94ConTSN-1178
❑ 94ConTSNB-1178

Killen, Brent
❑ 92NiaFalRC-23
❑ 92NiaFalRF-3332
❑ 93LakTigC-12
❑ 94LakTigC-12
❑ 94LakTigF-3044

Killen, Frank
❑ 98CamPepP-41

Killian, Ed
❑ 07TigACDPP-8
❑ 08RosComP-35
❑ 09ColChiE-153A
❑ 09ColChiE-153B
❑ 09T206-185
❑ 09T206-186
❑ 09TigTaCP-10
❑ 09WolNewDTPP-10
❑ 10CouT21-36
❑ 10SweCapPP-27
❑ 11MecDFT-21
❑ 11SpoLifCW-201
❑ 11T205-87
❑ 12ColRedB-153A
❑ 12ColRedB-153B
❑ 12ColTinT-153A
❑ 12ColTinT-153B
❑ 81TigDetN-87

Killifer, William
❑ 11PinT-5-123
❑ 11PinT-5-569
❑ 11SpoLifM-126
❑ 14PieStaT-58
❑ 21E121So8-49B

Killilay, John
❑ 12Zee-36
❑ 13Zee-37
❑ 14Zee-38
❑ 15Zee-110

Killingsworth, Kirk
❑ 83TulDriT-12
❑ 85TulDriT-32
❑ 86TulDriTI-3
❑ 87OklCit8P-9

Killingsworth, Sam
❑ 75BurBeeT-13

Kilner, John Steven
❑ 09ObaT21-25
❑ 86DurBulP-16
❑ 87GreBraB-14
❑ 88GreBraB-20
❑ 89GreBraS-11
❑ 89RicBraTI-12
❑ 90Bes-289
❑ 90GreBraB-21
❑ 90GreBraB-22
❑ 90GreBraP-1125
❑ 90GreBraS-10

Kilroy, Mathew
❑ 87BucN28-3
❑ 87OldJudN-280
❑ 88SpoTimM-16

Kilroy, Orville
❑ 11Zee-31

Kim, Bobby
❑ 93BoiHawC-17
❑ 93BoiHawF-3930

Kim, Byung-Hyun
❑ 99PacOme-14
❑ 99PacOmeC-14
❑ 99PacOmeG-14
❑ 99PacOmePB-14

Kim, David
❑ 97NewJerCB-14
❑ 98PeoChiM-12

Kim, Kwang Ung
❑ 87AncGlaP-18

Kim, Wendell
❑ 75LafDriT-2
❑ 77PhoGiaCC-15
❑ 77PhoGiaCP-15
❑ 77PhoGiaVNB-15
❑ 78PhoGiaC-13
❑ 81CliGiaT-2
❑ 82CliGiaF-2
❑ 85FreGiaSB-1
❑ 86ShrCapP-13
❑ 86ShrCapP-14
❑ 87PhoFirP-23
❑ 88PhoFirC-24
❑ 88PhoFirP-65
❑ 89GiaMot-28
❑ 90GiaMot-21
❑ 90GiaSmo-11
❑ 91GiaMot-27
❑ 92GiaMot-28
❑ 92GiaPacGaE-22
❑ 93GiaMot-28
❑ 93GiaPos-20
❑ 94GiaMot-28
❑ 95GiaMot-28
❑ 96GiaMot-28
❑ 97PhoFirDTTI-15

Kim, Yuni
❑ 97LanJet-13

Kimata, Tatsuhiko
❑ 79TCMJapPB-73

Kimball, Andrew
❑ 98ModA'sG-15

Kimball, Doug
❑ 92GreFalDSP-18

Kimball, Newt
❑ 40DodTeal-13
❑ 41DodTeal-4
❑ 42DodTeal-13
❑ 43PhiTeal-12
❑ 73Dod194T-16
❑ 78DodTCM4-28
❑ 90DodTar-409

Kimball, Ricky
❑ 88CapCodPPaLP-142
❑ 91SouOreAC-6
❑ 91SouOreAP-3838
❑ 92ProFS7-137

Kimball, Scott
❑ 90BelBreB-8
❑ 90BelBreS-11
❑ 90Bes-124
❑ 90MidLeaASGS-12

Kimber, Doug
❑ 95RocCubTI-30

Kimberlin, Keith
❑ 89NiaFalRP-13
❑ 90FloStaLAS-34
❑ 90LakTigS-15
❑ 90StaFS7-36
❑ 91Cla/Bes-170
❑ 91LinDriAA-389
❑ 91LonTigLD-389
❑ 91LonTigP-1885
❑ 93ReaPhiF-301
❑ 94ReaPhiF-2071
❑ 94ScrRedBF-926

Kimberling, Shannon
❑ 94ColSilBC-5
❑ 95ColSilB-15
❑ 95ColSilB9-5

Kimbler, Doug
❑ 90NiaFalRP-2
❑ 91FayGenC-19
❑ 91FayGenP-1178

Kimbrell, Mike
❑ 96ButCopKB-19
❑ 97HudValRB-17
❑ 98ChaRivDG-24

Kimbro, Henry
❑ 93NegLeaRL2-21
❑ 93UppDecS-17
❑ 95NegLeaL2-16
❑ 97NegLeaPC-8C

Kimbrough, Larry
❑ 86NegLeaF-37
❑ 86NegLeaF-61
❑ 92NegLeaRLI-35

Kimel, Jack
❑ 92ButCopKSP-11
❑ 93ChaRaiC-8
❑ 93ChaRaiF-1903
❑ 93SouAtlLAGF-7
❑ 94ClaGolF-30
❑ 94TulDriF-240
❑ 94TulDriTI-11
❑ 95TulDriTI-10

Kimler, Mike
❑ 92LetMouSP-17

Kimm, Bruce
❑ 76DetTigP-14
❑ 77Top-554
❑ 81Fle-355
❑ 81Top-272
❑ 83CedRapRF-22
❑ 83CedRapRT-1
❑ 84RedEnq-28
❑ 86RedTexG-NNO
❑ 87RedKah-NNO
❑ 88RedKah-NNO
❑ 89CedRapRAB-27
❑ 89PirVerFJ-36
❑ 90CedRapRDGB-27
❑ 91PadSmo-17
❑ 92PadMot-27
❑ 92PadPolD-28
❑ 92PadSmo-16
❑ 93GreBraF-364
❑ 94RicBraF-2864
❑ 95OrlCubF-25
❑ 96OrlCubB-1
❑ 97MarPac-27

Kimm, Tyson
❑ 95BatCliTI-19
❑ 96PieBolWB-15

Kimmick, Walt
❑ 24Zee-132
❑ 27Zee-139

Kimsey, Chad
❑ 92ConTSN-511

Kimsey, Keith
❑ 91BriTigC-12
❑ 91BriTigP-3618
❑ 92NiaFalRC-22
❑ 92NiaFalRF-3340
❑ 93FayGenC-12
❑ 93FayGenF-141
❑ 94Bow-561
❑ 94LakTigC-13
❑ 97LakTigB-18
❑ 98LakTigM-5

Kinard, Rudy
❑ 75SpolndC-3

Kindall, Jerry
❑ 58Top-221
❑ 59Top-274
❑ 60Top-444
❑ 61CubJayP-9
❑ 61Pos-199A
❑ 61Pos-199B
❑ 61Top-27
❑ 62AmeTraS-51A
❑ 62AmeTraS-51B
❑ 62Jel-191
❑ 62Pos-191
❑ 62PosCan-191
❑ 62Top-292
❑ 63Fle-13
❑ 63Jel-68
❑ 63Pos-68
❑ 63Top-36
❑ 78TCM60I-218
❑ 78TCM60I-271
❑ 78TwiFri-35
❑ 84AriWilP-9
❑ 86AriWilP-9
❑ 87AriWilP-7
❑ 88AriWilP-6
❑ 90AriWilP-10
❑ 92AriWilP-7

Kindelan, Orestes
❑ 90IBAWorA-41

Kindell, Scott
❑ 94KinMetC-5
❑ 94KinMetF-3815
❑ 95PitMetTI-45

Kinder, Ellis
❑ 46SeaSLP-29
❑ 47Exh-118
❑ 48RedSoxTI-13
❑ 49RedSoxTI-12
❑ 50Bow-152
❑ 50RedSoxTI-10
❑ 51Bow-128
❑ 51R42SmaS-55
❑ 52Top-78
❑ 53RedSoxFNSMS-2

❑ 53RedSoxTI-16
❑ 53Top-44
❑ 54Bow-98
❑ 54Top-47
❑ 55Top-115
❑ 55TopDouH-129
❑ 56Top-336
❑ 57Top-352
❑ 79TCM50-115
❑ 81RedSoxBG2S-32
❑ 83TopRep5-78
❑ 85TCMPpl1-26
❑ 91TopArc1-44
❑ 94TopArc1-47
❑ 94TopArc1G-47

Kindler, Tom
❑ 92SpoIndC-8
❑ 92SpoIndF-1289
❑ 93WatDiaC-20
❑ 93WatDiaF-1765
❑ 94SprSulC-15
❑ 94SprSulF-2033

Kindred, Curt
❑ 83VisOakF-22
❑ 84VisOakT-2
❑ 86CedRapRT-6
❑ 87CedRapRP-4

Kindred, Vincent L.
❑ 87SprCarB-23
❑ 89SavCarP-355
❑ 90Bes-302
❑ 90SprCarB-10

Kindsfather, Vern
❑ 54SeaPop-14

Kiner, Ralph
❑ 46SpoExcW-6-7
❑ 47Exh-119
❑ 47HomBon-28
❑ 47PM1StaP1-104
❑ 47TipTop-143
❑ 48BluTin-7
❑ 48Bow-3
❑ 49Bow-29
❑ 49EurSta-164
❑ 49IndVisEI-9
❑ 49Lea-91
❑ 49MPR302-2-110
❑ 50AmeNut&CCP-12
❑ 50Bow-33
❑ 50PirTeal-9
❑ 51BerRos-C1
❑ 51R42SmaS-58
❑ 51TopCurA-6
❑ 51TopRedB-15
❑ 52BerRos-30
❑ 52Bow-11
❑ 52DixLid-11
❑ 52DixPre-11
❑ 52RedMan-NL12
❑ 52StaCalL-77B
❑ 52StaCalS-89D
❑ 52Whe-16A
❑ 52Whe-16B
❑ 53BowC-80
❑ 53DixLid-10
❑ 53DixPre-10
❑ 53ExhCan-22
❑ 53MacSta-1
❑ 53RedMan-NL15
❑ 53Top-191
❑ 54Bow-45
❑ 54DixLid-7
❑ 54RedHeaF-13
❑ 55Bow-197
❑ 55IndCarBL-5
❑ 55IndGolS-16
❑ 60Fle-79
❑ 61Fle-50
❑ 74LauAllG-51
❑ 74NewYorNTDiS-7
❑ 75TCMAllG-18
❑ 76ShaPiz-151
❑ 76TayBow4-9
❑ 77GalGloG-2
❑ 77Top-437
❑ 79BasGre-80
❑ 79Pew-7
❑ 79TCM50-13
❑ 80PacLeg-81
❑ 80PerHaloFP-151
❑ 80PerHaloFPS-29
❑ 80PirGreT-7
❑ 80SSPHOF-151
❑ 82CraJac-11
❑ 82DiaCla-110
❑ 82GSGalAG-15
❑ 82TCMGreS-5
❑ 83DonHOFH-38
❑ 84SpoDesPW-36
❑ 85CirK-30
❑ 85TCMHomRC-5
❑ 85TCMPpl1-19
❑ 86PirGreT-5
❑ 86SpoDecG-35
❑ 86TCMSupS-14
❑ 87HygAllG-29
❑ 87MetColP-51
❑ 88PacLegI-9
❑ 89MetRinP69-32
❑ 89PerCelP-24
❑ 89TopBasT-36
❑ 90PacLeg-36
❑ 90PerGreM-75
❑ 90SweBasG-80
❑ 91Col-12
❑ 91Kel3D-15
❑ 91SweBasG-50
❑ 91TopArc1-191
❑ 92ActPacA-5
❑ 92ActPacA2-5G
❑ 92BazQua5A-17
❑ 93ActPacAC-5
❑ 93TedWil-76
❑ 93TedWil-127
❑ 94UppDecAH-49
❑ 94UppDecAH1-49
❑ 97TopStaHRR-8
❑ 97TopStaRRAU-8
❑ 98DonSigSS-7
❑ 98SpoIllTaN-16
❑ 98SpoIllTaNEE-16

King, A. V.
❑ 19Zee-72
❑ 21Zee-52
❑ 22Zee-48

King, Andre
❑ 93DanBraC-1
❑ 93DanBraF-3632
❑ 94Bow-217
❑ 94ClaGolF-48
❑ 94ExcFS7-157
❑ 94MacBraC-1
❑ 94MacBraF-2218
❑ 94SigRoo-13
❑ 94SigRooS-13
❑ 94Top-752
❑ 94TopGol-752
❑ 94TopSpa-752
❑ 94UppDecML-126
❑ 95DurBulTI-16
❑ 95UppDecML-109
❑ 95UppDecML-118
❑ 95UppDecMLFS-109
❑ 95UppDecMLFS-118
❑ 96BesAutSA-37
❑ 97BesAutAS-24
❑ 97St.PetDR-20
❑ 97St.PetDRUB-20

King, Anthony
❑ 93HunCubC-13
❑ 93HunCubF-3251

King, Bill
❑ 94SigRooDP-55
❑ 94SigRooDPS-55
❑ 94SouOreAC-14
❑ 94SouOreAF-3617
❑ 95MidLeaA-27
❑ 95WesMicWTI-34
❑ 96ModA'sB-22
❑ 97HunStaTI-13

King, Billie Jean
❑ 74NewYorNTDiS-10

King, Brad
❑ 97RocCub-19

King, Brett
❑ 93EveGiaC-15
❑ 93EveGiaF-3775
❑ 94Bow-603
❑ 94ClaGolF-62
❑ 94SanJosGC-13
❑ 94SanJosGF-2825
❑ 97ShrCap-14
❑ 97ShrCapB-14
❑ 98ShrCapM-19
❑ 98ShrCapWS-19

King, Brion
❑ 96DunBluJUTI-5

King, Bryan
❑ 88SanBerSB-22
❑ 88SanBerSCLC-28
❑ 89SanBerSB-20
❑ 89SanBerSCLC-80
❑ 90WilBilB-12
❑ 90WilBilP-1063
❑ 90WilBilS-13
❑ 91SanBerSC-17
❑ 91SanBerSP-1994

King, Cesar
❑ 96ChaRivTI-9616
❑ 98Bow-348
❑ 98BowBes-137
❑ 98BowBesAR-137
❑ 98BowBesR-137
❑ 98BowChr-348
❑ 98BowChrGA-348
❑ 98BowChrGAR-348
❑ 98BowChrI-348
❑ 98BowChrIR-348
❑ 98BowChrR-348
❑ 98BowGolA-348
❑ 98BowInt-348
❑ 98TexLeaC-10
❑ 98TexLeaTPG-18
❑ 98TulDriTI-22
❑ 99Bow-110
❑ 99BowChr-110
❑ 99BowChrG-110
❑ 99BowChrGR-110
❑ 99BowChrI-110
❑ 99BowChrIR-110
❑ 99BowChrR-110
❑ 99BowGol-110
❑ 99BowInt-110
❑ 99SP SigAuto-CKI
❑ 99SP SigAutoG-CKI
❑ 99SP TopP-65
❑ 99SP TopPC-CK
❑ 99SP TopPDtS-D16
❑ 99SP TopPGF-GF16
❑ 99SP TopPPE-65
❑ 99SPSig-88
❑ 99UppDec-284
❑ 99UppDecE-127
❑ 99UppDecEFXG-127
❑ 99UppDecEL1-284
❑ 99UppDecEL2-284
❑ 99Vic-395

King, Chick (Charles G.)
❑ 55Bow-133
❑ 59Top-538

King, Clarence
❑ 92NegLeaRLI-36

King, Clay
❑ 92EveGiaC-14
❑ 92EveGiaF-1697
❑ 93CliGiaC-14
❑ 94SanJosGC-14
❑ 94SanJosGF-2826

King, Clyde
❑ 47DodTeal-13
❑ 50WorWidGV-26
❑ 51Bow-299
❑ 52Bow-56
❑ 52Top-205
❑ 58JetPos-10
❑ 69Top-274
❑ 70Top-624
❑ 71RicBraTI-11
❑ 74dod195T-17
❑ 75AtlBraP-19
❑ 75OPC-589
❑ 75Top-589
❑ 75TopMin-589
❑ 81YanPhoA-1
❑ 82YanPhoA-2
❑ 83Top-486
❑ 83TopRep5-205
❑ 88DodRinP1-12A
❑ 90DodTar-410
❑ 90SweBasG-117
❑ 91SweBasG-51
❑ 95TopArcBD-12

King, Curtis
❑ 94NewJerCC-16
❑ 94NewJerCF-3414
❑ 97ArkTraB-7
❑ 98Don-259
❑ 98DonGolPP-259
❑ 98DonSilPP-259
❑ 98Fle-36
❑ 98PacInv-134
❑ 98PacInvPBlue-134
❑ 98PacInvSilv-134

King, David
❑ 90AppFoxBS-16
❑ 90AppFoxP-2101
❑ 91BasCitRC-18
❑ 91BasCitRP-1404

King, Douglas
❑ 90CedRapRB-21
❑ 90ChaWheP-2235
❑ 91ChaWheC-5
❑ 91ChaWheP-2882

King, Eric
❑ 86DonRoo-27
❑ 86SpoRoo-42
❑ 86TopTra-53T
❑ 86TopTraT-53T
❑ 87Don-250
❑ 87Fle-155
❑ 87FleGlo-155
❑ 87SpoTeaP-15
❑ 87TigCaiD-19
❑ 87Top-36
❑ 87TopRoo-8
❑ 87TopTif-36
❑ 87ToyRoo-16
❑ 88Don-50
❑ 88Fle-60
❑ 88FleGlo-60
❑ 88OPC-108
❑ 88Sco-471
❑ 88ScoGlo-471
❑ 88StaLinTi-10
❑ 88TigPep-25
❑ 88TolMudHC-5
❑ 88TolMudHP-592
❑ 88Top-499
❑ 88TopSti-271
❑ 88TopTif-499
❑ 89Don-535
❑ 89DonBasB-235
❑ 89DonTra-37
❑ 89Fle-136
❑ 89FleGlo-136
❑ 89FleUpd-19
❑ 89Sco-471
❑ 89ScoRoo-26T
❑ 89ScoYouS2-7
❑ 89Top-238
❑ 89TopTif-238
❑ 89TopTra-61T
❑ 89TopTraT-61T
❑ 89UppDec-493
❑ 89WhiSoxC-14
❑ 90Bow-304
❑ 90BowTif-304
❑ 90Don-337
❑ 90DonBesA-46
❑ 90Fle-537
❑ 90FleCan-537
❑ 90Lea-43
❑ 90OPC-786
❑ 90PubIntS-392
❑ 90Sco-28
❑ 90Top-786
❑ 90TopTif-786
❑ 90UppDec-651
❑ 90WhiSoxC-12
❑ 91Bow-63
❑ 91ClaGam-56
❑ 91Don-271
❑ 91Fle-126
❑ 91IndFanC-17
❑ 91Lea-382
❑ 91OPC-121
❑ 91Sco-124
❑ 91ScoRoo-60T
❑ 91StaClu-328
❑ 91Stu-47
❑ 91Top-121
❑ 91TopDesS-121
❑ 91TopMic-121
❑ 91TopTif-121
❑ 91UppDec-281
❑ 91UppDec-782
❑ 92Bow-317
❑ 92Fle-115
❑ 92OPC-326
❑ 92OPCPre-80
❑ 92Pin-503
❑ 92Sco-144
❑ 92ScoRoo-42T
❑ 92StaClu-125
❑ 92StaClu-638
❑ 92StaCluECN-638
❑ 92TigTeal-18
❑ 92Top-326
❑ 92TopGol-326
❑ 92TopGolW-326
❑ 92TopMic-326
❑ 92UppDec-679

King, Frank J.
❑ 09T206-496

King, Hal (Harold)
❑ 36GouWidPPR-D15
❑ 36WorWidGV-121
❑ 67Ast-15
❑ 69MilBra-146
❑ 70OPC-327
❑ 70Top-327
❑ 71MLBOffS-15
❑ 71OPC-88
❑ 71Top-88
❑ 72RanTeal-15
❑ 72Top-598
❑ 74OPC-362
❑ 74Top-362
❑ 76LauIndC-32
❑ 93RanKee-21

King, Hank
❑ 85PhiTas-8
❑ 93BoiHawC-18
❑ 93BoiHawF-3924
❑ 94LakElsSC-11
❑ 94LakElsSF-1671

King, Jake
❑ 91ColMetPI-18

King, Jason
❑ 90PitMetP-8
❑ 92St.LucMCB-23
❑ 92St.LucMF-1754
❑ 93St.LucMC-15

King, Jeff
❑ 87SalBucP-24
❑ 88EasLeaAP-16
❑ 88Fle-653
❑ 88FleGlo-653
❑ 88HarSenP-859
❑ 89BufBisC-16
❑ 89BufBisP-1671
❑ 89FleUpd-114
❑ 90Don-480
❑ 90Fle-469
❑ 90FleCan-469
❑ 90Hot50RS-25
❑ 90Lea-163
❑ 90OPC-454
❑ 90PirHomC-13
❑ 90Sco-549
❑ 90Sco100RS-71
❑ 90ScoYouS2-16
❑ 90Top-454
❑ 90TopBig-117
❑ 90TopDeb89-66
❑ 90TopRoo-17
❑ 90TopTif-454
❑ 90UppDec-557
❑ 91Bow-520
❑ 91Don-233
❑ 91Fle-39
❑ 91Lea-71
❑ 91OPC-272
❑ 91PanFreS-117
❑ 91Sco-244
❑ 91StaClu-528
❑ 91Top-272
❑ 91TopDesS-272
❑ 91TopMic-272
❑ 91TopTif-272
❑ 91Ult-280
❑ 91UppDec-687
❑ 92Don-468
❑ 92Fle-555
❑ 92Lea-420
❑ 92LeaBlaG-420
❑ 92OPC-693
❑ 92Pin-317
❑ 92PirNatI-9
❑ 92Sco-511
❑ 92StaClu-24
❑ 92Top-693
❑ 92TopGol-693
❑ 92TopGolW-693
❑ 92TopMic-693
❑ 92Ult-553
❑ 92UppDec-111
❑ 93Bow-654
❑ 93Don-252
❑ 93Fla-113
❑ 93Fle-113
❑ 93Lea-207
❑ 93OPC-96
❑ 93PacSpa-245
❑ 93PanSti-284
❑ 93Pin-355
❑ 93PirHil-4
❑ 93PirNatI-13
❑ 93Sco-159
❑ 93SP-185
❑ 93StaClu-93
❑ 93StaCluFDI-93
❑ 93StaCluMOP-93
❑ 93Stu-102
❑ 93Top-136
❑ 93TopGol-136
❑ 93TopInaM-136
❑ 93TopInaR-136
❑ 93TopMic-136
❑ 93TriPla-182
❑ 93Ult-97
❑ 93UppDec-240
❑ 93UppDecGold-240
❑ 94Bow-490
❑ 94ColC-163
❑ 94ColChoGS-163
❑ 94ColChoSS-163
❑ 94Don-538
❑ 94DonMVP-11
❑ 94Fin-65
❑ 94FinRef-65
❑ 94Fla-422
❑ 94Fle-611
❑ 94FleExtB-347
❑ 94FUnPac-128
❑ 94Lea-145
❑ 94LeaL-140
❑ 94OPC-151
❑ 94Pac-499
❑ 94PanSti-236
❑ 94Pin-208
❑ 94PinArtP-208
❑ 94PinMusC-208
❑ 94PirQui-9
❑ 94Sco-382
❑ 94ScoGolR-382
❑ 94Sel-56
❑ 94SP-142
❑ 94SPDieC-142
❑ 94StaClu-338
❑ 94StaCluFDI-338
❑ 94StaCluGR-338
❑ 94StaCluMOP-338
❑ 94Stu-146
❑ 94Top-44
❑ 94TopGol-44
❑ 94TopSpa-44
❑ 94TriPla-185
❑ 94Ult-256
❑ 94UppDec-238
❑ 94UppDecAJ-27
❑ 94UppDecAJG-27
❑ 94UppDecED-238
❑ 95ColCho-379
❑ 95ColChoGS-379
❑ 95ColChoSS-379
❑ 95Don-108
❑ 95DonPreP-108
❑ 95DonTopotO-317
❑ 95Emo-175
❑ 95Fin-133
❑ 95FinRef-133
❑ 95Fla-401
❑ 95Fle-480
❑ 95Lea-270
❑ 95LeaLim-46
❑ 95Pac-344
❑ 95Pin-35
❑ 95PinArtP-35
❑ 95PinMusC-35
❑ 95PirFil-14
❑ 95Sco-109
❑ 95ScoGolR-109
❑ 95ScoPlaTS-109
❑ 95StaClu-433
❑ 95StaClu-506
❑ 95StaCluMOP-433
❑ 95StaCluMOP-506
❑ 95StaCluSTWS-433
❑ 95StaCluSTWS-506
❑ 95StaCluVR-228
❑ 95StaCluVRMO-228
❑ 95Stu-180
❑ 95Top-501
❑ 95TopCyb-291
❑ 95Ult-216
❑ 95UltGolM-216
❑ 95UppDec-384
❑ 95UppDecED-384
❑ 95UppDecEDG-384
❑ 95UppDecSE-87
❑ 95UppDecSEG-87
❑ 95Zen-50
❑ 96Baz-75
❑ 96Cir-173

- 96CirRav-173
- 96ColCho-258
- 96ColChoGS-258
- 96ColChoSS-258
- 96Don-498
- 96DonDiaK-13
- 96DonPreP-498
- 96EmoXL-256
- 96Fin-S78
- 96FinRef-S78
- 96Fla-348
- 96Fle-523
- 96FleTeaL-25
- 96FleTif-523
- 96Lea-55
- 96LeaPrePB-55
- 96LeaPrePG-55
- 96LeaPrePS-55
- 96LeaSigA-128
- 96LeaSigAG-128
- 96LeaSigAS-128
- 96MetUni-216
- 96MetUniP-216
- 96MetUniProS-216
- 96Pac-172
- 96PanSti-68
- 96Pin-49
- 96PinAfi-34
- 96PinAfiAP-34
- 96PinAfiFPP-34
- 96Sco-462
- 96Sel-54
- 96SelArtP-54
- 96SelTeaN-3
- 96Spo-38
- 96SpoArtP-38
- 96StaClu-194
- 96StaClu-335
- 96StaCluEPB-335
- 96StaCluEPG-335
- 96StaCluEPS-335
- 96StaCluMOP-194
- 96StaCluMOP-335
- 96Stu-31
- 96StuPrePB-31
- 96StuPrePG-31
- 96StuPrePS-31
- 96Sum-27
- 96SumAbo&B-27
- 96SumArtP-27
- 96SumFoi-27
- 96Top-116
- 96TopChr-32
- 96TopChrR-32
- 96TopGal-20
- 96TopGalPPI-20
- 96TopLas-25
- 96Ult-534
- 96UltGolM-534
- 96UppDec-175
- 97Bow-68
- 97BowChr-49
- 97BowChrI-49
- 97BowChrIR-49
- 97BowChrR-49
- 97BowInt-68
- 97Cir-386
- 97CirRav-386
- 97ColChoU-U16
- 97Don-323
- 97DonGolPP-323
- 97DonSilPP-323
- 97Fin-244
- 97FinRef-244
- 97Fle-430
- 97Fle-656
- 97FleTeaL-25
- 97FleTif-430
- 97FleTif-656
- 97Lea-253
- 97LeaFraM-253
- 97LeaFraMDC-253
- 97MetUni-239
- 97NewPin-152
- 97NewPinAP-152
- 97NewPinMC-152
- 97NewPinPP-152
- 97Pac-395
- 97PacLigB-395
- 97PacSil-395
- 97Pin-74
- 97PinArtP-PP74
- 97PinMusC-74
- 97PinPrePla-74
- 97RoyPol-13
- 97Sco-17
- 97Sco-362
- 97ScoArtPWB-17
- 97ScoArtPWB-362
- 97ScoPreS-17
- 97ScoResC-362
- 97ScoShoS-17
- 97ScoShoS-362
- 97ScoShoSAP-17
- 97ScoShoSAP-362
- 97SP-91
- 97SpoIll-155
- 97SpoIllEE-155
- 97StaClu-326
- 97StaCluMOP-326
- 97Top-28
- 97TopChr-11
- 97TopChrR-11
- 97TopGal-74
- 97TopGalPPI-74
- 97TopIntF-ILM8
- 97TopIntFR-ILM8
- 97Ult-263
- 97Ult-412
- 97UltGolME-263
- 97UltGolME-412
- 97UltPlaME-263
- 97UltPlaME-412
- 97UppDec-539
- 98Bow-12
- 98BowBes-47
- 98BowBesAR-47
- 98BowBesR-47
- 98BowChr-12
- 98BowChrGA-12
- 98BowChrGAR-12
- 98BowChrI-12
- 98BowChrIR-12
- 98BowChrR-12
- 98BowGolA-12
- 98BowInt-12
- 98CirThu-105
- 98CirThuRav-105
- 98CirThuSupRav-105
- 98ColCho-139
- 98CroRoy-66
- 98E-X2-58
- 98E-X2ECFut-58
- 98E-X2ECNow-58
- 98Fin-221
- 98FinNo--221
- 98FinNo-R-221
- 98FinRef-221
- 98FlaShoLeg0-95
- 98FlaShoLeg1-95
- 98FlaShoLeg2-95
- 98FlaShoLeg3-95
- 98FlaShoLegM-95
- 98FlaShoR0-95
- 98FlaShoR1-95
- 98FlaShoR2-95
- 98FlaShoR3-95
- 98Fle-7
- 98MetUni-115
- 98MetUniPMG-115
- 98Pac-105
- 98PacAur-45
- 98PacOme-115
- 98PacOmeR-115
- 98PacOnl-343
- 98PacOnl-360
- 98PacOnlR-343
- 98PacOnlR-360
- 98PacOnlWC-343
- 98PacOnlWC-360
- 98PacPar-55
- 98PacParC-55
- 98PacParG-55
- 98PacParHS-55
- 98PacParPB-55
- 98PacParR-55
- 98PacPlaB-105
- 98PacRedT-105
- 98PacSil-105
- 98PinPlu-91
- 98Revo-70
- 98RevoSS-70
- 98ScoRT-105
- 98SP Aut-105
- 98SpoIll-76
- 98SpoIllEE-76
- 98SpoIllFE-76
- 98SPxFin-282
- 98SPxFinR-282
- 98SPxFinS-282
- 98StaCluFDI-36
- 98StaCluI-36
- 98StaCluOneK-36
- 98StaCluPP-36
- 98Top-286
- 98TopChr-286
- 98TopChrR-286
- 98TopDevR-286
- 98TopDia-286
- 98TopGal-57
- 98TopGalGP-57
- 98TopGalOPP-57
- 98TopGalPPI-57
- 98TopGalPPIA-57
- 98TopMiniC-286
- 98TopOpeD-113
- 98TopSta-84
- 98TopStaB-84
- 98TopStaG-84
- 98TopStaGR-84
- 98TopStaS-84
- 98TopTek-79
- 98TopTekD-79
- 98Ult-66
- 98UltGolM-66
- 98UltMas-66
- 98UltPlaM-66
- 98UppDec-109
- 98UppDecSF-67
- 99199Fin-52
- 99Bow-38
- 99BowChr-38
- 99BowChrG-38
- 99BowChrGR-38
- 99BowChrI-38
- 99BowChrIR-38
- 99BowChrR-38
- 99BowGol-38
- 99BowInt-38
- 99CroRoyB-70
- 99CroRoyL-70
- 99CroRoyOD-70
- 99FinGolRef-52
- 99FinRef-52
- 99Fle-127
- 99FleBri-40
- 99FleBri2G-40
- 99FleBriBlu-40
- 99FleBriGol-40
- 99FleSta9-127
- 99FleWarT-127
- 99MetUni-75
- 99MetUniGM-75
- 99MetUniPMG-75
- 99Pac-205
- 99PacAur-88
- 99PacAurOD-88
- 99PacCroC-132
- 99PacCroCPB-132
- 99PacCroCTC-14
- 99PacPar-112
- 99PacParC-112
- 99PacParG-112
- 99PacParHoloGold-112
- 99PacParHS-112
- 99PacParOD-112
- 99PacParPB-112
- 99PacParRed-112
- 99PacPlaB-205
- 99PacPri-71
- 99PacPriHB-71
- 99PacPriHG-71
- 99PacPriHM-71
- 99PacPriHP-71
- 99PacPriRed-71
- 99PacPriS-107
- 99PacPriS206-107
- 99PacPriS206R-107
- 99PacRed-205
- 99PacTeaC-7
- 99SkyThu-43
- 99SkyThuRant-43
- 99SkyThuRave-43
- 99SpoIll-156
- 99StaClu-123
- 99StaCluFDI-123
- 99StaCluOoaK-123
- 99StaCluPP-123
- 99ThuSkySupR-43
- 99Top-193
- 99TopChr-193
- 99TopChrR-193
- 99TopMVPP-193
- 99TopOpeD-102
- 99Ult-99
- 99UltGolM-99
- 99UltMas-99
- 99UltPlaM-99
- 99UppDec-115
- 99UppDecEL1-115
- 99UppDecEL2-115
- 99UppDecM-97
- 99UppDecMGS-97
- 99UppDecMHFS-97
- 99UppDecMP-97
- 99UppDecMSS-97
- 99Vic-186

King, Jerome
- 83TacTigT-6

King, Jerry
- 81BriRedST-13

King, Jim (James H.)
- 56Top-74
- 57Top-186
- 58Top-332
- 60MapLeaSF-11
- 61Top-351
- 62Top-42
- 62TopVen-42
- 63Top-176
- 64Top-217
- 64TopVen-217
- 65OPC-38
- 65Top-38
- 65TopEmbI-54
- 65TopTral-53
- 66Top-369
- 66TopVen-369
- 67CokCapS-8
- 67DexPre-117
- 67Top-509
- 78TCM60I-207

King, Joe
- 82DanSunF-22
- 83PeoSunF-2

King, John
- 90GeoColC-14

King, Kenny
- 87MiaMarP-1
- 88BakDodCLC-254

King, Kevin
- 80WauTimT-20
- 81WauTimT-27
- 83ChaLooT-18
- 84ChaLooT-1B
- 86MidAngP-12
- 87EdmTraP-2068
- 88EdmTraC-25
- 88EdmTraP-573
- 89TenTecGE-33

King, Kevin Ray
- 88CapCodPPaLP-99
- 88OklSoo-20
- 89OklSoo-19
- 90OklSoo-13
- 91PenPilC-6
- 91PenPilP-372
- 92SanBerC-22
- 92SanBerSF-948
- 93RivPilCLC-9
- 94MarMot-26
- 94Top-774
- 94TopGol-774
- 94TopSpa-774
- 94Ult-420
- 95Sco-590
- 95ScoGolR-590
- 95ScoPlaTS-590

King, Lee
- 21Nei-92
- 22E120-200
- 22W572-55
- 23WilChoV-81
- 23Zee-69

King, Louie the Lumber
- 97CliLumG-16

King, Lynn
- 40SolHug-11
- 43CenFlo-16

King, Mike
- 81QuaCitCT-17
- 84NasSouTI-11
- 87ChaRaiP-4
- 88ChaRaiP-1202
- 89WatDiaP-1787
- 89WatDiaS-15
- 96ButCopKB-20
- 97ChaRivDG-17

King, Nelson
- 55Top-112
- 56PirTeal-11
- 57Top-349
- 79TCM50-247

King, Randy
- 85NewOriT-2

King, Raymond
- 95BilMusTI-21
- 96DurBulBrB-3
- 96MacBraB-9
- 98WesTenDJM-1

King, Richard
- 76LauIndC-5
- 76LauIndC-31
- 91WavRedF-10
- 92SouOreAF-3412
- 93SouOreAC-12
- 93SouOreAF-4057

King, Ron
- 86SalRedBP-14

King, Silver (Charles F.)
- 87OldJudN-281
- 89EdgR.WG-15

King, Steve
- 86JamExpP-14
- 89BoiHawP-2002
- 90QuaCitAGS-10
- 91LinDriAA-439
- 91MidAngLD-439
- 91MidAngOHP-15
- 91MidAngP-432

King, Thomas
- 87WytCubP-28
- 93HunCubC-14
- 93HunCubF-3252
- 94WilCubC-12
- 94WilCubF-3779

King, Tiger
- 93ButCopKSP-3

King, Tom
- 74SacSolC-54
- 75AppFoxT-9
- 76CliPilT-22

King, Willie
- 96YakBeaTI-55
- 97YakBeaG-13
- 98RocCubM-16
- 98RocCubTI-17

Kingdon, Wescott
- 20Zee-48
- 21Zee-53

Kingery, Mike
- 82ChaRoyT-12
- 84MemChiT-7
- 85OmaRoyT-23
- 86OmaRoyP-13
- 86OmaRoyT-4
- 86RoyTeal-12
- 86SpoRoo-37
- 87Don-424
- 87DonOpeD-119
- 87Fle-371
- 87FleGlo-371
- 87FleUpd-57
- 87FleUpdG-57
- 87MarMot-17
- 87Top-203
- 87TopTif-203
- 87TopTra-58T
- 87TopTraT-58T
- 88Don-322
- 88Fle-376
- 88FleGlo-376
- 88Lea-104
- 88MarMot-17
- 88OPC-119
- 88PanSti-193
- 88Sco-178
- 88ScoGlo-178
- 88StaLinMa-7
- 88Top-532
- 88TopBig-160
- 88TopTif-532
- 89CalCanC-20
- 89CalCanP-545
- 89Top-413
- 89TopTif-413
- 90CMC-538
- 90Don-601
- 90PhoFirC-11
- 90PhoFirP-23
- 90ProAAAF-49
- 91Don-573
- 91GiaMot-21
- 91GiaPacGaE-16
- 91Lea-224
- 91OPC-657
- 91Sco-547
- 91Top-657
- 91TopDesS-657
- 91TopMic-657
- 91TopTif-657
- 92StaClu-862
- 92TacTigF-2516
- 93OmaRoyF-1690
- 94FleUpd-126
- 95ColCho-441
- 95ColChoGS-441
- 95ColChoSS-441
- 95Don-96
- 95DonPreP-96
- 95DonTopotO-229
- 95Fle-522
- 95Pac-139
- 95PacPri-46
- 95Pin-29
- 95PinArtP-29
- 95PinMusC-29
- 95RocPol-8
- 95Sco-156
- 95ScoGolR-156
- 95ScoPlaTS-156
- 95StaClu-307
- 95StaCluMOP-307
- 95StaCluSTWS-307
- 95StaCluVR-163
- 95StaCluVRMO-163
- 95Top-615
- 95TopCyb-383
- 95Ult-155
- 95UltGolM-155
- 95UppDec-411
- 95UppDecED-411
- 95UppDecEDG-411
- 96ColCho-684
- 96ColChoGS-684
- 96ColChoSS-684
- 96Don-400
- 96DonPreP-400
- 96Fla-349
- 96Fle-365
- 96FleTif-365
- 96FleUpd-U178
- 96FleUpdTC-U178
- 96LeaSigEA-100
- 96Pac-60
- 96Ult-535
- 96UltGolM-535
- 96UppDec-437
- 97PacPriGotD-GD193

Kingman, Brendan
- 94KanCouCC-12
- 94KanCouCF-164
- 94KanCouCTI-13
- 95AusFut-26
- 95AusFut-99
- 95AusFutGP-5
- 95AusFutSFP-SFFP8
- 95BreCouMF-248
- 98LanJetG-16
- 99SP TopP-66
- 99SP TopPPE-66

Kingman, Brian
- 77SanJosMC-19
- 79OgdA'sT-13
- 80Top-671
- 80VenLeaS-224
- 81Don-360
- 81Fle-579
- 81Top-284
- 82Don-87
- 82Fle-96
- 82OPC-231
- 82TacTigT-25
- 82Top-476
- 83Fle-522
- 83Top-312
- 84PhoGiaC-15

Kingman, Dave
- 72GiaTeal-11
- 72OPC-147
- 72Top-147
- 73Kel2D-44
- 73LinPor-159
- 73OPC-23
- 73Top-23
- 74MetTeal-9
- 74OPC-610
- 74Top-610
- 74TopSta-106
- 75Hos-85
- 75MetSSP-9
- 75OPC-156
- 75SSPSam-3
- 75Top-156

❑ 75TopMin-156
❑ 76BlaDis-26
❑ 76BucDis-26
❑ 76CarDis-26
❑ 76CraDis-26
❑ 76DailsID-26
❑ 76Hos-15
❑ 76HosTwi-15
❑ 76IsaDis-26
❑ 76MetMSAP-2
❑ 76OPC-40
❑ 76OPC-193
❑ 76OrbDis-26
❑ 76RedBarD-26
❑ 76SafDis-26
❑ 76Spo-1
❑ 76SSP-542
❑ 76Top-40
❑ 76Top-193
❑ 76TowCluD-26
❑ 77BurCheD-141
❑ 77ChiWilD-35
❑ 77DailsID-35
❑ 77DetCaeD-35
❑ 77HolInnD-35
❑ 77Hos-60
❑ 77Kel-35
❑ 77MetDaiPA-9
❑ 77MSADis-35
❑ 77OPC-98
❑ 77PepGloD-69
❑ 77RCColC-32
❑ 77SagDis-35
❑ 77sDis-35
❑ 77Spo-2721
❑ 77Spo-4208
❑ 77Top-500
❑ 77TopCloS-24
❑ 77WenDis-35
❑ 77ZipDis-35
❑ 78Hos-26
❑ 78Pep-33
❑ 78RCColC-5
❑ 78SagDis-19
❑ 78SSP270-252
❑ 78TasDis-19
❑ 78Top-570
❑ 78WifBalD-34
❑ 79Hos-146
❑ 79OPC-191
❑ 79Top-370
❑ 79TopCom-20
❑ 80Kel-6
❑ 80OPC-127
❑ 80Top-202
❑ 80Top-240
❑ 80TopSup-16
❑ 81AllGamPI-148
❑ 81CokTeaS-87
❑ 81Don-553
❑ 81Dra-19
❑ 81Fle-291
❑ 81FleStiC-111
❑ 81Kel-47
❑ 81OPC-361
❑ 81PerCreC-18
❑ 81Squ-14
❑ 81Top-450
❑ 81TopScr-69
❑ 81TopSti-151
❑ 81TopSupHT-26
❑ 81TopTra-781
❑ 82Don-17
❑ 82Don-182
❑ 82Dra-21
❑ 82Fle-530
❑ 82FleSta-85
❑ 82Kel-19
❑ 82MetPhoA-14
❑ 82OPC-276
❑ 82Top-690
❑ 82TopSti-72
❑ 83Don-301
❑ 83Dra-14
❑ 83Fle-548
❑ 83FleSti-232
❑ 83OPC-160
❑ 83OPC-161
❑ 83Top-160
❑ 83Top-161
❑ 83Top-702
❑ 83TopFol-2
❑ 83TopSti-11
❑ 83TopSti-207
❑ 83TopSti-259
❑ 84A'sMot-15
❑ 84Don-360
❑ 84DonCha-3
❑ 84Fle-590
❑ 84FleUpd-62
❑ 84FunFooP-36
❑ 84Nes792-573
❑ 84Nes792-703
❑ 84OPC-172
❑ 84Top-573
❑ 84Top-703
❑ 84TopTif-573
❑ 84TopTif-703
❑ 84TopTra-63T
❑ 84TopTraT-63T
❑ 85A'sMot-2
❑ 85CirK-26
❑ 85Don-54
❑ 85DonActA-32
❑ 85Fle-427
❑ 85FleLimE-15
❑ 85FleStaS-14
❑ 85FleStaS-29
❑ 85FleStaS-48
❑ 85Lea-182
❑ 85OPC-123
❑ 85Top-730
❑ 85Top3-D-12
❑ 85TopGloS-5
❑ 85TopSti-320
❑ 85TopSup-59
❑ 85TopTif-730
❑ 86A'sMot-2
❑ 86BasStaB-64
❑ 86Don-54
❑ 86Fle-423
❑ 86FleStiC-67
❑ 86OPC-322
❑ 86SevCoi-W9
❑ 86Spo-68
❑ 86Spo-116
❑ 86Spo-150
❑ 86Top-410
❑ 86TopSti-167
❑ 86TopTif-410
❑ 86Woo-16
❑ 87Don-425
❑ 87Fle-396
❑ 87FleGlo-396
❑ 87FleLeaL-27
❑ 87OPC-266
❑ 87RedFolSB-115
❑ 87Spo-178
❑ 87Top-709
❑ 87TopMinL-69
❑ 87TopSti-173
❑ 87TopTif-709
❑ 88AlaGolAA60TI-7
❑ 89PacLegI-175
❑ 89PacSenL-164
❑ 89PacSenL-186
❑ 89T/MSenL-59
❑ 89TopSenL-101
❑ 90EliSenL-24
❑ 90EliSenL-126
❑ 90PacLeg-87
❑ 90SouCalS-7
❑ 91MetWIZ-211
❑ 91SweBasG-52
❑ 91UppDecS-21
❑ 92ActPacA-56
❑ 92MCIAmb-7
❑ 92UppDecS-7
❑ 92YanWIZ7-90
❑ 93TedWil-57
❑ 94UppDecAH-86
❑ 94UppDecAH-208
❑ 94UppDecAH1-86
❑ 94UppDecAH1-208
❑ 97PhoFirDTTI-14
❑ 99SpollIGotG-64
❑ 99SpollIGotGA-40

Kingman, Eamon
❑ 88CapCodPPaLP-17

Kingrey, Jarrod
❑ 98St.CatSM-16
❑ 99TeaBesR-45
❑ 99TeaBesRFS-25
❑ 99TeaBesRG-45
❑ 99TeaBesRS-45

Kingsale, Eugene
❑ 96Bow-157
❑ 96BowFoi-157
❑ 96FreKeyB-12
❑ 97Bow-129
❑ 97BowBes-156
❑ 97BowBesAR-156
❑ 97BowBesR-156
❑ 97BowCerBlaIA-CA44
❑ 97BowCerBluIA-CA44
❑ 97BowCerGolIA-CA44
❑ 97BowChr-141
❑ 97BowChrI-141
❑ 97BowChrIR-141
❑ 97BowChrR-141
❑ 97BowInt-129
❑ 97Cir-223
❑ 97CirRav-223
❑ 97Sel-118
❑ 97SelArtP-118
❑ 97SelCom-118
❑ 97SelRegG-118
❑ 97UppDec-470
❑ 98BowBayM-18
❑ 98EasLeaTPM-15

Kingsbury, Willy
❑ 97LowSpiB-12

Kingsolver, Kurt
❑ 80BurBeeT-19
❑ 82ElPasDT-4

Kingston, Mark
❑ 92HelBreF-1721
❑ 92HelBreSP-3
❑ 93PeoChiTI-13
❑ 94DayCubC-13
❑ 94DayCubF-2359
❑ 96OrlCubB-14

Kingwood, Tyrone
❑ 88WesPalBES-15
❑ 90SanBerSCLC-102
❑ 90SanBerSP-2644
❑ 91Cla/Bes-304
❑ 91HagSunLD-234
❑ 91HagSunP-2467
❑ 91LinDriAA-234
❑ 92LonTigF-646
❑ 92LonTigS-411
❑ 92SkyAA F-175
❑ 92UppDecML-220

Kinkade, Mike
❑ 95HelBreTI-6
❑ 96BelSnaTI-19
❑ 96MidLeaAB-11
❑ 97El PasDB-4
❑ 97TexAllM-19
❑ 98Bes-72
❑ 98Bow-137
❑ 98BowBes-181
❑ 98BowBesAR-181
❑ 98BowBesR-181
❑ 98BowCerBlueAU-38
❑ 98BowCerGA-38
❑ 98BowCerSA-38
❑ 98BowChr-137
❑ 98BowChrGA-137
❑ 98BowChrGAR-137
❑ 98BowChrI-137
❑ 98BowChrIR-137
❑ 98BowChrR-137
❑ 98BowGolA-137
❑ 98BowInt-137
❑ 98ColCho-427
❑ 98ColChoPCR-427
❑ 98FleUpd-U84
❑ 98LeaRS-226
❑ 98LeaRSLHolo-226
❑ 98LeaRSLong-226
❑ 98LeaRTrue-226
❑ 98LouRedQ-5
❑ 98SP Aut-12
❑ 98SP MinDTSPE-DS29
❑ 98SP MinPE-71
❑ 98SPMin-71
❑ 98SPMinDTS-DS29
❑ 98SPxFin-207
❑ 98SPxFinR-207
❑ 98SPxFinS-207
❑ 98UD3-12
❑ 98UD3-102
❑ 98UD3-192
❑ 98UD3DieCut-12
❑ 98UD3DieCut-102
❑ 98UD3DieCut-192
❑ 98UppDec-546
❑ 98UppDecDS-DS6
❑ 99Fle-165
❑ 99FleSta9-165
❑ 99FleWarT-165
❑ 99SkyPreA-32
❑ 99SkyPreABlue-32
❑ 99SP Aut-111
❑ 99SP AutC-MK
❑ 99SP AutCG-MK
❑ 99SP SigAuto-MKI
❑ 99SP SigAutoG-MKI
❑ 99SP TopP-67
❑ 99SP TopPC-MK
❑ 99SP TopPDtS-D17
❑ 99SP TopPGF-GF17
❑ 99SP TopPPE-67
❑ 99SpoIll-58
❑ 99SPSig-78
❑ 99SPx-108
❑ 99SPxFinR-108
❑ 99SPxFinS-108
❑ 99UD Cho-21
❑ 99UD ChoPCR-21
❑ 99UDHoloUDA-MK
❑ 99UppDec-8
❑ 99UppDecE-98
❑ 99UppDecEFXG-98
❑ 99UppDecEL1-8
❑ 99UppDecEL2-8
❑ 99UppDecM-136
❑ 99UppDecMGS-136
❑ 99UppDecMHFS-136
❑ 99UppDecMSS-136
❑ 99UppDecO-70
❑ 99UppDecOSO-70
❑ 99Vic-249

Kinlaw, Jeff
❑ 92AlbPolCB-28

Kinnard, Ken (Kenneth Joe)
❑ 83KinBluJTI-9
❑ 86VenGulP-10
❑ 87GreBraB-27

Kinney, Brad
❑ 84ButCopKT-13

Kinney, Dennis
❑ 75SanAntBT-12
❑ 76WilTomT-14
❑ 78IndTeal-18
❑ 79HawIslC-17
❑ 79HawIslT-18
❑ 81Don-363
❑ 81EvaTriT-22
❑ 81Fle-505
❑ 81Top-599
❑ 82TacTigT-6

Kinney, Matt
❑ 96LowSpiB-13
❑ 97MicBatC-16
❑ 98Bow-421
❑ 98BowChr-421
❑ 98BowChrGA-421
❑ 98BowChrGAR-421
❑ 98BowChrI-421
❑ 98BowChrIR-421
❑ 98BowChrR-421
❑ 98BowGolA-421
❑ 98BowInt-421

Kinney, Michael
❑ 93GreFalDSP-11
❑ 94BakDodC-12

Kinney, Tom
❑ 91Cla/Bes-139
❑ 91SavCarC-8
❑ 91SavCarP-1649

Kinney, Walter
❑ 27Zee-71
❑ 28Zee-11

Kinnon, Duane
❑ 93NiaFalRF-3397

Kinnunen, Mike
❑ 81TolMudHT-6
❑ 83MemChiT-24
❑ 85OmaRoyT-18
❑ 86RocRedWP-12
❑ 88BlaYNPRWL-60
❑ 88ColCliC-9
❑ 88ColCliP-4
❑ 88ColCliP-316
❑ 88TriAAAP-10
❑ 89BlaYNPRWLU-6
❑ 89DenZepC-4
❑ 89DenZepP-33
❑ 91OriCro-239

Kinsel, David
❑ 83AppFoxFr-23

Kinsella, W.P.
❑ 90LitSunW-15

Kinslow, Thomas
❑ 90DodTar-1000
❑ 95May-16A
❑ 95May-16B

Kintana, L.
❑ 33Zee-60

Kinugasa, Sachio
❑ 79TCMJapPB-9
❑ 87JapPlaB-9
❑ 93UppDecS-22

Kinyoun, Tavis
❑ 89BriTigS-13
❑ 91BasCitRC-14
❑ 91BasCitRP-1400

Kinzer, Matt
❑ 85SprCarT-14
❑ 86St.PetCP-17
❑ 88ArkTraGS-14
❑ 88LouRedBTI-24
❑ 89BlaYNPRWL-92
❑ 89LouRedBC-7
❑ 89LouRedBP-1255
❑ 89LouRedBTI-25
❑ 90CMC-382
❑ 90Fle-652
❑ 90FleCan-652
❑ 90ProAAAF-374
❑ 90Sco-628
❑ 90SprCarDGB-13
❑ 90TolMudHC-5
❑ 90TolMudHP-144
❑ 90TopDeb89-67

Kiper, Kory
❑ 92GulCoaYF-3787

Kipfer, Greg
❑ 82WisRapTF-2

Kipila, Jeff
❑ 88BenBucL-2
❑ 89BenBucL-18
❑ 90PalSprACLC-205
❑ 90PalSprAP-2584
❑ 91QuaCitAC-18
❑ 91QuaCitAP-2637
❑ 92MidAngF-4038
❑ 92MidAngOHP-12
❑ 92MidAngS-462
❑ 92SkyAA F-196
❑ 93ExcFS7-144
❑ 93VanCanF-2610
❑ 94HarSenF-2099
❑ 97MidAngOHP-18

Kipp, Fred
❑ 59DodTeal-11
❑ 59Top-258
❑ 60Top-202
❑ 90DodTar-1001
❑ 92YanWIZ6-67

Kipper, Bob
❑ 83PeoSunF-25
❑ 83TriTriT-3
❑ 86Don-44
❑ 86DonRoo-46
❑ 86Fle-648
❑ 86TopTra-54T
❑ 86TopTraT-54T
❑ 87Don-572
❑ 87Fle-612
❑ 87FleGlo-612
❑ 87Top-289
❑ 87TopTif-289
❑ 88Don-115
❑ 88Fle-332
❑ 88FleGlo-332
❑ 88PirTeal-16
❑ 88Top-723
❑ 88TopBig-141
❑ 88TopClo-56
❑ 88TopTif-723
❑ 89Bow-414
❑ 89BowTif-414
❑ 89Don-409
❑ 89Fle-211
❑ 89FleGlo-211
❑ 89PirVerFJ-16
❑ 89Sco-354
❑ 89Top-114
❑ 89TopTif-114
❑ 89UppDec-520
❑ 90Don-362
❑ 90Fle-470
❑ 90FleCan-470
❑ 90OPC-441
❑ 90PirHomC-14
❑ 90Top-441
❑ 90TopTif-441
❑ 90UppDec-560
❑ 91Don-720
❑ 91Fle-40
❑ 91OPC-551
❑ 91Sco-646
❑ 91StaClu-334
❑ 91Top-551
❑ 91TopDesS-551
❑ 91TopMic-551
❑ 91TopTif-551
❑ 91UppDec-407
❑ 92Don-622
❑ 92Fle-556
❑ 92Lea-506
❑ 92LeaBlaG-506
❑ 92OPC-64
❑ 92Pin-495
❑ 92Sco-340
❑ 92StaClu-752
❑ 92Top-64
❑ 92TopGol-64
❑ 92TopGolW-64
❑ 92TopMic-64

Kipper, Thornton
❑ 54Top-108
❑ 55Top-62
❑ 55TopDouH-9
❑ 94TopArc1-108
❑ 94TopArc1G-108

Kippert, Ed
❑ 09ObaT21-216
❑ 09ObaT21-387
❑ 12ObaPreT-136

Kiraly, Jeff
❑ 92KinMetC-6
❑ 92KinMetF-1539
❑ 93CapCitBC-9
❑ 93CapCitBF-466
❑ 94CapCitBC-12
❑ 94CapCitBF-1756

Kirby, Butch
❑ 81BurBeeT-18
❑ 82BelBreFr-15
❑ 83BelBreFr-1

Kirby, Chris
❑ 78WauMetT-14

Kirby, Clay
❑ 69Top-637
❑ 70MLBOffS-115
❑ 70OPC-79
❑ 70Top-79
❑ 71MLBOffS-230
❑ 71OPC-333
❑ 71Top-333
❑ 72OPC-173
❑ 72OPC-174
❑ 72PadPos-16
❑ 72Top-173
❑ 72Top-174
❑ 73OPC-655
❑ 73PadDea-14
❑ 73Top-655
❑ 73TopCanL-26
❑ 74OPC-287
❑ 74Top-287
❑ 74TopSta-96
❑ 75OPC-423
❑ 75Top-423
❑ 75TopMin-423
❑ 76ExpRed-16
❑ 76MonExpP-15
❑ 76OPC-579
❑ 76SSP-28
❑ 76Top-579
❑ 76TopTra-579T
❑ 77PadSchC-34A
❑ 77PadSchC-34B

Kirby, Doug
❑ 96BilMusTI-17

Kirby, Scott
❑ 96HelBreTI-11
❑ 97HelBreB-17
❑ 98BelSnaM-16

Kirby, Wayne
❑ 76TusTorCr-15

Kirby, Wayne Edward
❑ 85VerBeaDT-8
❑ 86VerBeaDP-14
❑ 87BakDodP-23
❑ 88BakDodCLC-249
❑ 88SanAntMB-8
❑ 89SanAntMB-8
❑ 90AlbDukCm-23
❑ 90AlbDukP-359
❑ 90AlbDukTr-17
❑ 90CMC-425
❑ 90ProAAAF-80
❑ 91ColSprSSLD-87
❑ 91ColSprSSP-2197
❑ 91LinDriAAA-87
❑ 92ColSprSSF-764
❑ 92ColSprSSS-87
❑ 92Fle-670
❑ 92TopDeb91-101

❑ 92TriA AAS-87
❑ 93ChaKniF-557
❑ 93Don-380
❑ 93Fla-193
❑ 93FleFinE-201
❑ 93IndWUA-14
❑ 93JimDeaR-5
❑ 93Lea-528
❑ 93Sco-328
❑ 93SelRoo-56T
❑ 93SP-122
❑ 93SP-123
❑ 93StaClu-35
❑ 93StaCluFDI-35
❑ 93StaCluMOP-35
❑ 94ColC-164
❑ 94ColChoGS-164
❑ 94ColChoSS-164
❑ 94Don-125
❑ 94Fin-36
❑ 94FinRef-36
❑ 94Fla-40
❑ 94Fle-107
❑ 94FleExtB-59
❑ 94FleExtBSYS-10
❑ 94FleRooS-9
❑ 94Lea-283
❑ 94OPC-219
❑ 94OPCDiaD-3
❑ 94Pac-171
❑ 94PanSti-57
❑ 94Pin-132
❑ 94PinArtP-132
❑ 94PinMusC-132
❑ 94Sco-230
❑ 94ScoBoyoS-16
❑ 94ScoGolR-230
❑ 94Sel-342
❑ 94StaClu-43
❑ 94StaCluFDI-43
❑ 94StaCluGR-43
❑ 94StaCluMOP-43
❑ 94Top-508
❑ 94TopGol-508
❑ 94TopSpa-508
❑ 94TriPla-114
❑ 94Ult-43
❑ 94USPlaCR-8D
❑ 95ColCho-276
❑ 95ColChoGS-276
❑ 95ColChoSS-276
❑ 95Don-237
❑ 95DonPreP-237
❑ 95Fle-136
❑ 95Lea-176
❑ 95Pac-121
❑ 95Sco-517
❑ 95ScoGolR-517
❑ 95ScoPlaTS-517
❑ 95StaClu-377
❑ 95StaCluMOP-377
❑ 95StaCluSTWS-377
❑ 95Top-227
❑ 95UppDec-342
❑ 95UppDec-347
❑ 95UppDecED-342
❑ 95UppDecEDG-342
❑ 96LeaSigEA-101
❑ 97ColSprSATTI-24
❑ 97DodMot-16
❑ 97DodPol-16
❑ 97Ult-521
❑ 97UltGolME-521
❑ 97UltPlaME-521
❑ 98MemRedG-7

Kirchenwitz, Arno
❑ 78St.PetCT-15
❑ 79ArkTraT-1

Kirgan, Chris
❑ 94BluOriC-12
❑ 94BluOriF-3568
❑ 96HigDesMB-15
❑ 97BowBay-20
❑ 98NewHavRM-16
❑ 98NewHavRMA-16

Kirk, Chuck
❑ 90HunCubP-3277
❑ 91PeoChiC-6
❑ 91PeoChiP-1338
❑ 91PeoChiTI-9
❑ 92WinSpiC-17
❑ 92WinSpiF-1205
❑ 93DayCubC-11
❑ 93DayCubF-855

Kirk, Thomas
❑ 52Par-79

Kirk, Tim
❑ 86WatPirP-11
❑ 87SalBucP-8
❑ 88CarLeaAS-11
❑ 88SalBucS-9
❑ 89PenPilS-9

Kirke, Judson
❑ 12T207-90

Kirkland, Kris
❑ 93BatCliCB-15
❑ 93BatCliF-3142
❑ 94BatCliC-8
❑ 94BatCliF-3439

Kirkland, Willie
❑ 58GiaJayP-5
❑ 58GiaSFCB-12
❑ 58Top-128
❑ 59Top-484
❑ 60GiaJayP-7
❑ 60Top-172
❑ 60TopVen-172
❑ 61Kah-23
❑ 61Pos-146A
❑ 61Pos-146B
❑ 61Top-15
❑ 62IndJayP-6
❑ 62Jel-41
❑ 62Kah-23
❑ 62Pos-41
❑ 62PosCan-41
❑ 62SalPlaC-61
❑ 62ShiPlaC-61
❑ 62Top-447
❑ 63BasMagM-45
❑ 63IndJayP-9
❑ 63Jel-72
❑ 63Pos-72
❑ 63Top-187
❑ 64BalOriP-21
❑ 64OriJayP-6
❑ 64Top-17
❑ 64TopVen-17
❑ 65OPC-148
❑ 65Top-148
❑ 66Top-434
❑ 91OriCro-240

Kirkpatrick, Bill
❑ 75IntLeaAT-14

Kirkpatrick, Brian
❑ 98PorRocG-20

Kirkpatrick, Ed
❑ 63Top-386
❑ 64Top-296
❑ 64TopVen-296
❑ 65SeaPop-7
❑ 65Top-393
❑ 66AngDexP-5
❑ 66OPC-102
❑ 66Top-102
❑ 66TopVen-102
❑ 67CokCapDA-35
❑ 67SeaPop-9
❑ 67Top-293
❑ 68Top-552
❑ 69MilBra-147
❑ 69MLBOffS-59
❑ 69Top-529
❑ 70MLBOffS-223
❑ 70OPC-165
❑ 70RoyTeal-18
❑ 70Top-165
❑ 70TopPos-19
❑ 71MLBOffS-418
❑ 71OPC-299
❑ 71oySigST-11
❑ 71Top-299
❑ 72MilBra-183
❑ 72oyTeal-10
❑ 72Top-569
❑ 72Top-570
❑ 73LinPor-150
❑ 73OPC-233
❑ 73Top-233
❑ 74OPC-262
❑ 74Top-262
❑ 74TopSta-183
❑ 74TopTra-262T
❑ 75OPC-171
❑ 75PitPirP-10
❑ 75Top-171
❑ 75TopMin-171
❑ 76OPC-294
❑ 76PirPos-7
❑ 76SSP-580
❑ 76Top-294
❑ 77Top-582
❑ 78Top-77
❑ 86RoyGreT-8
❑ 93RanKee-218
❑ 94BreMilB-138

Kirkpatrick, Enos
❑ 90DodTar-411

Kirkpatrick, Jay
❑ 91GreFalDSP-18
❑ 92VerBeaDC-7
❑ 92VerBeaDF-2882
❑ 93AusFut-5
❑ 93BakDodCLC-14
❑ 93ClaGolF-98
❑ 93ExcFS7-52
❑ 94SanAntMF-2478
❑ 95AusFut-103
❑ 95SanBerSTI-10
❑ 96SanAntMB-11
❑ 96SigRooOJ-15
❑ 96SigRooOJS-15
❑ 97SanAntMB-18
❑ 98SanAntMM-18

Kirkpatrick, Michael
❑ 98BluOriQ-26

Kirkpatrick, Stephen
❑ 87UtiBluSP-18
❑ 88ClePhiS-16
❑ 88SpaPhiS-9
❑ 89ClePhiS-12
❑ 90ReaPhiB-22
❑ 90ReaPhiP-1232
❑ 90ReaPhiS-15

Kirkreit, Daron
❑ 92TopTra-60T
❑ 92TopTraG-60T
❑ 93StaCluM-21
❑ 94ActPac-9
❑ 94Bow-495
❑ 94CarLeaAF-CAR34
❑ 94Cla-163
❑ 94ClaGolF-186
❑ 94ClaGolN1PLF-LP7
❑ 94ClaGolREF-RE7
❑ 94ClaTriF-T22
❑ 94ExcFS7-45
❑ 94KinIndF-2638
❑ 94Pin-263
❑ 94PinArtP-263
❑ 94PinMusC-263
❑ 94Sco-527
❑ 94ScoGolR-527
❑ 94TedWil-126
❑ 94UppDec-534
❑ 94UppDecAHNIL-8
❑ 94UppDecED-534
❑ 94UppDecML-122
❑ 95ActPacF-38
❑ 95Bow-144
❑ 95Exc-41
❑ 95UppDecML-75
❑ 95UppDecMLFS-75
❑ 95UppDecMLOP-OP8
❑ 97AkrAer-13
❑ 98WicWraM-21

Kirkwood, Don
❑ 75CalAngP-21
❑ 76OPC-108
❑ 76Top-108
❑ 77Top-519
❑ 77WhiSoxT-13
❑ 78BluJayP-12
❑ 78Top-251
❑ 79OPC-334
❑ 79Top-632

Kirrene, Joe
❑ 75OakOak2A-19

Kirsch, Paul
❑ 82CedRapRT-14
❑ 84CedRapRT-5
❑ 85CedRapRT-26
❑ 86CedRapRT-24
❑ 87CedRapRP-24
❑ 91LinDriAAA-425
❑ 91PorBeaP-1584
❑ 92PorBeaF-2682
❑ 92PorBeaS-425
❑ 95ElmPioTI-13
❑ 95ElmPioUTI-13

Kirst, Mark
❑ 98BelSnaM-17

Kirt, Tim
❑ 90NiaFalRP-3

Kirtlan, Josh
❑ 94OgdRapF-3734
❑ 94OgdRapSP-20

Kirwin, Steve
❑ 88BenBucL-8

Kiser, Bob
❑ 88CapCodPB-10
❑ 88CapCodPPaLP-74

Kiser, Dan
❑ 84ModA'sC-26
❑ 89ModA'sC-4

Kiser, Garland
❑ 86BenPhiC-154
❑ 89WatIndS-12
❑ 90CarLeaA-37
❑ 90KinIndTI-12
❑ 91CanIndLD-84
❑ 91CanIndP-976
❑ 91CarLeaAP-CAR17
❑ 91LinDriAA-84
❑ 92CanIndF-687
❑ 92TopDeb91-102
❑ 93NewOrlZF-967

Kiser, Larry G.
❑ 76OklCit8TI-28

Kish, Bobby
❑ 82SprCarF-14
❑ 83St.PetCT-8
❑ 84SavCarT-12

Kisinger, Rube (Charles S.)
❑ 08BufBisFJO-6
❑ 09T206-434

Kison, Bruce
❑ 72OPC-72
❑ 72Top-72
❑ 73OPC-141
❑ 73Top-141
❑ 75OPC-598
❑ 75PitPirP-11
❑ 75Top-598
❑ 75TopMin-598
❑ 76OPC-161
❑ 76PirPos-8
❑ 76SSP-568
❑ 76Top-161
❑ 77PirPosP-12
❑ 77Top-563
❑ 78Top-223
❑ 79Top-661
❑ 80Top-28
❑ 81Fle-284
❑ 81Top-340
❑ 82Don-66
❑ 82Fle-467
❑ 82Top-442
❑ 83Don-267
❑ 83Fle-96
❑ 83FleSta-95
❑ 83FleSti-27
❑ 83Top-712
❑ 84AngSmo-15
❑ 84Don-499
❑ 84Fle-523
❑ 84Nes792-201
❑ 84OPC-201
❑ 84Top-201
❑ 84TopSti-235
❑ 84TopTif-201
❑ 85Don-377
❑ 85Fle-306
❑ 85FleUpd-65
❑ 85Top-544
❑ 85TopTif-544
❑ 85TopTifT-67T
❑ 85TopTra-67T
❑ 86Don-616
❑ 86Fle-353
❑ 86Top-117
❑ 86TopTif-117
❑ 89PacSenL-136
❑ 89T/MSenL-60
❑ 89TopSenL-11
❑ 90EliSenL-37
❑ 91UppDecS-13
❑ 92RoyPol-27
❑ 93RoyPol-27

Kissell, George
❑ 71CarTeal-14
❑ 71CarTeal-22
❑ 71CarTeal-23
❑ 72CarTeal-11
❑ 73OPC-497
❑ 73Top-497A
❑ 73Top-497B
❑ 74OPC-236
❑ 74Top-236
❑ 90JohCitCS-28

Kissick, David
❑ 91BriBanF-7

Kissinger, John
❑ 11SpoLifCW-202
❑ 12ImpTobC-72

Kistaitis, Dale
❑ 88NebCor-7
❑ 90MedHatBJB-18

Kisten, Dale
❑ 88HamRedP-1728
❑ 89SprCarB-20
❑ 90ArkTraGS-19
❑ 90LouRedBLBC-22
❑ 90SprCarDGB-19
❑ 91ArkTraLD-36
❑ 91ArkTraP-1279
❑ 91LinDriAA-36

Kitabeppu, Manabu
❑ 87JapPlaB-8

Kitagawa, Hirotoshi
❑ 96HilStaHWB-10

Kitchen, Ron
❑ 93BluOriF-4120

Kite, Dan
❑ 87LSUTigP-4
❑ 88ElmPioC-6
❑ 90LSUTigGM-3
❑ 90WinHavRSS-13
❑ 91WinHavRSC-3
❑ 91WinHavRSP-483

Kitson, Frank R.
❑ 03BreE10-82
❑ 90DodTar-412

Kittle, Hub
❑ 71AstTeal-14
❑ 72AstTeal-14
❑ 73OPC-624
❑ 73Top-624
❑ 74OPC-31
❑ 74Top-31
❑ 75AstPos-18
❑ 77St.PetCT-13
❑ 81Car5x7-14
❑ 83Car-13
❑ 95NewJerCTI-15

Kittle, Ron
❑ 77CliDodT-13
❑ 79KnoKnoST-12
❑ 80AppFoxT-9
❑ 81GleFalWST-19
❑ 82EdmTraT-13
❑ 83Fle-241
❑ 83TopTra-55T
❑ 83WhiSoxTV-42
❑ 84AllGamPI-147
❑ 84Don-18
❑ 84Don-18A
❑ 84Don-244
❑ 84Dra-17
❑ 84Fle-64
❑ 84FleSti-22
❑ 84FleSti-109
❑ 84FunFooP-53
❑ 84MilBra-15
❑ 84Nes792-480
❑ 84OCoandSI-56
❑ 84OPC-373
❑ 84SevCoi-C17
❑ 84Top-480
❑ 84TopRubD-2
❑ 84TopSti-382
❑ 84TopSup-11
❑ 84TopTif-480
❑ 84WhiSoxTV-19
❑ 85AllGamPI-60
❑ 85Don-180
❑ 85DonActA-13
❑ 85DonWaxBC-PC3
❑ 85Fle-518
❑ 85FleLimE-16
❑ 85Lea-210
❑ 85OPC-105
❑ 85Top-105
❑ 85TopRubD-2
❑ 85TopSti-232
❑ 85TopTif-105
❑ 85WhiSoxC-42
❑ 86Don-526
❑ 86Fle-210
❑ 86FleMin-45
❑ 86FleStiC-68
❑ 86Lea-257
❑ 86MSAJayPCD-11
❑ 86OPC-288
❑ 86Spo-67
❑ 86Spo-86
❑ 86Top-574
❑ 86TopSti-289
❑ 86TopTat-6
❑ 86TopTif-574
❑ 86WhiSoxC-42
❑ 87Don-351
❑ 87Fle-103
❑ 87FleGlo-103
❑ 87Top-584
❑ 87TopTif-584
❑ 88Don-422
❑ 88Fle-213
❑ 88FleGlo-213
❑ 88IndGat-33
❑ 88IndTeal-23
❑ 88Lea-251
❑ 88Sco-449
❑ 88ScoGlo-449
❑ 88ScoRoo-44T
❑ 88ScoRooG-44T
❑ 88Top-259
❑ 88TopTif-259
❑ 88TopTra-58T
❑ 88TopTraT-58T
❑ 89Bow-69
❑ 89BowTif-69
❑ 89Don-428
❑ 89DonBasB-249
❑ 89DonTra-51
❑ 89FleUpd-20
❑ 89OPC-268
❑ 89Sco-96
❑ 89Top-771
❑ 89TopTif-771
❑ 89TopTra-62T
❑ 89TopTraT-62T
❑ 89UppDec-228
❑ 89UppDec-711
❑ 89WhiSoxC-15
❑ 90BalOriP-14
❑ 90Don-148
❑ 90Fle-538
❑ 90FleCan-538
❑ 90Lea-405
❑ 90OPC-79
❑ 90PanSti-51
❑ 90PubIntS-393
❑ 90RedFolSB-54
❑ 90Sco-529
❑ 90Top-79
❑ 90TopSti-302
❑ 90TopTif-79
❑ 90UppDec-790
❑ 90WhiSoxC-13
❑ 90WhiSoxK-4
❑ 91Don-613
❑ 91Fle-480
❑ 91OPC-324
❑ 91OriCro-241
❑ 91Top-324A
❑ 91Top-324B
❑ 91TopDesS-324
❑ 91TopMic-324
❑ 91TopTif-324
❑ 92YanWIZ8-101

Kittredge, Malachi
❑ 03BreE10-83
❑ 03BreE10-84
❑ 11SpoLifCW-203
❑ 98CamPepP-42

Kiyohara, Kazuhiro
❑ 87JapPlaB-35

Kiyono, Masashi
❑ 98SalVol-19

Kizer, Bubba (Hal)
❑ 79QuaCitCT-15

Kizer, Craig
❑ 82AubAstT-14

Kizziah, Daren
❑ 89St.CatBJP-2076
❑ 90MyrBeaBJP-2772
❑ 91DunBluJC-4
❑ 91DunBluJP-200
❑ 92KnoBluJF-2985
❑ 92KnoBluJS-382
❑ 93KnoSmoF-1250

Kjos, Ryan
❑ 96SouOreTI-15
❑ 97ModA'sG-14

Klages, Fred
❑ 67Top-373
❑ 68Top-229
❑ 68TopVen-229
❑ 69MilBra-148

Klamm, Ted
❑ 92WelPirC-14
❑ 92WelPirF-1317
❑ 93AugPirC-10

❑ 93AugPirF-1537
❑ 94SalBucC-13
❑ 94SalBucF-2319
Klancnik, Joe
❑ 86AncGlaPTI-18
❑ 88JamExpP-1919
❑ 89JamExpP-2155
❑ 91QuaCitAP-2622
Klass, Klinton
❑ 93AubAstC-16
❑ 93AubAstF-3455
Klassen, Danny
❑ 94BelBreC-13
❑ 94BelBreFl-109
❑ 95BelBreTI-20
❑ 95Exc-70
❑ 95UppDecML-171
❑ 95UppDecMLFS-171
❑ 96Bow-328
❑ 96BowFoi-328
❑ 96StoPorB-1
❑ 97Bow-395
❑ 97BowChr-261
❑ 97BowChrI-261
❑ 97BowChrIR-261
❑ 97BowChrR-261
❑ 97BowInt-395
❑ 97El PasDB-5
❑ 97TexAllM-20
❑ 97TexLeaTP-4
❑ 98AriFalLTP-3
❑ 98Don-270
❑ 98DonGolPP-270
❑ 98DonSilPP-270
❑ 98SP MinPE-72
❑ 98SPMin-72
❑ 98TusSidM-23
❑ 98UppDec-598
❑ 99Bow-157
❑ 99BowBes-133
❑ 99BowBesAR-133
❑ 99BowBesR-133
❑ 99BowChr-157
❑ 99BowChrG-157
❑ 99BowChrGR-157
❑ 99BowChrI-157
❑ 99BowChrIR-157
❑ 99BowChrR-157
❑ 99BowGol-157
❑ 99BowInt-157
❑ 99Fle-433
❑ 99FleBri-162
❑ 99FleBri2G-162
❑ 99FleBriBlu-162
❑ 99FleBriGol-162
❑ 99FleSta9-433
❑ 99FleWarT-433
❑ 99SpoIll-51
❑ 99Top-212
❑ 99TopChr-212
❑ 99TopChrR-212
❑ 99UppDec-305
❑ 99UppDecEL1-305
❑ 99UppDecEL2-305
Klauke, Steve
❑ 97SalLakB-7
❑ 98SalLakBO-6
Klaus, Billy (William)
❑ 47Exh-120
❑ 55Bow-150
❑ 56BalOriP-29
❑ 56Top-217
❑ 57Top-292
❑ 58Top-89
❑ 59Top-299
❑ 60Top-406
❑ 61Pos-79
❑ 61Top-187
❑ 62Jel-67
❑ 62Pos-67
❑ 62PosCan-67
❑ 62SalPlaC-10
❑ 62ShiPlaC-10
❑ 62Top-571
❑ 63Top-551
❑ 79TCM50-251
❑ 81RedSoxBG2S-33
❑ 83Bra53F-2
❑ 91OriCro-242
Klaus, Robert
❑ 61TopStal-203
❑ 64Top-524
❑ 65OPC-227
❑ 65Top-227
❑ 66OPC-108
❑ 66Top-108
❑ 66TopVen-108
❑ 69Top-387
❑ 78TCM60I-19
❑ 91MetWIZ-212
Klaus, Todd
❑ 98MidAngO-23
Klavitter, Clay
❑ 91BelMarCB-2
❑ 91BelMarP-3668
❑ 91SanBerSC-13
❑ 91SanBerSP-1989
Klawitter, Albert
❑ 12HomRunKE-40
❑ 12Zee-63
❑ 13Zee-81
❑ 14Zee-85
❑ 15Zee-36
❑ 16Zee-36
Klawitter, Tom
❑ 84TolMudHT-14
❑ 85TwiPos-15
❑ 85TwiTeal-13
❑ 85TwiTeal-25
Klebba, Rob
❑ 79WatA'sT-13
❑ 80WesHavWCT-6
Klebe, Frank
❑ 98BatMucTI-13
Klee, Chuck
❑ 96BriWhiSB-21
❑ 97HicCraB-18
❑ 97HicCraRB-22
❑ 98HicCraM-18
Kleean, Tom
❑ 86BelBreP-12
Klein, Bob
❑ 75AppFoxT-10
Klein, Bruce
❑ 89AugPirP-513
Klein, Chuck
❑ 28PorandAR-A19
❑ 28PorandAR-B19
❑ 29PorandAR-52
❑ 30SchR33-17
❑ 30UncJac-18
❑ 30W554-9
❑ 31Exh-11
❑ 31W517-10
❑ 32USCar*-21
❑ 33ButCre-14
❑ 33DelR33-22
❑ 33DouDisP-26
❑ 33ExhFou-6
❑ 33GeoCMil-20
❑ 33Gou-128
❑ 33NatLeaAC-4
❑ 33RitCE-3D
❑ 33TatOrbSDR-157
❑ 33WorCig-60
❑ 34BatR31-185
❑ 34DiaMatCSB-104
❑ 34ExhFou-3
❑ 34Gou-10
❑ 34GouCanV-56
❑ 35AlDemDCR3-154
❑ 35DiaMatCS2-11
❑ 35DiaMatCS3T1-88
❑ 35ExhFou-3
❑ 35GouPuzR-1F
❑ 35GouPuzR-3D
❑ 35GouPuzR-14D
❑ 35GouPuzR-15D
❑ 35WheBB1-18
❑ 36CubTeal-18
❑ 36DiaMatCS4-8
❑ 36GouBWR-20
❑ 36GouWidPPR-A60
❑ 36R31PasP-31
❑ 36SandSW-38
❑ 36WorWidGV-13
❑ 38BasTabP-18
❑ 38ExhFou-6
❑ 39ExhSal-33
❑ 39PlaBal-82
❑ 40PhiTeal-10
❑ 40PlaBal-102
❑ 41PhiTeal-11
❑ 41PlaBal-60
❑ 43PhiTeal-13
❑ 60Fle-30
❑ 61Fle-51
❑ 72FleFamF-36
❑ 74Bra193NLA-4
❑ 76ISCHooHA-3
❑ 77BobParMBC-9
❑ 77GalGloG-48
❑ 77GalGloG-218
❑ 77PhiFav-18
❑ 80LauFamF-6
❑ 80PacLeg-112
❑ 80PerHaloFP-171
❑ 80SSPHOF-172
❑ 81ConTSN-88
❑ 81SpoHaloF-8
❑ 82DiaCla-22
❑ 82TCMGreS-26
❑ 83BigLeaCOA-27
❑ 83ConMar-25
❑ 83PhiPosGPaM-1
❑ 84OCoandSI-201
❑ 86PhiGreT-1
❑ 88ConNatA-12
❑ 88GreBasS-13
❑ 89HOFStiB-48
❑ 90PerGreM-60
❑ 91ConTSN-30
❑ 91ConTSN-300
❑ 92ConTSN-438
❑ 92ConTSN-531
❑ 93ConTSN-671
❑ 93DiaStaES-139
❑ 94ConTSN-1095
❑ 94ConTSNB-1095
❑ 94TedWil-74
Klein, Edward
❑ 09ObaT21-87
❑ 16Zee-37
Klein, Gary
❑ 83ButCopKT-6
Klein, Jeff
❑ 79WatIndT-4A
Klein, Larry
❑ 85BurRanT-3
❑ 86TulDriTI-24
❑ 88OklCit8C-17
❑ 88OklCit8P-32
Klein, Lou
❑ 46SeaSLP-30
❑ 49EurSta-188
❑ 51A'sTeal-15
❑ 60Top-457
❑ 83Car194T-3
Klein, Mark
❑ 77ReaPhiT-15
Klein, Matt
❑ 97UCLBruTI-10
❑ 98SouOreTG-16
Klein, Mike
❑ 96ButCopKB-6
Kleine, Harold
❑ 48AngTeal-15
Kleiner, Stacy
❑ 96NewJerCB-16
❑ 97PriWilC-16
❑ 98ArkTraM-16
Kleinhans, Ted
❑ 34DiaMatCSB-105
❑ 35DiaMatCS3T1-89
❑ 75YanDyn1T-28
Kleinke, Norbert
❑ 40SolHug-12
Kleinow, Red (John)
❑ 08RosComP-50
❑ 09BriE97-17
❑ 09RamT20-66
❑ 09T206-187
❑ 09T206-188
❑ 09T206-189
❑ 10E101-25
❑ 10E102-12
❑ 10MelMinE-25
❑ 10NadCarE-30
❑ 10PeoT21-30
❑ 10W555-40
❑ 11E94-17
❑ 11PinT-5-659
❑ 11SpoLifCW-204
❑ 11T205-88
❑ 11TurRedT-21
Klem, Bill
❑ 09SpoNewSM-38
❑ 21Exh-92
❑ 30SchR33-6
❑ 34DiaMatCSB-106
❑ 35AlDemDCR3-162
❑ 50CalHOFW-46
❑ 53ArtHaloFP-52
❑ 72FleFamF-31
❑ 76ShaPiz-68
❑ 77GalGloG-173
❑ 80PerHaloFP-67
❑ 80SSPHOF-67
❑ 84OCoandSI-106
❑ 86ConSer1-5
❑ 87SpoCubG-3
❑ 88ConSer4-15
❑ 89T/MUmp-63
❑ 92ConTSN-460
❑ 93ConTSNP-1190
❑ 94ConTSN-1190
❑ 94ConTSNB-1190
❑ 95ConTSN-1378
Klemyk, Jim
❑ 98BriBluM-15
Klenoshek, Bill
❑ 88CapCodPPaLP-50
Klepfer, Edward
❑ 14Zee-138
Klesko, Ryan
❑ 2000TopPre-PP3
❑ 89HigSchPLS-20
❑ 90Bes-236
❑ 90CMC-826
❑ 90DurBulUTI-7
❑ 90ProAaA-106
❑ 90SumBraB-9
❑ 90SumBraP-2441
❑ 91Bow-590
❑ 91Cla/Bes-388
❑ 91Cla2-T53
❑ 91ClaGolB-BC15
❑ 91GreBraC-17
❑ 91GreBraLD-209
❑ 91GreBraP-3011
❑ 91LeaGolR-BC21
❑ 91LinDriAA-209
❑ 91UppDecFE-1F
❑ 91UppDecFE-8F
❑ 92Bow-549
❑ 92Bow-623
❑ 92Don-13
❑ 92DonPre-9
❑ 92DonRooP-BC15
❑ 92OPC-126
❑ 92ProFS7-181
❑ 92RicBraBB-4
❑ 92RicBraF-383
❑ 92RicBraRC-8
❑ 92RicBraS-430
❑ 92SkyAAAF-197
❑ 92Top-126
❑ 92TopGol-126
❑ 92TopGolW-126
❑ 92TopMcD-39
❑ 92TopMic-126
❑ 92TriPlaG-GS10
❑ 92UppDec-1
❑ 92UppDec-24
❑ 93Bow-634
❑ 93BraLykP-15
❑ 93BraStaC-26
❑ 93ClaGam-43
❑ 93ClaGam-NNO
❑ 93Don-422
❑ 93Fle-6
❑ 93Lea-469
❑ 93OPC-189
❑ 93PacSpa-9
❑ 93Pin-251
❑ 93PinRooTP-4
❑ 93PinTea2-27
❑ 93RicBraBB-1
❑ 93RicBraF-191
❑ 93RicBraP-1
❑ 93RicBraRC-17
❑ 93RicBraRC-17
❑ 93Sco-294
❑ 93ScoBoyoS-8
❑ 93ScoProaG-5
❑ 93Sel-405
❑ 93StaClu-541
❑ 93StaCluFDI-541
❑ 93StaCluMOP-541
❑ 93Top-423
❑ 93TopGol-423
❑ 93TopInaM-423
❑ 93TopInaR-423
❑ 93TopMic-423
❑ 93Toy-4
❑ 93TriAAAGF-2
❑ 93Ult-7
❑ 93UppDec-376
❑ 93UppDecGold-376
❑ 94Bow-105
❑ 94BowBes-R84
❑ 94BowBesR-R84
❑ 94BraLykP-16
❑ 94BraLykS-16
❑ 94BraUSPC-3S
❑ 94BraUSPC-9H
❑ 94ColC-165
❑ 94ColChoGS-165
❑ 94ColChoSS-165
❑ 94Don-617
❑ 94Fin-437
❑ 94FinJum-437
❑ 94FinRef-437
❑ 94Fla-128
❑ 94FlaWavotF-A4
❑ 94Fle-362
❑ 94FleExtB-205
❑ 94FleExtBRS-11
❑ 94FUnPac-7
❑ 94Lea-286
❑ 94LeaL-85
❑ 94LeaLimRP-7
❑ 94OPC-75
❑ 94OPCHotP-9
❑ 94Pac-12
❑ 94Pin-157
❑ 94PinArtP-157
❑ 94PinMusC-157
❑ 94ProMag-2
❑ 94Sco-464
❑ 94ScoBoyoS-41
❑ 94ScoGolR-464
❑ 94ScoRoo-RT75
❑ 94ScoRooGR-RT75
❑ 94ScoRooSR-SU3
❑ 94Sel-197
❑ 94SelRooS-RS3
❑ 94SelSam-197
❑ 94SP-52
❑ 94SPDieC-52
❑ 94SPHol-21
❑ 94SPHolDC-21
❑ 94Spo-20
❑ 94SpoRoo-RO1
❑ 94SpoRooRS-TR9
❑ 94StaClu-148
❑ 94StaClu-628
❑ 94StaCluFDI-148
❑ 94StaCluFDI-628
❑ 94StaCluGR-148
❑ 94StaCluGR-628
❑ 94StaCluMOP-148
❑ 94StaCluMOP-628
❑ 94StaCluT-38
❑ 94StaCluTFDI-38
❑ 94Stu-37
❑ 94Top-777
❑ 94TopGol-777
❑ 94TopSpa-777
❑ 94TriPla-282
❑ 94Ult-444
❑ 94UltAllR-5
❑ 94UltAllRJ-5
❑ 94UppDec-64
❑ 94UppDecED-64
❑ 94UppDecNG-10
❑ 94UppDecNGED-10
❑ 95Baz-18
❑ 95Bow-309
❑ 95BraAtlC-5
❑ 95ColCho-155
❑ 95ColChoCtG-CG11
❑ 95ColChoCtG-CG11B
❑ 95ColChoCtG-CG11C
❑ 95ColChoCtGE-11
❑ 95ColChoCtGG-CG11
❑ 95ColChoCtGG-CG11B
❑ 95ColChoCtGG-CG11C
❑ 95ColChoCtGGE-11
❑ 95ColChoGS-155
❑ 95ColChoSE-62
❑ 95ColChoSEGS-62
❑ 95ColChoSESS-62
❑ 95ColChoSS-155
❑ 95Don-253
❑ 95DonPreP-253
❑ 95DonTopotO-187
❑ 95Emo-104
❑ 95Fin-8
❑ 95FinPowK-PK3
❑ 95FinRef-8
❑ 95Fla-103
❑ 95Fle-308
❑ 95FleRooS-10
❑ 95Lea-214
❑ 95LeaLim-145
❑ 95Pac-8
❑ 95PacPri-2
❑ 95PanSti-100
❑ 95Pin-224
❑ 95PinArtP-224
❑ 95PinMusC-224
❑ 95PinSam-224
❑ 95Sco-332
❑ 95Sco-RG1
❑ 95Sco-SG1
❑ 95ScoAi-AM9
❑ 95ScoGolR-332
❑ 95ScoHaloG-HG75
❑ 95ScoPlaTS-332
❑ 95ScoRul-SR28
❑ 95ScoRulJ-SR28
❑ 95Sel-41
❑ 95SelArtP-41
❑ 95SelCanM-CM2
❑ 95SelCer-53
❑ 95SelCerMG-53
❑ 95Spo-65
❑ 95SpoArtP-65
❑ 95SPSpeF-27
❑ 95StaClu-19
❑ 95StaCluFDI-19
❑ 95StaCluMO-50
❑ 95StaCluMOP-19
❑ 95StaCluSTDW-B19
❑ 95StaCluSTMP-5
❑ 95StaCluSTWS-19
❑ 95StaCluVR-13
❑ 95StaCluVRMO-13
❑ 95Stu-109
❑ 95Sum-89
❑ 95SumNthD-89
❑ 95Top-324
❑ 95TopCyb-177
❑ 95TopCybSiR-6
❑ 95TopEmb-21
❑ 95TopEmbGI-21
❑ 95UC3-54
❑ 95UC3ArtP-54
❑ 95Ult-349
❑ 95UltAllR-7
❑ 95UltAllRGM-7
❑ 95UltGolM-349
❑ 95UltSecYS-9
❑ 95UltSecYSGM-9
❑ 95UppDec-296
❑ 95UppDecED-296
❑ 95UppDecEDG-296
❑ 95UppDecSE-11
❑ 95UppDecSEG-11
❑ 95Zen-97
❑ 95ZenSam-97
❑ 96Baz-17
❑ 96Bow-11
❑ 96BowBes-19
❑ 96BowBesAR-19
❑ 96BowBesC-6
❑ 96BowBesCAR-6
❑ 96BowBesCR-6
❑ 96BowBesR-19
❑ 96BowFoi-11
❑ 96BraFle-8
❑ 96Cir-104
❑ 96CirBos-26
❑ 96CirRav-104
❑ 96ColCho-460
❑ 96ColChoGS-460
❑ 96ColChoSS-460
❑ 96Don-138
❑ 96DonLonBL-2
❑ 96DonPreP-138
❑ 96EmoXL-144
❑ 96Fin-B333
❑ 96Fin-G321
❑ 96Fin-S88
❑ 96FinRef-B333
❑ 96FinRef-G321
❑ 96FinRef-S88
❑ 96Fla-202
❑ 96Fle-296
❑ 96FleTif-296
❑ 96FleTomL-7
❑ 96FleUpd-U229
❑ 96FleUpdH-11
❑ 96FleUpdTC-U229
❑ 96Lea-176
❑ 96LeaLim-49
❑ 96LeaLimG-49
❑ 96LeaPre-66
❑ 96LeaPreP-66
❑ 96LeaPrePB-176
❑ 96LeaPrePG-176
❑ 96LeaPrePS-176
❑ 96LeaPreSG-55
❑ 96LeaPreSte-55
❑ 96LeaSig-43

❑ 96LeaSigEA-102
❑ 96LeaSigEACM-15
❑ 96LeaSigPPG-43
❑ 96LeaSigPPP-43
❑ 96MetUni-131
❑ 96MetUniP-131
❑ 96MetUniPP-6
❑ 96Pac-2
❑ 96PacOctM-OM10
❑ 96PacPri-P4
❑ 96PacPriG-P4
❑ 96PanSti-7
❑ 96Pin-253
❑ 96PinAfi-107
❑ 96PinAfiAP-107
❑ 96PinAfiP-107
❑ 96PinAfiSP-21
❑ 96PinArtP-153
❑ 96PinChrBC-2
❑ 96PinFoil-253
❑ 96PinProS-18
❑ 96PinSta-153
❑ 96ProMagA-15
❑ 96ProMagDM-2
❑ 96ProSta-22
❑ 96Sco-3
❑ 96Sco-368
❑ 96ScoDugC-A3
❑ 96ScoDugC-B93
❑ 96ScoDugCAP-A3
❑ 96ScoDugCAP-B93
❑ 96ScoDugCSamp-3
❑ 96ScoGolS-19
❑ 96ScoSam-3
❑ 96Sel-77
❑ 96SelArtP-77
❑ 96SelCer-82
❑ 96SelCer-144
❑ 96SelCerAP-82
❑ 96SelCerAP-144
❑ 96SelCerCB-82
❑ 96SelCerCB-144
❑ 96SelCerCR-82
❑ 96SelCerCR-144
❑ 96SelCerIP-5
❑ 96SelCerMB-82
❑ 96SelCerMB-144
❑ 96SelCerMG-82
❑ 96SelCerMG-144
❑ 96SelCerMR-82
❑ 96SelCerMR-144
❑ 96SelCerSF-11
❑ 96SelTeaN-12
❑ 96SP-22
❑ 96Spo-28
❑ 96SpoArtP-28
❑ 96StaClu-178
❑ 96StaCluEPB-178
❑ 96StaCluEPG-178
❑ 96StaCluEPS-178
❑ 96StaCluMOP-178
❑ 96Stu-150
❑ 96StuPrePB-150
❑ 96StuPrePG-150
❑ 96StuPrePS-150
❑ 96Sum-136
❑ 96Sum-157
❑ 96SumAbo&B-136
❑ 96SumAbo&B-157
❑ 96SumArtP-136
❑ 96SumArtP-157
❑ 96SumBigB-9
❑ 96SumBigBM-9
❑ 96SumFoi-136
❑ 96SumFoi-157
❑ 96SumHitI-11
❑ 96SumPos-7
❑ 96Top-193
❑ 96TopChr-61
❑ 96TopChrR-61
❑ 96TopGal-110
❑ 96TopGalPPI-110
❑ 96TopLas-10
❑ 96Ult-158
❑ 96Ult-597
❑ 96UltChe-B7
❑ 96UltCheGM-B7
❑ 96UltFreF-6
❑ 96UltFreFGM-6
❑ 96UltGolM-158
❑ 96UltGolM-597
❑ 96UltRisS-7
❑ 96UltRisSGM-7
❑ 96UppDec-272
❑ 96UppDecDD-DD4
❑ 96UppDecDDG-DD4
❑ 96UppDecDDS-DD4
❑ 96Zen-37
❑ 96Zen-139
❑ 96ZenArtP-37
❑ 96ZenArtP-139
❑ 96ZenDiaC-10
❑ 96ZenDiaCP-10
❑ 96ZenMoz-1
❑ 96ZenZ-9
❑ 97Bow-14
❑ 97BowBes-61
❑ 97BowBesAR-61
❑ 97BowBesR-61
❑ 97BowChr-10
❑ 97BowChrI-10
❑ 97BowChrIR-10
❑ 97BowChrR-10
❑ 97BowInt-14
❑ 97BraSco-1
❑ 97BraScoPl-1
❑ 97BraScoPr-1
❑ 97Cir-365
❑ 97CirRav-365
❑ 97ColCho-32
❑ 97ColChoCtG-1A
❑ 97ColChoCtG-1B
❑ 97ColChoCtG-1C
❑ 97ColChoCtGE-CG1
❑ 97ColChoCtGIW-CG1
❑ 97ColChoT-AB5
❑ 97Don-144
❑ 97DonEli-22
❑ 97DonEliGS-22
❑ 97DonGolPP-144
❑ 97DonLim-105
❑ 97DonLim-182
❑ 97DonLimE-105
❑ 97DonLimE-182
❑ 97DonLimENG-182
❑ 97DonLonL-14
❑ 97DonPre-43
❑ 97DonPreCttC-43
❑ 97DonSigA-61
❑ 97DonSigAC-74
❑ 97DonSigAM-74
❑ 97DonSilPP-144
❑ 97DonTea-21
❑ 97DonTeaSPE-21
❑ 97DurBulATI-2
❑ 97E-X2-55
❑ 97E-X2Cred-55
❑ 97E-X2EssCre-55
❑ 97Fin-116
❑ 97Fin-343
❑ 97FinEmb-116
❑ 97FinEmb-343
❑ 97FinEmbR-116
❑ 97FinEmbR-343
❑ 97FinRef-116
❑ 97FinRef-343
❑ 97FlaShoLC-118
❑ 97FlaShoLeg0-118
❑ 97FlaShoLeg1-118
❑ 97FlaShoM-A118
❑ 97FlaShoM-B118
❑ 97FlaShoM-C118
❑ 97FlaShoR0-118
❑ 97FlaShoR1-118
❑ 97FlaShoR2-118
❑ 97Fle-260
❑ 97FleLumC-11
❑ 97FleTif-260
❑ 97Lea-233
❑ 97LeaFraM-233
❑ 97LeaFraMDC-233
❑ 97LeaKnoG-10
❑ 97LeaKnoG-P10
❑ 97MetUni-32
❑ 97NewPin-127
❑ 97NewPinAP-127
❑ 97NewPinMC-127
❑ 97NewPinPP-127
❑ 97Pac-237
❑ 97PacCar-23
❑ 97PacCarM-23
❑ 97PacGolCD-23
❑ 97PacLigB-237
❑ 97PacPri-80
❑ 97PacPriLB-80
❑ 97PacPriP-80
❑ 97PacPriSL-SL8A
❑ 97PacSil-237
❑ 97Pin-38
❑ 97PinArtP-PP38
❑ 97PinCer-14
❑ 97PinCerMBla-14
❑ 97PinCerMBlu-14
❑ 97PinCerMG-14
❑ 97PinCerMR-14
❑ 97PinCerR-14
❑ 97PinIns-81
❑ 97PinInsC-14
❑ 97PinInsCE-81
❑ 97PinInsDE-81
❑ 97PinMin-28
❑ 97PinMin-P28
❑ 97PinMinB-28
❑ 97PinMinB-P28
❑ 97PinMinCB-28
❑ 97PinMinCB-P28
❑ 97PinMinCG-28
❑ 97PinMinCGR-28
❑ 97PinMinCN-28
❑ 97PinMinCSS-28
❑ 97PinMinG-28
❑ 97PinMinS-28
❑ 97PinMusC-38
❑ 97PinPrePla-38
❑ 97PinTotCPB-14
❑ 97PinTotCPG-14
❑ 97PinTotCPR-14
❑ 97PinX-P-92
❑ 97PinX-PMoS-92
❑ 97PinX-PSfF-34
❑ 97PinX-PSfFU-34
❑ 97RicBraBC-3
❑ 97RicBraBC-25
❑ 97Sco-7
❑ 97Sco-536
❑ 97ScoArtPWB-7
❑ 97ScoArtPWB-536
❑ 97ScoHeaotO-21
❑ 97ScoHigZ-16
❑ 97ScoPreS-7
❑ 97ScoResC-536
❑ 97ScoShoS-7
❑ 97ScoShoS-536
❑ 97ScoShoSAP-7
❑ 97ScoShoSAP-536
❑ 97ScoSteS-18
❑ 97ScoTitT-10
❑ 97Sel-20
❑ 97SelArtP-20
❑ 97SelCom-20
❑ 97SelRegG-20
❑ 97SP-26
❑ 97SpoIll-47
❑ 97SpoIllEE-47
❑ 97SpoIllGS-2
❑ 97SPSpeF-38
❑ 97StaClu-16
❑ 97StaCluMat-16
❑ 97StaCluMOP-16
❑ 97Stu-125
❑ 97StuPrePG-125
❑ 97StuPrePS-125
❑ 97Top-390
❑ 97TopChr-135
❑ 97TopChrR-135
❑ 97TopGal-101
❑ 97TopGalPPI-101
❑ 97TopMem05-28
❑ 97Ult-155
❑ 97UltGolME-155
❑ 97UltHRK-6
❑ 97UltPlaME-155
❑ 97UppDec-299
❑ 97UppDecPP-PP13
❑ 97UppDecPPJ-PP13
❑ 97UppDecRSF-RS7
❑ 98Bow-244
❑ 98BowBes-44
❑ 98BowBesAR-44
❑ 98BowBesR-44
❑ 98BowChr-244
❑ 98BowChrGA-244
❑ 98BowChrGAR-244
❑ 98BowChrI-244
❑ 98BowChrIR-244
❑ 98BowChrR-244
❑ 98BowChrR-31
❑ 98BowChrRR-31
❑ 98BowGolA-244
❑ 98BowInt-244
❑ 98BraSco-6
❑ 98BraScoP-6
❑ 98CirThu-181
❑ 98CirThuRav-181
❑ 98CirThuSupRav-181
❑ 98ColCho-302
❑ 98CroRoy-14
❑ 98Don-98
❑ 98DonCol-98
❑ 98DonColL-215
❑ 98DonColP-599
❑ 98DonColS-98
❑ 98DonGolPP-98
❑ 98DonPre-49
❑ 98DonPreSeat-49
❑ 98DonPriCD-98
❑ 98DonPriCL-215
❑ 98DonPriCP-599
❑ 98DonSig-4
❑ 98DonSigA-50
❑ 98DonSigAC-67
❑ 98DonSigAM-68
❑ 98DonSigP-4
❑ 98DonSilPP-98
❑ 98E-X2-65
❑ 98E-X2ECFut-65
❑ 98E-X2ECNow-65
❑ 98Fin-72
❑ 98FinNo--72
❑ 98FinNo-R-72
❑ 98FinRef-72
❑ 98FlaShoLeg0-40
❑ 98FlaShoLeg1-40
❑ 98FlaShoLeg2-40
❑ 98FlaShoLeg3-40
❑ 98FlaShoLegM-40
❑ 98FlaShoR0-40
❑ 98FlaShoR1-40
❑ 98FlaShoR2-40
❑ 98FlaShoR3-40
❑ 98Fle-382
❑ 98FleVin'-73
❑ 98FleVin'C-73
❑ 98Lea-15
❑ 98LeaFraDA-15
❑ 98LeaFraF-15
❑ 98LeaFraM-15
❑ 98LeaFraM-15
❑ 98LeaFraMDC-15
❑ 98LeaFraMDC-15
❑ 98LeaFraMS-15
❑ 98LeaFraMZ2-15
❑ 98LeaRS-20
❑ 98LeaRSLHolo-20
❑ 98LeaRSLong-20
❑ 98LeaRTrue-20
❑ 98MetUni-143
❑ 98MetUniPMG-143
❑ 98Pac-236
❑ 98PacAur-106
❑ 98PacAurPF-18
❑ 98PacAurPFC-18
❑ 98PacAurPFPB-18
❑ 98PacAurPFR-18
❑ 98PacAurPFS-18
❑ 98PacInv-78
❑ 98PacInvGems-119
❑ 98PacInvPBlue-78
❑ 98PacInvSilv-78
❑ 98PacInvTeam-2
❑ 98PacOme-21
❑ 98PacOmeR-21
❑ 98PacOnl-64
❑ 98PacOnlR-64
❑ 98PacOnlWC-64
❑ 98PacPar-131
❑ 98PacParC-131
❑ 98PacParG-131
❑ 98PacParHS-131
❑ 98PacParI-43
❑ 98PacParPB-131
❑ 98PacParR-131
❑ 98PacPlaB-236
❑ 98PacRedT-236
❑ 98PacSil-236
❑ 98PinIns-19
❑ 98PinInsCE-19
❑ 98PinInsDE-19
❑ 98PinPer-50
❑ 98PinPerPP-50
❑ 98PinPerSftF-40
❑ 98PinPlu-167
❑ 98PinSna-AB1
❑ 98Revo-14
❑ 98RevoSS-14
❑ 98Sco-30
❑ 98ScoRT-82
❑ 98ScoRTSS-PP62
❑ 98ScoRTSSAP-PP62
❑ 98ScoRTSSAP1-PP62
❑ 98ScoSS-PP10
❑ 98ScoSSAP-PP10
❑ 98SkyDugA-5
❑ 98SkyDugAIA-5
❑ 98SP Aut-48
❑ 98SpoIll-77
❑ 98SpoIllEE-77
❑ 98SpoIllFE-77
❑ 98SpoIllWSF-79
❑ 98SpoIllWSFEE-79
❑ 98SpoIllWSFFE-79
❑ 98SPxFin-56
❑ 98SPxFinR-56
❑ 98SPxFinS-56
❑ 98StaCluFDI-229
❑ 98StaCluI-229
❑ 98StaCluOneK-229
❑ 98StaCluPP-229
❑ 98Stu-158
❑ 98StuGPP-158
❑ 98StuSPP-158
❑ 98Top-65
❑ 98TopChr-65
❑ 98TopChrR-65
❑ 98TopDevR-65
❑ 98TopDia-65
❑ 98TopGal-137
❑ 98TopGalGP-137
❑ 98TopGalOPP-137
❑ 98TopGalPPI-137
❑ 98TopGalPPIA-137
❑ 98TopGolLabC1-82
❑ 98TopGolLabC1B-82
❑ 98TopGolLabC1One-82
❑ 98TopGolLabC1R-82
❑ 98TopGolLabC2-82
❑ 98TopGolLabC2B-82
❑ 98TopGolLabC2One-82
❑ 98TopGolLabC2R-82
❑ 98TopGolLabC3-82
❑ 98TopGolLabC3B-82
❑ 98TopGolLabC3One-82
❑ 98TopGolLabC3R-82
❑ 98TopMiniC-65
❑ 98TopOpeD-34
❑ 98TopSta-116
❑ 98TopStaB-116
❑ 98TopStaG-116
❑ 98TopStaGR-116
❑ 98TopStaS-116
❑ 98TopSup-10
❑ 98TopSup-10
❑ 98UD3-34
❑ 98UD3-124
❑ 98UD3-214
❑ 98UD3DieCut-34
❑ 98UD3DieCut-124
❑ 98UD3DieCut-214
❑ 98Ult-87
❑ 98UltGolM-87
❑ 98UltMas-87
❑ 98UltPlaM-87
❑ 98UppDec-303
❑ 99199Fin-192
❑ 99Bow-244
❑ 99BowBes-81
❑ 99BowBesAR-81
❑ 99BowBesR-81
❑ 99BowGol-244
❑ 99BowInt-244
❑ 99CroRoyB-14
❑ 99CroRoyL-14
❑ 99CroRoyOD-14
❑ 99FinGolRef-192
❑ 99FinRef-192
❑ 99Fle-144
❑ 99FleSta9-144
❑ 99FleWarT-144
❑ 99MetUni-157
❑ 99MetUniGM-157
❑ 99MetUniPMG-157
❑ 99Pac-33
❑ 99PacCroC-26
❑ 99PacCroCPB-26
❑ 99PacInv-15
❑ 99PacInvOD-15
❑ 99PacInvPB-15
❑ 99PacOme-24
❑ 99PacOmeC-24
❑ 99PacOmeG-24
❑ 99PacOmePB-24
❑ 99PacPar-26
❑ 99PacParC-26
❑ 99PacParG-26
❑ 99PacParHoloGold-26
❑ 99PacParHS-26
❑ 99PacParOD-26
❑ 99PacParPB-26
❑ 99PacParRed-26
❑ 99PacPlaB-33
❑ 99PacPri-14
❑ 99PacPriHB-14
❑ 99PacPriHG-14
❑ 99PacPriHM-14
❑ 99PacPriHP-14
❑ 99PacPriRed-14
❑ 99PacPriS-37
❑ 99PacPriS206-37
❑ 99PacPriS206R-37
❑ 99PacPriSP-37
❑ 99PacPriSV-37
❑ 99PacRed-33
❑ 99SkyMolM-26
❑ 99SkyMolMOA-18
❑ 99SkyMolMX-26
❑ 99SkyPre-173
❑ 99SkyPreR-173
❑ 99SkyThu-213
❑ 99SkyThuRant-213
❑ 99SkyThuRave-213
❑ 99StaClu-206
❑ 99StaCluFDI-206
❑ 99StaCluOoaK-206
❑ 99StaCluPP-206
❑ 99ThuSkySupR-213
❑ 99Top-370
❑ 99TopChr-370
❑ 99TopChrR-370
❑ 99TopMVPP-370
❑ 99TopOpeD-123
❑ 99TopSta-142
❑ 99TopStaFoil-142
❑ 99UppDec-34
❑ 99UppDecEL1-34
❑ 99UppDecEL2-34

Kleven, Jay
❑ 75TidTidTI-14
❑ 91MetWIZ-213

Kleven, Mark
❑ 88ChaRaiP-1205

Kliafas, Steve
❑ 92BakDodCLC-14
❑ 92SanAntMF-3984
❑ 92VerBeaDF-2883
❑ 94SanAntMF-2479

Klieman, Ed
❑ 47IndTeal-16
❑ 47IndVanPP-15
❑ 48IndTeal-19
❑ 79DiaGre-292
❑ 83TCMPla1944-13

Klimas, Phil
❑ 77CocAstT-9
❑ 80TulDriT-13
❑ 81TulDriT-3
❑ 82GleFalWST-7
❑ 90TulDriDGB-22

Klimchock, Lou
❑ 60Lea-116
❑ 60Top-137
❑ 60TopVen-137
❑ 61A'sTeal-10
❑ 61Top-462
❑ 62Top-259
❑ 63Top-542
❑ 65Top-542
❑ 66Top-589
❑ 70OPC-247
❑ 70Top-247
❑ 91MetWIZ-214

Klimek, Josh
❑ 96HelBreTI-12
❑ 97BelSnaB-17
❑ 97MidLeaTP-2
❑ 98StoPorG-13

Klimkowski, Ron
❑ 70Top-702
❑ 70YanPhoS-20
❑ 71MLBOffS-492
❑ 71OPC-28
❑ 71Top-28
❑ 72OPC-363
❑ 72Top-363
❑ 72TopCloT-18
❑ 73SyrChiTI-12
❑ 92YanWIZ6-68
❑ 92YanWIZ7-91

Kline, Bob
❑ 55Top-173
❑ 84NewOriT-24

Kline, Bob (Robert George)
❑ 34DiaMatCSB-107

Kline, Doug
❑ 88VisOakCLC-169
❑ 88VisOakP-107

❑ 89WesPalBES-14
❑ 90JacMetGS-2
❑ 91LinDriAA-636
❑ 91WilBilLD-636
❑ 91WilBilP-288
Kline, Greg
❑ 75CliPilT-5
❑ 76CliPilT-23
Kline, Jason
❑ 95OdgRapTI-13
Kline, Kris
❑ 83PeoSunF-7
Kline, Peter
❑ 94OgdRapSP-28
Kline, Ron
❑ 53Top-175
❑ 56PirTeal-12
❑ 56Top-94
❑ 57Kah-16
❑ 57Top-256
❑ 58Hir-31
❑ 58Kah-15
❑ 58PirTeal-5
❑ 58Top-82
❑ 59Kah-16
❑ 59Top-265
❑ 59Top-428
❑ 60CarJayP-5
❑ 60Kah-18A
❑ 60Kah-18B
❑ 60Lea-105
❑ 60Top-197
❑ 61Top-127
❑ 61TopStal-90
❑ 62TigPosCF-11
❑ 62Top-216
❑ 63Top-84
❑ 64Top-358
❑ 64TopVen-358
❑ 65OPC-56
❑ 65Top-56
❑ 65TopTral-54
❑ 66Top-453
❑ 67CokCapTw-1
❑ 67OPC-133
❑ 67Top-133
❑ 67TwiTeal-8
❑ 68PirKDK-27
❑ 68PirTeal-8
❑ 68Top-446
❑ 69MilBra-149
❑ 69PirTeal-10
❑ 69Top-243
❑ 69TopSta-86
❑ 78TCM60I-251
❑ 91TopArc1-175
Kline, Steve (Steven Jack)
❑ 70YanPhoS-21
❑ 71MLBOffS-493
❑ 71OPC-51
❑ 71Top-51
❑ 72OPC-467
❑ 72Top-467
❑ 73Kel2D-50
❑ 73LinPor-64
❑ 73OPC-172
❑ 73SyrChiTI-13
❑ 73Top-172
❑ 74OPC-324
❑ 74SyrChiTI-12
❑ 74Top-324
❑ 75OPC-639
❑ 75Top-639
❑ 75TopMin-639
❑ 76SSP-532
❑ 92YanWIZ7-92
Kline, Steve James
❑ 93BurIndC-14
❑ 93BurIndF-3292
❑ 94ColRedC-12
❑ 94ColRedF-439
❑ 94SouAtlLAF-SAL9
❑ 95Exc-42
❑ 95Top-635
❑ 95UppDecML-178
❑ 95UppDecMLFS-178
❑ 96CanIndB-14
❑ 97ColCho-315
❑ 97Fle-692
❑ 97FleTif-692
❑ 98PacOnl-451
❑ 98PacOnlR-451
❑ 98PacOnlWC-451
❑ 98Ult-171
❑ 98UltGolM-171
❑ 98UltMas-171
❑ 98UltPlaM-171
❑ 99Fle-454
❑ 99FleSta9-454
❑ 99FleWarT-454
❑ 99Pac-267
❑ 99PacPlaB-267
❑ 99PacRed-267
Klinefelter, David
❑ 88AubAstP-1972
Kling, Johnny (John)
❑ 06FanCraNL-24
❑ 07CubA.CDPP-5
❑ 07CubGFGCP-5
❑ 08AmeCarE91-12
❑ 08CubPos-3
❑ 08RosComP-105
❑ 09ColChiE-154
❑ 09SpoNewSM-41
❑ 09T206-190
❑ 10E98-17
❑ 10JHDABE-9
❑ 11BasBatEU-26
❑ 11HelSta-79
❑ 11MecDFT-12
❑ 11PinT-5-211
❑ 11PloCanE-38
❑ 11S74Sil-63
❑ 11SpoLifCW-205
❑ 11SpoLifM-172
❑ 11T205-89
❑ 11TurRedT-102
❑ 12ColRedB-154
❑ 12ColTinT-154A
❑ 12ColTinT-154B
❑ 12HasTriFT-20
❑ 12HasTriFT-50A
❑ 12HasTriFT-50B
❑ 12HasTriFT-50C
❑ 12HasTriFT-50D
❑ 12PhiCarE-15
❑ 12T207-91
❑ 50CubGreB-12
❑ 61Fle-52
❑ 87Cub190T-4
❑ 93ConTSN-867
❑ 93UppDecTR-3
Klingbell, Scott
❑ 85VisOakT-23
Klingenbeck, Scott
❑ 92FroRowDP-45
❑ 92FroRowDPG-45
❑ 92FroRowDPS-45
❑ 92KanCouCTI-17
❑ 93AusFut-65
❑ 93FreKeyC-12
❑ 93FreKeyF-1023
❑ 93StaCluM-80
❑ 94Bow-86
❑ 94BowBayF-2411
❑ 94ExcFS7-8
❑ 94OriPro-49
❑ 95RocRedWTI-20
❑ 95Top-631
❑ 96ColCho-203
❑ 96ColChoGS-203
❑ 96ColChoSS-203
❑ 96Don-137
❑ 96DonPreP-137
❑ 97IndInd-11
❑ 98IndIndQ-11
Klinger, Robert
❑ 37Zee-55
❑ 39PlaBal-90
❑ 40PlaBal-165
❑ 41DouPlaR-35
❑ 41DouPlaR-97
❑ 47RedSoxTI-13
❑ 48SmiClo-25
❑ 75RedSox1T-22
Klink, Joe
❑ 85LynMetT-13
❑ 86OrlTwiP-9
❑ 87SpoTeaP-17
❑ 87TwiPos-13
❑ 89HunStaB-27
❑ 90A'sMot-26
❑ 90ClaYel-T26
❑ 90Lea-503
❑ 90TopTra-51T
❑ 90TopTraT-51T
❑ 91A'sMot-26
❑ 91Don-591
❑ 91Fle-13
❑ 91Lea-461
❑ 91OPC-553
❑ 91Sco-588
❑ 91Top-553
❑ 91TopDesS-553
❑ 91TopMic-553
❑ 91TopTif-553
❑ 91UppDec-468
❑ 92Don-183
❑ 92OPC-678
❑ 92Sco-151
❑ 92StaClu-326
❑ 92Top-678
❑ 92TopGol-678
❑ 92TopGolW-678
❑ 92TopMic-678
❑ 92UppDec-530
❑ 93FleFinE-64
❑ 93MarPub-14
❑ 93MarUppD-715
❑ 93MarUSPC-5H
❑ 93TopTra-95T
❑ 93Ult-380
❑ 93UppDec-715
❑ 93UppDecGold-715
❑ 94Fle-470
❑ 94Sco-283
❑ 94ScoGolR-283
❑ 94StaClu-68
❑ 94StaCluFDI-68
❑ 94StaCluGR-68
❑ 94StaCluMOP-68
❑ 94StaCluT-87
❑ 94StaCluTFDI-87
❑ 94Top-409
❑ 94TopGol-409
❑ 94TopSpa-409
Klippstein, John
❑ 51Bow-248
❑ 52Top-148
❑ 53Top-46
❑ 54Bow-29
❑ 54Top-31
❑ 55Bow-152
❑ 56Kah-8
❑ 56Top-249
❑ 57Kah-17
❑ 57RedSoh-11
❑ 57Top-296
❑ 58RedEnq-22
❑ 58Top-242
❑ 59Top-152
❑ 59TopVen-152
❑ 60DodBelB-12
❑ 60Top-191
❑ 60TopVen-191
❑ 61Top-539
❑ 61TopStal-204
❑ 62RedEnq-20
❑ 62Top-151
❑ 62TopVen-151
❑ 63RedEnq-18
❑ 63Top-571
❑ 64Top-533
❑ 65Top-384
❑ 66Top-493
❑ 67Top-588
❑ 78TwiFri-36
❑ 79DiaGre-120
❑ 79TCM50-62
❑ 83TopRep5-148
❑ 90DodTar-413
❑ 91TopArc1-46
❑ 94TopArc1-31
❑ 94TopArc1G-31
Klipstein, Dave
❑ 84ElPasDT-18
❑ 86VanCanP-16
❑ 87DenZepP-12
❑ 88NasSouC-20
❑ 88NasSouP-474
Kloek, Kevin
❑ 92FroRowDP-30
❑ 92FroRowDPG-30
❑ 92FroRowDPS-30
❑ 93El PasDF-2948
❑ 95ElPasDTI-13
❑ 96El PasDB-13
Kloes, David
❑ 98OneYanG-19
Kloff, August
❑ 87OldJudN-282
Klonoski, Jason
❑ 87AriWilP-8
❑ 88AriWilP-7
❑ 88CapCodPPaLP-127
❑ 90BenBucL-10
❑ 91Cla/Bes-370
❑ 91KenTwiC-27
❑ 91KenTwiP-2069
❑ 92OrlSunRF-2843
❑ 92OrlSunRS-508
❑ 93NasXprF-396
Klopp, Betz
❑ 78ReaRem-9
Klopp, Frank
❑ 85PriWilPT-26
Klopper, Rod
❑ 88AlaGolTI-12
Kluge, Matt
❑ 92SanBerC-5
❑ 92SanBerSF-957
Klugman, Joe
❑ 90DodTar-1002
Klump, Ken
❑ 83WisRapTF-21
❑ 85OrlTwiT-17
Klumpp, Elmer
❑ 90DodTar-414
Klusener, Matt
❑ 90WicStaSGD-19
Klusman, William F.
❑ 87OldJudN-283
Kluss, Dennis
❑ 90WatIndS-12
Kluszewski, Ted
❑ 47Exh-121A
❑ 47Exh-121B
❑ 47Exh-121C
❑ 47PM1StaP1-105
❑ 47PM1StaP1-106
❑ 49EurSta-87
❑ 49Lea-38
❑ 50Bow-62
❑ 51Bow-143
❑ 51FisBakL-15
❑ 51TopRedB-39
❑ 52BasPho-3
❑ 52Top-29
❑ 53BowC-62
❑ 53DixLid-11
❑ 53DixPre-11
❑ 53MacSta-2
❑ 53NorBreL-15
❑ 53RedMan-NL6
❑ 53Top-162
❑ 54DixLid-8
❑ 54RedHeaF-14
❑ 54RedMan-NL6
❑ 54Top-7
❑ 55ArmCoi-11
❑ 55Kah-2
❑ 55RedMan-NL16
❑ 55RobGouS-10
❑ 55RobGouW-10
❑ 55Top-120
❑ 55TopDouH-121
❑ 56Kah-9
❑ 56Top-25
❑ 56TopHocF-A12
❑ 56TopHocF-B14
❑ 56TopPin-56
❑ 56YelBasP-17
❑ 57Kah-18
❑ 57RedSoh-12
❑ 57Top-165
❑ 58Hir-67
❑ 58Kah-16
❑ 58Top-178
❑ 58Top-321
❑ 59Kah-17
❑ 59Top-17
❑ 59Top-35
❑ 59TopVen-17
❑ 59TopVen-35
❑ 60Kah-19
❑ 60MacSta-10
❑ 60NuHi-57
❑ 60Top-505
❑ 60WhiSoxJP-4
❑ 60WhiSoxTS-8
❑ 61AngJayP-7
❑ 61Baz-18
❑ 61NuSco-457
❑ 61Pos-31
❑ 61Top-65
❑ 61TopStal-173
❑ 62AngJayP-6
❑ 62Pos-82
❑ 62PosCan-82
❑ 63BasMagM-47
❑ 67TopVen-183
❑ 73OPC-296
❑ 73Top-296
❑ 74OPC-326
❑ 74Top-326
❑ 76SSP-618
❑ 77RedCarP-1
❑ 79DiaGre-269
❑ 79TCM50-12
❑ 81TCM60I-439
❑ 81WhiSox1T-16
❑ 82DiaCla-62
❑ 82GSGalAG-17
❑ 82OhiHaloF-18
❑ 82TCMGreS-11
❑ 83TopRep5-29
❑ 84OCoandSI-213
❑ 84SpoDesPW-48
❑ 84TCMBruS-BS3
❑ 85AngStrH-10
❑ 85TCMPla1-16
❑ 86RedGreT-9
❑ 86SpoDecG-38
❑ 88PacLegI-72
❑ 89WhiSoxK-1
❑ 91TopArc1-162
❑ 92BazQua5A-17
❑ 93ActPacA-138
❑ 94TedWil-22
❑ 94TopArc1-7
❑ 94TopArc1G-7
Klutts, Mickey (Gene)
❑ 77Top-490
❑ 78SSP270-21
❑ 78Top-707
❑ 78YanSSPD-21
❑ 80Top-717
❑ 81Don-110
❑ 81Fle-584
❑ 81Top-232
❑ 82Fle-97
❑ 82Top-148
❑ 83Don-465
❑ 83Top-571
❑ 83TopTra-56T
❑ 92YanWIZ7-93
Kluttz, Clyde
❑ 46SeaSLP-31
❑ 50WorWidGV-41
❑ 52Top-132
❑ 83Car194T-35
❑ 83TCMPla1944-39
❑ 83TopRep5-132
Kluver, Hayden
❑ 98GreFalDG-18
Klvac, David
❑ 92LynRedSC-15
❑ 92LynRedSF-2902
❑ 93ForLauRSC-15
❑ 93ForLauRSFP-1593
Kmak, Joe
❑ 85EveGiaC-7
❑ 86FreGiaSB-6
❑ 88ShrCapP-1280
❑ 89CalLeaA-46
❑ 89FleUpd-127
❑ 89RenSilSCLC-252
❑ 90ElPasDGS-19
❑ 91DenZepLD-144
❑ 91DenZepP-125
❑ 91LinDriAAA-144
❑ 92Bow-545
❑ 92DenZepF-2643
❑ 92DenZepS-135
❑ 93Bow-15
❑ 93BrePol-14
❑ 93ExcFS7-190
❑ 93FleFinE-225
❑ 93Pin-575
❑ 93Ult-570
❑ 93UppDec-782
❑ 93UppDecGold-782
❑ 94BreMilB-139
❑ 94NorTidF-2924
❑ 94USPlaCR-3D
❑ 95IowCubTI-19
❑ 96IndIndB-13
❑ 97IndInd-12
Knabe, Otto (Franz Otto)
❑ 08RosComP-142
❑ 09ColChiE-156
❑ 09T206-191
❑ 10CouT21-37
❑ 10CouT21-160
❑ 10E101-26
❑ 10E102-13
❑ 10LuxCigPP-12
❑ 10MelMinE-26
❑ 10NadCarE-31
❑ 10NadE1-26
❑ 10PeoT21-31A
❑ 10PeoT21-31B
❑ 11HelSta-144
❑ 11PinT-5-307
❑ 11SpoLifM-232
❑ 12ColRedB-156
❑ 12ColTinT-156
❑ 12T207-92
❑ 14CraJacE-1
❑ 14TexTomE-25
❑ 15AmeCarE106-23
❑ 15CraJacE-1
Knabenshue, Chris
❑ 85SpoIndC-9
❑ 86ChaRaiP-12
❑ 87WicPilRD-7
❑ 88TexLeaAGS-34
❑ 88WicPilRD-14
❑ 89LasVegSC-23
❑ 89LasVegSP-19
❑ 90CMC-246
❑ 90ProAAAF-313
❑ 90ScrRedBC-20
❑ 90ScrRedBP-611
❑ 91LinDriAAA-485
❑ 91ScrRedBLD-485
❑ 91ScrRedBP-2551
❑ 92HunStaS-312
Knackert, Brent
❑ 88FloStaLAS-40
❑ 88TamTarS-11
❑ 89SarWhiSS-13
❑ 90DonRoo-52
❑ 90MarMot-18
❑ 90MetColP-37
❑ 90TopTra-52T
❑ 90TopTraT-52T
❑ 91Don-662
❑ 91MarCouH-17
❑ 91OPC-563
❑ 91Sco-774
❑ 91Top-563
❑ 91TopDeb90-78
❑ 91TopDesS-563
❑ 91TopMic-563
❑ 91TopTif-563
❑ 91UppDec-378
❑ 92Don-608
❑ 92JacSunS-372
❑ 92SkyAA F-153
❑ 93JacSunF-2708
❑ 95BinMetTI-34
❑ 96PawRedSDD-15
Knapland, Greg
❑ 91WatIndC-8
❑ 91WatIndP-3363
Knapp, Chris (Robert C.)
❑ 77Top-247
❑ 77WhiSoxJT-7
❑ 77WhiSoxT-14
❑ 78AngFamF-20
❑ 78SSP270-212
❑ 78Top-361
❑ 79Top-453
❑ 80Top-658
❑ 81Don-173
❑ 81SalLakCGT-7
❑ 81Top-557
❑ 82IowCubT-18
❑ 83KinBluJTI-10
Knapp, John
❑ 87ChaWheP-12
❑ 88BakDodCLC-236
❑ 89VerBeaDS-14
❑ 90VerBeaDS-17
❑ 91AdeGiaF-10
❑ 92GulCoaDF-3584
Knapp, Leri
❑ 08BufBisFJO-7
Knapp, Mike (Michael)
❑ 86SalAngC-87
❑ 87QuaCitAP-27
❑ 88MidAngGS-13
❑ 88TexLeaAGS-36
❑ 89MidAngGS-20
❑ 90MidAngGS-13
❑ 90TexLeaAGS-6
❑ 91ChaKniLD-136
❑ 91ChaKniP-1691
❑ 91LinDriAA-136
❑ 92IowCubF-4053
❑ 92IowCubS-210

❑ 93OmaRoyF-1681
❑ 94OmaRoyF-1225
❑ 96TacRaiB-16
Knapp, Rick
❑ 86TulDriTI-9B
❑ 88GasRanP-1000
❑ 92GulCoaRSP-29
❑ 93OklCit8F-1641
❑ 94OklCit8F-1510
Knauss, Tom
❑ 92ClaDraP-49
❑ 92FroRowDP-19
❑ 92FroRowDPG-19
❑ 92FroRowDPS-19
❑ 93ClaFS7-213
❑ 93EliTwiC-13
❑ 93EliTwiF-3420
❑ 93ForWayWC-13
❑ 93ForWayWF-1974
❑ 93StaCluM-38
❑ 94ForWayWC-12
❑ 94ForWayWF-2023
❑ 95ForMyeMTI-13
❑ 96FtMyeMB-25
Knecht, Bobby
❑ 88AppFoxP-161
❑ 88MidLeaAGS-41
Knell, Phillip
❑ 87OldJudN-284
Knepper, Bob
❑ 70RelPam-7
❑ 75PhoGiaC-16
❑ 75PhoGiaCK-10
❑ 76PheGiaCr-34
❑ 76PhoGiaCa-15
❑ 76PhoGiaCC-14
❑ 76PhoGiaVNB-13
❑ 77Gia-12
❑ 77GiaTeal-14
❑ 77PhoGiaCC-16
❑ 77PhoGiaCP-16
❑ 77PhoGiaVNB-16
❑ 78GiaTeal-15
❑ 78Top-589
❑ 79GiaPol-39
❑ 79Hos-52
❑ 79Kel-35
❑ 79OPC-255
❑ 79Top-486
❑ 80GiaPol-39
❑ 80GiaTeal-12
❑ 80OPC-61
❑ 80Top-111
❑ 81AllGamPI-170
❑ 81AstPos-9
❑ 81Don-194
❑ 81Fle-447
❑ 81OPC-279
❑ 81Top-279
❑ 81TopTra-782
❑ 82AstAstI-5
❑ 82AstPos-8
❑ 82Don-41
❑ 82Fle-219
❑ 82FleSta-49
❑ 82Kel-31
❑ 82OPC-389
❑ 82Top-672
❑ 82TopSti-45
❑ 82TopStiV-45
❑ 83AllGamPI-168
❑ 83AstPos-10
❑ 83Don-92
❑ 83Fle-451
❑ 83Top-382
❑ 84AstMot-16
❑ 84AstPos-11
❑ 84Don-572
❑ 84Fle-228
❑ 84Nes792-93
❑ 84OPC-93
❑ 84Top-93
❑ 84TopTif-93
❑ 85AstHouP-18
❑ 85AstMot-20
❑ 85Don-476
❑ 85Fle-352
❑ 85Lea-61
❑ 85OPC-289
❑ 85Top-455
❑ 85Top-721
❑ 85TopSti-62
❑ 85TopTif-455
❑ 85TopTif-721
❑ 86AstMilL-12
❑ 86AstMot-22
❑ 86AstPol-15
❑ 86AstTeal-9
❑ 86Don-161
❑ 86Fle-304
❑ 86Lea-90
❑ 86OPC-231
❑ 86Top-590
❑ 86TopTif-590
❑ 87AstMot-5
❑ 87AstPol-20
❑ 87AstShoSPT-6
❑ 87Don-112
❑ 87Fle-61
❑ 87FleAwaW-20
❑ 87FleGamW-23
❑ 87FleGlo-61
❑ 87FleMin-60
❑ 87Lea-249
❑ 87OPC-129
❑ 87RedFolSB-17
❑ 87Spo-29
❑ 87SpoTeaP-8
❑ 87Top-722
❑ 87TopGloS-13
❑ 87TopMinL-10
❑ 87TopSti-32
❑ 87TopTif-722
❑ 88AstMot-5
❑ 88AstPol-15
❑ 88Don-138
❑ 88DonBasB-176
❑ 88Fle-451
❑ 88FleGlo-451
❑ 88Sco-344
❑ 88ScoGlo-344
❑ 88Top-151
❑ 88TopTif-151
❑ 89AstLenH-10
❑ 89AstMot-7
❑ 89AstSmo-22
❑ 89Don-123
❑ 89DonAll-54
❑ 89Fle-360
❑ 89FleBasA-25
❑ 89FleGlo-360
❑ 89OPC-280
❑ 89PanSti-82
❑ 89Sco-273
❑ 89ScoHot1S-38
❑ 89Top-280
❑ 89TopSti-22
❑ 89TopStiB-63
❑ 89TopTif-280
❑ 89UppDec-422
❑ 90Don-485
❑ 90OPC-104
❑ 90PhoFirP-7
❑ 90ProAAAF-33
❑ 90PubIntS-97
❑ 90Top-104
❑ 90TopTif-104
❑ 90UppDec-599
Knerr, Lou
❑ 45A'sTeal-20
Knetzer, Elmer
❑ 11PinT-5-457
❑ 12T207-93
❑ 14CraJacE-84
❑ 15CraJacE-84
❑ 16FleBreD-52
❑ 90DodTar-1003
Kneuer, Frank
❑ 83NasSouTI-9
Knicely, Alan
❑ 75DubPacT-18
❑ 76DubPacT-17
❑ 80Top-678
❑ 80TucTorT-14
❑ 81Top-82
❑ 81TucTorT-4
❑ 82AstAstI-7
❑ 82AstPos-9
❑ 83Don-620
❑ 83Fle-452
❑ 83Top-117
❑ 83TopTra-57T
❑ 84Fle-473
❑ 84Nes792-323
❑ 84Top-323
❑ 84TopTif-323
❑ 84WicAerRD-18
❑ 85TopTifT-68T
❑ 85TopTra-68T
❑ 86LouRedTI-15
❑ 86OPC-316
❑ 86Top-418
❑ 86TopTif-418
❑ 87AstShoSPO-11
❑ 87OklCit8P-22
Knickerbocker, Bill (Wm.)
❑ 34BatR31-58
❑ 34DiaMatCSB-108
❑ 35DiaMatCS3T1-90
❑ 35GouPuzR-8I
❑ 35GouPuzR-9I
❑ 36GouWidPPR-B15
❑ 36NatChiFPR-49
❑ 40PlaBal-182
❑ 42A'sTeal-18
❑ 47A'sTeal-17
❑ 75YanDyn1T-29
❑ 91ConTSN-79
Knickerbocker, Tom
❑ 97SouOreTB-16
Knieper, Aaron
❑ 93JamExpC-12
❑ 93JamExpF-3321
❑ 94BurBeeC-11
❑ 94BurBeeF-1078
Kniffen, Chuck
❑ 88WauTimGS-2
❑ 89SanBerSB-10
❑ 89SanBerSCLC-89
❑ 90SanBerSB-8
❑ 90SanBerSCLC-115
❑ 90SanBerSP-2650
❑ 91SanBerSC-26
❑ 91SanBerSP-2004
❑ 92WesPalBEC-30
❑ 92WesPalBEF-2104
❑ 93HarSenF-286
❑ 94WesPalBEC-29
❑ 94WesPalBEF-59
Kniffin, Chuck
❑ 97HigDesMG-11
❑ 98TusSidM-2
Knight, Brandon
❑ 95ChaRivUTIS-37
❑ 96HudValRB-5
❑ 98TulDriTI-21
Knight, Brock
❑ 85ElmPioT-9
Knight, Brooke
❑ 95HelBreTI-1
Knight, Dennis
❑ 83TriTriT-5
Knight, E. R.
❑ 28Zee-157
❑ 30Zee-145
Knight, Grover
❑ 11Zee-32
❑ 12Zee-83
Knight, J. W.
❑ 26Zee-117
❑ 27Zee-93
Knight, Jack (John)
❑ 09AmeCarE90-1-65
❑ 09ColChiE-157A
❑ 09ColChiE-157B
❑ 09RamT20-67
❑ 09T206-192
❑ 09T206-193
❑ 10DomDisP-62A
❑ 10DomDisP-62B
❑ 10E101-27
❑ 10MelMinE-27
❑ 10NadCarE-32
❑ 10PeoT21-32
❑ 10SweCapPP-36A
❑ 10SweCapPP-36B
❑ 11HelSta-73
❑ 11PinT-5-805
❑ 11S74Sil-23
❑ 11SpoLifM-80
❑ 11T205-90
❑ 12ColRedB-157A
❑ 12ColRedB-157B
❑ 12ColTinT-157A
❑ 12ColTinT-157B
❑ 12HasTriFT-49
❑ 14PieStaT-60
❑ 20Zee-25
❑ 21Zee-29
❑ 22Zee-30
❑ 23Zee-41
❑ 23Zee-42
❑ 29Zee-92
❑ 93UppDecTR-4
Knight, Kittie
❑ 09ObaT21-276
❑ 12ObaPreT-25
Knight, Marcus
❑ 97ButCopKB-11
❑ 97ButCopKK-11
❑ 98CedRapKTI-14
Knight, Randy
❑ 89TenTecGE-12
Knight, Ray (C. Ray)
❑ 76IndIndTI-3
❑ 78Pep-16
❑ 78SSP270-110
❑ 78Top-674
❑ 79OPC-211
❑ 79Top-401
❑ 80OPC-98
❑ 80RedEnq-25
❑ 80Top-174
❑ 81AllGamPI-121
❑ 81CokTeaS-44
❑ 81Don-61
❑ 81Fle-198
❑ 81OPC-325
❑ 81Top-325
❑ 81TopSupHT-38
❑ 82AstAstI-6
❑ 82AstPos-10
❑ 82Don-374
❑ 82Fle-71
❑ 82FleSta-18
❑ 82OPC-319
❑ 82Top-525
❑ 82TopSti-39
❑ 82TopTra-57T
❑ 83AllGamPI-96
❑ 83AstPos-11
❑ 83Don-522
❑ 83Fle-453
❑ 83FleSta-96
❑ 83FleSti-145
❑ 83FleSti-147
❑ 83FleSti-208
❑ 83OPC-275
❑ 83Top-275
❑ 83Top-441
❑ 83TopGloS-18
❑ 83TopSti-238
❑ 84AllGamPI-7
❑ 84AstMot-6
❑ 84AstPos-12
❑ 84Don-12
❑ 84Don-12A
❑ 84Don-232
❑ 84Fle-229
❑ 84FleSti-10
❑ 84Nes792-660
❑ 84OPC-321
❑ 84Top-660
❑ 84TopRubD-3
❑ 84TopSti-68
❑ 84TopStiB-9
❑ 84TopTif-660
❑ 85AllGamPI-121
❑ 85Don-617
❑ 85Fle-86
❑ 85IndIndTI-28
❑ 85MetColP-11
❑ 85MetTCM-26
❑ 85OPC-274
❑ 85Top-590
❑ 85TopTif-590
❑ 86AstMot-24
❑ 86Don-597
❑ 86Fle-86
❑ 86MetColP-10
❑ 86MetTCM-20
❑ 86MetWorSC-29
❑ 86OPC-27
❑ 86Top-27
❑ 86TopTif-27
❑ 87AstShoSPO-12
❑ 87BalOriP-20
❑ 87Don-586
❑ 87DonOpeD-137
❑ 87Fle-14
❑ 87FleAwaW-21
❑ 87FleGlo-14
❑ 87FleGlo-WS11
❑ 87FleGlo-WS12
❑ 87FleRecS-18
❑ 87FleUpd-58
❑ 87FleUpdG-58
❑ 87FleWorS-11
❑ 87FleWorS-12
❑ 87Lea-166
❑ 87OPC-275
❑ 87OriFreB-25
❑ 87Spo-88
❑ 87SpoTeaP-21
❑ 87Top-488
❑ 87TopSti-24
❑ 87TopTif-488
❑ 87TopTra-59T
❑ 87TopTraT-59T
❑ 87Woo-30
❑ 87Woo-33
❑ 88Don-108
❑ 88Fle-564
❑ 88FleGlo-564
❑ 88FleUpd-28
❑ 88FleUpdG-28
❑ 88OPC-124
❑ 88PanSti-12
❑ 88RedFolSB-43
❑ 88Sco-96
❑ 88ScoGlo-96
❑ 88ScoRoo-17T
❑ 88ScoRooG-17T
❑ 88Spo-115
❑ 88StaLinO-7
❑ 88StaLinTi-11
❑ 88TigPep-22
❑ 88Top-124
❑ 88TopSti-229
❑ 88TopTif-124
❑ 88TopTra-59T
❑ 88TopTraT-59T
❑ 89Sco-135A
❑ 89Sco-135B
❑ 89UppDec-259
❑ 91MetWIZ-215
❑ 91OriCro-243
❑ 91UppDecS-8
❑ 92MDAMVP-16
❑ 93RedKah-8
❑ 94RedKah-33
❑ 95RedKah-34
Knight, Shawn
❑ 94SpoIndC-15
❑ 94SpoIndF-3330
Knight, Steve
❑ 80SanJosMJitB-12
Knight, Tim
❑ 82NasSouTI-15
❑ 83NasSouTI-10
❑ 84NasSouTI-12
❑ 85AlbYanT-33
❑ 85ColCliP-15
❑ 85ColCliT-20
❑ 86PorBeaP-12
Knighton, Toure'
❑ 94ChaRivC-11
❑ 94ChaRivF-2668
❑ 95ChaRivTI-11
Knoblauch, Chuck
❑ 88CapCodPB-15
❑ 88CapCodPPaLP-94
❑ 90Bes-146
❑ 90Bes-322
❑ 90Bow-415
❑ 90BowTif-415
❑ 90CMC-807
❑ 90OrlSunRB-3
❑ 90OrlSunRP-1090
❑ 90OrlSunRS-8
❑ 90ProAaA-56
❑ 90Sco-672
❑ 91Bow-330
❑ 91Cla3-T46
❑ 91DodPho-17
❑ 91Don-421
❑ 91DonRoo-39
❑ 91FleUpd-37
❑ 91Lea-396
❑ 91ScoAllF-10
❑ 91ScoRoo-93T
❑ 91StaClu-548
❑ 91StaCluMO-20
❑ 91TopTra-69T
❑ 91TopTraT-69T
❑ 91Ult-382
❑ 91UltUpd-37
❑ 91UppDec-40
❑ 92Bow-24
❑ 92Cla1-T50
❑ 92Cla2-T71
❑ 92ClaGam-181
❑ 92ColAllG-10
❑ 92ColAllP-10
❑ 92Don-390
❑ 92DonBonC-BC5
❑ 92DonCraJ1-24
❑ 92Fle-206
❑ 92FleRooS-10
❑ 92Fre-1
❑ 92JimDea-12
❑ 92Lea-230
❑ 92LeaBlaG-230
❑ 92MJBHolK-1
❑ 92MJBHolK-2
❑ 92MJBHolK-3
❑ 92MJBHolK-4
❑ 92MJBHolK-AU
❑ 92MJBHolP-R1
❑ 92MotKno-1
❑ 92MotKno-2
❑ 92MotKno-3
❑ 92MotKno-4
❑ 92OPC-23
❑ 92OPCPre-35
❑ 92PanSti-116
❑ 92Pin-119
❑ 92Pin-285
❑ 92Pin-307
❑ 92PinTea2-6
❑ 92Pos-6
❑ 92Sco-572
❑ 92Sco-792
❑ 92Sco-X672
❑ 92Sco100RS-11
❑ 92ScoCokD-14
❑ 92ScoImpP-1
❑ 92SpoIllFK1-433
❑ 92StaClu-601
❑ 92StaClu-830
❑ 92StaCluECN-601
❑ 92StaCluNC-830
❑ 92StaKno-1
❑ 92StaKno-2
❑ 92StaKno-3
❑ 92StaKno-4
❑ 92StaKno-5
❑ 92StaKno-6
❑ 92StaKno-7
❑ 92StaKno-8
❑ 92StaKno-9
❑ 92StaKno-10
❑ 92StaKno-11
❑ 92Top-23
❑ 92TopDeb91-103
❑ 92TopGol-23
❑ 92TopGolW-23
❑ 92TopKid-112
❑ 92TopMcD-35
❑ 92TopMic-23
❑ 92TriPla-171
❑ 92Ult-93
❑ 92UltAwaW-2
❑ 92UppDec-446
❑ 93Bow-481
❑ 93ClaGam-49
❑ 93DiaMar-61
❑ 93Don-415
❑ 93Fin-76
❑ 93FinRef-76
❑ 93Fla-237
❑ 93Fle-357
❑ 93Fle-639
❑ 93FleFruotL-32
❑ 93FunPac-193
❑ 93KinDis-24
❑ 93Lea-98
❑ 93LeaFas-6
❑ 93LeaGolA-R5
❑ 93OPC-175
❑ 93PacSpa-172
❑ 93PanSti-126
❑ 93Pin-107
❑ 93PinTea2-4
❑ 93RedFolS-51
❑ 93Sco-148
❑ 93Sel-36
❑ 93SP-248
❑ 93StaClu-314
❑ 93StaCluFDI-314
❑ 93StaCluM-8
❑ 93StaCluMMP-5
❑ 93StaCluMOP-314
❑ 93Stu-109
❑ 93Top-250
❑ 93TopGol-250
❑ 93TopInaM-250
❑ 93TopInaR-250
❑ 93TopMic-250
❑ 93TopPre-250
❑ 93Toy-39
❑ 93ToyMasP-7
❑ 93TriPla-48
❑ 93Ult-583
❑ 93UppDec-254

❑ 93UppDecGold-254
❑ 94Bow-229
❑ 94ColC-166
❑ 94ColChoGS-166
❑ 94ColChoSS-166
❑ 94Don-28
❑ 94DonSpeE-28
❑ 94Fin-324
❑ 94FinRef-324
❑ 94Fla-314
❑ 94Fle-210
❑ 94Fle-712
❑ 94FleExtB-118
❑ 94FUnPac-147
❑ 94Lea-64
❑ 94LeaL-49
❑ 94OPC-155
❑ 94Pac-357
❑ 94PanSti-92
❑ 94Pin-83
❑ 94PinArtP-83
❑ 94PinMusC-83
❑ 94ProMag-80
❑ 94Sco-89
❑ 94ScoGolR-89
❑ 94Sel-29
❑ 94SP-185
❑ 94SPDieC-185
❑ 94Spo-83
❑ 94StaClu-416
❑ 94StaCluFDI-416
❑ 94StaCluGR-416
❑ 94StaCluMOP-416
❑ 94Stu-197
❑ 94Top-555
❑ 94TopGol-555
❑ 94TopSpa-555
❑ 94TriPla-254
❑ 94Ult-89
❑ 94UppDec-152
❑ 94UppDecED-152
❑ 95Baz-112
❑ 95Bow-365
❑ 95BowBes-R44
❑ 95BowBesR-R44
❑ 95ColCho-490
❑ 95ColChoGS-490
❑ 95ColChoSE-28
❑ 95ColChoSE-226
❑ 95ColChoSEGS-28
❑ 95ColChoSEGS-226
❑ 95ColChoSESS-28
❑ 95ColChoSESS-226
❑ 95ColChoSS-490
❑ 95Don-286
❑ 95DonPreP-286
❑ 95DonTopotO-109
❑ 95Emo-57
❑ 95Fin-88
❑ 95FinRef-88
❑ 95Fla-57
❑ 95FlaTodS-4
❑ 95Fle-206
❑ 95FleAllS-10
❑ 95Kra-7
❑ 95Lea-238
❑ 95LeaLim-53
❑ 95Pac-250
❑ 95PanSti-47
❑ 95Pin-91
❑ 95PinArtP-91
❑ 95PinMusC-91
❑ 95Sco-431
❑ 95ScoGolR-431
❑ 95ScoHaloG-HG80
❑ 95ScoPlaTS-431
❑ 95Sel-122
❑ 95SelArtP-122
❑ 95SelCer-38
❑ 95SelCerMG-38
❑ 95SP-173
❑ 95SPCha-169
❑ 95SPChaDC-169
❑ 95Spo-91
❑ 95SpoArtP-91
❑ 95SPSil-173
❑ 95StaClu-249
❑ 95StaCluFDI-249
❑ 95StaCluMO-26
❑ 95StaCluMOP-249
❑ 95StaCluSTWS-249
❑ 95StaCluVR-123
❑ 95StaCluVRMO-123
❑ 95Stu-104
❑ 95Sum-71
❑ 95SumNthD-71
❑ 95Top-250
❑ 95TopCyb-138
❑ 95TopD3-8
❑ 95TopEmb-99
❑ 95TopEmbGI-99
❑ 95TopLeaL-LL44
❑ 95UC3-38
❑ 95UC3ArtP-38
❑ 95Ult-303
❑ 95UltAllS-9
❑ 95UltAllSGM-9
❑ 95UltGolM-303
❑ 95UltRisS-5
❑ 95UltRisSGM-5
❑ 95UppDec-193
❑ 95UppDecED-193
❑ 95UppDecEDG-193
❑ 95UppDecSE-218
❑ 95UppDecSEG-218
❑ 95USPlaCMLA-8H
❑ 95Zen-17
❑ 96Baz-65
❑ 96Bow-84
❑ 96BowBes-34
❑ 96BowBesAR-34
❑ 96BowBesR-34
❑ 96BowFoi-84
❑ 96Cir-57
❑ 96CirBos-12
❑ 96CirRav-57
❑ 96ColCho-205
❑ 96ColChoGS-205
❑ 96ColChoSS-205
❑ 96Don-536
❑ 96DonPreP-536
❑ 96EmoXL-82
❑ 96Fin-B49
❑ 96Fin-S261
❑ 96FinRef-B49
❑ 96FinRef-S261
❑ 96Fla-116
❑ 96Fle-166
❑ 96FleTif-166
❑ 96Lea-43
❑ 96LeaLim-19
❑ 96LeaLimG-19
❑ 96LeaPre-16
❑ 96LeaPreP-16
❑ 96LeaPrePB-43
❑ 96LeaPrePG-43
❑ 96LeaPrePS-43
❑ 96LeaPreSG-75
❑ 96LeaPreSte-75
❑ 96LeaSig-20
❑ 96LeaSigEA-103
❑ 96LeaSigEACM-16
❑ 96LeaSigPPG-20
❑ 96LeaSigPPP-20
❑ 96MetUni-76
❑ 96MetUniP-76
❑ 96Pac-367
❑ 96PacPri-P114
❑ 96PacPriG-P114
❑ 96PanSti-199
❑ 96Pin-8
❑ 96PinAfi-78
❑ 96PinAfiAP-78
❑ 96PinAfiFPP-78
❑ 96PinArtP-6
❑ 96PinSta-6
❑ 96PinTeaP-2
❑ 96ProSta-126
❑ 96Sco-285
❑ 96ScoDugC-B10
❑ 96ScoDugCAP-B10
❑ 96ScoRef-20
❑ 96Sel-5
❑ 96SelArtP-5
❑ 96SelCer-18
❑ 96SelCerAP-18
❑ 96SelCerCB-18
❑ 96SelCerCR-18
❑ 96SelCerMB-18
❑ 96SelCerMG-18
❑ 96SelCerMR-18
❑ 96SelTeaN-19
❑ 96SP-116
❑ 96StaClu-187
❑ 96StaClu-414
❑ 96StaCluEPB-414
❑ 96StaCluEPG-414
❑ 96StaCluEPS-414
❑ 96StaCluEWB-EW4
❑ 96StaCluEWG-EW4
❑ 96StaCluEWS-EW4
❑ 96StaCluMO-19
❑ 96StaCluMOP-187
❑ 96StaCluMOP-414
❑ 96Stu-21
❑ 96StuPrePB-21
❑ 96StuPrePG-21
❑ 96StuPrePS-21
❑ 96Sum-141
❑ 96SumAbo&B-141
❑ 96SumArtP-141
❑ 96SumFoi-141
❑ 96SumPos-2
❑ 96TeaOut-46
❑ 96Top-248
❑ 96TopChr-95
❑ 96TopChrR-95
❑ 96TopGal-170
❑ 96TopGalPPI-170
❑ 96TopLas-83
❑ 96Ult-89
❑ 96UltGolM-89
❑ 96UltOn-L-5
❑ 96UltOn-LGM-5
❑ 96UppDec-125
❑ 96UppDecDD-DD26
❑ 96UppDecDDG-DD26
❑ 96UppDecDDS-DD26
❑ 96UppDecPRE-R25
❑ 96UppDecPreR-R25
❑ 96Zen-72
❑ 96ZenArtP-72
❑ 96ZenMoz-19
❑ 97Bow-37
❑ 97BowBes-51
❑ 97BowBesAR-51
❑ 97BowBesMI-MI8
❑ 97BowBesMIAR-MI8
❑ 97BowBesMIARI-MI8
❑ 97BowBesMII-MI8
❑ 97BowBesMIR-MI8
❑ 97BowBesMIRI-MI8
❑ 97BowBesR-51
❑ 97BowChr-32
❑ 97BowChrI-32
❑ 97BowChrIR-32
❑ 97BowChrR-32
❑ 97BowInt-37
❑ 97Cir-350
❑ 97CirRav-350
❑ 97ColCho-153
❑ 97ColChoAC-2
❑ 97CraJac-2
❑ 97DenHol-9
❑ 97Don-25
❑ 97Don-444
❑ 97DonDiaK-4
❑ 97DonDiaKC-4
❑ 97DonEli-33
❑ 97DonEliGS-33
❑ 97DonEliLaL-8
❑ 97DonFraFea-4
❑ 97DonGolPP-25
❑ 97DonGolPP-444
❑ 97DonLim-12
❑ 97DonLim-54
❑ 97DonLim-149
❑ 97DonLimE-12
❑ 97DonLimE-54
❑ 97DonLimE-149
❑ 97DonLimENG-12
❑ 97DonLimFotG-24
❑ 97DonPre-4
❑ 97DonPre-189
❑ 97DonPreCttC-4
❑ 97DonPreCttC-189
❑ 97DonPreXP-2B
❑ 97DonSig-92
❑ 97DonSigAC-75
❑ 97DonSigAM-75
❑ 97DonSigPPP-92
❑ 97DonSilPP-25
❑ 97DonSilPP-444
❑ 97DonTeaSMVP-5
❑ 97DonVxP1-17
❑ 97E-X2-28
❑ 97E-X2Cred-28
❑ 97E-X2EssCre-28
❑ 97Fin-140
❑ 97Fin-214
❑ 97FinEmb-140
❑ 97FinEmbR-140
❑ 97FinRef-140
❑ 97FinRef-214
❑ 97FlaShoLC-45
❑ 97FlaShoLeg0-45
❑ 97FlaShoLeg1-45
❑ 97FlaShoM-A45
❑ 97FlaShoM-B45
❑ 97FlaShoM-C45
❑ 97FlaShoR0-45
❑ 97FlaShoR1-45
❑ 97FlaShoR2-45
❑ 97Fle-147
❑ 97FleTif-147
❑ 97KinB-20
❑ 97Lea-192
❑ 97Lea-220
❑ 97Lea-376
❑ 97LeaBanS-7
❑ 97LeaFraM-192
❑ 97LeaFraM-220
❑ 97LeaFraM-376
❑ 97LeaFraMDC-192
❑ 97LeaFraMDC-220
❑ 97LeaFraMDC-376
❑ 97LeaGolS-26
❑ 97LeaKnoG-1
❑ 97MetUni-210
❑ 97NewPin-108
❑ 97NewPin-179
❑ 97NewPinAP-108
❑ 97NewPinAP-179
❑ 97NewPinKtP-8
❑ 97NewPinMC-108
❑ 97NewPinMC-179
❑ 97NewPinPP-108
❑ 97NewPinPP-179
❑ 97NewPinPP-K8
❑ 97Pac-139
❑ 97PacCar-10
❑ 97PacCarM-10
❑ 97PacLigB-139
❑ 97PacPri-46
❑ 97PacPriGotD-GD62
❑ 97PacPriLB-46
❑ 97PacPriP-46
❑ 97PacSil-139
❑ 97Pin-188
❑ 97PinArtP-PP188
❑ 97PinCer-73
❑ 97PinCerLI-6
❑ 97PinCerMBla-73
❑ 97PinCerMBlu-73
❑ 97PinCerMG-73
❑ 97PinCerMR-73
❑ 97PinCerR-73
❑ 97PinFan-FF3
❑ 97PinIns-10
❑ 97PinInsCE-10
❑ 97PinInsDD-5
❑ 97PinInsDE-10
❑ 97PinMin-19
❑ 97PinMinB-19
❑ 97PinMinCB-19
❑ 97PinMinCG-19
❑ 97PinMinCGR-19
❑ 97PinMinCN-19
❑ 97PinMinCSS-19
❑ 97PinMinG-19
❑ 97PinMinS-19
❑ 97PinMusC-188
❑ 97PinPrePla-188
❑ 97PinTeaP-2
❑ 97PinTeaP-10
❑ 97PinTotCPB-73
❑ 97PinTotCPG-73
❑ 97PinTotCPR-73
❑ 97PinX-P-18
❑ 97PinX-PMoS-18
❑ 97Sco-165
❑ 97Sco-533
❑ 97ScoAllF-3
❑ 97ScoArtPWB-165
❑ 97ScoArtPWB-533
❑ 97ScoHeaotO-34
❑ 97ScoPreS-165
❑ 97ScoResC-533
❑ 97ScoShoS-165
❑ 97ScoShoS-533
❑ 97ScoShoSAP-165
❑ 97ScoShoSAP-533
❑ 97ScoSteS-2
❑ 97Sel-69
❑ 97SelArtP-69
❑ 97SelCom-69
❑ 97SelRegG-69
❑ 97SelToootT-18
❑ 97SelToootTMB-18
❑ 97SP-110
❑ 97SpoIll-145
❑ 97SpoIllEE-145
❑ 97StaClu-206
❑ 97StaCluMat-206
❑ 97StaCluMOP-206
❑ 97StrAll-36
❑ 97Stu-127
❑ 97StuHarH-4
❑ 97StuPrePG-127
❑ 97StuPrePS-127
❑ 97Top-65
❑ 97TopAll-AS5
❑ 97TopChr-22
❑ 97TopChrAS-AS5
❑ 97TopChrR-22
❑ 97TopChrSAR-AS5
❑ 97TopChrSB-5
❑ 97TopChrSBR-5
❑ 97TopGal-105
❑ 97TopGalPPI-105
❑ 97TopMem05-29
❑ 97TopSeaB-SB5
❑ 97TopSta-38
❑ 97TopStaAM-38
❑ 97Ult-87
❑ 97UltDouT-6
❑ 97UltFieC-9
❑ 97UltGolME-87
❑ 97UltPlaME-87
❑ 97UppDec-411
❑ 97Zen-32
❑ 98Bow-281
❑ 98BowBes-10
❑ 98BowBesA-10
❑ 98BowBesAAR-10
❑ 98BowBesAR-10
❑ 98BowBesAR-10
❑ 98BowBesMIF-MI2
❑ 98BowBesMIFAR-MI2
❑ 98BowBesMIFR-MI2
❑ 98BowBesR-10
❑ 98BowChr-281
❑ 98BowChrGA-281
❑ 98BowChrGAR-281
❑ 98BowChrI-281
❑ 98BowChrIR-281
❑ 98BowChrR-281
❑ 98BowChrR-21
❑ 98BowChrRR-21
❑ 98BowGolA-281
❑ 98BowInt-281
❑ 98CirThu-123
❑ 98CirThuRav-123
❑ 98CirThuSupRav-123
❑ 98ColCho-159
❑ 98ColChoSQ-SQ48
❑ 98CroRoy-95
❑ 98Don-55
❑ 98Don-196
❑ 98DonCol-55
❑ 98DonColE-421
❑ 98DonColE-538
❑ 98DonColL-362
❑ 98DonColP-587
❑ 98DonColS-55
❑ 98DonCruG-29
❑ 98DonCruP-29
❑ 98DonCruR-29
❑ 98DonDom-12
❑ 98DonEli-21
❑ 98DonEli-138
❑ 98DonEliA-21
❑ 98DonEliA-138
❑ 98DonEliS-21
❑ 98DonEliS-138
❑ 98DonGolPP-55
❑ 98DonGolPP-196
❑ 98DonPre-37
❑ 98DonPreSeat-37
❑ 98DonPriCD-55
❑ 98DonPriCE-421
❑ 98DonPriCE-538
❑ 98DonPriCL-362
❑ 98DonPriCP-587
❑ 98DonProLO-4
❑ 98DonSig-15
❑ 98DonSigAC-68
❑ 98DonSigAM-69
❑ 98DonSigP-15
❑ 98DonSigSP-14
❑ 98DonSilPP-55
❑ 98DonSilPP-196
❑ 98E-X2-32
❑ 98E-X2ECFut-32
❑ 98E-X2ECNow-32
❑ 98Fin-110
❑ 98FinNo--110
❑ 98FinNo-R-110
❑ 98FinRef-110
❑ 98FlaShoLeg0-77
❑ 98FlaShoLeg1-77
❑ 98FlaShoLeg2-77
❑ 98FlaShoLeg3-77
❑ 98FlaShoLegM-77
❑ 98FlaShoR0-77
❑ 98FlaShoR1-77
❑ 98FlaShoR2-77
❑ 98FlaShoR3-77
❑ 98Fle-11
❑ 98Fle-420
❑ 98FleVin'-33
❑ 98FleVin'-108
❑ 98FleVin'C-33
❑ 98FleVin'C-108
❑ 98KinDis-14
❑ 98Lea-163
❑ 98LeaFraDA-163
❑ 98LeaFraF-163
❑ 98LeaFraM-163
❑ 98LeaFraM-163
❑ 98LeaFraMDC-163
❑ 98LeaFraMDC-163
❑ 98LeaFraMS-163
❑ 98LeaFraMZ2-163
❑ 98LeaRS-10
❑ 98LeaRSLHolo-10
❑ 98LeaRSLMVP-2
❑ 98LeaRSLMVPPE-2
❑ 98LeaRSLong-10
❑ 98LeaRSTicMas-12
❑ 98LeaRSTicMasDC-12
❑ 98LeaRTrue-10
❑ 98LeaStaRep-24
❑ 98MetUni-25
❑ 98MetUniPMG-25
❑ 98Pac-135
❑ 98PacAur-59
❑ 98PacInv-46
❑ 98PacInvGems-64
❑ 98PacInvPBlue-46
❑ 98PacInvSilv-46
❑ 98PacInvTeam-16
❑ 98PacOme-166
❑ 98PacOmeR-166
❑ 98PacOnl-506
❑ 98PacOnlR-506
❑ 98PacOnlWC-506
❑ 98PacPar-70
❑ 98PacParC-70
❑ 98PacParG-70
❑ 98PacParHS-70
❑ 98PacParPB-70
❑ 98PacParR-70
❑ 98PacPlaB-135
❑ 98PacRedT-135
❑ 98PacSil-135
❑ 98PacTeaC-9
❑ 98PinIns-29
❑ 98PinInsCE-29
❑ 98PinInsDE-29
❑ 98PinInsSG-14AB
❑ 98PinInsSG-14CD
❑ 98PinInsSGS-14AB
❑ 98PinInsSGS-14CD
❑ 98PinPer-38
❑ 98PinPerPP-38
❑ 98PinPlu-17
❑ 98PinPluAP-PP10
❑ 98PinPluGAP-PP10
❑ 98PinPluMAP-PP10
❑ 98PinSna-NYY16
❑ 98Revo-100
❑ 98RevoSS-100
❑ 98Sco-123
❑ 98ScoLoaL-LL1
❑ 98ScoRT-29
❑ 98ScoRTSS-PP29
❑ 98ScoRTSSAP-PP29
❑ 98ScoRTSSAP1-PP29
❑ 98ScoSS-PP150
❑ 98ScoSSAP-PP150
❑ 98SkyDugA-146
❑ 98SkyDugAFF-FF3
❑ 98SkyDugAIA-146
❑ 98SP Aut-142
❑ 98SpoIll-78
❑ 98SpoIllEE-78
❑ 98SpoIllFE-78
❑ 98SpoIllTaN-45
❑ 98SpoIllTaN-103
❑ 98SpoIllTaNEE-45
❑ 98SpoIllTaNEE-103
❑ 98SpoIllWSF-67
❑ 98SpoIllWSFEE-67
❑ 98SpoIllWSFFE-67
❑ 98SPxFin-304

❑ 98SPxFin-343
❑ 98SPxFinR-304
❑ 98SPxFinR-343
❑ 98SPxFinS-304
❑ 98SPxFinS-343
❑ 98StaCluFDI-31
❑ 98StaCluFDI-358
❑ 98StaCluI-31
❑ 98StaCluI-358
❑ 98StaCluOneK-31
❑ 98StaCluOneK-358
❑ 98StaCluPP-31
❑ 98StaCluPP-358
❑ 98StaCluTIII-T12B
❑ 98StaCluTLme-T12B
❑ 98StaCluTLmo-T12B
❑ 98Stu-204
❑ 98StuFF-19
❑ 98StuFFDC-19
❑ 98StuGPP-204
❑ 98StuPor8x10-34
❑ 98StuPor8x10GP-34
❑ 98StuSPP-204
❑ 98Top-270
❑ 98Top-309
❑ 98TopChr-270
❑ 98TopChr-309
❑ 98TopChrR-270
❑ 98TopChrR-309
❑ 98TopDevR-270
❑ 98TopDevR-309
❑ 98TopDia-270
❑ 98TopDia-309
❑ 98TopFocP-FP11
❑ 98TopGal-11
❑ 98TopGalGP-11
❑ 98TopGalOPP-11
❑ 98TopGalPPI-11
❑ 98TopGalPPIA-11
❑ 98TopGolLabC1-68
❑ 98TopGolLabC1B-68
❑ 98TopGolLabC1One-68
❑ 98TopGolLabC1R-68
❑ 98TopGolLabC2-68
❑ 98TopGolLabC2B-68
❑ 98TopGolLabC2One-68
❑ 98TopGolLabC2R-68
❑ 98TopGolLabC3-68
❑ 98TopGolLabC3B-68
❑ 98TopGolLabC3One-68
❑ 98TopGolLabC3R-68
❑ 98TopMiniC-270
❑ 98TopMiniC-309
❑ 98TopOpeD-135
❑ 98TopSta-71
❑ 98TopStaB-71
❑ 98TopStaG-71
❑ 98TopStaGR-71
❑ 98TopStaLB-L7
❑ 98TopStaLG-L7
❑ 98TopStaLGR-L7
❑ 98TopStaLS-L7
❑ 98TopStaS-71
❑ 98TopTek-70
❑ 98TopTekD-70
❑ 98UD3-73
❑ 98UD3-163
❑ 98UD3-253
❑ 98UD3DieCut-73
❑ 98UD3DieCut-163
❑ 98UD3DieCut-253
❑ 98Ult-89
❑ 98Ult-296
❑ 98UltGolM-89
❑ 98UltGolM-296
❑ 98UltMas-89
❑ 98UltMas-296
❑ 98UltPlaM-89
❑ 98UltPlaM-296
❑ 98UltTop3-28
❑ 98UppDec-435
❑ 98UppDec-705
❑ 98UppDec10AP-27
❑ 98UppDec1APR-27
❑ 98YanUppD-705
❑ 98Zen-28
❑ 98Zen5 xx7-20
❑ 98Zen5x7GoldImp-20
❑ 98Zen5x7Imp-20
❑ 98ZenZ-G-28
❑ 98ZenZ-S-28
❑ 99199Fin-241
❑ 99Bow-13
❑ 99BowChr-13
❑ 99BowChrG-13
❑ 99BowChrGR-13
❑ 99BowChrI-13
❑ 99BowChrIR-13
❑ 99BowChrR-13
❑ 99BowGol-13
❑ 99BowInt-13
❑ 99CroRoyB-98
❑ 99CroRoyL-98
❑ 99CroRoyOD-98
❑ 99FinGolRef-241
❑ 99FinRef-241
❑ 99Fle-196
❑ 99FleBri-76
❑ 99FleBri2G-76
❑ 99FleBriBlu-76
❑ 99FleBriGol-76
❑ 99FleMys-10
❑ 99FleMysG-10
❑ 99FleMysM-10
❑ 99FleSta9-196
❑ 99FleWarT-196
❑ 99MetUni-76
❑ 99MetUniGM-76
❑ 99MetUniPMG-76
❑ 99Pac-295
❑ 99PacAur-129
❑ 99PacAurOD-129
❑ 99PacInv-101
❑ 99PacInvOD-101
❑ 99PacInvPB-101
❑ 99PacOme-164
❑ 99PacOmeC-164
❑ 99PacOmeG-164
❑ 99PacOmePB-164
❑ 99PacPar-163
❑ 99PacParC-163
❑ 99PacParG-163
❑ 99PacParHoloGold-163
❑ 99PacParHS-163
❑ 99PacParOD-163
❑ 99PacParPB-163
❑ 99PacParRed-163
❑ 99PacPlaB-295
❑ 99PacRed-295
❑ 99Rev-96
❑ 99RevPremDate-96
❑ 99RevRet-96
❑ 99RevShaSS-96
❑ 99SkyMolM-40
❑ 99SkyMolMX-40
❑ 99SkyPre-32
❑ 99SkyPreR-32
❑ 99SkyThu-25
❑ 99SkyThuRant-25
❑ 99SkyThuRave-25
❑ 99SpoIll-141
❑ 99StaClu-45
❑ 99StaCluFDI-45
❑ 99StaCluOoaK-45
❑ 99StaCluPP-45
❑ 99ThuSkySupR-25
❑ 99Top-51
❑ 99Top-234
❑ 99TopChr-51
❑ 99TopChr-234
❑ 99TopChrR-51
❑ 99TopChrR-234
❑ 99TopGal-30
❑ 99TopGalPP-30
❑ 99TopGalPPI-30
❑ 99TopMVPP-51
❑ 99TopOpeD-28
❑ 99TopSta-145
❑ 99TopStaFoil-145
❑ 99Ult-153
❑ 99UltGolM-153
❑ 99UltMas-153
❑ 99UltPlaM-153
❑ 99UppDec-155
❑ 99UppDecEL1-155
❑ 99UppDecEL2-155
❑ 99UppDecR-59
❑ 99UppDecRG-59
❑ 99UppDecRP-59
❑ 99Vic-273
❑ 99YanFle-5

Knoblauh, Jay
❑ 88OneYanP-2067
❑ 89PenPilS-10
❑ 90FloStaLAS-35
❑ 90Ft.LauYS-11
❑ 90StaFS7-40
❑ 91AlbYanLD-8
❑ 91AlbYanP-1019
❑ 91LinDriAA-8
❑ 92AlbYanF-2238
❑ 92ColCliS-106
❑ 93ColCliF-1122
❑ 93ColCliP-22
❑ 95LynHilTI-11

Knoll, Brian
❑ 95BelGiaTI-29
❑ 96BurBeeTI-8
❑ 97BakBlaB-11
❑ 97BakBlaTI-11
❑ 98SanJosGQ-25

Knoll, Randy
❑ 96PieBolWB-16
❑ 97ClePhi-10
❑ 98ClePhiM-13
❑ 98ClePhiUM-13

Knollin, Chris
❑ 98St.PauSTI-12

Knoop, Bobby
❑ 64Top-502
❑ 65OPC-26
❑ 65Top-26
❑ 65TopTraI-18
❑ 66AngDexP-6
❑ 66Top-280
❑ 66TopRubI-46
❑ 66TopVen-280
❑ 67CokCapDA-28
❑ 67OPC-175
❑ 67OPCPapI-17
❑ 67Top-175
❑ 67TopPos-17
❑ 67TopTesF-9
❑ 67TopVen-260
❑ 68Baz-3
❑ 68Top-271
❑ 68TopVen-271
❑ 69MilBra-150
❑ 69MLBOffS-23
❑ 69Top-445
❑ 69TopSta-145
❑ 69TopTeaP-17
❑ 69TraSta-17
❑ 70MLBOffS-188
❑ 70Top-695
❑ 70WhiSoxTI-9
❑ 71OPC-506
❑ 71Top-506
❑ 72MilBra-184
❑ 72oyTeal-11
❑ 72Top-664
❑ 75QuaCitAT-6
❑ 78TCM60I-234
❑ 85AngStrH-7
❑ 87CalAngPPS-20
❑ 89AngSmo-4
❑ 90El PasDAGTI-44
❑ 93AngMot-28
❑ 94AngMot-28
❑ 95AngMot-28
❑ 96AngMot-28

Knorr, Randy
❑ 87MyrBeaBJP-1446
❑ 88MyrBeaBJP-1182
❑ 89DunBluJS-10
❑ 90Bes-273
❑ 90CMC-813
❑ 90KnoBluJB-26
❑ 90KnoBluJP-1248
❑ 90KnoBluJS-9
❑ 91Cla/Bes-21
❑ 91KnoBluJLD-361
❑ 91KnoBluJP-1770
❑ 91LinDriAA-361
❑ 91SyrChiMB-10
❑ 92FleUpd-65
❑ 92SkyAAAF-226
❑ 92SyrChiF-1981
❑ 92SyrChiMB-9
❑ 92SyrChiS-508
❑ 92TopDeb91-104
❑ 93BluJayD-17
❑ 93BluJayD4-25
❑ 93BluJayFS-17
❑ 93Don-717
❑ 93Fle-695
❑ 93OPCPre-25
❑ 93StaClu-321
❑ 93StaCluFDI-321
❑ 93StaCluMOP-321
❑ 93Top-534
❑ 93TopGol-534
❑ 93TopInaM-534
❑ 93TopInaR-534
❑ 93TopMic-534
❑ 93Ult-643
❑ 93UppDec-682
❑ 93UppDecGold-682
❑ 94BluJayUSPC-3S
❑ 94BluJayUSPC-10D
❑ 94Fle-336
❑ 94Pac-645
❑ 94StaClu-174
❑ 94StaCluFDI-174
❑ 94StaCluGR-174
❑ 94StaCluMOP-174
❑ 94StaCluT-176
❑ 94StaCluTFDI-176
❑ 94Top-96
❑ 94TopGol-96
❑ 94TopSpa-96
❑ 95BluJayOH-22
❑ 95BluJayUSPC-10D
❑ 95Don-183
❑ 95DonPreP-183
❑ 95Fle-99
❑ 95Top-327
❑ 96ColCho-357
❑ 96ColChoGS-357
❑ 96ColChoSS-357
❑ 98ChaKniQ-17

Knose, Mark
❑ 75WesPalBES-26

Knothe, W. E.
❑ 28Zee-94
❑ 29Zee-93
❑ 30Zee-178
❑ 31Zee-119

Knott, Eric
❑ 97LetBlaDB-24
❑ 98HigDesMG-13

Knott, Jack
❑ 34DiaMatCSB-109
❑ 35DiaMatCS3T1-91
❑ 39WhiSoxTI-8
❑ 40PlaBal-13
❑ 40WhiSoxL-9
❑ 42A'sTeal-19
❑ 79DiaGre-181
❑ 91ConTSN-178
❑ 95ConTSN-1339

Knott, James
❑ 92GulCoaMF-3475

Knott, John
❑ 29Zee-48
❑ 31Zee-34
❑ 39PlaBal-91
❑ 41PlaBal-68
❑ 93MacBraC-13
❑ 93MacBraF-1408
❑ 94MacBraC-10
❑ 94MacBraF-2214
❑ 95AusFut-25
❑ 95DurBulTI-17
❑ 98FarRedHM-15

Knott, Shawn
❑ 93BluOriC-15

Knotts, Gary
❑ 98KanCouC-16
❑ 98KanCouCCP-16

Knout, Fred (Edward)
❑ 87OldJudN-285

Knowland, Sam
❑ 95DanBraTI-14

Knowles, Brian
❑ 94HigDesMC-18
❑ 94HigDesMF-2802

Knowles, Darold
❑ 64Top-418
❑ 65BalOriP-17
❑ 65Top-577
❑ 66OPC-27
❑ 66Top-27
❑ 66TopVen-27
❑ 67CokCapS-15
❑ 67SenPos-13
❑ 67Top-362
❑ 68Top-483
❑ 69SenTeal8-13
❑ 70OPC-106
❑ 70SenPolY-6
❑ 70Top-106
❑ 71MLBOffS-544
❑ 71OPC-261
❑ 71Top-261
❑ 72Top-583
❑ 73OPC-274
❑ 73Top-274
❑ 74OPC-57
❑ 74OPC-472
❑ 74Top-57
❑ 74Top-472
❑ 75OPC-352
❑ 75Top-352
❑ 75TopMin-352
❑ 76OPC-617
❑ 76SSP-307
❑ 76Top-617
❑ 77Top-169
❑ 78ExpPos-7
❑ 78Top-414
❑ 79Car5-13
❑ 79OPC-303
❑ 79Top-581
❑ 80Top-286
❑ 88LouRedBTI-3
❑ 89PhiTas-16
❑ 90PhiTas-34
❑ 91ClePhiC-10
❑ 91ClePhiP-1640
❑ 91OriCro-244
❑ 92ClePhiC-25
❑ 92ClePhiF-2075
❑ 93ClePhiC-28
❑ 93ClePhiF-2700
❑ 93RanKee-219
❑ 94ClePhiC-28
❑ 94ClePhiF-2543
❑ 95ClePhiF-232
❑ 97ClePhi-27
❑ 98ClePhiM-28
❑ 98ClePhiUM-28

Knowles, Eric
❑ 92OneYanC-24
❑ 93PriWilCC-16
❑ 93PriWilCF-665
❑ 94GreBatF-483
❑ 94SouAtlLAF-SAL14
❑ 95Bow-27
❑ 95TamYanYI-15
❑ 96NorNavB-13
❑ 97BinMetB-15
❑ 97GreBatC-10
❑ 98TamYanM-15

Knowles, Greg
❑ 91MiaHurBB-8
❑ 92SavCarF-661
❑ 93SprCarC-16
❑ 93SprCarF-1846
❑ 94St.PetCC-13
❑ 94St.PetCF-2580
❑ 95BowBayTI-35

Knox, Jeff
❑ 86ClePhiP-14
❑ 87AlbYanP-17
❑ 94BoiHawC-17
❑ 94BoiHawF-3351
❑ 94Bow-591
❑ 94CedRapKC-17
❑ 95CedRapKTI-35

Knox, John
❑ 74OPC-604
❑ 74Tig-7
❑ 74Top-604
❑ 75DetTigP-15
❑ 75OPC-546
❑ 75Top-546
❑ 75TopMin-546
❑ 76IndIndTI-21
❑ 76OPC-218
❑ 76SSP-361
❑ 76SSP-592
❑ 76Top-218

Knox, Kerry
❑ 89SpoIndSP-14
❑ 90Bes-221
❑ 90RivRedWB-14
❑ 90RivRedWP-2603
❑ 91LinDriAA-609
❑ 91WicWraLD-609
❑ 91WicWraP-2594
❑ 91WicWraRD-4
❑ 92BelBreCB-27
❑ 92BelBreFI-402
❑ 93ArkTraF-2811
❑ 94LouRedF-2979

Knox, Mike
❑ 83CedRapRF-9
❑ 83CedRapRT-4
❑ 83DurBulT-8
❑ 84DurBulT-15
❑ 85GreBraTI-10

Knox, Scott
❑ 85PriWilPT-29

Knuckles, Phil
❑ 66St.PetCTI-7

Knudsen, Kurt
❑ 89LakTigS-13
❑ 90LakTigS-16
❑ 91LonTigP-1874
❑ 92DonRoo-62
❑ 92FleUpd-25
❑ 92SkyAAAF-266
❑ 92TigKro-14
❑ 92TigTeal-19
❑ 92TolMudHS-592
❑ 93Don-145
❑ 93Fle-231
❑ 93Sco-264
❑ 93Sel-306
❑ 93StaClu-65
❑ 93StaCluFDI-65
❑ 93StaCluMOP-65
❑ 93TigGat-15
❑ 93TolMudHF-1652
❑ 93Top-272
❑ 93TopGol-272
❑ 93TopInaM-272
❑ 93TopInaR-272
❑ 93TopMic-272
❑ 94Fle-136
❑ 94TolMudHF-1025
❑ 95PhoFirTI-7
❑ 97MidAng-19

Knudson, Mark
❑ 83DayBeaAT-7
❑ 85TucTorC-60
❑ 86TucTorP-10
❑ 87DenZepP-20
❑ 88DenZepC-1
❑ 88DenZepP-1275
❑ 88Don-495
❑ 88Top-61
❑ 88TopTif-61
❑ 89BrePol-41
❑ 90BreMilB-12
❑ 90BrePol-41
❑ 90Don-575
❑ 90Fle-327
❑ 90FleCan-327
❑ 90Lea-348
❑ 90OPC-566
❑ 90Sco-539
❑ 90Top-566
❑ 90TopTif-566
❑ 91BreMilB-13
❑ 91BrePol-12
❑ 91Don-328
❑ 91Fle-587
❑ 91Lea-159
❑ 91OPC-267
❑ 91PanFreS-211
❑ 91PanSti-165
❑ 91Sco-239
❑ 91Top-267
❑ 91TopDesS-267
❑ 91TopMic-267
❑ 91TopTif-267
❑ 91Ult-176
❑ 91UppDec-393
❑ 92LasVegSF-2793
❑ 92LasVegSS-233
❑ 92Sco-373
❑ 94BreMilB-140

Knudtson, Jim
❑ 87CedRapRP-27
❑ 95ChaLooTI-27
❑ 96ChaLooB-4
❑ 97ChaLoo-4

Knupfer, Jason
❑ 96BatCliTI-1
❑ 97ClePhi-11
❑ 98ReaPhiM-28
❑ 98ReaPhiUM-14

Koba, Takeshi
❑ 79TCMJapPB-33

Kobayashi, Shigeru
❑ 79TCMJapPB-85

Kobbe, Eric
❑ 89GeoColC-16
❑ 90GeoColC-15

Kobel, Kevin
❑ 74OPC-605
❑ 74Top-605
❑ 75OPC-337
❑ 75Top-337
❑ 75TopMin-337
❑ 76OPC-588
❑ 76SpoIndC-8
❑ 76Top-588
❑ 77SpoIndC-22
❑ 79OPC-6
❑ 79Top-21
❑ 80OPC-106
❑ 80Top-189
❑ 91MetWIZ-216

❑ 94BreMilB-141
Kobernus, Jeff
❑ 82MadMusF-25
❑ 84ModA'sC-24
Kobetitsch, Kevin
❑ 91EugEmeC-16
❑ 91EugEmeP-3721
❑ 92AppFoxCB-22
❑ 92BasCitRF-3841
Kobza, Greg
❑ 89UtiBluSP-13
❑ 90SouBenWSB-15
❑ 90SouBenWSGS-24
❑ 91Cla/Bes-73
❑ 91SarWhiSC-14
❑ 91SarWhiSP-1116
❑ 92StoPorC-10
❑ 92StoPorF-36
Koch, Alan
❑ 77FriOneYW-99
Koch, Barney
❑ 90DodTar-1004
Koch, Billy
❑ 97BesLimA-19
❑ 97BluJayS-58
❑ 97Bow-73
❑ 97BowInt-73
❑ 97DunBluJTI-17
❑ 97FloStaLTPB-9
❑ 97Top-481
❑ 98BesAutPOY-8
❑ 98BesNumOP-30
❑ 98BesPreA-19
❑ 98Bow-302
❑ 98BowChr-302
❑ 98BowChrGA-302
❑ 98BowChrGAR-302
❑ 98BowChrI-302
❑ 98BowChrIR-302
❑ 98BowChrR-302
❑ 98BowGolA-302
❑ 98BowInt-302
❑ 98DunBluJSB-8
❑ 98DunBluJTI-14
❑ 99Bow-180
❑ 99BowAut-BA65
❑ 99BowBes-102
❑ 99BowBesAR-102
❑ 99BowBesR-102
❑ 99BowChr-180
❑ 99BowChrG-180
❑ 99BowChrGR-180
❑ 99BowChrI-180
❑ 99BowChrIR-180
❑ 99BowChrR-180
❑ 99BowGol-180
❑ 99BowInt-180
❑ 99PacOme-250
❑ 99PacOmeC-250
❑ 99PacOmeG-250
❑ 99PacOmePB-250
❑ 99Top-437
❑ 99TopChr-437
❑ 99TopChrR-437
❑ 99TopMVPP-437
❑ 99UppDecE-111
❑ 99UppDecEFXG-111
Koch, Donn
❑ 82AppFoxFr-17
Koch, Ken
❑ 86BirBarTI-24
❑ 87OrlTwiP-8
Kochanski, Mark
❑ 82IdaFalAT-9
Kocher, Bradley W.
❑ 12ImpTobC-82
❑ 16FleBreD-53
❑ 22MrsShePP-2
Koegel, Pete
❑ 71OPC-633
❑ 71Top-633
❑ 72OPC-14
❑ 72Top-14
❑ 77JacSunT-12
❑ 94BreMilB-142
Koehler, Arthur
❑ 19Zee-37
❑ 20Zee-49
❑ 21Zee-30
❑ 22Zee-31
❑ 23Zee-43
❑ 23Zee-88
❑ 25Zee-70
❑ 26Zee-118
❑ 27Zee-94
❑ 28Zee-112
❑ 29Zee-114
❑ 30Zee-126
❑ 31Zee-90
❑ 32Zee-60
Koehler, Ben
❑ 11SpoLifCW-206
Koehler, James
❑ 91ButCopKSP-1
❑ 93RivPilCLC-26
❑ 94RivPilCLC-26
Koehler, Jason
❑ 96StCatSB-14
Koehler, P.K.
❑ 95DanBraTI-15
❑ 96EugEmeB-14
Koehler, Russ
❑ 98LanJetG-15
Koehnke, Odie
❑ 75AppFoxT-11
Koelling, Brian
❑ 91BilMusP-3762
❑ 91BilMusSP-20
❑ 92Bow-65
❑ 92CedRapRC-26
❑ 92CedRapRF-1079
❑ 92ClaFS7-49
❑ 92MidLeaATI-25
❑ 92UppDecML-330
❑ 93Bow-554
❑ 93ChaLooF-2367
❑ 93ClaFS7-214
❑ 94Bow-542
❑ 94IndIndF-1818
❑ 94StaClu-503
❑ 94StaCluFDI-503
❑ 94StaCluGR-503
❑ 94StaCluMOP-503
❑ 94UppDec-217
❑ 94UppDecED-217
❑ 95ChaLooTI-9
❑ 97ChaLoo-12
Koeman, Matt
❑ 96BurIndB-9
❑ 98ColRedSM-5
Koenecke, Len (Leonard)
❑ 34ExhFou-2
❑ 72TCMthe3-43
❑ 90DodTar-415
Koenig, Fred
❑ 76St.LouCP-18
❑ 83CubThoAV-NNO
❑ 88PulBraP-1749
❑ 89PulBraP-1900
❑ 91PulBraC-23
❑ 91PulBraP-4024
❑ 91PulBraP-4025
❑ 92PulBraF-3198
❑ 93RanKee-220
Koenig, Gary
❑ 90BasCitRS-14
Koenig, Mark
❑ 28PorandAR-A20
❑ 28PorandAR-B20
❑ 28W513-83
❑ 29ExhFou-26
❑ 29PorandAR-53
❑ 31Exh-24
❑ 32CubTeal-15
❑ 32OrbPinNP-30
❑ 32OrbPinUP-39
❑ 33Gou-39
❑ 33GouCanV-39
❑ 33TatOrb-39
❑ 34DiaMatCSB-110
❑ 34Gou-56
❑ 35AlDemDCR3-102
❑ 35DiaMatCS3T1-92
❑ 35GouPuzR-8A
❑ 35GouPuzR-8M
❑ 37Zee-16
❑ 72TCMthe3-44
❑ 75Yan192T-13
❑ 79DiaGre-252
❑ 79Yan192T-16
❑ 84Yan192G-17
❑ 87ConSer2-41
❑ 88ConSer4-16
❑ 91ConTSN-125
❑ 92MegRut-154
❑ 93ConTSN-751
❑ 93ConTSNP-1230
❑ 94ConTSN-1121
❑ 94ConTSN-1230
❑ 94ConTSNB-1121
❑ 94ConTSNB-1230
Koenig, Matt
❑ 94KinMetC-6
❑ 94KinMetF-3816
❑ 95PitMetTI-44
Koenigsfeld, Ron
❑ 82ElPasDT-3
❑ 84VanCanC-25
Koerner, Mike
❑ 98VisOakG-17
Koerner, Philip
❑ 15Zee-37
❑ 16Zee-11
❑ 17Zee-92
❑ 18Zee-85
❑ 19Zee-98
❑ 20Zee-111
Koestner, Elmer
❑ 09ObaT21-292
❑ 11PinT-5-609
❑ 11Zee-48
❑ 12ObaPreT-41
❑ 12Zee-64
❑ 12Zee-65
❑ 13Zee-140
Koeyers, Ramsey
❑ 93JamExpC-1
❑ 93JamExpF-3331
❑ 94WesPalBEC-14
❑ 94WesPalBEF-43
❑ 96HarSenB-16
❑ 97PorSeaD-16
❑ 98TexLeaC-11
❑ 98TulDriTI-5
Kofler, Ed
❑ 97PriDevR-23
❑ 98HudValR-13
Kofler, Eric
❑ 97GreBatB-15
Koga, Hide
❑ 90SalSpuCLC-142
❑ 90SalSpuP-2735
❑ 91SalSpuC-24
❑ 91SalSpuP-2260
❑ 92SalSpuC-25
❑ 92SalSpuF-3773
Koh, Joe
❑ 87IdaFalBP-20
Kohl, Doug
❑ 98LetBlaDG-17
Kohl, Jim
❑ 92Ft.MyeMCB-25
❑ 92Ft.MyeMF-2741
❑ 93ForMyeMC-12
❑ 93ForMyeMF-2650
Kohli, John
❑ 87BelMarL-15
❑ 88NebCor-23
Kohlmeier, Ryan
❑ 97DelSho-23
❑ 98BowBayM-19
Kohlogi, Asst. (Acey)
❑ 89VisOakCLC-121
Kohno, Takayuki
❑ 90SalSpuCLC-143
❑ 90SalSpuP-2736
❑ 91SalSpuC-26
❑ 91SalSpuP-2262
❑ 92SalSpuF-3775
Koike, Takuichi
❑ 96HonShaHWB-12
Kojima, Keiichi
❑ 97TulDriTI-15
Kokinda, Steve
❑ 97EveAquG-14
Koklys, Wayne
❑ 91IdaFalBP-4322
Kokora, Pat
❑ 89AncGlaP-17
Kokos, Dick
❑ 49Bow-31
❑ 50Bow-50
❑ 51Bow-68
❑ 51TopRedB-19
❑ 53Top-232
❑ 54Bow-37
❑ 54OriEss-17
❑ 54Top-106
❑ 79DiaGre-196
❑ 85TCMPpl1-43
❑ 91OriCro-245
❑ 91TopArc1-232
❑ 94TopArc1-106
❑ 94TopArc1G-106
Kolarek, Frank
❑ 79OgdA'sT-19
❑ 79WatA'sT-8
Kolb, Brandon
❑ 96CliLumKTI-17
❑ 97CalLeaTP-18
❑ 97RanCucQG-15
❑ 98MobBayBTI-15
Kolb, Dan
❑ 96ChaRivTI-9617
❑ 97FloStaLTPB-3
❑ 98TexLeaC-12
❑ 98TulDriTI-9
Kolb, Gary
❑ 64Top-119
❑ 64TopVen-119
❑ 65BraTeal-7
❑ 65Top-287
❑ 68PirKDK-10
❑ 68PirTeal-9
❑ 68Top-407
❑ 69MilBra-151
❑ 69PirTeal-11
❑ 69Top-307
❑ 70PirTeal-9
❑ 78TCM60I-268
❑ 78TCM60I-283
❑ 91MetWIZ-217
Kolb, Pete
❑ 86ElPasDP-15
❑ 87ElPasDP-9
❑ 88DenZepP-1252
❑ 89DenZepP-50
❑ 97TucTorB-29
❑ 98TusSidM-4
Kolbe, Brian
❑ 82JacMetT-7
Kolinsky, Steve
❑ 93HunCubC-28
❑ 93HunCubF-3254
❑ 94HunCubC-28
❑ 94HunCubF-3569
Koller, Jerry
❑ 91IdaFalBP-4323
❑ 92MacBraF-263
❑ 93DurBulC-11
❑ 93DurBulF-481
❑ 93DurBulTI-27
❑ 94GreBraF-409
❑ 94GreBraTI-15
❑ 95BreBtaTI-30
Koller, Mark
❑ 87WatPirP-25
❑ 88WatPirP-7
Koller, Mike
❑ 88BriTigP-1880
❑ 89FayGenP-1576
❑ 90FayGenP-2403
Koller, Rodney
❑ 91BurIndP-3299
❑ 92BurIndC-7
❑ 92BurIndF-1651
❑ 93ColRedC-14
❑ 93ColRedF-593
Kolloway, Don
❑ 47Exh-122
❑ 48WhiSoxTI-14
❑ 49Bow-28
❑ 50Bow-133
❑ 51Bow-105
❑ 52Bow-91
❑ 52Top-104
❑ 53Top-97
❑ 77TCMTheWY-58
❑ 83TCMPla1943-10
❑ 83TopRep5-104
❑ 91TopArc1-97
Kolodny, Mike
❑ 80BatTroT-5
Kolotka, Chuck
❑ 82MadMusF-6
❑ 83MiaMarT-8
❑ 84BeaGolGT-22
Kolovitz, Mike
❑ 87SalSpuS-28
Kolp, Ray
❑ 23WilChoV-82
❑ 33Gou-150
❑ 33GouCanV-82
❑ 33WorCig(-53
❑ 94ConTSN-1160
❑ 94ConTSNB-1160
Kolstad, Hal (Harold)
❑ 62Top-276
❑ 63Top-574
❑ 64SeaPop-9
❑ 65SeaPop-8
Komadina, Tony
❑ 75AppFoxT-12
Komazaki, Yukiichi
❑ 83SanJosBC-9
Kominek, Tobias
❑ 95BelBreTI-21
❑ 95HelBreTI-29
❑ 96StoPorB-3
❑ 97StoPor-3
❑ 98El PasDG-18
Komminsk, Brad
❑ 80AndBraT-28
❑ 81DurBulT-10
❑ 83RicBraT-19
❑ 84Don-36
❑ 84FleUpd-63
❑ 84raPho-16
❑ 84RicBraT-10
❑ 84RicBraT-11
❑ 85BraHos-13
❑ 85BraPol-36
❑ 85BraTBSAT-1
❑ 85Don-321
❑ 85Fle-331
❑ 85Top-292
❑ 85TopTif-292
❑ 86Fle-520
❑ 86OPC-210
❑ 86RicBraP-11
❑ 86Top-698
❑ 86TopTif-698
❑ 87DenZepP-6
❑ 88DenZepC-21
❑ 88DenZepP-1263
❑ 88Don-583
❑ 89FleUpd-28
❑ 89IndTeal-17
❑ 90BalOriP-15
❑ 90Don-350
❑ 90Fle-496
❑ 90FleCan-496
❑ 90Lea-303
❑ 90OPC-476
❑ 90RicBra2ATI-14
❑ 90RocRedWGC-27
❑ 90Sco-496
❑ 90ScoRoo-53T
❑ 90Top-476
❑ 90TopTif-476
❑ 90TopTra-53T
❑ 90TopTraT-53T
❑ 90UppDec-428
❑ 91LinDriAAA-540
❑ 91OriCro-246
❑ 91Sco-259
❑ 91TacTigLD-540
❑ 92Sco-735
❑ 93NasSouF-581
❑ 94BreMilB-233
❑ 97TolMudHB-4
❑ 98TolMudHQ-3
Komprood, Brian
❑ 98CliLumG-29
Konderla, Mike
❑ 83CedRapRF-14
❑ 83CedRapRT-7
❑ 84CedRapRT-9
❑ 87NasSouTI-12
❑ 88DenZepC-2
❑ 88DenZepP-1276
Kondo, Akihiko
❑ 79TCMJapPB-23
Konemann, Troy
❑ 92SprCarC-12
❑ 92SprCarF-862
Konerko, Paul
❑ 94ClaUpdCotC-CC12
❑ 94SigRooDP-13
❑ 94SigRooDPS-13
❑ 94StaCluDP-80
❑ 94StaCluDPFDI-80
❑ 94TopTra-112T
❑ 94YakBeaC-8
❑ 94YakBeaF-3854
❑ 95Bes-79
❑ 95Bow-241
❑ 95BowBes-B28
❑ 95BowBesR-B28
❑ 95BowGolF-241
❑ 95Exc-214
❑ 95ExcFirYP-1
❑ 95Pin-170
❑ 95PinArtP-170
❑ 95PinMusC-170
❑ 95SanBerSTI-11
❑ 95ScoDraP-DP7
❑ 95SelSurS-SS4
❑ 95SPML-77
❑ 95SPMLDtS-DS8
❑ 95StaClu-102
❑ 95StaCluFDI-102
❑ 95StaCluMOP-102
❑ 95StaCluSTWS-102
❑ 95Top-139
❑ 95UppDecML-194
❑ 95UppDecML-222
❑ 95UppDecMLFS-194
❑ 95UppDecMLFS-222
❑ 95UppDecMLOP-OP14
❑ 96BesAutSA-38
❑ 96Bow-338
❑ 96BowBes-156
❑ 96BowBesAR-156
❑ 96BowBesR-156
❑ 96BowFoi-338
❑ 96DouAllB-51
❑ 96Exc-177
❑ 96SanAntMB-12
❑ 96TexLeaAB-27
❑ 96Top-432
❑ 97AlbDukGS-18
❑ 97Bes-6
❑ 97Bes-97
❑ 97BesAutAS-25
❑ 97BesAutP-H6
❑ 97BesAutSBPP-6
❑ 97BesAutSC-4
❑ 97BesDiaB-7
❑ 97BesLimA-20
❑ 97BesLum-8
❑ 97Bow-130
❑ 97Bow98ROY-ROY7
❑ 97BowBes-103
❑ 97BowBesAR-103
❑ 97BowBesMI-MI7
❑ 97BowBesMIAR-MI7
❑ 97BowBesMIARI-MI7
❑ 97BowBesMII-MI7
❑ 97BowBesMIR-MI7
❑ 97BowBesMIRI-MI7
❑ 97BowBesR-103
❑ 97BowCerBlaIA-CA45
❑ 97BowCerBluIA-CA45
❑ 97BowCerGolIA-CA45
❑ 97BowChr-142
❑ 97BowChr1RFR-ROY7
❑ 97BowChr98RF-ROY7
❑ 97BowChrI-142
❑ 97BowChrIR-142
❑ 97BowChrR-142
❑ 97BowChrSHR-SHR4
❑ 97BowChrSHRR-SHR4
❑ 97BowInt-130
❑ 97BowScoHR-4
❑ 97DonSigA-62
❑ 97DonSigAC-76
❑ 97DonSigAM-76
❑ 97Top-489
❑ 97TopSta-105
❑ 97TopStaAM-105
❑ 98BesCasT-7
❑ 98BesFulCA-8
❑ 98BesPauK-1
❑ 98BesPauK-2
❑ 98BesPauK-3
❑ 98BesPauK-4
❑ 98BesPauK-5
❑ 98BesPauK-6
❑ 98BesPauKA-1
❑ 98BesPauKA-2
❑ 98BesPauKA-3
❑ 98BesPauKA-4
❑ 98BesPauKA-5
❑ 98BesPauKA-6
❑ 98BesPlaotYP-2
❑ 98BesPreA-20
❑ 98Bow-294
❑ 98BowBes-110
❑ 98BowBesA-110
❑ 98BowBesAAR-110
❑ 98BowBesAR-110
❑ 98BowBesAR-110
❑ 98BowBesMIF-MI11
❑ 98BowBesMIFAR-MI11
❑ 98BowBesMIFR-MI11
❑ 98BowBesP-BP6
❑ 98BowBesPAR-BP6
❑ 98BowBesPR-BP6
❑ 98BowBesR-110
❑ 98BowCerBlueAU-62
❑ 98BowCerGA-62
❑ 98BowCerSA-62
❑ 98BowChr-294
❑ 98BowChrGA-294

❑ 98BowChrGAR-294
❑ 98BowChrI-294
❑ 98BowChrIR-294
❑ 98BowChrR-294
❑ 98BowChrR-45
❑ 98BowChrRR-45
❑ 98BowGolA-294
❑ 98BowInt-294
❑ 98BowScoC-SC1
❑ 98CirThu-139
❑ 98CirThuRav-139
❑ 98CirThuSupRav-139
❑ 98ColCho-100
❑ 98ColChoSQ-SQ20
❑ 98ColChoSQDouble-26
❑ 98ColChoSQHR-26
❑ 98ColChoSQSingle-26
❑ 98ColChoSQTriple-26
❑ 98DodPol-14
❑ 98Don-148
❑ 98Don-388
❑ 98DonCol-148
❑ 98DonCol-178
❑ 98DonColE-498
❑ 98DonColL-381
❑ 98DonColP-689
❑ 98DonColP-750
❑ 98DonColS-148
❑ 98DonColS-173
❑ 98DonEli-98
❑ 98DonEliA-98
❑ 98DonEliBttF-1
❑ 98DonEliBttFA-1A
❑ 98DonEliS-98
❑ 98DonGolPP-148
❑ 98DonGolPP-388
❑ 98DonPre-139
❑ 98DonPre-200
❑ 98DonPreGES-5
❑ 98DonPreGX-5
❑ 98DonPreGXDC-5
❑ 98DonPrePM-26
❑ 98DonPreSeat-139
❑ 98DonPreSeat-200
❑ 98DonPriCD-148
❑ 98DonPriCD-178
❑ 98DonPriCE-498
❑ 98DonPriCL-381
❑ 98DonPriCP-689
❑ 98DonPriCP-750
❑ 98DonRatR-3
❑ 98DonRatRM-3
❑ 98DonRooDK-8
❑ 98DonRooDKC-8
❑ 98DonSig-93
❑ 98DonSigP-93
❑ 98DonSigSB-16
❑ 98DonSilPP-148
❑ 98DonSilPP-388
❑ 98E-X2-91
❑ 98E-X2ECFut-91
❑ 98E-X2ECNow-91
❑ 98E-X2SD2001-3
❑ 98E-X2Sig2001-11
❑ 98Fin-174
❑ 98FinCen-C12
❑ 98FinCenR-C12
❑ 98FinNo--174
❑ 98FinNo-R-174
❑ 98FinRef-174
❑ 98FlaShoLeg0-11
❑ 98FlaShoLeg1-11
❑ 98FlaShoLeg2-11
❑ 98FlaShoLeg3-11
❑ 98FlaShoLegM-11
❑ 98FlaShoR0-11
❑ 98FlaShoR1-11
❑ 98FlaShoR2-11
❑ 98FlaShoR3-11
❑ 98FlaShoWotF-7
❑ 98Fle-69
❑ 98FleProF-PF9
❑ 98FleUpd-U96
❑ 98Lea-182
❑ 98LeaFraDA-182
❑ 98LeaFraF-182
❑ 98LeaFraM-182
❑ 98LeaFraM-182
❑ 98LeaFraMDC-182
❑ 98LeaFraMDC-182
❑ 98LeaFraMZ2-182
❑ 98LeaRCrusUP-102
❑ 98LeaRS-134
❑ 98LeaRS-191
❑ 98LeaRSCrusUG-102
❑ 98LeaRSCrusUR-102
❑ 98LeaRSFOSamp-4
❑ 98LeaRSFresh-4
❑ 98LeaRSHRDerby-8
❑ 98LeaRSLHolo-134
❑ 98LeaRSLHolo-191
❑ 98LeaRSLong-134
❑ 98LeaRSLong-191
❑ 98LeaRSTicMas-13
❑ 98LeaRSTicMasDC-13
❑ 98LeaRTrue-134
❑ 98LeaRTrue-191
❑ 98MetUni-76
❑ 98MetUniPMG-76
❑ 98PacAur-145
❑ 98PacAurPF-13
❑ 98PacAurPFC-13
❑ 98PacAurPFPB-13
❑ 98PacAurPFR-13
❑ 98PacAurPFS-13
❑ 98PacOme-124
❑ 98PacOmeR-124
❑ 98PacOmeRS-26
❑ 98PacOmeRST2-26
❑ 98PacOnl-376
❑ 98PacOnlR-376
❑ 98PacOnlWC-376
❑ 98PacPar-176
❑ 98PacParC-176
❑ 98PacParG-176
❑ 98PacParHS-176
❑ 98PacParPB-176
❑ 98PacParR-176
❑ 98Pin-159
❑ 98PinIns-129
❑ 98PinInsCE-129
❑ 98PinInsDE-129
❑ 98PinInsSG-13AB
❑ 98PinInsSG-13CD
❑ 98PinInsSGS-13AB
❑ 98PinInsSGS-13CD
❑ 98PinPer-117
❑ 98PinPerPP-117
❑ 98PinPluTP-15
❑ 98PinPluTPG-15
❑ 98PinPluTPM-15
❑ 98PinPreP-159
❑ 98PinSna-LAD8
❑ 98Sco-234
❑ 98ScoNewS-NS12
❑ 98ScoRT-250
❑ 98ScoRT-S250
❑ 98ScoRTSS-PP143
❑ 98ScoRTSSAP-PP143
❑ 98ScoRTSSAP1-PP143
❑ 98SkyDugA-118
❑ 98SkyDugAIA-118
❑ 98SP Aut-20
❑ 98SP Aut-SD28
❑ 98SP AutC-PK
❑ 98SP AutSD-SD28
❑ 98SP AutSDT-SD28
❑ 98SP MinDTSPE-DS16
❑ 98SP MinPE-2
❑ 98SP MinPE-70
❑ 98SP SPTSC-PK
❑ 98SPMin-2
❑ 98SPMin-70
❑ 98SPMinDTS-DS16
❑ 98SpoIll-162
❑ 98SpoIllAuto-5
❑ 98SpoIllEE-162
❑ 98SpoIllFE-162
❑ 98SpoIllTaN-147
❑ 98SpoIllTaNEE-147
❑ 98SpoIllWSF-86
❑ 98SpoIllWSFEE-86
❑ 98SpoIllWSFFE-86
❑ 98SPxFin-27
❑ 98SPxFinR-27
❑ 98SPxFinS-27
❑ 98StaCluC-CS9
❑ 98StaCluC-CS11
❑ 98StaCluC-CS12
❑ 98StaCluFDI-352
❑ 98StaCluI-352
❑ 98StaCluITW-W7
❑ 98StaCluOneK-352
❑ 98StaCluPP-352
❑ 98StaCluRC-RC12
❑ 98Stu-28
❑ 98StuGPP-28
❑ 98StuHitPar-20
❑ 98StuPor8x10-4
❑ 98StuPor8x10GP-4
❑ 98StuSPP-28
❑ 98TopChrRC-R4
❑ 98TopChrRCRef-R4
❑ 98TopGolLabC1-91
❑ 98TopGolLabC1B-91
❑ 98TopGolLabC1One-91
❑ 98TopGolLabC1R-91
❑ 98TopGolLabC2-91
❑ 98TopGolLabC2B-91
❑ 98TopGolLabC2One-91
❑ 98TopGolLabC2R-91
❑ 98TopGolLabC3-91
❑ 98TopGolLabC3B-91
❑ 98TopGolLabC3One-91
❑ 98TopGolLabC3R-91
❑ 98TopRooCla-R4
❑ 98TopSta-80
❑ 98TopStaB-80
❑ 98TopStaG-80
❑ 98TopStaGR-80
❑ 98TopStaS-80
❑ 98TopStaSB-S9
❑ 98TopStaSG-S9
❑ 98TopStaSGR-S9
❑ 98TopStaSS-S9
❑ 98TopTek-63
❑ 98TopTekD-63
❑ 98UD3-20
❑ 98UD3-110
❑ 98UD3-200
❑ 98UD3DieCut-20
❑ 98UD3DieCut-110
❑ 98UD3DieCut-200
❑ 98Ult-233
❑ 98UltGolM-233
❑ 98UltMas-233
❑ 98UltPlaM-233
❑ 98UltRoctS-12
❑ 98UppDec-285
❑ 98UppDec-629
❑ 98UppDecBCP-BC16
❑ 98UppDecDS-DS25
❑ 98UppDecR-24
❑ 98UppDecREP-5
❑ 98UppDecRSotT-PK
❑ 98Zen-94
❑ 98Zen5 xx7-68
❑ 98Zen5x7GoldImp-68
❑ 98Zen5x7Imp-68
❑ 98ZenRooT-9
❑ 98ZenZ-G-94
❑ 98ZenZ-S-94
❑ 98ZenZ-T-16
❑ 98ZenZ-TG-16
❑ 99199Fin-203
❑ 99BowBes-115
❑ 99BowBesAR-115
❑ 99BowBesR-115
❑ 99FinGolRef-203
❑ 99FinRef-203
❑ 99FlaShoLeg1-116
❑ 99FlaShoLeg2-116
❑ 99FlaShoLeg3-116
❑ 99FlaShoLegM1-116
❑ 99FlaShoLegM2-116
❑ 99FlaShoLegM3-116
❑ 99FlaShoR1-116
❑ 99FlaShoR2-116
❑ 99FlaShoR3-116
❑ 99Fle-240
❑ 99FleSta9-240
❑ 99FleWarT-240
❑ 99MetUni-111
❑ 99MetUniGM-111
❑ 99MetUniN-7
❑ 99MetUniPMG-111
❑ 99PacOme-56
❑ 99PacOmeC-56
❑ 99PacOmeG-56
❑ 99PacOmePB-56
❑ 99PacPar-56
❑ 99PacParC-56
❑ 99PacParG-56
❑ 99PacParHoloGold-56
❑ 99PacParHS-56
❑ 99PacParOD-56
❑ 99PacParPB-56
❑ 99PacParRed-56
❑ 99SkyMolM-59
❑ 99SkyMolMX-59
❑ 99SkyPre-202
❑ 99SkyPreR-202
❑ 99SkyThu-128
❑ 99SkyThuRant-128
❑ 99SkyThuRave-128
❑ 99SP Aut-23
❑ 99SP SigAuto-PK
❑ 99SPSig-134
❑ 99ThuSkySupR-128
❑ 99Top-24
❑ 99TopChr-24
❑ 99TopChrNB-NB13
❑ 99TopChrNBR-NB13
❑ 99TopChrR-24
❑ 99TopMVPP-24
❑ 99TopNewB-NB13
❑ 99TopOpeD-16
❑ 99TopSta-78
❑ 99TopSta1Foil-78
❑ 99TopStaFoil-78
❑ 99TopStaOS-78
❑ 99UD ChoMBH-B10
❑ 99Ult-138
❑ 99UltGolM-138
❑ 99UltMas-138
❑ 99UltPlaM-138
❑ 99UltWorP-12
❑ 99UppDec-73
❑ 99UppDec-338
❑ 99UppDecBD-23
❑ 99UppDecBDD-23
❑ 99UppDecBDDom-D12
❑ 99UppDecBDDomE-D12
❑ 99UppDecBDQ-23
❑ 99UppDecBDT-23
❑ 99UppDecCLM-C19
❑ 99UppDecE-21
❑ 99UppDecEFXG-21
❑ 99UppDecEL1-73
❑ 99UppDecEL1-338
❑ 99UppDecEL2-73
❑ 99UppDecEL2-338
❑ 99UppDecM-48
❑ 99UppDecMGS-48
❑ 99UppDecMHFS-48
❑ 99UppDecMSS-48
❑ 99Vic-98

Konetchy, Ed
❑ 08RosComP-167
❑ 09ColChiE-158
❑ 09PC7HHB-28
❑ 09RamT20-65
❑ 09SpoNewSM-34
❑ 09T206-194
❑ 09T206-195
❑ 10CouT21-161
❑ 10CouT21-162
❑ 10CouT21-163
❑ 10CouT21-296
❑ 10DarChoE-21
❑ 10DomDisP-63
❑ 10OrnOvaPP-8
❑ 10RedCroT-37
❑ 10RedCroT-126
❑ 10RedCroT-209
❑ 10SweCapPP-150
❑ 11HelSta-173
❑ 11PinT-5-360
❑ 11S74Sil-121
❑ 11SpoLifCW-207
❑ 11SpoLifM-272
❑ 11T205-91
❑ 11TurRedT-103
❑ 12ColRedB-158
❑ 12ColTinT-158
❑ 12HasTriFT-70C
❑ 12PhiCarE-16
❑ 12T207-94
❑ 13NatGamW-24
❑ 13TomBarW-23
❑ 14B18B-79A
❑ 14B18B-79B
❑ 14CraJacE-118
❑ 14PieStaT-59
❑ 15CraJacE-118
❑ 15SpoNewM-94
❑ 15VicT21-16
❑ 16FleBreD-54
❑ 16SpoNewM-96
❑ 17ColE13-94
❑ 19W514-93
❑ 21Exh-93
❑ 22MrsShePP-19
❑ 72ClaCar-107
❑ 90DodTar-416
❑ 91ConTSN-263
❑ 92ConTSN-638

Konieczki, Dominic
❑ 91EriSaiC-17
❑ 91EriSaiP-4062
❑ 92KenTwiC-23
❑ 92KenTwiF-599
❑ 93NasXprF-397
❑ 94ForMyeMC-10
❑ 94ForMyeMF-1164
❑ 95HarCitRCTI-9
❑ 96FtMyeMB-16
❑ 96HarCitRCB-17

Konieczny, Doug
❑ 75AstPos-19
❑ 75OPC-624
❑ 75Top-624
❑ 75TopMin-624
❑ 76OPC-602
❑ 76SSP-49
❑ 76Top-602
❑ 87AstShoSPT-17

Konikowski, Alex
❑ 75Gia195T-13

Konnick, Michael
❑ 18Zee-62

Konopa, Bob
❑ 80WisRapTT-7
❑ 82OrlTwi8SCT-18
❑ 82OrlTwiT-6
❑ 84ChaO'sT-15
❑ 90HagSunDGB-14

Konopki, Mark
❑ 91ElmPioC-22
❑ 91ElmPioP-3268
❑ 92LynRedSC-21
❑ 92LynRedSF-2903

Konrady, Dennis
❑ 96WatIndTI-12
❑ 98KinIndQ-16

Konstanty, Jim
❑ 47Exh-123
❑ 47PM1StaP1-107
❑ 49EurSta-139
❑ 49PhiBul-29
❑ 50Bow-226
❑ 51BerRos-D6
❑ 51Bow-27
❑ 51FisBakL-16
❑ 51R42SmaS-56
❑ 51TopCurA-7
❑ 52Top-108
❑ 53BowBW-58
❑ 53Dor-138
❑ 55Bow-231
❑ 56Top-321
❑ 60RawGloT-12
❑ 61Top-479
❑ 63GadFunC-27
❑ 70Houof J-12
❑ 75Phi195T-16
❑ 75TCMHouoJ-12
❑ 76SSPYanOD-6
❑ 79TCM50-53
❑ 80Phi195T-16
❑ 83TCMPla1944-30
❑ 83TopRep5-108
❑ 86PhiGreT-7
❑ 87Phi195T-3
❑ 90HOFStiB-44

Kontorinis, Andrew
❑ 92KenTwiF-614
❑ 93ForMyeMC-13
❑ 93ForMyeMF-2664
❑ 94FloStaLAF-FSL9
❑ 94ForMyeMC-11
❑ 94ForMyeMF-1173

Konuszewski, Dennis
❑ 92WelPirC-13
❑ 93ClaGolF-178
❑ 93SalBucC-13
❑ 93SalBucF-426
❑ 94CarMudF-1572
❑ 95CarMudF-151
❑ 96CarMudB-3

Koob, Ernie
❑ 92ConTSN-349

Kooiman, Bill
❑ 90IdaFalBP-3265

Kooman, Chris
❑ 87EveGiaC-14

Koonce, Cal
❑ 63Top-31
❑ 65OPC-34
❑ 65Top-34
❑ 66Top-278
❑ 66TopVen-278
❑ 67CokCapC-15
❑ 67DexPre-118
❑ 67OPC-171
❑ 67Top-171
❑ 68Top-486
❑ 69Top-303
❑ 70OPC-521
❑ 70Top-521
❑ 71MLBOffS-320
❑ 71OPC-254
❑ 71Top-254
❑ 72MilBra-185
❑ 89MetRinP69-18
❑ 91MetWIZ-218
❑ 94Met69CCPP-20
❑ 94Met69CS-19
❑ 94Met69T-28

Koonce, Graham
❑ 94BriTigC-16
❑ 96FayGenB-20

Koontz, Jim
❑ 81ElPasDT-10
❑ 82ElPasDT-20
❑ 84VanCanC-45

Koopman, Bob
❑ 86PriWilPP-14
❑ 87SalBucP-20

Koosman, Jerry
❑ 68OPC-177
❑ 68Top-177
❑ 68TopVen-177
❑ 69CitMetC-12
❑ 69EquSpoHoF-BB10
❑ 69MetCit-6
❑ 69MetNewYDN-11
❑ 69MetTeal-10
❑ 69MetTealC-2
❑ 69MLBOffS-168
❑ 69MLBPin-49
❑ 69OPC-90
❑ 69Top-90
❑ 69Top-434
❑ 69TopDec-25
❑ 69TopDecI-22
❑ 69TopSta-66
❑ 69TopSup-51
❑ 69TopTeaP-24
❑ 69TraSta-46
❑ 70DayDaiNM-44
❑ 70MetTeal-9
❑ 70MetTealC-2
❑ 70MetTra-22B
❑ 70MLBOffS-79
❑ 70OPC-309
❑ 70OPC-468
❑ 70Top-309
❑ 70Top-468
❑ 70Top-610
❑ 70TraSta-5C
❑ 71MetTeal-11
❑ 71MetTealC-6
❑ 71MLBOffS-157
❑ 71OPC-335
❑ 71Top-335
❑ 71TopCoi-23
❑ 71TopTat-22
❑ 72MetTeal-11
❑ 72MilBra-186
❑ 72Top-697
❑ 72Top-698
❑ 73LinPor-114
❑ 73MetAllEB-6
❑ 73MetTeal-6
❑ 73OPC-184
❑ 73Top-184
❑ 74MetDaiPA-17
❑ 74MetJapEB-4
❑ 74MetTeal-10
❑ 74OPC-356
❑ 74Top-356
❑ 74TopSta-65
❑ 75MetSSP-14
❑ 75OPC-19
❑ 75SSP42-17
❑ 75Top-19
❑ 75TopMin-19
❑ 76BlaDis-27
❑ 76BucDis-27
❑ 76CarDis-27
❑ 76CraDis-27
❑ 76DailsID-27
❑ 76IsaDis-27
❑ 76LauDiaJ-22
❑ 76MetMSAP-4
❑ 76OPC-64
❑ 76OrbDis-27
❑ 76RedBarD-27
❑ 76SafDis-27
❑ 76SSP-591
❑ 76SSP-609
❑ 76Top-64
❑ 76TowCluD-27
❑ 77BurCheD-143
❑ 77ChiWilD-36

❑ 77DailsID-36
❑ 77DetCaeD-36
❑ 77HollnnD-36
❑ 77Hos-77
❑ 77Kel-29
❑ 77MetDaiPA-10
❑ 77MSADis-36
❑ 77OPC-26
❑ 77SagDis-36
❑ 77sDis-36
❑ 77Top-300
❑ 77WenDis-36
❑ 77ZipDis-36
❑ 78Hos-80
❑ 78MetDaiPA-12
❑ 78Pep-34
❑ 78SagDis-12
❑ 78TasDis-12
❑ 78Top-565
❑ 78WifBalD-35
❑ 79Hos-149
❑ 79OPC-345
❑ 79Top-655
❑ 79TwiFriP-12
❑ 80BurKinPHR-5
❑ 80OPC-144
❑ 80Top-275
❑ 80TopSup-38
❑ 80TwiPos-14
❑ 81Don-531
❑ 81Fle-552
❑ 81FleStiC-19
❑ 81OPC-298
❑ 81Top-476
❑ 81TopSti-104
❑ 81TwiPos-17
❑ 82Don-603
❑ 82Fle-347
❑ 82OPC-63
❑ 82Top-714
❑ 83Don-39
❑ 83Fle-242
❑ 83FleSta-97
❑ 83FleSti-152
❑ 83OPC-153
❑ 83Top-153
❑ 83TopFol-1
❑ 83WhiSoxTV-36
❑ 84Don-501
❑ 84Fle-65
❑ 84FleUpd-64
❑ 84Nes792-311
❑ 84Nes792-716
❑ 84OPC-311
❑ 84PhiTas-23
❑ 84Top-311
❑ 84Top-716
❑ 84TopTif-311
❑ 84TopTif-716
❑ 84TopTra-64T
❑ 84TopTraT-64T
❑ 85Don-233
❑ 85Fle-256
❑ 85Lea-178
❑ 85OPC-15
❑ 85PhiCIG-7
❑ 85PhiTas-9
❑ 85PhiTas-21
❑ 85Top-15
❑ 85TopMin-15
❑ 85TopSti-117
❑ 85TopTif-15
❑ 86Don-23
❑ 86DonSupD-23
❑ 86Lea-23
❑ 86MetGreT-10
❑ 86OPC-343
❑ 86Spo-64
❑ 86Top-505
❑ 86TopTif-505
❑ 87Met196T-4
❑ 88PacLegI-66
❑ 89Met196C-8
❑ 89MetRinP69-19
❑ 89SweBasG-109
❑ 90MetHalof-5
❑ 90PacLeg-88
❑ 91MetWIZ-219
❑ 91PitMetC-26
❑ 91PitMetP-3440
❑ 91UppDocRH-10
❑ 92ColMetC-27
❑ 92ColMetPI-2
❑ 92UppDecS-10
❑ 93ActPacA-160
❑ 94Met69CCPP-21
❑ 94Met69CS-20
❑ 94Met69SP-P2
❑ 94Met69T-4
❑ 94Met69T-37
❑ 94Met69T-39
❑ 94Met69T-48
❑ 94Met69T-54
❑ 96Met69Y-6
❑ 99SpollIGotG-17
❑ 99SpollIGotGA-41
❑ 99SpollIGotGC-20

Kopacz, Derek
❑ 96FayGenB-21
❑ 98HicCraM-19

Kopacz, George
❑ 71OPC-204
❑ 71Top-204

Koperda, Mike
❑ 80AndBraT-21

Kopetsky, Brian
❑ 86BakDodP-18

Kopf, Dave
❑ 86PitCubP-11
❑ 87IowCubTI-10
❑ 88PitCubP-1373

Kopf, Larry (William)
❑ 19W514-118
❑ 20NatCarE-56
❑ 20RedWorCP-9
❑ 22E120-128
❑ 22W572-56
❑ 77RedCarP-22
❑ 88PacEigMO-91

Kopitzke, Chad
❑ 93HelBreF-4088
❑ 93HelBreSP-21
❑ 94BelBreC-14
❑ 94BelBreFI-95
❑ 95BelBreTI-13

Koplitz, Howard
❑ 62Top-114
❑ 62TopVen-114
❑ 63Top-406
❑ 64Top-372
❑ 66OPC-46
❑ 66Top-46
❑ 66TopVen-46
❑ 78TCM60I-221

Kopp, Merlin
❑ 20Zee-127
❑ 21Zee-72
❑ 23Zee-89
❑ 24Zee-64
❑ 25Zee-71
❑ 26Zee-119
❑ 27Zee-95
❑ 28Zee-113

Koppe, Clint
❑ 94BilMusF-3664
❑ 94BilMusSP-17
❑ 97ChaLoo-13

Koppe, Joe
❑ 59Top-517
❑ 60Top-319
❑ 61Top-179
❑ 62SalPlaC-209
❑ 62ShiPlaC-209
❑ 62Top-39
❑ 62TopVen-39
❑ 63Jel-26
❑ 63Pos-26A
❑ 63Pos-26B
❑ 63Top-396
❑ 64Top-279
❑ 64TopRooAB-8
❑ 64TopVen-279
❑ 65SeaPop-9

Kopriva, Dan
❑ 92PriRedC-25
❑ 92PriRedF-3095
❑ 93SouAtlLAGF-55
❑ 93WesVirWC-12
❑ 93WesVirWF-2873
❑ 94WinSpiC-12
❑ 94WinSpiF-279
❑ 95ChaLooTI-10
❑ 96PriWilCB-16

Kopyta, Jeff
❑ 86MedA'sC-66
❑ 86ModA'sC-27
❑ 87MadMusP-10
❑ 87MadMusP-18
❑ 88ModA'sCLC-63
❑ 88ModA'sTI-12
❑ 89ModA'sCLC-272

Koranda, Jim
❑ 58MonRoyF-12
❑ 59O'KAleMR-11

Korcheck, Steve
❑ 58SeaTeal-16
❑ 58Top-403
❑ 59Top-284
❑ 60Lea-79
❑ 60SenJayP-8
❑ 60Top-56
❑ 60TopVen-56

Korczyk, Steve
❑ 82TolMudHT-3
❑ 83TolMudHT-5

Kordish, Steve
❑ 83TriTriT-2
❑ 84TulDriTI-30
❑ 86SalRedBP-15

Kores, Arthur
❑ 13Zee-62
❑ 14Zee-64
❑ 20MrsShePP-10
❑ 70MetMusoAB-4

Korince, George
❑ 67OPC-72
❑ 67Top-72
❑ 67Top-526
❑ 68Top-447

Korn, Ray
❑ 91EriSaiC-27
❑ 91EriSaiP-4085
❑ 94HunCubC-29
❑ 94HunCubF-3570
❑ 97St.PauS-14
❑ 98St.PauSTI-13

Korneev, Leonid
❑ 89EasLeaDDP-DD15

Kornfeld, Craig
❑ 79QuaCitCT-16
❑ 80QuaCitCT-17

Korolev, Sergey
❑ 89EasLeaDDP-DD4

Koronka, John
❑ 98BilMusTI-17

Kortmeyer, Scott
❑ 95SpolndTI-10

Kortright, Jim
❑ 88IdaFalBP-1858
❑ 89IdaFalBP-2031

Korwan, Jim
❑ 90DodTar-1005

Kosc, Greg
❑ 88T/MUmp-25
❑ 89T/MUmp-23
❑ 90T/MUmp-22

Kosco, Andy
❑ 66Top-264
❑ 66TopVen-264
❑ 67CokCapTw-18
❑ 67Top-366
❑ 68Top-524
❑ 68YanPhoS-69
❑ 69MilBra-152
❑ 69OPC-139
❑ 69Top-139
❑ 69TopFou-8
❑ 69TopSta-204
❑ 69TopTeaP-22
❑ 70OPC-535
❑ 70Top-535
❑ 71MLBOffS-440
❑ 71OPC-746
❑ 71Top-746
❑ 72MilBra-187
❑ 72OPC-376
❑ 72Top-376
❑ 74OPC-34
❑ 74Top-34
❑ 90DodTar-417
❑ 92YanWIZ6-69
❑ 94BreMilB-234

Kosco, Bryn
❑ 88JamExpP-1896
❑ 89RocExpLC-16
❑ 90JacExpB-6
❑ 90JacExpP-1382
❑ 91HarSenLD-259
❑ 91HarSenP-633
❑ 91LinDriAA-259
❑ 92HarSenF-465
❑ 92HarSenS-285
❑ 93HigDesMC-8
❑ 93HigDesMF-47
❑ 94ExcFS7-192
❑ 94NewHavRF-1557
❑ 94SigRoo-31
❑ 94SigRooS-31
❑ 95IowCubTI-20
❑ 96IowCubB-18

Kosco, Dru (Andrew)
❑ 87WauTimP-14
❑ 88WauTimGS-26
❑ 89WilBilP-626
❑ 90WilBilB-13
❑ 90WilBilP-1068
❑ 90WilBilS-14

Kosek, Kory
❑ 95MarPhiTI-14
❑ 98St.PauSTI-14

Kosenski, John
❑ 88CapCodPPaLP-108
❑ 88OklSoo-13
❑ 89OklSoo-20
❑ 90OklSoo-15
❑ 91FayGenC-4
❑ 91FayGenP-1165
❑ 92LakTigC-14
❑ 92LakTigF-2273
❑ 93LakTigC-13
❑ 93LakTigF-1305

Koshevoy, Alexei
❑ 89EasLeaDDP-DD7

Koshorek, Clem
❑ 52Top-380
❑ 53BowC-147
❑ 53Top-8
❑ 83TopRep5-380
❑ 91TopArc1-8

Koskie, Corey
❑ 95ForWayWTI-17
❑ 95MidLeaA-28
❑ 96Exc-78
❑ 96FtMyeMB-17
❑ 97NewBriRC-17
❑ 97TexAllM-21
❑ 98Bes-20
❑ 98Bow-118
❑ 98BowBes-123
❑ 98BowBesAR-123
❑ 98BowBesR-123
❑ 98BowChr-118
❑ 98BowChrGA-118
❑ 98BowChrGAR-118
❑ 98BowChrI-118
❑ 98BowChrIR-118
❑ 98BowChrR-118
❑ 98BowGolA-118
❑ 98BowInt-118
❑ 98FleUpd-U93
❑ 98SalLakBO-16
❑ 98SPxFin-198
❑ 98SPxFinR-198
❑ 98SPxFinS-198
❑ 98UppDec-548
❑ 98UppDecDS-DS29
❑ 99Bow-100
❑ 99BowAut-BA20
❑ 99BowBes-145
❑ 99BowBesAR-145
❑ 99BowBesR-145
❑ 99BowChr-100
❑ 99BowChrG-100
❑ 99BowChrGR-100
❑ 99BowChrI-100
❑ 99BowChrIR-100
❑ 99BowChrR-100
❑ 99BowGol-100
❑ 99BowInt-100
❑ 99BowPreProd-PP4
❑ 99DumSet-116
❑ 99E-X Cen-113
❑ 99E-X CenECFut-113
❑ 99E-X CenECNow-113
❑ 99FlaShoLeg1-89
❑ 99FlaShoLeg2-89
❑ 99FlaShoLeg3-89
❑ 99FlaShoLegM1-89
❑ 99FlaShoLegM2-89
❑ 99FlaShoLegM3-89
❑ 99FlaShoR1-89
❑ 99FlaShoR2-89
❑ 99FlaShoR3-89
❑ 99Fle-130
❑ 99FleBri-136
❑ 99FleBri2G-136
❑ 99FleBriBlu-136
❑ 99FleBriGol-136
❑ 99FleBriI-14
❑ 99FleMys-116
❑ 99FleMysM-116
❑ 99FleSta9-130
❑ 99FleWarT-130
❑ 99MetUni-263
❑ 99MetUniGM-263
❑ 99MetUniPMG-263
❑ 99PacInv-84
❑ 99PacInvOD-84
❑ 99PacInvPB-84
❑ 99PacOme-138
❑ 99PacOmeC-138
❑ 99PacOmeG-138
❑ 99PacOmePB-138
❑ 99Rev-79
❑ 99RevPremDate-79
❑ 99RevRet-79
❑ 99RevShaSS-79
❑ 99SkyThu-81
❑ 99SkyThuRant-81
❑ 99SkyThuRave-81
❑ 99SP Aut-107
❑ 99SP AutC-CK
❑ 99SP AutCG-CK
❑ 99SP SigAuto-CK
❑ 99SP SigAutoG-CK
❑ 99SP TopP-68
❑ 99SP TopPDtS-D12
❑ 99SP TopPPE-68
❑ 99SpoIll-69
❑ 99SPSig-46
❑ 99SPx-104
❑ 99SPxFinR-104
❑ 99SPxFinS-104
❑ 99ThuSkySupR-81
❑ 99Top-435
❑ 99TopChr-435
❑ 99TopChrR-435
❑ 99UD Cho-17
❑ 99UD ChoPCR-17
❑ 99UD Ion-37
❑ 99UD IonR-37
❑ 99UDHolo-33
❑ 99UDHoloAUsome-33
❑ 99UDHoloUDA-CK
❑ 99Ult-250
❑ 99UltGolM-250
❑ 99UltMas-250
❑ 99UltPlaM-250
❑ 99UppDec-411
❑ 99UppDecE-53
❑ 99UppDecEFXG-53
❑ 99UppDecEL1-411
❑ 99UppDecEL2-411
❑ 99UppDecM-122
❑ 99UppDecMGS-122
❑ 99UppDecMHFS-122
❑ 99UppDecMP-CK
❑ 99UppDecMSS-122
❑ 99UppDecO-77
❑ 99UppDecOSO-77
❑ 99UppDecR-48
❑ 99UppDecRG-48
❑ 99UppDecRP-48
❑ 99Vic-221

Koslo, Dave (George B.)
❑ 47TipTop-126
❑ 48Bow-48
❑ 48GiaTeal-10
❑ 49Bow-34
❑ 49EurSta-114
❑ 49GiaTeal-16
❑ 50Bow-65
❑ 51Bow-90
❑ 52BerRos-31
❑ 52Bow-182
❑ 52Top-336
❑ 54OriEss-18
❑ 55BraGolS-12
❑ 55BraJohC-20
❑ 75Gia195T-14
❑ 79TCM50-231
❑ 83TopRep5-336
❑ 85TCMPla1-45
❑ 91OriCro-247

Koslofski, Kevin
❑ 86Ft.MyeRP-16
❑ 87Ft.MyeRP-24
❑ 88BasCitRS-15
❑ 89BasCitRS-14
❑ 90MemChiB-10
❑ 90MemChiP-1021
❑ 90MemChiS-12
❑ 91LinDriAA-408
❑ 91MemChiLD-408
❑ 91MemChiP-666
❑ 92DonRoo-63
❑ 92FleUpd-28
❑ 92OmaRoyF-2975
❑ 92OmaRoyS-332
❑ 92ProFS7-74
❑ 92SkyAAAF-152
❑ 93Don-205
❑ 93Fle-240
❑ 93OmaRoyF-1691
❑ 93RoyPol-15
❑ 93Sco-226
❑ 93Sel-394
❑ 93StaClu-505
❑ 93StaCluFDI-505
❑ 93StaCluMOP-505
❑ 93Top-158
❑ 93TopGol-158
❑ 93TopInaM-158
❑ 93TopInaR-158
❑ 93TopMic-158
❑ 93Ult-211
❑ 93UppDec-351
❑ 93UppDecGold-351
❑ 93USPlaCR-4D
❑ 94Pac-291
❑ 97LouRedB-17

Kosman, Cody
❑ 93EugEmeC-18
❑ 93EugEmeF-3852

Kosnik, Jim
❑ 87BelMarL-16

Kostich, Billy
❑ 89HigSchPLS-15
❑ 91PenPilC-7
❑ 91PenPilP-373
❑ 92PenPilC-21
❑ 92PenPilF-2928
❑ 93AppFoxCB-13
❑ 93AppFoxFI-2457

Kostickhka, Steve
❑ 87BelBreP-6

Kostro, Frank
❑ 63Top-407
❑ 65Top-459
❑ 68OPC-44
❑ 68Top-44
❑ 68TopVen-44
❑ 69Top-242

Kotarski, Mike
❑ 92BenRocCB-16
❑ 92BenRocF-1473
❑ 93CenValRC-15
❑ 93CenValRF-2891
❑ 93Top-621
❑ 93TopGol-621
❑ 93TopInaM-621
❑ 93TopInaR-621
❑ 93TopMic-621
❑ 94NewHavRF-1545
❑ 96NorNavB-14

Kotch, Darrin
❑ 22KolMotBPP-16
❑ 90JamExpP-19
❑ 91SumFlyC-6
❑ 91SumFlyP-2329
❑ 92RocExpC-5
❑ 92RocExpF-2110

Kotchman, Randy
❑ 89MiaMirIS-8
❑ 90BoiHawP-3325

Kotchman, Tom
❑ 86PalSprAP-19
❑ 86PalSprAS-2
❑ 87EdmTraP-2072
❑ 88EdmTraC-22
❑ 88EdmTraP-580
❑ 89EdmTraC-25
❑ 89EdmTraP-549
❑ 89TriAAAP-AAA28
❑ 90BoiHawP-3331
❑ 91BoiHawP-3899
❑ 92BoiHawF-3646
❑ 93BoiHawC-27
❑ 94BoiHawC-30
❑ 94BoiHawF-3372
❑ 95BoiHawTI-21
❑ 96BoiHawB-1
❑ 97BoiHawG-17

Kotes, Chris
❑ 91St.CatBJC-17
❑ 91St.CatBJP-3389
❑ 92MyrBeaHC-14
❑ 92MyrBeaHF-2192
❑ 93DunBluJC-13
❑ 93DunBluJF-1792
❑ 93DunBluJFFN-14
❑ 93SouAtlLAPI-19
❑ 94DunBluJC-16
❑ 94DunBluJF-2553
❑ 95KnoSmoF-40

Kotkas, Jim
❑ 90IBAWorA-27
Kotrany, Joe
❑ 76DalCon-6
Kotsay, Mark
❑ 96BesAutS1RP-FR2
❑ 96KanCouCUTI-9
❑ 96MauStiHWB-9
❑ 97BesLimA-21
❑ 97BesWhe-5
❑ 97Bow-108
❑ 97Bow98ROY-ROY8
❑ 97BowBes-197
❑ 97BowBesAR-197
❑ 97BowBesR-197
❑ 97BowChr-128
❑ 97BowChr1RFR-ROY8
❑ 97BowChr98RF-ROY8
❑ 97BowChrI-128
❑ 97BowChrIR-128
❑ 97BowChrR-128
❑ 97BowInt-108
❑ 97DonLim-88
❑ 97DonLimE-88
❑ 97DonSig-49
❑ 97DonSigA-63
❑ 97DonSigAC-77
❑ 97DonSigAM-77
❑ 97DonSigPPP-49
❑ 97EasLeaTPB-24
❑ 97PorSeaD-17
❑ 97Sel-165
❑ 97SelCom-165
❑ 97TexAllM-43
❑ 97Top-483
❑ 97TopSta-108
❑ 97TopStaAM-108
❑ 98Bes-21
❑ 98BesCon-6
❑ 98BesCon-7
❑ 98BesDiaB-4
❑ 98BesFulCA-9
❑ 98BesPlaotYP-3
❑ 98BesPreA-21
❑ 98BesYouG-6
❑ 98BesYouG-7
❑ 98Bow-218
❑ 98BowBes-149
❑ 98BowBesAR-149
❑ 98BowBesMIF-MI16
❑ 98BowBesMIFAR-MI16
❑ 98BowBesMIFR-MI16
❑ 98BowBesR-149
❑ 98BowChr-218
❑ 98BowChrGA-218
❑ 98BowChrGAR-218
❑ 98BowChrI-218
❑ 98BowChrIR-218
❑ 98BowChrR-218
❑ 98BowGolA-218
❑ 98BowInt-218
❑ 98BowScoC-SC3
❑ 98CirThu-108
❑ 98CirThuRav-108
❑ 98CirThuSupRav-108
❑ 98ColCho-115
❑ 98Don-298
❑ 98DonCol-176
❑ 98DonColE-507
❑ 98DonColL-387
❑ 98DonColP-695
❑ 98DonColS-171
❑ 98DonEli-107
❑ 98DonEliA-107
❑ 98DonEliS-107
❑ 98DonGolPP-298
❑ 98DonPre-145
❑ 98DonPreGES-11
❑ 98DonPreGX-11
❑ 98DonPreGXDC-11
❑ 98DonPrePM-30
❑ 98DonPreSeat-145
❑ 98DonPriCD-176
❑ 98DonPriCE-507
❑ 98DonPriCL-387
❑ 98DonPriCP-695
❑ 98DonRatR-1
❑ 98DonRatRM-1
❑ 98DonRooDK-10
❑ 98DonRooDKC-10
❑ 98DonSig-63
❑ 98DonSigA-51
❑ 98DonSigAC-69
❑ 98DonSigAM-70
❑ 98DonSigP-63
❑ 98DonSilPP-298
❑ 98E-X2-85
❑ 98E-X2ECFut-85
❑ 98E-X2ECNow-85
❑ 98E-X2Sig2001-3
❑ 98Fle-107
❑ 98FleProF-PF10
❑ 98Lea-188
❑ 98LeaFraDA-188
❑ 98LeaFraF-188
❑ 98LeaFraM-188
❑ 98LeaFraM-188
❑ 98LeaFraMDC-188
❑ 98LeaFraMDC-188
❑ 98LeaFraMZ2-188
❑ 98LeaRCrusUP-108
❑ 98LeaRS-193
❑ 98LeaRSCrusUG-108
❑ 98LeaRSCrusUR-108
❑ 98LeaRSFOSamp-11
❑ 98LeaRSFresh-11
❑ 98LeaRSLHolo-193
❑ 98LeaRSLong-193
❑ 98LeaRTrue-193
❑ 98MetUni-189
❑ 98MetUniPMG-189
❑ 98PacOme-98
❑ 98PacOmeR-98
❑ 98PacOmeRS-16
❑ 98PacOmeRST1-16
❑ 98PacOnl-298
❑ 98PacOnlR-298
❑ 98PacOnlWC-298
❑ 98PacPar-162
❑ 98PacParC-162
❑ 98PacParG-162
❑ 98PacParHS-162
❑ 98PacParPB-162
❑ 98PacParR-162
❑ 98Pin-169
❑ 98PinArtP-PP72
❑ 98PinIns-83
❑ 98PinInsCE-83
❑ 98PinInsDE-83
❑ 98PinMusC-PP72
❑ 98PinPer-113
❑ 98PinPerPP-113
❑ 98PinPlu-157
❑ 98PinPreP-169
❑ 98PorSeaD5AQ-8
❑ 98Sco-241
❑ 98ScoRT-61
❑ 98ScoRTSS-PP55
❑ 98ScoRTSSAP-PP55
❑ 98ScoRTSSAP1-PP55
❑ 98SkyDugA-106
❑ 98SkyDugAIA-106
❑ 98SP Aut-4
❑ 98SP AutC-MK
❑ 98SpoIll-158
❑ 98SpoIllEE-158
❑ 98SpoIllFE-158
❑ 98SPxFin-6
❑ 98SPxFinR-6
❑ 98SPxFinS-6
❑ 98StaCluBPP-BP4
❑ 98StaCluC-CS8
❑ 98StaCluC-CS10
❑ 98StaCluC-CS12
❑ 98StaCluFDI-227
❑ 98StaCluI-227
❑ 98StaCluITW-W8
❑ 98StaCluOneK-227
❑ 98StaCluPP-227
❑ 98StaCluRC-RC15
❑ 98Stu-145
❑ 98StuGPP-145
❑ 98StuSPP-145
❑ 98Top-411
❑ 98TopBabB-BB11
❑ 98TopChr-411
❑ 98TopChrBB-BB11
❑ 98TopChrBBR-BB11
❑ 98TopChrR-411
❑ 98TopChrRC-R5
❑ 98TopChrRCRef-R5
❑ 98TopDevR-411
❑ 98TopDia-411
❑ 98TopGolLabC1-86
❑ 98TopGolLabC1B-86
❑ 98TopGolLabC1One-86
❑ 98TopGolLabC1R-86
❑ 98TopGolLabC2-86
❑ 98TopGolLabC2B-86
❑ 98TopGolLabC2One-86
❑ 98TopGolLabC2R-86
❑ 98TopGolLabC3-86
❑ 98TopGolLabC3B-86
❑ 98TopGolLabC3One-86
❑ 98TopGolLabC3R-86
❑ 98TopMiniC-411
❑ 98TopRooCla-R5
❑ 98TopStaSB-S8
❑ 98TopStaSG-S8
❑ 98TopStaSGR-S8
❑ 98TopStaSS-S8
❑ 98TopTek-22
❑ 98TopTekD-22
❑ 98UD3-7
❑ 98UD3-97
❑ 98UD3-187
❑ 98UD3DieCut-7
❑ 98UD3DieCut-97
❑ 98UD3DieCut-187
❑ 98Ult-69
❑ 98UltBacttF-11
❑ 98UltGolM-69
❑ 98UltMas-69
❑ 98UltPlaM-69
❑ 98UppDec-254
❑ 98UppDecBCP-BC14
❑ 98UppDecDS-DS60
❑ 98UppDecR-115
❑ 98UppDecREP-3
❑ 98UppDecRNF-NF15
❑ 98UppDecSF-140
❑ 98Zen-79
❑ 98ZenZ-G-79
❑ 98ZenZ-S-79
❑ 99199Fin-162
❑ 99Bow-36
❑ 99BowBes-68
❑ 99BowBesAR-68
❑ 99BowBesR-68
❑ 99BowChr-36
❑ 99BowChrG-36
❑ 99BowChrGR-36
❑ 99BowChrI-36
❑ 99BowChrIR-36
❑ 99BowChrR-36
❑ 99BowGol-36
❑ 99BowInt-36
❑ 99CroRoyB-59
❑ 99CroRoyL-59
❑ 99CroRoyOD-59
❑ 99FinGolRef-162
❑ 99FinRef-162
❑ 99Fle-192
❑ 99FleSta9-192
❑ 99FleWarT-192
❑ 99KinDis-7
❑ 99Pac-179
❑ 99PacAur-76
❑ 99PacAurOD-76
❑ 99PacCroC-116
❑ 99PacCroCPB-116
❑ 99PacInv-61
❑ 99PacInvOD-61
❑ 99PacInvPB-61
❑ 99PacOme-100
❑ 99PacOmeC-100
❑ 99PacOmeG-100
❑ 99PacOmePB-100
❑ 99PacPar-97
❑ 99PacParC-97
❑ 99PacParG-97
❑ 99PacParHoloGold-97
❑ 99PacParHS-97
❑ 99PacParOD-97
❑ 99PacParPB-97
❑ 99PacParRed-97
❑ 99PacParTC-12
❑ 99PacPlaB-179
❑ 99PacPriS-108
❑ 99PacPriS206-108
❑ 99PacPriS206R-108
❑ 99PacRed-179
❑ 99PacTeaC-20
❑ 99Rev-58
❑ 99RevPremDate-58
❑ 99RevRet-58
❑ 99RevShaSS-58
❑ 99SkyMolM-7
❑ 99SkyMolMX-7
❑ 99SkyThu-103
❑ 99SkyThuRant-103
❑ 99SkyThuRave-103
❑ 99SP Aut-35
❑ 99SP SigAuto-MK
❑ 99SP SigAutoG-MK
❑ 99SPSig-71
❑ 99SPx-41
❑ 99SPxFinR-41
❑ 99SPxFinS-41
❑ 99StaClu-193
❑ 99StaCluFDI-193
❑ 99StaCluOoaK-193
❑ 99StaCluPP-193
❑ 99ThuSkySupR-103
❑ 99Top-91
❑ 99TopBlaLC1-59
❑ 99TopBlaLC2-59
❑ 99TopBlaLC3-59
❑ 99TopChr-91
❑ 99TopChrR-91
❑ 99TopGal-66
❑ 99TopGalPP-66
❑ 99TopGalPPI-66
❑ 99TopGolL-59
❑ 99TopGolLC1-59
❑ 99TopGolLC2-59
❑ 99TopGolLOtO-59
❑ 99TopMVPP-91
❑ 99TopOpeD-51
❑ 99TopRedLC1-59
❑ 99TopRedLC2-59
❑ 99TopRedLC3-59
❑ 99TopSta-60
❑ 99TopSta1Foil-60
❑ 99TopStaFoil-60
❑ 99TopStaOS-60
❑ 99UD Cho-88
❑ 99UD ChoP-88
❑ 99UD ChoPCR-88
❑ 99UDHolo-24
❑ 99UDHoloAUsome-24
❑ 99UppDec-379
❑ 99UppDecBD-34
❑ 99UppDecBDD-34
❑ 99UppDecBDQ-34
❑ 99UppDecBDT-34
❑ 99UppDecE-41
❑ 99UppDecEFXG-41
❑ 99UppDecEL1-379
❑ 99UppDecEL2-379
❑ 99UppDecM-86
❑ 99UppDecMGS-86
❑ 99UppDecMHFS-86
❑ 99UppDecMP-86
❑ 99UppDecMSS-86
❑ 99UppDecO-29
❑ 99UppDecOSO-29
❑ 99UppDecR-34
❑ 99UppDecRG-34
❑ 99UppDecRP-34
❑ 99Vic-156
Kouba, Curtis
❑ 82WauTimF-5
Koufax, Sandy
❑ 47Exh-124
❑ 55DodGolS-8
❑ 55Top-123
❑ 56Dod-15
❑ 56Top-79
❑ 57Top-302
❑ 58DodBelB-6
❑ 58DodTeal-12
❑ 58Top-187
❑ 59DodMor-5
❑ 59DodPos-6
❑ 59DodTeal-12
❑ 59Top-163
❑ 59TopVen-163
❑ 60DodBelB-9
❑ 60DodMor-6
❑ 60DodPos-6
❑ 60DodTeal-10
❑ 60DodUniO-10
❑ 60Top-343
❑ 61DodBelB-32
❑ 61DodMor-4
❑ 61DodUniO-11
❑ 61Top-49
❑ 61Top-207
❑ 61Top-344
❑ 62AurRec-9
❑ 62Baz-16
❑ 62DodBelB-32
❑ 62DodJayP-6
❑ 62DodVol-1
❑ 62ExhStaB-19
❑ 62Jel-109
❑ 62Pos-109A
❑ 62Pos-109B
❑ 62PosCan-109
❑ 62SalPlaC-109
❑ 62ShiPlaC-109
❑ 62Top-5
❑ 62Top-60
❑ 62TopBuc-45
❑ 62TopStal-136
❑ 62TopVen-5
❑ 62TopVen-60
❑ 63BasMagM-46
❑ 63DodJayP-8
❑ 63ExhStaB-36
❑ 63Fle-42
❑ 63Jel-121
❑ 63Pos-121
❑ 63SalMetC-4
❑ 63Top-5
❑ 63Top-9
❑ 63Top-210
❑ 63Top-412
❑ 63TopStil-23
❑ 64Baz-32
❑ 64DodHea-6
❑ 64Top-1
❑ 64Top-3
❑ 64Top-5
❑ 64Top-136
❑ 64Top-200
❑ 64TopCoi-106
❑ 64TopCoi-159
❑ 64TopGia-3
❑ 64TopSta-91
❑ 64TopStaU-40
❑ 64TopTatl-48
❑ 64TopVen-1
❑ 64TopVen-3
❑ 64TopVen-5
❑ 64TopVen-136
❑ 64TopVen-200
❑ 65Baz-32
❑ 65DodJayP-7
❑ 65DodTeal-10
❑ 65OPC-8
❑ 65Top-8
❑ 65Top-300
❑ 65TopEmbl-8
❑ 65TopTral-55
❑ 66Baz-1
❑ 66DodVolT-6
❑ 66OPC-100
❑ 66Top-100
❑ 66Top-221
❑ 66Top-223
❑ 66Top-225
❑ 66TopRubl-47
❑ 66TopVen-100
❑ 66TopVen-221
❑ 66TopVen-223
❑ 66TopVen-225
❑ 67Top-234
❑ 67Top-236
❑ 67Top-238
❑ 67TopTesF-10
❑ 67TopVen-162
❑ 68LauWorS-60
❑ 68LauWorS-62
❑ 72LauGreF-4
❑ 73HalofFPP-10
❑ 74NewYorNTDiS-5
❑ 75DodTCMA-7
❑ 75OPC-201
❑ 75TCMAllG-19
❑ 75Top-201
❑ 75TopMin-201
❑ 76JerJonPC-1
❑ 76LauDiaJ-4
❑ 76ShaPiz-131
❑ 76UPIS-6
❑ 77BobParHoF-95
❑ 77GalGloG-244
❑ 77Spo-2902
❑ 77Spo-6023
❑ 78DexHaloFP-29
❑ 78TCM60I-130
❑ 79Pew-8
❑ 79TCM50-49
❑ 80DodGreT-5
❑ 80PacLeg-10
❑ 80PerHaloFP-131
❑ 80PerHaloFPS-18
❑ 80SSPHOF-131
❑ 81AlbDukTc-23B
❑ 82BasCarN-17
❑ 82DavHaloFB-14
❑ 82DiaCla-60
❑ 82K-M-4
❑ 82TCMGreP-8
❑ 82TCMStaot5-2
❑ 83MLBPin-24
❑ 84OCoandSI-3
❑ 84OCoandSI-101
❑ 86SpoDesJM-17
❑ 86TCM-3
❑ 86TCMSupS-20
❑ 87DodSmoA-16
❑ 88DodSmo-4
❑ 88DodSmo-6
❑ 89DodSmoG-15
❑ 89HOFStiB-79
❑ 90DodTar-418
❑ 90HOFStiB-69
❑ 90OPC-665
❑ 90PerGreM-16
❑ 90Top-665
❑ 90TopTif-665
❑ 91DodUno7P-4
❑ 91DodUno7P-6
❑ 92DodStaTA-4
❑ 95TopArcBD-102
❑ 95TopArcBD-146
❑ 95TopArcBD-AU102
❑ 95TopArcBD-AU146
❑ 98DonSigSS-R3
Koukalik, Joe
❑ 90DodTar-1006
Kounas, Tony
❑ 88CapCodPPaLP-144
❑ 91PenPilC-14
❑ 91PenPilP-380
❑ 92SanBerC-8
❑ 92SanBerSF-958
❑ 93JacSunF-2715
❑ 94JacSunF-1414
❑ 95HarSenTI-20
Koupal, Lou
❑ 37Zee-78
❑ 90DodTar-1007
❑ 93ConTSN-713
Kovach, Ty
❑ 89WatIndS-13
❑ 90CarLeaA-34
❑ 90KinIndTI-4
❑ 91CanIndLD-85
❑ 91CanIndP-977
❑ 91Cla/Bes-309
❑ 91LinDriAA-85
❑ 92KinIndC-6
❑ 92KinIndF-2470
Kowalik, Fabian
❑ 35DiaMatCS3T1-93
❑ 36CubTeal-19
❑ 36OveCanR-28
Kowar, Frank
❑ 90St.CatBJP-3462
Kowitz, Brian
❑ 90ProAaA-192
❑ 90PulBraB-22
❑ 90PulBraP-3087
❑ 91Cla/Bes-66
❑ 91DurBulC-25
❑ 91DurBulP-1559
❑ 92DurBulF-1114
❑ 92GreBraS-237
❑ 93ClaGolF-90
❑ 93ExcFS7-4
❑ 93GreBraF-362
❑ 94RicBraF-2861
❑ 95RicBraRC-8
❑ 95RicBraTI-7
❑ 96SyrChiTI-19
❑ 96TolMudHB-15
Kown, John
❑ 97PriWilC-17
Koy, Ernest
❑ 37Zee-39
❑ 41DouPlaR-117
❑ 79DiaGre-161
❑ 90DodTar-419
❑ 92TexLon-28
Koza, Dave
❑ 77BriRedST-10
❑ 81PawRedST-16
❑ 83PawRedST-17
Kozar, Al
❑ 47SenGunBP-5
❑ 49Bow-16
❑ 49MPR302-2-xx
❑ 50Bow-15
❑ 85TCMPla1-32
Kozeniewski, Blaise
❑ 92OneYanC-21
❑ 93GreHorC-14
❑ 93GreHorF-894
❑ 93OneYanC-11
❑ 93OneYanF-3498
❑ 94GreBatF-468
❑ 95NorNagUTI-39

❑ 97GreBatC-11
Kozyrez, Alexander
❑ 89EasLeaDDP-DD18
Krablin, Justin
❑ 92GulCoaMF-3476
❑ 94KinMetC-7
❑ 94KinMetF-3817
Kracl, Darin
❑ 87BriYouC-10
❑ 89MedAthB-13
❑ 90CMC-867
❑ 90MadMusP-2262
❑ 90MidLeaASGS-55
❑ 91SouOreAAP-SOA6
Kraeger, Don
❑ 79AppFoxT-23
Kraemer, Joe
❑ 85MadMusP-17
❑ 85MadMusT-20
❑ 86ModA'sP-18
❑ 86PeoChiP-13
❑ 87HunStaTI-18
❑ 87IowCubTI-9
❑ 88IowCubC-7
❑ 88IowCubP-549
❑ 89IowCubC-3
❑ 89IowCubP-1715
❑ 90DonRoo-10
❑ 90FleUpd-8
❑ 90TopDeb89-68
❑ 90TopTVCu-10
❑ 90UppDec-740
❑ 91IowCubLD-207
❑ 91IowCubP-1054
❑ 91LinDriAAA-207
❑ 91Sco-755
❑ 92MidAngF-4023
❑ 92MidAngOHP-13
❑ 92MidAngS-463
❑ 92SkyAA F-197
Kraft, Bob
❑ 76SeaRaiC-8
Kraft, Clarence
❑ 80BraTCM1-10
Kraft, Ken
❑ 86ClePhiP-15
Kraft, Mike
❑ 89JohCitCS-15
❑ 90SprCarB-11
Krafve, Keith
❑ 86EveGiaC-24
❑ 86EveGiaPC-10
Krahenbuhl, Ken
❑ 90HunCubP-3278
❑ 91PeoChiC-26
❑ 91PeoChiTI-10
❑ 92PeoChiTI-10
❑ 92WinSpiC-15
Krajewski, Chris
❑ 80SanJosMJitB-13
Krakauskas, Joe
❑ 40PlaBal-188
❑ 41DouPlaR-77
❑ 47SigOil-10
❑ 91ConTSN-228
Kralick, Jack
❑ 61Top-36
❑ 61TwiCloD-11
❑ 61TwiJayP-6
❑ 61TwiPetM-6
❑ 61TwiUniMC-8
❑ 62Top-346
❑ 62TopStal-77
❑ 63Jel-11
❑ 63Pos-11
❑ 63Top-448
❑ 64IndJayP-8
❑ 64Kah-14
❑ 64Top-338
❑ 64TopVen-338
❑ 65Kah-20
❑ 65Top-535
❑ 65TopEmbl-72
❑ 66IndTeal-7
❑ 66OPC-129
❑ 66Top-129
❑ 66TopVen-129
❑ 67CokCapI-14
❑ 67Top-316
❑ 78TCM60I-134
❑ 78TwiFri-37
Krall, Eric
❑ 97GreBatB-16
❑ 98GreBatM-7
Kraly, Steve
❑ 54NewYorJA-47
❑ 55Top-139
Kramer, Jack (John)
❑ 41BroW75-18
❑ 41Gou-14
❑ 46SeaSLP-32
❑ 47TipTop-66
❑ 48RedSoxTI-14
❑ 49Bow-53
❑ 49RedSoxTI-13
❑ 50Bow-199
❑ 51Bow-200
❑ 52Whe-17A
❑ 52Whe-17B
❑ 75Gia195T-15
❑ 76TayBow4-32
❑ 79DiaGre-180
❑ 79TCM50-107
❑ 84TCMPla1-19
❑ 85TCMPla1-24
❑ 96Bro194F-14
Kramer, Jeff
❑ 94HelBreF-3611
❑ 94HelBreSP-24
❑ 95Exc-71
❑ 96El PasDB-14
Kramer, Mark
❑ 85BurRanT-18
❑ 86DayBealP-15
❑ 87PorChaRP-19
❑ 88ChaRanS-11
❑ 89MiaMirIS-9
Kramer, Matt
❑ 96YakBeaTI-24
Kramer, Randy
❑ 83BurRanF-5
❑ 83BurRanT-8
❑ 86KinEagP-13
❑ 86TulDriTI-23
❑ 87VanCanP-1613
❑ 88BlaYNPRWLU-39
❑ 88BufBisC-5
❑ 88BufBisP-1464
❑ 89BlaYNPRWL-158
❑ 89Don-480
❑ 89DonBasB-213
❑ 89DonRoo-48
❑ 89Fle-647
❑ 89FleGlo-647
❑ 89FleUpd-115
❑ 89PanSti-159
❑ 89ScoHot1R-57
❑ 89Top-522
❑ 89TopTif-522
❑ 90BufBisTI-12
❑ 90Don-409
❑ 90Fle-471
❑ 90FleCan-471
❑ 90Hot50RS-26
❑ 90OPC-126
❑ 90PanSti-327
❑ 90PirHomC-15
❑ 90Sco100RS-41
❑ 90Top-126
❑ 90TopTif-126
❑ 90UppDec-519
❑ 91LinDriAAA-432
❑ 91RicBraBC-8
❑ 91RicBraLD-432
❑ 91RicBraP-2561
❑ 91RicBraTI-17
❑ 92Bow-398
❑ 92CalCanS-62
❑ 92SkyAAAF-27
❑ 93EdmTraF-1132
❑ 98BelSnaM-27
Kramer, Scott
❑ 94WatIndC-18
❑ 94WatIndF-3932
Kramer, Tommy (Tom)
❑ 88MidLeaAGS-22
❑ 88WatIndP-689
❑ 89KinIndS-11
❑ 89Sta-76
❑ 90CarLeaA-38
❑ 90KinIndTI-2
❑ 91CanIndLD-86
❑ 91CanIndP-978
❑ 91LinDriAA-86
❑ 92ColSprSSF-748
❑ 92ColSprSSS-88
❑ 92SkyAAAF-38
❑ 92TopDeb91-105
❑ 93Bow-37
❑ 93FleFinE-202
❑ 93IndWUA-15
❑ 93Pin-585
❑ 93SelRoo-73T
❑ 94ChaKniF-890
❑ 94Don-384
❑ 94Fle-108
❑ 94Pac-172
❑ 94Sco-314
❑ 94ScoGolR-314
❑ 94Top-642
❑ 94TopGol-642
❑ 94TopSpa-642
❑ 94Ult-44
❑ 95ChaLooTI-11
❑ 96ColSprSSTI-22
❑ 97ColSprSTI-13
❑ 98ColSprSS-29
Kranepool, Ed
❑ 47Exh-125
❑ 47PM1StaP1-108
❑ 63Top-228
❑ 64Top-393
❑ 64Top-566
❑ 65MetJayP-9
❑ 65MetPos-6
❑ 65OPC-144
❑ 65Top-144
❑ 65TopEmbl-6
❑ 65TopTral-56
❑ 66Baz-9
❑ 66MetPos-3
❑ 66MetTeal-9
❑ 66MetVolC-7
❑ 66Top-212
❑ 66TopRubl-48
❑ 66TopVen-212
❑ 67AshOil-5
❑ 67CokCapYM-V21
❑ 67DexPre-119
❑ 67Kah-20A
❑ 67Kah-20B
❑ 67MetPos-4
❑ 67MetTeal-9
❑ 67OPC-186
❑ 67Top-186
❑ 67Top-452
❑ 67TopVen-282
❑ 68OPC-92
❑ 68Top-92
❑ 68TopActS-5C
❑ 68TopVen-92
❑ 69MetCit-5
❑ 69MetNewYDN-12
❑ 69MetTeal-11
❑ 69MetTealC-3
❑ 69MilBra-153
❑ 69MLBOffS-169
❑ 69Top-381
❑ 69TopSta-67
❑ 69TopTeaP-24
❑ 70Kel-1
❑ 70MetTealC-3
❑ 70MetTra-21A
❑ 70MLBOffS-80
❑ 70OPC-310
❑ 70Top-557
❑ 71MetTeal-12
❑ 71MLBOffS-158
❑ 71OPC-573
❑ 71Top-573
❑ 72MetTeal-12
❑ 72MilBra-188
❑ 72OPC-181
❑ 72OPC-182
❑ 72Top-181
❑ 72Top-182
❑ 73MetAllEB-7
❑ 73MetTeal-7
❑ 73OPC-329
❑ 73Top-329
❑ 74MetDaiPA-10
❑ 74MetJapEB-5
❑ 74MetTeal-11
❑ 74OPC-561
❑ 74Top-561
❑ 75MetSSP-10
❑ 75OPC-324
❑ 75Top-324
❑ 75TopMin-324
❑ 76MetMSAP-2
❑ 76OPC-314
❑ 76SSP-533
❑ 76Top-314
❑ 77BurCheD-136
❑ 77MetDaiPA-11
❑ 77OPC-60
❑ 77Top-201
❑ 78MetDaiPA-13
❑ 78OPC-205
❑ 78Top-49
❑ 78WifBalD-36
❑ 79OPC-265
❑ 79Top-505
❑ 80OPC-336
❑ 80Top-641
❑ 86MetGreT-1
❑ 87Met196T-1
❑ 89Met196C-9
❑ 89MetRinP69-17
❑ 89PacLegI-114
❑ 89SweBasG-28
❑ 90MetHaloF-6
❑ 91MetWIZ-220
❑ 92UppDecS-10
❑ 94Met69CCPP-22
❑ 94Met69CS-21
❑ 94Met69T-13
❑ 94Met69T-36
❑ 99SpollIGotG-55
❑ 99SpollIGotGA-42
Kranitz, Rick
❑ 80HolMilT-1
❑ 81ElPasDT-17
❑ 82VanCanT-19
❑ 86WinSpiP-11
❑ 87WytCubP-29
❑ 88PeoChiTI-19
❑ 89PeoChiTI-31
❑ 90ChaKniTI-25
❑ 91ChaKniLD-150
❑ 91ChaKniP-1705
❑ 91LinDriAA-150
❑ 92IowCubF-4066
❑ 92IowCubS-225
❑ 93OrlCubF-2802
Krapp, Gene
❑ 09ObaT21-120
❑ 10BisCoaLE99-14
❑ 13Zee-63
Krasovich, Anthony
❑ 29Zee-115
Kratochvil, Tim
❑ 96LowSpiB-14
❑ 97MicBatC-17
Krattli, Tom
❑ 77DayBealT-11
Kratz, Ron
❑ 92BatCliCB-15
❑ 92BatCliF-3273
Kraus, Jack
❑ 43PhiTeal-14
Kraus, Jake
❑ 97HelBreB-18
❑ 98BelSnaM-18
Kraus, Jeff
❑ 77SpaPhiT-18
❑ 80CarMudF-8
Kraus, Ralph
❑ 87PriWilYP-5
❑ 88Ft.LauYS-14
❑ 89Ft.LauYS-12
Kraus, Tim
❑ 96SouBenSHS-18
❑ 97HicCraRB-23
Krause, Andrew
❑ 85MadMusP-18
❑ 85MadMusT-21
Krause, Guy
❑ 75WesPalBES-28
❑ 75WesPalBES-29B
Krause, Harry
❑ 08AmeCarE91-50
❑ 09AmeCarE90-1-66
❑ 09PhiCarE-12
❑ 09SpoNewSM-27
❑ 09T206-196
❑ 09T206-197
❑ 10CouT21-164
❑ 10DomDisP-64
❑ 10E12AmeCDCE125-20
❑ 10LuxCigPP-13
❑ 10NadE1-27
❑ 10RedCroT-38
❑ 10RedCroT-127
❑ 10RedCroT-210
❑ 10SweCapPP-46
❑ 11A'sFirT20-8
❑ 11D35RocB-8
❑ 11HelSta-56
❑ 11PinT-5-513
❑ 11S74Sil-32
❑ 11SpoLifCW-208
❑ 11SpoLifM-95
❑ 11T205-92
❑ 11TurRedT-22
❑ 12HasTriFT-70D
❑ 12T207-95
❑ 13Zee-64
❑ 14Zee-65
❑ 15Zee-65
❑ 16Zee-57
❑ 17Zee-28
❑ 20WalMaiW-25
❑ 21Zee-31
❑ 23Zee-44
❑ 24Zee-30
❑ 25Zee-29
❑ 26Zee-78
❑ 27Zee-57
❑ 28ExhPCL-17
❑ 28Zee-82
❑ 29Zee-49
Krause, Kevin
❑ 94WilCubC-13
❑ 94WilCubF-3760
❑ 95RocCubTI-8
Krause, Ron
❑ 90RocExpLC-13
❑ 90RocExpP-2700
❑ 91WesPalBEC-21
❑ 92WesPalBEC-2
❑ 92WesPalBEF-2095
❑ 93HarSenF-275
Krause, Scott
❑ 95BelBreTI-17
❑ 96El PasDB-15
❑ 96StoPorB-9
❑ 97El PasDB-6
❑ 97TexLeaTP-5
❑ 98Bes-73
❑ 98LouRedQ-13
❑ 99BasAmeTP-58
❑ 99BasAmeTPG-58
Krause, Tom
❑ 87SalSpuS-21
Krauss, Ron
❑ 82ChaRoyT-15
Krauss, Timothy
❑ 81RedPioT-17
❑ 82HolMilT-17
❑ 84EdmTraC-98
❑ 85DomLeaS-92
❑ 85EdmTraC-17
❑ 86BufBisP-14
❑ 87HawIsIP-23
Krausse, Lew
❑ 63Top-104
❑ 64Top-334
❑ 64TopVen-334
❑ 65Top-462
❑ 66Top-256
❑ 66TopVen-256
❑ 67CokCapAt-16
❑ 67DexPre-120
❑ 67Top-565
❑ 67TopVen-205
❑ 68Top-458
❑ 69MilBra-154
❑ 69OPC-23
❑ 69Top-23
❑ 69TopSta-217
❑ 70BreMcD-14
❑ 70BreMil-11
❑ 70BreTeal-6
❑ 70OPC-233
❑ 70SunPin-12
❑ 70Top-233
❑ 71BreTeal-6
❑ 71MLBOffS-441
❑ 71OPC-372
❑ 71Top-372
❑ 71TopCoi-20
❑ 72RedSoxTI-11
❑ 72Top-592
❑ 73OPC-566
❑ 73Top-566
❑ 75OPC-603
❑ 75Top-603
❑ 75TopMin-603
❑ 75TucTorC-13
❑ 75TucTorTI-7
❑ 94BreMilB-235
Krausse, Lew Sr.
❑ 74A's192T-5
Krauza, Ron
❑ 89BufBisC-19
Kravec, Ken
❑ 77Top-389
❑ 77WhiSoxJT-8
❑ 77WhiSoxT-15
❑ 78Top-439
❑ 79OPC-141
❑ 79Top-283
❑ 80OPC-299
❑ 80Top-575
❑ 81Top-67
❑ 81TopTra-783
❑ 82CubRedL-37
❑ 82Don-378
❑ 82IowCubT-19
❑ 82Top-639
❑ 87Ft.MyeRP-28
❑ 88MemChiB-14
❑ 89PacSenL-151
❑ 91PacSenL-10
Kravitz, Dan
❑ 56PirTeal-13
❑ 57JetPos-10
❑ 57PirTeal-3
❑ 57Top-267
❑ 58Top-444
❑ 59Top-536
❑ 60Top-238
❑ 61Top-166
❑ 77PirTCM1WC-36
Krawczyk, Ray
❑ 82AleDukT-4
❑ 84HawIsIC-129
❑ 85DomLeaS-60
❑ 85HawIsIC-245
❑ 86HawIsIP-14
❑ 87HawIsIP-17
❑ 88BlaYNPRWL-120
❑ 89BlaYNPRWL-127
❑ 89DenZepC-7
❑ 89DenZepP-32
❑ 94BreMilB-236
Krebs, Dave
❑ 87SavCarP-3
❑ 88SavCarP-338
Kreevich, Mike
❑ 36R31PasP-38
❑ 36SandSW-39
❑ 38CloFotW-44
❑ 38ExhFou-10
❑ 39ExhSal-34
❑ 39GouPreR303A-29
❑ 39GouPreR303B-17
❑ 39WhiSoxTI-9
❑ 39WorWidGTP-29
❑ 40WhiSoxL-10
❑ 42A'sTeal-20
❑ 83TCMPla1944-3
❑ 93DiaStaES-140
❑ 96Bro194F-30
Kreitz, Ralph
❑ 12HomRunKE-50
❑ 12Zee-84
❑ 13Zee-141
Kremblas, Frank
❑ 90CedRapRP-2324
❑ 91ChaLooLD-160
❑ 91ChaLooP-1966
❑ 91LinDriAA-160
❑ 92ChaLooF-3828
❑ 92ChaLooS-188
❑ 93IndIndF-1497
❑ 94ChaLooF-1364
Kremblas, Kris
❑ 95IndIndF-110
Kremer, Ken
❑ 89BelBre2S-18
❑ 89BelBreIS-12
Kremer, Ray (Remy)
❑ 14Zee-86
❑ 18Zee-25
❑ 19Zee-21
❑ 19Zee-99
❑ 20WalMaiW-26
❑ 20Zee-26
❑ 21Zee-32
❑ 22Zee-32
❑ 23Zee-45
❑ 25Exh-53
❑ 26Exh-53
❑ 27Exh-26
❑ 28Exh-25
❑ 28W56PlaC-C9
❑ 29ExhFou-14
❑ 31Exh-14
❑ 33ButCre-15
❑ 33Gou-54
❑ 34GouCanV-38
❑ 85BigLeaC3-10
❑ 91ConTSN-279

Kremers, Jimmy
❑ 89BlaYNPRWLU-35
❑ 89GreBraB-24
❑ 89GreBraP-1163
❑ 89GreBraS-12
❑ 89SouLeaAJ-8
❑ 90BraDubS-17
❑ 90CMC-286
❑ 90FleUpd-4
❑ 90ProAAAF-406
❑ 90RicBraBC-12
❑ 90RicBraC-10
❑ 90RicBraP-261
❑ 90RicBraTI-17
❑ 91Don-739
❑ 91Fle-694
❑ 91IndIndLD-187
❑ 91IndIndP-464
❑ 91LinDriAAA-187
❑ 91Sco-736
❑ 91TopDeb90-79
❑ 91UppDec-262
❑ 92IndIndF-1862
❑ 92IndIndS-185
❑ 92SkyAAAF-91
❑ 94NewOrlZF-1472
❑ 94VenLinU-268
❑ 95PorSeaDTI-9
Kremmel, Jim
❑ 93RanKee-221
Kremmeyer, Charles
❑ 87OldJudN-286
Krenchicki, Wayne
❑ 78RocRedWT-11
❑ 80RocRedWT-16
❑ 80Top-661
❑ 81BalOriP-8
❑ 82Fle-168
❑ 82RedCok-12
❑ 82Top-107
❑ 82TopTra-58T
❑ 83Don-314
❑ 83Fle-594
❑ 83FleSti-220
❑ 83Top-374
❑ 84Don-334
❑ 84Fle-83
❑ 84FleUpd-65
❑ 84Nes792-223
❑ 84RedEnq-8
❑ 84Top-223
❑ 84TopTif-223
❑ 84TopTra-65T
❑ 84TopTraT-65T
❑ 84WicAerRD-7
❑ 85Don-140
❑ 85Fle-539
❑ 85RedYea-8
❑ 85Top-468
❑ 85TopTif-468
❑ 86Don-140
❑ 86ExpPos-6
❑ 86ExpProPa-20
❑ 86Fle-180
❑ 86FleUpd-60
❑ 86OPC-81
❑ 86Top-777
❑ 86TopTif-777
❑ 86TopTra-55T
❑ 86TopTraT-55T
❑ 87Don-406
❑ 87Fle-322
❑ 87FleGlo-322
❑ 87OPC-81
❑ 87TacTigP-6
❑ 87Top-774
❑ 87TopTif-774
❑ 88LouRedBTI-25
❑ 88TacTigC-14
❑ 88TacTigP-635
❑ 89PacSenL-157
❑ 89TopSenL-75
❑ 90EliSenL-38
❑ 91OriCro-248
❑ 91PacSenL-42
❑ 92BelBreCB-28
❑ 92BelBreFI-422
❑ 93BelBreCB-26
❑ 93BelBreFI-1726
❑ 94BelBreC-27
❑ 94BelBreFI-118
Krenke, Keith
❑ 92BenRocCB-17
❑ 92BenRocF-1487
❑ 92Min-9
❑ 93CenValRC-16
❑ 93CenValRF-2905
Krepfle, Keith
❑ 80PhiBul-12
Kress, Chuck (Charlie)
❑ 54Top-219
❑ 90DodTar-420
❑ 94TopArc1-219
❑ 94TopArc1G-219
Kress, Red (Ralph)
❑ 29ExhFou-29
❑ 29PorandAR-54
❑ 31Exh-30
❑ 33Gou-33
❑ 33GouCanV-33
❑ 34BatR31-169
❑ 35AlDemDCR3-20
❑ 35DiaMatCS3T1-94
❑ 35GouPuzR-4C
❑ 35GouPuzR-7C
❑ 35GouPuzR-12C
❑ 38BasTabP-19
❑ 38CloFotW-45
❑ 39PlaBal-115
❑ 39TigSpo-5
❑ 40PlaBal-45
❑ 54Top-160
❑ 55IndGolS-29
❑ 55Top-151
❑ 58IndTeal-11
❑ 60Top-460
❑ 82MetGal62-30
❑ 85BigLeaC3-75
❑ 92ConTSN-383
❑ 94TopArc1-160
❑ 94TopArc1G-160
Kretlow, Lou
❑ 52Bow-221
❑ 52Top-42
❑ 53BowC-50
❑ 54Bow-197
❑ 54OriEss-19
❑ 54OriTeal-11
❑ 55Bow-108
❑ 55OriEss-12
❑ 55SeaPop-13
❑ 56A'sPos-30
❑ 57Top-139
❑ 83TopRep5-42
❑ 91OriCro-249
❑ 97BalOriP-25
Kreuter, Chad
❑ 86SalRedBP-16
❑ 87PorChaRP-25
❑ 88TexLeaAGS-3
❑ 88TulDriTI-19
❑ 89ClaLigB-27
❑ 89Don-579
❑ 89Fle-526
❑ 89FleGlo-526
❑ 89PanSti-444
❑ 89RanSmo-17
❑ 89Sco-638
❑ 89ScoHot1R-51
❑ 89ScoYouS2-40
❑ 89Spo-43
❑ 89Top-432
❑ 89TopTif-432
❑ 89UppDec-312
❑ 90Don-520
❑ 90Fle-303
❑ 90FleCan-303
❑ 90OPC-562
❑ 90PubIntS-414
❑ 90Sco-406
❑ 90Sco100RS-51
❑ 90Top-562
❑ 90TopTif-562
❑ 90TulDriDGB-23
❑ 90UppDec-609
❑ 92Bow-515
❑ 92Lea-496
❑ 92LeaBlaG-496
❑ 92TigKro-15
❑ 92Ult-365
❑ 93Don-673
❑ 93Fla-205
❑ 93Fle-607
❑ 93Lea-463
❑ 93PacSpa-444
❑ 93RanKee-222
❑ 93TigGat-16
❑ 93Top-692
❑ 93TopGol-692
❑ 93TopInaM-692
❑ 93TopInaR-692
❑ 93TopMic-692
❑ 93Ult-201
❑ 94Bow-13
❑ 94ColC-167
❑ 94ColChoGS-167
❑ 94ColChoSS-167
❑ 94Don-224
❑ 94Fin-388
❑ 94FinRef-388
❑ 94Fle-137
❑ 94Lea-5
❑ 94Pac-223
❑ 94Pin-125
❑ 94PinArtP-125
❑ 94PinMusC-125
❑ 94Sco-503
❑ 94ScoGolR-503
❑ 94Sel-327
❑ 94StaClu-411
❑ 94StaCluFDI-411
❑ 94StaCluGR-411
❑ 94StaCluMOP-411
❑ 94Top-257
❑ 94TopGol-257
❑ 94TopSpa-257
❑ 94Ult-56
❑ 94UppDec-392
❑ 94UppDecED-392
❑ 95Don-219
❑ 95DonPreP-219
❑ 95Fle-57
❑ 95FleUpd-75
❑ 95MarMot-18
❑ 95Pac-156
❑ 95Sco-504
❑ 95ScoGolR-504
❑ 95ScoPlaTS-504
❑ 95Top-362
❑ 95Ult-48
❑ 95UltGolM-48
❑ 96LeaSigEA-104
❑ 97AngMot-18
❑ 98PacInvGems-6
❑ 98PacOnl-173
❑ 98PacOnlR-173
❑ 98PacOnlWC-173
❑ 99UppDec-394
❑ 99UppDecEL1-394
❑ 99UppDecEL2-394
❑ 99Vic-189
Kreutzer, Frank
❑ 63WhiSoxTS-14
❑ 64Top-107
❑ 64TopVen-107
❑ 65Top-371
❑ 66Top-211
❑ 66TopVen-211
❑ 78TCM60I-116
Krevokuch, Krev (James)
❑ 91WelPirC-8
❑ 91WelPirP-3579
❑ 92AugPirC-3
❑ 92AugPirF-246
❑ 93CarMudF-2062
❑ 93CarMudTI-18
❑ 94CarMudF-1586
❑ 95CarMudF-166
Krichell, Paul
❑ 07NewEveWS-5
❑ 09ColChiE-153
❑ 12ColRedB-159
❑ 12ColTinT-159
Krieg, William
❑ 87OldJudN-287
❑ 87OldJudN-288
Kries, John
❑ 89SalDodTI-14
Kringen, Jake
❑ 97PorRocG-14
❑ 98AshTouM-10
Kripner, Mike
❑ 80CedRapRT-23
❑ 82WatRedT-12
Krippner, Curt
❑ 88BelBreGS-16
❑ 89BelBre2S-19
❑ 90StoPorCLC-185
❑ 90StoPorP-2184
❑ 91Cla/Bes-403
❑ 91EriSaiP-4063
Krislock, Zak
❑ 92AubAstC-24
❑ 92AubAstF-1351
❑ 93AshTouC-10
❑ 93AshTouF-2271
Krist, Howie
❑ 41CarW75-12
❑ 46SeaSLP-33
❑ 79DiaGre-165
❑ 83Car194T-42
Kristan, Kevin
❑ 85LasVegSC-124
❑ 87WesPalBEP-673
Kritscher, Ryan
❑ 96JohCitCTI-18
Krivda, Rick
❑ 91BluOriC-18
❑ 91BluOriP-4123
❑ 92KanCouCC-14
❑ 92KanCouCF-87
❑ 92KanCouCTI-18
❑ 92MidLeaATI-26
❑ 92ProFS7-13
❑ 93ClaFS7-53
❑ 93ExcFS7-124
❑ 94ActPac-44
❑ 94Bow-159
❑ 94ExcFS7-9
❑ 94ExcLeaLF-12
❑ 94OriPro-50
❑ 94RocRedWF-993
❑ 94RocRedWTI-9
❑ 94TriAAF-AAA13
❑ 94Ult-306
❑ 94UppDecML-226
❑ 95BalOriP-28
❑ 95Fle-10
❑ 95RocRedWTI-21
❑ 96BalOriP-18
❑ 96ColCho-11
❑ 96ColChoGS-11
❑ 96ColChoSS-11
❑ 96Don-262
❑ 96DonPreP-262
❑ 96Fle-13
❑ 96FleTif-13
❑ 96OriFle-9
❑ 96StaClu-294
❑ 96StaCluMOP-294
❑ 96Top-352
❑ 96TopChr-142
❑ 96TopChrR-142
❑ 96UppDec-16
❑ 97ColCho-44
❑ 97RocRedW-15
❑ 97Top-323
Krizmanich, Mike
❑ 75IntLeaAT-3
❑ 75IntLeaAT-23
Kroc, Ray
❑ 77PadSchC-35
❑ 78PadFamF-17
❑ 91FouBal-23
Krock, August
❑ 87OldJudN-289
❑ 88AugBecN-21
❑ 88GandBCGCE-24
Kroener, Chris
❑ 86VisOakP-12
Kroh, Rube (Floyd)
❑ 09BriE97-18
❑ 09ColChiE-160
❑ 09T206-198
❑ 10SweCapPP-83
❑ 11SpoLifM-173
❑ 11T205-93
❑ 12ColRedB-160
❑ 12ColTinT-160
Krokroskia, Sean
❑ 90BenBucL-3
Krol, David
❑ 88CapCodPPaLP-180
Krol, Jack
❑ 76ArkTraT-4
❑ 77Car5-13
❑ 77CarTeal-13
❑ 78CarTeal-13
❑ 79Car5-14
❑ 81PadFamF-11
❑ 83PadTeal-12
❑ 84PadMot-27
❑ 84PadSmo-15
❑ 85PadMot-27
❑ 87LasVegSP-3
❑ 88ChaRaiP-1219
❑ 89ChaRaiP-991
❑ 90ChaRaiB-26
❑ 90ChaRaiP-2054
❑ 92LouRedF-1902
❑ 92LouRedS-274
Kroll, Gary
❑ 65Top-449
❑ 66Top-548
❑ 66TopRubI-49
❑ 78TCM60I-27B
❑ 78TCM60I-127
❑ 91MetWIZ-221
Kroll, Todd
❑ 87BakDodP-8
❑ 88BakDodCLC-255
Kromy, Ted
❑ 79WisRapTT-19
❑ 82OrlTwi8SCT-19
❑ 82OrlTwiT-19
❑ 83OrlTwiT-17
Kroon, Marc
❑ 92KinMetC-18
❑ 92KinMetF-1527
❑ 92StaCluD-99
❑ 93CapCitBC-10
❑ 93CapCitBF-456
❑ 94RanCucQC-18
❑ 94RanCucQF-1635
❑ 95Bow-207
❑ 95BowBes-B17
❑ 95BowBesR-B17
❑ 95MemChiTI-16
❑ 96BesAutS-46
❑ 96ColCho-699
❑ 96ColChoGS-29
❑ 96ColChoGS-699
❑ 96ColChoSS-29
❑ 96ColChoSS-699
❑ 96Fle-572
❑ 96FleTif-572
❑ 96MemChiB-20
❑ 96Sco-238
❑ 96Sco-498
❑ 96Top-433
❑ 97Bow-402
❑ 97BowCerBlaIA-CA46
❑ 97BowCerBluIA-CA46
❑ 97BowCerGolIA-CA46
❑ 97BowInt-402
❑ 97LasVegS1A-20
❑ 98Bow-202
❑ 98BowCerBlueAU-52
❑ 98BowCerGA-52
❑ 98BowCerSA-52
❑ 98BowChr-202
❑ 98BowChrGA-202
❑ 98BowChrGAR-202
❑ 98BowChrI-202
❑ 98BowChrIR-202
❑ 98BowChrR-202
❑ 98BowGolA-202
❑ 98BowInt-202
❑ 98IndIndQ-12
Kropke, Keri
❑ 95ColSilB-16
Krsnich, Joe
❑ 77BriRedST-11
Krsnich, Mike
❑ 62Top-289
Krsnich, Rocky (Rocco)
❑ 53Top-229
❑ 55SeaPop-14
❑ 91TopArc1-229
Krueger, Arthur T.
❑ 09ObaT21-293
❑ 09T206-435
❑ 10JuJuDE-23
❑ 11PinT-5-1068
❑ 11SpoLifCW-209
❑ 11SpoLifM-284
❑ 11Zee-49
❑ 12HomRunKE-41
❑ 12ObaPreT-42
❑ 12Zee-66
❑ 13Zee-65
Krueger, Bill
❑ 82WesHavAT-7
❑ 84Fle-450
❑ 84Nes792-178
❑ 84OPC-178
❑ 84TacTigC-84
❑ 84Top-178
❑ 84TopTif-178
❑ 85A'sMot-21
❑ 85Don-467
❑ 85Fle-428
❑ 85Top-528
❑ 85TopTif-528
❑ 86A'sMot-21
❑ 86Don-298
❑ 86Fle-424
❑ 86Top-58
❑ 86TopTif-58
❑ 87Top-238
❑ 87TopTif-238
❑ 88AlbDukCm-3
❑ 88AlbDukP-271
❑ 88TriAAC-42
❑ 90BreMilB-13
❑ 90BrePol-47
❑ 90DodTar-421
❑ 90Fle-328
❑ 90FleCan-328
❑ 90Lea-421
❑ 90OPC-518
❑ 90Sco-366
❑ 90Top-518
❑ 90TopTif-518
❑ 91Bow-248
❑ 91Don-647
❑ 91Fle-588
❑ 91FleUpd-54
❑ 91OPC-417
❑ 91Sco-598
❑ 91Top-417
❑ 91TopDesS-417
❑ 91TopMic-417
❑ 91TopTif-417
❑ 91TopTra-70T
❑ 91TopTraT-70T
❑ 91UltUpd-52
❑ 91UppDecFE-60F
❑ 92Don-672
❑ 92DonUpd-U16
❑ 92Fle-285
❑ 92Lea-477
❑ 92LeaBlaG-477
❑ 92OPC-368
❑ 92Pin-501
❑ 92Sco-253
❑ 92StaClu-861
❑ 92Top-368
❑ 92TopGol-368
❑ 92TopGolW-368
❑ 92TopMic-368
❑ 92TopTra-61T
❑ 92TopTraG-61T
❑ 92Ult-397
❑ 92UppDec-403
❑ 92UppDec-781
❑ 93Don-352
❑ 93FleFinE-211
❑ 93Lea-348
❑ 93OPCPre-38
❑ 93PacSpa-445
❑ 93Pin-547
❑ 93TigGat-17
❑ 93Ult-552
❑ 93UppDec-530
❑ 93UppDecGold-530
❑ 94BreMilB-237
❑ 94Don-252
❑ 94Fle-138
❑ 94Pac-222
❑ 94Top-552
❑ 94TopGol-552
❑ 94TopSpa-552
Krueger, Ernie
❑ 90DodTar-422
Krueger, Kirby
❑ 81WisRapTT-6
❑ 83OrlTwiT-18
Krueger, Rick
❑ 79TCMJapPB-58
Krueger, Robert
❑ 94AppFoxC-13
❑ 94AppFoxFI-1050
Krueger, Steve
❑ 81LynSaiT-7
❑ 82LynSaiT-5
Krug, Chris (Everett B.)
❑ 66CubTeal-9
❑ 66OPC-166
❑ 66Top-166
❑ 66TopVen-166
❑ 67SeaPop-10
Krug, Dustin
❑ 98WilCubM-17
Krug, Martin
❑ 20Zee-85
❑ 21Zee-54
❑ 22E120-162
❑ 23Zee-12
❑ 24Zee-12
❑ 25Zee-8
❑ 26Zee-30
❑ 27Zee-16

❑ 28Zee-35
❑ 29Zee-5
❑ 29Zee-24

Kruger, Andy
❑ 94BriTigC-17
❑ 94BriTigF-3519

Kruk, John
❑ 83BeaGolGT-11
❑ 84LasVegSC-228
❑ 84LasVegSC-250
❑ 85LasVegSC-103
❑ 86DonRoo-42
❑ 86FleUpd-61
❑ 86SpoRoo-1
❑ 86TopTra-56T
❑ 86TopTraT-56T
❑ 87Don-328
❑ 87Fle-420
❑ 87FleGlo-420
❑ 87Lea-217
❑ 87PadBohHB-8
❑ 87Spo-61
❑ 87SpoTeaP-16
❑ 87StuPan-12
❑ 87Top-123
❑ 87TopSti-113
❑ 87TopTif-123
❑ 87ToyRoo-17
❑ 88ClaBlu-203
❑ 88ClaRed-162
❑ 88Don-205
❑ 88DonBasB-245
❑ 88Fle-589
❑ 88FleGlo-589
❑ 88FleMin-113
❑ 88FleStiC-124
❑ 88FleSup-20
❑ 88Lea-176
❑ 88OPC-32
❑ 88OPCBoxB-G
❑ 88PadCok-8
❑ 88PadSmo-14
❑ 88PanSti-326
❑ 88PanSti-403
❑ 88RedFolSB-44
❑ 88Sco-36
❑ 88ScoGlo-36
❑ 88ScoYouSI-17
❑ 88Spo-64
❑ 88StaLinPa-7
❑ 88Top-596
❑ 88TopBig-60
❑ 88TopCoi-45
❑ 88TopMinL-75
❑ 88TopSti-110
❑ 88TopTif-596
❑ 88TopUKM-41
❑ 88TopUKMT-41
❑ 88TopWaxBC-G
❑ 89Bow-460
❑ 89BowTif-460
❑ 89Don-86
❑ 89DonBasB-240
❑ 89Fle-309
❑ 89FleGlo-309
❑ 89FleUpd-109
❑ 89OPC-235
❑ 89PadMag-5
❑ 89PanSti-200
❑ 89PhiTas-42
❑ 89RedFolSB-69
❑ 89Sco-148
❑ 89ScoRoo-70T
❑ 89Spo-184
❑ 89Top-235
❑ 89TopBasT-145
❑ 89TopBig-216
❑ 89TopSti-102
❑ 89TopTif-235
❑ 89TopTra-63T
❑ 89TopTraT-63T
❑ 89TVSpoM-48
❑ 89UppDec-280
❑ 90Bow-154
❑ 90BowTif-154
❑ 90ClaYel-T3
❑ 90Don-160
❑ 90DonBesN-69
❑ 90Fle-565
❑ 90FleCan-565
❑ 90Lea-284
❑ 90OPC-469
❑ 90PanSti-310
❑ 90PhiTas-18
❑ 90PubIntS-52
❑ 90Sco-467
❑ 90Spo-124
❑ 90Top-469
❑ 90TopBig-214
❑ 90TopMag-96
❑ 90TopSti-117
❑ 90TopTif-469
❑ 90UppDec-668
❑ 91Bow-503
❑ 91Cla3-T47
❑ 91Don-260
❑ 91Fle-402
❑ 91Lea-278
❑ 91OPC-689
❑ 91PanSti-107
❑ 91PhiMed-22
❑ 91Sco-94
❑ 91SimandSMLBL-23
❑ 91StaClu-227
❑ 91Top-689
❑ 91TopDesS-689
❑ 91TopMic-689
❑ 91TopTif-689
❑ 91TopTriH-N8
❑ 91Ult-266
❑ 91UppDec-199
❑ 91USPlaCA-4S
❑ 92Bow-541
❑ 92Don-230
❑ 92DonDiaK-DK12
❑ 92DonSupD-DK12
❑ 92Fle-537
❑ 92Hig5-78
❑ 92Lea-313
❑ 92LeaBlaG-313
❑ 92LeaGolP-8
❑ 92LeaPre-8
❑ 92OPC-30
❑ 92OPCPre-134
❑ 92PanSti-242
❑ 92PhiMed-17
❑ 92Pin-147
❑ 92Sco-235
❑ 92SpollIFK1-196
❑ 92StaClu-209
❑ 92StaCluD-100
❑ 92Stu-76
❑ 92StuPre-4
❑ 92Top-30
❑ 92TopGol-30
❑ 92TopGolW-30
❑ 92TopKid-18
❑ 92TopMic-30
❑ 92TriPla-38
❑ 92Ult-246
❑ 92UppDec-38
❑ 92UppDec-326
❑ 92UppDecHRH-HR23
❑ 92UppDecTMH-28
❑ 93Bow-540
❑ 93ClaGam-50
❑ 93ColAllG-4
❑ 93DiaMar-62
❑ 93Don-436
❑ 93DurPowP2-3
❑ 93Fin-38
❑ 93FinRef-38
❑ 93Fla-105
❑ 93Fle-104
❑ 93FleAtl-12
❑ 93FleFruotL-33
❑ 93FleTeaL-NL8
❑ 93FunPac-146
❑ 93Hos-4
❑ 93Lea-366
❑ 93LeaGolA-U3
❑ 93OPC-216
❑ 93OPCPre-76
❑ 93PacJugC-30
❑ 93PacSpa-238
❑ 93PanSti-270
❑ 93PhiMed-21
❑ 93PhiStaC-30
❑ 93Pin-8
❑ 93PinSlu-17
❑ 93Pos-29
❑ 93RedFolS-52
❑ 93RedFolS-118
❑ 93Sco-79
❑ 93Sel-33
❑ 93SelStaL-6
❑ 93SelStaL-53
❑ 93SP-14
❑ 93StaClu-83
❑ 93StaCluFDI-83
❑ 93StaCluM-84
❑ 93StaCluMOP-83
❑ 93Stu-183
❑ 93StuHer-12
❑ 93StuSil-7
❑ 93Top-340
❑ 93TopFulS-16
❑ 93TopGol-340
❑ 93TopInaM-340
❑ 93TopInaR-340
❑ 93TopMic-340
❑ 93TriPla-139
❑ 93Ult-90
❑ 93UppDec-247
❑ 93UppDec-485
❑ 93UppDecGold-247
❑ 93UppDecGold-485
❑ 93USPlaCA-10D
❑ 94Bow-412
❑ 94ColC-168
❑ 94ColC-326
❑ 94ColChoGS-168
❑ 94ColChoGS-326
❑ 94ColChoSS-168
❑ 94ColChoSS-326
❑ 94Don-7
❑ 94DonDiaK-DK9
❑ 94DonDiaKJ-DK9
❑ 94DonDom-B10
❑ 94DonDomJ-B10
❑ 94DonEli-41
❑ 94DonSpeE-7
❑ 94Fin-416
❑ 94FinRef-416
❑ 94Fla-415
❑ 94Fle-594
❑ 94FleAllS-44
❑ 94FleExtB-340
❑ 94FleSun-15
❑ 94FUnPac-120
❑ 94FUnPac-214
❑ 94FUnPac-230
❑ 94Lea-347
❑ 94LeaGam-11
❑ 94LeaL-138
❑ 94OPC-257
❑ 94OscMayR-25
❑ 94Pac-479
❑ 94PacSilP-32
❑ 94PacSilPC-32
❑ 94PanSti-229
❑ 94PhiMed-19
❑ 94PhiMel-14
❑ 94PhiUSPC-7D
❑ 94PhiUSPC-13C
❑ 94Pin-63
❑ 94PinArtP-63
❑ 94PinMusC-63
❑ 94PinRunC-RC25
❑ 94ProMag-104
❑ 94RedFolMI-13
❑ 94Sco-28
❑ 94ScoGolR-28
❑ 94ScoGolS-7
❑ 94Sel-24
❑ 94SelSam-24
❑ 94SP-138
❑ 94SPDieC-138
❑ 94SPHol-22
❑ 94SPHolDC-22
❑ 94Spo-101
❑ 94StaClu-361
❑ 94StaClu-533
❑ 94StaCluDD-DD3
❑ 94StaCluFDI-361
❑ 94StaCluFDI-533
❑ 94StaCluGR-361
❑ 94StaCluGR-533
❑ 94StaCluMO-3
❑ 94StaCluMOP-361
❑ 94StaCluMOP-533
❑ 94StaCluMOP-DD3
❑ 94StaCluT-226
❑ 94StaCluTFDI-226
❑ 94Stu-142
❑ 94TomPiz-12
❑ 94Top-401
❑ 94TopBlaG-37
❑ 94TopGol-401
❑ 94TopSpa-401
❑ 94TriPla-177
❑ 94Ult-249
❑ 94Ult-P249
❑ 94UltPhiF-6
❑ 94UltPhiF-7
❑ 94UltPhiF-8
❑ 94UltPhiF-9
❑ 94UltPhiF-10
❑ 94UltPhiF-16
❑ 94UltPhiF-17
❑ 94UltPhiF-18
❑ 94UltPhiF-19
❑ 94UltPhiF-20
❑ 94UltPhiF-M2
❑ 94UltPhiF-M4
❑ 94UltPhiF-AU2
❑ 94UppDec-276
❑ 94UppDec-410
❑ 94UppDecAJ-7
❑ 94UppDecAJG-7
❑ 94UppDecED-276
❑ 94UppDecED-410
❑ 94USPlaCA-2D
❑ 95ColCho-373
❑ 95ColCho-584T
❑ 95ColChoGS-373
❑ 95ColChoSS-373
❑ 95Don-61
❑ 95DonPreP-61
❑ 95Fin-132
❑ 95Fin-319
❑ 95FinRef-132
❑ 95FinRef-319
❑ 95Fle-398
❑ 95Lea300C-14
❑ 95Pac-331
❑ 95Pin-395
❑ 95PinArtP-395
❑ 95PinMusC-395
❑ 95RedFol-29
❑ 95ScoHaloG-HG76
❑ 95ScoHaloGYTE-HG76T
❑ 95StaClu-331
❑ 95StaCluMOP-331
❑ 95StaCluSTWS-331
❑ 95StaCluVR-171
❑ 95StaCluVRMO-171
❑ 95Top-572
❑ 95TopCyb-346
❑ 95TopTra-116T
❑ 95Ult-421
❑ 95UltGolM-421
❑ 95UppDec-145
❑ 95UppDecED-145
❑ 95UppDecEDG-145
❑ 95WhiSoxK-17
❑ 96ColCho-98
❑ 96ColChoGS-98
❑ 96ColChoSS-98

Krukow, Mike
❑ 76CubTri-13
❑ 77CubJewT-8
❑ 77Top-493
❑ 78SSP270-267
❑ 78Top-17
❑ 79Top-592
❑ 80OPC-223
❑ 80Top-431
❑ 81CokTeaS-18
❑ 81Fle-312
❑ 81OPC-176
❑ 81Top-176
❑ 81TopSupHT-27
❑ 82Don-351
❑ 82Fle-598
❑ 82FleSta-92
❑ 82OPC-215
❑ 82Top-215
❑ 82TopSti-31
❑ 82TopTra-59T
❑ 83Don-119
❑ 83Fle-163
❑ 83GiaMot-12
❑ 83GiaPos-12
❑ 83OPC-331
❑ 83Top-331
❑ 83TopTra-58T
❑ 84Don-509
❑ 84Fle-374
❑ 84GiaPos-8
❑ 84Nes792-633
❑ 84OPC-37
❑ 84Top-633
❑ 84TopTif-633
❑ 85AllGamPI-171
❑ 85Don-630
❑ 85Fle-609
❑ 85GiaMot-11
❑ 85GiaPos-16
❑ 85OPC-74
❑ 85Top-74
❑ 85TopSti-163
❑ 85TopTif-74
❑ 86Don-143
❑ 86DonHig-49
❑ 86Fle-546
❑ 86GiaMot-11
❑ 86GiaPos-15
❑ 86OPC-126
❑ 86Top-752
❑ 86TopSti-93
❑ 86TopTat-8
❑ 86TopTif-752
❑ 87BurKinA-12
❑ 87ClaGam-67
❑ 87Don-609
❑ 87DonAll-58
❑ 87DonAllB-PC15
❑ 87DonOpeD-98
❑ 87Fle-275
❑ 87Fle-630
❑ 87FleGamW-24
❑ 87FleGlo-275
❑ 87FleGlo-630
❑ 87FleLimE-24
❑ 87FleMin-61
❑ 87FleStiC-69
❑ 87GiaMot-6
❑ 87GiaPos-15
❑ 87HosSti-17
❑ 87Lea-86
❑ 87OPC-241
❑ 87SmoNatL-12
❑ 87Spo-62
❑ 87SpoTeaP-10
❑ 87Top-580
❑ 87TopMinL-36
❑ 87TopSti-92
❑ 87TopTif-580
❑ 88Don-116
❑ 88DonBasB-50
❑ 88Fle-85
❑ 88FleGlo-85
❑ 88GiaMot-6
❑ 88GiaPos-13
❑ 88OPC-393
❑ 88PanSti-417
❑ 88RedFolSB-45
❑ 88Sco-185
❑ 88ScoGlo-185
❑ 88Top-445
❑ 88TopTif-445
❑ 89ClaTraO-114
❑ 89Don-258
❑ 89DonBasB-135
❑ 89Fle-331
❑ 89FleGlo-331
❑ 89GiaMot-6
❑ 89OPC-125
❑ 89Sco-190
❑ 89Top-125
❑ 89TopSti-83
❑ 89TopTif-125
❑ 89UppDec-46
❑ 90OPC-241
❑ 90PubIntS-72
❑ 90Sco-215
❑ 90Top-241
❑ 90TopTif-241
❑ 90UppDec-639
❑ 98GiaMot-27

Krum, Sandy
❑ 88CedRapRP-1140
❑ 89ChaLooB-24
❑ 89ChaLooGS-3
❑ 90SalBucS-27
❑ 91SalBucC-24
❑ 95CarMudF-176
❑ 97CalCanB-4
❑ 98NasSouTI-19
❑ 98NasSouTISS-18

Krumback, Mark
❑ 88BoiHawP-1625
❑ 89GreHorP-425
❑ 90CedRapRB-12
❑ 90CedRapRP-2335
❑ 91CalLeLA-34
❑ 91RenSilSCLC-2

Krumm, Todd
❑ 90LakTigS-17
❑ 91LinDriAA-390
❑ 91LonTigLD-390
❑ 91LonTigP-1875

Krupenchemkov, Alex.
❑ 89EasLeaDDP-DD14

Kruppa, Ken
❑ 75ForLauYS-15
❑ 76ForLauYS-10

Krusch, Lawrence
❑ 80VenLeaS-155

Kruse, Kelly
❑ 96SouBenSHS-19

Krusinski, Clar
❑ 89PeoChiTI-33

Krusinski, Mark
❑ 91PeoChiTI-30

Krusinski, Scott
❑ 93PeoChiC-25

Kryhoski, Dick
❑ 49Bow-218
❑ 49RemBre-14
❑ 50Bow-242
❑ 52Bow-133
❑ 52Top-149
❑ 53BowC-127
❑ 54Bow-117
❑ 54OriEss-20
❑ 54OriTeal-12
❑ 54Top-150
❑ 55A'sTeal-12
❑ 55JetPos-7
❑ 79TCM50-241
❑ 83TopRep5-149
❑ 91OriCro-250
❑ 94TopArc1-150
❑ 94TopArc1G-150
❑ 97BalOriP-26

Kryka, Mark
❑ 77CliDodT-14
❑ 78CliDodT-18

Kryzanowski, Rusty
❑ 86AubAstP-15
❑ 87KenTwiP-9
❑ 88KenTwiP-1383
❑ 89KenTwiP-1077
❑ 89KenTwiS-10

Ksenich, Michael
❑ 91ElmPioC-29

Ksenich, Phil
❑ 91ElmPioC-29

Kubala, Brian
❑ 86SanJosBP-11
❑ 87SanJosBP-30

Kubek, Tony
❑ 47Exh-126A
❑ 47Exh-126B
❑ 57Top-312
❑ 58Top-393
❑ 58YanJayP-6
❑ 59Top-505
❑ 59Yoo-3
❑ 60Top-83
❑ 60TopVen-83
❑ 60YanJayP-5
❑ 61Pos-9A
❑ 61Pos-9B
❑ 61Top-265
❑ 61TopDicG-7
❑ 61TopStal-195
❑ 61Yan61RL-42
❑ 61YanJayP-7
❑ 62Jel-4
❑ 62Pos-4
❑ 62PosCan-4
❑ 62SalPlaC-18
❑ 62ShiPlaC-18
❑ 62Top-311
❑ 62Top-430
❑ 62TopStal-87
❑ 63Kah-18
❑ 63ReqKP-9
❑ 63Top-20
❑ 63YanJayP-6
❑ 64ChatheY-13
❑ 64Top-415
❑ 64YanJayP-6
❑ 65ChaTheY-11
❑ 65OPC-65
❑ 65Top-65
❑ 65TopEmbl-71
❑ 79DiaGre-19
❑ 79TCM50-244
❑ 81TCM60I-477
❑ 83FraBroR-16
❑ 83Yan196-3
❑ 87Yan196T-4
❑ 88PacLegl-29
❑ 89SweBasG-68
❑ 91YanRinP11-9
❑ 92YanWIZ6-70
❑ 92YanWIZA-37

Kubenka, Jeff
❑ 96YakBeaTI-37
❑ 97CalLeaATI-12
❑ 97SanBerS-8
❑ 98AlbDukG-15

❑ 98FleUpd-U99
❑ 99Fle-195
❑ 99FleSta9-195
❑ 99FleWarT-195
❑ 99SkyThu-136
❑ 99SkyThuRant-136
❑ 99SkyThuRave-136
❑ 99SpoIll-52
❑ 99ThuSkySupR-136
Kubes, Greg
❑ 98BatMucTI-14
Kubiak, Ted
❑ 68OPC-79
❑ 68Top-79
❑ 68TopVen-79
❑ 69Top-281
❑ 70BreMcD-15
❑ 70BreMil-12
❑ 70BreTeal-7
❑ 70SunPin-13
❑ 70Top-688
❑ 71BreTeal-7
❑ 71MLBOffS-442
❑ 71OPC-516
❑ 71Top-516
❑ 72MilBra-189
❑ 72OPC-23
❑ 72RanTeal-16
❑ 72Top-23
❑ 73OPC-652
❑ 73Top-652
❑ 74A'sPos-53
❑ 74OPC-228
❑ 74Top-228
❑ 75OPC-329
❑ 75PadDea-16
❑ 75Top-329
❑ 75TopMin-329
❑ 76OPC-578
❑ 76SSP-129
❑ 76Top-578
❑ 77Top-158
❑ 89ModA'sC-1
❑ 90ModA'sC-33
❑ 90ModA'sCLC-171
❑ 90ModA'sP-2229
❑ 91ModA'sC-17
❑ 91ModA'sP-3106
❑ 92CalLeaACL-21
❑ 92ModA'sC-25
❑ 92ModA'sF-3910
❑ 93ModA'sC-26
❑ 93ModA'sF-815
❑ 93RanKee-22
❑ 94BreMilB-238
❑ 94CanIndF-3133
❑ 96WatIndTI-13
❑ 97WatIndTI-14
❑ 98WatIndTI-15
Kubicki, Marc
❑ 91UtiBluSC-1
❑ 91UtiBluSP-3237
❑ 92ProFS7-48
❑ 92SalSpuC-6
Kubinski, Tim
❑ 94WesMicWC-12
❑ 94WesMicWF-2290
❑ 95ModA'sTI-12
❑ 96HunStaTI-14
❑ 99WesMicWAM-13
Kubiszyn, Jack
❑ 60MapLeaSF-12
❑ 77FriOneYW-42
Kubit, Joe
❑ 80WisRapTT-23
❑ 83VisOakF-17
Kuboto, Masahiro
❑ 90SalSpuCLC-148
Kubski, Gil
❑ 78SalLakCGC-16
❑ 79SalLakCGT-16B
❑ 80SalLakCGT-21
❑ 81SyrChiT-18
❑ 81VanCanT-9
❑ 82IndIndTI-28
❑ 91HunCubP-3354
❑ 92HunCubC-29
Kucab, John
❑ 51A'sTeal-16
❑ 52A'sTeal-15
❑ 52Top-358
❑ 83TopRep5-358
Kucek, Jack
❑ 75OPC-614
❑ 75Top-614
❑ 75TopMin-614
❑ 76OPC-597
❑ 76Top-597
❑ 77Top-623
❑ 77WhiSoxT-16
❑ 80SyrChiT-11
❑ 80SyrChiTI-13
❑ 81SyrChiT-6
❑ 81SyrChiTI-12
Kucharski, Joe
❑ 84RocRedWT-18
❑ 85RocRedWT-20
❑ 86ChaOriW-16
❑ 87ChaO'sW-37
❑ 87RocRedWT-27
Kucks, John
❑ 56Top-88
❑ 56YanTeal-11
❑ 57Top-185
❑ 57YanJayP-7
❑ 58Top-87
❑ 59Top-289
❑ 60A's-7
❑ 60A'sTeal-11
❑ 60Lea-96
❑ 60Top-177
❑ 60TopVen-177
❑ 61Top-94
❑ 62KahAtl-11
❑ 62Top-241
❑ 79DiaGre-23
❑ 83YanASFY-23
❑ 92YanWIZA-38
Kuder, Jeff
❑ 89AugPirP-491
❑ 89WelPirP-16
Kuecker, Mark
❑ 77CedRapGT-20
❑ 79PhoGiaVNB-20
Kuehl, John
❑ 88SpoIndP-1934
❑ 89ChaRaiP-986
❑ 89SouAtlLAGS-12
❑ 91Cla/Bes-354
❑ 91MidLeaAP-MWL30
❑ 91WatDiaC-17
❑ 91WatDiaP-1264
❑ 92ClaFS7-130
❑ 92HigDesMC-15
❑ 93HunStaF-2089
❑ 97SouOreTB-28
Kuehl, Karl
❑ 75IntLeaAT-25
❑ 76ExpRed-17
❑ 76MonExpP-16
❑ 76OPC-216
❑ 76SSP-611
❑ 76Top-216
❑ 79TwiFriP-13
❑ 80TwiPos-15
❑ 81TwiPos-18
❑ 82TwiPos-19
Kuehne, William
❑ 87OldJudN-290
❑ 88WG1CarG-60
❑ 89WelPirP-33
Kuen Kim, Bong
❑ 96HilStaHWB-14
Kuenn, Harvey
❑ 47Exh-127A
❑ 47Exh-127B
❑ 47Exh-127C
❑ 53TigGle-18
❑ 54Bow-23
❑ 54RedHeaF-15
❑ 54Top-25
❑ 54Wil-11
❑ 55ArmCoi-12A
❑ 55ArmCoi-12B
❑ 55BigLeaIS-9
❑ 55Bow-132A
❑ 55Bow-132B
❑ 55DaiQueS-9
❑ 56Top-155
❑ 57Top-88
❑ 58Top-304
❑ 58Top-434
❑ 59ArmCoi-11
❑ 59Baz-13
❑ 59TigGraASP-11
❑ 59Top-70
❑ 59TopVen-70
❑ 60Baz-34
❑ 60IndJayP-4
❑ 60Kah-20
❑ 60NuHi-59
❑ 60Top-330
❑ 60Top-429
❑ 60TopTat-27
❑ 61Baz-15
❑ 61GiaJayP-7
❑ 61NuSco-459
❑ 61Pos-57A
❑ 61Pos-57B
❑ 61Top-500
❑ 61TopStal-77
❑ 61WilSpoGH828-2
❑ 61WilSpoGH828-1-3
❑ 62GiaJayP-7
❑ 62Jel-135
❑ 62Pos-135
❑ 62PosCan-135
❑ 62SalPlaC-121
❑ 62ShiPlaC-121
❑ 62Top-480
❑ 62TopBuc-46
❑ 62TopStal-197
❑ 63ExhStaB-37
❑ 63Jel-105
❑ 63Pos-105
❑ 63Top-30
❑ 64Top-242
❑ 64TopVen-242
❑ 65OPC-103
❑ 65Top-103
❑ 66CubTeal-10
❑ 66Top-372
❑ 73OPC-646
❑ 73Top-646
❑ 74Top-99
❑ 75SSP42-41
❑ 76GrePlaG-34
❑ 78NewWayCT-24
❑ 78TigDeaCS-6
❑ 79DiaGre-399
❑ 79TCM50-104
❑ 80BreTeal-14
❑ 80PacLeg-66
❑ 81Gia196T-7
❑ 81TigDetN-96
❑ 82Don-578
❑ 82TCMGreH-11
❑ 83BreGar-1
❑ 83BrePol-32
❑ 83Don-608
❑ 83TigAlKS-15
❑ 83TigAlKS-16
❑ 83Top-726
❑ 84Nes792-321
❑ 84Top-321
❑ 84TopGloA-1
❑ 84TopTif-321
❑ 85TCMPhoC-31
❑ 86BreGreT-12
❑ 86TigSpoD-11
❑ 88PacLegI-56
❑ 89SweBasG-9
❑ 91SweBasG-114
❑ 91TopArc1-301
❑ 92BazQua5A-20
❑ 92BreCarT-11
❑ 92UppDecS-9
❑ 94TopArc1-25
❑ 94TopArc1G-25
Kuenzi, Kevin
❑ 89BoiHawP-1978
Kuhaulua, Fred
❑ 77SalLakCGC-12
❑ 79HawIslC-23
❑ 80HawIslT-25
❑ 81HawIslT-17
❑ 82HawIslT-17
❑ 82Top-731
Kuhel, Joe
❑ 31SenTealPW-20
❑ 33Gou-108
❑ 34BabRutG-39
❑ 34BatR31-80
❑ 34BatR31-128
❑ 34ButPreR-38
❑ 34DiaStaR-78
❑ 34ExhFou-16
❑ 34Gou-16
❑ 34GouCanV-52
❑ 35GouPuzR-8H
❑ 35GouPuzR-9H
❑ 36GouWidPPR-A61
❑ 36NatChiFPR-50
❑ 36WorWidGV-63
❑ 37ExhFou-16
❑ 37OPCBatUV-127
❑ 38GouHeaU-243
❑ 38GouHeaU-267
❑ 39ExhSal-35
❑ 39WhiSoxTI-10
❑ 40PlaBal-185
❑ 40WhiSoxL-11
❑ 41PlaBal-31
❑ 47SenGunBP-1
❑ 47TipTop-22
❑ 60SenUniMC-11
❑ 61Fle-119
❑ 82DiaCla-95
❑ 83ConMar-8
❑ 83TCMPla1945-4
❑ 88ConAmeA-18
❑ 88ConSer5-18
❑ 91ConTSN-188
Kuhlman, Eric
❑ 88IdaFalBP-1851
❑ 89IdaFalBP-2028
Kuhn, Bowie
❑ 69TopBowK-1
❑ 77PadSchC-31
❑ 83TigAlKS-64
Kuhn, Chad
❑ 88SpoIndP-1935
❑ 89WatDiaP-1797
❑ 89WatDiaS-16
❑ 90MadMusB-17
❑ 90MadMusP-2263
❑ 91HunStaC-13
❑ 91HunStaLD-287
❑ 91HunStaP-1790
❑ 91HunStaTI-12
❑ 91LinDriAA-287
❑ 92HunStaF-3944
Kuhn, Ken
❑ 57IndTeal-11
❑ 57Top-266
❑ 60Lea-115
Kuhn, Red (Walter)
❑ 09ObaT21-294
❑ 11PacCoaBD-33
❑ 11Zee-50
❑ 12ObaPreT-43
❑ 12T207-96
❑ 15Zee-38
❑ 16Zee-38
Kuhn, Todd
❑ 85FreGiaSB-21
Kuhnz, Les
❑ 65SeaPop-10
Kuilan, Hector
❑ 96KanCouCTI-17
❑ 96KanCouCUTI-10
❑ 97BreCouMB-21
❑ 98PorSeaDQ-13
Kuilan, Jorge
❑ 88WinHavRSS-11
Kuiper, Duane
❑ 76OPC-508
❑ 76SSP-522
❑ 76SSP-529
❑ 76Top-508
❑ 77BurCheD-55
❑ 77OPC-233
❑ 77PepGloD-19
❑ 77Top-85
❑ 78Hos-34
❑ 78IndTeal-19
❑ 78OPC-39
❑ 78Top-332
❑ 79Hos-13
❑ 79OPC-67
❑ 79Top-146
❑ 80IndTeal-16
❑ 80OPC-221
❑ 80Top-429
❑ 81AllGamPI-14
❑ 81Don-319A
❑ 81Don-319B
❑ 81OPC-226
❑ 81Top-612
❑ 82Don-198
❑ 82Fle-373
❑ 82Gia25tATI-13
❑ 82OPC-233
❑ 82Top-233
❑ 82TopTra-60T
❑ 83Fle-263
❑ 83FleSta-98
❑ 83FleSti-58
❑ 83GiaMot-11
❑ 83GiaPos-13
❑ 83Top-767
❑ 84Don-553
❑ 84Fle-375
❑ 84GiaPos-9
❑ 84Nes792-542
❑ 84OPC-338
❑ 84Top-542
❑ 84TopSti-169
❑ 84TopTif-542
❑ 85Fle-610
❑ 85Top-22
❑ 85TopTif-22
❑ 98GiaMot-27
Kuiper, Glen
❑ 85SpoIndC-10
❑ 86EriCarP-16
Kulakov, Vadim
❑ 89EasLeaDDP-DD5
Kuld, Pete
❑ 88WatIndP-682
❑ 89MiaMirIS-22
❑ 90HunStaB-14
❑ 91LinDriAA-610
❑ 91WicWraLD-610
❑ 91WicWraP-2602
❑ 91WicWraRD-12
❑ 92TulDriS-610
Kulle, Chuck
❑ 93WatIndC-14
❑ 93WatIndF-3576
Kulpa, Stephen
❑ 93GenCubC-18
❑ 93GenCubF-3184
Kume, Mike
❑ 52Par-100
Kummerfeldt, Jason
❑ 92BilMusF-3348
❑ 92BilMusSP-11
❑ 93ExcFS7-23
❑ 93WesVirWC-13
❑ 93WesVirWF-2861
❑ 94WinSpiC-13
❑ 94WinSpiF-266
Kunka, Tony
❑ 98FarRedHM-16
Kunkel, Bill (William)
❑ 61Top-322
❑ 62Top-147A
❑ 62Top-147B
❑ 62TopVen-147
❑ 63Top-523
❑ 85Top-136
❑ 85TopTif-136
❑ 92YanWIZ6-71
Kunkel, Jeff
❑ 84RanJarP-20
❑ 85Don-587
❑ 85Fle-561
❑ 85OklCit8T-3
❑ 85OPC-288
❑ 85Top-136
❑ 85Top-288
❑ 85TopSti-350
❑ 85TopTif-136
❑ 85TopTif-288
❑ 86OklCit8P-9
❑ 87RanMot-24
❑ 88OklCit8C-18
❑ 88OklCit8P-30
❑ 88Sco-407
❑ 88ScoGlo-407
❑ 89Bow-231
❑ 89BowTif-231
❑ 89Don-496
❑ 89Fle-527
❑ 89FleGlo-527
❑ 89RanMot-19
❑ 89RanSmo-18
❑ 89Sco-484
❑ 89Top-92
❑ 89TopTif-92
❑ 89UppDec-463
❑ 90Don-496
❑ 90Fle-304
❑ 90FleCan-304
❑ 90OPC-174
❑ 90PubIntS-415
❑ 90RanMot-18
❑ 90Sco-431
❑ 90Top-174
❑ 90TopSti-246
❑ 90TopTif-174
❑ 90UppDec-394
❑ 91Fle-292
❑ 91OPC-562
❑ 91Sco-783
❑ 91StaClu-580
❑ 91Stu-126
❑ 91Top-562
❑ 91TopDesS-562
❑ 91TopMic-562
❑ 91TopTif-562
❑ 92DenZepF-2648
❑ 92DenZepS-136
❑ 93ChaKniF-550
❑ 93RanKee-223
❑ 94TolMudHF-1032
Kunkel, Kevin
❑ 86MedA'sC-70
❑ 87MadMusP-11
❑ 87MadMusP-19
Kuntz, Lee
❑ 86WatIndP-16
❑ 88WilBilP-1303
❑ 90CanIndB-3
❑ 90CanIndS-21
Kuntz, Rusty
❑ 78KnoKnoST-10
❑ 81Don-282
❑ 81Top-112
❑ 82EdmTraT-20
❑ 82Fle-348
❑ 82Top-237
❑ 84Fle-568
❑ 84FleUpd-66
❑ 84Nes792-598
❑ 84TigTeal-21
❑ 84TigWavP-24
❑ 84Top-598
❑ 84TopTif-598
❑ 84TopTra-66T
❑ 84TopTraT-66T
❑ 85Don-516
❑ 85Fle-14
❑ 85NasSouTI-8
❑ 85TigWen-13
❑ 85Top-73
❑ 85TopTif-73
❑ 89MarMot-27
❑ 90MarMot-27
❑ 92MarMot-27
Kunz, Devin
❑ 93EriSaiC-13
❑ 93EriSaiF-3110
Kunz, Earl
❑ 20Zee-66
❑ 21Zee-73
❑ 22Zee-62
❑ 24Zee-31
❑ 25Zee-30
❑ 26Zee-79
❑ 27Zee-114
❑ 29Zee-116
❑ 30Zee-179
Kuoda, Masa
❑ 89SalSpuCLC-134
❑ 89SalSpuP-1804
Kupsey, John
❑ 89PulBraP-1913
❑ 90SumBraB-10
❑ 90SumBraP-2442
❑ 92SpaPhiC-11
❑ 92SpaPhiF-1270
❑ 94ReaPhiF-2072
Kurczewski, Tommy
❑ 88WatIndP-665
❑ 89BurBraP-1603
Kurek, Chris
❑ 94UtiBluSC-15
❑ 95MicBatCTI-16
Kurilla, Kevin
❑ 97BatCliTI-4
❑ 98PieBolWM-20
Kurosaki, Ryan
❑ 76ArkTraT-5
❑ 77ArkTraT-3A
❑ 77ArkTraT-3B
❑ 78ArkTraT-15
❑ 80ArkTraT-13
Kurowski, Whitey (George)
❑ 46SeaSLP-34
❑ 46SpoExcW-4-1A
❑ 47Exh-128
❑ 47TipTop-158
❑ 49Lea-81
❑ 50AmeNut&CCP-11
❑ 76TayBow4-96
❑ 78ReaRem-10
❑ 83Car194T-16
❑ 83TCMPla1943-26
❑ 92CarMcD-8
Kurpiel, Ed
❑ 76SalLakCGC-8
❑ 78TidTidT-12
Kurtz, Dan

❑ 96WisTimRB-13
Kurtz, John
❑ 89GeoColC-17
❑ 90GeoColC-16
Kurtz, Rodd
❑ 93HunCubC-15
❑ 93HunCubF-3232
❑ 94PeoChiC-14
❑ 94PeoChiF-2263
Kurtz, Tony
❑ 97FreKey-11
Kurys, Sophie
❑ 94TedWil-97
Kusel, Ed
❑ 09ObaT21-246
Kush, Emil
❑ 47TipTop-109
❑ 49EurSta-59
❑ 77CubAllT-9
❑ 80CubGreT-6
Kusick, Craig
❑ 73TacTwiC-13
❑ 74TacTwiC-3
❑ 75OPC-297
❑ 75Top-297
❑ 75TopMin-297
❑ 75TwiPos-15
❑ 75TwiTeal-19
❑ 76MinTwiP-10
❑ 76VenLeaS-14
❑ 77Top-38
❑ 78Top-137
❑ 78TwiFriP-11
❑ 79Top-472
❑ 79TwiFriP-14
❑ 80HawIsIT-7
❑ 80OPC-374
❑ 80Top-693
❑ 81EvaTriT-16
Kusiewicz, Mike
❑ 95AshTouTI-10
❑ 96BesAutS-47
❑ 96Bow-113
❑ 96BowFoi-113
❑ 96Exc-157
❑ 96NewHavRB-16
❑ 97NewHavRB-16
❑ 97SalAva-U2
❑ 98NewHavRM-17
❑ 98NewHavRMA-17
❑ 99Bow-397
❑ 99BowGol-397
❑ 99BowInt-397
❑ 99SP TopP-69
❑ 99SP TopPPE-69
Kusnyer, Art
❑ 72OPC-213
❑ 72Top-213
❑ 74SacSolC-47
❑ 75IntLeaASB-15
❑ 75PacCoaLAB-15
❑ 75SacSolC-10
❑ 76SpoIndC-12
❑ 77SpoIndC-10
❑ 79IowOakP-10
❑ 84WhiSoxTV-8
❑ 89A'sMot-27
❑ 90A'sMot-27
❑ 91A'sMot-28
❑ 92AthMot-28
❑ 93AthMot-27
❑ 93Don-396
❑ 94A'sMot-28
❑ 94BreMilB-324
❑ 95AthMot-28
Kustus, Joe
❑ 90DodTar-1008
Kutcher, Randy
❑ 80CliGiaT-14
❑ 83PhoGiaBHN-15
❑ 84PhoGiaC-18
❑ 85DomLeaS-94
❑ 85PhoGiaC-177
❑ 86PhoFirP-13
❑ 87Don-547
❑ 87Fle-276
❑ 87FleGlo-276
❑ 87PhoFirP-12
❑ 88PawRedSC-11
❑ 88PawRedSP-464
❑ 89Fle-98A
❑ 89TopTra-64T
❑ 89TopTraT-64T
❑ 90OPC-676
❑ 90PubIntS-459
❑ 90Sco-551
❑ 90Top-676
❑ 90TopTif-676
❑ 90TopTVRS-31
❑ 91Fle-100
❑ 91Sco-837
Kutina, Joe
❑ 12T207-97
Kutner, Mike
❑ 82MiaMarT-20
Kutsukos, Pete
❑ 84BeaGolGT-2
❑ 85BeaGolGT-7
Kutyna, Marty
❑ 58RedEnq-23
❑ 58SeaRalT-11
❑ 60A'sTeal-12
❑ 60Top-516
❑ 61SenJayP-5
❑ 61Top-546
❑ 62Top-566
Kutzler, Jerry
❑ 88TamTarS-12
❑ 89BirBarB-15
❑ 89BirBarP-117
❑ 89SouLeaAJ-15
❑ 90Don-503
❑ 90DonRoo-25
❑ 90ScoRoo-80T
❑ 90WhiSoxC-14
❑ 90WhiSoxC-28
❑ 91LinDriAAA-639
❑ 91Sco-749
❑ 91TopDeb90-80
❑ 91VanCanLD-639
❑ 91VanCanP-1592
❑ 93AlbDukF-1456
❑ 93LinVenB-203
❑ 94OmaRoyF-1219
❑ 95OmaRoyTI-16
Kuykendall, Kevin
❑ 87WatIndP-12
Kuzava, Bob (Robert)
❑ 50Bow-5
❑ 51Bow-97
❑ 51TopBluB-22
❑ 52BerRos-32
❑ 52Bow-233
❑ 52Top-85
❑ 53BowBW-33
❑ 54NewYorJA-48
❑ 54OriEss-21
❑ 54Top-230
❑ 55Bow-215
❑ 55OriEss-13
❑ 57JetPos-11
❑ 83TopRep5-85
❑ 91OriCro-251
❑ 94TopArc1-230
❑ 94TopArc1G-230
❑ 97BalOriP-27
Kuzma, Greg
❑ 88ButCopKSP-3
Kuzmic, Craig
❑ 98EveAquG-10
❑ 99TeaBesR-46
❑ 99TeaBesRG-46
❑ 99TeaBesRS-46
Kuzniar, Kooz (Paul)
❑ 87WatIndP-19
❑ 88WilBilP-1321
❑ 89CanIndB-20
❑ 89CanIndP-1305
❑ 89CanIndS-11
❑ 90NewBriRSS-7
Kvansnicka, Jay
❑ 89KenTwiP-1063
❑ 89KenTwiS-11
❑ 90VisOakP-2168
❑ 91LinDriAA-483
❑ 91OrlSunRLD-483
❑ 91OrlSunRP-1862
❑ 92OrlSunRF-2859
❑ 92PorBeaF-2679
❑ 92PorBeaS-412
Kwasny, Joe
❑ 75ForLauYS-18
Kwolek, Chuck
❑ 79AshTouT-24
Kwolek, Joe
❑ 86OscAstP-16
Kyles, Stan
❑ 81QuaCitCT-19
❑ 83MidCubT-19
❑ 84AlbA'sT-15
❑ 85TacTigC-138
❑ 86HunStaDJ-30
❑ 87TacTigP-3
❑ 88AlbDukCm-2
❑ 88AlbDukP-275
❑ 91BenBucCB-3
❑ 91BenBucP-3712
❑ 92GenCubC-27
❑ 92GenCubF-1577
❑ 93IowCubF-2150
❑ 93IowCubF-2151
❑ 96AshTouB-4
❑ 97OrlRayB-2
❑ 98RocCubM-17
❑ 98RocCubTI-18
Kynerd, Jay
❑ 89CarNewE-25
Kyslinger, Dan
❑ 92FroRowDP-95
❑ 92FroRowDPG-95
❑ 92FroRowDPS-95
❑ 92HelBreF-1712
❑ 92HelBreSP-1
❑ 93BelBreCB-13
❑ 93BelBreFI-1706
❑ 94StoPorC-13
❑ 94StoPorF-1690
Kyte, Frank
❑ 92BasCitRC-27
❑ 97WicWra-29
❑ 98OmaRoyM-3
Laabs, Chet (Chester)
❑ 40PlaBal-206
❑ 41BroW75-19
❑ 46SeaSLP-35
❑ 50WorWidGV-31
❑ 77TCMTheWY-60
❑ 79DiaGre-187
❑ 83TCMPla1943-16
❑ 94ConTSN-1278
❑ 94ConTSNB-1278
❑ 96Bro194F-33
Laake, Pete
❑ 91GasRanP-2694
Labarca, Argenis
❑ 93PriRedC-16
❑ 93PriRedF-4186
❑ 94PriRedC-13
❑ 94PriRedF-3269
LaBare, Jay
❑ 80ElmPioRST-40
Labastidas, Mario
❑ 93LinVenB-139
❑ 94VenLinU-258
Labay, Steve
❑ 86ReaPhiP-13
LaBelle, Henry
❑ 07NewEveWS-6
Labine, Clem
❑ 52Top-342
❑ 53Top-14
❑ 54Bow-106
❑ 54NewYorJA-9
❑ 54Top-121
❑ 55DodGolS-11
❑ 55Top-180
❑ 56Dod-16
❑ 56Dod-17
❑ 56Top-295
❑ 57Top-53
❑ 58DodJayP-7
❑ 58DodTeal-13
❑ 58DodVol-8
❑ 58Hir-34
❑ 58Top-305
❑ 59DodMor-6
❑ 59DodPos-11
❑ 59DodTeal-13
❑ 59DodVol-8
❑ 59Top-262
❑ 59Top-403
❑ 60DodBelB-6
❑ 60Lea-60
❑ 60Top-29
❑ 60TopVen-29
❑ 61Top-22
❑ 74dod195T-21
❑ 74MetOriEB-8
❑ 77PirTCM1WC-24
❑ 79TCM50-31
❑ 81TCM60I-482
❑ 83DodBoyoST-1
❑ 83TopRep5-342
❑ 87Dod195T-8
❑ 88DodRinP1-7B
❑ 89DodSmoG-61
❑ 90DodTar-423
❑ 90PacLeg-89
❑ 91MetWIZ-222
❑ 91SweBasG-54
❑ 91TopArc1-14
❑ 92ActPacA-59
❑ 94TopArc1-121
❑ 94TopArc1G-121
❑ 95TopArcBD-25
❑ 95TopArcBD-39
❑ 95TopArcBD-73
❑ 95TopArcBD-104
❑ 95TopArcBD-162
Labitzke, Jesse
❑ 98PorRocG-21
Labossiere, Dave
❑ 77BriRedST-12
❑ 80TucTorT-12
❑ 81TucTorT-14
❑ 82TucTorT-27
❑ 83TucTorT-25
❑ 88AstMot-28
❑ 89AstMot-28
❑ 90AstMot-28
❑ 92AstMot-28
❑ 94AstMot-28
Laboy, Carlos
❑ 87AubAstP-14
❑ 88AshTouP-1056
❑ 88BlaYNPRWL-166
❑ 89BlaYNPRWL-141
❑ 89OscAstS-10
❑ 91PalSprAP-2029
❑ 92SalSpuC-22
❑ 92SalSpuF-3769
Laboy, Coco (Jose A.)
❑ 69ExpFudP-6
❑ 69ExpPin-4
❑ 69Top-524
❑ 70ExpPin-9
❑ 70ExpPos-8
❑ 70Kel-66
❑ 70MLBOffS-67
❑ 70OPC-238
❑ 70Top-238
❑ 71ExpLaPR-5
❑ 71ExpPS-12
❑ 71MLBOffS-132
❑ 71OPC-132
❑ 71Top-132
❑ 72Dia-24
❑ 72MilBra-190
❑ 72Top-727
❑ 73OPC-642
❑ 73Top-642
❑ 87Ft.LauYP-20
❑ 88PriWilYS-14
❑ 89BlaYNPRWL-198
❑ 92Nab-9
Labozzetta, Al
❑ 86GleFalTP-11
LaCasse, Michael
❑ 79NewCoPT-10
Lacefield, Tim
❑ 97St.CatSB-19
Lacer, Mike
❑ 86PitCubP-12
LaCerra, Tony
❑ 88RenSilSCLC-270
Lacey, Kerry
❑ 91ButCopKSP-14
Lacey, Robert
❑ 76TucTorCa-7
❑ 76TusTorCr-19
❑ 77SanJosMC-14
❑ 78Top-29
❑ 79Top-647
❑ 80OPC-167
❑ 80Top-316
❑ 81Don-240A
❑ 81Don-240B
❑ 81Fle-578
❑ 81Top-481
❑ 81TopTra-784
❑ 82Top-103
❑ 85Fle-611
❑ 85PhoGiaC-191
❑ 93RanKee-224
LaChance, Candy (George)
❑ 03BreE10-85
❑ 04RedSoxUP-9
❑ 11SpoLifCW-210
❑ 90DodTar-424
❑ 98CamPepP-43
LaChance, Vince (Vincent)
❑ 93JamExpC-13
❑ 93JamExpF-3338
❑ 94BurBeeC-12
❑ 94BurBeeF-1095
LaChapelle, Yan
❑ 96StCatSB-15
❑ 97HagSunB-8
❑ 98DunBluJTI-15
LaChappa, Matt
❑ 94SprSulC-16
❑ 94SprSulF-2034
❑ 95RanCucQT-15
Lachemann, Bill
❑ 83CliGiaF-29
❑ 86QuaCitAP-18
❑ 87PalSprP-17
❑ 88CalLeaACLC-35
❑ 88PalSprACLC-112
❑ 88PalSprAP-1436
❑ 89PalSprACLC-63
❑ 89PalSprAP-489
❑ 95AngMot-28
❑ 96AngMot-28
❑ 97ButCopKB-30
❑ 97ButCopKK-30
❑ 98ButCopKG-17
Lachemann, Bret
❑ 91QuaCitAC-6
❑ 91QuaCitAP-2623
Lachemann, Marcel
❑ 71MLBOffS-518
❑ 71OPC-84
❑ 71Top-84
❑ 75WesPalBES-11
❑ 82DanSunF-14
❑ 87CalAngPPS-21
❑ 93MarPub-28
❑ 94AngLAT-26
❑ 94AngMot-1
❑ 95AngCHP-16
❑ 95AngMot-1
❑ 96AngMot-1
Lachemann, Rene
❑ 65Top-526
❑ 66OPC-157
❑ 66Top-157
❑ 66TopVen-157
❑ 67CokCapAt-10
❑ 67Top-471
❑ 67VanMouSO-15
❑ 68Top-422
❑ 76VenLeaS-242
❑ 77SanJosMC-2
❑ 78SanJosMMC-2
❑ 79SpoIndT-16
❑ 80SpoIndT-18
❑ 80VenLeaS-181
❑ 81MarPos-20
❑ 81SpoIndT-13
❑ 82Don-600
❑ 82MarPos-20
❑ 83Top-336
❑ 84BreGar-1
❑ 84BrePol-9
❑ 84Fle-655
❑ 84TopTra-67T
❑ 84TopTraT-67T
❑ 85Top-628
❑ 85TopTif-628
❑ 86MarGreT-12
❑ 87Top-556
❑ 87TopTif-556
❑ 88ChaLooLTI-19
❑ 89A'sMot-27
❑ 90A'sMot-27
❑ 91A'sMot-28
❑ 92AthMot-28
❑ 93MarPub-15
❑ 93Top-505
❑ 93TopGol-505
❑ 93TopInaM-505
❑ 93TopInaR-505
❑ 93TopMic-505
Lachmann, Tom
❑ 88OklSoo-22
❑ 89BurIndS-14
Lachowetz, Anthony J.
❑ 81VerBeaDT-8
❑ 82VerBeaDT-23
Lachowicz, Al
❑ 82TulDriT-7
❑ 84OklCit8T-1
❑ 85TulDriTI-36
❑ 93RanKee-225
Lackey, John
❑ 81BirBarT-1
❑ 82GleFalWST-20
❑ 83LynPirT-4
Lackey, Stephen
❑ 92GulCoaMF-3491
❑ 92HigSchPLS-23
❑ 93KinMetC-15
❑ 93KinMetF-3803
❑ 94KinMetF-3830
❑ 95PitMetTI-26
❑ 96FayGenB-22
❑ 97LakTigB-19
❑ 98JacSunM-15
❑ 98LakTigM-15
Lacko, Rich
❑ 87LakTigP-14
❑ 88GleFalTP-920
Lacks, Charles K.
❑ 54BraJohC-49
❑ 55BraGolS-31
❑ 55BraJohC-49
LaCock, R. Pete
❑ 73WicAerJPKB-5
❑ 74WicAerODF-124
❑ 75OPC-494
❑ 75Top-494
❑ 75TopMin-494
❑ 76OPC-101
❑ 76SSP-317
❑ 76Top-101
❑ 77Top-561
❑ 78Roy-10
❑ 78SSP270-223
❑ 78Top-157
❑ 79Top-248
❑ 80OPC-202
❑ 80Top-389
❑ 81Don-344
❑ 81Fle-47
❑ 81Top-9
❑ 89PacSenL-33
❑ 89TopSenL-99
❑ 90EliSenL-98
❑ 91PacSenL-53
❑ 91PacSenL-120
LaCorte, Frank
❑ 76OPC-597
❑ 76SSP-612
❑ 76Top-597
❑ 78RicBraT-6
❑ 80Top-411
❑ 81AstPos-10
❑ 81Don-143
❑ 81Fle-55
❑ 81OPC-348
❑ 81Top-513
❑ 82AstAstI-7
❑ 82AstPos-12
❑ 82Don-270
❑ 82Fle-220
❑ 82Top-248
❑ 83AstPos-12
❑ 83Don-218
❑ 83Fle-454
❑ 83Top-14
❑ 84AngSmo-16
❑ 84Don-283
❑ 84Fle-230
❑ 84FleUpd-67
❑ 84Nes792-301
❑ 84Top-301
❑ 84TopTif-301
❑ 84TopTra-68T
❑ 84TopTraT-68T
❑ 85OPC-153
❑ 85Top-153
❑ 85TopTif-153
❑ 87AstShoSPO-13
LaCoss, Mike
❑ 77IndIndTI-11
❑ 78IndIndTI-4
❑ 79Top-717
❑ 80OPC-111
❑ 80RedEnq-51
❑ 80Top-199
❑ 81Don-183
❑ 81OPC-134
❑ 81Top-474
❑ 82AstAstI-8
❑ 82AstPos-11
❑ 82Don-440
❑ 82Fle-72
❑ 82Top-294
❑ 82TopTra-61T
❑ 83AstPos-13
❑ 83Don-344
❑ 83Fle-455
❑ 83Top-92

❑ 84AstMot-24
❑ 84AstPos-13
❑ 84Don-206
❑ 84Fle-231
❑ 84Nes792-507
❑ 84Top-507
❑ 84TopTif-507
❑ 85Don-405
❑ 85Fle-353
❑ 85FleUpd-66
❑ 85RoyTeal-16
❑ 85Top-666
❑ 85TopTif-666
❑ 85TopTifT-69T
❑ 85TopTra-69T
❑ 86FleUpd-62
❑ 86GiaMot-17
❑ 86Top-359
❑ 86TopTif-359
❑ 86TopTra-57T
❑ 86TopTraT-57T
❑ 87AstShoSPO-14
❑ 87Don-636
❑ 87Fle-277
❑ 87FleGlo-277
❑ 87GiaMot-21
❑ 87GiaPos-16
❑ 87Top-151
❑ 87TopTif-151
❑ 88Don-436
❑ 88Fle-86
❑ 88FleGlo-86
❑ 88GiaMot-21
❑ 88GiaPos-14
❑ 88PanSti-418
❑ 88Sco-465
❑ 88ScoGlo-465
❑ 88Top-754
❑ 88TopTif-754
❑ 89Don-602
❑ 89FleUpd-129
❑ 89GiaMot-21
❑ 89RedFolSB-70
❑ 89Sco-500
❑ 89Top-417
❑ 89TopTif-417
❑ 89UppDec-48
❑ 90Don-652
❑ 90Fle-59
❑ 90FleCan-59
❑ 90GiaMot-11
❑ 90GiaSmo-12
❑ 90Lea-463
❑ 90OPC-53
❑ 90PubIntS-73
❑ 90Sco-253
❑ 90Top-53
❑ 90TopTif-53
❑ 90UppDec-140
❑ 91Fle-264
❑ 91GiaMot-11
❑ 91GiaPacGaE-17
❑ 91GiaSFE-9
❑ 91Lea-309
❑ 91OPC-242
❑ 91Sco-652
❑ 91StaClu-479
❑ 91Top-242
❑ 91TopDesS-242
❑ 91TopMic-242
❑ 91TopTif-242
❑ 91UppDec-691

Lacy, Kerry
❑ 92GasRanC-15
❑ 92GasRanF-2250
❑ 93ChaRaiC-9
❑ 93ChaRaiF-1904
❑ 93SouAtlLAGF-8
❑ 94Bow-241
❑ 94ClaGolF-31
❑ 94ExcFS7-135
❑ 94TulDriF-241
❑ 94TulDriTI-12
❑ 95SigRoo-28
❑ 95TulDriTI-11
❑ 96OklCit8B-12
❑ 97PawRedS-14

Lacy, Lee
❑ 73OPC-391
❑ 73Top-391
❑ 74OPC-658
❑ 74Top-658
❑ 75OPC-631
❑ 75Top-631
❑ 75TopMin-631
❑ 76AtlBraP-16
❑ 76OPC-99
❑ 76SSP-78
❑ 76Top-99
❑ 76TopTra-99T
❑ 77Top-272
❑ 78SSP270-69
❑ 78Top-104
❑ 79OPC-229
❑ 79Top-441
❑ 80Top-536
❑ 81Don-376
❑ 81Fle-374
❑ 81Top-332
❑ 82Don-276
❑ 82Fle-483
❑ 82FleSta-80
❑ 82Top-752
❑ 83Don-276
❑ 83Fle-308
❑ 83FleSti-78
❑ 83FleSti-142
❑ 83OPC-69
❑ 83Top-69
❑ 84Don-479
❑ 84Fle-252
❑ 84Nes792-462
❑ 84OPC-229
❑ 84Pir-8
❑ 84Top-462
❑ 84TopSti-138
❑ 84TopTif-462
❑ 85AllGamPI-61
❑ 85BalOriP-12
❑ 85Don-508
❑ 85Fle-467
❑ 85FleStaS-9
❑ 85FleUpd-67
❑ 85Lea-40
❑ 85OriHea-8
❑ 85Top-669
❑ 85TopSti-126
❑ 85TopTif-669
❑ 85TopTifT-70T
❑ 85TopTra-70T
❑ 86BalOriHMP-8
❑ 86Don-228
❑ 86Fle-277
❑ 86Lea-104
❑ 86OPC-226
❑ 86Spo-87
❑ 86Top-226
❑ 86TopSti-229
❑ 86TopTif-226
❑ 87BalOriP-21
❑ 87Don-336
❑ 87Fle-473
❑ 87FleGlo-473
❑ 87OPC-182
❑ 87OriFreB-27
❑ 87Spo-86
❑ 87SpoTeaP-21
❑ 87Top-182
❑ 87TopSti-231
❑ 87TopTif-182
❑ 88Fle-565
❑ 88FleGlo-565
❑ 88Sco-173
❑ 88ScoGlo-173
❑ 88StaLinO-8
❑ 88Top-598
❑ 88TopTif-598
❑ 89PacSenL-184
❑ 89T/MSenL-61
❑ 89TopSenL-72
❑ 90DodTar-425
❑ 90EliSenL-25
❑ 90SweBasG-94
❑ 91DodUno7P-2
❑ 91OriCro-252

Lacy, Steve
❑ 75WatRoyT-17
❑ 76WatRoyT-16
❑ 77DayBealT-12

Ladd, Jeff
❑ 92St.CatBJC-18
❑ 92St.CatBJF-3389
❑ 93HagSunC-16
❑ 93HagSunF-1882
❑ 94HagSunC-10
❑ 94HagSunF-2734
❑ 94St.CatBJC-14
❑ 94St.CatBJF-3646
❑ 95HagSunF-71

Ladd, Pete
❑ 80Top-678
❑ 80VenLeaS-83
❑ 81TucTorT-19
❑ 82VanCanT-17
❑ 83BrePol-27
❑ 83Fle-37
❑ 84BreGar-10
❑ 84BrePol-27
❑ 84Don-124
❑ 84Fle-204
❑ 84FleSti-77
❑ 84Nes792-243
❑ 84Top-243
❑ 84TopTif-243
❑ 85BreGar-10
❑ 85BrePol-27
❑ 85Don-271
❑ 85Fle-585
❑ 85Top-471
❑ 85TopTif-471
❑ 86Fle-492
❑ 86FleUpd-63
❑ 86MarMot-17
❑ 86Top-163
❑ 86TopTif-163
❑ 86TopTra-58T
❑ 86TopTraT-58T
❑ 87AlbDukD-12
❑ 87AstShoSPT-18
❑ 87Don-660
❑ 87Fle-588
❑ 87FleGlo-588
❑ 87Top-572
❑ 87TopTif-572
❑ 92BreCarT-12
❑ 94BreMilB-47

Lade, Doyle
❑ 49Bow-168
❑ 49EurSta-60
❑ 50Bow-196
❑ 51Bow-139
❑ 76TayBow4-76
❑ 85TCMPla1-31

Ladell, Cleveland
❑ 92PriRedC-4
❑ 92PriRedF-3098
❑ 93CarLeaAGF-43
❑ 93WinSpiC-12
❑ 93WinSpiF-1581
❑ 94Bow-46
❑ 94ChaLooF-1370
❑ 94Cla-191
❑ 94ExcFS7-177
❑ 95ChaLooTI-12
❑ 96ChaLooB-16

Ladjevich, Rick
❑ 94BelMarC-17
❑ 94BelMarF-3243
❑ 96PorCitRB-18

Ladnier, Deric
❑ 86Ft.MyeRP-17
❑ 87AppFoxP-8
❑ 89MemChiB-11
❑ 89MemChiP-1189
❑ 89MemChiS-13
❑ 89Sta-43
❑ 91LinDriAA-409
❑ 91MemChiLD-409
❑ 91MemChiP-662

Lafata, Joe
❑ 49EurSta-115

Lafayette, George
❑ 22Zee-33
❑ 23Zee-46
❑ 23Zee-47
❑ 24Zee-32
❑ 25Zee-31
❑ 26Zee-95

LaFever, Greg
❑ 86WatIndP-17
❑ 87WilBiIP-17
❑ 88SanAntMB-4

Lafitte, Doc (Edward)
❑ 09ColChiE-161A
❑ 09ColChiE-161B
❑ 11PinT-5-168
❑ 12ColRedB-161A
❑ 12ColRedB-161B
❑ 12ColTinT-161A
❑ 12ColTinT-161B

Lafitte, James A.
❑ 09T206-497

LaFountain, James
❑ 77VisOakT-7

LaFrancois, Roger
❑ 81PawRedST-23
❑ 83Don-534
❑ 83PawRedST-12
❑ 83Top-344
❑ 84RicBraT-14
❑ 85DurBulT-27
❑ 88JamExpP-1894
❑ 89SouBenWSGS-4
❑ 90CMC-671
❑ 90ProAAAF-185
❑ 90VanCanC-27
❑ 90VanCanP-507
❑ 91LinDriAAA-650
❑ 91VanCanLD-650
❑ 91VanCanP-1611
❑ 92VanCanF-2735
❑ 92VanCanS-650
❑ 93NasSouF-585
❑ 94NasSouF-1266
❑ 95NasSouTI-9
❑ 96NasSouB-3
❑ 98PitMetM-1

Laga, Mike
❑ 81BirBarT-8
❑ 82EvaTriT-16
❑ 83EvaTriT-15
❑ 84Don-491
❑ 84EvaTriT-16
❑ 85NasSouTI-9
❑ 86Don-578
❑ 86TopTra-59T
❑ 86TopTraT-59T
❑ 87CarSmo-15
❑ 87Don-293
❑ 87LouRedTI-23
❑ 87Top-321
❑ 87TopTif-321
❑ 88LouRedBTI-26
❑ 89BirBarADB-20
❑ 89PhoFirC-17
❑ 89PhoFirP-1493
❑ 89Sco-536
❑ 90BirBarADB-20
❑ 90CMC-548
❑ 90PhoFirC-21

Lagarde, Joe
❑ 93YakBeaC-16
❑ 95SanBerSTI-12
❑ 96VerBeaDB-16
❑ 97Bow-149
❑ 97BowInt-149
❑ 97SanAntMB-5
❑ 98AlbDukG-16
❑ 98SanAntMM-5

Lagattuta, Rico
❑ 96SouOreTI-7
❑ 97SouOreTB-17

Lagimas, Tracie
❑ 91HawWomS-5

Lago, Pete
❑ 89CarNewE-15

Lagrandeur, Yan
❑ 96DanBraB-13
❑ 97EugEmeB-8

LaGrow, Lerrin
❑ 71OPC-39
❑ 71Top-39
❑ 73OPC-369
❑ 73Top-369
❑ 74OPC-433
❑ 74Top-433
❑ 75DetTigP-16
❑ 75OPC-116
❑ 75Top-116
❑ 75TopMin-116
❑ 76OPC-138
❑ 76SSP-356
❑ 76Top-138
❑ 76TulOilGP-13
❑ 77WhiSoxJT-9
❑ 77WhiSoxT-17
❑ 78OPC-152
❑ 78SSP270-161
❑ 78Top-14
❑ 79Top-527
❑ 80Top-624
❑ 90DodTar-426
❑ 97AriStaBG-14

Lague, Raymond
❑ 52LavPro-14

Lahey, Kevin
❑ 75WatRoyT-18

Lahman, Cal
❑ 33Zee-92

LaHonta, Ken
❑ 76DubPacT-18

Lahoud, Joe
❑ 69OPC-189
❑ 69Top-189
❑ 69TopFou-14
❑ 70OPC-78
❑ 70Top-78
❑ 71MLBOffS-321
❑ 71OPC-622
❑ 71Top-622
❑ 72MilBra-191
❑ 72OPC-321
❑ 72RedSoxTI-12
❑ 72Top-321
❑ 72TopCloT-19
❑ 73OPC-212
❑ 73Top-212
❑ 74OPC-512
❑ 74Top-512
❑ 75CalAngP-22
❑ 75Hos-10
❑ 75HosTwi-10
❑ 75OPC-317
❑ 75Top-317
❑ 75TopMin-317
❑ 76OPC-612
❑ 76SSP-201
❑ 76Top-612
❑ 78SSP270-226
❑ 78Top-382
❑ 81RedSoxBG2S-89
❑ 93RanKee-226
❑ 94BreMilB-48

Lahrman, Tom
❑ 86PenWhiSP-15
❑ 87PenWhiSP-22
❑ 88TamTarS-13

Lahti, Jeffrey Allen
❑ 80WatRedT-2
❑ 81IndIndTI-16
❑ 82LouRedE-13
❑ 83Car-14
❑ 83Fle-12
❑ 83Top-284
❑ 84Car-15
❑ 84Don-327
❑ 84Fle-327
❑ 84Nes792-593
❑ 84Top-593
❑ 84TopTif-593
❑ 85CarTeal-19
❑ 85Fle-231
❑ 85Top-447
❑ 85TopTif-447
❑ 86CarIGAS-8
❑ 86CarKASD-18
❑ 86CarSchM-12
❑ 86CarTeal-23
❑ 86Don-475
❑ 86Fle-40
❑ 86Lea-233
❑ 86SevCoi-S12
❑ 86Top-33
❑ 86TopTif-33
❑ 87Don-577
❑ 87Fle-299
❑ 87FleGlo-299
❑ 87Top-367
❑ 87TopTif-367

Lail, Denny
❑ 97TamYan-17
❑ 98TamYanM-16

Lain, Marty
❑ 83BeaGolGT-9

Lair, Scott
❑ 94JohCitCC-17
❑ 94JohCitCF-3697

Laird, Tony
❑ 85NasPirT-13
❑ 86NasPirP-14

Lairsey, Eric
❑ 91PulBraC-24
❑ 91PulBraP-4001
❑ 92IdaFalGF-3507
❑ 92IdaFalGSP-26

Lajeskie, Dick
❑ 48SomandK-22
❑ 49BowPCL-16
❑ 49SomandK-12

Lajoie, Nap (Napoleon)
❑ 03BreE10-86
❑ 03WilCarE-19
❑ 04FanCraAL-32
❑ 05IndSouPSoCP-13
❑ 08AmeLeaPC-11
❑ 08RosComP-27
❑ 09AmeCarE90-1-67
❑ 09ColChiE-162
❑ 09SpoNewSM-4
❑ 09SpoNewSM-6
❑ 09T206-199
❑ 09T206-200
❑ 09T206-201
❑ 10CouT21-165
❑ 10CouT21-166
❑ 10CouT21-167
❑ 10CouT21-297
❑ 10DomDisP-65
❑ 10E-UOraBSC-13
❑ 10E101-28
❑ 10E102-14
❑ 10E98-18
❑ 10MelMinE-28
❑ 10NadCarE-33
❑ 10NotCov-6
❑ 10OrnOvaPP-10
❑ 10PeoT21-33A
❑ 10PeoT21-33B
❑ 10PeoT21-33C
❑ 10RedCroT-39
❑ 10RedCroT-128
❑ 10RedCroT-211
❑ 10SepAnoP-17
❑ 10StaCarE-19
❑ 10SweCapPP-18
❑ 10W555-41
❑ 11BasBatEU-27
❑ 11DiaGumP-17
❑ 11E94-18
❑ 11HelSta-24
❑ 11L1L-121
❑ 11MecDFT-20
❑ 11PinT-5-603
❑ 11PinT-5-627
❑ 11PloCanE-39
❑ 11S81LarS-96
❑ 11SpoLifCW-211
❑ 11SpoLifM-45
❑ 11TurRedT-23
❑ 12ColRedB-162
❑ 12ColTinT-162
❑ 12PhiCarE-17
❑ 12VasSwe-4
❑ 13NatGamW-25
❑ 13TomBarW-24
❑ 14CraJacE-66
❑ 14PolGroW-12
❑ 14TexTomE-26
❑ 15AmeCarE106-24
❑ 15CraJacE-66
❑ 15SpoNewM-95
❑ 15VicT21-17
❑ 16BF2FP-37
❑ 16SpoNewM-97
❑ 19W514-62
❑ 33Gou-106
❑ 36Halof FP-16
❑ 39PC7AlbHoF-8
❑ 40PlaBal-173
❑ 48ExhHoF-20
❑ 50CalHOFW-47
❑ 53ArtHaloFP-53
❑ 60Fle-1
❑ 61Fle-120
❑ 61GolPre-31
❑ 63BazA-8
❑ 63HalofFB-26
❑ 67SpoHobFC-10
❑ 67TopVen-159
❑ 69Baz-10
❑ 69Baz-11
❑ 72ClaCar-30
❑ 72ClaCar-45
❑ 72FleFamF-28
❑ 73FleWilD-35
❑ 74CapPub-43
❑ 75FlePio-18
❑ 76MotOldT-2
❑ 76ShaPiz-6
❑ 77BobParHoF-31
❑ 77GalGloG-137
❑ 77GalGloG-260
❑ 77PhiFav-2
❑ 77ShaPiz-15
❑ 78DexHaloFP-30
❑ 80Lau300-9
❑ 80PacLeg-74
❑ 80PerHaloFP-8
❑ 80SSPHOF-8
❑ 81SpoHaloF-12
❑ 82OhiHaloF-26
❑ 82TCMGreH-24
❑ 84GalHaloFRL-6
❑ 86IndGreT-2
❑ 89HOFStiB-10

❑ 92ConTSN-528
❑ 93ConMasC-2
❑ 93ConTSN-837
❑ 93CraJac-8
❑ 94ConTSN-1218
❑ 94ConTSNB-1218
❑ 94OriofB-83
❑ 94UppDecAH-25
❑ 94UppDecAH-103
❑ 94UppDecAH-175
❑ 94UppDecAH1-25
❑ 94UppDecAH1-103
❑ 94UppDecAH1-175
❑ 94UppDecTAE-22
❑ 96PitPosH-8
❑ 99UppDecCL-29
❑ 99UppDecCLCC-29

Lajszky, Werner
❑ 80WauTimT-21

Lak, Carlos
❑ 91CliGiaP-842

Lake, Dan
❑ 85AncGlaPTI-18

Lake, Edward
❑ 41CarW75-13
❑ 43RedSoxTI-12
❑ 47Exh-129
❑ 47TipTop-35
❑ 49Bow-107
❑ 50Bow-240
❑ 51Bow-140
❑ 83TCMPla1945-19

Lake, Fred
❑ 11SpoLifM-142

Lake, Joe
❑ 09T206-202
❑ 09T206-203
❑ 09T206-204
❑ 10RedCroT-129
❑ 10RedCroT-212
❑ 10W555-42
❑ 11E94-19
❑ 11HelSta-61
❑ 11MecDFT-48
❑ 11PinT-5-103
❑ 11SpoLifCW-212
❑ 11SpoLifM-112
❑ 72ClaCar-97

Lake, Ken
❑ 89JamExpP-2148
❑ 89MiaMirIS-10
❑ 90WesPalBES-12
❑ 91HarSenLD-260
❑ 91HarSenP-641
❑ 91LinDriAA-260

Lake, Kevin
❑ 94EveGiaC-17
❑ 94EveGiaF-3650
❑ 95BurBeeTI-8
❑ 96BurBeeTI-9

Lake, Mike
❑ 77LodDodT-8
❑ 78LodDodT-11

Lake, Steve
❑ 80HolMilT-17
❑ 81VanCanT-25
❑ 82TucTorT-5
❑ 83CubThoAV-16
❑ 84CubChiT-16
❑ 84Don-198
❑ 84Nes792-691
❑ 84Top-691
❑ 84TopTif-691
❑ 85CubLioP-14
❑ 85CubSev-16
❑ 85Top-98
❑ 85TopTif-98
❑ 86CubGat-29
❑ 86Top-588
❑ 86TopTif-588
❑ 87CarSmo-10
❑ 87CarTeal-14
❑ 87Don-604
❑ 87Fle-300
❑ 87FleGlo-300
❑ 87Top-84
❑ 87TopTif-84
❑ 88CarSmo-11
❑ 88CarTeal-13
❑ 88Don-510
❑ 88Fle-38
❑ 88FleGlo-38
❑ 88Sco-596
❑ 88ScoGlo-596
❑ 88StaLinCa-11
❑ 88Top-208
❑ 88TopTif-208
❑ 89Bow-399
❑ 89BowTif-399
❑ 89Fle-454
❑ 89FleGlo-454
❑ 89PhiTas-17
❑ 89Sco-363
❑ 89ScoRoo-12T
❑ 89Top-463
❑ 89TopTif-463
❑ 89TopTra-65T
❑ 89TopTraT-65T
❑ 90Don-431
❑ 90Fle-566
❑ 90FleCan-566
❑ 90Lea-395
❑ 90OPC-183
❑ 90PhiTas-19
❑ 90PubIntS-245
❑ 90Sco-435
❑ 90Top-183
❑ 90TopBig-191
❑ 90TopTif-183
❑ 90UppDec-491
❑ 91Don-334
❑ 91Fle-403
❑ 91Lea-385
❑ 91OPC-661
❑ 91PhiMed-23
❑ 91Sco-572
❑ 91StaClu-395
❑ 91Stu-216
❑ 91Top-661
❑ 91TopDesS-661
❑ 91TopMic-661
❑ 91TopTif-661
❑ 92OPC-331
❑ 92PhiMed-18
❑ 92Sco-467
❑ 92StaClu-54
❑ 92Top-331
❑ 92TopGol-331
❑ 92TopGolW-331
❑ 92TopMic-331
❑ 93CubMar-12
❑ 93CubStaC-10
❑ 93Sco-443
❑ 94Fle-388

Lakeman, Al
❑ 49EurSta-14
❑ 55JetPos-9

Laker, Tim
❑ 88JamExpP-1904
❑ 89JamExpP-2137
❑ 90MidLeaASGS-13
❑ 90RocExpLC-14
❑ 90RocExpP-2696
❑ 91Cla/Bes-205
❑ 91WesPalBEC-16
❑ 91WesPalBEP-1232
❑ 92ClaFS7-125
❑ 92HarSenF-463
❑ 92HarSenS-286
❑ 92SkyAA F-121
❑ 93Bow-156
❑ 93Don-440
❑ 93Fle-77
❑ 93Lea-367
❑ 93OPC-276
❑ 93OPCPre-120
❑ 93PacSpa-534
❑ 93Pin-583
❑ 93StaClu-18
❑ 93StaCluFDI-18
❑ 93StaCluMOP-18
❑ 93Top-816
❑ 93TopGol-816
❑ 93TopInaM-816
❑ 93TopInaR-816
❑ 93TopMic-816
❑ 93Toy-7
❑ 93Ult-416
❑ 94Pin-465
❑ 94PinArtP-465
❑ 94PinMusC-465
❑ 94Top-524
❑ 94TopGol-524
❑ 94TopSpa-524
❑ 94TriAAF-AAA39
❑ 96Don-211
❑ 96DonPreP-211
❑ 96Fle-460
❑ 96FleTif-460
❑ 96Sco-452
❑ 97RocRedW-16
❑ 98DurBulTI-15

Lakman, Jason
❑ 96AppLeaAB-5
❑ 96BriWhiSB-22
❑ 97HicCraB-19
❑ 97HicCraRB-24
❑ 98CarLeaTPQ-19
❑ 98WinWar-16

Lakovic, Greg
❑ 96ForWayWB-13

LaLonge, L. N.
❑ 09ObaT21-14
❑ 09ObaT21-144
❑ 09ObaT21-311
❑ 11BigEatEU-10
❑ 11PacCoaBD-34
❑ 11Zee-70
❑ 12ObaPreT-60
❑ 12Zee-67

Lamabe, Jack
❑ 62Top-593
❑ 63Top-251
❑ 64RedSoxTI-2
❑ 64Top-305
❑ 64TopVen-305
❑ 65OPC-88
❑ 65RedSoxTI-6
❑ 65Top-88
❑ 66Top-577
❑ 67Top-208
❑ 68Top-311
❑ 68TopVen-311
❑ 81RedSoxBG2S-90
❑ 85BeaGolGT-24
❑ 91MetWIZ-223
❑ 92ChaRaiC-23
❑ 92ChaRaiF-136
❑ 93CenValRC-27
❑ 93CenValRF-2910
❑ 94AshTouC-27
❑ 94AshTouF-1798
❑ 95AshTouTI-36
❑ 96NewHavRB-3
❑ 97AshTou-28
❑ 98SalAvaC-15

LaMacchia, Al
❑ 46SeaSLP-36

LaManna, Frank
❑ 77TCMTheWY-63

Lamanno, Ray
❑ 46SpoExcW-8-9
❑ 49Bow-113

Lamanske, Frank
❑ 30Zee-180
❑ 31Zee-120
❑ 37Zee-17
❑ 90DodTar-1009

Lamar, Bill
❑ 89CedRapRAB-35
❑ 90DodTar-427
❑ 93ConTSN-852

LaMar, Danny
❑ 82CedRapRT-12
❑ 83TamTarT-16
❑ 84CedRapRT-18

Lamar, Johnny
❑ 92BriTigC-24
❑ 92BriTigF-1425
❑ 93LakTigC-14
❑ 93LakTigF-1323
❑ 94ChaWheC-17
❑ 94ChaWheF-2712

Lamar, Mascot
❑ 90CedRapRDGB-35

LaMarche, Michel
❑ 87SpaPhiP-10

LaMarque, Jim
❑ 92NegLeaRLI-37
❑ 96NegLeaBMKC-4

LaMaster, Wayne
❑ 90DodTar-428

Lamattina, Ryan
❑ 98PorRocG-22

Lamb, David
❑ 94AlbPolF-2243
❑ 94Bow-36
❑ 94OriPro-51
❑ 96HigDesMB-16
❑ 97CalLeaATI-33
❑ 97CarLeaTP-20
❑ 97FreKey-12
❑ 98BowBayM-20
❑ 99PacOme-233
❑ 99PacOmeC-233
❑ 99PacOmeG-233
❑ 99PacOmePB-233

Lamb, Michael
❑ 98Cha-18

Lamb, Randy
❑ 77CocAstT-10
❑ 78WauMetT-15

Lamb, Ray
❑ 70OPC-131
❑ 70Top-131
❑ 71Ind-8
❑ 71MLBOffS-377
❑ 71OPC-727
❑ 71Top-727
❑ 72OPC-422
❑ 72Top-422
❑ 73IndTeal-16
❑ 73OPC-496
❑ 73Top-496
❑ 85SpoIndGC-11
❑ 90DodTar-429

Lamb, Todd
❑ 84DurBulT-19
❑ 85GreBraTI-11
❑ 86DurBulP-17

Lamber, Justin
❑ 97SpoIndG-15
❑ 98WilBluRC-15

Lambert, Clark
❑ 98PitMetM-15

Lambert, Don
❑ 20Zee-27

Lambert, Gene
❑ 82CliGiaF-17
❑ 83CliGiaF-10

Lambert, Jeremy
❑ 97JohCitCTI-19
❑ 98JohCCTI-19

Lambert, Ken
❑ 87VerBeaDP-10

Lambert, Kristopher
❑ 97EriSeaWB-21
❑ 98LynHilQ-9

Lambert, Layne
❑ 90AubAstP-3396
❑ 91BurAstC-16
❑ 91BurAstP-2810
❑ 92OscAstC-15

Lambert, Mark
❑ 90HigSchPLS-17
❑ 98BriBluM-2

Lambert, Reese
❑ 87HunStaTI-19
❑ 87MadMusP-23
❑ 88TacTigC-4
❑ 88TacTigP-631
❑ 89TacTigC-3
❑ 89TacTigP-1548
❑ 90CMC-585
❑ 90ProAAAF-134
❑ 90TacTigC-8
❑ 90TacTigP-87
❑ 92OmaRoyF-2957
❑ 92OmaRoyS-333

Lambert, Reggie
❑ 86PalSprAP-20
❑ 86PalSprAS-27
❑ 87PalSprP-5
❑ 88PalSprACLC-113
❑ 88PalSprAP-1461

Lambert, Rob
❑ 87PriWilYP-25
❑ 88ColCliC-14
❑ 88ColCliP-319

Lambert, Tim
❑ 82IdaFalAT-10
❑ 84AlbA'sT-17
❑ 85TacTigC-140
❑ 86TacTigP-11
❑ 87MemChiB-16
❑ 87MemChiP-13
❑ 90AlbDecGB-24

Lamkey, William
❑ 80WisRapTT-6

Lamle, Adam
❑ 88ChaRanS-12
❑ 88FloStaLAS-41
❑ 89MiaMirIS-10
❑ 89TulDriGS-12

Lamline, Fred
❑ 09ObaT21-363
❑ 12ObaPreT-112

Lammon, John
❑ 90ElmPioP-14
❑ 91ElmPioC-7
❑ 91ElmPioP-3272

Lamonde, Larry
❑ 82AleDukT-3
❑ 84HawIslC-124
❑ 85NasPirT-14

Lamont, Gene
❑ 71OPC-39
❑ 71Top-39
❑ 75DetTigP-17
❑ 75OPC-593
❑ 75Top-593
❑ 75TopMin-593
❑ 84OmaRoyT-2
❑ 85OmaRoyT-22
❑ 88PirTeal-17
❑ 89PirVerFJ-36
❑ 90PirHomC-16
❑ 92TopTra-62T
❑ 92TopTraG-62T
❑ 92WhiSoxK-33
❑ 92WhiSoxK-NNO
❑ 93Top-504
❑ 93TopGol-504
❑ 93TopInaM-504
❑ 93TopInaR-504
❑ 93TopMic-504
❑ 93WhiSoxK-16
❑ 93WhiSoxK-30
❑ 94WhiSoxK-18
❑ 94WhiSoxK-30
❑ 97PirPos-19

Lamp, Dennis
❑ 78SSP270-260
❑ 78Top-711
❑ 79Top-153
❑ 80OPC-129
❑ 80Top-54
❑ 81Don-573
❑ 81Fle-305
❑ 81Top-331
❑ 81TopTra-785
❑ 82Don-619
❑ 82Fle-349
❑ 82Top-216
❑ 82Top-622
❑ 83AllGamPI-81
❑ 83Don-165
❑ 83Fle-243
❑ 83OPC-26
❑ 83Top-434
❑ 83WhiSoxTV-53
❑ 84BluJayFS-21
❑ 84Don-526
❑ 84Fle-66
❑ 84FleUpd-68
❑ 84Nes792-541
❑ 84Top-541
❑ 84TopSti-239
❑ 84TopTif-541
❑ 84TopTra-69T
❑ 84TopTraT-69T
❑ 85BluJayFS-17
❑ 85Don-119
❑ 85Fle-111
❑ 85OPC-83
❑ 85Top-774
❑ 85TopTif-774
❑ 86BluJayAF-17
❑ 86BluJayFS-21
❑ 86Don-626
❑ 86Fle-64
❑ 86Lea-244
❑ 86OPC-219
❑ 86Top-219
❑ 86TopSti-193
❑ 86TopTat-12
❑ 86TopTif-219
❑ 87Fle-233
❑ 87FleGlo-233
❑ 87OPC-336
❑ 87Top-768
❑ 87TopTif-768
❑ 88DonTeaBRS-NEW
❑ 88Fle-284
❑ 88FleGlo-284
❑ 88Sco-616
❑ 88ScoGlo-616
❑ 88ScoRoo-6T
❑ 88ScoRooG-6T
❑ 89Don-633
❑ 89Fle-92
❑ 89FleGlo-92
❑ 89Sco-508
❑ 89Top-188
❑ 89TopBig-169
❑ 89TopTif-188
❑ 89UppDec-503
❑ 90Don-423
❑ 90Fle-280
❑ 90FleCan-280
❑ 90Lea-315
❑ 90OPC-338
❑ 90PubIntS-460
❑ 90RedSoxP-12
❑ 90Sco-471
❑ 90Top-338
❑ 90TopTif-338
❑ 90TopTVRS-13
❑ 91Don-138
❑ 91Fle-101
❑ 91OPC-14
❑ 91RedSoxP-11
❑ 91RedSoxP-17
❑ 91Sco-612
❑ 91Top-14
❑ 91TopDesS-14
❑ 91TopMic-14
❑ 91TopTif-14
❑ 92Fle-42
❑ 92OPC-653
❑ 92Sco-335
❑ 92Top-653
❑ 92TopGol-653
❑ 92TopGolW-653
❑ 92TopMic-653

Lampard, Keith (C. Keith)
❑ 70AstPho-12
❑ 70OPC-492
❑ 70Top-492
❑ 71OPC-728
❑ 71Top-728
❑ 72OPC-489
❑ 72Top-489

Lampe, Ed
❑ 88HamRedP-1742

Lampert, Ken
❑ 86VerBeaDP-15

Lamphere, Larry (Lawrence)
❑ 87PanAmTUBI-2
❑ 87PanAmTURB-11
❑ 88AubAstP-1947
❑ 89AshTouP-967
❑ 89SouAtlLAGS-4
❑ 90OscAstS-14

Lampkin, Steve
❑ 92LetMouSP-22

Lampkin, Tom
❑ 87WatIndP-23
❑ 88BasAmeAAB-7
❑ 88EasLeaAP-41
❑ 88WilBilP-1304
❑ 89ColSprSSP-254
❑ 89Don-639
❑ 89TriAAAP-AAA35
❑ 90CMC-464
❑ 90ColSprSSC-12
❑ 90ColSprSSP-39
❑ 90IndTeal-23
❑ 90OPC-172
❑ 90ProAAAF-220
❑ 90Top-172
❑ 90TopTif-172
❑ 91Lea-512
❑ 91PadMag-4
❑ 91PadSmo-18
❑ 91Sco-720
❑ 91Sco100RS-70
❑ 91StaClu-530
❑ 92Fle-610
❑ 92LasVegSS-234
❑ 92PadPolD-12
❑ 92PadSmo-15
❑ 92Sco-338
❑ 92StaClu-453
❑ 93Don-654
❑ 93FleFinE-226
❑ 93NewOrlZF-976
❑ 93Top-492
❑ 93TopGol-492
❑ 93TopInaM-492
❑ 93TopInaR-492
❑ 93TopMic-492
❑ 94BreMilB-49
❑ 94PhoFirF-1523
❑ 94StaClu-147
❑ 94StaCluFDI-147
❑ 94StaCluGR-147
❑ 94StaCluMOP-147
❑ 94Top-558
❑ 94TopGol-558
❑ 94TopSpa-558
❑ 95GiaMot-15
❑ 96GiaMot-22
❑ 96LeaSigEA-105

❑ 97CarPol-13
❑ 97ColSprSATTI-14
❑ 97PacPriGotD-GD218
❑ 98PacOnl-615
❑ 98PacOnlR-615
❑ 98PacOnlWC-615
❑ 99UppDec-185
❑ 99UppDec-488
❑ 99UppDecEL1-185
❑ 99UppDecEL1-488
❑ 99UppDecEL2-185
❑ 99UppDecEL2-488
Lampley, Danny
❑ 98LowSpiM-23
Lamplugh, Ian
❑ 92CalLeaACL-26
Lamson, Chuck
❑ 78AshTouT-14
❑ 80TulDriT-20
Lancaster, Brian
❑ 96EriSeaB-3
❑ 97AugGre-5
Lancaster, Les (Lester)
❑ 86WinSpiP-12
❑ 87CubCan-13
❑ 87DonRoo-10
❑ 88CubDavB-50
❑ 88Don-561
❑ 88DonBasB-172
❑ 88DonTeaBC-561
❑ 88Fle-421
❑ 88FleGlo-421
❑ 88Sco-602
❑ 88ScoGlo-602
❑ 88Top-112
❑ 88TopClo-57
❑ 88TopTif-112
❑ 89CubMar-50
❑ 89Don-341
❑ 89Fle-429
❑ 89FleGlo-429
❑ 89IowCubC-8
❑ 89IowCubP-1689
❑ 89Sco-60
❑ 89Top-694
❑ 89TopTif-694
❑ 89UppDec-84
❑ 90CubMar-11
❑ 90Don-628
❑ 90DonBesN-38
❑ 90Fle-35
❑ 90FleCan-35
❑ 90Lea-361
❑ 90OPC-437
❑ 90Sco-413
❑ 90Top-437
❑ 90TopTif-437
❑ 90TopTVCu-11
❑ 90UppDec-584
❑ 91CubMar-50
❑ 91CubVinL-16
❑ 91Don-256
❑ 91Fle-424
❑ 91OPC-86
❑ 91Sco-293A
❑ 91Sco-293B
❑ 91Top-86
❑ 91TopDesS-86
❑ 91TopMic-86
❑ 91TopTif-86
❑ 91Ult-63
❑ 92Don-296
❑ 92Fle-384
❑ 92Lea-402
❑ 92LeaBlaG-402
❑ 92OPC-213
❑ 92Sco-348
❑ 92StaClu-88
❑ 92TigKro-17
❑ 92Top-213
❑ 92TopGol-213
❑ 92TopGolW-213
❑ 92TopMic-213
❑ 92Ult-177
❑ 92UppDec-481
❑ 93CarStaC-26
❑ 93FleFinE-126
❑ 93PacSpa-111
❑ 94Fle-635
❑ 94Pac-594
❑ 94Sco-269
❑ 94ScoGolR-269
❑ 94StaCluT-330
❑ 94StaCluTFDI-330
❑ 94SyrChiF-969
❑ 94SyrChiTI-16
Lance, Gary
❑ 75OmaRoyTI-8
❑ 76OmaRoyTT-10
❑ 76VenLeaS-36
❑ 79SpoIndT-11
❑ 83IdaFalAT-32
❑ 84MadMusP-2
❑ 85HunStaJ-24
❑ 87ChaRaiP-9
❑ 88ChaRaiP-1212
❑ 89BlaYNPRWL-130
❑ 89WicStaR-28
❑ 89WicWraR-38
❑ 90CMC-526
❑ 90LasVegSC-23
❑ 90LasVegSP-138
❑ 90MarPhiP-3191
❑ 90ProAAAF-26
❑ 91PacSenL-62
❑ 91SumFlyC-27
❑ 91SumFlyP-2352
❑ 92AlbPolCB-29
❑ 92AlbPolF-2322
❑ 92AlbPolF-2323
❑ 93CarLeaAGF-14
❑ 93WilBluRC-28
❑ 93WilBluRF-2014
❑ 94CarLeaAF-CAR19
❑ 94WilBluRC-25
❑ 94WilBluRF-316
❑ 95WicWraTI-11
❑ 96WicWraB-29
❑ 97WicWra-26
❑ 98OmaRoyM-2
Lance, Mark
❑ 83DurBulT-19
❑ 84DurBulT-2
Lancellotti, Rick
❑ 78SalPirT-7
❑ 79BufBisT-3
❑ 80PorBeaT-20
❑ 81HawIslT-9
❑ 82HawIslT-11
❑ 84LasVegSC-230
❑ 85TidTidT-1
❑ 86PhoFirP-14
❑ 87JapPlaB-3
❑ 89PawRedSTI-13
❑ 90CMC-270
❑ 90PawRedSC-19
❑ 90PawRedSDD-12
❑ 90PawRedSP-472
❑ 90ProAAAF-444
❑ 90TopTVRS-48
❑ 91LinDriAAA-358
❑ 91PacSenL-122
❑ 91PawRedSDD-10
❑ 91PawRedSLD-358
❑ 91PawRedSP-47
Land, Grover
❑ 11PinT-5-617
❑ 19Zee-115
Landaker, Dave
❑ 92ClaDraP-26
❑ 92FroRowDP-94
❑ 92FroRowDPG-94
❑ 92FroRowDPS-94
❑ 92HigSchPLS-19
❑ 92HigSchPLS-NNO
❑ 93Top-743
❑ 93TopGol-743
❑ 93TopInaM-743
❑ 93TopInaR-743
❑ 93TopMic-743
❑ 94QuaCitRBF-542
❑ 96KisCobB-12
Landers, Hank
❑ 83BelBreFr-7
Landers, Lee
❑ 76TulOilGP-26
❑ 78SprRedWK-12
Landers, Mark
❑ 94MedHatBJF-3688
❑ 94MedHatBJSP-1
❑ 95StCatSTI-20
Landestoy, Rafael
❑ 75WatDodT-9
❑ 78AstPos-14
❑ 78SSP270-74
❑ 79AstPos-12
❑ 79AstTeal-8
❑ 79Top-14
❑ 80Top-268
❑ 81AllGamPI-103
❑ 81CokTeaS-65
❑ 81Don-19
❑ 81Fle-70
❑ 81OPC-326
❑ 81Top-597
❑ 81TopSti-168
❑ 81TopTra-786
❑ 82Fle-73
❑ 82RedCok-13
❑ 82Top-361
❑ 83Fle-595
❑ 83Top-684
❑ 83TopTra-59T
❑ 84DodPol-17
❑ 84Nes792-477
❑ 84Top-477
❑ 84TopTif-477
❑ 85AlbYanT-17
❑ 85DomLeaS-11
❑ 85TucTorC-61
❑ 87AstShoSPO-15
❑ 87PocGiaTB-2
❑ 89ExpPos-16
❑ 89PacSenL-60
❑ 89T/MSenL-62
❑ 89TopSenL-5
❑ 90DodTar-430
❑ 90EliSenL-85
❑ 90ExpPos-20
❑ 91PacSenL-24
❑ 94St.LucMC-27
❑ 94St.LucMF-1211
❑ 95StLucMTI-1
Landinez, Carlos
❑ 90SprCarB-12
❑ 91SavCarC-18
❑ 91SavCarP-1659
❑ 92St.PetCF-2035
❑ 93LinVenB-53
❑ 93SprCarC-17
❑ 93SprCarF-1861
Landingham, James B.
❑ 98BriBluM-16
Landis, Craig
❑ 78CedRapGT-13
❑ 80PhoGiaVNB-14
❑ 81RicBraT-5
Landis, Jim
❑ 47Exh-130
❑ 57Top-375
❑ 58Top-108A
❑ 58Top-108B
❑ 59Top-493
❑ 60MacSta-11
❑ 60Top-550
❑ 60WhiSoxJP-5
❑ 60WhiSoxTS-9
❑ 61Pos-27A
❑ 61Pos-27B
❑ 61Top-271
❑ 61TopStaI-122
❑ 61WhiSoxTS-6
❑ 62Baz-19
❑ 62ExhStaB-20
❑ 62Jel-50
❑ 62Pos-50
❑ 62PosCan-50
❑ 62SalPlaC-49
❑ 62ShiPlaC-49
❑ 62Top-540
❑ 62TopBuc-47
❑ 62TopStal-26
❑ 62WhiSoxJP-5
❑ 62WhiSoxTS-9
❑ 63BasMagM-48
❑ 63ExhStaB-38
❑ 63Fle-10
❑ 63Jel-40
❑ 63Pos-40
❑ 63SalMetC-60
❑ 63Top-485
❑ 63WhiSoxJP-7
❑ 63WhiSoxTS-15
❑ 64A's-11
❑ 64Top-264
❑ 64TopVen-264
❑ 64WhiSoxI-16
❑ 64WhiSoxTS-14
❑ 65AthJayP-9
❑ 65Top-376
❑ 66OPC-128
❑ 66Top-128
❑ 66TopVen-128
❑ 67CokCapAs-17
❑ 67DexPre-121
❑ 67Top-483
❑ 79DiaGre-148
❑ 81WhiSox1T-6
❑ 85WhiSoxC-8
❑ 87AstShowSTh-10
❑ 89WhiSoxK-4
Landis, Judge (Kenesaw M.)
❑ 39PC7AlbHoF-28
❑ 50CalHOFW-48
❑ 53ArtHaloFP-54
❑ 60Fle-64
❑ 61Fle-53
❑ 63BazA-30
❑ 68SCFOldT-35
❑ 70FleWorS-18
❑ 70SpoCarfCOP-15
❑ 75TCMAllG-20
❑ 76ShaPiz-28
❑ 77BobParHoF-63
❑ 77GalGloG-123
❑ 80PerHaloFP-28
❑ 80SSPHOF-28
❑ 82OhiHaloF-49
❑ 84GalHaloFRL-28
❑ 88LitSunBS-15
❑ 88PacEigMO-67
❑ 88PacEigMO-79
❑ 89HOFStiB-95
❑ 91FouBal-9
❑ 93DiaStaES-153
❑ 94UppDecTAE-33
Landis, William
❑ 68OPC-189
❑ 68Top-189
❑ 68TopVen-189
❑ 69RedSoxTI-5
❑ 69Top-264
❑ 72MilBra-192
Landmark, Neil
❑ 85VisOakT-20
Landphere, Ed
❑ 90SalSpuCLC-130
❑ 90SalSpuP-2728
Landreaux, Ken
❑ 78AngFamF-21
❑ 78SSP270-190
❑ 79Top-619
❑ 79TwiFriP-15
❑ 80OPC-49
❑ 80Top-88
❑ 80TwiPos-16
❑ 81AllGamPI-149
❑ 81Dod-16
❑ 81DodPol-44B
❑ 81DodPos-5
❑ 81Don-565
❑ 81Fle-553
❑ 81FleStiC-46
❑ 81Kel-30
❑ 81LonBeaPT-6
❑ 81OPC-219
❑ 81Top-219
❑ 81TopScr-41
❑ 81TopSti-101
❑ 81TopTra-787
❑ 82DodPol-44
❑ 82DodUniOV-9
❑ 82Don-388
❑ 82Fle-11
❑ 82OPC-114
❑ 82Top-114
❑ 82TopSti-49
❑ 82TopStiV-49
❑ 83AllGamPI-149
❑ 83DodPol-44
❑ 83DodPos-6
❑ 83Don-236
❑ 83Fle-210
❑ 83FleSta-99
❑ 83FleSti-120
❑ 83Top-376
❑ 83TopSti-246
❑ 84AllGamPI-54
❑ 84DodPol-44
❑ 84DodSmo-1
❑ 84Don-470
❑ 84Fle-104
❑ 84FleSti-2
❑ 84Nes792-533
❑ 84OPC-216
❑ 84Top-533
❑ 84TopSti-76
❑ 84TopTif-533
❑ 85DodCokP-17
❑ 85Don-494
❑ 85Fle-375
❑ 85Top-418
❑ 85TopSti-75
❑ 85TopTif-418
❑ 86DodCokP-15
❑ 86DodPol-44
❑ 86DodUniOP-11
❑ 86Don-470
❑ 86Fle-134
❑ 86OPC-2
❑ 86Top-782
❑ 86TopTif-782
❑ 87DodMot-24
❑ 87DodPol-23
❑ 87Don-352
❑ 87DonOpeD-81
❑ 87Fle-444
❑ 87FleGlo-444
❑ 87OPC-123
❑ 87Top-699
❑ 87TopTif-699
❑ 88RocRedWGCP-14
❑ 88Sco-247
❑ 88ScoGlo-247
❑ 88Top-23
❑ 88TopClo-58
❑ 88TopTif-23
❑ 89T/MSenL-63
❑ 89TopSenL-109
❑ 90DodTar-431
❑ 90El PasDAGTI-41
❑ 90EliSenL-9
❑ 91PacSenL-134
❑ 97AriStaBG-15
Landress, Roger
❑ 91EugEmeC-24
❑ 91EugEmeP-3722
❑ 92AppFoxCB-5
❑ 92AppFoxFI-980
❑ 92BasCitRF-3842
❑ 93WilBluRC-16
❑ 93WilBluRF-1994
Landreth, Harry
❑ 83ChaLooT-25
❑ 84ChaLooT-14
Landreth, Larry
❑ 78Top-701
Landrith, Dave
❑ 83ButCopKT-13
Landrith, Hobie
❑ 54Bow-220
❑ 55Bow-50
❑ 56Top-314
❑ 57Top-182
❑ 58Top-24A
❑ 58Top-24B
❑ 59Top-422
❑ 60Top-42
❑ 60TopVen-42
❑ 61Pos-150A
❑ 61Pos-150B
❑ 61Top-114
❑ 61TopStal-78
❑ 62BalOriP-15
❑ 62MetJayP-7
❑ 62SalPlaC-181
❑ 62ShiPlaC-181
❑ 62Top-279
❑ 62TopStal-157
❑ 63BalOriP-16
❑ 63Top-209
❑ 74MetOriEB-9
❑ 81TCM60I-344
❑ 91MetWIZ-224
❑ 91OriCro-253
Landrum, Bill
❑ 82WatRedT-1
❑ 83WatRedT-5
❑ 84WicAerRD-17
❑ 87RedKah-43
❑ 88BlaYNPRWL-59
❑ 88Fle-238
❑ 88FleGlo-238
❑ 88IowCubC-8
❑ 88IowCubP-541
❑ 88Top-42
❑ 88TopTif-42
❑ 89BufBisC-2
❑ 89BufBisP-1674
❑ 89FleUpd-116
❑ 89PirVerFJ-43
❑ 90Bow-166
❑ 90BowTif-166
❑ 90Don-668
❑ 90DonBesN-58
❑ 90Fle-472
❑ 90FleCan-472
❑ 90Lea-222
❑ 90OPC-425
❑ 90PanSti-326
❑ 90PirHomC-17
❑ 90PubIntS-157
❑ 90Sco-456
❑ 90Top-425
❑ 90TopBig-164
❑ 90TopSti-128
❑ 90TopTif-425
❑ 90UppDec-442
❑ 91Bow-523
❑ 91Don-350
❑ 91Fle-41
❑ 91OPC-595
❑ 91Sco-98
❑ 91SimandSMLBL-24
❑ 91StaClu-431
❑ 91Stu-225
❑ 91Top-595
❑ 91TopDesS-595
❑ 91TopMic-595
❑ 91TopTif-595
❑ 91Ult-281
❑ 91UppDec-614
❑ 92Don-221
❑ 92ExpDonD-17A
❑ 92ExpPos-20
❑ 92Fle-557
❑ 92Lea-333
❑ 92LeaBlaG-333
❑ 92OPC-661
❑ 92OPCPre-68
❑ 92Pin-116
❑ 92Sco-196
❑ 92StaClu-672
❑ 92StaCluECN-672
❑ 92Top-661
❑ 92TopGol-661
❑ 92TopGolW-661
❑ 92TopMic-661
❑ 92TriPla-248
❑ 92UppDec-636
❑ 93RedKah-12
❑ 94Fle-413
Landrum, Ced (Cedric)
❑ 86GenCubP-13
❑ 87WinSpiP-4
❑ 88PitCubP-1370
❑ 89ChaKniTI-4
❑ 90CMC-94
❑ 90IowCubC-19
❑ 90IowCubP-330
❑ 90ProAAAF-637
❑ 90TopTVCu-51
❑ 91Cla3-T49
❑ 91DonRoo-11
❑ 91IowCubLD-208
❑ 91IowCubP-1075
❑ 91LinDriAAA-208
❑ 92Don-662
❑ 92Fle-385
❑ 92IowCubS-211
❑ 92OPC-81
❑ 92Sco-418
❑ 92Sco100RS-30
❑ 92StaClu-334
❑ 92Top-81
❑ 92TopDeb91-106
❑ 92TopGol-81
❑ 92TopGolW-81
❑ 92TopMic-81
❑ 92UppDec-50
❑ 94Pac-409
Landrum, Darryl
❑ 86VenGulP-11
❑ 87DunBluJP-933
❑ 88WilBilP-1319
Landrum, Don
❑ 58Top-291
❑ 61Top-338
❑ 62Top-323
❑ 63CubJayP-8
❑ 63Jel-175
❑ 63Pos-175
❑ 63Top-113
❑ 64Top-286
❑ 64TopVen-286
❑ 65Top-596
❑ 66OPC-43
❑ 66Top-43A
❑ 66Top-43B
❑ 66Top-43C
❑ 66TopRubI-50
❑ 66TopVen-43

Landrum, Joe
❑ 74dod195T-20
Landrum, Tito (Terry)
❑ 76ArkTraT-6
❑ 77ArkTraT-4A
❑ 77ArkTraT-4B
❑ 78St.PetCT-16
❑ 79ArkTraT-4
❑ 81Fle-539
❑ 81Top-244
❑ 82Don-292
❑ 82Fle-118
❑ 82Top-658
❑ 83Don-498
❑ 83Fle-13
❑ 83LouRedR-12
❑ 83Top-337
❑ 84Car-16
❑ 84FleUpd-69
❑ 84TopSti-14
❑ 85CarTeal-20
❑ 85Don-168
❑ 85Fle-232
❑ 85OPC-33
❑ 85Top-33
❑ 85TopTif-33
❑ 86CarlGAS-7
❑ 86CarKASD-3
❑ 86CarSchM-13
❑ 86CarTeal-24
❑ 86Don-425
❑ 86Fle-41
❑ 86OPC-171
❑ 86Top-498
❑ 86TopSti-19
❑ 86TopTat-15
❑ 86TopTif-498
❑ 87CarSmo-23
❑ 87CarTeal-15
❑ 87Don-386
❑ 87DonOpeD-66
❑ 87Fle-301
❑ 87FleGlo-301
❑ 87OPC-288
❑ 87Top-288
❑ 87TopTif-288
❑ 88DodPol-21
❑ 88RocRedWC-22
❑ 88Top-581
❑ 88TopTif-581
❑ 89NasSouTI-11
❑ 89PacSenL-168
❑ 89T/MSenL-64
❑ 89TopSenL-94
❑ 90DodTar-432
❑ 90EliSenL-26
❑ 90MiaMirIS-15
❑ 91GreFalDSP-28
❑ 91OriCro-254
❑ 91PacSenL-149
❑ 92YakBeaC-11
❑ 92YakBeaF-3462
❑ 93VerBeaDC-13
❑ 93VerBeaDF-2231
❑ 94BakDodC-13
❑ 95SanAntMTI-32
❑ 96SanBerSB-14
Landry, Greg
❑ 89BelBrelS-13
❑ 89HelBreSP-10
❑ 90BelBreB-9
Landry, Howard
❑ 89WinHavRSS-11
❑ 90LynRedSTI-19
Landry, Jacques
❑ 97WesMicW-15
❑ 98LakTigM-16
Landry, Lonny
❑ 93BriTigC-14
❑ 93BriTigF-3664
❑ 94JamJamC-13
❑ 94JamJamF-3979
❑ 96LakTigB-15
Landry, Todd
❑ 93HelBreF-4101
❑ 93HelBreSP-9
❑ 94StoPorC-14
❑ 94StoPorF-1700
❑ 95ElPasDTI-14
❑ 96BesAutSA-39
❑ 97BesAutAS-26
❑ 97El PasDB-7
❑ 98BinMetQ-17
Landstad, Rob
❑ 96BurIndB-18
Landuyt, Doug
❑ 78CedRapGT-14
❑ 81ShrCapT-14
❑ 83PhoGiaBHN-25
Landy, Brian
❑ 88BilMusP-1820
❑ 89GreHorP-412
Landy, Ron
❑ 89GeoColC-18
Lane, Aaron
❑ 93AlbPolF-2024
❑ 94AlbPolC-15
❑ 94AlbPolF-2233
❑ 95AusFut-51
❑ 95BowBayTI-19
❑ 96RocRedWB-17
Lane, Andy
❑ 94DavLipB-13
Lane, Bill
❑ 21Zee-145
❑ 22Zee-131
❑ 23Zee-164
Lane, Brian
❑ 88GreHorP-1555
❑ 88SouAtlLAGS-7
❑ 89BasAmeAPB-AA16
❑ 89ChaLooB-4
❑ 89ChaLooGS-14
❑ 90Bow-48
❑ 90BowTif-48
❑ 90CMC-145
❑ 90NasSouC-20
❑ 90NasSouP-239
❑ 90ProAAAF-551
❑ 92ChaLooS-189
❑ 92ClaFS7-87
❑ 92NasSouF-1839
❑ 92SkyAA F-84
❑ 93ChaLooF-2368
❑ 93ClaFS7-215
Lane, Dan
❑ 94WesPalBEC-15
❑ 94WesPalBEF-50
❑ 95HarSenTI-7
Lane, Danny
❑ 92JamExpC-14
❑ 92JamExpF-1507
Lane, Frank
❑ 59Ind-9
❑ 61A'sTeal-11
❑ 83FraBroR-29
Lane, Gene
❑ 82DurBulT-24
❑ 90BurBraB-29
❑ 90BurBraS-31
Lane, Heath
❑ 87AriWilP-9
❑ 88AriWilP-8
❑ 89BelBrelS-14
❑ 90RivRedWB-26
❑ 90RivRedWCLC-19
❑ 90RivRedWP-2604
Lane, Ira
❑ 82DayBeaAT-14
Lane, Jerry
❑ 81ElPasDT-7
Lane, Jerry (Jerald H.)
❑ 54Top-97
❑ 94TopArc1-97
❑ 94TopArc1G-97
Lane, Kevin
❑ 91BurAstC-6
❑ 91BurAstP-2797
❑ 92OscAstC-25
❑ 92OscAstF-2528
❑ 93FloStaLAF-35
❑ 93OscAstC-15
❑ 93OscAstF-623
❑ 94ClaGolF-134
Lane, Marvin
❑ 77EvaTriT-17
Lane, Mike
❑ 94BluOriF-3559
Lane, Nolan
❑ 88CapCodPPaLP-46
❑ 89BurIndS-15
❑ 89Sta-179
❑ 90CarLeaA-42
❑ 90KinIndTI-10
❑ 91CanIndLD-87
❑ 91CanIndP-990
❑ 91LinDriAA-87
❑ 92CanIndS-111
❑ 92Ft.MyeMCB-20
❑ 92SkyAA F-52
Lane, Ryan
❑ 94EliTwiC-10
❑ 94EliTwiF-3739
❑ 95ForWayWTI-18
❑ 96FtMyeMB-18
❑ 97NewBriRC-18
Lane, Scott
❑ 88RocExpLC-19
Lane, William C.
❑ 16Zee-39
❑ 17Zee-29
❑ 19Zee-22
❑ 20Zee-28
❑ 26Zee-169
❑ 52Par-50
Lanfair, Dave
❑ 75WatDodT-10
Lanfranco, Luis
❑ 90SouOreAB-6
❑ 90SouOreAP-3432
❑ 91MadMusC-23
❑ 91MadMusP-2139
Lanfranco, Otoniel
❑ 97JohCitCTI-20
❑ 98NewJerCM-18
Lanfranco, Raphael
❑ 90AshTouC-19
❑ 91AshTouP-571
❑ 92BurAstC-8
❑ 92BurAstF-550
Lanfranconi, Walt
❑ 48AngTeal-16
❑ 49AngTeal-20
❑ 49W725AngTI-15
❑ 85TCMPla1-34
Lang, Bert
❑ 26Zee-144
Lang, Chip (Robert)
❑ 76ExpRed-18
❑ 76MonExpP-17
❑ 77OPC-216
❑ 77Top-132
Lang, Don
❑ 85TCMPla1-3
Lang, Perry
❑ 88PacEigMO-15
Lang, Stephen
❑ 91TopRut-2
Langaigne, Selwyn
❑ 96DunBluJUTI-6
❑ 96MedHatBJTI-15
❑ 97DunBluJTI-18
❑ 98DunBluJSB-5
❑ 98DunBluJTI-16
Langaine, Selwyn
❑ 97St.CatSB-20
Langbehn, Gregg
❑ 89PitMetS-14
❑ 90ColMetGS-16
❑ 90ColMetPPI-7
❑ 91St.LucMC-20
❑ 91St.LucMP-705
❑ 92BinMetF-512
❑ 92BinMetS-64
❑ 92SkyAA F-29
❑ 93NorTidF-2567
❑ 94BinMetF-700
❑ 94NorTidF-2916
Langdon, Ted
❑ 83TamTarT-17
❑ 84CedRapRT-2
❑ 86TamTarP-9
❑ 87VerRedP-3
Langdon, Tim
❑ 91KinIndC-4
❑ 91KinIndP-316
Lange, Clark
❑ 85OscAstTI-19
❑ 87VisOakP-26
Lange, Frank H.
❑ 09ColChiE-164
❑ 11T205-94
❑ 12ColRedB-164
❑ 12ColTinT-164
❑ 12T207-98
Lange, Fred
❑ 87OldJudN-291
Lange, Richard
❑ 74OPC-429
❑ 74Top-429
❑ 75CalAngP-23
❑ 75OPC-114
❑ 75Top-114
❑ 75TopMin-114
❑ 76OPC-176
❑ 76SalLakCGC-15
❑ 76Top-176
❑ 77SalLakCGC-20
Langen, Brian
❑ 98NewJerCM-19
Langerhans, Ryan
❑ 99Bow-416
❑ 99BowGol-416
❑ 99BowInt-416
Langfield, Paul
❑ 80UtiBluJT-28
Langford, Elton
❑ 29Zee-136
Langford, Rick
❑ 75ShrCapT-8
❑ 78Hos-120
❑ 78OPC-33
❑ 78Top-327
❑ 79Top-29
❑ 80OPC-284
❑ 80Top-546
❑ 81A'sGraG-22
❑ 81Don-238
❑ 81Fle-572
❑ 81FleStiC-27
❑ 81Kel-55
❑ 81OPC-154
❑ 81Top-154
❑ 81TopSti-121
❑ 82A'sGraG-7
❑ 82Don-161
❑ 82Fle-98
❑ 82FleSta-126
❑ 82OPC-43
❑ 82Top-454
❑ 83A'sGraG-22
❑ 83Don-365
❑ 83Fle-523
❑ 83FleSti-190
❑ 83Top-286
❑ 83Top-531
❑ 83TopSti-106
❑ 84Fle-451
❑ 84Nes792-629
❑ 84OPC-304
❑ 84Top-629
❑ 84TopTif-629
❑ 85SubDis-14
❑ 85ThoMcAD-14
❑ 85Top-347
❑ 85TopTif-347
❑ 86A'sMot-14
❑ 86Fle-425
❑ 86Top-766
❑ 86TopTif-766
❑ 88ColCliC-10
❑ 88ColCliP-5
❑ 88ColCliP-308
❑ 91BilMusP-3749
❑ 91BilMusSP-19
❑ 91CedRapRC-7
❑ 91CedRapRP-2715
❑ 91Cla/Bes-347
❑ 92BilMusF-3349
❑ 92BilMusSP-9
❑ 92ChaWheF-5
❑ 92ChaWVWC-9
❑ 93WesVirWC-14
❑ 93WesVirWF-2862
❑ 96KnoSmoB-2
❑ 97KnoSmo-3
❑ 98DunBluJSB-23
❑ 98DunBluJTI-17
Langiotti, Fred
❑ 89SprCarB-24
❑ 90SprCarB-13
❑ 91St.PetCC-16
❑ 91St.PetCP-2279
❑ 98TamYanM-3
Langley, Lee
❑ 87VerBeaDP-28
❑ 88BakDodCLC-256
❑ 89ClePhiS-13
❑ 90ClePhiS-10
❑ 91MiaMirC-14
❑ 91MiaMirP-404
❑ 92ClePhiC-11
❑ 92ClePhiF-2054
Langowski, Ted
❑ 91MedHatBJP-4107
Langston, Bruce
❑ 90MisStaB-44
Langston, Keith
❑ 88CapCodPPaLP-109
❑ 89NiaFalRP-14
Langston, Mark
❑ 83ChaLooT-11
❑ 84FleUpd-70
❑ 84FunFooP-18
❑ 84MarMot-13
❑ 84TopTra-70T
❑ 84TopTraT-70T
❑ 85AllGamPI-79
❑ 85Don-557
❑ 85Dra-38
❑ 85Fle-492
❑ 85FleLimE-17
❑ 85FleStaS-109
❑ 85Lea-56
❑ 85MarMot-3
❑ 85OPC-259
❑ 85Top-625
❑ 85Top3-D-22
❑ 85TopMin-625
❑ 85TopRubD-29
❑ 85TopSti-281
❑ 85TopSti-337
❑ 85TopSti-371
❑ 85TopSup-20
❑ 85TopTif-625
❑ 86Don-118
❑ 86Fle-467
❑ 86MarMot-3
❑ 86MarPacNB-7
❑ 86OPC-198
❑ 86Top-495
❑ 86TopSti-225
❑ 86TopTif-495
❑ 87ClaGam-89
❑ 87Don-568
❑ 87DonHig-34
❑ 87DonOpeD-116
❑ 87Fle-589
❑ 87FleAwaW-22
❑ 87FleGlo-589
❑ 87FleHotS-26
❑ 87FleMin-62
❑ 87FleStiC-70
❑ 87Lea-55
❑ 87MarMot-5
❑ 87OPC-215
❑ 87RedFolSB-45
❑ 87Spo-102
❑ 87SpoTeaP-25
❑ 87StuPan-25
❑ 87Top-215
❑ 87TopMinL-71
❑ 87TopSti-219
❑ 87TopTif-215
❑ 88ClaBlu-250
❑ 88Don-20
❑ 88Don-317
❑ 88DonAll-26
❑ 88DonBasB-136
❑ 88DonSupD-20
❑ 88Fle-377
❑ 88FleBasA-20
❑ 88FleBasM-21
❑ 88FleGlo-377
❑ 88FleHotS-23
❑ 88FleLeaL-24
❑ 88FleMin-52
❑ 88FleSlu-23
❑ 88FleStiC-60
❑ 88FleTeaL-18
❑ 88GreBasS-16
❑ 88Lea-20
❑ 88Lea-123
❑ 88MarMot-5
❑ 88OPC-80
❑ 88PanSti-181
❑ 88RedFolSB-46
❑ 88Sco-30
❑ 88ScoGlo-30
❑ 88ScoSam-30
❑ 88Spo-46
❑ 88StaLinMa-8
❑ 88TarPla-24
❑ 88Top-80
❑ 88TopBig-176
❑ 88TopCoi-18
❑ 88TopGaloC-8
❑ 88TopMinL-34
❑ 88TopRevLL-33
❑ 88TopSti-214
❑ 88TopStiB-63
❑ 88TopTif-80
❑ 88TopUKM-42
❑ 88TopUKMT-42
❑ 89Bow-205
❑ 89BowTif-205
❑ 89Don-227
❑ 89DonBasB-68
❑ 89ExpPos-17
❑ 89Fle-551
❑ 89FleExcS-29
❑ 89FleGlo-551
❑ 89FleSup-27
❑ 89FleUpd-97
❑ 89K-M-21
❑ 89MarMot-5
❑ 89OPC-355
❑ 89PanSti-430
❑ 89RedFolSB-71
❑ 89Sco-161
❑ 89ScoHot1S-67
❑ 89Scomast-13
❑ 89ScoRoo-25T
❑ 89Spo-159
❑ 89Top-355
❑ 89TopBasT-85
❑ 89TopHilTM-19
❑ 89TopMinL-73
❑ 89TopSti-221
❑ 89TopTif-355
❑ 89TopTra-66T
❑ 89TopTraT-66T
❑ 89TopUKM-47
❑ 89TVSpoM-121
❑ 89UppDec-526
❑ 90AngSmo-10
❑ 90Bow-284
❑ 90BowTif-284
❑ 90ClaBlu-72
❑ 90ClaUpd-T28
❑ 90Don-338
❑ 90DonBesA-17
❑ 90Fle-352
❑ 90FleCan-352
❑ 90FleUpd-78
❑ 90Lea-155
❑ 90LeaPre-6
❑ 90OPC-530
❑ 90PanSti-287
❑ 90PubIntS-179
❑ 90RedFolSB-55
❑ 90Sco-401
❑ 90Sco-688
❑ 90Sco100S-96
❑ 90ScoRoo-11T
❑ 90Spo-110
❑ 90Top-530
❑ 90TopBig-232
❑ 90TopMinL-62
❑ 90TopSti-70
❑ 90TopStiB-29
❑ 90TopTif-530
❑ 90TopTra-54T
❑ 90TopTraT-54T
❑ 90UppDec-647
❑ 90UppDec-783
❑ 91AngSmo-8
❑ 91Bow-202
❑ 91Don-190
❑ 91DonBonC-BC1
❑ 91Fle-318
❑ 91FleWaxBC-1
❑ 91Lea-67
❑ 91MajLeaCP-25
❑ 91OPC-755
❑ 91PanFreS-352
❑ 91PanSti-1
❑ 91Sco-21
❑ 91Sco-411
❑ 91Sco-699
❑ 91SimandSMLBL-25
❑ 91StaClu-27
❑ 91StaCluCM-17
❑ 91Stu-27
❑ 91Top-755
❑ 91TopCraJI-17
❑ 91TopDesS-755
❑ 91TopMic-755
❑ 91TopTif-755
❑ 91Ult-49
❑ 91UppDec-234
❑ 91USPlaCA-5H
❑ 92AngPol-14
❑ 92Bow-520
❑ 92Cla2-T6
❑ 92ClaGam-113
❑ 92Don-531
❑ 92DonCraJ2-20
❑ 92DonDiaK-DK20
❑ 92DonMcD-19
❑ 92DonSupD-DK20
❑ 92Fle-63
❑ 92Hig5-14
❑ 92Hig5S-22
❑ 92HitTheBB-19

❑ 92Lea-229
❑ 92LeaBlaG-229
❑ 92MVPPin-14
❑ 92OPC-165
❑ 92PanSti-11
❑ 92Pin-132
❑ 92Sco-12
❑ 92Sco100S-32
❑ 92ScoProP-2
❑ 92SpoStaCC-29
❑ 92StaClu-670
❑ 92StaCluD-101
❑ 92Stu-148
❑ 92Top-165
❑ 92TopGol-165
❑ 92TopGolW-165
❑ 92TopKid-98
❑ 92TopMic-165
❑ 92TriPla-36
❑ 92Ult-327
❑ 92UltAwaW-16
❑ 92UppDec-305
❑ 93AngMot-8
❑ 93AngPol-8
❑ 93AngStaCl-4
❑ 93Bow-469
❑ 93Don-593
❑ 93Fin-82
❑ 93FinRef-82
❑ 93Fla-175
❑ 93Fle-194
❑ 93FunPac-40
❑ 93JimDea-9
❑ 93Lea-324
❑ 93LeaGolA-U1
❑ 93OPC-232
❑ 93PacSpa-48
❑ 93PanSti-2
❑ 93Pin-56
❑ 93Sco-66
❑ 93ScoFra-3
❑ 93Sel-52
❑ 93SP-5
❑ 93StaClu-355
❑ 93StaCluFDI-355
❑ 93StaCluM-107
❑ 93StaCluMOP-355
❑ 93Top-210
❑ 93TopGol-210
❑ 93TopInaM-210
❑ 93TopInaR-210
❑ 93TopMic-210
❑ 93TriPla-235
❑ 93Ult-166
❑ 93UltAwaW-10
❑ 93UppDec-53
❑ 93UppDec-128
❑ 93UppDecGold-53
❑ 93UppDecGold-128
❑ 94AngLAT-14
❑ 94AngMot-2
❑ 94Bow-235
❑ 94ColC-169
❑ 94ColChoGS-169
❑ 94ColChoSS-169
❑ 94Don-31
❑ 94Don-660
❑ 94DonSpeE-31
❑ 94Fin-24
❑ 94FinRef-24
❑ 94Fla-271
❑ 94Fle-61
❑ 94FleAllS-14
❑ 94FleExtB-37
❑ 94FleSmo'nH-6
❑ 94FUnPac-112
❑ 94Kra-6
❑ 94Lea-162
❑ 94LeaL-17
❑ 94OPC-175
❑ 94Pac-81
❑ 94PanSti-38
❑ 94Pin-311
❑ 94PinArtP-311
❑ 94PinMusC-311
❑ 94ProMag-17
❑ 94RedFolMI-23
❑ 94Sco-71
❑ 94ScoGolR-71
❑ 94Sel-351
❑ 94SP-25
❑ 94SPDieC-25
❑ 94Spo-38
❑ 94StaClu-442
❑ 94StaCluFDI-442
❑ 94StaCluGR-442
❑ 94StaCluMO-16
❑ 94StaCluMOP-442
❑ 94Stu-13
❑ 94SucSav-11
❑ 94Top-665
❑ 94TopGol-665
❑ 94TopSpa-665
❑ 94TriPla-17
❑ 94Ult-331
❑ 94UltAwaW-9
❑ 94UltStrK-2
❑ 94UppDec-485
❑ 94UppDecED-485
❑ 95AngCHP-3
❑ 95AngMot-2
❑ 95Baz-108
❑ 95Bow-404
❑ 95ColCho-103
❑ 95ColChoGS-103
❑ 95ColChoSS-103
❑ 95Don-155
❑ 95DonPreP-155
❑ 95DonTopotO-37
❑ 95Fin-142
❑ 95FinRef-142
❑ 95Fla-236
❑ 95Fle-228
❑ 95Lea-236
❑ 95LeaLim-169
❑ 95Pac-62
❑ 95Pin-225
❑ 95PinArtP-225
❑ 95PinMusC-225
❑ 95Sco-126
❑ 95ScoGolR-126
❑ 95ScoPlaTS-126
❑ 95Sel-136
❑ 95SelArtP-136
❑ 95SP-132
❑ 95Spo-87
❑ 95SpoArtP-87
❑ 95SPSil-132
❑ 95StaClu-246
❑ 95StaCluFDI-246
❑ 95StaCluMOP-246
❑ 95StaCluSTWS-246
❑ 95Stu-87
❑ 95Top-95
❑ 95TopCyb-62
❑ 95TopEmb-122
❑ 95TopEmbGI-122
❑ 95UC3-79
❑ 95UC3ArtP-79
❑ 95Ult-22
❑ 95UltAwaW-9
❑ 95UltAwaWGM-9
❑ 95UltGolM-22
❑ 95UppDec-271
❑ 95UppDecED-271
❑ 95UppDecEDG-271
❑ 95UppDecSE-129
❑ 95UppDecSEG-129
❑ 96AngMot-3
❑ 96Baz-119
❑ 96ColCho-73
❑ 96ColChoGS-73
❑ 96ColChoSS-73
❑ 96Don-426
❑ 96DonPreP-426
❑ 96EmoXL-28
❑ 96Fin-B114
❑ 96FinRef-B114
❑ 96Fla-39
❑ 96Fle-51
❑ 96FleTif-51
❑ 96Lea-97
❑ 96LeaPrePB-97
❑ 96LeaPrePG-97
❑ 96LeaPrePS-97
❑ 96MetUni-29
❑ 96MetUniP-29
❑ 96Pac-261
❑ 96PanSti-214
❑ 96Pin-127
❑ 96Sco-291
❑ 96ScoDugC-B16
❑ 96ScoDugCAP-B16
❑ 96SP-47
❑ 96StaClu-385
❑ 96StaCluEPB-385
❑ 96StaCluEPG-385
❑ 96StaCluEPS-385
❑ 96StaCluMOP-385
❑ 96Top-423
❑ 96TopGal-4
❑ 96TopGalPPI-4
❑ 96TopLas-57
❑ 96Ult-31
❑ 96UltGolM-31
❑ 96UppDec-28
❑ 97AngMot-4
❑ 97Cir-166
❑ 97CirRav-166
❑ 97ColCho-261
❑ 97Don-228
❑ 97DonGolPP-228
❑ 97DonSilPP-228
❑ 97DonTea-6
❑ 97DonTeaSPE-6
❑ 97Fin-185
❑ 97FinRef-185
❑ 97Fle-48
❑ 97FleTif-48
❑ 97Lea-73
❑ 97LeaFraM-73
❑ 97LeaFraMDC-73
❑ 97Pac-10
❑ 97PacLigB-10
❑ 97PacSil-10
❑ 97Sco-287
❑ 97ScoArtPWB-287
❑ 97ScoPreS-287
❑ 97ScoShoS-287
❑ 97ScoShoSAP-287
❑ 97StaClu-334
❑ 97StaCluMOP-334
❑ 97Top-128
❑ 97UppDec-136
❑ 97UppDec-289
❑ 98ColCho-478
❑ 98Fle-535
❑ 98Pac-11
❑ 98PacPlaB-11
❑ 98PacRedT-11
❑ 98PacSil-11
❑ 98PadMot-16
❑ 98Top-379
❑ 98TopChr-379
❑ 98TopChrR-379
❑ 98TopDevR-379
❑ 98TopDia-379
❑ 98TopMiniC-379
❑ 98Ult-449
❑ 98UltGolM-449
❑ 98UltMas-449
❑ 98UltPlaM-449
❑ 98UppDec-718
❑ 99Ult-12
❑ 99UltGolM-12
❑ 99UltMas-12
❑ 99UltPlaM-12

Laniauskas, Vitas

❑ 89AshTouP-941

Lanier, H. Max

❑ 41CarW75-14
❑ 50Bow-207
❑ 51Bow-230
❑ 52Bow-110
❑ 52Top-101
❑ 79DiaGre-155
❑ 83Car194T-43
❑ 83TopRep5-101
❑ 92ConTSN-620

Lanier, Hal

❑ 47PM1StaP1-109
❑ 64TopRooAB-17
❑ 65OPC-118
❑ 65Top-118
❑ 66OPC-156
❑ 66Top-156
❑ 66Top-271
❑ 66TopVen-156
❑ 66TopVen-271
❑ 67CokCapG-8
❑ 67DexPre-122
❑ 67OPC-4
❑ 67Top-4
❑ 67TopVen-287
❑ 68Top-436
❑ 69MilBra-155
❑ 69MLBOffS-201
❑ 69Top-316
❑ 69TopSta-106
❑ 69TopTeaP-14
❑ 70Gia-6
❑ 70MLBOffS-126
❑ 70Top-583
❑ 71MLBOffS-255
❑ 71OPC-181
❑ 71Top-181
❑ 72MilBra-193
❑ 72Top-589
❑ 73OPC-479
❑ 73Top-479
❑ 74OPC-588
❑ 74Top-588
❑ 75TulOil7-8
❑ 78St.PetCT-29
❑ 81Car5x7-15
❑ 83Car-15
❑ 84Car-17
❑ 84Car5x7-14
❑ 85CarTeal-18
❑ 86AstMilL-13
❑ 86AstPol-6
❑ 86CarTeal-25
❑ 86TopTra-60T
❑ 86TopTraT-60T
❑ 87AstMot-1
❑ 87AstPol-7
❑ 87Top-343
❑ 87TopTif-343
❑ 88AstMot-1
❑ 88AstPol-25
❑ 88Top-684
❑ 88TopTif-684
❑ 89Top-164
❑ 89TopTif-164
❑ 90PhiTas-34
❑ 91PhiMed-24
❑ 92YanWIZ7-94

Lanier, Tom

❑ 94LSUTigMP-4

Lankard, Steve

❑ 86SalRedBP-17
❑ 87PorChaRP-3
❑ 88TulDriTI-20
❑ 89TexLeaAGS-35
❑ 89TulDriGS-13
❑ 90CMC-152
❑ 90OklCit8C-2
❑ 90OklCit8P-428
❑ 90ProAAAF-674

Lankford, Derrick

❑ 97EriSeaWB-22
❑ 98AugGreM-5

Lankford, Frank

❑ 93OneYanC-12
❑ 93OneYanF-3499
❑ 94GreBatF-469
❑ 95TamYanYI-16
❑ 96NorNavB-15
❑ 97EasLeaTPB-21
❑ 97GreBatC-12
❑ 97NorNav-21
❑ 97NorNavTI-17
❑ 98ColCliD-15
❑ 98ColCliM-19
❑ 98DodPol-15

Lankford, Ray

❑ 88MidLeaAGS-26
❑ 88SprCarB-14
❑ 89ArkTraGS-9
❑ 89BasAmeAPB-AA23
❑ 89BlaYNPRWL-93
❑ 89BlaYNPRWLU-62
❑ 89TexLeaAGS-22
❑ 90Bow-192
❑ 90BowTif-192
❑ 90ClaUpd-T29
❑ 90CMC-114
❑ 90Lea-308
❑ 90LouRedBC-14
❑ 90LouRedBLBC-23
❑ 90LouRedBP-416
❑ 90ProAAAF-530
❑ 90ScoRoo-84T
❑ 90SprCarDGB-24
❑ 90TopMag-56
❑ 90TopTVCa-53
❑ 90UppDec-755
❑ 91Bow-388
❑ 91CarPol-16
❑ 91Cla3-T48
❑ 91ClaGam-83
❑ 91Don-43
❑ 91DonRoo-8
❑ 91Fle-637
❑ 91Lea-523
❑ 91LeaPre-10
❑ 91MajLeaCP-50
❑ 91OPC-682
❑ 91OPCPre-72
❑ 91Sco-731
❑ 91ScoAllF-1
❑ 91ScoHotR-7
❑ 91ScoRoo-2
❑ 91SevCoi-M10
❑ 91StaClu-537
❑ 91StaCluMO-21
❑ 91Stu-234
❑ 91Top-682
❑ 91TopDeb90-81
❑ 91TopDesS-682
❑ 91TopMic-682
❑ 91TopTif-682
❑ 91Ult-290
❑ 91UppDec-346
❑ 92Bow-643
❑ 92CarPol-10
❑ 92Cla1-T51
❑ 92ClaGam-130
❑ 92Don-350
❑ 92Fle-583
❑ 92FleRooS-17
❑ 92Hig5-97
❑ 92Lea-195
❑ 92LeaBlaG-195
❑ 92MVPPin-32
❑ 92OPC-292
❑ 92OPCPre-148
❑ 92PanSti-177
❑ 92Pin-126
❑ 92PinTea2-51
❑ 92RedFolS-54
❑ 92Sco-223
❑ 92Sco100RS-43
❑ 92ScoImpP-8
❑ 92StaClu-8
❑ 92Top-292
❑ 92TopGol-292
❑ 92TopGolW-292
❑ 92TopMic-292
❑ 92TriPla-194
❑ 92Ult-265
❑ 92UppDec-262
❑ 92UppDecF-8
❑ 92UppDecFG-8
❑ 93Bow-404
❑ 93CadDis-38
❑ 93CarPol-9
❑ 93CarStaC-17
❑ 93ClaGam-51
❑ 93DenHol-7
❑ 93Don-366
❑ 93DonMVP-12
❑ 93Fin-187
❑ 93FinRef-187
❑ 93Fla-122
❑ 93Fle-127
❑ 93FleFruotL-34
❑ 93FleTeaL-NL3
❑ 93FunPac-76
❑ 93Hos-5
❑ 93JimDea-20
❑ 93Lea-297
❑ 93LeaFas-8
❑ 93OPC-191
❑ 93OPCPre-44
❑ 93PacSpa-296
❑ 93PanSti-196
❑ 93Pin-116
❑ 93PinTea2-19
❑ 93Sco-56
❑ 93ScoFra-24
❑ 93Sel-155
❑ 93SelStaL-17
❑ 93SP-76
❑ 93StaClu-49
❑ 93StaCluFDI-49
❑ 93StaCluMOP-49
❑ 93Stu-175
❑ 93Top-386
❑ 93TOPBLAG-10
❑ 93TopGol-386
❑ 93TopInaM-386
❑ 93TopInaR-386
❑ 93TopMic-386
❑ 93Toy-100
❑ 93TriPla-254
❑ 93Ult-108
❑ 93Ult-298
❑ 93UltAllS-7
❑ 93UppDec-244
❑ 93UppDec-461
❑ 93UppDec-482
❑ 93UppDecDG-7
❑ 93UppDecGold-244
❑ 93UppDecGold-461
❑ 93UppDecGold-482
❑ 93UppDecHRH-HR20
❑ 94Bow-96
❑ 94BowBes-R64
❑ 94BowBesR-R64
❑ 94CarMagG-4
❑ 94CarPol-9
❑ 94ColC-365
❑ 94ColChoGS-365
❑ 94ColChoSS-365
❑ 94Don-367
❑ 94DonSpeE-367
❑ 94Fin-347
❑ 94FinRef-347
❑ 94Fla-226
❑ 94Fle-636
❑ 94FleExtB-360
❑ 94Lea-384
❑ 94LeaL-146
❑ 94LeaMVPC-N8
❑ 94LeaMVPCG-N8
❑ 94OPC-251
❑ 94PanSti-245
❑ 94Pin-36
❑ 94PinArtP-36
❑ 94PinMusC-36
❑ 94ProMag-111
❑ 94RedFolMI-14
❑ 94Sco-16
❑ 94ScoGolR-16
❑ 94Sel-152
❑ 94SP-64
❑ 94SPDieC-64
❑ 94Spo-65
❑ 94StaClu-353
❑ 94StaCluFDI-353
❑ 94StaCluGR-353
❑ 94StaCluMOP-353
❑ 94StaCluT-310
❑ 94StaCluTFDI-310
❑ 94Stu-52
❑ 94Top-530
❑ 94TopGol-530
❑ 94TopSpa-530
❑ 94TriPla-64
❑ 94Ult-566
❑ 94UppDec-446
❑ 94UppDecED-446
❑ 95Baz-74
❑ 95Bow-299
❑ 95BowBes-R18
❑ 95BowBesR-R18
❑ 95ColCho-190
❑ 95ColChoGS-190
❑ 95ColChoSE-77
❑ 95ColChoSEGS-77
❑ 95ColChoSESS-77
❑ 95ColChoSS-190
❑ 95Don-324
❑ 95DonPreP-324
❑ 95DonTopotO-331
❑ 95Emo-182
❑ 95Fin-136
❑ 95FinRef-136
❑ 95Fla-411
❑ 95Fle-501
❑ 95Lea-79
❑ 95LeaLim-181
❑ 95Pac-408
❑ 95Pin-195
❑ 95PinArtP-195
❑ 95PinMusC-195
❑ 95Sco-264
❑ 95ScoGolR-264
❑ 95ScoPlaTS-264
❑ 95Sel-76
❑ 95SelArtP-76
❑ 95SelCer-63
❑ 95SelCerMG-63
❑ 95SP-104
❑ 95SPCha-87
❑ 95SPChaDC-87
❑ 95Spo-130
❑ 95SpoArtP-130
❑ 95SPSil-104
❑ 95StaClu-424
❑ 95StaClu-507
❑ 95StaCluMO-27
❑ 95StaCluMOP-424
❑ 95StaCluMOP-507
❑ 95StaCluSTWS-424
❑ 95StaCluSTWS-507
❑ 95StaCluVR-221
❑ 95StaCluVRMO-221
❑ 95Stu-190
❑ 95Sum-38
❑ 95SumNthD-38
❑ 95Top-82
❑ 95TopCyb-58
❑ 95TopEmb-25
❑ 95TopEmbGI-25

❑ 95UC3-66
❑ 95UC3ArtP-66
❑ 95Ult-431
❑ 95UltGolM-431
❑ 95UppDec-305
❑ 95UppDecED-305
❑ 95UppDecEDG-305
❑ 95UppDecSE-90
❑ 95UppDecSEG-90
❑ 95Zen-85
❑ 96ArkTraB-29
❑ 96Baz-11
❑ 96Bow-28
❑ 96BowBes-90
❑ 96BowBesAR-90
❑ 96BowBesR-90
❑ 96BowFoi-28
❑ 96CarPol-14
❑ 96Cir-178
❑ 96CirRav-178
❑ 96ColCho-690
❑ 96ColChoGS-690
❑ 96ColChoSS-690
❑ 96Don-379
❑ 96DonPreP-379
❑ 96EmoXL-268
❑ 96Fin-B334
❑ 96Fin-S10
❑ 96FinRef-B334
❑ 96FinRef-S10
❑ 96Fla-361
❑ 96Fle-546
❑ 96FleTeaL-26
❑ 96FleTif-546
❑ 96Lea-37
❑ 96LeaLim-7
❑ 96LeaLimG-7
❑ 96LeaPre-10
❑ 96LeaPreP-10
❑ 96LeaPrePB-37
❑ 96LeaPrePG-37
❑ 96LeaPrePS-37
❑ 96LeaPreSG-29
❑ 96LeaPreSte-29
❑ 96LeaSig-6
❑ 96LeaSigPPG-6
❑ 96LeaSigPPP-6
❑ 96MetUni-227
❑ 96MetUniP-227
❑ 96MLBPin-19
❑ 96Pac-219
❑ 96PanSti-73
❑ 96Pin-57
❑ 96PinAfi-57
❑ 96PinAfiAP-57
❑ 96PinAfiFPP-57
❑ 96PinArtP-22
❑ 96PinSta-22
❑ 96ProSta-32
❑ 96Sco-279
❑ 96ScoDugC-B4
❑ 96ScoDugCAP-B4
❑ 96Sel-18
❑ 96SelArtP-18
❑ 96SelCer-26
❑ 96SelCerAP-26
❑ 96SelCerCB-26
❑ 96SelCerCR-26
❑ 96SelCerIP-7
❑ 96SelCerMB-26
❑ 96SelCerMG-26
❑ 96SelCerMR-26
❑ 96SelTeaN-2
❑ 96SP-151
❑ 96Spo-77
❑ 96SpoArtP-77
❑ 96StaClu-209
❑ 96StaClu-283
❑ 96StaCluB&B-BB7
❑ 96StaCluEPB-283
❑ 96StaCluEPG-283
❑ 96StaCluEPS-283
❑ 96StaCluMOP-209
❑ 96StaCluMOP-283
❑ 96StaCluMOP-BB7
❑ 96Stu-112
❑ 96StuPrePB-112
❑ 96StuPrePG-112
❑ 96StuPrePS-112
❑ 96Sum-33
❑ 96SumAbo&B-33
❑ 96SumArtP-33
❑ 96SumFoi-33
❑ 96TeaOut-47
❑ 96Top-327
❑ 96TopChr-130
❑ 96TopChrR-130
❑ 96TopGal-5
❑ 96TopGalE-11
❑ 96TopGalPPI-5
❑ 96TopLas-71
❑ 96Ult-549
❑ 96UltGolM-549
❑ 96UppDec-441
❑ 96Zen-38
❑ 96ZenArtP-38
❑ 96ZenMoz-11
❑ 97Bow-33
❑ 97BowBes-24
❑ 97BowBesAR-24
❑ 97BowBesR-24
❑ 97BowChr-28
❑ 97BowChrI-28
❑ 97BowChrIR-28
❑ 97BowChrR-28
❑ 97BowInt-33
❑ 97CarPol-14
❑ 97Cir-28
❑ 97CirRav-28
❑ 97ColCho-202
❑ 97DenHol-25
❑ 97Don-67
❑ 97DonGolPP-67
❑ 97DonLim-148
❑ 97DonLim-150
❑ 97DonLimE-148
❑ 97DonLimE-150
❑ 97DonLimENG-150
❑ 97DonPre-80
❑ 97DonPreCttC-80
❑ 97DonSig-15
❑ 97DonSigA-64
❑ 97DonSigAC-78
❑ 97DonSigAM-78
❑ 97DonSigPPP-15
❑ 97DonSilPP-67
❑ 97DonTea-153
❑ 97DonTeaSPE-153
❑ 97E-X2-100
❑ 97E-X2Cred-100
❑ 97E-X2EssCre-100
❑ 97Fin-256
❑ 97FinRef-256
❑ 97FlaShoLC-116
❑ 97FlaShoLeg0-116
❑ 97FlaShoLeg1-116
❑ 97FlaShoM-A116
❑ 97FlaShoM-B116
❑ 97FlaShoM-C116
❑ 97FlaShoR0-116
❑ 97FlaShoR1-116
❑ 97FlaShoR2-116
❑ 97Fle-446
❑ 97FleTif-446
❑ 97KinB-17
❑ 97Lea-6
❑ 97LeaFraM-6
❑ 97LeaFraMDC-6
❑ 97MetUni-232
❑ 97NewPin-67
❑ 97NewPinAP-67
❑ 97NewPinMC-67
❑ 97NewPinPP-67
❑ 97Pac-412
❑ 97PacLigB-412
❑ 97PacSil-412
❑ 97PinCer-13
❑ 97PinCerMBla-13
❑ 97PinCerMBlu-13
❑ 97PinCerMG-13
❑ 97PinCerMR-13
❑ 97PinCerR-13
❑ 97PinTotCPB-13
❑ 97PinTotCPG-13
❑ 97PinTotCPR-13
❑ 97Sco-236
❑ 97ScoArtPWB-236
❑ 97ScoPreS-236
❑ 97ScoShoS-236
❑ 97ScoShoSAP-236
❑ 97Sel-163
❑ 97SelCom-163
❑ 97SP-145
❑ 97SpoIll-104
❑ 97SpoIllEE-104
❑ 97StaClu-236
❑ 97StaCluMat-236
❑ 97StaCluMOP-236
❑ 97StrAll-37
❑ 97Stu-28
❑ 97StuPrePG-28
❑ 97StuPrePS-28
❑ 97Top-87
❑ 97TopChr-33
❑ 97TopChrR-33
❑ 97TopGal-70
❑ 97TopGalPPI-70
❑ 97TopSta-89
❑ 97TopSta97AS-AS17
❑ 97TopStaAM-89
❑ 97Ult-273
❑ 97UltDouT-18
❑ 97UltGolME-273
❑ 97UltPlaME-273
❑ 97UppDec-485
❑ 98Bow-229
❑ 98BowBes-79
❑ 98BowBesAR-79
❑ 98BowBesR-79
❑ 98BowChr-229
❑ 98BowChrGA-229
❑ 98BowChrGAR-229
❑ 98BowChrI-229
❑ 98BowChrIR-229
❑ 98BowChrR-229
❑ 98BowGolA-229
❑ 98BowInt-229
❑ 98CarScoP-8
❑ 98CirThu-130
❑ 98CirThuRav-130
❑ 98CirThuSupRav-130
❑ 98ColCho-475
❑ 98ColChoSQ-SQ42
❑ 98CroRoy-114
❑ 98Don-13
❑ 98DonCol-13
❑ 98DonColE-458
❑ 98DonColL-342
❑ 98DonColP-627
❑ 98DonColS-13
❑ 98DonCruG-92
❑ 98DonCruP-92
❑ 98DonCruR-92
❑ 98DonEli-58
❑ 98DonEliA-58
❑ 98DonEliS-58
❑ 98DonGolPP-13
❑ 98DonPre-77
❑ 98DonPreSeat-77
❑ 98DonPriCD-13
❑ 98DonPriCE-458
❑ 98DonPriCL-342
❑ 98DonPriCP-627
❑ 98DonSig-22
❑ 98DonSigP-22
❑ 98DonSilPP-13
❑ 98E-X2-49
❑ 98E-X2ECFut-49
❑ 98E-X2ECNow-49
❑ 98Fin-169
❑ 98FinNo--169
❑ 98FinNo-R-169
❑ 98FinRef-169
❑ 98FlaShoLeg0-73
❑ 98FlaShoLeg1-73
❑ 98FlaShoLeg2-73
❑ 98FlaShoLeg3-73
❑ 98FlaShoLegM-73
❑ 98FlaShoR0-73
❑ 98FlaShoR1-73
❑ 98FlaShoR2-73
❑ 98FlaShoR3-73
❑ 98Fle-169
❑ 98FleVin'-49
❑ 98FleVin'C-49
❑ 98KinDis-23
❑ 98Lea-143
❑ 98LeaFraDA-143
❑ 98LeaFraF-143
❑ 98LeaFraM-143
❑ 98LeaFraM-143
❑ 98LeaFraMDC-143
❑ 98LeaFraMDC-143
❑ 98LeaFraMZ2-143
❑ 98LeaRS-79
❑ 98LeaRSLHolo-79
❑ 98LeaRSLong-79
❑ 98LeaRTrue-79
❑ 98MetUni-102
❑ 98MetUniPMG-102
❑ 98Pac-414
❑ 98PacAur-185
❑ 98PacInv-135
❑ 98PacInvPBlue-135
❑ 98PacInvSilv-135
❑ 98PacInvTeam-23
❑ 98PacOme-199
❑ 98PacOmeR-199
❑ 98PacOnl-616
❑ 98PacOnlR-616
❑ 98PacOnlWC-616
❑ 98PacPar-231
❑ 98PacParC-231
❑ 98PacParG-231
❑ 98PacParHS-231
❑ 98PacParPB-231
❑ 98PacParR-231
❑ 98PacPlaB-414
❑ 98PacRedT-414
❑ 98PacSil-414
❑ 98Pin-8
❑ 98Pin-195
❑ 98Pin-198
❑ 98PinArtP-PP8
❑ 98PinArtP-PP98
❑ 98PinIns-62
❑ 98PinInsCE-62
❑ 98PinInsDE-62
❑ 98PinMusC-PP8
❑ 98PinMusC-PP98
❑ 98PinPer-78
❑ 98PinPerPP-78
❑ 98PinPerSftF-41
❑ 98PinPlu-49
❑ 98PinPowPJ-14
❑ 98PinPowPJS-14
❑ 98PinPreP-8
❑ 98PinPreP-195
❑ 98PinPreP-198
❑ 98PinSna-SLC12
❑ 98Revo-120
❑ 98RevoSS-120
❑ 98Sco-104
❑ 98ScoCar-8
❑ 98ScoRT-168
❑ 98ScoRTSS-PP97
❑ 98ScoRTSSAP-PP97
❑ 98ScoRTSSAP1-PP97
❑ 98ScoSS-PP143
❑ 98ScoSSAP-PP143
❑ 98SkyDugA-42
❑ 98SkyDugAIA-42
❑ 98SP Aut-161
❑ 98SP AutC-RL
❑ 98SpoIll-79
❑ 98SpoIllEE-79
❑ 98SpoIllFE-79
❑ 98SpoIllTaN-104
❑ 98SpoIllTaNEE-104
❑ 98SpoIllWSF-87
❑ 98SpoIllWSFEE-87
❑ 98SpoIllWSFFE-87
❑ 98SPxFin-119
❑ 98SPxFinR-119
❑ 98SPxFinS-119
❑ 98StaCluFDI-156
❑ 98StaCluI-156
❑ 98StaCluOneK-156
❑ 98StaCluPP-156
❑ 98StaCluTIII-T16C
❑ 98StaCluTLme-T16C
❑ 98StaCluTLmo-T16C
❑ 98Stu-39
❑ 98StuGPP-39
❑ 98StuSPP-39
❑ 98Top-180
❑ 98TopChr-180
❑ 98TopChrR-180
❑ 98TopDevR-180
❑ 98TopDia-180
❑ 98TopGal-52
❑ 98TopGalGP-52
❑ 98TopGalOPP-52
❑ 98TopGalPPI-52
❑ 98TopGalPPIA-52
❑ 98TopGolLabC1-66
❑ 98TopGolLabC1B-66
❑ 98TopGolLabC1One-66
❑ 98TopGolLabC1R-66
❑ 98TopGolLabC2-66
❑ 98TopGolLabC2B-66
❑ 98TopGolLabC2One-66
❑ 98TopGolLabC2R-66
❑ 98TopGolLabC3-66
❑ 98TopGolLabC3B-66
❑ 98TopGolLabC3One-66
❑ 98TopGolLabC3R-66
❑ 98TopMiniC-180
❑ 98TopOpeD-96
❑ 98TopSta-67
❑ 98TopSta'S-23
❑ 98TopSta'SGH-23
❑ 98TopStaB-67
❑ 98TopStaG-67
❑ 98TopStaGR-67
❑ 98TopStaS-67
❑ 98TopStaSteG-23
❑ 98TopTek-90
❑ 98TopTekD-90
❑ 98Ult-169
❑ 98UltDouT-13
❑ 98UltGolM-169
❑ 98UltMas-169
❑ 98UltPlaM-169
❑ 98UppDec-490
❑ 98UppDecR-80
❑ 98Zen-76
❑ 98ZenZ-G-76
❑ 98ZenZ-S-76
❑ 99199Fin-154
❑ 99Bow-57
❑ 99BowBes-45
❑ 99BowBesAR-45
❑ 99BowBesR-45
❑ 99BowChr-57
❑ 99BowChrG-57
❑ 99BowChrGR-57
❑ 99BowChrI-57
❑ 99BowChrIR-57
❑ 99BowChrR-57
❑ 99BowGol-57
❑ 99BowInt-57
❑ 99CroRoyB-115
❑ 99CroRoyL-115
❑ 99CroRoyOD-115
❑ 99E-X Cen-46
❑ 99E-X CenECFut-46
❑ 99E-X CenECNow-46
❑ 99FinGolRef-154
❑ 99FinRef-154
❑ 99FlaShoLeg1-60
❑ 99FlaShoLeg2-60
❑ 99FlaShoLeg3-60
❑ 99FlaShoLegM1-60
❑ 99FlaShoLegM2-60
❑ 99FlaShoLegM3-60
❑ 99FlaShoR1-60
❑ 99FlaShoR2-60
❑ 99FlaShoR3-60
❑ 99Fle-139
❑ 99FleBri-55
❑ 99FleBri2G-55
❑ 99FleBriBlu-55
❑ 99FleBriGol-55
❑ 99FleMys-87
❑ 99FleMysG-87
❑ 99FleMysM-87
❑ 99FleSta9-139
❑ 99FleWarT-139
❑ 99KinDis-22
❑ 99MetUni-209
❑ 99MetUniGM-209
❑ 99MetUniPMG-209
❑ 99Pac-355
❑ 99PacAur-154
❑ 99PacAurOD-154
❑ 99PacCroC-231
❑ 99PacCroCPB-231
❑ 99PacInv-119
❑ 99PacInvOD-119
❑ 99PacInvPB-119
❑ 99PacOme-195
❑ 99PacOmeC-195
❑ 99PacOmeG-195
❑ 99PacOmePB-195
❑ 99PacPar-192
❑ 99PacParC-192
❑ 99PacParG-192
❑ 99PacParHoloGold-192
❑ 99PacParHS-192
❑ 99PacParOD-192
❑ 99PacParPB-192
❑ 99PacParRed-192
❑ 99PacPlaB-355
❑ 99PacPriS-109
❑ 99PacPriS206-109
❑ 99PacPriS206R-109
❑ 99PacRed-355
❑ 99Rev-115
❑ 99RevPremDate-115
❑ 99RevRet-115
❑ 99RevShaSS-115
❑ 99SkyMolM-33
❑ 99SkyMolMX-33
❑ 99SkyPre-150
❑ 99SkyPreA-33
❑ 99SkyPreABlue-33
❑ 99SkyPreR-150
❑ 99SkyThu-89
❑ 99SkyThuRant-89
❑ 99SkyThuRave-89
❑ 99SP AutHRC-HR33
❑ 99SP SigAuto-RL
❑ 99SPAutHRCDC-HR33
❑ 99SpoIll-93
❑ 99SPSig-108
❑ 99StaClu-95
❑ 99StaCluFDI-95
❑ 99StaCluOoaK-95
❑ 99StaCluPP-95
❑ 99StaCluTI-T5B
❑ 99StaCluTL-T5B
❑ 99StaCluTL-T5B
❑ 99ThuSkySupR-89
❑ 99Top-35
❑ 99TopBlaLC1-24
❑ 99TopBlaLC2-24
❑ 99TopBlaLC3-24
❑ 99TopChr-35
❑ 99TopChrR-35
❑ 99TopGal-87
❑ 99TopGalPP-87
❑ 99TopGalPPI-87
❑ 99TopGolL-24
❑ 99TopGolLC1-24
❑ 99TopGolLC2-24
❑ 99TopGolLOtO-24
❑ 99TopMVPP-35
❑ 99TopOpeD-22
❑ 99TopRedLC1-24
❑ 99TopRedLC2-24
❑ 99TopRedLC3-24
❑ 99TopSta-130
❑ 99TopStaFoil-130
❑ 99UD Cho-131
❑ 99UD ChoPCR-131
❑ 99Ult-27
❑ 99UltGolM-27
❑ 99UltMas-27
❑ 99UltPlaM-27
❑ 99UppDec-186
❑ 99UppDecCf7-36
❑ 99UppDecCo7CE-36
❑ 99UppDecEL1-186
❑ 99UppDecEL2-186
❑ 99UppDecM-175
❑ 99UppDecMGS-175
❑ 99UppDecMHFS-175
❑ 99UppDecMSS-175
❑ 99UppDecO-53
❑ 99UppDecOSO-53
❑ 99Vic-326

Lanning, David P.

❑ 81VerBeaDT-9

Lanning, Johnny

❑ 38CloFotW-46
❑ 79DiaGre-202
❑ 94ConTSN-1301
❑ 94ConTSNB-1301

Lanok, Dale

❑ 85BurRanT-7

Lanoux, Marty

❑ 86KenTwiP-11
❑ 87VisOakP-23
❑ 88CalLeaACLC-39
❑ 88VisOakCLC-153
❑ 88VisOakP-104
❑ 89OrlTwiB-26
❑ 89OrlTwiP-1328
❑ 90PorBeaP-186
❑ 90ProAAAF-256

Lansford, Carney

❑ 76QuaCitAT-18
❑ 78AngFamF-22
❑ 78SSP270-207
❑ 79Top-212
❑ 80OPC-177
❑ 80Top-337
❑ 81AllGamPI-35
❑ 81CokTeaS-6
❑ 81Don-409
❑ 81Fle-270
❑ 81FleStiC-12
❑ 81OPC-245
❑ 81Top-639
❑ 81TopScr-25
❑ 81TopSti-43
❑ 81TopSupHT-6
❑ 81TopTra-788
❑ 82Don-82
❑ 82Fle-298
❑ 82FleSta-164
❑ 82Kel-41
❑ 82OPC-91
❑ 82PerCreC-15
❑ 82PerCreCG-15

❑ 82RedSoxC-10
❑ 82SevSluC-16
❑ 82Top-91
❑ 82Top-161
❑ 82Top-786
❑ 82TopSti-2
❑ 82TopSti-156
❑ 82TopStiV-156
❑ 83A'sGraG-4
❑ 83AllGamPl-34
❑ 83Don-408
❑ 83Fle-187
❑ 83FleSta-100
❑ 83FleSti-67
❑ 83OPC-318
❑ 83Top-523
❑ 83TopSti-32
❑ 83TopTra-60T
❑ 84A'sMot-7
❑ 84AllGamPl-124
❑ 84Don-176
❑ 84DonActAS-39
❑ 84Fle-452
❑ 84FunFooP-55
❑ 84Nes792-767
❑ 84OPC-59
❑ 84Top-767
❑ 84TopRubD-18
❑ 84TopSti-328
❑ 84TopTif-767
❑ 85A'sMot-8
❑ 85AllGamPl-34
❑ 85Don-8
❑ 85Don-345
❑ 85DonSupD-8
❑ 85Fle-429
❑ 85Lea-8
❑ 85OPC-347
❑ 85Top-422
❑ 85TopRubD-17
❑ 85TopSti-330
❑ 85TopTif-422
❑ 86A'sMot-8
❑ 86Don-131
❑ 86Fle-426
❑ 86Lea-55
❑ 86OPC-134
❑ 86SevCoi-W10
❑ 86Spo-75
❑ 86Top-134
❑ 86TopSti-169
❑ 86TopTat-7
❑ 86TopTif-134
❑ 86Woo-17
❑ 87A'sSmoC-8
❑ 87Don-158
❑ 87DonOpeD-20
❑ 87Fle-397
❑ 87FleBasA-24
❑ 87FleGlo-397
❑ 87FleMin-63
❑ 87FleStiC-71
❑ 87OPC-69
❑ 87RedFolSB-37
❑ 87Spo-138
❑ 87SpoTeaP-23
❑ 87StuPan-24
❑ 87Top-678
❑ 87TopSti-171
❑ 87TopTif-678
❑ 88A'sMot-6
❑ 88ActPacT-4
❑ 88Don-178
❑ 88DonBasB-246
❑ 88DonTeaBA-178
❑ 88Fle-285
❑ 88FleGlo-285
❑ 88FleSluBC-C3
❑ 88FleStiC-55
❑ 88Lea-195
❑ 88OPC-292
❑ 88PanSti-169
❑ 88Sco-253
❑ 88ScoGlo-253
❑ 88Spo-202
❑ 88StaLinAs-9
❑ 88Top-292
❑ 88TopBig-221
❑ 88TopSti-167
❑ 88TopTif-292
❑ 89A'sMot-5
❑ 89Bow-198
❑ 89BowTif-198
❑ 89Don-243
❑ 89DonAll-17
❑ 89DonBasB-22
❑ 89Fle-16
❑ 89Fle-633
❑ 89FleGlo-16
❑ 89FleGlo-633
❑ 89OPC-47
❑ 89PanSti-421
❑ 89RedFolSB-72
❑ 89Sco-179
❑ 89ScoHot1S-12
❑ 89Spo-53
❑ 89Top-47
❑ 89TopBasT-103
❑ 89TopBatL-20
❑ 89TopBig-57
❑ 89TopSti-170
❑ 89TopTif-47
❑ 89TVSpoM-99
❑ 89UppDec-562
❑ 90A'sMot-8
❑ 90Bow-452
❑ 90BowTif-452
❑ 90ClaBlu-12
❑ 90Don-95
❑ 90DonBesA-117
❑ 90El PasDAGTI-40
❑ 90Fle-14
❑ 90FleCan-14
❑ 90Lea-213
❑ 90MLBBasB-73
❑ 90OPC-316
❑ 90PanSti-134
❑ 90PanSti-184
❑ 90PubIntS-309
❑ 90RedFolSB-56
❑ 90Sco-296
❑ 90Sco-702
❑ 90Sco100S-20
❑ 90Spo-84
❑ 90Top-316
❑ 90TopBatL-12
❑ 90TopBig-83
❑ 90TopDou-39
❑ 90TopGloS-6
❑ 90TopMinL-29
❑ 90TopSti-183
❑ 90TopStiB-42
❑ 90TopTif-316
❑ 90TopTVA-4
❑ 90UppDec-253
❑ 91A'sMot-8
❑ 91BasBesHM-12
❑ 91Don-273
❑ 91Fle-14
❑ 91OPC-502
❑ 91PanFreS-194
❑ 91Sco-630
❑ 91StaClu-231
❑ 91Top-502
❑ 91TopDesS-502
❑ 91TopMic-502
❑ 91TopTif-502
❑ 91Ult-250
❑ 91UppDec-194
❑ 92AthMot-8
❑ 92Bow-78
❑ 92Don-775
❑ 92Fle-261
❑ 92Lea-148
❑ 92LeaBlaG-148
❑ 92OPC-495
❑ 92PanSti-17
❑ 92Pin-455
❑ 92Sco-648
❑ 92StaClu-45
❑ 92Stu-225
❑ 92Top-495
❑ 92TopGol-495
❑ 92TopGolW-495
❑ 92TopMic-495
❑ 92Ult-423
❑ 92UppDec-682
❑ 93PanSti-17
❑ 93Sel-156
❑ 93Top-127
❑ 93TopGol-127
❑ 93TopInaM-127
❑ 93TopInaR-127
❑ 93TopMic-127
❑ 94A'sMot-28
❑ 95AthMot-28

Lansford, Joe
❑ 82HawIslT-6
❑ 83LasVegSBHN-13
❑ 84LasVegSC-220
❑ 85TacTigC-146
❑ 87LasVegSP-4

Lansing, Mike
❑ 90MiaMirlS-16
❑ 90WicStaSGD-20
❑ 91Cla/Bes-45
❑ 91FloStaLAP-FSL24
❑ 91MiaMirC-21
❑ 91MiaMirP-415
❑ 92HarSenF-466
❑ 92HarSenS-287
❑ 92UppDecML-131
❑ 93Bow-184
❑ 93ExcFS7-61
❑ 93ExpPosN-15
❑ 93Fin-186
❑ 93FinRef-186
❑ 93Fla-85
❑ 93FleFinE-95
❑ 93JimDeaR-6
❑ 93Lea-464
❑ 93OPCPre-82
❑ 93PacSpa-535
❑ 93Pin-620
❑ 93SelRoo-60T
❑ 93SelRooAR-3
❑ 93SP-105
❑ 93StaClu-691
❑ 93StaCluFDI-691
❑ 93StaCluMOP-691
❑ 93Stu-46
❑ 93TopTra-99T
❑ 93Ult-417
❑ 93UltAllR-4
❑ 93UppDec-677
❑ 93UppDecGold-677
❑ 94Bow-228
❑ 94ColC-170
❑ 94ColChoGS-170
❑ 94ColChoSS-170
❑ 94Don-208
❑ 94Fin-10
❑ 94FinJum-10
❑ 94FinRef-10
❑ 94Fla-402
❑ 94Fle-543
❑ 94FleExtB-308
❑ 94FleRooS-10
❑ 94Lea-89
❑ 94OPC-218
❑ 94Pac-384
❑ 94PanSti-212
❑ 94Pin-455
❑ 94PinArtP-455
❑ 94PinMusC-455
❑ 94Sco-488
❑ 94ScoBoyoS-17
❑ 94ScoGolR-488
❑ 94Sel-88
❑ 94StaClu-577
❑ 94StaCluFDI-577
❑ 94StaCluGR-577
❑ 94StaCluMO-48
❑ 94StaCluMOP-577
❑ 94Top-287
❑ 94TopGol-287
❑ 94TopSpa-287
❑ 94TriPla-97
❑ 94Ult-230
❑ 94UppDec-244
❑ 94UppDecED-244
❑ 94USPlaCR-7H
❑ 94USPlaCR-12D
❑ 95ColCho-233
❑ 95ColChoGS-233
❑ 95ColChoSS-233
❑ 95Don-15
❑ 95DonPreP-15
❑ 95DonTopotO-281
❑ 95Fla-163
❑ 95Fle-355
❑ 95Lea-11
❑ 95Pin-408
❑ 95PinArtP-408
❑ 95PinMusC-408
❑ 95Sco-127
❑ 95ScoGolR-127
❑ 95ScoPlaTS-127
❑ 95StaClu-431
❑ 95StaCluMOP-431
❑ 95StaCluSTWS-431
❑ 95Top-548
❑ 95TopCyb-329
❑ 95Ult-404
❑ 95UltGolM-404
❑ 95UppDec-328
❑ 95UppDecED-328
❑ 95UppDecEDG-328
❑ 96ColCho-615
❑ 96ColChoGS-615
❑ 96ColChoSS-615
❑ 96Don-252
❑ 96DonPreP-252
❑ 96ExpDis-11
❑ 96Fla-308
❑ 96Fle-461
❑ 96FleTif-461
❑ 96Lea-206
❑ 96LeaPrePB-206
❑ 96LeaPrePG-206
❑ 96LeaPrePS-206
❑ 96LeaSigA-129
❑ 96LeaSigAG-129
❑ 96LeaSigAS-129
❑ 96Pac-118
❑ 96SP-119
❑ 96StaClu-369
❑ 96StaCluMOP-369
❑ 96TeaOut-48
❑ 96Top-86
❑ 96Ult-232
❑ 96UltGolM-232
❑ 96UppDec-133
❑ 97Bow-21
❑ 97BowChr-17
❑ 97BowChrI-17
❑ 97BowChrIR-17
❑ 97BowChrR-17
❑ 97BowInt-21
❑ 97Cir-118
❑ 97CirRav-118
❑ 97ColCho-164
❑ 97Fin-69
❑ 97FinRef-69
❑ 97Fle-381
❑ 97FleTif-381
❑ 97Lea-37
❑ 97LeaFraM-37
❑ 97LeaFraMDC-37
❑ 97MetUni-157
❑ 97Pac-346
❑ 97PacLigB-346
❑ 97PacSil-346
❑ 97Sco-289
❑ 97ScoArtPWB-289
❑ 97ScoPreS-289
❑ 97ScoShoS-289
❑ 97ScoShoSAP-289
❑ 97SP-112
❑ 97StaClu-145
❑ 97StaCluMOP-145
❑ 97Stu-123
❑ 97StuPrePG-123
❑ 97StuPrePS-123
❑ 97Top-83
❑ 97TopChr-31
❑ 97TopChrR-31
❑ 97TopGal-106
❑ 97TopGalPPI-106
❑ 97Ult-384
❑ 97UltGolME-384
❑ 97UltPlaME-384
❑ 97UppDec-428
❑ 98CirThu-128
❑ 98CirThuRav-128
❑ 98CirThuSupRav-128
❑ 98ColCho-361
❑ 98Don-256
❑ 98DonGolPP-256
❑ 98DonSilPP-256
❑ 98Fin-153
❑ 98FinNo--153
❑ 98FinNo-R-153
❑ 98FinRef-153
❑ 98Fle-135
❑ 98Fle-392
❑ 98FleVin'-90
❑ 98FleVin'C-90
❑ 98MetUni-151
❑ 98MetUniPMG-151
❑ 98Pac-348
❑ 98PacOme-84
❑ 98PacOmeR-84
❑ 98PacOnl-249
❑ 98PacOnlR-249
❑ 98PacOnlWC-249
❑ 98PacPlaB-348
❑ 98PacRedT-348
❑ 98PacSil-348
❑ 98PinPlu-55
❑ 98PinSna-CR7
❑ 98Sco-169
❑ 98ScoRT-187
❑ 98SP Aut-83
❑ 98SpollIWSF-74
❑ 98SpollIWSFEE-74
❑ 98SpollIWSFFE-74
❑ 98SPxFin-270
❑ 98SPxFin-339
❑ 98SPxFinR-270
❑ 98SPxFinR-339
❑ 98SPxFinS-270
❑ 98SPxFinS-339
❑ 98StaCluFDI-360
❑ 98StaClul-360
❑ 98StaCluOneK-360
❑ 98StaCluPP-360
❑ 98Top-136
❑ 98Top-459
❑ 98TopChr-136
❑ 98TopChr-459
❑ 98TopChrR-136
❑ 98TopChrR-459
❑ 98TopDevR-136
❑ 98TopDevR-459
❑ 98TopDia-136
❑ 98TopDia-459
❑ 98TopGal-16
❑ 98TopGalGP-16
❑ 98TopGalOPP-16
❑ 98TopGalPPI-16
❑ 98TopGalPPIA-16
❑ 98TopMiniC-136
❑ 98TopMiniC-459
❑ 98TopOpeD-69
❑ 98TopSta-134
❑ 98TopStaB-134
❑ 98TopStaG-134
❑ 98TopStaGR-134
❑ 98TopStaS-134
❑ 98Ult-44
❑ 98Ult-265
❑ 98UltGolM-44
❑ 98UltGolM-265
❑ 98UltMas-44
❑ 98UltMas-265
❑ 98UltPlaM-44
❑ 98UltPlaM-265
❑ 98UppDec-154
❑ 98UppDec-674
❑ 99199Fin-238
❑ 99FinGolRef-238
❑ 99FinRef-238
❑ 99Fle-123
❑ 99FleSta9-123
❑ 99FleWarT-123
❑ 99Pac-149
❑ 99PacPar-84
❑ 99PacParC-84
❑ 99PacParG-84
❑ 99PacParHoloGold-84
❑ 99PacParHS-84
❑ 99PacParOD-84
❑ 99PacParPB-84
❑ 99PacParRed-84
❑ 99PacPlaB-149
❑ 99PacRed-149
❑ 99SkyThu-73
❑ 99SkyThuRant-73
❑ 99SkyThuRave-73
❑ 99StaClu-204
❑ 99StaCluFDI-204
❑ 99StaCluOoaK-204
❑ 99StaCluPP-204
❑ 99ThuSkySupR-73
❑ 99Top-342
❑ 99TopChr-342
❑ 99TopChrR-342
❑ 99TopMVPP-342
❑ 99Ult-8
❑ 99UltGolM-8
❑ 99UltMas-8
❑ 99UltPlaM-8
❑ 99UppDec-89
❑ 99UppDecEL1-89
❑ 99UppDecEL2-89
❑ 99Vic-138

Lantigua, Eduardo
❑ 92GulCoaDF-3573
❑ 93VerBeaDC-14
❑ 93VerBeaDF-2229
❑ 94Bow-266

Lantigua, Manny
❑ 75SanAntBT-13
❑ 79PorBeaT-16

Lantrip, Joe
❑ 92BluOriC-16
❑ 92BluOriF-2357

Lantrip, Rick
❑ 88AriWilP-9
❑ 90FreStaS-9
❑ 90OneYanP-3387
❑ 91GreHorP-3066
❑ 92GreHorC-15
❑ 92GreHorF-788

Lantz, Tom
❑ 75CliPilT-14

Lanza, Mike
❑ 94BelMarC-18
❑ 94BelMarF-3244
❑ 96LanJetB-16

Lanzetta, Tobin
❑ 97VerExpB-17
❑ 98CapFeaCM-10

LaPalme, Paul
❑ 52Top-166
❑ 53BowBW-19
❑ 53Top-201
❑ 54Bow-107
❑ 54DanDee-14
❑ 55Bow-61
❑ 55CarHunW-12
❑ 57Top-344
❑ 58MonRoyF-15
❑ 59O'KAleMR-12
❑ 83TopRep5-166
❑ 91TopArc1-201

Lapan, Peter
❑ 17Zee-11
❑ 18Zee-10
❑ 19Zee-11

Lapenta, Jerry
❑ 86GenCubP-14
❑ 87PeoChiP-6
❑ 88PeoChiTI-20
❑ 88PitCubP-1366

Lapka, Rick
❑ 94PriRedC-14
❑ 94PriRedF-3258
❑ 95BilMusTI-5
❑ 97St.PauS-15

LaPlante, Michel
❑ 92WelPirC-15
❑ 92WelPirF-1318
❑ 93AugPirC-11
❑ 93AugPirF-1538
❑ 94CarMudF-1573
❑ 98MadBlaW-10

LaPoint, Dave
❑ 77NewCoPT-21
❑ 78BurBeeT-18
❑ 79CliDodT-19
❑ 80VanCanT-7
❑ 81Car5x7-16
❑ 83Car-16
❑ 83Don-544
❑ 83Fle-14
❑ 83Top-438
❑ 84AllGamPl-81
❑ 84Car-18
❑ 84Car5x7-15
❑ 84Don-290
❑ 84Fle-328
❑ 84Nes792-627
❑ 84Top-627
❑ 84TopSti-146
❑ 84TopTif-627
❑ 85Don-138
❑ 85Fle-233
❑ 85FleUpd-68
❑ 85GiaMot-16
❑ 85GiaPos-17
❑ 85OPC-229
❑ 85Top-229
❑ 85TopMin-229
❑ 85TopSti-143
❑ 85TopTif-229
❑ 85TopTifT-71T
❑ 85TopTra-71T
❑ 86Don-387
❑ 86Fle-547
❑ 86FleUpd-64
❑ 86OPC-162
❑ 86TigCaiD-10
❑ 86Top-551
❑ 86TopTif-551
❑ 86TopTra-61T
❑ 86TopTraT-61T
❑ 87Don-607
❑ 87Fle-421
❑ 87FleGlo-421
❑ 87OPC-319
❑ 87Top-754
❑ 87TopTif-754
❑ 88Don-552
❑ 88DonBasB-123

❑ 88Fle-402
❑ 88FleBasA-21
❑ 88FleGlo-402
❑ 88FleSlu-24
❑ 88Sco-589
❑ 88ScoGlo-589
❑ 88StaLinWS-11
❑ 88Top-334
❑ 88TopTif-334
❑ 88WhiSoxC-13
❑ 89Bow-165
❑ 89BowTif-165
❑ 89Don-488
❑ 89DonBasB-244
❑ 89DonTra-27
❑ 89Fle-212
❑ 89FleGlo-212
❑ 89OPC-89
❑ 89Sco-384
❑ 89ScoRoo-4T
❑ 89Top-89
❑ 89TopTif-89
❑ 89TopTra-67T
❑ 89TopTraT-67T
❑ 89UppDec-600
❑ 89UppDec-706
❑ 89YanScoNW-15
❑ 90Don-72
❑ 90OPC-186
❑ 90PubIntS-539
❑ 90Sco-357
❑ 90Top-186
❑ 90TopTif-186
❑ 90TopTVY-11
❑ 90UppDec-507
❑ 90YanScoNW-12
❑ 91Don-481
❑ 91Fle-669
❑ 91OPC-484
❑ 91Sco-218
❑ 91Top-484
❑ 91TopDesS-484
❑ 91TopMic-484
❑ 91TopTif-484
❑ 91UppDec-483
❑ 92YanWIZ8-102
❑ 93PorBeaF-2381
❑ 94BreMilB-50

LaPoint, Tony (J. Anthony)
❑ 86GenCubP-15
❑ 87ChaWheP-19

LaPorte, Frank
❑ 08RosComP-3
❑ 09ColChiE-165A
❑ 09ColChiE-165B
❑ 09T206-205
❑ 10CouT21-38
❑ 10DomDisP-66
❑ 10E-UOraBSC-12
❑ 10JHDABE-10
❑ 10SweCapPP-53A
❑ 10SweCapPP-53B
❑ 11HelSta-62
❑ 11MecDFT-42
❑ 11PinT-5-802
❑ 11SpoLifCW-213
❑ 11SpoLifM-81
❑ 11T205-95
❑ 12ColRedB-165A
❑ 12ColRedB-165B
❑ 12ColTinT-165A
❑ 12ColTinT-165B
❑ 12HasTriFT-1A
❑ 14CraJacE-98
❑ 14PieStaT-61
❑ 15CraJacE-98

Lapp, John
❑ 10NadE1-28
❑ 11A'sFirT20-9
❑ 11D35RocB-9
❑ 11MecDFT-2
❑ 11PinT-5-516
❑ 11PloCanE-40
❑ 11SpoLifM-96
❑ 12T207-99
❑ 14FatPlaT-22
❑ 15SpoNewM-96
❑ 16BF2FP-14
❑ 16SpoNewM-98
❑ 74A'sTCM1P-6

Lapple, Bob
❑ 80CedRapRT-10

Lara, Carlos
❑ 91PulBraC-3
❑ 91PulBraP-4009

Lara, Crucito
❑ 87St.PetCP-20
❑ 88St.PetCS-11
❑ 89St.LucMS-12
❑ 90JacMetGS-25

Lara, Eddie
❑ 96WesMicWB-13
❑ 97SouOreTB-7
❑ 98VisOakG-18

Lara, Felix
❑ 97EriSeaWB-23
❑ 98EriSeaWM-15

Lara, Giovanni
❑ 96VerExpB-15
❑ 98CapFeaCM-11

Lara, Luis
❑ 85DomLeaS-61

Lara, Nelson
❑ 98Bow-307
❑ 98BowChr-307
❑ 98BowChrGA-307
❑ 98BowChrGAR-307
❑ 98BowChrI-307
❑ 98BowChrIR-307
❑ 98BowChrR-307
❑ 98BowGolA-307
❑ 98BowInt-307
❑ 99Bow-190
❑ 99BowChr-190
❑ 99BowChrG-190
❑ 99BowChrGR-190
❑ 99BowChrI-190
❑ 99BowChrIR-190
❑ 99BowChrR-190
❑ 99BowGol-190
❑ 99BowInt-190

Larcom, Mark
❑ 82WisRapTF-22
❑ 83WisRapTF-12

Lardizabal, Ruben
❑ 90ModA'sC-17
❑ 91ModA'sC-7
❑ 91ModA'sP-3082

Lardner, Ring
❑ 88PacEigMO-30
❑ 88PacEigMO-35
❑ 88PacEigMO-42

Largusa, Levon
❑ 92ClaDraP-70
❑ 92St.CatBJC-25
❑ 92St.CatBJF-3384
❑ 93HagSunC-17
❑ 93HagSunF-1876
❑ 93StaCluM-23
❑ 94DunBluJF-2554
❑ 95DunBluJTI-11

Laribee, Russ
❑ 81PawRedST-20

Larios, John
❑ 86EugEmeC-35
❑ 87AppFoxP-3

Lariviere, Chris
❑ 88RocExpLC-20

Lariviere, Jason
❑ 95NewJerCTI-16
❑ 96PeoChiB-18
❑ 97ArkTraB-22
❑ 98ArkTraM-17

Larker, Norm
❑ 53ExhCan-37
❑ 59DodMor-7
❑ 59DodPos-10
❑ 59DodTeal-14
❑ 59Top-107
❑ 59TopVen-107
❑ 60DodBelB-1
❑ 60DodJayP-8
❑ 60DodTeal-11
❑ 60DodUniO-11
❑ 60KeyChal-29
❑ 60Top-394
❑ 61Baz-34
❑ 61DodBelB-5
❑ 61DodJayP-5
❑ 61DodMor-5
❑ 61DodUniO-12
❑ 61Pos-156A
❑ 61Pos-156B
❑ 61Top-41
❑ 61Top-130
❑ 61TopStal-28
❑ 62Baz-39
❑ 62Col.45B-11
❑ 62Col45'HC-10
❑ 62Col45'JP-8
❑ 62Jel-113
❑ 62Pos-113
❑ 62PosCan-113
❑ 62SalPlaC-194
❑ 62ShiPlaC-194
❑ 62Top-23
❑ 62TopBuc-48
❑ 62TopVen-23
❑ 63BraJayP-6
❑ 63Jel-188
❑ 63Pos-188
❑ 63Top-536
❑ 89AstCol4S-14
❑ 89DodSmoG-67
❑ 90DodTar-433

Larkin, Andy
❑ 93ElmPioC-9
❑ 93ElmPioF-3818
❑ 94Bow-262
❑ 94Cla-62
❑ 94KanCouCC-13
❑ 94KanCouCF-157
❑ 94KanCouCTI-14
❑ 94MidLeaAF-MDW16
❑ 95Bow-166
❑ 95BowBes-B9
❑ 95BowBesR-B9
❑ 95Exc-195
❑ 95KanCouCLTI-8
❑ 95PorSeaDTI-10
❑ 95UppDecML-64
❑ 95UppDecMLFS-64
❑ 96SigRooOJTP-T8
❑ 97Bow-132
❑ 97BowInt-132
❑ 97ChaKni-17
❑ 97UppDec-478
❑ 98ChaKniQ-18
❑ 98LeaRS-299
❑ 98LeaRSLHolo-299
❑ 98LeaRSLong-299
❑ 98LeaRTrue-299
❑ 98PacOmeRS-5
❑ 98PacOmeRST5-5
❑ 98PacOnl-299
❑ 98PacOnlR-299
❑ 98PacOnlWC-299
❑ 99UppDec-103
❑ 99UppDecEL1-103
❑ 99UppDecEL2-103

Larkin, Barry
❑ 86SpoRoo-34
❑ 87ClaGam-18
❑ 87ClaUpdY-133
❑ 87Don-492
❑ 87DonOpeD-191
❑ 87Fle-204
❑ 87FleGlo-204
❑ 87RedKah-15
❑ 87SpoTeaP-4
❑ 87Top-648
❑ 87TopTif-648
❑ 87ToyRoo-18
❑ 88Don-492
❑ 88DonBasB-222
❑ 88Fle-239
❑ 88FleGlo-239
❑ 88Lea-226
❑ 88OPC-102
❑ 88PanSti-280
❑ 88RedKah-11
❑ 88Sco-72
❑ 88ScoGlo-72
❑ 88ScoSam-72
❑ 88ScoYouS2-34
❑ 88StaLinRe-12
❑ 88Top-102
❑ 88TopBig-74
❑ 88TopSti-140
❑ 88TopTif-102
❑ 89Bow-311
❑ 89BowTif-311
❑ 89CadEllD-32
❑ 89ClaLigB-70
❑ 89ClaTraP-165
❑ 89Don-257
❑ 89DonAll-47
❑ 89DonBasB-110
❑ 89Fle-164
❑ 89FleBasA-26
❑ 89FleGlo-164
❑ 89OPC-363
❑ 89PanSti-74
❑ 89RedFolSB-73
❑ 89RedKah-11
❑ 89Sco-31
❑ 89ScoHot1S-52
❑ 89Scomast-24
❑ 89Spo-136
❑ 89Top-515
❑ 89TopBasT-90
❑ 89TopBig-199
❑ 89TopMinL-11
❑ 89TopSti-137
❑ 89TopStiB-44
❑ 89TopTif-515
❑ 89TVSpoM-39
❑ 89UppDec-270
❑ 89UppDecS-2
❑ 90Bow-50
❑ 90BowTif-50
❑ 90ClaBlu-48
❑ 90Don-71
❑ 90DonBesN-52
❑ 90DonLeaS-51
❑ 90Fle-423
❑ 90FleBasA-23
❑ 90FleBasAC-23
❑ 90FleCan-423
❑ 90FleLeaL-22
❑ 90FleLeaLC-22
❑ 90FleLeaS-1
❑ 90Lea-18
❑ 90LeaPre-5
❑ 90MLBBasB-21
❑ 90OPC-10
❑ 90PanSti-253
❑ 90PubIntS-33
❑ 90PubIntS-266
❑ 90RedFolSB-57
❑ 90RedKah-12
❑ 90Sco-155
❑ 90Sco-689
❑ 90Spo-160
❑ 90StaLar-1
❑ 90StaLar-2
❑ 90StaLar-3
❑ 90StaLar-4
❑ 90StaLar-5
❑ 90StaLar-6
❑ 90StaLar-7
❑ 90StaLar-8
❑ 90StaLar-9
❑ 90StaLar-10
❑ 90StaLar-11
❑ 90Top-10
❑ 90TopBig-189
❑ 90TopCoi-51
❑ 90TopDou-40
❑ 90TopGloS-5
❑ 90TopMag-18
❑ 90TopMag-81
❑ 90TopSti-136
❑ 90TopStiB-11
❑ 90TopTif-10
❑ 90TopTVA-36
❑ 90UppDec-99
❑ 90UppDec-167
❑ 90USPlaCA-6D
❑ 91BasBesHM-13
❑ 91Bow-379
❑ 91Bow-673
❑ 91CadEllD-34
❑ 91Cla2-T33
❑ 91ClaGam-142
❑ 91Col-31
❑ 91Don-5
❑ 91Don-471
❑ 91DonSupD-5
❑ 91Fle-68
❑ 91Fle-711
❑ 91FleAll-2
❑ 91JimDea-10
❑ 91Lea-168
❑ 91LeaPre-3
❑ 91OPC-400
❑ 91OPC-730
❑ 91PanCanT1-28
❑ 91PanFreS-130
❑ 91PanSti-129
❑ 91Pos-18
❑ 91RedFolS-58
❑ 91RedKah-11
❑ 91RedPep-11
❑ 91Sco-505
❑ 91Sco-666
❑ 91Sco-795
❑ 91Sco-888
❑ 91Sco100S-20
❑ 91ScoCoo-B2
❑ 91SevCoi-F10
❑ 91SimandSMLBL-26
❑ 91StaClu-92
❑ 91StaPinB-28
❑ 91Stu-167
❑ 91SunSee-16
❑ 91Top-400
❑ 91Top-730
❑ 91TopCraJ2-11
❑ 91TopDesS-400
❑ 91TopDesS-730
❑ 91TopMic-400
❑ 91TopMic-730
❑ 91TopTif-400
❑ 91TopTif-730
❑ 91TopTriH-N3
❑ 91Ult-96
❑ 91UppDec-353
❑ 91UppDecSS-SS18
❑ 91USPlaCA-6C
❑ 91Woo-30
❑ 92Bow-353
❑ 92Bow-694
❑ 92Cla2-T74
❑ 92ClaGam-76
❑ 92Don-185
❑ 92DonCraJ1-19
❑ 92DonMcD-15
❑ 92Fle-411
❑ 92Fle-704
❑ 92FleAll-16
❑ 92FleCitTP-14
❑ 92Hig5-32
❑ 92HitTheBB-20
❑ 92Lea-73
❑ 92LeaBlaG-73
❑ 92MVPPin-43
❑ 92New-14
❑ 92OPC-465
❑ 92OPCPre-96
❑ 92PanSti-265
❑ 92PepDieM-18
❑ 92Pin-5
❑ 92PinRool-9
❑ 92PinTeaP-7
❑ 92Pos-23
❑ 92RedFolS-55
❑ 92RedKah-11
❑ 92Sco-100
❑ 92Sco-775
❑ 92Sco100S-77
❑ 92ScoImpP-50
❑ 92SevCoi-13
❑ 92SpoIllFK1-402
❑ 92StaClu-100
❑ 92StaClu-596
❑ 92StaCluD-102
❑ 92Stu-23
❑ 92Top-389
❑ 92Top-465
❑ 92TopDaiQTU-4
❑ 92TopGol-389
❑ 92TopGol-465
❑ 92TopGolW-389
❑ 92TopGolW-465A
❑ 92TopGolW-465B
❑ 92TopKid-37
❑ 92TopMcD-21
❑ 92TopMic-389
❑ 92TopMic-465
❑ 92TriPla-31
❑ 92Ult-191
❑ 92UltAllS-13
❑ 92UppDec-144
❑ 92UppDecF-30
❑ 92UppDecFG-30
❑ 92UppDecTMH-29
❑ 93Bow-470
❑ 93ClaGam-52
❑ 93ColAllG-20
❑ 93DiaMar-63
❑ 93Don-426
❑ 93DonEli-23
❑ 93DonEliS-5
❑ 93DonPre-3
❑ 93DonSpiotG-SG13
❑ 93DurPowP2-17
❑ 93Fin-114
❑ 93FinJum-114
❑ 93FinRef-114
❑ 93Fla-27
❑ 93Fle-394
❑ 93FleAll-NL4
❑ 93FleFruotL-35
❑ 93FunPac-167
❑ 93FunPac-170
❑ 93Hos-8
❑ 93JimDea-2
❑ 93Kra-25
❑ 93Lea-311
❑ 93LeaGolA-R14
❑ 93LeaGolA-U6
❑ 93MetBak-32
❑ 93MilBonSS-3
❑ 93OPC-147
❑ 93OPCPre-103
❑ 93PacSpa-84
❑ 93PanSti-293
❑ 93Pin-22
❑ 93Pin-300
❑ 93Pin-306
❑ 93PinCoo-26
❑ 93PinCooD-26
❑ 93Pos-28
❑ 93PosCan-15
❑ 93RedFolS-53
❑ 93RedKah-13
❑ 93Sco-16
❑ 93ScoFra-17
❑ 93Sel-23
❑ 93SP-15
❑ 93StaClu-415
❑ 93StaCluFDI-415
❑ 93StaCluMOP-415
❑ 93Stu-43
❑ 93StuHer-7
❑ 93Top-110
❑ 93Top-404
❑ 93TOPBLAG-11
❑ 93TopFulS-17
❑ 93TopGol-110
❑ 93TopGol-404
❑ 93TopInaM-110
❑ 93TopInaM-404
❑ 93TopInaR-110
❑ 93TopInaR-404
❑ 93TopMic-110
❑ 93TopMic-404
❑ 93TriPla-31
❑ 93TriPlaA-8
❑ 93Ult-30
❑ 93UltAllS-4
❑ 93UppDec-245
❑ 93UppDec-473
❑ 93UppDecCP-R13
❑ 93UppDecDG-22
❑ 93UppDecGold-245
❑ 93UppDecGold-473
❑ 93UppDecIC-WI21
❑ 93UppDecICJ-WI21
❑ 94Bow-471
❑ 94BowBes-X95
❑ 94BowBesR-X95
❑ 94ChuHomS-12
❑ 94ChuHomSG-12
❑ 94ColC-171
❑ 94ColC-349
❑ 94ColChoGS-171
❑ 94ColChoGS-349
❑ 94ColChoSS-171
❑ 94ColChoSS-349
❑ 94ColChoT-8
❑ 94Don-45
❑ 94DonDiaK-DK17
❑ 94DonDiaKJ-DK17
❑ 94DonSpeE-45
❑ 94Fin-240
❑ 94FinJum-240
❑ 94FinRef-240
❑ 94Fla-146
❑ 94Fle-414
❑ 94FleAllS-45
❑ 94FleExtB-233
❑ 94FleTeaL-17
❑ 94FUnPac-111
❑ 94KinDis-17
❑ 94Kra-26
❑ 94Lea-126
❑ 94LeaL-95
❑ 94LeaMVPC-N9
❑ 94LeaMVPCG-N9
❑ 94OPC-125
❑ 94Pac-150
❑ 94PanSti-163
❑ 94Pin-12
❑ 94PinArtP-12
❑ 94PinMusC-12
❑ 94Pos-12
❑ 94ProMag-32
❑ 94RedFolMI-15
❑ 94RedKah-17
❑ 94Sco-74
❑ 94ScoDreT-5
❑ 94ScoGolR-74
❑ 94ScoGolS-15

❑ 94ScoSam-DT5
❑ 94Sel-7
❑ 94SelSki-SK2
❑ 94SP-159
❑ 94SPDieC-159
❑ 94SPHol-23
❑ 94SPHolDC-23
❑ 94Spo-109
❑ 94StaClu-414
❑ 94StaCluFDI-414
❑ 94StaCluGR-414
❑ 94StaCluMOP-414
❑ 94StaCluMOP-ST3
❑ 94StaCluST-ST3
❑ 94Stu-168
❑ 94TomPiz-13
❑ 94Top-250
❑ 94TopGol-250
❑ 94TopSpa-250
❑ 94TopSupS-25
❑ 94TriPla-214
❑ 94TriPlaM-8
❑ 94Ult-474
❑ 94UppDec-269
❑ 94UppDec-385
❑ 94UppDecAJ-26
❑ 94UppDecAJG-26
❑ 94UppDecDC-C3
❑ 94UppDecED-269
❑ 94UppDecED-385
❑ 95Baz-40
❑ 95BazRedH-RH8
❑ 95Bow-415
❑ 95BowBes-R25
❑ 95BowBesR-R25
❑ 95ClaPhoC-15
❑ 95ColCho-430
❑ 95ColChoGS-430
❑ 95ColChoSE-200
❑ 95ColChoSEGS-200
❑ 95ColChoSESS-200
❑ 95ColChoSS-430
❑ 95DenHol-13
❑ 95Don-241
❑ 95DonDom-6
❑ 95DonPreP-241
❑ 95DonTopotO-214
❑ 95Emo-117
❑ 95Fin-96
❑ 95FinRef-96
❑ 95Fla-339
❑ 95FlaHotG-5
❑ 95Fle-439
❑ 95Kra-24
❑ 95Lea-283
❑ 95LeaGreG-9
❑ 95LeaLim-49
❑ 95LeaLimIBP-18
❑ 95Pac-108
❑ 95PacPri-33
❑ 95PanSti-62
❑ 95Pin-382
❑ 95PinArtP-382
❑ 95PinMusC-382
❑ 95RedFol-15
❑ 95RedKah-16
❑ 95Sco-254
❑ 95ScoGolR-254
❑ 95ScoHaloG-HG8
❑ 95ScoPlaTS-254
❑ 95Sel-52
❑ 95SelArtP-52
❑ 95SelCer-27
❑ 95SelCerMG-27
❑ 95SP-45
❑ 95SPCha-36
❑ 95SPChaDC-36
❑ 95Spo-94
❑ 95SpoArtP-94
❑ 95SPSil-45
❑ 95SPSpeF-32
❑ 95StaClu-35
❑ 95StaClu-211
❑ 95StaClu-407
❑ 95StaClu-498
❑ 95StaCluFDI-35
❑ 95StaCluFDI-211
❑ 95StaCluMOP-35
❑ 95StaCluMOP-211
❑ 95StaCluMOP-407
❑ 95StaCluMOP-498
❑ 95StaCluMOP-SS17
❑ 95StaCluSS-SS17
❑ 95StaCluSTDW-RE3T
❑ 95StaCluSTDW-RE35
❑ 95StaCluSTWS-35
❑ 95StaCluSTWS-211
❑ 95StaCluSTWS-407
❑ 95StaCluSTWS-498
❑ 95StaCluVR-24
❑ 95StaCluVRMO-24
❑ 95Stu-37
❑ 95StuGolS-37
❑ 95Sum-10
❑ 95SumNthD-10
❑ 95SumSam-10
❑ 95TomPiz-25
❑ 95Top-350
❑ 95TopCyb-189
❑ 95TopD3-48
❑ 95TopEmb-129
❑ 95TopEmbGI-129
❑ 95UC3-26
❑ 95UC3ArtP-26
❑ 95Ult-145
❑ 95UltAllS-10
❑ 95UltAllSGM-10
❑ 95UltAwaW-14
❑ 95UltAwaWGM-14
❑ 95UltGolM-145
❑ 95UppDec-405
❑ 95UppDecED-405
❑ 95UppDecEDG-405
❑ 95UppDecSE-163
❑ 95UppDecSEG-163
❑ 95Zen-4
❑ 96Baz-97
❑ 96Bow-18
❑ 96BowBes-66
❑ 96BowBesAR-66
❑ 96BowBesMI-4
❑ 96BowBesMIAR-4
❑ 96BowBesMIR-4
❑ 96BowBesP-BBP17
❑ 96BowBesPAR-BBP17
❑ 96BowBesPR-BBP17
❑ 96BowBesR-66
❑ 96BowFoi-18
❑ 96Cir-117
❑ 96CirAcc-17
❑ 96CirBos-31
❑ 96CirRav-117
❑ 96ColCho-276
❑ 96ColCho-401
❑ 96ColCho-520
❑ 96ColCho-707
❑ 96ColChoGS-276
❑ 96ColChoGS-401
❑ 96ColChoGS-520
❑ 96ColChoGS-707
❑ 96ColChoSS-276
❑ 96ColChoSS-401
❑ 96ColChoSS-520
❑ 96ColChoSS-707
❑ 96ColChoYMtP-20
❑ 96ColChoYMtP-20A
❑ 96ColChoYMtPGS-20
❑ 96ColChoYMtPGS-20A
❑ 96DenHol-13
❑ 96Don-442
❑ 96DonPreP-442
❑ 96EmoXL-165
❑ 96Fin-B167
❑ 96Fin-B319
❑ 96Fin-S7
❑ 96FinRef-B167
❑ 96FinRef-B319
❑ 96FinRef-S7
❑ 96Fla-234
❑ 96Fle-345
❑ 96FleTeaL-17
❑ 96FleTif-345
❑ 96FleUpd-U230
❑ 96FleUpdTC-U230
❑ 96Kin-15
❑ 96Lea-122
❑ 96LeaGolS-13
❑ 96LeaHatO-2
❑ 96LeaLim-43
❑ 96LeaLimG-43
❑ 96LeaPre-38
❑ 96LeaPreP-38
❑ 96LeaPrePB-122
❑ 96LeaPrePG-122
❑ 96LeaPrePS-122
❑ 96LeaPreSG-69
❑ 96LeaPreSte-69
❑ 96LeaSig-42
❑ 96LeaSigPPG-42
❑ 96LeaSigPPP-42
❑ 96LibSpo-12
❑ 96MetUni-149
❑ 96MetUniP-149
❑ 96Pac-40
❑ 96Pac-50
❑ 96PacPri-P16
❑ 96PacPriG-P16
❑ 96PanSti-49
❑ 96Pin-90
❑ 96PinAfi-38
❑ 96PinAfiAP-38
❑ 96PinAfiFPP-38
❑ 96PinArtP-51
❑ 96PinFan-18
❑ 96PinFirR-15
❑ 96PinSta-51
❑ 96PinTeaP-4
❑ 96ProMagA-19
❑ 96ProMagDM-9
❑ 96ProSta-101
❑ 96RedF-23
❑ 96Sco-5
❑ 96Sco-362
❑ 96Sco-516
❑ 96ScoDugC-A5
❑ 96ScoDugC-B87
❑ 96ScoDugCAP-A5
❑ 96ScoDugCAP-B87
❑ 96ScoDugCSamp-5
❑ 96ScoGolS-14
❑ 96ScoRef-10
❑ 96ScoSam-5
❑ 96Sel-32
❑ 96SelArtP-32
❑ 96SelCer-41
❑ 96SelCerAP-41
❑ 96SelCerCB-41
❑ 96SelCerCR-41
❑ 96SelCerIP-24
❑ 96SelCerMB-41
❑ 96SelCerMG-41
❑ 96SelCerMR-41
❑ 96SelTeaN-25
❑ 96SP-63
❑ 96SPMarM-MM11
❑ 96SPMarMDC-11
❑ 96Spo-60
❑ 96SpoArtP-60
❑ 96SpoDouT-1
❑ 96SPSpeFX-9
❑ 96SPSpeFXDC-9
❑ 96SPx-17
❑ 96SPxGol-17
❑ 96StaClu-197
❑ 96StaClu-271
❑ 96StaCluEPB-271
❑ 96StaCluEPG-271
❑ 96StaCluEPS-271
❑ 96StaCluEWB-EW6
❑ 96StaCluEWG-EW6
❑ 96StaCluEWS-EW6
❑ 96StaCluMM-MM6
❑ 96StaCluMO-20
❑ 96StaCluMOP-197
❑ 96StaCluMOP-271
❑ 96StaCluMOP-MM6
❑ 96Stu-26
❑ 96StuPrePB-26
❑ 96StuPrePG-26
❑ 96StuPrePS-26
❑ 96Sum-108
❑ 96SumAbo&B-108
❑ 96SumArtP-108
❑ 96SumFoi-108
❑ 96SumPos-4
❑ 96TeaOut-49
❑ 96Top-6
❑ 96Top-293
❑ 96TopBroLL-1
❑ 96TopChr-6
❑ 96TopChr-116
❑ 96TopChrR-6
❑ 96TopChrR-116
❑ 96TopGal-169
❑ 96TopGalE-20
❑ 96TopGalPPI-169
❑ 96TopLas-84
❑ 96TopLasSS-5
❑ 96TopPowB-6
❑ 96TopPro-NL17
❑ 96Ult-179
❑ 96Ult-583
❑ 96UltGolM-179
❑ 96UltGolM-583
❑ 96UltPriL-13
❑ 96UltPriLGM-13
❑ 96UppDec-219
❑ 96UppDec-310
❑ 96UppDecA-11
❑ 96UppDecDD-DD15
❑ 96UppDecDDG-DD15
❑ 96UppDecDDS-DD15
❑ 96UppDecPHE-H37
❑ 96UppDecPRE-R58
❑ 96UppDecPreH-H37
❑ 96UppDecPreR-R58
❑ 96Zen-19
❑ 96ZenArtP-19
❑ 96ZenMoz-10
❑ 97Bow-9
❑ 97BowBes-30
❑ 97BowBesAR-30
❑ 97BowBesMI-MI1
❑ 97BowBesMIAR-MI1
❑ 97BowBesMIARI-MI1
❑ 97BowBesMII-MI1
❑ 97BowBesMIR-MI1
❑ 97BowBesMIRI-MI1
❑ 97BowBesR-30
❑ 97BowChr-7
❑ 97BowChrI-7
❑ 97BowChrIR-7
❑ 97BowChrR-7
❑ 97BowInt-9
❑ 97Cir-332
❑ 97CirRav-332
❑ 97ColCho-80
❑ 97ColChoAC-22
❑ 97ColChoS-11
❑ 97ColChoSR-15
❑ 97ColChoTBS-17
❑ 97ColChoTBSWH-17
❑ 97ColChoTotT-T12
❑ 97CraJac-6
❑ 97DenHol-17
❑ 97Don-23
❑ 97Don-441
❑ 97DonArmaD-15
❑ 97DonDom-17
❑ 97DonEli-88
❑ 97DonEliGS-88
❑ 97DonGolPP-23
❑ 97DonGolPP-441
❑ 97DonLim-10
❑ 97DonLim-61
❑ 97DonLim-131
❑ 97DonLim-153
❑ 97DonLimE-10
❑ 97DonLimE-61
❑ 97DonLimE-131
❑ 97DonLimE-153
❑ 97DonLimENG-10
❑ 97DonLimFotG-41
❑ 97DonPre-109
❑ 97DonPre-185
❑ 97DonPreCttC-109
❑ 97DonPreCttC-185
❑ 97DonSig-25
❑ 97DonSigA-65
❑ 97DonSigAC-79
❑ 97DonSigAM-79
❑ 97DonSigPPP-25
❑ 97DonSilPP-23
❑ 97DonSilPP-441
❑ 97DonTeaSMVP-8
❑ 97DonVxP1-14
❑ 97E-X2-64
❑ 97E-X2Cred-64
❑ 97E-X2EssCre-64
❑ 97Fin-66
❑ 97Fin-157
❑ 97Fin-323
❑ 97FinEmb-157
❑ 97FinEmb-323
❑ 97FinEmbR-157
❑ 97FinEmbR-323
❑ 97FinRef-66
❑ 97FinRef-157
❑ 97FinRef-323
❑ 97FlaShoHG-8
❑ 97FlaShoLC-32
❑ 97FlaShoLeg0-32
❑ 97FlaShoLeg1-32
❑ 97FlaShoM-A32
❑ 97FlaShoM-B32
❑ 97FlaShoM-C32
❑ 97FlaShoR0-32
❑ 97FlaShoR1-32
❑ 97FlaShoR2-32
❑ 97Fle-296
❑ 97Fle-706
❑ 97Fle-727
❑ 97FleTeaL-17
❑ 97FleTif-296
❑ 97FleTif-706
❑ 97FleTif-727
❑ 97KinB-25
❑ 97Lea-55
❑ 97Lea-365
❑ 97LeaFraM-55
❑ 97LeaFraM-365
❑ 97LeaFraMDC-55
❑ 97LeaFraMDC-365
❑ 97LeaGolS-23
❑ 97LeaKnoG-11
❑ 97LeaLeaotN-8
❑ 97MetUni-47
❑ 97NewPin-116
❑ 97NewPinAP-116
❑ 97NewPinMC-116
❑ 97NewPinPP-116
❑ 97Pac-271
❑ 97PacLigB-271
❑ 97PacPri-93
❑ 97PacPriLB-93
❑ 97PacPriP-93
❑ 97PacSil-271
❑ 97Pin-109
❑ 97PinArtP-PP109
❑ 97PinCer-25
❑ 97PinCerMBla-25
❑ 97PinCerMBlu-25
❑ 97PinCerMG-25
❑ 97PinCerMR-25
❑ 97PinCerR-25
❑ 97PinEpixGO-E12
❑ 97PinIns-112
❑ 97PinInsCE-112
❑ 97PinInsDD-11
❑ 97PinInsDE-112
❑ 97PinMin-27
❑ 97PinMinB-27
❑ 97PinMinCB-27
❑ 97PinMinCG-27
❑ 97PinMinCGR-27
❑ 97PinMinCN-27
❑ 97PinMinCSS-27
❑ 97PinMinG-27
❑ 97PinMinS-27
❑ 97PinMusC-109
❑ 97PinPrePla-109
❑ 97PinTotCPB-25
❑ 97PinTotCPG-25
❑ 97PinTotCPR-25
❑ 97PinX-P-31
❑ 97PinX-PMoS-31
❑ 97PinX-PSfF-35
❑ 97PinX-PSfFU-35
❑ 97Sco-242
❑ 97Sco-538
❑ 97ScoArtPWB-242
❑ 97ScoArtPWB-538
❑ 97ScoPreS-242
❑ 97ScoResC-538
❑ 97ScoShoS-242
❑ 97ScoShoS-538
❑ 97ScoShoSAP-242
❑ 97ScoShoSAP-538
❑ 97Sel-92
❑ 97SelArtP-92
❑ 97SelCom-92
❑ 97SelRegG-92
❑ 97SP-55
❑ 97SPMarM-MM18
❑ 97SpoIll-99
❑ 97SpoIllEE-99
❑ 97SPSpeF-19
❑ 97SPx-19
❑ 97SPxBro-19
❑ 97SPxGol-19
❑ 97SPxGraF-19
❑ 97SPxSil-19
❑ 97SPxSte-19
❑ 97StaClu-17
❑ 97StaCluI-I8
❑ 97StaCluMat-17
❑ 97StaCluMOP-17
❑ 97StaCluMOP-I8
❑ 97StaCluMOP-PL9
❑ 97StaCluPL-PL9
❑ 97StrAll-38
❑ 97Stu-9
❑ 97StuHarH-11
❑ 97StuPrePG-9
❑ 97StuPrePS-9
❑ 97Top-420
❑ 97TopAll-AS10
❑ 97TopChr-149
❑ 97TopChrAS-AS10
❑ 97TopChrR-149
❑ 97TopChrSAR-AS10
❑ 97TopGal-34
❑ 97TopGalPG-PG16
❑ 97TopGalPPI-34
❑ 97TopIntF-ILM6
❑ 97TopIntFR-ILM6
❑ 97TopMem05-30
❑ 97TopSta-15
❑ 97TopStaAM-15
❑ 97UD3-34
❑ 97Ult-177
❑ 97UltFieC-10
❑ 97UltGolME-177
❑ 97UltPlaME-177
❑ 97UppDec-45
❑ 97Zen-9
❑ 98Bow-63
❑ 98BowBes-92
❑ 98BowBesAR-92
❑ 98BowBesR-92
❑ 98BowChr-63
❑ 98BowChrGA-63
❑ 98BowChrGAR-63
❑ 98BowChrI-63
❑ 98BowChrIR-63
❑ 98BowChrR-63
❑ 98BowGolA-63
❑ 98BowInt-63
❑ 98CirThu-11
❑ 98CirThuRav-11
❑ 98CirThuSupRav-11
❑ 98ColCho-345
❑ 98ColChoER-ER7
❑ 98CroRoy-40
❑ 98Don-20
❑ 98Don-394
❑ 98DonCol-20
❑ 98DonColE-423
❑ 98DonColE-540
❑ 98DonColL-367
❑ 98DonColP-600
❑ 98DonColS-20
❑ 98DonCruG-63
❑ 98DonCruP-63
❑ 98DonCruR-63
❑ 98DonDiaK-15
❑ 98DonDiaKC-15
❑ 98DonEli-23
❑ 98DonEli-140
❑ 98DonEliA-23
❑ 98DonEliA-140
❑ 98DonEliC-27
❑ 98DonEliMC-27
❑ 98DonEliS-23
❑ 98DonEliS-140
❑ 98DonGolPP-20
❑ 98DonGolPP-394
❑ 98DonPre-50
❑ 98DonPreSeat-50
❑ 98DonPriCD-20
❑ 98DonPriCE-423
❑ 98DonPriCE-540
❑ 98DonPriCL-367
❑ 98DonPriCP-600
❑ 98DonProLO-6
❑ 98DonSig-11
❑ 98DonSigP-11
❑ 98DonSilPP-20
❑ 98DonSilPP-394
❑ 98E-X2-25
❑ 98E-X2ECFut-25
❑ 98E-X2ECNow-25
❑ 98Fin-231
❑ 98FinNo--231
❑ 98FinNo-R-231
❑ 98FinRef-231
❑ 98FlaShoLeg0-65
❑ 98FlaShoLeg1-65
❑ 98FlaShoLeg2-65
❑ 98FlaShoLeg3-65
❑ 98FlaShoLegM-65
❑ 98FlaShoR0-65
❑ 98FlaShoR1-65
❑ 98FlaShoR2-65
❑ 98FlaShoR3-65
❑ 98Fle-98
❑ 98KinDis-25
❑ 98Lea-168
❑ 98LeaFraDA-168
❑ 98LeaFraF-168
❑ 98LeaFraM-168
❑ 98LeaFraM-168
❑ 98LeaFraMDC-168
❑ 98LeaFraMDC-168
❑ 98LeaFraMZ2-168
❑ 98LeaHeaftH-10

❑ 98LeaHeaftHS-10
❑ 98LeaRS-21
❑ 98LeaRS-172
❑ 98LeaRSGAHSamp-19
❑ 98LeaRSGreAH-19
❑ 98LeaRSLHolo-21
❑ 98LeaRSLHolo-172
❑ 98LeaRSLMVP-14
❑ 98LeaRSLMVPPE-14
❑ 98LeaRSLong-21
❑ 98LeaRSLong-172
❑ 98LeaRTrue-21
❑ 98LeaRTrue-172
❑ 98MetUni-190
❑ 98MetUniPMG-190
❑ 98Pac-265
❑ 98PacAur-120
❑ 98PacInv-86
❑ 98PacInvPBlue-86
❑ 98PacInvSilv-86
❑ 98PacInvTeam-7
❑ 98PacOme-64
❑ 98PacOmeOnIns-27
❑ 98PacOmeR-64
❑ 98PacOnl-195
❑ 98PacOnl-209
❑ 98PacOnlR-195
❑ 98PacOnlR-209
❑ 98PacOnlWC-195
❑ 98PacOnlWC-209
❑ 98PacPar-147
❑ 98PacParC-147
❑ 98PacParG-147
❑ 98PacParHS-147
❑ 98PacParI-3
❑ 98PacParPB-147
❑ 98PacParR-147
❑ 98PacParTC-18
❑ 98PacPlaB-265
❑ 98PacRedT-265
❑ 98PacSil-265
❑ 98PacTeaC-17
❑ 98Pin-9
❑ 98PinArtP-PP9
❑ 98PinEpixGE-E12
❑ 98PinEpixGP-E12
❑ 98PinEpixME-E12
❑ 98PinEpixMO-E12
❑ 98PinEpixMP-E12
❑ 98PinEpixSE-E12
❑ 98PinEpixSO-E12
❑ 98PinEpixSP-E12
❑ 98PinIns-11
❑ 98PinInsCE-11
❑ 98PinInsDE-11
❑ 98PinInsSG-6AB
❑ 98PinInsSG-6CD
❑ 98PinInsSGS-6AB
❑ 98PinInsSGS-6CD
❑ 98PinMusC-PP9
❑ 98PinPer-51
❑ 98PinPerPP-51
❑ 98PinPlu-40
❑ 98PinPluAE-12
❑ 98PinPluAEE-12
❑ 98PinPluAEP-12
❑ 98PinPluAP-PP21
❑ 98PinPluGAP-PP21
❑ 98PinPluLM-12
❑ 98PinPluMAP-PP21
❑ 98PinPluTP-4
❑ 98PinPluTPG-4
❑ 98PinPluTPM-4
❑ 98PinPreP-9
❑ 98PinPreP-E12
❑ 98Revo-40
❑ 98RevoSS-40
❑ 98Sco-64
❑ 98ScoAllST-8
❑ 98ScoEpix-E12
❑ 98ScoRT-5
❑ 98ScoRTASEpix-12
❑ 98ScoRTSS-PP5
❑ 98ScoRTSSAP-PP5
❑ 98ScoRTSSAP1-PP5
❑ 98ScoSS-PP28
❑ 98ScoSSAP-PP28
❑ 98SkyDugA-10
❑ 98SkyDugAIA-10
❑ 98SP Aut-70
❑ 98SpoIll-80
❑ 98SpoIllEE-80
❑ 98SpoIllFE-80
❑ 98SpoIllODMP-OD8
❑ 98SpoIllTaN-105
❑ 98SpoIllTaNEE-105
❑ 98SpoIllWSF-73
❑ 98SpoIllWSFEE-73
❑ 98SpoIllWSFFE-73
❑ 98SPxFin-265
❑ 98SPxFinR-265
❑ 98SPxFinS-265
❑ 98StaCluFDI-30
❑ 98StaCluI-30
❑ 98StaCluNC-NC15
❑ 98StaCluOneK-30
❑ 98StaCluPP-30
❑ 98Stu-7
❑ 98StuGPP-7
❑ 98StuPor8x10-35
❑ 98StuPor8x10GP-35
❑ 98StuSPP-7
❑ 98Top-302
❑ 98TopChr-302
❑ 98TopChrR-302
❑ 98TopDevR-302
❑ 98TopDia-302
❑ 98TopGal-45
❑ 98TopGalGP-45
❑ 98TopGalOPP-45
❑ 98TopGalPPI-45
❑ 98TopGalPPIA-45
❑ 98TopGolLabC1-74
❑ 98TopGolLabC1B-74
❑ 98TopGolLabC1One-74
❑ 98TopGolLabC1R-74
❑ 98TopGolLabC2-74
❑ 98TopGolLabC2B-74
❑ 98TopGolLabC2One-74
❑ 98TopGolLabC2R-74
❑ 98TopGolLabC3-74
❑ 98TopGolLabC3B-74
❑ 98TopGolLabC3One-74
❑ 98TopGolLabC3R-74
❑ 98TopMiniC-302
❑ 98TopOpeD-129
❑ 98TopSta-65
❑ 98TopSta'S-24
❑ 98TopSta'SGH-24
❑ 98TopStaB-65
❑ 98TopStaG-65
❑ 98TopStaGR-65
❑ 98TopStaS-65
❑ 98TopStaSteG-24
❑ 98TopSup-6
❑ 98TopSup-6
❑ 98TopTek-57
❑ 98TopTekD-57
❑ 98UD3-67
❑ 98UD3-157
❑ 98UD3-247
❑ 98UD3DieCut-67
❑ 98UD3DieCut-157
❑ 98UD3DieCut-247
❑ 98Ult-180
❑ 98UltGolM-180
❑ 98UltMas-180
❑ 98UltPlaM-180
❑ 98UppDec-65
❑ 98UppDec10AP-43
❑ 98UppDec1APR-43
❑ 98UppDec5x7-65
❑ 98UppDecR-25
❑ 98UppDecRTC-TC35
❑ 98UppDecSF-40
❑ 98Zen-21
❑ 98Zen5 xx7-51
❑ 98Zen5x7GoldImp-51
❑ 98Zen5x7Imp-51
❑ 98ZenEpi-E12
❑ 98ZenZ-G-21
❑ 98ZenZ-S-21
❑ 99199Fin-97
❑ 99Bow-23
❑ 99BowBes-34
❑ 99BowBesAR-34
❑ 99BowBesR-34
❑ 99BowChr-23
❑ 99BowChrG-23
❑ 99BowChrGR-23
❑ 99BowChrI-23
❑ 99BowChrIR-23
❑ 99BowChrR-23
❑ 99BowGol-23
❑ 99BowInt-23
❑ 99CroRoyB-38
❑ 99CroRoyL-38
❑ 99CroRoyOD-38
❑ 99DumSet-BL
❑ 99DumSet-BL
❑ 99E-X Cen-34
❑ 99E-X CenECFut-34
❑ 99E-X CenECNow-34
❑ 99FinGolRef-97
❑ 99FinRef-97
❑ 99FlaShoLeg1-74
❑ 99FlaShoLeg2-74
❑ 99FlaShoLeg3-74
❑ 99FlaShoLegM1-74
❑ 99FlaShoLegM2-74
❑ 99FlaShoLegM3-74
❑ 99FlaShoR1-74
❑ 99FlaShoR2-74
❑ 99FlaShoR3-74
❑ 99Fle-14
❑ 99FleBri-103
❑ 99FleBri2G-103
❑ 99FleBriBlu-103
❑ 99FleBriGol-103
❑ 99FleMys-41
❑ 99FleMysFI-20
❑ 99FleMysG-41
❑ 99FleMysM-41
❑ 99FleSta9-14
❑ 99FleVin'-14
❑ 99FleWarT-14
❑ 99KinDis-19
❑ 99MetUni-98
❑ 99MetUniGM-98
❑ 99MetUniPMG-98
❑ 99Pac-114
❑ 99PacAur-45
❑ 99PacAurOD-45
❑ 99PacCroC-75
❑ 99PacCroCPB-75
❑ 99PacCroCTC-8
❑ 99PacInv-39
❑ 99PacInvOD-39
❑ 99PacInvPB-39
❑ 99PacOme-65
❑ 99PacOmeC-65
❑ 99PacOmeG-65
❑ 99PacOmePB-65
❑ 99PacPar-63
❑ 99PacParC-63
❑ 99PacParG-63
❑ 99PacParHoloGold-63
❑ 99PacParHS-63
❑ 99PacParOD-63
❑ 99PacParPB-63
❑ 99PacParRed-63
❑ 99PacParTC-8
❑ 99PacPlaB-114
❑ 99PacPri-38
❑ 99PacPriHB-38
❑ 99PacPriHG-38
❑ 99PacPriHM-38
❑ 99PacPriHP-38
❑ 99PacPriRed-38
❑ 99PacPriS-110
❑ 99PacPriS206-110
❑ 99PacPriS206R-110
❑ 99PacRed-114
❑ 99PacTeaC-18
❑ 99Pin-16
❑ 99Rev-39
❑ 99RevPremDate-39
❑ 99RevRet-39
❑ 99RevShaSS-39
❑ 99SkyMolM-71
❑ 99SkyMolMX-71
❑ 99SkyPre-87
❑ 99SkyPreA-34
❑ 99SkyPreABlue-34
❑ 99SkyPreR-87
❑ 99SkyThu-160
❑ 99SkyThuRant-160
❑ 99SkyThuRave-160
❑ 99SP Aut-25
❑ 99SpoIll-79
❑ 99SPx-31
❑ 99SPxFinR-31
❑ 99SPxFinS-31
❑ 99StaClu-181
❑ 99StaCluFDI-181
❑ 99StaCluOoaK-181
❑ 99StaCluPP-181
❑ 99ThuSkySupR-160
❑ 99Top-345
❑ 99TopBlaLC1-18
❑ 99TopBlaLC2-18
❑ 99TopBlaLC3-18
❑ 99TopChr-345
❑ 99TopChrR-345
❑ 99TopGal-22
❑ 99TopGalPP-22
❑ 99TopGalPPI-22
❑ 99TopGolL-18
❑ 99TopGolLC1-18
❑ 99TopGolLC2-18
❑ 99TopGolLOtO-18
❑ 99TopMVPP-345
❑ 99TopOpeD-143
❑ 99TopRedLC1-18
❑ 99TopRedLC2-18
❑ 99TopRedLC3-18
❑ 99TopSta-57
❑ 99TopSta'S-16
❑ 99TopSta'SG-16
❑ 99TopSta'SGDH-16
❑ 99TopSta1Foil-57
❑ 99TopStaFoil-57
❑ 99TopStaOS-57
❑ 99Ult-7
❑ 99UltGolM-7
❑ 99UltMas-7
❑ 99UltPlaM-7
❑ 99UppDec-71
❑ 99UppDecCL-72
❑ 99UppDecCLCC-72
❑ 99UppDecCLM-C23
❑ 99UppDecE-23
❑ 99UppDecEFXG-23
❑ 99UppDecEL1-71
❑ 99UppDecEL2-71
❑ 99UppDecM-57
❑ 99UppDecMGS-57
❑ 99UppDecMHFS-57
❑ 99UppDecMP-57
❑ 99UppDecMSS-57
❑ 99UppDecO-21
❑ 99UppDecOSO-21
❑ 99UppDecR-23
❑ 99UppDecRG-23
❑ 99UppDecRP-23
❑ 99Vic-112

Larkin, Earl
❑ 19Zee-53
❑ 20Zee-67

Larkin, Gene
❑ 85VisOakT-14
❑ 86OrlTwiP-10
❑ 87DonRoo-23
❑ 87FleUpd-59
❑ 87FleUpdG-59
❑ 87PorBeaP-19
❑ 87SpoRoo2-34
❑ 87TopTra-60T
❑ 87TopTraT-60T
❑ 87TwiTeal-6
❑ 88Don-564
❑ 88DonBasB-158
❑ 88Fle-14
❑ 88FleGlo-14
❑ 88OPC-384
❑ 88PanSti-145
❑ 88RedFolSB-47
❑ 88Sco-276
❑ 88ScoGlo-276
❑ 88Spo-107
❑ 88StaLinTw-11
❑ 88Top-746
❑ 88TopBig-264
❑ 88TopSti-279
❑ 88TopTif-746
❑ 88TwiSmoC-5
❑ 89Bow-160
❑ 89BowTif-160
❑ 89Don-355
❑ 89Fle-117
❑ 89FleGlo-117
❑ 89PanSti-388
❑ 89Sco-280
❑ 89ScoYouS2-6
❑ 89Top-318
❑ 89TopBig-226
❑ 89TopSti-294
❑ 89TopTif-318
❑ 89UppDec-580
❑ 90ClaYel-T53
❑ 90Don-436
❑ 90Fle-379
❑ 90FleCan-379
❑ 90Lea-215
❑ 90OPC-556
❑ 90PubIntS-331
❑ 90Sco-276
❑ 90Top-556
❑ 90TopBig-302
❑ 90TopSti-291
❑ 90TopTif-556
❑ 90UppDec-471
❑ 91DodPho-19
❑ 91DodPho-29
❑ 91Don-152
❑ 91Fle-615
❑ 91Lea-157
❑ 91OPC-102
❑ 91PanFreS-306
❑ 91PanSti-246
❑ 91Sco-471
❑ 91StaClu-132
❑ 91Top-102
❑ 91TopDesS-102
❑ 91TopMic-102
❑ 91TopTif-102
❑ 91Ult-190
❑ 91UppDec-501
❑ 92Bow-479
❑ 92Don-496
❑ 92Fle-207
❑ 92Lea-415
❑ 92LeaBlaG-415
❑ 92OPC-284
❑ 92Pin-435
❑ 92Sco-272
❑ 92ScoFacI-B7
❑ 92StaClu-66
❑ 92Top-284
❑ 92TopGol-284
❑ 92TopGolW-284
❑ 92TopMic-284
❑ 92UppDec-187
❑ 93Don-575
❑ 93Fle-269
❑ 93PacSpa-173
❑ 93Sco-444
❑ 93StaClu-42
❑ 93StaCluFDI-42
❑ 93StaCluMOP-42
❑ 93Top-61
❑ 93TopGol-61
❑ 93TopInaM-61
❑ 93TopInaR-61
❑ 93TopMic-61
❑ 93Ult-584
❑ 93UppDec-540
❑ 93UppDecGold-540
❑ 94Fle-211
❑ 94Pac-358
❑ 94Sco-288
❑ 94ScoGolR-288

Larkin, Jim
❑ 94UtiBluSF-3828

Larkin, Pat
❑ 84EvaTriT-5

Larkin, Stephen
❑ 94HudValRC-10
❑ 94HudValRF-3399
❑ 94TopTra-56T
❑ 95ChaRivTI-6

Larkin, Steve (Steven Patrick)
❑ 34Gou-92
❑ 98ChaLooG-15

Larkin, Ted (Henry)
❑ 87OldJudN-292
❑ 90KalBatN-28
❑ 90KalBatN-40

Larman, Jayson
❑ 98BilMusTI-18

Larned, Andy
❑ 98LowSpiM-10

LaRocca, Greg
❑ 94SpoIndC-16
❑ 94SpoIndF-3331
❑ 95Bes-98
❑ 95RanCucQT-18
❑ 95SPML-142
❑ 96Exc-237
❑ 96MemChiB-21
❑ 97MobBayBB-17
❑ 98Las-13

LaRocca, Todd
❑ 95SigRoo-29
❑ 95SigRooSig-29

LaRoche, Dave
❑ 71OPC-174
❑ 71Top-174
❑ 72OPC-352
❑ 72Top-352
❑ 72TwiPos-9
❑ 72TwiTeal-5
❑ 73OPC-426
❑ 73Top-426
❑ 74OPC-502
❑ 74Top-502
❑ 74WicAerODF-107
❑ 75CleIndP-16
❑ 75OPC-258
❑ 75Top-258
❑ 75TopMin-258
❑ 76IndTeal-6
❑ 76OPC-21
❑ 76SSP-510
❑ 76Top-21
❑ 77BurCheD-60
❑ 77ChiWilD-37
❑ 77DailsID-37
❑ 77DetCaeD-37
❑ 77HolInnD-37
❑ 77IndTeal-14
❑ 77MSADis-37
❑ 77OPC-61
❑ 77PepGloD-15
❑ 77RCColC-33
❑ 77SagDis-37
❑ 77sDis-37
❑ 77Top-385
❑ 77WenDis-37
❑ 77ZipDis-37
❑ 78AngFamF-23
❑ 78RCColC-22
❑ 78SSP270-197
❑ 78Top-454
❑ 79OPC-317
❑ 79Top-601
❑ 80Top-263
❑ 81Fle-285
❑ 81Top-529
❑ 81TopTra-789
❑ 81YanPhoA-11
❑ 82Don-569
❑ 82Top-142
❑ 82YanPhoA-1
❑ 83Fle-384
❑ 83OPC-333
❑ 83OPC-334
❑ 83Top-333
❑ 83Top-334
❑ 85AlbYanT-24
❑ 86ColCliP-25
❑ 86ColCliP-13
❑ 87SyrChiP-1946
❑ 87SyrChiT-24
❑ 89PacSenL-97
❑ 89T/MSenL-65
❑ 89TopSenL-89
❑ 90SweBasG-108
❑ 90WhiSoxC-30
❑ 91WhiSoxK-NNO
❑ 92MetColP-36
❑ 92MetKah-28
❑ 94PitMetC-26
❑ 94PitMetF-3539

LaRock, Scott
❑ 94BenRocC-14
❑ 94BenRocF-3588
❑ 95SalAvaTI-20
❑ 96SalAvaB-18

LaRocque, Gary
❑ 76BurBeeT-20
❑ 77HolMilT-18
❑ 88BakDodCLC-262

LaRosa, Bill
❑ 78AshTouT-13

Larosa, John
❑ 87UtiBluSP-23
❑ 88SpaPhiP-1031
❑ 88SpaPhiS-10
❑ 89PacSenL-43
❑ 89SpaPhiP-1054
❑ 89SpaPhiS-12

LaRosa, Mark
❑ 88CapCodPPaLP-77
❑ 91JamExpC-15
❑ 91JamExpP-3541
❑ 91LSUTigP-9
❑ 92AlbPolCB-9
❑ 92AlbPolF-2300
❑ 93WesPalBEC-11
❑ 93WesPalBEF-1334
❑ 94ExcFS7-227

Larosa, Tom
❑ 97ForMyeM-16
❑ 98Bow-337
❑ 98BowChr-337
❑ 98BowChrGA-337
❑ 98BowChrGAR-337
❑ 98BowChrI-337
❑ 98BowChrIR-337
❑ 98BowChrR-337
❑ 98BowGolA-337
❑ 98BowInt-337
❑ 98ForMyeMTI-18

Larose, Steve

❑ 87LitFalMP-2387
❑ 88ColMetGS-6
❑ 89St.LucMS-13
❑ 90JacMetGS-8
❑ 91JacGenLD-566
❑ 91JacGenP-924
❑ 91LinDriAA-566
❑ 92JacGenS-337

LaRose, Vic
❑ 66SeaPop-10
❑ 69Top-404

LaRoy, Louis
❑ 15Zee-83

Larreal, Guillermo
❑ 96-97LinVen-190
❑ 96BelGiaTI-25
❑ 97BakBlaB-13
❑ 97BakBlaTI-13

Larregui, Ed
❑ 90HunCubP-3300
❑ 91GenCubC-11
❑ 91GenCubP-4231
❑ 92ClaFS7-221
❑ 92MidLeaATI-27
❑ 92PeoChiC-13
❑ 92PeoChiTI-11
❑ 93DayCubC-12
❑ 93DayCubF-869
❑ 94DayCubC-14
❑ 94DayCubF-2366
❑ 95OrlCubF-22
❑ 96Exc-139
❑ 96OrlCubB-15
❑ 96SigRooOJ-16
❑ 96SigRooOJS-16

Larsen, Bill
❑ 88RocExpLC-21

Larsen, Don
❑ 47Exh-131
❑ 54Bow-101
❑ 54OriEss-22
❑ 54OriTeal-13
❑ 55Bow-67
❑ 56Top-251
❑ 56Top-332
❑ 56YanTeal-12
❑ 57Top-175
❑ 57YanJayP-8
❑ 58Top-161
❑ 58YanJayP-7
❑ 59Top-205
❑ 59Top-383
❑ 60A's-5
❑ 60A'sJayP-6
❑ 60NuHi-18
❑ 60Top-353
❑ 61A'sTeal-12
❑ 61NuSco-418
❑ 61Top-177
❑ 61Top-402
❑ 62Top-33
❑ 62TopVen-33
❑ 63Top-163
❑ 64Top-513
❑ 65BalOriP-18
❑ 65Top-389
❑ 68LauWorS-53
❑ 72LauGreF-45
❑ 76ISCHooHA-13
❑ 76LauDiaJ-17
❑ 77BobParMBC-10
❑ 77GalGloG-3
❑ 77Spo-6204
❑ 78TCM60I-211
❑ 78TCM60I-266
❑ 79DiaGre-21
❑ 79TCM50-272
❑ 81Gia196T-26
❑ 82ASAMicM-68
❑ 86TCMSupS-45
❑ 87AstSer1-15
❑ 87AstSer1-24
❑ 87AstShoSTw-28
❑ 87HygAllG-30
❑ 88PacLegI-42A
❑ 88PacLegI-42B
❑ 90BasWit-7
❑ 90HOFStiB-54
❑ 91OriCro-255
❑ 93ActPacA-144
❑ 94UppDecTAE-64
❑ 95SkiBra-1
❑ 97BalOriP-28
❑ 97FleMilDM-23
❑ 97FleMilDMR-23
❑ 97NewYorL-5
❑ 98BowChrR-7
❑ 98BowChrRR-7
❑ 98SpollIWSFAE-10
❑ 98SpollIWSFAEG-10
❑ 99UppDecCL-131
❑ 99UppDecCLCC-131
❑ 99UppDecCLES-DL
❑ 99UppDecCLESC-DL

Larsen, Frank
❑ 16Zee-12

Larsen, Jim
❑ 86EugEmeC-36

Larson, Dan
❑ 77Top-641
❑ 81OklCit8T-7
❑ 83IowCubT-6
❑ 84ButCopKT-14
❑ 84OklCit8T-6
❑ 86KinEagP-14
❑ 86WauTimP-12
❑ 87AstShoSPT-7
❑ 87BurExpP-1092

Larson, Danny
❑ 87SalSpuS-15
❑ 91MarPhiC-3
❑ 91MarPhiP-3468
❑ 93SpaPhiC-17
❑ 93SpaPhiF-1068

Larson, Duane
❑ 80KnoBluJT-27
❑ 82SyrChiT-27A

Larson, Jamie
❑ 85AncGlaPTI-36
❑ 86AncGlaPTI-40

Larson, Joe
❑ 92JohCitCC-16
❑ 92JohCitCF-3110
❑ 93GleFalRC-18
❑ 93GleFalRF-3999

Larson, Kirk
❑ 92AubAstC-13
❑ 92AubAstF-1360

Larson, Lance
❑ 89AncBucTI-6

Larson, Mike (Michael)
❑ 88BoiHawP-1620
❑ 89BoiHawP-2003
❑ 90EriSaiS-12

Larson, Toby
❑ 94PitMetC-13
❑ 94PitMetF-3519
❑ 95StLucMTI-20

LaRue, Jason
❑ 95BilMusTI-3
❑ 98AriFalLTP-5
❑ 98Bow-309
❑ 98BowChr-309
❑ 98BowChrGA-309
❑ 98BowChrGAR-309
❑ 98BowChrI-309
❑ 98BowChrIR-309
❑ 98BowChrR-309
❑ 98BowGolA-309
❑ 98BowInt-309
❑ 98ChaLooG-16
❑ 98IndIndQ-21
❑ 98LeaRS-223
❑ 98LeaRSLHolo-223
❑ 98LeaRSLong-223
❑ 98LeaRTrue-223
❑ 98SouLeaTPG-22
❑ 99BasAmeTP-59
❑ 99BasAmeTPA-23
❑ 99BasAmeTPG-59
❑ 99Bow-215
❑ 99BowAut-BA51
❑ 99BowChr-215
❑ 99BowChrG-215
❑ 99BowChrGR-215
❑ 99BowChrI-215
❑ 99BowChrIR-215
❑ 99BowChrR-215
❑ 99BowGol-215
❑ 99BowInt-215
❑ 99SP TopP-71
❑ 99SP TopPPE-71
❑ 99Top-431
❑ 99TopChr-431
❑ 99TopChrR-431
❑ 99TopMVPP-431

LaRussa, Tony
❑ 64Top-244
❑ 64TopVen-244
❑ 68Top-571
❑ 72OPC-451
❑ 72Top-451
❑ 73WicAerJPKB-6
❑ 78KnoKnoST-11
❑ 78TCM60I-229
❑ 79IowOakP-1
❑ 80Top-112
❑ 81Don-402
❑ 81Fle-344
❑ 81Top-664
❑ 82Don-319
❑ 83Don-571
❑ 83Top-216
❑ 83WhiSoxTV-10
❑ 84Fle-649
❑ 84FleSti-126
❑ 84Nes792-591
❑ 84Top-591
❑ 84TopTif-591
❑ 84WhiSoxTV-8
❑ 84WhiSoxTV-20
❑ 85Top-466
❑ 85TopTif-466
❑ 85WhiSoxC-10
❑ 86Top-531
❑ 86TopTif-531
❑ 86WhiSoxC-NNO
❑ 87ModA'sC-A1
❑ 87Top-68
❑ 87TopTif-68
❑ 88A'sMot-1
❑ 88Top-344
❑ 88TopTif-344
❑ 89A'sMot-1
❑ 89PacLegI-140
❑ 89Top-224
❑ 89TopBasT-132
❑ 89TopTif-224
❑ 90A'sMot-1
❑ 90K-M-33
❑ 90OPC-639
❑ 90PacLeg-90
❑ 90Top-639
❑ 90TopGloA-12
❑ 90TopTif-639
❑ 90TopTVA-33
❑ 91A'sMot-1
❑ 91OPC-171
❑ 91Stu-263
❑ 91Top-171
❑ 91TopDesS-171
❑ 91TopGloA-1
❑ 91TopMic-171
❑ 91TopTif-171
❑ 92AthMot-1
❑ 92OPC-429
❑ 92RedFolS-121
❑ 92Top-429
❑ 92TopGol-429
❑ 92TopGolW-429
❑ 92TopMic-429
❑ 93AthMot-1
❑ 93Top-511
❑ 93TopGol-511
❑ 93TopInaM-511
❑ 93TopInaR-511
❑ 93TopMic-511
❑ 94A'sMot-1
❑ 95AthMot-1
❑ 96CarPol-15
❑ 97CarPol-15

Lary, Al
❑ 77FriOneYW-118

Lary, Frank
❑ 55Bow-154
❑ 56Top-191
❑ 57Top-168
❑ 58Top-245
❑ 59Top-393
❑ 60Lea-3
❑ 60TigJayP-8
❑ 60Top-85
❑ 60TopTat-28
❑ 60TopVen-85
❑ 61Pos-38A
❑ 61Pos-38B
❑ 61TigJayP-10
❑ 61Top-48
❑ 61Top-50
❑ 61Top-243
❑ 61TopStal-153
❑ 62Jel-22
❑ 62Pos-22
❑ 62PosCan-22
❑ 62SalPlaC-58
❑ 62ShiPlaC-58
❑ 62TigJayP-8
❑ 62Top-57
❑ 62Top-474
❑ 62TopBuc-49
❑ 62TopStal-48
❑ 62TopVen-57
❑ 63Fle-14
❑ 63Jel-55
❑ 63Pos-55
❑ 63TigJayP-9
❑ 63Top-140
❑ 63Top-218
❑ 64TigJayP-7
❑ 64TigLid-8
❑ 64Top-197
❑ 64TopVen-197
❑ 65OPC-127
❑ 65Top-127
❑ 78TCM60I-253
❑ 79DiaGre-398
❑ 79TCM50-183
❑ 81TigDetN-125
❑ 82TCMGreP-27
❑ 91MetWIZ-225

Lary, Lyn (Lynford H.)
❑ 26Zee-80
❑ 27Zee-58
❑ 28ExhPCL-18
❑ 28Zee-83
❑ 31Exh-26
❑ 33Gou-193
❑ 35GouPuzR-1C
❑ 35GouPuzR-2C
❑ 35GouPuzR-16C
❑ 35GouPuzR-17C
❑ 36GouWidPPR-A62
❑ 38CloFotW-47
❑ 72TCMthe3-90
❑ 72TCMthe3-91
❑ 72TCMthe3-92
❑ 72TCMthe3-93
❑ 72TCMthe3-116
❑ 90DodTar-434
❑ 91ConTSN-318

Lasbury, Robert
❑ 93BenRocCB-15
❑ 93BenRocF-3263
❑ 94AshTouC-14
❑ 94AshTouF-1774

Lasek, Jim
❑ 77SpaPhiT-8

Laseke, Eric
❑ 85ElmPioT-10
❑ 86WinHavRSP-14
❑ 87WinHavRSP-7
❑ 89WinHavRSS-12

Laseter, Tom
❑ 75WatRoyT-19
❑ 76WatRoyT-17

Lash, Herbie
❑ 52LaPat-8

Lasher, Fred
❑ 68TigDetFPB-9
❑ 68Top-447
❑ 69TigTealC-8
❑ 69Top-373
❑ 70OPC-356
❑ 70Top-356
❑ 71MLBOffS-347
❑ 71OPC-707
❑ 71Top-707
❑ 72MilBra-194
❑ 88TigDom-10

Lashley, Mickey
❑ 77CliDodT-15
❑ 78LodDodT-12

Laskey, Bill
❑ 80OmaRoyP-16
❑ 81OmaRoyT-10
❑ 82Gia25tATI-14
❑ 83Don-424
❑ 83Fle-264
❑ 83FleSta-101
❑ 83FleSti-57
❑ 83GiaMot-15
❑ 83GiaPos-14
❑ 83OPC-218
❑ 83Top-171
❑ 83Top-518
❑ 83TopSti-325
❑ 84Don-358
❑ 84Fle-376
❑ 84GiaPos-10
❑ 84Nes792-129
❑ 84OPC-129
❑ 84Top-129
❑ 84TopSti-172
❑ 84TopTif-129
❑ 85Don-387
❑ 85Fle-612
❑ 85GiaMot-9
❑ 85GiaPos-18
❑ 85OPC-331
❑ 85Top-331
❑ 85TopTif-331
❑ 86Don-585
❑ 86Fle-251
❑ 86GiaMot-24
❑ 86GiaPos-16
❑ 86OPC-281
❑ 86Top-603
❑ 86TopTif-603
❑ 87TolMudHP-21
❑ 87TolMudHT-4
❑ 88IndGat-17
❑ 88IndTeal-24
❑ 90CMC-300
❑ 90ProAAAF-399
❑ 90RicBraBC-3
❑ 90RicBraC-24
❑ 90RicBraP-254
❑ 90RicBraTI-18

Lasky, Larry
❑ 85OscAstTI-27
❑ 86AshTouP-17
❑ 87ColAstP-21
❑ 88ColAstB-15
❑ 89TucTorP-182

Lasorda, Tom
❑ 50WorWidGV-45
❑ 52Par-58
❑ 53ExhCan-50
❑ 54Top-132
❑ 55DodGolS-23
❑ 58MonRoyF-13
❑ 59O'KAleMR-13
❑ 73OPC-569
❑ 73Top-569
❑ 74OPC-144
❑ 74Top-144
❑ 77DodPho-6
❑ 77Spo-7509
❑ 77Top-504
❑ 78SSP270-63
❑ 78Top-189
❑ 79DodBlu-7
❑ 79Top-526
❑ 80Top-302
❑ 81Dod-17
❑ 81DodPol-2
❑ 81DodPol-NNO
❑ 81Don-420
❑ 81Fle-116
❑ 81LonBeaPT-26
❑ 81Top-679
❑ 82DodPol-2
❑ 82DodPos-5
❑ 82DodUniOV-10
❑ 82DogBuiE-5
❑ 82Don-110
❑ 82FleSta-111
❑ 83DodPol-2
❑ 83DodPos-7
❑ 83Don-136
❑ 83Top-306
❑ 84DodPol-2
❑ 84Fle-651
❑ 84FleSti-124
❑ 84Nes792-681
❑ 84Top-681
❑ 84TopTif-681
❑ 85DodCokP-18
❑ 85SpoIndGC-12
❑ 85Top-601
❑ 85TopTif-601
❑ 86DodCokP-16
❑ 86DodPol-2
❑ 86DodUniOP-10
❑ 86Top-291
❑ 86TopTif-291
❑ 87DodMot-1
❑ 87DodPho-8
❑ 87DodPol-1
❑ 87DodPol-29
❑ 87DodSmoA-17
❑ 87Top-493
❑ 87TopTif-493
❑ 88DodMot-1
❑ 88DodPol-2
❑ 88DodPol-NNO
❑ 88DodRinP1-1B
❑ 88DodSmo-23
❑ 88Top-74
❑ 88TopTif-74
❑ 89DodMot-1
❑ 89DodPol-1
❑ 89DodPol-2
❑ 89DodStaSV-10
❑ 89OPCBoxB-H
❑ 89Top-254
❑ 89TopBasT-54
❑ 89TopTif-254
❑ 89TopWaxBC-H
❑ 90DodMot-1
❑ 90DodPol-1
❑ 90DodPol-NNO
❑ 90DodTar-435
❑ 90OPC-669
❑ 90OPCBoxB-G
❑ 90PerGreM-102
❑ 90Top-669
❑ 90TopGloA-1
❑ 90TopTif-669
❑ 90TopWaxBC-G
❑ 91DodMot-1
❑ 91DodPol-NNO
❑ 91DodSt.V-14
❑ 91OPC-789
❑ 91Stu-262
❑ 91Top-789
❑ 91TopDesS-789
❑ 91TopMic-789
❑ 91TopTif-789
❑ 92DodMot-1
❑ 92DodPol-2
❑ 92DodPol-NNO
❑ 92DodSmo-5092
❑ 92DodStaTA-18
❑ 92DodStaTA-22
❑ 92DodUno7P-5
❑ 92OPC-261
❑ 92Top-261
❑ 92TopGol-261
❑ 92TopGolPS-261
❑ 92TopGolW-261
❑ 92TopMic-261
❑ 92TopPreS-798
❑ 93DodMot-1
❑ 93DodPol-14
❑ 93DodPol-30
❑ 93Top-507
❑ 93TopGol-507
❑ 93TopInaM-507
❑ 93TopInaR-507
❑ 93TopMic-507
❑ 94DodMot-1
❑ 94DodPol-15
❑ 94DodPol-30
❑ 94TopArc1-132
❑ 94TopArc1G-132
❑ 95DodMot-1
❑ 95DodPol-13
❑ 95DodPol-30
❑ 95TopArcBD-75
❑ 95TopArcBD-115
❑ 96DodMot-1
❑ 96DodPol-8
❑ 96DodPol-22
❑ 96UppDec-478
❑ 97UppDec-221
❑ 98SpollITaN-17
❑ 98SpollITaNEE-17

Lassard, Paul
❑ 87Ft.LauYP-14

Lassiter, David
❑ 94BurIndC-30

Lata, Tim
❑ 88CapCodPPaLP-129
❑ 89HamRedS-20
❑ 90Bes-267
❑ 90SprCarB-16
❑ 91St.PetCC-29
❑ 91St.PetCP-2273

Latarola, Aaron
❑ 94CedRapKC-15

Latham, Bill
❑ 83LynMetT-3
❑ 84TidTidT-6
❑ 85MetColP-16
❑ 85TidTidT-10
❑ 86TwiTeal-25
❑ 87PorBeaP-18
❑ 87TidTidP-22
❑ 87TidTidT-28
❑ 91ColMetPI-2
❑ 91MetWIZ-226
❑ 92St.LucMCB-28
❑ 92St.LucMF-1765
❑ 93St.LucMC-27

❑ 93St.LuMF-2938
❑ 94St.LucMC-28
❑ 94St.LucMF-1213
❑ 95BinMetTI-39
❑ 96BinMetB-14
Latham, Chris
❑ 91KisDodP-4194
❑ 92GreFalDSP-7
❑ 93YakBeaC-17
❑ 93YakBeaF-3899
❑ 94YakBeaC-9
❑ 94YakBeaF-3862
❑ 95Bes-76
❑ 95SPML-74
❑ 95VerBeaDTI-14
❑ 96Exc-178
❑ 96ExcCli-5
Latham, John
❑ 89WelPirP-17
❑ 90SalBucS-9
❑ 91AugPirC-9
❑ 91AugPirP-801
Latham, W. Arlie
❑ 09T206-206
❑ 10RedCroT-40
❑ 10SweCapPP-115
❑ 11T205-96
❑ 12HasTriFT-69
❑ 12T207-100
❑ 76SSP188WS-3
❑ 87BucN28-99
❑ 87LonJacN-8
❑ 87OldJudN-293
❑ 87OldJudN-294
❑ 87ScrDC-6
❑ 88SpoTimM-17
❑ 89EdgR.WG-2
❑ 89SFHaCN-11
❑ 94OriofB-55
❑ 95ConTSN-1383
❑ 95May-17
Lathers, Charles
❑ 11SpoLifM-62
Latimer, Tacks
❑ 90DodTar-1010
Latimer, William
❑ 92HunCubC-20
❑ 92HunCubF-3144
Latman, Barry
❑ 59Top-477
❑ 60IndJayP-5
❑ 60Top-41
❑ 60TopVen-41
❑ 60WhiSoxTS-10
❑ 61Top-560
❑ 61TopStal-137
❑ 62IndJayP-7
❑ 62Kah-24
❑ 62Top-37
❑ 62Top-145
❑ 62TopStal-36
❑ 62TopVen-37
❑ 62TopVen-145
❑ 63IndJayP-10
❑ 63Top-426
❑ 64Top-227
❑ 64TopVen-227
❑ 65Top-307
❑ 66Top-451
❑ 67CokCapAs-5
❑ 67OPC-28
❑ 67Top-28
❑ 81WhiSox1T-33
❑ 87AstShowSTh-11
Latmore, Bob
❑ 86MiaMarP-14
❑ 87MiaMarP-10
❑ 88HagSunS-10
❑ 89HagSunB-4
❑ 89HagSunP-271
❑ 89HagSunS-12
❑ 90EasLeaAP-EL34
❑ 90HagSunB-7
❑ 90HagSunP-1422
❑ 90HagSunS-12
Latta, Greg
❑ 85BufBisT-3
❑ 86BufBisP-15
❑ 87HawIsIP-25
❑ 89VanCanP-574
❑ 95NasSouTI-10
❑ 96NasSouB-4
Latter, Dave
❑ 89MedAthB-12
❑ 90MadMusB-18
❑ 90MadMusP-2264
❑ 91HunStaC-14
❑ 91HunStaLD-288
❑ 91HunStaP-1791
❑ 91HunStaTI-13
❑ 91LinDriAA-288
❑ 92HunStaF-3945
❑ 92HunStaS-313
❑ 93HunStaF-2080
Lattimore, William
❑ 09T206-436
Lau, Charley
❑ 58Top-448
❑ 60Top-312
❑ 61Top-261
❑ 62BalOriP-16
❑ 62Top-533
❑ 63BalOriP-17
❑ 63Top-41
❑ 64AthJayP-8
❑ 64BalOriP-22
❑ 64Top-229
❑ 64TopVen-229
❑ 65BalOriP-19
❑ 65OPC-94
❑ 65Top-94
❑ 66BalOriP-20
❑ 66Top-368
❑ 66TopVen-368
❑ 67BalOriP-58
❑ 67Top-329
❑ 71oySigST-13
❑ 72oyTeal-12
❑ 73OPC-593
❑ 73Top-593
❑ 74RoyPos-14
❑ 74Top-166
❑ 75RoyPos-15
❑ 76KanCitRP-14
❑ 79YanPicA-23
❑ 91OriCro-256
❑ 94FUnPac-189
Lau, David
❑ 87ColMetP-5
❑ 88ColMetGS-13
❑ 89St.LucMS-14
Laubhan, John
❑ 77CedRapGT-NNO
Lauck, Jeff
❑ 84SavCarT-2
Laudenslager, Kevin
❑ 90GeoColC-17
Laudner, Tim
❑ 80OrlTwiT-12
❑ 82Don-549
❑ 82OrlTwi8SCT-8
❑ 82Top-766
❑ 83Don-177
❑ 83Fle-618
❑ 83Top-529
❑ 83TopSti-93
❑ 83TopSti-314
❑ 83TwiTeal-10
❑ 83TwiTeal-31
❑ 83TwiTeal-32
❑ 84Fle-569
❑ 84MinTwiP-18
❑ 84Nes792-363
❑ 84Top-363
❑ 84TopTif-363
❑ 84TwiTeal-11
❑ 85Don-652
❑ 85Fle-283
❑ 85Top-71
❑ 85TopTif-71
❑ 85Twi7-12
❑ 85TwiPos-16
❑ 85TwiTeal-11
❑ 85TwiTeal-14
❑ 86Don-391
❑ 86Fle-398
❑ 86Top-184
❑ 86TopTif-184
❑ 86TwiTeal-10
❑ 87Don-320
❑ 87Fle-546
❑ 87FleGlo-546
❑ 87OPC-392
❑ 87Top-206
❑ 87Top-478
❑ 87TopTif-206
❑ 87TopTif-478
❑ 87TwiPos-14
❑ 87TwiTeal-9
❑ 88Don-631
❑ 88Fle-15
❑ 88FleGlo-15
❑ 88OPC-78
❑ 88PanSti-135
❑ 88Sco-153
❑ 88ScoGlo-153
❑ 88StaLinTw-12
❑ 88Top-671
❑ 88TopBig-243
❑ 88TopSti-278
❑ 88TopTif-671
❑ 88TwiMasBD-5
❑ 88TwiSmoC-7
❑ 89Bow-154
❑ 89BowTif-154
❑ 89Don-615
❑ 89DonAll-19
❑ 89Fle-118
❑ 89FleGlo-118
❑ 89OPC-239
❑ 89PanSti-384
❑ 89Sco-134
❑ 89Spo-152
❑ 89Top-239
❑ 89TopSti-290
❑ 89TopTif-239
❑ 89UppDec-62
❑ 90Don-419
❑ 90Fle-380
❑ 90FleCan-380
❑ 90OPC-777
❑ 90PubIntS-332
❑ 90Sco-318
❑ 90Top-777
❑ 90TopBig-218
❑ 90TopTif-777
❑ 90UppDec-419
Lauer, John Charles
❑ 87OldJudN-295
Laureano, Frank (Francisco)
❑ 86BurExpP-13
❑ 87AppFoxP-7
❑ 88VirGenS-13
❑ 89BasCitRS-15
❑ 90MemChiB-7
❑ 90MemChiP-1018
❑ 90MemChiS-13
❑ 91LinDriAAA-338
❑ 91OmaRoyLD-338
❑ 91OmaRoyP-1043
Laurent, Rick (Milfred)
❑ 93NegLeaRL2-22
Lauterhahn, Dan
❑ 98WesMicWM-9
Lauterhahn, Michael
❑ 94HunCubC-18
❑ 94HunCubF-3568
Lauzerique, George
❑ 69Top-358
❑ 70BreMcD-16
❑ 70OPC-41
❑ 70Top-41
❑ 75DubPacT-27
❑ 76DubPacT-19
❑ 76DubPacT-40
❑ 94BreMilB-51
Lavagetto, Cookie (Harry)
❑ 34BatR31-51
❑ 36GouWidPPR-A63
❑ 36NatChiFPR-51
❑ 36OveCanR-29
❑ 38CloFotW-48
❑ 39PlaBal-74
❑ 40DodTeal-14
❑ 40PlaBal-69
❑ 41DouPlaR-17
❑ 46DodTeal-15
❑ 46SpoExcW-7-7
❑ 47TipTop-99
❑ 48SigOil-13
❑ 49RemBre-15
❑ 50RemBre-15
❑ 52Top-365
❑ 58SeaTeal-17
❑ 58SenJayP-5
❑ 59Top-74
❑ 59TopVen-74
❑ 60SenJayP-9
❑ 60Top-221
❑ 61Top-226
❑ 61TwiPetM-10
❑ 61TwiUniMC-9
❑ 72TCMthe3-45
❑ 73Dod194T-17
❑ 74dod195T-28
❑ 78DodTCM4-32
❑ 81TCM60I-482
❑ 82Bow195E-266
❑ 82MetGal62-27
❑ 83TopRep5-365
❑ 88DodRinP1-10A
❑ 88DodRinP1-11C
❑ 89DodSmoG-40
❑ 90DodTar-436
❑ 90HOFStiB-43
❑ 95ConTSN-1411
❑ 95TopArcBD-27
LaValley, Todd
❑ 92YakBeaC-17
❑ 92YakBeaF-3444
LaValliere, Mike
❑ 83ReaPhiT-12
❑ 85LouRedR-22
❑ 86CarSchM-14
❑ 86DonRoo-35
❑ 86FleUpd-65
❑ 87Don-331
❑ 87Fle-302
❑ 87FleGlo-302
❑ 87FleUpd-60
❑ 87FleUpdG-60
❑ 87Top-162
❑ 87TopTif-162
❑ 87TopTra-61T
❑ 87TopTraT-61T
❑ 87ToyRoo-19
❑ 88Don-312
❑ 88DonBasB-129
❑ 88Fle-333
❑ 88FleGlo-333
❑ 88FleSlu-25
❑ 88Lea-112
❑ 88OPC-57
❑ 88PanSti-369
❑ 88PirTeal-18
❑ 88Sco-421
❑ 88ScoGlo-421
❑ 88Spo-193
❑ 88StaLinPi-13
❑ 88Top-539
❑ 88TopBig-61
❑ 88TopSti-131
❑ 88TopTif-539
❑ 89Bow-417
❑ 89BowTif-417
❑ 89Don-244
❑ 89DonBasB-201
❑ 89Fle-213
❑ 89FleGlo-213
❑ 89OPC-218
❑ 89PanSti-168
❑ 89PirVerFJ-12
❑ 89RedFolSB-74
❑ 89Sco-33
❑ 89Spo-98
❑ 89Top-218
❑ 89TopBasT-126
❑ 89TopBig-306
❑ 89TopSti-128
❑ 89TopStiB-56
❑ 89TopTif-218
❑ 89UppDec-417
❑ 90Bow-172
❑ 90BowTif-172
❑ 90ClaBlu-42
❑ 90Don-211
❑ 90DonBesN-107
❑ 90DonLeaS-43
❑ 90Fle-473
❑ 90FleCan-473
❑ 90Lea-32
❑ 90OPC-478
❑ 90PanSti-333
❑ 90PirHomC-18
❑ 90PubIntS-158
❑ 90Sco-116
❑ 90Spo-157
❑ 90Top-478
❑ 90TopBig-104
❑ 90TopSti-133
❑ 90TopTif-478
❑ 90TopTVA-57
❑ 90UppDec-578
❑ 91Bow-514
❑ 91Don-121
❑ 91Fle-42
❑ 91Lea-15
❑ 91OPC-665
❑ 91PanFreS-114
❑ 91Sco-222
❑ 91StaClu-279
❑ 91Stu-226
❑ 91Top-665
❑ 91TopDesS-665
❑ 91TopMic-665
❑ 91TopTif-665
❑ 91Ult-282
❑ 91UppDec-129
❑ 92Bow-245
❑ 92Don-121
❑ 92Fle-558
❑ 92FleAll-5
❑ 92Lea-228
❑ 92LeaBlaG-228
❑ 92OPC-312
❑ 92PanSti-251
❑ 92Pin-146
❑ 92PirNatl-10
❑ 92Sco-38
❑ 92StaClu-216
❑ 92StaCluD-103
❑ 92Stu-85
❑ 92Top-312
❑ 92TopGol-312
❑ 92TopGolW-312
❑ 92TopMic-312
❑ 92TriPla-232
❑ 92Ult-254
❑ 92UppDec-113
❑ 93Don-306
❑ 93Fle-114
❑ 93FleFinE-196
❑ 93Lea-510
❑ 93OPC-145
❑ 93PacSpa-246
❑ 93PanSti-280
❑ 93Pin-219
❑ 93Sco-83
❑ 93Sel-203
❑ 93StaClu-496
❑ 93StaCluFDI-496
❑ 93StaCluMOP-496
❑ 93Top-54
❑ 93TopGol-54
❑ 93TopInaM-54
❑ 93TopInaR-54
❑ 93TopMic-54
❑ 93TriPla-110
❑ 93Ult-98
❑ 93UppDec-120
❑ 93UppDecGold-120
❑ 93WhiSoxK-17
❑ 94Don-201
❑ 94Fle-87
❑ 94Pac-131
❑ 94Sco-181
❑ 94ScoGolR-181
❑ 94StaClu-118
❑ 94StaCluFDI-118
❑ 94StaCluGR-118
❑ 94StaCluMOP-118
❑ 94StaCluT-124
❑ 94StaCluTFDI-124
❑ 94Top-147
❑ 94TopGol-147
❑ 94TopSpa-147
❑ 94WhiSoxK-19
❑ 95Don-517
❑ 95DonPreP-517
❑ 95Fla-26
❑ 95Fle-123
❑ 95Sco-168
❑ 95ScoGolR-168
❑ 95ScoPlaTS-168
❑ 95WhiSoxK-18
Lavan, Doc (John)
❑ 15SpoNewM-97
❑ 16BF2FP-44
❑ 16SpoNewM-99
❑ 17ColE13-95
❑ 19W514-4
❑ 21E121So1-54
❑ 21E121So8-50
❑ 21Exh-94
❑ 21Nei-102
❑ 22AmeCarE122-39
❑ 22E120-233
❑ 22W573-72
❑ 22W575-70
❑ 23W501-109
❑ 23WilChoV-83
Lavelle, Gary
❑ 70RelPam-8
❑ 75OPC-624
❑ 75Top-624
❑ 75TopMin-624
❑ 76OPC-105
❑ 76SanFraGP-11
❑ 76SSP-96
❑ 76Top-105
❑ 77Gia-13
❑ 77GiaTeal-15
❑ 77Top-423
❑ 78GiaTeal-16
❑ 78Hos-32
❑ 78Top-671
❑ 79GiaPol-46
❑ 79Top-311
❑ 80GiaEurFS-2
❑ 80GiaPol-46
❑ 80GiaTeal-13
❑ 80Top-84
❑ 81Don-314
❑ 81Fle-448
❑ 81GiaTeal-8
❑ 81OPC-62
❑ 81Top-588
❑ 82Don-60
❑ 82Fle-392
❑ 82Gia25tATI-16
❑ 82OPC-209
❑ 82Top-209
❑ 83Don-60
❑ 83Fle-265
❑ 83FleSta-102
❑ 83FleSti-52
❑ 83GiaMot-14
❑ 83GiaPos-15
❑ 83OPC-376
❑ 83Top-791
❑ 83TopFol-4
❑ 84AllGamPI-82
❑ 84Don-573
❑ 84DonActAS-1
❑ 84Fle-377
❑ 84GiaMot-10
❑ 84GiaPos-11
❑ 84Nes792-145
❑ 84OPC-145
❑ 84Top-145
❑ 84TopSti-164
❑ 84TopTif-145
❑ 85BluJayFS-18
❑ 85Don-265
❑ 85Fle-613
❑ 85FleUpd-69
❑ 85Lea-114
❑ 85OPC-2
❑ 85OPCPos-24
❑ 85Top-462
❑ 85TopSti-159
❑ 85TopTif-462
❑ 85TopTifT-72T
❑ 85TopTra-72T
❑ 86BluJayAF-18
❑ 86BluJayFS-22
❑ 86Don-621
❑ 86Fle-65
❑ 86OPC-22
❑ 86Top-622
❑ 86TopTif-622
❑ 87BluJayFS-17
Lavenda, John
❑ 91CalLeLA-27
Lavender, Jeff
❑ 89TenTecGE-13
Lavender, Jimmy (James)
❑ 09SpoNewSM-91
❑ 09T206-437
❑ 14CraJacE-105
❑ 14E&SP-4
❑ 14PolGroW-13
❑ 15CraJacE-105
❑ 15SpoNewM-98
❑ 16BF2FP-68
❑ 16SpoNewM-100
❑ 17ColE13-96
❑ 92ConTSN-344
Lavender, Robert
❑ 88GasRanP-996
❑ 89ChaRanS-11
Lavenia, Mark
❑ 93HunCubC-16
❑ 93HunCubF-3233
❑ 94HunCubC-19
❑ 94HunCubF-3548
❑ 95MacBraTI-16
Laverty, Pat
❑ 93LetMouSP-23
❑ 95KanCouCTI-NNO
Laviano, Frank
❑ 90TamYanD-13

❑ 91OneYanP-4151
❑ 92GreHorC-6
Lavigne, Ben
❑ 92IdaFalGF-3515
Lavigne, Martin
❑ 91KisDodP-4179
❑ 93VerBeaDC-15
❑ 93VerBeaDF-2214
LaVigne, Randy
❑ 82IowCubT-6
❑ 83MidCubT-24
Lavoie, Marc
❑ 90AriWilP-11
Lavrusky, Chuck
❑ 87IdaFalBP-7
❑ 88BoiHawP-1621
Law, Joe
❑ 83IdaFalAT-14
❑ 84ModA'sC-17
❑ 85HunStaJ-40
❑ 87ModA'sC-10
❑ 87ModA'sP-19
❑ 89TacTigC-6
❑ 89TacTigP-1550
❑ 90CMC-587
❑ 90ProAAAF-135
❑ 90TacTigC-10
❑ 90TacTigP-88
Law, Rudy
❑ 77LodDodT-9
❑ 79AlbDukTc-19
❑ 79Top-719
❑ 81AlbDukTc-20
❑ 81Dod-18
❑ 81DodPol-3
❑ 81Don-180
❑ 81Fle-139
❑ 81Top-127
❑ 83Don-521
❑ 83Fle-244
❑ 83FleSti-150
❑ 83Top-514
❑ 83WhiSoxTV-11
❑ 84Don-257
❑ 84Fle-67
❑ 84FleSti-93
❑ 84Nes792-47
❑ 84OPC-47
❑ 84Top-47
❑ 84TopSti-245
❑ 84TopTif-47
❑ 84WhiSoxTV-21
❑ 85Don-244
❑ 85Fle-519
❑ 85Lea-117
❑ 85OPC-286
❑ 85Top-286
❑ 85TopSti-241
❑ 85TopTif-286
❑ 85WhiSoxC-23
❑ 86Don-632
❑ 86Fle-211
❑ 86FleUpd-66
❑ 86OPC-6
❑ 86RoyTeal-13
❑ 86Top-637
❑ 86TopSti-291
❑ 86TopTif-637
❑ 86TopTra-62T
❑ 86TopTraT-62T
❑ 87Don-343
❑ 87Fle-372
❑ 87FleGlo-372
❑ 87Top-382
❑ 87TopTif-382
❑ 90DodTar-437
Law, Travis
❑ 88ButCopKSP-23
❑ 89ChaRanS-12
Law, Vance
❑ 79PorBeaT-5
❑ 80PorBeaT-9
❑ 81PorBeaT-14
❑ 81Top-551
❑ 82Don-582
❑ 82Fle-484
❑ 82Top-291
❑ 83Don-117
❑ 83Fle-245
❑ 83OPC-98
❑ 83Top-98
❑ 83WhiSoxTV-5
❑ 84AllGamPI-125
❑ 84Don-546
❑ 84Fle-68
❑ 84Nes792-667
❑ 84Top-667
❑ 84TopSti-249
❑ 84TopTif-667
❑ 84WhiSoxTV-22
❑ 85Don-122
❑ 85ExpPos-11
❑ 85Fle-520
❑ 85FleUpd-70
❑ 85Lea-183
❑ 85OPC-81
❑ 85Top-137
❑ 85Top-413
❑ 85TopSti-242
❑ 85TopTif-137
❑ 85TopTif-413
❑ 85TopTifT-73T
❑ 85TopTra-73T
❑ 86Don-132
❑ 86ExpProPa-23
❑ 86ExpProPo-12
❑ 86Fle-252
❑ 86GenMilB-6D
❑ 86Lea-57
❑ 86OPC-99
❑ 86Top-787
❑ 86TopSti-81
❑ 86TopTif-787
❑ 87Don-212
❑ 87DonOpeD-94
❑ 87ExpPos-13
❑ 87Fle-323
❑ 87FleGlo-323
❑ 87GenMilB-4D
❑ 87OPC-127
❑ 87Top-127
❑ 87TopTif-127
❑ 88CubDavB-2
❑ 88CubVanLS-1
❑ 88CubVanLS-2
❑ 88CubVanLS-3
❑ 88Don-212
❑ 88DonBasB-60
❑ 88DonTeaBC-NEW
❑ 88Fle-187
❑ 88FleGlo-187
❑ 88FleUpd-79
❑ 88FleUpdG-79
❑ 88OPC-346
❑ 88PanSti-324
❑ 88Sco-85
❑ 88ScoGlo-85
❑ 88ScoRoo-16T
❑ 88ScoRooG-16T
❑ 88Spo-41
❑ 88StaLinE-9
❑ 88Top-111
❑ 88Top-346
❑ 88TopTif-111
❑ 88TopTif-346
❑ 88TopTra-60T
❑ 88TopTraT-60T
❑ 89Bow-293
❑ 89BowTif-293
❑ 89CubMar-2
❑ 89Don-276
❑ 89DonAll-49
❑ 89Fle-430
❑ 89FleBasA-27
❑ 89FleGlo-430
❑ 89MSAHolD-12
❑ 89Nis-12A
❑ 89OPC-338
❑ 89PanSti-57
❑ 89Sco-102
❑ 89Spo-162
❑ 89Top-501
❑ 89TopBig-143
❑ 89TopSti-46
❑ 89TopStiB-42
❑ 89TopTif-501
❑ 89TVSpoM-24
❑ 89UppDec-473
❑ 90Don-629
❑ 90Fle-36
❑ 90FleCan-36
❑ 90OPC-287
❑ 90PubIntS-197
❑ 90Sco-73
❑ 90Top-287
❑ 90TopTif-287
❑ 90UppDec-380
❑ 91A'sMot-12
❑ 91Bow-222
❑ 91Lea-355
❑ 91UppDec-760
Law, Vern (Vernon)
❑ 50PirTeal-10
❑ 51Bow-203
❑ 52Bow-71
❑ 52Top-81
❑ 54Bow-187
❑ 54Top-235
❑ 55Bow-199
❑ 56PirTeal-14
❑ 56Top-252
❑ 57PirTeal-4
❑ 57Top-199
❑ 58HirTes-5
❑ 58Kah-17
❑ 58Top-132
❑ 59Kah-18
❑ 59Top-12
❑ 59Top-428
❑ 59TopVen-12
❑ 60Kah-21
❑ 60KeyChal-30
❑ 60Top-453
❑ 60TopTat-29
❑ 61Kah-24
❑ 61NuSco-406
❑ 61PirJayP-7
❑ 61PirRigF-5
❑ 61Pos-126A
❑ 61Pos-126B
❑ 61Top-47
❑ 61Top-250
❑ 61Top-400
❑ 61TopStal-66
❑ 62Jel-179
❑ 62Pos-179
❑ 62PosCan-179
❑ 62Top-295
❑ 63Fle-58
❑ 63PirJayP-8
❑ 63Top-184
❑ 64PirKDK-15
❑ 64Top-472
❑ 65Top-515
❑ 66Baz-18
❑ 66OPC-15
❑ 66PirEasH-32
❑ 66Top-15
❑ 66Top-221
❑ 66TopRubl-51
❑ 66TopVen-15
❑ 66TopVen-221
❑ 67CokCapPi-16
❑ 67DexPre-123
❑ 67PirTeal-9
❑ 67Top-351
❑ 67TopPirS-11
❑ 69PirTeal-12
❑ 77PirTCM1WC-17
❑ 78TCM60I-239
❑ 79DiaGre-371
❑ 79TCM50-42
❑ 79TCMJapPB-17
❑ 82PorBeaT-24
❑ 83TopRep5-81
❑ 85Top-137
❑ 85TopTif-137
❑ 87Pir196T-9
❑ 90PacLeg-37
❑ 91SweBasG-55
❑ 91TopArc1-324
❑ 92ActPacA-19
❑ 92BazQua5A-18
❑ 93UppDecAH-81
❑ 94TopArc1-235
❑ 94TopArc1G-235
Lawler, Brian
❑ 93SpaPhiF-1062
Lawler, Chris
❑ 92Min-10
Lawler, Scott
❑ 97AubDouTI-13
Lawless, Thomas
❑ 80WatRedT-18
❑ 81WatRedT-14
❑ 82IndIndTI-15
❑ 83Don-400
❑ 83IndIndTI-12
❑ 83Top-423
❑ 84RedEnq-4
❑ 85CarTeal-21
❑ 86CarSchM-15
❑ 86CarTeal-26
❑ 86Top-228
❑ 86TopTif-228
❑ 87CarSmo-19
❑ 87CarTeal-16
❑ 87Top-647
❑ 87TopTif-647
❑ 88CarSmo-15
❑ 88CarTeal-14
❑ 88Top-183
❑ 88TopSti-22
❑ 88TopTif-183
❑ 88Woo-25
❑ 89BluJayFS-15
❑ 89Bow-255
❑ 89BowTif-255
❑ 89Top-312
❑ 89TopTif-312
❑ 90BluJayFS-15
❑ 90Don-681
❑ 90OPC-49
❑ 90PubIntS-519
❑ 90Top-49
❑ 90TopTif-49
❑ 94CedRapKC-23
❑ 94CedRapKF-1124
❑ 96CedRapKTI-27
❑ 97NorTid-2
❑ 97NorTidB-2
❑ 98NorTidP-15
❑ 98NorTidQ-33
Lawn, Mike
❑ 91HelBreSP-4
❑ 92SalSpuC-8
❑ 92SalSpuF-3770
❑ 92StoPorF-49
Lawrence, Andy
❑ 85LynMetT-22
❑ 86JacMetT-16
❑ 87JacExpP-435
❑ 88JacExpB-19
❑ 88JacExpP-972
Lawrence, Bill
❑ 30Zee-181
❑ 34DiaMatCSB-111
❑ 43CenFlo-17
Lawrence, Brooks
❑ 55Bow-75
❑ 55CarHunW-13
❑ 55RedMan-NL4
❑ 56Kah-10
❑ 56Top-305
❑ 57Kah-19
❑ 57RedSoh-13
❑ 57Top-66
❑ 58Kah-18
❑ 58RedEnq-24
❑ 58Top-374
❑ 59RedEnq-12
❑ 59RedShiBS-10
❑ 59Top-67
❑ 59TopVen-67
❑ 60Kah-22
❑ 60Lea-25A
❑ 60Lea-36
❑ 60Top-434
❑ 75OakOak2A-20
❑ 79TCM50-217
❑ 93UppDecS-8
Lawrence, Chip
❑ 96BluOriB-17
❑ 97FreKey-13
❑ 98FreKey-M-26
Lawrence, Clint
❑ 96StCatSB-16
❑ 97HagSunB-9
❑ 98DunBluJTI-18
❑ 98KnoSG-9
Lawrence, Joe
❑ 96BesAutS1RP-FR6
❑ 97BesLimA-22
❑ 97Bow-368
❑ 97BowChr-246
❑ 97BowChrI-246
❑ 97BowChrIR-246
❑ 97BowChrR-246
❑ 97BowInt-368
❑ 97HagSunB-15
❑ 97SouAtlTPB-20
❑ 97Top-480
❑ 98BesPreA-22
❑ 98Bow-366
❑ 98BowChr-366
❑ 98BowChrGA-366
❑ 98BowChrGAR-366
❑ 98BowChrI-366
❑ 98BowChrIR-366
❑ 98BowChrR-366
❑ 98BowGolA-366
❑ 98BowInt-366
❑ 98DunBluJSB-4
❑ 98DunBluJTI-19
❑ 99Bow-104
❑ 99BowChr-104
❑ 99BowChrG-104
❑ 99BowChrGR-104
❑ 99BowChrI-104
❑ 99BowChrIR-104
❑ 99BowChrR-104
❑ 99BowGol-104
❑ 99BowInt-104
❑ 99SP SigAuto-JLA
❑ 99SP SigAutoG-JLA
❑ 99SP TopP-72
❑ 99SP TopPPE-72
❑ 99SPSig-59
❑ 99UppDec-280
❑ 99UppDecE-123
❑ 99UppDecEFXG-123
❑ 99UppDecEL1-280
❑ 99UppDecEL2-280
Lawrence, Leigh
❑ 60SeaPop-6
Lawrence, Matt
❑ 92HunCubC-14
❑ 92HunCubF-3145
Lawrence, Mike
❑ 97ButCopKB-12
❑ 97ButCopKK-12
❑ 98CedRapKTI-15
Lawrence, Randy
❑ 92ElmPioC-7
❑ 92ElmPioF-1379
❑ 93ForLauRSC-16
❑ 93ForLauRSFP-1594
❑ 93UtiBluSC-13
❑ 93UtiBluSF-3529
Lawrence, Richard
❑ 95BilMusTI-26
Lawrence, Scott
❑ 86EriCarP-17
❑ 87SavCarP-25
❑ 88St.PetCS-12
❑ 89SprCarB-13
Lawrence, Sean
❑ 92WelPirC-16
❑ 92WelPirF-1319
❑ 93AugPirC-12
❑ 94CarLeaAF-CAR41
❑ 94SalBucC-14
❑ 94SalBucF-2320
❑ 95LynHilTI-12
❑ 95SigRoo-30
❑ 95SigRooSig-30
❑ 96CarMudB-4
❑ 97CalCanB-15
❑ 98NasSouTI-20
❑ 98NasSouTISS-19
❑ 99SpoIll-62
Lawrence, Tony
❑ 97IdaFalBTI-8
❑ 98CliLumG-10
Lawrenson, Scott
❑ 87LynMetP-27
❑ 90CMC-687
❑ 90TidTidC-30
Lawson, Cale
❑ 91BurIndP-3304
Lawson, David
❑ 92BelMarCB-24
❑ 92BelMarF-1457
❑ 93AppFoxCB-14
❑ 93AppFoxFI-2472
❑ 94AppFoxFI-1067
Lawson, Jarrod
❑ 98MarPhiG-15
Lawson, Jim (James)
❑ 88SouOreAP-1712
❑ 89MadMusS-12
❑ 90MadMusB-19
❑ 90ModA'sCLC-152
❑ 90ModA'sP-2209
Lawson, Roxie (Alfred V.)
❑ 33MrsShePP-6
❑ 36WorWidGV-104
❑ 72TCMthe3-46
❑ 74TigTCM1AC-18
❑ 92ConTSN-513
Lawson, Steve
❑ 73OPC-612
❑ 73Top-612
❑ 93RanKee-23
Lawton, Alycia
❑ 91FreStaLBS-13
Lawton, Jack
❑ 88SFHesCreN32-14
Lawton, Marcus
❑ 86LynMetP-14
❑ 87JacMetF-16
❑ 87MetColP-37
❑ 87TexLeaAF-24
❑ 88MetColP-30
❑ 88TidTidP-1591
❑ 89TidTidC-23
❑ 89TidTidP-1967
❑ 90CMC-643
❑ 90OPC-302
❑ 90ProAAAF-178
❑ 90Top-302
❑ 90TopDeb89-69
❑ 90TopTif-302
❑ 90VanCanC-16
❑ 90VanCanP-500
❑ 91LinDriAA-440
❑ 91MidAngLD-440
❑ 91MidAngOHP-16
❑ 91MidAngP-446
❑ 92MemChiS-438
❑ 92MidAngOHP-14
❑ 92SkyAA F-184
❑ 92YanWIZ8-103
Lawton, Matt
❑ 93ForWayWC-14
❑ 93ForWayWF-1982
❑ 94FloStaLAF-FSL10
❑ 94ForMyeMC-12
❑ 94ForMyeMF-1180
❑ 95HarCitRCTI-10
❑ 96Bow-261
❑ 96BowFoi-261
❑ 96ColCho-34
❑ 96ColChoGS-34
❑ 96ColChoSS-34
❑ 96Don-432
❑ 96DonPreP-432
❑ 96Fin-B312
❑ 96FinRef-B312
❑ 96Fla-117
❑ 96Fle-167
❑ 96FleTif-167
❑ 96Lea-10
❑ 96LeaPre-145
❑ 96LeaPreP-145
❑ 96LeaPrePB-10
❑ 96LeaPrePG-10
❑ 96LeaPrePS-10
❑ 96LeaSigA-130
❑ 96LeaSigAG-130
❑ 96LeaSigAS-130
❑ 96Pac-354
❑ 96Pin-168
❑ 96PinAfi-184
❑ 96PinAfiAP-184
❑ 96Sco-495
❑ 96SelCer-131
❑ 96SelCerAP-131
❑ 96SelCerCB-131
❑ 96SelCerCR-131
❑ 96SelCerMB-131
❑ 96SelCerMG-131
❑ 96SelCerMR-131
❑ 96Spo-136
❑ 96SpoArtP-136
❑ 96StaClu-437
❑ 96StaCluMOP-437
❑ 96Ult-376
❑ 96UltGolM-376
❑ 96UppDecPHE-H27
❑ 96UppDecPreH-H27
❑ 97ColCho-381
❑ 97Don-344
❑ 97DonGolPP-344
❑ 97DonLim-35
❑ 97DonLimE-35
❑ 97DonPre-53
❑ 97DonPreCttC-53
❑ 97DonSilPP-344
❑ 97Fle-148
❑ 97FleTif-148
❑ 97Lea-217
❑ 97LeaFraM-217
❑ 97LeaFraMDC-217
❑ 97NewPin-126
❑ 97NewPinAP-126
❑ 97NewPinMC-126
❑ 97NewPinPP-126
❑ 97Pac-140
❑ 97PacLigB-140
❑ 97PacSil-140
❑ 97Sco-394
❑ 97ScoArtPWB-394
❑ 97ScoResC-394
❑ 97ScoShoS-394

❑ 97ScoShoSAP-394
❑ 97Top-428
❑ 97Ult-88
❑ 97UltGolME-88
❑ 97UltPlaME-88
❑ 98CirThu-213
❑ 98CirThuRav-213
❑ 98CirThuSupRav-213
❑ 98ColCho-409
❑ 98Fin-117
❑ 98FinNo--117
❑ 98FinNo-R-117
❑ 98FinRef-117
❑ 98Fle-368
❑ 98FleVin'-102
❑ 98FleVin'C-102
❑ 98Pac-136
❑ 98PacOnl-423
❑ 98PacOnlR-423
❑ 98PacOnlWC-423
❑ 98PacPlaB-136
❑ 98PacRedT-136
❑ 98PacSil-136
❑ 98Top-208
❑ 98TopChr-208
❑ 98TopChrR-208
❑ 98TopDevR-208
❑ 98TopDia-208
❑ 98TopMiniC-208
❑ 98UppDec-129
❑ 99199Fin-44
❑ 99Bow-283
❑ 99BowGol-283
❑ 99BowInt-283
❑ 99CroRoyB-81
❑ 99CroRoyL-81
❑ 99CroRoyOD-81
❑ 99FinGolRef-44
❑ 99FinRef-44
❑ 99Fle-162
❑ 99FleBri-57
❑ 99FleBri2G-57
❑ 99FleBriBlu-57
❑ 99FleBriGol-57
❑ 99FleSta9-162
❑ 99FleWarT-162
❑ 99Pac-248
❑ 99PacAur-105
❑ 99PacAurOD-105
❑ 99PacInv-85
❑ 99PacInvOD-85
❑ 99PacInvPB-85
❑ 99PacPar-134
❑ 99PacParC-134
❑ 99PacParG-134
❑ 99PacParHoloGold-134
❑ 99PacParHS-134
❑ 99PacParOD-134
❑ 99PacParPB-134
❑ 99PacParRed-134
❑ 99PacPlaB-248
❑ 99PacRed-248
❑ 99SkyPreA-35
❑ 99SkyPreABlue-35
❑ 99SkyThu-108
❑ 99SkyThuRant-108
❑ 99SkyThuRave-108
❑ 99StaClu-37
❑ 99StaCluFDI-37
❑ 99StaCluOoaK-37
❑ 99StaCluPP-37
❑ 99ThuSkySupR-108
❑ 99Top-94
❑ 99TopChr-94
❑ 99TopChrR-94
❑ 99TopMVPP-94
❑ 99TopOpeD-53
❑ 99UppDec-134
❑ 99UppDecEL1-134
❑ 99UppDecEL2-134
❑ 99Vic-227

Laxamana, Brian
❑ 90CalLeaACLC-34
❑ 91CalLeLA-50

Laxton, Brett
❑ 93LSUTigM-15
❑ 94LSUTig-8
❑ 94LSUTigMP-5
❑ 96SouOreTI-20
❑ 97VisOakG-17
❑ 98HunStaTI-8
❑ 99Bow-371
❑ 99BowGol-371
❑ 99BowInt-371

Laxton, William
❑ 75TidTidTI-15
❑ 76DetTigP-15
❑ 76SSP-615
❑ 77Top-394

Lay, Shane
❑ 92HelBreF-1728
❑ 92HelBreSP-6

Laya, Jesus
❑ 87PocGiaTB-28
❑ 88PocGiaP-2096
❑ 89EveGiaS-19
❑ 93LinVenB-113
❑ 96-97LinVen-30

Layana, Tim
❑ 87AlbYanP-11
❑ 88AlbYanP-1333
❑ 89AlbYanB-5
❑ 89AlbYanP-329
❑ 89AlbYanSt-9
❑ 89EasLeaAP-14
❑ 90AlbDecGB-11
❑ 90Bow-41
❑ 90BowTif-41
❑ 90ClaYel-T46
❑ 90DonRoo-23
❑ 90FleUpd-14
❑ 90Lea-410
❑ 90RedKah-14
❑ 90ScoRoo-107T
❑ 90TopTra-55T
❑ 90TopTraT-55T
❑ 90UppDec-717
❑ 91Bow-689
❑ 91Don-516
❑ 91Fle-69
❑ 91OPC-627
❑ 91Sco-64
❑ 91Sco100RS-54
❑ 91StaClu-396
❑ 91Top-627
❑ 91TopDeb90-82
❑ 91TopDesS-627
❑ 91TopMic-627
❑ 91TopTif-627
❑ 91UppDec-396
❑ 92RocRedWF-1933
❑ 92RocRedWS-460
❑ 92Sco-628
❑ 92StaClu-419
❑ 93PhoFirF-1512
❑ 94SanBerSF-2752

Layne, Hillis
❑ 47CenFlo-15
❑ 47SigOil-80
❑ 88ChaLooLTI-21

Layne, Jason
❑ 96SpoIndB-15
❑ 97LanLugTS-11
❑ 98CarLeaAC-5
❑ 98WilBluRC-16

Layne, Jerry
❑ 90T/MUmp-58

Layne, Roger
❑ 97BurIndG-16
❑ 98ColRedSM-6

Layton, Blane
❑ 98BilMusTI-19

Layton, Tom
❑ 83KinBluJTI-11
❑ 87IowCubTI-8

Lazar, John Dan
❑ 69Top-439
❑ 70Top-669
❑ 72MilBra-195

Lazor, Joe
❑ 87CedRapRP-5
❑ 88ChaLooB-4
❑ 88SouLeaAJ-35
❑ 89ChaLooB-5
❑ 89ChaLooGS-15
❑ 90ChaLooGS-18

Lazor, John Paul
❑ 43RedSoxTI-13
❑ 49BowPCL-30
❑ 75RedSox1T-23
❑ 83TCMPla1945-20

Lazorko, Jack
❑ 80TulDriT-6
❑ 81TulDriT-19
❑ 83ElPasDT-23
❑ 84VanCanC-48
❑ 85PhoGiaC-176
❑ 85Top-317
❑ 85TopTif-317
❑ 86Don-628
❑ 86NasSouTI-15
❑ 87EdmTraP-2062
❑ 87FleUpd-61
❑ 87FleUpdG-61
❑ 87TopTra-62T
❑ 87TopTraT-62T
❑ 88Don-160
❑ 88EdmTraC-3
❑ 88EdmTraP-556
❑ 88Fle-494
❑ 88FleGlo-494
❑ 88Sco-437
❑ 88ScoGlo-437
❑ 88Top-601
❑ 88TopTif-601
❑ 89EdmTraC-1
❑ 89Fle-482
❑ 89FleGlo-482
❑ 89Top-362
❑ 89TopTif-362
❑ 90TulDriDGB-13
❑ 91PacSenL-113
❑ 93HolLeg-10
❑ 94BreMilB-143

Lazzaro, Sam
❑ 93SalBucC-29
❑ 94SalBucC-28
❑ 95SalAvaTI-30

Lazzeri, Tony (Anthony)
❑ 22Zee-82
❑ 25Zee-91
❑ 26Exh-100
❑ 26SpoComoA-26
❑ 26SpoNewSM-4
❑ 27Exh-50
❑ 28PorandAR-A21
❑ 28PorandAR-B21
❑ 28StaPlaCE-43
❑ 28W502-29
❑ 28W513-79
❑ 28Yue-29
❑ 29ExhFou-25
❑ 30UncJac-19
❑ 31Exh-25
❑ 31W517-27
❑ 32OrbPinNP-107
❑ 32USCar*-18
❑ 33CraJacP-15
❑ 33ExhFou-13
❑ 33Gou-31
❑ 33GouCanV-31
❑ 33WorCig-61
❑ 33WorCig-62
❑ 34BatR31-45
❑ 34DiaStaR-74
❑ 35AlDemDCR3-6
❑ 35ExhFou-13
❑ 35GouPuzR-4D
❑ 35GouPuzR-7D
❑ 35GouPuzR-12D
❑ 36ExhFou-13
❑ 36OveCanR-30
❑ 36R31Pre-L12
❑ 37ExhFou-13
❑ 37OPCBatUV-117
❑ 38BasTabP-20
❑ 40PlaBal-233
❑ 51R42SmaS-62
❑ 60ExhWriH-14
❑ 60Fle-31
❑ 61Fle-54
❑ 68LauWorS-23
❑ 69Baz-3
❑ 70FleWorS-23
❑ 71FleWorS-35
❑ 72TCMthe3-47
❑ 74CapPub-14
❑ 75ShaPiz-16
❑ 75Yan192T-14
❑ 75YanAllTT-5
❑ 75YanDyn1T-30
❑ 75YanDyn1T-51
❑ 75YanDyn1T-52
❑ 77GalGloG-116
❑ 77GalGloG-191
❑ 79Yan192T-17
❑ 80LauFamF-26
❑ 80PerHaloFP-209
❑ 80YanGreT-2
❑ 81ConTSN-11
❑ 83BigLeaCOA-18
❑ 83ConMar-18
❑ 83TCMRuT-5
❑ 84Yan192G-16
❑ 87Yan192T-3
❑ 88ConAmeA-19
❑ 88ConSer3-17
❑ 90DodTar-438
❑ 91ConTSN-113
❑ 92YanWIZA-39
❑ 92YanWIZH-20
❑ 93ActPacA-101
❑ 93ActPacA2-35G
❑ 93ConTSN-761
❑ 93ConTSN-762
❑ 93ConTSN-911
❑ 93LegFoi-7
❑ 94ConTSN-1053
❑ 94ConTSNB-1053
❑ 95ConTSN-1412

Le Grand, Todd
❑ 95AusFut-19

Lea, Charles
❑ 79MemChiT-8
❑ 80ExpPos-13
❑ 80MemChiT-2
❑ 81ExpPos-3
❑ 81Fle-165
❑ 81OPC-293
❑ 81Top-293
❑ 82Don-320
❑ 82ExpHygM-11
❑ 82ExpPos-19
❑ 82Fle-193
❑ 82OPC-38
❑ 82Top-38
❑ 83AllGamPI-169
❑ 83Don-414
❑ 83ExpPos-15
❑ 83ExpStu-23
❑ 83Fle-286
❑ 83FleSta-103
❑ 83FleSti-266
❑ 83OPC-253
❑ 83Top-629
❑ 84AllGamPI-83
❑ 84Don-376
❑ 84ExpPos-16
❑ 84ExpStu-8
❑ 84Fle-278
❑ 84Nes792-421
❑ 84Nes792-516
❑ 84OPC-142
❑ 84OPC-332
❑ 84Top-421
❑ 84Top-516
❑ 84TopSti-98
❑ 84TopTif-421
❑ 84TopTif-516
❑ 85Don-21
❑ 85Don-177
❑ 85DonSupD-21
❑ 85Fle-401
❑ 85Fle-632
❑ 85Lea-21
❑ 85OPC-345
❑ 85OPCPos-10
❑ 85Top-345
❑ 85TopGloA-10
❑ 85TopGloS-30
❑ 85TopMin-345
❑ 85TopSti-84
❑ 85TopSti-182
❑ 85TopTif-345
❑ 86Don-376
❑ 86Fle-253
❑ 86Lea-172
❑ 86OPC-376
❑ 86Top-526
❑ 86TopTat-21
❑ 86TopTif-526
❑ 87WesPalBEP-668
❑ 88FleUpd-44
❑ 88FleUpdG-44
❑ 89Don-473
❑ 89Fle-119
❑ 89FleGlo-119
❑ 89Sco-501
❑ 89UppDec-81
❑ 91UppDecS-23
❑ 93ExpDonM-23

Lea, Corey
❑ 93LetMouF-4162
❑ 93LetMouSP-18

Leach, Chris
❑ 89WinHavRSS-13
❑ 90LynRedSTI-2
❑ 91LynRedSC-21
❑ 91LynRedSP-1211

Leach, Don
❑ 80ElmPioRST-19

Leach, Fred
❑ 09T206-207
❑ 09T206-208
❑ 10W555-43
❑ 11SpoLifM-252
❑ 11TurRedT-3
❑ 28Exh-21
❑ 28PorandAR-A22
❑ 28PorandAR-B22
❑ 29PorandAR-55
❑ 33Gou-179
❑ 79DiaGre-28
❑ 94ConTSN-1130
❑ 94ConTSNB-1130

Leach, Jay (Jalal)
❑ 90OneYanP-3420
❑ 90ProAaA-183
❑ 91Cla/Bes-270
❑ 91Ft.LauYC-27
❑ 91Ft.LauYP-2441
❑ 92PriWilCC-5
❑ 92PriWilCF-161
❑ 94ColCliF-2964
❑ 94ColCliP-17
❑ 94VenLinU-179
❑ 95ColCliMCTI-21
❑ 95ColCliP-15
❑ 95ColCliTI-15
❑ 96HarSenB-17
❑ 97TacRai-19

Leach, Jumaane
❑ 94SpoIndC-17
❑ 94SpoIndF-3320

Leach, Martin
❑ 82TulDriT-3
❑ 85WatIndT-13

Leach, Matthew
❑ 94EliTwiC-11
❑ 94EliTwiF-3725

Leach, Nick
❑ 96GreFalDB-18
❑ 96GreFalDTI-23
❑ 97YakBeaG-14
❑ 98SanBerS-16
❑ 98SanBerSTIS-15

Leach, Rick
❑ 80EvaTriT-24
❑ 82Don-583
❑ 82Fle-272
❑ 82Top-266
❑ 83Don-81
❑ 83Fle-334
❑ 83TigPos-18
❑ 83Top-147
❑ 84BluJayFS-22
❑ 84Fle-84
❑ 84FleUpd-71
❑ 84Nes792-427
❑ 84SyrChiT-6
❑ 84Top-427
❑ 84TopTif-427
❑ 84TopTra-71T
❑ 84TopTraT-71T
❑ 85Fle-112
❑ 85IntLeaAT-29
❑ 85OPC-52
❑ 85SyrChiT-11
❑ 85Top-593
❑ 85TopTif-593
❑ 86BluJayFS-23
❑ 86TopTra-63T
❑ 86TopTraT-63T
❑ 87BluJayFS-18
❑ 87Don-567
❑ 87Fle-234
❑ 87FleGlo-234
❑ 87FleUpd-63
❑ 87FleUpdG-63
❑ 87OPC-5
❑ 87SyrChi1A-7
❑ 87Top-716
❑ 87TopTif-716
❑ 88BluJayFS-17
❑ 88Don-518
❑ 88Fle-115
❑ 88FleGlo-115
❑ 88Lea-247
❑ 88OPC-323
❑ 88Sco-257
❑ 88ScoGlo-257
❑ 88StaLinBJ-11
❑ 88Top-323
❑ 88TopTif-323
❑ 89Bow-234
❑ 89BowTif-234
❑ 89Don-638
❑ 89Fle-237
❑ 89FleGlo-237
❑ 89OPC-284
❑ 89RanMot-16
❑ 89RanSmo-19
❑ 89Sco-540
❑ 89Top-682
❑ 89TopTif-682
❑ 89TopTra-68T
❑ 89TopTraT-68T
❑ 89UppDec-554
❑ 90Don-613
❑ 90Fle-305
❑ 90FleCan-305
❑ 90GiaMot-14
❑ 90Lea-436
❑ 90OPC-27
❑ 90PubIntS-416
❑ 90Sco-426
❑ 90Top-27
❑ 90TopTif-27
❑ 90TopTra-56T
❑ 90TopTraT-56T
❑ 90UppDec-640
❑ 91Lea-136
❑ 93RanKee-227

Leach, Ron
❑ 80WatIndT-3

Leach, Terry
❑ 76BatRouCT-14
❑ 79SavBraT-19
❑ 81TidTidT-29
❑ 82TidTidT-14
❑ 82Top-623
❑ 83Don-634
❑ 83TidTidT-5
❑ 83Top-187
❑ 84RicBraT-19
❑ 84TidTidT-26
❑ 85TidTidT-2
❑ 86Fle-87
❑ 86TidTidP-15
❑ 86Top-774
❑ 86TopTif-774
❑ 87FleUpd-62
❑ 87FleUpdG-62
❑ 87MetColP-38
❑ 87TopTra-63T
❑ 87TopTraT-63T
❑ 88Don-603
❑ 88DonTeaBM-603
❑ 88Fle-139
❑ 88FleGlo-139
❑ 88MetColP-31
❑ 88MetKah-26
❑ 88OPC-391
❑ 88Sco-203
❑ 88ScoGlo-203
❑ 88Spo-139
❑ 88Top-457
❑ 88TopTif-457
❑ 89Don-502
❑ 89Fle-40
❑ 89FleGlo-40
❑ 89MetColP-38
❑ 89Sco-431
❑ 89ScoRoo-24T
❑ 89Top-207
❑ 89TopBig-96
❑ 89TopTif-207
❑ 89TopTra-69T
❑ 89TopTraT-69T
❑ 89UppDec-288
❑ 90Don-534
❑ 90Fle-111
❑ 90FleCan-111
❑ 90Lea-360
❑ 90OPC-508
❑ 90Sco-502
❑ 90ScoRoo-43T
❑ 90Top-508
❑ 90TopTif-508
❑ 90TopTra-57T
❑ 90TopTraT-57T
❑ 90UppDec-642
❑ 91Bow-340
❑ 91DodPho-18
❑ 91Don-715
❑ 91Fle-616
❑ 91MetWIZ-227
❑ 91Sco-556
❑ 91StaClu-397
❑ 92Don-484
❑ 92Fle-208
❑ 92Lea-486
❑ 92LeaBlaG-486
❑ 92OPC-644
❑ 92Sco-296

❑ 92StaClu-778
❑ 92StaCluECN-778
❑ 92Top-644
❑ 92TopGol-644
❑ 92TopGolW-644
❑ 92TopMic-644
❑ 92UppDec-311
❑ 92WhiSoxK-34
❑ 93Don-720
❑ 93Fle-585
❑ 93Sco-479
❑ 93Top-443
❑ 93TopGol-443
❑ 93TopInaM-443
❑ 93TopInaR-443
❑ 93TopMic-443
❑ 93UppDec-418
❑ 93UppDecGold-418
❑ 93WhiSoxK-18
❑ 93WhiSoxSC-29
❑ 94Don-441

Leach, Thomas
❑ 03BreE10-87
❑ 03WilCarE-20
❑ 06FanCraNL-25
❑ 08AmeCarE91-81
❑ 08RosComP-153
❑ 09AmeCarE90-1-68
❑ 09AmeCarE90-1-69
❑ 09ColChiE-166
❑ 09PhiCarE-13
❑ 09SpoNewSM-24
❑ 10CouT21-168
❑ 10CouT21-169
❑ 10CouT21-170
❑ 10DarChoE-22
❑ 10DomDisP-67
❑ 10E12AmeCDCE125-21
❑ 10JuJuDE-24
❑ 10NadE1-29
❑ 10PirAmeCE-5
❑ 10PirHerICP-7
❑ 10PirTipTD-5
❑ 10RedCroT-41
❑ 10RedCroT-130
❑ 10StaCarE-20
❑ 10SweCapPP-138
❑ 10SweCapPP-138
❑ 11E94-20
❑ 11HelSta-161
❑ 11MecDFT-23
❑ 11PinT-5-859
❑ 11S74Sil-111
❑ 11SpoLifCW-215
❑ 11T205-97
❑ 12ColRedB-166
❑ 12ColTinT-166
❑ 12HasTriFT-30C
❑ 12T207-101
❑ 14CraJacE-41
❑ 14FatPlaT-23
❑ 14PieStaT-62
❑ 15CraJacE-41
❑ 95ConTSN-1368

Leader, Ramon
❑ 77CocAstT-11
❑ 78DayBeaAT-13

Leahy, Pat
❑ 92ClaDraP-114
❑ 92EriSaiC-14
❑ 92EriSaiF-1615
❑ 93KanCouCC-10
❑ 93KanCouCF-912
❑ 93KanCouCTI-11
❑ 93Top-641
❑ 93TopGol-641
❑ 93TopInaM-641
❑ 93TopInaR-641
❑ 93TopMic-641
❑ 94BreCouMC-7
❑ 94BreCouMF-5
❑ 94FloStaLAF-FSL27
❑ 95PorSeaDTI-11

Leahy, Tom (Thomas)
❑ 91MacBraC-3
❑ 91MacBraP-857
❑ 92DurBulC-18
❑ 92DurBulF-1095
❑ 92DurBulTI-25
❑ 93DurBulC-12
❑ 93DurBulF-482
❑ 93DurBulTI-20

Leake, Albert
❑ 17Zee-51
❑ 18Zee-47

Leake, Jon
❑ 85MiaHur-8
❑ 87SalLakTTT-24

Leal, Carlos
❑ 80UtiBluJT-27
❑ 80VenLeaS-54

Leal, Luis
❑ 80SyrChiTI-14
❑ 80VenLeaS-64
❑ 81OPC-238
❑ 81Top-577
❑ 82Don-255
❑ 82Fle-617
❑ 82OPC-368
❑ 82OPCPos-9
❑ 82Top-412
❑ 83Don-129
❑ 83Fle-432
❑ 83OPC-109
❑ 83Top-109
❑ 84AllGamPI-173
❑ 84BluJayFS-23
❑ 84Don-485
❑ 84Fle-160
❑ 84Nes792-783
❑ 84OPC-207
❑ 84Top-783
❑ 84TopSti-371
❑ 84TopTif-783
❑ 85BluJayFS-19
❑ 85Don-317
❑ 85Fle-113
❑ 85Lea-29
❑ 85OPC-31
❑ 85Top-622
❑ 85TopSti-361
❑ 85TopTif-622
❑ 86Don-315
❑ 86OPC-365
❑ 86SyrChiP-16
❑ 86Top-459
❑ 86TopTif-459
❑ 88SyrChiP-806
❑ 93LinVenB-112
❑ 95LinVen-190
❑ 96-97LinVen-57

Leaman, Jeff
❑ 95BatCliTI-20

Leandro, Francisco
❑ 80VenLeaS-195

Leard, Bill
❑ 09ObaT21-373
❑ 12HomRunKE-23
❑ 12ObaPreT-122
❑ 12PCLPin-12
❑ 12Zee-37
❑ 13Zee-38
❑ 14Zee-139
❑ 15Zee-111
❑ 27Zee-29
❑ 70MetMusoAB-5
❑ 90DodTar-1011

Leary, Rob
❑ 87WesPalBEP-652
❑ 88RocExpLC-22
❑ 89WesPalBES-15
❑ 90LSUTigGM-8
❑ 90RocExpLC-15
❑ 90RocExpP-2697
❑ 92MadMusC-6
❑ 92MadMusF-1243
❑ 92RocExpC-28
❑ 92RocExpF-2131
❑ 93MadMusC-18
❑ 93MadMusF-1829
❑ 93WesPalBEC-26
❑ 93WesPalBEF-1357
❑ 94WesPalBEC-28
❑ 94WesPalBEF-58
❑ 95LynHilTI-13

Leary, Tim
❑ 97UCLBruTI-29

Leary, Timothy
❑ 82Top-623
❑ 83TidTidT-9
❑ 84JacMetF-7
❑ 85VanCanC-203
❑ 86BrePol-39
❑ 86Don-577
❑ 86TopTra-64T
❑ 86TopTraT-64T
❑ 87DodMot-21
❑ 87DodPho-9
❑ 87DodPol-11
❑ 87Don-232
❑ 87Fle-348
❑ 87FleGlo-348
❑ 87Top-32
❑ 87TopTif-32
❑ 87TopTra-64T
❑ 87TopTraT-64T
❑ 88AlaGolAA70TI-20
❑ 88DodMot-21
❑ 88DodPol-54
❑ 88Fle-521
❑ 88FleGlo-521
❑ 88Sco-224
❑ 88ScoGlo-224
❑ 88Top-367
❑ 88TopTif-367
❑ 89Bow-339
❑ 89BowTif-339
❑ 89DodMot-21
❑ 89DodPol-28
❑ 89Don-552
❑ 89DonBasB-309
❑ 89Fle-65
❑ 89FleExcS-30
❑ 89FleGlo-65
❑ 89OPC-249
❑ 89PanSti-99
❑ 89Sco-429
❑ 89ScoHot1S-9
❑ 89ScoRoo-52T
❑ 89Spo-81
❑ 89Top-249
❑ 89TopBig-17
❑ 89TopSti-62
❑ 89TopTif-249
❑ 89UppDec-94
❑ 90Bow-429
❑ 90BowTif-429
❑ 90DodTar-439
❑ 90Don-670
❑ 90DonBesA-53
❑ 90Fle-424
❑ 90FleCan-424
❑ 90Lea-148
❑ 90OPC-516
❑ 90PubIntS-12
❑ 90Sco-504
❑ 90ScoRoo-27T
❑ 90Top-516
❑ 90TopTif-516
❑ 90TopTra-58T
❑ 90TopTraT-58T
❑ 90TopTVY-12
❑ 90UppDec-662
❑ 90UppDec-705
❑ 90YanScoNW-13
❑ 91Don-67
❑ 91Fle-670
❑ 91Lea-206
❑ 91MetWIZ-228
❑ 91OPC-161
❑ 91Sco-631
❑ 91StaClu-423
❑ 91Stu-95
❑ 91Top-161
❑ 91TopDesS-161
❑ 91TopMic-161
❑ 91TopTif-161
❑ 91Ult-236
❑ 91UppDec-693
❑ 92Don-433
❑ 92Fle-235
❑ 92OPC-778
❑ 92Pin-349
❑ 92Sco-286
❑ 92StaClu-291
❑ 92Top-778
❑ 92TopGol-778
❑ 92TopGolW-778
❑ 92TopMic-778
❑ 92Ult-411
❑ 93Don-289
❑ 93Fle-677
❑ 93MarMot-21
❑ 93PacSpa-624
❑ 94BreMilB-144
❑ 94Don-240
❑ 94Fle-291
❑ 94Sco-240
❑ 94ScoGolR-240

Leatherman, Jeff
❑ 91WelPirC-17
❑ 91WelPirP-3580
❑ 92AugPirC-22

Leathers, Harold
❑ 18Zee-11

Leatherwood, Anthony
❑ 90GeoColC-18

Leatherwood, Del
❑ 78DayBeaAT-14
❑ 80ColAstT-5
❑ 81TucTorT-2

Leavell, Gregg
❑ 91WelPirC-12
❑ 91WelPirP-3586

Lebak, David
❑ 91SpoIndC-7
❑ 91SpoIndP-3960
❑ 92ChaRaiC-14
❑ 92ChaRaiF-133

Lebejko, David
❑ 97EugEmeB-9

LeBlanc, Eric
❑ 98BurBeeM-12

LeBlanc, Michael
❑ 88CapCodPPaLP-61
❑ 89BelMarL-7

LeBlanc, Richie
❑ 88BasCitRS-16
❑ 88FloStaLAS-42
❑ 90MemChiB-16
❑ 90MemChiP-1024
❑ 90MemChiS-14

Lebo, Mike
❑ 78DunBluJT-15

LeBoeuf, Alan
❑ 85PorBeaC-32
❑ 86PorBeaP-13
❑ 87MaiGuiP-22
❑ 87MaiGuiT-13
❑ 88ReaPhiP-864
❑ 89MarPhiS-35
❑ 90ClePhiS-27
❑ 91LinDriAA-525
❑ 91ReaPhiLD-525
❑ 91ReaPhiP-1386
❑ 92ScrRedBF-2463
❑ 92ScrRedBS-500
❑ 93BatCliCB-29
❑ 93BatCliF-3163
❑ 94BatCliC-27
❑ 94BatCliF-3464
❑ 97ReaPhi-1
❑ 98ReaPhiM-2
❑ 98ReaPhiUM-28

LeBourveau, DeWitt
❑ 28Zee-95

Lebron, David
❑ 78NewWayCT-25

LeBron, Jesus
❑ 98St.CatSM-27

LeBron, Jose
❑ 89BlaYNPRWL-142
❑ 89WatDiaP-1775
❑ 89WatDiaS-17
❑ 90Bes-37
❑ 90WatDiaB-27
❑ 90WatDiaP-2375
❑ 91HigDesMC-6
❑ 91HigDesMP-2389
❑ 92HigDesMC-22

LeBron, Juan
❑ 95Bes-127
❑ 95BowBes-X5
❑ 95BowBesR-X5
❑ 95SPML-108
❑ 95TopTra-12T
❑ 96Exc-61
❑ 96Top-17
❑ 96TopPowB-17
❑ 97SpoIndG-16
❑ 98BesAutSS-28
❑ 98Bow-414
❑ 98BowChr-414
❑ 98BowChrGA-414
❑ 98BowChrGAR-414
❑ 98BowChrI-414
❑ 98BowChrIR-414
❑ 98BowChrR-414
❑ 98BowGolA-414
❑ 98BowInt-414
❑ 98LanLugQ-27
❑ 99SP TopP-23
❑ 99SP TopPPE-23

Lebron, Ruben
❑ 96LowSpiB-15
❑ 96MicBatCB-14
❑ 97LowSpiB-13

Leclair, Keith
❑ 88IdaFalBP-1850

LeClair, Morgan
❑ 90WicStaSGD-22

LeClair, Paul
❑ 94KinMetC-8
❑ 94KinMetF-3835
❑ 95PitMetTI-35

LeClaire, Frenchy (George)
❑ 12ImpTobC-3

LeCronier, Jason
❑ 96HigDesMB-17
❑ 97FreKey-14
❑ 98FreKeyM-29
❑ 98St.PetDRM-25

LeCroy, Matt
❑ 98BesNumOP-31
❑ 98Bow-405
❑ 98BowChr-405
❑ 98BowChrGA-405
❑ 98BowChrGAR-405
❑ 98BowChrI-405
❑ 98BowChrIR-405
❑ 98BowChrR-405
❑ 98BowGolA-405
❑ 98BowInt-405
❑ 98ForWayW!-4
❑ 98MidLeaPM-10
❑ 99BasAmeTPA-24
❑ 99Bow-210
❑ 99BowChr-210
❑ 99BowChrG-210
❑ 99BowChrGR-210
❑ 99BowChrI-210
❑ 99BowChrIR-210
❑ 99BowChrR-210
❑ 99BowGol-210
❑ 99BowInt-210
❑ 99TeaBesRA-14
❑ 99Top-431
❑ 99TopChr-431
❑ 99TopChrR-431
❑ 99TopMVPP-431

Ledbetter, Blake
❑ 97JohCitCTI-21
❑ 98JohCCTI-20

Ledbetter, Gary
❑ 77CedRapGT-9

Ledbetter, Jeff
❑ 86ArkTraP-11

Leddon, Charles
❑ 95PitMetTI-NNO

Ledduke, Dan
❑ 79WesHavYT-9
❑ 80NasSouTI-12
❑ 81NasSouTI-7

Ledee, Ricky
❑ 90TamYanD-14
❑ 92GulCoaYF-3702
❑ 93OneYanC-13
❑ 93OneYanF-3516
❑ 94GreBatF-488
❑ 94SouAtlLAF-SAL15
❑ 95GreBatTI-14
❑ 96NorNavB-16
❑ 97Bes-81
❑ 97BesAutSBPP-14
❑ 97BesAutSC-5
❑ 97BesLum-9
❑ 97Bow98ROY-ROY9
❑ 97BowBes-191
❑ 97BowBesAR-191
❑ 97BowBesR-191
❑ 97BowChr-103
❑ 97BowChr1RFR-ROY9
❑ 97BowChr98RF-ROY9
❑ 97BowChrI-103
❑ 97BowChrIR-103
❑ 97BowChrR-103
❑ 97ColCliB-15
❑ 97ColCliD-11
❑ 97Fle-560
❑ 97FleTif-560
❑ 97GreBatC-13
❑ 97Ult-458
❑ 97UltGolME-458
❑ 97UltPlaME-458
❑ 98Bes-22
❑ 98Bow-105
❑ 98BowBes-139
❑ 98BowBesAR-139
❑ 98BowBesR-139
❑ 98BowCerBlueAU-3
❑ 98BowCerGA-3
❑ 98BowCerSA-3
❑ 98BowChr-105
❑ 98BowChrGA-105
❑ 98BowChrGAR-105
❑ 98BowChrI-105
❑ 98BowChrIR-105
❑ 98BowChrR-105
❑ 98BowGolA-105
❑ 98BowInt-105
❑ 98BowScoC-SC11
❑ 98CirThu-36
❑ 98CirThuRav-36
❑ 98CirThuSupRav-36
❑ 98ColCliD-16
❑ 98ColCliM-20
❑ 98CroRoy-96
❑ 98CroRoyDK-16
❑ 98Don-314
❑ 98DonColE-513
❑ 98DonColL-389
❑ 98DonEli-113
❑ 98DonEliA-113
❑ 98DonEliS-113
❑ 98DonGolPP-314
❑ 98DonPriCE-513
❑ 98DonPriCL-389
❑ 98DonSig-95
❑ 98DonSigA-52
❑ 98DonSigAC-70
❑ 98DonSigAM-71
❑ 98DonSigP-95
❑ 98DonSilPP-314
❑ 98E-X2-90
❑ 98E-X2ECFut-90
❑ 98E-X2ECNow-90
❑ 98E-X2Sig2001-1
❑ 98FlaShoLeg0-29
❑ 98FlaShoLeg1-29
❑ 98FlaShoLeg2-29
❑ 98FlaShoLeg3-29
❑ 98FlaShoLegM-29
❑ 98FlaShoR0-29
❑ 98FlaShoR1-29
❑ 98FlaShoR2-29
❑ 98FlaShoR3-29
❑ 98Lea-190
❑ 98LeaFraDA-190
❑ 98LeaFraF-190
❑ 98LeaFraM-190
❑ 98LeaFraM-190
❑ 98LeaFraMDC-190
❑ 98LeaFraMDC-190
❑ 98LeaFraMZ2-190
❑ 98LeaRCrusUP-120
❑ 98LeaRS-261
❑ 98LeaRSCrusUG-120
❑ 98LeaRSCrusUR-120
❑ 98LeaRSLHolo-261
❑ 98LeaRSLong-261
❑ 98LeaRTrue-261
❑ 98MetUni-43
❑ 98MetUniPMG-43
❑ 98PinPer-133
❑ 98PinPerPP-133
❑ 98RevoRooHH-14
❑ 98RevoRooHHG-14
❑ 98SkyDugA-110
❑ 98SkyDugAIA-110
❑ 98SP MinPE-87
❑ 98SP SPTSC-RL
❑ 98SPMin-87
❑ 98SpoIll-166
❑ 98SpoIllEE-166
❑ 98SpoIllFE-166
❑ 98Stu-22
❑ 98StuGPP-22
❑ 98StuSPP-22
❑ 98Ult-238
❑ 98UltGolM-238
❑ 98UltMas-238
❑ 98UltPlaM-238
❑ 98UppDecDS-DS36
❑ 99Bow-101
❑ 99BowAut-BA44
❑ 99BowBes-131
❑ 99BowBesAR-131
❑ 99BowBesR-131
❑ 99BowChr-101
❑ 99BowChrG-101
❑ 99BowChrGR-101
❑ 99BowChrI-101
❑ 99BowChrIR-101
❑ 99BowChrR-101
❑ 99BowChrSC-SC18
❑ 99BowChrSCR-SC18
❑ 99BowGol-101
❑ 99BowInt-101
❑ 99BowScoC-SC18
❑ 99DumSet-128
❑ 99E-X Cen-45
❑ 99E-X CenECFut-45
❑ 99E-X CenECNow-45
❑ 99E-XCenA-7
❑ 99FlaShoLeg1-118

❑ 99FlaShoLeg2-118
❑ 99FlaShoLeg3-118
❑ 99FlaShoLegM1-118
❑ 99FlaShoLegM2-118
❑ 99FlaShoLegM3-118
❑ 99FlaShoR1-118
❑ 99FlaShoR2-118
❑ 99FlaShoR3-118
❑ 99FlaShoWotF-8
❑ 99Fle-225
❑ 99FleBri-158
❑ 99FleBri2G-158
❑ 99FleBriBlu-158
❑ 99FleBriGol-158
❑ 99FleBril-8
❑ 99FleMys-128
❑ 99FleMysM-128
❑ 99FleSta9-225
❑ 99FleWarT-225
❑ 99MetUniN-4
❑ 99PacCroC-191
❑ 99PacCroCPB-191
❑ 99SkyMolM-41
❑ 99SkyMolMX-41
❑ 99SkyPreA-36
❑ 99SkyPreABlue-36
❑ 99SkyThu-275
❑ 99SkyThuRant-275
❑ 99SkyThuRave-275
❑ 99SP Aut-112
❑ 99SP AutC-RL
❑ 99SP AutCG-RL
❑ 99SPSig-118
❑ 99SPx-110
❑ 99SPxFinR-110
❑ 99SPxFinS-110
❑ 99StaClu-354
❑ 99StaCluFDI-354
❑ 99StaCluOoaK-354
❑ 99StaCluPP-354
❑ 99ThuSkySupR-275
❑ 99Top-206
❑ 99Top-233
❑ 99Top-421
❑ 99TopChr-206
❑ 99TopChr-233
❑ 99TopChr-421
❑ 99TopChrR-206
❑ 99TopChrR-233
❑ 99TopChrR-421
❑ 99TopMVPP-421
❑ 99UD Cho-4
❑ 99UD ChoPCR-4
❑ 99UppDec-434
❑ 99UppDecEL1-434
❑ 99UppDecEL2-434
❑ 99UppDecM-147
❑ 99UppDecMGS-147
❑ 99UppDecMHFS-147
❑ 99UppDecMP-RL
❑ 99UppDecMSS-147
❑ 99Vic-263
❑ 99YanFle-23

Ledeit, Richard

❑ 96OgdRapTI-49

Ledesma, Aaron

❑ 90KinMetB-1
❑ 90KinMetS-13
❑ 91ColMetPI-13
❑ 91ColMetPPI-6
❑ 91ColMetPPI-6
❑ 92ClaFS7-275
❑ 92St.LucMCB-17
❑ 92St.LucMF-1755
❑ 93BinMetF-2342
❑ 93Bow-102
❑ 94NorTidF-2927
❑ 95NorTidTI-17
❑ 95SigRoo-31
❑ 95SigRooSig-31
❑ 96MetKah-20
❑ 96Sco-507
❑ 96VanCanB-19
❑ 97RocRedW-17
❑ 98DevRayP-16
❑ 98Pac-27
❑ 98PacOnl-711
❑ 98PacOnlR-711
❑ 98PacOnlWC-711
❑ 98PacPlaB-27
❑ 98PacRedT-27
❑ 98PacSil-27
❑ 99Fle-413
❑ 99FleSta9-413
❑ 99FleWarT-413
❑ 99Pac-412
❑ 99PacAur-185
❑ 99PacAurOD-185
❑ 99PacCroC-275
❑ 99PacCroCPB-275
❑ 99PacPlaB-412
❑ 99PacPri-139
❑ 99PacPriHB-139
❑ 99PacPriHG-139
❑ 99PacPriHM-139
❑ 99PacPriHP-139
❑ 99PacPriRed-139
❑ 99PacRed-412

Ledesma, Phil

❑ 98LowSpiM-11

Ledezma, Carlos

❑ 75WesPalBES-8
❑ 81BufBisT-8
❑ 82PorBeaT-26
❑ 84HawIsIC-143
❑ 86HawIsIP-15
❑ 87VanCanP-1601
❑ 88BufBisP-1481
❑ 88TriAAAP-48
❑ 89BufBisC-3
❑ 89BufBisP-1678
❑ 90BufBisTI-13

Ledinsky, Ray

❑ 91MiaMirC-22
❑ 91MiaMirP-416

Leduc, Jean

❑ 78ChaPirT-12

Ledwick, Shannon

❑ 91IdaFalBP-4324
❑ 91IdaFalBSP-16

Lee, Annabel

❑ 94UppDecTAE-53
❑ 94UppDecTAELD-LD8

Lee, Anthony

❑ 92AppFoxCB-7
❑ 92AppFoxFI-981
❑ 93PeoChiC-11
❑ 93PeoChiF-1081
❑ 93PeoChiTI-14
❑ 94DayCubC-15

Lee, Ben

❑ 87AppFoxP-13

Lee, Bob

❑ 64Top-502
❑ 65OPC-46
❑ 65Top-46
❑ 66AngDexP-7
❑ 66Top-481
❑ 67Top-313
❑ 68Kah-B20
❑ 68Top-543
❑ 85VisOakT-15
❑ 86AngGreT-11
❑ 86KenTwiP-12
❑ 87VisOakP-6
❑ 88KenTwiP-1403
❑ 89KenTwiP-1058
❑ 90DodTar-440

Lee, Calvin

❑ 95OdgRapTI-14

Lee, Carlos

❑ 96BesAutS-48
❑ 96Exc-33
❑ 96HicCraB-11
❑ 96HicCraB-30
❑ 97CalLeaATI-34
❑ 97CarLeaTP-25
❑ 98Bes-23
❑ 98BirBarG-16
❑ 98BirBarG-17
❑ 98Bow-428
❑ 98BowBes-154
❑ 98BowBesAR-154
❑ 98BowBesR-154
❑ 98BowChr-428
❑ 98BowChrGA-428
❑ 98BowChrGAR-428
❑ 98BowChrI-428
❑ 98BowChrIR-428
❑ 98BowChrR-428
❑ 98BowGolA-428
❑ 98BowInt-428
❑ 98DonSig-135
❑ 98DonSigP-135
❑ 98LeaRS-227
❑ 98LeaRSLHolo-227
❑ 98LeaRSLong-227
❑ 98LeaRTrue-227
❑ 98SouLeaTPG-14
❑ 98SP MinPE-38
❑ 98SP MinSTHPE-H7
❑ 98SPMin-38
❑ 98SPMinSTH-H7
❑ 98UppDec-556
❑ 98UppDecDS-DS33
❑ 99199Fin-279
❑ 99BasAmeTP-60
❑ 99BasAmeTPA-25
❑ 99BasAmeTPG-60
❑ 99Bow-320
❑ 99BowBes-123
❑ 99BowBesAR-123
❑ 99BowBesR-123
❑ 99BowChrSC-SC10
❑ 99BowChrSCR-SC10
❑ 99BowGol-320
❑ 99BowInt-320
❑ 99BowScoC-SC10
❑ 99FinGolRef-279
❑ 99FinRef-279
❑ 99PacOme-57
❑ 99PacOme5T-6
❑ 99PacOme5TT-6
❑ 99PacOmeC-57
❑ 99PacOmeG-57
❑ 99PacOmePB-57
❑ 99Rev-33
❑ 99RevPremDate-33
❑ 99RevRet-33
❑ 99RevShaSS-33
❑ 99SkyPre-249
❑ 99SkyPre-249
❑ 99SkyPreDD-14
❑ 99SkyPreR-249
❑ 99SkyPreR-249
❑ 99SP SigAuto-CL
❑ 99SP SigAutoG-CL
❑ 99SP TopP-73
❑ 99SP TopPC-CL
❑ 99SP TopPDtS-D18
❑ 99SP TopPGF-GF18
❑ 99SP TopPPE-73
❑ 99SPSig-27
❑ 99StaClu-355
❑ 99StaCluFDI-355
❑ 99StaCluOoaK-355
❑ 99StaCluPP-355
❑ 99Top-425
❑ 99TopAll-AM23
❑ 99TopChr-425
❑ 99TopChrA-AE23
❑ 99TopChrAR-AE23
❑ 99TopChrR-425
❑ 99TopGal-143
❑ 99TopGalPP-143
❑ 99TopGalPPI-143
❑ 99TopTekFP-F5
❑ 99UppDec-340
❑ 99UppDecEL1-340
❑ 99UppDecEL2-340
❑ 99UppDecM-51
❑ 99UppDecMGS-51
❑ 99UppDecMHFS-51
❑ 99UppDecMSS-51
❑ 99Vic-89

Lee, Charles

❑ 92JamExpC-12
❑ 92JamExpF-1513
❑ 94BurBeeC-13
❑ 94WesPalBEC-16
❑ 94WesPalBEF-56

Lee, Chong Bum

❑ 90IBAWorA-18

Lee, Chris

❑ 88AshTouP-1059

Lee, Corey

❑ 97Bow-376
❑ 97BowChr-250
❑ 97BowChrI-250
❑ 97BowChrIR-250
❑ 97BowChrR-250
❑ 97BowInt-376
❑ 97Top-270
❑ 98Bes-24
❑ 98Bow-198
❑ 98BowCerBlueAU-37
❑ 98BowCerGA-37
❑ 98BowCerSA-37
❑ 98BowChr-198
❑ 98BowChrGA-198
❑ 98BowChrGAR-198
❑ 98BowChrI-198
❑ 98BowChrIR-198
❑ 98BowChrR-198
❑ 98BowGolA-198
❑ 98BowInt-198
❑ 98SP MinDTSPE-DS23
❑ 98SP MinPE-123
❑ 98SP SPTSC-CL
❑ 98SPMin-123
❑ 98SPMinDTS-DS23
❑ 98TexLeaTPG-19
❑ 98Top-486
❑ 98TopChr-486
❑ 98TopChrR-486
❑ 98TopDevR-486
❑ 98TopDia-486
❑ 98TopMiniC-486
❑ 98TulDriTI-7
❑ 99BasAmeTP-61
❑ 99BasAmeTPA-26
❑ 99BasAmeTPG-61
❑ 99Bow-122
❑ 99BowChr-122
❑ 99BowChrG-122
❑ 99BowChrGR-122
❑ 99BowChrI-122
❑ 99BowChrIR-122
❑ 99BowChrR-122
❑ 99BowGol-122
❑ 99BowInt-122
❑ 99JustheS-31
❑ 99JustheSJB-31
❑ 99JustheSJD-7
❑ 99TeaBesRA-15

Lee, David

❑ 87RocRedWT-14
❑ 88RocRedWC-17
❑ 96PorRocB-18
❑ 97AshTou-14
❑ 98CarLeaAC-26
❑ 98CarLeaTPQ-16
❑ 98SalAvaC-16

Lee, Derek

❑ 88UtiBluSP-7
❑ 89SouBenWSGS-27
❑ 90Bes-144
❑ 90BirBarB-10
❑ 90BirBarP-1118
❑ 90CMC-769
❑ 91BirBarLD-66
❑ 91BirBarP-1466
❑ 91Cla/Bes-272
❑ 91LinDriAA-66
❑ 92Bow-210
❑ 92SkyAAAF-285
❑ 92UppDecML-148
❑ 92VanCanF-2733
❑ 92VanCanS-642
❑ 93Bow-335
❑ 93PorBeaF-2394
❑ 94OttLynF-2908
❑ 95NorTidTI-18
❑ 96OklCit8B-13
❑ 97LasVegS1A-21
❑ 98RocRedWQ-17
❑ 98StoPorG-15

Lee, Derrek

❑ 94ActPac-35
❑ 94Bow-232
❑ 94Cla-130
❑ 94ClaGolF-64
❑ 94ClaGolN1PLF-LP8
❑ 94ClaGolREF-RE8
❑ 94ClaTriF-T67
❑ 94ColC-645
❑ 94ColChoGS-645
❑ 94ColChoSS-645
❑ 94Pin-438
❑ 94PinArtP-438
❑ 94PinMusC-438
❑ 94RanCucQC-1
❑ 94RanCucQF-1645
❑ 94Sco-585
❑ 94ScoGolR-585
❑ 94SP-10
❑ 94SPDieC-10
❑ 94UppDec-539
❑ 94UppDecED-539
❑ 94UppDecML-116
❑ 95ARuFalLS-13
❑ 95Bes-100
❑ 95Bes-102
❑ 95BesFra-F10
❑ 95Bow-25
❑ 95BowBes-B22
❑ 95BowBesR-B22
❑ 95Exc-286
❑ 95RanCucQT-34
❑ 95SPML-140
❑ 95SPMLA-17
❑ 95SPMLDtS-DS12
❑ 95UppDecML-66
❑ 95UppDecMLFS-66
❑ 96Bow-278
❑ 96BowBes-160
❑ 96BowBesAR-160
❑ 96BowBesR-160
❑ 96BowFoi-278
❑ 96DouAllB-36
❑ 96Exc-238
❑ 96MemChiB-22
❑ 96Top-424
❑ 97Bes-8
❑ 97BesAutSBPP-19
❑ 97BesAutSC-11
❑ 97BesCarCSP-10
❑ 97BesDiaB-9
❑ 97BesLum-3
❑ 97Bow-292
❑ 97Bow98ROY-ROY11
❑ 97BowBes-178
❑ 97BowBesAR-178
❑ 97BowBesMI-MI2
❑ 97BowBesMIAR-MI2
❑ 97BowBesMIARI-MI2
❑ 97BowBesMII-MI2
❑ 97BowBesMIR-MI2
❑ 97BowBesMIRI-MI2
❑ 97BowBesR-178
❑ 97BowCerBlaIA-CA47
❑ 97BowCerBluIA-CA47
❑ 97BowCerGolIA-CA47
❑ 97BowChr-200
❑ 97BowChr1RFR-ROY11
❑ 97BowChr98RF-ROY11
❑ 97BowChrI-200
❑ 97BowChrIR-200
❑ 97BowChrR-200
❑ 97BowChrSHR-SHR9
❑ 97BowChrSHRR-SHR9
❑ 97BowInt-292
❑ 97BowScoHR-9
❑ 97ColCho-476
❑ 97Don-383
❑ 97DonGolPP-383
❑ 97DonLim-96
❑ 97DonLim-100
❑ 97DonLimE-96
❑ 97DonLimE-100
❑ 97DonLimENG-96
❑ 97DonSigA-66
❑ 97DonSigAC-80
❑ 97DonSigAM-80
❑ 97DonSilPP-383
❑ 97FlaShoLC-80
❑ 97FlaShoLeg0-80
❑ 97FlaShoLeg1-80
❑ 97FlaShoM-A80
❑ 97FlaShoM-B80
❑ 97FlaShoM-C80
❑ 97FlaShoR0-80
❑ 97FlaShoR1-80
❑ 97FlaShoR2-80
❑ 97Fle-620
❑ 97FleTif-620
❑ 97LasVegS1A-22
❑ 97Lea-321
❑ 97LeaFraM-321
❑ 97LeaFraMDC-321
❑ 97Sel-128
❑ 97SelArtP-128
❑ 97SelCom-128
❑ 97SelRegG-128
❑ 97SP-9
❑ 97Top-489
❑ 97Ult-541
❑ 97UltGolME-541
❑ 97UltGolP-10
❑ 97UltPlaME-541
❑ 97UppDec-543
❑ 98Bow-267
❑ 98BowBes-192
❑ 98BowBesAR-192
❑ 98BowBesR-192
❑ 98BowCerBlueAU-69
❑ 98BowCerGA-69
❑ 98BowCerSA-69
❑ 98BowChr-267
❑ 98BowChrGA-267
❑ 98BowChrGAR-267
❑ 98BowChrI-267
❑ 98BowChrIR-267
❑ 98BowChrR-267
❑ 98BowGolA-267
❑ 98BowInt-267
❑ 98CirThu-272
❑ 98CirThuRav-272
❑ 98CirThuSupRav-272
❑ 98ColCho-226
❑ 98ColCho-375
❑ 98ColChoSQ-SQ19
❑ 98CroRoy-59
❑ 98Don-280
❑ 98DonCol-189
❑ 98DonColE-511
❑ 98DonColL-298
❑ 98DonColP-713
❑ 98DonColS-184
❑ 98DonEli-111
❑ 98DonEliA-111
❑ 98DonEliS-111
❑ 98DonGolPP-280
❑ 98DonPre-163
❑ 98DonPreSeat-163
❑ 98DonPriCD-189
❑ 98DonPriCE-511
❑ 98DonPriCL-298
❑ 98DonPriCP-713
❑ 98DonRatR-14
❑ 98DonRatRM-14
❑ 98DonRooDK-5
❑ 98DonRooDKC-5
❑ 98DonSig-96
❑ 98DonSigA-53
❑ 98DonSigAC-71
❑ 98DonSigAM-72
❑ 98DonSigP-96
❑ 98DonSilPP-280
❑ 98Fin-245
❑ 98FinNo--245
❑ 98FinNo-R-245
❑ 98FinRef-245
❑ 98FlaShoWotF-8
❑ 98Fle-24
❑ 98Fle-383
❑ 98FleProF-PF11
❑ 98FleVin'-94
❑ 98FleVin'C-94
❑ 98Lea-99
❑ 98LeaFraDA-99
❑ 98LeaFraF-99
❑ 98LeaFraM-99
❑ 98LeaFraM-99
❑ 98LeaFraMDC-99
❑ 98LeaFraMDC-99
❑ 98LeaFraMS-99
❑ 98LeaFraMZ2-99
❑ 98LeaRCrusUP-122
❑ 98LeaRS-263
❑ 98LeaRSCrusUG-122
❑ 98LeaRSCrusUR-122
❑ 98LeaRSFOSamp-18
❑ 98LeaRSFresh-18
❑ 98LeaRSLHolo-263
❑ 98LeaRSLong-263
❑ 98LeaRTrue-263
❑ 98MetUni-10
❑ 98MetUniPMG-10
❑ 98PacAur-132
❑ 98PacOme-99
❑ 98PacOmeOnIns-29
❑ 98PacOmeR-99
❑ 98PacOmeRS-27
❑ 98PacOmeRST2-27
❑ 98PacOnl-300
❑ 98PacOnl-308
❑ 98PacOnlR-300
❑ 98PacOnlR-308
❑ 98PacOnlWC-300
❑ 98PacOnlWC-308
❑ 98PacPar-163
❑ 98PacParC-163
❑ 98PacParG-163
❑ 98PacParHS-163
❑ 98PacParPB-163
❑ 98PacParR-163
❑ 98Pin-164
❑ 98PinArtP-PP67
❑ 98PinIns-117
❑ 98PinInsCE-117
❑ 98PinInsDE-117
❑ 98PinMusC-PP67
❑ 98PinPer-112
❑ 98PinPerPP-112
❑ 98PinPlu-71
❑ 98PinPreP-164
❑ 98Revo-62
❑ 98RevoRooHH-7
❑ 98RevoRooHHG-7
❑ 98RevoSS-62
❑ 98Sco-235
❑ 98ScoRT-220
❑ 98ScoRTSS-PP122
❑ 98ScoRTSSAP-PP122
❑ 98ScoRTSSAP1-PP122

❑ 98SkyDugA-112
❑ 98SkyDugAIA-112
❑ 98SP Aut-22
❑ 98SpolllTaN-148
❑ 98SpolllTaNEE-148
❑ 98SpolllWSF-126
❑ 98SpolllWSFEE-126
❑ 98SpolllWSFFE-126
❑ 98SPxFin-210
❑ 98SPxFinR-210
❑ 98SPxFinS-210
❑ 98StaCluFDI-85
❑ 98StaClul-85
❑ 98StaCluITW-W9
❑ 98StaCluOneK-85
❑ 98StaCluPP-85
❑ 98StaCluPP-336
❑ 98Stu-129
❑ 98StuGPP-129
❑ 98StuSPP-129
❑ 98TopChrRC-R6
❑ 98TopChrRCRef-R6
❑ 98TopRooCla-R6
❑ 98TopSta-98
❑ 98TopStaB-98
❑ 98TopStaG-98
❑ 98TopStaGR-98
❑ 98TopStaS-98
❑ 98TopStaSB-S5
❑ 98TopStaSG-S5
❑ 98TopStaSGR-S5
❑ 98TopStaSS-S5
❑ 98TopTek-76
❑ 98TopTekD-76
❑ 98UD3-30
❑ 98UD3-120
❑ 98UD3-210
❑ 98UD3DieCut-30
❑ 98UD3DieCut-120
❑ 98UD3DieCut-210
❑ 98Ult-241
❑ 98Ult-294
❑ 98UltGolM-241
❑ 98UltGolM-294
❑ 98UltMas-241
❑ 98UltMas-294
❑ 98UltPlaM-241
❑ 98UltPlaM-294
❑ 98UppDec-213
❑ 98UppDec-680
❑ 98UppDecDS-DS38
❑ 98UppDecR-116
❑ 98UppDecRNF-NF16
❑ 98Zen-87
❑ 98Zen5 xx7-73
❑ 98Zen5x7GoldImp-73
❑ 98Zen5x7Imp-73
❑ 98ZenRooT-3
❑ 98ZenZ-G-87
❑ 98ZenZ-S-87
❑ 98ZenZ-T-11
❑ 98ZenZ-TG-11
❑ 99CroRoyB-60
❑ 99CroRoyL-60
❑ 99CroRoyOD-60
❑ 99Fle-216
❑ 99FleBri-53
❑ 99FleBri2G-53
❑ 99FleBriBlu-53
❑ 99FleBriGol-53
❑ 99FleSta9-216
❑ 99FleWarT-216
❑ 99MetUni-232
❑ 99MetUniGM-232
❑ 99MetUniPMG-232
❑ 99Pac-180
❑ 99PacAur-77
❑ 99PacAurOD-77
❑ 99PacCroC-117
❑ 99PacCroCPB-117
❑ 99PacInv-62
❑ 99PacInvOD-62
❑ 99PacInvPB-62
❑ 99PacPar-98
❑ 99PacParC-98
❑ 99PacParG-98
❑ 99PacParHoloGold-98
❑ 99PacParHS-98
❑ 99PacParOD-98
❑ 99PacParPB-98
❑ 99PacParRed-98
❑ 99PacPlaB-180
❑ 99PacPri-63
❑ 99PacPriHB-63
❑ 99PacPriHG-63
❑ 99PacPriHM-63
❑ 99PacPriHP-63
❑ 99PacPriRed-63
❑ 99PacRed-180
❑ 99SkyMolM-18
❑ 99SkyMolMX-18
❑ 99SkyPre-97
❑ 99SkyPreR-97
❑ 99SkyThu-76
❑ 99SkyThuRant-76
❑ 99SkyThuRave-76
❑ 99SP SigAuto-DL
❑ 99SP SigAutoG-DL
❑ 99SPSig-24
❑ 99SPx-40
❑ 99SPxFinR-40
❑ 99SPxFinS-40
❑ 99StaClu-103
❑ 99StaCluFDI-103
❑ 99StaCluOoaK-103
❑ 99StaCluPP-103
❑ 99ThuSkySupR-76
❑ 99Top-22
❑ 99TopChr-22
❑ 99TopChrR-22
❑ 99TopMVPP-22
❑ 99Ult-87
❑ 99UltGolM-87
❑ 99UltMas-87
❑ 99UltPlaM-87
❑ 99UppDec-104
❑ 99UppDecBD-35
❑ 99UppDecBDD-35
❑ 99UppDecBDQ-35
❑ 99UppDecBDT-35
❑ 99UppDecCLM-C39
❑ 99UppDecEL1-104
❑ 99UppDecEL2-104
❑ 99UppDecM-85
❑ 99UppDecMGS-85
❑ 99UppDecMHFS-85
❑ 99UppDecMP-85
❑ 99UppDecMSS-85
❑ 99Vic-162

Lee, Don
❑ 57Top-379
❑ 59Top-132
❑ 59TopVen-132
❑ 60Top-503
❑ 61Top-153
❑ 61TwiCloD-12
❑ 61TwiJayP-7
❑ 61TwiPetM-9
❑ 62Top-166
❑ 62TopVen-166
❑ 63AngJayP-7
❑ 63Fle-18
❑ 63Top-372
❑ 64Top-493
❑ 65Top-595

Lee, Dudley
❑ 21Exh-95
❑ 28ExhPCL-19
❑ 28Zee-12
❑ 29Zee-6
❑ 30Zee-10
❑ 31Zee-5
❑ 32Zee-9

Lee, Eddie
❑ 79ElmPioRST-11

Lee, Garret
❑ 97DanBraB-20
❑ 98EugEme-16

Lee, Greg
❑ 88PocGiaP-2086
❑ 89SalSpuCLC-141
❑ 89SalSpuP-1806

Lee, Hal
❑ 33ButCanV-30
❑ 34BabRutG-40
❑ 34ButPreR-39
❑ 90DodTar-441

Lee, Harvey
❑ 86Ft.LauYP-14
❑ 87SanJosBP-5

Lee, Jason
❑ 96JohCitCTI-19
❑ 97NewJerCB-15
❑ 98PeoChiM-13

Lee, Jeremy
❑ 94ClaGolF-69
❑ 94St.CatBJC-15
❑ 94St.CatBJF-3639
❑ 94Top-206
❑ 94TopGol-206
❑ 94TopSpa-206
❑ 95HagSunF-64
❑ 96DunBluJUTI-7
❑ 97DunBluJTI-19
❑ 98KnoSG-10

Lee, John
❑ 76DubPacT-20
❑ 89CarNewE-17

Lee, John Wayne
❑ 98SpoIndG-17

Lee, Larry
❑ 47PadTeal-13

Lee, Leon
❑ 72CedRapCT-24
❑ 75TulOil7-2
❑ 76TulOilGP-12
❑ 79TCMJapPB-70
❑ 87JapPlaB-4

Lee, Leron
❑ 70CarTeal-17
❑ 70CarTeal-18
❑ 70DayDaiNM-140
❑ 70OPC-96
❑ 70Top-96
❑ 71MLBOffS-276
❑ 71OPC-521
❑ 71Top-521
❑ 72OPC-238
❑ 72PadPos-17
❑ 72Top-238
❑ 73OPC-83
❑ 73PadDea-15
❑ 73SevTraC-37
❑ 73Top-83
❑ 74OPC-651
❑ 74Top-651
❑ 75CleIndP-17
❑ 75OPC-506
❑ 75Top-506
❑ 75TopMin-506
❑ 76OPC-487
❑ 76Top-487
❑ 79TCMJapPB-67
❑ 86SyrChiP-17
❑ 87JapPlaB-21
❑ 90DodTar-442

Lee, Manny
❑ 85BluJayFS-20
❑ 85FleUpd-71
❑ 86KnoBluJP-14
❑ 86OPC-23
❑ 86Top-23
❑ 86TopTif-23
❑ 87Don-518
❑ 87OPC-289
❑ 87SyrChiP-1941
❑ 87SyrChiT-16
❑ 87Top-574
❑ 87TopTif-574
❑ 88BluJayFS-18
❑ 88Don-650
❑ 88Fle-116
❑ 88FleGlo-116
❑ 88OPC-303
❑ 88Sco-561
❑ 88ScoGlo-561
❑ 88StaLinBJ-12
❑ 88Top-722
❑ 88TopTif-722
❑ 89BluJayFS-16
❑ 89Don-504
❑ 89Fle-238
❑ 89FleGlo-238
❑ 89OPC-371
❑ 89PanSti-468
❑ 89Sco-326
❑ 89Top-371
❑ 89TopBig-70
❑ 89TopTif-371
❑ 89UppDec-271
❑ 90BluJayFS-16
❑ 90Bow-512
❑ 90BowTif-512
❑ 90Don-620
❑ 90Fle-86
❑ 90FleCan-86
❑ 90Lea-370
❑ 90OPC-113
❑ 90PubIntS-520
❑ 90Sco-482
❑ 90Top-113
❑ 90TopBig-219
❑ 90TopTif-113
❑ 90UppDec-285
❑ 91BluJayFS-16
❑ 91BluJayFS-17
❑ 91BluJayS-16
❑ 91Bow-21
❑ 91Don-211
❑ 91Fle-179
❑ 91Lea-399
❑ 91OPC-297
❑ 91PanFreS-337
❑ 91Sco-534
❑ 91StaClu-168
❑ 91Top-297
❑ 91TopDesS-297
❑ 91TopMic-297
❑ 91TopTif-297
❑ 91Ult-365
❑ 91UppDec-142
❑ 92Bow-421
❑ 92Don-499
❑ 92Fle-333
❑ 92Lea-382
❑ 92LeaBlaG-382
❑ 92OPC-634
❑ 92PanSti-28
❑ 92Pin-245
❑ 92Sco-518
❑ 92StaClu-283
❑ 92Top-634
❑ 92TopGol-634
❑ 92TopGolW-634
❑ 92TopMic-634
❑ 92Ult-148
❑ 92UppDec-118
❑ 93BluJayD4-8
❑ 93Don-688
❑ 93Fle-337
❑ 93Lea-381
❑ 93OPC-320
❑ 93OPCWorC-9
❑ 93PacSpa-325
❑ 93Pin-493
❑ 93RanKee-413
❑ 93RanStaC-18
❑ 93Sco-205
❑ 93Sel-380
❑ 93SelRoo-119T
❑ 93StaClu-713
❑ 93StaCluFDI-713
❑ 93StaCluM-118
❑ 93StaCluMOP-713
❑ 93Top-488
❑ 93TopGol-488
❑ 93TopInaM-488
❑ 93TopInaR-488
❑ 93TopMic-488
❑ 93Ult-631
❑ 93UppDec-205
❑ 93UppDec-637
❑ 93UppDecGold-205
❑ 93UppDecGold-637
❑ 94ColC-172
❑ 94ColChoGS-172
❑ 94ColChoSS-172
❑ 94Fin-188
❑ 94FinRef-188
❑ 94Fla-113
❑ 94Fle-310
❑ 94FleExtB-182
❑ 94Lea-372
❑ 94PanSti-129
❑ 94RanMagM-23
❑ 94Sel-364
❑ 94StaClu-423
❑ 94StaCluFDI-423
❑ 94StaCluGR-423
❑ 94StaCluMOP-423
❑ 94StaCluT-248
❑ 94StaCluTFDI-248
❑ 94Top-51
❑ 94TopGol-51
❑ 94TopSpa-51
❑ 94UppDec-216
❑ 94UppDecED-216
❑ 95BluJayUSPC-8D
❑ 95ColCho-404
❑ 95ColChoGS-404
❑ 95ColChoSS-404
❑ 95Don-215
❑ 95DonPreP-215
❑ 95Fle-290
❑ 95Pac-430

Lee, Mark
❑ 97ColSprSTI-14

Lee, Mark L.
❑ 78PadFamF-18
❑ 79PadFamF-35
❑ 79Top-138
❑ 80HawIslT-17
❑ 80Top-557
❑ 81PorBeaT-15

Lee, Mark Owen
❑ 82EvaTriT-4
❑ 86LakTigP-8
❑ 87GleFalTP-15
❑ 87LakTigP-17
❑ 88LakTigS-17
❑ 89MemChiB-4
❑ 89MemChiP-1190
❑ 89MemChiS-14
❑ 91BreMilB-14
❑ 91BrePol-11
❑ 91FleUpd-30
❑ 91Lea-343
❑ 91OPC-721
❑ 91Sco-372
❑ 91Top-721
❑ 91TopDesS-721
❑ 91TopMic-721
❑ 91TopTif-721
❑ 92DenZepF-2637
❑ 92DenZepS-137
❑ 92Don-313
❑ 92Fle-180
❑ 92OPC-384
❑ 92Sco-277
❑ 92StaClu-32
❑ 92Top-384
❑ 92TopGol-384
❑ 92TopGolW-384
❑ 92TopMic-384
❑ 92UppDec-507
❑ 93OklCit8F-1622
❑ 94BreMilB-145
❑ 94IowCubF-1272
❑ 94TriAAF-AAA33
❑ 95BalOriP-29
❑ 95RocRedWTI-22
❑ 96NorTidB-19
❑ 96RicBraUB-16

Lee, Michael
❑ 60Top-521

Lee, Richard
❑ 98St.CatSM-8

Lee, Robert D.
❑ 74BroClu-3

Lee, Ronnie
❑ 50WorWidGV-25
❑ 53ExhCan-51

Lee, Terry
❑ 75CedRapGT-9
❑ 80HolMilT-21
❑ 81VanCanT-14
❑ 83CedRapRF-13
❑ 83CedRapRT-19

Lee, Terry James
❑ 89ChaLooB-10
❑ 89ChaLooGS-16
❑ 90ChaLooGS-19
❑ 91Bow-683
❑ 91Don-752
❑ 91Fle-70
❑ 91LinDriAAA-266
❑ 91NasSouLD-266
❑ 91NasSouP-2165
❑ 91TopDeb90-83
❑ 91TriA AAGP-AAA23
❑ 91UppDec-37
❑ 92ColSprSSS-89
❑ 92OPC-262
❑ 92Top-262
❑ 92TopGol-262
❑ 92TopGolW-262
❑ 92TopMic-262

Lee, Thomas
❑ 91EugEmeC-23
❑ 91EugEmeP-3723
❑ 92LetMouSP-18

Lee, Thornton
❑ 34BatR31-109
❑ 34DiaMatCSB-112
❑ 36NatChiFPR-52
❑ 38CloFotW-49
❑ 39WhiSoxTI-11
❑ 40WhiSoxL-12
❑ 47TipTop-23
❑ 48GiaTeal-11
❑ 85WhiSoxC-37
❑ 89PacLegI-158

Lee, Tod
❑ 98DelShoM-18

Lee, Tony
❑ 94DayCubF-2349

Lee, Travis
❑ 97Bes-3
❑ 97Bes-95
❑ 97BesAll-15
❑ 97BesAutSBPP-50
❑ 97BesAutSC-1
❑ 97BesBetP-6
❑ 97BesCarCSP-1
❑ 97BesCarCSP-5
❑ 97BesDiaB-4
❑ 97BesFiv-3
❑ 97BesLum-10
❑ 97Bow-389
❑ 97Bow98ROY-ROY10
❑ 97BowBes-187
❑ 97BowBesAR-187
❑ 97BowBesMI-MI2
❑ 97BowBesMIAR-MI2
❑ 97BowBesMIARI-MI2
❑ 97BowBesMII-MI2
❑ 97BowBesMIR-MI2
❑ 97BowBesMIRI-MI2
❑ 97BowBesR-187
❑ 97BowCerBlaIA-CA48
❑ 97BowCerBluIA-CA48
❑ 97BowCerGolIA-CA48
❑ 97BowChr-257
❑ 97BowChr1RFR-ROY10
❑ 97BowChr98RF-ROY10
❑ 97BowChrI-257
❑ 97BowChrIR-257
❑ 97BowChrR-257
❑ 97BowChrSHR-SHR12
❑ 97BowChrSHRR-SHR12
❑ 97BowInt-389
❑ 97BowScoHR-12
❑ 97CalLeaATI-13
❑ 97CalLeaTP-4
❑ 97HigDesMG-12
❑ 97HigDesMUG-1
❑ 97HigDesMUG-2
❑ 97HigDesMUG-16
❑ 97TopSta-106
❑ 97TopStaAM-106
❑ 97TucTorB-19
❑ 98Bow-292
❑ 98BowBes-101
❑ 98BowBesAR-101
❑ 98BowBesMIF-MI12
❑ 98BowBesMIFAR-MI12
❑ 98BowBesMIFR-MI12
❑ 98BowBesP-BP2
❑ 98BowBesPAR-BP2
❑ 98BowBesPR-BP2
❑ 98BowBesR-101
❑ 98BowCerBlueAU-48
❑ 98BowCerGA-48
❑ 98BowCerSA-48
❑ 98BowChr-292
❑ 98BowChrGA-292
❑ 98BowChrGAR-292
❑ 98BowChrI-292
❑ 98BowChrIR-292
❑ 98BowChrR-292
❑ 98BowGolA-292
❑ 98BowInt-292
❑ 98BowScoC-SC12
❑ 98CirThu-81
❑ 98CirThuB-11
❑ 98CirThuFT-7
❑ 98CirThuRav-81
❑ 98CirThuSupRav-81
❑ 98ColCho-266
❑ 98ColCho-430
❑ 98ColChoCtG-CG2A
❑ 98ColChoCtG-CG2B
❑ 98ColChoCtG-CG2C
❑ 98ColChoCtGExch-CG2
❑ 98ColChoCtGIW-CG2
❑ 98ColChoMBH-2
❑ 98ColChoPCR-430
❑ 98ColChoSQDouble-30
❑ 98ColChoSQHR-30
❑ 98ColChoSQSingle-30
❑ 98ColChoSQTriple-30
❑ 98CroRoy-7
❑ 98CroRoyCCPA-5
❑ 98CroRoyCCPrem-5
❑ 98CroRoyFoB-1
❑ 98CroRoyFoBA-1
❑ 98CroRoyPotG-2
❑ 98DiaBacP-18
❑ 98DiaMcD-14
❑ 98Don-334
❑ 98DonColP-694
❑ 98DonDay-7
❑ 98DonFANT-5
❑ 98DonFANTDC-5
❑ 98DonGolPP-334
❑ 98DonPre-144

❑ 98DonPreGB-8
❑ 98DonPreGES-1
❑ 98DonPreGoB-8
❑ 98DonPreGX-1
❑ 98DonPreGXDC-1
❑ 98DonPrePM-29
❑ 98DonPreSeat-144
❑ 98DonPreTP-8
❑ 98DonPreTPD-4
❑ 98DonPreTPG-8
❑ 98DonPreTPS-8
❑ 98DonPriCP-694
❑ 98DonRooDK-1
❑ 98DonRooDKC-1
❑ 98DonSig-97
❑ 98DonSigA-54
❑ 98DonSigA-NNO
❑ 98DonSigAC-72
❑ 98DonSigAM-73
❑ 98DonSigP-97
❑ 98DonSigSB-17
❑ 98DonSigSP-15
❑ 98DonSilPP-334
❑ 98E-X2-100
❑ 98E-X2Cheap-17
❑ 98E-X2ECFut-100
❑ 98E-X2ECNow-100
❑ 98E-X2SD2001-1
❑ 98Fin-263
❑ 98FinCen-C15
❑ 98FinCenR-C15
❑ 98FinMysF2-M25
❑ 98FinMysF2-M28
❑ 98FinMysF2-M29
❑ 98FinMysF2-M38
❑ 98FinMysF2R-M25
❑ 98FinMysF2R-M28
❑ 98FinMysF2R-M29
❑ 98FinMysF2R-M38
❑ 98FinNo--263
❑ 98FinNo-R-263
❑ 98FinRef-263
❑ 98FinTheM-TM15
❑ 98FinTheMR-TM15
❑ 98FlaShoLeg0-2
❑ 98FlaShoLeg1-2
❑ 98FlaShoLeg2-2
❑ 98FlaShoLeg3-2
❑ 98FlaShoLegM-2
❑ 98FlaShoR0-2
❑ 98FlaShoR1-2
❑ 98FlaShoR2-2
❑ 98FlaShoR3-2
❑ 98FlaShoWotF-1
❑ 98Fle-515
❑ 98FleProF-PF12
❑ 98FleVin'-69
❑ 98FleVin'C-69
❑ 98LeaRCrusUP-105
❑ 98LeaRS-139
❑ 98LeaRS-161
❑ 98LeaRS-202
❑ 98LeaRSCrusUG-105
❑ 98LeaRSCrusUR-105
❑ 98LeaRSFOSamp-3
❑ 98LeaRSFresh-3
❑ 98LeaRSGreHit-20
❑ 98LeaRSHRDerby-9
❑ 98LeaRSLHolo-139
❑ 98LeaRSLHolo-161
❑ 98LeaRSLHolo-202
❑ 98LeaRSLong-139
❑ 98LeaRSLong-161
❑ 98LeaRSLong-202
❑ 98LeaRSTicMas-19
❑ 98LeaRSTicMasDC-19
❑ 98LeaRTrue-139
❑ 98LeaRTrue-161
❑ 98LeaRTrue-202
❑ 98PacAur-99
❑ 98PacAurCube-1
❑ 98PacAurHC-1
❑ 98PacAurODLC-1
❑ 98PacAurPF-16
❑ 98PacAurPFC-16
❑ 98PacAurPFPB-16
❑ 98PacAurPFR-16
❑ 98PacAurPFS-16
❑ 98PacOme-14
❑ 98PacOmeEP-11
❑ 98PacOmeEP1o1-11
❑ 98PacOmeFTF-8
❑ 98PacOmeOnIns-20
❑ 98PacOmeP-12
❑ 98PacOmeR-14
❑ 98PacOmeRS-29
❑ 98PacOmeRST4-29
❑ 98PacOnl-41A
❑ 98PacOnl-41B
❑ 98PacOnl-52
❑ 98PacOnlR-41A
❑ 98PacOnlR-41B
❑ 98PacOnlR-52
❑ 98PacOnlWC-41A
❑ 98PacOnlWC-41B
❑ 98PacOnlWC-52
❑ 98PacPar-123
❑ 98PacParC-123
❑ 98PacParG-123
❑ 98PacParHS-123
❑ 98PacParPB-123
❑ 98PacParR-123
❑ 98PinPer-122
❑ 98PinPerLP-5
❑ 98PinPerPP-122
❑ 98PinPerSftF-14
❑ 98PinPlu-68
❑ 98PinPluAP-PP28
❑ 98PinPluGAP-PP28
❑ 98PinPluMAP-PP28
❑ 98PinSna-AD1
❑ 98PinSna-AD17
❑ 98PinSnaS-3
❑ 98Revo-7
❑ 98RevoFP-12
❑ 98RevoPTP-12
❑ 98RevoRooHH-3
❑ 98RevoRooHHG-3
❑ 98RevoShow-21
❑ 98RevoSS-7
❑ 98ScoNewS-NS10
❑ 98ScoRT-236
❑ 98ScoRTSS-PP129
❑ 98ScoRTSSAP-PP129
❑ 98ScoRTSSAP1-PP129
❑ 98SelSelSamp-4
❑ 98SkyDugA-1
❑ 98SkyDugA-114
❑ 98SkyDugADH-DH19
❑ 98SkyDugAIA-1
❑ 98SkyDugAIA-114
❑ 98SP Aut-1
❑ 98SP Aut-SD5
❑ 98SP AutC-TL
❑ 98SP AutSD-SD5
❑ 98SP AutSDT-SD5
❑ 98SP MinDTSPE-DS1
❑ 98SP MinPE-1
❑ 98SP MinPE-15
❑ 98SP MinSTHPE-H1
❑ 98SP SPTSC-TL
❑ 98SPMin-1
❑ 98SPMin-15
❑ 98SPMinDTS-DS1
❑ 98SPMinSTH-H1
❑ 98SpoIll-201
❑ 98SpoIllEE-201
❑ 98SpoIllFE-201
❑ 98SpoIllWSF-91
❑ 98SpoIllWSFEE-91
❑ 98SpoIllWSFFE-91
❑ 98SPxFin-200
❑ 98SPxFin-229
❑ 98SPxFin-351
❑ 98SPxFinR-200
❑ 98SPxFinR-229
❑ 98SPxFinR-351
❑ 98SPxFinS-200
❑ 98SPxFinS-229
❑ 98SPxFinS-351
❑ 98StaCluC-CS7
❑ 98StaCluC-CS8
❑ 98StaCluC-CS9
❑ 98StaCluFDI-302
❑ 98StaCluFDI-379
❑ 98StaCluI-302
❑ 98StaCluI-379
❑ 98StaCluITW-W10
❑ 98StaCluOneK-302
❑ 98StaCluOneK-379
❑ 98StaCluPP-302
❑ 98StaCluPP-379
❑ 98StaCluRC-RC11
❑ 98Stu-147
❑ 98Stu8x10S-1
❑ 98StuAuto8X10-1
❑ 98StuFF-26
❑ 98StuFFDC-26
❑ 98StuGPP-147
❑ 98StuMast-1
❑ 98StuPor8x10-1
❑ 98StuPor8x10GP-1
❑ 98StuSPP-147
❑ 98TopChrRC-R1
❑ 98TopChrRCRef-R1
❑ 98TopGal-20
❑ 98TopGalGP-20
❑ 98TopGalOPP-20
❑ 98TopGalPPI-20
❑ 98TopGalPPIA-20
❑ 98TopGolLabC1-84
❑ 98TopGolLabC1B-84
❑ 98TopGolLabC1One-84
❑ 98TopGolLabC1R-84
❑ 98TopGolLabC2-84
❑ 98TopGolLabC2B-84
❑ 98TopGolLabC2One-84
❑ 98TopGolLabC2R-84
❑ 98TopGolLabC3-84
❑ 98TopGolLabC3B-84
❑ 98TopGolLabC3One-84
❑ 98TopGolLabC3R-84
❑ 98TopRooCla-R1
❑ 98TopSta-85
❑ 98TopStaB-85
❑ 98TopStaG-85
❑ 98TopStaGR-85
❑ 98TopStaS-85
❑ 98TopStaSB-S2
❑ 98TopStaSG-S2
❑ 98TopStaSGR-S2
❑ 98TopStaSS-S2
❑ 98TopTek-59
❑ 98TopTekD-59
❑ 98UD3-1
❑ 98UD3-91
❑ 98UD3-181
❑ 98UD3DieCut-1
❑ 98UD3DieCut-91
❑ 98UD3DieCut-181
❑ 98Ult-453
❑ 98UltGolM-453
❑ 98UltMas-453
❑ 98UltPlaM-453
❑ 98UltRoctS-3
❑ 98UltTicS-1
❑ 98UltTop3-26
❑ 98UppDec-600
❑ 98UppDec-612
❑ 98UppDec-750
❑ 98UppDec5x7-612
❑ 98UppDecAC-AS2
❑ 98UppDecAPA3-TL
❑ 98UppDecDS-DS1
❑ 98UppDecR-103
❑ 98UppDecRBBop-BB19
❑ 98UppDecRGKoG-G12
❑ 98UppDecRL-4
❑ 98UppDecRNF-NF3
❑ 98UppDecRQL-Q12
❑ 98UppDecRSotT-TLE
❑ 98UppDecRTC-TC28
❑ 98UppDecU-2
❑ 98Zen-90
❑ 98Zen5 xx7-67
❑ 98Zen5x7GoldImp-67
❑ 98Zen5x7Imp-67
❑ 98ZenRooT-1
❑ 98ZenZ-G-90
❑ 98ZenZ-S-90
❑ 98ZenZ-T-14
❑ 98ZenZ-TG-14
❑ 99199Fin-125
❑ 99199Fin-177
❑ 99AllMysFR-M22
❑ 99Bow-17
❑ 99BowBes-62
❑ 99BowBesAR-62
❑ 99BowBesR-62
❑ 99BowChr-17
❑ 99BowChrG-17
❑ 99BowChrGR-17
❑ 99BowChrI-17
❑ 99BowChrIR-17
❑ 99BowChrR-17
❑ 99BowGol-17
❑ 99BowInt-17
❑ 99CroRoyB-9
❑ 99CroRoyL-9
❑ 99CroRoyOD-9
❑ 99E-X Cen-20
❑ 99E-X CenECFut-20
❑ 99E-X CenECNow-20
❑ 99E-X CenEQ-15
❑ 99E-XCenA-2
❑ 99E-XCenMotC-10
❑ 99FinGolRef-125
❑ 99FinGolRef-177
❑ 99FinMil-M7
❑ 99FinPeelHyp-18
❑ 99FinPeelSpark-18
❑ 99FinPeeSS-18
❑ 99FinRef-125
❑ 99FinRef-177
❑ 99FinSplS-SS14
❑ 99FinSplSDR-SS14
❑ 99FinTeaFB-TF6
❑ 99FinTeaFBR-TF6
❑ 99FinTeaFG-TF6
❑ 99FinTeaFGR-TF6
❑ 99FinTeaFR-TF6
❑ 99FinTeaFRR-TF6
❑ 99FlaShoLeg1-11
❑ 99FlaShoLeg2-11
❑ 99FlaShoLeg3-11
❑ 99FlaShoLegM1-11
❑ 99FlaShoLegM2-11
❑ 99FlaShoLegM3-11
❑ 99FlaShoR1-11
❑ 99FlaShoR2-11
❑ 99FlaShoR3-11
❑ 99FlaShoWotF-5
❑ 99Fle-10
❑ 99Fle-586
❑ 99FleBri-4
❑ 99FleBri2G-4
❑ 99FleBriBlu-4
❑ 99FleBriGol-4
❑ 99FleBril-5
❑ 99FleMys-97
❑ 99FleMysG-97
❑ 99FleMysM-97
❑ 99FleMysP-8
❑ 99FleRooFla-13
❑ 99FleSta9-10
❑ 99FleSta9-586
❑ 99FleVin'-10
❑ 99FleWarT-10
❑ 99FleWarT-586
❑ 99MetUni-146
❑ 99MetUni-282
❑ 99MetUniBWTW-7
❑ 99MetUniDS-15
❑ 99MetUniGM-146
❑ 99MetUniGM-282
❑ 99MetUniN-2
❑ 99MetUniPM-8
❑ 99MetUniPMG-146
❑ 99MetUniPMG-282
❑ 99Pac-22
❑ 99Pac-22A
❑ 99PacAur-12
❑ 99PacAurOD-12
❑ 99PacCroC-17
❑ 99PacCroCPB-17
❑ 99PacCroCTC-2
❑ 99PacDynaD-9
❑ 99PacDynaDT-9
❑ 99PacGolCDC-20
❑ 99PacInv-8
❑ 99PacInvOD-8
❑ 99PacInvPB-8
❑ 99PacOme-15
❑ 99PacOmeC-15
❑ 99PacOmeG-15
❑ 99PacOmePB-15
❑ 99PacPar-16
❑ 99PacParC-16
❑ 99PacParG-16
❑ 99PacParHoloGold-16
❑ 99PacParHS-16
❑ 99PacParOD-16
❑ 99PacParPB-3
❑ 99PacParPB-16
❑ 99PacParRed-16
❑ 99PacParTC-2
❑ 99PacPlaB-22
❑ 99PacPlaB-22A
❑ 99PacPri-8
❑ 99PacPriAotG-2
❑ 99PacPriDG-2
❑ 99PacPriHB-8
❑ 99PacPriHG-8
❑ 99PacPriHM-8
❑ 99PacPriHP-8
❑ 99PacPriRed-8
❑ 99PacPriS-10
❑ 99PacPriS206-10
❑ 99PacPriS206R-10
❑ 99PacPriSE-10
❑ 99PacPriSP-10
❑ 99PacPriSP-10
❑ 99PacPriSV-10
❑ 99PacRed-22
❑ 99PacRed-22A
❑ 99PacTeaC-15
❑ 99Rev-9
❑ 99RevPremDate-9
❑ 99RevRet-9
❑ 99RevShaSS-9
❑ 99SkyMolM-109
❑ 99SkyMolMF-9
❑ 99SkyMolMFS-9
❑ 99SkyMolMFT-9
❑ 99SkyMolMX-109
❑ 99SkyPre-39
❑ 99SkyPre-290
❑ 99SkyPreA-37
❑ 99SkyPreABlue-37
❑ 99SkyPreLB-9
❑ 99SkyPreR-39
❑ 99SkyPreR-290
❑ 99SkyThu-271
❑ 99SkyThuRant-271
❑ 99SkyThuRave-271
❑ 99SkyThuUnl-U12
❑ 99SP Aut-4
❑ 99SP AutC-TL
❑ 99SP AutCG-TL
❑ 99SP AutEF-E2
❑ 99SP AutR-R2
❑ 99SP SigAutoG-TL
❑ 99SpoIll-21
❑ 99SpoIll-159
❑ 99SPSig-52
❑ 99SPx-13
❑ 99SPxFinR-13
❑ 99SPxFinS-13
❑ 99SPxPowE-PE3
❑ 99SPxPreS-PS29
❑ 99SPxWinM-TL
❑ 99StaClu-85
❑ 99StaCluFDI-85
❑ 99StaCluOoaK-85
❑ 99StaCluPP-85
❑ 99StaCluTI-T10B
❑ 99StaCluTL-T10B
❑ 99StaCluTL-T10B
❑ 99ThuSkySupR-271
❑ 99Top-25
❑ 99Top-457
❑ 99TopAllMF-M22
❑ 99TopBlaLC1-84
❑ 99TopBlaLC2-84
❑ 99TopBlaLC3-84
❑ 99TopChr-25
❑ 99TopChr-457
❑ 99TopChrNB-NB5
❑ 99TopChrNBR-NB5
❑ 99TopChrR-25
❑ 99TopChrR-457
❑ 99TopGal-15
❑ 99TopGal-123
❑ 99TopGalHer-TH5
❑ 99TopGalHerP-TH5
❑ 99TopGalPP-15
❑ 99TopGalPP-123
❑ 99TopGalPPI-15
❑ 99TopGalPPI-123
❑ 99TopGolL-84
❑ 99TopGolLC1-84
❑ 99TopGolLC2-84
❑ 99TopGolLOtO-84
❑ 99TopMVPP-25
❑ 99TopMVPP-457
❑ 99TopNewB-NB5
❑ 99TopOpeD-17
❑ 99TopRedLC1-84
❑ 99TopRedLC2-84
❑ 99TopRedLC3-84
❑ 99TopSta-39
❑ 99TopSta'S-27
❑ 99TopSta'SG-27
❑ 99TopSta'SGDH-27
❑ 99TopSta1Foil-39
❑ 99TopSta2Foil-39
❑ 99TopStaFoil-39
❑ 99TopStaOS-39
❑ 99TopStaTS-39
❑ 99TopSupC-6
❑ 99TopSupCR-6
❑ 99TopTek-3A
❑ 99TopTek-3B
❑ 99TopTekG-3A
❑ 99TopTekG-3B
❑ 99UD Cho-52
❑ 99UD ChoP-52
❑ 99UD ChoPCR-52
❑ 99UD ChoS-16
❑ 99UD ChoSD-16
❑ 99UD ChoSHR-16
❑ 99UD ChoST-16
❑ 99UD Ion-3
❑ 99UD Ion-61
❑ 99UD IonC-C17
❑ 99UD IonH-H17
❑ 99UD IonR-3
❑ 99UD IonR-61
❑ 99UDHolo-5
❑ 99UDHoloAUsome-5
❑ 99Ult-98
❑ 99Ult-225
❑ 99UltDamI-15
❑ 99UltGolM-98
❑ 99UltGolM-225
❑ 99UltMas-98
❑ 99UltMas-225
❑ 99UltPlaM-98
❑ 99UltPlaM-225
❑ 99UltRBIK-24
❑ 99UltTheBook-12
❑ 99UltThu-13
❑ 99UltWorP-13
❑ 99UppDec-32
❑ 99UppDec-253
❑ 99UppDecBD-93
❑ 99UppDecBDD-93
❑ 99UppDecBDDom-D16
❑ 99UppDecBDDomE-D16
❑ 99UppDecBDMN-M24
❑ 99UppDecBDMNE-M24
❑ 99UppDecBDQ-93
❑ 99UppDecBDT-93
❑ 99UppDecCf7-37
❑ 99UppDecCf7-85
❑ 99UppDecCf7-C27
❑ 99UppDecCf7Cf7P-C27
❑ 99UppDecCf7SftF-S11
❑ 99UppDecCL-106
❑ 99UppDecCLCC-106
❑ 99UppDecCLM-C5
❑ 99UppDecCo7CE-37
❑ 99UppDecCo7CE-85
❑ 99UppDecCo7SftFA-TL
❑ 99UppDecE-3
❑ 99UppDecEFXG-3
❑ 99UppDecEL1-32
❑ 99UppDecEL1-253
❑ 99UppDecEL2-32
❑ 99UppDecEL2-253
❑ 99UppDecEPE-P3
❑ 99UppDecGJ-TL
❑ 99UppDecIP-I13
❑ 99UppDecIPD-I13
❑ 99UppDecIPHR-I13
❑ 99UppDecIPT-I13
❑ 99UppDecM-10
❑ 99UppDecMGS-10
❑ 99UppDecMHFS-10
❑ 99UppDecMP-10
❑ 99UppDecMSC-SC13
❑ 99UppDecMSS-10
❑ 99UppDecO-37
❑ 99UppDecOSO-37
❑ 99UppDecR-5
❑ 99UppDecRG-5
❑ 99UppDecRP-5
❑ 99UppDecVtaT-V3
❑ 99UppDecVtaTD-V3
❑ 99UppDecVtaTQ-V3
❑ 99UppDecVtaTT-V3
❑ 99UppDecWY-W2
❑ 99UppDecWYD-W2
❑ 99UppDecWYHR-W2
❑ 99UppDecWYT-W2
❑ 99Vic-18

Lee, Watty (Wyatt)

❑ 03BreE10-88
❑ 03BreE10-89
❑ 11SpoLifCW-216
❑ 11T205-193
❑ 12ColRedB-167
❑ 12ColTinT-167
❑ 12ImpTobC-71

Lee, Wiley

❑ 87SalAngP-19
❑ 88MidLeaAGS-24
❑ 88QuaCitAGS-4
❑ 89CalLeaA-11
❑ 89PalSprACLC-39
❑ 89PalSprAP-485
❑ 90MidAngGS-11

Lee, William C.

❑ 34BatR31-140
❑ 34DiaMatCSB-113
❑ 35DiaMatCS3T1-95

❑ 36CubTeal-20
❑ 36DiaMatCS3T2-16
❑ 36SandSW-40
❑ 36WorWidGV-109
❑ 37ExhFou-3
❑ 39CubTeal-13
❑ 39ExhSal-36
❑ 39WheBB12-4
❑ 41CubTeal-10
❑ 41DouPlaR-103
❑ 42CubTeal-10
❑ 43CubTeal-12
❑ 47PM1StaP1-110
❑ 47TipTop-110
❑ 75TCMLarFP-3
❑ 89ChaLooLITI-15
❑ 91ConTSN-128
❑ 92CubOldS-17
❑ 93ConTSN-724

Lee, William F.
❑ 70OPC-279
❑ 70Top-279
❑ 71MLBOffS-322
❑ 71OPC-58
❑ 71Top-58
❑ 72Dia-25
❑ 72RedSoxTI-13
❑ 72Top-636
❑ 73LinPor-25
❑ 73OPC-224
❑ 73Top-224
❑ 74OPC-118
❑ 74Top-118
❑ 74TopSta-135
❑ 75Hos-66
❑ 75OPC-128
❑ 75Top-128
❑ 75TopMin-128
❑ 76Kel-29
❑ 76LinSup-111
❑ 76OPC-396
❑ 76RedSoxSM-9
❑ 76SSP-421
❑ 76Top-396
❑ 77BurCheD-32
❑ 77Top-503
❑ 78PapGinD-9
❑ 78SSP270-167
❑ 78Top-295
❑ 79ExpPos-13
❑ 79ExpPos-14
❑ 79OPC-237
❑ 79Top-455
❑ 80ExpPos-14
❑ 80OPC-53
❑ 80Top-97
❑ 81Don-211
❑ 81ExpPos-4
❑ 81Fle-157
❑ 81OPC-371
❑ 81Top-633
❑ 82Don-194
❑ 82ExpPos-20
❑ 82Fle-194
❑ 82OPC-323
❑ 82Top-323
❑ 88AlaGolAA60TI-6
❑ 89PacSenL-28
❑ 89T/MSenL-66
❑ 89TopSenL-33
❑ 90EliSenL-99
❑ 90SouCalS-8
❑ 91PacSenL-146
❑ 92Nab-1
❑ 93ExpDonM-24
❑ 95MCIAmb-11
❑ 99SpolllGotG-23
❑ 99SpolllGotGA-43

Lee, William PCL
❑ 17Zee-30
❑ 19Zee-23

Leech, Skip
❑ 77ChaPatT-7

Leek, Eugene
❑ 61Top-527
❑ 62SalPlaC-82A
❑ 62SalPlaC-82B
❑ 62ShiPlaC-82

Leenam, Rick
❑ 97ForWayW-17

Leeper, Dave
❑ 83OmaRoyT-22
❑ 84OmaRoyT-22
❑ 85OmaRoyT-24
❑ 86Don-461
❑ 86HawIsIP-16
❑ 87VanCanP-1611

Leese, Brandon
❑ 96BelGiaTI-24
❑ 97SanJosG-18

Leever, Sam
❑ 03BreE10-90
❑ 08AmeCarE91-82
❑ 09AmeCarE90-1-70
❑ 10DomDisP-68
❑ 10NadE1-30
❑ 10PirAmeCE-6
❑ 10PirHerICP-8
❑ 10PirTipTD-18
❑ 10SweCapPP-139
❑ 11PinT-5-871
❑ 11SpoLifCW-217
❑ 11SpoLifM-253
❑ 11T205-98

Lefebvre, Jim
❑ 65DodJayP-8
❑ 65Top-561
❑ 66OPC-57
❑ 66Top-57
❑ 66TopVen-57
❑ 67CokCapD-12
❑ 67CokCapDA-12
❑ 67DexPre-124
❑ 67Top-260
❑ 67TopVen-286
❑ 68Baz-2
❑ 68Top-457
❑ 68TopActS-4A
❑ 68TopActS-13A
❑ 69MilBra-156
❑ 69MLBOffS-149
❑ 69OPC-140
❑ 69Top-140
❑ 69TopFou-9
❑ 69TopSta-46
❑ 69TopTeaP-22
❑ 69TraSta-47
❑ 70MLBOffS-52
❑ 70Top-553
❑ 71Dod-6
❑ 71DodTic-8
❑ 71MLBOffS-106
❑ 71OPC-459
❑ 71Top-459
❑ 72MilBra-196
❑ 72OPC-369
❑ 72Top-369
❑ 72TopCloT-20
❑ 78TCM60I-263
❑ 80GiaPol-5
❑ 85PhoGiaC-187
❑ 86PhoFirP-15
❑ 86StaoftFT-37
❑ 87DodSmoA-18
❑ 88A'sMot-27
❑ 89DodSmoG-71
❑ 89MarMot-1
❑ 89TopTra-70T
❑ 89TopTraT-70T
❑ 90DodTar-443
❑ 90MarMot-1
❑ 90OPC-459
❑ 90Top-459
❑ 90TopTif-459
❑ 91MarCouH-1
❑ 91OPC-699
❑ 91Top-699
❑ 91TopDesS-699
❑ 91TopMic-699
❑ 91TopTif-699
❑ 92CubMar-5
❑ 92DodStaTA-5
❑ 92TopTra-63T
❑ 92TopTraG-63T
❑ 93CubMar-13
❑ 93Top-502
❑ 93TopGol-502
❑ 93TopInaM-502
❑ 93TopInaR-502
❑ 93TopMic-502
❑ 94A'sMot-28
❑ 95AthMot-28
❑ 95DodROY-6

Lefebvre, Joe
❑ 77ForLauYS-6
❑ 79WesHavYT-25
❑ 80ColCliP-14
❑ 80ColCliT-26
❑ 80YanPhoA-15
❑ 81Don-571
❑ 81Fle-103
❑ 81OPC-88
❑ 81PadFamF-12
❑ 81Top-88
❑ 81TopTra-790
❑ 82Don-373
❑ 82Fle-575
❑ 82Top-434
❑ 83Don-523
❑ 83Fle-363
❑ 83Top-644
❑ 83TopTra-61T
❑ 84AllGamPI-55
❑ 84Don-82
❑ 84Fle-37
❑ 84Nes792-148
❑ 84PhiTas-37
❑ 84Top-148
❑ 84TopTif-148
❑ 85Don-285
❑ 85Fle-257
❑ 85PhiTas-12
❑ 85PhiTas-37
❑ 85Top-531
❑ 85TopTif-531
❑ 86PhiTas-23
❑ 87ReaPhiP-3
❑ 88MaiPhiC-25
❑ 88MaiPhiP-301
❑ 89ScrRedBC-18
❑ 89ScrRedBP-722
❑ 90AlbYanB-25
❑ 90AlbYanP-1181
❑ 90AlbYanSt-25
❑ 92YanWIZ8-104
❑ 96PhoFirB-4
❑ 97PhoFirTI-14
❑ 98FreGriG-15

Lefebvre, Ryan
❑ 92Min-11

Lefebvre, Tip
❑ 84PhoGiaC-14

Lefevre, Alfred
❑ 23Zee-136
❑ 23Zee-165

Lefevre, Ross
❑ 22Zee-102

Lefferts, Craig
❑ 82IowCubT-20
❑ 83CubThoAV-32
❑ 84Don-388
❑ 84Fle-496
❑ 84FleUpd-72
❑ 84Nes792-99
❑ 84PadMot-19
❑ 84Top-99
❑ 84TopTif-99
❑ 84TopTra-72T
❑ 84TopTraT-72T
❑ 85Don-261
❑ 85Fle-38
❑ 85OPC-76
❑ 85PadMot-15
❑ 85Top-608
❑ 85TopMin-608
❑ 85TopTif-608
❑ 86Don-307
❑ 86Fle-328
❑ 86OPC-244
❑ 86Top-244
❑ 86TopTif-244
❑ 87Don-387
❑ 87Fle-422
❑ 87FleGlo-422
❑ 87FleRecS-19
❑ 87FleUpd-64
❑ 87FleUpdG-64
❑ 87OPC-287
❑ 87PadBohHB-37
❑ 87SpoTeaP-16
❑ 87Top-501
❑ 87TopTif-501
❑ 88Don-515
❑ 88DonBasB-330
❑ 88Fle-87
❑ 88FleGlo-87
❑ 88GiaMot-24
❑ 88GiaPos-15
❑ 88Sco-553
❑ 88ScoGlo-553
❑ 88StaLinG-9
❑ 88Top-734
❑ 88TopClo-59
❑ 88TopTif-734
❑ 89Bow-464
❑ 89BowTif-464
❑ 89Don-59
❑ 89Fle-332
❑ 89FleGlo-332
❑ 89GiaMot-24
❑ 89Sco-178
❑ 89Top-372
❑ 89TopTif-372
❑ 89UppDec-541
❑ 90Bow-206
❑ 90BowTif-206
❑ 90ClaBlu-109
❑ 90Don-376
❑ 90DonBesN-23
❑ 90Fle-60
❑ 90FleCan-60
❑ 90FleUpd-57
❑ 90Lea-339
❑ 90OPC-158
❑ 90PadCok-9
❑ 90PadMag-11
❑ 90PanSti-362
❑ 90PubIntS-74
❑ 90Sco-209
❑ 90ScoRoo-22T
❑ 90Spo-130
❑ 90Top-158
❑ 90TopSti-80
❑ 90TopTif-158
❑ 90TopTra-59T
❑ 90TopTraT-59T
❑ 90UppDec-399
❑ 90UppDec-792
❑ 91Bow-650
❑ 91Don-515
❑ 91Fle-534
❑ 91Lea-390
❑ 91OPC-448
❑ 91PadCok-4
❑ 91PadMag-21
❑ 91PadSmo-19
❑ 91PanCanT1-84
❑ 91RedFolS-59
❑ 91Sco-184
❑ 91StaClu-533
❑ 91Top-448
❑ 91TopDesS-448
❑ 91TopMic-448
❑ 91TopTif-448
❑ 91Ult-307
❑ 91UppDec-228
❑ 92Bow-105
❑ 92Don-162
❑ 92Fle-611
❑ 92Lea-408
❑ 92LeaBlaG-408
❑ 92OPC-41
❑ 92PadCarJ-11
❑ 92PadMot-24
❑ 92PadPolD-13
❑ 92PadSmo-17
❑ 92PanSti-239
❑ 92Pin-478
❑ 92Sco-175
❑ 92StaClu-618
❑ 92StaCluNC-618
❑ 92Top-41
❑ 92TopGol-41
❑ 92TopGolW-41
❑ 92TopMic-41
❑ 92Ult-577
❑ 92UppDec-589
❑ 93Bow-249
❑ 93Don-1
❑ 93Fle-544
❑ 93Lea-309
❑ 93Pin-522
❑ 93RanKee-414
❑ 93Sco-435
❑ 93Sel-373
❑ 93SelRoo-112T
❑ 93Top-617
❑ 93TopGol-617
❑ 93TopInaM-617
❑ 93TopInaR-617
❑ 93TopMic-617
❑ 93Ult-632
❑ 93UppDec-718
❑ 93UppDecGold-718
❑ 94AngLAT-17
❑ 94AngMot-18
❑ 94Don-472
❑ 94Fle-311
❑ 94Pac-621
❑ 94Top-288
❑ 94TopGol-288
❑ 94TopSpa-288

Lefler, Wade
❑ 75SenTCM1-15

LeFlore, Ron
❑ 75DetTigP-18
❑ 75OPC-628
❑ 75Top-628
❑ 75TopMin-628
❑ 76DetTigP-16
❑ 76GreHeroBP-3
❑ 76Hos-69
❑ 76Kel-17
❑ 76OPC-61
❑ 76SSP-363
❑ 76Top-61
❑ 77BurCheD-98
❑ 77Hos-50
❑ 77Kel-25
❑ 77OPC-167
❑ 77PepGloD-28
❑ 77RCColC-34
❑ 77Spo-3601
❑ 77TigBurK-2
❑ 77Top-240
❑ 78Hos-95
❑ 78OPC-88
❑ 78RCColC-12
❑ 78TigBurK-19
❑ 78TigTeal-17
❑ 78Top-480
❑ 78WifBalD-37
❑ 79Hos-34
❑ 79OPC-348
❑ 79TigFreP-4
❑ 79Top-4
❑ 79Top-660
❑ 79TopCom-8
❑ 80BurKinPHR-27
❑ 80ExpPos-15
❑ 80OPC-45
❑ 80Top-80
❑ 81AllGamPI-55
❑ 81CokTeaS-31
❑ 81Don-576
❑ 81Fle-154
❑ 81FleStiC-2
❑ 81MSAMinD-20
❑ 81OPC-104
❑ 81Squ-26
❑ 81Top-4
❑ 81Top-204
❑ 81Top-710
❑ 81TopSti-23
❑ 81TopSupHT-17
❑ 81TopTra-791
❑ 82Don-165
❑ 82Fle-350
❑ 82FleSta-182
❑ 82OnDecD-20
❑ 82OPC-140
❑ 82Top-140
❑ 82TopSti-172
❑ 83Don-543
❑ 83Fle-246
❑ 83FleSta-104
❑ 83FleSti-151
❑ 83OPC-297
❑ 83Top-560
❑ 83TopFol-5
❑ 89PacSenL-4
❑ 89T/MSenL-67
❑ 89TopSenL-111
❑ 90EliSenL-39
❑ 91PacSenL-63
❑ 94MCIAmb-8

Leftwich, Phil
❑ 90BoiHawP-3306
❑ 90ProAaA-158
❑ 91Cla/Bes-247
❑ 91MidLeaAP-MWL27
❑ 91QuaCitAC-7
❑ 91QuaCitAP-2624
❑ 92MidAngF-4024
❑ 93VanCanF-2592
❑ 94AngAdoF-2
❑ 94AngLAT-9
❑ 94ColC-173
❑ 94ColChoGS-173
❑ 94ColChoSS-173
❑ 94Don-403
❑ 94Fin-391
❑ 94FinRef-391
❑ 94Fla-272
❑ 94Fle-62
❑ 94Lea-132
❑ 94Pac-82
❑ 94Pin-441
❑ 94PinArtP-441
❑ 94PinMusC-441
❑ 94Top-471
❑ 94TopGol-471
❑ 94TopSpa-471
❑ 94Ult-23
❑ 94UppDec-139
❑ 94UppDecED-139
❑ 95ColCho-106
❑ 95ColChoGS-106
❑ 95ColChoSS-106
❑ 95Don-199
❑ 95DonPreP-199
❑ 95Fle-229
❑ 95Top-619
❑ 95TopCyb-387

Legault, Kevin
❑ 92EliTwiC-8
❑ 92EliTwiF-3675
❑ 93ClaFS7-216
❑ 93ForWayWC-15
❑ 93ForWayWF-1964
❑ 94ForMyeMC-13
❑ 94ForMyeMF-1165
❑ 95HarCitRCTI-11
❑ 97NewBriRC-19

Legendre, Rob
❑ 91YakBeaC-25
❑ 91YakBeaP-4245
❑ 92YakBeaC-10
❑ 92YakBeaF-3445

Legends, Hollywood
❑ 93HolLeg-19

Leger, Frank
❑ 83LynPirT-24

Leger, Tim
❑ 92FroRowDP-23
❑ 92FroRowDPG-23
❑ 92FroRowDPS-23
❑ 93StaCluM-67
❑ 94WelPirC-12
❑ 94WelPirF-3508

Legett, Lou
❑ 35DiaMatCS3T1-96

Legg, Greg
❑ 83ReaPhiT-14
❑ 85PorBeaC-48
❑ 87MaiGuiP-4
❑ 87MaiGuiT-14
❑ 87PhiTas-11
❑ 88ReaPhiP-882
❑ 89ScrRedBC-19
❑ 89ScrRedBP-708
❑ 90ProAAAF-311
❑ 90ScrRedBP-609
❑ 91LinDriAAA-486
❑ 91ScrRedBLD-486
❑ 91ScrRedBP-2546
❑ 92ScrRedBF-2452
❑ 92ScrRedBS-486
❑ 93ScrRedBF-2547
❑ 93ScrRedBTI-12
❑ 94ClePhiC-29
❑ 94ClePhiF-2544
❑ 95ClePhiF-233
❑ 96ScrRedBB-3
❑ 97BatCliTI-29
❑ 98ScrRedB1ATI-7
❑ 98ScrRedB1ATI-8

Leggatt, Rich
❑ 82BufBisT-1
❑ 83DurBulT-20
❑ 84DurBulT-18
❑ 85GreBraTI-12
❑ 86TolMudHP-13

Leggett, Adam
❑ 97BoiHawG-18
❑ 98CedRapKTI-16

Legree, Keith
❑ 92EliTwiF-3686
❑ 95HarCitRCTI-12
❑ 97NewBriRC-20

Legrow, Brett
❑ 94BatCliC-9
❑ 94BatCliF-3440

Legumina, Gary
❑ 83SanJosBC-15
❑ 85VerBeaDT-9

Lehew, Jim
❑ 62BalOriP-17
❑ 91OriCro-257

Lehman, Bill
❑ 76AppFoxT-11

Lehman, Ken
❑ 50W720HolS-16
❑ 55Bow-310
❑ 56BalOriP-30
❑ 57Top-366

□ 58Hir-52
□ 58Top-141
□ 59Top-31
□ 59TopVen-31
□ 74dod195T-19
□ 79TCM50-258
□ 90DodTar-444
□ 91OriCro-258
□ 95TopArcBD-140
Lehman, Mike
□ 87NewOriP-2
□ 89FreKeyS-12
□ 90FreKeyTI-16
□ 91HagSunLD-235
□ 91HagSunP-2459
□ 91LinDriAA-235
□ 92RocRedWS-455
□ 92SkyAAAF-207
Lehman, Toby
□ 93HicCraC-12
□ 93HicCraF-1274
□ 94SouBenSHC-7
□ 94SouBenSHF-588
□ 96HigDesMB-18
Lehmann, Arthur
□ 63GadFunC-70
Lehner, Ken
□ 95BreCouMF-265
Lehner, Paul
□ 47TipTop-67
□ 49Bow-131
□ 50A'sTeal-16
□ 50Bow-158
□ 51A'sTeal-17
□ 51Bow-8
□ 85TCMPla1-18
Lehnerz, Daniel
□ 88IdaFalBP-1857
Lehnerz, Mike
□ 89KinMetS-15
□ 91PitMetC-20
□ 91PitMetP-3417
Lehoisky, Russ
□ 93EliTwiC-14
□ 93EliTwiF-3413
□ 94ForWayWC-13
□ 94ForWayWF-2005
□ 95ForMyeMTI-14
Lehr, Ryan
□ 98MacBraM-13
Leibee, Skye
□ 94SouOreAC-15
□ 94SouOreAF-3618
□ 95WesMicWTI-21
Leiber, Hank
□ 38ExhFou-5
□ 39CubTeal-14
□ 41CubTeal-11
□ 79DiaGre-37
□ 95ConTSN-1426
Leibert, Allen
□ 90CanIndS-10
Leibold, Nemo (Harry)
□ 14B18B-5A
□ 14B18B-5B
□ 14FatPlaT-24
□ 15SpoNewM-99
□ 16SpoNewM-101
□ 17ColE13-97
□ 17HolBreD-60
□ 17HolBreD-61
□ 21E121So8-51
□ 22E120-6
□ 22W575-71
□ 23WilChoV-84
□ 75WhiSox1T-13
□ 88PacEigMO-101
□ 94ConTSN-1036
□ 94ConTSN-1042
□ 94ConTSNB-1036
□ 94ConTSNB-1042
Leibrandt, Charles
□ 79IndIndTI-7
□ 80RedEnq-44
□ 81Don-421
□ 81Fle-208
□ 81IndIndTI-5
□ 81OPC-126
□ 81Top-126
□ 82Fle-74
□ 82RedCok-14
□ 82Top-169
□ 83Don-421
□ 83Fle-596
□ 83IndIndTI-4
□ 83Top-607
□ 84OmaRoyT-1
□ 84RoyPos-18
□ 85AllGamPI-80
□ 85Don-399
□ 85DonHig-4
□ 85DonHig-46
□ 85Fle-206
□ 85IndIndTI-33
□ 85RoyTeal-17
□ 85Top-459
□ 85TopTif-459
□ 86BasStaB-67
□ 86Don-297
□ 86Fle-13
□ 86FleLeaL-21
□ 86FleSlu-20
□ 86FleStiC-69
□ 86Lea-171
□ 86OPC-77
□ 86RoyKitCD-10
□ 86RoyNatP-37
□ 86RoyTeal-14
□ 86Spo-159
□ 86Spo-186
□ 86Top-77
□ 86TopMinL-19
□ 86TopSti-262
□ 86TopSup-37
□ 86TopTat-1
□ 86TopTif-77
□ 87Don-220
□ 87Fle-373
□ 87FleGlo-373
□ 87OPC-223
□ 87SpoTeaP-13
□ 87Top-223
□ 87TopSti-258
□ 87TopTif-223
□ 88Don-157
□ 88DonBasB-151
□ 88Fle-263
□ 88FleGlo-263
□ 88FleStiC-31
□ 88Lea-76
□ 88OPC-218
□ 88PanSti-100
□ 88RoySmo-13
□ 88RoyTeal-17
□ 88Sco-61
□ 88ScoGlo-61
□ 88Spo-21
□ 88StaLinRo-8
□ 88Top-569
□ 88TopSti-260
□ 88TopTif-569
□ 89Bow-116
□ 89BowTif-116
□ 89ClaLigB-82
□ 89Don-89
□ 89DonBasB-231
□ 89Fle-286
□ 89FleGlo-286
□ 89OPC-301
□ 89PanSti-351
□ 89RoyTasD-10
□ 89Sco-133
□ 89Top-301
□ 89TopTif-301
□ 89UppDec-637
□ 90Bow-8
□ 90BowTif-8
□ 90BraDubP-15
□ 90BraDubS-18
□ 90Don-208
□ 90Fle-112
□ 90FleCan-112
□ 90Lea-428
□ 90MLBBasB-103
□ 90OPC-776
□ 90PubIntS-351
□ 90Sco-82
□ 90Top-776
□ 90TopTif-776
□ 90TopTra-60T
□ 90TopTraT-60T
□ 90UppDec-658
□ 91Bow-573
□ 91BraDubP-17
□ 91BraSubS-22
□ 91Don-562
□ 91Fle-695
□ 91Lea-209
□ 91OPC-456
□ 91PanFreS-27
□ 91PanSti-23
□ 91Sco-536
□ 91StaClu-527
□ 91Top-456
□ 91TopDesS-456
□ 91TopMic-456
□ 91TopTif-456
□ 91UppDec-460
□ 92BraLykP-17
□ 92BraLykS-20
□ 92Don-84
□ 92Fle-361
□ 92Lea-113
□ 92LeaBlaG-113
□ 92OPC-152
□ 92Pin-423
□ 92Sco-105
□ 92StaClu-366
□ 92Top-152
□ 92TopGol-152
□ 92TopGolW-152
□ 92TopMic-152
□ 92Ult-459
□ 92UppDec-170
□ 93Bow-433
□ 93Don-630
□ 93Fle-7
□ 93FleFinE-280
□ 93Lea-407
□ 93OPC-204
□ 93OPCPre-116
□ 93PacSpa-642
□ 93Pin-115
□ 93RanKee-415
□ 93RanStaC-16
□ 93Sco-393
□ 93Sel-209
□ 93SelRoo-91T
□ 93StaClu-723
□ 93StaCluFDI-723
□ 93StaCluMOP-723
□ 93Top-677
□ 93TopGol-677
□ 93TopInaM-677
□ 93TopInaR-677
□ 93TopMic-677
□ 93UppDec-678
□ 93UppDecGold-678
□ 94Don-190
□ 94Fle-312
□ 94Sco-467
□ 94ScoGolR-467
Leiby, Brent
□ 90PriPatD-30
□ 91SpaPhiC-30
□ 95ReaPhiELC-24
□ 96ReaPhiB-29
Leifer, Elmer
□ 18Zee-26
Leifield, Lefty (Albert)
□ 09T206-209
□ 09T206-210
□ 10DomDisP-69
□ 10PirTipTD-10
□ 10RedCroT-42
□ 10RedCroT-131
□ 10RedCroT-213
□ 10SweCapPP-140
□ 11HelSta-162
□ 11MecDFT-40
□ 11PinT-5-860
□ 11S74Sil-112
□ 11SpoLifM-254
□ 11T205-99
□ 12HasTriFT-16C
□ 12T207-102
□ 13Zee-114
□ 14Zee-114
Leighton, John
□ 87OldJudN-296
Leimeister, Eric
□ 90NiaFalRP-20
□ 91LakTigC-7
□ 91LakTigP-263
Lein, Chris
□ 82NasSouTI-16
□ 83AleDukT-14
□ 85PriWilPT-13
□ 87SalBucP-28
□ 89HarSenP-301
□ 90SalBucS-26
□ 91BluOriC-25
□ 91BluOriP-4142
□ 95BowBayTI-25
□ 96BowBayB-2
Leinen, Michael
□ 90WauTimS-13
Leinen, Pat
□ 88NebCor-13
□ 89EriOriS-11
□ 90Bes-96
□ 90WauTimB-3
□ 90WauTimP-2116
□ 91FreKeyP-2359
□ 91HagSunP-2452
□ 91PerHeaF-7
□ 92RocRedWF-1934
□ 92RocRedWS-456
Leinhard, Steve
□ 90ShrCapS-14
□ 94CliLumF-1998
Leiper, Dave
□ 82IdaFalAT-11
□ 83MadMusF-27
□ 84ModA'sC-18
□ 86TacTigP-12
□ 87Don-472
□ 87Fle-398
□ 87FleGlo-398
□ 87ModA'sC-A4
□ 87Top-441
□ 87TopTif-441
□ 88Don-557
□ 88FleUpd-123
□ 88FleUpdG-123
□ 88PadSmo-15
□ 88Sco-348
□ 88ScoGlo-348
□ 89Don-465
□ 89DonBasB-133
□ 89Fle-310
□ 89FleGlo-310
□ 89PadPos-17
□ 89Sco-515
□ 89Top-82
□ 89TopTif-82
□ 89UppDec-363
□ 90OPC-773
□ 90PubIntS-53
□ 90Sco-212
□ 90Top-773
□ 90TopTif-773
□ 91EdmTraLD-166
□ 91EdmTraP-1514
□ 91LinDriAAA-166
□ 94TacTigF-3169
□ 95AthMot-16
□ 96PhiTeal-19
Leiper, Tim (Timothy)
□ 86FloStaLAP-29
□ 86LakTigP-9
□ 87GleFalTP-9
□ 88GleFalTP-938
□ 88TolMudHC-21
□ 88TolMudHP-603
□ 89LonTigP-1373
□ 90CMC-838
□ 90EasLeaAP-EL5
□ 90LonTigP-1281
□ 91LinDriAAA-561
□ 91TidTidLD-561
□ 91TidTidP-2523
□ 92MemChiF-2431
□ 92MemChiS-441
□ 93CarMudF-2063
□ 93CarMudTI-23
□ 94BufBisF-1849
□ 95JacSunTI-18
□ 96BinMetB-15
□ 98arSenW1-25
□ 98HarSenM-25
Leishman, Edwin
□ 30Zee-11
□ 33WorCig(-54
□ 37Zee-36
□ 37Zee-97
Leister, John
□ 86PawRedSP-12
□ 87PawRedSP-55
□ 87PawRedST-26
□ 88PawRedSC-4
□ 88PawRedSP-470
□ 89PawRedSC-5
□ 89PawRedSP-681
□ 89PawRedSTI-14
□ 90CMC-257
□ 90PawRedSC-6
□ 90PawRedSDD-13
□ 90PawRedSP-459
□ 90ProAAAF-431
□ 90TopTVRS-49
Leiter, Al
□ 82RegGloT-2
□ 87ColCliP-15
□ 87ColCliP-26
□ 87IntLeaAT-38
□ 88ClaBlu-238
□ 88Don-43
□ 88DonBasB-132
□ 88DonReaBY-43
□ 88DonRoo-27
□ 88FleUpd-49
□ 88FleUpdG-49
□ 88Lea-43
□ 88ScoRoo-97T
□ 88ScoRooG-97T
□ 88Top-18A
□ 88Top-18B
□ 88TopTif-18
□ 89Bow-170
□ 89BowTif-170
□ 89ClaTraO-112
□ 89Don-315
□ 89Fle-257
□ 89FleGlo-257
□ 89FleUpd-70
□ 89PanSti-396
□ 89Sco-580
□ 89ScoHot1R-80
□ 89ScoYouSI-17
□ 89Top-659
□ 89TopBig-125
□ 89TopRoo-15
□ 89TopTif-659
□ 89TopTra-71T
□ 89TopTraT-71T
□ 89ToyRoo-19
□ 89UppDec-588
□ 89UppDec-705
□ 90BluJayFS-17
□ 90Don-543
□ 90OPC-138
□ 90PubIntS-521
□ 90Top-138
□ 90TopTif-138
□ 91BluJayFS-17
□ 91BluJayS-4
□ 91Don-697
□ 91OPC-233
□ 91Top-233
□ 91TopDesS-233
□ 91TopMic-233
□ 91TopTif-233
□ 92Fle-334
□ 92OPC-394
□ 92SkyAAAF-227
□ 92StaClu-231
□ 92SyrChiF-1963
□ 92SyrChiMB-10
□ 92SyrChiS-509
□ 92YanWIZ8-105
□ 93BluJayD-18
□ 93BluJayD4-34
□ 93BluJayFS-18
□ 93FleFinE-294
□ 93PacSpa-652
□ 93Pin-568
□ 93StaClu-670
□ 93StaCluFDI-670
□ 93StaCluMOP-670
□ 93UppDec-638
□ 93UppDecGold-638
□ 94BluJayUSPC-2C
□ 94BluJayUSPC-10H
□ 94ColC-512
□ 94ColChoGS-512
□ 94ColChoSS-512
□ 94Don-229
□ 94Fle-337
□ 94Lea-95
□ 94Pac-646
□ 94Pin-334
□ 94PinArtP-334
□ 94PinMusC-334
□ 94StaClu-667
□ 94StaCluFDI-667
□ 94StaCluGR-667
□ 94StaCluMOP-667
□ 94StaCluT-171
□ 94StaCluTFDI-171
□ 94Top-732
□ 94TopGol-732
□ 94TopSpa-732
□ 94Ult-139
□ 95BluJayOH-23
□ 95Don-419
□ 95DonPreP-419
□ 95Fle-100
□ 95StaClu-256
□ 95StaCluFDI-256
□ 95StaCluMOP-256
□ 95StaCluSTWS-256
□ 95TopTra-135T
□ 95Ult-341
□ 95UltGolM-341
□ 96Cir-130
□ 96CirRav-130
□ 96ColCho-356
□ 96ColCho-772
□ 96ColChoGS-356
□ 96ColChoSS-356
□ 96Don-89
□ 96DonPreP-89
□ 96Fin-B208
□ 96FinRef-B208
□ 96Fla-264
□ 96Fle-277
□ 96FleTif-277
□ 96FleUpd-U132
□ 96FleUpdTC-U132
□ 96LeaSigA-131
□ 96LeaSigAG-131
□ 96LeaSigAS-131
□ 96MetUni-167
□ 96MetUniP-167
□ 96Pac-444
□ 96PanSti-165
□ 96Pin-24
□ 96Sco-464
□ 96StaClu-236
□ 96StaCluMOP-236
□ 96Ult-479
□ 96UltGolM-479
□ 96UppDec-339
□ 97Cir-319
□ 97CirRav-319
□ 97ColCho-111
□ 97ColChoT-FM2
□ 97Don-213
□ 97DonEli-149
□ 97DonEliGS-149
□ 97DonGolPP-213
□ 97DonSilPP-213
□ 97Fin-183
□ 97FinRef-183
□ 97Fle-331
□ 97FleTif-331
□ 97Lea-118
□ 97LeaFraM-118
□ 97LeaFraMDC-118
□ 97LeaGet-14
□ 97MarPac-16
□ 97MetUni-176
□ 97NewPin-35
□ 97NewPinAP-35
□ 97NewPinMC-35
□ 97NewPinPP-35
□ 97Pac-302
□ 97PacLigB-302
□ 97PacSil-302
□ 97PinCer-81
□ 97PinCerMBla-81
□ 97PinCerMBlu-81
□ 97PinCerMG-81
□ 97PinCerMR-81
□ 97PinCerR-81
□ 97PinTotCPB-81
□ 97PinTotCPG-81
□ 97PinTotCPR-81
□ 97Sco-124
□ 97ScoArtPWB-124
□ 97ScoPreS-124
□ 97ScoShoS-124
□ 97ScoShoSAP-124
□ 97SpoIll-81
□ 97SpoIllEE-81
□ 97StaClu-110
□ 97StaCluMOP-110
□ 97Top-101
□ 97Top-280
□ 97Ult-198
□ 97UltGolME-198
□ 97UltPlaME-198
□ 97UppDec-78
□ 98CirThu-212
□ 98CirThuRav-212
□ 98CirThuSupRav-212
□ 98ColCho-438
□ 98Fle-419
□ 98Pac-305
□ 98PacOnl-481
□ 98PacOnlR-481
□ 98PacOnlWC-481
□ 98PacPlaB-305
□ 98PacRedT-305
□ 98PacSil-305

❑ 98PinPlu-41
❑ 98StaCluFDI-162
❑ 98StaClul-162
❑ 98StaCluOneK-162
❑ 98StaCluPP-162
❑ 98Top-444
❑ 98TopChr-444
❑ 98TopChrR-444
❑ 98TopDevR-444
❑ 98TopDia-444
❑ 98TopMiniC-444
❑ 98Ult-398
❑ 98UltGolM-398
❑ 98UltMas-398
❑ 98UltPlaM-398
❑ 98UppDec-376
❑ 98UppDec-702
❑ 99199Fin-173
❑ 99Bow-16
❑ 99BowBes-64
❑ 99BowBesAR-64
❑ 99BowBesR-64
❑ 99BowChr-16
❑ 99BowChrG-16
❑ 99BowChrGR-16
❑ 99BowChrl-16
❑ 99BowChrlR-16
❑ 99BowChrR-16
❑ 99BowGol-16
❑ 99Bowlnt-16
❑ 99FinGolRef-173
❑ 99FinRef-173
❑ 99FlaShoLeg1-129
❑ 99FlaShoLeg2-129
❑ 99FlaShoLeg3-129
❑ 99FlaShoLegM1-129
❑ 99FlaShoLegM2-129
❑ 99FlaShoLegM3-129
❑ 99FlaShoR1-129
❑ 99FlaShoR2-129
❑ 99FlaShoR3-129
❑ 99Fle-132
❑ 99FleBri-38
❑ 99FleBri2G-38
❑ 99FleBriBlu-38
❑ 99FleBriGol-38
❑ 99FleSta9-132
❑ 99FleWarT-132
❑ 99MetUni-166
❑ 99MetUniGM-166
❑ 99MetUniPMG-166
❑ 99Pac-280
❑ 99PacPlaB-280
❑ 99PacRed-280
❑ 99SkyPre-15
❑ 99SkyPreR-15
❑ 99SkyThu-58
❑ 99SkyThuRant-58
❑ 99SkyThuRave-58
❑ 99SP SigAuto-AL
❑ 99Spolll-122
❑ 99SPSig-124
❑ 99StaClu-60
❑ 99StaCluFDI-60
❑ 99StaCluOoaK-60
❑ 99StaCluPP-60
❑ 99ThuSkySupR-58
❑ 99Top-320
❑ 99TopBlaLC1-57
❑ 99TopBlaLC2-57
❑ 99TopBlaLC3-57
❑ 99TopChr-320
❑ 99TopChrR-320
❑ 99TopGal-100
❑ 99TopGalPP-100
❑ 99TopGalPPI-100
❑ 99TopGolL-57
❑ 99TopGolLC1-57
❑ 99TopGolLC2-57
❑ 99TopGolLOtO-57
❑ 99TopMVPP-320
❑ 99TopOpeD-148
❑ 99TopRedLC1-57
❑ 99TopRedLC2-57
❑ 99TopRedLC3-57
❑ 99TopSta-133
❑ 99TopStaFoil-133
❑ 99Ult-97
❑ 99UltGolM-97
❑ 99UltMas-97
❑ 99UltPlaM-97
❑ 99UppDec-427
❑ 99UppDecEL1-427
❑ 99UppDecEL2-427
❑ 99UppDecM-137
❑ 99UppDecMGS-137
❑ 99UppDecMHFS-137
❑ 99UppDecMP-137
❑ 99UppDecMSS-137
❑ 99Vic-256

Leiter, Kurt

❑ 83SanJosBC-24
❑ 84ChaO'sT-23
❑ 86MiaMarP-15

Leiter, Mark

❑ 89ColCliC-29
❑ 89Ft.LauYS-13
❑ 90CMC-204
❑ 90ColCliC-4
❑ 90ColCliP-11
❑ 90ColCliP-673
❑ 90ProAAAF-323
❑ 90TopTVY-51
❑ 91Bow-138
❑ 91DonRoo-29
❑ 91LinDriAAA-588
❑ 91Sco-727
❑ 91TigCok-23
❑ 91TolMudHLD-588
❑ 91TopDeb90-84
❑ 92Bow-476
❑ 92Cla1-T52
❑ 92Don-633
❑ 92Fle-140
❑ 92Lea-207
❑ 92LeaBlaG-207
❑ 92OPC-537
❑ 92OPCPre-48
❑ 92Sco-626
❑ 92StaClu-889
❑ 92TigKro-16
❑ 92Top-537
❑ 92TopGol-537
❑ 92TopGolW-537
❑ 92TopMic-537
❑ 92Ult-366
❑ 92UppDec-319
❑ 93Don-495
❑ 93Fle-608
❑ 93OPC-174
❑ 93PacSpa-112
❑ 93StaClu-116
❑ 93StaCluFDI-116
❑ 93StaCluMOP-116
❑ 93TigGat-18
❑ 93Top-216
❑ 93TopGol-216
❑ 93TopInaM-216
❑ 93TopInaR-216
❑ 93TopMic-216
❑ 93UppDec-95
❑ 93UppDecGold-95
❑ 94AngLAT-13
❑ 94AngMot-24
❑ 94Fla-24
❑ 94FleUpd-19
❑ 94Pac-224
❑ 94StaClu-663
❑ 94StaCluFDI-663
❑ 94StaCluGR-663
❑ 94StaCluMOP-663
❑ 94Top-133
❑ 94TopGol-133
❑ 94TopSpa-133
❑ 94TopTra-117T
❑ 95Fle-230
❑ 95GiaMot-11
❑ 95Sco-225
❑ 95ScoGolR-225
❑ 95ScoPlaTS-225
❑ 95Top-41
❑ 96ColCho-301
❑ 96ColChoGS-301
❑ 96ColChoSS-301
❑ 96Don-296
❑ 96DonPreP-296
❑ 96EmoXL-292
❑ 96Fin-B34
❑ 96FinRef-B34
❑ 96Fla-390
❑ 96Fle-589
❑ 96FleTif-589
❑ 96GiaMot-12
❑ 96LeaSigA-132
❑ 96LeaSigAG-132
❑ 96LeaSigAS-132
❑ 96MetUni-244
❑ 96MetUniP-244
❑ 96Pac-205
❑ 96ProSta-54
❑ 96Sco-459
❑ 96StaClu-165
❑ 96StaCluMOP-165
❑ 96Top-107
❑ 96Ult-295
❑ 96UltGolM-295
❑ 96UppDec-452
❑ 97Cir-170
❑ 97CirRav-170
❑ 97ColCho-417
❑ 97Fle-627
❑ 97FleTif-627
❑ 97PacPriGotD-GD169
❑ 97PhiCopQ-14
❑ 97PhiTeal-31B
❑ 97Sco-453
❑ 97ScoArtPWB-453
❑ 97ScoResC-453
❑ 97ScoShoS-453
❑ 97ScoShoSAP-453
❑ 97Top-327
❑ 97Ult-453
❑ 97UltGolME-453
❑ 97UltPlaME-453
❑ 98Pac-383
❑ 98PacOnl-565
❑ 98PacOnlR-565
❑ 98PacOnlWC-565
❑ 98PacPlaB-383
❑ 98PacRedT-383
❑ 98PacSil-383
❑ 98PhiTeal-20
❑ 98Pin-118
❑ 98PinPreP-118
❑ 98Top-60
❑ 98TopChr-60
❑ 98TopChrR-60
❑ 98TopDevR-60
❑ 98TopDia-60
❑ 98TopMiniC-60
❑ 98UppDec-477
❑ 99Pac-328
❑ 99PacPlaB-328
❑ 99PacRed-328
❑ 99Top-294
❑ 99TopChr-294
❑ 99TopChrR-294
❑ 99TopMVPP-294

Leitner, Ted

❑ 90PadMag-16
❑ 91PadCok-5

Leius, Scott

❑ 87KenTwiP-21
❑ 88VisOakCLC-154
❑ 88VisOakP-102
❑ 89BasAmeAPB-AA18
❑ 89OrlTwiB-16
❑ 89OrlTwiP-1332
❑ 89SouLeaAJ-6
❑ 90Bow-423
❑ 90BowTif-423
❑ 90CMC-568
❑ 90Fle-647
❑ 90FleCan-647
❑ 90PorBeaC-16
❑ 90PorBeaP-185
❑ 90ProAAAF-255
❑ 91Bow-337
❑ 91DodPho-24
❑ 91DonRoo-4
❑ 91FleUpd-38
❑ 91LeaGolR-BC1
❑ 91LeaGolRNV-265
❑ 91Sco-370
❑ 91StaClu-338
❑ 91TopDeb90-85
❑ 91TopTra-71T
❑ 91TopTraT-71T
❑ 91UltUpd-38
❑ 91UppDec-35
❑ 92Bow-209
❑ 92Don-359
❑ 92Fle-209
❑ 92FleRooS-20
❑ 92Lea-214
❑ 92LeaBlaG-214
❑ 92OPC-74
❑ 92OPCPre-118
❑ 92Pin-365
❑ 92Sco-320
❑ 92ScoFacl-B2
❑ 92StaClu-350
❑ 92StaCluD-104
❑ 92Stu-206
❑ 92Top-74
❑ 92TopGol-74
❑ 92TopGolW-74
❑ 92TopMic-74
❑ 92Ult-94
❑ 92UppDec-313
❑ 93Don-369
❑ 93Fle-270
❑ 93Lea-208
❑ 93PacSpa-522
❑ 93PanSti-128
❑ 93Pin-192
❑ 93Sco-178
❑ 93Sel-251
❑ 93StaClu-254
❑ 93StaCluFDI-254
❑ 93StaCluMOP-254
❑ 93Top-146
❑ 93TopGol-146
❑ 93TopInaM-146
❑ 93TopInaR-146
❑ 93TopMic-146
❑ 93TriPla-165
❑ 93Ult-233
❑ 93UppDec-212
❑ 93UppDecGold-212
❑ 94ColC-382
❑ 94ColChoGS-382
❑ 94ColChoSS-382
❑ 94Fin-377
❑ 94FinRef-377
❑ 94Fla-76
❑ 94FleExtB-119
❑ 94FleUpd-62
❑ 94Lea-337
❑ 94Pac-359
❑ 94Sco-545
❑ 94ScoGolR-545
❑ 94StaClu-670
❑ 94StaCluFDI-670
❑ 94StaCluGR-670
❑ 94StaCluMOP-670
❑ 94Top-517
❑ 94TopGol-517
❑ 94TopSpa-517
❑ 94UppDec-322
❑ 94UppDecED-322
❑ 95ColCho-486
❑ 95ColChoGS-486
❑ 95ColChoSS-486
❑ 95Don-247
❑ 95DonPreP-247
❑ 95DonTopotO-110
❑ 95Fin-57
❑ 95FinRef-57
❑ 95Fla-58
❑ 95Fle-207
❑ 95Lea-49
❑ 95LeaLim-175
❑ 95Pac-251
❑ 95Pin-44
❑ 95PinArtP-44
❑ 95PinMusC-44
❑ 95Sco-142
❑ 95ScoGolR-142
❑ 95ScoPlaTS-142
❑ 95StaClu-292
❑ 95StaCluMOP-292
❑ 95StaCluSTWS-292
❑ 95StaCluVR-151
❑ 95StaCluVRMO-151
❑ 95Top-573
❑ 95TopCyb-347
❑ 95TopD3-18
❑ 95Ult-74
❑ 95UltGolM-74
❑ 96Don-240
❑ 96DonPreP-240
❑ 96LeaSigEA-106
❑ 96Pac-362
❑ 96PacPri-P115
❑ 96PacPriG-P115
❑ 96Sco-392
❑ 96StaClu-338
❑ 96StaCluMOP-338
❑ 96Top-78
❑ 98OmaRoyM-12

Leiva, Jose

❑ 86ReaPhiP-14
❑ 87ReaPhiP-22
❑ 88ReaPhiP-884
❑ 89CanIndB-22
❑ 89CanIndP-1312
❑ 89CanIndS-24
❑ 93LinVenB-165

Leix, Tom

❑ 81WisRapTT-2

Leja, Frank

❑ 54NewYorJA-49
❑ 54Top-175
❑ 55Top-99
❑ 60Lea-121
❑ 94TopArc1-175
❑ 94TopArc1G-175

LeJeune, Larry

❑ 90DodTar-1105

LeJohn, Ducky (Don)

❑ 66OPC-41
❑ 66Top-41
❑ 66TopVen-41
❑ 75WatDodT-11
❑ 77CliDodT-16
❑ 78CliDodT-19
❑ 86BakDodP-19
❑ 90DodTar-445

Lekew, Jim

❑ 77FriOneYW-88

Leland, Stan

❑ 78DayBeaAT-15
❑ 80ColAstT-4
❑ 81TucTorT-15

Lelivelt, John Frank

❑ 11PinT-5-555
❑ 14FatPlaT-25
❑ 30Zee-34
❑ 31Zee-20
❑ 33Zee-8

Lelivelt, William

❑ 09ColChiE-168
❑ 12ColRedB-168
❑ 12ColTinT-168

Lemanczyk, Dave

❑ 75DetTigP-19
❑ 75OPC-571
❑ 75Top-571
❑ 75TopMin-571
❑ 76DetTigP-17
❑ 76OPC-409
❑ 76SSP-355
❑ 76Top-409
❑ 77OPC-229
❑ 77Top-611
❑ 78BluJayP-13
❑ 78OPC-85
❑ 78Top-33
❑ 79BluJayBY-15
❑ 79OPC-102
❑ 79Top-207
❑ 80OPC-68
❑ 80Top-124
❑ 81Don-292
❑ 81Top-391
❑ 86BluJayGT-9

LeMaster, Denny

❑ 63Top-74
❑ 64BraJayP-5
❑ 64Top-152
❑ 64TopVen-152
❑ 65Kah-21
❑ 65Top-441
❑ 66BraPos-16
❑ 66Kah-17
❑ 66Top-252
❑ 66TopVen-252
❑ 67Ast-16
❑ 67BraPho-19
❑ 67CokCapB-7
❑ 67Top-288
❑ 68CokCapA-16
❑ 68DexPre-47
❑ 68Top-491
❑ 69MilBra-157
❑ 69OPC-96
❑ 69Top-96
❑ 69TopSta-34
❑ 69TopTeaP-6
❑ 70AstPho-13
❑ 70AstTeal-6
❑ 70MLBOffS-42
❑ 70OPC-178
❑ 70Top-178
❑ 71MLBOffS-84
❑ 71OPC-636
❑ 71Top-636
❑ 72MilBra-197
❑ 72OPC-371
❑ 72Top-371
❑ 78AtlCon-13
❑ 78TCM60I-17
❑ 87AstShoSO-14
❑ 87AstShowSTh-28

LeMaster, Frank

❑ 80PhiBul-14

LeMaster, Johnnie

❑ 75IntLeaASB-16
❑ 75PacCoaLAB-16
❑ 75PhoGiaC-12
❑ 75PhoGiaCK-12
❑ 76OPC-596
❑ 76PheGiaCr-2
❑ 76PhoGiaCa-1
❑ 76PhoGiaCC-15
❑ 76PhoGiaVNB-14
❑ 76Top-596
❑ 77GiaTeal-16
❑ 77Top-151
❑ 78GiaTeal-17
❑ 78Top-538
❑ 79GiaPol-10
❑ 79Top-284
❑ 80GiaEurFS-3
❑ 80GiaPol-10
❑ 80GiaTeal-14
❑ 80OPC-224
❑ 80Top-434
❑ 81Don-432
❑ 81Fle-450
❑ 81OPC-84
❑ 81Top-84
❑ 82Don-524
❑ 82Fle-393
❑ 82Gia25tATI-15
❑ 82Top-304
❑ 82TopSti-108
❑ 83Don-125
❑ 83Fle-266
❑ 83GiaMot-4
❑ 83GiaPos-16
❑ 83OPC-154
❑ 83Top-154
❑ 83TopSti-304
❑ 84AllGamPI-22
❑ 84Don-649
❑ 84Fle-378
❑ 84GiaPos-12
❑ 84Nes792-663
❑ 84OPC-107
❑ 84Top-663
❑ 84TopRubD-2
❑ 84TopSti-168
❑ 84TopTif-663
❑ 85Don-114
❑ 85Fle-614
❑ 85GiaMot-14
❑ 85GiaPos-19
❑ 85OPC-302
❑ 85Top-772
❑ 85TopRubD-2
❑ 85TopSti-164
❑ 85TopTif-772
❑ 85TopTifT-74T
❑ 85TopTra-74T
❑ 86OPC-289
❑ 86Top-289
❑ 86TopTif-289
❑ 90SweBasG-68

LeMasters, Jim

❑ 87SumBraP-20
❑ 88BurBraP-13
❑ 88MidLeaAGS-20
❑ 89GreBraB-10
❑ 89GreBraP-1176
❑ 89GreBraS-13
❑ 89Sta-36
❑ 90CMC-180
❑ 90OmaRoyC-5
❑ 90OmaRoyP-63
❑ 90ProAAAF-598
❑ 91LinDriAAA-339
❑ 91OmaRoyLD-339
❑ 91OmaRoyP-1032

Lemay, Bob

❑ 91NiaFalRC-27
❑ 91NiaFalRP-3629
❑ 92FayGenC-8
❑ 92FayGenF-2165

Lemay, Richard

❑ 62Top-71
❑ 62TopVen-71
❑ 63Top-459
❑ 81Gia196T-23

Lembo, Steve

❑ 50WorWidGV-7
❑ 53ExhCan-36
❑ 74dod195T-18
❑ 90DodTar-446

Lemke, Mark

❑ 86SumBraP-16
❑ 87DurBulP-26
❑ 88BasAmeAAB-16
❑ 88GreBraB-10
❑ 88SouLeaAJ-15

❑ 89ClaLigB-52
❑ 89Don-523
❑ 89RicBraBC-13
❑ 89RicBraC-19
❑ 89RicBraP-830
❑ 89RicBraTI-13
❑ 89Top-327
❑ 89TopTif-327
❑ 89TriAAAP-AAA55
❑ 89UppDec-19
❑ 90Bow-11
❑ 90BowTif-11
❑ 90BraDubP-16
❑ 90BraDubS-19
❑ 90Don-624
❑ 90DonRoo-43
❑ 90Fle-587
❑ 90FleCan-587
❑ 90OPC-451
❑ 90Sco-593
❑ 90ScoRooDT-B5
❑ 90ScoYouS2-22
❑ 90Top-451
❑ 90TopBig-120
❑ 90TopTif-451
❑ 90TriAAAC-18
❑ 90UppDec-665
❑ 91BraDubP-18
❑ 91BraSubS-23
❑ 91Don-604
❑ 91Fle-696
❑ 91OPC-251
❑ 91Sco-779
❑ 91Sco100RS-89
❑ 91StaClu-203
❑ 91Top-251
❑ 91TopDesS-251
❑ 91TopMic-251
❑ 91TopTif-251
❑ 91UppDec-419
❑ 92Bow-663
❑ 92BraLykP-18
❑ 92BraLykS-21
❑ 92Don-606
❑ 92Fle-362
❑ 92Lea-94
❑ 92LeaBlaG-94
❑ 92OPC-689
❑ 92PanSti-163
❑ 92Pin-426
❑ 92Sco-386
❑ 92ScoFacI-B3
❑ 92StaClu-316
❑ 92StaCluD-105
❑ 92Stu-6
❑ 92Top-689
❑ 92TopGol-689
❑ 92TopGolW-689
❑ 92TopMic-689
❑ 92Ult-165
❑ 92UppDec-47
❑ 93BraFloA-6
❑ 93BraLykP-16
❑ 93BraLykS-19
❑ 93BraStaC-4
❑ 93Don-316
❑ 93Fla-6
❑ 93Fle-368
❑ 93Lea-68
❑ 93OPC-236
❑ 93PacSpa-334
❑ 93PanSti-182
❑ 93Pin-368
❑ 93Sco-147
❑ 93Sel-161
❑ 93StaClu-172
❑ 93StaCluFDI-172
❑ 93StaCluM-37
❑ 93StaCluMOP-172
❑ 93Top-116
❑ 93TopGol-116
❑ 93TopInaM-116
❑ 93TopInaR-116
❑ 93TopMic-116
❑ 93TriPla-215
❑ 93Ult-8
❑ 93UppDec-109
❑ 93UppDecGold-109
❑ 94BraLykP-17
❑ 94BraLykS-17
❑ 94BraUSPC-2H
❑ 94BraUSPC-12D
❑ 94ColC-501
❑ 94ColChoGS-501
❑ 94ColChoSS-501
❑ 94Don-147
❑ 94Fin-95
❑ 94FinRef-95
❑ 94Fla-354
❑ 94Fle-363
❑ 94FleExtB-206
❑ 94Lea-392
❑ 94Pac-13
❑ 94Pin-447
❑ 94PinArtP-447
❑ 94PinMusC-447
❑ 94Sco-392
❑ 94ScoGolR-392
❑ 94Sel-60
❑ 94StaClu-402
❑ 94StaCluFDI-402
❑ 94StaCluGR-402
❑ 94StaCluMOP-402
❑ 94StaCluT-46
❑ 94StaCluTFDI-46
❑ 94Top-23
❑ 94TopGol-23
❑ 94TopSpa-23
❑ 94Ult-153
❑ 94UppDec-489
❑ 94UppDecED-489
❑ 95BraAtlC-6
❑ 95ColCho-164
❑ 95ColChoGS-164
❑ 95ColChoSS-164
❑ 95Don-146
❑ 95DonPreP-146
❑ 95DonTopotO-188
❑ 95Fla-327
❑ 95Fle-309
❑ 95Lea-174
❑ 95Pac-9
❑ 95Pin-126
❑ 95PinArtP-126
❑ 95PinMusC-126
❑ 95Sco-87
❑ 95ScoGolR-87
❑ 95ScoPlaTS-87
❑ 95StaClu-285
❑ 95StaCluMOP-285
❑ 95StaCluSTWS-285
❑ 95StaCluVR-147
❑ 95StaCluVRMO-147
❑ 95Top-486
❑ 95TopCyb-278
❑ 95Ult-128
❑ 95UltGolM-128
❑ 96BraFle-9
❑ 96ColCho-44
❑ 96ColChoGS-44
❑ 96ColChoSS-44
❑ 96Don-279
❑ 96DonPreP-279
❑ 96Fla-203
❑ 96Fle-297
❑ 96FleTif-297
❑ 96MetUni-132
❑ 96MetUniP-132
❑ 96Pac-12
❑ 96Sco-124
❑ 96ScoDugC-A78
❑ 96ScoDugCAP-A78
❑ 96StaClu-382
❑ 96StaCluEPB-382
❑ 96StaCluEPG-382
❑ 96StaCluEPS-382
❑ 96StaCluMOP-382
❑ 96Top-83
❑ 96Ult-439
❑ 96UltGolM-439
❑ 96UppDec-7
❑ 97BraSco-8
❑ 97BraScoPl-8
❑ 97BraScoPr-8
❑ 97Cir-48
❑ 97CirRav-48
❑ 97ColCho-269
❑ 97Fle-261
❑ 97FleTif-261
❑ 97Pac-238
❑ 97PacLigB-238
❑ 97PacSil-238
❑ 97Sco-163
❑ 97ScoArtPWB-163
❑ 97ScoPreS-163
❑ 97ScoShoS-163
❑ 97ScoShoSAP-163
❑ 97StaClu-322
❑ 97StaCluMOP-322
❑ 97Top-94
❑ 97Ult-419
❑ 97UltGolME-419
❑ 97UltPlaME-419
❑ 97UppDec-13
❑ 98Pac-237
❑ 98PacOnl-118
❑ 98PacOnlR-118
❑ 98PacOnlWC-118
❑ 98PacPlaB-237
❑ 98PacRedT-237
❑ 98PacSil-237
❑ 98Top-36
❑ 98TopChr-36
❑ 98TopChrR-36
❑ 98TopDevR-36
❑ 98TopDia-36
❑ 98TopMiniC-36
❑ 98UppDec-302

Lemke, Steve
❑ 92SouOreAC-4
❑ 92SouOreAF-3413
❑ 93SouOreAC-13
❑ 93SouOreAF-4058
❑ 94MidLeaAF-MDW31
❑ 94WesMicWC-13
❑ 94WesMicWF-2291
❑ 95Exc-110
❑ 95HunStaTI-17

Lemle, Rob
❑ 87LitFalMP-2403
❑ 88ColMetGS-21
❑ 89ColMetB-4
❑ 89ColMetGS-14

Lemon, Bob (Robert)
❑ 46SpoExcW-5-12
❑ 47Exh-132A
❑ 47Exh-132B
❑ 47IndTeal-17
❑ 47IndVanPP-16
❑ 47PM1StaP1-111
❑ 47PM1StaP1-112
❑ 48IndTeal-20
❑ 49Bow-238
❑ 49IndTeal-17
❑ 49IndVisEl-11
❑ 49MPR302-2-119
❑ 50Bow-40
❑ 50IndNumN-15
❑ 50IndTeal-17
❑ 51BerRos-A2
❑ 51Bow-53
❑ 51FisBakL-17
❑ 51R42SmaS-59
❑ 51TopCurA-8
❑ 52BerRos-33
❑ 52Bow-23
❑ 52IndNumN-4
❑ 52StaCalL-74C
❑ 52StaCalS-88A
❑ 52Top-268
❑ 52Whe-18A
❑ 52Whe-18B
❑ 53BowBW-27
❑ 53DixLid-12
❑ 53DixPre-12
❑ 53ExhCan-31
❑ 53IndPenCBP-19
❑ 53NorBreL-16
❑ 53RedMan-AL17
❑ 54Bow-196
❑ 54DanDee-15
❑ 54RedHeaF-16
❑ 54RedMan-AL21
❑ 55BigLeaIS-10
❑ 55Bow-191
❑ 55DaiQueS-10
❑ 55Ind-4
❑ 55IndCarBL-6
❑ 55IndGolS-2
❑ 55RedMan-AL8
❑ 56Top-255
❑ 57IndSoh-7
❑ 57IndTeal-12
❑ 57Top-120
❑ 58Top-2A
❑ 58Top-2B
❑ 60RawGloT-13
❑ 60Top-460
❑ 65SeaPop-11
❑ 70Houof J-13
❑ 70RoyTeal-19
❑ 71OPC-91
❑ 71oySigST-14
❑ 71Top-91
❑ 72OPC-449
❑ 72oyTeal-13
❑ 72Top-449
❑ 74SacSolC-62
❑ 75TCM195Cl-18
❑ 75TCM195Cl-39
❑ 75TCMHouoJ-13
❑ 76RowExh-5
❑ 76ShaPiz-155
❑ 76TayBow4-104
❑ 77Top-418
❑ 78SSP270-139
❑ 78Top-574
❑ 78YanPhoA-16
❑ 79TCM50-19
❑ 79Top-626
❑ 79YanBurK-1
❑ 80PacLeg-120
❑ 80PerHaloFP-155
❑ 80PerHaloFPS-31
❑ 80SSPHOF-155
❑ 82DiaCla-79
❑ 82Don-635
❑ 82OhiHaloF-32
❑ 82TCMGreP-2
❑ 83DonHOFH-30
❑ 83TopRep5-268
❑ 84SpoDesPW-45
❑ 85TCMPla1-16
❑ 86SpoDecG-39
❑ 88PacLegI-32
❑ 89HOFStiB-68
❑ 89PerCelP-25
❑ 90PerGreM-67
❑ 91TopArc1-284
❑ 92BazQua5A-1
❑ 93ActPacA-113
❑ 93ActPacA2-47G

Lemon, Chet
❑ 75TucTorTI-8
❑ 76OPC-590
❑ 76Top-590
❑ 77BurCheD-73
❑ 77OPC-195
❑ 77Top-58
❑ 77WhiSoxJT-10
❑ 77WhiSoxT-18
❑ 78Hos-124
❑ 78OPC-224
❑ 78SSP270-146
❑ 78Top-127
❑ 79BasPat-45
❑ 79Hos-40
❑ 79OPC-169
❑ 79Top-333
❑ 79TopCom-5
❑ 80Kel-46
❑ 80OPC-309
❑ 80Top-589
❑ 80TopSup-57
❑ 81AllGamPI-56
❑ 81CokTeaS-32
❑ 81Don-281
❑ 81Fle-354
❑ 81Kel-19
❑ 81OPC-242
❑ 81Squ-33
❑ 81Top-242
❑ 81TopScr-34
❑ 81TopSti-57
❑ 81TopSupHT-18
❑ 82Don-291
❑ 82Fle-351
❑ 82FleSta-191
❑ 82Kel-54
❑ 82OPC-13
❑ 82Top-216
❑ 82Top-493
❑ 82TopSti-168
❑ 82TopTra-62T
❑ 83AllGamPI-58
❑ 83Don-511
❑ 83Fle-335
❑ 83FleSti-251
❑ 83OPC-53
❑ 83TigPos-19
❑ 83Top-727
❑ 84AllGamPI-148
❑ 84Don-171
❑ 84Fle-85
❑ 84FunFooP-97
❑ 84Nes792-611
❑ 84OPC-86
❑ 84TigFarJ-9
❑ 84TigTeal-22
❑ 84TigWavP-23
❑ 84Top-611
❑ 84TopSti-271
❑ 84TopTif-611
❑ 85AllGamPI-62
❑ 85Don-90
❑ 85Fle-15
❑ 85Lea-77
❑ 85OPC-20
❑ 85SevCoi-D11
❑ 85SevCoi-G9
❑ 85TigCaiD-12
❑ 85TigWen-14
❑ 85Top-20
❑ 85TopGloA-18
❑ 85TopSti-21
❑ 85TopSti-190
❑ 85TopSti-260
❑ 85TopTif-20
❑ 86BasStaB-65
❑ 86Don-90
❑ 86Fle-230
❑ 86Lea-85
❑ 86OPC-160
❑ 86SevCoi-C14
❑ 86TigCaiD-11
❑ 86Top-160
❑ 86TopSti-274
❑ 86TopTat-10
❑ 86TopTif-160
❑ 87Don-353
❑ 87DonOpeD-213
❑ 87Fle-156
❑ 87FleGlo-156
❑ 87Lea-227
❑ 87OPC-206
❑ 87SevCoi-D6
❑ 87SpoTeaP-15
❑ 87TigCaiD-10
❑ 87TigCok-10
❑ 87Top-739
❑ 87TopSti-268
❑ 87TopTif-739
❑ 88Don-215
❑ 88DonBasB-147
❑ 88Fle-61
❑ 88FleGlo-61
❑ 88Lea-166
❑ 88OPC-366
❑ 88PanSti-96
❑ 88Sco-119
❑ 88ScoGlo-119
❑ 88StaLinTi-12
❑ 88TigPep-34
❑ 88TigPol-7
❑ 88Top-366
❑ 88TopBig-147
❑ 88TopTif-366
❑ 89Bow-108
❑ 89BowTif-108
❑ 89Don-209
❑ 89DonBasB-69
❑ 89Fle-137
❑ 89FleGlo-137
❑ 89OPC-328
❑ 89PanSti-344
❑ 89Sco-44
❑ 89Spo-171
❑ 89TigMar-34
❑ 89TigPol-34
❑ 89Top-514
❑ 89TopBig-202
❑ 89TopSti-283
❑ 89TopTif-514
❑ 89UppDec-128
❑ 90Bow-354
❑ 90BowTif-354
❑ 90Don-60
❑ 90DonBesA-76
❑ 90Fle-608
❑ 90FleCan-608
❑ 90Lea-133
❑ 90M.Vpin-35
❑ 90MLBBasB-87
❑ 90OPC-271
❑ 90PanSti-77
❑ 90PubIntS-475
❑ 90Sco-106
❑ 90TigCok-10
❑ 90Top-271
❑ 90TopBig-86
❑ 90TopSti-278
❑ 90TopTif-271
❑ 90UppDec-348
❑ 91Don-301
❑ 91Fle-341
❑ 91OPC-469
❑ 91PanFreS-292
❑ 91Sco-557
❑ 91StaClu-23
❑ 91Top-469
❑ 91TopDesS-469
❑ 91TopMic-469
❑ 91TopTif-469
❑ 91UppDec-389

Lemon, Don
❑ 89IdaFalBP-2033

Lemon, Don (Donald)
❑ 92EriSaiC-5
❑ 92EriSaiF-1616
❑ 93AusFut-52
❑ 93HigDesMC-9
❑ 93HigDesMF-35
❑ 93Top-441
❑ 93TopGol-441
❑ 93TopInaM-441
❑ 93TopInaR-441
❑ 93TopMic-441
❑ 94PorSeaDF-674
❑ 94PorSeaDTI-19

Lemon, Jim
❑ 47PM1StaP1-113
❑ 54Top-103
❑ 55Bow-262
❑ 57Top-57
❑ 58SeaTeal-18
❑ 58SenJayP-6
❑ 58Top-15
❑ 59HomRunD-11
❑ 59Top-74
❑ 59Top-215
❑ 59TopVen-74
❑ 60SenJayP-10
❑ 60Top-440
❑ 61Baz-12
❑ 61Pos-93A
❑ 61Pos-93B
❑ 61Top-44
❑ 61Top-450
❑ 61TopStal-182
❑ 61TwiCloD-13
❑ 61TwiJayP-8
❑ 61TwiPetM-17
❑ 61TwiUniMC-10
❑ 62Jel-89
❑ 62Pos-89
❑ 62PosCan-89
❑ 62SalPlaC-9A
❑ 62SalPlaC-9B
❑ 62ShiPlaC-9
❑ 62Top-510
❑ 63Top-369
❑ 67SenTeal-7
❑ 67TwiTeal-9
❑ 68SenTeal-7
❑ 68Top-341
❑ 68TopVen-341
❑ 69Top-294
❑ 78TwiFri-9
❑ 79TCM50-180
❑ 82TwiPos-20
❑ 83TwiTeal-29
❑ 83TwiTeal-34
❑ 84MinTwiP-20
❑ 84TwiTeal-30
❑ 89EliTwiS-30
❑ 90EliTwiS-25
❑ 91EliTwiP-4316
❑ 94TopArc1-103
❑ 94TopArc1G-103

Lemon, Leo
❑ 81RedPioT-19

Lemon, Timothy
❑ 98JohCCTI-21
❑ 99TeaBesR-47
❑ 99TeaBesRG-47
❑ 99TeaBesRS-47

Lemonds, Dave
❑ 71OPC-458
❑ 71Top-458
❑ 72OPC-413
❑ 72Top-413
❑ 73OPC-534
❑ 73Top-534

Lemongello, Mark
❑ 77Top-478
❑ 78AstBurK-9
❑ 78AstPos-15
❑ 78Top-358
❑ 79Top-187
❑ 80WicAerT-22
❑ 87AstShoSPT-19

Lemonis, Chris
❑ 97WesMicW-16
❑ 98LakTigM-17

Lemons, Richard
❑ 92AriWilP-8

❑ 93BurIndC-15
❑ 93BurIndF-3312
❑ 94ColRedC-13
❑ 94ColRedF-455
Lemons, Tim
❑ 86BurExpP-14
❑ 87SprCarB-7
Lemp, Chris
❑ 91BluOriC-21
❑ 91BluOriP-4124
❑ 92KanCouCC-11
❑ 92KanCouCF-88
❑ 92KanCouCTI-19
❑ 92ProFS7-12
❑ 93FreKeyC-13
❑ 93FreKeyF-1024
❑ 94FreKeyC-13
❑ 94FreKeyF-2609
❑ 94OriPro-52
❑ 95Exc-7
❑ 96BowBayB-19
Lemperle, John
❑ 85AlbYanT-30
❑ 86AlbYanT-19
Lemuth, Steve
❑ 89MedAthB-19
Lenderman, Dave
❑ 86PitCubP-13
Lenhardt, Don
❑ 51TopBluB-33
❑ 52Top-4
❑ 53BowC-20
❑ 54Bow-53
❑ 54OriEss-23
❑ 54Top-157
❑ 73OPC-131
❑ 73Top-131A
❑ 73Top-131B
❑ 79DiaGre-144
❑ 81RedSoxBG2S-34
❑ 83TopRep5-4
❑ 91OriCro-259
❑ 94TopArc1-157
❑ 94TopArc1G-157
Lennon, Ed
❑ 24Zee-49
Lennon, Patrick
❑ 86BelMarCr-128
❑ 87WauTimP-7
❑ 88VerMarP-947
❑ 89WilBilP-632
❑ 89WilBilS-12
❑ 90Bes-153
❑ 90SanBerSB-9
❑ 90SanBerSCLC-101
❑ 90SanBerSP-2645
❑ 91Bow-250
❑ 91CalCanLD-63
❑ 91CalCanP-528
❑ 91LinDriAAA-63
❑ 91UppDecFE-43F
❑ 92Bow-192
❑ 92CalCanS-64
❑ 92ClaGam-172
❑ 92Don-17
❑ 92Pin-542
❑ 92SkyAAAF-28
❑ 92StaClu-679
❑ 92StaCluECN-679
❑ 92TopDeb91-107
❑ 92UppDec-13
❑ 94NewBriRSF-657
❑ 95PawRedSDD-17
❑ 95PawRedTI-22
❑ 95TreThuTI-26
❑ 98PacInvGems-85
❑ 98SyrSkyG-18
Lennon, Robert
❑ 55Top-119
❑ 56Top-104
❑ 57Top-371
❑ 58MonRoyF-14
❑ 59O'KAleMR-14
Lennox, Ed (James E.)
❑ 09T206-211
❑ 10CouT21-39
❑ 10CouT21-171
❑ 11HelSta-97
❑ 11PinT-5-454
❑ 11SpoLifM-159
❑ 11T205-100
❑ 11TurRedT-104
❑ 12HasTriFT-42
❑ 12T207-103
❑ 14PieStaT-63
❑ 15VicT21-18
❑ 72ClaCar-13
❑ 90DodTar-447
Lenti, Mike
❑ 81CliGiaT-23
Lentine, James
❑ 78ArkTraT-16
❑ 81ChaChaT-17
❑ 81Don-250
❑ 81Fle-476
Lentz, Harry
❑ 09T206-498
❑ 10CouT21-40
Lentz, Ryan
❑ 98VerExpO-24
❑ 99TeaBesR-48
❑ 99TeaBesRG-48
❑ 99TeaBesRS-48
Leon, Angel
❑ 93LinVenB-242
❑ 95LinVen-130
Leon, Carlos
❑ 98MicBatCM-19
Leon, Danny (Danilo)
❑ 87JamExpP-2560
❑ 88JamExpP-1913
❑ 88WesPalBES-16
❑ 89JacExpB-21
❑ 89JacExpP-169
❑ 92DonRoo-64
❑ 92FleUpd-61
❑ 92TopTra-64T
❑ 92TopTraG-64T
❑ 92TulDriF-2691
❑ 93Don-387
❑ 93LinVenB-247
❑ 93OklCit8F-1623
❑ 93RanKee-228
❑ 94VenLinU-247
❑ 95LinVen-64
❑ 96-97LinVen-119
Leon, Donny
❑ 97Bow-360
❑ 97BowChr-241
❑ 97BowChrI-241
❑ 97BowChrIR-241
❑ 97BowChrR-241
❑ 97BowInt-360
❑ 97GreBatB-17
❑ 98TamYanM-17
❑ 99Bow-410
❑ 99BowGol-410
❑ 99BowInt-410
Leon, Eddie (Eduardo)
❑ 70OPC-292
❑ 70Top-292
❑ 71MLBOffS-378
❑ 71OPC-252
❑ 71Top-252
❑ 72Top-721
❑ 72WhiSox-7
❑ 73LinPor-49
❑ 73OPC-287
❑ 73Top-287
❑ 74OPC-501
❑ 74Top-501
❑ 75OPC-528
❑ 75Top-528
❑ 75TopMin-528
❑ 92YanWIZ7-95
Leon, Felix
❑ 93LinVenB-4
Leon, Henry
❑ 95LinVen-259
Leon, Johnny
❑ 90TamYanD-15
Leon, Jose
❑ 89EliTwiS-14
❑ 93LinVenB-171
❑ 94VenLinU-176
❑ 96JohCitCTI-20
❑ 97PeoChi-15
❑ 98PriWilCQ-23
Leon, Maximino
❑ 75OPC-442
❑ 75Top-442
❑ 75TopMin-442
❑ 76AtlBraP-17
❑ 76OPC-576
❑ 76SSP-3
❑ 76Top-576
❑ 77Top-213
❑ 98GreFalDG-19
Leon, Mike
❑ 87AppFoxP-22
❑ 88AppFoxP-163
❑ 89MemChiB-27
❑ 89MemChiP-1191
❑ 90MemChiB-27
❑ 90MemChiS-27
❑ 95ChaKniTI-4
❑ 96ChaKniB-4
❑ 98ChaKniQ-5
Leon, Mike (Michael)
❑ 93JamExpC-14
❑ 93JamExpF-3322
❑ 97ChaKni-6
Leon, Richard
❑ 75TulOil7-5
❑ 98PorRocG-23
Leon, Ron
❑ 85SprCarT-15
❑ 87EriCarP-5
Leon, Scott
❑ 96HudValRB-12
❑ 97ChaRivDG-18
❑ 98St.PetDRM-10
Leonard, Andy
❑ 86BurExpP-15
Leonard, Bernardo
❑ 78HolMilT-15
Leonard, Buck (Walter)
❑ 74LauOldTBS-11
❑ 76ShaPiz-132
❑ 80PerHaloFP-132
❑ 80PerHaloFPS-19
❑ 80SSPHOF-132
❑ 83ConMar-56
❑ 86NegLeaF-1
❑ 87NegLeaPD-30
❑ 88ConNegA-7
❑ 88NegLeaD-16
❑ 89NegLeaRP-11
❑ 89PerCelP-26
❑ 90NegLeaS-26
❑ 90PerGreM-58
❑ 90PomBlaBNLP-2542
❑ 91NegLeaRL-22
❑ 91PomBlaBPB-2
❑ 91PomBlaBPB-12
❑ 91PomBlaBPB-15
❑ 91PomBlaBPB-19
❑ 91PomBlaBPB-29
❑ 92FroRowBL-1
❑ 92FroRowBL-1AU
❑ 92FroRowBL-2
❑ 92FroRowBL-3
❑ 92FroRowBL-4
❑ 92FroRowBL-5
❑ 92NegLeaK-16
❑ 92NegLeaPL-2
❑ 92NegLeaRLI-38
❑ 93NegLeaRL2-41
❑ 93TedWil-108
❑ 93UppDecS-17
❑ 94PomNegLB-2
❑ 95NegLeaL2-3
❑ 95NegLeaLI-22
❑ 95S.FExaNLT-1
❑ 97NegLeaPC-11H
❑ 99UppDecCL-47
❑ 99UppDecCLCC-47
Leonard, Dennis
❑ 75OPC-615
❑ 75RoyPos-16
❑ 75Top-615
❑ 75TopMin-615
❑ 76KanCitRP-15
❑ 76OPC-334
❑ 76RoyAaP-6
❑ 76SSP-164
❑ 76Top-334
❑ 77BurCheD-70
❑ 77Hos-72
❑ 77OPC-91
❑ 77Top-75
❑ 78Hos-88
❑ 78OPC-5
❑ 78OPC-41
❑ 78Roy-11
❑ 78SSP270-220
❑ 78Top-205
❑ 78Top-665
❑ 79Hos-109
❑ 79OPC-109
❑ 79RoyTeal-4
❑ 79Top-218
❑ 80OPC-293
❑ 80Top-565
❑ 81AllGamPI-86
❑ 81CokTeaS-76
❑ 81Don-102
❑ 81Fle-42
❑ 81OPC-185
❑ 81RoyPol-5
❑ 81RoyProPS-9
❑ 81Top-185
❑ 81TopSti-87
❑ 82Don-264
❑ 82Fle-413
❑ 82FleSta-208
❑ 82OPC-369
❑ 82Roy-11
❑ 82Squ-10
❑ 82Top-495
❑ 82TopSti-191
❑ 82TopStiV-191
❑ 83Don-412
❑ 83Fle-116
❑ 83FleSta-105
❑ 83FleSti-95
❑ 83OPC-87
❑ 83RoyPol-3
❑ 83RoyPos-16
❑ 83Top-785
❑ 84Fle-349
❑ 84Nes792-375
❑ 84OPC-375
❑ 84RoyPos-19
❑ 84Top-375
❑ 84TopTif-375
❑ 85RoyTeal-18
❑ 86FleUpd-67
❑ 86RoyNatP-22
❑ 86RoyTeal-15
❑ 86TopTra-65T
❑ 86TopTraT-65T
❑ 87Fle-374
❑ 87FleGlo-374
❑ 87OPC-38
❑ 87RedFolSB-33
❑ 87Top-38
❑ 87TopTif-38
❑ 89PacSenL-84
❑ 89T/MSenL-68
❑ 89TopSenL-125
❑ 90EliSenL-72
❑ 90PacLeg-91
❑ 93RoySta2-5
❑ 93UppDecAH-82
❑ 93UppDecS-20
Leonard, Dutch (Emil)
❑ 34DiaMatCSB-114
❑ 35DiaMatCS3T1-97
❑ 39PlaBal-21
❑ 40PlaBal-23
❑ 41PlaBal-24
❑ 48Bow-24
❑ 49Bow-115
❑ 49EurSta-61
❑ 49Lea-113
❑ 50Bow-170
❑ 51Bow-102
❑ 52Bow-159
❑ 52StaCalL-80B
❑ 52StaCalS-92A
❑ 52TipTop-20
❑ 52Top-110
❑ 53BowBW-50
❑ 55Bow-247
❑ 61Fle-121
❑ 79DiaGre-55
❑ 83TCMPla1943-4
❑ 83TopRep5-110
❑ 85TCMPla1-14
❑ 90DodTar-448
❑ 91TopArc1-155
❑ 94ConTSNB-1276
Leonard, Dutch (Hubert)
❑ 15SpoNewM-100
❑ 16BF2FP-5
❑ 16FleBreD-56
❑ 16SpoNewM-102
❑ 17ColE13-98
❑ 17HolBreD-62
❑ 20NatCarE-57
❑ 34TarThoBD-18
❑ 53Top-155
❑ 67SpoHobFC-25
❑ 72FleFamF-17
❑ 72LauGreF-34
❑ 76GrePlaG-28
❑ 79Top-418
❑ 85Woo-22
❑ 91ConTSN-142
❑ 91ConTSN-276
❑ 92ConTSN-346
❑ 93ConTSN-712
❑ 94ConTSN-1276
Leonard, Jeff (Jeffrey)
❑ 79AstPos-13
❑ 80Top-106
❑ 81Don-264
❑ 81Fle-67
❑ 81Top-469
❑ 82Don-438
❑ 82Gia25tATI-17
❑ 82RegGloT-3
❑ 82RegGloT-4
❑ 82RegGloT-5
❑ 82Top-47
❑ 83Don-474
❑ 83GiaMot-8
❑ 83GiaPos-17
❑ 83Top-309
❑ 84AllGamPI-56
❑ 84Don-567
❑ 84Fle-379
❑ 84GiaPos-13
❑ 84Nes792-576
❑ 84Nes792-748
❑ 84Top-576
❑ 84Top-748
❑ 84TopRubD-29
❑ 84TopSti-166
❑ 84TopTif-576
❑ 84TopTif-748
❑ 85AllGamPI-147
❑ 85Don-358
❑ 85Fle-615
❑ 85FleLimE-18
❑ 85GenMilS-4
❑ 85GiaMot-4
❑ 85GiaPos-20
❑ 85Lea-92
❑ 85OPC-132
❑ 85SevCoi-W14
❑ 85SubDis-35
❑ 85ThoMcAD-35
❑ 85Top-619
❑ 85Top-718
❑ 85TopMin-619
❑ 85TopRubD-30
❑ 85TopSti-161
❑ 85TopTif-619
❑ 85TopTif-718
❑ 86BasStaB-66
❑ 86Don-79
❑ 86Fle-548
❑ 86GiaMot-4
❑ 86GiaPos-17
❑ 86Lea-74
❑ 86OPC-381
❑ 86Top-490
❑ 86TopSti-84
❑ 86TopTat-15
❑ 86TopTif-490
❑ 87AstShoSPO-16
❑ 87ClaGam-64
❑ 87Don-391
❑ 87DonOpeD-103
❑ 87Fle-278
❑ 87FleGamW-25
❑ 87FleGlo-278
❑ 87FleSlu-23
❑ 87GiaMot-8
❑ 87GiaPos-17
❑ 87OPC-280
❑ 87RedFolSB-102
❑ 87SpoTeaP-10
❑ 87StuPan-13
❑ 87Top-280
❑ 87TopSti-90
❑ 87TopTif-280
❑ 88BreTeal-22
❑ 88ClaRed-175
❑ 88Don-327
❑ 88DonAll-54
❑ 88Fle-88
❑ 88FleGlo-88
❑ 88FleMin-117
❑ 88FleRecS-23
❑ 88FleStiC-128
❑ 88FleSup-21
❑ 88FleUpd-39
❑ 88FleUpdG-39
❑ 88GiaMot-8
❑ 88GiaPos-16
❑ 88GreBasS-31
❑ 88Lea-118
❑ 88OPC-152
❑ 88PanSti-246
❑ 88PanSti-427
❑ 88PanSti-446
❑ 88RedFolSB-48
❑ 88Sco-580
❑ 88ScoGlo-580
❑ 88Spo-82
❑ 88StaLinG-10
❑ 88Top-570
❑ 88TopCoi-46
❑ 88TopRitTM-32
❑ 88TopSti-16
❑ 88TopSti-86
❑ 88TopStiB-17
❑ 88TopTif-570
❑ 88TopTra-61T
❑ 88TopTraT-61T
❑ 88TopUKM-43
❑ 88TopUKMT-43
❑ 88Woo-17
❑ 89Bow-218
❑ 89BowTif-218
❑ 89Don-457
❑ 89DonBasB-107
❑ 89DonTra-1
❑ 89Fle-190
❑ 89FleGlo-190
❑ 89FleUpd-60
❑ 89MarMot-8
❑ 89OPC-160
❑ 89Sco-557
❑ 89ScoRoo-7T
❑ 89Top-160
❑ 89TopAme2C-19
❑ 89TopSti-199
❑ 89TopTif-160
❑ 89TopTra-72T
❑ 89TopTraT-72T
❑ 89UppDec-263
❑ 89UppDec-789
❑ 90Bow-472
❑ 90BowTif-472
❑ 90ClaBlu-93
❑ 90DodTar-449
❑ 90Don-93
❑ 90DonBesA-125
❑ 90DonGraS-2
❑ 90Fle-519
❑ 90FleCan-519
❑ 90Lea-219
❑ 90M.Vpin-95
❑ 90MarMot-4
❑ 90OPC-455
❑ 90PanSti-150
❑ 90PubIntS-436
❑ 90RedFolSB-58
❑ 90Sco-98
❑ 90Sco100S-91
❑ 90Spo-20
❑ 90Top-455
❑ 90TopBig-303
❑ 90TopSti-223
❑ 90TopTif-455
❑ 90UppDec-331
❑ 91Fle-456
❑ 91OPC-55
❑ 91Sco-44
❑ 91Top-55
❑ 91TopDesS-55
❑ 91TopMic-55
❑ 91TopTif-55
❑ 91UppDec-107
❑ 94BreMilB-146
❑ 96ModA'sB-28
❑ 97ModA'sG-16
❑ 98HunStaTI-5
Leonard, Kathy
❑ 81RedPioT-24
Leonard, Mark
❑ 86EveGiaC-182
❑ 86EveGiaPC-11
❑ 87CliGiaP-14
❑ 88CalLeaACLC-3
❑ 88SanJosGCLC-122
❑ 88SanJosGP-134
❑ 89PhoFirC-5
❑ 89PhoFirP-1498
❑ 90CMC-546
❑ 90PhoFirC-19
❑ 90PhoFirP-24
❑ 90ProAAAF-50
❑ 90TriAllGP-AAA52
❑ 91Bow-624
❑ 91Don-526
❑ 91Fle-265
❑ 91GiaMot-13
❑ 91GiaPacGaE-22
❑ 91Lea-369

❑ 91Sco-719
❑ 91ScoRoo-18
❑ 91TopDeb90-86
❑ 91Ult-322
❑ 91UppDec-557
❑ 92Don-761
❑ 92GiaMot-13
❑ 92GiaPacGaE-23
❑ 92GiaPacGaE-24
❑ 92PhoFirF-2833
❑ 92Pin-233
❑ 92Sco-499
❑ 92Sco100RS-62
❑ 92StaClu-538
❑ 92Ult-591
❑ 93Don-288
❑ 93Fle-532
❑ 93PanSti-241
❑ 93RocRedWF-253
❑ 93Sco-381
❑ 93StaClu-497
❑ 93StaCluFDI-497
❑ 93StaCluMOP-497
❑ 93Top-729
❑ 93TopGol-729
❑ 93TopInaM-729
❑ 93TopInaR-729
❑ 93TopMic-729
❑ 94PhoFirF-1533
❑ 95PhoFirTI-27

Leonard, Mathew
❑ 88GenCubP-1645
❑ 88WytCubP-1996
❑ 89ChaWheB-9
❑ 89ChaWheP-1758

Leonard, Tom
❑ 81RedPioT-23

Leonard, Wilfred
❑ 48SomandK-20

Leonardo, Juan
❑ 75AppFoxT-13

Leonette, Mark
❑ 83IdaFalAT-8
❑ 84IdaFalATI-16
❑ 85MadMusP-19
❑ 85MadMusT-22
❑ 86HunStaDJ-26
❑ 87PitCubP-16
❑ 88PitCubP-1371

Leonhard, Dave
❑ 67BalOriP-59
❑ 67BalOriP-60
❑ 67BalOriP-61
❑ 67BalOriP-62
❑ 68OPC-56
❑ 68Top-56
❑ 68TopVen-56
❑ 69MilBra-158
❑ 69Top-228
❑ 70BalOriP-17
❑ 70Top-674
❑ 71MLBOffS-302
❑ 71OPC-716
❑ 71OriCha-8
❑ 71Top-716
❑ 72MilBra-198
❑ 72OriPos-20
❑ 72Top-527
❑ 91OriCro-260

Leonhardt, Dave
❑ 92FayGenC-21
❑ 92FayGenF-2175
❑ 94PitMetC-14
❑ 94PitMetF-3520

Leopold, Jim
❑ 83BeaGolGT-6
❑ 84BeaGolGT-14
❑ 85LasVegSC-119
❑ 86NasPirP-15
❑ 88LouRedBC-10
❑ 88LouRedBP-437
❑ 88LouRedBTI-27

Lepcio, Ted
❑ 52Top-335
❑ 53RedSoxTI-17
❑ 53Top-18
❑ 54Bow-162
❑ 54Top-66
❑ 55Top-128
❑ 55TopDouH-125
❑ 57Top-288
❑ 58Top-29
❑ 59Top-348
❑ 60Top-97
❑ 60TopVen-97
❑ 61Top-234
❑ 81RedSoxBG2S-35
❑ 83TopRep5-335
❑ 91TopArc1-18
❑ 94TopArc1-66
❑ 94TopArc1G-66

Lepel, Joel
❑ 91KenTwiC-19
❑ 91KenTwiP-2091

Lepley, John
❑ 88HamRedP-1737
❑ 88NebCor-8
❑ 89ArkTraGS-10
❑ 90ArkTraGS-20
❑ 91ArkTraLD-37
❑ 91ArkTraP-1280
❑ 91LinDriAA-37

Leppert, Don
❑ 62Top-36
❑ 62TopVen-36
❑ 63Top-243
❑ 64Top-463
❑ 64WheSta-26
❑ 73OPC-517
❑ 73Top-517A
❑ 73Top-517B
❑ 74OPC-489
❑ 74Top-489
❑ 75PitPirP-12
❑ 76PirPos-9
❑ 76VenLeaS-145
❑ 77OPC-58
❑ 77Top-113
❑ 78BluJayP-14
❑ 78TCM60I-101
❑ 78TCM60I-110
❑ 81AstPos-11
❑ 82AstPos-13
❑ 83AstPos-14
❑ 84AstMot-27
❑ 84AstPos-14
❑ 85AstMot-27
❑ 86KenTwiP-13
❑ 87KenTwiP-27
❑ 88KenTwiP-1399
❑ 89KenTwiP-1070
❑ 91OriCro-261
❑ 97BalOriP-29

Lepson, Mark
❑ 79BurBeeT-11
❑ 80BurBeeT-4
❑ 81BurBeeT-9

Lerch, Randy
❑ 76OklCit8TI-15
❑ 76OPC-595
❑ 76Top-595
❑ 77Top-489
❑ 78SSP270-44
❑ 78Top-271
❑ 79PhiBurK-8
❑ 79Top-52
❑ 80OPC-181
❑ 80PhiBurK-18
❑ 80Top-344
❑ 81Don-574
❑ 81Fle-25
❑ 81Top-584
❑ 81TopTra-792
❑ 82BrePol-35
❑ 82Don-595A
❑ 82Don-595B
❑ 82Fle-147
❑ 82Top-466
❑ 83ExpPos-16
❑ 83ExpStu-28
❑ 83Fle-287
❑ 83OPC-22
❑ 83Top-686
❑ 84Fle-380
❑ 84GiaPos-14
❑ 85Don-309
❑ 85Fle-616
❑ 85Top-103
❑ 85TopTif-103
❑ 86PhiTas-35
❑ 86PorBeaP-14
❑ 89PacSenL-23
❑ 89TopSenL-23
❑ 90EliSenL-10
❑ 94BreMilB-147

Lerchen, Bertran
❑ 09ObaT21-312
❑ 11BigEatEU-11
❑ 11Zee-71
❑ 12ObaPreT-61

LeRoy, John
❑ 95DurBulTI-18
❑ 96CarLeaA1B-7
❑ 96CarLeaA2B-7
❑ 96DurBulBIB-8
❑ 96DurBulBrB-9
❑ 97Bow-337
❑ 97BowInt-337
❑ 97GreBraG-16
❑ 98BesAutSS-29
❑ 98Fle-245
❑ 98St.PetDRM-9

LeRoy, Louis
❑ 11SpoLifCW-214

Lersch, Barry
❑ 69OPC-206
❑ 69Top-206
❑ 69TopFoc-22
❑ 71MLBOffS-183
❑ 71OPC-739
❑ 71Top-739
❑ 72OPC-453
❑ 72Top-453
❑ 73OPC-559
❑ 73PhiTeal-10
❑ 73Top-559
❑ 74OPC-313
❑ 74Top-313
❑ 74TopTra-313T
❑ 75OklCit8TI-2

Lesch, J.R.
❑ 93EriSaiC-14

Lesch, Paul
❑ 92ButCopKSP-29
❑ 93EriSaiF-3111

Leshay, Maney
❑ 96HelBreTI-13

Lesher, Brian
❑ 92SouOreAC-6
❑ 92SouOreAF-3434
❑ 93MadMusC-19
❑ 93MadMusF-1837
❑ 94ModA'sC-18
❑ 94ModA'sF-3077
❑ 95HunStaTI-18
❑ 96BesAutS-49
❑ 97ColCho-24
❑ 97Pac-171
❑ 97PacLigB-171
❑ 97PacSil-171
❑ 98PacInvGems-86

Leshnock, Don
❑ 75ShrCapT-9

Leshnock, Donnie
❑ 91TopTra-72T
❑ 91TopTraT-72T
❑ 92ClaDraP-81
❑ 92OneYanC-8
❑ 92StaCluD-106
❑ 93StaCluM-137
❑ 93Top-701
❑ 93TopGol-701
❑ 93TopInaM-701
❑ 93TopInaR-701
❑ 93TopMic-701
❑ 94GreBatF-470
❑ 95TamYanYI-17
❑ 97GreBatC-14

Leskanic, Curt (Curtis)
❑ 90KinIndTI-5
❑ 91Cla/Bes-297
❑ 91KinIndC-5
❑ 91KinIndP-317
❑ 92OrlSunRF-2844
❑ 92OrlSunRS-509
❑ 92ProFS7-57
❑ 92SkyAA F-218
❑ 93ColSprSSF-3082
❑ 93Lea-527
❑ 93Top-774
❑ 93TopGol-774
❑ 93TopInaM-774
❑ 93TopInaR-774
❑ 93TopMic-774
❑ 94ColSprSSF-728
❑ 94Don-580
❑ 94Pac-200
❑ 94StaClu-507
❑ 94StaCluFDI-507
❑ 94StaCluGR-507
❑ 94StaCluMOP-507
❑ 94StaCluT-118
❑ 94StaCluTFDI-118
❑ 94Top-191
❑ 94TopGol-191
❑ 94TopSpa-191
❑ 95ColCho-442
❑ 95ColChoGS-442
❑ 95ColChoSS-442
❑ 95Don-533
❑ 95DonPreP-533
❑ 96ColCho-537
❑ 96ColChoGS-537
❑ 96ColChoSS-537
❑ 96Don-268
❑ 96DonPreP-268
❑ 96Fla-248
❑ 96Fle-366
❑ 96FleTif-366
❑ 96LeaSigA-133
❑ 96LeaSigAG-133
❑ 96LeaSigAS-133
❑ 96Pac-62
❑ 96RocFle-7
❑ 96RocPol-11
❑ 96Sco-485
❑ 96StaClu-290
❑ 96StaCluMOP-290
❑ 96Ult-469
❑ 96UltGolM-469
❑ 97ColSprSTI-15
❑ 97Fle-311
❑ 97FleTif-311
❑ 97PacPriGotD-GD135
❑ 97Ult-186
❑ 97UltGolME-186
❑ 97UltPlaME-186
❑ 97UppDec-56
❑ 98PacInvGems-145
❑ 98PacOnl-250
❑ 98PacOnlR-250
❑ 98PacOnlWC-250
❑ 99UppDec-365
❑ 99UppDecEL1-365
❑ 99UppDecEL2-365

Lesley, Brad
❑ 81CedRapRT-3
❑ 82IndIndTI-5
❑ 83Don-547
❑ 83IndIndTI-26
❑ 85Top-597
❑ 85TopTif-597
❑ 85VanCanC-202
❑ 87JapPlaB-16
❑ 89CedRapRAB-21
❑ 90CedRapRDGB-21
❑ 94BreMilB-148

Leslie, Reggie
❑ 91ChaWheC-6
❑ 91ChaWheP-2883
❑ 92CedRapRC-9
❑ 92CedRapRF-1070
❑ 92ChaLooS-190

Leslie, Roy Reid
❑ 22E120-201
❑ 23Zee-109
❑ 24Zee-80
❑ 25Zee-92
❑ 26Zee-9

Leslie, Sam
❑ 34BatR31-46
❑ 34DiaStaR-68
❑ 34ExhFou-2
❑ 34Gou-49
❑ 35AlDemDCR3-100
❑ 35GouPuzR-1G
❑ 35GouPuzR-3E
❑ 35GouPuzR-5E
❑ 35GouPuzR-14E
❑ 36GouWidPPR-A64
❑ 36OveCanR-31
❑ 36WorWidGV-4
❑ 37ExhFou-5
❑ 72TCMthe3-102
❑ 79DiaGre-27
❑ 92ConTSN-504

Leslie, Sean
❑ 96DelShoB-19
❑ 96VerExpB-16

Lesperance, Frank
❑ 94ButCopKSP-12

Lesslie, Bob
❑ 75WatDodT-12

Lester, Jimmy
❑ 88WicPilRD-22
❑ 89ChaRaiP-989
❑ 90ChaRaiB-27
❑ 90ChaRaiP-2056
❑ 91WatDiaC-11
❑ 91WatDiaP-1273

Letchas, Charlie
❑ 89ChaLooLITI-16

Letendre, Mark
❑ 79ColCliT-11
❑ 80ColCliP-NNO
❑ 80ColCliT-18
❑ 81ColCliP-NNO
❑ 81ColCliT-25
❑ 91GiaMot-28

Letourneau, Jeff
❑ 91EriSaiC-18
❑ 91EriSaiP-4064

Lett, Jim
❑ 80CedRapRT-22
❑ 82WatRedT-23
❑ 83WatRedT-19
❑ 84CedRapRT-12
❑ 86RedTexG-NNO
❑ 87RedKah-NNO
❑ 88RedKah-NNO
❑ 89RedKah-xx
❑ 90ChaWheB-26
❑ 90ChaWheP-2257
❑ 91LinDriAAA-275
❑ 91NasSouP-2174
❑ 92NasSouF-1850
❑ 97BluJayOH-17
❑ 97BluJayS-23

Letterio, Shane
❑ 88GreHorP-1556
❑ 89MiaMirIS-11
❑ 89MiaMirIS-11
❑ 90CMC-758
❑ 90WilBilB-14
❑ 90WilBilP-1064
❑ 90WilBilS-15
❑ 91CalCanLD-64
❑ 91CalCanP-522
❑ 91LinDriAAA-64
❑ 92JacSunF-3716
❑ 92JacSunS-361

Levan, Jesse
❑ 78ReaRem-12
❑ 88ChaLooLTI-20

Levan, Matt
❑ 98KanCouC-17
❑ 98KanCouCCP-17

LeVander, Scott
❑ 84IdaFalATI-17

Levangie, Dana
❑ 91ElmPioC-8
❑ 91ElmPioP-3273
❑ 92WinHavRSC-20
❑ 92WinHavRSF-1781
❑ 93ForLauRSC-17
❑ 93ForLauRSFP-1600
❑ 94LynRedSC-16
❑ 94LynRedSF-1894
❑ 95TreThuTI-17
❑ 96TreThuB-17

LeVasseur, Tom
❑ 86SpoIndC-169
❑ 88RivRedWCLC-223
❑ 88RivRedWP-1417
❑ 89WicChaR-9
❑ 89WicStaR-26
❑ 89WicWraR-21
❑ 90CMC-520
❑ 90LasVegSC-17
❑ 90LasVegSP-129
❑ 90ProAAAF-17
❑ 94CalCanF-796
❑ 97CliLumG-13
❑ 98CliLumG-26

Levenda, John
❑ 90CalLeaACLC-31

Leverenz, Walter
❑ 11Zee-15
❑ 12HomRunKE-10
❑ 12Zee-13
❑ 17Zee-71
❑ 18Zee-63
❑ 20Zee-86
❑ 21Zee-101
❑ 23Zee-70
❑ 24Zee-50
❑ 25Zee-44

Leverette, Dixie (Gorham)
❑ 22W572-57
❑ 22W573-73

Leverette, Horace
❑ 22E120-23

Levey, James
❑ 32OrbPinNP-52
❑ 32OrbPinUP-40
❑ 33TatOrb-40
❑ 92ConTSN-395

Levey, Josh
❑ 97NewJerCB-16

Levi, Stan
❑ 80BurBeeT-27
❑ 83ElPasDT-11

Levias, Andres
❑ 94HicCraC-13
❑ 94HicCraF-2188
❑ 95ButCopKtl-14
❑ 96PriWilCB-17

Levine, Al
❑ 91UtiBluSC-21
❑ 91UtiBluSP-3238
❑ 93SarWhiSF-1367
❑ 94BirBarC-16
❑ 94BirBarF-620
❑ 94VenLinU-139
❑ 98PacInvGems-30

Levine, Alan
❑ 92SouBenWSC-18
❑ 92SouBenWSF-174
❑ 93SarWhiSC-17
❑ 95LinVen-138
❑ 96NasSouB-15

Levinson, Davis
❑ 81RedPioT-25

Levinson, Steve
❑ 81RedPioT-30

Levis, Jesse
❑ 88CapCodPB-13
❑ 88CapCodPPaLP-116
❑ 89BurIndS-16
❑ 90CarLeaA-39
❑ 90KinIndTI-8
❑ 91CanIndLD-88
❑ 91CanIndP-981
❑ 91LinDriAA-88
❑ 92ColSprSSF-755
❑ 92ColSprSSS-90
❑ 92DonRoo-65
❑ 92FleUpd-16
❑ 93ChaKniF-546
❑ 93Don-669
❑ 93FleFinE-203
❑ 93FleMajLP-A14
❑ 93Pin-288
❑ 93PinRooTP-3
❑ 93Sco-330
❑ 93StaClu-468
❑ 93StaCluFDI-468
❑ 93StaCluMOP-468
❑ 93Top-801
❑ 93TopGol-801
❑ 93TopInaM-801
❑ 93TopInaR-801
❑ 93TopMic-801
❑ 94ChaKniF-898
❑ 94Pac-174
❑ 94VenLinU-222
❑ 96BrePol-12
❑ 97BrePol-14
❑ 97Fle-131
❑ 97FleTif-131
❑ 97Pac-121
❑ 97PacLigB-121
❑ 97PacSil-121
❑ 98Pac-119
❑ 98PacOnl-403
❑ 98PacOnlR-403
❑ 98PacOnlWC-403
❑ 98PacPlaB-119
❑ 98PacRedT-119
❑ 98PacSil-119

Levrault, Allen
❑ 96HelBreTI-14
❑ 97BelSnaB-18
❑ 98StoPorG-16
❑ 99Bow-385
❑ 99BowGol-385
❑ 99BowInt-385

Levsen, Dutch
❑ 94ConTSN-1304
❑ 94ConTSNB-1304

Levy, Ed
❑ 40PhiTeal-11
❑ 41PhiTeal-12

Levy, Lenny
❑ 77PirTCM1WC-40

Levy, Rube
❑ 87OldJudN-297
❑ 88SFHesCreN32-15

Levy, Tye
❑ 98ChaAllCM-7

Lewallyn, Dennis
❑ 75AlbDukCa-20
❑ 76VenLeaS-200
❑ 79AlbDukTc-7
❑ 80AlbDukTc-8

❑ 82Ind-22
❑ 82IndWhe-7
❑ 82Top-356
❑ 83VerBeaDT-29
❑ 85VerBeaDT-25
❑ 89VerBeaDS-28
❑ 90DodTar-451
❑ 90VerBeaDS-30
❑ 91VerBeaDP-793
❑ 92VerBeaDC-30
❑ 92VerBeaDF-2896
❑ 93RanKee-229
❑ 93VerBeaDC-30
❑ 94VerBeaDC-28
❑ 95SanBerSTI-30
❑ 96AriBlaDB-2
❑ 96HonShaHWB-26
❑ 97SouBenSH-6
❑ 98HigDesMG-14

Lewandowski, John
❑ 92BurIndC-1
❑ 92BurIndF-1659

Lewis, A.D.
❑ 94ChaRivF-2684

Lewis, Alan
❑ 88BakDodCLC-237
❑ 89VerBeaDS-15
❑ 90VerBeaDS-18
❑ 91BakDodCLC-9
❑ 92ElPasDF-3931
❑ 92ElPasDS-216
❑ 93El PasDF-2957
❑ 96SanBerSB-3

Lewis, Amos
❑ 79AshTouT-17

Lewis, Andreaus
❑ 94BurIndC-10
❑ 94BurIndF-3809
❑ 94ChaRivC-12
❑ 97OmaRoyB-33

Lewis, Anthony
❑ 90SavCarP-2083
❑ 91Cla/Bes-137
❑ 91St.PetCC-27
❑ 91St.PetCP-2290
❑ 92St.PetCC-17
❑ 92St.PetCF-2040
❑ 93ArkTraF-2823
❑ 93ExcFS7-101
❑ 94ArkTraF-3102
❑ 95ArkTraTI-17
❑ 96HarCitRCB-18

Lewis, Bill
❑ 81TCM60I-362

Lewis, Bob
❑ 93WatIndC-15
❑ 93WatIndF-3565
❑ 94ColRedC-14
❑ 94ColRedF-446

Lewis, Bob 30s
❑ 31CubTeal-13
❑ 36CubTeal-21

Lewis, Brett
❑ 87PocGiaTB-3

Lewis, Brian
❑ 92GulCoaYF-3703
❑ 93OneYanC-14
❑ 93OneYanF-3517

Lewis, Buddy (John K.)
❑ 37OPCBatUV-101
❑ 37WheBB6-7
❑ 38OurNatGPP-17
❑ 38WheBB15-7
❑ 39PlaBal-47
❑ 40PlaBal-20
❑ 41PlaBal-47
❑ 47Exh-133
❑ 60SenUniMC-12
❑ 79DiaGre-60
❑ 84TCMPla1-12
❑ 89PacLegI-119
❑ 95ConTSN-1348

Lewis, Chris
❑ 92DavLipB-4
❑ 93DavLipB-15

Lewis, Craig
❑ 88WatPirP-8
❑ 98GreBatM-8

Lewis, Curt
❑ 78OrlTwiT-10

Lewis, Dan
❑ 87AubAstP-8
❑ 88AshTouP-1061
❑ 89OscAstS-11
❑ 90CalLeaACLC-40
❑ 91LinDriAA-310
❑ 91ShrCapLD-310
❑ 91ShrCapP-1830
❑ 92PhoFirF-2828
❑ 92PhoFirS-385
❑ 93IowCubF-2140
❑ 94JacSunF-1417

Lewis, Darren
❑ 89CalLeaA-33
❑ 89ModA'sC-30
❑ 89ModA'sCLC-278
❑ 90Bes-22
❑ 90Bow-463
❑ 90BowTif-463
❑ 90HunStaB-1
❑ 91Cla2-T54
❑ 91DonRoo-35
❑ 91Fle-15
❑ 91LinDriAAA-384
❑ 91OPC-239
❑ 91OPCPre-73
❑ 91PhoFirLD-384
❑ 91PhoFirP-80
❑ 91Sco-350
❑ 91ScoRoo-28
❑ 91StaClu-362
❑ 91Top-239
❑ 91TopDeb90-87
❑ 91TopDesS-239
❑ 91TopMic-239
❑ 91TopTif-239
❑ 91TriA AAGP-AAA33
❑ 91Ult-323
❑ 91UppDec-564
❑ 91UppDecFE-38F
❑ 92Bow-683
❑ 92Cla1-T53
❑ 92Don-615
❑ 92Fle-639
❑ 92FleRooS-6
❑ 92GiaMot-11
❑ 92GiaPacGaE-25
❑ 92Lea-441
❑ 92LeaBlaG-441
❑ 92OPC-743
❑ 92OPCPre-151
❑ 92Pin-408
❑ 92PinTea2-63
❑ 92ProFS7-340
❑ 92Sco-562
❑ 92Sco100RS-10
❑ 92StaClu-31
❑ 92Stu-117
❑ 92Top-743
❑ 92TopGol-743
❑ 92TopGolW-743
❑ 92TopMic-743
❑ 92TriPla-111
❑ 92Ult-292
❑ 92UppDec-565
❑ 93Don-392
❑ 93Fla-143
❑ 93Fle-157
❑ 93GiaMot-13
❑ 93GiaPos-21
❑ 93GiaStaC-25
❑ 93Lea-369
❑ 93OPC-193
❑ 93PacSpa-273
❑ 93Pin-94
❑ 93Sco-203
❑ 93SP-113
❑ 93StaClu-143
❑ 93StaCluFDI-143
❑ 93StaCluMO-13
❑ 93StaCluMOP-143
❑ 93Top-176
❑ 93TopGol-176
❑ 93TopInaM-176
❑ 93TopInaR-176
❑ 93TopMic-176
❑ 93Ult-134
❑ 93UppDec-173
❑ 93UppDecGold-173
❑ 94Bow-659
❑ 94ColC-174
❑ 94ColChoGS-174
❑ 94ColChoSS-174
❑ 94Don-424
❑ 94Fin-85
❑ 94FinRef-85
❑ 94Fla-244
❑ 94Fle-693
❑ 94FleExtB-388
❑ 94GiaAMC-11
❑ 94GiaMot-12
❑ 94GiaTarBC-13
❑ 94GiaTeal-8
❑ 94GiaUSPC-6S
❑ 94GiaUSPC-12D
❑ 94Lea-399
❑ 94OPC-132
❑ 94Pac-548
❑ 94Pin-169
❑ 94PinArtP-169
❑ 94PinMusC-169
❑ 94ProMag-124
❑ 94Sco-480
❑ 94ScoGolR-480
❑ 94Sel-304
❑ 94Spo-8
❑ 94StaClu-453
❑ 94StaCluFDI-453
❑ 94StaCluGR-453
❑ 94StaCluMOP-453
❑ 94StaCluT-19
❑ 94StaCluTFDI-19
❑ 94Stu-85
❑ 94Top-354
❑ 94TopGol-354
❑ 94TopSpa-354
❑ 94TriPla-105
❑ 94Ult-291
❑ 94UppDec-207
❑ 94UppDecED-207
❑ 94USPlaCA-5H
❑ 95Bow-341
❑ 95ColCho-256
❑ 95ColChoGS-256
❑ 95ColChoSE-106
❑ 95ColChoSEGS-106
❑ 95ColChoSESS-106
❑ 95ColChoSS-256
❑ 95Don-311
❑ 95DonPreP-311
❑ 95DonTopotO-215
❑ 95Emo-195
❑ 95Fin-157
❑ 95FinRef-157
❑ 95Fla-209
❑ 95FlaHotG-6
❑ 95Fle-582
❑ 95FleUpdSL-5
❑ 95GiaMot-14
❑ 95Lea-76
❑ 95Pac-379
❑ 95Pin-199
❑ 95PinArtP-199
❑ 95PinMusC-199
❑ 95Sco-274
❑ 95ScoGolR-274
❑ 95ScoPlaTS-274
❑ 95Sel-191
❑ 95SelArtP-191
❑ 95Spo-95
❑ 95SpoArtP-95
❑ 95StaClu-74
❑ 95StaCluFDI-74
❑ 95StaCluMO-28
❑ 95StaCluMOP-74
❑ 95StaCluSTWS-74
❑ 95Top-39
❑ 95TopCyb-31
❑ 95TopD3-36
❑ 95TopEmb-140
❑ 95TopEmbGI-140
❑ 95TopLeaL-LL45
❑ 95Ult-241
❑ 95UltAwaW-17
❑ 95UltAwaWGM-17
❑ 95UltGolM-241
❑ 95UppDec-87
❑ 95UppDec-487
❑ 95UppDecED-87
❑ 95UppDecEDG-87
❑ 95UppDecSE-204
❑ 95UppDecSEG-204
❑ 95USPlaCMLA-5H
❑ 96Don-287
❑ 96DonPreP-287
❑ 96EmoXL-38
❑ 96Fla-54
❑ 96Fle-346
❑ 96FleTif-346
❑ 96FleUpd-U25
❑ 96FleUpdTC-U25
❑ 96LeaSigA-134
❑ 96LeaSigAG-134
❑ 96LeaSigAS-134
❑ 96Sco-41
❑ 96Ult-180
❑ 96Ult-332
❑ 96UltGolM-180
❑ 96UltGolM-332
❑ 96UppDec-303
❑ 96WhiSoxF-10
❑ 97Fle-64
❑ 97FleTif-64
❑ 97Pac-56
❑ 97PacLigB-56
❑ 97PacSil-56
❑ 97Sco-374
❑ 97ScoArtPWB-374
❑ 97ScoResC-374
❑ 97ScoShoS-374
❑ 97ScoShoSAP-374
❑ 97Top-292
❑ 97Ult-41
❑ 97UltGolME-41
❑ 97UltPlaME-41
❑ 97WhiSoxTI-10
❑ 98PacOnl-119
❑ 98PacOnlR-119
❑ 98PacOnlWC-119
❑ 98Ult-317
❑ 98UltGolM-317
❑ 98UltMas-317
❑ 98UltPlaM-317
❑ 99Fle-476
❑ 99FleSta9-476
❑ 99FleWarT-476
❑ 99Pac-69
❑ 99PacAur-29
❑ 99PacAurOD-29
❑ 99PacCroC-46
❑ 99PacCroCPB-46
❑ 99PacPar-40
❑ 99PacParC-40
❑ 99PacParG-40
❑ 99PacParHoloGold-40
❑ 99PacParHS-40
❑ 99PacParOD-40
❑ 99PacParPB-40
❑ 99PacParRed-40
❑ 99PacPlaB-69
❑ 99PacRed-69
❑ 99Top-157
❑ 99TopChr-157
❑ 99TopChrR-157
❑ 99TopMVPP-157
❑ 99Ult-26
❑ 99UltGolM-26
❑ 99UltMas-26
❑ 99UltPlaM-26
❑ 99Vic-66

Lewis, Derrick
❑ 97DanBraB-21

Lewis, Duffy (George)
❑ 09ObaT21-15
❑ 11PinT-5-658
❑ 12T207-104
❑ 15SpoNewM-101
❑ 16BF2FP-6
❑ 16FleBreD-57
❑ 16SpoNewM-103
❑ 17ColE13-99
❑ 17HolBreD-63
❑ 21E121So8-52
❑ 22AmeCarE122-40
❑ 22W575-72
❑ 22Zee-83
❑ 23Zee-110
❑ 24Zee-81
❑ 25Zee-45
❑ 55BraJohC-50
❑ 79DiaGre-10
❑ 81ConTSN-16
❑ 87ConSer2-36
❑ 88ConSer4-17
❑ 91ConTSN-146

Lewis, Dwayne
❑ 95SpoIndTI-11

Lewis, Dwight
❑ 94IdaFalBF-3599
❑ 94IdaFalBSP-3

Lewis, Ed
❑ 94QuaCitRBC-13
❑ 94QuaCitRBF-530
❑ 95TenVolW-6

Lewis, Herman
❑ 80UtiBluJT-26

Lewis, Irving
❑ 12T207-105A
❑ 12T207-105B

Lewis, J.J.
❑ 98ShrCapM-7
❑ 98ShrCapWS-7

Lewis, James
❑ 09ObaT21-160
❑ 11PacCoaBD-35
❑ 11Zee-72
❑ 12HomRunKE-51
❑ 12Zee-85
❑ 13Zee-82

Lewis, Jay
❑ 83PeoSunF-18

Lewis, Jeremy
❑ 96RocCubTI-16

Lewis, Jerry
❑ 78NewWayCT-26

Lewis, Jim
❑ 11BigEatEU-12
❑ 94OscAstC-13
❑ 96BufBisB-12

Lewis, Jim L.
❑ 80ColCliP-21
❑ 80ColCliT-16
❑ 81ColCliP-21
❑ 81ColCliT-6
❑ 82ColCliP-21
❑ 82ColCliT-22
❑ 83TolMudHT-6
❑ 85CalCanC-77

Lewis, Jim M.
❑ 79SpoIndT-13
❑ 84SalLakCGC-180
❑ 92YanWIZ8-106

Lewis, Jim S.
❑ 86ChaRaiP-13
❑ 88RivRedWCLC-212
❑ 88RivRedWP-1423
❑ 89WicStaR-14
❑ 89WicWraR-20
❑ 90CMC-509
❑ 90LasVegSC-6
❑ 90LasVegSP-114
❑ 90ProAAAF-2
❑ 91AubAstC-3
❑ 91AubAstP-4269
❑ 91Cla/Bes-411
❑ 91LinDriAA-611
❑ 91WicWraLD-611
❑ 91WicWraRD-5
❑ 92Fle-612
❑ 92JacGenF-3999
❑ 92OscAstC-20
❑ 92OscAstF-2529
❑ 92RocRedWF-1935
❑ 92RocRedWS-457
❑ 92TopDeb91-108

Lewis, Jimmy
❑ 91ClaDraP-44
❑ 91FroRowDP-28
❑ 91FroRowDPG-28
❑ 91FroRowDPS-28
❑ 92Sco-852
❑ 92StaCluD-107
❑ 94OscAstF-1134

Lewis, Joe
❑ 89GasRanP-1007
❑ 89GasRanS-10
❑ 90GasRanB-20
❑ 90GasRanP-2523
❑ 90GasRanS-12

Lewis, John
❑ 86PeoChiP-14
❑ 87WinSpiP-16
❑ 88WinSpiS-8

Lewis, Johnny
❑ 62KahAtl-12
❑ 64Top-479
❑ 65OPC-277
❑ 65Top-277
❑ 66MetVolC-8
❑ 66Top-282
❑ 66TopRubI-52
❑ 66TopVen-282
❑ 67CokCapYM-V20
❑ 67DexPre-125
❑ 67OPC-91
❑ 67Top-91
❑ 74OPC-236
❑ 74Top-236
❑ 76St.LouCP-19
❑ 85CarTeal-22
❑ 86CarTeal-27
❑ 87CarTeal-17
❑ 88CarTeal-15
❑ 89CarTeal-14
❑ 91MetWIZ-229

Lewis, Ken
❑ 89BriTigS-14
❑ 89Sta-188

Lewis, Kevin
❑ 93PitMetC-13
❑ 93PitMetF-3713
❑ 94CapCitBC-13
❑ 94CapCitBF-1755

Lewis, Marc
❑ 96CarLeaAIB-B8
❑ 96DurBulBrB-19
❑ 96MacBraB-23
❑ 97BesAll-9
❑ 97BesBetP-9
❑ 97Bow-393
❑ 97BowInt-393
❑ 97GreBraG-17
❑ 97SouLeaTP-10
❑ 98SalLakBO-17

Lewis, Mark
❑ 88BurIndP-1800
❑ 89Bow-87
❑ 89BowTif-87
❑ 89KinIndS-12
❑ 89Sta-168
❑ 89StaFutS-3
❑ 89StaFutS-4
❑ 89Top-222
❑ 89TopTif-222
❑ 90Bes-4
❑ 90Bes-320
❑ 90Bow-338
❑ 90BowTif-338
❑ 90CanIndB-1
❑ 90CanIndP-1299
❑ 90CanIndS-9
❑ 90CMC-831
❑ 90EasLeaAP-EL36
❑ 90ProAaA-27
❑ 90StaFS7-13
❑ 91Bow-70
❑ 91Cla1-T37
❑ 91Cla2-T11
❑ 91ClaGam-185
❑ 91ColSprSSLD-88
❑ 91ColSprSSP-2190
❑ 91Don-29
❑ 91DonRoo-42
❑ 91FleUpd-19
❑ 91Lea-289
❑ 91LinDriAAA-88
❑ 91ScoRoo-106T
❑ 91StaClu-492
❑ 91StaLewRG-1
❑ 91StaLewRG-2
❑ 91StaLewRG-3
❑ 91StaLewRG-4
❑ 91StaLewRG-5
❑ 91StaLewRG-6
❑ 91StaLewRG-7
❑ 91StaLewRG-8
❑ 91StaLewRG-9
❑ 91StaLewRG-10
❑ 91StaLewRG-11
❑ 91Stu-48
❑ 91TopTra-73T
❑ 91TopTraT-73T
❑ 91TopTriH-A5
❑ 91UppDec-17
❑ 92Bow-439
❑ 92ClaGam-48
❑ 92Don-273
❑ 92Fle-116
❑ 92IndFanC-15
❑ 92Lea-49
❑ 92LeaBlaG-49
❑ 92OPC-446
❑ 92PanSti-46
❑ 92Pin-91
❑ 92PinTea2-57
❑ 92ProFS7-49
❑ 92RedFolS-56
❑ 92Sco-528
❑ 92Sco100RS-50
❑ 92ScoImpP-82
❑ 92ScoProP-25
❑ 92StaClu-193
❑ 92Stu-167
❑ 92Top-446
❑ 92TopDeb91-109
❑ 92TopGol-446
❑ 92TopGolW-446
❑ 92TopMic-446
❑ 92TriPla-205
❑ 92Ult-51
❑ 92UppDec-235
❑ 93ChaKniF-551
❑ 93ClaFS7-217
❑ 93Don-125
❑ 93Fle-216

❑ 93IndWUA-16
❑ 93OPC-194
❑ 93PacSpa-96
❑ 93PanSti-49
❑ 93Pin-374
❑ 93Sco-164
❑ 93Sel-150
❑ 93StaClu-337
❑ 93StaCluFDI-337
❑ 93StaCluMOP-337
❑ 93Top-762
❑ 93TopGol-762
❑ 93TopInaM-762
❑ 93TopInaR-762
❑ 93TopMic-762
❑ 93TriPla-155
❑ 93Ult-186
❑ 93UppDec-88
❑ 93UppDecGold-88
❑ 94ColC-533
❑ 94ColChoGS-533
❑ 94ColChoSS-533
❑ 94Don-464
❑ 94Fin-91
❑ 94FinRef-91
❑ 94Fle-109
❑ 94Lea-423
❑ 94Sco-483
❑ 94ScoGolR-483
❑ 94Top-678
❑ 94TopGol-678
❑ 94TopSpa-678
❑ 94UppDec-381
❑ 94UppDecED-381
❑ 94VerExpC-16
❑ 94VerExpF-3917
❑ 95RedKah-17
❑ 96ColCho-373T
❑ 96ColCho-551
❑ 96ColChoGS-551
❑ 96ColChoSS-551
❑ 96Fla-83
❑ 96Fle-114
❑ 96FleTif-114
❑ 96FleUpd-U34
❑ 96FleUpdTC-U34
❑ 96LeaSigA-135
❑ 96LeaSigAG-135
❑ 96LeaSigAS-135
❑ 96Pin-328
❑ 96PinFoil-328
❑ 96Sco-144
❑ 96Sum-150
❑ 96SumAbo&B-150
❑ 96SumArtP-150
❑ 96SumFoi-150
❑ 96TigHebN-9
❑ 96Ult-347
❑ 96UltGolM-347
❑ 97Cir-348
❑ 97CirRav-348
❑ 97ColCho-109
❑ 97ColCho-456
❑ 97Don-236
❑ 97DonGolPP-236
❑ 97DonSilPP-236
❑ 97Fle-100
❑ 97Fle-570
❑ 97FleTif-100
❑ 97FleTif-570
❑ 97MetUni-111
❑ 97Pac-89
❑ 97PacLigB-89
❑ 97PacSil-89
❑ 97Sco-48
❑ 97Sco-339
❑ 97ScoArtPWB-48
❑ 97ScoArtPWB-339
❑ 97ScoPreS-48
❑ 97ScoResC-339
❑ 97ScoShoS-48
❑ 97ScoShoS-339
❑ 97ScoShoSAP-48
❑ 97ScoShoSAP-339
❑ 97Top-442
❑ 97Ult-523
❑ 97UltGolME-523
❑ 97UltPlaME-523
❑ 97UppDec-61
❑ 98Fle-560
❑ 98PacOnl-566
❑ 98PacOnlR-566
❑ 98PacOnlWC-566
❑ 98PhiTeal-21
❑ 98Top-412
❑ 98TopChr-412
❑ 98TopChrR-412
❑ 98TopDevR-412
❑ 98TopDia-412
❑ 98TopMiniC-412
❑ 98Ult-335
❑ 98UltGolM-335
❑ 98UltMas-335
❑ 98UltPlaM-335
❑ 98UppDec-712
❑ 99Fle-518
❑ 99FleSta9-518
❑ 99FleWarT-518

Lewis, Matt
❑ 94FayGenC-30
❑ 95FayGenTI-15
❑ 96FayGenB-4
❑ 98JacSunM-28

Lewis, Mica
❑ 88AubAstP-1974
❑ 89AshTouP-966
❑ 89AubAstP-2186
❑ 90OscAstS-15
❑ 91VisOakC-16
❑ 91VisOakP-1748
❑ 92ClaFS7-71
❑ 92OrlSunRF-2858
❑ 92OrlSunRS-510
❑ 92SkyAA F-219
❑ 93ReaPhiF-302

Lewis, Mike
❑ 92ClaFS7-296
❑ 92VisOakC-15
❑ 92VisOakF-1009
❑ 95BreCouMF-243

Lewis, Phil
❑ 11SpoLifCW-218
❑ 90DodTar-1012

Lewis, Richie
❑ 88JacExpB-10
❑ 88JacExpP-992
❑ 90JacExpB-20
❑ 90WesPalBES-13
❑ 91HarSenP-621
❑ 92RocRedWF-1936
❑ 92RocRedWS-458
❑ 92SkyAAAF-208
❑ 93Bow-502
❑ 93Don-265
❑ 93FleFinE-65
❑ 93MarFloA-5
❑ 93MarPub-16
❑ 93MarUSPC-4D
❑ 93MarUSPC-13S
❑ 93Pin-608
❑ 93SelRoo-139T
❑ 93StaClu-619
❑ 93StaCluFDI-619
❑ 93StaCluMOP-619
❑ 93TopTra-90T
❑ 93Ult-381
❑ 94Don-297
❑ 94Fle-471
❑ 94Lea-14
❑ 94MarTeal-9
❑ 94Pac-245
❑ 94Sco-280
❑ 94ScoGolR-280
❑ 94StaClu-427
❑ 94StaCluFDI-427
❑ 94StaCluGR-427
❑ 94StaCluMOP-427
❑ 94StaCluT-74
❑ 94StaCluTFDI-74
❑ 94Top-47
❑ 94TopGol-47
❑ 94TopSpa-47
❑ 94Ult-196
❑ 95Fle-335
❑ 95Top-373
❑ 96TigHebN-10
❑ 97A'sMot-20
❑ 98RocRedWQ-18

Lewis, Rickey Jr
❑ 98HelBreM-22

Lewis, Rufus
❑ 91NegLeaRL-30
❑ 95NegLeaLI-30

Lewis, Sam
❑ 21Zee-124
❑ 22Zee-84

Lewis, Scott
❑ 89MidAngGS-21
❑ 89TexLeaAGS-5
❑ 90CMC-487
❑ 90EdmTraC-10
❑ 90EdmTraP-516
❑ 90ProAAAF-92
❑ 91AngSmo-19
❑ 91Bow-192
❑ 91Sco-759
❑ 91ScoRoo-9
❑ 91TopDeb90-88
❑ 91UppDec-594
❑ 92EdmTraF-3537
❑ 92Sco-165
❑ 92StaClu-43
❑ 92Ult-328
❑ 93AngMot-19
❑ 93AngStaCl-14
❑ 93Don-167
❑ 93Fle-575
❑ 93PacSpa-49
❑ 93Top-668
❑ 93TopGol-668
❑ 93TopInaM-668
❑ 93TopInaR-668
❑ 93TopMic-668
❑ 94AngMot-19
❑ 96LasVegSB-16

Lewis, Steve
❑ 83AleDukT-25
❑ 84PriWilPT-19
❑ 85PriWilPT-9

Lewis, T.R.
❑ 89BluOriS-13
❑ 90Bes-10
❑ 90CMC-869
❑ 90StaFS7-32
❑ 90WauTimB-1
❑ 90WauTimP-2133
❑ 90WauTimS-14
❑ 91Cla/Bes-238
❑ 91FreKeyC-18
❑ 91FreKeyP-2372
❑ 91PerHeaF-10
❑ 92FreKeyF-1811
❑ 92KanCouCC-8
❑ 92KanCouCF-99
❑ 92UppDecML-183
❑ 93Bow-85
❑ 93BowBayF-2196
❑ 93ClaFS7-54
❑ 94ExcFS7-10
❑ 94OriPro-53
❑ 94RocRedWF-1004
❑ 94RocRedWTI-10
❑ 94UppDecML-11
❑ 95BowBayTI-44
❑ 95RocRedWTI-23
❑ 96PawRedSDD-16
❑ 97RicBra-16
❑ 98OklRedM-8

Lewis, Tim
❑ 76ForLauYS-25
❑ 79WesHavYT-18
❑ 94DavLipB-19
❑ 95DavLipB-16

Lewis, Timothy
❑ 77WesHavYT-13

Lewis, Tony
❑ 87SpoIndP-3
❑ 88ChaRaiP-1214
❑ 89RivRedWB-9
❑ 89RivRedWCLC-24
❑ 89RivRedWP-1395
❑ 90WatDiaB-9
❑ 90WatDiaP-2376

Lewis, Tyrone
❑ 92GulCoaDF-3574
❑ 93BakDodCLC-15
❑ 96SanBerSB-15

Lewright, Cleo
❑ 52LavPro-23

Lexa, Michael
❑ 87KenTwiP-10
❑ 88KenTwiP-1395

Ley, Terry
❑ 72OPC-506
❑ 72Top-506
❑ 92YanWIZ7-96

Leyland, Jim
❑ 75CliPilT-1
❑ 80EvaTriT-17
❑ 81EvaTriT-1
❑ 84WhiSoxTV-8
❑ 86TopTra-66T
❑ 86TopTraT-66T
❑ 87Top-93
❑ 87TopTif-93
❑ 88PirTeal-19
❑ 88Top-624
❑ 88TopClo-60
❑ 88TopTif-624
❑ 89PirVerFJ-10
❑ 89Top-284
❑ 89TopTif-284
❑ 90OPC-699
❑ 90PirHomC-19
❑ 90Top-699
❑ 90TopTif-699
❑ 91OPC-381
❑ 91Top-381
❑ 91TopDesS-381
❑ 91TopMic-381
❑ 91TopTif-381
❑ 92OPC-141
❑ 92PirNatl-11
❑ 92Top-141
❑ 92TopGol-141
❑ 92TopGolW-141
❑ 92TopMic-141
❑ 93PirHil-5
❑ 93PirNatl-14
❑ 93Top-511
❑ 93TopGol-511
❑ 93TopInaM-511
❑ 93TopInaR-511
❑ 93TopMic-511
❑ 94PirQui-10
❑ 95PirCocP-24
❑ 95PirFil-15
❑ 96UppDec-479
❑ 97MarPac-25

Leyritz, Jim
❑ 87Ft.LauYP-24
❑ 88AlbYanP-1344
❑ 89AlbYanB-2
❑ 89AlbYanP-325
❑ 89AlbYanSt-10
❑ 89EasLeaAP-9
❑ 90AlbDecGB-6
❑ 90ClaYel-T60
❑ 90CMC-211
❑ 90ColCliC-11
❑ 90ColCliP-5
❑ 90ColCliP-681
❑ 90FleUpd-112
❑ 90Lea-465
❑ 90ProAAAF-331
❑ 90ScoRoo-83T
❑ 90TopTra-61T
❑ 90TopTraT-61T
❑ 90TopTVY-50
❑ 90UppDec-723
❑ 90YanScoNW-10
❑ 91Bow-171
❑ 91Don-219
❑ 91Fle-671
❑ 91OPC-202
❑ 91PanFreS-326
❑ 91Sco-65
❑ 91Sco100RS-29
❑ 91Top-202
❑ 91TopDeb90-89
❑ 91TopDesS-202
❑ 91TopMic-202
❑ 91TopRoo-16
❑ 91TopTif-202
❑ 91Ult-237
❑ 91UppDec-243
❑ 92Don-649
❑ 92StaClu-198
❑ 92Ult-412
❑ 92UppDec-117
❑ 93Don-477
❑ 93Fla-248
❑ 93FleFinE-248
❑ 93Lea-468
❑ 93PacSpa-559
❑ 93StaClu-234
❑ 93StaCluFDI-234
❑ 93StaCluMOP-234
❑ 93Top-385
❑ 93TopGol-385
❑ 93TopInaM-385
❑ 93TopInaR-385
❑ 93TopMic-385
❑ 93Ult-597
❑ 94ColC-453
❑ 94ColChoGS-453
❑ 94ColChoSS-453
❑ 94Don-146
❑ 94Fla-83
❑ 94Fle-237
❑ 94Lea-158
❑ 94Pac-428
❑ 94Pin-517
❑ 94PinArtP-517
❑ 94PinMusC-517
❑ 94Sco-213
❑ 94ScoGolR-213
❑ 94Sel-350
❑ 94StaClu-283
❑ 94StaCluFDI-283
❑ 94StaCluGR-283
❑ 94StaCluMOP-283
❑ 94StaCluT-192
❑ 94StaCluTFDI-192
❑ 94Top-728
❑ 94TopGol-728
❑ 94TopSpa-728
❑ 94Ult-97
❑ 95ColCho-521
❑ 95ColChoGS-521
❑ 95ColChoSE-242
❑ 95ColChoSEGS-242
❑ 95ColChoSESS-242
❑ 95ColChoSS-521
❑ 95Don-401
❑ 95DonPreP-401
❑ 95Fla-65
❑ 95Fle-75
❑ 95Lea-168
❑ 95Sco-102
❑ 95ScoGolR-102
❑ 95ScoPlaTS-102
❑ 95StaClu-341
❑ 95StaCluMOP-341
❑ 95StaCluSTWS-341
❑ 95StaCluVR-180
❑ 95StaCluVRMO-180
❑ 95Top-450
❑ 95TopCyb-246
❑ 95Ult-310
❑ 95UltGolM-310
❑ 95UppDecSE-8
❑ 95UppDecSEG-8
❑ 96ColCho-369T
❑ 96ColCho-629
❑ 96ColChoGS-629
❑ 96ColChoSS-629
❑ 96Fla-131
❑ 96Fle-187
❑ 96FleTif-187
❑ 96MetUni-88
❑ 96MetUniP-88
❑ 96Sco-181
❑ 96Ult-100
❑ 96UltGolM-100
❑ 97AngMot-11
❑ 97Cir-353
❑ 97CirRav-353
❑ 97ColCho-179
❑ 97ColCho-224
❑ 97ColChoU-U1
❑ 97Don-339
❑ 97DonGolPP-339
❑ 97DonSilPP-339
❑ 97DonTea-9
❑ 97DonTeaSPE-9
❑ 97Fin-209
❑ 97FinRef-209
❑ 97Fle-170
❑ 97Fle-610
❑ 97FleTif-170
❑ 97FleTif-610
❑ 97Lea-264
❑ 97LeaFraM-264
❑ 97LeaFraMDC-264
❑ 97Pac-153
❑ 97PacLigB-153
❑ 97PacSil-153
❑ 97Sco-466
❑ 97ScoArtPWB-466
❑ 97ScoResC-466
❑ 97ScoShoS-466
❑ 97ScoShoSAP-466
❑ 97SpoIll-165
❑ 97SpoIllEE-165
❑ 97StaClu-288
❑ 97StaCluI-I22
❑ 97StaCluMOP-288
❑ 97StaCluMOP-I22
❑ 97Top-98
❑ 97Ult-338
❑ 97UltGolME-338
❑ 97UltPlaME-338
❑ 97UppDec-265
❑ 97UppDec-523
❑ 98CirThu-141
❑ 98CirThuRav-141
❑ 98CirThuSupRav-141
❑ 98ColCho-319
❑ 98Fle-489
❑ 98PacOnl-120
❑ 98PacOnlR-120
❑ 98PacOnlWC-120
❑ 98PinPlu-118
❑ 98PinSna-BRS6
❑ 98Sco-180
❑ 98ScoRT-225
❑ 98StaCluFDI-380
❑ 98StaCluI-380
❑ 98StaCluOneK-380
❑ 98StaCluPP-380
❑ 98Top-438
❑ 98TopChr-438
❑ 98TopChrR-438
❑ 98TopDevR-438
❑ 98TopDia-438
❑ 98TopMiniC-438
❑ 98Ult-209
❑ 98Ult-336
❑ 98UltGolM-209
❑ 98UltGolM-336
❑ 98UltMas-209
❑ 98UltMas-336
❑ 98UltPlaM-209
❑ 98UltPlaM-336
❑ 98UppDec-656
❑ 99Fle-394
❑ 99FleSta9-394
❑ 99FleWarT-394
❑ 99Pac-373
❑ 99PacAur-163
❑ 99PacAurOD-163
❑ 99PacPar-202
❑ 99PacParC-202
❑ 99PacParG-202
❑ 99PacParHoloGold-202
❑ 99PacParHS-202
❑ 99PacParOD-202
❑ 99PacParPB-202
❑ 99PacParRed-202
❑ 99PacPlaB-373
❑ 99PacRed-373
❑ 99SkyThu-87
❑ 99SkyThuRant-87
❑ 99SkyThuRave-87
❑ 99SP SigAuto-JLE
❑ 99SpoIll-8
❑ 99SPSig-162
❑ 99ThuSkySupR-87
❑ 99Top-5
❑ 99TopChr-5
❑ 99TopChrR-5
❑ 99TopMVPP-5
❑ 99Ult-152
❑ 99UltGolM-152
❑ 99UltMas-152
❑ 99UltPlaM-152
❑ 99UppDec-475
❑ 99UppDecEL1-475
❑ 99UppDecEL2-475
❑ 99UppDecM-181
❑ 99UppDecMGS-181
❑ 99UppDecMHFS-181
❑ 99UppDecMSS-181
❑ 99Vic-348

Leystra, Jeff
❑ 93MedHatBJF-3732
❑ 93MedHatBJSP-18
❑ 94St.CatBJC-16
❑ 94St.CatBJF-3640

Leyva, Damian
❑ 92BurIndC-19
❑ 92BurIndF-1652
❑ 93BurIndC-16
❑ 93BurIndF-3293

Leyva, Edgar
❑ 97CedRapK-15
❑ 98LakElsSG-20

Leyva, Juslian
❑ 97ModA'sG-15
❑ 98ModA'sG-16

Leyva, Nick
❑ 77ArkTraT-5A
❑ 77ArkTraT-5B
❑ 83ArkTraT-23
❑ 84Car-19
❑ 84Car5x7-16
❑ 85CarTeal-23
❑ 86CarTeal-28
❑ 87CarTeal-18
❑ 88CarTeal-16
❑ 89PhiTas-18
❑ 89Top-74
❑ 89TopTif-74
❑ 90OPC-489
❑ 90PhiTas-20

❑ 90Top-489
❑ 90TopTif-489
❑ 91OPC-141
❑ 91Top-141
❑ 91TopDesS-141
❑ 91TopMic-141
❑ 91TopTif-141
❑ 92SyrChiF-1986
❑ 92SyrChiMB-11
❑ 92SyrChiS-524
❑ 93SyrChiF-1013
❑ 95BluJayOH-24
❑ 96BluJayOH-18
❑ 97BluJayOH-18
❑ 97BluJayS-26

Lezcano, Carlos
❑ 81Don-521
❑ 81Fle-307
❑ 81Top-381
❑ 82Top-51
❑ 83IowCubT-23
❑ 84TacTigC-79
❑ 88BlaYNPRWLU-5
❑ 89BlaYNPRWL-199
❑ 91PenPilP-395
❑ 93AppFoxCB-26
❑ 93AppFoxFI-2476
❑ 94AppFoxC-22
❑ 94AppFoxFI-1069
❑ 96SanJosGB-27
❑ 97ShrCap-2
❑ 97ShrCapB-2

Lezcano, Sixto
❑ 74SacSolC-57
❑ 76BreA&P-7
❑ 76OPC-353
❑ 76SSP-241
❑ 76Top-353
❑ 77BurCheD-89
❑ 77Hos-12
❑ 77Kel-27
❑ 77OPC-71
❑ 77Top-185
❑ 78Hos-35
❑ 78OPC-102
❑ 78Top-595
❑ 78WifBalD-38
❑ 79Hos-136
❑ 79OPC-364
❑ 79Top-685
❑ 80BreTeal-15
❑ 80OPC-114
❑ 80Top-215
❑ 80TopSup-31
❑ 81AllGamPI-150
❑ 81CokTeaS-125
❑ 81Don-207
❑ 81Fle-513
❑ 81OPC-25
❑ 81Top-25
❑ 81TopScr-45
❑ 81TopSti-218
❑ 81TopTra-793
❑ 82Don-64
❑ 82Fle-119
❑ 82OPC-271
❑ 82Top-727
❑ 82TopSti-95
❑ 82TopTra-63T
❑ 83AllGamPI-150
❑ 83Don-499
❑ 83Fle-364
❑ 83FleSta-106
❑ 83FleSti-229
❑ 83OPC-244
❑ 83PadTeal-13
❑ 83Top-455
❑ 83TopSti-298
❑ 84Fle-38
❑ 84Nes792-185
❑ 84OPC-185
❑ 84PhiTas-38
❑ 84Top-185
❑ 84TopTif-185
❑ 85Don-529
❑ 85Fle-258
❑ 85FleUpd-72
❑ 85OPC-89
❑ 85Pir-9
❑ 85Top-556
❑ 85TopMin-556
❑ 85TopTif-556
❑ 85TopTifT-75T
❑ 85TopTra-75T
❑ 86BreGreT-5
❑ 86Top-278
❑ 86TopTif-278
❑ 88BlaYNPRWL-167
❑ 88BlaYNPRWLU-18
❑ 94BreMilB-149
❑ 94CarLeaAF-CAR20
❑ 94WilBluRC-26
❑ 94WilBluRF-317
❑ 95WilBluRTI-16
❑ 96OmaRoyB-2

Lezeau, Jim
❑ 94BenRocC-15
❑ 94BenRocF-3610

Libke, Al
❑ 44CenFlo-14
❑ 47SigOil-11
❑ 83TCMPla1945-40

Liborio, Dennis
❑ 88AstMot-28
❑ 89AstMot-28
❑ 90AstMot-28
❑ 92AstMot-28
❑ 94AstMot-28

Liburdi, John
❑ 84AlbA'sT-10
❑ 85AlbYanT-34
❑ 86AlbYanT-13

Licciardi, Ron
❑ 97WilCubB-13

Lich, Rod
❑ 84CedRapRT-23
❑ 85CedRapRT-29
❑ 86TamTarP-10
❑ 87VerRedP-27
❑ 92AugPirC-27
❑ 93AugPirC-28
❑ 93AugGenF-28
❑ 95LynHilTI-14

Lichtenberger, Tom
❑ 96SarRedSB-4

Lichtenstein, R.C.
❑ 98HelBreM-2

Lickert, John
❑ 83PawRedST-13
❑ 85RicBraT-11

Licursi, Richard
❑ 92SalLakTSP-1
❑ 93VerBeaDC-16
❑ 94HigDesMC-19
❑ 94HigDesMF-2785

Liddell, Dave
❑ 86PeoChiP-15
❑ 87ColMetP-13
❑ 88RenSilSCLC-287
❑ 89JacMetGS-25
❑ 89MetColP-39
❑ 89TidTidC-18
❑ 90CMC-371
❑ 90ProAAAF-278
❑ 90TidTidC-20
❑ 90TidTidP-547
❑ 90TopTVM-49
❑ 91MetWIZ-230
❑ 91TopDeb90-90
❑ 92DenZepF-2644
❑ 92DenZepS-138

Liddle, Don
❑ 53BraJohC-9
❑ 53BraMer-10
❑ 53BraSpiaS3-15
❑ 54NewYorJA-29
❑ 54Top-225
❑ 55Bow-303
❑ 55GiaGolS-12
❑ 56Top-325
❑ 83Bra53F-43
❑ 94TopArc1-225
❑ 94TopArc1G-225

Liddle, Steve
❑ 82RedPioT-7
❑ 83NasAngT-10
❑ 84EdmTraC-107
❑ 85EdmTraC-13
❑ 86EdmTraP-17
❑ 87PorBeaP-10
❑ 88PorBeaC-12
❑ 88PorBeaP-655
❑ 89KenTwiP-1084
❑ 89KenTwiS-25
❑ 90KenTwiB-27
❑ 90KenTwiP-2310
❑ 90KenTwiS-25
❑ 91VisOakC-24
❑ 91VisOakP-1757
❑ 92VisOakC-24
❑ 92VisOakF-1029
❑ 93ForMyeMC-26
❑ 93ForMyeMF-2672
❑ 94ForMyeMC-26
❑ 94ForMyeMF-1183

Lidge, Brad
❑ 99BowBes-173
❑ 99BowBesAR-173
❑ 99BowBesR-173
❑ 99StaClu-336
❑ 99StaCluFDI-336
❑ 99StaCluOoaK-336
❑ 99StaCluPP-336
❑ 99Top-441
❑ 99TopChr-441
❑ 99TopChrR-441
❑ 99TopMVPP-441

Lidle, Cory
❑ 92EliTwiC-15
❑ 92EliTwiF-3676
❑ 93PocPosF-4205
❑ 93PocPosSP-10
❑ 94StoPorC-15
❑ 94StoPorF-1691
❑ 95ElPasDTI-15
❑ 96BinMetB-16
❑ 97NorTid-20
❑ 97NorTidB-20
❑ 98Top-348
❑ 98TopChr-348
❑ 98TopChrR-348
❑ 98TopDevR-348
❑ 98TopDia-348
❑ 98TopMiniC-348

Lidle, Kevin
❑ 92BriTigF-1414
❑ 93FayGenC-13
❑ 93FayGenF-132
❑ 94LakTigC-14
❑ 94LakTigF-3038
❑ 95JacSunTI-19
❑ 96LakTigB-16
❑ 96WesOahCHWB-40
❑ 97JacSun-15
❑ 98SalAvaC-17

Lieber, Charles
❑ 30Zee-58
❑ 31Zee-35
❑ 32Zee-39
❑ 33Zee-30

Lieber, Jon
❑ 92ClaDraP-29
❑ 92ClaFS7-421
❑ 92EugEmeC-16
❑ 92EugEmeF-3027
❑ 92FroRowDP-76
❑ 92FroRowDPG-76
❑ 92FroRowDPS-76
❑ 93CarLeaAGF-15
❑ 93ClaFS7-110
❑ 93StaCluM-57
❑ 93WilBluRC-17
❑ 93WilBluRF-1995
❑ 94BowBes-B18
❑ 94BowBesR-B18
❑ 94CarMudF-1574
❑ 94ExcFS7-68
❑ 94Fla-423
❑ 94FlaWavotF-B5
❑ 94FleUpd-174
❑ 94LeaLimR-34
❑ 94PirQui-11
❑ 94TopTra-67T
❑ 94UppDecML-132
❑ 95Bow-301
❑ 95ColCho-385
❑ 95ColChoGS-385
❑ 95ColChoSE-177
❑ 95ColChoSEGS-177
❑ 95ColChoSESS-177
❑ 95ColChoSS-385
❑ 95Don-163
❑ 95DonPreP-163
❑ 95Fin-7
❑ 95FinRef-7
❑ 95Fla-402
❑ 95Fle-481
❑ 95Lea-38
❑ 95Pac-345
❑ 95Pin-153
❑ 95PinArtP-153
❑ 95PinMusC-153
❑ 95PirFil-16
❑ 95Sco-461
❑ 95ScoGolR-461
❑ 95ScoPlaTS-461
❑ 95StaClu-386
❑ 95StaCluMOP-386
❑ 95StaCluSTWS-386
❑ 95Stu-136
❑ 95Top-537
❑ 95TopCyb-320
❑ 95Ult-217
❑ 95UltGolM-217
❑ 95UppDec-146
❑ 95UppDecED-146
❑ 95UppDecEDG-146
❑ 95UppDecSE-223
❑ 95UppDecSEG-223
❑ 96ColCho-262
❑ 96ColChoGS-262
❑ 96ColChoSS-262
❑ 96FleUpd-U179
❑ 96FleUpdTC-U179
❑ 96LeaSigEA-107
❑ 97Cir-4
❑ 97CirRav-4
❑ 97ColCho-431
❑ 97Fle-431
❑ 97FleTif-431
❑ 97Pac-396
❑ 97PacLigB-396
❑ 97PacSil-396
❑ 97PirPos-20
❑ 97UppDec-462
❑ 98ColCho-468
❑ 98Pac-397
❑ 98PacOnl-586
❑ 98PacOnlR-586
❑ 98PacOnlWC-586
❑ 98PacPlaB-397
❑ 98PacRedT-397
❑ 98PacSil-397
❑ 98StaCluFDI-290
❑ 98StaCluI-290
❑ 98StaCluOneK-290
❑ 98StaCluPP-290
❑ 98UppDec-194
❑ 98UppDecSF-104
❑ 99Fle-425
❑ 99FleSta9-425
❑ 99FleWarT-425

Liebert, Allen
❑ 86LakTigP-10
❑ 87FayGenP-15
❑ 88CarLeaAS-29
❑ 88KinIndS-15
❑ 89CanIndB-21
❑ 89CanIndP-1314
❑ 89CanIndS-12
❑ 90Bes-188
❑ 90CanIndB-6
❑ 90CanIndP-1294
❑ 90EasLeaAP-EL35
❑ 92BirBarF-2586
❑ 92BirBarS-88

Lieberthal, Mike
❑ 90ClaDraP-3
❑ 90ClaYel-T62
❑ 90HigSchPLS-2
❑ 90MarPhiP-3197
❑ 90ProAaA-193
❑ 91Bow-506
❑ 91Cla/Bes-290
❑ 91OPC-471
❑ 91Sco-683
❑ 91SouAtlLAGP-SAL44
❑ 91SpaPhiC-14
❑ 91SpaPhiP-899
❑ 91Top-471
❑ 91TopDesS-471
❑ 91TopMic-471
❑ 91TopTif-471
❑ 91UppDec-67
❑ 92ClaDraP-93
❑ 92ClaFS7-231
❑ 92ProFS7-302
❑ 92ReaPhiF-578
❑ 92ReaPhiS-532
❑ 92SkyAA F-230
❑ 92UppDecML-184
❑ 92UppDecMLPotY-PY17
❑ 93Bow-20
❑ 93ClaFisN-11
❑ 93ClaYouG-YG8
❑ 93ExcAllF-4
❑ 93ExcFS7-86
❑ 93PhiStaC-19
❑ 93ScrRedBF-2546
❑ 93ScrRedBTI-13
❑ 94Bow-112
❑ 94Cla-74
❑ 94ExcFS7-246
❑ 94FleMajLP-21
❑ 94FleUpd-166
❑ 94LeaLimR-27
❑ 94ScrRedBF-922
❑ 94StaCluT-233
❑ 94StaCluTFDI-233
❑ 94Ult-550
❑ 94UppDecML-54
❑ 95Bow-419
❑ 95ColCho-371
❑ 95ColChoGS-371
❑ 95ColChoSE-24
❑ 95ColChoSEGS-24
❑ 95ColChoSESS-24
❑ 95ColChoSS-371
❑ 95Don-240
❑ 95DonPreP-240
❑ 95Fin-13
❑ 95FinRef-13
❑ 95Fle-399
❑ 95Lea-65
❑ 95PacPri-108
❑ 95Pin-156
❑ 95PinArtP-156
❑ 95PinMusC-156
❑ 95Sco-309
❑ 95ScoGolR-309
❑ 95ScoPlaTS-309
❑ 95ScrRedBTI-18
❑ 95StaClu-203
❑ 95StaCluFDI-203
❑ 95StaCluMOP-203
❑ 95StaCluSTWS-203
❑ 95Top-554
❑ 95TopCyb-333
❑ 95Ult-206
❑ 95UltGolM-206
❑ 96FleUpd-U167
❑ 96FleUpdTC-U167
❑ 96PhiTeal-20
❑ 97Cir-258
❑ 97CirRav-258
❑ 97ColCho-419
❑ 97Don-343
❑ 97DonGolPP-343
❑ 97DonSilPP-343
❑ 97Fin-82
❑ 97FinRef-82
❑ 97Fle-414
❑ 97FleTif-414
❑ 97PhiCopQ-15
❑ 97PhiTeal-24
❑ 97PinX-PSfF-36
❑ 97PinX-PSfFU-36
❑ 97SpoIll-93
❑ 97SpoIllEE-93
❑ 97StaClu-364
❑ 97StaCluMOP-364
❑ 97Top-56
❑ 97Ult-251
❑ 97UltGolME-251
❑ 97UltPlaME-251
❑ 97UppDec-452
❑ 98CirThu-279
❑ 98CirThuRav-279
❑ 98CirThuSupRav-279
❑ 98ColCho-464
❑ 98E-X2-51
❑ 98E-X2ECFut-51
❑ 98E-X2ECNow-51
❑ 98Fin-252
❑ 98FinNo--252
❑ 98FinNo-R-252
❑ 98FinRef-252
❑ 98FlaShoLeg0-119
❑ 98FlaShoLeg1-119
❑ 98FlaShoLeg2-119
❑ 98FlaShoLeg3-119
❑ 98FlaShoLegM-119
❑ 98FlaShoR0-119
❑ 98FlaShoR1-119
❑ 98FlaShoR2-119
❑ 98FlaShoR3-119
❑ 98Fle-72
❑ 98KinDis-22
❑ 98MetUni-191
❑ 98MetUniPMG-191
❑ 98Pac-384
❑ 98PacOme-184
❑ 98PacOmeR-184
❑ 98PacOnl-567
❑ 98PacOnlR-567
❑ 98PacOnlWC-567
❑ 98PacPar-214
❑ 98PacParC-214
❑ 98PacParG-214
❑ 98PacParHS-214
❑ 98PacParPB-214
❑ 98PacParR-214
❑ 98PacPlaB-384
❑ 98PacRedT-384
❑ 98PacSil-384
❑ 98PhiTeal-22
❑ 98Pin-128
❑ 98PinPreP-128
❑ 98ScrRedB1ATI-9
❑ 98SP Aut-153
❑ 98StaCluFDI-106
❑ 98StaCluI-106
❑ 98StaCluOneK-106
❑ 98StaCluPP-106
❑ 98Top-94
❑ 98TopChr-94
❑ 98TopChrR-94
❑ 98TopDevR-94
❑ 98TopDia-94
❑ 98TopMiniC-94
❑ 98Ult-45
❑ 98UltGolM-45
❑ 98UltMas-45
❑ 98UltPlaM-45
❑ 98UppDec-190
❑ 98UppDecSF-100
❑ 99199Fin-197
❑ 99FinGolRef-197
❑ 99FinRef-197
❑ 99Fle-537
❑ 99FleSta9-537
❑ 99FleWarT-537
❑ 99MetUni-39
❑ 99MetUniGM-39
❑ 99MetUniPMG-39
❑ 99PacOme-180
❑ 99PacOmeC-180
❑ 99PacOmeG-180
❑ 99PacOmePB-180
❑ 99SkyPre-64
❑ 99SkyPreR-64
❑ 99SkyThu-85
❑ 99SkyThuRant-85
❑ 99SkyThuRave-85
❑ 99StaClu-201
❑ 99StaCluFDI-201
❑ 99StaCluOoaK-201
❑ 99StaCluPP-201
❑ 99ThuSkySupR-85
❑ 99Top-159
❑ 99TopChr-159
❑ 99TopChrR-159
❑ 99TopMVPP-159
❑ 99Ult-151
❑ 99UltGolM-151
❑ 99UltMas-151
❑ 99UltPlaM-151

Liebhardt, Glenn
❑ 08AmeLeaPC-12
❑ 08RosComP-28
❑ 09T206-212
❑ 11PinT-5-1059

Liebold, Harry
❑ 18WhiSoxTI-14
❑ 20NatCarE-58
❑ 21Exh-96
❑ 21Exh-97
❑ 75SenTCM1-16
❑ 92Man191BSR-15

Liebovitz, Neil
❑ 75ForLauYS-4

Liefer, Jeff
❑ 96MidLeaAB-53
❑ 96SouBenSHS-20
❑ 96Top-243
❑ 97BesAutAS-27
❑ 97BirBarB-1
❑ 97Bow-82
❑ 97BowBes-168
❑ 97BowBesAR-168
❑ 97BowBesR-168
❑ 97BowChr-109
❑ 97BowChrI-109
❑ 97BowChrIR-109
❑ 97BowChrR-109
❑ 97BowInt-82
❑ 97SouLeaTP-3
❑ 98BirBarG-18
❑ 98Bow-117
❑ 98BowCerBlueAU-43
❑ 98BowCerGA-43
❑ 98BowCerSA-43
❑ 98BowChr-117
❑ 98BowChrGA-117
❑ 98BowChrGAR-117
❑ 98BowChrI-117
❑ 98BowChrIR-117

❑ 98BowChrR-117
❑ 98BowGolA-117
❑ 98BowInt-117
❑ 98SP MinPE-36
❑ 98SPMin-36
❑ 99Bow-128
❑ 99BowChr-128
❑ 99BowChrG-128
❑ 99BowChrGR-128
❑ 99BowChrI-128
❑ 99BowChrIR-128
❑ 99BowChrR-128
❑ 99BowGol-128
❑ 99BowInt-128
❑ 99DumSet-123
❑ 99FleMys-123
❑ 99FleMysM-123
❑ 99PacInv-36
❑ 99PacInvOD-36
❑ 99PacInvPB-36
❑ 99Rev-34
❑ 99RevPremDate-34
❑ 99RevRet-34
❑ 99RevShaSS-34
❑ 99SP TopP-74
❑ 99SP TopPPE-74
❑ 99Top-434
❑ 99TopChr-434
❑ 99TopChrR-434
Lien, Al
❑ 48SomandK-7
❑ 49SomandK-5
❑ 52MotCoo-47
❑ 53SanFraSTI-10
Liendo, Temis
❑ 93LinVenB-201
❑ 94VenLinU-191
❑ 95LinVen-114
❑ 96-97LinVen-64
Lienhard, Steve
❑ 87PocGiaTB-5
❑ 88CliGiaP-694
❑ 89CalLeaA-47
❑ 89SanJosGB-20
❑ 89SanJosGCLC-214
❑ 89SanJosGP-456
❑ 89SanJosGS-17
❑ 90ShrCapP-1440
❑ 91ElPasDLD-185
❑ 91ElPasDP-2745
❑ 91LinDriAA-185
❑ 92ElPasDS-217
❑ 93CliGiaC-28
❑ 93CliGiaF-2506
❑ 94CliLumC-27
❑ 95ButCopKtl-24
Liepa, John
❑ 94LetMouF-3882
❑ 94LetMouSP-20
Lieppman, Keith
❑ 75TucTorC-10
❑ 76TucTorCa-3
❑ 76TusTorCr-6
❑ 79OgdA'sT-26
❑ 82IdaFalAT-30
❑ 82WesHavAT-27
❑ 84AlbA'sT-7
❑ 85TacTigC-126
❑ 86TacTigP-13
❑ 87TacTigP-14
Lifgren, Kelly
❑ 88SpoIndP-1925
❑ 89RivRedWB-10
❑ 89RivRedWCLC-16
❑ 89RivRedWP-1392
❑ 90Bes-190
❑ 90RivRedWB-15
❑ 90RivRedWCLC-22
❑ 90RivRedWP-2605
❑ 91Cla/Bes-120
❑ 91HigDesMC-7
❑ 91HigDesMP-2390
❑ 92HigDesMC-8
❑ 93WicWraF-2977
Liggett, Troy
❑ 89TenTecGE-14
Light, Tal
❑ 95AshTouUTI-26
❑ 96AshTouB-23
❑ 97SalAva-34
❑ 98NewHavRM-13
❑ 98NewHavRMA-13
Lightenburg, Kerry
❑ 97GreBraG-18
Lightner, Ed
❑ 91BenBucCB-23
❑ 91BenBucP-3701
Lightner, Fred
❑ 48BabRutS-11
Lignitz, Jeremiah
❑ 98WesMicWM-10
Ligons, Merrell
❑ 97SpoIndG-17
❑ 98SpoIndG-18
Ligtenberg, Kerry
❑ 96DurBulBlB-16
❑ 96DurBulBrB-16
❑ 99StaClu-305
❑ 99StaCluFDI-305
❑ 99StaCluOoaK-305
❑ 99StaCluPP-305
❑ 99Top-368
❑ 99TopChr-368
❑ 99TopChrR-368
❑ 99TopMVPP-368
Liles, Greyson
❑ 90ArkRaz-19
Liilard, Robert E.
❑ 36CubTeal-22
❑ 37WheBB7-29P
❑ 37Zee-79
❑ 39CubTeal-15
❑ 46SunBre-10
❑ 47RemBre-22
❑ 47SigOil-48
❑ 47SmiClo-6
❑ 48SigOil-14
❑ 48SmiClo-8
Lilliquist, Derek
❑ 88BobCamRB-7
❑ 88RicBraC-2
❑ 88RicBraP-21
❑ 89Bow-264
❑ 89BowTif-264
❑ 89BraDub-15
❑ 89ClaTraP-172
❑ 89Don-653
❑ 89DonBasB-226
❑ 89DonRoo-54
❑ 89FleUpd-73
❑ 89Sco-631
❑ 89ScoHot1R-23
❑ 89TopTra-73T
❑ 89TopTraT-73T
❑ 89UppDec-753
❑ 90Bow-7
❑ 90BowTif-7
❑ 90BraDubP-17
❑ 90Don-286
❑ 90Fle-588
❑ 90FleCan-588
❑ 90Hot50RS-27
❑ 90OPC-282
❑ 90PanSti-223
❑ 90PubIntS-116
❑ 90Sco-243
❑ 90Sco100RS-19
❑ 90ScoYouSI-30
❑ 90Spo-24
❑ 90Top-282
❑ 90TopBig-192
❑ 90TopDeb89-70
❑ 90TopRoo-18
❑ 90TopTif-282
❑ 90ToyRoo-17
❑ 90UppDec-234
❑ 91Don-570
❑ 91Fle-535
❑ 91LasVegSLD-287
❑ 91LasVegSP-231
❑ 91LinDriAAA-287
❑ 91OPC-683
❑ 91Sco-571
❑ 91StaClu-268
❑ 91Top-683
❑ 91TopDesS-683
❑ 91TopMic-683
❑ 91TopTif-683
❑ 91UppDec-251
❑ 92IndFanC-16
❑ 92Lea-451
❑ 92LeaBlaG-451
❑ 92ScoRoo-44T
❑ 92StaClu-864
❑ 92StaCluECN-864
❑ 93Don-9
❑ 93Fla-194
❑ 93Fle-217
❑ 93IndWUA-17
❑ 93Lea-444
❑ 93OPC-211
❑ 93PacSpa-413
❑ 93Sco-548
❑ 93StaClu-441
❑ 93StaCluFDI-441
❑ 93StaCluMOP-441
❑ 93Top-31
❑ 93TopGol-31
❑ 93TopInaM-31
❑ 93TopInaR-31
❑ 93TopMic-31
❑ 93Ult-187
❑ 93UppDec-70
❑ 93UppDecGold-70
❑ 94ColC-175
❑ 94ColChoGS-175
❑ 94ColChoSS-175
❑ 94Don-154
❑ 94Fle-110
❑ 94Pin-219
❑ 94PinArtP-219
❑ 94PinMusC-219
❑ 94Sco-194
❑ 94ScoGolR-194
❑ 94StaClu-508
❑ 94StaCluFDI-508
❑ 94StaCluGR-508
❑ 94StaCluMOP-508
❑ 94Top-301
❑ 94TopGol-301
❑ 94TopSpa-301
❑ 94Ult-344
❑ 95Top-189
Lillis, Bob
❑ 59DarFar-10
❑ 59DodTeal-15
❑ 59Top-133
❑ 59TopVen-133
❑ 60Top-354
❑ 61DodBelB-11
❑ 61Top-38
❑ 62Col.45B-12
❑ 62SalPlaC-108A
❑ 62SalPlaC-108B
❑ 62ShiPlaC-108
❑ 62Top-74
❑ 62TopVen-74
❑ 63Col45"P-10
❑ 63Col45'JP-5
❑ 63Jel-191
❑ 63Pos-191
❑ 63Top-119
❑ 64Top-321
❑ 64TopVen-321
❑ 65AstJayP-10
❑ 67AstTeal2-15
❑ 74OPC-31
❑ 74Top-31
❑ 75AstPos-20
❑ 76HouAstP-19
❑ 78AstPos-16
❑ 78TCM60I-42
❑ 81AstPos-12
❑ 82AstPos-14
❑ 83AstPos-15
❑ 83Top-66
❑ 84AstMot-15
❑ 84AstPos-15
❑ 84Don-84
❑ 84Fle-656
❑ 84Nes792-441
❑ 84Top-441
❑ 84TopTif-441
❑ 85AstMot-1
❑ 85Top-186
❑ 85TopTif-186
❑ 86GiaMot-28
❑ 86GiaPos-18
❑ 86Top-561
❑ 86TopTif-561
❑ 87AstSer1-16
❑ 87AstShoSPO-17
❑ 87AstShoSPO-31
❑ 87GiaMot-27
❑ 87GiaPos-18
❑ 88GiaMot-27
❑ 88GiaPos-17
❑ 89AstCol4S-17
❑ 89GiaMot-28
❑ 90DodTar-452
❑ 90GiaMot-21
❑ 90GiaSmo-13
❑ 91GiaMot-27
❑ 92GiaMot-28
❑ 92GiaPacGaE-26
❑ 93GiaMot-28
❑ 93GiaPos-22
❑ 94GiaMot-28
❑ 95GiaMot-28
❑ 96GiaMot-28
Lilly, Ted
❑ 96YakBeaTI-10
❑ 97Bes-72
❑ 97CalLeaATI-14
❑ 97CalLeaTP-20
❑ 97SanBerS-9
❑ 98Bow-183
❑ 98BowChr-183
❑ 98BowChrGA-183
❑ 98BowChrGAR-183
❑ 98BowChrI-183
❑ 98BowChrIR-183
❑ 98BowChrR-183
❑ 98BowGolA-183
❑ 98BowInt-183
❑ 98SanAntMG-14
❑ 98TexLeaTPG-20
❑ 99Bow-366
❑ 99BowGol-366
❑ 99BowInt-366
Lim, Ron
❑ 90LSUTigP-12
Lima, Cory
❑ 98KanCouC-18
❑ 98KanCouCCP-18
Lima, Jose
❑ 90BriTigP-3156
❑ 90BriTigS-14
❑ 92LakTigC-9
❑ 92LakTigF-2274
❑ 93LimRocDWB-87
❑ 93LimRocDWB-143
❑ 93LonTigF-2303
❑ 94Bow-481
❑ 94ScoRoo-RT158
❑ 94ScoRooGR-RT158
❑ 94TolMudHF-1026
❑ 94UppDecML-101
❑ 95Bow-427
❑ 95Don-137
❑ 95DonPreP-137
❑ 95Lea-113
❑ 95Pin-148
❑ 95PinArtP-148
❑ 95PinMusC-148
❑ 95Sco-292
❑ 95ScoGolR-292
❑ 95ScoPlaTS-292
❑ 95ScoRooDT-RDT10
❑ 95Sel-205
❑ 95SelArtP-205
❑ 95TolMudHTI-17
❑ 96ColCho-547
❑ 96ColChoGS-547
❑ 96ColChoSS-547
❑ 96Don-502
❑ 96DonPreP-502
❑ 96Fle-115
❑ 96FleTif-115
❑ 96Pac-310
❑ 96Sco-466
❑ 96TigHebN-2
❑ 96TolMudHB-16
❑ 96Top-366
❑ 96Ult-348
❑ 96UltGolM-348
❑ 96UppDec-332
❑ 97AstMot-25
❑ 97Pac-90
❑ 97PacLigB-90
❑ 97PacSil-90
❑ 98Pac-323
❑ 98PacOnl-327
❑ 98PacOnlR-327
❑ 98PacOnlWC-327
❑ 98PacPlaB-323
❑ 98PacRedT-323
❑ 98PacSil-323
❑ 99Fle-159
❑ 99FleSta9-159
❑ 99FleWarT-159
❑ 99PacCroC-128
❑ 99PacCroCPB-128
❑ 99PacOme-108
❑ 99PacOmeC-108
❑ 99PacOmeG-108
❑ 99PacOmePB-108
❑ 99SkyThu-70
❑ 99SkyThuRant-70
❑ 99SkyThuRave-70
❑ 99StaClu-11
❑ 99StaCluFDI-11
❑ 99StaCluOoaK-11
❑ 99StaCluPP-11
❑ 99ThuSkySupR-70
❑ 99Top-87
❑ 99TopChr-87
❑ 99TopChrR-87
❑ 99TopMVPP-87
❑ 99UppDec-111
❑ 99UppDecEL1-111
❑ 99UppDecEL2-111
Limbach, Chris
❑ 86BenPhiC-147
❑ 88ClePhiS-17
❑ 88FloStaLAS-10
❑ 90SouAtlLAS-15
❑ 90SpaPhiB-7
❑ 90SpaPhiP-2488
❑ 90SpaPhiS-13
❑ 91ClePhiC-6
❑ 91ClePhiP-1617
❑ 92ReaPhiF-571
❑ 92ReaPhiS-533
❑ 92SkyAA F-231
❑ 93MemChiF-371
Limmer, Lou
❑ 51A'sTeal-18
❑ 52Par-86
❑ 54A'STEAI-14
❑ 54Top-232
❑ 55Bow-80
❑ 55Top-54
❑ 55TopDouH-15
❑ 79DiaGre-342
❑ 94TopArc1-232
❑ 94TopArc1G-232
Limon, Vinny
❑ 88NebCor-24
Limoncelli, Bill
❑ 79ElmPioRST-23
❑ 80ElmPioRST-35
❑ 87ElmPioBC-2
❑ 87ElmPioRC-2
❑ 88ElmPioC-27
Limoncelli, Jeff
❑ 90ElmPioP-7
Lina, Estivinson
❑ 98SavSanGM-17
Linarelli, Tom
❑ 98LowSpiM-24
Linares, Antonio
❑ 88MarPhiS-22
❑ 89SpaPhiP-1046
❑ 89SpaPhiS-13
❑ 89Sta-55
❑ 90SpaPhiB-20
❑ 90SpaPhiP-2503
❑ 90SpaPhiS-14
Linares, Ifrain
❑ 93LinVenB-39
❑ 94VenLinU-24
❑ 95LinVen-92
❑ 96-97LinVen-19
Linares, Julio
❑ 94AstMot-27
❑ 95AstMot-28
❑ 96AstMot-28
Linares, Mario
❑ 91AubAstC-15
❑ 91AubAstP-4277
❑ 92AshTouC-22
❑ 93QuaCitRBC-11
❑ 93QuaCitRBF-103
❑ 93QuaCitRBF-130
Linares, Omar
❑ 90IBAWorA-4
❑ 90IBAWorA-43
Linares, Ramon
❑ 85DomLeaS-109
Linares, Rich
❑ 93FloStaLAF-48
❑ 93VerBeaDC-17
❑ 93VerBeaDF-2215
❑ 94BakDodC-14
❑ 94ClaGolF-185
❑ 94ExcFS7-217
❑ 95BakBlaTI-17
❑ 96SanBerSB-16
❑ 97SanAntMB-6
❑ 98SanAntMM-6
Linares, Rufino
❑ 79SavBraT-3
❑ 81BraPol-25
❑ 82BraBurKL-15
❑ 82BraPol-25
❑ 82Don-310
❑ 82Fle-439
❑ 82Top-244
❑ 83Don-275
❑ 83Fle-140
❑ 83Top-467
❑ 84raPho-17
❑ 84RicBraT-2
❑ 85DomLeaS-180
❑ 85Top-167
❑ 85TopTif-167
❑ 86EdmTraP-18
Linares, Yfrain
❑ 95BelBreTI-4
Linarez, Jose
❑ 87PocGiaTB-32
Lincoln, Abraham
❑ 39WheBB13-2
❑ 88WilMulP-10
❑ 94OriofB-13
Lincoln, Lance
❑ 84AriWilP-10
❑ 86BelBreP-13
❑ 87BelBreP-14
Lincoln, Mike
❑ 97ForMyeM-17
❑ 98Bow-347
❑ 98BowChr-347
❑ 98BowChrGA-347
❑ 98BowChrGAR-347
❑ 98BowChrI-347
❑ 98BowChrIR-347
❑ 98BowChrR-347
❑ 98BowGolA-347
❑ 98BowInt-347
❑ 98NewBriRCM-17
❑ 99Bow-105
❑ 99BowAut-BA45
❑ 99BowChr-105
❑ 99BowChrG-105
❑ 99BowChrGR-105
❑ 99BowChrI-105
❑ 99BowChrIR-105
❑ 99BowChrR-105
❑ 99BowGol-105
❑ 99BowInt-105
❑ 99SP TopP-75
❑ 99SP TopPPE-75
❑ 99Top-211
❑ 99TopChr-211
❑ 99TopChrR-211
❑ 99UppDecMP-ML
Lind, Carl
❑ 29ExhFou-21
❑ 94ConTSN-1262
❑ 94ConTSNB-1262
Lind, Jack
❑ 74SacSolC-60
❑ 75SacSolC-4
❑ 83RedPioT-30
❑ 87NasSouTI-13
❑ 88NasSouC-23
❑ 88NasSouP-486
❑ 94BreMilB-239
❑ 97PirPos-21
Lind, Jose
❑ 85PriWilPT-17
❑ 86NasPirP-16
❑ 87VanCanP-1616
❑ 88BlaYNPRWL-168
❑ 88ClaRed-195
❑ 88Don-38
❑ 88DonBasB-145
❑ 88Fle-334
❑ 88FleGlo-334
❑ 88Lea-38
❑ 88PanSti-371
❑ 88PirTeal-20
❑ 88Sco-597
❑ 88ScoGlo-597
❑ 88ScoYouS2-4
❑ 88StaLinPi-14
❑ 88Top-767
❑ 88TopBig-106
❑ 88TopClo-61
❑ 88TopSti-127
❑ 88TopTif-767
❑ 89BimBreD-7
❑ 89BlaYNPRWL-143
❑ 89Bow-421
❑ 89BowTif-421
❑ 89ClaLigB-20
❑ 89Don-290
❑ 89DonBasB-101
❑ 89Fle-214
❑ 89FleGlo-214
❑ 89OPC-273
❑ 89PanSti-170
❑ 89PirVerFJ-13
❑ 89RedFolSB-75

❑ 89Sco-87
❑ 89Spo-62
❑ 89Top-273
❑ 89TopBig-25
❑ 89TopSti-126
❑ 89TopTif-273
❑ 89UppDec-334
❑ 90Bow-170
❑ 90BowTif-170
❑ 90Don-172
❑ 90DonBesN-82
❑ 90Fle-474
❑ 90FleCan-474
❑ 90Lea-77
❑ 90OPC-168
❑ 90PanSti-328
❑ 90PirHomC-20
❑ 90PublntS-159
❑ 90PublntS-616
❑ 90Sco-83
❑ 90Spo-58
❑ 90Top-168
❑ 90TopBig-196
❑ 90TopSti-131
❑ 90TopTif-168
❑ 90UppDec-424
❑ 91Bow-530
❑ 91Don-58
❑ 91Fle-43
❑ 91Lea-146
❑ 91OPC-537
❑ 91PanFreS-116
❑ 91PanSti-117
❑ 91Sco-461
❑ 91Sco100S-33
❑ 91StaClu-233
❑ 91Stu-227
❑ 91Top-537
❑ 91TopDesS-537
❑ 91TopMic-537
❑ 91TopTif-537
❑ 91Ult-283
❑ 91UppDec-258
❑ 92Bow-351
❑ 92ClaGam-178
❑ 92Don-189
❑ 92Fle-559
❑ 92Lea-175
❑ 92LeaBlaG-175
❑ 92OPC-43
❑ 92PanSti-253
❑ 92Pin-49
❑ 92Pin-603
❑ 92PirNatl-12
❑ 92Sco-265
❑ 92StaClu-859
❑ 92Stu-86
❑ 92Top-43
❑ 92TopGol-43
❑ 92TopGolW-43
❑ 92TopMic-43
❑ 92Ult-255
❑ 92UppDec-205
❑ 93Bow-153
❑ 93Don-675
❑ 93Fla-219
❑ 93Fle-115
❑ 93FleFinE-221
❑ 93Lea-402
❑ 93OPC-120
❑ 93OPCPre-42
❑ 93PacBeiA-8
❑ 93PacSpa-489
❑ 93PacSpaPl-2
❑ 93Pin-103
❑ 93RoyPol-16
❑ 93RoyStaC-10
❑ 93Sco-660
❑ 93Sel-105
❑ 93SelRoo-22T
❑ 93StaClu-729
❑ 93StaCluFDI-729
❑ 93StaCluMOP-729
❑ 93Stu-189
❑ 93Top-108
❑ 93TopGol-108
❑ 93ToplnaM-108
❑ 93ToplnaR-108
❑ 93TopMic-108
❑ 93Ult-563
❑ 93UltAwaW-4
❑ 93UppDec-309
❑ 93UppDec-513
❑ 93UppDecGold-309
❑ 93UppDecGold-513
❑ 94Bow-611
❑ 94ColC-176
❑ 94ColChoGS-176
❑ 94ColChoSS-176
❑ 94Don-306
❑ 94Fin-46
❑ 94FinRef-46
❑ 94Fla-301
❑ 94Fle-163
❑ 94FleExtB-94
❑ 94Lea-65
❑ 94OPC-68
❑ 94Pac-292
❑ 94PanSti-76
❑ 94Pin-199
❑ 94PinArtP-199
❑ 94PinMusC-199
❑ 94Sco-39
❑ 94ScoGolR-39
❑ 94Sel-51
❑ 94SelSam-51
❑ 94StaClu-135
❑ 94StaCluFDI-135
❑ 94StaCluGR-135
❑ 94StaCluMOP-135
❑ 94StaCluMOP-ST21
❑ 94StaCluP-135
❑ 94StaCluST-ST21
❑ 94Top-332
❑ 94TopGol-332
❑ 94TopSpa-332
❑ 94TriPla-237
❑ 94Ult-68
❑ 94UppDec-161
❑ 94UppDecED-161
❑ 95ColCho-454
❑ 95ColChoGS-454
❑ 95ColChoSS-454
❑ 95Don-225
❑ 95DonPreP-225
❑ 95Fla-265
❑ 95Fle-164
❑ 95Lea-32
❑ 95Pac-207
❑ 95PanSti-48
❑ 95Pin-108
❑ 95PinArtP-108
❑ 95PinMusC-108
❑ 95Sco-172
❑ 95ScoGolR-172
❑ 95ScoPlaTS-172
❑ 95StaClu-232
❑ 95StaCluFDI-232
❑ 95StaCluMOP-232
❑ 95StaCluSTWS-232
❑ 95Top-578
❑ 95TopCyb-352
❑ 95Ult-58
❑ 95UltGolM-58
❑ 95UppDec-183
❑ 95UppDecED-183
❑ 95UppDecEDG-183
Lind, Orlando
❑ 85PriWilPT-1
❑ 86NasPirP-17
❑ 87HarSenP-14
❑ 88BlaYNPRWL-135
❑ 88HarSenP-847
❑ 89BlaYNPRWL-7
❑ 89HarSenP-300
❑ 89HarSenS-9
❑ 90OrlSunRS-9
❑ 90PorBeaP-175
❑ 90ProAAAF-245
❑ 91LinDriAA-484
❑ 91OrlSunRLD-484
❑ 91OrlSunRP-1845
❑ 92PorBeaF-2663
❑ 92PorBeaS-413
Lind, Randy
❑ 87EveGiaC-11
Lindaman, Vivian
❑ 08RosComP-92
❑ 09ColChiE-170A
❑ 09ColChiE-170B
❑ 09ColChiE-170C
❑ 09RamT20-68
❑ 09T206-213
❑ 11SpoLifCW-219
❑ 12ColRedB-170A
❑ 12ColRedB-170B
❑ 12ColRedB-170C
❑ 12ColTinT-170A
❑ 12ColTinT-170B
❑ 12ColTinT-170C
Lindamore, Howard
❑ 21Zee-13
❑ 22Zee-10
❑ 23Zee-13
❑ 25Zee-93
❑ 26Zee-10
Lindbeck, Em
❑ 77FriOneYW-111
Lindblad, Paul
❑ 66Top-568
❑ 67Top-227
❑ 68OPC-127
❑ 68Top-127
❑ 68TopVen-127
❑ 69Top-449
❑ 70OPC-408
❑ 70Top-408
❑ 71MLBOffS-519
❑ 71OPC-658
❑ 71SenTealW-14
❑ 71Top-658
❑ 72OPC-396
❑ 72RanTeal-17
❑ 72Top-396
❑ 73OPC-406
❑ 73Top-406
❑ 74OPC-369
❑ 74Top-369
❑ 75OPC-278
❑ 75Top-278
❑ 75TopMin-278
❑ 76Kel-52A
❑ 76Kel-52B
❑ 76OPC-9
❑ 76SSP-479
❑ 76Top-9
❑ 77BurCheD-117
❑ 77Top-583
❑ 78SSP270-85
❑ 78Top-314
❑ 79Top-634
❑ 87ElPasDP-20
❑ 88ElPasDB-10
❑ 89ElPasDGS-2
❑ 90ElPasDGS-2
❑ 91ElPasDLD-200
❑ 91ElPasDP-2763
❑ 91LinDriAA-200
❑ 92PenPilC-29
❑ 92PenPilF-2950
❑ 92YanWIZ7-97
❑ 93AppFoxCB-28
❑ 93RanKee-24
Lindell, Johnny (John)
❑ 43YanSta-17
❑ 46SpoExcW-5-3
❑ 47Exh-134
❑ 47HomBon-30
❑ 47TipTop-53
❑ 47YanTeaT-17
❑ 48BluTin-5
❑ 48Bow-11
❑ 48SweSpoT-17
❑ 48YanTeal-17
❑ 49Bow-197
❑ 49Lea-82
❑ 49YanTeal-12
❑ 50Bow-209
❑ 50W720HolS-17
❑ 52MotCoo-1
❑ 53Top-230
❑ 54Bow-159
❑ 54Top-51
❑ 76TayBow4-106
❑ 77TCMTheWY-55
❑ 79DiaGre-17
❑ 83TCMPla1943-3
❑ 85TCMPhoC-7
❑ 91TopArc1-230
❑ 92YanWIZA-40
❑ 93ConTSN-715
❑ 94TopArc1-51
❑ 94TopArc1G-51
Lindell, Rick
❑ 91PacSenL-72
Lindeman, Jim
❑ 86LouRedTI-16
❑ 87CarSmo-14
❑ 87CarTeal-19
❑ 87ClaUpdY-111
❑ 87Don-37
❑ 87DonOpeD-59
❑ 87DonRoo-41
❑ 87FleMin-64
❑ 87FleUpd-65
❑ 87FleUpdG-65
❑ 87Lea-37
❑ 87SpoRoo2-43
❑ 87TopTra-65T
❑ 87TopTraT-65T
❑ 88CarTeal-17
❑ 88Don-540
❑ 88Fle-39
❑ 88FleGlo-39
❑ 88LouRedBTI-28
❑ 88OPC-16
❑ 88Sco-302
❑ 88ScoGlo-302
❑ 88StaLinCa-12
❑ 88Top-562
❑ 88TopTif-562
❑ 89BlaYNPRWL-94
❑ 89CarSmo-11
❑ 89CarTeal-15
❑ 89LouRedBTI-26
❑ 89Top-791
❑ 89TopTif-791
❑ 90CMC-392
❑ 90ProAAAF-386
❑ 90SprCarDGB-29
❑ 90TolMudHC-15
❑ 90TolMudHP-156
❑ 91LinDriAAA-487
❑ 91ScrRedBLD-487
❑ 92Don-701
❑ 92Fle-538
❑ 92OPC-258
❑ 92PhiMed-19
❑ 92Sco-321
❑ 92StaClu-893
❑ 92StaCluECN-893
❑ 92Top-258
❑ 92TopGol-258
❑ 92TopGolW-258
❑ 92TopMic-258
❑ 93TucTorF-3066
❑ 94NorTidF-2933
❑ 95ColCho-317
❑ 95ColChoGS-317
❑ 95ColChoSS-317
❑ 95Fla-173
❑ 95Fle-374
❑ 95Sco-216
❑ 95ScoGolR-216
❑ 95ScoPlaTS-216
❑ 95StaClu-380
❑ 95StaCluMOP-380
❑ 95StaCluSTWS-380
Lindemann, Skip
❑ 89GeoColC-19
❑ 89GeoColC-28
Lindemann, Wayne
❑ 93HicCraC-13
❑ 93HicCraF-1275
❑ 94SouBenSHC-8
❑ 94SouBenSHF-589
❑ 95PriWilCTI-20
Lindemuth, John
❑ 90BasWit-87
Linden, Mark
❑ 89GenCubP-1878
Lindner, Brian
❑ 96EveAquB-14
Lindquist, Dan
❑ 83TriTriT-11
❑ 84VisOakT-25
Lindquist, John
❑ 95OdgRapTI-15
Lindros, Eric
❑ 90ScoRoo-100T
Lindsay, Chuck
❑ 80LynSaiT-5
Lindsay, Darian
❑ 90KinMetB-2
❑ 90KinMetS-14
❑ 91ParPatF-4
❑ 91PitMetC-19
❑ 91PitMetP-3418
❑ 92ColMetC-8
❑ 92ColMetF-290
❑ 92ColMetPI-12
Lindsay, John
❑ 84WilMay-38
Lindsay, Jon
❑ 91GulCoaRSP-16
Lindsay, Tim
❑ 91St.CatBJC-21
❑ 91St.CatBJP-3390
❑ 92MyrBeaHC-18
❑ 92MyrBeaHF-2193
❑ 93DunBluJC-14
❑ 93DunBluJFFN-15
Lindsay, William
❑ 09ObaT21-184
❑ 11Zee-51
❑ 12HomRunKE-42
❑ 12Zee-68
❑ 13Zee-66
❑ 15Zee-39
Lindsey, Bill (William D.)
❑ 85AlbYanT-12
❑ 86AlbYanT-22
❑ 87BirBarB-26
❑ 88Fle-403
❑ 88FleGlo-403
❑ 88VanCanC-16
❑ 88VanCanP-758
Lindsey, Chris
❑ 08IndPos-14
Lindsey, Darrell
❑ 88MarPhiS-21
❑ 89SpaPhiP-1040
❑ 89SpaPhiS-14
❑ 90ClePhiS-11
❑ 91LinDriAA-511
❑ 91ReaPhiLD-511
❑ 91ReaPhiP-1369
❑ 92ClePhiF-2055
Lindsey, Dave
❑ 75SacSolC-2
Lindsey, Don
❑ 89EugEmeB-5
Lindsey, Doug (Douglas)
❑ 82DanSunF-12
Lindsey, Doug (Michael Douglas)
❑ 87UtiBluSP-10
❑ 88SpaPhiP-1042
❑ 88SpaPhiS-11
❑ 90CMC-776
❑ 90ReaPhiB-12
❑ 90ReaPhiP-1223
❑ 90ReaPhiS-16
❑ 91Cla/Bes-100
❑ 91LinDriAA-512
❑ 91ReaPhiLD-512
❑ 91ReaPhiP-1372
❑ 92ScrRedBF-2449
❑ 92ScrRedBS-487
❑ 92TopDeb91-110
❑ 93PhiStaC-10
❑ 93ScrRedBTI-14
❑ 94NasSouF-1254
Lindsey, Jim
❑ 31CarMet-19
❑ 74Car193T-16
❑ 90DodTar-453
Lindsey, John
❑ 85CloHSS-24
Lindsey, John William
❑ 96PorRocB-19
❑ 97AshTou-15
❑ 98AshTouM-11
Lindsey, Jon
❑ 82ReaPhiT-16
Lindsey, Joseph
❑ 75TulOil7-18
Lindsey, Rodney L.
❑ 95IdaFalBTI-7
❑ 96IdaFalB-13
❑ 97CliLumG-14
❑ 98CliLumG-11
Lindsey, Shawn
❑ 98SalVol-20
Lindstrom, David
❑ 97LakTigB-20
❑ 98LakTigM-12
Lindstrom, Fred
❑ 26Exh-36
❑ 27Exh-20
❑ 28Exh-19
❑ 28PorandAR-A23
❑ 28PorandAR-B23
❑ 28W56PlaC-D8
❑ 29ExhFou-10
❑ 29PorandAR-56
❑ 30UncJac-20
❑ 31Exh-9
❑ 31W517-24
❑ 32USCar*-16
❑ 33ButCre-16
❑ 33DelR33-11
❑ 33ExhFou-5
❑ 33Gou-133
❑ 34BatR31-122
❑ 34GouCanV-17
❑ 35DiaMatCS3T1-98
❑ 36ExhFou-2
❑ 36GouWidPPR-A64
❑ 36R31PasP-31
❑ 36WorWidGV-65
❑ 73SpoScoHC-8
❑ 73SpoScoHC-9
❑ 73SpoScoHC-10
❑ 75GiaAllT-4
❑ 76GrePlaG-23
❑ 76RowExh-9
❑ 76ShaPiz-156
❑ 77BobParHoF-32
❑ 77GalGloG-127
❑ 79DiaGre-351
❑ 80GiaGreT-11
❑ 80PacLeg-100
❑ 80PerHaloFP-156
❑ 80SSPHOF-156
❑ 83ConMar-35
❑ 85BigLeaC3-84
❑ 88ConNatA-13
❑ 89DodSmoG-103
❑ 90DodTar-454
❑ 91ConTSN-58
❑ 92ConTSN-596
❑ 93DiaStaES-141
Linduyt, Doug
❑ 79CedRapGT-31
Linebarger, Keith
❑ 92EliTwiC-2
❑ 92EliTwiF-3677
❑ 93ForWayWC-16
❑ 93ForWayWF-1965
❑ 94ForWayWC-14
❑ 94ForWayWF-2006
❑ 95ForMyeMTI-15
❑ 96HarCitRCB-19
❑ 97SalLakB-14
❑ 98WesTenDJM-15
Linebrink, Scott
❑ 98ShrCapM-20
❑ 98ShrCapWS-20
❑ 98TexLeaTPG-21
Linehan, Andrew
❑ 94ElmPioC-11
❑ 94ElmPioF-3468
Linemann, Wayne
❑ 92UtiBluSC-20
Lines, Richard
❑ 61UniOil-SD6
❑ 67CokCapS-10
❑ 67SenPos-14
❑ 67Top-273
❑ 68Top-291
❑ 68TopVen-291
Lineweaver, Aaron
❑ 96SpoIndB-16
❑ 98CarLeaAC-1
❑ 98CarLeaAC-34
❑ 98WilBluRC-17
Linfante, Rob
❑ 91OklStaC-14
❑ 92OklStaC-15
❑ 94ButCopKSP-5
Linfonte, Ron
❑ 79WatIndT-3B
Ling, Holly
❑ 91HawWomS-6
Lingerman, Nemo
❑ 78WisRapTT-11
Lingrel, Ray
❑ 27Zee-72
Liniak, Cole
❑ 96MicBatCB-15
❑ 97Bes-94
❑ 97BesAutSBPP-46
❑ 97BesDiaB-18
❑ 97Bow-417
❑ 97BowChr-277
❑ 97BowChrI-277
❑ 97BowChrIR-277
❑ 97BowChrR-277
❑ 97BowInt-417
❑ 97FloStaLTPB-21
❑ 97SarRedS-1
❑ 98Bow-404
❑ 98BowCerBlueAU-8
❑ 98BowCerGA-8
❑ 98BowCerSA-8
❑ 98BowChr-404
❑ 98BowChrGA-404
❑ 98BowChrGAR-404
❑ 98BowChrI-404
❑ 98BowChrIR-404
❑ 98BowChrR-404
❑ 98BowGolA-404
❑ 98BowInt-404

❑ 98PawRedSQ-18
❑ 98SP MinPE-29
❑ 98SPMin-29
❑ 99BowAut-BA52
❑ 99BowChr-108
❑ 99BowChrG-108
❑ 99BowChrGR-108
❑ 99BowChrI-108
❑ 99BowChrIR-108
❑ 99BowChrR-108
Link, Bryan
❑ 93BluOriC-16
❑ 93BluOriF-4132
❑ 94Bow-349
❑ 94ExcFirYPF-2
❑ 94ExcFS7-11
❑ 94FreKeyC-14
❑ 94FreKeyF-2629
❑ 94OriPro-54
❑ 95HudValRTI-12
Link, Dave
❑ 83St.PetCT-30
Link, Robert
❑ 86WatIndP-14
❑ 87WilBilP-7
❑ 88GleFalTP-937
❑ 89TolMudHC-6
❑ 89TolMudHP-778
Linke, Ed
❑ 35DiaMatCS3T1-99
❑ 93ConTSN-961
Linke, Fred
❑ 11SpoLifM-46
Linnert, Tom
❑ 75SanAntBT-14
❑ 76WilTomT-9
Lino, Rivera Ortiz
❑ 87GasRanP-9
Linseman, Kenny
❑ 80PhiBul-25
Linskey, Mike
❑ 89FreKeyS-13
❑ 90Bes-21
❑ 90HagSunB-20
❑ 90HagSunDGB-15
❑ 90HagSunP-1407
❑ 90ProAaA-1
❑ 90ProAAAF-475
❑ 90RocRedWGC-20
❑ 90RocRedWP-718
❑ 91Bow-105
❑ 91LinDriAAA-468
❑ 91RocRedWLD-468
❑ 91RocRedWP-1897
❑ 92Fle-663
❑ 92WicWraF-3655
❑ 92WicWraS-638
❑ 93LasVegSF-940
Lint, Royce
❑ 54CarHunW-10
❑ 55Bow-62
Lintern, Cory
❑ 94EveGiaC-18
❑ 94EveGiaF-3651
❑ 95BurBeeTI-9
Linton, Dave
❑ 85UtiBluST-3
❑ 86DayBealP-16
Linton, Doug
❑ 87MyrBeaBJP-1439
❑ 88KnoBluJB-15
❑ 90CMC-331
❑ 90ProAAAF-347
❑ 90SyrChiC-5
❑ 90SyrChiMB-14
❑ 90SyrChiP-567
❑ 91LinDriAAA-507
❑ 91SyrChiLD-507
❑ 91SyrChiMB-11
❑ 91SyrChiP-2478
❑ 92Bow-277
❑ 92SkyAAAF-228
❑ 92SyrChiF-1964
❑ 92SyrChiMB-12
❑ 92SyrChiS-510
❑ 93BluJayD4-35
❑ 93Don-321
❑ 93LinVenB-261
❑ 93Sco-295
❑ 93SyrChiF-996
❑ 93Top-159
❑ 93TopGol-159
❑ 93TopInaM-159
❑ 93TopInaR-159
❑ 93TopMic-159
❑ 94MetColP-15
❑ 94VenLinU-126
❑ 95ColCho-323
❑ 95ColChoGS-323
❑ 95ColChoSS-323
❑ 95LinVen-187
❑ 95OmaRoyTI-17
❑ 96OmaRoyB-15
Lintz, Larry
❑ 72Dia-26
❑ 74OPC-121
❑ 74Top-121
❑ 75OPC-416
❑ 75Top-416
❑ 75TopMin-416
❑ 76OPC-109
❑ 76SSP-286
❑ 76Top-109
❑ 77Top-323
Lintz, Ricky
❑ 81WatIndT-11
❑ 82WatIndF-5
❑ 82WatIndT-6
Linz, Phil
❑ 47Exh-135
❑ 62Top-596
❑ 63ReqKP-10
❑ 63Top-264
❑ 64ChatheY-14
❑ 64Top-344
❑ 64TopVen-344
❑ 65ChaTheY-12
❑ 65Top-369
❑ 66PhiTeal-9
❑ 66Top-522
❑ 67CokCapPh-8
❑ 67OPC-14
❑ 67Top-14
❑ 68Top-594
❑ 78TCM60I-97
❑ 91MetWIZ-231
❑ 92YanWIZ6-72
Linzy, Frank
❑ 65Top-589
❑ 66OPC-78
❑ 66Top-78
❑ 66TopVen-78
❑ 67CokCapG-13
❑ 67Top-279
❑ 68DexPre-48
❑ 68OPC-147
❑ 68Top-147
❑ 68TopVen-147
❑ 69MLBOffS-202
❑ 69Top-345
❑ 70CarTeal-19
❑ 70Gia-7
❑ 70MLBOffS-127
❑ 70OPC-77
❑ 70Top-77
❑ 71CarTeal-15
❑ 71CarTeal-24
❑ 71MLBOffS-277
❑ 71OPC-551
❑ 71Top-551
❑ 72MilBra-199
❑ 72OPC-243
❑ 72Top-243
❑ 73OPC-286
❑ 73Top-286
❑ 75HawIsIC-13
❑ 94BreMilB-240
Lipanovich, Edward
❑ 31Zee-69
Lipe, Perry H.
❑ 09T206-499
Lipon, John
❑ 51Bow-285
❑ 52Bow-163
❑ 52Top-89
❑ 53BowC-123
❑ 53RedSoxTI-18
❑ 53Top-40
❑ 54Top-19
❑ 57JetPos-12
❑ 58JetPos-11
❑ 61MapLeaBH-12
❑ 76ShrCapT-13
❑ 77ShrCapT-12
❑ 78ColCliT-13
❑ 79DiaGre-382
❑ 79PorBeaT-9
❑ 81BufBisT-1
❑ 81TigDetN-26
❑ 82AleDukT-21
❑ 83AleDukT-11
❑ 83TopRep5-89
❑ 84PriWilPT-29
❑ 85NasPirT-27
❑ 87FayGenP-17
❑ 88FloStaLAS-28
❑ 89LakTigS-26
❑ 90FloStaLAS-49
❑ 90LakTigS-26
❑ 91LakTigC-29
❑ 91LakTigP-282
❑ 91TopArc1-40
❑ 92LakTigC-27
❑ 92LakTigF-2293
❑ 94TopArc1-19
❑ 94TopArc1G-19
Lipscomb, Bruce
❑ 89ChaRanS-13
Lipski, Robert
❑ 63Top-558
Lipson, Marc
❑ 90Bes-101
❑ 90KenTwiB-20
❑ 90KenTwiP-2289
❑ 90KenTwiS-9
❑ 90MidLeaASGS-14
❑ 90ProAaA-113
❑ 91Cla/Bes-229
❑ 91VisOakC-4
❑ 91VisOakP-1738
❑ 92OrlSunRF-2845
Lipson, Stefan
❑ 83ButCopKT-7
Lira, Felipe
❑ 90BriTigP-3165
❑ 90BriTigS-15
❑ 92LakTigC-16
❑ 92LakTigF-2275
❑ 93Bow-643
❑ 93LinVenB-177
❑ 93LonTigF-2304
❑ 94Cla-2
❑ 94ExcFS7-57
❑ 94TolMudHF-1027
❑ 94VenLinU-78
❑ 95Fin-329
❑ 95FinRef-329
❑ 95Fla-259
❑ 95FleUpd-21
❑ 95LinVen-242
❑ 95LinVen-305
❑ 95StaClu-585
❑ 95StaCluMOP-585
❑ 95StaCluSTWS-585
❑ 95TopTra-68T
❑ 95UppDec-422
❑ 95UppDecED-422
❑ 95UppDecEDG-422
❑ 96-97LinVen-253
❑ 96ColCho-138
❑ 96ColChoGS-138
❑ 96ColChoSS-138
❑ 96Don-207
❑ 96DonPreP-207
❑ 96EmoXL-62
❑ 96Fla-84
❑ 96Fle-116
❑ 96FleTif-116
❑ 96LeaSigA-136
❑ 96LeaSigAG-136
❑ 96LeaSigAS-136
❑ 96MetUni-61
❑ 96MetUniP-61
❑ 96Pac-322
❑ 96PacPri-P102
❑ 96PacPriG-P102
❑ 96PanSti-145
❑ 96Sco-47
❑ 96StaClu-302
❑ 96StaCluMOP-302
❑ 96TigHebN-11
❑ 96Top-71
❑ 96Ult-63
❑ 96UltGolM-63
❑ 96UppDec-71
❑ 97Cir-86
❑ 97CirRav-86
❑ 97ColCho-106
❑ 97Fle-101
❑ 97FleTif-101
❑ 97Pac-91
❑ 97PacLigB-91
❑ 97PacSil-91
❑ 97Top-31
❑ 97UppDec-73
❑ 98TacRaiQ-19
Liranzo, Rafael
❑ 77RocRedWM-3
❑ 78RocRedWT-12
Liriano, Felix
❑ 88FayGenP-1093
Liriano, Julio
❑ 88WatIndP-675
Liriano, Nelson
❑ 85KinBluJT-13
❑ 86KnoBluJP-15
❑ 87IntLeaAT-8
❑ 87SyrChiP-1929
❑ 87SyrChiT-17
❑ 88BluJay5-8
❑ 88BluJayFS-19
❑ 88Don-32
❑ 88Fle-117
❑ 88FleGlo-117
❑ 88Lea-32
❑ 88OPC-205
❑ 88Sco-621
❑ 88ScoGlo-621
❑ 88ScoYouSI-13
❑ 88StaLinBJ-13
❑ 88Top-205
❑ 88TopBig-155
❑ 88TopTif-205
❑ 89BluJayFS-17
❑ 89ClaTraP-196
❑ 89Don-627
❑ 89DonBasB-160
❑ 89Fle-239
❑ 89FleGlo-239
❑ 89OPC-76
❑ 89Sco-577
❑ 89Top-776
❑ 89TopBig-207
❑ 89TopTif-776
❑ 89UppDec-109
❑ 90BluJayFS-18
❑ 90Bow-518
❑ 90BowTif-518
❑ 90Don-267
❑ 90Fle-87
❑ 90FleCan-87
❑ 90OPC-543
❑ 90PanSti-182
❑ 90PubIntS-522
❑ 90Sco-77
❑ 90Top-543
❑ 90TopBig-142
❑ 90TopSti-197
❑ 90TopTif-543
❑ 90UppDec-134
❑ 91Don-603
❑ 91Fle-617
❑ 91OPC-18
❑ 91Sco-288
❑ 91Top-18
❑ 91TopDesS-18
❑ 91TopMic-18
❑ 91TopTif-18
❑ 91UppDec-360
❑ 92ColSprSSF-758
❑ 92ColSprSSS-91
❑ 93ColSprSSF-3095
❑ 93LimRocDWB-21
❑ 93TopTra-53T
❑ 94Fla-375
❑ 94FleUpd-127
❑ 94RocPol-16
❑ 94StaCluT-110
❑ 94StaCluTFDI-110
❑ 95DonTopotO-318
❑ 95Fle-523
❑ 95Pac-140
❑ 95PirFil-17
❑ 96ColCho-678
❑ 96ColChoGS-678
❑ 96ColChoSS-678
❑ 96Don-91
❑ 96DonPreP-91
❑ 96Fle-524
❑ 96FleTif-524
❑ 96LeaSigEA-108
❑ 96Pac-175
❑ 96Ult-536
❑ 96UltGolM-536
❑ 97DodMot-26
❑ 97DodPol-17
❑ 97Pac-397
❑ 97PacLigB-397
❑ 97PacSil-397
❑ 98PacOnl-251
❑ 98PacOnlR-251
❑ 98PacOnlWC-251
Lis, Joe
❑ 91St.CatBJC-9
❑ 91St.CatBJP-3404
❑ 92MyrBeaHC-15
❑ 92MyrBeaHF-2204
❑ 93ClaGolF-129
❑ 93KnoSmoF-1260
❑ 93SouAtlLAPI-20
❑ 94SyrChiF-979
❑ 94SyrChiTI-17
❑ 95SyrChiTI-15
❑ 96BufBisB-13
Lis, Joe (Joseph)
❑ 70OPC-56
❑ 70Top-56
❑ 71OPC-138
❑ 71Top-138
❑ 74OPC-659
❑ 74Top-659
❑ 75OklCit8TI-20
❑ 75OPC-86
❑ 75Top-86
❑ 75TopMin-86
❑ 76SSP-523
❑ 77Hos-125
❑ 77Top-269
Lisanti, Bob
❑ 97RocCub-20
Liscio, Joe
❑ 60DarFar-5
Lisenbee, Hod (Horace)
❑ 33Gou-68
❑ 34GouCanV-45
❑ 92ConTSN-540
Lisi, Rick
❑ 75AndRanT-2
❑ 76AshTouT-7
❑ 79TulDriT-14
❑ 80ChaChaT-9
❑ 80VenLeaS-214
❑ 82RocRedWT-14
❑ 83RocRedWT-21
❑ 84RicBraT-7
❑ 93RanKee-230
Lisiecki, David
❑ 91BelMarCB-22
❑ 91BelMarP-3658
❑ 92ProFS7-147
Lisio, Joe
❑ 94KinMetC-9
❑ 94KinMetF-3818
❑ 95PitMetTI-42
❑ 97St.LucM-13
❑ 98TamYanM-18
Liska, Ad
❑ 29PorandAR-57
Liss, Tom
❑ 87BelMarL-17
❑ 89BelMarL-8
List, Joe
❑ 95NewHavRTI-7
List, Lew
❑ 94NewHavRF-1561
List, Paul
❑ 87SalAngP-20
❑ 88BenBucL-32
❑ 91AugPirC-21
❑ 91AugPirP-820
❑ 92GasRanF-2264
❑ 93TulDriF-2747
❑ 93TulDriTI-14
Listach, Pat
❑ 89StoPorB-22
❑ 89StoPorCLC-173
❑ 89StoPorP-379
❑ 89StoPorS-4
❑ 90CalLeaACLC-36
❑ 90StoPorB-5
❑ 90StoPorCLC-191
❑ 90StoPorP-2190
❑ 90TopMag-98
❑ 91ElPasDLD-191
❑ 91ElPasDP-2753
❑ 91LinDriAA-191
❑ 92Bow-526
❑ 92BrePol-13
❑ 92DonRooP-BC7
❑ 92DonUpd-U1
❑ 92FleUpd-36
❑ 92JimDeaRS-2
❑ 92Lea-370
❑ 92LeaBlaG-370
❑ 92Pin-562
❑ 92PinRoo-5
❑ 92ScoRoo-80T
❑ 92StaClu-757
❑ 92StaCluECN-757
❑ 92TopTra-65T
❑ 92TopTraG-65T
❑ 92Ult-385
❑ 92UppDec-775
❑ 92UppDecSR-SR13
❑ 93Bow-395
❑ 93BrePol-15
❑ 93BreSen5-1
❑ 93ClaGam-53
❑ 93DiaMar-64
❑ 93Don-309
❑ 93DonDiaK-DK29
❑ 93Fin-109
❑ 93FinJum-109
❑ 93FinRef-109
❑ 93Fla-226
❑ 93Fle-253
❑ 93FleAll-AL4
❑ 93FleFruotL-36
❑ 93FleRooS-RSA3
❑ 93FleTeaL-AL3
❑ 93FunPac-71
❑ 93Hos-32
❑ 93JimDea-28
❑ 93Lea-264
❑ 93LeaFas-10
❑ 93OPC-205
❑ 93OPCPreSP-15
❑ 93OPCPreSPF-15
❑ 93PacSpa-160
❑ 93PanSti-39
❑ 93PanSti-163
❑ 93Pin-33
❑ 93PinTeaP-7
❑ 93Sco-357
❑ 93Sco-485
❑ 93Sel-273
❑ 93SelChaR-1
❑ 93SelStaL-56
❑ 93SP-67
❑ 93StaClu-293
❑ 93StaClu-432
❑ 93StaCluFDI-293
❑ 93StaCluFDI-432
❑ 93StaCluMOP-293
❑ 93StaCluMOP-432
❑ 93Stu-146
❑ 93Top-480
❑ 93TOPBLAG-35
❑ 93TopGol-480
❑ 93TopInaM-480
❑ 93TopInaR-480
❑ 93TopMic-480
❑ 93Toy-5
❑ 93TriPla-116
❑ 93TriPlaLL-L3
❑ 93Ult-571
❑ 93UltAwaW-19
❑ 93UltPer-5
❑ 93UppDec-43
❑ 93UppDec-253
❑ 93UppDec-491
❑ 93UppDec-817
❑ 93UppDecFA-A13
❑ 93UppDecFAJ-A13
❑ 93UppDecGold-43
❑ 93UppDecGold-253
❑ 93UppDecGold-491
❑ 93UppDecGold-817
❑ 93USPlaCA-12H
❑ 93USPlaCR-1H
❑ 93USPlaCR-JK
❑ 94Bow-617
❑ 94BreMilB-241
❑ 94BrePol-16
❑ 94BreSen-3
❑ 94BreTeal-14
❑ 94ColC-333
❑ 94ColC-520
❑ 94ColChoGS-333
❑ 94ColChoGS-520
❑ 94ColChoSS-333
❑ 94ColChoSS-520
❑ 94ColChoT-9
❑ 94Don-148
❑ 94Fin-79
❑ 94FinPre-79P
❑ 94FinRef-79
❑ 94Fla-305
❑ 94Fle-181
❑ 94FleExtB-105
❑ 94FUnPac-92
❑ 94Lea-420
❑ 94LeaL-45
❑ 94OPC-216
❑ 94Pac-332

❑ 94PanSti-83
❑ 94Pin-449
❑ 94PinArtP-449
❑ 94PinMusC-449
❑ 94Sco-371
❑ 94ScoGolR-371
❑ 94Sel-220
❑ 94SP-59
❑ 94SPDieC-59
❑ 94SPHol-24
❑ 94SPHolDC-24
❑ 94StaClu-354
❑ 94StaCluFDI-354
❑ 94StaCluGR-354
❑ 94StaCluMOP-354
❑ 94StaCluMOP-ST22
❑ 94StaCluST-ST22
❑ 94Top-130
❑ 94TopGol-130
❑ 94TopSpa-130
❑ 94TriPla-55
❑ 94Ult-374
❑ 94UppDec-305
❑ 94UppDecAJ-9
❑ 94UppDecAJG-9
❑ 94UppDecED-305
❑ 95ColCho-179
❑ 95ColChoGS-179
❑ 95ColChoSS-179
❑ 95Don-410
❑ 95DonPreP-410
❑ 95DonTopotO-98
❑ 95Fla-52
❑ 95Fle-182
❑ 95Lea-120
❑ 95LeaLim-33
❑ 95PacPri-75
❑ 95Pin-433
❑ 95PinArtP-433
❑ 95PinMusC-433
❑ 95Sco-417
❑ 95ScoGolR-417
❑ 95ScoPlaTS-417
❑ 95StaClu-244
❑ 95StaCluFDI-244
❑ 95StaCluMOP-244
❑ 95StaCluSTWS-244
❑ 95Stu-185
❑ 95TopTra-144T
❑ 95Ult-296
❑ 95UltGolM-296
❑ 95UppDec-54
❑ 95UppDecED-54
❑ 95UppDecEDG-54
❑ 96BrePol-13
❑ 96ColCho-597
❑ 96ColChoGS-597
❑ 96ColChoSS-597
❑ 96Don-80
❑ 96DonPreP-80
❑ 96Fle-150
❑ 96FleTif-150
❑ 96Lea-194
❑ 96LeaPrePB-194
❑ 96LeaPrePG-194
❑ 96LeaPrePS-194
❑ 96LeaSigA-137
❑ 96LeaSigAG-137
❑ 96LeaSigAS-137
❑ 96Pac-342
❑ 96ProSta-29
❑ 96Sco-81
❑ 97AstMot-26
❑ 97ColCho-353
❑ 97Fle-648
❑ 97FleTif-648
❑ 97Sco-52
❑ 97Sco-405
❑ 97ScoArtPWB-52
❑ 97ScoArtPWB-405
❑ 97ScoPreS-52
❑ 97ScoResC-405
❑ 97ScoShoS-52
❑ 97ScoShoS-405
❑ 97ScoShoSAP-52
❑ 97ScoShoSAP-405
❑ 97Ult-405
❑ 97UltGolME-405
❑ 97UltPlaME-405
❑ 98BufBisG-17

Lister, Martin
❑ 92BilMusF-3350
❑ 92BilMusSP-18
❑ 93WesVirWC-15
❑ 93WesVirWF-2863
❑ 94ExcFS7-178
❑ 94WinSpiC-14
❑ 94WinSpiF-267
❑ 95JacGenTI-5

Litschi, Louis
❑ 12HomRunKE-88
❑ 12Zee-150
❑ 13Zee-142
❑ 14Zee-140
❑ 15Zee-40

Littell, Mark
❑ 74OPC-596
❑ 74Top-596
❑ 75OmaRoyTI-9
❑ 76KanCitRP-16
❑ 76OPC-593
❑ 76SSP-181
❑ 76Top-593
❑ 77Top-141
❑ 78CarTeal-14
❑ 78Top-331
❑ 79Car5-15
❑ 79Top-466
❑ 80Top-631
❑ 81Don-580
❑ 81Fle-544
❑ 81Top-255
❑ 82Don-442
❑ 82Fle-120
❑ 82Top-56
❑ 86RoyGreT-11
❑ 89WatDiaP-1784
❑ 89WatDiaS-27
❑ 90ChaRaiB-25
❑ 90ChaRaiP-2055
❑ 90SweBasG-112
❑ 91HigDesMC-30
❑ 91HigDesMP-2414
❑ 92StoPorC-24
❑ 92StoPorF-52
❑ 93StoPorC-29
❑ 93StoPorF-762
❑ 94StoPorC-28
❑ 94StoPorF-1709
❑ 97TucTorB-28

Littimer, Dave
❑ 91CalLeLA-54

Little, Bryan
❑ 82ExpPos-21
❑ 83ExpPos-17
❑ 83ExpStu-24
❑ 83TopTra-62T
❑ 84Don-157
❑ 84ExpPos-17
❑ 84ExpStu-30
❑ 84Fle-279
❑ 84Nes792-188
❑ 84OPC-188
❑ 84Top-188
❑ 84TopTif-188
❑ 85BufBisT-9
❑ 85Fle-402
❑ 85OPC-257
❑ 85Top-257
❑ 85TopTif-257
❑ 86Don-452
❑ 86Fle-212
❑ 86Top-346
❑ 86TopTif-346
❑ 87ColCliP-16
❑ 87ColCliP-10
❑ 87ColCliT-14
❑ 88BufBisC-16
❑ 88BufBisP-1491
❑ 88BufBisTI-3
❑ 89WicStaR-27
❑ 89WicWraR-4
❑ 90WatDiaB-19
❑ 90WatDiaP-2393
❑ 91WatDiaC-25
❑ 91WatDiaP-1272
❑ 92HigDesMC-29
❑ 92YanWIZ8-107

Little, Dick
❑ 91SalSpuC-25
❑ 91SalSpuP-2263
❑ 92SalSpuC-27
❑ 92SalSpuF-3776

Little, Dick (Richard)
❑ 82WicAerTI-9

Little, Doug
❑ 87DayBeaAP-8
❑ 88BirBarB-26
❑ 89BirBarB-22
❑ 89BirBarP-93

Little, Grady
❑ 84ChaO'sT-10
❑ 85KinBluJT-24
❑ 88BurBraP-11
❑ 89DurBullS-26
❑ 89DurBullS-26
❑ 89DurBulTI-28
❑ 90DurBulTI-29
❑ 90HagSunDGB-16
❑ 91DurBulC-15
❑ 91DurBulP-1676
❑ 92GreBraF-1168
❑ 92GreBraS-249
❑ 93RicBraBB-25
❑ 93RicBraF-201
❑ 93RicBraP-25
❑ 93RicBraRC-25
❑ 93RicBraRC-1
❑ 94RicBraF-2862
❑ 95RicBraRC-9
❑ 95RicBraTI-1
❑ 96PadMot-28

Little, Jeff
❑ 75LafDriT-19
❑ 78PhoGiaC-14
❑ 79PhoGiaVNB-4
❑ 82TolMudHT-4
❑ 83Fle-619
❑ 83TolMudHT-7
❑ 83Top-499

Little, Marc
❑ 92WinSpiC-10

Little, Mark
❑ 94HudValRC-11
❑ 94HudValRF-3400
❑ 94StaCluDP-73
❑ 94StaCluDPFDI-73
❑ 96TexLeaAB-11
❑ 96TulDriTI-15
❑ 97OklCit8-18
❑ 98OklRedM-25
❑ 99SpolII-48

Little, Martin
❑ 80WauTimT-5

Little, Mike
❑ 89WytCubS-20
❑ 90HunCubP-3301
❑ 91PeoChiC-21
❑ 91PeoChiP-1358
❑ 91PeoChiTI-27
❑ 92WinSpiF-1221

Little, Randy
❑ 86BelMarCr-119

Little, Ronald
❑ 82WatRedT-21
❑ 83IndIndTI-20

Little, Scott
❑ 84LitFalMT-4
❑ 85LynMetT-27
❑ 86JacMetT-21
❑ 88HarSenP-838
❑ 89BufBisC-20
❑ 89BufBisP-1681
❑ 90BufBisC-25
❑ 90BufBisP-388
❑ 90BufBisTI-14
❑ 90CMC-25
❑ 90ProAAAF-503
❑ 90TopDeb89-71
❑ 91BufBisLD-31
❑ 91BufBisP-552
❑ 91LinDriAAA-31
❑ 92AugPirC-25
❑ 92AugPirF-255
❑ 93SalBucC-26
❑ 93SalBucF-448
❑ 93SouAtlLAPI-21
❑ 94AugGreC-28
❑ 94AugGreF-3024
❑ 97AugGre-3

Little, Thomas
❑ 86BelMarCr-109

Littlefield, Dick (Richard)
❑ 50RedSoxTI-11
❑ 52Bow-209
❑ 54Bow-213
❑ 54OriEss-24
❑ 55Bow-200
❑ 57Top-346
❑ 58Top-241
❑ 79DiaGre-123
❑ 79TCM50-14
❑ 91OriCro-262

Littlefield, John
❑ 77St.PetCT-4
❑ 78ArkTraT-17
❑ 79ArkTraT-6
❑ 81Don-309
❑ 81Fle-535
❑ 81Top-489
❑ 81TopTra-794
❑ 82Don-412
❑ 82Fle-576A
❑ 82Fle-576B
❑ 82SyrChiT-5
❑ 82SyrChiTI-15
❑ 82Top-278

Littlejohn, Carlisle
❑ 27MidBre-31

Littlejohn, Dennis
❑ 78PhoGiaC-15
❑ 79PhoGiaVNB-19
❑ 80GiaTeal-15
❑ 80PhoGiaVNB-16
❑ 80Top-686
❑ 81Don-313
❑ 81Fle-455
❑ 81PhoGiaVNB-18
❑ 81Top-561

Littleton, Larry
❑ 77ShrCapT-13
❑ 79PorBeaT-19
❑ 80TacTigT-3
❑ 82ChaChaT-20

Littlewood, Mike
❑ 87BriYouC-9

Litton, Greg
❑ 84EveGiaC-1
❑ 85FreGiaSB-12
❑ 86ShrCapP-15
❑ 87ShrCapP-8
❑ 89FleUpd-130
❑ 89ScoRoo-86T
❑ 90Don-453
❑ 90Fle-61
❑ 90FleCan-61
❑ 90GiaMot-18
❑ 90GiaSmo-14
❑ 90Hot50RS-28
❑ 90Lea-331
❑ 90OPC-66
❑ 90PhoFirP-20
❑ 90ProAAAF-46
❑ 90Sco-497
❑ 90Sco100RS-91
❑ 90ScoYouSI-33
❑ 90Top-66
❑ 90TopBig-308
❑ 90TopDeb89-72
❑ 90TopTif-66
❑ 90UppDec-677
❑ 91Bow-621
❑ 91Don-198
❑ 91Fle-266
❑ 91GiaMot-18
❑ 91GiaPacGaE-8
❑ 91OPC-628
❑ 91Sco-532
❑ 91StaClu-45
❑ 91Top-628
❑ 91TopDesS-628
❑ 91TopMic-628
❑ 91TopTif-628
❑ 91Ult-324
❑ 92Fle-640
❑ 92GiaMot-18
❑ 92OPC-238
❑ 92PhoFirS-386
❑ 92Sco-603
❑ 92StaClu-439
❑ 92Top-238
❑ 92TopGol-238
❑ 92TopGolW-238
❑ 92TopMic-238
❑ 93CalCanF-1171
❑ 93Don-340
❑ 93Fle-533
❑ 93FleFinE-273
❑ 93MariStaClu-10
❑ 94Fle-292
❑ 94Pac-575
❑ 94PawRedSDD-10
❑ 94PawRedSF-950
❑ 94Top-111
❑ 94TopGol-111
❑ 94TopSpa-111
❑ 95TacRaiTI-10

Littrell, Jack
❑ 78CliDodT-20
❑ 79WauTimT-15

Littrell, Jack Sr.
❑ 49PorBeaP-2
❑ 55A'sRodM-22
❑ 55A'sTeal-13
❑ 76A'sRodMC-14

Litwhiler, Dan
❑ 36OveCanR-32
❑ 40PhiTeal-12
❑ 41DouPlaR-45
❑ 41DouPlaR-99
❑ 41PhiTeal-13
❑ 47TipTop-81
❑ 49Bow-97
❑ 49EurSta-88
❑ 50Bow-198
❑ 51Bow-179
❑ 79DiaGre-313
❑ 83Car194T-4

Litzinger, Jeff
❑ 88CapCodPB-8
❑ 88CapCodPPaLP-185

Livchak, Robert
❑ 87St.PetCP-27
❑ 88St.PetCS-13

Lively, Everett
❑ 49EurSta-89

Lively, Henry
❑ 09ObaT21-103
❑ 12T207-106
❑ 13Zee-83

Livengood, Wes
❑ 38RedOraW-16
❑ 77CinRedT-38

Livernois, Derek
❑ 85ElmPioT-11
❑ 86GreHorP-13
❑ 87WinHavRSP-23
❑ 89LynRedSS-12
❑ 90Bes-307
❑ 90CMC-805
❑ 90NewBriRSB-24
❑ 90NewBriRSP-1314
❑ 90NewBriRSS-8
❑ 90TopTVRS-50
❑ 91Bow-123
❑ 91LinDriAAA-359
❑ 91PawRedSDD-11
❑ 91PawRedSLD-359
❑ 91PawRedSP-34
❑ 92ClaFS7-197
❑ 92NewBriRSF-428
❑ 92NewBriRSS-488
❑ 92SkyAA F-208
❑ 93PawRedSDD-13
❑ 93PawRedSF-2405
❑ 93PawRedSTI-13

Liverziani, Claudio
❑ 97WisTimR-17
❑ 98WisTimRM-18

Livesey, Jeff
❑ 87AncGlaP-19
❑ 88OneYanP-2052
❑ 89PriWilCS-11
❑ 90Ft.LauYS-12
❑ 91AlbYanLD-10
❑ 91AlbYanP-1011
❑ 91LinDriAA-10
❑ 92AlbYanF-2229
❑ 92ColCliS-107
❑ 93AlbYanF-2165
❑ 94AlbYanF-1444
❑ 95ColCliP-16
❑ 95ColCliTI-16
❑ 96HarSenB-2
❑ 97HarSen-26
❑ 98LynHilQ-26

Livesey, Steve
❑ 91OneYanP-4162
❑ 92PriWilCC-19
❑ 92PriWilCF-158
❑ 93SanBerSC-22
❑ 93SanBerSF-788
❑ 94SanBerSC-27
❑ 94SanBerSF-2776
❑ 96HudValRB-26
❑ 96WesOahCHWB-30
❑ 97HudValRB-29

Livesy, Shawn
❑ 95RocCubTI-12

Livin, Jeff
❑ 86OscAstP-17
❑ 87ColAstP-20

Livingston, Bob
❑ 89SanDieSAS-14

Livingston, Clyde
❑ 95MarPhiTI-15

Livingston, Dennis
❑ 86AlbDukP-13
❑ 86StaoftFT-14
❑ 87AlbDukD-13

Livingston, Doug
❑ 96PorRocB-20
❑ 97AshTou-16
❑ 98CarLeaAC-35
❑ 98SalAvaC-18

Livingston, Mickey (T.)
❑ 43PhiTeal-15
❑ 47TipTop-111
❑ 48GiaTeal-12
❑ 49GiaTeal-17
❑ 83TCMPla1943-42
❑ 90DodTar-1013

Livingston, Paddy
❑ 08IndPos-15
❑ 09T206-214
❑ 10DomDisP-70
❑ 10LuxCigPP-14
❑ 10NadE1-31
❑ 10SweCapPP-47
❑ 11A'sFirT20-10
❑ 11D35RocB-10
❑ 11HelSta-25
❑ 11PinT-5-520
❑ 11PinT-5-523
❑ 11SpoLifCW-220
❑ 11SpoLifM-97
❑ 11T205-101
❑ 12T207-107
❑ 12T207-108
❑ 12T207-109

Livingstone, Scott
❑ 87PanAmTUBI-30
❑ 87PanAmTURB-4
❑ 89LonTigP-1381
❑ 90CMC-393
❑ 90ProAAAF-387
❑ 90TolMudHC-16
❑ 90TolMudHP-157
❑ 91Cla3-T50
❑ 91LinDriAAA-589
❑ 91TolMudHLD-589
❑ 91TolMudHP-1940
❑ 91TriA AAGP-AAA46
❑ 91UppDecFE-53F
❑ 92Bow-3
❑ 92Cla1-T54
❑ 92Don-675
❑ 92Fle-141
❑ 92Lea-127
❑ 92LeaBlaG-127
❑ 92OPC-685
❑ 92OPCPre-56
❑ 92Pin-490
❑ 92ProFS7-64
❑ 92Sco-414
❑ 92Sco100RS-57
❑ 92StaClu-317
❑ 92TigKro-18
❑ 92Top-685
❑ 92TopDeb91-111
❑ 92TopGol-685
❑ 92TopGolW-685
❑ 92TopMic-685
❑ 92Ult-61
❑ 92UppDec-538
❑ 92UppDecSR-SR14
❑ 93Bow-235
❑ 93Don-409
❑ 93Fla-206
❑ 93Fle-232
❑ 93FleRooS-RSB6
❑ 93Lea-375
❑ 93OPC-219
❑ 93PacSpa-446
❑ 93PanSti-116
❑ 93Pin-106
❑ 93Sco-196
❑ 93Sel-320
❑ 93StaClu-328
❑ 93StaCluFDI-328
❑ 93StaCluMOP-328
❑ 93TigGat-19
❑ 93Top-298
❑ 93TopGol-298
❑ 93TopInaM-298
❑ 93TopInaR-298
❑ 93TopMic-298
❑ 93Toy-71
❑ 93ToyMasP-8
❑ 93Ult-202
❑ 93UppDec-63
❑ 93UppDecGold-63
❑ 93USPlaCR-12H
❑ 94ColC-421

- 94ColChoGS-421
- 94ColChoSS-421
- 94Don-597
- 94Fle-139
- 94Lea-202
- 94Sco-171
- 94ScoGolR-171
- 94StaClu-351
- 94StaCluFDI-351
- 94StaCluGR-351
- 94StaCluMOP-351
- 94Stu-134
- 94Top-19
- 94TopGol-19
- 94TopSpa-19
- 95Don-218
- 95DonPreP-218
- 95Lea-99
- 95PadMot-11
- 95Sco-211
- 95ScoGolR-211
- 95ScoPlaTS-211
- 95StaClu-196
- 95StaCluFDI-196
- 95StaCluMOP-196
- 95StaCluSTWS-196
- 95Top-483
- 95TopCyb-275
- 96Fle-573
- 96FleTif-573
- 96LeaSigEA-109
- 96PadMot-16
- 96Ult-560
- 96UltGolM-560
- 97Pac-430
- 97PacLigB-430
- 97PacSil-430
- 97PadMot-17
- 98PacOnl-452
- 98PacOnlR-452
- 98PacOnlWC-452

Livsey, Shawn
- 91Cla/Bes-434
- 91ClaDraP-25
- 91FroRowDP-38
- 91FroRowDPG-38
- 91FroRowDPS-38
- 92OPC-124
- 92Pin-545
- 92StaCluD-108
- 92Top-124
- 92TopGol-124
- 92TopGolW-124
- 92TopMic-124
- 93AshTouC-11
- 93AshTouF-2290
- 94OscAstC-14
- 94OscAstF-1150
- 96DayCubB-15

Liz, Jesus
- 95SpoIndTI-12

Llanes, Pedro
- 86MiaMarP-16
- 87SavCarP-13

Llano, Jorge
- 82MiaMarT-11

Llanos, Alexis
- 97ButCopKB-13
- 97ButCopKK-13
- 98HudValR-14

Llanos, Aurelio
- 88MarPhiS-23
- 89MarPhiS-17
- 90PriPatD-13
- 95HagSunF-80

Llanos, Bobby
- 92BelMarCB-29
- 92BelMarF-1453
- 93AppFoxCB-15
- 93AppFoxFI-2473

Llanos, Victor
- 93GleFalRC-19
- 93GleFalRF-4012
- 94SavCarC-16
- 94SavCarF-516
- 95PeoChiTI-24

Llenas, Chilote
- 85DomLeaS-77

Llenas, Winston
- 71OPC-152
- 71Top-152
- 74OPC-467
- 74Top-467
- 75CalAngP-24
- 75OPC-597
- 75Top-597
- 75TopMin-597
- 76SSP-195
- 83NasAngT-20
- 85EdmTraC-14
- 86EdmTraP-19
- 88BluJayFS-20

Llewellyn, Paul
- 83AndBraT-28

Llewlyn, Herbert
- 18Zee-86

Llibre, Brian
- 97JohCitCTI-22

Llig, Brett
- 96GreFalDTI-22

Llodrat, Fernando
- 76WatRoyT-18

Lloyd, Brian
- 97CliLumG-17

Lloyd, Graeme
- 88MyrBeaBJP-1167
- 91DunBluJC-5
- 91DunBluJP-201
- 92KnoBluJF-2986
- 92KnoBluJS-383
- 92SkyAA F-161
- 93Bow-423
- 93BrePol-16
- 93Fla-227
- 93FleFinE-227
- 93Lea-459
- 93OPCPre-71
- 93PacSpa-512
- 93Pin-616
- 93SelRoo-76T
- 93Ult-572
- 93UppDec-725
- 93UppDecGold-725
- 94BreMilB-242
- 94BrePol-17
- 94BreTeal-15
- 94ColC-518
- 94ColChoGS-518
- 94ColChoSS-518
- 94Don-176
- 94Fin-48
- 94FinRef-48
- 94Fle-182
- 94Lea-351
- 94Pac-333
- 94Sco-284
- 94ScoGolR-284
- 94Sel-262
- 94Top-187
- 94TopGol-187
- 94TopSpa-187
- 94Ult-78
- 94UppDec-332
- 94UppDecED-332
- 95Fla-273
- 95Fle-183
- 95Pac-235
- 95Sco-275
- 95ScoGolR-275
- 95ScoPlaTS-275
- 95Ult-66
- 95UltGolM-66
- 96BrePol-14
- 96FleUpd-U47
- 96FleUpdTC-U47
- 96LeaSigEA-110
- 97Fle-663
- 97FleTif-663
- 97Sco-443
- 97ScoArtPWB-443
- 97ScoResC-443
- 97ScoShoS-443
- 97ScoShoSAP-443
- 98PacInvGems-75
- 98PacOnl-507
- 98PacOnlR-507
- 98PacOnlWC-507
- 99YanFle-6

Lloyd, John
- 93BoiHawC-19
- 93BoiHawF-3912
- 94CedRapKF-1106
- 96CedRapKTI-15

Lloyd, Mike
- 89EliTwiS-15
- 90KenTwiB-6
- 90KenTwiP-2301
- 90KenTwiS-10

Lloyd, Pop (John Henry)
- 74LauOldTBS-33
- 78DexHaloFP-31
- 80PerHaloFP-160
- 80SSPHOF-160
- 83ConMar-54
- 86NegLeaF-16
- 88ConNegA-8
- 88NegLeaD-6
- 90NegLeaS-5
- 91PomBlaBPB-21
- 93TedWil-109
- 94PomNegLB-9
- 94UppDecTAE-19
- 95S.FExaNLT-5
- 97NegLeaPC-6D

Loaiza, Esteban
- 93SalBucC-14
- 93SalBucF-427
- 94Bow-134
- 95Bow-162
- 95BowBes-R82
- 95BowBesR-R82
- 95Exc-256
- 95Fin-253
- 95FinRef-253
- 95Fla-403
- 95FleUpd-150
- 95FleUpdRU-6
- 95PirFil-18
- 95SigRoo-32
- 95SigRooSig-32
- 95StaClu-531
- 95StaCluMOP-531
- 95StaCluSTWS-531
- 95Sum-147
- 95SumNthD-147
- 95Top-655
- 95UppDec-260
- 95UppDecED-260
- 95UppDecEDG-260
- 96ColCho-263
- 96ColChoGS-263
- 96ColChoSS-263
- 96Don-273
- 96DonPreP-273
- 96Fle-525
- 96FleTif-525
- 96Pac-166
- 96PacEstL-EL14
- 96PacPri-P58
- 96PacPriG-P58
- 96Sco-439
- 96StaClu-288
- 96StaCluMOP-288
- 96Top-172
- 96TopGal-101
- 96TopGalPPI-101
- 96Ult-265
- 96UltGolM-265
- 96UppDec-174
- 97ColCho-424
- 97Don-312
- 97DonGolPP-312
- 97DonLim-98
- 97DonLimE-98
- 97DonLimENG-98
- 97DonSigA-67
- 97DonSigAC-81
- 97DonSigAM-81
- 97DonSilPP-312
- 97Pac-398
- 97PacLigB-398
- 97PacSil-398
- 97PirPos-22
- 97Sco-459
- 97ScoArtPWB-459
- 97ScoResC-459
- 97ScoShoS-459
- 97ScoShoSAP-459
- 98ColCho-212
- 98Don-206
- 98DonGolPP-206
- 98DonSilPP-206
- 98Fle-375
- 98Pac-398
- 98PacInv-129
- 98PacInvPBlue-129
- 98PacInvSilv-129
- 98PacInvTeam-22
- 98PacOnl-587
- 98PacOnlR-587
- 98PacOnlWC-587
- 98PacPlaB-398
- 98PacRedT-398
- 98PacSil-398
- 98Pin-148
- 98PinPreP-148
- 98ScoRT-115
- 98StaCluFDI-141
- 98StaCluI-141
- 98StaCluOneK-141
- 98StaCluPP-141
- 98Stu-30
- 98StuGPP-30
- 98StuSPP-30
- 98Top-115
- 98TopChr-115
- 98TopChrR-115
- 98TopDevR-115
- 98TopDia-115
- 98TopMiniC-115
- 98UppDec-481
- 99Fle-485
- 99FleSta9-485
- 99FleWarT-485
- 99PacCroC-287
- 99PacCroCPB-287
- 99UppDec-509
- 99UppDecEL1-509
- 99UppDecEL2-509

Loaiza, Steve
- 92AugPirC-4
- 92AugPirF-233
- 94CarMudF-1575

Lobaton, Jose
- 94OneYanC-11
- 94OneYanF-3800
- 95GreBatTI-15
- 96TamYanY-16
- 97NorNav-22

Lobaton, Pedro
- 76VenLeaS-44

Lobb, Dave
- 71RicBraTI-12

Lobe, Bill
- 55IndGolS-31
- 75TCM195CI-38

Lober, Elmer
- 11Zee-16
- 12HomRunKE-11
- 12Zee-14
- 13Zee-67
- 14Zee-66
- 15Zee-66

Loberg, Tim
- 77TacTwiDQ-8A

Lobert, Hans (John)
- 08RosComP-119
- 09AmeCarE90-1-71
- 09RamT20-69
- 09SpoNewSM-97
- 09T206-215
- 10DomDisP-71
- 10E101-29
- 10E102-15
- 10MelMinE-29
- 10NadCarE-34
- 10PeoT21-34A
- 10PeoT21-34B
- 10SweCapPP-127
- 11E94-21
- 11HelSta-145
- 11MecDFT-36
- 11PinT-5-412
- 11S74Sil-101
- 11SpoLifCW-221
- 11SpoLifM-197
- 11T205-102
- 11TurRedT-105
- 12HasTriFT-31B
- 12HasTriFT-50A
- 12HasTriFT-50B
- 12HasTriFT-50C
- 12HasTriFT-50D
- 12HasTriFT-51
- 14FatPlaT-26
- 14PieStaT-64
- 15AmeCarE106-25
- 15CraJacE-170
- 15SpoNewM-102
- 16BF2FP-80
- 16SpoNewM-104
- 17ColE13-91
- 40PhiTeal-13
- 40PlaBal-160
- 41PhiTeal-14
- 91ConTSN-172
- 92ConTSN-392

Lobozzetta, Al
- 87CedRapRP-1

Locanto, Pat
- 70RoyTeal-20

Locey, Tony
- 93GenCubC-19
- 93GenCubF-3171
- 94PeoChiC-15
- 94PeoChiF-2264

Lochner, Dave
- 83CedRapRF-8
- 83CedRapRT-3

Lock, Dan
- 94SigRooDP-44
- 94SigRooDPS-44
- 94StaCluDP-8
- 94StaCluDPFDI-8
- 95QuaCitRBTI-13
- 96KisCobB-13
- 97KisCob-16

Lock, Don
- 47Exh-136
- 63Top-47
- 64Top-114
- 64TopCoi-53
- 64TopSta-24
- 64TopStaU-41
- 64TopTatI-49
- 64TopVen-114
- 65ChaTheY-31
- 65OldLonC-29
- 65Top-445
- 66OPC-165
- 66SenTeal-9
- 66Top-165
- 66TopRubI-53
- 66TopVen-165
- 67CokCapPh-18
- 67DexPre-126
- 67Top-376
- 68OPC-59
- 68Top-59
- 68TopVen-59
- 69MilBra-159
- 69Top-229
- 69TopSta-76
- 73TCM60I-34

Locke, Bobby
- 60Top-44
- 60TopVen-44
- 61Top-537
- 62Top-359
- 65SeaPop-12
- 65Top-324
- 66SeaPop-11
- 67SeaPop-11
- 68OPC-24
- 68Top-24
- 68TopVen-24

Locke, Charlie
- 91OriCro-263

Locke, Roger Dale
- 88AshTouP-1064

Locke, Ron
- 64Top-556
- 65Top-511
- 91MetWIZ-232

Locke, William H.
- 10PirTipTD-2

Lockenmeyer, Mark
- 84JacMetT-3

Locker, Dallas
- 22Zee-157
- 23Zee-191

Locker, John
- 89ElmPioP-29
- 90ElmPioP-18

Locker, Robert
- 65Top-541
- 66Top-374
- 67CokCapWS-16
- 67DexPre-127
- 67Top-338
- 68OPC-51
- 68Top-51
- 68TopVen-51
- 69Top-548
- 70BreMcD-17
- 70BreMil-13
- 70MLBOffS-274
- 70OPC-249
- 70Top-249
- 71MLBOffS-520
- 71OPC-356
- 71Top-356
- 72Top-537
- 73LinPor-42
- 73OPC-645
- 73Top-645
- 74OPC-62
- 74Top-62
- 74TopTra-62T
- 75OPC-434
- 75Top-434
- 75TopMin-434
- 83Pil69G-19
- 94BreMilB-243

Lockett, Lester
- 91NegLeaRL-28
- 92NegLeaK-3
- 93TedWil-110
- 95NegLeaL2-2
- 95NegLeaLI-28

Lockett, Ron
- 90PriPatD-14
- 91Cla/Bes-348
- 91ClePhiC-17
- 91ClePhiP-1628
- 91FloStaLAP-FSL7
- 92Bow-303
- 92ClaFS7-232
- 92ReaPhiF-588
- 92ReaPhiS-534
- 92SkyAA F-232
- 92UppDecML-231
- 93PhiStaC-26
- 93ReaPhiF-303
- 94ScrRedBF-933

Lockhart, Bruce
- 85GreHorT-6
- 86WinHavRSP-15
- 87WinHavRSP-13

Lockhart, Keith
- 87CedRapRP-13
- 88ChaLooB-9
- 88SouLeaAJ-5
- 89CedRapRAB-12
- 89NasSouC-16
- 89NasSouP-1278
- 89NasSouTI-12
- 90CedRapRDGB-12
- 90CMC-144
- 90NasSouC-19
- 90NasSouP-247
- 90ProAAAF-559
- 91LinDriAAA-264
- 91NasSouLD-264
- 91NasSouP-2166
- 92TacTigF-2510
- 92TacTigS-538
- 93LouRedF-223
- 93TriAAAGF-23
- 94Bow-111
- 94PadMot-19
- 94ScoRoo-RT146
- 94ScoRooGR-RT146
- 94Sel-395
- 94SpoRoo-56
- 94SpoRooAP-56
- 94Ult-580
- 94VenLinU-82
- 95Sco-306
- 95ScoGolR-306
- 95ScoPlaTS-306
- 96Cir-45
- 96CirRav-45
- 96ColCho-574
- 96ColChoGS-574
- 96ColChoSS-574
- 96Don-386
- 96DonPreP-386
- 96Fla-91
- 96Fle-133
- 96FleTif-133
- 96LeaSigA-138
- 96LeaSigAG-138
- 96LeaSigAS-138
- 96Pin-56
- 96ProSta-117
- 96RoyPol-15
- 96Sco-114
- 96StaClu-305
- 96StaCluMOP-305
- 96Ult-357
- 96UltGolM-357
- 96UppDec-498U
- 97Fle-115
- 97FleTif-115
- 97Lea-45
- 97LeaFraM-45
- 97LeaFraMDC-45
- 97MetUni-94
- 97Pac-104
- 97PacLigB-104
- 97PacSil-104
- 97Sco-59
- 97Sco-472
- 97ScoArtPWB-59

❑ 97ScoArtPWB-472
❑ 97ScoPreS-59
❑ 97ScoResC-472
❑ 97ScoShoS-59
❑ 97ScoShoS-472
❑ 97ScoShoSAP-59
❑ 97ScoShoSAP-472
❑ 97StaClu-159
❑ 97StaCluMOP-159
❑ 97Top-312
❑ 97Ult-67
❑ 97UltGolME-67
❑ 97UltPlaME-67
❑ 97UppDec-84
❑ 98ColCho-307
❑ 98PacInvGems-120
❑ 98PacOnl-65
❑ 98PacOnlR-65
❑ 98PacOnlWC-65
❑ 98StaCluFDI-99
❑ 98StaCluI-99
❑ 98StaCluOneK-99
❑ 98StaCluPP-99
❑ 98UppDec-298
❑ 99UppDec-35
❑ 99UppDecEL1-35
❑ 99UppDecEL2-35
Lockhart, Mike
❑ 92WatIndC-19
❑ 92WatIndF-3238
Lockhart, Tim
❑ 89FreStaBS-12
Lockie, Randy
❑ 83QuaCitCT-13
Locklear, Dean
❑ 91Cla/Bes-206
❑ 91SouBenWSC-18
❑ 91SouBenWSP-2854
❑ 92SarWhiSCB-7
❑ 92SarWhiSF-201
❑ 93SarWhiSC-18
❑ 94MidAngOHP-15
❑ 94PriWilCC-13
❑ 94PriWilCF-1917
Locklear, Gene
❑ 74HawIsIC-101
❑ 74PadDea-17
❑ 75OPC-13
❑ 75PadDea-17
❑ 75Top-13
❑ 75TopMin-13
❑ 76OPC-447
❑ 76Top-447
❑ 92YanWIZ7-98
Locklear, Jeff
❑ 92CliGiaF-3593
❑ 93CliGiaC-15
❑ 93CliGiaF-2486
❑ 94CliLumC-13
❑ 94CliLumF-1976
❑ 94SanJosGC-15
❑ 94SanJosGF-2812
Lockley, Blain
❑ 86WatPirP-12
❑ 87MacPirP-12
Lockman, Whitey (Carroll)
❑ 47Exh-137
❑ 47HomBon-31
❑ 47PM1StaP1-114
❑ 47TipTop-127
❑ 48Bow-30
❑ 48GiaTeal-13
❑ 49Bow-2
❑ 49EurSta-116
❑ 49GiaTeal-18
❑ 50Bow-82
❑ 50Dra-8
❑ 50JJKCopP-8
❑ 51Bow-37
❑ 51R42SmaS-60
❑ 51TopRedB-41
❑ 52BerRos-34
❑ 52Bow-38
❑ 52H-OInsOR-2
❑ 52RedMan-NL13
❑ 52StaCalL-78G
❑ 52TipTop-21
❑ 53BowC-128
❑ 53Bri-33
❑ 53RedMan-NL7
❑ 53StaMey-5
❑ 54Bow-153
❑ 54NewYorJA-30
❑ 54StaMey-5
❑ 55Bow-219
❑ 55GiaGolS-16
❑ 55StaMey-5
❑ 56BalOriP-32
❑ 56GiaJayP-5
❑ 56Top-205
❑ 57Top-232
❑ 58GiaArmT-4
❑ 58GiaJayP-6
❑ 58GiaSFCB-13
❑ 58Hir-62
❑ 58Top-195
❑ 59Top-411
❑ 60Top-535
❑ 73OPC-81
❑ 73Top-81A
❑ 73Top-81B
❑ 74OPC-354
❑ 74Top-354
❑ 75Gia195T-16
❑ 79TCM50-26
❑ 81Gia196T-2
❑ 84FifNatCT-9
❑ 85TCMPhoC-37
❑ 85TCMPla1-22
❑ 91OriCro-264
❑ 91TopArc1-292
Lockwood, Rick
❑ 85ChaO'sT-4
❑ 86JacMetT-18
❑ 88LouRedBTI-29
Lockwood, Skip (Claude)
❑ 65Top-526
❑ 70OPC-499
❑ 70Top-499
❑ 71MLBOffS-443
❑ 71OPC-433
❑ 71Top-433
❑ 72OPC-118
❑ 72Top-118
❑ 73OPC-308
❑ 73Top-308
❑ 74MetTeal-12
❑ 74OPC-532
❑ 74Top-532
❑ 75OPC-417
❑ 75Top-417
❑ 75TopMin-417
❑ 75TucTorC-16
❑ 75TucTorTI-9
❑ 76OPC-166
❑ 76SSP-549
❑ 76Top-166
❑ 77BurCheD-139
❑ 77MetDaiPA-12
❑ 77Top-65
❑ 78MetDaiPA-14
❑ 78Top-379
❑ 79OPC-250
❑ 79Top-481
❑ 80OPC-295
❑ 80Top-567
❑ 81Don-217
❑ 81Top-233
❑ 91MetWIZ-233
❑ 94BreMilB-244
Locurto, Gary
❑ 97MicBatC-18
❑ 98MicBatCM-20
Lodbell, Dick
❑ 87AncGlaP-38
Lodding, Richard
❑ 89BelMarL-9
❑ 91PenPilC-8
❑ 91PenPilP-374
❑ 92SanBerC-6
❑ 92SanBerSF-949
Lodes, Lance
❑ 90ArkRaz-32
Lodgek, Scott
❑ 89BelMarL-10
❑ 90PenPilS-11
Lodigiani, Dario
❑ 41Gou-15
❑ 47RemBre-19
❑ 47SigOil-49
❑ 48SigOil-15
❑ 48SmiClo-15
❑ 49RemBre-16
❑ 79DiaGre-339
❑ 84TCMPla1-14
LoDuca, Paul
❑ 94BakDodC-15
❑ 94Bow-594
❑ 95AusFut-52
❑ 95SanAntMTI-17
❑ 96VerBeaDB-17
❑ 97AriStaBG-16
❑ 97SanAntMB-14
❑ 97TexAllM-44
❑ 98AlbDukG-17
❑ 98SanAntMM-14
❑ 99Bow-336
❑ 99BowAut-BA36
❑ 99BowGol-336
❑ 99BowInt-336
❑ 99DodPol-14
❑ 99PacInv-76
❑ 99PacInvOD-76
❑ 99PacInvPB-76
❑ 99SpoIll-52
Loe, Darin
❑ 89BelMarL-11
❑ 90PenPilS-12
❑ 91SanBerSC-8
❑ 91SanBerSP-1984
Loeb, Marc
❑ 90MedHatBJB-24
❑ 91MyrBeaHC-14
❑ 91MyrBeaHP-2948
❑ 93DunBluJC-15
❑ 93DunBluJF-1799
❑ 93DunBluJFFN-16
❑ 94DunBluJC-17
❑ 94DunBluJF-2560
❑ 95DunBluJTI-12
Loehr, Ted
❑ 75AppFoxT-14
Loera, Javier
❑ 89GreFalDSP-7
Loes, Billy
❑ 47StaPinP2-18
❑ 52Bow-240
❑ 52Top-20
❑ 53BowC-14
❑ 53Top-174
❑ 54Bow-42
❑ 54NewYorJA-10
❑ 55Bow-240
❑ 55DodGolS-5
❑ 56BalOriP-33
❑ 56BalOriP-31
❑ 56Top-270
❑ 57Top-244
❑ 58Hir-48
❑ 58OriJayP-5
❑ 58Top-359
❑ 59Top-336A
❑ 59Top-336B
❑ 60Top-181
❑ 60TopVen-181
❑ 61Top-237
❑ 73BooProC-8
❑ 74dod195T-27
❑ 79TCM50-50
❑ 90DodTar-455
❑ 91DodRinP2-10
❑ 91OriCro-265
❑ 91TopArc1-174
❑ 95TopArcBD-3
❑ 95TopArcBD-49
❑ 95TopArcBD-136
❑ 95TopArcBD-160
Loew, Jeremy
❑ 98VisOakG-19
Loewer, Carlton
❑ 92MisStaB-25
❑ 93BazTeaU-21
❑ 93MisStaB-26
❑ 93TopTra-4T
❑ 94SigRooDPBSDP-6
❑ 95Bes-88
❑ 95ClePhiF-214
❑ 95ReaPhiELC-25
❑ 95SPML-131
❑ 95UppDecML-202
❑ 95UppDecMLFS-202
❑ 96Exc-207
❑ 96ExcFirYP-8
❑ 96ReaPhiB-8
❑ 97Bow-218
❑ 97BowInt-218
❑ 97ScrRedB-14
❑ 98FleUpd-U51
❑ 98RevoRooHH-16
❑ 98RevoRooHHG-16
❑ 98ScrRedBQ-18
❑ 98UppDec-596
❑ 98UppDecDS-DS23
❑ 99Fle-213
❑ 99FleSta9-213
❑ 99FleWarT-213
❑ 99MetUni-271
❑ 99MetUniGM-271
❑ 99MetUniPMG-271
❑ 99Ult-236
❑ 99UltGolM-236
❑ 99UltMas-236
❑ 99UltPlaM-236
❑ 99UppDec-452
❑ 99UppDecBD-112
❑ 99UppDecBDD-112
❑ 99UppDecBDQ-112
❑ 99UppDecBDT-112
❑ 99UppDecEL1-452
❑ 99UppDecEL2-452
❑ 99Vic-303
Loewer, Stan
❑ 87LSUTigP-5
Lofthus, Kevin
❑ 90ModA'sCLC-170
❑ 90ModA'sP-2219
Loftin, Bo
❑ 90LSUTigA-10
❑ 91BilMusP-3757
❑ 91BilMusSP-5
❑ 92BilMusF-3351
❑ 92BilMusSP-1
❑ 93ExcFS7-24
❑ 93WinSpiC-13
❑ 93WinSpiF-1566
Lofton, James
❑ 93PriRedC-17
❑ 93PriRedF-4187
❑ 94BilMusF-3679
❑ 94BilMusSP-8
❑ 95Exc-177
❑ 97BurBeeB-14
Lofton, Kenny (Kenneth)
❑ 88AubAstP-1953
❑ 89AubAstP-2166
❑ 90FloStaLAS-11
❑ 90OscAstS-16
❑ 90StaFS7-3
❑ 91Bow-565
❑ 91LinDriAAA-614
❑ 91TriA AAGP-AAA52
❑ 91TucTorLD-614
❑ 91TucTorP-2225
❑ 91UppDecFE-24F
❑ 92Bow-110
❑ 92Cla2-T46
❑ 92ClaGam-177
❑ 92Don-5
❑ 92DonRooP-BC8
❑ 92DonUpd-U6
❑ 92Fle-655
❑ 92FleUpd-17
❑ 92IndFanC-17
❑ 92JimDeaRS-8
❑ 92LeaGolR-BC4
❑ 92OPC-69
❑ 92OPCPre-72
❑ 92Pin-290
❑ 92Pin-582
❑ 92PinRoo-3
❑ 92PinRool-7
❑ 92PinTea2-35
❑ 92ProFS7-223
❑ 92Sco-845
❑ 92ScoHotR-3
❑ 92ScoImpP-32
❑ 92ScoRoo-14T
❑ 92ScoRoo-10
❑ 92SpoIllFK1-359
❑ 92SpoIllFK1-703
❑ 92StaClu-695
❑ 92StaCluNC-695
❑ 92Stu-168
❑ 92Top-69
❑ 92TopDeb91-112
❑ 92TopGol-69
❑ 92TopGolW-69
❑ 92TopMic-69
❑ 92TopTra-66T
❑ 92TopTraG-66T
❑ 92Ult-350
❑ 92UltAllR-7
❑ 92UppDec-25
❑ 92UppDec-766
❑ 92UppDecSR-SR15
❑ 93Bow-417
❑ 93ClaGam-54
❑ 93DiaMar-65
❑ 93Don-537
❑ 93DonSpiotG-SG11
❑ 93Fin-43
❑ 93FinRef-43
❑ 93Fla-195
❑ 93Fle-218
❑ 93Fle-346
❑ 93FleFruotL-37
❑ 93FleRooS-RSA1
❑ 93FunPac-109
❑ 93IndWUA-18
❑ 93JimDea-23
❑ 93Lea-40
❑ 93LeaFas-3
❑ 93OPC-251
❑ 93OPCPreSP-17
❑ 93OPCPreSPF-17
❑ 93PacJugC-9
❑ 93PacSpa-97
❑ 93PanSti-53
❑ 93Pin-40
❑ 93PinTea2-18
❑ 93RedFolS-54
❑ 93Sco-58
❑ 93Sel-275
❑ 93SelChaR-4
❑ 93SelStaL-55
❑ 93StaClu-277
❑ 93StaCluFDI-277
❑ 93StaCluMOP-277
❑ 93Stu-180
❑ 93Top-331
❑ 93TOPBLAG-36
❑ 93TopGol-331
❑ 93TopInaM-331
❑ 93TopInaR-331
❑ 93TopMic-331
❑ 93Toy-69
❑ 93TriPla-144
❑ 93TriPla-181
❑ 93Ult-542
❑ 93UppDec-45
❑ 93UppDec-262
❑ 93UppDecGold-45
❑ 93UppDecGold-262
❑ 93UppDecSH-HI11
❑ 93USPlaCA-13H
❑ 93USPlaCR-1C
❑ 94Bow-195
❑ 94BowBes-R68
❑ 94BowBesR-R68
❑ 94ColC-315
❑ 94ColC-565
❑ 94ColChoGS-315
❑ 94ColChoGS-565
❑ 94ColChoSS-315
❑ 94ColChoSS-565
❑ 94Don-39
❑ 94DonSpeE-39
❑ 94Fin-218
❑ 94FinJum-218
❑ 94FinRef-218
❑ 94Fla-283
❑ 94FlaHotG-4
❑ 94Fle-111
❑ 94FleExtB-60
❑ 94FleLeaL-4
❑ 94FUnPac-107
❑ 94Lea-350
❑ 94LeaL-28
❑ 94O-PJumAF-25
❑ 94OPC-237
❑ 94OPCAllR-25
❑ 94OPCJumA-25
❑ 94OscMayR-7
❑ 94Pac-173
❑ 94PacSilP-17
❑ 94PacSilPC-17
❑ 94PanSti-58
❑ 94Pin-179
❑ 94PinArtP-179
❑ 94PinMusC-179
❑ 94PinRunC-RC14
❑ 94PinTheN-7
❑ 94Sco-81
❑ 94ScoCyc-TC2
❑ 94ScoGolR-81
❑ 94ScoGolS-41
❑ 94Sel-231
❑ 94SelSki-SK4
❑ 94SP-98
❑ 94SPDieC-98
❑ 94Spo-43
❑ 94SpoSha-SH1
❑ 94StaClu-301
❑ 94StaCluFDI-301
❑ 94StaCluGR-301
❑ 94StaCluMO-27
❑ 94StaCluMOP-301
❑ 94StaCluMOP-ST19
❑ 94StaCluST-ST19
❑ 94Stu-93
❑ 94Top-149
❑ 94TopBlaG-11
❑ 94TopGol-149
❑ 94TopPre-331
❑ 94TopSpa-149
❑ 94TopTraFI-6
❑ 94TriPla-115
❑ 94Ult-45
❑ 94UltAwaW-7
❑ 94UltLeaL-3
❑ 94UltRisS-7
❑ 94UppDec-215
❑ 94UppDecAJ-29
❑ 94UppDecAJG-29
❑ 94UppDecED-215
❑ 94USPlaCA-1H
❑ 94USPlaCA-8D
❑ 95Baz-22
❑ 95BazRedH-RH4
❑ 95Bow-305
❑ 95BowBes-R20
❑ 95BowBes-X10
❑ 95BowBesR-R20
❑ 95BowBesR-X10
❑ 95ClaPhoC-22
❑ 95ColCho-81
❑ 95ColChoGS-81
❑ 95ColChoSE-119
❑ 95ColChoSE-139
❑ 95ColChoSE-258
❑ 95ColChoSEGS-119
❑ 95ColChoSEGS-139
❑ 95ColChoSEGS-258
❑ 95ColChoSESS-119
❑ 95ColChoSESS-139
❑ 95ColChoSESS-258
❑ 95ColChoSS-81
❑ 95Don-371
❑ 95DonDiaK-DK11
❑ 95DonDom-8
❑ 95DonPreP-371
❑ 95DonTopotO-59
❑ 95Emo-34
❑ 95EmoMas-5
❑ 95Fin-56
❑ 95FinRef-56
❑ 95FlaHotG-7
❑ 95FlaHotN-5
❑ 95FlaTodS-5
❑ 95Fle-137
❑ 95FleAllS-16
❑ 95FleUpdH-12
❑ 95FleUpdSL-6
❑ 95FleUpdSS-6
❑ 95Kra-8
❑ 95Lea-8
❑ 95Lea300C-18
❑ 95LeaGreG-8
❑ 95LeaLim-12
❑ 95LeaLimG-18
❑ 95LeaLimIBP-9
❑ 95NatPac-16
❑ 95Pac-122
❑ 95PacGolP-24
❑ 95PacPri-39
❑ 95PanSti-81
❑ 95PanSti-125
❑ 95Pin-189
❑ 95Pin-284
❑ 95PinArtP-189
❑ 95PinArtP-284
❑ 95PinGatA-GA17
❑ 95PinMusC-189
❑ 95PinMusC-284
❑ 95PinRedH-RH21
❑ 95PinWhiH-WH21
❑ 95Sco-422
❑ 95ScoDouGC-GC8
❑ 95ScoGolR-422
❑ 95ScoHaloG-HG57
❑ 95ScoPlaTS-422
❑ 95ScoRul-SR14
❑ 95ScoRulJ-SR14
❑ 95Sel-120
❑ 95SelArtP-120
❑ 95SelCer-91
❑ 95SelCerMG-91
❑ 95SP-150
❑ 95SPCha-149
❑ 95SPChaDC-149
❑ 95Spo-81
❑ 95SpoArtP-81
❑ 95SpoDouT-8

❑ 95SpoHamT-HT16
❑ 95SPSil-150
❑ 95SPSpeF-10
❑ 95StaClu-470
❑ 95StaCluMO-29
❑ 95StaCluMOP-470
❑ 95StaCluMOP-SS14
❑ 95StaCluMOP-VRE7
❑ 95StaCluSS-SS14
❑ 95StaCluSTDW-I19T
❑ 95StaCluSTDW-I470
❑ 95StaCluSTMP-14
❑ 95StaCluSTWS-470
❑ 95StaCluVE-VRE7
❑ 95StaCluVR-257
❑ 95StaCluVRMO-257
❑ 95Stu-11
❑ 95StuGolS-11
❑ 95StuPlaS-11
❑ 95Sum-48
❑ 95SumNthD-48
❑ 95TomPiz-11
❑ 95Top-104
❑ 95TopCyb-67
❑ 95TopCybSiR-7
❑ 95TopD3Z-6
❑ 95TopEmb-1
❑ 95TopEmbGI-1
❑ 95TopFinIns-10
❑ 95TopLeaL-LL16
❑ 95TopLeaL-LL30
❑ 95UC3-85
❑ 95UC3-143
❑ 95UC3ArtP-85
❑ 95UC3ArtP-143
❑ 95UC3CycS-CS19
❑ 95Ult-38
❑ 95UltAllS-11
❑ 95UltAllSGM-11
❑ 95UltAwaW-7
❑ 95UltAwaWGM-7
❑ 95UltGolM-38
❑ 95UltLeaL-2
❑ 95UltLeaLGM-2
❑ 95UltRisS-6
❑ 95UltRisSGM-6
❑ 95UppDec-90
❑ 95UppDecED-90
❑ 95UppDecEDG-90
❑ 95UppDecPAW-H24
❑ 95UppDecPAWE-H24
❑ 95UppDecPLL-R22
❑ 95UppDecPLLE-R22
❑ 95UppDecSE-159
❑ 95UppDecSEG-159
❑ 95UppDecSoaD-SD3
❑ 95USPlaCMLA-1H
❑ 95USPlaCMLA-9D
❑ 95Zen-62
❑ 95ZenZ-15
❑ 96Baz-12
❑ 96Bow-55
❑ 96BowBes-23
❑ 96BowBesAR-23
❑ 96BowBesMI-6
❑ 96BowBesMIAR-6
❑ 96BowBesMIR-6
❑ 96BowBesR-23
❑ 96BowFoi-55
❑ 96Cir-33
❑ 96CirAcc-6
❑ 96CirBos-9
❑ 96CirRav-33
❑ 96ColCho-5
❑ 96ColCho-127
❑ 96ColCho-385T
❑ 96ColCho-388T
❑ 96ColCho-410
❑ 96ColChoGS-5
❑ 96ColChoGS-127
❑ 96ColChoGS-410
❑ 96ColChoSS-5
❑ 96ColChoSS-127
❑ 96ColChoSS-410
❑ 96ColChoYMtP-21
❑ 96ColChoYMtP-21A
❑ 96ColChoYMtPGS-21
❑ 96ColChoYMtPGS-21A
❑ 96Don-396
❑ 96DonPreP-396
❑ 96EmoXL-49
❑ 96EmoXLD-5
❑ 96Fin-B233
❑ 96Fin-G81
❑ 96Fin-S327
❑ 96FinRef-B233
❑ 96FinRef-G81
❑ 96FinRef-S327
❑ 96Fla-67
❑ 96FlaHotG-5
❑ 96Fle-89
❑ 96FleTeaL-5
❑ 96FleTif-89
❑ 96FleUpd-U231
❑ 96FleUpdH-12
❑ 96FleUpdSL-5
❑ 96FleUpdTC-U231
❑ 96FleZon-6
❑ 96IndFle-6
❑ 96Lea-127
❑ 96LeaAllGMC-12
❑ 96LeaAllGMCG-12
❑ 96LeaLim-29
❑ 96LeaLimG-29
❑ 96LeaPre-24
❑ 96LeaPreP-24
❑ 96LeaPrePB-127
❑ 96LeaPrePG-127
❑ 96LeaPrePS-127
❑ 96LeaPreSG-3
❑ 96LeaPreSte-3
❑ 96LeaSig-55
❑ 96LeaSigA-139
❑ 96LeaSigAG-139
❑ 96LeaSigAS-139
❑ 96LeaSigEA-111
❑ 96LeaSigEACM-17
❑ 96LeaSigPPG-55
❑ 96LeaSigPPP-55
❑ 96MetUni-46
❑ 96MetUniML-4
❑ 96MetUniP-46
❑ 96Pac-303
❑ 96PacBaeS-7
❑ 96PacOctM-OM11
❑ 96PacPri-P95
❑ 96PacPriG-P95
❑ 96PanSti-123
❑ 96PanSti-180
❑ 96Pin-105
❑ 96Pin-312
❑ 96PinAfi-114
❑ 96PinAfiAP-114
❑ 96PinAfiSP-23
❑ 96PinArtP-40
❑ 96PinArtP-194
❑ 96PinChrBC-16
❑ 96PinFoil-312
❑ 96PinSta-40
❑ 96PinSta-194
❑ 96ProMagA-4
❑ 96ProSta-56
❑ 96SchDis-12
❑ 96Sco-325
❑ 96ScoBigB-16
❑ 96ScoDugC-B50
❑ 96ScoDugCAP-B50
❑ 96ScoNumG-22
❑ 96ScoRef-4
❑ 96Sel-14
❑ 96SelArtP-14
❑ 96SelCer-4
❑ 96SelCerAP-4
❑ 96SelCerCB-4
❑ 96SelCerCR-4
❑ 96SelCerIP-20
❑ 96SelCerMB-4
❑ 96SelCerMG-4
❑ 96SelCerMR-4
❑ 96SP-73
❑ 96Spo-39
❑ 96SpoArtP-39
❑ 96SPSpeFX-23
❑ 96SPSpeFXDC-23
❑ 96SPx-18
❑ 96SPxGol-18
❑ 96StaClu-208
❑ 96StaClu-325
❑ 96StaCluEPB-325
❑ 96StaCluEPG-325
❑ 96StaCluEPS-325
❑ 96StaCluMM-MM8
❑ 96StaCluMO-21
❑ 96StaCluMOP-208
❑ 96StaCluMOP-325
❑ 96StaCluMOP-MM8
❑ 96Stu-45
❑ 96StuPrePB-45
❑ 96StuPrePG-45
❑ 96StuPrePS-45
❑ 96StuStaGS-12
❑ 96Sum-39
❑ 96SumAbo&B-39
❑ 96SumArtP-39
❑ 96SumFoi-39
❑ 96TeaOut-50
❑ 96Top-420
❑ 96TopChr-164
❑ 96TopChrR-164
❑ 96TopGal-161
❑ 96TopGalPPI-161
❑ 96TopLas-108
❑ 96TopLasSS-13
❑ 96TopPro-AL15
❑ 96Ult-48
❑ 96Ult-584
❑ 96UltGolM-48
❑ 96UltGolM-584
❑ 96UltPriL-7
❑ 96UltPriLGM-7
❑ 96UltPro-SC4
❑ 96UltRaw-5
❑ 96UltRawGM-5
❑ 96UltSeaC-4
❑ 96UltSeaCGM-4
❑ 96UppDec-319
❑ 96UppDecA-12
❑ 96UppDecDD-DD18
❑ 96UppDecDDG-DD18
❑ 96UppDecDDS-DD18
❑ 96UppDecHC-HC18
❑ 96UppDecPHE-H2
❑ 96UppDecPRE-R26
❑ 96UppDecPreH-H2
❑ 96UppDecPreR-R26
❑ 96UppDecRunP-RP9
❑ 96Zen-66
❑ 96ZenArtP-66
❑ 97Bow-224
❑ 97BowBes-11
❑ 97BowBesAR-11
❑ 97BowBesJ-11
❑ 97BowBesJAR-11
❑ 97BowBesJR-11
❑ 97BowBesMI-MI10
❑ 97BowBesMIAR-MI10
❑ 97BowBesMIARI-MI10
❑ 97BowBesMII-MI10
❑ 97BowBesMIR-MI10
❑ 97BowBesMIRI-MI10
❑ 97BowBesP-8
❑ 97BowBesPAR-8
❑ 97BowBesPR-8
❑ 97BowBesR-11
❑ 97BowChr-54
❑ 97BowChrI-54
❑ 97BowChrIR-54
❑ 97BowChrR-54
❑ 97BowInt-224
❑ 97Cir-1
❑ 97CirRav-1
❑ 97ColCho-59
❑ 97ColCho-264
❑ 97ColChoAC-25
❑ 97ColChoS-7
❑ 97ColChoSR-16
❑ 97ColChoT-AB2
❑ 97ColChoTBS-18
❑ 97ColChoTBSWH-18
❑ 97ColChoTotT-T5
❑ 97CraJac-9
❑ 97Don-50
❑ 97Don-276
❑ 97Don-411
❑ 97DonArmaD-9
❑ 97DonDom-16
❑ 97DonEli-19
❑ 97DonEliGS-19
❑ 97DonFraFea-12
❑ 97DonGolPP-50
❑ 97DonGolPP-276
❑ 97DonGolPP-411
❑ 97DonLim-73
❑ 97DonLim-94
❑ 97DonLim-141
❑ 97DonLimE-73
❑ 97DonLimE-94
❑ 97DonLimE-141
❑ 97DonLimENG-73
❑ 97DonLimFotG-31
❑ 97DonPowA-15
❑ 97DonPowADC-15
❑ 97DonPre-24
❑ 97DonPre-174
❑ 97DonPreCttC-24
❑ 97DonPreCttC-174
❑ 97DonPrePM-6
❑ 97DonPreTB-11
❑ 97DonPreTBG-11
❑ 97DonPreTF-11
❑ 97DonPreTP-11
❑ 97DonPreTPG-11
❑ 97DonSig-2
❑ 97DonSigPPP-2
❑ 97DonSilPP-50
❑ 97DonSilPP-276
❑ 97DonSilPP-411
❑ 97DonTea-24
❑ 97DonTeaSMVP-14
❑ 97DonTeaSPE-24
❑ 97DonVxP1-33
❑ 97E-X2-56
❑ 97E-X2Cred-56
❑ 97E-X2EssCre-56
❑ 97E-X2Hall-20
❑ 97Fin-174
❑ 97Fin-283
❑ 97FinEmb-174
❑ 97FinEmb-283
❑ 97FinEmbR-174
❑ 97FinEmbR-283
❑ 97FinRef-174
❑ 97FinRef-283
❑ 97FlaShoHG-9
❑ 97FlaShoLC-7
❑ 97FlaShoLeg0-7
❑ 97FlaShoLeg1-7
❑ 97FlaShoM-A7
❑ 97FlaShoM-B7
❑ 97FlaShoM-C7
❑ 97FlaShoR0-7
❑ 97FlaShoR1-7
❑ 97FlaShoR2-7
❑ 97Fle-80
❑ 97Fle-501
❑ 97FleGouG-6
❑ 97FleGouGF-6
❑ 97FleTif-80
❑ 97FleTif-501
❑ 97IndSco-7
❑ 97IndScoPl-7
❑ 97IndScoPr-7
❑ 97IndScoU-7
❑ 97IndScoUTC-7
❑ 97KinB-5
❑ 97Lea-110
❑ 97Lea-363
❑ 97LeaBanS-6
❑ 97LeaFraM-110
❑ 97LeaFraM-363
❑ 97LeaFraMDC-110
❑ 97LeaFraMDC-363
❑ 97LeaGolS-17
❑ 97LeaLeaotN-4
❑ 97LeaWarT-5
❑ 97MetUni-82
❑ 97MetUniMF-6
❑ 97MetUniML-7
❑ 97NewPin-25
❑ 97NewPinAP-25
❑ 97NewPinKtP-11
❑ 97NewPinMC-25
❑ 97NewPinPP-25
❑ 97NewPinPP-K11
❑ 97Pac-73
❑ 97PacLigB-73
❑ 97PacPri-26
❑ 97PacPriGA-GA5
❑ 97PacPriLB-26
❑ 97PacPriP-26
❑ 97PacPriSH-SH4A
❑ 97PacPriSL-SL3C
❑ 97PacSil-73
❑ 97Pin-186
❑ 97PinArtP-PP186
❑ 97PinCer-58
❑ 97PinCerLI-14
❑ 97PinCerMBla-58
❑ 97PinCerMBlu-58
❑ 97PinCerMG-58
❑ 97PinCerMR-58
❑ 97PinCerR-58
❑ 97PinIns-71
❑ 97PinInsC-1
❑ 97PinInsCE-71
❑ 97PinInsDD-12
❑ 97PinInsDE-71
❑ 97PinMusC-186
❑ 97PinPrePla-186
❑ 97PinTotCPB-58
❑ 97PinTotCPG-58
❑ 97PinTotCPR-58
❑ 97PinX-P-6
❑ 97PinX-PMoS-6
❑ 97PinX-PMW-19
❑ 97PinX-PMWG-19
❑ 97PinX-PMWS-19
❑ 97Sco-157
❑ 97Sco-340
❑ 97Sco-540
❑ 97ScoArtPWB-157
❑ 97ScoArtPWB-340
❑ 97ScoArtPWB-540
❑ 97ScoPreS-157
❑ 97ScoResC-340
❑ 97ScoResC-540
❑ 97ScoShoS-157
❑ 97ScoShoS-340
❑ 97ScoShoS-540
❑ 97ScoShoSAP-157
❑ 97ScoShoSAP-340
❑ 97ScoShoSAP-540
❑ 97Sel-27
❑ 97SelArtP-27
❑ 97SelCom-27
❑ 97SelRegG-27
❑ 97SelToootT-11
❑ 97SelToootTMB-11
❑ 97SP-24
❑ 97SPInsI-3
❑ 97SpoIII-77
❑ 97SpoIIIEE-77
❑ 97SpoIIIGS-3
❑ 97SPSpeF-12
❑ 97SPx-8
❑ 97SPxBoufG-4
❑ 97SPxBro-8
❑ 97SPxGol-8
❑ 97SPxGraF-8
❑ 97SPxSil-8
❑ 97SPxSte-8
❑ 97StaClu-3
❑ 97StaCluMat-3
❑ 97StaCluMOP-3
❑ 97StaCluMOP-PG13
❑ 97StaCluMOP-PL8
❑ 97StaCluPG-PG13
❑ 97StaCluPL-PL8
❑ 97StaCluPP-PP2
❑ 97StrAll-39
❑ 97Stu-85
❑ 97StuMasS-10
❑ 97StuMasS8-10
❑ 97StuPor8-17
❑ 97StuPrePG-85
❑ 97StuPrePS-85
❑ 97Top-350
❑ 97TopChr-117
❑ 97TopChrDD-DD4
❑ 97TopChrDDR-DD4
❑ 97TopChrR-117
❑ 97TopChrSB-21
❑ 97TopChrSBR-21
❑ 97TopGal-117
❑ 97TopGalPG-PG9
❑ 97TopGalPPI-117
❑ 97TopHobM-HM10
❑ 97TopMem05-31
❑ 97TopScr-13
❑ 97TopScrT-13
❑ 97TopSeaB-SB21
❑ 97TopSta-64
❑ 97TopStaAM-64
❑ 97UD3-37
❑ 97Ult-50
❑ 97Ult-406
❑ 97UltDiaP-5
❑ 97UltDouT-5
❑ 97UltFamGam-14
❑ 97UltFieC-11
❑ 97UltGolME-50
❑ 97UltGolME-406
❑ 97UltHitM-12
❑ 97UltLeaS-11
❑ 97UltPlaME-50
❑ 97UltPlaME-406
❑ 97UltSeaC-4
❑ 97UltTop3-17
❑ 97UltTop3GM-17
❑ 97UppDec-52
❑ 97UppDec-153
❑ 97UppDec-525
❑ 97UppDecAG-AG7
❑ 97UppDecAWJ-7
❑ 97UppDecHTH-HT11
❑ 97UppDecP-12
❑ 97UppDecPE-12
❑ 97UppDecRP-RP17
❑ 97UppDecSA-10
❑ 97UppDecSAG-10
❑ 97Zen-37
❑ 98Bow-231
❑ 98BowBes-81
❑ 98BowBesAR-81
❑ 98BowBesR-81
❑ 98BowChr-231
❑ 98BowChrGA-231
❑ 98BowChrGAR-231
❑ 98BowChrI-231
❑ 98BowChrIR-231
❑ 98BowChrR-231
❑ 98BowChrR-28
❑ 98BowChrRR-28
❑ 98BowGolA-231
❑ 98BowInt-231
❑ 98BraSco-8
❑ 98BraScoP-8
❑ 98CirThu-7
❑ 98CirThuRav-7
❑ 98CirThuSupRav-7
❑ 98ColCho-350
❑ 98ColChoMBH-11
❑ 98ColChoSQ-SQ57
❑ 98ColChoSQDouble-11
❑ 98ColChoSQHR-11
❑ 98ColChoSQSingle-11
❑ 98ColChoSQTriple-11
❑ 98CroRoy-44
❑ 98CroRoyAS-3
❑ 98Don-16
❑ 98Don-195
❑ 98Don-350
❑ 98DonCol-16
❑ 98DonColE-417
❑ 98DonColE-534
❑ 98DonColL-349
❑ 98DonColP-572
❑ 98DonColS-16
❑ 98DonCruG-52
❑ 98DonCruP-52
❑ 98DonCruR-52
❑ 98DonDiaK-6
❑ 98DonDiaKC-6
❑ 98DonDom-28
❑ 98DonEli-17
❑ 98DonEli-134
❑ 98DonEliA-17
❑ 98DonEliA-134
❑ 98DonEliC-24
❑ 98DonEliMC-24
❑ 98DonEliPN-12A
❑ 98DonEliPN-12B
❑ 98DonEliPN-12C
❑ 98DonEliPNDC-12A
❑ 98DonEliPNDC-12B
❑ 98DonEliPNDC-12C
❑ 98DonEliPNS-12A
❑ 98DonEliPNS-12B
❑ 98DonEliPNS-12C
❑ 98DonEliS-17
❑ 98DonEliS-134
❑ 98DonGolPP-16
❑ 98DonGolPP-195
❑ 98DonGolPP-350
❑ 98DonPre-22
❑ 98DonPrePM-20
❑ 98DonPreSeat-22
❑ 98DonPreTW-27
❑ 98DonPriCD-16
❑ 98DonPriCE-417
❑ 98DonPriCE-534
❑ 98DonPriCL-349
❑ 98DonPriCP-572
❑ 98DonProLO-7
❑ 98DonSig-39
❑ 98DonSigP-39
❑ 98DonSilPP-16
❑ 98DonSilPP-195
❑ 98DonSilPP-350
❑ 98DonSonM9-8
❑ 98E-X2-21
❑ 98E-X2ECFut-21
❑ 98E-X2ECNow-21
❑ 98Fin-210
❑ 98FinNo--210
❑ 98FinNo-R-210
❑ 98FinRef-210
❑ 98FlaShoLeg0-39
❑ 98FlaShoLeg1-39
❑ 98FlaShoLeg2-39
❑ 98FlaShoLeg3-39
❑ 98FlaShoLegM-39
❑ 98FlaShoR0-39
❑ 98FlaShoR1-39
❑ 98FlaShoR2-39
❑ 98FlaShoR3-39

❑ 98Fle-104
❑ 98Fle-358
❑ 98FleDiaS-12
❑ 98FleVin'-5
❑ 98FleVin'-88
❑ 98FleVin'C-5
❑ 98FleVin'C-88
❑ 98Lea-150
❑ 98LeaFraDA-150
❑ 98LeaFraF-150
❑ 98LeaFraM-150
❑ 98LeaFraM-150
❑ 98LeaFraMDC-150
❑ 98LeaFraMDC-150
❑ 98LeaFraMZ2-150
❑ 98LeaHeaftH-11
❑ 98LeaHeaftHS-11
❑ 98LeaRCMLHDSamp-18
❑ 98LeaRS-47
❑ 98LeaRS-147
❑ 98LeaRSCross-1
❑ 98LeaRSGAHSamp-15
❑ 98LeaRSGreAH-15
❑ 98LeaRSLHolo-47
❑ 98LeaRSLHolo-147
❑ 98LeaRSLong-47
❑ 98LeaRSLong-147
❑ 98LeaRSMLHD-18
❑ 98LeaRSTicMas-16
❑ 98LeaRSTicMasDC-16
❑ 98LeaRTrue-47
❑ 98LeaRTrue-147
❑ 98LeaStaS-20
❑ 98LeaStaSDC-20
❑ 98MetUni-44
❑ 98MetUniPMG-44
❑ 98MetUniUL-18
❑ 98Pac-238
❑ 98PacAur-31
❑ 98PacInv-24
❑ 98PacInvPBlue-24
❑ 98PacInvSilv-24
❑ 98PacOme-72
❑ 98PacOmeR-72
❑ 98PacOnl-223
❑ 98PacOnlR-223
❑ 98PacOnlWC-223
❑ 98PacPar-38
❑ 98PacParC-38
❑ 98PacParG-38
❑ 98PacParHS-38
❑ 98PacParPB-38
❑ 98PacParR-38
❑ 98PacPlaB-238
❑ 98PacRedT-238
❑ 98PacSil-238
❑ 98Pin-3
❑ 98PinArtP-PP3
❑ 98PinIns-6
❑ 98PinIns-136
❑ 98PinInsCE-6
❑ 98PinInsCE-136
❑ 98PinInsDE-6
❑ 98PinInsDE-136
❑ 98PinInsSG-20AB
❑ 98PinInsSG-20CD
❑ 98PinInsSGS-20AB
❑ 98PinInsSGS-20CD
❑ 98PinMusC-PP3
❑ 98PinPer-22
❑ 98PinPerPP-22
❑ 98PinPlu-50
❑ 98PinPluAP-PP22
❑ 98PinPluGAP-PP22
❑ 98PinPluLM-20
❑ 98PinPluMAP-PP22
❑ 98PinPluTP-9
❑ 98PinPluTPG-9
❑ 98PinPluTPM-9
❑ 98PinPreP-3
❑ 98PinSna-CI6
❑ 98Revo-45
❑ 98RevoSS-45
❑ 98Sco-94
❑ 98ScoNewS-NS1
❑ 98ScoRT-44
❑ 98ScoRTSS-PP44
❑ 98ScoRTSSAP-PP44
❑ 98ScoRTSSAP1-PP44
❑ 98ScoSS-PP140
❑ 98ScoSSAP-PP140
❑ 98SkyDugA-128
❑ 98SkyDugADH-DH10
❑ 98SkyDugAFF-FF2
❑ 98SkyDugAIA-128
❑ 98SP Aut-75
❑ 98SP Aut-SD6
❑ 98SP AutSD-SD6
❑ 98SP AutSDT-SD6
❑ 98SpoIll-81
❑ 98SpoIll-130
❑ 98SpoIllEE-81
❑ 98SpoIllEE-130
❑ 98SpoIllFE-81
❑ 98SpoIllFE-130
❑ 98SpoIllTaN-106
❑ 98SpoIllTaNEE-106
❑ 98SpoIllWSF-83
❑ 98SpoIllWSFEE-83
❑ 98SpoIllWSFFE-83
❑ 98SPxFin-75
❑ 98SPxFin-152
❑ 98SPxFinR-75
❑ 98SPxFinR-152
❑ 98SPxFinS-75
❑ 98SPxFinS-152
❑ 98StaCluFDI-364
❑ 98StaCluI-364
❑ 98StaCluOneK-364
❑ 98StaCluPP-364
❑ 98StaCluTIII-T1C
❑ 98StaCluTLme-T1C
❑ 98StaCluTLmo-T1C
❑ 98Stu-5
❑ 98StuFF-17
❑ 98StuFFDC-17
❑ 98StuGPP-5
❑ 98StuMast-2
❑ 98StuPor8x10-36
❑ 98StuPor8x10GP-36
❑ 98StuSony99-8
❑ 98StuSPP-5
❑ 98Top-175
❑ 98TopChr-175
❑ 98TopChrF-FB7
❑ 98TopChrFR-FB7
❑ 98TopChrR-175
❑ 98TopDevR-175
❑ 98TopDia-175
❑ 98TopFla-FB7
❑ 98TopFruR-3
❑ 98TopGal-12
❑ 98TopGalGP-12
❑ 98TopGalOPP-12
❑ 98TopGalPPI-12
❑ 98TopGalPPIA-12
❑ 98TopGolLabC1-64
❑ 98TopGolLabC1B-64
❑ 98TopGolLabC1One-64
❑ 98TopGolLabC1R-64
❑ 98TopGolLabC2-64
❑ 98TopGolLabC2B-64
❑ 98TopGolLabC2One-64
❑ 98TopGolLabC2R-64
❑ 98TopGolLabC3-64
❑ 98TopGolLabC3B-64
❑ 98TopGolLabC3One-64
❑ 98TopGolLabC3R-64
❑ 98TopMiniC-175
❑ 98TopOpeD-94
❑ 98TopSta-142
❑ 98TopSta'S-25
❑ 98TopSta'SGH-25
❑ 98TopStaB-142
❑ 98TopStaG-142
❑ 98TopStaGR-142
❑ 98TopStaLB-L8
❑ 98TopStaLG-L8
❑ 98TopStaLGR-L8
❑ 98TopStaLS-L8
❑ 98TopStaS-142
❑ 98TopStaSteG-25
❑ 98TopTek-45
❑ 98TopTekD-45
❑ 98UD3-85
❑ 98UD3-175
❑ 98UD3-265
❑ 98UD3DieCut-85
❑ 98UD3DieCut-175
❑ 98UD3DieCut-265
❑ 98Ult-203
❑ 98Ult-337
❑ 98Ult-498
❑ 98UltArtT-18
❑ 98UltDouT-3
❑ 98UltGolM-203
❑ 98UltGolM-337
❑ 98UltGolM-498
❑ 98UltMas-203
❑ 98UltMas-337
❑ 98UltMas-498
❑ 98UltPlaM-203
❑ 98UltPlaM-337
❑ 98UltPlaM-498
❑ 98UltPriL-17
❑ 98UltTop3-3
❑ 98UppDec-27
❑ 98UppDec-148
❑ 98UppDec-345
❑ 98UppDec-621
❑ 98UppDec10AP-50
❑ 98UppDec1APR-50
❑ 98UppDec5x7-27
❑ 98UppDecAC-AS27
❑ 98UppDecAG-AG7
❑ 98UppDecAGDC-AG7
❑ 98UppDecCD-CD7
❑ 98UppDecR-29
❑ 98UppDecR-26
❑ 98UppDecRGKoG-G7
❑ 98UppDecRQL-Q5
❑ 98UppDecRTC-TC10
❑ 98UppDecSFPD-PZ16
❑ 98UppDecSFPZOB-PZ14
❑ 98UppDecU-7
❑ 98Zen-38
❑ 98Zen5 xx7-13
❑ 98Zen5x7GoldImp-13
❑ 98Zen5x7Imp-13
❑ 98ZenZ-G-38
❑ 98ZenZ-S-38
❑ 99199Fin-225
❑ 99Bow-61
❑ 99BowBes-59
❑ 99BowBesAR-59
❑ 99BowBesR-59
❑ 99BowChr-61
❑ 99BowChrG-61
❑ 99BowChrGR-61
❑ 99BowChrI-61
❑ 99BowChrIR-61
❑ 99BowChrR-61
❑ 99BowGol-61
❑ 99BowInt-61
❑ 99BowLatB-LB7
❑ 99CroRoyB-44
❑ 99CroRoyL-44
❑ 99CroRoyOD-44
❑ 99FinGolRef-225
❑ 99FinRef-225
❑ 99Fle-188
❑ 99FleMys-84
❑ 99FleMysG-84
❑ 99FleMysM-84
❑ 99FleSta9-188
❑ 99FleWarT-188
❑ 99MetUni-159
❑ 99MetUniGM-159
❑ 99MetUniPMG-159
❑ 99Pac-131
❑ 99PacAur-53
❑ 99PacAurOD-53
❑ 99PacCroC-87
❑ 99PacCroCPB-87
❑ 99PacGolCDC-7
❑ 99PacInv-45
❑ 99PacInvOD-45
❑ 99PacInvPB-45
❑ 99PacOme-74
❑ 99PacOmeC-74
❑ 99PacOmeDM-12
❑ 99PacOmeG-74
❑ 99PacOmePB-74
❑ 99PacPar-74
❑ 99PacParC-74
❑ 99PacParG-74
❑ 99PacParHoloGold-74
❑ 99PacParHS-74
❑ 99PacParOD-74
❑ 99PacParPB-74
❑ 99PacParRed-74
❑ 99PacPlaB-131
❑ 99PacPri-44
❑ 99PacPriHB-44
❑ 99PacPriHG-44
❑ 99PacPriHM-44
❑ 99PacPriHP-44
❑ 99PacPriRed-44
❑ 99PacPriS-38
❑ 99PacPriS206-38
❑ 99PacPriS206R-38
❑ 99PacPriSP-38
❑ 99PacPriSV-38
❑ 99PacRed-131
❑ 99Rev-44
❑ 99RevPremDate-44
❑ 99RevRet-44
❑ 99RevShaSS-44
❑ 99SkyMolM-118
❑ 99SkyMolMF-18
❑ 99SkyMolMFS-18
❑ 99SkyMolMFT-18
❑ 99SkyMolMOA-1
❑ 99SkyMolMX-118
❑ 99SkyPre-184
❑ 99SkyPreR-184
❑ 99SkyThu-189
❑ 99SkyThuRant-189
❑ 99SkyThuRave-189
❑ 99SP Aut-26
❑ 99SP AutEF-E12
❑ 99SP AutR-R12
❑ 99SPx-34
❑ 99SPxFinR-34
❑ 99SPxFinS-34
❑ 99SPxPreS-PS7
❑ 99SPxStaF-SF10
❑ 99StaClu-71
❑ 99StaCluFDI-71
❑ 99StaCluOoaK-71
❑ 99StaCluPP-71
❑ 99ThuSkySupR-189
❑ 99Top-68
❑ 99TopBlaLC1-81
❑ 99TopBlaLC2-81
❑ 99TopBlaLC3-81
❑ 99TopChr-68
❑ 99TopChrR-68
❑ 99TopGal-72
❑ 99TopGalPP-72
❑ 99TopGalPPI-72
❑ 99TopGolL-81
❑ 99TopGolLC1-81
❑ 99TopGolLC2-81
❑ 99TopGolLOtO-81
❑ 99TopMVPP-68
❑ 99TopOpeD-38
❑ 99TopRedLC1-81
❑ 99TopRedLC2-81
❑ 99TopRedLC3-81
❑ 99TopSta-88
❑ 99TopSta'S-23
❑ 99TopSta'SG-23
❑ 99TopSta'SGDH-23
❑ 99TopSta1Foil-88
❑ 99TopStaFoil-88
❑ 99TopStaOS-88
❑ 99UD Cho-80
❑ 99UD ChoMBH-B12
❑ 99UD ChoP-80
❑ 99UD ChoPCR-80
❑ 99UD ChoS-26
❑ 99UD ChoSD-26
❑ 99UD ChoSHR-26
❑ 99UD ChoST-26
❑ 99UD Ion-20
❑ 99UD Ion-72
❑ 99UD IonC-C23
❑ 99UD IonR-20
❑ 99UD IonR-72
❑ 99UDHolo-17
❑ 99UDHoloAUsome-17
❑ 99Ult-113
❑ 99UltGolM-113
❑ 99UltMas-113
❑ 99UltPlaM-113
❑ 99UltPromo-NNO
❑ 99UppDec-354
❑ 99UppDec10AT-X27
❑ 99UppDec10ATD-X27
❑ 99UppDec10ATHR-X27
❑ 99UppDec10ATT-X27
❑ 99UppDecBD-26
❑ 99UppDecBDD-26
❑ 99UppDecBDDom-D11
❑ 99UppDecBDDomE-D11
❑ 99UppDecBDQ-26
❑ 99UppDecBDT-26
❑ 99UppDecCL-87
❑ 99UppDecCLCC-87
❑ 99UppDecCLM-C25
❑ 99UppDecE-30
❑ 99UppDecEFXG-30
❑ 99UppDecEL1-354
❑ 99UppDecEL2-354
❑ 99UppDecIP-I14
❑ 99UppDecIPD-I14
❑ 99UppDecIPHR-I14
❑ 99UppDecIPT-I14
❑ 99UppDecM-62
❑ 99UppDecMGS-62
❑ 99UppDecMHFS-62
❑ 99UppDecMP-62
❑ 99UppDecMSS-62
❑ 99UppDecMST-T8
❑ 99UppDecO-59
❑ 99UppDecOMP-S18
❑ 99UppDecOSO-59
❑ 99UppDecR-27
❑ 99UppDecRG-27
❑ 99UppDecRP-27
❑ 99UppDecWY-W16
❑ 99UppDecWYD-W16
❑ 99UppDecWYHR-W16
❑ 99UppDecWYT-W16
❑ 99Vic-125

Lofton, Rodney
❑ 89FreKeyS-14
❑ 90CMC-765
❑ 90HagSunB-9
❑ 90HagSunP-1423
❑ 90HagSunS-13
❑ 91HagSunLD-236
❑ 91HagSunP-2464
❑ 91LinDriAA-236
❑ 92HagSunS-262
❑ 92RocRedWF-1946
❑ 92SkyAA F-107
❑ 92UppDecML-327
❑ 93Bow-258
❑ 93El PasDF-2958
❑ 94ElPasDF-3152

Loftus, Dick
❑ 90DodTar-1014

Loftus, Thomas
❑ 87OldJudN-298

Logan, Chris
❑ 94SpoIndC-18
❑ 94SpoIndF-3321
❑ 96RanCucQB-18

Logan, H. Dan
❑ 80RocRedWT-4
❑ 81RocRedWT-11
❑ 81RocRedWW-11
❑ 82RocRedWT-15
❑ 83RocRedWT-17

Logan, Joe
❑ 88CapCodPPaLP-19
❑ 89JamExpP-2158
❑ 90RocExpLC-16
❑ 90RocExpP-2689
❑ 91FloStaLAP-FSL44
❑ 91WesPalBEC-7
❑ 91WesPalBEP-1223

Logan, Johnny
❑ 47Exh-138
❑ 53BraJohC-20
❑ 53BraMer-11
❑ 53BraSpiaS3-16
❑ 53BraSpiaS7-7
❑ 53Top-158
❑ 54Bow-80
❑ 54BraJohC-23
❑ 54BraMer-5
❑ 54BraSpiaSP-12
❑ 54RedMan-NL20
❑ 54Top-122
❑ 55Bow-180
❑ 55BraGolS-19
❑ 55BraJohC-23
❑ 55BraSpiaSD-11
❑ 55RedMan-NL5
❑ 56Top-136
❑ 56YelBasP-18
❑ 57Bra8x1-6
❑ 57BraSpiaS4-12
❑ 57SwiFra-12
❑ 57Top-4
❑ 58BraJayP-7
❑ 58Top-110
❑ 59Top-225
❑ 60BraLaktL-13
❑ 60BraSpiaS-10
❑ 60Top-205
❑ 61Pos-105A
❑ 61Pos-105B
❑ 61Top-524
❑ 62Top-573
❑ 63PirIDL-12
❑ 63Top-259
❑ 78BraTCC-8
❑ 79TCM50-158
❑ 80Bra195T-10
❑ 83Bra53F-23
❑ 87Bra195T-4
❑ 91TopArc1-158
❑ 92BazQua5A-3
❑ 93UppDecAH-83
❑ 94TopArc1-122
❑ 94TopArc1G-122
❑ 94UppDecAH-83
❑ 94UppDecAH1-83

Logan, Kyle
❑ 98QuaCitRBG-12

Logan, Lefty (Robert Dean)
❑ 77SerSta-16
❑ 86IndIndTI-18
❑ 90DodTar-456

Logan, Marcus
❑ 94NewJerCC-17
❑ 94NewJerCF-3415
❑ 96StPetCB-15
❑ 97ArkTraB-8
❑ 98ArkTraM-18

Logan, Stephen
❑ 97AubDouTI-15

Logan, Todd
❑ 90VisOakCLC-76
❑ 90VisOakP-2157
❑ 92VisOakC-13

Loggins, Mike
❑ 86Ft.MyeRP-18
❑ 87MemChiB-18
❑ 87MemChiP-4
❑ 88OmaRoyC-13
❑ 88OmaRoyP-1504
❑ 89OmaRoyC-20
❑ 89OmaRoyP-1738
❑ 90CMC-187
❑ 90OmaRoyC-12
❑ 90OmaRoyP-76
❑ 90ProAAAF-611
❑ 91LinDriAAA-433
❑ 91RicBraBC-26
❑ 91RicBraLD-433
❑ 91RicBraTI-2

LoGrande, Angelo
❑ 78WatIndT-14
❑ 81ChaChaT-14
❑ 82ChaChaT-15
❑ 83ChaChaT-10

Logsdon, Kevin
❑ 91WatIndC-9
❑ 91WatIndP-3364
❑ 92ColRedC-11
❑ 92ColRedF-2387
❑ 93KinIndC-13
❑ 93KinIndF-2243
❑ 93KinIndTI-13
❑ 94CanIndF-3117

Logue, Matt
❑ 89NiaFalRP-15

Lohman, Claude
❑ 13Zee-39

Lohrke, Jack
❑ 47TipTop-128
❑ 48Bow-16
❑ 48GiaTeal-14
❑ 49Bow-59
❑ 49EurSta-117
❑ 51Bow-235
❑ 52Bow-251
❑ 53BowBW-47
❑ 56SeaPop-10
❑ 57HygMea-8
❑ 57SeaPop-13
❑ 75Gia195T-17
❑ 76TayBow4-61
❑ 85TCMPla1-44

Lohrman, Bill
❑ 40PlaBal-210
❑ 79DiaGre-40
❑ 83Car194T-49
❑ 90DodTar-457

Lohrman, David
❑ 97PitMet-15
❑ 98St.LucMM-4

Lohry, Adin
❑ 90OneYanP-3367
❑ 92PriWilCC-8
❑ 92PriWilCF-151
❑ 93SanBerSC-11
❑ 93SanBerSF-775
❑ 94SanBerSC-9
❑ 94SanBerSF-2762

Lohse, Kyle
❑ 98RocCubM-18
❑ 98RocCubTI-19

Lohuis, Mark
❑ 81ShrCapT-21

Lois, Alberto
❑ 77ColCliT-10A
❑ 77ColCliT-10B
❑ 78ColCliT-14
❑ 79PorBeaT-14

❑ 80Top-683
Loiselle, Rich
❑ 92ChaRaiC-13
❑ 92ChaRaiF-116
❑ 93WatDiaC-21
❑ 93WatDiaF-1766
❑ 94RanCucQC-19
❑ 94RanCucQF-1636
❑ 95MemChiTI-17
❑ 96JacGenB-16
❑ 97PirPos-23
❑ 98Fin-47
❑ 98FinNo--47
❑ 98FinNo-R-47
❑ 98FinRef-47
❑ 98StaCluFDI-161
❑ 98StaCluI-161
❑ 98StaCluOneK-161
❑ 98StaCluPP-161
❑ 98Top-59
❑ 98TopChr-59
❑ 98TopChrR-59
❑ 98TopDevR-59
❑ 98TopDia-59
❑ 98TopMiniC-59
Loiz, Niuman
❑ 96QuaCitRB-18
❑ 98StoPorG-17
Lolich, Mickey
❑ 64Top-128
❑ 64TopVen-128
❑ 65TigJayP-8
❑ 65Top-335
❑ 65TopEmbl-55
❑ 66TigVolC-7
❑ 66Top-226
❑ 66Top-455
❑ 66TopRubl-54
❑ 66TopVen-226
❑ 67CokCapTi-14
❑ 67DexPre-128
❑ 67OPC-88
❑ 67Top-88
❑ 67TopVen-239
❑ 68CokCapT-14
❑ 68TigDetFPB-10
❑ 68Top-414
❑ 69KelPin-10
❑ 69MilBra-160
❑ 69MLBOffS-50
❑ 69MLBPin-15
❑ 69OPC-168
❑ 69TigTeal-6
❑ 69TigTealC-9
❑ 69Top-168
❑ 69Top-270
❑ 69TopFou-14
❑ 69TopSta-175
❑ 69TopTeaP-1
❑ 70DayDaiNM-35
❑ 70Kel-65
❑ 70MilBra-13
❑ 70MLBOffS-210
❑ 70OPC-72
❑ 70Top-72
❑ 70Top-715
❑ 71MLBOffS-398
❑ 71OPC-71
❑ 71OPC-133
❑ 71Top-71
❑ 71Top-133
❑ 71TopCoi-106
❑ 71TopGreM-23
❑ 71TopTat-105
❑ 72Kel-38
❑ 72MilBra-200
❑ 72OPC-94
❑ 72OPC-96
❑ 72OPC-450
❑ 72ProStaP-29
❑ 72SevTraC-27
❑ 72Top-94
❑ 72Top-96
❑ 72Top-450
❑ 72TopPos-5
❑ 73Kel2D-3
❑ 73LinPor-73
❑ 73OPC-390
❑ 73SevTraC-38
❑ 73TigJew-11
❑ 73Top-390
❑ 73TopCanL-27
❑ 73TopCom-10
❑ 73TopPin-10
❑ 74MetTeal-13
❑ 74OPC-166
❑ 74Top-9
❑ 74TopSta-178
❑ 75DetTigP-20
❑ 75Hos-6
❑ 75HosTwi-6
❑ 75OPC-245
❑ 75SSP42-21
❑ 75Top-245
❑ 75TopMin-245
❑ 76BlaDis-28
❑ 76BucDis-28
❑ 76CarDis-28
❑ 76CraDis-28
❑ 76DaiIsID-28
❑ 76IsaDis-28
❑ 76LauDiaJ-3
❑ 76MetMSAP-4
❑ 76OPC-3
❑ 76OPC-385
❑ 76OrbDis-28
❑ 76RedBarD-28
❑ 76SafDis-28
❑ 76SSP-354
❑ 76Top-3
❑ 76Top-385
❑ 76TopTra-385T
❑ 76TowCluD-28
❑ 77Spo-5209
❑ 77Top-565
❑ 78PadFamF-19
❑ 79PadFamF-21
❑ 79Top-164
❑ 80Top-459
❑ 81TCM60I-347
❑ 81TigDetN-55
❑ 83TigAIKS-62
❑ 84OCoandSI-156
❑ 86TigSpoD-20
❑ 88PacLegI-39
❑ 88TigDom-11
❑ 89SweBasG-97
❑ 90SweBasG-81
❑ 91MetWIZ-234
❑ 91SweBasG-56
❑ 91UppDecS-22
❑ 92ActPacA-36
❑ 93MetIma-11
❑ 93TedWil-40
❑ 93TigLitC-7
❑ 93UppDecAH-84
❑ 93UppDecS-26
❑ 94TedWilM-M31
❑ 94UppDecAH-91
❑ 94UppDecAH1-91
❑ 97FleMilDM-33
❑ 97FleMilDMR-33
❑ 98SpoIllWSF-27
❑ 98SpoIllWSFEE-27
❑ 98SpoIllWSFFE-27
Lolich, Ron
❑ 71OPC-458
❑ 71Top-458
❑ 73IndTeal-17
Lollar, Sherm
❑ 50Bow-142
❑ 51Bow-100
❑ 51TopBluB-24
❑ 52Bow-237
❑ 52NatTeaL-16
❑ 52Top-117
❑ 52WhiSoxHDP-5
❑ 53BowC-157
❑ 53Top-53
❑ 54Bow-182
❑ 54RedHeaF-17
❑ 54RedMan-AL5
❑ 54Top-39
❑ 55Bow-174
❑ 55Top-201
❑ 56Top-243
❑ 57Top-23
❑ 58Top-267
❑ 58Top-491
❑ 58WhiSoxJP-6
❑ 59Top-385
❑ 60Top-495
❑ 60Top-567
❑ 60WhiSoxJP-6
❑ 60WhiSoxTS-11
❑ 61Pos-28A
❑ 61Pos-28B
❑ 61Top-285
❑ 61TopStal-123
❑ 61WhiSoxTS-7
❑ 62Jel-53
❑ 62Pos-53
❑ 62PosCan-53
❑ 62SalPlaC-55
❑ 62ShiPlaC-55
❑ 62Top-514
❑ 62WhiSoxJP-6
❑ 62WhiSoxTS-10
❑ 63Jel-42
❑ 63Pos-42
❑ 63Top-118
❑ 63WhiSoxTS-16
❑ 65BalOriP-20
❑ 66BalOriP-21
❑ 66BalOriP-22
❑ 67BalOriP-63
❑ 76ChiGre-10
❑ 79TCM50-73
❑ 81Ori6F-21
❑ 81WhiSox1T-8
❑ 83TopRep5-117
❑ 85WhiSoxC-7
❑ 89WhiSoxK-3
❑ 91TopArc1-53
❑ 94TopArc1-39
❑ 94TopArc1G-39
Lollar, Tim
❑ 79WesHavYT-20
❑ 80ColCliP-23
❑ 80ColCliT-1
❑ 81Fle-108
❑ 81PadFamF-13
❑ 81Top-424
❑ 82Top-587
❑ 83Don-61
❑ 83DonActA-37
❑ 83Fle-365
❑ 83FleSti-228
❑ 83OPC-185
❑ 83PadTeal-14
❑ 83Top-185
❑ 83Top-742
❑ 83TopSti-296
❑ 84Don-284
❑ 84Fle-305
❑ 84Nes792-644
❑ 84OPC-267
❑ 84PadMot-3
❑ 84PadSmo-16
❑ 84Top-644
❑ 84TopTif-644
❑ 85Don-324
❑ 85Fle-39
❑ 85FleUpd-73
❑ 85Lea-111
❑ 85OPC-13
❑ 85Top-13
❑ 85TopSti-153
❑ 85TopTif-13
❑ 85TopTifT-76T
❑ 85TopTra-76T
❑ 85WhiSoxC-46
❑ 86Don-620
❑ 86Fle-354
❑ 86Top-297
❑ 86TopTif-297
❑ 87Fle-38
❑ 87FleGlo-38
❑ 87Top-396
❑ 87TopTif-396
❑ 92YanWIZ8-108
Loman, Doug
❑ 78BurBeeT-19
❑ 80HolMilT-15
❑ 81ElPasDT-8
❑ 82VanCanT-10
❑ 84VanCanC-28
❑ 85BrePol-5
❑ 85Don-46
❑ 94BreMilB-325
Loman, Kevin
❑ 95RicBraRC-10
❑ 96RicBraUB-17
Lomasney, Steve
❑ 96LowSpiB-16
❑ 97MicBatC-19
❑ 98Bow-397
❑ 98BowChr-397
❑ 98BowChrGA-397
❑ 98BowChrGAR-397
❑ 98BowChrI-397
❑ 98BowChrIR-397
❑ 98BowChrR-397
❑ 98BowGolA-397
❑ 98BowInt-397
❑ 99Bow-383
❑ 99BowGol-383
❑ 99BowInt-383
Lomastro, Jerry
❑ 83OrlTwiT-12
❑ 85TolMudHT-24
❑ 86StaoftFT-25
❑ 86TolMudHP-14
❑ 87HagSunP-7
❑ 87RocRedWT-26
Lombard, George
❑ 94StaCluDP-14
❑ 94StaCluDPFDI-14
❑ 95EugEmeTI-1
❑ 96BesAutS-50
❑ 96Bow-204
❑ 96BowFoi-204
❑ 96Exc-131
❑ 96MacBraB-24
❑ 97Bes-52
❑ 97BesAutSBPP-27
❑ 97Bow-168
❑ 97BowChr-164
❑ 97BowChrI-164
❑ 97BowChrIR-164
❑ 97BowChrR-164
❑ 97BowInt-168
❑ 97CalLeaATI-35
❑ 97CarLeaTP-23
❑ 97DurBulTI-27
❑ 98AriFalLTP-2
❑ 98BesBet-8
❑ 98BesCor-8
❑ 98BesDiaB-18
❑ 98Bow-193
❑ 98BowBes-144
❑ 98BowBesAR-144
❑ 98BowBesMIF-MI17
❑ 98BowBesMIFAR-MI17
❑ 98BowBesMIFR-MI17
❑ 98BowBesR-144
❑ 98BowChr-193
❑ 98BowChrGA-193
❑ 98BowChrGAR-193
❑ 98BowChrI-193
❑ 98BowChrIR-193
❑ 98BowChrR-193
❑ 98BowGolA-193
❑ 98BowInt-193
❑ 98FleUpd-U28
❑ 98GreBraG-12
❑ 98LeaRS-329
❑ 98LeaRSLHolo-329
❑ 98LeaRSLong-329
❑ 98LeaRTrue-329
❑ 98SouLeaTPG-1
❑ 98SP MinPE-21
❑ 98SPMin-21
❑ 99199Fin-280
❑ 99BasAmeTPSC-6
❑ 99Bow-340
❑ 99Bow200RF-ROY9
❑ 99BowAut-BA61
❑ 99BowBes-117
❑ 99BowBesAR-117
❑ 99BowBesR-117
❑ 99BowChrSC-SC11
❑ 99BowChrSCR-SC11
❑ 99BowGol-340
❑ 99BowInt-340
❑ 99BowScoC-SC11
❑ 99DumSet-GL
❑ 99E-X Cen-94
❑ 99E-X CenECFut-94
❑ 99E-X CenECNow-94
❑ 99FinGolRef-280
❑ 99FinRef-280
❑ 99FlaShoWotF-11
❑ 99Fle-181
❑ 99FleBri-133
❑ 99FleBri2G-133
❑ 99FleBriBlu-133
❑ 99FleBriGol-133
❑ 99FleBriI-11
❑ 99FleSta9-181
❑ 99FleWarT-181
❑ 99Pac-34
❑ 99PacPlaB-34
❑ 99PacRed-34
❑ 99SkyThu-242
❑ 99SkyThuRant-242
❑ 99SkyThuRave-242
❑ 99SP Aut-92
❑ 99SP AutC-GL
❑ 99SP AutCG-GL
❑ 99SP TopP-76
❑ 99SP TopPC-GL
❑ 99SP TopPDtS-D19
❑ 99SP TopPGF-GF19
❑ 99SP TopPPE-76
❑ 99SpoIll-46
❑ 99SPSig-106
❑ 99SPx-83
❑ 99SPxFinR-83
❑ 99SPxFinS-83
❑ 99StaClu-165
❑ 99StaCluC-SCC35
❑ 99StaCluCR-SCC35
❑ 99StaCluFDI-165
❑ 99StaCluOoaK-165
❑ 99StaCluPP-165
❑ 99TeaBesR-6
❑ 99ThuSkySupR-242
❑ 99Top-207
❑ 99TopChr-207
❑ 99TopChrR-207
❑ 99TopGal-150
❑ 99TopGalPP-150
❑ 99TopGalPPI-150
❑ 99TopSta-43
❑ 99TopSta1Foil-43
❑ 99TopSta2Foil-43
❑ 99TopStaFoil-43
❑ 99TopStaOS-43
❑ 99TopStaTS-43
❑ 99UD Cho-25
❑ 99UD ChoPCR-25
❑ 99UDHoloUDA-GL
❑ 99Ult-247
❑ 99UltGolM-247
❑ 99UltMas-247
❑ 99UltPlaM-247
❑ 99UppDec-7
❑ 99UppDecBD-120
❑ 99UppDecBDD-120
❑ 99UppDecBDQ-120
❑ 99UppDecBDT-120
❑ 99UppDecCf7-86
❑ 99UppDecCo7CE-86
❑ 99UppDecE-97
❑ 99UppDecEFXG-97
❑ 99UppDecEL1-7
❑ 99UppDecEL2-7
❑ 99UppDecM-21
❑ 99UppDecMGS-21
❑ 99UppDecMHFS-21
❑ 99UppDecMP-GL
❑ 99UppDecMSS-21
❑ 99UppDecO-68
❑ 99UppDecOSO-68
❑ 99Vic-28
Lombardi, Al
❑ 89PenPilS-11
Lombardi, Dominick
❑ 98ButCopKG-18
Lombardi, Ernie
❑ 28Zee-84
❑ 29Zee-77
❑ 30Zee-88
❑ 32OrbPinNP-58
❑ 32OrbPinUP-41
❑ 33TatOrb-41
❑ 33WorCig-63
❑ 34BatR31-129
❑ 34DiaMatCSB-115
❑ 34DiaStaR-36A
❑ 34DiaStaR-36B
❑ 34DiaStaR-105
❑ 34ExhFou-4
❑ 34Gou-35
❑ 34GouCanV-82
❑ 35DiaMatCS2-12
❑ 35DiaMatCS3T1-100
❑ 35ExhFou-4
❑ 36ExhFou-4
❑ 36GouWidPPR-A66
❑ 36NatChiFPR-111
❑ 36R31PasP-15
❑ 37ExhFou-4
❑ 37WheBB14-8
❑ 37WheBB7-29E
❑ 38CloFotW-50
❑ 38ExhFou-4
❑ 38GouHeaU-246
❑ 38GouHeaU-270
❑ 38RedOraW-17
❑ 38WheBB10-8
❑ 38WheBB11-6
❑ 39ExhSal-37A
❑ 39ExhSal-38B
❑ 39GouPreR303A-30
❑ 39GouPreR303B-18
❑ 39OrcPhoAP-30
❑ 39OrcPhoAP-32
❑ 39RedTeal-13
❑ 39WheBB12-1
❑ 39WorWidGTP-30
❑ 40WheM4-8A
❑ 40WheM4-8B
❑ 41DouPlaR-11
❑ 41HarHarW-13
❑ 47TipTop-129
❑ 48SigOil-16
❑ 60Fle-17
❑ 61Fle-55
❑ 75JohMiz-1
❑ 75ShaPiz-5
❑ 77CinRedT-4
❑ 77GalGloG-64
❑ 77RedCarP-23
❑ 80PacLeg-11
❑ 80PerHaloFP-195
❑ 80SSPHOF-191
❑ 81ConTSN-28
❑ 82DiaCla-32
❑ 82OhiHaloF-8
❑ 82TCMGreH-39
❑ 86DonHig-33
❑ 86SpoDecG-23
❑ 89DodSmoG-102
❑ 89HOFStiB-58
❑ 91ConTSN-27
❑ 92ConTSN-427
❑ 93ConTSN-877
❑ 94ConTSN-1064
❑ 94ConTSNB-1064
Lombardi, John
❑ 91MedHatBJP-4102
❑ 94AlbPolC-16
❑ 94AlbPolF-2234
❑ 94OriPro-55
Lombardi, Phil
❑ 83GreHorT-15
❑ 85AlbYanT-13
❑ 86ColCliP-12
❑ 86ColCliP-14
❑ 86StaoftFT-4
❑ 87ColCliP-17
❑ 87ColCliP-12
❑ 87ColCliT-15
❑ 87Don-401
❑ 87Fle-648
❑ 87FleGlo-648
❑ 87Spo-118
❑ 87SpoTeaP-7
❑ 88MetColP-32
❑ 88TidTidCa-10
❑ 88TidTidCM-12
❑ 88TidTidP-1578
❑ 88Top-283
❑ 88TopTif-283
❑ 89MetColP-40
❑ 89TidTidC-12
❑ 89TidTidP-1975
❑ 90MetColP-38
❑ 91MetWIZ-235
❑ 92YanWIZ8-109
Lombardi, Vic
❑ 46DodTeal-16
❑ 46SpoExcW-8-7
❑ 47DodTeal-14
❑ 47TipTop-100
❑ 49EurSta-165
❑ 50PirTeal-11
❑ 51Bow-204
❑ 52Par-7
❑ 56SeaPop-11
❑ 79DiaGre-88
❑ 84TCMPla1-27
❑ 90DodTar-459
Lombardi, Vince
❑ 87SpoCubG-1
Lombardo, Chris
❑ 78St.PetCT-17
Lombardozzi, Chris
❑ 87PriWilYP-13
❑ 89CedRapRB-28
❑ 89CedRapRP-935
❑ 89ChaLooB-17
❑ 89ChaLooGS-25
❑ 90NasSouP-240
❑ 90ProAAAF-552
Lombardozzi, Steve
❑ 83OrlTwiT-6
❑ 84TolMudHT-1
❑ 85TolMudHT-17
❑ 86Don-598
❑ 86DonRoo-18
❑ 86FleUpd-68
❑ 86Spo-178
❑ 86SpoRoo-17

❑ 86TwiTeal-2
❑ 87Don-318
❑ 87DonOpeD-227
❑ 87Fle-547
❑ 87FleGlo-547
❑ 87SpoTeaP-17
❑ 87TopTra-66T
❑ 87TopTraT-66T
❑ 87TwiPos-15
❑ 87TwiTeal-1
❑ 88Don-196
❑ 88Fle-16
❑ 88FleGlo-16
❑ 88PanSti-137
❑ 88Sco-174
❑ 88ScoGlo-174
❑ 88StaLinTw-13
❑ 88Top-697
❑ 88TopTif-697
❑ 88TwiMasBD-6
❑ 89AstSmo-23
❑ 89Don-554
❑ 89Fle-120
❑ 89FleGlo-120
❑ 89OPC-376
❑ 89Sco-421
❑ 89Top-376
❑ 89TopTif-376
❑ 89TucTorC-23
❑ 89TucTorJP-13
❑ 89TucTorP-181
❑ 89UppDec-179
❑ 90Don-688
Lombarski, Tom
❑ 80CarMudF-12
❑ 81ReaPhiT-16
❑ 82OklCit8T-14
❑ 83MidCubT-14
❑ 84IowCubT-17
❑ 85IowCubT-4
❑ 86PeoChiP-16
❑ 87TidTidP-17
❑ 87TidTidT-14
Lomeli, Michael
❑ 87IdaFalBP-14
❑ 88BoiHawP-1622
❑ 89BoiHawP-2004
❑ 90EriSaiS-13
Lomon, Kevin
❑ 92DurBulC-8
❑ 92DurBulTI-14
❑ 93DurBulF-483
❑ 93DurBulTI-21
❑ 94Bow-401
❑ 94RicBraF-2844
❑ 95FleUpd-114
❑ 95MetColP-19
❑ 95RicBraTI-8
❑ 96RicBraB-18
❑ 96RicBraRC-1
❑ 97ColCliB-16
❑ 97ColCliD-12
❑ 98Las-14
Lonborg, Jim
❑ 65Top-573
❑ 66OPC-93
❑ 66RedSoxTI-6
❑ 66Top-93
❑ 66TopVen-93
❑ 67CokCapRS-16
❑ 67DexPre-129
❑ 67Top-371
❑ 67TopGiaSU-4
❑ 67TopRedSS-9
❑ 67TopVen-213
❑ 68AtlOilPBCC-24
❑ 68Baz-11
❑ 68CokCapRS-16
❑ 68DexPre-49
❑ 68OPC-10
❑ 68OPC-12
❑ 68OPC-155
❑ 68RedSoxTI-5
❑ 68Top-10A
❑ 68Top-10B
❑ 68Top-12
❑ 68Top-155
❑ 68Top-460
❑ 68Top3-D-5
❑ 68TopActS-4C
❑ 68TopActS-15C
❑ 68TopGamI-14
❑ 68TopPla-8
❑ 68TopPos-11
❑ 68TopVen-10
❑ 68TopVen-12
❑ 68TopVen-155
❑ 69CitMetC-3
❑ 69MilBra-161
❑ 69MLBOffS-14
❑ 69MLBPin-16
❑ 69NabTeaF-13
❑ 69OPC-109
❑ 69RedSoxAO-6
❑ 69RedSoxTI-6
❑ 69RedSoxTI-5
❑ 69Top-109
❑ 69TopSta-135
❑ 69TopTeaP-3
❑ 70Kel-49
❑ 70MLBOffS-159
❑ 70RedSoxCPPC-17
❑ 70Top-665
❑ 71MLBOffS-323
❑ 71OPC-577
❑ 71RedSoxTI-5
❑ 71Top-577
❑ 72MilBra-201
❑ 72OPC-255
❑ 72SevTraC-28
❑ 72Top-255
❑ 73OPC-3
❑ 73PhiTeal-11
❑ 73Top-3
❑ 74OPC-342
❑ 74PhiJohP-41
❑ 74Top-342
❑ 74TopSta-75
❑ 75OPC-94
❑ 75PhiPhiP-19
❑ 75PhiProPS-8
❑ 75Top-94
❑ 75TopMin-94
❑ 76OPC-271
❑ 76PhiPhiP-15
❑ 76SSP-462
❑ 76Top-271
❑ 77Kel-41
❑ 77Top-569
❑ 78SSP270-52
❑ 78Top-52
❑ 79OPC-233
❑ 79Top-446
❑ 81RedSoxBG2S-66
❑ 81RedSoxBG2S-91
❑ 82TCMGreP-26
❑ 83PhiPosGM-12
❑ 88PacLegI-80A
❑ 88PacLegI-80B
❑ 89SweBasG-48
❑ 90SweBasG-124
❑ 91LinDri-16
❑ 91SweBasG-57
❑ 92ActPacA-50
❑ 92UppDecS-6
❑ 93TedWil-3
❑ 93UppDecAH-85
❑ 94BreMilB-326
❑ 94UppDecAH-128
❑ 94UppDecAH1-128
❑ 94UppDecS-8
❑ 99SpoIllGotG-77
❑ 99SpoIllGotGA-44
Lonchar, John
❑ 77TacTwiDQ-9
Lond, Joel
❑ 86FloStaLAP-30
London, Darren
❑ 90PriWilCTI-3
Long, Bill (William)
❑ 82AmaGolST-18
❑ 83LasVegSBHN-14
❑ 84BeaGolGT-11
❑ 85BufBisT-21
❑ 86BufBisP-16
❑ 87DonRoo-48
❑ 87FleUpd-66
❑ 87FleUpdG-66
❑ 87HawIsIP-16
❑ 87TopTra-67T
❑ 87TopTraT-67T
❑ 88Don-306
❑ 88Fle-404
❑ 88FleGlo-404
❑ 88OPC-309
❑ 88RedFolSB-49
❑ 88Sco-539
❑ 88ScoGlo-539
❑ 88Top-309
❑ 88TopTif-309
❑ 88WhiSoxC-14
❑ 89Bow-56
❑ 89BowTif-56
❑ 89Don-573
❑ 89Fle-501
❑ 89FleGlo-501
❑ 89OPC-133
❑ 89Sco-351
❑ 89Top-133
❑ 89TopTif-133
❑ 89UppDec-499
❑ 89WhiSoxC-16
❑ 90CubMar-12
❑ 90OPC-499
❑ 90PubIntS-394
❑ 90Sco-526
❑ 90ScoRoo-62T
❑ 90Top-499
❑ 90TopTif-499
❑ 90TopTVCu-52
❑ 91Fle-425
❑ 91OPC-668
❑ 91Sco-559
❑ 91Top-668
❑ 91TopDesS-668
❑ 91TopMic-668
❑ 91TopTif-668
❑ 91UppDec-495
❑ 94ElmPioC-25
❑ 94ElmPioF-3490
Long, Bob
❑ 52LavPro-22
Long, Bob (Robert E.)
❑ 75LynRanT-15
❑ 78SalPirT-8
❑ 79BufBisT-20
❑ 80PorBeaT-21
❑ 81PorBeaT-16
❑ 82PorBeaT-5
❑ 82Top-291
❑ 84SalLakCGC-179
❑ 85CalCanC-95
❑ 86Fle-468
❑ 86RicBraP-12
❑ 87ChaO'sW-14
❑ 89ChaLooLITI-17
Long, Bruce
❑ 86ReaPhiP-15
❑ 87ReaPhiP-10
Long, Dale
❑ 47Exh-139A
❑ 47Exh-139B
❑ 55DonWin-30
❑ 55Top-127
❑ 55TopDouH-115
❑ 56PirTeal-15
❑ 56Top-56
❑ 56TopPin-43
❑ 56YelBasP-19
❑ 57Kah-20
❑ 57PirTeal-5
❑ 57SwiFra-3
❑ 57Top-3
❑ 58Top-7
❑ 59Top-147
❑ 59Top-414
❑ 59TopVen-147
❑ 60CubJayP-8
❑ 60Top-375
❑ 61Top-117
❑ 61TopStaI-205
❑ 62Jel-65
❑ 62Pos-65
❑ 62PosCan-65
❑ 62SalPlaC-35
❑ 62ShiPlaC-35
❑ 62Top-228
❑ 63BasMagM-49
❑ 63Top-484
❑ 72LauGreF-48
❑ 78TCM60I-223
❑ 79TCM50-41
❑ 80MarExh-16
❑ 84CubBriPC-10D
❑ 87SpoRea-15
❑ 90HOFStiB-53
❑ 90PacLeg-92
❑ 92YanWIZ6-73
Long, Danny
❑ 87OldJudN-300
❑ 88SFHesCreN32-16
Long, Dennis
❑ 81TulDriT-14
❑ 82TulDriT-4
❑ 83TulDriT-8
Long, Don
❑ 87QuaCitAP-19
❑ 88BenBucL-27
❑ 89BenBucL-26
❑ 89PalSprACLC-60
❑ 89PalSprAP-476
❑ 90QuaCitAGS-1
❑ 91LinDriAA-449
❑ 91MidAngLD-449
❑ 91MidAngOHP-17
❑ 91MidAngP-449
❑ 92MidAngF-4040
❑ 92MidAngS-474
❑ 93MidAngF-337
❑ 94VanCanF-1878
❑ 96VanCanB-1
❑ 97LakElsSG-19
❑ 98MidAngG-20
Long, Garrett
❑ 96EriSeaB-14
❑ 96Exc-219
❑ 96Top-241
❑ 97AugGre-27
❑ 98LynHilQ-17
Long, Germany (Herman)
❑ 03BreE10-91
❑ 11SpoLifCW-222
❑ 87OldJudN-299
❑ 95May-18
❑ 98CamPepP-44
Long, James V.
❑ 88PalSprACLC-89
❑ 88PalSprAP-1460
Long, Jeoff
❑ 64Top-497
Long, Joe
❑ 91SpoIndP-3946
❑ 92GulCoaYF-3788
❑ 93GreHorC-15
❑ 93GreHorF-883
❑ 94TamYanC-16
❑ 94TamYanF-2379
❑ 95NorNavTI-43
❑ 96Bow-295
❑ 96BowFoi-295
❑ 97Bow-152
❑ 97BowInt-152
Long, Joey
❑ 91SpoIndC-2
❑ 93WatDiaC-22
❑ 93WatDiaF-1767
❑ 94RanCucQC-20
❑ 94RanCucQF-1637
❑ 96LasVegSB-17
❑ 97LasVegS1A-23
Long, Justin
❑ 95ElmPioTI-14
❑ 95ElmPioUTI-14
Long, Kevin
❑ 88AriWilP-10
❑ 88CapCodPPaLP-98
❑ 89EugEmeB-14
❑ 90BasCitRS-15
❑ 92OmaRoyF-2976
❑ 92OmaRoyS-334
❑ 92SkyAAAF-153
❑ 93OmaRoyF-1692
❑ 94MemChiF-369
❑ 96WicWraB-3
❑ 98CarLeaAC-21
❑ 98WilBluRC-18
Long, R.D.
❑ 92OneYanC-15
❑ 93GreHorC-16
❑ 93GreHorF-895
❑ 94TamYanC-17
❑ 94TamYanF-2394
❑ 95NorNavTI-24
❑ 95TamYanYI-18
❑ 97NorNav-23
❑ 97NorNavTI-18
Long, Rich (Richard)
❑ 89UtiBluSP-14
❑ 90SouBenWSB-10
❑ 90SouBenWSGS-9
Long, Ryan
❑ 91ClaDraP-40
❑ 91FroRowDP-18
❑ 91FroRowDPG-18
❑ 91FroRowDPS-18
❑ 91HigSchPLS-30
❑ 92Bow-79
❑ 92EugEmeC-2
❑ 92EugEmeF-3035
❑ 92StaCluD-109
❑ 93RocRoyC-16
❑ 93RocRoyF-722
❑ 94WilBluRC-12
❑ 94WilBluRF-305
❑ 95WicWraTI-9
❑ 96WicWraB-13
❑ 97OmaRoyB-23
❑ 98Fle-168
❑ 98OmaRoyM-13
❑ 98WicWraM-27
Long, Steve
❑ 90JamExpP-20
❑ 91SumFlyC-7
❑ 91SumFlyP-2330
❑ 92WesPalBEC-11
❑ 92WesPalBEF-2085
❑ 93BinMetF-2330
❑ 94EdmTraF-2872
❑ 95ChaKniTI-13
Long, Terrence
❑ 94ClaUpdCotC-CC17
❑ 94KinMetC-10
❑ 94KinMetF-3836
❑ 94SigRooDP-20
❑ 94SigRooDPS-20
❑ 94StaCluDP-83
❑ 94StaCluDPFDI-83
❑ 94TopTra-33T
❑ 95Exc-232
❑ 95Pin-173
❑ 95PinArtP-173
❑ 95PinMusC-173
❑ 95PitMetTI-23
❑ 95ScoDraP-DP10
❑ 95SelSurS-SS10
❑ 95SPML-99
❑ 95StaClu-98
❑ 95StaCluFDI-98
❑ 95StaCluMOP-98
❑ 95StaCluSTWS-98
❑ 95Top-112
❑ 95UppDecML-175
❑ 95UppDecMLFS-175
❑ 96Bow-368
❑ 96BowFoi-368
❑ 96HilStaHWB-12
❑ 97Bow-187
❑ 97BowBes-157
❑ 97BowBesAR-157
❑ 97BowBesR-157
❑ 97BowCerBlaIA-CA49
❑ 97BowCerBluIA-CA49
❑ 97BowCerGolIA-CA49
❑ 97BowInt-187
❑ 97FloStaLTPB-17
❑ 97St.LucM-14
❑ 98BinMetQ-18
❑ 98EasLeaTPM-16
❑ 99Bow-156
❑ 99BowChr-156
❑ 99BowChrG-156
❑ 99BowChrGR-156
❑ 99BowChrI-156
❑ 99BowChrIR-156
❑ 99BowChrR-156
❑ 99BowGol-156
❑ 99BowInt-156
❑ 99DumSet-148
❑ 99FleMys-148
❑ 99FleMysM-148
Long, The Kid (Ernest)
❑ 93NegLeaRL2-23
Long, Thomas
❑ 15SpoNewM-103
❑ 16SpoNewM-105
❑ 17ColE13-100
❑ 19Zee-140
❑ 20Zee-144
Long, Tony
❑ 86LakTigP-11
❑ 90EugEmeGS-18
❑ 91BasCitRC-9
❑ 91BasCitRP-1396
❑ 91FloStaLAP-FSL2
❑ 92BasCitRF-3843
❑ 95ArkTraTI-18
Longaker, Scott
❑ 91HamRedC-9
❑ 91HamRedP-4035
Longenecker, Jere
❑ 83ButCopKT-18
❑ 86MemChiSTOS-13
❑ 86MemChiTOS-13
❑ 87MemChiB-19
❑ 87MemChiP-9
Longmire, Marcel
❑ 97RocCub-21
❑ 98RocCubM-19
❑ 98RocCubTI-20
Longmire, Tony
❑ 87MacPirP-8
❑ 88SalBucS-10
❑ 91Bow-489
❑ 91Cla/Bes-98
❑ 91LinDriAA-513
❑ 91ReaPhiLD-513
❑ 91ReaPhiP-1382
❑ 92ProFS7-297
❑ 93Bow-596
❑ 93ClaFS7-67
❑ 93ScrRedBF-2555
❑ 93ScrRedBTI-15
❑ 93TriAAAGF-20
❑ 94Bow-168
❑ 94FleUpd-167
❑ 94LeaLimR-37
❑ 94Pac-480
❑ 94PhiMed-20
❑ 94PhiMel-15
❑ 94PhiUSPC-2H
❑ 94PhiUSPC-8S
❑ 94Pin-528
❑ 94PinArtP-528
❑ 94PinMusC-528
❑ 94ScoRoo-RT148
❑ 94ScoRooGR-RT148
❑ 94Sel-382
❑ 94SpoRoo-57
❑ 94SpoRooAP-57
❑ 94StaClu-394
❑ 94StaCluFDI-394
❑ 94StaCluGR-394
❑ 94StaCluMOP-394
❑ 94StaCluT-213
❑ 94StaCluTFDI-213
❑ 94Top-28
❑ 94TopGol-28
❑ 94TopSpa-28
❑ 94Ult-551
❑ 95Don-420
❑ 95DonPreP-420
❑ 95Fla-181
❑ 95Fle-400
❑ 95Pac-332
❑ 95PacPri-109
❑ 95Phi-18
❑ 95PhiMel-15
❑ 95Sco-242
❑ 95ScoGolR-242
❑ 95ScoPlaTS-242
❑ 95Top-608
❑ 95TopCyb-362
❑ 96ColCho-252
❑ 96ColChoGS-252
❑ 96ColChoSS-252
❑ 96Don-90
❑ 96DonPreP-90
❑ 96Fle-502
❑ 96FleTif-502
❑ 96Ult-255
❑ 96UltGolM-255
❑ 97PacPriGotD-GD183
Longo, Neil
❑ 98EveAquG-11
❑ 99TeaBesR-49
❑ 99TeaBesRG-49
❑ 99TeaBesRS-49
Longueira, Tony
❑ 97WilBluR-8
❑ 98LanLugQ-18
Longuil, Rich
❑ 87SumBraP-15
❑ 88DurBulS-10
❑ 89BurBraP-1624
❑ 89BurBraS-14
❑ 90DurBulTI-21
Lonigro, Greg
❑ 87CedRapRP-15
❑ 88CedRapRP-1152
❑ 88MidLeaAGS-9
❑ 89ChaLooB-16
❑ 89ChaLooGS-17
❑ 90ChaLooGS-20
❑ 91ChaLooLD-161
❑ 91ChaLooP-1967
❑ 91LinDriAA-161
❑ 93IowCubF-2141
❑ 93OrlCubF-2794
Lonnett, Joe
❑ 57Top-241
❑ 58Top-64
❑ 73OPC-356
❑ 73Top-356
❑ 74OPC-221
❑ 74Top-221

❑ 77PirPosP-13
❑ 93CarMudF-2071
❑ 98EriSeaWM-30

Lono, Joel
❑ 86TamTarP-11
❑ 87CedRapRP-6

Look, Bruce
❑ 69Top-317

Lookout, Chief
❑ 83ChaLooT-24

Lookout, Looie the
❑ 98ChaLooG-17

Lookouts, Chattanooga
❑ 83ChaLooT-28

Loomis, Albert
❑ 14Zee-39

Loomis, Geoff
❑ 92SouOreAC-10
❑ 92SouOreAF-3425
❑ 93SouOreAC-14
❑ 93SouOreAF-4072

Looney, Brian
❑ 91JamExpC-17
❑ 91JamExpP-3542
❑ 92ProFS7-269
❑ 92RocExpC-18
❑ 92RocExpF-2111
❑ 93WesPalBEC-12
❑ 93WesPalBEF-1335
❑ 94Bow-472
❑ 94Fle-544
❑ 94UppDec-125
❑ 94UppDecED-125
❑ 95PawRedSDD-18
❑ 95PawRedTI-17
❑ 96PawRedSDD-17
❑ 97SalLakB-15
❑ 98ColCliD-17
❑ 98ColCliM-22

Looney, Steve
❑ 91FayGenC-24
❑ 91FayGenP-1183

Looper, Aaron
❑ 98EveAquG-12

Looper, Braden
❑ 97Bes-22
❑ 97BesLimA-23
❑ 97Bow-77
❑ 97BowBes-172
❑ 97BowBesAR-172
❑ 97BowBesR-172
❑ 97BowChr-105
❑ 97BowChrI-105
❑ 97BowChrIR-105
❑ 97BowChrR-105
❑ 97BowInt-77
❑ 97CarLeaTP-9
❑ 97PriWilC-1
❑ 97Top-477
❑ 98AriFalLTP-1
❑ 98BesAutPOY-9
❑ 98BesDiaB-5
❑ 98BesDiaBA-7
❑ 98BesFulCA-10
❑ 98BesPos-2
❑ 98BesPreA-23
❑ 98Bow-138
❑ 98BowBes-146
❑ 98BowBesAR-146
❑ 98BowBesR-146
❑ 98BowChr-138
❑ 98BowChrGA-138
❑ 98BowChrGAR-138
❑ 98BowChrI-138
❑ 98BowChrIR-138
❑ 98BowChrR-138
❑ 98BowGolA-138
❑ 98BowInt-138
❑ 98Fle-415
❑ 98LeaRS-291
❑ 98LeaRSLHolo-291
❑ 98LeaRSLong-291
❑ 98LeaRTrue-291
❑ 98PacOnl-617
❑ 98PacOnlR-617
❑ 98PacOnlWC-617
❑ 98PriWilCASM-5
❑ 98SP MinPE-103
❑ 98SPMin-103
❑ 98SPxFin-208
❑ 98SPxFinR-208
❑ 98SPxFinS-208
❑ 98Top-485
❑ 98TopChr-485
❑ 98TopChrR-485
❑ 98TopDevR-485
❑ 98TopDia-485
❑ 98TopMiniC-485
❑ 98UppDec-593
❑ 99Bow-353
❑ 99BowGol-353
❑ 99BowInt-353
❑ 99PacInv-63
❑ 99PacInvOD-63
❑ 99PacInvPB-63
❑ 99UppDec-375
❑ 99UppDecEL1-375
❑ 99UppDecEL2-375

Looper, Eddie
❑ 87SavCarP-18
❑ 88SavCarP-350
❑ 89SprCarB-23

Lootens, Brian
❑ 93EveGiaC-16
❑ 93EveGiaF-3783

Lopat, Ed
❑ 47Exh-140
❑ 47StaPinP2-19
❑ 47TipTop-24
❑ 48BluTin-40
❑ 48YanTeal-16
❑ 49Bow-229
❑ 49YanTeal-13
❑ 50Bow-215
❑ 50YanTeal-13
❑ 51BerRos-C6
❑ 51Bow-218
❑ 51R42SmaS-61
❑ 51TopBluB-39
❑ 52BerRos-35
❑ 52Bow-17
❑ 52CokTip-4
❑ 52StaCalL-70B
❑ 52StaCalS-84B
❑ 52TipTop-22
❑ 52Top-57
❑ 53Dor-103
❑ 53ExhCan-15
❑ 53Top-87
❑ 54NewYorJA-50
❑ 54Top-5
❑ 55Top-109
❑ 55TopDouH-41
❑ 56TopHocF-A2
❑ 60RawGloT-14
❑ 60Top-465
❑ 61TwiPetM-2
❑ 63AthJayP-7
❑ 63Top-23
❑ 64AthJayP-9
❑ 64Top-348
❑ 64TopVen-348
❑ 70Houof J-14
❑ 71FleWorS-49
❑ 75TCMHouoJ-14
❑ 79DiaGre-135
❑ 81TCM60I-345
❑ 83ASAJohM-11
❑ 83TCMPla1945-17
❑ 83TopRep5-57
❑ 83YanASFY-24
❑ 84FifNatC-4
❑ 90PacLeg-38
❑ 90SweBasG-24
❑ 91OriCro-266
❑ 91SweBasG-58
❑ 91TopArc1-87
❑ 92ActPacA-67
❑ 92BazQua5A-12
❑ 92YanWIZA-41
❑ 93TedWil-65
❑ 94TopArc1-5
❑ 94TopArc1G-5
❑ 94UppDecAH-68
❑ 94UppDecAH1-68
❑ 97BalOriP-30

Lopata, Stan
❑ 47PM1StaP1-115
❑ 49Bow-177
❑ 49EurSta-140
❑ 49PhiBul-30
❑ 50Bow-206
❑ 50PhiPhil-14
❑ 51BerRos-B9
❑ 51Bow-76
❑ 54Bow-207
❑ 55Bow-18
❑ 56PhiPos-4
❑ 56Top-183
❑ 57Top-119
❑ 58Hir-29
❑ 58HirTes-6
❑ 58PhiJayP-7
❑ 58PhiTeal-11
❑ 58Top-353
❑ 59Top-412
❑ 60BraJayP-7
❑ 60RawGloT-15
❑ 60Top-515
❑ 75Phi195T-17
❑ 75TCMHouoJ-15
❑ 79TCM50-151
❑ 80Phi195T-17
❑ 83PhiPosGPaM-3

Lopes, Dave
❑ 73LinPor-95
❑ 73OPC-609
❑ 73Top-609
❑ 74GreHeroBP-4
❑ 74GreHeroBP-6
❑ 74OPC-112
❑ 74Top-112
❑ 74TopSta-46
❑ 75GreHeroBP-2
❑ 75GreHeroBP-6
❑ 75Hos-67
❑ 75HosTwi-67
❑ 75OPC-93
❑ 75Top-93
❑ 75TopMin-93
❑ 76DodPos-9
❑ 76GreHeroBP-2
❑ 76GreHeroBP-6
❑ 76Hos-105
❑ 76LinSup-114
❑ 76OPC-4
❑ 76OPC-197
❑ 76OPC-660
❑ 76Spo-10
❑ 76SSP-79
❑ 76Top-4
❑ 76Top-197
❑ 76Top-660
❑ 77BurCheD-145
❑ 77DodPho-7
❑ 77Hos-14
❑ 77OPC-4
❑ 77OPC-96
❑ 77Spo-5102
❑ 77Spo-7401
❑ 77Top-4
❑ 77Top-180
❑ 78Hos-112
❑ 78OPC-222
❑ 78SSP270-67
❑ 78Top-412
❑ 78Top-440
❑ 78WifBalD-39
❑ 79BasPat-46
❑ 79DodBlu-8
❑ 79Hos-114
❑ 79Kel-52
❑ 79OPC-144
❑ 79Pew-9
❑ 79Top-290
❑ 80BurKinPHR-28
❑ 80DodPol-15
❑ 80Kel-29
❑ 80OPC-291
❑ 80Top-560
❑ 80TopSup-60
❑ 81AllGamPI-104
❑ 81Dod-7
❑ 81Dod-19
❑ 81DodPol-15
❑ 81DodPos-6
❑ 81Don-416
❑ 81Fle-114A
❑ 81Fle-114B
❑ 81FleStiC-67
❑ 81Kel-29
❑ 81LonBeaPT-2
❑ 81OPC-50
❑ 81PerAll-5
❑ 81Top-50
❑ 81TopScr-92
❑ 81TopSti-175
❑ 81TopSupHT-48
❑ 82A'sGraG-8
❑ 82Don-327
❑ 82Fle-12
❑ 82FleSta-10
❑ 82OPC-85
❑ 82OPC-218
❑ 82OPC-338
❑ 82Top-338
❑ 82Top-740
❑ 82Top-741
❑ 82TopTra-64T
❑ 83A'sGraG-15
❑ 83Don-339
❑ 83Fle-524
❑ 83FleSta-107
❑ 83FleSti-188
❑ 83OPC-365
❑ 83Top-365
❑ 83TopFol-5
❑ 83TopSti-105
❑ 84A'sMot-21
❑ 84CubChiT-17
❑ 84Don-400
❑ 84Fle-453
❑ 84Nes792-669
❑ 84Nes792-714
❑ 84OPC-17
❑ 84Top-669
❑ 84Top-714
❑ 84TopRubD-19
❑ 84TopSti-331
❑ 84TopTif-669
❑ 84TopTif-714
❑ 85CubLioP-15
❑ 85CubSev-15
❑ 85Don-604
❑ 85Fle-60
❑ 85OPC-12
❑ 85SpoIndGC-13
❑ 85Top-12
❑ 85TopMin-12
❑ 85TopTif-12
❑ 86CubGat-15
❑ 86CubUno-11
❑ 86Don-9
❑ 86Don-388
❑ 86DonSupD-9
❑ 86Fle-372
❑ 86Lea-9
❑ 86OPC-125
❑ 86Spo-144
❑ 86Spo-194
❑ 86Top-125
❑ 86TopTif-125
❑ 87AstMot-16
❑ 87AstPol-8
❑ 87DodSmoA-19
❑ 87Don-455
❑ 87Fle-62
❑ 87FleGlo-62
❑ 87OPC-311
❑ 87Top-4
❑ 87Top-445
❑ 87TopSti-7
❑ 87TopTif-4
❑ 87TopTif-445
❑ 88DodSmo-15
❑ 88DodSmo-18
❑ 88RanMot-27
❑ 88Sco-489
❑ 88ScoGlo-489
❑ 88Top-226
❑ 88TopTif-226
❑ 89DodSmoG-96
❑ 89RanMot-27
❑ 89RanSmo-20
❑ 90DodTar-460
❑ 90RanMot-27
❑ 91DodUno7P-1
❑ 91RanMot-28
❑ 92BalOriP-16
❑ 92DodStaTA-20
❑ 92UppDecS-15
❑ 93RanKee-231
❑ 94BalOriP-16
❑ 95PadMot-28
❑ 96PadMot-28
❑ 98PadMot-28

Lopez, Al
❑ 33DouDisP-27
❑ 33ExhFou-2
❑ 33WorCig-64
❑ 34BatR31-3
❑ 34DiaMatCSB-116
❑ 34DiaStaR-28
❑ 34DiaStaR-97
❑ 34ExhFou-2
❑ 35DiaMatCS2-13
❑ 35DiaMatCS3T1-101
❑ 35ExhFou-2
❑ 36DiaMatCS4-9
❑ 36GouWidPPR-A67
❑ 36R31PasP-44
❑ 36WorWidGV-131
❑ 37ExhFou-1
❑ 38CldFotW-51
❑ 38GouHeaU-257
❑ 38GouHeaU-281
❑ 47IndTeal-18
❑ 47IndVanPP-17
❑ 51Bow-295
❑ 52IndNumN-20
❑ 53BowC-143
❑ 53IndPenCBP-20
❑ 54DanDee-16
❑ 55Bow-308
❑ 55Ind-5
❑ 55IndGolS-1
❑ 60MacSta-12
❑ 60Top-222
❑ 60WhiSoxJP-7
❑ 60WhiSoxTS-12
❑ 61Top-132
❑ 61Top-337
❑ 61WhiSoxTS-8
❑ 62Top-286
❑ 62WhiSoxJP-7
❑ 62WhiSoxTS-11
❑ 63Top-458
❑ 63WhiSoxJP-8
❑ 63WhiSoxTS-17
❑ 64Top-232
❑ 64TopVen-232
❑ 64WhiSoxTS-15
❑ 65Top-414
❑ 65WhiSoxJP-2
❑ 69Top-527
❑ 69WhiSoxTI-8
❑ 72TCMthe3-96
❑ 75TCM195CI-19
❑ 76ChiGre-11
❑ 76RowExh-14
❑ 76WhiSoxTAG-5
❑ 77GalGloG-32
❑ 77TCMTheWY-10
❑ 79DiaGre-80
❑ 80PacLeg-98
❑ 80PerHaloFP-161
❑ 80PerHaloFPS-34
❑ 80SSPHOF-161
❑ 80WhiSoxGT-3
❑ 81TCM60I-348
❑ 81WhiSox1T-41
❑ 82OhiHaloF-27
❑ 83TCMPla1942-39
❑ 84OCoandSI-116
❑ 85BigLeaC3-60
❑ 85TCMPhoC-13
❑ 85WhiSoxC-10
❑ 86IndGreT-12
❑ 86IndIndTI-21
❑ 89DodSmoG-38
❑ 89PacLegI-197
❑ 89PerCelP-27
❑ 89SweBasG-90
❑ 90DodTar-461
❑ 90PerGreM-64
❑ 91TopArc1-329
❑ 91TopGloA-11
❑ 93ActPacA-104
❑ 93ActPacA2-38G
❑ 93ConTSN-844
❑ 93ConTSN-873
❑ 94ConTSN-1010
❑ 94ConTSN-1104
❑ 94ConTSNB-1010
❑ 94ConTSNB-1104

Lopez, Albie
❑ 91BurIndP-3300
❑ 92ColRedC-19
❑ 92ColRedF-2388
❑ 92ProFS7-60
❑ 93Bow-613
❑ 93CanIndF-2835
❑ 93ClaFS7-141
❑ 93ClaGolF-12
❑ 93SouAtlLAPI-22
❑ 94Bow-635
❑ 94ChaKniF-891
❑ 94ColC-177
❑ 94ColChoGS-177
❑ 94ColChoSS-177
❑ 94Don-648
❑ 94FleMajLP-22
❑ 94Pin-426
❑ 94PinArtP-426
❑ 94PinMusC-426
❑ 94Top-178
❑ 94TopGol-178
❑ 94TopSpa-178
❑ 95ColCho-278
❑ 95ColChoGS-278
❑ 95ColChoSS-278
❑ 95Fle-138
❑ 95Pin-442
❑ 95PinArtP-442
❑ 95PinMusC-442
❑ 95Sco-512
❑ 95ScoGolR-512
❑ 95ScoPlaTS-512
❑ 95Sel-183
❑ 95SelArtP-183
❑ 95SigRoo-33
❑ 95SigRooSig-33
❑ 95Spo-70
❑ 95SpoArtP-70
❑ 95StaClu-353
❑ 95StaCluMOP-353
❑ 95StaCluSTWS-353
❑ 95Top-478
❑ 95TopCyb-271
❑ 95UppDecSE-23
❑ 95UppDecSEG-23
❑ 96BufBisB-14
❑ 96Sco-447
❑ 97PacPriGotD-GD36
❑ 97Sco-377
❑ 97ScoArtPWB-377
❑ 97ScoResC-377
❑ 97ScoShoS-377
❑ 97ScoShoSAP-377
❑ 97StaClu-260
❑ 97StaCluMOP-260
❑ 97Ult-474
❑ 97UltGolME-474
❑ 97UltPlaME-474
❑ 98ColCho-507
❑ 98DevRayP-6
❑ 98Pac-74
❑ 98PacOnl-712
❑ 98PacOnlR-712
❑ 98PacOnlWC-712
❑ 98PacPlaB-74
❑ 98PacRedT-74
❑ 98PacSil-74
❑ 98PinSna-TBDR13
❑ 98UppDec-728
❑ 99Pac-413
❑ 99PacCroC-276
❑ 99PacCroCPB-276
❑ 99PacPlaB-413
❑ 99PacRed-413

Lopez, Andres
❑ 93EugEmeC-19
❑ 93EugEmeF-3853
❑ 93LimRocDWB-115
❑ 94EugEmeC-12
❑ 94EugEmeF-3707

Lopez, Antonio
❑ 79WisRapTT-1
❑ 80VenLeaS-23
❑ 93LinVenB-61

Lopez, Art
❑ 65Top-566
❑ 92YanWIZ6-74

Lopez, Aurelio
❑ 78CarTeal-15
❑ 78SprRedWK-22
❑ 79Top-444
❑ 80Top-101
❑ 81CokTeaS-53
❑ 81OPC-291
❑ 81TigDetN-75
❑ 81Top-291
❑ 82Don-359
❑ 82Fle-273
❑ 82Top-728
❑ 83TigPos-20
❑ 83TopTra-63T
❑ 84AllGamPI-181
❑ 84Don-516
❑ 84Fle-86
❑ 84FunFooP-98
❑ 84Nes792-95
❑ 84OPC-95
❑ 84TigTeal-23
❑ 84TigWavP-25
❑ 84Top-95
❑ 84TopSti-268
❑ 84TopTif-95
❑ 85Don-349
❑ 85Fle-16
❑ 85Lea-160
❑ 85SevCoi-D9
❑ 85TigCaiD-13
❑ 85TigWen-15
❑ 85Top-539

❑ 85TopSti-265
❑ 85TopTif-539
❑ 86AstTeal-10
❑ 86Don-293
❑ 86Fle-231
❑ 86FleUpd-69
❑ 86Top-367
❑ 86TopTif-367
❑ 87AstMot-18
❑ 87AstPol-13
❑ 87Don-629
❑ 87Fle-63
❑ 87FleGlo-63
❑ 87Top-659
❑ 87TopTif-659
Lopez, Carlos
❑ 76SalLakCGC-5
❑ 77Top-492
❑ 78BalOriP-15
❑ 78OPC-219
❑ 78Top-166
❑ 79RocRedWT-8
❑ 79Top-568
❑ 89GeoColC-20
❑ 90GeoColC-19
❑ 90GeoColC-34
❑ 91OriCro-267
❑ 93LinVenB-134
❑ 94VenLinU-151
❑ 95LinVen-146
Lopez, Craig
❑ 87NewOriP-10
Lopez, Dina
❑ 91FreStaLBS-4
Lopez, Felipe
❑ 99BasAmeTPA-27
❑ 99Bow-346
❑ 99BowGol-346
❑ 99BowInt-346
❑ 99TeaBesR-50
❑ 99TeaBesRFS-24
❑ 99TeaBesRG-50
❑ 99TeaBesRS-50
Lopez, Francisco
❑ 74WicAerODF-101
Lopez, Fred
❑ 89IdaFalBP-2016
❑ 90SumBraB-19
❑ 90SumBraP-2437
❑ 91GreBraC-13
❑ 91GreBraP-3007
❑ 91MedHatBJP-4095
❑ 91MedHatBJSP-13
Lopez, Gil
❑ 96WesMicWB-3
❑ 97HunStaTI-14
❑ 98SouOreTG-17
Lopez, Hector
❑ 47StaPinP2-20
❑ 52LavPro-56
❑ 55A'sRodM-23
❑ 55A'sTeal-14
❑ 56A'sPos-31
❑ 56A'sRodM-6
❑ 56Top-16
❑ 56TopPin-13
❑ 57Top-6
❑ 58A'sJayP-6
❑ 58Top-155
❑ 59Top-402
❑ 60Top-163
❑ 60TopVen-163
❑ 60YanJayP-6
❑ 61Pos-12A
❑ 61Pos-12B
❑ 61Top-28
❑ 61Yan61RL-10
❑ 62Top-502
❑ 63Top-92
❑ 64ChatheY-15
❑ 64Top-325
❑ 64TopVen-325
❑ 65Top-532
❑ 66OPC-177
❑ 66Top-177
❑ 66TopVen-177
❑ 66YanTeal-6
❑ 76A'sRodMC-15
❑ 78TCM60I-272
❑ 79TCM50-195
❑ 83Yan196-10
❑ 91YanRinP11-8
❑ 92YanWIZ6-75
Lopez, Javier
❑ 78CedRapGT-15
❑ 88BlaYNPRWL-136
❑ 89BlaYNPRWL-8
❑ 89PulBraP-1892
❑ 90BurBraP-2352
❑ 92GreBraS-238
❑ 93RicBraRC-10
❑ 93StaCluMOP-630
❑ 93TopInaM-811
❑ 93TopInaR-811
❑ 93TopMic-811
❑ 93TriAAAGF-3
❑ 94BraUSPC-3H
❑ 94BraUSPC-7S
❑ 94ColChoSS-178
❑ 94FinJum-425
❑ 94ScoGolR-620
❑ 94ScoRooGR-RT78
❑ 94StaCluMOP-630
❑ 94StaCluMOP-703
❑ 94StaCluTFDI-52
❑ 94TopGol-194
❑ 94TopSpa-194
❑ 94UppDecED-255
❑ 94UppDecNGED-11
❑ 95ScoRulJ-SR27
❑ 95StaCluMOP-200
❑ 95StaCluSTWS-200
❑ 96BraFle-10
❑ 96ColChoGS-46
❑ 96ColChoSS-46
❑ 96FleTif-298
❑ 96LeaSig-128
❑ 96LeaSigPPG-128
❑ 96LeaSigPPP-128
❑ 96PacPriG-P5
❑ 96PanSti-3
❑ 96PinFoil-326
❑ 96ScoDugCAP-A89
❑ 96StaCluMOP-103
❑ 96TeaOut-51
❑ 97BraSco-5
❑ 97BraScoPl-5
❑ 97BraScoPr-5
❑ 97ColCho-33
❑ 97ColChoT-AB6
❑ 97Don-301
❑ 97DonGolPP-301
❑ 97DonPre-14
❑ 97DonPreCttC-14
❑ 97DonSig-62
❑ 97DonSigA-68
❑ 97DonSigAC-82
❑ 97DonSigAM-82
❑ 97DonSigPPP-62
❑ 97DonSilPP-301
❑ 97DonTea-25
❑ 97DonTeaSPE-25
❑ 97DurBulATI-8
❑ 97Fle-262
❑ 97FleTif-262
❑ 97Lea-93
❑ 97LeaFraM-93
❑ 97LeaFraMDC-93
❑ 97NewPin-13
❑ 97NewPinAP-13
❑ 97NewPinMC-13
❑ 97NewPinPP-13
❑ 97Pac-239
❑ 97PacLatotML-24
❑ 97PacLigB-239
❑ 97PacPri-81
❑ 97PacPriLB-81
❑ 97PacPriP-81
❑ 97PacSil-239
❑ 97PinCer-42
❑ 97PinPasttM-11
❑ 97PinTotCPB-42
❑ 97PinTotCPG-42
❑ 97PinTotCPR-42
❑ 97PinX-P-53
❑ 97PinX-PMoS-53
❑ 97PinX-PSfF-37
❑ 97Sco-105
❑ 97ScoArtPWB-105
❑ 97ScoPreS-105
❑ 97ScoShoS-105
❑ 97ScoShoSAP-105
❑ 97SP-27
❑ 97Stu-110
❑ 97StuPrePG-110
❑ 97StuPrePS-110
❑ 97Ult-156
❑ 97UltGolME-156
❑ 97UltPlaME-156
❑ 97UppDec-255
❑ 97UppDec-301
❑ 97Zen-27
❑ 98BraSco-5
❑ 98BraScoP-5
❑ 98CirThu-228
❑ 98CirThuRav-228
❑ 98CirThuSupRav-228
❑ 98ColCho-34
❑ 98ColCho-184
❑ 98Don-29
❑ 98DonCol-29
❑ 98DonColE-462
❑ 98DonColL-256
❑ 98DonColP-624
❑ 98DonColS-29
❑ 98DonCruG-58
❑ 98DonCruP-58
❑ 98DonCruR-58
❑ 98DonEli-62
❑ 98DonEliA-62
❑ 98DonEliS-62
❑ 98DonGolPP-29
❑ 98DonPre-74
❑ 98DonPreSeat-74
❑ 98DonPriCD-29
❑ 98DonPriCE-462
❑ 98DonPriCL-256
❑ 98DonPriCP-624
❑ 98DonSigA-55
❑ 98DonSigAC-73
❑ 98DonSigAM-74
❑ 98DonSilPP-29
❑ 98Fle-227
❑ 98Lea-57
❑ 98LeaCruG-58
❑ 98LeaCruP-58
❑ 98LeaCruR-58
❑ 98LeaFraDA-57
❑ 98LeaFraF-57
❑ 98LeaFraM-57
❑ 98LeaFraM-57
❑ 98LeaFraMDC-57
❑ 98LeaFraMDC-57
❑ 98LeaFraMZ2-57
❑ 98LeaRS-71
❑ 98LeaRSLHolo-71
❑ 98LeaRSLong-71
❑ 98LeaRTrue-71
❑ 98Pac-239
❑ 98PacInv-79
❑ 98PacInvGems-121
❑ 98PacInvPBlue-79
❑ 98PacInvSilv-79
❑ 98PacLatotML-2
❑ 98PacPlaB-239
❑ 98PacRedT-239
❑ 98PacSil-239
❑ 98Pin-19
❑ 98PinArtP-PP19
❑ 98PinIns-69
❑ 98PinInsCE-69
❑ 98PinInsDE-69
❑ 98PinMusC-PP19
❑ 98PinPer-75
❑ 98PinPerPP-75
❑ 98PinPreP-19
❑ 98PinSna-AB7
❑ 98Sco-28
❑ 98ScoRT-167
❑ 98ScoRTSS-PP96
❑ 98ScoRTSSAP-PP96
❑ 98ScoRTSSAP1-PP96
❑ 98ScoSS-PP122
❑ 98ScoSSAP-PP122
❑ 98Stu-184
❑ 98StuGPP-184
❑ 98StuSPP-184
❑ 98UppDec-28
❑ 98UppDecSF-17
❑ 98Zen-40
❑ 98Zen5 xx7-62
❑ 98Zen5x7GoldImp-62
❑ 98Zen5x7Imp-62
❑ 98ZenZ-G-40
❑ 98ZenZ-S-40
❑ 99SP AutHRC-HR28
❑ 99SPAutHRCDC-HR28
❑ 99TeaBesR-51
❑ 99TeaBesRG-51
❑ 99TeaBesRS-51
❑ 99UppDec-42
❑ 99UppDecEL1-42
❑ 99UppDecEL2-42
Lopez, Javier A.
❑ 99TeaBesRFS-1
Lopez, Javy (Javier Torres)
❑ 90Bes-107
❑ 90BurBraB-20
❑ 90BurBraS-16
❑ 90MidLeaASGS-38
❑ 90ProAaA-132
❑ 91Bow-587
❑ 91CarLeaAP-CAR2
❑ 91Cla/Bes-62
❑ 91DurBulC-19
❑ 91DurBulP-1547
❑ 92Bow-452
❑ 92ClaBluBF-BC10
❑ 92ClaFS7-117
❑ 92ClaRedB-BC10
❑ 92GreBraF-1156
❑ 92ProFS7-186
❑ 92SkyAA F-101
❑ 93Bow-343
❑ 93Bow-466
❑ 93BraLykS-20
❑ 93BraStaC-27
❑ 93ClaMVPF-2
❑ 93Don-782
❑ 93FleMajLP-B15
❑ 93RicBraBB-15
❑ 93RicBraF-187
❑ 93RicBraP-2
❑ 93RicBraRC-18
❑ 93SP-281
❑ 93StaClu-630
❑ 93StaCluFDI-630
❑ 93Top-811
❑ 93TopGol-811
❑ 93Toy-92
❑ 93Ult-9
❑ 93UppDec-29
❑ 93UppDecGold-29
❑ 94Bow-273
❑ 94BowBes-R85
❑ 94BowBes-X106
❑ 94BowBesR-R85
❑ 94BowBesR-X106
❑ 94BowPre-4
❑ 94BraLykP-18
❑ 94BraLykS-18
❑ 94ColC-178
❑ 94ColChoGS-178
❑ 94Don-613
❑ 94Fin-425
❑ 94FinRef-425
❑ 94Fla-129
❑ 94FlaWavotF-A5
❑ 94Fle-364
❑ 94FleExtB-207
❑ 94FleExtBRS-12
❑ 94FUnPac-6
❑ 94LeaGolR-1
❑ 94LeaL-86
❑ 94LeaLimRP-8
❑ 94OPC-162
❑ 94OPCHotP-7
❑ 94Pac-14
❑ 94Pin-239
❑ 94PinArtP-239
❑ 94PinMusC-239
❑ 94PinNewG-NG15
❑ 94PinRooTP-1
❑ 94Sco-620
❑ 94ScoBoyoS-20
❑ 94ScoRoo-RT78
❑ 94ScoRooSR-SU11
❑ 94Sel-188
❑ 94SelRooS-RS9
❑ 94SP-53
❑ 94SPDieC-53
❑ 94Spo-172
❑ 94SpoRooRS-TR5
❑ 94SpoSam-7
❑ 94SpoSha-SH7
❑ 94SPPre-ER3
❑ 94StaClu-630
❑ 94StaClu-703
❑ 94StaCluFDI-630
❑ 94StaCluFDI-703
❑ 94StaCluGR-630
❑ 94StaCluGR-703
❑ 94StaCluT-52
❑ 94Stu-38
❑ 94StuHer-6
❑ 94Top-194
❑ 94TriPla-283
❑ 94Ult-445
❑ 94UltAllR-6
❑ 94UltAllRJ-6
❑ 94UppDec-255
❑ 94UppDecNG-11
❑ 95Baz-123
❑ 95ColCho-160
❑ 95ColChoGS-160
❑ 95ColChoSE-63
❑ 95ColChoSEGS-63
❑ 95ColChoSESS-63
❑ 95ColChoSS-160
❑ 95Don-166
❑ 95DonPreP-166
❑ 95DonTopotO-189
❑ 95Emo-105
❑ 95Fin-25
❑ 95FinRef-25
❑ 95Fla-104
❑ 95FlaTodS-6
❑ 95Fle-310
❑ 95FleRooS-11
❑ 95Lea-140
❑ 95LeaLim-172
❑ 95Pac-10
❑ 95PacGolP-33
❑ 95PacLatD-20
❑ 95PacPri-3
❑ 95Pin-229
❑ 95PinArtP-229
❑ 95PinMusC-229
❑ 95PinUps-US4
❑ 95Sco-119
❑ 95ScoGolR-119
❑ 95ScoPlaTS-119
❑ 95ScoRul-SR27
❑ 95Sel-51
❑ 95SelArtP-51
❑ 95SelCer-37
❑ 95SelCerMG-37
❑ 95Spo-78
❑ 95SpoArtP-78
❑ 95StaClu-200
❑ 95StaCluFDI-200
❑ 95StaCluSTDW-B200
❑ 95StaCluSTMP-6
❑ 95Stu-61
❑ 95Sum-78
❑ 95SumNthD-78
❑ 95Top-567
❑ 95TopCyb-343
❑ 95TopEmb-36
❑ 95TopEmbGI-36
❑ 95Ult-350
❑ 95UltGolM-350
❑ 95UppDec-48
❑ 95UppDecED-48
❑ 95UppDecEDG-48
❑ 95UppDecSE-149
❑ 95UppDecSEG-149
❑ 95Zen-44
❑ 96Bow-32
❑ 96BowFoi-32
❑ 96ColCho-46
❑ 96ColCho-376T
❑ 96ColCho-387T
❑ 96Don-230
❑ 96DonPreP-230
❑ 96EmoXL-145
❑ 96Fin-B158
❑ 96FinRef-B158
❑ 96Fla-204
❑ 96Fle-298
❑ 96Lea-119
❑ 96LeaPrePB-119
❑ 96LeaPrePG-119
❑ 96LeaPrePS-119
❑ 96MetUni-133
❑ 96MetUniP-133
❑ 96Pac-14
❑ 96PacEstL-EL15
❑ 96PacOctM-OM12
❑ 96PacPri-P5
❑ 96Pin-326
❑ 96PinChrBC-7
❑ 96Sco-154
❑ 96ScoDugC-A89
❑ 96SP-21
❑ 96StaClu-103
❑ 96StaCluEPB-103
❑ 96StaCluEPG-103
❑ 96StaCluEPS-103
❑ 96Stu-47
❑ 96StuPrePB-47
❑ 96StuPrePG-47
❑ 96StuPrePS-47
❑ 96Top-367
❑ 96TopChr-149
❑ 96TopChrR-149
❑ 96TopGal-125
❑ 96TopGalPPI-125
❑ 96TopLas-26
❑ 96Ult-159
❑ 96UltGolM-159
❑ 96UppDec-6
❑ 97Cir-266
❑ 97CirRav-266
❑ 97ColCho-222
❑ 97ColChoAC-44
❑ 97DonEli-53
❑ 97DonEliGS-53
❑ 97DonLim-81
❑ 97DonLim-175
❑ 97DonLimE-81
❑ 97DonLimE-175
❑ 97DonLimENG-175
❑ 97Fin-52
❑ 97FinRef-52
❑ 97PinCerMBla-42
❑ 97PinCerMBlu-42
❑ 97PinCerMG-42
❑ 97PinCerMR-42
❑ 97PinCerR-42
❑ 97PinIns-82
❑ 97PinInsCE-82
❑ 97PinInsDE-82
❑ 97PinX-PSfFU-37
❑ 97Sel-28
❑ 97SelArtP-28
❑ 97SelCom-28
❑ 97SelRegG-28
❑ 97StaClu-215
❑ 97StaCluMat-215
❑ 97StaCluMOP-215
❑ 97StrAll-40
❑ 97Top-395
❑ 97TopChr-137
❑ 97TopChrR-137
❑ 97TopGal-100
❑ 97TopGal-129
❑ 97TopGalPPI-100
❑ 97TopGalPPI-129
❑ 97TopSta-95
❑ 97TopStaAM-95
❑ 97UppDecRSF-RS15
❑ 98Bow-291
❑ 98BowBes-32
❑ 98BowBesAR-32
❑ 98BowBesR-32
❑ 98BowChr-291
❑ 98BowChrGA-291
❑ 98BowChrGAR-291
❑ 98BowChrI-291
❑ 98BowChrIR-291
❑ 98BowChrR-291
❑ 98BowChrR-30
❑ 98BowChrRR-30
❑ 98BowGolA-291
❑ 98BowInt-291
❑ 98CroRoy-15
❑ 98DonSig-82
❑ 98DonSigP-82
❑ 98Fin-86
❑ 98FinNo--86
❑ 98FinNo-R-86
❑ 98FinRef-86
❑ 98MetUni-26
❑ 98MetUniPMG-26
❑ 98PacAur-107
❑ 98PacAurPF-22
❑ 98PacAurPFC-22
❑ 98PacAurPFPB-22
❑ 98PacAurPFR-22
❑ 98PacAurPFS-22
❑ 98PacInvTeam-2
❑ 98PacNes-12
❑ 98PacOme-22
❑ 98PacOmeR-22
❑ 98PacOnl-66
❑ 98PacOnlR-66
❑ 98PacOnlWC-66
❑ 98PacPar-132
❑ 98PacParC-132
❑ 98PacParG-132
❑ 98PacParHS-132
❑ 98PacParI-20
❑ 98PacParPB-132
❑ 98PacParR-132
❑ 98PinInsSG-3AB
❑ 98PinInsSG-3CD
❑ 98PinInsSG-7AB
❑ 98PinInsSG-7CD
❑ 98PinInsSGS-3AB
❑ 98PinInsSGS-3CD
❑ 98PinInsSGS-7AB
❑ 98PinInsSGS-7CD
❑ 98Revo-15
❑ 98RevoSS-15

❑ 98SP Aut-43
❑ 98SpoIllWSF-82
❑ 98SpoIllWSFEE-82
❑ 98SpoIllWSFFE-82
❑ 98SPxFin-60
❑ 98SPxFinR-60
❑ 98SPxFinS-60
❑ 98StaCluFDI-67
❑ 98StaCluI-67
❑ 98StaCluOneK-67
❑ 98StaCluPP-67
❑ 98Top-183
❑ 98TopChr-183
❑ 98TopChrR-183
❑ 98TopDevR-183
❑ 98TopDia-183
❑ 98TopGal-54
❑ 98TopGalGP-54
❑ 98TopGalOPP-54
❑ 98TopGalPPI-54
❑ 98TopGalPPIA-54
❑ 98TopGolLabC1-39
❑ 98TopGolLabC1B-39
❑ 98TopGolLabC1One-39
❑ 98TopGolLabC1R-39
❑ 98TopGolLabC2-39
❑ 98TopGolLabC2B-39
❑ 98TopGolLabC2One-39
❑ 98TopGolLabC2R-39
❑ 98TopGolLabC3-39
❑ 98TopGolLabC3B-39
❑ 98TopGolLabC3One-39
❑ 98TopGolLabC3R-39
❑ 98TopMiniC-183
❑ 98TopOpeD-98
❑ 98TopSta-30
❑ 98TopStaB-30
❑ 98TopStaG-30
❑ 98TopStaGR-30
❑ 98TopStaS-30
❑ 98TopTek-65
❑ 98TopTekD-65
❑ 98Ult-98
❑ 98UltGolM-98
❑ 98UltMas-98
❑ 98UltPlaM-98
❑ 99199Fin-2
❑ 99BowBes-60
❑ 99BowBesAR-60
❑ 99BowBesR-60
❑ 99CroRoyB-15
❑ 99CroRoyL-15
❑ 99CroRoyOD-15
❑ 99E-X Cen-60
❑ 99E-X CenECFut-60
❑ 99E-X CenECNow-60
❑ 99FinGolRef-2
❑ 99FinPre-PP2
❑ 99FinRef-2
❑ 99Fle-344
❑ 99FleBri-83
❑ 99FleBri2G-83
❑ 99FleBriBlu-83
❑ 99FleBriGol-83
❑ 99FleSta9-344
❑ 99FleWarT-344
❑ 99MetUni-228
❑ 99MetUniGM-228
❑ 99MetUniPMG-228
❑ 99Pac-35
❑ 99PacAur-19
❑ 99PacAurOD-19
❑ 99PacCroC-27
❑ 99PacCroC-26
❑ 99PacCroCPB-27
❑ 99PacInv-16
❑ 99PacInvOD-16
❑ 99PacInvPB-16
❑ 99PacOme-25
❑ 99PacOmeC-25
❑ 99PacOmeG-25
❑ 99PacOmePB-25
❑ 99PacPar-27
❑ 99PacParC-27
❑ 99PacParG-27
❑ 99PacParHoloGold-27
❑ 99PacParHS-27
❑ 99PacParOD-27
❑ 99PacParPB-27
❑ 99PacParRed-27
❑ 99PacPlaB-35
❑ 99PacPri-15
❑ 99PacPriHB-15
❑ 99PacPriHG-15
❑ 99PacPriHM-15
❑ 99PacPriHP-15
❑ 99PacPriRed-15
❑ 99PacPriS-39
❑ 99PacPriS206-39
❑ 99PacPriS206R-39
❑ 99PacPriSP-39
❑ 99PacPriSV-39
❑ 99PacRed-35
❑ 99Rev-14
❑ 99RevPremDate-14
❑ 99RevRet-14
❑ 99RevShaSS-14
❑ 99SkyMolM-46
❑ 99SkyMolMOA-24
❑ 99SkyMolMX-46
❑ 99SkyPre-102
❑ 99SkyPreR-102
❑ 99SkyThu-91
❑ 99SkyThuRant-91
❑ 99SkyThuRave-91
❑ 99SpoIll-150
❑ 99StaClu-265
❑ 99StaCluFDI-265
❑ 99StaCluOoaK-265
❑ 99StaCluPP-265
❑ 99ThuSkySupR-91
❑ 99Top-72
❑ 99TopBlaLC1-31
❑ 99TopBlaLC2-31
❑ 99TopBlaLC3-31
❑ 99TopChr-72
❑ 99TopChrR-72
❑ 99TopGal-33
❑ 99TopGalPP-33
❑ 99TopGalPPI-33
❑ 99TopGolL-31
❑ 99TopGolLC1-31
❑ 99TopGolLC2-31
❑ 99TopGolLOtO-31
❑ 99TopMVPP-72
❑ 99TopOpeD-40
❑ 99TopRedLC1-31
❑ 99TopRedLC2-31
❑ 99TopRedLC3-31
❑ 99TopSta-94
❑ 99TopSta1Foil-94
❑ 99TopStaFoil-94
❑ 99TopStaOS-94
❑ 99TopSupC-12
❑ 99TopSupCR-12
❑ 99UD Cho-57
❑ 99UD ChoPCR-57
❑ 99UppDecCf7-25
❑ 99UppDecCo7CE-25
❑ 99UppDecM-19
❑ 99UppDecMGS-19
❑ 99UppDecMHFS-19
❑ 99UppDecMP-19
❑ 99UppDecMSS-19
❑ 99UppDecR-11
❑ 99UppDecRG-11
❑ 99UppDecRP-11
❑ 99Vic-33

Lopez, Johann
❑ 94AubAstF-3753
❑ 95LinVen-31
❑ 96-97LinVen-156
❑ 96KisCobB-14
❑ 97JacGen-14
❑ 97JacGenS-13
❑ 98NewOrlZM-12

Lopez, Jose
❑ 90JohCitCS-17
❑ 91SavCarC-9
❑ 91SavCarP-1650
❑ 92JohCitCC-15
❑ 92JohCitCF-3111
❑ 96StLucMTI-19
❑ 97BriWhiSB-6
❑ 98BriWhiSQ-17
❑ 98HicCraUO-20

Lopez, Jose Muisi
❑ 76VenLeaS-41

Lopez, Jose Rafael
❑ 97BinMetB-16
❑ 98BinMetQ-19

Lopez, Juan
❑ 74SacSolC-59
❑ 75SacSolC-22
❑ 76SpoIndC-7
❑ 77SpoIndC-14
❑ 78SpoIndC-13
❑ 79VanCanT-12
❑ 80EvaTriT-23
❑ 81EvaTriT-17
❑ 82EvaTriT-17
❑ 83EvaTriT-16
❑ 83WatIndF-6
❑ 84EvaTriT-1
❑ 87FayGenP-18
❑ 87OscAstP-2
❑ 88ColAstB-10
❑ 89BlaYNPRWL-65
❑ 89BlaYNPRWL-78
❑ 89NiaFalRP-26
❑ 90EveGiaP-3147
❑ 90NiaFalRP-28
❑ 91BriTigC-20
❑ 91BriTigP-3622
❑ 94EveGiaC-30
❑ 95BelGiaTI-13
❑ 96GiaMot-28
❑ 96PitMetB-3
❑ 98CapCitBF5-30
❑ 98CapCitBM-30
❑ 98GiaMot-28

Lopez, Louis
❑ 95OdgRapTI-17

Lopez, Luis
❑ 97HagSunB-16
❑ 98KnoSG-11

Lopez, Luis (Luis Santos)
❑ 88SpoIndP-1930
❑ 89BlaYNPRWL-79
❑ 89BlaYNPRWLU-28
❑ 89ChaRaiP-984
❑ 89SanAntMB-15
❑ 90AlbDukCm-21
❑ 90RivRedWCLC-5
❑ 91ColSprSSLD-90
❑ 91ColSprSSP-2191
❑ 91LinDriAA-612
❑ 91WicWraLD-612
❑ 91WicWraP-2604
❑ 91WicWraRD-14
❑ 92LasVegSF-2803
❑ 92LasVegSS-235
❑ 93Bow-250
❑ 93ClaFS7-218
❑ 93LasVegSF-952
❑ 94ColC-669
❑ 94ColChoGS-669
❑ 94ColChoSS-669
❑ 94Don-393
❑ 94Fla-439
❑ 94FleAllR-M8
❑ 94FleUpd-187
❑ 94LeaLimR-38
❑ 94Pac-529
❑ 94PadMot-24
❑ 94Pin-259
❑ 94PinArtP-259
❑ 94PinMusC-259
❑ 94RicBraF-2853
❑ 94SigRooDP-96
❑ 94SigRooDPS-96
❑ 94Spo-159
❑ 94SpoRoo-147
❑ 94SpoRooAP-147
❑ 94Top-336
❑ 94TopGol-336
❑ 94TopSpa-336
❑ 94TriAAF-AAA42
❑ 95ColCho-348
❑ 95ColChoGS-348
❑ 95ColChoSS-348
❑ 95Don-4
❑ 95DonPreP-4
❑ 95Fle-563
❑ 95Pac-365
❑ 95PacLatD-21
❑ 95PacPri-117
❑ 95Sco-117
❑ 95ScoGolR-117
❑ 95ScoPlaTS-117
❑ 95SigRoo-34
❑ 95SigRooSig-34
❑ 95StaClu-306
❑ 95StaCluMOP-306
❑ 95StaCluSTWS-306
❑ 95StaCluVR-162
❑ 95StaCluVRMO-162
❑ 95Top-118
❑ 95TopCyb-75
❑ 95Ult-235
❑ 95UltGolM-235
❑ 95UppDec-138
❑ 95UppDecED-138
❑ 95UppDecEDG-138
❑ 96LeaSigEA-112
❑ 96PadMot-23
❑ 97NorTid-21
❑ 97NorTidB-21
❑ 97SalVolG-20
❑ 98Bow-391
❑ 98BowChr-391
❑ 98BowChrGA-391
❑ 98BowChrGAR-391
❑ 98BowChrI-391
❑ 98BowChrIR-391
❑ 98BowChrR-391
❑ 98BowGolA-391
❑ 98BowInt-391
❑ 98PacInvGems-183
❑ 98PacOnl-482
❑ 98PacOnlR-482
❑ 98PacOnlWC-482
❑ 99PacCroC-180
❑ 99PacCroCPB-180

Lopez, Luis Antonio
❑ 85VerBeaDT-21
❑ 86FloStaLAP-31
❑ 86VerBeaDP-16
❑ 87BakDodP-10
❑ 88BlaYNPRWL-71
❑ 88BlaYNPRWL-169
❑ 88SanAntMB-26
❑ 88TexLeaAGS-37
❑ 89BlaYNPRWL-144
❑ 90AlbDukP-360
❑ 90AlbDukTr-18
❑ 90CMC-423
❑ 90CMC-852
❑ 90ProAAAF-81
❑ 90RivRedWP-2616
❑ 91LinDriAAA-90
❑ 91ScoRoo-109T
❑ 91TopDeb90-91
❑ 92Sco-716
❑ 92Sco100RS-84
❑ 92StaClu-556
❑ 93CanIndF-2846
❑ 93LinVenB-319
❑ 96StCatSB-17

Lopez, Manny
❑ 97ForWayW-18
❑ 98ForWayW!-5

Lopez, Marcelino
❑ 63Top-549
❑ 65Top-537
❑ 66AngDexP-8
❑ 66OPC-155
❑ 66Top-155
❑ 66TopVen-155
❑ 67BalOriP-64
❑ 67CokCapA-4
❑ 67CokCapAAm-31
❑ 67CokCapDA-32
❑ 67Top-513
❑ 70BalOriP-18
❑ 70OPC-344
❑ 70Top-344
❑ 71MLBOffS-303
❑ 71OPC-137
❑ 71Top-137
❑ 72Top-652
❑ 91OriCro-268
❑ 94BreMilB-327

Lopez, Marcos
❑ 87UtiBluSP-16
❑ 88ChaWheB-16
❑ 89PeoChiTI-4

Lopez, Mendy
❑ 95Bow-173
❑ 95SPML-69
❑ 95WilBluRTI-27
❑ 96BesAutSA-40
❑ 96ColCho-427
❑ 96ColChoGS-427
❑ 96ColChoSS-427
❑ 96TexLeaAB-28
❑ 96UppDec-253
❑ 96WicWraB-19
❑ 97BesAutAS-28
❑ 97BesAutP-R7
❑ 97Bow-134
❑ 97BowInt-134
❑ 97OmaRoyB-17
❑ 97Sel-130
❑ 97SelArtP-130
❑ 97SelCom-130
❑ 97SelRegG-130
❑ 98OmaRoyM-14
❑ 99Fle-417
❑ 99FleSta9-417
❑ 99FleWarT-417
❑ 99PacCroC-133
❑ 99PacCroCPB-133
❑ 99SkyThu-15
❑ 99SkyThuRant-15
❑ 99SkyThuRave-15
❑ 99ThuSkySupR-15

Lopez, Mickey
❑ 95HelBreTI-17
❑ 96BelSnaTI-20
❑ 96LibSpo-NNO
❑ 97El PasDB-8
❑ 99BowBes-183
❑ 99BowBesAR-183
❑ 99BowBesR-183
❑ 99Top-433
❑ 99TopChr-433
❑ 99TopChrR-433
❑ 99TopMVPP-433

Lopez, Mike
❑ 92NiaFalRC-11
❑ 92NiaFalRF-3318
❑ 98ChaRivDG-8

Lopez, Omar
❑ 96BriWhiSB-23
❑ 97BriWhiSB-18

Lopez, Orangel
❑ 92GulCoaYF-3798
❑ 93LinVenB-238

Lopez, Orlando
❑ 93HunCubC-17
❑ 93HunCubF-3234
❑ 94PeoChiC-16
❑ 94PeoChiF-2265
❑ 96RocCubTI-17

Lopez, Pancho
❑ 73CedRapAT-27

Lopez, Pedro
❑ 88BlaYNPRWL-107
❑ 89BlaYNPRWL-118
❑ 89WatDiaP-1790
❑ 89WatDiaS-18
❑ 90ChaRaiB-13
❑ 90ChaRaiP-2043
❑ 92WicWraS-639
❑ 94WicWraF-192
❑ 95ElPasDTI-16
❑ 96El PasDB-16
❑ 98JacGenM-9

Lopez, Pee Wee
❑ 96AppLeaAB-24
❑ 97Bow-169
❑ 97BowInt-169
❑ 97St.LucM-15

Lopez, Rene
❑ 93ForWayWC-17
❑ 93ForWayWF-1972
❑ 94ForMyeMC-14
❑ 94ForMyeMF-1171
❑ 95HarCitRCTI-13
❑ 96HarCitRCB-20

Lopez, Rich
❑ 94JohCitCC-18
❑ 94JohCitCF-3617

Lopez, Rob
❑ 86FloStaLAP-32
❑ 86TamTarP-12
❑ 87VerRedP-9
❑ 88NasSouC-8
❑ 88NasSouP-487
❑ 89NasSouC-6
❑ 89NasSouP-1295
❑ 89NasSouTI-13
❑ 90CMC-133
❑ 90NasSouC-8
❑ 90NasSouP-228
❑ 90ProAAAF-540
❑ 91LinDriAAA-267
❑ 91NasSouLD-267

Lopez, Robert
❑ 92OklStaC-16

Lopez, Roberto
❑ 95ElPasDTI-17
❑ 96BesAutS-51
❑ 96BesAutSA-41
❑ 96Exc-72
❑ 97BesAutAS-29
❑ 98El PasDG-19

Lopez, Rodrigo
❑ 96IdaFalB-14
❑ 97CliLumG-15

Lopez, Steve
❑ 88IdaFalBP-1859
❑ 89SumBraP-1096

Lopez-Cao, Mike
❑ 97HudValRB-15

Lopiccolo, Gina
❑ 91FreStaLBS-5

Lopiccolo, Jamie
❑ 95OdgRapTI-16
❑ 96BelSnaTI-21
❑ 96Bow-250
❑ 96BowFoi-250
❑ 97BelSnaB-19
❑ 98LakTigM-21

Lopresti, Tom
❑ 98LynHilQ-28

Lora, Jose
❑ 90ElmPioP-10
❑ 91ElmPioC-9
❑ 91ElmPioP-3284
❑ 91WinHavRSC-28

Lora, Luis
❑ 85DomLeaS-113

Lora, Ramon Antonio
❑ 81SyrChiT-10
❑ 81SyrChiTI-13
❑ 82SyrChiT-12
❑ 85DomLeaS-18

Loranger, Bob
❑ 52LavPro-53

Lord, Bristol
❑ 08RosComP-4
❑ 09ColChiE-171
❑ 10NadE1-32
❑ 11A'sFirT20-11
❑ 11D35RocB-11
❑ 11HelSta-11
❑ 11PinT-5-507
❑ 11SpoLifCW-223
❑ 11SpoLifM-47
❑ 11T205-103
❑ 11TurRedT-106
❑ 12ColRedB-171
❑ 12ColTinT-171
❑ 12ColTinT-172A
❑ 12T207-110
❑ 14PieStaT-65
❑ 14TexTomE-27

Lord, Harry
❑ 03WilCarE-21
❑ 08AmeCarE91-83
❑ 09ColChiE-172A
❑ 09ColChiE-172B
❑ 09PhiCarE-14
❑ 09RamT20-70
❑ 09SpoNewSM-51
❑ 09T206-216
❑ 10DomDisP-72
❑ 10E-UOraBSC-14
❑ 10E12AmeCDCE125-22
❑ 10RedCroT-43
❑ 10RedCroT-132
❑ 10RedCroT-214
❑ 10SepAnoP-18
❑ 10SweCapPP-11A
❑ 10SweCapPP-11B
❑ 11DiaGumP-18
❑ 11E94-22
❑ 11MecDFT-15
❑ 11PinT-5-656
❑ 11SpoLifCW-224
❑ 11SpoLifM-12
❑ 11T205-104
❑ 12ColRedB-172A
❑ 12ColRedB-172B
❑ 12ColTinT-172B
❑ 12HasTriFT-42
❑ 12HasTriFT-45
❑ 12HasTriFT-52
❑ 12HasTriFT-57
❑ 12HasTriFT-60
❑ 12T207-111
❑ 14CraJacE-48
❑ 72ClaCar-108

Lorenz, Joe
❑ 82DurBulT-4

Lorenzana, Jose
❑ 90IBAWorA-40

Lorenzana, Luis
❑ 97AugGre-21
❑ 98LynHilQ-16

Lorenzo, Martin
❑ 96HelBreTI-15

Loretta, Mark
❑ 94Bow-149
❑ 94ElPasDF-3153
❑ 95Bow-150
❑ 95Exc-72
❑ 96Bow-372
❑ 96BowFoi-372
❑ 96BrePol-15
❑ 96ColCho-591
❑ 96ColChoGS-591
❑ 96ColChoSS-591

❑ 96Fle-151
❑ 96FleTif-151
❑ 96Lea-219
❑ 96LeaPre-136
❑ 96LeaPreP-136
❑ 96LeaPrePB-219
❑ 96LeaPrePG-219
❑ 96LeaPrePS-219
❑ 96Sco-493
❑ 96SelCer-121
❑ 96SelCerAP-121
❑ 96SelCerCB-121
❑ 96SelCerCR-121
❑ 96SelCerMB-121
❑ 96SelCerMG-121
❑ 96SelCerMR-121
❑ 96StaClu-440
❑ 96StaCluMOP-440
❑ 96Top-340
❑ 96TopChr-134
❑ 96TopChrR-134
❑ 96TopGal-139
❑ 96TopGalPPI-139
❑ 96Ult-365
❑ 96UltGolM-365
❑ 96UppDec-499U
❑ 97BrePol-15
❑ 97ColCho-147
❑ 97Don-256
❑ 97DonGolPP-256
❑ 97DonSilPP-256
❑ 97Fle-132
❑ 97FleTif-132
❑ 97Pac-122
❑ 97PacLigB-122
❑ 97PacSil-122
❑ 97Pin-129
❑ 97PinArtP-PP129
❑ 97PinMusC-129
❑ 97PinPrePla-129
❑ 97StaClu-369
❑ 97StaCluMOP-369
❑ 97Top-112
❑ 97UppDec-101
❑ 98ColCho-401
❑ 98Fin-108
❑ 98FinNo--108
❑ 98FinNo-R-108
❑ 98FinRef-108
❑ 98Pac-120
❑ 98PacOnl-404
❑ 98PacOnlR-404
❑ 98PacOnlWC-404
❑ 98PacPlaB-120
❑ 98PacRedT-120
❑ 98PacSil-120
❑ 98Top-225
❑ 98TopChr-225
❑ 98TopChrR-225
❑ 98TopDevR-225
❑ 98TopDia-225
❑ 98TopMiniC-225
❑ 98UppDec-404
❑ 99Fle-486
❑ 99FleSta9-486
❑ 99FleWarT-486
❑ 99Pac-237
❑ 99PacPlaB-237
❑ 99PacPriS-111
❑ 99PacPriS206-111
❑ 99PacPriS206R-111
❑ 99PacRed-237
❑ 99Top-36
❑ 99TopChr-36
❑ 99TopChrR-36
❑ 99TopMVPP-36
❑ 99UD Cho-104
❑ 99UD ChoP-104
❑ 99UD ChoPCR-104
❑ 99UppDec-132
❑ 99UppDecEL1-132
❑ 99UppDecEL2-132
Lorms, John
❑ 90WatIndS-13
❑ 91CollndC-20
❑ 91CollndP-1487
❑ 92KinIndC-10
❑ 92KinIndF-2478
Lorraine, Andrew
❑ 94Bow-675
❑ 94Cla-186
❑ 94SigRooTPD-T3
❑ 94SigRooTPS-T3
❑ 94TriAAF-AAA23
❑ 94VanCanF-1863
❑ 94VenLinU-67
❑ 95ActPacF-40
❑ 95Bow-420
❑ 95BowBes-B57
❑ 95BowBesR-B57
❑ 95ColCho-13
❑ 95ColChoGS-13
❑ 95ColChoSS-13
❑ 95Don-524
❑ 95DonPreP-524
❑ 95Fla-19
❑ 95LeaGolR-16
❑ 95NasSouTI-11
❑ 95Pin-406
❑ 95PinArtP-406
❑ 95PinMusC-406
❑ 95Sel-194
❑ 95SelArtP-194
❑ 95SigRooMOP-P1
❑ 95SigRooMOPS-P1
❑ 95SigRooOJHP-HP3
❑ 95SigRooOJHPS-HP3
❑ 95StaClu-492
❑ 95StaCluMOP-492
❑ 95StaCluSTWS-492
❑ 95Top-221
❑ 95Ult-270
❑ 95UltGolM-270
❑ 96ColCho-647
❑ 96ColCho-665
❑ 96ColChoGS-647
❑ 96ColChoGS-665
❑ 96ColChoSS-647
❑ 96ColChoSS-665
❑ 98TacRaiQ-20
Losa, Bill
❑ 88ButCopKSP-13
❑ 88GasRanP-1013
❑ 89ChaRanS-14
❑ 90ChaRanS-23
❑ 91KinIndC-14
❑ 91KinIndP-325
Losauro, Carmelo
❑ 86DayBealP-17
❑ 88VirGenS-14
Loscalzo, Bob
❑ 82IdaFalAT-24
❑ 83MadMusF-15
❑ 84MadMusP-13
❑ 85ModA'sC-24
Loscrey, Mike
❑ 89ChaLooGS-18
Loseke, Scott
❑ 84CedRapRT-22
Lotshaw, Andy
❑ 31CubTeal-14
❑ 36CubTeal-23
Lott, Billy (Bill)
❑ 89HigSchPLS-4
❑ 90BakDodCLC-259
❑ 90YakBeaTI-18
❑ 91BakDodCLC-15
❑ 92ClaFS7-357
❑ 92VerBeaDC-13
❑ 92VerBeaDF-2891
❑ 93SanAntMF-3018
❑ 94SanAntMF-2481
❑ 97CalCanB-16
Lott, Brian
❑ 94PriRedC-15
❑ 94PriRedF-3259
❑ 97ChaLoo-14
Lotzar, Greg
❑ 85ElmPioT-12
❑ 86FloStaLAP-33
❑ 86WinHavRSP-16
❑ 87NewBriRSP-6
Loubier, Scott
❑ 97VerExpB-18
Loubier, Stephen
❑ 88RivRedWCLC-213
❑ 88RivRedWP-1432
❑ 89RivRedWB-11
❑ 89RivRedWCLC-20
❑ 89RivRedWP-1389
❑ 89WicStaR-24
❑ 89WicUpdR-14
❑ 90WicWraRD-13
❑ 91PalSprAP-2008
Loucks, Scott
❑ 78DayBeaAT-16
❑ 80ColAstT-17
❑ 81TucTorT-11
❑ 82AstAstl-3
❑ 82AstAstl-10
❑ 83TucTorT-22
❑ 85HawIslC-228
❑ 87AstShoSPT-8
Louden, William
❑ 17ColE13-101
Loudenslager, Charlie
❑ 90DodTar-1015
Loudermilk, Darren
❑ 96BurlndB-10
Loughlin, Larry
❑ 77FriOneYW-96
Loughlin, Mark
❑ 91AubAstC-1
❑ 91AubAstP-4270
❑ 92AshTouC-25
❑ 92ProFS7-236
❑ 93QuaCitRBC-12
❑ 93QuaCitRBF-95
Louie, Mascot
❑ 98BowBayM-30
Louis, Albert
❑ 76ShrCapT-14
Louis, Joe
❑ 87SpoCubG-3
Loun, Don
❑ 65OPC-181
❑ 65Top-181
Loury, Sam
❑ 43A'STEAI-14
Loux, Shane
❑ 98MidLeaPM-25
❑ 98WesMicWM-11
Lovdal, Stewart
❑ 89MarPhiS-18
❑ 90BatCliP-3062
Love, Farley
❑ 98QuaCitRBG-13
Love, James
❑ 92ElmPioC-26
❑ 93ForLauRSC-30
Love, Jeff
❑ 96NewJerCB-17
Love, John
❑ 87MacPirP-6
❑ 88SalBucS-11
Love, Slim (Edward H.)
❑ 14Zee-14
❑ 15Zee-11
❑ 16FleBreD-58
❑ 20Zee-112
❑ 21Zee-162
Love, Steve
❑ 76WauMetT-15
Love, Sylvester
❑ 90StoPorB-9
❑ 90StoPorCLC-194
❑ 90StoPorP-2194
Love, Will (William)
❑ 89MadMusS-13
❑ 89Sta-66
❑ 90ModA'sC-18
❑ 90ModA'sCLC-157
❑ 90ModA'sP-2210
❑ 91ModA'sP-3083
❑ 92RenSilSCLC-45
Lovekamp, Scott
❑ 97AugGre-4
❑ 98AugGreM-27
Lovelace, Dan
❑ 94WilCubC-30
Lovelace, Vance
❑ 82QuaCitCT-10
❑ 83VerBeaDT-7
❑ 86MidAngP-13
❑ 87MidAngP-24
❑ 88EdmTraC-4
❑ 88EdmTraP-557
❑ 89EdmTraP-559
❑ 89Fle-651
❑ 89FleGlo-651
❑ 90CalCanC-7
❑ 90CalCanP-647
❑ 90CMC-434
❑ 90ProAAAF-112
❑ 91CalCanLD-65
❑ 91CalCanP-514
❑ 91LinDriAAA-65
❑ 92TolMudHF-1041
❑ 92TolMudHS-593
❑ 93GreBraF-343
Lovell, Don
❑ 86WatIndP-15
❑ 87BufBisP-1
❑ 88ColSprSSC-15
❑ 88ColSprSSP-1523
❑ 88IndTeal-25
Lovell, Jim
❑ 88GreBraB-11
❑ 89GreBraB-22
❑ 89GreBraP-1167
❑ 91GreBraC-29
❑ 93RicBraRC-19
❑ 95RicBraTI-30
❑ 96RicBraB-4
❑ 97RicBra-4
❑ 98RicBraQ-30
Lovenguth, Lynn
❑ 61TacBan-11
Lovett, Tom (Thomas)
❑ 74BroClu-10
❑ 87OldJudN-301
❑ 90DodTar-1016
❑ 95May-19
Loviglio, Jay (John)
❑ 81EdmTraRR-23
❑ 81Top-526
❑ 82EdmTraT-8
❑ 82Top-599
❑ 83IowCubT-15
❑ 86GenCubP-16
❑ 87WinSpiP-13
❑ 89WinSpiS-19
❑ 90ChaKniTI-16
❑ 91ChaKniLD-149
❑ 91ChaKniP-1704
❑ 91LinDriAA-149
❑ 96AugGreB-1
❑ 97NewHavRB-27
❑ 98SalAvaC-19
Lovinger, Allan
❑ 90PenPilS-27
Lovingier, Kevin
❑ 94NewJerCC-18
❑ 94NewJerCF-3416
❑ 94StaCluDP-5
❑ 94StaCluDPFDI-5
❑ 95Exc-268
❑ 96ArkTraB-16
❑ 97AppLeaTPB-17
❑ 97ArkTraB-9
❑ 97NewJerCB-6
❑ 98ArkTraM-19
Lovingood, Ray
❑ 98CapCitBF5-11
❑ 98CapCitBM-11
❑ 98PitMetM-16
Lovins, Sarge (Steve)
❑ 79MemChiT-1
❑ 80MemChiT-1
Lovitto, Joe
❑ 73OPC-276
❑ 73Top-276
❑ 74OPC-639
❑ 74Top-639
❑ 75OPC-36
❑ 75RanPos-19
❑ 75Top-36
❑ 75TopMin-36
❑ 76OPC-604
❑ 76SSP-271
❑ 76Top-604
❑ 93RanKee-25
Lovrich, Pete
❑ 63Top-549
❑ 64Top-212
❑ 64TopVen-212
❑ 65Top-462
Lovrich, Tom
❑ 54SeaPop-15
Lovullo, Torey
❑ 88EasLeaAP-8
❑ 88GleFalTP-923
❑ 89DonRoo-17
❑ 89Fle-648
❑ 89FleGlo-648
❑ 89PanSti-332
❑ 89ScoHot1R-17
❑ 89TigMar-23
❑ 89UppDec-782
❑ 90CMC-401
❑ 90ProAAAF-388
❑ 90TolMudHC-24
❑ 90TolMudHP-158
❑ 90UppDec-332
❑ 91Bow-175
❑ 91ColCliP-603
❑ 92ColCliF-359
❑ 92ColCliP-17
❑ 92ColCliS-108
❑ 92SkyAAAF-48
❑ 92StaClu-809
❑ 92StaCluNC-809
❑ 93AngMot-18
❑ 93AngStaCl-29
❑ 93FleFinE-184
❑ 93Lea-476
❑ 93Ult-521
❑ 94ColC-179
❑ 94ColChoGS-179
❑ 94ColChoSS-179
❑ 94Don-612
❑ 94Fle-63
❑ 94Lea-204
❑ 94MarMot-27
❑ 94Pac-83
❑ 94PanSti-39
❑ 94Sco-179
❑ 94ScoGolR-179
❑ 94StaClu-506
❑ 94StaCluFDI-506
❑ 94StaCluGR-506
❑ 94StaCluMOP-506
❑ 94Top-634
❑ 94TopGol-634
❑ 94TopSpa-634
❑ 94Ult-24
❑ 96A'sMot-20
❑ 96LeaSigEA-113
❑ 98BufBisG-18
Lowdermilk, Grover
❑ 75WhiSox1T-24
Lowdermilk, Louis
❑ 12T207-112
Lowe, Benny
❑ 95StCatSTI-4
❑ 96HagSunB-13
❑ 97KnoSmo-14
❑ 98DunBluJTI-20
Lowe, Chris
❑ 88MarPhiS-24
❑ 89MarPhiS-19
❑ 90HamRedS-14
Lowe, Derek
❑ 92BelMarCB-11
❑ 92BelMarF-1439
❑ 92Bow-98
❑ 92UppDecML-192
❑ 93Bow-107
❑ 93ClaGolF-213
❑ 93ExcFS7-226
❑ 93RivPilCLC-2
❑ 94Bow-585
❑ 94Cla-138
❑ 94JacSunF-1408
❑ 94UppDecML-89
❑ 95SigRooOJ-22
❑ 95SigRooOJP-22
❑ 95SigRooOJPS-22
❑ 95SigRooOJS-22
❑ 96Bow-228
❑ 96BowFoi-228
❑ 96PorCitRB-19
❑ 97TacRai-20
❑ 98Don-191
❑ 98DonGolPP-191
❑ 98DonSilPP-191
❑ 98Fle-463
❑ 98LeaRS-234
❑ 98LeaRSLHolo-234
❑ 98LeaRSLong-234
❑ 98LeaRTrue-234
❑ 98PacOme-39
❑ 98PacOmeR-39
❑ 98PacOnl-121
❑ 98PacOnlR-121
❑ 98PacOnlWC-121
❑ 99Fle-499
❑ 99FleSta9-499
❑ 99FleWarT-499
Lowe, Doc (Steve)
❑ 78WauMetT-16
Lowe, Donald
❑ 79WauTimT-17
Lowe, Jamie
❑ 89OrlTwiB-29
Lowe, Jason
❑ 92HigSchPLS-15
❑ 93SouOreAC-15
❑ 93SouOreAF-4059
❑ 94SouOreAC-16
❑ 94SouOreAF-3619
Lowe, Kevin
❑ 95DanBraTI-16
Lowe, Q.V.
❑ 82OneYanT-6
❑ 83GreHorT-29
❑ 85ColCliP-25
❑ 86JacExpT-10
❑ 87JamExpP-2678
❑ 88JamExpP-2039
❑ 89JamExpP-2152
❑ 90JamExpP-28
❑ 91JamExpC-28
❑ 91JamExpP-3561
❑ 92JamExpC-26
❑ 92JamExpF-1516
Lowe, Robert
❑ 87OldJudN-302
❑ 95May-20
❑ 98CamPepP-45
Lowe, Sean
❑ 92ClaDraP-11
❑ 92ClaDraPFB-BC11
❑ 92ClaFS7-404
❑ 92UppDecML-119
❑ 93Bow-572
❑ 93CarStaC-27
❑ 93ClaFS7-244
❑ 93ClaGolF-119
❑ 93Pin-461
❑ 93Sco-493
❑ 93Sel-356
❑ 93St.PetCC-17
❑ 93St.PetCF-2624
❑ 93StaCluM-121
❑ 93Top-191
❑ 93TopGol-191
❑ 93TopInaM-191
❑ 93TopInaR-191
❑ 93TopMic-191
❑ 94SigRoo-40
❑ 94SigRooS-40
❑ 94St.PetCC-14
❑ 94St.PetCF-2581
❑ 95ArkTraTI-19
❑ 97LouRedB-18
❑ 98MemRedG-8
Lowell, Mike
❑ 96GreBatB-14
❑ 97NorNav-24
❑ 97NorNavTI-19
❑ 98Bes-25
❑ 98Bes-74
❑ 98BesDiaB-19
❑ 98Bow-85
❑ 98BowBes-104
❑ 98BowBesAR-104
❑ 98BowBesR-104
❑ 98BowCerBlueAU-21
❑ 98BowCerGA-21
❑ 98BowCerSA-21
❑ 98BowChr-85
❑ 98BowChrGA-85
❑ 98BowChrGAR-85
❑ 98BowChrI-85
❑ 98BowChrIR-85
❑ 98BowChrR-85
❑ 98BowGolA-85
❑ 98BowInt-85
❑ 98CirThu-133
❑ 98CirThuRav-133
❑ 98CirThuSupRav-133
❑ 98ColCliD-18
❑ 98ColCliM-21
❑ 98Don-327
❑ 98DonGolPP-327
❑ 98DonSig-132
❑ 98DonSigA-56
❑ 98DonSigAC-74
❑ 98DonSigAM-75
❑ 98DonSigP-132
❑ 98DonSigSB-18
❑ 98DonSigSP-16
❑ 98DonSilPP-327
❑ 98E-X2Sig2001-17
❑ 98FlaShoWotF-9
❑ 98Fle-558
❑ 98LeaRS-214
❑ 98LeaRSLHolo-214
❑ 98LeaRSLong-214
❑ 98LeaRTrue-214
❑ 98ScoRT-252
❑ 98ScoRTSS-PP145
❑ 98ScoRTSSAP-PP145
❑ 98ScoRTSSAP1-PP145
❑ 98SkyDugA-93
❑ 98SkyDugAIA-93
❑ 98SPxFin-199
❑ 98SPxFinR-199
❑ 98SPxFinS-199
❑ 98StaCluBPP-BP8
❑ 98StaCluFDI-332
❑ 98StaClul-332
❑ 98StaCluOneK-332
❑ 98StaCluPP-332

❑ 98Stu-104
❑ 98StuGPP-104
❑ 98StuSPP-104
❑ 98Ult-375
❑ 98UltGolM-375
❑ 98UltMas-375
❑ 98UltPlaM-375
❑ 98UppDec-589
❑ 98UppDecDS-DS51
❑ 99Bow-292
❑ 99BowAut-BA43
❑ 99BowGol-292
❑ 99BowInt-292
❑ 99DumSet-143
❑ 99Fle-254
❑ 99FleBri-165
❑ 99FleBri2G-165
❑ 99FleBriBlu-165
❑ 99FleBriGol-165
❑ 99FleMys-143
❑ 99FleMysM-143
❑ 99FleSta9-254
❑ 99FleWarT-254
❑ 99Pac-296
❑ 99Pac-296A
❑ 99PacPlaB-296
❑ 99PacPlaB-296A
❑ 99PacRed-296
❑ 99PacRed-296A
❑ 99SkyThu-155
❑ 99SkyThuRant-155
❑ 99SkyThuRave-155
❑ 99SP Aut-113
❑ 99SP AutC-ML
❑ 99SP AutCG-ML
❑ 99SP TopP-77
❑ 99SP TopPC-ML
❑ 99SP TopPDtS-D26
❑ 99SP TopPPE-77
❑ 99SpoIll-71
❑ 99SPSig-110
❑ 99SPx-109
❑ 99SPxFinR-109
❑ 99SPxFinS-109
❑ 99StaCluC-CS23
❑ 99StaCluC-CS29
❑ 99StaCluC-CS34
❑ 99StaCluC-CS40
❑ 99ThuSkySupR-155
❑ 99Top-425
❑ 99TopChr-425
❑ 99TopChrR-425
❑ 99TopMVPP-425
❑ 99UD Cho-23
❑ 99UD ChoPCR-23
❑ 99UppDecMP-MLO
❑ 99UppDecO-66
❑ 99UppDecOSO-66

Lowenstein, John
❑ 70WicAerM-11
❑ 71OPC-231
❑ 71Top-231
❑ 72OPC-486
❑ 72Top-486
❑ 73IndTeal-18
❑ 73OPC-327
❑ 73Top-327
❑ 74OPC-176
❑ 74Top-176
❑ 75CleIndP-18
❑ 75OPC-424
❑ 75Top-424
❑ 75TopMin-424
❑ 76OPC-646
❑ 76SSP-528
❑ 76Top-646
❑ 77IndTeal-15
❑ 77OPC-175
❑ 77Top-393
❑ 78RanBurK-21
❑ 78SSP270-87
❑ 78Top-87
❑ 79BalOriP-9
❑ 79Top-173
❑ 80BalOriP-11
❑ 80Top-287
❑ 81Don-235
❑ 81Fle-186
❑ 81OPC-199
❑ 81Top-591
❑ 82Don-599
❑ 82Fle-169
❑ 82Top-747
❑ 83Don-153
❑ 83Fle-63
❑ 83FleSta-108
❑ 83FleSti-197
❑ 83OPC-337
❑ 83OriPos-14
❑ 83Top-473
❑ 83TopSti-24
❑ 84AllGamPl-149
❑ 84BalOriP-17
❑ 84Don-228
❑ 84DonActAS-26
❑ 84Fle-10
❑ 84FleSti-116
❑ 84Nes792-604
❑ 84OriEng-6
❑ 84Top-604
❑ 84TopSti-20
❑ 84TopSti-209
❑ 84TopTif-604
❑ 85Don-245
❑ 85Fle-180
❑ 85OPC-316
❑ 85Top-316
❑ 85TopSti-206
❑ 85TopTif-316
❑ 91OriCro-269
❑ 93RanKee-232

Lowery, David
❑ 91GasRanC-18
❑ 91GasRanP-2695
❑ 91SouAtlLAGP-SAL23
❑ 92ChaRanC-1
❑ 92ChaRanF-2233
❑ 93BinMetF-2343

Lowery, John
❑ 92CliGiaF-3594
❑ 92Min-12

Lowery, Josh
❑ 89BatCliP-1942

Lowery, Phill
❑ 99TeaBesR-52
❑ 99TeaBesRG-52
❑ 99TeaBesRS-52

Lowery, Terrell
❑ 91ButCopKSP-17
❑ 92UppDecML-81
❑ 93Bow-373
❑ 93ChaRanC-1
❑ 93ChaRanF-1952
❑ 93FloStaLAF-6
❑ 94Bow-17
❑ 94Cla-18
❑ 94ClaTriF-T79
❑ 94TulDriF-255
❑ 94TulDriTI-13
❑ 94UppDecML-216
❑ 95Bow-260
❑ 95BowGolF-260
❑ 95Exc-129
❑ 95Top-643
❑ 95UppDecML-67
❑ 95UppDecMLFS-67
❑ 96BinMetB-17
❑ 97IowCub-16
❑ 98IowCubQ-14

Lowman, Mel
❑ 77DayBealT-13

Lown, Turk (Omar)
❑ 50WorWidGV-14
❑ 52Bow-16
❑ 52Top-330
❑ 53BowC-154
❑ 53Top-130
❑ 54Bow-157
❑ 57Top-247
❑ 58Top-261
❑ 59Top-277
❑ 60Top-57
❑ 60Top-313
❑ 60TopVen-57
❑ 60WhiSoxTS-13
❑ 61Pos-32
❑ 61Top-424
❑ 61TopMagR-35
❑ 62Top-528
❑ 62WhiSoxTS-12
❑ 79DiaGre-147
❑ 81WhiSox1T-30
❑ 83TopRep5-330
❑ 91TopArc1-130

Lowrey, Peanuts (Harry)
❑ 42CubTeal-11
❑ 43CubTeal-13
❑ 46SpoExcW-6-11
❑ 47Exh-141A
❑ 47Exh-141B
❑ 47TipTop-112
❑ 49Bow-22
❑ 49EurSta-62
❑ 49Lea-33
❑ 50Bow-172
❑ 51Bow-194
❑ 52Bow-102
❑ 52Top-111
❑ 53CarHunW-12
❑ 53ExhCan-29
❑ 53Top-16
❑ 54CarHunW-11
❑ 54Top-158
❑ 59SeaPop-25
❑ 60RawGloT-16
❑ 70Houof J-15
❑ 72TopTes5-7
❑ 75TCMHouoJ-16
❑ 83TCMPla1943-37
❑ 83TopRep5-111
❑ 91TopArc1-16
❑ 94TopArc1-158
❑ 94TopArc1G-158

Lowrey, Steve
❑ 82CedRapRT-4

Lowry, Curt
❑ 96CliLumKTI-18

Lowry, Dwight
❑ 81BirBarT-3
❑ 83BirBarT-4
❑ 84TigTeal-24
❑ 85DomLeaS-133
❑ 85NasSouTI-10
❑ 87Don-338
❑ 87Fle-157
❑ 87FleGlo-157
❑ 87SevCoi-D7
❑ 87SpoTeaP-15
❑ 87TigCaiD-5
❑ 87TigCok-11
❑ 87TolMudHT-25
❑ 87Top-483
❑ 87TopTif-483
❑ 89PacSenL-21
❑ 89TopSenL-2
❑ 90CMC-64
❑ 90IndIndC-14
❑ 90IndIndP-297
❑ 90ProAAAF-580
❑ 91FayGenC-11
❑ 91FayGenP-1188
❑ 92FayGenC-25
❑ 92FayGenF-2185
❑ 93FayGenC-26
❑ 93FayGenF-146
❑ 94FayGenC-27
❑ 94FayGenF-2164
❑ 95FayGenTI-16
❑ 96FayGenB-1

Lowry, Elliot
❑ 94BurIndC-11

Lowry, Mike
❑ 78WauMetT-17

Loy, Darren
❑ 86ReaPhiP-16
❑ 87MaiGuiP-21
❑ 87MaiGuiT-9
❑ 87PhiTas-xx
❑ 88ChaRanS-13
❑ 89OklCit8C-20
❑ 89OklCit8P-1526
❑ 89TulDriTI-12

Loyd, Brian
❑ 98RanCucQG-17
❑ 98RanCucQG-16

Loynd, Mike
❑ 86RanPer-46
❑ 86TulDriTI-8
❑ 87Don-506
❑ 87FleUpd-67
❑ 87FleUpdG-67
❑ 87RanMot-21
❑ 87RanSmo-27
❑ 87SpoTeaP-1
❑ 87Top-126
❑ 87TopTif-126
❑ 88Don-550
❑ 88Fle-472
❑ 88FleGlo-472
❑ 88Sco-491
❑ 88ScoGlo-491
❑ 88Top-319
❑ 88TopTif-319
❑ 88TucTorC-3
❑ 88TucTorP-185
❑ 89ColMudP-147
❑ 89ColMudS-16
❑ 90CMC-332
❑ 90ProAAAF-348
❑ 90SyrChiC-6
❑ 90SyrChiMB-15
❑ 90SyrChiP-568
❑ 91LouRedTI-11
❑ 92LouRedF-1886
❑ 92LouRedS-259
❑ 93RanKee-233
❑ 93RicBraP-13
❑ 93RicBraRC-21

Loyola, Juan
❑ 91PriRedC-2
❑ 91PriRedP-3526

Lozado, Willie
❑ 79BurBeeT-7
❑ 81ElPasDT-2
❑ 82VanCanT-5
❑ 83IndIndTI-10
❑ 85Don-595
❑ 85Fle-644
❑ 85LouRedR-19
❑ 86OklCit8P-10
❑ 88BlaYNPRWL-7
❑ 94BreMilB-328

Lozano, Steve
❑ 89FreStaBS-13

Lozinski, Tony
❑ 89BatCliP-1916
❑ 90ClePhiS-12

Lubert, Dennis
❑ 83DurBulT-21

Lubratich, Steve
❑ 80SalLakCGT-14
❑ 81SalLakCGT-19
❑ 82SpoIndT-17
❑ 84Don-377
❑ 84EdmTraC-112
❑ 84EdmTraC-249
❑ 84Fle-524
❑ 84Nes792-266
❑ 84Top-266
❑ 84TopTif-266
❑ 85LasVegSC-106
❑ 86BeaGolGP-14
❑ 86LasVegSP-11
❑ 87SpoIndP-10
❑ 88LasVegSP-243
❑ 88SpoIndP-1928
❑ 89RivRedWB-22
❑ 89RivRedWCLC-25
❑ 89RivRedWP-1411
❑ 90WicWraRD-25
❑ 91LinDriAA-624
❑ 91WicWraLD-624
❑ 91WicWraP-2614
❑ 91WicWraRD-24

Luby, Hugh
❑ 48SomandK-23
❑ 72TCMthe1-196

Lucadello, John
❑ 41BroW75-20
❑ 46SeaSLP-32
❑ 72TCMthe1-203
❑ 84TCMPla1-20

Lucarelli, Vito
❑ 79AppFoxT-3
❑ 80AppFoxT-8

Lucas, Arbrey
❑ 85OscAstTI-8

Lucas, Brian
❑ 78ChaPirT-13

Lucas, Charles S.
❑ 36GouWidPPR-D16

Lucas, Dave
❑ 86AncGlaPTI-19

Lucas, Gary
❑ 79HawIsIC-26
❑ 79HawIsIT-9
❑ 81Don-243
❑ 81Fle-502
❑ 81OPC-259
❑ 81PadFamF-14
❑ 81Top-436
❑ 82Don-296
❑ 82Don-422A
❑ 82Fle-577
❑ 82OPC-120
❑ 82Top-120
❑ 82TopSti-102
❑ 83Don-187
❑ 83Fle-366
❑ 83OPC-364
❑ 83PadTeal-15
❑ 83Top-761
❑ 84Don-307
❑ 84ExpPos-18
❑ 84ExpSta-12
❑ 84Fle-306
❑ 84FleUpd-73
❑ 84Nes792-7
❑ 84OPC-7
❑ 84Top-7
❑ 84TopSti-161
❑ 84TopTif-7
❑ 84TopTra-73T
❑ 84TopTraT-73T
❑ 85Don-498
❑ 85Fle-403
❑ 85OPC-297
❑ 85Top-297
❑ 85TopTif-297
❑ 86Don-453
❑ 86Fle-254
❑ 86OPC-351
❑ 86Top-601
❑ 86TopTif-601
❑ 87AngSmo-4
❑ 87CalAngPPS-22
❑ 87Don-618
❑ 87Fle-87
❑ 87FleGlo-87
❑ 87OPC-382
❑ 87Top-696
❑ 87TopTif-696
❑ 88Don-579
❑ 88Fle-495
❑ 88FleGlo-495
❑ 88Top-524
❑ 88TopClo-62
❑ 88TopTif-524
❑ 91CalLeLA-48
❑ 91SanJosGC-24
❑ 91SanJosGP-29
❑ 92CliGiaC-28
❑ 92CliGiaF-3614
❑ 93QuaCitRBC-27
❑ 93QuaCitRBF-117
❑ 94QuaCitRBC-26
❑ 94QuaCitRBF-552

Lucas, Pepe
❑ 85DomLeaS-142

Lucas, Ray
❑ 33DouDisP-28
❑ 90DodTar-462

Lucas, Red (Charles Fred.)
❑ 29ExhFou-8
❑ 29PorandAR-58
❑ 30SchR33-43
❑ 31Exh-8
❑ 32OrbPinNP-40
❑ 32OrbPinUP-42
❑ 33DouDisP-29
❑ 33ExhFou-4
❑ 33Gou-137
❑ 33TatOrb-42
❑ 33WorCig-65
❑ 34DiaMatCSB-117
❑ 34DiaStaR-46
❑ 34DiaStaR-106
❑ 34GouCanV-7
❑ 35GouPuzR-4B
❑ 35GouPuzR-7B
❑ 35GouPuzR-12B
❑ 36NatChiFPR-53
❑ 72TCMthe1-195
❑ 77RedCarP-12
❑ 79DiaGre-352
❑ 82DiaCla-98
❑ 85BigLeaC3-74
❑ 91ConTSN-190

Lucas, Scott
❑ 91HelBreSP-6

Lucca, Lou
❑ 91OklStaC-15
❑ 92EriSaiC-16
❑ 92EriSaiF-1631
❑ 92OklStaC-17
❑ 93ExcFS7-37
❑ 93KanCouCC-11
❑ 93KanCouCF-923
❑ 93KanCouCTI-12
❑ 93Top-494
❑ 93TopGol-494
❑ 93TopInaM-494
❑ 93TopInaR-494
❑ 93TopMic-494
❑ 94BreCouMC-8
❑ 94BreCouMF-19
❑ 95PorSeaDTI-12
❑ 96ChaKniB-16
❑ 98ChaKniQ-19
❑ 98PorSeaD5AQ-11

Lucchesi, Frank
❑ 70Top-662
❑ 71OPC-119
❑ 71Top-119
❑ 72OPC-188
❑ 72Top-188
❑ 74OPC-379
❑ 74Top-379
❑ 75RanPos-20
❑ 76OPC-172
❑ 76SSP-272
❑ 76Top-172
❑ 77Top-428
❑ 87CubCan-14
❑ 88ChaLooLTI-22
❑ 88NasSouTI-25
❑ 88Top-564
❑ 88TopClo-63
❑ 88TopTif-564
❑ 89NasSouC-25
❑ 89NasSouP-1284
❑ 89NasSouTI-30
❑ 91FouBal-13
❑ 93RanKee-234

Lucchetti, Larry
❑ 92SavCarC-4
❑ 92SavCarF-663
❑ 93SavCarC-16
❑ 93SavCarF-684
❑ 94St.PetCC-15
❑ 94St.PetCF-2582

Luce, Robert
❑ 96EveAquB-15
❑ 97CalLeaATI-15
❑ 97LanJet-14
❑ 98Bow-403
❑ 98BowChr-403
❑ 98BowChrGA-403
❑ 98BowChrGAR-403
❑ 98BowChrI-403
❑ 98BowChrIR-403
❑ 98BowChrR-403
❑ 98BowGolA-403
❑ 98BowInt-403
❑ 98OrlRayM-11
❑ 98SouLeaTPG-9
❑ 98SP MinPE-116
❑ 98SPMin-116

Luce, Roger
❑ 92ChaRanC-4
❑ 92ChaRanF-2227
❑ 92ClaFS7-111
❑ 93TulDriF-2735
❑ 93TulDriTI-15
❑ 94TulDriF-246
❑ 94TulDriTI-14
❑ 96JacGenB-17
❑ 96TusTorB-15

Lucero, Kevin
❑ 91HamRedC-4
❑ 91HamRedP-4036
❑ 92SavCarC-3
❑ 92SavCarF-662

Lucero, Nathan
❑ 95QuaCitRBTI-14
❑ 96QuaCitRB-4
❑ 97QuaCitRBB-13
❑ 98KisCobQ-5

Lucero, Robert
❑ 88CliGiaP-714

Lucia, Danny
❑ 78GreBraT-14
❑ 81DurBulT-20

Luciani, Randy
❑ 88FayGenP-1098

Luciano, Medina
❑ 89PitMetS-15

Luciano, Ron
❑ 77Spo-8021

Luciano, Suliban
❑ 91KinMetC-5
❑ 91KinMetP-3825

Luciano, Virgilio
❑ 95ChaRivTI-26

Lucier, Lou
❑ 43RedSoxTI-14

Luckham, Ken
❑ 89SalDodTI-15
❑ 90OscAstS-17
❑ 91OscAstC-7
❑ 91OscAstP-679
❑ 92JacGenS-338

Luderus, Fred
❑ 10DarChoE-23

❏ 11HelSta-146
❏ 11PinT-5-301
❏ 11PloCanE-41
❏ 14CraJacE-45
❏ 15CraJacE-45
❏ 15SpoNewM-104
❏ 16BF2FP-90
❏ 16FleBreD-55
❏ 16SpoNewM-106
❏ 17ColE13-102
❏ 22MrsShePP-17
Ludolph, Willie
❏ 21Zee-125
❏ 25Zee-158
❏ 26Zee-51
❏ 27Zee-30
❏ 33Zee-22
❏ 33Zee-61
❏ 35PebBea-3
Ludvigsen, Marc
❏ 98PitMetM-17
Ludwick, Bob
❏ 53ExhCan-38
Ludwick, Eric
❏ 93PitMetC-1
❏ 93PitMetF-3705
❏ 94ExcFS7-236
❏ 94St.LucMC-16
❏ 94St.LucMF-1191
❏ 95AusFut-41
❏ 95Bes-74
❏ 95BinMetTI-38
❏ 96BesAutSA-42
❏ 96Bow-222
❏ 96BowFoi-222
❏ 96Exc-188
❏ 97CarPol-16
❏ 97LouRedB-19
❏ 98Don-294
❏ 98DonGolPP-294
❏ 98DonSilPP-294
Ludwig, Jeff
❏ 89GenCubP-1869
Ludwig, William
❏ 09ColChiE-173A
❏ 09ColChiE-173B
❏ 12ColRedB-173A
❏ 12ColRedB-173B
❏ 12ColTinT-173A
❏ 12ColTinT-173B
Ludy, John
❏ 85BelBreT-19
❏ 86StoPorP-13
❏ 87StoPorP-16
Luebber, Steve
❏ 72Top-678
❏ 76VenLeaS-123
❏ 77TacTwiDQ-18
❏ 77Top-457
❏ 79SyrChiT-20
❏ 79SyrChiTI-31
❏ 80RocRedWT-15
❏ 81RocRedWT-12
❏ 81RocRedWW-12
❏ 83EvaTriT-5
❏ 86BeaGolGP-15
❏ 87WicPilRD-23
❏ 88WicPilRD-42
❏ 89LasVegSC-25
❏ 89LasVegSP-26
❏ 89PacSenL-94
❏ 90RivRedWB-20
❏ 90RivRedWCLC-25
❏ 90RivRedWP-2623
❏ 91HagSunLD-240
❏ 91HagSunP-2473
❏ 91LinDriAA-240
❏ 91OriCro-270
❏ 91PacSenL-7
❏ 92RocRedWF-1956
❏ 92RocRedWS-475
❏ 93RocRedWF-258
❏ 94RocRedWF-1014
❏ 94RocRedWTI-11
❏ 98KanCouC-19
❏ 98KanCouCCP-19
Luebbers, Larry
❏ 90BilMusP-3217
❏ 91CedRapRC-8
❏ 91CedRapRP-2716
❏ 91Cla/Bes-373
❏ 91MidLeaAP-MWL22
❏ 92CedRapRC-11
❏ 92CedRapRF-1071
❏ 92ChaLooF-3815
❏ 92ClaFS7-50
❏ 93IndIndF-1484
❏ 94Don-192
❏ 94Fle-415
❏ 94IowCubF-1273
❏ 94Pac-151
❏ 94Sco-603
❏ 94ScoGolR-603
❏ 94StaCluT-335
❏ 94StaCluTFDI-335
❏ 94Top-221
❏ 94TopGol-221
❏ 94TopSpa-221
❏ 94Ult-172
❏ 95ChaLooTI-13
❏ 96ChaLooB-17
❏ 97RicBra-17
❏ 98MemRedG-9
Luebke, Dick
❏ 77FriOneYW-66
❏ 91OriCro-271
Luecken, Rick
❏ 84ChaLooT-18
❏ 85CalCanC-98
❏ 86ChaLooP-16
❏ 87MemChiB-22
❏ 87MemChiP-18
❏ 88MemChiB-20
❏ 89OmaRoyC-7
❏ 89OmaRoyP-1734
❏ 89TriAAAP-AAA38
❏ 90Bow-5
❏ 90BowTif-5
❏ 90BraDubP-18
❏ 90CMC-656
❏ 90Don-562
❏ 90Fle-113
❏ 90FleCan-113
❏ 90OPC-87
❏ 90RicBraC-26
❏ 90RicBraTI-19
❏ 90Top-87
❏ 90TopDeb89-73
❏ 90TopTif-87
❏ 90UppDec-621
Luedtke, John
❏ 90ArkRaz-27
Lugo, Angel
❏ 89EliTwiS-16
❏ 90MiaMirlS-14
❏ 91St.CatBJC-23
❏ 91St.CatBJP-3391
Lugo, Arquimedes
❏ 93AubAstC-17
❏ 93AubAstF-3440
Lugo, Elias
❏ 76VenLeaS-87
❏ 93LinVenB-232
❏ 95LinVen-130
❏ 96-97LinVen-93
Lugo, Jesus
❏ 95LinVen-144
❏ 95PeoChiTI-32
❏ 96-97LinVen-209
❏ 96JohCitCTI-21
❏ 96StPetCB-16
Lugo, Julio
❏ 95AubAstTI-8
❏ 96QuaCitRB-19
❏ 97KisCob-17
❏ 98KisCobQ-19
❏ 99Bow-378
❏ 99BowGol-378
❏ 99BowInt-378
Lugo, Urbano (Rafael)
❏ 82DanSunF-26
❏ 83PeoSunF-20
❏ 85EdmTraC-9
❏ 85FleUpd-74
❏ 86Don-329
❏ 86Fle-162
❏ 86Top-373
❏ 86TopTif-373
❏ 87AngSmo-9
❏ 87CalAngPPS-23
❏ 87Top-92A
❏ 87Top-92B
❏ 87TopTif-92A
❏ 87TopTif-92B
❏ 88EdmTraC-6
❏ 88EdmTraP-581
❏ 88TriAAAP-15
❏ 89IndIndP-1232
❏ 90TigCok-11
❏ 93LinVenB-8
❏ 93LinVenB-322
❏ 94VenLinU-40
❏ 95LinVen-8
❏ 95LinVen-299
❏ 95LinVen-308
❏ 95LinVen-319
❏ 96-97LinVen-150
Luis, Bevan
❏ 76ForLauYS-26
❏ 77ForLauYS-7
Luis, Joe
❏ 91LynRedSC-12
❏ 91LynRedSP-1202
❏ 92WinHavRSC-12
Lujack, Johnny
❏ 51Whe-2
❏ 52Whe-19A
❏ 52Whe-19B
Lukachyk, Rob
❏ 88UtiBluSP-1
❏ 89SouBenWSGS-22
❏ 90SarWhiSS-14
❏ 91FloStaLAP-FSL29
❏ 91SarWhiSC-23
❏ 91SarWhiSP-1124
❏ 92StoPorC-13
❏ 92StoPorF-50
❏ 93El PasDF-2964
❏ 93ExcFS7-191
❏ 94BowBayF-2424
❏ 94ClaGolF-61
❏ 94OriPro-56
❏ 95TolMudHTI-18
❏ 96HarSenB-18
❏ 97HarSen-15
Lukasiewicz, Mark
❏ 92OklStaC-18
❏ 94HagSunC-11
❏ 94HagSunF-2723
❏ 95DunBluJTI-13
❏ 96DunBluJB-15
❏ 96DunBluJTI-18
❏ 97KnoSmo-15
❏ 98SyrSkyG-19
Luke, Matt
❏ 92ClaDraP-115
❏ 92FroRowDP-69
❏ 92FroRowDPG-69
❏ 92FroRowDPS-69
❏ 92OneYanC-1
❏ 93GreHorC-17
❏ 93GreHorF-899
❏ 94ClaGolF-85
❏ 94ExcFS7-109
❏ 94FloStaLAF-FSL23
❏ 94TamYanC-18
❏ 94TamYanF-2397
❏ 95Exc-99
❏ 95NorNagUTI-48
❏ 95NorNavTI-48
❏ 95SigRooOJ-23
❏ 95SigRooOJP-23
❏ 95SigRooOJPS-23
❏ 95SigRooOJS-23
❏ 95UppDecML-184
❏ 95UppDecMLFS-184
❏ 96Bow-217
❏ 96BowFoi-217
❏ 96ColCliB-17
❏ 96FleUpd-U63
❏ 96FleUpdTC-U63
❏ 96Sel-190
❏ 96SelArtP-190
❏ 96Ult-389
❏ 96UltGolM-389
❏ 97ColCliB-17
❏ 97ColCliD-13
❏ 98DodMot-23
❏ 98DodPol-16
❏ 98PacOmeRS-26
❏ 98PacOnl-377
❏ 98PacOnlR-377
❏ 98PacOnlWC-377
❏ 99Fle-484
❏ 99FleSta9-484
❏ 99FleWarT-484
❏ 99Pac-223
❏ 99PacAur-4
❏ 99PacAurOD-4
❏ 99PacPlaB-223
❏ 99PacRed-223
❏ 99UppDec-122
❏ 99UppDecEL1-122
❏ 99UppDecEL2-122
Lukens, Doug
❏ 66St.PetCTI-8
Luketich, Stan
❏ 91NiaFalRC-30
❏ 91NiaFalRP-3651
❏ 92NiaFalRC-29
❏ 92NiaFalRF-3343
Lukevics, Mitch
❏ 76AppFoxT-12
❏ 78KnoKnoST-12
❏ 79KnoKnoST-11
Lukish, Tom
❏ 80UtiBluJT-25
❏ 82KnoBluJT-5
❏ 83SyrChiT-9
❏ 84SyrChiT-20
Lukon, Eddie
❏ 48AngTeal-17
❏ 79DiaGre-260
❏ 85TCMPla1-38
Lum, Mike
❏ 68BraPos-20
❏ 68Top-579
❏ 69AtlBraBPPS-15
❏ 69MilBra-162
❏ 69Top-514
❏ 70OPC-367
❏ 70Top-367
❏ 71MLBOffS-16
❏ 71OPC-194
❏ 71Top-194
❏ 72Top-641
❏ 73LinPor-5
❏ 73OPC-266
❏ 73Top-266
❏ 74OPC-227
❏ 74Top-227
❏ 74TopSta-7
❏ 75AtlBraP-21
❏ 75Hos-33
❏ 75HosTwi-33
❏ 75OPC-154
❏ 75Top-154
❏ 75TopMin-154
❏ 76LinSup-93
❏ 76OPC-208
❏ 76RedParC-15
❏ 76SSP-11
❏ 76Top-208
❏ 76TopTra-208T
❏ 77Top-601
❏ 78Pep-17
❏ 78SSP270-119
❏ 78Top-326
❏ 79OPC-286
❏ 79Top-556
❏ 80Top-7
❏ 81Fle-258
❏ 81Top-457
❏ 81TopTra-795
❏ 82Don-300
❏ 82Fle-599
❏ 82Top-732
❏ 88RoySmo-2
❏ 88RoyTeal-18
Luman, Charley
❏ 83ButCopKT-8
LumberKing, Louie the
❏ 98CliLumG-30
Lumenti, Ralph
❏ 58Top-369
❏ 59SenTealW-10
❏ 59Top-316A
❏ 59Top-316B
❏ 60Lea-130
❏ 61Top-469
Lumley, Harry G.
❏ 06FanCraNL-26
❏ 08RosComP-96
❏ 09AmeCarE90-1-72
❏ 09RamT20-71
❏ 09T206-217
❏ 11SpoLifCW-225
❏ 72ClaCar-74
❏ 90DodTar-464
Lumley, Mike
❏ 89LakTigS-14
❏ 90CMC-837
❏ 90LonTigP-1265
❏ 91LakTigC-9
❏ 91LakTigP-264
❏ 92ClaFS7-173
❏ 92LonTigF-630
❏ 92LonTigS-412
❏ 93ClaGolF-63
❏ 93TolMudHF-1653
Lumpe, Jerry
❏ 56YanTeal-13
❏ 58Top-193
❏ 58YanJayP-8
❏ 59Top-272
❏ 60A'sJayP-7
❏ 60A'sTeal-13
❏ 60Lea-47
❏ 60Top-290
❏ 61A'sTeal-13
❏ 61AthJayP-12
❏ 61AthJayP-13
❏ 61Pos-81A
❏ 61Pos-81B
❏ 61Top-119
❏ 61Top-365
❏ 61TopStal-164
❏ 62Jel-93
❏ 62Pos-93
❏ 62PosCan-93
❏ 62SalPlaC-25
❏ 62ShiPlaC-25
❏ 62Top-127
❏ 62Top-305
❏ 62TopBuc-50
❏ 62TopStal-54
❏ 62TopVen-127
❏ 63AthJayP-8
❏ 63BasMagM-50
❏ 63Fle-16
❏ 63Jel-86
❏ 63Pos-86
❏ 63Top-256
❏ 63TopStil-24
❏ 64A's-12
❏ 64TigJayP-8
❏ 64TigLid-9
❏ 64Top-165
❏ 64TopCoi-28
❏ 64TopCoi-124
❏ 64TopSta-86
❏ 64TopStaU-42
❏ 64TopVen-165
❏ 65TigJayP-9
❏ 65Top-353
❏ 66OPC-161
❏ 66Top-161
❏ 66TopVen-161
❏ 67CokCapTi-3
❏ 67DexPre-130
❏ 67TigDexP-5
❏ 67Top-247
❏ 78TCM60I-55
Luna, Alexis
❏ 92MedHatBJF-3215
❏ 92MedHatBJSP-17
Luna, Memo (Guillermo)
❏ 52MotCoo-26
❏ 54Bow-222
❏ 54CarHunW-12
Luna, Rich
❏ 93WelPirC-11
❏ 93WelPirF-3367
❏ 94AugGreF-3017
Lunar, Fernando
❏ 95Bow-201
❏ 95EugEmeTI-2
❏ 95MacBraTI-17
❏ 96-97LinVen-210
❏ 96BesAutS-52
❏ 96MacBraB-15
❏ 97MacBra-10
❏ 98CarLeaAC-29
❏ 98DanQ-C-6
Lunar, Luis
❏ 76VenLeaS-111
❏ 76WauMetT-16
❏ 77WauMetT-11
❏ 79JacMetT-13
❏ 80VenLeaS-204
❏ 93LinVenB-42
❏ 95LinVen-211
❏ 96-97LinVen-185
Lunar, Manuel
❏ 80VenLeaS-243
❏ 80WisRapTT-5
Lunar, Victor
❏ 95LinVen-239
Lund, Don
❏ 48DodTeal-15
❏ 53TigGle-19
❏ 53Top-277
❏ 54Bow-87
❏ 54Top-167
❏ 90DodTar-465
❏ 91TopArc1-277
❏ 94TopArc1-167
❏ 94TopArc1G-167
Lund, Ed
❏ 90GreFalDSP-4
❏ 91BakDodCLC-13
❏ 92VerBeaDF-2879
❏ 93BakDodCLC-16
Lund, Gordy (Gordon)
❏ 70Top-642
❏ 75AppFoxT-15
❏ 79KnoKnoST-4
❏ 80AppFoxT-29
❏ 81EdmTraRR-8
❏ 82EdmTraT-22
Lund, Greg
❏ 89EveGiaS-27
Lundahl, Rich
❏ 86LitFalMP-17
❏ 87ColMetP-7
Lundberg, Bryan
❏ 93MarPhiC-17
❏ 93MarPhiF-3469
❏ 94BatCliC-10
❏ 94BatCliF-3441
Lundberg, David
❏ 98SavSanGM-18
Lundblade, Rick
❏ 87PhiTas-xx
❏ 87ReaPhiP-13
❏ 88MaiPhiC-15
❏ 88MaiPhiP-291
❏ 89TidTidC-19
❏ 89TidTidP-1968
❏ 90HagSunP-1424
Lundeen, Larry
❏ 88BoiHawP-1615
Lundgren, Carl
❏ 06FanCraNL-27
❏ 07CubA.CDPP-6
❏ 07CubGFGCP-6
❏ 09T206-218
❏ 09T206-438
❏ 11SpoLifCW-226
Lundgren, Jason
❏ 89BenBucL-25
Lundgren, Kurt
❏ 86JacMetT-7
❏ 87JacMetF-8
Lundquist, David
❏ 94HicCraC-14
❏ 94HicCraF-2173
❏ 99SkyPre-227
❏ 99SkyPre-227
❏ 99SkyPreR-227
❏ 99SkyPreR-227
Lundstedt, Thomas
❏ 73WicAerJPKB-7
❏ 74OPC-603
❏ 74Top-603
❏ 75TacTwiK-4
❏ 75TwiPos-16
❏ 75TwiTeal-20
Lundy, Dick
❏ 78LauLonABS-6
❏ 86NegLeaF-75
❏ 90NegLeaS-25
❏ 91PomBlaBPB-23
Lunetta, Dan
❏ 90RocRedWGC-33
Lung, Rod
❏ 88QuaCitAGS-16
Lunte, Harry
❏ 77Ind192T-11
Lupica, Charles
❏ 73BooProC-24
Lupien, Tony (Ulysses)
❏ 42RedSoxTI-16
❏ 43RedSoxTI-15
❏ 47SigOil-12
❏ 48WhiSoxTI-15
❏ 49Bow-141
❏ 77TCMTheWY-11
❏ 79DiaGre-230
❏ 83TCMPla1943-18
Luplow, Al
❏ 62Top-598
❏ 63Jel-73
❏ 63Pos-73
❏ 63Top-351
❏ 64Top-184
❏ 64TopVen-184
❏ 66OPC-188
❏ 66Top-188
❏ 66TopVen-188
❏ 67CokCapYM-V22
❏ 67Top-433
❏ 91MetWIZ-236

Luque, Dolph (Adolpho)
❑ 19W514-17
❑ 20RedWorCP-10
❑ 21Exh-98
❑ 21Nei-72
❑ 22E120-174
❑ 22WilPatV-9
❑ 23W503-43
❑ 27YorCarE-18
❑ 28Exh-15
❑ 28StaPlaCE-44
❑ 28W502-18
❑ 28W513-71
❑ 28Yue-18
❑ 33Gou-209
❑ 40PlaBal-231
❑ 61Fle-56
❑ 77RedCarP-17
❑ 87ConSer2-46
❑ 88ConSer5-19
❑ 88PacEigMO-90
❑ 90DodTar-466
❑ 92ConTSN-413
❑ 94ConTSN-1021
❑ 94ConTSNB-1021
Lusader, Scott
❑ 86GleFalTP-12
❑ 87IntLeaAT-16
❑ 87TolMudHP-3
❑ 87TolMudHT-8
❑ 88Don-615
❑ 88Fle-62
❑ 88FleGlo-62
❑ 88TolMudHC-13
❑ 88TolMudHP-594
❑ 89ScoHot1R-15
❑ 89Top-487
❑ 89TopTif-487
❑ 90CMC-396
❑ 90Don-696
❑ 90OPC-632
❑ 90ProAAAF-393
❑ 90Sco-575
❑ 90Sco100RS-42
❑ 90TolMudHC-19
❑ 90TolMudHP-163
❑ 90Top-632
❑ 90TopTif-632
❑ 91Bow-174
❑ 91UppDec-241
Luse, Kelly
❑ 92SalSpuC-28
Lush, Ernie
❑ 09RamT20-72
Lush, John Charles
❑ 08RosComP-168
❑ 09PC7HHB-29
❑ 11MecDFT-25
❑ 11PinT-5-363
❑ 11SpoLifCW-227
❑ 11SpoLifM-273
❑ 11T205-105
❑ 12ColRedB-174
❑ 12ColTinT-174
❑ 12ImpTobC-33
❑ 15Zee-67
❑ 16Zee-58
Lush, William L.
❑ 03BreE10-92
❑ 03BreE10-93
Lussier, Pat
❑ 92WelPirC-17
❑ 92WelPirF-1339
❑ 93LetMouF-4163
❑ 93LetMouSP-22
Lusted, Chuck
❑ 84ShrCapFB-10
Luster, Jeremy
❑ 98SalVol-21
Lutes, Brian
❑ 89SanDieSAS-15
Luther, Brad
❑ 83St.PetCT-18
❑ 85SprCarT-16
Luther, Tim
❑ 91EveGiaC-15
❑ 91EveGiaP-3910
❑ 92EveGiaC-3
❑ 92EveGiaF-1683
Lutt, Jeff
❑ 93WelPirC-12
❑ 93WelPirF-3351
❑ 94AugGreC-10
❑ 94AugGreF-3002
Lutticken, Bob
❑ 86SpoIndC-156
❑ 87SpoIndP-18
❑ 88ChaRaiP-1217
❑ 89RivRedWB-1
❑ 89RivRedWCLC-11
❑ 89RivRedWP-1403
❑ 90WicWraRD-14
❑ 91HigDesMC-16
❑ 91HigDesMP-2399
Luttig, Chris
❑ 98EriSeaWM-16
Luttrell, Lyle
❑ 57Top-386
Luttrull, Bruce
❑ 85BenPhiC-14
Lutz, Brent
❑ 91MedHatBJP-4103
❑ 92MyrBeaHC-21
❑ 92MyrBeaHF-2200
❑ 93DunBluJC-16
❑ 93DunBluJF-1800
❑ 93DunBluJFFN-17
❑ 94KnoSmoF-1306
Lutz, Chris
❑ 88GenCubP-1653
❑ 89ChaWheP-1760
❑ 90MidLeaASGS-39
❑ 90PeoChiTI-25
❑ 91WinSpiC-9
Lutz, Manuel
❑ 96BriWhiSB-24
❑ 97BriWhiSB-19
❑ 98BriWhiSQ-18
Lutz, Rollin Joseph
❑ 52Par-74
❑ 73OPC-449
❑ 73Top-449A
❑ 73Top-449B
Lutzke, Rube (Walter)
❑ 25Exh-83
❑ 26Exh-82
❑ 27Exh-42
❑ 94ConTSN-1045
❑ 94ConTSNB-1045
Luuloa, Keith
❑ 95LakElsSTI-18
❑ 96MidAngB-21
❑ 96MidAngOHP-16
❑ 96TexLeaAB-29
❑ 97MidAng-20
❑ 98MidAngG-21
❑ 98MidAngO-24
❑ 99Bow-179
❑ 99BowChr-179
❑ 99BowChrG-179
❑ 99BowChrGR-179
❑ 99BowChrI-179
❑ 99BowChrIR-179
❑ 99BowChrR-179
❑ 99BowGol-179
❑ 99BowInt-179
Luzinski, Bill
❑ 80AppFoxT-25
Luzinski, Greg
❑ 71OPC-439
❑ 71Top-439
❑ 72OPC-112
❑ 72Top-112
❑ 73LinPor-146
❑ 73OPC-189
❑ 73PhiTeal-12
❑ 73SevTraC-39
❑ 73Top-189
❑ 73TopCanL-28
❑ 74Kel-9
❑ 74OPC-360
❑ 74PhiJohP-19
❑ 74Top-360
❑ 74TopDecE-24
❑ 74TopSta-76
❑ 75Hos-27
❑ 75HosTwi-27
❑ 75OPC-630
❑ 75PhiPhiP-20
❑ 75PhiProPS-9
❑ 75SSPPuzB-14
❑ 75Top-630
❑ 75TopMin-630
❑ 76BlaDis-29
❑ 76BucDis-29
❑ 76CarDis-29
❑ 76CraDis-29
❑ 76DailsID-29
❑ 76Hos-125
❑ 76IsaDis-29
❑ 76Kel-18
❑ 76OPC-193
❑ 76OPC-195
❑ 76OPC-610
❑ 76OrbDis-29
❑ 76PhiPhiP-16
❑ 76RedBarD-29
❑ 76SafDis-29
❑ 76SSP-467
❑ 76Top-193
❑ 76Top-195
❑ 76Top-610
❑ 76TowCluD-29
❑ 77BobParMBC-7
❑ 77BurCheD-163
❑ 77ChiWilD-38
❑ 77DailsID-38
❑ 77DetCaeD-38
❑ 77HollnnD-38
❑ 77Hos-25
❑ 77Kel-12
❑ 77MSADis-38
❑ 77OPC-118
❑ 77PepGloD-72
❑ 77RCColC-35
❑ 77SagDis-38
❑ 77sDis-38
❑ 77Spo-3424
❑ 77Top-30
❑ 77WenDis-38
❑ 77ZipDis-38
❑ 78Hos-8
❑ 78Kel-33
❑ 78OPC-42
❑ 78RCColC-42
❑ 78SagDis-5
❑ 78SSP270-31
❑ 78TasDis-5
❑ 78Top-420
❑ 78WifBalD-40
❑ 79BasPat-47
❑ 79Hos-30
❑ 79OPC-278
❑ 79PhiBurK-19
❑ 79PhiTeal-4
❑ 79Top-540
❑ 80OPC-66
❑ 80PhiBurK-11
❑ 80Top-120
❑ 81AllGamPI-57
❑ 81CokTeaS-100
❑ 81Don-175
❑ 81Fle-10
❑ 81FleStiC-75
❑ 81OPC-270
❑ 81Top-270
❑ 81TopScr-74
❑ 81TopSupHT-82
❑ 81TopTra-796
❑ 82Don-193
❑ 82Dra-22
❑ 82Fle-352
❑ 82FleSta-187
❑ 82OPC-69
❑ 82OPC-152
❑ 82Top-720
❑ 82Top-721
❑ 82TopSti-165
❑ 83AllGamPI-59
❑ 83Don-395
❑ 83DonActA-4
❑ 83Fle-247
❑ 83FleSta-109
❑ 83FleSti-158
❑ 83Kel-50
❑ 83OPC-310
❑ 83PhiPosGM-12
❑ 83PhiPosGPaM-6
❑ 83Top-310
❑ 83Top-591
❑ 83TopFol-2
❑ 83TopSti-51
❑ 83WhiSoxTV-19
❑ 84AllGamPI-150
❑ 84Don-122
❑ 84DonActAS-41
❑ 84DonCha-13
❑ 84Dra-18
❑ 84Fle-69
❑ 84FleSti-47
❑ 84FunFooP-34
❑ 84Nes792-20
❑ 84Nes792-712
❑ 84OCoandSI-8
❑ 84OPC-20
❑ 84RalPur-5
❑ 84Top-20
❑ 84Top-712
❑ 84TopCer-5
❑ 84TopRubD-12
❑ 84TopSti-7
❑ 84TopSti-8
❑ 84TopSti-244
❑ 84TopTif-20
❑ 84TopTif-712
❑ 84WhiSoxTV-23
❑ 85Don-546
❑ 85Fle-521
❑ 85Lea-75
❑ 85OPC-328
❑ 85Top-650
❑ 85TopRubD-15
❑ 85TopSti-238
❑ 85TopTif-650
❑ 89SweBasG-24
❑ 92UppDecS-24
❑ 93AthMot-27
Luzinski, Ryan
❑ 92ClaDraP-23
❑ 92ClaDraPFB-BC16
❑ 92GreFalDSP-1
❑ 92UppDecML-144
❑ 93BakDodCLC-2
❑ 93StaCluM-140
❑ 93Top-481
❑ 93TopGol-481
❑ 93TopInaM-481
❑ 93TopInaR-481
❑ 93TopMic-481
❑ 93YakBeaC-1
❑ 93YakBeaF-3885
❑ 94ActPac-53
❑ 94ClaGolF-197
❑ 94ExcFS7-218
❑ 94FloStaLAF-FSL47
❑ 94VerBeaDC-1
❑ 94VerBeaDF-75
❑ 95SanAntMTI-42
❑ 95UppDecML-68
❑ 95UppDecMLFS-68
❑ 97BowBay-21
❑ 98BowBayM-21
Luzon, Bob
❑ 82DurBulT-5
❑ 83DurBulT-9
❑ 85GreBraTI-13
Lychak, Perry
❑ 83KinBluJTI-12
❑ 85KinBluJT-6
❑ 86KinEagP-15
Lyden, Mitch
❑ 87ColCliP-18
❑ 87ColCliP-5
❑ 87ColCliT-11
❑ 89AlbYanB-14
❑ 89AlbYanP-320
❑ 89AlbYanSt-11
❑ 89Sta-98
❑ 90AlbDecGB-34
❑ 90AlbYanB-11
❑ 90AlbYanP-1037
❑ 90AlbYanSt-9
❑ 90Bes-179
❑ 90EasLeaAP-EL15
❑ 90ProAaA-33
❑ 90StaFS7-52
❑ 91LinDriAAA-590
❑ 91TolMudHLD-590
❑ 91TolMudHP-1935
❑ 92TidTidF-901
❑ 92TidTidS-561
❑ 93EdmTraF-1139
❑ 93FleFinE-66
❑ 93TopTra-61T
❑ 94EdmTraF-2877
❑ 94Pac-246
❑ 95OmaRoyTI-18
❑ 96SigRooOJ-17
❑ 96SigRooOJS-17
Lydy, Scott
❑ 89MedAthB-8
❑ 91Cla/Bes-436
❑ 91MadMusC-20
❑ 91MadMusP-2142
❑ 92HunStaF-3963
❑ 92RenSilSCLC-34
❑ 92UppDecML-171
❑ 92UppDecMLPotY-PY3
❑ 93AthStaC-24
❑ 93Bow-49
❑ 93ClaFS7-144
❑ 93FleFinE-256
❑ 93TacTigF-3047
❑ 94Cla-47
❑ 94ColC-180
❑ 94ColChoGS-180
❑ 94ColChoSS-180
❑ 94Don-226
❑ 94Fle-267
❑ 94Lea-27
❑ 94Pac-455
❑ 94Pin-232
❑ 94PinArtP-232
❑ 94PinMusC-232
❑ 94Spo-175
❑ 94StaClu-391
❑ 94StaCluFDI-391
❑ 94StaCluGR-391
❑ 94StaCluMOP-391
❑ 94TacTigF-3187
❑ 94Top-160
❑ 94TopGol-160
❑ 94TopSpa-160
❑ 94Ult-110
❑ 94UppDec-218
❑ 94UppDecED-218
❑ 95EdmTraTI-14
Lyle, Don
❑ 79IndIndTI-15
❑ 80IndIndTI-24
❑ 80VenLeaS-177
Lyle, Jeff
❑ 90WelPirP-22
❑ 91AugPirP-802
Lyle, Sparky (Albert)
❑ 69MilBra-163
❑ 69RedSoxAO-7
❑ 69RedSoxTI-7
❑ 69Top-311
❑ 70MLBOffS-160
❑ 70OPC-116
❑ 70RedSoxCPPC-7
❑ 70Top-116
❑ 71MLBOffS-324
❑ 71OPC-649
❑ 71RedSoxTI-6
❑ 71Top-649
❑ 72MilBra-202
❑ 72OPC-259
❑ 72Top-259
❑ 73Kel2D-15
❑ 73LinPor-130
❑ 73NewYorSNM-21
❑ 73OPC-68
❑ 73OPC-394
❑ 73SevTraC-40
❑ 73SyrChiTI-14
❑ 73Top-68
❑ 73Top-394
❑ 73Yan-2
❑ 74Kel-41
❑ 74OPC-66
❑ 74SyrChiTI-13
❑ 74Top-66
❑ 74TopSta-212
❑ 75Hos-134
❑ 75Kel-47
❑ 75OPC-485
❑ 75SSP42-28
❑ 75SyrChiTI-8
❑ 75Top-485
❑ 75TopMin-485
❑ 75YanSSP-22
❑ 76OPC-545
❑ 76SSP-429
❑ 76Top-545
❑ 77OPC-89
❑ 77Top-598
❑ 77YanBurK-10
❑ 78Hos-68
❑ 78Kel-43
❑ 78OPC-214
❑ 78OPC-237
❑ 78RCColC-84
❑ 78SSP270-11
❑ 78Top-2
❑ 78Top-35
❑ 78YanBurK-9
❑ 78YanPhoA-17
❑ 78YanSSPD-11
❑ 79Hos-143
❑ 79OPC-188
❑ 79Top-365
❑ 80OPC-62
❑ 80Top-115
❑ 81Don-284
❑ 81Fle-17
❑ 81FleStiC-91
❑ 81OPC-337
❑ 81RedSoxBG2S-92
❑ 81Top-719
❑ 82Don-189
❑ 82Fle-247
❑ 82OPC-285
❑ 82Top-285
❑ 83OPC-92
❑ 83OPC-208
❑ 83Top-693
❑ 83Top-694
❑ 83YanASFY-25
❑ 90PacLeg-93
❑ 92YanWIZ7-99
❑ 92YanWIZA-42
❑ 93MCIAmb-13
❑ 93RanKee-235
❑ 94MCIAmb-1
❑ 94TedWil-60
❑ 94TedWil-138
❑ 95MCIAmb-7
❑ 95SonGre-7
❑ 99SpollIGotG-28
❑ 99SpollIGotGA-45
❑ 99SpollIGotGC-24
Lyman, Billy
❑ 44CenFlo-15
❑ 45CenFlo-15
Lyman, Jason
❑ 93WatIndC-16
❑ 93WatIndF-3569
❑ 94ColRedC-15
❑ 94ColRedF-450
Lymberpoulos, Nick
❑ 93PocPosF-4206
❑ 93PocPosSP-11
Lynch, Charlie
❑ 80ElmPioRST-41
Lynch, David
❑ 89TulDriGS-14
❑ 90CMC-154
❑ 90OklCit8C-4
❑ 90OklCit8P-429
❑ 90ProAAAF-675
❑ 90TulDriDGB-16
❑ 90TulDriTI-14
❑ 91AlbDukLD-13
❑ 91AlbDukP-1137
❑ 91LinDriAAA-13
❑ 92ChaLooF-3816
❑ 92ChaLooS-191
❑ 93IndIndF-1485
❑ 94ChaKniF-892
Lynch, Ed
❑ 78AshTouT-15
❑ 78ChaPirT-14
❑ 79TucTorT-20
❑ 80TidTidT-21
❑ 81TidTidT-16
❑ 82Don-641
❑ 82Fle-531
❑ 82MetPhoA-15
❑ 82Top-121
❑ 83Don-308
❑ 83Fle-549
❑ 83Top-601
❑ 84Don-75
❑ 84Fle-591
❑ 84Nes792-293
❑ 84Top-293
❑ 84TopTif-293
❑ 85Don-623
❑ 85Fle-87
❑ 85MetColP-3
❑ 85MetTCM-14
❑ 85Top-467
❑ 85TopTif-467
❑ 86Don-631
❑ 86Fle-88
❑ 86MetTCM-7
❑ 86OPC-68
❑ 86Top-68
❑ 86TopTif-68
❑ 87CubCan-15
❑ 87CubDavB-37
❑ 87Don-516
❑ 87Fle-567
❑ 87FleGlo-567
❑ 87OPC-16
❑ 87Top-697
❑ 87TopTif-697
❑ 88Don-77
❑ 88Fle-422
❑ 88FleGlo-422
❑ 88Sco-506
❑ 88ScoGlo-506
❑ 88Top-336

❑ 88TopTif-336
❑ 91MetWIZ-237
❑ 94MetColP-16
Lynch, Jerry
❑ 54Top-234
❑ 55Top-142
❑ 55TopDouH-73
❑ 56PirTeal-16
❑ 56RedBurB-12
❑ 56Top-97
❑ 57Top-358
❑ 58RedEnq-25
❑ 58Top-103
❑ 59Kah-19
❑ 59RedShiBS-11
❑ 59Top-97
❑ 59TopVen-97
❑ 60Kah-23
❑ 60Lea-45
❑ 60Top-198
❑ 60Top-352
❑ 61Kah-25
❑ 61Pos-187A
❑ 61Pos-187B
❑ 61RedJayP-9
❑ 61Top-97
❑ 61TopStal-19
❑ 62Jel-127
❑ 62Kah-25
❑ 62Pos-127
❑ 62PosCan-127
❑ 62RedEnq-21
❑ 62RedJayP-8
❑ 62SalPlaC-198
❑ 62ShiPlaC-198
❑ 62Top-487
❑ 63Jel-129
❑ 63Kah-19
❑ 63Pos-129
❑ 63RedEnq-19
❑ 63RedJayP-7
❑ 63Top-37
❑ 64Kah-15
❑ 64PirKDK-16
❑ 64Top-193
❑ 64TopVen-193
❑ 65Kah-22
❑ 65Top-291
❑ 66OPC-182
❑ 66PirEasH-24
❑ 66Top-182
❑ 66TopVen-182
❑ 72LauGreF-22
❑ 79DiaGre-275
❑ 80Red196T-35
❑ 94TopArc1-234
❑ 94TopArc1G-234
Lynch, Jim
❑ 96QuaCitRB-20
❑ 97QuaCitRBB-14
❑ 98QuaCitRBG-14
Lynch, Joe
❑ 85SpoIndC-11
❑ 87TexLeaAF-3
❑ 87WicPilRD-10
❑ 88LasVegSC-9
❑ 88LasVegSP-223
❑ 89LasVegSC-3
❑ 89LasVegSP-22
❑ 90CMC-513
❑ 90LasVegSC-10
❑ 90LasVegSP-115
❑ 90ProAAAF-3
Lynch, John
❑ 92ClaDraP-122
❑ 92ClaFS7-434
❑ 92EriSaiC-17
❑ 92EriSaiF-1617
❑ 92UppDecML-21
❑ 93ExcFS7-38
❑ 93KanCouCC-12
Lynch, John H.
❑ 87OldJudN-303A
❑ 87OldJudN-303B
❑ 90KalBatN-29
Lynch, Mike
❑ 09ObaT21-197
❑ 91EriSaiC-19
❑ 91EriSaiP-4065
❑ 92WinHavRSF-1771
❑ 94LetMouF-3890
❑ 94LetMouSP-2
Lynch, Rich
❑ 80WesHavWCT-21B
❑ 81WesHavAT-22
Lynch, Ryan
❑ 98CliLumG-12
Lynch, Ty
❑ 92UtiBluSC-24
Lynes, Mike
❑ 83AlbA'sT-6
Lynn, Byrd
❑ 14Zee-87
❑ 18WhiSoxTI-15
❑ 21Zee-102
❑ 75WhiSox1T-14
❑ 92Man191BSR-16
Lynn, Chuck
❑ 86LynMetP-15
Lynn, Fred
❑ 75BlaBacD-4
❑ 75OPC-622
❑ 75SSPPuzB-15
❑ 75Top-622
❑ 75TopMin-622
❑ 76BlaDis-30
❑ 76BucDis-30
❑ 76CarDis-30
❑ 76CraDis-30
❑ 76DailsID-30
❑ 76Hos-1
❑ 76HosTwi-1
❑ 76IsaDis-30
❑ 76Kel-31
❑ 76LinSup-103
❑ 76OPC-50
❑ 76OPC-192
❑ 76OPC-196
❑ 76OrbDis-30
❑ 76RedBarD-30
❑ 76RedSox-5
❑ 76RedSoxSM-10
❑ 76SafDis-30
❑ 76SafSupLB-2
❑ 76SafSupLB-8
❑ 76SafSupLB-11
❑ 76SafSupLB-13
❑ 76SafSupLB-14A
❑ 76SafSupLB-14B
❑ 76SSP-402
❑ 76Top-50
❑ 76Top-192
❑ 76Top-196
❑ 76TowCluD-30
❑ 77BobParMBC-11
❑ 77BurCheD-35
❑ 77ChiWilD-39
❑ 77DailsID-39
❑ 77DetCaeD-39
❑ 77HollnnD-39
❑ 77Hos-51
❑ 77MSADis-39
❑ 77OPC-163
❑ 77PepGloD-21
❑ 77RCColC-36
❑ 77SagDis-39
❑ 77sDis-39
❑ 77Top-210
❑ 77WenDis-39
❑ 77ZipDis-39
❑ 78OPC-62
❑ 78PapGinD-19
❑ 78SSP270-174
❑ 78Top-320
❑ 78WifBalD-41
❑ 79BasPat-48
❑ 79Kel-30
❑ 79OPC-249
❑ 79Top-480
❑ 80BurKinPHR-18
❑ 80Kel-40
❑ 80OPC-60
❑ 80Top-110
❑ 80Top-201
❑ 80TopSup-10
❑ 80WilGloT-4
❑ 81AllGamPI-58
❑ 81Don-218
❑ 81Dra-9
❑ 81Fle-223
❑ 81FleStiC-98
❑ 81Kel-40
❑ 81LonBeaPT-6
❑ 81MSAMinD-21
❑ 81OPC-313
❑ 81PerCreC-20
❑ 81Squ-25
❑ 81Top-720
❑ 81TopScr-5
❑ 81TopSti-42
❑ 81TopSupHT-60
❑ 81TopTra-797
❑ 82Don-367
❑ 82Fle-468
❑ 82Fle-642
❑ 82FleSta-214
❑ 82K-M-27
❑ 82LouSlu-3
❑ 82OnDecD-21
❑ 82OPC-251
❑ 82OPC-252
❑ 82PerAll-8
❑ 82PerAllG-8
❑ 82Top-251
❑ 82Top-252
❑ 82TopSti-161
❑ 82TopStiV-161
❑ 82WilSpoG-5A
❑ 82WilSpoG-5B
❑ 83AllGamPI-60
❑ 83Don-241
❑ 83DonActA-59
❑ 83Fle-97
❑ 83FleSta-110
❑ 83FleSti-31
❑ 83Kel-51
❑ 83OPC-182
❑ 83OPC-392
❑ 83PerAll-3
❑ 83PerAllG-3
❑ 83SevCoi-3
❑ 83Top-392
❑ 83Top-520
❑ 83TopFol-3
❑ 83TopSti-44
❑ 83TopSti-158
❑ 84AllGamPI-151
❑ 84AngSmo-18
❑ 84Don-17
❑ 84Don-17A
❑ 84Don-108
❑ 84DonActAS-27
❑ 84DonCha-59
❑ 84Dra-19
❑ 84Fle-525
❑ 84Fle-626
❑ 84FunFooP-54
❑ 84Nes792-680
❑ 84OCoandSI-61
❑ 84OPC-247
❑ 84RalPur-29
❑ 84SevCoi-W16
❑ 84Top-680
❑ 84TopCer-29
❑ 84TopGloA-7
❑ 84TopRubD-15
❑ 84TopSti-5
❑ 84TopSti-6
❑ 84TopSti-230
❑ 84TopSup-23
❑ 84TopTif-680
❑ 85AllGamPI-63
❑ 85BalOriP-13
❑ 85BalOriP-14
❑ 85Don-133
❑ 85Fle-307
❑ 85FleUpd-75
❑ 85Lea-198
❑ 85OPC-220
❑ 85OriHea-9
❑ 85SevCoi-S9
❑ 85Top-220
❑ 85TopRubD-13
❑ 85TopSti-225
❑ 85TopTif-220
❑ 85TopTifT-77T
❑ 85TopTra-77T
❑ 86BalOriHMP-9
❑ 86BasStaB-68
❑ 86Don-245
❑ 86Fle-278
❑ 86FleStiC-70
❑ 86Lea-120
❑ 86OPC-55
❑ 86SevCoi-E16
❑ 86Spo-38
❑ 86Spo-63
❑ 86Spo-71
❑ 86Spo-73
❑ 86Spo-137
❑ 86Spo-150
❑ 86SpoRoo-46
❑ 86Top-55
❑ 86TopSti-228
❑ 86TopTat-8
❑ 86TopTif-55
❑ 86Woo-18
❑ 87BalOriP-22
❑ 87ClaGam-23
❑ 87Don-9
❑ 87Don-108
❑ 87DonOpeD-135
❑ 87DonSupD-9
❑ 87Fle-474
❑ 87FleBasA-25
❑ 87FleExcS-32
❑ 87FleGlo-474
❑ 87FleStiC-72
❑ 87Lea-9
❑ 87Lea-83
❑ 87OPC-370
❑ 87OriFreB-19
❑ 87Spo-49
❑ 87Spo-198
❑ 87SpoTeaP-21
❑ 87StuPan-14
❑ 87Top-370
❑ 87TopSti-226
❑ 87TopTif-370
❑ 88Don-248
❑ 88DonBasB-297
❑ 88Fle-566
❑ 88FleGlo-566
❑ 88Lea-163
❑ 88OriFreB-19
❑ 88OriPos-18
❑ 88PanSti-15
❑ 88RedFolSB-50
❑ 88Sco-42
❑ 88ScoBoxC-T2
❑ 88ScoGlo-42
❑ 88Spo-23
❑ 88StaLinO-9
❑ 88Top-707
❑ 88TopBig-169
❑ 88TopTif-707
❑ 89AngSmo-14
❑ 89Don-563
❑ 89Fle-138
❑ 89FleGlo-138
❑ 89OPC-27
❑ 89RedFolSB-76
❑ 89Sco-126
❑ 89Spo-68
❑ 89TigMar-9
❑ 89TigPol-9
❑ 89Top-416
❑ 89TopBasT-163
❑ 89TopTif-416
❑ 89UppDec-761
❑ 90BasWit-28
❑ 90Bow-216
❑ 90BowTif-216
❑ 90ClaYel-T59
❑ 90Fle-609
❑ 90FleCan-609
❑ 90HOFStiB-83
❑ 90Lea-188
❑ 90MLBBasB-90
❑ 90OPC-107
❑ 90OPC-663
❑ 90OPCBoxB-H
❑ 90PadCok-10
❑ 90PadMag-17
❑ 90PanSti-73
❑ 90PubIntS-476
❑ 90Sco-131
❑ 90ScoRoo-20T
❑ 90SouCalS-9
❑ 90Top-107
❑ 90Top-663
❑ 90TopAmeA-10
❑ 90TopBig-277
❑ 90TopHilHM-14
❑ 90TopSti-279
❑ 90TopTif-107
❑ 90TopTif-663
❑ 90TopTra-62T
❑ 90TopTraT-62T
❑ 90TopWaxBC-H
❑ 90UppDec-247
❑ 90UppDec-771
❑ 91Don-673
❑ 91Fle-536
❑ 91OPC-586
❑ 91OriCro-272
❑ 91Sco-554
❑ 91Top-586
❑ 91TopDesS-586
❑ 91TopMic-586
❑ 91TopTif-586
❑ 91UppDec-273
❑ 94TedWil-4
❑ 94TedWilM-M34
❑ 95SonGre-8
❑ 99UppDecRI-FL
❑ 99UppDecRIL2-FL
Lynn, Greg
❑ 83CliGiaF-6
❑ 91GiaMot-28
Lynn, Ken
❑ 83AndBraT-11
Lynn, Red (Japhet)
❑ 47SigOil-28
❑ 48AngTeal-18
❑ 49AngTeal-21
❑ 49W725AngTI-16
❑ 53MotCoo-58
Lynn, Thomas
❑ 83LynPirT-26
Lyons, Albert
❑ 52MotCoo-42
❑ 53SanFraSTI-11
Lyons, Barry
❑ 86MetColP-24
❑ 86MetTCM-15
❑ 86TidTidP-16
❑ 87MetColP-55
❑ 87TopTra-68T
❑ 87TopTraT-68T
❑ 88Don-619
❑ 88DonTeaBM-619
❑ 88Fle-140
❑ 88FleGlo-140
❑ 88MetColP-33
❑ 88MetKah-33
❑ 88Sco-387
❑ 88ScoGlo-387
❑ 88StaLinMe-11
❑ 88Top-633
❑ 88TopClo-64
❑ 88TopTif-633
❑ 89Don-572
❑ 89FleUpd-101
❑ 89MetColP-41
❑ 89MetKah-15
❑ 89Sco-456
❑ 89Top-412
❑ 89TopTif-412
❑ 89UppDec-176
❑ 90Bow-139
❑ 90BowTif-139
❑ 90Don-526
❑ 90Fle-209
❑ 90FleCan-209
❑ 90Lea-119
❑ 90MetColP-16
❑ 90MetKah-33
❑ 90OPC-258
❑ 90Sco-29
❑ 90Top-258
❑ 90TopBig-97
❑ 90TopTif-258
❑ 90TopTVM-20
❑ 90UppDec-473
❑ 91DodMot-25
❑ 91DodPol-40
❑ 91MetWIZ-238
❑ 92TucTorF-490
❑ 92TucTorS-612
❑ 93LouRedF-218
❑ 94IndIndF-1814
❑ 94TriAAF-AAA32
❑ 95NasSouTI-12
❑ 98ChaAllCM-26
Lyons, Bill (William Allen)
❑ 82LouRedE-14
❑ 82SprCarF-4
❑ 83LouRedR-27
❑ 84Car-20
❑ 84Car5x7-17
❑ 84LouRedR-14
❑ 85LouRedR-17
❑ 86LouRedTI-17
❑ 87LouRedTI-24
❑ 88LouRedBC-12
❑ 88LouRedBP-432
❑ 88LouRedBTI-30
❑ 90SprCarDGB-32
Lyons, Bobby
❑ 83AleDukT-1
Lyons, Curt
❑ 92PriRedC-11
❑ 92PriRedF-3083
❑ 93BilMusF-3940
❑ 93BilMusSP-6
❑ 96ChaLooB-18
❑ 97BowCerBlaIA-CA50
❑ 97BowCerBluIA-CA50
❑ 97BowCerGolIA-CA50
❑ 97Cir-41
❑ 97CirRav-41
❑ 97IowCub-17
❑ 97MetUniMfG-7
❑ 97UppDec-469
Lyons, Dennis
❑ 87OldJudN-304
❑ 90KalBatN-2
❑ 90KalBatN-30
❑ 90KalBatN-31
❑ 98CamPepP-46
Lyons, Eddie
❑ 90MisStaB-23
❑ 91MisStaB-30
❑ 92MisStaB-26
❑ 93MisStaB-27
Lyons, Edward Hoyte
❑ 47SenGunBP-9
Lyons, George
❑ 21Zee-14
❑ 22Zee-11
❑ 23Zee-14
Lyons, Harry P.
❑ 87OldJudN-305
Lyons, Jimmie
❑ 74LauOldTBS-14
❑ 86NegLeaF-114
Lyons, Jonathan
❑ 97SarRedS-13
❑ 98MicBatCM-21
Lyons, Mario
❑ 90BenBucL-23
Lyons, Mike
❑ 97CapCitB-7
❑ 98St.LucMM-3
Lyons, Steve
❑ 92ClaDraP-78
❑ 93CapCitBC-11
❑ 93CapCitBF-457
❑ 93StaCluM-45
❑ 94St.LucMC-17
❑ 94St.LucMF-1192
❑ 98WatIndTI-16
Lyons, Steve (Stephen John)
❑ 84PawRedST-18
❑ 85Don-29
❑ 85FleUpd-76
❑ 86Don-579
❑ 86Fle-355
❑ 86SevCoi-E9
❑ 86Top-233
❑ 86TopTif-233
❑ 86TopTra-67T
❑ 86TopTraT-67T
❑ 87Don-409
❑ 87Fle-502
❑ 87FleGlo-502
❑ 87Top-511
❑ 87TopTif-511
❑ 87WhiSoxC-19
❑ 88Don-532
❑ 88DonBasB-291
❑ 88Fle-405
❑ 88FleGlo-405
❑ 88PanSti-60
❑ 88StaLinWS-12
❑ 88Top-108
❑ 88TopTif-108
❑ 88WhiSoxC-15
❑ 89Bow-63
❑ 89BowTif-63
❑ 89Don-253
❑ 89Fle-502
❑ 89FleGlo-502
❑ 89OPC-334
❑ 89PanSti-308
❑ 89Sco-388
❑ 89Top-334
❑ 89TopBig-105
❑ 89TopSti-298
❑ 89TopTif-334
❑ 89UppDec-224
❑ 89WhiSoxC-17
❑ 89WhiSoxK-2
❑ 90Bow-321
❑ 90BowTif-321
❑ 90Don-651
❑ 90Fle-539
❑ 90FleCan-539
❑ 90OPC-751
❑ 90PanSti-40
❑ 90PubIntS-395
❑ 90Sco-88
❑ 90Top-751

❑ 90TopBig-32
❑ 90TopSti-301
❑ 90TopTif-751
❑ 90UppDec-390
❑ 90WhiSoxC-15
❑ 91Fle-127
❑ 91FleUpd-6
❑ 91OPC-612
❑ 91RedSoxP-18
❑ 91Sco-269
❑ 91Top-612
❑ 91TopDesS-612
❑ 91TopMic-612
❑ 91TopTif-612
❑ 91Ult-77
❑ 91UltUpd-7
❑ 91UppDec-601
❑ 92Don-758
❑ 92OPC-349
❑ 92Sco-294
❑ 92Top-349
❑ 92TopGol-349
❑ 92TopGolW-349
❑ 92TopMic-349
❑ 93PawRedSDD-14
❑ 93PawRedSF-2420
Lyons, Ted
❑ 28Exh-39
❑ 28StaPlaCE-45
❑ 30SchR33-33
❑ 30UncJac-21
❑ 30WhiSoxTI-17
❑ 31Exh-19
❑ 31W517-45
❑ 32OrbPinUP-43
❑ 33ButCre-17
❑ 33CraJacP-16
❑ 33DouDisP-30
❑ 33ExhFou-10
❑ 33Gou-7
❑ 33GouCanV-7
❑ 33TatOrb-43
❑ 33TatOrbSDR-172
❑ 34BatR31-36
❑ 34BatR31-111
❑ 34BatR31-119
❑ 34DiaMatCSB-118
❑ 34DiaStaR-43
❑ 35AlDemDCR3-19
❑ 35ExhFou-10
❑ 35GouPuzR-8B
❑ 35GouPuzR-9B
❑ 36ExhFou-10
❑ 36OveCanR-33
❑ 38BasTabP-21
❑ 38CloFotW-52
❑ 38ExhFou-10
❑ 39WhiSoxTI-12
❑ 40WhiSoxL-13
❑ 46SpoExcW-4-5
❑ 48BabRutS-22
❑ 48WhiSoxTI-16
❑ 50CalHOFW-49
❑ 53ArtHaloFP-55
❑ 61Fle-122
❑ 63BazA-38
❑ 67TopVen-174
❑ 76ChiGre-12
❑ 76RowExh-1
❑ 76ShaPiz-76
❑ 76TayBow4-92
❑ 76WhiSoxTAG-6
❑ 77GalGloG-110
❑ 80PacLeg-77
❑ 80PerHaloFP-77
❑ 80PerHaloFPS-6
❑ 80SSPHOF-77
❑ 80WhiSoxGT-1
❑ 81ConTSN-92
❑ 82DiaCla-41
❑ 83TCMPla1942-18
❑ 85WhiSoxC-41
❑ 91ConTSN-19
❑ 92ConTSN-359
❑ 93ConTSN-822
❑ 93ConTSN-935
❑ 94ConTSN-1248
❑ 94ConTSNB-1248
Lyons, Tim
❑ 97DanBraB-22
Lysander, Rick (Richard)
❑ 76TucTorCa-17
❑ 76TusTorCr-28
❑ 79OgdA'sT-11
❑ 80OgdA'sT-6
❑ 80VenLeaS-8
❑ 81TacTigT-23
❑ 82TucTorT-16
❑ 83TwiTeal-13
❑ 84Don-560
❑ 84Fle-570
❑ 84Nes792-639
❑ 84TolMudHT-23
❑ 84Top-639
❑ 84TopTif-639
❑ 85Don-560
❑ 85Fle-284
❑ 85Top-383
❑ 85TopTif-383
❑ 85TwiPos-17
❑ 85TwiTeal-14
❑ 85TwiTeal-15
❑ 86Fle-399
❑ 86Top-482
❑ 86TopTif-482
❑ 89PacSenL-143
❑ 89TopSenL-68
❑ 90CMC-338
❑ 90ProAAAF-349
❑ 90SyrChiC-12
❑ 90SyrChiMB-16
❑ 90SyrChiP-569
❑ 91PacSenL-39
❑ 91PacSenL-52
Lysgaard, Jim
❑ 76ForLauYS-8
❑ 77WesHavYT-14
❑ 78TacYanC-18
Lytle, Wade
❑ 89PriPirS-11
Lyttle, Jim
❑ 70OPC-516
❑ 70Top-516
❑ 70YanPhoS-22
❑ 71OPC-234
❑ 71Top-234
❑ 71YanCliDP-9
❑ 72Top-648
❑ 74OPC-437
❑ 74Top-437
❑ 75ExpPos-18
❑ 76ExpRed-19
❑ 76MonExpP-18
❑ 76SSP-337
❑ 79TCMJapPB-32
❑ 90DodTar-467
❑ 92YanWIZ6-76
❑ 92YanWIZ7-100
Maack, B.J.
❑ 98ArkTraM-29
Maack, Mike
❑ 83WisRapTF-18
❑ 98TenKry-3
Maas, Duke (Duane)
❑ 56Top-57
❑ 57Top-405
❑ 58Top-228
❑ 59Top-167
❑ 59TopVen-167
❑ 60Top-421
❑ 61Top-387
❑ 61TopMagR-28
❑ 61Yan61RL-30
❑ 79TCM50-117
❑ 91YanRinP13-5
❑ 92YanWIZ6-77
Maas, Jason
❑ 86Ft.LauYP-15
❑ 87PriWilYP-24
❑ 88AlbYanP-1346
❑ 89AlbYanB-24
❑ 89AlbYanP-334
❑ 89AlbYanSt-12
❑ 90CMC-215
❑ 90ColCliC-15
❑ 90ColCliP-8
❑ 90ColCliP-690
❑ 90ProAAAF-340
❑ 90TopTVY-52
❑ 91ColCliLD-111
❑ 91ColCliP-11
❑ 91ColCliP-609
❑ 91LinDriAAA-111
Maas, Kevin
❑ 87Ft.LauYP-19
❑ 88EasLeaAP-2
❑ 88PriWilYS-15
❑ 89ColCliC-17
❑ 89ColCliP-22
❑ 89ColCliP-737
❑ 89TriAAAP-AAA18
❑ 90AlbDecGB-12
❑ 90Bow-440
❑ 90BowTif-440
❑ 90ClaUpd-T30
❑ 90CMC-217
❑ 90ColCliC-17
❑ 90ColCliP-4
❑ 90ColCliP-691
❑ 90ColMaa-1
❑ 90ColMaa-2
❑ 90ColMaa-3
❑ 90ColMaa-4
❑ 90ColMaa-5
❑ 90ColMaa-6
❑ 90ColMaa-7
❑ 90ColMaa-8
❑ 90ColMaa-9
❑ 90ColMaa-10
❑ 90ColMaa-11
❑ 90ColMaa-12
❑ 90Fle-641
❑ 90FleCan-641
❑ 90FleUpd-113
❑ 90Lea-446
❑ 90ProAAAF-341
❑ 90Sco-606
❑ 90Sco100RS-27
❑ 90StaFS7-19
❑ 90StaMaa-1
❑ 90StaMaa-2
❑ 90StaMaa-3
❑ 90StaMaa-4
❑ 90StaMaa-5
❑ 90StaMaa-6
❑ 90StaMaa-7
❑ 90StaMaa-8
❑ 90StaMaa-9
❑ 90StaMaa-10
❑ 90StaMaa-11
❑ 90TopMag-31
❑ 90TopTra-63T
❑ 90TopTraT-63T
❑ 90TopTVY-53
❑ 90TriAAAC-24
❑ 90UppDec-70
❑ 90UppDecS-2
❑ 91Bow-158
❑ 91Cla1-T63
❑ 91Cla1-NNO
❑ 91Cla3-T51
❑ 91ClaGam-130
❑ 91Col-21
❑ 91Don-554
❑ 91Fle-672
❑ 91JimDea-23
❑ 91KinDis-3
❑ 91Lea-393
❑ 91MajLeaCP-2
❑ 91MLBKeyC-2
❑ 91OPC-4
❑ 91OPC-435
❑ 91OPCPre-74
❑ 91PanSti-264
❑ 91Pos-30
❑ 91PosCan-20
❑ 91Sco-600
❑ 91Sco100RS-40
❑ 91ScoHotR-2
❑ 91Sev3DCN-10
❑ 91SevCoi-NE10
❑ 91StaClu-282
❑ 91StaCluCM-18
❑ 91StaCluP-21
❑ 91Stu-96
❑ 91Top-4
❑ 91Top-435
❑ 91TopCraJI-20
❑ 91TopDeb90-92
❑ 91TopDesS-4
❑ 91TopDesS-435
❑ 91TopMic-4
❑ 91TopMic-435
❑ 91TopRoo-17
❑ 91TopSta-22
❑ 91TopTif-4
❑ 91TopTif-435
❑ 91ToyRoo-16
❑ 91Ult-238
❑ 91UppDec-375
❑ 91Woo-13
❑ 92Bow-205
❑ 92ClaGam-55
❑ 92ColPro-10
❑ 92Don-153
❑ 92Fle-236
❑ 92Hig5-88
❑ 92Lea-284
❑ 92LeaBlaG-284
❑ 92MooSna-5
❑ 92MVPPin-2
❑ 92OPC-710
❑ 92Pin-90
❑ 92RedFolS-57
❑ 92Sco-613
❑ 92Sco100S-46
❑ 92ScoProP-24
❑ 92SpoStaCC-30
❑ 92StaClu-35
❑ 92StaPro-6
❑ 92Stu-215
❑ 92Top-710
❑ 92TopGol-710
❑ 92TopGolW-710
❑ 92TopKid-86
❑ 92TopMic-710
❑ 92TriPla-225
❑ 92Ult-104
❑ 92UppDec-98
❑ 92UppDec-377
❑ 93Don-635
❑ 93Fle-652
❑ 93Lea-206
❑ 93PacSpa-207
❑ 93PanSti-147
❑ 93Pin-165
❑ 93Sco-634
❑ 93Sel-142
❑ 93StaClu-395
❑ 93StaCluFDI-395
❑ 93StaCluMOP-395
❑ 93Top-168
❑ 93TopGol-168
❑ 93TopInaM-168
❑ 93TopInaR-168
❑ 93TopMic-168
❑ 93TriPla-57
❑ 93Ult-243
❑ 93UppDec-594
❑ 93UppDecGold-594
❑ 93YanStaC-8
❑ 94Fle-238
❑ 94Pac-429
❑ 94Sco-425
❑ 94ScoGolR-425
❑ 94WicWraF-199
❑ 95ColCliP-17
❑ 95ColCliTI-17
❑ 95FleUpd-60
❑ 97IndInd-13
Maas, Steve
❑ 98LanLugQ-8
Maasberg, Gary
❑ 88SpaPhiP-1041
Mabe, Bobby (Robert)
❑ 59RedEnq-13
❑ 59SeaPop-26
❑ 59Top-356
❑ 60Top-288
❑ 91OriCro-273
Mabe, Todd
❑ 85Ft.MyeRT-2
Mabee, Vic
❑ 77AshTouT-13
❑ 79WauTimT-6
Maberry, Louis
❑ 92PriRedC-17
❑ 92PriRedF-3084
❑ 93WesVirWC-16
❑ 93WesVirWF-2864
❑ 94ClaGolF-192
Maberry, Mark
❑ 98CapCitBF5-12
❑ 98CapCitBM-12
Mabry, John
❑ 91HamRedC-17
❑ 91HamRedP-4053
❑ 92ProFS7-331
❑ 92SprCarC-19
❑ 92SprCarF-883
❑ 92UppDecML-234
❑ 93ArkTraF-2824
❑ 94Bow-124
❑ 94ExcFS7-269
❑ 94LeaLimR-29
❑ 94LouRedF-2993
❑ 94ScoRoo-RT130
❑ 94ScoRooGR-RT130
❑ 94SigRooDP-97
❑ 94SigRooDPS-97
❑ 94SpoRoo-100
❑ 94SpoRooAP-100
❑ 95Bow-185
❑ 95BowBes-R77
❑ 95BowBesR-R77
❑ 95ColCho-21
❑ 95ColChoGS-21
❑ 95ColChoSS-21
❑ 95Don-260
❑ 95DonPreP-260
❑ 95DonTopotO-332
❑ 95Fin-303
❑ 95FinRef-303
❑ 95Fla-412
❑ 95Fle-502
❑ 95Lea-6
❑ 95Pin-151
❑ 95PinArtP-151
❑ 95PinMusC-151
❑ 95Sco-301
❑ 95ScoAi-AM2
❑ 95ScoGolR-301
❑ 95ScoPlaTS-301
❑ 95SelCer-126
❑ 95SelCerMG-126
❑ 95TopTra-83T
❑ 95UC3-119
❑ 95UC3ArtP-119
❑ 95Ult-432
❑ 95UltGolM-432
❑ 95UppDec-56
❑ 95UppDecED-56
❑ 95UppDecEDG-56
❑ 96CarPol-16
❑ 96Cir-179
❑ 96CirRav-179
❑ 96ColCho-693
❑ 96ColChoGS-693
❑ 96ColChoSS-693
❑ 96Don-253
❑ 96DonPreP-253
❑ 96EmoXL-269
❑ 96Fla-362
❑ 96Fle-547
❑ 96FleRooS-11
❑ 96FleTif-547
❑ 96Lea-197
❑ 96LeaPre-98
❑ 96LeaPreP-98
❑ 96LeaPrePB-197
❑ 96LeaPrePG-197
❑ 96LeaPrePS-197
❑ 96LeaSig-56
❑ 96LeaSigA-140
❑ 96LeaSigAG-140
❑ 96LeaSigAS-140
❑ 96LeaSigPPG-56
❑ 96LeaSigPPP-56
❑ 96MetUni-228
❑ 96MetUniP-228
❑ 96Pac-222
❑ 96PanSti-76
❑ 96Pin-12
❑ 96PinAfi-126
❑ 96PinAfiAP-126
❑ 96PinArtP-60
❑ 96PinSta-60
❑ 96Sco-293
❑ 96ScoDugC-B18
❑ 96ScoDugCAP-B18
❑ 96Sel-40
❑ 96SelArtP-40
❑ 96Spo-88
❑ 96SpoArtP-88
❑ 96StaClu-46
❑ 96StaCluMOP-46
❑ 96Sum-112
❑ 96SumAbo&B-112
❑ 96SumArtP-112
❑ 96SumFoi-112
❑ 96Top-73
❑ 96TopGal-102
❑ 96TopGalPPI-102
❑ 96Ult-276
❑ 96UltGolM-276
❑ 96UppDec-184
❑ 97CarPol-17
❑ 97Cir-346
❑ 97CirRav-346
❑ 97ColCho-203
❑ 97Don-90
❑ 97DonEli-94
❑ 97DonEliGS-94
❑ 97DonGolPP-90
❑ 97DonLim-97
❑ 97DonLimE-97
❑ 97DonLimENG-97
❑ 97DonPre-127
❑ 97DonPreCttC-127
❑ 97DonSilPP-90
❑ 97DonTea-154
❑ 97DonTeaSPE-154
❑ 97Fin-97
❑ 97FinRef-97
❑ 97Fle-447
❑ 97FleTif-447
❑ 97Lea-35
❑ 97LeaFraM-35
❑ 97LeaFraMDC-35
❑ 97MetUni-233
❑ 97Pac-413
❑ 97PacLigB-413
❑ 97PacPri-140
❑ 97PacPriLB-140
❑ 97PacPriP-140
❑ 97PacSil-413
❑ 97PinIns-15
❑ 97PinInsCE-15
❑ 97PinInsDE-15
❑ 97Sco-118
❑ 97ScoArtPWB-118
❑ 97ScoPreS-118
❑ 97ScoShoS-118
❑ 97ScoShoSAP-118
❑ 97StaClu-167
❑ 97StaCluMOP-167
❑ 97Stu-86
❑ 97StuPrePG-86
❑ 97StuPrePS-86
❑ 97Top-102
❑ 97Top-171
❑ 97Ult-274
❑ 97UltGolME-274
❑ 97UltPlaME-274
❑ 97UppDec-163
❑ 97UppDec-316
❑ 98CarScoP-9
❑ 98ColCho-474
❑ 98Fin-127
❑ 98FinNo--127
❑ 98FinNo-R-127
❑ 98FinRef-127
❑ 98Fle-516
❑ 98PacInvGems-204
❑ 98PacOnl-618
❑ 98PacOnlR-618
❑ 98PacOnlWC-618
❑ 98PinSna-SLC15
❑ 98Sco-122
❑ 98ScoCar-9
❑ 98Top-56
❑ 98TopChr-56
❑ 98TopChrR-56
❑ 98TopDevR-56
❑ 98TopDia-56
❑ 98TopMiniC-56
❑ 98UppDec-493
❑ 99Fle-470
❑ 99FleSta9-470
❑ 99FleWarT-470
❑ 99StaClu-118
❑ 99StaCluFDI-118
❑ 99StaCluOoaK-118
❑ 99StaCluPP-118
❑ 99UppDec-493
❑ 99UppDecEL1-493
❑ 99UppDecEL2-493
Macaluso, Nick
❑ 88MarPhiS-25
Macalutas, Jon
❑ 96OgdRapTI-39
❑ 97BelSnaB-20
❑ 98StoPorG-18
MacArthur, John
❑ 84AriWilP-11
MacArthur, Mark
❑ 90HamRedB-21
❑ 90HamRedS-15
❑ 91SavCarC-19
❑ 91SavCarP-1660
❑ 92VisOakC-11
❑ 92VisOakF-1022
Macauley, Drew
❑ 80BufBisT-6
❑ 81BufBisT-7
Macavage, Joe
❑ 87WatPirP-26
❑ 88AugPirP-372
Macca, Chris
❑ 96AshTouB-24
❑ 96MauStiHWB-14
❑ 97NewHavRB-17
MacCauley, John
❑ 92SouOreAC-21
❑ 92SouOreAF-3414

❑ 93SouOreAC-16
❑ 93SouOreAF-4060
MacCormack, Franc
❑ 76DetTigP-18
❑ 78SanJosMMC-4
MacDonald, Bill
❑ 50PirTeal-12
❑ 51Bow-239
❑ 52Top-138
❑ 83TopRep5-138
MacDonald, Jim
❑ 78DayBeaAT-17
❑ 80ColAstT-20
❑ 81TucTorT-23
MacDonald, Ken
❑ 91BriBanF-10
❑ 93AusFut-19
❑ 95AusFut-73
MacDonald, Kevin
❑ 79NewCoPT-11
MacDonald, Mike
❑ 95MidLeaA-29
❑ 95SprSulTI-12
MacDonald, Robert
❑ 88MyrBeaBJP-1191
❑ 89KnoBluJB-13
❑ 89KnoBluJP-1139
❑ 89KnoBluJS-11
❑ 90KnoBluJP-1247
❑ 90KnoBluJS-10
❑ 90ProAaA-44
❑ 91BluJayFS-18
❑ 91BluJayS-32
❑ 91Don-636
❑ 91LinDriAAA-508
❑ 91StaClu-585
❑ 91SyrChiLD-508
❑ 91SyrChiMB-15
❑ 91TopDeb90-93
❑ 91UltUpd-61
❑ 92Don-588
❑ 92Fle-335
❑ 92OPC-87
❑ 92OPCPre-152
❑ 92Sco-405
❑ 92Sco100RS-46
❑ 92StaClu-372
❑ 92Top-87
❑ 92TopGol-87
❑ 92TopGolW-87
❑ 92TopMic-87
❑ 93BluJayD4-36
❑ 93Don-689
❑ 93Fle-696
❑ 93FleFinE-212
❑ 93OPC-131
❑ 93PacSpa-447
❑ 93StaClu-434
❑ 93StaCluFDI-434
❑ 93StaCluMOP-434
❑ 93TigGat-20
❑ 93Top-427
❑ 93TopGol-427
❑ 93TopInaM-427
❑ 93TopInaR-427
❑ 93TopMic-427
❑ 93Ult-289
❑ 94CalCanF-785
❑ 94Don-415
❑ 94Fle-140
❑ 94Pac-225
❑ 94Sco-286
❑ 94ScoGolR-286
❑ 94Top-162
❑ 94TopGol-162
❑ 94TopSpa-162
❑ 94Ult-57
MacDonald, Ronald
❑ 79JacMetT-23
❑ 80TidTidT-9
❑ 82TidTidT-10
MacDonald, Stew
❑ 62SeaPop-4
Mace, Jeff
❑ 83BurRanF-24
❑ 83BurRanT-21
❑ 85TulDriTI-24
❑ 88BoiHawP-1616
❑ 89BoiHawP-1977
Macey, Fausto
❑ 95Bow-218
❑ 97VanCanB-19
Macfarlane, Mike
❑ 86MemChiSTOS-16
❑ 86MemChiTOS-16
❑ 87OmaRoyP-24
❑ 88DonRoo-55
❑ 88FleUpd-31
❑ 88FleUpdG-31
❑ 88RoySmo-17
❑ 88RoyTeal-19
❑ 88ScoRoo-76T
❑ 88ScoRooG-76T
❑ 88StaLinRo-9
❑ 88TopTra-62T
❑ 88TopTraT-62T
❑ 89Bow-118
❑ 89BowTif-118
❑ 89Don-416
❑ 89Fle-287
❑ 89FleGlo-287
❑ 89Sco-319
❑ 89ScoHot1R-97
❑ 89ScoYouSI-13
❑ 89Top-479
❑ 89TopBig-86
❑ 89TopTif-479
❑ 89UppDec-546
❑ 90Don-498
❑ 90Fle-114
❑ 90FleCan-114
❑ 90Lea-389
❑ 90OPC-202
❑ 90PubIntS-352
❑ 90RoyPos-15
❑ 90Top-202
❑ 90TopTif-202
❑ 90UppDec-307
❑ 91Bow-301
❑ 91Don-313
❑ 91Fle-562
❑ 91Lea-30
❑ 91OPC-638
❑ 91PanFreS-275
❑ 91RoyPol-13
❑ 91Sco-839
❑ 91StaClu-15
❑ 91Top-638
❑ 91TopDesS-638
❑ 91TopMic-638
❑ 91TopTif-638
❑ 91Ult-151
❑ 91UppDec-570
❑ 92Bow-589
❑ 92Don-161
❑ 92Fle-161
❑ 92Lea-83
❑ 92LeaBlaG-83
❑ 92OPC-42
❑ 92Pin-517
❑ 92RoyPol-15
❑ 92Sco-27
❑ 92StaClu-74
❑ 92Top-42
❑ 92TopGol-42
❑ 92TopGolW-42
❑ 92TopMic-42
❑ 92TriPla-144
❑ 92Ult-73
❑ 92UppDec-497
❑ 93Bow-505
❑ 93DiaMar-66
❑ 93Don-525
❑ 93Fla-220
❑ 93Fle-241
❑ 93Lea-422
❑ 93OPC-265
❑ 93PanSti-102
❑ 93Pin-332
❑ 93RoyPol-17
❑ 93RoyStaC-2
❑ 93Sco-323
❑ 93SP-232
❑ 93StaClu-470
❑ 93StaCluFDI-470
❑ 93StaCluMOP-470
❑ 93Top-768
❑ 93TopGol-768
❑ 93TopInaM-768
❑ 93TopInaR-768
❑ 93TopMic-768
❑ 93Ult-564
❑ 93UppDec-327
❑ 93UppDecGold-327
❑ 93UppDecHRH-HR25
❑ 94Bow-227
❑ 94ColC-181
❑ 94ColChoGS-181
❑ 94ColChoSS-181
❑ 94Don-324
❑ 94Fin-300
❑ 94FinRef-300
❑ 94Fla-61
❑ 94Fle-164
❑ 94FleExtB-95
❑ 94Lea-159
❑ 94OPC-154
❑ 94Pac-294
❑ 94PanSti-77
❑ 94Pin-488
❑ 94PinArtP-488
❑ 94PinMusC-488
❑ 94Sco-459
❑ 94ScoGolR-459
❑ 94Sel-27
❑ 94StaClu-250
❑ 94StaCluFDI-250
❑ 94StaCluGR-250
❑ 94StaCluMOP-250
❑ 94Stu-187
❑ 94Top-578
❑ 94TopGol-578
❑ 94TopSpa-578
❑ 94TriPla-239
❑ 94Ult-69
❑ 94UppDec-107
❑ 94UppDecED-107
❑ 95ColCho-459
❑ 95ColCho-574T
❑ 95ColChoGS-459
❑ 95ColChoSE-213
❑ 95ColChoSEGS-213
❑ 95ColChoSESS-213
❑ 95ColChoSS-459
❑ 95Don-439
❑ 95DonPreP-439
❑ 95DonTopotO-22
❑ 95Fin-165
❑ 95Fin-227
❑ 95FinRef-165
❑ 95FinRef-227
❑ 95Fla-228
❑ 95Fle-165
❑ 95FleUpd-11
❑ 95Lea-379
❑ 95Pac-208
❑ 95Pin-113
❑ 95PinArtP-113
❑ 95PinMusC-113
❑ 95Sco-96
❑ 95ScoGolR-96
❑ 95ScoPlaTS-96
❑ 95SP-126
❑ 95SPSil-126
❑ 95StaClu-175
❑ 95StaClu-530
❑ 95StaCluFDI-175
❑ 95StaCluMOP-175
❑ 95StaCluMOP-530
❑ 95StaCluSTDW-RS530
❑ 95StaCluSTWS-175
❑ 95StaCluSTWS-530
❑ 95Top-296
❑ 95TopCyb-159
❑ 95TopTra-37T
❑ 95Ult-292
❑ 95UltGolM-292
❑ 95UppDec-396
❑ 95UppDecED-396
❑ 95UppDecEDG-396
❑ 95UppDecSE-54
❑ 95UppDecSEG-54
❑ 96ColCho-64
❑ 96ColCho-575
❑ 96ColChoGS-64
❑ 96ColChoGS-575
❑ 96ColChoSS-64
❑ 96ColChoSS-575
❑ 96Don-119
❑ 96DonPreP-119
❑ 96Fle-30
❑ 96FleTif-30
❑ 96FleUpd-U41
❑ 96FleUpdTC-U41
❑ 96LeaSigA-141
❑ 96LeaSigAG-141
❑ 96LeaSigAS-141
❑ 96Pac-257
❑ 96RoyPol-16
❑ 96Sco-108
❑ 96StaClu-108
❑ 96StaCluEPB-108
❑ 96StaCluEPG-108
❑ 96StaCluEPS-108
❑ 96StaCluMOP-108
❑ 96TeaOut-52
❑ 96Top-33
❑ 96Ult-18
❑ 96Ult-358
❑ 96UltGolM-18
❑ 96UltGolM-358
❑ 96UppDec-347
❑ 97Cir-35
❑ 97CirRav-35
❑ 97ColCho-355
❑ 97Fin-227
❑ 97FinRef-227
❑ 97Fle-116
❑ 97FleTif-116
❑ 97Pac-105
❑ 97PacLigB-105
❑ 97PacSil-105
❑ 97RoyPol-14
❑ 97StaClu-281
❑ 97StaCluMOP-281
❑ 97Top-198
❑ 97Ult-482
❑ 97UltGolME-482
❑ 97UltPlaME-482
❑ 97UppDec-88
❑ 98A'sMot-18
❑ 98Pac-106
❑ 98PacOnl-535
❑ 98PacOnlR-535
❑ 98PacOnlWC-535
❑ 98PacPlaB-106
❑ 98PacRedT-106
❑ 98PacSil-106
❑ 98UppDec-111
❑ 99Fle-458
❑ 99FleSta9-458
❑ 99FleWarT-458
❑ 99UppDec-447
❑ 99UppDecEL1-447
❑ 99UppDecEL2-447
MacFayden, Dan
❑ 31Exh-18
❑ 33ExhFou-9
❑ 33Gou-156
❑ 33GouCanV-87
❑ 34DiaMatCSB-119
❑ 35GouPuzR-4F
❑ 35GouPuzR-7F
❑ 35GouPuzR-12F
❑ 36ExhFou-1
❑ 36GouWidPPR-A68
❑ 37ExhFou-1
❑ 38CloFotW-53
❑ 38ExhFou-1
❑ 79RedSoxEF-7
❑ 85BigLeaC3-12
❑ 91ConTSN-215
Macha, Ken
❑ 72Dia-27
❑ 76VenLeaS-168
❑ 77ColCliT-11
❑ 78ColCliT-15
❑ 78Top-483
❑ 79ExpPos-16
❑ 80ExpPos-16
❑ 81Don-540
❑ 81Fle-167
❑ 82Fle-618
❑ 82OPC-282
❑ 82Top-282
❑ 86ExpPos-7
❑ 86ExpProPa-28
❑ 87ExpPos-16
❑ 89ExpPos-18
❑ 90ExpPos-21
❑ 93AngMot-28
❑ 94AngMot-28
❑ 95TreThuTI-1
❑ 96DouAllB-1
❑ 96TreThuB-1
❑ 97PawRedS-2
❑ 98PawRedSQ-2
Macha, Mike
❑ 78RicBraT-7
❑ 80VenLeaS-127
Machado, Albenis
❑ 98VerExpO-25
Machado, Gregorio
❑ 76VenLeaS-146
❑ 80VenLeaS-138
❑ 93LinVenB-142
❑ 96-97LinVen-31
Machado, Julio
❑ 87ClePhiP-21
❑ 89JacMetGS-11
❑ 89PenPilS-12
❑ 90ClaUpd-T31
❑ 90Don-47
❑ 90DonRoo-41
❑ 90FleUpd-37
❑ 90MetColP-39
❑ 90MetKah-48
❑ 90OPC-684
❑ 90ScoRoo-92T
❑ 90Top-684
❑ 90TopDeb89-74
❑ 90TopTif-684
❑ 90TopTVM-14
❑ 90TriAAAC-28
❑ 90UppDec-93
❑ 91Bow-50
❑ 91BreMilB-15
❑ 91BrePol-13
❑ 91Don-764
❑ 91FleUpd-31
❑ 91Lea-247
❑ 91MetWIZ-240
❑ 91OPC-434
❑ 91Sco100RS-87
❑ 91Top-434
❑ 91TopDesS-434
❑ 91TopMic-434
❑ 91TopTif-434
❑ 91UppDec-716
❑ 92Don-262
❑ 92Fle-181
❑ 92OPC-208
❑ 92Sco-353
❑ 92Top-208
❑ 92TopGol-208
❑ 92TopGolW-208
❑ 92TopMic-208
❑ 92UppDec-479
❑ 93LinVenB-59
❑ 94BreMilB-52
❑ 94VenLinU-211
❑ 96-97LinVen-117
Machado, Robert
❑ 92UtiBluSC-14
❑ 93LinVenB-156
❑ 93MidLeaAGF-24
❑ 93SouBenWSC-14
❑ 93SouBenWSF-1433
❑ 94PriWilCC-14
❑ 94PriWilCF-1924
❑ 94VenLinU-251
❑ 95LinVen-197
❑ 95LinVen-258
❑ 95PriWilCTI-14
❑ 96-97LinVen-167
❑ 96-97LinVen-281
❑ 96BirBarB-10
❑ 98PacInvGems-31
❑ 98PriWilCASM-13
❑ 98SpoIll-149
❑ 98SpoIllEE-149
❑ 98SpoIllFE-149
❑ 99MetUni-264
❑ 99MetUniGM-264
❑ 99MetUniPMG-264
Machalec, Mark
❑ 84ButCopKT-15
Machemer, Dave
❑ 77SalLakCGC-11
❑ 78SalLakCGC-3
❑ 80EvaTriT-16
❑ 81TolMudHT-13
❑ 82TolMudHT-14
❑ 85BelBreT-26
❑ 86StoPorP-14
❑ 87StoPorP-3
❑ 88ElPasDB-6
❑ 89DenZepC-25
❑ 89DenZepP-37
❑ 90CMC-50
❑ 90DenZepC-25
❑ 90DenZepP-641
❑ 90ProAAAF-666
❑ 90TriAllGP-AAA26
❑ 96El PasDB-4
❑ 97El PasDB-24
❑ 98DelShoM-2
Machold, A. D.
❑ 16Zee-113
Machuca, Freddy
❑ 82DanSunF-19
Macias, Angel
❑ 91EugEmeC-19
❑ 91EugEmeP-3724
Macias, Bob
❑ 82AmaGolST-6
Macias, Henry
❑ 77CedRapGT-8
❑ 78CedRapGT-16
Macias, Jaime
❑ 96CedRapKTI-30
❑ 97CedRapK-16
❑ 98ButCopKG-19
Macias, Jose
❑ 96DelShoB-20
❑ 97LakTigB-21
❑ 98JacSunM-16
❑ 99Bow-309
❑ 99BowGol-309
❑ 99BowInt-309
❑ 99DumSet-115
❑ 99FleMys-115
❑ 99FleMysM-115
❑ 99SkyPre-235
❑ 99SkyPre-235
❑ 99SkyPreR-235
❑ 99SkyPreR-235
Mack, Connie
❑ 04FanCraAL-33
❑ 09SpoNewSM-37
❑ 10E98-19
❑ 10JHDABE-11
❑ 10NadE1-33
❑ 11A'sFirT20-12
❑ 11D35RocB-12
❑ 11PinT-5-505
❑ 11SpoLifCW-228
❑ 11SpoLifM-98
❑ 12PhiCarE-18
❑ 13LawSemC-5
❑ 13NatGamW-26
❑ 13TomBarW-25
❑ 14CraJacE-12
❑ 14TexTomE-28
❑ 14TexTomE-56
❑ 15CraJacE-12
❑ 15SpoNewM-105
❑ 16BF2FP-38
❑ 16SpoNewM-107
❑ 23WilChoV-85
❑ 32OrbPinUP-44
❑ 33TatOrb-44
❑ 33TatOrbSDR-188
❑ 36Halof FP-17
❑ 36NatChiFPR-94
❑ 36R31PasP-36
❑ 36R31Pre-L8
❑ 36WorWidGV-110
❑ 39PC7AlbHoF-9
❑ 40PlaBal-132
❑ 42A'sTeal-21
❑ 43A'STEAI-15
❑ 43A'STEAI-16
❑ 46A'sTeal-10
❑ 47A'sTeal-18
❑ 48A'sTeal-14
❑ 48ExhHoF-21
❑ 49A'sTeal-20
❑ 49PhiBul-31
❑ 50CalHOFW-50
❑ 50H80FouMH-1
❑ 51A'sTeal-19
❑ 51R42SmaS-67
❑ 51TopConMA-7
❑ 52A'sTeal-16
❑ 53A'sTeal-16
❑ 60Fle-14
❑ 61Fle-123
❑ 63BasMagM-51
❑ 63BazA-18
❑ 68SCFOldT-19
❑ 68SpoMemAG-2
❑ 69Baz-10
❑ 74A's192T-17
❑ 74CapPub-56
❑ 76ShaPiz-12
❑ 76TayBow4-47
❑ 76TayBow4-81
❑ 77BobParHoF-33
❑ 77GalGloG-145
❑ 77GalGloG-194
❑ 77PhiFav-1
❑ 77ShaPiz-1
❑ 78DexHaloFP-32
❑ 80LauFamF-37
❑ 80PerHaloFP-9
❑ 80SSPHOF-9
❑ 81ConTSN-58
❑ 81SpoHaloF-4
❑ 82BHCRSpoL-9
❑ 83A'sGreT-12
❑ 83BigLeaCOA-2
❑ 84GalHaloFRL-12
❑ 84SpoDesPW-39
❑ 86ConSer1-18
❑ 87OldJudN-306

❑ 88AugBecN-22
❑ 88ConHar-4
❑ 88GandBCGCE-25
❑ 88WG1CarG-67
❑ 89HOFStiB-85
❑ 90BasWit-99
❑ 90HOFStiB-45
❑ 91ConTSN-45
❑ 91ConTSN-46
❑ 91ConTSN-47
❑ 92ConTSN-439
❑ 92ConTSN-599
❑ 92ConTSNCI-14
❑ 93ConTSN-824
❑ 93CraJac-10
❑ 93DiaStaES-142
❑ 94ConTSN-1159
❑ 94ConTSN-1217
❑ 94ConTSNB-1159
❑ 94ConTSNB-1217
❑ 94OriofB-84
❑ 94TedWil-69
❑ 94UppDecTAE-43

Mack, Connie III
❑ 76TayBow4-81

Mack, Earle
❑ 42A'sTeal-22
❑ 43A'STEAl-17
❑ 45A'sTeal-24
❑ 49A'sTeal-21
❑ 49PhiBul-32
❑ 51A'sTeal-20
❑ 74A's192T-17
❑ 76TayBow4-82
❑ 81ConTSN-57
❑ 92ConTSN-453

Mack, Frank
❑ 22Zee-133

Mack, Henry
❑ 77SpaPhiT-7

Mack, Jerry
❑ 86KenTwiP-14

Mack, Joseph
❑ 87OldJudN-307

Mack, Quinn
❑ 88WesPalBES-17
❑ 89JacExpB-14
❑ 89JacExpP-153
❑ 90CMC-66
❑ 90IndIndC-16
❑ 90IndIndP-299
❑ 90ProAAAF-582
❑ 91IndIndLD-188
❑ 91IndIndP-475
❑ 91LinDriAAA-188
❑ 92IndIndF-1874
❑ 92IndIndS-186
❑ 93LinVenB-41
❑ 94CalCanF-801
❑ 95LinVen-207
❑ 95TacRaiTI-11
❑ 98HelBreM-3

Mack, Ray
❑ 72TCMthe1-200
❑ 77TCMTheWY-2
❑ 83TCMPla1943-6

Mack, Raymond
❑ 89WytCubS-21
❑ 90PulBraP-3090
❑ 91MacBraC-4
❑ 91MacBraP-858

Mack, Roy
❑ 76TayBow4-81

Mack, Shane
❑ 85BeaGolGT-4
❑ 85Top-398
❑ 85TopTif-398
❑ 86BeaGolGP-16
❑ 87DonRoo-42
❑ 87LasVegSP-18
❑ 87SpoRoo2-31
❑ 87SpoTeaP-16
❑ 87TopTra-69T
❑ 87TopTraT-69T
❑ 88Don-411
❑ 88Fle-590
❑ 88FleGlo-590
❑ 88LasVegSC-10
❑ 88LasVegSP-233
❑ 88OPC-283
❑ 88PadSmo-16
❑ 88Sco-414
❑ 88ScoGlo-414
❑ 88ScoYouS2-36
❑ 88Top-548
❑ 88TopTif-548
❑ 89Don-538
❑ 89Sco-270
❑ 89UppDec-182
❑ 90ClaYel-T17
❑ 90DonBesA-122
❑ 90Lea-136
❑ 90TopTra-64T
❑ 90TopTraT-64T
❑ 91Bow-326
❑ 91DodPho-22
❑ 91Don-320
❑ 91Fle-618
❑ 91Lea-40
❑ 91OPC-672
❑ 91Sco-284
❑ 91StaClu-259
❑ 91StaCluP-22
❑ 91Stu-88
❑ 91Top-672
❑ 91TopDesS-672
❑ 91TopMic-672
❑ 91TopTif-672
❑ 91Ult-191
❑ 91UppDec-188
❑ 92Bow-592
❑ 92Cla1-T55
❑ 92Don-345
❑ 92Fle-210
❑ 92Lea-82
❑ 92LeaBlaG-82
❑ 92OPC-164
❑ 92PanSti-119
❑ 92Pin-230
❑ 92Sco-284
❑ 92ScoSam-6
❑ 92StaClu-47
❑ 92Stu-207
❑ 92Top-164
❑ 92TopDaiQTU-8
❑ 92TopGol-164
❑ 92TopGolW-164
❑ 92TopMic-164
❑ 92TriPla-197
❑ 92Ult-95
❑ 92UppDec-428
❑ 93Bow-101
❑ 93ClaGam-55
❑ 93Don-395
❑ 93Fin-61
❑ 93FinRef-61
❑ 93Fla-238
❑ 93Fle-640
❑ 93FleFruotL-38
❑ 93FunPac-194
❑ 93Lea-315
❑ 93OPC-263
❑ 93PacSpa-174
❑ 93PanSti-129
❑ 93Pin-78
❑ 93Sco-19
❑ 93Sel-104
❑ 93SP-249
❑ 93StaClu-420
❑ 93StaCluFDI-420
❑ 93StaCluMOP-420
❑ 93Top-282
❑ 93TopGol-282
❑ 93TopInaM-282
❑ 93TopInaR-282
❑ 93TopMic-282
❑ 93TriPla-180
❑ 93Ult-585
❑ 93UppDec-236
❑ 93UppDec-837
❑ 93UppDecGold-236
❑ 93UppDecGold-837
❑ 93USPlaCA-5D
❑ 94ColC-182
❑ 94ColChoGS-182
❑ 94ColChoSS-182
❑ 94Don-253
❑ 94Fin-105
❑ 94FinRef-105
❑ 94Fla-315
❑ 94Fle-212
❑ 94FleExtB-120
❑ 94Lea-435
❑ 94LeaL-50
❑ 94Pac-360
❑ 94PanSti-93
❑ 94Pin-148
❑ 94PinArtP-148
❑ 94PinMusC-148
❑ 94Sco-383
❑ 94ScoGolR-383
❑ 94Sel-274
❑ 94StaClu-429
❑ 94StaCluFDI-429
❑ 94StaCluGR-429
❑ 94StaCluMOP-429
❑ 94Stu-198
❑ 94Top-337
❑ 94TopGol-337
❑ 94TopSpa-337
❑ 94TriPla-255
❑ 94Ult-390
❑ 94UppDec-197
❑ 94UppDecED-197
❑ 95ColChoSE-228
❑ 95ColChoSEGS-228
❑ 95ColChoSESS-228
❑ 95Don-526
❑ 95DonPreP-526
❑ 95Fle-208
❑ 95PacPri-80
❑ 95Sco-43
❑ 95ScoGolR-43
❑ 95ScoHaloG-HG54
❑ 95ScoPlaTS-43
❑ 95StaClu-362
❑ 95StaCluMOP-362
❑ 95StaCluSTWS-362
❑ 95StaCluVR-189
❑ 95StaCluVRMO-189
❑ 95Top-8
❑ 95TopCyb-6
❑ 95UppDec-190
❑ 95UppDecED-190
❑ 95UppDecEDG-190
❑ 97ColCho-282
❑ 97DonTea-56
❑ 97DonTeaSPE-56
❑ 97Fle-603
❑ 97FleTif-603
❑ 97Ult-463
❑ 97UltGolME-463
❑ 97UltPlaME-463
❑ 98PacInvGems-22
❑ 98RedSoxS-15
❑ 98RedSoxSP-15
❑ 98Sco-231
❑ 99Pac-206
❑ 99PacPlaB-206
❑ 99PacRed-206

Mack, Toby (Tony Lynn)
❑ 83RedPioT-17
❑ 85EdmTraC-6
❑ 86EdmTraP-20
❑ 87MidAngP-19
❑ 88SanAntMB-5
❑ 89MiaMirIS-12

MacKanin, Pete
❑ 74OPC-597
❑ 74SpoIndC-42
❑ 74Top-597
❑ 75ExpPos-19
❑ 76ExpRed-20
❑ 76MonExpP-20
❑ 76OPC-287
❑ 76SSP-324
❑ 76Top-287
❑ 76VenLeaS-55
❑ 77ExpPos-20
❑ 77OPC-260
❑ 77Top-156
❑ 78Top-399
❑ 79PhiBurK-17
❑ 80TwiPos-17
❑ 81Fle-565
❑ 81Top-509
❑ 81TwiPos-19
❑ 82Don-354
❑ 82Fle-556
❑ 82Top-438
❑ 83OklCit8T-12
❑ 84IowCubT-12
❑ 86PeoChiP-17
❑ 88IowCubC-24
❑ 88IowCubP-543
❑ 89IowCubC-25
❑ 89IowCubP-1707
❑ 89TriAAAP-AAA43
❑ 90CMC-149
❑ 90NasSouC-24
❑ 90NasSouP-249
❑ 90ProAAAF-561
❑ 91LinDriAAA-274
❑ 91NasSouLD-274
❑ 91NasSouP-2172
❑ 91PacSenL-66
❑ 91TriA AAGP-AAA24
❑ 92NasSouF-1848
❑ 92NasSouS-299
❑ 93FreKeyC-26
❑ 93FreKeyF-1042
❑ 93RanKee-236
❑ 94BowBayF-2427

MacKay, Bill
❑ 83AndBraT-1

MacKay, Joey
❑ 83GreHorT-25
❑ 84GreHorT-8

MacKenzie, Gordon
❑ 75WesPalBES-17
❑ 77JacSunT-13
❑ 82CubRedL-NNO
❑ 83EvaTriT-22
❑ 84EvaTriT-4
❑ 85NasSouTI-13
❑ 86GiaMot-28
❑ 86GiaPos-22
❑ 87GiaMot-27
❑ 87GiaPos-19
❑ 88GiaMot-27
❑ 88GiaPos-18
❑ 89PhoFirC-25
❑ 89PhoFirP-1504
❑ 95KinIndTI-17

MacKenzie, Kenneth P.
❑ 60Top-534
❑ 61Top-496
❑ 62Top-421
❑ 63Top-393
❑ 64Top-297
❑ 64TopVen-297
❑ 67AstTeal2-16
❑ 81TCM60I-433
❑ 82MetGal62-14
❑ 91MetWIZ-239

MacKenzie, Shaun
❑ 86EveGiaC-20
❑ 86EveGiaPC-12
❑ 87EveGiaC-20

Mackey, Biz
❑ 74LauOldTBS-27
❑ 86NegLeaF-91
❑ 90NegLeaS-4
❑ 91PomBlaBPB-23

Mackey, Jason
❑ 93BurIndC-17
❑ 93BurIndF-3294

Mackie, Bart
❑ 81BatTroT-9
❑ 82WauTimF-6

Mackie, Ed
❑ 93HelBreF-4102
❑ 93HelBreSP-18

Mackie, Scott
❑ 89MiaMirIS-12

Mackiewicz, Felix
❑ 42A'sTeal-23
❑ 48SomandK-15
❑ 83TCMPla1945-14

Mackin, Jeff
❑ 90MisStaB-24
❑ 91MisStaB-31
❑ 92MisStaB-27
❑ 93MisStaB-28

MacKinnon, Tim
❑ 88BoiHawP-1629

Macko, Joe
❑ 76DalCon-7
❑ 90RanMot-28

Macko, Steve
❑ 80Top-676
❑ 80WicAerT-18
❑ 81Don-535
❑ 81Top-381

Mackowiak, Robert
❑ 97EriSeaWB-24
❑ 98LynHilQ-18

MacLeish, Rick
❑ 80PhiBul-17

MacLeod, Bill
❑ 62SeaPop-5

MacLeod, Kevin
❑ 88SouOreAP-1709
❑ 89ModA'sCLC-273
❑ 90HunStaB-8

Maclin, Lonnie
❑ 88St.PetCS-14
❑ 89SprCarB-25
❑ 90LouRedBLBC-24
❑ 90St.PetCS-14
❑ 91LinDriAAA-239
❑ 91LouRedLD-239
❑ 91LouRedP-2928
❑ 91LouRedTI-25
❑ 92LouRedF-1901
❑ 92LouRedS-267
❑ 92SkyAAAF-127
❑ 93LouRedF-227
❑ 94Pin-407
❑ 94PinArtP-407
❑ 94PinMusC-407

MacMillan, Chris
❑ 98WatIndTI-17

MacMillan, Darrell
❑ 89BoiHawP-1986
❑ 90EriSaiS-14

MacNeil, Doug
❑ 92ElmPioC-16
❑ 92ElmPioF-1380
❑ 92WinHavRSC-11

MacNeil, Tim
❑ 88ButCopKSP-4
❑ 89GasRanP-1024
❑ 89GasRanS-11
❑ 90MiaMirIS-15

Macon, Leland
❑ 94Bow-569
❑ 94ChaRivC-13
❑ 94ChaRivF-2685

Macon, Max
❑ 38CloFotW-54
❑ 43DodTeal-15
❑ 77TCMTheWY-48
❑ 79DiaGre-218
❑ 90DodTar-468

MacPhail, Larry
❑ 78DexHaloFP-33
❑ 80PerHaloFP-165
❑ 82OhiHaloF-62
❑ 88DodRinP1-8B
❑ 92YanWIZH-21

MacPherson, Bruce
❑ 77OrlTwiT-14
❑ 78OrlTwiT-11
❑ 80TolMudHT-4
❑ 81TolMudHT-7
❑ 82RocRedWT-3

MacQuarrie, Dave
❑ 75WesPalBES-24

MacRae, Scott
❑ 95BilMusTI-23
❑ 97BurBeeB-15
❑ 98ChaLooG-18

Macrina, Eric
❑ 91SalLakTP-3218

Macrory, Robert
❑ 98PeoChiM-14

Macu, Andres
❑ 90KisDodD-15

Macullar, James
❑ 87OldJudN-308

MacWhorter, Keith
❑ 80VenLeaS-162
❑ 81Top-689
❑ 83PawRedST-8
❑ 84MaiGuiT-21

Macy, Frank
❑ 82IowCubT-30
❑ 84IowCubT-10

Madden, Billy
❑ 81TCM60I-391

Madden, Bob
❑ 76AppFoxT-13
❑ 77AppFoxT-13
❑ 79QuaCitCT-17
❑ 80QuaCitCT-11

Madden, Joey
❑ 93BatCliCB-16
❑ 93BatCliF-3159
❑ 94BatCliC-11
❑ 94BatCliF-3458

Madden, Kid (Michael)
❑ 87OldJudN-309
❑ 88AugBecN-23
❑ 89N526N7C-9

Madden, Mike
❑ 81ElPasDT-14
❑ 82VanCanT-14
❑ 83AstPos-16
❑ 83TopTra-64T
❑ 84AstMot-25
❑ 84AstPos-16
❑ 84Don-161
❑ 84Fle-232
❑ 84Nes792-127
❑ 84Top-127
❑ 84TopTif-127
❑ 85Top-479
❑ 85TopTif-479
❑ 86AstMilL-14
❑ 86AstPol-18
❑ 86Top-691
❑ 86TopTif-691

Madden, Morris
❑ 83VerBeaDT-8
❑ 86GleFalTP-13
❑ 87TolMudHP-18
❑ 87TolMudHT-15
❑ 88BlaYNPRWL-153
❑ 88BufBisC-6
❑ 88BufBisP-1466
❑ 88BufBisTI-8
❑ 89BlaYNPRWLU-29
❑ 89ScoHot1R-32
❑ 90AlbDukCm-5
❑ 90AlbDukP-340
❑ 90AlbDukTr-19
❑ 90CMC-407
❑ 90ProAAAF-61
❑ 90TriAAAC-11

Madden, Scott
❑ 86ClePhiP-16
❑ 88RenSilSCLC-273

Madden, Thomas
❑ 09ColChiE-175
❑ 09ObaT21-324
❑ 11PacCoaBD-36
❑ 11PinT-5-665
❑ 11SpoLifM-13
❑ 11Zee-89
❑ 12ColRedB-175
❑ 12ColTinT-175
❑ 12ObaPreT-73
❑ 12Zee-86

Maddern, Clarence
❑ 49AngTeal-22
❑ 49Bow-152
❑ 49W725AngTI-17
❑ 52MotCoo-44
❑ 53MotCoo-34
❑ 54SeaPop-16
❑ 85TCMPpl1-8

Maddon, Joe
❑ 76QuaCitAT-19
❑ 85MidAngT-10
❑ 86MidAngP-14
❑ 94AngMot-28
❑ 95AngMot-28
❑ 96AngMot-28

Maddox, Derrick
❑ 98BatMucTI-15

Maddox, Elliott
❑ 71MLBOffS-545
❑ 71OPC-11
❑ 71SenPolP-7
❑ 71SenTealW-15
❑ 71Top-11
❑ 72OPC-277
❑ 72RanTeal-18
❑ 72Top-277
❑ 72TopCloT-21
❑ 73OPC-658
❑ 73RanTeal-16
❑ 73Top-658
❑ 74OPC-401
❑ 74Top-401
❑ 75Hos-90
❑ 75Kel-9
❑ 75OPC-113
❑ 75Top-113
❑ 75TopMin-113
❑ 75YanSSP-10
❑ 76OPC-503
❑ 76SSP-451
❑ 76Top-503
❑ 77Top-332
❑ 78Hos-40
❑ 78MetDaiPA-15
❑ 78Top-442
❑ 79OPC-28
❑ 79Top-69
❑ 80OPC-357
❑ 80Top-707
❑ 81Don-397
❑ 81Fle-326
❑ 81OPC-299
❑ 81Top-299
❑ 90SweBasG-109
❑ 91MetWIZ-241
❑ 91OriCro-274
❑ 92YanWIZ7-101
❑ 93RanKee-26

Maddox, Garry

❑ 72GiaTeal-12
❑ 73LinPor-160
❑ 73OPC-322
❑ 73Top-322
❑ 74OPC-178
❑ 74Top-178
❑ 74TopSta-107
❑ 75Hos-43
❑ 75HosTwi-43
❑ 75Kel-37
❑ 75OPC-240
❑ 75PhiPhiP-21
❑ 75Top-240
❑ 75TopMin-240
❑ 76OPC-38
❑ 76PhiPhiP-17
❑ 76Top-38
❑ 77BurCheD-167
❑ 77Kel-37
❑ 77OPC-42
❑ 77Top-520
❑ 78Hos-133
❑ 78Kel-28
❑ 78OPC-93
❑ 78RCColC-78
❑ 78SSP270-28
❑ 78Top-610
❑ 78WifBalD-42
❑ 79BasPat-49
❑ 79Kel-16
❑ 79OPC-245
❑ 79PhiBurK-20
❑ 79PhiTeal-5
❑ 79Top-470
❑ 80OPC-198
❑ 80PhiBul-36
❑ 80PhiBurK-10
❑ 80Top-380
❑ 81AllGamPI-151
❑ 81CokTeaS-101
❑ 81Don-55
❑ 81Fle-19
❑ 81FleStiC-70
❑ 81OPC-160
❑ 81Top-160
❑ 81TopSti-204
❑ 81TopSupHT-83
❑ 82Don-315
❑ 82Fle-248
❑ 82FleSta-57
❑ 82OPC-20
❑ 82Top-20
❑ 82TopSti-73
❑ 82TopStiV-73
❑ 83AllGamPI-151
❑ 83Don-63
❑ 83Fle-164
❑ 83FleSta-111
❑ 83FleSti-173
❑ 83OPC-41
❑ 83PhiTas-15
❑ 83Top-615
❑ 83TopFol-5
❑ 84Don-305
❑ 84Fle-39
❑ 84FleSti-122
❑ 84Nes792-755
❑ 84OPC-187
❑ 84PhiTas-39
❑ 84Top-755
❑ 84TopSti-123
❑ 84TopTif-755
❑ 85Don-137
❑ 85Fle-259
❑ 85OPC-235
❑ 85PhiCIG-11
❑ 85PhiTas-38
❑ 85Top-235
❑ 85TopMin-235
❑ 85TopSti-121
❑ 85TopTif-235
❑ 86Don-407
❑ 86Fle-445
❑ 86OPC-362
❑ 86PhiTas-31
❑ 86Top-585
❑ 86TopSti-117
❑ 86TopTat-14
❑ 86TopTif-585
❑ 88PhiTas-39
❑ 90PhiTas-36
❑ 97CalLeaATI-16
❑ 97HigDesMG-13
❑ 97HigDesMUG-14
❑ 98JacGenM-10

Maddox, Jerry

❑ 78RicBraT-8
❑ 79RicBraT-6

Maddox, Leland

❑ 87MadMusP-13

Maddox, Nicholas

❑ 08RosComP-154
❑ 09ColChiE-176A
❑ 09ColChiE-176B
❑ 09PhiCarE-15
❑ 09T206-219
❑ 10DomDisP-73
❑ 10NadE1-34
❑ 10PirAmeCE-7
❑ 10PirTipTD-11
❑ 10SweCapPP-141
❑ 11PinT-5-861
❑ 11SpoLifCW-229
❑ 11SpoLifM-255
❑ 11T205-106
❑ 12ColRedB-176A
❑ 12ColRedB-176B
❑ 12ColTinT-176A
❑ 12ColTinT-176B
❑ 72ClaCar-75

Maddux, Greg

❑ 86PitCubP-14
❑ 87CubCan-16
❑ 87CubDavB-31
❑ 87Don-36
❑ 87DonRoo-52
❑ 87FleUpd-68
❑ 87FleUpdG-68
❑ 87Lea-36
❑ 87SpoTeaP-22
❑ 87TopTra-70T
❑ 87TopTraT-70T
❑ 88CubDavB-31
❑ 88Don-539
❑ 88DonBasB-82
❑ 88DonTeaBC-539
❑ 88Fle-423
❑ 88FleGlo-423
❑ 88OPC-361
❑ 88PeoChiTI-21
❑ 88Top-361
❑ 88TopSti-59
❑ 88TopTif-361
❑ 89Bow-284
❑ 89BowTif-284
❑ 89CadElID-33
❑ 89ClaTraO-121
❑ 89CubMar-31
❑ 89Don-373
❑ 89DonAll-56
❑ 89DonBasB-37
❑ 89Fle-431
❑ 89FleBasM-24
❑ 89FleForTR-5
❑ 89FleGlo-431
❑ 89FleSup-28
❑ 89OPC-240
❑ 89PanSti-49
❑ 89PeoChiTI-28
❑ 89RedFolSB-77
❑ 89Sco-119
❑ 89ScoHot1S-48
❑ 89ScoYouSI-39
❑ 89Spo-108
❑ 89Top-240
❑ 89TopMinL-4
❑ 89TopSti-48
❑ 89TopTif-240
❑ 89TVSpoM-23
❑ 89UppDec-241
❑ 90Bow-27
❑ 90BowTif-27
❑ 90ClaUpd-T32
❑ 90CubMar-13
❑ 90Don-158
❑ 90DonBesN-14
❑ 90Fle-37
❑ 90FleCan-37
❑ 90Lea-25
❑ 90MLBBasB-49
❑ 90OPC-715
❑ 90PanSti-237
❑ 90PeoChiTI-20
❑ 90PubIntS-198
❑ 90Sco-403
❑ 90Spo-211
❑ 90Top-715
❑ 90TopBig-204
❑ 90TopDou-41
❑ 90TopMinL-50
❑ 90TopSti-51
❑ 90TopTif-715
❑ 90TopTVCu-12
❑ 90UppDec-213
❑ 91Bow-426
❑ 91Cla3-T52
❑ 91ClaGam-68
❑ 91CubMar-31
❑ 91CubVinL-17
❑ 91Don-374
❑ 91Fle-426
❑ 91Lea-127
❑ 91OPC-35
❑ 91PanCanT1-98
❑ 91PanFreS-50
❑ 91PanSti-43
❑ 91Sco-317
❑ 91StaClu-126
❑ 91Top-35
❑ 91TopDesS-35
❑ 91TopMic-35
❑ 91TopTif-35
❑ 91Ult-64
❑ 91UppDec-115
❑ 92Bow-148
❑ 92ClaGam-30
❑ 92CubMar-31
❑ 92Don-520
❑ 92Fle-386
❑ 92Hig5-29
❑ 92Lea-294
❑ 92LeaBlaG-294
❑ 92OPC-580
❑ 92PanSti-189
❑ 92Pin-65
❑ 92Pin-608
❑ 92PinTea2-32
❑ 92RedFolS-58
❑ 92Sco-269
❑ 92ScoImpP-77
❑ 92SpoIllFK1-162
❑ 92SpoIllFK1-737
❑ 92StaClu-665
❑ 92StaCluECN-665
❑ 92Stu-15
❑ 92Top-580
❑ 92TopGol-580
❑ 92TopGolW-580
❑ 92TopMic-580
❑ 92TriPla-19
❑ 92Ult-178
❑ 92UltAwaW-24
❑ 92UppDec-353
❑ 92UppDecTMH-30
❑ 93Bow-550
❑ 93BraLykP-17
❑ 93BraLykS-21
❑ 93BraStaC-18
❑ 93ClaGam-56
❑ 93ClaGam-NNO
❑ 93Don-608
❑ 93DonEliD-3
❑ 93DurPowP2-12
❑ 93Fin-85
❑ 93FinJum-85
❑ 93FinRef-85
❑ 93Fla-7
❑ 93Fle-380
❑ 93Fle-707
❑ 93FleAll-NL10
❑ 93FleAtl-13
❑ 93FleFinE-3
❑ 93FleFruotL-39
❑ 93FunPac-65
❑ 93Lea-326
❑ 93LeaGolA-R19
❑ 93MSABenSPD-4
❑ 93OPC-135
❑ 93OPCPre-126
❑ 93OPCPreSP-19
❑ 93OPCPreSPF-19
❑ 93PacSpa-335
❑ 93PanSti-159
❑ 93PanSti-164
❑ 93Pin-517
❑ 93PinTeaP-1
❑ 93RedFolS-55
❑ 93Sco-484
❑ 93Sco-527
❑ 93Sco-576
❑ 93Sel-31
❑ 93SelAce-4
❑ 93SelChaS-9
❑ 93SelDufIP-9
❑ 93SelRoo-123T
❑ 93SelStaL-66
❑ 93SelStaL-78
❑ 93SelStaL-84
❑ 93SelStaL-88
❑ 93SP-59
❑ 93StaClu-2
❑ 93StaClu-665
❑ 93StaClu-750
❑ 93StaCluFDI-2
❑ 93StaCluFDI-665
❑ 93StaCluFDI-750
❑ 93StaCluM-126
❑ 93StaCluMO-14
❑ 93StaCluMOP-2
❑ 93StaCluMOP-665
❑ 93StaCluMOP-750
❑ 93StaCluMP-27
❑ 93Stu-196
❑ 93Top-183
❑ 93Top-409
❑ 93TOPBLAG-12
❑ 93TopComotH-17
❑ 93TopComotH-19
❑ 93TopGol-183
❑ 93TopGol-409
❑ 93TopInaM-183
❑ 93TopInaM-409
❑ 93TopInaR-183
❑ 93TopInaR-409
❑ 93TopMic-183
❑ 93TopMic-409
❑ 93TopTra-54T
❑ 93TriPlaG-GS4
❑ 93TriPlaLL-L2
❑ 93Ult-307
❑ 93UltAllS-9
❑ 93UltAwaW-1
❑ 93UltAwaW-22
❑ 93UltPer-6
❑ 93UppDec-472
❑ 93UppDec-488
❑ 93UppDec-535
❑ 93UppDecGold-472
❑ 93UppDecGold-488
❑ 93UppDecGold-535
❑ 93USPlaCA-13S
❑ 94Bow-245
❑ 94BowBes-R36
❑ 94BowBes-X101
❑ 94BowBesR-R36
❑ 94BowBesR-X101
❑ 94BraLykP-19
❑ 94BraLykS-19
❑ 94BraUSPC-1D
❑ 94BraUSPC-8S
❑ 94ChuHomS-4
❑ 94ChuHomSG-4
❑ 94ColC-183
❑ 94ColChoGS-183
❑ 94ColChoSS-183
❑ 94Don-380
❑ 94DonAwaWJ-2
❑ 94DonSpeE-380
❑ 94Fin-209
❑ 94FinJum-209
❑ 94FinRef-209
❑ 94Fla-130
❑ 94FlaHotG-5
❑ 94Fle-365
❑ 94FleAwaW-4
❑ 94FleExtB-208
❑ 94FleExtBGB-16
❑ 94FleExtBPD-7
❑ 94FleLeaL-12
❑ 94FleSmo'nH-7
❑ 94FleSun-16
❑ 94FUnPac-131
❑ 94FUnPac-184
❑ 94FUnPac-207
❑ 94KinDis-18
❑ 94Lea-94
❑ 94LeaGolS-8
❑ 94LeaL-87
❑ 94LeaLimGA-18
❑ 94LeaStaS-5
❑ 94O-PJumAF-22
❑ 94OPC-101
❑ 94OPCAllR-22
❑ 94OPCJumA-22
❑ 94OscMayR-26
❑ 94Pac-15
❑ 94Pac-656
❑ 94PacPro-P5
❑ 94PacSilP-30
❑ 94PacSilPC-30
❑ 94PanSti-147
❑ 94Pin-11
❑ 94PinArtP-11
❑ 94PinMusC-11
❑ 94PinSam-11
❑ 94PinTeaP-9
❑ 94PinTheN-15
❑ 94PinTri-TR12
❑ 94ProMag-5
❑ 94ProMagP-2
❑ 94RedFolMI-16
❑ 94Sco-524
❑ 94Sco-634
❑ 94ScoGolR-524
❑ 94ScoGolR-634
❑ 94Sel-2
❑ 94SelCroC-CC2
❑ 94SP-54
❑ 94SPDieC-54
❑ 94Spo-53
❑ 94Spo-193
❑ 94SpoFanA-AS9
❑ 94SpoSam-193
❑ 94StaClu-544
❑ 94StaClu-716
❑ 94StaCluFDI-544
❑ 94StaCluFDI-716
❑ 94StaCluGR-544
❑ 94StaCluGR-716
❑ 94StaCluMO-42
❑ 94StaCluMOP-544
❑ 94StaCluMOP-716
❑ 94StaCluT-31
❑ 94StaCluTFDI-31
❑ 94Stu-39
❑ 94StuSerS-8
❑ 94StuSerSG-8
❑ 94TomPiz-14
❑ 94Top-392
❑ 94Top-499
❑ 94TopBlaG-38
❑ 94TopGol-392
❑ 94TopGol-499
❑ 94TopSpa-392
❑ 94TopSpa-499
❑ 94TopSupS-26
❑ 94TopTraFI-1
❑ 94TriPla-46
❑ 94TriPlaM-14
❑ 94TriPlaP-10
❑ 94Ult-446
❑ 94UltAllS-20
❑ 94UltAwaW-18
❑ 94UltAwaW-23
❑ 94UltStrK-3
❑ 94UppDec-320
❑ 94UppDecAJ-18
❑ 94UppDecAJG-18
❑ 94UppDecED-320
❑ 94USPlaCA-1S
❑ 95Baz-1
❑ 95BazRedH-RH1
❑ 95Bow-406
❑ 95BowBes-R15
❑ 95BowBesJR-4
❑ 95BowBesR-R15
❑ 95ClaPhoC-3
❑ 95ColCho-63
❑ 95ColCho-67
❑ 95ColChoGS-63
❑ 95ColChoGS-67
❑ 95ColChoSE-60
❑ 95ColChoSE-142
❑ 95ColChoSE-249
❑ 95ColChoSEGS-60
❑ 95ColChoSEGS-142
❑ 95ColChoSEGS-249
❑ 95ColChoSESS-60
❑ 95ColChoSESS-142
❑ 95ColChoSESS-249
❑ 95ColChoSS-63
❑ 95ColChoSS-67
❑ 95DenHol-14
❑ 95Don-331
❑ 95DonAll-NL1
❑ 95DonDiaK-DK22
❑ 95DonDom-1
❑ 95DonEli-51
❑ 95DonMouM-1
❑ 95DonPreP-331
❑ 95DonTopotO-190
❑ 95Emo-106
❑ 95EmoMas-6
❑ 95Fin-213
❑ 95FinRef-213
❑ 95Fla-105
❑ 95FlaHotN-6
❑ 95Fle-311
❑ 95FleAllF-9
❑ 95FleAllS-9
❑ 95FleAwaW-4
❑ 95FleLeaL-9
❑ 95FlePro-4
❑ 95FleTeaL-15
❑ 95FleUpdDT-8
❑ 95FleUpdH-13
❑ 95KinDis-23
❑ 95Kra-25
❑ 95Lea-115
❑ 95LeaChe-6
❑ 95LeaGolS-9
❑ 95LeaGreG-11
❑ 95LeaLim-115
❑ 95LeaLimG-15
❑ 95NatPac2-4
❑ 95Pac-11
❑ 95PacGolCDC-1
❑ 95PacPri-4
❑ 95PanSti-6
❑ 95PanSti-109
❑ 95PanSti-120
❑ 95Pin-244
❑ 95PinArtP-244
❑ 95PinFan-21
❑ 95PinGatA-GA16
❑ 95PinMusC-244
❑ 95PinPer-PP12
❑ 95PinPin-1
❑ 95PinPinR-1
❑ 95PinRedH-RH12
❑ 95PinTeaP-TP1
❑ 95PinWhiH-WH12
❑ 95Pos-3
❑ 95PosCan-15
❑ 95RedFol-9
❑ 95Sco-32
❑ 95ScoDouGC-GC6
❑ 95ScoDreT-DG11
❑ 95ScoGolR-32
❑ 95ScoHaloG-HG18
❑ 95ScoPlaTS-32
❑ 95ScoRul-SR15
❑ 95ScoRulJ-SR15
❑ 95Sel-21
❑ 95SelArtP-21
❑ 95SelCer-59
❑ 95SelCerMG-59
❑ 95SP-31
❑ 95SPCha-25
❑ 95SPChaDC-25
❑ 95SPChaDFC-7
❑ 95SPChaFCDC-7
❑ 95Spo-45
❑ 95SpoArtP-45
❑ 95SpoDouT-12
❑ 95SPSil-31
❑ 95SPSpeF-29
❑ 95StaClu-46
❑ 95StaClu-425
❑ 95StaCluFDI-46
❑ 95StaCluMO-30
❑ 95StaCluMOP-46
❑ 95StaCluMOP-425
❑ 95StaCluSTDW-B425
❑ 95StaCluSTMP-7
❑ 95StaCluSTWS-46
❑ 95StaCluSTWS-425
❑ 95StaCluVR-222
❑ 95StaCluVRMO-222
❑ 95Stu-6
❑ 95StuGolS-6
❑ 95StuPlaS-6
❑ 95Sum-30
❑ 95Sum-189
❑ 95SumNthD-30
❑ 95SumNthD-189
❑ 95TomPiz-5
❑ 95Top-295
❑ 95Top-392
❑ 95TopCyb-158
❑ 95TopEmb-109
❑ 95TopEmbGI-109
❑ 95TopLeaL-LL24
❑ 95UC3-61
❑ 95UC3-129
❑ 95UC3ArtP-61
❑ 95UC3ArtP-129
❑ 95UC3InM-IM8
❑ 95Ult-129
❑ 95UltAllS-12
❑ 95UltAllSGM-12
❑ 95UltAwaW-18
❑ 95UltAwaW-22
❑ 95UltAwaWGM-18
❑ 95UltAwaWGM-22
❑ 95UltGolM-129

❑ 95UltLeaL-8
❑ 95UltLeaLGM-8
❑ 95UltStrK-4
❑ 95UltStrKGM-4
❑ 95UppDec-49
❑ 95UppDec-101
❑ 95UppDecC-5A
❑ 95UppDecC-3B
❑ 95UppDecED-49
❑ 95UppDecED-101
❑ 95UppDecEDG-49
❑ 95UppDecEDG-101
❑ 95UppDecPAW-H27
❑ 95UppDecPAWE-H27
❑ 95UppDecSE-151
❑ 95UppDecSEG-151
❑ 95USPlaCMLA-1S
❑ 95Zen-37
❑ 95ZenZ-8
❑ 96Baz-79
❑ 96Bow-67
❑ 96BowBes-85
❑ 96BowBesAR-85
❑ 96BowBesMI-9
❑ 96BowBesMIAR-9
❑ 96BowBesMIR-9
❑ 96BowBesP-BBP14
❑ 96BowBesPAR-BBP14
❑ 96BowBesPR-BBP14
❑ 96BowBesR-85
❑ 96BowFoi-67
❑ 96BraFle-11
❑ 96Cir-105
❑ 96CirAcc-14
❑ 96CirBos-27
❑ 96CirRav-105
❑ 96Cla7/1PC-6
❑ 96ColCho-6
❑ 96ColCho-8
❑ 96ColCho-40
❑ 96ColCho-268
❑ 96ColCho-386T
❑ 96ColCho-396
❑ 96ColCho-709
❑ 96ColCho-754
❑ 96ColChoGS-6
❑ 96ColChoGS-8
❑ 96ColChoGS-40
❑ 96ColChoGS-268
❑ 96ColChoGS-396
❑ 96ColChoGS-709
❑ 96ColChoGS-754
❑ 96ColChoSS-6
❑ 96ColChoSS-8
❑ 96ColChoSS-40
❑ 96ColChoSS-268
❑ 96ColChoSS-396
❑ 96ColChoSS-709
❑ 96ColChoSS-754
❑ 96ColChoYMtP-22
❑ 96ColChoYMtP-22A
❑ 96ColChoYMtPGS-22
❑ 96ColChoYMtPGS-22A
❑ 96DenHol-1
❑ 96Don-394
❑ 96DonDiaK-15
❑ 96DonEli-68
❑ 96DonFreF-5
❑ 96DonPreP-394
❑ 96DonSam-8
❑ 96DonSho-3
❑ 96EmoN-7
❑ 96EmoXL-146
❑ 96EmoXLD-6
❑ 96Fin-G145
❑ 96Fin-S1
❑ 96Fin-S235
❑ 96FinLan-1
❑ 96FinRef-G145
❑ 96FinRef-S1
❑ 96FinRef-S235
❑ 96Fla-205
❑ 96FlaDiaC-6
❑ 96FlaHotG-6
❑ 96Fle-299
❑ 96FleChe-4
❑ 96FleGolM-3
❑ 96FleRoaW-3
❑ 96FleSmo'H-6
❑ 96FleTeaL-15
❑ 96FleTif-299
❑ 96FleUpd-U232
❑ 96FleUpd-6
❑ 96FleUpdH-13
❑ 96FleUpdSL-6
❑ 96FleUpdSS-6
❑ 96FleUpdTC-U232
❑ 96FleZon-7
❑ 96Kin-18
❑ 96Lea-192
❑ 96LeaAllGMC-19
❑ 96LeaAllGMCG-19
❑ 96LeaGolS-15
❑ 96LeaHatO-8
❑ 96LeaLim-10
❑ 96LeaLimG-10
❑ 96LeaLimPC-6
❑ 96LeaPicP-3
❑ 96LeaPre-12
❑ 96LeaPreP-12
❑ 96LeaPrePB-192
❑ 96LeaPrePG-192
❑ 96LeaPrePS-192
❑ 96LeaPreSG-53
❑ 96LeaPreSta-8
❑ 96LeaPreSte-53
❑ 96LeaSig-3
❑ 96LeaSigEA-114
❑ 96LeaSigEACM-18
❑ 96LeaSigPPG-3
❑ 96LeaSigPPP-3
❑ 96LeaStaS-6
❑ 96LeaTotB-12
❑ 96LibSpo-9
❑ 96MetUni-134
❑ 96MetUniP-134
❑ 96MetUniT-5
❑ 96Pac-6
❑ 96Pac-18
❑ 96PacCraC-CC4
❑ 96PacGolCD-DC28
❑ 96PacHom-HP2
❑ 96PacMil-M7
❑ 96PacOctM-OM13
❑ 96PacPri-P6
❑ 96PacPriFT-FT7
❑ 96PacPriG-P6
❑ 96PacPriRHS-RH8
❑ 96PanSti-4
❑ 96PanSti-118
❑ 96Pin-1
❑ 96Pin-254
❑ 96Pin-397
❑ 96Pin-399
❑ 96PinAfi-22
❑ 96PinAfi-199
❑ 96PinAfiAP-22
❑ 96PinAfiAP-199
❑ 96PinAfiFPP-22
❑ 96PinAfiMN-2
❑ 96PinAfiSP-14
❑ 96PinArtP-1
❑ 96PinArtP-154
❑ 96PinChrBC-1
❑ 96PinEssotG-2
❑ 96PinFan-2
❑ 96PinFoil-254
❑ 96PinFoil-397
❑ 96PinFoil-399
❑ 96PinSam-1
❑ 96PinSky-3
❑ 96PinSta-1
❑ 96PinSta-154
❑ 96PinTeaP-9
❑ 96PinTeaS-1
❑ 96Pro-8
❑ 96ProMagA-12
❑ 96ProSta-24
❑ 96RedF-17
❑ 96SchDis-3
❑ 96Sco-194
❑ 96Sco-275
❑ 96Sco-276
❑ 96Sco-515
❑ 96ScoAll-10
❑ 96ScoDiaA-7
❑ 96ScoDreT-9
❑ 96ScoDugC-B1
❑ 96ScoDugCAP-B1
❑ 96ScoGolS-17
❑ 96ScoNumG-6
❑ 96ScoRef-17
❑ 96Sel-7
❑ 96Sel-159
❑ 96Sel-198
❑ 96SelArtP-7
❑ 96SelArtP-159
❑ 96SelArtP-198
❑ 96SelCer-32
❑ 96SelCer-137
❑ 96SelCerAP-32
❑ 96SelCerAP-137
❑ 96SelCerCB-32
❑ 96SelCerCB-137
❑ 96SelCerCR-32
❑ 96SelCerCR-137
❑ 96SelCerIP-2
❑ 96SelCerMB-32
❑ 96SelCerMB-137
❑ 96SelCerMG-32
❑ 96SelCerMG-137
❑ 96SelCerMR-32
❑ 96SelCerMR-137
❑ 96SelCerSF-6
❑ 96SelClaTF-2
❑ 96SelEnF-4
❑ 96SelTeaN-12
❑ 96SP-25
❑ 96SPBasH-89
❑ 96SPMarM-MM10
❑ 96SPMarMDC-10
❑ 96Spo-8
❑ 96Spo-143
❑ 96SpoArtP-8
❑ 96SpoArtP-143
❑ 96SpoDouT-5
❑ 96SpoPro-2
❑ 96SPSpeFX-1
❑ 96SPSpeFXDC-1
❑ 96SPx-1
❑ 96SPxBoufG-5
❑ 96SPxGol-1
❑ 96StaClu-132
❑ 96StaClu-245
❑ 96StaCluEPB-132
❑ 96StaCluEPG-132
❑ 96StaCluEPS-132
❑ 96StaCluEWB-EW1
❑ 96StaCluEWG-EW1
❑ 96StaCluEWS-EW1
❑ 96StaCluMet-M6
❑ 96StaCluMO-22
❑ 96StaCluMOF-2
❑ 96StaCluMOP-132
❑ 96StaCluMOP-245
❑ 96StaCluMOP-M6
❑ 96StaCluMOP-TSCA7
❑ 96StaCluTA-7
❑ 96Stu-18
❑ 96StuMas-8
❑ 96StuPrePB-18
❑ 96StuPrePG-18
❑ 96StuPrePS-18
❑ 96StuStaGS-4
❑ 96Sum-91
❑ 96Sum-199
❑ 96SumAbo&B-91
❑ 96SumAbo&B-199
❑ 96SumArtP-91
❑ 96SumArtP-199
❑ 96SumBal-8
❑ 96SumFoi-91
❑ 96SumFoi-199
❑ 96SumPos-6
❑ 96TeaOut-53
❑ 96TeaOut-C96
❑ 96Top-3
❑ 96Top-318
❑ 96TopBigC-5
❑ 96TopBroLL-2
❑ 96TopChr-3
❑ 96TopChr-125
❑ 96TopChrMotG-19
❑ 96TopChrMotGR-19
❑ 96TopChrR-3
❑ 96TopChrR-125
❑ 96TopClaC-CC15
❑ 96TopGal-145
❑ 96TopGalPPI-145
❑ 96TopLas-121
❑ 96TopMasotG-19
❑ 96TopMysF-M2
❑ 96TopMysFR-M2
❑ 96TopPowB-3
❑ 96TopPro-NL4
❑ 96Ult-160
❑ 96Ult-585
❑ 96UltCalttH-5
❑ 96UltCalttHGM-5
❑ 96UltChe-B8
❑ 96UltCheGM-B8
❑ 96UltDiaP-5
❑ 96UltDiaPGM-5
❑ 96UltGolM-160
❑ 96UltGolM-585
❑ 96UltRaw-6
❑ 96UltRawGM-6
❑ 96UltRes-4
❑ 96UltResGM-4
❑ 96UltSeaC-5
❑ 96UltSeaCGM-5
❑ 96UppDec-10
❑ 96UppDec-379
❑ 96UppDec-422
❑ 96UppDecDD-DD5
❑ 96UppDecDDG-DD5
❑ 96UppDecDDS-DD5
❑ 96UppDecG-GF10
❑ 96UppDecHC-HC10
❑ 96UppDecPHE-H44
❑ 96UppDecPreH-H44
❑ 96UppDecVJLS-VJ5
❑ 96Zen-3
❑ 96Zen-134
❑ 96ZenArtP-3
❑ 96ZenArtP-134
❑ 96ZenDiaC-18
❑ 96ZenDiaCP-18
❑ 96ZenMoz-1
❑ 96ZenZ-5
❑ 97Bow-256
❑ 97BowBes-40
❑ 97BowBesAR-40
❑ 97BowBesMI-MI3
❑ 97BowBesMIAR-MI3
❑ 97BowBesMIARI-MI3
❑ 97BowBesMII-MI3
❑ 97BowBesMIR-MI3
❑ 97BowBesMIRI-MI3
❑ 97BowBesR-40
❑ 97BowChr-79
❑ 97BowChrI-79
❑ 97BowChrIR-79
❑ 97BowChrR-79
❑ 97BowInt-256
❑ 97BraSco-12
❑ 97BraScoPl-12
❑ 97BraScoPr-12
❑ 97Cir-337
❑ 97Cir-400
❑ 97CirBos-11
❑ 97CirIco-6
❑ 97CirLimA-9
❑ 97CirRav-337
❑ 97CirRav-400
❑ 97CirRavR-6
❑ 97CirSupB-11
❑ 97ColCho-266
❑ 97ColChoAC-36
❑ 97ColChoNF-NF36
❑ 97ColChoS-23
❑ 97ColChoSR-17
❑ 97ColChoT-AB12
❑ 97ColChoTBS-1
❑ 97ColChoTBSWH-1
❑ 97ColChoTotT-T3
❑ 97Don-7
❑ 97Don-423
❑ 97Don-449
❑ 97DonArmaD-13
❑ 97DonDom-3
❑ 97DonEli-4
❑ 97DonEliGS-4
❑ 97DonGolPP-7
❑ 97DonGolPP-423
❑ 97DonGolPP-449
❑ 97DonLim-2
❑ 97DonLim-46
❑ 97DonLim-121
❑ 97DonLimE-2
❑ 97DonLimE-46
❑ 97DonLimE-121
❑ 97DonLimENG-2
❑ 97DonPre-6
❑ 97DonPre-196
❑ 97DonPreCttC-6
❑ 97DonPreCttC-196
❑ 97DonPrePM-3
❑ 97DonPreS-13
❑ 97DonPreSS-13
❑ 97DonPreTB-12
❑ 97DonPreTBG-12
❑ 97DonPreTF-12
❑ 97DonPreTP-12
❑ 97DonPreTPG-12
❑ 97DonSig-8
❑ 97DonSigAC-83
❑ 97DonSigAM-83
❑ 97DonSigPPP-8
❑ 97DonSilPP-7
❑ 97DonSilPP-423
❑ 97DonSilPP-449
❑ 97DonTea-16
❑ 97DonTeaSMVP-18
❑ 97DonTeaSPE-16
❑ 97DonVxP1-4
❑ 97DonVxP1CD-2
❑ 97E-X2-57
❑ 97E-X2Cred-57
❑ 97E-X2EssCre-57
❑ 97E-X2Hall-12
❑ 97Fin-158
❑ 97Fin-294
❑ 97FinEmb-158
❑ 97FinEmb-294
❑ 97FinEmbR-158
❑ 97FinEmbR-294
❑ 97FinRef-158
❑ 97FinRef-294
❑ 97FlaShoDC-10
❑ 97FlaShoHG-10
❑ 97FlaShoLC-44
❑ 97FlaShoLeg0-44
❑ 97FlaShoLeg1-44
❑ 97FlaShoM-A44
❑ 97FlaShoM-B44
❑ 97FlaShoM-C44
❑ 97FlaShoR0-44
❑ 97FlaShoR1-44
❑ 97FlaShoR2-44
❑ 97Fle-263
❑ 97Fle-707
❑ 97Fle-722
❑ 97FleDecoE-6
❑ 97FleDecoERT-6
❑ 97FleDiaT-6
❑ 97FleGouG-7
❑ 97FleGouGF-7
❑ 97FleHea-11
❑ 97FleMilDM-44
❑ 97FleMilDMR-44
❑ 97FleSoaS-8
❑ 97FleSoaSG-8
❑ 97FleTif-263
❑ 97FleTif-707
❑ 97FleTif-722
❑ 97FleZon-10
❑ 97HigMinM-65
❑ 97HigMinM-66
❑ 97HigMinM-67
❑ 97HigMinMCP-6
❑ 97HigMinMCP-7
❑ 97HigMinMM-9
❑ 97HigMinMM-11
❑ 97HigMinMM-13
❑ 97Lea-85
❑ 97Lea-351
❑ 97Lea-372
❑ 97LeaDrefS-1
❑ 97LeaFraM-85
❑ 97LeaFraM-351
❑ 97LeaFraM-372
❑ 97LeaFraMDC-85
❑ 97LeaFraMDC-351
❑ 97LeaFraMDC-372
❑ 97LeaGet-1
❑ 97LeaGolS-11
❑ 97LeaStaS-7
❑ 97MetUni-33
❑ 97MetUniT-5
❑ 97NewPin-3
❑ 97NewPinAP-3
❑ 97NewPinIE-7
❑ 97NewPinKtP-2
❑ 97NewPinMC-3
❑ 97NewPinPP-3
❑ 97NewPinPP-I7A
❑ 97NewPinPP-K2
❑ 97Pac-240
❑ 97PacCar-24
❑ 97PacCarM-24
❑ 97PacCerCGT-19
❑ 97PacCerCGT-P19
❑ 97PacCerCGT-S19
❑ 97PacLigB-240
❑ 97PacPri-82
❑ 97PacPriGA-GA19
❑ 97PacPriGotD-GD113
❑ 97PacPriLB-82
❑ 97PacPriP-82
❑ 97PacPriSH-SH8B
❑ 97PacSil-240
❑ 97Pin-189
❑ 97PinAllFP-3
❑ 97PinArtP-PP189
❑ 97PinCar-1
❑ 97PinCer-83
❑ 97PinCer-143
❑ 97PinCerCMGT-19
❑ 97PinCerCT-19
❑ 97PinCerMBla-83
❑ 97PinCerMBla-143
❑ 97PinCerMBlu-83
❑ 97PinCerMBlu-143
❑ 97PinCerMG-83
❑ 97PinCerMG-143
❑ 97PinCerMR-83
❑ 97PinCerMR-143
❑ 97PinCerR-83
❑ 97PinCerR-143
❑ 97PinEpixGO-E21
❑ 97PinEpixPE-E21
❑ 97PinFan-FF20
❑ 97PinIns-16
❑ 97PinInsC-10
❑ 97PinInsCE-16
❑ 97PinInsDD-15
❑ 97PinInsDE-16
❑ 97PinMin-11
❑ 97PinMinB-11
❑ 97PinMinCB-11
❑ 97PinMinCG-11
❑ 97PinMinCGR-11
❑ 97PinMinCN-11
❑ 97PinMinCSS-11
❑ 97PinMinG-11
❑ 97PinMinS-11
❑ 97PinMusC-189
❑ 97PinPasttM-1
❑ 97PinPrePla-189
❑ 97PinTotCPB-83
❑ 97PinTotCPB-143
❑ 97PinTotCPG-83
❑ 97PinTotCPG-143
❑ 97PinTotCPR-83
❑ 97PinTotCPR-143
❑ 97PinX-P-9
❑ 97PinX-P-149
❑ 97PinX-PMoS-9
❑ 97PinX-PMoS-149
❑ 97PinX-PMW-10
❑ 97PinX-PMWG-10
❑ 97PinX-PMWS-10
❑ 97PreCon-4
❑ 97Sco-215
❑ 97Sco-520
❑ 97ScoArtPWB-215
❑ 97ScoArtPWB-520
❑ 97ScoHigZ-7
❑ 97ScoPreS-215
❑ 97ScoResC-520
❑ 97ScoShoS-215
❑ 97ScoShoS-520
❑ 97ScoShoSAP-215
❑ 97ScoShoSAP-520
❑ 97ScoStaaD-2
❑ 97Sel-23
❑ 97Sel-P23
❑ 97SelArtP-23
❑ 97SelCom-23
❑ 97SelRegG-23
❑ 97SelSam-P23
❑ 97SelToootT-2
❑ 97SelToootTMB-2
❑ 97SP-23
❑ 97SPInsI-6
❑ 97SPMarM-MM13
❑ 97SpollI-75
❑ 97SpollI-173
❑ 97SpollIEE-75
❑ 97SpollIEE-173
❑ 97SpollIGS-4
❑ 97SPSpeF-6
❑ 97SPSpxF-5
❑ 97SPSPxFA-5
❑ 97SPx-7
❑ 97SPxBoufG-3
❑ 97SPxBro-7
❑ 97SPxCorotG-3
❑ 97SPxGol-7
❑ 97SPxGraF-7
❑ 97SPxSil-7
❑ 97SPxSte-7
❑ 97StaClu-196
❑ 97StaCluMat-196
❑ 97StaCluMOP-196
❑ 97StaCluMOP-PL5
❑ 97StaCluPL-PL5
❑ 97StrAll-41
❑ 97Stu-88
❑ 97StuMasS-12
❑ 97StuMasS8-12
❑ 97StuPor8-6
❑ 97StuPrePG-88
❑ 97StuPrePS-88
❑ 97Top-130

❑ 97TopChr-49
❑ 97TopChrR-49
❑ 97TopGal-26
❑ 97TopGalPPI-26
❑ 97TopHobM-HM3
❑ 97TopMem05-32
❑ 97TopSta-17
❑ 97TopSta97AS-AS1
❑ 97TopStaAM-17
❑ 97UD3-31
❑ 97Ult-157
❑ 97UltBasR-5
❑ 97UltChe-A4
❑ 97UltChe-B7
❑ 97UltDiaP-6
❑ 97UltDouT-11
❑ 97UltFamGam-6
❑ 97UltFieC-12
❑ 97UltGolME-157
❑ 97UltPlaME-157
❑ 97UltStaR-7
❑ 97UltTop3-7
❑ 97UltTop3GM-7
❑ 97UppDec-65
❑ 97UppDec-137
❑ 97UppDec-260
❑ 97UppDec-263
❑ 97UppDec-302
❑ 97UppDecAG-AG11
❑ 97UppDecHC-HC19
❑ 97UppDecMM-B4
❑ 97UppDecP-3
❑ 97UppDecPE-3
❑ 97UppDecSA-18
❑ 97UppDecSAG-18
❑ 97Zen-8
❑ 97Zen8x10-6
❑ 97Zen8x1D-6
❑ 98Bow-16
❑ 98BowBes-60
❑ 98BowBesAR-60
❑ 98BowBesMIF-MI19
❑ 98BowBesMIFAR-MI19
❑ 98BowBesMIFR-MI19
❑ 98BowBesR-60
❑ 98BowChr-16
❑ 98BowChrGA-16
❑ 98BowChrGAR-16
❑ 98BowChrI-16
❑ 98BowChrIR-16
❑ 98BowChrR-16
❑ 98BowGolA-16
❑ 98BowInt-16
❑ 98BraSco-2
❑ 98BraScoP-2
❑ 98CirThu-31
❑ 98CirThuB-12
❑ 98CirThuLA-9
❑ 98CirThuQS-6
❑ 98CirThuRav-31
❑ 98CirThuRR-10
❑ 98CirThuSupRav-31
❑ 98ColCho-305
❑ 98ColChoER-ER2
❑ 98ColChoMBH-5
❑ 98ColChoSQ-SQ25
❑ 98ColChoSQ-SQ88
❑ 98ColChoSQDouble-13
❑ 98ColChoSQHR-13
❑ 98ColChoSQSingle-13
❑ 98ColChoSQTriple-13
❑ 98CroRoy-16
❑ 98CroRoyAS-13
❑ 98CroRoyCCPA-7
❑ 98CroRoyCCPrem-7
❑ 98CroRoyDK-3
❑ 98CroRoyFoB-3
❑ 98CroRoyFoBA-3
❑ 98CroRoyPotG-4
❑ 98Don-35
❑ 98Don-161
❑ 98Don-380
❑ 98Don-406
❑ 98DonCol-35
❑ 98DonCol-161
❑ 98DonColE-405
❑ 98DonColE-522
❑ 98DonColL-354
❑ 98DonColP-555
❑ 98DonColP-722
❑ 98DonColS-35
❑ 98DonColS-161
❑ 98DonCruG-55
❑ 98DonCruP-55
❑ 98DonCruR-55
❑ 98DonDay-14
❑ 98DonDiaK-2
❑ 98DonDiaKC-2
❑ 98DonDom-22
❑ 98DonEli-5
❑ 98DonEli-122
❑ 98DonEliA-5
❑ 98DonEliA-122
❑ 98DonEliBttF-7
❑ 98DonEliBttFA-7
❑ 98DonEliC-5
❑ 98DonEliI-15
❑ 98DonEliMC-5
❑ 98DonEliS-5
❑ 98DonEliS-122
❑ 98DonFANT-6
❑ 98DonFANTDC-6
❑ 98DonGolPP-35
❑ 98DonGolPP-161
❑ 98DonGolPP-380
❑ 98DonGolPP-406
❑ 98DonPre-5
❑ 98DonPre-172
❑ 98DonPreGB-5
❑ 98DonPreGES-7
❑ 98DonPreGoB-5
❑ 98DonPreGX-7
❑ 98DonPreGXDC-7
❑ 98DonPrePM-5
❑ 98DonPreSeat-5
❑ 98DonPreSeat-172
❑ 98DonPreTP-5
❑ 98DonPreTPD-3
❑ 98DonPreTPG-5
❑ 98DonPreTPS-5
❑ 98DonPreTW-23
❑ 98DonPriCD-35
❑ 98DonPriCD-161
❑ 98DonPriCE-405
❑ 98DonPriCE-522
❑ 98DonPriCL-354
❑ 98DonPriCP-555
❑ 98DonPriCP-722
❑ 98DonSig-49
❑ 98DonSig-110
❑ 98DonSigA-57
❑ 98DonSigAC-75
❑ 98DonSigAM-76
❑ 98DonSigP-49
❑ 98DonSigP-110
❑ 98DonSigSP-17
❑ 98DonSilPP-35
❑ 98DonSilPP-161
❑ 98DonSilPP-380
❑ 98DonSilPP-406
❑ 98E-X2-3
❑ 98E-X2DesCoop-5
❑ 98E-X2ECFut-3
❑ 98E-X2ECNow-3
❑ 98Fin-16
❑ 98FinMysF1-M23
❑ 98FinMysF1-M26
❑ 98FinMysF1-M28
❑ 98FinMysF1-M30
❑ 98FinMysFR-M23
❑ 98FinMysFR-M26
❑ 98FinMysFR-M28
❑ 98FinMysFR-M30
❑ 98FinNo--16
❑ 98FinNo-R-16
❑ 98FinOve-A5
❑ 98FinOveR-A5
❑ 98FinRef-16
❑ 98FinTheM-TM20
❑ 98FinTheMR-TM20
❑ 98FlaShoLeg0-13
❑ 98FlaShoLeg1-13
❑ 98FlaShoLeg2-13
❑ 98FlaShoLeg3-13
❑ 98FlaShoLegM-13
❑ 98FlaShoP1-5
❑ 98FlaShoR0-13
❑ 98FlaShoR1-13
❑ 98FlaShoR2-13
❑ 98FlaShoR3-13
❑ 98Fle-31
❑ 98Fle-305
❑ 98Fle-346
❑ 98Fle-589
❑ 98FleDecERT-9
❑ 98FleDecoE-9
❑ 98FleDiamInk-7
❑ 98FleDiaS-13
❑ 98FleIn TC-IC11
❑ 98FlePowG-12
❑ 98FleVin'-6
❑ 98FleVin'C-6
❑ 98FleZon-10
❑ 98Lea-155
❑ 98LeaFraDA-155
❑ 98LeaFraF-155
❑ 98LeaFraM-155
❑ 98LeaFraM-155
❑ 98LeaFraMDC-155
❑ 98LeaFraMDC-155
❑ 98LeaFraMZ2-155
❑ 98LeaHeaftH-12
❑ 98LeaHeaftHS-12
❑ 98LeaRS-31
❑ 98LeaRS-145
❑ 98LeaRSCross-4
❑ 98LeaRSExtM-8
❑ 98LeaRSExtMDC-8
❑ 98LeaRSGAHSamp-5
❑ 98LeaRSGreAH-5
❑ 98LeaRSLHolo-31
❑ 98LeaRSLHolo-145
❑ 98LeaRSLMVP-19
❑ 98LeaRSLMVPPE-19
❑ 98LeaRSLong-31
❑ 98LeaRSLong-145
❑ 98LeaRSSOSamp-7
❑ 98LeaRSStaOva-7
❑ 98LeaRSTicMas-4
❑ 98LeaRSTicMasDC-4
❑ 98LeaRTrue-31
❑ 98LeaRTrue-145
❑ 98LeaStaRep-28
❑ 98LeaStaS-5
❑ 98LeaStaSDC-5
❑ 98MetUni-133
❑ 98MetUniAT-12
❑ 98MetUniPMG-133
❑ 98MetUniPP-9
❑ 98MetUniT-12
❑ 98MetUniUL-12
❑ 98Pac-241
❑ 98PacAur-108
❑ 98PacAurCube-3
❑ 98PacAurHC-3
❑ 98PacAurKotML-2
❑ 98PacAurODLC-3
❑ 98PacAurPF-46
❑ 98PacAurPFC-46
❑ 98PacAurPFPB-46
❑ 98PacAurPFR-46
❑ 98PacAurPFS-46
❑ 98PacCraCh-1
❑ 98PacGolCDC-2
❑ 98PacInv-80
❑ 98PacInvCCDB-1
❑ 98PacInvCCG-1
❑ 98PacInvCCG-1
❑ 98PacInvCCLB-1
❑ 98PacInvCCP-1
❑ 98PacInvCCR-1
❑ 98PacInvGems-122
❑ 98PacInvInt-12N
❑ 98PacInvPBlue-80
❑ 98PacInvPhoto-1
❑ 98PacInvSilv-80
❑ 98PacInvTeam-2
❑ 98PacOme-23
❑ 98PacOmeEP-12
❑ 98PacOmeEP1o1-12
❑ 98PacOmeOnIns-24
❑ 98PacOmeP-14
❑ 98PacOmeR-23
❑ 98PacOnl-67A
❑ 98PacOnl-67B
❑ 98PacOnlR-67A
❑ 98PacOnlR-67B
❑ 98PacOnlWC-67A
❑ 98PacOnlWC-67B
❑ 98PacPar-133
❑ 98PacParC-133
❑ 98PacParCB-1
❑ 98PacParCBPP-1
❑ 98PacParFC-2
❑ 98PacParG-133
❑ 98PacParHS-133
❑ 98PacParI-17
❑ 98PacParPB-133
❑ 98PacParR-133
❑ 98PacParSD-2
❑ 98PacPlaB-241
❑ 98PacRedT-241
❑ 98PacSil-241
❑ 98PacTeaC-15
❑ 98Pin-14
❑ 98PinArtP-PP14
❑ 98PinEpixGE-E21
❑ 98PinEpixGP-E21
❑ 98PinEpixME-E21
❑ 98PinEpixMO-E21
❑ 98PinEpixMP-E21
❑ 98PinEpixPO-E21
❑ 98PinEpixPP-E21
❑ 98PinIns-31
❑ 98PinIns-142
❑ 98PinInsBtN-12
❑ 98PinInsC-12
❑ 98PinInsCE-31
❑ 98PinInsCE-142
❑ 98PinInsCG-12
❑ 98PinInsDE-31
❑ 98PinInsDE-142
❑ 98PinInsSG-3AB
❑ 98PinInsSG-3CD
❑ 98PinInsSG-12AB
❑ 98PinInsSG-12CD
❑ 98PinInsSGS-3AB
❑ 98PinInsSGS-3CD
❑ 98PinInsSGS-12AB
❑ 98PinInsSGS-12CD
❑ 98PinMinB-12
❑ 98PinMinCB-12
❑ 98PinMinCBAP-12
❑ 98PinMinCBS-12
❑ 98PinMinCGP-12
❑ 98PinMinCGPAP-12
❑ 98PinMinCN-12
❑ 98PinMinCNAP-12
❑ 98PinMinCSGR-12
❑ 98PinMinDC-12
❑ 98PinMinG-12
❑ 98PinMinMCSS-12
❑ 98PinMinS-12
❑ 98PinMinS-12
❑ 98PinMusC-PP14
❑ 98PinPer-5
❑ 98PinPer-142
❑ 98PinPerPP-5
❑ 98PinPerPP-142
❑ 98PinPlu-156
❑ 98PinPlu-191
❑ 98PinPluAE-21
❑ 98PinPluAEE-21
❑ 98PinPluAEP-21
❑ 98PinPluAP-PP51
❑ 98PinPluGAP-PP51
❑ 98PinPluLM-21
❑ 98PinPluMAP-PP51
❑ 98PinPluPieGame-7
❑ 98PinPluTP-12
❑ 98PinPluTPG-12
❑ 98PinPluTPM-12
❑ 98PinPowPJ-19
❑ 98PinPowPJS-19
❑ 98PinPreP-14
❑ 98PinPreP-E21
❑ 98PinSna-AB8
❑ 98PinSna-AB13
❑ 98PinSnaS-1
❑ 98Revo-16
❑ 98RevoPTP-14
❑ 98RevoRooHH-22
❑ 98RevoShow-24
❑ 98RevoSS-16
❑ 98Sco-9
❑ 98Sco-265
❑ 98ScoAllST-19
❑ 98ScoEpix-E21
❑ 98ScoFirP-17
❑ 98ScoLoaL-LL10
❑ 98ScoRT-4
❑ 98ScoRTComPla-6A
❑ 98ScoRTComPla-6B
❑ 98ScoRTComPla-6C
❑ 98ScoRTCPSamp-6A
❑ 98ScoRTCPSamp-6B
❑ 98ScoRTCPSamp-6C
❑ 98ScoRTSS-PP4
❑ 98ScoRTSSAP-PP4
❑ 98ScoRTSSAP1-PP4
❑ 98ScoRTStarGaz-18
❑ 98ScoSS-PP115
❑ 98ScoSSAP-PP115
❑ 98SkyDugA-6
❑ 98SkyDugA-129
❑ 98SkyDugAAR-9
❑ 98SkyDugAD-D1
❑ 98SkyDugAIA-6
❑ 98SkyDugAIA-129
❑ 98SP Aut-45
❑ 98SP Aut-SD31
❑ 98SP AutSD-SD31
❑ 98SP AutSDT-SD31
❑ 98SP AutTrade-11
❑ 98SPAutGJ5x7-3
❑ 98SpoIll-82
❑ 98SpoIll-142
❑ 98SpoIllEC-EC5
❑ 98SpoIllEE-82
❑ 98SpoIllEE-142
❑ 98SpoIllFE-82
❑ 98SpoIllFE-142
❑ 98SpoIllODMP-OD3
❑ 98SpoIllTaN-38
❑ 98SpoIllTaN-107
❑ 98SpoIllTaNEE-38
❑ 98SpoIllTaNEE-107
❑ 98SpoIllTaNGS-9
❑ 98SpoIllTaNRtC-RC6
❑ 98SpoIllWSF-90
❑ 98SpoIllWSFEE-90
❑ 98SpoIllWSFFE-90
❑ 98SpoIllWSFRJP-5
❑ 98SPxFin-142
❑ 98SPxFin-171
❑ 98SPxFin-250
❑ 98SPxFinR-142
❑ 98SPxFinR-171
❑ 98SPxFinR-250
❑ 98SPxFinS-142
❑ 98SPxFinS-171
❑ 98SPxFinS-250
❑ 98StaCluFDI-116
❑ 98StaCluI-116
❑ 98StaCluNC-NC8
❑ 98StaCluOneK-116
❑ 98StaCluPP-116
❑ 98StaCluTIII-T9B
❑ 98StaCluTLme-T9B
❑ 98StaCluTLmo-T9B
❑ 98Stu-199
❑ 98Stu-CL3
❑ 98StuFF-6
❑ 98StuFFDC-6
❑ 98StuGPP-199
❑ 98StuGPP-CL3
❑ 98StuMast-16
❑ 98StuPor8x10-15
❑ 98StuPor8x10GP-15
❑ 98StuSPP-199
❑ 98StuSPP-CL3
❑ 98Top-296
❑ 98TopChr-296
❑ 98TopChrHB-HB7
❑ 98TopChrHBR-HB7
❑ 98TopChrM-MS7
❑ 98TopChrMR-MS7
❑ 98TopChrR-296
❑ 98TopDevR-296
❑ 98TopDia-296
❑ 98TopEtc-ES4
❑ 98TopFocP-FP13
❑ 98TopGal-60
❑ 98TopGalGoH-GH15
❑ 98TopGalGoHJ-GH15
❑ 98TopGalGP-60
❑ 98TopGalOPP-60
❑ 98TopGalPPI-60
❑ 98TopGalPPIA-60
❑ 98TopGolLabC1-2
❑ 98TopGolLabC1B-2
❑ 98TopGolLabC1One-2
❑ 98TopGolLabC1R-2
❑ 98TopGolLabC2-2
❑ 98TopGolLabC2B-2
❑ 98TopGolLabC2One-2
❑ 98TopGolLabC2R-2
❑ 98TopGolLabC3-2
❑ 98TopGolLabC3B-2
❑ 98TopGolLabC3One-2
❑ 98TopGolLabC3R-2
❑ 98TopHal-HB7
❑ 98TopMil-MS7
❑ 98TopMiniC-296
❑ 98TopMysF-ILM3
❑ 98TopMysFB-M12
❑ 98TopMysFB-M12
❑ 98TopMysFBR-M12
❑ 98TopMysFBR-M12
❑ 98TopMysFR-ILM3
❑ 98TopOpeD-123
❑ 98TopSta-1
❑ 98TopSta'S-26
❑ 98TopSta'SGH-26
❑ 98TopStaB-1
❑ 98TopStaG-1
❑ 98TopStaGR-1
❑ 98TopStaS-1
❑ 98TopStaSteG-26
❑ 98TopSup-19
❑ 98TopSup-19
❑ 98TopTek-50
❑ 98TopTekD-50
❑ 98UD3-75
❑ 98UD3-165
❑ 98UD3-255
❑ 98UD3DieCut-75
❑ 98UD3DieCut-165
❑ 98UD3DieCut-255
❑ 98Ult-122
❑ 98Ult-484
❑ 98UltArtT-8
❑ 98UltDial-7
❑ 98UltDiaP-8
❑ 98UltDouT-4
❑ 98UltFalC-8
❑ 98UltGolM-122
❑ 98UltGolM-484
❑ 98UltMas-122
❑ 98UltMas-484
❑ 98UltMilM-12
❑ 98UltPlaM-122
❑ 98UltPlaM-484
❑ 98UltPriL-8
❑ 98UltTop3-15
❑ 98UltWinN-8
❑ 98UppDec-5
❑ 98UppDec-16
❑ 98UppDec-30
❑ 98UppDec-147
❑ 98UppDec-602
❑ 98UppDec10AP-1
❑ 98UppDec1APR-1
❑ 98UppDec5x7-30
❑ 98UppDecAC-AS22
❑ 98UppDecAG-AG11
❑ 98UppDecAGDC-AG11
❑ 98UppDecAPA1-6
❑ 98UppDecCD-CD18
❑ 98UppDecPN-PN56
❑ 98UppDecPN-PN57
❑ 98UppDecPN-PN58
❑ 98UppDecPN-PN59
❑ 98UppDecPN-PN60
❑ 98UppDecR-9
❑ 98UppDecR-12
❑ 98UppDecRGKoG-G14
❑ 98UppDecRQL-Q14
❑ 98UppDecRTC-TC33
❑ 98UppDecSF-8
❑ 98UppDecSF-20
❑ 98UppDecSFPD-PZ7
❑ 98UppDecSFPZOB-PZ10
❑ 98UppDecSFPZSX-PZ7
❑ 98UppDecU-13
❑ 98Zen-12
❑ 98Zen5 xx7-3
❑ 98Zen5x7GoldImp-3
❑ 98Zen5x7Imp-3
❑ 98ZenEpi-E21
❑ 98ZenRaitB-8
❑ 98ZenSampL-Z3
❑ 98ZenSamS-12
❑ 98ZenZ-G-12
❑ 98ZenZ-S-12
❑ 98ZenZ-T-6
❑ 98ZenZ-T5x7-6
❑ 98ZenZ-TG-6
❑ 99199Fin-100
❑ 99199Fin-120
❑ 99199Fin-262
❑ 99AllMysFR-M33
❑ 99AurPenF-2
❑ 99AurPenF-2
❑ 99AurPenFB-2
❑ 99AurPenFS-2
❑ 99AurSty-2
❑ 99Bow-10
❑ 99BowBes-67
❑ 99BowBes-93
❑ 99BowBesAR-67
❑ 99BowBesAR-93
❑ 99BowBesMI-M5
❑ 99BowBesMIAR-M5
❑ 99BowBesMIR-M5
❑ 99BowBesR-67
❑ 99BowBesR-93
❑ 99BowChr-10
❑ 99BowChrG-10
❑ 99BowChrGR-10
❑ 99BowChrI-10
❑ 99BowChrIR-10
❑ 99BowChrR-10
❑ 99BowGol-10
❑ 99BowInt-10
❑ 99CroRoyB-16

❑ 99CroRoyL-16
❑ 99CroRoyLL-1
❑ 99CroRoyMP-2
❑ 99CroRoyOD-16
❑ 99CroRoyPotG-3
❑ 99CroRoyPP-3
❑ 99CroRoyPPN-3
❑ 99DumSet-158
❑ 99E-X Cen-14
❑ 99E-X CenECFut-14
❑ 99E-X CenECNow-14
❑ 99FinGolRef-100
❑ 99FinGolRef-120
❑ 99FinGolRef-262
❑ 99FinPeelHyp-6
❑ 99FinPeelSpark-6
❑ 99FinPeeSS-6
❑ 99FinRef-100
❑ 99FinRef-120
❑ 99FinRef-262
❑ 99FinSplS-SS11
❑ 99FinSplSDR-SS11
❑ 99FinTeaFB-TF1
❑ 99FinTeaFBR-TF1
❑ 99FinTeaFG-TF1
❑ 99FinTeaFGR-TF1
❑ 99FinTeaFR-TF1
❑ 99FinTeaFRR-TF1
❑ 99FlaShoLeg1-31
❑ 99FlaShoLeg2-31
❑ 99FlaShoLeg3-31
❑ 99FlaShoLegM1-31
❑ 99FlaShoLegM2-31
❑ 99FlaShoLegM3-31
❑ 99FlaShoR1-31
❑ 99FlaShoR2-31
❑ 99FlaShoR3-31
❑ 99Fle-49
❑ 99FleBri-95
❑ 99FleBri2G-95
❑ 99FleBriBlu-95
❑ 99FleBriGol-95
❑ 99FleBriSS-12
❑ 99FleBriSSP-12
❑ 99FleDatWD-5
❑ 99FleDiaM-10
❑ 99FleGolM-8
❑ 99FleMys-81
❑ 99FleMys-158
❑ 99FleMysE-4
❑ 99FleMysG-81
❑ 99FleMysM-81
❑ 99FleMysM-158
❑ 99FleSta9-49
❑ 99FleVin'-49
❑ 99FleWarT-49
❑ 99MetUni-215
❑ 99MetUni-243
❑ 99MetUni-291
❑ 99MetUniDS-6
❑ 99MetUniGM-215
❑ 99MetUniGM-243
❑ 99MetUniGM-291
❑ 99MetUniL-5
❑ 99MetUniPMG-215
❑ 99MetUniPMG-243
❑ 99MetUniPMG-291
❑ 99Pac-36
❑ 99Pac-36A
❑ 99PacAur-20
❑ 99PacAurOD-20
❑ 99PacCraCho-6
❑ 99PacCroC-28
❑ 99PacCroCPB-28
❑ 99PacCroCPC-6
❑ 99PacDynaD-11
❑ 99PacDynaDT-11
❑ 99PacGolCDC-22
❑ 99PacInv-17
❑ 99PacInvFP-3
❑ 99PacInvOD-17
❑ 99PacInvPB-17
❑ 99PacInvSF-3
❑ 99PacInvSF-3B
❑ 99PacInvSH-3
❑ 99PacInvSH-3B
❑ 99PacOme-26
❑ 99PacOme5T-2
❑ 99PacOme5TT-2
❑ 99PacOmeC-26
❑ 99PacOmeDM-6
❑ 99PacOmeEP-3
❑ 99PacOmeEP1o1-3
❑ 99PacOmeG-26
❑ 99PacOmePB-26
❑ 99PacPar-28
❑ 99PacParC-28
❑ 99PacParCB-1
❑ 99PacParCBPP-1
❑ 99PacParFC-2
❑ 99PacParG-28
❑ 99PacParHoloGold-28
❑ 99PacParHS-28
❑ 99PacParOD-28
❑ 99PacParPB-5
❑ 99PacParPB-28
❑ 99PacParRed-28
❑ 99PacPlaB-36
❑ 99PacPlaB-36A
❑ 99PacPri-16
❑ 99PacPriBL-6
❑ 99PacPriDG-4
❑ 99PacPriEP-9
❑ 99PacPriHB-16
❑ 99PacPriHG-16
❑ 99PacPriHM-16
❑ 99PacPriHP-16
❑ 99PacPriRed-16
❑ 99PacPriS-11
❑ 99PacPriS206-11
❑ 99PacPriS206R-11
❑ 99PacPriSE-11
❑ 99PacPriSP-11
❑ 99PacPriSP-11
❑ 99PacPriSV-11
❑ 99PacRed-36
❑ 99PacRed-36A
❑ 99PacTim-14
❑ 99Pin-17
❑ 99Rev-15
❑ 99RevDiaL-6
❑ 99RevPremDate-15
❑ 99RevRet-15
❑ 99RevShaSS-15
❑ 99RevThoitS-3
❑ 99RevTri-1
❑ 99RevTri-1
❑ 99SkyMolM-136
❑ 99SkyMolMF-36
❑ 99SkyMolMFS-36
❑ 99SkyMolMFT-36
❑ 99SkyMolMOA-22
❑ 99SkyMolMX-136
❑ 99SkyPre-140
❑ 99SkyPre-284
❑ 99SkyPreIN-9
❑ 99SkyPreR-140
❑ 99SkyPreR-284
❑ 99SkyPreSB-10
❑ 99SkyThu-274
❑ 99SkyThuRant-274
❑ 99SkyThuRave-274
❑ 99SP Aut-8
❑ 99SP AutC-GM
❑ 99SP AutCG-GM
❑ 99SP AutEF-E6
❑ 99SP AutR-R6
❑ 99SP SigAuto-GM
❑ 99SP SigAutoG-GM
❑ 99SpoIll-7
❑ 99SpoIll-16
❑ 99SpoIll-153
❑ 99SpoIllDD-4
❑ 99SpoIllH-19
❑ 99SPSig-7
❑ 99SPx-17
❑ 99SPxDom-FB2
❑ 99SPxFinR-17
❑ 99SPxFinS-17
❑ 99SPxPreS-PS17
❑ 99SPxStaF-SF2
❑ 99StaClu-100
❑ 99StaCluC-SCC29
❑ 99StaCluCR-SCC29
❑ 99StaCluFDI-100
❑ 99StaCluNC-NC4
❑ 99StaCluOoaK-100
❑ 99StaCluPP-100
❑ 99StaCluTI-T11A
❑ 99StaCluTL-T11A
❑ 99StaCluTL-T11A
❑ 99ThuSkySupR-274
❑ 99Top-16
❑ 99Top-231
❑ 99Top-460
❑ 99TopActF-7
❑ 99TopActFAU-7
❑ 99TopActFCU-7
❑ 99TopAllMF-M33
❑ 99TopBlaLC1-72
❑ 99TopBlaLC2-72
❑ 99TopBlaLC3-72
❑ 99TopChr-16
❑ 99TopChr-231
❑ 99TopChr-460
❑ 99TopChrF1-FF9
❑ 99TopChrF1R-FF9
❑ 99TopChrLotD-LD15
❑ 99TopChrLotDR-LD15
❑ 99TopChrR-16
❑ 99TopChrR-231
❑ 99TopChrR-460
❑ 99TopGal-9
❑ 99TopGal-114
❑ 99TopGalE-E3
❑ 99TopGalHer-TH18
❑ 99TopGalHerP-TH18
❑ 99TopGalPP-9
❑ 99TopGalPP-114
❑ 99TopGalPPI-9
❑ 99TopGalPPI-114
❑ 99TopGolL-72
❑ 99TopGolLC1-72
❑ 99TopGolLC2-72
❑ 99TopGolLOtO-72
❑ 99TopLorotD-LD15
❑ 99TopMVPP-16
❑ 99TopMVPP-460
❑ 99TopOpeD-11
❑ 99TopOver-A2
❑ 99TopPicP-P5
❑ 99TopRedLC1-72
❑ 99TopRedLC2-72
❑ 99TopRedLC3-72
❑ 99TopSta-51
❑ 99TopSta-151
❑ 99TopSta'S-38
❑ 99TopSta'SG-38
❑ 99TopSta'SGDH-38
❑ 99TopSta1Foil-51
❑ 99TopStaFoil-51
❑ 99TopStaFoil-151
❑ 99TopStaOS-51
❑ 99TopSupC-4
❑ 99TopSupCR-4
❑ 99TopTek-43A
❑ 99TopTek-43B
❑ 99TopTekG-43A
❑ 99TopTekG-43B
❑ 99UD Cho-35
❑ 99UD Cho-56
❑ 99UD ChoBU-10
❑ 99UD ChoP-56
❑ 99UD ChoPCR-35
❑ 99UD ChoPCR-56
❑ 99UD ChoS-11
❑ 99UD ChoSD-11
❑ 99UD ChoSHR-11
❑ 99UD ChoST-11
❑ 99UD Ion-6
❑ 99UD Ion-65
❑ 99UD IonC-C4
❑ 99UD IonH-HG4
❑ 99UD IonH-H4
❑ 99UD IonN-N4
❑ 99UD IonR-6
❑ 99UD IonR-65
❑ 99UD IonWZ-WZ4
❑ 99UDHolo-7
❑ 99UDHoloAUsome-7
❑ 99UDHoloFF-F5
❑ 99UDHoloFFG-F5
❑ 99UDHoloStar-S6
❑ 99UDHoloStarG-S6
❑ 99Ult-1
❑ 99Ult-217
❑ 99UltDamI-2
❑ 99UltDiaP-7
❑ 99UltGolM-1
❑ 99UltGolM-217
❑ 99UltMas-1
❑ 99UltMas-217
❑ 99UltPlaM-1
❑ 99UltPlaM-217
❑ 99UltTheBook-14
❑ 99UppDec-308
❑ 99UppDec10AT-X20
❑ 99UppDec10ATD-X20
❑ 99UppDec10ATHR-X20
❑ 99UppDec10ATT-X20
❑ 99UppDecBD-9
❑ 99UppDecBDD-9
❑ 99UppDecBDDom-D29
❑ 99UppDecBDDomE-D29
❑ 99UppDecBDMN-M11
❑ 99UppDecBDMNE-M11
❑ 99UppDecBDQ-9
❑ 99UppDecBDT-9
❑ 99UppDecCL-39
❑ 99UppDecCL-56
❑ 99UppDecCLCC-39
❑ 99UppDecCLCC-56
❑ 99UppDecCLES-GM
❑ 99UppDecCLESC-GM
❑ 99UppDecCLJotC-GM
❑ 99UppDecCLM-C7
❑ 99UppDecE-7
❑ 99UppDecEFXG-7
❑ 99UppDecEL1-308
❑ 99UppDecEL2-308
❑ 99UppDecEPE-P5
❑ 99UppDecEUR-U9
❑ 99UppDecF-F4
❑ 99UppDecFD-F4
❑ 99UppDecFQ-F4
❑ 99UppDecFT-F4
❑ 99UppDecGJ-GM
❑ 99UppDecIP-I15
❑ 99UppDecIPD-I15
❑ 99UppDecIPHR-I15
❑ 99UppDecIPT-I15
❑ 99UppDecM-17
❑ 99UppDecMGS-17
❑ 99UppDecMHFS-17
❑ 99UppDecMP-17
❑ 99UppDecMSS-17
❑ 99UppDecO-45
❑ 99UppDecOMP-S14
❑ 99UppDecOSO-45
❑ 99UppDecOWP-R12
❑ 99UppDecR-7
❑ 99UppDecRDR-D4
❑ 99UppDecRDRL2-D4
❑ 99UppDecRG-7
❑ 99UppDecROSS-S7
❑ 99UppDecROSS-S7
❑ 99UppDecRP-7
❑ 99UppDecRTA-T7
❑ 99UppDecRTAL2-T7
❑ 99UppDecTE-T2
❑ 99UppDecTED-T2
❑ 99UppDecTEQ-T2
❑ 99UppDecTET-T2
❑ 99UppDecVtaT-V5
❑ 99UppDecVtaTD-V5
❑ 99UppDecVtaTQ-V5
❑ 99UppDecVtaTT-V5
❑ 99UppDecWY-W17
❑ 99UppDecWYD-W17
❑ 99UppDecWYHR-W17
❑ 99UppDecWYT-W17
❑ 99Vic-31
❑ 99Vic-455

Maddux, Mike
❑ 85PhiTas-42
❑ 85PorBeaC-38
❑ 86PhiTas-NNO
❑ 86PorBeaP-15
❑ 87Don-535
❑ 87Fle-179
❑ 87FleGlo-179
❑ 87MaiGuiT-5
❑ 87PhiTas-44
❑ 87Top-553
❑ 87TopTif-553
❑ 88Fle-309
❑ 88FleGlo-309
❑ 88PhiTas-16
❑ 88Top-756
❑ 88TopTif-756
❑ 89Bow-391
❑ 89BowTif-391
❑ 89Don-487
❑ 89Fle-576
❑ 89FleGlo-576
❑ 89OPC-39
❑ 89PhiTas-19
❑ 89Sco-393
❑ 89Top-39
❑ 89TopBig-74
❑ 89TopTif-39
❑ 89UppDec-338
❑ 90AlbDukCm-8
❑ 90AlbDukP-341
❑ 90AlbDukTr-20
❑ 90CMC-410
❑ 90Don-312
❑ 90OPC-154
❑ 90ProAAAF-62
❑ 90PubIntS-246
❑ 90Top-154
❑ 90TopTif-154
❑ 91Lea-300
❑ 91PadSmo-20
❑ 91UltUpd-113
❑ 92Don-450
❑ 92Fle-613
❑ 92Lea-393
❑ 92LeaBlaG-393
❑ 92OPC-438
❑ 92PadCarJ-12
❑ 92PadMot-26
❑ 92PadPolD-29
❑ 92PadSmo-18
❑ 92Pin-489
❑ 92Sco-313
❑ 92StaClu-26
❑ 92Top-438
❑ 92TopGol-438
❑ 92TopGolW-438
❑ 92TopMic-438
❑ 92TriPla-196
❑ 92Ult-281
❑ 92UppDec-330
❑ 93Don-286
❑ 93Fle-142
❑ 93FleFinE-103
❑ 93Lea-305
❑ 93MetColP-39
❑ 93MetKah-51
❑ 93OPC-168
❑ 93PacSpa-260
❑ 93Sco-451
❑ 93StaClu-103
❑ 93StaCluFDI-103
❑ 93StaCluMOP-103
❑ 93Top-329
❑ 93TopGol-329
❑ 93TopInaM-329
❑ 93TopInaR-329
❑ 93TopMic-329
❑ 93Ult-430
❑ 93UppDec-58
❑ 93UppDec-650
❑ 93UppDecGold-58
❑ 93UppDecGold-650
❑ 94Don-213
❑ 94Fla-201
❑ 94Fle-571
❑ 94MetColP-17
❑ 94MetShuST-5
❑ 94Pac-410
❑ 94StaClu-33
❑ 94StaCluFDI-33
❑ 94StaCluGR-33
❑ 94StaCluMOP-33
❑ 94Top-217
❑ 94TopGol-217
❑ 94TopSpa-217
❑ 95Pac-284
❑ 96LeaSigEA-115
❑ 97PacPriGotD-GD23
❑ 98PacOnl-453
❑ 98PacOnlR-453
❑ 98PacOnlWC-453

Mader, Chris
❑ 93HicCraC-14
❑ 93HicCraF-1285
❑ 93SouAtlLAGF-28
❑ 94ClaGolF-92
❑ 94HicCraC-15

Mader, Perry
❑ 83KinBluJTI-13

Madera, Wil
❑ 97LetBlaDB-15
❑ 97SouBenSH-15

Maderas, A. J.
❑ 23Zee-49
❑ 24Zee-34

Maderfield, Steve
❑ 78NewWayCT-27

Madison, Dave
❑ 52Top-366
❑ 53TigGle-20
❑ 53Top-99
❑ 83TopRep5-366
❑ 91TopArc1-99

Madison, Jerry
❑ 90NebCor-14

Madison, Scott
❑ 96ButCopKB-21
❑ 97HudValRB-4
❑ 98ChaRivDG-17
❑ 98St.PetDRM-11

Madison, Scotti
❑ 83AlbDukTc-12
❑ 85NasSouTI-11
❑ 86NasSouTI-16
❑ 87OmaRoyP-17
❑ 88RoySmo-18
❑ 88TopTra-63T
❑ 88TopTraT-63T
❑ 89NasSouC-21
❑ 89NasSouP-1271
❑ 89NasSouTI-14
❑ 89TriAAAP-AAA2

Madlock, Bill
❑ 74OPC-600
❑ 74Top-600
❑ 75Hos-125A
❑ 75Hos-125B
❑ 75HosTwi-125
❑ 75OPC-104
❑ 75SSPPuzB-16
❑ 75Top-104
❑ 75TopMin-104
❑ 76BlaDis-31
❑ 76BucDis-31
❑ 76CarDis-31
❑ 76CraDis-31
❑ 76DailsID-31
❑ 76Hos-100
❑ 76IsaDis-31
❑ 76Kel-20
❑ 76OPC-191
❑ 76OPC-640
❑ 76OrbDis-31
❑ 76RedBarD-31
❑ 76SafDis-31
❑ 76Spo-3
❑ 76SSP-309
❑ 76Top-191
❑ 76Top-640
❑ 76TowCluD-31
❑ 77BobParMBC-22
❑ 77BurCheD-198
❑ 77ChiWilD-40
❑ 77DailsID-40
❑ 77DetCaeD-40
❑ 77Gia-14
❑ 77GiaTeal-17
❑ 77HolInnD-40
❑ 77Hos-118
❑ 77Kel-43
❑ 77MSADis-40
❑ 77OPC-1
❑ 77OPC-56
❑ 77RCColC-37
❑ 77SagDis-40
❑ 77sDis-40
❑ 77Top-1
❑ 77Top-250
❑ 77TopCloS-25
❑ 77WenDis-40
❑ 77ZipDis-40
❑ 78GiaTeal-18
❑ 78Hos-117
❑ 78OPC-89
❑ 78Pep-35
❑ 78RCColC-54
❑ 78SagDis-15
❑ 78TasDis-15
❑ 78Top-410
❑ 79BasPat-50
❑ 79GiaPol-18
❑ 79Hos-138
❑ 79OPC-96
❑ 79Top-195
❑ 80OPC-30
❑ 80Top-55
❑ 81AllGamPI-122
❑ 81CokTeaS-114
❑ 81Don-252
❑ 81Fle-381
❑ 81OPC-137
❑ 81Top-715
❑ 81TopSti-213
❑ 82Don-653
❑ 82Dra-23
❑ 82Fle-485
❑ 82FleSta-77
❑ 82Kel-55
❑ 82OPC-365
❑ 82PerCreC-7
❑ 82PerCreCG-7
❑ 82SevSluC-17
❑ 82Top-161
❑ 82Top-365
❑ 82Top-696
❑ 82TopSti-1
❑ 82TopSti-83
❑ 83AllGamPI-123
❑ 83Don-311
❑ 83DonActA-30
❑ 83Dra-15
❑ 83Fle-309

- 83FleSta-112
- 83FleSti-71
- 83Kel-18
- 83OPC-335
- 83PerCreC-8
- 83PerCreCG-8
- 83Top-291
- 83Top-645
- 83TopFol-3
- 83TopGloS-26
- 83TopSti-275
- 84AllGamPI-32
- 84CubBriPC-11S
- 84Don-20
- 84Don-20A
- 84Don-113
- 84DonActAS-33
- 84DonCha-22
- 84Dra-20
- 84Fle-253
- 84FleSti-6
- 84FunFooP-31
- 84MilBra-16
- 84Nes792-131
- 84Nes792-250
- 84Nes792-696
- 84Nes792-701
- 84OCoandSI-71
- 84OPC-250
- 84Pir-9
- 84RalPur-26
- 84SevCoi-E11
- 84Top-131
- 84Top-250
- 84Top-696
- 84Top-701
- 84TopCer-26
- 84TopGloS-19
- 84TopRubD-25
- 84TopSti-99
- 84TopSti-131
- 84TopStiB-12
- 84TopSup-8
- 84TopTif-131
- 84TopTif-250
- 84TopTif-696
- 84TopTif-701
- 85AllGamPI-122
- 85Don-200
- 85Fle-468
- 85FleLimE-19
- 85Lea-185
- 85OPC-157
- 85Pir-10
- 85SevCoi-E11
- 85Top-560
- 85TopMin-560
- 85TopRubD-25
- 85TopSti-122
- 85TopTif-560
- 86DodCokP-17
- 86DodPol-12
- 86DodUniOP-12
- 86Don-617
- 86Fle-135
- 86FleMin-29
- 86Lea-238
- 86OPC-47
- 86SevCoi-W14
- 86Spo-58
- 86Spo-88
- 86Spo-131
- 86Spo-181
- 86Top-470
- 86TopSti-12
- 86TopSti-70
- 86TopTat-19
- 86TopTif-470
- 86TruVal-23
- 86Woo-19
- 87DodMot-8
- 87DodPol-5
- 87Don-155
- 87DonOpeD-78
- 87Fle-445
- 87FleGlo-445
- 87FleMin-65
- 87FleStiC-73
- 87FleUpd-69
- 87FleUpdG-69
- 87Lea-120
- 87OPC-276
- 87RedFolSB-109
- 87Spo-130
- 87Top-734
- 87TopSti-67
- 87TopTif-734
- 87TopTra-71T
- 87TopTraT-71T
- 88Don-496
- 88Fle-63
- 88FleGlo-63
- 88Lea-232
- 88OPC-145
- 88Sco-445
- 88ScoGlo-445
- 88Spo-123
- 88StaLinTi-13
- 88Top-145
- 88TopSti-266
- 88TopTif-145
- 89PacSenL-214
- 89T/MSenL-69
- 89TopSenL-71
- 90DodTar-469
- 90EliSenL-116
- 92ActPacA-82
- 92KelAll-7
- 92MCIAmb-5
- 92MVP-15
- 92MVP2H-16
- 93RanKee-237
- 93TedWil-77
- 93UppDecAH-86
- 93UppDecS-9
- 93UppDecS-22
- 93UppDecS-24
- 94UppDecAH-74
- 94UppDecAH-216
- 94UppDecAH1-74
- 94UppDecAH1-216
- 98MicBatCM-2

Madonna, Chris
- 97MicBatC-20

Madrid, Alex
- 85BelBreT-18
- 87DenZepP-10
- 88BlaYNPRWL-91
- 88DenZepC-3
- 88DenZepP-1251
- 89Don-604
- 89PhiTas-20
- 89ScoHot1R-58
- 89ScrRedBC-5
- 89ScrRedBP-720
- 94BreMilB-53

Madrigal, Victor
- 91ButCopKSP-18
- 91Cla/Bes-266
- 91GasRanC-8
- 91GasRanP-2685
- 92ButCopKSP-21
- 93AshTouC-12
- 93AshTouF-2272

Madril, Bill
- 91ElmPioC-10
- 91ElmPioP-3274
- 91WinHavRSP-494
- 92WinHavRSC-5

Madril, Mike
- 83RedPioT-18
- 85EdmTraC-3
- 86MidAngP-15

Madritsch, Bob
- 98BilMusTI-20

Madsen, Dan
- 92GenCubC-11
- 92GenCubF-1573
- 93PeoChiC-12
- 93PeoChiF-1096
- 93PeoChiTI-15
- 94PeoChiC-17
- 94PeoChiF-2280

Madsen, Dave
- 94MadHatC-13
- 94MadHatF-141
- 96ModA'sB-20

Madsen, Erik
- 89GreFalDSP-24
- 90YakBeaTI-9

Madsen, Lance
- 89AubAstP-2164
- 90OscAstS-18
- 91JacGenLD-567
- 91JacGenP-933
- 91LinDriAA-567
- 92JacGenF-4006
- 92JacGenS-339
- 93JacGenF-2115
- 94TucTorF-769

Madson, Ryan
- 98MarPhiG-16

Maduro, Calvin
- 93BluOriC-17
- 93BluOriF-4121
- 94FreKeyC-15
- 94FreKeyF-2610
- 94OriPro-57
- 95Bow-121
- 96BowBayB-20
- 96DouAllB-24
- 97BowBes-158
- 97BowBesAR-158
- 97BowBesR-158
- 97ColCho-416
- 97Fle-575
- 97FleTif-575
- 97PhiTeal-50
- 97PinCer-133
- 97PinCerMBla-133
- 97PinCerMBlu-133
- 97PinCerMG-133
- 97PinCerMR-133
- 97PinCerR-133
- 97PinTotCPB-133
- 97PinTotCPG-133
- 97PinTotCPR-133
- 97Ult-522
- 97UltGolME-522
- 97UltPlaME-522
- 98ScoRT-103
- 98ScrRedBQ-19

Maduro, Noe
- 93LinVenB-162
- 95LinVen-70
- 96-97LinVen-123

Maebe, Art
- 80CliGiaT-11

Maeda, Katsuhiro
- 96Bow-121
- 96BowFoi-121
- 97Bow-91
- 97BowBes-167
- 97BowBesAR-167
- 97BowBesP-20
- 97BowBesPAR-20
- 97BowBesPR-20
- 97BowBesR-167
- 97BowChr-115
- 97BowChrl-115
- 97BowChrlR-115
- 97BowChrR-115
- 97BowInt-91
- 97BowIntB-BBI18
- 97BowIntBAR-BBI18
- 97BowIntBR-BBI18
- 97NorNav-25
- 97NorNavTI-20
- 97StaClu-189
- 97StaCluM-M27
- 97StaCluMOP-189
- 97StaCluMOP-M27
- 98NorNavQ-15
- 98SP MinPE-86
- 98SP SPTSC-KM
- 98SPMin-86

Maeda, Koji
- 88SanJosGCLC-133
- 88SanJosGP-108

Maeda, Tomonori
- 93GolCar-5
- 94Cal-1

Maema, Takashi
- 90GatCitPP-3358
- 90GatCitPSP-14

Maestas, Mickey
- 96YakBeaTI-35
- 97YakBeaG-15

Maffett, Chris
- 91BurIndP-3301
- 92BurIndC-12
- 92BurIndF-1653

Mag, Rick
- 88BriTigP-1862

Magadan, Dave
- 86MetWorSC-19
- 86StaoftFT-32
- 86TidTidP-17
- 87ClaGam-19
- 87Don-575
- 87DonRoo-34
- 87Fle-648
- 87FleGlo-648
- 87FleUpd-70
- 87FleUpdG-70
- 87MetColP-16
- 87SpoRooI-10
- 87SpoRooP-3
- 87SpoTeaP-2
- 87Top-512
- 87TopRoo-9
- 87TopTif-512
- 88ClaBlu-230
- 88Don-323
- 88DonTeaBM-323
- 88Fle-141
- 88FleGlo-141
- 88KeyFooD-13
- 88Lea-108
- 88MetColP-34
- 88MetKah-29
- 88MSAIceTD-13
- 88OPC-58
- 88OurOwnTD-13
- 88RedFolSB-51
- 88Sco-41
- 88ScoGlo-41
- 88ScoYouSI-23
- 88Spo-83
- 88StaLinMe-12
- 88TetTeaD-13
- 88Top-58
- 88TopSti-104
- 88TopTif-58
- 88WeiMarD-13
- 89Bow-384
- 89BowTif-384
- 89Don-408
- 89DonBasB-264
- 89Fle-41
- 89FleGlo-41
- 89MetColP-42
- 89MetKah-16
- 89OPC-81
- 89Sco-312
- 89Top-655
- 89TopBig-71
- 89TopTif-655
- 89UppDec-388
- 90Don-383
- 90DonBesN-56
- 90Fle-210
- 90FleCan-210
- 90Lea-330
- 90MetColP-18
- 90MetKah-10
- 90OPC-135
- 90PanSti-300
- 90PubIntS-138
- 90Sco-46
- 90Spo-173
- 90Top-135
- 90TopBig-24
- 90TopSti-99
- 90TopTif-135
- 90TopTVM-26
- 90UppDec-243
- 91Bow-484
- 91Cla1-T67
- 91Cla2-T72
- 91ClaGam-100
- 91Don-17
- 91Don-362
- 91DonSupD-17
- 91Fle-153
- 91Lea-20
- 91MajLeaCP-76
- 91MetColP-6
- 91MetKah-10
- 91MetPerPA-21
- 91MetTro-6
- 91MetWIZ-242
- 91MooSna-13
- 91OPC-480
- 91PanCanT1-3
- 91PanFreS-79
- 91PanSti-81
- 91PosCan-4
- 91Sco-190
- 91Sco100S-34
- 91SimandSMLBL-27
- 91StaClu-210
- 91Stu-208
- 91Top-480
- 91TopDesS-480
- 91TopMic-480
- 91TopTif-480
- 91Ult-223
- 91UppDec-177
- 92Bow-263
- 92Don-45
- 92Fle-510
- 92Lea-306
- 92LeaBlaG-306
- 92MetColP-7
- 92MetKah-29
- 92OPC-745
- 92PanSti-222
- 92Pin-201
- 92Sco-201
- 92StaClu-118
- 92Top-745
- 92TopGol-745
- 92TopGolW-745
- 92TopMic-745
- 92TriPla-82
- 92Ult-236
- 92UppDec-112
- 93Bow-614
- 93ClaGam-57
- 93Don-486
- 93Fle-477
- 93Lea-391
- 93MarlStaClu-10
- 93MarUppD-479
- 93MarUppD-528
- 93MarUSPC-1D
- 93MarUSPC-2C
- 93MarUSPC-4C
- 93OPC-253
- 93OPCPre-61
- 93PacJugC-31
- 93PacSpa-466
- 93PanSti-250
- 93Pin-237
- 93PinExpOD-5
- 93Sco-631
- 93Sel-149
- 93SelRoo-116T
- 93StaClu-452
- 93StaCluFDI-452
- 93StaCluMOP-452
- 93Stu-154
- 93Top-578
- 93TopGol-578
- 93TopInaM-578
- 93TopInaR-578
- 93TopMic-578
- 93TopTra-106T
- 93Ult-382
- 93UppDec-479
- 93UppDec-528
- 93UppDecGold-479
- 93UppDecGold-528
- 94Bow-450
- 94ColC-184
- 94ColC-367
- 94ColChoGS-184
- 94ColChoGS-367
- 94ColChoSS-184
- 94ColChoSS-367
- 94Don-658
- 94Fin-130
- 94FinPre-130P
- 94FinRef-130
- 94Fla-165
- 94Fle-293
- 94FleExtB-264
- 94FleUpd-136
- 94Lea-386
- 94MarTeal-10
- 94OPC-107
- 94Pac-247
- 94PacAll-2
- 94Pin-187
- 94PinArtP-187
- 94PinMusC-187
- 94ProMag-55
- 94Sco-14
- 94ScoGolR-14
- 94ScoRoo-RT23
- 94ScoRooGR-RT23
- 94Sel-143
- 94StaClu-365
- 94StaCluFDI-365
- 94StaCluGR-365
- 94StaCluMOP-365
- 94StaCluT-81
- 94StaCluTFDI-81
- 94Top-347
- 94TopGol-347
- 94TopSpa-347
- 94TopTra-80T
- 94TriPla-138
- 94Ult-197
- 94UppDec-73
- 94UppDecED-73
- 95AstMot-8
- 95ColCho-302
- 95ColCho-532T
- 95ColChoGS-302
- 95ColChoSS-302
- 95Don-489
- 95DonPreP-489
- 95DonTopotO-257
- 95Fle-336
- 95Pin-397
- 95PinArtP-397
- 95PinMusC-397
- 95Sco-475
- 95ScoGolR-475
- 95ScoPlaTS-475
- 95Top-283
- 95TopCyb-154
- 95TopTra-134T
- 96ColCho-163
- 96ColCho-766
- 96ColChoGS-163
- 96ColChoSS-163
- 96Don-280
- 96DonPreP-280
- 96Fla-219
- 96Fle-414
- 96FleTif-414
- 96FleUpd-U113
- 96FleUpdTC-U113
- 96LeaSigEA-116
- 96Pac-98
- 96Sco-116
- 96Ult-452
- 96UltGolM-452
- 97A'sMot-8
- 97Ult-545
- 97UltGolME-545
- 97UltPlaME-545
- 98A'sMot-16
- 98ColCho-197
- 98Pac-167
- 98PacOnl-536
- 98PacOnlR-536
- 98PacOnlWC-536
- 98PacPlaB-167
- 98PacRedT-167
- 98PacSil-167
- 98StaCluFDI-44
- 98StaCluI-44
- 98StaCluOneK-44
- 98StaCluPP-44
- 98UppDec-469

Magallanes, Bobby (William)
- 86AppFoxP-13
- 90SanBerSB-12
- 90SanBerSCLC-107
- 90SanBerSP-2640
- 91Cla/Bes-263
- 91SanBerSC-18
- 91SanBerSP-1995
- 92PenPilF-2939
- 93LinVenB-209
- 94VenLinU-165
- 95LinVen-149
- 96-97LinVen-240

Magallanes, Ever
- 88KinIndS-16
- 89CanIndB-23
- 89CanIndP-1309
- 89CanIndS-13
- 90CMC-465
- 90ColSprSSC-13
- 90ColSprSSP-42
- 90ProAAAF-223
- 91Bow-61
- 91ColSprSSLD-91
- 91ColSprSSP-2192
- 91LinDriAAA-91
- 92SkyAAAF-286
- 92TopDeb91-113
- 92VanCanF-2731
- 92VanCanS-643
- 93TulDriF-2742
- 93TulDriTI-16
- 94TulDriF-252
- 94TulDriTI-15

Magallanes, Willie
- 88BirBarB-25
- 90Bes-125
- 90BirBarB-11
- 90BirBarP-1396

Magdaleno, Rick
- 92ClaDraP-36
- 93ClaFS7-106
- 93StaCluM-71
- 93WesVirWC-17
- 93WesVirWF-2874
- 94CarLeaAF-CAR49

❑ 94WinSpiC-15
❑ 94WinSpiF-280
❑ 96ChaLooB-19
❑ 97ChaLoo-15
❑ 98RicBraQ-19

Magee, Bo
❑ 91ButCopKSP-22
❑ 92GasRanC-14
❑ 92GasRanF-2251
❑ 93ChaRanC-17
❑ 93ChaRanF-1938
❑ 94KinIndC-11
❑ 94KinIndF-2639

Magee, Danny
❑ 94MacBraC-11
❑ 94MacBraF-2215
❑ 95DurBulTI-19
❑ 96DurBulBIB-28
❑ 96DurBulBrB-28

Magee, Lee
❑ 09PC7HHB-30
❑ 14FatPlaT-27
❑ 15CraJacE-147
❑ 15SpoNewM-106
❑ 16SpoNewM-108
❑ 17ColE13-103
❑ 90DodTar-470
❑ 94ConTSN-1273
❑ 94ConTSNB-1273

Magee, Sherry
❑ 08RosComP-143
❑ 09SpoNewSM-7
❑ 09T206-220
❑ 09T206-221
❑ 09T206-222
❑ 10CouT21-172
❑ 10CouT21-173
❑ 10CouT21-174
❑ 10CouT21-298
❑ 10DomDisP-74
❑ 10E101-30
❑ 10E102-16
❑ 10MelMinE-30
❑ 10NadCarE-35
❑ 10PeoT21-35
❑ 10RedCroT-44
❑ 10RedCroT-215
❑ 10SweCapPP-128
❑ 10W555-44
❑ 11E94-23
❑ 11HelSta-147
❑ 11L1L-123
❑ 11PinT-5-306
❑ 11PloCanE-42
❑ 11S81LarS-98
❑ 11SpoLifCW-230
❑ 11SpoLifM-233
❑ 11T205-107
❑ 11TurRedT-31
❑ 12HasTriFT-9
❑ 12HasTriFT-17
❑ 12HasTriFT-30D
❑ 14CraJacE-108
❑ 14FatPlaT-28
❑ 14PieStaT-66
❑ 15CraJacE-108
❑ 15VicT21-19
❑ 16BF2FP-55
❑ 16SpoNewM-109
❑ 17ColE13-104
❑ 20RedWorCP-11
❑ 83PhiPosGPaM-5
❑ 88FriBasCM-6
❑ 92ConTSN-449
❑ 93ConTSN-897
❑ 94ConTSN-1025
❑ 94ConTSN-1267
❑ 94ConTSNB-1025
❑ 94ConTSNB-1267

Magee, Warren
❑ 87ClePhiP-14
❑ 88EasLeaAP-33
❑ 88ReaPhiP-871
❑ 89ReaPhiB-2
❑ 89ReaPhiP-674
❑ 89ReaPhiS-16
❑ 90ReaPhiB-9
❑ 90ReaPhiP-1218
❑ 90ReaPhiS-17

Magee, Wendell
❑ 94BatCliC-12
❑ 94BatCliF-3459
❑ 95Bes-86
❑ 95ClePhiF-229
❑ 95ReaPhiELC-26
❑ 95SPML-132
❑ 96Bow-226
❑ 96BowFoi-226
❑ 96Exc-208
❑ 96ExcCli-6
❑ 96ExcTL-6
❑ 96ReaPhiB-23
❑ 97Bow-114
❑ 97BowInt-114
❑ 97ColCho-14
❑ 97Don-378
❑ 97DonGolPP-378
❑ 97DonPre-163
❑ 97DonPreCttC-163
❑ 97DonSilPP-378
❑ 97Fin-229
❑ 97FinRef-229
❑ 97FlaShoLC-168
❑ 97FlaShoLeg0-168
❑ 97FlaShoLeg1-168
❑ 97FlaShoM-A168
❑ 97FlaShoM-B168
❑ 97FlaShoM-C168
❑ 97FlaShoR0-168
❑ 97FlaShoR1-168
❑ 97FlaShoR2-168
❑ 97Fle-415
❑ 97FleRooS-16
❑ 97FleTif-415
❑ 97Lea-183
❑ 97LeaFraM-183
❑ 97LeaFraMDC-183
❑ 97MetUni-202
❑ 97NewPin-163
❑ 97NewPinAP-163
❑ 97NewPinMC-163
❑ 97NewPinPP-163
❑ 97PacPriGotD-GD184
❑ 97PhiCopQ-16
❑ 97PhiTeal-29
❑ 97PinCer-130
❑ 97PinCerMBla-130
❑ 97PinCerMBlu-130
❑ 97PinCerMG-130
❑ 97PinCerMR-130
❑ 97PinCerR-130
❑ 97PinTotCPB-130
❑ 97PinTotCPG-130
❑ 97PinTotCPR-130
❑ 97PinX-P-132
❑ 97PinX-PMoS-132
❑ 97Sco-322
❑ 97ScoArtPWB-322
❑ 97ScoPreS-322
❑ 97ScoShoS-322
❑ 97ScoShoSAP-322
❑ 97StaClu-372
❑ 97StaCluM-M25
❑ 97StaCluMOP-372
❑ 97StaCluMOP-M25
❑ 97Top-302
❑ 97Ult-252
❑ 97UltGolME-252
❑ 97UltPlaME-252
❑ 97UppDec-472
❑ 98ScrRedB1ATI-10
❑ 98ScrRedBQ-20
❑ 98UppDec-184
❑ 99Fle-227
❑ 99FleSta9-227
❑ 99FleWarT-227
❑ 99Pac-329
❑ 99PacPlaB-329
❑ 99PacRed-329

Magers, Matthew
❑ 97WilCubB-14
❑ 98RocCubM-20
❑ 98RocCubTI-21

Maggert, Harl
❑ 09ObaT21-277
❑ 10BisCoaLE99-16
❑ 11PacCoaBD-37
❑ 11Zee-33
❑ 12ObaPreT-26
❑ 13Zee-14
❑ 14Zee-15
❑ 15Zee-14
❑ 16Zee-14
❑ 17Zee-12
❑ 20Zee-88

Maggio, Aggie
❑ 80WesHavWCT-22A

Magill, Jim
❑ 93HigDesMC-10
❑ 93HigDesMF-36

Magistri, Greg
❑ 85ElmPioT-13

Maglie, Sal
❑ 47Exh-142
❑ 47PM1StaP1-116
❑ 51Bow-127
❑ 52BerRos-36
❑ 52Bow-66
❑ 52RedMan-NL14
❑ 52StaCalL-78C
❑ 52StaCalS-90B
❑ 52TipTop-23
❑ 53BowC-96
❑ 53RedMan-NL8
❑ 54Bow-105
❑ 54NewYorJA-31
❑ 55Bow-95
❑ 55GiaGolS-4
❑ 55RedMan-NL6
❑ 56Dod-18
❑ 56GiaJayP-6
❑ 57Top-5
❑ 57YanJayP-9
❑ 58Top-43
❑ 59Top-309
❑ 60NuHi-70
❑ 60Top-456
❑ 61NuSco-470
❑ 67TopRedSS-17
❑ 69PilPos-32
❑ 74NewYorNTDiS-23
❑ 75Gia195T-18
❑ 77GalGloG-28
❑ 77PilPosR-32
❑ 79TCM50-256
❑ 80MarExh-17
❑ 83DodBoyoST-2
❑ 83Pil69G-21
❑ 84FifNatCT-10
❑ 88DodRinP1-11A
❑ 88PacLegI-85
❑ 89NiaFalRP-29
❑ 89SweBasG-99
❑ 90DodTar-471
❑ 90SweBasG-38
❑ 91SweBasG-59
❑ 91TopArc1-303
❑ 92BazQua5A-16
❑ 94TedWil-53
❑ 94TedWilM-M22

Magnante, Mike (Michael)
❑ 89MemChiB-21
❑ 89MemChiP-1198
❑ 89MemChiS-15
❑ 90CMC-181
❑ 90OmaRoyC-6
❑ 90OmaRoyP-64
❑ 90ProAAAF-599
❑ 91LinDriAAA-340
❑ 91OmaRoyLD-340
❑ 91OmaRoyP-1033
❑ 92Don-706
❑ 92OPC-597
❑ 92OPCPre-57
❑ 92RoyPol-16
❑ 92Sco-739
❑ 92StaClu-448
❑ 92Top-597
❑ 92TopDeb91-114
❑ 92TopGol-597
❑ 92TopGolW-597
❑ 92TopMic-597
❑ 93Fle-620
❑ 93OmaRoyF-1677
❑ 93RoyStaC-13
❑ 93StaClu-12
❑ 93StaCluFDI-12
❑ 93StaCluMOP-12
❑ 93Top-186
❑ 93TopGol-186
❑ 93TopInaM-186
❑ 93TopInaR-186
❑ 93TopMic-186
❑ 93UppDec-180
❑ 93UppDecGold-180
❑ 94Fle-165
❑ 94StaClu-607
❑ 94StaCluFDI-607
❑ 94StaCluGR-607
❑ 94StaCluMOP-607
❑ 95Fle-166
❑ 95OmaRoyTI-19
❑ 95Top-415
❑ 95TopCyb-215
❑ 96LeaSigEA-117
❑ 98PacOnl-328
❑ 98PacOnlR-328
❑ 98PacOnlWC-328

Magnante, Rick
❑ 89NiaFalRP-25

Magnelli, Tony
❑ 93GleFalRC-20
❑ 93GleFalRF-4000

Magner, Rich
❑ 75WatDodT-13
❑ 79AlbDukTc-17

Magno, Chris
❑ 85MiaHur-9

Magnuson, Jim
❑ 72Top-597
❑ 92YanWIZ7-102

Magnusson, Brett
❑ 88GreFalDTI-3
❑ 89Sta-30
❑ 89VerBeaDS-16
❑ 90BakDodCLC-254
❑ 90CalLeaACLC-2
❑ 91AdeGiaF-9
❑ 91LinDriAA-537
❑ 91SanAntMLD-537
❑ 91SanAntMP-2988
❑ 92YakBeaC-25
❑ 93SanAntMF-3022
❑ 94SanAntMF-2487

Magoon, George
❑ 11SpoLifCW-231
❑ 90DodTar-472

Magrane, Joe
❑ 84AriWilP-12
❑ 86ArkTraP-12
❑ 87CarTeal-20
❑ 87ClaUpdY-117
❑ 87DonRoo-40
❑ 87FleSlu-24
❑ 87FleUpd-71
❑ 87FleUpdG-71
❑ 87LouRedTI-25
❑ 87SpoRooI-11
❑ 87SpoTeaP-12
❑ 87TopTra-72T
❑ 87TopTraT-72T
❑ 88CarSmo-6
❑ 88CarTeal-18
❑ 88ClaBlu-240
❑ 88Don-140
❑ 88DonBasB-100
❑ 88Fle-40
❑ 88FleGlo-40
❑ 88LouRedBTI-31
❑ 88OPC-380
❑ 88PanSti-385
❑ 88RedFolSB-52
❑ 88Sco-94
❑ 88ScoGlo-94
❑ 88ScoYouSI-9
❑ 88Spo-128
❑ 88Top-380
❑ 88TopGloS-40
❑ 88TopRoo-20
❑ 88TopSti-51
❑ 88TopTif-380
❑ 88ToyRoo-15
❑ 89Bow-432
❑ 89BowTif-432
❑ 89CarSmo-12
❑ 89CarTeal-16
❑ 89ClaTraO-148
❑ 89Don-201
❑ 89DonBasB-131
❑ 89Fle-455
❑ 89FleGlo-455
❑ 89FleLeaL-24
❑ 89OPC-264
❑ 89PanSti-178
❑ 89Sco-460
❑ 89Top-657
❑ 89TopBasT-94
❑ 89TopBig-203
❑ 89TopMinL-36
❑ 89TopTif-657
❑ 89UppDec-103
❑ 90Bow-183
❑ 90BowTif-183
❑ 90CarSmo-12
❑ 90ClaBlu-145
❑ 90Don-13
❑ 90Don-163
❑ 90DonBesN-46
❑ 90DonLeaS-34
❑ 90DonSupD-13
❑ 90Fle-252
❑ 90FleAll-5
❑ 90FleCan-252
❑ 90K-M-12
❑ 90Lea-11
❑ 90OPC-406
❑ 90OPC-578
❑ 90PanSti-346
❑ 90PubIntS-220
❑ 90PubIntS-267
❑ 90Sco-17
❑ 90Spo-151
❑ 90Top-406
❑ 90Top-578
❑ 90TopBig-271
❑ 90TopCoi-52
❑ 90TopDou-42
❑ 90TopGloS-36
❑ 90TopMinL-76
❑ 90TopSti-41
❑ 90TopStiB-30
❑ 90TopTif-406
❑ 90TopTif-578
❑ 90TopTVA-64
❑ 90TopTVCa-16
❑ 90UppDec-242
❑ 91ClaGam-29
❑ 91Don-295
❑ 91Fle-638
❑ 91OPC-185
❑ 91PanFreS-38
❑ 91PanSti-31
❑ 91Sco-575
❑ 91StaClu-85
❑ 91StaCluP-23
❑ 91Stu-235
❑ 91Top-185
❑ 91TopDesS-185
❑ 91TopMic-185
❑ 91TopTif-185
❑ 91Ult-291
❑ 91UppDec-465
❑ 92CarPol-11
❑ 92Don-767
❑ 92OPC-783
❑ 92Pin-494
❑ 92StaClu-622
❑ 92StaCluECN-622
❑ 92Top-783
❑ 92TopGol-783
❑ 92TopGolW-783
❑ 92TopMic-783
❑ 93CarStaC-8
❑ 93Don-492
❑ 93FleFinE-127
❑ 93PacSpa-633
❑ 93Pin-342
❑ 93StaClu-646
❑ 93StaCluFDI-646
❑ 93StaCluMOP-646
❑ 93Ult-464
❑ 93UppDec-703
❑ 93UppDecGold-703
❑ 94AngAdoF-3
❑ 94AngLAT-8
❑ 94AngMot-17
❑ 94ColC-185
❑ 94ColChoGS-185
❑ 94ColChoSS-185
❑ 94Fle-64
❑ 94Pac-84
❑ 94Pin-114
❑ 94PinArtP-114
❑ 94PinMusC-114
❑ 94SpoRoo-3
❑ 94SpoRooAP-3
❑ 94StaClu-509
❑ 94StaCluFDI-509
❑ 94StaCluGR-509
❑ 94StaCluMOP-509
❑ 94Top-27
❑ 94TopGol-27
❑ 94TopSpa-27
❑ 94UppDec-159
❑ 94UppDecED-159
❑ 96LeaSigEA-118

Magrann, Tom
❑ 86HagSunP-8
❑ 87MiaMarP-24
❑ 89CanIndB-10
❑ 89CanIndP-1313
❑ 89CanIndS-14
❑ 90CMC-466
❑ 90ColSprSSC-14
❑ 90ColSprSSP-40
❑ 90Don-374
❑ 90IndTeal-24
❑ 90ProAAAF-221
❑ 90TopDeb89-75
❑ 91BufBisLD-32
❑ 91BufBisP-545
❑ 91LinDriAAA-32

Magre, Pete
❑ 93BilMusF-3941
❑ 94ChaWheF-2700

Magria, Javier
❑ 89WelPirP-18
❑ 90MiaMirIS-16

Magrini, Paul
❑ 91BriTigC-27
❑ 91BriTigP-3598
❑ 92BriTigC-4
❑ 92BriTigF-1404
❑ 93NiaFalRF-3381

Magrini, Pete
❑ 66Top-558

Magruder, Chris
❑ 98SalVol-22
❑ 99Bow-424
❑ 99BowGol-424
❑ 99BowInt-424
❑ 99TeaBesR-53
❑ 99TeaBesRG-53
❑ 99TeaBesRS-53

Maguire, Chris
❑ 91DaiDolF-8

Maguire, Fred
❑ 29ExhFou-2
❑ 29PorandAR-59
❑ 31Exh-2
❑ 33ExhFou-1
❑ 93ConTSN-791

Maguire, Jack
❑ 75Gia195T-19

Maguire, Kevin
❑ 92AugPirC-20
❑ 92AugPirF-242

Maguire, Mike
❑ 91WelPirC-22
❑ 91WelPirP-3569

Mahaffey, Alan
❑ 96ForWayWB-14
❑ 97ForMyeM-18
❑ 98NewBriRCM-18

Mahaffey, Art
❑ 47Exh-143
❑ 58PhiTeal-12
❑ 60Top-138
❑ 60TopVen-138
❑ 61Baz-1
❑ 61Top-433
❑ 61TopStal-57
❑ 62Baz-22
❑ 62ExhStaB-21
❑ 62Jel-199
❑ 62Pos-199
❑ 62PosCan-199
❑ 62SalPlaC-112
❑ 62ShiPlaC-112
❑ 62Top-550
❑ 62TopBuc-51
❑ 62TopStal-171
❑ 63BasMagM-52
❑ 63Baz-35
❑ 63ExhStaB-39
❑ 63Fle-54
❑ 63Jel-183
❑ 63Pos-183
❑ 63SalMetC-10
❑ 63Top-7
❑ 63Top-385
❑ 63TopStil-25
❑ 64ChatheY-32
❑ 64PhiJayP-7
❑ 64PhiPhiB-16
❑ 64Top-104
❑ 64TopVen-104
❑ 65ChaTheY-32
❑ 65PhiJayP-7
❑ 65Top-446
❑ 66Top-570
❑ 83PhiPosGM-3
❑ 94CarLeaA-DJ11

Mahaffey, Leroy
❑ 29Zee-94
❑ 33Gou-196
❑ 33RitCE-4H
❑ 33TatOrbSDR-175
❑ 34BatR31-15
❑ 34DiaMatCSB-121
❑ 34DiaStaR-10A
❑ 34DiaStaR-10B
❑ 35ExhFou-14
❑ 35GouPuzR-1B
❑ 35GouPuzR-2B

❑ 35GouPuzR-16B
❑ 35GouPuzR-17B
❑ 74A's192T-18
❑ 92ConTSN-603
Mahalik, John
❑ 93ButCopKSP-7
❑ 94BurBeeF-1088
❑ 95BinMetTI-11
❑ 96BinMetB-18
❑ 97BinMetB-17
Mahambitov, Igor
❑ 89EasLeaDDP-DD20
Mahan, George
❑ 76WilTomT-15
Mahan, Russ
❑ 88MisStaB-16
❑ 89MisStaB-23
Mahar, Eddie
❑ 87SyrChiT-32
Maharg, Billy
❑ 88PacEigMO-17
Mahay, Ron
❑ 92WinHavRSC-14
❑ 93LynRedSC-15
❑ 93LynRedSF-2530
❑ 94SarRedSC-17
❑ 94SarRedSF-1966
❑ 95TreThuTI-25
❑ 97TreThuB-20
❑ 98PawRedSQ-19
Maher, Kim
❑ 91FreStaLBS-6
Mahlberg, Greg
❑ 76SacSolC-23
❑ 77TucTorC-8
❑ 78TucTorC-24
❑ 79TucTorT-15
❑ 80ChaChaT-6
❑ 80Top-673
❑ 81IndIndTI-12
❑ 87SalSpuS-32
❑ 88ChaWheB-3
❑ 89ChaWheB-25
❑ 89ChaWheP-1755
❑ 90PeoChiTI-31
❑ 91GenCubC-19
❑ 91GenCubP-4234
❑ 92GenCubC-26
❑ 93RanKee-238
❑ 93SanBerSC-21
❑ 93SanBerSF-786
❑ 94SanBerSC-25
❑ 94SanBerSF-2774
❑ 95BakBlaTI-31
❑ 96StoPorB-27
❑ 97CalLeaATI-1
❑ 97StoPor-26
❑ 98ChaRivDG-18
Mahlberg, John
❑ 96PorRocB-21
❑ 97AshTou-17
❑ 97PorRocG-15
Mahler, Jim
❑ 81SpoIndT-22
Mahler, Mickey
❑ 78Top-703
❑ 79Top-331
❑ 80PorBeaT-10
❑ 81SalLakCGT-8
❑ 82SpoIndT-4
❑ 84LouRedR-28
❑ 85DomLeaS-130
❑ 85ExpPos-12
❑ 85FleUpd-77
❑ 85IndIndTI-16
❑ 86FleUpd-70
❑ 86TopTra-68T
❑ 86TopTraT-68T
❑ 87LouRedTI-18
❑ 89T/MSenL-70
❑ 89TopSenL-82
❑ 91PacSenL-37
❑ 93RanKee-239
Mahler, Rick
❑ 78RicBraT-9
❑ 80RicBraT-11
❑ 80VenLeaS-189
❑ 81BraPol-42
❑ 82BraBurKL-16
❑ 82BraPol-42
❑ 82Don-349
❑ 82Fle-440
❑ 82Top-126
❑ 82Top-579
❑ 83Don-527
❑ 83Fle-141
❑ 83OPC-76
❑ 83Top-76
❑ 84BraPol-42
❑ 84raPho-18
❑ 85AllGamPI-172
❑ 85BraHos-14
❑ 85BraPol-42
❑ 85Don-385
❑ 85Fle-332
❑ 85OPC-79
❑ 85Top-79
❑ 85TopSti-26
❑ 85TopTif-79
❑ 86BraPol-42
❑ 86Don-21
❑ 86Don-77
❑ 86DonSupD-21
❑ 86Fle-521
❑ 86Lea-21
❑ 86OPC-39
❑ 86Top-437
❑ 86TopSti-43
❑ 86TopTat-11
❑ 86TopTif-437
❑ 87BraSmo-5
❑ 87Don-190
❑ 87DonOpeD-41
❑ 87Fle-520
❑ 87FleGlo-520
❑ 87OPC-242
❑ 87SpoTeaP-24
❑ 87Top-242
❑ 87TopSti-43
❑ 87TopTif-242
❑ 88Don-389
❑ 88DonBasB-114
❑ 88OPC-171
❑ 88PanSti-239
❑ 88Sco-319
❑ 88ScoGlo-319
❑ 88StaLinBra-11
❑ 88Top-706
❑ 88TopTif-706
❑ 89Bow-302
❑ 89BowTif-302
❑ 89Don-222
❑ 89DonBasB-286
❑ 89DonTra-24
❑ 89Fle-595
❑ 89FleGlo-595
❑ 89FleUpd-85
❑ 89OPC-393
❑ 89PanSti-35
❑ 89RedKah-42
❑ 89Sco-229
❑ 89ScoRoo-79T
❑ 89Top-621
❑ 89TopSti-29
❑ 89TopTif-621
❑ 89TopTra-74T
❑ 89TopTraT-74T
❑ 89UppDec-74
❑ 89UppDec-760
❑ 90Don-375
❑ 90Fle-425
❑ 90FleCan-425
❑ 90OPC-151
❑ 90PubIntS-34
❑ 90RedKah-15
❑ 90RicBra2ATI-15
❑ 90Sco-87
❑ 90Top-151
❑ 90TopSti-139
❑ 90TopTif-151
❑ 90UppDec-220
❑ 91ExpPos-12
❑ 91Fle-71
❑ 91Lea-284
❑ 91OPC-363
❑ 91Sco-464
❑ 91Top-363
❑ 91TopDesS-363
❑ 91TopMic-363
❑ 91TopTif-363
❑ 91UppDec-613
❑ 96ArkTraB-1
❑ 97ArkTraB-26
❑ 98SpoIndG-19
Mahling, William
❑ 07NewEveWS-7
Mahnke, Jason
❑ 96YakBeaTI-NNO
❑ 97YakBeaG-16
Mahomes, Pat
❑ 89KenTwiP-1067
❑ 89KenTwiS-12
❑ 90CMC-861
❑ 90ProAaA-141
❑ 90VisOakCLC-60
❑ 90VisOakP-2149
❑ 91LinDriAA-485
❑ 91OrlSunRLD-485
❑ 91OrlSunRP-1846
❑ 92Bow-131
❑ 92Cla2-T97
❑ 92Don-403
❑ 92FleUpd-40
❑ 92LeaGolR-BC17
❑ 92OPC-676
❑ 92Pin-472
❑ 92PinRoo-11
❑ 92PinTea2-80
❑ 92PorBeaF-2664
❑ 92ProFS7-93
❑ 92ScoRoo-102T
❑ 92SkyAA F-295
❑ 92Stu-208
❑ 92Top-676
❑ 92TopGol-676
❑ 92TopGolW-676
❑ 92TopMic-676
❑ 92Ult-398
❑ 92UltAllR-9
❑ 92UppDec-776
❑ 92UppDecSR-SR16
❑ 93Bow-157
❑ 93Don-357
❑ 93Fle-271
❑ 93Lea-344
❑ 93PacSpa-523
❑ 93Pin-408
❑ 93Sco-337
❑ 93Sel-324
❑ 93StaClu-740
❑ 93StaCluFDI-740
❑ 93StaCluMOP-740
❑ 93Top-684
❑ 93TopGol-684
❑ 93TopInaM-684
❑ 93TopInaR-684
❑ 93TopMic-684
❑ 93Toy-11
❑ 93Ult-234
❑ 93UppDec-337
❑ 93UppDecGold-337
❑ 93USPlaCR-2H
❑ 94Bow-160
❑ 94ColC-577
❑ 94ColChoGS-577
❑ 94ColChoSS-577
❑ 94FleExtB-121
❑ 94FleUpd-63
❑ 94Lea-413
❑ 94StaClu-688
❑ 94StaCluFDI-688
❑ 94StaCluGR-688
❑ 94StaCluMOP-688
❑ 94Top-43
❑ 94TopGol-43
❑ 94TopSpa-43
❑ 95ColCho-493
❑ 95ColChoGS-493
❑ 95ColChoSS-493
❑ 95Don-512
❑ 95DonPreP-512
❑ 95Fla-59
❑ 95Fle-209
❑ 95Lea-366
❑ 95Pin-252
❑ 95PinArtP-252
❑ 95PinMusC-252
❑ 95Sco-500
❑ 95ScoGolR-500
❑ 95ScoPlaTS-500
❑ 95Top-217
❑ 95Ult-304
❑ 95UltGolM-304
❑ 95UppDec-429
❑ 95UppDecED-429
❑ 95UppDecEDG-429
❑ 96ColCho-606
❑ 96ColChoGS-606
❑ 96ColChoSS-606
❑ 96Don-180
❑ 96DonPreP-180
❑ 96LeaSigEA-119
Mahon, Frank
❑ 96LowSpiB-3
Mahoney, Chris
❑ 09ObaT21-313
❑ 11BigEatEU-13
❑ 11Zee-73
❑ 12ObaPreT-62
❑ 12Zee-87
❑ 89TexLeaAGS-19
Mahoney, Daniel
❑ 87OldJudN-310
Mahoney, Jim
❑ 68SeaPop-9
❑ 73OPC-356
❑ 73Top-356
❑ 74OPC-221
❑ 74Top-221
❑ 77ChaPatT-8
❑ 78SalPirT-9
❑ 80PorBeaT-6
❑ 81GleFalWST-22
❑ 82GleFalWST-25
❑ 85MarMot-27
❑ 88PorBeaC-24
❑ 88PorBeaP-650
Mahoney, Mike
❑ 95EugEmeTI-14
❑ 96DurBulBIB-21
❑ 96DurBulBrB-22
❑ 97GreBraG-19
❑ 98RicBraQ-20
Mahoney, Ricardo
❑ 98PorRocG-24
Mahoney, Robert
❑ 52Top-58
❑ 83TopRep5-58
Mahoney, Sean
❑ 98HudValR-15
Mahony, Dan
❑ 91EriSaiC-7
❑ 91EriSaiP-4072
Maier, Taber
❑ 97NewJerCB-17
❑ 98PeoChiM-15
Maietta, Bub (Ron)
❑ 89BriTigS-15
❑ 89HigSchPLS-7
❑ 90BriTigP-3158
❑ 90BriTigS-16
Mailho, Emil
❑ 32Zee-61
❑ 33Zee-65
Mails, Duster (Walter)
❑ 20NatCarE-59
❑ 20WalMaiW-27
❑ 20Zee-69
❑ 21E121So1-55
❑ 21Exh-99
❑ 23WilChoV-86
❑ 23Zee-50
❑ 24Zee-35
❑ 28ExhPCL-20
❑ 33Zee-128
❑ 35PebBea-4
❑ 90DodTar-473
❑ 95ConTSN-1365
Mails, John
❑ 19Zee-116
❑ 22E120-36
❑ 23W501-23
❑ 27Zee-116
❑ 28Zee-135
❑ 29Zee-137
❑ 30Zee-147
❑ 77Ind192T-12
Main, Forrest
❑ 52Top-397
❑ 53Top-198
❑ 83TopRep5-397
❑ 91TopArc1-198
Main, Kevin
❑ 87ChaWheP-16
❑ 87GenCubP-21
Mainini, Marco
❑ 52LavPro-93
Mains, Miles
❑ 19Zee-117
Mains, Willard
❑ 87OldJudN-311
❑ 98CamPepP-50
Mainville, Martin
❑ 94ClaGolF-72
Mainville, Peter Jr
❑ 98BluOriQ-5
Mairena, Oswaldo
❑ 97GreBatB-18
❑ 98TamYanM-19
Maisel, Fritz
❑ 14B18B-25
❑ 14FatPlaT-29
❑ 14PolGroW-14
❑ 15CraJacE-158
Maisel, George
❑ 17Zee-93
❑ 19Zee-39
❑ 20Zee-51
❑ 21Exh-100
Maitland, Bill
❑ 92IdaFalGF-3508
❑ 92IdaFalGSP-6
Maitland, Mike
❑ 79AppFoxT-20
❑ 80AppFoxT-28
❑ 81GleFalWST-5
❑ 82GleFalWST-25
❑ 83GleFalWST-14
Maize, Dave
❑ 92WelPirC-18
❑ 92WelPirF-1326
❑ 93PitMetF-3714
Majcherek, Matt
❑ 96HudValRB-19
Majer, Steffen
❑ 90St.PetCS-15
❑ 91ArkTraP-1281
❑ 92ArkTraF-1125
❑ 92ArkTraS-36
Majeski, Brian
❑ 94GreFalDSP-11
❑ 95VerBeaDTI-16
❑ 96VerBeaDB-18
Majeski, Carl
❑ 91IdaFalBP-4325
❑ 91IdaFalBSP-22
Majeski, Ed
❑ 34DiaMatCSB-120
Majeski, Henry (Hank)
❑ 41DouPlaR-119
❑ 47A'sTeal-19
❑ 47Exh-144
❑ 48A'sTeal-15
❑ 48BluTin-23
❑ 49A'sTeal-22
❑ 49Bow-127A
❑ 49Bow-127B
❑ 49Lea-149
❑ 49PhiBul-33
❑ 50A'sTeal-17
❑ 50Bow-92
❑ 51A'sTeal-21
❑ 51Bow-12
❑ 51TopBluB-2
❑ 52Bow-58
❑ 52Top-112
❑ 55Bow-127
❑ 55IndGolS-21
❑ 75TCM195CI-20
❑ 79DiaGre-206
❑ 83TopRep5-112
❑ 84TCMPla1-21
❑ 91OriCro-275
Majia, Roberto
❑ 96IndIndB-14
Majtyka, Roy
❑ 64TulOil-4
❑ 77BobParMBC-12
❑ 77IndIndTI-2
❑ 78IndIndTI-2
❑ 79IndIndTI-2
❑ 81BirBarT-2
❑ 82EvaTriT-25
❑ 83BirBarT-25
❑ 85IntLeaAT-22
❑ 85RicBraT-26
❑ 86RicBraP-13
❑ 87RicBraC-6
❑ 87RicBraT-21
❑ 89BirBarADB-21
❑ 89BraDub-16
❑ 90BirBarADB-21
❑ 90BraDubS-20
❑ 91MacBraC-28
❑ 91MacBraP-881
❑ 91SouAtlLAGP-SAL34
❑ 92SpaPhiC-22
❑ 92SpaPhiF-1280
❑ 93SpaPhiC-25
❑ 93SpaPhiF-1071
❑ 94SpaPhiF-1738
❑ 94SparPhiC-25
❑ 95PiePhiF-202
❑ 96PieBolWB-1
❑ 97ClePhi-26
Makarewicz, Scott
❑ 89AubAstP-2163
❑ 90FloStaLAS-12
❑ 90OscAstS-19
❑ 90StaFS7-4
❑ 91JacGenLD-568
❑ 91JacGenP-929
❑ 91LinDriAA-568
❑ 92JacGenF-4001
❑ 92JacGenS-340
❑ 93JacGenF-2111
❑ 94TucTorF-764
❑ 95TucTotTI-14
❑ 96JacSunB-18
❑ 97TolMudHB-26
❑ 98ChaKniQ-20
Makemson, Jay
❑ 87OneYanP-18
❑ 88OneYanP-2063
❑ 89PenPilS-13
Maki, Timothy
❑ 82BurRanF-29
❑ 82BurRanT-6
❑ 83BurRanF-19
❑ 83BurRanT-9
Makin, George
❑ 25Zee-34
❑ 26Zee-83
❑ 27Zee-59
Makosky, Frank
❑ 75YanDyn1T-31
Maksudian, Mike (Michael)
❑ 88MidLeaAGS-48
❑ 88SouBenWSGS-10
❑ 89MiaMirIS-15
❑ 89Sta-142
❑ 90Bes-111
❑ 90KnoBluJB-11
❑ 90KnoBluJP-1258
❑ 90KnoBluJS-11
❑ 90StaFS7-88
❑ 91LinDriAAA-509
❑ 91SyrChiLD-509
❑ 91SyrChiMB-12
❑ 91SyrChiP-2494
❑ 92SyrChiF-1982
❑ 92SyrChiMB-13
❑ 92SyrChiS-511
❑ 93BluJayD4-39
❑ 93Bow-297
❑ 93FleFinE-237
❑ 93LinVenB-103
❑ 94IowCubF-1279
❑ 95EdmTraTI-15
Malangone, John
❑ 52LavPro-96
Malarcher, Dave
❑ 74LauOldTBS-20
❑ 83ConMar-53
❑ 86NegLeaF-108
❑ 88ConNegA-9
Malarkey, John
❑ 11SpoLifCW-232
Malarkey, William
❑ 09T206-439
❑ 12HomRunKE-24
❑ 12ImpTobC-73
❑ 12PCLPin-13
❑ 12Zee-38
❑ 13Zee-40
❑ 14Zee-40
❑ 15Zee-42
Malave, Benito
❑ 86WauTimP-13
❑ 87St.PetCP-22
❑ 88ArkTraGS-17
❑ 93LinVenB-67
❑ 94VenLinU-253
❑ 95LinVen-213
❑ 96-97LinVen-187
Malave, Jaime
❑ 95YakBeaTI-17
❑ 96YakBeaTI-30
Malave, Jose
❑ 90ElmPioP-11
❑ 92ElmPioC-13
❑ 92ElmPioF-1390
❑ 93Bow-696
❑ 93CarLeaAGF-10
❑ 93ClaFS7-11
❑ 93ExcFS7-133
❑ 93LinVenB-258
❑ 93LynRedSC-16
❑ 93LynRedSF-2531
❑ 94Bow-671
❑ 94BowBes-B22
❑ 94BowBes-X107
❑ 94BowBesR-B22
❑ 94BowBesR-X107
❑ 94Cla-137

- ❑ 94NewBriRSF-663
- ❑ 94UppDecML-204
- ❑ 95ActPac2G-14G
- ❑ 95ActPacF-34
- ❑ 95ActPacF-75
- ❑ 95Bow-106
- ❑ 95Exc-11
- ❑ 95LinVen-84
- ❑ 95PawRedSDD-19
- ❑ 95PawRedTI-41
- ❑ 95Pin-429
- ❑ 95PinArtP-429
- ❑ 95PinMusC-429
- ❑ 95Sel-161
- ❑ 95SelArtP-161
- ❑ 95SelCer-101
- ❑ 95SelCerMG-101
- ❑ 95SP-13
- ❑ 95SPML-22
- ❑ 95SPSil-13
- ❑ 95Top-237
- ❑ 95UppDec-256
- ❑ 95UppDecED-256
- ❑ 95UppDecEDG-256
- ❑ 95UppDecML-18
- ❑ 95UppDecMLFS-18
- ❑ 95UppDecSE-211
- ❑ 95UppDecSEG-211
- ❑ 96-97LinVen-9
- ❑ 96Exc-13
- ❑ 96Fla-21
- ❑ 96FlaWavotF-16
- ❑ 96FleUpd-U14
- ❑ 96FleUpdTC-U14
- ❑ 96Ult-316
- ❑ 96UltGolM-316
- ❑ 97Fle-26
- ❑ 97FleTif-26
- ❑ 97PacPriGotD-GD24
- ❑ 97PawRedS-15
- ❑ 97Sel-186
- ❑ 97SelCom-186
- ❑ 97Ult-15
- ❑ 97UltGolME-15
- ❑ 97UltPlaME-15
- ❑ 98PacInvGems-23

Malave, Omar
- ❑ 80VenLeaS-69
- ❑ 85KinBluJT-17
- ❑ 86VenGulP-12
- ❑ 87KnoBluJP-1497
- ❑ 88MyrBeaBJP-1181
- ❑ 89KnoBluJB-14
- ❑ 89KnoBluJP-1127
- ❑ 89KnoBluJS-13
- ❑ 93LinVenB-122
- ❑ 93MedHatBJF-3752
- ❑ 93MedHatBJSP-23
- ❑ 94HagSunC-26
- ❑ 94HagSunF-2746
- ❑ 94SouAtlLAF-SAL17
- ❑ 95HagSunF-84
- ❑ 95LinVen-191
- ❑ 96-97LinVen-59
- ❑ 96KnoSmoB-1
- ❑ 97KnoSmo-1
- ❑ 98KnoSG-12

Malaver, Johnny
- ❑ 93HicCraC-15
- ❑ 93HicCraF-1276
- ❑ 93LinVenB-36

Malay, Charlie
- ❑ 90DodTar-1017

Malchesky, Tom
- ❑ 88HamRedP-1741
- ❑ 89SprCarB-19

Malcolm, Trevor
- ❑ 91PerHeaF-12

Malden, Chris
- ❑ 79LodDodT-18

Maldonado, Al
- ❑ 90KisDodD-16
- ❑ 91GreFalDSP-2
- ❑ 92BakDodCLC-15

Maldonado, Candy
- ❑ 79CliDodT-26
- ❑ 81AlbDukTc-21
- ❑ 82AlbDukTc-21
- ❑ 82RegGloT-6
- ❑ 83AlbDukTc-14
- ❑ 83DodPol-20
- ❑ 83Don-262
- ❑ 83Fle-212
- ❑ 84DodPol-20
- ❑ 84Don-93
- ❑ 84Nes792-244
- ❑ 84Top-244
- ❑ 84TopTif-244
- ❑ 85DodCokP-19
- ❑ 85Don-250
- ❑ 85Fle-376
- ❑ 85Top-523
- ❑ 85TopSti-81
- ❑ 85TopTif-523
- ❑ 86Fle-136
- ❑ 86FleUpd-71
- ❑ 86GiaMot-9
- ❑ 86GiaPos-19
- ❑ 86Top-87
- ❑ 86TopTif-87
- ❑ 86TopTra-69T
- ❑ 86TopTraT-69T
- ❑ 87Don-327
- ❑ 87DonOpeD-102
- ❑ 87Fle-279
- ❑ 87FleAwaW-23
- ❑ 87FleGlo-279
- ❑ 87GiaMot-7
- ❑ 87GiaPos-20
- ❑ 87Lea-216
- ❑ 87OPC-335
- ❑ 87Spo-78
- ❑ 87SpoTeaP-10
- ❑ 87Top-335
- ❑ 87TopMinL-37
- ❑ 87TopSti-94
- ❑ 87TopTif-335
- ❑ 88BlaYNPRWLU-6
- ❑ 88Don-391
- ❑ 88DonBasB-247
- ❑ 88Fle-89
- ❑ 88FleBasA-22
- ❑ 88FleGlo-89
- ❑ 88FleMin-118
- ❑ 88FleStiC-129
- ❑ 88GiaMot-7
- ❑ 88GiaPos-19
- ❑ 88KinDis-16
- ❑ 88Lea-239
- ❑ 88OPC-190
- ❑ 88PanSti-428
- ❑ 88Sco-54
- ❑ 88ScoGlo-54
- ❑ 88Spo-126
- ❑ 88StaLinG-11
- ❑ 88TarPla-25
- ❑ 88Top-190
- ❑ 88TopBig-35
- ❑ 88TopSti-95
- ❑ 88TopTif-190
- ❑ 88TopUKM-44
- ❑ 88TopUKMT-44
- ❑ 89BimBreD-2
- ❑ 89Bow-478
- ❑ 89BowTif-478
- ❑ 89Don-177
- ❑ 89Fle-333
- ❑ 89FleGlo-333
- ❑ 89GiaMot-7
- ❑ 89OPC-269
- ❑ 89PanSti-221
- ❑ 89RedFolSB-78
- ❑ 89Sco-47
- ❑ 89Top-495
- ❑ 89TopBasT-137
- ❑ 89TopBig-197
- ❑ 89TopSti-89
- ❑ 89TopTif-495
- ❑ 89UppDec-502
- ❑ 90Bow-335
- ❑ 90BowTif-335
- ❑ 90ClaYel-T34
- ❑ 90DodTar-474
- ❑ 90Don-611
- ❑ 90DonBesA-132
- ❑ 90DonLeaS-42
- ❑ 90Fle-62
- ❑ 90FleCan-62
- ❑ 90FleUpd-93
- ❑ 90IndTeal-25
- ❑ 90Lea-338
- ❑ 90OPC-628
- ❑ 90PubIntS-75
- ❑ 90Sco-138
- ❑ 90ScoRoo-8T
- ❑ 90Top-628
- ❑ 90TopBig-248
- ❑ 90TopTif-628
- ❑ 90TopTra-65T
- ❑ 90TopTraT-65T
- ❑ 90UppDec-136
- ❑ 90UppDec-780
- ❑ 91BluJayFS-19
- ❑ 91BluJayS-29
- ❑ 91BreMilB-16
- ❑ 91BrePol-14
- ❑ 91Don-391
- ❑ 91Don-480
- ❑ 91Fle-373
- ❑ 91Lea-434
- ❑ 91OPC-723
- ❑ 91PanFreS-220
- ❑ 91PanSti-179
- ❑ 91RedFolS-60
- ❑ 91Sco-93
- ❑ 91Sco100S-76
- ❑ 91ScoRoo-28T
- ❑ 91StaClu-350
- ❑ 91Stu-72
- ❑ 91Top-723
- ❑ 91TopDesS-723
- ❑ 91TopMic-723
- ❑ 91TopTif-723
- ❑ 91TopTra-74T
- ❑ 91TopTraT-74T
- ❑ 91UppDec-138
- ❑ 91UppDec-739
- ❑ 91UppDecFE-28F
- ❑ 92Don-664
- ❑ 92Fle-336
- ❑ 92OPC-507
- ❑ 92PanSti-31
- ❑ 92Sco-591
- ❑ 92StaClu-179
- ❑ 92Top-507
- ❑ 92TopGol-507
- ❑ 92TopGolW-507
- ❑ 92TopMic-507
- ❑ 92TriPla-15
- ❑ 92Ult-451
- ❑ 92UppDec-393
- ❑ 93BluJayD4-9
- ❑ 93BluJayDM-13
- ❑ 93BluJayDM-21
- ❑ 93BluJayDWS-4
- ❑ 93Bow-312
- ❑ 93CubMar-14
- ❑ 93CubStaC-4
- ❑ 93Don-684
- ❑ 93Fle-338
- ❑ 93FleFinE-9
- ❑ 93Lea-329
- ❑ 93OPC-382
- ❑ 93OPCPre-83
- ❑ 93OPCWorC-10
- ❑ 93PacBeiA-20
- ❑ 93PacSpa-379
- ❑ 93Pin-422
- ❑ 93Sco-615
- ❑ 93Sel-110
- ❑ 93StaClu-669
- ❑ 93StaCluFDI-669
- ❑ 93StaCluMOP-669
- ❑ 93Top-213
- ❑ 93TopGol-213
- ❑ 93TopInaM-213
- ❑ 93TopInaR-213
- ❑ 93TopMic-213
- ❑ 93Ult-316
- ❑ 93UppDec-741
- ❑ 93UppDecGold-741
- ❑ 94BreMilB-54
- ❑ 94Don-659
- ❑ 94Fle-112
- ❑ 94Pac-175
- ❑ 94Sco-154
- ❑ 94ScoGolR-154
- ❑ 94StaClu-464
- ❑ 94StaCluFDI-464
- ❑ 94StaCluGR-464
- ❑ 94StaCluMOP-464
- ❑ 94Top-667
- ❑ 94TopGol-667
- ❑ 94TopSpa-667
- ❑ 95BluJayUSPC-2H
- ❑ 95BluJayUSPC-8H
- ❑ 95DonTopotO-174
- ❑ 95Pac-123

Maldonado, Carlos
- ❑ 88BriTigP-1863
- ❑ 90Bes-117
- ❑ 90CMC-779
- ❑ 90MemChiB-21
- ❑ 90MemChiP-1007
- ❑ 90MemChiS-15
- ❑ 90ProAaA-35
- ❑ 91FayGenC-20
- ❑ 91FayGenP-1179
- ❑ 91LinDriAAA-341
- ❑ 91OmaRoyLD-341
- ❑ 91OmaRoyP-1034
- ❑ 91TopDeb90-94
- ❑ 92OmaRoyF-2958
- ❑ 92OmaRoyS-335
- ❑ 92SkyAAAF-154
- ❑ 92StaClu-569
- ❑ 93FleFinE-228
- ❑ 93PacSpa-513
- ❑ 93Ult-573
- ❑ 94BreMilB-55
- ❑ 94Pac-334
- ❑ 94TacTigF-3170
- ❑ 97MidLeaTP-29
- ❑ 97WisTimR-18
- ❑ 98EveAquG-13
- ❑ 98WisTimRM-13

Maldonado, Efrain
- ❑ 89BlaYNPRWL-131

Maldonado, Esteban
- ❑ 96AubDouB-22
- ❑ 97QuaCitRBB-15
- ❑ 98KisCobQ-20

Maldonado, Felix
- ❑ 64SeaPop-11
- ❑ 87ElmPioBC-30
- ❑ 92WinHavRSC-26
- ❑ 92WinHavRSF-1794

Maldonado, Jay
- ❑ 93St.CatBJC-12
- ❑ 93St.CatBJF-3970
- ❑ 94BowBes-B88
- ❑ 94BowBesR-B88
- ❑ 94HagSunC-12
- ❑ 94HagSunF-2724

Maldonado, Jerry
- ❑ 89RenSilSCLC-264
- ❑ 90RenSilSCLC-290

Maldonado, Johnny
- ❑ 89BlaYNPRWLU-3
- ❑ 89SumBraP-1105

Maldonado, Pete
- ❑ 87SpaPhiP-2
- ❑ 88ClePhiS-18

Maldonado, Phil
- ❑ 87IdaFalBP-3
- ❑ 88DurBulS-11
- ❑ 89DurBullS-13
- ❑ 89DurBullS-13
- ❑ 89DurBulTI-13
- ❑ 90DurBulTI-22

Malejko, Matt
- ❑ 94LSUTig-6

Malenfant, David
- ❑ 97LakTigB-22

Maler, Jim (James)
- ❑ 80SpoIndT-14
- ❑ 80VenLeaS-119
- ❑ 82MarPos-21
- ❑ 83SalLakCGT-17
- ❑ 83Top-54
- ❑ 84Nes792-461
- ❑ 84Top-461
- ❑ 84TopTif-461
- ❑ 85OklCit8T-20
- ❑ 86OklCit8P-11

Malerich, William
- ❑ 97SalVolG-21

Malespin, Gus
- ❑ 79ElmPioRST-19
- ❑ 82SprCarF-10
- ❑ 83SprCarF-25

Maley, Dennis
- ❑ 83MiaMarT-27

Malinak, Mike (Michael)
- ❑ 87SalLakTTT-2
- ❑ 88CedRapRP-1164
- ❑ 89CedRapRP-911
- ❑ 89CedRapRS-29

Malinoski, Chris
- ❑ 91RocExpC-20
- ❑ 91RocExpP-2055
- ❑ 92WesPalBEC-15
- ❑ 92WesPalBEF-2096
- ❑ 93ClaGolF-47
- ❑ 93HigDesMC-11
- ❑ 93HigDesMF-48
- ❑ 94ClaGolF-95
- ❑ 94PorSeaDF-686
- ❑ 94PorSeaDTI-20

Malinosky, Tony
- ❑ 72TCMthe3-95
- ❑ 72TCMthe3-98
- ❑ 90DodTar-475

Malkin, John
- ❑ 81WatIndT-19
- ❑ 82WatIndF-20
- ❑ 82WatIndT-12
- ❑ 83BufBisT-10
- ❑ 84HawIslC-145
- ❑ 85HawIslC-247

Malkmus, Robert
- ❑ 58SeaTeal-19
- ❑ 58Top-356
- ❑ 59Top-151
- ❑ 59TopVen-151
- ❑ 60Top-251
- ❑ 61Top-530

Malko, Bryan
- ❑ 97ForWayW-19
- ❑ 98ForWayW!-19

Mallard, Randi
- ❑ 96AppLeaAB-29
- ❑ 98BesAutSS-30
- ❑ 98BurBeeM-13

Mallea, Luis
- ❑ 87EugEmeP-2666
- ❑ 88AppFoxP-138

Mallee, Johnny
- ❑ 91MarPhiC-8
- ❑ 91MarPhiP-3463
- ❑ 92SpaPhiC-3
- ❑ 92SpaPhiF-1271
- ❑ 96BelSnaTI-22
- ❑ 97BelSnaB-4
- ❑ 98StoPorG-19

Mallette, Brian
- ❑ 97HelBreB-19
- ❑ 98BelSnaM-5

Mallette, Mal (Malcolm)
- ❑ 52LaPat-9
- ❑ 52Par-60
- ❑ 90DodTar-1018

Malley, Mike
- ❑ 89GreHorP-424
- ❑ 90ChaWheB-3
- ❑ 90ChaWheP-2236
- ❑ 91KinIndC-6
- ❑ 91KinIndP-318
- ❑ 91WatIndC-10
- ❑ 91WatIndP-3365

Mallicoat, Rob
- ❑ 85OscAstTI-9
- ❑ 86ColAstP-17
- ❑ 86TucTorP-11
- ❑ 87ColAstP-22
- ❑ 87SouLeaAJ-15
- ❑ 88Fle-452
- ❑ 88FleGlo-452
- ❑ 89ColMudP-131
- ❑ 89ColMudS-17
- ❑ 91JacGenLD-569
- ❑ 91JacGenP-925
- ❑ 91LinDriAA-569
- ❑ 92AstMot-23
- ❑ 92Don-673
- ❑ 92Fle-440
- ❑ 92OPC-501
- ❑ 92Sco-819
- ❑ 92SkyAAAF-273
- ❑ 92Top-501
- ❑ 92TopGol-501
- ❑ 92TopGolW-501
- ❑ 92TopMic-501
- ❑ 92TucTorS-613
- ❑ 93AstStaC-16
- ❑ 93Sco-253
- ❑ 94RanCucQF-1638

Mallinak, Mel
- ❑ 87HagSunP-24

Mallon, Jim
- ❑ 90WelPirP-32

Mallory, Andrew
- ❑ 98RocCubM-21
- ❑ 98RocCubTI-22

Mallory, Sheldon
- ❑ 76OmaRoyTT-11
- ❑ 78SyrChiT-13
- ❑ 79TacTugT-21

Mallory, Steve
- ❑ 76VenLeaS-202

Mallory, Trevor
- ❑ 91ClaDraP-50
- ❑ 91FroRowDP-53
- ❑ 91FroRowDPG-53
- ❑ 91FroRowDPS-53
- ❑ 92MyrBeaHC-3
- ❑ 92St.CatBJC-6
- ❑ 92St.CatBJF-3385
- ❑ 92StaCluD-110
- ❑ 93HagSunC-18
- ❑ 93HagSunF-1877
- ❑ 94HagSunC-13
- ❑ 94HagSunF-2725
- ❑ 95DunBluJTI-14

Mallott, Don
- ❑ 54SeaPop-17

Malloy, Bill
- ❑ 96BelGiaTI-23
- ❑ 97BakBlaB-3
- ❑ 97BakBlaTI-3
- ❑ 98SanJosGQ-5

Malloy, Bob
- ❑ 87GasRanP-11
- ❑ 88TulDriTI-22
- ❑ 89TexLeaAGS-37
- ❑ 89TulDriGS-15
- ❑ 89TulDriTI-13
- ❑ 90Bes-43
- ❑ 90JacExpB-19
- ❑ 90JacExpP-1370
- ❑ 93RanKee-240

Malloy, Charles
- ❑ 94UtiBluSC-16
- ❑ 94UtiBluSF-3814

Malloy, Marty
- ❑ 93MacBraC-14
- ❑ 93MacBraF-1409
- ❑ 93SouAtlLAGF-39
- ❑ 94ClaGolF-114
- ❑ 94DurBulC-11
- ❑ 94DurBulF-334
- ❑ 94DurBulTI-11
- ❑ 96Bow-224
- ❑ 96BowFoi-224
- ❑ 96GreBraB-18
- ❑ 96GreBraTI-4
- ❑ 96RicBraB-19
- ❑ 96Ult-440
- ❑ 96UltGolM-440
- ❑ 97RicBra-18
- ❑ 98RicBraQ-21
- ❑ 99Pac-37
- ❑ 99Pac-37A
- ❑ 99PacPlaB-37
- ❑ 99PacPlaB-37A
- ❑ 99PacRed-37
- ❑ 99PacRed-37A

Malloy, Pat
- ❑ 97BurIndG-17

Malmberg, Harry
- ❑ 59SeaPop-7
- ❑ 59SeaPop-27
- ❑ 60HenHouW-2
- ❑ 61SeaPop-10
- ❑ 61SeaPop-11
- ❑ 61UniOil-S4

Malone, Chuck (Charles)
- ❑ 86BenPhiC-136
- ❑ 87ClePhiP-4
- ❑ 88BasAmeAAB-6
- ❑ 88EasLeaAP-34
- ❑ 88ReaPhiP-869
- ❑ 89ReaPhiB-3
- ❑ 89ReaPhiP-656
- ❑ 89ReaPhiS-17
- ❑ 90Bow-144
- ❑ 90BowTif-144
- ❑ 90CMC-230
- ❑ 90ProAAAF-298
- ❑ 90ScrRedBC-4
- ❑ 90ScrRedBP-596
- ❑ 91Bow-497
- ❑ 91Fle-404
- ❑ 91LinDriAAA-488
- ❑ 91Sco-724
- ❑ 91ScoRoo-21
- ❑ 91ScrRedBLD-488
- ❑ 91ScrRedBP-2534
- ❑ 91TopDeb90-95
- ❑ 91UppDec-649

Malone, Earl
- ❑ 88BoiHawP-1617

Malone, Ed
- ❑ 47SigOil-29
- ❑ 48AngTeal-19
- ❑ 49AngTeal-23
- ❑ 49BowPCL-31
- ❑ 49W725AngTI-18
- ❑ 50RemBre-16
- ❑ 53MotCoo-20

Malone, Eddie
- ❑ 82IdaFalAT-25

Malone, Jack

❑ 89BoiHawP-1990
Malone, Kevin
❑ 80BatTroT-19
❑ 88JamExpP-1893
Malone, Lew
❑ 90DodTar-476
Malone, Pat (Perce)
❑ 29PorandAR-60
❑ 30CubTeal-11
❑ 31CubTeal-15
❑ 32CubTeal-16
❑ 32OrbPinNP-13
❑ 32OrbPinUP-45
❑ 33Gou-55
❑ 33TatOrb-45
❑ 33TatOrbSDR-192
❑ 34DiaMatCSB-122
❑ 34GouCanV-30
❑ 35GouPuzR-4D
❑ 35GouPuzR-7D
❑ 35GouPuzR-12D
❑ 75YanDyn1T-32
❑ 91ConTSN-219
Malone, Rubio
❑ 79WisRapTT-18
Malone, Scott
❑ 92ButCopKSP-2
❑ 93ChaRaiC-25
❑ 93ChaRaiF-1920
❑ 94ChaRanF-2503
Malone, Todd
❑ 89OneYanP-2122
❑ 90Bes-18
❑ 90CMC-824
❑ 90GreHorB-1
❑ 90GreHorP-2659
❑ 90GreHorS-13
❑ 90OneYanP-3368
❑ 91GreHorP-3054
❑ 92PriWilCC-23
❑ 92PriWilCF-142
❑ 93SanBerSC-12
❑ 93SanBerSF-766
Maloney, Bill
❑ 08RosComP-97
❑ 96MicBatCB-3
Maloney, Chris
❑ 85LynMetT-17
❑ 88SprCarB-25
❑ 89ArkTraGS-2
❑ 90HamRedB-4
❑ 90HamRedS-27
❑ 91JohCitCC-29
❑ 91JohCitCP-3994
❑ 93SavCarC-26
❑ 93SavCarF-702
❑ 93SouAtlLAGF-48
❑ 94ArkTraF-3104
❑ 96StPetCB-1
❑ 97LouRedB-3
❑ 98ArkTraM-27
Maloney, Jeffrey
❑ 96MedHatBJTI-16
❑ 97HagSunB-24
❑ 98DunBluJSB-16
❑ 98DunBluJTI-21
Maloney, Jim
❑ 56RedBurB-13
❑ 59RedBurBP-10
❑ 61Kah-26
❑ 61Top-436
❑ 62Kah-26
❑ 62RedEnq-22
❑ 63Kah-20
❑ 63RedEnq-20
❑ 63RedFreBC-13
❑ 63Top-444
❑ 64Baz-19
❑ 64Kah-16
❑ 64RedJayP-6
❑ 64Top-3
❑ 64Top-5
❑ 64Top-420
❑ 64TopCoi-60
❑ 64TopCoi-158
❑ 64TopGia-34
❑ 64TopSta-32
❑ 64TopStaU-43
❑ 64TopVen-3
❑ 64TopVen-5
❑ 65Kah-23
❑ 65RedEnq-17
❑ 65Top-530
❑ 65TopEmbl-68
❑ 65TopTral-19
❑ 66Baz-45
❑ 66Kah-18
❑ 66OPC-140
❑ 66RedVolC-7
❑ 66Top-140
❑ 66TopRubl-55
❑ 66TopVen-140
❑ 67AshOil-6
❑ 67Baz-45
❑ 67CokCapR-7
❑ 67DexPre-131
❑ 67Kah-21A
❑ 67Kah-21B
❑ 67OPC-80
❑ 67Top-80
❑ 67TopVen-325
❑ 68AtlOilPBCC-25
❑ 68Kah-A7
❑ 68Kah-B21
❑ 68Top-425
❑ 68Top3-D-6
❑ 68TopActS-3A
❑ 68TopActS-16A
❑ 69Kah-A2
❑ 69Kah-B12
❑ 69MilBra-164
❑ 69MLBOffS-130
❑ 69MLBPin-50
❑ 69Top-362
❑ 69TopSta-26
❑ 69TopTeaP-20
❑ 70DayDaiNM-150
❑ 70Kel-10
❑ 70MLBOffS-29
❑ 70OPC-320
❑ 70Top-320
❑ 71MLBOffS-348
❑ 71OPC-645
❑ 71Top-645
❑ 72MilBra-203
❑ 72Top-645
❑ 77RedCarP-3
❑ 78TCM60I-10
❑ 80Red196T-33
Maloney, Kevin
❑ 89ColMetB-28
❑ 89ColMetGS-5
Maloney, Mark
❑ 88KinIndS-17
Maloney, Mike
❑ 29Zee-8
❑ 30Zee-12
Maloney, Rich
❑ 87SumBraP-18
❑ 88DurBulS-12
❑ 89DurBullS-14
❑ 89DurBullS-14
❑ 89DurBulTI-14
❑ 90GreBraB-14
❑ 90GreBraP-1139
❑ 90GreBraS-11
❑ 91GreBraC-18
❑ 91GreBraLD-210
❑ 91GreBraP-3012
❑ 91LinDriAA-210
Maloney, Ryan
❑ 92WinHavRSC-17
❑ 92WinHavRSF-1772
❑ 93LynRedSC-17
❑ 93LynRedSF-2515
Maloney, Sean
❑ 93HelBreF-4089
❑ 93HelBreSP-17
❑ 94BelBreC-15
❑ 94BelBreFI-96
❑ 94MidLeaAF-MDW9
❑ 95ElPasDTI-18
❑ 96DouAllB-47
❑ 96El PasDB-17
❑ 96TexLeaAB-30
❑ 97Bow-121
❑ 97BowInt-121
❑ 97TucTorB-8
Maloney, William A.
❑ 06FanCraNL-28
❑ 09T206-440
❑ 11SpoLifCW-233
Maloof, Jack
❑ 76TacTwiDQ-10
❑ 77IndIndTI-24
❑ 79TCMJapPB-14
❑ 83BeaGolGT-21
❑ 85SpoIndC-12
❑ 91LinDriAA-625
❑ 91WicWraP-2616
❑ 91WicWraRD-26
Malpeso, Dave
❑ 84PawRedST-17
❑ 85PawRedST-7
Malpica, Omar
❑ 91PriRedC-3
❑ 91PriRedP-3527
Malseed, Jim (James)
❑ 87PocGiaTB-10
❑ 88FreSunCLC-12
❑ 88FreSunP-1232
❑ 89SanJosGB-22
❑ 89SanJosGCLC-223
❑ 89SanJosGP-437
❑ 89SanJosGS-18
Maltzberger, Gordon
❑ 49BowPCL-12
❑ 49W72HolS-10
❑ 50W720HolS-18
❑ 52LavPro-36
❑ 77TCMTheWY-38
Maluchnik, Gregg
❑ 98EugEme-17
Malzone, Frank
❑ 47Exh-145
❑ 47PM1StaP1-117
❑ 47PM1StaP1-118
❑ 55Bow-302
❑ 56Top-304
❑ 57Top-355
❑ 58JayPubA-10
❑ 58RedSoxJP-6
❑ 58Top-260
❑ 58Top-481
❑ 59ArmCoi-12
❑ 59RedSoxJP-5
❑ 59Top-220
❑ 59Top-519
❑ 59Top-558
❑ 60ArmCoi-13A
❑ 60ArmCoi-13B
❑ 60Baz-12
❑ 60RedSoxJP-7
❑ 60Top-310
❑ 60Top-557
❑ 60TopTat-30
❑ 61Baz-9
❑ 61ChePat-7
❑ 61Pos-48A
❑ 61Pos-48B
❑ 61Top-173
❑ 61Top-445
❑ 61TopStal-113
❑ 62ExhStaB-22
❑ 62Jel-58
❑ 62Pos-58
❑ 62PosCan-58
❑ 62RedSoxJP-5
❑ 62SalPlaC-14
❑ 62ShiPlaC-14
❑ 62Top-225
❑ 62TopBuc-52
❑ 62TopStal-14
❑ 63BasMagM-53
❑ 63ExhStaB-40
❑ 63Jel-79
❑ 63Pos-79
❑ 63Top-232
❑ 64ChatheY-33
❑ 64RedSoxTI-3
❑ 64Top-60
❑ 64TopCoi-7
❑ 64TopCoi-126
❑ 64TopSta-6
❑ 64TopStaU-44
❑ 64TopTatl-50
❑ 64TopVen-60
❑ 64WheSta-27
❑ 65ChaTheY-33
❑ 65RedSoxTI-7
❑ 65Top-315
❑ 65TopEmbl-37
❑ 66OPC-152
❑ 66Top-152
❑ 66TopVen-152
❑ 78TCM60I-177
❑ 80ElmPioRST-38
❑ 81RedSoxBG2S-36
❑ 86RedSoxGT-7
❑ 87ElmPioBC-31
Malzone, John
❑ 91WinHavRSC-20
❑ 91WinHavRSP-499
❑ 92LynRedSC-22
❑ 92LynRedSF-2914
❑ 93PawRedSDD-15
❑ 93PawRedSF-2414
❑ 93PawRedSTI-14
❑ 94NewBriRSF-658
Mamaux, Al (Albert L.)
❑ 15SpoNewM-107
❑ 16BF2FP-94
❑ 16FleBreD-59
❑ 16SpoNewM-110
❑ 17ColE13-105
❑ 17HolBreD-64
❑ 19W514-19
❑ 21E121So8-53
❑ 22AmeCarE122-41
❑ 22E120-143
❑ 22KolMotBPP-19
❑ 22W572-58
❑ 22W575-73
❑ 23W515-2
❑ 90DodTar-477
Mammola, Mark
❑ 91BoiHawC-13
❑ 91BoiHawP-3873
❑ 92QuaCitRBC-19
Mamott, Joe
❑ 94UtiBluSC-17
❑ 94UtiBluSF-3815
❑ 96LowSpiB-17
Manabe, Bullet
❑ 88FreSunCLC-21
❑ 88FreSunP-1235
Manahan, Anthony
❑ 89AriStaB-18
❑ 90Bes-83
❑ 91JacSunP-158
❑ 92ClaFS7-329
❑ 92JacSunF-3717
❑ 92JacSunS-362
❑ 92SkyAA F-154
❑ 93CalCanF-1172
❑ 93TriAAAGF-52
❑ 94CalCanF-797
❑ 94ClaGolF-23
❑ 94Ult-421
❑ 95ScrRedBTI-19
❑ 96ScrRedBB-19
Manahan, Austin
❑ 89Bow-420
❑ 89BowTif-420
❑ 90AugPirP-2473
❑ 90CMC-850
❑ 90ProAaA-97
❑ 90SouAtlLAS-36
❑ 91Bow-527
❑ 91Cla/Bes-218
❑ 91ParPatF-20
❑ 91SalBucC-6
❑ 91SalBucP-960
❑ 92CarMudF-1188
❑ 92CarMudS-137
❑ 92ClaFS7-44
❑ 92SkyAA F-64
❑ 92UppDecML-78
❑ 93WesPalBEC-13
❑ 93WesPalBEF-1348
❑ 94RanCucQF-1646
❑ 95OrlCubF-19
Manaure, Johanne
❑ 93LinVenB-47
❑ 94VenLinU-76
❑ 95LinVen-246
Manbeck, Mark
❑ 98PieBolWM-21
Mancini, Joe
❑ 88BoiHawP-1626
❑ 88FreSunCLC-3
❑ 88FreSunP-1247
❑ 89BoiHawP-1991
Mancini, Pete
❑ 85NewOriT-21
Mancuso, Frank
❑ 84OmaRoyT-28
❑ 85OmaRoyT-4
Mancuso, Frank Octavius
❑ 46SeaSLP-38
❑ 83TCMPla1945-8
❑ 96Bro194F-23
Mancuso, Gus (August)
❑ 30SchR33-24
❑ 31CarMet-20
❑ 33ButCanV-31
❑ 33Gou-41
❑ 33Gou-237
❑ 33GouCanV-41
❑ 33RitCE-2H
❑ 34BabRutG-41
❑ 34BatR31-67
❑ 34ButPreR-40
❑ 35AlDemDCR3-82
❑ 35GouPuzR-1K
❑ 35GouPuzR-3B
❑ 35GouPuzR-4A
❑ 35GouPuzR-7A
❑ 35GouPuzR-12A
❑ 35GouPuzR-14B
❑ 35GouPuzR-15B
❑ 35WheBB1-19
❑ 36ExhFou-5
❑ 36WorWidGV-9
❑ 37ExhFou-5
❑ 38OurNatGPP-18
❑ 39CubTeal-16
❑ 39GouPreR303A-31
❑ 39GouPreR303B-19
❑ 39WorWidGTP-31
❑ 40DodTeal-15
❑ 40PlaBal-207
❑ 41CarW75-15
❑ 41DouPlaR-37
❑ 72TCMthe3-48
❑ 77TCMTheWY-31
❑ 79DiaGre-34
❑ 85BigLeaC3-30
❑ 90DodTar-478
❑ 91ConTSN-129
Mancuso, Paul
❑ 83WisRapTF-22
❑ 84VisOakT-18
❑ 85OrlTwiT-18
❑ 86BeaGolGP-17
Manda, Carl
❑ 15Zee-43
Mandel, Brett
❑ 94OgdRapF-3743
❑ 94OgdRapSP-12
Mandel, Mike
❑ 75TopPho-24
Manderbach, Gary
❑ 75TidTidTI-16
Manderfield, Steve
❑ 77NewCoPT-23
❑ 79BurBeeT-25
❑ 80BurBeeT-8
❑ 82ElPasDT-15
Manders, Jack
❑ 40WheM4-8A
Mandeville, Bob
❑ 86PeoChiP-18
Mandia, Sam
❑ 90St.CatBJP-3459
❑ 91MyrBeaHC-9
❑ 91MyrBeaHP-2943
Mandl, Steve
❑ 89JamExpP-2151
❑ 91HigSchPLS-33
Maneely, Bob
❑ 76TacTwiDQ-11
❑ 76VenLeaS-28
Manering, Mark
❑ 87Ft.LauYP-27
Maness, Chris
❑ 98MarPhiG-17
Maness, Don
❑ 89TenTecGE-15
Maness, Dwight
❑ 92ClaDraP-56
❑ 92GulCoaDF-3581
❑ 93ClaGolF-111
❑ 93VerBeaDC-18
❑ 93VerBeaDF-2232
❑ 94BakDodC-16
❑ 94SanAntMF-2482
❑ 95SanAntMTI-20
❑ 96BinMetB-19
❑ 97BinMetB-18
Manfre, Mike
❑ 83CedRapRF-20
❑ 83CedRapRT-20
❑ 84CedRapRT-21
❑ 86VerRedP-12
❑ 87NasSouTI-14
Manfred, Jim
❑ 91PitMetC-18
❑ 91PitMetP-3419
❑ 92ColMetC-6
❑ 92ColMetF-291
❑ 92ColMetPI-26
Manfredi, Joel
❑ 95GreFalDTI-12
Mangham, Eric
❑ 87BakDodP-19
❑ 88VerBeaDS-13
❑ 89SanAntMB-3
❑ 91LinDriAAA-591
❑ 91TolMudHLD-591
❑ 91TolMudHP-1945
Mangham, Mark
❑ 85OscAstTI-10
Mangiardi, Paul
❑ 83EriCarT-1
Mangrum, Lloyd
❑ 52Whe-20A
❑ 52Whe-20B
Mangual, Angel
❑ 70Top-654
❑ 71OPC-317
❑ 71Top-317
❑ 72OPC-62
❑ 72Top-62
❑ 73OPC-625
❑ 73Top-625
❑ 75OPC-452
❑ 75Top-452
❑ 75TopMin-452
❑ 76SSP-503
❑ 76TucTorCa-6
❑ 76TusTorCr-8
Mangual, Pepe (Jose)
❑ 75ExpPos-20
❑ 75OPC-616
❑ 75Top-616
❑ 75TopMin-616
❑ 76ExpRed-21
❑ 76MonExpP-19
❑ 76OPC-164
❑ 76SSP-335
❑ 76Top-164
❑ 77Top-552
❑ 78TidTidT-13
❑ 79SalLakCGT-22A
❑ 80SalLakCGT-22
❑ 81SalLakCGT-22
❑ 82SpoIndT-22
❑ 91MetWIZ-243
Mangual, Victor
❑ 87BelMarL-18
❑ 87BelMarTI-8
Mangum, Leo
❑ 26Zee-96
❑ 28LaPre-27
❑ 33Gou-162
❑ 33GouCanV-92
❑ 34DiaMatCSB-123
Mangum, Mark
❑ 97Bow-435
❑ 97BowChr-295
❑ 97BowChrI-295
❑ 97BowChrIR-295
❑ 97BowChrR-295
❑ 97BowInt-435
❑ 98BesNumOP-32
❑ 98Bow-139
❑ 98BowChr-139
❑ 98BowChrGA-139
❑ 98BowChrGAR-139
❑ 98BowChrI-139
❑ 98BowChrIR-139
❑ 98BowChrR-139
❑ 98BowGolA-139
❑ 98BowInt-139
❑ 98StaCluFDI-391
❑ 98StaCluI-391
❑ 98StaCluOneK-391
❑ 98StaCluPP-391
❑ 98Top-491
❑ 98TopChr-491
❑ 98TopChrR-491
❑ 98TopDevR-491
❑ 98TopDia-491
❑ 98TopMiniC-491
❑ 98VerExpO-14
Mangum, Wade
❑ 83IdaFalAT-9
Maniac, Miami
❑ 85AncGlaPTI-42
❑ 85MiaHur-10
❑ 91MiaHurBB-9
Manias, James
❑ 96ButCopKB-22
❑ 97Bow-345
❑ 97BowInt-345
❑ 97St.PetDR-21
❑ 97St.PetDRUB-21
❑ 98Bow-109
❑ 98BowChr-109
❑ 98BowChrGA-109
❑ 98BowChrGAR-109
❑ 98BowChrI-109

❑ 98BowChrIR-109
❑ 98BowChrR-109
❑ 98BowGolA-109
❑ 98BowInt-109
❑ 98SP MinPE-119
❑ 98SPMin-119
❑ 98St.PetDRM-12
❑ 98Top-251
❑ 98TopChr-251
❑ 98TopChrR-251
❑ 98TopDevR-251
❑ 98TopDia-251
❑ 98TopMiniC-251

Manicchia, Bryan
❑ 90PriPatD-15
❑ 91BatCliCB-16
❑ 91BatCliP-3481
❑ 91SpaPhiC-8
❑ 91SpaPhiP-893
❑ 92SpaPhiC-7
❑ 92SpaPhiF-1263

Manion, Clyde
❑ 33Gou-80
❑ 34GouCanV-35
❑ 34TarThoBD-19
❑ 67SpoHobFC-26
❑ 94ConTSN-1161
❑ 94ConTSNB-1161

Manion, George A.
❑ 09T206-500

Mankowski, Phil
❑ 77Top-477
❑ 78TigBurK-17
❑ 78TigTeal-18
❑ 78Top-559
❑ 79Top-93
❑ 80Top-216
❑ 81TidTidT-6
❑ 82TidTidT-9
❑ 91MetWIZ-244

Manley, Effie
❑ 97NegLeaPC-12D

Manley, Greg
❑ 85Fle-280
❑ 90GeoColC-20

Mann, Bill
❑ 88JacExpB-15

Mann, Dave
❑ 61SeaPop-12
❑ 61UniOil-S5
❑ 62SeaPop-6
❑ 62SeaPop-7

Mann, Fred
❑ 87OldJudN-312
❑ 90KalBatN-32
❑ 90KalBatN-48

Mann, Gordon
❑ 37Zee-80

Mann, Jim
❑ 96StCatSB-18
❑ 97HagSunB-10
❑ 98DunBluJSB-17
❑ 98DunBluJTI-22

Mann, Kelly
❑ 86GenCubP-17
❑ 87PeoChiP-25
❑ 88CarLeaAS-30
❑ 88WinSpiS-9
❑ 89BlaYNPRWL-193
❑ 89ChaKniTI-9
❑ 89SouLeaAJ-4
❑ 90Bes-157
❑ 90Don-46
❑ 90Fle-642
❑ 90FleCan-642
❑ 90GreBraB-9
❑ 90GreBraP-1132
❑ 90GreBraS-12
❑ 90Hot50RS-29
❑ 90OPC-744
❑ 90ProAaA-63
❑ 90RicBraBC-21
❑ 90Sco-627
❑ 90Sco100RS-56
❑ 90Top-744
❑ 90TopDeb89-76
❑ 90TopTif-744
❑ 90UppDec-33
❑ 91Don-736
❑ 91LinDriAAA-434
❑ 91RicBraBC-3
❑ 91RicBraLD-434
❑ 91RicBraP-2571
❑ 91RicBraTI-24
❑ 91Stu-147

Mann, Les
❑ 14B18B-51A
❑ 14B18B-51B
❑ 14B18B-51C
❑ 15SpoNewM-108
❑ 16SpoNewM-111
❑ 17ColE13-106
❑ 19W514-49
❑ 80BraTCM1-29
❑ 94ConTSN-1134
❑ 94ConTSNB-1134

Mann, Mark
❑ 93BilMusSP-26

Mann, Red (Garth)
❑ 44CubTeal-14
❑ 46SunBre-11
❑ 47SigOil-63
❑ 47SigOil-81
❑ 47SunBre-9

Mann, Scott
❑ 86WesPalBEP-23
❑ 87JacExpP-436
❑ 88JacExpP-964

Mann, Skip
❑ 79LodDodT-5
❑ 81VerBeaDT-10

Mann, Tom
❑ 90HunCubP-3279
❑ 91PeoChiC-7
❑ 91PeoChiP-1339
❑ 91PeoChiTI-11

Manning, Al (Melvin)
❑ 77BurBeeT-14
❑ 78BurBeeT-20
❑ 81ElPasDT-3

Manning, Archie
❑ 74NewYorNTDiS-27

Manning, Brian
❑ 96BelGiaTI-12
❑ 97BakBlaB-9
❑ 97BakBlaTI-9
❑ 98BirBarG-19
❑ 98WinWar-17

Manning, Dave
❑ 92ClaDraP-68
❑ 93StaCluM-198
❑ 96TulDriTI-16
❑ 97TulDriTI-16

Manning, Derek
❑ 93SouOreAC-17
❑ 93SouOreAF-4061
❑ 94WesMicWC-14
❑ 94WesMicWF-2292
❑ 95ModA'sTI-13
❑ 96HunStaTI-15
❑ 97HunStaTI-15

Manning, Dick
❑ 83GleFalWST-24

Manning, Henry
❑ 88CapCodPPaLP-150
❑ 92SouBenWSC-22
❑ 92SouBenWSF-180
❑ 93SarWhiSC-19
❑ 94PriWilCC-15
❑ 94PriWilCF-1925

Manning, James
❑ 87BucN28-32
❑ 87OldJudN-313

Manning, Len
❑ 94MarPhiC-11
❑ 94MarPhiF-3287
❑ 95PiePhiF-185
❑ 96BesAutS-53
❑ 96Exc-209
❑ 97ReaPhi-20

Manning, Max
❑ 86NegLeaF-54
❑ 91NegLeaRL-13
❑ 92NegLeaRLI-39
❑ 93TedWil-111
❑ 95NegLeaL2-4
❑ 95NegLeaLI-13

Manning, Mike
❑ 94HudValRC-12
❑ 94HudValRF-3379

Manning, Rick
❑ 76Hos-12
❑ 76HosTwi-12
❑ 76OPC-275
❑ 76SSP-522
❑ 76SSP-529
❑ 76Top-275
❑ 77BurCheD-56
❑ 77ChiWilD-41
❑ 77DailsID-41
❑ 77DetCaeD-41
❑ 77HollnnD-41
❑ 77Hos-53
❑ 77IndTeal-16
❑ 77Kel-15
❑ 77MSADis-41
❑ 77OPC-190
❑ 77PepGloD-12
❑ 77SagDis-41
❑ 77sDis-41
❑ 77Top-115
❑ 77WenDis-41
❑ 77ZipDis-41
❑ 78Hos-91
❑ 78IndTeal-20
❑ 78OPC-151
❑ 78Top-11
❑ 79Hos-76
❑ 79OPC-220
❑ 79Top-425
❑ 80IndTeal-17
❑ 80OPC-292
❑ 80Top-564
❑ 80TopSup-44
❑ 81Don-202
❑ 81Fle-403
❑ 81OPC-308
❑ 81Top-308
❑ 81TopScr-19
❑ 81TopSti-69
❑ 82Don-85
❑ 82Fle-374
❑ 82FleSta-195
❑ 82Ind-23
❑ 82IndWhe-8
❑ 82OPC-202
❑ 82Top-202
❑ 82TopSti-179
❑ 83AllGamPI-61
❑ 83Don-198
❑ 83Fle-413
❑ 83FleSta-113
❑ 83FleSti-246
❑ 83IndPos-21
❑ 83IndWhe-20
❑ 83OPC-147
❑ 83Top-757
❑ 83TopSti-60
❑ 83TopTra-65T
❑ 84BreGar-11
❑ 84BrePol-28
❑ 84Don-170
❑ 84Fle-205
❑ 84Nes792-128
❑ 84OPC-128
❑ 84Top-128
❑ 84TopSti-299
❑ 84TopTif-128
❑ 85BreGar-11
❑ 85BrePol-28
❑ 85Don-237
❑ 85Fle-586
❑ 85OPC-389
❑ 85Top-603
❑ 85TopMin-603
❑ 85TopSti-291
❑ 85TopTif-603
❑ 86BrePol-28
❑ 86Don-368
❑ 86Fle-493
❑ 86OPC-49
❑ 86Top-49
❑ 86TopTif-49
❑ 87BrePol-28
❑ 87Don-521
❑ 87Fle-349
❑ 87FleGlo-349
❑ 87OPC-196
❑ 87Top-706
❑ 87TopTif-706
❑ 88Don-486
❑ 88Fle-168
❑ 88FleGlo-168
❑ 88Sco-593
❑ 88ScoGlo-593
❑ 88Top-441
❑ 88TopTif-441
❑ 89PacSenL-86
❑ 89T/MSenL-71
❑ 89TopSenL-39
❑ 90EliSenL-73
❑ 94BreMilB-56
❑ 96-97PinFan-PC6

Manning, Rube
❑ 09RamT20-73
❑ 09T206-223
❑ 09T206-224
❑ 11PinT-5-810
❑ 11TurRedT-107

Manning, Tony
❑ 75SanAntBT-15

Mannion, Greg
❑ 90SalSpuCLC-132

Manno, Don
❑ 77TCMTheWY-29

Manon, Julio
❑ 94JohCitCF-3698

Manon, Ramon
❑ 87PriWilYP-23
❑ 89Ft.LauYS-14
❑ 90AlbYanB-3
❑ 90AlbYanP-1175
❑ 90AlbYanSt-10
❑ 90CedRapRB-17
❑ 90CedRapRP-2316
❑ 90FleUpd-124
❑ 91CedRapRC-9
❑ 91Ft.LauYC-6
❑ 91Ft.LauYP-2420
❑ 91TopDeb90-96
❑ 92PriWilCC-3
❑ 92PriWilCF-143
❑ 93BirBarF-1187
❑ 93LimRocDWB-12
❑ 93RanKee-241

Manos, Pete Charles
❑ 77ReaPhiT-16

Manrique, Fred
❑ 80VenLeaS-50
❑ 82SyrChiT-18
❑ 82SyrChiTI-16
❑ 83SyrChiT-17
❑ 84SyrChiT-12
❑ 85IndIndTI-12
❑ 86LouRedTI-18
❑ 87FleUpd-72
❑ 87FleUpdG-72
❑ 87WhiSoxC-20
❑ 88Don-493
❑ 88Fle-406
❑ 88FleGlo-406
❑ 88PanSti-57
❑ 88Sco-139
❑ 88ScoGlo-139
❑ 88StaLinWS-13
❑ 88Top-437
❑ 88TopRoo-6
❑ 88TopTif-437
❑ 88ToyRoo-16
❑ 88WhiSoxC-17
❑ 89Bow-66
❑ 89BowTif-66
❑ 89Don-489
❑ 89Fle-503
❑ 89FleGlo-503
❑ 89OPC-108
❑ 89Sco-457
❑ 89Top-108
❑ 89TopBig-84
❑ 89TopSti-300
❑ 89TopTif-108
❑ 89UppDec-628A
❑ 89UppDec-628B
❑ 90Don-165
❑ 90Fle-306
❑ 90FleCan-306
❑ 90Lea-518
❑ 90OPC-242
❑ 90PanSti-158
❑ 90PubIntS-396
❑ 90Sco-166
❑ 90Top-242
❑ 90TopTif-242
❑ 90TopTra-66T
❑ 90TopTraT-66T
❑ 90UppDec-392
❑ 93RanKee-242
❑ 94VenLinU-155

Manrique, Marco
❑ 92BluOriC-19
❑ 92BluOriF-2363
❑ 93AlbPolCB-16
❑ 93AlbPolF-2028
❑ 93LinVenB-54
❑ 94FreKeyC-16
❑ 94FreKeyF-2617
❑ 94VenLinU-137
❑ 95LinVen-154
❑ 96-97LinVen-199

Mansavage, Jay
❑ 96AubDouB-12
❑ 97AubDouTI-10
❑ 98QuaCitRBG-15

Manser, James
❑ 16Zee-40

Manship, Jeff
❑ 92BilMusF-3368
❑ 92BilMusSP-19

Manship, Ray
❑ 78NewWayCT-28

Mansolino, Doug
❑ 85PhoGiaC-192
❑ 89VanCanP-575
❑ 92WhiSoxK-NNO
❑ 93WhiSoxK-30
❑ 94WhiSoxK-30
❑ 95WhiSoxK-31

Mansur, Jeff
❑ 92KenTwiC-2
❑ 92VisOakF-1010
❑ 93NasXprF-398
❑ 94NasXprF-381

Mantei, Matt
❑ 93BelMarCB-17
❑ 93BelMarF-3204
❑ 94AppFoxFl-1051
❑ 94MidLeaAF-MDW4
❑ 95Exc-119
❑ 96FleUpd-U133
❑ 96FleUpdTC-U133
❑ 96LeaSigEA-120
❑ 97PacPriGotD-GD142
❑ 98ChaKniQ-21
❑ 99Fle-479
❑ 99FleSta9-479
❑ 99FleWarT-479
❑ 99MetUni-59
❑ 99MetUniGM-59
❑ 99MetUniPMG-59
❑ 99Pac-181
❑ 99PacPlaB-181
❑ 99PacRed-181
❑ 99SkyPre-88
❑ 99SkyPreR-88
❑ 99UppDec-380
❑ 99UppDecEL1-380
❑ 99UppDecEL2-380
❑ 99Vic-161

Manti, Sam
❑ 89PenPilS-14

Mantick, Dennis
❑ 77OrlTwiT-15
❑ 78OrlTwiT-12
❑ 79TolMudHT-21

Mantilla, Felix
❑ 57BraSpiaS4-13
❑ 57Top-188
❑ 58Top-17
❑ 59Top-157
❑ 59TopVen-157
❑ 60BraJayP-8
❑ 60BraLaktL-14
❑ 60BraSpiaS-11
❑ 60Top-19
❑ 60TopVen-19
❑ 61Top-164
❑ 61TopStal-44
❑ 62SalPlaC-183
❑ 62ShiPlaC-183
❑ 62Top-436
❑ 62TopBuc-53
❑ 62TopStal-158
❑ 63Jel-198
❑ 63Pos-198
❑ 63Top-447
❑ 64Top-228
❑ 64TopVen-228
❑ 65OPC-29
❑ 65RedSoxTI-8
❑ 65Top-29
❑ 66Top-557
❑ 66TopRubI-56
❑ 67Top-524
❑ 80Bra195T-23
❑ 81RedSoxBG2S-93
❑ 81TCM60I-327
❑ 82MetGal62-13
❑ 91MetWIZ-245

Mantle, Billy
❑ 82ASAMicM-56

Mantle, Butch
❑ 82ASAMicM-69

Mantle, David
❑ 82ASAMicM-56

Mantle, Merlyn
❑ 82ASAMicM-56

Mantle, Mickey
❑ 47Exh-146A
❑ 47Exh-146B
❑ 47Exh-146C
❑ 47Exh-146D
❑ 47PM1StaP1-119
❑ 47PM1StaP1-120
❑ 47PM1StaP1-121
❑ 47PM1StaP1-122
❑ 47PM1StaP1-123
❑ 47PM1StaP1-124
❑ 47PM1StaP1-125
❑ 47StaPinP2-21
❑ 51Bow-253
❑ 52BerRos-37
❑ 52Bow-101
❑ 52StaCalL-70G
❑ 52TipTop-24
❑ 52Top-311
❑ 53BowC-44
❑ 53BowC-59
❑ 53Bri-34
❑ 53Dor-111
❑ 53Dor-111A
❑ 53Dor-111B
❑ 53Dor-111C
❑ 53StaMey-6
❑ 53Top-82
❑ 54Bow-65
❑ 54DanDee-17
❑ 54NewYorJA-51
❑ 54RedHeaF-18
❑ 54StaMey-6
❑ 55ArmCoi-13A
❑ 55ArmCoi-13B
❑ 55BigLeaIS-11
❑ 55Bow-202
❑ 55DaiQueS-11
❑ 55DonWin-31
❑ 55StaMey-6
❑ 56MicManHIP-1
❑ 56Top-135
❑ 56YanJayP-8
❑ 56YanTeal-14
❑ 56YelBasP-20
❑ 57Top-95
❑ 57Top-407
❑ 57YanJayP-10
❑ 58HarSta-1
❑ 58JayPubA-11
❑ 58JayPubS-5
❑ 58Top-150
❑ 58Top-418
❑ 58Top-487
❑ 58YanJayP-9
❑ 58YooMatBC-2
❑ 59Baz-14
❑ 59HomRunD-12
❑ 59OklTodML-12
❑ 59Top-10
❑ 59Top-461
❑ 59Top-564
❑ 59TopVen-10
❑ 59Yoo-4
❑ 60ArmCoi-14
❑ 60Baz-31
❑ 60KeyChal-31
❑ 60NuHi-22
❑ 60NuHi-50
❑ 60Pos-7
❑ 60RawGloT-17
❑ 60Top-160
❑ 60Top-350
❑ 60Top-563
❑ 60TopTat-31
❑ 60TopTat-92
❑ 60TopVen-160
❑ 60YanJayP-7
❑ 61Baz-2
❑ 61NuSco-422
❑ 61NuSco-450
❑ 61Pos-4A
❑ 61Pos-4B
❑ 61Raw-5
❑ 61Top-44
❑ 61Top-300
❑ 61Top-307
❑ 61Top-406
❑ 61Top-475
❑ 61Top-578
❑ 61TopDicG-8
❑ 61TopStal-196
❑ 61Yan61RL-7
❑ 61YanJayP-8
❑ 62AurRec-10
❑ 62BasPen-3
❑ 62Baz-23
❑ 62ExhStaB-23
❑ 62Jel-5
❑ 62Pos-5A

❑ 62Pos-5B
❑ 62PosCan-5
❑ 62SalPlaC-41
❑ 62ShiPlaC-41
❑ 62Top-18
❑ 62Top-53
❑ 62Top-200
❑ 62Top-318
❑ 62Top-471
❑ 62TopBuc-54
❑ 62TopStal-88
❑ 62TopVen-18
❑ 62TopVen-53
❑ 62YanJayP-9
❑ 63BasMagM-54
❑ 63Baz-1
❑ 63ExhStaB-41
❑ 63Jel-15
❑ 63Pos-15
❑ 63SalMetC-56
❑ 63Top-2
❑ 63Top-173
❑ 63Top-200
❑ 63TopStil-26
❑ 63YanJayP-7
❑ 64Baz-1
❑ 64ChatheY-16
❑ 64Raw-5
❑ 64Top-50
❑ 64Top-331
❑ 64TopCoi-120
❑ 64TopCoi-131A
❑ 64TopCoi-131B
❑ 64TopGia-25
❑ 64TopSta-53
❑ 64TopStaU-45
❑ 64TopTatl-51
❑ 64TopVen-50
❑ 64TopVen-331
❑ 64YanJayP-7
❑ 65Baz-1
❑ 65ChaTheY-13
❑ 65OldLonC-30
❑ 65OPC-3
❑ 65OPC-5
❑ 65OPC-134
❑ 65Top-3
❑ 65Top-5
❑ 65Top-134
❑ 65Top-350
❑ 65TopEmbl-11
❑ 65TopTral-57
❑ 66Baz-7
❑ 66OPC-50
❑ 66Top-50
❑ 66TopRubl-57
❑ 66TopVen-50
❑ 66YanTeal-7
❑ 67Baz-7
❑ 67CokCapYM-V8
❑ 67DexPre-132
❑ 67OPC-103
❑ 67OPC-150
❑ 67OPCPapl-6
❑ 67Top-103
❑ 67Top-150
❑ 67TopGiaSU-8
❑ 67TopPos-6
❑ 67TopTesF-11
❑ 67TopVen-192
❑ 68AtlOil-7
❑ 68Baz-11
❑ 68LauWorS-61
❑ 68Top-280
❑ 68Top-490
❑ 68TopActS-7B
❑ 68TopActS-10A
❑ 68TopGaml-2
❑ 68TopPla-9
❑ 68TopPos-18
❑ 68TopVen-280
❑ 69EquSpoHoF-BB11
❑ 69Top-412
❑ 69Top-500A
❑ 69Top-500B
❑ 69TopDecl-23
❑ 69TopSta-205
❑ 69TopSup-24
❑ 69TopTeaP-19
❑ 69TraSta-30
❑ 69YanMal-5
❑ 70YanCliDP-13
❑ 70YanPhoS-23
❑ 71YanCliDP-10
❑ 72LauGreF-33
❑ 73BooProC-16
❑ 73SevTraC-41
❑ 73SyrChiTI-15
❑ 74NewYorNTDiS-18
❑ 74SyrChiTI-14
❑ 75OPC-194
❑ 75OPC-195
❑ 75OPC-200
❑ 75SSP42-37
❑ 75SSPSam-4
❑ 75SyrChiTI-9
❑ 75TCMAllG-21
❑ 75TCMHouoJ-17
❑ 75Top-194
❑ 75Top-195
❑ 75Top-200
❑ 75TopMin-194
❑ 75TopMin-195
❑ 75TopMin-200
❑ 75YanAllTT-6
❑ 76GalBasGHoF-17
❑ 76GrePlaG-41
❑ 76ShaPiz-145
❑ 76Spo-D
❑ 76SSPYanOD-7
❑ 76UPIS-7
❑ 77BobParHoF-34
❑ 77GalGloG-7
❑ 77GalGloG-232
❑ 77Spo-716
❑ 78DexHaloFP-34
❑ 78TCM60I-262
❑ 79BasGre-72
❑ 79TCM50-7
❑ 80Lau300-18
❑ 80MicManRL-1
❑ 80PacLeg-6
❑ 80PerHaloFP-145
❑ 80PerHaloFPS-26
❑ 80SSPHOF-145
❑ 80YanGreT-6
❑ 81SanDieSC-10
❑ 81SanDieSC-11
❑ 81SanDieSC-12
❑ 81SanDieSC-13
❑ 81SpoHaloF-15
❑ 81TCM60I-303
❑ 81TCM60I-474
❑ 82ASAMicM-1
❑ 82ASAMicM-1AU
❑ 82ASAMicM-2
❑ 82ASAMicM-3
❑ 82ASAMicM-4
❑ 82ASAMicM-5
❑ 82ASAMicM-6
❑ 82ASAMicM-7
❑ 82ASAMicM-8
❑ 82ASAMicM-9
❑ 82ASAMicM-10
❑ 82ASAMicM-11
❑ 82ASAMicM-12
❑ 82ASAMicM-13
❑ 82ASAMicM-14
❑ 82ASAMicM-15
❑ 82ASAMicM-16
❑ 82ASAMicM-17
❑ 82ASAMicM-18
❑ 82ASAMicM-19
❑ 82ASAMicM-20
❑ 82ASAMicM-21
❑ 82ASAMicM-22
❑ 82ASAMicM-23
❑ 82ASAMicM-24
❑ 82ASAMicM-25
❑ 82ASAMicM-26
❑ 82ASAMicM-27
❑ 82ASAMicM-28
❑ 82ASAMicM-29
❑ 82ASAMicM-30
❑ 82ASAMicM-31
❑ 82ASAMicM-32
❑ 82ASAMicM-33
❑ 82ASAMicM-34
❑ 82ASAMicM-35
❑ 82ASAMicM-36
❑ 82ASAMicM-37
❑ 82ASAMicM-38
❑ 82ASAMicM-39
❑ 82ASAMicM-40
❑ 82ASAMicM-41
❑ 82ASAMicM-42
❑ 82ASAMicM-43
❑ 82ASAMicM-44
❑ 82ASAMicM-45
❑ 82ASAMicM-46
❑ 82ASAMicM-47
❑ 82ASAMicM-48
❑ 82ASAMicM-49
❑ 82ASAMicM-50
❑ 82ASAMicM-51
❑ 82ASAMicM-52
❑ 82ASAMicM-53
❑ 82ASAMicM-54
❑ 82ASAMicM-55
❑ 82ASAMicM-57
❑ 82ASAMicM-58
❑ 82ASAMicM-59
❑ 82ASAMicM-60
❑ 82ASAMicM-61
❑ 82ASAMicM-62
❑ 82ASAMicM-63
❑ 82ASAMicM-64
❑ 82ASAMicM-65
❑ 82ASAMicM-66
❑ 82ASAMicM-67
❑ 82ASAMicM-68
❑ 82ASAMicM-69
❑ 82ASAMicM-70
❑ 82ASAMicM-71
❑ 82ASAMicM-72
❑ 82BasCarN-1
❑ 82CraJac-6
❑ 82DavHaloFB-15
❑ 82DiaCla-55
❑ 82K-M-1
❑ 82TCMGreS-3
❑ 82TCMStaot5-19
❑ 83DonHOFH-7
❑ 83DonHOFH-43
❑ 83MLBPin-12
❑ 83Oco& SSBG-10
❑ 83TigAlKS-14
❑ 83TigAlKS-16
❑ 83TigAlKS-35
❑ 83TopRep5-311
❑ 83TopTraBP-4
❑ 83Yan196-7
❑ 83YanASFY-1
❑ 83YanASFY-26
❑ 83YanYealT-15
❑ 84DonCha-50
❑ 84FifNatCT-11
❑ 84OCoandSI-25
❑ 84OCoandSI-100
❑ 84OCoandSI-140
❑ 84OCoandSI-150
❑ 84OCoandSI-207
❑ 84SpoDesPW-4
❑ 84WilMay-29
❑ 85CirK-6
❑ 85DonHOFS-6
❑ 85GeoSteM-5
❑ 85Woo-23
❑ 86BigLeaC-6
❑ 86DonHig-10
❑ 86SpoDecG-26
❑ 86SpoDesJM-4
❑ 86TCM-20
❑ 86TCMSupS-4
❑ 86TCMSupS-7
❑ 86TCMSupS-9
❑ 86TCMSupS-11
❑ 86TCMSupS-18
❑ 86TCMSupS-23
❑ 86TCMSupS-24
❑ 87AstShoSO-26
❑ 87HygAllG-31
❑ 87K-M-5
❑ 87LeaSpeO*-H1
❑ 87NesDreT-17
❑ 87Yan196T-2
❑ 88GreBasS-46
❑ 88HouSho-9
❑ 88PacLegl-7
❑ 88WilMulP-23
❑ 89BowInsT-5
❑ 89BowInsT-6
❑ 89BowRepl-5
❑ 89BowRepl-6
❑ 89BowTif-R5
❑ 89BowTif-R6
❑ 89CMCMan-1
❑ 89CMCMan-2
❑ 89CMCMan-3
❑ 89CMCMan-4
❑ 89CMCMan-5
❑ 89CMCMan-6
❑ 89CMCMan-7
❑ 89CMCMan-8
❑ 89CMCMan-9
❑ 89CMCMan-10
❑ 89CMCMan-11
❑ 89CMCMan-12
❑ 89CMCMan-13
❑ 89CMCMan-14
❑ 89CMCMan-15
❑ 89CMCMan-16
❑ 89CMCMan-17
❑ 89CMCMan-18
❑ 89CMCMan-19
❑ 89CMCMan-20
❑ 89HOFStiB-40
❑ 89PerCelP-28
❑ 90BasWit-3
❑ 90HOFStiB-49
❑ 90PerGreM-19
❑ 90PerGreM-87
❑ 90PerMasW-6
❑ 90PerMasW-7
❑ 90PerMasW-8
❑ 90PerMasW-9
❑ 90PerMasW-10
❑ 90YanMomPRP-6
❑ 91ManVid-1
❑ 91ScoMan-1
❑ 91ScoMan-2
❑ 91ScoMan-3
❑ 91ScoMan-4
❑ 91ScoMan-5
❑ 91ScoMan-6
❑ 91ScoMan-7
❑ 91ScoMan-AU0
❑ 91TopArc1-82
❑ 91TopEasCN-2
❑ 91YanRinP13-1
❑ 92PinMan-1
❑ 92PinMan-2
❑ 92PinMan-3
❑ 92PinMan-4
❑ 92PinMan-5
❑ 92PinMan-6
❑ 92PinMan-7
❑ 92PinMan-8
❑ 92PinMan-9
❑ 92PinMan-10
❑ 92PinMan-11
❑ 92PinMan-12
❑ 92PinMan-13
❑ 92PinMan-14
❑ 92PinMan-15
❑ 92PinMan-16
❑ 92PinMan-17
❑ 92PinMan-18
❑ 92PinMan-19
❑ 92PinMan-20
❑ 92PinMan-21
❑ 92PinMan-22
❑ 92PinMan-23
❑ 92PinMan-24
❑ 92PinMan-25
❑ 92PinMan-26
❑ 92PinMan-27
❑ 92PinMan-28
❑ 92PinMan-29
❑ 92PinMan-30
❑ 92ScoFra-2
❑ 92ScoFra-4
❑ 92ScoFra-AU2
❑ 92ScoFra-AU4
❑ 92TVSpoMF5HRC-6
❑ 92YanWIZ6-78
❑ 92YanWIZA-43
❑ 92YanWIZH-22
❑ 93Ble-19
❑ 93Ble-20
❑ 93Ble-21
❑ 93Ble-22
❑ 93Ble-23
❑ 93Ble-24
❑ 93SelTriC-1
❑ 93UppDecAH-87
❑ 93UppDecAH-134
❑ 93UppDecAH-135
❑ 93UppDecAH-137
❑ 93UppDecAH-140
❑ 93UppDecAH-141
❑ 93UppDecAH-165
❑ 93UppDecAHP-1
❑ 93UppDecAHP-2
❑ 93UppDecAHP-4
❑ 93UppDecTAN-TN17
❑ 94MetImpM-1
❑ 94MetImpM-2
❑ 94MetImpM-3
❑ 94MetImpM-4
❑ 94MetImpM-5
❑ 94MetImpM-6
❑ 94MetImpM-7
❑ 94MetImpM-8
❑ 94MetImpM-9
❑ 94MetImpM-10
❑ 94TedWil5C-4
❑ 94UppDec-GM1
❑ 94UppDec-MM1
❑ 94UppDecAH-7
❑ 94UppDecAH-10
❑ 94UppDecAH-100
❑ 94UppDecAH-116
❑ 94UppDecAH-135
❑ 94UppDecAH-168
❑ 94UppDecAH-222
❑ 94UppDecAH-225
❑ 94UppDecAH1-7
❑ 94UppDecAH1-10
❑ 94UppDecAH1-100
❑ 94UppDecAH1-116
❑ 94UppDecAH1-135
❑ 94UppDecAH1-168
❑ 94UppDecAH1-222
❑ 94UppDecAH1-225
❑ 94UppDecAH1A-259
❑ 94UppDecAHA-3
❑ 94UppDecAJ-46
❑ 94UppDecAJG-46
❑ 94UppDecMH-64
❑ 94UppDecMH-65
❑ 94UppDecMH-66
❑ 94UppDecMH-67
❑ 94UppDecMH-68
❑ 94UppDecMH-69
❑ 94UppDecMH-70
❑ 94UppDecMH-71
❑ 94UppDecMH-72
❑ 94UppDecMH-NNO0
❑ 94UppDecMLS-MM21
❑ 94UppDecMLS-NNO
❑ 94UppDecMLS-NNO
❑ 94UppDecMLSED-MM21
❑ 94UppDecMPC-1
❑ 94UppDecMPC-2
❑ 94UppDecMPC-3
❑ 94UppDecMPC-4
❑ 94UppDecMPC-5
❑ 94UppDecMPC-6
❑ 94UppDecMPC-7
❑ 94UppDecMPC-8
❑ 94UppDecMPC-9
❑ 94UppDecMPC-10
❑ 94UppDecS-10
❑ 94UppDecTAE-63
❑ 94UppDecTAE-BC1
❑ 94UppDecTAEGM-5
❑ 94UppDecTAELD-LD12
❑ 95UppDecMMI-1
❑ 95UppDecMMI-2
❑ 95UppDecMMI-3
❑ 95UppDecMMI-4
❑ 95UppDecMMI-5
❑ 95UppDecMMI-6
❑ 95UppDecMMI-7
❑ 95UppDecMMI-8
❑ 96Baz-NNO
❑ 96Bow-M20
❑ 96BowBes-NNO
❑ 96BowBes-NNO
❑ 96BowBes-NNO
❑ 96BowBesAR-NNO
❑ 96BowBesR-NNO
❑ 96ManDonC-1
❑ 96StaCluMa-MM1
❑ 96StaCluMa-MM2
❑ 96StaCluMa-MM3
❑ 96StaCluMa-MM4
❑ 96StaCluMa-MM5
❑ 96StaCluMa-MM6
❑ 96StaCluMa-MM7
❑ 96StaCluMa-MM8
❑ 96StaCluMa-MM9
❑ 96StaCluMa-MM10
❑ 96StaCluMa-MM11
❑ 96StaCluMa-MM12
❑ 96StaCluMa-MM13
❑ 96StaCluMa-MM14
❑ 96StaCluMa-MM15
❑ 96StaCluMa-MM16
❑ 96StaCluMa-MM17
❑ 96StaCluMa-MM18
❑ 96StaCluMa-MM19
❑ 96Top-7
❑ 96Top-F7
❑ 96TopChr-7
❑ 96TopChrR-7
❑ 96TopGal-NNO
❑ 96TopMan-1
❑ 96TopMan-2
❑ 96TopMan-3
❑ 96TopMan-4
❑ 96TopMan-5
❑ 96TopMan-6
❑ 96TopMan-7
❑ 96TopMan-8
❑ 96TopMan-9
❑ 96TopMan-10
❑ 96TopMan-11
❑ 96TopMan-12
❑ 96TopMan-13
❑ 96TopMan-14
❑ 96TopMan-15
❑ 96TopMan-16
❑ 96TopMan-17
❑ 96TopMan-18
❑ 96TopMan-19
❑ 96TopManC-1
❑ 96TopManC-2
❑ 96TopManC-3
❑ 96TopManC-4
❑ 96TopManC-5
❑ 96TopManC-6
❑ 96TopManC-7
❑ 96TopManC-8
❑ 96TopManC-9
❑ 96TopManC-10
❑ 96TopManC-11
❑ 96TopManC-12
❑ 96TopManC-13
❑ 96TopManC-14
❑ 96TopManC-15
❑ 96TopManC-16
❑ 96TopManC-17
❑ 96TopManC-18
❑ 96TopManC-19
❑ 96TopManC-1
❑ 96TopManC-2
❑ 96TopManC-3
❑ 96TopManC-4
❑ 96TopManC-5
❑ 96TopManC-6
❑ 96TopManC-7
❑ 96TopManC-8
❑ 96TopManF-1
❑ 96TopManF-2
❑ 96TopManF-3
❑ 96TopManF-4
❑ 96TopManF-5
❑ 96TopManF-6
❑ 96TopManF-7
❑ 96TopManF-8
❑ 96TopManF-9
❑ 96TopManF-10
❑ 96TopManF-11
❑ 96TopManF-12
❑ 96TopManF-13
❑ 96TopManF-14
❑ 96TopManF-15
❑ 96TopManF-16
❑ 96TopManF-17
❑ 96TopManF-18
❑ 96TopManF-19
❑ 96TopManFR-1
❑ 96TopManFR-2
❑ 96TopManFR-3
❑ 96TopManFR-4
❑ 96TopManFR-5
❑ 96TopManFR-6
❑ 96TopManFR-7
❑ 96TopManFR-8
❑ 96TopManFR-9
❑ 96TopManFR-10
❑ 96TopManFR-11
❑ 96TopManFR-12
❑ 96TopManFR-13
❑ 96TopManFR-14
❑ 96TopManFR-15
❑ 96TopManFR-16
❑ 96TopManFR-17
❑ 96TopManFR-18
❑ 96TopManFR-19
❑ 96TopManR-1
❑ 96TopManR-2
❑ 96TopManR-3
❑ 96TopManR-4
❑ 96TopManR-5
❑ 96TopManR-6
❑ 96TopManR-7
❑ 96TopManR-8
❑ 96TopManR-9
❑ 96TopManR-10
❑ 96TopManR-11
❑ 96TopManR-12
❑ 96TopManR-13

❑ 96TopManR-14
❑ 96TopManR-15
❑ 96TopManR-16
❑ 96TopManR-17
❑ 96TopManR-18
❑ 96TopManR-19
❑ 97HigMinESC-20
❑ 97HigMinESC-21
❑ 97HigMinESC-22
❑ 97HigMinM-69
❑ 97HigMinMCP-8
❑ 97HigMinMCP-9
❑ 97HigMinMCP-10
❑ 97HigMinMSM-5
❑ 97HigMinMSM-6
❑ 97HigMinMSM-7
❑ 97ScoMan-1
❑ 97ScoMan-2
❑ 97ScoMan-3
❑ 97ScoMan-4
❑ 97ScoMan-5
❑ 97ScoMan-6
❑ 97ScoMan-7
❑ 97ScoMan-8
❑ 97ScoMan-9
❑ 97ScoMan-10
❑ 97ScoMan-11
❑ 97ScoMan-12
❑ 97ScoMan-13
❑ 97ScoMan-14
❑ 97ScoMan-15
❑ 97ScoMan-16
❑ 97ScoMan-17
❑ 97ScoMan-18
❑ 97ScoMan-19
❑ 97ScoMan-20
❑ 97ScoMan-21
❑ 97ScoMan-22
❑ 97ScoMan-23
❑ 97ScoMan-24
❑ 97ScoMan-25
❑ 97ScoMan-26
❑ 97ScoMan-27
❑ 97ScoMan-28
❑ 97ScoMan-29
❑ 97ScoMan-30
❑ 97ScoMan-31
❑ 97ScoMan-32
❑ 97ScoMan-33
❑ 97ScoMan-34
❑ 97ScoMan-35
❑ 97ScoMan-36
❑ 97ScoMan-37
❑ 97ScoMan-38
❑ 97ScoMan-39
❑ 97ScoMan-40
❑ 97ScoMan-41
❑ 97ScoMan-42
❑ 97ScoMan-43
❑ 97ScoMan-44
❑ 97ScoMan-45
❑ 97ScoMan-46
❑ 97ScoMan-47
❑ 97ScoMan-48
❑ 97ScoMan-49
❑ 97ScoMan-50
❑ 97ScoMan-51
❑ 97ScoMan-52
❑ 97ScoMan-53
❑ 97ScoMan-54
❑ 97ScoMan-55
❑ 97ScoMan-56A
❑ 97ScoMan-56B
❑ 97ScoMan-57
❑ 97ScoMan-58
❑ 97ScoMan-59
❑ 97ScoMan-60
❑ 97ScoMan-61
❑ 97ScoMan-62
❑ 97ScoMan-63
❑ 97ScoMan-64
❑ 97ScoMan-65
❑ 97ScoMan-66
❑ 97ScoMan-67
❑ 97ScoMan-68
❑ 97ScoMan-69
❑ 97ScoMan-70
❑ 97ScoMan-71
❑ 97ScoMan-72
❑ 97ScoMan-73
❑ 97ScoMan-74
❑ 97ScoMan-P1
❑ 97ScoMan-P7
❑ 97ScoManI-1
❑ 97ScoManI-2
❑ 97ScoManI-3
❑ 97ScoManI-4
❑ 97ScoManI-5
❑ 97ScoManI-6
❑ 97ScoManI-7
❑ 97TopMan-21
❑ 97TopMan-22
❑ 97TopMan-23
❑ 97TopMan-24
❑ 97TopMan-25
❑ 97TopMan-26
❑ 97TopMan-27
❑ 97TopMan-28
❑ 97TopMan-29
❑ 97TopMan-30
❑ 97TopMan-31
❑ 97TopMan-32
❑ 97TopMan-33
❑ 97TopMan-34
❑ 97TopMan-35
❑ 97TopMan-36
❑ 97TopManF-21
❑ 97TopManF-22
❑ 97TopManF-23
❑ 97TopManF-24
❑ 97TopManF-25
❑ 97TopManF-26
❑ 97TopManF-27
❑ 97TopManF-28
❑ 97TopManF-29
❑ 97TopManF-30
❑ 97TopManF-31
❑ 97TopManF-32
❑ 97TopManF-33
❑ 97TopManF-34
❑ 97TopManF-35
❑ 97TopManF-36
❑ 97TopManFR-21
❑ 97TopManFR-22
❑ 97TopManFR-23
❑ 97TopManFR-24
❑ 97TopManFR-25
❑ 97TopManFR-26
❑ 97TopManFR-27
❑ 97TopManFR-28
❑ 97TopManFR-29
❑ 97TopManFR-30
❑ 97TopManFR-31
❑ 97TopManFR-32
❑ 97TopManFR-33
❑ 97TopManFR-34
❑ 97TopManFR-35
❑ 97TopManFR-36
❑ 98Fle-536
❑ 98Fle2PostMantle-1
❑ 98FleManaS-NNO
❑ 98FleManaS-NNO
❑ 98FleMicMMM-1
❑ 98FleMicMMM-2
❑ 98FleMicMMM-3
❑ 98FleMicMMM-4
❑ 98FleMicMMM-5
❑ 98FleMicMMM-6
❑ 98FleMicMMM-7
❑ 98FleMicMMM-8
❑ 98FleMicMMM-9
❑ 98FleMicMMM-10
❑ 98FleMicMMMG-1
❑ 98FleMicMMMG-2
❑ 98FleMicMMMG-3
❑ 98FleMicMMMG-4
❑ 98FleMicMMMG-5
❑ 98FleMicMMMG-6
❑ 98FleMicMMMG-7
❑ 98FleMicMMMG-8
❑ 98FleMicMMMG-9
❑ 98FleMicMMMG-10
❑ 98FleVin'-67
❑ 98FleVin'C-67
❑ 98SpoIIIWSF-1
❑ 98SpoIIIWSFAE-7
❑ 98SpoIIIWSFAEG-7
❑ 98SpoIIIWSFEE-1
❑ 98SpoIIIWSFFE-1
❑ 99SpoIIIGotG-7
❑ 99SpoIIIGotGC-2
❑ 99SpoIIIGotGC-9
❑ 99SpoIIIGotGC-50
❑ 99SpoIIIGotGRB-1
❑ 99SpoIIIGotGRBG-1
❑ 99UppDecAP-MM
❑ 99UppDecCL-17
❑ 99UppDecCLA-1950
❑ 99UppDecCLCC-17
❑ 99UppDecCLMS-HR8
❑ 99UppDecO-MICL
❑ 99UppDecR-98
❑ 99UppDecRG-98
❑ 99UppDecRL-3
❑ 99UppDecRL-10
❑ 99UppDecRL-14
❑ 99UppDecRL-15
❑ 99UppDecRP-98

Mantle, Mickey Jr
❑ 82ASAMicM-56

Mantle, Roy
❑ 82ASAMicM-69

Manto, Jeff
❑ 86QuaCitAP-19
❑ 87PalSprP-4
❑ 88BasAmeAAB-29
❑ 88BlaYNPRWL-185
❑ 88MidAngGS-21
❑ 88TexLeaAGS-39
❑ 89EdmTraC-20
❑ 89EdmTraP-570
❑ 89FleUpd-13
❑ 90CMC-467
❑ 90ColSprSSC-15
❑ 90ColSprSSP-43
❑ 90Fle-137
❑ 90FleCan-137
❑ 90FleUpd-94
❑ 90IndTeal-26
❑ 90ProAAAF-224
❑ 91Bow-75
❑ 91Don-602
❑ 91IndFanC-18
❑ 91OPC-488
❑ 91Sco-337
❑ 91StaClu-582
❑ 91Top-488
❑ 91TopDeb90-97
❑ 91TopDesS-488
❑ 91TopMic-488
❑ 91TopTif-488
❑ 91UppDec-238
❑ 92RicBraBB-1
❑ 92RicBraF-384
❑ 92RicBraRC-9
❑ 92RicBraS-431
❑ 92Sco-666
❑ 92StaClu-699
❑ 93ScrRedBF-2548
❑ 93ScrRedBTI-16
❑ 94NorTidF-2928
❑ 94Pac-481
❑ 94RocRedWTI-12
❑ 95BalOriP-30
❑ 95Fin-299
❑ 95FinRef-299
❑ 95StaClu-597
❑ 95StaCluMOP-597
❑ 95StaCluSTWS-597
❑ 96ColCho-58
❑ 96ColChoGS-58
❑ 96ColChoSS-58
❑ 96Don-38
❑ 96DonPreP-38
❑ 96Fle-14
❑ 96FleTif-14
❑ 96Pac-233
❑ 96Ult-8
❑ 96UltGolM-8
❑ 96UppDec-17
❑ 97ColSprSATTI-10
❑ 97RicBraBC-12
❑ 98PacOnl-278
❑ 98PacOnlR-278
❑ 98PacOnlWC-278

Mantrana, Manny
❑ 87FayGenP-12
❑ 88ColMetGS-19
❑ 88St.LucMS-15

Manuare, Jose
❑ 91MedHatBJP-4096
❑ 91MedHatBJSP-3

Manuel, Barry
❑ 87LSUTigP-6
❑ 88ChaRanS-14
❑ 89TulDriGS-16
❑ 90ChaRanS-12
❑ 90FloStaLAS-36
❑ 90LSUTigGM-16
❑ 90StaFS7-24
❑ 91LinDriAA-586
❑ 91TulDriLD-586
❑ 91TulDriP-2768
❑ 91TulDriTI-16
❑ 92Don-401
❑ 92OklCit8F-1913
❑ 92ProFS7-154
❑ 92TopDeb91-115
❑ 93LinVenB-230
❑ 93Pin-257
❑ 93RanKee-243
❑ 93Sco-225
❑ 94OriPro-58
❑ 94RocRedWF-994
❑ 94RocRedWTI-13
❑ 97Fle-382
❑ 97FleTif-382
❑ 97Ult-231
❑ 97UltGolME-231
❑ 97UltPlaME-231
❑ 98DiaBacP-7
❑ 98PacOnl-42
❑ 98PacOnlR-42
❑ 98PacOnlWC-42

Manuel, Charlie (Charles)
❑ 70OPC-194
❑ 70Top-194
❑ 71MLBOffS-466
❑ 71OPC-744
❑ 71Top-744
❑ 72TwiTeal-6
❑ 74AlbDukCa-72
❑ 74AlbDukTI-9
❑ 76SSP-86
❑ 79TCMJapPB-44
❑ 83WisRapTF-27
❑ 85OrlTwiT-22
❑ 86TolMudHP-15
❑ 87PorBeaP-22
❑ 88IndGat-9
❑ 88IndTeal-26
❑ 89IndTeal-28
❑ 90DodTar-479
❑ 91ColSprSSLD-99
❑ 91ColSprSSP-2200
❑ 91LinDriAAA-99
❑ 92ColSprSSF-766
❑ 92ColSprSSS-99
❑ 93ChaKniF-559
❑ 93TriAAAGF-37
❑ 97ColSprSATTI-29

Manuel, Jerry
❑ 76DetTigP-19
❑ 76OPC-596
❑ 76Top-596
❑ 77EvaTriT-18
❑ 81ExpPos-5
❑ 82Fle-195
❑ 83IowCubT-17
❑ 86IndIndTI-36
❑ 87IndIndTI-5
❑ 89TopSenL-90
❑ 90JacExpB-25
❑ 90JacExpP-1391
❑ 91IndIndLD-199
❑ 91IndIndP-477
❑ 91LinDriAAA-199
❑ 92ExpPos-21
❑ 97MarPac-28

Manuel, Jose
❑ 88SanAntMB-18

Manush, Heinie
❑ 26SpoNewSM-5
❑ 29ExhFou-29
❑ 29PorandAR-61
❑ 31Exh-31
❑ 31SenTealPW-21
❑ 31W517-28
❑ 32R33So2-416
❑ 33ExhFou-16
❑ 33Gou-47
❑ 33Gou-107
❑ 33Gou-187
❑ 33GouCanV-47
❑ 33TatOrbSDR-178
❑ 33WorCig-66
❑ 34BabRutG-42
❑ 34BatR31-77
❑ 34ButPreR-41
❑ 34DiaStaR-30A
❑ 34DiaStaR-30B
❑ 34ExhFou-16
❑ 34Gou-18
❑ 34GouCanV-68
❑ 35ExhFou-16
❑ 35GouPuzR-1C
❑ 35GouPuzR-2C
❑ 35GouPuzR-16C
❑ 35GouPuzR-17C
❑ 36GouWidPPR-B16
❑ 36WorWidGV-73
❑ 37WheBB6-8
❑ 38WheBB15-8
❑ 39PlaBal-94
❑ 40PlaBal-176
❑ 46SpoExcW-6-11
❑ 54Top-187
❑ 60Fle-18
❑ 61Fle-57
❑ 72TCMthe3-119
❑ 74CapPub-62
❑ 76RowExh-10
❑ 76ShaPiz-100
❑ 77BobParHoF-35
❑ 77GalGloG-56
❑ 78DexHaloFP-35
❑ 79RedSoxEF-16
❑ 80PacLeg-2
❑ 80PerHaloFP-100
❑ 80SSPHOF-100
❑ 81ConTSN-77
❑ 81TigDetN-82A
❑ 81TigDetN-82B
❑ 81TigSecNP-3
❑ 82TCMGreH-30
❑ 83ConMar-2
❑ 83TCMRut-1
❑ 85BigLeaC3-23
❑ 86ConSer1-19
❑ 88ConAmeA-20
❑ 89DodSmoG-16
❑ 89HOFStiB-36
❑ 90DodTar-480
❑ 91ConTSN-63
❑ 91ConTSN-270
❑ 94ConTSN-1077
❑ 94ConTSNB-1077
❑ 94TopArc1-187
❑ 94TopArc1G-187

Manwaring, Kirt
❑ 87ShrCapP-10
❑ 87TexLeaAF-22
❑ 88BlaYNPRWL-92
❑ 88Don-39
❑ 88Fle-651
❑ 88FleGlo-651
❑ 88FleMin-119
❑ 88Lea-39
❑ 88PhoFirC-12
❑ 88PhoFirP-61
❑ 88Sco-627
❑ 88ScoGlo-627
❑ 88TopTra-64T
❑ 88TopTraT-64T
❑ 89Bow-469
❑ 89BowTif-469
❑ 89Don-494
❑ 89DonBasB-330
❑ 89Fle-334
❑ 89FleGlo-334
❑ 89GiaMot-23
❑ 89PanSti-208
❑ 89Sco-619
❑ 89ScoHot1R-46
❑ 89ScoYouSI-22
❑ 89Top-506
❑ 89TopTif-506
❑ 89UppDec-500
❑ 90CMC-537
❑ 90Don-59
❑ 90Fle-63
❑ 90FleCan-63
❑ 90OPC-678
❑ 90PhoFirC-10
❑ 90PhoFirP-14
❑ 90ProAAAF-40
❑ 90PublntS-76
❑ 90Sco-146
❑ 90Top-678
❑ 90TopTif-678
❑ 90UppDec-457
❑ 91GiaMot-23
❑ 91GiaPacGaE-25
❑ 91OPC-472
❑ 91Sco-101
❑ 91Top-472
❑ 91TopDesS-472
❑ 91TopMic-472
❑ 91TopTif-472
❑ 92Bow-361
❑ 92Don-494
❑ 92Fle-641
❑ 92GiaMot-23
❑ 92GiaPacGaE-27
❑ 92Lea-208
❑ 92LeaBlaG-208
❑ 92OPC-726
❑ 92Pin-181
❑ 92Sco-636
❑ 92StaClu-271
❑ 92Top-726
❑ 92TopGol-726
❑ 92TopGolW-726
❑ 92TopMic-726
❑ 92TriPla-61
❑ 92Ult-293
❑ 92UppDec-740
❑ 93Bow-688
❑ 93Don-122
❑ 93Don-364
❑ 93Fla-144
❑ 93Fle-158
❑ 93GiaMot-9
❑ 93GiaPos-23
❑ 93GiaStaC-6
❑ 93Lea-66
❑ 93PacSpa-612
❑ 93PanSti-235
❑ 93Pin-122
❑ 93Sco-179
❑ 93Sel-247
❑ 93StaClu-690
❑ 93StaCluFDI-690
❑ 93StaCluMOP-690
❑ 93Stu-151
❑ 93Top-337
❑ 93TopGol-337
❑ 93TopInaM-337
❑ 93TopInaR-337
❑ 93TopMic-337
❑ 93Ult-135
❑ 93UppDec-179
❑ 93UppDecGold-179
❑ 94Bow-275
❑ 94ColC-186
❑ 94ColChoGS-186
❑ 94ColChoSS-186
❑ 94Don-209
❑ 94Fin-415
❑ 94FinRef-415
❑ 94Fla-245
❑ 94Fle-694
❑ 94FleExtB-389
❑ 94GiaAMC-12
❑ 94GiaMot-13
❑ 94GiaTarBC-14
❑ 94GiaTeal-6
❑ 94GiaUSPC-6C
❑ 94GiaUSPC-12H
❑ 94Lea-55
❑ 94OPC-2
❑ 94Pac-549
❑ 94Pin-53
❑ 94PinArtP-53
❑ 94PinMusC-53
❑ 94Sco-344
❑ 94ScoGolR-344
❑ 94Sel-370
❑ 94StaClu-218
❑ 94StaCluFDI-218
❑ 94StaCluGR-218
❑ 94StaCluMOP-218
❑ 94StaCluMOP-ST14
❑ 94StaCluST-ST14
❑ 94StaCluT-3
❑ 94StaCluTFDI-3
❑ 94Top-30
❑ 94TopGol-30
❑ 94TopSpa-30
❑ 94TriPla-106
❑ 94TriPlaM-2
❑ 94Ult-292
❑ 94UltAwaW-10
❑ 94UppDec-100
❑ 94UppDecED-100
❑ 95ColCho-257
❑ 95ColChoGS-257
❑ 95ColChoSS-257
❑ 95Don-187
❑ 95DonPreP-187
❑ 95DonTopotO-352
❑ 95Fla-425
❑ 95Fle-583
❑ 95GiaMot-12
❑ 95Lea-190
❑ 95Pac-380
❑ 95Pin-203
❑ 95PinArtP-203
❑ 95PinMusC-203
❑ 95Sco-368
❑ 95ScoGolR-368
❑ 95ScoPlaTS-368
❑ 95StaClu-465
❑ 95StaCluMOP-465
❑ 95StaCluSTWS-465

❑ 95StaCluVR-254
❑ 95StaCluVRMO-254
❑ 95Top-211
❑ 95TopCyb-120
❑ 95Ult-242
❑ 95UltGolM-242
❑ 95UppDec-332
❑ 95UppDecED-332
❑ 95UppDecEDG-332
❑ 96ColCho-304
❑ 96ColChoGS-304
❑ 96ColChoSS-304
❑ 96Don-35
❑ 96DonPreP-35
❑ 96EmoXL-293
❑ 96Fla-391
❑ 96Fle-590
❑ 96FleTif-590
❑ 96GiaMot-7
❑ 96LeaSigA-142
❑ 96LeaSigAG-142
❑ 96LeaSigAS-142
❑ 96Pac-212
❑ 96Pin-69
❑ 96Sco-406
❑ 96StaClu-78
❑ 96StaCluMOP-78
❑ 96Top-260
❑ 96Ult-296
❑ 96UltGolM-296
❑ 96UppDec-454
❑ 97Cir-138
❑ 97CirRav-138
❑ 97ColCho-317
❑ 97ColChoT-CR12
❑ 97DonTea-105
❑ 97DonTeaSPE-105
❑ 97PacPriGotD-GD153
❑ 97PhoFirDTTI-5
❑ 97RocPol-7
❑ 97Sco-39
❑ 97ScoArtPWB-39
❑ 97ScoPreS-39
❑ 97ScoShoS-39
❑ 97ScoShoSAP-39
❑ 97Top-364
❑ 97Ult-413
❑ 97UltGolME-413
❑ 97UltPlaME-413
❑ 97UppDec-352
❑ 98ColCho-362
❑ 98Pac-285
❑ 98PacOnl-252
❑ 98PacOnlR-252
❑ 98PacOnlWC-252
❑ 98PacPlaB-285
❑ 98PacRedT-285
❑ 98PacSil-285
❑ 98PinSna-CR5
❑ 98StaCluFDI-236
❑ 98StaCluI-236
❑ 98StaCluOneK-236
❑ 98StaCluPP-236
❑ 98UppDec-353
❑ 99Fle-506
❑ 99FleSta9-506
❑ 99FleWarT-506
❑ 99StaClu-302
❑ 99StaCluFDI-302
❑ 99StaCluOoaK-302
❑ 99StaCluPP-302
❑ 99UppDec-362
❑ 99UppDecEL1-362
❑ 99UppDecEL2-362
❑ 99UppDecM-69
❑ 99UppDecMGS-69
❑ 99UppDecMHFS-69
❑ 99UppDecMP-69
❑ 99UppDecMSS-69
❑ 99Vic-139

Manwarren, Marc
❑ 96KisCobB-15

Manwiller, Tim
❑ 97SouOreTB-25
❑ 98ModA'sG-17

Manz, George
❑ 74WicAerODF-105

Manzanillo, Josias
❑ 85ElmPioT-14
❑ 87NewBriRSP-21
❑ 89EasLeaAP-17
❑ 89NewBriRSP-606
❑ 89NewBriRSS-8
❑ 90Bes-70
❑ 90CMC-879
❑ 90NewBriRSB-4
❑ 90NewBriRSP-1315
❑ 90NewBriRSS-9
❑ 90TopTVRS-51
❑ 91PawRedSP-35
❑ 92MemChiS-429
❑ 92OmaRoyF-2959
❑ 92OmaRoyS-336
❑ 92Sco-838
❑ 92StaClu-504
❑ 92TopDeb91-116
❑ 93LimRocDWB-42
❑ 93PacSpa-514
❑ 93Ult-574
❑ 94BreMilB-150
❑ 94Fla-408
❑ 94FleUpd-157
❑ 94NorTidF-2917
❑ 94Pac-411
❑ 94TopTra-9T
❑ 94Ult-239
❑ 95Don-190
❑ 95DonPreP-190
❑ 95Fle-375
❑ 95MetCoIP-20
❑ 95StaClu-413
❑ 95StaCluMOP-413
❑ 95StaCluSTWS-413
❑ 95Top-308
❑ 95Ult-199
❑ 95UltGolM-199
❑ 98DurBulTI-16
❑ 98NorTidQ-14

Manzanillo, Ravelo
❑ 83AleDukT-27
❑ 85NasPirT-15
❑ 88FloStaLAS-43
❑ 88TamTarS-14
❑ 89BirBarB-13
❑ 90CMC-631
❑ 90ProAAAF-164
❑ 90VanCanC-4
❑ 90VanCanP-486
❑ 91LinDriAAA-510
❑ 91SyrChiLD-510
❑ 91SyrChiMB-13
❑ 94Bow-302
❑ 94Fla-424
❑ 94FleUpd-175
❑ 94PirQui-12
❑ 94SpoRoo-59
❑ 94SpoRooAP-59
❑ 94Ult-556
❑ 95Fla-186
❑ 95Fle-482
❑ 95Pac-346
❑ 95StaClu-490
❑ 95StaCluMOP-490
❑ 95StaCluSTWS-490

Manzano, Adrian
❑ 98GreBraG-13

Manzon, Howard
❑ 86KenTwiP-15

Mapel, Steve
❑ 79WisRapTT-9
❑ 80OrlTwiT-6
❑ 80TolMudHT-1
❑ 82OrlTwi8SCT-20

Mapes, Cliff
❑ 48BluTin-33
❑ 48YanTeal-18
❑ 50Bow-218
❑ 50YanTeal-14
❑ 51BerRos-D2
❑ 51Bow-289
❑ 51R42SmaS-64
❑ 52Bow-13
❑ 52Top-103
❑ 83TopRep5-103

Maples, Steve
❑ 79CliDodT-23

Maples, Tim
❑ 81MiaOriT-18

Mapp, Eric
❑ 96BilMusTI-18

Marabell, Scott
❑ 89BakDodCLC-195
❑ 90VerBeaDS-19
❑ 91SanAntMP-2989

Marabella, Tony
❑ 90GatCitPP-3347
❑ 90GatCitPSP-15
❑ 91SumFlyC-16
❑ 91SumFlyP-2341
❑ 94BurBeeC-14
❑ 94BurBeeF-1089

Marak, Paul
❑ 87SumBraP-9
❑ 88DurBulS-13
❑ 89GreBraB-17
❑ 89GreBraP-1174
❑ 89GreBraS-14
❑ 90CMC-284
❑ 90ProAAAF-400
❑ 90RicBraBC-10
❑ 90RicBraC-8
❑ 90RicBraP-255
❑ 90RicBraTI-20
❑ 91Cla2-T52
❑ 91Don-413
❑ 91Lea-260
❑ 91OPC-753
❑ 91RicBraP-2562
❑ 91Sco-712
❑ 91ScoRoo-13
❑ 91Top-753
❑ 91TopDeb90-98
❑ 91TopDesS-753
❑ 91TopMic-753
❑ 91TopTif-753
❑ 92ChaKniF-2768
❑ 93LinVenB-74

Maranda, Georges
❑ 52LaPat-10
❑ 52LavPro-5
❑ 60Top-479
❑ 61TacBan-12
❑ 61TwiCloD-15
❑ 61UniOil-T20

Maranville, Rabbit (Walter)
❑ 14B18B-52A
❑ 14B18B-52B
❑ 14B18B-52C
❑ 14CraJacE-136
❑ 14PolGroW-15
❑ 15CraJacE-136
❑ 15SpoNewM-109
❑ 16BF2FP-56
❑ 16FleBreD-60
❑ 16SpoNewM-112
❑ 17ColE13-107
❑ 17HolBreD-65
❑ 19W514-21
❑ 20NatCarE-60
❑ 20WalMaiW-28
❑ 21E121So1-56
❑ 21E121So8-54
❑ 21Exh-101
❑ 21Nei-90
❑ 22AmeCarE122-42
❑ 22E120-220
❑ 22W572-59
❑ 22W573-74
❑ 22W575-74
❑ 22WilPatV-42
❑ 23W501-83
❑ 23W503-46
❑ 23W515-50
❑ 23WilChoV-87
❑ 24MrsShePP-5
❑ 25Exh-23
❑ 26Exh-15
❑ 26SpoComoA-27
❑ 29PorandAR-62
❑ 31Exh-1
❑ 32USCar*-10
❑ 33CraJacP-17
❑ 33DelR33-13
❑ 33GeoCMil-21
❑ 33Gou-117
❑ 34BatR31-37
❑ 34DiaMatCSB-124
❑ 34DiaStaR-3
❑ 34GouCanV-4
❑ 35DiaMatCS2-14
❑ 35GouPuzR-1J
❑ 35GouPuzR-3A
❑ 35GouPuzR-14A
❑ 35GouPuzR-15A
❑ 36WorWidGV-129
❑ 50CalHOFW-51
❑ 53ArtHaloFP-57
❑ 60ExhWriH-15
❑ 60Fle-21
❑ 61Fle-124
❑ 63BazA-14
❑ 68SCFOldT-20
❑ 69Baz-10
❑ 69Baz-12
❑ 70SpoCarfCOP-7
❑ 76RowExh-14
❑ 76ShaPiz-72
❑ 77BobParHoF-96
❑ 77GalGloG-114
❑ 80BraTCM1-16
❑ 80PacLeg-3
❑ 80PerHaloFP-72
❑ 80SSPHOF-72
❑ 82DiaCla-78
❑ 86BraGreT-3
❑ 87ConSer2-47
❑ 89DodSmoG-18
❑ 89HOFStiB-17
❑ 90DodTar-481
❑ 91ConTSN-4
❑ 93ConTSN-914
❑ 93CraJac-20
❑ 94ConTSN-1060
❑ 94ConTSNB-1060
❑ 95ConTSN-1329
❑ 95ConTSNCMP-1387
❑ 95ConTSNP-1500

Marberry, Firpo (Fred)
❑ 26SpoComoA-28
❑ 28PorandAR-A24
❑ 28PorandAR-B24
❑ 28W56PlaC-S7A
❑ 30SchR33-47
❑ 31Exh-31
❑ 31SenTealPW-22
❑ 33DouDisP-31
❑ 33ExhFou-16
❑ 33Gou-104
❑ 33WorCig-67
❑ 34BabRutG-43
❑ 34BatR31-66
❑ 34ButPreR-42
❑ 34ExhFou-12
❑ 34GouCanV-8
❑ 35AlDemDCR3-26
❑ 35GolMedFR-8
❑ 35GouPuzR-5F
❑ 35GouPuzR-6F
❑ 35GouPuzR-11H
❑ 35GouPuzR-13F
❑ 36WorWidGV-10
❑ 61Fle-125
❑ 74TigTCM1AC-19
❑ 74TigTCM1AC-35
❑ 75SenTCM1-17
❑ 75SenTCM1-40
❑ 76TigOldTS-15
❑ 78TigDeaCS-15
❑ 81TigSecNP-19
❑ 91ConTSN-326

Marble, Harry
❑ 37Zee-2
❑ 37Zee-18

Marcan, Arthur
❑ 15Zee-44

Marcano, Gilberto
❑ 76VenLeaS-185
❑ 80VenLeaS-231

Marcano, Raul
❑ 96-97LinVen-198

Marcano, Roberto
❑ 74SalLakCAC-92
❑ 76VenLeaS-142
❑ 79TCMJapPB-11
❑ 80VenLeaS-211
❑ 94VenLinU-10

Marcano, Tucupita
❑ 95LinVen-72

Marcell, Ziggy
❑ 86NegLeaF-56

Marcelle, Oliver
❑ 74LauOldTBS-3
❑ 90NegLeaS-17

Marcero, Doug
❑ 89NiaFalRP-16
❑ 90NiaFalRP-21
❑ 91LakTigP-265

Marchan, Jose
❑ 93LinVenB-24
❑ 94VenLinU-95
❑ 95LinVen-198

Marchant, Nick
❑ 98MarPhiG-18

Marchese, Joe (Joseph)
❑ 86ElmPioRSP-11
❑ 87GreHorP-11
❑ 88CarLeaAS-12
❑ 88LynRedSS-10
❑ 89NewBriRSP-616
❑ 89NewBriRSS-9
❑ 91WinHavRSC-26
❑ 91WinHavRSP-506
❑ 92WinHavRSC-28
❑ 92WinHavRSF-1795
❑ 93LynRedSC-26
❑ 93LynRedSF-2535
❑ 94LynRedSC-28
❑ 94LynRedSF-1910
❑ 95AshTouTI-11
❑ 96SalAvaB-28

Marchese, John
❑ 88BenBucL-24
❑ 89QuaCitAB-18
❑ 89QuaCitAGS-10
❑ 90QuaCitAGS-15

Marchesi, Jim
❑ 92JohCitCC-21
❑ 92JohCitCF-3112
❑ 93JohCitCC-12
❑ 93JohCitCF-3672

Marcheskie, Lee
❑ 82AleDukT-2
❑ 83LynPirT-5
❑ 85NasPirT-16

Marchiano, Mike
❑ 97EveAquG-15
❑ 98WisTimRM-23

Marchildon, Phil
❑ 39WorWidGV-17
❑ 42A'sTeal-24
❑ 46A'sTeal-11
❑ 47A'sTeal-20
❑ 48A'sTeal-16
❑ 49A'sTeal-23
❑ 49Bow-187
❑ 49PhiBul-34
❑ 50A'sTeal-18
❑ 60RawGloT-18
❑ 70Houof J-16
❑ 75TCMHouoJ-18
❑ 76TayBow4-100

Marchio, Frank
❑ 53ExhCan-53

Marchok, Chris
❑ 87JamExpP-2565
❑ 88RocExpLC-23
❑ 89JacExpB-4
❑ 89JacExpP-166
❑ 90CMC-55
❑ 90IndIndC-5
❑ 90IndIndP-300
❑ 90ProAAAF-583
❑ 91HarSenLD-262
❑ 91HarSenP-622
❑ 91LinDriAA-262
❑ 92HarSenF-457
❑ 92HarSenS-288

Marciano, Rocky
❑ 83FraBroR-20

Marcinczyk, T.R.
❑ 96SouOreTI-10
❑ 97ModA'sG-17
❑ 98Bes-26
❑ 98HunStaTI-6

Marcon, Dave
❑ 90St.CatBJP-3463
❑ 91SalLakTP-3206
❑ 91SalLakTSP-23
❑ 93CedRapKC-12
❑ 93CedRapKF-1733

Marcucci, Lilo
❑ 46SunBre-12

Marcum, John
❑ 34Gou-69
❑ 35DiaMatCS3T1-102
❑ 35GouPuzR-8J
❑ 35GouPuzR-9J
❑ 36GouWidPPR-A69
❑ 36WorWidGV-58
❑ 79RedSoxEF-4
❑ 92ConTSN-574

Mardsen, Steve
❑ 84BufBisT-17

Marenghi, Matt
❑ 94BluOriC-13
❑ 94BluOriF-3560
❑ 96HigDesMB-19
❑ 97HigDesMG-14

Marett, John
❑ 89BluOriS-14
❑ 90WauTimP-2127
❑ 90WauTimS-15

Marge, Pete
❑ 93BilMusSP-15

Margenau, Eric
❑ 92ColMetPI-34
❑ 93ForWayWC-29
❑ 94ForWayWC-29
❑ 95ForWayWTI-31
❑ 96ForWayWB-30

Margheim, Greg
❑ 90BilMusP-3218
❑ 91CedRapRC-10
❑ 91CedRapRP-2717

Margoneri, Joe
❑ 57Top-191

Marguardt, Chuck
❑ 88GasRanP-1023

Maria, Esteban
❑ 75BurBeeT-14

Mariano, Bob
❑ 84ChaO'sT-12
❑ 85ChaO'sT-18
❑ 89AlbYanB-28
❑ 89AlbYanP-324
❑ 91AlbYanP-1025
❑ 91LinDriAA-25
❑ 92ForLauYTI-20
❑ 92Ft.LauYF-2630
❑ 93BelBreCB-28
❑ 93BelBreFI-1728
❑ 94ElPasDF-3163
❑ 94ElPasDF-3164
❑ 97TucTorB-27

Marichal, Juan
❑ 47PM1StaP1-126
❑ 60TacBan-9
❑ 61GiaJayP-8
❑ 61Top-417
❑ 61TopStal-79
❑ 62GiaJayP-8
❑ 62Jel-140
❑ 62Pos-140
❑ 62PosCan-140
❑ 62Top-505
❑ 62TopStal-198
❑ 63Jel-109
❑ 63Pos-109
❑ 63SalMetC-5
❑ 63Top-440
❑ 64ChatheY-34
❑ 64GiaJayP-6
❑ 64Top-3
❑ 64Top-280
❑ 64TopCoi-36
❑ 64TopCoi-157
❑ 64TopGia-37
❑ 64TopSta-39
❑ 64TopStaU-46
❑ 64TopVen-3
❑ 64TopVen-280
❑ 64WheSta-28
❑ 65Baz-24
❑ 65ChaTheY-34
❑ 65GiaTeal-5
❑ 65OPC-10
❑ 65OPC-50
❑ 65Top-10
❑ 65Top-50
❑ 65TopTral-20
❑ 66Baz-10
❑ 66Top-221
❑ 66Top-420
❑ 66TopRubl-58
❑ 66TopVen-221
❑ 67Baz-10
❑ 67CokCapA-14
❑ 67CokCapG-7
❑ 67CokCapNLA-34
❑ 67OPCPapl-28
❑ 67Top-234
❑ 67Top-236
❑ 67Top-454A
❑ 67Top-454B
❑ 67Top-500
❑ 67TopPos-28
❑ 67TopTesF-12
❑ 67TopVen-300
❑ 68Baz-5
❑ 68DexPre-50
❑ 68OPC-107
❑ 68Top-107A
❑ 68Top-107B
❑ 68Top-205
❑ 68TopVen-107
❑ 68TopVen-205
❑ 69KelPin-11
❑ 69MilBra-165
❑ 69MLBOffS-203
❑ 69MLBPin-51
❑ 69NabTeaF-14
❑ 69OPC-10
❑ 69OPCDec-15
❑ 69Top-10

❑ 69Top-370
❑ 69Top-572
❑ 69TopDec-32
❑ 69TopSta-107
❑ 69TopSup-64
❑ 69TopTeaP-14
❑ 69TraSta-32
❑ 70Gia-8
❑ 70Kel-13
❑ 70MilBra-14
❑ 70MLBOffS-128
❑ 70OPC-67
❑ 70OPC-69
❑ 70OPC-210
❑ 70OPC-466
❑ 70Top-67
❑ 70Top-69
❑ 70Top-210
❑ 70Top-466
❑ 70TopCanL-14
❑ 70TopScr-12
❑ 70TraSta-3A
❑ 71BazNumT-19
❑ 71BazUnn-19
❑ 71GiaTic-6
❑ 71MLBOffS-256
❑ 71OPC-325
❑ 71Top-325
❑ 71TopCoi-125
❑ 71TopTat-5
❑ 72EssCoi-7
❑ 72GiaTeal-13
❑ 72Kel-47
❑ 72MilBra-204
❑ 72ProStaP-17
❑ 72SevTraC-29
❑ 72Top-567
❑ 72Top-568
❑ 73OPC-480
❑ 73Top-480
❑ 74OPC-330
❑ 74Top-330
❑ 74TopTra-330T
❑ 78TCM60I-2
❑ 80PerHaloFP-183
❑ 80PerHaloFPS-48
❑ 80SSPHOF-182
❑ 81Gia196T-31
❑ 82DiaCla-70
❑ 82TCMGreP-9
❑ 83ASAJuaM-1
❑ 83ASAJuaM-2
❑ 83ASAJuaM-3
❑ 83ASAJuaM-4
❑ 83ASAJuaM-5
❑ 83ASAJuaM-6
❑ 83ASAJuaM-7
❑ 83ASAJuaM-8
❑ 83ASAJuaM-9
❑ 83ASAJuaM-10
❑ 83ASAJuaM-11
❑ 83ASAJuaM-12
❑ 83MLBPin-25
❑ 84GiaMot-3
❑ 85DomLeaS-1
❑ 85DomLeaS-2
❑ 85DomLeaS-3
❑ 85DomLeaS-4
❑ 85DomLeaS-5
❑ 85DomLeaS-6
❑ 85DomLeaS-7
❑ 85DomLeaS-8
❑ 85DomLeaS-9
❑ 86SpoDecG-46
❑ 86SpoDesJM-13
❑ 87K-M-6
❑ 88PacLegI-54
❑ 89DodSmoG-17
❑ 89PerCelP-29
❑ 90DodTar-482
❑ 90PerGreM-56
❑ 91FouBal-8
❑ 91TopGloA-22
❑ 92UppDecS-7
❑ 93ActPacA-124
❑ 93ActPacA2-58G
❑ 93UppDecS-7
❑ 93UppDecS-21
❑ 94TedWil-54
❑ 94TopSpa-L7
❑ 95TopLegot6M-9
❑ 97SpoIllCC-5
❑ 98SpoIllTaN-18
❑ 98SpoIllTaNEE-18
❑ 98SpoIllTaNGS-20

Marichal, Victor
❑ 75BurBeeT-15

Marie, Larry
❑ 90RicBra2ATI-16

Marietta, Lou
❑ 78CedRapGT-17
❑ 82WesHavAT-8

Marietta, Ron
❑ 98WatIndTI-18

Marifian, John
❑ 98MarPhiG-19

Marigny, Ron
❑ 87GleFalTP-11
❑ 87LakTigP-9
❑ 89LakTigS-15
❑ 90LakTigS-18
❑ 91LakTigC-20
❑ 91LakTigP-273

Marin, Jose
❑ 91ElmPioC-11
❑ 91ElmPioP-3278
❑ 92LynRedSC-4
❑ 92LynRedSF-2915

Marina, Juan
❑ 87ColMetP-18
❑ 88BlaYNPRWL-8
❑ 88ColMetGS-7
❑ 89St.LucMS-15

Marina, Vega
❑ 90St.LucMS-14

Marinaro, Bob
❑ 90PriWilCTI-4

Marine, Del
❑ 92BriTigC-16
❑ 92BriTigF-1415
❑ 93NiaFalRF-3393
❑ 94FayGenC-15
❑ 94FayGenF-2149
❑ 97JacSun-16
❑ 98TolMudHQ-23

Marine, Justin
❑ 95BilMusTI-25
❑ 96BilMusTI-19

Mariners, Bellingham
❑ 87BelMarTI-33

Mariners, Harwich
❑ 88CapCodPB-29

Mariners, Seattle
❑ 78Top-499
❑ 83FleSta-248
❑ 83FleSti-NNO
❑ 83FleSti-NNO
❑ 87SpoTeaL-25
❑ 87Top-156
❑ 87TopTif-156
❑ 88PanSti-466
❑ 88RedFolSB-122
❑ 90PubIntS-641
❑ 90RedFolSB-113
❑ 92UppDecS-22
❑ 94ImpProP-12
❑ 94Sco-328
❑ 94ScoGolR-328
❑ 95MarPac-4
❑ 95PacPriTL-12
❑ 95PanSti-148
❑ 96PanSti-227
❑ 97ColChoT-SM
❑ 99Vic-364

Marini, Marc
❑ 92ColRedC-10
❑ 92ColRedF-2406
❑ 93ClaGolF-16
❑ 93ExcFS7-160
❑ 93KinIndC-14
❑ 93KinIndF-2261
❑ 93KinIndTI-14
❑ 93SouAtlLAIPI-11
❑ 93SouAtlLAPI-23
❑ 94CanIndF-3131
❑ 95SigRoo-35
❑ 95SigRooSig-35
❑ 96ColCliB-18

Marino, Bob
❑ 92ForLauYC-25

Marino, Larry
❑ 98MicBatCM-22

Marino, Mark
❑ 86QuaCitAP-20
❑ 87PalSprP-30
❑ 89StoPorP-402
❑ 89StoPorS-28

Marion, Mark
❑ 89StoPorB-31

Marion, Marty
❑ 39ExhSal-39
❑ 41CarW75-16
❑ 46SeaSLP-39
❑ 46SpoExcW-5-1A
❑ 47Exh-147
❑ 47PM1StaP1-127
❑ 47TipTop-159
❑ 48BluTin-3
❑ 48Bow-40
❑ 49Bow-54
❑ 49EurSta-189
❑ 49Lea-97
❑ 50Bow-88
❑ 51Bow-34
❑ 52Bow-85
❑ 53BowC-52
❑ 60Fle-19
❑ 61Fle-58
❑ 61NuSco-473
❑ 66CarCoi-5
❑ 77TCMTheWY-26
❑ 79TCM50-99
❑ 82DiaCla-86
❑ 83Car194T-21
❑ 83CarGreT-4
❑ 83TCMPla1942-27
❑ 90BasWit-47
❑ 91TopArc1-302
❑ 92CarMcD-6
❑ 92ConTSN-626
❑ 93ActPacA-134

Maris, Roger
❑ 47Exh-148
❑ 47PM1StaP1-128
❑ 47PM1StaP1-129
❑ 47PM1StaP1-130
❑ 47StaPinP2-22
❑ 47StaPinP2-23
❑ 55DonWin-32
❑ 56A'sPos-32
❑ 57IndSoh-8
❑ 57IndTeal-13
❑ 58HarSta-18
❑ 58IndTeal-12
❑ 58Top-47
❑ 59Top-202
❑ 60KeyChal-32
❑ 60Top-377
❑ 60Top-565
❑ 60TopTat-32
❑ 60YanJayP-8
❑ 61Baz-5
❑ 61NuSco-416
❑ 61Pos-7A
❑ 61Pos-7B
❑ 61SevElev-25
❑ 61Top-2
❑ 61Top-44
❑ 61Top-478
❑ 61Top-576
❑ 61TopStal-197
❑ 61Yan61RL-3
❑ 61YanJayP-9
❑ 62AurRec-11
❑ 62BasPen-4
❑ 62Baz-14
❑ 62ExhStaB-24
❑ 62Gol-1
❑ 62Jel-6
❑ 62Pos-6A
❑ 62Pos-6B
❑ 62PosCan-6
❑ 62SalPlaC-23
❑ 62ShiPlaC-23
❑ 62Top-1
❑ 62Top-53
❑ 62Top-234
❑ 62Top-313
❑ 62Top-401
❑ 62TopBuc-55
❑ 62TopStal-89
❑ 62TopVen-1
❑ 62TopVen-53
❑ 62YanJayP-10
❑ 63BasMagM-55
❑ 63ExhStaB-42
❑ 63Jel-16
❑ 63Pos-16
❑ 63SalMetC-57
❑ 63Top-4
❑ 63Top-120
❑ 63Top-144
❑ 63YanJayP-8
❑ 64ChatheY-17
❑ 64Top-225
❑ 64Top-331
❑ 64TopVen-225
❑ 64TopVen-331
❑ 64YanJayP-8
❑ 65ChaTheY-14
❑ 65OldLonC-31
❑ 65OPC-155
❑ 65Top-155
❑ 66Top-365
❑ 66TopVen-365
❑ 66YanTeal-8
❑ 67OPC-45
❑ 67Top-45
❑ 67TopVen-328
❑ 68AtlOilPBCC-26
❑ 68Top-330
❑ 68TopVen-330
❑ 69OPC-164
❑ 69Top-164
❑ 72LauGreF-50
❑ 75OPC-198
❑ 75OPC-199
❑ 75Top-198
❑ 75Top-199
❑ 75TopMin-198
❑ 75TopMin-199
❑ 76GrePlaG-18
❑ 76LauDiaJ-30
❑ 76UPIS-8
❑ 77GalGloG-226
❑ 77Spo-716
❑ 78ReaRem-14
❑ 78TCM60I-11
❑ 79DiaGre-25
❑ 79TCM50-161
❑ 79Top-413
❑ 80MarExh-18
❑ 80PacLeg-101
❑ 81SanDieSC-15
❑ 81SanDieSC-16
❑ 81TCM60I-303
❑ 81TCM60I-382
❑ 81TCM60I-474
❑ 82ASAMicM-42
❑ 82BasCarN-5
❑ 82GSGalAG-16
❑ 82TCMGreS-2
❑ 83Yan196-1
❑ 83YanASFY-27
❑ 84OCoandSI-28
❑ 85GeoSteM-6
❑ 85TCMPhoC-22
❑ 85Woo-24
❑ 86SpoDesJM-5
❑ 86TCMSupS-9
❑ 86TCMSupS-32
❑ 86Top-405
❑ 86TopTif-405
❑ 87K-M-7
❑ 87Yan196T-8
❑ 88PacLegI-89
❑ 89CMCMan-6
❑ 89CMCMan-10
❑ 90AGFA-10
❑ 90HOFStiB-63
❑ 90YanMomPRP-11
❑ 91YanRinP12-1
❑ 92YanWIZ6-79
❑ 92YanWIZA-44
❑ 94TedWil-139
❑ 94TedWilM-M27
❑ 94TedWilRM-ES1
❑ 94TedWilRM-ES2
❑ 94TedWilRM-ES3
❑ 94TedWilRM-ES4
❑ 94TedWilRM-ES5
❑ 94TedWilRM-ES6
❑ 94TedWilRM-ES7
❑ 94TedWilRM-ES8
❑ 94TedWilRM-ES9
❑ 94UppDecTAE-67
❑ 94Yoo-9
❑ 96StaCluMa-MM12
❑ 97TopMan-36
❑ 97TopManF-36
❑ 97TopManFR-36
❑ 98TopGolLHRR-HR1
❑ 98TopGolLHRRB-HR1
❑ 98TopGolLHRRR-HR1

Markell, Duke
❑ 52Par-19

Markert, Jim
❑ 86PenWhiSP-16
❑ 88BirBarB-5

Markert, Josh
❑ 95YakBeaTI-18

Markham, Andy
❑ 94BurBeeC-15
❑ 94BurBeeF-1079
❑ 97FreKey-15

Markham, Bobby
❑ 80WesHavWCT-12

Markham, Dan
❑ 92GulCoaDF-3562
❑ 93GreFalDSP-3

Markiewicz, Brandon
❑ 91BoiHawC-18
❑ 91BoiHawP-3887
❑ 92QuaCitRBC-5
❑ 92QuaCitRBF-819
❑ 93CedRapKC-13
❑ 93CedRapKF-1747
❑ 94BoiHawC-18
❑ 94BoiHawF-3364
❑ 94LakElsSC-12
❑ 94LakElsSF-1672

Markland, Gene
❑ 50WorWidGV-37

Markle, Cliff
❑ 22E120-175
❑ 22W573-75

Markley, Scot
❑ 86AshTouP-18
❑ 87OscAstP-23

Markray, Thad
❑ 98BilMusTI-21
❑ 98ChaAllCM-19

Marks, John
❑ 82CliGiaF-28
❑ 83WisRapTF-26

Marks, Lance
❑ 91PulBraC-9
❑ 91PulBraP-4015
❑ 92MacBraC-3
❑ 92MacBraF-276
❑ 92ProFS7-193
❑ 93DurBulC-13
❑ 93DurBulF-493
❑ 93DurBulTI-23

Markulike, Joe
❑ 90IdaFalBP-3253

Markwell, Diegomar
❑ 97St.CatSB-21
❑ 98St.CatSM-17

Marlin, Billy the
❑ 93MarFloA-2
❑ 93MarPub-29
❑ 94MasMan-2
❑ 97MarPac-32

Marlina, Mario
❑ 89PalSprACLC-37

Marlins, Florida
❑ 92DonBonC-BC8
❑ 92HitTheBB-14
❑ 93TedWilPC-11
❑ 94BreCouMC-29B
❑ 94ElmPioC-29A
❑ 94ImpProP-19
❑ 94Sco-651
❑ 94ScoGolR-651
❑ 95PacPriTL-19
❑ 95PanSti-137
❑ 95UDAUnsBC-NNO
❑ 96PanSti-13
❑ 97ColChoT-FM
❑ 98PinInsC-22
❑ 98PinInsCG-22
❑ 98SpoIllFE-199
❑ 98SpoIllFE-199
❑ 99Vic-154

Marlowe, Dick
❑ 53TigGle-21
❑ 55Bow-91

Marn, Josh
❑ 98HudValR-16

Marn, Kevin
❑ 96BilMusTI-20
❑ 98ChaAllCM-22

Marnell, Dean
❑ 96PorRocB-22
❑ 97PorRocG-16
❑ 97SalAva-U9

Marone, Lou
❑ 70Top-703
❑ 71MLBOffS-206

Maropis, Pete
❑ 76AppFoxT-14

Maroth, Mike
❑ 99TeaBesR-54
❑ 99TeaBesRFS-5
❑ 99TeaBesRG-54
❑ 99TeaBesRS-54

Marotta, Chris
❑ 95StCatSTI-33

Marquard, Rube
(Richard)
❑ 08AmeCarE91-51
❑ 08IndPos-16
❑ 09AmeCarE90-1-73
❑ 09ColChiE-178
❑ 09MaxPubP-5
❑ 09SpoNewSM-72
❑ 09T206-225
❑ 09T206-226
❑ 09T206-227
❑ 10CouT21-41
❑ 10CouT21-175
❑ 10CouT21-176
❑ 10CouT21-177
❑ 10CouT21-178
❑ 10CouT21-299
❑ 10CouT21-300
❑ 10DomDisP-75
❑ 10PeoT21-36
❑ 10RedCroT-45
❑ 10RedCroT-46
❑ 10RedCroT-133
❑ 10RedCroT-216
❑ 10RedCroT-217
❑ 10SweCapPP-116
❑ 11HelSta-130
❑ 11L1L-111
❑ 11PloCanE-43
❑ 11S74Sil-87
❑ 11S81LarS-86
❑ 11T205-108
❑ 12ColRedB-178
❑ 12ColTinT-178
❑ 12HasTriFT-48F
❑ 12HasTriFT-74E
❑ 12PhiCarE-19
❑ 12T207-113
❑ 12T22SeroC-4
❑ 13LawSemC-6
❑ 13NatGamW-27
❑ 13TomBarW-26
❑ 14CraJacE-43
❑ 14FatPlaT-30
❑ 14PieStaT-67
❑ 14PolGroW-16
❑ 14TexTomE-57
❑ 15AmeCarE106-26
❑ 15CraJacE-43
❑ 15SpoNewM-110
❑ 15SpoNewP-6
❑ 16BF2FP-61
❑ 16FleBreD-61
❑ 16SpoNewM-113
❑ 17ColE13-108
❑ 22E120-129
❑ 22W572-60
❑ 22W575-75
❑ 22WilPatV-2
❑ 23W503-37
❑ 23WilChoV-88
❑ 26SpoComoA-29
❑ 68SCFOldT-2
❑ 70SpoCarfCOP-20
❑ 72LauGreF-14
❑ 76ShaPiz-124
❑ 77BobParHoF-64
❑ 77GalGloG-158
❑ 79DiaGre-26
❑ 80PerHaloFP-124
❑ 80SSPHOF-124
❑ 81ConTSN-45
❑ 82OhiHaloF-57
❑ 86ConSer1-27
❑ 89DodSmoG-19
❑ 89HOFStiB-66
❑ 90BasWit-91
❑ 90DodTar-483
❑ 90PerGreM-30
❑ 91ConTSN-252
❑ 92ConTSN-342
❑ 92ConTSNCI-6
❑ 93CraJac-9
❑ 94ConTSN-1015
❑ 94ConTSNB-1015
❑ 96PitPosH-9

Marquardt, Chuck
❑ 89GasRanP-1010
❑ 91ButCopKSP-28
❑ 93EriSaiC-30

Marquardt, John
❑ 84MadMusP-12
❑ 85HunStaJ-18
❑ 86OrlTwiP-11

Marquardt, Scott
❑ 93JohCitCC-13
❑ 93JohCitCF-3673

❑ 94SavCarC-17
❑ 94SavCarF-503
Marquess, Mark
❑ 88TopTra-65T
❑ 88TopTraT-65T
Marquez, Edgar
❑ 88MyrBeaBJP-1170
❑ 88St.CatBJP-2025
❑ 90St.CatBJP-3455
❑ 93LinVenB-117
Marquez, Edwin
❑ 86QuaCitAP-21
❑ 87MidAngP-12
❑ 88EdmTraC-19
❑ 88EdmTraP-575
❑ 89EdmTraC-13
❑ 89EdmTraP-552
❑ 90Bes-109
❑ 90CMC-62
❑ 90IndIndC-12
❑ 90IndIndP-301
❑ 90JacExpB-29
❑ 90ProAAAF-584
❑ 94VenLinU-96
❑ 95LinVen-235
❑ 96-97LinVen-200
Marquez, Gonzalo
❑ 73OPC-605
❑ 73Top-605
❑ 74OPC-422
❑ 74Top-422
❑ 76VenLeaS-91
❑ 80VenLeaS-98
Marquez, Ishovany
❑ 92BluOriC-6
❑ 92BluOriF-2358
❑ 92KanCouCC-23
❑ 92KanCouCF-89
Marquez, Isidrio
❑ 89SanAntMB-16
❑ 90SanAntMGS-17
❑ 91SanAntMP-2970
❑ 93SanAntMF-3000
❑ 94NasSouF-1248
❑ 95NasSouTI-13
Marquez, Jesus
❑ 93AppFoxCB-16
❑ 93AppFoxFI-2474
❑ 93LinVenB-197
❑ 94VenLinU-103
❑ 95LinVen-175
❑ 96-97LinVen-44
❑ 96LanJetB-17
❑ 97JacSun-17
❑ 98FarRedHM-17
Marquez, Luis
❑ 83Bra53F-29
Marquez, Robert
❑ 96DelShoB-21
❑ 98JupHamQ-8
Marquez, Ruben
❑ 98BriBluM-17
Marquis, Jason
❑ 97Bow-401
❑ 97BowChr-265
❑ 97BowChrI-265
❑ 97BowChrIR-265
❑ 97BowChrR-265
❑ 97BowInt-401
❑ 97MacBra-4
❑ 97SouAtlTPB-26
❑ 97Top-274
❑ 98Bow-157
❑ 98BowCerBlueAU-20
❑ 98BowCerGA-20
❑ 98BowCerSA-20
❑ 98BowChr-157
❑ 98BowChrGA-157
❑ 98BowChrGAR-157
❑ 98BowChrI-157
❑ 98BowChrIR-157
❑ 98BowChrR-157
❑ 98BowGolA-157
❑ 98BowInt-157
❑ 98CarLeaTPQ-6
❑ 98DanQ-C-3
❑ 98SP MinPE-20
❑ 98SPMin-20
❑ 98Top-486
❑ 98TopChr-486
❑ 98TopChrR-486
❑ 98TopDevR-486
❑ 98TopDia-486
❑ 98TopMiniC-486
❑ 99Bow-296
❑ 99BowAut-BA60
❑ 99BowGol-296
❑ 99BowInt-296
Marquis, Roger
❑ 91OriCro-276
Marr, Alan
❑ 83CliGiaF-18
❑ 85EveGiaC-8
Marr, Charles
❑ 87OldJudN-314
Marr, Jason
❑ 98JohCCTI-22
Marrero, Conrado
❑ 51Bow-206
❑ 52Top-317
❑ 53Bri-9
❑ 53Top-13
❑ 54Bow-200
❑ 67TopVen-188
❑ 83TopRep5-317
❑ 91TopArc1-13
Marrero, Eli
❑ 94SavCarC-18
❑ 94SavCarF-508
❑ 94SouAtlLAF-SAL50
❑ 95Bow-172
❑ 95Exc-269
❑ 96ArkTraB-17
❑ 96Bow-238
❑ 96BowFoi-238
❑ 96TexLeaAB-12
❑ 97Bes-25
❑ 97Bow-93
❑ 97Bow98ROY-ROY12
❑ 97BowBes-112
❑ 97BowBesAR-112
❑ 97BowBesMI-MI4
❑ 97BowBesMIAR-MI4
❑ 97BowBesMIARI-MI4
❑ 97BowBesMII-MI4
❑ 97BowBesMIR-MI4
❑ 97BowBesMIRI-MI4
❑ 97BowBesR-112
❑ 97BowCerBlaIA-CA51
❑ 97BowCerBluIA-CA51
❑ 97BowCerGolIA-CA51
❑ 97BowChr-117
❑ 97BowChr1RFR-ROY12
❑ 97BowChr98RF-ROY12
❑ 97BowChrI-117
❑ 97BowChrIR-117
❑ 97BowChrR-117
❑ 97BowInt-93
❑ 97ColCho-477
❑ 97FlaShoWotF-23
❑ 97Fle-559
❑ 97FleTif-559
❑ 97LouRedB-20
❑ 97Ult-549
❑ 97UltGolME-549
❑ 97UltPlaME-549
❑ 98Bow-132
❑ 98BowBes-108
❑ 98BowBesAR-108
❑ 98BowBesR-108
❑ 98BowCerBlueAU-19
❑ 98BowCerGA-19
❑ 98BowCerSA-19
❑ 98BowChr-132
❑ 98BowChrGA-132
❑ 98BowChrGAR-132
❑ 98BowChrI-132
❑ 98BowChrIR-132
❑ 98BowChrR-132
❑ 98BowGolA-132
❑ 98BowInt-132
❑ 98BowScoC-SC8
❑ 98CirThu-191
❑ 98CirThuRav-191
❑ 98CirThuSupRav-191
❑ 98ColCho-219
❑ 98Don-344
❑ 98DonColL-393
❑ 98DonColP-696
❑ 98DonGolPP-344
❑ 98DonPre-146
❑ 98DonPreGES-18
❑ 98DonPreGX-18
❑ 98DonPreGXDC-18
❑ 98DonPreSeat-146
❑ 98DonPriCL-393
❑ 98DonPriCP-696
❑ 98DonSigA-58
❑ 98DonSigAC-76
❑ 98DonSigAM-77
❑ 98DonSigSB-19
❑ 98DonSilPP-344
❑ 98FlaShoWotF-12
❑ 98Fle-120
❑ 98Lea-194
❑ 98LeaFraDA-194
❑ 98LeaFraF-194
❑ 98LeaFraM-194
❑ 98LeaFraM-194
❑ 98LeaFraMDC-194
❑ 98LeaFraMDC-194
❑ 98LeaFraMS-194
❑ 98LeaFraMZ2-194
❑ 98LeaRCrusUP-109
❑ 98LeaRS-236
❑ 98LeaRSCrusUG-109
❑ 98LeaRSCrusUR-109
❑ 98LeaRSLHolo-236
❑ 98LeaRSLong-236
❑ 98LeaRTrue-236
❑ 98PacInvGems-205
❑ 98PacOmeRS-19
❑ 98PacOmeRST1-19
❑ 98PacOnl-619
❑ 98PacOnlR-619
❑ 98PacOnlWC-619
❑ 98PinPer-124
❑ 98PinPerPP-124
❑ 98PinSna-SLC4
❑ 98ScoRT-237
❑ 98ScoRTSS-PP130
❑ 98ScoRTSSAP-PP130
❑ 98ScoRTSSAP1-PP130
❑ 98SkyDugA-92
❑ 98SkyDugAIA-92
❑ 98SpoIll-174
❑ 98SpoIllEE-174
❑ 98SpoIllFE-174
❑ 98SPxFin-29
❑ 98SPxFinR-29
❑ 98SPxFinS-29
❑ 98StaCluFDI-276
❑ 98StaCluI-276
❑ 98StaCluITW-W11
❑ 98StaCluOneK-276
❑ 98StaCluPP-276
❑ 98Stu-24
❑ 98StuGPP-24
❑ 98StuSPP-24
❑ 98Top-261
❑ 98TopChr-261
❑ 98TopChrR-261
❑ 98TopChrRC-R7
❑ 98TopChrRCRef-R7
❑ 98TopDevR-261
❑ 98TopDia-261
❑ 98TopMiniC-261
❑ 98TopRooCla-R7
❑ 98UD3-27
❑ 98UD3-117
❑ 98UD3-207
❑ 98UD3DieCut-27
❑ 98UD3DieCut-117
❑ 98UD3DieCut-207
❑ 98Ult-278
❑ 98UltGolM-278
❑ 98UltMas-278
❑ 98UltPlaM-278
❑ 98UppDec-256
❑ 98UppDecSF-138
❑ 99Bow-335
❑ 99BowAut-BA59
❑ 99BowGol-335
❑ 99BowInt-335
❑ 99Fle-174
❑ 99FleSta9-174
❑ 99FleWarT-174
❑ 99MetUni-40
❑ 99MetUniGM-40
❑ 99MetUniPMG-40
❑ 99Pac-356
❑ 99PacAur-155
❑ 99PacAurOD-155
❑ 99PacCroC-232
❑ 99PacCroCPB-232
❑ 99PacPar-193
❑ 99PacParC-193
❑ 99PacParG-193
❑ 99PacParHoloGold-193
❑ 99PacParHS-193
❑ 99PacParOD-193
❑ 99PacParPB-193
❑ 99PacParRed-193
❑ 99PacPlaB-356
❑ 99PacPri-120
❑ 99PacPriHB-120
❑ 99PacPriHG-120
❑ 99PacPriHM-120
❑ 99PacPriHP-120
❑ 99PacPriRed-120
❑ 99PacRed-356
❑ 99Rev-116
❑ 99RevPremDate-116
❑ 99RevRet-116
❑ 99RevShaSS-116
❑ 99SkyMolM-53
❑ 99SkyMolMX-53
❑ 99SkyPre-59
❑ 99SkyPreA-38
❑ 99SkyPreABlue-38
❑ 99SkyPreR-59
❑ 99SkyThu-118
❑ 99SkyThuRant-118
❑ 99SkyThuRave-118
❑ 99SP Aut-80
❑ 99SP SigAuto-ELI
❑ 99SPSig-142
❑ 99StaClu-23
❑ 99StaCluC-CS5
❑ 99StaCluC-CS12
❑ 99StaCluC-CS18
❑ 99StaCluC-CS21
❑ 99StaCluFDI-23
❑ 99StaCluOoaK-23
❑ 99StaCluPP-23
❑ 99ThuSkySupR-118
❑ 99Top-358
❑ 99TopChr-358
❑ 99TopChrR-358
❑ 99TopMVPP-358
❑ 99UD Cho-132
❑ 99UD ChoP-132
❑ 99UD ChoPCR-132
❑ 99Ult-45
❑ 99UltGolM-45
❑ 99UltMas-45
❑ 99UltPlaM-45
❑ 99UppDec-184
❑ 99UppDecEL1-184
❑ 99UppDecEL2-184
❑ 99UppDecM-174
❑ 99UppDecMGS-174
❑ 99UppDecMHFS-174
❑ 99UppDecMSS-174
❑ 99Vic-329
Marrero, Kenny
❑ 91EriSaiC-8
❑ 91EriSaiP-4073
❑ 92BriTigC-17
❑ 92BriTigF-1416
❑ 93NiaFalRF-3394
❑ 94JamJamC-14
❑ 94JamJamF-3960
❑ 96LakTigB-17
❑ 97JacSun-18
❑ 98TusSidM-12
Marrero, Oreste
❑ 88BlaYNPRWL-41
❑ 89BelBreIS-15
❑ 89Sta-5
❑ 90BelBreB-18
❑ 90BelBreS-12
❑ 90Bes-292
❑ 91Cla/Bes-194
❑ 91StoPorC-6
❑ 91StoPorP-3040
❑ 92ElPasDS-218
❑ 92SkyAA F-95
❑ 92StoPorF-41
❑ 93HarSenF-276
❑ 94OttLynF-2904
❑ 94Pac-385
❑ 95SanAntMTI-28
❑ 97AlbDukGS-19
❑ 97Pac-333
❑ 97PacLigB-333
❑ 97PacSil-333
Marrero, Roger
❑ 89AubAstP-2181
Marrero, Vilato
❑ 88BlaYNPRWL-42
❑ 89BelBre2S-20
❑ 89BelBreIS-16
❑ 90BelBreB-12
❑ 90BelBreS-13
❑ 90Bes-172
❑ 91StoPorC-21
❑ 91StoPorP-3041
Marrett, Scott
❑ 86PalSprAP-21
❑ 86PalSprAS-13
❑ 87SanBerSP-15
Marriot, Michael
❑ 98KanCouC-20
❑ 98KanCouCCP-20
Marriott, Bill
❑ 22Zee-34
❑ 23Zee-51
❑ 90DodTar-484
Marris, Moose (Mark)
❑ 87OneYanP-26
❑ 88PriWilYS-16
❑ 89PriWilCS-12
❑ 91Ft.LauYC-7
❑ 91Ft.LauYP-2421
Marrow, Buck
❑ 34DiaMatCSB-125
❑ 90DodTar-485
Marrs, Terry
❑ 87ElmPioBC-10
❑ 87ElmPioRC-10
❑ 88ElmPioC-22
❑ 89WinHavRSS-14
Marsans, Armando
❑ 12T207-114
❑ 14CraJacE-134
❑ 14TexTomE-29
❑ 15CraJacE-134
❑ 15SpoNewM-111
❑ 17ColE13-109
❑ 95ConTSN-1379
Marsh, Frank
❑ 93NegLeaRL2-24
Marsh, Freddie (Fred)
❑ 49SolSunP-7
❑ 52Top-8
❑ 53Top-240
❑ 54Top-218
❑ 55OriEss-14
❑ 55Top-13
❑ 55TopDouH-39
❑ 56BalOriP-27
❑ 56Top-23
❑ 83TopRep5-8
❑ 91OriCro-277
❑ 91TopArc1-240
❑ 94TopArc1-218
❑ 94TopArc1G-218
❑ 97BalOriP-31
Marsh, Mary Ann
❑ 98JohCCTI-23
Marsh, Quinn
❑ 88GreHorP-1552
❑ 89CedRapRB-4
❑ 89CedRapRP-929
❑ 89CedRapRS-10
❑ 90SalSpuCLC-124
❑ 90SalSpuP-2721
Marsh, Randy
❑ 88T/MUmp-43
❑ 89T/MUmp-41
❑ 89T/MUmp-60
❑ 90T/MUmp-39
Marsh, Roy
❑ 94AubAstC-7
❑ 94AubAstF-3770
❑ 94StaCluDP-66
❑ 94StaCluDPFDI-66
❑ 97SarRedS-14
Marsh, Tom
❑ 88BatCliP-1676
❑ 89SpaPhiP-1047
❑ 89SpaPhiS-15
❑ 90ReaPhiB-23
❑ 90ReaPhiP-1233
❑ 90ReaPhiS-18
❑ 90SpaPhiB-28
❑ 90SpaPhiP-2495
❑ 90SpaPhiS-15
❑ 91LinDriAA-514
❑ 91ReaPhiLD-514
❑ 91ReaPhiP-1383
❑ 92DonRoo-66
❑ 92PhiMed-43
❑ 92ScrRedBS-488
❑ 93Fle-494
❑ 93Pin-256
❑ 93Sco-263
❑ 93ScrRedBF-2556
❑ 93ScrRedBTI-17
❑ 93StaClu-466
❑ 93StaCluFDI-466
❑ 93StaCluMOP-466
❑ 93Top-649
❑ 93TopGol-649
❑ 93TopInaM-649
❑ 93TopInaR-649
❑ 93TopMic-649
❑ 94ScoRoo-RT147
❑ 94ScoRooGR-RT147
❑ 94Ult-552
❑ 95Pac-333
❑ 95PacPri-110
❑ 95ScrRedBTI-20
❑ 96BufBisB-15
❑ 96Fle-503
❑ 96FleTif-503
❑ 96Pac-156
❑ 98ScrRedB1ATI-11
Marsh, Trent
❑ 89StoPorS-26
Marshall, Bret
❑ 89SouBenWSGS-13
Marshall, Charlie
❑ 50WorWidGV-35
Marshall, Clarence
❑ 43CenFlo-18
❑ 52NatTeaL-17
❑ 52Top-174
❑ 83TopRep5-174
Marshall, Dave
❑ 69Top-464A
❑ 69Top-464B
❑ 70OPC-58
❑ 70Top-58
❑ 71MetTeal-13
❑ 71MLBOffS-159
❑ 71OPC-259
❑ 71Top-259
❑ 72MilBra-205
❑ 72Top-673
❑ 73OPC-513
❑ 73PadDea-16
❑ 73Top-513
❑ 77PadSchC-36
❑ 91MetWIZ-247
Marshall, Doc (William R.)
❑ 09T206-228
❑ 10CouT21-42
❑ 11SpoLifCW-234
Marshall, Gary
❑ 96RocCubTI-18
Marshall, George
❑ 48BabRutS-12
Marshall, Jason
❑ 92EugEmeC-17
❑ 92EugEmeF-3036
❑ 93LetMouF-4152
❑ 93LetMouSP-12
❑ 93WilBluRC-18
❑ 93WilBluRF-2006
❑ 94WilBluRF-306
❑ 95WicWraTI-6
Marshall, Jim (R. James)
❑ 52MotCoo-9
❑ 56BalOriP-33
❑ 58Top-441
❑ 59Top-153
❑ 59TopVen-153
❑ 60Top-267
❑ 61Top-188
❑ 62Top-337
❑ 73WicAerJPKB-9
❑ 74OPC-354
❑ 74Top-354
❑ 75OakOak2A-21
❑ 75OPC-638
❑ 75Top-638
❑ 75TopMin-638
❑ 76OPC-277
❑ 76SSP-308
❑ 76Top-277
❑ 80Top-96
❑ 84NasSouTI-13
❑ 86BufBisP-17
❑ 91MetWIZ-248
❑ 91OriCro-278
❑ 91PacSenL-54
❑ 91PacSenL-127
❑ 91PacSenL-133
Marshall, John
❑ 88MarPhiS-26
❑ 89SanDieSAS-16
❑ 89SpaPhiP-1045
❑ 89SpaPhiS-16
❑ 89Sta-56
Marshall, Keith
❑ 75OmaRoyTI-10
❑ 76IndIndTI-19
Marshall, Lee
❑ 98ForWayW!-20
Marshall, Max
❑ 40SolHug-13
❑ 47SmiClo-22

Marshall, Mike A.
❑ 79LodDodT-6
❑ 81AlbDukTc-16
❑ 82AlbDukTc-22
❑ 82DodUniOV-11
❑ 82Don-562
❑ 82Fle-13
❑ 82Top-681
❑ 83DodPol-5
❑ 83DodPos-8
❑ 83Don-362
❑ 83Fle-211
❑ 83OPC-324
❑ 83Top-324
❑ 84AllGamPI-58
❑ 84DodPol-5
❑ 84Don-348
❑ 84Fle-105
❑ 84FunFooP-64
❑ 84Nes792-634
❑ 84OPC-52
❑ 84Top-634
❑ 84TopSti-85
❑ 84TopTif-634
❑ 85AllGamPI-148
❑ 85DodCokP-20
❑ 85Don-12
❑ 85Don-296
❑ 85DonActA-22
❑ 85DonSupD-12
❑ 85Fle-377
❑ 85Lea-12
❑ 85OPC-85
❑ 85Top-85
❑ 85TopSti-72
❑ 85TopTif-85
❑ 86BasStaB-69
❑ 86DodCokP-18
❑ 86DodPol-5
❑ 86DodUniOP-13
❑ 86Don-52
❑ 86Dra-8
❑ 86Fle-137
❑ 86FleMin-30
❑ 86FleStiC-71
❑ 86Lea-40
❑ 86OPC-26
❑ 86SevCoi-W11
❑ 86Spo-89
❑ 86Top-728
❑ 86TopSti-71
❑ 86TopTat-17
❑ 86TopTif-728
❑ 87DodMot-5
❑ 87DodPol-3
❑ 87DodSmoA-21
❑ 87Don-176
❑ 87DonOpeD-77
❑ 87Fle-446
❑ 87FleGlo-446
❑ 87FleLimE-25
❑ 87OPC-186
❑ 87RedFolSB-31
❑ 87SevCoi-W8
❑ 87Spo-82
❑ 87SpoTeaP-14
❑ 87StuPan-6
❑ 87Top-664
❑ 87TopSti-66
❑ 87TopTif-664
❑ 88DodMot-5
❑ 88DodPol-5
❑ 88DodSmo-16
❑ 88DodSmo-29
❑ 88Don-229
❑ 88DonBasB-178
❑ 88Fle-522
❑ 88FleGlo-522
❑ 88OPC-249
❑ 88PanSti-315
❑ 88Sco-135
❑ 88ScoGlo-135
❑ 88Spo-220
❑ 88StaLinD-11
❑ 88Top-249
❑ 88TopBig-133
❑ 88TopSti-69
❑ 88TopTif-249
❑ 89Bow-350
❑ 89BowTif-350
❑ 89DodMot-5
❑ 89DodPol-4
❑ 89DodSmoG-101
❑ 89DodStaSV-4
❑ 89Don-110
❑ 89Don-552
❑ 89DonBasB-204
❑ 89DonGraS-2
❑ 89Fle-66
❑ 89FleBasM-25
❑ 89FleGlo-66
❑ 89FleGlo-WS7
❑ 89FleWorS-7
❑ 89OPC-323
❑ 89PanSti-108
❑ 89Sco-186
❑ 89Spo-54
❑ 89Top-582
❑ 89TopBasT-138
❑ 89TopBig-48
❑ 89TopCoi-18
❑ 89TopSti-67
❑ 89TopTif-582
❑ 89TopUKM-48
❑ 89TVSpoM-35
❑ 89UppDec-70
❑ 89Woo-26
❑ 90Bow-132
❑ 90BowTif-132
❑ 90ClaYel-T57
❑ 90DodTar-486
❑ 90Don-84
❑ 90Fle-401
❑ 90FleCan-401
❑ 90Lea-224
❑ 90MetColP-19
❑ 90MetKah-6
❑ 90OPC-198
❑ 90PanSti-272
❑ 90PubIntS-13
❑ 90Sco-384
❑ 90Top-198
❑ 90TopSti-62
❑ 90TopTif-198
❑ 90TopTra-67T
❑ 90TopTraT-67T
❑ 90TopTVM-27
❑ 90UppDec-262
❑ 90UppDec-781
❑ 91Don-625
❑ 91Fle-102
❑ 91MetWIZ-249
❑ 91OPC-356
❑ 91Sco-617
❑ 91StaClu-226
❑ 91Top-356
❑ 91TopDesS-356
❑ 91TopMic-356
❑ 91TopTif-356
❑ 91Ult-35
❑ 91UppDec-681
❑ 92DodStaTA-23

Marshall, Mike G.
❑ 68CokCapT-3
❑ 68Top-201
❑ 68TopVen-201
❑ 69OPC-17
❑ 69PilPos-29
❑ 69Top-17
❑ 71ExpPS-13
❑ 71MLBOffS-133
❑ 71OPC-713
❑ 71Top-713
❑ 72Dia-28
❑ 72OPC-505
❑ 72Top-505
❑ 73OPC-355
❑ 73SevTraC-42
❑ 73Top-355
❑ 73TopCanL-30
❑ 74OPC-73
❑ 74OPC-208
❑ 74Top-73
❑ 74Top-208
❑ 74TopSta-57
❑ 74TopTra-73T
❑ 75Kel-36
❑ 75OPC-6
❑ 75OPC-313
❑ 75OPC-330
❑ 75Top-6
❑ 75Top-313
❑ 75Top-330
❑ 75TopMin-6
❑ 75TopMin-313
❑ 75TopMin-330
❑ 76DodPos-10
❑ 76LinSup-122
❑ 76OPC-465
❑ 76Top-465
❑ 77PilPosR-29
❑ 77Spo-4103
❑ 77Top-263
❑ 79TwiFriP-16
❑ 80TwiPos-18
❑ 82Fle-532
❑ 83Pil69G-6
❑ 86ExpGreT-11
❑ 87AstShowSTh-12
❑ 87DodSmoA-20
❑ 89DodSmoG-84
❑ 90DodTar-487
❑ 90HOFStiB-79
❑ 91MetWIZ-246
❑ 92DodStaTA-13
❑ 93ExpDonM-25
❑ 93RanKee-244

Marshall, Monte
❑ 96GreFalDTI-24
❑ 97GreFalDTI-17
❑ 97VerBeaD-14
❑ 98SanBerS-18

Marshall, Randy
❑ 89ButCopKSP-20
❑ 89FayGenP-1581
❑ 90FayGenP-2404
❑ 90GasRanB-18
❑ 90GasRanP-2528
❑ 90GasRanS-13
❑ 90ProAaA-83
❑ 91GasRanC-19
❑ 91GasRanP-2696
❑ 91LinDriAA-391
❑ 91LonTigLD-391
❑ 91LonTigP-1876
❑ 92TidTidF-892
❑ 92TidTidS-562
❑ 92TriA AAS-562
❑ 94ColSprSSF-729
❑ 95TolMudHTI-19
❑ 96TolMudHB-17

Marshall, Steve
❑ 89CarNewE-2

Marshall, Todd
❑ 92SpoIndC-6
❑ 92SpoIndF-1290

Marshall, Willard
❑ 47Exh-149
❑ 47HomBon-33
❑ 47TipTop-130
❑ 48Bow-13
❑ 48GiaTeal-15
❑ 49Bow-48
❑ 49EurSta-118
❑ 49GiaTeal-19
❑ 50Bow-73
❑ 50Dra-17
❑ 50JJKCopP-9
❑ 50RoyDes-17
❑ 51Bow-98
❑ 51R42SmaS-65
❑ 52Bow-97
❑ 52Top-96
❑ 53BowC-58
❑ 53Top-95
❑ 54Bow-70
❑ 55Bow-131
❑ 75JohMiz-1
❑ 76TayBow4-107
❑ 79DiaGre-43
❑ 79TCM50-124
❑ 83TCMPla1942-33
❑ 83TopRep5-96
❑ 84FifNatC-8
❑ 91TopArc1-95

Marsland, David
❑ 93MisStaB-32

Marsonek, Sam
❑ 97AppLeaTPB-9
❑ 97Bow-305
❑ 97BowInt-305
❑ 98BesAutSS-31
❑ 98SavSanGM-19
❑ 99SP TopP-79
❑ 99SP TopPPE-79

Marsters, Brandon
❑ 96BatCliTI-6
❑ 97PieBolWB-17
❑ 98ClePhiM-14
❑ 98ClePhiUM-14

Marte, Alexis
❑ 83KinBluJTI-14
❑ 84VisOakT-4
❑ 85DomLeaS-174
❑ 85OrlTwiT-7
❑ 86TolMudHP-16
❑ 87PorBeaP-17
❑ 89TulDriTI-14

Marte, Damaso
❑ 95EveAqaTI-12
❑ 96WisTimRB-14
❑ 97CalLeaTP-11
❑ 97LanJet-15
❑ 99Bow-181
❑ 99BowChr-181
❑ 99BowChrG-181
❑ 99BowChrGR-181
❑ 99BowChrI-181
❑ 99BowChrIR-181
❑ 99BowChrR-181
❑ 99BowGol-181
❑ 99BowInt-181

Marte, Pedro
❑ 93WatIndC-17
❑ 93WatIndF-3577
❑ 94ColRedF-456

Marte, Roberto
❑ 86EriCarP-18
❑ 87EriCarP-10
❑ 88SavCarP-341
❑ 89SprCarB-21
❑ 91EriSaiC-26
❑ 91EriSaiP-4086

Marte, Vic
❑ 78ChaPirT-15

Martel, Ed
❑ 87OneYanP-30
❑ 88OneYanP-2040
❑ 89Ft.LauYS-15
❑ 90PriWilCTI-14
❑ 91AlbYanLD-11
❑ 91AlbYanP-1004
❑ 91LinDriAA-11
❑ 92Bow-607
❑ 92ColCliF-347
❑ 92ColCliP-6
❑ 92ColCliS-109
❑ 92DonRoo-67
❑ 92LeaGolR-BC14
❑ 92ProFS7-112
❑ 92SkyAAAF-49

Martel, Jay
❑ 87SavCarP-7

Marten, Greg
❑ 93Sou-2

Marten, Tom
❑ 88KenTwiP-1405

Marteniz, Ivan
❑ 88WytCubP-1995

Martes, Sixto
❑ 84EveGiaC-14

Martig, Rich
❑ 86ModA'sC-14
❑ 86ModA'sP-19

Martin, Al
❑ 86SumBraP-17
❑ 87SumBraP-24
❑ 88BurBraP-19
❑ 88MidLeaAGS-19
❑ 89DurBullS-15
❑ 89DurBullS-15
❑ 89DurBulTI-15
❑ 90Bes-220
❑ 90GreBraB-17
❑ 90GreBraP-1141
❑ 90TopMag-102
❑ 91GreBraC-23
❑ 91GreBraLD-211
❑ 91GreBraP-3015
❑ 91LinDriAA-211
❑ 91RicBraBC-27
❑ 92BufBisBS-11
❑ 92BufBisF-333
❑ 92BufBisS-35
❑ 92DonRoo-68
❑ 92FleUpd-114
❑ 93Bow-246
❑ 93DiaMar-67
❑ 93Don-716
❑ 93Fin-155
❑ 93FinRef-155
❑ 93Fla-114
❑ 93FleFinE-113
❑ 93Lea-189
❑ 93OPCPre-57
❑ 93PacSpa-587
❑ 93Pin-614
❑ 93PirHil-6
❑ 93PirNatl-15
❑ 93Sco-322
❑ 93ScoBoyoS-27
❑ 93SelRoo-47T
❑ 93StaClu-579
❑ 93StaCluFDI-579
❑ 93StaCluMOP-579
❑ 93Stu-159
❑ 93Top-623
❑ 93TopGol-623
❑ 93TopInaM-623
❑ 93TopInaR-623
❑ 93TopMic-623
❑ 93TriPla-242
❑ 93Ult-451
❑ 93UltAllR-5
❑ 93UppDec-340
❑ 93UppDecGold-340
❑ 94Bow-330
❑ 94ColC-187
❑ 94ColChoGS-187
❑ 94ColChoSS-187
❑ 94Don-494
❑ 94Fin-11
❑ 94FinJum-11
❑ 94FinRef-11
❑ 94Fla-217
❑ 94Fle-612
❑ 94FleExtB-348
❑ 94FleExtBSYS-11
❑ 94FleRooS-11
❑ 94FUnPac-76
❑ 94Lea-49
❑ 94LeaL-141
❑ 94OPC-241
❑ 94Pac-500
❑ 94Pin-211
❑ 94PinArtP-211
❑ 94PinMusC-211
❑ 94PirQui-13
❑ 94Sco-546
❑ 94ScoGolR-546
❑ 94Sel-50
❑ 94StaClu-6
❑ 94StaCluFDI-6
❑ 94StaCluGR-6
❑ 94StaCluMOP-6
❑ 94StaCluP-6
❑ 94Stu-147
❑ 94Top-366
❑ 94TopGol-366
❑ 94TopSpa-366
❑ 94TriPla-186
❑ 94Ult-257
❑ 94UppDec-243
❑ 94UppDecED-243
❑ 94USPlaCR-5H
❑ 94USPlaCR-7D
❑ 94USPlaCR-11C
❑ 95ColCho-381
❑ 95ColChoGS-381
❑ 95ColChoSS-381
❑ 95Don-147
❑ 95DonDiaK-DK26
❑ 95DonPreP-147
❑ 95DonTopotO-319
❑ 95Emo-176
❑ 95Fla-187
❑ 95Fle-483
❑ 95Lea-364
❑ 95LeaLim-135
❑ 95Pac-347
❑ 95Pin-275
❑ 95PinArtP-275
❑ 95PinMusC-275
❑ 95PirFil-19
❑ 95RedFol-30
❑ 95Sco-380
❑ 95ScoGolR-380
❑ 95ScoPlaTS-380
❑ 95Sel-3
❑ 95SelArtP-3
❑ 95StaClu-218
❑ 95StaClu-253
❑ 95StaCluFDI-218
❑ 95StaCluFDI-253
❑ 95StaCluMOP-218
❑ 95StaCluMOP-253
❑ 95StaCluSTWS-218
❑ 95StaCluSTWS-253
❑ 95Stu-163
❑ 95Top-51
❑ 95Ult-424
❑ 95UltGolM-424
❑ 95UppDec-383
❑ 95UppDecED-383
❑ 95UppDecEDG-383
❑ 95UppDecSE-219
❑ 95UppDecSEG-219
❑ 96Cir-174
❑ 96CirRav-174
❑ 96ColCho-682
❑ 96ColChoGS-682
❑ 96ColChoSS-682
❑ 96Don-127
❑ 96DonPreP-127
❑ 96EmoXL-257
❑ 96Fla-350
❑ 96Fle-526
❑ 96FleTif-526
❑ 96Lea-201
❑ 96LeaPrePB-201
❑ 96LeaPrePG-201
❑ 96LeaPrePS-201
❑ 96LeaSig-131
❑ 96LeaSigA-143
❑ 96LeaSigAG-143
❑ 96LeaSigAS-143
❑ 96LeaSigPPG-131
❑ 96LeaSigPPP-131
❑ 96MetUni-217
❑ 96MetUniP-217
❑ 96Pac-180
❑ 96PanSti-71
❑ 96ProSta-94
❑ 96Sco-123
❑ 96StaClu-26
❑ 96StaCluMOP-26
❑ 96Stu-94
❑ 96StuPrePB-94
❑ 96StuPrePG-94
❑ 96StuPrePS-94
❑ 96TeaOut-54
❑ 96Top-53
❑ 96Ult-266
❑ 96UltGolM-266
❑ 96UppDec-434
❑ 97Bow-30
❑ 97BowBes-36
❑ 97BowBesAR-36
❑ 97BowBesR-36
❑ 97BowChr-26
❑ 97BowChrI-26
❑ 97BowChrIR-26
❑ 97BowChrR-26
❑ 97BowInt-30
❑ 97Cir-354
❑ 97CirRav-354
❑ 97ColCho-435
❑ 97Don-211
❑ 97DonGolPP-211
❑ 97DonLim-166
❑ 97DonLim-192
❑ 97DonLimE-166
❑ 97DonLimE-192
❑ 97DonLimENG-166
❑ 97DonPre-70
❑ 97DonPreCttC-70
❑ 97DonSig-66
❑ 97DonSigPPP-66
❑ 97DonSilPP-211
❑ 97DurBulATI-10
❑ 97Fin-6
❑ 97FinRef-6
❑ 97FlaShoLC-93
❑ 97FlaShoLeg0-93
❑ 97FlaShoLeg1-93
❑ 97FlaShoM-A93
❑ 97FlaShoM-B93
❑ 97FlaShoM-C93
❑ 97FlaShoR0-93
❑ 97FlaShoR1-93
❑ 97FlaShoR2-93
❑ 97Fle-432
❑ 97FleTif-432
❑ 97KinB-24
❑ 97Lea-134
❑ 97LeaFraM-134
❑ 97LeaFraMDC-134
❑ 97MetUni-240
❑ 97Pac-399
❑ 97PacLigB-399
❑ 97PacPri-136
❑ 97PacPriLB-136
❑ 97PacPriP-136
❑ 97PacSil-399
❑ 97PinX-P-86
❑ 97PinX-PMoS-86
❑ 97PirPos-24
❑ 97Sco-282
❑ 97ScoArtPWB-282
❑ 97ScoPreS-282
❑ 97ScoShoS-282
❑ 97ScoShoSAP-282
❑ 97SP-142
❑ 97SpoIll-106
❑ 97SpoIllEE-106
❑ 97StaClu-316

❑ 97StaCluMOP-316
❑ 97Stu-90
❑ 97StuPrePG-90
❑ 97StuPrePS-90
❑ 97Top-356
❑ 97TopChr-121
❑ 97TopChrR-121
❑ 97TopGal-129
❑ 97TopGalPPI-129
❑ 97Ult-264
❑ 97UltGolME-264
❑ 97UltPlaME-264
❑ 97UppDec-460
❑ 98Bow-258
❑ 98BowChr-258
❑ 98BowChrGA-258
❑ 98BowChrGAR-258
❑ 98BowChrI-258
❑ 98BowChrIR-258
❑ 98BowChrR-258
❑ 98BowGolA-258
❑ 98BowInt-258
❑ 98CirThu-217
❑ 98CirThuRav-217
❑ 98CirThuSupRav-217
❑ 98ColCho-469
❑ 98ColChoER-ER22
❑ 98Don-121
❑ 98DonCol-121
❑ 98DonColL-400
❑ 98DonColP-646
❑ 98DonColS-121
❑ 98DonGolPP-121
❑ 98DonPre-96
❑ 98DonPreSeat-96
❑ 98DonPriCD-121
❑ 98DonPriCL-400
❑ 98DonPriCP-646
❑ 98DonSigA-59
❑ 98DonSigAC-77
❑ 98DonSigAM-78
❑ 98DonSilPP-121
❑ 98E-X2-50
❑ 98E-X2ECFut-50
❑ 98E-X2ECNow-50
❑ 98Fin-234
❑ 98FinNo--234
❑ 98FinNo-R-234
❑ 98FinRef-234
❑ 98FlaShoLeg0-71
❑ 98FlaShoLeg1-71
❑ 98FlaShoLeg2-71
❑ 98FlaShoLeg3-71
❑ 98FlaShoLegM-71
❑ 98FlaShoR0-71
❑ 98FlaShoR1-71
❑ 98FlaShoR2-71
❑ 98FlaShoR3-71
❑ 98Fle-507
❑ 98FleVin'-114
❑ 98FleVin'C-114
❑ 98KinDis-18
❑ 98Lea-201
❑ 98LeaFraDA-201
❑ 98LeaFraF-201
❑ 98LeaFraM-201
❑ 98LeaFraM-201
❑ 98LeaFraMDC-201
❑ 98LeaFraMDC-201
❑ 98LeaFraMS-201
❑ 98LeaFraMZ2-201
❑ 98MetUni-162
❑ 98MetUniPMG-162
❑ 98Pac-399
❑ 98PacAur-177
❑ 98PacInv-130
❑ 98PacInvPBlue-130
❑ 98PacInvSilv-130
❑ 98PacInvTeam-22
❑ 98PacOme-191
❑ 98PacOmeR-191
❑ 98PacOnl-588
❑ 98PacOnlR-588
❑ 98PacOnlWC-588
❑ 98PacPar-222
❑ 98PacParC-222
❑ 98PacParG-222
❑ 98PacParHS-222
❑ 98PacParPB-222
❑ 98PacParR-222
❑ 98PacPlaB-399
❑ 98PacRedT-399
❑ 98PacSil-399
❑ 98PacTeaC-25
❑ 98PinPer-85
❑ 98PinPerPP-85
❑ 98PinPlu-152
❑ 98Revo-114
❑ 98RevoSS-114
❑ 98ScoRT-119
❑ 98ScoRTSS-PP75
❑ 98ScoRTSSAP-PP75
❑ 98ScoRTSSAP1-PP75
❑ 98SkyDugA-38
❑ 98SkyDugAIA-38
❑ 98SpoIll-83
❑ 98SpoIllEE-83
❑ 98SpoIllFE-83
❑ 98SpoIllTaN-108
❑ 98SpoIllTaNEE-108
❑ 98SpoIllWSF-76
❑ 98SpoIllWSFEE-76
❑ 98SpoIllWSFFE-76
❑ 98SPxFin-309
❑ 98SPxFinR-309
❑ 98SPxFinS-309
❑ 98StaCluFDI-132
❑ 98StaCluI-132
❑ 98StaCluOneK-132
❑ 98StaCluPP-132
❑ 98Stu-54
❑ 98StuGPP-54
❑ 98StuSPP-54
❑ 98Top-311
❑ 98TopChr-311
❑ 98TopChrR-311
❑ 98TopDevR-311
❑ 98TopDia-311
❑ 98TopGal-49
❑ 98TopGalGP-49
❑ 98TopGalOPP-49
❑ 98TopGalPPI-49
❑ 98TopGalPPIA-49
❑ 98TopMiniC-311
❑ 98TopOpeD-137
❑ 98Ult-174
❑ 98UltGolM-174
❑ 98UltMas-174
❑ 98UltPlaM-174
❑ 98UppDec-486
❑ 99Fle-460
❑ 99FleSta9-460
❑ 99FleWarT-460
❑ 99KinDis-17
❑ 99MetUni-151
❑ 99MetUniGM-151
❑ 99MetUniPMG-151
❑ 99Pac-342
❑ 99PacCroC-222
❑ 99PacCroCPB-222
❑ 99PacOme-188
❑ 99PacOmeC-188
❑ 99PacOmeG-188
❑ 99PacOmePB-188
❑ 99PacPar-187
❑ 99PacParC-187
❑ 99PacParG-187
❑ 99PacParHoloGold-187
❑ 99PacParHS-187
❑ 99PacParOD-187
❑ 99PacParPB-187
❑ 99PacParRed-187
❑ 99PacPlaB-342
❑ 99PacPri-114
❑ 99PacPriHB-114
❑ 99PacPriHG-114
❑ 99PacPriHM-114
❑ 99PacPriHP-114
❑ 99PacPriRed-114
❑ 99PacRed-342
❑ 99StaClu-269
❑ 99StaCluFDI-269
❑ 99StaCluOoaK-269
❑ 99StaCluPP-269
❑ 99Top-287
❑ 99TopChr-287
❑ 99TopChrR-287
❑ 99TopMVPP-287
❑ 99UppDec-178
❑ 99UppDecEL1-178
❑ 99UppDecEL2-178

Martin, Andy (Andrew)
❑ 92HamRedC-11
❑ 92HamRedF-1601
❑ 94MadHatC-14
❑ 94MadHatF-142

Martin, Ariel
❑ 93HunCubC-18
❑ 93HunCubF-3242

Martin, Babe (Boris)
❑ 49Bow-167
❑ 96Bro194F-21

Martin, Bill
❑ 97PinFan-PC2

Martin, Billy (Alfred)
❑ 47StaPinP2-24
❑ 48SigOil-17
❑ 48SmiClo-17
❑ 49RemBre-17
❑ 52BerRos-38
❑ 52Top-175
❑ 53BowC-93
❑ 53BowC-118
❑ 53Dor-130
❑ 53Top-86
❑ 54Bow-145
❑ 54RedHeaF-19
❑ 54Top-13
❑ 56Top-181
❑ 56YanJayP-9
❑ 56YanTeal-15
❑ 57Top-62
❑ 57YanJayP-11
❑ 58Top-271
❑ 59Ind-10
❑ 59Kah-20
❑ 59TigGraASP-12
❑ 59Top-295
❑ 60Kah-24
❑ 60Top-173
❑ 60TopVen-173
❑ 61Pos-190A
❑ 61Pos-190B
❑ 61Top-89
❑ 61TopMagR-26
❑ 62Jel-84
❑ 62Pos-84
❑ 62PosCan-84
❑ 62SalPlaC-43
❑ 62ShiPlaC-43
❑ 62Top-208
❑ 67TwiTeal-10
❑ 69Top-547
❑ 69TwiTealC-7
❑ 71OPC-208
❑ 71Top-208
❑ 72OPC-33
❑ 72OPC-34
❑ 72Top-33
❑ 72Top-34
❑ 73BooProC-15
❑ 73OPC-323
❑ 73TigJew-12
❑ 73Top-323
❑ 74OPC-379
❑ 74Top-379
❑ 75OPC-511
❑ 75RanPos-21
❑ 75Top-511
❑ 75TopMin-511
❑ 76SSP-453
❑ 76Top-17
❑ 77Spo-8309
❑ 77Top-387
❑ 77YanBurK-1
❑ 78SSP270-14
❑ 78Top-721
❑ 78TwiFri-10
❑ 78YanBurK-1
❑ 78YanSSPD-14
❑ 79TCM50-143
❑ 79YanPicA-24
❑ 81A'sGraG-1
❑ 81Don-479
❑ 81Fle-581
❑ 81TCM60I-364
❑ 81TigDetN-67
❑ 81TigDetN-107
❑ 81Top-671
❑ 82A'sGraG-9
❑ 82ASAMicM-67
❑ 82Don-491
❑ 82TopSti-115
❑ 83Don-575
❑ 83TigAlKS-15
❑ 83TigAlKS-16
❑ 83TigAlKS-43
❑ 83Top-156
❑ 83TopRep5-175
❑ 83TopTra-66T
❑ 83YanASFY-28
❑ 83YanPhoA-14
❑ 83YanYealT-5
❑ 84Fle-652
❑ 84Nes792-81
❑ 84OCoandSI-65
❑ 84Top-81
❑ 84TopTif-81
❑ 85PolMet-Y6
❑ 85TopTifT-78T
❑ 85TopTra-78T
❑ 86TCMSupS-17
❑ 86Top-651
❑ 86TopTif-651
❑ 87A'sMot-23
❑ 90YanScoNW-30
❑ 91ScoMan-1
❑ 91TopArc1-86
❑ 92BazQua5A-8
❑ 92PinMan-26
❑ 92RevLeg1-13
❑ 92RevLeg1-14
❑ 92RevLeg1-15
❑ 92YanWIZA-45
❑ 93ActPacA-140
❑ 93RanKee-245
❑ 93UppDecAH-88
❑ 93UppDecAH-141
❑ 93UppDecS-25
❑ 94TedWil-61
❑ 94TopArc1-13
❑ 94TopArc1G-13
❑ 94UppDecAH-99
❑ 94UppDecAH1-99

Martin, Casey
❑ 97BoiHawG-19
❑ 98CedRapKTI-17

Martin, Chandler
❑ 96AshTouB-25
❑ 97SalAva-20
❑ 98SalAvaC-20

Martin, Chris
❑ 88KenTwiP-1397
❑ 91HarSenLD-263
❑ 91HarSenP-634
❑ 91LinDriAA-263
❑ 92Bow-493
❑ 92ClaFS7-126
❑ 92HarSenF-467
❑ 92HarSenS-289
❑ 92SkyAA F-122
❑ 92UppDecML-235
❑ 93HarSenF-277
❑ 94OttLynF-2905
❑ 94UppDecML-104
❑ 98DurBulTI-17

Martin, Darryl
❑ 87FayGenP-10
❑ 89FayGenP-1585
❑ 89SouAtlLAGS-39
❑ 90LakTigS-19
❑ 93CenValRC-17
❑ 93CenValRF-2906

Martin, Derrell
❑ 59SeaPop-28
❑ 60SeaPop-7
❑ 61SeaPop-13
❑ 61UniOil-S6

Martin, Doug
❑ 91NiaFalRC-23
❑ 91NiaFalRP-3630
❑ 92NiaFalRF-3319

Martin, Eric
❑ 94EveGiaC-20
❑ 94EveGiaF-3668

Martin, Francine
❑ 91HawWomS-7

Martin, Fred
❑ 46SeaSLP-40
❑ 79TCM50-121

Martin, Gene
❑ 90GreBraS-13
❑ 90SumBraB-11
❑ 90SumBraP-2446

Martin, Gregg
❑ 89St.CatBJP-2070
❑ 90MyrBeaBJP-2773
❑ 90ProAaA-91
❑ 91Cla/Bes-193
❑ 91DunBluJC-6
❑ 91DunBluJP-202
❑ 92MyrBeaHF-2194

Martin, Heber
❑ 32Zee-105

Martin, Herschel
❑ 39PlaBal-12
❑ 40PhiTeal-14
❑ 40PlaBal-100
❑ 41PhiTeal-15
❑ 46RemBre-5
❑ 47RemBre-12
❑ 47SigOil-50
❑ 83TCMPla1944-9

Martin, J.C. (Joseph C.)
❑ 60Lea-92
❑ 60Top-346
❑ 60Top-407
❑ 61Top-124
❑ 61TopStal-124
❑ 61WhiSoxTS-10
❑ 62Top-91
❑ 62TopStal-27
❑ 62TopVen-91
❑ 62WhiSoxJP-8
❑ 62WhiSoxTS-13
❑ 63Top-499
❑ 63WhiSoxTS-18
❑ 64Top-148
❑ 64TopRooAB-10
❑ 64TopVen-148
❑ 64WhiSoxI-17
❑ 64WhiSoxTS-16
❑ 65Top-382
❑ 65WhiSoxJP-3
❑ 66OPC-47
❑ 66Top-47
❑ 66TopVen-47
❑ 67Top-538
❑ 68Top-211
❑ 68TopVen-211
❑ 69MilBra-166
❑ 69OPC-112
❑ 69Top-112
❑ 69TopFou-17
❑ 70OPC-308
❑ 70OPC-488
❑ 70Top-308
❑ 70Top-488
❑ 71MLBOffS-37
❑ 71OPC-704
❑ 71Top-704
❑ 72MilBra-206
❑ 72Top-639
❑ 73OPC-552
❑ 73Top-552
❑ 73WicAerJPKB-8
❑ 74OPC-354
❑ 74Top-354
❑ 81TCM60I-419
❑ 81TCM60I-438
❑ 81WhiSox1T-25
❑ 85WhiSoxC-22
❑ 89MetRinP69-22
❑ 91MetWIZ-250
❑ 94Met69CCPP-23
❑ 94Met69CS-22
❑ 94Met69T-19

Martin, Jake
❑ 56Top-129

Martin, James
❑ 92GreFalDSP-25
❑ 92OklStaC-19
❑ 95AusFut-69
❑ 95SanAntMTI-45
❑ 97BinMetB-19

Martin, Jared
❑ 80WicAerT-16
❑ 82IowCubT-7

Martin, Jared W.
❑ 97LetBlaDB-9
❑ 98HigDesMG-15

Martin, Jason
❑ 98MarPhiG-20

Martin, Jeff
❑ 93EveGiaC-17
❑ 93EveGiaF-3766
❑ 93LynRedSC-18
❑ 93LynRedSF-2519
❑ 94CliLumC-14
❑ 94CliLumF-1977
❑ 94LynRedSC-17
❑ 94LynRedSF-1895
❑ 95Exc-291
❑ 95TreThuTI-18
❑ 96HonShaHWB-21
❑ 96SanJosGB-14
❑ 96WilBluRB-14
❑ 97LynHil-11
❑ 97SanJosG-21
❑ 98ShrCapM-21
❑ 98ShrCapWS-21

Martin, Jerry
❑ 92GulCoaRSP-8
❑ 93ChaRaiC-11
❑ 93ChaRaiF-1906
❑ 94ChaRanF-2494
❑ 94FloStaLAF-FSL3
❑ 95Bow-122
❑ 95Exc-130
❑ 95TulDriTI-12
❑ 96TulDriTI-17

Martin, Jerry Lindsey
❑ 76PhiPhiP-18
❑ 76SSP-475
❑ 77Top-596
❑ 78SSP270-51
❑ 78Top-222
❑ 79Top-382
❑ 80OPC-256
❑ 80Top-493
❑ 81AllGamPI-152
❑ 81Don-555A
❑ 81Don-555B
❑ 81Fle-295
❑ 81GiaTeal-9
❑ 81OPC-103
❑ 81RoyProPS-10
❑ 81Top-103
❑ 81TopScr-98
❑ 81TopTra-798
❑ 82Don-298
❑ 82Fle-394
❑ 82Roy-12
❑ 82Top-722
❑ 82TopTra-65T
❑ 83Don-138
❑ 83Fle-117
❑ 83OPC-309
❑ 83RoyPos-18
❑ 83Top-626
❑ 84FleUpd-74
❑ 84Nes792-74
❑ 84Top-74
❑ 84TopTif-74
❑ 84TopTra-74T
❑ 84TopTraT-74T
❑ 85Top-517
❑ 85TopTif-517
❑ 89PacSenL-6
❑ 89PacSenL-197
❑ 89TopSenL-14
❑ 91MetWIZ-251
❑ 91PacSenL-14

Martin, Jim
❑ 91SalLakTP-3226
❑ 91SalLakTSP-14
❑ 92AugPirF-234
❑ 93BakDodCLC-17
❑ 93SalBucC-15
❑ 93SalBucF-428

Martin, Joey
❑ 75LafDriT-3
❑ 76PhoGiaCa-17
❑ 76PhoGiaVNB-15
❑ 77PhoGiaCC-17
❑ 77PhoGiaCP-17
❑ 77PhoGiaVNB-17

Martin, John A.
❑ 87LouRedTI-19
❑ 88LouRedBTI-32

Martin, John Robert
❑ 77AppFoxT-14
❑ 80EvaTriT-14
❑ 81Car5x7-17
❑ 82Don-343
❑ 82Fle-121
❑ 82LouRedE-15
❑ 82Top-236
❑ 83Car-18
❑ 83Don-617
❑ 83St.PetCT-9
❑ 83Top-721
❑ 84ArkTraT-17
❑ 84Nes792-24
❑ 84Top-24
❑ 84TopTif-24
❑ 86ArkTraP-13
❑ 88LouRedBC-3
❑ 88LouRedBP-423
❑ 89ScrRedBC-3
❑ 89ScrRedBP-719
❑ 90ClePhiS-27
❑ 91LinDriAA-509
❑ 91ReaPhiLD-509
❑ 91ReaPhiP-1387
❑ 92BatCliCB-29
❑ 92BatCliF-3283
❑ 95PiePhiF-203
❑ 96PieBolWB-2
❑ 97PieBolWB-3
❑ 98BatMucTI-16

Martin, Jon
❑ 90WelPirP-4

Martin, Justin
❑ 88BenBucL-25

❑ 89QuaCitAB-11
❑ 90QuaCitAGS-9
❑ 91QuaCitAC-8
❑ 91QuaCitAP-2625

Martin, Lefty
❑ 49EurSta-40

Martin, Lincoln
❑ 93BluOriC-18
❑ 93BluOriF-4133
❑ 94FreKeyC-17
❑ 94FreKeyF-2621
❑ 94OriPro-59
❑ 96CarLeaA1B-16
❑ 96CarLeaA2B-16
❑ 96FreKeyB-13
❑ 97FreKey-16

Martin, Louis
❑ 28Zee-55
❑ 30Zee-89
❑ 32Zee-62

Martin, Mark
❑ 87IdaFalBP-4
❑ 88OneYanP-2068

Martin, Matt
❑ 91BilMusP-3763
❑ 91BilMusSP-8
❑ 92BilMusF-3365
❑ 92BilMusSP-27
❑ 93WesVirWC-18
❑ 93WesVirWF-2875
❑ 94WinSpiC-16
❑ 94WinSpiF-281
❑ 95BilMusTI-29
❑ 96BilMusTI-21
❑ 98JacSunM-27

Martin, Mike
❑ 81VerBeaDT-12
❑ 82AmaGolST-9
❑ 83BeaGolGT-1
❑ 84LasVegSC-227
❑ 85VanCanC-217
❑ 86PitCubP-15

Martin, Mike David
❑ 93BazTeaU-20
❑ 93TopTra-128T
❑ 94JamJamC-15
❑ 94JamJamF-3973
❑ 94JohCitCC-19
❑ 94JohCitCF-3699
❑ 95AusFut-7
❑ 96CliLumKTI-19
❑ 97LanJet-16

Martin, Morrie (Morris)
❑ 51A'sTeal-22
❑ 52A'sTeal-17
❑ 52Top-131
❑ 53A'sTeal-15
❑ 53BowBW-53
❑ 53Top-227
❑ 54Bow-179
❑ 54Top-168
❑ 58Top-53A
❑ 58Top-53B
❑ 59Top-38
❑ 59TopVen-38
❑ 82Bow195E-256
❑ 83TopRep5-131
❑ 90DodTar-488
❑ 91OriCro-279
❑ 91TopArc1-227
❑ 94TopArc1-168
❑ 94TopArc1G-168

Martin, Norberto
❑ 87ChaWheP-25
❑ 88TamTarS-15
❑ 90CMC-648
❑ 90ProAAAF-173
❑ 90VanCanC-21
❑ 90VanCanP-495
❑ 91Bow-346
❑ 91LinDriAAA-640
❑ 91VanCanLD-640
❑ 91VanCanP-1603
❑ 92SkyAAAF-287
❑ 92VanCanF-2732
❑ 92VanCanS-644
❑ 93LimRocDWB-34
❑ 93NasSouF-578
❑ 94FleUpd-29
❑ 94LeaLimR-23
❑ 94NasSouF-1257
❑ 94Pac-132
❑ 94Pin-228
❑ 94PinArtP-228
❑ 94PinMusC-228
❑ 94ScoRoo-RT131
❑ 94ScoRooGR-RT131
❑ 94Spo-161
❑ 94StaCluT-139
❑ 94StaCluTFDI-139
❑ 94Top-527
❑ 94TopGol-527
❑ 94TopSpa-527
❑ 94WhiSoxK-20
❑ 95ColCho-508
❑ 95ColChoGS-508
❑ 95ColChoSS-508
❑ 95Don-165
❑ 95DonPreP-165
❑ 95Fle-124
❑ 95Pac-93
❑ 95Sco-503
❑ 95ScoGolR-503
❑ 95ScoPlaTS-503
❑ 95Top-258
❑ 95Ult-275
❑ 95UltGolM-275
❑ 95WhiSoxK-19
❑ 96Fle-71
❑ 96FleTif-71
❑ 96LeaSigA-144
❑ 96LeaSigAG-144
❑ 96LeaSigAS-144
❑ 96Ult-333
❑ 96UltGolM-333
❑ 97Pac-57
❑ 97PacLigB-57
❑ 97PacSil-57
❑ 97WhiSoxTI-7
❑ 98Pac-59
❑ 98PacInv-19
❑ 98PacInvPBlue-19
❑ 98PacInvSilv-19
❑ 98PacOnl-15
❑ 98PacOnlR-15
❑ 98PacOnlWC-15
❑ 98PacPlaB-59
❑ 98PacRedT-59
❑ 98PacSil-59
❑ 98UppDec-328
❑ 99PacCroC-6
❑ 99PacCroCPB-6

Martin, Pepper (John Leonard)
❑ 30SchR33-36
❑ 30UncJac-22
❑ 31CarMet-21
❑ 32OrbPinNP-21
❑ 32OrbPinUP-46
❑ 33ButCre-18
❑ 33DelR33-17
❑ 33Gou-62
❑ 33GouCanV-62
❑ 33NatLeaAC-17
❑ 33TatOrb-46
❑ 33TatOrbSDR-159
❑ 33WorCig-68
❑ 34BabRutG-44
❑ 34BatR31-7
❑ 34BatR31-125
❑ 34ButPreR-43
❑ 34DiaStaR-26
❑ 34ExhFou-8
❑ 35AlDemDCR3-127
❑ 35ExhFou-8
❑ 35GolMedFR-9
❑ 35GouPuzR-4F
❑ 35GouPuzR-7F
❑ 35GouPuzR-12F
❑ 35WheBB1-20A
❑ 35WheBB1-20B
❑ 36GouBWR-21
❑ 36GouWidPPR-A70
❑ 36NatChiFPR-54
❑ 36R31PasP-16
❑ 36R31Pre-G12
❑ 36WheBB3-8
❑ 37WheBB14-9
❑ 37WheBB7-29F
❑ 37WheBB9-11
❑ 38CloFotW-55
❑ 55DesMoiHB-10
❑ 59OklTodML-11
❑ 60Fle-80A
❑ 60Fle-80B
❑ 68LauWorS-28
❑ 70FleWorS-28
❑ 71FleWorS-29
❑ 74Bra193NLA-17
❑ 74Car193T-17
❑ 74NewYorNTDiS-28
❑ 77BobParMBC-13
❑ 77GalGloG-66
❑ 77GalGloG-203
❑ 80PacLeg-106
❑ 81ConTSN-24
❑ 83BigLeaCOA-23
❑ 83Car194T-28
❑ 83ConMar-31
❑ 84OCoandSI-143
❑ 86ConSer1-22
❑ 87Car193T-3
❑ 88ConNatA-14
❑ 88ConSer3-18
❑ 91ConTSN-274
❑ 92CarMcD-12
❑ 92ConTSN-637
❑ 93ActPacA-132
❑ 93ConTSN-680
❑ 93ConTSNP-991
❑ 94ConTSN-991
❑ 94ConTSN-1108
❑ 94ConTSNB-991
❑ 94ConTSNB-1108

Martin, R. Hollis
❑ 81VerBeaDT-11

Martin, Renie
❑ 79RoyTeal-5
❑ 80Top-667
❑ 81Don-103
❑ 81Fle-39
❑ 81OPC-266
❑ 81Top-452
❑ 82Don-238
❑ 82Fle-414
❑ 82Gia25tATI-18
❑ 82Top-594
❑ 82TopTra-66T
❑ 83Don-272
❑ 83Fle-267
❑ 83GiaPos-18
❑ 83Top-263
❑ 84Don-445
❑ 84Fle-381
❑ 84GiaPos-15
❑ 84Nes792-603
❑ 84Top-603
❑ 84TopTif-603
❑ 85OmaRoyT-14
❑ 86OmaRoyP-14
❑ 91PacSenL-65

Martin, Rep. (Joe)
❑ 59FleWil-78

Martin, Russ
❑ 87JamExpP-2538

Martin, Ryan
❑ 94DanBraC-17
❑ 94DanBraF-3535
❑ 95DanBraTI-17

Martin, Sam
❑ 81BatTroT-17
❑ 82WatIndF-21
❑ 82WatIndT-17
❑ 83SprCarF-4

Martin, Sid
❑ 27Zee-140

Martin, Speed (Elwood)
❑ 16Zee-41
❑ 18Zee-27
❑ 21E121So1-57
❑ 23W501-55
❑ 25Zee-74
❑ 26Zee-121
❑ 28Zee-158

Martin, Steve
❑ 82VerBeaDT-8
❑ 85AlbDukCr-172

Martin, Steve ASU
❑ 89AriStaB-19

Martin, Steve W.
❑ 89SpoIndSP-18
❑ 90Bes-209
❑ 90CMC-878
❑ 90WatDiaB-10
❑ 90WatDiaP-2385
❑ 91Bow-662
❑ 91Cla/Bes-85
❑ 91HigDesMC-25
❑ 91HigDesMP-2408
❑ 92HagSunS-263
❑ 92WicWraF-3668

Martin, Stuart
❑ 37ExhFou-8
❑ 38ExhFou-8
❑ 43CubTeal-14
❑ 79DiaGre-157

Martin, T. Eugene
❑ 70Top-599
❑ 79TCMJapPB-51

Martin, Todd
❑ 90UtiBluSP-2

Martin, Tom (Thomas Edgar)
❑ 89BluOriS-15
❑ 90Bes-178
❑ 90WauTimB-4
❑ 90WauTimP-2117
❑ 90WauTimS-16
❑ 91KanCouCC-7
❑ 91KanCouCP-2655
❑ 91KanCouCTI-12
❑ 92HigDesMC-24
❑ 92WatDiaF-2140
❑ 93RanCucQC-20
❑ 93RanCucQF-831
❑ 94GreBraF-410
❑ 94GreBraTI-16
❑ 96JacGenB-18
❑ 97AstMot-22
❑ 98BufBisG-19
❑ 98Top-238
❑ 98TopChr-238
❑ 98TopChrR-238
❑ 98TopDevR-238
❑ 98TopDia-238
❑ 98TopMiniC-238

Martin, Tony
❑ 77LodDodT-10

Martin, Trey
❑ 97VerExpB-19

Martin, Troy
❑ 91SydWavF-4

Martin, Vic
❑ 83ChaLooT-7
❑ 86CalCanP-13

Martina, Joe
❑ 75SenTCM1-18

Martindale, Denzel
❑ 77St.PetCT-5

Martindale, Ryan
❑ 88MisStaB-17
❑ 91WatIndC-13
❑ 91WatIndP-3368
❑ 92KinIndC-2
❑ 92KinIndF-2479
❑ 93CanIndF-2842
❑ 94CanIndF-3121

Martine, Chris
❑ 97NewJerCB-18
❑ 98PriWilCQ-24

Martineau, Brian
❑ 95HudValRTI-19

Martineau, Paul Peter
❑ 86JamExpP-15

Martineau, Yves
❑ 92IdaFalGF-3509
❑ 92IdaFalGSP-27
❑ 93IdaFalBF-4026
❑ 93IdaFalBSP-3

Martines, Jason
❑ 97LetBlaDB-25

Martinez, Abraham
❑ 89BlaYNPRWL-132

Martinez, Alex
❑ 98MarPhiG-21

Martinez, Angel
❑ 88ModA'sTI-24
❑ 88VerBeaDS-14
❑ 89MadMusS-14
❑ 91MedHatBJP-4104
❑ 91MedHatBJSP-2
❑ 92MedHatBJF-3210
❑ 92MedHatBJSP-6
❑ 93HagSunC-19
❑ 93HagSunF-1883
❑ 94Bow-141
❑ 94Cla-7
❑ 94DunBluJC-18
❑ 94DunBluJF-2561
❑ 94FloStaLAF-FSL7
❑ 95BluJayOH-25
❑ 95Bow-216
❑ 95BowBes-B81
❑ 95BowBesR-B81
❑ 95Exc-139
❑ 95KnoSmoF-44
❑ 95Top-644
❑ 95UppDecML-69
❑ 95UppDecMLFS-69
❑ 96ColCho-13
❑ 96ColChoGS-13
❑ 96ColChoSS-13
❑ 96Sco-227
❑ 96UppDec-212

Martinez, Art
❑ 84MemChiT-4
❑ 86MemChiSTOS-14
❑ 86MemChiTOS-14

Martinez, Belvani
❑ 98LetBlaDG-18

Martinez, Ben
❑ 92MarPhiC-7
❑ 92MarPhiF-3072

Martinez, Bert
❑ 83TriTriT-20

Martinez, Bill
❑ 92RocExpF-2112

Martinez, Buck (John Albert)
❑ 70Top-609
❑ 71OPC-163
❑ 71Top-163
❑ 72OPC-332
❑ 72Top-332
❑ 74RoyPos-15
❑ 75OPC-314
❑ 75RoyPos-17
❑ 75Top-314
❑ 75TopMin-314
❑ 76KanCitRP-17
❑ 76OPC-616
❑ 76RoyAaP-7
❑ 76SSP-165
❑ 76Top-616
❑ 77Top-46
❑ 78Top-571
❑ 79Top-243
❑ 80BreTeal-16
❑ 80Top-477
❑ 81Don-444A
❑ 81Don-444B
❑ 81Fle-526
❑ 81RoyProPS-11
❑ 81Top-56
❑ 81TopTra-799
❑ 82BluJayS-10
❑ 82Don-561
❑ 82OPC-314
❑ 82Top-314
❑ 83Don-178
❑ 83Fle-433
❑ 83OPC-308
❑ 83Top-733
❑ 84BluJayFS-24
❑ 84Don-612
❑ 84Fle-161
❑ 84Nes792-179
❑ 84OPC-179
❑ 84Top-179
❑ 84TopTif-179
❑ 85BluJayFS-21
❑ 85Fle-114
❑ 85OPC-119
❑ 85OPCPos-13
❑ 85Top-673
❑ 85TopMin-673
❑ 85TopTif-673
❑ 86BluJayAF-19
❑ 86BluJayFS-24
❑ 86Fle-66
❑ 86OPC-363
❑ 86Top-518
❑ 86TopTif-518
❑ 87Fle-235
❑ 87FleGlo-235
❑ 92Nab-24
❑ 94BreMilB-151

Martinez, Caleb
❑ 97PieBolWB-18
❑ 98PieBolWM-22

Martinez, Carlos
❑ 86AlbYanT-9
❑ 87HawIslP-21
❑ 88BirBarB-16
❑ 89BirBarADB-22
❑ 89DonRoo-14
❑ 89ScoRoo-103T
❑ 89VanCanC-17
❑ 89VanCanP-579
❑ 90Baz-13
❑ 90BirBarADB-22
❑ 90Bow-322
❑ 90BowTif-322
❑ 90Don-531
❑ 90Fle-540
❑ 90FleCan-540
❑ 90Lea-438
❑ 90OPC-461
❑ 90PanSti-374
❑ 90Sco-314
❑ 90Sco100RS-70
❑ 90ScoYouSI-35
❑ 90Spo-213
❑ 90Top-461
❑ 90TopBig-116
❑ 90TopCoi-20
❑ 90TopGloS-9
❑ 90TopRoo-19
❑ 90TopSti-300
❑ 90TopSti-325
❑ 90TopTif-461
❑ 90ToyRoo-18
❑ 90UppDec-347
❑ 90WhiSoxC-16
❑ 91CanIndLD-89
❑ 91CanIndP-987
❑ 91Don-465
❑ 91Fle-128
❑ 91LinDriAA-89
❑ 91OPC-156
❑ 91PanFreS-312
❑ 91Sco-274
❑ 91Top-156
❑ 91TopDesS-156
❑ 91TopMic-156
❑ 91TopTif-156
❑ 91UppDec-625
❑ 92Don-521
❑ 92Fle-117
❑ 92OPC-280
❑ 92Sco-593
❑ 92Sco100RS-71
❑ 92StaClu-482
❑ 92Top-280
❑ 92TopGol-280
❑ 92TopGolW-280
❑ 92TopMic-280
❑ 92Ult-52
❑ 92UppDec-598
❑ 93Don-682
❑ 93Fla-196
❑ 93Fle-595
❑ 93IndWUA-19
❑ 93Lea-347
❑ 93LinVenB-251
❑ 93PacBeiA-6
❑ 93PacSpa-98
❑ 93SP-124
❑ 93StaClu-255
❑ 93StaCluFDI-255
❑ 93StaCluMOP-255
❑ 93Stu-125
❑ 93Top-59
❑ 93TopGol-59
❑ 93TopInaM-59
❑ 93TopInaR-59
❑ 93TopMic-59
❑ 93Ult-188
❑ 93UppDec-520
❑ 93UppDecGold-520
❑ 94Pac-176
❑ 94VenLinU-61
❑ 95LinVen-222
❑ 95LinVen-268
❑ 95LinVen-288
❑ 95LinVen-289
❑ 96-97LinVen-233

Martinez, Carmelo
❑ 80QuaCitCT-29
❑ 83IowCubT-16
❑ 84Don-623
❑ 84Fle-497
❑ 84FleUpd-75
❑ 84Nes792-267
❑ 84PadMot-20
❑ 84Top-267
❑ 84TopSti-383
❑ 84TopTif-267
❑ 84TopTra-75T
❑ 84TopTraT-75T
❑ 85Don-478
❑ 85Fle-40
❑ 85OPC-365
❑ 85PadMot-24
❑ 85Top-558
❑ 85TopSti-157
❑ 85TopSti-375
❑ 85TopTif-558
❑ 86Don-324
❑ 86Fle-329
❑ 86OPC-67
❑ 86Top-67
❑ 86TopSti-109
❑ 86TopTif-67

❑ 87DonOpeD-151
❑ 87Fle-423
❑ 87FleGlo-423
❑ 87OPC-348
❑ 87PadBohHB-14
❑ 87Top-348
❑ 87TopTif-348
❑ 88Don-287
❑ 88Fle-591
❑ 88FleGlo-591
❑ 88Lea-142
❑ 88OPC-148
❑ 88PadCok-14
❑ 88PadSmo-17
❑ 88PanSti-412
❑ 88Sco-181
❑ 88ScoGlo-181
❑ 88StaLinPa-8
❑ 88Top-148
❑ 88TopBig-238
❑ 88TopCoi-47
❑ 88TopSti-106
❑ 88TopTif-148
❑ 89BimBreD-1
❑ 89Bow-459
❑ 89BowTif-459
❑ 89Don-601
❑ 89Fle-311
❑ 89FleGlo-311
❑ 89OPC-332
❑ 89PadCok-9
❑ 89PadMag-10
❑ 89PadPos-18
❑ 89PanSti-204
❑ 89Sco-517
❑ 89Top-449
❑ 89TopBig-11
❑ 89TopTif-449
❑ 89UppDec-365
❑ 90Bow-162
❑ 90BowTif-162
❑ 90ClaBlu-56
❑ 90Don-482
❑ 90Fle-162
❑ 90FleCan-162
❑ 90FleUpd-44
❑ 90Lea-448
❑ 90OPC-686
❑ 90PhiTas-21
❑ 90PubIntS-54
❑ 90Sco-114
❑ 90ScoRoo-10T
❑ 90Top-686
❑ 90TopBig-287
❑ 90TopTif-686
❑ 90TopTra-68T
❑ 90TopTraT-68T
❑ 90UppDec-592
❑ 91Fle-44
❑ 91Lea-160
❑ 91Lea-467
❑ 91OPC-779
❑ 91Sco-792
❑ 91Top-779
❑ 91TopDesS-779
❑ 91TopMic-779
❑ 91TopTif-779
❑ 91UppDec-92
❑ 92Sco-686
❑ 92UppDec-696
❑ 93CalCanF-1178

Martinez, Cesar

❑ 92ElmPioC-12
❑ 92ElmPioF-1381
❑ 93ForLauRSC-18
❑ 93ForLauRSFP-1595
❑ 96SarRedSB-22

Martinez, Chito

❑ 85Ft.MyeRT-16
❑ 86MemChiSTOS-15
❑ 86MemChiTOS-15
❑ 87OmaRoyP-7
❑ 88MemChiB-21
❑ 89BlaYNPRWLU-36
❑ 89MemChiB-12
❑ 89MemChiP-1200
❑ 89MemChiS-16
❑ 90CMC-188
❑ 90OmaRoyC-13
❑ 90OmaRoyP-77
❑ 90ProAAAF-612
❑ 91BalOriP-16
❑ 91DonRoo-54
❑ 91LinDriAAA-458
❑ 91RocRedWLD-458
❑ 91RocRedWP-1914
❑ 91TriA AAGP-AAA40
❑ 91UltUpd-2
❑ 91UppDecFE-30F
❑ 92BalOriP-17
❑ 92Bow-19
❑ 92Cla1-T56
❑ 92Don-558
❑ 92Fle-13
❑ 92FleRooS-18
❑ 92Lea-300
❑ 92LeaBlaG-300
❑ 92OPC-479
❑ 92OPCPre-77
❑ 92Pin-380
❑ 92ProFS7-4
❑ 92Sco-400
❑ 92Sco100RS-76
❑ 92StaClu-438
❑ 92Top-479
❑ 92TopDeb91-117
❑ 92TopGol-479
❑ 92TopGolW-479
❑ 92TopMcD-40
❑ 92TopMic-479
❑ 92TriPla-192
❑ 92Ult-7
❑ 92UppDec-672
❑ 93Don-221
❑ 93Fle-545
❑ 93Lea-274
❑ 93PacSpa-19
❑ 93Pin-214
❑ 93Sco-638
❑ 93StaClu-362
❑ 93StaCluFDI-362
❑ 93StaCluMOP-362
❑ 93Top-772
❑ 93TopGol-772
❑ 93TopInaM-772
❑ 93TopInaR-772
❑ 93TopMic-772
❑ 93Ult-141
❑ 93UppDec-514
❑ 93UppDecGold-514
❑ 94ColCliF-2965
❑ 94ColCliP-18

Martinez, Christian

❑ 83St.PetCT-10

Martinez, Dalvis

❑ 93BriTigC-15
❑ 93BriTigF-3654
❑ 94JamJamC-16
❑ 94JamJamF-3974

Martinez, Dave

❑ 83QuaCitCT-26
❑ 86IowCubP-17
❑ 86StaoftFT-8
❑ 87CubCan-17
❑ 87CubDavB-1
❑ 87Don-488
❑ 87SpoTeaP-22
❑ 87TopTra-73T
❑ 87TopTraT-73T
❑ 88Don-438
❑ 88DonBasB-149
❑ 88DonTeaBC-438
❑ 88ExpPos-18
❑ 88Fle-424
❑ 88FleGlo-424
❑ 88PanSti-266
❑ 88Sco-223
❑ 88ScoGlo-223
❑ 88StaLinCu-6
❑ 88Top-439
❑ 88TopTif-439
❑ 89Bow-370
❑ 89BowTif-370
❑ 89Don-102
❑ 89ExpPos-19
❑ 89Fle-384
❑ 89FleGlo-384
❑ 89OPC-395
❑ 89Sco-77
❑ 89Top-763
❑ 89TopTif-763
❑ 89UppDec-444
❑ 90Bow-121
❑ 90BowTif-121
❑ 90Don-452
❑ 90DonBesN-79
❑ 90ExpPos-22
❑ 90Fle-353A
❑ 90Fle-353B
❑ 90FleCan-353
❑ 90Lea-318
❑ 90OPC-228
❑ 90PanSti-293
❑ 90PubIntS-180
❑ 90Sco-27
❑ 90Top-228
❑ 90TopSti-71
❑ 90TopTif-228
❑ 90UppDec-470
❑ 91Bow-455
❑ 91Don-237
❑ 91ExpPos-13
❑ 91Fle-237
❑ 91Lea-8
❑ 91OPC-24
❑ 91PanFreS-144
❑ 91PanSti-66
❑ 91Sco-82
❑ 91StaClu-346
❑ 91Top-24
❑ 91TopDesS-24
❑ 91TopMic-24
❑ 91TopTif-24
❑ 91Ult-205
❑ 91UppDec-186
❑ 92Bow-220
❑ 92Don-732
❑ 92Fle-485
❑ 92Lea-457
❑ 92LeaBlaG-457
❑ 92OPC-309
❑ 92OPCPre-75
❑ 92Pin-397
❑ 92RedFolS-59
❑ 92RedKah-30
❑ 92Sco-501
❑ 92ScoRoo-33T
❑ 92StaClu-723
❑ 92StaCluNC-723
❑ 92Top-309
❑ 92TopGol-309
❑ 92TopGolW-309
❑ 92TopMic-309
❑ 92TopTra-67T
❑ 92TopTraG-67T
❑ 92Ult-484
❑ 92UppDec-382
❑ 92UppDec-784
❑ 93Don-534
❑ 93Fle-395
❑ 93FleFinE-153
❑ 93GiaMot-16
❑ 93GiaPos-24
❑ 93GiaStaC-19
❑ 93Lea-301
❑ 93OPC-172
❑ 93OPCPre-22
❑ 93PacSpa-613
❑ 93Pin-132
❑ 93Sco-501
❑ 93SelRoo-126T
❑ 93StaClu-640
❑ 93StaCluFDI-640
❑ 93StaCluMOP-640
❑ 93Top-671
❑ 93TopGol-671
❑ 93TopInaM-671
❑ 93TopInaR-671
❑ 93TopMic-671
❑ 93Ult-486
❑ 93UppDec-400
❑ 93UppDec-700
❑ 93UppDecGold-400
❑ 93UppDecGold-700
❑ 94Don-463
❑ 94Fle-695
❑ 94GiaAMC-13
❑ 94GiaMot-16
❑ 94GiaTarBC-15
❑ 94GiaUSPC-5S
❑ 94GiaUSPC-11D
❑ 94Lea-15
❑ 94Pac-550
❑ 94StaCluT-15
❑ 94StaCluTFDI-15
❑ 94Top-174
❑ 94TopGol-174
❑ 94TopSpa-174
❑ 94Ult-293
❑ 95HudValRTI-16
❑ 95Pac-381
❑ 95WhiSoxK-20
❑ 96ColCho-499
❑ 96ColChoGS-499
❑ 96ColChoSS-499
❑ 96Don-95
❑ 96DonPreP-95
❑ 96Fle-72
❑ 96FleTif-72
❑ 96Pac-289
❑ 96StaClu-398
❑ 96StaCluMOP-398
❑ 96WhiSoxF-11
❑ 97ColCho-293
❑ 97DonTea-74
❑ 97DonTeaSPE-74
❑ 97Fle-65
❑ 97FleTif-65
❑ 97Pac-58
❑ 97PacLatotML-7
❑ 97PacLigB-58
❑ 97PacSil-58
❑ 97Sco-447
❑ 97ScoArtPWB-447
❑ 97ScoResC-447
❑ 97ScoShoS-447
❑ 97ScoShoSAP-447
❑ 97Top-197
❑ 97UppDec-334
❑ 97WhiSoxTI-14
❑ 98CirThu-268
❑ 98CirThuRav-268
❑ 98CirThuSupRav-268
❑ 98ColCho-502
❑ 98DevRayP-23
❑ 98Fle-552
❑ 98Pac-60
❑ 98PacAur-81
❑ 98PacOnl-713
❑ 98PacOnlR-713
❑ 98PacOnlWC-713
❑ 98PacPar-97
❑ 98PacParC-97
❑ 98PacParG-97
❑ 98PacParHS-97
❑ 98PacParPB-97
❑ 98PacParR-97
❑ 98PacPlaB-60
❑ 98PacRedT-60
❑ 98PacSil-60
❑ 98PinSna-TBDR8
❑ 98Sco-134
❑ 98Top-134
❑ 98TopChr-134
❑ 98TopChrR-134
❑ 98TopDevR-134
❑ 98TopDia-134
❑ 98TopMiniC-134
❑ 98UppDec-729
❑ 98WhiSoxS-11
❑ 98WhiSoxSP-11
❑ 99Pac-414
❑ 99PacAur-186
❑ 99PacAurOD-186
❑ 99PacOme-230
❑ 99PacOmeC-230
❑ 99PacOmeG-230
❑ 99PacOmePB-230
❑ 99PacPar-227
❑ 99PacParC-227
❑ 99PacParG-227
❑ 99PacParHoloGold-227
❑ 99PacParHS-227
❑ 99PacParOD-227
❑ 99PacParPB-227
❑ 99PacParRed-227
❑ 99PacPlaB-414
❑ 99PacRed-414
❑ 99Top-107
❑ 99TopChr-107
❑ 99TopChrR-107
❑ 99TopMVPP-107
❑ 99UppDec-498
❑ 99UppDecEL1-498
❑ 99UppDecEL2-498

Martinez, David

❑ 86PalSprAP-22
❑ 87AriWilP-10
❑ 87MidAngP-2
❑ 88MidAngGS-20
❑ 89MidAngGS-22
❑ 90PalSprACLC-217
❑ 90PalSprAP-2573
❑ 91LinDriAAA-459
❑ 91RocRedWLD-459
❑ 91RocRedWP-1898
❑ 92ElPasDF-3916
❑ 92ElPasDS-219
❑ 96OgdRapTI-8

Martinez, Dennis Jr.

❑ 95SPML-104
❑ 96WatIndTI-15

Martinez, Denny (J. Dennis)

❑ 77BalOriP-12
❑ 77Top-491
❑ 78BalOriP-16
❑ 78Top-119
❑ 79Hos-32
❑ 79OPC-105
❑ 79Top-211
❑ 80OPC-2
❑ 80Top-10
❑ 81BalOriP-9
❑ 81Don-533
❑ 81Fle-180
❑ 81OPC-367
❑ 81Top-367
❑ 82Don-79
❑ 82Fle-170
❑ 82OPC-135
❑ 82Top-165
❑ 82Top-712
❑ 82TopSti-10
❑ 83Don-231
❑ 83Fle-64
❑ 83FleSta-114
❑ 83FleSti-199
❑ 83OPC-167
❑ 83OriPos-15
❑ 83Top-553
❑ 84BalOriP-18
❑ 84Don-633
❑ 84Fle-11
❑ 84Nes792-631
❑ 84Top-631
❑ 84TopTif-631
❑ 85BalOriP-15
❑ 85Don-514
❑ 85Fle-181
❑ 85OriHea-10
❑ 85Top-199
❑ 85TopTif-199
❑ 86BalOriHMP-10
❑ 86Don-454
❑ 86Fle-280
❑ 86Top-416
❑ 86TopTif-416
❑ 87Fle-324
❑ 87FleGlo-324
❑ 87IndIndTI-31
❑ 87OPC-252
❑ 87Top-252
❑ 87TopTif-252
❑ 88Don-549
❑ 88DonBasB-146
❑ 88ExpPos-19
❑ 88Fle-188
❑ 88FleGlo-188
❑ 88Lea-262
❑ 88OPC-76
❑ 88Sco-601
❑ 88ScoGlo-601
❑ 88Top-76
❑ 88TopSti-84
❑ 88TopTif-76
❑ 89Bow-359
❑ 89BowTif-359
❑ 89ClaLigB-45
❑ 89Don-106
❑ 89DonBasB-90
❑ 89ExpPos-20
❑ 89Fle-385
❑ 89FleGlo-385
❑ 89OPC-313
❑ 89PanSti-114
❑ 89Sco-114
❑ 89ScoHot1S-13
❑ 89Spo-106
❑ 89Top-313
❑ 89TopSti-74
❑ 89TopTif-313
❑ 89UppDec-377
❑ 90Bow-111
❑ 90BowTif-111
❑ 90Don-156
❑ 90DonBesN-30
❑ 90ExpPos-23
❑ 90Fle-354
❑ 90FleCan-354
❑ 90Lea-54
❑ 90M.Vpin-60
❑ 90OPC-763
❑ 90PanSti-288
❑ 90PubIntS-181
❑ 90Sco-47
❑ 90Spo-53
❑ 90Top-763
❑ 90TopBig-133
❑ 90TopSti-68
❑ 90TopTif-763
❑ 90UppDec-413
❑ 90USPlaCA-3D
❑ 91BasBesAotM-11
❑ 91Bow-434
❑ 91Cla3-T53
❑ 91ClaGam-30
❑ 91Don-139
❑ 91ExpPos-14
❑ 91Fle-238
❑ 91Lea-274
❑ 91OPC-528
❑ 91OPCPre-75
❑ 91OriCro-280
❑ 91PanFreS-150
❑ 91PanSti-68
❑ 91Sco-454
❑ 91StaClu-273
❑ 91StaCluMO-5
❑ 91StaCluP-24
❑ 91Top-528
❑ 91TopDesS-528
❑ 91TopMic-528
❑ 91TopTif-528
❑ 91TopTriH-N6
❑ 91Ult-206
❑ 91UppDec-385
❑ 91UppDecFE-50F
❑ 91USPlaCA-7S
❑ 92Bow-305
❑ 92Cla1-T57
❑ 92ClaGam-134
❑ 92Don-276
❑ 92Don-686
❑ 92DonDiaK-DK24
❑ 92DonMcD-16
❑ 92DonSupD-DK24
❑ 92ExpDonD-12
❑ 92ExpPos-22
❑ 92Fle-486
❑ 92Fle-683
❑ 92Fle-695
❑ 92Hig5-59
❑ 92Lea-190
❑ 92LeaBlaG-190
❑ 92MVPPin-46
❑ 92OPC-15
❑ 92OPCPre-13
❑ 92PanSti-149
❑ 92PanSti-209
❑ 92PepDieM-4
❑ 92Pin-77
❑ 92PosCan-1
❑ 92Sco-470
❑ 92Sco-783
❑ 92Sco-784
❑ 92Sco100S-97
❑ 92ScoProP-17
❑ 92StaClu-860
❑ 92StaCluD-111
❑ 92StaCluNC-860
❑ 92Stu-57
❑ 92Top-15
❑ 92Top-394
❑ 92TopGol-15
❑ 92TopGol-394
❑ 92TopGolPS-15
❑ 92TopGolW-15
❑ 92TopGolW-394
❑ 92TopKid-10
❑ 92TopMic-15
❑ 92TopMic-394
❑ 92TopPreS-273
❑ 92TriPla-92
❑ 92Ult-223
❑ 92UppDec-365
❑ 92UppDecTMH-31
❑ 93Bow-480
❑ 93DiaMar-68
❑ 93Don-168
❑ 93DurPowP2-14
❑ 93ExpColP7-5
❑ 93ExpDonM-10
❑ 93Fla-86
❑ 93Fle-462
❑ 93FleFruotL-40
❑ 93FunPac-97
❑ 93HumDumC-41
❑ 93Lea-300
❑ 93MSABenSPD-5
❑ 93OPC-300
❑ 93PacBeiA-25
❑ 93PacSpa-187
❑ 93PacSpaGE-5
❑ 93PacSpaPI-3
❑ 93PanSti-228

❑ 93Pin-38
❑ 93Pin-291
❑ 93RedFolS-56
❑ 93Sco-75
❑ 93Sel-147
❑ 93SelAce-6
❑ 93SelStaL-90
❑ 93SP-106
❑ 93StaClu-140
❑ 93StaCluFDI-140
❑ 93StaCluM-58
❑ 93StaCluMOP-140
❑ 93Top-610
❑ 93TopComotH-23
❑ 93TopGol-610
❑ 93TopInaM-610
❑ 93TopInaR-610
❑ 93TopMic-610
❑ 93TriPla-74
❑ 93Ult-418
❑ 93UppDec-232
❑ 93UppDec-481
❑ 93UppDec-821
❑ 93UppDecGold-232
❑ 93UppDecGold-481
❑ 93UppDecGold-821
❑ 93USPlaCA-9S
❑ 94Bow-523
❑ 94ColC-546
❑ 94ColChoGS-546
❑ 94ColChoSS-546
❑ 94Don-422
❑ 94Fin-412
❑ 94FinRef-412
❑ 94Fla-41
❑ 94Fle-545
❑ 94FleExtB-61
❑ 94FleUpd-32
❑ 94FUnPac-132
❑ 94Lea-310
❑ 94OPC-21
❑ 94Pac-386
❑ 94PacAll-7
❑ 94Pin-516
❑ 94PinArtP-516
❑ 94PinMusC-516
❑ 94Sco-514
❑ 94ScoGolR-514
❑ 94ScoRoo-RT24
❑ 94ScoRooGR-RT24
❑ 94Sel-346
❑ 94SP-99
❑ 94SPDieC-99
❑ 94SpoRoo-92
❑ 94SpoRooAP-92
❑ 94StaClu-187
❑ 94StaClu-682
❑ 94StaCluFDI-187
❑ 94StaCluFDI-682
❑ 94StaCluGR-187
❑ 94StaCluGR-682
❑ 94StaCluMOP-187
❑ 94StaCluMOP-682
❑ 94Top-440
❑ 94TopGol-440
❑ 94TopSpa-440
❑ 94TopTra-7T
❑ 94Ult-345
❑ 94UppDec-358
❑ 94UppDecED-358
❑ 95Baz-13
❑ 95ColCho-65
❑ 95ColCho-274
❑ 95ColChoGS-65
❑ 95ColChoGS-274
❑ 95ColChoSE-122
❑ 95ColChoSEGS-122
❑ 95ColChoSESS-122
❑ 95ColChoSS-65
❑ 95ColChoSS-274
❑ 95Don-92
❑ 95DonPreP-92
❑ 95DonTopotO-60
❑ 95Emo-35
❑ 95Fin-188
❑ 95FinRef-188
❑ 95Fla-32
❑ 95Fle-139
❑ 95FleTeaL-5
❑ 95Lea-195
❑ 95LeaLim-190
❑ 95Pac-124
❑ 95PacLatD-22
❑ 95PacPri-40
❑ 95PanSti-20
❑ 95Pin-374
❑ 95PinArtP-374
❑ 95PinMusC-374
❑ 95ScoHaloG-HG88
❑ 95Sel-130
❑ 95SelArtP-130
❑ 95SelCer-86
❑ 95SelCerMG-86
❑ 95SP-147
❑ 95SPCha-147
❑ 95SPChaDC-147
❑ 95SPSil-147
❑ 95StaClu-484
❑ 95StaCluMOP-484
❑ 95StaCluSTDW-I484
❑ 95StaCluSTMP-15
❑ 95StaCluSTWS-484
❑ 95StaCluVR-264
❑ 95StaCluVRMO-264
❑ 95Stu-77
❑ 95Top-20
❑ 95TopCyb-16
❑ 95TopD3-5
❑ 95Ult-280
❑ 95UltGolM-280
❑ 95UppDec-94
❑ 95UppDecED-94
❑ 95UppDecEDG-94
❑ 95UppDecSE-158
❑ 95UppDecSEG-158
❑ 96Cir-34
❑ 96CirRav-34
❑ 96ColCho-122
❑ 96ColCho-335
❑ 96ColChoGS-122
❑ 96ColChoGS-335
❑ 96ColChoSS-122
❑ 96ColChoSS-335
❑ 96Don-284
❑ 96DonPreP-284
❑ 96EmoXL-50
❑ 96Fin-B131
❑ 96FinRef-B131
❑ 96Fla-68
❑ 96Fle-90
❑ 96FleTif-90
❑ 96IndFle-7
❑ 96Lea-139
❑ 96LeaPrePB-139
❑ 96LeaPrePG-139
❑ 96LeaPrePS-139
❑ 96LeaSigA-145
❑ 96LeaSigAG-145
❑ 96LeaSigAS-145
❑ 96MetUni-47
❑ 96MetUniP-47
❑ 96Pac-299
❑ 96PacEstL-EL16
❑ 96PacHom-HP16
❑ 96PacPri-P96
❑ 96PacPriG-P96
❑ 96Pin-112
❑ 96PinAfi-39
❑ 96PinAfi-157
❑ 96PinAfiAP-39
❑ 96PinAfiAP-157
❑ 96PinAfiFPP-39
❑ 96PinArtP-44
❑ 96PinSta-44
❑ 96SchDis-7
❑ 96Sco-306
❑ 96ScoDugC-B31
❑ 96ScoDugCAP-B31
❑ 96Sel-142
❑ 96SelArtP-142
❑ 96SP-71
❑ 96StaClu-100
❑ 96StaClu-253
❑ 96StaCluEPB-100
❑ 96StaCluEPG-100
❑ 96StaCluEPS-100
❑ 96StaCluMOP-100
❑ 96StaCluMOP-253
❑ 96Top-181
❑ 96TopChrMotG-2
❑ 96TopChrMotGR-2
❑ 96TopGalE-13
❑ 96TopLas-58
❑ 96TopMasotG-2
❑ 96Ult-49
❑ 96UltGolM-49
❑ 96UppDec-103
❑ 96UppDec-314
❑ 97ColCho-91
❑ 97Fle-81
❑ 97FleTif-81
❑ 97IndSco-4
❑ 97IndScoPl-4
❑ 97Lea-265
❑ 97LeaFraM-265
❑ 97LeaFraMDC-265
❑ 97Pac-74
❑ 97PacLigB-74
❑ 97PacSil-74
❑ 97Sco-115
❑ 97Sco-345
❑ 97ScoArtPWB-115
❑ 97ScoArtPWB-345
❑ 97ScoPreS-115
❑ 97ScoResC-345
❑ 97ScoShoS-115
❑ 97ScoShoS-345
❑ 97ScoShoSAP-115
❑ 97ScoShoSAP-345
❑ 97StaClu-62
❑ 97StaCluMOP-62
❑ 97Top-181
❑ 97UppDec-198
❑ 98ColCho-236
❑ 98FleUpd-U45
❑ 98PacOnl-68
❑ 98PacOnlR-68
❑ 98PacOnlWC-68
❑ 98Ult-315
❑ 98UltGolM-315
❑ 98UltMas-315
❑ 98UltPlaM-315
❑ 98UppDec-224
❑ 99Pac-38
❑ 99PacCroC-29
❑ 99PacCroCPB-29
❑ 99PacPlaB-38
❑ 99PacRed-38
❑ 99SpoIll-39
❑ 99UppDec-41
❑ 99UppDecEL1-41
❑ 99UppDecEL2-41

Martinez, Domingo

❑ 86VenGulP-13
❑ 87DunBluJP-945
❑ 88KnoBluJB-6
❑ 88SouLeaAJ-25
❑ 89KnoBluJB-15
❑ 89KnoBluJP-1148
❑ 89KnoBluJS-12
❑ 90KnoBluJB-15
❑ 90KnoBluJP-1254
❑ 90KnoBluJS-12
❑ 91LinDriAAA-511
❑ 91SyrChiLD-511
❑ 91SyrChiMB-14
❑ 91SyrChiP-2485
❑ 92ProFS7-160
❑ 92SkyAAAF-229
❑ 92SyrChiF-1975
❑ 92SyrChiMB-14
❑ 92SyrChiS-512
❑ 93BluJayD4-38
❑ 93BluJayFS-19
❑ 93Bow-203
❑ 93Don-363
❑ 93Lea-356
❑ 93LimRocDWB-24
❑ 93PacSpa-653
❑ 93Pin-596
❑ 93PinRooTP-6
❑ 93Sco-257
❑ 93StaClu-727
❑ 93StaCluFDI-727
❑ 93StaCluMOP-727
❑ 93SyrChiF-1004
❑ 93Top-810
❑ 93TopGol-810
❑ 93TopInaM-810
❑ 93TopInaR-810
❑ 93TopMic-810
❑ 93Ult-644
❑ 93UppDec-651
❑ 93UppDecGold-651
❑ 94Don-584
❑ 94NasSouF-1258
❑ 94Pac-647
❑ 94StaCluT-157
❑ 94StaCluTFDI-157
❑ 95LouRedF-283

Martinez, Eddy

❑ 93BelMarCB-18
❑ 96BesAutS-54
❑ 96Exc-5
❑ 96FreKeyB-14
❑ 97BowBay-22
❑ 98DelShoM-19

Martinez, Edgar

❑ 86ChaLooP-17
❑ 87CalCanP-2309
❑ 88CalCanC-16
❑ 88CalCanP-782
❑ 88DonRoo-36
❑ 88Fle-378
❑ 88FleGlo-378
❑ 88TriAAC-34
❑ 89BlaYNPRWL-9
❑ 89BlaYNPRWLU-40
❑ 89BlaYNPRWLU-48
❑ 89BlaYNPRWLU-56
❑ 89Bow-216
❑ 89BowTif-216
❑ 89Don-645
❑ 89DonRoo-15
❑ 89Fle-552
❑ 89FleGlo-552
❑ 89MarMot-11
❑ 89PanSti-428
❑ 89Sco-637
❑ 89ScoHot1R-40
❑ 89SpollIFKI-279
❑ 89UppDec-768
❑ 90ClaYel-T23
❑ 90CMC-439
❑ 90DonLeaS-45
❑ 90Fle-520
❑ 90FleCan-520
❑ 90Lea-299
❑ 90MarMot-10
❑ 90OPC-148
❑ 90PubIntS-437
❑ 90Sco-324
❑ 90Top-148
❑ 90TopTif-148
❑ 90UppDec-532
❑ 91Bow-243
❑ 91Cla3-T54
❑ 91Don-16
❑ 91Don-606
❑ 91DonSupD-16
❑ 91Fle-457
❑ 91Lea-477
❑ 91MarCouH-7
❑ 91OPC-607
❑ 91PanFreS-230
❑ 91PanSti-187
❑ 91Sco-264
❑ 91Sco100S-17
❑ 91SevCoi-NW11
❑ 91StaClu-47
❑ 91Stu-117
❑ 91Top-607
❑ 91TopDesS-607
❑ 91TopMic-607
❑ 91TopTif-607
❑ 91Ult-340
❑ 91UppDec-574
❑ 92Bow-33
❑ 92Don-286
❑ 92DonCraJ2-24
❑ 92Fle-286
❑ 92Hig5-109
❑ 92Lea-197
❑ 92LeaBlaG-197
❑ 92MarMot-20
❑ 92OPC-553
❑ 92PanSti-57
❑ 92Pin-13
❑ 92RedFolS-60
❑ 92Sco-485
❑ 92Sco100S-17
❑ 92SpollIFK1-407
❑ 92StaClu-267
❑ 92Stu-235
❑ 92Top-553
❑ 92TopGol-553
❑ 92TopGolW-553
❑ 92TopKid-125
❑ 92TopMic-553
❑ 92TriPla-127
❑ 92Ult-126
❑ 92UppDec-91
❑ 92UppDec-367
❑ 93Bow-515
❑ 93ClaGam-58
❑ 93DenHol-13
❑ 93DiaMar-69
❑ 93Don-421
❑ 93DonEli-27
❑ 93DonEliS-9
❑ 93DurPowP1-6
❑ 93Fin-190
❑ 93FinRef-190
❑ 93Fla-273
❑ 93Fle-309
❑ 93Fle-344
❑ 93Fle-716
❑ 93FleAll-AL3
❑ 93FleFruotL-41
❑ 93FunPac-116
❑ 93Lea-386
❑ 93LeaGolA-R15
❑ 93MarDaiQ-2
❑ 93MariStaClu-24
❑ 93MarMot-11
❑ 93OPC-164
❑ 93OPCPreSP-5
❑ 93OPCPreSPF-5
❑ 93PacBeiA-1
❑ 93PacBeiA-11
❑ 93PacSpa-290
❑ 93PacSpaGE-16
❑ 93PacSpaPI-17
❑ 93PanSti-62
❑ 93PanSti-155
❑ 93Pin-17
❑ 93PinTeaP-6
❑ 93RedFolS-57
❑ 93Sco-49
❑ 93Sco-502
❑ 93Sel-82
❑ 93SolChaS-16
❑ 93SelStaL-1
❑ 93SelStaL-13
❑ 93SelStaL-44
❑ 93SP-133
❑ 93StaClu-331
❑ 93StaCluFDI-331
❑ 93StaCluM-159
❑ 93StaCluMOP-331
❑ 93Stu-126
❑ 93Top-315
❑ 93Top-403
❑ 93TOPBLAG-37
❑ 93TopGol-315
❑ 93TopGol-403
❑ 93TopInaM-315
❑ 93TopInaM-403
❑ 93TopInaR-315
❑ 93TopInaR-403
❑ 93TopMic-315
❑ 93TopMic-403
❑ 93TriPla-20
❑ 93TriPlaLL-L6
❑ 93Ult-270
❑ 93UltAllS-15
❑ 93UppDec-495
❑ 93UppDec-553
❑ 93UppDecGold-495
❑ 93UppDecGold-553
❑ 93USPlaCA-1D
❑ 94Bow-61
❑ 94ChuHomS-21
❑ 94ChuHomSG-21
❑ 94ColC-477
❑ 94ColC-480
❑ 94ColChoGS-477
❑ 94ColChoGS-480
❑ 94ColChoSS-480
❑ 94Don-268
❑ 94DonDom-B4
❑ 94DonDomJ-B4
❑ 94Fin-154
❑ 94FinPre-154P
❑ 94FinRef-154
❑ 94Fla-338
❑ 94Fle-294
❑ 94FleExtB-169
❑ 94Lea-344
❑ 94LeaL-68
❑ 94MarMot-13
❑ 94OPC-44
❑ 94Pac-576
❑ 94PanSti-121
❑ 94Pin-302
❑ 94PinArtP-302
❑ 94PinMusC-302
❑ 94ProMag-130
❑ 94Sco-465
❑ 94ScoGolR-465
❑ 94Sel-72
❑ 94SP-107
❑ 94SPDieC-107
❑ 94Spo-115
❑ 94StaClu-364
❑ 94StaCluFDI-364
❑ 94StaCluGR-364
❑ 94StaCluMOP-364
❑ 94Stu-103
❑ 94Top-195
❑ 94TopGol-195
❑ 94TopSpa-195
❑ 94TriPla-129
❑ 94Ult-422
❑ 94UppDec-424
❑ 94UppDecED-424
❑ 95Bow-333
❑ 95ColCho-287
❑ 95ColChoGS-287
❑ 95ColChoSE-129
❑ 95ColChoSEGS-129
❑ 95ColChoSESS-129
❑ 95ColChoSS-287
❑ 95Don-151
❑ 95DonPreP-151
❑ 95DonTopotO-152
❑ 95Emo-79
❑ 95Fin-36
❑ 95FinRef-36
❑ 95Fla-301
❑ 95Fle-272
❑ 95Lea-271
❑ 95Lea300C-8
❑ 95LeaLim-150
❑ 95MarMot-5
❑ 95MarPac-7
❑ 95MarPac-8
❑ 95MarPac-35
❑ 95Pac-400
❑ 95PacPri-128
❑ 95Pin-97
❑ 95PinArtP-97
❑ 95PinMusC-97
❑ 95Sco-478
❑ 95ScoGolR-478
❑ 95ScoPlaTS-478
❑ 95SelCer-24
❑ 95SelCerMG-24
❑ 95SP-193
❑ 95SPCha-188
❑ 95SPChaDC-188
❑ 95SPSil-193
❑ 95StaClu-354
❑ 95StaCluMOP-354
❑ 95StaCluMOP-RL37
❑ 95StaCluRL-RL37
❑ 95StaCluSTDW-M354
❑ 95StaCluSTWS-354
❑ 95StaCluVR-185
❑ 95StaCluVRMO-185
❑ 95Stu-183
❑ 95Sum-17
❑ 95SumNthD-17
❑ 95Top-55
❑ 95TopCyb-40
❑ 95Ult-104
❑ 95UltGolM-104
❑ 95UppDec-349
❑ 95UppDecED-349
❑ 95UppDecEDG-349
❑ 95UppDecSE-119
❑ 95UppDecSEG-119
❑ 95Zen-30
❑ 96Baz-100
❑ 96Bow-20
❑ 96BowBes-2
❑ 96BowBesAR-2
❑ 96BowBesR-2
❑ 96BowFoi-20
❑ 96Cir-80
❑ 96CirRav-80
❑ 96ColCho-2
❑ 96ColCho-275
❑ 96ColCho-371T
❑ 96ColCho-725
❑ 96ColChoGS-2
❑ 96ColChoGS-275
❑ 96ColChoGS-725
❑ 96ColChoSS-2
❑ 96ColChoSS-275
❑ 96ColChoSS-725
❑ 96Don-471
❑ 96DonDiaK-26
❑ 96DonHitL-22
❑ 96DonPreP-471
❑ 96EmoXL-116
❑ 96Fin-B323
❑ 96Fin-G335
❑ 96Fin-S35
❑ 96FinRef-B323
❑ 96FinRef-G335
❑ 96FinRef-S35
❑ 96Fla-163
❑ 96Fle-241
❑ 96FleGolM-4
❑ 96FleTif-241

❑ 96FleZon-8
❑ 96Lea-115
❑ 96LeaLim-42
❑ 96LeaLimG-42
❑ 96LeaPre-71
❑ 96LeaPreP-71
❑ 96LeaPrePB-115
❑ 96LeaPrePG-115
❑ 96LeaPrePS-115
❑ 96LeaSig-61
❑ 96LeaSigPPG-61
❑ 96LeaSigPPP-61
❑ 96MarMot-7
❑ 96MetUni-109
❑ 96MetUniP-109
❑ 96Pac-408
❑ 96Pac-419
❑ 96PacBaeS-6
❑ 96PacCraC-CC10
❑ 96PacEstL-EL17
❑ 96PacGolCD-DC5
❑ 96PacHom-HP20
❑ 96PacOctM-OM14
❑ 96PacPri-P133
❑ 96PacPriFB-FB10
❑ 96PacPriG-P133
❑ 96PacPriRHS-RH13
❑ 96PanSti-120
❑ 96PanSti-230
❑ 96Pin-67
❑ 96Pin-147
❑ 96Pin-313
❑ 96PinAfi-21
❑ 96PinAfiAP-21
❑ 96PinAfiFPP-21
❑ 96PinArtP-26
❑ 96PinArtP-74
❑ 96PinArtP-195
❑ 96PinFoil-313
❑ 96PinSta-26
❑ 96PinSta-74
❑ 96PinSta-195
❑ 96ProSta-64
❑ 96Sco-117
❑ 96Sco-376
❑ 96ScoAll-15
❑ 96ScoBigB-17
❑ 96ScoDugC-A77
❑ 96ScoDugC-B101
❑ 96ScoDugCAP-A77
❑ 96ScoDugCAP-B101
❑ 96ScoGolS-13
❑ 96ScoNumG-16
❑ 96ScoRef-13
❑ 96Sel-70
❑ 96SelArtP-70
❑ 96SelCer-61
❑ 96SelCerAP-61
❑ 96SelCerCB-61
❑ 96SelCerCR-61
❑ 96SelCerIP-22
❑ 96SelCerMB-61
❑ 96SelCerMG-61
❑ 96SelCerMR-61
❑ 96SelTeaN-9
❑ 96SP-172
❑ 96Spo-23
❑ 96Spo-111
❑ 96SpoArtP-23
❑ 96SpoArtP-111
❑ 96SpoPowS-15
❑ 96SPSpeFX-45
❑ 96SPSpeFXDC-45
❑ 96StaClu-221
❑ 96StaClu-300
❑ 96StaCluEPB-300
❑ 96StaCluEPG-300
❑ 96StaCluEPS-300
❑ 96StaCluMM-MM10
❑ 96StaCluMO-23
❑ 96StaCluMOP-221
❑ 96StaCluMOP-300
❑ 96StaCluMOP-MM10
❑ 96StaCluMOP-PC5
❑ 96StaCluPC-PC5
❑ 96Stu-34
❑ 96StuPrePB-34
❑ 96StuPrePG-34
❑ 96StuPrePS-34
❑ 96Sum-142
❑ 96SumAbo&B-142
❑ 96SumArtP-142
❑ 96SumFoi-142
❑ 96Top-247
❑ 96TopChr-94
❑ 96TopChrR-94
❑ 96TopClaC-CC3
❑ 96TopGal-158
❑ 96TopGalE-16
❑ 96TopGalPPI-158
❑ 96TopLas-27
❑ 96TopLasSS-14
❑ 96TopPro-AL16
❑ 96TopRoaW-RW9
❑ 96Ult-128
❑ 96UltGolM-128
❑ 96UltHitM-5
❑ 96UltHitMGM-5
❑ 96UltOn-L-6
❑ 96UltOn-LGM-6
❑ 96UltSeaC-6
❑ 96UltSeaCGM-6
❑ 96UppDec-205
❑ 96UppDec-218
❑ 96UppDecPRE-R16
❑ 96UppDecPRE-R27
❑ 96UppDecPreR-R16
❑ 96UppDecPreR-R27
❑ 96UppDecRunP-RP10
❑ 96Zen-35
❑ 96ZenArtP-35
❑ 97Bow-40
❑ 97BowBes-10
❑ 97BowBesAR-10
❑ 97BowBesR-10
❑ 97BowChr-34
❑ 97BowChrI-34
❑ 97BowChrIR-34
❑ 97BowChrR-34
❑ 97BowInt-40
❑ 97Cir-232
❑ 97CirRav-232
❑ 97ColCho-232
❑ 97ColChoT-SM3
❑ 97Don-126
❑ 97Don-408
❑ 97DonEli-42
❑ 97DonEliGS-42
❑ 97DonGolPP-126
❑ 97DonGolPP-408
❑ 97DonLim-65
❑ 97DonLim-120
❑ 97DonLimE-65
❑ 97DonLimE-120
❑ 97DonLimENG-65
❑ 97DonLimFotG-15
❑ 97DonPre-32
❑ 97DonPreCttC-32
❑ 97DonSig-97
❑ 97DonSigA-69
❑ 97DonSigAC-84
❑ 97DonSigAM-84
❑ 97DonSigPPP-97
❑ 97DonSilPP-126
❑ 97DonSilPP-408
❑ 97DonTea-141
❑ 97DonTeaSPE-141
❑ 97E-X2-42
❑ 97E-X2Cred-42
❑ 97E-X2EssCre-42
❑ 97Fin-99
❑ 97Fin-329
❑ 97FinEmb-329
❑ 97FinEmbR-329
❑ 97FinRef-99
❑ 97FinRef-329
❑ 97FlaShoLC-137
❑ 97FlaShoLeg0-137
❑ 97FlaShoLeg1-137
❑ 97FlaShoM-A137
❑ 97FlaShoM-B137
❑ 97FlaShoM-C137
❑ 97FlaShoR0-137
❑ 97FlaShoR1-137
❑ 97FlaShoR2-137
❑ 97Fle-211
❑ 97FleTif-211
❑ 97Lea-246
❑ 97LeaFraM-246
❑ 97LeaFraMDC-246
❑ 97MarSco-2
❑ 97MarScoPl-2
❑ 97MarScoPr-2
❑ 97MetUni-148
❑ 97NewPin-155
❑ 97NewPinAP-155
❑ 97NewPinMC-155
❑ 97NewPinPP-155
❑ 97Pac-190
❑ 97PacGolCD-17
❑ 97PacLatotML-19
❑ 97PacLigB-190
❑ 97PacPri-64
❑ 97PacPriLB-64
❑ 97PacPriP-64
❑ 97PacSil-190
❑ 97Pin-29
❑ 97PinArtP-PP29
❑ 97PinCer-84
❑ 97PinCerMBla-84
❑ 97PinCerMBlu-84
❑ 97PinCerMG-84
❑ 97PinCerMR-84
❑ 97PinCerR-84
❑ 97PinIns-42
❑ 97PinInsCE-42
❑ 97PinInsDE-42
❑ 97PinMusC-29
❑ 97PinPasttM-10
❑ 97PinPrePla-29
❑ 97PinTotCPB-84
❑ 97PinTotCPG-84
❑ 97PinTotCPR-84
❑ 97PinX-P-27
❑ 97PinX-PMoS-27
❑ 97PinX-PSfF-38
❑ 97PinX-PSfFU-38
❑ 97Sco-56
❑ 97ScoArtPWB-56
❑ 97ScoHigZ-14
❑ 97ScoPitP-4
❑ 97ScoPreS-56
❑ 97ScoShoS-56
❑ 97ScoShoSAP-56
❑ 97Sel-64
❑ 97SelArtP-64
❑ 97SelCom-64
❑ 97SelRegG-64
❑ 97SP-168
❑ 97StaClu-233
❑ 97StaCluMat-233
❑ 97StaCluMOP-233
❑ 97StrAll-42
❑ 97Stu-68
❑ 97StuPrePG-68
❑ 97StuPrePS-68
❑ 97Top-95
❑ 97TopChr-38
❑ 97TopChrR-38
❑ 97TopGal-21
❑ 97TopGalPPI-21
❑ 97TopSta-25
❑ 97TopSta97AS-AS10
❑ 97TopStaAM-25
❑ 97TopSweS-SS9
❑ 97Ult-125
❑ 97UltGolME-125
❑ 97UltPlaME-125
❑ 97UltSeaC-5
❑ 97UppDec-179
❑ 97UppDec-202
❑ 97UppDec-318
❑ 97UppDec-384
❑ 97UppDecMP-P6
❑ 97Zen-40
❑ 98Bow-19
❑ 98BowBes-62
❑ 98BowBesAR-62
❑ 98BowBesR-62
❑ 98BowChr-19
❑ 98BowChrGA-19
❑ 98BowChrGAR-19
❑ 98BowChrI-19
❑ 98BowChrIR-19
❑ 98BowChrR-19
❑ 98BowGolA-19
❑ 98BowInt-19
❑ 98CirThu-233
❑ 98CirThuRav-233
❑ 98CirThuSupRav-233
❑ 98ColChoSQ-SQ26
❑ 98CroRoy-126
❑ 98Don-56
❑ 98DonCol-56
❑ 98DonColE-455
❑ 98DonColL-330
❑ 98DonColP-603
❑ 98DonColS-56
❑ 98DonCruG-42
❑ 98DonCruP-42
❑ 98DonCruR-42
❑ 98DonEli-55
❑ 98DonEliA-55
❑ 98DonEliS-55
❑ 98DonGolPP-56
❑ 98DonPre-53
❑ 98DonPreSeat-53
❑ 98DonPriCD-56
❑ 98DonPriCE-455
❑ 98DonPriCL-330
❑ 98DonPriCP-603
❑ 98DonProLO-2
❑ 98DonSig-42
❑ 98DonSigP-42
❑ 98DonSilPP-56
❑ 98E-X2-69
❑ 98E-X2ECFut-69
❑ 98E-X2ECNow-69
❑ 98Fin-35
❑ 98FinNo--35
❑ 98FinNo-R-35
❑ 98FinRef-35
❑ 98FlaShoLeg0-103
❑ 98FlaShoLeg1-103
❑ 98FlaShoLeg2-103
❑ 98FlaShoLeg3-103
❑ 98FlaShoLegM-103
❑ 98FlaShoR0-103
❑ 98FlaShoR1-103
❑ 98FlaShoR2-103
❑ 98FlaShoR3-103
❑ 98Fle-249
❑ 98FleVin'-57
❑ 98FleVin'C-57
❑ 98Lea-131
❑ 98LeaFraDA-131
❑ 98LeaFraF-131
❑ 98LeaFraM-131
❑ 98LeaFraM-131
❑ 98LeaFraMDC-131
❑ 98LeaFraMDC-131
❑ 98LeaFraMZ2-131
❑ 98LeaRS-54
❑ 98LeaRSLHolo-54
❑ 98LeaRSLong-54
❑ 98LeaRTrue-54
❑ 98MarSco-8
❑ 98MarScoP-8
❑ 98MetUni-74
❑ 98MetUniPMG-74
❑ 98Pac-190
❑ 98PacAur-74
❑ 98PacAurPF-11
❑ 98PacAurPFC-11
❑ 98PacAurPFPB-11
❑ 98PacAurPFR-11
❑ 98PacAurPFS-11
❑ 98PacGolCDC-31
❑ 98PacInCage-17
❑ 98PacInv-66
❑ 98PacInvGems-93
❑ 98PacInvPBlue-66
❑ 98PacInvSilv-66
❑ 98PacInvTeam-26
❑ 98PacLatotML-32
❑ 98PacNes-4A
❑ 98PacOme-223
❑ 98PacOmeOnIns-14
❑ 98PacOmeR-223
❑ 98PacOnl-690
❑ 98PacOnlR-690
❑ 98PacOnlWC-690
❑ 98PacPar-89
❑ 98PacParC-89
❑ 98PacParG-89
❑ 98PacParHS-89
❑ 98PacParPB-89
❑ 98PacParR-89
❑ 98PacPlaB-190
❑ 98PacRedT-190
❑ 98PacSil-190
❑ 98PinIns-60
❑ 98PinInsCE-60
❑ 98PinInsDE-60
❑ 98PinPer-54
❑ 98PinPerPP-54
❑ 98PinPerSftF-15
❑ 98PinPlu-11
❑ 98PinSna-SM18
❑ 98PinSnaS-7
❑ 98Revo-134
❑ 98RevoSS-134
❑ 98Sco-110
❑ 98ScoRT-46
❑ 98ScoRTSS-PP46
❑ 98ScoRTSSAP-PP46
❑ 98ScoRTSSAP1-PP46
❑ 98ScoSS-PP146
❑ 98ScoSSAP-PP146
❑ 98SP Aut-177
❑ 98SpoIll-84
❑ 98SpoIllEE-84
❑ 98SpoIllFE-84
❑ 98SpoIllTaN-109
❑ 98SpoIllTaNEE-109
❑ 98SpoIllWSF-71
❑ 98SpoIllWSFEE-71
❑ 98SpoIllWSFFE-71
❑ 98SPxFin-132
❑ 98SPxFinR-132
❑ 98SPxFinS-132
❑ 98StaCluFDI-271
❑ 98StaCluI-271
❑ 98StaCluOneK-271
❑ 98StaCluPP-271
❑ 98StaCluTIll-T3B
❑ 98StaCluTIll-T18B
❑ 98StaCluTLme-T3B
❑ 98StaCluTLme-T18B
❑ 98StaCluTLmo-T3B
❑ 98StaCluTLmo-T18B
❑ 98Stu-118
❑ 98StuGPP-118
❑ 98StuSPP-118
❑ 98Top-297
❑ 98TopChr-297
❑ 98TopChrC9-C1
❑ 98TopChrC9R-C1
❑ 98TopChrR-297
❑ 98TopClo9-C1
❑ 98TopDevR-297
❑ 98TopDia-297
❑ 98TopGal-148
❑ 98TopGalGP-148
❑ 98TopGalOPP-148
❑ 98TopGalPPI-148
❑ 98TopGalPPIA-148
❑ 98TopGolLabC1-75
❑ 98TopGolLabC1B-75
❑ 98TopGolLabC1One-75
❑ 98TopGolLabC1R-75
❑ 98TopGolLabC2-75
❑ 98TopGolLabC2B-75
❑ 98TopGolLabC2One-75
❑ 98TopGolLabC2R-75
❑ 98TopGolLabC3-75
❑ 98TopGolLabC3B-75
❑ 98TopGolLabC3One-75
❑ 98TopGolLabC3R-75
❑ 98TopMiniC-297
❑ 98TopOpeD-124
❑ 98TopSta-62
❑ 98TopSta'S-27
❑ 98TopSta'SGH-27
❑ 98TopStaB-62
❑ 98TopStaG-62
❑ 98TopStaGR-62
❑ 98TopStaS-62
❑ 98TopStaSteG-27
❑ 98TopTek-64
❑ 98TopTekD-64
❑ 98UD3-63
❑ 98UD3-153
❑ 98UD3-243
❑ 98UD3DieCut-63
❑ 98UD3DieCut-153
❑ 98UD3DieCut-243
❑ 98Ult-157
❑ 98UltGolM-157
❑ 98UltMas-157
❑ 98UltPlaM-157
❑ 98UppDec-226
❑ 98UppDec10AP-58
❑ 98UppDec1APR-58
❑ 98UppDecNP-NP32
❑ 98UppDecSF-127
❑ 98Zen-34
❑ 98Zen5 xx7-28
❑ 98Zen5x7GoldImp-28
❑ 98Zen5x7Imp-28
❑ 98ZenZ-G-34
❑ 98ZenZ-S-34
❑ 99199Fin-160
❑ 99Bow-241
❑ 99BowGol-241
❑ 99BowInt-241
❑ 99CroRoyB-129
❑ 99CroRoyL-129
❑ 99CroRoyOD-129
❑ 99FinGolRef-160
❑ 99FinRef-160
❑ 99FlaShoLeg1-102
❑ 99FlaShoLeg2-102
❑ 99FlaShoLeg3-102
❑ 99FlaShoLegM1-102
❑ 99FlaShoLegM2-102
❑ 99FlaShoLegM3-102
❑ 99FlaShoR1-102
❑ 99FlaShoR2-102
❑ 99FlaShoR3-102
❑ 99Fle-173
❑ 99FleBri-89
❑ 99FleBri2G-89
❑ 99FleBriBlu-89
❑ 99FleBriGol-89
❑ 99FleMys-54
❑ 99FleMysG-54
❑ 99FleMysM-54
❑ 99FleSta9-173
❑ 99FleWarT-173
❑ 99MetUni-77
❑ 99MetUniGM-77
❑ 99MetUniPMG-77
❑ 99Pac-399
❑ 99PacAur-178
❑ 99PacAurOD-178
❑ 99PacCroC-265
❑ 99PacCroC-16
❑ 99PacCroCITC-17
❑ 99PacCroCPB-265
❑ 99PacInv-135
❑ 99PacInvOD-135
❑ 99PacInvPB-135
❑ 99PacOme-222
❑ 99PacOmeC-222
❑ 99PacOmeG-222
❑ 99PacOmePB-222
❑ 99PacPar-219
❑ 99PacParC-219
❑ 99PacParG-219
❑ 99PacParHoloGold-219
❑ 99PacParHS-219
❑ 99PacParOD-219
❑ 99PacParPB-219
❑ 99PacParRed-219
❑ 99PacPlaB-399
❑ 99PacPri-134
❑ 99PacPriHB-134
❑ 99PacPriHG-134
❑ 99PacPriHM-134
❑ 99PacPriHP-134
❑ 99PacPriRed-134
❑ 99PacPriS-112
❑ 99PacPriS206-112
❑ 99PacPriS206R-112
❑ 99PacRed-399
❑ 99Rev-132
❑ 99RevPremDate-132
❑ 99RevRet-132
❑ 99RevShaSS-132
❑ 99SkyMolM-57
❑ 99SkyMolMX-57
❑ 99SkyPre-124
❑ 99SkyPreR-124
❑ 99SkyThu-149
❑ 99SkyThuRant-149
❑ 99SkyThuRave-149
❑ 99SP Aut-78
❑ 99SP AutHRC-HR18
❑ 99SP SigAuto-EM
❑ 99SPAutHRCDC-HR18
❑ 99SpoIll-171
❑ 99SPSig-131
❑ 99StaClu-268
❑ 99StaCluFDI-268
❑ 99StaCluOoaK-268
❑ 99StaCluPP-268
❑ 99ThuSkySupR-149
❑ 99Top-190
❑ 99TopChr-190
❑ 99TopChrR-190
❑ 99TopGal-51
❑ 99TopGalPP-51
❑ 99TopGalPPI-51
❑ 99TopMVPP-190
❑ 99TopOpeD-100
❑ 99UD Cho-145
❑ 99UD ChoPCR-145
❑ 99Ult-121
❑ 99UltGolM-121
❑ 99UltMas-121
❑ 99UltPlaM-121
❑ 99UppDec-491
❑ 99UppDecBD-78
❑ 99UppDecBDD-78
❑ 99UppDecBDQ-78
❑ 99UppDecBDT-78
❑ 99UppDecCf7-31
❑ 99UppDecCf7LL-L21
❑ 99UppDecCLM-C89
❑ 99UppDecCo7CE-31
❑ 99UppDecEL1-491
❑ 99UppDecEL2-491
❑ 99UppDecM-194
❑ 99UppDecMGS-194
❑ 99UppDecMHFS-194

❑ 99UppDecMSS-194
❑ 99Vic-375
Martinez, Eric
❑ 91AubAstC-13
❑ 91AubAstP-4280
❑ 91BoiHawC-24
❑ 91BoiHawP-3874
❑ 92AshTouC-9
❑ 92QuaCitRBC-9
❑ 92QuaCitRBF-804
Martinez, Erik
❑ 94SpoIndC-19
❑ 94SpoIndF-3332
❑ 95OdgRapTI-18
Martinez, Ernest
❑ 92AubAstC-12
❑ 92AubAstF-1361
Martinez, Felix Anthony
❑ 94Bow-162
❑ 94WilBluRC-13
❑ 94WilBluRF-307
❑ 95Bow-133
❑ 95WicWraTI-16
❑ 96Bow-383
❑ 96BowFoi-383
❑ 96OmaRoyB-16
❑ 97Bow-88
❑ 97BowChr-112
❑ 97BowChrI-112
❑ 97BowChrIR-112
❑ 97BowChrR-112
❑ 97BowInt-88
❑ 97OmaRoyB-18
❑ 98Bow-209
❑ 98BowChr-209
❑ 98BowChrGA-209
❑ 98BowChrGAR-209
❑ 98BowChrI-209
❑ 98BowChrIR-209
❑ 98BowChrR-209
❑ 98BowGolA-209
❑ 98BowInt-209
❑ 98ColCho-138
❑ 98Don-343
❑ 98DonGolPP-343
❑ 98DonSilPP-343
❑ 98Fle-148
❑ 98LeaRS-292
❑ 98LeaRSLHolo-292
❑ 98LeaRSLong-292
❑ 98LeaRTrue-292
❑ 98Pac-107
❑ 98PacOmeRS-7
❑ 98PacOmeRST3-7
❑ 98PacPlaB-107
❑ 98PacRedT-107
❑ 98PacSil-107
❑ 98StaCluFDI-150
❑ 98StaCluI-150
❑ 98StaCluOneK-150
❑ 98StaCluPP-150
Martinez, Fili
❑ 89BenBucL-7
❑ 90MidLeaASGS-40
❑ 90QuaCitAGS-25
❑ 91MidAngOHP-18
Martinez, Francisco
❑ 97HelBreB-20
Martinez, Frank
❑ 92SprCarC-11
❑ 92SprCarF-863
❑ 93SavCarC-17
❑ 93SavCarF-685
❑ 94ArkTraF-3086
❑ 94ExcFS7-270
Martinez, Fred
❑ 85LouRedR-20
❑ 86LouRedTI-19
Martinez, Fred (Alfredo)
❑ 79JacMetT-24
❑ 81Don-172
❑ 81Fle-288
❑ 81SalLakCGT-9
❑ 81Top-227
❑ 82SpoIndT-5
❑ 82Top-659
Martinez, Gabby
❑ 92UppDecML-143
❑ 93BelBreCB-14
❑ 93BelBreFI-1718
❑ 93ClaFS7-283
❑ 94Bow-317
❑ 94Cla-24
❑ 94ClaTriF-T43
❑ 94StoPorC-16
❑ 94StoPorF-1701
❑ 96El PasDB-18
❑ 97Bow-341
❑ 97BowChr-233
❑ 97BowChrI-233
❑ 97BowChrIR-233
❑ 97BowChrR-233
❑ 97BowInt-341
❑ 97NorNav-26
❑ 97NorNavTI-21
Martinez, Gil
❑ 87GreHorP-15
❑ 88LynRedSS-11
❑ 89BlaYNPRWL-43
❑ 89LynRedSS-13
Martinez, Greg
❑ 93HelBreF-4111
❑ 94BelBreC-16
❑ 94BelBreFI-116
❑ 96StoPorB-5
❑ 97El PasDB-9
❑ 98LouRedQ-9
Martinez, Hector
❑ 93MedHatBJF-3739
❑ 93MedHatBJSP-4
Martinez, Hipolito
❑ 97SouOreTB-12
❑ 98ModA'sG-18
Martinez, Jacen
❑ 93CapCitBC-12
❑ 93CapCitBF-467
Martinez, Jaime
❑ 93BelMarF-3218
Martinez, Javier
❑ 92BoiHawC-16
❑ 92BoiHawF-3638
❑ 94HunCubC-20
❑ 94HunCubF-3549
❑ 95RocCubTI-32
❑ 97FloStaLTPB-8
❑ 98Fle-402
❑ 98PacOmeRS-11
❑ 98PacOmeRST4-11
❑ 98PacOnl-589
❑ 98PacOnlR-589
❑ 98PacOnlWC-589
Martinez, Jesus
❑ 92ClaFS7-447
❑ 92GreFalDSP-10
❑ 92GulCoaDF-3563
❑ 93BakDodCLC-18
❑ 93ClaGolF-133
❑ 93LimRocDWB-118
❑ 94VerBeaDF-67
❑ 95AusFut-27
❑ 95SanAntMTI-47
❑ 96BesAutS-55
❑ 96SanAntMB-13
❑ 96TexLeaAB-31
❑ 97AlbDukGS-20
❑ 98IndIndQ-13
Martinez, Joe
❑ 92ModA'sF-3896
Martinez, John
❑ 90BurIndP-3012
❑ 91PocPioP-3785
❑ 91PocPioSP-8
Martinez, Johnny Antonio
❑ 93BurIndC-18
❑ 93BurIndF-3295
❑ 94BurIndC-12
❑ 94BurIndF-3787
❑ 96CanIndB-15
❑ 97AkrAer-14
❑ 97BesAutAS-30
Martinez, Jose
❑ 88St.CatBJP-2024
❑ 98Cha-5
Martinez, Jose Luis
❑ 69PirTeal-13
❑ 70OPC-8
❑ 70Top-8
❑ 71MLBOffS-207
❑ 71OPC-712
❑ 71Top-712
❑ 77DayBealT-14
❑ 83RoyPos-17
❑ 84RoyPos-20
❑ 85RoyTeal-19
❑ 88CubDavB-NNO
❑ 89CubMar-NNO
❑ 90CubMar-28
❑ 90TopTVCu-4
❑ 91CubMar-NNO
❑ 92CubMar-NNO
❑ 93CubMar-15
Martinez, Jose Miguel
❑ 91ColMetPI-28
❑ 91ColMetPI-31
❑ 91ColMetPPI-6
❑ 91CubVinL-18
❑ 91SouAtlLAGP-SAL17
❑ 92ClaFS7-276
❑ 92ColMetPI-41
❑ 92ColMetPIISPI-1
❑ 92ColMetPIISPI-3
❑ 92ModA'sC-23
❑ 92ProFS7-287
❑ 92St.LucMCB-14
❑ 92St.LucMF-1743
❑ 92UppDecML-248
❑ 93Bow-331
❑ 93ClaFS7-219
❑ 93EdmTraF-1133
❑ 93ExcFS7-76
❑ 93LimRocDWB-104
❑ 93MarlStaClu-28
❑ 93MarUppD-506
❑ 93UppDec-506
❑ 93UppDecGold-506
❑ 94WicWraF-186
❑ 95Pac-366
❑ 95Pin-160
❑ 95PinArtP-160
❑ 95PinMusC-160
❑ 96ChaRivTI-9618
❑ 96HudValRB-10
Martinez, Julian
❑ 87SavCarP-19
❑ 88St.PetCS-15
❑ 89ArkTraGS-11
❑ 89TexLeaAGS-20
❑ 90CMC-111
❑ 90LouRedBC-11
❑ 90LouRedBLBC-25
❑ 90LouRedBP-410
❑ 90ProAAAF-524
❑ 90TopTVCa-54
❑ 91LinDriAAA-240
❑ 91LouRedLD-240
❑ 91LouRedP-2929
❑ 91LouRedTI-26
❑ 92ArkTraF-1142
❑ 92ArkTraS-37
❑ 93LimRocDWB-33
Martinez, Julio
❑ 93MadMusC-20
❑ 93MadMusF-1820
Martinez, Leo
❑ 96ButCopKB-23
Martinez, Louie
❑ 91AubAstC-6
❑ 91AubAstP-4271
Martinez, Louie (Louis)
❑ 89SanAntMB-14
Martinez, Luis
❑ 80VenLeaS-21
❑ 86MedA'sC-57
❑ 87MadMusP-12
❑ 87MadMusP-8
❑ 88BlaYNPRWL-72
❑ 88BlaYNPRWLU-34
❑ 88FloStaLAS-11
❑ 88ModA'sCLC-74
❑ 89BlaYNPRWL-119
❑ 89SavCarP-350
❑ 90Bes-56
❑ 90SanAntMGS-18
❑ 90SprCarB-14
❑ 91AlbDukLD-14
❑ 91AlbDukP-1147
❑ 91ArkTraLD-38
❑ 91ArkTraP-1300
❑ 91LinDriAA-38
❑ 91LinDriAAA-14
❑ 92AlbDukF-727
❑ 92AlbDukS-12
❑ 93ClaGolF-138
❑ 98HelBreM-23
Martinez, Manny (Manuel)
❑ 90SouOreAB-12
❑ 90SouOreAP-3433
❑ 91CalLeLA-44
❑ 91Cla/Bes-145
❑ 91ModA'sC-24
❑ 91ModA'sP-3104
❑ 92ClaFS7-35
❑ 92ModA'sC-17
❑ 93SanBerSC-13
❑ 93SanBerSF-785
❑ 94ClaGolF-149
❑ 94TacTigF-3188
❑ 95IowCubTI-21
❑ 96TacRaiB-17
❑ 97CalCanB-17
❑ 98NasSouTI-21
❑ 98NasSouTISS-20
Martinez, Martin
❑ 90RocExpLC-17
❑ 90RocExpP-2693
❑ 91Cla/Bes-252
❑ 91RocExpC-8
❑ 91RocExpP-2043
Martinez, Marty (Orlando)
❑ 61TwiCloD-16
❑ 67BraPho-20
❑ 67Top-504
❑ 68BraPos-21
❑ 68CokCapB-11
❑ 68Top-578
❑ 69MilBra-167
❑ 69Top-337
❑ 70AstPho-14
❑ 70OPC-126
❑ 70Top-126
❑ 71MLBOffS-85
❑ 71OPC-602
❑ 71Top-602
❑ 72MilBra-207
❑ 72OPC-336
❑ 72Top-336
❑ 72TopCloT-22
❑ 74SpoIndC-44
❑ 76SanAntBTI-14
❑ 80WauTimT-23
❑ 81SpoIndT-32
❑ 85MarMot-27
❑ 86MarMot-28
❑ 87AstShowSTh-13
❑ 92MarMot-27
❑ 93RanKee-27
Martinez, Matt
❑ 93ElmPioC-10
❑ 93ElmPioF-3830
Martinez, Nicio
❑ 88BatCliP-1667
❑ 90SavCarP-2076
Martinez, Obed R.
❑ 95IdaFalBTI-26
❑ 96IdaFalB-15
Martinez, Osvaldo
❑ 94BriTigC-18
❑ 94BriTigF-3499
Martinez, Pablo
❑ 90ChaRaiB-14
❑ 90ChaRaiP-2044
❑ 91ChaRaiC-19
❑ 91ChaRaiP-104
❑ 92HigDesMC-5
❑ 93WicWraF-2986
❑ 94NorTidF-2929
❑ 95BreBtaTI-5
❑ 96RicBraB-20
❑ 96RicBraRC-18
❑ 96RicBraUB-18
❑ 97RicBra-19
❑ 98LouRedQ-20
Martinez, Pedro A.
❑ 89ChaRaiP-992
❑ 89SouAtlLAGS-11
❑ 90WicWraRD-15
❑ 91WicWraLD-613
❑ 91WicWraP-2595
❑ 91WicWraRD-6
❑ 92WicWraF-3656
❑ 92WicWraS-640
❑ 93ExcFS7-110
❑ 93LasVegSF-941
❑ 93LimRocDWB-126
❑ 94Bow-4
❑ 94ColC-188
❑ 94ColChoGS-188
❑ 94ColChoSS-188
❑ 94Don-526
❑ 94Fin-101
❑ 94FinRef-101
❑ 94Fle-669
❑ 94FleExtB-375
❑ 94OPC-26
❑ 94Pac-530
❑ 94PadMot-27
❑ 94StaClu-611
❑ 94StaClu-684
❑ 94StaCluFDI-684
❑ 94StaCluGR-684
❑ 94StaCluMOP-684
❑ 94Top-676
❑ 94TopGol-676
❑ 94TopSpa-676
❑ 94TriPla-169
❑ 94Ult-581
❑ 95AstMot-16
❑ 95Don-202
❑ 95DonPreP-202
❑ 95Fle-564
❑ 95FleUpd-141
❑ 95Pac-367
❑ 95Top-410
❑ 95TopCyb-210
❑ 95Ult-236
❑ 95UltGolM-236
❑ 96ColCho-358
❑ 96ColChoGS-358
❑ 96ColChoSS-358
❑ 96NorTidB-20
❑ 96Pac-92
❑ 97IndInd-14
❑ 98Pac-266
❑ 98PacPlaB-266
❑ 98PacRedT-266
❑ 98PacSil-266
❑ 98TolMudHQ-24
❑ 99PacOmeDD-5
Martinez, Pedro J.
❑ 90GreFalDSP-12
❑ 91BakDodCLC-32
❑ 91CalLeLA-2
❑ 91Cla/Bes-355
❑ 91Cla3-T55
❑ 91LinDriAA-613
❑ 91SanAntMP-2971
❑ 91UppDecFE-2F
❑ 92AlbDukF-716
❑ 92AlbDukS-13
❑ 92Bow-82
❑ 92DonRoo-69
❑ 92LeaGolR-BC3
❑ 92ProFS7-244
❑ 92SkyAAAF-5
❑ 92SpollIFK1-758
❑ 92TriA AAS-13
❑ 92UppDec-18
❑ 92UppDec-79
❑ 93Bow-154
❑ 93DodMot-16
❑ 93DodPol-15
❑ 93DodStaC-2
❑ 93Don-326
❑ 93Fla-72
❑ 93Fle-354
❑ 93FleMajLP-B4
❑ 93Lea-163
❑ 93PacSpa-500
❑ 93Pin-259
❑ 93PinRooTP-1
❑ 93PinTea2-14
❑ 93Sco-321
❑ 93ScoBoyoS-3
❑ 93ScoProaG-2
❑ 93SelRoo-36T
❑ 93StaClu-365
❑ 93StaCluFDI-365
❑ 93StaCluMOP-365
❑ 93Top-557
❑ 93TopGol-557
❑ 93TopInaM-557
❑ 93TopInaR-557
❑ 93TopMic-557
❑ 93Ult-57
❑ 93UppDec-324
❑ 93UppDecGold-324
❑ 94ColC-189
❑ 94ColC-588
❑ 94ColChoGS-189
❑ 94ColChoGS-588
❑ 94ColChoSS-189
❑ 94ColChoSS-588
❑ 94Don-179
❑ 94Fin-362
❑ 94FinRef-362
❑ 94Fla-193
❑ 94Fle-515
❑ 94FleExtB-309
❑ 94FleExtBSYS-12
❑ 94FleUpd-153
❑ 94FUnPac-88
❑ 94Lea-367
❑ 94OPC-41
❑ 94Pac-313
❑ 94Pin-501
❑ 94PinArtP-501
❑ 94PinMusC-501
❑ 94ProMag-84
❑ 94Sco-554
❑ 94ScoBoyoS-49
❑ 94ScoGolR-554
❑ 94ScoRoo-RT62
❑ 94ScoRooGR-RT62
❑ 94Sel-332
❑ 94SP-85
❑ 94SPDieC-85
❑ 94SpoRoo-16
❑ 94SpoRooAP-16
❑ 94StaCluFDI-611
❑ 94StaCluGR-611
❑ 94StaCluMOP-611
❑ 94Top-268
❑ 94TopGol-268
❑ 94TopSpa-268
❑ 94TopTra-42T
❑ 94Ult-524
❑ 94UppDec-318
❑ 94UppDecAJ-32
❑ 94UppDecAJG-32
❑ 94UppDecED-318
❑ 94USPlaCR-11S
❑ 95Bow-350
❑ 95ColCho-244
❑ 95ColChoGS-244
❑ 95ColChoSE-101
❑ 95ColChoSEGS-101
❑ 95ColChoSESS-101
❑ 95ColChoSS-244
❑ 95Don-315
❑ 95DonPreP-315
❑ 95DonTopotO-282
❑ 95Emo-153
❑ 95Fin-189
❑ 95FinFlaT-FT6
❑ 95FinRef-189
❑ 95Fla-164
❑ 95Fle-356
❑ 95Lea-88
❑ 95LeaLim-37
❑ 95Pac-271
❑ 95PacPri-88
❑ 95PanSti-4
❑ 95Pin-235
❑ 95PinArtP-235
❑ 95PinMusC-235
❑ 95Sco-170
❑ 95Sco-444
❑ 95ScoGolR-170
❑ 95ScoGolR-444
❑ 95ScoPlaTS-170
❑ 95ScoPlaTS-444
❑ 95Sel-87
❑ 95SelArtP-87
❑ 95SP-77
❑ 95SPCha-68
❑ 95SPChaDC-68
❑ 95Spo-99
❑ 95SpoArtP-99
❑ 95SPSil-77
❑ 95StaClu-485
❑ 95StaCluMOP-485
❑ 95StaCluSTWS-485
❑ 95StaCluVR-265
❑ 95StaCluVRMO-265
❑ 95Stu-73
❑ 95Top-622
❑ 95TopCyb-389
❑ 95TopEmb-94
❑ 95TopEmbGI-94
❑ 95TopLeaL-LL25
❑ 95Ult-405
❑ 95UltGolM-405
❑ 95UltStrK-5
❑ 95UltStrKGM-5
❑ 95UppDec-329
❑ 95UppDecED-329
❑ 95UppDecEDG-329
❑ 95UppDecSE-3
❑ 95UppDecSEG-3
❑ 96Baz-76
❑ 96Bow-37
❑ 96BowFoi-37
❑ 96Cir-150
❑ 96CirRav-150
❑ 96ColCho-610
❑ 96ColChoGS-360
❑ 96ColChoGS-610
❑ 96ColChoSS-360
❑ 96ColChoSS-610
❑ 96Don-343

- ❑ 96DonDiaK-12
- ❑ 96DonPreP-343
- ❑ 96DonSho-6
- ❑ 96EmoXL-223
- ❑ 96ExpDis-12
- ❑ 96ExpDis-13
- ❑ 96Fin-B27
- ❑ 96FinRef-B27
- ❑ 96Fla-309
- ❑ 96Fle-462
- ❑ 96FleSmo'H-7
- ❑ 96FleTif-462
- ❑ 96Lea-92
- ❑ 96LeaLim-59
- ❑ 96LeaLimG-59
- ❑ 96LeaPre-53
- ❑ 96LeaPreP-53
- ❑ 96LeaPrePB-92
- ❑ 96LeaPrePG-92
- ❑ 96LeaPrePS-92
- ❑ 96LeaSigA-146
- ❑ 96LeaSigAG-146
- ❑ 96LeaSigAS-146
- ❑ 96MetUni-192
- ❑ 96MetUniP-192
- ❑ 96Pac-123
- ❑ 96PacEstL-EL9
- ❑ 96PacPri-P42
- ❑ 96PacPriG-P42
- ❑ 96PanSti-18
- ❑ 96Pin-79
- ❑ 96PinAfi-120
- ❑ 96PinAfiAP-120
- ❑ 96PinArtP-29
- ❑ 96PinSta-29
- ❑ 96ProSta-49
- ❑ 96Sco-277
- ❑ 96ScoDugC-B2
- ❑ 96ScoDugCAP-B2
- ❑ 96Sel-74
- ❑ 96SelArtP-74
- ❑ 96SelCer-93
- ❑ 96SelCerAP-93
- ❑ 96SelCerCB-93
- ❑ 96SelCerCR-93
- ❑ 96SelCerMB-93
- ❑ 96SelCerMG-93
- ❑ 96SelCerMR-93
- ❑ 96SP-118
- ❑ 96Spo-69
- ❑ 96SpoArtP-69
- ❑ 96StaClu-80
- ❑ 96StaCluEPB-80
- ❑ 96StaCluEPG-80
- ❑ 96StaCluEPS-80
- ❑ 96StaCluMOP-80
- ❑ 96Stu-92
- ❑ 96StuPrePB-92
- ❑ 96StuPrePG-92
- ❑ 96StuPrePS-92
- ❑ 96Top-303
- ❑ 96TopChr-121
- ❑ 96TopChrR-121
- ❑ 96TopGal-111
- ❑ 96TopGalPPI-111
- ❑ 96TopLas-122
- ❑ 96Ult-233
- ❑ 96UltGolM-233
- ❑ 96UppDec-136
- ❑ 96UppDecPHE-H45
- ❑ 96UppDecPreH-H45
- ❑ 96Zen-85
- ❑ 96ZenArtP-85
- ❑ 97Bow-223
- ❑ 97BowChr-53
- ❑ 97BowChrI-53
- ❑ 97BowChrIR-53
- ❑ 97BowChrR-53
- ❑ 97BowInt-223
- ❑ 97Cir-347
- ❑ 97CirRav-347
- ❑ 97ColCho-162
- ❑ 97Don-263
- ❑ 97DonGolPP-263
- ❑ 97DonLim-16
- ❑ 97DonLimE-16
- ❑ 97DonLimENG-16
- ❑ 97DonSig-81
- ❑ 97DonSigA-70
- ❑ 97DonSigAC-85
- ❑ 97DonSigAM-85
- ❑ 97DonSigPPP-81
- ❑ 97DonSilPP-263
- ❑ 97Fin-40
- ❑ 97FinRef-40
- ❑ 97Fle-383
- ❑ 97FleTif-383
- ❑ 97KinB-18
- ❑ 97Lea-44
- ❑ 97LeaFraM-44
- ❑ 97LeaFraMDC-44
- ❑ 97MetUni-158
- ❑ 97NewPin-40
- ❑ 97NewPin-182
- ❑ 97NewPinAP-40
- ❑ 97NewPinAP-182
- ❑ 97NewPinMC-40
- ❑ 97NewPinMC-182
- ❑ 97NewPinPP-40
- ❑ 97NewPinPP-182
- ❑ 97Pac-347
- ❑ 97PacLatotML-31
- ❑ 97PacLigB-347
- ❑ 97PacPri-119
- ❑ 97PacPriLB-119
- ❑ 97PacPriP-119
- ❑ 97PacSil-347
- ❑ 97Sco-72
- ❑ 97ScoArtPWB-72
- ❑ 97ScoPreS-72
- ❑ 97ScoShoS-72
- ❑ 97ScoShoSAP-72
- ❑ 97SP-113
- ❑ 97SpoIll-87
- ❑ 97SpoIllEE-87
- ❑ 97StaClu-12
- ❑ 97StaCluMat-12
- ❑ 97StaCluMOP-12
- ❑ 97StrAll-43
- ❑ 97Stu-139
- ❑ 97StuPrePG-139
- ❑ 97StuPrePS-139
- ❑ 97Top-158
- ❑ 97TopGal-132
- ❑ 97TopGalPPI-132
- ❑ 97TopSta-77
- ❑ 97TopStaAM-77
- ❑ 97Ult-232
- ❑ 97UltGolME-232
- ❑ 97UltPlaME-232
- ❑ 97UppDec-111
- ❑ 97UppDecRSF-RS16
- ❑ 98Bow-234
- ❑ 98BowBes-38
- ❑ 98BowBesAR-38
- ❑ 98BowBesR-38
- ❑ 98BowChr-234
- ❑ 98BowChrGA-234
- ❑ 98BowChrGAR-234
- ❑ 98BowChrI-234
- ❑ 98BowChrIR-234
- ❑ 98BowChrR-234
- ❑ 98BowGolA-234
- ❑ 98BowInt-234
- ❑ 98CirThu-264
- ❑ 98CirThuB-13
- ❑ 98CirThuLA-10
- ❑ 98CirThuQS-7
- ❑ 98CirThuRav-264
- ❑ 98CirThuSupRav-264
- ❑ 98ColCho-259
- ❑ 98ColCho-325
- ❑ 98ColChoS'-17
- ❑ 98ColChoSQ-SQ24
- ❑ 98ColChoSQDouble-12
- ❑ 98ColChoSQHR-12
- ❑ 98ColChoSQSingle-12
- ❑ 98ColChoSQTriple-12
- ❑ 98CroRoy-25
- ❑ 98Don-18
- ❑ 98Don-235
- ❑ 98Don-384
- ❑ 98DonCol-18
- ❑ 98DonColL-320
- ❑ 98DonColP-597
- ❑ 98DonColS-18
- ❑ 98DonCruG-85
- ❑ 98DonCruP-85
- ❑ 98DonCruR-85
- ❑ 98DonGolPP-18
- ❑ 98DonGolPP-235
- ❑ 98DonGolPP-384
- ❑ 98DonPre-47
- ❑ 98DonPreSeat-47
- ❑ 98DonPriCD-18
- ❑ 98DonPriCL-320
- ❑ 98DonPriCP-597
- ❑ 98DonSig-56
- ❑ 98DonSigP-56
- ❑ 98DonSilPP-18
- ❑ 98DonSilPP-235
- ❑ 98DonSilPP-384
- ❑ 98DonSonM9-5
- ❑ 98E-X2-39
- ❑ 98E-X2ECFut-39
- ❑ 98E-X2ECNow-39
- ❑ 98Fin-154
- ❑ 98FinNo--154
- ❑ 98FinNo-R-154
- ❑ 98FinRef-154
- ❑ 98FlaShoLeg0-85
- ❑ 98FlaShoLeg1-85
- ❑ 98FlaShoLeg2-85
- ❑ 98FlaShoLeg3-85
- ❑ 98FlaShoLegM-85
- ❑ 98FlaShoR0-85
- ❑ 98FlaShoR1-85
- ❑ 98FlaShoR2-85
- ❑ 98FlaShoR3-85
- ❑ 98Fle-45
- ❑ 98Fle-306
- ❑ 98Fle-381
- ❑ 98FleDiaS-14
- ❑ 98FlePowG-13
- ❑ 98FleVin'-36
- ❑ 98FleVin'-81
- ❑ 98FleVin'C-36
- ❑ 98FleVin'C-81
- ❑ 98Lea-121
- ❑ 98LeaFraDA-121
- ❑ 98LeaFraF-121
- ❑ 98LeaFraM-121
- ❑ 98LeaFraM-121
- ❑ 98LeaFraMDC-121
- ❑ 98LeaFraMDC-121
- ❑ 98LeaFraMZ2-121
- ❑ 98LeaRS-16
- ❑ 98LeaRSLHolo-16
- ❑ 98LeaRSLong-16
- ❑ 98LeaRTrue-16
- ❑ 98MetUni-65
- ❑ 98MetUniPMG-65
- ❑ 98Pac-349
- ❑ 98PacAur-18
- ❑ 98PacAurPF-45
- ❑ 98PacAurPFC-45
- ❑ 98PacAurPFPB-45
- ❑ 98PacAurPFR-45
- ❑ 98PacAurPFS-45
- ❑ 98PacInv-115
- ❑ 98PacInvGems-178
- ❑ 98PacInvInt-14N
- ❑ 98PacInvMiT-11
- ❑ 98PacInvPBlue-115
- ❑ 98PacInvPhoto-8
- ❑ 98PacInvSilv-115
- ❑ 98PacInvTeam-17
- ❑ 98PacLatotML-22
- ❑ 98PacNes-8
- ❑ 98PacOme-40
- ❑ 98PacOmeOnIns-3
- ❑ 98PacOmeP-3
- ❑ 98PacOmeR-40
- ❑ 98PacOnl-122
- ❑ 98PacOnlR-122
- ❑ 98PacOnlWC-122
- ❑ 98PacPar-22
- ❑ 98PacParC-22
- ❑ 98PacParG-22
- ❑ 98PacParHS-22
- ❑ 98PacParPB-22
- ❑ 98PacParR-22
- ❑ 98PacParSD-5
- ❑ 98PacPlaB-349
- ❑ 98PacRedT-349
- ❑ 98PacSil-349
- ❑ 98PacTeaC-22
- ❑ 98Pin-2
- ❑ 98PinArtP-PP2
- ❑ 98PinIns-98
- ❑ 98PinInsCE-98
- ❑ 98PinInsDE-98
- ❑ 98PinMinMG-4
- ❑ 98PinMinMGC-4
- ❑ 98PinMusC-PP2
- ❑ 98PinPer-48
- ❑ 98PinPerPP-48
- ❑ 98PinPlu-29
- ❑ 98PinPluAP-PP16
- ❑ 98PinPluGAP-PP16
- ❑ 98PinPluMAP-PP16
- ❑ 98PinPluTP-13
- ❑ 98PinPluTPG-13
- ❑ 98PinPluTPM-13
- ❑ 98PinPreP-2
- ❑ 98PinSna-BRS4
- ❑ 98Revo-26
- ❑ 98RevoShow-3
- ❑ 98RevoSS-26
- ❑ 98Sco-86
- ❑ 98ScoRT-45
- ❑ 98ScoRTSS-PP45
- ❑ 98ScoRTSSAP-PP45
- ❑ 98ScoRTSSAP1-PP45
- ❑ 98ScoSS-PP137
- ❑ 98ScoSSAP-PP137
- ❑ 98SkyDugA-56
- ❑ 98SkyDugAD-D3
- ❑ 98SkyDugAIA-56
- ❑ 98SP Aut-61
- ❑ 98SP Aut-SD24
- ❑ 98SP AutSD-SD24
- ❑ 98SP AutSDT-SD24
- ❑ 98SpoIll-85
- ❑ 98SpoIll-194
- ❑ 98SpoIllEE-85
- ❑ 98SpoIllEE-194
- ❑ 98SpoIllFE-85
- ❑ 98SpoIllFE-194
- ❑ 98SpoIllTaN-110
- ❑ 98SpoIllTaNEE-110
- ❑ 98SpoIllWSF-96
- ❑ 98SpoIllWSFEE-96
- ❑ 98SpoIllWSFFE-96
- ❑ 98SPxFin-215
- ❑ 98SPxFin-254
- ❑ 98SPxFin-335
- ❑ 98SPxFinR-215
- ❑ 98SPxFinR-254
- ❑ 98SPxFinR-335
- ❑ 98SPxFinS-215
- ❑ 98SPxFinS-254
- ❑ 98SPxFinS-335
- ❑ 98StaCluFDI-398
- ❑ 98StaCluI-398
- ❑ 98StaCluOneK-398
- ❑ 98StaCluPP-398
- ❑ 98Stu-57
- ❑ 98StuGPP-57
- ❑ 98StuSony99-5
- ❑ 98StuSPP-57
- ❑ 98Top-271
- ❑ 98Top-338
- ❑ 98TopChr-271
- ❑ 98TopChr-338
- ❑ 98TopChrR-271
- ❑ 98TopChrR-338
- ❑ 98TopDevR-271
- ❑ 98TopDevR-338
- ❑ 98TopDia-271
- ❑ 98TopDia-338
- ❑ 98TopGal-4
- ❑ 98TopGalAG-AG4
- ❑ 98TopGalGP-4
- ❑ 98TopGalOPP-4
- ❑ 98TopGalPPI-4
- ❑ 98TopGalPPIA-4
- ❑ 98TopGolLabC1-45
- ❑ 98TopGolLabC1B-45
- ❑ 98TopGolLabC1One-45
- ❑ 98TopGolLabC1R-45
- ❑ 98TopGolLabC2-45
- ❑ 98TopGolLabC2B-45
- ❑ 98TopGolLabC2One-45
- ❑ 98TopGolLabC2R-45
- ❑ 98TopGolLabC3-45
- ❑ 98TopGolLabC3B-45
- ❑ 98TopGolLabC3One-45
- ❑ 98TopGolLabC3R-45
- ❑ 98TopMiniC-271
- ❑ 98TopMiniC-338
- ❑ 98TopOpeD-165
- ❑ 98TopSta-144
- ❑ 98TopStaB-144
- ❑ 98TopStaG-144
- ❑ 98TopStaGR-144
- ❑ 98TopStaPre-PP6
- ❑ 98TopStaS-144
- ❑ 98TopTek-41
- ❑ 98TopTekD-41
- ❑ 98UD3-87
- ❑ 98UD3-177
- ❑ 98UD3-267
- ❑ 98UD3DieCut-87
- ❑ 98UD3DieCut-177
- ❑ 98UD3DieCut-267
- ❑ 98Ult-34
- ❑ 98Ult-324
- ❑ 98UltDouT-2
- ❑ 98UltGolM-34
- ❑ 98UltGolM-324
- ❑ 98UltMas-34
- ❑ 98UltMas-324
- ❑ 98UltPlaM-34
- ❑ 98UltPlaM-324
- ❑ 98UppDec-6
- ❑ 98UppDec-157
- ❑ 98UppDec-361
- ❑ 98UppDec-655
- ❑ 98UppDecNP-NP13
- ❑ 98UppDecR-14
- ❑ 98UppDecRTC-TC5
- ❑ 98Zen-66
- ❑ 98ZenZ-G-66
- ❑ 98ZenZ-S-66
- ❑ 99199Fin-170
- ❑ 99Bow-19
- ❑ 99BowBes-53
- ❑ 99BowBesAR-53
- ❑ 99BowBesR-53
- ❑ 99BowChr-19
- ❑ 99BowChrG-19
- ❑ 99BowChrGR-19
- ❑ 99BowChrI-19
- ❑ 99BowChrIR-19
- ❑ 99BowChrR-19
- ❑ 99BowGol-19
- ❑ 99BowInt-19
- ❑ 99CroRoyB-24
- ❑ 99CroRoyL-24
- ❑ 99CroRoyOD-24
- ❑ 99E-X Cen-23
- ❑ 99E-X CenECFut-23
- ❑ 99E-X CenECNow-23
- ❑ 99FinGolRef-170
- ❑ 99FinRef-170
- ❑ 99FlaShoLeg1-58
- ❑ 99FlaShoLeg2-58
- ❑ 99FlaShoLeg3-58
- ❑ 99FlaShoLegM1-58
- ❑ 99FlaShoLegM2-58
- ❑ 99FlaShoLegM3-58
- ❑ 99FlaShoR1-58
- ❑ 99FlaShoR2-58
- ❑ 99FlaShoR3-58
- ❑ 99Fle-116
- ❑ 99FleBri-7
- ❑ 99FleBri2G-7
- ❑ 99FleBriBlu-7
- ❑ 99FleBriGol-7
- ❑ 99FleMys-94
- ❑ 99FleMysG-94
- ❑ 99FleMysM-94
- ❑ 99FleSta9-116
- ❑ 99FleWarT-116
- ❑ 99KinDis-18
- ❑ 99MetUni-210
- ❑ 99MetUniGM-210
- ❑ 99MetUniPMG-210
- ❑ 99Pac-71
- ❑ 99PacAur-30
- ❑ 99PacAurOD-30
- ❑ 99PacCroC-47
- ❑ 99PacCroC-4
- ❑ 99PacCroCPB-47
- ❑ 99PacGolCDC-4
- ❑ 99PacInv-24
- ❑ 99PacInvOD-24
- ❑ 99PacInvPB-24
- ❑ 99PacOme-41
- ❑ 99PacOme5T-3
- ❑ 99PacOme5TT-3
- ❑ 99PacOmeC-41
- ❑ 99PacOmeDM-9
- ❑ 99PacOmeG-41
- ❑ 99PacOmePB-41
- ❑ 99PacPar-41
- ❑ 99PacParC-41
- ❑ 99PacParG-41
- ❑ 99PacParHoloGold-41
- ❑ 99PacParHS-41
- ❑ 99PacParOD-41
- ❑ 99PacParPB-41
- ❑ 99PacParRed-41
- ❑ 99PacPlaB-71
- ❑ 99PacPri-23
- ❑ 99PacPriHB-23
- ❑ 99PacPriHG-23
- ❑ 99PacPriHM-23
- ❑ 99PacPriHP-23
- ❑ 99PacPriRed-23
- ❑ 99PacPriS-40
- ❑ 99PacPriS206-40
- ❑ 99PacPriS206R-40
- ❑ 99PacPriSP-40
- ❑ 99PacPriSV-40
- ❑ 99PacRed-71
- ❑ 99Pin-18
- ❑ 99Rev-25
- ❑ 99RevPremDate-25
- ❑ 99RevRet-25
- ❑ 99RevShaSS-25
- ❑ 99SkyMolM-20
- ❑ 99SkyMolMX-20
- ❑ 99SkyPre-16
- ❑ 99SkyPreR-16
- ❑ 99SkyThu-260
- ❑ 99SkyThuRant-260
- ❑ 99SkyThuRave-260
- ❑ 99SP Aut-17
- ❑ 99SP SigAuto-PM
- ❑ 99SP SigAutoG-PM
- ❑ 99SpoIll-175
- ❑ 99SpoIllDD-5
- ❑ 99SpoIllH-24
- ❑ 99SPSig-22
- ❑ 99SPx-24
- ❑ 99SPxFinR-24
- ❑ 99SPxFinS-24
- ❑ 99StaClu-115
- ❑ 99StaClu-290
- ❑ 99StaCluC-SCC15
- ❑ 99StaCluCR-SCC15
- ❑ 99StaCluFDI-115
- ❑ 99StaCluFDI-290
- ❑ 99StaCluOoaK-115
- ❑ 99StaCluOoaK-290
- ❑ 99StaCluPP-115
- ❑ 99StaCluPP-290
- ❑ 99StaCluTI-T7B
- ❑ 99StaCluTL-T7B
- ❑ 99StaCluTL-T7B
- ❑ 99ThuSkySupR-260
- ❑ 99Top-95
- ❑ 99Top-449
- ❑ 99TopAll-AM29
- ❑ 99TopBlaLC1-44
- ❑ 99TopBlaLC2-44
- ❑ 99TopBlaLC3-44
- ❑ 99TopChr-95
- ❑ 99TopChr-449
- ❑ 99TopChrA-AE29
- ❑ 99TopChrAR-AE29
- ❑ 99TopChrR-95
- ❑ 99TopChrR-449
- ❑ 99TopGal-91
- ❑ 99TopGalPP-91
- ❑ 99TopGalPPI-91
- ❑ 99TopGolL-44
- ❑ 99TopGolLC1-44
- ❑ 99TopGolLC2-44
- ❑ 99TopGolLOtO-44
- ❑ 99TopMVPP-95
- ❑ 99TopMVPP-449
- ❑ 99TopOpeD-54
- ❑ 99TopPicP-P3
- ❑ 99TopRedLC1-44
- ❑ 99TopRedLC2-44
- ❑ 99TopRedLC3-44
- ❑ 99TopSta-56
- ❑ 99TopSta'S-24
- ❑ 99TopSta'SG-24
- ❑ 99TopSta'SGDH-24
- ❑ 99TopSta1Foil-56
- ❑ 99TopStaFoil-56
- ❑ 99TopStaOS-56
- ❑ 99TopSupC-16
- ❑ 99TopSupCR-16
- ❑ 99UD Cho-64
- ❑ 99UD ChoMBH-B6
- ❑ 99UD ChoP-64
- ❑ 99UD ChoPCR-64
- ❑ 99UD Ion-14
- ❑ 99UD IonR-14
- ❑ 99UDHolo-13
- ❑ 99UDHoloAUsome-13
- ❑ 99Ult-150
- ❑ 99UltGolM-150
- ❑ 99UltMas-150
- ❑ 99UltPlaM-150
- ❑ 99UppDec-234
- ❑ 99UppDec-328
- ❑ 99UppDecBD-17
- ❑ 99UppDecBDD-17
- ❑ 99UppDecBDMN-M19
- ❑ 99UppDecBDMNE-M19
- ❑ 99UppDecBDQ-17
- ❑ 99UppDecBDT-17
- ❑ 99UppDecCL-76
- ❑ 99UppDecCLCC-76
- ❑ 99UppDecCLM-C14
- ❑ 99UppDecE-16
- ❑ 99UppDecEFXG-16
- ❑ 99UppDecEL1-234
- ❑ 99UppDecEL1-328
- ❑ 99UppDecEL2-234

❑ 99UppDecEL2-328
❑ 99UppDecM-32
❑ 99UppDecMGS-32
❑ 99UppDecMHFS-32
❑ 99UppDecMP-32
❑ 99UppDecMSS-32
❑ 99UppDecO-43
❑ 99UppDecOSO-43
❑ 99UppDecOWP-R13
❑ 99UppDecR-16
❑ 99UppDecRG-16
❑ 99UppDecRP-16
❑ 99Vic-62
Martinez, Porfi
❑ 86LakTigP-12
Martinez, Rafael
❑ 88St.CatBJP-2026
❑ 89MyrBeaBJP-1468
❑ 95GreFalDTI-30
❑ 96VerBeaDB-19
❑ 97St.LucM-16
Martinez, Ramiro
❑ 92GulCoaRSP-6
❑ 93ChaRaiC-12
❑ 93ChaRaiF-1907
❑ 93StaCluM-173
❑ 94TulDriF-242
❑ 94TulDriTI-16
❑ 95TulDriTI-13
❑ 97HarSen-16
❑ 98arSenW1-13
❑ 98HarSenM-13
Martinez, Ramon
❑ 87SalAngP-12
❑ 88BenBucL-5
❑ 89PalSprACLC-38
❑ 89PalSprAP-467
❑ 89PriPirS-12
❑ 92SalBucC-2
Martinez, Ramon Dario
❑ 90AugPirP-2458
❑ 91AugPirC-16
❑ 91AugPirP-812
❑ 91PalSprAP-2024
❑ 92EdmTraF-3546
❑ 92SalBucF-71
❑ 93Bow-66
❑ 93ExcFS7-92
❑ 93HigDesMC-12
❑ 93HigDesMF-49
❑ 93MarlStaClu-17
❑ 93StaClu-322
❑ 93StaCluFDI-322
❑ 93StaCluMOP-322
❑ 93VanCanF-2604
❑ 94PorSeaDF-687
❑ 94PorSeaDTI-22
❑ 94UppDecML-223
❑ 94WilBluRC-14
❑ 94WilBluRF-308
❑ 95FinRef-200
❑ 95WicWraTI-15
❑ 96ColCho-360
❑ 96LynHilB-14
❑ 96OmaRoyB-17
❑ 96SanAntMB-14
❑ 97ShrCap-15
❑ 97ShrCapB-15
Martinez, Ramon E.
❑ 98BesAutSS-32
❑ 98FreGriG-16
❑ 99PacCroC-253
❑ 99PacCroCPB-253
❑ 99Rev-127
❑ 99RevPremDate-127
❑ 99RevRet-127
❑ 99RevShaSS-127
❑ 99SkyPre-256
❑ 99SkyPre-256
❑ 99SkyPreR-256
❑ 99SkyPreR-256
❑ 99SpoIll-54
❑ 99SPx-116
❑ 99SPxFinR-116
❑ 99SPxFinS-116
❑ 99UD Cho-10
❑ 99UD ChoPCR-10
❑ 99UppDec-16
❑ 99UppDecE-106
❑ 99UppDecEFXG-106
❑ 99UppDecEL1-16
❑ 99UppDecEL2-16
❑ 99UppDecM-187
❑ 99UppDecMGS-187
❑ 99UppDecMHFS-187
❑ 99UppDecMSS-187
Martinez, Ramon J.
❑ 86BakDodP-20
❑ 87VerBeaDP-7
❑ 88BasAmeAAB-21
❑ 88SanAntMB-1
❑ 88TexLeaAGS-28
❑ 88TriAAC-45
❑ 89AlbDukCm-7
❑ 89AlbDukP-69
❑ 89ClaTraO-130
❑ 89DodPol-24
❑ 89DodStaSV-16
❑ 89Don-464
❑ 89DonRoo-45
❑ 89Fle-67
❑ 89FleGlo-67
❑ 89Sco-635
❑ 89ScoHot1R-55
❑ 89ScoYouSI-40
❑ 89Spo-224
❑ 89SpoIllFKI-303
❑ 89Top-225
❑ 89TopTif-225
❑ 89TriAAAP-AAA47
❑ 89UppDec-18
❑ 90Bow-88
❑ 90BowTif-88
❑ 90ClaBlu-76
❑ 90DodMot-17
❑ 90DodTar-489
❑ 90Don-685
❑ 90DonBesN-141
❑ 90Fle-402
❑ 90FleCan-402
❑ 90Hot50RS-30
❑ 90Lea-147
❑ 90OPC-62
❑ 90PanSti-380
❑ 90Sco-461
❑ 90Sco100RS-59
❑ 90ScoMcD-13
❑ 90Spo-68
❑ 90Top-62
❑ 90TopRoo-20
❑ 90TopSti-61
❑ 90TopTif-62
❑ 90ToyRoo-19
❑ 90TriAAAC-40
❑ 90UppDec-675
❑ 90USPlaCA-1H
❑ 91BasBesRB-10
❑ 91Bow-610
❑ 91CadEllD-35
❑ 91Cla1-T52
❑ 91ClaGam-99
❑ 91Col-18
❑ 91DodMot-10
❑ 91DodPho-18
❑ 91DodPol-48
❑ 91DodSt.V-15
❑ 91DodUno7P-6
❑ 91Don-15
❑ 91Don-557
❑ 91DonSupD-15
❑ 91Fle-212
❑ 91KinDis-12
❑ 91Lea-61
❑ 91LeaPre-5
❑ 91MajLeaCP-52
❑ 91OPC-340
❑ 91PanCanT1-58
❑ 91PanCanT1-75
❑ 91PanFreS-62
❑ 91PanSti-50
❑ 91Sco-300
❑ 91Sco-408
❑ 91Sco-419
❑ 91Sco100S-16
❑ 91SevCoi-F11
❑ 91SevCoi-SC8
❑ 91StaClu-516
❑ 91StaCluCM-19
❑ 91Stu-184
❑ 91Top-340
❑ 91TopCraJ2-25
❑ 91TopDesS-340
❑ 91TopMic-340
❑ 91TopSta-23
❑ 91TopTif-340
❑ 91TopTriH-N5
❑ 91Ult-164
❑ 91UltGol-7
❑ 91UppDec-78
❑ 91UppDec-136
❑ 92Bow-255
❑ 92Cla2-T40
❑ 92ClaGam-35
❑ 92DodMot-7
❑ 92DodPol-48
❑ 92DodSmo-4592
❑ 92DodStaTA-29
❑ 92Don-656
❑ 92DonCraJ1-30
❑ 92Fle-463
❑ 92Fle-706
❑ 92FleAll-7
❑ 92FleCitTP-21
❑ 92Hig5-53
❑ 92Hig5S-23
❑ 92Lea-297
❑ 92LeaBlaG-297
❑ 92MVPPin-35
❑ 92OPC-730
❑ 92Pin-429
❑ 92PinTea2-49
❑ 92PinTeaP-1
❑ 92Sco-610
❑ 92Sco-780
❑ 92Sco100S-75
❑ 92ScoImpP-75
❑ 92SpoStaCC-31
❑ 92StaClu-207
❑ 92Stu-46
❑ 92Top-730
❑ 92TopGol-730
❑ 92TopGolW-730
❑ 92TopKid-48
❑ 92TopMic-730
❑ 92TriPla-55
❑ 92Ult-213
❑ 92UppDec-79
❑ 92UppDec-346
❑ 92UppDecTMH-32
❑ 93Bow-590
❑ 93CadDis-39
❑ 93DiaMar-70
❑ 93DodMot-12
❑ 93DodPol-16
❑ 93DodStaC-10
❑ 93Don-298
❑ 93Fin-29
❑ 93FinRef-29
❑ 93Fla-73
❑ 93Fle-65
❑ 93Fle-354
❑ 93FleFruotL-42
❑ 93FunPac-90
❑ 93FunPac-213
❑ 93Lea-335
❑ 93OPC-275
❑ 93PacSpa-152
❑ 93PacSpaPI-4
❑ 93PanSti-212
❑ 93Pin-377
❑ 93Sco-199
❑ 93Sel-213
❑ 93SP-95
❑ 93StaClu-71
❑ 93StaCluFDI-71
❑ 93StaCluMOP-71
❑ 93Stu-149
❑ 93Top-120
❑ 93TopGol-120
❑ 93TopInaM-120
❑ 93TopInaR-120
❑ 93TopMic-120
❑ 93TriPla-161
❑ 93Ult-401
❑ 93UppDec-133
❑ 93UppDecGold-133
❑ 94Bow-398
❑ 94ColC-190
❑ 94ColChoGS-190
❑ 94ColChoSS-190
❑ 94DodDaiN-7
❑ 94DodMot-11
❑ 94DodPol-17
❑ 94Don-368
❑ 94DonSpeE-368
❑ 94Fin-405
❑ 94FinRef-405
❑ 94Fla-398
❑ 94Fle-516
❑ 94FleExtB-290
❑ 94Lea-303
❑ 94OPC-76
❑ 94Pac-314
❑ 94Pin-353
❑ 94PinArtP-353
❑ 94PinMusC-353
❑ 94Sco-233
❑ 94ScoGolR-233
❑ 94Sel-107
❑ 94Spo-99
❑ 94StaClu-276
❑ 94StaCluFDI-276
❑ 94StaCluGR-276
❑ 94StaCluMOP-276
❑ 94Top-545
❑ 94TopGol-545
❑ 94TopSpa-545
❑ 94TriPla-86
❑ 94Ult-519
❑ 94UppDec-349
❑ 94UppDecAJ-32
❑ 94UppDecAJG-32
❑ 94UppDecED-349
❑ 95Bow-358
❑ 95ColCho-227
❑ 95ColChoGS-227
❑ 95ColChoSE-93
❑ 95ColChoSEGS-93
❑ 95ColChoSESS-93
❑ 95ColChoSS-227
❑ 95DodMot-4
❑ 95DodPol-14
❑ 95Don-481
❑ 95DonPreP-481
❑ 95DonTopotO-267
❑ 95Emo-142
❑ 95Fin-200
❑ 95Fla-367
❑ 95Fle-544
❑ 95FleTeaL-21
❑ 95Lea-104
❑ 95LeaLim-114
❑ 95Pac-221
❑ 95PacPri-70
❑ 95Pin-274
❑ 95PinArtP-274
❑ 95PinMusC-274
❑ 95Sco-155
❑ 95ScoGolR-155
❑ 95ScoPlaTS-155
❑ 95SP-69
❑ 95SPCha-61
❑ 95SPChaDC-61
❑ 95SPSil-69
❑ 95StaClu-434
❑ 95StaCluMOP-434
❑ 95StaCluSTDW-D434
❑ 95StaCluSTWS-434
❑ 95StaCluVR-229
❑ 95StaCluVRMO-229
❑ 95Stu-74
❑ 95Top-275
❑ 95TopCyb-148
❑ 95Ult-182
❑ 95UltGolM-182
❑ 95UppDec-321
❑ 95UppDecED-321
❑ 95UppDecEDG-321
❑ 95UppDecSE-37
❑ 95UppDecSEG-37
❑ 96Baz-68
❑ 96Cir-142
❑ 96CirRav-142
❑ 96ColCho-186
❑ 96ColCho-360
❑ 96ColChoGS-186
❑ 96ColChoGS-360
❑ 96ColChoSS-186
❑ 96ColChoSS-360
❑ 96DodFle-11
❑ 96DodMot-21
❑ 96DodPol-23
❑ 96Don-151
❑ 96DonPreP-151
❑ 96EmoXL-211
❑ 96Fin-B71
❑ 96FinRef-B71
❑ 96Fla-295
❑ 96Fle-440
❑ 96FleGolM-5
❑ 96FleTif-440
❑ 96Lea-198
❑ 96LeaPrePB-198
❑ 96LeaPrePG-198
❑ 96LeaPrePS-198
❑ 96MetUni-184
❑ 96MetUniP-184
❑ 96Pac-104
❑ 96PacPri-P35
❑ 96PacPriFT-FT9
❑ 96PacPriG-P35
❑ 96PanSti-94
❑ 96Pin-45
❑ 96PinAfi-93
❑ 96PinAfiAP-93
❑ 96PinAfiFPP-93
❑ 96Sco-294
❑ 96ScoDugC-B19
❑ 96ScoDugCAP-B19
❑ 96Sel-109
❑ 96SelArtP-109
❑ 96SP-103
❑ 96StaClu-140
❑ 96StaCluEPB-140
❑ 96StaCluEPG-140
❑ 96StaCluEPS-140
❑ 96StaCluMOP-140
❑ 96Stu-30
❑ 96StuPrePB-30
❑ 96StuPrePG-30
❑ 96StuPrePS-30
❑ 96Sum-103
❑ 96SumAbo&B-103
❑ 96SumArtP-103
❑ 96SumFoi-103
❑ 96Top-206
❑ 96TopChr-71
❑ 96TopChrR-71
❑ 96TopGal-8
❑ 96TopGalPPI-8
❑ 96Ult-221
❑ 96UltGolM-221
❑ 96UppDec-354
❑ 97Bow-238
❑ 97BowInt-238
❑ 97Cir-370
❑ 97CirRav-370
❑ 97ColCho-362
❑ 97ColChoT-LA8
❑ 97DodMot-9
❑ 97DodPol-18
❑ 97DodSco-12
❑ 97DodScoPI-12
❑ 97DodScoPr-12
❑ 97Don-198
❑ 97DonGolPP-198
❑ 97DonLim-25
❑ 97DonLimE-25
❑ 97DonLimENG-25
❑ 97DonSilPP-198
❑ 97DonTea-114
❑ 97DonTeaSPE-114
❑ 97Fin-31
❑ 97FinRef-31
❑ 97Fle-366
❑ 97FleTif-366
❑ 97Lea-109
❑ 97LeaFraM-109
❑ 97LeaFraMDC-109
❑ 97MetUni-102
❑ 97NewPin-79
❑ 97NewPinAP-79
❑ 97NewPinMC-79
❑ 97NewPinPP-79
❑ 97Pac-334
❑ 97PacLatotML-28
❑ 97PacLigB-334
❑ 97PacPri-112
❑ 97PacPriLB-112
❑ 97PacPriP-112
❑ 97PacSil-334
❑ 97Sco-248
❑ 97ScoArtPWB-248
❑ 97ScoPreS-248
❑ 97ScoShoS-248
❑ 97ScoShoSAP-248
❑ 97SP-96
❑ 97SpoIll-117
❑ 97SpoIllEE-117
❑ 97StaClu-205
❑ 97StaCluMat-205
❑ 97StaCluMOP-205
❑ 97Top-182
❑ 97TopGal-53
❑ 97TopGalPPI-53
❑ 97Ult-219
❑ 97UltGolME-219
❑ 97UltPlaME-219
❑ 97UppDec-374
❑ 97UppDec-395
❑ 98CirThu-287
❑ 98CirThuRav-287
❑ 98CirThuSupRav-287
❑ 98ColCho-146
❑ 98DodMot-6
❑ 98DodPol-17
❑ 98DodSco-10
❑ 98DodScoP-10
❑ 98Don-189
❑ 98DonGolPP-189
❑ 98DonSilPP-189
❑ 98Fin-3
❑ 98FinNo--3
❑ 98FinNo-R-3
❑ 98FinRef-3
❑ 98Fle-161
❑ 98Pac-333
❑ 98PacInv-108
❑ 98PacInvPBlue-108
❑ 98PacInvSilv-108
❑ 98PacInvTeam-14
❑ 98PacOme-125
❑ 98PacOmeR-125
❑ 98PacOnl-378
❑ 98PacOnlR-378
❑ 98PacOnlWC-378
❑ 98PacPar-177
❑ 98PacParC-177
❑ 98PacParG-177
❑ 98PacParHS-177
❑ 98PacParPB-177
❑ 98PacParR-177
❑ 98PacPlaB-333
❑ 98PacRedT-333
❑ 98PacSil-333
❑ 98PinPlu-85
❑ 98PinSna-LAD12
❑ 98Sco-140
❑ 98ScoRT-126
❑ 98ScoSS-PP58
❑ 98ScoSSAP-PP58
❑ 98SP Aut-111
❑ 98SpoIllTaN-111
❑ 98SpoIllTaNEE-111
❑ 98SPxFin-91
❑ 98SPxFinR-91
❑ 98SPxFinS-91
❑ 98StaCluFDI-251
❑ 98StaCluI-251
❑ 98StaCluOneK-251
❑ 98StaCluPP-251
❑ 98Top-397
❑ 98TopChr-397
❑ 98TopChrR-397
❑ 98TopDevR-397
❑ 98TopDia-397
❑ 98TopMiniC-397
❑ 98Ult-382
❑ 98UltGolM-382
❑ 98UltMas-382
❑ 98UltPlaM-382
❑ 98UppDec-397
❑ 99Fle-543
❑ 99FleSta9-543
❑ 99FleWarT-543
❑ 99Pac-224
❑ 99PacPlaB-224
❑ 99PacRed-224
❑ 99Top-316
❑ 99TopChr-316
❑ 99TopChrR-316
❑ 99TopMVPP-316
❑ 99UppDec-123
❑ 99UppDecEL1-123
❑ 99UppDecEL2-123
❑ 99UppDecEM-MC4
❑ 99UppDecEMFXG-MC4
Martinez, Randy
❑ 83SprCarF-19
Martinez, Ray
❑ 81BatTroT-13
❑ 83WatIndF-19
Martinez, Rey
❑ 85LynMetT-23
❑ 90KinMetB-8
❑ 90KinMetS-15
❑ 90MadMusP-2265
❑ 90QuaCitAGS-23
❑ 92MidAngOHP-15
❑ 92MidAngS-464
❑ 92SkyAA F-198
Martinez, Rick
❑ 92NiaFalRC-6
❑ 92NiaFalRF-3333
Martinez, Roger
❑ 95PitMetTI-12
❑ 96PitMetB-14
Martinez, Romulo
❑ 97WesMicW-17
❑ 98LakTigM-6
Martinez, Sandy
❑ 91KisDodP-4195
❑ 92YakBeaF-3459
❑ 96BluJayOH-19
❑ 96Don-295

❑ 96DonPreP-295
❑ 96Fla-188
❑ 96Fle-278
❑ 96FleTif-278
❑ 96LeaSigA-147
❑ 96LeaSigAG-147
❑ 96LeaSigAS-147
❑ 96MetUni-123
❑ 96MetUniP-123
❑ 96StaClu-157
❑ 96StaCluMOP-157
❑ 96Top-321
❑ 96Ult-148
❑ 96UltGolM-148
❑ 97BluJayS-54
❑ 97Fle-244
❑ 97FleTif-244
❑ 97PacPriGotD-GD102
❑ 97StaClu-371
❑ 97StaCluMOP-371
❑ 97SyrSkyCB-14
❑ 97Top-418
❑ 98PacOnl-145
❑ 98PacOnlR-145
❑ 98PacOnlWC-145
❑ 98Ult-410
❑ 98UltGolM-410
❑ 98UltMas-410
❑ 98UltPlaM-410

Martinez, Silvio
❑ 76ShrCapT-15
❑ 76VenLeaS-198
❑ 78CarTeal-16
❑ 78SprRedWK-18
❑ 79Car5-16
❑ 79Top-609
❑ 80OPC-258
❑ 80Top-496
❑ 81Don-429
❑ 81Fle-546
❑ 81Top-586
❑ 82ChaChaT-7
❑ 82Don-469
❑ 82Fle-122
❑ 82Top-181

Martinez, Ted
❑ 71OPC-648
❑ 71Top-648
❑ 72Top-544
❑ 73LinPor-115
❑ 73OPC-161
❑ 73Top-161
❑ 74OPC-487
❑ 74Top-487
❑ 75OPC-637
❑ 75St.LouCP-16
❑ 75Top-637
❑ 75TopMin-637
❑ 76OPC-356
❑ 76SSP-499
❑ 76Top-356
❑ 78SSP270-64
❑ 78Top-546
❑ 79OPC-59
❑ 79Top-128
❑ 80AlbDukTc-14
❑ 80DodPol-23
❑ 80Top-191
❑ 85DomLeaS-38
❑ 90DodTar-490
❑ 91MetWIZ-252

Martinez, Thomas
❑ 83AleDukT-17

Martinez, Tino
❑ 87PanAmTUBI-19
❑ 87PanAmTURB-1
❑ 88TopTra-66T
❑ 88TopTraT-66T
❑ 89BasAmeAPB-AA6
❑ 89Bow-211
❑ 89BowTif-211
❑ 89EasLeaAP-18
❑ 89Sta-124
❑ 89TopBig-93
❑ 89WilBilP-635
❑ 89WilBilS-13
❑ 90Bow-484
❑ 90BowTif-484
❑ 90CalCanC-12
❑ 90CalCanP-659
❑ 90FleUpd-119
❑ 90ProAAAF-124
❑ 90Sco-596
❑ 90TopMag-46
❑ 90UppDec-37
❑ 91Bow-257
❑ 91CalCanLD-66
❑ 91CalCanP-523
❑ 91Cla1-T2
❑ 91ClaGam-150
❑ 91Don-28
❑ 91DonPre-6
❑ 91Fle-458
❑ 91LeaPre-24
❑ 91LinDriAAA-66
❑ 91MajLeaCP-7
❑ 91MarCouH-10
❑ 91OPC-482
❑ 91OPCPre-76
❑ 91Sco-798
❑ 91ScoRoo-38
❑ 91SevCoi-NW12
❑ 91StaClu-179
❑ 91Stu-118
❑ 91Top-482
❑ 91TopDeb90-99
❑ 91TopDesS-482
❑ 91TopMic-482
❑ 91TopTif-482
❑ 91TriA AAGP-AAA5
❑ 91Ult-341
❑ 91UppDec-553
❑ 92Bow-483
❑ 92Bow-626
❑ 92Cla2-T42
❑ 92ClaGam-50
❑ 92Don-410
❑ 92Don-525
❑ 92Fle-287
❑ 92Lea-329
❑ 92LeaBlaG-329
❑ 92MarMot-11
❑ 92MVPPin-4
❑ 92OPC-481
❑ 92OPCPre-64
❑ 92Pin-123
❑ 92PinTea2-62
❑ 92ProFS7-138
❑ 92Sco-596
❑ 92Sco100RS-51
❑ 92ScoHotR-7
❑ 92SpollIFK1-613
❑ 92StaClu-573
❑ 92Stu-236
❑ 92Top-481
❑ 92TopGol-481
❑ 92TopGolW-481
❑ 92TopMic-481
❑ 92TriPla-259
❑ 92Ult-127
❑ 92UppDec-554
❑ 93Bow-303
❑ 93Don-217
❑ 93Fla-274
❑ 93Fle-310
❑ 93Lea-406
❑ 93MariStaClu-18
❑ 93MarMot-17
❑ 93OPC-212
❑ 93PacBeiA-11
❑ 93PacSpa-289
❑ 93PanSti-66
❑ 93Pin-213
❑ 93RedFolS-58
❑ 93Sco-76
❑ 93Sel-246
❑ 93SP-134
❑ 93StaClu-273
❑ 93StaCluFDI-273
❑ 93StaCluMOP-273
❑ 93Stu-204
❑ 93Top-232
❑ 93TopGol-232
❑ 93TopInaM-232
❑ 93TopInaR-232
❑ 93TopMic-232
❑ 93TriPla-35
❑ 93Ult-623
❑ 93UppDec-287
❑ 93UppDecGold-287
❑ 94Bow-669
❑ 94ColC-191
❑ 94ColChoGS-191
❑ 94ColChoSS-191
❑ 94Don-296
❑ 94Fin-55
❑ 94FinRef-55
❑ 94Fla-106
❑ 94Fle-295
❑ 94FleExtB-170
❑ 94Lea-92
❑ 94LeaL-69
❑ 94MarMot-16
❑ 94Pac-577
❑ 94PanSti-122
❑ 94Pin-129
❑ 94PinArtP-129
❑ 94PinMusC-129
❑ 94Sco-59
❑ 94ScoGolR-59
❑ 94Sel-163
❑ 94StaClu-60
❑ 94StaCluFDI-60
❑ 94StaCluGR-60
❑ 94StaCluMOP-60
❑ 94Stu-104
❑ 94Top-693
❑ 94TopGol-693
❑ 94TopSpa-693
❑ 94TriPla-130
❑ 94Ult-121
❑ 94UppDec-94
❑ 94UppDecED-94
❑ 95ColCho-283
❑ 95ColChoGS-283
❑ 95ColChoSE-127
❑ 95ColChoSEGS-127
❑ 95ColChoSESS-127
❑ 95ColChoSS-283
❑ 95Don-63
❑ 95DonPreP-63
❑ 95DonTopotO-153
❑ 95Emo-80
❑ 95Fin-51
❑ 95FinRef-51
❑ 95Fla-83
❑ 95Fle-273
❑ 95Lea-90
❑ 95LeaLim-96
❑ 95MarMot-23
❑ 95MarPac-7
❑ 95MarPac-36
❑ 95Pac-401
❑ 95Pin-310
❑ 95PinArtP-310
❑ 95PinMusC-310
❑ 95Sco-128
❑ 95ScoGolR-128
❑ 95ScoPlaTS-128
❑ 95SP-191
❑ 95SPSil-191
❑ 95StaClu-227
❑ 95StaCluFDI-227
❑ 95StaCluMOP-227
❑ 95StaCluSTDW-M227
❑ 95StaCluSTWS-227
❑ 95StaCluVR-115
❑ 95StaCluVRMO-115
❑ 95Stu-82
❑ 95Top-377
❑ 95TopCyb-198
❑ 95TopEmb-73
❑ 95TopEmbGI-73
❑ 95Ult-328
❑ 95UltGolM-328
❑ 95UppDec-99
❑ 95UppDecED-99
❑ 95UppDecEDG-99
❑ 95UppDecSE-256
❑ 95UppDecSEG-256
❑ 95Zen-103
❑ 96Baz-113
❑ 96Bow-49
❑ 96BowBes-59
❑ 96BowBesAR-59
❑ 96BowBesR-59
❑ 96BowFoi-49
❑ 96Cir-66
❑ 96CirRav-66
❑ 96ColCho-318
❑ 96ColCho-780
❑ 96ColChoGS-318
❑ 96ColChoSS-318
❑ 96Don-43
❑ 96DonPreP-43
❑ 96EmoXL-91
❑ 96Fin-B260
❑ 96Fin-S357
❑ 96FinRef-B260
❑ 96FinRef-S357
❑ 96Fla-132
❑ 96Fle-188
❑ 96FleTif-188
❑ 96FleUpd-U64
❑ 96FleUpdTC-U64
❑ 96LeaLim-4
❑ 96LeaLimG-4
❑ 96LeaPre-7
❑ 96LeaPreP-7
❑ 96LeaSig-123
❑ 96LeaSigPPG-123
❑ 96LeaSigPPP-123
❑ 96MetUni-89
❑ 96MetUniP-89
❑ 96MLBPin-20
❑ 96Pac-404
❑ 96PacEstL-EL18
❑ 96PacPri-P134
❑ 96PacPriG-P134
❑ 96PanSti-225
❑ 96Pin-27
❑ 96Pin-361
❑ 96PinAfi-64
❑ 96PinAfiAP-64
❑ 96PinAfiFPP-64
❑ 96PinAfiSP-24
❑ 96PinArtP-13
❑ 96PinFoil-361
❑ 96PinSta-13
❑ 96Sco-354
❑ 96ScoDugC-B79
❑ 96ScoDugCAP-B79
❑ 96Sel-104
❑ 96SelArtP-104
❑ 96SelCer-2
❑ 96SelCerAP-2
❑ 96SelCerCB-2
❑ 96SelCerCR-2
❑ 96SelCerMB-2
❑ 96SelCerMG-2
❑ 96SelCerMR-2
❑ 96Spo-84
❑ 96SpoArtP-84
❑ 96StaClu-185
❑ 96StaCluMO-24
❑ 96StaCluMOP-185
❑ 96Stu-144
❑ 96StuPrePB-144
❑ 96StuPrePG-144
❑ 96StuPrePS-144
❑ 96Sum-3
❑ 96SumAbo&B-3
❑ 96SumArtP-3
❑ 96SumFoi-3
❑ 96Top-168
❑ 96TopChr-48
❑ 96TopChrR-48
❑ 96TopLas-85
❑ 96TopRoaW-RW10
❑ 96Ult-129
❑ 96Ult-390
❑ 96UltGolM-129
❑ 96UltGolM-390
❑ 96UppDec-503U
❑ 96Zen-14
❑ 96ZenArtP-14
❑ 97Bow-48
❑ 97BowBes-66
❑ 97BowBesAR-66
❑ 97BowBesR-66
❑ 97BowChr-38
❑ 97BowChrI-38
❑ 97BowChrIR-38
❑ 97BowChrR-38
❑ 97BowInt-48
❑ 97Cir-104
❑ 97CirRav-104
❑ 97ColCho-181
❑ 97ColChoT-NY6
❑ 97Don-55
❑ 97DonEli-105
❑ 97DonEliGS-105
❑ 97DonGolPP-55
❑ 97DonLim-56
❑ 97DonLim-93
❑ 97DonLimE-56
❑ 97DonLimE-93
❑ 97DonLimENG-56
❑ 97DonLimFotG-35
❑ 97DonPre-79
❑ 97DonPreCttC-79
❑ 97DonSig-34
❑ 97DonSigAC-86
❑ 97DonSigAM-86
❑ 97DonSigPPP-34
❑ 97DonSilPP-55
❑ 97DonTea-124
❑ 97DonTeaSPE-124
❑ 97DonVxP1-27
❑ 97Fin-204
❑ 97FinRef-204
❑ 97Fle-171
❑ 97FleTif-171
❑ 97Lea-254
❑ 97LeaFraM-254
❑ 97LeaFraMDC-254
❑ 97LeaLeaotN-13
❑ 97MetUni-119
❑ 97NewPin-66
❑ 97NewPinAP-66
❑ 97NewPinMC-66
❑ 97NewPinPP-66
❑ 97Pac-154
❑ 97PacLatotML-13
❑ 97PacLigB-154
❑ 97PacPri-52
❑ 97PacPriLB-52
❑ 97PacPriP-52
❑ 97PacSil-154
❑ 97PhiCopQ-17
❑ 97PinIns-55
❑ 97PinInsCE-55
❑ 97PinInsDE-55
❑ 97PinX-P-44
❑ 97PinX-P-144
❑ 97PinX-PMoS-44
❑ 97PinX-PMoS-144
❑ 97PinX-PSfF-39
❑ 97PinX-PSfFU-39
❑ 97Sco-208
❑ 97ScoArtPWB-208
❑ 97ScoPreS-208
❑ 97ScoShoS-208
❑ 97ScoShoSAP-208
❑ 97SP-126
❑ 97SpolII-29
❑ 97SpolII-129
❑ 97SpolIIEE-29
❑ 97SpolIIEE-129
❑ 97StaClu-220
❑ 97StaCluMat-220
❑ 97StaCluMOP-220
❑ 97StrAll-44
❑ 97Stu-31
❑ 97StuPrePG-31
❑ 97StuPrePS-31
❑ 97Top-187
❑ 97TopChr-72
❑ 97TopChrR-72
❑ 97TopGal-89
❑ 97TopGalPPI-89
❑ 97TopSta-2
❑ 97TopSta97AS-AS3
❑ 97TopStaAM-2
❑ 97Ult-100
❑ 97UltGolME-100
❑ 97UltPlaME-100
❑ 97UppDec-123
❑ 97UppDecSA-8
❑ 97UppDecSAG-8
❑ 97YanMcDP-2
❑ 97YanSco-13
❑ 97YanScoPI-13
❑ 97YanScoPr-13
❑ 97Zen-23
❑ 98Bow-43
❑ 98BowBes-65
❑ 98BowBesAR-65
❑ 98BowBesR-65
❑ 98BowChr-43
❑ 98BowChrGA-43
❑ 98BowChrGAR-43
❑ 98BowChrI-43
❑ 98BowChrIR-43
❑ 98BowChrR-43
❑ 98BowChrR-12
❑ 98BowChrRR-12
❑ 98BowGolA-43
❑ 98BowInt-43
❑ 98BowMinLM-MVP8
❑ 98CirThu-195
❑ 98CirThuRav-195
❑ 98CirThuSupRav-195
❑ 98CirThuTB-7
❑ 98ColCho-9
❑ 98ColCho-23
❑ 98ColCho-180
❑ 98ColCho-276
❑ 98ColChoCG-9
❑ 98ColChoCtG-CG26A
❑ 98ColChoCtG-CG26B
❑ 98ColChoCtG-CG26C
❑ 98ColChoCtGExch-CG26
❑ 98ColChoCtGIW-CG26
❑ 98ColChoER-ER19
❑ 98ColChoGJ5-276
❑ 98ColChoRJ-180
❑ 98ColChoS'-20
❑ 98ColChoSQ-SQ45
❑ 98ColChoSQ-SQ87
❑ 98ColChoSQDouble-21
❑ 98ColChoSQHR-21
❑ 98ColChoSQSingle-21
❑ 98ColChoSQTriple-21
❑ 98CroRoy-97
❑ 98Don-25
❑ 98Don-168
❑ 98Don-358
❑ 98DonCol-25
❑ 98DonCol-168
❑ 98DonColE-471
❑ 98DonColE-550
❑ 98DonColL-202
❑ 98DonColP-585
❑ 98DonColP-744
❑ 98DonColS-25
❑ 98DonColS-168
❑ 98DonCruG-33
❑ 98DonCruP-33
❑ 98DonCruR-33
❑ 98DonDom-10
❑ 98DonEli-71
❑ 98DonEli-150
❑ 98DonEliA-71
❑ 98DonEliA-150
❑ 98DonEliC-30
❑ 98DonEliMC-30
❑ 98DonEliS-71
❑ 98DonEliS-150
❑ 98DonGolPP-25
❑ 98DonGolPP-168
❑ 98DonGolPP-358
❑ 98DonLonL-3
❑ 98DonPre-35
❑ 98DonPre-194
❑ 98DonPreSeat-35
❑ 98DonPreSeat-194
❑ 98DonPriCD-25
❑ 98DonPriCD-168
❑ 98DonPriCE-471
❑ 98DonPriCE-550
❑ 98DonPriCL-202
❑ 98DonPriCP-585
❑ 98DonPriCP-744
❑ 98DonProLPI-19
❑ 98DonProLS-12
❑ 98DonSig-69
❑ 98DonSigP-69
❑ 98DonSilPP-25
❑ 98DonSilPP-168
❑ 98DonSilPP-358
❑ 98E-X2-38
❑ 98E-X2Cheap-4
❑ 98E-X2ECFut-38
❑ 98E-X2ECNow-38
❑ 98Fin-9
❑ 98FinMysF1-M43
❑ 98FinMysF1-M46
❑ 98FinMysF1-M48
❑ 98FinMysF1-M50
❑ 98FinMysFR-M43
❑ 98FinMysFR-M46
❑ 98FinMysFR-M48
❑ 98FinMysFR-M50
❑ 98FinNo--9
❑ 98FinNo-R-9
❑ 98FinPowZ-P18
❑ 98FinRef-9
❑ 98FinStaS-SS21
❑ 98FlaShoLeg0-60
❑ 98FlaShoLeg1-60
❑ 98FlaShoLeg2-60
❑ 98FlaShoLeg3-60
❑ 98FlaShoLegM-60
❑ 98FlaShoR0-60
❑ 98FlaShoR1-60
❑ 98FlaShoR2-60
❑ 98FlaShoR3-60
❑ 98Fle-278
❑ 98Fle-331
❑ 98FleLumC-9
❑ 98FlePowG-14
❑ 98FleVin'-39
❑ 98FleVin'C-39
❑ 98HamHel-3
❑ 98Lea-2
❑ 98LeaFraDA-2
❑ 98LeaFraF-2
❑ 98LeaFraM-2
❑ 98LeaFraM-2
❑ 98LeaFraMDC-2
❑ 98LeaFraMDC-2
❑ 98LeaFraMZ2-2
❑ 98LeaRS-8
❑ 98LeaRSGreHit-11
❑ 98LeaRSHRDerby-1

❑ 98LeaRSLHolo-8
❑ 98LeaRSLong-8
❑ 98LeaRSTicMas-12
❑ 98LeaRSTicMasDC-12
❑ 98LeaRTrue-8
❑ 98LeaStaRep-13
❑ 98MetUni-122
❑ 98MetUniPMG-122
❑ 98Pac-152
❑ 98PacAur-60
❑ 98PacGolCDC-23
❑ 98PacHomRH-14
❑ 98PacInCage-11
❑ 98PacInv-53
❑ 98PacInvGems-76
❑ 98PacInvInt-9A
❑ 98PacInvPBlue-53
❑ 98PacInvPhoto-10
❑ 98PacInvSilv-53
❑ 98PacInvTeam-19
❑ 98PacLatotML-26
❑ 98PacNes-2A
❑ 98PacOme-167
❑ 98PacOmeR-167
❑ 98PacOnl-508
❑ 98PacOnlR-508
❑ 98PacOnlWC-508
❑ 98PacPar-71
❑ 98PacParC-71
❑ 98PacParG-71
❑ 98PacParHS-71
❑ 98PacParI-47
❑ 98PacParPB-71
❑ 98PacParR-71
❑ 98PacPlaB-152
❑ 98PacRedT-152
❑ 98PacSil-152
❑ 98PacTeaC-10
❑ 98Pin-189
❑ 98Pin-198
❑ 98Pin-199
❑ 98PinArtP-PP92
❑ 98PinHitIH-7
❑ 98PinHitHS-7
❑ 98PinIns-77
❑ 98PinInsCE-77
❑ 98PinInsDE-77
❑ 98PinInsSG-19AB
❑ 98PinInsSG-19CD
❑ 98PinInsSGS-19AB
❑ 98PinInsSGS-19CD
❑ 98PinMinB-13
❑ 98PinMinCB-13
❑ 98PinMinCBAP-13
❑ 98PinMinCGP-13
❑ 98PinMinCGPAP-13
❑ 98PinMinCN-13
❑ 98PinMinCNAP-13
❑ 98PinMinCSGR-13
❑ 98PinMinDC-13
❑ 98PinMinG-13
❑ 98PinMinMCSS-13
❑ 98PinMinS-13
❑ 98PinMusC-PP92
❑ 98PinPer-36
❑ 98PinPerBB-13
❑ 98PinPerBBSamp-13
❑ 98PinPerBBSO-13
❑ 98PinPerPP-36
❑ 98PinPerSftF-16
❑ 98PinPlu-12
❑ 98PinPluAP-PP6
❑ 98PinPluGAP-PP6
❑ 98PinPluMAP-PP6
❑ 98PinPluTP-10
❑ 98PinPluTPG-10
❑ 98PinPluTPM-10
❑ 98PinPluY-6
❑ 98PinPowPJ-8
❑ 98PinPowPJS-8
❑ 98PinPreP-189
❑ 98PinPreP-198
❑ 98PinPreP-199
❑ 98PinPreP-H7
❑ 98PinSna-NYY8
❑ 98PinSna-NYY11
❑ 98PreCon-18
❑ 98Revo-101
❑ 98RevoSS-101
❑ 98Sco-42
❑ 98ScoRT-41
❑ 98ScoRTSS-PP41
❑ 98ScoRTSSAP-PP41
❑ 98ScoRTSSAP1-PP41
❑ 98ScoSS-PP127
❑ 98ScoSSAP-PP127
❑ 98SP Aut-140
❑ 98SP Aut-SD39
❑ 98SP AutSD-SD39
❑ 98SP AutSDT-SD39
❑ 98SpoIll-86
❑ 98SpoIllEE-86
❑ 98SpoIllFE-86
❑ 98SpoIllTaN-112
❑ 98SpoIllTaNEE-112
❑ 98SpoIllWSF-99
❑ 98SpoIllWSFEE-99
❑ 98SpoIllWSFFE-99
❑ 98SPxFin-44
❑ 98SPxFin-105
❑ 98SPxFin-160
❑ 98SPxFin-236
❑ 98SPxFinR-44
❑ 98SPxFinR-105
❑ 98SPxFinR-160
❑ 98SPxFinR-236
❑ 98SPxFinS-44
❑ 98SPxFinS-105
❑ 98SPxFinS-160
❑ 98SPxFinS-236
❑ 98StaCluBP-BP8
❑ 98StaCluC-CS21
❑ 98StaCluC-CS23
❑ 98StaCluC-CS24
❑ 98StaCluFDI-202
❑ 98StaCluI-202
❑ 98StaCluOneK-202
❑ 98StaCluPP-202
❑ 98StaCluPWP-P8
❑ 98StaCluTIII-T2C
❑ 98StaCluTIII-T11B
❑ 98StaCluTLme-T2C
❑ 98StaCluTLme-T11B
❑ 98StaCluTLmo-T2C
❑ 98StaCluTLmo-T11B
❑ 98Stu-139
❑ 98StuGPP-139
❑ 98StuHitPar-14
❑ 98StuPor8x10-25
❑ 98StuPor8x10GP-25
❑ 98StuSPP-139
❑ 98Top-269
❑ 98Top-284
❑ 98Top-483
❑ 98TopChr-269
❑ 98TopChr-284
❑ 98TopChr-483
❑ 98TopChrR-269
❑ 98TopChrR-284
❑ 98TopChrR-483
❑ 98TopDevR-269
❑ 98TopDevR-284
❑ 98TopDevR-483
❑ 98TopDia-269
❑ 98TopDia-284
❑ 98TopDia-483
❑ 98TopGal-145
❑ 98TopGalGP-145
❑ 98TopGalOPP-145
❑ 98TopGalPPI-145
❑ 98TopGalPPIA-145
❑ 98TopGolLabC1-95
❑ 98TopGolLabC1B-95
❑ 98TopGolLabC1One-95
❑ 98TopGolLabC1R-95
❑ 98TopGolLabC2-95
❑ 98TopGolLabC2B-95
❑ 98TopGolLabC2One-95
❑ 98TopGolLabC2R-95
❑ 98TopGolLabC3-95
❑ 98TopGolLabC3B-95
❑ 98TopGolLabC3One-95
❑ 98TopGolLabC3R-95
❑ 98TopMiniC-269
❑ 98TopMiniC-284
❑ 98TopMiniC-483
❑ 98TopMysF-ILM8
❑ 98TopMysFB-M11
❑ 98TopMysFB-M11
❑ 98TopMysFBR-M11
❑ 98TopMysFBR-M11
❑ 98TopMysFR-ILM8
❑ 98TopOpeD-111
❑ 98TopSta-82
❑ 98TopSta'S-28
❑ 98TopSta'SGH-28
❑ 98TopStaB-82
❑ 98TopStaG-82
❑ 98TopStaGR-82
❑ 98TopStaS-82
❑ 98TopStaSteG-28
❑ 98TopSup-16
❑ 98TopSup-16
❑ 98TopTek-25
❑ 98TopTekD-25
❑ 98UD3-39
❑ 98UD3-129
❑ 98UD3-219
❑ 98UD3DieCut-39
❑ 98UD3DieCut-129
❑ 98UD3DieCut-219
❑ 98Ult-139
❑ 98UltBigS-13
❑ 98UltDouT-5
❑ 98UltGolM-139
❑ 98UltMas-139
❑ 98UltNot-13
❑ 98UltPlaM-139
❑ 98UppDec-1
❑ 98UppDec-12
❑ 98UppDec-244
❑ 98UppDec-460
❑ 98UppDec-606
❑ 98UppDecAC-AS24
❑ 98UppDecAG-AG18
❑ 98UppDecAGDC-AG18
❑ 98UppDecCD-CD24
❑ 98UppDecR-68
❑ 98UppDecR-23
❑ 98UppDecRBBop-BB11
❑ 98UppDecRTC-TC14
❑ 98UppDecSF-5
❑ 98UppDecSFPZPD-PZ9
❑ 98UppDecTMT-20
❑ 98UppDecTMTG-20
❑ 98YanSco-3
❑ 98YanScoP-3
❑ 98YanUppD-460
❑ 98YanUppDWSC-1
❑ 98Zen-42
❑ 98Zen5 xx7-47
❑ 98Zen5x7GoldImp-47
❑ 98Zen5x7Imp-47
❑ 98ZenZ-G-42
❑ 98ZenZ-S-42
❑ 99199Fin-5
❑ 99AllMysFR-M6
❑ 99Bow-288
❑ 99BowBes-56
❑ 99BowBesAR-56
❑ 99BowBesR-56
❑ 99BowGol-288
❑ 99BowInt-288
❑ 99CroRoyB-99
❑ 99CroRoyL-99
❑ 99CroRoyOD-99
❑ 99E-X Cen-73
❑ 99E-X CenECFut-73
❑ 99E-X CenECNow-73
❑ 99FinGolRef-5
❑ 99FinPre-PP5
❑ 99FinRef-5
❑ 99FlaShoLeg1-49
❑ 99FlaShoLeg2-49
❑ 99FlaShoLeg3-49
❑ 99FlaShoLegM1-49
❑ 99FlaShoLegM2-49
❑ 99FlaShoLegM3-49
❑ 99FlaShoR1-49
❑ 99FlaShoR2-49
❑ 99FlaShoR3-49
❑ 99Fle-268
❑ 99FleBri-31
❑ 99FleBri2G-31
❑ 99FleBriBlu-31
❑ 99FleBriGol-31
❑ 99FleMys-29
❑ 99FleMysG-29
❑ 99FleMysM-29
❑ 99FleSta9-268
❑ 99FleWarT-268
❑ 99MetUni-60
❑ 99MetUniGM-60
❑ 99MetUniPMG-60
❑ 99Pac-297
❑ 99PacAur-130
❑ 99PacAurOD-130
❑ 99PacCroC-192
❑ 99PacCroC-13
❑ 99PacCroCPB-192
❑ 99PacInv-102
❑ 99PacInvOD-102
❑ 99PacInvPB-102
❑ 99PacOme-165
❑ 99PacOmeC-165
❑ 99PacOmeG-165
❑ 99PacOmePB-165
❑ 99PacPar-164
❑ 99PacParC-164
❑ 99PacParG-164
❑ 99PacParHoloGold-164
❑ 99PacParHS-164
❑ 99PacParOD-164
❑ 99PacParPB-164
❑ 99PacParRed-164
❑ 99PacPlaB-297
❑ 99PacPri-101
❑ 99PacPriHB-101
❑ 99PacPriHG-101
❑ 99PacPriHM-101
❑ 99PacPriHP-101
❑ 99PacPriRed-101
❑ 99PacPriS-113
❑ 99PacPriS206-113
❑ 99PacPriS206R-113
❑ 99PacRed-297
❑ 99Rev-97
❑ 99RevPremDate-97
❑ 99RevRet-97
❑ 99RevShaSS-97
❑ 99SkyMolM-80
❑ 99SkyMolMX-80
❑ 99SkyPre-185
❑ 99SkyPreR-185
❑ 99SkyThu-230
❑ 99SkyThuRant-230
❑ 99SkyThuRave-230
❑ 99SP Aut-58
❑ 99SP AutEF-E19
❑ 99SP AutR-R19
❑ 99SpoIll-135
❑ 99SPx-56
❑ 99SPxFinR-56
❑ 99SPxFinS-56
❑ 99SPxPowE-PE20
❑ 99SPxStaF-SF19
❑ 99StaClu-219
❑ 99StaCluA-SCA4
❑ 99StaCluFDI-219
❑ 99StaCluOoaK-219
❑ 99StaCluPP-219
❑ 99StaCluTI-T4B
❑ 99StaCluTI-T15C
❑ 99StaCluTL-T4B
❑ 99StaCluTL-T15C
❑ 99StaCluTL-T4B
❑ 99StaCluTL-T15C
❑ 99ThuSkySupR-230
❑ 99Top-236
❑ 99Top-290
❑ 99Top-451
❑ 99TopAllMF-M6
❑ 99TopBlaLC1-89
❑ 99TopBlaLC2-89
❑ 99TopBlaLC3-89
❑ 99TopChr-236
❑ 99TopChr-290
❑ 99TopChr-451
❑ 99TopChrR-236
❑ 99TopChrR-290
❑ 99TopChrR-451
❑ 99TopGal-69
❑ 99TopGalPP-69
❑ 99TopGalPPI-69
❑ 99TopGolL-89
❑ 99TopGolLC1-89
❑ 99TopGolLC2-89
❑ 99TopGolLOtO-89
❑ 99TopMVPP-290
❑ 99TopMVPP-451
❑ 99TopOpeD-157
❑ 99TopRedLC1-89
❑ 99TopRedLC2-89
❑ 99TopRedLC3-89
❑ 99TopSta-150
❑ 99TopStaFoil-150
❑ 99TopTek-33A
❑ 99TopTek-33B
❑ 99TopTekG-33A
❑ 99TopTekG-33B
❑ 99UD Cho-119
❑ 99UD ChoMBH-B18
❑ 99UD ChoPCR-119
❑ 99UD ChoYW-Y20
❑ 99UD Ion-42
❑ 99UD Ion-79
❑ 99UD IonR-42
❑ 99UD IonR-79
❑ 99Ult-4
❑ 99UltGolM-4
❑ 99UltMas-4
❑ 99UltPlaM-4
❑ 99UltRBIK-28
❑ 99UppDec-436
❑ 99UppDecBD-58
❑ 99UppDecBDD-58
❑ 99UppDecBDDom-D28
❑ 99UppDecBDDomE-D28
❑ 99UppDecBDQ-58
❑ 99UppDecBDT-58
❑ 99UppDecCf7-23
❑ 99UppDecCf7-60
❑ 99UppDecCf7-C20
❑ 99UppDecCf7Cf7P-C20
❑ 99UppDecCf7LL-L30
❑ 99UppDecCL-96
❑ 99UppDecCLCC-96
❑ 99UppDecCLM-C65
❑ 99UppDecCo7CE-23
❑ 99UppDecCo7CE-60
❑ 99UppDecE-62
❑ 99UppDecE-159
❑ 99UppDecEFXG-62
❑ 99UppDecEFXG-159
❑ 99UppDecEL1-436
❑ 99UppDecEL2-436
❑ 99UppDecM-143
❑ 99UppDecMGS-143
❑ 99UppDecMHFS-143
❑ 99UppDecMP-143
❑ 99UppDecMSS-143
❑ 99UppDecO-15
❑ 99UppDecOSO-15
❑ 99UppDecR-57
❑ 99UppDecRG-57
❑ 99UppDecRP-57
❑ 99UppDecWY-W18
❑ 99UppDecWYD-W18
❑ 99UppDecWYHR-W18
❑ 99UppDecWYT-W18
❑ 99Vic-274
❑ 99YanFle-11

Martinez, Tippy (Felix)

❑ 75SyrChiTI-10
❑ 76BalOriP-23
❑ 76OPC-41
❑ 76Top-41
❑ 77BalOriP-13
❑ 77OPC-254
❑ 77Top-238
❑ 78BalOriP-17
❑ 78Top-393
❑ 79Top-491
❑ 80Top-706
❑ 81BalOriP-10
❑ 81Don-354
❑ 81Fle-179
❑ 81OPC-119
❑ 81Top-119
❑ 82Don-205
❑ 82Fle-171
❑ 82Top-583
❑ 83Don-357
❑ 83Fle-65
❑ 83FleSta-115
❑ 83FleSti-201
❑ 83OPC-263
❑ 83OriPos-16
❑ 83Top-631
❑ 84AllGamPI-182
❑ 84BalOriP-19
❑ 84Don-472
❑ 84Fle-12
❑ 84Fle-635
❑ 84Nes792-215
❑ 84OPC-215
❑ 84OriEng-7
❑ 84Top-215
❑ 84TopSti-208
❑ 84TopTif-215
❑ 85BalOriP-16
❑ 85Don-210
❑ 85Fle-182
❑ 85OPC-247
❑ 85OriHea-11
❑ 85Top-445
❑ 85TopMin-445
❑ 85TopSti-200
❑ 85TopTif-445
❑ 86BalOriHMP-11
❑ 86Don-514
❑ 86Fle-279
❑ 86OPC-82
❑ 86Top-82
❑ 86TopTif-82
❑ 87OPC-269
❑ 87RedFolSB-14
❑ 87Top-728
❑ 87TopTif-728
❑ 89PacSenL-144
❑ 89T/MSenL-72
❑ 90EliSenL-40
❑ 91OriCro-281
❑ 91PacSenL-28
❑ 92YanWIZ7-103
❑ 93OriCroASU-6
❑ 95BalOriP-31

Martinez, Tommy

❑ 79WatIndT-26
❑ 80WatIndT-28

Martinez, Tony (Gabriel)

❑ 63Top-466
❑ 64Top-404
❑ 66Top-581
❑ 97SouBenSH-16

Martinez, Victor

❑ 97EveAquG-16
❑ 98EveAquG-14

Martinez, Wilfredo

❑ 83EriCarT-5

Martinez, William

❑ 90GatCitPP-3344
❑ 91SouAtlLAGP-SAL46
❑ 91SumFlyC-8
❑ 91SumFlyP-2331
❑ 92RocExpC-19
❑ 96-97LinVen-216

Martinez, Willie

❑ 96WatIndTI-16
❑ 97Bow-172
❑ 97BowBes-131
❑ 97BowBesAR-131
❑ 97BowBesR-131
❑ 97BowInt-172
❑ 97CarLeaTP-8
❑ 97KinIndB-12
❑ 98AkrAerM-11
❑ 98Bes-27
❑ 98Bes-75
❑ 98Bow-325
❑ 98BowBes-182
❑ 98BowBesAR-182
❑ 98BowBesR-182
❑ 98BowChr-325
❑ 98BowChrGA-325
❑ 98BowChrGAR-325
❑ 98BowChrI-325
❑ 98BowChrIR-325
❑ 98BowChrR-325
❑ 98BowGolA-325
❑ 98BowInt-325
❑ 98EasLeaTPM-17
❑ 98SP MinPE-48
❑ 98SPMin-48
❑ 99BasAmeTP-62
❑ 99BasAmeTPG-62
❑ 99Bow-319
❑ 99BowAut-BA22
❑ 99BowGol-319
❑ 99BowInt-319

Marting, Tim

❑ 71OPC-423
❑ 71Top-423
❑ 90ColMetGS-28

Martinke, Felix

❑ 09ObaT21-73
❑ 09ObaT21-185

Martino, R.J.

❑ 95AshTouTI-NNO

Martinoni, Elmer

❑ 11Zee-34
❑ 12HomRunKE-25
❑ 12PCLPin-14
❑ 12Zee-39
❑ 14Zee-67
❑ 15Zee-45

Martins, Eric

❑ 94SouOreAC-17
❑ 94SouOreAF-3630
❑ 95Exc-111
❑ 95ModA'sTI-14
❑ 96HunStaTI-16
❑ 97HunStaTI-16
❑ 98HunStaTI-14
❑ 99WesMicWAM-15

Martinson, Evon

❑ 78CliDodT-21
❑ 79LodDodT-21

Martinson, Mike

❑ 75QuaCitAT-33
❑ 76QuaCitAT-20
❑ 76SalLakCGC-7

Martorana, Mutta (Dave)

❑ 91UtiBluSC-12
❑ 91UtiBluSP-3249
❑ 92SouBenWSF-186
Marty, Joe
❑ 33Zee-129
❑ 33Zee-130
❑ 36DiaMatCS3T2-17
❑ 38CloFotW-56
❑ 40PhiTeal-15
❑ 40PlaBal-216
❑ 41PhiTeal-16
❑ 41PlaBal-28
❑ 46SunBre-13
❑ 47SigOil-64
❑ 47SunBre-10
❑ 49BowPCL-26
❑ 49SolSunP-8
❑ 52MotCoo-20
❑ 79DiaGre-308
❑ 93ConTSN-896
Martyn, Bob
❑ 58Top-39
❑ 59Top-41
❑ 59TopVen-41
❑ 79TCM50-254
Martz, Gary
❑ 75OmaRoyTI-11
❑ 76OmaRoyTT-12
❑ 76VenLeaS-203
Martz, Randy
❑ 80VenLeaS-166
❑ 80WicAerT-7
❑ 81Fle-300
❑ 81Top-381
❑ 82CubRedL-34
❑ 82Don-126
❑ 82Fle-600
❑ 82Top-188
❑ 82Top-456
❑ 83Don-151
❑ 83Fle-501
❑ 83FleSta-116
❑ 83FleSti-129
❑ 83Top-22
❑ 84RicBraT-18
❑ 85TucTorC-66
Martz, Tom
❑ 66TolMudHTI-16
Marval, Raul
❑ 94CliLumC-15
❑ 94CliLumF-1987
❑ 94EveGiaC-21
❑ 94EveGiaF-3660
❑ 95BurBeeTI-10
❑ 96-97LinVen-183
❑ 96BurBeeTI-21
❑ 97BakBlaB-17
❑ 97BakBlaTI-17
❑ 98ShrCapM-22
❑ 98ShrCapWS-22
Marx, Bill
❑ 86ChaRaiP-14
❑ 88RivRedWCLC-214
❑ 88RivRedWP-1424
❑ 89RivRedWB-12
❑ 89RivRedWCLC-14
❑ 89RivRedWP-1416
❑ 90RivRedWCLC-20
❑ 90RivRedWP-2606
Marx, Tim
❑ 93SalBucC-16
❑ 93SalBucF-436
❑ 97CalCanB-18
Marx, William
❑ 90ChaRaiB-16
Marzan, Jose
❑ 88BlaYNPRWLU-50
❑ 88VisOakCLC-155
❑ 88VisOakP-89
❑ 89BlaYNPRWL-145
❑ 89VisOakCLC-111
❑ 89VisOakP-1443
❑ 90OrlSunRB-6
❑ 90OrlSunRP-1091
❑ 90OrlSunRS-10
❑ 91LinDriAA-486
❑ 91OrlSunRLD-486
❑ 91OrlSunRP-1857
❑ 95ForMyeMTI-29
❑ 98ForWayW!-26
Marzano, John
❑ 85Top-399
❑ 85TopTif-399
❑ 86NewBriRSP-16
❑ 87IntLeaAT-19
❑ 87PawRedSP-51
❑ 87PawRedST-11
❑ 87SpoRoo2-49
❑ 88ClaRed-189
❑ 88Don-421
❑ 88DonTeaBRS-421
❑ 88Fle-357
❑ 88FleGlo-357
❑ 88Lea-245
❑ 88Sco-584
❑ 88ScoGlo-584
❑ 88StaLinRS-13
❑ 88Top-757
❑ 88TopClo-65
❑ 88TopTif-757
❑ 88ToyRoo-17
❑ 89PawRedSC-17
❑ 89PawRedSP-687
❑ 89PawRedSTI-15
❑ 90CMC-263
❑ 90PawRedSC-12
❑ 90PawRedSP-465
❑ 90ProAAAF-437
❑ 90TopTra-69T
❑ 90TopTraT-69T
❑ 90TopTVRS-19
❑ 91Bow-119
❑ 91Don-346
❑ 91Fle-103
❑ 91Lea-179
❑ 91OPC-574
❑ 91RedSoxP-12
❑ 91RedSoxP-19
❑ 91Sco-831
❑ 91StaClu-201
❑ 91Top-574
❑ 91TopDesS-574
❑ 91TopMic-574
❑ 91TopTif-574
❑ 92Don-448
❑ 92OPC-677
❑ 92RedSoxDD-18
❑ 92Sco-539
❑ 92StaClu-424
❑ 92Top-677
❑ 92TopDaiQTU-3
❑ 92TopGol-677
❑ 92TopGolW-677
❑ 92TopMic-677
❑ 92Ult-316
❑ 93Don-487
❑ 93RedSoxWHP-17
❑ 93StaClu-73
❑ 93StaCluFDI-73
❑ 93StaCluMOP-73
❑ 94ScrRedBF-923
❑ 96LeaSigEA-121
❑ 96MarMot-12
❑ 97PacPriGotD-GD89
❑ 97UppDecMP-P19
❑ 98PacInvGems-94
❑ 98PacOnl-691
❑ 98PacOnlR-691
❑ 98PacOnlWC-691
Marze, Dickey
❑ 90BurBraB-15
❑ 90BurBraP-2357
❑ 90BurBraS-17
Marzetta, Angie
❑ 95ColSilB-17
❑ 96ColSilB-17
Masaoka, Onan
❑ 95YakBeaTI-19
❑ 96BesAutS-56
❑ 96Bow-119
❑ 96BowFoi-119
❑ 96Exc-179
❑ 96SavSanB-18
❑ 97Bow-205
❑ 97BowInt-205
❑ 97FloStaLTPB-26
❑ 97VerBeaD-15
❑ 98Bow-388
❑ 98BowChr-388
❑ 98BowChrGA-388
❑ 98BowChrGAR-388
❑ 98BowChrI-388
❑ 98BowChrIR-388
❑ 98BowChrR-388
❑ 98BowGolA-388
❑ 98BowInt-388
❑ 98SanAntMG-15
❑ 98TexLeaTPG-22
❑ 99Bow-85
❑ 99BowChr-85
❑ 99BowChrG-85
❑ 99BowChrGR-85
❑ 99BowChrI-85
❑ 99BowChrIR-85
❑ 99BowChrR-85
❑ 99BowGol-85
❑ 99BowInt-85
❑ 99DodPol-15
Mascia, Dan
❑ 92ButCopKSP-1
Mashanic, Mike
❑ 97OmaRoyB-30
Mashore, Clyde
❑ 71ExpPS-14
❑ 71OPC-376
❑ 71Top-376
❑ 72Dia-29
❑ 73OPC-401
❑ 73Top 401
Mashore, Damon
❑ 90AriWilP-12
❑ 91SouOreAC-2
❑ 91SouOreAP-3863
❑ 92CalLeaACL-12
❑ 92ClaFS7-189
❑ 92ModA'sC-4
❑ 92ModA'sF-3909
❑ 92UppDecML-300
❑ 93HunStaF-2095
❑ 94HunStaF-1344
❑ 95EdmTraTI-16
❑ 96A'sMot-27
❑ 97A'sMot-26
❑ 97ColChoU-U21
❑ 97Don-377
❑ 97DonGolPP-377
❑ 97DonLim-190
❑ 97DonLimE-190
❑ 97DonRatR-30
❑ 97DonSilPP-377
❑ 97Fle-192
❑ 97FleTif-192
❑ 97Lea-327
❑ 97LeaFraM-327
❑ 97LeaFraMDC-327
❑ 97NewPin-167
❑ 97NewPinAP-167
❑ 97NewPinMC-167
❑ 97NewPinPP-167
❑ 97Pac-172
❑ 97PacLigB-172
❑ 97PacSil-172
❑ 97PinCer-113
❑ 97PinCerMBla-113
❑ 97PinCerMBlu-113
❑ 97PinCerMG-113
❑ 97PinCerMR-113
❑ 97PinCerR-113
❑ 97PinTotCPB-113
❑ 97PinTotCPG-113
❑ 97PinTotCPR-113
❑ 97PinX-P-131
❑ 97PinX-PMoS-131
❑ 97Sco-321
❑ 97ScoArtPWB-321
❑ 97ScoPreS-321
❑ 97ScoShoS-321
❑ 97ScoShoSAP-321
❑ 97SpoIll-14
❑ 97SpoIllEE-14
❑ 97Ult-113
❑ 97UltGolME-113
❑ 97UltPlaME-113
❑ 98PacOnl-16
❑ 98PacOnlR-16
❑ 98PacOnlWC-16
❑ 98Sco-130
❑ 98UppDec-179
❑ 98UppDecSF-96
Mashore, Justin
❑ 91BriTigC-3
❑ 91BriTigP-3619
❑ 92FayGenC-17
❑ 92FayGenF-2182
❑ 92StaCluD-112
❑ 92UppDecML-139
❑ 93Bow-447
❑ 93LakTigC-15
❑ 93LakTigF-1324
❑ 94Cla-104
❑ 94TreThuF-2131
❑ 94UppDecML-31
❑ 95TolMudHTI-20
❑ 96JacSunB-19
❑ 97MobBayBB-21
Masi, Phil
❑ 46SpoExcW-7-10
❑ 47TipTop-82
❑ 48BluTin-12
❑ 49Bow-153
❑ 49EurSta-15
❑ 50Bow-128
❑ 51Bow-160
❑ 51TopBluB-19
❑ 52Top-283
❑ 77TCMTheWY-14
❑ 79DiaGre-207
❑ 83TCMPla1943-38
❑ 83TopRep5-283
Masino, Ron
❑ 87BriYouC-7
Maskery, Sam
❑ 87OldJudN-316
Maskivish, Joe
❑ 94WelPirC-13
❑ 94WelPirF-3491
❑ 95Exc-257
❑ 96BesAutS-57
❑ 96Exc-220
❑ 96LynHilB-15
❑ 97CalLeaATI-36
❑ 97LynHil-12
Maskovich, George
❑ 52Par-97
Mason, Andy
❑ 93EveGiaC-18
❑ 93EveGiaF-3784
Mason, Charlie
❑ 90KalBatN-33
Mason, Chris
❑ 97PriDevR-24
Mason, Dan
❑ 95RocRedWTI-44
Mason, Don
❑ 66Top-524
❑ 69Top-584
❑ 71MLBOffS-231
❑ 71OPC-548
❑ 71Top-548
❑ 72Top-739
❑ 73PadDea-17
Mason, Henry
❑ 60Lea-80
❑ 60Top-331
❑ 96NegLeaBMKC-5
Mason, Jim
❑ 72Dia-30
❑ 72OPC-334
❑ 72Top-334
❑ 73OPC-458
❑ 73Top-458
❑ 74OPC-618
❑ 74Top-618
❑ 74TopTra-618T
❑ 75OPC-136
❑ 75Top-136
❑ 75TopMin-136
❑ 75YanSSP-18
❑ 76SSP-448
❑ 77OPC-211
❑ 77Top-212
❑ 78SSP270-94
❑ 78Top-588
❑ 79ExpPos-15
❑ 79Top-67
❑ 80OPC-259
❑ 80Top-497
❑ 92YanWIZ7-104
❑ 93RanKee-28
Mason, Kevin
❑ 89TenTecGE-16
❑ 89TenTecGE-35
Mason, Larry
❑ 81TCM60I-387
Mason, Marty (Martin)
❑ 82SprCarF-16
❑ 83SprCarF-7
❑ 84ArkTraT-19
❑ 86St.PetCP-18
❑ 87St.PetCP-19
❑ 88SavCarP-336
❑ 89St.PetCS-28
❑ 90ArkTraGS-2
❑ 91ArkTraP-1303
❑ 91LinDriAA-50
❑ 92ArkTraF-1145
❑ 92ArkTraS-50
❑ 93ArkTraF-2828
❑ 94ArkTraF-3105
❑ 95ArkTraTI-20
❑ 96ArkTraB-3
❑ 97LouRedB-4
❑ 98MemRedG-10
Mason, Mike
❑ 82TulDriT-5
❑ 83OklCit8T-20
❑ 84FleUpd-76
❑ 84RanJarP-16
❑ 84TopTra-76T
❑ 84TopTraT-76T
❑ 85Don-281
❑ 85Fle-562
❑ 85OPC-144
❑ 85RanPer-16
❑ 85Top-464
❑ 85TopMin-464
❑ 85TopSti-354
❑ 85TopTif-464
❑ 86Don-422
❑ 86Fle-565
❑ 86OPC-189
❑ 86RanPer-16
❑ 86Top-189
❑ 86TopTif-189
❑ 87Don-284
❑ 87Fle-129
❑ 87FleGlo-129
❑ 87FleUpd-73
❑ 87FleUpdG-73
❑ 87OPC-208
❑ 87RanSmo-4
❑ 87Top-646
❑ 87TopTif-646
❑ 88Top-87
❑ 88TopTif-87
❑ 91AppFoxCB-28
❑ 91AppFoxP-1733
❑ 91AppFoxP-1734
❑ 92AppFoxCB-28
❑ 92AppFoxFl-1002
❑ 93MemChiF-392
❑ 93RanKee-246
❑ 94MemChiF-374
❑ 95SprSulTI-13
❑ 96LanLugB-3
❑ 97LanLugTS-12
❑ 98WicWraM-23
Mason, Raymond
❑ 52LavPro-69
Mason, Rob
❑ 88WesPalBES-18
❑ 89RocExpLC-17
❑ 90WesPalBES-14
Mason, Roger
❑ 83BirBarT-24
❑ 84EvaTriT-21
❑ 85PhoGiaC-190
❑ 86Don-633
❑ 86FleUpd-72
❑ 86GiaMot-23
❑ 86GiaPos-20
❑ 86TopTra-70T
❑ 86TopTraT-70T
❑ 87Don-204
❑ 87Fle-280
❑ 87FleGlo-280
❑ 87GiaMot-23
❑ 87Top-526
❑ 87TopTif-526
❑ 88BlaYNPRWLU-7
❑ 88PhoFirC-4
❑ 88PhoFirP-62
❑ 89AstSmo-24
❑ 89TucTorC-4
❑ 89TucTorJP-14
❑ 89TucTorP-195
❑ 90BufBisTI-15
❑ 91BufBisLD-33
❑ 91BufBisP-536
❑ 91LinDriAAA-33
❑ 91TriA AAGP-AAA3
❑ 92Don-715
❑ 92FleUpd-115
❑ 92Lea-454
❑ 92LeaBlaG-454
❑ 92PirNatl-13
❑ 92Sco-727
❑ 92StaClu-266
❑ 92Ult-554
❑ 93Don-358
❑ 93Fle-116
❑ 93PadMot-25
❑ 93Sco-441
❑ 94Fle-595
❑ 94PhiMed-21
❑ 94PhiUSPC-3D
❑ 94PhiUSPC-10C
❑ 94Sco-123
❑ 94ScoGolR-123
❑ 94StaCluT-221
❑ 94StaCluTFDI-221
❑ 94Top-533
❑ 94TopGol-533
❑ 94TopSpa-533
❑ 95Don-430
❑ 95DonPreP-430
❑ 95Fle-376
Masone, Tony
❑ 80CedRapRT-9
Massarelli, John
❑ 87AubAstP-1
❑ 88AubAstP-1961
❑ 89AshTouP-945
❑ 90FloStaLAS-13
❑ 90OscAstS-20
❑ 91Cla/Bes-165
❑ 91OscAstC-15
❑ 91OscAstP-688
❑ 92JacGenS-341
❑ 92TucTorF-491
❑ 93TucTorF-3073
❑ 94EdmTraF-2887
❑ 95ChaKniTI-14
Massaro, Justo
❑ 80VenLeaS-240
❑ 93LinVenB-212
❑ 96-97LinVen-195
Masse, Billy (Bill)
❑ 88TopTra-67T
❑ 88TopTraT-67T
❑ 89PriWilCS-13
❑ 89Sta-90
❑ 89TopBig-179
❑ 90AlbYanB-21
❑ 90AlbYanP-1045
❑ 90AlbYanSt-11
❑ 91AlbYanLD-9
❑ 91AlbYanP-1020
❑ 91LinDriAA-9
❑ 92ColCliF-364
❑ 92ColCliP-23
❑ 92ColCliS-110
❑ 92SkyAAAF-50
❑ 93ColCliF-1123
❑ 93ColCliP-23
❑ 93TriAAAGF-49
❑ 94ClaGolF-43
❑ 94ColCliF-2966
❑ 94ColCliP-19
❑ 94Top-79
❑ 94TopGol-79
❑ 94TopSpa-79
❑ 95ColCliMCTI-19
❑ 95ColCliP-18
❑ 95ColCliTI-18
❑ 97VerExpB-4
Masse, Daniel
❑ 94BilMusF-3665
Massengale, Stan
❑ 84JacMetT-11
Massey, Jim
❑ 86EveGiaC-17
❑ 86EveGiaPC-13
❑ 87EveGiaC-21
Massey, Seth
❑ 95DavLipB-17
Massicotte, Jeff
❑ 87GenCubP-19
❑ 88PeoChiTI-15
❑ 89PeoChiTI-5
❑ 90WinSpiTI-20
Massie, Bret
❑ 88SpaPhiS-8
Massimo, Ryan
❑ 98DanBraQ-15
Masson, Todd
❑ 93Sou-13
Massuci, Tony
❑ 33Zee-131
❑ 33Zee-132
Mast, Brian
❑ 92DavLipB-17
❑ 93DavLipB-16
❑ 93KinMetC-16
❑ 93KinMetF-3792
Masteller, Dan
❑ 90VisOakCLC-67
❑ 90VisOakP-2162
❑ 91Cla/Bes-330
❑ 91LinDriAA-487
❑ 91OrlSunRLD-487
❑ 91OrlSunRP-1858
❑ 92OrlSunRF-2854
❑ 92OrlSunRS-511
❑ 93NasXprF-409
❑ 94SalLakBF-830

- 94VenLinU-223

Masters, Burke
- 88CapCodPPaLP-101
- 88MisStaB-18
- 89MisStaB-24
- 90MisStaB-25

Masters, Dave (David)
- 86WinSpiP-13
- 87PitCubP-14
- 88IowCubC-9
- 88IowCubP-533
- 89IowCubC-6
- 89IowCubP-1698
- 90CMC-77
- 90IowCubC-2
- 90IowCubP-315
- 90ProAAAF-622
- 91IndIndLD-189
- 91IndIndP-458
- 91LinDriAAA-189
- 92PhoFirF-2816
- 92PhoFirS-387
- 93LinVenB-45
- 93ShrCapF-2755

Masters, Frank
- 86GleFalTP-14
- 87ModA'sC-20
- 88MadMusP-15
- 89MadMusS-15

Masters, Walt
- 31SenTealPW-24
- 79DiaGre-332

Masters, Wayne
- 90AugPirP-2459

Masterson, Walt
- 47SenGunBP-6
- 49Bow-157
- 50Bow-153
- 50RedSoxTI-12
- 51Bow-307
- 52Bow-205
- 52Top-186
- 53BowBW-9
- 53Bri-11
- 60RawGloT-19
- 70Houof J-17
- 75TCMHouoJ-19
- 76TayBow4-108
- 79DiaGre-68
- 83TopRep5-186

Mastrolonardo, David
- 98FreKeyM-11

Mastropietro, Dave
- 90NiaFalRP-5

Mastrullo, Michael
- 94BurIndC-13
- 94BurIndF-3810

Masuyama, Daryl
- 86ShrCapP-16

Masuzawa, Hideki
- 90GatCitPP-3342

Mata, Vic
- 83NasSouTI-11
- 84ColCliP-14
- 84ColCliT-10
- 85ColCliT-1
- 85DomLeaS-15
- 85Don-629
- 85Fle-644
- 85YanTCMP-36
- 86ColCliP-13
- 86ColCliP-15
- 86YanTCM-34
- 88RocRedWC-23
- 88RocRedWGCP-15
- 88RocRedWP-197
- 88RocRedWTI-12
- 92YanWIZ8-110

Matachun, Paul
- 90ButCopKSP-11
- 91GasRanC-20
- 91GasRanP-2697
- 92GasRanC-18
- 92GasRanF-2261

Matan, James A.
- 98BilMusTI-22

Matas, Jim
- 86GenCubP-18
- 87WinSpiP-26
- 88WinSpiS-10

Matchett, Steve
- 89BriTigS-16

Matchick, J. Tom
- 67OPC-72
- 67Top-72
- 68OPC-113
- 68TigDetFPB-14
- 68Top-113
- 68TopVen-113
- 69MilBra-168
- 69TigTealC-10
- 69Top-344
- 70RoyTeal-21
- 70Top-647
- 71MLBOffS-419
- 71OPC-321
- 71Top-321
- 72MilBra-208
- 73OPC-631
- 73Top-631
- 81TCM60I-397
- 88TigDom-12
- 91OriCro-282
- 94BreMilB-152

Matcuk, Steven
- 96PorRocB-23
- 97AshTou-18
- 98AshTouM-12
- 98SalAvaC-21

Mateo, Henry
- 97VerExpB-20
- 98CapFeaCM-12

Mateo, Huascar
- 88BenBucL-13

Mateo, Jose
- 90ChaRaiB-15
- 90ChaRaiP-2047
- 95GreFalDTI-22
- 96SavSanB-25
- 98DanQ-C-23

Mateo, Julio
- 98EveAquG-15

Mateo, Luis
- 89MadMusS-16

Mateo, Ruben
- 96ChaRivTI-9619
- 97BesAll-7
- 97FloStaLTPB-4
- 98BesAutSS-33
- 98Bow-396
- 98BowBes-177
- 98BowBesAR-177
- 98BowBesMIF-MI8
- 98BowBesMIFAR-MI8
- 98BowBesMIFR-MI8
- 98BowBesR-177
- 98BowChr-396
- 98BowChrGA-396
- 98BowChrGAR-396
- 98BowChrI-396
- 98BowChrIR-396
- 98BowChrR-396
- 98BowGolA-396
- 98BowInt-396
- 98LeaRS-316
- 98LeaRSLHolo-316
- 98LeaRSLong-316
- 98LeaRTrue-316
- 98SP MinPE-122
- 98SPMin-122
- 98TexLeaC-13
- 98TulDriTI-27
- 99199Fin-144
- 99BasAmeTP-63
- 99BasAmeTPG-63
- 99BasAmeTPSC-7
- 99Bow-98
- 99Bow200RF-ROY4
- 99BowAut-BA1
- 99BowBes-120
- 99BowBesAR-120
- 99BowBesFFMI-FF1
- 99BowBesFFMI-FF1
- 99BowBesFFMII-FF1
- 99BowBesMI-M2
- 99BowBesMIAR-M2
- 99BowBesMIR-M2
- 99BowBesR-120
- 99BowChr-98
- 99BowChrDA-DA5
- 99BowChrDAR-DA5
- 99BowChrG-98
- 99BowChrGR-98
- 99BowChrI-98
- 99BowChrIR-98
- 99BowChrR-98
- 99BowChrSC-SC1
- 99BowChrSCR-SC1
- 99BowGol-98
- 99BowInt-98
- 99BowScoC-SC1
- 99DumSet-21
- 99DumSet-101
- 99FinFutF-FF5
- 99FinGolRef-144
- 99FinRef-144
- 99FleMys-101
- 99FleMysM-101
- 99PacOme-237
- 99PacOme5T-10
- 99PacOme5TT-10
- 99PacOmeC-237
- 99PacOmeDM-34
- 99PacOmeG-237
- 99PacOmePB-237
- 99SkyPre-251
- 99SkyPre-251
- 99SkyPreA-39
- 99SkyPreABlue-39
- 99SkyPreR-251
- 99SkyPreR-251
- 99SP SigAuto-RMA
- 99SP SigAutoG-RMA
- 99SP TopP-80
- 99SP TopPC-RM
- 99SP TopPDtS-D20
- 99SP TopPGF-GF20
- 99SP TopPPE-80
- 99SPSig-63
- 99StaClu-167
- 99StaCluC-SCC37
- 99StaCluCR-SCC37
- 99StaCluFDI-167
- 99StaCluOoaK-167
- 99StaCluPP-167
- 99Top-430
- 99TopAll-AM17
- 99TopBlaLC1-26
- 99TopBlaLC2-26
- 99TopBlaLC3-26
- 99TopChr-430
- 99TopChrA-AE17
- 99TopChrAR-AE17
- 99TopChrR-430
- 99TopGal-139
- 99TopGalPP-139
- 99TopGalPPI-139
- 99TopGolL-26
- 99TopGolLC1-26
- 99TopGolLC2-26
- 99TopGolLOtO-26
- 99TopMVPP-430
- 99TopRedLC1-26
- 99TopRedLC2-26
- 99TopRedLC3-26
- 99TopSta-19
- 99TopSta1Foil-19
- 99TopSta2Foil-19
- 99TopSta3Foil-19
- 99TopStaBF-BF9
- 99TopStaBFFoil-BF9
- 99TopStaFoil-19
- 99TopStaFoil-164
- 99TopStaOS-19
- 99TopStaTS-19
- 99TopStaTS-19
- 99TopTekFP-F6
- 99UppDec-270
- 99UppDecE-113
- 99UppDecEFXG-113
- 99UppDecEL1-270
- 99UppDecEL2-270
- 99UppDecMSC-SC14
- 99Vic-394

Matew, Francisco
- 98JohCCTI-24

Matheny, Mike (Michael)
- 91HelBreSP-11
- 92ClaFS7-393
- 92StoPorC-15
- 92StoPorF-37
- 93El PasDF-2953
- 94Bow-673
- 94BreMilB-329
- 94ExcFS7-83
- 94Sel-204
- 94SpoRoo-127
- 94SpoRooAP-127
- 94Ult-375
- 95Pin-144
- 95PinArtP-144
- 95PinMusC-144
- 96BrePol-16
- 96Don-541
- 96DonPreP-541
- 96Fla-102
- 96Fle-152
- 96FleTif-152
- 96LeaSigA-148
- 96LeaSigAG-148
- 96LeaSigAS-148
- 96StaClu-446
- 96StaCluMOP-446
- 96Ult-366
- 96UltGolM-366
- 97BrePol-16
- 97ColCho-372
- 97Fle-133
- 97FleTif-133
- 97Pac-123
- 97PacLigB-123
- 97PacSil-123
- 97Top-485
- 97Ult-78
- 97UltGolME-78
- 97UltPlaME-78
- 98ColCho-406
- 98PacInvGems-59
- 98PacOnl-405
- 98PacOnlR-405
- 98PacOnlWC-405
- 98StaCluFDI-97
- 98StaCluI-97
- 98StaCluOneK-97
- 98StaCluPP-97
- 98UppDec-408
- 99Fle-510
- 99FleSta9-510
- 99FleWarT-510
- 99Pac-238
- 99PacPlaB-238
- 99PacRed-238

Mathes, Joseph
- 19Zee-141

Matheson, Bill
- 43CenFlo-19
- 44CenFlo-16
- 45CenFlo-16

Mathews, Byron
- 90OklSoo-11
- 92ClaDraP-120
- 92UtiBluSC-7
- 93MidLeaAGF-25
- 93SouBenWSC-15
- 93SouBenWSF-1445
- 93StaCluM-186
- 93Top-612
- 93TopGol-612
- 93TopInaM-612
- 93TopInaR-612
- 93TopMic-612
- 94SouBenSHC-9
- 94SouBenSHF-607

Mathews, Chuck
- 85OscAstTI-11
- 86ColAstP-18

Mathews, Del
- 94MacBraC-12
- 94MacBraF-2199
- 95DurBulTI-20
- 96DurBulBIB-10
- 96DurBulBrB-11
- 97LynHil-13

Mathews, Eddie (Edwin Lee)
- 47Exh-150A
- 47Exh-150B
- 50JJKCopP-10
- 52Top-407
- 53BowC-97
- 53BraJohC-21
- 53BraMer-12
- 53BraSpiaS3-17
- 53BraSpiaS7-8
- 53Top-37
- 54Bow-64
- 54BraJohC-41
- 54BraMer-6
- 54BraSpiaSP-13
- 54RedMan-NL23
- 54Top-30
- 55BigLeaIS-12
- 55Bow-103
- 55BraGolS-18
- 55BraJohC-41
- 55BraSpiaSD-12
- 55DaiQueS-12
- 55Top-155
- 56BraBilaBP-13
- 56Top-107
- 56TopHocF-B21
- 56TopPin-18
- 56YelBasP-21
- 57Bra8x1-7
- 57BraSpiaS4-14
- 57Top-250
- 58BraJayP-8
- 58HarSta-4
- 58JayPubS-6
- 58Top-351
- 58Top-440
- 58Top-480
- 59HomRunD-13
- 59Top-212
- 59Top-450
- 60ArmCoi-15
- 60BraDav-2
- 60BraSpiaS-12
- 60KeyChal-33
- 60Pos-6
- 60RawGloT-20
- 60Top-420
- 60Top-558
- 60TopTat-33
- 61Baz-11
- 61NuSco-412
- 61Pos-106
- 61Top-43
- 61Top-120
- 61TopStaI-45
- 62Baz-2
- 62BraJayP-6
- 62ExhStaB-25
- 62Jel-147
- 62Pos-147
- 62PosCan-147
- 62SalPlaC-111
- 62ShiPlaC-111
- 62Top-30
- 62TopBuc-56
- 62TopStaI-148
- 62TopVen-30
- 63BasMagM-56
- 63BraJayP-7
- 63ExhStaB-43
- 63Jel-151
- 63Pos-151
- 63SalMetC-28
- 63Top-275
- 64BraJayP-6
- 64ChatheY-35
- 64Top-35
- 64TopCoi-33
- 64TopSta-97
- 64TopStaU-47
- 64TopTatI-52
- 64TopVen-35
- 65ChaTheY-35
- 65Top-500
- 65TopEmbl-26
- 66BraPos-17
- 66Top-200
- 66TopRubI-59
- 66TopVen-200
- 67AstTeal1-9
- 67CokCapAs-18
- 67DexPre-133
- 67OPC-166
- 67Top-166
- 67TopVen-214
- 68CokCapT-16
- 68OPC-58
- 68Top-58
- 68TopVen-58
- 69EquSpoHoF-BB12
- 69MilBra-169
- 70Houof J-18
- 73OPC-237
- 73Top-237A
- 73Top-237B
- 74BraPhoC-4
- 74OPC-634
- 74Top-634
- 75TCMHouoJ-20
- 77BobParHoF-66
- 77GalGloG-34
- 78AtlCon-14
- 78BraTCC-9
- 78DexHaloFP-36
- 79BasGre-78
- 79DiaGre-400
- 79TCM50-157
- 80Bra195T-27
- 80Lau300-25
- 80PerHaloFP-166
- 80PerHaloFPS-36
- 80SSPHOF-166
- 82CraJac-12
- 82TCMGreS-7
- 82TCMStaot5-7
- 83Bra53F-41
- 83MLBPin-26
- 83TopRep5-407
- 84OCoandSI-22
- 84OCoandSI-121
- 84SpoDesPW-17
- 85CirK-11
- 85TCMHomRC-6
- 86BigLeaC-10
- 86BraGreT-4
- 86SpoDecG-34
- 86SpoDesJM-16
- 86SumBraP-18
- 86TCM-19
- 86TCMSupS-40
- 87AstShoSTw-23
- 87Bra195T-2
- 87DurBulP-16
- 87NesDreT-25
- 88GreBraB-22
- 88TigDom-13
- 89HOFStiB-25
- 89KahCoo-8
- 89PacLegI-116
- 89PerCelP-30
- 89RicBraBC-14
- 89RicBraC-10
- 89RicBraP-845
- 89RicBraTI-14
- 89TopBasT-32
- 90PacLeg-66
- 90PerGreM-28
- 90SumBraB-12
- 90SweBasG-65
- 91LinDri-40
- 91SweBasG-147
- 91TopArc1-37
- 91UppDecS-15
- 92BazQua5A-3
- 92TVSpoMF5HRC-7
- 93ActPacA-117
- 93ActPacA2-51G
- 94TedWil-43
- 94TopArc1-30
- 94TopArc1G-30
- 97TopStaHRR-9
- 97TopStaRRAU-9
- 98DonEliBttF-3
- 98DonEliBttFA-3
- 98DonSigSB-20
- 98DonSigSS-9
- 98SpollITaN-19
- 98SpollITaNC-C4
- 98SpollITaNEE-19
- 98UppDecR-49
- 98UppDecRSotT-EM
- 99SP SigAuto-EMA
- 99SpollIGotG-40
- 99SpollIGotGA-46
- 99SpollIGotGC-4
- 99SPSig-176
- 99TopHaloFC-HOF5
- 99UppDecAP-EM
- 99UppDecAPH5AU-EMAU
- 99UppDecCLES-EMA
- 99UppDecCLESC-EMA

Mathews, Greg
- 86CarTeal-29
- 86DonRoo-26
- 86FleUpd-73
- 86SpoRoo-41
- 87CarSmo-8
- 87Don-208
- 87Fle-303
- 87FleGlo-303
- 87Top-567
- 87TopGloS-60
- 87TopTif-567
- 87ToyRoo-20
- 88CarSmo-7
- 88CarTeal-19
- 88Don-84
- 88DonBasB-324
- 88Fle-41
- 88FleGlo-41
- 88LouRedBTI-33
- 88Sco-226
- 88ScoGlo-226
- 88ScoYouS2-35
- 88StaLinCa-13
- 88Top-133
- 88TopBig-177
- 88TopTif-133

❑ 89CarTeal-17
❑ 89Don-281
❑ 89Fle-456
❑ 89FleGlo-456
❑ 89Sco-286
❑ 89Top-97
❑ 89TopTif-97
❑ 89UppDec-531
❑ 90CarSmo-13
❑ 90LouRedBLBC-26
❑ 90OPC-209
❑ 90PubIntS-221
❑ 90Sco-537
❑ 90Top-209
❑ 90TopTif-209
❑ 90TopTVCa-17
❑ 90UppDec-678
❑ 92ScrRedBF-2443
❑ 92ScrRedBS-489
❑ 93Fle-495
Mathews, Jeremy
❑ 89BelMarL-22
Mathews, Jim
❑ 78AshTouT-16
Mathews, Jon
❑ 94BenRocC-16
❑ 94BenRocF-3604
Mathews, Michael
❑ 92ClaDraP-27
❑ 93WatIndF-3558
Mathews, Nelson
❑ 63Top-54A
❑ 63Top-54B
❑ 64Top-366
❑ 64TopVen-366
❑ 65OPC-87
❑ 65Top-87
❑ 81TCM60I-394
Mathews, Rick
❑ 81ChaRoyT-26
❑ 82ForMyeRT-22
❑ 84MemChiT-1
Mathews, Robert
❑ 87OldJudN-317
❑ 90KalBatN-34
Mathews, T.J.
❑ 92HamRedC-19
❑ 92HamRedF-1588
❑ 93ClaGolF-120
❑ 93ExcFS7-102
❑ 93MidLeaAGF-52
❑ 93SprCarC-18
❑ 93SprCarF-1847
❑ 94Bow-236
❑ 94ClaGolF-165
❑ 94ExcFS7-271
❑ 94FloStaLAF-FSL42
❑ 94St.PetCC-16
❑ 94St.PetCF-2583
❑ 95LouRedF-274
❑ 96Bow-255
❑ 96BowFoi-255
❑ 96CarPol-17
❑ 96Fin-B297
❑ 96FinRef-B297
❑ 96Fla-363
❑ 96Fle-548
❑ 96FleTif-548
❑ 96LeaSigA-149
❑ 96LeaSigAG-149
❑ 96LeaSigAS-149
❑ 96SigRooOJ-18
❑ 96SigRooOJS-18
❑ 96Top-102
❑ 96Ult-550
❑ 96UltGolM-550
❑ 97CarPol-18
❑ 97Fle-448
❑ 97FleTif-448
❑ 97PacPriGotD-GD200
❑ 97Top-343
❑ 97Ult-275
❑ 97UltGolME-275
❑ 97UltPlaME-275
❑ 98A'sMot-21
❑ 98Fle-199
❑ 98PacOnl-537
❑ 98PacOnlR-537
❑ 98PacOnlWC-537
❑ 98Top-420
❑ 98TopChr-420
❑ 98TopChrR-420
❑ 98TopDevR-420
❑ 98TopDia-420
❑ 98TopMiniC-420
Mathews, Terry
❑ 88ChaRanS-15
❑ 89TulDriGS-17
❑ 89TulDriTI-15
❑ 90TulDriP-1171
❑ 90TulDriTI-15
❑ 91LinDriAAA-311
❑ 91OklCit8LD-311
❑ 91OklCit8P-173
❑ 92Don-694
❑ 92Fle-310
❑ 92ProFS7-151
❑ 92RanMot-20
❑ 92RanTeal-12
❑ 92Sco-737
❑ 92TopDeb91-118
❑ 92TopGol-131
❑ 92TopGolW-131
❑ 92Ult-135
❑ 93Fle-684
❑ 93JacGenF-2107
❑ 93RanKee-247
❑ 94EdmTraF-2873
❑ 95Fle-337
❑ 95Top-623
❑ 95TopCyb-390
❑ 95Ult-164
❑ 95UltGolM-164
❑ 96Fle-389
❑ 96FleTif-389
❑ 96LeaSigEA-122
❑ 97BalOriP-20
❑ 98PacOnl-93
❑ 98PacOnlR-93
❑ 98PacOnlWC-93
Mathews, Tom
❑ 86FreGiaSB-22
Mathewson, Christy
❑ 03BreE10-94
❑ 03WilCarE-22
❑ 06GiaUllAFS-6
❑ 08AmeCarE91-13
❑ 08AmeCarE91-52
❑ 08RosComP-129
❑ 09AmeCarE90-1-74
❑ 09MaxPubP-6
❑ 09PhiCarE-16
❑ 09SpoNewSM-3
❑ 09T206-229
❑ 09T206-230
❑ 09T206-231
❑ 10CouT21-43
❑ 10CouT21-179
❑ 10CouT21-301
❑ 10DomDisP-76
❑ 10E-UOraBSC-15
❑ 10E101-31
❑ 10E102-17
❑ 10E12AmeCDCE125-23
❑ 10E98-20
❑ 10JHDABE-12
❑ 10JuJuDE-25
❑ 10MelMinE-31
❑ 10NadCarE-36
❑ 10NotCov-7
❑ 10OrnOvaPP-11
❑ 10PeoT21-37A
❑ 10PeoT21-37B
❑ 10RedCroT-47
❑ 10RedCroT-48
❑ 10RedCroT-134
❑ 10SepAnoP-19
❑ 10StaCarE-21
❑ 10SweCapPP-117A
❑ 10SweCapPP-117B
❑ 10W555-45
❑ 11DiaGumP-19
❑ 11HelSta-131
❑ 11L1L-133
❑ 11MecDFT-6
❑ 11PinT-5-251
❑ 11PloCanE-44
❑ 11S74Sil-88
❑ 11S81LarS-108
❑ 11SpoLifCW-235
❑ 11SpoLifM-211
❑ 11T205-109
❑ 11TurRedT-27
❑ 12HasTriFT-29A
❑ 12HasTriFT-29B
❑ 12HasTriFT-29C
❑ 12HasTriFT-29D
❑ 12HasTriFT-48E
❑ 12HasTriFT-48H
❑ 12HasTriFT-74C
❑ 12HasTriFT-74D
❑ 13NatGamW-28
❑ 13TomBarW-27
❑ 14CraJacE-88
❑ 14PieStaT-68
❑ 14PolGroW-17
❑ 14TexTomE-30
❑ 14TexTomE-58
❑ 15AmeCarE106-27
❑ 15CraJacE-88
❑ 16FleBreD-62
❑ 19W514-72
❑ 20W516-24
❑ 20W52-2
❑ 30SchR33-10
❑ 36Halof FP-18
❑ 36Halof FP-28
❑ 39PC7AlbHoF-3
❑ 39PC7AlbHoF-64
❑ 40PlaBal-175
❑ 48ExhHoF-22
❑ 49LeaPre-5
❑ 50CalHOFW-52
❑ 50H80FouMH-2
❑ 51R42SmaS-68
❑ 51TopConMA-8
❑ 53ArtHaloFP-58
❑ 58JayPubAG-7
❑ 60ExhWriH-16
❑ 60Fle-2
❑ 60NuHi-8
❑ 61Fle-59
❑ 61GolPre-24
❑ 61NuSco-477
❑ 61Top-408
❑ 63BasMagM-57
❑ 63BazA-4
❑ 63HalofFB-13
❑ 67SpoHobFC-4
❑ 67TopVen-151
❑ 68LauWorS-2
❑ 68SpoMemAG-5
❑ 69Baz-3
❑ 69Baz-12
❑ 70FleWorS-2
❑ 71FleWorS-3
❑ 71FleWorS-11
❑ 72ClaCar-24
❑ 72FleFamF-3
❑ 72LauGreF-25
❑ 73FleWilD-22
❑ 73HalofFPP-11
❑ 73TCMAllG-12
❑ 74CapPub-19
❑ 75GiaAllT-5
❑ 76ShaPiz-4
❑ 77BobParHoF-65
❑ 77BobParMBC-14
❑ 77GalGloG-152
❑ 77GalGloG-242
❑ 77ShaPiz-6
❑ 79Pew-10
❑ 80GiaGreT-10
❑ 80Lau300-5
❑ 80LauFamF-22
❑ 80PacLeg-34
❑ 80PerHaloFP-3
❑ 80SSPHOF-4
❑ 81ConTSN-9
❑ 82BHCRSpoL-6
❑ 82DavHaloFB-16
❑ 82TCMGreP-33
❑ 83DonHOFH-3
❑ 84GalHaloFRL-4
❑ 84OCoandSI-119
❑ 84OCoandSI-172
❑ 85Woo-25
❑ 86ConSer1-23
❑ 86ConSer1-32
❑ 86ConSer1-46
❑ 87ConSer2-3
❑ 87HygAllG-32
❑ 89HOFStiB-65
❑ 90BasWit-104
❑ 90HOFStiB-10
❑ 90PerGreM-6
❑ 90SweBasG-134
❑ 91ConTSN-57
❑ 91ConTSNP-331
❑ 91SweBasG-141
❑ 91USGamSBL-12C
❑ 91USGamSBL-12D
❑ 91USGamSBL-12H
❑ 91USGamSBL-12S
❑ 92ConTSN-331
❑ 92ConTSNCI-9
❑ 93ActPacA-87
❑ 93ActPacA2-21G
❑ 93CokCasI-CM1
❑ 93ConMasC-8
❑ 93ConTSN-910
❑ 93CraJac-4
❑ 93UppDecAH-89
❑ 93UppDecAH-143
❑ 93UppDecAH-144
❑ 93UppDecAH-155
❑ 93UppDecAH-156
❑ 93UppDecTR-1
❑ 94ConTSN-1220
❑ 94ConTSNB-1220
❑ 94UppDecAH-35
❑ 94UppDecAH-104
❑ 94UppDecAH-153
❑ 94UppDecAH1-35
❑ 94UppDecAH1-104
❑ 94UppDecAH1-153
❑ 94UppDecTAE-14
❑ 94UppDecTAELD-LD5
❑ 95ConTSN-1322
❑ 96BalHOF1C-3
❑ 96ColCho-503
❑ 96ColChoGS-503
❑ 96ColChoSS-503
❑ 99SpollIGotG-13
❑ 99SpollIGotGRB-4
❑ 99SpollIGotGRBG-4
❑ 99UppDecCL-7
❑ 99UppDecCLCC-7
Mathewson, Harry
❑ 06GiaUllAFS-7
Mathias, Carl
❑ 60Top-139
❑ 60TopVen-139
❑ 61MapLeaBH-13
❑ 78ReaRem-13
Mathieu, Franz
❑ 82MonNew-9
Mathile, Mike
❑ 89AncBucTI-7
❑ 91RocExpC-9
❑ 91RocExpP-2044
❑ 92ClaFS7-127
❑ 92HarSenF-458
❑ 92HarSenS-290
❑ 92SkyAA F-123
❑ 93OttLynF-2432
❑ 94IndIndF-1807
❑ 95IndIndF-91
Mathiot, Mike
❑ 89KenTwiP-1059
❑ 89KenTwiS-13
❑ 90KenTwiB-7
❑ 90KenTwiP-2302
❑ 90KenTwiS-11
Mathis, Jared
❑ 98StoPorUG-3
Mathis, Joe
❑ 94BelMarC-19
❑ 94BelMarF-3251
❑ 96WisTimRB-15
❑ 97CalLeaTP-12
❑ 97LanJet-17
❑ 98OrlRayM-12
❑ 98SouLeaTPG-18
Mathis, Lefty (Verdell)
❑ 86NegLeaF-62
❑ 91NegLeaRL-7
❑ 91PomBlaBPB-2
❑ 92NegLeaRLI-40
❑ 93UppDecS-17
❑ 95NegLeaLI-7
❑ 97NegLeaPC-10C
Mathis, Monte
❑ 92SarWhiSCB-23
Mathis, Ron
❑ 81BirBarT-5
❑ 83TucTorT-4
❑ 84TucTorC-72
❑ 85AstMot-26
❑ 85FleUpd-78
❑ 85TopTifT-79T
❑ 85TopTra-79T
❑ 86Fle-305
❑ 86Top-476
❑ 86TopTif-476
❑ 86TucTorP-12
❑ 87TucTorP-14
❑ 88ColSprSSC-5
❑ 88ColSprSSP-1548
Mathis, Sammie
❑ 95WatIndTI-18
Mathis, Wayne
❑ 90KinMetB-4
❑ 90KinMetS-16
Mathison, Chuck
❑ 84GreHorT-15
Matias, John
❑ 70OPC-444
❑ 70Top-444
❑ 71OPC-546
❑ 71Top-546
❑ 73TacTwiC-14
❑ 87HawRai-8
Matilla, Pedro
❑ 88ElmPioC-14
❑ 89WinHavRSS-15
❑ 90WinHavRSS-14
❑ 91WinHavRSC-14
Matlack, Jon
❑ 71OPC-648
❑ 71Top-648
❑ 72OPC-141
❑ 72Top-141
❑ 73Kel2D-12
❑ 73LinPor-116
❑ 73OPC-55
❑ 73Top-55
❑ 74MetJapEB-6
❑ 74MetTeal-14
❑ 74OPC-153
❑ 74OPC-471
❑ 74Top-153
❑ 74Top-471
❑ 74TopDecE-44
❑ 74TopSta-66
❑ 75Kel-10
❑ 75MetSSP-21
❑ 75OPC-290
❑ 75Top-290
❑ 75TopMin-290
❑ 76Hos-97
❑ 76Kel-49A
❑ 76Kel-49B
❑ 76MetMSAP-4
❑ 76OPC-190
❑ 76SSP-554
❑ 76Top-190
❑ 77BurCheD-137
❑ 77ChiWilD-42
❑ 77DailsID-42
❑ 77DetCaeD-42
❑ 77HolInnD-42
❑ 77Hos-114
❑ 77MetDaiPA-14
❑ 77MSADis-42
❑ 77OPC-132
❑ 77PepGloD-68
❑ 77RCColC-38
❑ 77SagDis-42
❑ 77sDis-42
❑ 77Top-440
❑ 77WenDis-42
❑ 77ZipDis-42
❑ 78OPC-98
❑ 78RanBurK-5
❑ 78RCColC-38
❑ 78SSP270-99
❑ 78Top-25
❑ 78WifBalD-43
❑ 79BasPat-51
❑ 79Hos-122
❑ 79Kel-58
❑ 79OPC-159
❑ 79Top-315
❑ 80OPC-312
❑ 80Top-592
❑ 81Don-266
❑ 81Fle-621
❑ 81FleStiC-51
❑ 81OPC-339
❑ 81Top-656
❑ 81TopSti-135
❑ 81TopSupHT-92
❑ 82Don-215
❑ 82Fle-323
❑ 82FleSta-176
❑ 82OPC-239
❑ 82Top-239
❑ 83Don-195
❑ 83Fle-572
❑ 83FleSta-117
❑ 83FleSti-165
❑ 83RanAffF-32
❑ 83Top-749
❑ 84Don-378
❑ 84Fle-422
❑ 84Nes792-149
❑ 84Top-149
❑ 84TopTif-149
❑ 86RanGreT-2
❑ 89PacLegI-214
❑ 89PacSenL-9
❑ 89RivRedWB-23
❑ 89RivRedWCLC-26
❑ 89RivRedWP-1408
❑ 89T/MSenL-73
❑ 89TidTidC-3
❑ 89TopSenL-102
❑ 90EliSenL-11
❑ 90WicWraRD-27
❑ 91LasVegSLD-300
❑ 91LasVegSP-254
❑ 91LinDriAAA-300
❑ 91MetWIZ-253
❑ 92LasVegSF-2811
❑ 93RanKee-248
❑ 93SarWhiSC-29
❑ 93SarWhiSF-1387
❑ 94PriWilCC-26
❑ 94PriWilCF-1938
Matlock, Leroy
❑ 78LauLonABS-32
Matney, Ron
❑ 74WicAerODF-115
Matoian, Chad
❑ 97UCLBruTI-11
Matos, Alberto
❑ 93SpoIndC-12
❑ 93SpoIndF-3588
Matos, Carlos
❑ 82DanSunF-11
Matos, Domingo
❑ 90JamExpP-3
❑ 91JamExpC-14
❑ 91JamExpP-3554
❑ 92RocExpC-10
❑ 92RocExpF-2125
❑ 93WesPalBEC-14
❑ 93WesPalBEF-1349
❑ 94WesPalBEC-17
❑ 94WesPalBEF-51
Matos, Francisco
❑ 89ModA'sC-24
❑ 89ModA'sCLC-283
❑ 90ModA'sC-19
❑ 90ModA'sCLC-168
❑ 90ModA'sP-2220
❑ 91HunStaC-15
❑ 91HunStaLD-289
❑ 91HunStaP-1804
❑ 91LinDriAA-289
❑ 92HunStaS-314
❑ 92SkyAA F-133
❑ 93HunStaF-2090
❑ 94TacTigF-3183
❑ 95Pac-315
❑ 97RocRedW-18
❑ 98DurBulTI-18
Matos, Jose
❑ 94AshTouC-15
❑ 94AshTouF-1775
❑ 94BenRocF-3589
Matos, Julius
❑ 94WatIndC-19
❑ 94WatIndF-3945
❑ 98HigDesMG-16
Matos, Luis
❑ 92HunCubF-3146
❑ 98DelShoM-20
Matos, Malvin
❑ 90ButCopKSP-12
❑ 91GasRanC-24
❑ 91GasRanP-2701
❑ 92GasRanC-23
❑ 92GasRanF-2265
❑ 93ChaRaiC-13
❑ 93ChaRaiF-1924
❑ 93LinVenB-33
❑ 94ChaRanF-2508
❑ 94VenLinU-83
❑ 95LinVen-202
❑ 96-97LinVen-168
Matos, Pascual
❑ 94IdaFalBF-3588
❑ 94IdaFalBSP-15
❑ 94MacBraC-13
❑ 94MacBraF-2209
❑ 95MacBraTI-18
❑ 96DurBulBlB-24
❑ 96DurBulBrB-25
❑ 97DurBulTI-18
❑ 98GreBraG-14
❑ 99SkyPre-224
❑ 99SkyPre-224
❑ 99SkyPreR-224
❑ 99SkyPreR-224

Matos, Rafael
❑ 84ButCopKT-16
❑ 85DomLeaS-96
Matouzas, Jeff
❑ 90TamYanD-16
Matranga, Dave
❑ 90NebCor-18
❑ 98AubDouTI-15
Matranga, Jeff
❑ 92JohCitCF-3113
❑ 94St.PetCC-17
❑ 94St.PetCF-2584
❑ 96ArkTraB-18
❑ 97LouRedB-21
Matrisciano, Ron
❑ 80CliGiaT-7
Matsko, Rick
❑ 98WatIndTI-19
Matsubara, Makoto
❑ 79TCMJapPB-5
Matsukubo, Shingo
❑ 89SalLakTTI-12
Matsumoto, Akira
❑ 96MauStiHWB-7
Matsunaga, Hiromi
❑ 87JapPlaB-29
Matsuo, Hideharu
❑ 87MiaMarP-22
Mattern, Al
❑ 09ColChiE-179
❑ 09T206-232
❑ 10DomDisP-77
❑ 10SweCapPP-68A
❑ 10SweCapPP-68B
❑ 11HelSta-80
❑ 11MecDFT-24
❑ 11PinT-5-709
❑ 11S74Sil-45
❑ 11SpoLifM-274
❑ 11T205-110
❑ 12ColRedB-179
❑ 12ColTinT-179
❑ 12HasTriFT-50C
Mattern, Erik
❑ 98SalVol-23
Matterson, Henry
❑ 20Zee-89
Mattes, Troy
❑ 96DelShoB-22
❑ 98JupHamQ-9
Matteson, Eddie
❑ 20Zee-90
Matthews, Fran (Francis)
❑ 93NegLeaRL2-25
❑ 97NegLeaPC-3C
Matthews, Gary
❑ 73LinPor-161
❑ 73OPC-606
❑ 73Top-606
❑ 74OPC-386
❑ 74Top-386
❑ 75Gia-4
❑ 75GiaTeal-8
❑ 75Hos-31
❑ 75HosTwi-31
❑ 75OPC-79
❑ 75Top-79
❑ 75TopMin-79
❑ 76Hos-142
❑ 76OPC-133
❑ 76SanFraGP-12
❑ 76SSP-110
❑ 76Top-133
❑ 77BurCheD-210
❑ 77Hos-142
❑ 77RCColC-39
❑ 77Top-194
❑ 78BraCok-8
❑ 78Hos-19
❑ 78OPC-209
❑ 78RCColC-27
❑ 78Top-475
❑ 78WifBalD-44
❑ 79Hos-42
❑ 79OPC-35
❑ 79Top-85
❑ 80Kel-48
❑ 80OPC-186
❑ 80PhiBul-35
❑ 80Top-355
❑ 81AllGamPI-153
❑ 81Don-306A
❑ 81Don-306B
❑ 81Fle-251A
❑ 81Fle-251B
❑ 81OPC-186
❑ 81Top-528
❑ 81TopScr-76
❑ 81TopSti-144
❑ 81TopTra-800
❑ 82Don-441
❑ 82Fle-249
❑ 82FleSta-58
❑ 82OPC-151
❑ 82Top-680
❑ 82TopSti-79
❑ 83AllGamPI-152
❑ 83Don-420
❑ 83Dra-16
❑ 83Fle-165
❑ 83FleSta-118
❑ 83FleSti-178
❑ 83OPC-64
❑ 83PhiPosGPaM-6
❑ 83PhiTas-16
❑ 83Top-780
❑ 83TopSti-269
❑ 84AllGamPI-59
❑ 84CubBriPC-3S
❑ 84CubChiT-18
❑ 84CubSev-36
❑ 84Don-233
❑ 84Dra-21
❑ 84Fle-40
❑ 84FleSti-121
❑ 84FleUpd-77
❑ 84FunFooP-70
❑ 84Nes792-70
❑ 84Nes792-637
❑ 84OCoandSI-41
❑ 84OPC-70
❑ 84SevCoi-E23
❑ 84Top-70
❑ 84Top-637
❑ 84TopRubD-16
❑ 84TopSti-18
❑ 84TopSti-118
❑ 84TopTif-70
❑ 84TopTif-637
❑ 84TopTra-77T
❑ 84TopTraT-77T
❑ 85AllGamPI-149
❑ 85CubLioP-16
❑ 85CubSev-36
❑ 85Don-239
❑ 85Dra-18
❑ 85Fle-61
❑ 85FleStaS-24
❑ 85Lea-220
❑ 85OPC-210
❑ 85SevCoi-S10
❑ 85Top-210
❑ 85TopMin-210
❑ 85TopRubD-30
❑ 85TopSti-44
❑ 85TopSup-19
❑ 85TopTif-210
❑ 86BasStaB-70
❑ 86CubGat-36
❑ 86CubUno-12
❑ 86Don-76
❑ 86Fle-373
❑ 86GenMilB-4E
❑ 86OPC-292
❑ 86Spo-66
❑ 86Top-485
❑ 86TopSti-59
❑ 86TopTat-5
❑ 86TopTif-485
❑ 87CubCan-18
❑ 87CubDavB-36
❑ 87Fle-568
❑ 87FleGlo-568
❑ 87OPC-390
❑ 87SevCoi-C10
❑ 87Top-390
❑ 87TopSti-62
❑ 87TopTif-390
❑ 88OPC-156
❑ 88Sco-599
❑ 88ScoGlo-599
❑ 88Top-156
❑ 88TopClo-66
❑ 88TopSti-223
❑ 88TopTif-156
❑ 89SweBasG-118
❑ 93UppDecS-2
❑ 93UppDecS-12
❑ 97PhoFirDTTI-16
❑ 98UppDecRSotT-GMS
Matthews, Gary Jr.
❑ 94SpoIndF-3337
❑ 96RanCucQB-19
❑ 97CalLeaATI-17
❑ 97RanCucQUG-5
❑ 98MobBayBTI-16
❑ 98SP MinDTSPE-DS12
❑ 98SP MinPE-109
❑ 98SP SPTSC-GM
❑ 98SPMin-109
❑ 98SPMinDTS-DS12
❑ 98SPxFin-184
❑ 98SPxFinR-184
❑ 98SPxFinS-184
❑ 98UD3-29
❑ 98UD3-119
❑ 98UD3-209
❑ 98UD3DieCut-29
❑ 98UD3DieCut-119
❑ 98UD3DieCut-209
❑ 98UppDec-545
❑ 98UppDecDS-DS8
❑ 98UppDecR-18
❑ 98UppDecR-128
❑ 98UppDecRNF-NF28
❑ 98UppDecRSotT-GMJ
❑ 99Bow-306
❑ 99BowGol-306
❑ 99BowInt-306
❑ 99PacOme-205
❑ 99PacOmeC-205
❑ 99PacOmeG-205
❑ 99PacOmePB-205
❑ 99SP AutC-GMJ
❑ 99SP AutCG-GMJ
❑ 99SP SigAuto-GMJ
❑ 99SP TopP-82
❑ 99SP TopPC-GM
❑ 99SP TopPDtS-D21
❑ 99SP TopPGF-GF21
❑ 99SP TopPPE-82
❑ 99SPSig-125
❑ 99Vic-336
Matthews, Jeff
❑ 78GreBraT-15
Matthews, Jeremy
❑ 89WauTimGS-15
Matthews, Joel
❑ 89MisStaB-25
❑ 90MisStaB-26
❑ 91MisStaB-32
❑ 92MisStaB-28
❑ 93MisStaB-29
Matthews, Jon
❑ 97ForMyeM-3
Matthews, Michael
❑ 92ClaFS7-419
❑ 93Bow-261
❑ 93StaCluM-149
❑ 93Top-787
❑ 93TopGol-787
❑ 93TopInaM-787
❑ 93TopInaR-787
❑ 93TopMic-787
❑ 93WatIndC-18
❑ 94ColRedF-440
❑ 96CanIndB-18
❑ 97BufBis-20
❑ 98BufBisG-20
Matthews, Ron
❑ 92LetMouSP-24
❑ 93PocPosSP-14
Matthews, Tom
❑ 90KisDodD-17
Matthews, Wid (W.C.)
❑ 21Exh-102
❑ 75SenTCM1-19
Matthias, Brother
❑ 92MegRut-118
Mattick, Robert
❑ 39CubTeal-17
❑ 80Top-577
❑ 81Don-570
❑ 81Fle-431
❑ 81Top-674
Mattick, Walter
❑ 16Zee-136
❑ 17Zee-112
Mattimore, Michael
❑ 87OldJudN-318
Mattingly, Dennis
❑ 89AncBucTI-25
Mattingly, Don
❑ 81NasSouTI-8
❑ 82ColCliP-19
❑ 82ColCliT-21
❑ 83YanPhoA-1
❑ 84AllGamPI-183
❑ 84Don-248
❑ 84Fle-131
❑ 84FunFooP-77
❑ 84Nes792-8
❑ 84OCoandSI-103
❑ 84OPC-8
❑ 84Top-8
❑ 84TopPewB-3
❑ 84TopSti-325
❑ 84TopTif-8
❑ 85AllGamPI-6
❑ 85Don-7
❑ 85Don-295
❑ 85Don-651A
❑ 85Don-651B
❑ 85DonActA-48
❑ 85DonHig-36
❑ 85DonHig-44
❑ 85DonHig-45
❑ 85DonSupD-7
❑ 85Dra-19
❑ 85Fle-133
❑ 85FleLimE-20
❑ 85FleStaS-4
❑ 85FleStaS-37
❑ 85Lea-7
❑ 85Lea-140
❑ 85OPC-324
❑ 85SevCoi-E12
❑ 85Top-665
❑ 85Top3-D-8
❑ 85TopGaloC-6
❑ 85TopGloS-27
❑ 85TopRubD-22
❑ 85TopSti-171
❑ 85TopSti-310
❑ 85TopSup-4
❑ 85TopTif-665
❑ 85YanTCMP-27
❑ 86BasStaB-71
❑ 86BurKinA-19
❑ 86Don-173
❑ 86DonAll-50
❑ 86DonHig-48
❑ 86DonHig-53
❑ 86DorChe-13
❑ 86Dra-7
❑ 86Fle-109
❑ 86Fle-627
❑ 86Fle-639
❑ 86FleAll-1
❑ 86FleLeaL-22
❑ 86FleLimE-27
❑ 86FleMin-24
❑ 86FleSlu-21
❑ 86FleStiC-72
❑ 86FraGloT-2
❑ 86FraGloT-3
❑ 86GenMilB-1D
❑ 86KayB-19
❑ 86Lea-103
❑ 86MeaGolBB-8
❑ 86MeaGolM-5
❑ 86MeaGolSB-5
❑ 86MSAJifPD-6
❑ 86OPC-180
❑ 86OPCBoxB-J
❑ 86QuaGra-18
❑ 86SevCoi-C3
❑ 86SevCoi-E3
❑ 86SevCoi-S3
❑ 86SevCoi-W3
❑ 86Spo-2
❑ 86Spo-54
❑ 86Spo-75
❑ 86Spo-176
❑ 86Spo-179
❑ 86Spo-180
❑ 86Spo-183
❑ 86Spo-184
❑ 86SpoDecG-65
❑ 86Top-180
❑ 86Top-712
❑ 86Top3-D-15
❑ 86TopGaloC-6
❑ 86TopGloS-31
❑ 86TopMinL-28
❑ 86TopSti-296
❑ 86TopSup-1
❑ 86TopTat-7
❑ 86TopTif-180
❑ 86TopTif-712
❑ 86TopWaxBC-J
❑ 86TruVal-5
❑ 86Woo-20
❑ 86YanTCM-24
❑ 87BoaandB-32
❑ 87BurKinA-13
❑ 87ClaGam-10
❑ 87ClaUpdY-104
❑ 87Don-52
❑ 87DonAll-33
❑ 87DonHig-17
❑ 87DonHig-23
❑ 87DonHig-48
❑ 87DonOpeD-241
❑ 87Dra-8
❑ 87Fle-104
❑ 87Fle-638
❑ 87FleAll-1
❑ 87FleAwaW-24
❑ 87FleBasA-26
❑ 87FleExcS-33
❑ 87FleGamW-26
❑ 87FleGlo-104
❑ 87FleGlo-638
❑ 87FleHotS-27
❑ 87FleLeaL-28
❑ 87FleLimE-26
❑ 87FleMin-66
❑ 87FleRecS-20
❑ 87FleSlu-25
❑ 87FleStiC-74
❑ 87FleStiC-131
❑ 87FleStiWBC-S8
❑ 87GenMilB-2E
❑ 87HosSti-27
❑ 87K-M-28
❑ 87KayB-19
❑ 87KeyFooD-6
❑ 87KraFoo-29
❑ 87Lea-150
❑ 87MandMSL-11
❑ 87MSAIceTD-6
❑ 87MSAJifPD-6
❑ 87OPC-229
❑ 87OurOwnTD-6
❑ 87RalPur-5
❑ 87RedFolSB-106
❑ 87SevCoi-E12
❑ 87Spo-1
❑ 87Spo-75
❑ 87Spo-159
❑ 87SpoDeaP-1
❑ 87SpoIllS-8
❑ 87SpoRea-21
❑ 87SpoTeaP-7
❑ 87StaBlaM-1
❑ 87StaBlaM-2
❑ 87StaBlaM-3
❑ 87StaBlaM-4
❑ 87StaBlaM-5
❑ 87StaBlaM-6
❑ 87StaMat-1
❑ 87StaMat-2
❑ 87StaMat-3
❑ 87StaMat-4
❑ 87StaMat-5
❑ 87StaMat-6
❑ 87StaMat-7
❑ 87StaMat-8
❑ 87StaMat-9
❑ 87StaMat-10
❑ 87StaMat-11
❑ 87StaMat-12
❑ 87StaMat-1
❑ 87StaMat-2
❑ 87StaMat-3
❑ 87StaMat-4
❑ 87StaMat-5
❑ 87StaMat-6
❑ 87StaMat-7
❑ 87StaMat-8
❑ 87StaMat-9
❑ 87StaMat-10
❑ 87StaMat-11
❑ 87StaMat-12
❑ 87StaMat-13
❑ 87StaMat-14
❑ 87StaMat-15
❑ 87StaMat-16
❑ 87StaMat-17
❑ 87StaMat-18
❑ 87StaMat-19
❑ 87StaMat-20
❑ 87StaMat-21
❑ 87StaMat-22
❑ 87StaMat-23
❑ 87StaMat-24
❑ 87StuPan-23
❑ 87Top-406
❑ 87Top-500
❑ 87Top-606
❑ 87Top-606A
❑ 87TopCoi-17
❑ 87TopGaloC-7
❑ 87TopGloS-1
❑ 87TopMinL-65
❑ 87TopSti-294
❑ 87TopTif-406
❑ 87TopTif-500
❑ 87TopTif-606A
❑ 87TopTif-606B
❑ 87WeiMarD-6
❑ 87Woo-15
❑ 88ActPacT-5
❑ 88Baz-11
❑ 88CheBoy-16
❑ 88ClaBlu-211
❑ 88ClaBlu-247
❑ 88ClaRed-151
❑ 88ClaRed-152
❑ 88CMCMat-1
❑ 88CMCMat-2
❑ 88CMCMat-3
❑ 88CMCMat-4
❑ 88CMCMat-5
❑ 88CMCMat-6
❑ 88CMCMat-7
❑ 88CMCMat-8
❑ 88CMCMat-9
❑ 88CMCMat-10
❑ 88CMCMat-11
❑ 88CMCMat-12
❑ 88CMCMat-13
❑ 88CMCMat-14
❑ 88CMCMat-15
❑ 88CMCMat-16
❑ 88CMCMat-17
❑ 88CMCMat-18
❑ 88CMCMat-19
❑ 88CMCMat-20
❑ 88CMCMat-P1
❑ 88Don-217
❑ 88DonAll-1
❑ 88DonBasB-1
❑ 88DonBonM-BC21
❑ 88DonPop-1
❑ 88DonReaBY-217
❑ 88Dra-1
❑ 88Fle-214
❑ 88FleAwaW-23
❑ 88FleBasA-23
❑ 88FleBasM-22
❑ 88FleExcS-25
❑ 88FleGlo-214
❑ 88FleHea-1
❑ 88FleHotS-24
❑ 88FleLeaL-25
❑ 88FleMin-41
❑ 88FleRecS-24
❑ 88FleSlu-26
❑ 88FleStiC-48
❑ 88FleSup-22
❑ 88FleTeaL-19
❑ 88GreBasS-14
❑ 88K-M-15
❑ 88KayB-16
❑ 88KeyFooD-3
❑ 88KinDis-15
❑ 88Lea-177
❑ 88MSAFanSD-9
❑ 88MSAIceTD-3
❑ 88Nes-15
❑ 88OPC-300
❑ 88OurOwnTD-3
❑ 88PanSti-152
❑ 88PanSti-155
❑ 88PanSti-227
❑ 88PanSti-430
❑ 88RedFolSB-53
❑ 88Sco-1
❑ 88Sco-650
❑ 88Sco-658
❑ 88ScoBoxC-2
❑ 88ScoGlo-1
❑ 88ScoGlo-650
❑ 88ScoGlo-658
❑ 88ScoYouS2-1
❑ 88Spo-1
❑ 88Spo-222
❑ 88SpoGam-1
❑ 88StaLinAl-17
❑ 88StaLinY-8
❑ 88StaMat-1
❑ 88StaMat-2
❑ 88StaMat-3

❑ 88StaMat-4
❑ 88StaMat-5
❑ 88StaMat-6
❑ 88StaMat-7
❑ 88StaMat-8
❑ 88StaMat-9
❑ 88StaMat-10
❑ 88StaMat-11
❑ 88StaMat/S-1
❑ 88StaMat/S-3
❑ 88StaMat/S-5
❑ 88StaMat/S-7
❑ 88StaMat/S-9
❑ 88StaMat/S-11
❑ 88TarPla-26
❑ 88TetTeaD-3
❑ 88Top-2
❑ 88Top-300
❑ 88Top-386
❑ 88TopBig-229
❑ 88TopClo-67
❑ 88TopCoi-19
❑ 88TopGloA-2
❑ 88TopGloS-11
❑ 88TopMatW-1
❑ 88TopMinL-27
❑ 88TopRitTM-22
❑ 88TopSti-3
❑ 88TopSti-156
❑ 88TopSti-299
❑ 88TopStiB-35
❑ 88TopTif-2
❑ 88TopTif-300
❑ 88TopTif-386
❑ 88TopUKM-45
❑ 88TopUKMT-45
❑ 88WeiMarD-3
❑ 88Woo-4
❑ 89Bow-176
❑ 89BowTif-176
❑ 89CadEllD-34
❑ 89CerSup-11
❑ 89ClaLigB-5
❑ 89ClaTraO-106
❑ 89Don-26
❑ 89Don-74
❑ 89DonAll-21
❑ 89DonBasB-1
❑ 89DonSupD-26
❑ 89Fle-258
❑ 89FleBasA-28
❑ 89FleBasM-26
❑ 89FleExcS-31
❑ 89FleForTR-6
❑ 89FleGlo-258
❑ 89FleHeroB-26
❑ 89FleLeaL-25
❑ 89FleSup-29
❑ 89K-M-12
❑ 89KayB-20
❑ 89KeyFooD-1
❑ 89MasBreD-6
❑ 89MSAHolD-4
❑ 89MSAIceTD-1
❑ 89Nis-4
❑ 89OPC-26
❑ 89OurOwnTD-1
❑ 89PanSti-404
❑ 89RedFolSB-79
❑ 89RinPosM-1
❑ 89RinPosM-2
❑ 89RinPosM-3
❑ 89RinPosM-4
❑ 89RinPosM-5
❑ 89RinPosM-6
❑ 89RinPosM-7
❑ 89RinPosM-8
❑ 89RinPosM-9
❑ 89RinPosM-10
❑ 89RinPosM-11
❑ 89RinPosM-12
❑ 89Sco-100
❑ 89ScoHot1S-10
❑ 89Scomast-6
❑ 89Spo-50
❑ 89SpollIFKI-37
❑ 89TetTeaD-1
❑ 89Top-397
❑ 89Top-700
❑ 89TopBasT-123
❑ 89TopBatL-3
❑ 89TopBig-50
❑ 89TopCapC-8
❑ 89TopCoi-43
❑ 89TopDouA-1
❑ 89TopDouM-14
❑ 89TopGloS-51
❑ 89TopHeaUT-19
❑ 89TopRitM-1
❑ 89TopRitM-2
❑ 89TopRitM-3
❑ 89TopRitM-4
❑ 89TopRitM-5
❑ 89TopRitM-6
❑ 89TopRitM-7
❑ 89TopRitM-8
❑ 89TopRitM-9
❑ 89TopSti-314
❑ 89TopStiB-2
❑ 89TopTif-397
❑ 89TopTif-700
❑ 89TopUKM-49
❑ 89TVSpoM-82
❑ 89UppDec-200
❑ 89UppDec-693
❑ 89UppDecS-3
❑ 89WeiMarD-1
❑ 89YanScoNW-1
❑ 90AllBasT-11
❑ 90Bow-443
❑ 90BowIns-5
❑ 90BowInsL-5
❑ 90BowInsT-5
❑ 90BowTif-443
❑ 90BowTif-A5
❑ 90ClaBlu-16
❑ 90ClaYel-T12
❑ 90ClaYel-NNO0
❑ 90Col-13
❑ 90ColMat-1
❑ 90ColMat-2
❑ 90ColMat-3
❑ 90ColMat-4
❑ 90ColMat-5
❑ 90ColMat-6
❑ 90ColMat-7
❑ 90ColMat-8
❑ 90ColMat-9
❑ 90ColMat-10
❑ 90ColMat-11
❑ 90ColMat-12
❑ 90ColtheSBM-97
❑ 90Don-190
❑ 90DonBesA-38
❑ 90DonLeaS-12
❑ 90Fle-447
❑ 90Fle-626
❑ 90Fle-638
❑ 90FleAwaW-21
❑ 90FleBasA-24
❑ 90FleBasAC-24
❑ 90FleBasM-23
❑ 90FleBasMC-23
❑ 90FleCan-447
❑ 90FleCan-626
❑ 90FleCan-638
❑ 90FleLeaL-23
❑ 90FleLeaLC-23
❑ 90FleLeaS-2
❑ 90FleWaxBC-C19
❑ 90GooHumICBLS-13
❑ 90HOFStiB-90
❑ 90Hot50PS-25
❑ 90K-M-17
❑ 90KayB-18
❑ 90KinDis-14
❑ 90Lea-69
❑ 90M.Vpin-68
❑ 90MLBBasB-63
❑ 90MSAIceTD-14
❑ 90OPC-200
❑ 90PanSti-125
❑ 90Pos-1
❑ 90PubIntS-291
❑ 90PubIntS-540
❑ 90RedFolSB-59
❑ 90Sco-1
❑ 90Sco100S-10
❑ 90Spo-150
❑ 90StaLonJS-1
❑ 90StaLonJS-28
❑ 90StaLonJS-35
❑ 90SunSee-8
❑ 90Top-200
❑ 90TopAmeA-18
❑ 90TopBatL-4
❑ 90TopBig-85
❑ 90TopCoi-21
❑ 90TopDou-43
❑ 90TopGloS-11
❑ 90TopHeaU-19
❑ 90TopHilHM-3
❑ 90TopMag-17
❑ 90TopMinL-24
❑ 90TopSti-308
❑ 90TopStiB-34
❑ 90TopTif-200
❑ 90TopTVA-17
❑ 90TopTVY-25
❑ 90UppDec-191
❑ 90WonBreS-6
❑ 90YanScoNW-2
❑ 91BasBesHM-14
❑ 91BasBesRB-11
❑ 91Bow-178
❑ 91CadEllD-36
❑ 91Cla1-T33
❑ 91Cla3-T56
❑ 91ClaGam-98
❑ 91CokMat-1
❑ 91CokMat-2
❑ 91CokMat-3
❑ 91CokMat-4
❑ 91CokMat-5
❑ 91CokMat-6
❑ 91CokMat-7
❑ 91CokMat-8
❑ 91CokMat-9
❑ 91CokMat-10
❑ 91CokMat-11
❑ 91CokMat-12
❑ 91CokMat-13
❑ 91CokMat-14
❑ 91CokMat-15
❑ 91DenHol-8
❑ 91Don-107
❑ 91Fle-673
❑ 91FlePro-11
❑ 91Lea-425
❑ 91LeaPre-22
❑ 91MajLeaCP-1
❑ 91MooSna-15
❑ 91OPC-100
❑ 91OPCPre-77
❑ 91PanFreS-324
❑ 91PanSti-267
❑ 91PepSup-11
❑ 91PetSta-19
❑ 91PlaMat-26
❑ 91PlaMat-27
❑ 91PlaMat-28
❑ 91PlaMat-29
❑ 91PlaMat-30
❑ 91PlaMat-44
❑ 91PlaMat-45
❑ 91PlaMat-46
❑ 91PlaMat-47
❑ 91PlaMat-48
❑ 91PlaMatG-4
❑ 91PlaMatG-5
❑ 91Pos-29
❑ 91RedFolS-61
❑ 91RinPosM2-1
❑ 91RinPosM2-2
❑ 91RinPosM2-3
❑ 91RinPosM2-4
❑ 91RinPosM2-5
❑ 91RinPosM2-6
❑ 91RinPosM2-7
❑ 91RinPosM2-8
❑ 91RinPosM2-9
❑ 91RinPosM2-10
❑ 91RinPosM2-11
❑ 91RinPosM2-12
❑ 91Sco-23
❑ 91Sco-856
❑ 91Sco100S-23
❑ 91Sev3DCN-11
❑ 91SevCoi-NE11
❑ 91SimandSMLBL-28
❑ 91StaClu-21
❑ 91StaCluP-25
❑ 91StaPinB-29
❑ 91Stu-97
❑ 91Top-100
❑ 91Top-100A
❑ 91TopCraJI-7
❑ 91TopDesS-100
❑ 91TopMic-100
❑ 91TopSta-24
❑ 91TopTif-100
❑ 91TopTriH-A10
❑ 91Ult-239
❑ 91UppDec-354
❑ 92Bow-340
❑ 92Cla1-T58
❑ 92Cla2-T49
❑ 92ClaGam-105
❑ 92ColPro-11
❑ 92Don-596
❑ 92DonCraJ1-36
❑ 92DonMat#-1
❑ 92Fle-237
❑ 92FleCitTP-16
❑ 92FleTeaL-1
❑ 92Fre-11
❑ 92Hig5-89
❑ 92HitTheBB-21
❑ 92JimDea-8
❑ 92LaKdec-21
❑ 92Lea-57
❑ 92LeaBlaG-57
❑ 92LeaGolP-22
❑ 92LeaPre-22
❑ 92Mr.TurS-16
❑ 92MVPPin-1
❑ 92New-15
❑ 92OPC-300
❑ 92OPCPre-92
❑ 92PanSti-135
❑ 92Pin-23
❑ 92Pin-584
❑ 92Pos-3
❑ 92RedFolS-61
❑ 92Sco-23
❑ 92Sco100S-23
❑ 92ScoProP-7
❑ 92SevCoi-2
❑ 92SpoStaCC-32
❑ 92StaClu-420
❑ 92StaPro-7
❑ 92Stu-216
❑ 92StuHer-BC5
❑ 92StuPre-9
❑ 92Top-300
❑ 92TopGol-300
❑ 92TopGolW-300
❑ 92TopKid-84
❑ 92TopMic-300
❑ 92TopMic-G300
❑ 92TriPla-159
❑ 92TriPlaP-4
❑ 92Ult-105
❑ 92UltAwaW-19
❑ 92UppDec-356
❑ 92UppDecF-31
❑ 92UppDecFG-31
❑ 92UppDecS-1
❑ 92UppDecTMH-33
❑ 92YanWIZ8-111
❑ 92YanWIZA-46
❑ 93Ble-25
❑ 93Bow-595
❑ 93CadDis-40
❑ 93ClaGam-59
❑ 93DiaMar-71
❑ 93Don-264
❑ 93Don-609
❑ 93DonEli-24
❑ 93DonEliD-6
❑ 93DonEliD-AU6
❑ 93DonEliS-6
❑ 93DonMVP-5
❑ 93DonPre-18
❑ 93DurPowP1-19
❑ 93Fin-98
❑ 93FinJum-98
❑ 93FinPro-98
❑ 93FinProR-98
❑ 93FinRef-98
❑ 93Fla-249
❑ 93Fle-281
❑ 93FleAtl-14
❑ 93FleFruotL-43
❑ 93FunPac-208
❑ 93Hos-28
❑ 93JimDea-6
❑ 93Kra-9
❑ 93Lea-237
❑ 93LeaGolA-R2
❑ 93MetBak-14
❑ 93OPC-103
❑ 93OPCPre-46
❑ 93PacSpa-208
❑ 93PanSti-154
❑ 93Pin-23
❑ 93Pin-470
❑ 93PinCoo-14
❑ 93PinCooD-14
❑ 93PinSlu-23
❑ 93Pos-12
❑ 93RedFolS-59
❑ 93Sco-23
❑ 93ScoFra-10
❑ 93Sel-24
❑ 93SelSam-24
❑ 93SelStaL-14
❑ 93SP-265
❑ 93StaClu-557
❑ 93StaCluFDI-557
❑ 93StaCluI-B2
❑ 93StaCluMOP-557
❑ 93StaCluMOP-MB2
❑ 93Stu-193
❑ 93Top-32
❑ 93TopGol-32
❑ 93TopInaM-32
❑ 93TopInaR-32
❑ 93TopMic-32
❑ 93TopMic-P32
❑ 93TopPre-32
❑ 93TriPla-120
❑ 93TriPlaA-19
❑ 93Ult-244
❑ 93UltAwaW-12
❑ 93UppDec-47
❑ 93UppDec-134
❑ 93UppDecCP-R14
❑ 93UppDecDG-28
❑ 93UppDecGold-47
❑ 93UppDecGold-134
❑ 93UppDecIC-WI26
❑ 93UppDecICJ-WI26
❑ 93UppDecTAN-TN13
❑ 93YanStaC-1
❑ 94Bow-25
❑ 94Bow-386
❑ 94BowBes-R45
❑ 94BowBesR-R45
❑ 94ColC-192
❑ 94ColC-355
❑ 94ColChoGS-192
❑ 94ColChoGS-355
❑ 94ColChoSS-192
❑ 94ColChoSS-355
❑ 94ColChoT-3
❑ 94Don-340
❑ 94DonAnn8-8
❑ 94DonDiaK-DK16
❑ 94DonDiaKJ-DK16
❑ 94DonMVP-24
❑ 94DonPro-9
❑ 94DonSpeE-340
❑ 94DonSpiotG-9
❑ 94DonSpiotGJ-9
❑ 94Fin-392
❑ 94FinRef-392
❑ 94Fla-84
❑ 94FlaHotG-6
❑ 94FlaInfP-4
❑ 94Fle-239
❑ 94FleExtB-133
❑ 94FleExtBGB-17
❑ 94FleSun-17
❑ 94FleTeaL-10
❑ 94FleUpdDT-6
❑ 94FUnPac-123
❑ 94FUnPac-200
❑ 94Lea-121
❑ 94LeaGam-4
❑ 94LeaGolS-6
❑ 94LeaL-56
❑ 94LeaPro-5
❑ 94OPC-54
❑ 94Pac-430
❑ 94PacSilP-10
❑ 94PacSilPC-10
❑ 94PanSti-102
❑ 94Pin-23
❑ 94PinArtP-23
❑ 94PinMusC-23
❑ 94Pos-2
❑ 94ProMag-88
❑ 94RedFolMI-17
❑ 94Sco-23
❑ 94ScoDreT-3
❑ 94ScoGolR-23
❑ 94ScoGolS-49
❑ 94Sel-23
❑ 94SP-198
❑ 94SPDieC-198
❑ 94SPHol-25
❑ 94SPHolDC-25
❑ 94Spo-127
❑ 94SpoMov-MM9
❑ 94SPPre-ER4
❑ 94StaClu-195
❑ 94StaCluFDI-195
❑ 94StaCluGR-195
❑ 94StaCluMOP-195
❑ 94StaCluMOP-ST24
❑ 94StaCluST-ST24
❑ 94StaCluT-181
❑ 94StaCluTF-7
❑ 94StaCluTFDI-181
❑ 94Stu-215
❑ 94StuHer-4
❑ 94StuSerS-10
❑ 94StuSerSG-10
❑ 94Top-600
❑ 94TopGol-600
❑ 94TopSpa-600
❑ 94TopSupS-27
❑ 94TriPla-276
❑ 94TriPlaP-9
❑ 94Ult-400
❑ 94UltAwaW-2
❑ 94UppDec-90
❑ 94UppDec-290
❑ 94UppDecAJ-8
❑ 94UppDecAJG-8
❑ 94UppDecDC-E8
❑ 94UppDecED-90
❑ 94UppDecED-290
❑ 94Yoo-10
❑ 95Baz-47
❑ 95Bow-282
❑ 95BowBes-R46
❑ 95BowBesR-R46
❑ 95ClaPhoC-38
❑ 95ColCho-510
❑ 95ColChoGS-510
❑ 95ColChoSE-240
❑ 95ColChoSEGS-240
❑ 95ColChoSESS-240
❑ 95ColChoSS-510
❑ 95DenHol-15
❑ 95Don-55
❑ 95Don-220
❑ 95Don-440
❑ 95DonPreP-55
❑ 95DonPreP-220
❑ 95DonPreP-440
❑ 95DonTopotO-120
❑ 95Emo-62
❑ 95Fin-126
❑ 95FinRef-126
❑ 95Fla-66
❑ 95FlaHotG-8
❑ 95Fle-76
❑ 95FleTeaL-10
❑ 95FleUpdSL-7
❑ 95Lea-303
❑ 95Lea300C-15
❑ 95LeaCor-3
❑ 95LeaGolS-6
❑ 95LeaGreG-10
❑ 95LeaLim-55
❑ 95LeaLimG-12
❑ 95LeaLimIBP-21
❑ 95LeaStaS-3
❑ 95MegRut-13
❑ 95NatPac2-5
❑ 95Pac-299
❑ 95PacGolP-10
❑ 95PacPri-97
❑ 95PanSti-38
❑ 95Pin-21
❑ 95Pin-295
❑ 95PinArtP-21
❑ 95PinArtP-295
❑ 95PinFan-3
❑ 95PinGatA-GA12
❑ 95PinMusC-21
❑ 95PinMusC-295
❑ 95PinRedH-RH10
❑ 95PinWhiH-WH10
❑ 95RedFol-27
❑ 95Sco-239
❑ 95Sco-564
❑ 95ScoDouGC-GC5
❑ 95ScoGolR-239
❑ 95ScoGolR-564
❑ 95ScoHaloG-HG22
❑ 95ScoPlaTS-239
❑ 95ScoPlaTS-564
❑ 95ScoRul-SR25
❑ 95ScoRulJ-SR25
❑ 95Sel-101
❑ 95SelArtP-101
❑ 95SelBigS-BS5
❑ 95SelCer-21
❑ 95SelCerGT-8
❑ 95SelCerMG-21
❑ 95SP-175
❑ 95SPCha-171

❑ 95SPCha-175
❑ 95SPChaDC-171
❑ 95SPChaDC-175
❑ 95SPChaDFC-5
❑ 95SPChaFCDC-5
❑ 95Spo-13
❑ 95SpoArtP-13
❑ 95SpoHamT-HT8
❑ 95SpoPro-PM9
❑ 95SPSil-175
❑ 95SPSpeF-15
❑ 95StaClu-212
❑ 95StaClu-381
❑ 95StaCluFDI-212
❑ 95StaCluMOP-212
❑ 95StaCluMOP-381
❑ 95StaCluMOP-RL33
❑ 95StaCluMOP-SS5
❑ 95StaCluRL-RL33
❑ 95StaCluSS-SS5
❑ 95StaCluSTWS-212
❑ 95StaCluSTWS-381
❑ 95StaCluVR-200
❑ 95StaCluVRMO-200
❑ 95Stu-3
❑ 95StuGolS-3
❑ 95StuPlaS-3
❑ 95Sum-21
❑ 95Sum-181
❑ 95SumBigB-BB8
❑ 95SumNthD-21
❑ 95SumNthD-181
❑ 95Top-399
❑ 95TopCyb-200
❑ 95TopD3-37
❑ 95TopEmb-115
❑ 95TopEmbGI-115
❑ 95UC3-20
❑ 95UC3-139
❑ 95UC3ArtP-20
❑ 95UC3ArtP-139
❑ 95UC3CycS-CS11
❑ 95UC3InM-IM9
❑ 95Ult-311
❑ 95UltAwaW-2
❑ 95UltAwaWGM-2
❑ 95UltGolM-311
❑ 95UppDec-210
❑ 95UppDecED-210
❑ 95UppDecEDG-210
❑ 95UppDecPAW-H22
❑ 95UppDecPAWE-H22
❑ 95UppDecPC-MLB11
❑ 95UppDecPLL-R53
❑ 95UppDecPLLE-R53
❑ 95UppDecSE-145
❑ 95UppDecSEG-145
❑ 95UppDecSoaD-SD13
❑ 95Zen-29
❑ 95ZenZ-17
❑ 96Baz-23
❑ 96ColCho-100
❑ 96ColCho-237
❑ 96ColCho-368T
❑ 96ColChoGS-100
❑ 96ColChoGS-237
❑ 96ColChoSS-100
❑ 96ColChoSS-237
❑ 96ColChoYMtP-23
❑ 96ColChoYMtP-23A
❑ 96ColChoYMtPGS-23
❑ 96ColChoYMtPGS-23A
❑ 96Don-301
❑ 96DonDiaK-16
❑ 96DonHitL-15
❑ 96DonPreP-301
❑ 96Fle-189
❑ 96FleTeaL-10
❑ 96FleTif-189
❑ 96MetUni-90
❑ 96MetUniP-90
❑ 96MetUniProS-90
❑ 96Pac-376
❑ 96PacGolCD-DC4
❑ 96PacHom-HP5
❑ 96PacMil-M2
❑ 96PacOctM-OM15
❑ 96PacPri-P119
❑ 96PacPriG-P119
❑ 96PacPriRHS-RH18
❑ 96PanSti-151
❑ 96Pin-99
❑ 96Pin-157
❑ 96Pin-307
❑ 96PinArtP-37
❑ 96PinArtP-84
❑ 96PinArtP-192
❑ 96PinEssotG-15
❑ 96PinFoil-307
❑ 96PinSta-37
❑ 96PinSta-84
❑ 96PinSta-192
❑ 96Pro-9
❑ 96ProMagDM-18
❑ 96Sco-8
❑ 96Sco-377
❑ 96ScoDugC-A8
❑ 96ScoDugC-B102
❑ 96ScoDugCAP-A8
❑ 96ScoDugCAP-B102
❑ 96ScoNumG-23
❑ 96ScoRef-5
❑ 96SpoPro-12
❑ 96StaClu-73
❑ 96StaCluEPB-73
❑ 96StaCluEPG-73
❑ 96StaCluEPS-73
❑ 96StaCluMOP-73
❑ 96Top-185
❑ 96TopChr-56
❑ 96TopChrMotG-13
❑ 96TopChrMotGR-13
❑ 96TopChrR-56
❑ 96TopMasotG-13
❑ 96TopPro-AL17
❑ 96Ult-101
❑ 96UltGolM-101
❑ 96UppDec-154
❑ 97DonSigSS-14
❑ 97HigMinM-70
❑ 97HigMinM-71
❑ 97HigMinMCT-22
❑ 97HigMinMCT-23
❑ 98DonSigSS-10
❑ 99BowBesFF-FR1B
❑ 99BowBesFF-FR1C
❑ 99BowBesFFA-FR1B
❑ 99BowBesFFA-FR1C
❑ 99UppDecR-97
❑ 99UppDecRG-97
❑ 99UppDecRI-DM
❑ 99UppDecRIL2-DM
❑ 99UppDecRP-97

Mattingly, Earl
❑ 90DodTar-491

Mattingly, Shane
❑ 89AncBucTI-21

Mattingly, Steve
❑ 89BoiHawP-1989

Mattocks, Rich
❑ 84GreHorT-24

Mattos, Tony
❑ 94EveGiaC-22
❑ 95BurBeeTI-11

Mattox, Frank
❑ 85BelBreT-11
❑ 86StoPorP-18
❑ 87ElPasDP-8
❑ 88ElPasDB-29
❑ 88TexLeaAGS-38
❑ 89ElPasDGS-23
❑ 90CMC-39
❑ 90DenZepC-14
❑ 90DenZepP-632
❑ 90ProAAAF-657

Mattson, Craig
❑ 94AugGreC-11
❑ 94AugGreF-3003
❑ 95Bow-101
❑ 96LynHilB-16

Mattson, Don
❑ 91MacBraC-5

Mattson, John
❑ 98PitMetM-18

Mattson, Kurt
❑ 83CliGiaF-22
❑ 84ShrCapFB-11

Mattson, Rob
❑ 91DurBulUP-3
❑ 91MacBraP-859
❑ 95MemChiTI-18
❑ 96MemChiB-23

Mattson, Ronnie
❑ 77SpaPhiT-13

Matuella, Joe
❑ 97OmaRoyB-34

Matula, Rick
❑ 80Top-596
❑ 81Don-317
❑ 81Fle-263
❑ 81Top-611
❑ 82EvaTriT-5

Matulevich, Jeff
❑ 92JohCitCC-20
❑ 92JohCitCF-3114
❑ 94MadHatC-15
❑ 94MadHatF-127
❑ 95Exc-270
❑ 96ArkTraB-19
❑ 96BesAutS-58
❑ 96Exc-229

Matusyavichus, Edmuntas
❑ 89EasLeaDDP-DD9

Matuszak, Mick
❑ 91AubAstC-23

Matuszek, Len
❑ 81OklCit8T-10
❑ 82OklCit8T-8
❑ 83PorBeaT-8
❑ 83Top-357
❑ 84Don-549
❑ 84Fle-41
❑ 84Nes792-275
❑ 84OPC-275
❑ 84PhiTas-31
❑ 84Top-275
❑ 84TopTif-275
❑ 85BluJayFS-22
❑ 85Don-259
❑ 85Fle-260
❑ 85FleUpd-79
❑ 85OPC-226
❑ 85Top-688
❑ 85TopTif-688
❑ 85TopTifT-80T
❑ 85TopTra-80T
❑ 86DodCokP-19
❑ 86DodPol-17
❑ 86Don-494
❑ 86Fle-138
❑ 86Top-109
❑ 86TopTif-109
❑ 87DodMot-20
❑ 87DodPho-10
❑ 87DodPol-8
❑ 87Don-423
❑ 87Fle-447
❑ 87FleGlo-447
❑ 87Top-457
❑ 87TopTif-457
❑ 88DodPol-21
❑ 88Sco-424
❑ 88ScoGlo-424
❑ 88Top-92
❑ 88TopClo-68
❑ 88TopTif-92
❑ 90DodTar-492

Matvey, Mike
❑ 93GleFalRC-21
❑ 93GleFalRF-4013
❑ 94SavCarC-19
❑ 94SavCarF-517
❑ 94SouAtlLAF-SAL51
❑ 96StPetCB-17
❑ 97PriWilC-18

Matz, Brian
❑ 96VerExpB-17
❑ 98CapFeaCM-13

Matzen, Charles
❑ 23Zee-112

Matzen, Mark
❑ 82CedRapRT-13

Matznick, Danny
❑ 90Bes-256
❑ 90MidLeaASGS-15
❑ 90SouBenWSB-20
❑ 90SouBenWSGS-10
❑ 91SarWhiSC-7
❑ 91SarWhiSP-1110

Mauch, Dennis
❑ 95GreFalDTI-20

Mauch, Gene
❑ 49EurSta-63
❑ 51Bow-312
❑ 57Top-342
❑ 58PhiTeal-13
❑ 59RedSoxJP-6
❑ 61Top-219
❑ 62Top-374
❑ 63Top-318
❑ 64PhiJayP-8
❑ 64PhiPhiB-17
❑ 64Top-157
❑ 64TopVen-157
❑ 65PhiJayP-8
❑ 65Top-489
❑ 66Top-411
❑ 67PhiPol-10
❑ 67Top-248
❑ 68OPC-122
❑ 68Top-122
❑ 68TopVen-122
❑ 69ExpPin-5
❑ 69Top-606
❑ 70OPC-442
❑ 70Top-442
❑ 71ExpLaPR-6
❑ 71ExpPS-15
❑ 71OPC-59
❑ 71Top-59
❑ 72Dia-31
❑ 72OPC-276
❑ 72Top-276
❑ 73OPC-377
❑ 73Top-377
❑ 74OPC-531
❑ 74Top-531
❑ 75ExpPos-21
❑ 75OPC-101
❑ 75Top-101
❑ 75TopMin-101
❑ 76OPC-556
❑ 76SSP-597
❑ 76Top-556
❑ 77Top-228
❑ 78Top-601
❑ 78TwiFri-11
❑ 79Top-41
❑ 79TwiFriP-17
❑ 80Top-328
❑ 80TwiPos-19
❑ 81RedSoxBG2S-37
❑ 81TCM60I-359
❑ 82Don-141
❑ 83Top-276
❑ 85AngSmo-24
❑ 85TopTifT-81T
❑ 85TopTra-81T
❑ 86AngSmo-24
❑ 86Top-81
❑ 86TopTif-81
❑ 87CalAngPPS-24
❑ 87Top-518
❑ 87TopTif-518
❑ 88Top-774
❑ 88TopTif-774
❑ 90DodTar-493
❑ 93ExpDonM-30
❑ 93UppDecS-27

Mauch, Thomas
❑ 87St.PetCP-17
❑ 88St.PetCS-16

Maul, Al
❑ 87OldJudN-319
❑ 88WG1CarG-61
❑ 90DodTar-494
❑ 90KalBatN-26
❑ 90KalBatN-35

Mauldin, Eric
❑ 91MarPhiC-2
❑ 91MarPhiP-3469

Mauney, Terry
❑ 84ChaO'sT-2
❑ 85ChaO'sT-28
❑ 86ChaOriW-17
❑ 87ChaO'sW-NNO

Mauramatsu, Arihito
❑ 91SalSpuP-2257

Maurer, Dave
❑ 98RanCucQG-18
❑ 98RanCucQG-18

Maurer, Mike
❑ 94SouOreAC-18
❑ 94SouOreAF-3620
❑ 95ModA'sTI-15
❑ 96BesAutSA-43
❑ 96HunStaTI-17
❑ 97BesAutAS-31
❑ 97HunStaTI-17

Maurer, Rob
❑ 88ButCopKSP-15
❑ 89ChaRanS-15
❑ 89Sta-7
❑ 90CMC-798
❑ 90ProAaA-69
❑ 90TexLeaAGS-20
❑ 90TulDriP-1163
❑ 90TulDriTI-16
❑ 91LinDriAAA-312
❑ 91OklCit8LD-312
❑ 91OklCit8P-186
❑ 91TriA AAGP-AAA26
❑ 92Bow-437
❑ 92ClaGam-184
❑ 92Don-703
❑ 92Fle-659A
❑ 92Fle-659B
❑ 92Fle-720A
❑ 92Fle-720B
❑ 92OklCit8F-1922
❑ 92OklCit8S-314
❑ 92Pin-273
❑ 92ProFS7-149
❑ 92Sco-767
❑ 92SkyAAAF-144
❑ 92StaClu-462
❑ 92TopDeb91-119
❑ 92UppDec-10
❑ 93Don-584
❑ 93PacSpa-313
❑ 93RanKee-249
❑ 93RanStaC-13
❑ 93Top-763
❑ 93TopGol-763
❑ 93TopInaM-763
❑ 93TopInaR-763
❑ 93TopMic-763
❑ 94OklCit8F-1500

Maurer, Ron
❑ 90GreFalDSP-27
❑ 91BakDodCLC-2
❑ 91CalLeLA-21
❑ 92SanAntMF-3985
❑ 92SanAntMS-569
❑ 92SkyAA F-248
❑ 93AlbDukF-1469
❑ 93AusFut-6
❑ 93SanAntMF-3012
❑ 94AlbDukF-851
❑ 97AlbDukGS-21

Mauriello, Ralph
❑ 90DodTar-1019

Mauro, Carmen
❑ 49AngTeal-24
❑ 49W725AngTI-19
❑ 52LaPat-11
❑ 52Par-71
❑ 53Bri-10
❑ 53ExhCan-47
❑ 55SeaPop-15
❑ 56SeaPop-12
❑ 57SeaPop-14
❑ 79TCM50-109
❑ 90DodTar-495

Mauro, Mike
❑ 90BriTigS-17

Mauser, Tim (Timothy)
❑ 88SpaPhiS-12
❑ 89ClePhiS-14
❑ 89EasLeaAP-24
❑ 89Sta-13
❑ 90Bes-115
❑ 90CMC-801
❑ 90ReaPhiB-8
❑ 90ReaPhiP-1217
❑ 90ReaPhiS-19
❑ 91LinDriAAA-489
❑ 91PhiMed-25
❑ 91ScrRedBLD-489
❑ 91ScrRedBP-2535
❑ 92Sco-744
❑ 92ScrRedBF-2444
❑ 92ScrRedBS-490
❑ 92SkyAAAF-221
❑ 92StaClu-558
❑ 92TopDeb91-120
❑ 93ScrRedBF-2543
❑ 93ScrRedBTI-18
❑ 94Don-215
❑ 94Fle-670
❑ 94PadMot-20
❑ 94StaClu-200
❑ 94StaCluFDI-200
❑ 94StaCluGR-200
❑ 94StaCluMOP-200
❑ 94Top-99
❑ 94TopGol-99
❑ 94TopSpa-99
❑ 94Ult-281
❑ 95Fla-204
❑ 95Fle-565
❑ 95Top-356
❑ 98ScrRedB1ATI-12

Mawhinney, Mindy
❑ 91FreStaLBS-13

Max (Mascot), Miner
❑ 97LetBlaDB-5

Max, Bill
❑ 82BelBreFr-21
❑ 83ElPasDT-13
❑ 84JacMetT-12

Maxcy, Brian
❑ 92BriTigC-5
❑ 92BriTigF-1405
❑ 93FayGenC-14
❑ 93FayGenF-125
❑ 95TopTra-16T
❑ 96ColCho-143
❑ 96ColChoGS-143
❑ 96ColChoSS-143
❑ 96Don-213
❑ 96DonPreP-213
❑ 96Fle-117
❑ 96FleTif-117
❑ 96SigRooOJ-19
❑ 96SigRooOJS-19
❑ 96TolMudHB-18
❑ 96Ult-64
❑ 96UltGolM-64
❑ 97LouRedB-22
❑ 98NorTidQ-15

Maxey, Kevin
❑ 88St.PetCS-17

Maxie, Larry
❑ 64Top-94
❑ 64TopVen-94
❑ 71RicBraTI-13
❑ 78TCM60I-59

Maxson, Dan
❑ 78NewWayCT-29

Maxvill, Dal
❑ 63CarJayP-13
❑ 63Top-49
❑ 64Raw-6
❑ 64Top-563
❑ 65CarTeal-15
❑ 65OPC-78
❑ 65Top-78
❑ 66Top-338
❑ 66TopVen-338
❑ 67Top-421
❑ 68OPC-141
❑ 68Top-141
❑ 68TopVen-141
❑ 69MilBra-174
❑ 69MLBOffS-213
❑ 69Top-320
❑ 69TopSta-117
❑ 69TopTeaP-18
❑ 70CarTeal-20
❑ 70MLBOffS-141
❑ 70OPC-503
❑ 70Top-503
❑ 71CarTeal-16
❑ 71CarTeal-25
❑ 71CarTeal-26
❑ 71MLBOffS-278
❑ 71OPC-476
❑ 71Top-476
❑ 72CarTeal-12
❑ 72MilBra-214
❑ 72OPC-206
❑ 72Top-206
❑ 73OPC-483
❑ 73Top-483
❑ 74OPC-358
❑ 74Top-358
❑ 78CarTeal-17
❑ 78TCM60I-241
❑ 79Car5-17
❑ 82BraPol-53
❑ 83BraPol-53
❑ 84BraPol-53
❑ 84raPho-19

Maxwell, Billy
❑ 92PriRedC-29
❑ 94BilMusSP-25
❑ 98ChaLooG-19

Maxwell, Charlie
❑ 52Top-180
❑ 55Bow-162
❑ 55OriEss-15
❑ 57Top-205
❑ 58Top-380
❑ 59Top-34
❑ 59Top-481
❑ 59TopVen-34
❑ 60Lea-48
❑ 60TigJayP-9
❑ 60Top-443
❑ 61Pos-37A
❑ 61Pos-37B
❑ 61TigJayP-11
❑ 61Top-37

❑ 61TopMagR-22
❑ 61TopStal-154
❑ 62Jel-25
❑ 62Pos-25
❑ 62PosCan-25
❑ 62TigJayP-9
❑ 62Top-506
❑ 63Jel-41
❑ 63Pos-41
❑ 63Top-86
❑ 63WhiSoxTS-19
❑ 64Top-401
❑ 64WhiSoxI-18
❑ 79DiaGre-246
❑ 81TCM60I-320
❑ 81TigDetN-76
❑ 83TopRep5-180
❑ 91OriCro-283

Maxwell, Jason
❑ 93HunCubC-19
❑ 93HunCubF-3243
❑ 94DayCubC-16
❑ 94DayCubF-2360
❑ 96Exc-140
❑ 96FleUpd-U114
❑ 96FleUpdTC-U114
❑ 96OrlCubB-16
❑ 96Ult-453
❑ 96UltGolM-453
❑ 96UltGolP-12
❑ 96UltGolPHGM-12
❑ 97OrlRayB-16
❑ 97SouLeaTP-29
❑ 97Ult-167
❑ 97UltGolME-167
❑ 97UltPlaME-167
❑ 98IowCubQ-15
❑ 98SP MinPE-33
❑ 98SPMin-33
❑ 99Pac-87
❑ 99Pac-87A
❑ 99PacPlaB-87
❑ 99PacPlaB-87A
❑ 99PacRed-87
❑ 99PacRed-87A
❑ 99SpoIll-49

Maxwell, Jim
❑ 80AshTouT-16

Maxwell, John
❑ 90ChaRaiB-24
❑ 91ChaRaiC-28
❑ 92WatDiaC-28
❑ 95IdaFalBTI-NNO
❑ 96IdaFalB-16
❑ 97IdaFalBTI-9

Maxwell, Keith
❑ 97EriSeaWB-25
❑ 98EriSeaWM-17

Maxwell, Marty
❑ 78OrlTwiT-13

Maxwell, Pat
❑ 91WatIndC-20
❑ 91WatIndP-3374
❑ 92ColRedC-5
❑ 92ColRedF-2397
❑ 93CarLeaAGF-32
❑ 93KinIndC-15
❑ 93KinIndF-2253
❑ 93KinIndTI-15
❑ 94CanIndF-3123

Maxwell, Vernon
❑ 98GreBatM-9

May, Carlos
❑ 69Top-654
❑ 69WhiSoxTI-9
❑ 70DayDaiNM-85
❑ 70Kel-16
❑ 70OPC-18
❑ 70Top-18
❑ 70WhiSoxTI-10
❑ 71Kel-45
❑ 71OPC-243
❑ 71Top-243
❑ 71TopCoi-144
❑ 72MilBra-209
❑ 72OPC-525
❑ 72Top-525
❑ 72WhiSox-8
❑ 72WhiSoxC-4
❑ 72WhiSoxDS-4
❑ 72WhiSoxTI1-10
❑ 73Kel2D-45
❑ 73OPC-105
❑ 73SevTraC-43
❑ 73Top-105
❑ 74OPC-195
❑ 74Top-195
❑ 74TopSta-157
❑ 75Hos-44
❑ 75OPC-480
❑ 75Top-480
❑ 75TopMin-480
❑ 76BlaDis-32A
❑ 76BlaDis-32B
❑ 76BucDis-32A
❑ 76BucDis-32B
❑ 76CarDis-32A
❑ 76CarDis-32B
❑ 76CraDis-32A
❑ 76CraDis-32B
❑ 76DailsID-32A
❑ 76DailsID-32B
❑ 76Hos-34
❑ 76HosTwi-34
❑ 76IsaDis-32A
❑ 76IsaDis-32B
❑ 76OPC-110
❑ 76OrbDis-32A
❑ 76OrbDis-32B
❑ 76RedBarD-32A
❑ 76RedBarD-32B
❑ 76SafDis-32A
❑ 76SafDis-32B
❑ 76SSP-148
❑ 76Top-110
❑ 76TowCluD-32A
❑ 76TowCluD-32B
❑ 77Top-568
❑ 77Top-633
❑ 77YanBurK-22
❑ 79TCMJapPB-68
❑ 85WhiSoxC-20
❑ 87SpoRea-1
❑ 92UppDecS-5
❑ 92YanWIZ7-105
❑ 94TedWil-21

May, Darrell
❑ 93MacBraC-15
❑ 93MacBraF-1396
❑ 93SouAtlLAGF-40
❑ 94CarLeaAF-CAR29
❑ 94ClaGolF-115
❑ 94DurBulTI-12
❑ 94ExcFS7-158
❑ 95BreBtaTI-25
❑ 95Exc-154
❑ 95RicBraRC-11
❑ 96RicBraRC-3
❑ 97VanCanB-20

May, Dave
❑ 67BalOriP-65
❑ 67BalOriP-66
❑ 68CokCapO-7
❑ 68OPC-56
❑ 68Top-56
❑ 68TopVen-56
❑ 69OPC-113
❑ 69Top-113
❑ 69TopFou-17
❑ 70BreTeal-8
❑ 70OPC-81
❑ 70Top-81
❑ 71BreTeal-8
❑ 71MLBOffS-444
❑ 71OPC-493
❑ 71OriCha-9
❑ 71Top-493
❑ 72Top-549
❑ 73LinPor-101
❑ 73OPC-152
❑ 73Top-152
❑ 74Kel-13
❑ 74OPC-12
❑ 74Top-12
❑ 74TopDecE-58
❑ 74TopSta-196
❑ 75AtlBraP-22
❑ 75OPC-650
❑ 75Top-650
❑ 75TopMin-650
❑ 76AtlBraP-18
❑ 76Hos-148
❑ 76OPC-281
❑ 76SSP-19
❑ 76Top-281
❑ 76VenLeaS-133
❑ 78SSP270-92
❑ 78Top-362
❑ 81TCM60I-385
❑ 83PinArtP-5
❑ 86BreGreT-7
❑ 91OriCro-284
❑ 93RanKee-250
❑ 94BreMilB-153

May, Davis
❑ 76TacTwiDQ-12
❑ 77TacTwiDQ-12
❑ 79SyrChiT-16
❑ 79SyrChiTI-22
❑ 80KnoBluJT-7

May, Derrick
❑ 87PeoChiP-12
❑ 88WinSpiS-11
❑ 89ChaKniTI-5
❑ 90CMC-89
❑ 90Fle-645
❑ 90FleCan-645
❑ 90IowCubC-14
❑ 90IowCubP-331
❑ 90ProAAAF-638
❑ 90TopTVCu-53
❑ 90UppDec-736
❑ 91Cla1-T28
❑ 91ClaGam-153
❑ 91Don-36
❑ 91Fle-427
❑ 91IowCubLD-209
❑ 91LinDriAAA-209
❑ 91MajLeaCP-69
❑ 91OPC-288
❑ 91Sco-379
❑ 91ScoRoo-36
❑ 91StaClu-73
❑ 91Top-288
❑ 91TopDeb90-100
❑ 91TopDesS-288
❑ 91TopMic-288
❑ 91TopTif-288
❑ 91Ult-65
❑ 91UppDec-334
❑ 92Cla2-T22
❑ 92CubMar-27
❑ 92DonRoo-70
❑ 92Fle-387
❑ 92IowCubS-212
❑ 92Pin-534
❑ 92SkyAAAF-108
❑ 92StaClu-148
❑ 92TopTra-68T
❑ 92TopTraG-68T
❑ 93CubMar-16
❑ 93CubStaC-12
❑ 93Don-318
❑ 93Fla-16
❑ 93Fle-21
❑ 93FleRooS-RSA8
❑ 93Lea-200
❑ 93OPC-159
❑ 93PacBeiA-19
❑ 93PacJugC-32
❑ 93PacSpa-380
❑ 93PanSti-209
❑ 93Pin-371
❑ 93Sco-213
❑ 93Sel-402
❑ 93SP-85
❑ 93StaClu-109
❑ 93StaCluFDI-109
❑ 93StaCluMOP-109
❑ 93Stu-148
❑ 93Top-391
❑ 93TopGol-391
❑ 93TopInaM-391
❑ 93TopInaR-391
❑ 93TopMic-391
❑ 93Toy-79
❑ 93Ult-19
❑ 93UppDec-248
❑ 93UppDecGold-248
❑ 93USPlaCR-10H
❑ 94ColC-193
❑ 94ColChoGS-193
❑ 94ColChoSS-193
❑ 94Don-178
❑ 94Fin-162
❑ 94FinRef-162
❑ 94Fla-361
❑ 94Fle-389
❑ 94FleExtB-220
❑ 94Lea-139
❑ 94LeaL-91
❑ 94OPC-40
❑ 94Pac-103
❑ 94PanSti-154
❑ 94Pin-196
❑ 94PinArtP-196
❑ 94PinMusC-196
❑ 94ProMag-24
❑ 94Sco-68
❑ 94ScoGolR-68
❑ 94Sel-38
❑ 94StaClu-287
❑ 94StaCluFDI-287
❑ 94StaCluGR-287
❑ 94StaCluMOP-287
❑ 94StaCluMOP-ST2
❑ 94StaCluST-ST2
❑ 94StaCluT-332
❑ 94StaCluTFDI-332
❑ 94Stu-61
❑ 94Top-6
❑ 94TopGol-6
❑ 94TopSpa-6
❑ 94TriPla-74
❑ 94Ult-461
❑ 94UppDec-328
❑ 94UppDecED-328
❑ 95AstMot-10
❑ 95ColCho-209
❑ 95ColCho-538T
❑ 95ColChoGS-209
❑ 95ColChoSE-84
❑ 95ColChoSEGS-84
❑ 95ColChoSESS-84
❑ 95ColChoSS-209
❑ 95Don-441
❑ 95DonPreP-441
❑ 95Fla-113
❑ 95Fle-419
❑ 95FleUpd-54
❑ 95Pac-74
❑ 95Pin-28
❑ 95PinArtP-28
❑ 95PinMusC-28
❑ 95Sco-334
❑ 95ScoGolR-334
❑ 95ScoPlaTS-334
❑ 95Spo-5
❑ 95SpoArtP-5
❑ 95StaClu-243
❑ 95StaCluFDI-243
❑ 95StaCluMOP-243
❑ 95StaCluSTWS-243
❑ 95Top-579
❑ 95TopCyb-353
❑ 95Ult-360
❑ 95UltGolM-360
❑ 95UppDec-68
❑ 95UppDecED-68
❑ 95UppDecEDG-68
❑ 96AstMot-8
❑ 96ColCho-567
❑ 96ColChoGS-567
❑ 96ColChoSS-567
❑ 96Don-489
❑ 96DonPreP-489
❑ 96EmoXL-201
❑ 96Fla-281
❑ 96Fle-415
❑ 96FleTif-415
❑ 96Pac-85
❑ 96Sco-476
❑ 96Ult-489
❑ 96UltGolM-489
❑ 97Fle-350
❑ 97Fle-505
❑ 97FleTif-350
❑ 97FleTif-505
❑ 97Pac-321
❑ 97PacLigB-321
❑ 97PacSil-321
❑ 97PhiTeal-34
❑ 97Ult-476
❑ 97UltGolME-476
❑ 97UltPlaME-476
❑ 98ColCho-414
❑ 98PacOnl-454
❑ 98PacOnlR-454
❑ 98PacOnlWC-454
❑ 98UppDec-700

May, Frank
❑ 31CubTeal-16

May, Freddy
❑ 96AugGreB-17
❑ 97AugGre-28
❑ 98CarLeaAC-13
❑ 98CarLeaAC-16
❑ 98LynHilQ-21

May, Herb
❑ 22Zee-134
❑ 27Zee-117

May, Jakie
❑ 27AmeCarE126-56
❑ 32CubTeal-17
❑ 91ConTSN-319

May, Jerry
❑ 65OPC-143
❑ 65Top-143
❑ 66OPC-123
❑ 66PirEasH-12
❑ 66Top-123
❑ 66TopVen-123
❑ 67PirTeal-10
❑ 67Top-379
❑ 67TopPirS-13
❑ 68PirKDK-12
❑ 68PirTeal-10
❑ 68Top-598
❑ 69MilBra-170
❑ 69MLBOffS-186
❑ 69PirGre-5
❑ 69PirJacitB-5
❑ 69PirTeal-14
❑ 69Top-263
❑ 69TopSta-87
❑ 69TopTeaP-16
❑ 70MLBOffS-102
❑ 70OPC-423
❑ 70PirTeal-10
❑ 70Top-423
❑ 71MLBOffS-420
❑ 71OPC-719
❑ 71oySigST-15
❑ 71Top-719
❑ 72MilBra-210
❑ 72OPC-109
❑ 72oyTeal-14
❑ 72Top-109
❑ 73OPC-558
❑ 73Top-558
❑ 91MetWIZ-254

May, Ken
❑ 76SeaRaiC-9

May, Kevin
❑ 81CliGiaT-9

May, Larry
❑ 80WisRapTT-4
❑ 82OrlTwiT-20

May, Lee
❑ 88LitFalMP-1
❑ 89ColMetB-10
❑ 89ColMetGS-15
❑ 89PitMetS-16
❑ 90St.LucMS-15
❑ 91LinDriAAA-562
❑ 91TidTidLD-562
❑ 91WilBilP-307
❑ 92SkyAAAF-254
❑ 92TidTidF-911
❑ 92TidTidS-563
❑ 93MemChiF-389

May, Lee Sr.
❑ 66Top-424
❑ 67Kah-22
❑ 67Top-222
❑ 68Kah-A8
❑ 68Kah-B22
❑ 68Top-487
❑ 69Kah-B13
❑ 69MilBra-171
❑ 69MLBOffS-131
❑ 69Top-405
❑ 69TopSta-27
❑ 69TopTeaP-20
❑ 69TraSta-52
❑ 70DayDaiNM-19
❑ 70MLBOffS-30
❑ 70OPC-65
❑ 70OPC-225
❑ 70Top-65
❑ 70Top-225
❑ 71MLBOffS-62
❑ 71OPC-40
❑ 71Top-40
❑ 71TopCoi-29
❑ 71TopTat-38
❑ 72AstTeal-15
❑ 72Kel-37
❑ 72MilBra-211
❑ 72OPC-89
❑ 72OPC-480
❑ 72Top-89
❑ 72Top-480
❑ 73LinPor-11
❑ 73OPC-135
❑ 73SevTraC-44
❑ 73Top-135
❑ 73TopCanL-31
❑ 74AstFouTIP-4
❑ 74OPC-500
❑ 74Top-500
❑ 74TopSta-33
❑ 75BalOriP-20
❑ 75Hos-35
❑ 75Hos-142
❑ 75HosTwi-35
❑ 75OPC-25
❑ 75Top-25
❑ 75TopMin-25
❑ 76BalOriP-24
❑ 76Hos-98
❑ 76OPC-210
❑ 76SSP-389
❑ 76Top-210
❑ 77BurCheD-45
❑ 77Hos-55
❑ 77OPC-3
❑ 77OPC-125
❑ 77Top-3
❑ 77Top-380
❑ 77Top-633
❑ 77TopCloS-26
❑ 78BalOriP-18
❑ 78Hos-53
❑ 78OPC-47
❑ 78Top-640
❑ 78WifBalD-45
❑ 79OPC-1
❑ 79Top-10
❑ 80OPC-255
❑ 80Top-490
❑ 81Fle-183
❑ 82AstAstI-2
❑ 82Don-570
❑ 82Fle-415
❑ 82Top-132
❑ 83Don-538
❑ 83Fle-118
❑ 83FraBroR-36
❑ 83OPC-377
❑ 83OPC-378
❑ 83Top-377
❑ 83Top-378
❑ 83TopSti-9
❑ 84RoyPos-21
❑ 85CirK-34
❑ 85RoyTeal-20
❑ 86AstMot-12
❑ 87AstShoSO-15
❑ 87AstShowSTh-25
❑ 88RedKah-NNO
❑ 89RedKah-xx
❑ 90PacLeg-55
❑ 90SweBasG-67
❑ 91OriCro-285
❑ 92RoyPol-27
❑ 93RoyPol-27
❑ 93UppDecAH-90
❑ 94UppDecAH-193
❑ 94UppDecAH1-193
❑ 95BalOriP-32

May, Malcolm
❑ 91MelBusF-12

May, Milt
❑ 71OPC-343
❑ 71PirActP-8
❑ 71Top-343
❑ 72OPC-247
❑ 72Top-247
❑ 73OPC-529
❑ 73Top-529
❑ 74AstFouTIP-3
❑ 74OPC-293
❑ 74Top-293
❑ 75AstPos-21
❑ 75Hos-35
❑ 75HosTwi-35
❑ 75OPC-279
❑ 75Top-279
❑ 75TopMin-279
❑ 76DetTigP-20
❑ 76OPC-532
❑ 76SSP-53
❑ 76Top-532
❑ 76TopTra-532T
❑ 77OPC-14
❑ 77Top-98
❑ 78Hos-115
❑ 78OPC-115
❑ 78TigBurK-2
❑ 78TigTeal-19
❑ 78Top-176
❑ 79TigFreP-8
❑ 79Top-316
❑ 80GiaEurFS-4
❑ 80GiaPol-7

❑ 80GiaTeal-16
❑ 80OPC-340
❑ 80Top-647
❑ 81AllGamPl-132
❑ 81Don-193
❑ 81Fle-442
❑ 81GiaTeal-10
❑ 81OPC-273
❑ 81Top-463
❑ 81TopSti-237
❑ 82Don-503
❑ 82Fle-395
❑ 82FleSta-62
❑ 82Gia25tATI-23
❑ 82OPC-242
❑ 82SevSluC-18
❑ 82Top-242
❑ 82Top-576
❑ 82TopSti-110
❑ 83Don-312
❑ 83Fle-268
❑ 83FleSta-119
❑ 83GiaPos-19
❑ 83Top-84
❑ 83TopSti-301
❑ 84Don-386
❑ 84Fle-254
❑ 84Nes792-788
❑ 84Pir-10
❑ 84Top-788
❑ 84TopTif-788
❑ 85Don-410
❑ 85Top-509
❑ 85TopTif-509
❑ 87AstShoSPO-18
❑ 87AstShowSTh-14
❑ 88PirTeal-21
❑ 89PirVerFJ-39
❑ 90PirHomC-21
❑ 92PirNatl-14
❑ 93PirNatl-16
❑ 94PirQui-14
❑ 97MarPac-29

May, Pinky (Merrill)
❑ 39ExhSal-40
❑ 39PlaBal-45
❑ 40PlaBal-98
❑ 41DouPlaR-45
❑ 41PhiTeal-17
❑ 41PlaBal-9
❑ 43PhiTeal-16
❑ 75TCMGua-4
❑ 77TCMTheWY-32

May, Rudy
❑ 65Top-537
❑ 66SeaPop-12
❑ 69AngJacitB-6
❑ 70MLBOffS-175
❑ 70OPC-203
❑ 70Top-203
❑ 71AngJacitB-6
❑ 71MLBOffS-349
❑ 71OPC-318
❑ 71Top-318
❑ 72Top-656
❑ 73OPC-102
❑ 73Top-102
❑ 74OPC-302
❑ 74Top-302
❑ 75OPC-321
❑ 75Top-321
❑ 75TopMin-321
❑ 76BalOriP-25
❑ 76OPC-481
❑ 76SSP-427
❑ 76Top-481
❑ 77Top-56
❑ 78ExpPos-8
❑ 78Top-262
❑ 79OPC-318
❑ 79Top-603
❑ 80OPC-281
❑ 80Top-539
❑ 80YanPhoA-16
❑ 81Fle-90
❑ 81OPC-179
❑ 81Top-7
❑ 81Top-179
❑ 81TopSti-3
❑ 81TopSupHT-68
❑ 81YanPhoA-12
❑ 82Don-325
❑ 82Fle-41
❑ 82OPC-128
❑ 82Top-735
❑ 82YanPhoA-13
❑ 83Don-135
❑ 83Fle-385
❑ 83Top-408
❑ 83YanPhoA-15
❑ 84Don-626
❑ 84Nes792-652
❑ 84Top-652
❑ 84TopTif-652
❑ 91OriCro-286
❑ 92YanWIZ7-106
❑ 92YanWIZ8-112

May, Scott
❑ 86AlbDukP-14
❑ 87SanAntDTI-11
❑ 88OklCit8C-3
❑ 88OklCit8P-27
❑ 89Don-636
❑ 89OklCit8C-5
❑ 89OklCit8P-1523
❑ 90ElPasDGS-20
❑ 91IowCubLD-210
❑ 91IowCubP-1055
❑ 91LinDriAAA-210
❑ 92IowCubF-4049
❑ 92IowCubS-213
❑ 93RanKee-251
❑ 96EriSeaB-15
❑ 97AugGre-18

May, Steve
❑ 93PocPosF-4207
❑ 93PocPosSP-16

May, Ted
❑ 79QuaCitCT-7

May, William
❑ 28Zee-136

Mayber, Chan
❑ 95AshTouTI-9
❑ 96SalAvaB-19

Mayberry, Germaine
❑ 92BurIndC-4
❑ 92BurIndF-1671

Mayberry, Greg
❑ 85VerBeaDT-20
❑ 88VerBeaDS-15
❑ 89SanAntMB-19
❑ 90AlbDukCm-7
❑ 90AlbDukP-342
❑ 90AlbDukTr-21
❑ 90CMC-409
❑ 90ProAAAF-63

Mayberry, John
❑ 70AstPho-15
❑ 70OPC-227
❑ 70Top-227
❑ 71MLBOffS-86
❑ 71OPC-148
❑ 71Top-148
❑ 72OPC-373
❑ 72oyTeal-15
❑ 72Top-373
❑ 73LinPor-87
❑ 73OPC-118
❑ 73SevTraC-45
❑ 73Top-118
❑ 73TopCanL-32
❑ 74Kel-29
❑ 74OPC-150
❑ 74RoyPos-16
❑ 74Top-150
❑ 74TopDecE-51
❑ 74TopSta-184
❑ 75Hos-92
❑ 75OPC-95
❑ 75RoyPos-18
❑ 75SSP42-31
❑ 75Top-95
❑ 75TopMin-95
❑ 76BlaDis-33
❑ 76BucDis-33
❑ 76CarDis-33
❑ 76CraDis-33
❑ 76DailsID-33
❑ 76Hos-91
❑ 76IsaDis-33
❑ 76KanCitRP-18
❑ 76Kel-46
❑ 76OPC-194
❑ 76OPC-196
❑ 76OPC-440
❑ 76OrbDis-33
❑ 76RedBarD-33
❑ 76RoyAaP-8
❑ 76SafDis-33
❑ 76SSP-169
❑ 76Top-194
❑ 76Top-196
❑ 76Top-440
❑ 76TowCluD-33
❑ 77BurCheD-69
❑ 77ChiWilD-43
❑ 77DailsID-43
❑ 77DetCaeD-43
❑ 77HollnnD-43
❑ 77Hos-56
❑ 77MSADis-43
❑ 77OPC-16
❑ 77SagDis-43
❑ 77sDis-43
❑ 77Top-244
❑ 77TopCloS-27
❑ 77WenDis-43
❑ 77ZipDis-43
❑ 78BluJayP-15
❑ 78OPC-168
❑ 78PapGinD-40
❑ 78Roy-12
❑ 78Top-550
❑ 78WifBalD-46
❑ 79BasPat-52
❑ 79BluJayBY-16
❑ 79Hos-82
❑ 79OPC-199
❑ 79Top-380
❑ 79TopCom-17
❑ 80OPC-338
❑ 80Top-643
❑ 81AllGamPl-7
❑ 81Don-29
❑ 81Dra-31
❑ 81Fle-416
❑ 81OPC-169
❑ 81OPCPos-13
❑ 81Top-169
❑ 81TopScr-15
❑ 81TopSti-139
❑ 82BluJayS-11
❑ 82Don-25
❑ 82Don-306
❑ 82Dra-24
❑ 82FBIDis-14
❑ 82Fle-619
❑ 82FleSta-235
❑ 82OPC-53
❑ 82OPC-382
❑ 82OPCPos-1
❑ 82SevSluC-19
❑ 82Top-470
❑ 82Top-606
❑ 82TopSti-248
❑ 82TopTra-67T
❑ 82YanPhoA-14
❑ 83Fle-386
❑ 83OPC-45
❑ 83Top-45
❑ 83TopFol-2
❑ 85SyrChiT-20
❑ 86BluJayGT-1
❑ 86RoyGreT-1
❑ 87AstShoSTw-22
❑ 87AstShowSTh-15
❑ 90RoyPos-16
❑ 92UppDecS-3
❑ 92YanWIZ8-113
❑ 93RoySta2-6

Maye, Lee (A. Lee)
❑ 60BraLaktL-15
❑ 60BraSpiaS-13
❑ 60Top-246
❑ 61Top-84
❑ 62BraJayP-7
❑ 62Jel-156
❑ 62PC7HFGSS-3
❑ 62Pos-156
❑ 62PosCan-156
❑ 62SalPlaC-216
❑ 62ShiPlaC-216
❑ 62Top-518
❑ 63Top-109
❑ 64BraJayP-7
❑ 64Top-416
❑ 65Kah-24
❑ 65Top-407
❑ 65TopEmbl-62
❑ 65TopTral-21
❑ 66OPC-162
❑ 66Top-162
❑ 66TopVen-162
❑ 67CokCapl-10
❑ 67Top-258
❑ 68OPC-94
❑ 68Top-94
❑ 68TopVen-94
❑ 69MilBra-172
❑ 69SenTeal-10
❑ 69Top-595
❑ 69TopSta-165
❑ 70OPC-439
❑ 70SenPolY-7
❑ 70Top-439
❑ 71OPC-733
❑ 71Top-733
❑ 72MilBra-212
❑ 78AtlCon-15
❑ 78TCM60I-51
❑ 78TCM60I-107

Maye, Steve (Stephen)
❑ 86WinSpiP-14
❑ 88ModA'sCLC-66
❑ 88ModA'sTI-13
❑ 89HunStaB-10
❑ 90SalSpuCLC-128
❑ 91SalSpuC-17
❑ 91SalSpuP-2238
❑ 94SanBerSC-10

Mayer, Aaron
❑ 95BoiHawTI-22
❑ 96BoiHawB-19
❑ 97LakElsSG-20

Mayer, Bob
❑ 79NaSouTI-14

Mayer, Ed
❑ 58Top-461

Mayer, James Erskine
❑ 15CraJacE-172
❑ 15SpoNewM-112
❑ 16SpoNewM-114
❑ 17ColE13-110
❑ 75WhiSox1T-15

Mayers, Jerry
❑ 52LavPro-35

Mayes, Craig
❑ 92EveGiaC-26
❑ 92EveGiaF-1693
❑ 93CliGiaC-16
❑ 93CliGiaF-2493
❑ 94CliLumC-16
❑ 94CliLumF-1983
❑ 96SanJosGB-11
❑ 96WesOahCHWB-29
❑ 97ShrCap-16
❑ 97ShrCapB-16
❑ 98FreGriG-17

Mayhew, Keith
❑ 95EugEmeTI-24

Maynard, Scott
❑ 97EveAquG-17
❑ 98WisTimRM-14

Maynard, Tow (Ellerton)
❑ 87BelMarL-4
❑ 89WauTimGS-7
❑ 90Bes-84
❑ 90SanBerSB-13
❑ 90SanBerSCLC-111
❑ 90SanBerSP-2646
❑ 91SanBerSC-22
❑ 91SanBerSP-1999
❑ 92ClaFS7-141
❑ 92JacSunF-3719
❑ 92JacSunS-363
❑ 92SkyAA F-155
❑ 93CalCanF-1179
❑ 93ExcFS7-227
❑ 93RivPilCLC-10
❑ 94VenLinU-134

Mayne, Brent
❑ 90Bes-8
❑ 90Bow-372
❑ 90BowTif-372
❑ 90CMC-780
❑ 90MemChiB-1
❑ 90MemChiP-1012
❑ 90MemChiS-16
❑ 90ProAaA-52
❑ 90Sco-669
❑ 91Cla1-T50
❑ 91Don-617
❑ 91DonRoo-43
❑ 91FleUpd-28
❑ 91OPC-776
❑ 91Sco-765
❑ 91ScoRoo-8
❑ 91StaClu-418
❑ 91Top-776
❑ 91TopDeb90-101
❑ 91TopDesS-776
❑ 91TopMic-776
❑ 91TopTif-776
❑ 91Ult-150
❑ 91UppDec-72
❑ 92Don-265
❑ 92Fle-162
❑ 92Lea-200
❑ 92LeaBlaG-200
❑ 92OPC-183
❑ 92OPCPre-40
❑ 92Pin-469
❑ 92RoyPol-17
❑ 92Sco-84
❑ 92Sco100RS-85
❑ 92ScoImpP-18
❑ 92ScoProP-23
❑ 92StaClu-229
❑ 92Stu-186
❑ 92Top-183
❑ 92TopGol-183
❑ 92TopGolW-183
❑ 92TopMic-183
❑ 92Ult-74
❑ 93Don-261
❑ 93Fle-621
❑ 93Lea-36
❑ 93PacSpa-490
❑ 93Pin-359
❑ 93RoyPol-18
❑ 93RoyStaC-18
❑ 93StaClu-25
❑ 93StaCluFDI-25
❑ 93StaCluMOP-25
❑ 93Top-294
❑ 93TopGol-294
❑ 93TopInaM-294
❑ 93TopInaR-294
❑ 93TopMic-294
❑ 93TriPla-36
❑ 93Ult-212
❑ 93UppDec-604
❑ 93UppDecGold-604
❑ 94Don-511
❑ 94Fle-166
❑ 94Pac-293
❑ 94Sco-183
❑ 94ScoGolR-183
❑ 94StaClu-333
❑ 94StaCluFDI-333
❑ 94StaCluGR-333
❑ 94StaCluMOP-333
❑ 94Top-38
❑ 94TopGol-38
❑ 94TopSpa-38
❑ 94Ult-367
❑ 95Don-238
❑ 95DonPreP-238
❑ 95DonTopotO-93
❑ 95Fle-167
❑ 95Lea-336
❑ 95Top-264
❑ 95Ult-59
❑ 95UltGolM-59
❑ 96ColCho-622
❑ 96ColChoGS-622
❑ 96ColChoSS-622
❑ 96Don-244
❑ 96DonPreP-244
❑ 96Fle-134
❑ 96FleTif-134
❑ 96FleUpd-U159
❑ 96FleUpdTC-U159
❑ 96MetKah-21
❑ 96Pac-333
❑ 96Sco-187
❑ 96Ult-73
❑ 96UltGolM-73
❑ 97A'sMot-17
❑ 97Pac-370
❑ 97PacLigB-370
❑ 97PacSil-370
❑ 98GiaMot-16
❑ 98Pac-168
❑ 98PacOnl-666
❑ 98PacOnlR-666
❑ 98PacOnlWC-666
❑ 98PacPlaB-168
❑ 98PacRedT-168
❑ 98PacSil-168
❑ 98Ult-427
❑ 98UltGolM-427
❑ 98UltMas-427
❑ 98UltPlaM-427

Maynor, Tonka
❑ 94WelPirC-14
❑ 94WelPirF-3509

Mayo, Blake
❑ 92MisStaB-29
❑ 96YakBeaTI-43
❑ 97SanBerS-10
❑ 98VerBeaDM-13

Mayo, Eddie (Edward)
❑ 43A'STEAI-18
❑ 47Exh-151
❑ 47TipTop-36
❑ 49Bow-75
❑ 54Top-247
❑ 75Phi195T-18
❑ 83TCMPla1945-1
❑ 94TopArc1-247
❑ 94TopArc1G-247
❑ 95ConTSN-1427

Mayo, Jackie (John)
❑ 49Bow-228
❑ 49EurSta-141
❑ 49PhiBul-35
❑ 50WorWidGV-36
❑ 55JetPos-10
❑ 80Phi195T-18

Mayo, Todd
❑ 88CapCodPPaLP-119
❑ 89JamExpP-2146
❑ 90WesPalBES-15
❑ 91WesPalBEC-26
❑ 91WesPalBEP-1241
❑ 92HarSenS-291

Mays, Al
❑ 87FouBasHN-7
❑ 87OldJudN-320A
❑ 87OldJudN-320B
❑ 90KalBatN-36

Mays, Carl W.
❑ 19W514-103
❑ 20NatCarE-61
❑ 21E121So1-58
❑ 21E121So8-55A
❑ 21E121So8-55B
❑ 21Exh-103
❑ 21KoBreWSI-38
❑ 21Nei-7
❑ 22AmeCarE122-43
❑ 22E120-66
❑ 22W573-76
❑ 22W575-76
❑ 23W501-29
❑ 23W503-20
❑ 23W515-20
❑ 23WilChoV-89
❑ 27YorCarE-17
❑ 28W502-17
❑ 28Yue-17
❑ 30SchR33-8
❑ 77GalGloG-126
❑ 87ConSer2-48
❑ 88ConSer4-18
❑ 91ConTSN-150

Mays, David
❑ 89TenTecGE-17

Mays, Henry
❑ 77St.PetCT-16

Mays, Jarrod
❑ 96WatIndTI-14
❑ 97KinIndB-13
❑ 98AkrAerM-12

Mays, Jeff
❑ 86SalRedBP-18
❑ 87PorChaRP-11
❑ 88ChaRanS-16

Mays, Joe
❑ 97WisTimR-19
❑ 98BesAutSS-34
❑ 98ForMyeMTI-19
❑ 99DumSet-137
❑ 99FleMys-137
❑ 99FleMysM-137
❑ 99SkyPre-236
❑ 99SkyPre-236
❑ 99SkyPreR-236
❑ 99SkyPreR-236
❑ 99SP TopP-83
❑ 99SP TopPPE-83

Mays, Mae
❑ 84WilMay-43

Mays, Marcus
❑ 94KanCouCC-14
❑ 94KanCouCF-158
❑ 94KanCouCTI-15

Mays, Mrs. (Willie)
❑ 84WilMay-46

Mays, Willie
❑ 47Exh-152A
❑ 47Exh-152B
❑ 47PM1StaP1-131

❑ 47PM1StaP1-132
❑ 47PM1StaP1-133
❑ 47PM1StaP1-134
❑ 47PM1StaP1-135
❑ 47PM1StaP1-136
❑ 47PM1StaP1-137
❑ 47StaPinP2-25
❑ 47StaPinP2-26
❑ 51Bow-305
❑ 52BerRos-39
❑ 52Bow-218
❑ 52RedMan-NL15
❑ 52StaCalL-78E
❑ 52StaCalS-90A
❑ 52Top-261
❑ 53Bri-35
❑ 53Top-244
❑ 54Bow-89
❑ 54NewYorJA-32
❑ 54RedMan-NL25
❑ 54StaMey-7
❑ 54Top-90
❑ 55Bow-184
❑ 55DonWin-33
❑ 55GiaGolS-21
❑ 55RedMan-NL7
❑ 55RobGouS-1
❑ 55RobGouW-1
❑ 55Top-194
❑ 56GiaJayP-7
❑ 56Top-31
❑ 56Top-130
❑ 56TopPin-41
❑ 57GiaJayP-5
❑ 57Top-10
❑ 58GiaArmT-5
❑ 58GiaJayP-7
❑ 58GiaSFCB-14
❑ 58HarSta-9
❑ 58Hir-25
❑ 58HirTes-7
❑ 58JayPubS-7
❑ 58PacBel-5
❑ 58Top-5
❑ 58Top-436
❑ 58Top-486
❑ 59Baz-15
❑ 59HomRunD-14
❑ 59HowPhoSP-1
❑ 59Top-50
❑ 59Top-317
❑ 59Top-464
❑ 59Top-563
❑ 59TopVen-50
❑ 60ArmCoi-16
❑ 60Baz-13
❑ 60GiaJayP-8
❑ 60KeyChal-34
❑ 60MacSta-13
❑ 60NuHi-27
❑ 60RawGloT-21
❑ 60Top-7
❑ 60Top-200
❑ 60Top-564
❑ 60TopTat-34
❑ 60TopTat-93
❑ 60TopVen-7
❑ 61Baz-23
❑ 61ChePat-8
❑ 61GiaJayP-9
❑ 61NuSco-404
❑ 61NuSco-427
❑ 61Pos-145A
❑ 61Pos-145B
❑ 61SevElev-17
❑ 61Top-41
❑ 61Top-150
❑ 61Top-482
❑ 61Top-579
❑ 61TopDicG-9
❑ 62AurRec-12
❑ 62Baz-38
❑ 62ExhStaB-26
❑ 62GiaJayP-9
❑ 62Jel-142
❑ 62Pos-142
❑ 62PosCan-142
❑ 62SalPlaC-149
❑ 62ShiPlaC-149
❑ 62Top-18
❑ 62Top-54
❑ 62Top-300
❑ 62Top-395
❑ 62TopBuc-57
❑ 62TopStal-199
❑ 62TopVen-18
❑ 62TopVen-54
❑ 63BasMagM-58
❑ 63Baz-12
❑ 63ExhStaB-44
❑ 63Fle-5
❑ 63GiaJayP-7
❑ 63Jel-106
❑ 63Pos-106
❑ 63SalMetC-22
❑ 63Top-3
❑ 63Top-138
❑ 63Top-300
❑ 63TopStil-27
❑ 64Baz-12
❑ 64GiaJayP-7
❑ 64Top-9
❑ 64Top-150
❑ 64Top-306
❑ 64Top-423
❑ 64TopCoi-80
❑ 64TopCoi-151
❑ 64TopGia-51
❑ 64TopSta-20
❑ 64TopStaU-48
❑ 64TopTatl-53
❑ 64TopVen-9
❑ 64TopVen-150
❑ 64TopVen-306
❑ 64WheSta-29
❑ 65Baz-12
❑ 65GiaTeal-6
❑ 65MacSta-6
❑ 65OldLonC-14
❑ 65OPC-4
❑ 65OPC-6
❑ 65OPC-250
❑ 65Top-4
❑ 65Top-6
❑ 65Top-250
❑ 65TopEmbl-27
❑ 65TopTral-58
❑ 66AurSpoMK-3
❑ 66Baz-16
❑ 66OPC-1
❑ 66Top-1
❑ 66Top-215
❑ 66Top-217
❑ 66Top-219
❑ 66TopRubl-60
❑ 66TopVen-1
❑ 66TopVen-215
❑ 66TopVen-217
❑ 66TopVen-219
❑ 67Baz-16
❑ 67CokCapA-10
❑ 67CokCapG-17
❑ 67DexPre-134
❑ 67DexPre-135
❑ 67OPC-191
❑ 67OPCPapl-12
❑ 67Top-191A
❑ 67Top-191B
❑ 67Top-200
❑ 67Top-244
❑ 67Top-423
❑ 67TopGiaSU-19
❑ 67TopPos-12
❑ 67TopTesF-13
❑ 67TopVen-273
❑ 68AtlOil-8
❑ 68Baz-14
❑ 68DexPre-51
❑ 68OPC-50
❑ 68Top-50
❑ 68Top-490
❑ 68TopActS-5B
❑ 68TopActS-9C
❑ 68TopGaml-8
❑ 68TopPla-19
❑ 68TopPos-20
❑ 68TopVen-50
❑ 69EquSpoHoF-BB13
❑ 69KelPin-12
❑ 69MilBra-173
❑ 69MLBOffS-204
❑ 69MLBPin-52
❑ 69NabTeaF-15
❑ 69OPC-190
❑ 69OPCDec-16
❑ 69Top-190
❑ 69TopDec-33
❑ 69TopDecl-24
❑ 69TopFou-1
❑ 69TopSta-108
❑ 69TopSup-65
❑ 69TopTeaP-14
❑ 69TraSta-34
❑ 70DayDaiNM-6
❑ 70Gia-9
❑ 70Houof J-19
❑ 70Kel-12
❑ 70MilBra-15
❑ 70MLBOffS-129
❑ 70Top-600
❑ 70TopBoo-24
❑ 70TopSup-18
❑ 70TraSta-1B
❑ 71AllBasA-15
❑ 71BazNumT-47
❑ 71BazUnn-17
❑ 71GiaTic-7
❑ 71Kel-10
❑ 71MatMin-7
❑ 71MatMin-8
❑ 71MilDud-51
❑ 71MLBOffS-257
❑ 71MLBOffS-567
❑ 71OPC-600
❑ 71Top-600
❑ 71TopCoi-153
❑ 71TopGreM-41
❑ 71TopSup-56
❑ 71TopTat-130
❑ 71TopTat-131
❑ 72Kel-54A
❑ 72Kel-54B
❑ 72MilBra-213
❑ 72OPC-49
❑ 72OPC-50
❑ 72ProStaP-18
❑ 72SevTraC-30
❑ 72Top-49
❑ 72Top-50
❑ 72TopPos-17
❑ 73MetTeal-8
❑ 73NewYorSNM-17
❑ 73OPC-1
❑ 73OPC-305
❑ 73SevTraC-46
❑ 73Top-1
❑ 73Top-305
❑ 73TopCanL-33
❑ 74LauAllG-60
❑ 74OPC-473
❑ 74Top-473
❑ 75Gia195T-20
❑ 75Gia195T-34
❑ 75GiaAllT-6
❑ 75OPC-192
❑ 75OPC-203
❑ 75SSP42-35
❑ 75SSPSam-5
❑ 75TCMHouoJ-21
❑ 75Top-192
❑ 75Top-203
❑ 75TopMin-192
❑ 75TopMin-203
❑ 76GalBasGHoF-18
❑ 76JerJonPC-3
❑ 76LauDiaJ-18
❑ 76Spo-A
❑ 76SSP-595
❑ 76SSP-616
❑ 76UPIS-9
❑ 77BobParHoF-67
❑ 77GalGloG-8
❑ 77GalGloG-245
❑ 77SerSta-17
❑ 77Spo-1106
❑ 78DexHaloFP-37
❑ 78HalHalR-20
❑ 78TCM60I-280
❑ 79BasGre-70
❑ 79DiaGre-50
❑ 79Pew-11
❑ 79TCM50-6
❑ 80GiaGreT-1
❑ 80Lau300-10
❑ 80MarExh-19
❑ 80PacLeg-48
❑ 80PerHaloFP-168
❑ 80PerHaloFPS-37
❑ 80SSPHOF-168
❑ 81Gia196T-8
❑ 81SanDieSC-12
❑ 82BasCarN-7
❑ 82CraJac-13
❑ 82DavHaloFB-17
❑ 82DiaCla-18
❑ 82K-M-8
❑ 82TCMGreH-6
❑ 82TCMGreS-43
❑ 82TCMStaot5-9
❑ 83ASAWilM1-1
❑ 83ASAWilM1-2
❑ 83ASAWilM1-3
❑ 83ASAWilM1-4
❑ 83ASAWilM1-5
❑ 83ASAWilM1-6
❑ 83ASAWilM1-7
❑ 83ASAWilM1-8
❑ 83ASAWilM1-9
❑ 83ASAWilM1-10
❑ 83ASAWilM1-11
❑ 83ASAWilM1-12
❑ 83KelCerB-5
❑ 83KelCerB-6
❑ 83MLBPin-27
❑ 83TopRep5-261
❑ 83TopSti-3
❑ 83TopTraBP-5
❑ 84FifNatCT-12
❑ 84GiaMot-1
❑ 84OCoandSI-20
❑ 84OCoandSI-131
❑ 84OCoandSI-165
❑ 84OCoandSI-216
❑ 84SpoDesPW-13
❑ 84WilMay-1A
❑ 84WilMay-1B
❑ 84WilMay-2
❑ 84WilMay-3
❑ 84WilMay-4
❑ 84WilMay-5
❑ 84WilMay-6
❑ 84WilMay-7
❑ 84WilMay-8
❑ 84WilMay-9
❑ 84WilMay-10
❑ 84WilMay-11
❑ 84WilMay-12
❑ 84WilMay-13
❑ 84WilMay-14
❑ 84WilMay-15
❑ 84WilMay-16
❑ 84WilMay-17
❑ 84WilMay-18
❑ 84WilMay-19
❑ 84WilMay-20
❑ 84WilMay-21
❑ 84WilMay-22
❑ 84WilMay-23
❑ 84WilMay-24
❑ 84WilMay-25
❑ 84WilMay-26
❑ 84WilMay-27
❑ 84WilMay-28
❑ 84WilMay-29
❑ 84WilMay-30
❑ 84WilMay-31
❑ 84WilMay-32
❑ 84WilMay-33
❑ 84WilMay-34
❑ 84WilMay-35
❑ 84WilMay-36
❑ 84WilMay-37
❑ 84WilMay-38
❑ 84WilMay-39
❑ 84WilMay-40
❑ 84WilMay-41
❑ 84WilMay-42
❑ 84WilMay-43
❑ 84WilMay-44
❑ 84WilMay-45
❑ 84WilMay-46
❑ 84WilMay-47
❑ 84WilMay-48
❑ 84WilMay-49
❑ 84WilMay-50
❑ 84WilMay-51
❑ 84WilMay-52
❑ 84WilMay-53
❑ 84WilMay-54
❑ 84WilMay-55
❑ 84WilMay-56
❑ 84WilMay-57
❑ 84WilMay-58
❑ 84WilMay-59
❑ 84WilMay-60
❑ 84WilMay-61
❑ 84WilMay-62
❑ 84WilMay-63
❑ 84WilMay-64
❑ 84WilMay-65
❑ 84WilMay-66
❑ 84WilMay-67
❑ 84WilMay-68
❑ 84WilMay-69
❑ 84WilMay-70
❑ 84WilMay-71
❑ 84WilMay-72
❑ 84WilMay-73
❑ 84WilMay-74
❑ 84WilMay-75
❑ 84WilMay-76
❑ 84WilMay-77
❑ 84WilMay-78
❑ 84WilMay-79
❑ 84WilMay-80
❑ 84WilMay-81
❑ 84WilMay-82
❑ 84WilMay-83
❑ 84WilMay-84
❑ 84WilMay-85
❑ 84WilMay-86
❑ 84WilMay-87
❑ 84WilMay-88
❑ 84WilMay-89
❑ 84WilMay-90
❑ 85CirK-3
❑ 85TCMPhoC-35
❑ 85TCMPhoC-37
❑ 85Woo-26
❑ 86BigLeaC-3
❑ 86GiaPos-21
❑ 86SpoDecG-50
❑ 86SpoDesJM-22
❑ 86SpoRoo-46
❑ 86TCM-6
❑ 86TCMSupS-29
❑ 86Top-403
❑ 86TopTif-403
❑ 87AstShoSTw-21
❑ 87AstShoSTw-25
❑ 87GiaPos-21
❑ 87HygAllG-33
❑ 87K-M-8
❑ 87NesDreT-28
❑ 88GiaPos-20
❑ 88GreBasS-52
❑ 88HouSho-5
❑ 88PacLegl-24
❑ 88PhiTopAS-8
❑ 88WilMulP-22
❑ 89BowInsT-7
❑ 89BowRepl-7
❑ 89BowTif-R7
❑ 90AGFA-1
❑ 90BasWit-18
❑ 90El PasDAGTI-43
❑ 90HOFStiB-65
❑ 90PerGreM-65
❑ 90PerGreM-87
❑ 90PerMasW-11
❑ 90PerMasW-12
❑ 90PerMasW-13
❑ 90PerMasW-14
❑ 90PerMasW-15
❑ 91Kel3D-3
❑ 91MetWIZ-255
❑ 91NegLeaRL-21
❑ 91SweBasG-106
❑ 91TopArc1-244
❑ 92ActPacA-14
❑ 92ActPacA2-14G
❑ 92ActPacAP-3
❑ 92BazQua5A-1
❑ 92GiaCheHoFP-1
❑ 92GiaFanFFB-3
❑ 92MVP-16
❑ 92MVP2H-1
❑ 92RevLeg1-1
❑ 92RevLeg1-2
❑ 92RevLeg1-3
❑ 92TVSpoMF5HRC-8
❑ 92Zip-8
❑ 93ActPacAC-14
❑ 93MetIma-12
❑ 93MetIma-P1
❑ 93StaCluU-1
❑ 93StaCluU-2
❑ 93StaCluU-6
❑ 93StaCluU-8
❑ 93StaCluU-9
❑ 93TedWil-55
❑ 93TedWil-126
❑ 93TedWil-138
❑ 93TedWil-144
❑ 93TedWilLC-3
❑ 93UppDecAH-91
❑ 93UppDecAH-137
❑ 93UppDecAH-150
❑ 93UppDecAH-151
❑ 93UppDecAH-163
❑ 93UppDecAH-164
❑ 93UppDecMH-46
❑ 93UppDecMH-47
❑ 93UppDecMH-48
❑ 93UppDecMH-49
❑ 93UppDecMH-50
❑ 93UppDecMH-51
❑ 93UppDecMH-52
❑ 93UppDecMH-53
❑ 93UppDecMH-54
❑ 93UppDecTAN-TN18
❑ 94TedWil-150
❑ 94TopArc1-90
❑ 94TopArc1G-90
❑ 94UppDecAH-10
❑ 94UppDecAH-17
❑ 94UppDecAH-24
❑ 94UppDecAH-117
❑ 94UppDecAH-150
❑ 94UppDecAH-166
❑ 94UppDecAH1-10
❑ 94UppDecAH1-17
❑ 94UppDecAH1-24
❑ 94UppDecAH1-117
❑ 94UppDecAH1-150
❑ 94UppDecAH1-166
❑ 95NegLeaL2-1
❑ 95NegLeaLI-21
❑ 95TopLegot6M-1
❑ 95UppDecA-3
❑ 97NegLeaPC-13C
❑ 97SpollIAM-4
❑ 97SpollICC-11
❑ 97TopMan-33
❑ 97TopManF-33
❑ 97TopManFR-33
❑ 97TopMay-1
❑ 97TopMay-2
❑ 97TopMay-3
❑ 97TopMay-4
❑ 97TopMay-5
❑ 97TopMay-6
❑ 97TopMay-7
❑ 97TopMay-8
❑ 97TopMay-9
❑ 97TopMay-10
❑ 97TopMay-11
❑ 97TopMay-12
❑ 97TopMay-13
❑ 97TopMay-14
❑ 97TopMay-15
❑ 97TopMay-16
❑ 97TopMay-17
❑ 97TopMay-18
❑ 97TopMay-19
❑ 97TopMay-20
❑ 97TopMay-21
❑ 97TopMay-22
❑ 97TopMay-23
❑ 97TopMay-24
❑ 97TopMay-25
❑ 97TopMay-26
❑ 97TopMay-27
❑ 97TopMay-J261
❑ 97TopMay-NNO
❑ 97TopMayF-1
❑ 97TopMayF-2
❑ 97TopMayF-3
❑ 97TopMayF-4
❑ 97TopMayF-5
❑ 97TopMayF-6
❑ 97TopMayF-7
❑ 97TopMayF-8
❑ 97TopMayF-9
❑ 97TopMayF-10
❑ 97TopMayF-11
❑ 97TopMayF-12
❑ 97TopMayF-13
❑ 97TopMayF-14
❑ 97TopMayF-15
❑ 97TopMayF-16
❑ 97TopMayF-17
❑ 97TopMayF-18
❑ 97TopMayF-19
❑ 97TopMayF-20
❑ 97TopMayF-21
❑ 97TopMayF-22
❑ 97TopMayF-23
❑ 97TopMayF-24
❑ 97TopMayF-25
❑ 97TopMayF-26
❑ 97TopMayF-27
❑ 97TopMayFR-1
❑ 97TopMayFR-2
❑ 97TopMayFR-3
❑ 97TopMayFR-4

❑ 97TopMayFR-5
❑ 97TopMayFR-6
❑ 97TopMayFR-7
❑ 97TopMayFR-8
❑ 97TopMayFR-9
❑ 97TopMayFR-10
❑ 97TopMayFR-11
❑ 97TopMayFR-12
❑ 97TopMayFR-13
❑ 97TopMayFR-14
❑ 97TopMayFR-15
❑ 97TopMayFR-16
❑ 97TopMayFR-17
❑ 97TopMayFR-18
❑ 97TopMayFR-19
❑ 97TopMayFR-20
❑ 97TopMayFR-21
❑ 97TopMayFR-22
❑ 97TopMayFR-23
❑ 97TopMayFR-24
❑ 97TopMayFR-25
❑ 97TopMayFR-26
❑ 97TopMayFR-27
❑ 98BowChrR-5
❑ 98BowChrRR-5
❑ 98SpollITaN-20
❑ 98SpollITaNA-5
❑ 98SpollITaNAR-5
❑ 98SpollITaNC-C5
❑ 98SpollITaNEE-20
❑ 98SpollITaNGS-24
❑ 98SpollIWSFAE-1
❑ 98SpollIWSFAEG-1
❑ 99SpollIGotG-24
❑ 99SpollIGotGA-47
❑ 99SpollIGotGC-6
❑ 99UppDecAP-WM
❑ 99UppDecAPH5AU-WMAU
❑ 99UppDecCL-2
❑ 99UppDecCL-122
❑ 99UppDecCLA-1950
❑ 99UppDecCLCC-2
❑ 99UppDecCLCC-122
❑ 99UppDecCLESC-WM
❑ 99UppDecCLJotC-AC3
❑ 99UppDecR-103
❑ 99UppDecRG-103
❑ 99UppDecRP-103
Mayse, Gary
❑ 91CliGiaC-15
Maysey, Matt
❑ 85SpoIndC-13
❑ 86ChaRaiP-15
❑ 87ChaRaiP-14
❑ 88WicPilRD-43
❑ 89LasVegSC-6
❑ 89LasVegSP-5
❑ 90CMC-505
❑ 90LasVegSC-3
❑ 90LasVegSP-116
❑ 90ProAAAF-4
❑ 91HarSenLD-264
❑ 91HarSenP-623
❑ 91LinDriAA-264
❑ 92DonRoo-71
❑ 92IndIndF-1855
❑ 92IndIndS-187
❑ 92SkyAAAF-92
❑ 93LinVenB-183
❑ 93NewOrlZF-968
❑ 93Sco-316
❑ 94BreMilB-154
❑ 94Sco-610
❑ 94ScoGolR-610
Mayumi, Akinobu
❑ 87JapPlaB-23
Mazeroski, Bill
❑ 47Exh-153A
❑ 47Exh-153B
❑ 56PirTeal-17
❑ 57Kah-21
❑ 57PirTeal-6
❑ 57Top-24
❑ 58Hir-36
❑ 58JayPubA-12
❑ 58Kah-19
❑ 58PirTeal-6
❑ 58Top-238
❑ 59Baz-16
❑ 59Kah-21
❑ 59Top-415
❑ 59Top-555
❑ 60Kah-25
❑ 60MacSta-14
❑ 60PirJayP-9
❑ 60PirTag-9
❑ 60Top-55
❑ 60TopVen-55
❑ 61Baz-24
❑ 61Kah-27
❑ 61NuSco-403
❑ 61PirJayP-8
❑ 61PirRigF-6
❑ 61Pos-128A
❑ 61Pos-128B
❑ 61Top-312
❑ 61Top-430
❑ 61Top-571
❑ 61TopDicG-10
❑ 61TopStal-67
❑ 62AurRec-13
❑ 62Jel-170
❑ 62Kah-27
❑ 62Pos-170
❑ 62PosCan-170
❑ 62SalPlaC-131
❑ 62ShiPlaC-131
❑ 62Top-353
❑ 62Top-391
❑ 62TopStal-179
❑ 63Baz-6
❑ 63ExhStaB-45
❑ 63Fle-59
❑ 63Jel-138
❑ 63Kah-21
❑ 63PirIDL-13
❑ 63PirJayP-9
❑ 63Pos-138
❑ 63SalMetC-14
❑ 63Top-323
❑ 63TopStil-28
❑ 64ChatheY-36
❑ 64Kah-17
❑ 64PirKDK-17
❑ 64Top-570
❑ 64TopCoi-27
❑ 64TopCoi-143
❑ 64TopSta-40
❑ 64TopStaU-49
❑ 64TopTatl-54
❑ 65ChaTheY-36
❑ 65Kah-25
❑ 65OldLonC-15
❑ 65OPC-95
❑ 65Top-95
❑ 65TopEmbl-23
❑ 65TopTral-59
❑ 66Kah-19
❑ 66PirEasH-9
❑ 66Top-210
❑ 66TopRubl-61
❑ 66TopVen-210
❑ 67AshOil-7
❑ 67CokCapA-27
❑ 67CokCapNLA-28
❑ 67CokCapPi-6
❑ 67DexPre-136
❑ 67Kah-23A
❑ 67Kah-23B
❑ 67PirTeal-11
❑ 67Top-510
❑ 67TopPirS-14
❑ 67TopVen-313
❑ 68Baz-7
❑ 68DexPre-52
❑ 68Kah-A9
❑ 68Kah-B23
❑ 68PirKDK-9
❑ 68PirTeal-11
❑ 68Top-390
❑ 68TopActS-1A
❑ 68TopActS-14A
❑ 69Kah-B14
❑ 69MilBra-175
❑ 69MLBOffS-187
❑ 69PirGre-6
❑ 69PirJacitB-6
❑ 69PirTeal-15
❑ 69Top-335
❑ 69TopSta-88
❑ 69TopTeaP-16
❑ 69TraSta-60
❑ 70DayDaiNM-138
❑ 70MLBOffS-103
❑ 70OPC-440
❑ 70PirTeal-11
❑ 70Top-440
❑ 70TopCanL-13
❑ 71BazNumT-3
❑ 71MLBOffS-208
❑ 71OPC-110
❑ 71PirActP-19
❑ 71PirArc-6
❑ 71Top-110
❑ 71TopCoi-15
❑ 71TopTat-90
❑ 72MilBra-215
❑ 72Top-760
❑ 73OPC-517
❑ 73Top-517A
❑ 73Top-517B
❑ 74OPC-489
❑ 74Top-489
❑ 76LauDiaJ-6
❑ 76UPIS-10
❑ 77GalGloG-261
❑ 77PirTCM1WC-3
❑ 78TCM60I-62
❑ 80PirGreT-2
❑ 86PirGreT-2
❑ 87Pir196T-2
❑ 88PacLegI-60
❑ 89SweBasG-67
❑ 89TopBasT-19
❑ 90HOFStiB-62
❑ 90PacLeg-39
❑ 90SweBasG-93
❑ 91Col-24
❑ 91LinDri-13
❑ 91MDAA-4
❑ 91SweBasG-60
❑ 92ActPacA-69
❑ 92MVP-17
❑ 92MVP2H-14
❑ 93TedWil-78
❑ 93UppDecAH-92
❑ 94TedWil-79
❑ 94UppDecAH-8
❑ 94UppDecAH-76
❑ 94UppDecAH-118
❑ 94UppDecAH1-8
❑ 94UppDecAH1-76
❑ 94UppDecAH1-118
❑ 94UppDecS-5
❑ 94UppDecS-8
❑ 94UppDecTAE-66
❑ 95SkiBra-2
❑ 97FleMilDM-9
❑ 97FleMilDMR-9
❑ 98SpollIWSF-21
❑ 98SpollIWSFEE-21
❑ 98SpollIWSFFE-21
❑ 99UppDecCLES-BM
❑ 99UppDecCLESC-BM
❑ 99UppDecCLMS-HR5
Mazey, Randy
❑ 88BurIndP-1776
❑ 89MiaMirIS-13
Mazion, Rodney
❑ 93PitMetC-14
❑ 93PitMetF-3724
Mazone, Brian
❑ 98EugEme-18
Mazur, Bob
❑ 77SalPirT-14
Mazurek, Brian
❑ 96NewJerCB-18
❑ 97PriWilC-19
Mazurek, Danny
❑ 52LavPro-18
Mazzella, Joe
❑ 72CedRapCT-22
Mazzilli, Lee
❑ 77MetDaiPA-15
❑ 77Spo-8712
❑ 77Top-488
❑ 78MetDaiPA-16
❑ 78OPC-26
❑ 78Top-147
❑ 79BasPat-53
❑ 79Hos-7
❑ 79Kel-42
❑ 79OPC-183
❑ 79Top-355
❑ 80Kel-38
❑ 80OPC-11
❑ 80Top-25
❑ 80TopSup-8
❑ 81AllGamPI-154
❑ 81CokTeaS-90
❑ 81Don-34
❑ 81Dra-33
❑ 81Fle-316
❑ 81FleStiC-42
❑ 81Kel-46
❑ 81MSAMinD-22
❑ 81OPC-167
❑ 81Squ-21
❑ 81Top-510
❑ 81TopScr-75
❑ 81TopSti-191
❑ 81TopSupHT-75
❑ 82Don-49
❑ 82Fle-533
❑ 82FleSta-90
❑ 82OnDecD-22
❑ 82OPC-243
❑ 82Top-465
❑ 82TopSti-67
❑ 82TopTra-68T
❑ 83Don-638
❑ 83Fle-387
❑ 83FleSta-120
❑ 83FleSti-40
❑ 83OPC-306
❑ 83Top-685
❑ 83TopTra-67T
❑ 84Don-166
❑ 84Fle-255
❑ 84JacMetF-8
❑ 84Nes792-225
❑ 84OPC-225
❑ 84Pir-11
❑ 84Top-225
❑ 84TopTif-225
❑ 85Don-386
❑ 85Fle-469
❑ 85OPC-323
❑ 85Pir-11
❑ 85Top-748
❑ 85TopMin-748
❑ 85TopTif-748
❑ 86Don-288
❑ 86Fle-612
❑ 86MetWorSC-13
❑ 86OPC-373
❑ 86Top-578
❑ 86TopTif-578
❑ 87Don-562
❑ 87Fle-15
❑ 87FleGlo-15
❑ 87MetColP-6
❑ 87Top-198
❑ 87TopTif-198
❑ 88Don-614
❑ 88DonBasB-209
❑ 88DonTeaBM-614
❑ 88Lea-223
❑ 88MetColP-35
❑ 88MetKah-13
❑ 88OPC-308
❑ 88Sco-158A
❑ 88Sco-158B
❑ 88ScoGlo-158A
❑ 88ScoGlo-158B
❑ 88StaLinMe-13
❑ 88Top-308
❑ 88TopTif-308
❑ 89MetColP-12
❑ 89MetKah-17
❑ 89Sco-217
❑ 89Top-58
❑ 89TopTif-58
❑ 89UppDec-657
❑ 90BasWit-8
❑ 90Don-584
❑ 90Fle-88
❑ 90FleCan-88
❑ 90OPC-721
❑ 90PubIntS-139
❑ 90Sco-459
❑ 90Top-721
❑ 90TopTif-721
❑ 91MetWIZ-256
❑ 92YanWIZ8-114
❑ 93RanKee-252
❑ 97TamYan-1
❑ 98TamYanM-1
Mazzone, Leo
❑ 75TucTorC-15
❑ 75TucTorTI-10
❑ 79SavBraT-17
❑ 83DurBulT-29
❑ 84DurBulT-9
❑ 85BraPol-52
❑ 86SumBraP-19
❑ 87GreBraB-2
❑ 87SouLeaAJ-25
❑ 88RicBraC-24
❑ 88RicBraP-16
❑ 89RicBraBC-15
❑ 89RicBraC-24
❑ 89RicBraP-833
❑ 89RicBraTI-25
❑ 90BraDubS-21
❑ 90CMC-278
❑ 90ProAAAF-421
❑ 90RicBraC-2
❑ 90RicBraP-276
❑ 90RicBraTI-21
❑ 91BraSubS-24
❑ 92BraLykS-22
❑ 93BraLykS-22
❑ 94BraLykP-20
❑ 94BraLykS-20
Mazzone, Tony
❑ 94IdaFalBF-3580
❑ 94IdaFalBSP-13
❑ 95EugEmeTI-25
Mazzotti, Mauro
❑ 89BelMarL-31
McAbee, Monte R.
❑ 82MadMusF-15
❑ 82WesHavAT-15
❑ 83GleFalWST-4
McAdams, Dennis
❑ 94AshTouC-16
❑ 94AshTouF-1776
McAfee, Bill
❑ 28LaPre-23
McAfee, Bret
❑ 82WauTimF-13
McAfee, Josh
❑ 97SouBenSH-17
❑ 98LetBlaDG-19
McAleer, James
❑ 04FanCraAL-34
❑ 09PC7HHB-31
❑ 09RamT20-74
❑ 09SpoNewSM-17
❑ 11SpoLifCW-236
❑ 11SpoLifM-127
❑ 74CapPub-16
❑ 87OldJudN-321
❑ 98CamPepP-49
McAleese, John
❑ 09T206-233
❑ 11PinT-5-118
McAllester, Bill
❑ 14B18B-32A
❑ 14B18B-32B
McAllister, Sport (Lewis)
❑ 03BreE10-95
❑ 08BufBisFJO-8
❑ 11SpoLifCW-237
❑ 11T205-194
❑ 12ColRedB-181
❑ 12ColTinT-181
❑ 12ImpTobC-57
McAllister, Steve
❑ 83DayBeaAT-21
❑ 85NasPirT-17
❑ 86NasPirP-18
McAllister, Troy
❑ 92EugEmeC-18
❑ 92EugEmeF-3037
McAlpin, Mike
❑ 88St.CatBJP-2015
❑ 89St.CatBJP-2093
❑ 90St.CatBJP-3483
❑ 91KnoBluJLD-375
❑ 91KnoBluJP-1785
❑ 91LinDriAA-375
❑ 92KnoBluJF-3007
❑ 93KnoSmoF-1266
McAnally, Ernie
❑ 71OPC-376
❑ 71Top-376
❑ 72Dia-32
❑ 72OPC-58
❑ 72ProStaP-8
❑ 72Top-58
❑ 73OPC-484
❑ 73Top-484
❑ 74ExpWes-7
❑ 74OPC-322
❑ 74Top-322
❑ 75OPC-318
❑ 75Top-318
❑ 75TopMin-318
McAnany, Jim
❑ 81WhiSox1T-5
❑ 88PalSprACLC-104
❑ 88PalSprAP-1452
McAnany, Michele
❑ 95ColSilB-18
❑ 96ColSilB-18
McAnarney, James
❑ 87LitFalMP-2388
❑ 88ColMetGS-8
McAndrew, Jamie
❑ 89GreFalDSP-5
❑ 90BakDodCLC-237
❑ 90CalLeaACLC-22
❑ 91AlbDukLD-15
❑ 91AlbDukP-1138
❑ 91Bow-601
❑ 91LinDriAAA-15
❑ 92AlbDukS-14
❑ 92Bow-591
❑ 92ProFS7-242
❑ 92SanAntMF-3971
❑ 92SkyAAAF-6
❑ 92UppDecML-197
❑ 93Don-774
❑ 93NewOrlZF-969
❑ 93Top-412
❑ 93TopGol-412
❑ 93TopInaM-412
❑ 93TopInaR-412
❑ 93TopMic-412
❑ 94NewOrlZF-1465
❑ 97TucTorB-7
McAndrew, Jim (James)
❑ 69MetNewYDN-13
❑ 69Top-321
❑ 69TopTeaP-24
❑ 70DayDaiNM-147
❑ 70OPC-246
❑ 70Top-246
❑ 71MetTeal-14
❑ 71MetTealA-4
❑ 71MLBOffS-160
❑ 71OPC-428
❑ 71Top-428
❑ 72Top-781
❑ 73LinPor-117
❑ 73OPC-436
❑ 73Top-436
❑ 89MetRinP69-20
❑ 91MetWIZ-257
❑ 94Met69CCPP-24
❑ 94Met69CS-23
❑ 94Met69T-24
McAninch, John
❑ 95BoiHawTI-23
❑ 96CedRapKTI-16
❑ 97LakElsSG-21
McArdle, Harry
❑ 10BisCoaLE99-17
❑ 11PacCoaBD-38
❑ 11Zee-90
❑ 12HomRunKE-66
❑ 12Zee-116
❑ 13Zee-115
❑ 14Zee-141
McArdle, Roy
❑ 09ObaT21-54
❑ 09ObaT21-161
❑ 09ObaT21-325
❑ 12ObaPreT-74
McArn, Brian
❑ 90NebCor-15
❑ 96VerExpB-3
❑ 98ModA'sG-19
McArthur, Kennon
❑ 98MarPhiG-22
❑ 99TeaBesR-55
❑ 99TeaBesRG-55
❑ 99TeaBesRS-55
McAulay, John
❑ 95HudValRTI-22
McAuley, James
❑ 20Zee-14
❑ 21Zee-15
❑ 22Zee-12
❑ 23Zee-15
❑ 24Zee-13
McAuliffe, David
❑ 89GreHorP-411
❑ 89SouAtlLAGS-32
❑ 90CedRapRB-22
❑ 90CedRapRP-2320
❑ 90MidLeaASGS-41
❑ 90ProAaA-123
❑ 91ChaLooLD-162
❑ 91ChaLooP-1956
❑ 91LinDriAA-162
❑ 91WavRedF-2
McAuliffe, Dick
❑ 62Top-527
❑ 63Jel-48
❑ 63Pos-48

❑ 63Top-64
❑ 64TigLid-10
❑ 64Top-363
❑ 64TopVen-363
❑ 65OPC-53
❑ 65TigJayP-10
❑ 65Top-53
❑ 66TigVolC-8
❑ 66Top-495
❑ 66TopRubl-62
❑ 67CokCapTi-6
❑ 67DexPre-137
❑ 67OPC-170
❑ 67TigDexP-6
❑ 67Top-170
❑ 67TopVen-241
❑ 68CokCapT-6
❑ 68Kah-B24
❑ 68TigDetFPB-11
❑ 68Top-285
❑ 68TopVen-285
❑ 69MilBra-176
❑ 69MLBOffS-51
❑ 69OPC-169
❑ 69TigTeal-7
❑ 69TigTealC-11
❑ 69Top-169
❑ 69Top-305
❑ 69TopFou-23
❑ 69TopSta-176
❑ 69TopTeaP-1
❑ 70MLBOffS-211
❑ 70OPC-475
❑ 70Top-475
❑ 71MLBOffS-399
❑ 71OPC-3
❑ 71Top-3
❑ 71TopCoi-10
❑ 71TopTat-75
❑ 72MilBra-216
❑ 72Top-725
❑ 73LinPor-74
❑ 73OPC-349
❑ 73TigJew-13
❑ 73Top-349
❑ 74OPC-495
❑ 74Top-495
❑ 78TCM60I-94
❑ 81TigDetN-134
❑ 88TigDom-14
❑ 89SweBasG-14
McAuliffe, Jack
❑ 23Zee-16
McAvoy, Charles
❑ 15Zee-41
McAvoy, George
❑ 12Zee-117
McAvoy, Thomas
❑ 60Lea-108
McBean, Al (Alvin)
❑ 62Top-424
❑ 63Jel-146
❑ 63PirIDL-14
❑ 63Pos-146
❑ 63Top-387
❑ 64Kah-18
❑ 64PirKDK-18
❑ 64Top-525
❑ 64TopCoi-66
❑ 64TopSta-17
❑ 65Kah-26
❑ 65OPC-25
❑ 65Top-25
❑ 65TopEmbl-14
❑ 66PirEasH-34
❑ 66Top-353
❑ 66TopVen-353
❑ 67CokCapPi-1
❑ 67PirTeal-12
❑ 67Top-203
❑ 67TopPirS-12
❑ 67TopVen-301
❑ 68PirKDK-34
❑ 68PirTeal-12
❑ 68Top-514
❑ 69MilBra-177
❑ 69OPC-14
❑ 69Top-14
❑ 69TopSta-96
❑ 69TopTeaP-12
❑ 70Top-641
❑ 72MilBra-217
❑ 81TCM60I-435
❑ 90DodTar-496
McBean, Douglas
❑ 52LavPro-71
McBride, Bake
❑ 74OPC-601
❑ 74Top-601
❑ 75Hos-41
❑ 75Kel-13
❑ 75OPC-174
❑ 75St.LouCP-17
❑ 75Top-174
❑ 75TopMin-174
❑ 76BlaDis-34
❑ 76BucDis-34
❑ 76CarDis-34
❑ 76CraDis-34
❑ 76DailsID-34
❑ 76Hos-93
❑ 76IsaDis-34
❑ 76OPC-135
❑ 76OrbDis-34
❑ 76RedBarD-34
❑ 76SafDis-34
❑ 76SSP-277
❑ 76St.LouCP-20
❑ 76Top-135
❑ 76TowCluD-34
❑ 77BurCheD-17
❑ 77Hos-97
❑ 77Kel-34
❑ 77RCColC-40
❑ 77Top-516
❑ 78OPC-156
❑ 78RCColC-26
❑ 78SSP270-53
❑ 78Top-340
❑ 78WifBalD-47
❑ 79OPC-332
❑ 79PhiBurK-21
❑ 79PhiTeal-6
❑ 79Top-630
❑ 80OPC-257
❑ 80PhiBul-37
❑ 80PhiBurK-9
❑ 80Top-495
❑ 81AllGamPI-155
❑ 81CokTeaS-102
❑ 81Don-404
❑ 81Fle-9
❑ 81FleStiC-31
❑ 81OPC-90
❑ 81Top-90
❑ 81TopScr-58
❑ 81TopSti-202
❑ 81TopSupHT-84
❑ 82Don-497
❑ 82Fle-250
❑ 82Ind-24
❑ 82IndWhe-26
❑ 82OPC-92
❑ 82Top-745
❑ 82TopTra-69T
❑ 83Fle-414
❑ 83IndPos-22
❑ 83IndWhe-21
❑ 83OPC-248
❑ 83Top-248
❑ 83TopFol-3
❑ 84Fle-547
❑ 84Nes792-569
❑ 84OPC-81
❑ 84Top-569
❑ 84TopSti-256
❑ 84TopTif-569
❑ 89PacSenL-19
❑ 89PacSenL-201
❑ 89T/MSenL-74
❑ 90EliSenL-58
❑ 92CarMcD-44
McBride, Charles
❑ 93IdaFalBF-4040
❑ 93IdaFalBSP-4
McBride, Chris
❑ 94SigRooDP-71
❑ 94SigRooDPS-71
❑ 94St.CatBJC-1
❑ 94St.CatBJF-3641
❑ 94StaCluDP-42
❑ 94StaCluDPFDI-42
❑ 95HagSunF-65
❑ 96StCatSB-19
❑ 97DunBluJTI-20
❑ 98KnoSG-13
McBride, Gator
❑ 95DurBulTI-21
❑ 96DurBulBIB-7
❑ 96DurBulBrB-8
❑ 96GreBraB-19
❑ 96GreBraTI-2
❑ 97GreBraG-20
McBride, George
❑ 08AmeCarE91-84
❑ 08RosComP-82
❑ 09ColChiE-182
❑ 09SenBarP-7
❑ 09T206-234
❑ 10CouT21-44
❑ 10DomDisP-78
❑ 10SenWasT-3
❑ 10SweCapPP-61
❑ 11HelSta-74
❑ 11MecDFT-19
❑ 11PinT-5-568
❑ 11SpoLifM-128
❑ 11T205-111
❑ 11TurRedT-110
❑ 12ColRedB-182
❑ 12ColTinT-182
❑ 12HasTriFT-58
❑ 12HasTriFT-59
❑ 12T207-115
❑ 14B18B-42
❑ 14FatPlaT-31
❑ 14PieStaT-69
❑ 14TexTomE-31
❑ 15SpoNewM-113
❑ 16BF2FP-49
❑ 16SpoNewM-115
❑ 17ColE13-111
❑ 17HolBreD-66
❑ 23WilChoV-90
McBride, Ivan
❑ 88WatIndP-677
McBride, Jason
❑ 98GreBatM-10
McBride, Ken
❑ 47Exh-154
❑ 60Top-276
❑ 61Top-209
❑ 62Baz-25
❑ 62SalPlaC-91A
❑ 62SalPlaC-91B
❑ 62ShiPlaC-91
❑ 62Top-268
❑ 62TopBuc-58
❑ 62TopStal-66
❑ 63AngJayP-8
❑ 63ExhStaB-46
❑ 63Jel-33
❑ 63Pos-33
❑ 63SalMetC-41
❑ 63Top-510
❑ 64Baz-4
❑ 64ChatheY-37
❑ 64Top-405
❑ 64TopCoi-52
❑ 64TopSta-89
❑ 64TopStaU-50
❑ 64TopTatI-55
❑ 64WheSta-30
❑ 65AngMatSA-3
❑ 65ChaTheY-37
❑ 65OPC-268
❑ 65Top-268
❑ 65TopEmbl-30
❑ 81WhiSox1T-37
McBride, Loy
❑ 89VisOakCLC-107
❑ 89VisOakP-1449
❑ 90St.LucMS-16
❑ 91LinDriAA-637
❑ 91WilBilLD-637
❑ 91WilBilP-308
McBride, Rodney
❑ 96ForWayWB-15
❑ 97ForWayW-20
McBride, Thomas
❑ 47SenGunBP-7
❑ 49Bow-74
❑ 75RedSox1T-24
❑ 79DiaGre-237
McCabe, Bill
❑ 22Zee-13
❑ 23Zee-17
❑ 90DodTar-1020
McCabe, Brett
❑ 93GenCubC-20
❑ 93GenCubF-3185
McCabe, James
❑ 11MecDFT-41
McCabe, Joseph
❑ 64Top-564
❑ 65OPC-181
❑ 65Top-181
McCabe, R. J.
❑ 23Zee-111
❑ 25Zee-94
❑ 27Zee-5
❑ 28Zee-13
❑ 29Zee-7
McCabe, Timothy
❑ 18Zee-64
McCafferty, Charles
❑ 07NewEveWS-8
McCaffery, Dennis
❑ 92QuaCitRBC-16
❑ 92QuaCitRBF-822
❑ 93PalSprAC-13
❑ 93PalSprAF-82
McCahan, Bill
❑ 47A'sTeal-21
❑ 48A'sTeal-17
❑ 48Bow-31
❑ 49Bow-80
❑ 49PhiBul-36
McCain, Marcus
❑ 97St.PetDR-22
❑ 97St.PetDRUB-22
❑ 97Top-472
❑ 98Bow-195
❑ 98BowChr-195
❑ 98BowChrGA-195
❑ 98BowChrGAR-195
❑ 98BowChrI-195
❑ 98BowChrIR-195
❑ 98BowChrR-195
❑ 98BowGolA-195
❑ 98BowInt-195
❑ 98Top-501
❑ 98TopChr-501
❑ 98TopChrR-501
❑ 98TopDevR-501
❑ 98TopDia-501
❑ 98TopMiniC-501
McCain, Mike
❑ 83OrlTwiT-7
❑ 83TolMudHT-27
McCall, Brian
❑ 77FriOneYW-79
McCall, Dutch (Robert)
❑ 47SigOil-30
❑ 49Lea-57
McCall, Larry
❑ 78TacYanC-29
❑ 79TucTorT-23
❑ 80TacTigT-8
❑ 91KanCouCC-27
❑ 91KanCouCP-2676
❑ 91KanCouCTI-26
❑ 92KanCouCC-27
❑ 92KanCouCF-109
❑ 92KanCouCTI-20
❑ 92YanWIZ7-107
❑ 93FreKeyC-28
❑ 93FreKeyF-1044
❑ 93RanKee-253
❑ 94FreKeyC-26
❑ 94FreKeyF-2632
❑ 96HigDesMB-2
❑ 97BowBay-2
❑ 98RocRedWQ-3
McCall, Rod
❑ 91Cla/Bes-175
❑ 91ColIndC-26
❑ 91ColIndP-1493
❑ 91SouAtlLAGP-SAL18
❑ 92ColRedC-22
❑ 92ColRedF-2398
❑ 93ClaGolF-13
❑ 93KinIndC-16
❑ 93KinIndF-2254
❑ 93KinIndTI-16
❑ 93SouAtlLAPI-24
❑ 94KinIndC-12
❑ 94KinIndF-2651
❑ 95BakBlaTI-2
❑ 96CanIndB-16
❑ 97BufBis-21
❑ 98IowCubQ-16
McCall, Travis
❑ 97SouBenSH-18
❑ 98SouBenSHM-19
McCall, Trey
❑ 85BenPhiC-15
❑ 87SpaPhiP-14
❑ 88ClePhiS-19
❑ 89ClePhiS-15
McCall, Windy (John)
❑ 53SanFraSTI-12
❑ 55GiaGolS-13
❑ 55Top-42
❑ 55TopDouH-87
❑ 56Top-44
❑ 57Top-291
❑ 59SeaPop-29
❑ 77RocRedWM-19
❑ 79TCM50-200
McCallum, John D.
❑ 75McCCob-14
McCalmont, James
❑ 94EliTwiC-12
❑ 94EliTwiF-3740
❑ 95ForMyeMTI-19
❑ 96FtMyeMB-19
McCament, Randy
❑ 85EveGialC-9
❑ 86FreGiaSB-11
❑ 87ShrCapP-16
❑ 88PhoFirC-9
❑ 88PhoFirP-71
❑ 89BlaYNPRWLU-15
❑ 89ShrCapP-1853
❑ 90CMC-529
❑ 90Fle-64
❑ 90FleCan-64
❑ 90OPC-361
❑ 90PhoFirC-2
❑ 90PhoFirP-8
❑ 90ProAAAF-34
❑ 90Sco-580
❑ 90Top-361
❑ 90TopDeb89-77
❑ 90TopTif-361
❑ 90UppDec-657
McCann, Brian
❑ 82AleDukT-19
❑ 83LynPirT-25
❑ 86WauTimP-14
❑ 87PitCubP-6
❑ 88EasLeaAP-49
❑ 88PitCubP-1364
❑ 89ChaKniTI-23
❑ 90CMC-100
❑ 90IowCubC-25
McCann, Emmett
❑ 22Zee-49
❑ 23Zee-71
❑ 24Zee-51
❑ 25Zee-47
❑ 33WorCig(-57
McCann, Frank
❑ 77JacSunT-14
❑ 82BirBarT-19
McCann, Gene
❑ 90DodTar-1021
McCann, Joe
❑ 79NewCoPT-12
❑ 89PitMetS-17
❑ 90ColMetGS-6
❑ 90ColMetPPI-5
❑ 91St.LucMC-19
❑ 91St.LucMP-706
❑ 92St.LucMCB-9
❑ 92St.LucMF-1744
❑ 93WinSpiC-14
❑ 93WinSpiF-1567
McCardell, Roger
❑ 52LavPro-52
McCarl, George
❑ 13Zee-116
McCarren, Bill
❑ 25Zee-32
❑ 90DodTar-497
McCarter, Edward
❑ 86SanJosBP-12
McCarter, Jason Ray
❑ 97AubDouTI-8
❑ 98QuaCitRBG-16
McCarthy, Alex
❑ 09ColChiE-183
❑ 12ColRedB-183
❑ 12ColTinT-183
❑ 12T207-116
McCarthy, Dave
❑ 75AndRanT-20
❑ 76AshTouT-10
❑ 77AshTouT-14
McCarthy, Drew
❑ 96BatCliTI-28
❑ 98PeoChiM-30
McCarthy, Greg
❑ 87UtiBluSP-33
❑ 88SpaPhiP-1028
❑ 88SpaPhiS-13
❑ 89SpaPhiP-1034
❑ 89SpaPhiS-17
❑ 90ClePhiS-13
❑ 92KinIndC-21
❑ 92KinIndF-2471
❑ 93CanIndF-2836
❑ 93KinIndC-17
❑ 93KinIndF-2244
❑ 93KinIndTI-17
❑ 94CanIndF-3118
❑ 97PacPriGotD-GD90
❑ 97UppDecMP-P11
❑ 98PacInvGems-95
McCarthy, J.D.
❑ 86SpoDesJM-1
McCarthy, Jack (John Arthur)
❑ 03BreE10-96
❑ 11SpoLifCW-238
❑ 90DodTar-498
McCarthy, Joe
❑ 11PinT-5-1113
❑ 30ChiEveAP-7
❑ 30CubTeal-12
❑ 36GouWidPPR-A117
❑ 38OurNatGPP-19
❑ 43YanSta-18
❑ 48RedSoxTI-15
❑ 49RedSoxTI-14
❑ 50CubGreB-13
❑ 50RedSoxTI-13
❑ 53ArtHaloFP-59
❑ 68LauWorS-40
❑ 75TCMAllG-22
❑ 75YanDyn1T-33
❑ 76ShaPiz-83
❑ 77DanBurG-8
❑ 77GalGloG-70
❑ 80LauFamF-33
❑ 80PacLeg-58
❑ 80PerHaloFP-83
❑ 80SSPHOF-83
❑ 83TCMPla1942-4
❑ 84CubBriPC-8H
❑ 84CubUno-8
❑ 85TCMPhoC-5
❑ 86ConSer1-28
❑ 89HOFStiB-87
❑ 91ConTSN-28
❑ 92ConTSN-589
❑ 92YanWIZH-23
❑ 93ConTSN-823
❑ 93DiaStaES-143
❑ 93PinDiM-21
❑ 95ConTSN-1398
McCarthy, John A.
❑ 87OldJudN-323
McCarthy, John J.
❑ 36WorWidGV-53
❑ 40PlaBal-215
❑ 48GiaTeal-16
❑ 49Bow-220
❑ 72TCMthe3-49
❑ 93ConTSN-726
McCarthy, Kevin
❑ 97CapCitB-27
❑ 97PitMet-16
McCarthy, Shaun
❑ 76BurBeeT-21
❑ 80KnoBluJT-10
McCarthy, Steve
❑ 88BilMusP-1817
❑ 89CedRapRB-10
❑ 89CedRapRP-914
❑ 89CedRapRS-11
❑ 89Sta-192
❑ 90CedRapRP-2319
❑ 90ChaWheB-4
❑ 91ChaLooLD-163
❑ 91ChaLooP-1957
❑ 91LinDriAA-163
McCarthy, Thomas F.
❑ 07NewEveWS-9
❑ 39PC7AlbHoF-44
❑ 50CalHOFW-53
❑ 75FlePio-13
❑ 76ShaPiz-44
❑ 80PerHaloFP-44
❑ 80SSPHOF-44
❑ 87OldJudN-322
❑ 89DodSmoG-20
❑ 90DodTar-499
❑ 94OriofB-86
❑ 95May-21
McCarthy, Tom
❑ 53ArtHaloFP-60
❑ 72ClaCar-10
❑ 79ElmPioRST-8

❑ 80ElmPioRST-17
❑ 85PawRedST-17
❑ 86TidTidP-19
❑ 87JacMetF-5
❑ 87MetColP-39
❑ 87TidTidP-13
❑ 87TidTidT-6
❑ 88BlaYNPRWL-93
❑ 88MetColP-36
❑ 88TidTidCa-22
❑ 88TidTidCM-7
❑ 88TidTidP-1599
❑ 89TopTra-75T
❑ 89TopTraT-75T
❑ 89VanCanC-4
❑ 89VanCanP-593
❑ 90Fle-541
❑ 90FleCan-541
❑ 90OPC-326
❑ 90Sco100RS-57
❑ 90Top-326
❑ 90TopTif-326
❑ 91LinDriAAA-435
❑ 91RicBraBC-10
❑ 91RicBraLD-435
❑ 91RicBraP-2563
❑ 91RicBraTI-14
❑ 92RicBraBB-24
❑ 92RicBraF-372
❑ 92RicBraRC-10
❑ 92RicBraS-432
❑ 93ChaKniF-538
❑ 97RicBraBC-15

McCartney, Sommer
❑ 94ElmPioC-12
❑ 94ElmPioF-3478
❑ 95ElmPioTI-15
❑ 95ElmPioUTI-15
❑ 96KanCouCTI-18
❑ 97BreCouMB-22

McCartney, Steve
❑ 74SacSolC-58

McCarty, David
❑ 91Cla/Bes-400
❑ 91ClaDraP-3
❑ 91ClaGolB-BC18
❑ 91VisOakUP-1
❑ 91VisOakUP-3
❑ 92ClaBluBF-BC17
❑ 92ClaDraP-88
❑ 92ClaFS7-350
❑ 92ClaRedB-BC17
❑ 92DEL-AU2
❑ 92OrlSunRF-2860
❑ 92OrlSunRS-512
❑ 92ProFS7-95
❑ 92SkyAA F-220
❑ 92UppDec-75
❑ 92UppDecCPH-CP1
❑ 92UppDecML-47
❑ 92UppDecML-255
❑ 92UppDecMLTPHF-TP5
❑ 93Bow-369
❑ 93Bow-649
❑ 93ClaFisN-15
❑ 93ClaGolF-93
❑ 93ClaGolLF-1
❑ 93ClaGolP-2
❑ 93ClaYouG-YG9
❑ 93ExcFS7-202
❑ 93Fla-239
❑ 93FlaWavotF-9
❑ 93FleFinE-238
❑ 93FunPac-5
❑ 93FunPac-221
❑ 93LeaGolR-U3
❑ 93LeaGolRJ-U3
❑ 93PacSpa-524
❑ 93PorBeaF-2388
❑ 93SelRoo-45T
❑ 93SP-250
❑ 93StaClu-569
❑ 93StaCluFDI-569
❑ 93StaCluMOP-569
❑ 93TopFulS-12
❑ 93TopTra-17T
❑ 93Ult-586
❑ 93UppDec-450
❑ 93UppDec-462
❑ 93UppDecGold-450
❑ 93UppDecGold-462
❑ 94Bow-516
❑ 94ColC-194
❑ 94ColChoGS-194
❑ 94ColChoSS-194
❑ 94Don-281
❑ 94Fin-17
❑ 94FinJum-17
❑ 94FinRef-17
❑ 94Fle-213
❑ 94FUnPac-167
❑ 94Lea-78
❑ 94OPC-247
❑ 94OPCDiaD-7
❑ 94Pac-361
❑ 94Pin-333
❑ 94PinArtP-333
❑ 94PinMusC-333
❑ 94Sco-290
❑ 94ScoBoyoS-27
❑ 94ScoGolR-290
❑ 94Sel-154
❑ 94Spo-9
❑ 94StaClu-134
❑ 94StaCluFDI-134
❑ 94StaCluGR-134
❑ 94StaCluMOP-134
❑ 94Top-156
❑ 94TopGol-156
❑ 94TopSpa-156
❑ 94TriPla-256
❑ 94Ult-391
❑ 94UppDec-200
❑ 94UppDecED-200
❑ 95ColCho-485
❑ 95ColChoGS-485
❑ 95ColChoSS-485
❑ 95Don-217
❑ 95DonPreP-217
❑ 95FleUpd-61
❑ 95Lea-14
❑ 95Pac-252
❑ 95Pin-323
❑ 95PinArtP-323
❑ 95PinMusC-323
❑ 95Sel-12
❑ 95SelArtP-12
❑ 95StaClu-8
❑ 95StaCluFDI-8
❑ 95StaCluMOP-8
❑ 95StaCluSTWS-8
❑ 95Stu-65
❑ 95Top-98
❑ 95UppDec-427
❑ 95UppDecED-427
❑ 95UppDecEDG-427
❑ 96Fle-591
❑ 96FleTif-591
❑ 96GiaMot-21
❑ 96LeaSigA-150
❑ 96LeaSigAG-150
❑ 96LeaSigAS-150
❑ 96Sco-468
❑ 97Pac-445
❑ 97PacLigB-445
❑ 97PacSil-445
❑ 97PhoFirTI-15
❑ 98TacRaiQ-21

McCarty, G. Lewis
❑ 17ColE13-112
❑ 19W514-37
❑ 90DodTar-500
❑ 94ConTSN-1267
❑ 94ConTSNB-1267

McCarty, Matt
❑ 96GreFalDB-19
❑ 96GreFalDTI-29
❑ 96SanBerSB-17

McCarty, Scott
❑ 91MadMusC-10
❑ 91MadMusP-2127

McCarty, Tom
❑ 11MecDFT-31
❑ 12ImpTobC-89

McCarver, Tim
❑ 62KahAtl-13
❑ 62Top-167
❑ 62TopStal-186
❑ 62TopVen-167
❑ 63CarJayP-14
❑ 63Top-394
❑ 64CarTeal-6
❑ 64Top-429
❑ 64TopCoi-156
❑ 65CarJayP-6
❑ 65CarTeal-16
❑ 65ChaTheY-38
❑ 65OPC-136
❑ 65Top-136
❑ 65Top-294
❑ 65TopEmbl-7
❑ 66CarTeal-8
❑ 66Top-275
❑ 66TopRubl-63
❑ 66TopVen-275
❑ 67Top-485
❑ 67TopGiaSU-14
❑ 68Baz-3
❑ 68Top-275
❑ 68Top-376
❑ 68TopActS-6C
❑ 68TopGamI-18
❑ 68TopPla-20
❑ 68TopPos-19
❑ 68TopVen-275
❑ 69KelPin-13
❑ 69MilBra-178
❑ 69MLBOffS-214
❑ 69MLBPin-53
❑ 69OPC-164
❑ 69Top-164
❑ 69Top-475
❑ 69TopDecI-25
❑ 69TopFou-7
❑ 69TopSta-118
❑ 69TopSup-61
❑ 69TopTeaP-18
❑ 69TraSta-35
❑ 70Kel-34
❑ 70MLBOffS-92
❑ 70OPC-90
❑ 70PhiTeal-8
❑ 70Top-90
❑ 70TopCanL-15
❑ 70TopScr-13
❑ 70TopSup-23
❑ 71BazNumT-1
❑ 71MLBOffS-184
❑ 71OPC-465
❑ 71PhiArcO-8
❑ 71Top-465
❑ 71TopCoi-107
❑ 71TopGreM-25
❑ 71TopSup-34
❑ 72Dia-33
❑ 72MilBra-218
❑ 72OPC-139
❑ 72Top-139
❑ 73OPC-269
❑ 73Top-269
❑ 74OPC-520
❑ 74Top-520
❑ 74TopSta-115
❑ 75OPC-586
❑ 75PhiPhiP-22
❑ 75Top-586
❑ 75TopMin-586
❑ 76OPC-502
❑ 76PhiPhiP-19
❑ 76Top-502
❑ 77Top-357
❑ 78SSP270-48
❑ 78Top-235
❑ 79PhiBurK-3
❑ 79Top-675
❑ 80Top-178
❑ 81Fle-27
❑ 81TCM60I-386
❑ 83CarGreT-10
❑ 92CarMcD-36
❑ 92SkyAA F-300

McCaskill, Kirk
❑ 83RedPioT-19
❑ 85EdmTraC-7
❑ 86AngSmo-5
❑ 86Don-474
❑ 86Fle-163
❑ 86Top-628
❑ 86TopTif-628
❑ 87AngSmo-5
❑ 87CalAngPPS-25
❑ 87Don-381
❑ 87Fle-88
❑ 87FleGamW-27
❑ 87FleGlo-88
❑ 87FleHotS-29
❑ 87FleMin-67
❑ 87FleStiC-75
❑ 87GenMilB-3G
❑ 87Lea-223
❑ 87OPC-194
❑ 87SevCoi-W5
❑ 87Spo-127
❑ 87SpoTeaP-11
❑ 87Top-194
❑ 87TopSti-181
❑ 87TopTif-194
❑ 88AngSmo-12
❑ 88Don-381
❑ 88DonBasB-83
❑ 88Fle-496
❑ 88FleGlo-496
❑ 88PanSti-36
❑ 88Sco-552
❑ 88ScoGlo-552
❑ 88Spo-78
❑ 88StaLinAn-12
❑ 88Top-16
❑ 88TopBig-168
❑ 88TopClo-69
❑ 88TopTif-16
❑ 89Bow-38
❑ 89BowTif-38
❑ 89Don-136
❑ 89DonBasB-83
❑ 89Fle-483
❑ 89FleGlo-483
❑ 89OPC-348
❑ 89PanSti-285
❑ 89Sco-181
❑ 89Spo-214
❑ 89Top-421
❑ 89TopBig-149
❑ 89TopSti-184
❑ 89TopTif-421
❑ 89UppDec-223
❑ 90AngSmo-11
❑ 90Bow-283
❑ 90BowTif-283
❑ 90Don-170A
❑ 90Don-170B
❑ 90Fle-138
❑ 90FleCan-138
❑ 90Lea-247
❑ 90OPC-215
❑ 90PanSti-37
❑ 90PubIntS-373
❑ 90PubIntS-598
❑ 90Sco-217
❑ 90Sco100S-38
❑ 90Spo-169
❑ 90Top-215
❑ 90TopMinL-9
❑ 90TopSti-167
❑ 90TopTif-215
❑ 90UppDec-506
❑ 91AngSmo-10
❑ 91Don-637
❑ 91Fle-319
❑ 91Lea-199
❑ 91OPC-532
❑ 91Sco-590
❑ 91StaClu-313
❑ 91Stu-28
❑ 91Top-532
❑ 91TopDesS-532
❑ 91TopMic-532
❑ 91TopTif-532
❑ 91Ult-50
❑ 91UppDec-539
❑ 92Bow-2
❑ 92Don-340
❑ 92Fle-64
❑ 92Lea-517
❑ 92LeaBlaG-517
❑ 92OPC-301
❑ 92OPCPre-60
❑ 92Pin-391
❑ 92Sco-79
❑ 92ScoProP-18
❑ 92ScoRoo-29T
❑ 92StaClu-688
❑ 92StaCluECN-688
❑ 92Stu-155
❑ 92Top-301
❑ 92TopGol-301
❑ 92TopGolW-301
❑ 92TopMic-301
❑ 92TopTra-69T
❑ 92TopTraG-69T
❑ 92Ult-338
❑ 92UppDec-128
❑ 92UppDec-722
❑ 92WhiSoxK-25
❑ 93Don-227
❑ 93Fle-206
❑ 93Lea-151
❑ 93OPC-230
❑ 93PacSpa-392
❑ 93Pin-560
❑ 93Sco-469
❑ 93Sel-387
❑ 93StaClu-166
❑ 93StaCluFDI-166
❑ 93StaCluMOP-166
❑ 93Top-175
❑ 93TopGol-175
❑ 93TopInaM-175
❑ 93TopInaR-175
❑ 93TopMic-175
❑ 93TriPla-82
❑ 93Ult-535
❑ 93UppDec-608
❑ 93UppDecGold-608
❑ 93WhiSoxK-19
❑ 93WhiSoxSC-28
❑ 94Don-540
❑ 94Fla-34
❑ 94Fle-88
❑ 94Pac-133
❑ 94StaCluT-135
❑ 94StaCluTFDI-135
❑ 94Top-724
❑ 94TopGol-724
❑ 94TopSpa-724
❑ 94Ult-37
❑ 94WhiSoxK-21
❑ 95ColCho-496
❑ 95ColChoGS-496
❑ 95ColChoSS-496
❑ 95Don-425
❑ 95DonPreP-425
❑ 95Fle-125
❑ 95Sco-544
❑ 95ScoGolR-544
❑ 95ScoPlaTS-544
❑ 95Ult-32
❑ 95UltGolM-32
❑ 95WhiSoxK-21
❑ 96ColCho-511
❑ 96ColChoGS-511
❑ 96ColChoSS-511
❑ 96Fle-73
❑ 96FleTif-73

McCatty, Steve
❑ 78Top-701
❑ 80Top-231
❑ 81A'sGraG-54
❑ 81Don-478
❑ 81Fle-589
❑ 81OPC-59
❑ 81Top-503
❑ 82A'sGraG-10
❑ 82Don-35
❑ 82Fle-99
❑ 82FleSta-131
❑ 82OPC-113
❑ 82Top-113
❑ 82Top-156
❑ 82Top-165
❑ 82Top-167
❑ 82TopSti-10
❑ 82TopSti-14
❑ 82TopSti-228
❑ 83A'sGraG-54
❑ 83Don-491
❑ 83Fle-525
❑ 83Top-493
❑ 84A'sMot-8
❑ 84Don-420
❑ 84Fle-454
❑ 84Nes792-369
❑ 84OPC-369
❑ 84Top-369
❑ 84TopTif-369
❑ 85A'sMot-20
❑ 85Don-497
❑ 85Fle-430
❑ 85Top-63
❑ 85TopSti-324
❑ 85TopTif-63
❑ 86BufBisP-18
❑ 86Fle-427
❑ 86Top-624
❑ 86TopTif-624
❑ 87SanJosBP-26
❑ 89PacSenL-89
❑ 89T/MSenL-75
❑ 89TopSenL-110
❑ 91PacSenL-16
❑ 97WesMicW-3
❑ 98WesMicWM-12

McCauley, Drew
❑ 82BufBisT-4

McCawley, Bill
❑ 52MotCoo-11
❑ 53MotCoo-22
❑ 53SanFraSTI-13

McCawley, James
❑ 87OldJudN-324

McCerod, George
❑ 86PawRedSP-13

McCladdie, Tony
❑ 97PitMet-17

McClain, Charles
❑ 91BilMusP-3750
❑ 91BilMusSP-1
❑ 92ChaWheF-6
❑ 92ChaWVWC-2
❑ 93WinSpiC-15
❑ 93WinSpiF-1568

McClain, Joe
❑ 79QuaCitCT-8

McClain, Joe Sr.
❑ 61SenJayP-6
❑ 61Top-488
❑ 62SalPlaC-54
❑ 62ShiPlaC-54
❑ 62Top-324
❑ 62TopStal-98
❑ 63Top-311

McClain, Michael
❑ 82OrlTwiT-10
❑ 83MiaMarT-2
❑ 85BeaGolGT-12
❑ 86BeaGolGP-18

McClain, Ron
❑ 76IndIndTI-25
❑ 77IndIndTI-26
❑ 78IndIndTI-26
❑ 79IndIndTI-30
❑ 83ExpPos-18

McClain, Scott
❑ 92KanCouCC-10
❑ 92KanCouCF-100
❑ 92KanCouCTI-21
❑ 93CarLeaAGF-3
❑ 93FreKeyC-14
❑ 93FreKeyF-1032
❑ 94BowBayF-2419
❑ 94ExcFS7-12
❑ 94OriPro-60
❑ 95RocRedWTI-24
❑ 96Bow-245
❑ 96BowFoi-245
❑ 96FleUpd-U3
❑ 96FleUpdTC-U3
❑ 96RocRedWB-18
❑ 96Ult-306
❑ 96UltGolM-306
❑ 96UltGolP-13
❑ 96UltGolPHGM-13
❑ 97NorTid-22
❑ 97NorTidB-22
❑ 98DurBulTI-19
❑ 99SpoIll-50

McClain, Terrence
❑ 95YakBeaTI-20

McClaskey, Tim
❑ 98KanCouC-21
❑ 98KanCouCCP-21

McClatchy, Kevin
❑ 96ModA'sB-30

McClear, Michael
❑ 86Ft.LauYP-16

McClellan, Bobby
❑ 75AppFoxT-16

McClellan, Dan
❑ 74LauOldTBS-32

McClellan, Garth
❑ 85CloHSS-25

McClellan, Harvey
❑ 22E120-24
❑ 22W573-77
❑ 23WilChoV-91
❑ 75WhiSox1T-16

McClellan, Matt
❑ 98HagSunM-18

McClellan, Paul
❑ 86EveGiaC-2
❑ 86EveGiaPC-14
❑ 87CliGiaP-21
❑ 88ShrCapP-1290
❑ 89BlaYNPRWL-26
❑ 89ShrCapP-1850
❑ 90CMC-528
❑ 90PhoFirC-1
❑ 90PhoFirP-9
❑ 90ProAAAF-35
❑ 91LinDriAA-311
❑ 91Sco-726
❑ 91ShrCapLD-311
❑ 91ShrCapP-1817
❑ 91TopDeb90-102
❑ 92Cla1-T59
❑ 92Don-700

❑ 92Fle-642
❑ 92OPC-424
❑ 92PhoFirF-2817
❑ 92PhoFirS-388
❑ 92ProFS7-344
❑ 92Sco-703
❑ 92SkyAAAF-177
❑ 92StaClu-566
❑ 92Top-424
❑ 92TopGol-424
❑ 92TopGolW-424
❑ 92TopMic-424
❑ 92UppDec-563
McClellan, Sean
❑ 96MedHatBJTI-17
❑ 97HagSunB-11
❑ 98DunBluJTI-23
McClellan, William
❑ 87BucN28-14
❑ 87OldJudN-325
McClelland, Tim
❑ 88T/MUmp-46
❑ 89T/MUmp-44
❑ 90T/MUmp-42
McClendon, Lloyd
❑ 82LynMetT-16
❑ 83WatRedT-9
❑ 87FleUpd-74
❑ 87FleUpdG-74
❑ 87RedKah-23
❑ 88RedKah-30
❑ 88Top-172
❑ 88TopTif-172
❑ 89Bow-287
❑ 89BowTif-287
❑ 89CubMar-10
❑ 89Don-595
❑ 89DonBasB-228
❑ 89FleUpd-77
❑ 89IowCubC-12
❑ 89IowCubP-1695
❑ 89Sco-521
❑ 89Top-644
❑ 89TopTif-644
❑ 89TopTra-76T
❑ 89TopTraT-76T
❑ 89UppDec-446
❑ 90Bow-36
❑ 90BowTif-36
❑ 90CubMar-14
❑ 90Don-341
❑ 90DonBesN-134
❑ 90Fle-38
❑ 90FleCan-38
❑ 90OPC-337
❑ 90Sco-176A
❑ 90Sco-176B
❑ 90Top-337
❑ 90TopBig-5
❑ 90TopTif-337
❑ 90TopTVCu-32
❑ 90UppDec-398
❑ 91FleUpd-111
❑ 91StaClu-385
❑ 92Don-338
❑ 92Fle-560
❑ 92OPC-209
❑ 92PirNatl-15
❑ 92Sco-566
❑ 92StaClu-302
❑ 92Top-209
❑ 92TopGol-209
❑ 92TopGolW-209
❑ 92TopMic-209
❑ 92Ult-256
❑ 93Don-384
❑ 93Fle-502
❑ 93PacSpa-247
❑ 93PirHil-7
❑ 93PirNatl-17
❑ 93Sco-380
❑ 93StaClu-66
❑ 93StaCluFDI-66
❑ 93StaCluM-69
❑ 93StaCluMOP-66
❑ 93Top-81
❑ 93TopGol-81
❑ 93TopInaM-81
❑ 93TopInaR-81
❑ 93TopMic-81
❑ 93Ult-99
❑ 93UppDec-559
❑ 93UppDecGold-559
❑ 94Fle-613
❑ 94Pac-501
❑ 94PirQui-15
❑ 94StaClu-511
❑ 94StaCluFDI-511
❑ 94StaCluGR-511
❑ 94StaCluMOP-511
❑ 94Top-518
❑ 94TopGol-518
❑ 94TopSpa-518
❑ 97PirPos-25
McClendon, Travis
❑ 95NewJerCTI-17
❑ 96PeoChiB-19
❑ 97PeoChi-16
McClinic, Nath
❑ 92NegLeaRLI-41
McClinton, Patrick
❑ 93BenRocCB-16
❑ 93BenRocF-3264
❑ 94AshTouC-17
❑ 94AshTouF-1777
❑ 95AshTouUTI-21
❑ 96SalAvaB-20
McClinton, Tim
❑ 89KinMetS-16
❑ 90ColMetGS-3
❑ 90ColMetPPI-7
❑ 90PitMetP-10
❑ 91ColMetPI-21
❑ 91ColMetPPI-1
❑ 92St.LucMCB-21
❑ 92St.LucMF-1756
❑ 93St.LucMC-16
❑ 93St.LuMF-2934
McClochlin, Mike
❑ 91CollndP-1481
McCloskey, John
❑ 11SpoLifCW-239
McCloughan, Scot
❑ 90WicStaSGD-23
❑ 92St.CatBJC-20
❑ 92St.CatBJF-3398
❑ 93HagSunC-20
❑ 93HagSunF-1893
McClure, Bob (Robert)
❑ 76OmaRoyTT-13
❑ 76OPC-599
❑ 76SSP-182
❑ 76Top-599
❑ 77Top-472
❑ 78Top-243
❑ 79Top-623
❑ 80Top-357
❑ 81Don-510
❑ 81Fle-520
❑ 81OPC-156
❑ 81Top-156
❑ 82BrePol-10
❑ 82Top-487
❑ 83BreGar-10
❑ 83BrePol-10
❑ 83Don-582
❑ 83Fle-38
❑ 83FleSta-121
❑ 83FleSti-17
❑ 83Top-62
❑ 84BreGar-12
❑ 84BrePol-10
❑ 84Don-359
❑ 84Fle-206
❑ 84Nes792-582
❑ 84Top-582
❑ 84TopTif-582
❑ 85BreGar-12
❑ 85BrePol-10
❑ 85Don-536
❑ 85Fle-587
❑ 85Top-203
❑ 85TopTif-203
❑ 86BrePol-10
❑ 86Fle-494
❑ 86Top-684
❑ 86TopTif-684
❑ 86TopTra-71T
❑ 86TopTraT-71T
❑ 87ExpPos-14
❑ 87Fle-325
❑ 87FleGlo-325
❑ 87OPC-133
❑ 87Top-707
❑ 87TopTif-707
❑ 88Don-529
❑ 88ExpPos-20
❑ 88Fle-189
❑ 88FleGlo-189
❑ 88OPC-313
❑ 88Sco-381
❑ 88ScoGlo-381
❑ 88StaLinE-10
❑ 88Top-313
❑ 88TopTif-313
❑ 89Bow-43
❑ 89BowTif-43
❑ 89Fle-42
❑ 89FleGlo-42
❑ 89FleUpd-14
❑ 89Sco-572
❑ 89ScoRoo-58T
❑ 89Top-182
❑ 89TopTif-182
❑ 90AngSmo-20
❑ 90Don-470
❑ 90Fle-139
❑ 90FleCan-139
❑ 90OPC-458
❑ 90PubIntS-374
❑ 90Sco-117
❑ 90Top-458
❑ 90TopTif-458
❑ 90UppDec-81
❑ 91MetWIZ-258
❑ 91OPC-84
❑ 91Top-84
❑ 91TopDesS-84
❑ 91TopMic-84
❑ 91TopTif-84
❑ 92BreCarT-13
❑ 92Don-661
❑ 92Sco-717
❑ 92StaClu-484
❑ 93Fle-128
❑ 93MarlStaClu-3
❑ 93MarUSPC-5C
❑ 93PacSpa-467
❑ 93Sco-434
❑ 93Ult-383
❑ 94BreMilB-155
McClure, Brian
❑ 96IdaFalB-17
❑ 97CliLumG-18
❑ 98RanCucQG-19
❑ 98RanCucQG-19
McClure, Craig
❑ 94Top-79
❑ 94TopGol-79
❑ 94TopSpa-79
❑ 96AppLeaAB-6
❑ 96BriWhiSB-25
McClure, Jack
❑ 44CenFlo-17
❑ 65Top-553
McClure, Rich
❑ 79QuaCitCT-9
McClure, Todd
❑ 87AshTouP-21
❑ 87AubAstP-3
❑ 88FloStaLAS-12
❑ 88OscAstS-17
❑ 89KenTwiS-14
❑ 89Sta-52
❑ 89VisOakP-1436
McClurg, Clint
❑ 94MarPhiC-12
❑ 94MarPhiF-3288
❑ 95BatCliTI-21
McCollom, Jim
❑ 87QuaCitAP-21
❑ 88MidAngGS-22
❑ 88TexLeaAGS-27
McCollough, Adam
❑ 96BluOriB-18
McCollough, Mike
❑ 91GulCoaRSP-1
❑ 92GasRanC-22
McCollum, Greg
❑ 87ElmPioBC-23
❑ 87ElmPioRC-23
❑ 88LynRedSS-12
McCollum, Lou
❑ 47SunBre-11
McCommon, Jason
❑ 94VerExpC-17
❑ 94VerExpF-3908
❑ 96HarSenB-19
❑ 97HarSen-17
❑ 98BowBayM-22
McConachie, Dale
❑ 89AlbYanB-26
McConathy, Doug
❑ 91BluOriC-15
❑ 91BluOriP-4135
❑ 92FreKeyC-21
❑ 92FreKeyF-1812
❑ 93FreKeyC-15
❑ 93FreKeyF-1033
McConnell, Ambrose
❑ 08AmeCarE91-85
❑ 09BriE97-19
❑ 09ColChiE-184
❑ 09ColChiE-185
❑ 09RamT20-75
❑ 10E12AmeCDCE125-24
❑ 10W555-46
❑ 11HelSta-12
❑ 11S74Sil-6
❑ 11SpoLifCW-240
❑ 11SpoLifM-14A
❑ 11SpoLifM-14B
❑ 11T205-112
❑ 11TurRedT-29
❑ 12ColRedB-184
❑ 12ColRedB-185
❑ 12ColTinT-184
❑ 12ColTinT-185
❑ 12HasTriFT-4
❑ 12HasTriFT-41A
❑ 12HasTriFT-53
❑ 12HasTriFT-54
❑ 72ClaCar-11
McConnell, Chad
❑ 92Bow-587
❑ 92ClaDraP-10
❑ 92ClaDraPFB-BC10
❑ 92TopTra-70T
❑ 92TopTraG-70T
❑ 92UppDecML-8
❑ 93Bow-132
❑ 93ClaFS7-245
❑ 93ClePhiF-2696
❑ 93PhiStaC-4
❑ 93StaCluM-35
❑ 93StaCluM-81
❑ 93Top-161
❑ 93TopGol-161
❑ 93TopInaM-161
❑ 93TopInaR-161
❑ 93TopMic-161
❑ 93UppDec-439
❑ 93UppDecGold-439
❑ 94Cla-21
❑ 94ClePhiC-19
❑ 94ClePhiF-2541
❑ 94SigRoo-39
❑ 94SigRooS-39
❑ 94UppDecML-39
❑ 95ReaPhiELC-27
❑ 95ReaPhiTI-14
❑ 96ReaPhiB-24
McConnell, George N.
❑ 08BufBisFJO-9
McConnell, Jason
❑ 98ForWayW!-6
McConnell, Sam
❑ 97EriSeaWB-26
❑ 98AugGreM-22
McConnell, Tim
❑ 92FayGenF-2171
❑ 93LakTigC-16
❑ 93LakTigF-1314
❑ 94LakTigC-15
❑ 94LakTigF-3039
❑ 94TreThuF-2122
McConnell, Walt
❑ 86FloStaLAP-34
❑ 86VerBeaDP-17
❑ 87SanAntDTI-14
❑ 88SanAntMB-16
❑ 89AlbDukCm-21
❑ 89AlbDukP-83
❑ 90AlbDukCm-28
❑ 90AlbDukP-353
❑ 90AlbDukTr-22
❑ 90CMC-658
❑ 90ProAAAF-74
❑ 91AlbDukP-1148
❑ 91MidAngOHP-19
❑ 92MidAngF-4033
❑ 92MidAngS-465
McCool, Bill
❑ 64Top-356
❑ 64TopRooAB-31
❑ 64TopVen-356
❑ 65Kah-27
❑ 65OPC-18
❑ 65RedEnq-18
❑ 65Top-18
❑ 66Kah-20
❑ 66RedVolC-8
❑ 66Top-459
❑ 67CokCapR-14
❑ 67DexPre-138
❑ 67Kah-24
❑ 67Top-353
❑ 67TopVen-334
❑ 68Kah-B25
❑ 68Top-597
❑ 69MilBra-179
❑ 69MLBOffS-194
❑ 69OPC-129
❑ 69Top-129
❑ 69TopFou-15
❑ 70MLBOffS-116
❑ 70OPC-314
❑ 70Top-314
❑ 72MilBra-219
❑ 81TCM60I-351
McCord, Clinton
❑ 92NegLeaRLI-42
McCord, Tom
❑ 88SFHesCreN32-17
McCorkle, Dave
❑ 86WauTimP-15
❑ 87SalSpuS-12
❑ 88VerMarP-963
McCorkle, Shawn
❑ 98EveAquG-16
❑ 99TeaBesR-56
❑ 99TeaBesRG-56
❑ 99TeaBesRS-56
McCormack, Andy
❑ 94SouBenSHC-10
❑ 94SouBenSHF-590
❑ 96CanIndB-37
McCormack, Brian
❑ 87EugEmeP-2661
❑ 88AppFoxP-152
❑ 89BasCitRS-16
❑ 90MemChiB-19
❑ 90MemChiP-1009
❑ 90MemChiS-17
McCormack, Don R.
❑ 81OklCit8T-9
❑ 82EvaTriT-12
❑ 88BatCliP-1664
❑ 89BatCliP-1935
❑ 90ReaPhiB-24
❑ 90ReaPhiP-1234
❑ 90ReaPhiS-26
❑ 91LinDriAA-524
❑ 91ReaPhiLD-524
❑ 91ReaPhiP-1385
❑ 92ReaPhiF-591
❑ 92ReaPhiS-549
❑ 93ReaPhiF-310
❑ 94ClePhiC-27
❑ 95ClePhiF-231
McCormack, John
❑ 87OldJudN-326
McCormack, Mark
❑ 83NasAngT-23
McCormack, Ron
❑ 83ChaRoyT-21
McCormack, Tim
❑ 86JacExpT-26
❑ 87IndIndTI-32
❑ 88IndIndP-498
❑ 89IndIndC-9
❑ 89IndIndP-1226
McCormick, Andrew
❑ 96DunBluJB-16
❑ 96DunBluJTI-19
❑ 96HagSunB-14
McCormick, Barry
❑ 03BreE10-97
McCormick, Buck (Frank A.)
❑ 38CloFotW-57
❑ 38RedOraW-18
❑ 39ExhSal-41A
❑ 39ExhSal-41B
❑ 39OrcPhoAP-15
❑ 39PlaBal-36
❑ 39RedTeal-14
❑ 40PlaBal-75
❑ 41DouPlaR-9
❑ 41HarHarW-14
❑ 41PlaBal-5
❑ 49Bow-239
❑ 77CinRedT-34
❑ 77RedCarP-18
❑ 79DiaGre-256
❑ 83TCMPla1942-35
❑ 85BigLeaC3-50
❑ 91ConTSN-306
McCormick, Cody
❑ 96GreBatB-15
McCormick, Glenn
❑ 90BenBucL-17
❑ 90MadMusP-2277
McCormick, Jim
❑ 87BucN28-89
❑ 87OldJudN-327
❑ 87TobLit-9
McCormick, John
❑ 89AppFoxP-873
❑ 90BasCitRS-16
❑ 91BasCitRC-10
❑ 91BasCitRP-1397
McCormick, Kid (Michael J.)
❑ 13Zee-68
❑ 90DodTar-501
McCormick, Mike
❑ 79ArkTraT-14
❑ 80ArkTraT-24
McCormick, Mike (Myron W.)
❑ 41DouPlaR-115
❑ 41HarHarW-15
❑ 49Bow-146
❑ 49EurSta-41
❑ 52MotCoo-57
❑ 76TayBow4-69
❑ 77TCMTheWY-65
❑ 85TCMPla1-11
❑ 90DodTar-1022
McCormick, Mike F.
❑ 58GiaSFCB-15
❑ 58Top-37
❑ 59Top-148
❑ 59TopVen-148
❑ 60GiaJayP-10
❑ 60MacSta-15
❑ 60Top-530
❑ 61GiaJayP-10
❑ 61Pos-141A
❑ 61Pos-141B
❑ 61Top-45
❑ 61Top-305
❑ 61Top-383
❑ 61TopStal-81
❑ 62GiaJayP-10
❑ 62Jel-139
❑ 62Pos-139
❑ 62PosCan-139
❑ 62SalPlaC-134
❑ 62ShiPlaC-134
❑ 62Top-56
❑ 62Top-107
❑ 62Top-319
❑ 62TopBuc-59
❑ 62TopStal-200
❑ 62TopVen-56
❑ 62TopVen-107
❑ 63BalOriP-18
❑ 63Top-563
❑ 64BalOriP-23
❑ 64Top-487
❑ 65Top-343
❑ 66OPC-118
❑ 66Top-118
❑ 66TopVen-118
❑ 67CokCapG-12
❑ 67DexPre-139
❑ 67OPC-86
❑ 67Top-86A
❑ 67Top-86B
❑ 67TopVen-289
❑ 68AtlOilPBCC-27
❑ 68Baz-12
❑ 68DexPre-53
❑ 68OPC-9
❑ 68Top-9
❑ 68Top-400A
❑ 68Top-400B
❑ 68TopActS-2A
❑ 68TopActS-15A
❑ 68TopGamI-17
❑ 68TopVen-9
❑ 69MilBra-180
❑ 69MLBOffS-205
❑ 69Top-517
❑ 70MLBOffS-130
❑ 70OPC-337
❑ 70Top-337
❑ 70YanPhoS-24
❑ 71MLBOffS-494
❑ 71OPC-438
❑ 71Top-438
❑ 72MilBra-220
❑ 72Top-682
❑ 73TacTwiC-15

❑ 79TCM50-245
❑ 81Gia196T-27
❑ 84GiaMot-16
❑ 88PacLegI-67
❑ 91OriCro-287
❑ 92YanWIZ7-108

McCormick, Moose (Harry)

❑ 09ColChiE-186
❑ 09RamT20-76
❑ 09T206-235
❑ 11SpoLifCW-241
❑ 12ColRedB-186
❑ 12ColTinT-186
❑ 72ClaCar-14

McCorry, William

❑ 12HomRunKE-67
❑ 12Zee-118
❑ 13Zee-117

McCosky, W. Barney

❑ 39TigSpo-6
❑ 40PlaBal-201
❑ 41DouPlaR-53
❑ 41PlaBal-36
❑ 41WheM5-20
❑ 47A'sTeal-22
❑ 47Exh-155A
❑ 47Exh-155B
❑ 48A'sTeal-18
❑ 48Bow-25
❑ 49A'sTeal-24
❑ 49Bow-203
❑ 49Lea-63
❑ 49OlmStu-5
❑ 49PhiBul-37
❑ 50A'sTeal-19
❑ 51Bow-84
❑ 52Top-300
❑ 73SpoScoHC-11
❑ 75TCMGua-17
❑ 76TayBow4-93
❑ 79DiaGre-390
❑ 81TigDetN-114
❑ 81TigSecNP-25
❑ 82Bow195E-254
❑ 83TCMPla1942-14
❑ 83TopRep5-300
❑ 85BigLeaC3-9

McCovey, Willie

❑ 47PM1StaP1-138
❑ 60GiaJayP-9
❑ 60NuHi-67
❑ 60Top-316
❑ 60Top-554
❑ 61Pos-147A
❑ 61Pos-147B
❑ 61Top-517
❑ 61TopStal-82
❑ 62Jel-131
❑ 62Pos-131
❑ 62PosCan-131
❑ 62SalPlaC-142
❑ 62ShiPlaC-142
❑ 62Top-544
❑ 63GiaJayP-8
❑ 63Jel-112
❑ 63Pos-112
❑ 63Top-490
❑ 64Baz-21
❑ 64ChatheY-38
❑ 64GiaJayP-8
❑ 64Top-9
❑ 64Top-41
❑ 64Top-350
❑ 64TopCoi-22
❑ 64TopRooAB-8
❑ 64TopSta-94
❑ 64TopStaU-51
❑ 64TopVen-9
❑ 64TopVen-41
❑ 64TopVen-350
❑ 64WheSta-31
❑ 65ChaTheY-39
❑ 65GiaTeal-7
❑ 65OPC-176
❑ 65Top-176
❑ 66Baz-14
❑ 66Top-217
❑ 66Top-550
❑ 66TopRubI-64
❑ 66TopVen-217
❑ 67Baz-14
❑ 67CokCapG-11
❑ 67DexPre-140
❑ 67OPCPapI-32
❑ 67Top-423
❑ 67Top-480
❑ 67TopPos-32
❑ 67TopVen-303
❑ 68AtlOilPBCC-28
❑ 68Baz-13
❑ 68OPC-5
❑ 68Top-5
❑ 68Top-290
❑ 68TopActS-7A
❑ 68TopVen-5
❑ 68TopVen-290
❑ 69CitMetC-19
❑ 69MilBra-181
❑ 69MLBOffS-206
❑ 69MLBPin-54
❑ 69OPC-4
❑ 69OPC-6
❑ 69OPCDec-13
❑ 69Top-4
❑ 69Top-6
❑ 69Top-416
❑ 69Top-440A
❑ 69Top-440B
❑ 69Top-572
❑ 69TopDec-31
❑ 69TopDecI-26
❑ 69TopSta-109
❑ 69TopSup-66
❑ 69TopTeaP-14
❑ 69TraSta-36
❑ 70Gia-10
❑ 70Kel-4
❑ 70MilBra-16
❑ 70MLBOffS-131
❑ 70OPC-63
❑ 70OPC-65
❑ 70OPC-250
❑ 70OPC-450
❑ 70Top-63
❑ 70Top-65
❑ 70Top-250
❑ 70Top-450
❑ 70TopPos-7
❑ 70TopSup-13
❑ 70TraSta-2C
❑ 71BazNumT-4
❑ 71BazUnn-22
❑ 71GiaTic-8
❑ 71Kel-33
❑ 71MatMin-9
❑ 71MatMin-10
❑ 71MilDud-52
❑ 71MLBOffS-258
❑ 71OPC-50
❑ 71Top-50
❑ 71TopCoi-57
❑ 71TopGreM-52
❑ 71TopSup-46
❑ 71TopTat-106
❑ 71TopTat-107
❑ 72Dia-61
❑ 72GiaTeal-14
❑ 72Kel-7A
❑ 72Kel-7B
❑ 72MilBra-221
❑ 72OPC-280
❑ 72ProStaP-19
❑ 72SevTraC-31
❑ 72Top-280
❑ 72TopCloT-23
❑ 72TopPos-24
❑ 73LinPor-162
❑ 73OPC-410
❑ 73Top-410
❑ 73TopCanL-29
❑ 73TopCom-11
❑ 73TopPin-11
❑ 74LauAllG-69
❑ 74OPC-250
❑ 74PadDea-18
❑ 74PadMcDD-9
❑ 74PadTeal-8
❑ 74PadTeal-9
❑ 74Top-250A
❑ 74Top-250B
❑ 74TopDecE-28
❑ 74TopSta-97
❑ 75Hos-19
❑ 75HosTwi-19
❑ 75OPC-207
❑ 75OPC-450
❑ 75PadDea-18
❑ 75Top-207
❑ 75Top-450
❑ 75TopMin-207
❑ 75TopMin-450
❑ 76Hos-124
❑ 76OPC-520
❑ 76Top-520
❑ 77GalGloG-263
❑ 77Gia-15
❑ 77PadSchC-37A
❑ 77PadSchC-37B
❑ 77Spo-7816
❑ 77Top-547
❑ 78GiaTeal-21
❑ 78Hos-73
❑ 78Kel-23
❑ 78OPC-185
❑ 78OPC-238
❑ 78RCColC-83
❑ 78Top-3
❑ 78Top-34
❑ 79GiaPol-44
❑ 79Kel-17
❑ 79OPC-107
❑ 79Pew-12
❑ 79Top-215
❑ 80GiaEurFS-5
❑ 80GiaPol-44
❑ 80GiaTeal-18
❑ 80Lau300-30
❑ 80OPC-176
❑ 80PerHaloFP-196
❑ 80PerHaloFPS-59
❑ 80SSPHOF-190
❑ 80Top-2
❑ 80Top-335
❑ 81Fle-434
❑ 81Gia196T-14
❑ 82DiaCla-90
❑ 82Gia25tATI-24
❑ 82K-M-16
❑ 82TCMGreS-6
❑ 83MLBPin-28
❑ 84GiaMot-2
❑ 84OCoandSI-14
❑ 84SpoDesPW-14
❑ 85CirK-8
❑ 85TCMHomRC-7
❑ 85TopGloA-11
❑ 86DonHig-34
❑ 86GreAmeSDFSB-2
❑ 86SpoDecG-48
❑ 87GiaPos-22
❑ 87LeaSpeO*-H11
❑ 88GiaPos-21
❑ 89HOFStiB-4
❑ 89PadMag-4
❑ 89PerCelP-31
❑ 89TopBasT-29
❑ 90AGFA-20
❑ 90PerGreM-22
❑ 92GiaCheHoFP-2
❑ 92TVSpoMF5HRC-9
❑ 92Zip-7
❑ 93ActPacA-123
❑ 93ActPacA2-57G
❑ 93Yoo-9
❑ 94CarLeaA-DJ4
❑ 95TopLegot6M-7
❑ 97CalLot-4
❑ 97PhoFirDTTI-1
❑ 97St.VinHHS-11
❑ 98DonSigSS-11
❑ 98SpollITaN-21
❑ 98SpollITaNEE-21
❑ 98UppDecR-89
❑ 98UppDecRSotT-WM
❑ 99SP SigAuto-WMC
❑ 99SPSig-174
❑ 99TopHaloFC-HOF4
❑ 99UppDecAP-WM
❑ 99UppDecAPH5AU-WMAU
❑ 99UppDecCLES-WMC
❑ 99UppDecCLESC-WMC

McCoy, Benjamin

❑ 41DouPlaR-129
❑ 42A'sTeal-25
❑ 79DiaGre-334

McCoy, Brent

❑ 88PulBraP-1762
❑ 89PulBraP-1894
❑ 90Bes-59
❑ 90BurBraB-27
❑ 90BurBraP-2358
❑ 90BurBraS-18
❑ 90MidLeaASGS-42
❑ 90ProAaA-130
❑ 90StaFS7-57
❑ 91DurBulC-23
❑ 91DurBulP-1556

McCoy, Kevin

❑ 80BurBeeT-2
❑ 81BurBeeT-3
❑ 83ElPasDT-20

McCoy, Larry

❑ 88T/MUmp-10
❑ 89T/MUmp-8
❑ 90T/MUmp-8

McCoy, Tim (Timothy)

❑ 86EveGiaC-13
❑ 86EveGiaPC-15
❑ 88ShrCapP-1300
❑ 89PalSprACLC-57
❑ 89PalSprAP-468
❑ 90ModA'sC-20
❑ 90ModA'sCLC-156
❑ 90ModA'sP-2208
❑ 91LinDriAAA-541
❑ 91TacTigLD-541

McCoy, Tommy

❑ 93SavCarC-29

McCoy, Trey

❑ 88ButCopKSP-18
❑ 89GasRanP-1012
❑ 89GasRanS-12
❑ 89SouAtlLAGS-28
❑ 89Sta-138
❑ 89StaFutS-21
❑ 89StaFutS-22
❑ 90ChaRanS-13
❑ 91LinDriAA-587
❑ 91TulDriLD-587
❑ 91TulDriP-2781
❑ 91TulDriTI-17
❑ 92TulDriF-2702
❑ 92TulDriS-611
❑ 93TulDriF-2743
❑ 93TulDriTI-17
❑ 94ClaGolF-182
❑ 94ExcFS7-136
❑ 94ExcLeaLF-13
❑ 94OklCit8F-1506

McCrabb, Les

❑ 49A'sTeal-25
❑ 79DiaGre-333

McCracken, Quinton

❑ 92BenRocCB-18
❑ 92BenRocF-1480
❑ 93Bow-260
❑ 93CenValRC-18
❑ 93CenValRF-2899
❑ 93RocStaC-2
❑ 93Top-451
❑ 93TopGol-451
❑ 93TopInaM-451
❑ 93TopInaR-451
❑ 93TopMic-451
❑ 94ExcFS7-185
❑ 94NewHavRF-1562
❑ 94UppDecML-6
❑ 95ARuFalLS-14
❑ 95NewHavRTI-1
❑ 95UppDecML-119
❑ 95UppDecMLFS-119
❑ 96Bow-306
❑ 96BowFoi-306
❑ 96ColCho-538
❑ 96ColCho-661
❑ 96ColChoGS-37
❑ 96ColChoGS-538
❑ 96ColChoGS-661
❑ 96ColChoSS-37
❑ 96ColChoSS-538
❑ 96ColChoSS-661
❑ 96Fle-367
❑ 96FleTif-367
❑ 96Lea-44
❑ 96LeaPrePB-44
❑ 96LeaPrePG-44
❑ 96LeaPrePS-44
❑ 96Pin-391
❑ 96PinFoil-391
❑ 96RocFle-8
❑ 96RocPol-12
❑ 96Sco-504
❑ 96Sel-171
❑ 96SelArtP-171
❑ 96Sum-179
❑ 96SumAbo&B-179
❑ 96SumArtP-179
❑ 96SumFoi-179
❑ 96Ult-470
❑ 96UltGolM-470
❑ 96UppDec-234
❑ 96UppDecFSP-FS14
❑ 97Cir-327
❑ 97CirRav-327
❑ 97ColCho-101
❑ 97ColChoT-CR6
❑ 97Don-385
❑ 97DonEli-130
❑ 97DonEliGS-130
❑ 97DonGolPP-385
❑ 97DonLim-123
❑ 97DonLimE-123
❑ 97DonLimENG-123
❑ 97DonPre-75
❑ 97DonPreCttC-75
❑ 97DonRatR-8
❑ 97DonSilPP-385
❑ 97DonTea-99
❑ 97DonTeaSPE-99
❑ 97Fle-312
❑ 97FleTif-312
❑ 97Lea-21
❑ 97LeaFraM-21
❑ 97LeaFraMDC-21
❑ 97Pac-283
❑ 97PacLigB-283
❑ 97PacSil-283
❑ 97Pin-176
❑ 97PinArtP-PP176
❑ 97PinIns-101
❑ 97PinInsCE-101
❑ 97PinInsDE-101
❑ 97PinMusC-176
❑ 97PinPrePla-176
❑ 97RocPol-8
❑ 97RocSco-10
❑ 97RocScoPl-10
❑ 97RocScoPr-10
❑ 97Sco-189
❑ 97ScoArtPWB-189
❑ 97ScoPreS-189
❑ 97ScoShoS-189
❑ 97ScoShoSAP-189
❑ 97Top-443
❑ 97Ult-187
❑ 97UltGolME-187
❑ 97UltPlaME-187
❑ 97UppDec-57
❑ 98Bow-274
❑ 98BowChr-274
❑ 98BowChrGA-274
❑ 98BowChrGAR-274
❑ 98BowChrI-274
❑ 98BowChrIR-274
❑ 98BowChrR-274
❑ 98BowGolA-274
❑ 98BowInt-274
❑ 98CirThu-129
❑ 98CirThuRav-129
❑ 98CirThuSupRav-129
❑ 98ColCho-83
❑ 98ColCho-511
❑ 98CroRoy-132
❑ 98DevRayP-24
❑ 98Fin-222
❑ 98FinNo--222
❑ 98FinNo-R-222
❑ 98FinRef-222
❑ 98Fle-462
❑ 98FleVin'-122
❑ 98FleVin'C-122
❑ 98Pac-286
❑ 98PacOme-232
❑ 98PacOmeR-232
❑ 98PacOnl-714
❑ 98PacOnlR-714
❑ 98PacOnlWC-714
❑ 98PacPar-98
❑ 98PacParC-98
❑ 98PacParG-98
❑ 98PacParHS-98
❑ 98PacParPB-98
❑ 98PacParR-98
❑ 98PacPlaB-286
❑ 98PacRedT-286
❑ 98PacSil-286
❑ 98PinPlu-53
❑ 98PinSna-TBDR12
❑ 98Revo-139
❑ 98RevoSS-139
❑ 98Sco-32
❑ 98ScoRT-171
❑ 98SPxFin-321
❑ 98SPxFinR-321
❑ 98SPxFinS-321
❑ 98StaCluFDI-328
❑ 98StaCluI-328
❑ 98StaCluOneK-328
❑ 98StaCluPP-328
❑ 98Top-206
❑ 98Top-462
❑ 98TopChr-206
❑ 98TopChr-462
❑ 98TopChrR-206
❑ 98TopChrR-462
❑ 98TopDevR-206
❑ 98TopDevR-462
❑ 98TopDia-206
❑ 98TopDia-462
❑ 98TopGal-13
❑ 98TopGalGP-13
❑ 98TopGalOPP-13
❑ 98TopGalPPI-13
❑ 98TopGalPPIA-13
❑ 98TopGolLabC1-55
❑ 98TopGolLabC1B-55
❑ 98TopGolLabC1One-55
❑ 98TopGolLabC1R-55
❑ 98TopGolLabC2-55
❑ 98TopGolLabC2B-55
❑ 98TopGolLabC2One-55
❑ 98TopGolLabC2R-55
❑ 98TopGolLabC3-55
❑ 98TopGolLabC3B-55
❑ 98TopGolLabC3One-55
❑ 98TopGolLabC3R-55
❑ 98TopMiniC-206
❑ 98TopMiniC-462
❑ 98TopSta-54
❑ 98TopStaB-54
❑ 98TopStaG-54
❑ 98TopStaGR-54
❑ 98TopStaS-54
❑ 98TopTek-82
❑ 98TopTekD-82
❑ 98Ult-472
❑ 98UltGolM-472
❑ 98UltMas-472
❑ 98UltPlaM-472
❑ 98UppDec-81
❑ 98UppDec-731
❑ 98UppDecR-93
❑ 99199Fin-18
❑ 99CroRoyB-135
❑ 99CroRoyL-135
❑ 99CroRoyOD-135
❑ 99FinGolRef-18
❑ 99FinRef-18
❑ 99FlaShoLeg1-92
❑ 99FlaShoLeg2-92
❑ 99FlaShoLeg3-92
❑ 99FlaShoLegM1-92
❑ 99FlaShoLegM2-92
❑ 99FlaShoLegM3-92
❑ 99FlaShoR1-92
❑ 99FlaShoR2-92
❑ 99FlaShoR3-92
❑ 99Fle-175
❑ 99FleBri-13
❑ 99FleBri2G-13
❑ 99FleBriBlu-13
❑ 99FleBriGol-13
❑ 99FleSta9-175
❑ 99FleWarT-175
❑ 99MetUni-99
❑ 99MetUniGM-99
❑ 99MetUniPMG-99
❑ 99Pac-415
❑ 99PacAur-187
❑ 99PacAurOD-187
❑ 99PacCroC-277
❑ 99PacCroCPB-277
❑ 99PacInv-141
❑ 99PacInvOD-141
❑ 99PacInvPB-141
❑ 99PacPar-228
❑ 99PacParC-228
❑ 99PacParG-228
❑ 99PacParHoloGold-228
❑ 99PacParHS-228
❑ 99PacParOD-228
❑ 99PacParPB-228
❑ 99PacParRed-228
❑ 99PacPlaB-415
❑ 99PacPri-53
❑ 99PacPriHB-53
❑ 99PacPriHG-53
❑ 99PacPriHM-53
❑ 99PacPriHP-53
❑ 99PacPriRed-53
❑ 99PacPriS-114
❑ 99PacPriS206-114
❑ 99PacPriS206R-114
❑ 99PacRed-415

❑ 99Rev-137
❑ 99RevPremDate-137
❑ 99RevRet-137
❑ 99RevShaSS-137
❑ 99SkyPre-33
❑ 99SkyPreR-33
❑ 99SkyThu-178
❑ 99SkyThuRant-178
❑ 99SkyThuRave-178
❑ 99SP Aut-83
❑ 99SpoIll-167
❑ 99SPx-74
❑ 99SPxFinR-74
❑ 99SPxFinS-74
❑ 99StaClu-199
❑ 99StaCluFDI-199
❑ 99StaCluOoaK-199
❑ 99StaCluPP-199
❑ 99ThuSkySupR-178
❑ 99Top-39
❑ 99TopChr-39
❑ 99TopChrR-39
❑ 99TopMVPP-39
❑ 99UD Cho-148
❑ 99UD ChoP-148
❑ 99UD ChoPCR-148
❑ 99Ult-80
❑ 99UltGolM-80
❑ 99UltMas-80
❑ 99UltPlaM-80
❑ 99UppDec-213
❑ 99UppDecBD-83
❑ 99UppDecBDD-83
❑ 99UppDecBDQ-83
❑ 99UppDecBDT-83
❑ 99UppDecEL1-213
❑ 99UppDecEL2-213
❑ 99UppDecM-201
❑ 99UppDecMGS-201
❑ 99UppDecMHFS-201
❑ 99UppDecMSS-201
❑ 99UppDecO-11
❑ 99UppDecOSO-11
❑ 99Vic-392

McCrary, Arnold
❑ 77AshTouT-15
❑ 78AshTouT-17
❑ 79WauTimT-23
❑ 80WauTimT-22

McCrary, Sam
❑ 86JacMetT-23
❑ 87JacMetF-13
❑ 88TidTidCa-1
❑ 88TidTidP-1580
❑ 89TidTidC-28
❑ 89TidTidP-1947

McCrary, Scott
❑ 98St.LucMM-7

McCraw, Tom
❑ 64Top-283
❑ 64TopVen-283
❑ 65Top-586
❑ 65WhiSoxJP-4
❑ 66OPC-141
❑ 66Top-141
❑ 66TopVen-141
❑ 66WhiSoxTI-9
❑ 67CokCapWS-11
❑ 67DexPre-141
❑ 67OPC-29
❑ 67Top-29
❑ 68Top-413
❑ 69MilBra-182
❑ 69MLBOffS-33
❑ 69Top-388
❑ 69TopTeaP-11
❑ 70MLBOffS-189
❑ 70Top-561
❑ 71OPC-373
❑ 71SenPolP-8
❑ 71Top-373
❑ 72MilBra-222
❑ 72Top-767
❑ 73Kel2D-21
❑ 73OPC-86
❑ 73Top-86
❑ 74OPC-449
❑ 74Top-449
❑ 75OPC-482
❑ 75Top-482
❑ 75TopMin-482
❑ 80IndTeal-18
❑ 81TCM60I-353
❑ 82Ind-25
❑ 82IndBurK-5
❑ 82IndBurK-6
❑ 82IndBurK-7
❑ 82IndWhe-9
❑ 83GiaPos-8
❑ 84GiaPos-16
❑ 85GiaMot-27
❑ 85GiaPos-21
❑ 89BalOriP-16
❑ 89OriFreB-40
❑ 92MetColP-37
❑ 92MetKah-27
❑ 96MetKah-21
❑ 96MetKah-22

McCray, Eric
❑ 89GasRanP-1008
❑ 89GasRanS-13
❑ 90CMC-766
❑ 90TulDriP-1151
❑ 90TulDriTI-17
❑ 91Bow-281
❑ 91TulDriTI-18

McCray, Justin
❑ 90AshTouP-2756
❑ 91SarWhiSC-17
❑ 91SarWhiSP-1119

McCray, Rod (Rodney)
❑ 86ChaRaiP-16
❑ 88SouBenWSGS-8
❑ 89SarWhiSS-14
❑ 90Bes-204
❑ 90BirBarB-12
❑ 90BirBarP-1119
❑ 91LinDriAAA-641
❑ 91OPC-523
❑ 91Sco-763
❑ 91Top-523
❑ 91TopDeb90-103
❑ 91TopDesS-523
❑ 91TopMic-523
❑ 91TopTif-523
❑ 91VanCanLD-641
❑ 91VanCanP-1607
❑ 92Sco-517
❑ 92StaClu-829
❑ 92StaCluNC-829
❑ 94LetMouF-3895
❑ 94LetMouSP-29
❑ 98LanLugQ-30

McCray, Todd
❑ 90BoiHawP-3307
❑ 91RenSilSCLC-18

McCrea, Francis
❑ 28Zee-134

McCreadie, Brant
❑ 89HigSchPLS-16
❑ 91SalSpuC-8
❑ 91SalSpuP-2239

McCready, Aaron
❑ 96BriWhiSB-6

McCready, Jim
❑ 92ColMetC-22
❑ 92ColMetF-292
❑ 92ColMetPI-16
❑ 93St.LucMC-17
❑ 93St.LuMF-2919
❑ 94BinMetF-701
❑ 95BinMetTI-17

McCreary, Bob
❑ 88CapCodPPaLP-82
❑ 89EliTwiS-17
❑ 90VisOakCLC-69
❑ 90VisOakP-2163
❑ 91Cla/Bes-308
❑ 91LinDriAA-488
❑ 91OrlSunRLD-488
❑ 91OrlSunRP-1859
❑ 92CalLeaACL-33
❑ 92OrlSunRF-2846
❑ 92VisOakF-1011
❑ 93NasXprF-399

McCreedie, Judge
❑ 09ObaT21-29
❑ 09ObaT21-121
❑ 09ObaT21-295
❑ 11Zee-52
❑ 12ObaPreT-44
❑ 12PCLPin-15
❑ 12Zee-69
❑ 13Zee-69
❑ 14Zee-68
❑ 15Zee-69
❑ 16Zee-59
❑ 17Zee-52
❑ 18Zee-65
❑ 19Zee-38
❑ 20Zee-50
❑ 21Zee-55
❑ 22Zee-132
❑ 26Zee-52
❑ 90DodTar-502

McCreery, Tom
❑ 90DodTar-503

McCreight, Kenneth
❑ 47SenGunBP-10

McCroskey, Jackie
❑ 93PriRedC-18
❑ 93PriRedF-4195
❑ 94PriRedC-16
❑ 94PriRedF-3278

McCrotty, Will
❑ 97YakBeaG-17
❑ 98SanBerS-19
❑ 98SanBerSTIS-16

McCubbin, Shane
❑ 93BurBeeC-13
❑ 93BurBeeF-161
❑ 93ButCopKSP-6
❑ 94BurBeeC-16
❑ 94BurBeeF-1084
❑ 94VerExpC-18
❑ 94VerExpF-3913

McCue, Deron
❑ 85FreGiaSB-9
❑ 86ShrCapP-17
❑ 87ShrCapP-19
❑ 88PhoFirC-23
❑ 88PhoFirP-58
❑ 90EveGiaP-3145
❑ 91CliGiaC-28
❑ 91CliGiaP-852

McCulla, Harry
❑ 82SprCarF-22
❑ 83SprCarF-17
❑ 84SavCarT-16
❑ 85SprCarT-17
❑ 86ArkTraP-14
❑ 90SprCarDGB-3

McCullers, Lance
❑ 85LasVegSC-109
❑ 86Don-41
❑ 86Fle-330
❑ 86PadFirPTB-4
❑ 86SpoRoo-8
❑ 86Top-44
❑ 86TopTif-44
❑ 87ClaGam-80
❑ 87Don-237
❑ 87Fle-424
❑ 87FleGlo-424
❑ 87FleMin-68
❑ 87FleStiC-76
❑ 87OPC-71
❑ 87PadBohHB-41
❑ 87SpoTeaP-16
❑ 87Top-559
❑ 87TopSti-111
❑ 87TopTif-559
❑ 88Don-451
❑ 88DonBasB-210
❑ 88Fle-592
❑ 88FleGlo-592
❑ 88FleMin-114
❑ 88OPC-197
❑ 88PadCok-41
❑ 88PadSmo-18
❑ 88PanSti-399
❑ 88Sco-150
❑ 88ScoGlo-150
❑ 88Spo-85
❑ 88StaLinPa-9
❑ 88Top-197
❑ 88TopBig-38
❑ 88TopSti-114
❑ 88TopTif-197
❑ 89Bow-168
❑ 89BowTif-168
❑ 89Don-129
❑ 89DonBasB-220
❑ 89DonTra-13
❑ 89Fle-312
❑ 89FleGlo-312
❑ 89OPC-307
❑ 89Sco-158
❑ 89ScoRoo-63T
❑ 89ScoYouS2-19
❑ 89Spo-76
❑ 89Top-307
❑ 89TopSti-108
❑ 89TopTif-307
❑ 89TopTra-77T
❑ 89TopTraT-77T
❑ 89UppDec-382
❑ 89UppDec-710
❑ 89YanScoNW-14
❑ 90Don-433
❑ 90Fle-448
❑ 90FleCan-448
❑ 90Lea-456
❑ 90OPC-259
❑ 90PubIntS-541
❑ 90Sco-186
❑ 90Top-259
❑ 90TopTif-259
❑ 90TopTVY-13
❑ 90UppDec-615
❑ 91Don-133
❑ 91Fle-342
❑ 91Sco-313
❑ 91UppDec-203
❑ 92OklCit8S-315
❑ 92YanWIZ8-115
❑ 93CalCanF-1163
❑ 93RanKee-254

McCullock, Alec
❑ 84BufBisT-10

McCullough, Carol
❑ 84IowCubT-15

McCullough, Clyde
❑ 41CubTeal-12
❑ 42CubTeal-12
❑ 43CubTeal-15
❑ 47TipTop-113
❑ 49Bow-163
❑ 49EurSta-166
❑ 50Bow-124
❑ 50PirTeal-13
❑ 51Bow-94
❑ 51R42SmaS-66
❑ 52Bow-99
❑ 52Top-218
❑ 55Bow-280
❑ 61TwiPetM-21
❑ 72TopTes5-6
❑ 83TopRep5-218
❑ 84TCMPla1-32

McCune, Gary
❑ 83KnoBluJT-22
❑ 88KnoBluJB-21
❑ 89KnoBluJP-1121

McCurdy, Harry
❑ 27Zee-73
❑ 28Exh-40
❑ 31Exh-12
❑ 33Gou-170
❑ 94ConTSN-1242
❑ 94ConTSNB-1242

McCurine, Jim
❑ 93NegLeaRL2-26

McCurry, Jeff
❑ 92AugPirC-17
❑ 92AugPirF-235
❑ 92UppDecML-207
❑ 93CarLeaAGF-50
❑ 93SalBucC-17
❑ 93SalBucF-429
❑ 94CarMudF-1576
❑ 94ExcFS7-253
❑ 95PirFil-20
❑ 95Sum-173
❑ 95SumNthD-173
❑ 96TolMudHB-19
❑ 98NasSouTI-22
❑ 98NasSouTISS-21
❑ 98PacInvGems-146

McCutcheon, Greg
❑ 88St.CatBJP-2020
❑ 89St.CatBJP-2094
❑ 90EriSaiS-15

McCutcheon, James
❑ 87GasRanP-21
❑ 88GasRanP-1004
❑ 89GasRanP-1011
❑ 89GasRanS-14
❑ 93AshTouC-13
❑ 93AshTouF-2273
❑ 93QuaCitRBF-96

McCutcheon, Mike
❑ 96HonShaHWB-19
❑ 97SouBenSH-19
❑ 98LetBlaDG-20

McDade, Neal
❑ 96EriSeaB-16
❑ 97AugGre-13
❑ 98LynHilQ-10

McDaniel, Cannonball (Booker T.)
❑ 49AngTeal-25
❑ 49W725AngTI-20
❑ 87NegLeaPD-40

McDaniel, Denny
❑ 98SpoIndG-20

McDaniel, Donna
❑ 91FreStaLBS-7

McDaniel, Jim
❑ 55DesMoiHB-11
❑ 59Top-134
❑ 59TopVen-134

McDaniel, Joey
❑ 93DavLipB-17

McDaniel, Lindy
❑ 47Exh-156
❑ 57Top-79
❑ 58CarJayP-9
❑ 58Top-180
❑ 59OklTodML-10
❑ 59Top-479
❑ 60CarJayP-6
❑ 60Top-195
❑ 60TopVen-195
❑ 61CarJayP-8
❑ 61Pos-175A
❑ 61Pos-175B
❑ 61Top-75
❑ 61Top-266
❑ 61TopStal-91
❑ 62CarJayP-8
❑ 62Jel-163
❑ 62Pos-163
❑ 62PosCan-163
❑ 62SalPlaC-144
❑ 62ShiPlaC-144
❑ 62Top-306
❑ 62Top-522
❑ 62TopStal-187
❑ 63CubJayP-9
❑ 63Jel-167
❑ 63Pos-167A
❑ 63Pos-167B
❑ 63Top-329
❑ 64CubJayP-9
❑ 64Top-510
❑ 65GiaTeal-8
❑ 65OPC-244
❑ 65Top-244
❑ 66Top-496
❑ 67CokCapG-16
❑ 67OPC-46
❑ 67Top-46
❑ 68Top-545
❑ 68YanPhoS-70
❑ 69MilBra-183
❑ 69OPC-191
❑ 69Top-191
❑ 69TopFou-10
❑ 69YanPhoS-44
❑ 70OPC-493
❑ 70Top-493
❑ 70YanPhoS-25
❑ 71MLBOffS-495
❑ 71OPC-303
❑ 71Top-303
❑ 71YanCliDP-11
❑ 72MilBra-223
❑ 72OPC-513
❑ 72Top-513
❑ 73OPC-46
❑ 73SyrChiTI-16
❑ 73Top-46
❑ 74OPC-182
❑ 74RoyPos-17
❑ 74Top-182
❑ 74TopTra-182T
❑ 75OPC-652
❑ 75RoyPos-19
❑ 75Top-652
❑ 75TopMin-652
❑ 79TCM50-280
❑ 84CubUno-9
❑ 92YanWIZ6-80
❑ 92YanWIZ7-109

McDaniel, M. Von
❑ 58CarJayP-10
❑ 58Top-65A
❑ 58Top-65B
❑ 59OklTodML-9
❑ 89AstCol4S-21

McDaniel, Marty
❑ 89CarNewE-22

McDaniel, Osborne
❑ 27Zee-31
❑ 28Zee-54
❑ 29Zee-163

McDaniel, Ryan
❑ 97IdaFalBTI-10
❑ 98CliLumG-13

McDaniel, Terry
❑ 87LitFalMP-2404
❑ 88ColMetGS-22
❑ 89St.LucMS-16
❑ 90JacMetGS-27
❑ 90MetColP-40
❑ 90TexLeaAGS-28
❑ 90TopTVM-50
❑ 91MetColP-38
❑ 91TidTidP-2524
❑ 92Fle-511
❑ 92Sco-765
❑ 92TopDeb91-121
❑ 92TopGol-527
❑ 92TopGolW-527

McDaniels, Paul
❑ 98LowSpiM-12

McDarrah, Fred
❑ 75TopPho-52

McDavid, Ray
❑ 91ChaRaiC-21
❑ 91ChaRaiP-107
❑ 92CalLeaACL-29
❑ 92ClaFS7-131
❑ 92HigDesMC-9
❑ 92UppDecML-64
❑ 92UppDecML-256
❑ 92UppDecMLPotY-PY16
❑ 93Bow-26
❑ 93Bow-359
❑ 93ClaGolF-58
❑ 93ClaYouG-YG10
❑ 93SP-170
❑ 93UppDec-438
❑ 93UppDecGold-438
❑ 93WicWraF-2991
❑ 94Bow-260
❑ 94BowBes-B67
❑ 94BowBesR-B67
❑ 94Cla-92
❑ 94ExcFS7-285
❑ 94FleUpd-188
❑ 94LasVegSF-880
❑ 94LeaLimR-70
❑ 94SigRoo-12
❑ 94SigRooHP-S6
❑ 94SigRooHPS-S6
❑ 94SigRooS-12
❑ 94Top-152
❑ 94TopGol-152
❑ 94TopSpa-152
❑ 94Ult-582
❑ 94UppDecML-160
❑ 94UppDecML-165
❑ 94UppDecMLPotYF-PY17
❑ 95Bow-84
❑ 95ColCho-353
❑ 95ColChoGS-353
❑ 95ColChoSE-20
❑ 95ColChoSEGS-20
❑ 95ColChoSESS-20
❑ 95ColChoSS-353
❑ 95Don-117
❑ 95DonPreP-117
❑ 95LeaGolR-11
❑ 95Pin-409
❑ 95PinArtP-409
❑ 95PinMusC-409
❑ 95Sel-175
❑ 95SelArtP-175
❑ 95StaClu-43
❑ 95StaCluFDI-43
❑ 95StaCluMOP-43
❑ 95StaCluSTWS-43
❑ 95StaCluVR-31
❑ 95StaCluVRMO-31
❑ 95Top-147
❑ 95UppDec-139
❑ 95UppDecED-139
❑ 95UppDecEDG-139
❑ 96Don-482
❑ 96DonPreP-482

McDermont, Jim
❑ 92UtiBluSC-19
❑ 93SouBenWSF-1427

McDermott, Mickey (Maurice)
❑ 48RedSoxTI-16
❑ 50Bow-97
❑ 50Dra-31
❑ 50RedSoxTI-14
❑ 51Bow-16
❑ 51TopRedB-43
❑ 52Bow-25
❑ 52Top-119

❑ 53BowC-35
❑ 53Bri-12
❑ 53NorBreL-17
❑ 53RedSoxTI-19
❑ 53Top-55
❑ 54Bow-56
❑ 55Bow-165
❑ 56Top-340
❑ 56YanTeal-16
❑ 57Top-318
❑ 79TCM50-207
❑ 81RedSoxBG2S-38
❑ 83TopRep5-119
❑ 91TopArc1-55

McDermott, Randall
❑ 92GulCoaYF-3789

McDermott, Ryan
❑ 96AppLeaAB-9
❑ 96BurIndB-11
❑ 97BurIndG-18

McDermott, Terry
❑ 74AlbDukCa-67
❑ 74AlbDukTI-10
❑ 75AlbDukCa-7
❑ 90DodTar-1023

McDermott, Toby
❑ 97PriDevR-25

McDevitt, Danny
❑ 58DodTeal-14
❑ 58Top-357
❑ 59DodTeal-16
❑ 59Top-364
❑ 60DodBelB-3
❑ 60Lea-50
❑ 60Top-333
❑ 61Top-349
❑ 61Yan61RL-29
❑ 62Top-493
❑ 90DodTar-504
❑ 91YanRinP12-3
❑ 92YanWIZ6-81

McDevitt, Terry
❑ 86SpoIndC-170
❑ 87ChaRaiP-12
❑ 88RivRedWCLC-224
❑ 88RivRedWP-1430
❑ 89WatDiaS-31
❑ 90ClePhiS-14

McDill, Allen
❑ 92GulCoaMF-3477
❑ 92KinMetC-12
❑ 92KinMetF-1528
❑ 93PitMetF-3706
❑ 94CapCitBC-14
❑ 94CapCitBF-1748
❑ 95AusFut-30
❑ 95StLucMTI-21
❑ 96WicWraB-8
❑ 97OmaRoyB-10
❑ 98OmaRoyM-15

McDonald, Ashanti
❑ 96RocCubTI-19

McDonald, Ben
❑ 87AncGlaP-20
❑ 89BalOriP-17
❑ 89Sta-200
❑ 90BalOriP-16
❑ 90Baz-10
❑ 90Bes-7
❑ 90Bow-243
❑ 90BowTif-243
❑ 90ClaBlu-130
❑ 90CMC-302
❑ 90Don-32
❑ 90DonBesA-114
❑ 90DonPre-2
❑ 90DonRoo-30
❑ 90Fle-180
❑ 90FleCan-180
❑ 90HagSunB-1
❑ 90HagSunP-1408
❑ 90Lea-249
❑ 90LSUMcDM-1
❑ 90LSUMcDM-2
❑ 90LSUMcDM-3
❑ 90LSUMcDM-4
❑ 90LSUMcDM-5
❑ 90LSUMcDM-6
❑ 90LSUMcDM-7
❑ 90LSUMcDM-8
❑ 90LSUMcDM-9
❑ 90LSUMcDM-10
❑ 90LSUMcDM-11
❑ 90LSUMcDM-12
❑ 90LSUMcDM-13
❑ 90LSUMcDM-14
❑ 90LSUMcDM-15
❑ 90LSUMcDM-16
❑ 90LSUTigGM-7
❑ 90OPC-774
❑ 90PanSti-373
❑ 90ProAaA-2
❑ 90ProAAAF-456
❑ 90RocRedWC-1
❑ 90RocRedWGC-3
❑ 90RocRedWP-699
❑ 90Sco-680
❑ 90Sco100RS-93
❑ 90ScoYouS2-2
❑ 90StaFS7-28
❑ 90StaMcD-1
❑ 90StaMcD-2
❑ 90StaMcD-3
❑ 90StaMcD-4
❑ 90StaMcD-5
❑ 90StaMcD-6
❑ 90StaMcD-7
❑ 90StaMcD-8
❑ 90StaMcD-9
❑ 90StaMcD-10
❑ 90StaMcD-11
❑ 90Top-774
❑ 90TopBig-228
❑ 90TopDeb89-78
❑ 90TopMag-15
❑ 90TopTif-774
❑ 90TopTra-70T
❑ 90TopTraT-70T
❑ 90UppDec-54A
❑ 90UppDec-54B
❑ 91BalOriP-17
❑ 91Bow-86
❑ 91Cla1-T14
❑ 91ClaGam-132
❑ 91Col-9
❑ 91Don-485
❑ 91Fle-481
❑ 91KinDis-4
❑ 91Lea-117
❑ 91MajLeaCP-31
❑ 91OPC-497
❑ 91OriCro-288
❑ 91PanFreS-247
❑ 91PanSti-197
❑ 91RedFolS-109
❑ 91Sco-645
❑ 91Sco100RS-50
❑ 91SevCoi-A8
❑ 91StaClu-264
❑ 91StaCluP-26
❑ 91Stu-6
❑ 91SunSee-17
❑ 91Top-497
❑ 91TopCraJ2-6
❑ 91TopDesS-497
❑ 91TopMic-497
❑ 91TopRoo-18
❑ 91TopSta-25
❑ 91TopTif-497
❑ 91TopTriH-A1
❑ 91ToyRoo-17
❑ 91Ult-19
❑ 91UppDec-446
❑ 92BalOriP-18
❑ 92Bow-359
❑ 92ClaGam-59
❑ 92Don-436
❑ 92Fle-14
❑ 92Hig5-2
❑ 92HitTheBB-22
❑ 92Lea-145
❑ 92LeaBlaG-145
❑ 92MVPPin-19
❑ 92OPC-540
❑ 92Pin-44
❑ 92PinTea2-41
❑ 92RedFolS-62
❑ 92Sco-658
❑ 92Sco100S-94
❑ 92ScoImpP-81
❑ 92StaClu-490
❑ 92Stu-126
❑ 92Top-540
❑ 92TopDaiQTU-10
❑ 92TopGol-540
❑ 92TopGolW-540
❑ 92TopKid-64
❑ 92TopMic-540
❑ 92TriPla-105
❑ 92Ult-303
❑ 92UppDec-93
❑ 92UppDec-163
❑ 92UppDecCPH-CP3
❑ 93BalOriP-16
❑ 93Bow-437
❑ 93ClaGam-60
❑ 93Don-249
❑ 93Fin-65
❑ 93FinRef-65
❑ 93Fla-152
❑ 93Fle-169
❑ 93FunPac-133
❑ 93Lea-1
❑ 93MilBonSS-14
❑ 93OPC-254
❑ 93PacSpa-20
❑ 93PanSti-68
❑ 93Pin-72
❑ 93Sco-202
❑ 93Sel-224
❑ 93SP-158
❑ 93StaClu-259
❑ 93StaCluFDI-259
❑ 93StaCluMOP-259
❑ 93Top-218
❑ 93TopGol-218
❑ 93TopInaM-218
❑ 93TopInaR-218
❑ 93TopMic-218
❑ 93TriPla-145
❑ 93Ult-142
❑ 93UppDec-276
❑ 93UppDecGold-276
❑ 94BalOriP-17
❑ 94Bow-459
❑ 94BowBes-R22
❑ 94BowBesR-R22
❑ 94ColC-195
❑ 94ColChoGS-195
❑ 94ColChoSS-195
❑ 94Don-158
❑ 94Fin-161
❑ 94FinRef-161
❑ 94Fla-4
❑ 94Fle-8
❑ 94FleExtB-7
❑ 94FleExtBGB-18
❑ 94FleExtBPD-2
❑ 94Lea-127
❑ 94LeaL-2
❑ 94OPC-122
❑ 94OriPro-61
❑ 94OriUSPC-8C
❑ 94OriUSPC-13H
❑ 94Pac-35
❑ 94Pin-184
❑ 94PinArtP-184
❑ 94PinMusC-184
❑ 94ProMag-7
❑ 94Sco-111
❑ 94ScoGolR-111
❑ 94Sel-117
❑ 94SP-123
❑ 94SPDieC-123
❑ 94Spo-11
❑ 94StaClu-413
❑ 94StaCluFDI-413
❑ 94StaCluGR-413
❑ 94StaCluMOP-413
❑ 94StaCluT-284
❑ 94StaCluTFDI-284
❑ 94Stu-124
❑ 94Top-636
❑ 94TopGol-636
❑ 94TopSpa-636
❑ 94TriPla-155
❑ 94Ult-3
❑ 94UppDec-456
❑ 94UppDecED-456
❑ 95Baz-38
❑ 95Bow-311
❑ 95ColCho-339
❑ 95ColChoGS-339
❑ 95ColChoSE-159
❑ 95ColChoSEGS-159
❑ 95ColChoSESS-159
❑ 95ColChoSS-339
❑ 95Don-412
❑ 95DonPreP-412
❑ 95DonTopotO-12
❑ 95Emo-5
❑ 95Fin-83
❑ 95FinRef-83
❑ 95Fla-223
❑ 95Fle-11
❑ 95Lea-197
❑ 95Pac-24
❑ 95Pin-120
❑ 95PinArtP-120
❑ 95PinMusC-120
❑ 95Sco-273
❑ 95ScoGolR-273
❑ 95ScoHaloG-HG90
❑ 95ScoPlaTS-273
❑ 95Sel-144
❑ 95SelArtP-144
❑ 95Spo-49
❑ 95SpoArtP-49
❑ 95StaClu-84
❑ 95StaCluFDI-84
❑ 95StaCluMOP-84
❑ 95StaCluSTWS-84
❑ 95StaCluVR-51
❑ 95StaCluVRMO-51
❑ 95Stu-176
❑ 95Sum-4
❑ 95SumNthD-4
❑ 95Top-165
❑ 95TopCyb-99
❑ 95UC3-62
❑ 95UC3ArtP-62
❑ 95Ult-5
❑ 95UltGolM-5
❑ 95UppDec-127
❑ 95UppDecED-127
❑ 95UppDecEDG-127
❑ 95UppDecSE-49
❑ 95UppDecSEG-49
❑ 95Zen-6
❑ 96BrePol-17
❑ 96ColCho-56
❑ 96ColCho-776
❑ 96ColChoGS-56
❑ 96ColChoSS-56
❑ 96Don-82
❑ 96DonPreP-82
❑ 96EmoXL-74
❑ 96Fin-B210
❑ 96FinRef-B210
❑ 96Fla-103
❑ 96Fle-15
❑ 96FleTif-15
❑ 96FleUpd-U48
❑ 96FleUpdTC-U48
❑ 96LeaLim-22
❑ 96LeaLimG-22
❑ 96LeaPre-23
❑ 96LeaPreP-23
❑ 96LeaSigA-151
❑ 96LeaSigAG-151
❑ 96LeaSigAS-151
❑ 96MetUni-5
❑ 96MetUniP-5
❑ 96Pac-240
❑ 96PanSti-130
❑ 96Pin-120
❑ 96Pin-331
❑ 96PinAfi-56
❑ 96PinAfiAP-56
❑ 96PinAfiFPP-56
❑ 96PinFoil-331
❑ 96Sco-341
❑ 96ScoDugC-B66
❑ 96ScoDugCAP-B66
❑ 96Sel-102
❑ 96SelArtP-102
❑ 96SelCer-45
❑ 96SelCerAP-45
❑ 96SelCerCB-45
❑ 96SelCerCR-45
❑ 96SelCerMB-45
❑ 96SelCerMG-45
❑ 96SelCerMR-45
❑ 96SP-108
❑ 96Sum-80
❑ 96SumAbo&B-80
❑ 96SumArtP-80
❑ 96SumFoi-80
❑ 96Top-320
❑ 96Ult-367
❑ 96UltGolM-367
❑ 96UppDec-361
❑ 96Zen-28
❑ 96ZenArtP-28
❑ 96ZenMoz-14
❑ 97BrePol-17
❑ 97Cir-14
❑ 97CirRav-14
❑ 97ColCho-376
❑ 97Don-178
❑ 97DonGolPP-178
❑ 97DonLim-151
❑ 97DonLimE-151
❑ 97DonLimENG-151
❑ 97DonSilPP-178
❑ 97E-X2-27
❑ 97E-X2Cred-27
❑ 97E-X2EssCre-27
❑ 97Fin-96
❑ 97FinRef-96
❑ 97Fle-134
❑ 97FleTif-134
❑ 97Lea-139
❑ 97LeaFraM-139
❑ 97LeaFraMDC-139
❑ 97MetUni-67
❑ 97Pac-124
❑ 97PacLigB-124
❑ 97PacSil-124
❑ 97Pin-28
❑ 97PinArtP-PP28
❑ 97PinMusC-28
❑ 97PinPrePla-28
❑ 97Sco-27
❑ 97ScoArtPWB-27
❑ 97ScoPreS-27
❑ 97ScoShoS-27
❑ 97ScoShoSAP-27
❑ 97SP-104
❑ 97StaClu-166
❑ 97StaCluMOP-166
❑ 97Top-25
❑ 97Ult-79
❑ 97UltGolME-79
❑ 97UltPlaME-79
❑ 97UppDec-99
❑ 98Fle-40
❑ 98Pac-121
❑ 98PacPlaB-121
❑ 98PacRedT-121
❑ 98PacSil-121
❑ 98Sco-207
❑ 98ScoSS-PP99
❑ 98ScoSSAP-PP99
❑ 98Top-55
❑ 98TopChr-55
❑ 98TopChrR-55
❑ 98TopDevR-55
❑ 98TopDia-55
❑ 98TopMiniC-55
❑ 98Ult-58
❑ 98UltGolM-58
❑ 98UltMas-58
❑ 98UltPlaM-58

McDonald, Chad
❑ 91WesPalBEC-22
❑ 91WesPalBEP-1237
❑ 92HarSenF-468
❑ 92HarSenS-292

McDonald, Clarence
❑ 14Zee-142

McDonald, Clown (Ronald)
❑ 74PadMcDD-14
❑ 81TidTidT-3
❑ 93IndWUA-35

McDonald, Dan
❑ 93BatCliCB-17
❑ 93BatCliF-3160

McDonald, Darnell
❑ 98Bes-28
❑ 98BesDiaB-1
❑ 98BesNumOP-33
❑ 98BesPlaotYP-4
❑ 98Bow-420
❑ 98BowBes-130
❑ 98BowBesAR-130
❑ 98BowBesR-130
❑ 98BowChr-420
❑ 98BowChrGA-420
❑ 98BowChrGAR-420
❑ 98BowChrI-420
❑ 98BowChrIR-420
❑ 98BowChrR-420
❑ 98BowGolA-420
❑ 98BowInt-420
❑ 98DelShoM-1
❑ 98SouAtlLPM-15
❑ 98Top-490
❑ 98TopChr-490
❑ 98TopChrR-490
❑ 98TopDevR-490
❑ 98TopDia-490
❑ 98TopMiniC-490
❑ 99BasAmeTP-64
❑ 99BasAmeTPA-28
❑ 99BasAmeTPG-64
❑ 99Bow-76
❑ 99BowAut-BA6
❑ 99BowChr-76
❑ 99BowChrG-76
❑ 99BowChrGR-76
❑ 99BowChrI-76
❑ 99BowChrIR-76
❑ 99BowChrR-76
❑ 99BowGol-76
❑ 99BowInt-76
❑ 99TeaBesRFS-4
❑ 99TeaBesRFS-21

McDonald, Dave
❑ 91SanBerSC-9
❑ 91SanBerSP-1985

McDonald, David B.
❑ 70OPC-189
❑ 70Top-189
❑ 92YanWIZ6-82

McDonald, Donzell
❑ 97Bow-347
❑ 97BowChr-235
❑ 97BowChrI-235
❑ 97BowChrIR-235
❑ 97BowChrR-235
❑ 97BowInt-347
❑ 97FloStaLTPB-24
❑ 97TamYan-18
❑ 98Bes-76
❑ 98Bow-350
❑ 98BowBes-114
❑ 98BowBesAR-114
❑ 98BowBesR-114
❑ 98BowChr-350
❑ 98BowChrGA-350
❑ 98BowChrGAR-350
❑ 98BowChrI-350
❑ 98BowChrIR-350
❑ 98BowChrR-350
❑ 98BowGolA-350
❑ 98BowInt-350
❑ 98EasLeaTPM-18
❑ 98NorNavQ-1
❑ 99TeaBesRFS-21

McDonald, Ed
❑ 12T207-117

McDonald, George
❑ 45CenFlo-17

McDonald, Grant
❑ 93AusFut-25

McDonald, Hank
❑ 31Zee-70
❑ 33Zee-25

McDonald, James
❑ 86JamExpP-16

McDonald, Jason
❑ 91TopTra-75T
❑ 91TopTraT-75T
❑ 92StaCluD-113
❑ 94WesMicWC-15
❑ 94WesMicWF-2306
❑ 95ModA'sTI-16
❑ 95SPML-122
❑ 96Bow-288
❑ 96BowFoi-288
❑ 96Exc-99
❑ 96ExcTL-7
❑ 97DonLim-190
❑ 97DonLimE-190
❑ 97Fle-758
❑ 97FleTif-758
❑ 97SpoIll-15
❑ 97SpoIllEE-15
❑ 98A'sMot-23
❑ 98ColCho-196
❑ 98Fle-42
❑ 98Pac-169
❑ 98PacOnl-538
❑ 98PacOnlR-538
❑ 98PacOnlWC-538
❑ 98PacPar-81
❑ 98PacParC-81
❑ 98PacParG-81
❑ 98PacParHS-81
❑ 98PacParPB-81
❑ 98PacParR-81
❑ 98PacPlaB-169
❑ 98PacRedT-169
❑ 98PacSil-169
❑ 98PinPlu-52
❑ 98Top-236
❑ 98TopChr-236
❑ 98TopChrR-236
❑ 98TopDevR-236
❑ 98TopDia-236
❑ 98TopMiniC-236
❑ 98Ult-365
❑ 98UltGolM-365
❑ 98UltMas-365

❑ 98UltPlaM-365
❑ 98UppDec-180
❑ 99Fle-490
❑ 99FleSta9-490
❑ 99FleWarT-490
❑ 99Pac-314
❑ 99PacPlaB-314
❑ 99PacRed-314
❑ 99Top-119
❑ 99TopChr-119
❑ 99TopChrR-119
❑ 99TopMVPP-119
❑ 99WesMicWAM-16
McDonald, Jeff
❑ 84ChaLooT-28
❑ 86ChaLooP-18
McDonald, Jerry
❑ 77SalPirT-15A
❑ 77SalPirT-15B
❑ 79BufBisT-6
❑ 80PorBeaT-4
McDonald, Jim
❑ 76ForLauYS-5
❑ 77ForLauYS-14
❑ 79WesHavYT-10
❑ 80ColCliP-31
❑ 80ColCliT-11
❑ 82TucTorT-12
❑ 83ColAstT-15
❑ 86AriWilP-10
McDonald, Jimmie LeRoy
❑ 53Dor-117
❑ 55Bow-77
❑ 55OriEss-16
❑ 91OriCro-289
❑ 97BalOriP-32
McDonald, John
❑ 96WatIndTI-17
❑ 97CalLeaATI-37
❑ 97KinIndB-14
❑ 98AkrAerM-23
McDonald, Keith
❑ 94JohCitCC-20
❑ 94JohCitCF-3706
❑ 95PeoChiTI-7
❑ 96StPetCB-18
❑ 97ArkTraB-12
❑ 98MemRedG-11
McDonald, Kevin
❑ 90HelBreSP-5
❑ 91SalLakTP-3207
❑ 91SalLakTSP-5
❑ 92WesPalBEC-8
❑ 92WesPalBEF-2086
❑ 93WesPalBEC-15
❑ 93WesPalBEF-1336
McDonald, Kirk
❑ 86MadMusP-14
❑ 86MadMusP-14
❑ 88HunStaTI-11
❑ 89ModA'sC-13
❑ 89ModA'sCLC-274
McDonald, Mac (Mark)
❑ 82MadMusF-29
McDonald, Manny
❑ 81OklCit8T-12
McDonald, Matt
❑ 96SavSanB-27
❑ 97VerBeaD-16
❑ 98SanBerS-20
❑ 98SanBerSTIS-17
McDonald, Mike (Michael)
❑ 86BelMarCr-103
❑ 86HunStaDJ-42
❑ 87WauTimP-20
❑ 88MidLeaAGS-55
❑ 88WauTimGS-11
❑ 89EveGiaS-20
❑ 89SanBerSB-22
❑ 89SanBerSCLC-87
❑ 90Bes-226
❑ 90CMC-794
❑ 90WilBilB-15
❑ 90WilBilP-1069
❑ 90WilBilS-16
❑ 91JacSunLD-338
❑ 91JacSunP-162
❑ 91LinDriAA-338
❑ 92JacSunF-3720
❑ 92JacSunS-364
❑ 92SkyAA F-156
❑ 93NasXprF-416
McDonald, Rob
❑ 91MisStaB-54
McDonald, Rod
❑ 82WatIndF-8
❑ 82WatIndT-7
❑ 83BufBisT-5
McDonald, Ron
❑ 25Zee-33
McDonald, Russ
❑ 83TacTigT-7
McDonald, Rusty
❑ 78CliDodT-22
McDonald, Shelby
❑ 87UtiBluSP-6
❑ 88SpaPhiP-1030
❑ 88SpaPhiS-14
❑ 89ClePhiS-16
❑ 90ClePhiS-15
McDonald, T.J.
❑ 84EveGiaC-22B
❑ 86FreGiaSB-24
❑ 87ShrCapP-18
❑ 88ShrCapP-1302
❑ 89SanJosGB-25
❑ 89SanJosGCLC-224
❑ 89SanJosGP-436
❑ 89SanJosGS-19
McDonald, Tony
❑ 80CarMudF-21
❑ 82OklCit8T-15
❑ 82ReaPhiT-21
McDonald, Webster
❑ 78LauLonABS-10
❑ 91PomBlaBPB-23
❑ 94TedWil-108
McDonnell, Clarence
❑ 09ObaT21-351
❑ 11PacCoaBD-40
❑ 11Zee-118
❑ 12ObaPreT-100
❑ 12Zee-151
❑ 13Zee-143
❑ 15Zee-12
McDonnell, Gary
❑ 98HelBreM-24
McDonnell, Mack (James William)
❑ 47PadTeal-14
❑ 77TCMTheWY-69
McDonnell, Shawn
❑ 94PeoChiC-18
❑ 94PeoChiF-2269
McDonough, Brian
❑ 82MiaMarT-4
❑ 83SanJosBC-5
McDonough, Neil
❑ 91TopRut-6
McDougal, Art
❑ 30Zee-146
❑ 31Zee-109
McDougal, John
❑ 90DodTar-1024
McDougal, Julius
❑ 86WinSpiP-15
❑ 87PorBeaP-12
❑ 88EasLeaAP-9
❑ 88GleFalTP-919
❑ 89CanIndB-2
❑ 89CanIndP-1321
❑ 89CanIndS-15
❑ 90CMC-267
❑ 90NewBriRSB-3
❑ 90NewBriRSP-1326
❑ 90NewBriRSS-10
❑ 90PawRedSC-16
❑ 90PawRedSDD-14
❑ 90TopTVRS-53
❑ 91LinDriAAA-503
❑ 91SyrChiLD-503
❑ 91SyrChiMB-16
❑ 91SyrChiP-2486
McDougal, Mike
❑ 96NewJerCB-19
❑ 97NewJerCB-19
❑ 98PriWilCQ-9
McDougald, Gil
❑ 47Exh-157
❑ 47PM1StaP1-139
❑ 47StaPinP2-27
❑ 52BerRos-40
❑ 52Bow-33
❑ 52CokTip-5
❑ 52RedMan-AL14
❑ 52TipTop-25
❑ 52Top-372
❑ 53BowC-63
❑ 53Bri-36
❑ 53Dor-110
❑ 53Dor-110A
❑ 53RedMan-AL23
❑ 53Top-43
❑ 54Bow-97
❑ 54DixLid-9
❑ 54NewYorJA-52
❑ 54RedHeaF-20
❑ 54RedMan-AL25
❑ 54StaMey-8
❑ 55Bow-9
❑ 55StaMey-7
❑ 56Top-225
❑ 56YanJayP-10
❑ 56YanTeal-17
❑ 57SwiFra-9
❑ 57Top-200
❑ 57YanJayP-12
❑ 58Top-20A
❑ 58Top-20B
❑ 58YanJayP-10
❑ 59Top-237
❑ 59Top-345
❑ 59Yoo-5
❑ 60MacSta-16
❑ 60Top-247
❑ 60YanJayP-9
❑ 61Pos-10
❑ 79TCM50-155
❑ 83TopRep5-372
❑ 85TCMPhoC-14
❑ 90PacLeg-94
❑ 91TopArc1-43
❑ 92ActPacA-33
❑ 92YanWIZ6-83
❑ 92YanWIZA-47
❑ 93UppDecAH-93
❑ 94UppDecAH-26
❑ 94UppDecAH1-26
❑ 98BowChrR-6
❑ 98BowChrRR-6
McDowell, Arturo
❑ 98SalVol-24
❑ 99Bow-91
❑ 99BowBes-185
❑ 99BowBesAR-185
❑ 99BowBesR-185
❑ 99BowChr-91
❑ 99BowChrG-91
❑ 99BowChrGR-91
❑ 99BowChrI-91
❑ 99BowChrIR-91
❑ 99BowChrR-91
❑ 99BowGol-91
❑ 99BowInt-91
❑ 99TeaBesR-57
❑ 99TeaBesRG-57
❑ 99TeaBesRS-57
❑ 99Top-214
❑ 99TopChr-214
❑ 99TopChrR-214
McDowell, Jack
❑ 88Don-47
❑ 88DonRoo-40
❑ 88Fle-407
❑ 88FleGlo-407
❑ 88FleHotS-25
❑ 88FleMin-16
❑ 88Lea-47
❑ 88ScoRoo-85T
❑ 88ScoRooG-85T
❑ 88TopTra-68T
❑ 88TopTraT-68T
❑ 88WhiSoxC-16
❑ 89Bow-61
❑ 89BowTif-61
❑ 89Don-531
❑ 89Fle-504
❑ 89FleGlo-504
❑ 89OPC-143
❑ 89PanSti-302
❑ 89Sco-289
❑ 89Top-486
❑ 89TopSti-302
❑ 89TopTif-486
❑ 89ToyRoo-20
❑ 89UppDec-530
❑ 89VanCanP-577
❑ 90Bow-305
❑ 90BowTif-305
❑ 90TopTra-71T
❑ 90TopTraT-71T
❑ 90UppDec-625
❑ 90WhiSoxC-17
❑ 91Bow-352
❑ 91Cla3-T66
❑ 91Don-57A
❑ 91Don-57B
❑ 91Fle-129
❑ 91Lea-340
❑ 91OPC-219
❑ 91Sco-27
❑ 91StaClu-87
❑ 91Stu-36
❑ 91Top-219
❑ 91TopDesS-219
❑ 91TopMic-219
❑ 91TopTif-219
❑ 91Ult-78
❑ 91UppDec-323
❑ 91USPlaCA-3H
❑ 91WhiSoxK-29
❑ 91WhiSoxK-NNO
❑ 92Bow-371
❑ 92Bow-605
❑ 92Cla2-T82
❑ 92Don-352
❑ 92DonCraJ2-36
❑ 92Fle-89
❑ 92FleSmo'nH-S2
❑ 92Hig5-17
❑ 92Lea-422
❑ 92LeaBlaG-422
❑ 92OPC-11
❑ 92Pin-107
❑ 92Pin-291
❑ 92Pin-607
❑ 92RedFolS-63
❑ 92Sco-62
❑ 92Sco100S-22
❑ 92ScoImpP-73
❑ 92ScoProP-16
❑ 92SpoIllFK1-136
❑ 92StaClu-52
❑ 92StaCluD-114
❑ 92Top-11
❑ 92TopGol-11
❑ 92TopGolW-11
❑ 92TopMic-11
❑ 92TriPla-129
❑ 92Ult-40
❑ 92UltAllS-10
❑ 92UppDec-553
❑ 92UppDecTMH-34
❑ 92WhiSoxK-29
❑ 93Bow-527
❑ 93ClaGam-61
❑ 93Don-433
❑ 93DurPowP2-20
❑ 93Fin-172
❑ 93FinRef-172
❑ 93Fla-188
❑ 93Fle-207
❑ 93FleAll-AL12
❑ 93FleFruotL-44
❑ 93FunPac-200
❑ 93Hos-31
❑ 93Lea-400
❑ 93MetBak-15
❑ 93MSABenSPD-10
❑ 93OPC-264
❑ 93PacSpa-73
❑ 93PanSti-134
❑ 93Pin-80
❑ 93RedFolS-60
❑ 93Sco-70
❑ 93Sel-196
❑ 93SelAce-3
❑ 93SelStaL-61
❑ 93SelStaL-86
❑ 93SP-258
❑ 93StaClu-75
❑ 93StaCluFDI-75
❑ 93StaCluM-157
❑ 93StaCluMO-15
❑ 93StaCluMOP-75
❑ 93Stu-200
❑ 93Top-344
❑ 93TOPBLAG-38
❑ 93TopComotH-5
❑ 93TopGol-344
❑ 93TopInaM-344
❑ 93TopInaR-344
❑ 93TopMic-344
❑ 93TriPla-158
❑ 93Ult-176
❑ 93UppDec-357
❑ 93UppDecGold-357
❑ 93WhiSoxK-20
❑ 93WhiSoxSC-18
❑ 94Bow-455
❑ 94BowBes-R23
❑ 94BowBesR-R23
❑ 94ColC-306
❑ 94ColC-309
❑ 94ColC-445
❑ 94ColChoGS-306
❑ 94ColChoGS-309
❑ 94ColChoGS-445
❑ 94ColChoSS-306
❑ 94ColChoSS-309
❑ 94ColChoSS-445
❑ 94Don-20
❑ 94DonAwaWJ-7
❑ 94DonEli-47
❑ 94DonSpeE-20
❑ 94Fin-226
❑ 94FinJum-226
❑ 94FinRef-226
❑ 94Fla-280
❑ 94Fle-89
❑ 94Fle-708
❑ 94FleAllS-15
❑ 94FleAwaW-3
❑ 94FleExtB-51
❑ 94FleExtBPD-1
❑ 94FleLeaL-5
❑ 94FlePro-7
❑ 94FleSun-18
❑ 94FUnPac-129
❑ 94KinDis-3
❑ 94Lea-125
❑ 94LeaGolS-15
❑ 94LeaL-22
❑ 94O-PJumAF-14
❑ 94OPC-173
❑ 94OPCAllR-14
❑ 94OPCJumA-14
❑ 94OscMayR-8
❑ 94Pac-134
❑ 94Pac-657
❑ 94PanSti-8
❑ 94PanSti-50
❑ 94Pin-57
❑ 94PinArtP-57
❑ 94PinMusC-57
❑ 94PinTeaP-9
❑ 94Pos-7
❑ 94ProMag-26
❑ 94Sco-6
❑ 94Sco-633
❑ 94ScoGolR-6
❑ 94ScoGolR-633
❑ 94ScoGolS-39
❑ 94ScoSam-6
❑ 94ScoSam-6GR
❑ 94Sel-97
❑ 94SP-192
❑ 94SPDieC-192
❑ 94Spo-92
❑ 94Spo-184
❑ 94StaClu-24
❑ 94StaCluDD-DD5
❑ 94StaCluFDI-24
❑ 94StaCluGR-24
❑ 94StaCluMO-21
❑ 94StaCluMOP-24
❑ 94StaCluT-122
❑ 94StaCluTFDI-122
❑ 94Stu-207
❑ 94SupMcDP-1
❑ 94SupMcDP-2
❑ 94TomPiz-22
❑ 94Top-392
❑ 94Top-515
❑ 94TopBlaG-12
❑ 94TopGol-392
❑ 94TopGol-515
❑ 94TopSpa-392
❑ 94TopSpa-515
❑ 94TopSupS-28
❑ 94TriPla-267
❑ 94TriPlaM-13
❑ 94Ult-340
❑ 94UltAllS-10
❑ 94UltAwaW-22
❑ 94UltLeaL-4
❑ 94UppDec-395
❑ 94UppDecAJ-42
❑ 94UppDecAJG-42
❑ 94UppDecED-395
❑ 94USPlaCA-4S
❑ 94WhiSoxK-22
❑ 95Baz-106
❑ 95Bow-418
❑ 95ColCho-515
❑ 95ColChoGS-515
❑ 95ColChoSE-232
❑ 95ColChoSEGS-232
❑ 95ColChoSESS-232
❑ 95ColChoSS-515
❑ 95Don-418
❑ 95DonPreP-418
❑ 95DonTopotO-121
❑ 95Emo-63
❑ 95Fin-207
❑ 95Fin-258
❑ 95FinRef-207
❑ 95FinRef-258
❑ 95Fla-286
❑ 95Fle-126
❑ 95FleTeaL-4
❑ 95FleUpd-26
❑ 95Lea-399
❑ 95LeaLim-143
❑ 95Pac-94
❑ 95PacPri-30
❑ 95Pin-365
❑ 95PinArtP-365
❑ 95PinMusC-365
❑ 95Sco-255
❑ 95ScoGolR-255
❑ 95ScoPlaTS-255
❑ 95Sel-108
❑ 95SelArtP-108
❑ 95SP-176
❑ 95SPCha-176
❑ 95SPChaDC-176
❑ 95Spo-126
❑ 95SpoArtP-126
❑ 95SPSil-176
❑ 95StaClu-155
❑ 95StaClu-622
❑ 95StaCluFDI-155
❑ 95StaCluMOP-155
❑ 95StaCluMOP-622
❑ 95StaCluSTWS-155
❑ 95StaCluSTWS-622
❑ 95StaCluVR-81
❑ 95StaCluVRMO-81
❑ 95Stu-100
❑ 95Top-561
❑ 95TopCyb-337
❑ 95TopTra-36T
❑ 95UC3-42
❑ 95UC3ArtP-42
❑ 95Ult-312
❑ 95UltGolM-312
❑ 95UppDec-206
❑ 95UppDecED-206
❑ 95UppDecEDG-206
❑ 95UppDecSE-143
❑ 95UppDecSEG-143
❑ 96Baz-117
❑ 96Bow-24
❑ 96BowFoi-24
❑ 96ColCho-233
❑ 96ColCho-771
❑ 96ColChoGS-233
❑ 96ColChoSS-233
❑ 96Don-418
❑ 96DonPreP-418
❑ 96EmoXL-51
❑ 96Fin-B203
❑ 96FinRef-B203
❑ 96Fla-69
❑ 96Fle-190
❑ 96FleTif-190
❑ 96FleUpd-U32
❑ 96FleUpdTC-U32
❑ 96LeaLim-90
❑ 96LeaLimG-90
❑ 96LeaPre-84
❑ 96LeaPreP-84
❑ 96MetUni-48
❑ 96MetUniP-48
❑ 96Pac-372
❑ 96PacPri-P120
❑ 96PacPriG-P120
❑ 96PanSti-157
❑ 96Pin-108
❑ 96Pin-359
❑ 96PinAfi-1
❑ 96PinAfiAP-1
❑ 96PinAfiFPP-1
❑ 96PinArtP-42
❑ 96PinFoil-359
❑ 96PinSta-42
❑ 96SchDis-11
❑ 96Sco-46
❑ 96ScoDugC-A40
❑ 96ScoDugCAP-A40
❑ 96Sel-117
❑ 96SelArtP-117

❑ 96SelCer-88
❑ 96SelCerAP-88
❑ 96SelCerCB-88
❑ 96SelCerCR-88
❑ 96SelCerMB-88
❑ 96SelCerMG-88
❑ 96SelCerMR-88
❑ 96SP-72
❑ 96Spo-87
❑ 96SpoArtP-87
❑ 96StaClu-8
❑ 96StaCluEPB-8
❑ 96StaCluEPG-8
❑ 96StaCluEPS-8
❑ 96StaCluMeg-MH6
❑ 96StaCluMOP-8
❑ 96StaCluMOP-MH6
❑ 96Stu-135
❑ 96StuPrePB-135
❑ 96StuPrePG-135
❑ 96StuPrePS-135
❑ 96Sum-62
❑ 96SumAbo&B-62
❑ 96SumArtP-62
❑ 96SumFoi-62
❑ 96Top-203
❑ 96TopChr-69
❑ 96TopChrR-69
❑ 96TopGal-28
❑ 96TopGalPPI-28
❑ 96TopLas-59
❑ 96Ult-102
❑ 96Ult-342
❑ 96UltGolM-102
❑ 96UltGolM-342
❑ 96UppDec-493U
❑ 96Zen-74
❑ 96ZenArtP-74
❑ 97Bow-12
❑ 97BowInt-12
❑ 97Cir-303
❑ 97CirRav-303
❑ 97ColCho-312
❑ 97Don-85
❑ 97DonGolPP-85
❑ 97DonSilPP-85
❑ 97DonTea-77
❑ 97DonTeaSPE-77
❑ 97Fin-55
❑ 97FinRef-55
❑ 97Fle-82
❑ 97FleTif-82
❑ 97IndSco-2
❑ 97IndScoPl-2
❑ 97IndScoPr-2
❑ 97IndScoU-2
❑ 97IndScoUTC-2
❑ 97MetUni-83
❑ 97NewPin-70
❑ 97NewPinAP-70
❑ 97NewPinMC-70
❑ 97NewPinPP-70
❑ 97Pac-75
❑ 97PacLigB-75
❑ 97PacSil-75
❑ 97PinCar-19
❑ 97Sco-85
❑ 97ScoArtPWB-85
❑ 97ScoPreS-85
❑ 97ScoShoS-85
❑ 97ScoShoSAP-85
❑ 97SP-62
❑ 97StaClu-75
❑ 97StaCluMOP-75
❑ 97Top-307
❑ 97TopChr-103
❑ 97TopChrR-103
❑ 97TopGal-56
❑ 97TopGalPPI-56
❑ 97Ult-51
❑ 97UltGolME-51
❑ 97UltPlaME-51
❑ 97UppDec-342
❑ 98IndSco-1
❑ 98IndScoP-1
❑ 98PacInvGems-39
❑ 98PacOnl-17
❑ 98PacOnlR-17
❑ 98PacOnlWC-17
❑ 98Sco-6
❑ 98UppDec-632
❑ 99UppDecM-3
❑ 99UppDecMGS-3
❑ 99UppDecMHFS-3
❑ 99UppDecMP-3
❑ 99UppDecMSS-3

McDowell, James
❑ 24Zee-133
❑ 26Zee-53

McDowell, Mike (Michael)
❑ 89AubAstP-2173
❑ 90AshTouP-2743
❑ 91BurAstC-7
❑ 91BurAstP-2798

McDowell, Oddibe
❑ 85DonHig-24
❑ 85FleUpd-80
❑ 85OklCit8T-18
❑ 85RanPer-0
❑ 85Top-400
❑ 85TopTif-400
❑ 85TopTifT-82T
❑ 85TopTra-82T
❑ 86Don-56
❑ 86Fle-566
❑ 86FleLeaL-23
❑ 86FleLimE-28
❑ 86FleMin-111
❑ 86FleStiC-73
❑ 86KayB-20
❑ 86Lea-46
❑ 86OPC-192
❑ 86OPCBoxB-K
❑ 86RanPer-0
❑ 86SevCoi-S9
❑ 86Spo-160
❑ 86Top-480
❑ 86TopGloS-1
❑ 86TopSti-237
❑ 86TopSti-307
❑ 86TopTat-20
❑ 86TopTif-480
❑ 86TopWaxBC-K
❑ 87ClaUpdY-115
❑ 87Don-161
❑ 87DonOpeD-177
❑ 87Fle-130
❑ 87FleGlo-130
❑ 87FleLimE-27
❑ 87FleStiC-77
❑ 87Lea-51
❑ 87OPC-95
❑ 87RanMot-4
❑ 87RanSmo-16
❑ 87RedFolSB-78
❑ 87Spo-131
❑ 87SpoTeaP-1
❑ 87Top-95
❑ 87TopSti-243
❑ 87TopTif-95
❑ 88Don-382
❑ 88Fle-473
❑ 88FleGlo-473
❑ 88FleStiC-66
❑ 88Lea-154
❑ 88OPC-234
❑ 88PanSti-208
❑ 88RanMot-4
❑ 88RanSmo-5
❑ 88Sco-215
❑ 88ScoGlo-215
❑ 88ScoYouS2-27
❑ 88Spo-175
❑ 88StaLinRa-8
❑ 88Top-617
❑ 88TopBig-198
❑ 88TopSti-237
❑ 88TopTif-617
❑ 89Bow-90
❑ 89BowTif-90
❑ 89BraDub-17
❑ 89Don-378
❑ 89DonTra-49
❑ 89Fle-528
❑ 89FleGlo-528
❑ 89IndTeal-18
❑ 89OPC-183
❑ 89PanSti-456
❑ 89Sco-59
❑ 89ScoRoo-72T
❑ 89Top-183
❑ 89TopBasT-113
❑ 89TopBig-245
❑ 89TopTif-183
❑ 89TopTra-78T
❑ 89TopTraT-78T
❑ 89UppDec-333
❑ 89UppDec-796
❑ 90Bow-13
❑ 90BowTif-13
❑ 90BraDubP-19
❑ 90BraDubS-22
❑ 90Don-340
❑ 90DonBesN-100
❑ 90Fle-589
❑ 90FleCan-589
❑ 90Lea-112
❑ 90OPC-329
❑ 90PanSti-221
❑ 90PubIntS-563
❑ 90Sco-476
❑ 90Spo-207
❑ 90Top-329
❑ 90TopBig-148
❑ 90TopSti-32
❑ 90TopTif-329
❑ 90UppDec-145
❑ 91Don-450
❑ 91Fle-697
❑ 91OPC-533
❑ 91RedFolS-62
❑ 91RocRedWP-1915
❑ 91Sco-121
❑ 91Top-533
❑ 91TopDesS-533
❑ 91TopMic-533
❑ 91TopTif-533
❑ 91Ult-8
❑ 91UppDec-497
❑ 92EdmTraS-163
❑ 93RanKee-255
❑ 94FleUpd-94
❑ 94RanMagM-24
❑ 94RedFolMI-25
❑ 94TopTra-14T
❑ 95Fle-291
❑ 97AriStaBG-17

McDowell, Roger
❑ 85FleUpd-81
❑ 85MetColP-10
❑ 85MetTCM-40
❑ 85TopTifT-83T
❑ 85TopTra-83T
❑ 86BasStaB-72
❑ 86Don-629
❑ 86Fle-89
❑ 86KayB-21
❑ 86Lea-248
❑ 86MetColP-9
❑ 86MetFanC-7
❑ 86MetTCM-8
❑ 86MetWorSC-5
❑ 86OPC-139
❑ 86SevCoi-E15
❑ 86Spo-161
❑ 86Top-547
❑ 86TopGloS-39
❑ 86TopSti-103
❑ 86TopSti-312
❑ 86TopTat-20
❑ 86TopTif-547
❑ 87ClaGam-76
❑ 87Don-241
❑ 87Fle-16
❑ 87FleAwaW-25
❑ 87FleGlo-16
❑ 87Lea-49
❑ 87MetColP-7
❑ 87MetFanC-4
❑ 87OPC-185
❑ 87SmoNatL-6
❑ 87Spo-160
❑ 87Top-185
❑ 87TopGloS-8
❑ 87TopSti-104
❑ 87TopTif-185
❑ 88Don-651
❑ 88DonBasB-126
❑ 88DonTeaBM-651
❑ 88Fle-142
❑ 88FleBasA-24
❑ 88FleGlo-142
❑ 88FleMin-96
❑ 88FleStiC-105
❑ 88Lea-243
❑ 88MetColP-7
❑ 88MetFanC-42
❑ 88MetKah-42
❑ 88OPC-355
❑ 88Sco-188
❑ 88ScoGlo-188
❑ 88Spo-42
❑ 88StaLinMe-14
❑ 88Top-355
❑ 88TopBig-101
❑ 88TopMinL-62
❑ 88TopSti-100
❑ 88TopTif-355
❑ 89Don-265
❑ 89DonBasB-16
❑ 89Fle-43
❑ 89FleGlo-43
❑ 89FleUpd-110
❑ 89MetColP-43
❑ 89MetFanC-42
❑ 89OPC-296
❑ 89PanSti-132
❑ 89PhiTas-43
❑ 89Sco-281
❑ 89ScoRoo-53T
❑ 89Spo-79
❑ 89Top-735
❑ 89TopBasT-93
❑ 89TopSti-92
❑ 89TopTif-735
❑ 89TopTra-79T
❑ 89TopTraT-79T
❑ 89UppDec-296
❑ 90Bow-146
❑ 90BowTif-146
❑ 90ClaYel-T69
❑ 90Don-251
❑ 90DonBesN-57
❑ 90Fle-567
❑ 90FleCan-567
❑ 90Lea-20
❑ 90M.Vpin-80
❑ 90OPC-625
❑ 90PanSti-308
❑ 90PhiTas-22
❑ 90PubIntS-140
❑ 90Sco-445
❑ 90Spo-75
❑ 90Top-625
❑ 90TopBig-230
❑ 90TopSti-121
❑ 90TopTif-625
❑ 90UppDec-416
❑ 91Bow-500
❑ 91ClaGam-80
❑ 91Don-166
❑ 91Fle-405
❑ 91Lea-410
❑ 91MetWIZ-259
❑ 91OPC-43
❑ 91PanFreS-111
❑ 91PhiMed-26
❑ 91RedFolS-63
❑ 91Sco-537
❑ 91StaClu-506
❑ 91Stu-217
❑ 91Top-43
❑ 91TopDesS-43
❑ 91TopMic-43
❑ 91TopTif-43
❑ 91Ult-267
❑ 91UppDec-406
❑ 91UppDecFE-57F
❑ 92Bow-657
❑ 92DodMot-22
❑ 92DodPol-31
❑ 92DodSmo-10192
❑ 92Don-750
❑ 92Fle-464
❑ 92Lea-58
❑ 92LeaBlaG-58
❑ 92OPC-713
❑ 92Pin-445
❑ 92Sco-597
❑ 92StaClu-804
❑ 92StaCluNC-804
❑ 92Top-713
❑ 92TopGol-713
❑ 92TopGolW-713
❑ 92TopMic-713
❑ 92TriPla-80
❑ 92Ult-214
❑ 92UppDec-484
❑ 93DodMot-25
❑ 93DodPol-17
❑ 93DodStaC-25
❑ 93Don-350
❑ 93Fla-74
❑ 93Fle-451
❑ 93Lea-537
❑ 93PacSpa-501
❑ 93Pin-528
❑ 93Sco-605
❑ 93Sel-375
❑ 93StaClu-251
❑ 93StaCluFDI-251
❑ 93StaCluMOP-251
❑ 93Top-39
❑ 93TopGol-39
❑ 93TopInaM-39
❑ 93TopInaR-39
❑ 93TopMic-39
❑ 93TriPla-263
❑ 93Ult-58
❑ 93UppDec-250
❑ 93UppDecGold-250
❑ 94ColC-196
❑ 94ColChoGS-196
❑ 94ColChoSS-196
❑ 94DodDaiN-15
❑ 94DodMot-25
❑ 94DodPol-18
❑ 94Don-207
❑ 94Fle-517
❑ 94Pac-315
❑ 94Pin-339
❑ 94PinArtP-339
❑ 94PinMusC-339
❑ 94StaClu-38
❑ 94StaCluFDI-38
❑ 94StaCluGR-38
❑ 94StaCluMOP-38
❑ 94Top-296
❑ 94TopGol-296
❑ 94TopSpa-296
❑ 95RanCra-17
❑ 96BalOriP-19
❑ 96BalOriP-20
❑ 96Fle-253
❑ 96FleTif-253
❑ 96FleUpd-U4
❑ 96FleUpdTC-U4

McDowell, Sam
❑ 62Top-591
❑ 63Top-317
❑ 64Top-391
❑ 65Kah-28
❑ 65OPC-76
❑ 65Top-76
❑ 66Baz-17
❑ 66IndTeal-8
❑ 66IndVolC-8
❑ 66Kah-21
❑ 66Top-222
❑ 66Top-226
❑ 66Top-470
❑ 66TopRubl-65
❑ 66TopVen-222
❑ 66TopVen-226
❑ 67Baz-17
❑ 67CokCapl-15
❑ 67DexPre-142
❑ 67Kah-25
❑ 67OPCPapl-8
❑ 67Top-237
❑ 67Top-295
❑ 67Top-463
❑ 67TopPos-8
❑ 67TopTesF-14
❑ 67TopVen-259
❑ 68AtlOilPBCC-29
❑ 68Kah-B26
❑ 68OPC-12
❑ 68OPC-115
❑ 68Top-12
❑ 68Top-115
❑ 68TopActS-12C
❑ 68TopVen-12
❑ 68TopVen-115
❑ 69Kah-B15
❑ 69MilBra-184
❑ 69MLBOffS-42
❑ 69MLBPin-17
❑ 69OPC-7
❑ 69OPC-11
❑ 69Top-7
❑ 69Top-11
❑ 69Top-220
❑ 69Top-435
❑ 69TopDecl-27
❑ 69TopSta-166
❑ 69TopSup-14
❑ 69TopTeaP-13
❑ 70DayDaiNM-9
❑ 70Ind-8
❑ 70Kel-50
❑ 70MilBra-17
❑ 70MLBOffS-201
❑ 70OPC-72
❑ 70OPC-469
❑ 70Top-72
❑ 70Top-469
❑ 70Top-650
❑ 70TopCanL-16
❑ 70TopScr-14
❑ 70TopSup-10
❑ 70TraSta-14C
❑ 71AllBasA-16
❑ 71BazNumT-11
❑ 71BazUnn-29
❑ 71Ind-9
❑ 71Kel-37
❑ 71MilDud-15
❑ 71MLBOffS-379
❑ 71MLBOffS-568
❑ 71OPC-71
❑ 71OPC-150
❑ 71Top-71
❑ 71Top-150
❑ 71TopCoi-86
❑ 71TopGreM-50
❑ 71TopSup-16
❑ 71TopTat-29
❑ 71TopTat-30
❑ 72Kel-33A
❑ 72Kel-33B
❑ 72MilBra-224
❑ 72Top-720
❑ 73LinPor-163
❑ 73OPC-342
❑ 73OPC-511
❑ 73Top-342
❑ 73Top-511
❑ 74OPC-550
❑ 74SyrChiTI-15
❑ 74Top-550
❑ 75SSP18-8
❑ 78TCM60I-103
❑ 86IndGreT-10
❑ 89PacLegI-155
❑ 89SweBasG-71
❑ 92ActPacA-48
❑ 92YanWIZ7-110
❑ 93UppDecAH-94
❑ 94TedWil-27
❑ 94UppDecAH-127
❑ 94UppDecAH1-127
❑ 99SpollIGotG-62
❑ 99SpollIGotGA-48
❑ 99SpollIGotGC-12

McDowell, Tim
❑ 90SalBucS-10
❑ 91ParPatF-19
❑ 91SalBucC-16
❑ 91SalBucP-946

McDowell, Ward
❑ 12HomRunKE-43
❑ 12Zee-70

McElfish, Shawn
❑ 90BurIndP-3007

McElligott, Bob
❑ 94KinIndC-27
❑ 95KinIndTI-18

McElroy, Chuck (Charles)
❑ 87SpaPhiP-5
❑ 88ReaPhiP-875
❑ 89ReaPhiB-1
❑ 89ReaPhiP-669
❑ 89ReaPhiS-18
❑ 90Bow-150
❑ 90BowTif-150
❑ 90Fle-650
❑ 90FleCan-650
❑ 90PhiTas-23
❑ 90TopDeb89-79
❑ 90UppDec-706
❑ 91CubMar-33
❑ 91CubVinL-19
❑ 91Don-709
❑ 91DonRoo-49
❑ 91Fle-406
❑ 91FleUpd-79
❑ 91Sco-374
❑ 91ScoRoo-34
❑ 91StaClu-407
❑ 91UltUpd-71
❑ 91UppDecFE-29F
❑ 92Cla1-T60
❑ 92CubMar-35
❑ 92Don-650
❑ 92Fle-388
❑ 92Lea-158
❑ 92LeaBlaG-158
❑ 92OPC-727
❑ 92OPCPre-85
❑ 92Pin-329
❑ 92Sco-366
❑ 92Sco100RS-63
❑ 92StaClu-474

❑ 92Stu-16
❑ 92Top-727
❑ 92TopGol-727
❑ 92TopGolW-727
❑ 92TopMic-727
❑ 92TriPla-245
❑ 92Ult-470
❑ 92UppDec-220
❑ 93CubStaC-18
❑ 93Don-236
❑ 93Fla-17
❑ 93Fle-22
❑ 93Pin-341
❑ 93Sco-389
❑ 93StaClu-472
❑ 93StaCluFDI-472
❑ 93StaCluMOP-472
❑ 93Top-346
❑ 93TopGol-346
❑ 93TopInaM-346
❑ 93TopInaR-346
❑ 93TopMic-346
❑ 93Ult-20
❑ 93UppDec-130
❑ 93UppDecGold-130
❑ 94ColC-503
❑ 94ColChoGS-503
❑ 94ColChoSS-503
❑ 94Don-639
❑ 94Fla-367
❑ 94Fle-390
❑ 94FleUpd-120
❑ 94RedKah-18
❑ 94Top-613
❑ 94TopGol-613
❑ 94TopSpa-613
❑ 94TopTra-19T
❑ 94Ult-163
❑ 95Don-290
❑ 95DonPreP-290
❑ 95Fle-440
❑ 95RedKah-18
❑ 95Top-141
❑ 95TopCyb-93
❑ 95Ult-146
❑ 95UltGolM-146
❑ 96LeaSigEA-123
❑ 97WhiSoxTI-26
❑ 98PacOnl-253
❑ 98PacOnlR-253
❑ 98PacOnlWC-253
❑ 98Sco-12
❑ 98WhiSoxS-2
❑ 98WhiSoxSP-2
❑ 99Pac-150
❑ 99PacPlaB-150
❑ 99PacRed-150
McElroy, Glen
❑ 86PenWhiSP-17
❑ 87DayBeaAP-26
❑ 89BirBarP-116
McElveen, Pryor
❑ 09T206-236
❑ 10CouT21-45
❑ 11SpoLifM-160
❑ 11T205-113
❑ 90DodTar-1025
McElwain, Tim
❑ 85CloHSS-26
McEnaney, Will
❑ 75OPC-481
❑ 75Top-481
❑ 75TopMin-481
❑ 76OPC-362
❑ 76RedIceL-8
❑ 76Top-362
❑ 77ExpPos-21
❑ 77OPC-50
❑ 77Top-160
❑ 78OPC-81
❑ 78Top-603
❑ 80Top-563
❑ 91MiaMirC-2
❑ 91MiaMirP-424
McEntire, Ethan
❑ 94KinMetC-11
❑ 94KinMetF-3819
❑ 95PitMetTI-40
❑ 97St.LucM-17
❑ 98St.LucMM-25
Mcevoy, Casey
❑ 98BilMusTI-23
McEvoy, Lou
❑ 29Zee-78
❑ 33Zee-62
McEwing, Joe
❑ 93SavCarC-18
❑ 93SavCarF-701
❑ 94MadHatC-16
❑ 94MadHatF-147
❑ 94MidLeaAF-MDW44
❑ 95Exc-271
❑ 96ArkTraB-20
❑ 97ArkTraB-15
❑ 98ArkTraH-5
❑ 98ArkTraM-20
❑ 99Bow-399
❑ 99BowBes-149
❑ 99BowBesAR-149
❑ 99BowBesR-149
❑ 99BowGol-399
❑ 99BowInt-399
❑ 99DumSet-135
❑ 99FleMys-135
❑ 99FleMysM-135
❑ 99PacOme-196
❑ 99PacOmeC-196
❑ 99PacOmeG-196
❑ 99PacOmePB-196
❑ 99Rev-117
❑ 99RevPremDate-117
❑ 99RevRet-117
❑ 99RevShaSS-117
❑ 99SkyPre-258
❑ 99SkyPre-258
❑ 99SkyPreA-40
❑ 99SkyPreABlue-40
❑ 99SkyPreDD-8
❑ 99SkyPreR-258
❑ 99SkyPreR-258
❑ 99UppDecE-101
❑ 99UppDecEFXG-101
McFadden, Leon
❑ 69OPC-156
❑ 69Top-156
❑ 69TopFou-2
❑ 70Top-672
❑ 72MilBra-225
McFarland, Chappie (Charles A.)
❑ 11SpoLifCW-242
❑ 90DodTar-505
McFarland, Dustin
❑ 85AncGlaPTI-19
❑ 86AncGlaPTI-20
❑ 87AncGlaP-21
McFarland, Ed
❑ 03BreE10-98
❑ 07WhiSoxGWH-7
McFarland, Herm
❑ 03BreE10-99
❑ 11SpoLifCW-243
McFarland, Kelly
❑ 85AncGlaPTI-43
❑ 86AncGlaPTI-21
McFarland, Steve
❑ 85AncGlaPTI-20
❑ 86AncGlaPTI-22
❑ 87AncGlaP-22
❑ 95ElmPioTI-16
❑ 95ElmPioUTI-16
McFarland, Toby
❑ 92BriTigC-6
❑ 92BriTigF-1406
❑ 93NiaFalRF-3382
❑ 94FayGenC-16
❑ 94FayGenF-2141
McFarlane, Hemmy
❑ 85NewOriT-6
McFarlane, Orlando
❑ 62Top-229
❑ 64PirKDK-19
❑ 64Top-509
❑ 66Top-569
❑ 67Top-496
❑ 69MilBra-185
McFarlin, Jason
❑ 89EveGiaS-28
❑ 90CliGiaB-13
❑ 90CliGiaP-2563
❑ 90CMC-845
❑ 91CalLeLA-43
❑ 91Cla/Bes-70
❑ 91SanJosGC-10
❑ 91SanJosGP-24
❑ 91SanJosGP-26
❑ 92ClaFS7-249
❑ 92SanJosGC-15
❑ 94ShrCapF-1619
❑ 96GreBraB-20
❑ 96GreBraTI-50
McFarlin, Terry
❑ 91BakDodCLC-31
❑ 91CalLeLA-9
❑ 93SanAntMF-3001
❑ 94WicWraF-187
McFerrin, Chris
❑ 96AubDouB-13
❑ 97QuaCitRBB-16
McGaffigan, Andy
❑ 79WesHavYT-14
❑ 80NasSouTI-13
❑ 81ColCliT-8
❑ 82PhoGiaVNB-19
❑ 82Top-83
❑ 83GiaMot-20
❑ 83GiaPos-20
❑ 83TopTra-68T
❑ 84Don-309
❑ 84ExpPos-19
❑ 84ExpStu-34
❑ 84Fle-382
❑ 84FleUpd-78
❑ 84Nes792-31
❑ 84Top-31
❑ 84TopTif-31
❑ 84TopTra-78T
❑ 84TopTraT-78T
❑ 85Don-646
❑ 85Fle-540
❑ 85Top-323
❑ 85TopTif-323
❑ 86ExpPos-8
❑ 86ExpProPa-4
❑ 86ExpProPo-8
❑ 86Fle-181
❑ 86FleUpd-74
❑ 86Top-133
❑ 86TopTif-133
❑ 86TopTra-72T
❑ 86TopTraT-72T
❑ 87Don-380
❑ 87ExpPos-15
❑ 87Fle-326
❑ 87FleGlo-326
❑ 87GenMilB-4E
❑ 87Lea-220
❑ 87OPC-351
❑ 87Top-742
❑ 87TopTif-742
❑ 88Don-380
❑ 88ExpPos-21
❑ 88Fle-190
❑ 88FleGlo-190
❑ 88OPC-56
❑ 88Sco-366
❑ 88ScoGlo-366
❑ 88StaLinE-11
❑ 88Top-488
❑ 88TopTif-488
❑ 89Bow-356
❑ 89BowTif-356
❑ 89Don-338
❑ 89ExpPos-21
❑ 89Fle-386
❑ 89FleGlo-386
❑ 89OPC-278
❑ 89Sco-138
❑ 89Top-278
❑ 89TopBig-315
❑ 89TopSti-75
❑ 89TopTif-278
❑ 89UppDec-359
❑ 90CMC-185
❑ 90Don-574
❑ 90Fle-355
❑ 90FleCan-355
❑ 90OmaRoyC-10
❑ 90OPC-559
❑ 90PubIntS-182
❑ 90Sco-224
❑ 90Top-559
❑ 90TopTif-559
❑ 90UppDec-597A
❑ 90UppDec-597B
❑ 91LinDriAAA-342
❑ 91OmaRoyLD-342
❑ 91OPC-671
❑ 91RoyPol-14
❑ 91Sco-619
❑ 91Top-671
❑ 91TopDesS-671
❑ 91TopMic-671
❑ 91TopTif-671
❑ 92YanWIZ8-116
McGaffigan, Mark
❑ 16Zee-135
❑ 19Zee-54
❑ 20Zee-68
❑ 21Zee-74
❑ 23Zee-48
McGah, Ed
❑ 46RedSoxTI-15
❑ 75RedSox1T-25
McGaha, Mel
❑ 60MapLeaSF-13
❑ 62IndJayP-8
❑ 62Top-242
❑ 64A's-13
❑ 65AthJayP-10
❑ 65Top-391
❑ 67Ast-17
McGann, Dan
❑ 06FanCraNL-29
❑ 06GiaUllAFS-8
❑ 11SpoLifCW-244
❑ 90DodTar-1026
McGann, Dennis
❑ 09ColChiE-187
❑ 09T206-441
❑ 12ColRedB-187
❑ 12ColTinT-187
McGann, Don
❑ 83GreHorT-30
❑ 84NasSouTI-14
❑ 85NasSouTI-12
❑ 86NasSouTI-17
❑ 87TolMudHP-23
❑ 88TolMudHP-606
❑ 89EdmTraP-560
❑ 97VanCanB-4
McGannon, Paul
❑ 81OmaRoyT-3
❑ 82OmaRoyT-27
❑ 83OmaRoyT-26
McGarity, Jeremy
❑ 90JohCitCS-18
❑ 91SavCarC-10
❑ 91SavCarP-1651
❑ 92Bow-26
❑ 92ClaFS7-280
❑ 92St.PetCC-16
❑ 92St.PetCF-2025
❑ 93St.PetCC-18
❑ 93St.PetCF-2625
❑ 94MadHatC-17
❑ 94MadHatF-128
McGarr, Chippy (James)
❑ 87OldJudN-329
❑ 90KalBatN-37
❑ 98CamPepP-52
McGeachy, Jack (John)
❑ 87BucN28-44
❑ 87OldJudN-330
McGee, Brian
❑ 91BenBucCB-22
❑ 91BenBucP-3697
❑ 92PeoChiC-26
❑ 92PeoChiTI-12
McGee, Francis
❑ 27Zee-96
McGee, Mickey
❑ 98DunBluJTI-24
McGee, Ron
❑ 80SpoIndT-6
McGee, Tim
❑ 86WinHavRSP-17
❑ 87GreHorP-16
❑ 88LynRedSS-13
❑ 88NewBriRSP-901
McGee, Tom
❑ 98DelShoM-21
McGee, Tony
❑ 89SpoIndSP-5
❑ 90RivRedWB-16
❑ 90RivRedWCLC-4
❑ 90RivRedWP-2611
McGee, Willie D.
❑ 79WesHavYT-13
❑ 80NasSouTI-14
❑ 81NasSouTI-9
❑ 82LouRedE-16
❑ 83AllGamPI-153
❑ 83Car-19
❑ 83CarPanP-4
❑ 83Don-190
❑ 83Fle-15
❑ 83FleSti-2
❑ 83OPC-49
❑ 83Top-49
❑ 83TopSti-147
❑ 83TopSti-326
❑ 84AllGamPI-57
❑ 84Car-21
❑ 84Car5x7-18
❑ 84Don-353
❑ 84Don-625
❑ 84DonActAS-2
❑ 84Fle-329
❑ 84FunFooP-33
❑ 84Nes792-310
❑ 84OPC-310
❑ 84SevCoi-C9
❑ 84Top-310
❑ 84TopSti-141
❑ 84TopStiB-8
❑ 84TopTif-310
❑ 85AllGamPI-150
❑ 85CarTeal-24
❑ 85Don-475
❑ 85DonHig-29
❑ 85DonHig-38
❑ 85DonHig-52
❑ 85Fle-234
❑ 85KASDis-8
❑ 85KitCloD-8
❑ 85Lea-125
❑ 85OPC-57
❑ 85SubDis-36
❑ 85ThoMcAD-36
❑ 85Top-757
❑ 85TopMin-757
❑ 85TopSti-141
❑ 85TopTif-757
❑ 86BasStaB-73
❑ 86BurKinA-16
❑ 86CarIGAS-9
❑ 86CarKASD-20
❑ 86CarSchM-16
❑ 86CarTeal-30
❑ 86Don-3
❑ 86Don-109
❑ 86Don-651
❑ 86DonAll-36
❑ 86DonSupD-3
❑ 86DorChe-15
❑ 86Dra-23
❑ 86Fle-42
❑ 86Fle-636
❑ 86FleLeaL-24
❑ 86FleLimE-29
❑ 86FleMin-9
❑ 86FleSlu-22
❑ 86FleStiC-74
❑ 86GenMilB-4F
❑ 86Lea-3
❑ 86Lea-225
❑ 86MeaGolBB-9
❑ 86MeaGolM-6
❑ 86MeaGolSB-10
❑ 86MSAJifPD-15
❑ 86OPC-117
❑ 86OPCBoxB-L
❑ 86QuaGra-1
❑ 86SevCoi-S16
❑ 86Spo-19
❑ 86Spo-176
❑ 86Spo-179
❑ 86Spo-183
❑ 86Spo-184
❑ 86Top-580
❑ 86Top-707
❑ 86Top3-D-14
❑ 86TopGaloC-7
❑ 86TopGloS-9
❑ 86TopMinL-63
❑ 86TopSti-45
❑ 86TopSti-144
❑ 86TopSup-2
❑ 86TopTat-23
❑ 86TopTif-580
❑ 86TopTif-707
❑ 86TopWaxBC-L
❑ 86Woo-21
❑ 87CarSmo-22
❑ 87CarTeal-21
❑ 87ClaGam-31
❑ 87Don-84
❑ 87Dra-9
❑ 87Fle-304
❑ 87FleBasA-27
❑ 87FleGlo-304
❑ 87FleHotS-30
❑ 87FleLeaL-29
❑ 87GenMilB-5D
❑ 87Lea-113
❑ 87OPC-357
❑ 87RedFolSB-86
❑ 87Spo-74
❑ 87SpoTeaP-12
❑ 87Top-440
❑ 87TopSti-48
❑ 87TopTif-440
❑ 88Baz-12
❑ 88CarSmo-21
❑ 88CarTeal-20
❑ 88ClaRed-173
❑ 88Don-307
❑ 88DonAll-44
❑ 88DonBasB-131
❑ 88Fle-42
❑ 88FleGlo-42
❑ 88FleMin-108
❑ 88FleStiC-118
❑ 88FleTeaL-20
❑ 88KayB-17
❑ 88Lea-103
❑ 88OPC-160
❑ 88PanSti-396
❑ 88Sco-40
❑ 88ScoGlo-40
❑ 88Spo-91
❑ 88StaLinCa-14
❑ 88Top-160
❑ 88TopBig-79
❑ 88TopGloS-36
❑ 88TopMinL-71
❑ 88TopSti-55
❑ 88TopTif-160
❑ 88TopUKM-46
❑ 88TopUKMT-46
❑ 88Woo-26
❑ 89Bow-442
❑ 89BowTif-442
❑ 89CarSmo-13
❑ 89CarTeal-18
❑ 89ClaLigB-98
❑ 89Don-161
❑ 89DonAll-51
❑ 89Fle-457
❑ 89FleGlo-457
❑ 89LouRedBTI-27
❑ 89OPC-225
❑ 89PanSti-189
❑ 89Sco-88
❑ 89ScoHot1S-93
❑ 89Spo-206
❑ 89Top-640
❑ 89TopBasT-84
❑ 89TopBatL-12
❑ 89TopBig-183
❑ 89TopSti-36
❑ 89TopTif-640
❑ 89UppDec-621
❑ 90Bow-194
❑ 90BowTif-194
❑ 90CarSmo-14
❑ 90Don-632
❑ 90DonBesN-131
❑ 90Fle-253
❑ 90FleCan-253
❑ 90Lea-367
❑ 90MLBBasB-33
❑ 90OPC-285
❑ 90PanSti-339
❑ 90PubIntS-222
❑ 90Sco-374
❑ 90Top-285
❑ 90TopBatL-14
❑ 90TopBig-158
❑ 90TopTif-285
❑ 90TopTVCa-34
❑ 90UppDec-505
❑ 91Baz-11
❑ 91Bow-640
❑ 91Cla1-T74
❑ 91Cla2-T76
❑ 91ClaGam-162
❑ 91Don-666
❑ 91DonBonC-BC22
❑ 91Fle-16
❑ 91FleUpd-130
❑ 91GiaMot-6
❑ 91GiaPacGaE-23
❑ 91GiaSFE-10
❑ 91KinDis-1
❑ 91Lea-360
❑ 91OPC-380
❑ 91OPCBoxB-I
❑ 91OPCPre-78
❑ 91PanCanT1-1
❑ 91RedFolS-64
❑ 91Sco-597
❑ 91Sco100S-37

❑ 91ScoRoo-19T
❑ 91StaClu-335
❑ 91StaCluCM-20
❑ 91Stu-256
❑ 91Top-380
❑ 91TopDesS-380
❑ 91TopGaloC-9
❑ 91TopMic-380
❑ 91TopTif-380
❑ 91TopTra-76T
❑ 91TopTraT-76T
❑ 91TopWaxBC-I
❑ 91Ult-325
❑ 91UltUpd-118
❑ 91UppDec-584
❑ 91UppDec-721
❑ 92Bow-604
❑ 92CarMcD-43
❑ 92ClaGam-42
❑ 92Don-60
❑ 92Fle-643
❑ 92GiaMot-6
❑ 92GiaPacGaE-28
❑ 92Hig5-127
❑ 92KinDis-15
❑ 92Lea-47
❑ 92LeaBlaG-47
❑ 92OPC-65
❑ 92PanSti-217
❑ 92Pin-7
❑ 92RedFolS-64
❑ 92Sco-112
❑ 92Sco100S-18
❑ 92ScoProP-1
❑ 92StaClu-239
❑ 92SunSee-24
❑ 92Top-65
❑ 92TopGol-65
❑ 92TopGolW-65
❑ 92TopKid-61
❑ 92TopMic-65
❑ 92TriPla-101
❑ 92Ult-294
❑ 92UppDec-34
❑ 92UppDec-194
❑ 93Bow-196
❑ 93Don-355
❑ 93Fla-145
❑ 93Fle-159
❑ 93GiaMot-8
❑ 93GiaPos-25
❑ 93GiaStaC-11
❑ 93Lea-396
❑ 93OPC-210
❑ 93PacSpa-274
❑ 93PanSti-240
❑ 93Pin-39
❑ 93Pin-490
❑ 93RedFolS-61
❑ 93Sco-93
❑ 93Sel-119
❑ 93SP-114
❑ 93StaClu-91
❑ 93StaCluFDI-91
❑ 93StaCluMOP-91
❑ 93Stu-179
❑ 93Top-435
❑ 93TopGol-435
❑ 93TopInaM-435
❑ 93TopInaR-435
❑ 93TopMic-435
❑ 93TriPla-227
❑ 93Ult-487
❑ 93UppDec-281
❑ 93UppDecGold-281
❑ 94ColC-587
❑ 94ColChoGS-587
❑ 94ColChoSS-587
❑ 94Don-238
❑ 94DonDom-B8
❑ 94DonDomJ-B8
❑ 94Fin-184
❑ 94FinRef-184
❑ 94Fle-696
❑ 94FleExtB-390
❑ 94GiaAMC-14
❑ 94GiaMot-15
❑ 94GiaTarBC-16
❑ 94GiaTeal-9
❑ 94GiaUSPC-7S
❑ 94GiaUSPC-13D
❑ 94Lea-366
❑ 94Pac-551
❑ 94PanSti-265
❑ 94Pin-274
❑ 94PinArtP-274
❑ 94PinMusC-274
❑ 94ProMag-125
❑ 94Sco-70
❑ 94ScoGolR-70
❑ 94Sel-221
❑ 94StaClu-686
❑ 94StaCluFDI-686
❑ 94StaCluGR-686
❑ 94StaCluMOP-686
❑ 94StaCluT-6
❑ 94StaCluTFDI-6
❑ 94Stu-86
❑ 94Top-574
❑ 94TopGol-574
❑ 94TopSpa-574
❑ 94TriPla-107
❑ 94Ult-589
❑ 94UppDec-258
❑ 94UppDecED-258
❑ 95Sco-466
❑ 95ScoGolR-466
❑ 95ScoPlaTS-466
❑ 95StaCluMOP-RL39
❑ 95StaCluRL-RL39
❑ 95UppDec-484
❑ 96CarPol-18
❑ 96Cir-180
❑ 96CirRav-180
❑ 96Don-521
❑ 96DonPreP-521
❑ 96FleUpd-U191
❑ 96FleUpdTC-U191
❑ 96Ult-551
❑ 96UltGolM-551
❑ 97CarPol-19
❑ 97ColCho-199
❑ 97Don-281
❑ 97DonGolPP-281
❑ 97DonSilPP-281
❑ 97DonTea-162
❑ 97DonTeaSPE-162
❑ 97Fle-449
❑ 97FleTif-449
❑ 97Pac-414
❑ 97PacLigB-414
❑ 97PacSil-414
❑ 98ColCho-217
❑ 98Pac-415
❑ 98PacAur-186
❑ 98PacInvGems-206
❑ 98PacInvTeam-23
❑ 98PacOnl-620
❑ 98PacOnlR-620
❑ 98PacOnlWC-620
❑ 98PacPlaB-415
❑ 98PacRedT-415
❑ 98PacSil-415
❑ 98StaCluFDI-287
❑ 98StaCluI-287
❑ 98StaCluOneK-287
❑ 98StaCluPP-287
❑ 98Ult-288
❑ 98UltGolM-288
❑ 98UltMas-288
❑ 98UltPlaM-288
❑ 98UppDec-202
❑ 98UppDec-363
❑ 98UppDecSF-109
❑ 99Ult-58
❑ 99UltGolM-58
❑ 99UltMas-58
❑ 99UltPlaM-58
❑ 99UppDec-187
❑ 99UppDecEL1-187
❑ 99UppDecEL2-187
❑ 99Vic-327

McGeehee, Connor
❑ 82BufBisT-3
❑ 83LynPirT-21

McGehee, Kevin
❑ 90EveGiaP-3123
❑ 91CalLeLA-37
❑ 91SanJosGC-18
❑ 91SanJosGP-7
❑ 92Bow-616
❑ 92ClaFS7-256
❑ 92ProFS7-351
❑ 92ShrCapF-3866
❑ 92ShrCapS-587
❑ 92SkyAA F-259
❑ 92UppDecML-227
❑ 93ExcFS7-120
❑ 93PhoFirF-1513
❑ 94OriPro-62
❑ 94OriUSPC-3S
❑ 94RocRedWF-995
❑ 94RocRedWTI-14
❑ 94StaCluT-281
❑ 94StaCluTFDI-281
❑ 95RocRedWTI-25

McGehee, Mike
❑ 96ButCopKB-24
❑ 97PriDevR-11

McGhee, Bill
❑ 45A'sTeal-21

McGhee, Ed (Warren E.)
❑ 53A'sTeal-17
❑ 53Top-195
❑ 54Top-215
❑ 55Top-32
❑ 55TopDouH-77
❑ 91TopArc1-195
❑ 94TopArc1-215
❑ 94TopArc1G-215

McGilberry, Randy
❑ 77JacSunT-15
❑ 78SSP270-222
❑ 79Top-707
❑ 80OmaRoyP-17
❑ 80TidTidT-25

McGinley, James
❑ 09ColChiE-188
❑ 09T206-442
❑ 12ColRedB-188
❑ 12ColTinT-188
❑ 12ImpTobC-2

McGinn, Dan
❑ 69ExpFudP-7
❑ 69Top-646
❑ 70ExpPin-10
❑ 70ExpPos-3
❑ 70OPC-364
❑ 70Top-364
❑ 71ExpPS-16
❑ 71MLBOffS-134
❑ 71OPC-21
❑ 71Top-21
❑ 72MilBra-226
❑ 72OPC-473
❑ 72Top-473
❑ 73OPC-527
❑ 73Top-527

McGinn, Mark
❑ 92GulCoaMF-3478
❑ 94LetMouF-3876

McGinn, Shaun
❑ 90NebCor-16
❑ 93BatCliCB-18
❑ 93BatCliF-3153
❑ 94BatCliC-13
❑ 94BatCliF-3454

McGinnis, Jumbo (George Washington)
❑ 23Zee-90
❑ 25Zee-48
❑ 25Zee-72
❑ 87BucN28-100

McGinnis, Ronnie
❑ 98BatMucTI-17

McGinnis, Russ
❑ 86BelBreP-14
❑ 87BelBreP-13
❑ 89TacTigC-16
❑ 89TacTigP-1556
❑ 90CMC-598
❑ 90ProAAAF-143
❑ 90TacTigC-21
❑ 90TacTigP-96
❑ 91IowCubLD-211
❑ 91IowCubP-1063
❑ 91LinDriAAA-211
❑ 91TriA AAGP-AAA18
❑ 92DonRoo-72
❑ 92OklCit8S-316
❑ 92SkyAAAF-145
❑ 93OmaRoyF-1685
❑ 93RanKee-256
❑ 93TopGol-824
❑ 94OmaRoyF-1226

McGinnis, Shane
❑ 93GenCubC-21
❑ 93GenCubF-3186

McGinnity, Iron Man (Joe)
❑ 03BreE10-100
❑ 05RotCP-8
❑ 05RotCP-9
❑ 06FanCraNL-30
❑ 06GiaUllAFS-9
❑ 08AmeCarE91-14
❑ 08RosComP-130
❑ 09ColChiE-189
❑ 09T206-443
❑ 10RedCroT-49
❑ 10RedCroT-218
❑ 11MecDFT-31
❑ 11SpoLifCW-245
❑ 12ColRedB-189
❑ 12ColTinT-189
❑ 12ImpTobC-77
❑ 39PC7AlbHoF-45
❑ 50CalHOFW-54
❑ 53ArtHaloFP-61
❑ 61Fle-126
❑ 72ClaCar-72
❑ 72FleFamF-1
❑ 72LauGreF-6
❑ 76ShaPiz-45
❑ 77BobParHoF-36
❑ 80PerHaloFP-45
❑ 80SSPHOF-45
❑ 82TCMGreP-32
❑ 89DodSmoG-21
❑ 90DodTar-506
❑ 90HOFStiB-11
❑ 94ConTSN-1252
❑ 94ConTSNB-1252

McGivney, Tom
❑ 79AshTouT-3

McGlawn, Thomas
❑ 93MarPhiC-18
❑ 93MarPhiF-3483

McGlinchy, Kevin
❑ 96AppLeaAB-12
❑ 96DanBraB-14
❑ 97Bes-26
❑ 97Bow-307
❑ 97BowBes-122
❑ 97BowBesAR-122
❑ 97BowBesR-122
❑ 97BowInt-307
❑ 97CarLeaTP-22
❑ 97DurBulTI-11
❑ 98BesPreA-24
❑ 98Bow-98
❑ 98BowChr-98
❑ 98BowChrGA-98
❑ 98BowChrGAR-98
❑ 98BowChrI-98
❑ 98BowChrIR-98
❑ 98BowChrR-98
❑ 98BowGolA-98
❑ 98BowInt-98
❑ 98CarLeaAC-22
❑ 98CarLeaTPQ-7
❑ 98DanQ-C-2
❑ 98StaCluFDI-369
❑ 98StaCluI-369
❑ 98StaCluOneK-369
❑ 98StaCluPP-369
❑ 99BasAmeTPA-29
❑ 99Bow-357
❑ 99BowGol-357
❑ 99BowInt-357
❑ 99JustheS-32
❑ 99JustheSJB-32
❑ 99JustheSJN-3
❑ 99JustheSJP-7
❑ 99Rev-16
❑ 99RevPremDate-16
❑ 99RevRet-16
❑ 99RevShaSS-16

McGlone, Brian
❑ 91AubAstC-20
❑ 91AubAstP-4281
❑ 92BurAstC-16
❑ 92BurAstF-556
❑ 93QuaCitRBC-13
❑ 93QuaCitRBF-108

McGlone, John
❑ 87OldJudN-331

McGlothen, Lynn
❑ 72RedSoxTI-14
❑ 73LinPor-168
❑ 73OPC-114
❑ 73Top-114
❑ 75Kel-20
❑ 75OPC-272
❑ 75St.LouCP-18
❑ 75Top-272
❑ 75TopMin-272
❑ 76OPC-478
❑ 76SSP-297
❑ 76St.LouCP-21
❑ 76Top-478
❑ 77GiaTeal-18
❑ 77Top-47
❑ 78GiaTeal-22
❑ 78Top-581
❑ 79Top-323
❑ 80Top-716
❑ 81Don-562
❑ 81Fle-302
❑ 81Top-609
❑ 82Top-85
❑ 92YanWIZ8-117

McGlothin, Pat (Ezra)
❑ 50WorWidGV-10
❑ 52Par-53
❑ 90DodTar-1027

McGlothlin, Jim
❑ 65SeaPop-13
❑ 66Top-417
❑ 67OPC-19
❑ 67Top-19
❑ 67TopVen-225
❑ 68Baz-8
❑ 68Top-493
❑ 68TopActS-12A
❑ 69AngJacitB-7
❑ 69MilBra-186
❑ 69MLBOffS-24
❑ 69Top-386
❑ 69TopSta-146
❑ 69TopTeaP-17
❑ 70DayDaiNM-37
❑ 70MLBOffS-31
❑ 70OPC-132
❑ 70Top-132
❑ 71MLBOffS-63
❑ 71OPC-556
❑ 71Top-556
❑ 71TopCoi-9
❑ 72MilBra-227
❑ 72OPC-236
❑ 72Top-236
❑ 73OPC-318
❑ 73Top-318
❑ 74OPC-557
❑ 74Top-557

McGlynn, Stoney (Ulysses)
❑ 08RosComP-169
❑ 09T206-444
❑ 11MecDFT-32

McGonigle, Bill
❑ 96StoPorB-22

McGonnigal, Brett
❑ 91CliGiaC-4
❑ 91EveGiaC-5
❑ 91EveGiaP-3932
❑ 92CliGiaF-3611
❑ 92SanJosGC-24

McGorkle, Robbie
❑ 82DayBeaAT-18

McGough, Greg
❑ 91SarWhiSC-13
❑ 91SarWhiSP-1117
❑ 92SalSpuC-14
❑ 92SalSpuF-3758

McGough, Keith
❑ 91ButCopKSP-24
❑ 91GasRanC-9
❑ 91GasRanP-2686

McGough, Tom
❑ 75OklCit8TI-3
❑ 76WilTomT-10

McGovern, Steve
❑ 90BatCliP-3063

McGowan, Bill
❑ 80PerHaloFP-213
❑ 93ConTSN-737
❑ 94ConTSN-1212
❑ 94ConTSNB-1212

McGowan, Donnie
❑ 85ElmPioT-15
❑ 86GreHorP-14
❑ 87WinHavRSP-5
❑ 88WinHavRSS-12

McGowan, Earl
❑ 48GiaTeal-17

McGowan, Mike
❑ 93HigDesMC-29
❑ 93HigDesMF-NNO
❑ 94KanCouCC-30
❑ 94KanCouCTI-16
❑ 95PorSeaDTI-13

McGrath, Chuck (Charles)
❑ 83EriCarT-15
❑ 84SavCarT-6
❑ 85SprCarT-20
❑ 86St.PetCP-19
❑ 87ArkTraP-3
❑ 89ArkTraGS-12
❑ 89LouRedBTI-28
❑ 90CMC-48
❑ 90DenZepC-23
❑ 90DenZepP-622
❑ 90ElPasDGS-21
❑ 90ProAAAF-647

McGrath, Sean
❑ 98PitMetM-19

McGraw, Bob
❑ 21Zee-163
❑ 27MidBre-12
❑ 90DodTar-507

McGraw, Doug
❑ 92UtiBluSC-18
❑ 94OscAstF-1135

McGraw, Gary
❑ 82IdaFalAT-26

McGraw, Hank
❑ 71RicBraTI-14

McGraw, John J.
❑ 03BreE10-101
❑ 05RotCP-5
❑ 06FanCraNL-31
❑ 06GiaUllAFS-10
❑ 08AmeCarE91-15
❑ 08AmeCarE91-53
❑ 09MaxPubP-7
❑ 09SpoNewSM-57
❑ 09T206-237
❑ 09T206-238
❑ 09T206-239
❑ 09T206-240
❑ 10CouT21-180
❑ 10CouT21-181
❑ 10CouT21-302
❑ 10CouT21-303
❑ 10DomDisP-79
❑ 10E-UOraBSC-16
❑ 10E101-32
❑ 10E98-21
❑ 10JuJuDE-26
❑ 10MelMinE-32
❑ 10NadCarE-37
❑ 10NadE1-35
❑ 10PeoT21-38A
❑ 10PeoT21-38B
❑ 10RedCroT-50
❑ 10RedCroT-51
❑ 10RedCroT-135
❑ 10RedCroT-136
❑ 10RedCroT-219
❑ 10RedCroT-220
❑ 10StaCarE-22
❑ 10SweCapPP-118A
❑ 10SweCapPP-118B
❑ 10W555-47
❑ 11E94-24
❑ 11HelSta-132
❑ 11JonKeyaAC-345
❑ 11L1L-116
❑ 11S74Sil-89
❑ 11S81LarS-91
❑ 11SpoLifCW-246
❑ 11SpoLifM-212
❑ 11T205-114
❑ 11TurRedT-26
❑ 12HasTriFT-48B
❑ 12HasTriFT-48G
❑ 12T207-118
❑ 13LawSemC-7
❑ 13NatGamW-29
❑ 13TomBarW-28
❑ 14CraJacE-69
❑ 14PieStaT-70
❑ 14PolGroW-18
❑ 14TexTomE-32
❑ 14TexTomE-59
❑ 15AmeCarE106-28
❑ 15CraJacE-69
❑ 15SpoNewM-114
❑ 16BF2FP-81
❑ 16SpoNewM-116
❑ 17ColE13-113
❑ 17HolBreD-67
❑ 19W514-52
❑ 21E121So1-59
❑ 21E121So8-56
❑ 21Exh-104
❑ 21KoBreWSI-15
❑ 22AmeCarE122-44
❑ 22W575-77
❑ 22WilPatV-40
❑ 23W501-73
❑ 23W501-104

❑ 23W515-45
❑ 23WilChoV-92
❑ 27YorCarE-42
❑ 28W502-42
❑ 28Yue-42
❑ 30SchR33-41
❑ 35ClaBreD3-3
❑ 36Halof FP-19
❑ 36NatChiFPR-94
❑ 39PC7AlbHoF-10
❑ 40PlaBal-235
❑ 48ExhHoF-23
❑ 49LeaPre-6
❑ 50CalHOFW-55
❑ 53ArtHaloFP-62
❑ 60ExhWriH-17
❑ 60Fle-66
❑ 61Fle-60
❑ 61GolPre-23
❑ 63BazA-20
❑ 63HalofFB-14
❑ 67SpoHobFC-11
❑ 68LauWorS-8
❑ 69Baz-5
❑ 69Baz-6
❑ 70FleWorS-8
❑ 70FleWorS-21
❑ 71FleWorS-2
❑ 72ClaCar-85
❑ 72KelATG-3
❑ 73SevTraC-47
❑ 73TCMAllG-13
❑ 75FlePio-15
❑ 75GiaAllT-7
❑ 75McCCob-13
❑ 75TCMAllG-23
❑ 76ShaPiz-11
❑ 77BobParHoF-37
❑ 77GalGloG-98
❑ 77GalGloG-215
❑ 77ShaPiz-2
❑ 80GiaGreT-12
❑ 80PacLeg-43
❑ 80PerHaloFP-10
❑ 80SSPHOF-10
❑ 81ConTSN-6
❑ 83BigLeaCOA-22
❑ 83DonHOFH-35
❑ 84GalHaloFRL-11
❑ 84OCoandSI-175
❑ 85FegMurCG-13
❑ 85UltBasC-10
❑ 86ConSer1-29
❑ 88ConSer5-20
❑ 89HOFStiB-89
❑ 90BasWit-59
❑ 91ConTSN-65
❑ 91FouBal-9
❑ 92ConTSN-584
❑ 92ConTSNGI-820
❑ 93ConMasC-7
❑ 93ConMasC-8
❑ 93ConTSN-820
❑ 93CraJac-21
❑ 93UppDecTR-5
❑ 94ConTSN-1001
❑ 94ConTSNB-1001
❑ 94OriofB-87
❑ 94OriTeal-11
❑ 94UppDecTAE-12
❑ 94UppDecTAELD-LD4

McGraw, Tom

❑ 64WhiSoxI-19
❑ 90BelBreS-14
❑ 91ElPasDLD-192
❑ 91ElPasDP-2746
❑ 91LinDriAA-192
❑ 92ElPasDF-3917
❑ 92StoPorF-32
❑ 93HigDesMF-37
❑ 93LinVenB-65
❑ 95PorSeaDTI-14
❑ 97LouRedB-23

McGraw, Tug (Frank E.)

❑ 65Top-533
❑ 66MetPos-6
❑ 66MetVolC-9
❑ 66OPC-124
❑ 66Top-124
❑ 66TopVen-124
❑ 67CokCapYM-V33
❑ 67Top-348
❑ 68AtlOilPBCC-30
❑ 68Top-236
❑ 68TopVen-236
❑ 69MetNewYDN-14
❑ 69Top-601
❑ 70MetTra-24B
❑ 70OPC-26
❑ 70OPC-310
❑ 70Top-26
❑ 71MetTeal-15
❑ 71MLBOffS-161
❑ 71OPC-618
❑ 71Top-618
❑ 72MilBra-228
❑ 72OPC-163
❑ 72OPC-164
❑ 72Top-163
❑ 72Top-164
❑ 73LinPor-118
❑ 73MetAllEB-8
❑ 73MetTeal-9
❑ 73NewYorSNM-22
❑ 73OPC-30
❑ 73Top-30
❑ 74OPC-265
❑ 74Top-265
❑ 74TopSta-67
❑ 75Hos-149
❑ 75OPC-67
❑ 75PhiPhiP-23
❑ 75PhiProPS-10
❑ 75Top-67
❑ 75TopMin-67
❑ 76OPC-565
❑ 76PhiPhiP-20
❑ 76SSP-457
❑ 76Top-565
❑ 77BurCheD-165
❑ 77OPC-142
❑ 77Top-164
❑ 78RCColC-85
❑ 78SSP270-42
❑ 78Top-446
❑ 78WifBalD-48
❑ 79OPC-176
❑ 79PhiBurK-10
❑ 79Top-345
❑ 80OPC-346
❑ 80PhiBul-2
❑ 80PhiBurK-20
❑ 80Top-655
❑ 81CokTeaS-103
❑ 81Don-273
❑ 81Fle-7
❑ 81Fle-657A
❑ 81Fle-657B
❑ 81FleStiC-83
❑ 81Kel-37
❑ 81Top-40
❑ 81Top-404
❑ 81TopSti-205
❑ 81TopSti-262
❑ 81TopSupHT-85
❑ 82Don-420
❑ 82Fle-251
❑ 82FleSta-55
❑ 82OPC-250
❑ 82Top-250
❑ 83Don-371
❑ 83Fle-166
❑ 83FleSta-122
❑ 83FleSti-171
❑ 83OPC-166
❑ 83OPC-187
❑ 83PhiPosGM-10
❑ 83PhiTas-17
❑ 83Top-510
❑ 83Top-511
❑ 83TopFol-4
❑ 84Don-547
❑ 84DonCha-53
❑ 84Fle-42
❑ 84Nes792-709
❑ 84Nes792-728
❑ 84OPC-161
❑ 84PhiTas-24
❑ 84Top-709
❑ 84Top-728
❑ 84TopTif-709
❑ 84TopTif-728
❑ 85Fle-261
❑ 85Top-157
❑ 85TopTif-157
❑ 86MetGreT-11
❑ 87Met196T-6
❑ 88PacLegI-96
❑ 89Met196C-10
❑ 89MetRinP69-21
❑ 89SweBasG-96
❑ 91MetWIZ-260
❑ 91UppDecS-8
❑ 92MCIAmb-12
❑ 92UppDecS-24
❑ 94MCIAmb-6
❑ 94Met69CCPP-25
❑ 94Met69CS-24
❑ 94Met69T-12
❑ 94TedWil-58
❑ 95MCIAmb-3
❑ 95MrTurBG-3
❑ 99SpoIllGotG-75
❑ 99SpoIllGotGA-49

McGregor, Scott

❑ 75OPC-618
❑ 75SyrChiTI-11
❑ 75Top-618
❑ 75TopMin-618
❑ 77BalOriP-14
❑ 77Top-475
❑ 78BalOriP-19
❑ 78Top-491
❑ 79BalOriP-10
❑ 79OPC-206
❑ 79Top-393
❑ 80BalOriP-12
❑ 80Top-237
❑ 81AllGamPI-87
❑ 81Don-114
❑ 81Fle-174
❑ 81FleStiC-10
❑ 81OPC-65
❑ 81Top-65
❑ 81TopSti-37
❑ 82Don-331
❑ 82Fle-172
❑ 82FleSta-149
❑ 82OPC-246
❑ 82OPC-316
❑ 82Top-555
❑ 82Top-617
❑ 82TopSti-143
❑ 82TopStiV-143
❑ 83Don-483
❑ 83Fle-66
❑ 83FleSta-123
❑ 83FleSti-194
❑ 83OPC-216
❑ 83OriPos-17
❑ 83Top-745
❑ 84BalOriP-20
❑ 84Don-594
❑ 84Fle-13
❑ 84Fle-646
❑ 84FleSti-64
❑ 84FunFooP-102
❑ 84Nes792-260
❑ 84OPC-260
❑ 84OriEng-8
❑ 84Top-260
❑ 84TopSti-207
❑ 84TopTif-260
❑ 85BalOriP-17
❑ 85Don-413
❑ 85Fle-183
❑ 85Lea-72
❑ 85OPC-228
❑ 85OriHea-12
❑ 85Top-550
❑ 85TopSti-198
❑ 85TopTif-550
❑ 86BalOriHMP-12
❑ 86BalOriP-11
❑ 86Don-291
❑ 86Fle-281
❑ 86FleStiC-75
❑ 86Lea-165
❑ 86OPC-110
❑ 86Top-110
❑ 86TopSti-230
❑ 86TopTat-6
❑ 86TopTif-110
❑ 87BalOriP-23
❑ 87Don-520
❑ 87Fle-475
❑ 87FleGlo-475
❑ 87Lea-243
❑ 87OPC-347
❑ 87OriFreB-16
❑ 87Top-708
❑ 87TopTif-708
❑ 88OPC-254
❑ 88OriPos-19
❑ 88Sco-315
❑ 88ScoGlo-315
❑ 88Top-419
❑ 88TopTif-419
❑ 89SweBasG-56
❑ 91OriCro-290

McGrew, Charley

❑ 86BelBreP-15
❑ 87StoPorP-12
❑ 88BelBreGS-7
❑ 89ModA'sCLC-284

McGriff, Fred

❑ 85DomLeaS-149
❑ 85SyrChiT-2
❑ 85SyrChiT-25
❑ 86Don-28
❑ 86Lea-28
❑ 86StaoftFT-26
❑ 86SyrChiP-18
❑ 87BluJayFS-20
❑ 87Don-621
❑ 87DonHig-39
❑ 87DonOpeD-38
❑ 87DonRoo-31
❑ 87FleUpd-75
❑ 87FleUpdG-75
❑ 87SpoRool-12
❑ 87SpoTeaP-5
❑ 87TopTra-74T
❑ 87TopTraT-74T
❑ 88BluJayFS-21
❑ 88Don-195
❑ 88DonBasB-160
❑ 88Fle-118
❑ 88FleGlo-118
❑ 88MSAHosD-15
❑ 88OPC-395
❑ 88RedFolSB-54
❑ 88Sco-107
❑ 88ScoGlo-107
❑ 88ScoYouS2-28
❑ 88Spo-168
❑ 88StaLinBJ-14
❑ 88Top-463
❑ 88Top-729
❑ 88TopClo-70
❑ 88TopTif-463
❑ 88TopTif-729
❑ 88ToyRoo-18
❑ 89BluJayFS-18
❑ 89Bow-253
❑ 89BowTif-253
❑ 89CadEllD-35
❑ 89ClaTraO-116
❑ 89Don-16
❑ 89Don-70
❑ 89DonBasB-104
❑ 89DonBonM-BC19
❑ 89DonSupD-16
❑ 89Fle-240
❑ 89FleBasM-27
❑ 89FleGlo-240
❑ 89FleHeroB-27
❑ 89FleLeaL-26
❑ 89FleSup-30
❑ 89FleWaxBC-C19
❑ 89OPC-258
❑ 89PanSti-467
❑ 89Sco-6
❑ 89ScoHot1S-65
❑ 89Spo-14
❑ 89SpoIllFKI-172
❑ 89Top-745
❑ 89TopBig-15
❑ 89TopCoi-44
❑ 89TopHilTM-20
❑ 89TopMinL-77
❑ 89TopSti-185
❑ 89TopTif-745
❑ 89TopUKM-50
❑ 89TVSpoM-77
❑ 89UppDec-572
❑ 89UppDec-671
❑ 90Baz-5
❑ 90BluJayFS-19
❑ 90BluJayHS-3
❑ 90BluJayHS-5
❑ 90Bow-513
❑ 90BowTif-513
❑ 90ClaBlu-19
❑ 90Don-188
❑ 90DonBesA-56
❑ 90DonGraS-9
❑ 90Fle-89
❑ 90FleAwaW-22
❑ 90FleBasM-24
❑ 90FleBasMC-24
❑ 90FleCan-89
❑ 90FleLeaL-24
❑ 90FleLeaLC-24
❑ 90Hot50PS-26
❑ 90K-M-31
❑ 90KinDis-13
❑ 90Lea-132
❑ 90M.Vpin-107
❑ 90MSAHolD-13
❑ 90OPC-295
❑ 90OPC-385
❑ 90PanSti-170
❑ 90PubIntS-523
❑ 90PubIntS-599
❑ 90RedFolSB-60
❑ 90Sco-271
❑ 90Sco100S-45
❑ 90Spo-13
❑ 90SupActM-9
❑ 90Top-295
❑ 90Top-385
❑ 90TopBig-134
❑ 90TopCoi-22
❑ 90TopDou-44
❑ 90TopGaloC-4
❑ 90TopGloS-55
❑ 90TopMag-86
❑ 90TopMinL-43
❑ 90TopSti-187
❑ 90TopStiB-35
❑ 90TopTif-295
❑ 90TopTif-385
❑ 90TopTVA-26
❑ 90UppDec-108
❑ 90VicPos-3
❑ 91Bow-659
❑ 91CadEllD-37
❑ 91Cla1-T88
❑ 91Cla2-T46
❑ 91ClaGam-163
❑ 91Don-261
❑ 91Don-389
❑ 91Fle-180
❑ 91FleUpd-125
❑ 91Lea-342
❑ 91OPC-140
❑ 91OPCPre-79
❑ 91PadMag-24
❑ 91PadSmo-21
❑ 91PanCanT1-16
❑ 91PanCanT1-40
❑ 91PanFreS-336
❑ 91PanSti-157
❑ 91RedFolS-65
❑ 91Sco-404
❑ 91Sco-480
❑ 91Sco100S-71
❑ 91ScoRoo-58T
❑ 91SevCoi-SC9
❑ 91StaClu-357
❑ 91Stu-247
❑ 91Top-140
❑ 91TopDesS-140
❑ 91TopMic-140
❑ 91TopTif-140
❑ 91TopTra-77T
❑ 91TopTraT-77T
❑ 91TopTriH-N10
❑ 91Ult-308
❑ 91UppDec-565
❑ 91UppDec-775
❑ 92Bow-650
❑ 92Cla1-T61
❑ 92ClaGam-149
❑ 92ColAllG-16
❑ 92ColAllP-16
❑ 92DenHol-3
❑ 92Don-283
❑ 92DonCraJ2-12
❑ 92DonDiaK-DK26
❑ 92DonMcD-9
❑ 92DonSupD-DK26
❑ 92Fle-614
❑ 92Hig5-124
❑ 92LaKdec-22
❑ 92Lea-274
❑ 92LeaBlaG-274
❑ 92LeaGolP-11
❑ 92LeaPre-11
❑ 92MooSna-17
❑ 92New-16
❑ 92OPC-660
❑ 92OPCPre-166
❑ 92PadCarJ-13
❑ 92PadMot-4
❑ 92PadPolD-14
❑ 92PadPolD-30
❑ 92PadSmo-19
❑ 92PanSti-232
❑ 92Pin-112
❑ 92RedFolS-65
❑ 92Sco-7
❑ 92Sco100S-65
❑ 92ScoImpP-56
❑ 92ScoProaG-11
❑ 92StaClu-580
❑ 92Stu-106
❑ 92SyrChiTT-5
❑ 92Top-660
❑ 92TopGol-660
❑ 92TopGolW-660
❑ 92TopKid-55
❑ 92TopMic-660
❑ 92TriPla-87
❑ 92Ult-282
❑ 92UppDec-33
❑ 92UppDec-344
❑ 92UppDecHRH-HR10
❑ 92UppDecTMH-35
❑ 92UppDecWB-T8
❑ 93BluJayDM-3
❑ 93Bow-686
❑ 93BraLykP-18
❑ 93BraLykS-23
❑ 93ClaGam-62
❑ 93DiaMar-72
❑ 93Don-390
❑ 93DonEli-19
❑ 93DonEliD-2
❑ 93DonEliS-1
❑ 93DonLonBL-LL2
❑ 93DonMasotG-4
❑ 93DonSpiotG-SG12
❑ 93DurPowP2-9
❑ 93Fin-106
❑ 93FinJum-106
❑ 93FinRef-106
❑ 93Fla-8
❑ 93Fle-143
❑ 93Fle-349
❑ 93FleAll-NL1
❑ 93FleAtl-15
❑ 93FleFruotL-45
❑ 93FunPac-136
❑ 93FunPac-139
❑ 93FunPacA-AS1
❑ 93HumDumC-48
❑ 93Lea-46
❑ 93LeaGolA-R2
❑ 93OPC-255
❑ 93OPCPreSP-2
❑ 93OPCPreSPF-2
❑ 93PacSpa-261
❑ 93PadMot-4
❑ 93PanSti-258
❑ 93Pin-71
❑ 93PinHomRC-2
❑ 93PinSlu-5
❑ 93PinTeaP-4
❑ 93Pos-5
❑ 93RedFolS-62
❑ 93RedFolS-119
❑ 93Sco-44
❑ 93Sco-528
❑ 93Sel-19
❑ 93SelChaS-1
❑ 93SelRoo-5T
❑ 93SelStaL-28
❑ 93SelStaL-36
❑ 93SelStaL-48
❑ 93SP-60
❑ 93SPPlaP-PP12
❑ 93StaClu-510
❑ 93StaClu-594
❑ 93StaCluFDI-510
❑ 93StaCluFDI-594
❑ 93StaCluM-78
❑ 93StaCluMOP-510
❑ 93StaCluMOP-594
❑ 93Stu-157
❑ 93Top-30
❑ 93Top-401
❑ 93TOPBLAG-13
❑ 93TopFulS-21
❑ 93TopGol-30
❑ 93TopGol-401
❑ 93TopInaM-30
❑ 93TopInaM-401
❑ 93TopInaR-30
❑ 93TopInaR-401
❑ 93TopMic-30
❑ 93TopMic-401
❑ 93TopTra-88T
❑ 93TriPla-95

❑ 93TriPlaLL-L4
❑ 93TriPlaN-10
❑ 93Ult-119
❑ 93UltHomRK-4
❑ 93UppDec-474
❑ 93UppDec-496
❑ 93UppDec-577
❑ 93UppDecCP-R15
❑ 93UppDecGold-474
❑ 93UppDecGold-496
❑ 93UppDecGold-577
❑ 93UppDecHRH-HR4
❑ 93UppDecIC-WI16
❑ 93UppDecICJ-WI16
❑ 93UppDecTriCro-TC5
❑ 93USPlaCA-11C
❑ 94Bow-405
❑ 94BowBes-R15
❑ 94BowBes-X92
❑ 94BowBesR-R15
❑ 94BowBesR-X92
❑ 94BraLykP-21
❑ 94BraLykS-21
❑ 94BraUSPC-7D
❑ 94BraUSPC-13C
❑ 94ChuShoS-6
❑ 94ColC-197
❑ 94ColChoGS-197
❑ 94ColChoSS-197
❑ 94Don-342
❑ 94DonDom-A3
❑ 94DonDomJ-A3
❑ 94DonPro-8
❑ 94DonSpeE-342
❑ 94Fin-224
❑ 94FinJum-224
❑ 94FinRef-224
❑ 94Fla-131
❑ 94FlaHotN-4
❑ 94FlaInfP-5
❑ 94Fle-366
❑ 94Fle-706
❑ 94FleExtB-209
❑ 94FleExtBGB-19
❑ 94FleGolM-8
❑ 94FleGolMJ-8
❑ 94FleLumC-7
❑ 94FleUpdDT-7
❑ 94FUnPac-27
❑ 94FUnPac-186
❑ 94KinDis-1
❑ 94Lea-345
❑ 94LeaCleC-9
❑ 94LeaGolS-14
❑ 94LeaL-88
❑ 94LeaMVPC-N10
❑ 94LeaMVPCG-N10
❑ 94LeaPowB-8
❑ 94O-PJumAF-13
❑ 94OPC-13
❑ 94OPCAllR-13
❑ 94OPCJumA-13
❑ 94Pac-16
❑ 94PacGolP-14
❑ 94PanSti-148
❑ 94Pin-384
❑ 94PinArtP-384
❑ 94PinMusC-384
❑ 94PinRunC-RC26
❑ 94PinTheN-13
❑ 94ProMag-3
❑ 94RedFolMI-34
❑ 94Sco-82
❑ 94ScoGolR-82
❑ 94ScoGolS-18
❑ 94Sel-268
❑ 94SP-55
❑ 94SPDieC-55
❑ 94Spo-32
❑ 94Spo-185
❑ 94SpoFanA-AS1
❑ 94SpoRooGGG-GG9
❑ 94StaClu-111
❑ 94StaClu-180
❑ 94StaClu-264
❑ 94StaClu-665
❑ 94StaCluFDI-111
❑ 94StaCluFDI-180
❑ 94StaCluFDI-264
❑ 94StaCluFDI-665
❑ 94StaCluGR-111
❑ 94StaCluGR-180
❑ 94StaCluGR-264
❑ 94StaCluGR-665
❑ 94StaCluMO-30
❑ 94StaCluMOP-111
❑ 94StaCluMOP-180
❑ 94StaCluMOP-264
❑ 94StaCluMOP-665
❑ 94StaCluT-47
❑ 94StaCluTFDI-47
❑ 94Stu-40
❑ 94Top-384
❑ 94Top-565
❑ 94TopBlaG-39
❑ 94TopGol-384
❑ 94TopGol-565
❑ 94TopSpa-384
❑ 94TopSpa-565
❑ 94TopSupS-29
❑ 94TriPla-47
❑ 94TriPlaBS-6
❑ 94TriPlaM-4
❑ 94Ult-154
❑ 94UltAllS-12
❑ 94UltHomRK-10
❑ 94UppDec-225
❑ 94UppDecAJ-11
❑ 94UppDecAJG-11
❑ 94UppDecED-225
❑ 94UppDecMLS-MM12
❑ 94UppDecMLSED-MM12
❑ 94USPlaCA-7C
❑ 95Baz-63
❑ 95BluJayUSPC-5S
❑ 95BluJayUSPC-12D
❑ 95Bow-331
❑ 95BowBes-R56
❑ 95BowBesR-R56
❑ 95ClaPhoC-4
❑ 95ColCho-69
❑ 95ColCho-530
❑ 95ColChoCtA-3
❑ 95ColChoCtAGR-3
❑ 95ColChoCtG-CG12
❑ 95ColChoCtG-CG12B
❑ 95ColChoCtG-CG12C
❑ 95ColChoCtGE-12
❑ 95ColChoCtGG-CG12
❑ 95ColChoCtGG-CG12B
❑ 95ColChoCtGG-CG12C
❑ 95ColChoCtGGE-12
❑ 95ColChoGS-69
❑ 95ColChoGS-530
❑ 95ColChoSE-65
❑ 95ColChoSEGS-65
❑ 95ColChoSESS-65
❑ 95ColChoSS-69
❑ 95ColChoSS-530
❑ 95Don-349
❑ 95DonBomS-4
❑ 95DonDom-3
❑ 95DonEli-58
❑ 95DonLonBL-2
❑ 95DonPreP-349
❑ 95DonTopotO-191
❑ 95Emo-107
❑ 95Fin-103
❑ 95FinPowK-PK16
❑ 95FinRef-103
❑ 95Fla-106
❑ 95FlaInfP-5
❑ 95Fle-312
❑ 95FleAllS-15
❑ 95FleLumC-7
❑ 95FleUpdH-14
❑ 95KinDis-13
❑ 95Lea-232
❑ 95LeaLim-184
❑ 95LeaLimIBP-22
❑ 95LeaLimL-5
❑ 95LeaSli-3A
❑ 95LeaSli-3B
❑ 95LeaStaS-4
❑ 95NatPac-14
❑ 95Pac-12
❑ 95PacGolCDC-2
❑ 95PacGolP-3
❑ 95PacPri-5
❑ 95PanSti-35
❑ 95Pin-12
❑ 95Pin-276
❑ 95PinArtP-12
❑ 95PinArtP-276
❑ 95PinMusC-12
❑ 95PinMusC-276
❑ 95RedFol-6
❑ 95Sco-316
❑ 95Sco-459
❑ 95ScoGolR-316
❑ 95ScoGolR-459
❑ 95ScoHaloG-HG67
❑ 95ScoPlaTS-316
❑ 95ScoPlaTS-459
❑ 95ScoRul-SR13
❑ 95ScoRulJ-SR13
❑ 95Sel-42
❑ 95SelArtP-42
❑ 95SelCer-62
❑ 95SelCerMG-62
❑ 95SP-30
❑ 95SPCha-21
❑ 95SPCha-23
❑ 95SPChaDC-21
❑ 95SPChaDC-23
❑ 95SPChaDFC-8
❑ 95SPChaFCDC-8
❑ 95Spo-3
❑ 95SpoArtP-3
❑ 95SpoDouT-2
❑ 95SpoHamT-HT14
❑ 95SpoSam-3
❑ 95SPPlaP-PP4
❑ 95SPSil-30
❑ 95SPSpeF-28
❑ 95StaClu-363
❑ 95StaClu-496
❑ 95StaCluCC-CC5
❑ 95StaCluCT-13
❑ 95StaCluMO-31
❑ 95StaCluMOP-363
❑ 95StaCluMOP-496
❑ 95StaCluMOP-CC5
❑ 95StaCluMOP-PZ9
❑ 95StaCluMOP-RL13
❑ 95StaCluPZ-PZ9
❑ 95StaCluRL-RL13
❑ 95StaCluSTDW-B393
❑ 95StaCluSTMP-8
❑ 95StaCluSTWS-363
❑ 95StaCluSTWS-496
❑ 95StaCluVR-190
❑ 95StaCluVRMO-190
❑ 95Stu-23
❑ 95StuGolS-23
❑ 95StuPlaS-23
❑ 95Sum-3
❑ 95SumBigB-BB17
❑ 95SumNthD-3
❑ 95SumSam-BB17
❑ 95TomPiz-26
❑ 95Top-355
❑ 95TopCyb-191
❑ 95TopCybSiR-4
❑ 95TopD3Z-4
❑ 95TopEmb-127
❑ 95TopEmbGI-127
❑ 95TopLeaL-LL15
❑ 95TopLeaL-LL34
❑ 95TopTra-156T
❑ 95UC3-65
❑ 95UC3-142
❑ 95UC3ArtP-65
❑ 95UC3ArtP-142
❑ 95UC3CycS-CS17
❑ 95Ult-351
❑ 95UltAllS-13
❑ 95UltAllSGM-13
❑ 95UltGolM-351
❑ 95UltHitM-8
❑ 95UltHitMGM-8
❑ 95UltHomRK-9
❑ 95UltHomRKGM-9
❑ 95UltRBIK-9
❑ 95UltRBIKGM-9
❑ 95UppDec-45
❑ 95UppDec-108
❑ 95UppDecC-2A
❑ 95UppDecED-45
❑ 95UppDecED-108
❑ 95UppDecEDG-45
❑ 95UppDecEDG-108
❑ 95UppDecPAW-H28
❑ 95UppDecPAWE-H28
❑ 95UppDecPC-MLB2
❑ 95UppDecPLL-R8
❑ 95UppDecPLL-R48
❑ 95UppDecPLLE-R8
❑ 95UppDecPLLE-R48
❑ 95UppDecSE-150
❑ 95UppDecSEG-150
❑ 95UppDecSoaD-SD2
❑ 95USPlaCMLA-8C
❑ 95Zen-34
❑ 96Baz-109
❑ 96Bow-4
❑ 96BowBes-61
❑ 96BowBesAR-61
❑ 96BowBesR-61
❑ 96BowFoi-4
❑ 96BraFle-12
❑ 96Cir-106
❑ 96CirRav-106
❑ 96ColCho-45
❑ 96ColCho-107
❑ 96ColCho-375T
❑ 96ColCho-377T
❑ 96ColChoCtG-CG2
❑ 96ColChoCtG-CG2B
❑ 96ColChoCtG-CG2C
❑ 96ColChoCtGE-CR2
❑ 96ColChoCtGG-CG2
❑ 96ColChoCtGG-CG2B
❑ 96ColChoCtGG-CG2C
❑ 96ColChoCtGGE-CR2
❑ 96ColChoGS-45
❑ 96ColChoGS-107
❑ 96ColChoSS-45
❑ 96ColChoSS-107
❑ 96ColChoYMtP-24
❑ 96ColChoYMtP-24A
❑ 96ColChoYMtPGS-24
❑ 96ColChoYMtPGS-24A
❑ 96Don-349
❑ 96DonPreP-349
❑ 96EmoXL-147
❑ 96Fin-B40
❑ 96Fin-S218
❑ 96FinRef-B40
❑ 96FinRef-S218
❑ 96Fla-206
❑ 96Fle-300
❑ 96FleTif-300
❑ 96Lea-33
❑ 96LeaLim-37
❑ 96LeaLimG-37
❑ 96LeaPre-62
❑ 96LeaPreP-62
❑ 96LeaPrePB-33
❑ 96LeaPrePG-33
❑ 96LeaPrePS-33
❑ 96LeaPreSG-27
❑ 96LeaPreSte-27
❑ 96LeaSig-38
❑ 96LeaSigEA-124
❑ 96LeaSigEACM-19
❑ 96LeaSigPPG-38
❑ 96LeaSigPPP-38
❑ 96LeaTotB-8
❑ 96MetUni-135
❑ 96MetUniP-135
❑ 96Pac-9
❑ 96PacPri-P7
❑ 96PacPriG-P7
❑ 96Pin-161
❑ 96Pin-209
❑ 96PinAfi-8
❑ 96PinAfiAP-8
❑ 96PinAfiFPP-8
❑ 96PinArtP-88
❑ 96PinArtP-109
❑ 96PinChrBC-6
❑ 96PinFoil-209
❑ 96PinPow-12
❑ 96PinSta-88
❑ 96PinSta-109
❑ 96ProMagDM-3
❑ 96ProSta-21
❑ 96SchDis-10
❑ 96Sco-84
❑ 96ScoDugC-A67
❑ 96ScoDugCAP-A67
❑ 96Sel-68
❑ 96SelArtP-68
❑ 96SelCer-66
❑ 96SelCerAP-66
❑ 96SelCerCB-66
❑ 96SelCerCR-66
❑ 96SelCerMB-66
❑ 96SelCerMG-66
❑ 96SelCerMR-66
❑ 96SP-27
❑ 96SPMarM-MM20
❑ 96SPMarMDC-20
❑ 96Spo-36
❑ 96SpoArtP-36
❑ 96SPSpeFX-19
❑ 96SPSpeFXDC-19
❑ 96SPx-3
❑ 96SPxGol-3
❑ 96StaClu-407
❑ 96StaCluEPB-407
❑ 96StaCluEPG-407
❑ 96StaCluEPS-407
❑ 96StaCluMM-MM3
❑ 96StaCluMOP-407
❑ 96StaCluMOP-MM3
❑ 96StaCluMOP-PP13
❑ 96StaCluPP-PP13
❑ 96Stu-50
❑ 96StuPrePB-50
❑ 96StuPrePG-50
❑ 96StuPrePS-50
❑ 96Sum-69
❑ 96SumAbo&B-69
❑ 96SumArtP-69
❑ 96SumFoi-69
❑ 96Top-389
❑ 96TopChr-156
❑ 96TopChrR-156
❑ 96TopChrWC-WC10
❑ 96TopChrWCR-WC10
❑ 96TopGal-172
❑ 96TopGalPPI-172
❑ 96TopLas-72
❑ 96TopLasPC-3
❑ 96TopPro-NL5
❑ 96TopWreC-WC10
❑ 96Ult-441
❑ 96UltGolM-441
❑ 96UltThu-12
❑ 96UltThuGM-12
❑ 96UppDec-270
❑ 96UppDec-380
❑ 96UppDecDD-DD2
❑ 96UppDecDDG-DD2
❑ 96UppDecDDS-DD2
❑ 96UppDecPD-PD9
❑ 96UppDecPRE-R35
❑ 96UppDecPreR-R35
❑ 96UppDecRunP-RP11
❑ 96Zen-10
❑ 96ZenArtP-10
❑ 97BluJayS-49
❑ 97Bow-263
❑ 97BowBes-94
❑ 97BowBesAR-94
❑ 97BowBesR-94
❑ 97BowChr-84
❑ 97BowChrI-84
❑ 97BowChrIR-84
❑ 97BowChrR-84
❑ 97BowInt-263
❑ 97BraSco-9
❑ 97BraScoPI-9
❑ 97BraScoPr-9
❑ 97Cir-16
❑ 97CirRav-16
❑ 97ColCho-30
❑ 97ColChoT-AB3
❑ 97Don-170
❑ 97Don-440
❑ 97DonEli-44
❑ 97DonEliGS-44
❑ 97DonGolPP-170
❑ 97DonGolPP-440
❑ 97DonLim-102
❑ 97DonLim-105
❑ 97DonLim-199
❑ 97DonLimE-102
❑ 97DonLimE-105
❑ 97DonLimE-199
❑ 97DonLimENG-102
❑ 97DonLimFotG-54
❑ 97DonPre-78
❑ 97DonPreCttC-78
❑ 97DonRocL-7
❑ 97DonSig-53
❑ 97DonSigPPP-53
❑ 97DonSilPP-170
❑ 97DonSilPP-440
❑ 97DonTea-22
❑ 97DonTeaSPE-22
❑ 97E-X2-58
❑ 97E-X2ACA-10
❑ 97E-X2Cred-58
❑ 97E-X2EssCre-58
❑ 97Fin-186
❑ 97Fin-325
❑ 97FinEmb-325
❑ 97FinEmbR-325
❑ 97FinRef-186
❑ 97FinRef-325
❑ 97FlaShoLC-127
❑ 97FlaShoLeg0-127
❑ 97FlaShoLeg1-127
❑ 97FlaShoM-A127
❑ 97FlaShoM-B127
❑ 97FlaShoM-C127
❑ 97FlaShoR0-127
❑ 97FlaShoR1-127
❑ 97FlaShoR2-127
❑ 97Fle-264
❑ 97FleTif-264
❑ 97Lea-97
❑ 97Lea-391
❑ 97LeaFraM-97
❑ 97LeaFraM-391
❑ 97LeaFraMDC-97
❑ 97LeaFraMDC-391
❑ 97MetUni-34
❑ 97NewPin-65
❑ 97NewPinAP-65
❑ 97NewPinMC-65
❑ 97NewPinPP-65
❑ 97Pac-241
❑ 97PacLigB-241
❑ 97PacSil-241
❑ 97PinCer-8
❑ 97PinCerMBla-8
❑ 97PinCerMBlu-8
❑ 97PinCerMG-8
❑ 97PinCerMR-8
❑ 97PinCerR-8
❑ 97PinIns-49
❑ 97PinInsCE-49
❑ 97PinInsDD-9
❑ 97PinInsDE-49
❑ 97PinTotCPB-8
❑ 97PinTotCPG-8
❑ 97PinTotCPR-8
❑ 97PinX-P-37
❑ 97PinX-PMoS-37
❑ 97PinX-PSfF-40
❑ 97PinX-PSfFU-40
❑ 97Sco-172
❑ 97Sco-512
❑ 97ScoArtPWB-172
❑ 97ScoArtPWB-512
❑ 97ScoPreS-172
❑ 97ScoResC-512
❑ 97ScoShoS-172
❑ 97ScoShoS-512
❑ 97ScoShoSAP-172
❑ 97ScoShoSAP-512
❑ 97SP-28
❑ 97SpoIll-78
❑ 97SpoIllEE-78
❑ 97StaClu-47
❑ 97StaCluMat-47
❑ 97StaCluMOP-47
❑ 97Stu-81
❑ 97StuPrePG-81
❑ 97StuPrePS-81
❑ 97Top-352
❑ 97TopChr-119
❑ 97TopChrR-119
❑ 97TopGal-33
❑ 97TopGalPPI-33
❑ 97TopSta-52
❑ 97TopStaAM-52
❑ 97TopStaASM-ASM6
❑ 97Ult-158
❑ 97UltGolME-158
❑ 97UltPlaME-158
❑ 97UppDec-15
❑ 97UppDecP-4
❑ 97UppDecPE-4
❑ 97UppDecPP-PP6
❑ 97UppDecPPJ-PP6
❑ 98Bow-260
❑ 98BowBes-34
❑ 98BowBesAR-34
❑ 98BowBesR-34
❑ 98BowChr-260
❑ 98BowChrGA-260
❑ 98BowChrGAR-260
❑ 98BowChrI-260
❑ 98BowChrIR-260
❑ 98BowChrR-260
❑ 98BowGolA-260
❑ 98BowInt-260
❑ 98BraSco-14
❑ 98BraScoP-14
❑ 98CirThu-6
❑ 98CirThuRav-6
❑ 98CirThuSupRav-6
❑ 98ColCho-270
❑ 98ColCho-510
❑ 98ColChoCtG-CG8A
❑ 98ColChoCtG-CG8B
❑ 98ColChoCtG-CG8C
❑ 98ColChoCtGExch-CG8
❑ 98ColChoCtGIW-CG8
❑ 98ColChoMBH-27

❑ 98CroRoy-133
❑ 98DevRayP-17
❑ 98Don-64
❑ 98Don-230
❑ 98DonCol-64
❑ 98DonColE-463
❑ 98DonColL-336
❑ 98DonColP-604
❑ 98DonColS-64
❑ 98DonCruG-59
❑ 98DonCruP-59
❑ 98DonCruR-59
❑ 98DonEli-63
❑ 98DonEliA-63
❑ 98DonEliS-63
❑ 98DonGolPP-64
❑ 98DonGolPP-230
❑ 98DonPre-54
❑ 98DonPreSeat-54
❑ 98DonPriCD-64
❑ 98DonPriCE-463
❑ 98DonPriCL-336
❑ 98DonPriCP-604
❑ 98DonSig-59
❑ 98DonSigP-59
❑ 98DonSilPP-64
❑ 98DonSilPP-230
❑ 98E-X2-76
❑ 98E-X2ECFut-76
❑ 98E-X2ECNow-76
❑ 98Fin-225
❑ 98FinMysF2-M27
❑ 98FinMysF2-M29
❑ 98FinMysF2-M30
❑ 98FinMysF2-M39
❑ 98FinMysF2R-M27
❑ 98FinMysF2R-M29
❑ 98FinMysF2R-M30
❑ 98FinMysF2R-M39
❑ 98FinNo--225
❑ 98FinNo-R-225
❑ 98FinRef-225
❑ 98FlaShoLeg0-108
❑ 98FlaShoLeg1-108
❑ 98FlaShoLeg2-108
❑ 98FlaShoLeg3-108
❑ 98FlaShoLegM-108
❑ 98FlaShoR0-108
❑ 98FlaShoR1-108
❑ 98FlaShoR2-108
❑ 98FlaShoR3-108
❑ 98Fle-130
❑ 98Fle-540
❑ 98FleVin'-123
❑ 98FleVin'C-123
❑ 98Lea-137
❑ 98LeaCruG-59
❑ 98LeaCruP-59
❑ 98LeaCruR-59
❑ 98LeaFraDA-137
❑ 98LeaFraF-137
❑ 98LeaFraM-137
❑ 98LeaFraM-137
❑ 98LeaFraMDC-137
❑ 98LeaFraMDC-137
❑ 98LeaFraMS-137
❑ 98LeaFraMZ2-137
❑ 98LeaRS-55
❑ 98LeaRSLHolo-55
❑ 98LeaRSLong-55
❑ 98LeaRTrue-55
❑ 98Pac-240
❑ 98PacAur-82
❑ 98PacInvTeam-30
❑ 98PacOme-233
❑ 98PacOmeR-233
❑ 98PacOnl-715
❑ 98PacOnlR-715
❑ 98PacOnlWC-715
❑ 98PacPar-99
❑ 98PacParC-99
❑ 98PacParG-99
❑ 98PacParHS-99
❑ 98PacParPB-99
❑ 98PacParR-99
❑ 98PacPlaB-240
❑ 98PacRedT-240
❑ 98PacSil-240
❑ 98PacTeaC-30
❑ 98PinIns-81
❑ 98PinInsCE-81
❑ 98PinInsDE-81
❑ 98PinPer-55
❑ 98PinPerPP-55
❑ 98PinPerSftF-26
❑ 98PinPlu-120
❑ 98PinPluAP-PP39
❑ 98PinPluGAP-PP39
❑ 98PinPluMAP-PP39
❑ 98PinSna-TBDR15
❑ 98PinSna-TBDR18
❑ 98Revo-140
❑ 98RevoSS-140
❑ 98Sco-195
❑ 98ScoRT-212
❑ 98ScoRTSS-PP117
❑ 98ScoRTSSAP-PP117
❑ 98ScoRTSSAP1-PP117
❑ 98ScoSS-PP91
❑ 98ScoSSAP-PP91
❑ 98SkyDugA-82
❑ 98SkyDugA-137
❑ 98SkyDugAIA-82
❑ 98SkyDugAIA-137
❑ 98SP Aut-185
❑ 98SP Aut-SD12
❑ 98SP AutSD-SD12
❑ 98SP AutSDT-SD12
❑ 98SpoIllODMP-OD28
❑ 98SpoIllWSF-81
❑ 98SpoIllWSFEE-81
❑ 98SpoIllWSFFE-81
❑ 98SPxFin-325
❑ 98SPxFin-348
❑ 98SPxFinR-325
❑ 98SPxFinR-348
❑ 98SPxFinS-325
❑ 98SPxFinS-348
❑ 98StaCluFDI-318
❑ 98StaCluI-318
❑ 98StaCluOneK-318
❑ 98StaCluPP-318
❑ 98Stu-116
❑ 98StuGPP-116
❑ 98StuSPP-116
❑ 98Top-349
❑ 98TopChr-349
❑ 98TopChrR-349
❑ 98TopDevR-349
❑ 98TopDia-349
❑ 98TopGal-2
❑ 98TopGalGP-2
❑ 98TopGalOPP-2
❑ 98TopGalPPI-2
❑ 98TopGalPPIA-2
❑ 98TopGolLabC1-32
❑ 98TopGolLabC1B-32
❑ 98TopGolLabC1One-32
❑ 98TopGolLabC1R-32
❑ 98TopGolLabC2-32
❑ 98TopGolLabC2B-32
❑ 98TopGolLabC2One-32
❑ 98TopGolLabC2R-32
❑ 98TopGolLabC3-32
❑ 98TopGolLabC3B-32
❑ 98TopGolLabC3One-32
❑ 98TopGolLabC3R-32
❑ 98TopMiniC-349
❑ 98TopSta-104
❑ 98TopStaB-104
❑ 98TopStaG-104
❑ 98TopStaGR-104
❑ 98TopStaS-104
❑ 98UD3-64
❑ 98UD3-154
❑ 98UD3-244
❑ 98UD3DieCut-64
❑ 98UD3DieCut-154
❑ 98UD3DieCut-244
❑ 98Ult-61
❑ 98Ult-468
❑ 98UltGolM-61
❑ 98UltGolM-468
❑ 98UltMas-61
❑ 98UltMas-468
❑ 98UltPlaM-61
❑ 98UltPlaM-468
❑ 98UppDec-29
❑ 98UppDec-730
❑ 98UppDec-749
❑ 98UppDec10AP-22
❑ 98UppDec1APR-22
❑ 98UppDecR-94
❑ 98UppDecR-13
❑ 98UppDecRTC-TC21
❑ 98UppDecTMT-24
❑ 98UppDecTMTG-24
❑ 98Zen-31
❑ 98ZenZ-G-31
❑ 98ZenZ-S-31
❑ 99199Fin-217
❑ 99Bow-239
❑ 99BowGol-239
❑ 99BowInt-239
❑ 99CroRoyB-136
❑ 99CroRoyL-136
❑ 99CroRoyOD-136
❑ 99DumSet-FM
❑ 99DumSet-FM
❑ 99FinGolRef-217
❑ 99FinRef-217
❑ 99Fle-201
❑ 99FleSta9-201
❑ 99FleWarT-201
❑ 99KinDis-15
❑ 99MetUni-78
❑ 99MetUniGM-78
❑ 99MetUniPMG-78
❑ 99Pac-416
❑ 99PacAur-188
❑ 99PacAurOD-188
❑ 99PacCroC-278
❑ 99PacCroCPB-278
❑ 99PacInv-142
❑ 99PacInvOD-142
❑ 99PacInvPB-142
❑ 99PacOme-231
❑ 99PacOmeC-231
❑ 99PacOmeG-231
❑ 99PacOmePB-231
❑ 99PacPar-229
❑ 99PacParC-229
❑ 99PacParG-229
❑ 99PacParHoloGold-229
❑ 99PacParHS-229
❑ 99PacParOD-229
❑ 99PacParPB-229
❑ 99PacParRed-229
❑ 99PacPlaB-416
❑ 99PacPri-140
❑ 99PacPriHB-140
❑ 99PacPriHG-140
❑ 99PacPriHM-140
❑ 99PacPriHP-140
❑ 99PacPriRed-140
❑ 99PacPriS-115
❑ 99PacPriS206-115
❑ 99PacPriS206R-115
❑ 99PacRed-416
❑ 99Rev-138
❑ 99RevPremDate-138
❑ 99RevRet-138
❑ 99RevShaSS-138
❑ 99SkyMolM-89
❑ 99SkyMolMOA-10
❑ 99SkyMolMX-89
❑ 99SkyPre-186
❑ 99SkyPreR-186
❑ 99SkyThu-150
❑ 99SkyThuRant-150
❑ 99SkyThuRave-150
❑ 99SpoIll-95
❑ 99StaClu-63
❑ 99StaCluFDI-63
❑ 99StaCluOoaK-63
❑ 99StaCluPP-63
❑ 99ThuSkySupR-150
❑ 99Top-139
❑ 99TopChr-139
❑ 99TopChrR-139
❑ 99TopGal-88
❑ 99TopGalPP-88
❑ 99TopGalPPI-88
❑ 99TopMVPP-139
❑ 99TopOpeD-82
❑ 99TopSta-148
❑ 99TopStaFoil-148
❑ 99Ult-202
❑ 99UltGolM-202
❑ 99UltMas-202
❑ 99UltPlaM-202
❑ 99UppDec-497
❑ 99UppDecBD-84
❑ 99UppDecBDD-84
❑ 99UppDecBDQ-84
❑ 99UppDecBDT-84
❑ 99UppDecCf7LL-L7
❑ 99UppDecCL-75
❑ 99UppDecCLCC-75
❑ 99UppDecCLM-C93
❑ 99UppDecE-84
❑ 99UppDecEFXG-84
❑ 99UppDecEL1-497
❑ 99UppDecEL2-497
❑ 99UppDecM-200
❑ 99UppDecMGS-200
❑ 99UppDecMHFS-200
❑ 99UppDecMSS-200
❑ 99UppDecO-39
❑ 99UppDecOSO-39
❑ 99Vic-386
❑ 99Vic-470

McGriff, Terry (Terrence)

❑ 83TamTarT-18
❑ 87Don-512
❑ 88Don-556
❑ 88Fle-240
❑ 88FleGlo-240
❑ 88NasSouTI-16
❑ 88RedKah-8
❑ 88Sco-281
❑ 88ScoGlo-281
❑ 88Top-644
❑ 88TopTif-644
❑ 89BlaYNPRWL-159
❑ 89BlaYNPRWLU-61
❑ 89NasSouTI-15
❑ 89Top-151
❑ 89TopTif-151
❑ 90CMC-129
❑ 90NasSouC-4
❑ 90NasSouP-236
❑ 90ProAAAF-548
❑ 91LinDriAAA-615
❑ 91TucTorLD-615
❑ 91TucTorP-2215
❑ 93EdmTraF-1140
❑ 94FleUpd-180
❑ 95Fle-503
❑ 95Pac-409
❑ 95StaClu-202
❑ 95StaCluFDI-202
❑ 95StaCluMOP-202
❑ 95StaCluSTWS-202
❑ 95TolMudHTI-21
❑ 96SyrChiTI-20
❑ 98BriBluM-18

McGuire, Bill

❑ 87ChaLooB-15
❑ 88BasAmeAAB-10
❑ 88VerMarP-943
❑ 89CalCanC-21
❑ 89CalCanP-533
❑ 89Fle-553
❑ 89FleGlo-553
❑ 90CalCanC-14
❑ 90CalCanP-653
❑ 90CMC-441
❑ 90ProAAAF-118
❑ 92PeoChiC-29
❑ 92PeoChiTI-13
❑ 93BenRocCB-28
❑ 93BenRocF-3285
❑ 94AshTouC-28
❑ 94AshTouF-1799
❑ 94AshTouF-1800
❑ 95AshTouTI-32
❑ 96SalAvaB-26
❑ 97SalAva-2

McGuire, Brandon

❑ 97ButCopKB-14
❑ 97ButCopKK-14
❑ 98CedRapKTI-18

McGuire, Deacon (James)

❑ 03BreE10-102
❑ 04FanCraAL-35
❑ 10JuJuDE-27
❑ 11SpoLifM-48
❑ 87OldJudN-332
❑ 90DodTar-508
❑ 90KalBatN-20
❑ 90KalBatN-38
❑ 90KalBatN-39

McGuire, Matt

❑ 96BelGiaTI-11

McGuire, Mickey

❑ 68SeaPop-10
❑ 91OriCro-291

McGuire, Mike

❑ 87BelMarTI-22
❑ 88WauTimGS-20
❑ 89WauTimGS-1

McGuire, Ryan

❑ 94Bow-559
❑ 94Cla-185
❑ 94ExcFS7-20
❑ 94LynRedSC-18
❑ 94LynRedSF-1900
❑ 94Top-746
❑ 94TopGol-746
❑ 94TopSpa-746
❑ 94UppDecML-16
❑ 95Bes-4
❑ 95SPML-23
❑ 95TreThuTI-20
❑ 95UppDecML-71
❑ 95UppDecMLFS-71
❑ 96Bow-216
❑ 96BowFoi-216
❑ 96ColCho-778
❑ 96Exc-14
❑ 96Fla-310
❑ 96FleUpd-U148
❑ 96FleUpdNH-16
❑ 96FleUpdTC-U148
❑ 96Ult-505
❑ 96UltGolM-505
❑ 96UppDec-266
❑ 97DonLim-56
❑ 97DonLimE-56
❑ 97DonLimENG-56
❑ 97Fle-757
❑ 97FleTif-757
❑ 97Lea-328
❑ 97LeaFraM-328
❑ 97LeaFraMDC-328
❑ 97Sel-176
❑ 97SelCom-176
❑ 97SpoIll-16
❑ 97SpoIllEE-16
❑ 98Bow-196
❑ 98BowChr-196
❑ 98BowChrGA-196
❑ 98BowChrGAR-196
❑ 98BowChrI-196
❑ 98BowChrIR-196
❑ 98BowChrR-196
❑ 98ColCho-436
❑ 98E-X2-81
❑ 98E-X2ECFut-81
❑ 98E-X2ECNow-81
❑ 98Fle-196
❑ 98MetUni-103
❑ 98MetUniPMG-103
❑ 98Pac-350
❑ 98PacOnl-455
❑ 98PacOnlR-455
❑ 98PacOnlWC-455
❑ 98PacPlaB-350
❑ 98PacRedT-350
❑ 98PacSil-350
❑ 98Pin-167
❑ 98PinArtP-PP70
❑ 98PinIns-120
❑ 98PinInsCE-120
❑ 98PinInsDE-120
❑ 98PinMusC-PP70
❑ 98PinPreP-167
❑ 98Sco-245
❑ 98ScoRT-183
❑ 98StaCluFDI-183
❑ 98StaCluI-183
❑ 98StaCluOneK-183
❑ 98StaCluPP-183
❑ 98Top-413
❑ 98TopChr-413
❑ 98TopChrR-413
❑ 98TopDevR-413
❑ 98TopDia-413
❑ 98TopMiniC-413
❑ 98Ult-25
❑ 98UltGolM-25
❑ 98UltMas-25
❑ 98UltPlaM-25
❑ 98UppDec-158
❑ 98Zen-92
❑ 98Zen5 xx7-72
❑ 98Zen5x7GoldImp-72
❑ 98Zen5x7Imp-72
❑ 98ZenRooT-5
❑ 98ZenZ-G-92
❑ 98ZenZ-S-92
❑ 99Top-303
❑ 99TopChr-303
❑ 99TopChrR-303
❑ 99TopMVPP-303
❑ 99UppDec-144
❑ 99UppDecEL1-144
❑ 99UppDecEL2-144

McGuire, Steve

❑ 86QuaCitAP-22
❑ 87MidAngP-26
❑ 88MidAngGS-12
❑ 89PalSprACLC-54
❑ 89QuaCitAB-14
❑ 89QuaCitAGS-17

McGunnigle, William

❑ 74BroClu-11
❑ 87OldJudN-333
❑ 90DodTar-509

McGwire, Mark

❑ 82AncGlaPM-1
❑ 84TopPewB-5
❑ 85ModA'sC-17A
❑ 85ModA'sC-17B
❑ 85Top-401
❑ 85TopTif-401
❑ 86HunStaDJ-33
❑ 86SouLeaAJ-3
❑ 87ClaUpdY-121
❑ 87ClaUpdY-150
❑ 87Don-46
❑ 87DonHig-27
❑ 87DonHig-40
❑ 87DonHig-46
❑ 87DonHig-54
❑ 87DonRoo-1
❑ 87FleSlu-26
❑ 87FleUpd-76
❑ 87FleUpdG-76
❑ 87Lea-46
❑ 87MotMcG-1
❑ 87MotMcG-2
❑ 87MotMcG-3
❑ 87MotMcG-4
❑ 87SpoRooI-13
❑ 87SpoTeaP-23
❑ 87Top-366
❑ 87TopTif-366
❑ 88A'sMot-2
❑ 88A'sMot-28
❑ 88Baz-13
❑ 88CheBoy-1
❑ 88ClaBlu-212
❑ 88ClaBlu-247
❑ 88ClaRed-151
❑ 88ClaRed-153
❑ 88ClaRed-197
❑ 88Don-1
❑ 88Don-256
❑ 88DonAll-19
❑ 88DonBasB-169
❑ 88DonBonM-BC23
❑ 88DonSupD-1
❑ 88DonTeaBA-256
❑ 88Dra-6
❑ 88Fle-286
❑ 88Fle-624
❑ 88Fle-629
❑ 88Fle-633
❑ 88FleAwaW-24
❑ 88FleBasA-25
❑ 88FleBasM-23
❑ 88FleExcS-26
❑ 88FleGlo-286
❑ 88FleGlo-624
❑ 88FleGlo-629
❑ 88FleGlo-633
❑ 88FleHea-2
❑ 88FleHotS-26
❑ 88FleLeaL-26
❑ 88FleMin-46
❑ 88FleRecS-25
❑ 88FleSlu-27
❑ 88FleStiC-56
❑ 88FleStiWBC-S1
❑ 88FleSup-23
❑ 88FleTeaL-21
❑ 88GreBasS-77
❑ 88K-M-16
❑ 88KayB-18
❑ 88KeyFooD-4
❑ 88KinDis-6
❑ 88Lea-1
❑ 88Lea-194
❑ 88MotMcG-1
❑ 88MotMcG-2
❑ 88MotMcG-3
❑ 88MotMcG-4
❑ 88MSAFanSD-3
❑ 88MSAIceTD-4
❑ 88Nes-10
❑ 88OPC-394
❑ 88OurOwnTD-4
❑ 88PanSti-167
❑ 88PanSti-438
❑ 88RedFolSB-55
❑ 88Sco-5
❑ 88Sco-648
❑ 88Sco-659
❑ 88ScoBoxC-T3
❑ 88ScoGlo-5
❑ 88ScoGlo-648
❑ 88ScoGlo-659

❑ 88ScoYouSI-1
❑ 88Spo-100
❑ 88Spo-221
❑ 88SpoGam-2
❑ 88StaDav-1
❑ 88StaDav-3
❑ 88StaDav-5
❑ 88StaDav-7
❑ 88StaDav-9
❑ 88StaDav-11
❑ 88StaLinAs-10
❑ 88StaMcG-1
❑ 88StaMcG-2
❑ 88StaMcG-3
❑ 88StaMcG-4
❑ 88StaMcG-5
❑ 88StaMcG-6
❑ 88StaMcG-7
❑ 88StaMcG-8
❑ 88StaMcG-9
❑ 88StaMcG-10
❑ 88StaMcG-11
❑ 88StaMcGG-1
❑ 88StaMcGG-2
❑ 88StaMcGG-3
❑ 88StaMcGG-4
❑ 88StaMcGG-5
❑ 88StaMcGG-6
❑ 88StaMcGG-7
❑ 88StaMcGG-8
❑ 88StaMcGG-9
❑ 88StaMcGG-10
❑ 88StaMcGG-11
❑ 88TarPla-27
❑ 88TetTeaD-4
❑ 88Top-3
❑ 88Top-3A
❑ 88Top-580
❑ 88Top-759
❑ 88TopBig-179
❑ 88TopClo-71
❑ 88TopCoi-3
❑ 88TopGaloC-9
❑ 88TopGloS-39
❑ 88TopMinL-31
❑ 88TopRevLL-17
❑ 88TopRitTM-23
❑ 88TopRoo-13
❑ 88TopSti-1
❑ 88TopSti-164
❑ 88TopSti-309
❑ 88TopStiB-36
❑ 88TopTif-3
❑ 88TopTif-580
❑ 88TopTif-759
❑ 88TopUKM-47
❑ 88TopUKMT-47
❑ 88ToyRoo-19
❑ 88WeiMarD-4
❑ 88Woo-15
❑ 89A'sMot-2
❑ 89A'sMot-28
❑ 89A'sMotR-2
❑ 89A'sMotR-4
❑ 89Bow-197
❑ 89BowTif-197
❑ 89CadEllD-36
❑ 89ClaLigB-4
❑ 89ClaTraO-104
❑ 89ClaTraP-190
❑ 89CMCCan-12
❑ 89ColPosMc-1
❑ 89ColPosMc-2
❑ 89ColPosMc-3
❑ 89ColPosMc-4
❑ 89ColPosMc-5
❑ 89ColPosMc-6
❑ 89ColPosMc-7
❑ 89ColPosMc-8
❑ 89Don-95
❑ 89DonAll-1
❑ 89DonBasB-43
❑ 89DonGraS-7
❑ 89DonPop-1
❑ 89Fle-17
❑ 89Fle-634
❑ 89FleBasA-29
❑ 89FleBasM-28
❑ 89FleExcS-32
❑ 89FleGlo-17
❑ 89FleGlo-634
❑ 89FleGlo-WS8
❑ 89FleHeroB-28
❑ 89FleLeaL-27
❑ 89FleSup-31
❑ 89FleWorS-8
❑ 89KayB-21
❑ 89KeyFooD-3
❑ 89KinDis-4
❑ 89ModA'sC-35
❑ 89MotMcG-1
❑ 89MotMcG-2
❑ 89MotMcG-3
❑ 89MotMcG-4
❑ 89MSAHolD-14
❑ 89MSAIceTD-3
❑ 89Nis-14
❑ 89OPC-70
❑ 89OPC-174
❑ 89OurOwnTD-3
❑ 89PanSti-20
❑ 89PanSti-244
❑ 89PanSti-420
❑ 89PepMcG-1
❑ 89PepMcG-2
❑ 89PepMcG-3
❑ 89PepMcG-4
❑ 89PepMcG-5
❑ 89PepMcG-6
❑ 89PepMcG-7
❑ 89PepMcG-8
❑ 89PepMcG-9
❑ 89PepMcG-10
❑ 89PepMcG-11
❑ 89PepMcG-12
❑ 89RedFolSB-80
❑ 89Sco-3
❑ 89ScoHot1S-25
❑ 89Scomast-32
❑ 89Spo-200
❑ 89SpollIFKI-146
❑ 89TacTigP-1537
❑ 89TetTeaD-3
❑ 89Top-70
❑ 89TopBasT-64
❑ 89TopBig-34
❑ 89TopCapC-22
❑ 89TopCoi-45
❑ 89TopDouA-12
❑ 89TopGloA-2
❑ 89TopGloS-41
❑ 89TopHeaUT-14
❑ 89TopMinL-70
❑ 89TopSti-151
❑ 89TopSti-172
❑ 89TopStiB-3
❑ 89TopTif-70
❑ 89TopUKM-51
❑ 89TVSpoM-98
❑ 89TVSpoM-137
❑ 89UppDec-300
❑ 89UppDecS-2
❑ 89WeiMarD-3
❑ 89Woo-27
❑ 90A'sMot-2
❑ 90AllBasT-2
❑ 90Bow-454
❑ 90BowTif-454
❑ 90ClaBlu-59A
❑ 90ClaBlu-59B
❑ 90ClaUpd-T33
❑ 90Don-185
❑ 90Don-697A
❑ 90Don-697B
❑ 90DonBesA-54
❑ 90DonGraS-4
❑ 90Fle-15
❑ 90Fle-638
❑ 90FleBasA-25
❑ 90FleBasAC-25
❑ 90FleBasM-25
❑ 90FleBasMC-25
❑ 90FleCan-15
❑ 90FleCan-638
❑ 90FleLeaL-25
❑ 90FleLeaLC-25
❑ 90FleWaxBC-C20
❑ 90HOFStiB-91
❑ 90K-M-32
❑ 90Lea-62
❑ 90M.Vpin-75
❑ 90MLBBasB-77
❑ 90MotMcG-1
❑ 90MotMcG-2
❑ 90MotMcG-3
❑ 90MotMcG-4
❑ 90MSAIceTD-15
❑ 90OPC-690
❑ 90OPCBoxB-I
❑ 90PanSti-132
❑ 90PanSti-204
❑ 90Pos-12
❑ 90PubIntS-310
❑ 90PubIntS-600
❑ 90RedFolSB-61
❑ 90Sco-385
❑ 90Sco100S-25
❑ 90SouCalS-10
❑ 90Spo-141
❑ 90StaLonJS-9
❑ 90StaLonJS-11
❑ 90StaLonJS-27
❑ 90Top-690
❑ 90TopBig-28
❑ 90TopDou-45
❑ 90TopGloA-13
❑ 90TopGloS-42
❑ 90TopHeaU-14
❑ 90TopMag-34
❑ 90TopMag-94
❑ 90TopMinL-30
❑ 90TopSti-162
❑ 90TopSti-176
❑ 90TopStiB-36
❑ 90TopTif-690
❑ 90TopTVA-1
❑ 90TopWaxBC-I
❑ 90UppDec-36
❑ 90UppDec-171
❑ 90UppDecS-1
❑ 90USPlaCA-WCO
❑ 91A'sMot-2
❑ 91A'sSFE-8
❑ 91BasBesHRK-13
❑ 91Bow-234
❑ 91CadEllD-38
❑ 91Cla1-T73
❑ 91ClaGam-131
❑ 91DenHol-10
❑ 91Don-56
❑ 91Don-105
❑ 91DonBonC-BC9
❑ 91DonGraS-11
❑ 91Fle-17
❑ 91FlePro-4
❑ 91Lea-487
❑ 91MajLeaCP-39
❑ 91MLBKeyC-3
❑ 91MSAHolD-16
❑ 91OPC-270
❑ 91PanCanT1-14
❑ 91PanCanT1-23
❑ 91PanCanT1-110
❑ 91PanFreS-167
❑ 91PanFreS-192
❑ 91PanSti-145
❑ 91Pos-2
❑ 91RedFolS-122
❑ 91Sco-324
❑ 91Sco100S-39
❑ 91SevCoi-NC9
❑ 91SimandSMLBL-29
❑ 91StaClu-399
❑ 91StaPinB-30
❑ 91Stu-106
❑ 91SunSee-18
❑ 91Top-270
❑ 91Top-270A
❑ 91TopCraJI-27
❑ 91TopDesS-270
❑ 91TopGloA-2
❑ 91TopMic-270
❑ 91TopSta-26
❑ 91TopTif-270
❑ 91Ult-251
❑ 91UppDec-174
❑ 91UppDec-656
❑ 92A'sUno7P-1
❑ 92AthMot-2
❑ 92Bow-384
❑ 92Bow-620
❑ 92Cla2-T10
❑ 92ClaGam-119
❑ 92ColAllG-1
❑ 92ColAllP-1
❑ 92ColMcG-1
❑ 92ColMcG-2
❑ 92ColMcG-3
❑ 92ColMcG-4
❑ 92ColMcG-5
❑ 92ColMcG-6
❑ 92ColMcG-7
❑ 92ColMcG-8
❑ 92ColMcG-9
❑ 92ColMcG-10
❑ 92ColMcG-11
❑ 92ColMcG-12
❑ 92ColMcG-AU
❑ 92Don-348
❑ 92DonUpd-U7
❑ 92Fle-262
❑ 92Lea-16
❑ 92LeaBlaG-16
❑ 92LeaGolP-32
❑ 92New-17
❑ 92OPC-450
❑ 92OPCPre-99
❑ 92PanSti-15
❑ 92Pin-217
❑ 92PinSlu-2
❑ 92PolMcG-1
❑ 92PolMcG-2
❑ 92PolMcG-3
❑ 92PolMcG-4
❑ 92PolMcG-5
❑ 92PolMcG-6
❑ 92PolMcG-7
❑ 92PolMcG-8
❑ 92PolMcG-9
❑ 92PolMcG-10
❑ 92PolMcG-11
❑ 92PolMcG-12
❑ 92PolMcG-13
❑ 92PolMcG-14
❑ 92PolMcG-15
❑ 92PolMcG-16
❑ 92PolMcG-17
❑ 92PolMcG-18
❑ 92PolMcG-19
❑ 92PolMcG-20
❑ 92PolMcG-21
❑ 92PolMcG-22
❑ 92PolMcG-23
❑ 92PolMcG-24
❑ 92RedFolS-67
❑ 92Sco-20
❑ 92Sco100S-63
❑ 92ScoProaG-2
❑ 92SpollIFK1-412
❑ 92SpollIFK1-608
❑ 92SpollIFK1-790
❑ 92StaClu-475
❑ 92Stu-226
❑ 92StuPre-17
❑ 92Top-450
❑ 92TopDaiQTU-1
❑ 92TopGol-450
❑ 92TopGolW-450
❑ 92TopKid-121
❑ 92TopMic-450
❑ 92TriPla-231
❑ 92TriPla-262
❑ 92Ult-115
❑ 92UltAllS-1
❑ 92UppDec-153
❑ 92UppDecF-32
❑ 92UppDecFG-32
❑ 93A'sSmoM-1
❑ 93A'sSmoM-2
❑ 93AthMot-2
❑ 93AthStaC-7
❑ 93Bow-161
❑ 93CadDis-41
❑ 93ClaGam-63
❑ 93ClaGam-NNO
❑ 93ColAllG-23
❑ 93DiaMar-73
❑ 93Don-479
❑ 93DonDiaK-DK18
❑ 93DonEli-33
❑ 93DonEliS-15
❑ 93DonLonBL-LL4
❑ 93DonMVP-19
❑ 93DurPowP1-9
❑ 93Fin-92
❑ 93FinJum-92
❑ 93FinRef-92
❑ 93Fla-261
❑ 93Fle-296
❑ 93Fle-710
❑ 93FleAtl-16
❑ 93FleFruotL-46
❑ 93FleTeaL-AL2
❑ 93FunPac-17
❑ 93FunPac-48
❑ 93FunPac-51
❑ 93FunPacA-AS3
❑ 93JimDea-22
❑ 93Kra-10
❑ 93Lea-323
❑ 93LeaGolA-R11
❑ 93MilBonSS-4
❑ 93OPC-201
❑ 93OPCPreSP-16
❑ 93OPCPreSPF-16
❑ 93PacJugC-10
❑ 93PacSpa-224
❑ 93PanSti-15
❑ 93Pin-58
❑ 93PinCoo-30
❑ 93PinCooD-30
❑ 93PinHomRC-8
❑ 93PinSlu-2
❑ 93Pos-19
❑ 93RedFolS-63
❑ 93RedFolS-120
❑ 93Sco-557
❑ 93Sel-16
❑ 93SelStaL-26
❑ 93SelStaL-43
❑ 93SP-41
❑ 93SPPlaP-PP13
❑ 93StaClu-478
❑ 93StaClu-595
❑ 93StaCluFDI-478
❑ 93StaCluFDI-595
❑ 93StaClul-B1
❑ 93StaCluM-153
❑ 93StaCluMOP-478
❑ 93StaCluMOP-595
❑ 93StaCluMOP-MB1
❑ 93StaCluMP-20
❑ 93Stu-141
❑ 93StuHer-4
❑ 93StuSupoC-3
❑ 93Top-100
❑ 93TOPBLAG-39
❑ 93TopGol-100
❑ 93TopInaM-100
❑ 93TopInaR-100
❑ 93TopMic-100
❑ 93TopPre-100
❑ 93TriPla-68
❑ 93TriPla-87
❑ 93TriPla-245
❑ 93TriPlaA-23
❑ 93Ult-609
❑ 93UltAllS-12
❑ 93UltHomRK-2
❑ 93UppDec-41
❑ 93UppDec-49
❑ 93UppDec-420
❑ 93UppDec-493
❑ 93UppDec-566
❑ 93UppDecDG-3
❑ 93UppDecFH-60
❑ 93UppDecGold-41
❑ 93UppDecGold-49
❑ 93UppDecGold-420
❑ 93UppDecGold-493
❑ 93UppDecGold-566
❑ 93UppDecHRH-HR2
❑ 93UppDecIC-WI3
❑ 93UppDecICJ-WI3
❑ 93UppDecOD-D18
❑ 93USPlaCA-13C
❑ 94A'sMot-2
❑ 94Bow-192
❑ 94ColC-330
❑ 94ColC-525
❑ 94ColChoGS-330
❑ 94ColChoGS-525
❑ 94ColChoSS-330
❑ 94ColChoSS-525
❑ 94ColChoT-10
❑ 94Don-335
❑ 94DonDom-A10
❑ 94DonDomJ-A10
❑ 94DonSpeE-335
❑ 94Fin-78
❑ 94FinPre-78P
❑ 94FinRef-78
❑ 94Fla-94
❑ 94Fle-268
❑ 94FleExtB-153
❑ 94FleTeaL-11
❑ 94FUnPac-125
❑ 94Lea-391
❑ 94LeaL-61
❑ 94OPC-74
❑ 94Pac-456
❑ 94PanSti-110
❑ 94Pin-300
❑ 94PinArtP-300
❑ 94PinMusC-300
❑ 94ProMag-97
❑ 94RedFolMI-18
❑ 94Sco-550
❑ 94ScoGolR-550
❑ 94Sel-57
❑ 94SP-36
❑ 94SPDieC-36
❑ 94SPHol-26
❑ 94SPHolDC-26
❑ 94Spo-4
❑ 94StaClu-358
❑ 94StaCluFDI-358
❑ 94StaCluGR-358
❑ 94StaCluMOP-358
❑ 94Stu-4
❑ 94Top-340
❑ 94TopGol-340
❑ 94TopSpa-340
❑ 94TriPla-5
❑ 94TriPlaN-7
❑ 94Ult-111
❑ 94UppDec-67
❑ 94UppDecDC-W8
❑ 94UppDecED-67
❑ 94UppDecMLS-MM13
❑ 94UppDecMLSED-MM13
❑ 95A'sCHP-2
❑ 95AthMot-2
❑ 95Baz-27
❑ 95Bow-303
❑ 95BowBes-R69
❑ 95BowBesR-R69
❑ 95ClaPhoC-41
❑ 95ColCho-130
❑ 95ColChoCtA-4
❑ 95ColChoCtAGR-4
❑ 95ColChoCtG-CG13
❑ 95ColChoCtG-CG13B
❑ 95ColChoCtG-CG13C
❑ 95ColChoCtGE-13
❑ 95ColChoCtGG-CG13
❑ 95ColChoCtGG-CG13B
❑ 95ColChoCtGG-CG13C
❑ 95ColChoCtGGE-13
❑ 95ColChoGS-130
❑ 95ColChoSE-45
❑ 95ColChoSEGS-45
❑ 95ColChoSESS-45
❑ 95ColChoSS-130
❑ 95DenHol-16
❑ 95Don-460
❑ 95DonPreP-460
❑ 95DonTopotO-139
❑ 95Emo-72
❑ 95EmoN-7
❑ 95Fin-169
❑ 95FinRef-169
❑ 95Fla-76
❑ 95Fle-249
❑ 95Lea-240
❑ 95LeaLim-166
❑ 95Pac-316
❑ 95Pin-196
❑ 95PinArtP-196
❑ 95PinMusC-196
❑ 95RedFol-28
❑ 95Sco-377
❑ 95ScoGolR-377
❑ 95ScoPlaTS-377
❑ 95Sel-14
❑ 95SelArtP-14
❑ 95SelCer-50
❑ 95SelCerMG-50
❑ 95SelCerS-50
❑ 95SP-185
❑ 95SPCha-177
❑ 95SPCha-181
❑ 95SPChaDC-177
❑ 95SPChaDC-181
❑ 95Spo-121
❑ 95SpoArtP-121
❑ 95SPPlaP-PP13
❑ 95SPSil-185
❑ 95StaClu-289
❑ 95StaCluMOP-289
❑ 95StaCluMOP-RL2
❑ 95StaCluRL-RL2
❑ 95StaCluSTWS-289
❑ 95StaCluVR-176
❑ 95StaCluVRMO-176
❑ 95Stu-141
❑ 95Sum-27
❑ 95SumNthD-27
❑ 95Top-472
❑ 95TopCyb-266
❑ 95TopEmb-107
❑ 95TopEmbGI-107
❑ 95UC3-51
❑ 95UC3-137
❑ 95UC3ArtP-51

❑ 95UC3ArtP-137
❑ 95Ult-94
❑ 95UltGolM-94
❑ 95UppDec-35
❑ 95UppDecED-35
❑ 95UppDecEDG-35
❑ 95UppDecPAW-H26
❑ 95UppDecPAWE-H26
❑ 95UppDecSE-247
❑ 95UppDecSEG-247
❑ 95Zen-71
❑ 96A'sMot-2
❑ 96Baz-74
❑ 96Bow-22
❑ 96BowBes-75
❑ 96BowBesAR-75
❑ 96BowBesR-75
❑ 96BowFoi-22
❑ 96Cir-73
❑ 96CirAcc-11
❑ 96CirBos-18
❑ 96CirRav-73
❑ 96ColCho-418
❑ 96ColCho-640
❑ 96ColCho-710
❑ 96ColChoGS-418
❑ 96ColChoGS-640
❑ 96ColChoGS-710
❑ 96ColChoSS-418
❑ 96ColChoSS-640
❑ 96ColChoSS-710
❑ 96ColChoYMtP-25
❑ 96ColChoYMtP-25A
❑ 96ColChoYMtPGS-25
❑ 96ColChoYMtPGS-25A
❑ 96DenHol-25
❑ 96Don-511
❑ 96DonDiaK-4
❑ 96DonLonBL-3
❑ 96DonPreP-511
❑ 96EmoLegoB-5
❑ 96EmoXL-104
❑ 96Fin-B162
❑ 96Fin-B236
❑ 96Fin-G74
❑ 96FinRef-B162
❑ 96FinRef-B236
❑ 96FinRef-G74
❑ 96Fla-150
❑ 96FlaPow-5
❑ 96Fle-213
❑ 96FleGolM-6
❑ 96FleLumC-5
❑ 96FleRoaW-4
❑ 96FleTeaL-11
❑ 96FleTif-213
❑ 96Kin-24
❑ 96Lea-15
❑ 96LeaLim-21
❑ 96LeaLimG-21
❑ 96LeaLimL-10
❑ 96LeaLimLB-10
❑ 96LeaPre-15
❑ 96LeaPreP-15
❑ 96LeaPrePB-15
❑ 96LeaPrePG-15
❑ 96LeaPrePS-15
❑ 96LeaPreSG-14
❑ 96LeaPreSte-14
❑ 96LeaSig-23
❑ 96LeaSigPPG-23
❑ 96LeaSigPPP-23
❑ 96LibSpo-15
❑ 96MetUni-101
❑ 96MetUniHM-5
❑ 96MetUniP-101
❑ 96Pac-385
❑ 96PacGolCD-DC34
❑ 96PacPri-P126
❑ 96PacPriFB-FB11
❑ 96PacPriG-P126
❑ 96PanSti-218
❑ 96Pin-130
❑ 96Pin-158
❑ 96PinAfi-6
❑ 96PinAfiAP-6
❑ 96PinAfiFPP-6
❑ 96PinArtP-55
❑ 96PinArtP-85
❑ 96PinFan-27
❑ 96PinFirR-18
❑ 96PinSta-55
❑ 96PinSta-85
❑ 96ProSta-6
❑ 96RedF-4
❑ 96Sco-310
❑ 96ScoDugC-B35
❑ 96ScoDugCAP-B35
❑ 96ScoPowP-1
❑ 96ScoRef-16
❑ 96ScoTitT-6
❑ 96Sel-31
❑ 96SelArtP-31
❑ 96SelCer-20
❑ 96SelCerAP-20
❑ 96SelCerCB-20
❑ 96SelCerCR-20
❑ 96SelCerIP-23
❑ 96SelCerMB-20
❑ 96SelCerMG-20
❑ 96SelCerMR-20
❑ 96SelTeaN-5
❑ 96SP-140
❑ 96SPMarM-MM7
❑ 96SPMarMDC-7
❑ 96Spo-16
❑ 96Spo-117
❑ 96SpoArtP-16
❑ 96SpoArtP-117
❑ 96SpoPowS-21
❑ 96SPSpeFX-27
❑ 96SPSpeFXDC-27
❑ 96SPx-45
❑ 96SPxGol-45
❑ 96StaClu-104
❑ 96StaCluEPB-104
❑ 96StaCluEPG-104
❑ 96StaCluEPS-104
❑ 96StaCluMO-25
❑ 96StaCluMOP-104
❑ 96StaCluMOP-PP2
❑ 96StaCluMOP-PS7
❑ 96StaCluPP-PP2
❑ 96StaCluPS-PS7
❑ 96Stu-118
❑ 96StuPrePB-118
❑ 96StuPrePG-118
❑ 96StuPrePS-118
❑ 96Sum-20
❑ 96SumAbo&B-20
❑ 96SumArtP-20
❑ 96SumFoi-20
❑ 96TeaOut-55
❑ 96TeaOut-C97
❑ 96Top-145
❑ 96TopChr-41
❑ 96TopChrR-41
❑ 96TopChrWC-WC11
❑ 96TopChrWCR-WC11
❑ 96TopGal-155
❑ 96TopGalE-8
❑ 96TopGalPPI-155
❑ 96TopLas-46
❑ 96TopPro-AL18
❑ 96TopRoaW-RW11
❑ 96TopWreC-WC11
❑ 96Ult-115
❑ 96UltGolM-115
❑ 96UltHomRK-7
❑ 96UltHomRKGM-7
❑ 96UltHomRKR-7
❑ 96UltHomRKRGM-7
❑ 96UltThu-13
❑ 96UltThuGM-13
❑ 96UppDec-151
❑ 96UppDec-425
❑ 96UppDecDD-DD30
❑ 96UppDecDDG-DD30
❑ 96UppDecDDS-DD30
❑ 96UppDecPD-PD10
❑ 96UppDecPHE-H7
❑ 96UppDecPRE-R5
❑ 96UppDecPreH-H7
❑ 96UppDecPreR-R5
❑ 96UppDecRunP-RP12
❑ 96UppDecVJLS-VJ6
❑ 96Zen-5
❑ 96ZenArtP-5
❑ 96ZenMoz-21
❑ 97A'sMot-2
❑ 97A'sPinST-1
❑ 97A'sPinST-2
❑ 97Bow-15
❑ 97BowBes-45
❑ 97BowBesAR-45
❑ 97BowBesBC-BC5
❑ 97BowBesBCAR-BC5
❑ 97BowBesBCR-BC5
❑ 97BowBesJ-45
❑ 97BowBesJAR-45
❑ 97BowBesJR-45
❑ 97BowBesMI-MI7
❑ 97BowBesMIAR-MI7
❑ 97BowBesMIARI-MI7
❑ 97BowBesMII-MI7
❑ 97BowBesMIR-MI7
❑ 97BowBesMIRI-MI7
❑ 97BowBesP-6
❑ 97BowBesPAR-6
❑ 97BowBesPR-6
❑ 97BowBesR-45
❑ 97BowChr-11
❑ 97BowChrI-11
❑ 97BowChrIR-11
❑ 97BowChrR-11
❑ 97BowInt-15
❑ 97Cir-50
❑ 97CirBos-12
❑ 97CirIco-7
❑ 97CirLimA-10
❑ 97CirRav-50
❑ 97CirRavR-7
❑ 97CirSupB-12
❑ 97ColCho-57
❑ 97ColCho-190
❑ 97ColCho-330
❑ 97ColChoAC-1
❑ 97ColChoCtG-24A
❑ 97ColChoCtG-24B
❑ 97ColChoCtG-24C
❑ 97ColChoCtGE-CG24
❑ 97ColChoCtGIW-CG24
❑ 97ColChoNF-NF5
❑ 97ColChoPP-PP1
❑ 97ColChoPPG-PP1
❑ 97ColChoPPJ-PP1
❑ 97ColChoS-25
❑ 97ColChoSR-18
❑ 97ColChoTBS-36
❑ 97ColChoTBSWH-36
❑ 97ColChoTotT-T22
❑ 97CraJac-19
❑ 97DenHol-10
❑ 97Don-12
❑ 97Don-270
❑ 97Don-413
❑ 97DonDom-7
❑ 97DonEli-21
❑ 97DonEliGS-21
❑ 97DonEliLaL-10
❑ 97DonFraFea-8
❑ 97DonGolPP-12
❑ 97DonGolPP-270
❑ 97DonGolPP-413
❑ 97DonLim-64
❑ 97DonLim-101
❑ 97DonLim-106
❑ 97DonLimE-64
❑ 97DonLimE-101
❑ 97DonLimE-106
❑ 97DonLimENG-64
❑ 97DonLimFotG-27
❑ 97DonLonL-12
❑ 97DonPowA-14
❑ 97DonPowADC-14
❑ 97DonPre-50
❑ 97DonPre-176
❑ 97DonPreCttC-50
❑ 97DonPreCttC-176
❑ 97DonPrePM-9
❑ 97DonPreS-14
❑ 97DonPreSS-14
❑ 97DonPreTB-13
❑ 97DonPreTBG-13
❑ 97DonPreTF-13
❑ 97DonPreTP-13
❑ 97DonPreTPG-13
❑ 97DonSig-1
❑ 97DonSigPPP-1
❑ 97DonSilPP-12
❑ 97DonSilPP-270
❑ 97DonSilPP-413
❑ 97DonVxP1-42
❑ 97E-X2-38
❑ 97E-X2ACA-6
❑ 97E-X2Cred-38
❑ 97E-X2EssCre-38
❑ 97E-X2Hall-10
❑ 97Fin-30
❑ 97Fin-155
❑ 97Fin-305
❑ 97FinEmb-155
❑ 97FinEmb-305
❑ 97FinEmbR-155
❑ 97FinEmbR-305
❑ 97FinPro-30
❑ 97FinRef-30
❑ 97FinRef-155
❑ 97FinRef-305
❑ 97FlaShoDC-11
❑ 97FlaShoLC-52
❑ 97FlaShoLeg0-52
❑ 97FlaShoLeg1-52
❑ 97FlaShoM-A52
❑ 97FlaShoM-B52
❑ 97FlaShoM-C52
❑ 97FlaShoR0-52
❑ 97FlaShoR1-52
❑ 97FlaShoR2-52
❑ 97Fle-193
❑ 97Fle-495
❑ 97Fle-708
❑ 97Fle-740
❑ 97FleBleB-5
❑ 97FleDecoE-7
❑ 97FleDecoERT-7
❑ 97FleDiaT-7
❑ 97FleGolM-4
❑ 97FleGouG-8
❑ 97FleGouGF-8
❑ 97FleHea-12
❑ 97FleLumC-12
❑ 97FleNig&D-5
❑ 97FleSoaS-9
❑ 97FleSoaSG-9
❑ 97FleTeaL-11
❑ 97FleTif-193
❑ 97FleTif-495
❑ 97FleTif-708
❑ 97FleTif-740
❑ 97FleZon-11
❑ 97HigMinM-72
❑ 97KinB-6
❑ 97Lea-38
❑ 97Lea-355
❑ 97LeaDrefS-9
❑ 97LeaFraM-38
❑ 97LeaFraM-355
❑ 97LeaFraMDC-38
❑ 97LeaFraMDC-355
❑ 97LeaGolS-22
❑ 97LeaLeaotN-3
❑ 97LeaStaS-10
❑ 97MetUni-131
❑ 97MetUniBF-8
❑ 97MetUniT-6
❑ 97NewPin-142
❑ 97NewPin-188
❑ 97NewPinAP-142
❑ 97NewPinAP-188
❑ 97NewPinMC-142
❑ 97NewPinMC-188
❑ 97NewPinPP-142
❑ 97NewPinPP-188
❑ 97Pac-173
❑ 97PacCar-15
❑ 97PacCarM-15
❑ 97PacFirD-10
❑ 97PacGolCD-15
❑ 97PacLigB-173
❑ 97PacPri-59
❑ 97PacPriGA-GA13
❑ 97PacPriGotD-GD80
❑ 97PacPriLB-59
❑ 97PacPriP-59
❑ 97PacPriSL-SL5A
❑ 97PacSil-173
❑ 97PacTriCD-8
❑ 97Pin-52
❑ 97PinArtP-PP52
❑ 97PinCar-4
❑ 97PinCer-49
❑ 97PinCer-139
❑ 97PinCerLI-5
❑ 97PinCerMBla-49
❑ 97PinCerMBla-139
❑ 97PinCerMBlu-49
❑ 97PinCerMBlu-139
❑ 97PinCerMG-49
❑ 97PinCerMG-139
❑ 97PinCerMR-49
❑ 97PinCerMR-139
❑ 97PinCerR-49
❑ 97PinCerR-139
❑ 97PinEpixPE-E18
❑ 97PinHom-19
❑ 97PinHom-20
❑ 97PinIns-78
❑ 97PinInsC-23
❑ 97PinInsCE-78
❑ 97PinInsDD-9
❑ 97PinInsDE-78
❑ 97PinInsFS-4
❑ 97PinMin-15
❑ 97PinMinB-15
❑ 97PinMinCB-15
❑ 97PinMinCG-15
❑ 97PinMinCGR-15
❑ 97PinMinCN-15
❑ 97PinMinCSS-15
❑ 97PinMinG-15
❑ 97PinMinS-15
❑ 97PinMusC-52
❑ 97PinPrePla-52
❑ 97PinTotCPB-49
❑ 97PinTotCPB-139
❑ 97PinTotCPG-49
❑ 97PinTotCPG-139
❑ 97PinTotCPR-49
❑ 97PinTotCPR-139
❑ 97PinX-P-42
❑ 97PinX-P-143
❑ 97PinX-PF&A-2
❑ 97PinX-PMoS-42
❑ 97PinX-PMoS-143
❑ 97PinX-PMW-14
❑ 97PinX-PMWG-14
❑ 97PinX-PMWS-14
❑ 97PinX-PSfF-41
❑ 97PinX-PSfF-U41
❑ 97PinX-PSfFU-41
❑ 97PreCon-19
❑ 97Sco-187
❑ 97Sco-511
❑ 97ScoArtPWB-187
❑ 97ScoArtPWB-511
❑ 97ScoBla-2
❑ 97ScoPitP-6
❑ 97ScoPreS-187
❑ 97ScoResC-511
❑ 97ScoShoS-187
❑ 97ScoShoS-511
❑ 97ScoShoSAP-187
❑ 97ScoShoSAP-511
❑ 97ScoSteS-5
❑ 97ScoTitT-1
❑ 97Sel-75
❑ 97SelArtP-75
❑ 97SelCom-75
❑ 97SelRegG-75
❑ 97SelToootT-19
❑ 97SelToootTMB-19
❑ 97SP-130
❑ 97SPGamF-GF7
❑ 97SPInsI-2
❑ 97SPMarM-MM4
❑ 97SpoIll-168
❑ 97SpoIll-175
❑ 97SpoIllEE-168
❑ 97SpoIllEE-175
❑ 97SpoIllGS-17
❑ 97SPSpeF-11
❑ 97SPSpxF-2
❑ 97SPSPxFA-2
❑ 97SPx-38
❑ 97SPxBoufG-14
❑ 97SPxBro-38
❑ 97SPxCorotG-9
❑ 97SPxGol-38
❑ 97SPxGraF-38
❑ 97SPxSil-38
❑ 97SPxSte-38
❑ 97StaClu-5
❑ 97StaClu-384
❑ 97StaCluFR-F7
❑ 97StaCluFW-F7
❑ 97StaCluI-I6
❑ 97StaCluMat-5
❑ 97StaCluMOP-5
❑ 97StaCluMOP-384
❑ 97StaCluMOP-I6
❑ 97StaCluMOP-FB7
❑ 97StaCluMOP-PG8
❑ 97StaCluPG-PG8
❑ 97StrAll-45
❑ 97Stu-8
❑ 97StuMasS-22
❑ 97StuMasS8-22
❑ 97StuPor8-13
❑ 97StuPrePG-8
❑ 97StuPrePS-8
❑ 97Top-62
❑ 97TopChr-21
❑ 97TopChrR-21
❑ 97TopChrSB-6
❑ 97TopChrSBR-6
❑ 97TopGal-37
❑ 97TopGalGoH-GH6
❑ 97TopGalPG-PG8
❑ 97TopGalPMS-8
❑ 97TopGalPMSSS-8
❑ 97TopGalPPI-37
❑ 97TopIntF-ILM1
❑ 97TopIntFR-ILM1
❑ 97TopMem05-33
❑ 97TopScr-14
❑ 97TopScrT-14
❑ 97TopSeaB-SB6
❑ 97TopSta-51
❑ 97TopStaAM-51
❑ 97TopSweS-SS10
❑ 97TopTeaT-TT12
❑ 97UD3-1
❑ 97UD3Marq-MA2
❑ 97Ult-114
❑ 97UltBasR-6
❑ 97UltChe-A5
❑ 97UltDiaP-7
❑ 97UltDouT-8
❑ 97UltFamGam-12
❑ 97UltGolME-114
❑ 97UltHitM-11
❑ 97UltHRK-7
❑ 97UltPlaME-114
❑ 97UltPowP-A6
❑ 97UltPowP-B10
❑ 97UltSeaC-6
❑ 97UltThu-3
❑ 97UltTop3-14
❑ 97UltTop3GM-14
❑ 97UppDec-320
❑ 97UppDec-386
❑ 97UppDec-420
❑ 97UppDec-450
❑ 97UppDecAWJ-3
❑ 97UppDecHC-HC10
❑ 97UppDecLDC-LD1
❑ 97UppDecMM-A7
❑ 97UppDecP-21
❑ 97UppDecPE-21
❑ 97UppDecPP-PP10
❑ 97UppDecPPJ-PP10
❑ 97UppDecRP-RP4
❑ 97UppDecSA-12
❑ 97UppDecSAG-12
❑ 97Zen-28
❑ 97Zen8x10-11
❑ 97Zen8x1D-11
❑ 98Bow-5
❑ 98BowBes-1
❑ 98BowBesAR-1
❑ 98BowBesMIF-MI12
❑ 98BowBesMIFAR-MI12
❑ 98BowBesMIFR-MI12
❑ 98BowBesR-1
❑ 98BowChr-5
❑ 98BowChrGA-5
❑ 98BowChrGAR-5
❑ 98BowChrI-5
❑ 98BowChrIR-5
❑ 98BowChrR-5
❑ 98BowGolA-5
❑ 98BowInt-5
❑ 98CarScoP-4
❑ 98CirThu-25
❑ 98CirThuB-14
❑ 98CirThuLA-11
❑ 98CirThuQS-8
❑ 98CirThuRav-25
❑ 98CirThuRR-11
❑ 98CirThuSupRav-25
❑ 98CirThuTB-8
❑ 98ColCho-5
❑ 98ColCho-22
❑ 98ColCho-220
❑ 98ColCho-254
❑ 98ColCho-268
❑ 98ColChoCG-5
❑ 98ColChoCtG-CG10A
❑ 98ColChoCtG-CG10B
❑ 98ColChoCtG-CG10C
❑ 98ColChoCtGExch-CG10
❑ 98ColChoCtGIW-CG10
❑ 98ColChoER-ER23
❑ 98ColChoMBH-22
❑ 98ColChoRJ-5
❑ 98ColChoRJ-220
❑ 98ColChoS'-22
❑ 98ColChoSQ-SQ40
❑ 98ColChoSQ-SQ89
❑ 98ColChoSQDouble-10
❑ 98ColChoSQHR-10
❑ 98ColChoSQSingle-10
❑ 98ColChoSQTriple-10
❑ 98CroRoy-115
❑ 98CroRoyAS-18

❑ 98CroRoyCCPA-9
❑ 98CroRoyCCPrem-9
❑ 98CroRoyDK-17
❑ 98CroRoyFoB-16
❑ 98CroRoyFoBA-16
❑ 98CroRoyHRF-5
❑ 98CroRoyPotG-20
❑ 98Don-62
❑ 98Don-164
❑ 98Don-365
❑ 98Don-401
❑ 98Don-417
❑ 98DonCol-62
❑ 98DonCol-164
❑ 98DonColE-413
❑ 98DonColE-530
❑ 98DonColL-370
❑ 98DonColP-566
❑ 98DonColP-733
❑ 98DonColS-62
❑ 98DonColS-164
❑ 98DonCruG-93
❑ 98DonCruP-93
❑ 98DonCruR-93
❑ 98DonDay-6
❑ 98DonDom-11
❑ 98DonEli-13
❑ 98DonEli-130
❑ 98DonEliA-13
❑ 98DonEliA-130
❑ 98DonEliC-19
❑ 98DonEliI-6
❑ 98DonEliMC-19
❑ 98DonEliPN-3A
❑ 98DonEliPN-3B
❑ 98DonEliPN-3C
❑ 98DonEliPNDC-3A
❑ 98DonEliPNDC-3B
❑ 98DonEliPNDC-3C
❑ 98DonEliPNS-3A
❑ 98DonEliPNS-3B
❑ 98DonEliPNS-3C
❑ 98DonEliS-13
❑ 98DonEliS-130
❑ 98DonFANT-8
❑ 98DonFANTDC-8
❑ 98DonGolPP-62
❑ 98DonGolPP-164
❑ 98DonGolPP-365
❑ 98DonGolPP-401
❑ 98DonGolPP-417
❑ 98DonLonL-2
❑ 98DonPre-16
❑ 98DonPre-183
❑ 98DonPreGB-12
❑ 98DonPreGES-25
❑ 98DonPreGoB-12
❑ 98DonPreGX-25
❑ 98DonPreGXDC-25
❑ 98DonPrePM-16
❑ 98DonPreSeat-16
❑ 98DonPreSeat-183
❑ 98DonPreTP-12
❑ 98DonPreTPD-6
❑ 98DonPreTPG-12
❑ 98DonPreTPS-12
❑ 98DonPreTW-17
❑ 98DonPriCD-62
❑ 98DonPriCD-164
❑ 98DonPriCE-413
❑ 98DonPriCE-530
❑ 98DonPriCL-370
❑ 98DonPriCP-566
❑ 98DonPriCP-733
❑ 98DonProLO-12
❑ 98DonProLPI-2
❑ 98DonProLS-1
❑ 98DonSig-52
❑ 98DonSig-140
❑ 98DonSigP-52
❑ 98DonSigP-140
❑ 98DonSilPP-62
❑ 98DonSilPP-164
❑ 98DonSilPP-365
❑ 98DonSilPP-401
❑ 98DonSilPP-417
❑ 98DonSonM9-17
❑ 98E-X2-11
❑ 98E-X2Cheap-3
❑ 98E-X2DesCoop-8
❑ 98E-X2ECFut-11
❑ 98E-X2ECNow-11
❑ 98Fin-145
❑ 98FinCen-C8
❑ 98FinCenR-C8
❑ 98FinMysF1-M3
❑ 98FinMysF1-M6
❑ 98FinMysF1-M8
❑ 98FinMysF1-M10
❑ 98FinMysF2-M19
❑ 98FinMysF2-M20
❑ 98FinMysF2-M21
❑ 98FinMysF2R-M19
❑ 98FinMysF2R-M20
❑ 98FinMysF2R-M21
❑ 98FinMysFO-3
❑ 98FinMysFOR-3
❑ 98FinMysFR-M3
❑ 98FinMysFR-M6
❑ 98FinMysFR-M8
❑ 98FinMysFR-M10
❑ 98FinNo--145
❑ 98FinNo-R-145
❑ 98FinOve-A1
❑ 98FinOveR-A1
❑ 98FinPowZ-P5
❑ 98FinRef-145
❑ 98FinStaS-SS19
❑ 98FinStaSJ-6
❑ 98FinTheM-TM7
❑ 98FinTheMR-TM7
❑ 98FlaShoLeg0-9
❑ 98FlaShoLeg1-9
❑ 98FlaShoLeg2-9
❑ 98FlaShoLeg3-9
❑ 98FlaShoLegM-9
❑ 98FlaShoP1-7
❑ 98FlaShoR0-9
❑ 98FlaShoR1-9
❑ 98FlaShoR2-9
❑ 98FlaShoR3-9
❑ 98Fle-25
❑ 98Fle-318
❑ 98Fle-332
❑ 98Fle-573
❑ 98Fle-590
❑ 98FleDecERT-10
❑ 98FleDecoE-10
❑ 98FleDiaS-15
❑ 98FleDiaSCS-NNO
❑ 98FleDiaT-DT6
❑ 98FleIn TC-IC12
❑ 98FleLumC-10
❑ 98FlePowG-15
❑ 98FleUpd-U1
❑ 98FleVin'-50
❑ 98FleVin'C-50
❑ 98FleZon-11
❑ 98HamHel-1
❑ 98Lea-171
❑ 98LeaFraDA-171
❑ 98LeaFraF-171
❑ 98LeaFraM-171
❑ 98LeaFraM-171
❑ 98LeaFraMDC-171
❑ 98LeaFraMDC-171
❑ 98LeaFraMS-171
❑ 98LeaFraMZ2-171
❑ 98LeaHeaftH-13
❑ 98LeaHeaftHS-13
❑ 98LeaRS-41
❑ 98LeaRS-159
❑ 98LeaRS-185
❑ 98LeaRS-338
❑ 98LeaRS-339
❑ 98LeaRSExtM-4
❑ 98LeaRSExtMDC-4
❑ 98LeaRSGAHSamp-13
❑ 98LeaRSGreAH-13
❑ 98LeaRSGreHit-14
❑ 98LeaRSHRDerby-11
❑ 98LeaRSLHolo-41
❑ 98LeaRSLHolo-159
❑ 98LeaRSLHolo-185
❑ 98LeaRSLHolo-338
❑ 98LeaRSLHolo-339
❑ 98LeaRSLMVP-20
❑ 98LeaRSLMVPPE-20
❑ 98LeaRSLong-41
❑ 98LeaRSLong-159
❑ 98LeaRSLong-185
❑ 98LeaRSLong-338
❑ 98LeaRSLong-339
❑ 98LeaRSSOSamp-2
❑ 98LeaRSStaOva-2
❑ 98LeaRSTicMas-15
❑ 98LeaRSTicMasDC-15
❑ 98LeaRTrue-41
❑ 98LeaRTrue-159
❑ 98LeaRTrue-185
❑ 98LeaRTrue-338
❑ 98LeaRTrue-339
❑ 98LeaStaRep-22
❑ 98LeaStaS-10
❑ 98LeaStaSDC-10
❑ 98MarMcGLL-1
❑ 98McGDen-1
❑ 98MetUni-110
❑ 98MetUniAT-17
❑ 98MetUniPMG-110
❑ 98Pac-416
❑ 98PacAur-187
❑ 98PacAurCube-13
❑ 98PacAurHC-14
❑ 98PacAurKotML-7
❑ 98PacAurODLC-13
❑ 98PacAurPF-25
❑ 98PacAurPFC-25
❑ 98PacAurPFPB-25
❑ 98PacAurPFR-25
❑ 98PacAurPFS-25
❑ 98PacCraCh-7
❑ 98PacGolCDC-26
❑ 98PacHomRH-1
❑ 98PacHomRH-1
❑ 98PacHomRH-3
❑ 98PacHomRH-5
❑ 98PacHomRH-7
❑ 98PacHomRH-9
❑ 98PacHomRH-11
❑ 98PacHomRH-13
❑ 98PacHomRH-15
❑ 98PacHomRH-17
❑ 98PacHomRH-19
❑ 98PacHomRH-21
❑ 98PacHomRH-23
❑ 98PacHomRH-25
❑ 98PacHomRH-27
❑ 98PacHomRH-29
❑ 98PacHomRH-31
❑ 98PacHomRH-33
❑ 98PacHomRH-35
❑ 98PacHomRH-37
❑ 98PacHomRH-39
❑ 98PacHomRH-41
❑ 98PacHomRH-43
❑ 98PacHomRH-45
❑ 98PacHomRH-47
❑ 98PacHomRH-49
❑ 98PacHomRH-51
❑ 98PacHomRH-53
❑ 98PacHomRH-55
❑ 98PacHomRH-57
❑ 98PacHomRH-59
❑ 98PacHomRH-61
❑ 98PacHomRH-63
❑ 98PacHomRH-65
❑ 98PacHomRH-67
❑ 98PacHomRH-68
❑ 98PacHomRH-69
❑ 98PacHomRH-70
❑ 98PacHomRH-HRC1
❑ 98PacHomRH-15
❑ 98PacInCage-13
❑ 98PacInv-136
❑ 98PacInvCCDB-7
❑ 98PacInvCCG-7
❑ 98PacInvCCG-7
❑ 98PacInvCCLB-7
❑ 98PacInvCCP-7
❑ 98PacInvCCR-7
❑ 98PacInvGems-207
❑ 98PacInvInt-9N
❑ 98PacInvMiT-15
❑ 98PacInvPBlue-136
❑ 98PacInvPhoto-11
❑ 98PacInvSilv-136
❑ 98PacInvTeam-23
❑ 98PacOme-200
❑ 98PacOmeEP-18
❑ 98PacOmeEP1o1-18
❑ 98PacOmeFTF-2
❑ 98PacOmeOnIns-34
❑ 98PacOmeP-19
❑ 98PacOmeR-200
❑ 98PacOnl-621A
❑ 98PacOnl-621B
❑ 98PacOnl-629
❑ 98PacOnlR-621A
❑ 98PacOnlR-621B
❑ 98PacOnlR-629
❑ 98PacOnlWC-621A
❑ 98PacOnlWC-621B
❑ 98PacOnlWC-629
❑ 98PacPar-232
❑ 98PacParC-232
❑ 98PacParCB-6
❑ 98PacParCBPP-6
❑ 98PacParFC-13
❑ 98PacParG-232
❑ 98PacParHS-232
❑ 98PacParI-32
❑ 98PacParPB-232
❑ 98PacParR-232
❑ 98PacParSD-15
❑ 98PacParTC-28
❑ 98PacPlaB-416
❑ 98PacRedT-416
❑ 98PacSil-416
❑ 98PacTeaC-26
❑ 98Pin-63
❑ 98Pin-188
❑ 98Pin-198
❑ 98PinArtP-PP56
❑ 98PinArtP-PP91
❑ 98PinEpixME-E18
❑ 98PinEpixMO-E18
❑ 98PinEpixMP-E18
❑ 98PinEpixPO-E18
❑ 98PinEpixPP-E18
❑ 98PinEpixSE-E18
❑ 98PinEpixSO-E18
❑ 98PinEpixSP-E18
❑ 98PinHitIH-8
❑ 98PinHitIHS-8
❑ 98PinIns-40
❑ 98PinIns-145
❑ 98PinInsBtN-10
❑ 98PinInsC-13
❑ 98PinInsCE-40
❑ 98PinInsCE-145
❑ 98PinInsCG-13
❑ 98PinInsDE-40
❑ 98PinInsDE-145
❑ 98PinInsSG-5AB
❑ 98PinInsSG-5CD
❑ 98PinInsSG-22AB
❑ 98PinInsSG-22CD
❑ 98PinInsSGS-5AB
❑ 98PinInsSGS-5CD
❑ 98PinInsSGS-22AB
❑ 98PinInsSGS-22CD
❑ 98PinMinB-14
❑ 98PinMinCB-14
❑ 98PinMinCBAP-14
❑ 98PinMinCBS-14
❑ 98PinMinCGP-14
❑ 98PinMinCGPAP-14
❑ 98PinMinCN-14
❑ 98PinMinCNAP-14
❑ 98PinMinCSGR-14
❑ 98PinMinDC-14
❑ 98PinMinG-14
❑ 98PinMinMCSS-14
❑ 98PinMinS-14
❑ 98PinMinS-14
❑ 98PinMusC-PP56
❑ 98PinMusC-PP91
❑ 98PinPer-16
❑ 98PinPerBB-10
❑ 98PinPerBBSamp-10
❑ 98PinPerBBSO-10
❑ 98PinPerLP-16
❑ 98PinPerPP-16
❑ 98PinPerPT-9
❑ 98PinPerSftF-42
❑ 98PinPerSftFShop-7
❑ 98PinPlu-14
❑ 98PinPlu-193
❑ 98PinPlu-196
❑ 98PinPluAE-18
❑ 98PinPluAEE-18
❑ 98PinPluAEP-18
❑ 98PinPluAP-PP8
❑ 98PinPluGAP-PP8
❑ 98PinPluLM-11
❑ 98PinPluMAP-PP8
❑ 98PinPluTP-2
❑ 98PinPluTPG-2
❑ 98PinPluTPM-2
❑ 98PinPluY-14
❑ 98PinPowPJ-7
❑ 98PinPowPJS-7
❑ 98PinPreP-63
❑ 98PinPreP-188
❑ 98PinPreP-198
❑ 98PinPreP-E18
❑ 98PinPreP-H8
❑ 98PinPreP-S1
❑ 98PinPreP-S2
❑ 98PinPreP-S3
❑ 98PinPreP-S5
❑ 98PinPreP-S6
❑ 98PinPreP-S7
❑ 98PinSna-SLC5
❑ 98PinSna-SLC9
❑ 98PinSpe-1
❑ 98PinSpe-2
❑ 98PinSpe-3
❑ 98PinSpe-4
❑ 98PinSpe-5
❑ 98PinSpe-6
❑ 98PinSpe-7
❑ 98PreCon-19
❑ 98Revo-121
❑ 98RevoFP-19
❑ 98RevoMLI-9
❑ 98RevoPTP-19
❑ 98RevoRooHH-26
❑ 98RevoShow-34
❑ 98RevoSS-121
❑ 98Sco-41
❑ 98Sco-270
❑ 98ScoAllST-4
❑ 98ScoCar-4
❑ 98ScoComP-2A
❑ 98ScoComP-2B
❑ 98ScoComP-2C
❑ 98ScoComPG-2A
❑ 98ScoComPG-2B
❑ 98ScoComPG-2C
❑ 98ScoEpix-E18
❑ 98ScoFirP-16
❑ 98ScoRT-25
❑ 98ScoRTSS-PP25
❑ 98ScoRTSSAP-PP25
❑ 98ScoRTSSAP1-PP25
❑ 98ScoRTStarGaz-4
❑ 98ScoSS-PP126
❑ 98ScoSSAP-PP126
❑ 98SkyDugA-41
❑ 98SkyDugA-127
❑ 98SkyDugADH-DH11
❑ 98SkyDugAG-G5
❑ 98SkyDugAIA-41
❑ 98SkyDugAIA-127
❑ 98SP Aut-160
❑ 98SP Aut-SD10
❑ 98SP AutSD-SD10
❑ 98SP AutSDT-SD10
❑ 98SpoIll-87
❑ 98SpoIll-132
❑ 98SpoIll-184
❑ 98SpoIllEC-EC4
❑ 98SpoIllEE-87
❑ 98SpoIllEE-132
❑ 98SpoIllEE-184
❑ 98SpoIllFE-87
❑ 98SpoIllFE-132
❑ 98SpoIllFE-184
❑ 98SpoIllODMP-OD24
❑ 98SpoIllTaN-52
❑ 98SpoIllTaN-113
❑ 98SpoIllTaNC-C10
❑ 98SpoIllTaNEE-52
❑ 98SpoIllTaNEE-113
❑ 98SpoIllTaNGS-7
❑ 98SpoIllWSF-80
❑ 98SpoIllWSFEE-80
❑ 98SpoIllWSFFE-80
❑ 98SpoIllWSFPP-1
❑ 98SpoIllWSFRJP-13
❑ 98SPxFin-40
❑ 98SPxFin-120
❑ 98SPxFin-162
❑ 98SPxFin-176
❑ 98SPxFin-225
❑ 98SPxFin-355
❑ 98SPxFinHRH-HR2
❑ 98SPxFinR-40
❑ 98SPxFinR-120
❑ 98SPxFinR-162
❑ 98SPxFinR-176
❑ 98SPxFinR-225
❑ 98SPxFinR-355
❑ 98SPxFinS-40
❑ 98SPxFinS-120
❑ 98SPxFinS-162
❑ 98SPxFinS-176
❑ 98SPxFinS-225
❑ 98SPxFinS-355
❑ 98StaCluBP-BP9
❑ 98StaCluFDI-203
❑ 98StaCluI-203
❑ 98StaCluNC-NC17
❑ 98StaCluOneK-203
❑ 98StaCluPP-203
❑ 98StaCluRC-RC5
❑ 98StaCluTIII-T11A
❑ 98StaCluTLme-T11A
❑ 98StaCluTLmo-T11A
❑ 98Stu-161
❑ 98StuGPP-161
❑ 98StuHitPar-15
❑ 98StuMast-6
❑ 98StuPor8x10-22
❑ 98StuPor8x10GP-22
❑ 98StuSony99-17
❑ 98StuSPP-161
❑ 98Top-325
❑ 98Top-478
❑ 98TopChr-325
❑ 98TopChr-478
❑ 98TopChrHB-HB11
❑ 98TopChrHBR-HB11
❑ 98TopChrM-MS8
❑ 98TopChrMR-MS8
❑ 98TopChrR-325
❑ 98TopChrR-478
❑ 98TopDevR-325
❑ 98TopDevR-478
❑ 98TopDia-325
❑ 98TopDia-478
❑ 98TopFruR-4
❑ 98TopGal-50
❑ 98TopGalAG-AG9
❑ 98TopGalGoH-GH7
❑ 98TopGalGoHJ-GH7
❑ 98TopGalGP-50
❑ 98TopGalOPP-50
❑ 98TopGalPPI-50
❑ 98TopGalPPIA-50
❑ 98TopGolLabC1-15
❑ 98TopGolLabC1B-15
❑ 98TopGolLabC1One-15
❑ 98TopGolLabC1R-15
❑ 98TopGolLabC2-15
❑ 98TopGolLabC2B-15
❑ 98TopGolLabC2One-15
❑ 98TopGolLabC2R-15
❑ 98TopGolLabC3-15
❑ 98TopGolLabC3B-15
❑ 98TopGolLabC3One-15
❑ 98TopGolLabC3R-15
❑ 98TopGolLHRR-HR2
❑ 98TopGolLHRRB-HR2
❑ 98TopGolLHRRR-HR2
❑ 98TopHal-HB11
❑ 98TopMil-MS8
❑ 98TopMiniC-325
❑ 98TopMiniC-478
❑ 98TopMysFB-M7
❑ 98TopMysFB-M7
❑ 98TopMysFBR-M7
❑ 98TopMysFBR-M7
❑ 98TopOpeD-151
❑ 98TopSta-135
❑ 98TopSta'S-29
❑ 98TopSta'SGH-29
❑ 98TopStaB-135
❑ 98TopStaG-135
❑ 98TopStaGR-135
❑ 98TopStaLB-L2
❑ 98TopStaLG-L2
❑ 98TopStaLGR-L2
❑ 98TopStaLS-L2
❑ 98TopStaS-135
❑ 98TopStaSteG-29
❑ 98TopSup-30
❑ 98TopSup-30
❑ 98TopTek-13
❑ 98TopTekD-13
❑ 98TopTekP-13
❑ 98UD3-50
❑ 98UD3-140
❑ 98UD3-230
❑ 98UD3DieCut-50
❑ 98UD3DieCut-140
❑ 98UD3DieCut-230
❑ 98UD3PCBlowup-50
❑ 98Ult-208
❑ 98Ult-218
❑ 98Ult-494
❑ 98UltArtT-15
❑ 98UltBigS-7
❑ 98UltDial-6
❑ 98UltDiaP-13
❑ 98UltDouT-13
❑ 98UltFalC-14
❑ 98UltGolM-208
❑ 98UltGolM-218
❑ 98UltGolM-494
❑ 98UltMas-208
❑ 98UltMas-218
❑ 98UltMas-494

❑ 98UltNot-7
❑ 98UltPlaM-208
❑ 98UltPlaM-218
❑ 98UltPlaM-494
❑ 98UltTicS-6
❑ 98UltTop3-7
❑ 98UltWinN-14
❑ 98UppDec-9
❑ 98UppDec-150
❑ 98UppDec-205
❑ 98UppDec-454
❑ 98UppDec-535
❑ 98UppDec-610
❑ 98UppDec10AP-20
❑ 98UppDec1APR-20
❑ 98UppDec5x7-205
❑ 98UppDec5x7-610
❑ 98UppDecAC-AS10
❑ 98UppDecAG-AG25
❑ 98UppDecAGDC-AG25
❑ 98UppDecCD-CD1
❑ 98UppDecMJ-1
❑ 98UppDecMMCf6-1
❑ 98UppDecMMCf6-2
❑ 98UppDecMMCf6-3
❑ 98UppDecMMCf6-4
❑ 98UppDecMMCf6-5
❑ 98UppDecMMCf6-6
❑ 98UppDecMMCf6-7
❑ 98UppDecMMCf6-8
❑ 98UppDecMMCf6-9
❑ 98UppDecMMCf6-10
❑ 98UppDecMMCf6-11
❑ 98UppDecMMCf6-12
❑ 98UppDecMMCf6-13
❑ 98UppDecMMCf6-14
❑ 98UppDecMMCf6-15
❑ 98UppDecMMCf6-16
❑ 98UppDecMMCf6-17
❑ 98UppDecMMCf6-18
❑ 98UppDecMMCf6-19
❑ 98UppDecMMCf6-20
❑ 98UppDecMMCf6-21
❑ 98UppDecMMCf6-22
❑ 98UppDecMMCf6-23
❑ 98UppDecMMCf6-24
❑ 98UppDecMMCf6-25
❑ 98UppDecMMCf6-26
❑ 98UppDecMMCf6-27
❑ 98UppDecMMCf6-28
❑ 98UppDecMMCf6-29
❑ 98UppDecMMCf6-30
❑ 98UppDecMMCf6-NNO
❑ 98UppDecPN-PN22
❑ 98UppDecPN-PN23
❑ 98UppDecPN-PN24
❑ 98UppDecPN-PN25
❑ 98UppDecPN-PN26
❑ 98UppDecPN-PN27
❑ 98UppDecPN-PN28
❑ 98UppDecR-81
❑ 98UppDecR-11
❑ 98UppDecRBBop-BB29
❑ 98UppDecRGKoG-G26
❑ 98UppDecRL-5
❑ 98UppDecRQL-Q19
❑ 98UppDecRTC-TC47
❑ 98UppDecSF-2
❑ 98UppDecSF-110
❑ 98UppDecSFPD-PZ5
❑ 98UppDecSFPZOB-PZ4
❑ 98UppDecSFPZPD-PZ5
❑ 98UppDecSFPZSX-PZ5
❑ 98UppDecTMT-1
❑ 98UppDecTMTG-1
❑ 98UppDecU-20
❑ 98Zen-60
❑ 98Zen5 xx7-5
❑ 98Zen5x7GoldImp-5
❑ 98Zen5x7Imp-5
❑ 98ZenEpi-E18
❑ 98ZenRaitB-10
❑ 98ZenZ-G-60
❑ 98ZenZ-S-60
❑ 99199Fin-70
❑ 99199Fin-104
❑ 99199Fin-252
❑ 99199Fin-300
❑ 99AllMysFR-M3
❑ 99AurComP-7A
❑ 99AurComP-7B
❑ 99AurKinotML-7
❑ 99AurOn DL-15
❑ 99AurPenF-15
❑ 99AurPenF-15
❑ 99AurPenFB-15
❑ 99AurPenFS-15
❑ 99AurSty-15
❑ 99Bow-6
❑ 99BowBes-70
❑ 99BowBes-90
❑ 99BowBesAR-70
❑ 99BowBesAR-90
❑ 99BowBesFBMI-FB1
❑ 99BowBesFBMII-FB1
❑ 99BowBesFBMIII-FB1
❑ 99BowBesMI-M10
❑ 99BowBesMIAR-M10
❑ 99BowBesMIR-M10
❑ 99BowBesR-70
❑ 99BowBesR-90
❑ 99BowChr-6
❑ 99BowChrDA-DA14
❑ 99BowChrDAR-DA14
❑ 99BowChrG-6
❑ 99BowChrGR-6
❑ 99BowChrI-6
❑ 99BowChrIR-6
❑ 99BowChrR-6
❑ 99BowEarR-ER6
❑ 99BowGol-6
❑ 99BowInt-6
❑ 99CroRoyB-116
❑ 99CroRoyC2-7
❑ 99CroRoyCCDB-8
❑ 99CroRoyCCG-8
❑ 99CroRoyCCG-8
❑ 99CroRoyCCLB-8
❑ 99CroRoyCCP-8
❑ 99CroRoyCCP-8
❑ 99CroRoyCCR-8
❑ 99CroRoyL-116
❑ 99CroRoyLL-7
❑ 99CroRoyMP-14
❑ 99CroRoyOD-116
❑ 99CroRoyPotG-19
❑ 99CroRoyPP-20
❑ 99CroRoyPPN-20
❑ 99DumSet-152
❑ 99DumSet-ER6
❑ 99E-X Cen-16
❑ 99E-X CenECFut-16
❑ 99E-X CenECNow-16
❑ 99E-XCenFoF'-20
❑ 99E-XCenMotC-2
❑ 99FinAarAwC-HA9
❑ 99FinAarAwCR-HA9
❑ 99FinCom-C6
❑ 99FinComDualR-C6
❑ 99FinFraR-FR3
❑ 99FinFraRR-FR3
❑ 99FinGolRef-70
❑ 99FinGolRef-104
❑ 99FinGolRef-252
❑ 99FinGolRef-300
❑ 99FinLeaL-L1
❑ 99FinMil-M11
❑ 99FinMil-M27
❑ 99FinPeelHyp-2
❑ 99FinPeelSpark-2
❑ 99FinPeeSS-2
❑ 99FinProF-PF1
❑ 99FinProF-PF11
❑ 99FinProF-PF33
❑ 99FinProF-PF42
❑ 99FinRef-70
❑ 99FinRef-104
❑ 99FinRef-252
❑ 99FinRef-300
❑ 99FinSplS-SS1
❑ 99FinSplSDR-SS1
❑ 99FinTeaFB-TF2
❑ 99FinTeaFBR-TF2
❑ 99FinTeaFG-TF2
❑ 99FinTeaFGR-TF2
❑ 99FinTeaFR-TF2
❑ 99FinTeaFRR-TF2
❑ 99FlaShoLeg1-1
❑ 99FlaShoLeg2-1
❑ 99FlaShoLeg3-1
❑ 99FlaShoLegM1-1
❑ 99FlaShoLegM2-1
❑ 99FlaShoLegM3-1
❑ 99FlaShoMoG-9
❑ 99FlaShoR1-1
❑ 99FlaShoR2-1
❑ 99FlaShoR3-1
❑ 99Fle-1
❑ 99Fle-595
❑ 99FleBri-1
❑ 99FleBri2G-1
❑ 99FleBriBlu-1
❑ 99FleBriGol-1
❑ 99FleBriSS-2
❑ 99FleBriSSP-2
❑ 99FleDatWD-6
❑ 99FleDiaM-11
❑ 99FleDiaSkiSheet-NNO
❑ 99FleGoiYar-9
❑ 99FleGolM-9
❑ 99FleMys-70
❑ 99FleMys-152
❑ 99FleMysE-5
❑ 99FleMysG-70
❑ 99FleMysM-70
❑ 99FleMysM-152
❑ 99FleSta9-1
❑ 99FleSta9-595
❑ 99FleVin'-1
❑ 99FleWarT-1
❑ 99FleWarT-595
❑ 99HomHer-1
❑ 99HomHer-5
❑ 99HomHer-9
❑ 99HomHer-13
❑ 99MarMcG5HRS-1
❑ 99MarMcG5HRS-2
❑ 99MarMcG5HRS-3
❑ 99MarMcG5HRS-4
❑ 99MarMcG5HRS-5
❑ 99MarMcG5HRS-6
❑ 99MarMcG5HRS-7
❑ 99MarMcG5HRS-8
❑ 99MarMcG5HRS-9
❑ 99MarMcG5HRS-10
❑ 99MarMcG5HRS-11
❑ 99MarMcG5HRS-12
❑ 99MarMcG5HRS-13
❑ 99MarMcG5HRS-14
❑ 99MarMcG5HRS-15
❑ 99MarMcG5HRS-16
❑ 99MarMcG5HRS-17
❑ 99MarMcG5HRS-18
❑ 99MarMcG5HRS-19
❑ 99MarMcG5HRS-20
❑ 99MarMcG5HRS-21
❑ 99MarMcG5HRS-22
❑ 99MarMcG5HRS-23
❑ 99MarMcG5HRS-24
❑ 99MarMcG5HRS-25
❑ 99MarMcG5HRS-26
❑ 99MarMcG5HRS-27
❑ 99MarMcG5HRS-28
❑ 99MarMcG5HRS-29
❑ 99MarMcG5HRS-NNO
❑ 99MetUni-1
❑ 99MetUni-244
❑ 99MetUni-295
❑ 99MetUniBWTW-5
❑ 99MetUniDS-10
❑ 99MetUniGM-1
❑ 99MetUniGM-244
❑ 99MetUniGM-295
❑ 99MetUniL-2
❑ 99MetUniPM-12
❑ 99MetUniPMG-1
❑ 99MetUniPMG-244
❑ 99MetUniPMG-295
❑ 99Pac-70
❑ 99Pac-70A
❑ 99PacAur-156
❑ 99PacAurOD-156
❑ 99PacCraCho-9
❑ 99PacCroC-233
❑ 99PacCroCITC-14
❑ 99PacCroCPB-233
❑ 99PacCroCPC-9
❑ 99PacCroCTC-24
❑ 99PacCroCTM-14
❑ 99PacDynaD-18
❑ 99PacDynaDT-18
❑ 99PacGolCDC-34
❑ 99PacInv-120
❑ 99PacInvDM-7
❑ 99PacInvFP-16
❑ 99PacInvGotG-7
❑ 99PacInvOD-120
❑ 99PacInvPB-120
❑ 99PacInvSF-15
❑ 99PacInvSF-15B
❑ 99PacInvSH-16
❑ 99PacInvSH-16B
❑ 99PacInvTA-15
❑ 99PacOme-197
❑ 99PacOme5T-15
❑ 99PacOme5TT-15
❑ 99PacOmeC-197
❑ 99PacOmeDD-9
❑ 99PacOmeDM-26
❑ 99PacOmeEP-14
❑ 99PacOmeEP1o1-14
❑ 99PacOmeG-197
❑ 99PacOmeH'-14
❑ 99PacOmePB-197
❑ 99PacPar-194
❑ 99PacParC-194
❑ 99PacParCB-7
❑ 99PacParCBPP-7
❑ 99PacParFC-15
❑ 99PacParG-194
❑ 99PacParHoloGold-194
❑ 99PacParHS-194
❑ 99PacParOD-194
❑ 99PacParPB-29
❑ 99PacParPB-194
❑ 99PacParRed-194
❑ 99PacParTC-24
❑ 99PacPlaB-70
❑ 99PacPlaB-70A
❑ 99PacPri-121
❑ 99PacPriAotG-16
❑ 99PacPriBL-9
❑ 99PacPriDG-16
❑ 99PacPriEP-10
❑ 99PacPriHB-121
❑ 99PacPriHG-121
❑ 99PacPriHM-121
❑ 99PacPriHP-121
❑ 99PacPriRed-121
❑ 99PacPriS-12
❑ 99PacPriS206-12
❑ 99PacPriS206R-12
❑ 99PacPriSE-12
❑ 99PacPriSHRH-1
❑ 99PacPriSHRH-3
❑ 99PacPriSHRH-5
❑ 99PacPriSHRH-7
❑ 99PacPriSHRH-9
❑ 99PacPriSHRH-11
❑ 99PacPriSHRH-13
❑ 99PacPriSHRH-15
❑ 99PacPriSHRH-17
❑ 99PacPriSHRH-19
❑ 99PacPriSHRH-20
❑ 99PacPriSHRH-21
❑ 99PacPriSP-12
❑ 99PacPriSP-12
❑ 99PacPriSV-12
❑ 99PacRed-70
❑ 99PacRed-70A
❑ 99PacTeaC-28
❑ 99PacTim-19
❑ 99Pin-19
❑ 99Rev-118
❑ 99RevDiaL-27
❑ 99RevFouP-16
❑ 99RevMLBIcon-7
❑ 99RevPremDate-118
❑ 99RevRet-118
❑ 99RevShaSS-118
❑ 99RevThoitS-14
❑ 99RevTri-7
❑ 99RevTri-7
❑ 99SkyMolM-134
❑ 99SkyMolMF-34
❑ 99SkyMolMFS-34
❑ 99SkyMolMFT-34
❑ 99SkyMolMX-134
❑ 99SkyPre-47
❑ 99SkyPre-273
❑ 99SkyPre-300
❑ 99SkyPreIN-6
❑ 99SkyPreLB-2
❑ 99SkyPreR-47
❑ 99SkyPreR-273
❑ 99SkyPreR-300
❑ 99SkyPreSB-1
❑ 99SkyPreSotG-8
❑ 99SkyThu-270
❑ 99SkyThuDial1-D5
❑ 99SkyThuHip-H8
❑ 99SkyThuInD-ID6
❑ 99SkyThuRant-270
❑ 99SkyThuRave-270
❑ 99SkyThuTur-TC5
❑ 99SkyThuwww-WB6
❑ 99SP Aut-79
❑ 99SP Aut-121
❑ 99SP Aut-122
❑ 99SP AutEF-E23
❑ 99SP AutHRC-HR1
❑ 99SP AutHRC-HR4
❑ 99SP AutHRC-HR5
❑ 99SP AutHRC-HR43
❑ 99SP AutHRC-HR45
❑ 99SP AutHRC-HR48
❑ 99SP AutHRC-HR52
❑ 99SP AutHRC-HR54
❑ 99SP AutHRC-HR58
❑ 99SP AutHRC-HR60
❑ 99SP AutHRC-HR61
❑ 99SP AutHRC-HR62
❑ 99SP AutHRC-HR63
❑ 99SP AutHRC-HR64
❑ 99SP AutHRC-HR65
❑ 99SP AutHRC-HR67
❑ 99SP AutHRC-HR68
❑ 99SP AutHRC-HR69
❑ 99SP AutHRC-HR70
❑ 99SP AutR-R23
❑ 99SP AutRC-5
❑ 99SP AutRC-6
❑ 99SPAutHRCDC-HR1
❑ 99SPAutHRCDC-HR4
❑ 99SPAutHRCDC-HR5
❑ 99SPAutHRCDC-HR43
❑ 99SPAutHRCDC-HR45
❑ 99SPAutHRCDC-HR48
❑ 99SPAutHRCDC-HR52
❑ 99SPAutHRCDC-HR54
❑ 99SPAutHRCDC-HR58
❑ 99SPAutHRCDC-HR60
❑ 99SPAutHRCDC-HR61
❑ 99SPAutHRCDC-HR62
❑ 99SPAutHRCDC-HR63
❑ 99SPAutHRCDC-HR64
❑ 99SPAutHRCDC-HR65
❑ 99SPAutHRCDC-HR67
❑ 99SPAutHRCDC-HR68
❑ 99SPAutHRCDC-HR69
❑ 99SPAutHRCDC-HR70
❑ 99SpoIll-10
❑ 99SpoIll-33
❑ 99SpoIll-123
❑ 99SpoIllDD-9
❑ 99SpoIllF4-1
❑ 99SpoIllF4E-1
❑ 99SpoIllH-7
❑ 99SPx-1
❑ 99SPx-2
❑ 99SPx-3
❑ 99SPx-4
❑ 99SPx-5
❑ 99SPx-6
❑ 99SPx-7
❑ 99SPx-8
❑ 99SPx-9
❑ 99SPx-10
❑ 99SPx-72
❑ 99SPxDom-FB18
❑ 99SPxFinR-1
❑ 99SPxFinR-2
❑ 99SPxFinR-3
❑ 99SPxFinR-4
❑ 99SPxFinR-5
❑ 99SPxFinR-6
❑ 99SPxFinR-7
❑ 99SPxFinR-8
❑ 99SPxFinR-9
❑ 99SPxFinR-10
❑ 99SPxFinR-72
❑ 99SPxFinS-1
❑ 99SPxFinS-2
❑ 99SPxFinS-3
❑ 99SPxFinS-4
❑ 99SPxFinS-5
❑ 99SPxFinS-6
❑ 99SPxFinS-7
❑ 99SPxFinS-8
❑ 99SPxFinS-9
❑ 99SPxFinS-10
❑ 99SPxFinS-72
❑ 99SPxPowE-PE27
❑ 99SPxPreS-PS1
❑ 99SPxStaF-SF26
❑ 99StaClu-70
❑ 99StaCluC-SCC27
❑ 99StaCluCR-SCC27
❑ 99StaCluFDI-70
❑ 99StaCluNC-NC1
❑ 99StaCluOoaK-70
❑ 99StaCluPP-70
❑ 99StaCluTI-T5C
❑ 99StaCluTI-T16A
❑ 99StaCluTL-T5C
❑ 99StaCluTL-T16A
❑ 99StaCluTL-T5C
❑ 99StaCluTL-T16A
❑ 99StaCluVR-VR1
❑ 99ThuSkySupR-270
❑ 99Top-70
❑ 99Top-201
❑ 99Top-220A
❑ 99Top-220B
❑ 99Top-220C
❑ 99Top-220D
❑ 99Top-220E
❑ 99Top-220F
❑ 99Top-220G
❑ 99Top-220H
❑ 99Top-220I
❑ 99Top-220J
❑ 99Top-220K
❑ 99Top-220L
❑ 99Top-220M
❑ 99Top-220N
❑ 99Top-220O
❑ 99Top-220P
❑ 99Top-220Q
❑ 99Top-220R
❑ 99Top-220S
❑ 99Top-220T
❑ 99Top-220U
❑ 99Top-220V
❑ 99Top-220W
❑ 99Top-220X
❑ 99Top-220Y
❑ 99Top-220Z
❑ 99Top-220AA
❑ 99Top-220AB
❑ 99Top-220AC
❑ 99Top-220AD
❑ 99Top-220AE
❑ 99Top-220AF
❑ 99Top-220AG
❑ 99Top-220AH
❑ 99Top-220AI
❑ 99Top-220AJ
❑ 99Top-220AK
❑ 99Top-220AL
❑ 99Top-220AM
❑ 99Top-220AN
❑ 99Top-220AO
❑ 99Top-220AP
❑ 99Top-220AQ
❑ 99Top-220AR
❑ 99Top-220AS
❑ 99Top-220AT
❑ 99Top-220AU
❑ 99Top-220AV
❑ 99Top-220AW
❑ 99Top-220AX
❑ 99Top-220AY
❑ 99Top-220AZ
❑ 99Top-220BB
❑ 99Top-220CC
❑ 99Top-220DD
❑ 99Top-220EE
❑ 99Top-220FF
❑ 99Top-220GG
❑ 99Top-220HH
❑ 99Top-220II
❑ 99Top-220JJ
❑ 99Top-220KK
❑ 99Top-220LL
❑ 99Top-220MM
❑ 99Top-220NN
❑ 99Top-220OO
❑ 99Top-220PP
❑ 99Top-220QQ
❑ 99Top-220RR
❑ 99Top-220SS
❑ 99Top-223
❑ 99Top-450
❑ 99TopActF-8
❑ 99TopActFAU-8
❑ 99TopActFCU-8
❑ 99TopAll-AM1
❑ 99TopAllMF-M3
❑ 99TopBlaLC1-70
❑ 99TopBlaLC2-70
❑ 99TopBlaLC3-70
❑ 99TopChr-70
❑ 99TopChr-201
❑ 99TopChr-220A
❑ 99TopChr-220B
❑ 99TopChr-220C
❑ 99TopChr-220D
❑ 99TopChr-220E
❑ 99TopChr-220F
❑ 99TopChr-220G
❑ 99TopChr-220H
❑ 99TopChr-220I
❑ 99TopChr-220J
❑ 99TopChr-220K
❑ 99TopChr-220L

❑ 99TopChr-220M
❑ 99TopChr-220N
❑ 99TopChr-220O
❑ 99TopChr-220P
❑ 99TopChr-220Q
❑ 99TopChr-220R
❑ 99TopChr-220S
❑ 99TopChr-220T
❑ 99TopChr-220U
❑ 99TopChr-220V
❑ 99TopChr-220W
❑ 99TopChr-220X
❑ 99TopChr-220Y
❑ 99TopChr-220Z
❑ 99TopChr-220AA
❑ 99TopChr-220AB
❑ 99TopChr-220AC
❑ 99TopChr-220AD
❑ 99TopChr-220AE
❑ 99TopChr-220AF
❑ 99TopChr-220AG
❑ 99TopChr-220AH
❑ 99TopChr-220AI
❑ 99TopChr-220AJ
❑ 99TopChr-220AK
❑ 99TopChr-220AL
❑ 99TopChr-220AM
❑ 99TopChr-220AN
❑ 99TopChr-220AO
❑ 99TopChr-220AP
❑ 99TopChr-220AQ
❑ 99TopChr-220AR
❑ 99TopChr-220AS
❑ 99TopChr-220AT
❑ 99TopChr-220AU
❑ 99TopChr-220AV
❑ 99TopChr-220AW
❑ 99TopChr-220AX
❑ 99TopChr-220AY
❑ 99TopChr-220AZ
❑ 99TopChr-220BB
❑ 99TopChr-220CC
❑ 99TopChr-220DD
❑ 99TopChr-220EE
❑ 99TopChr-220FF
❑ 99TopChr-220GG
❑ 99TopChr-220HH
❑ 99TopChr-220II
❑ 99TopChr-220JJ
❑ 99TopChr-220KK
❑ 99TopChr-220LL
❑ 99TopChr-220MM
❑ 99TopChr-220NN
❑ 99TopChr-220OO
❑ 99TopChr-220PP
❑ 99TopChr-220QQ
❑ 99TopChr-220RR
❑ 99TopChr-220SS
❑ 99TopChr-223
❑ 99TopChr-450
❑ 99TopChrA-AE1
❑ 99TopChrAR-AE1
❑ 99TopChrF1-FF12
❑ 99TopChrF1R-FF12
❑ 99TopChrLotD-LD5
❑ 99TopChrLotDR-LD5
❑ 99TopChrR-70
❑ 99TopChrR-201
❑ 99TopChrR-220
❑ 99TopChrR-220A
❑ 99TopChrR-220B
❑ 99TopChrR-220C
❑ 99TopChrR-220D
❑ 99TopChrR-220E
❑ 99TopChrR-220F
❑ 99TopChrR-220G
❑ 99TopChrR-220H
❑ 99TopChrR-220I
❑ 99TopChrR-220J
❑ 99TopChrR-220K
❑ 99TopChrR-220L
❑ 99TopChrR-220M
❑ 99TopChrR-220N
❑ 99TopChrR-220O
❑ 99TopChrR-220P
❑ 99TopChrR-220Q
❑ 99TopChrR-220R
❑ 99TopChrR-220S
❑ 99TopChrR-220T
❑ 99TopChrR-220U
❑ 99TopChrR-220V
❑ 99TopChrR-220W
❑ 99TopChrR-220X
❑ 99TopChrR-220Y
❑ 99TopChrR-220Z
❑ 99TopChrR-220AA
❑ 99TopChrR-220AB
❑ 99TopChrR-220AC
❑ 99TopChrR-220AD
❑ 99TopChrR-220AE
❑ 99TopChrR-220AF
❑ 99TopChrR-220AG
❑ 99TopChrR-220AH
❑ 99TopChrR-220AI
❑ 99TopChrR-220AJ
❑ 99TopChrR-220AK
❑ 99TopChrR-220AL
❑ 99TopChrR-220AM
❑ 99TopChrR-220AN
❑ 99TopChrR-220AO
❑ 99TopChrR-220AP
❑ 99TopChrR-220AQ
❑ 99TopChrR-220AR
❑ 99TopChrR-220AS
❑ 99TopChrR-220AT
❑ 99TopChrR-220AU
❑ 99TopChrR-220AV
❑ 99TopChrR-220AW
❑ 99TopChrR-220AX
❑ 99TopChrR-220AY
❑ 99TopChrR-220AZ
❑ 99TopChrR-220BB
❑ 99TopChrR-220CC
❑ 99TopChrR-220DD
❑ 99TopChrR-220EE
❑ 99TopChrR-220FF
❑ 99TopChrR-220GG
❑ 99TopChrR-220HH
❑ 99TopChrR-220II
❑ 99TopChrR-220JJ
❑ 99TopChrR-220KK
❑ 99TopChrR-220LL
❑ 99TopChrR-220MM
❑ 99TopChrR-220NN
❑ 99TopChrR-220OO
❑ 99TopChrR-220PP
❑ 99TopChrR-220QQ
❑ 99TopChrR-220RR
❑ 99TopChrR-220SS
❑ 99TopChrR-223
❑ 99TopChrR-450
❑ 99TopChrRN-RN1
❑ 99TopChrRN-RN10
❑ 99TopChrRNR-RN1
❑ 99TopChrRNR-RN10
❑ 99TopGal-1
❑ 99TopGal-103
❑ 99TopGalAG-AG8
❑ 99TopGalE-E2
❑ 99TopGalGoH-GH1
❑ 99TopGalHer-TH20
❑ 99TopGalHerP-TH20
❑ 99TopGalPP-1
❑ 99TopGalPP-103
❑ 99TopGalPPI-1
❑ 99TopGalPPI-103
❑ 99TopGolL-70
❑ 99TopGolLC1-70
❑ 99TopGolLC2-70
❑ 99TopGolLOtO-70
❑ 99TopGolLRtA-RA1
❑ 99TopGolLRtAB-RA1
❑ 99TopGolLRtAOtO-RA1
❑ 99TopGolLRtAR-RA1
❑ 99TopLorotD-LD5
❑ 99TopMVPP-70
❑ 99TopMVPP-450
❑ 99TopOpeD-39
❑ 99TopOpeD-163
❑ 99TopOpeDO-2
❑ 99TopOver-A6
❑ 99TopPicP-P4
❑ 99TopPowB-PB1
❑ 99TopPowBR-PB1
❑ 99TopRecN-RN1
❑ 99TopRecN-RN10
❑ 99TopRecNG-RN1
❑ 99TopRecNG-RN10
❑ 99TopRedLC1-70
❑ 99TopRedLC2-70
❑ 99TopRedLC3-70
❑ 99TopSta-8
❑ 99TopSta-180
❑ 99TopSta'S-21
❑ 99TopSta'SG-21
❑ 99TopSta'SGDH-21
❑ 99TopSta1Foil-8
❑ 99TopSta2Foil-8
❑ 99TopSta3Foil-8
❑ 99TopSta4Foil-8
❑ 99TopStaFoil-8
❑ 99TopStaFoil-180
❑ 99TopStaFS-8
❑ 99TopStaG-G1
❑ 99TopStaGFoil-G1
❑ 99TopStaOS-8
❑ 99TopStaTS-8
❑ 99TopStaTS-8
❑ 99TopSupC-11
❑ 99TopSupC-34
❑ 99TopSupCR-11
❑ 99TopSupCR-34
❑ 99TopTek-7A
❑ 99TopTek-7B
❑ 99TopTekG-7A
❑ 99TopTekG-7B
❑ 99TopTekT-T2
❑ 99UD Cho-28
❑ 99UD Cho-130
❑ 99UD ChoBU-3
❑ 99UD ChoBUCG-1
❑ 99UD ChoMBH-B28
❑ 99UD ChoP-130
❑ 99UD ChoPCR-28
❑ 99UD ChoPCR-130
❑ 99UD ChoS-22
❑ 99UD ChoSD-22
❑ 99UD ChoSHR-22
❑ 99UD ChoST-22
❑ 99UD ChoYW-Y27
❑ 99UD Ion-54
❑ 99UD Ion-83
❑ 99UD IonC-C9
❑ 99UD IonH-HG9
❑ 99UD IonH-H9
❑ 99UD IonN-N9
❑ 99UD IonR-54
❑ 99UD IonR-83
❑ 99UD IonWZ-WZ9
❑ 99UDHolo-48
❑ 99UDHoloAUsome-48
❑ 99UDHoloFF-F3
❑ 99UDHoloFFG-F3
❑ 99UDHoloLau-L1
❑ 99UDHoloLauG-L1
❑ 99UDHoloStar-S1
❑ 99UDHoloStarG-S1
❑ 99Ult-70
❑ 99Ult-221
❑ 99UltDamI-10
❑ 99UltDiaP-6
❑ 99UltGolM-70
❑ 99UltGolM-221
❑ 99UltMas-70
❑ 99UltMas-221
❑ 99UltPlaM-70
❑ 99UltPlaM-221
❑ 99UltPromo-NNO
❑ 99UltRBIK-7
❑ 99UltTheBook-7
❑ 99UltThu-11
❑ 99UppDec-182
❑ 99UppDec-248
❑ 99UppDec-518
❑ 99UppDec-527
❑ 99UppDec10AT-X2
❑ 99UppDec10ATD-X2
❑ 99UppDec10ATHR-X2
❑ 99UppDec10ATT-X2
❑ 99UppDecBD-80
❑ 99UppDecBDAPH-MM
❑ 99UppDecBDD-80
❑ 99UppDecBDDom-D25
❑ 99UppDecBDDomE-D25
❑ 99UppDecBDMN-M4
❑ 99UppDecBDMNE-M4
❑ 99UppDecBDQ-80
❑ 99UppDecBDT-80
❑ 99UppDecCf7-1
❑ 99UppDecCf7-46
❑ 99UppDecCf7-50
❑ 99UppDecCf7-61
❑ 99UppDecCf7-62
❑ 99UppDecCf7-63
❑ 99UppDecCf7-64
❑ 99UppDecCf7-65
❑ 99UppDecCf7-67
❑ 99UppDecCf7-68
❑ 99UppDecCf7-69
❑ 99UppDecCf7-70
❑ 99UppDecCf7-71
❑ 99UppDecCf7-C1
❑ 99UppDecCf7Cf7P-C1
❑ 99UppDecCf7LL-L2
❑ 99UppDecCf7MoH-M1
❑ 99UppDecCf7MoH-M2
❑ 99UppDecCf7MoH-M3
❑ 99UppDecCf7MoH-M4
❑ 99UppDecCf7MoH-M5
❑ 99UppDecCf7MoH-M6
❑ 99UppDecCf7MoH-M7
❑ 99UppDecCf7MoH-M8
❑ 99UppDecCf7MoH-M9
❑ 99UppDecCf7MoH-M10
❑ 99UppDecCf7MoH-M11
❑ 99UppDecCf7MoH-M12
❑ 99UppDecCf7MoH-M13
❑ 99UppDecCf7MoH-M14
❑ 99UppDecCf7MoH-M15
❑ 99UppDecCf7MoH-M16
❑ 99UppDecCf7MoH-M17
❑ 99UppDecCf7MoH-M18
❑ 99UppDecCf7MoH-M19
❑ 99UppDecCf7MoH-M20
❑ 99UppDecCf7MoH-M21
❑ 99UppDecCf7MoH-M22
❑ 99UppDecCf7MoH-M23
❑ 99UppDecCf7MoH-M24
❑ 99UppDecCf7MoH-M25
❑ 99UppDecCf7MoHP-M1
❑ 99UppDecCf7MoHP-M2
❑ 99UppDecCf7MoHP-M3
❑ 99UppDecCf7MoHP-M4
❑ 99UppDecCf7MoHP-M5
❑ 99UppDecCf7MoHP-M6
❑ 99UppDecCf7MoHP-M7
❑ 99UppDecCf7MoHP-M8
❑ 99UppDecCf7MoHP-M9
❑ 99UppDecCf7MoHP-M10
❑ 99UppDecCf7MoHP-M11
❑ 99UppDecCf7MoHP-M12
❑ 99UppDecCf7MoHP-M13
❑ 99UppDecCf7MoHP-M14
❑ 99UppDecCf7MoHP-M15
❑ 99UppDecCf7MoHP-M16
❑ 99UppDecCf7MoHP-M17
❑ 99UppDecCf7MoHP-M18
❑ 99UppDecCf7MoHP-M19
❑ 99UppDecCf7MoHP-M20
❑ 99UppDecCf7MoHP-M21
❑ 99UppDecCf7MoHP-M22
❑ 99UppDecCf7MoHP-M23
❑ 99UppDecCf7MoHP-M24
❑ 99UppDecCf7MoHP-M25
❑ 99UppDecCf7SftF-S2
❑ 99UppDecCG-CG2
❑ 99UppDecCG-CG3
❑ 99UppDecCGD-CG2
❑ 99UppDecCGD-CG3
❑ 99UppDecCGHR-CG2
❑ 99UppDecCGHR-CG3
❑ 99UppDecCGT-CG2
❑ 99UppDecCGT-CG3
❑ 99UppDecCL-58
❑ 99UppDecCL-125
❑ 99UppDecCLCC-58
❑ 99UppDecCLCC-125
❑ 99UppDecCLEM-EM4
❑ 99UppDecCLM-C76
❑ 99UppDecCLMS-HR7
❑ 99UppDecCLMS-HR10
❑ 99UppDecCo7CE-1
❑ 99UppDecCo7CE-46
❑ 99UppDecCo7CE-50
❑ 99UppDecCo7CE-61
❑ 99UppDecCo7CE-62
❑ 99UppDecCo7CE-63
❑ 99UppDecCo7CE-64
❑ 99UppDecCo7CE-65
❑ 99UppDecCo7CE-67
❑ 99UppDecCo7CE-68
❑ 99UppDecCo7CE-69
❑ 99UppDecCo7CE-70
❑ 99UppDecCo7CE-71
❑ 99UppDecE-73
❑ 99UppDecE-137
❑ 99UppDecE-169
❑ 99UppDecE2C-2K9
❑ 99UppDecEDF-D2
❑ 99UppDecEDFFXG-D2
❑ 99UppDecEFXG-73
❑ 99UppDecEFXG-137
❑ 99UppDecEFXG-169
❑ 99UppDecEL1-182
❑ 99UppDecEL1-248
❑ 99UppDecEL1-518
❑ 99UppDecEL1-527
❑ 99UppDecEL2-182
❑ 99UppDecEL2-248
❑ 99UppDecEL2-518
❑ 99UppDecEL2-527
❑ 99UppDecEM-MC1
❑ 99UppDecEM-MC2
❑ 99UppDecEM-MC3
❑ 99UppDecEM-MC4
❑ 99UppDecEM-MC5
❑ 99UppDecEM-MC6
❑ 99UppDecEM-MC7
❑ 99UppDecEM-MC8
❑ 99UppDecEM-MC9
❑ 99UppDecEM-MC10
❑ 99UppDecEMFXG-MC1
❑ 99UppDecEMFXG-MC2
❑ 99UppDecEMFXG-MC3
❑ 99UppDecEMFXG-MC4
❑ 99UppDecEMFXG-MC5
❑ 99UppDecEMFXG-MC6
❑ 99UppDecEMFXG-MC7
❑ 99UppDecEMFXG-MC8
❑ 99UppDecEMFXG-MC9
❑ 99UppDecEMFXG-MC10
❑ 99UppDecEPE-P23
❑ 99UppDecEUR-U2
❑ 99UppDecF-F21
❑ 99UppDecFD-F21
❑ 99UppDecFQ-F21
❑ 99UppDecFT-F21
❑ 99UppDecIP-I16
❑ 99UppDecIPD-I16
❑ 99UppDecIPHR-I16
❑ 99UppDecIPT-I16
❑ 99UppDecM-169
❑ 99UppDecM-220
❑ 99UppDecM-P1
❑ 99UppDecMD-D5
❑ 99UppDecMGS-169
❑ 99UppDecMGS-220
❑ 99UppDecMHFS-169
❑ 99UppDecMHFS-220
❑ 99UppDecMP-169
❑ 99UppDecMSS-169
❑ 99UppDecMSS-220
❑ 99UppDecMST-S2
❑ 99UppDecO-36
❑ 99UppDecO-82
❑ 99UppDecOMP-S2
❑ 99UppDecORM-MM1
❑ 99UppDecORM-MM2
❑ 99UppDecORM-MM3
❑ 99UppDecORM-MM4
❑ 99UppDecORM-MM5
❑ 99UppDecORM-MM6
❑ 99UppDecORM-MM7
❑ 99UppDecORM-MM8
❑ 99UppDecORM-MM9
❑ 99UppDecORM-MM10
❑ 99UppDecORM-MM11
❑ 99UppDecORM-MM12
❑ 99UppDecORM-MM13
❑ 99UppDecORM-MM14
❑ 99UppDecORM-MM15
❑ 99UppDecOSO-36
❑ 99UppDecOSO-82
❑ 99UppDecOWP-R1
❑ 99UppDecR-69
❑ 99UppDecRDR-D2
❑ 99UppDecRDRL2-D2
❑ 99UppDecRG-69
❑ 99UppDecRL-4
❑ 99UppDecRL-11
❑ 99UppDecRL-15
❑ 99UppDecRL-16
❑ 99UppDecRL-17
❑ 99UppDecROSS-S10
❑ 99UppDecROSS-S10
❑ 99UppDecRP-69
❑ 99UppDecRTA-T2
❑ 99UppDecRTAL2-T2
❑ 99UppDecTE-T21
❑ 99UppDecTED-T21
❑ 99UppDecTEQ-T21
❑ 99UppDecTET-T21
❑ 99UppDecVtaT-V23
❑ 99UppDecVtaTD-V23
❑ 99UppDecVtaTQ-V23
❑ 99UppDecVtaTT-V23
❑ 99UppDecWY-W19
❑ 99UppDecWYD-W19
❑ 99UppDecWYHR-W19
❑ 99UppDecWYT-W19
❑ 99Vic-319
❑ 99Vic-321
❑ 99Vic-322
❑ 99Vic-323
❑ 99Vic-421
❑ 99Vic-422
❑ 99Vic-423
❑ 99Vic-424
❑ 99Vic-425
❑ 99Vic-426
❑ 99Vic-427
❑ 99Vic-428
❑ 99Vic-429
❑ 99Vic-430
❑ 99Vic-431
❑ 99Vic-432
❑ 99Vic-433
❑ 99Vic-434
❑ 99Vic-435
❑ 99Vic-436
❑ 99Vic-437
❑ 99Vic-438
❑ 99Vic-439
❑ 99Vic-440
❑ 99Vic-441
❑ 99Vic-442
❑ 99Vic-443
❑ 99Vic-444
❑ 99Vic-445
❑ 99Vic-446
❑ 99Vic-447
❑ 99Vic-448
❑ 99Vic-449
❑ 99Vic-450
❑ 99Vic-461

McHale, Marty
❑ 11PinT-5-668

McHenry, Austin
❑ 22E120-234
❑ 23WilChoV-93

McHenry, Frank
❑ 19Zee-55
❑ 20Zee-87

McHenry, Vance
❑ 80SpoIndT-9
❑ 81SpoIndT-20
❑ 82SalLakCGT-12
❑ 85SyrChiT-23

McHugh, Chip
❑ 86LakTigP-13
❑ 87GleFalTP-25

McHugh, Mike
❑ 88GreFalDTI-6
❑ 95HudValRTI-21
❑ 96ChaRivTI-9620

McHugh, Ryan
❑ 97PriWilC-20

McHugh, Scott
❑ 87JamExpP-2541

McHugh, Tom
❑ 82ChaRoyT-4

McIlvaine, Joe
❑ 91PadSmo-22

McIlwain, W. Stover
❑ 60Lea-114

McInerney, Steve
❑ 86GleFalTP-15
❑ 87GleFalTP-7
❑ 89TolMudHC-24
❑ 89TolMudHP-762
❑ 90CMC-476
❑ 90TolMudHC-27
❑ 95SyrChiTI-17

McInerny, Dan
❑ 83SanJosBC-7

McInnes, Chris
❑ 93HelBreF-4103
❑ 93HelBreSP-25
❑ 94BelBreC-17
❑ 94BelBreFI-110
❑ 97St.PauS-16

McInnis, Bill
❑ 86NewBriRSP-17
❑ 87NewBriRSP-8
❑ 88PawRedSC-12
❑ 88PawRedSP-456

McInnis, Macie
❑ 97PinFan-PC1

McInnis, Stuffy (John)
❑ 09AmeCarE90-1-75

❑ 09SpoNewSM-73
❑ 11PinT-5-508
❑ 11PloCanE-45
❑ 11SpoLifM-99
❑ 14CraJacE-10
❑ 14FatPlaT-32
❑ 14PolGroW-19
❑ 14TexTomE-33
❑ 15CraJacE-10
❑ 15SpoNewM-115
❑ 16BF2FP-39
❑ 16SpoNewM-117
❑ 17ColE13-114
❑ 19W514-20
❑ 20WalMaiW-29
❑ 21E121So1-60
❑ 21E121So8-57
❑ 21Exh-105
❑ 21Exh-106
❑ 22AmeCarE122-45
❑ 22E120-37
❑ 22W575-78
❑ 23W501-18
❑ 23WilChoV-94
❑ 25Exh-29
❑ 26SpoComoA-30
❑ 27AmeCarE126-41
❑ 27Exh-22
❑ 27YorCarE-60
❑ 28W502-60
❑ 28Yue-60
❑ 68SCFOldT-33
❑ 74A'sTCM1P-7
❑ 77GalGloG-180
❑ 80LauFamF-29
❑ 88ConSer5-21
❑ 91ConTSN-191
McIntire, Harry (John Reed)
❑ 06FanCraNL-32
❑ 08RosComP-98
❑ 09AmeCarE90-1-76
❑ 10DomDisP-81
❑ 10SweCapPP-84
❑ 11HelSta-98
❑ 11S74Sil-64
❑ 11SpoLifCW-247
❑ 11SpoLifM-174
❑ 11T205-115
❑ 11TurRedT-28
❑ 12T207-119
❑ 72ClaCar-73
❑ 90DodTar-510
McIntosh, Joe
❑ 75PadDea-19
❑ 76HouAstP-20
❑ 76OPC-497
❑ 76Top-497
❑ 76TopTra-497T
McIntosh, Tim
❑ 87BelBreP-26
❑ 88CalLeaACLC-12
❑ 88StoPorCLC-189
❑ 88StoPorP-733
❑ 89ElPasDGS-18
❑ 89TexLeaAGS-13
❑ 90Bow-394
❑ 90BowTif-394
❑ 90CMC-40
❑ 90DenZepC-15
❑ 90DenZepP-628
❑ 90El PasDAGTI-24
❑ 90Fle-329
❑ 90FleCan-329
❑ 90ProAAAF-653
❑ 90TriAllGP-AAA24
❑ 91Bow-36
❑ 91Cla1-T55
❑ 91DenZepLD-145
❑ 91DenZepP-126
❑ 91Don-414
❑ 91Fle-589
❑ 91LinDriAAA-145
❑ 91OPC-561
❑ 91Sco-347
❑ 91ScoRoo-35
❑ 91StaClu-321
❑ 91Stu-71
❑ 91Top-561
❑ 91TopDeb90-104
❑ 91TopDesS-561
❑ 91TopMic-561
❑ 91TopTif-561
❑ 91TriA AAGP-AAA10
❑ 91Ult-177
❑ 91UppDec-547
❑ 92Bow-402
❑ 92BrePol-14
❑ 92DonRoo-73
❑ 92Sco-469
❑ 92Sco100RS-93
❑ 92ScoRoo-20
❑ 92StaClu-477
❑ 92Ult-386
❑ 93BrePol-17
❑ 93Don-367
❑ 93ExpPosN-16
❑ 93Lea-78
❑ 93Sel-334
❑ 93StaClu-502
❑ 93StaCluFDI-502
❑ 93StaCluMOP-502
❑ 93Top-234
❑ 93TopGol-234
❑ 93TopInaM-234
❑ 93TopInaR-234
❑ 93TopMic-234
❑ 94BreMilB-156
❑ 94SalLakBF-820
❑ 94TriAAF-AAA16
❑ 96ColCliB-19
❑ 97IowCub-18
McIntosh, Troy
❑ 94BatCliC-30
❑ 94BatCliF-3464
❑ 97LanJet-4
❑ 98LanJetG-17
McIntyre, James J.
❑ 80ArkTraT-12
McIntyre, Joe (Joseph)
❑ 92BatCliCB-19
❑ 92BatCliF-3260
McIntyre, Matthew
❑ 07TigACDPP-23
❑ 08RosComP-36
❑ 09BriE97-20
❑ 09ColChiE-190A
❑ 09ColChiE-190B
❑ 09PhiCarE-17
❑ 09RamT20-77
❑ 09T206-241
❑ 09T206-242
❑ 09T206-243
❑ 09TigMorBBBP-10
❑ 09TigMorPWBPP-7
❑ 09TigTaCP-11
❑ 10CouT21-46
❑ 10DomDisP-82
❑ 10JHDABE-13
❑ 10NadE1-36
❑ 10RedCroT-52
❑ 10RedCroT-221
❑ 10RedCroT-222
❑ 10SweCapPP-12A
❑ 10SweCapPP-12B
❑ 11BasBatEU-28
❑ 11HelSta-13
❑ 11PinT-5-151
❑ 11PinT-5-213
❑ 11SpoLifCW-248
❑ 11SpoLifM-63
❑ 11T205-116
❑ 11TurRedT-25
❑ 12ColRedB-190A
❑ 12ColRedB-190B
❑ 12ColTinT-190A
❑ 12ColTinT-190B
❑ 12HasTriFT-13B
❑ 12HasTriFT-41A
❑ 12HasTriFT-54
❑ 12T207-120
McIntyre, Remer
❑ 97JohCitCTI-23
❑ 98JohCCTI-25
McIntyre, Rich
❑ 86AncGlaPTI-23
McIsaacs, Gus
❑ 29Zee-79
❑ 33Zee-63
McIver, Edward
❑ 12HomRunKE-68
❑ 12Zee-119
McIver, Jeryl
❑ 76WauMetT-18
❑ 77LynMetT-19
McIver, Larry
❑ 82AubAstT-9
McJames, Doc
❑ 90DodTar-1028
McKain, Archie
❑ 93ConTSN-945
McKain, Hal
❑ 30WhiSoxTI-18
McKamie, Sean
❑ 91VerBeaDC-22
❑ 91VerBeaDP-783
❑ 92VerBeaDC-10
❑ 92VerBeaDF-2884
❑ 93BakDodCLC-19
McKay, Alan
❑ 85KinBluJT-7
❑ 86PitCubP-16
McKay, Cody
❑ 96SouOreTI-5
❑ 97ModA'sG-18
❑ 98ModA'sG-20
❑ 99BasAmeTP-65
❑ 99BasAmeTPG-65
McKay, Dave
❑ 75IntLeaASB-17
❑ 75PacCoaLAB-17
❑ 75TacTwiK-2
❑ 76MinTwiP-11
❑ 76OPC-592
❑ 76TacTwiDQ-13
❑ 76Top-592
❑ 77Hos-130
❑ 77OPC-40
❑ 77Top-377
❑ 79OPC-322
❑ 79Top-608
❑ 81A'sGraG-39
❑ 81Don-350
❑ 81Fle-592
❑ 81Top-461
❑ 82Don-391
❑ 82Fle-100
❑ 82Top-534
❑ 83Don-213
❑ 83Fle-526
❑ 83TacTigT-29B
❑ 83Top-47
❑ 85A'sMot-27
❑ 86A'sMot-27
❑ 88A'sMot-27
❑ 89A'sMot-27
❑ 90A'sMot-27
❑ 91A'sMot-28
❑ 92AthMot-28
❑ 92Nab-12
❑ 93AthMot-27
❑ 94A'sMot-28
❑ 95AthMot-28
McKay, Karl
❑ 80BurBeeT-28
❑ 81BurBeeT-26
McKay, Tripp
❑ 96VerExpB-18
McKay, Troy
❑ 86JacExpT-16
McKean, Edward
❑ 87OldJudN-334
❑ 89EdgR.WG-12
❑ 93JusSo-7
❑ 98CamPepP-53
McKean, Jim
❑ 88T/MUmp-20
❑ 89T/MUmp-16
❑ 90T/MUmp-15
McKechnie, Bill (William B.)
❑ 11PinT-5-874
❑ 12T207-121
❑ 16FleBreD-63
❑ 23MapCriV-25
❑ 34DiaMatCSB-126
❑ 35DiaMatCS3T1-103
❑ 36WorWidGV-108
❑ 38CloFotW-58
❑ 38RedOraW-19
❑ 39OrcPhoAP-16
❑ 39RedTeal-15
❑ 40PlaBal-153
❑ 41HarHarW-16
❑ 48IndTeal-21
❑ 49IndTeal-29
❑ 53ArtHaloFP-63
❑ 75TCMAllG-24
❑ 76RedParC-16
❑ 76RowExh-8
❑ 76ShaPiz-89
❑ 77BobParHoF-68
❑ 77CinRedT-45
❑ 77GalGloG-213
❑ 80PacLeg-86
❑ 80PerHaloFP-88
❑ 80SSPHOF-88
❑ 82OhiHaloF-58
❑ 86RedGreT-2
❑ 89HOFStiB-88
❑ 91ConTSN-34
❑ 92ConTSN-592
❑ 93ConTSN-831
❑ 93DiaStaES-144
❑ 94ConTSN-1066
❑ 94ConTSNB-1066
McKee, Bob
❑ 55DesMoiHB-12
McKee, Matt
❑ 89AshTouP-940
McKee, Raymond
❑ 18Zee-87
McKee, Ron
❑ 80AshTouT-9
❑ 88AshTouP-1077
❑ 89AshTouP-942
❑ 94AshTouC-30
❑ 95AshTouTI-NNO
❑ 96AshTouB-1
McKeel, Walt
❑ 92ClaFS7-389
❑ 92LynRedSC-9
❑ 92LynRedSF-2911
❑ 93LynRedSC-19
❑ 93LynRedSF-2520
❑ 94SarRedSC-18
❑ 94SarRedSF-1954
❑ 96DouAllB-8
❑ 96TreThuB-18
❑ 97PawRedS-16
❑ 98PawRedSQ-20
McKelvey, Mitch
❑ 84PriWilPT-24
❑ 85NasPirT-18
❑ 86Ft.MyeRP-19
❑ 86MemChiSTOS-17
❑ 86MemChiTOS-17
McKelvie, Ron
❑ 83VisOakF-12
McKenna, Chris
❑ 96MedHatBJTI-18
McKenna, Kit
❑ 90DodTar-1029
McKenna, Sean
❑ 90NebCor-17
McKenry, Frank
❑ 26Zee-81
McKenzie, David
❑ 93BilMusF-3942
❑ 93BilMusSP-25
McKenzie, Don
❑ 81WauTimT-10
McKenzie, Doug
❑ 83PeoSunF-8
❑ 85MidAngT-7
McKenzie, Jason
❑ 96ForWayWB-16
McKenzie, Scott
❑ 96ChaLooB-20
❑ 97ChaLoo-16
McKeon, Brian
❑ 90Bes-264
❑ 90ProAaA-109
❑ 90WatDiaB-11
❑ 90WatDiaP-2377
❑ 91HigDesMC-8
❑ 91HigDesMP-2391
❑ 92HigDesMC-28
❑ 93StoPorC-18
❑ 93StoPorF-743
McKeon, Jack
❑ 73OPC-593
❑ 73Top-593
❑ 74RoyPos-18
❑ 74Top-166
❑ 75OPC-72
❑ 75RoyPos-20
❑ 75SSP18-7
❑ 75Top-72
❑ 75TopMin-72
❑ 77A'sPos-84
❑ 77Top-74
❑ 79Top-328
❑ 83PadTeal-16
❑ 84PadSmo-17
❑ 88PadCok-15
❑ 88TopTra-69T
❑ 88TopTraT-69T
❑ 89PadCok-10
❑ 89PadMag-1
❑ 89PadPos-19
❑ 89Top-624
❑ 89TopTif-624
❑ 90OPC-231
❑ 90PadCok-11
❑ 90PadMag-25
❑ 90Top-231
❑ 90TopTif-231
❑ 94CarLeaA-DJ36
McKeon, Joel
❑ 83AppFoxFr-5
❑ 85BufBisT-22
❑ 86DonRoo-55
❑ 86FleUpd-75
❑ 87Fle-503
❑ 87FleGlo-503
❑ 87WhiSoxC-21
❑ 88LasVegSC-4
❑ 88LasVegSP-225
❑ 88Top-409
❑ 88TopTif-409
❑ 89IndIndP-1212
❑ 89RicBraBC-16
❑ 90HagSunB-22
❑ 90HagSunP-1409
❑ 90HagSunS-14
❑ 90RocRedWGC-26
❑ 91HagSunLD-238
❑ 91HagSunP-2453
❑ 91LinDriAA-238
McKeon, Kasey
❑ 89BriTigS-17
❑ 89SanDieSAS-17
❑ 90FayGenP-2411
McKeown, Dan
❑ 85AncGlaPTI-37
McKercher, Tim
❑ 88SalLakCTTI-24
McKinion, Mickey
❑ 93HicCraC-16
❑ 93HicCraF-1277
❑ 94HicCraC-16
❑ 94HicCraF-2174
McKinley, Dan
❑ 98Bow-329
❑ 98BowBes-194
❑ 98BowBesAR-194
❑ 98BowBesR-194
❑ 98BowChr-329
❑ 98BowChrGA-329
❑ 98BowChrGAR-329
❑ 98BowChrI-329
❑ 98BowChrIR-329
❑ 98BowChrR-329
❑ 98BowGolA-329
❑ 98BowInt-329
❑ 98ShrCapM-23
❑ 98ShrCapWS-23
❑ 99BasAmeTP-66
❑ 99BasAmeTPG-66
McKinley, Josh
❑ 99199Fin-134
❑ 99Bow-155
❑ 99BowBes-188
❑ 99BowBesAR-188
❑ 99BowBesR-188
❑ 99BowChr-155
❑ 99BowChrG-155
❑ 99BowChrGR-155
❑ 99BowChrI-155
❑ 99BowChrIR-155
❑ 99BowChrR-155
❑ 99BowGol-155
❑ 99BowInt-155
❑ 99FinGolRef-134
❑ 99FinRef-134
❑ 99StaClu-152
❑ 99StaCluFDI-152
❑ 99StaCluOoaK-152
❑ 99StaCluPP-152
❑ 99TeaBesR-58
❑ 99TeaBesRFS-12
❑ 99TeaBesRG-58
❑ 99TeaBesRS-58
❑ 99Top-215
❑ 99TopChr-215
❑ 99TopChrR-215
McKinley, Leif
❑ 92ElmPioC-14
❑ 92ElmPioF-1382
❑ 93UtiBluSC-14
❑ 93UtiBluSF-3530
McKinley, Michael
❑ 96LowSpiB-18
McKinley, Pat
❑ 88VirGenS-15
McKinley, Tim
❑ 88SalBucS-12
❑ 89HarSenP-312
❑ 89HarSenS-11
❑ 90MiaMirIS-17
McKinley, W.F.
❑ 55Bow-226
McKinley, William F. President
❑ 82OhiHaloF-19
McKinney, Charlie
❑ 80CedRapRT-12
McKinney, Greg
❑ 81CedRapRT-25
McKinney, Jay
❑ 90MisStaB-44
McKinney, John
❑ 85BenPhiC-16
McKinney, Lynn
❑ 76OmaRoyTT-14
❑ 78SpoIndC-24
❑ 79HawIslC-20
❑ 79HawIslT-2
McKinney, Rich (C. Rich)
❑ 71OPC-37
❑ 71Top-37
❑ 72Top-619
❑ 73OPC-587
❑ 73Top-587
❑ 75TucTorC-11
❑ 75TucTorTI-11
❑ 76SSP-587
❑ 76TucTorCa-8
❑ 76TusTorCr-22
❑ 92YanWIZ7-111
McKinnis, Bo
❑ 88MisStaB-39
❑ 89MisStaB-45
McKinnis, Leroy
❑ 93SpoIndF-3595
❑ 94SprSulC-17
❑ 94SprSulF-2040
❑ 95RanCucQT-24
❑ 96RanCucQB-20
❑ 97FreKey-17
McKinnis, Roy
❑ 93SpoIndC-13
McKinnis, Tim
❑ 88QuaCitAGS-26
McKinnon, Alex
❑ 87OldJudN-335
McKinnon, Sandy
❑ 94SouBenSHC-11
❑ 94SouBenSHF-608
❑ 95PriWilCTI-2
❑ 96PriWilCB-18
❑ 97BirBarB-21
McKinnon, Tom
❑ 91Cla/Bes-426
❑ 91ClaDraP-24
❑ 91FroRowDP-41
❑ 91FroRowDPG-41
❑ 91FroRowDPS-41
❑ 91HigSchPLS-16
❑ 91JohCitCC-28
❑ 91JohCitCP-3975
❑ 92OPC-96
❑ 92ProFS7-326
❑ 92StaCluD-115
❑ 92Top-96
❑ 92TopGol-96
❑ 92TopGolW-96
❑ 92TopMic-96
❑ 93JohCitCC-14
❑ 93JohCitCF-3688
❑ 97ChaRivDG-19
McKinzie, Phil
❑ 87AppFoxP-29
McKitrick, Greg
❑ 90OklSoo-21
McKnight, Chris
❑ 95EugEmeTI-10
McKnight, Jack
❑ 83KnoBluJT-5
❑ 86PhoFirP-16
❑ 87PhoFirP-14
McKnight, James
❑ 62SalPlaC-199
❑ 62ShiPlaC-199
❑ 62Top-597
❑ 81TCM60I-383
❑ 82DayBeaAT-21
McKnight, Jeff
❑ 86JacMetT-17
❑ 87JacMetF-2
❑ 87TidTidP-4
❑ 87TidTidT-15
❑ 88TidTidCa-16

❑ 88TidTidCM-19
❑ 88TidTidP-1587
❑ 89TidTidC-13
❑ 89TidTidP-1953
❑ 90CMC-320
❑ 90ProAAAF-467
❑ 90RocRedWC-12
❑ 90RocRedWGC-7
❑ 90RocRedWP-710
❑ 90TopDeb89-80
❑ 90UppDec-162
❑ 91BalOriP-18
❑ 91LinDriAAA-460
❑ 91MetWIZ-261
❑ 91OPC-319
❑ 91OriCro-292
❑ 91RocRedWLD-460
❑ 91RocRedWP-1909
❑ 91Sco-369
❑ 91Top-319
❑ 91TopDesS-319
❑ 91TopMic-319
❑ 91TopTif-319
❑ 92StaClu-633
❑ 92StaCluECN-633
❑ 92TidTidF-906
❑ 92TidTidS-565
❑ 93MetColP-40
❑ 93MetKah-7
❑ 93PacSpa-544
❑ 94Don-634
❑ 94Fle-572
❑ 94MetColP-18
❑ 94Pac-412
❑ 94StaClu-324
❑ 94StaCluFDI-324
❑ 94StaCluGR-324
❑ 94StaCluMOP-324
❑ 94Top-331
❑ 94TopGol-331
❑ 94TopSpa-331
McKnight, Toby
❑ 95BowBes-X6
❑ 95BowBesR-X6
McKnight, Tony
❑ 95Bes-123
❑ 95TopTra-38T
❑ 96Exc-172
❑ 96SigRooOJPP-P6
❑ 96SigRooOJPPS-P6
❑ 96Top-18
❑ 96TopPowB-18
❑ 97MidLeaTP-20
❑ 97QuaCitRBB-17
❑ 98KisCobQ-21
McKown, Steven
❑ 76CedRapGT-14
McKoy, Keith
❑ 90SpoIndSP-1
❑ 91ChaRaiC-22
❑ 91ChaRaiP-108
❑ 92WatDiaC-20
❑ 92WatDiaF-2152
McKune, Jerry
❑ 81ArkTraT-22
❑ 82LouRedE-17
❑ 83LouRedR-3
❑ 84LouRedR-3
❑ 85LouRedR-4
McKune, Terry
❑ 09ObaT21-17
❑ 11Zee-53
McLain, Brian
❑ 93SpoIndC-14
❑ 93SpoIndF-3589
McLain, Dennis
❑ 65OPC-236
❑ 65Top-236
❑ 66TigVolC-9
❑ 66Top-226
❑ 66Top-540
❑ 66TopVen-226
❑ 67Baz-13
❑ 67OPCPapI-20
❑ 67Top-235
❑ 67Top-420
❑ 67TopPos-20
❑ 67TopTesF-15
❑ 67TopVen-261
❑ 68CokCapT-15
❑ 68OPC-40
❑ 68TigDetFPB-12
❑ 68Top-40
❑ 68TopVen-40
❑ 69CitMetC-1
❑ 69KelPin-14
❑ 69MilBra-187
❑ 69MLBOffS-52
❑ 69MLBPin-18
❑ 69OPC-9
❑ 69OPC-11
❑ 69OPC-57
❑ 69OPC-150
❑ 69OPC-169
❑ 69OPCDec-14
❑ 69TigTeal-8
❑ 69TigTealC-12
❑ 69Top-9
❑ 69Top-11
❑ 69Top-57
❑ 69Top-150
❑ 69Top-169
❑ 69Top-433
❑ 69TopDec-8
❑ 69TopDecl-28
❑ 69TopFou-21
❑ 69TopFou-23
❑ 69TopSta-177
❑ 69TopSup-17
❑ 69TopTeaP-1
❑ 69TraSta-4
❑ 70DayDaiNM-87
❑ 70Kel-73
❑ 70MLBOffS-212
❑ 70OPC-70
❑ 70OPC-400
❑ 70OPC-467
❑ 70Top-70
❑ 70Top-400
❑ 70Top-467
❑ 70TopCanL-17
❑ 70TopPos-24
❑ 70TopSup-17
❑ 70TraSta-11A
❑ 71AllBasA-17
❑ 71MLBOffS-546
❑ 71MLBOffS-569
❑ 71OPC-750
❑ 71SenPolP-9
❑ 71SenTealW-16
❑ 71Top-750
❑ 71TopGreM-20
❑ 72MilBra-229
❑ 72OPC-210
❑ 72SevTraC-32
❑ 72Top-210
❑ 72Top-753
❑ 73OPC-630
❑ 73Top-630
❑ 75OPC-206
❑ 75Top-206
❑ 75TopMin-206
❑ 76GrePlaG-42
❑ 77GalGloG-239
❑ 78TCM60I-210
❑ 80TigGreT-10
❑ 81TigDetN-15
❑ 81TigDetN-79
❑ 81TigDetN-94
❑ 82K-M-13
❑ 82TCMGreP-24
❑ 83TigAlKS-39
❑ 84SpoDesPW-43
❑ 86TigSpoD-21
❑ 88TigDom-15
❑ 90HOFStiB-72
❑ 91FouBal-6
❑ 93ActPacA-154
❑ 93TigLitC-5
❑ 94TedWil-33
❑ 94TedWilM-M32
McLain, Mike
❑ 92CliGiaF-3595
❑ 92EveGiaC-10
❑ 92EveGiaF-1684
❑ 94SanJosGC-16
❑ 94SanJosGF-2813
McLain, Ron
❑ 81ExpPos-7
McLain, Tim
❑ 86WauTimP-16
❑ 88SanBerSCLC-46
McLamb, Brian
❑ 93OneYanC-15
❑ 93OneYanF-3511
❑ 94GreBatF-484
❑ 94OneYanC-12
❑ 94OneYanF-3801
❑ 95GreBatTI-16
❑ 96TamYanY-17
❑ 97GreBatC-15
❑ 98NorNavQ-16
McLane, Larry
❑ 82BurRanF-20
❑ 82BurRanT-7
❑ 83TulDriT-6
McLaren, John
❑ 75DubPacT-9
❑ 83KnoBluJT-19
❑ 86BluJayFS-25
❑ 87BluJayFS-21
❑ 88BluJayFS-22
❑ 89BluJayFS-19
❑ 90BluJayFS-20
❑ 92RedKah-NNO
❑ 93MarMot-28
❑ 94MarMot-28
❑ 95MarMot-28
❑ 96MarMot-28
McLarnan, John
❑ 87ReaPhiP-23
❑ 88MaiPhiC-6
❑ 88MaiPhiP-281
❑ 90ReaPhiB-4
❑ 90ReaPhiP-1219
❑ 90ReaPhiS-20
McLarry, Howard
❑ 16Zee-13
❑ 17Zee-111
McLauchlin, Dick
❑ 81AlbDukTc-26
McLaughlin, Bo (Michael)
❑ 77Top-184
❑ 78ChaChaT-9
❑ 78Top-437
❑ 79AstPos-14
❑ 80RicBraT-23
❑ 80Top-326
❑ 82Top-217
❑ 87AstShoSPT-9
❑ 98BowBayM-2
McLaughlin, Burke
❑ 52Par-12
McLaughlin, Byron
❑ 77MarPos-10
❑ 78SanJosMMC-17
❑ 79Top-712
❑ 80MarPos-14
❑ 80Top-197
❑ 81Don-287
❑ 81Top-344
❑ 84Nes792-442
❑ 84Top-442
❑ 84TopTif-442
McLaughlin, Colin
❑ 82KnoBluJT-6
❑ 83SyrChiT-10
❑ 85SyrChiT-15
❑ 86KnoBluJP-16
❑ 87SyrChiT-6
❑ 88SyrChiC-3
❑ 88SyrChiP-823
❑ 89CalCanC-3
❑ 89CalCanP-532
McLaughlin, Dave
❑ 83AppFoxFr-3
McLaughlin, Denis
❑ 94UtiBluSC-18
❑ 94UtiBluSF-3816
❑ 96MicBatCB-16
McLaughlin, James
❑ 25Zee-73
❑ 26Zee-120
❑ 27Zee-97
❑ 28Zee-114
❑ 30Zee-127
❑ 31Zee-91
❑ 88KimN18-23
McLaughlin, Joey
❑ 78RicBraT-10
❑ 79RicBraT-1
❑ 80Top-384
❑ 81Don-271
❑ 81Fle-420
❑ 81OPC-248
❑ 81Top-248
❑ 82BluJayS-12
❑ 82Don-507
❑ 82Fle-620
❑ 82OPC-376
❑ 82OPCPos-8
❑ 82Top-739
❑ 83Don-255
❑ 83Fle-434
❑ 83FleSti-107
❑ 83OPC-9
❑ 83Top-9
❑ 84Don-617
❑ 84Fle-162
❑ 84FleUpd-79
❑ 84Nes792-556
❑ 84OPC-11
❑ 84RanJarP-53
❑ 84Top-556
❑ 84TopTif-556
❑ 85Top-678
❑ 85TopTif-678
❑ 86BluJayGT-11
❑ 86TacTigP-14
❑ 87HawIslP-19
❑ 93RanKee-257
McLaughlin, Jud (Justin)
❑ 34DiaMatCSB-127
McLaughlin, Mac (Dick)
❑ 77CliDodT-17
❑ 78CliDodT-23
❑ 79CliDodT-17
❑ 82AlbDukTc-26
❑ 83AlbDukTc-25
❑ 84AlbDukCr-169
❑ 85AlbDukCr-160
❑ 86AlbDukP-15
McLaughlin, Mike
❑ 87BelMarL-5
McLaughlin, Steve
❑ 86AppFoxP-14
McLaughlin, Thomas
❑ 87OldJudN-336
McLaughlin, Tom
❑ 81CliGiaT-24
McLaughlin, Wm.
❑ 40SolHug-14
McLaurine, Bill (William)
❑ 77SpoIndC-2
❑ 78SpoIndC-2
McLean, Larry (John R.)
❑ 03WilCarE-23
❑ 08RosComP-120
❑ 09AmeCarE90-1-77
❑ 09ColChiE-191A
❑ 09ColChiE-191B
❑ 09RamT20-78
❑ 09SpoNewSM-45
❑ 09T206-244
❑ 10CouT21-182
❑ 10DomDisP-80
❑ 10E101-33
❑ 10E98-22
❑ 10MelMinE-33
❑ 10NadCarE-38
❑ 10PeoT21-39
❑ 10RedCroT-137
❑ 10RedCroT-223
❑ 10SweCapPP-103A
❑ 10SweCapPP-103B
❑ 11HelSta-117
❑ 11MecDFT-33
❑ 11PinT-5-423
❑ 11PloCanE-46
❑ 11SpoLifCW-249
❑ 11SpoLifM-198
❑ 11T205-117
❑ 12ColRedB-191A
❑ 12ColRedB-191B
❑ 12ColTinT-191A
❑ 12ColTinT-191B
❑ 12HasTriFT-10A
❑ 12HasTriFT-41B
❑ 12HasTriFT-73A
❑ 12HasTriFT-73B
❑ 12T207-122
❑ 13NatGamW-30
❑ 14FatPlaT-33
❑ 14PieStaT-71
❑ 72ClaCar-117
McLeary, Marty
❑ 97LowSpiB-20
❑ 98MicBatCM-23
McLellan, Sean
❑ 98DunBluJSB-18
McLemore, Mark
❑ 83PeoSunF-9
❑ 85MidAngT-17
❑ 86Don-35
❑ 86Fle-650
❑ 86MidAngP-16
❑ 87AngSmo-13
❑ 87CalAngPPS-26
❑ 87ClaUpdY-119
❑ 87Don-479
❑ 87DonOpeD-8
❑ 87DonRoo-7
❑ 87FleUpd-77
❑ 87FleUpdG-77
❑ 87SpoRooI-14
❑ 87TopTra-75T
❑ 87TopTraT-75T
❑ 88AngSmo-22
❑ 88Don-181
❑ 88DonBasB-251
❑ 88Fle-497
❑ 88FleGlo-497
❑ 88Lea-159
❑ 88OPC-162
❑ 88PanSti-41
❑ 88Sco-152
❑ 88ScoGlo-152
❑ 88ScoYouS2-29
❑ 88StaLinAn-13
❑ 88Top-162
❑ 88TopTif-162
❑ 89Don-94
❑ 89Fle-484
❑ 89FleGlo-484
❑ 89Sco-208
❑ 89Top-51
❑ 89Top-547
❑ 89TopBig-30
❑ 89TopTif-51
❑ 89TopTif-547
❑ 89UppDec-245
❑ 90AngSmo-22
❑ 90TopBig-310
❑ 91AstMot-17
❑ 91Lea-86
❑ 92BalOriP-19
❑ 92Bow-446
❑ 92Lea-427
❑ 92LeaBlaG-427
❑ 92Ult-304
❑ 93BalOriP-17
❑ 93Don-485
❑ 93Fla-153
❑ 93Fle-546
❑ 93Lea-512
❑ 93PacSpa-344
❑ 93Pin-184
❑ 93SP-159
❑ 93Top-55
❑ 93TopGol-55
❑ 93TopInaM-55
❑ 93TopInaR-55
❑ 93TopMic-55
❑ 93UppDec-801
❑ 93UppDecGold-801
❑ 94BalOriP-18
❑ 94ColC-198
❑ 94ColChoGS-198
❑ 94ColChoSS-198
❑ 94Don-186
❑ 94Fin-115
❑ 94FinRef-115
❑ 94Fla-5
❑ 94Fle-9
❑ 94FleExtB-8
❑ 94Lea-36
❑ 94OriUSPC-1S
❑ 94OriUSPC-8H
❑ 94Pac-36
❑ 94Pin-379
❑ 94PinArtP-379
❑ 94PinMusC-379
❑ 94Sco-415
❑ 94ScoGolR-415
❑ 94Sel-80
❑ 94StaClu-342
❑ 94StaCluFDI-342
❑ 94StaCluGR-342
❑ 94StaCluMOP-342
❑ 94StaCluT-272
❑ 94StaCluTFDI-272
❑ 94Top-379
❑ 94TopGol-379
❑ 94TopSpa-379
❑ 94TriPla-156
❑ 94Ult-4
❑ 94UppDec-248
❑ 94UppDecED-248
❑ 95ColCho-569T
❑ 95Don-399
❑ 95DonPreP-399
❑ 95DonTopotO-162
❑ 95Fin-229
❑ 95FinRef-229
❑ 95Fla-307
❑ 95Fle-12
❑ 95FleUpd-84
❑ 95Lea-322
❑ 95Pac-25
❑ 95RanCra-18
❑ 95Sco-162
❑ 95ScoGolR-162
❑ 95ScoPlaTS-162
❑ 95StaClu-593
❑ 95StaCluMOP-593
❑ 95StaCluSTWS-593
❑ 95Top-602
❑ 95TopCyb-373
❑ 95TopTra-114T
❑ 96Cir-89
❑ 96CirRav-89
❑ 96ColCho-324
❑ 96ColChoGS-324
❑ 96ColChoSS-324
❑ 96Don-238
❑ 96DonPreP-238
❑ 96Fla-175
❑ 96Fle-254
❑ 96FleTif-254
❑ 96LeaSigEA-125
❑ 96Pac-421
❑ 96RanDr P-19
❑ 96RanFle-11
❑ 96RanMot-14
❑ 96Top-166
❑ 96Ult-137
❑ 96UltGolM-137
❑ 96UppDec-466
❑ 97Cir-133
❑ 97CirRav-133
❑ 97ColCho-489
❑ 97ColChoT-TR9
❑ 97Don-308
❑ 97DonGolPP-308
❑ 97DonSilPP-308
❑ 97Fin-243
❑ 97FinRef-243
❑ 97Fle-227
❑ 97FleTif-227
❑ 97Lea-271
❑ 97LeaFraM-271
❑ 97LeaFraMDC-271
❑ 97MetUni-165
❑ 97Pac-205
❑ 97PacLigB-205
❑ 97PacSil-205
❑ 97RanCup-3
❑ 97RanDr P-16
❑ 97RanMot-14
❑ 97RanSco-7
❑ 97RanScoPl-7
❑ 97RanScoPr-7
❑ 97Sco-145
❑ 97ScoArtPWB-145
❑ 97ScoPreS-145
❑ 97ScoShoS-145
❑ 97ScoShoSAP-145
❑ 97StaClu-99
❑ 97StaCluMOP-99
❑ 97Top-139
❑ 97Ult-137
❑ 97UltGolME-137
❑ 97UltPlaME-137
❑ 97UppDec-509
❑ 98Fle-526
❑ 98PacOnl-739
❑ 98PacOnlR-739
❑ 98PacOnlWC-739
❑ 98Pin-88
❑ 98PinPreP-88
❑ 98PinSna-TR13
❑ 98Sco-74
❑ 98ScoRT-69
❑ 98StaCluFDI-168
❑ 98StaClul-168
❑ 98StaCluOneK-168
❑ 98StaCluPP-168
❑ 98Top-71
❑ 98TopChr-71
❑ 98TopChrR-71
❑ 98TopDevR-71
❑ 98TopDia-71
❑ 98TopMiniC-71
❑ 98Ult-91
❑ 98UltGolM-91
❑ 98UltMas-91
❑ 98UltPlaM-91
❑ 98UppDec-740
❑ 99Fle-522
❑ 99FleSta9-522

❑ 99FleWarT-522
❑ 99Pac-428
❑ 99PacPlaB-428
❑ 99PacRed-428
❑ 99Top-396
❑ 99TopChr-396
❑ 99TopChrR-396
❑ 99TopMVPP-396
❑ 99UD Cho-151
❑ 99UD ChoPCR-151
❑ 99UppDec-219
❑ 99UppDecEL1-219
❑ 99UppDecEL2-219
McLeod, Bill
❑ 63MilSau-4
McLeod, Brian
❑ 90EveGiaB-8
❑ 90EveGiaP-3124
❑ 91CliGiaP-830
❑ 92SanJosGC-6
❑ 93SanJosGC-15
❑ 93SanJosGF-4
McLeod, Jason
❑ 97RanCucQG-16
❑ 98RanCucQG-20
❑ 98RanCucQG-20
McLeod, Jessie
❑ 41WheM5-15
McLeod, Kevin
❑ 90HamRedB-6
❑ 90HamRedS-16
McLin, Joe
❑ 91WelPirC-13
❑ 91WelPirP-3581
McLintock, Ron
❑ 87PocGiaTB-18
McLish, Cal
❑ 49AngTeal-26
❑ 49EurSta-64
❑ 57Top-364
❑ 58IndTeal-13
❑ 58Top-208
❑ 59Ind-11
❑ 59Kah-22
❑ 59OklTodML-8
❑ 59Top-445
❑ 60Kah-26
❑ 60Top-110
❑ 60TopTat-35
❑ 60TopVen-110
❑ 61Top-157
❑ 61WhiSoxTS-9
❑ 62Top-453
❑ 62WhiSoxTS-14
❑ 63Top-512
❑ 64Top-365
❑ 64TopVen-365
❑ 69ExpFudP-8
❑ 72Dia-34
❑ 73OPC-377
❑ 73Top-377
❑ 74OPC-531
❑ 74Top-531
❑ 75ExpPos-22
❑ 79TCM50-221
❑ 80BreTeal-17
❑ 81TCM60I-411
❑ 82BrePol-NNO
❑ 90DodTar-511
❑ 92BreCarT-xx
McLish, Tom
❑ 78NewWayCT-30
McLochlin, Mike
❑ 91ColIndC-14
McLoughlin, Tim
❑ 86SalRedBP-19
McMahon, David
❑ 88MisStaB-19
McMahon, Don
❑ 58BraJayP-9
❑ 58Top-147
❑ 59Top-3
❑ 59TopVen-3
❑ 60BraLaktL-16
❑ 60BraSpiaS-14
❑ 60Top-189
❑ 60TopVen-189
❑ 61Top-278
❑ 62Col.45B-13
❑ 62Top-483
❑ 63Col45"P-11
❑ 63Col45'JP-6
❑ 63Top-395
❑ 64Top-122
❑ 64TopVen-122
❑ 65Kah-29
❑ 65Top-317
❑ 66IndTeal-9
❑ 66IndVolC-9
❑ 66OPC-133
❑ 66Top-133
❑ 66TopVen-133
❑ 67CokCapRS-7
❑ 67OPC-7
❑ 67Top-7
❑ 67TopRedSS-10
❑ 68TigDetFPB-13
❑ 68Top-464
❑ 69Top-616
❑ 70OPC-519
❑ 70Top-519
❑ 71GiaTic-9
❑ 71MLBOffS-259
❑ 71OPC-354
❑ 71Top-354
❑ 72OPC-509
❑ 72Top-509
❑ 73OPC-252
❑ 73Top-252A
❑ 73Top-252B
❑ 74OPC-78
❑ 74Top-78
❑ 80Bra195T-1
❑ 80GiaPol-47
❑ 81RedSoxBG2S-95
❑ 82Gia25tATI-19
❑ 83IndPos-23
❑ 83IndWhe-22
❑ 84Ind-21
❑ 84IndWhe-NNO
❑ 85Ind-21
❑ 85IndPol-NNO
❑ 86DodPol-NNO
❑ 87DodMot-27
❑ 87DodPol-29
❑ 88TigDom-16
McMahon, Jack
❑ 83VisOakF-9
McMahon, John
❑ 94OriTeal-12
McMahon, Pat
❑ 88MisStaB-20
❑ 89MisStaB-42
McMahon, Sadie
❑ 90DodTar-1030
❑ 98CamPepP-54
McMakin, Rex
❑ 89AriStaB-20
McManaman, Steve
❑ 80OrlTwiT-17
McManus, Hugh
❑ 40WheM4-12
McManus, Jim (James M.)
❑ 61UniOil-H2
❑ 77FriOneYW-70
❑ 87RicBraT-24
McManus, Marty (Martin)
❑ 20WalMaiW-30
❑ 21Nei-41
❑ 22E120-98
❑ 22W572-61
❑ 22W573-78
❑ 25Exh-115
❑ 26Exh-115
❑ 27YorCarE-48
❑ 29ExhFou-23
❑ 31Exh-23
❑ 32OrbPinNP-7
❑ 32OrbPinUP-47
❑ 33DelR33-1
❑ 33Gou-48
❑ 33GouCanV-48
❑ 33TatOrb-47
❑ 34DiaMatCSB-128
❑ 34Gou-80
❑ 35GouPuzR-1J
❑ 35GouPuzR-3A
❑ 35GouPuzR-14A
❑ 35GouPuzR-15A
❑ 91ConTSN-189
McMath, Shelton
❑ 80AshTouT-27
McMichael, Chuck
❑ 81ChaRoyT-14
McMichael, Greg (Gregory)
❑ 88BurIndP-1796
❑ 89CanIndB-24
❑ 89CanIndP-1315
❑ 89CanIndS-16
❑ 90CanIndS-11
❑ 90CMC-459
❑ 90ColSprSSC-7
❑ 90ColSprSSP-31
❑ 90ProAAAF-212
❑ 91DurBulUP-7
❑ 92GreBraS-239
❑ 93Bow-317
❑ 93BraLykP-19
❑ 93BraLykS-24
❑ 93FleFinE-4
❑ 93Lea-489
❑ 93OPCPre-127
❑ 93SelRoo-59T
❑ 93SelRooAR-10
❑ 93TopTra-6T
❑ 93Ult-308
❑ 93UppDec-652
❑ 93UppDecGold-652
❑ 94BraLykP-22
❑ 94BraLykS-22
❑ 94BraUSPC-4D
❑ 94BraUSPC-11C
❑ 94ColC-199
❑ 94ColChoGS-199
❑ 94ColChoSS-199
❑ 94Don-175
❑ 94Fin-3
❑ 94FinJum-3
❑ 94FinRef-3
❑ 94Fla-355
❑ 94Fle-367
❑ 94FleExtB-210
❑ 94FleExtBSYS-13
❑ 94FleRooS-12
❑ 94Lea-207
❑ 94OPCDiaD-14
❑ 94Pac-17
❑ 94Pin-69
❑ 94PinArtP-69
❑ 94PinMusC-69
❑ 94Sco-551
❑ 94ScoBoyoS-21
❑ 94ScoGolR-551
❑ 94Sel-247
❑ 94StaClu-241
❑ 94StaCluFDI-241
❑ 94StaCluGR-241
❑ 94StaCluMOP-241
❑ 94StaCluT-55
❑ 94StaCluTFDI-55
❑ 94Top-81
❑ 94TopGol-81
❑ 94TopSpa-81
❑ 94Ult-155
❑ 94UltSecYS-8
❑ 94UppDec-407
❑ 94UppDecED-407
❑ 94USPlaCR-1S
❑ 95Baz-55
❑ 95ColCho-162
❑ 95ColChoGS-162
❑ 95ColChoSS-162
❑ 95Don-191
❑ 95DonPreP-191
❑ 95DonTopotO-192
❑ 95Fin-49
❑ 95FinRef-49
❑ 95Fle-313
❑ 95Pac-13
❑ 95Sco-250
❑ 95ScoGolR-250
❑ 95ScoPlaTS-250
❑ 95StaClu-449
❑ 95StaCluMOP-449
❑ 95StaCluSTWS-449
❑ 95StaCluVR-240
❑ 95StaCluVRMO-240
❑ 95Top-512
❑ 95TopCyb-300
❑ 95Ult-130
❑ 95UltGolM-130
❑ 96BraFle-13
❑ 96ColCho-458
❑ 96ColChoGS-458
❑ 96ColChoSS-458
❑ 96Don-281
❑ 96DonPreP-281
❑ 96Fla-207
❑ 96Fle-301
❑ 96FleTif-301
❑ 96LeaSigEA-126
❑ 96Pac-7
❑ 96Ult-442
❑ 96UltGolM-442
❑ 97Fle-265
❑ 97Fle-527
❑ 97FleTif-265
❑ 97FleTif-527
❑ 97Ult-329
❑ 97UltGolME-329
❑ 97UltPlaME-329
❑ 98Pac-370
❑ 98PacPlaB-370
❑ 98PacRedT-370
❑ 98PacSil-370
❑ 99Pac-281
❑ 99PacPlaB-281
❑ 99PacRed-281
❑ 99SkyMolMOA-14
McMillan, Leonard
❑ 95BurBeeTI-12
McMillan, Norm
❑ 23W503-10
McMillan, Roy
❑ 52Bow-238
❑ 52Top-137
❑ 53BowC-26
❑ 53Top-259
❑ 54Bow-12
❑ 54RedHeaF-21
❑ 54Top-120
❑ 54Wil-12
❑ 55Kah-3
❑ 55Top-181
❑ 56Kah-11
❑ 56RedBurB-14
❑ 56Top-123
❑ 56TopPin-57
❑ 57Kah-22
❑ 57RedSoh-14
❑ 57Top-69
❑ 58JayPubA-13
❑ 58Kah-20
❑ 58RedEnq-26
❑ 58RedJayP-9
❑ 58Top-360
❑ 59Baz-17
❑ 59Kah-23
❑ 59RedEnq-14
❑ 59RedShiBS-12
❑ 59Top-405
❑ 60Baz-33
❑ 60Kah-27
❑ 60RedJayP-5
❑ 60Top-45
❑ 60TopVen-45
❑ 61Pos-183
❑ 61Top-465
❑ 61TopStal-46
❑ 61WilSpoGH828-1-4
❑ 62BraJayP-8
❑ 62Jel-148
❑ 62Pos-148
❑ 62PosCan-148
❑ 62SalPlaC-159
❑ 62ShiPlaC-159
❑ 62Top-211
❑ 62Top-393
❑ 62TopStal-149
❑ 63BraJayP-8
❑ 63Jel-150
❑ 63Pos-150
❑ 63Top-156
❑ 64BraJayP-8
❑ 64Top-238
❑ 64TopCoi-148
❑ 64TopGia-8
❑ 64TopVen-238
❑ 65MetJayP-10
❑ 65MetPos-7
❑ 65OPC-45
❑ 65Top-45
❑ 65TopEmbl-44
❑ 66Baz-13
❑ 66MetVolC-10
❑ 66Top-421
❑ 67CokCapYM-V31
❑ 70BreMcD-18
❑ 70BreMil-14
❑ 73OPC-257
❑ 73Top-257A
❑ 73Top-257B
❑ 74OPC-179
❑ 74Top-179
❑ 77VisOakT-8
❑ 79DiaGre-272
❑ 79TCM50-154
❑ 80OrlTwiT-22
❑ 83TopRep5-137
❑ 91MetWIZ-262
❑ 91TopArc1-259
❑ 94TopArc1-120
❑ 94TopArc1G-120
McMillan, Stu
❑ 90IdaFalBP-3261
McMillan, Thomas E.
❑ 75OklCit8TI-16
❑ 77Top-490
❑ 78SanJosMMC-18
❑ 79BufBisT-15
❑ 89PacSenL-40
❑ 90EliSenL-100
McMillan, Thomas Law
❑ 11PinT-5-405
❑ 11SpoLifM-161
❑ 90DodTar-1032
McMillan, Tim
❑ 86PriWilPP-15
❑ 87ChaWheP-17
❑ 88SalBucS-13
McMillin, Darrell
❑ 90GeoColC-21
❑ 92EugEmeC-19
❑ 92EugEmeF-3043
McMillon, Billy
❑ 91TopTra-78T
❑ 91TopTraT-78T
❑ 92StaCluD-116
❑ 93ElmPioC-11
❑ 93ElmPioF-3836
❑ 94KanCouCC-15
❑ 94KanCouCF-175
❑ 94KanCouCTI-17
❑ 94MidLeaAF-MDW17
❑ 95Bes-71
❑ 95Exc-196
❑ 95KanCouCLTI-9
❑ 95PorSeaDTI-15
❑ 95SPML-60
❑ 95UppDecML-183
❑ 95UppDecMLFS-183
❑ 96Bow-209
❑ 96BowFoi-209
❑ 96ChaKniB-17
❑ 96Exc-163
❑ 96Top-435
❑ 96UppDec-236
❑ 96UppDecFSP-FS15
❑ 97ChaKni-18
❑ 97PacPriGotD-GD143
❑ 97Sco-311
❑ 97ScoArtPWB-311
❑ 97ScoShoS-311
❑ 97ScoShoSAP-311
❑ 97StaClu-104
❑ 97StaClu-186
❑ 97StaCluMOP-104
❑ 97StaCluMOP-186
❑ 97Top-206
❑ 98Don-275
❑ 98DonGolPP-275
❑ 98DonSilPP-275
❑ 98LeaRS-213
❑ 98LeaRSLHolo-213
❑ 98LeaRSLong-213
❑ 98LeaRTrue-213
❑ 98PhiTeal-23
❑ 98PorSeaD5AQ-17
❑ 98ScrRedBQ-21
McMorran, Pat
❑ 94HagSunC-29
❑ 95KnoSmoF-57
McMorris, Mark
❑ 86WinSpiP-16
❑ 87WinSpiP-1
McMullen, Dale
❑ 78MemChiBC-6
McMullen, Hugh
❑ 28StaPlaCE-46
❑ 33Zee-64
❑ 33Zee-127
McMullen, Jerry
❑ 95EugEmeTI-18
❑ 97SarRedS-15
McMullen, Jon
❑ 92ClaDraP-116
❑ 93BatCliCB-19
❑ 93BatCliF-3154
❑ 94SpaPhiF-1730
❑ 95ClePhiF-225
McMullen, Ken
❑ 63Top-537
❑ 64Top-214
❑ 64TopVen-214
❑ 65Top-319
❑ 66Top-401
❑ 66TopRubI-66
❑ 67CokCapS-12
❑ 67DexPre-143
❑ 67OPC-47
❑ 67SenPos-15
❑ 67SenTeal-8
❑ 67Top-47
❑ 68OPC-116
❑ 68SenTeal-8
❑ 68Top-116
❑ 68TopActS-8C
❑ 68TopVen-116
❑ 69MilBra-188
❑ 69MLBOffS-106
❑ 69SenTeal-11
❑ 69SenTeal8-14
❑ 69Top-319
❑ 69TopSta-239
❑ 69TopTeaP-23
❑ 70MLBOffS-284
❑ 70OPC-420
❑ 70Top-420
❑ 71MLBOffS-350
❑ 71OPC-485
❑ 71Top-485
❑ 72MilBra-230
❑ 72Top-765
❑ 73OPC-196
❑ 73Top-196
❑ 74OPC-434
❑ 74Top-434
❑ 75OPC-473
❑ 75Top-473
❑ 75TopMin-473
❑ 76OPC-566
❑ 76SSP-80
❑ 76Top-566
❑ 77Top-181
❑ 81TCM60I-338
❑ 90DodTar-512
❑ 94BreMilB-245
❑ 94BreMilB-330
McMullen, Kevin
❑ 91GreHorP-3063
McMullen, Mac
❑ 94SparPhiC-15
McMullen, Mike
❑ 95BurBeeTI-13
❑ 96BurBeeTI-11
❑ 97SanJosG-22
❑ 98ShrCapM-24
❑ 98ShrCapWS-24
McMullen, Rick
❑ 82JacMetT-15
McMullin, Fred
❑ 15Zee-13
❑ 18WhiSoxTI-16
❑ 75WhiSox1T-17
❑ 88LitSunBS-9
❑ 88PacEigMO-15
❑ 88PacEigMO-105
❑ 92Man191BSR-17
❑ 94ConTSN-1039
❑ 94ConTSNB-1039
McMurray, Brock
❑ 88GreFalDTI-16
❑ 89SalDodTI-16
❑ 90BakDodCLC-250
❑ 91VerBeaDC-28
❑ 91VerBeaDP-788
❑ 92BakDodCLC-16
McMurray, Steve
❑ 79WatIndT-9
McMurtrie, Dan
❑ 86LitFalMP-18
❑ 87ColMetP-24
McMurtry, Craig
❑ 82RicBraT-6
❑ 83BraPol-29
❑ 83TopTra-69T
❑ 84BraPol-29
❑ 84Don-599
❑ 84Fle-184
❑ 84FleSti-105
❑ 84Nes792-126
❑ 84Nes792-543
❑ 84OPC-219
❑ 84raPho-20
❑ 84Top-126
❑ 84Top-543
❑ 84TopRubD-30
❑ 84TopSti-384
❑ 84TopTif-126
❑ 84TopTif-543
❑ 85BraHos-15
❑ 85BraPol-29

❑ 85Don-188
❑ 85Fle-333
❑ 85Lea-45
❑ 85OPC-362
❑ 85Top-362
❑ 85TopMin-362
❑ 85TopRubD-31
❑ 85TopSti-28
❑ 85TopTif-362
❑ 86BraPol-29
❑ 86Top-194
❑ 86TopTif-194
❑ 87BluJayFS-22
❑ 87Top-461
❑ 87TopTif-461
❑ 88OklCit8C-4
❑ 88OklCit8P-44
❑ 89Don-520
❑ 89RanMot-20
❑ 89RanSmo-21
❑ 89Top-779
❑ 89TopTif-779
❑ 90OklCit8P-430
❑ 90OPC-294
❑ 90ProAAAF-676
❑ 90Top-294
❑ 90TopTif-294
❑ 91Sco-602
❑ 92PhoFirF-2818
❑ 92PhoFirS-389
❑ 93RanKee-258
❑ 94TriAAF-AAA46
❑ 94TucTorF-757
❑ 95TucTotTI-15

McMurtry, Orville
❑ 27Zee-115

McNabb, Buck
❑ 91Cla/Bes-441
❑ 91ClaDraP-43
❑ 91FroRowDP-42
❑ 91FroRowDPG-42
❑ 91FroRowDPS-42
❑ 92BurAstC-25
❑ 92BurAstF-558
❑ 92MidLeaATI-28
❑ 92StaCluD-117
❑ 92UppDecML-328
❑ 93ClaFS7-107
❑ 93FloStaLAF-36
❑ 93OscAstC-1
❑ 93OscAstF-639
❑ 94ClaGolF-135
❑ 94JacGenF-229
❑ 95BakBlaTI-27
❑ 97JacGen-15
❑ 97JacGenS-14
❑ 98WesTenDJM-16

McNabb, Glenn
❑ 89AugPirP-508
❑ 89SouAtlLAGS-6
❑ 90SalBucS-11

McNabb, Kevin
❑ 97OmaRoyB-35

McNair, Bob
❑ 80UtiBluJT-24

McNair, Donald Eric
❑ 33RitCE-12H
❑ 34BatR31-61
❑ 34DiaMatCSB-129
❑ 34TarThoBD-20
❑ 35DiaMatCS3T1-104
❑ 36GouWidPPR-A71
❑ 39GouPreR303A-32
❑ 39PlaBal-105
❑ 39WhiSoxTI-13
❑ 39WorWidGTP-32
❑ 40PlaBal-14
❑ 40WhiSoxL-14
❑ 74A's192T-19
❑ 92ConTSN-477
❑ 94ConTSN-1144
❑ 94ConTSNB-1144

McNair, Fred
❑ 92BelMarCB-6
❑ 92BelMarF-1458
❑ 93ExcFS7-228
❑ 93RivPilCLC-11
❑ 94JacSunF-1418
❑ 95ReaPhiELC-28
❑ 95ReaPhiTI-19
❑ 96Exc-210

McNair, Hurley Allen
❑ 87NegLeaPD-17

McNally, Andrew
❑ 97WatIndTI-15
❑ 98ColRedSM-7

McNally, Bob
❑ 86SumBraP-20
❑ 87SumBraP-5

McNally, Dave
❑ 63BalOriP-19
❑ 63Top-562
❑ 64BalOriP-24
❑ 64Top-161
❑ 64TopVen-161
❑ 65BalOriP-21
❑ 65OPC-249
❑ 65Top-249
❑ 66BalOriP-23
❑ 66OPC-193
❑ 66Top-193
❑ 66TopVen-193
❑ 67BalOriP-67
❑ 67BalOriP-68
❑ 67CokCapO-1
❑ 67DexPre-144
❑ 67OPC-154
❑ 67Top-154
❑ 67Top-382
❑ 67TopVen-248
❑ 68BalOriDPCP-8
❑ 68CokCapO-1
❑ 68DexPre-54
❑ 68Top-478
❑ 69CitMetC-2
❑ 69MilBra-189
❑ 69MLBOffS-5
❑ 69OPC-7
❑ 69OPC-9
❑ 69Top-7
❑ 69Top-9
❑ 69Top-340
❑ 69Top-532
❑ 69TopDecl-29
❑ 69TopSta-126
❑ 69TopSup-1
❑ 69TopTeaP-5
❑ 69TraSta-15
❑ 70BalOriP-19
❑ 70BalOriP-20
❑ 70DayDaiNM-52
❑ 70Kel-14
❑ 70MLBOffS-151
❑ 70OPC-20
❑ 70OPC-70
❑ 70Ori-7
❑ 70Top-20
❑ 70Top-70
❑ 71BalOriP-18
❑ 71BazNumT-27
❑ 71BazUnn-15
❑ 71Kel-59
❑ 71MilDud-16
❑ 71MLBOffS-304
❑ 71OPC-69
❑ 71OPC-196
❑ 71OPC-320
❑ 71OriCha-10
❑ 71Top-69
❑ 71Top-196
❑ 71Top-320
❑ 71TopCoi-26
❑ 71TopSup-18
❑ 71TopTat-96
❑ 72Kel-29A
❑ 72Kel-29B
❑ 72MilBra-231
❑ 72OPC-223
❑ 72OPC-344
❑ 72OPC-490
❑ 72OriDMV-6
❑ 72OriPos-21
❑ 72ProStaP-30
❑ 72SevTraC-33
❑ 72Top-223
❑ 72Top-344
❑ 72Top-490
❑ 72TopPos-1
❑ 73BalOriP-28
❑ 73BalOriP-29
❑ 73OPC-600
❑ 73OriJohP-19
❑ 73OriTeal-21
❑ 73Top-600
❑ 74OPC-235
❑ 74Top-235
❑ 74TopSta-127
❑ 75ExpPos-23
❑ 75Hos-150
❑ 75OPC-26
❑ 75Top-26
❑ 75TopMin-26
❑ 78TCM60I-270
❑ 81Ori6F-22
❑ 86OriGreT-4
❑ 88PacLegl-38
❑ 91OriCro-293
❑ 93ActPacA-153

McNally, Mike
❑ 20GasAmeMBD-12
❑ 21E121So1-61
❑ 21E121So8-58
❑ 21KoBreWSI-39
❑ 22E120-67
❑ 22W575-79
❑ 22WilPatV-39
❑ 23W501-33
❑ 75SenTCM1-20

McNally, Sean
❑ 94EugEmeC-13
❑ 94EugEmeF-3721
❑ 95MidLeaA-30
❑ 95NewJerCTI-18
❑ 95SprSulTI-14
❑ 96Exc-62
❑ 96PeoChiB-20
❑ 96WilBluRB-11
❑ 97PriWilC-21
❑ 97WicWra-15
❑ 98WicWraM-18

McNamara, Denny (Dennis)
❑ 90NiaFalRP-4
❑ 91LakTigC-25
❑ 91LakTigP-279
❑ 92ClaFS7-166
❑ 92LakTigC-8
❑ 92LakTigF-2291
❑ 93ClaGolF-163

McNamara, James
❑ 86EveGiaC-10
❑ 86EveGiaPC-16
❑ 87CliGiaP-9
❑ 88SanJosGCLC-123
❑ 88SanJosGP-133
❑ 89SalSpuCLC-145
❑ 89SalSpuP-1811
❑ 91LinDriAA-303
❑ 91LinDriAA-312
❑ 91ShrCapLD-312
❑ 91ShrCapP-1824
❑ 92DonRoo-74
❑ 92GiaMot-20
❑ 92GiaPacGaE-29
❑ 92Lea-514
❑ 92LeaBlaG-514
❑ 92Ult-592
❑ 92UltAllR-5
❑ 93PacSpa-275
❑ 93PhoFirF-1518
❑ 93TopGol-395
❑ 94OklCit8F-1497
❑ 97BatCliTI-32

McNamara, John
❑ 70Top-706
❑ 73OPC-252
❑ 73Top-252A
❑ 73Top-252B
❑ 74OPC-78
❑ 74PadDea-19
❑ 74PadMcDD-10
❑ 74Top-78
❑ 75OPC-146
❑ 75PadDea-20
❑ 75Top-146
❑ 75TopMin-146
❑ 76OPC-331
❑ 76SSP-123
❑ 76Top-331
❑ 77PadSchC-38A
❑ 77PadSchC-38B
❑ 77PadSchC-38C
❑ 77Top-134
❑ 78AngFamF-24
❑ 80RedEnq-3
❑ 80Top-606
❑ 81Top-677
❑ 82Don-526
❑ 83TopTra-70T
❑ 84AngSmo-19
❑ 84Nes792-651
❑ 84Top-651
❑ 84TopTif-651
❑ 85Top-732
❑ 85TopTif-732
❑ 85TopTifT-84T
❑ 85TopTra-84T
❑ 86Top-771
❑ 86TopTif-771
❑ 87Top-306
❑ 87Top-368
❑ 87TopTif-306
❑ 87TopTif-368
❑ 88DonAll-10
❑ 88DonPop-10
❑ 88Top-414
❑ 88TopGloA-1
❑ 88TopTif-414
❑ 90IndTeal-27
❑ 90TopTra-72T
❑ 90TopTraT-72T
❑ 91IndFanC-19
❑ 91OPC-549
❑ 91Top-549
❑ 91TopDesS-549
❑ 91TopMic-549
❑ 91TopTif-549

McNamara, Mike
❑ 88CapCodPPaLP-85

McNamara, Rusty
❑ 98ClePhiM-15
❑ 98ClePhiUM-15

McNamara, Tom
❑ 87BelMarL-6

McNamee, Graham
❑ 63GadFunC-31

McNaney, Scott
❑ 89WatDiaS-32

McNary, Mike
❑ 88CapCodPPaLP-32

McNatt, John
❑ 97DelSho-29
❑ 98CarLeaAC-7
❑ 98CarLeaAC-20
❑ 98FreKeyM-10

McNaughton, Troy
❑ 98NewJerCM-20

McNeal, Aaron
❑ 98MidLeaPM-19
❑ 98QuaCitRBG-17

McNeal, Clyde
❑ 91NegLeaRL-9
❑ 92NegLeaRLI-43
❑ 95NegLeaLI-9

McNeal, Paul
❑ 86HagSunP-10
❑ 87HagSunP-2

McNeal, Pepe
❑ 94BurIndC-14
❑ 94BurIndF-3798
❑ 94StaCluDP-59
❑ 94StaCluDPFDI-59
❑ 96JohCitCTI-22
❑ 97PeoChi-17
❑ 98PriWilCQ-25

McNealy, Derwin
❑ 83NasSouTI-12
❑ 85SyrChiT-29
❑ 86ColCliP-14
❑ 86ColCliP-16

McNealy, Rusty
❑ 82WesHavAT-23
❑ 83TacTigT-17
❑ 86ChaLooP-19
❑ 87SanJosBP-27

McNeely, Al
❑ 32Zee-10

McNeely, Earl
❑ 23Zee-91
❑ 24Zee-65
❑ 25Exh-127
❑ 26Exh-127
❑ 26Zee-82
❑ 91ConTSN-177

McNeely, George
❑ 33Zee-33

McNeely, Jeff
❑ 89ElmPioP-30
❑ 90ElmPioP-12
❑ 90WinHavRSS-15
❑ 91Bow-113
❑ 91CarLeaAP-CAR23
❑ 91Cla/Bes-169
❑ 91Cla3-T67
❑ 91LynRedSC-22
❑ 91LynRedSP-1212
❑ 91UppDecFE-20F
❑ 92Bow-193
❑ 92ClaFS7-198
❑ 92DonRoo-75
❑ 92NewBriRSF-447
❑ 92NewBriRSS-489
❑ 92OPC-618
❑ 92ProFS7-20
❑ 92SkyAA F-209
❑ 92StaClu-577
❑ 92Top-618
❑ 92TopGol-618
❑ 92TopGolW-618
❑ 92TopMic-618
❑ 92UppDecML-258
❑ 93ClaFS7-12
❑ 93ExcFS7-134
❑ 93PawRedSDD-16
❑ 93PawRedSF-2421
❑ 93PawRedSTI-15
❑ 93RedSoxWHP-18
❑ 94Bow-175
❑ 94Cla-98
❑ 94ColC-200
❑ 94ColChoGS-200
❑ 94ColChoSS-200
❑ 94Don-609
❑ 94FleMajLP-23
❑ 94Pac-58
❑ 94PawRedSDD-11
❑ 94PawRedSF-955
❑ 94Pin-231
❑ 94PinArtP-231
❑ 94PinMusC-231
❑ 94PinNewG-NG11
❑ 94Sco-646
❑ 94ScoBoyoS-33
❑ 94ScoGolR-646
❑ 94Spo-171
❑ 94StaClu-48
❑ 94StaCluFDI-48
❑ 94StaCluGR-48
❑ 94StaCluMOP-48
❑ 94TriPla-285
❑ 94UppDec-21
❑ 94UppDecED-21
❑ 94USPlaCR-2D
❑ 95LouRedF-289
❑ 96MidAngOHP-18
❑ 96SigRooOJ-20
❑ 96SigRooOJS-20

McNeely, Mitch
❑ 95YakBeaTI-21
❑ 97VerBeaD-17

McNeely, Rod
❑ 77ModA'sC-18
❑ 79WatA'sT-21

McNees, Kevin
❑ 87IdaFalBP-8
❑ 88HagSunS-11

McNeese, John
❑ 96DayCubB-16

McNeill, Kevin
❑ 94JohCitCC-21
❑ 94JohCitCF-3700
❑ 96StPetCB-19
❑ 97PriWilC-22

McNertney, Jerry (Gerald)
❑ 64Top-564
❑ 67CokCapWS-9
❑ 67DexPre-145
❑ 68OPC-14
❑ 68Top-14
❑ 68TopVen-14
❑ 69MilBra-190
❑ 69PilPos-4
❑ 69PilWhe-4
❑ 69Top-534
❑ 69TopSta-226
❑ 69TopTeaP-9
❑ 70BreMcD-19
❑ 70BreMil-15
❑ 70BreTeal-9
❑ 70MLBOffS-275
❑ 70OPC-158
❑ 70Top-158
❑ 71BreTeal-9
❑ 71CarTeal-17
❑ 71CarTeal-28
❑ 71MLBOffS-279
❑ 71OPC-286
❑ 71Top-286
❑ 71TopCoi-68
❑ 72MilBra-232
❑ 72Top-584
❑ 77PilPosR-4
❑ 79ColCliT-9
❑ 80ColCliT-22
❑ 81ColCliT-28
❑ 82ColCliP-NNO
❑ 82ColCliT-24
❑ 83Pil69G-15
❑ 85ColCliP-25
❑ 87AlbYanP-10
❑ 87ColCliP-25
❑ 87ColCliP-2
❑ 87ColCliT-24
❑ 94BreMilB-246

McNichol, Brian
❑ 96DayCubB-17
❑ 96Top-239
❑ 98WesTenDJM-17

McNickle, Rusty
❑ 89MisStaB-44

McNulty, Bill
❑ 73OPC-603
❑ 73Top-603
❑ 74SacSolC-49
❑ 75SacSolC-6

McNulty, J. M.
❑ 18Zee-48
❑ 19Zee-56

McNulty, Pat
❑ 28Zee-14
❑ 93ConTSN-978

McNutt, Brent
❑ 92DavLipB-18
❑ 92DavLipB-23

McNutt, Larry
❑ 83LynMetT-2

McPhail, Larry
❑ 80SSPHOF-165

McPhail, Lee
❑ 83TigAlKS-54

McPhail, Marlin
❑ 86TidTidP-18
❑ 87BirBarB-5
❑ 88VanCanC-25
❑ 88VanCanP-777
❑ 89VanCanC-15
❑ 89VanCanP-596
❑ 90CMC-645
❑ 90ProAAAF-179
❑ 90VanCanC-18
❑ 90VanCanP-501
❑ 91IndIndLD-190
❑ 91IndIndP-470
❑ 91LinDriAAA-190
❑ 92ColMetC-28
❑ 92ColMetF-313
❑ 92ColMetPI-3
❑ 93NorTidF-2587
❑ 94NorTidF-2938

McPhee, Bid (John)
❑ 87OldJudN-337
❑ 94OriofB-28
❑ 98CamPepP-55

McPhee, Walter
❑ 26Zee-11

McPheeters, Kourtney
❑ 87AncGlaP-35

McPherson, Barry
❑ 84SavCarT-3

McPherson, John
❑ 86DavLipB-16
❑ 88KimN18-24

McQuaid, Jack (John H.)
❑ 20Zee-113
❑ 21Zee-126
❑ 22Zee-103
❑ 29Zee-50
❑ 30Zee-59
❑ 33Zee-34
❑ 87OldJudN-338
❑ 87OldJudN-339

McQueen, David
❑ 93EliTwiC-26

McQueen, Mike
❑ 70Top-621
❑ 71OPC-8
❑ 71Top-8
❑ 72OPC-214
❑ 72Top-214

McQuillan, George
❑ 03WilCarE-24
❑ 08RosComP-144
❑ 09AmeCarE90-1-78
❑ 09T206-245
❑ 09T206-246
❑ 10CouT21-183
❑ 10CouT21-184
❑ 10CouT21-185
❑ 10CouT21-304
❑ 10LuxCigPP-15
❑ 10PeoT21-40
❑ 11PinT-5-402
❑ 11SpoLifM-234A
❑ 11SpoLifM-234B

❑ 12PhiCarE-20
❑ 15AmeCarE106-29
❑ 15CraJacE-152
❑ 16TanBraE-12
❑ 46SeaSLP-41

McQuillan, Hugh

❑ 22E120-130
❑ 22WilPatV-14
❑ 23W515-33
❑ 26Exh-37
❑ 93ConTSN-807

McQuillen, Carl

❑ 52LavPro-59

McQuillen, Glenn

❑ 75TCMGua-10

McQuinn, George

❑ 36NatChiFPR-106
❑ 36NatChiFPR-112
❑ 36OveCanR-34
❑ 39ExhSal-42A
❑ 39ExhSal-42B
❑ 39PlaBal-122
❑ 40PlaBal-53
❑ 41BroW75-21
❑ 41Gou-5
❑ 41PlaBal-23
❑ 46SpoExcW-5-1B
❑ 47YanTeaT-18
❑ 48YanTeaI-20
❑ 49Bow-232
❑ 52LavPro-1
❑ 76TayBow4-68
❑ 77TCMTheWY-60
❑ 83TCMPla1943-17
❑ 92ConTSN-391
❑ 92YanWIZA-48
❑ 96Bro194F-19

McRae, Brian

❑ 86EugEmeC-28
❑ 87Ft.MyeRP-26
❑ 88BasCitRS-17
❑ 89MemChiB-13
❑ 89MemChiP-1205
❑ 89MemChiS-17
❑ 89Sta-44
❑ 90Bes-276
❑ 90CMC-829
❑ 90MemChiB-13
❑ 90MemChiP-1022
❑ 90MemChiS-18
❑ 90ProAaA-50
❑ 90StaFS7-68
❑ 91Bow-292
❑ 91Cla1-T49
❑ 91Cla3-T68
❑ 91ClaGam-157
❑ 91Don-575
❑ 91DonRoo-31
❑ 91Fle-563
❑ 91Lea-235
❑ 91OPC-222
❑ 91RoyPol-15
❑ 91Sco-331
❑ 91StaClu-478
❑ 91Stu-68
❑ 91Top-222
❑ 91TopDeb90-105
❑ 91TopDesS-222
❑ 91TopMic-222
❑ 91TopTif-222
❑ 91ToyRoo-18
❑ 91Ult-152
❑ 91UppDec-543
❑ 92Bow-66
❑ 92Cla2-T77
❑ 92ClaGam-85
❑ 92DenHol-15
❑ 92Don-387
❑ 92DonCraJ1-20
❑ 92DonDiaK-DK16
❑ 92DonSupD-DK16
❑ 92Fle-163
❑ 92FleRooS-9
❑ 92Hig5-63
❑ 92Lea-123
❑ 92LeaBlaG-123
❑ 92MVPPin-13
❑ 92OPC-659
❑ 92OPCPre-12
❑ 92PanSti-99
❑ 92Pin-117
❑ 92PinTea2-20
❑ 92RedFolS-66
❑ 92RoyPol-18
❑ 92Sco-478
❑ 92StaClu-270
❑ 92Stu-187
❑ 92Top-659
❑ 92TopGol-659
❑ 92TopGolW-659
❑ 92TopKid-108
❑ 92TopMic-659
❑ 92TriPla-69
❑ 92Ult-75
❑ 92UppDec-157
❑ 93Bow-589
❑ 93Bow-704
❑ 93CadDis-42
❑ 93DiaMar-74
❑ 93Don-411
❑ 93Fla-221
❑ 93Fle-242
❑ 93Hos-12
❑ 93Lea-58
❑ 93OPC-287
❑ 93PacSpa-139
❑ 93PanSti-108
❑ 93Pin-367
❑ 93RedFolS-64
❑ 93RoyPol-19
❑ 93RoyStaC-25
❑ 93Sco-128
❑ 93Sel-250
❑ 93SP-233
❑ 93StaClu-33
❑ 93StaCluFDI-33
❑ 93StaCluMOP-33
❑ 93StaCluMP-3
❑ 93Stu-137
❑ 93Top-49
❑ 93TopGol-49
❑ 93TopInaM-49
❑ 93TopInaR-49
❑ 93TopMic-49
❑ 93TriPla-21
❑ 93Ult-213
❑ 93UppDec-238
❑ 93UppDecGold-238
❑ 94Bow-115
❑ 94ChuHomS-1
❑ 94ChuHomSG-1
❑ 94ColC-201
❑ 94ColChoGS-201
❑ 94ColChoSS-201
❑ 94ColChoT-12
❑ 94Don-43
❑ 94DonDiaK-DK12
❑ 94DonDiaKJ-DK12
❑ 94DonSpeE-43
❑ 94Fin-62
❑ 94FinPre-62P
❑ 94FinRef-62
❑ 94Fla-302
❑ 94Fle-167
❑ 94FleExtB-96
❑ 94FleTeaL-7
❑ 94FUnPac-56
❑ 94Kra-7
❑ 94Lea-306
❑ 94LeaL-41
❑ 94OPC-245
❑ 94Pac-295
❑ 94PanSti-78
❑ 94Pin-18
❑ 94PinArtP-18
❑ 94PinMusC-18
❑ 94ProMag-62
❑ 94RedFolMI-19
❑ 94Sco-19
❑ 94ScoCyc-TC15
❑ 94ScoGolR-19
❑ 94ScoGolS-60
❑ 94Sel-47
❑ 94SP-175
❑ 94SPDieC-175
❑ 94StaClu-520
❑ 94StaCluFDI-520
❑ 94StaCluGR-520
❑ 94StaCluMOP-520
❑ 94Stu-188
❑ 94Top-425
❑ 94TopGol-425
❑ 94TopSpa-425
❑ 94TriPla-238
❑ 94Ult-368
❑ 94UppDec-253
❑ 94UppDecAJ-13
❑ 94UppDecAJG-13
❑ 94UppDecED-253
❑ 95Bow-328
❑ 95ColCho-460
❑ 95ColCho-543T
❑ 95ColChoGS-460
❑ 95ColChoSE-216
❑ 95ColChoSEGS-216
❑ 95ColChoSESS-216
❑ 95ColChoSS-460
❑ 95Don-167
❑ 95DonPreP-167
❑ 95DonTopotO-200
❑ 95Emo-111
❑ 95Fin-175
❑ 95Fin-256
❑ 95FinRef-175
❑ 95FinRef-256
❑ 95Fla-333
❑ 95Fle-168
❑ 95FleUpd-126
❑ 95Lea-347
❑ 95LeaLim-35
❑ 95Pac-209
❑ 95PacPri-67
❑ 95Pin-319
❑ 95PinArtP-319
❑ 95PinMusC-319
❑ 95RedFol-21
❑ 95Sco-493
❑ 95ScoGolR-493
❑ 95ScoHaloG-HG77
❑ 95ScoHaloGYTE-HG77T
❑ 95ScoPlaTS-493
❑ 95ScoYouTE-493T
❑ 95SP-40
❑ 95SPCha-32
❑ 95SPChaDC-32
❑ 95Spo-79
❑ 95SpoArtP-79
❑ 95SPSil-40
❑ 95StaClu-273
❑ 95StaClu-624
❑ 95StaCluMOP-273
❑ 95StaCluMOP-624
❑ 95StaCluSTWS-273
❑ 95StaCluSTWS-624
❑ 95StaCluVR-138
❑ 95StaCluVRMO-138
❑ 95Stu-154
❑ 95Top-624
❑ 95TopCyb-391
❑ 95TopTra-26T
❑ 95UC3-57
❑ 95UC3ArtP-57
❑ 95Ult-60
❑ 95UltGolM-60
❑ 95UppDec-457
❑ 95UppDecSE-55
❑ 95UppDecSEG-55
❑ 95USPlaCMLA-2H
❑ 96Baz-90
❑ 96Bow-63
❑ 96BowFoi-63
❑ 96Cir-110
❑ 96CirRav-110
❑ 96ColCho-84
❑ 96ColChoGS-84
❑ 96ColChoSS-84
❑ 96CubFle-12
❑ 96Don-55
❑ 96DonPreP-55
❑ 96EmoXL-156
❑ 96Fin-B26
❑ 96FinRef-B26
❑ 96Fla-220
❑ 96Fle-322
❑ 96FleTif-322
❑ 96Lea-109
❑ 96LeaPrePB-109
❑ 96LeaPrePG-109
❑ 96LeaPrePS-109
❑ 96MetUni-142
❑ 96MetUniP-142
❑ 96Pac-30
❑ 96PacPri-P11
❑ 96PacPriG-P11
❑ 96PanSti-41
❑ 96Pin-109
❑ 96ProSta-38
❑ 96Sco-68
❑ 96SP-52
❑ 96StaClu-180
❑ 96StaCluMO-26
❑ 96StaCluMOP-180
❑ 96Stu-148
❑ 96StuPrePB-148
❑ 96StuPrePG-148
❑ 96StuPrePS-148
❑ 96TeaOut-56
❑ 96Top-184
❑ 96TopChr-55
❑ 96TopChrR-55
❑ 96TopGal-56
❑ 96TopGalPPI-56
❑ 96TopLas-47
❑ 96Ult-454
❑ 96UltGolM-454
❑ 96UltPriL-17
❑ 96UltPriLGM-17
❑ 96UppDec-33
❑ 96UppDecRCJ-6
❑ 96UppDecRipC-6
❑ 97Bow-257
❑ 97BowBes-55
❑ 97BowBesAR-55
❑ 97BowBesR-55
❑ 97BowInt-257
❑ 97Cir-374
❑ 97CirRav-374
❑ 97ColCho-285
❑ 97Don-328
❑ 97DonGolPP-328
❑ 97DonSilPP-328
❑ 97Fin-26
❑ 97FinRef-26
❑ 97FlaShoLC-95
❑ 97FlaShoLeg0-95
❑ 97FlaShoLeg1-95
❑ 97FlaShoM-A95
❑ 97FlaShoM-B95
❑ 97FlaShoM-C95
❑ 97FlaShoR0-95
❑ 97FlaShoR1-95
❑ 97FlaShoR2-95
❑ 97Fle-280
❑ 97FleTif-280
❑ 97Lea-2
❑ 97LeaFraM-2
❑ 97LeaFraMDC-2
❑ 97MetUni-12
❑ 97Pac-253
❑ 97PacLigB-253
❑ 97PacSil-253
❑ 97Sco-99
❑ 97ScoArtPWB-99
❑ 97ScoPreS-99
❑ 97ScoShoS-99
❑ 97ScoShoSAP-99
❑ 97SP-41
❑ 97StaClu-175
❑ 97StaCluMOP-175
❑ 97Stu-78
❑ 97StuPrePG-78
❑ 97StuPrePS-78
❑ 97Top-74
❑ 97TopChr-27
❑ 97TopChrR-27
❑ 97TopGal-77
❑ 97TopGalPPI-77
❑ 97Ult-448
❑ 97UltGolME-448
❑ 97UltPlaME-448
❑ 97UppDec-326
❑ 98CirThu-245
❑ 98CirThuRav-245
❑ 98CirThuSupRav-245
❑ 98ColCho-437
❑ 98Fin-12
❑ 98FinNo--12
❑ 98FinNo-R-12
❑ 98FinRef-12
❑ 98Fle-60
❑ 98Pac-371
❑ 98PacAur-165
❑ 98PacOme-159
❑ 98PacOmeR-159
❑ 98PacOnl-483
❑ 98PacOnlR-483
❑ 98PacOnlWC-483
❑ 98PacPar-207
❑ 98PacParC-207
❑ 98PacParG-207
❑ 98PacParHS-207
❑ 98PacParPB-207
❑ 98PacParR-207
❑ 98PacPlaB-371
❑ 98PacRedT-371
❑ 98PacSil-371
❑ 98Pin-121
❑ 98PinPreP-121
❑ 98PinSna-NYM13
❑ 98Sco-194
❑ 98ScoSS-PP90
❑ 98ScoSSAP-PP90
❑ 98StaCluFDI-90
❑ 98StaCluI-90
❑ 98StaCluOneK-90
❑ 98StaCluPP-90
❑ 98Top-386
❑ 98TopChr-386
❑ 98TopChrR-386
❑ 98TopDevR-386
❑ 98TopDia-386
❑ 98TopMiniC-386
❑ 98Ult-406
❑ 98UltGolM-406
❑ 98UltMas-406
❑ 98UltPlaM-406
❑ 98UppDec-442
❑ 99199Fin-13
❑ 99FinGolRef-13
❑ 99FinRef-13
❑ 99Fle-164
❑ 99FleSta9-164
❑ 99FleWarT-164
❑ 99Pac-282
❑ 99PacPar-151
❑ 99PacParC-151
❑ 99PacParG-151
❑ 99PacParHoloGold-151
❑ 99PacParHS-151
❑ 99PacParOD-151
❑ 99PacParPB-151
❑ 99PacParRed-151
❑ 99PacPlaB-282
❑ 99PacRed-282
❑ 99SkyThu-110
❑ 99SkyThuRant-110
❑ 99SkyThuRave-110
❑ 99StaClu-62
❑ 99StaCluFDI-62
❑ 99StaCluOoaK-62
❑ 99StaCluPP-62
❑ 99ThuSkySupR-110
❑ 99Top-269
❑ 99TopChr-269
❑ 99TopChrR-269
❑ 99TopMVPP-269
❑ 99UD Cho-112
❑ 99UD ChoP-112
❑ 99UD ChoPCR-112
❑ 99UppDec-429
❑ 99UppDecEL1-429
❑ 99UppDecEL2-429
❑ 99UppDecM-138
❑ 99UppDecMGS-138
❑ 99UppDecMHFS-138
❑ 99UppDecMP-138
❑ 99UppDecMSS-138
❑ 99Vic-257

McRae, Hal

❑ 68Top-384
❑ 70DayDaiNM-64
❑ 70Top-683
❑ 71MLBOffS-64
❑ 71OPC-177
❑ 71Top-177
❑ 72OPC-291
❑ 72OPC-292
❑ 72Top-291
❑ 72Top-292
❑ 72TopCloT-24
❑ 73OPC-28
❑ 73Top-28
❑ 74OPC-563
❑ 74RoyPos-19
❑ 74Top-563
❑ 75Hos-104
❑ 75Kel-53
❑ 75OPC-268
❑ 75RoyPos-21
❑ 75Top-268
❑ 75TopMin-268
❑ 76Hos-135
❑ 76KanCitRP-19
❑ 76OPC-72
❑ 76RoyAaP-9
❑ 76SSP-176
❑ 76Top-72
❑ 77BurCheD-72
❑ 77ChiWilD-44
❑ 77DailsID-44
❑ 77DetCaeD-44
❑ 77HolInnD-44
❑ 77Hos-17
❑ 77Kel-10
❑ 77MSADis-44
❑ 77OPC-215
❑ 77RCColC-41
❑ 77SagDis-44
❑ 77sDis-44
❑ 77Top-340
❑ 77WenDis-44
❑ 77ZipDis-44
❑ 78Hos-6
❑ 78Kel-20
❑ 78RCColC-33
❑ 78Roy-13
❑ 78SSP270-219
❑ 78Top-465
❑ 78WifBalD-49
❑ 79Hos-90
❑ 79OPC-306
❑ 79RoyTeal-6
❑ 79Top-585
❑ 80OPC-104
❑ 80Top-185
❑ 81AllGamPI-59
❑ 81CokTeaS-77
❑ 81Don-463
❑ 81Fle-41A
❑ 81Fle-41B
❑ 81OPC-295
❑ 81RoyPol-6
❑ 81RoyProPS-12
❑ 81Top-295
❑ 81TopSti-86
❑ 82Don-196
❑ 82Fle-416
❑ 82FleSta-210
❑ 82OPC-384
❑ 82Roy-13
❑ 82Top-625
❑ 83AllGamPI-62
❑ 83Don-238
❑ 83DonActA-16
❑ 83Dra-17
❑ 83Fle-119
❑ 83FleSta-124
❑ 83FleSti-102
❑ 83FleSti-146
❑ 83Kel-5
❑ 83OPC-25
❑ 83PerCreC-28
❑ 83PerCreCG-28
❑ 83RoyPol-4
❑ 83RoyPos-19
❑ 83Top-25
❑ 83Top-703
❑ 83TopSti-19
❑ 83TopSti-75
❑ 84AllGamPI-152
❑ 84Don-11
❑ 84Don-11A
❑ 84Don-297
❑ 84DonActAS-25
❑ 84DonCha-17
❑ 84Fle-350
❑ 84FleSti-44
❑ 84FunFooP-63
❑ 84Nes792-96
❑ 84Nes792-340
❑ 84OPC-340
❑ 84RoyPos-22
❑ 84Top-96
❑ 84Top-340
❑ 84TopRubD-14
❑ 84TopSti-278
❑ 84TopStiB-3
❑ 84TopTif-96
❑ 84TopTif-340
❑ 85Don-588
❑ 85Fle-207
❑ 85Lea-34
❑ 85OPC-284
❑ 85RoyTeal-21
❑ 85Top-773
❑ 85TopRubD-12
❑ 85TopSti-270
❑ 85TopTif-773
❑ 86Don-521
❑ 86Fle-14
❑ 86Lea-251
❑ 86OPC-278
❑ 86RoyKitCD-4
❑ 86RoyNatP-11
❑ 86RoyTeal-16
❑ 86Top-415
❑ 86Top-606
❑ 86TopTat-15
❑ 86TopTif-415
❑ 86TopTif-606
❑ 86Woo-22
❑ 87Don-471
❑ 87Fle-375
❑ 87FleGlo-375
❑ 87OPC-246
❑ 87RedFolSB-59

❑ 87SpoTeaP-13
❑ 87Top-573
❑ 87TopTif-573
❑ 88ClaBlu-235
❑ 89PacSenL-133
❑ 89T/MSenL-76
❑ 89TopSenL-122
❑ 90ExpPos-24
❑ 91TopTra-79T
❑ 91TopTraT-79T
❑ 92OPC-519
❑ 92RoyPol-19
❑ 92Top-519
❑ 92TopGol-519
❑ 92TopGolW-519
❑ 92TopMic-519
❑ 93Bow-704
❑ 93RoyPol-1
❑ 93RoySta2-7
❑ 93Top-507
❑ 93TopGol-507
❑ 93TopInaM-507
❑ 93TopInaR-507
❑ 93TopMic-507
❑ 95RedKah-34
❑ 97PhiTeal-56
❑ 98PhiTeal-24

McRae, Norm
❑ 70OPC-207
❑ 70Top-207
❑ 71OPC-93
❑ 71Top-93

McReynolds, Kevin
❑ 83LasVegSBHN-15
❑ 83PadTeal-17
❑ 84Don-34
❑ 84Fle-307
❑ 84PadMot-13
❑ 84PadSmo-18
❑ 85AllGamPl-151
❑ 85Don-139
❑ 85Fle-41
❑ 85Lea-43
❑ 85PadMot-3
❑ 86Don-80
❑ 86Fle-331
❑ 86Lea-76
❑ 87ClaUpdY-126
❑ 87Don-14A
❑ 87Don-14B
❑ 87Don-451
❑ 87DonOpeD-125
❑ 87DonSupD-14
❑ 87Fle-425
❑ 87FleGamW-28
❑ 87FleGlo-425
❑ 87FleUpd-78
❑ 87FleUpdG-78
❑ 87Lea-14
❑ 87Lea-214
❑ 87MetColP-17
❑ 87MetFanC-5
❑ 87RedFolSB-35
❑ 87Spo-135
❑ 87Spo-155
❑ 87SpoTeaP-2
❑ 87TopTra-76T
❑ 87TopTraT-76T
❑ 88Don-617
❑ 88DonBasB-153
❑ 88DonTeaBM-617
❑ 88Fle-143
❑ 88FleGlo-143
❑ 88FleSup-24
❑ 88Lea-228
❑ 88MetColP-37
❑ 88MetKah-22
❑ 88OPC-37
❑ 88PanSti-346
❑ 88RedFolSB-56
❑ 88Sco-21
❑ 88ScoGlo-21
❑ 88Spo-56
❑ 88SpoGam-22
❑ 88StaLinMe-15
❑ 88StaMcR-1
❑ 88StaMcR-2
❑ 88StaMcR-3
❑ 88StaMcR-4
❑ 88StaMcR-5
❑ 88StaMcR-6
❑ 88StaMcR-7
❑ 88StaMcR-8
❑ 88StaMcR-9
❑ 88StaMcR-10
❑ 88StaMcR-11
❑ 88Top-579
❑ 88Top-735
❑ 88TopBig-158
❑ 88TopSti-102
❑ 88TopTif-579
❑ 88TopTif-735
❑ 89Bow-388
❑ 89BowTif-388
❑ 89ClaLigB-24
❑ 89Don-99
❑ 89DonBasB-70
❑ 89DonGraS-4
❑ 89Fle-44
❑ 89FleBasM-29
❑ 89FleGlo-44
❑ 89FleHeroB-29
❑ 89MetColP-13
❑ 89MetFanC-22
❑ 89MetKah-18
❑ 89OPC-85
❑ 89PanSti-139
❑ 89Sco-93
❑ 89ScoHot1S-96
❑ 89Spo-97
❑ 89Top-7
❑ 89Top-85
❑ 89TopAme2C-20
❑ 89TopBig-116
❑ 89TopDouM-3
❑ 89TopGloS-26
❑ 89TopMinL-27
❑ 89TopSti-10
❑ 89TopSti-95
❑ 89TopStiB-51
❑ 89TopTif-7
❑ 89TopTif-85
❑ 89TopTif-291
❑ 89TopUKM-52
❑ 89TVSpoM-5
❑ 89UppDec-367
❑ 89Woo-15
❑ 90Bow-138
❑ 90BowTif-138
❑ 90ClaYel-T56
❑ 90Don-218
❑ 90DonBesN-129
❑ 90Fle-211
❑ 90FleBasA-26
❑ 90FleBasAC-26
❑ 90FleCan-211
❑ 90Lea-198
❑ 90MetColP-17
❑ 90MetKah-22
❑ 90MLBBasB-15
❑ 90OPC-545
❑ 90PanSti-305
❑ 90PubIntS-141
❑ 90PubIntS-268
❑ 90RedFolSB-62
❑ 90Sco-5
❑ 90Spo-127
❑ 90Top-545
❑ 90TopBig-194
❑ 90TopDou-46
❑ 90TopSti-94
❑ 90TopTif-545
❑ 90TopTVM-31
❑ 90UppDec-265
❑ 91Bow-479
❑ 91Cla3-T69
❑ 91ClaGam-31
❑ 91Don-191
❑ 91Fle-154
❑ 91Lea-151
❑ 91MetCol8-2
❑ 91MetColP-19
❑ 91MetKah-22
❑ 91MetPerPA-22
❑ 91MetTro-7
❑ 91MetWIZ-263
❑ 91OPC-105
❑ 91PanFreS-83
❑ 91Sco-327
❑ 91StaClu-35
❑ 91StaPinB-31
❑ 91Stu-209
❑ 91Top-105
❑ 91TopDesS-105
❑ 91TopMic-105
❑ 91TopTif-105
❑ 91Ult-224
❑ 91UppDec-105
❑ 92Bow-337
❑ 92ClaGam-170
❑ 92Don-288
❑ 92Fle-512
❑ 92FleUpd-29
❑ 92Hig5-75
❑ 92Lea-522
❑ 92LeaBlaG-522
❑ 92OPC-625
❑ 92OPCPre-54
❑ 92PanSti-228
❑ 92Pin-427
❑ 92RoyPol-20
❑ 92Sco-168
❑ 92ScoRoo-31T
❑ 92StaClu-619
❑ 92StaCluECN-619
❑ 92Stu-188
❑ 92Top-625
❑ 92TopGol-625
❑ 92TopGolW-625
❑ 92TopKid-15
❑ 92TopMic-625
❑ 92TopTra-71T
❑ 92TopTraG-71T
❑ 92Ult-374
❑ 92UppDec-362
❑ 92UppDec-742
❑ 93Bow-321
❑ 93ClaGam-64
❑ 93Don-233
❑ 93Fle-622
❑ 93Lea-80
❑ 93OPC-359
❑ 93PacSpa-491
❑ 93PanSti-107
❑ 93Pin-164
❑ 93RoyPol-20
❑ 93RoyStaC-15
❑ 93Sco-69
❑ 93Sel-176
❑ 93StaClu-348
❑ 93StaCluFDI-348
❑ 93StaCluMOP-348
❑ 93Stu-75
❑ 93Top-442
❑ 93TopGol-442
❑ 93TopInaM-442
❑ 93TopInaR-442
❑ 93TopMic-442
❑ 93TriPla-104
❑ 93Ult-214
❑ 93UppDec-592
❑ 93UppDecGold-592
❑ 94Bow-568
❑ 94ColC-549
❑ 94ColChoGS-549
❑ 94ColChoSS-549
❑ 94Don-565
❑ 94Fin-334
❑ 94FinRef-334
❑ 94Fle-168
❑ 94FleExtB-321
❑ 94FleUpd-158
❑ 94Lea-280
❑ 94MetColP-19
❑ 94MetShuST-6
❑ 94Pac-296
❑ 94PanSti-79
❑ 94Sco-487
❑ 94ScoGolR-487
❑ 94ScoRoo-RT30
❑ 94ScoRooGR-RT30
❑ 94Sel-293
❑ 94StaClu-566
❑ 94StaCluFDI-566
❑ 94StaCluGR-566
❑ 94StaCluMOP-566
❑ 94Stu-118
❑ 94Top-218
❑ 94TopGol-218
❑ 94TopSpa-218
❑ 94Ult-531
❑ 94UppDec-319
❑ 94UppDecED-319
❑ 95Fle-377
❑ 95Sco-105
❑ 95ScoGolR-105
❑ 95ScoPlaTS-105
❑ 96MetTeal-5

McRoberts, Brian
❑ 98St.PauSTI-16

McSherry, John
❑ 88T/MUmp-12
❑ 89T/MUmp-10
❑ 90T/MUmp-10

McSpadden, Gaylen
❑ 76HawIslC-12

McSparin, Paul
❑ 96AugGreB-18

McSparron, Greg
❑ 81CliGiaT-25

McTammy, James
❑ 87OldJudN-340

McVey, Cal
❑ 77BobParMBC-15

McVey, George
❑ 87OldJudN-341

McWane, Rick
❑ 87LitFalMP-2411
❑ 88LitFalMP-28
❑ 89VisOakCLC-122
❑ 89VisOakP-1431
❑ 90OrlSunRB-25
❑ 90OrlSunRS-27
❑ 95HarCitRCTI-29
❑ 97SalLakB-6
❑ 98SalLakBO-5

McWeeny, Douglas
❑ 23WilChoV-95
❑ 23Zee-137
❑ 26Exh-13
❑ 29PorandAR-63
❑ 30W554-10
❑ 90DodTar-513

McWhirter, Kevin
❑ 78OrlTwiT-14
❑ 80OrlTwiT-20
❑ 81PawRedST-4

McWhite, Raymond
❑ 94DanBraC-18
❑ 94DanBraF-3541
❑ 95DanBraTI-18

McWilliam, Tim
❑ 89RivRedWB-13
❑ 89RivRedWCLC-2
❑ 89RivRedWP-1401
❑ 90WicWraRD-16
❑ 91LinDriAA-614
❑ 91WicWraLD-614
❑ 91WicWraP-2612
❑ 91WicWraRD-22
❑ 92WicWraS-641
❑ 94SpoIndC-26
❑ 94SpoIndF-3340

McWilliams, Bill
❑ 33WorCig(-59

McWilliams, Jim
❑ 79AshTouT-13

McWilliams, Larry
❑ 78BraCok-9
❑ 79Top-504
❑ 80Top-309
❑ 81Fle-267
❑ 81RicBraT-14
❑ 81Top-44
❑ 82BraBurKL-17
❑ 82BraPol-27
❑ 82Don-527
❑ 82Top-733
❑ 83AllGamPl-170
❑ 83Don-45
❑ 83Fle-310
❑ 83Top-253
❑ 84Don-566
❑ 84Fle-256
❑ 84FleSti-58
❑ 84FleSti-80
❑ 84Nes792-668
❑ 84OPC-341
❑ 84Pir-12
❑ 84Top-668
❑ 84TopSti-133
❑ 84TopTif-668
❑ 85Don-78
❑ 85Fle-470
❑ 85Lea-247
❑ 85OPC-183
❑ 85Pir-12
❑ 85Top-183
❑ 85TopSti-132
❑ 85TopTif-183
❑ 86Don-264
❑ 86Fle-613
❑ 86Lea-136
❑ 86OPC-204
❑ 86Top-425
❑ 86TopTif-425
❑ 87Fle-613
❑ 87FleGlo-613
❑ 87OPC-14
❑ 87Top-564
❑ 87TopTif-564
❑ 88CarSmo-22
❑ 88CarTeal-21
❑ 88ScoRoo-23T
❑ 88ScoRooG-23T
❑ 88TopBig-261
❑ 88TopTra-70T
❑ 88TopTraT-70T
❑ 89Bow-397
❑ 89BowTif-397
❑ 89Don-516
❑ 89Fle-458
❑ 89FleGlo-458
❑ 89PhiTas-21
❑ 89Sco-259
❑ 89Top-259
❑ 89TopTif-259
❑ 89TopTra-80T
❑ 89TopTraT-80T
❑ 89UppDec-143
❑ 90Don-709
❑ 90PubIntS-247

McWilliams, Matt
❑ 95EugEmeTI-6

McWilliams, Ryan
❑ 92BatCliCB-20
❑ 92BatCliF-3261

Meacham, Bobby
❑ 83ColCliT-20
❑ 83YanPhoA-1
❑ 84Don-336
❑ 84Nes792-204
❑ 84Top-204
❑ 84TopTif-204
❑ 85Don-126
❑ 85Fle-134
❑ 85Lea-147
❑ 85OPC-16
❑ 85Top-16
❑ 85TopSti-315
❑ 85TopTif-16
❑ 85YanTCMP-28
❑ 86Don-638
❑ 86Fle-110
❑ 86OPC-379
❑ 86Top-379
❑ 86TopSti-304
❑ 86TopTif-379
❑ 86YanTCM-25
❑ 87ColCliP-19
❑ 87ColCliP-6
❑ 87ColCliT-16
❑ 87Fle-105
❑ 87FleGlo-105
❑ 87Top-62
❑ 87TopTif-62
❑ 88Don-616
❑ 88DonReaBY-616
❑ 88Fle-215
❑ 88FleGlo-215
❑ 88SanDieS-11
❑ 88SanDieS-12
❑ 88SanDieSAAG-11
❑ 88SanDieSAAG-12
❑ 88Sco-137
❑ 88ScoGlo-137
❑ 88StaLinY-9
❑ 88Top-659
❑ 88TopTif-659
❑ 89BufBisC-17
❑ 89BufBisP-1663
❑ 89SanDieSAG-10
❑ 89SanDieSAG-11
❑ 89Sco-509
❑ 89Top-436
❑ 89TopTif-436
❑ 89UppDec-77
❑ 90CMC-189
❑ 90OmaRoyC-14
❑ 90OmaRoyP-72
❑ 90ProAAAF-607
❑ 92YanWIZ8-118
❑ 93ColSprSSF-3103
❑ 94CarMudF-1594

Meacham, Buddy
❑ 87SalSpuS-18

Meacham, Rusty
❑ 88BriTigP-1868
❑ 89FayGenP-1575
❑ 90EasLeaAP-EL6
❑ 90LonTigP-1266
❑ 90ProAaA-17
❑ 91Bow-149
❑ 91DonRoo-53
❑ 91LinDriAAA-592
❑ 91TolMudHLD-592
❑ 91TolMudHP-1928
❑ 91UppDecFE-44F
❑ 92Bow-486
❑ 92Don-654
❑ 92DonRoo-76
❑ 92FleUpd-30
❑ 92Pin-600
❑ 92Sco-395
❑ 92Sco100RS-67
❑ 92StaClu-768
❑ 92TopDeb91-122
❑ 92TopTra-72T
❑ 92TopTraG-72T
❑ 92UppDec-453
❑ 93Don-439
❑ 93Fle-243
❑ 93Lea-14
❑ 93OPC-173
❑ 93Pin-149
❑ 93RoyPol-21
❑ 93RoyStaC-29
❑ 93Sco-378
❑ 93Sel-277
❑ 93StaClu-439
❑ 93StaCluFDI-439
❑ 93StaCluMOP-439
❑ 93Top-321
❑ 93TopGol-321
❑ 93TopInaM-321
❑ 93TopInaR-321
❑ 93TopMic-321
❑ 93Toy-76
❑ 93Ult-215
❑ 93UppDec-59
❑ 93UppDecGold-59
❑ 93USPlaCR-12S
❑ 94FleUpd-50
❑ 94OmaRoyF-1220
❑ 94StaClu-610
❑ 94StaCluFDI-610
❑ 94StaCluGR-610
❑ 94StaCluMOP-610
❑ 95Don-386
❑ 95DonPreP-386
❑ 95Fla-48
❑ 95Fle-169
❑ 95Sco-83
❑ 95ScoGolR-83
❑ 95ScoPlaTS-83
❑ 95Top-513
❑ 95TopCyb-301
❑ 96OmaRoyB-18
❑ 96RoyPol-17
❑ 98MemRedG-12

Mead, Timber
❑ 85EveGialC-10
❑ 86CliGiaP-12
❑ 87TamTarP-16
❑ 88ChaLooB-1
❑ 89ChaLooB-13
❑ 89ChaLooGS-24
❑ 90CMC-550
❑ 90PhoFirC-23
❑ 90PhoFirP-10
❑ 90ProAAAF-36
❑ 91CalLeLA-56

Meade, Paul
❑ 92ColRedC-12
❑ 92ColRedF-2399
❑ 93KinIndC-18
❑ 93KinIndF-2255
❑ 93KinIndTI-18
❑ 94CanIndF-3124
❑ 95BakBlaTI-28

Meador, Paul
❑ 91OklStaC-16
❑ 92OklStaC-20

Meadows, Brian
❑ 94SigRooDP-60
❑ 94SigRooDPS-60
❑ 94StaCluDP-37
❑ 94StaCluDPFDI-37
❑ 95Bow-158
❑ 95KanCouCLTI-10
❑ 95KanCouCTI-44
❑ 95MidLeaA-31
❑ 95Top-570
❑ 96BesAutS-59
❑ 96BesAutSA-44
❑ 96BreCouMB-19
❑ 97BesAutAS-32
❑ 97PorSeaD-18
❑ 98Bow-419
❑ 98BowChr-419
❑ 98BowChrGA-419
❑ 98BowChrGAR-419
❑ 98BowChrl-419
❑ 98BowChrIR-419
❑ 98BowChrR-419
❑ 98BowGolA-419

- 98BowInt-419
- 98Fle-544
- 98LeaRS-293
- 98LeaRSLHolo-293
- 98LeaRSLong-293
- 98LeaRTrue-293
- 98PacOmeRS-5
- 98PacOmeRST5-5
- 98PacOnl-301
- 98PacOnlR-301
- 98PacOnlWC-301
- 98PorSeaD5AQ-25
- 98UppDec-597
- 99Fle-536
- 99FleSta9-536
- 99FleWarT-536
- 99MetUni-46
- 99MetUniGM-46
- 99MetUniPMG-46
- 99Pac-182
- 99PacPlaB-182
- 99PacRed-182
- 99StaClu-47
- 99StaClu-309
- 99StaCluFDI-47
- 99StaCluFDI-309
- 99StaCluOoaK-47
- 99StaCluOoaK-309
- 99StaCluPP-47
- 99StaCluPP-309
- 99Top-129
- 99TopChr-129
- 99TopChrR-129
- 99TopMVPP-129
- 99Ult-68
- 99UltGolM-68
- 99UltMas-68
- 99UltPlaM-68
- 99UppDec-105
- 99UppDecEL1-105
- 99UppDecEL2-105

Meadows, Chuck
- 83AleDukT-3

Meadows, Henry
- 22E120-202

Meadows, Jeff
- 82AubAstT-7

Meadows, Jim
- 86DayBealP-18
- 86FloStaLAP-35

Meadows, Lee
- 17ColE13-115
- 20NatCarE-62
- 21Exh-107
- 21OxfConE-11
- 22W572-62
- 22W573-79
- 23W503-49
- 23W515-23
- 27AmeCarE126-4
- 88ConSer3-19
- 93ConTSN-697

Meadows, Louie
- 83DayBeaAT-26
- 86TucTorP-13
- 87TucTorP-9
- 88FleUpd-92
- 88FleUpdG-92
- 88TucTorC-20
- 88TucTorP-177
- 89AstSmo-25
- 89Fle-361
- 89FleGlo-361
- 89Top-643
- 89TopTif-643
- 89TucTorC-14
- 89TucTorJP-15
- 89TucTorP-191
- 89UppDec-401
- 90CMC-614
- 90OPC-534
- 90ProAAAF-205
- 90Top-534
- 90TopTif-534
- 90TucTorC-12
- 90TucTorP-215
- 90UppDec-160
- 91LinDriAAA-490
- 91ScrRedBLD-490
- 91ScrRedBP-2552
- 91Top-603A

Meadows, Scott
- 89FreKeyS-15
- 89WatDiaP-1773
- 89WatDiaS-20
- 90Bes-294
- 90CMC-735
- 90EasLeaAP-EL9
- 90HagSunB-13
- 90HagSunP-1428
- 90HagSunS-15
- 90ProAaA-25
- 90StaFS7-75
- 91HagSunLD-239
- 91HagSunP-2468
- 91LinDriAA-239
- 92RocRedWF-1951
- 92RocRedWS-459
- 92SkyAAAF-209

Meads, Dave
- 86AshTouP-19
- 87AstMot-17
- 87AstPol-9
- 87DonRoo-46
- 87FleUpd-79
- 87FleUpdG-79
- 87TopTra-77T
- 87TopTraT-77T
- 88BlaYNPRWL-121
- 88Don-455
- 88Fle-453
- 88FleGlo-453
- 88RedFolSB-57
- 88Sco-243
- 88ScoGlo-243
- 88Top-199
- 88TopTif-199
- 88TucTorC-4
- 88TucTorJP-16
- 88TucTorP-183
- 89AstMot-26
- 89AstSmo-26
- 89Don-424
- 89Fle-362
- 89FleGlo-362
- 89Sco-593
- 89Top-589
- 89TopTif-589
- 89TucTorC-5
- 89TucTorJP-16
- 89TucTorP-180

Meady, Todd
- 97LanLugTS-13

Meagher, Adrian
- 86AlbDukP-16
- 88ElPasDB-24
- 91DaiDolF-15
- 93AusFut-41
- 95AusFut-29
- 95AusFut-94
- 95AusFutSFP-SFFP4

Meagher, Brad
- 77BurBeeT-15

Meagher, Tom
- 85SpoIndC-14
- 86ChaRaiP-17
- 88SanJosGCLC-134
- 88SanJosGP-120

Mealing, Allen
- 94HelBreF-3625
- 94HelBreSP-17
- 95HelBreTI-9
- 96BelSnaTI-23

Mealy, Tony
- 87MacPirP-5
- 88GreHorP-1563
- 89CedRapRB-21
- 89CedRapRP-926
- 89CedRapRS-12

Meamber, Tim
- 87EriCarP-14
- 88SavCarP-344
- 89SprCarB-22
- 90St.PetCS-16

Mean, Rick
- 79CedRapGT-19

Mear, Richard
- 96JohCitCTI-23

Meares, Pat
- 89AlaGol-8
- 90WicStaSGD-24
- 91VisOakC-17
- 91VisOakP-1749
- 92ClaFS7-201
- 92OrlSunRF-2855
- 92OrlSunRS-513
- 92SkyAA F-221
- 93Bow-45
- 93FleFinE-239
- 93Lea-451
- 93PorBeaF-2389
- 93SelRoo-67T
- 93TopTra-98T
- 94Bow-432
- 94ColC-202
- 94ColChoGS-202
- 94ColChoSS-202
- 94Don-392
- 94Fin-119
- 94FinRef-119
- 94Fla-316
- 94Fle-214
- 94FleExtB-122
- 94Lea-157
- 94Pac-362
- 94PanSti-94
- 94Pin-304
- 94PinArtP-304
- 94PinMusC-304
- 94Sco-238
- 94ScoBoyoS-4
- 94ScoGolR-238
- 94Sel-122
- 94StaClu-210
- 94StaClu-624
- 94StaCluFDI-210
- 94StaCluFDI-624
- 94StaCluGR-210
- 94StaCluGR-624
- 94StaCluMOP-210
- 94StaCluMOP-624
- 94Stu-199
- 94Top-223
- 94TopGol-223
- 94TopSpa-223
- 94TriPla-257
- 94Ult-90
- 94UppDec-501
- 94UppDecED-501
- 95ColCho-487
- 95ColChoGS-487
- 95ColChoSS-487
- 95Don-185
- 95DonPreP-185
- 95DonTopotO-111
- 95Fla-60
- 95Fle-210
- 95Lea-333
- 95Pac-253
- 95Sco-100
- 95ScoGolR-100
- 95ScoPlaTS-100
- 95StaClu-352
- 95StaCluMOP-352
- 95StaCluSTWS-352
- 95Top-432
- 95TopCyb-229
- 95Ult-75
- 95UltGolM-75
- 96ColCho-204
- 96ColChoGS-204
- 96ColChoSS-204
- 96Don-302
- 96DonPreP-302
- 96EmoXL-83
- 96Fla-118
- 96Fle-168
- 96FleTif-168
- 96LeaSigA-152
- 96LeaSigAG-152
- 96LeaSigAS-152
- 96MetUni-77
- 96MetUniP-77
- 96Pac-360
- 96PanSti-202
- 96Sco-135
- 96StaClu-111
- 96StaCluMOP-111
- 96Top-285
- 96Ult-90
- 96UltGolM-90
- 96UppDec-127
- 97ColCho-157
- 97Fle-149
- 97FleTif-149
- 97MetUni-211
- 97Pac-141
- 97PacLigB-141
- 97PacSil-141
- 97StaClu-116
- 97StaCluMOP-116
- 97Top-281
- 97Ult-89
- 97UltGolME-89
- 97UltPlaME-89
- 97UppDec-412
- 98ColCho-411
- 98CroRoy-78
- 98Fin-43
- 98FinNo--43
- 98FinNo-R-43
- 98FinRef-43
- 98Fle-545
- 98Pac-137
- 98PacOme-141
- 98PacOmeR-141
- 98PacOnl-424
- 98PacOnlR-424
- 98PacOnlWC-424
- 98PacPar-62
- 98PacParC-62
- 98PacParG-62
- 98PacParHS-62
- 98PacParPB-62
- 98PacParR-62
- 98PacPlaB-137
- 98PacRedT-137
- 98PacSil-137
- 98Revo-83
- 98RevoSS-83
- 98StaCluFDI-146
- 98StaCluI-146
- 98StaCluOneK-146
- 98StaCluPP-146
- 98Top-49
- 98TopChr-49
- 98TopChrR-49
- 98TopDevR-49
- 98TopDia-49
- 98TopMiniC-49
- 98Ult-17
- 98UltGolM-17
- 98UltMas-17
- 98UltPlaM-17
- 98UppDec-413
- 99Fle-421
- 99FleSta9-421
- 99FleWarT-421
- 99Pac-249
- 99PacPlaB-249
- 99PacRed-249
- 99Rev-112
- 99RevPremDate-112
- 99RevRet-112
- 99RevShaSS-112
- 99Top-148
- 99TopChr-148
- 99TopChrR-148
- 99TopMVPP-148
- 99Ult-67
- 99UltGolM-67
- 99UltMas-67
- 99UltPlaM-67
- 99UppDec-135
- 99UppDec-459
- 99UppDecEL1-135
- 99UppDecEL1-459
- 99UppDecEL2-135
- 99UppDecEL2-459
- 99UppDecM-166
- 99UppDecMGS-166
- 99UppDecMHFS-166
- 99UppDecMSS-166
- 99Vic-309

Mears, Chris
- 97EveAquG-18
- 98EveAquG-17

Mears, Ronnie
- 78WisRapTT-12

Mecerod, George
- 80ElmPioRST-16

Meche, Carl
- 75QuaCitAT-15

Meche, Gil
- 96BesAutS1RP-FR9
- 96EveAquB-30
- 97Bes-100
- 97BesLimA-24
- 97EveAquG-19
- 97Top-271
- 98Bes-77
- 98BesAutPOY-10
- 98BesFulCA-11
- 98BesPreA-25
- 98Bow-80
- 98BowChr-80
- 98BowChrGA-80
- 98BowChrGAR-80
- 98BowChrI-80
- 98BowChrIR-80
- 98BowChrR-80
- 98BowGolA-80
- 98BowInt-80
- 98MidLeaPM-28
- 98Top-256
- 98TopChr-256
- 98TopChrR-256
- 98TopDevR-256
- 98TopDia-256
- 98TopMiniC-256
- 98WisTimRM-30
- 99Bow-193
- 99BowAut-BA13
- 99BowChr-193
- 99BowChrG-193
- 99BowChrGR-193
- 99BowChrI-193
- 99BowChrIR-193
- 99BowChrR-193
- 99BowGol-193
- 99BowInt-193
- 99JustheS-33
- 99JustheSJB-33
- 99JustheSJP-8
- 99PacOme-216
- 99PacOmeC-216
- 99PacOmeG-216
- 99PacOmePB-216

Mecir, Jim
- 92SanBerC-11
- 92SanBerSF-950
- 92StaCluD-118
- 93RivPilCLC-12
- 94JacSunF-1409
- 95TacRaiTI-12
- 96ColCliB-20
- 97ColCliB-18
- 97ColCliD-14
- 98DevRayP-7
- 98PacOnl-716
- 98PacOnlR-716
- 98PacOnlWC-716
- 99Fle-473
- 99FleSta9-473
- 99FleWarT-473

Meckes, Tim
- 83ColAstT-16
- 84TulDriTI-24

Mecrina, Eric
- 91SalLakTSP-13

Meddaugh, Dean
- 89BurIndS-17

Medeiros, Jody
- 91HawWomS-8

Mediavilla, Rick
- 91HamRedC-26
- 91HamRedP-4054
- 92ClaFS7-365
- 92SavCarF-675
- 94SavCarC-20
- 94SavCarF-521

Medich, Doc (George)
- 73OPC-608
- 73SyrChiTI-17
- 73Top-608
- 74OPC-445
- 74SyrChiTI-16
- 74Top-445
- 74TopSta-213
- 75Hos-78
- 75OPC-426
- 75SSP42-25
- 75SyrChiTI-12
- 75Top-426
- 75TopMin-426
- 75YanSSP-15
- 76BlaDis-35
- 76BucDis-35
- 76CarDis-35
- 76CraDis-35
- 76DailsID-35
- 76IsaDis-35
- 76OPC-146
- 76OrbDis-35
- 76PirPos-10
- 76RedBarD-35
- 76SafDis-35
- 76SSP-430
- 76Top-146
- 76TopTra-146T
- 76TowCluD-35
- 77OPC-222
- 77Top-294
- 78Hos-86
- 78RanBurK-7
- 78SSP270-102
- 78Top-583
- 79OPC-347
- 79Top-657
- 80Top-336
- 81Don-386
- 81Fle-627
- 81Top-702
- 82Don-142
- 82Fle-324
- 82Top-36
- 82Top-78
- 83Fle-39
- 89SweBasG-18
- 91MetWIZ-264
- 92BreCarT-14
- 92YanWIZ7-112
- 93RanKee-259
- 94BreMilB-247

Medina, Alger
- 95RocCubTI-22

Medina, Amilcar
- 95LinVen-220

Medina, Facanel
- 89MarPhiS-20
- 90MarPhiP-3180
- 91BatCliCB-14
- 91BatCliP-3497

Medina, Julio
- 90IBAWorA-8

Medina, Luis
- 86WatIndP-18
- 87WilBilP-24
- 88ColSprSSC-21
- 88ColSprSSP-1543
- 88TriAAAP-8
- 88TriAAC-38
- 89ClaLigB-67
- 89Don-36
- 89DonRoo-20
- 89Fle-411
- 89FleGlo-411
- 89IndTeal-19
- 89PanSti-315
- 89Sco-633
- 89ScoHot1R-5
- 89ScoYouS2-26
- 89Top-528
- 89TopTif-528
- 89UppDec-2
- 90ClaBlu-103
- 90CMC-468
- 90ColSprSSC-16
- 90ColSprSSP-44
- 90Hot50RS-31
- 90ProAAAF-225
- 90PubIntS-564
- 91ColSprSSLD-92
- 91ColSprSSP-2193
- 91LinDriAAA-92
- 91TriA AAGP-AAA6
- 92OmaRoyF-2969
- 92OmaRoyS-337
- 92SkyAAAF-157
- 97ColSprSATTI-28
- 98WilCubM-18

Medina, Patrico
- 90MarPhiP-3186

Medina, Pedro
- 82OneYanT-17
- 83GreHorT-20
- 84GreHorT-23

Medina, Rafael
- 94OneYanC-13
- 94OneYanF-3787
- 95GreBatTI-17
- 96BowBes-179
- 96BowBesAR-179
- 96BowBesR-179
- 96DouAllB-23
- 96NorNavB-17
- 97Bes-42
- 97Bow-133
- 97BowCerBlaIA-CA52
- 97BowCerBluIA-CA52
- 97BowCerGolIA-CA52
- 97BowInt-133
- 97DonSigA-71
- 97DonSigAC-87
- 97DonSigAM-87
- 97RanCucQUG-6
- 97Sel-119
- 97SelArtP-119
- 97SelCom-119
- 97SelRegG-119
- 98Bow-390
- 98BowCerBlueAU-36
- 98BowCerGA-36
- 98BowCerSA-36
- 98BowChr-390
- 98BowChrGA-390

- 98BowChrGAR-390
- 98BowChrI-390
- 98BowChrIR-390
- 98BowChrR-390
- 98BowGolA-390
- 98BowInt-390
- 98Don-295
- 98DonGolPP-295
- 98DonSigA-60
- 98DonSigAC-78
- 98DonSigAM-79
- 98DonSilPP-295
- 98Fle-428
- 98LeaRS-232
- 98LeaRSLHolo-232
- 98LeaRSLong-232
- 98LeaRTrue-232
- 98PacOnl-302
- 98PacOnlR-302
- 98PacOnlWC-302
- 98ScoRT-235
- 98ScoRTSS-PP128
- 98ScoRTSSAP-PP128
- 98ScoRTSSAP1-PP128
- 98Stu-150
- 98StuGPP-150
- 98StuSPP-150
- 98UppDec-584
- 99Fle-475
- 99FleSta9-475
- 99FleWarT-475
- 99UppDecBD-102
- 99UppDecBDD-102
- 99UppDecBDQ-102
- 99UppDecBDT-102
- 99Vic-165

Medina, Ricardo
- 89WytCubS-22
- 90GenCubP-3031
- 90GenCubS-17
- 91GenCubC-12
- 91GenCubP-4225
- 92MidLeaATI-29
- 92PeoChiC-12
- 92PeoChiTI-14
- 93ClaGolF-121
- 93PeoChiC-13
- 93PeoChiF-1091
- 93PeoChiTI-16

Medina, Robert
- 96MedHatBJTI-19
- 97St.CatSB-22

Medina, Tomas
- 97AubDouTI-3
- 98LanLugQ-9

Medina, Val
- 82DayBeaAT-22

Medina, Victor
- 89BluOriS-16

Medlinger, Irving
- 50WorWidGV-33
- 52Par-11

Medosch, Keith
- 97BoiHawG-20
- 98CedRapKTI-19

Medrano, Anthony
- 94ClaGolF-70
- 95WilBluRTI-4
- 96Exc-63
- 96TexLeaAB-32
- 96WicWraB-9
- 97TexLeaTP-28
- 97WicWra-16
- 98WicWraM-11

Medrano, Ricardo
- 98BriWhiSQ-19

Medrano, Ryan
- 98ChaAllCM-20

Medrano, Steve
- 97LanLugTS-14
- 98LanLugQ-19

Medrano, Theodoro
- 96WisTimRB-16

Medrick, John
- 91EugEmeC-18
- 91EugEmeP-3725

Medvin, Scott
- 86ShrCapP-18
- 87ShrCapP-7
- 88BufBisC-10
- 88BufBisP-1484
- 89Bow-412
- 89BowTif-412
- 89BufBisC-6
- 89BufBisP-1680
- 89Don-597
- 89PanSti-160
- 89ScoHot1R-38
- 89Top-756
- 89TopTif-756
- 90BufBisC-6
- 90BufBisP-369
- 90CMC-6
- 90ProAAAF-484

Medwick, Ducky (Joe)
- 33WorCig-69
- 34BatR31-145
- 34DiaMatCSB-130
- 34DiaStaR-66
- 35AlDemDCR3-128
- 35DiaMatCS3T1-105
- 35GolMedFR-10
- 35WheBB1-21
- 36DiaMatCS4-10
- 36ExhFou-8
- 36GouWidPPR-A72
- 36NatChiFPR-55
- 36SandSW-41
- 36WheBB4-7
- 36WheBB5-5
- 36WorWidGV-75
- 37DixLid-5
- 37DixPre-5
- 37ExhFou-8
- 37GouThuMR-11
- 37KelPepS-BB10
- 37WheBB6-12
- 37WheBB8-8
- 38BasTabP-22
- 38CloFotW-59
- 38ExhFou-8
- 38GouFliMR-11A
- 38GouFliMR-11B
- 38GouHeaU-262
- 38GouHeaU-286
- 38OurNatGPP-20
- 38WheBB10-3
- 38WheBB11-7
- 38WheBB15-9
- 39ExhSal-43
- 39WheBB12-6
- 40DodTeal-16
- 40WheM4-5
- 41DouPlaR-21
- 42DodTeal-14
- 43DodTeal-16
- 43MPR302-1-16
- 51R42SmaS-69
- 60Fle-22
- 61Fle-61
- 66CarCoi-10
- 72TCMthe3-50
- 73Dod194T-18
- 73SevTraC-48
- 74Car193T-18
- 74Car193T-30
- 74LauAllG-37
- 74TCMNic-4
- 75TCMAllG-25
- 76RowExh-11
- 76ShaPiz-108
- 77GalGloG-63
- 78DexHaloFP-38
- 78DodTCM4-27
- 78DodTCM4-38
- 80LauFamF-19
- 80PerHaloFP-110
- 80SSPHOF-110
- 81ConTSN-84
- 82TCMGreH-45
- 83CarGreT-5
- 83ConMar-39
- 83TCMPla1943-44
- 85BigLeaC3-32
- 86SpoDecG-15
- 87Car193T-7
- 88ConNatA-15
- 89DodSmoG-22
- 89PacLegI-160
- 90DodTar-514
- 91ConTSN-18
- 92CarMcD-9
- 92ConTSN-629
- 93ActPacA-108
- 93ActPacA2-42G
- 94ConTSN-1094
- 94ConTSNB-1094

Mee, Jimmy
- 88GreHorP-1571

Mee, Tommy
- 64TopRooAB-26
- 78GreBraT-16

Meegan, Pete
- 87OldJudN-342
- 88SFHesCreN32-18

Meek, Darryl
- 92JohCitCC-19
- 92JohCitCF-3115
- 93BelBreCB-15
- 93BelBreFI-1707

Meek, Herman
- 14Zee-16
- 15Zee-15

Meek, Rich
- 89EriOriS-12

Meek, Stan
- 88OklSoo-5
- 89OklSoo-2
- 90OklSoo-24

Meeker, Charles
- 26Zee-97

Meekin, Jouett
- 95NewN566-182

Meeks, Tim
- 85AlbDukCr-169
- 86AlbDukP-17
- 87AlbDukD-14
- 88TacTigC-5
- 88TacTigP-633
- 89BlaYNPRWL-95
- 90PalSprACLC-227
- 91BufBisLD-34
- 91BufBisP-537
- 91LinDriAAA-34

Megabyte, Mascot
- 96HonShaHWB-NNO

Meggers, Mike
- 92BilMusF-3369
- 92BilMusSP-8
- 93WesVirWC-19
- 93WesVirWF-2878
- 94WinSpiC-17
- 94WinSpiF-284
- 96ChaLooB-21

Mehl, Steve
- 87ChaWheP-9
- 88UtiBluSP-8
- 89SouBenWSGS-18

Mehrtens, Pat
- 88TamTarS-16
- 88UtiBluSP-21
- 89UtiBluSP-15

Meier, Brad
- 86RedWinA-25

Meier, Brian
- 80BatTroT-14
- 80WatIndT-15

Meier, Dave
- 82OrlTwiT-9
- 83TolMudHT-22
- 84MinTwiP-21
- 84TwiTeal-4
- 85Don-147
- 85Fle-285
- 85Top-356
- 85TopTif-356
- 85TwiPos-18
- 85TwiTeal-4
- 85TwiTeal-16
- 86Fle-400
- 87OklCit8P-6
- 88IowCubC-20
- 88IowCubP-536
- 93RanKee-260

Meier, Jeff
- 89SumBraP-1118

Meier, Kevin
- 87PocGiaTB-6
- 88SanJosGCLC-135
- 88SanJosGP-132
- 89CalLeaA-40
- 89SanJosGB-18
- 89SanJosGCLC-215
- 89SanJosGP-447
- 89SanJosGS-20
- 90ShrCapP-1441
- 90ShrCapS-15
- 91LinDriAA-313
- 91ShrCapLD-313
- 91ShrCapP-1818
- 92ArkTraF-1126
- 92ArkTraS-38
- 92ClaFS7-440
- 93ExcFS7-103
- 93LouRedF-210
- 94ColSprSSF-730
- 95OrlCubF-6

Meier, Pat
- 94PriRedC-17
- 94PriRedF-3260

Meier, Randy
- 81ChaRoyT-20
- 82WauTimF-8
- 83WauTimF-15

Meier, Scott
- 81AppFoxT-19
- 82AppFoxFr-9
- 83GleFalWST-5

Meikle, Williard
- 09ObaT21-326
- 11Zee-91
- 12ObaPreT-75
- 12Zee-120

Meilan, Tony
- 94GreFalDSP-17

Meine, Heinie
- 30SchR33-50
- 33Gou-205

Meiners, Doug
- 93St.CatBJC-13
- 93St.CatBJF-3971
- 94HagSunC-14
- 94HagSunF-2726
- 96DunBluJUTI-8
- 97KnoSmo-16
- 98KnoSG-14

Meinershagen, Adam
- 92St.CatBJC-5
- 92St.CatBJF-3386
- 93St.CatBJC-14
- 93St.CatBJF-3972
- 94Bow-29
- 94Cla-69
- 94DunBluJC-19
- 94DunBluJF-2555
- 95AusFut-43
- 98BriBluM-19

Meischner, Otto
- 64TulOil-5

Meissner, Scooter
- 90BelBreB-22
- 90BelBreS-27
- 92HelBreSP-25
- 93StoPorC-30

Meister, Ralph
- 88SumBraP-418

Meizosa, Gus
- 87GasRanP-12
- 88BlaYNPRWL-43
- 88St.LucMS-16
- 89BlaYNPRWL-44
- 89JacMetGS-9

Mejia, Alfredo
- 79LodDodT-4

Mejia, Carlos
- 94UtiBluSC-19
- 94UtiBluSF-3817

Mejia, Cesar
- 88EasLeaAP-10
- 88GleFalTP-924
- 89RocRedWC-4
- 89RocRedWP-1635
- 90CMC-358
- 90ProAAAF-271
- 90TidTidC-7
- 90TidTidP-540
- 90TopTVM-51

Mejia, Delfino
- 91ModA'sC-12
- 92RenSilSCLC-47

Mejia, Diaz (Roberto)
- 91GreFalDSP-7
- 92ClaFS7-355
- 92UppDecML-209
- 92VerBeaDC-3
- 92VerBeaDF-2885
- 93Bow-692
- 93ClaFS7-13
- 93ColSprSSF-3096
- 93LeaGolR-U5
- 93LeaGolRJ-U5
- 93RocStaC-8
- 93SelRoo-87T
- 93SP-223
- 93StaClu-406
- 93StaCluFDI-406
- 93StaCluMOP-406
- 94Bow-638
- 94ColC-203
- 94ColChoGS-203
- 94ColChoSS-203
- 94Don-250
- 94Fin-153
- 94FinRef-153
- 94Fla-155
- 94Fle-446
- 94FleExtB-249
- 94FUnPac-171
- 94Lea-63
- 94OPC-190
- 94OPCDiaD-2
- 94Pac-201
- 94PanSti-177
- 94Pin-181
- 94PinArtP-181
- 94PinMusC-181
- 94RocPol-17
- 94Sco-615
- 94ScoBoyoS-23
- 94ScoGolR-615
- 94Sel-75
- 94StaClu-21
- 94StaCluFDI-21
- 94StaCluGR-21
- 94StaCluMOP-21
- 94StaCluT-93
- 94StaCluTFDI-93
- 94Stu-180
- 94Top-258
- 94TopGol-258
- 94TopSpa-258
- 94TriPla-228
- 94Ult-186
- 94UppDec-105
- 94UppDecED-105
- 95ActPacF-27
- 95ColCho-439
- 95ColChoGS-439
- 95ColChoSS-439
- 95Don-383
- 95DonPreP-383
- 95FleUpd-168
- 95Lea-5
- 95Pac-141
- 95Pin-311
- 95PinArtP-311
- 95PinMusC-311
- 95Sco-521
- 95ScoGolR-521
- 95ScoPlaTS-521
- 95Top-169
- 95UppDec-412
- 95UppDecED-412
- 95UppDecEDG-412
- 95UppDecSE-104
- 95UppDecSEG-104
- 98MemRedG-13

Mejia, Javier
- 96MarPhiB-13
- 97ClePhi-12
- 98ClePhiM-16
- 98ClePhiUM-16

Mejia, Juan
- 96MarPhiB-14
- 97ClePhi-13
- 98PieBolWM-23

Mejia, Leandro
- 90MadMusB-13
- 90MadMusP-2266
- 91MadMusC-11
- 91MadMusP-2128

Mejia, Marlon
- 96AubDouB-8

Mejia, Max
- 98VerBeaDM-28

Mejia, Miguel
- 94AlbPolC-17
- 94AlbPolF-2251
- 94BluOriC-14
- 94BluOriF-3576
- 94OriPro-64
- 96BowBes-110
- 96BowBesAR-110
- 96BowBesR-110
- 96FleUpd-U192
- 96FleUpdNH-17
- 96FleUpdTC-U192
- 96Ult-552
- 96UltGolM-552
- 97CarLeaTP-11
- 97NewJerCB-20
- 97NewJerCB-5
- 97PacPriGotD-GD201
- 97PriWilC-23
- 98FreKeyM-30

Mejia, Oscar
- 82TulDriT-16
- 84TulDriTI-7
- 85TulDriTI-7
- 86WatIndP-16
- 87WilBilP-4

Mejia, Secar
- 87MyrBeaBJP-1448

Mejias, Fernando
- 91MarPhiC-21
- 91MarPhiP-3450
- 92MarPhiC-27
- 92MarPhiF-3052
- 93MarPhiC-19
- 93MarPhiF-3470
- 95LinVen-125
- 95LinVen-285
- 96-97LinVen-85

Mejias, Marcos
- 75BurBeeT-16

Mejias, Roman
- 57Top-362
- 58PirTeal-7
- 58Top-452
- 59Top-218
- 60Top-2
- 60TopVen-2
- 62Col.45B-14
- 62Col45'HC-11
- 62Col45'JP-9
- 62Top-354
- 63Jel-186
- 63Pos-186
- 63Top-432
- 64Top-186
- 64TopVen-186
- 77PirTCM1WC-33
- 81RedSoxBG2S-94

Mejias, Sam
- 77ExpPos-22
- 77Top-479
- 78OPC-99
- 78Top-576
- 79OPC-42
- 79Top-97
- 80RedEnq-28
- 81Fle-219
- 81Top-521
- 82Don-295
- 82Fle-75
- 82Top-228
- 91PriRedC-28
- 91PriRedP-3531
- 93MarMot-28
- 94MarMot-28
- 95MarMot-28
- 96MarMot-28

Mejias, Simeon
- 87GenCubP-20
- 87PeoChiP-21

Mejias, Stan
- 76TulOilGP-8

Mejias, Teodulo
- 91CliGiaC-19
- 91CliGiaP-838
- 94VenLinU-252

Melchior, Henry
- 09ObaT21-55
- 09ObaT21-162
- 09ObaT21-327
- 10BisCoaLE99-19
- 11Zee-92
- 12ObaPreT-76

Melconian, Alex
- 98KanCouC-22
- 98KanCouCCP-22

Mele, Dutch (Albert)
- 47Exh-158
- 50WorWidGV-48

Mele, Sam (Sabath)
- 47Exh-159
- 47RedSoxTI-14
- 48RedSoxTI-17
- 49Bow-118
- 49RedSoxTI-15
- 50Bow-52
- 51Bow-168
- 51TopBluB-25
- 52Bow-15
- 52StaCalL-73H
- 52Top-94
- 54Bow-22
- 54OriEss-25
- 54RedMan-AL6A
- 54RedMan-AL6B
- 54Top-240
- 55Bow-147
- 60Top-470
- 61TwiJayP-9
- 61TwiPetM-16
- 62Top-482

❑ 63Top-531
❑ 63TwiJayP-7
❑ 63TwiVol-11
❑ 64Top-54
❑ 64TopVen-54
❑ 65Top-506
❑ 65TwiPos-6
❑ 66OPC-3
❑ 66Top-3
❑ 66TopVen-3
❑ 67Top-418
❑ 76TayBow4-64
❑ 78TwiFri-12
❑ 80ElmPioRST-37
❑ 81TCM60I-354
❑ 83TopRep5-94
❑ 86TwiGreT-12
❑ 91OriCro-294
❑ 94TopArc1-240
❑ 94TopArc1G-240
❑ 97BalOriP-33

Melendez, Angel
❑ 98SanJosGQ-12

Melendez, Dan
❑ 91TopTra-80T
❑ 91TopTraT-80T
❑ 92ClaDraP-41
❑ 92FroRowDP-1
❑ 92FroRowDPG-1
❑ 92FroRowDPS-1
❑ 92StaCluD-119
❑ 92TopDaiQTU-22
❑ 93Bow-562
❑ 93ClaFS7-142
❑ 93SanAntMF-3013
❑ 95SanAntMTI-46
❑ 96SanAntMB-15
❑ 97SanAntMB-19
❑ 98AlbDukG-18
❑ 98SanAntMM-19

Melendez, David
❑ 96FayGenB-23
❑ 98BesAutSS-35
❑ 98JacSunM-17

Melendez, Diego
❑ 77CocAstT-12
❑ 78DayBeaAT-18
❑ 80AppFoxT-3

Melendez, Esteban
❑ 94DayCubC-29

Melendez, Francisco
❑ 83ReaPhiT-15
❑ 84PorBeaC-199
❑ 85PhiTas-44
❑ 85PorBeaC-43
❑ 86PhiTas-NNO
❑ 86PorBeaP-16
❑ 87PhoFirP-25
❑ 88BlaYNPRWL-9
❑ 88PhoFirP-64
❑ 88TriAAC-32
❑ 89BlaYNPRWL-178
❑ 89Don-611
❑ 89OriFreB-43
❑ 89RocRedWC-3
❑ 89RocRedWP-1654
❑ 90CanIndB-16
❑ 90CanIndP-1300
❑ 90CanIndS-12
❑ 91OriCro-295

Melendez, Jorge
❑ 92GulCoaRSP-18
❑ 93EriSaiC-15
❑ 93EriSaiF-3120
❑ 95LinVen-238

Melendez, Jose
❑ 85PriWilPT-4
❑ 86PriWilPP-16
❑ 87HarSenP-5
❑ 88BlaYNPRWL-44
❑ 88HarSenP-848
❑ 89BlaYNPRWL-45
❑ 89WilBilP-633
❑ 89WilBilS-14
❑ 90CalCanC-22
❑ 90CalCanP-648
❑ 90CMC-449
❑ 90ProAAAF-113
❑ 91DonRoo-23
❑ 91LasVegSLD-288
❑ 91LasVegSP-232
❑ 91LinDriAAA-288
❑ 91PadSmo-23
❑ 91TopDeb90-106
❑ 92Don-572
❑ 92Fle-615
❑ 92Lea-507
❑ 92LeaBlaG-507
❑ 92OPC-518
❑ 92OPCPre-139
❑ 92PadCarJ-14
❑ 92PadMot-14
❑ 92PadPolD-29
❑ 92PadSmo-20
❑ 92Pin-536
❑ 92ProFS7-332
❑ 92Sco-397
❑ 92Sco100RS-19
❑ 92StaClu-342
❑ 92Top-518
❑ 92TopGol-518
❑ 92TopGolW-518
❑ 92TopMic-518
❑ 92Ult-578
❑ 92UppDec-566
❑ 93Don-626
❑ 93Fle-144
❑ 93FleFinE-175
❑ 93Lea-371
❑ 93PacSpa-361
❑ 93PawRedSDD-17
❑ 93PawRedSF-2406
❑ 93RedSoxP-21
❑ 93StaClu-87
❑ 93StaCluFDI-87
❑ 93StaCluMOP-87
❑ 93Top-58
❑ 93TopGol-58
❑ 93TopInaM-58
❑ 93TopInaR-58
❑ 93TopMic-58
❑ 93UppDec-288
❑ 93UppDecGold-288
❑ 94Pac-59
❑ 94PawRedSDD-12
❑ 94PawRedSF-945
❑ 95OmaRoyTI-20
❑ 95Pac-40

Melendez, Luis A.
❑ 71CarTeal-18
❑ 71CarTeal-27
❑ 71OPC-216
❑ 71Top-216
❑ 72Top-606
❑ 73CedRapAT-17
❑ 73OPC-47
❑ 73Top-47
❑ 74OPC-307
❑ 74Top-307
❑ 75OPC-353
❑ 75St.LouCP-19
❑ 75Top-353
❑ 75TopMin-353
❑ 76OPC-399
❑ 76SSP-282
❑ 76St.LouCP-22
❑ 76Top-399
❑ 77PadSchC-39
❑ 78SyrChiT-14
❑ 87FayGenP-22
❑ 88FayGenP-1083
❑ 88HamRedP-1733
❑ 89BlaYNPRWL-133
❑ 90HamRedB-27
❑ 90HamRedS-26
❑ 94SavCarC-29
❑ 94SavCarF-523
❑ 94SouAtlLAF-SAL52
❑ 95LinVen-304
❑ 95NewJerCTI-19
❑ 97ArkTraB-28
❑ 98ArkTraM-28

Melendez, Steve
❑ 86GenCubP-19
❑ 87GenCubP-5
❑ 88PeoChiTI-16
❑ 89WinSpiS-21
❑ 90WinSpiTI-27
❑ 91WinSpiC-28
❑ 92WinSpiC-28
❑ 93DayCubC-27
❑ 95OrlCubF-28
❑ 96OrlCubB-4
❑ 97OrlRayB-4

Melendez, William
❑ 76DubPacT-21

Meleski, Mark
❑ 86NewBriRSP-18
❑ 87PawRedSP-75
❑ 87PawRedST-28
❑ 88PawRedSC-25
❑ 88PawRedSP-454
❑ 89PawRedSC-24
❑ 89PawRedSP-696
❑ 89PawRedSTI-16
❑ 90CMC-259
❑ 90PawRedSC-8
❑ 90PawRedSDD-15
❑ 90PawRedSP-478
❑ 90ProAAAF-450
❑ 90TopTVRS-35
❑ 91LinDriAAA-360
❑ 91PawRedSDD-12
❑ 91PawRedSLD-360
❑ 91PawRedSP-56
❑ 92PawRedSF-940
❑ 93LynRedSC-25
❑ 93LynRedSF-2533
❑ 94LynRedSC-26
❑ 94LynRedSF-1908
❑ 95JacSunTI-20
❑ 96JacSunB-4
❑ 97DunDonPPS-13
❑ 97LakTigB-1
❑ 98LakTigM-27

Melhuse, Adam
❑ 93St.CatBJC-15
❑ 93St.CatBJF-3981
❑ 94HagSunC-15
❑ 94HagSunF-2735
❑ 95DunBluJTI-15
❑ 96DunBluJB-17
❑ 96DunBluJTI-20
❑ 96DunBluJUTI-9
❑ 97KnoSmo-17
❑ 97SyrSkyCB-15
❑ 98KnoSG-15

Melhuse, Mike
❑ 94WilCubC-28

Melian, Jackson
❑ 98Bes-29
❑ 98GreBatM-11
❑ 98SouAtlLPM-14
❑ 98SP MinDTSPE-DS5
❑ 98SP MinPE-7
❑ 98SP MinPE-85
❑ 98SP MinSTHPE-H5
❑ 98SPMin-7
❑ 98SPMin-85
❑ 98SPMinDTS-DS5
❑ 98SPMinSTH-H5
❑ 99BasAmeTP-67
❑ 99BasAmeTPG-67
❑ 99JustheS-34
❑ 99JustheSJB-34
❑ 99JustheSJD-8
❑ 99JustheSJN-4
❑ 99SP TopP-84
❑ 99SP TopPC-JAM
❑ 99SP TopPGF-GF22
❑ 99SP TopPPE-84

Melillo, Ski (Oscar)
❑ 26Exh-116
❑ 27MidBre-32
❑ 29ExhFou-30
❑ 29PorandAR-64
❑ 30SchR33-39
❑ 31Exh-29
❑ 33ButCanV-32
❑ 33DelR33-3
❑ 33DouDisP-32
❑ 33ExhFou-15
❑ 33GeoCMil-22
❑ 34BabRutG-45
❑ 34BatR31-151
❑ 34ButPreR-44
❑ 34DiaStaR-53
❑ 34ExhFou-15
❑ 34Gou-45
❑ 34GouCanV-94
❑ 34TarThoBD-21
❑ 35DiaMatCS3T1-106
❑ 35ExhFou-15
❑ 35GouPreR-13
❑ 35GouPuzR-5D
❑ 35GouPuzR-6D
❑ 35GouPuzR-11F
❑ 35GouPuzR-13D
❑ 36NatChiFPR-56
❑ 55A'sRodM-24
❑ 55A'sTeal-15
❑ 56A'sPos-33
❑ 61Fle-127
❑ 72TCMthe3-108
❑ 76A'sRodMC-16
❑ 91ConTSN-81
❑ 93ConTSN-890

Melito, Chuck
❑ 80BatTroT-17

Melito, Mark
❑ 95SpoIndTI-13
❑ 96LanLugB-16
❑ 96MidLeaAB-37

Mellana, Joe
❑ 28Zee-96
❑ 30Zee-90

Mellix, Lefty (Ralph)
❑ 88NegLeaD-18

Mello, John
❑ 88MidLeaAGS-43
❑ 88RocExpLC-24
❑ 89WesPalBES-16
❑ 90FloStaLAS-14
❑ 90WesPalBES-16

Melo, Juan
❑ 95Bow-237
❑ 95BowGolF-237
❑ 96Bow-127
❑ 96BowFoi-127
❑ 96RanCucQB-21
❑ 97Bes-24
❑ 97BesAutSBPP-23
❑ 97BesDiaB-17
❑ 97Bow-182
❑ 97Bow98ROY-ROY13
❑ 97BowBes-121
❑ 97BowBesAR-121
❑ 97BowBesR-121
❑ 97BowCerBlaIA-CA53
❑ 97BowCerBluIA-CA53
❑ 97BowCerGolIA-CA53
❑ 97BowChr-173
❑ 97BowChr1RFR-ROY13
❑ 97BowChr98RF-ROY13
❑ 97BowChrI-173
❑ 97BowChrIR-173
❑ 97BowChrR-173
❑ 97BowInt-182
❑ 97ColCho-462
❑ 97MobBayBB-14
❑ 97SouLeaTP-25
❑ 97TexAllM-45
❑ 98Bes-78
❑ 98BesDiaBA-8
❑ 98BesFulCA-12
❑ 98BesPreA-26
❑ 98Bow-89
❑ 98BowBes-126
❑ 98BowBesAR-126
❑ 98BowBesR-126
❑ 98BowChr-89
❑ 98BowChrGA-89
❑ 98BowChrGAR-89
❑ 98BowChrI-89
❑ 98BowChrIR-89
❑ 98BowChrR-89
❑ 98BowGolA-89
❑ 98BowInt-89
❑ 98Las-15
❑ 98SP MinDTSPE-DS28
❑ 98SP MinPE-106
❑ 98SP MinSTHPE-H27
❑ 98SP SPTSC-JM
❑ 98SPMin-106
❑ 98SPMinDTS-DS28
❑ 98SPMinSTH-H27
❑ 98UppDec-261
❑ 99Bow-116
❑ 99BowChr-116
❑ 99BowChrG-116
❑ 99BowChrGR-116
❑ 99BowChrI-116
❑ 99BowChrIR-116
❑ 99BowChrR-116
❑ 99BowGol-116
❑ 99BowInt-116
❑ 99JustheSAC-17
❑ 99SP SigAuto-JM
❑ 99SP SigAutoG-JM
❑ 99SP TopP-85
❑ 99SP TopPC-JM
❑ 99SP TopPDtS-D5
❑ 99SP TopPPE-85
❑ 99SPSig-61

Meloan, Paul
❑ 11SpoLifM-25
❑ 13Zee-144
❑ 14Zee-143
❑ 15Zee-112

Melrose, Jeff
❑ 86DayBealP-19
❑ 86TulDriTI-21
❑ 88GasRanP-1012

Melson, Gary
❑ 79TacTugT-9
❑ 80RicBraT-8

Melton, Bill (William)
❑ 69Top-481
❑ 69TopTeaP-11
❑ 69WhiSoxTI-10
❑ 70MLBOffS-190
❑ 70OPC-518
❑ 70Top-518
❑ 70WhiSoxTI-11
❑ 71BazNumT-21
❑ 71BazUnn-21
❑ 71MilDud-17
❑ 71OPC-80
❑ 71Top-80
❑ 71TopCoi-76
❑ 71TopGreM-33
❑ 71TopSup-47
❑ 71TopTat-111
❑ 72Kel-12
❑ 72MilBra-233
❑ 72OPC-90
❑ 72OPC-183
❑ 72OPC-184
❑ 72OPC-495
❑ 72ProStaP-31
❑ 72SevTraC-34
❑ 72Top-90
❑ 72Top-183
❑ 72Top-184
❑ 72Top-495
❑ 72TopPos-3
❑ 72WhiSox-9
❑ 72WhiSoxC-5
❑ 72WhiSoxDS-5
❑ 72WhiSoxTI1-11
❑ 73LinPor-50
❑ 73OPC-455
❑ 73Top-455
❑ 74OPC-170
❑ 74Top-170
❑ 74TopDecE-68
❑ 74TopSta-158
❑ 75Hos-8
❑ 75HosTwi-8
❑ 75OPC-11
❑ 75SSP42-3
❑ 75Top-11
❑ 75TopMin-11
❑ 76OPC-309
❑ 76SSP-155
❑ 76Top-309
❑ 76TopTra-309T
❑ 77IndTeal-17
❑ 77Top-107
❑ 85WhiSoxC-3
❑ 92UppDecS-5

Melton, Cliff
❑ 38CloFotW-60
❑ 39PlaBal-125
❑ 40PlaBal-83
❑ 41DouPlaR-25
❑ 41DouPlaR-93
❑ 47PM1StaP1-140
❑ 48SomandK-8
❑ 49SomandK-6
❑ 72TCMthe3-51
❑ 79DiaGre-42
❑ 92ConTSN-613
❑ 95ConTSN-1389

Melton, David
❑ 58Top-391

Melton, Larry
❑ 86PriWilPP-17
❑ 87SalBucP-3
❑ 88EasLeaAP-17
❑ 88HarSenP-857
❑ 89BufBisC-8
❑ 89BufBisP-1673

Melton, Rube (Reuben)
❑ 43DodTeal-17
❑ 47DodTeal-15
❑ 47TipTop-101
❑ 83TCMPla1942-45
❑ 90DodTar-515

Melton, Sam
❑ 87ElmPioBC-11
❑ 87ElmPioRC-11

Meltz, Rich
❑ 75ForLauYS-6

Meluskey, Mitch
❑ 92BurIndC-22
❑ 92BurIndF-1660
❑ 93ClaFS7-220
❑ 93ColRedC-15
❑ 93ColRedF-601
❑ 94KinIndC-13
❑ 94KinIndF-2647
❑ 96KisCobB-16
❑ 97JacGen-16
❑ 97JacGenS-15
❑ 97TexLeaTP-9
❑ 98FleUpd-U61
❑ 98NewOrlZM-13
❑ 99Bow-125
❑ 99BowBes-127
❑ 99BowBesAR-127
❑ 99BowBesR-127
❑ 99BowChr-125
❑ 99BowChrG-125
❑ 99BowChrGR-125
❑ 99BowChrI-125
❑ 99BowChrIR-125
❑ 99BowChrR-125
❑ 99BowGol-125
❑ 99BowInt-125
❑ 99Fle-508
❑ 99FleBri-148
❑ 99FleBri2G-148
❑ 99FleBriBlu-148
❑ 99FleBriGol-148
❑ 99FleSta9-508
❑ 99FleWarT-508
❑ 99PacInv-69
❑ 99PacInvOD-69
❑ 99PacInvPB-69
❑ 99SP SigAuto-MME
❑ 99SP SigAutoG-MME
❑ 99SpoIll-43
❑ 99SPSig-69
❑ 99StaClu-163
❑ 99StaCluC-SCC33
❑ 99StaCluCR-SCC33
❑ 99StaCluFDI-163
❑ 99StaCluOoaK-163
❑ 99StaCluPP-163
❑ 99Top-431
❑ 99TopChr-431
❑ 99TopChrR-431
❑ 99TopMVPP-431
❑ 99UppDec-286
❑ 99UppDecE-129
❑ 99UppDecEFXG-129
❑ 99UppDecEL1-286
❑ 99UppDecEL2-286
❑ 99Vic-168

Melvin, Bill
❑ 87GenCubP-16
❑ 88PeoChiTI-17
❑ 89WinSpiS-NNO
❑ 90WinSpiTI-5
❑ 91WinSpiC-7
❑ 91WinSpiP-2826
❑ 92ChaKniF-2769
❑ 92ChaKniS-162
❑ 93OrlCubF-2781

Melvin, Bob
❑ 82BirBarT-7
❑ 83BirBarT-12
❑ 84EvaTriT-11
❑ 86Don-456
❑ 86GiaMot-12
❑ 86GiaPos-23
❑ 86Top-479
❑ 86TopTif-479
❑ 87Don-239
❑ 87Fle-281
❑ 87FleGlo-281
❑ 87GiaMot-12
❑ 87GiaPos-23
❑ 87Top-549
❑ 87TopTif-549
❑ 88Don-638
❑ 88Fle-91
❑ 88FleGlo-91
❑ 88GiaMot-12
❑ 88GiaPos-22
❑ 88OPC-41
❑ 88Sco-477
❑ 88ScoGlo-477
❑ 88StaLinG-12
❑ 88Top-41
❑ 88TopTif-41
❑ 89BalOriP-18
❑ 89BirBarADB-23
❑ 89Bow-8
❑ 89BowTif-8
❑ 89Fle-335
❑ 89FleGlo-335
❑ 89OPC-329
❑ 89OriFreB-36

❑ 89Sco-617
❑ 89ScoRoo-61T
❑ 89Top-329
❑ 89Top-351
❑ 89TopTif-329
❑ 89TopTif-351
❑ 89UppDec-227
❑ 90BirBarADB-23
❑ 90Don-451
❑ 90Fle-181
❑ 90FleCan-181
❑ 90Lea-382
❑ 90OPC-626
❑ 90PubIntS-579
❑ 90Sco-453
❑ 90Top-626
❑ 90TopTif-626
❑ 90UppDec-644
❑ 91Bow-89
❑ 91Don-335
❑ 91Fle-482
❑ 91Lea-240
❑ 91OPC-249
❑ 91OriCro-296
❑ 91StaClu-312
❑ 91Top-249
❑ 91TopDesS-249
❑ 91TopMic-249
❑ 91TopTif-249
❑ 91UltUpd-3
❑ 91UppDec-310
❑ 92Don-231
❑ 92Fle-15
❑ 92OPC-733
❑ 92RoyPol-21
❑ 92Sco-208
❑ 92ScoRoo-73T
❑ 92StaClu-642
❑ 92Top-733
❑ 92TopGol-733
❑ 92TopGolW-733
❑ 92TopMic-733
❑ 92UppDec-692
❑ 93RedSoxP-22
❑ 93RedSoxWHP-22
❑ 93Ult-513
❑ 94Fle-36
Melvin, Doug
❑ 75ForLauYS-17
❑ 76ForLauYS-27
❑ 77WesHavYT-15
Melvin, Ken
❑ 75ShrCapT-10
Melvin, Scott
❑ 86KinEagP-16
❑ 87SprCarB-24
❑ 88St.PetCS-18
❑ 89St.PetCS-20
❑ 90ArkTraGS-21
❑ 91ArkTraLD-50
❑ 91ArkTraP-1295
❑ 91LinDriAA-50
❑ 92HamRedC-30
❑ 92HamRedF-1609
❑ 93SprCarC-29
❑ 96NewJerCB-1
Melvin, William
❑ 87ChaWheP-1
Mena, Andres
❑ 87SanAntDTI-2
Menard, Dyrryl
❑ 86OscAstP-18
Mendazona, Mike
❑ 89GasRanP-1026
❑ 89GasRanS-15
Mendek, William
❑ 87ChaLooB-24
❑ 88VerMarP-958
Mendenhall, Casey
❑ 90OklSoo-22
❑ 92NiaFalRC-15
❑ 92NiaFalRF-3320
❑ 93ClaFS7-221
❑ 93LakTigC-17
❑ 93LakTigF-1306
Mendenhall, Kirk
❑ 90NiaFalRP-6
❑ 91FloStaLAP-FSL21
❑ 91LakTigC-21
❑ 91LakTigP-274
❑ 92LonTigF-640
❑ 92LonTigS-413
❑ 93LonTigF-2315
❑ 94TreThuF-2127
Mendenhall, Monte
❑ 78QuaCitAT-13
Mendenhall, Shannon
❑ 86ModA'sC-15
❑ 88LynRedSS-14
Mendes, Jaime
❑ 95BatCliTI-22
❑ 96PieBolWB-17
❑ 97PieBolWB-19
❑ 98ClePhiM-17
❑ 98ClePhiUM-17
Mendez, Carlos
❑ 94RocRoyC-16
❑ 94RocRoyF-568
❑ 95LinVen-6
❑ 95WilBluRTI-28
❑ 96-97LinVen-146
❑ 96CarLeaA1B-11
❑ 96CarLeaA2B-11
❑ 96WilBluRB-2
❑ 97TexAllM-22
❑ 97WicWra-17
❑ 98OmaRoyM-16
Mendez, Eddie
❑ 89MyrBeaBJP-1453
Mendez, Emilio
❑ 93GenCubC-22
❑ 93GenCubF-3187
❑ 93PeoChiC-14
❑ 93PeoChiF-1092
❑ 94PeoChiC-19
❑ 94PeoChiF-2276
❑ 94WilCubC-14
❑ 94WilCubF-3771
Mendez, Francisco
❑ 98LetBlaDG-21
Mendez, Jaime
❑ 90IBAWorA-29
Mendez, Jesus
❑ 86St.PetCP-20
❑ 87St.PetCP-3
❑ 88ArkTraGS-15
❑ 90CMC-118
❑ 90LouRedBC-18
❑ 90LouRedBLBC-27
❑ 90LouRedBP-411
❑ 90ProAAAF-525
❑ 90TopTVCa-55
❑ 91LouRedP-2930
❑ 92ArkTraF-1138
❑ 92ArkTraS-39
❑ 93LinVenB-70
❑ 94VenLinU-174
❑ 95LinVen-108
❑ 96-97LinVen-67
Mendez, John
❑ 96StPetCB-20
Mendez, Jose D.
❑ 74LauOldTBS-9
❑ 87NegLeaPD-7
❑ 90NegLeaS-32
Mendez, Julio
❑ 89SavCarP-361
Mendez, Mauro
❑ 93LinVenB-202
❑ 95LinVen-220
Mendez, Miguel
❑ 90SumBraB-13
❑ 90SumBraP-2443
Mendez, Raul
❑ 86BelMarCr-124
Mendez, Ricardo
❑ 92MadMusC-10
❑ 92MadMusF-1244
❑ 92SouOreAF-3426
Mendez, Roberto
❑ 85MexCitTT-2
Mendez, Rodolfo
❑ 95MidLeaA-32
❑ 95SprSulTI-15
❑ 96Exc-64
Mendez, Sergio
❑ 93WelPirC-13
❑ 93WelPirF-3360
❑ 94AugGreC-12
❑ 94AugGreF-3012
❑ 94SouAtlLAF-SAL34
❑ 95LynHilTI-15
❑ 97CarMudC-12
Mendon, Kevin
❑ 80MemChiT-14
Mendonca, Robert
❑ 89BatCliP-1918
Mendoza, Alonso
❑ 93PocPosF-4219
❑ 93PocPosSP-2
Mendoza, Angel
❑ 98LowSpiM-13
Mendoza, Carlos
❑ 96-97LinVen-12
❑ 96Exc-189
❑ 97BinMetB-20
❑ 97CapCitB-28
❑ 97EasLeaTPB-5
❑ 97SalVolG-22
❑ 98Don-338
❑ 98DonGolPP-338
❑ 98DonSilPP-338
❑ 98DurBulTI-20
❑ 98Fle-149
❑ 98LeaRS-216
❑ 98LeaRSLHolo-216
❑ 98LeaRSLong-216
❑ 98LeaRTrue-216
❑ 98SanJosGQ-9
❑ 98Stu-136
❑ 98StuGPP-136
❑ 98StuSPP-136
Mendoza, Dave
❑ 76CedRapGT-15
Mendoza, Francisco
❑ 92BelBreCB-13
❑ 92BelBreFI-413
❑ 93BelBreCB-16
❑ 93BelBreFI-1719
❑ 95SprSulTI-16
Mendoza, Geronimo
❑ 98BriWhiSQ-20
Mendoza, Hatuey
❑ 98LetBlaDG-22
Mendoza, Jesus
❑ 88SumBraP-398
❑ 89BurBraP-1605
❑ 89BurBraS-13
❑ 95LinVen-159
❑ 96-97LinVen-203
Mendoza, Mario
❑ 75OPC-457
❑ 75PitPirP-13
❑ 75Top-457
❑ 75TopMin-457
❑ 76PirPos-11
❑ 76SSP-606
❑ 77PirPosP-14
❑ 78Top-383
❑ 79Top-509
❑ 80MarPos-15
❑ 80OPC-344
❑ 80Top-653
❑ 81Don-45
❑ 81Fle-613
❑ 81OPC-76
❑ 81Top-76
❑ 81TopTra-801
❑ 82Don-394
❑ 82Fle-325
❑ 82OPC-212
❑ 82Top-212
❑ 91PalSprAP-2035
❑ 92CalLeaACL-49
❑ 92PalSprAC-28
❑ 92PalSprAF-855
❑ 93PalSprAC-26
❑ 93PalSprAF-86
❑ 93RanKee-261
❑ 94MidAngF-2453
❑ 94MidAngOHP-16
❑ 95MidAngOHP-21
❑ 95MidAngTI-19
❑ 96MidAngB-1
❑ 96MidAngOHP-17
❑ 97CedRapK-17
❑ 98LakElsSG-21
Mendoza, Mike
❑ 75DubPacT-8
❑ 76DubPacT-22
❑ 79ChaChaT-19
❑ 80TucTorT-21
❑ 81TidTidT-19
Mendoza, Minnie
❑ 70TwiTeal-5
❑ 80ChaO'sP-12
❑ 80ChaO'sW-13
❑ 81MiaOriT-6
❑ 88OriFreB-40
❑ 88OriPos-20
❑ 96CanIndB-3
❑ 97AkrAer-3
Mendoza, Ramiro
❑ 95NorNavTI-18
❑ 95SPML-119
❑ 96ColCliB-21
❑ 97ColCliB-19
❑ 97ColCliD-15
❑ 97Fle-172
❑ 97FleTif-172
❑ 97Ult-101
❑ 97UltGolME-101
❑ 97UltPlaME-101
❑ 97UppDec-475
❑ 98ColCho-193
❑ 98Pac-153
❑ 98PacOnl-509
❑ 98PacOnlR-509
❑ 98PacOnlWC-509
❑ 98PacPlaB-153
❑ 98PacRedT-153
❑ 98PacSil-153
❑ 98StaCluFDI-148
❑ 98StaCluI-148
❑ 98StaCluOneK-148
❑ 98StaCluPP-148
❑ 98Ult-285
❑ 98UltGolM-285
❑ 98UltMas-285
❑ 98UltPlaM-285
❑ 98UppDec-462
❑ 98YanUppD-462
❑ 99Fle-483
❑ 99FleSta9-483
❑ 99FleWarT-483
❑ 99Pac-298
❑ 99PacCroC-193
❑ 99PacCroCPB-193
❑ 99PacPlaB-298
❑ 99PacRed-298
❑ 99Top-313
❑ 99TopChr-313
❑ 99TopChrR-313
❑ 99TopMVPP-313
❑ 99UppDec-162
❑ 99UppDecEL1-162
❑ 99UppDecEL2-162
❑ 99YanFle-14
Mendoza, Reynol
❑ 92EriSaiC-10
❑ 92EriSaiF-1618
❑ 93KanCouCC-13
❑ 93KanCouCF-913
❑ 93KanCouCTI-13
❑ 93MidLeaAGF-9
❑ 93Top-782
❑ 93TopGol-782
❑ 93TopInaM-782
❑ 93TopInaR-782
❑ 93TopMic-782
❑ 94BreCouMF-6
❑ 94ExcFS7-193
❑ 95PorSeaDTI-16
❑ 96PorSeaDB-17
❑ 97ChaKni-19
❑ 98ChaKniQ-22
Menechino, Frank
❑ 94MidLeaAF-MDW27
❑ 94SouBenSHC-12
❑ 94SouBenSHF-599
❑ 95PriWilCTI-9
❑ 96BirBarB-6
❑ 96DouAllB-32
❑ 96Exc-34
Menees, Gene
❑ 79NaSouTI-15
❑ 80IndIndTI-21
❑ 81IndIndTI-18
❑ 82WatRedT-5
Menefee, John
❑ 03BreE10-103
Menendez, Daniel
❑ 50W720HolS-19
Menendez, Tony (Antonio G.)
❑ 86BirBarTI-6
❑ 87BirBarB-10
❑ 88BirBarB-20
❑ 89BirBarADB-24
❑ 89BirBarB-3
❑ 89BirBarP-103
❑ 90BirBarADB-24
❑ 92DonRoo-77
❑ 92NasSouF-1830
❑ 92NasSouS-286
❑ 92SkyAAAF-133
❑ 93Bow-106
❑ 93BufBisF-513
❑ 94GiaTarBC-17
❑ 94PhoFirF-1517
❑ 94StaCluT-27
❑ 94StaCluTFDI-27
❑ 95PhoFirTI-36
Menendez, William
❑ 86WinSpiP-17
Mengel, Brad
❑ 90MyrBeaBJP-2782
❑ 91DunBluJC-17
❑ 91DunBluJP-214
❑ 92KnoBluJF-2997
Menges, William
❑ 14Zee-41
❑ 16Zee-83
Mengwasser, Brad
❑ 82TulDriT-2
Menhart, Paul
❑ 90St.CatBJP-3464
❑ 91DunBluJC-7
❑ 91DunBluJP-203
❑ 91FloStaLAP-FSL9
❑ 92KnoBluJF-2987
❑ 92KnoBluJS-384
❑ 92SkyAA F-162
❑ 93SyrChiF-997
❑ 95SyrChiTI-16
❑ 96Don-323
❑ 96DonPreP-323
❑ 96Fle-279
❑ 96FleTif-279
❑ 96MarMot-25
❑ 96StaClu-62
❑ 96StaCluMOP-62
❑ 97TacRai-21
❑ 98Las-16
Menke, Denis
❑ 62Top-597
❑ 63Top-433
❑ 64BraJayP-9
❑ 64Top-53
❑ 64TopCoi-90
❑ 64TopVen-53
❑ 65Kah-30
❑ 65Top-327
❑ 66BraPos-18
❑ 66Kah-22
❑ 66OPC-184
❑ 66Top-184
❑ 66TopRubI-67
❑ 66TopVen-184
❑ 67Ast-18
❑ 67BraIrvD-3
❑ 67BraPho-21
❑ 67CokCapB-6
❑ 67DexPre-146
❑ 67Kah-26
❑ 67Top-396
❑ 67Top-518
❑ 68CokCapA-8
❑ 68CokCapB-6
❑ 68DexPre-55
❑ 68Top-232
❑ 68TopVen-232
❑ 69MilBra-191
❑ 69MLBOffS-140
❑ 69Top-487
❑ 69TopSta-35
❑ 69TopTeaP-6
❑ 70AstPho-16
❑ 70AstTeal-7
❑ 70DayDaiNM-63
❑ 70MilBra-18
❑ 70MLBOffS-43
❑ 70OPC-155
❑ 70Top-155
❑ 70TopBoo-16
❑ 71AstCok-6
❑ 71Kel-8
❑ 71MilDud-53
❑ 71MLBOffS-87
❑ 71OPC-130
❑ 71Top-130
❑ 71TopCoi-89
❑ 72MilBra-234
❑ 72Top-586
❑ 73OPC-52
❑ 73Top-52
❑ 74OPC-134
❑ 74Top-134
❑ 77BurBeeT-16
❑ 78AtlCon-16
❑ 78DunBluJT-16
❑ 78TCM60I-58
❑ 82TucTorT-26
❑ 83AstPos-17
❑ 84AstMot-27
❑ 84AstPos-17
❑ 85AstMot-27
❑ 86AstMot-9
❑ 86AstPol-26
❑ 87AstMot-27
❑ 87AstPol-26
❑ 87AstShoSO-16
❑ 87AstShoSTw-24
❑ 87AstShoSTw-27
❑ 88AstMot-27
❑ 89PhiTas-22
❑ 90PhiTas-34
❑ 91PhiMed-27
❑ 92PhiMed-20
❑ 93PhiMed-22
❑ 94PhiMed-22
❑ 95Phi-19
❑ 96PhiTeal-21
Menking, Paul
❑ 55DesMoiHB-13
Menosky, Mike
❑ 21Nei-46
❑ 22E120-7
❑ 22W572-63
❑ 22W573-80
❑ 23WilChoV-96
❑ 24Zee-134
Mensik, Todd
❑ 96SouOreTI-3
❑ 98ModA'sG-21
Mensink, Brian
❑ 95BatCliTI-23
Mensor, Edward
❑ 09ObaT21-364
❑ 12ObaPreT-113
❑ 17Zee-31
❑ 18Zee-28
Mentzer, Troy
❑ 89EveGiaS-21
❑ 90SanJosGB-10
❑ 90SanJosGCLC-41
❑ 90SanJosGP-2013
❑ 90SanJosGS-15
Meola, Mike
❑ 39WorWidGV-18
Meoli, Rudy
❑ 74OPC-188
❑ 74SalLakCAC-91
❑ 74Top-188
❑ 75CalAngP-25
❑ 75OPC-533
❑ 75Top-533
❑ 75TopMin-533
❑ 76IndIndTI-10
❑ 76OPC-254
❑ 76SSP-196
❑ 76Top-254
❑ 77IndIndTI-18
❑ 78SSP270-270
❑ 78Top-489
Mepri, Sal
❑ 94PriRedC-18
❑ 94PriRedF-3264
Mercado, Brian
❑ 90ButCopKSP-15
Mercado, Candy
❑ 75AppFoxT-17
❑ 76AppFoxT-15
❑ 77AppFoxT-15
❑ 77BurBeeT-17
Mercado, Gabby
❑ 95BelBreTI-7
❑ 96OgdRapTI-22
Mercado, Hector
❑ 94FloStaLAF-FSL35
❑ 94OscAstC-15
❑ 94OscAstF-1136
❑ 96KisCobB-17
❑ 97PorSeaD-19
Mercado, Manny
❑ 86WatIndP-19
❑ 87WatIndP-2
Mercado, Orlando
❑ 80LynSaiT-9
❑ 81SpoIndT-5
❑ 82SalLakCGT-13
❑ 83TopTra-71T
❑ 84Don-318
❑ 84Fle-613
❑ 84MarMot-14
❑ 84Nes792-314
❑ 84Top-314
❑ 84TopTif-314
❑ 85OklCit8T-1
❑ 85Top-58
❑ 85TopTif-58
❑ 86OklCit8P-12
❑ 87AlbDukD-16
❑ 87DonOpeD-209
❑ 87Top-514
❑ 87TopTif-514

❑ 88BlaYNPRWL-45
❑ 88TacTigC-22
❑ 88TacTigP-624
❑ 89BlaYNPRWL-46
❑ 89PorBeaC-12
❑ 89PorBeaP-209
❑ 89UppDec-624
❑ 90CMC-372
❑ 90DodTar-517
❑ 90MetColP-41
❑ 90MetKah-35
❑ 90ProAAAF-279
❑ 90TidTidC-21
❑ 90TidTidP-548
❑ 90TopTra-73T
❑ 90TopTraT-73T
❑ 90TopTVM-21
❑ 91LinDriAAA-563
❑ 91MetColP-39
❑ 91MetWIZ-265
❑ 91TidTidLD-563
❑ 91TidTidP-2514
❑ 92TidTidF-900
❑ 92TidTidS-566
❑ 93lowCubF-2136
❑ 93RanKee-262
❑ 97MidAng-3
❑ 98ButCopKG-20

Mercado, Rafael
❑ 90SouOreAP-3434
❑ 91MadMusC-27
❑ 91MadMusP-2140
❑ 91MidLeaAP-MWL42
❑ 92RenSilSCLC-48
❑ 93ColRedC-16
❑ 93ColRedF-605

Merced, Orlando
❑ 86MacPirP-15
❑ 88AugPirP-364
❑ 88BlaYNPRWLU-8
❑ 89BlaYNPRWL-179
❑ 89HarSenP-299
❑ 89HarSenS-10
❑ 90BufBisC-18
❑ 90BufBisP-380
❑ 90BufBisTI-16
❑ 90CMC-18
❑ 90ProAAAF-495
❑ 90TopMag-64
❑ 90TriAAAC-15
❑ 91Bow-512
❑ 91BufBisLD-35
❑ 91Cla3-T57
❑ 91DonRoo-22
❑ 91FleUpd-112
❑ 91Lea-489
❑ 91LinDriAAA-35
❑ 91MajLeaCP-58
❑ 91Sco-747
❑ 91TopDeb90-107
❑ 91TopTra-81T
❑ 91TopTraT-81T
❑ 91Ult-284
❑ 91UppDec-84
❑ 92Bow-291
❑ 92Cla1-T62
❑ 92ClaGam-154
❑ 92Don-310
❑ 92Fle-561
❑ 92FleRooS-3
❑ 92Lea-363
❑ 92LeaBlaG-363
❑ 92OPC-637
❑ 92OPCPre-22
❑ 92PanSti-252
❑ 92Pin-62
❑ 92PirNatI-16
❑ 92Sco-153
❑ 92Sco100RS-75
❑ 92ScoImpP-7
❑ 92StaClu-134
❑ 92Top-637
❑ 92TopGol-637
❑ 92TopGolW-637
❑ 92TopMic-637
❑ 92TriPla-16
❑ 92Ult-257
❑ 92UppDec-517
❑ 93Bow-190
❑ 93DiaMar-75
❑ 93Don-282
❑ 93Fla-115
❑ 93Fle-117
❑ 93Lea-97
❑ 93PacJugC-33
❑ 93PacSpa-248
❑ 93PacSpaGE-6
❑ 93PanSti-281
❑ 93Pin-160
❑ 93PirHil-8
❑ 93PirNatI-18
❑ 93Sco-137
❑ 93Sel-183
❑ 93SP-186
❑ 93StaClu-372
❑ 93StaCluFDI-372
❑ 93StaCluMOP-372
❑ 93Stu-184
❑ 93Top-378
❑ 93TopGol-378
❑ 93TopInaM-378
❑ 93TopInaR-378
❑ 93TopMic-378
❑ 93Ult-100
❑ 93UppDec-150
❑ 93UppDecGold-150
❑ 94Bow-546
❑ 94ColC-204
❑ 94ColChoGS-204
❑ 94ColChoSS-204
❑ 94Don-334
❑ 94DonDiaK-DK19
❑ 94DonDiaKJ-DK19
❑ 94DonSpeE-334
❑ 94Fin-61
❑ 94FinPre-61P
❑ 94FinRef-61
❑ 94Fla-218
❑ 94Fle-614
❑ 94FleExtB-349
❑ 94FUnPac-83
❑ 94Lea-388
❑ 94LeaL-142
❑ 94OPC-48
❑ 94Pac-502
❑ 94PacAll-9
❑ 94PacSilP-34
❑ 94PacSilPC-34
❑ 94PanSti-237
❑ 94Pin-76
❑ 94PinArtP-76
❑ 94PinMusC-76
❑ 94PirQui-16
❑ 94Pos-30
❑ 94ProMag-110
❑ 94Sco-58
❑ 94ScoGolR-58
❑ 94ScoGolS-2
❑ 94Sel-361
❑ 94SP-143
❑ 94SPDieC-143
❑ 94Spo-19
❑ 94StaClu-277
❑ 94StaCluFDI-277
❑ 94StaCluGR-277
❑ 94StaCluMOP-277
❑ 94Stu-148
❑ 94Top-281
❑ 94TopGol-281
❑ 94TopSpa-281
❑ 94TriPla-187
❑ 94Ult-557
❑ 94UltOnBL-8
❑ 94UppDec-182
❑ 94UppDecAJ-37
❑ 94UppDecAJG-37
❑ 94UppDecED-182
❑ 95Bow-335
❑ 95ColCho-375
❑ 95ColChoGS-375
❑ 95ColChoSE-179
❑ 95ColChoSEGS-179
❑ 95ColChoSESS-179
❑ 95ColChoSS-375
❑ 95DenHol-17
❑ 95Don-351
❑ 95DonPreP-351
❑ 95DonTopotO-320
❑ 95Fin-204
❑ 95FinRef-204
❑ 95Fla-404
❑ 95Fle-484
❑ 95Lea-251
❑ 95LeaLim-165
❑ 95Pac-348
❑ 95PacPri-113
❑ 95Pin-60
❑ 95PinArtP-60
❑ 95PinMusC-60
❑ 95PirFil-21
❑ 95Sco-44
❑ 95ScoGolR-44
❑ 95ScoPlaTS-44
❑ 95SP-96
❑ 95SPCha-81
❑ 95SPChaDC-81
❑ 95Spo-31
❑ 95SpoArtP-31
❑ 95SPSil-96
❑ 95StaClu-198
❑ 95StaCluFDI-198
❑ 95StaCluMOP-198
❑ 95StaCluSTWS-198
❑ 95StaCluVR-104
❑ 95StaCluVRMO-104
❑ 95Stu-179
❑ 95TomPiz-27
❑ 95Top-21
❑ 95TopCyb-17
❑ 95TopD3-57
❑ 95TopEmb-92
❑ 95TopEmbGI-92
❑ 95Ult-218
❑ 95UltGolM-218
❑ 95UppDec-385
❑ 95UppDecED-385
❑ 95UppDecEDG-385
❑ 95UppDecSE-86
❑ 95UppDecSEG-86
❑ 96Baz-92
❑ 96ColCho-265
❑ 96ColChoGS-265
❑ 96ColChoSS-265
❑ 96Don-168
❑ 96DonPreP-168
❑ 96EmoXL-258
❑ 96Fin-B104
❑ 96FinRef-B104
❑ 96Fla-351
❑ 96Fle-527
❑ 96FleTif-527
❑ 96Lea-35
❑ 96LeaLim-62
❑ 96LeaLimG-62
❑ 96LeaPrePB-35
❑ 96LeaPrePG-35
❑ 96LeaPrePS-35
❑ 96LeaSigA-153
❑ 96LeaSigAG-153
❑ 96LeaSigAS-153
❑ 96MetUni-218
❑ 96MetUniP-218
❑ 96Pac-170
❑ 96PacEstL-EL19
❑ 96PacPri-P59
❑ 96PacPriG-P59
❑ 96PanSti-67
❑ 96Pin-71
❑ 96ProSta-91
❑ 96Sco-423
❑ 96SelCer-48
❑ 96SelCerAP-48
❑ 96SelCerCB-48
❑ 96SelCerCR-48
❑ 96SelCerMB-48
❑ 96SelCerMG-48
❑ 96SelCerMR-48
❑ 96SP-147
❑ 96StaClu-408
❑ 96StaCluEPB-408
❑ 96StaCluEPG-408
❑ 96StaCluEPS-408
❑ 96StaCluMOP-408
❑ 96Stu-90
❑ 96StuPrePB-90
❑ 96StuPrePG-90
❑ 96StuPrePS-90
❑ 96Sum-120
❑ 96SumAbo&B-120
❑ 96SumArtP-120
❑ 96SumFoi-120
❑ 96Top-265
❑ 96Ult-267
❑ 96UltGolM-267
❑ 96UppDec-178
❑ 96Zen-70
❑ 96ZenArtP-70
❑ 96ZenMoz-23
❑ 97BluJayOH-19
❑ 97BluJayS-11
❑ 97Cir-37
❑ 97CirRav-37
❑ 97ColCho-496
❑ 97Don-77
❑ 97Don-284
❑ 97DonGolPP-77
❑ 97DonGolPP-284
❑ 97DonSilPP-77
❑ 97DonSilPP-284
❑ 97Fin-196
❑ 97FinRef-196
❑ 97Fle-433
❑ 97Fle-577
❑ 97FleTif-433
❑ 97FleTif-577
❑ 97Lea-166
❑ 97LeaFraM-166
❑ 97LeaFraMDC-166
❑ 97MetUni-187
❑ 97Pac-400
❑ 97PacLigB-400
❑ 97PacSil-400
❑ 97StaClu-127
❑ 97StaCluMOP-127
❑ 97Top-278
❑ 97Ult-434
❑ 97UltGolME-434
❑ 97UltPlaME-434
❑ 97UppDec-549
❑ 98Pac-224
❑ 98PacOnl-425
❑ 98PacOnlR-425
❑ 98PacOnlWC-425
❑ 98PacPlaB-224
❑ 98PacRedT-224
❑ 98PacSil-224
❑ 98Sco-146
❑ 98ScoSS-PP134
❑ 98ScoSSAP-PP134
❑ 98Top-119
❑ 98TopChr-119
❑ 98TopChrR-119
❑ 98TopDevR-119
❑ 98TopDia-119
❑ 98TopMiniC-119
❑ 98Ult-353
❑ 98UltGolM-353
❑ 98UltMas-353
❑ 98UltPlaM-353
❑ 98UppDec-695

Mercedes, Carlos
❑ 96BluOriB-19
❑ 97AubDouTI-9
❑ 98QuaCitRBG-18

Mercedes, Feliciano
❑ 92BluOriC-9
❑ 92BluOriF-2366
❑ 92KanCouCC-17
❑ 92KanCouCF-101
❑ 93FreKeyC-16
❑ 93FreKeyF-1034
❑ 94FreKeyF-2622
❑ 94OriPro-65

Mercedes, Fernando
❑ 92BurAstC-2
❑ 92BurAstF-539

Mercedes, Guillermo
❑ 86MacPirP-14
❑ 92GulCoaRSP-19
❑ 93ChaRaiC-14
❑ 93ChaRaiF-1921
❑ 94ChaRanF-2504
❑ 94Cla-43
❑ 95TulDriTI-14
❑ 96KenIndB-15
❑ 97AkrAer-15

Mercedes, Hector
❑ 89St.CatBJP-2080
❑ 90MyrBeaBJP-2783

Mercedes, Henry
❑ 89MadMusS-26
❑ 89ModA'sC-20
❑ 90MadMusP-2272
❑ 90MidLeaASGS-16
❑ 91CalLeLA-38
❑ 91Cla/Bes-154
❑ 91ModA'sC-22
❑ 91ModA'sP-3091
❑ 92DonRoo-78
❑ 92ProFS7-131
❑ 92TacTigF-2507
❑ 92Ult-424
❑ 93Don-551
❑ 93FleFinE-257
❑ 93FleMajLP-B12
❑ 93LimRocDWB-131
❑ 93Pin-268
❑ 93Sco-290
❑ 93ScoBoyoS-24
❑ 93StaClu-733
❑ 93StaCluFDI-733
❑ 93StaCluMOP-733
❑ 93TacTigF-3035
❑ 93Top-602
❑ 93TopGol-602
❑ 93TopInaM-602
❑ 93TopInaR-602
❑ 93TopMic-602
❑ 94Don-602
❑ 94Pac-457
❑ 94TacTigF-3179
❑ 95OmaRoyTI-21
❑ 96OmaRoyB-19
❑ 97RanDr P-17
❑ 97RanMot-25
❑ 98FreGriG-18

Mercedes, Jose
❑ 93Bow-309
❑ 93BowBayF-2185
❑ 93ClaFS7-55
❑ 93LimRocDWB-43
❑ 94BreMilB-331
❑ 94FleUpd-55
❑ 94Ult-376
❑ 95Don-250
❑ 95DonPreP-250
❑ 95Fle-184
❑ 95Pac-236
❑ 95Top-638
❑ 95Ult-297
❑ 95UltGolM-297
❑ 97BrePol-18
❑ 98Fle-501
❑ 98Pac-122
❑ 98PacInvGems-60
❑ 98PacOnl-406
❑ 98PacOnlR-406
❑ 98PacOnlWC-406
❑ 98PacPlaB-122
❑ 98PacRedT-122
❑ 98PacSil-122

Mercedes, Juan
❑ 91BluOriC-6
❑ 91BluOriP-4125
❑ 92KanCouCC-16
❑ 92KanCouCF-90
❑ 92KanCouCTI-22
❑ 93HunCubC-20
❑ 93HunCubF-3244

Mercedes, Luis
❑ 89FreKeyS-16
❑ 89Sta-102
❑ 90Bes-313
❑ 90EasLeaAP-EL44
❑ 90HagSunB-12
❑ 90HagSunP-1429
❑ 90HagSunS-16
❑ 90ProAaA-24
❑ 90StaFS7-76
❑ 91Bow-94
❑ 91LinDriAAA-461
❑ 91RocRedWLD-461
❑ 91RocRedWP-1916
❑ 91UppDec-745
❑ 92Bow-163
❑ 92Cla1-T63
❑ 92ClaGam-173
❑ 92Don-6
❑ 92Fle-16
❑ 92Lea-130
❑ 92LeaBlaG-130
❑ 92OPC-603
❑ 92Pin-248
❑ 92PinRoo-1
❑ 92PinRooI-5
❑ 92PinTea2-71
❑ 92ProFS7-2
❑ 92RocRedWF-1952
❑ 92Sco-826
❑ 92StaClu-242
❑ 92Top-603
❑ 92TopDeb91-123
❑ 92TopGol-603
❑ 92TopGolW-603
❑ 92TopMic-603
❑ 92TriPla-145
❑ 92UppDec-652
❑ 93Don-645
❑ 93Fle-547
❑ 93GiaPos-26
❑ 93LimRocDWB-52
❑ 93OPC-43
❑ 93PacSpa-345
❑ 93Pin-376
❑ 93ScoBoyoS-4
❑ 93Sel-331
❑ 93StaClu-391
❑ 93StaCluFDI-391
❑ 93StaCluMOP-391
❑ 93Top-446
❑ 93TopGol-446
❑ 93TopInaM-446
❑ 93TopInaR-446
❑ 93TopMic-446
❑ 93Ult-496
❑ 94GiaUSPC-2D
❑ 94GiaUSPC-9C
❑ 94StaCluT-24
❑ 94StaCluTFDI-24

Mercedes, Manuel
❑ 76QuaCitAT-21

Mercer, Mark
❑ 78AshTouT-18
❑ 79TulDriT-10
❑ 80ChaChaT-11
❑ 83OklCit8T-13
❑ 93RanKee-263

Mercerod, George
❑ 85PawRedST-21

Merchant, Andy (James A.)
❑ 76OPC-594
❑ 76Top-594

Merchant, John
❑ 81BatTroT-18

Merchant, Mark
❑ 88AugPirP-1576
❑ 89AugPirP-496
❑ 89CalLeaA-3
❑ 89SanBerSB-27
❑ 89SanBerSCLC-93
❑ 90Bes-277
❑ 90CMC-791
❑ 90WilBilB-16
❑ 90WilBilP-1070
❑ 90WilBilS-17
❑ 91PenPilC-24
❑ 91PenPilP-389
❑ 92JacSunF-3721
❑ 92JacSunS-366
❑ 93ChaLooF-2374
❑ 94ChaLooF-1371
❑ 95ChaLooTI-14
❑ 96NasSouB-16

Mercker, Kent
❑ 87DurBulP-12
❑ 88CarLeaAS-31
❑ 88DurBulS-14
❑ 89RicBraBC-17
❑ 89RicBraC-5
❑ 89RicBraP-835
❑ 89RicBraTI-16
❑ 89TriAAAP-AAA5
❑ 90Bow-6
❑ 90BowTif-6
❑ 90ClaBlu-15
❑ 90CMC-657
❑ 90Don-31
❑ 90Fle-590
❑ 90FleCan-590
❑ 90RicBraBC-8
❑ 90RicBraC-27
❑ 90RicBraTI-22
❑ 90ScoRoo-72T
❑ 90TopDeb89-81
❑ 90UppDec-63
❑ 91Bow-568
❑ 91BraDubP-19
❑ 91BraSubS-25
❑ 91ClaGam-67
❑ 91Don-299
❑ 91FleUpd-74
❑ 91Lea-41
❑ 91OPC-772
❑ 91Sco-79
❑ 91Sco100RS-58
❑ 91StaClu-341
❑ 91StaCluMO-30
❑ 91Top-772
❑ 91TopDesS-772
❑ 91TopMic-772
❑ 91TopRoo-19
❑ 91TopTif-772
❑ 91ToyRoo-19
❑ 91UltUpd-68
❑ 91UppDec-642
❑ 92BraLykP-19
❑ 92BraLykS-23
❑ 92Cla1-T18
❑ 92Don-116
❑ 92Don-616
❑ 92Fle-363
❑ 92Fle-700
❑ 92OPC-596
❑ 92Sco-178
❑ 92Sco-787

- 92StaClu-147
- 92Top-596
- 92TopGol-596
- 92TopGolW-596
- 92TopMic-596
- 92Ult-460
- 92UppDec-472
- 93BraLykP-20
- 93BraLykS-25
- 93BraStaC-11
- 93Don-2
- 93Fle-8
- 93Lea-521
- 93PacSpa-336
- 93Pin-418
- 93StaClu-111
- 93StaCluFDI-111
- 93StaCluMOP-111
- 93Top-144
- 93TopGol-144
- 93TopInaM-144
- 93TopInaR-144
- 93TopMic-144
- 93Ult-309
- 93UppDec-393
- 93UppDecGold-393
- 94BraLykP-23
- 94BraLykS-23
- 94BraUSPC-3D
- 94BraUSPC-11S
- 94ColC-446
- 94ColChoGS-446
- 94ColChoSS-446
- 94Don-203
- 94Fla-132
- 94Fle-368
- 94FleExtB-211
- 94Lea-410
- 94Pac-18
- 94Pin-440
- 94PinArtP-440
- 94PinMusC-440
- 94Sco-126
- 94ScoGolR-126
- 94SpoRoo-28
- 94SpoRooAP-28
- 94StaClu-360
- 94StaCluFDI-360
- 94StaCluGR-360
- 94StaCluMOP-360
- 94StaCluT-39
- 94StaCluTFDI-39
- 94Top-718
- 94TopGol-718
- 94TopSpa-718
- 94Ult-447
- 94UppDec-442
- 94UppDecED-442
- 95ColCho-163
- 95ColChoGS-163
- 95ColChoSS-163
- 95Don-54
- 95DonPreP-54
- 95Fla-328
- 95Fle-314
- 95Lea-98
- 95Pin-436
- 95PinArtP-436
- 95PinMusC-436
- 95Sco-313
- 95Sco-525
- 95ScoGolR-313
- 95ScoGolR-525
- 95ScoPlaTS-313
- 95ScoPlaTS-525
- 95StaClu-304
- 95StaCluMOP-304
- 95StaCluSTWS-304
- 95StaCluVR-160
- 95StaCluVRMO-160
- 95Top-202
- 95TopCyb-115
- 95Ult-131
- 95UltGolM-131
- 95UppDec-291
- 95UppDecED-291
- 95UppDecEDG-291
- 96BalOriP-21
- 96ColCho-761
- 96Don-522
- 96DonPreP-522
- 96Fla-8
- 96Fle-302
- 96FleTif-302
- 96FleUpd-U5
- 96FleUpdTC-U5
- 96OriFle-10
- 96Pac-5
- 96Pin-340
- 96PinFoil-340
- 96Sco-219
- 96Top-266
- 96Ult-307
- 96UltGolM-307
- 96UppDec-482U
- 97Cir-210
- 97CirRav-210
- 97DurBulATI-9
- 97Fle-566
- 97FleTif-566
- 97Ult-435
- 97UltGolME-435
- 97UltPlaME-435
- 98Fle-397
- 98PacInvGems-137
- 98PacOnl-622
- 98PacOnlR-622
- 98PacOnlWC-622
- 98Sco-220
- 98Top-124
- 98TopChr-124
- 98TopChrR-124
- 98TopDevR-124
- 98TopDia-124
- 98TopMiniC-124
- 98Ult-395
- 98UltGolM-395
- 98UltMas-395
- 98UltPlaM-395
- 98UppDec-715
- 99Fle-469
- 99FleSta9-469
- 99FleWarT-469
- 99Pac-357
- 99PacPlaB-357
- 99PacRed-357
- 99SkyMolMOA-13
- 99UppDec-471
- 99UppDecEL1-471
- 99UppDecEL2-471

Mercurio, Tony
- 88TidTidCa-30

Meredith, Ryan
- 93BriTigF-3645

Meredith, Steve
- 90SalSpuCLC-136

Merejo, Domingo
- 87WatPirP-13
- 88WatPirP-21
- 89SalBucS-12
- 90SalBucS-12

Merejo, Jesus
- 88UtiBluSP-9
- 89UtiBluSP-16

Merejo, Luis
- 86SalAngC-92
- 87QuaCitAP-11
- 88PalSprACLC-90
- 88PalSprAP-1437
- 89MidAngGS-23
- 89TexLeaAGS-6
- 90MidAngGS-23

Meridith, Ron
- 80ColAstT-19
- 81TucTorT-16
- 82HawIslT-16
- 83TucTorT-5
- 84IowCubT-27
- 85IowCubT-17
- 86Don-533
- 86Fle-374
- 86IowCubP-18
- 87OklCit8P-13
- 87RanMot-16
- 88LouRedBTI-34
- 93RanKee-264

Merietta, Lou
- 79CedRapGT-22

Merigliano, Frank
- 88UtiBluSP-22
- 89SouBenWSGS-8
- 90SarWhiSS-15
- 91BirBarLD-67
- 91BirBarP-1453
- 91LinDriAA-67
- 92BirBarF-2579
- 92BirBarS-89
- 93BirBarF-1188
- 94VenLinU-146

Merila, Mark
- 92Min-13
- 93BazTeaU-15
- 93TopTra-70T
- 94SpoIndC-20
- 94SpoIndF-3333
- 95IdaFalBTI-22

Merkle, Fred
- 09ColChiE-192
- 09PhiCarE-18
- 09RamT20-79
- 09SpoNewSM-32
- 09T206-247
- 09T206-248
- 10CouT21-186
- 10CouT21-305
- 10DomDisP-83
- 10E12AmeCDCE125-25
- 10RedCroT-53
- 10RedCroT-224
- 10SweCapPP-119
- 11BasBatEU-29
- 11HelSta-133
- 11MecDFT-34
- 11PinT-5-252
- 11PloCanE-47
- 11S74Sil-90
- 11SpoLifCW-250
- 11SpoLifM-213
- 11T205-118
- 11TurRedT-108
- 12ColRedB-192
- 12ColTinT-192
- 12HasTriFT-30B
- 12HasTriFT-32
- 14CraJacE-78
- 14PieStaT-73
- 15CraJacE-78
- 15SpoNewM-116
- 16BF2FP-82
- 16SpoNewM-118
- 17ColE13-116
- 19W514-74
- 60NuHi-17
- 61NuSco-417
- 67SpoHobFC-17
- 68SCFOldT-31
- 72ClaCar-15
- 74CapPub-37
- 81ConTSN-27
- 86ConSer1-49
- 88ConSer4-19
- 90DodTar-516
- 94ConTSN-1260
- 94ConTSNB-1260
- 94UppDecTAE-17
- 95ConTSN-1406

Merloni, Lou
- 94SarRedSC-19
- 94SarRedSF-1959
- 95TreThuTI-21
- 96Bow-322
- 96BowFoi-322
- 96TreThuB-22
- 97TreThuB-21
- 98LeaRS-306
- 98LeaRSLHolo-306
- 98LeaRSLong-306
- 98LeaRTrue-306
- 98PawRedSQ-21
- 98PawRedSQ-30

Merrell, Philip
- 96BilMusTI-22
- 98ChaAllCM-8

Merrick, Brett
- 95WatIndTI-19
- 97KinIndB-15
- 98AkrAerM-13

Merrick, Jim
- 96HelBreTI-31
- 97HelBreB-2

Merrifield, Bill
- 85MidAngT-19
- 86MidAngP-17
- 87EdmTraP-2074
- 88OklCit8C-15
- 88OklCit8P-36

Merrifield, Doug
- 81SpoIndT-12
- 82SalLakCGT-1
- 83SalLakCGT-26
- 86CalCanP-14
- 88CalCanC-22
- 88CalCanP-787
- 90KnoBluJB-7
- 97HagSunB-30

Merrill, Durwood
- 88T/MUmp-30
- 89T/MUmp-28
- 90T/MUmp-27

Merrill, Ethan
- 94UtiBluSC-20
- 96SarRedSB-23
- 97SarRedS-16

Merrill, Mike
- 86DurBulP-18
- 87DurBulP-17

Merrill, Stump (Carl)
- 77WesHavYT-16
- 79WesHavYT-8
- 80NasSouTI-15
- 84ColCliP-15
- 84ColCliT-23
- 85ColCliP-16
- 85YanTCMP-3
- 86YanTCM-8
- 89EasLeaDDP-DD44
- 90CMC-224
- 90CMC-225
- 90ColCliC-24
- 90ColCliC-25
- 90ColCliP-3
- 90ColCliP-693
- 90ProAAAF-343
- 90TopTra-74T
- 90TopTraT-74T
- 90YanScoNW-1
- 91OPC-429
- 91Top-429
- 91TopDesS-429
- 91TopMic-429
- 91TopTif-429
- 93ColCliF-1126
- 93ColCliP-14
- 93ColCliP-24
- 94ColCliF-2967
- 94ColCliP-20
- 96ColCliB-1
- 97ColCliB-2
- 97ColCliD-16
- 98ColCliM-2
- 98ColCliM-3

Merriman, Brett
- 88BurIndP-1795
- 89MiaMirIS-14
- 89Sta-182
- 89WatIndS-14
- 90PalSprAP-2574
- 91PalSprAP-2009
- 92MidAngF-4025
- 92MidAngOHP-16
- 92MidAngS-466
- 93Top-593
- 93TopGol-593
- 93TopInaM-593
- 93TopInaR-593
- 93TopMic-593
- 94SalLakBF-813
- 95Sco-279
- 95ScoGolR-279
- 95ScoPlaTS-279

Merriman, Damione
- 98BriWhiSQ-21

Merriman, Lloyd
- 49EurSta-90
- 50Bow-173
- 51Bow-72
- 52Bow-78
- 55Bow-135
- 85TCMPpl1-16

Merritt, Bill
- 98CamPepP-56

Merritt, Ed
- 66TolMudHTI-17

Merritt, George
- 09ColChiE-193A
- 09ColChiE-193B
- 09T206-445
- 11T205-189
- 12ColRedB-193A
- 12ColRedB-193B
- 12ColTinT-193A
- 12ColTinT-193B

Merritt, Jim
- 66OPC-97
- 66Top-97
- 66TopVen-97
- 66TwiFaiG-8
- 67CokCapTw-4
- 67DexPre-147
- 67Top-523
- 67TwiTeal-11
- 68OPC-64
- 68Top-64
- 68TopVen-64
- 69MLBOffS-132
- 69Top-661
- 70DayDaiNM-29
- 70MLBOffS-32
- 70Top-616
- 71BazNumT-7
- 71BazUnn-25
- 71Kel-25
- 71MilDud-54
- 71MLBOffS-65
- 71OPC-420
- 71Top-420
- 71TopCoi-129
- 71TopTat-124
- 72Top-738
- 73RanTeal-17
- 74OPC-318
- 74Top-318
- 75OPC-83
- 75RanPos-22
- 75Top-83
- 75TopMin-83
- 78TwiFri-38
- 93RanKee-265

Merritt, John
- 21Zee-127

Merritt, Lloyd
- 58Top-231
- 59DarFar-11
- 84SavCarT-21
- 85SprCarT-10

Merriweather, James
- 92FayGenC-10
- 92FayGenF-2176

Mersh, Neil
- 78TacYanC-54
- 79WesHavYT-30

Merson, John
- 52Top-375
- 53RedSoxTI-20
- 82Bow195E-263
- 83TopRep5-375

Mertens, Warren
- 78OrlTwiT-15

Mertes, Sam
- 03BreE10-104
- 11SpoLifCW-251

Merullo, Lenny
- 42CubTeal-14
- 43CubTeal-16
- 44CubTeal-15
- 48AngTeal-20
- 77TCMTheWY-84
- 79DiaGre-107
- 83TCMPla1945-25

Merullo, Matt
- 87DayBeaAP-14
- 88BirBarB-22
- 88SouLeaAJ-7
- 89BirBarADB-25
- 89DonRoo-50
- 89FleUpd-21
- 90Bes-167
- 90BirBarADB-25
- 90BirBarB-3
- 90BirBarP-1112
- 90CMC-819
- 90Fle-542
- 90FleCan-542
- 90Sco-605
- 90TopDeb89-82
- 90UppDec-67
- 91FleUpd-13
- 91StaClu-382
- 91WhiSoxK-5
- 92Don-264
- 92Fle-90
- 92OPC-615
- 92Sco-367
- 92StaClu-404
- 92Top-615
- 92TopGol-615
- 92TopGolW-615
- 92TopMic-615
- 92TriPla-121
- 92VanCanF-2725
- 92WhiSoxK-5
- 94StaCluT-148
- 94StaCluTFDI-148
- 96IowCubB-19

Mesa, Audy
- 90BenBucL-29
- 91PocPioP-3790
- 91PocPioSP-24

Mesa, Baltazar
- 90BakDodCLC-232

Mesa, Ivan
- 79AppFoxT-12
- 81GleFalWST-13
- 82TolMudHT-15

Mesa, Jose
- 85KinBluJT-8
- 86VenGulP-14
- 87KnoBluJP-1494
- 88Don-601
- 88RocRedWC-3
- 88RocRedWP-206
- 88RocRedWTI-13
- 89HagSunB-3
- 89RocRedWP-1636
- 90BalOriP-17
- 90HagSunB-28
- 90HagSunP-1410
- 90HagSunS-17
- 90ProAaA-4
- 91BalOriP-19
- 91Bow-91
- 91Don-765
- 91FleUpd-3
- 91Lea-166
- 91OPC-512
- 91OriCro-297
- 91StaClu-380
- 91Top-512
- 91TopDesS-512
- 91TopMic-512
- 91TopTif-512
- 91UppDec-703
- 92BalOriP-20
- 92Don-773
- 92Fle-17
- 92Lea-351
- 92LeaBlaG-351
- 92OPC-310
- 92Pin-496
- 92Sco-707
- 92SpoIllFK1-485
- 92StaClu-888
- 92Top-310
- 92TopGol-310
- 92TopGolW-310
- 92TopMic-310
- 92Ult-305
- 93Don-465
- 93Fla-197
- 93Fle-596
- 93IndWUA-20
- 93Lea-374
- 93LimRocDWB-62
- 93PacBeiA-6
- 93PacSpa-414
- 93Pin-436
- 93Sco-424
- 93Top-696
- 93TopGol-696
- 93TopInaM-696
- 93TopInaR-696
- 93TopMic-696
- 93UppDec-798
- 93UppDecGold-798
- 94ColC-205
- 94ColChoGS-205
- 94ColChoSS-205
- 94Don-182
- 94Fin-138
- 94FinRef-138
- 94Fla-284
- 94Fle-113
- 94FleExtB-62
- 94Lea-438
- 94Pac-177
- 94Pin-337
- 94PinArtP-337
- 94PinMusC-337
- 94Sco-419
- 94ScoGolR-419
- 94Top-7
- 94TopGol-7
- 94TopSpa-7
- 94TriPla-116
- 94Ult-46
- 95Don-58
- 95DonPreP-58
- 95DonTopotO-61
- 95Fin-267
- 95FinRef-267
- 95Fle-140
- 95Sco-196
- 95ScoGolR-196
- 95ScoPlaTS-196
- 95StaClu-550
- 95StaCluMOP-550

- 95StaCluSTDW-I550
- 95StaCluSTMP-16
- 95StaCluSTWS-550
- 95Top-161
- 95TopCyb-96
- 96Baz-55
- 96Cir-35
- 96CirRav-35
- 96ColCho-9
- 96ColCho-121
- 96ColCho-271
- 96ColChoGS-9
- 96ColChoGS-121
- 96ColChoGS-271
- 96ColChoSS-9
- 96ColChoSS-121
- 96ColChoSS-271
- 96Don-315
- 96DonPreP-315
- 96EmoXL-52
- 96Fin-B177
- 96FinRef-B177
- 96Fla-70
- 96Fle-91
- 96FleTif-91
- 96IndFle-8
- 96Lea-46
- 96LeaPrePB-46
- 96LeaPrePG-46
- 96LeaPrePS-46
- 96LeaSigA-154
- 96LeaSigAG-154
- 96LeaSigAS-154
- 96MetUni-49
- 96MetUniP-49
- 96Pac-297
- 96PacEstL-EL20
- 96PacPriFT-FT10
- 96PanSti-126
- 96PanSti-182
- 96SchDis-14
- 96Sco-186
- 96ScoDugC-A101
- 96ScoDugCAP-A101
- 96StaClu-4
- 96StaClu-262
- 96StaCluEPB-4
- 96StaCluEPG-4
- 96StaCluEPS-4
- 96StaCluMO-27
- 96StaCluMOP-4
- 96StaCluMOP-262
- 96StaCluMOP-TSCA10
- 96StaCluTA-10
- 96Stu-70
- 96StuPrePB-70
- 96StuPrePG-70
- 96StuPrePS-70
- 96Top-231
- 96Top-276
- 96TopChr-91
- 96TopChr-111
- 96TopChrR-91
- 96TopChrR-111
- 96TopGal-19
- 96TopGalPPI-19
- 96TopLas-123
- 96Ult-50
- 96UltGolM-50
- 96UppDec-57
- 96UppDecPHE-H13
- 96UppDecPreH-H13
- 97Cir-132
- 97CirRav-132
- 97ColCho-92
- 97ColChoT-CI7
- 97Don-136
- 97DonGolPP-136
- 97DonSilPP-136
- 97DonTea-79
- 97DonTeaSPE-79
- 97Fin-93
- 97FinRef-93
- 97FlaShoLC-136
- 97FlaShoLeg0-136
- 97FlaShoLeg1-136
- 97FlaShoM-A136
- 97FlaShoM-B136
- 97FlaShoM-C136
- 97FlaShoR0-136
- 97FlaShoR1-136
- 97FlaShoR2-136
- 97Fle-83
- 97FleTif-83
- 97Lea-153
- 97LeaFraM-153
- 97LeaFraMDC-153
- 97MetUni-84
- 97Pac-76
- 97PacLigB-76
- 97PacSil-76
- 97StaClu-230
- 97StaCluMat-230
- 97StaCluMOP-230
- 97Top-153
- 97TopChr-59
- 97TopChrR-59
- 97TopGal-81
- 97TopGalPPI-81
- 97Ult-52
- 97UltGolME-52
- 97UltPlaME-52
- 98ColCho-76
- 98Fin-161
- 98FinNo--161
- 98FinNo-R-161
- 98FinRef-161
- 98Fle-517
- 98Pac-75
- 98PacOnl-224
- 98PacOnlR-224
- 98PacOnlWC-224
- 98PacPlaB-75
- 98PacRedT-75
- 98PacSil-75
- 98PinSna-CI10
- 98Top-216
- 98TopChr-216
- 98TopChrR-216
- 98TopDevR-216
- 98TopDia-216
- 98TopMiniC-216
- 98UppDec-346
- 99Pac-384
- 99PacCroC-254
- 99PacCroCPB-254
- 99PacPlaB-384
- 99PacRed-384
- 99SkyPre-125
- 99SkyPreR-125
- 99UppDec-489
- 99UppDecEL1-489
- 99UppDecEL2-489
- 99UppDecM-196
- 99UppDecMGS-196
- 99UppDecMHFS-196
- 99UppDecMSS-196

Mesa, Pablo
- 91PomBlaBPB-9

Mesa, Rafael
- 94BurIndC-15
- 94BurIndF-3788
- 95KinIndTI-19
- 96KenIndB-16
- 97AkrAer-16

Mesewicz, Mark
- 92WelPirF-1320
- 93AugPirC-13
- 93AugPirF-1539
- 94CarMudF-1577
- 95LynHilTI-16

Mesh, Mike
- 85PawRedST-8
- 86PawRedSP-14
- 87PawRedSP-68
- 87PawRedST-15
- 88PawRedSC-18
- 88PawRedSP-463
- 89OmaRoyC-16
- 89OmaRoyP-1730

Meskauskas, John
- 94BenRocC-17
- 94BenRocF-3597
- 95AshTouUTI-27

Mesner, Steve
- 41CarW75-17
- 46SunBre-14
- 47SigOil-65
- 47SunBre-12

Messaros, Mike
- 80CedRapRT-20

Messenger, Bobby
- 11PinT-5-762

Messer, Doug
- 87PocGiaTB-1
- 89SalSpuCLC-125
- 89SalSpuP-1817
- 91RenSilSCLC-11

Messerly, Mike (Michael)
- 88SouOreAP-1704
- 89MadMusS-7
- 90ModA'sC-21
- 90ModA'sCLC-160
- 90ModA'sP-2221
- 91Cla/Bes-44
- 91ModA'sC-20
- 91ModA'sP-3097

Messersmith, Andy (John)
- 66SeaPop-13
- 69AngJacitB-8
- 69Top-296
- 70DayDaiNM-53
- 70MLBOffS-176
- 70OPC-72
- 70OPC-430
- 70Top-72
- 70Top-430
- 70TopPos-9
- 70TopSup-25
- 71AngJacitB-7
- 71MilDud-18
- 71MLBOffS-351
- 71OPC-15
- 71Top-15
- 71TopCoi-112
- 72Kel-42
- 72MilBra-235
- 72OPC-160
- 72SevTraC-35
- 72Top-160
- 72TopPos-18
- 73OPC-515
- 73Top-515
- 74OPC-267
- 74Top-267
- 74TopSta-47
- 75Hos-79
- 75HosTwi-79
- 75Kel-30
- 75OPC-310
- 75OPC-440
- 75SSPPuzB-17
- 75Top-310
- 75Top-440
- 75TopMin-310
- 75TopMin-440
- 76AtlBraP-19
- 76BlaDis-36A
- 76BlaDis-36B
- 76BucDis-36A
- 76BucDis-36B
- 76CarDis-36A
- 76CarDis-36B
- 76CraDis-36A
- 76CraDis-36B
- 76DailsID-36A
- 76DailsID-36B
- 76IsaDis-36A
- 76IsaDis-36B
- 76OPC-199
- 76OPC-201
- 76OPC-203
- 76OPC-305
- 76OrbDis-36A
- 76OrbDis-36B
- 76RedBarD-36A
- 76RedBarD-36B
- 76SafDis-36A
- 76SafDis-36B
- 76SSP-70
- 76Top-199
- 76Top-201
- 76Top-203
- 76Top-305
- 76TowCluD-36A
- 76TowCluD-36B
- 77BurCheD-213
- 77ChiWilD-45
- 77DailsID-45
- 77DetCaeD-45
- 77HolInnD-45
- 77Hos-150
- 77Kel-54
- 77MSADis-45
- 77OPC-155
- 77RCColC-42
- 77SagDis-45
- 77sDis-45
- 77Top-80
- 77TopCloS-28
- 77WenDis-45
- 77ZipDis-45
- 78OPC-79
- 78RCColC-17
- 78Top-156
- 78WifBalD-50
- 79OPC-139
- 79Top-278
- 87DodSmoA-22
- 88AlaGolAA60TI-5
- 89DodSmoG-85
- 90DodTar-518
- 92DodStaTA-14
- 92YanWIZ7-113

Messick, J.T.
- 95ButCopKtl-15

Messier, Tom
- 84EveGiaC-30A
- 86FreGiaSB-10

Messitt, John
- 87OldJudN-343

Messman, Joseph
- 97AubDouTI-19
- 98QuaCitRBG-19

Messner, Jake
- 96BurIndB-26
- 97BurIndG-19
- 98ColRedSM-24

Mestek, Barney
- 75WatDodT-14

Metcalf, Clyde
- 90HigSchPLS-24

Metcalf, Scott
- 91PerHeaF-16
- 92BluOriC-10
- 92BluOriF-2367
- 93AlbPolCB-17
- 93AlbPolF-2033
- 93AusFut-64

Metcalf, Thomas
- 64ChatheY-18
- 64Top-281
- 64TopVen-281
- 65ChaTheY-15
- 92YanWIZ6-84

Metcalfe, Mike
- 94BakDodC-17
- 94SigRooDP-63
- 94SigRooDPS-63
- 94StaCluDP-39
- 94StaCluDPFDI-39
- 95Top-571
- 95VerBeaDTI-15
- 96BesAutS-60
- 96Exc-180
- 97CalLeaATI-18
- 97SanBerS-23
- 98FleUpd-U81
- 98SanAntMG-16

Metheney, Michael
- 93BatCliCB-20

Metheney, Nelson
- 93BatCliF-3143
- 94ClePhiC-20
- 94ClePhiF-2525
- 95ClePhiF-215

Metheny, Bud
- 43YanSta-19
- 77TCMTheWY-55
- 83TCMPla1944-7

Methven, Marlin
- 81WatIndT-23
- 82ChaLooT-12
- 82WatIndF-18

Metil, Bill
- 82CedRapRT-18

Metkovich, George
- 46RedSoxTI-16
- 47IndTeal-19
- 47IndVanPP-18
- 48SigOil-18
- 49BowPCL-2
- 49RemBre-18
- 50RemBre-17
- 51Bow-274
- 52Bow-108
- 52Top-310
- 53Top-58
- 54BraJohC-27
- 55BraGolS-27
- 75OakOak2A-22
- 75RedSox1T-26
- 79DiaGre-236
- 83TopRep5-310
- 91TopArc1-58

Metkovich, John
- 52Par-89

Metoyer, Tony
- 86AshTouP-20
- 87OscAstP-12
- 89MiaMirIS-13

Metro, Charles
- 45A'sTeal-22
- 46RemBre-11
- 70OPC-16
- 70RoyTeal-22
- 70Top-16

Metropolitans, New York
- 94OriofB-40

Mets, Columbia
- 90ColMetGS-30
- 90ColMetPPI-7
- 92ColMetPI-36
- 92ColMetPI-37

Mets, Hyannis
- 88CapCodPB-30

Mets, Kingsport
- 93KinMetC-28

Mets, New York
- 62GuyPotCP-14
- 63Top-473
- 64Top-27
- 64TopTatl-14
- 64TopVen-27
- 65Top-551
- 66OPC-172
- 66Top-172
- 66TopRubl-114
- 66TopVen-172
- 67OPC-42
- 67Top-42
- 68Top-401
- 69FleCloS-15
- 69FleCloS-34
- 69TopStaA-15
- 70FleWorS-66
- 70OPC-1
- 70Top-1
- 71FleWorS-67
- 71OPC-641
- 71Top-641
- 71TopTat-16
- 72OPC-362
- 72Top-362
- 73OPC-389
- 73OPCBTC-16
- 73Top-389
- 73TopBluTC-16
- 74OPC-56
- 74OPCTC-16
- 74Top-56
- 74TopTeaC-16
- 78Top-356
- 81MetMagM-1
- 81MetMagM-2
- 81MetMagM-3
- 81MetMagM-4
- 82MetGal62-24
- 83FleSta-240
- 83FleSti-NNO
- 83FleSti-NNO
- 85MetColP-29
- 86MetColP-1
- 87FleGlo-WS8
- 87FleWaxBC-C1
- 87FleWorS-8
- 87MetColP-1
- 87MetFanC-9
- 87SpoTeaL-2
- 88MetColP-12
- 88MetKah-NNO
- 88PanSti-475
- 88RedFolSB-126
- 89FleWaxBC-C1
- 89MetColP-1
- 89MetFanC-NNO
- 89MetKah-31
- 90FleWaxBC-C17
- 90MetColP-1
- 90MetKah-NNO
- 90PubIntS-629
- 90RedFolSB-128
- 91MetColP-2
- 91MetKah-NNO
- 91PanCanT1-118
- 91PanCanT1-119
- 91PanCanT1-130
- 92MetColP-1
- 92MetKah-NNO
- 93MetColP-21
- 93MetKah-NNO
- 94ImpProP-23
- 94Met69T-2
- 94MetColP-1
- 94Sco-655
- 94ScoGolR-655
- 95MetColP-1
- 95PacPriTL-23
- 95PanSti-133
- 96Met69Y-9
- 96PanSti-29
- 99Vic-248

Mettler, Bradley
- 85GreHorT-27

Metts, Carey
- 89EriOriS-13

Metz, Leonard
- 26Zee-98
- 27Zee-74

Metzger, Butch (Clarence E.)
- 75HawIslC-19
- 76OPC-593
- 76Top-593
- 77BurCheD-127
- 77Car5-14
- 77CarTeal-14
- 77Hos-99
- 77PadSchC-40
- 77Top-215
- 78MetDaiPA-17
- 78Top-431
- 80RicBraT-13
- 91MetWIZ-266

Metzger, Curt
- 86ArkTraP-15

Metzger, Erik
- 96LowSpiB-19
- 97LowSpiB-14

Metzger, George
- 09ObaT21-263
- 11PacCoaBD-41
- 11Zee-17
- 12HomRunKE-12
- 12ObaPreT-12
- 12Zee-15
- 13Zee-15
- 14Zee-17
- 15Zee-16

Metzger, Roger
- 70AstPho-17
- 71AstCok-7
- 71AstTeal-15
- 71OPC-404
- 71Top-404
- 72AstTeal-16
- 72OPC-217
- 72Top-217
- 73LinPor-82
- 73OPC-395
- 73Top-395
- 74AstFouTIP-4
- 74OPC-224
- 74Top-224
- 74TopSta-34
- 75AstPos-22
- 75Hos-115
- 75OPC-541
- 75Top-541
- 75TopMin-541
- 76Hos-67
- 76HouAstP-22
- 76OPC-297
- 76SSP-57
- 76Top-297
- 77BurCheD-5
- 77Hos-20
- 77OPC-44
- 77Top-481
- 78AstBurK-15
- 78Hos-85
- 78Top-697
- 79GiaPol-16
- 79Top-167
- 80GiaPol-16
- 80GiaTeal-17
- 80OPC-164
- 80Top-311
- 82AstAstI-1
- 86AstGreT-3
- 87AstShoSPO-20
- 87AstShoSTw-27
- 87AstShowSTh-25

Metzler, Alex
- 29ExhFou-20
- 94ConTSN-1265
- 94ConTSNB-1265

Metzler, Rod
- 97SpoIndG-18
- 98LanLugQ-20

Meulens, Hensley
- 87PriWilYP-1
- 88AlbYanP-1349

❑ 88BasAmeAAB-1
❑ 88EasLeaAP-3
❑ 89AlbYanB-17
❑ 89AlbYanP-337
❑ 89AlbYanSt-13
❑ 89ClaTraO-110
❑ 89Don-547
❑ 89FleUpd-51
❑ 89ScoHot1R-12
❑ 89Sta-99
❑ 89StaFutS-19
❑ 89StaFutS-20
❑ 89UppDec-746
❑ 90AlbDecGB-23
❑ 90ClaBlu-133A
❑ 90ClaBlu-133B
❑ 90CMC-209
❑ 90ColCliC-9
❑ 90ColCliP-23
❑ 90ColCliP-682
❑ 90Fle-449
❑ 90FleCan-449
❑ 90OPC-83
❑ 90ProAAAF-332
❑ 90Sco-636
❑ 90Sco100RS-53
❑ 90Top-83
❑ 90TopDeb89-83
❑ 90TopTif-83
❑ 90TopTVY-54
❑ 90TriAllGP-AAA13
❑ 90UppDec-546
❑ 91Bow-181
❑ 91Cla1-T69
❑ 91ClaGam-179
❑ 91Don-31
❑ 91FleUpd-47
❑ 91Lea-349
❑ 91MajLeaCP-3
❑ 91OPC-259
❑ 91OPCPre-80
❑ 91Sco-828
❑ 91Sco100RS-84
❑ 91ScoAllF-4
❑ 91ScoRoo-39
❑ 91StaClu-503
❑ 91Stu-98
❑ 91Top-259
❑ 91TopDesS-259
❑ 91TopMic-259
❑ 91TopTif-259
❑ 91Ult-240
❑ 91UppDec-675
❑ 92Bow-338
❑ 92ColCliP-360
❑ 92ColCliP-18
❑ 92ColCliS-111
❑ 92Don-711
❑ 92Fle-238
❑ 92OPC-154
❑ 92Pin-366
❑ 92Sco-89
❑ 92Sco100RS-72
❑ 92ScoProP-25
❑ 92SkyAAAF-51
❑ 92StaClu-64
❑ 92Top-154
❑ 92TopGol-154
❑ 92TopGolW-154
❑ 92TopMic-154
❑ 92TriA AAS-111
❑ 92Ult-106
❑ 92UppDec-606
❑ 92YanWIZ8-119
❑ 93ColCliF-1124
❑ 93ColCliP-19
❑ 93LimRocDWB-139
❑ 93Pin-124
❑ 93Sco-595
❑ 93Top-549
❑ 93TopGol-549
❑ 93TopInaM-549
❑ 93TopInaR-549
❑ 93TopMic-549
❑ 93Ult-245
❑ 98TusSidM-27

Meury, Bill
❑ 91Cla/Bes-339
❑ 91WatDiaC-18
❑ 91WatDiaP-1265
❑ 92HigDesMC-4

Meusel, Bob (Robert W.)
❑ 19Zee-142
❑ 20GasAmeMBD-13
❑ 20NatCarE-63
❑ 20WalMaiW-31
❑ 21E121So1-63
❑ 21E121So8-60
❑ 21Exh-114
❑ 21KoBreWSI-40
❑ 22E120-68
❑ 22W572-64
❑ 22W575-80
❑ 22WilPatV-19
❑ 23Lec-5
❑ 23W501-35
❑ 23W503-19
❑ 23W515-21
❑ 23WilChoV-98
❑ 25Exh-98
❑ 26Exh-101
❑ 27AmeCarE126-39
❑ 27Exh-51
❑ 27YorCarE-7
❑ 28StaPlaCE-47
❑ 28W502-7
❑ 28Yue-7
❑ 31W517-49
❑ 75Yan192T-15
❑ 77GalGloG-133
❑ 79Yan192T-18
❑ 81ConTSN-43
❑ 84Yan192G-6
❑ 86ConSer1-34
❑ 87ConSer2-21
❑ 87Yan192T-7
❑ 88ConSer5-22
❑ 91ConTSN-122
❑ 92MegRut-159

Meusel, Irish (Emil)
❑ 17Zee-13
❑ 20NatCarE-64
❑ 21E121So1-62
❑ 21E121So8-59
❑ 21KoBreWSI-16
❑ 21Nei-55
❑ 22E120-188
❑ 22W572-65
❑ 22W573-81
❑ 22W575-81
❑ 22WilPatV-20
❑ 23Lec-6
❑ 23MapCriV-17
❑ 23W501-36
❑ 23W501-114
❑ 23W503-18
❑ 23W515-21
❑ 23WilChoV-97
❑ 25Exh-36
❑ 26Exh-38
❑ 27AmeCarE126-34
❑ 28Zee-85
❑ 81ConTSN-42
❑ 87ConSer2-22
❑ 90DodTar-519

Meyer, Alfred
❑ 77St.PetCT-22

Meyer, Allen
❑ 86AncGlaPTI-24

Meyer, Basil
❑ 88KenTwiP-1404
❑ 89VisOakCLC-94
❑ 89VisOakP-1445
❑ 90CMC-755
❑ 90OrlSunRB-17
❑ 90OrlSunRP-1079
❑ 90OrlSunRS-11

Meyer, Benny
❑ 90DodTar-520

Meyer, Bob B.
❑ 64Top-488
❑ 65OPC-219
❑ 65Top-219
❑ 67VanMouSO-16
❑ 70BreMcD-20
❑ 70BreMil-16
❑ 70Top-667
❑ 71MLBOffS-445
❑ 71OPC-456
❑ 71Top-456
❑ 92YanWIZ6-85
❑ 94BreMilB-248

Meyer, Bobby
❑ 95GreFalDTI-14
❑ 96GreFalDB-20
❑ 96YakBeaTI-5

Meyer, Brad
❑ 88GasRanP-1015

Meyer, Brian
❑ 86AubAstP-16
❑ 87OscAstP-13
❑ 88ColAstB-5
❑ 88SouLeaAJ-31
❑ 89AstSmo-27
❑ 89Bow-319
❑ 89BowTif-319
❑ 89Don-640
❑ 89TucTorC-9
❑ 89TucTorJP-17
❑ 89TucTorP-189
❑ 90CMC-604
❑ 90Don-648
❑ 90Fle-232
❑ 90FleCan-232
❑ 90OPC-766
❑ 90ProAAAF-192
❑ 90Top-766
❑ 90TopTif-766
❑ 90TucTorC-2
❑ 90TucTorP-202
❑ 90UppDec-22
❑ 91Fle-510

Meyer, Dan
❑ 75DetTigP-21
❑ 75OPC-620
❑ 75Top-620
❑ 75TopMin-620
❑ 76DetTigP-21
❑ 76Hos-132
❑ 76OPC-242
❑ 76SSP-365
❑ 76Top-242
❑ 77Hos-135
❑ 77MarPos-11
❑ 77OPC-186
❑ 77Top-527
❑ 78Hos-97
❑ 78Kel-12
❑ 78OPC-55
❑ 78Top-57
❑ 79OPC-363
❑ 79Top-683
❑ 80MarPos-16
❑ 80OPC-207
❑ 80Top-396
❑ 81Don-43
❑ 81Fle-603
❑ 81MarPol-5
❑ 81MarPos-21
❑ 81OPC-143
❑ 81Top-143
❑ 81TopScr-40
❑ 81TopSti-125
❑ 82Don-176
❑ 82Fle-512
❑ 82Top-413
❑ 82TopTra-70T
❑ 83Don-413
❑ 83Fle-527
❑ 83Top-208
❑ 83TopSti-110
❑ 84Fle-455
❑ 84Nes792-609
❑ 84TacTigC-96
❑ 84Top-609
❑ 84TopTif-609
❑ 85A'sMot-23
❑ 85NasSouTI-14
❑ 86MarGreT-7
❑ 89PacSenL-155
❑ 89T/MSenL-77
❑ 89TopSenL-97

Meyer, David
❑ 94OneYanC-14
❑ 94OneYanF-3788
❑ 94StaCluDP-64
❑ 94StaCluDPFDI-64
❑ 96TamYanY-18
❑ 98MadBlaW-11

Meyer, Jack
❑ 56Top-269
❑ 57Top-162
❑ 58Top-186
❑ 59Top-269
❑ 60Lea-137
❑ 60Top-64
❑ 60TopVen-64
❑ 61Top-111

Meyer, Jake
❑ 97AppLeaTPB-25
❑ 97BriWhiSB-7
❑ 97UCLBruTI-12
❑ 98HicCraM-20

Meyer, Jay
❑ 91HunCubC-14
❑ 91HunCubP-3330
❑ 92PeoChiC-22
❑ 92PeoChiTI-15

Meyer, Joey
❑ 86VanCanP-17
❑ 87DenZepP-5
❑ 87Don-460
❑ 88BrePol-23
❑ 88BreTeal-23
❑ 88Don-36
❑ 88DonBasB-239
❑ 88DonRoo-38
❑ 88Fle-645
❑ 88FleGlo-645
❑ 88FleUpd-40
❑ 88FleUpdG-40
❑ 88Lea-36
❑ 88ScoRoo-75T
❑ 88ScoRooG-75T
❑ 88Top-312
❑ 88TopClo-72
❑ 88TopTif-312
❑ 89Bow-138
❑ 89BowTif-138
❑ 89BreGar-13
❑ 89BrePol-23
❑ 89ClaLigB-10
❑ 89Don-339
❑ 89Fle-191
❑ 89FleGlo-191
❑ 89OPC-136
❑ 89PanSti-363
❑ 89Sco-374
❑ 89ScoHot1R-93
❑ 89ScoYouSI-33
❑ 89Spo-135
❑ 89Top-136
❑ 89TopBig-153
❑ 89TopTif-136
❑ 89UppDec-403
❑ 90OPC-673
❑ 90PubIntS-498
❑ 90Sco-532
❑ 90Top-673
❑ 90TopTif-673
❑ 91BufBisLD-36
❑ 91BufBisP-547
❑ 91LinDriAAA-36
❑ 94BreMilB-249

Meyer, Lee
❑ 09ColChiE-194
❑ 12ColRedB-194
❑ 12ColTinT-194

Meyer, Matt
❑ 96YakBeaTI-18

Meyer, Paul
❑ 91KinMetC-9
❑ 91KinMetP-3823

Meyer, Rick
❑ 89MarPhiS-21
❑ 90MarPhiP-3178
❑ 92ClePhiC-21
❑ 92ClePhiF-2063

Meyer, Russ
❑ 49PhiBul-38
❑ 49PhiLumPB-6
❑ 50PhiPhil-15
❑ 51BerRos-D7
❑ 51Bow-75
❑ 52Bow-220
❑ 52Top-339
❑ 53BowC-129
❑ 54Bow-186
❑ 54NewYorJA-11
❑ 55Bow-196
❑ 55DodGolS-6
❑ 56Top-227
❑ 59Top-482
❑ 75Phi195T-19
❑ 79TCM50-194
❑ 80Phi195T-19
❑ 83TopRep5-339
❑ 88FloStaLAS-29
❑ 89AlbYanB-27
❑ 89AlbYanP-322
❑ 90AlbYanB-6
❑ 90AlbYanP-1182
❑ 90DodTar-521
❑ 91LinDriAAA-125
❑ 95TopArcBD-65
❑ 95TopArcBD-135

Meyer, Scott
❑ 79WatA'sT-23
❑ 80WesHavWCT-9
❑ 81WesHavAT-21

Meyer, Stephen W.
❑ 86EriCarP-19
❑ 87SprCarB-4
❑ 88SprCarB-18

Meyer, Travis
❑ 95YakBeaTI-22

Meyer, William
❑ 16TanBraE-13
❑ 46SpoExcW-6-12
❑ 47PM1StaP1-141
❑ 49EurSta-167
❑ 50PirTeal-14
❑ 51Bow-272
❑ 52Bow-155
❑ 52Top-387
❑ 83TopRep5-387

Meyers, Benny
❑ 12ImpTobC-28

Meyers, Brian
❑ 88AppFoxP-139

Meyers, Chad
❑ 97RocCub-22
❑ 98Bes-30
❑ 99SP TopP-86
❑ 99SP TopPPE-86

Meyers, Chief (John)
❑ 08AmeCarE91-54
❑ 09BriE97-21
❑ 09ColChiE-195
❑ 09MaxPubP-8
❑ 09SpoNewSM-63
❑ 09T206-249
❑ 09T206-250
❑ 09T206-264
❑ 10CouT21-187
❑ 10CouT21-188
❑ 10CouT21-189
❑ 10CouT21-190
❑ 10DomDisP-84
❑ 10E98-23
❑ 10JuJuDE-28
❑ 10RedCroT-54
❑ 10RedCroT-225
❑ 10SweCapPP-120
❑ 10W555-48
❑ 11HelSta-134
❑ 11MecDFT-35
❑ 11PloCanE-51
❑ 11S74Sil-91
❑ 11SpoLifM-215
❑ 11T205-119
❑ 12ColRedB-195
❑ 12ColTinT-195
❑ 12HasTriFT-29D
❑ 12HasTriFT-48A
❑ 12HasTriFT-48C
❑ 12HasTriFT-48F
❑ 12HasTriFT-48H
❑ 12HasTriFT-48J
❑ 12HasTriFT-74A
❑ 12HasTriFT-74B
❑ 12HasTriFT-74E
❑ 12HasTriFT-74F
❑ 12PhiCarE-21
❑ 13NatGamW-31
❑ 13TomBarW-29
❑ 14B18B-69
❑ 14CraJacE-71
❑ 14PieStaT-72
❑ 14PolGroW-20
❑ 14TexTomE-34
❑ 14TexTomE-60
❑ 15CraJacE-71
❑ 15SpoNewM-117
❑ 15VicT21-20
❑ 16BF2FP-62
❑ 16FleBreD-64
❑ 16SpoNewM-119
❑ 17ColE13-117
❑ 23W501-95
❑ 90DodTar-522
❑ 91ConTSN-171
❑ 92ConTSN1N-775
❑ 93ConTSN-775

Meyers, Don
❑ 90GreFalDSP-17
❑ 91YakBeaC-12
❑ 91YakBeaP-4251
❑ 92BakDodCLC-17

Meyers, George
❑ 87BucN28-43
❑ 88WG1CarG-34

Meyers, Glenn
❑ 86QuaCitAP-23

Meyers, Henry W.
❑ 23WilChoV-99

Meyers, Jim
❑ 11TurRedT-50
❑ 98OklRedM-11

Meyers, Loren
❑ 54SeaPop-18

Meyers, Paul
❑ 87ShrCapP-2
❑ 88ShrCapP-1288
❑ 89PhoFirC-22
❑ 89PhoFirP-1490

Meyers, Ryan
❑ 95TenVolW-7
❑ 96StCatSB-20

Meyett, Don
❑ 89BelBre2S-21
❑ 89BelBreIS-17

Meyhoff, Jason
❑ 94EliTwiC-13
❑ 94EliTwiF-3726
❑ 95ForWayWTI-7

Meyl, Brian
❑ 77ModA'sC-20

Meza, Lorenzo (Larry)
❑ 91HamRedC-28
❑ 91HamRedP-4046
❑ 92SprCarC-26
❑ 92SprCarF-874
❑ 93St.PetCC-19
❑ 93St.PetCF-2635
❑ 94St.PetCC-18
❑ 94St.PetCF-2594

Mezzanotte, Tom
❑ 91BriTigC-4
❑ 91BriTigP-3607
❑ 92ProFS7-70

Miceli, Dan
❑ 91EugEmeC-21
❑ 91EugEmeP-3726
❑ 92AppFoxCB-6
❑ 92AppFoxFI-982
❑ 92MemChiF-2415
❑ 92ProFS7-77
❑ 93Bow-293
❑ 93ClaFS7-222
❑ 93MemChiF-372
❑ 93RoyStaC-30
❑ 94Bow-574
❑ 94BufBisF-1832
❑ 94FleMajLP-24
❑ 94FleUpd-176
❑ 94LeaLimR-44
❑ 94PirQui-17
❑ 94ScoRoo-RT126
❑ 94ScoRooGR-RT126
❑ 94Sel-378
❑ 94SpoRoo-64
❑ 94SpoRooAP-64
❑ 94Top-224
❑ 94TopGol-224
❑ 94TopSpa-224
❑ 94Ult-258
❑ 95Don-444
❑ 95DonPreP-444
❑ 95DonTopotO-321
❑ 95Emo-177
❑ 95Fle-485
❑ 95Lea-344
❑ 95PirFil-22
❑ 95Sco-534
❑ 95ScoGolR-534
❑ 95ScoPlaTS-534
❑ 95Top-109
❑ 96ColCho-264
❑ 96ColChoGS-264
❑ 96ColChoSS-264
❑ 96Don-114
❑ 96DonPreP-114
❑ 96EmoXL-259
❑ 96Fin-B15
❑ 96FinRef-B15
❑ 96Fla-352
❑ 96Fle-528
❑ 96FleTif-528
❑ 96MetUni-219
❑ 96MetUniP-219
❑ 96Pac-176
❑ 96PanSti-66
❑ 96StaClu-57
❑ 96StaCluMOP-57
❑ 96Top-322
❑ 96TopGal-117
❑ 96TopGalPPI-117
❑ 96Ult-268
❑ 96UltGolM-268
❑ 96UppDec-433
❑ 97Cir-349
❑ 97CirRav-349
❑ 97Ult-490
❑ 97UltGolME-490

❑ 97UltPlaME-490
❑ 98Pac-92
❑ 98PacOnl-643
❑ 98PacOnlR-643
❑ 98PacOnlWC-643
❑ 98PacPlaB-92
❑ 98PacRedT-92
❑ 98PacSil-92
❑ 98PadMot-18
❑ 99Fle-408
❑ 99FleSta9-408
❑ 99FleWarT-408

Micelotta, Mickey (Robert Peter)
❑ 54Top-212
❑ 94TopArc1-212
❑ 94TopArc1G-212

Michael, Bill
❑ 75CliPilT-7

Michael, Gene
❑ 66PirEasH-45
❑ 67Top-428
❑ 68Top-299
❑ 68TopVen-299
❑ 68YanPhoS-71
❑ 69Top-626
❑ 70DayDaiNM-122
❑ 70OPC-114
❑ 70Top-114
❑ 70YanCliDP-7
❑ 70YanPhoS-26
❑ 71MLBOffS-496
❑ 71OPC-483
❑ 71Top-483
❑ 71YanArcO-7
❑ 71YanCliDP-4
❑ 72Top-713
❑ 72Top-714
❑ 73LinPor-131
❑ 73NewYorSNM-10
❑ 73OPC-265
❑ 73SyrChiTI-18
❑ 73Top-265
❑ 74OPC-299
❑ 74SyrChiTI-17
❑ 74Top-299
❑ 74TopSta-214
❑ 75DetTigP-22
❑ 75OPC-608
❑ 75Top-608
❑ 75TopMin-608
❑ 76SSP-369
❑ 79ColCliT-7
❑ 81Don-500
❑ 81TCM60I-384
❑ 81Top-670
❑ 81YanPhoA-13
❑ 82YanPhoA-15
❑ 85YanTCMP-4
❑ 86CubGat-4
❑ 86TopTra-73T
❑ 86TopTraT-73T
❑ 86YanTCM-18
❑ 87CubCan-19
❑ 87CubDavB-4
❑ 87Top-43
❑ 87TopTif-43
❑ 90DodTar-523
❑ 92YanWIZ6-86
❑ 92YanWIZ7-114
❑ 94CarLeaA-DJ35

Michael, Jeff
❑ 94FreKeyC-18
❑ 94FreKeyF-2623

Michael, Matt
❑ 89PenPilS-15

Michael, Steve
❑ 79MemChiT-2
❑ 82ElPasDT-12
❑ 84ElPasDT-4
❑ 87ElmPioBC-19
❑ 87ElmPioRC-19
❑ 88ElmPioC-3
❑ 89ElmPioP-7
❑ 90WinHavRSS-16

Michaels, Bill
❑ 98QuaCitRBG-6

Michaels, Cass
❑ 47TipTop-25
❑ 48WhiSoxTI-17
❑ 49Bow-12
❑ 49Lea-13
❑ 50Bow-91
❑ 51Bow-132
❑ 51FisBakL-18
❑ 51R42SmaS-63
❑ 52Bow-36
❑ 52DixLid-12
❑ 52DixPre-12
❑ 52Top-178
❑ 53A'sTeal-18
❑ 53BowC-130
❑ 54Bow-150
❑ 55Bow-85
❑ 79DiaGre-142
❑ 83TopRep5-178

Michaels, Jason
❑ 98BatMucTI-18
❑ 99TeaBesR-59
❑ 99TeaBesRFS-16
❑ 99TeaBesRG-59
❑ 99TeaBesRS-59

Michaels, John
❑ 35DiaMatCS3T1-107

Michalak, Chris
❑ 93SouOreAC-18
❑ 93SouOreAF-4062
❑ 94Top-316
❑ 94TopGol-316
❑ 94TopSpa-316
❑ 94WesMicWC-16
❑ 94WesMicWF-2293
❑ 95ModA'sTI-17
❑ 96HunStaTI-18
❑ 96ModA'sB-21
❑ 97HigDesMG-15
❑ 99WesMicWAM-17

Michalak, Tony
❑ 87EveGiaC-15
❑ 88CliGiaP-710

Michel, Domingo
❑ 86VerBeaDP-18
❑ 87SanAntDTI-7
❑ 88SanAntMB-6
❑ 89AlbDukCm-22
❑ 89AlbDukP-81
❑ 90CMC-389
❑ 90ProAAAF-389
❑ 90TolMudHC-12
❑ 90TolMudHP-159
❑ 91LinDriAA-392
❑ 91LonTigLD-392
❑ 91LonTigP-1886
❑ 93LimRocDWB-120

Michel, John
❑ 82IdaFalAT-19
❑ 83MadMusF-19

Michel, Larry
❑ 98Cha-28

Micheu, Buddy
❑ 89ButCopKSP-25
❑ 90GasRanB-8
❑ 90GasRanP-2524
❑ 90GasRanS-14

Michlovitz, Doug
❑ 94HelBreSP-27

Michno, Tim
❑ 88WinSpiS-12

Michno, Tom
❑ 87NewOriP-8
❑ 89ChaKniTI-15
❑ 91FloStaLAP-FSL25
❑ 91MiaMirC-9
❑ 91MiaMirP-405

Mickan, Dan
❑ 84NewOriT-5

Mickens, Glenn
❑ 90DodTar-1033

Micknich, Steve
❑ 95ElmPioTI-17
❑ 95ElmPioUTI-17

MiCucci, Mike
❑ 94WilCubC-15
❑ 94WilCubF-3769
❑ 96DayCubB-18
❑ 98WesTenDJM-18

Middaugh, Scott
❑ 90SarWhiSS-16
❑ 91BirBarLD-68
❑ 91BirBarP-1454
❑ 91LinDriAA-68

Middlebrook, Jason
❑ 98RanCucQG-21
❑ 98RanCucQG-21
❑ 99BasAmeTP-68
❑ 99BasAmeTPG-68

Middlekauff, Craig
❑ 89NiaFalRP-17

Middleton, Damon
❑ 77CliDodT-18

Middleton, J. B.
❑ 23Zee-72
❑ 28Zee-159

Middleton, Robert
❑ 14Zee-42
❑ 15Zee-46
❑ 16Zee-42
❑ 17Zee-32
❑ 18Zee-29
❑ 19Zee-57
❑ 21Zee-146

Miedreich, Kevin
❑ 95NewJerCTI-20

Mielke, Gary
❑ 88OklCit8C-5
❑ 88OklCit8P-35
❑ 89OklCit8C-6
❑ 89OklCit8P-1528
❑ 90Don-679
❑ 90FleUpd-125
❑ 90OPC-221
❑ 90RanMot-17
❑ 90Sco-574
❑ 90Top-221
❑ 90TopTif-221
❑ 90UppDec-612
❑ 91Fle-293
❑ 91OPC-54
❑ 91Sco-167
❑ 91Top-54
❑ 91TopDesS-54
❑ 91TopMic-54
❑ 91TopTif-54
❑ 92GasRanF-2270
❑ 93ChaRaiF-1928
❑ 93RanKee-266

Mientkiewicz, Doug
❑ 95ForMyeMTI-32
❑ 96FtMyeMB-20
❑ 97NewBriRC-21
❑ 98NewBriRCM-19
❑ 99199Fin-291
❑ 99Bow-186
❑ 99BowBes-156
❑ 99BowBesAR-156
❑ 99BowBesR-156
❑ 99BowChr-186
❑ 99BowChrG-186
❑ 99BowChrGR-186
❑ 99BowChrI-186
❑ 99BowChrIR-186
❑ 99BowChrR-186
❑ 99BowGol-186
❑ 99BowInt-186
❑ 99CroRoyB-82
❑ 99CroRoyL-82
❑ 99CroRoyOD-82
❑ 99DumSet-141
❑ 99FinGolRef-291
❑ 99FinRef-291
❑ 99FleBri-161
❑ 99FleBri2G-161
❑ 99FleBriBlu-161
❑ 99FleBriGol-161
❑ 99FleMys-141
❑ 99FleMysFI-21
❑ 99FleMysM-141
❑ 99PacInv-88
❑ 99PacInvOD-88
❑ 99PacInvPB-88
❑ 99Rev-80
❑ 99RevPremDate-80
❑ 99RevRet-80
❑ 99RevShaSS-80
❑ 99SkyPre-268
❑ 99SkyPre-268
❑ 99SkyPreA-41
❑ 99SkyPreABlue-41
❑ 99SkyPreR-268
❑ 99SkyPreR-268
❑ 99SkyThu-138
❑ 99SkyThuRant-138
❑ 99SkyThuRave-138
❑ 99SP SigAuto-DOM
❑ 99SPSig-93
❑ 99TeaBesR-7
❑ 99ThuSkySupR-138
❑ 99Top-435
❑ 99TopChr-435
❑ 99TopChrR-435
❑ 99TopMVPP-435

Mieses, Melanio
❑ 91EliTwiP-4297

Mieske, Matt
❑ 90SpoIndSP-19
❑ 91Bow-694
❑ 91CalLeLA-4
❑ 91Cla/Bes-8
❑ 91ClaGolB-BC3
❑ 91HigDesMC-26
❑ 91HigDesMP-2409
❑ 92Bow-608
❑ 92DenZepF-2654
❑ 92DenZepS-139
❑ 92ProFS7-335
❑ 92SkyAAAF-67
❑ 92UppDecML-113
❑ 93Bow-99
❑ 93ExcFS7-192
❑ 93FleFinE-229
❑ 93NewOrlZF-984
❑ 93StaClu-687
❑ 93StaCluFDI-687
❑ 93StaCluMOP-687
❑ 93Top-616
❑ 93TopGol-616
❑ 93TopInaM-616
❑ 93TopInaR-616
❑ 93TopMic-616
❑ 93TopTra-72T
❑ 93Ult-575
❑ 93UppDec-704
❑ 93UppDecGold-704
❑ 94Bow-589
❑ 94BreMilB-250
❑ 94BrePol-18
❑ 94BreTeal-16
❑ 94Don-522
❑ 94Fin-399
❑ 94FinRef-399
❑ 94Fla-306
❑ 94FlaWavotF-B6
❑ 94Fle-183
❑ 94FUnPac-160
❑ 94LeaLimR-6
❑ 94Pin-258
❑ 94PinArtP-258
❑ 94PinMusC-258
❑ 94ScoRoo-RT156
❑ 94ScoRooGR-RT156
❑ 94Sel-206
❑ 94SpoRoo-89
❑ 94SpoRooAP-89
❑ 94StaClu-126
❑ 94StaCluFDI-126
❑ 94StaCluGR-126
❑ 94StaCluMOP-126
❑ 94Top-339
❑ 94TopGol-339
❑ 94TopSpa-339
❑ 95ColCho-180
❑ 95ColChoGS-180
❑ 95ColChoSE-73
❑ 95ColChoSEGS-73
❑ 95ColChoSESS-73
❑ 95ColChoSS-180
❑ 95Don-189
❑ 95DonPreP-189
❑ 95DonTopotO-99
❑ 95Fla-53
❑ 95Fle-185
❑ 95FleRooS-12
❑ 95Lea-89
❑ 95Pin-73
❑ 95PinArtP-73
❑ 95PinMusC-73
❑ 95Sco-402
❑ 95ScoGolR-402
❑ 95ScoPlaTS-402
❑ 95Sel-83
❑ 95SelArtP-83
❑ 95Spo-63
❑ 95SpoArtP-63
❑ 95StaClu-226
❑ 95StaCluFDI-226
❑ 95StaCluMOP-226
❑ 95StaCluSTWS-226
❑ 95StaCluVR-114
❑ 95StaCluVRMO-114
❑ 95Stu-170
❑ 95Top-64
❑ 95TopCyb-46
❑ 95Ult-67
❑ 95UltGolM-67
❑ 95UppDec-50
❑ 95UppDecED-50
❑ 95UppDecEDG-50
❑ 95UppDecSE-236
❑ 95UppDecSEG-236
❑ 96BrePol-18
❑ 96ColCho-193
❑ 96ColChoGS-193
❑ 96ColChoSS-193
❑ 96Don-243
❑ 96DonPreP-243
❑ 96EmoXL-75
❑ 96Fla-104
❑ 96Fle-153
❑ 96FleTif-153
❑ 96LeaSigA-155
❑ 96LeaSigAG-155
❑ 96LeaSigAS-155
❑ 96Pac-352
❑ 96Pin-35
❑ 96Sco-421
❑ 96Ult-368
❑ 96UltGolM-368
❑ 96UppDec-364
❑ 97BrePol-19
❑ 97Cir-211
❑ 97CirRav-211
❑ 97ColCho-145
❑ 97Don-52
❑ 97DonGolPP-52
❑ 97DonSilPP-52
❑ 97Fle-135
❑ 97FleTif-135
❑ 97KinB-28
❑ 97Pac-125
❑ 97PacLigB-125
❑ 97PacSil-125
❑ 97Sco-285
❑ 97ScoArtPWB-285
❑ 97ScoPreS-285
❑ 97ScoShoS-285
❑ 97ScoShoSAP-285
❑ 97Top-168
❑ 97Ult-80
❑ 97UltGolME-80
❑ 97UltPlaME-80
❑ 97UppDec-402
❑ 98KinDis-26
❑ 98Pac-123
❑ 98PacOnl-146
❑ 98PacOnlR-146
❑ 98PacOnlWC-146
❑ 98PacPlaB-123
❑ 98PacRedT-123
❑ 98PacSil-123

Mifune, Hideyuki
❑ 91CalLeLA-32
❑ 91SalSpuC-4
❑ 91SalSpuP-2252

Miggins, Larry
❑ 53BowC-142
❑ 53CarHunW-13
❑ 79TCM50-285

Miggins, Mark
❑ 77CocAstT-13
❑ 79ChaChaT-10A
❑ 79ChaChaT-10B
❑ 79ChaChaT-11A
❑ 80ColAstT-21
❑ 81TucTorT-9
❑ 82TucTorT-17
❑ 83MiaMarT-26

Miglio, John
❑ 81QuaCitCT-21
❑ 82WatIndF-16
❑ 82WatIndT-8
❑ 83WatIndF-11
❑ 85WatIndT-8
❑ 87ElPasDP-12
❑ 87TexLeaAF-20
❑ 88DenZepC-4
❑ 88DenZepP-1260
❑ 89ElPasDGS-10

Mijares, Willie
❑ 85EveGiaC-9
❑ 86EveGiaPC-17
❑ 87CliGiaP-6
❑ 88SanJosGCLC-124
❑ 88SanJosGP-110

Mikan, George
❑ 51Whe-3
❑ 52Whe-21A
❑ 52Whe-21B

Mikesell, Larry James
❑ 82WisRapTF-12

Mikesell, Steve
❑ 97SanBerS-16

Mikkelsen, Lincoln
❑ 90EriSaiS-16
❑ 91StoPorC-5
❑ 91StoPorP-3029
❑ 92StoPorC-9
❑ 92StoPorF-33
❑ 95HarSenTI-37

Mikkelsen, Pete
❑ 64Top-488
❑ 65ChaTheY-16
❑ 65OPC-177
❑ 65Top-177
❑ 66PirEasH-19
❑ 66Top-248
❑ 66TopVen-248
❑ 67CokCapPi-5
❑ 67PirTeal-13
❑ 67Top-425
❑ 67TopPirS-15
❑ 68Top-516
❑ 71Dod-7
❑ 71DodTic-9
❑ 71MLBOffS-107
❑ 81TCM60I-431
❑ 90DodTar-524
❑ 92YanWIZ6-87

Miklos, John
❑ 44CubTeal-16
❑ 69PilPos-26
❑ 77PilPosR-26

Miksis, Eddie
❑ 47DodTeal-16
❑ 47TipTop-102
❑ 48DodTeal-16
❑ 49EurSta-42
❑ 51Bow-117
❑ 52Bow-32
❑ 52StaCalL-80A
❑ 52StaCalS-92B
❑ 52Top-172
❑ 53Top-39
❑ 54Bow-61
❑ 55Bow-181
❑ 56Top-285
❑ 57Top-350
❑ 58Top-121
❑ 59RedShiBS-13
❑ 59Top-58
❑ 59TopVen-58
❑ 83TopRep5-172
❑ 88DodRinP1-12B
❑ 90DodTar-525
❑ 91OriCro-298
❑ 91TopArc1-39

Mikulik, Joe
❑ 86ColAstP-19
❑ 87ColAstP-15
❑ 88TucTorC-18
❑ 88TucTorJP-17
❑ 88TucTorP-176
❑ 90ColMudB-22
❑ 90ColMudP-1360
❑ 90ColMudS-16
❑ 91JacGenLD-570
❑ 91JacGenP-939
❑ 91LinDriAA-570
❑ 92JacGenF-4007
❑ 92TucTorF-499
❑ 92TucTorS-614
❑ 93TucTorF-3074

Milacki, Bob
❑ 86HagSunP-11
❑ 87ChaO'sW-30
❑ 88RocRedWGCP-16
❑ 88TriAAAP-35
❑ 89BalOriP-19
❑ 89ClaLigB-92
❑ 89Don-651
❑ 89DonBasB-254
❑ 89DonRoo-22
❑ 89Fle-649
❑ 89FleGlo-649
❑ 89FleUpd-6
❑ 89OriFreB-18
❑ 89PanSti-251
❑ 89Sco-651
❑ 89Spo-224
❑ 89Top-324
❑ 89TopTif-324
❑ 89UppDec-735
❑ 90Don-333
❑ 90DonBesA-2
❑ 90Fle-182
❑ 90FleCan-182
❑ 90Lea-402
❑ 90OPC-73
❑ 90PanSti-6
❑ 90PubIntS-580
❑ 90PubIntS-601
❑ 90Sco-239
❑ 90Sco100RS-68
❑ 90ScoYouSI-20
❑ 90Top-73
❑ 90TopRoo-21
❑ 90TopSti-240

❑ 90TopTif-73
❑ 90ToyRoo-20
❑ 90UppDec-635
❑ 91BalOriP-20
❑ 91Bow-101
❑ 91Don-69
❑ 91Fle-483
❑ 91HagSunP-2454
❑ 91OPC-788
❑ 91OriCro-299
❑ 91Sco-512
❑ 91StaCluMO-10
❑ 91Top-788
❑ 91TopDesS-788
❑ 91TopMic-788
❑ 91TopTif-788
❑ 91UppDec-328
❑ 92BalOriP-21
❑ 92Bow-61
❑ 92Don-101
❑ 92Fle-18
❑ 92Lea-262
❑ 92LeaBlaG-262
❑ 92OPC-408
❑ 92Pin-339
❑ 92Sco-314
❑ 92Sco-427
❑ 92StaClu-331
❑ 92Top-408
❑ 92TopGol-408
❑ 92TopGolW-408
❑ 92TopMic-408
❑ 92Ult-306
❑ 92UppDec-480
❑ 93ChaKniF-539
❑ 93Don-587
❑ 93Fle-548
❑ 93Top-192
❑ 93TopGol-192
❑ 93TopInaM-192
❑ 93TopInaR-192
❑ 93TopMic-192
❑ 94OmaRoyF-1221
❑ 95OmaRoyTI-22
❑ 96TacRaiB-18
❑ 98NewOrlZM-14

Milan, J. Clyde
❑ 08AmeCarE91-86
❑ 08RosComP-84
❑ 09ColChiE-196
❑ 09RamT20-80
❑ 09SpoNewSM-62
❑ 09T206-252
❑ 10DomDisP-85
❑ 10SweCapPP-62
❑ 11HelSta-75
❑ 11PinT-5-566
❑ 11SpoLifCW-252
❑ 11SpoLifM-129
❑ 11T205-120
❑ 12ColRedB-196
❑ 12ColTinT-196
❑ 12HasTriFT-33
❑ 12HasTriFT-34
❑ 12HasTriFT-58
❑ 12SenNatPC-2
❑ 12T207-123
❑ 13NatGamW-32
❑ 13TomBarW-30
❑ 14B18B-43
❑ 14CraJacE-56
❑ 14PieStaT-74
❑ 15CraJacE-56
❑ 15SpoNewM-118
❑ 16BF2FP-50
❑ 16SpoNewM-120
❑ 17ColE13-118
❑ 17HolBreD-68
❑ 20GasAmeMBD-20
❑ 20NatCarE-65
❑ 20W516-25
❑ 21E121So1-64
❑ 21E121So8-61
❑ 21Exh-108
❑ 22AmeCarE122-46
❑ 22E120-112
❑ 22W573-82
❑ 22W575-82
❑ 22WilPatV-34
❑ 23W501-15
❑ 23WilChoV-100
❑ 40PlaBal-130
❑ 60SenUniMC-13
❑ 77GalGloG-141
❑ 93ConTSN-806

Milani, Terry
❑ 66St.PetCTI-9

Milbourne, Larry
❑ 75AstPos-23
❑ 75OPC-512
❑ 75Top-512
❑ 75TopMin-512
❑ 76HouAstP-21
❑ 76SSP-58
❑ 77MarPos-12
❑ 78Top-366
❑ 79OPC-100
❑ 79Top-199
❑ 80Top-422
❑ 81Don-486
❑ 81Fle-611
❑ 81Top-583
❑ 81TopTra-802
❑ 81YanPhoA-14
❑ 82Don-614
❑ 82Fle-42
❑ 82Top-669
❑ 82TopTra-71T
❑ 83Don-411
❑ 83Fle-415
❑ 83PhiTas-18
❑ 83Top-91
❑ 83TopTra-72T
❑ 84MarMot-10
❑ 84Nes792-281
❑ 84Top-281
❑ 84TopTif-281
❑ 84TopTra-79T
❑ 84TopTraT-79T
❑ 85Fle-493
❑ 85Top-754
❑ 85TopTif-754
❑ 86MarGreT-2
❑ 87AstShoSPO-19
❑ 87AstShowSTh-16
❑ 89PacSenL-112
❑ 89PacSenL-203
❑ 90EliSenL-86
❑ 91SavCarC-27
❑ 91SavCarP-1668
❑ 92YanWIZ8-120

Milburn, Adam
❑ 96EugEmeB-15
❑ 97MacBra-18
❑ 98DanQ-C-12

Milburn, Glyn
❑ 95TopD3-PF1

Milchin, Mike
❑ 89HamRedS-21
❑ 90SprCarDGB-26
❑ 90St.PetCS-17
❑ 90TopTVCa-56
❑ 91ArkTraLD-39
❑ 91ArkTraP-1282
❑ 91Bow-397
❑ 91Cla/Bes-107
❑ 91LinDriAA-39
❑ 91LouRedP-2910
❑ 91LouRedTI-9
❑ 92Bow-567
❑ 92LouRedS-273
❑ 92SkyAAAF-128
❑ 92UppDecML-79
❑ 93Bow-516
❑ 93ClaFS7-80
❑ 93LouRedF-211

Milene, Jeff
❑ 89EliTwiS-18
❑ 90KenTwiB-8
❑ 90KenTwiP-2296
❑ 90KenTwiS-12

Miles, Aaron
❑ 97QuaCitRBB-18
❑ 98QuaCitRBG-20

Miles, Chad
❑ 94ElmPioC-13
❑ 94ElmPioF-3469
❑ 95ElmPioTI-18
❑ 95ElmPioUTI-18
❑ 95KanCouCTI-28
❑ 96BreCouMB-20
❑ 97BreCouMB-23
❑ 98LakTigM-7

Miles, Dee (Wilson)
❑ 40PlaBal-195
❑ 42A'sTeal-26
❑ 43RedSoxTI-16
❑ 93ConTSN-743

Miles, Don
❑ 90DodTar-1034

Miles, Eddie
❑ 82AppFoxFr-20
❑ 83GleFalWST-6

Miles, James
❑ 69Top-658
❑ 70OPC-154
❑ 70Top-154
❑ 76WauMetT-17

Miles, John
❑ 92NegLeaRLI-44

Mileur, Jerome
❑ 83NasAngT-25
❑ 85NasPirT-29

Miley, Dave
❑ 81CedRapRT-9
❑ 83WatRedT-10
❑ 84WicAerRD-2
❑ 87VerRedP-17
❑ 89CedRapRB-22
❑ 89CedRapRP-927
❑ 89CedRapRS-22
❑ 90CedRapRB-19
❑ 90CedRapRP-2337
❑ 91ChaWheP-2902
❑ 91SouAtlLAGP-SAL8
❑ 92ChaLooS-199
❑ 93RedKah-8
❑ 95ChaLooTI-28
❑ 96IndIndB-2
❑ 97IndInd-1
❑ 98IndIndQ-2

Miley, Mike (Michael)
❑ 75CalAngP-26
❑ 75SalLakCC-8
❑ 76OPC-387
❑ 76SalLakCGC-6
❑ 76Top-387
❑ 77Top-257
❑ 90LSUTigGM-13

Milhaven, McGraw
❑ 88NebCor-25

Milholland, Eric
❑ 86AppFoxP-15
❑ 87DayBeaAP-3
❑ 88TamTarS-17

Militello, Sam
❑ 90OneYanP-3378
❑ 90ProAaA-176
❑ 91Bow-693
❑ 91CarLeaAP-CAR34
❑ 91Cla/Bes-150
❑ 91ClaGolB-BC8
❑ 91PriWilCC-7
❑ 91PriWilCP-1423
❑ 92Bow-21
❑ 92ColCliF-348
❑ 92ColCliP-7
❑ 92ColCliS-112
❑ 92Don-407
❑ 92DonRooP-BC16
❑ 92FleUpd-43
❑ 92OPC-676
❑ 92ProFS7-122
❑ 92ScoRoo-82T
❑ 92SkyAAAF-52
❑ 92Top-676
❑ 92TopGol-676
❑ 92TopGolW-676
❑ 92TopMic-676
❑ 92TriA AAS-112
❑ 93Bow-243
❑ 93ClaGam-65
❑ 93ClaGam-NNO
❑ 93ColCliF-1109
❑ 93ColCliP-9
❑ 93Don-371
❑ 93Fle-282
❑ 93FleRooS-RSB7
❑ 93Lea-52
❑ 93OPC-127
❑ 93Pin-225
❑ 93PinTea2-25
❑ 93Sco-351
❑ 93Sel-315
❑ 93SelChaR-8
❑ 93StaClu-11
❑ 93StaCluFDI-11
❑ 93StaCluMOP-11
❑ 93StaCluMP-4
❑ 93Top-624
❑ 93TopGol-624
❑ 93TopInaM-624
❑ 93TopInaR-624
❑ 93TopMic-624
❑ 93Toy-72
❑ 93ToyMasP-9
❑ 93TriPla-75
❑ 93Ult-246
❑ 93UppDec-383
❑ 93UppDecGold-383
❑ 93YanStaC-27
❑ 94ColCliF-2950

Milius, Dennis
❑ 92HamRedC-13
❑ 92HamRedF-1589

Miljus, John
❑ 23WilChoV-101
❑ 27Zee-141
❑ 28W513-65
❑ 30Zee-148
❑ 30Zee-149
❑ 32Zee-11
❑ 90DodTar-526

Mill, Steve
❑ 91PocPioP-3778
❑ 91PocPioSP-3

Millan, Adan
❑ 94BatCliF-3449
❑ 95PiePhiF-190
❑ 97ReaPhi-21
❑ 98ReaPhiM-21
❑ 98ReaPhiUM-15

Millan, Bernie
❑ 90KinMetB-5
❑ 90KinMetS-17
❑ 91ColMetPI-17
❑ 91ColMetPPI-3
❑ 91PitMetC-11
❑ 91PitMetP-3430
❑ 92St.LucMCB-2
❑ 92St.LucMF-1757
❑ 93FloStaLAF-40
❑ 93St.LucMC-18
❑ 93St.LuMF-2929
❑ 94ClaGolF-168
❑ 94StoPorC-17
❑ 94StoPorF-1702

Millan, Felix
❑ 66BraPos-19
❑ 67BraPho-22
❑ 67OPC-89
❑ 67Top-89
❑ 68BraPos-22
❑ 68CokCapB-7
❑ 68Top-241
❑ 68TopVen-241
❑ 69AtlBraBPPS-16
❑ 69MilBra-192
❑ 69MLBOffS-115
❑ 69OPC-210
❑ 69Top-210
❑ 69TopFou-10
❑ 69TopSta-7
❑ 69TopTeaP-2
❑ 70AtlBraS-6
❑ 70MLBOffS-8
❑ 70OPC-452
❑ 70Top-452
❑ 70Top-710
❑ 71MilDud-55
❑ 71MLBOffS-17
❑ 71OPC-81
❑ 71Top-81
❑ 71TopCoi-5
❑ 71TopSup-33
❑ 71TopTat-97
❑ 72EssCoi-8
❑ 72MilBra-236
❑ 72Top-540
❑ 73LinPor-119
❑ 73MetTeal-10
❑ 73NewYorSNM-8
❑ 73OPC-407
❑ 73Top-407
❑ 74Kel-53
❑ 74MetJapEB-7
❑ 74MetTeal-15
❑ 74OPC-132
❑ 74Top-132
❑ 74TopDecE-26
❑ 74TopSta-68
❑ 75Hos-111
❑ 75MetSSP-16
❑ 75OPC-445
❑ 75Top-445
❑ 75TopMin-445
❑ 76Hos-120
❑ 76Kel-9
❑ 76MetMSAP-3
❑ 76OPC-245
❑ 76SSP-536
❑ 76Top-245
❑ 77BurCheD-138
❑ 77Hos-96
❑ 77MetDaiPA-16
❑ 77OPC-249
❑ 77Top-605
❑ 78AtlCon-17
❑ 78TCM60I-31
❑ 78Top-505
❑ 79TCMJapPB-52
❑ 86BraGreT-2
❑ 89T/MSenL-78
❑ 89TopSenL-85
❑ 91MetWIZ-267
❑ 92GulCoaMF-3498
❑ 93UppDecS-10

Millan, Jorge
❑ 94JohCitCC-22
❑ 94JohCitCF-3710

Millar, Kevin
❑ 94ActPac-45
❑ 94KanCouCC-16
❑ 94KanCouCF-170
❑ 94KanCouCTI-18
❑ 94MidLeaAF-MDW18
❑ 95ActPacF-51
❑ 95BreCouMF-255
❑ 95Exc-197
❑ 96PorSeaDB-18
❑ 97BesAutSBPP-32
❑ 97PorSeaD-20
❑ 97TexAllM-46
❑ 98Bow-424
❑ 98BowBes-122
❑ 98BowBesAR-122
❑ 98BowBesR-122
❑ 98BowChr-424
❑ 98BowChrGA-424
❑ 98BowChrGAR-424
❑ 98BowChrI-424
❑ 98BowChrIR-424
❑ 98BowChrR-424
❑ 98BowGolA-424
❑ 98BowInt-424
❑ 98PorSeaD5AQ-3

Millares, Jose
❑ 91KanCouCC-17
❑ 91KanCouCP-2664
❑ 91KanCouCTI-13
❑ 92FreKeyC-17
❑ 92FreKeyF-1813
❑ 93ClaFS7-284
❑ 93FreKeyC-17
❑ 93FreKeyF-1035
❑ 94BowBayF-2420
❑ 94OriPro-66
❑ 95BowBayTI-14
❑ 96BowBayB-21

Millay, Gar
❑ 84AriWilP-13
❑ 86AriWilP-11
❑ 87PorChaRP-23
❑ 88OklCit8C-13
❑ 88OklCit8P-40
❑ 88TulDriTI-21
❑ 89TulDriGS-18
❑ 89TulDriTI-16
❑ 90CMC-168
❑ 90OklCit8C-18
❑ 90OklCit8P-445
❑ 90ProAAAF-691
❑ 91LinDriAAA-313
❑ 91OklCit8LD-313
❑ 91OklCit8P-191

Millay, Keith
❑ 92MadMusF-1229

Miller, Barry
❑ 91CliGiaC-21
❑ 91CliGiaP-843
❑ 92CalLeaACL-10
❑ 92ClaFS7-248
❑ 92SanJosGC-9
❑ 93ShrCapF-2770
❑ 94ShrCapF-1615
❑ 95PhoFirTI-23

Miller, Ben
❑ 98SalVol-25

Miller, Bill
❑ 89GreFalDSP-31
❑ 89IdaFalBP-2020
❑ 89SalDodTI-17
❑ 89SanDieSAS-18
❑ 90MiaMirIS-18
❑ 90MiaMirIS-18
❑ 92CalLeaACL-25

Miller, Bill (William Paul)
❑ 47StaPinP2-28
❑ 52Top-403
❑ 53BowBW-54
❑ 53Dor-107
❑ 53Top-100
❑ 54NewYorJA-53
❑ 55Bow-245
❑ 55OriEss-17
❑ 79TCM50-209
❑ 83TopRep5-403
❑ 91OriCro-300
❑ 91TopArc1-100

Miller, Bing (Edmund)
❑ 21Exh-109
❑ 21Nei-23
❑ 22E120-84
❑ 22W573-83
❑ 23WilChoV-102
❑ 25Exh-109
❑ 26Exh-109
❑ 27MidBre-33
❑ 28PorandAR-A25
❑ 28PorandAR-B25
❑ 29A'sVil-4
❑ 29PorandAR-65
❑ 31Exh-27
❑ 31W517-31
❑ 33Gou-59
❑ 33GouCanV-59
❑ 33RitCE-2C
❑ 40PlaBal-137
❑ 48WhiSoxTI-18
❑ 50A'sTeal-20
❑ 51A'sTeal-23
❑ 52A'sTeal-18
❑ 53A'sTeal-19
❑ 60Fle-39
❑ 61Fle-62
❑ 74A's192T-20
❑ 74TCMNic-20
❑ 76GrePlaG-14
❑ 83A'sGreT-7
❑ 85BigLeaC3-29
❑ 91ConTSN-192
❑ 94ConTSN-1139
❑ 94ConTSNB-1139

Miller, Bob (Robert G.)
❑ 54Top-241
❑ 55Top-9
❑ 56Top-263
❑ 62RedEnq-23
❑ 62Top-572
❑ 91MetWIZ-268
❑ 94TopArc1-241
❑ 94TopArc1G-241

Miller, Bob (Robert J.)
❑ 50Bow-227
❑ 50PhiPhil-16
❑ 51Bow-220
❑ 52Top-187
❑ 55Bow-110
❑ 55Top-157
❑ 55TopDouH-59
❑ 56Top-334
❑ 57Top-46
❑ 58Top-326
❑ 59Top-379
❑ 75Phi195T-20
❑ 79TCM50-289
❑ 80Phi195T-20
❑ 83TopRep5-187

Miller, Bob (Robert L.)
❑ 60Top-101
❑ 60TopVen-101
❑ 61Top-314
❑ 62MetJayP-8
❑ 62SalPlaC-185
❑ 62ShiPlaC-185
❑ 62Top-293
❑ 62TopStal-159
❑ 63Top-261
❑ 64Top-394
❑ 65DodTeal-11
❑ 65OPC-98
❑ 65Top-98
❑ 66Top-208
❑ 66TopVen-208
❑ 67CokCapD-14
❑ 67CokCapDA-14
❑ 67Top-461
❑ 68Top-534
❑ 69Top-403
❑ 70OPC-47
❑ 70Top-47
❑ 71MLBOffS-38
❑ 71OPC-542

❑ 71Top-542
❑ 72OPC-414
❑ 72Top-414
❑ 73OPC-277
❑ 73Top-277
❑ 74MetOriEB-10
❑ 74OPC-624
❑ 74Top-624
❑ 75HawIsIC-21
❑ 77OPC-58
❑ 77PadSchC-41
❑ 77Top-113
❑ 78BluJayP-16
❑ 81TCM60I-468
❑ 82MetGal62-18
❑ 85DomLeaS-111
❑ 85GiaMot-27
❑ 85GiaPos-22
❑ 90DodTar-527
❑ 91MetWIZ-269

Miller, Brent
❑ 91KanCouCC-18
❑ 91KanCouCP-2665
❑ 91KanCouCTI-14
❑ 92Bow-150
❑ 92HagSunF-2563
❑ 92HagSunS-264
❑ 92SkyAA F-108
❑ 93BowBayF-2197
❑ 94BowBayF-2421
❑ 94OriPro-67
❑ 97St.PauS-17

Miller, Brian
❑ 95MarPhiTI-16
❑ 96BatCliTI-7
❑ 97PieBolWB-20

Miller, Corky
❑ 98BilMusTI-24

Miller, Damian
❑ 90EliTwiS-13
❑ 92KenTwiC-12
❑ 92KenTwiF-608
❑ 93FloStaLAF-16
❑ 93ForMyeMC-14
❑ 93ForMyeMF-2659
❑ 94NasXprF-390
❑ 97SalLakB-16
❑ 98DiaMcD-15
❑ 98TusSidM-17

Miller, Danny
❑ 94OgdRapF-3735
❑ 94OgdRapSP-22

Miller, Danny 70's
❑ 75QuaCitAT-28
❑ 76SeaRaiC-10

Miller, Darrell
❑ 81HolMilT-17
❑ 82HolMilT-22
❑ 84EdmTraC-109
❑ 85Don-644
❑ 86AngSmo-18
❑ 86Top-524
❑ 86TopTif-524
❑ 87AngSmo-11
❑ 87CalAngPPS-27
❑ 87SpoTeaP-11
❑ 87Top-337
❑ 87TopTif-337
❑ 88Don-551
❑ 88EdmTraC-12
❑ 88EdmTraP-579
❑ 88Fle-498
❑ 88FleGlo-498
❑ 88Sco-463
❑ 88ScoGlo-463
❑ 88StaLinAn-14
❑ 88Top-679
❑ 88TopTif-679
❑ 89ColCliC-19
❑ 89ColCliP-14
❑ 89ColCliP-733
❑ 89Sco-499
❑ 89Top-68
❑ 89TopTif-68
❑ 89UppDec-462
❑ 90CMC-324
❑ 90ProAAAF-462
❑ 90RocRedWC-23
❑ 90RocRedWP-705

Miller, Dave
❑ 79AshTouT-11
❑ 87DurBulP-11
❑ 88BobCamRB-20
❑ 88GreBraB-14
❑ 89FreKeyS-17
❑ 89OklCit8C-7
❑ 89OklCit8P-1522
❑ 89Sta-103
❑ 90CMC-156
❑ 90HagSunB-24
❑ 90HagSunP-1411
❑ 90HagSunS-18
❑ 90OklCit8C-6
❑ 90OklCit8P-431
❑ 90ProAAAF-677
❑ 92HagSunF-2551
❑ 92HagSunS-265
❑ 96WatIndTI-18
❑ 98KinIndQ-27

Miller, David C.
❑ 96Bow-329
❑ 96BowFoi-329
❑ 96BreCouMB-21
❑ 96KenIndB-17
❑ 97AkrAer-17
❑ 98Bow-203
❑ 98BowChr-203
❑ 98BowChrGA-203
❑ 98BowChrGAR-203
❑ 98BowChrI-203
❑ 98BowChrIR-203
❑ 98BowChrR-203
❑ 98BowGolA-203
❑ 98BowInt-203
❑ 98BufBisG-21

Miller, Doc (Roy)
❑ 09MaxPubP-21
❑ 10JuJuDE-29
❑ 11HelSta-163
❑ 11PinT-5-702
❑ 12T207-127
❑ 93BelMarCB-19
❑ 93BelMarF-3219
❑ 94RivPilCLC-7

Miller, Dots (John B.)
❑ 08AmeCarE91-87
❑ 09AmeCarE90-1-79
❑ 09ColChiE-197
❑ 09T206-253
❑ 10CouT21-191
❑ 10CouT21-306
❑ 10DomDisP-86
❑ 10E-UOraBSC-17
❑ 10E101-34A
❑ 10E101-34B
❑ 10E102-18A
❑ 10E102-18B
❑ 10E12AmeCDCE125-26
❑ 10MelMinE-34A
❑ 10MelMinE-34B
❑ 10NadCarE-39A
❑ 10NadCarE-39B
❑ 10NadE1-37
❑ 10PeoT21-41A
❑ 10PeoT21-41B
❑ 10PeoT21-41C
❑ 10PirAmeCE-8
❑ 10PirHerICP-9
❑ 10PirTipTD-7
❑ 10RedCroT-55
❑ 10RedCroT-138
❑ 10SweCapPP-142
❑ 11DiaGumP-20
❑ 11MecDFT-26
❑ 11PinT-5-862
❑ 11S74Sil-113
❑ 11SpoLifCW-253
❑ 11SpoLifM-256
❑ 11T205-121
❑ 12ColRedB-197
❑ 12ColRedB-198
❑ 12ColTinT-197
❑ 12ColTinT-198
❑ 12HasTriFT-62
❑ 12T207-124
❑ 14B18B-86A
❑ 14B18B-86B
❑ 14CraJacE-49
❑ 14PieStaT-75
❑ 15AmeCarE106-30
❑ 15CraJacE-49
❑ 16SpoNewM-121

Miller, Dyar
❑ 75IntLeaAT-2
❑ 75OPC-614
❑ 75Top-614
❑ 75TopMin-614
❑ 76BalOriP-26
❑ 76OPC-555
❑ 76SSP-379
❑ 76Top-555
❑ 77Top-77
❑ 78AngFamF-25
❑ 78SSP270-206
❑ 78Top-239
❑ 79Top-313
❑ 80TidTidT-10
❑ 81Top-472
❑ 82Fle-534
❑ 82LouRedE-18
❑ 82Top-178
❑ 83LouRedR-4
❑ 84LouRedR-4
❑ 86LouRedTI-2
❑ 89PacSenL-211
❑ 89TopSenL-129
❑ 90EliSenL-59
❑ 91ColIndP-1505
❑ 91MetWIZ-270
❑ 91OriCro-301
❑ 91PacSenL-12
❑ 92ColSprSSF-768
❑ 92ColSprSSS-100
❑ 93ChaKniF-561
❑ 94ChaKniF-910
❑ 95LouRedF-293
❑ 96LouRedB-3

Miller, Edward Lee
❑ 76AshTouT-24
❑ 78RicBraT-11
❑ 79RicBraT-24
❑ 80RicBraT-22
❑ 80Top-675
❑ 80VenLeaS-120
❑ 81BraPol-45
❑ 81Top-192
❑ 82Don-425
❑ 82Fle-441
❑ 82Top-451
❑ 83PorBeaT-20
❑ 85BeaGolGT-13
❑ 93RanKee-267

Miller, Edward R.
❑ 40PlaBal-56
❑ 41PlaBal-1
❑ 49Lea-68
❑ 49PhiBul-39
❑ 83TCMPla1943-27

Miller, Edward S.
❑ 36GouWidPPR-D17
❑ 39PlaBal-49

Miller, Elmer
❑ 21E121So1-65
❑ 21E121So8-62
❑ 21KoBreWSI-41
❑ 22E120-69
❑ 22W573-84
❑ 22W575-83
❑ 23WilChoV-103

Miller, Eric
❑ 92JohCitCC-18
❑ 92JohCitCF-3116
❑ 93SprCarC-19
❑ 93SprCarF-1848
❑ 94FloStaLAF-FSL43
❑ 94St.PetCC-19
❑ 94St.PetCF-2585
❑ 95Exc-272
❑ 98WicWraM-5

Miller, Ernie
❑ 97ButCopKB-15
❑ 97ButCopKK-15
❑ 98CedRapKTI-20

Miller, Frank
❑ 93RicBraRC-30

Miller, Frank L.
❑ 09ObaT21-163
❑ 09ObaT21-198
❑ 09ObaT21-328
❑ 11Zee-93
❑ 12HomRunKE-69
❑ 12ObaPreT-77
❑ 12Zee-121

Miller, Gary
❑ 91St.CatBJC-15
❑ 91St.CatBJP-3392
❑ 92St.CatBJC-19
❑ 92St.CatBJF-3387

Miller, George
❑ 87BucN28-90
❑ 87OldJudN-344
❑ 88AllandGN-4
❑ 88AllandGN-4
❑ 88AugBecN-24
❑ 88GandBCGCE-26
❑ 88SpoTimM-18

Miller, Gerry
❑ 81BurBeeT-24
❑ 82BelBreFr-3

Miller, Gregg
❑ 90WicStaSGD-43

Miller, Hack (Lawrence H.)
❑ 17Zee-33
❑ 17Zee-34
❑ 18Zee-30
❑ 20WalMaiW-32
❑ 20Zee-29
❑ 21Exh-110
❑ 21Nei-86
❑ 21Zee-33
❑ 22E120-163
❑ 22W573-86
❑ 26Zee-84
❑ 90DodTar-1035
❑ 94ConTSN-1054
❑ 94ConTSNB-1054

Miller, Hugh
❑ 12Zee-88
❑ 13Zee-84A
❑ 13Zee-84B

Miller, Jeff
❑ 24Zee-52
❑ 87BelMarL-9
❑ 89WauTimGS-23
❑ 92BurAstC-3
❑ 92BurAstF-540

Miller, Jerrod
❑ 94IdaFalBF-3581
❑ 94IdaFalBSP-19

Miller, Jerry
❑ 86MiaMarP-17

Miller, Jessica
❑ 93RicBraRC-30

Miller, Jim
❑ 55JetPos-11
❑ 77ChaPatT-9
❑ 91PriRedC-7
❑ 91PriRedP-3509
❑ 92PriRedC-8
❑ 92PriRedF-3085
❑ 97HelBreB-21

Miller, Joe
❑ 97St.PauS-18
❑ 98St.PauSTI-17

Miller, Joey
❑ 92EliTwiC-22
❑ 92EliTwiF-3695
❑ 93ForWayWC-18
❑ 93ForWayWF-1983

Miller, John Allen
❑ 69Top-641
❑ 90DodTar-1036
❑ 92YanWIZ6-88

Miller, John E.
❑ 63BalOriP-20
❑ 63Top-208
❑ 65BalOriP-22
❑ 65Top-49
❑ 66BalOriP-24
❑ 66Top-427
❑ 67OPC-141
❑ 67Top-141
❑ 81Ori6F-23
❑ 81TCM60I-392
❑ 91OriCro-302

Miller, John PCL
❑ 22Zee-104
❑ 23Zee-138

Miller, Johnny
❑ 74NewYorNTDiS-4

Miller, Jon
❑ 90BalOriP-18
❑ 95BalOriP-33
❑ 98GiaMot-27

Miller, Joseph
❑ 87OldJudN-345

Miller, Justin
❑ 98AshTouM-13
❑ 98BesAutSS-36

Miller, Keith (Neal Keith)
❑ 86PorBeaP-17
❑ 86ReaPhiP-17
❑ 87MaiGuiP-8
❑ 87MaiGuiT-15
❑ 88MaiPhiC-20
❑ 88MaiPhiP-290
❑ 88PhiTas-27
❑ 88PhiTas-36
❑ 89ScrRedBC-13
❑ 89ScrRedBP-716
❑ 89Top-268
❑ 89TopTif-268
❑ 90ProAAAF-314
❑ 90ScrRedBC-21
❑ 90ScrRedBP-612
❑ 90TriAllGP-AAA7
❑ 91BufBisLD-37
❑ 91BufBisP-553
❑ 91LinDriAAA-37
❑ 91MetKah-25
❑ 92OklCit8F-1923
❑ 93OklCit8F-1633

Miller, Keith Alan
❑ 85LynMetT-18
❑ 86JacMetT-27
❑ 87IntLeaAT-18
❑ 87IntLeaAT-36
❑ 87MetColP-40
❑ 87SpoRoo2-50
❑ 87TidTidP-10
❑ 87TidTidT-16
❑ 88Don-562
❑ 88DonTeaBM-562
❑ 88Fle-144
❑ 88FleGlo-144
❑ 88MetColP-38
❑ 88Sco-639
❑ 88ScoGlo-639
❑ 88Spo-225
❑ 88TidTidCa-11
❑ 88TidTidCM-20
❑ 88TidTidP-1604
❑ 88Top-382
❑ 88TopTif-382
❑ 89Bow-380
❑ 89BowTif-380
❑ 89ClaLigB-16
❑ 89Don-623
❑ 89Fle-45
❑ 89FleGlo-45
❑ 89MetFanC-25
❑ 89MetKah-U2
❑ 89Sco-464
❑ 89ScoHot1R-62
❑ 89ScoYouSI-23
❑ 89TidTidC-14
❑ 89TidTidP-1948
❑ 89Top-557
❑ 89TopTif-557
❑ 89TriAAAP-AAA24
❑ 89UppDec-739
❑ 90Bow-136
❑ 90BowTif-136
❑ 90CMC-247
❑ 90Don-507
❑ 90Lea-462
❑ 90MetColP-20
❑ 90MetColP-42
❑ 90MetFanC-25
❑ 90MetKah-25
❑ 90OPC-58
❑ 90Sco-559
❑ 90Top-58
❑ 90TopTif-58
❑ 90TopTVM-32
❑ 90UppDec-190
❑ 91Don-248
❑ 91Fle-155
❑ 91MetColP-40
❑ 91MetPerPA-23
❑ 91MetWIZ-272
❑ 91OPC-719
❑ 91Sco-318
❑ 91StaClu-239
❑ 91Top-719
❑ 91TopDesS-719
❑ 91TopMic-719
❑ 91TopTif-719
❑ 91Ult-225
❑ 91UppDec-196
❑ 92Bow-285
❑ 92Don-657
❑ 92Fle-513
❑ 92FleUpd-31
❑ 92Lea-459
❑ 92LeaBlaG-459
❑ 92OPC-157
❑ 92OPCPre-94
❑ 92Pin-403
❑ 92RoyPol-22
❑ 92Sco-462
❑ 92ScoRoo-50T
❑ 92StaClu-786
❑ 92StaCluNC-786
❑ 92Stu-189
❑ 92Top-157
❑ 92TopGol-157
❑ 92TopGolW-157
❑ 92TopMic-157
❑ 92TopTra-73T
❑ 92TopTraG-73T
❑ 92Ult-375
❑ 92UppDec-383
❑ 92UppDec-704
❑ 93Bow-209
❑ 93Don-543
❑ 93Fle-244
❑ 93Lea-168
❑ 93PacSpa-492
❑ 93PanSti-109
❑ 93Pin-384
❑ 93RoyPol-22
❑ 93RoyStaC-7
❑ 93Sco-96
❑ 93Sel-54
❑ 93StaClu-401
❑ 93StaCluFDI-401
❑ 93StaCluMOP-401
❑ 93Top-267
❑ 93TopGol-267
❑ 93TopInaM-267
❑ 93TopInaR-267
❑ 93TopMic-267
❑ 93Ult-565
❑ 93UppDec-302
❑ 93UppDecGold-302
❑ 94ColC-409
❑ 94ColChoGS-409
❑ 94ColChoSS-409
❑ 94Fle-169
❑ 94Pac-297
❑ 94Top-454
❑ 94TopGol-454
❑ 94TopSpa-454
❑ 95Top-29

Miller, Ken
❑ 75LynRanT-16

Miller, Kenny
❑ 86BenPhiC-142
❑ 87SpaPhiP-9
❑ 97PitMet-18
❑ 98CapCitBF5-23
❑ 98CapCitBM-23
❑ 98PitMetM-20

Miller, Kevin
❑ 80WisRapTT-19
❑ 89MetColP-14
❑ 90BriTigP-3151
❑ 90BriTigS-18
❑ 91NiaFalRC-11
❑ 91NiaFalRP-3636
❑ 92FayGenC-7
❑ 92FayGenF-2172
❑ 97Bes-68

Miller, Killer (Don)
❑ 79Yan192T-19
❑ 88StoPorCLC-204
❑ 88StoPorP-750
❑ 89StoPorB-27
❑ 89StoPorCLC-175
❑ 89StoPorP-397
❑ 89StoPorS-24

Miller, Kumandae
❑ 95ElmPioTI-19
❑ 95ElmPioUTI-19

Miller, Kurt
❑ 90ClaDraP-5
❑ 90WelPirP-1
❑ 91AugPirC-28
❑ 91AugPirP-803
❑ 91Bow-521
❑ 91OPC-491
❑ 91Sco-682
❑ 91Top-491
❑ 91TopDesS-491
❑ 91TopMic-491
❑ 91TopTif-491
❑ 91UppDec-68
❑ 92ChaRanC-21
❑ 92ClaBluBF-BC5
❑ 92ClaFS7-67
❑ 92ClaRedB-BC5
❑ 92ProFS7-309
❑ 92UppDec-70
❑ 92UppDecML-42
❑ 92UppDecML-58
❑ 92UppDecML-166
❑ 92UppDecMLPotY-PY19
❑ 93Bow-53
❑ 93ClaYouG-YG11
❑ 93TulDriF-2731
❑ 93TulDriTI-18
❑ 93UppDec-9
❑ 93UppDec-20

❑ 93UppDecGold-9
❑ 93UppDecGold-20
❑ 94ActPac-54
❑ 94Bow-357
❑ 94Bow-478
❑ 94Cla-103
❑ 94EdmTraF-2874
❑ 94Fla-383
❑ 94FleUpd-137
❑ 94SigRoo-38
❑ 94SigRooHP-S7
❑ 94SigRooHPS-S7
❑ 94SigRooS-38
❑ 94TopTra-111T
❑ 94UppDec-307
❑ 94UppDecED-307
❑ 94UppDecML-51
❑ 95ChaKniTI-15
❑ 95ColCho-298
❑ 95ColChoGS-298
❑ 95ColChoSS-298
❑ 95Pin-161
❑ 95PinArtP-161
❑ 95PinMusC-161
❑ 95Sco-591
❑ 95ScoGolR-591
❑ 95ScoPlaTS-591
❑ 95Sel-193
❑ 95SelArtP-193
❑ 95Spo-164
❑ 95SpoArtP-164
❑ 95Top-251
❑ 95Ult-381
❑ 95UltGolM-381
❑ 96ChaKniB-18
❑ 97PacPriGotD-GD144
❑ 98IowCubQ-17

Miller, Larry Don
❑ 59DarFar-12
❑ 65Top-349
❑ 69Top-323
❑ 81TCM60I-373
❑ 90DodTar-528
❑ 91MetWIZ-271

Miller, Lemmie
❑ 83AlbDukTc-22
❑ 84AlbDukCr-150
❑ 85AlbDukCr-165
❑ 90DodTar-1037

Miller, Mark
❑ 75AndRanT-3
❑ 76AshTouT-17
❑ 78QuaCitAT-14
❑ 79NaSouTI-16
❑ 80CedRapRT-16
❑ 80ElPasDT-8
❑ 80IndIndTI-18

Miller, Marvin
❑ 94UppDecTAE-74

Miller, Matt
❑ 97JohCitCTI-24
❑ 97LakTigB-23
❑ 98WesMicWM-13
❑ 99Bow-418
❑ 99BowGol-418
❑ 99BowInt-418
❑ 99SP TopP-87
❑ 99SP TopPPE-87

Miller, Michael
❑ 87ReaPhiP-25

Miller, Mickey
❑ 76BatRouCT-15

Miller, Mike
❑ 79SavBraT-25
❑ 83ButCopKT-19
❑ 86ClePhiP-17
❑ 86MemChiSTOS-18
❑ 86MemChiTOS-18
❑ 86OmaRoyP-15
❑ 87LitFalMP-2389
❑ 87MemChiB-15
❑ 87PitCubP-9
❑ 87WinSpiP-20
❑ 88ColMetGS-9
❑ 88MemChiB-22
❑ 88SouAtlLAGS-14
❑ 89St.LucMS-17
❑ 90JacMetGS-18

Miller, Molly (Charles B.)
❑ 09T206-502
❑ 98CamPepP-56

Miller, Nancy
❑ 76LauIndC-9

Miller, Norm
❑ 67Ast-19
❑ 67Top-412
❑ 68OPC-161
❑ 68Top-161
❑ 68TopVen-161
❑ 69OPC-76
❑ 69Top-76
❑ 69TopTeaP-6
❑ 70AstPho-19
❑ 70Top-619
❑ 71MLBOffS-88
❑ 71OPC-18
❑ 71Top-18
❑ 72AstTeal-17
❑ 72MilBra-237
❑ 72OPC-466
❑ 72Top-466
❑ 73OPC-637
❑ 73Top-637
❑ 74OPC-439
❑ 74Top-439
❑ 87AstSer1-26
❑ 87AstShoSO-17
❑ 87AstShoSTw-26

Miller, Orlando
❑ 89OneYanP-2124
❑ 90AshTouP-2757
❑ 90CMC-668
❑ 90ProAaA-101
❑ 90SouAtlLAS-16
❑ 91Cla/Bes-377
❑ 91JacGenLD-571
❑ 91JacGenP-934
❑ 91LinDriAA-571
❑ 92Bow-555
❑ 92ClaFS7-140
❑ 92JacGenS-342
❑ 92SkyAA F-143
❑ 92UppDecML-237
❑ 93Bow-588
❑ 93ExcFS7-203
❑ 93TucTorF-3067
❑ 94Bow-146
❑ 94Bow-358
❑ 94BowBes-B28
❑ 94BowBesR-B28
❑ 94Cla-109
❑ 94ExcFS7-203
❑ 94Fla-391
❑ 94FlaWavotF-B7
❑ 94FleExtB-278
❑ 94FleExtBMLH-6
❑ 94FleUpd-145
❑ 94LeaLimR-71
❑ 94SigRoo-11
❑ 94SigRooS-11
❑ 94Top-158
❑ 94TopGol-158
❑ 94TopSpa-158
❑ 94TucTorF-770
❑ 94Ult-508
❑ 94UppDecML-208
❑ 95AstMot-17
❑ 95Bow-436
❑ 95BowBes-R84
❑ 95BowBesR-R84
❑ 95ColCho-19
❑ 95ColChoGS-19
❑ 95ColChoSE-17
❑ 95ColChoSEGS-17
❑ 95ColChoSESS-17
❑ 95ColChoSS-19
❑ 95Don-94
❑ 95DonPreP-94
❑ 95DonTopotO-258
❑ 95Emo-139
❑ 95Fin-29
❑ 95FinRef-29
❑ 95Fla-361
❑ 95FleMajLP-9
❑ 95FleUpd-142
❑ 95Lea-221
❑ 95LeaGolR-6
❑ 95LinVen-77
❑ 95Pac-190
❑ 95PacLatD-23
❑ 95Pin-137
❑ 95PinArtP-137
❑ 95PinMusC-137
❑ 95Sco-291
❑ 95ScoGolR-291
❑ 95ScoPlaTS-291
❑ 95Sel-192
❑ 95SelArtP-192
❑ 95SelCer-129
❑ 95SelCerMG-129
❑ 95Spo-142
❑ 95SpoArtP-142
❑ 95StaClu-330
❑ 95StaCluMOP-330
❑ 95StaCluSTWS-330
❑ 95Sum-117
❑ 95SumNthD-117
❑ 95Top-371
❑ 95UC3-103
❑ 95UC3ArtP-103
❑ 95UC3CleS-CS5
❑ 95Ult-389
❑ 95UltGolM-389
❑ 95UppDec-211
❑ 95UppDecED-211
❑ 95UppDecEDG-211
❑ 95UppDecSE-42
❑ 95UppDecSEG-42
❑ 95Zen-135
❑ 96AstMot-9
❑ 96ColCho-166
❑ 96ColChoGS-166
❑ 96ColChoSS-166
❑ 96Don-328
❑ 96DonPreP-328
❑ 96EmoXL-202
❑ 96Fla-282
❑ 96Fle-416
❑ 96FleTif-416
❑ 96LeaSigA-156
❑ 96LeaSigAG-156
❑ 96LeaSigAS-156
❑ 96MetUni-179
❑ 96MetUniP-179
❑ 96Pac-91
❑ 96PanSti-64
❑ 96Sco-419
❑ 96StaClu-48
❑ 96StaCluMOP-48
❑ 96Top-64
❑ 96Ult-212
❑ 96UltGolM-212
❑ 96UppDec-81
❑ 97Cir-13
❑ 97CirRav-13
❑ 97Don-197
❑ 97DonGolPP-197
❑ 97DonSilPP-197
❑ 97Fle-351
❑ 97Fle-615
❑ 97FleTif-351
❑ 97FleTif-615
❑ 97Lea-108
❑ 97LeaFraM-108
❑ 97LeaFraMDC-108
❑ 97MetUni-139
❑ 97Pac-322
❑ 97PacLigB-322
❑ 97PacSil-322
❑ 97Pin-12
❑ 97PinArtP-PP12
❑ 97PinMusC-12
❑ 97PinPrePla-12
❑ 97Sco-80
❑ 97Sco-367
❑ 97ScoArtPWB-80
❑ 97ScoArtPWB-367
❑ 97ScoPreS-80
❑ 97ScoResC-367
❑ 97ScoShoS-80
❑ 97ScoShoS-367
❑ 97ScoShoSAP-80
❑ 97ScoShoSAP-367
❑ 97StaClu-335
❑ 97StaCluMOP-335
❑ 97TolMudHB-27
❑ 97Top-255
❑ 97Ult-210
❑ 97Ult-531
❑ 97UltGolME-210
❑ 97UltGolME-531
❑ 97UltPlaME-210
❑ 97UltPlaME-531
❑ 98PacInvGems-47

Miller, Oscar
❑ 37Zee-81

Miller, Otis
❑ 27MidBre-34

Miller, Otto (Lowell)
❑ 12T207-126
❑ 14B18B-59
❑ 14CraJacE-53
❑ 15CraJacE-53
❑ 15SpoNewM-119
❑ 16BF2FP-63
❑ 16FleBreD-65
❑ 16SpoNewM-122
❑ 17ColE13-119
❑ 17HolBreD-69
❑ 20W52-17
❑ 21E121So1-66
❑ 21E121So8-63
❑ 22AmeCarE122-47
❑ 22W575-84
❑ 23W501-96
❑ 23WilChoV-104
❑ 90DodTar-529

Miller, Ox (John Anthony)
❑ 46SeaSLP-42

Miller, Pat
❑ 90HelBreSP-7
❑ 91BelBreCB-5
❑ 91BelBreP-2100
❑ 92StoPorC-18
❑ 92StoPorF-34
❑ 93St.LucMC-19

Miller, Paul
❑ 89SalBucS-13
❑ 90CarLeaA-26
❑ 90SalBucS-13
❑ 91CarMudLD-112
❑ 91CarMudP-1083
❑ 91LinDriAA-112
❑ 92Bow-686
❑ 92BufBisBS-13
❑ 92BufBisF-319
❑ 92DonRoo-79
❑ 92Lea-492
❑ 92LeaBlaG-492
❑ 92ProFS7-307
❑ 92TopDeb91-124
❑ 92Ult-555
❑ 93PacSpa-249
❑ 93Pin-258
❑ 93Sco-239
❑ 93ScoBoyoS-29
❑ 94BufBisF-1833

Miller, Pic (C. Bruce)
❑ 75OPC-606
❑ 75Top-606
❑ 75TopMin-606
❑ 76OPC-367
❑ 76PheGiaCr-14
❑ 76PhoGiaCa-20
❑ 76PhoGiaCC-17
❑ 76PhoGiaVNB-16
❑ 76SSP-102
❑ 76Top-367
❑ 82SprCarF-3

Miller, Ralph
❑ 77St.PetCT-25
❑ 78St.PetCT-18
❑ 83St.PetCT-27

Miller, Ralph Darwin
❑ 90DodTar-530

Miller, Ralph Joseph
❑ 22W573-85
❑ 75SenTCM1-21

Miller, Randall
❑ 77RocRedWM-15
❑ 80OPC-351
❑ 80Top-680
❑ 91OriCro-303

Miller, Ray
❑ 78BalOriP-20
❑ 79BalOriP-11
❑ 80BalOriP-13
❑ 81BalOriP-11
❑ 83OriPos-18
❑ 84BalOriP-21
❑ 84BalOriP-22
❑ 85BalOriP-18
❑ 86Top-381
❑ 86TopTif-381
❑ 86TwiTeal-31
❑ 88PirTeal-22
❑ 89BlaYNPRWL-136
❑ 89PirVerFJ-31
❑ 90PirHomC-22
❑ 93PirNatl-19
❑ 94PirQui-18
❑ 97BalOriP-21

Miller, Rich (Richard)
❑ 76DubPacT-23
❑ 78TidTidT-14
❑ 79JacMetT-18
❑ 86LitFalMP-19
❑ 87LitFalMP-2409
❑ 88TidTidCa-4
❑ 88TidTidCM-26
❑ 88TidTidP-1585
❑ 89TidTidC-25
❑ 90CMC-686
❑ 90ProAAAF-293
❑ 90TidTidC-29
❑ 90TidTidP-562

Miller, Rick (Richard A.)
❑ 72RedSoxTI-15
❑ 72Top-741
❑ 73LinPor-26
❑ 74OPC-247
❑ 74Top-247
❑ 74TopSta-136
❑ 75OPC-103
❑ 75Top-103
❑ 75TopMin-103
❑ 76OPC-302
❑ 76RedSoxSM-11
❑ 76SSP-416
❑ 76Top-302
❑ 77Top-566
❑ 78AngFamF-26
❑ 78SSP270-199
❑ 78Top-482
❑ 79Top-654
❑ 80OPC-27
❑ 80Top-48
❑ 81Don-294
❑ 81Fle-279
❑ 81OPC-239
❑ 81Top-239
❑ 81TopTra-803
❑ 82Don-334
❑ 82Fle-299
❑ 82RedSoxC-11
❑ 82RegGloT-7
❑ 82Top-717
❑ 83Don-82
❑ 83Fle-188
❑ 83OPC-188
❑ 83Top-188
❑ 84Don-493
❑ 84Fle-403
❑ 84Nes792-344
❑ 84Top-344
❑ 84TopTif-344
❑ 85Don-517
❑ 85Fle-163
❑ 85Top-502
❑ 85TopTif-502
❑ 86Top-424
❑ 86TopTif-424
❑ 91ModA'sC-8
❑ 92SanJosGC-27

Miller, Roger
❑ 88CapCodPPaLP-184
❑ 90Bes-120
❑ 90CliGiaB-19
❑ 90CliGiaP-2553
❑ 90MidLeaASGS-43
❑ 91SanJosGC-2
❑ 91SanJosGP-13
❑ 94SanJosGC-17
❑ 94SanJosGF-2821
❑ 96NewHavRB-17
❑ 96NewHavRUSTI-13

Miller, Roger Wesley
❑ 74SacSolC-53
❑ 75SacSolC-19
❑ 77SpoIndC-25
❑ 94BreMilB-251

Miller, Roscoe
❑ 03BreE10-105

Miller, Russ
❑ 29Zee-25
❑ 90BenBucL-15

Miller, Ryan
❑ 94PitMetC-15
❑ 94PitMetF-3529
❑ 95StLucMTI-22
❑ 96StLucMTI-25
❑ 97St.LucM-18
❑ 98JacGenM-11

Miller, Scott
❑ 82QuaCitCT-23
❑ 88CapCodPPaLP-87
❑ 90MedHatBJB-15
❑ 90MyrBeaBJP-2784
❑ 91MyrBeaHC-21
❑ 91MyrBeaHP-2955
❑ 92ClaDraP-66
❑ 92DunBluJC-25
❑ 92FroRowDP-47
❑ 92FroRowDPG-47
❑ 92FroRowDPS-47
❑ 92MedHatBJF-3223
❑ 92MedHatBJSP-27
❑ 93MedHatBJF-3754
❑ 93MedHatBJSP-25
❑ 94KnoSmoF-1321
❑ 95HagSunF-86

Miller, Shawn
❑ 92EliTwiC-1
❑ 92EliTwiF-3678
❑ 92StaCluD-120
❑ 93EliTwiC-15
❑ 93EliTwiF-3414
❑ 93ForWayWC-19
❑ 93ForWayWF-1966
❑ 94ForWayWC-15
❑ 94ForWayWF-2007
❑ 95ForMyeMTI-16
❑ 95HelBreTI-14
❑ 96OgdRapTI-35

Miller, Steve
❑ 86ShrCapP-19
❑ 87PhoFirP-26

Miller, Stu
❑ 53BowBW-16
❑ 53CarHunW-14
❑ 53Top-183
❑ 54Bow-158
❑ 54CarHunW-13
❑ 54Top-164
❑ 56Top-293
❑ 58GiaSFCB-16
❑ 58Top-111
❑ 59Top-183
❑ 59TopVen-183
❑ 60Top-378
❑ 61GiaJayP-11
❑ 61Top-72
❑ 62GiaJayP-11
❑ 62Jel-143
❑ 62Pos-143
❑ 62PosCan-143
❑ 62SalPlaC-205
❑ 62ShiPlaC-205
❑ 62Top-155
❑ 62TopBuc-60
❑ 62TopStal-201
❑ 62TopVen-155
❑ 63BalOriP-21
❑ 63Top-286
❑ 64BalOriP-25
❑ 64Top-565
❑ 65BalOriP-23
❑ 65Top-499
❑ 66BalOriP-25
❑ 66Top-265
❑ 66TopVen-265
❑ 67BalOriP-69
❑ 67CokCapO-7
❑ 67Top-345
❑ 67TopVen-229
❑ 78TCM60I-254
❑ 81Gia196T-28
❑ 81Ori6F-24
❑ 84GiaMot-18
❑ 91OriCro-304
❑ 91TopArc1-183
❑ 94TopArc1-164
❑ 94TopArc1G-164

Miller, Ted
❑ 86KenTwiP-16

Miller, Terry
❑ 92BurIndC-24
❑ 92BurIndF-1672

Miller, Thomas R.
❑ 97LowSpiB-21
❑ 98MicBatCM-24

Miller, Todd
❑ 85EveGiaC-10
❑ 86CliGiaP-13
❑ 88CliGiaP-706
❑ 91ElmPioC-24
❑ 91ElmPioP-3269
❑ 92WinHavRSC-24
❑ 92WinHavRSF-1773
❑ 93LynRedSC-20
❑ 93LynRedSF-2516

Miller, Tom
❑ 82LynMetT-11
❑ 87OmaRoyP-26
❑ 98LowSpiM-25

Miller, Tony
❑ 91AubAstC-2
❑ 91AubAstP-4272

Miller, Travis
❑ 94SigRooDP-32
❑ 94SigRooDPS-32
❑ 94StaCluDP-16
❑ 94StaCluDPFDI-16

❑ 95Bow-48
❑ 95ColCho-44
❑ 95ColChoGS-44
❑ 95ColChoSS-44
❑ 95HarCitRCTI-14
❑ 95SPML-87
❑ 95Top-194
❑ 96Bow-143
❑ 96BowFoi-143
❑ 97Cir-165
❑ 97CirRav-165
❑ 97Fle-150
❑ 97FleTif-150
❑ 97HudValRB-11
❑ 97SalLakB-17
❑ 97UppDec-285
❑ 98ColCho-161
❑ 98HudValR-17
❑ 98SalLakBO-18
❑ 98Top-339
❑ 98TopChr-339
❑ 98TopChrR-339
❑ 98TopDevR-339
❑ 98TopDia-339
❑ 98TopMiniC-339
Miller, Trever
❑ 91BriTigC-14
❑ 91BriTigP-3599
❑ 91Cla/Bes-406
❑ 91ClaDraP-37
❑ 91FroRowDP-7
❑ 91FroRowDPG-7
❑ 91FroRowDPS-7
❑ 92BriTigC-7
❑ 92BriTigF-1407
❑ 92OPC-684
❑ 92Pin-579
❑ 92ProFS7-72
❑ 92StaCluD-121
❑ 92Top-684
❑ 92TopGol-684
❑ 92TopGolW-684
❑ 92TopMic-684
❑ 93FayGenC-15
❑ 93FayGenF-126
❑ 94TreThuF-2118
❑ 95JacSunTI-21
❑ 96TolMudHB-20
❑ 98PacOmeRS-17
❑ 98PacOmeRST3-17
❑ 98PacOnl-329
❑ 98PacOnlR-329
❑ 98PacOnlWC-329
Miller, Wade
❑ 97MidLeaTP-21
❑ 97QuaCitRBB-19
❑ 98Bes-79
❑ 98Bow-385
❑ 98BowChr-385
❑ 98BowChrGA-385
❑ 98BowChrGAR-385
❑ 98BowChrI-385
❑ 98BowChrIR-385
❑ 98BowChrR-385
❑ 98BowGolA-385
❑ 98BowInt-385
❑ 98JacGenM-12
❑ 98TexLeaTPG-23
❑ 99Bow-202
❑ 99BowChr-202
❑ 99BowChrG-202
❑ 99BowChrGR-202
❑ 99BowChrI-202
❑ 99BowChrIR-202
❑ 99BowChrR-202
❑ 99BowGol-202
❑ 99BowInt-202
Miller, Walt
❑ 90DodTar-531
Miller, Ward
❑ 11PinT-5-415
❑ 12T207-125
❑ 14CraJacE-5
❑ 15CraJacE-5
❑ 18Zee-66
Miller, Warren
❑ 11SpoLifM-130
Miller, Wayne
❑ 75AlbDukCa-21
Miller-Jones, Gary
❑ 85PawRedST-9
❑ 86PawRedSP-15
❑ 87PawRedSP-69
❑ 87PawRedST-16
❑ 88PawRedSC-19
❑ 88PawRedSP-459
❑ 89PawRedSC-12
❑ 89PawRedSP-689
❑ 89PawRedSTI-17
Millerick, Edwin
❑ 91EriSaiC-20
❑ 91EriSaiP-4066
Millette, Joe
❑ 89BatCliP-1922
❑ 90ClePhiS-16
❑ 90FloStaLAS-15
❑ 90StaFS7-71
❑ 91ClePhiP-1629
❑ 91ReaPhiP-1374
❑ 92DonRoo-80
❑ 92ScrRedBF-2453
❑ 92ScrRedBS-491
❑ 93ScrRedBF-2549
❑ 93ScrRedBTI-19
❑ 93StaClu-360
❑ 93StaCluFDI-360
❑ 93StaCluMOP-360
❑ 93Top-531
❑ 93TopGol-531
❑ 93TopInaM-531
❑ 93TopInaR-531
❑ 93TopMic-531
❑ 94EdmTraF-2879
❑ 95ChaKniTI-16
Millhauser, Glenn
❑ 80QuaCitCT-19
Milliard, Ralph
❑ 94KanCouCC-17
❑ 94KanCouCF-171
❑ 94KanCouCTI-19
❑ 94MidLeaAF-MDW19
❑ 95KanCouCLTI-11
❑ 95PorSeaDTI-17
❑ 96BesAutSA-45
❑ 96Bow-379
❑ 96BowFoi-379
❑ 96ChaKniB-19
❑ 96LeaPre-146
❑ 96LeaPreP-146
❑ 96Zen-110
❑ 96ZenArtP-110
❑ 97ChaKni-20
❑ 97Fle-332
❑ 97FleTif-332
❑ 97PacPriGotD-GD145
❑ 97Sco-288
❑ 97ScoArtPWB-288
❑ 97ScoPreS-288
❑ 97ScoShoS-288
❑ 97ScoShoSAP-288
❑ 97Ult-199
❑ 97UltGolME-199
❑ 97UltPlaME-199
❑ 97UppDec-279
❑ 98Bow-344
❑ 98BowChr-344
❑ 98BowChrGA-344
❑ 98BowChrGAR-344
❑ 98BowChrI-344
❑ 98BowChrIR-344
❑ 98BowChrR-344
❑ 98BowGolA-344
❑ 98BowInt-344
❑ 98NorTidP-16
❑ 98NorTidQ-16
❑ 98PorSeaD5AQ-5
Millican, Kevin
❑ 94HudValRC-13
❑ 94HudValRF-3388
❑ 95ChaRivTI-14
Millies, Walter
❑ 40PhiTeal-16
❑ 40PlaBal-218
❑ 41PhiTeal-18
❑ 79DiaGre-306
❑ 90DodTar-532
Milligan, John
❑ 87OldJudN-346
❑ 90KalBatN-40
❑ 90KalBatN-52
❑ 90KalBatN-54
Milligan, John Alexander
❑ 35DiaMatCS3T1-111
Milligan, Randy
❑ 82LynMetT-15
❑ 83LynMetT-7
❑ 84JacMetT-25
❑ 86JacMetT-26
❑ 86TidTidP-20
❑ 87IntLeaAT-5
❑ 87TidTidP-28
❑ 87TidTidT-17
❑ 88BlaYNPRWL-122
❑ 88DonRoo-32
❑ 88FleUpd-113
❑ 88FleUpd-115
❑ 88FleUpdG-113
❑ 88FleUpdG-115
❑ 88MetColP-39
❑ 88PirTeal-23
❑ 88Sco-623
❑ 88ScoGlo-623
❑ 89BalOriP-20
❑ 89Bow-10
❑ 89BowTif-10
❑ 89FleUpd-7
❑ 89OriFreB-15
❑ 89TidTidC-13
❑ 89TopTra-81T
❑ 89TopTraT-81T
❑ 89UppDec-559
❑ 89UppDec-740
❑ 90BalOriP-19
❑ 90BalOriP-20
❑ 90Bow-257
❑ 90BowTif-257
❑ 90Don-519
❑ 90DonBesA-85
❑ 90Fle-183
❑ 90FleCan-183
❑ 90Lea-92
❑ 90OPC-153
❑ 90PanSti-1
❑ 90Sco-252
❑ 90Top-153
❑ 90TopBig-263
❑ 90TopSti-233
❑ 90TopTif-153
❑ 90UppDec-663
❑ 91BalOriP-21
❑ 91Don-542
❑ 91Fle-484
❑ 91Lea-109
❑ 91MetWIZ-273
❑ 91OPC-416
❑ 91OriCro-305
❑ 91PanFreS-240
❑ 91PanSti-201
❑ 91Sco-86
❑ 91Sco100S-43
❑ 91SevCoi-A9
❑ 91StaClu-80
❑ 91Stu-7
❑ 91Top-416
❑ 91TopDesS-416
❑ 91TopMic-416
❑ 91TopTif-416
❑ 91Ult-20
❑ 91UppDec-548
❑ 92BalOriP-22
❑ 92Don-222
❑ 92Fle-19
❑ 92OPC-17
❑ 92PanSti-65
❑ 92Pin-179
❑ 92Sco-87
❑ 92StaClu-587
❑ 92Top-17
❑ 92TopGol-17
❑ 92TopGolW-17
❑ 92TopMic-17
❑ 92Ult-8
❑ 92UppDec-181
❑ 93Don-191
❑ 93Fle-170
❑ 93FleFinE-16
❑ 93Lea-513
❑ 93PacSpa-402
❑ 93PanSti-71
❑ 93Pin-157
❑ 93RedFolS-65
❑ 93RedKah-14
❑ 93Sco-112
❑ 93Sel-212
❑ 93StaClu-158
❑ 93StaCluFDI-158
❑ 93StaCluMOP-158
❑ 93Stu-105
❑ 93Top-678
❑ 93TopGol-678
❑ 93TopInaM-678
❑ 93TopInaR-678
❑ 93TopMic-678
❑ 93Ult-330
❑ 93UppDec-228
❑ 93UppDec-622
❑ 93UppDecGold-228
❑ 93UppDecGold-622
❑ 94Don-210
❑ 94FleUpd-154
❑ 94Lea-343
❑ 94Pin-485
❑ 94PinArtP-485
❑ 94PinMusC-485
❑ 94Sco-498
❑ 94ScoGolR-498
❑ 94ScoRoo-RT28
❑ 94ScoRooGR-RT28
❑ 95Sco-193
❑ 95ScoGolR-193
❑ 95ScoPlaTS-193
❑ 95Top-226
Milligan, Ricky
❑ 93UtiBluSC-15
❑ 93UtiBluSF-3547
Milligan, Sean
❑ 93RanCucQF-836
Milligan, William J.
❑ 09T206-446
❑ 11SpoLifCW-254
Milliken, Bob
❑ 53ExhCan-44
❑ 53Top-221
❑ 54Top-177
❑ 55Top-111
❑ 55TopDouH-117
❑ 62KahAtl-14
❑ 65CarTeal-17
❑ 76St.LouCP-23
❑ 79TCM50-234
❑ 90DodTar-533
❑ 90JohCitCS-28
❑ 91TopArc1-221
❑ 94TopArc1-177
❑ 94TopArc1G-177
❑ 95TopArcBD-52
❑ 95TopArcBD-79
❑ 95TopArcBD-101
Million, Doug
❑ 94BenRocC-18
❑ 94BenRocF-3590
❑ 94ClaUpdCotC-CC6
❑ 94SigRooDP-7
❑ 94SigRooDPS-7
❑ 94StaCluDP-3
❑ 94StaCluDPFDI-3
❑ 94TopTra-85T
❑ 95ActPacF-57
❑ 95Bow-265
❑ 95BowBes-B88
❑ 95BowBesR-B88
❑ 95BowGolF-265
❑ 95ColCho-38
❑ 95ColChoGS-38
❑ 95ColChoSS-38
❑ 95Exc-189
❑ 95SalAvaTI-22
❑ 95ScoDraP-DP13
❑ 95SPML-48
❑ 95StaClu-109
❑ 95StaCluFDI-109
❑ 95StaCluMOP-109
❑ 95StaCluSTWS-109
❑ 95Top-286
❑ 95UppDecML-125
❑ 95UppDecML-223
❑ 95UppDecMLFS-125
❑ 95UppDecMLFS-223
❑ 96Bow-218
❑ 96BowBes-150
❑ 96BowBesAR-150
❑ 96BowBesR-150
❑ 96BowFoi-218
❑ 96CarLeaA1B-9
❑ 96CarLeaA2B-9
❑ 96MauStiHWB-30
❑ 96SalAvaB-1
❑ 96Top-428
❑ 97NewHavRB-22
❑ 97SalAva-U4
❑ 97Top-200
Million, Ten
❑ 09ObaT21-424
❑ 12ObaPreT-173
Millner, Tim
❑ 80QuaCitCT-3
❑ 83MidCubT-9
Mills, Alan
❑ 86SalAngC-81
❑ 87PriWilYP-7
❑ 88PriWilYS-17
❑ 89Ft.LauYS-16
❑ 90Bow-428
❑ 90BowTif-428
❑ 90DonRoo-44
❑ 90FleUpd-114
❑ 90Lea-491
❑ 90ScoRoo-89T
❑ 90TopTra-75T
❑ 90TopTraT-75T
❑ 90TopTVY-14
❑ 90YanScoNW-29
❑ 91Cla1-T64
❑ 91ColCliLD-112
❑ 91ColCliP-12
❑ 91ColCliP-595
❑ 91Don-338
❑ 91LinDriAAA-112
❑ 91OPC-651
❑ 91Sco-73
❑ 91Sco100RS-62
❑ 91StaClu-473
❑ 91Top-651
❑ 91TopDeb90-108
❑ 91TopDesS-651
❑ 91TopMic-651
❑ 91TopTif-651
❑ 91UppDec-222
❑ 92BalOriP-23
❑ 92Bow-342
❑ 92FleUpd-2
❑ 92StaClu-871
❑ 93BalOriP-18
❑ 93Don-691
❑ 93Fle-171
❑ 93Lea-111
❑ 93OPC-195
❑ 93PacSpa-346
❑ 93Sco-440
❑ 93Sel-367
❑ 93StaClu-643
❑ 93StaCluFDI-643
❑ 93StaCluMOP-643
❑ 93Top-137
❑ 93TopGol-137
❑ 93TopInaM-137
❑ 93TopInaR-137
❑ 93TopMic-137
❑ 93Ult-143
❑ 93UppDec-312
❑ 93UppDecGold-312
❑ 93USPlaCR-11C
❑ 94BalOriP-19
❑ 94ColC-608
❑ 94ColChoGS-608
❑ 94ColChoSS-608
❑ 94Don-214
❑ 94Fle-10
❑ 94OriPro-68
❑ 94OriUSPC-5H
❑ 94OriUSPC-11S
❑ 94Pac-37
❑ 94StaClu-693
❑ 94StaCluFDI-693
❑ 94StaCluGR-693
❑ 94StaCluMOP-693
❑ 94StaCluT-277
❑ 94StaCluTFDI-277
❑ 94Top-324
❑ 94TopGol-324
❑ 94TopSpa-324
❑ 94Ult-5
❑ 95BalOriP-34
❑ 95Fla-4
❑ 95Fle-13
❑ 96BalOriP-22
❑ 97BalOriP-22
❑ 97PacPriGotD-GD11
❑ 98PacOnl-94
❑ 98PacOnlR-94
❑ 98PacOnlWC-94
❑ 99DodPol-16
Mills, Art
❑ 47TipTop-37
Mills, Brad
❑ 80MemChiT-15
❑ 82ExpHygM-12
❑ 82ExpPos-22
❑ 82Fle-196
❑ 82OPC-118
❑ 82Top-118
❑ 83Don-366
❑ 83ExpPos-19
❑ 83ExpStu-30
❑ 83Fle-288
❑ 83OPC-199
❑ 83Top-744
❑ 83WicAerDS-13
❑ 84IndIndTI-9
❑ 85TucTorC-75
❑ 86IowCubP-19
❑ 87WytCubP-30
❑ 88ChaWheB-2
❑ 89PeoChiTI-30
❑ 90CarLeaA-51
❑ 90WinSpiTI-29
❑ 91CarLeaAP-CAR44
❑ 91WinSpiC-12
❑ 91WinSpiP-2845
❑ 92IowCubF-4065
❑ 92IowCubS-224
❑ 93ColSprSSF-3101
❑ 94ColSprSSF-748
❑ 96ColSprSSTI-23
❑ 97ColSprSATTI-30
❑ 97PhiTeal-9
❑ 98PhiTeal-25
Mills, Buster (Colonel)
❑ 48WhiSoxTI-19
❑ 54Top-227
❑ 79DiaGre-234
❑ 90DodTar-534
❑ 94TopArc1-227
❑ 94TopArc1G-227
Mills, Craig
❑ 86GleFalTP-16
❑ 87LakTigP-3
Mills, E.L.
❑ 87OldJudN-347
Mills, Gil
❑ 52Par-59
❑ 53ExhCan-55
Mills, Gotay
❑ 82LouRedE-19
❑ 83ArkTraT-21
❑ 84ArkTraT-21
Mills, Howard
❑ 33WorCig(-60
Mills, Jethro
❑ 72CedRapCT-5
Mills, Ken
❑ 83CliGiaF-19
Mills, Lefty
❑ 93ConTSN-966
Mills, Michael
❑ 85BeaGolGT-17
❑ 86BeaGolGP-19
❑ 88WicPilRD-31
❑ 89DunBluJS-11
❑ 89KnoBluJB-16
❑ 89KnoBluJP-1141
❑ 89KnoBluJS-23
Mills, Pinckney
❑ 37Zee-82
Mills, Rhadames
❑ 81ArkTraT-6
❑ 85DomLeaS-157
Mills, Richard Allen
❑ 71OPC-512
❑ 71Top-512
Mills, Ryan
❑ 99199Fin-132
❑ 99Bow-131
❑ 99BowAut-BA28
❑ 99BowBes-192
❑ 99BowBesAR-192
❑ 99BowBesR-192
❑ 99BowChr-131
❑ 99BowChrG-131
❑ 99BowChrGR-131
❑ 99BowChrI-131
❑ 99BowChrIR-131
❑ 99BowChrR-131
❑ 99BowGol-131
❑ 99BowInt-131
❑ 99FinGolRef-132
❑ 99FinRef-132
❑ 99Top-218
❑ 99TopChr-218
❑ 99TopChrR-218
Mills, Tony
❑ 90WicStaSGD-25
Mills, William
❑ 80AppFoxT-4
Millwood, Kevin
❑ 94DanBraC-27
❑ 94DanBraF-3528
❑ 94MacBraC-14
❑ 94MacBraF-2200
❑ 95MacBraTI-19
❑ 96DurBulBlB-12
❑ 96DurBulBrB-13
❑ 97GreBraG-21
❑ 97SouLeaTP-11

❑ 98Bow-91
❑ 98BowChr-91
❑ 98BowChrGA-91
❑ 98BowChrGAR-91
❑ 98BowChrI-91
❑ 98BowChrIR-91
❑ 98BowChrR-91
❑ 98BowGolA-91
❑ 98BowInt-91
❑ 98ColCho-123
❑ 98Don-302
❑ 98DonGolPP-302
❑ 98DonSig-106
❑ 98DonSigP-106
❑ 98DonSigSP-18
❑ 98DonSilPP-302
❑ 98E-X2Sig2001-4
❑ 98Fle-294
❑ 98LeaRCrusUP-126
❑ 98LeaRS-195
❑ 98LeaRSCrusUG-126
❑ 98LeaRSCrusUR-126
❑ 98LeaRSFOSamp-15
❑ 98LeaRSFresh-15
❑ 98LeaRSLHolo-195
❑ 98LeaRSLong-195
❑ 98LeaRTrue-195
❑ 98PacInvGems-123
❑ 98PacOme-24
❑ 98PacOmeR-24
❑ 98PacOnl-69
❑ 98PacOnlR-69
❑ 98PacOnlWC-69
❑ 98PinPlu-35
❑ 98PinSna-AB18
❑ 98SPxFin-201
❑ 98SPxFinR-201
❑ 98SPxFinS-201
❑ 98StaCluFDI-298
❑ 98StaCluI-298
❑ 98StaCluOneK-298
❑ 98StaCluPP-298
❑ 98Stu-124
❑ 98StuGPP-124
❑ 98StuSPP-124
❑ 98TopGolLabC1-93
❑ 98TopGolLabC1B-93
❑ 98TopGolLabC1One-93
❑ 98TopGolLabC1R-93
❑ 98TopGolLabC2-93
❑ 98TopGolLabC2B-93
❑ 98TopGolLabC2One-93
❑ 98TopGolLabC2R-93
❑ 98TopGolLabC3-93
❑ 98TopGolLabC3B-93
❑ 98TopGolLabC3One-93
❑ 98TopGolLabC3R-93
❑ 98Ult-121
❑ 98UltGolM-121
❑ 98UltMas-121
❑ 98UltPlaM-121
❑ 98UppDec-284
❑ 99199Fin-79
❑ 99Bow-287
❑ 99BowGol-287
❑ 99BowInt-287
❑ 99E-XCenA-3
❑ 99FinGolRef-79
❑ 99FinRef-79
❑ 99FlaShoLeg1-135
❑ 99FlaShoLeg2-135
❑ 99FlaShoLeg3-135
❑ 99FlaShoLegM1-135
❑ 99FlaShoLegM2-135
❑ 99FlaShoLegM3-135
❑ 99FlaShoR1-135
❑ 99FlaShoR2-135
❑ 99FlaShoR3-135
❑ 99Fle-206
❑ 99FleMysFtG-5
❑ 99FleSta9-206
❑ 99FleWarT-206
❑ 99MetUni-20
❑ 99MetUniGM-20
❑ 99MetUniPMG-20
❑ 99Pac-39
❑ 99PacPlaB-39
❑ 99PacRed-39
❑ 99SkyMolMOA-2
❑ 99SkyPre-143
❑ 99SkyPreR-143
❑ 99SkyThu-21
❑ 99SkyThuRant-21
❑ 99SkyThuRave-21
❑ 99SpoIll-103
❑ 99StaClu-131
❑ 99StaCluFDI-131
❑ 99StaCluOoaK-131
❑ 99StaCluPP-131
❑ 99ThuSkySupR-21
❑ 99Top-405
❑ 99TopChr-405
❑ 99TopChrR-405
❑ 99TopGal-120
❑ 99TopGalPP-120
❑ 99TopGalPPI-120
❑ 99TopMVPP-405
❑ 99TopOpeD-124
❑ 99TopSta-147
❑ 99TopStaFoil-147
❑ 99UppDec-36
❑ 99UppDecEL1-36
❑ 99UppDecEL2-36

Millwood, Terry
❑ 93AusFut-8

Milnar, Al
❑ 40PlaBal-202
❑ 41PlaBal-33
❑ 46SeaSLP-43
❑ 79DiaGre-290

Milne, Blaine
❑ 92HamRedC-4
❑ 92HamRedF-1594
❑ 94MadHatF-135

Milne, Darren
❑ 92BriTigC-25
❑ 92BriTigF-1426
❑ 93LakTigC-18
❑ 94TreThuF-2132

Milne, Pete (William J.)
❑ 49EurSta-119
❑ 53MotCoo-28

Milner, Brian
❑ 78BluJayP-17
❑ 81OPC-238
❑ 81Top-577
❑ 82KnoBluJT-10
❑ 82OPC-203
❑ 82Top-203
❑ 90OneYanP-3392
❑ 91GreHorP-3076
❑ 92GreHorC-28
❑ 92GreHorF-797
❑ 93PriWilCC-28
❑ 93PriWilCF-674
❑ 94GreBatF-492
❑ 95GreBatTI-30
❑ 97GreBatC-29

Milner, Eddie
❑ 79IndIndTI-10
❑ 79NaSouTI-17
❑ 80IndIndTI-10
❑ 81IndIndTI-9
❑ 82TopTra-72T
❑ 83Don-169
❑ 83Fle-597
❑ 83FleSta-125
❑ 83OPC-363
❑ 83RedYea-20
❑ 83Top-449
❑ 84Don-365
❑ 84Fle-474
❑ 84Nes792-34
❑ 84OPC-34
❑ 84RedBor-20
❑ 84RedEnq-11
❑ 84Top-34
❑ 84TopSti-60
❑ 84TopTif-34
❑ 85Don-428
❑ 85Fle-541
❑ 85OPC-198
❑ 85RedYea-9
❑ 85Top-198
❑ 85TopMin-198
❑ 85TopSti-53
❑ 85TopTif-198
❑ 86Don-325
❑ 86Fle-182
❑ 86RedTexG-20
❑ 86Top-544
❑ 86TopTif-544
❑ 87Don-433
❑ 87Fle-205
❑ 87FleGlo-205
❑ 87GiaMot-15
❑ 87GiaPos-24
❑ 87OPC-253
❑ 87Top-253
❑ 87TopSti-144
❑ 87TopTif-253
❑ 87TopTra-78T
❑ 87TopTraT-78T
❑ 88Fle-90
❑ 88FleGlo-90
❑ 88RedKah-9
❑ 88Sco-548
❑ 88ScoGlo-548
❑ 88Top-677
❑ 88TopTif-677
❑ 91PacSenL-25

Milner, John
❑ 72Top-741
❑ 73LinPor-120
❑ 73NewYorSNM-6
❑ 73OPC-4
❑ 73Top-4
❑ 74MetJapEB-5
❑ 74MetJapEB-8
❑ 74MetTeal-16
❑ 74OPC-234
❑ 74Top-234
❑ 74TopSta-69
❑ 75Hos-15
❑ 75HosTwi-15
❑ 75MetSSP-1
❑ 75OPC-264
❑ 75Top-264
❑ 75TopMin-264
❑ 76OPC-517
❑ 76SSP-547
❑ 76Top-517
❑ 77MetDaiPA-17
❑ 77Top-172
❑ 78Top-304
❑ 79Top-523
❑ 80OPC-38
❑ 80Top-71
❑ 81Don-377
❑ 81Fle-386
❑ 81Top-618
❑ 82Don-266
❑ 82ExpHygM-13
❑ 82ExpPos-23
❑ 82Fle-197
❑ 82OPC-331
❑ 82Top-638
❑ 83Fle-311
❑ 91MetWIZ-274
❑ 95PirCocP-18

Milner, Ted
❑ 84SavCarT-9
❑ 86SanJosBP-13

Miloszewski, Frank
❑ 78SalPirT-10

Milstead, George
❑ 25Zee-9

Milstien, David
❑ 86ElmPioRSP-12
❑ 87WinHavRSP-14
❑ 88WinHavRSS-13
❑ 89EasLeaDDP-DD23
❑ 89NewBriRSP-621
❑ 89NewBriRSS-10
❑ 90NewBriRSB-5
❑ 90NewBriRSP-1327
❑ 90NewBriRSS-11
❑ 91LinDriAA-466
❑ 91NewBriRSLD-466
❑ 91NewBriRSP-358
❑ 92PawRedSF-931
❑ 92PawRedSS-359
❑ 92SkyAAAF-163
❑ 93PawRedSDD-18
❑ 93PawRedSF-2415
❑ 93PawRedSTI-16
❑ 97DunDonPPS-14

Milton, Eric
❑ 97Bes-80
❑ 97BesAutSC-9
❑ 97BesLimA-25
❑ 97Bow-159
❑ 97BowBes-198
❑ 97BowBesAR-198
❑ 97BowBesR-198
❑ 97BowChr-157
❑ 97BowChrI-157
❑ 97BowChrIR-157
❑ 97BowChrR-157
❑ 97BowInt-159
❑ 97FloStaLTPB-23
❑ 97TamYan-19
❑ 97Top-272
❑ 98BesAutPOY-11
❑ 98BesFulCA-13
❑ 98BesPreA-27
❑ 98Bow-298
❑ 98BowBes-184
❑ 98BowBesAR-184
❑ 98BowBesR-184
❑ 98BowCerBlueAU-44
❑ 98BowCerGA-44
❑ 98BowCerSA-44
❑ 98BowChr-298
❑ 98BowChrGA-298
❑ 98BowChrGAR-298
❑ 98BowChrI-298
❑ 98BowChrIR-298
❑ 98BowChrR-298
❑ 98BowGolA-298
❑ 98BowInt-298
❑ 98CirThu-41
❑ 98CirThuRav-41
❑ 98CirThuSupRav-41
❑ 98Don-241
❑ 98DonGolPP-241
❑ 98DonSilPP-241
❑ 98Fle-410
❑ 98FleProF-PF13
❑ 98LeaRCrusUP-116
❑ 98LeaRS-240
❑ 98LeaRSCrusUG-116
❑ 98LeaRSCrusUR-116
❑ 98LeaRSLHolo-240
❑ 98LeaRSLong-240
❑ 98LeaRTrue-240
❑ 98PacOmeRS-23
❑ 98PacOmeRST2-23
❑ 98PacOnl-426
❑ 98PacOnlR-426
❑ 98PacOnlWC-426
❑ 98SkyDugA-109
❑ 98SkyDugAIA-109
❑ 98SP MinPE-88
❑ 98SPMin-88
❑ 98SPxFin-204
❑ 98SPxFinR-204
❑ 98SPxFinS-204
❑ 98StaCluFDI-375
❑ 98StaCluI-375
❑ 98StaCluOneK-375
❑ 98StaCluPP-375
❑ 98Stu-169
❑ 98StuGPP-169
❑ 98StuSPP-169
❑ 98Top-486
❑ 98TopChr-486
❑ 98TopChrR-486
❑ 98TopDevR-486
❑ 98TopDia-486
❑ 98TopMiniC-486
❑ 98TopSta-49
❑ 98TopStaB-49
❑ 98TopStaG-49
❑ 98TopStaGR-49
❑ 98TopStaS-49
❑ 98UD3-6
❑ 98UD3-96
❑ 98UD3-186
❑ 98UD3DieCut-6
❑ 98UD3DieCut-96
❑ 98UD3DieCut-186
❑ 98Ult-358
❑ 98UltGolM-358
❑ 98UltMas-358
❑ 98UltPlaM-358
❑ 98UppDec-544
❑ 98UppDecR-120
❑ 98UppDecRNF-NF20
❑ 99199Fin-98
❑ 99FinGolRef-98
❑ 99FinRef-98
❑ 99Fle-189
❑ 99FleSta9-189
❑ 99FleWarT-189
❑ 99MetUni-229
❑ 99MetUniGM-229
❑ 99MetUniPMG-229
❑ 99SkyMolM-60
❑ 99SkyMolMX-60
❑ 99SkyPre-204
❑ 99SkyPreR-204
❑ 99SkyThu-167
❑ 99SkyThuRant-167
❑ 99SkyThuRave-167
❑ 99SP SigAuto-EMI
❑ 99SPSig-146
❑ 99StaClu-182
❑ 99StaCluFDI-182
❑ 99StaCluOoaK-182
❑ 99StaCluPP-182
❑ 99ThuSkySupR-167
❑ 99Top-156
❑ 99TopChr-156
❑ 99TopChrR-156
❑ 99TopMVPP-156
❑ 99TopSta-135
❑ 99TopStaFoil-135
❑ 99Ult-57
❑ 99UltGolM-57
❑ 99UltMas-57
❑ 99UltPlaM-57
❑ 99UppDec-136
❑ 99UppDecBD-107
❑ 99UppDecBDD-107
❑ 99UppDecBDQ-107
❑ 99UppDecBDT-107
❑ 99UppDecCLM-C54
❑ 99UppDecEL1-136
❑ 99UppDecEL2-136
❑ 99UppDecM-118
❑ 99UppDecMGS-118
❑ 99UppDecMHFS-118
❑ 99UppDecMP-118
❑ 99UppDecMSS-118
❑ 99Vic-229

Milton, Herb
❑ 90AppFoxBS-17
❑ 90AppFoxP-2092
❑ 91AppFoxCB-6
❑ 91AppFoxP-1712

Milton, Prinz
❑ 98DanBraQ-17

Mimbs, Mark
❑ 90GreFalDSP-9
❑ 91BakDodCLC-12
❑ 92AlbDukF-717
❑ 92AlbDukS-15
❑ 92SkyAAAF-7
❑ 92UppDecML-77
❑ 94AlbDukF-839
❑ 97PawRedS-17
❑ 98NorTidP-17
❑ 98NorTidQ-17

Mimbs, Mike (Michael)
❑ 90GreFalDSP-10
❑ 91FloStaLAP-FSL40
❑ 91VerBeaDC-9
❑ 91VerBeaDP-770
❑ 92ProFS7-247
❑ 92SanAntMF-3972
❑ 92SanAntMS-570
❑ 92SkyAA F-249
❑ 94HarSenF-2087
❑ 95Emo-169
❑ 95Fin-232
❑ 95FinRef-232
❑ 95Fla-393
❑ 95FleUpd-123
❑ 95Phi-20
❑ 95PhiMel-16
❑ 95StaClu-586
❑ 95StaCluMOP-586
❑ 95StaCluSTWS-586
❑ 95TopTra-19T
❑ 96ColCho-254
❑ 96ColChoGS-254
❑ 96ColChoSS-254
❑ 96Don-264
❑ 96DonPreP-264
❑ 96Fle-504
❑ 96FleTif-504
❑ 96LeaSigA-157
❑ 96LeaSigAG-157
❑ 96LeaSigAS-157
❑ 96Pac-150
❑ 96PhiTeal-22
❑ 96Sco-418
❑ 96Top-97
❑ 96Ult-256
❑ 96UltGolM-256
❑ 96UppDec-429
❑ 97PhiTeal-47
❑ 98VanCanG-16

Mims, Fred
❑ 73CedRapAT-6
❑ 74CedRapAT-16

Mims, Gerry
❑ 80QuaCitCT-2

Mims, Larry
❑ 87MiaMarP-23
❑ 88HagSunS-12
❑ 89HagSunP-264
❑ 89WicStaR-6
❑ 89WicUpdR-13

Minarcin, John
❑ 78WisRapTT-13
❑ 79WisRapTT-10

Minarcin, Rudy
❑ 55Top-174
❑ 56Top-36

Minaya, Omar
❑ 81WauTimT-22

Minaya, Robert
❑ 88PulBraP-1767
❑ 89SumBraP-1111

Minch, John
❑ 87ModA'sC-11
❑ 87ModA'sP-7
❑ 88HunStaTI-12

Mincher, Don (Donald)
❑ 60Top-548
❑ 61Top-336
❑ 61TwiCloD-17
❑ 61TwiPetM-5
❑ 62Top-386
❑ 63Top-269
❑ 63TwiVol-12
❑ 64Top-542
❑ 65OPC-108
❑ 65Top-108
❑ 66Top-388
❑ 66TwiFaiG-9
❑ 67CokCapDA-25
❑ 67Top-312
❑ 67TopVen-223
❑ 68Baz-12
❑ 68OPC-75
❑ 68Top-75
❑ 68TopActS-8A
❑ 69MilBra-193
❑ 69MLBOffS-96
❑ 69PilPos-1
❑ 69PilWhe-5
❑ 69Top-285
❑ 69TopDecl-30
❑ 69TopSta-227
❑ 69TopSup-33
❑ 69TopTeaP-9
❑ 70Kel-75
❑ 70MilBra-19
❑ 70MLBOffS-261
❑ 70OPC-185
❑ 70Top-185
❑ 70TopPos-17
❑ 71Kel-27
❑ 71MLBOffS-521
❑ 71OPC-680
❑ 71SenTealW-17
❑ 71Top-680
❑ 72MilBra-238
❑ 72OPC-242
❑ 72RanTeal-19
❑ 72Top-242
❑ 77PilPosR-1
❑ 78TCM60I-54
❑ 78TwiFri-14
❑ 83Pil69G-10
❑ 89AngSmo-5
❑ 93RanKee-29

Minchey, Nate
❑ 88OPC-6
❑ 88RocExpLC-25
❑ 89RocExpLC-18
❑ 90DurBulTI-27
❑ 91DurBulUP-5
❑ 91MiaMirC-10
❑ 91MiaMirP-406
❑ 92GreBraS-240
❑ 93Bow-31
❑ 93PawRedSDD-19
❑ 93PawRedSF-2407
❑ 93PawRedSTI-17
❑ 94Don-484
❑ 94FleMajLP-25
❑ 94PawRedSDD-13
❑ 94PawRedSF-946
❑ 94Pin-406
❑ 94PinArtP-406
❑ 94PinMusC-406
❑ 94ScoRoo-RT121
❑ 94ScoRooGR-RT121
❑ 94SpoRoo-136
❑ 94SpoRooAP-136
❑ 94Top-716
❑ 94TopGol-716
❑ 94TopSpa-716
❑ 95LouRedF-275
❑ 95Pac-41
❑ 95Sco-586
❑ 95ScoGolR-586
❑ 95ScoPlaTS-586
❑ 95SigRoo-36

❑ 95SigRooSig-36
❑ 96PawRedSDD-18
❑ 97ColSprSTI-16
Minchk, Kevin
❑ 92SpoIndC-13
❑ 92SpoIndF-1303
❑ 93WatDiaC-23
❑ 93WatDiaF-1777
Mincho, Tom
❑ 90MiaMirIS-17
Minear, Clint
❑ 91KisDodP-4180
❑ 92YakBeaC-8
❑ 92YakBeaF-3446
❑ 93ButCopKSP-20
Miner, Gary
❑ 87BriYouC-17
Miner, J.R.
❑ 86BurExpP-16
❑ 87BurExpP-1090
❑ 87TucTorP-13
Miner, James
❑ 82ChaRoyT-1
❑ 84MemChiT-16
❑ 85TucTorC-72
❑ 86TucTorP-14
Miner, Richard
❑ 90IBAWorA-36
Miner, Tony
❑ 97WatIndTI-16
Minetto, Craig
❑ 77ModA'sC-3
❑ 80OgdA'sT-3
❑ 80Top-494
❑ 81Top-316
❑ 82RocRedWT-4
❑ 83RocRedWT-5
❑ 84TucTorC-69
Minford, Mitchell
❑ 96CarLeaA2B-23
Minford, Rich
❑ 96CarLeaA2B-23
Mingori, Steve
❑ 69Top-339
❑ 71OPC-612
❑ 71Top-612
❑ 72OPC-261
❑ 72Top-261
❑ 73IndTeal-19
❑ 73OPC-532
❑ 73Top-532
❑ 74OPC-537
❑ 74RoyPos-20
❑ 74Top-537
❑ 75OPC-544
❑ 75RoyPos-22
❑ 75Top-544
❑ 75TopMin-544
❑ 76KanCitRP-20
❑ 76OPC-541
❑ 76SSP-161
❑ 76Top-541
❑ 77Top-314
❑ 78Roy-14
❑ 78SSP270-242
❑ 78Top-696
❑ 79Top-72
❑ 80Top-219
❑ 86SyrChiP-19
❑ 87DunBluJP-935
❑ 90MyrBeaBJP-2793
❑ 91KnoBluJP-1786
❑ 91KnoBluJP-1787
❑ 91LinDriAA-375
❑ 92KnoBluJF-3008
❑ 92KnoBluJS-400
❑ 93KnoSmoF-1267
Minici, Jason
❑ 95WatIndTI-20
Minick, Jeff
❑ 86LakTigP-14
Minier, Pablo
❑ 77SpaPhiT-1
Minik, Tim
❑ 91BenBucCB-8
❑ 91BenBucP-3693
❑ 92MadMusF-1230
Minissale, Frank
❑ 88LitFalMP-29
Minium, Matt
❑ 80BatTroT-24
Minker, Al
❑ 79WatA'sT-16
❑ 80WesHavWCT-1
Minnehan, Dan
❑ 87OldJudN-348
Minnema, Dave
❑ 86LakTigP-15
Minner, Paul
❑ 49EurSta-43
❑ 52Bow-211
❑ 52Top-127
❑ 53BowC-71
❑ 53Top-92
❑ 54Bow-13
❑ 54Top-28
❑ 56Top-182
❑ 79TCM50-163
❑ 83TopRep5-127
❑ 90DodTar-535
❑ 91TopArc1-92
❑ 94TopArc1-28
❑ 94TopArc1G-28
Minnich, Bill
❑ 92AubAstC-5
❑ 92AubAstF-1366
Minnick, Don
❑ 80LynSaiT-8
Minnifield, Wallace
❑ 89KinMetS-17
❑ 90PitMetP-4
Minnis, Billy
❑ 91MidLeaAP-MWL28
❑ 91QuaCitAC-19
❑ 91QuaCitAP-2638
Minor, Blas
❑ 89SalBucS-14
❑ 90CMC-738
❑ 90HarSenP-1189
❑ 90HarSenS-11
❑ 90StaFS7-29
❑ 91BufBisLD-38
❑ 91BufBisP-538
❑ 91LinDriAAA-38
❑ 92BufBisBS-12
❑ 92BufBisF-320
❑ 92BufBisS-36
❑ 92DonRoo-81
❑ 92FleUpd-116
❑ 92SkyAAAF-15
❑ 93Bow-486
❑ 93FleFinE-114
❑ 93Lea-539
❑ 93PacSpa-588
❑ 93Pin-283
❑ 93PirHil-9
❑ 93PirNatl-20
❑ 93Sco-304
❑ 93SelRoo-71T
❑ 93TopTra-82T
❑ 93Ult-452
❑ 93UppDec-745
❑ 93UppDecGold-745
❑ 94ColC-206
❑ 94ColChoGS-206
❑ 94ColChoSS-206
❑ 94Don-189
❑ 94Fle-615
❑ 94Pac-503
❑ 94Pin-160
❑ 94PinArtP-160
❑ 94PinMusC-160
❑ 94Sco-211
❑ 94ScoGolR-211
❑ 94StaClu-465
❑ 94StaCluFDI-465
❑ 94StaCluGR-465
❑ 94StaCluMOP-465
❑ 94Top-253
❑ 94TopGol-253
❑ 94TopSpa-253
❑ 94Ult-259
❑ 95FleUpd-115
❑ 95MetColP-21
❑ 95Top-166
❑ 96LeaSigEA-127
❑ 96MetKah-23
Minor, Damon
❑ 96BelGiaTI-10
❑ 97BakBlaB-2
❑ 97BakBlaTI-2
❑ 97CalLeaATI-19
❑ 97CalLeaTP-2
❑ 98Bow-411
❑ 98BowChr-411
❑ 98BowChrGA-411
❑ 98BowChrGAR-411
❑ 98BowChrI-411
❑ 98BowChrIR-411
❑ 98BowChrR-411
❑ 98BowGolA-411
❑ 98BowInt-411
❑ 98ShrCapM-25
❑ 98ShrCapWS-25
❑ 98TexLeaTPG-24
❑ 99SP SigAuto-DAM
❑ 99SP SigAutoG-DAM
❑ 99SP TopP-88
❑ 99SP TopPPE-88
❑ 99SPSig-84
❑ 99Top-435
❑ 99TopChr-435
❑ 99TopChrR-435
❑ 99UppDec-275
❑ 99UppDecE-118
❑ 99UppDecEFXG-118
❑ 99UppDecEL1-275
❑ 99UppDecEL2-275
Minor, Ryan
❑ 97DelSho-28
❑ 97SouAtlTPB-16
❑ 98AriFalLTP-10
❑ 98Bes-31
❑ 98Bes-80
❑ 98BesAutSS-37
❑ 98BesBet-9
❑ 98BesCor-9
❑ 98BesPro-5
❑ 98Bow-107
❑ 98Bow99ROYF-ROY9
❑ 98BowBayM-23
❑ 98BowBes-152
❑ 98BowBesAR-152
❑ 98BowBesP-BP3
❑ 98BowBesPAR-BP3
❑ 98BowBesPR-BP3
❑ 98BowBesR-152
❑ 98BowCerBlueAU-18
❑ 98BowCerGA-18
❑ 98BowCerSA-18
❑ 98BowChr-107
❑ 98BowChrGA-107
❑ 98BowChrGAR-107
❑ 98BowChrI-107
❑ 98BowChrIR-107
❑ 98BowChrR-107
❑ 98BowGolA-107
❑ 98BowInt-107
❑ 98DonSig-124
❑ 98DonSigP-124
❑ 98EasLeaTPM-19
❑ 98FleUpd-U92
❑ 98LeaRS-317
❑ 98LeaRSLHolo-317
❑ 98LeaRSLong-317
❑ 98LeaRTrue-317
❑ 98SP MinDTSPE-DS9
❑ 98SP MinPE-25
❑ 98SP MinSTHPE-H12
❑ 98SPMin-25
❑ 98SPMinDTS-DS9
❑ 98SPMinSTH-H12
❑ 98Top-254
❑ 98TopChr-254
❑ 98TopChrR-254
❑ 98TopDevR-254
❑ 98TopDia-254
❑ 98TopMiniC-254
❑ 99199Fin-61
❑ 99199Fin-123
❑ 99BasAmeTP-69
❑ 99BasAmeTPBP-3
❑ 99BasAmeTPG-69
❑ 99BasAmeTPSC-8
❑ 99Bow-338
❑ 99BowAut-BA8
❑ 99BowGol-338
❑ 99BowInt-338
❑ 99E-X Cen-95
❑ 99E-X CenECFut-95
❑ 99E-X CenECNow-95
❑ 99FinGolRef-61
❑ 99FinGolRef-123
❑ 99FinRef-61
❑ 99FinRef-123
❑ 99Fle-182
❑ 99FleBri-127
❑ 99FleBri2G-127
❑ 99FleBriBlu-127
❑ 99FleBriGol-127
❑ 99FleSta9-182
❑ 99FleWarT-182
❑ 99MetUni-252
❑ 99MetUniGM-252
❑ 99MetUniPMG-252
❑ 99Pac-54
❑ 99Pac-54A
❑ 99PacPlaB-54
❑ 99PacPlaB-54A
❑ 99PacPri-18
❑ 99PacPriHB-18
❑ 99PacPriHG-18
❑ 99PacPriHM-18
❑ 99PacPriHP-18
❑ 99PacPriRed-18
❑ 99PacPriS-116
❑ 99PacPriS206-116
❑ 99PacPriS206R-116
❑ 99PacRed-54
❑ 99PacRed-54A
❑ 99SkyThu-264
❑ 99SkyThuRant-264
❑ 99SkyThuRave-264
❑ 99SP Aut-93
❑ 99SP AutC-RM
❑ 99SP AutCG-RM
❑ 99SP SigAuto-RM
❑ 99SP SigAutoG-RM
❑ 99SP TopP-89
❑ 99SP TopPC-RYM
❑ 99SP TopPDtS-D23
❑ 99SP TopPGF-GF23
❑ 99SP TopPPE-89
❑ 99SpoIll-59
❑ 99SpoIllOTW-14
❑ 99SPSig-42
❑ 99SPx-85
❑ 99SPxFinR-85
❑ 99SPxFinS-85
❑ 99ThuSkySupR-264
❑ 99Top-293
❑ 99TopChr-293
❑ 99TopChrR-293
❑ 99TopMVPP-293
❑ 99TopMVPP-435
❑ 99UD Cho-7
❑ 99UD ChoPCR-7
❑ 99UD Ion-11
❑ 99UD IonR-11
❑ 99UDHoloUDA-RM
❑ 99Ult-243
❑ 99UltGolM-243
❑ 99UltMas-243
❑ 99UltPlaM-243
❑ 99UppDec-276
❑ 99UppDecCL-105
❑ 99UppDecCLCC-105
❑ 99UppDecE-119
❑ 99UppDecEFXG-119
❑ 99UppDecEL1-276
❑ 99UppDecEL2-276
❑ 99UppDecM-29
❑ 99UppDecMGS-29
❑ 99UppDecMHFS-29
❑ 99UppDecMP-RM
❑ 99UppDecMSC-SC9
❑ 99UppDecMSS-29
❑ 99UppDecO-76
❑ 99UppDecOSO-76
❑ 99Vic-42
Minor, Tom
❑ 94NewJerCC-19
❑ 94NewJerCF-3417
❑ 95Exc-273
Minoso, Minnie (Orestes)
❑ 47Exh-160A
❑ 47Exh-160B
❑ 47PM1StaP1-142
❑ 52BerRos-41
❑ 52Bow-5
❑ 52RedMan-AL15
❑ 52StaCalL-73E
❑ 52StaCalS-87B
❑ 52Top-195
❑ 53BowC-36
❑ 53NorBreL-18
❑ 53Top-66
❑ 54Bow-38
❑ 54DixLid-10
❑ 54RedHeaF-22
❑ 54RedMan-AL7
❑ 55BigLeaIS-13
❑ 55Bow-25
❑ 55DaiQueS-13
❑ 55RedMan-AL24
❑ 56Top-125
❑ 56YelBasP-22
❑ 57Top-138
❑ 58IndTeal-14
❑ 58Top-295
❑ 59Ind-12
❑ 59Kah-24
❑ 59Top-80
❑ 59Top-166
❑ 59TopVen-80
❑ 59TopVen-166
❑ 60Top-365
❑ 60WhiSoxJP-8
❑ 60WhiSoxTS-14
❑ 61Baz-7
❑ 61Pos-25A
❑ 61Pos-25B
❑ 61Top-42
❑ 61Top-380
❑ 61TopStal-125
❑ 61WhiSoxTS-11
❑ 62CarJayP-9
❑ 62Jel-51
❑ 62Pos-51
❑ 62PosCan-51
❑ 62SalPlaC-39A
❑ 62SalPlaC-39B
❑ 62ShiPlaC-39
❑ 62Top-28
❑ 62TopBuc-61
❑ 62TopStal-188
❑ 62TopVen-28
❑ 63BasMagM-59
❑ 63Top-190
❑ 64Top-538
❑ 67TopVen-187
❑ 76ChiGre-13
❑ 77OPC-262
❑ 77Top-232
❑ 78SSP270-160
❑ 79DiaGre-150
❑ 79TCM50-286
❑ 80MarExh-20
❑ 80PacLeg-96
❑ 83TopRep5-195
❑ 84OCoandSI-2
❑ 84WhiSoxTV-24
❑ 85WhiSoxC-42
❑ 86WhiSoxC-NNO
❑ 87SpoRea-23
❑ 87WhiSoxC-22
❑ 88PacLegI-51
❑ 88WhiSoxC-18
❑ 89SweBasG-59
❑ 89WhiSoxC-30
❑ 89WhiSoxK-4
❑ 91KelLey-9
❑ 91TopArc1-66
❑ 92ActPacA-37
❑ 92BazQua5A-8
❑ 93TedWil-27
❑ 93UppDecAH-95
❑ 93UppDecAH-153
❑ 93UppDecS-6
❑ 93UppDecS-22
❑ 93UppDecS-28
❑ 94TopSpa-L8
❑ 94UppDecAH-205
❑ 94UppDecAH1-205
❑ 95NegLeaL2-5
❑ 95UppDecSHoB-14
❑ 96IllLot-3
❑ 97NegLeaPC-5D
Minoso, Orestes
❑ 77AppFoxT-16A
❑ 77AppFoxT-16B
Minter, Larry
❑ 91PocPioP-3797
❑ 91PocPioSP-1
Minter, Matthew
❑ 96WatIndTI-19
❑ 97WatIndTI-17
Minton, Greg
❑ 75PhoGiaC-15
❑ 75PhoGiaCK-8
❑ 76PhoGiaVNB-17
❑ 77PhoGiaCC-18
❑ 77PhoGiaCP-18
❑ 77PhoGiaVNB-18
❑ 77Top-489
❑ 78PhoGiaC-16
❑ 78Top-312
❑ 79Top-84
❑ 80GiaPol-38
❑ 80GiaTeal-19
❑ 80Top-588
❑ 81Don-579
❑ 81Fle-449
❑ 81OPC-111
❑ 81Top-111
❑ 81TopSti-238
❑ 82Don-348
❑ 82Fle-396
❑ 82Gia25tATI-20
❑ 82OPC-144
❑ 82Top-687
❑ 82TopSti-107
❑ 83Don-186
❑ 83DonActA-10
❑ 83Fle-269
❑ 83FleSta-126
❑ 83FleSti-54
❑ 83GiaMot-5
❑ 83GiaPos-21
❑ 83Kel-46
❑ 83OPC-107
❑ 83Top-3
❑ 83Top-470
❑ 83TopFol-4
❑ 83TopSti-137
❑ 83TopSti-138
❑ 83TopSti-299
❑ 84Don-187
❑ 84Fle-383
❑ 84FleSti-69
❑ 84GiaMot-8
❑ 84GiaPos-17
❑ 84Nes792-205
❑ 84OPC-205
❑ 84Top-205
❑ 84TopTif-205
❑ 85Don-143
❑ 85Fle-617
❑ 85GiaMot-8
❑ 85GiaPos-23
❑ 85OPC-45
❑ 85Top-45
❑ 85TopSti-167
❑ 85TopTif-45
❑ 86Don-480
❑ 86Fle-549
❑ 86GiaMot-8
❑ 86GiaPos-24
❑ 86Top-310
❑ 86Top-516
❑ 86TopTif-310
❑ 86TopTif-516
❑ 87Fle-282
❑ 87FleGlo-282
❑ 87FleUpd-80
❑ 87FleUpdG-80
❑ 87GiaMot-9
❑ 87OPC-333
❑ 87Top-724
❑ 87TopTif-724
❑ 87TopTra-79T
❑ 87TopTraT-79T
❑ 88AngSmo-11
❑ 88Don-505
❑ 88Fle-499
❑ 88FleGlo-499
❑ 88OPC-129
❑ 88Sco-176
❑ 88ScoGlo-176
❑ 88StaLinAn-15
❑ 88Top-129
❑ 88TopSti-176
❑ 88TopTif-129
❑ 89Don-490
❑ 89DonBasB-283
❑ 89Fle-485
❑ 89FleGlo-485
❑ 89OPC-306
❑ 89Sco-543
❑ 89Top-576
❑ 89TopTif-576
❑ 89UppDec-635
❑ 90Don-116
❑ 90Fle-140
❑ 90FleCan-140
❑ 90OPC-421
❑ 90PubIntS-375
❑ 90Sco-48
❑ 90Top-421
❑ 90TopTif-421
❑ 90UppDec-83
❑ 91Sco-823
❑ 97MidAng-2
❑ 97PhoFirDTTI-24
❑ 98VanCanG-17
Minton, Jesse
❑ 87SumBraP-17
Mintz, Alan
❑ 80ElmPioRST-42
Mintz, Steve
❑ 90YakBeaTI-29
❑ 91BakDodCLC-11
❑ 92VerBeaDC-25
❑ 92VerBeaDF-2871
❑ 93NewBriRSF-1215

❑ 94ShrCapF-1601
❑ 96PhoFirB-20
❑ 98NasSouTI-23
❑ 98NasSouTISS-22

Minutelli, Gino
❑ 86CedRapRT-7
❑ 87TamTarP-20
❑ 88ChaLooB-16
❑ 90ChaLooGS-21
❑ 91Bow-677
❑ 91LinDriAAA-268
❑ 91NasSouLD-268
❑ 91NasSouP-2153
❑ 91TopDeb90-109
❑ 92NasSouF-1831
❑ 92NasSouS-287
❑ 92Pin-261
❑ 92Sco-408
❑ 92SkyAAAF-134
❑ 92StaClu-452
❑ 93GiaMot-27
❑ 94TucTorF-758

Minyard, Sam
❑ 93ElmPioC-12
❑ 93ElmPioF-3819

Mirabella, Geno
❑ 91SalLakTP-3208
❑ 91SalLakTSP-17

Mirabella, Paul
❑ 76AshTouT-3
❑ 78TucTorC-10
❑ 79ColCliT-26
❑ 81Don-151
❑ 81OPC-11
❑ 81SyrChiTI-14
❑ 81Top-382
❑ 82Don-629
❑ 82OPC-163
❑ 82Top-499
❑ 83Don-541
❑ 83Fle-573
❑ 83Top-12
❑ 84MarMot-17
❑ 85CalCanC-89
❑ 85Fle-494
❑ 85Top-766
❑ 85TopTif-766
❑ 86MarMot-13
❑ 87DenZepP-9
❑ 88BreTeal-24
❑ 88DenZepC-5
❑ 88DenZepP-1258
❑ 89BrePol-27
❑ 89Don-654
❑ 89Fle-192
❑ 89FleGlo-192
❑ 89PacSenL-165
❑ 89Sco-569
❑ 89T/MSenL-79
❑ 89Top-192
❑ 89TopSenL-51
❑ 89TopTif-192
❑ 89UppDec-322
❑ 90BreMilB-14
❑ 90BrePol-27
❑ 90EliSenL-27
❑ 90PubIntS-499
❑ 91Fle-590
❑ 91OriCro-306
❑ 91Sco-558
❑ 92YanWIZ7-115
❑ 93RanKee-268
❑ 94BreMilB-252

Mirabelli, Doug
❑ 90WicStaSGD-26
❑ 93SanJosGC-16
❑ 93SanJosGF-14
❑ 93StaCluM-40
❑ 94ClaGolF-151
❑ 94ShrCapF-1610
❑ 97PhoFirTI-16
❑ 98FreGriG-19

Mirabito, Tim
❑ 86TamTarP-13
❑ 87VerRedP-8

Miracle, Miami
❑ 89MiaMirIS-22
❑ 90MiaMirIS-31

Miran, Tory
❑ 92YakBeaC-13
❑ 92YakBeaF-3463
❑ 93BakDodCLC-20

Miranda, Alex
❑ 94SouOreAC-19
❑ 94SouOreAF-3631
❑ 95WesMicWTI-33
❑ 96WesMicWB-14

Miranda, Angel
❑ 88BlaYNPRWL-10
❑ 88StoPorCLC-180
❑ 88StoPorP-749
❑ 89BelBre2S-22
❑ 89BlaYNPRWL-180
❑ 90CalLeaACLC-51
❑ 90ProAaA-139
❑ 90StoPorB-25
❑ 90StoPorCLC-175
❑ 90StoPorP-2175
❑ 91Bow-53
❑ 91ElPasDLD-193
❑ 91ElPasDP-2747
❑ 91LinDriAA-193
❑ 92Bow-63
❑ 92DenZepF-2638
❑ 92DenZepS-140
❑ 92SkyAAAF-68
❑ 93FleFinE-230
❑ 93SelRoo-72T
❑ 94BreMilB-253
❑ 94BreTeal-17
❑ 94ColC-207
❑ 94ColChoGS-207
❑ 94ColChoSS-207
❑ 94Don-488
❑ 94Fle-184
❑ 94Pac-335
❑ 94Pin-341
❑ 94PinArtP-341
❑ 94PinMusC-341
❑ 94Top-709
❑ 94TopGol-709
❑ 94TopSpa-709
❑ 94Ult-79
❑ 94USPlaCR-6S
❑ 96BrePol-19
❑ 96Pac-350
❑ 96Ult-369
❑ 96UltGolM-369
❑ 97BrePol-20
❑ 97Pac-126
❑ 97PacLigB-126
❑ 97PacSil-126

Miranda, Giovanni
❑ 90AppFoxBS-18
❑ 90AppFoxP-2102
❑ 90CMC-723
❑ 90EugEmeGS-19
❑ 91AppFoxCB-19
❑ 91AppFoxP-1725
❑ 92BasCitRC-18
❑ 92SarWhiSF-214
❑ 93BirBarF-1199
❑ 93SarWhiSF-1378
❑ 94PriWilCC-16
❑ 94PriWilCF-1929

Miranda, Tony
❑ 95SpoIndTI-14
❑ 96SpoIndB-17
❑ 97LanLugTS-15

Miranda, Walter
❑ 95KanCouCTI-43
❑ 96BreCouMB-22
❑ 97BreCouMB-24

Miranda, Willie
❑ 53Dor-123
❑ 53Top-278
❑ 54Top-56
❑ 55Bow-79
❑ 55OriEss-18
❑ 55Top-154
❑ 56BalOriP-5
❑ 56BalOriP-34
❑ 56BalOriP-35
❑ 56Top-103
❑ 56TopPin-2
❑ 57Top-151
❑ 58Hir-32
❑ 58OriJayP-6
❑ 58Top-179
❑ 59Top-540
❑ 91OriCro-307
❑ 91TopArc1-278
❑ 94TopArc1-56
❑ 94TopArc1G-56
❑ 97BalOriP-34

Mirizzi, Marc
❑ 98GreBatM-12

Misa, Joe
❑ 91SouOreAC-28
❑ 91SouOreAP-3839
❑ 92RenSilSCLC-57

Miscik, Bob
❑ 82BufBisT-2
❑ 84HawIslC-136
❑ 85HawIslC-239
❑ 86HawIslP-17
❑ 87EdmTraP-2064
❑ 88EdmTraC-15
❑ 88EdmTraP-577
❑ 90FreKeyTI-3
❑ 91KanCouCC-26
❑ 91KanCouCP-2674
❑ 91KanCouCTI-26
❑ 92FreKeyF-1822
❑ 93RocRedWF-257
❑ 94RocRedWF-1013
❑ 94RocRedWTI-15
❑ 95BowBayTI-10

Miscik, Dennis
❑ 77CocAstT-14
❑ 80TucTorT-13
❑ 81OklCit8T-11

Mishkin, Sol
❑ 28LaPre-18
❑ 28Zee-137

Miskolczi, Levi
❑ 96BelGiaTI-9

Missions, San Jose
❑ 77SanJosMC-1
❑ 89SanAntMB-28

Misuraca, Mike
❑ 89EliTwiS-19
❑ 89KenTwiP-1071
❑ 89KenTwiS-15
❑ 89Sta-148
❑ 90Bes-272
❑ 90KenTwiB-21
❑ 90KenTwiP-2290
❑ 90KenTwiS-13
❑ 91VisOakC-5
❑ 91VisOakP-1739
❑ 92Ft.MyeMCB-18
❑ 92Ft.MyeMF-2742
❑ 93NasXprF-400
❑ 94NasXprF-382
❑ 97TucTorB-9

Mitchell, Alvin
❑ 94UtiBluSC-21
❑ 94UtiBluSF-3818
❑ 95MicBatCTI-17

Mitchell, Andres
❑ 97PorRocG-17
❑ 98AshTouM-14

Mitchell, Bill
❑ 76BatTroTI-14

Mitchell, Bob
❑ 79HawIslT-1
❑ 80HawIslT-10

Mitchell, Bobby (Robert Van)
❑ 79AlbDukTc-18
❑ 80AlbDukTc-20
❑ 81AlbDukTc-22
❑ 81PorBeaT-18
❑ 82Fle-14
❑ 82PorBeaT-15
❑ 82TolMudHT-28
❑ 82TwiPos-21
❑ 83Fle-620
❑ 83Top-647
❑ 83TopSti-91
❑ 83TwiTeal-7
❑ 84Fle-571
❑ 84Nes792-307
❑ 84PorBeaC-202
❑ 84TolMudHT-10
❑ 84Top-307
❑ 84TopTif-307
❑ 85NasSouTI-15
❑ 90DodTar-536

Mitchell, Bobby (Robert Vance)
❑ 71OPC-111
❑ 71Top-111
❑ 74OPC-497
❑ 74Top-497
❑ 75OPC-468
❑ 75Top-468
❑ 75TopMin-468
❑ 76OPC-479
❑ 76SSP-242
❑ 76Top-479
❑ 79HawIslC-12
❑ 79TCMJapPB-41
❑ 92YanWIZ7-116
❑ 94BreMilB-254

Mitchell, Charlie
❑ 84PawRedST-1
❑ 85Don-40
❑ 85IntLeaAT-18
❑ 85PawRedST-20
❑ 86TolMudHP-17
❑ 88NasSouTI-17
❑ 89NasSouC-1
❑ 89NasSouP-1273
❑ 89NasSouTI-16
❑ 90CMC-131
❑ 90NasSouC-6
❑ 90NasSouP-229
❑ 90ProAAAF-541
❑ 91LinDriAAA-260
❑ 91NasSouLD-260
❑ 91NasSouP-2154

Mitchell, Chic
❑ 94MarPhiF-3289

Mitchell, Clarence
❑ 11HelSta-118
❑ 17ColE13-120
❑ 22E120-144
❑ 22W573-87
❑ 27YorCarE-15
❑ 28W502-15
❑ 28Yue-15
❑ 33Zee-31
❑ 90DodTar-537
❑ 91ConTSN-202

Mitchell, Claude
❑ 20Zee-30

Mitchell, Courtney
❑ 94MarPhiC-13
❑ 95BatCliTI-24
❑ 96BatCliTI-16
❑ 97PieBolWB-21
❑ 98ClePhiM-18
❑ 98ClePhiUM-18

Mitchell, Craig
❑ 75TucTorC-14
❑ 75TucTorTI-12
❑ 76OPC-591
❑ 76Top-591
❑ 76TucTorCa-15
❑ 76TusTorCr-32
❑ 76VenLeaS-166
❑ 77SanJosMC-15
❑ 77Top-491
❑ 78Top-711
❑ 79OgdA'sT-5
❑ 79OgdA'sT-21

Mitchell, David
❑ 88MisStaB-21
❑ 89MisStaB-26
❑ 90MisStaB-27

Mitchell, Dean
❑ 96YakBeaTI-14
❑ 98SanAntMG-17

Mitchell, Derek
❑ 97WesMicW-18
❑ 98JacSunM-18
❑ 99WesMicWAM-18

Mitchell, Donovan
❑ 92AubAstC-6
❑ 92AubAstF-1362
❑ 94ExcFS7-204
❑ 94OscAstC-16
❑ 94OscAstF-1145
❑ 95MidLeaA-33
❑ 95QuaCitRBTI-15
❑ 96JacGenB-19
❑ 97JacGen-17
❑ 97JacGenS-16
❑ 98NewOrlZM-15

Mitchell, Fred F.
❑ 03BreE10-106
❑ 09AmeCarE90-1-81
❑ 09T206-447
❑ 11SpoLifCW-255
❑ 12ImpTobC-47
❑ 19W514-96
❑ 23WilChoV-105
❑ 80BraTCM1-24
❑ 90DodTar-539

Mitchell, Glenn
❑ 88IdaFalBP-1837
❑ 88SumBraP-408
❑ 89SumBraP-1116
❑ 92QuaCitRBC-11
❑ 92QuaCitRBF-805

Mitchell, Howie
❑ 78PhoGiaC-17

Mitchell, J.W.
❑ 79QuaCitCT-10

Mitchell, Jackie
❑ 88ChaLooLTI-23

Mitchell, Joe
❑ 77NewCoPT-22

Mitchell, Joe (Joseph)
❑ 85BelBreT-3
❑ 86StoPorP-15
❑ 87ElPasDP-2
❑ 88ElPasDB-25
❑ 89DenZepC-20
❑ 89DenZepP-43
❑ 90CMC-37
❑ 90DenZepC-12
❑ 90DenZepP-633
❑ 90ProAAAF-658

Mitchell, John
❑ 93NegLeaRL2-27

Mitchell, John Franklin
❑ 18Zee-101
❑ 19Zee-143
❑ 20Zee-145
❑ 21KoBreWSI-42
❑ 22W575-85
❑ 26Zee-31
❑ 90DodTar-540

Mitchell, John Kyle
❑ 83BelBreFr-5
❑ 86StaoftFT-34
❑ 86TidTidP-21
❑ 87DonRoo-37
❑ 87FleUpd-81
❑ 87FleUpdG-81
❑ 87IdaFalBP-24
❑ 87TidTidP-20
❑ 87TidTidT-7
❑ 87TopTra-80T
❑ 87TopTraT-80T
❑ 88BurBraP-28
❑ 88Fle-145
❑ 88FleGlo-145
❑ 88MetColP-40
❑ 88Sco-249
❑ 88ScoGlo-249
❑ 88TidTidCa-23
❑ 88TidTidCM-8
❑ 88TidTidP-1577
❑ 88Top-207
❑ 88TopClo-73
❑ 88TopTif-207
❑ 89MetColP-44
❑ 89TidTidC-4
❑ 89TidTidP-1970
❑ 90BalOriP-21
❑ 90CMC-322
❑ 90ProAAAF-457
❑ 90RocRedWC-21
❑ 90RocRedWP-700
❑ 91CalCanLD-67
❑ 91CalCanP-513
❑ 91Don-710
❑ 91Fle-485
❑ 91LinDriAAA-67
❑ 91MetWIZ-275
❑ 91OPC-708
❑ 91OriCro-308
❑ 91Sco-569
❑ 91Top-708
❑ 91TopDesS-708
❑ 91TopMic-708
❑ 91TopTif-708

Mitchell, Johnny
❑ 93WelPirC-14
❑ 93WelPirF-3374

Mitchell, Jorge
❑ 87JamExpP-2548
❑ 88JamExpP-1916
❑ 93LinVenB-274
❑ 94VenLinU-156

Mitchell, Keith
❑ 88SumBraP-390
❑ 89BurBraP-1609
❑ 89BurBraS-15
❑ 90CarLeaA-29
❑ 90DurBulTI-2
❑ 91Bow-575
❑ 91BraSubS-26
❑ 91Cla/Bes-224
❑ 91Cla3-T58
❑ 91GreBraC-21
❑ 91GreBraLD-212
❑ 91GreBraP-3016
❑ 91LinDriAA-212
❑ 91RicBraBC-33
❑ 91UppDecFE-56F
❑ 92Bow-62
❑ 92Don-508
❑ 92Fle-364
❑ 92OPC-542
❑ 92Pin-258
❑ 92PinRool-8
❑ 92ProFS7-182
❑ 92RicBraBB-10
❑ 92RicBraF-387
❑ 92RicBraRC-11
❑ 92RicBraS-433
❑ 92Sco-748
❑ 92SkyAAAF-198
❑ 92StaClu-551
❑ 92Top-542
❑ 92TopDeb91-125
❑ 92TopGol-542
❑ 92TopGolW-542
❑ 92TopMic-542
❑ 92UppDec-80
❑ 92UppDec-454
❑ 92UppDecML-185
❑ 93RicBraBB-3
❑ 93RicBraF-198
❑ 93RicBraP-18
❑ 93RicBraRC-18
❑ 93RicBraRC-20
❑ 94FleUpd-84
❑ 94MarMot-19
❑ 94Pin-524
❑ 94PinArtP-524
❑ 94PinMusC-524
❑ 94ScoRoo-RT149
❑ 94ScoRooGR-RT149
❑ 94Sel-202
❑ 94SpoRoo-134
❑ 94SpoRooAP-134
❑ 94TopTra-51T
❑ 94Ult-423
❑ 95Pin-24
❑ 95PinArtP-24
❑ 95PinMusC-24
❑ 95Sco-410
❑ 95ScoGolR-410
❑ 95ScoPlaTS-410
❑ 96IndIndB-15
❑ 97IndInd-15
❑ 97RicBraBC-1

Mitchell, Kelvin
❑ 95EveAqaTI-13

Mitchell, Kendrick
❑ 95BakBlaTI-18
❑ 96VerBeaDB-20

Mitchell, Kevin
❑ 82LynMetT-6
❑ 84OCoandSI-205
❑ 84TidTidT-23
❑ 85IntLeaAT-4
❑ 85MetTCM-27
❑ 85TidTidT-18
❑ 86DonRoo-17
❑ 86FleUpd-76
❑ 86MetTCM-21
❑ 86MetWorSC-28
❑ 86SpoRoo-49
❑ 86TopTra-74T
❑ 86TopTraT-74T
❑ 87Don-599
❑ 87DonOpeD-145
❑ 87Fle-17
❑ 87FleGlo-17
❑ 87FleRecS-21
❑ 87FleUpd-82
❑ 87FleUpdG-82
❑ 87Lea-170
❑ 87MetColP-41
❑ 87OPC-307
❑ 87PadBohHB-7
❑ 87Spo-144
❑ 87SpoTeaP-16
❑ 87Top-653
❑ 87TopGloS-50
❑ 87TopTif-653
❑ 87TopTra-81T
❑ 87TopTraT-81T
❑ 87ToyRoo-21
❑ 88Don-66
❑ 88Fle-92
❑ 88FleGlo-92
❑ 88FleHotS-27
❑ 88FleStiWBC-S5
❑ 88GiaMot-3
❑ 88GiaPos-23
❑ 88Lea-87
❑ 88OPC-387
❑ 88PanSti-424
❑ 88PanSti-448
❑ 88Sco-481
❑ 88ScoGlo-481
❑ 88StaLinG-13

❑ 88Top-497
❑ 88TopBig-57
❑ 88TopSti-88
❑ 88TopTif-497
❑ 88TopUKM-48
❑ 88TopUKMT-48
❑ 89Bow-474
❑ 89BowTif-474
❑ 89ClaLigB-31
❑ 89ClaTraP-198
❑ 89ColPosM-1
❑ 89ColPosM-2
❑ 89ColPosM-3
❑ 89ColPosM-4
❑ 89ColPosM-5
❑ 89ColPosM-6
❑ 89ColPosM-7
❑ 89ColPosM-8
❑ 89Don-485
❑ 89DonBasB-281
❑ 89Fle-336
❑ 89FleGlo-336
❑ 89GiaMot-3
❑ 89OPC-189
❑ 89PanSti-216
❑ 89Sco-39
❑ 89Scomast-12
❑ 89ScoYouS2-38
❑ 89Spo-142
❑ 89SpoIllFKI-112
❑ 89StaMit-1
❑ 89StaMit-2
❑ 89StaMit-3
❑ 89StaMit-4
❑ 89StaMit-5
❑ 89StaMit-6
❑ 89StaMit-7
❑ 89StaMit-8
❑ 89StaMit-9
❑ 89StaMit-10
❑ 89StaMit-11
❑ 89StaMit/C-1
❑ 89StaMit/C-2
❑ 89StaMit/C-4
❑ 89StaMit/C-6
❑ 89StaMit/C-8
❑ 89StaMit/C-10
❑ 89Top-189
❑ 89TopAwaW-2
❑ 89TopBasT-159
❑ 89TopBig-129
❑ 89TopSti-84
❑ 89TopTif-189
❑ 89TVSpoM-51
❑ 89UppDec-163
❑ 89UppDecS-1
❑ 89UppDecS-3
❑ 90Baz-1
❑ 90Bow-232
❑ 90BowIns-6
❑ 90BowInsL-6
❑ 90BowInsT-6
❑ 90BowTif-232
❑ 90BowTif-A6
❑ 90ClaBlu-64
❑ 90ClaBlu-150A
❑ 90ClaBlu-150B
❑ 90Col-16
❑ 90Don-11
❑ 90Don-98
❑ 90Don-715A
❑ 90Don-715B
❑ 90DonBesN-85
❑ 90DOnBonM-BC11
❑ 90DonLeaS-2
❑ 90DonPre-6
❑ 90DonSupD-11
❑ 90Fle-65
❑ 90Fle-637
❑ 90FleAll-6
❑ 90FleAwaW-23
❑ 90FleBasA-27
❑ 90FleBasAC-27
❑ 90FleBasM-26
❑ 90FleBasMC-26
❑ 90FleCan-65
❑ 90FleCan-637
❑ 90FleLeaL-26
❑ 90FleLeaLC-26
❑ 90FleWaxBC-C21
❑ 90FleWorS-2
❑ 90GiaMot-5
❑ 90GiaSmo-15
❑ 90Hot50PS-27
❑ 90K-M-6
❑ 90KinDis-2
❑ 90Lea-120
❑ 90M.Vpin-91
❑ 90MLBBasB-24
❑ 90MSAHolD-9
❑ 90MSAIceTD-6
❑ 90OPC-401
❑ 90OPC-500
❑ 90PanSti-208
❑ 90PanSti-214
❑ 90PanSti-361
❑ 90Pos-15
❑ 90PubIntS-77
❑ 90PubIntS-617
❑ 90RedFolSB-64
❑ 90Sco-343
❑ 90Sco100S-50
❑ 90Spo-1
❑ 90StaMit-1
❑ 90StaMit-2
❑ 90StaMit-4
❑ 90StaMit-6
❑ 90StaMit-8
❑ 90StaMit-10
❑ 90SunSee-1
❑ 90Top-401
❑ 90Top-500
❑ 90TopBig-137
❑ 90TopCoi-33
❑ 90TopDou-47
❑ 90TopGaloC-5
❑ 90TopGloA-6
❑ 90TopGloS-21
❑ 90TopHeaU-15
❑ 90TopHilHM-5
❑ 90TopMag-7
❑ 90TopMinL-86
❑ 90TopSti-79
❑ 90TopSti-148
❑ 90TopStiB-17
❑ 90TopTif-401
❑ 90TopTif-500
❑ 90TopTVA-40
❑ 90UppDec-40
❑ 90UppDec-117
❑ 90USPlaCA-12H
❑ 90WonBreS-7
❑ 90Woo-2
❑ 90Woo-32
❑ 91BasBesHRK-14
❑ 91Bow-636
❑ 91CadEllD-39
❑ 91Cla1-T10
❑ 91Cla3-T59
❑ 91ClaGam-129
❑ 91Col-6
❑ 91Don-255
❑ 91Don-407
❑ 91Don-438
❑ 91Fle-267
❑ 91GiaActIS-2
❑ 91GiaMot-5
❑ 91GiaPacGaE-1
❑ 91GiaSFE-11
❑ 91JimDea-13
❑ 91Lea-85
❑ 91MajLeaCP-64
❑ 91MetWIZ-276
❑ 91MooSna-23
❑ 91MSAHolD-4
❑ 91OPC-40
❑ 91OPCPre-81
❑ 91PanCanT1-11
❑ 91PanCanT1-35
❑ 91PanFreS-71
❑ 91PanFreS-162
❑ 91PanSti-71
❑ 91Pos-24
❑ 91RedFolS-66
❑ 91RedFolS-123
❑ 91Sco-406
❑ 91Sco-451
❑ 91Sco100S-98
❑ 91SevCoi-NC10
❑ 91SimandSMLBL-30
❑ 91StaClu-250
❑ 91StaPinB-32
❑ 91Stu-257
❑ 91Top-40
❑ 91TopCraJI-30
❑ 91TopDesS-40
❑ 91TopGloA-17
❑ 91TopMic-40
❑ 91TopSta-27
❑ 91TopTif-40
❑ 91TopTriH-N11
❑ 91Ult-326
❑ 91UppDec-247
❑ 92Bow-276
❑ 92Cla1-T64
❑ 92Cla2-T91
❑ 92ClaGam-165
❑ 92Don-583
❑ 92Fle-644
❑ 92FleUpd-56
❑ 92Hig5-128
❑ 92Lea-185
❑ 92LeaBlaG-185
❑ 92MarMot-4
❑ 92OPC-180
❑ 92OPCPre-97
❑ 92PanSti-218
❑ 92Pin-393
❑ 92RedFolS-68
❑ 92Sco-640
❑ 92Sco100S-93
❑ 92ScoRoo-18T
❑ 92SpoStaCC-33
❑ 92StaClu-215
❑ 92StaClu-765
❑ 92StaCluECN-765
❑ 92Stu-237
❑ 92Top-180
❑ 92TopGol-180
❑ 92TopGolW-180
❑ 92TopKid-59
❑ 92TopMic-180
❑ 92TopTra-74T
❑ 92TopTraG-74T
❑ 92Ult-434
❑ 92UppDec-80
❑ 92UppDec-266
❑ 92UppDec-735
❑ 93Bow-386
❑ 93DiaMar-76
❑ 93Don-157
❑ 93Fin-136
❑ 93FinRef-136
❑ 93Fla-28
❑ 93Fle-396
❑ 93FleFinE-17
❑ 93FunPac-171
❑ 93Lea-321
❑ 93OPC-252
❑ 93PacSpa-403
❑ 93PanSti-296
❑ 93Pin-551
❑ 93PinHomRC-23
❑ 93PinSlu-21
❑ 93RedFolS-66
❑ 93RedKah-15
❑ 93Sco-407
❑ 93Sel-108
❑ 93SelRoo-29T
❑ 93SP-210
❑ 93StaClu-694
❑ 93StaCluFDI-694
❑ 93StaCluMOP-694
❑ 93Stu-162
❑ 93Top-217
❑ 93TopGol-217
❑ 93TopInaM-217
❑ 93TopInaR-217
❑ 93TopMic-217
❑ 93TopTra-112T
❑ 93Ult-331
❑ 93UppDec-55
❑ 93UppDec-213
❑ 93UppDec-646
❑ 93UppDecGold-55
❑ 93UppDecGold-213
❑ 93UppDecGold-646
❑ 94Bow-514
❑ 94BowBes-R33
❑ 94BowBesR-R33
❑ 94ColC-470
❑ 94ColChoGS-470
❑ 94ColChoSS-470
❑ 94Don-377
❑ 94DonSpeE-377
❑ 94Fin-323
❑ 94FinRef-323
❑ 94Fla-368
❑ 94Fle-416
❑ 94FleExtB-234
❑ 94Lea-370
❑ 94LeaL-96
❑ 94OPC-29
❑ 94Pac-152
❑ 94PanSti-164
❑ 94Pin-70
❑ 94PinArtP-70
❑ 94PinMusC-70
❑ 94ProMag-35
❑ 94RedKah-19
❑ 94Sco-24
❑ 94ScoGolR-24
❑ 94Sel-112
❑ 94SP-160
❑ 94SPDieC-160
❑ 94Spo-126
❑ 94StaClu-422
❑ 94StaCluFDI-422
❑ 94StaCluGR-422
❑ 94StaCluMOP-422
❑ 94Stu-169
❑ 94Top-335
❑ 94TopGol-335
❑ 94TopSpa-335
❑ 94TriPla-215
❑ 94Ult-173
❑ 94UppDec-58
❑ 94UppDecED-58
❑ 95Baz-7
❑ 95ColCho-435
❑ 95ColChoSE-203
❑ 95ColChoSEGS-203
❑ 95ColChoSESS-203
❑ 95Don-469
❑ 95DonBomS-6
❑ 95DonPreP-469
❑ 95Fin-146
❑ 95FinRef-146
❑ 95Fle-441
❑ 95FleLumC-8
❑ 95FleTeaL-17
❑ 95Pac-109
❑ 95Sco-336
❑ 95ScoGolR-336
❑ 95ScoHaloG-HG70
❑ 95ScoPlaTS-336
❑ 95StaClu-430
❑ 95StaCluMO-32
❑ 95StaCluMOP-430
❑ 95StaCluMOP-RL17
❑ 95StaCluRL-RL17
❑ 95StaCluSTWS-430
❑ 95StaCluVR-226
❑ 95StaCluVRMO-226
❑ 95Top-568
❑ 95TopCyb-344
❑ 95TopLeaL-LL2
❑ 95UppDec-169
❑ 95UppDecED-169
❑ 95UppDecEDG-169
❑ 95USPlaCMLA-3D
❑ 95USPlaCMLA-5C
❑ 96Fin-S293
❑ 96FinRef-S293
❑ 96FleRedS-9
❑ 96FleUpd-U15
❑ 96FleUpdTC-U15
❑ 96SP-42
❑ 96Sum-57
❑ 96SumAbo&B-57
❑ 96SumArtP-57
❑ 96SumFoi-57
❑ 96Ult-317
❑ 96UltGolM-317
❑ 96UppDec-484U
❑ 97ColCho-313
❑ 97Fle-297
❑ 97FleTif-297
❑ 97Pin-33
❑ 97PinArtP-PP33
❑ 97PinMusC-33
❑ 97PinPrePla-33
❑ 97Sco-296
❑ 97Sco-366
❑ 97ScoArtPWB-296
❑ 97ScoArtPWB-366
❑ 97ScoPreS-296
❑ 97ScoResC-366
❑ 97ScoShoS-296
❑ 97ScoShoS-366
❑ 97ScoShoSAP-296
❑ 97ScoShoSAP-366
❑ 97Ult-378
❑ 97UltGolME-378
❑ 97UltPlaME-378
❑ 98A'sMot-9
❑ 98PacOnl-539
❑ 98PacOnlR-539
❑ 98PacOnlWC-539

Mitchell, L. Dale
❑ 46SpoExcW-7-12
❑ 47Exh-161
❑ 47IndTeal-20
❑ 47IndVanPP-19
❑ 48IndTeal-22
❑ 49Bow-43
❑ 49IndTeal-18
❑ 49IndVisEl-12
❑ 49Lea-165
❑ 50Bow-130
❑ 50IndNumN-16
❑ 50IndTeal-18
❑ 51Bow-5
❑ 51TopRedB-13
❑ 52Bow-239
❑ 52IndNumN-15
❑ 52StaCalL-74F
❑ 52StaCalS-88C
❑ 52TipTop-26
❑ 52Top-92
❑ 53BowC-119
❑ 53IndPenCBP-21
❑ 53RedMan-AL9
❑ 53Top-26
❑ 54Bow-148
❑ 54DanDee-18
❑ 55Bow-314
❑ 55IndGolS-26
❑ 56Top-268
❑ 59OklTodML-7
❑ 75TCM195Cl-21
❑ 79TCM50-140
❑ 83ASAWS-3
❑ 83TopRep5-92
❑ 85TCMPla1-15
❑ 90DodTar-538
❑ 91TopArc1-26

Mitchell, Larry
❑ 92FroRowDP-22
❑ 92FroRowDPG-22
❑ 92FroRowDPS-22
❑ 92MarPhiC-1
❑ 92MarPhiF-3053
❑ 93SpaPhiC-18
❑ 93SpaPhiF-1053
❑ 93StaCluM-39
❑ 94Bow-664
❑ 94ReaPhiF-2059
❑ 95ReaPhiELC-29
❑ 95ReaPhiTI-37
❑ 96ReaPhiB-9
❑ 97NorNav-27
❑ 97NorNavTI-22

Mitchell, Mark
❑ 87OneYanP-22
❑ 88Ft.LauYS-15

Mitchell, Michael F.
❑ 08RosComP-121
❑ 09AmeCarE90-1-80
❑ 09ColChiE-199A
❑ 09ColChiE-199B
❑ 09RamT20-81
❑ 09T206-254
❑ 10CouT21-47
❑ 10CouT21-192
❑ 10DomDisP-87
❑ 10RedCroT-139
❑ 10RedCroT-226
❑ 10SweCapPP-104
❑ 11L1L-118
❑ 11PinT-5-424
❑ 11S74Sil-78
❑ 11S81LarS-93
❑ 11SpoLifCW-256
❑ 11SpoLifM-199
❑ 11T205-122
❑ 11TurRedT-24
❑ 12ColRedB-199A
❑ 12ColRedB-199B
❑ 12ColTinT-199A
❑ 12ColTinT-199B
❑ 12HasTriFT-15A
❑ 12T207-128
❑ 14PieStaT-76

Mitchell, Mike Peter
❑ 94OneYanF-3802
❑ 95TamYanYI-19
❑ 97RanCucQG-17
❑ 97RanCucQG-18
❑ 98MobBayBTI-17
❑ 99SP TopP-90
❑ 99SP TopPPE-90

Mitchell, Oliver
❑ 22Zee-105
❑ 23Zee-139
❑ 23Zee-140
❑ 24Zee-96
❑ 25Zee-114
❑ 26Zee-145
❑ 27Zee-118
❑ 28Zee-138

Mitchell, Parris
❑ 90IBAWorA-20
❑ 90IBAWorA-46
❑ 91PerHeaF-13

Mitchell, Paul
❑ 76OPC-393
❑ 76Top-393
❑ 77MarPos-13
❑ 77SanJosMC-25
❑ 77Top-53
❑ 78Top-558
❑ 79OPC-118
❑ 79Top-233
❑ 80Top-131
❑ 81Don-205
❑ 81Top-449
❑ 91OriCro-309
❑ 94BreMilB-255
❑ 97PieBolWB-4

Mitchell, Rivers
❑ 94BriTigC-19
❑ 94BriTigF-3520

Mitchell, Robert
❑ 91MarPhiC-20
❑ 91MarPhiP-3451
❑ 92MarPhiC-12
❑ 92MarPhiF-3054
❑ 93SpaPhiC-19
❑ 93SpaPhiF-1054

Mitchell, Ron
❑ 75ShrCapT-11
❑ 76ShrCapT-21
❑ 77ColCliT-12
❑ 78ColCliT-16
❑ 79PorBeaT-8
❑ 80BufBisT-2

Mitchell, Roy (Albert)
❑ 09ColChiE-201
❑ 12ColRedB-200
❑ 12ColRedB-201
❑ 12ColTinT-201
❑ 15Zee-139
❑ 16Zee-137
❑ 17Zee-113
❑ 18Zee-102
❑ 20RedWorCP-12

Mitchell, Scot
❑ 82MadMusF-11

Mitchell, Scott
❑ 88MisStaB-22
❑ 89MisStaB-27
❑ 90MisStaB-37
❑ 96DelShoB-23
❑ 98arSenW1-14
❑ 98HarSenM-14

Mitchell, Thomas
❑ 90EriSaiS-17
❑ 91RenSilSCLC-14

Mitchell, Tony (Antonio)
❑ 91WelPirC-5
❑ 91WelPirP-3587
❑ 92AugPirC-13
❑ 92AugPirF-252
❑ 92ClaFS7-18
❑ 93Bow-121
❑ 93ClaFS7-223
❑ 93ExcFS7-93
❑ 93KinIndC-19
❑ 93KinIndF-2262
❑ 93KinIndTI-19
❑ 93SouAtlLAPI-25
❑ 94CanIndF-3132
❑ 94Cla-195
❑ 95Exc-43
❑ 95JacGenTI-17
❑ 96JacSunB-20
❑ 96SigRooOJ-21
❑ 96SigRooOJS-21

Mitchell, Wes
❑ 80WatIndT-34

Mitchell, William
❑ 11PinT-5-611
❑ 12T207-129
❑ 14B18B-6A
❑ 14B18B-6B
❑ 15CraJacE-62
❑ 15SpoNewM-120
❑ 16SpoNewM-123
❑ 20Zee-146
❑ 21Zee-164

Mitchelson, Mark
❑ 91Cla/Bes-168
❑ 91ElmPioC-25
❑ 91ElmPioP-3270

❑ 91WinHavRSC-4
❑ 91WinHavRSP-484
❑ 92WinHavRSC-25
Mitchem, Shannan
❑ 95ColSilB-19
❑ 96ColSilB-19
Mitchener, Mike
❑ 89SouBenWSGS-14
❑ 90Bes-131
❑ 90SouBenWSB-17
❑ 90SouBenWSGS-11
Mitta, Chris
❑ 88PulBraP-1763
Mittauer, Casey
❑ 94OneYanC-15
❑ 94OneYanF-3789
❑ 95GreBatTI-18
❑ 96TamYanY-19
Mitterwald, George
❑ 68Top-301
❑ 68TopVen-301
❑ 69Top-491A
❑ 69Top-491B
❑ 70OPC-118
❑ 70Top-118
❑ 70TwiSupV-6
❑ 71MLBOffS-467
❑ 71OPC-189
❑ 71Top-189
❑ 72OPC-301
❑ 72OPC-302
❑ 72Top-301
❑ 72Top-302
❑ 72TwiPos-10
❑ 72TwiTeal-7
❑ 74OPC-249
❑ 74Top-249
❑ 74TopSta-209
❑ 74TopTra-249T
❑ 75OPC-411
❑ 75Top-411
❑ 75TopMin-411
❑ 76CubTri-14
❑ 76OPC-506
❑ 76SSP-318
❑ 76Top-506
❑ 77CubJewT-9
❑ 77Top-124
❑ 78SanJosMMC-20
❑ 78Top-688
❑ 84ModA'sC-23
❑ 85ModA'sC-26
❑ 86OrlTwiP-12
❑ 87OrlTwiP-9
Mitze, Carl
❑ 09ObaT21-105
❑ 09ObaT21-279
❑ 11PacCoaBD-42
❑ 11Zee-35
❑ 12ObaPreT-28
❑ 12PCLPin-16
❑ 12Zee-40
❑ 13Zee-41
❑ 14Zee-43
❑ 15Zee-133
❑ 16Zee-138
❑ 17Zee-114
❑ 18Zee-31
❑ 19Zee-24
❑ 20Zee-31
❑ 21Zee-34
❑ 22Zee-35
❑ 23Zee-52
Mix, Derek
❑ 93SpoIndC-15
❑ 93SpoIndF-3590
❑ 94SpoIndC-21
❑ 94SpoIndF-3322
Mix, Greg
❑ 93ElmPioC-13
❑ 93ElmPioF-3820
❑ 94BreCouMC-9
❑ 94BreCouMF-7
❑ 95PorSeaDTI-18
❑ 96PorSeaDB-19
❑ 97PorSeaD-21
❑ 98GreBraG-15
Mix, Steve
❑ 80PhiBul-26
Miyake, Chris
❑ 96AugGreB-19
❑ 97LynHil-14
❑ 98LynHilQ-19
Miyamoto, Shinya
❑ 96MauStiHWB-2
Miyauchi, Hector
❑ 88FreSunCLC-15
❑ 88FreSunP-1233
Mize, Johnny (John)
❑ 36OveCanR-35
❑ 36R31PasP-17
❑ 38CloFotW-62
❑ 38ExhFou-8
❑ 39ExhSal-44A
❑ 39ExhSal-44B
❑ 40WheM4-6A
❑ 40WheM4-6B
❑ 41CarW75-18
❑ 41DouPlaR-39
❑ 41DouPlaR-99
❑ 42GilRazL-1
❑ 43MPR302-1-17
❑ 46SpoExcW-6-3
❑ 47HomBon-34
❑ 47TipTop-131
❑ 48BluTin-30
❑ 48Bow-4
❑ 48GiaTeal-18
❑ 49Bow-85A
❑ 49Bow-85B
❑ 49EurSta-120
❑ 49GiaTeal-20
❑ 49Lea-46
❑ 50Bow-139
❑ 51BerRos-A7
❑ 51Bow-50
❑ 51FisBakL-19
❑ 51R42SmaS-70
❑ 51TopBluB-50
❑ 52BerRos-42
❑ 52Bow-145
❑ 52Top-129
❑ 53BowBW-15
❑ 53Dor-112
❑ 53NorBreL-19
❑ 53RedMan-AL18
❑ 53Top-77
❑ 58JayPubAG-8
❑ 60Fle-38
❑ 61Fle-63
❑ 66CarCoi-3
❑ 67TopVen-182
❑ 68LauWorS-49
❑ 70FleWorS-49
❑ 70SpoCarfCOP-25
❑ 71FleWorS-50
❑ 72LauGreF-17
❑ 72TopTes5-8
❑ 73BooProC-9
❑ 73SpoScoHC-12
❑ 73SpoScoHC-13
❑ 73SpoScoHC-14
❑ 74LauAllG-47
❑ 75JohMiz-1
❑ 75JohMiz-2
❑ 75JohMiz-3
❑ 75JohMiz-4
❑ 75JohMiz-5
❑ 75JohMiz-6
❑ 75JohMiz-7
❑ 75JohMiz-8
❑ 75JohMiz-9
❑ 75JohMiz-10
❑ 75JohMiz-11
❑ 75JohMiz-12
❑ 75JohMiz-13
❑ 75JohMiz-14
❑ 75JohMiz-15
❑ 75JohMiz-16
❑ 75JohMiz-17
❑ 75JohMiz-18
❑ 75JohMiz-19
❑ 75JohMiz-20
❑ 76GalBasGHoF-19
❑ 76TayBow4-15
❑ 77ShaPiz-B
❑ 78AtlCon-18
❑ 79DiaGre-73
❑ 80PacLeg-49
❑ 80PerHaloFP-176
❑ 80PerHaloFPS-41
❑ 80SSPHOF-176
❑ 82DiaCla-24
❑ 82TCMGreS-25
❑ 83ASAJohM-1
❑ 83ASAJohM-2
❑ 83ASAJohM-3
❑ 83ASAJohM-4
❑ 83ASAJohM-5
❑ 83ASAJohM-6
❑ 83ASAJohM-7
❑ 83ASAJohM-8
❑ 83ASAJohM-9
❑ 83ASAJohM-10
❑ 83ASAJohM-11
❑ 83ASAJohM-12
❑ 83DonHOFH-10
❑ 83TCMPla1942-31
❑ 83TopRep5-129
❑ 83YanASFY-29
❑ 84OCoandSI-58
❑ 84SpoDesPW-44
❑ 85BigLeaC3-16
❑ 85CirK-32
❑ 85DonHOFS-4
❑ 85TCMPhoC-17
❑ 85UltBasC-12
❑ 86SpoDecG-24
❑ 88PacLegI-63
❑ 89HOFStiB-3
❑ 89PacLegI-180
❑ 89PerCelP-32
❑ 89SweBasG-55
❑ 90PerGreM-23
❑ 90PerMasW-31
❑ 90PerMasW-32
❑ 90PerMasW-33
❑ 90PerMasW-34
❑ 90PerMasW-35
❑ 90SweBasG-90
❑ 91ConTSN-53
❑ 91SweBasG-62
❑ 91TopArc1-77
❑ 92ActPacA-13
❑ 92ActPacA2-13G
❑ 92BazQua5A-9
❑ 92CarMcD-3
❑ 92ConTSN-435
❑ 92ConTSN-628
❑ 92YanWIZA-49
❑ 92YanWIZH-24
❑ 93ActPacAC-13
❑ 93ConTSN-918
❑ 93DiaStaES-145
❑ 93MetIma-13
❑ 93TedWil-66
❑ 93TedWil-129
❑ 93TedWil-145
❑ 93TedWilLC-4
❑ 93UppDecAH-96
❑ 94ConTSN-1126
❑ 94ConTSNB-1126
❑ 94ConTSNCI-28
❑ 94UppDecAH-48
❑ 94UppDecAH-161
❑ 94UppDecAH1-48
❑ 94UppDecAH1-161
Mize, Paul
❑ 79WatA'sT-18
❑ 80WesHavWCT-8
❑ 81TacTigT-16
❑ 82TacTigT-15
❑ 82WesHavAT-16
Mizell, Wilmer
❑ 52Top-334
❑ 53BowBW-23
❑ 53CarHunW-15
❑ 53Top-128
❑ 54Top-249
❑ 56Top-193
❑ 57Top-113
❑ 58CarJayP-11
❑ 58Top-385
❑ 60CarJayP-7
❑ 61Kah-28
❑ 61Pos-140
❑ 74MetOriEB-11
❑ 77PirTCM1WC-19
❑ 82MetGal62-20
❑ 83TopRep5-334
❑ 91MetWIZ-277
❑ 91TopArc1-128
❑ 92BazQua5A-16
❑ 94TopArc1-249
❑ 94TopArc1G-249
Mizerock, John
❑ 84Don-380
❑ 85TucTorC-68
❑ 86Don-502
❑ 86TucTorP-15
❑ 87Don-653
❑ 87RicBraBC-14
❑ 87RicBraC-8
❑ 87RicBraT-10
❑ 87Top-408
❑ 87TopTif-408
❑ 88BobCamRB-10
❑ 88RicBraC-21
❑ 88RicBraP-19
❑ 89RicBraBC-18
❑ 89RicBraC-12
❑ 89RicBraP-827
❑ 89RicBraTI-15
❑ 90CMC-297
❑ 90ProAAAF-407
❑ 90RicBraBC-6
❑ 90RicBraC-21
❑ 90RicBraP-262
❑ 90RicBraTI-23
❑ 94RocRoyC-28
❑ 94RocRoyF-581
❑ 95WilBluRTI-7
❑ 96WilBluRB-28
❑ 97CalLeaATI-26
❑ 97WilBluR-27
❑ 98WicWraM-22
Mizusawa, Hideki
❑ 90GatCitPSP-17
Mizutani, Jitsuo
❑ 79TCMJapPB-30
Mizutani, Shintaro
❑ 79TCMJapPB-24
Mlicki, Dave
❑ 91ColIndC-6
❑ 92Bow-413
❑ 92CanIndF-688
❑ 92CanIndS-112
❑ 92ClaFS7-39
❑ 92SkyAA F-53
❑ 93Bow-451
❑ 93ClaGolF-6
❑ 93Don-273
❑ 93FleMajLP-B9
❑ 93Pin-275
❑ 93Sco-285
❑ 93Top-571
❑ 93TopGol-571
❑ 93TopInaM-571
❑ 93TopInaR-571
❑ 93TopMic-571
❑ 93UppDec-17
❑ 93UppDecGold-17
❑ 94ChaKniF-893
❑ 95Fin-248
❑ 95FinRef-248
❑ 95Fla-386
❑ 95FleUpd-116
❑ 95MetColP-22
❑ 95TopTra-46T
❑ 96ColCho-621
❑ 96ColChoGS-621
❑ 96ColChoSS-621
❑ 96Don-121
❑ 96DonPreP-121
❑ 96Fle-485
❑ 96FleTif-485
❑ 96LeaSigEA-128
❑ 96MetKah-22
❑ 96MetKah-23
❑ 96Pac-136
❑ 96UppDec-138
❑ 98ColCho-441
❑ 98DodMot-16
❑ 98Fle-512
❑ 98PacOnl-484
❑ 98PacOnlR-484
❑ 98PacOnlWC-484
❑ 98Top-191
❑ 98TopChr-191
❑ 98TopChrR-191
❑ 98TopDevR-191
❑ 98TopDia-191
❑ 98TopMiniC-191
❑ 98UppDec-446
❑ 99Fle-565
❑ 99FleSta9-565
❑ 99FleWarT-565
❑ 99Top-374
❑ 99TopChr-374
❑ 99TopChrR-374
❑ 99TopMVPP-374
Mlicki, Doug
❑ 90ArkRaz-33
❑ 92AubAstC-18
❑ 92AubAstF-1352
❑ 93ClaFS7-108
❑ 93OscAstC-16
❑ 93OscAstF-624
❑ 94JacGenF-216
❑ 95Exc-206
❑ 95JacGenTI-6
❑ 95SigRoo-37
❑ 95SigRooSig-37
❑ 96BesAutS-61
❑ 96BesAutSA-46
❑ 96TusTorB-16
❑ 97BesAutAS-33
❑ 97BesAutP-R8
Mlodik, Kevin
❑ 96WesMicWB-15
❑ 97VisOakG-18
❑ 98FarRedHM-18
Mmahat, Kevin
❑ 88FloStaLAS-44
❑ 88Ft.LauYS-16
❑ 89AlbYanB-23
❑ 89AlbYanP-341
❑ 89AlbYanSt-14
❑ 90AlbDecGB-25
❑ 90CMC-205
❑ 90ColCliC-5
❑ 90ColCliP-20
❑ 90ColCliP-674
❑ 90Don-481
❑ 90ProAAAF-324
❑ 90Sco-643
❑ 90TopDeb89-84
❑ 90TopTVY-55
❑ 90TriAllGP-AAA15
❑ 91ColCliP-13
❑ 92YanWIZ8-121
Moates, Dave
❑ 74SpoIndC-37
❑ 75SpoIndC-2
❑ 76OPC-327
❑ 76Top-327
❑ 77Top-588
❑ 77TucTorC-2
❑ 93RanKee-269
Moberg, Mike
❑ 91Cla/Bes-317
❑ 91RocExpC-23
❑ 91RocExpP-2058
Mobilia, Bill
❑ 92Min-14
❑ 94BatCliC-14
❑ 94BatCliF-3455
❑ 95PiePhiF-193
Mobley, Anton
❑ 89St.CatBJP-2084
❑ 90MyrBeaBJP-2789
❑ 90St.CatBJP-3479
Mobley, Kevin
❑ 98LakTigM-8
Moccia, Mario
❑ 89NiaFalRP-18
❑ 90NiaFalRP-7
Modrell, Gary
❑ 64SeaPop-10
Moeder, Tony
❑ 94CedRapKC-18
❑ 94CedRapKF-1117
❑ 94MidLeaAF-MDW39
❑ 95AusFut-71
❑ 96LakElsSB-18
❑ 96MidAngB-22
Moehler, Brian
❑ 93NiaFalRF-3383
❑ 94LakTigC-16
❑ 94LakTigF-3033
❑ 95JacSunTI-22
❑ 96JacSunB-21
❑ 97ColChoU-U11
❑ 97Don-384
❑ 97DonGolPP-384
❑ 97DonSilPP-384
❑ 97Fle-658
❑ 97FleTif-658
❑ 97Lea-332
❑ 97LeaFraM-332
❑ 97LeaFraMDC-332
❑ 98ColCho-372
❑ 98Fle-475
❑ 98Pac-93
❑ 98PacOnl-279
❑ 98PacOnlR-279
❑ 98PacOnlWC-279
❑ 98PacPlaB-93
❑ 98PacRedT-93
❑ 98PacSil-93
❑ 98UppDec-373
❑ 99Fle-501
❑ 99FleSta9-501
❑ 99FleWarT-501
❑ 99StaClu-297
❑ 99StaCluFDI-297
❑ 99StaCluOoaK-297
❑ 99StaCluPP-297
❑ 99UppDec-98
❑ 99UppDecEL1-98
❑ 99UppDecEL2-98
Moeller, Chad
❑ 96AppLeaAB-17
❑ 97ForWayW-21
❑ 97MidLeaTP-9
❑ 98ForMyeMTI-20
❑ 99BowBes-193
❑ 99BowBesAR-193
❑ 99BowBesR-193
❑ 99StaClu-141
❑ 99StaCluFDI-141
❑ 99StaCluOoaK-141
❑ 99StaCluPP-141
Moeller, Daniel
❑ 09T206-448
❑ 12ImpTobC-76
❑ 14B18B-44
Moeller, Dennis
❑ 86EugEmeC-50
❑ 87AppFoxP-26
❑ 88AppFoxP-160
❑ 89BasCitRS-17
❑ 90MemChiS-19
❑ 92DonRoo-82
❑ 92OmaRoyF-2960
❑ 92OmaRoyS-338
❑ 92SkyAAAF-155
❑ 92TriA AAS-338
❑ 93Bow-50
❑ 93Don-648
❑ 93FleFinE-115
❑ 93FleMajLP-B14
❑ 93OPCPre-54
❑ 93PacSpa-589
❑ 93Pin-600
❑ 93PirNatI-21
❑ 93Ult-453
❑ 93UppDec-779
❑ 93UppDecGold-779
❑ 94OmaRoyF-1222
❑ 94VenLinU-79
Moeller, Joe
❑ 62DodVol-18
❑ 63Top-53
❑ 64DodHea-7
❑ 64Top-549
❑ 65OPC-238
❑ 65Top-238
❑ 66Top-449
❑ 67CokCapD-4
❑ 67CokCapDA-4
❑ 67OPC-149
❑ 67Top-149
❑ 68Top-359
❑ 68TopVen-359
❑ 69Top-444A
❑ 69Top-444B
❑ 70OPC-97
❑ 70Top-97
❑ 71Dod-8
❑ 71DodTic-10
❑ 71MLBOffS-108
❑ 71OPC-288
❑ 71Top-288
❑ 81TCM60I-448
❑ 85SpoIndGC-14
❑ 90DodTar-541
Moeller, Ron
❑ 61Top-466
❑ 63Top-541
❑ 91OriCro-310
Moen, Eric
❑ 90YakBeaTI-21
❑ 91BenBucCB-27
Moen, Robbie
❑ 90AriWilP-13
❑ 92AriWilP-9
❑ 93ElmPioC-14
❑ 93ElmPioF-3837
❑ 94KanCouCC-18
❑ 94KanCouCF-176
Moesche, Carl
❑ 84ButCopKT-7
Moffat, Donald
❑ 91TopRut-5
Moffet, Samuel
❑ 87OldJudN-349
Moffitt, G. Scott
❑ 76QuaCitAT-22
❑ 77QuaCitAT-21
❑ 80SalLakCGT-4
❑ 81SalLakCGT-23
Moffitt, Randy
❑ 73OPC-43
❑ 73Top-43
❑ 74OPC-156

❑ 74Top-156
❑ 75Gia-5
❑ 75GiaTeal-9
❑ 75OPC-132
❑ 75Top-132
❑ 75TopMin-132
❑ 76OPC-553
❑ 76SanFraGP-13
❑ 76Top-553
❑ 77BurCheD-101
❑ 77Gia-16
❑ 77GiaTeal-19
❑ 77Top-464
❑ 78GiaTeal-19
❑ 78Top-284
❑ 78WifBalD-51
❑ 79GiaPol-17
❑ 79Top-62
❑ 80GiaPol-17
❑ 80GiaTeal-20
❑ 80Top-359
❑ 81Don-195
❑ 81Fle-446
❑ 81GiaTeal-11
❑ 81Top-622
❑ 82AstAstI-9
❑ 82AstPos-15
❑ 83Don-545
❑ 83Fle-456
❑ 83Top-723
❑ 83TopFol-4
❑ 83TopTra-73T
❑ 84Don-390
❑ 84Fle-163
❑ 84Nes792-108
❑ 84OPC-108
❑ 84Top-108
❑ 84TopTif-108
Moffitt, Shawn
❑ 97KisCob-29
❑ 98AubDouTI-16
Moford, Herb
❑ 59Top-91
❑ 59TopVen-91
❑ 91MetWIZ-278
Mogridge, George
❑ 12T207-130
❑ 22E120-113
❑ 22W572-66
❑ 22W573-88
❑ 23WilChoV-106
❑ 75SenTCM1-22
❑ 92ConTSN-376
Mohart, George
❑ 90DodTar-1038
Moharter, Dave
❑ 75SpoIndC-19
❑ 76SacSolC-3
❑ 77TucTorC-13
❑ 78TucTorC-13
❑ 79TucTorT-16
❑ 80ChaChaT-7
❑ 87MacPirP-25
❑ 88AugPirP-383
Mohler, Ernest
❑ 09ObaT21-56
❑ 09ObaT21-164
❑ 09ObaT21-329
❑ 10BisCoaLE99-20
❑ 11PacCoaBD-43
❑ 11Zee-94
❑ 12ObaPreT-78
❑ 12Zee-122
❑ 14Zee-88
Mohler, Mike
❑ 90MadMusB-20
❑ 90MadMusP-2267
❑ 91CalLeLA-42
❑ 91ModA'sC-9
❑ 91ModA'sP-3084
❑ 92ClaFS7-137
❑ 92HunStaF-3946
❑ 92HunStaS-315
❑ 92SkyAA F-134
❑ 93AthMot-23
❑ 93AthStaC-3
❑ 93Bow-105
❑ 93FleFinE-258
❑ 93PacSpa-570
❑ 93Pin-592
❑ 93Ult-610
❑ 94Don-505
❑ 94Fle-269
❑ 94Pac-458
❑ 94Top-282
❑ 94TopGol-282
❑ 94TopSpa-282
❑ 95EdmTraTI-17
❑ 96A'sMot-19
❑ 96LeaSigEA-129
❑ 97A'sMot-9
❑ 97Fle-194
❑ 97FleTif-194
❑ 97Lea-161
❑ 97LeaFraM-161
❑ 97LeaFraMDC-161
❑ 97Top-19
❑ 98A'sMot-22
❑ 98PacOnl-540
❑ 98PacOnlR-540
❑ 98PacOnlWC-540
Mohn, Solly
❑ 52LaPat-12
Mohorcic, Dale
❑ 81PorBeaT-17
❑ 85OklCit8T-26
❑ 86OklCit8P-13
❑ 86RanPer-34
❑ 87Don-531
❑ 87Fle-131
❑ 87FleGlo-131
❑ 87RanMot-15
❑ 87RanSmo-5
❑ 87Top-497
❑ 87TopTif-497
❑ 88Don-470
❑ 88DonBasB-144
❑ 88Fle-474
❑ 88FleGlo-474
❑ 88OPC-163
❑ 88RanMot-15
❑ 88RanSmo-6
❑ 88Sco-452
❑ 88ScoGlo-452
❑ 88StaLinRa-9
❑ 88Top-163
❑ 88TopSti-242
❑ 88TopTif-163
❑ 89Don-630
❑ 89Fle-259
❑ 89FleGlo-259
❑ 89Sco-420
❑ 89Top-26
❑ 89TopTif-26
❑ 89UppDec-727
❑ 89YanScoNW-16
❑ 90CMC-58
❑ 90Fle-450
❑ 90FleCan-450
❑ 90IndIndC-8
❑ 90IndIndP-298
❑ 90ProAAAF-581
❑ 90Sco-191
❑ 90UppDec-530
❑ 91Fle-239
❑ 91Sco-596
❑ 92YanWIZ8-122
❑ 93RanKee-270
Mohr, Dustan
❑ 97WatIndTI-18
❑ 98CarLeaTPQ-27
❑ 98KinIndQ-17
Mohr, Ed
❑ 79QuaCitCT-2
Mohr, Tommy
❑ 83ButCopKT-25
❑ 85Ft.MyeRT-19
Moisan, William
❑ 52MotCoo-64
Moitoza, Don
❑ 75OakOak2A-23
Mojica, Gonzalo
❑ 94BurIndF-3789
❑ 96BurIndB-12
Mokan, John
❑ 22E120-221
❑ 25Exh-46
❑ 26Exh-46
❑ 27Exh-23
Moldes, Orestes
❑ 80BatTroT-11
Moler, Dick
❑ 52LavPro-16
Moler, Jason
❑ 92FroRowDP-29
❑ 92FroRowDPG-29
❑ 92FroRowDPS-29
❑ 92TopTra-75T
❑ 92TopTraG-75T
❑ 93ClaFS7-285
❑ 93ClePhiC-1
❑ 93ClePhiF-2686
❑ 93FloStaLAF-28
❑ 93StaCluM-36
❑ 94Bow-636
❑ 94Cla-149
❑ 94ClaGolF-39
❑ 94ExcFS7-247
❑ 94ExcLeaLF-14
❑ 94ReaPhiF-2065
❑ 94TedWil-127
❑ 94UppDecML-111
❑ 94UppDecMLPotYF-PY18
❑ 95ReaPhiTI-22
❑ 95UppDecML-207
❑ 95UppDecMLFS-207
❑ 96ReaPhiB-20
Molero, Juan
❑ 87GreHorP-13
❑ 88LynRedSS-15
❑ 89LynRedSS-14
Molesworth, Carlton
❑ 09ColChiE-202
❑ 09T206-503
❑ 10CouT21-48
❑ 12ColRedB-202
❑ 12ColTinT-202
Molina, Albert
❑ 89SalBucS-15
Molina, Ben
❑ 95CedRapKTI-27
❑ 95MidLeaA-34
❑ 96MidAngB-23
❑ 96MidAngOHP-19
❑ 96TexLeaAB-33
❑ 97LakElsSG-22
❑ 97VanCanB-21
❑ 98MidAngO-25
❑ 98VanCanG-18
❑ 99SpoIll-42
Molina, Gabe
❑ 96BluOriB-20
❑ 97DelSho-27
❑ 98BowBayM-24
❑ 99Bow-170
❑ 99BowChr-170
❑ 99BowChrG-170
❑ 99BowChrGR-170
❑ 99BowChrI-170
❑ 99BowChrIR-170
❑ 99BowChrR-170
❑ 99BowGol-170
❑ 99BowInt-170
Molina, Izzy (Islay)
❑ 91MadMusC-16
❑ 91MadMusP-2136
❑ 91MidLeaAP-MWL43
❑ 92CalLeaACL-16
❑ 92RenSilSCLC-49
❑ 93AthStaC-17
❑ 93ModA'sC-13
❑ 93ModA'sF-802
❑ 94Bow-164
❑ 94ClaGolF-126
❑ 94ExcFS7-121
❑ 94HunStaF-1335
❑ 94UppDecML-79
❑ 95HunStaTI-19
❑ 97A'sMot-24
❑ 98Pac-170
❑ 98PacPlaB-170
❑ 98PacRedT-170
❑ 98PacSil-170
Molina, Jim
❑ 98NewJerCM-21
Molina, Jose
❑ 94PeoChiC-20
❑ 94PeoChiF-2270
❑ 96RocCubTI-20
❑ 98WesTenDJM-19
Molina, Luis
❑ 96LanJetB-18
❑ 97LanJet-18
Molina, Mario
❑ 87SalAngP-7
❑ 88QuaCitAGS-18
❑ 89PalSprAP-477
Molina, Norberto
❑ 80WisRapTT-20
Molina, Primitivo
❑ 98LowSpiM-26
Molinaro, Bob
❑ 77EvaTriT-19
❑ 78SSP270-158
❑ 79IowOakP-11
❑ 79Top-88
❑ 81CokTeaS-33
❑ 81Fle-340
❑ 81Top-466
❑ 81TopSti-61
❑ 81TopSupHT-19
❑ 82CubRedL-29
❑ 82Don-417
❑ 82Fle-353
❑ 82Top-363
❑ 83Don-596
❑ 83Fle-167
❑ 83PhiTas-19
❑ 83Top-664
❑ 85RocRedWT-12
❑ 86HagSunP-12
❑ 87RocRedWP-27
❑ 89CanIndB-17
❑ 89CanIndP-1319
❑ 89CanIndS-2
❑ 89PacSenL-80
❑ 89TopSenL-118
❑ 90CMC-477
❑ 90ColSprSSC-24
❑ 90ColSprSSP-54
❑ 90EliSenL-87
❑ 90HagSunDGB-17
❑ 90ProAAAF-235
❑ 91ChaRanC-27
❑ 91ChaRanP-1330
❑ 91OriCro-311
❑ 91PacSenL-13
Moline, Stan
❑ 76CedRapGT-16
Molitor, Paul
❑ 78Top-707
❑ 79Kel-20
❑ 79OPC-8
❑ 79Top-24
❑ 80OPC-211
❑ 80Top-406
❑ 81AllGamPI-60
❑ 81Don-203
❑ 81Fle-515
❑ 81FleStiC-82
❑ 81Kel-53
❑ 81OPC-300
❑ 81Top-300
❑ 81TopScr-35
❑ 81TopSti-91
❑ 82BrePol-4
❑ 82Don-78
❑ 82Fle-148
❑ 82FleSta-136
❑ 82OPC-195
❑ 82Top-195
❑ 82TopSti-200
❑ 83AllGamPI-35
❑ 83BreGar-11
❑ 83BrePol-4
❑ 83Don-484
❑ 83Fle-40
❑ 83FleSta-127
❑ 83FleSti-19
❑ 83OPC-371
❑ 83Top-630
❑ 83TopSti-83
❑ 83TopSti-139
❑ 83TopSti-140
❑ 83TopSti-156
❑ 84AllGamPI-126
❑ 84BreGar-13
❑ 84BrePol-4
❑ 84Don-107
❑ 84DonActAS-35
❑ 84DonCha-54
❑ 84Fle-207
❑ 84FunFooP-105
❑ 84Nes792-60
❑ 84OPC-60
❑ 84SevCoi-C18
❑ 84Top-60
❑ 84TopRubD-6
❑ 84TopSti-294
❑ 84TopTif-60
❑ 85AllGamPI-35
❑ 85BreGar-13
❑ 85BrePol-4
❑ 85Don-359
❑ 85Fle-588
❑ 85OPC-395
❑ 85Top-522
❑ 85TopRubD-7
❑ 85TopTif-522
❑ 86BrePol-4
❑ 86Don-124
❑ 86DonAll-39
❑ 86Fle-495
❑ 86FleLimE-30
❑ 86FleMin-101
❑ 86FleStiC-76
❑ 86Lea-70
❑ 86MSAJayPCD-12
❑ 86OPC-267
❑ 86SevCoi-C16
❑ 86Spo-39
❑ 86Spo-128
❑ 86Top-267
❑ 86TopSti-203
❑ 86TopTat-23
❑ 86TopTif-267
❑ 87BrePol-4
❑ 87BreTeal-8
❑ 87ClaGam-45
❑ 87Don-117
❑ 87DonHig-29
❑ 87DonOpeD-54
❑ 87Fle-350
❑ 87FleGlo-350
❑ 87FleStiC-78
❑ 87Lea-71
❑ 87OPC-184
❑ 87RedFolSB-22
❑ 87Spo-54
❑ 87SpoTeaP-19
❑ 87StuPan-21
❑ 87Top-56
❑ 87Top-741
❑ 87TopSti-200
❑ 87TopTif-56
❑ 87TopTif-741
❑ 88BrePol-4
❑ 88BreTeal-25
❑ 88ClaBlu-232
❑ 88Don-7
❑ 88Don-249
❑ 88DonBasB-165
❑ 88DonBonM-BC3
❑ 88DonSupD-7
❑ 88Dra-11
❑ 88Fle-169
❑ 88FleAll-12
❑ 88FleAwaW-25
❑ 88FleGlo-169
❑ 88FleLeaL-27
❑ 88FleMin-31
❑ 88FleStiC-38
❑ 88FleTeaL-22
❑ 88GreBasS-29
❑ 88K-M-17
❑ 88KayB-19
❑ 88KinDis-23
❑ 88Lea-7
❑ 88Lea-168
❑ 88MSAFanSD-5
❑ 88MSAJifPD-12
❑ 88OPC-231
❑ 88PanSti-125
❑ 88PanSti-432
❑ 88Sco-340
❑ 88Sco-660
❑ 88ScoBoxC-T6
❑ 88ScoGlo-340
❑ 88ScoGlo-660
❑ 88Spo-79
❑ 88Spo-221
❑ 88StaLinBre-11
❑ 88TarPla-28
❑ 88Top-465
❑ 88TopBig-1
❑ 88TopCoi-20
❑ 88TopGloS-57
❑ 88TopMinL-19
❑ 88TopRevLL-20
❑ 88TopRitTM-20
❑ 88TopSti-194
❑ 88TopStiB-42
❑ 88TopTif-465
❑ 88TopUKM-49
❑ 88TopUKMT-49
❑ 89Bow-140
❑ 89BowTif-140
❑ 89BreGar-1
❑ 89BrePol-4
❑ 89BreYea-4
❑ 89CadEllD-37
❑ 89ClaLigB-12
❑ 89Don-291
❑ 89DonAll-3
❑ 89DonBasB-15
❑ 89DonBonM-BC9
❑ 89DonPop-3
❑ 89Fle-193
❑ 89FleAll-8
❑ 89FleBasA-30
❑ 89FleGlo-193
❑ 89MasBreD-8
❑ 89OPC-110
❑ 89PanSti-243
❑ 89PanSti-373
❑ 89RedFolSB-81
❑ 89Sco-565
❑ 89ScoHot1S-57
❑ 89Spo-209
❑ 89SpoIllFKI-271
❑ 89Top-110
❑ 89TopBasT-153
❑ 89TopBatL-10
❑ 89TopBig-330
❑ 89TopCoi-46
❑ 89TopGloA-3
❑ 89TopGloS-43
❑ 89TopMinL-58
❑ 89TopSti-146
❑ 89TopSti-204
❑ 89TopStiB-9
❑ 89TopTif-110
❑ 89TopUKM-53
❑ 89TVSpoM-73
❑ 89UppDec-525
❑ 89UppDec-673
❑ 90AllBasT-22
❑ 90Bow-399
❑ 90BowTif-399
❑ 90BreMilB-15
❑ 90BrePol-4
❑ 90ClaUpd-T34
❑ 90Don-103
❑ 90DonBesA-64
❑ 90DOnBonM-BC15
❑ 90Fle-330
❑ 90FleBasM-27
❑ 90FleBasMC-27
❑ 90FleCan-330
❑ 90Hot50PS-28
❑ 90Lea-242
❑ 90M.Vpin-52
❑ 90MLBBasB-79
❑ 90OPC-360
❑ 90PanSti-98
❑ 90PubIntS-500
❑ 90RedFolSB-65
❑ 90Sco-460
❑ 90Sco100S-98
❑ 90Spo-183
❑ 90Top-360
❑ 90TopAmeA-14
❑ 90TopBatL-8
❑ 90TopBig-103
❑ 90TopCoi-23
❑ 90TopMag-68
❑ 90TopMinL-20
❑ 90TopSti-199
❑ 90TopTif-360
❑ 90TopTVA-29
❑ 90UppDec-254
❑ 91Bow-32
❑ 91BreMilB-17
❑ 91BrePol-15
❑ 91Cla2-T14
❑ 91Cla3-T60
❑ 91ClaGam-79
❑ 91Don-85
❑ 91Fle-591
❑ 91Lea-302
❑ 91LeaPre-20
❑ 91MajLeaCP-42
❑ 91OPC-95
❑ 91OPCPre-82
❑ 91PanFreS-205
❑ 91PanSti-168
❑ 91PetSta-15
❑ 91Sco-49
❑ 91Sco100S-13
❑ 91StaClu-245
❑ 91StaCluMO-6
❑ 91StaPinB-33
❑ 91Stu-73
❑ 91Top-95
❑ 91TopCraJI-2
❑ 91TopDesS-95
❑ 91TopMic-95
❑ 91TopTif-95
❑ 91TopTriH-A8
❑ 91Ult-178
❑ 91UppDec-324
❑ 91USPlaCA-8H
❑ 92Bow-375
❑ 92Bow-645
❑ 92BreCarT-15

❑ 92BrePol-15
❑ 92BreUSO-2
❑ 92ClaGam-21
❑ 92Don-51
❑ 92DonCraJ2-22
❑ 92DonDiaK-DK1
❑ 92DonSupD-DK1
❑ 92Fle-182
❑ 92Fle-702
❑ 92Hig5-67
❑ 92HitTheBB-23
❑ 92KinDis-14
❑ 92Lea-238
❑ 92LeaBlaG-238
❑ 92MooSna-14
❑ 92MSABenSHD-8
❑ 92OPC-600
❑ 92OPCPre-141
❑ 92Pin-8
❑ 92Pos-17
❑ 92Sco-61
❑ 92Sco100S-8
❑ 92ScoCokD-15
❑ 92ScoProP-2
❑ 92StaClu-230
❑ 92StaCluD-122
❑ 92Stu-194
❑ 92StuHer-BC11
❑ 92SunSee-13
❑ 92Top-600
❑ 92TopGol-600
❑ 92TopGolW-600
❑ 92TopKid-81
❑ 92TopMic-600
❑ 92TriPla-254
❑ 92Ult-81
❑ 92UppDec-423
❑ 92UppDecTMH-36
❑ 93BluJayCP1-13
❑ 93BluJayD-4
❑ 93BluJayDM-35
❑ 93BluJayFS-20
❑ 93Bow-167
❑ 93BreSen-1
❑ 93ClaGam-66
❑ 93DiaMar-77
❑ 93Don-75
❑ 93DonEli-22
❑ 93DonEliD-18
❑ 93DonEliD-AU18
❑ 93DonEliS-4
❑ 93DonMVP-4
❑ 93DurPowP2-24
❑ 93Fin-70
❑ 93FinRef-70
❑ 93Fla-292
❑ 93Fle-254
❑ 93FleFinE-295
❑ 93FleFinEDT-5
❑ 93FunPac-58
❑ 93HumDumC-18
❑ 93Lea-262
❑ 93LeaGolA-U10
❑ 93MetBak-33
❑ 93MilBonSS-1
❑ 93OPC-237
❑ 93OPCPre-124
❑ 93PacSpa-654
❑ 93Pin-428
❑ 93Pin-481
❑ 93PinCoo-23
❑ 93PinCooD-23
❑ 93Pos-16
❑ 93RedFolS-67
❑ 93Sco-598
❑ 93Sel-42
❑ 93SelChaS-23
❑ 93SelRoo-16T
❑ 93SelStaL-9
❑ 93SP-50
❑ 93StaClu-627
❑ 93StaCluFDI-627
❑ 93StaCluM-131
❑ 93StaCluMO-16
❑ 93StaCluMOP-627
❑ 93Stu-172
❑ 93Top-207
❑ 93TopGol-207
❑ 93TopInaM-207
❑ 93TopInaR-207
❑ 93TopMic-207
❑ 93TopTra-48T
❑ 93TriPla-97
❑ 93TriPlaG-GS6
❑ 93Ult-645
❑ 93UppDec-43
❑ 93UppDec-333
❑ 93UppDec-705
❑ 93UppDecGold-43
❑ 93UppDecGold-333
❑ 93UppDecGold-705
❑ 93UppDecIC-WI6
❑ 93UppDecICJ-WI6
❑ 93USPlaCA-7D
❑ 94BluJayP-6
❑ 94BluJayUSPC-1S
❑ 94BluJayUSPC-6D
❑ 94BluJayUSPC-7H
❑ 94Bow-281
❑ 94BowBes-R1
❑ 94BowBesR-R1
❑ 94BreMilB-256
❑ 94BreMilB-332
❑ 94BreSen-4
❑ 94BreSen-5
❑ 94BreUSO-1
❑ 94ColC-208
❑ 94ColChoGS-208
❑ 94ColChoSS-208
❑ 94Don-24
❑ 94DonAwaWJ-10
❑ 94DonDom-B3
❑ 94DonDomJ-B3
❑ 94DonSpeE-24
❑ 94Fin-239
❑ 94FinJum-239
❑ 94FinRef-239
❑ 94Fla-119
❑ 94FlaHotN-5
❑ 94Fle-338
❑ 94Fle-707
❑ 94FleAllS-16
❑ 94FleExtB-192
❑ 94FleExtB-P1
❑ 94FleExtBGB-20
❑ 94FleTeaL-1
❑ 94FUnPac-150
❑ 94KinDis-2
❑ 94Kra-8
❑ 94Lea-395
❑ 94LeaGolS-10
❑ 94LeaL-78
❑ 94LeaMVPC-A9
❑ 94LeaMVPCG-A9
❑ 94O-PJumAF-2
❑ 94OPC-1
❑ 94OPCAllR-2
❑ 94OPCJumA-2
❑ 94OPCWorC-3
❑ 94OscMayR-9
❑ 94Pac-648
❑ 94PacSilP-4
❑ 94PacSilPC-4
❑ 94PanSti-140
❑ 94Pin-27
❑ 94PinArtP-27
❑ 94PinMusC-27
❑ 94PinRunC-RC4
❑ 94PinSam-TR1
❑ 94PinTri-TR1
❑ 94PosCan-2
❑ 94ProMag-139
❑ 94Sco-427
❑ 94ScoCyc-TC3
❑ 94ScoGolR-427
❑ 94ScoGolS-57
❑ 94Sel-3
❑ 94Sel-MVP1
❑ 94SelSam-3
❑ 94SP-44
❑ 94SPDieC-44
❑ 94Spo-106
❑ 94Spo-NNO
❑ 94StaClu-110
❑ 94StaClu-526
❑ 94StaClu-645
❑ 94StaCluFDI-110
❑ 94StaCluFDI-526
❑ 94StaCluFDI-645
❑ 94StaCluGR-110
❑ 94StaCluGR-526
❑ 94StaCluGR-645
❑ 94StaCluMO-4
❑ 94StaCluMOP-110
❑ 94StaCluMOP-526
❑ 94StaCluMOP-645
❑ 94StaCluT-161
❑ 94StaCluTFDI-161
❑ 94Stu-29
❑ 94Top-540
❑ 94Top-609
❑ 94TopBlaG-13
❑ 94TopGol-540
❑ 94TopGol-609
❑ 94TopSpa-540
❑ 94TopSpa-609
❑ 94TopSupS-30
❑ 94TriPla-35
❑ 94TriPlaM-15
❑ 94TriPlaP-5
❑ 94Ult-140
❑ 94UltAwaW-21
❑ 94UltCarA-2
❑ 94UltHitM-7
❑ 94UltOnBL-9
❑ 94UppDec-294
❑ 94UppDec-470
❑ 94UppDecAJ-16
❑ 94UppDecAJG-16
❑ 94UppDecED-294
❑ 94UppDecED-470
❑ 94USPlaCA-10D
❑ 95Baz-102
❑ 95BazRedH-RH19
❑ 95BluJayB-3
❑ 95BluJayOH-26
❑ 95BluJayP-4
❑ 95BluJayUSPC-1S
❑ 95BluJayUSPC-7H
❑ 95Bow-324
❑ 95BowBes-R17
❑ 95BowBesR-R17
❑ 95BurBeeTI-21
❑ 95ColCho-145
❑ 95ColChoGS-145
❑ 95ColChoSE-55
❑ 95ColChoSEGS-55
❑ 95ColChoSESS-55
❑ 95ColChoSS-145
❑ 95Don-110
❑ 95Don-162
❑ 95DonPreP-110
❑ 95DonPreP-162
❑ 95DonTopotO-175
❑ 95Emo-96
❑ 95Fin-115
❑ 95FinRef-115
❑ 95Fla-317
❑ 95Fle-101
❑ 95FleAllS-13
❑ 95KinDis-14
❑ 95Lea-181
❑ 95Lea300C-2
❑ 95LeaHeaftH-8
❑ 95LeaLim-100
❑ 95LeaStaS-5
❑ 95Pac-447
❑ 95PacGolP-25
❑ 95PacPri-143
❑ 95PanSti-98
❑ 95Pin-260
❑ 95Pin-297
❑ 95PinArtP-260
❑ 95PinArtP-297
❑ 95PinGatA-GA14
❑ 95PinMusC-260
❑ 95PinMusC-297
❑ 95PinPer-PP7
❑ 95PinRedH-RH14
❑ 95PinWhiH-WH14
❑ 95PosCan-3
❑ 95Sco-247
❑ 95Sco-566
❑ 95ScoDreT-DG9
❑ 95ScoGolR-247
❑ 95ScoGolR-566
❑ 95ScoHaloG-HG25
❑ 95ScoPlaTS-247
❑ 95ScoPlaTS-566
❑ 95Sel-35
❑ 95SelArtP-35
❑ 95SelBigS-BS10
❑ 95SelCer-23
❑ 95SelCerMG-23
❑ 95SP-203
❑ 95SPCha-110
❑ 95SPCha-195
❑ 95SPCha-198
❑ 95SPChaDC-110
❑ 95SPChaDC-195
❑ 95SPChaDC-198
❑ 95Spo-8
❑ 95SpoArtP-8
❑ 95SPSil-203
❑ 95SPSpeF-26
❑ 95StaClu-39
❑ 95StaCluCT-7
❑ 95StaCluFDI-39
❑ 95StaCluMO-33
❑ 95StaCluMOP-39
❑ 95StaCluMOP-PZ8
❑ 95StaCluMOP-RL4
❑ 95StaCluPZ-PZ8
❑ 95StaCluRL-RL4
❑ 95StaCluSTWS-39
❑ 95StaCluVR-28
❑ 95StaCluVRMO-28
❑ 95Stu-10
❑ 95StuGolS-10
❑ 95StuPlaS-10
❑ 95Sum-58
❑ 95Sum-186
❑ 95SumBigB-BB13
❑ 95SumNthD-58
❑ 95SumNthD-186
❑ 95TomPiz-12
❑ 95Top-30
❑ 95TopCyb-23
❑ 95TopEmb-19
❑ 95TopEmbGI-19
❑ 95UC3-22
❑ 95UC3ArtP-22
❑ 95Ult-122
❑ 95UltGolM-122
❑ 95UppDec-107
❑ 95UppDec-285
❑ 95UppDecED-107
❑ 95UppDecED-285
❑ 95UppDecEDG-107
❑ 95UppDecEDG-285
❑ 95UppDecPLL-R23
❑ 95UppDecPLLE-R23
❑ 95UppDecSE-65
❑ 95UppDecSEG-65
❑ 95USPlaCMLA-7D
❑ 95Zen-81
❑ 96Baz-64
❑ 96Bow-88
❑ 96BowBes-87
❑ 96BowBesAR-87
❑ 96BowBesR-87
❑ 96BowFoi-88
❑ 96Cir-58
❑ 96CirAcc-8
❑ 96CirBos-13
❑ 96CirRav-58
❑ 96ColCho-355
❑ 96ColCho-414
❑ 96ColCho-600
❑ 96ColChoGS-355
❑ 96ColChoGS-414
❑ 96ColChoGS-600
❑ 96ColChoSS-355
❑ 96ColChoSS-414
❑ 96ColChoSS-600
❑ 96ColChoYMtP-26
❑ 96ColChoYMtP-26A
❑ 96ColChoYMtPGS-26
❑ 96ColChoYMtPGS-26A
❑ 96Don-325
❑ 96Don-419
❑ 96DonPreP-325
❑ 96DonPreP-419
❑ 96EmoXL-84
❑ 96Fin-B194
❑ 96Fin-G279
❑ 96FinRef-B194
❑ 96FinRef-G279
❑ 96Fla-119
❑ 96Fle-169
❑ 96FleTif-169
❑ 96FleUpd-U56
❑ 96FleUpdTC-U56
❑ 96Lea-80
❑ 96LeaLim-83
❑ 96LeaLimG-83
❑ 96LeaLimPC-7
❑ 96LeaPre-105
❑ 96LeaPreP-105
❑ 96LeaPrePB-80
❑ 96LeaPrePG-80
❑ 96LeaPrePS-80
❑ 96LeaPreSG-2
❑ 96LeaPreSte-2
❑ 96LeaSig-57
❑ 96LeaSigA-158
❑ 96LeaSigAG-158
❑ 96LeaSigAS-158
❑ 96LeaSigEA-130
❑ 96LeaSigEACM-20
❑ 96LeaSigPPG-57
❑ 96LeaSigPPP-57
❑ 96LeaTotB-7
❑ 96MetUni-78
❑ 96MetUniP-78
❑ 96Pac-435
❑ 96PacPri-P144
❑ 96PacPriG-P144
❑ 96PanSti-160
❑ 96Pin-61
❑ 96Pin-305A
❑ 96Pin-335
❑ 96PinAfi-48
❑ 96PinAfiAP-48
❑ 96PinAfiFPP-48
❑ 96PinArtP-24
❑ 96PinArtP-189
❑ 96PinFoil-305A
❑ 96PinFoil-335
❑ 96PinSta-24
❑ 96PinSta-189
❑ 96Sco-283
❑ 96ScoDugC-B8
❑ 96ScoDugCAP-B8
❑ 96Sel-110
❑ 96SelArtP-110
❑ 96SelCer-81
❑ 96SelCerAP-81
❑ 96SelCerCB-81
❑ 96SelCerCR-81
❑ 96SelCerMB-81
❑ 96SelCerMG-81
❑ 96SelCerMR-81
❑ 96SP-117
❑ 96Spo-27
❑ 96SpoArtP-27
❑ 96SPSpeFX-39
❑ 96SPSpeFXDC-39
❑ 96SPx-37
❑ 96SPxGol-37
❑ 96StaClu-2
❑ 96StaCluMOP-2
❑ 96Stu-138
❑ 96StuPrePB-138
❑ 96StuPrePG-138
❑ 96StuPrePS-138
❑ 96Sum-137
❑ 96SumAbo&B-137
❑ 96SumArtP-137
❑ 96SumFoi-137
❑ 96Top-30
❑ 96TopChr-14
❑ 96TopChrMotG-4
❑ 96TopChrMotGR-4
❑ 96TopChrR-14
❑ 96TopGal-51
❑ 96TopGalPPI-51
❑ 96TopLas-11
❑ 96TopMasotG-4
❑ 96Ult-149
❑ 96Ult-377
❑ 96UltGolM-149
❑ 96UltGolM-377
❑ 96UppDec-109
❑ 96UppDec-381
❑ 96UppDec-500U
❑ 96UppDecDD-DD25
❑ 96UppDecDDG-DD25
❑ 96UppDecDDS-DD25
❑ 96Zen-67
❑ 96ZenArtP-67
❑ 96ZenMoz-19
❑ 97BluJayS-37
❑ 97BluJayS-48
❑ 97Bow-10
❑ 97BowBes-33
❑ 97BowBesA-33
❑ 97BowBesAAR-33
❑ 97BowBesAR-33
❑ 97BowBesAR-33
❑ 97BowBesJ-33
❑ 97BowBesJAR-33
❑ 97BowBesJR-33
❑ 97BowBesR-33
❑ 97BowChr-8
❑ 97BowChrl-8
❑ 97BowChrIR-8
❑ 97BowChrR-8
❑ 97BowInt-10
❑ 97Cir-300
❑ 97CirRav-300
❑ 97ColCho-155
❑ 97ColChoS-4
❑ 97ColChoSR-19
❑ 97ColChoTBS-29
❑ 97ColChoTBSWH-29
❑ 97ColChoTotT-T16
❑ 97CraJac-12
❑ 97Don-39
❑ 97Don-268
❑ 97Don-417
❑ 97DonEli-34
❑ 97DonEli-2
❑ 97DonEliGS-34
❑ 97DonGolPP-39
❑ 97DonGolPP-268
❑ 97DonGolPP-417
❑ 97DonLim-20
❑ 97DonLim-35
❑ 97DonLim-112
❑ 97DonLimE-20
❑ 97DonLimE-35
❑ 97DonLimE-112
❑ 97DonLimENG-20
❑ 97DonLimFotG-22
❑ 97DonPowA-21
❑ 97DonPowADC-21
❑ 97DonPre-71
❑ 97DonPre-178
❑ 97DonPreCttC-71
❑ 97DonPreCttC-178
❑ 97DonPreXP-2A
❑ 97DonSig-22
❑ 97DonSigPPP-22
❑ 97DonSilPP-39
❑ 97DonSilPP-268
❑ 97DonSilPP-417
❑ 97DonVxP1-12
❑ 97E-X2-29
❑ 97E-X2Cred-29
❑ 97E-X2EssCre-29
❑ 97Fin-173
❑ 97Fin-181
❑ 97FinEmb-173
❑ 97FinEmbR-173
❑ 97FinRef-173
❑ 97FinRef-181
❑ 97FlaShoLC-4
❑ 97FlaShoLeg0-4
❑ 97FlaShoLeg1-4
❑ 97FlaShoM-A4
❑ 97FlaShoM-B4
❑ 97FlaShoM-C4
❑ 97FlaShoR0-4
❑ 97FlaShoR1-4
❑ 97FlaShoR2-4
❑ 97Fle-151
❑ 97Fle-496
❑ 97Fle-709
❑ 97Fle-736
❑ 97FleDecoE-8
❑ 97FleDecoERT-8
❑ 97FleGolM-5
❑ 97FleHea-13
❑ 97FleTeaL-9
❑ 97FleTif-151
❑ 97FleTif-496
❑ 97FleTif-709
❑ 97FleTif-736
❑ 97HigMinMCT-24
❑ 97HigMinMCT-25
❑ 97Lea-24
❑ 97Lea-362
❑ 97LeaFraM-24
❑ 97LeaFraM-362
❑ 97LeaFraMDC-24
❑ 97LeaFraMDC-362
❑ 97LeaGolS-18
❑ 97LeaKnoG-12
❑ 97LeaLeaotN-8
❑ 97LeaStaS-15
❑ 97MetUni-212
❑ 97NewPin-129
❑ 97NewPinAP-129
❑ 97NewPinMC-129
❑ 97NewPinPP-129
❑ 97Pac-142
❑ 97PacCar-11
❑ 97PacCarM-11
❑ 97PacLigB-142
❑ 97PacPri-47
❑ 97PacPriGA-GA7
❑ 97PacPriGotD-GD63
❑ 97PacPriLB-47
❑ 97PacPriP-47
❑ 97PacSil-142
❑ 97Pin-78
❑ 97PinArtP-PP78
❑ 97PinCer-30
❑ 97PinCerLI-13
❑ 97PinCerMBla-30
❑ 97PinCerMBlu-30
❑ 97PinCerMG-30
❑ 97PinCerMR-30
❑ 97PinCerR-30
❑ 97PinEpixGO-E23

❑ 97PinEpixPE-E23
❑ 97PinIns-14
❑ 97PinInsCE-14
❑ 97PinInsDE-14
❑ 97PinMusC-78
❑ 97PinPrePla-78
❑ 97PinTotCPB-30
❑ 97PinTotCPG-30
❑ 97PinTotCPR-30
❑ 97PinX-P-94
❑ 97PinX-PMoS-94
❑ 97Sco-243
❑ 97Sco-329
❑ 97Sco-541
❑ 97ScoArtPWB-243
❑ 97ScoArtPWB-329
❑ 97ScoArtPWB-541
❑ 97ScoHeaotO-35
❑ 97ScoPreS-243
❑ 97ScoPreS-329
❑ 97ScoResC-541
❑ 97ScoShoS-243
❑ 97ScoShoS-329
❑ 97ScoShoS-541
❑ 97ScoShoSAP-243
❑ 97ScoShoSAP-329
❑ 97ScoShoSAP-541
❑ 97Sel-15
❑ 97SelArtP-15
❑ 97SelCom-15
❑ 97SelRegG-15
❑ 97SelToootT-15
❑ 97SelToootTMB-15
❑ 97SP-105
❑ 97SPInsI-4
❑ 97SpollI-146
❑ 97SpollIEE-146
❑ 97SPSpeF-40
❑ 97SPSpxF-9
❑ 97SPSPxFA-9
❑ 97SPx-31
❑ 97SPxBro-31
❑ 97SPxCorotG-4
❑ 97SPxGol-31
❑ 97SPxGraF-31
❑ 97SPxSil-31
❑ 97SPxSte-31
❑ 97StaClu-10
❑ 97StaCluI-I2
❑ 97StaCluMat-10
❑ 97StaCluMOP-10
❑ 97StaCluMOP-I2
❑ 97Stu-11
❑ 97StuMasS-24
❑ 97StuMasS8-24
❑ 97StuPrePG-11
❑ 97StuPrePS-11
❑ 97Top-138
❑ 97Top-463
❑ 97TopChr-53
❑ 97TopChr-164
❑ 97TopChrR-53
❑ 97TopChrR-164
❑ 97TopChrSB-4
❑ 97TopChrSBR-4
❑ 97TopGal-1
❑ 97TopGalPG-PG2
❑ 97TopGalPPI-1
❑ 97TopIntF-ILM8
❑ 97TopIntFR-ILM8
❑ 97TopMem05-34
❑ 97TopScr-15
❑ 97TopScrT-15
❑ 97TopSeaB-SB4
❑ 97TopSta-21
❑ 97TopStaAM-21
❑ 97UD3-30
❑ 97Ult-90
❑ 97UltGolME-90
❑ 97UltPlaME-90
❑ 97UppDec-102
❑ 97UppDec-222
❑ 97UppDecAG-AG4
❑ 97UppDecRP-RP24
❑ 97Zen-4
❑ 98Bow-223
❑ 98BowBes-90
❑ 98BowBesAR-90
❑ 98BowBesR-90
❑ 98BowChr-223
❑ 98BowChrGA-223
❑ 98BowChrGAR-223
❑ 98BowChrI-223
❑ 98BowChrIR-223
❑ 98BowChrR-223
❑ 98BowGolA-223
❑ 98BowInt-223
❑ 98CirThu-4
❑ 98CirThuRav-4
❑ 98CirThuSupRav-4
❑ 98ColCho-160
❑ 98ColChoER-ER16
❑ 98ColChoRJ-160
❑ 98ColChoS'-16
❑ 98ColChoSQ-SQ47
❑ 98CroRoy-79
❑ 98CroRoyDK-12
❑ 98CroRoyFoB-12
❑ 98CroRoyFoBA-12
❑ 98Don-1
❑ 98Don-356
❑ 98DonCol-1
❑ 98DonColE-422
❑ 98DonColE-539
❑ 98DonColL-278
❑ 98DonColL-374
❑ 98DonColP-582
❑ 98DonColP-742
❑ 98DonColS-1
❑ 98DonCruG-28
❑ 98DonCruP-28
❑ 98DonCruR-28
❑ 98DonDiaK-5
❑ 98DonDiaKC-5
❑ 98DonEli-22
❑ 98DonEli-139
❑ 98DonEliA-22
❑ 98DonEliA-139
❑ 98DonEliC-26
❑ 98DonEliI-8
❑ 98DonEliMC-26
❑ 98DonEliS-22
❑ 98DonEliS-139
❑ 98DonGolPP-1
❑ 98DonGolPP-356
❑ 98DonPre-32
❑ 98DonPre-192
❑ 98DonPreGB-16
❑ 98DonPreGES-17
❑ 98DonPreGoB-16
❑ 98DonPreGX-17
❑ 98DonPreGXDC-17
❑ 98DonPrePM-24
❑ 98DonPreSeat-32
❑ 98DonPreSeat-192
❑ 98DonPreTP-16
❑ 98DonPreTPD-8
❑ 98DonPreTPG-16
❑ 98DonPreTPS-16
❑ 98DonPreTW-29
❑ 98DonPriCD-1
❑ 98DonPriCE-422
❑ 98DonPriCE-539
❑ 98DonPriCL-278
❑ 98DonPriCL-374
❑ 98DonPriCP-582
❑ 98DonPriCP-742
❑ 98DonSig-43
❑ 98DonSigAC-79
❑ 98DonSigAM-80
❑ 98DonSigP-43
❑ 98DonSigSB-21
❑ 98DonSilPP-1
❑ 98DonSilPP-356
❑ 98E-X2-71
❑ 98E-X2ECFut-71
❑ 98E-X2ECNow-71
❑ 98Fin-259
❑ 98FinNo--259
❑ 98FinNo-R-259
❑ 98FinRef-259
❑ 98FlaShoLeg0-47
❑ 98FlaShoLeg1-47
❑ 98FlaShoLeg2-47
❑ 98FlaShoLeg3-47
❑ 98FlaShoLegM-47
❑ 98FlaShoR0-47
❑ 98FlaShoR1-47
❑ 98FlaShoR2-47
❑ 98FlaShoR3-47
❑ 98Fle-136
❑ 98Fle-591
❑ 98FleUpd-U6
❑ 98FleVin'-34
❑ 98FleVin'C-34
❑ 98Lea-79
❑ 98Lea-175
❑ 98LeaCruG-28
❑ 98LeaCruP-28
❑ 98LeaCruR-28
❑ 98LeaFraDA-79
❑ 98LeaFraDA-175
❑ 98LeaFraF-79
❑ 98LeaFraF-175
❑ 98LeaFraM-79
❑ 98LeaFraM-175
❑ 98LeaFraM-79
❑ 98LeaFraM-175
❑ 98LeaFraMDC-79
❑ 98LeaFraMDC-175
❑ 98LeaFraMDC-79
❑ 98LeaFraMDC-175
❑ 98LeaFraMZ2-79
❑ 98LeaFraMZ2-175
❑ 98LeaHeaftH-14
❑ 98LeaHeaftHS-14
❑ 98LeaRS-5
❑ 98LeaRS-178
❑ 98LeaRSGAHSamp-17
❑ 98LeaRSGreAH-17
❑ 98LeaRSLHolo-5
❑ 98LeaRSLHolo-178
❑ 98LeaRSLong-5
❑ 98LeaRSLong-178
❑ 98LeaRSSOSamp-9
❑ 98LeaRSStaOva-9
❑ 98LeaRTrue-5
❑ 98LeaRTrue-178
❑ 98MetUni-45
❑ 98MetUniPMG-45
❑ 98Pac-138
❑ 98PacAur-52
❑ 98PacAurPF-4
❑ 98PacAurPFC-4
❑ 98PacAurPFPB-4
❑ 98PacAurPFR-4
❑ 98PacAurPFS-4
❑ 98PacInv-47
❑ 98PacInvGems-65
❑ 98PacInvPBlue-47
❑ 98PacInvSilv-47
❑ 98PacInvTeam-16
❑ 98PacOme-142
❑ 98PacOmeFTF-5
❑ 98PacOmeOnIns-9
❑ 98PacOmeR-142
❑ 98PacOnl-427
❑ 98PacOnl-442
❑ 98PacOnlR-427
❑ 98PacOnlR-442
❑ 98PacOnlWC-427
❑ 98PacOnlWC-442
❑ 98PacPar-63
❑ 98PacParC-63
❑ 98PacParCB-5
❑ 98PacParCBPP-5
❑ 98PacParG-63
❑ 98PacParHS-63
❑ 98PacParI-37
❑ 98PacParPB-63
❑ 98PacParR-63
❑ 98PacParTC-8
❑ 98PacPlaB-138
❑ 98PacRedT-138
❑ 98PacSil-138
❑ 98PacTeaC-9
❑ 98Pin-67
❑ 98PinArtP-PP60
❑ 98PinEpixGE-E23
❑ 98PinEpixGP-E23
❑ 98PinEpixME-E23
❑ 98PinEpixMO-E23
❑ 98PinEpixMP-E23
❑ 98PinEpixPO-E23
❑ 98PinEpixPP-E23
❑ 98PinIns-58
❑ 98PinInsCE-58
❑ 98PinInsDE-58
❑ 98PinInsSG-21AB
❑ 98PinInsSG-21CD
❑ 98PinInsSGS-21AB
❑ 98PinInsSGS-21CD
❑ 98PinMusC-PP60
❑ 98PinPer-33
❑ 98PinPerPP-33
❑ 98PinPluAE-23
❑ 98PinPluAEE-23
❑ 98PinPluAEP-23
❑ 98PinPreP-67
❑ 98PinPreP-E23
❑ 98Revo-84
❑ 98RevoShow-9
❑ 98RevoSS-84
❑ 98ScoAllST-9
❑ 98ScoEpix-E23
❑ 98ScoLoaL-LL8
❑ 98SkyDugA-70
❑ 98SkyDugAIA-70
❑ 98SP Aut-125
❑ 98SP Aut-SD14
❑ 98SP AutC-PM
❑ 98SP AutSD-SD14
❑ 98SP AutSDT-SD14
❑ 98SpollI-88
❑ 98SpollIEE-88
❑ 98SpollIFE-88
❑ 98SpollIODMP-OD17
❑ 98SpollITaN-44
❑ 98SpollITaNEE-44
❑ 98SpollITaNRtC-RC7
❑ 98SpollIWSFMC-7
❑ 98SPxFin-95
❑ 98SPxFin-158
❑ 98SPxFinR-95
❑ 98SPxFinR-158
❑ 98SPxFinS-95
❑ 98SPxFinS-158
❑ 98StaCluFDI-6
❑ 98StaCluI-6
❑ 98StaCluNC-NC20
❑ 98StaCluOneK-6
❑ 98StaCluPP-6
❑ 98StaCluTIII-T18A
❑ 98StaCluTLme-T18A
❑ 98StaCluTLmo-T18A
❑ 98Stu-12
❑ 98StuGPP-12
❑ 98StuPor8x10-31
❑ 98StuPor8x10GP-31
❑ 98StuSPP-12
❑ 98Top-291
❑ 98TopChr-291
❑ 98TopChrF-FB3
❑ 98TopChrFR-FB3
❑ 98TopChrHB-HB1
❑ 98TopChrHBR-HB1
❑ 98TopChrR-291
❑ 98TopDevR-291
❑ 98TopDia-291
❑ 98TopFla-FB3
❑ 98TopGal-141
❑ 98TopGalGP-141
❑ 98TopGalOPP-141
❑ 98TopGalPPI-141
❑ 98TopGalPPIA-141
❑ 98TopGolLabC1-73
❑ 98TopGolLabC1B-73
❑ 98TopGolLabC1One-73
❑ 98TopGolLabC1R-73
❑ 98TopGolLabC2-73
❑ 98TopGolLabC2B-73
❑ 98TopGolLabC2One-73
❑ 98TopGolLabC2R-73
❑ 98TopGolLabC3-73
❑ 98TopGolLabC3B-73
❑ 98TopGolLabC3One-73
❑ 98TopGolLabC3R-73
❑ 98TopHal-HB1
❑ 98TopMiniC-291
❑ 98TopOpeD-118
❑ 98TopSta-123
❑ 98TopSta'S-30
❑ 98TopSta'SGH-30
❑ 98TopStaB-123
❑ 98TopStaG-123
❑ 98TopStaGR-123
❑ 98TopStaS-123
❑ 98TopStaSteG-30
❑ 98TopTek-54
❑ 98TopTekD-54
❑ 98UD3-70
❑ 98UD3-160
❑ 98UD3-250
❑ 98UD3DieCut-70
❑ 98UD3DieCut-160
❑ 98UD3DieCut-250
❑ 98Ult-78
❑ 98UltGolM-78
❑ 98UltMas-78
❑ 98UltPlaM-78
❑ 98UppDec-130
❑ 98UppDec-630
❑ 98UppDec10AP-57
❑ 98UppDec1APR-57
❑ 98UppDec5x7-130
❑ 98UppDecAG-AG4
❑ 98UppDecAGDC-AG4
❑ 98UppDecCD-CD4
❑ 98UppDecR-54
❑ 98UppDecSF-80
❑ 98Zen-35
❑ 98Zen5 xx7-11
❑ 98Zen5x7GoldImp-11
❑ 98Zen5x7Imp-11
❑ 98ZenEpi-E23
❑ 98ZenZ-G-35
❑ 98ZenZ-S-35
❑ 99Fle-222
❑ 99FleSta9-222
❑ 99FleWarT-222
❑ 99MetUni-10
❑ 99MetUniGM-10
❑ 99MetUniPMG-10
❑ 99Pac-250
❑ 99Pac-250A
❑ 99PacCroC-161
❑ 99PacCroCPB-161
❑ 99PacGolCDC-9
❑ 99PacPlaB-250
❑ 99PacPlaB-250A
❑ 99PacPri-83
❑ 99PacPriHB-83
❑ 99PacPriHG-83
❑ 99PacPriHM-83
❑ 99PacPriHP-83
❑ 99PacPriRed-83
❑ 99PacPriS-41
❑ 99PacPriS206-41
❑ 99PacPriS206R-41
❑ 99PacPriSP-41
❑ 99PacPriSV-41
❑ 99PacRed-250
❑ 99PacRed-250A
❑ 99PacTeaC-8
❑ 99PacTim-4
❑ 99SP AutEF-E16
❑ 99SP AutR-R16
❑ 99SpollI-25
❑ 99UD Ion-77
❑ 99UD IonR-77
❑ 99UppDec-137
❑ 99UppDecBD-48
❑ 99UppDecBDD-48
❑ 99UppDecBDQ-48
❑ 99UppDecBDT-48
❑ 99UppDecEL1-137
❑ 99UppDecEL2-137
❑ 99UppDecR-92
❑ 99UppDecRG-92
❑ 99UppDecRI-PM
❑ 99UppDecRIL2-PM
❑ 99UppDecRP-92
❑ 99UppDecWY-W20
❑ 99UppDecWYD-W20
❑ 99UppDecWYHR-W20
❑ 99UppDecWYT-W20

Mollwitz, Fred
❑ 15SpoNewM-121
❑ 16FleBreD-66
❑ 16SpoNewM-124
❑ 20Zee-70
❑ 21Zee-75
❑ 22Zee-64
❑ 94ConTSN-1271
❑ 94ConTSNB-1271

Moloney, Bill
❑ 81BriRedST-2
❑ 83PawRedST-9
❑ 95MicBatCTI-20

Moloney, Richard
❑ 71OPC-13
❑ 71Top-13

Molta, Sal
❑ 96MarPhiB-15

Mompres, Danilo
❑ 91ColMetPI-20
❑ 91ColMetPPI-3
❑ 91PitMetC-10
❑ 91PitMetP-3431
❑ 92ColMetC-16
❑ 92ColMetF-304
❑ 92ColMetPI-5
❑ 93CapCitBC-13
❑ 93CapCitBF-468

Monahan, Ed
❑ 53A'sTeal-20

Monahan, Pat
❑ 22Zee-36

Monahan, Shane
❑ 96BowBes-174
❑ 96BowBesAR-174
❑ 96BowBesR-174
❑ 96LanJetB-19
❑ 96Top-238
❑ 97Bow-180
❑ 97BowCerBlaIA-CA54
❑ 97BowCerBluIA-CA54
❑ 97BowCerGolIA-CA54
❑ 97BowChr-172
❑ 97BowChrI-172
❑ 97BowChrIR-172
❑ 97BowChrR-172
❑ 97BowInt-180
❑ 97Top-491
❑ 98AriFalLTP-19
❑ 98Bow-150
❑ 98BowBes-191
❑ 98BowBesAR-191
❑ 98BowBesR-191
❑ 98BowCerBlueAU-63
❑ 98BowCerGA-63
❑ 98BowCerSA-63
❑ 98BowChr-150
❑ 98BowChrGA-150
❑ 98BowChrGAR-150
❑ 98BowChrI-150
❑ 98BowChrIR-150
❑ 98BowChrR-150
❑ 98BowGolA-150
❑ 98BowInt-150
❑ 98ColCho-431
❑ 98ColChoPCR-431
❑ 98CroRoy-127
❑ 98Don-308
❑ 98DonColP-711
❑ 98DonGolPP-308
❑ 98DonPre-161
❑ 98DonPreSeat-161
❑ 98DonPriCP-711
❑ 98DonSilPP-308
❑ 98FleUpd-U44
❑ 98PinSna-SM10
❑ 98TacRaiQ-22
❑ 98UppDec-542
❑ 99Fle-199
❑ 99FleSta9-199
❑ 99FleWarT-199
❑ 99Pac-400
❑ 99PacPlaB-400
❑ 99PacRed-400
❑ 99SkyThu-117
❑ 99SkyThuRant-117
❑ 99SkyThuRave-117
❑ 99SP Aut-116
❑ 99SP AutC-SM
❑ 99SP AutCG-SM
❑ 99SPx-118
❑ 99SPxFinR-118
❑ 99SPxFinS-118
❑ 99ThuSkySupR-117
❑ 99Top-284
❑ 99TopChr-284
❑ 99TopChrR-284
❑ 99TopMVPP-284
❑ 99UDHoloUDA-SM
❑ 99UppDec-206
❑ 99UppDecBD-118
❑ 99UppDecBDD-118
❑ 99UppDecBDQ-118
❑ 99UppDecBDT-118
❑ 99UppDecEL1-206
❑ 99UppDecEL2-206
❑ 99UppDecM-192
❑ 99UppDecMGS-192
❑ 99UppDecMHFS-192
❑ 99UppDecMP-SM
❑ 99UppDecMSS-192

Monarchs, Kansas City
❑ 90PomBlaBNLP-2541
❑ 91PomBlaBPB-13
❑ 92NegLeaRLI-85
❑ 92NegLeaRLI-86
❑ 93NegLeaRL2-47
❑ 93NegLeaRL2-69
❑ 93NegLeaRL2-70
❑ 93NegLeaRL2-71
❑ 93NegLeaRL2-72

Monarchs, Melbourne
❑ 93AusFut-104

Monasterio, Juan
❑ 76VenLeaS-144
❑ 76WauMetT-19
❑ 77LynMetT-20
❑ 80VenLeaS-201

Monastro, Frank
❑ 90BurIndP-3015

Monbouquette, Bill
❑ 47PM1StaP1-143
❑ 59Top-173
❑ 59TopVen-173
❑ 60Top-544
❑ 61Pos-54A
❑ 61Pos-54B
❑ 61Top-562
❑ 61TopStaI-114

❑ 62RedSoxJP-6
❑ 62SalPlaC-99
❑ 62ShiPlaC-99
❑ 62Top-580
❑ 62TopStal-15
❑ 63Baz-21
❑ 63Fle-7
❑ 63Jel-84
❑ 63Pos-84
❑ 63SalMetC-35
❑ 63Top-480
❑ 63TopStil-29
❑ 64RedSoxTI-4
❑ 64Top-25
❑ 64TopCoi-47
❑ 64TopSta-19
❑ 64TopTatl-56
❑ 64TopVen-25
❑ 65OPC-142
❑ 65RedSoxTI-9
❑ 65Top-142
❑ 66Top-429
❑ 66TopRubl-68
❑ 67CokCapTi-16
❑ 67Top-482
❑ 67YanPhoS-92
❑ 68Top-234
❑ 68TopVen-234
❑ 68YanPhoS-72
❑ 69OPC-64
❑ 69Top-64
❑ 76WauMetT-20
❑ 78TCM60I-111
❑ 81RedSoxBG2S-39
❑ 82MetPhoA-28
❑ 86AlbYanT-8
❑ 86AlbYanT-32
❑ 89MyrBeaBJP-1467
❑ 90DunBluJS-27
❑ 90SweBasG-106
❑ 91DunBluJC-26
❑ 91DunBluJP-224
❑ 92DunBluJC-29
❑ 92DunBluJF-2015
❑ 92YanWIZ6-89
❑ 93DunBluJC-27
❑ 93DunBluJF-1812
❑ 93DunBluJFFN-18
❑ 94DunBluJC-28
❑ 94DunBluJF-2573
❑ 95SyrChiTI-18
❑ 96SyrChiTI-21
❑ 97St.CatSB-3
❑ 98KnoSG-16

Moncallo, Bernie
❑ 95HelBreTI-19
❑ 96OgdRapTI-24
❑ 98StoPorG-20

Moncerratt, Pablo
❑ 84ButCopKT-17
❑ 86WauTimP-17
❑ 87SalSpuS-23

Monchak, Al
❑ 73OPC-356
❑ 73Top-356
❑ 74OPC-221
❑ 74Top-221
❑ 77PirPosP-15
❑ 86BraPol-52

Moncier, John
❑ 95BakBlaTI-30

Moncrief, Charles
❑ 33Zee-9

Moncrief, Homer
❑ 82BirBarT-4
❑ 83GleFalWST-15

Moncrief, Tony
❑ 83IdaFalAT-29
❑ 84ModA'sC-19

Monda, Greg
❑ 85CedRapRT-17
❑ 86VerRedP-13
❑ 88NasSouC-13
❑ 88NasSouP-491

Monday, Rick
❑ 67Top-542
❑ 68Baz-10
❑ 68Top-282
❑ 68TopActS-7A
❑ 68TopGaml-26
❑ 68TopVen-282
❑ 69A'sJacitB-10
❑ 69MilBra-194
❑ 69MLBOffS-88
❑ 69MLBPin-19
❑ 69NabTeaF-16
❑ 69OPC-105
❑ 69Top-105
❑ 69TopDec-14
❑ 69TopDecl-31
❑ 69TopSta-218
❑ 69TopSup-27
❑ 69TopTeaP-21
❑ 69TraSta-10
❑ 70MLBOffS-262
❑ 70Top-547
❑ 71Kel-73A
❑ 71Kel-73B
❑ 71Kel-73C
❑ 71MLBOffS-522
❑ 71OPC-135
❑ 71Top-135
❑ 71TopCoi-40
❑ 71TopTat-125
❑ 72CubTeal-8
❑ 72MilBra-239
❑ 72Top-730
❑ 73LinPor-43
❑ 73OPC-44
❑ 73Top-44
❑ 74Kel-2
❑ 74OPC-295
❑ 74Top-295
❑ 74TopSta-17
❑ 75Hos-113
❑ 75HosTwi-113
❑ 75OPC-129
❑ 75Top-129
❑ 75TopMin-129
❑ 76BlaDis-37
❑ 76BucDis-37
❑ 76CarDis-37
❑ 76CraDis-37
❑ 76DailsID-37
❑ 76Hos-80
❑ 76IsaDis-37
❑ 76OPC-251
❑ 76OrbDis-37
❑ 76RedBarD-37
❑ 76SafDis-37
❑ 76SSP-311
❑ 76Top-251
❑ 76TowCluD-37
❑ 77BurCheD-146
❑ 77ChiWilD-46
❑ 77DailsID-46
❑ 77DetCaeD-46
❑ 77DodPho-8
❑ 77HollnnD-46
❑ 77Hos-30
❑ 77MSADis-46
❑ 77OPC-230
❑ 77RCColC-43
❑ 77SagDis-46
❑ 77sDis-46
❑ 77Spo-4622
❑ 77Top-360
❑ 77WenDis-46
❑ 77ZipDis-46
❑ 78RCColC-29
❑ 78SSP270-77
❑ 78Top-145
❑ 79BasPat-54
❑ 79Kel-57
❑ 79OPC-320
❑ 79Top-605
❑ 80DodPol-16
❑ 80OPC-243
❑ 80Top-465
❑ 81Dod-8
❑ 81Dod-20
❑ 81DodPol-16
❑ 81Don-60
❑ 81Fle-122
❑ 81LonBeaPT-20
❑ 81OPC-177
❑ 81Top-726
❑ 81TopSupHT-49
❑ 82DodPol-16
❑ 82DodUniOV-12
❑ 82Don-514
❑ 82Fle-15
❑ 82FleSta-2
❑ 82OPC-6
❑ 82Top-577
❑ 83DodPol-16
❑ 83DodPos-9
❑ 83Don-643
❑ 83Fle-213
❑ 83FleSta-128
❑ 83FleSti-114
❑ 83OPC-63
❑ 83SevCoi-10
❑ 83Top-63
❑ 83TopFol-2
❑ 84DodPol-16
❑ 84Fle-106
❑ 84Nes792-274
❑ 84Top-274
❑ 84TopSti-83
❑ 84TopTif-274
❑ 86A'sGreT-6
❑ 87A'sMot-2
❑ 87DodSmoA-23
❑ 88AlaGolAA60TI-1
❑ 89DodSmoG-90
❑ 90DodTar-542
❑ 90PacLeg-40
❑ 90PadMag-8
❑ 91PadCok-6
❑ 91SweBasG-65
❑ 92DodStaTA-17
❑ 93UppDecAH-97
❑ 94TedWil-13
❑ 97AriStaBG-18

Mondello, Peter
❑ 97BatCliTI-20
❑ 98BatMucTI-19

Mondesi, Raul
❑ 90GreFalDSP-6
❑ 91BakDodCLC-1
❑ 91Bow-593
❑ 91CalLeLA-3
❑ 92AlbDukS-16
❑ 92Bow-64
❑ 92DonRoo-83
❑ 92LeaGolR-BC16
❑ 92SanAntMF-3987
❑ 92SkyAAAF-8
❑ 92SpollIFK1-362
❑ 92UppDec-60
❑ 92UppDecML-32
❑ 92UppDecML-163
❑ 93AlbDukF-1475
❑ 93Bow-353
❑ 93Bow-618
❑ 93ClaYouG-YG12
❑ 93DodStaC-15
❑ 93ExcFS7-53
❑ 93FleFinE-82
❑ 93Lea-473
❑ 93LimRocDWB-27
❑ 93LimRocDWB-142
❑ 93SP-96
❑ 93Ult-402
❑ 94Bow-538
❑ 94BowBes-R86
❑ 94BowBes-X99
❑ 94BowBesR-R86
❑ 94BowBesR-X99
❑ 94ColC-209
❑ 94ColChoGS-209
❑ 94ColChoSS-209
❑ 94DodDaiN-1
❑ 94DodMot-9
❑ 94DodPol-19
❑ 94Don-313
❑ 94Fin-74
❑ 94FinRef-74
❑ 94Fla-179
❑ 94FlaWavotF-A6
❑ 94Fle-518
❑ 94FleExtB-291
❑ 94FleExtBRS-13
❑ 94FUnPac-143
❑ 94Lea-93
❑ 94LeaL-119
❑ 94LeaLimRP-1
❑ 94OPC-199
❑ 94OPCHotP-4
❑ 94Pac-316
❑ 94Pin-242
❑ 94PinArtP-242
❑ 94PinMusC-242
❑ 94Sco-618
❑ 94ScoBoyoS-47
❑ 94ScoGolR-618
❑ 94ScoRoo-RT82
❑ 94ScoRooGR-RT82
❑ 94ScoRooSR-SU4
❑ 94Sel-183
❑ 94SelRooS-RS17
❑ 94SP-79
❑ 94SPDieC-79
❑ 94SPHol-27
❑ 94SPHolDC-27
❑ 94Spo-162
❑ 94SpoRooRS-TR7
❑ 94StaClu-390
❑ 94StaCluFDI-390
❑ 94StaCluGR-390
❑ 94StaCluMOP-390
❑ 94Stu-70
❑ 94Top-783
❑ 94TopGol-783
❑ 94TopSpa-783
❑ 94TopSupS-31
❑ 94TopTraFl-4
❑ 94TriPla-288
❑ 94Ult-216
❑ 94UltAllR-7
❑ 94UltAllRJ-7
❑ 94UppDec-59
❑ 94UppDecED-59
❑ 94UppDecNG-12
❑ 94UppDecNGED-12
❑ 95Baz-58
❑ 95Bow-348
❑ 95BowBes-R53
❑ 95BowBesR-R53
❑ 95ClaPhoC-34
❑ 95ColCho-79
❑ 95ColChoCtA-5
❑ 95ColChoCtAGR-5
❑ 95ColChoCtG-CG14
❑ 95ColChoCtG-CG14B
❑ 95ColChoCtG-CG14C
❑ 95ColChoCtGE-14
❑ 95ColChoCtGG-CG14
❑ 95ColChoCtGG-CG14B
❑ 95ColChoCtGG-CG14C
❑ 95ColChoCtGGE-14
❑ 95ColChoGS-79
❑ 95ColChoSE-95
❑ 95ColChoSEGS-95
❑ 95ColChoSESS-95
❑ 95ColChoSS-79
❑ 95DodMot-3
❑ 95DodPol-15
❑ 95DodROY-14
❑ 95Don-543
❑ 95DonDiaK-DK16
❑ 95DonPreP-543
❑ 95DonTopotO-268
❑ 95Emo-143
❑ 95EmoMas-7
❑ 95Fin-1
❑ 95FinPowK-PK2
❑ 95FinRef-1
❑ 95Fla-154
❑ 95FlaTodS-7
❑ 95Fle-545
❑ 95FleAwaW-6
❑ 95FlePro-2
❑ 95FleRooS-13
❑ 95FleUpdSS-7
❑ 95KinDis-10
❑ 95Lea-60
❑ 95LeaChe-5
❑ 95LeaGolS-7
❑ 95LeaLim-138
❑ 95LeaLimG-3
❑ 95LeaLimL-13
❑ 95LeaSli-1A
❑ 95LeaSli-1B
❑ 95LinVen-308
❑ 95LinVen-315
❑ 95LinVen-323
❑ 95NatPac-11
❑ 95Pac-222
❑ 95PacGolCDC-12
❑ 95PacGolP-15
❑ 95PacLatD-24
❑ 95PacPri-71
❑ 95PanSti-76
❑ 95PanSti-99
❑ 95PanSti-111
❑ 95Pin-292
❑ 95Pin-316
❑ 95PinArtP-292
❑ 95PinArtP-316
❑ 95PinFan-16
❑ 95PinGatA-GA10
❑ 95PinMusC-292
❑ 95PinMusC-316
❑ 95PinPer-PP6
❑ 95PinRedH-RH13
❑ 95PinUps-US9
❑ 95PinWhiH-WH13
❑ 95Sco-233
❑ 95Sco-567
❑ 95ScoAi-AM14
❑ 95ScoGolR-233
❑ 95ScoGolR-567
❑ 95ScoHaloG-HG33
❑ 95ScoPlaTS-233
❑ 95ScoPlaTS-567
❑ 95ScoRul-SR10
❑ 95ScoRulJ-SR10
❑ 95Sel-103
❑ 95Sel-247
❑ 95SelArtP-103
❑ 95SelArtP-247
❑ 95SelCanM-CM4
❑ 95SelCer-78
❑ 95SelCer-80
❑ 95SelCerC-7
❑ 95SelCerMG-78
❑ 95SelCerMG-80
❑ 95SelCerPU-3
❑ 95SelCerPU9-3
❑ 95SP-65
❑ 95SPCha-58
❑ 95SPChaDC-58
❑ 95Spo-21
❑ 95SpoArtP-21
❑ 95SpoDouT-10
❑ 95SpoHamT-HT17
❑ 95SPPlaP-PP5
❑ 95SPSil-65
❑ 95SPSpeF-42
❑ 95StaClu-57
❑ 95StaCluFDI-57
❑ 95StaCluMO-48
❑ 95StaCluMOP-57
❑ 95StaCluMOP-SS6
❑ 95StaCluSS-SS6
❑ 95StaCluSTDW-D57
❑ 95StaCluSTWS-57
❑ 95StaCluVR-35
❑ 95StaCluVRMO-35
❑ 95Stu-19
❑ 95StuGolS-19
❑ 95StuPlaS-19
❑ 95Sum-47
❑ 95SumNewA-NA3
❑ 95SumNthD-47
❑ 95TomPiz-6
❑ 95Top-180
❑ 95TopCyb-103
❑ 95TopD3Z-5
❑ 95TopEmb-102
❑ 95TopEmbGI-102
❑ 95UC3-84
❑ 95UC3-135
❑ 95UC3ArtP-84
❑ 95UC3ArtP-135
❑ 95UC3CycS-CS14
❑ 95Ult-183
❑ 95UltAllR-8
❑ 95UltAllRGM-8
❑ 95UltAwaW-24
❑ 95UltAwaWGM-24
❑ 95UltGolM-183
❑ 95UltRisS-7
❑ 95UltRisSGM-7
❑ 95UltSecYS-10
❑ 95UltSecYSGM-10
❑ 95UppDec-322
❑ 95UppDecA-4
❑ 95UppDecED-322
❑ 95UppDecEDG-322
❑ 95UppDecPLL-R56
❑ 95UppDecPLLE-R56
❑ 95UppDecSE-32
❑ 95UppDecSEG-32
❑ 95Zen-84
❑ 95ZenAllS-10
❑ 95ZenZ-7
❑ 96Baz-121
❑ 96Bow-104
❑ 96BowBes-46
❑ 96BowBesAR-46
❑ 96BowBesC-7
❑ 96BowBesCAR-7
❑ 96BowBesCR-7
❑ 96BowBesR-46
❑ 96BowFoi-104
❑ 96Cir-143
❑ 96CirRav-143
❑ 96ColCho-102
❑ 96ColCho-328
❑ 96ColCho-580
❑ 96ColChoGS-102
❑ 96ColChoGS-328
❑ 96ColChoGS-580
❑ 96ColChoSS-102
❑ 96ColChoSS-328
❑ 96ColChoSS-580
❑ 96ColChoYMtP-27
❑ 96ColChoYMtP-27A
❑ 96ColChoYMtPGS-27
❑ 96ColChoYMtPGS-27A
❑ 96DodFle-12
❑ 96DodMot-4
❑ 96DodPol-24
❑ 96Don-160
❑ 96DonLonBL-4
❑ 96DonPreP-160
❑ 96DonPurP-1
❑ 96EmoRarB-7
❑ 96EmoXL-212
❑ 96EmoXLD-7
❑ 96Fin-B199
❑ 96Fin-S130
❑ 96FinRef-B199
❑ 96FinRef-S130
❑ 96Fla-296
❑ 96Fle-441
❑ 96FleTif-441
❑ 96FleUpd-U233
❑ 96FleUpdSL-7
❑ 96FleUpdTC-U233
❑ 96Lea-49
❑ 96LeaAllGMC-15
❑ 96LeaAllGMCG-15
❑ 96LeaLim-51
❑ 96LeaLimG-51
❑ 96LeaPre-33
❑ 96LeaPreP-33
❑ 96LeaPrePB-49
❑ 96LeaPrePG-49
❑ 96LeaPrePS-49
❑ 96LeaPreSG-38
❑ 96LeaPreSte-38
❑ 96LeaSig-41
❑ 96LeaSigA-159
❑ 96LeaSigAG-159
❑ 96LeaSigAS-159
❑ 96LeaSigPPG-41
❑ 96LeaSigPPP-41
❑ 96MetUni-185
❑ 96MetUniML-5
❑ 96MetUniP-185
❑ 96Pac-107
❑ 96PacEstL-EL21
❑ 96PacGolCD-DC16
❑ 96PacHom-HP18
❑ 96PacPri-P36
❑ 96PacPriG-P36
❑ 96PanSti-89
❑ 96Pin-132
❑ 96Pin-229
❑ 96Pin-283
❑ 96PinAfi-129
❑ 96PinAfiAP-129
❑ 96PinAfiSP-12
❑ 96PinArtP-129
❑ 96PinArtP-183
❑ 96PinFoil-229
❑ 96PinFoil-283
❑ 96PinProS-17
❑ 96PinSky-18
❑ 96PinSta-129
❑ 96PinSta-183
❑ 96PinTeaT-3
❑ 96ProSta-43
❑ 96Sco-7
❑ 96Sco-369
❑ 96ScoBigB-8
❑ 96ScoDiaA-9
❑ 96ScoDugC-A7
❑ 96ScoDugC-B94
❑ 96ScoDugCAP-A7
❑ 96ScoDugCAP-B94
❑ 96ScoFutF-16
❑ 96ScoNumG-11
❑ 96ScoRef-6
❑ 96ScoSam-7
❑ 96Sel-50
❑ 96SelArtP-50
❑ 96SelCer-57
❑ 96SelCerAP-57
❑ 96SelCerCB-57
❑ 96SelCerCR-57
❑ 96SelCerIP-17
❑ 96SelCerMB-57
❑ 96SelCerMG-57
❑ 96SelCerMR-57
❑ 96SelTeaN-11
❑ 96SP-102
❑ 96Spo-14
❑ 96SpoArtP-14
❑ 96SPSpeFX-4
❑ 96SPSpeFXDC-4
❑ 96SPx-34

❑ 96SPxGol-34
❑ 96StaClu-430
❑ 96StaCluB&B-BB5
❑ 96StaCluEPB-430
❑ 96StaCluEPG-430
❑ 96StaCluEPS-430
❑ 96StaCluMOF-4
❑ 96StaCluMOP-430
❑ 96StaCluMOP-BB5
❑ 96Stu-63
❑ 96Sum-32
❑ 96Sum-160
❑ 96SumAbo&B-32
❑ 96SumAbo&B-160
❑ 96SumArtP-32
❑ 96SumArtP-160
❑ 96SumBigB-14
❑ 96SumBigBM-14
❑ 96SumFoi-32
❑ 96SumFoi-160
❑ 96TeaOut-57
❑ 96TeaOut-C93
❑ 96Top-175
❑ 96TopChr-51
❑ 96TopChrR-51
❑ 96TopGal-115
❑ 96TopGalPPI-115
❑ 96TopLas-86
❑ 96TopLasSS-6
❑ 96TopMysF-M14
❑ 96TopMysFR-M14
❑ 96TopPro-NL6
❑ 96Ult-222
❑ 96Ult-586
❑ 96Ult-598
❑ 96UltFreF-7
❑ 96UltFreFGM-7
❑ 96UltGolM-222
❑ 96UltGolM-586
❑ 96UltGolM-598
❑ 96UltPowP-4
❑ 96UltPowPGM-4
❑ 96UltPriL-18
❑ 96UltPriLGM-18
❑ 96UltRaw-7
❑ 96UltRawGM-7
❑ 96UppDec-99
❑ 96UppDecVJLS-VJ9
❑ 96Zen-47
❑ 96ZenArtP-47
❑ 96ZenMoz-13
❑ 97Bow-51
❑ 97BowBes-97
❑ 97BowBesAR-97
❑ 97BowBesR-97
❑ 97BowChr-39
❑ 97BowChrI-39
❑ 97BowChrIR-39
❑ 97BowChrR-39
❑ 97BowInt-51
❑ 97Cir-296
❑ 97CirRav-296
❑ 97ColCho-135
❑ 97ColChoT-LA1
❑ 97ColChoTBS-26
❑ 97ColChoTBSWH-26
❑ 97DodDWPM-3
❑ 97DodMot-4
❑ 97DodPol-19
❑ 97DodSco-7
❑ 97DodScoPl-7
❑ 97DodScoPr-7
❑ 97Don-6
❑ 97Don-447
❑ 97DonArmaD-2
❑ 97DonEli-71
❑ 97DonEliGS-71
❑ 97DonGolPP-6
❑ 97DonGolPP-447
❑ 97DonLim-26
❑ 97DonLim-128
❑ 97DonLimE-26
❑ 97DonLimE-128
❑ 97DonLimENG-128
❑ 97DonLimFotG-33
❑ 97DonPre-105
❑ 97DonPreCttC-105
❑ 97DonPreXP-9B
❑ 97DonSig-39
❑ 97DonSigA-72
❑ 97DonSigAC-88
❑ 97DonSigAM-88
❑ 97DonSigPPP-39
❑ 97DonSilPP-6
❑ 97DonSilPP-447
❑ 97DonTea-106
❑ 97DonTeaSPE-106
❑ 97DonVxP1-39
❑ 97E-X2-80
❑ 97E-X2Cred-80
❑ 97E-X2EssCre-80
❑ 97Fin-13
❑ 97Fin-328
❑ 97FinEmb-328
❑ 97FinEmbR-328
❑ 97FinRef-13
❑ 97FinRef-328
❑ 97FlaShoLC-43
❑ 97FlaShoLeg0-43
❑ 97FlaShoLeg1-43
❑ 97FlaShoM-A43
❑ 97FlaShoM-B43
❑ 97FlaShoM-C43
❑ 97FlaShoR0-43
❑ 97FlaShoR1-43
❑ 97FlaShoR2-43
❑ 97Fle-367
❑ 97FleTif-367
❑ 97HigMinM-75
❑ 97Lea-78
❑ 97Lea-383
❑ 97LeaFraM-78
❑ 97LeaFraM-383
❑ 97LeaFraMDC-78
❑ 97LeaFraMDC-383
❑ 97LeaWarT-12
❑ 97MetUni-103
❑ 97NewPin-101
❑ 97NewPinAP-101
❑ 97NewPinMC-101
❑ 97NewPinPP-101
❑ 97Pac-335
❑ 97PacLatotML-29
❑ 97PacLigB-335
❑ 97PacPri-113
❑ 97PacPriLB-113
❑ 97PacPriP-113
❑ 97PacPriSL-SL11B
❑ 97PacSil-335
❑ 97PinCer-74
❑ 97PinCerMBla-74
❑ 97PinCerMBlu-74
❑ 97PinCerMG-74
❑ 97PinCerMR-74
❑ 97PinCerR-74
❑ 97PinIns-40
❑ 97PinInsCE-40
❑ 97PinInsDE-40
❑ 97PinPasttM-17
❑ 97PinTotCPB-74
❑ 97PinTotCPG-74
❑ 97PinTotCPR-74
❑ 97PinX-P-104
❑ 97PinX-PMoS-104
❑ 97PinX-PSfF-42
❑ 97PinX-PSfFU-42
❑ 97Sco-202
❑ 97ScoArtPWB-202
❑ 97ScoHeaotO-24
❑ 97ScoPreS-202
❑ 97ScoShoS-202
❑ 97ScoShoSAP-202
❑ 97ScoStaaD-15
❑ 97Sel-57
❑ 97SelArtP-57
❑ 97SelCom-57
❑ 97SelRegG-57
❑ 97SP-98
❑ 97SpoIll-115
❑ 97SpoIllEE-115
❑ 97SPSpxF-7
❑ 97SPSPxFA-7
❑ 97SPx-28
❑ 97SPxBro-28
❑ 97SPxGol-28
❑ 97SPxGraF-28
❑ 97SPxSil-28
❑ 97SPxSte-28
❑ 97StaClu-216
❑ 97StaCluC-CO7
❑ 97StaCluMat-216
❑ 97StaCluMOP-216
❑ 97Stu-112
❑ 97StuPrePG-112
❑ 97StuPrePS-112
❑ 97Top-67
❑ 97TopChr-23
❑ 97TopChrR-23
❑ 97TopDodRotY-4
❑ 97TopGal-91
❑ 97TopGalPPI-91
❑ 97TopHobM-HM8
❑ 97TopMemO5-35
❑ 97TopSta-23
❑ 97TopStaAM-23
❑ 97UD3-32
❑ 97Ult-220
❑ 97UltFieC-13
❑ 97UltGolME-220
❑ 97UltPlaME-220
❑ 97UppDec-187
❑ 97UppDec-375
❑ 97UppDec-401
❑ 97UppDecRSF-RS20
❑ 98Bow-69
❑ 98BowBes-68
❑ 98BowBesAR-68
❑ 98BowBesR-68
❑ 98BowChr-69
❑ 98BowChrGA-69
❑ 98BowChrGAR-69
❑ 98BowChrI-69
❑ 98BowChrIR-69
❑ 98BowChrR-69
❑ 98BowChrR-32
❑ 98BowChrRR-32
❑ 98BowGolA-69
❑ 98BowInt-69
❑ 98CirThu-43
❑ 98CirThuRav-43
❑ 98CirThuSupRav-43
❑ 98ColCho-147
❑ 98ColChoSQ-SQ34
❑ 98CroRoy-71
❑ 98CroRoyPotG-14
❑ 98DodFanA-3
❑ 98DodMot-4
❑ 98DodPol-18
❑ 98DodSco-13
❑ 98DodScoP-13
❑ 98Don-46
❑ 98Don-361
❑ 98DonCol-46
❑ 98DonColE-460
❑ 98DonColL-350
❑ 98DonColP-594
❑ 98DonColS-46
❑ 98DonCruG-80
❑ 98DonCruP-80
❑ 98DonCruR-80
❑ 98DonDay-13
❑ 98DonEli-60
❑ 98DonEliA-60
❑ 98DonEliS-60
❑ 98DonGolPP-46
❑ 98DonGolPP-361
❑ 98DonLonL-13
❑ 98DonPre-44
❑ 98DonPreSeat-44
❑ 98DonPriCD-46
❑ 98DonPriCE-460
❑ 98DonPriCL-350
❑ 98DonPriCP-594
❑ 98DonProLS-15
❑ 98DonSig-54
❑ 98DonSigP-54
❑ 98DonSilPP-46
❑ 98DonSilPP-361
❑ 98DonSonM9-10
❑ 98E-X2-30
❑ 98E-X2ECFut-30
❑ 98E-X2ECNow-30
❑ 98Fin-265
❑ 98FinNo--265
❑ 98FinNo-R-265
❑ 98FinRef-265
❑ 98FlaShoLeg0-78
❑ 98FlaShoLeg1-78
❑ 98FlaShoLeg2-78
❑ 98FlaShoLeg3-78
❑ 98FlaShoLegM-78
❑ 98FlaShoR0-78
❑ 98FlaShoR1-78
❑ 98FlaShoR2-78
❑ 98FlaShoR3-78
❑ 98Fle-22
❑ 98FleVin'-31
❑ 98FleVin'C-31
❑ 98Lea-151
❑ 98LeaFraDA-151
❑ 98LeaFraF-151
❑ 98LeaFraM-151
❑ 98LeaFraM-151
❑ 98LeaFraMDC-151
❑ 98LeaFraMDC-151
❑ 98LeaFraMZ2-151
❑ 98LeaRS-23
❑ 98LeaRSLHolo-23
❑ 98LeaRSLong-23
❑ 98LeaRSTicMas-13
❑ 98LeaRSTicMasDC-13
❑ 98LeaRTrue-23
❑ 98LeaStaRep-26
❑ 98MetUni-91
❑ 98MetUniPMG-91
❑ 98Pac-334
❑ 98PacAur-146
❑ 98PacGolCDC-19
❑ 98PacInv-109
❑ 98PacInvGems-170
❑ 98PacInvPBlue-109
❑ 98PacInvSilv-109
❑ 98PacInvTeam-14
❑ 98PacLatotML-19
❑ 98PacOme-126
❑ 98PacOmeR-126
❑ 98PacOnl-379
❑ 98PacOnlR-379
❑ 98PacOnlWC-379
❑ 98PacPar-178
❑ 98PacParC-178
❑ 98PacParG-178
❑ 98PacParHS-178
❑ 98PacParl-39
❑ 98PacParPB-178
❑ 98PacParR-178
❑ 98PacPlaB-334
❑ 98PacRedT-334
❑ 98PacSil-334
❑ 98Pin-66
❑ 98PinArtP-PP59
❑ 98PinIns-84
❑ 98PinInsCE-84
❑ 98PinInsDE-84
❑ 98PinInsSG-17AB
❑ 98PinInsSG-17CD
❑ 98PinInsSGS-17AB
❑ 98PinInsSGS-17CD
❑ 98PinMusC-PP59
❑ 98PinPer-45
❑ 98PinPerPP-45
❑ 98PinPerSftF-43
❑ 98PinPreP-66
❑ 98PinSna-LAD3
❑ 98PinSna-LAD18
❑ 98Revo-76
❑ 98RevoShow-30
❑ 98RevoSS-76
❑ 98Sco-181
❑ 98ScoRT-38
❑ 98ScoRTSS-PP38
❑ 98ScoRTSSAP-PP38
❑ 98ScoRTSSAP1-PP38
❑ 98ScoSS-PP81
❑ 98ScoSSAP-PP81
❑ 98SkyDugA-24
❑ 98SkyDugAIA-24
❑ 98SP Aut-109
❑ 98SP Aut-SD7
❑ 98SP AutSD-SD7
❑ 98SP AutSDT-SD7
❑ 98SP AutTrade-12
❑ 98SpoIll-89
❑ 98SpoIllEE-89
❑ 98SpoIllFE-89
❑ 98SpoIllTaN-114
❑ 98SpoIllTaNEE-114
❑ 98SpoIllWSF-97
❑ 98SpoIllWSFEE-97
❑ 98SpoIllWSFFE-97
❑ 98SPxFin-92
❑ 98SPxFinR-92
❑ 98SPxFinS-92
❑ 98StaCluFDI-130
❑ 98StaCluI-130
❑ 98StaCluOneK-130
❑ 98StaCluPP-130
❑ 98StaCluTIll-T6B
❑ 98StaCluTLme-T6B
❑ 98StaCluTLmo-T6B
❑ 98Stu-186
❑ 98StuFF-29
❑ 98StuFFDC-29
❑ 98StuGPP-186
❑ 98StuSony99-10
❑ 98StuSPP-186
❑ 98Top-333
❑ 98TopChr-333
❑ 98TopChrR-333
❑ 98TopDevR-333
❑ 98TopDia-333
❑ 98TopGal-118
❑ 98TopGalGP-118
❑ 98TopGalOPP-118
❑ 98TopGalPPI-118
❑ 98TopGalPPIA-118
❑ 98TopGolLabC1-54
❑ 98TopGolLabC1B-54
❑ 98TopGolLabC1One-54
❑ 98TopGolLabC1R-54
❑ 98TopGolLabC2-54
❑ 98TopGolLabC2B-54
❑ 98TopGolLabC2One-54
❑ 98TopGolLabC2R-54
❑ 98TopGolLabC3-54
❑ 98TopGolLabC3B-54
❑ 98TopGolLabC3One-54
❑ 98TopGolLabC3R-54
❑ 98TopMiniC-333
❑ 98TopOpeD-160
❑ 98TopSta-15
❑ 98TopStaB-15
❑ 98TopStaG-G10
❑ 98TopStaG-15
❑ 98TopStaGG-G10
❑ 98TopStaGGR-G10
❑ 98TopStaGR-15
❑ 98TopStaGS-G10
❑ 98TopStaLB-L11
❑ 98TopStaLG-L11
❑ 98TopStaLGR-L11
❑ 98TopStaLS-L11
❑ 98TopStaS-15
❑ 98TopTek-56
❑ 98TopTekD-56
❑ 98TopTekP-76
❑ 98UD3-47
❑ 98UD3-137
❑ 98UD3-227
❑ 98UD3DieCut-47
❑ 98UD3DieCut-137
❑ 98UD3DieCut-227
❑ 98Ult-35
❑ 98UltGolM-35
❑ 98UltMas-35
❑ 98UltPlaM-35
❑ 98UppDec-115
❑ 98UppDecNP-NP11
❑ 98UppDecR-47
❑ 98UppDecRGKoG-G21
❑ 98UppDecSF-70
❑ 98Zen-43
❑ 98Zen5 xx7-46
❑ 98Zen5x7GoldImp-46
❑ 98Zen5x7Imp-46
❑ 98ZenZ-G-43
❑ 98ZenZ-S-43
❑ 99199Fin-249
❑ 99Bow-65
❑ 99BowBes-42
❑ 99BowBesAR-42
❑ 99BowBesR-42
❑ 99BowChr-65
❑ 99BowChrG-65
❑ 99BowChrGR-65
❑ 99BowChrI-65
❑ 99BowChrIR-65
❑ 99BowChrR-65
❑ 99BowEarR-ER11
❑ 99BowGol-65
❑ 99BowInt-65
❑ 99BowPreProd-PP2
❑ 99CroRoyB-74
❑ 99CroRoyL-74
❑ 99CroRoyMP-7
❑ 99CroRoyOD-74
❑ 99CroRoyPotG-11
❑ 99CroRoyPP-11
❑ 99CroRoyPPN-11
❑ 99DodPol-17
❑ 99DumSet-ER11
❑ 99E-X Cen-56
❑ 99E-X CenECFut-56
❑ 99E-X CenECNow-56
❑ 99FinGolRef-249
❑ 99FinRef-249
❑ 99FlaShoLeg1-98
❑ 99FlaShoLeg2-98
❑ 99FlaShoLeg3-98
❑ 99FlaShoLegM1-98
❑ 99FlaShoLegM2-98
❑ 99FlaShoLegM3-98
❑ 99FlaShoR1-98
❑ 99FlaShoR2-98
❑ 99FlaShoR3-98
❑ 99Fle-19
❑ 99FleBri-35
❑ 99FleBri2G-35
❑ 99FleBriBlu-35
❑ 99FleBriGol-35
❑ 99FleMys-23
❑ 99FleMysG-23
❑ 99FleMysM-23
❑ 99FleSta9-19
❑ 99FleVin'-19
❑ 99FleWarT-19
❑ 99KinDis-25
❑ 99MetUni-167
❑ 99MetUniGM-167
❑ 99MetUniPMG-167
❑ 99Pac-225
❑ 99PacAur-94
❑ 99PacAurOD-94
❑ 99PacCroC-142
❑ 99PacCroC-32
❑ 99PacCroCPB-142
❑ 99PacCroCTC-15
❑ 99PacCroCTM-10
❑ 99PacGolCDC-29
❑ 99PacInv-77
❑ 99PacInvOD-77
❑ 99PacInvPB-77
❑ 99PacOme-122
❑ 99PacOmeC-122
❑ 99PacOmeDD-4
❑ 99PacOmeDM-18
❑ 99PacOmeG-122
❑ 99PacOmeH'-10
❑ 99PacOmePB-122
❑ 99PacPar-119
❑ 99PacParC-119
❑ 99PacParG-119
❑ 99PacParHoloGold-119
❑ 99PacParHS-119
❑ 99PacParOD-119
❑ 99PacParPB-18
❑ 99PacParPB-119
❑ 99PacParRed-119
❑ 99PacParTC-15
❑ 99PacPlaB-225
❑ 99PacPri-75
❑ 99PacPriHB-75
❑ 99PacPriHG-75
❑ 99PacPriHM-75
❑ 99PacPriHP-75
❑ 99PacPriRed-75
❑ 99PacPriS-42
❑ 99PacPriS206-42
❑ 99PacPriS206R-42
❑ 99PacPriSP-42
❑ 99PacPriSV-42
❑ 99PacRed-225
❑ 99PacTeaC-22
❑ 99Rev-72
❑ 99RevDiaL-18
❑ 99RevFouP-9
❑ 99RevPremDate-72
❑ 99RevRet-72
❑ 99RevShaSS-72
❑ 99RevTri-25
❑ 99RevTri-25
❑ 99SkyMolM-69
❑ 99SkyMolMX-69
❑ 99SkyPre-215
❑ 99SkyPreR-215
❑ 99SkyThu-168
❑ 99SkyThuRant-168
❑ 99SkyThuRave-168
❑ 99SP Aut-45
❑ 99SP AutHRC-HR35
❑ 99SP SigAutoG-RMO
❑ 99SPAutHRCDC-HR35
❑ 99SpoIll-81
❑ 99SPSig-45
❑ 99SPx-48
❑ 99SPxFinR-48
❑ 99SPxFinS-48
❑ 99StaClu-30
❑ 99StaCluFDI-30
❑ 99StaCluOoaK-30
❑ 99StaCluPP-30
❑ 99ThuSkySupR-168
❑ 99Top-365
❑ 99TopBlaLC1-61
❑ 99TopBlaLC2-61
❑ 99TopBlaLC3-61
❑ 99TopChr-365
❑ 99TopChrR-365
❑ 99TopGal-7
❑ 99TopGalPP-7
❑ 99TopGalPPI-7
❑ 99TopGolL-61
❑ 99TopGolLC1-61
❑ 99TopGolLC2-61
❑ 99TopGolLOtO-61
❑ 99TopMVPP-365

❑ 99TopOpeD-110
❑ 99TopRedLC1-61
❑ 99TopRedLC2-61
❑ 99TopRedLC3-61
❑ 99TopSta-87
❑ 99TopSta'S-11
❑ 99TopSta'SG-11
❑ 99TopSta'SGDH-11
❑ 99TopSta1Foil-87
❑ 99TopStaFoil-87
❑ 99TopStaOS-87
❑ 99UD Cho-99
❑ 99UD ChoPCR-99
❑ 99UDHolo-30
❑ 99UDHoloAUsome-30
❑ 99Ult-181
❑ 99UltGolM-181
❑ 99UltMas-181
❑ 99UltPlaM-181
❑ 99UppDec-232
❑ 99UppDec-402
❑ 99UppDecBD-43
❑ 99UppDecBDD-43
❑ 99UppDecBDQ-43
❑ 99UppDecBDT-43
❑ 99UppDecCf7-38
❑ 99UppDecCL-97
❑ 99UppDecCLCC-97
❑ 99UppDecCLM-C49
❑ 99UppDecCo7CE-38
❑ 99UppDecE-49
❑ 99UppDecE-151
❑ 99UppDecEFXG-49
❑ 99UppDecEFXG-151
❑ 99UppDecEL1-232
❑ 99UppDecEL1-402
❑ 99UppDecEL2-232
❑ 99UppDecEL2-402
❑ 99UppDecM-105
❑ 99UppDecMGS-105
❑ 99UppDecMHFS-105
❑ 99UppDecMP-105
❑ 99UppDecMSS-105
❑ 99UppDecO-51
❑ 99UppDecOSO-51
❑ 99UppDecR-43
❑ 99UppDecRG-43
❑ 99UppDecRP-43
❑ 99Vic-203

Mondile, Steve
❑ 89FreKeyS-18
❑ 90FreKeyTI-7

Mondroff, Perhsing
❑ 50W720HolS-20

Monds, Wonderful
❑ 94MacBraC-15
❑ 94MacBraF-2219
❑ 95DurBulTI-22
❑ 95Exc-155
❑ 95SPML-13
❑ 95SPMLA-18
❑ 95UppDecML-47
❑ 95UppDecMLFS-47
❑ 96Fla-208
❑ 96FlaWavotF-17
❑ 96FleUpd-U105
❑ 96FleUpdNH-18
❑ 96FleUpdTC-U105
❑ 96Ult-443
❑ 96UltGolM-443
❑ 96UltGolP-14
❑ 96UltGolPHGM-14
❑ 97GreBraG-22
❑ 97Ult-159
❑ 97UltGolME-159
❑ 97UltPlaME-159
❑ 98NewHavRM-19
❑ 98NewHavRMA-19

Monegro, David
❑ 88ElmPioC-15

Monegro, Miguel
❑ 87ElmPioBC-4
❑ 87ElmPioRC-4
❑ 88WinHavRSS-14
❑ 90LynRedSTI-6

Monell, Johnny
❑ 85LitFalMT-26
❑ 86ColMetP-18
❑ 87ColMetP-9
❑ 88BlaYNPRWL-108
❑ 89JacMetGS-16
❑ 95TulDriTI-15

Monette, Jacques
❑ 52LaPat-13
❑ 52LavPro-114

Money, Don
❑ 69PhiTeal-6
❑ 69Top-454A
❑ 69Top-454B
❑ 69TopTeaP-8
❑ 70DayDaiNM-61
❑ 70PhiTeal-9
❑ 70Top-645
❑ 71MLBOffS-185
❑ 71OPC-49
❑ 71PhiArcO-9
❑ 71Top-49
❑ 71TopCoi-31
❑ 71TopTat-55
❑ 72MilBra-240
❑ 72Top-635
❑ 73LinPor-102
❑ 73OPC-386
❑ 73Top-386
❑ 74OPC-413
❑ 74Top-413
❑ 74TopSta-197
❑ 75Hos-112
❑ 75HosTwi-112
❑ 75OPC-175
❑ 75Top-175
❑ 75TopMin-175
❑ 76BreA&P-9
❑ 76Hos-136
❑ 76OPC-402
❑ 76SSP-236
❑ 76Top-402
❑ 77Top-79
❑ 78Top-24
❑ 79BasPat-55
❑ 79OPC-133
❑ 79Top-265
❑ 80BreTeal-18
❑ 80OPC-313
❑ 80Top-595
❑ 81Don-443
❑ 81Fle-524
❑ 81OPC-106
❑ 81Top-106
❑ 82BrePol-7
❑ 82Don-384
❑ 82Fle-149
❑ 82OPC-294
❑ 82Top-709
❑ 83BreGar-12
❑ 83BrePol-7
❑ 83Don-132
❑ 83Fle-41
❑ 83OPC-259
❑ 83Top-608
❑ 84Fle-208
❑ 84Nes792-374
❑ 84Top-374
❑ 84TopTif-374
❑ 86BreGreT-4
❑ 91UppDecS-17
❑ 92BreCarT-16
❑ 94BreMilB-333
❑ 94BreMilB-334
❑ 98BelSnaM-30

Money, Kyle
❑ 82ReaPhiT-4
❑ 83PorBeaT-4
❑ 86PorBeaP-18

Moneypenny, Bubba
❑ 92DavLipB-19
❑ 93DavLipB-24

Monge, Christine
❑ 95ColSilB-20
❑ 96ColSilB-20

Monge, Sid (Isidro)
❑ 75IntLeaASB-18
❑ 75PacCoaLAB-18
❑ 75SalLakCC-17
❑ 76OPC-595
❑ 76Top-595
❑ 77IndTeal-18
❑ 77Top-282
❑ 78IndTeal-21
❑ 78Top-101
❑ 79Top-459
❑ 80IndTeal-19
❑ 80OPC-39
❑ 80Top-74
❑ 81Don-81
❑ 81Fle-395
❑ 81OPC-333
❑ 81Top-333
❑ 82Don-620
❑ 82Fle-375
❑ 82Top-601
❑ 82TopTra-73T
❑ 83Don-245
❑ 83Fle-168
❑ 83PadTeal-18
❑ 83PhiTas-20
❑ 83Top-564
❑ 83TopSti-274
❑ 83TopTra-74T
❑ 84Don-139
❑ 84Fle-308
❑ 84Nes792-224
❑ 84PadMot-21
❑ 84PadSmo-19
❑ 84TigWavP-26
❑ 84Top-224
❑ 84TopTif-224
❑ 84TopTra-80T
❑ 84TopTraT-80T
❑ 85Fle-17
❑ 85Top-408
❑ 85TopTif-408
❑ 89PacSenL-180
❑ 90EliSenL-88
❑ 90RocExpLC-18
❑ 90RocExpP-2711
❑ 92FayGenC-26
❑ 92FayGenF-2186
❑ 93LonTigF-2323
❑ 94JamJamC-28
❑ 95FayGenTI-17
❑ 96FayGenB-2
❑ 97LasVegS1A-3

Mongiello, Michael
❑ 90Bes-282
❑ 90SouBenWSB-21
❑ 90SouBenWSGS-12
❑ 91SarWhiSC-8
❑ 91SarWhiSP-1111
❑ 92BirBarF-2580
❑ 92BirBarS-90
❑ 92ClaFS7-31
❑ 92SkyAA F-42
❑ 93BirBarF-1189
❑ 94NasSouF-1249
❑ 95NasSouTI-14

Monheimer, Len
❑ 88AugPirP-389

Monico, Mario
❑ 86StoPorP-16
❑ 87StoPorP-7
❑ 88ElPasDB-26
❑ 88TexLeaAGS-24
❑ 89ElPasDGS-30
❑ 90CMC-38
❑ 90DenZepC-13
❑ 90DenZepP-638
❑ 90ProAAAF-663

Monita, Greg
❑ 87VerRedP-21

Monroe, Bill
❑ 74LauOldTBS-31
❑ 86NegLeaF-110

Monroe, Craig
❑ 96ChaRivTI-9621
❑ 98Cha-19

Monroe, Darryl
❑ 94JamJamC-17
❑ 94JamJamF-3980
❑ 95FayGenTI-18

Monroe, Gary
❑ 81QuaCitCT-14

Monroe, John
❑ 26Zee-122
❑ 27Zee-98
❑ 28Zee-115
❑ 29Zee-117
❑ 30Zee-60
❑ 31Zee-36
❑ 32Zee-74

Monroe, Larry
❑ 75AppFoxT-18
❑ 78KnoKnoST-13
❑ 79KnoKnoST-14

Monroe, Zack
❑ 59Top-108
❑ 59TopVen-108
❑ 60Top-329
❑ 79TCM50-219

Mons, Jeffrey
❑ 88VerBeaDS-17

Monson, Mo (Steve)
❑ 87BelBreP-5
❑ 88StoPorCLC-175
❑ 88StoPorP-722
❑ 89ElPasDGS-11
❑ 89StoPorB-4
❑ 89StoPorCLC-160
❑ 89StoPorP-384
❑ 90ElPasDGS-22
❑ 91StoPorC-3
❑ 91StoPorP-3030

Montague, Ed
❑ 88T/MUmp-27
❑ 89T/MUmp-25
❑ 90T/MUmp-24

Montague, John
❑ 72Dia-35
❑ 75ExpPos-24
❑ 75OPC-405
❑ 75Top-405
❑ 75TopMin-405
❑ 76OklCit8TI-25
❑ 78Top-117
❑ 79OPC-172
❑ 79Top-337
❑ 80Top-253
❑ 81Top-652
❑ 86MarGreT-10

Montalvo, Rafael
❑ 83VerBeaDT-9
❑ 85AlbDukCr-173
❑ 86TucTorP-16
❑ 87TucTorP-5
❑ 88BlaYNPRWL-137
❑ 88TucTorC-6
❑ 88TucTorJP-18
❑ 88TucTorP-170
❑ 89BlaYNPRWL-10
❑ 90CMC-488
❑ 90EdmTraC-11
❑ 90EdmTraP-517
❑ 90ProAAAF-93
❑ 91Bow-189
❑ 91EdmTraLD-167
❑ 91EdmTraP-1515
❑ 91LinDriAAA-167

Montalvo, Robert
❑ 88St.CatBJP-2021
❑ 90MyrBeaBJP-2875
❑ 90St.CatBJP-3466
❑ 91DunBluJC-28
❑ 91DunBluJP-215
❑ 92KnoBluJF-2998
❑ 92KnoBluJS-385
❑ 92SyrChiF-1976
❑ 93SyrChiF-1005
❑ 94DunBluJC-20
❑ 94SyrChiTI-18

Montanari, Dave
❑ 86PalSprAP-23
❑ 86PalSprAS-21

Montane, Ivan
❑ 93BelMarCB-20
❑ 93BelMarF-3205
❑ 94AppFoxC-14
❑ 94AppFoxFl-1052
❑ 96LanJetB-20

Montanez, Willie
❑ 71OPC-138
❑ 71Top-138
❑ 72Dia-62
❑ 72EssCoi-9
❑ 72Top-690
❑ 73LinPor-147
❑ 73OPC-97
❑ 73PhiTeal-13
❑ 73Top-97
❑ 74OPC-515
❑ 74PhiJohP-27
❑ 74Top-515
❑ 74TopSta-77
❑ 75Gia-6
❑ 75GiaTeal-11
❑ 75Hos-137
❑ 75Kel-31
❑ 75OPC-162
❑ 75PhiProPS-11
❑ 75Top-162
❑ 75TopMin-162
❑ 76OPC-181
❑ 76SSP-103
❑ 76Top-181
❑ 77BurCheD-211
❑ 77Hos-19
❑ 77Kel-31
❑ 77OPC-79
❑ 77Top-410
❑ 77TopCloS-29
❑ 78Hos-143
❑ 78MetDaiPA-18
❑ 78OPC-43
❑ 78Top-38
❑ 78TopZes-4
❑ 79BasPat-56
❑ 79Hos-100
❑ 79OPC-153
❑ 79Top-305
❑ 80OPC-119
❑ 80Top-224
❑ 81AllGamPI-97
❑ 81ExpPos-6
❑ 81Fle-506
❑ 81OPC-63
❑ 81OPCPos-1
❑ 81Top-559
❑ 82Fle-486
❑ 82Top-458
❑ 89BlaYNPRWL-164
❑ 91MetWIZ-279
❑ 91UppDecS-17
❑ 93RanKee-271

Montano, Francisco
❑ 85MexCitTT-8

Montano, Martin
❑ 85BelBreT-22
❑ 86StoPorP-17
❑ 87StoPorP-13
❑ 88FreSunP-1245

Montas, Rico
❑ 97SpolndG-19
❑ 98LanLugQ-21
❑ 98SpolndG-21

Montaya, Ramon
❑ 93LinVenB-316

Montazvo, Rafael
❑ 91MidAngOHP-20

Monteagudo, Aurelio
❑ 64Top-466
❑ 65Top-286
❑ 66Top-532
❑ 67Top-453
❑ 70RoyTeal-23
❑ 71MLBOffS-421
❑ 71OPC-129
❑ 71Top-129
❑ 72OPC-458
❑ 72Top-458
❑ 74OPC-139
❑ 74Top-139
❑ 74TopTra-139T
❑ 76VenLeaS-114
❑ 80VenLeaS-203
❑ 81TCM60I-432
❑ 85MidAngT-20
❑ 86MidAngP-18
❑ 87KnoBluJP-1498

Monteau, Sam
❑ 75BurBeeT-17
❑ 76BurBeeT-22

Montefusco, John
❑ 75GiaTeal-10
❑ 76BlaDis-38
❑ 76BucDis-38
❑ 76CarDis-38
❑ 76CraDis-38
❑ 76DailsID-38
❑ 76Hos-41
❑ 76HosTwi-41
❑ 76IsaDis-38
❑ 76OPC-30
❑ 76OPC-203
❑ 76OrbDis-38
❑ 76RedBarD-38
❑ 76SafDis-38
❑ 76SanFraGP-14
❑ 76SSP-97
❑ 76Top-30
❑ 76Top-203
❑ 76TowCluD-38
❑ 77BurCheD-106
❑ 77ChiWilD-47
❑ 77DailsID-47
❑ 77DetCaeD-47
❑ 77Gia-17
❑ 77GiaTeal-20
❑ 77HollnnD-47
❑ 77Hos-31
❑ 77Kel-5
❑ 77MSADis-47
❑ 77OPC-232
❑ 77PepGloD-42
❑ 77RCColC-44
❑ 77SagDis-47
❑ 77sDis-47
❑ 77Top-370
❑ 77TopCloS-30
❑ 77WenDis-47
❑ 77ZipDis-47
❑ 78GiaTeal-20
❑ 78OPC-59
❑ 78Top-142
❑ 79BasPat-57
❑ 79GiaPol-26
❑ 79OPC-288
❑ 79Top-560
❑ 80GiaEurFS-6
❑ 80GiaPol-26
❑ 80GiaTeal-21
❑ 80OPC-109
❑ 80Top-195
❑ 81BraPol-24
❑ 81Don-434
❑ 81Fle-439
❑ 81Top-438
❑ 81TopTra-804
❑ 82Fle-442
❑ 82Top-697
❑ 82TopTra-74T
❑ 83Don-313
❑ 83Fle-367
❑ 83FleSta-129
❑ 83FleSti-270
❑ 83OPC-223
❑ 83PadTeal-19
❑ 83Top-223
❑ 83TopSti-297
❑ 84Don-126
❑ 84Fle-132
❑ 84GiaMot-24
❑ 84Nes792-761
❑ 84OPC-265
❑ 84Top-761
❑ 84TopTif-761
❑ 85Don-580
❑ 85Fle-135
❑ 85OPC-301
❑ 85Top-301
❑ 85TopSti-319
❑ 85TopTif-301
❑ 85YanTCMP-13
❑ 86Fle-111
❑ 87Spo-71A
❑ 92UppDecS-7
❑ 92YanWIZ8-123
❑ 93UppDecS-9

Monteguedo, Rene
❑ 83TCMPla1945-45

Monteiro, Dave
❑ 87UtiBluSP-15
❑ 88IdaFalBP-1841

Montejo, Steve
❑ 88WatPirP-22

Monteleone, Rich
❑ 85NasSouTI-16
❑ 86CalCanP-15
❑ 87CalCanP-2332
❑ 87MarMot-24
❑ 88CalCanC-3
❑ 88CalCanP-797
❑ 89EdmTraC-2
❑ 89EdmTraP-564
❑ 89ScoRoo-92T
❑ 90CMC-208
❑ 90ColCliC-8
❑ 90ColCliP-675
❑ 90Don-462
❑ 90Fle-648
❑ 90FleCan-648
❑ 90OPC-99
❑ 90ProAAAF-325
❑ 90Sco-565
❑ 90Top-99
❑ 90TopTif-99
❑ 90TopTVY-56
❑ 91ColCliLD-113
❑ 91ColCliP-14
❑ 91ColCliP-596
❑ 91LinDriAAA-113
❑ 91TriA AAGP-AAA7
❑ 92Lea-352
❑ 92LeaBlaG-352
❑ 92Sco-690
❑ 92StaClu-157
❑ 93Don-445
❑ 93Fle-653
❑ 93OPC-152
❑ 93StaClu-493
❑ 93StaCluFDI-493
❑ 93StaCluMOP-493
❑ 93Top-779
❑ 93TopGol-779
❑ 93TopInaM-779
❑ 93TopInaR-779
❑ 93TopMic-779
❑ 93YanStaC-23

❑ 94Fle-240
❑ 94FleUpd-194
❑ 94GiaAMC-15
❑ 94GiaMot-19
❑ 94GiaTarBC-18
❑ 94StaCluT-14
❑ 94StaCluTFDI-14
❑ 94Top-326
❑ 94TopGol-326
❑ 94TopSpa-326
❑ 95Fle-584
❑ 95Top-453
❑ 95TopCyb-249
❑ 96ColCliB-22
Montelongo, Joseph
❑ 94WilCubC-16
❑ 94WilCubF-3761
❑ 95RocCubTI-3
Montero, Alberto
❑ 90AshTouC-15
❑ 91AshTouP-576
❑ 92BurAstC-17
❑ 92BurAstF-557
Montero, Augustin
❑ 98SouOreTG-18
Montero, Cesar
❑ 90HunCubP-3289
Montero, Danny
❑ 92HunCubC-4
❑ 92HunCubF-3151
❑ 93DayCubC-13
❑ 93DayCubF-863
❑ 93GenCubC-23
❑ 93GenCubF-3177
❑ 94DayCubC-17
❑ 94DayCubF-2356
Montero, Francisco
❑ 96MarPhiB-16
Montero, Jorge
❑ 87SalAngP-11
Montero, Sixto
❑ 89MarPhiS-22
Montes, Dan
❑ 89EveGiaS-22
Montgomery, Al
❑ 30Zee-150
❑ 80UtiBluJT-23
Montgomery, Andre
❑ 95BilMusTI-4
❑ 98BurBeeM-14
Montgomery, Damin
❑ 91BilMusP-3768
❑ 91BilMusSP-12
❑ 92BilMusSP-28
Montgomery, Dan
❑ 87BakDodP-2
❑ 88BakDodCLC-238
❑ 89VerBeaDS-17
Montgomery, Don
❑ 91EveGiaC-6
❑ 91EveGiaP-3919
❑ 92SanJosGC-14
❑ 93SanJosGC-17
❑ 93SanJosGF-19
Montgomery, Greg
❑ 97PeoChi-18
❑ 98PriWilCQ-10
Montgomery, Jeff
❑ 87NasSouTI-15
❑ 88Fle-642
❑ 88FleGlo-642
❑ 88FleUpd-32
❑ 88FleUpdG-32
❑ 88OmaRoyC-7
❑ 88OmaRoyP-1501
❑ 88RoyTeal-20
❑ 88Sco-497
❑ 88ScoGlo-497
❑ 88ScoRoo-71T
❑ 88ScoRooG-71T
❑ 88Top-447
❑ 88TopClo-74
❑ 88TopTif-447
❑ 89Bow-113
❑ 89BowTif-113
❑ 89Don-440
❑ 89DonBasB-319
❑ 89Fle-288
❑ 89FleGlo-288
❑ 89Sco-367
❑ 89Top-116
❑ 89TopTif-116
❑ 89UppDec-618
❑ 90Bow-370
❑ 90BowTif-370
❑ 90Don-380
❑ 90Fle-115
❑ 90FleCan-115
❑ 90Lea-520
❑ 90OPC-638
❑ 90PanSti-85
❑ 90PubIntS-353
❑ 90RoyPos-17
❑ 90Sco-365
❑ 90Top-638
❑ 90TopSti-273
❑ 90TopTif-638
❑ 90UppDec-698
❑ 91Bow-308
❑ 91Don-505
❑ 91Fle-564
❑ 91OPC-371
❑ 91RoyPol-16
❑ 91Sco-143
❑ 91StaClu-369
❑ 91Top-371
❑ 91TopDesS-371
❑ 91TopMic-371
❑ 91TopTif-371
❑ 91Ult-153
❑ 91UppDec-637
❑ 92Bow-122
❑ 92Don-666
❑ 92Fle-164
❑ 92Hig5-64
❑ 92Lea-136
❑ 92LeaBlaG-136
❑ 92OPC-16
❑ 92Pin-173
❑ 92RoyPol-23
❑ 92Sco-14
❑ 92ScoProP-5
❑ 92StaClu-12
❑ 92Stu-190
❑ 92Top-16
❑ 92TopGol-16
❑ 92TopGolW-16
❑ 92TopMic-16
❑ 92Ult-76
❑ 92UppDec-627
❑ 93Bow-533
❑ 93ClaGam-67
❑ 93Don-175
❑ 93Fin-42
❑ 93FinRef-42
❑ 93Fla-222
❑ 93Fle-245
❑ 93FleFruotL-47
❑ 93Lea-124
❑ 93OPC-261
❑ 93PacSpa-140
❑ 93Pin-336
❑ 93RoyPol-23
❑ 93RoyStaC-19
❑ 93Sco-212
❑ 93Sel-264
❑ 93SelStaL-69
❑ 93SP-234
❑ 93StaClu-125
❑ 93StaCluFDI-125
❑ 93StaCluM-184
❑ 93StaCluMOP-125
❑ 93Top-130
❑ 93TopGol-130
❑ 93TopInaM-130
❑ 93TopInaR-130
❑ 93TopMic-130
❑ 93TriPla-236
❑ 93Ult-566
❑ 93UppDec-62
❑ 93UppDecGold-62
❑ 94Bow-59
❑ 94BowBes-R73
❑ 94BowBesR-R73
❑ 94ColC-210
❑ 94ColChoGS-210
❑ 94ColChoSS-210
❑ 94Don-362
❑ 94DonSpeE-362
❑ 94Fin-387
❑ 94FinRef-387
❑ 94Fla-62
❑ 94Fle-170
❑ 94FleAllS-17
❑ 94FleExtB-97
❑ 94FUnPac-53
❑ 94Lea-25
❑ 94OPC-7
❑ 94Pac-298
❑ 94PanSti-10
❑ 94Pin-106
❑ 94PinArtP-106
❑ 94PinMusC-106
❑ 94ProMag-65
❑ 94Sco-155
❑ 94ScoGolR-155
❑ 94Sel-109
❑ 94StaClu-49
❑ 94StaCluFDI-49
❑ 94StaCluGR-49
❑ 94StaCluMO-41
❑ 94StaCluMOP-49
❑ 94TomPiz-23
❑ 94Top-394
❑ 94Top-535
❑ 94TopBlaG-14
❑ 94TopGol-394
❑ 94TopGol-535
❑ 94TopSpa-394
❑ 94TopSpa-535
❑ 94TriPla-240
❑ 94Ult-70
❑ 94UltFir-1
❑ 94UppDec-339
❑ 94UppDecED-339
❑ 95Baz-94
❑ 95Bow-345
❑ 95ColCho-455
❑ 95ColChoGS-455
❑ 95ColChoSE-211
❑ 95ColChoSEGS-211
❑ 95ColChoSESS-211
❑ 95ColChoSS-455
❑ 95DenHol-18
❑ 95Don-321
❑ 95DonPreP-321
❑ 95DonTopotO-94
❑ 95Emo-50
❑ 95Fin-214
❑ 95FinRef-214
❑ 95Fla-49
❑ 95Fle-170
❑ 95Lea-29
❑ 95Pac-210
❑ 95Pin-90
❑ 95PinArtP-90
❑ 95PinMusC-90
❑ 95Sco-400
❑ 95ScoGolR-400
❑ 95ScoPlaTS-400
❑ 95SP-161
❑ 95SPCha-159
❑ 95SPChaDC-159
❑ 95SPSil-161
❑ 95SPSpeF-12
❑ 95StaClu-286
❑ 95StaCluMOP-286
❑ 95StaCluSTWS-286
❑ 95StaCluVR-148
❑ 95StaCluVRMO-148
❑ 95Stu-86
❑ 95Top-210
❑ 95TopCyb-119
❑ 95TopD3-19
❑ 95TopEmb-89
❑ 95TopEmbGI-89
❑ 95Ult-293
❑ 95UltGolM-293
❑ 95UppDec-182
❑ 95UppDecED-182
❑ 95UppDecEDG-182
❑ 95UppDecSE-188
❑ 95UppDecSEG-188
❑ 96Baz-5
❑ 96Cir-46
❑ 96CirRav-46
❑ 96ColCho-174
❑ 96ColChoGS-174
❑ 96ColChoSS-174
❑ 96Don-271
❑ 96DonPreP-271
❑ 96EmoXL-68
❑ 96Fin-B129
❑ 96FinRef-B129
❑ 96Fla-92
❑ 96Fle-135
❑ 96FleTif-135
❑ 96Lea-17
❑ 96LeaPrePB-17
❑ 96LeaPrePG-17
❑ 96LeaPrePS-17
❑ 96LeaSigA-160
❑ 96LeaSigAG-160
❑ 96LeaSigAS-160
❑ 96MetUni-66
❑ 96MetUniP-66
❑ 96PanSti-189
❑ 96RoyPol-18
❑ 96Sco-313
❑ 96ScoDugC-B38
❑ 96ScoDugCAP-B38
❑ 96SP-97
❑ 96StaClu-69
❑ 96StaCluEPB-69
❑ 96StaCluEPG-69
❑ 96StaCluEPS-69
❑ 96StaCluMOP-69
❑ 96Top-308
❑ 96TopGal-22
❑ 96TopGalPPI-22
❑ 96TopLas-124
❑ 96Ult-74
❑ 96UltGolM-74
❑ 96UppDec-348
❑ 97Cir-363
❑ 97CirRav-363
❑ 97ColCho-127
❑ 97Fin-300
❑ 97FinEmb-300
❑ 97FinEmbR-300
❑ 97FinRef-300
❑ 97Fle-117
❑ 97FleTif-117
❑ 97KinB-12
❑ 97MetUni-95
❑ 97Pac-106
❑ 97PacLigB-106
❑ 97PacPri-37
❑ 97PacPriLB-37
❑ 97PacPriP-37
❑ 97PacSil-106
❑ 97RoyPol-15
❑ 97StaClu-135
❑ 97StaCluMOP-135
❑ 97Top-399
❑ 97Ult-68
❑ 97UltGolME-68
❑ 97UltPlaME-68
❑ 97UppDec-85
❑ 98Fin-129
❑ 98FinNo--129
❑ 98FinNo-R-129
❑ 98FinRef-129
❑ 98KinDis-12
❑ 98Pac-108
❑ 98PacAur-46
❑ 98PacOme-116
❑ 98PacOmeR-116
❑ 98PacOnl-344
❑ 98PacOnlR-344
❑ 98PacOnlWC-344
❑ 98PacPar-56
❑ 98PacParC-56
❑ 98PacParG-56
❑ 98PacParHS-56
❑ 98PacParPB-56
❑ 98PacParR-56
❑ 98PacPlaB-108
❑ 98PacRedT-108
❑ 98PacSil-108
❑ 98StaCluFDI-165
❑ 98StaClul-165
❑ 98StaCluOneK-165
❑ 98StaCluPP-165
❑ 98Top-184
❑ 98TopChr-184
❑ 98TopChrR-184
❑ 98TopDevR-184
❑ 98TopDia-184
❑ 98TopMiniC-184
❑ 98TopOpeD-99
❑ 98UppDec-392
❑ 99Fle-442
❑ 99FleSta9-442
❑ 99FleWarT-442
❑ 99KinDis-17
❑ 99Pac-207
❑ 99PacAur-89
❑ 99PacAurOD-89
❑ 99PacPar-113
❑ 99PacParC-113
❑ 99PacParG-113
❑ 99PacParHoloGold-113
❑ 99PacParHS-113
❑ 99PacParOD-113
❑ 99PacParPB-113
❑ 99PacParRed-113
❑ 99PacPlaB-207
❑ 99PacRed-207
❑ 99SkyPre-174
❑ 99SkyPreR-174
❑ 99StaClu-207
❑ 99StaCluFDI-207
❑ 99StaCluOoaK-207
❑ 99StaCluPP-207
❑ 99Top-179
❑ 99TopChr-179
❑ 99TopChrR-179
❑ 99TopMVPP-179
❑ 99UppDec-116
❑ 99UppDecEL1-116
❑ 99UppDecEL2-116
❑ 99Vic-192
Montgomery, Josh
❑ 94ButCopKSP-21
Montgomery, Larry
❑ 77BurBeeT-18
❑ 78BurBeeT-21
❑ 80HolMilT-20
❑ 81ElPasDT-12
❑ 85TucTorC-58
❑ 91DaiDolF-2
Montgomery, Matt
❑ 97YakBeaG-18
❑ 98SanBerS-21
❑ 98SanBerSTIS-18
Montgomery, Mike
❑ 90BatCliP-3064
Montgomery, Monty
❑ 72OPC-372
❑ 72Top-372
❑ 73OPC-164
❑ 73Top-164
Montgomery, Ray
❑ 90AubAstP-3394
❑ 91BurAstC-21
❑ 91BurAstP-2815
❑ 92JacGenF-4012
❑ 93JacGenF-2121
❑ 94TucTorF-775
❑ 95JacGenTI-18
❑ 95TucTotTI-16
❑ 96TusTorB-17
❑ 97AstMot-14
❑ 97Don-229
❑ 97DonGolPP-229
❑ 97DonSilPP-229
❑ 97Fle-611
❑ 97FleTif-611
❑ 97PinCer-134
❑ 97PinCerMBla-134
❑ 97PinCerMBlu-134
❑ 97PinCerMG-134
❑ 97PinCerMR-134
❑ 97PinCerR-134
❑ 97PinTotCPB-134
❑ 97PinTotCPG-134
❑ 97PinTotCPR-134
❑ 97Sco-274
❑ 97Sco-491
❑ 97ScoArtPWB-274
❑ 97ScoArtPWB-491
❑ 97ScoResC-491
❑ 97ScoShoS-274
❑ 97ScoShoS-491
❑ 97ScoShoSAP-274
❑ 97ScoShoSAP-491
❑ 98NewOrlZM-16
❑ 98PacInvGems-164
Montgomery, Reggie
❑ 85MidAngT-24
❑ 86EdmTraP-21
❑ 88RocRedWP-207
Montgomery, Robert
❑ 71OPC-176
❑ 71RedSoxA-6
❑ 71Top-176
❑ 72OPC-411
❑ 72RedSoxTI-16
❑ 72Top-411
❑ 73LinPor-27
❑ 73OPC-491
❑ 73Top-491
❑ 74OPC-301
❑ 74Top-301
❑ 75OPC-559
❑ 75Top-559
❑ 75TopMin-559
❑ 76OPC-523
❑ 76SSP-414
❑ 76Top-523
❑ 77Top-288
❑ 78PapGinD-10
❑ 78Top-83
❑ 79OPC-219
❑ 79Top-423
❑ 80Top-618
Montgomery, Steve
❑ 92ClaDraP-61
❑ 92FroRowDP-87
❑ 92FroRowDPG-87
❑ 92FroRowDPS-87
❑ 93StaCluM-193
❑ 94ArkTraF-3087
❑ 95ArkTraTI-21
❑ 96BesAutS-62
❑ 96Exc-230
❑ 96HigDesMB-20
❑ 96LeaSigEA-131
❑ 96Top-431
❑ 97BowBay-23
❑ 98RocRedWQ-19
Montgomery, Wilbert
❑ 80PhiBul-4
Montiel, David
❑ 95BelBreTI-26
❑ 95LinVen-45
❑ 96-97LinVen-112
Montiel, Ivan
❑ 95LinVen-216
❑ 96-97LinVen-246
Montilla, Felix
❑ 98EriSeaWM-18
Montilla, Jose
❑ 94VenLinU-122
❑ 95LinVen-179
Montilla, Julio
❑ 93RocRoyC-17
❑ 93RocRoyF-723
❑ 96WilBluRB-24
Montilla, Miguel
❑ 98TamYanM-20
Montoya, Albert
❑ 91MedHatBJP-4097
❑ 91MedHatBJSP-16
❑ 92MyrBeaHC-24
❑ 92MyrBeaHF-2195
❑ 93DunBluJC-17
❑ 93DunBluJF-1793
❑ 93DunBluJFFN-19
❑ 94KnoSmoF-1301
Montoya, Charlie
❑ 89StoPorCLC-172
❑ 90TexLeaAGS-4
Montoya, Norman
❑ 91QuaCitAC-9
❑ 91QuaCitAP-2626
❑ 92PalSprAC-3
❑ 92PalSprAF-835
❑ 95ElPasDTI-19
❑ 96El PasDB-19
❑ 97TucTorB-10
Montoya, Wilmer
❑ 94VenLinU-157
❑ 94WatIndC-20
❑ 94WatIndF-3933
❑ 95LinVen-136
❑ 96-97LinVen-217
Montoyo, Charlie
❑ 88BlaYNPRWL-73
❑ 88CalLeaACLC-16
❑ 88StoPorCLC-199
❑ 88StoPorP-737
❑ 89BlaYNPRWL-80
❑ 89CalLeaA-29
❑ 89StoPorB-14
❑ 89StoPorP-381
❑ 89StoPorS-12
❑ 90ElPasDGS-23
❑ 91DenZepLD-146
❑ 91DenZepP-131
❑ 91LinDriAAA-146
❑ 92DenZepF-2649
❑ 92DenZepS-141
❑ 93OttLynF-2443
❑ 94ScrRedBF-927
❑ 95ScrRedBTI-21
❑ 96HarSenB-20
❑ 97PriDevR-1
❑ 98HudValR-18
Montreuil, Al
❑ 73WicAerJPKB-10
❑ 74WicAerODF-114
Monzant, Ray
❑ 56Top-264
❑ 58GiaSFCB-17
❑ 58Top-37
❑ 58Top-447
❑ 59Top-332
❑ 60TacBan-10
❑ 60Top-338
❑ 79TCM50-199
Monzo, Vincent
❑ 33Zee-133
❑ 37Zee-83
Monzon, Dan

❑ 72TwiPos-11
❑ 73OPC-469
❑ 73Top-469
❑ 74OPC-613
❑ 74Top-613
❑ 78WauMetT-19
❑ 90UtiBluSP-3
❑ 91SouBenWSC-3
Monzon, Daniel F.
❑ 82LynMetT-1
Monzon, Jose
❑ 89MyrBeaBJP-1459
❑ 91KnoBluJLD-362
❑ 91KnoBluJP-1771
❑ 91LinDriAA-362
❑ 92KnoBluJF-2992
❑ 92KnoBluJS-386
❑ 92SyrChiF-1971
❑ 93LinVenB-99
❑ 93SyrChiF-1000
❑ 94MidAngF-2441
❑ 94MidAngOHP-17
❑ 94VenLinU-62
❑ 95LinVen-232
❑ 95MidAngOHP-22
❑ 95MidAngTI-20
❑ 96-97LinVen-235
❑ 96MidAngB-24
❑ 96MidAngOHP-20
❑ 97VanCanB-22
Moock, Chris
❑ 92LSUTigM-3
❑ 92PeoChiTI-16
Moock, Joe
❑ 77FriOneYW-32
❑ 81TCM60I-340
❑ 91MetWIZ-280
Moock, Pat
❑ 76AshTouT-16
Moody, Eric
❑ 93EriSaiC-16
❑ 93EriSaiF-3112
❑ 94HudValRC-14
❑ 94HudValRF-3380
❑ 96TulDriTI-18
❑ 97OklCit8-19
❑ 98OklRedM-9
Moody, James
❑ 89OneYanP-2105
❑ 90PriWilCTI-15
Moody, Jason
❑ 98GreFalDG-20
Moody, Kyle
❑ 91SpoIndC-6
❑ 91SpoIndP-3957
❑ 92ChaRaiF-127
Moody, Lee
❑ 93NegLeaRL2-28
Moody, Ritchie
❑ 91OklStaC-17
❑ 92ClaDraP-43
❑ 92ClaFS7-429
❑ 92FroRowDP-79
❑ 92FroRowDPG-79
❑ 92FroRowDPS-79
❑ 92GasRanF-2252
❑ 92OklStaC-21
❑ 93Bow-377
❑ 93ClaFS7-224
❑ 93RanStaC-2
❑ 93StaCluM-195
❑ 93Top-438
❑ 93TopGol-438
❑ 93TopInaM-438
❑ 93TopInaR-438
❑ 93TopMic-438
❑ 93TulDriF-2732
❑ 93TulDriTI-19
❑ 94Bow-457
❑ 94OklCit8F-1494
❑ 97TulDriTI-17
Moody, Willis
❑ 88NegLeaD-18
Moon Yang, Sang
❑ 96WesOahCHWB-37
Moon, Bradley
❑ 96MedHatBJTI-20
❑ 97St.CatSB-23
❑ 98St.CatSM-28
Moon, Brian
❑ 97HelBreB-22
❑ 98BelSnaM-2
❑ 98MidLeaPM-2
Moon, Glen
❑ 80CliGiaT-19
Moon, Jared
❑ 97YakBeaG-19
❑ 98GreFalDG-21
Moon, Ray
❑ 92PriRedC-5
❑ 92PriRedF-3099
❑ 93BilMusF-3958
❑ 93BilMusSP-3
Moon, Wally
❑ 47Exh-162
❑ 54Top-137
❑ 55CarHunW-14
❑ 55Top-67
❑ 55TopDouH-37
❑ 56Top-55
❑ 56TopPin-48
❑ 57Top-65
❑ 58CarJayP-12
❑ 58Top-210
❑ 59DodTeal-17
❑ 59DodVol-9
❑ 59Top-530
❑ 60Baz-3
❑ 60DodJayP-9
❑ 60DodMor-7
❑ 60DodPos-7
❑ 60DodTeal-12
❑ 60DodUniO-12
❑ 60Top-5
❑ 60TopTat-36
❑ 60TopVen-5
❑ 61DodBelB-9
❑ 61DodJayP-6
❑ 61DodUniO-13
❑ 61Pos-159A
❑ 61Pos-159B
❑ 61Raw-6
❑ 61Top-325
❑ 61TopStal-29
❑ 62DodBelB-9
❑ 62DodJayP-7
❑ 62DodVol-2
❑ 62ExhStaB-27
❑ 62SalPlaC-124
❑ 62ShiPlaC-124
❑ 62Top-52
❑ 62Top-190A
❑ 62Top-190B
❑ 62TopBuc-62
❑ 62TopStal-137
❑ 62TopVen-52
❑ 62TopVen-190
❑ 63BasMagM-60
❑ 63DodJayP-10
❑ 63ExhStaB-47
❑ 63Top-279
❑ 64Top-353
❑ 64TopVen-353
❑ 65OPC-247
❑ 65Top-247
❑ 79TCM50-137
❑ 81TCM60I-372
❑ 82GSGalAG-18
❑ 88PacLegI-81
❑ 89DodSmoG-65
❑ 89SweBasG-81
❑ 90CarLeaA-7
❑ 90DodTar-543
❑ 90FreKeyTI-1
❑ 91FreKeyC-26
❑ 91FreKeyP-2381
❑ 91SweBasG-64
❑ 92ActPacA-22
❑ 93UppDecAH-98
❑ 94TopArc1-137
❑ 94TopArc1G-137
Mooney, Eric
❑ 94EugEmeC-14
❑ 94EugEmeF-3708
Mooney, James
❑ 34DiaMatCSB-131
❑ 34Gou-83
❑ 74Car193T-19
Mooney, John
❑ 90MisStaB-44
Mooney, Troy
❑ 89PriPirS-13
❑ 90WelPirP-23
❑ 91AugPirC-10
❑ 91AugPirP-804
❑ 92SalBucC-22
❑ 92SalBucF-61
Mooneyham, Bill
❑ 81HolMilT-23
❑ 82HolMilT-6
❑ 83NasAngT-5
❑ 84EdmTraC-110
❑ 85HunStaJ-21
❑ 86DonRoo-50
❑ 86FleUpd-77
❑ 87Don-302
❑ 87Fle-399
❑ 87FleGlo-399
❑ 87TacTigP-18
❑ 87Top-548
❑ 87TopTif-548
❑ 88DenZepP-1254
❑ 88ElPasDB-9
Moore, Andy
❑ 92ElmPioC-22
❑ 92ElmPioF-1391
❑ 93UtiBluSC-16
❑ 93UtiBluSF-3541
Moore, Archie
❑ 64Top-581
❑ 66TolMudHTI-18
❑ 81TCM60I-479
❑ 92YanWIZ6-90
Moore, Austin
❑ 33ButCanV-33
Moore, Balor
❑ 71OPC-747
❑ 71Top-747
❑ 72Dia-36
❑ 73OPC-211
❑ 73Top-211
❑ 74OPC-453
❑ 74Top-453
❑ 75OPC-592
❑ 75Top-592
❑ 75TopMin-592
❑ 78AngFamF-27
❑ 78BluJayP-18
❑ 78SSP270-202
❑ 78Top-368
❑ 79BluJayBY-17
❑ 79OPC-122
❑ 79Top-238
❑ 80OPC-6
❑ 80Top-19
❑ 80VenLeaS-29
❑ 81VanCanT-10
❑ 92UppDecS-3
Moore, Barry (R. Barry)
❑ 67OPC-11
❑ 67Top-11
❑ 68Top-462
❑ 69Top-639
❑ 70OPC-366
❑ 70Top-366
❑ 72MilBra-241
❑ 81TCM60I-360
Moore, Bart
❑ 89ElmPioP-9
❑ 90WinHavRSS-17
Moore, Billy
❑ 86IndIndTI-35
❑ 87IndIndTI-18
❑ 88BlaYNPRWLU-40
❑ 88IndIndC-13
❑ 88IndIndP-497
❑ 88TriAAC-6
❑ 89IndIndC-13
❑ 89IndIndP-1211
❑ 89RocRedWP-1647
❑ 90CMC-36
❑ 90DenZepC-11
❑ 90DenZepP-639
❑ 90ProAAAF-664
Moore, Bobby
❑ 95HudValRTI-27
❑ 97EugEmeB-3
❑ 97TulDriTI-18
❑ 98Cha-10
Moore, Bobby (Robert Vincent)
❑ 88BasCitRS-18
❑ 89BasCitRS-18
❑ 90Bes-231
❑ 90MemChiB-9
❑ 90MemChiP-1019
❑ 90MemChiS-20
❑ 90ProAaA-51
❑ 90StaFS7-86
❑ 91LinDriAAA-343
❑ 91OmaRoyLD-343
❑ 91OmaRoyP-1047
❑ 92RicBraBB-9
❑ 92RicBraF-388
❑ 92RicBraRC-12
❑ 92RicBraS-434
❑ 92SkyAAAF-199
❑ 92TopDeb91-126
❑ 94MemChiF-370
❑ 95RicBraRC-12
❑ 95RicBraTI-9
❑ 96ChaRivTI-9622
❑ 96RicBraB-21
❑ 96RicBraRC-5
❑ 97RicBraBC-19
❑ 98DanQ-C-30
Moore, Bobby (Robert)
❑ 84ShrCapFB-12
❑ 86PhoFirP-17
❑ 87EugEmeP-2653
Moore, Boo
❑ 90WinHavRSS-18
❑ 91CarLeaAP-CAR24
❑ 91Cla/Bes-43
❑ 91LynRedSC-23
❑ 91LynRedSP-1213
❑ 92LynRedSC-19
❑ 92LynRedSF-2920
❑ 92UppDecML-200
❑ 93NewBriRSF-1233
❑ 94LynRedSC-19
❑ 94LynRedSF-1906
Moore, Brad
❑ 86BenPhiC-144
❑ 87ClePhiP-2
❑ 88PhiTas-27
❑ 88ReaPhiP-866
❑ 89BlaYNPRWL-61
❑ 89BlaYNPRWLU-67
❑ 89OPC-202
❑ 89ScrRedBC-8
❑ 89ScrRedBP-709
❑ 89Top-202
❑ 89TopTif-202
❑ 90FleUpd-45
❑ 90ProAAAF-299
❑ 90ScrRedBP-597
❑ 91LinDriAAA-564
❑ 91TidTidLD-564
❑ 91TidTidP-2506
❑ 92TidTidF-893
❑ 92TidTidS-567
❑ 98SouOreTG-19
Moore, Brandon
❑ 96PriWilCB-19
❑ 97BirBarB-5
Moore, Brian
❑ 95MicBatCTI-21
❑ 96MicBatCB-4
Moore, Bud
❑ 96WatIndTI-20
❑ 97WatIndTI-19
Moore, Calvin
❑ 75CedRapGT-29
Moore, Cary
❑ 89EriOriS-14
Moore, Charley
❑ 09ObaT21-264
❑ 11PacCoaBD-44
❑ 11Zee-18
❑ 12ObaPreT-13
❑ 12Zee-16
❑ 13Zee-16
❑ 14Zee-18
Moore, Charlie
❑ 74OPC-603
❑ 74Top-603
❑ 75OPC-636
❑ 75Top-636
❑ 75TopMin-636
❑ 76BreA&P-8
❑ 76OPC-116
❑ 76SSP-231
❑ 76Top-116
❑ 76VenLeaS-201
❑ 77BurCheD-84
❑ 77Top-382
❑ 78Top-51
❑ 79Top-408
❑ 80OPC-302
❑ 80Top-579
❑ 81Don-324
❑ 81Fle-521
❑ 81OPC-237
❑ 81Top-237
❑ 82BrePol-22
❑ 82Don-280
❑ 82Fle-150
❑ 82OPC-308
❑ 82Top-308
❑ 83BreGar-13
❑ 83BrePol-22
❑ 83Don-206
❑ 83Fle-42
❑ 83Top-659
❑ 83TopSti-157
❑ 84BreGar-14
❑ 84BrePol-22
❑ 84Don-292
❑ 84Fle-209
❑ 84Nes792-751
❑ 84OPC-138
❑ 84Top-751
❑ 84TopSti-301
❑ 84TopTif-751
❑ 85BreGar-14
❑ 85BrePol-22
❑ 85Don-351
❑ 85Fle-589
❑ 85Top-83
❑ 85TopTif-83
❑ 86BrePol-22
❑ 86Don-246
❑ 86Fle-496
❑ 86OPC-137
❑ 86Top-137
❑ 86Top-426
❑ 86TopSti-204
❑ 86TopTif-137
❑ 86TopTif-426
❑ 87Don-372
❑ 87Fle-351
❑ 87FleGlo-351
❑ 87OPC-93
❑ 87SanJosBP-6
❑ 87Top-676
❑ 87TopTif-676
❑ 87TopTra-82T
❑ 87TopTraT-82T
❑ 88ScoGlo-444
❑ 88ScoGlo-444
❑ 91UppDecS-10
❑ 92BreCarT-17
❑ 94BreMilB-335
Moore, Charlton
❑ 92MarPhiC-4
❑ 92MarPhiF-3073
❑ 93BatCliCB-21
❑ 93BatCliF-3161
Moore, Cy (William Wilcey)
❑ 28StaPlaCE-48
❑ 28W513-77
❑ 75Yan192T-16
❑ 79RedSoxEF-21
❑ 79Yan192T-20
❑ 84Yan192G-13
❑ 87Yan192T-5
❑ 90DodTar-544
❑ 91ConTSN-109
❑ 94ConTSN-1007
❑ 94ConTSNB-1007
Moore, Daryl
❑ 90Bes-121
❑ 90ProAaA-107
❑ 90WauTimB-5
❑ 90WauTimP-2118
❑ 91FreKeyP-2360
❑ 92HagSunS-266
❑ 92ProFS7-8
❑ 92RocRedWF-1937
❑ 92SkyAA F-110
Moore, Dave
❑ 78IndIndTI-11
❑ 79IndIndTI-4
❑ 80VenLeaS-25
❑ 81AlbDukTc-1
❑ 82AlbDukTc-6
Moore, Dee
❑ 43DodTeal-18
❑ 90DodTar-545
Moore, Don
❑ 81ArkTraT-3
❑ 82ArkTraT-17
❑ 87GenCubP-11
Moore, Donnie
❑ 96OgdRapTI-44
❑ 98BelSnaM-19
Moore, Donnie Ray
❑ 76CubTri-15
❑ 78SSP270-263
❑ 78Top-523
❑ 79Top-17
❑ 82RicBraT-7
❑ 84BraPol-31
❑ 84Fle-185
❑ 84Nes792-207
❑ 84Top-207
❑ 84TopTif-207
❑ 85AngSmo-21
❑ 85Don-650
❑ 85Fle-334
❑ 85FleUpd-82
❑ 85OPC-61
❑ 85Top-699
❑ 85TopTif-699
❑ 85TopTifT-85T
❑ 85TopTra-85T
❑ 86AngSmo-21
❑ 86Don-255
❑ 86DonAll-46
❑ 86Fle-164
❑ 86FleStiC-77
❑ 86Lea-130
❑ 86OPC-345
❑ 86SevCoi-W15
❑ 86Top-345
❑ 86TopSti-182
❑ 86TopTat-16
❑ 86TopTif-345
❑ 87AngSmo-8
❑ 87CalAngPPS-28
❑ 87Don-110
❑ 87Fle-89
❑ 87FleGlo-89
❑ 87FleLeaL-30
❑ 87OPC-115
❑ 87RedFolSB-56
❑ 87SpoTeaP-11
❑ 87Top-115
❑ 87TopMinL-46
❑ 87TopSti-177
❑ 87TopTif-115
❑ 88AngSmo-20
❑ 88Don-621
❑ 88Fle-500
❑ 88FleGlo-500
❑ 88OPC-204
❑ 88Sco-195
❑ 88ScoGlo-195
❑ 88Top-471
❑ 88TopTif-471
❑ 89Sco-535
❑ 94BreMilB-336
Moore, Earl A.
❑ 03BreE10-107
❑ 04FanCraAL-36
❑ 05IndSouPSoCP-14
❑ 09BriE97-22
❑ 10LuxCigPP-16
❑ 10NadE1-38
❑ 10W555-49
❑ 11E94-25
❑ 11HelSta-148
❑ 11MecDFT-36
❑ 11PinT-5-309
❑ 11SpoLifCW-257
❑ 11SpoLifM-235
❑ 12T207-131
❑ 14CraJacE-124
❑ 14TexTomE-35
❑ 15CraJacE-124
❑ 92ConTSN-373
Moore, Ed
❑ 79QuaCitCT-3
❑ 80QuaCitCT-4
Moore, Eddie (Graham E.)
❑ 33Gou-180
❑ 90DodTar-546
❑ 93ConTSN-850
Moore, Euel
❑ 93ConTSN-772
Moore, Gary D.
❑ 90DodTar-1039
Moore, Gene (Eugene)
❑ 36GouWidPPR-A73
❑ 39PlaBal-160
❑ 40PlaBal-143
❑ 41DouPlaR-121
❑ 41PlaBal-25
❑ 77TCMTheWY-27
❑ 81DiaStaCD-115
❑ 83TCMPla1945-7
❑ 90DodTar-547
❑ 91ConTSN-77
❑ 96Bro194F-32
Moore, Greg
❑ 86KnoBluJP-17
Moore, Henry
❑ 18Zee-103
❑ 88SFHesCreN32-19
Moore, J.B.
❑ 85PriWilPT-27

Moore, Jackie S.
❑ 65Top-593
❑ 70BreMcD-21
❑ 73OPC-549
❑ 73Top-549
❑ 74OPC-379
❑ 74Top-379
❑ 75RanPos-23
❑ 77OPC-58
❑ 77Top-113
❑ 84A'sMot-27
❑ 84TopTra-81T
❑ 84TopTraT-81T
❑ 85A'sMot-1
❑ 85Top-38
❑ 85TopTif-38
❑ 86A'sMot-1
❑ 86Top-591
❑ 86TopTif-591
❑ 87ExpPos-17
❑ 88ExpPos-22
❑ 89ExpPos-22
❑ 90RedKah-27
❑ 91RedKah-NNO
❑ 92RedKah-NNO
❑ 93RanKee-438
❑ 94RanMagM-11
❑ 94RanMagM-25
Moore, Jason
❑ 96AriBlaDB-22
❑ 97SouBenSH-20
Moore, Jeramie
❑ 94LSUTig-16
Moore, Jim
❑ 85Ft.MyeRT-25
Moore, Jim William
❑ 30ChiEveAP-18
❑ 30WhiSoxTI-19
❑ 74A's192T-28
Moore, Jo-Jo (Joe G.)
❑ 33Gou-126
❑ 33Gou-231
❑ 33WorCig-70
❑ 34DiaMatCSB-132
❑ 35DiaMatCS2-15
❑ 35DiaMatCS3T1-108
❑ 36WorWidGV-8
❑ 37WheBB14-10
❑ 37WheBB7-29D
❑ 38OurNatGPP-21
❑ 39PlaBal-79
❑ 40PlaBal-84
❑ 41DouPlaR-29
❑ 79DiaGre-31
❑ 85BigLeaC3-78
❑ 94ConTSN-1182
❑ 94ConTSNB-1182
Moore, Joel
❑ 93BenRocCB-17
❑ 93BenRocF-3265
❑ 94Bow-151
❑ 94CenValRC-1
❑ 94CenValRF-3199
❑ 95NewHavRTI-13
❑ 95SPML-49
❑ 96Exc-158
❑ 97NewHavRB-18
❑ 98NewHavRM-18
❑ 98NewHavRMA-18
Moore, John
❑ 90WauTimS-17
❑ 91PerHeaF-5
❑ 93AusFut-71
Moore, Johnny (John F.)
❑ 30Zee-35
❑ 31CubTeal-17
❑ 32CubTeal-18
❑ 34BabRutG-46
❑ 34ButPreR-45
❑ 34DiaMatCSB-133
❑ 35DiaMatCS3T1-109
❑ 36ExhFou-6
❑ 37ExhFou-2
❑ 37ExhFou-6
❑ 37WheBB9-12
❑ 79DiaGre-103
❑ 93DiaStaES-146
❑ 94ConTSN-1184
❑ 94ConTSNB-1184
Moore, Junior (Alvin)
❑ 78GreBraT-17
❑ 78SSP270-159
❑ 78Top-421
❑ 79Top-275
❑ 80Top-186
❑ 81DurBulT-13
Moore, Kelvin
❑ 80OgdA'sT-20
❑ 81TacTigT-18
❑ 82Don-534
❑ 82TacTigT-31
❑ 82Top-531
❑ 83Don-87
❑ 83TacTigT-32
❑ 84ElPasDT-13
❑ 84VanCanC-31
❑ 85BufBisT-10
Moore, Kenderick
❑ 96SpoIndB-18
❑ 97LanLugTS-16
❑ 98Bes-32
❑ 98WilBluRC-20
Moore, Kerwin
❑ 89EugEmeB-17
❑ 90AppFoxBS-19
❑ 90AppFoxP-2109
❑ 90CMC-873
❑ 91BasCitRC-26
❑ 91BasCitRP-1412
❑ 91Bow-312
❑ 91Cla/Bes-38
❑ 91UppDecFE-19F
❑ 92BasCitRC-14
❑ 92Bow-593
❑ 92ClaFS7-22
❑ 92UppDecML-278
❑ 93ClaGolF-82
❑ 93HigDesMC-13
❑ 93HigDesMF-55
❑ 94Bow-319
❑ 94Cla-61
❑ 94ExcFS7-194
❑ 94HunStaF-1345
❑ 94UppDecML-123
❑ 96SigRooOJ-22
❑ 96SigRooOJS-22
❑ 98HunStaTI-9
Moore, LaCarlo
❑ 98LakTigM-22
Moore, Lenny
❑ 78ReaRem-15
Moore, Marcus
❑ 89BenBucL-8
❑ 90QuaCitAGS-13
❑ 91DunBluJC-8
❑ 91DunBluJP-204
❑ 91MelBusF-6
❑ 92ClaFS7-160
❑ 92KnoBluJF-2988
❑ 92KnoBluJS-387
❑ 92SkyAA F-163
❑ 93Bow-288
❑ 93CenValRC-19
❑ 93CenValRF-2892
❑ 94Bow-2
❑ 94ColC-536
❑ 94ColChoGS-536
❑ 94ColChoSS-536
❑ 94Fla-156
❑ 94FleExtB-250
❑ 94FleUpd-128
❑ 94LeaGolR-12
❑ 94LeaLimR-61
❑ 94ScoRoo-RT157
❑ 94ScoRooGR-RT157
❑ 94SpoRoo-60
❑ 94SpoRooAP-60
❑ 94Top-186
❑ 94TopGol-186
❑ 94TopSpa-186
❑ 94Ult-485
❑ 94UppDec-234
❑ 94UppDecED-234
❑ 95Don-169
❑ 95DonPreP-169
❑ 95Lea-175
❑ 96FleUpd-U123
❑ 96FleUpdTC-U123
Moore, Mark
❑ 80CedRapRT-1
❑ 92SouOreAC-9
❑ 92SouOreAF-3420
❑ 93SouOreAC-19
❑ 93SouOreAF-4066
❑ 94WesMicWC-17
❑ 94WesMicWF-2299
❑ 95ModA'sTI-18
Moore, Meredith
❑ 89WinHavRSS-16
Moore, Michael
❑ 88BoiHawP-1608
❑ 92ClaBluBF-BC30
❑ 92ClaFS7-418
❑ 92YakBeaF-3464
❑ 93ClaGolF-183
❑ 93DodStaC-21
❑ 93StaCluM-26
❑ 93Top-576
❑ 93TopGol-576
❑ 93TopInaM-576
❑ 93TopInaR-576
❑ 93TopMic-576
❑ 93UppDec-430
❑ 93UppDecGold-430
❑ 94BakDodC-18
❑ 94BowBesR-B60
❑ 94Cla-121
❑ 94UppDecML-250
❑ 94UppDecML-263
❑ 96SanAntMB-16
❑ 97BinMetB-21
Moore, Mike (Michael W.)
❑ 80LynSaiT-1
❑ 82MarPos-22
❑ 83Don-428
❑ 83Fle-482
❑ 83SalLakCGT-7
❑ 83Top-209
❑ 84Don-634
❑ 84Fle-614
❑ 84MarMot-5
❑ 84Nes792-547
❑ 84Top-547
❑ 84TopTif-547
❑ 85Don-440
❑ 85Fle-495
❑ 85MarMot-8
❑ 85Top-279
❑ 85Top-373
❑ 85TopTif-279
❑ 85TopTif-373
❑ 86Don-240
❑ 86Fle-469
❑ 86Lea-114
❑ 86MarMot-21
❑ 86MarPacNB-8
❑ 86PenWhiSP-18
❑ 86Spo-162
❑ 86Top-646
❑ 86TopMinL-30
❑ 86TopSti-221
❑ 86TopTat-2
❑ 86TopTif-646
❑ 87Don-70
❑ 87Fle-590
❑ 87FleGlo-590
❑ 87MarMot-3
❑ 87OPC-102
❑ 87SmoAmeL-11
❑ 87SpoTeaP-25
❑ 87Top-727
❑ 87TopSti-215
❑ 87TopTif-727
❑ 88Don-75
❑ 88DonBasB-192
❑ 88Fle-379
❑ 88FleGlo-379
❑ 88MarMot-3
❑ 88Sco-464
❑ 88ScoGlo-464
❑ 88StaLinMa-9
❑ 88Top-432
❑ 88TopBig-241
❑ 88TopTif-432
❑ 89A'sMot-12
❑ 89Bow-189
❑ 89BowTif-189
❑ 89Don-448
❑ 89DonBasB-246
❑ 89DonTra-21
❑ 89Fle-554
❑ 89FleGlo-554
❑ 89FleUpd-55
❑ 89OPC-28
❑ 89PanSti-431
❑ 89PAORelT-3
❑ 89Sco-274
❑ 89ScoRoo-5T
❑ 89Spo-77
❑ 89Top-28
❑ 89TopSti-220
❑ 89TopTif-28
❑ 89TopTra-82T
❑ 89TopTraT-82T
❑ 89UppDec-123
❑ 89UppDec-758
❑ 90A'sMot-9
❑ 90Bow-445
❑ 90BowTif-445
❑ 90ClaBlu-104
❑ 90Don-214
❑ 90Fle-16
❑ 90FleCan-16
❑ 90FleWorS-1
❑ 90Lea-293
❑ 90OPC-175
❑ 90PanSti-136
❑ 90PubIntS-311
❑ 90Sco-190
❑ 90Sco-700
❑ 90Sco100S-42
❑ 90Spo-185
❑ 90Top-175
❑ 90TopBig-200
❑ 90TopMinL-31
❑ 90TopSti-178
❑ 90TopTif-175
❑ 90UppDec-275
❑ 90Woo-27
❑ 91A'sMot-11
❑ 91A'sSFE-9
❑ 91Bow-212
❑ 91Don-161
❑ 91Fle-18
❑ 91Lea-218
❑ 91OPC-294
❑ 91Sco-516
❑ 91StaClu-464
❑ 91Top-294
❑ 91TopDesS-294
❑ 91TopMic-294
❑ 91TopTif-294
❑ 91Ult-252
❑ 91UppDec-423
❑ 91WatIndC-14
❑ 91WatIndP-3369
❑ 92AthMot-11
❑ 92Bow-216
❑ 92Don-337
❑ 92Fle-263
❑ 92Lea-164
❑ 92LeaBlaG-164
❑ 92OPC-359
❑ 92Pin-109
❑ 92Sco-91
❑ 92StaClu-669
❑ 92Stu-227
❑ 92Top-359
❑ 92TopGol-359
❑ 92TopGolW-359
❑ 92TopMic-359
❑ 92Ult-425
❑ 92UppDec-661
❑ 92WatIndC-23
❑ 92WatIndF-3239
❑ 93BakDodCLC-1
❑ 93Bow-179
❑ 93Don-683
❑ 93Fle-666
❑ 93FleFinE-213
❑ 93Lea-401
❑ 93OPC-186
❑ 93OPCPre-110
❑ 93PacSpa-448
❑ 93Pin-202
❑ 93Sco-641
❑ 93Sel-270
❑ 93StaClu-693
❑ 93StaCluFDI-693
❑ 93StaCluMOP-693
❑ 93TigGat-21
❑ 93Top-73
❑ 93TopGol-73
❑ 93TopInaM-73
❑ 93TopInaR-73
❑ 93TopMic-73
❑ 93Ult-553
❑ 93UppDec-182
❑ 93UppDec-512
❑ 93UppDecGold-182
❑ 93UppDecGold-512
❑ 94Bow-565
❑ 94BowBes-B60
❑ 94ColC-459
❑ 94ColChoGS-459
❑ 94ColChoSS-459
❑ 94Don-554
❑ 94Fin-83
❑ 94FinRef-83
❑ 94Fla-51
❑ 94Fle-141
❑ 94FleExtB-78
❑ 94Lea-197
❑ 94Pac-226
❑ 94PanSti-66
❑ 94Pin-212
❑ 94PinArtP-212
❑ 94PinMusC-212
❑ 94SanAntMF-2483
❑ 94Sco-143
❑ 94ScoGolR-143
❑ 94Sel-224
❑ 94StaClu-99
❑ 94StaCluFDI-99
❑ 94StaCluGR-99
❑ 94StaCluMOP-99
❑ 94Top-523
❑ 94TopGol-523
❑ 94TopSpa-523
❑ 94Ult-58
❑ 94UppDec-316
❑ 94UppDecED-316
❑ 95ColCho-469
❑ 95ColChoGS-469
❑ 95ColChoSS-469
❑ 95Don-154
❑ 95DonPreP-154
❑ 95Fle-58
❑ 95FleTeaL-6
❑ 95Lea-278
❑ 95Pac-157
❑ 95Sco-174
❑ 95ScoGolR-174
❑ 95ScoPlaTS-174
❑ 95Top-576
❑ 95TopCyb-350
❑ 95Ult-49
❑ 95UltGolM-49
❑ 95UppDec-187
❑ 95UppDecED-187
❑ 95UppDecEDG-187
Moore, Pat
❑ 87EriCarP-27
Moore, Randy
❑ 88BelBreGS-21
Moore, Randy (Randolph)
❑ 31Exh-1
❑ 33ButCanV-34
❑ 33Gou-69
❑ 33TatOrbSDR-171
❑ 34DiaMatCSB-134
❑ 34GouCanV-26
❑ 35GouPuzR-4E
❑ 35GouPuzR-7E
❑ 35GouPuzR-12E
❑ 36GouWidPPR-A74
❑ 36NatChiFPR-113
❑ 90DodTar-548
❑ 93ConTSN-924
Moore, Ray
❑ 55OriEss-19
❑ 55Top-208
❑ 56BalOriP-16
❑ 56BalOriP-36
❑ 56Top-43
❑ 57Top-106
❑ 58Top-249
❑ 58WhiSoxJP-7
❑ 59Top-293
❑ 60Top-447
❑ 61Top-289
❑ 61TopMagR-20
❑ 61TwiCloD-18
❑ 61TwiPetM-13
❑ 62Top-437
❑ 63Top-26
❑ 63TwiVol-13
❑ 74dod195T-22
❑ 78HalHalR-9
❑ 81WhiSox1T-34
❑ 90DodTar-549
❑ 91OriCro-312
Moore, Red (James)
❑ 95NegLeaL2-30
❑ 97NegLeaPC-3S
Moore, Rick
❑ 86ChaLooP-20
❑ 87SalSpuS-10
Moore, Robert
❑ 79WatA'sT-25
❑ 80WesHavWCT-21C
❑ 83GleFalWST-16
❑ 90CMC-127
❑ 90NasSouC-2
❑ 90NasSouP-230
❑ 90ProAAAF-542
Moore, Rod
❑ 90ArkRaz-29
Moore, Ron
❑ 90ArkRaz-20
Moore, Ronald
❑ 86SpoIndC-159
Moore, Roy Daniel
❑ 22E120-85
Moore, Sam
❑ 86FreGiaSB-8
❑ 87CliGiaP-23
❑ 95ElmPioTI-20
❑ 95ElmPioUTI-20
Moore, Steve
❑ 82TulDriT-13
Moore, Terry
❑ 36GouWidPPR-A75
❑ 36NatChiFPR-114
❑ 38CloFotW-63
❑ 41CarW75-19
❑ 41DouPlaR-37
❑ 46SeaSLP-44
❑ 49Bow-174
❑ 51R42SmaS-71
❑ 66CarCoi-9
❑ 72TCMthe3-52
❑ 75JohMiz-11
❑ 76TayBow4-91
❑ 79DiaGre-154
❑ 82Bow195E-261
❑ 83Car194T-18
❑ 83TCMPla1942-25
❑ 92CarMcD-10
❑ 92ConTSN-641
Moore, Tim
❑ 90HunCubP-3290
❑ 90WinSpiTI-19
❑ 91EliTwiP-4312
❑ 91GenCubC-13
❑ 91GenCubP-4226
❑ 91PeoChiC-17
❑ 91PeoChiP-1350
❑ 91PeoChiTI-18
❑ 92FroRowDP-4
❑ 92FroRowDPG-4
❑ 92FroRowDPS-4
❑ 92KenTwiC-7
❑ 92KenTwiF-618
❑ 92PeoChiC-11
❑ 92PeoChiTI-17
❑ 92UtiBluSC-1
❑ 93ForMyeMC-15
❑ 93ForMyeMF-2669
❑ 93SouBenWSC-16
❑ 93SouBenWSF-1428
❑ 93StaCluM-127
❑ 94NasXprF-400
❑ 94PriWilCC-17
❑ 94PriWilCF-1918
❑ 95HarCitRCTI-15
❑ 96BirBarB-15
Moore, Tommy J.
❑ 75St.LouCP-20
❑ 89PacSenL-148
❑ 91MetWIZ-281
❑ 93RanKee-272
Moore, Tony
❑ 90KinMetB-9
❑ 90KinMetS-18
Moore, Trey
❑ 94SigRooDP-42
❑ 94SigRooDPS-42
❑ 94StaCluDP-32
❑ 94StaCluDPFDI-32
❑ 95SPML-151
❑ 95Top-538
❑ 96BesAutS-63
❑ 96PorCitRB-20
❑ 97HarSen-18
❑ 98Fle-411
❑ 98PacOmeRS-6
❑ 98PacOmeRST4-6
❑ 98PacOnl-456
❑ 98PacOnlR-456
❑ 98PacOnlWC-456
❑ 98UppDec-699
Moore, Vince (Vincent)
❑ 92Bow-443
❑ 92MacBraC-18
❑ 92StaCluD-123
❑ 94Bow-476
❑ 94TedWil-128
❑ 94UppDecML-56
❑ 97RanCucQG-19
Moore, Whitey (Lloyd)
❑ 38CloFotW-64

❑ 38RedOraW-20
❑ 39OrcPhoAP-18
❑ 39PlaBal-162
❑ 39RedTeal-16
❑ 40PlaBal-150
❑ 41HarHarW-17
❑ 77CinRedT-44
❑ 94ConTSN-1227
❑ 94ConTSNB-1227
Moorhead, Bob
❑ 62Top-593
❑ 82MetGal62-16
❑ 91MetWIZ-282
Moose, Bob
❑ 68OPC-36
❑ 68PirKDK-38
❑ 68PirTeal-13
❑ 68Top-36
❑ 68TopVen-36
❑ 69PirTeal-16
❑ 69Top-409
❑ 70DayDaiNM-144
❑ 70MLBOffS-104
❑ 70OPC-110
❑ 70PirTeal-12
❑ 70Top-110
❑ 70TopBoo-21
❑ 71MLBOffS-209
❑ 71OPC-690
❑ 71PirActP-20
❑ 71PirArc-7
❑ 71Top-690
❑ 71TopCoi-147
❑ 72MilBra-242
❑ 72Top-647
❑ 73OPC-499
❑ 73Top-499
❑ 74OPC-382
❑ 74Top-382
❑ 75OPC-536
❑ 75PitPirP-14
❑ 75Top-536
❑ 75TopMin-536
❑ 76OPC-476
❑ 76PirPos-12
❑ 76SSP-570
❑ 76Top-476
❑ 81TCM60I-350
Moose, Juice
❑ 90MidAngGS-NNO
❑ 95MidAngTI-30
Moose, Mariner
❑ 91MarCouH-29
❑ 94MasMan-8
Mooty, Jake (J.T.)
❑ 36GouWidPPR-D18
❑ 41CubTeal-13
❑ 42CubTeal-13
❑ 49BowPCL-23
Mora, Andres
❑ 76BalOriP-27
❑ 77Top-646
❑ 78BalOriP-21
❑ 78Top-517
❑ 79Top-287
❑ 80IndTeal-20
❑ 91OriCro-313
Mora, Juan Carlos
❑ 98WesMicWM-14
Mora, Melvin
❑ 93AshTouC-14
❑ 93AshTouF-2284
❑ 93LinVenB-79
❑ 93SouAtlLAGF-31
❑ 94ClaGolF-15
❑ 94OscAstC-17
❑ 94OscAstF-1151
❑ 94VenLinU-18
❑ 95JacGenTI-16
❑ 95LinVen-75
❑ 96-97LinVen-7
❑ 96JacGenB-20
❑ 96TusTorB-18
Moraga, David
❑ 96WesPalBEB-11
❑ 98JupHamQ-10
Moraga, Omar
❑ 98WatIndTI-20
Morales, Alex
❑ 95BelGiaTI-9
❑ 95HelBreTI-18
❑ 96BurBeeTI-22
❑ 96HelBreTI-30
❑ 97HelBreB-1
❑ 97SanJosG-25
Morales, Allen
❑ 94IdaFalBSP-30
Morales, Armando
❑ 91PriRedC-11
❑ 91PriRedP-3510
❑ 92ChaWheF-7
❑ 92ChaWVWC-13
❑ 93PriRedC-19
❑ 93PriRedF-4175
Morales, Edwin
❑ 87PorChaRP-8
Morales, Eric
❑ 94KinMetC-12
❑ 94KinMetF-3826
❑ 95PitMetTI-31
❑ 97St.LucM-19
❑ 98BinMetQ-20
Morales, Francisco
❑ 92HunCubF-3152
❑ 96StPetCB-21
❑ 96WesPalBEB-19
❑ 98arSenW1-15
❑ 98HarSenM-15
Morales, Heriberto
❑ 92GulCoaMF-3485
Morales, Jerry (Julio)
❑ 70OPC-262
❑ 70Top-262
❑ 71OPC-696
❑ 71Top-696
❑ 72PadPos-18
❑ 73OPC-268
❑ 73PadDea-18
❑ 73Top-268
❑ 74OPC-258
❑ 74Top-258
❑ 74TopSta-98
❑ 75OPC-282
❑ 75Top-282
❑ 75TopMin-282
❑ 76BlaDis-39
❑ 76BucDis-39
❑ 76CarDis-39
❑ 76CraDis-39
❑ 76CubTri-16
❑ 76DailsID-39
❑ 76Hos-140
❑ 76IsaDis-39
❑ 76OPC-79
❑ 76OrbDis-39
❑ 76RedBarD-39
❑ 76SafDis-39
❑ 76SSP-312
❑ 76Top-79
❑ 76TowCluD-39
❑ 77BurCheD-196
❑ 77CubJewT-10
❑ 77Hos-49
❑ 77Top-639
❑ 78CarTeal-18
❑ 78OPC-23
❑ 78Top-175
❑ 79OPC-235
❑ 79Top-452
❑ 80Top-572
❑ 81Fle-338
❑ 81Top-377
❑ 81TopTra-805
❑ 82CubRedL-24
❑ 82Don-309
❑ 82Fle-601
❑ 82FleSta-93
❑ 82Top-33
❑ 83CubThoAV-24
❑ 83Fle-502
❑ 83Top-729
❑ 84Fle-498
❑ 89BlaYNPRWL-33
❑ 91MetWIZ-283
Morales, Joe Edwin
❑ 82BelBreFr-16
❑ 84ElPasDT-21
Morales, Jorge
❑ 91PenPilC-15
❑ 91PenPilP-381
❑ 92PenPilC-6
❑ 92PenPilF-2936
❑ 93AppFoxCB-17
❑ 93AppFoxFI-2463
Morales, Jose
❑ 75ExpPos-25
❑ 76ExpRed-22
❑ 76MonExpP-21
❑ 76OPC-418
❑ 76SSP-323
❑ 76Top-418
❑ 77ExpPos-23
❑ 77OPC-90
❑ 77OPC-263
❑ 77Top-102
❑ 77Top-233
❑ 78OPC-63
❑ 78Top-374
❑ 78TwiFriP-12
❑ 79Top-552
❑ 79TwiFriP-18
❑ 80OPC-116
❑ 80Top-218
❑ 80TwiPos-20
❑ 81BalOriP-12
❑ 81Don-495
❑ 81Fle-571
❑ 81Top-43
❑ 81TopTra-806
❑ 82DodUniOV-13
❑ 82Don-203
❑ 82Fle-173
❑ 82Top-648
❑ 82TopTra-75T
❑ 83DodPol-43
❑ 83TopTra-75T
❑ 84DodPol-43
❑ 84Don-275
❑ 84Fle-107
❑ 84Nes792-143
❑ 84Top-143
❑ 84TopTif-143
❑ 86GiaMot-28
❑ 86GiaPos-25
❑ 87GiaMot-27
❑ 87GiaPos-25
❑ 88GiaMot-27
❑ 88GiaPos-24
❑ 89SweBasG-38
❑ 90DodTar-550
❑ 90IndTeal-28
❑ 91IndFanC-30
❑ 91OriCro-314
❑ 92IndFanC-30
❑ 93IndWUA-33
Morales, Lester
❑ 76VenLeaS-112
Morales, Manuel
❑ 85MexCitTT-20
Morales, Rich
❑ 69Top-654
❑ 70OPC-91
❑ 70Top-91
❑ 71OPC-267
❑ 71Top-267
❑ 72Top-593
❑ 73OPC-494
❑ 73Top-494
❑ 74OPC-387
❑ 74PadDea-20
❑ 74Top-387A
❑ 74Top-387B
❑ 81QuaCitCT-30
❑ 88VerMarP-954
❑ 89CalCanC-24
❑ 89CalCanP-538
❑ 90SanBerSCLC-109
❑ 90WilBilB-25
❑ 90WilBilP-1072
❑ 90WilBilS-25
❑ 91PocPioP-3800
❑ 91PocPioSP-30
❑ 92SalSpuC-30
❑ 92SalSpuF-3777
❑ 94OgdRapF-3751
❑ 94OgdRapSP-25
❑ 95OdgRapTI-19
❑ 98VerExpO-3
Morales, William
❑ 87PriWilYP-29
❑ 88PriWilYS-18
Morales, Willie
❑ 92AriWilP-10
❑ 93SouOreAC-20
❑ 93SouOreAF-4067
❑ 94WesMicWC-18
❑ 94WesMicWF-2300
❑ 95ModA'sTI-19
❑ 95SPML-127
❑ 96HunStaTI-19
❑ 97HunStaTI-18
Moralez, Paul
❑ 86KinEagP-17
❑ 87BakDodP-24
Moran, Al (Richard Alan)
❑ 63Top-558
❑ 64Top-288
❑ 64TopVen-288
❑ 76Met63 S-10
❑ 81TCM60I-430
❑ 91MetWIZ-284
Moran, Billy (William Nelson)
❑ 58Top-388
❑ 59Top-196
❑ 59TopVen-196
❑ 62Top-539
❑ 63AngJayP-9
❑ 63SalMetC-48
❑ 63Top-57
❑ 64Top-333
❑ 64TopSta-67
❑ 64TopVen-333
❑ 65Top-562
❑ 76VenLeaS-175
❑ 81TCM60I-429
Moran, Bugs (Bill)
❑ 58IndTeal-15
❑ 60MapLeaSF-14
❑ 61MapLeaBH-14
❑ 63Jel-25
❑ 63Pos-25
❑ 78KnoKnoST-14
Moran, Charles
❑ 94ConTSN-1189
❑ 94ConTSNB-1189
Moran, Cyril
❑ 49AngTeal-27
❑ 49W725AngTI-21
Moran, Dino
❑ 86WatPirP-13
Moran, Frank
❑ 88HamRedP-1746
Moran, Jim
❑ 53MotCoo-12
❑ 53SanFraSTI-14
Moran, John Herbert
❑ 09ColChiE-203
❑ 09T206-449
❑ 12ColRedB-203
❑ 12ColTinT-203
❑ 15CraJacE-111
❑ 15SpoNewM-122
❑ 16FleBreD-67
❑ 80BraTCM1-25
❑ 80BraTCM1-30
❑ 90DodTar-1040
Moran, Opie
❑ 87EriCarP-2
❑ 89ArkTraGS-13
Moran, Pat J.
❑ 07CubA.CDPP-7
❑ 07CubGFGCP-7
❑ 09ColChiE-204
❑ 09RamT20-82
❑ 09T206-255
❑ 10DomDisP-88A
❑ 10DomDisP-88B
❑ 10LuxCigPP-17
❑ 10SweCapPP-129
❑ 11HelSta-149
❑ 11S74Sil-102
❑ 11SpoLifCW-258
❑ 11SpoLifM-236
❑ 11T205-123A
❑ 11T205-123B
❑ 11TurRedT-109
❑ 12ColRedB-204
❑ 12ColTinT-204
❑ 12HasTriFT-9
❑ 12T207-132
❑ 14PieStaT-77
❑ 15SpoNewM-123
❑ 16BF2FP-91
❑ 16SpoNewM-125
❑ 19W514-12
❑ 20RedWorCP-13
❑ 20WalMaiW-33
❑ 23WilChoV-107
❑ 24MrsShePP-6
❑ 72ClaCar-29
❑ 74CapPub-48
❑ 76RedParC-17
❑ 83PhiPosGPaM-11
❑ 88PacEigMO-89
Moran, Roy
❑ 13Zee-85
❑ 14Zee-89
Moran, Steve
❑ 86AppFoxP-16
Morandini, Mickey
❑ 88TopTra-71T
❑ 88TopTraT-71T
❑ 89SpaPhiP-1030
❑ 89SpaPhiS-18
❑ 89Sta-57
❑ 89Sta-120
❑ 89TopBig-162
❑ 90Bow-153
❑ 90BowTif-153
❑ 90CMC-240
❑ 90ProAAAF-308
❑ 90ScrRedBC-14
❑ 90ScrRedBP-606
❑ 91Bow-492
❑ 91Cla1-T79
❑ 91ClaGam-187
❑ 91Don-44
❑ 91Fle-407
❑ 91Lea-383
❑ 91LinDriAAA-491
❑ 91MajLeaCP-61
❑ 91OPC-342
❑ 91OPCPre-83
❑ 91PhiMed-28
❑ 91Sco-376
❑ 91ScoRoo-33
❑ 91ScrRedBLD-491
❑ 91Sev3DCN-12
❑ 91SevCoi-NE12
❑ 91StaClu-535
❑ 91Stu-218
❑ 91Top-342
❑ 91TopDeb90-110
❑ 91TopDesS-342
❑ 91TopMic-342
❑ 91TopTif-342
❑ 91Ult-268
❑ 91UppDec-18
❑ 92Bow-628
❑ 92Don-669
❑ 92Fle-539
❑ 92Lea-330
❑ 92LeaBlaG-330
❑ 92OPC-587
❑ 92PanSti-243
❑ 92PhiMed-21
❑ 92Pin-103
❑ 92Sco-143
❑ 92StaClu-369
❑ 92Stu-77
❑ 92Top-587
❑ 92TopGol-587
❑ 92TopGolW-587
❑ 92TopMic-587
❑ 92Ult-247
❑ 92UppDec-449
❑ 93Bow-428
❑ 93Don-224
❑ 93Fle-105
❑ 93FleGolM-A2
❑ 93Lea-77
❑ 93OPC-256
❑ 93PacSpa-239
❑ 93PanSti-271
❑ 93PhiMed-23
❑ 93PhiStaC-8
❑ 93Pin-156
❑ 93Sco-415
❑ 93Sco-512
❑ 93Sel-245
❑ 93SP-177
❑ 93StaClu-449
❑ 93StaCluFDI-449
❑ 93StaCluMOP-449
❑ 93Stu-208
❑ 93Top-262
❑ 93TopGol-262
❑ 93TopInaM-262
❑ 93TopInaR-262
❑ 93TopMic-262
❑ 93TriPla-53
❑ 93Ult-91
❑ 93UppDec-285
❑ 93UppDecGold-285
❑ 93UppDecSH-HI12
❑ 94ColC-211
❑ 94ColChoGS-211
❑ 94ColChoSS-211
❑ 94Don-498
❑ 94Fin-273
❑ 94FinRef-273
❑ 94Fle-596
❑ 94Lea-424
❑ 94Pac-482
❑ 94PhiMed-23
❑ 94PhiMel-16
❑ 94PhiUSPC-4C
❑ 94PhiUSPC-12D
❑ 94Pin-159
❑ 94PinArtP-159
❑ 94PinMusC-159
❑ 94Sco-460
❑ 94ScoCyc-TC15
❑ 94ScoGolR-460
❑ 94StaClu-120
❑ 94StaCluFDI-120
❑ 94StaCluGR-120
❑ 94StaCluMOP-120
❑ 94StaCluMOP-ST10
❑ 94StaCluST-ST10
❑ 94StaCluT-234
❑ 94StaCluTFDI-234
❑ 94Top-692
❑ 94TopGol-692
❑ 94TopSpa-692
❑ 94Ult-250
❑ 94UppDec-463
❑ 94UppDecED-463
❑ 95Don-278
❑ 95DonPreP-278
❑ 95DonTopotO-308
❑ 95Fla-394
❑ 95Fle-401
❑ 95Lea-87
❑ 95Pac-334
❑ 95Phi-21
❑ 95PhiMel-17
❑ 95Pin-16
❑ 95PinArtP-16
❑ 95PinMusC-16
❑ 95PinSam-16
❑ 95Sco-494
❑ 95ScoGolR-494
❑ 95ScoPlaTS-494
❑ 95StaClu-291
❑ 95StaCluMOP-291
❑ 95StaCluSTWS-291
❑ 95Top-2
❑ 95TopCyb-2
❑ 95Ult-207
❑ 95UltGolM-207
❑ 96Cir-167
❑ 96CirRav-167
❑ 96ColCho-256
❑ 96ColChoGS-256
❑ 96ColChoSS-256
❑ 96Don-248
❑ 96DonPreP-248
❑ 96EmoXL-247
❑ 96Fla-336
❑ 96Fle-505
❑ 96FleTif-505
❑ 96Lea-42
❑ 96LeaPrePB-42
❑ 96LeaPrePG-42
❑ 96LeaPrePS-42
❑ 96LeaSigA-161
❑ 96LeaSigAG-161
❑ 96LeaSigAS-161
❑ 96MetUni-212
❑ 96MetUniP-212
❑ 96Pac-154
❑ 96PanSti-38
❑ 96PhiTeal-23
❑ 96ProSta-88
❑ 96SP-144
❑ 96StaClu-139
❑ 96StaCluMOP-139
❑ 96Top-370
❑ 96Ult-257
❑ 96UltGolM-257
❑ 96UppDec-168
❑ 97Cir-12
❑ 97CirRav-12
❑ 97ColCho-415
❑ 97FlaShoLC-134
❑ 97FlaShoLeg0-134
❑ 97FlaShoLeg1-134
❑ 97FlaShoM-A134
❑ 97FlaShoM-B134
❑ 97FlaShoM-C134
❑ 97FlaShoR0-134
❑ 97FlaShoR1-134
❑ 97FlaShoR2-134
❑ 97Fle-416
❑ 97FleTif-416
❑ 97KinB-16
❑ 97MetUni-203
❑ 97Pac-382
❑ 97PacLigB-382
❑ 97PacSil-382
❑ 97PhiCopQ-18
❑ 97PhiTeal-12
❑ 97SP-139

❑ 97StaClu-320
❑ 97StaCluMOP-320
❑ 97Top-64
❑ 97Ult-253
❑ 97UltGolME-253
❑ 97UltPlaME-253
❑ 97UppDec-154
❑ 98CirThu-122
❑ 98CirThuRav-122
❑ 98CirThuSupRav-122
❑ 98ColCho-207
❑ 98ColCho-329
❑ 98CroRoy-30
❑ 98Fle-270
❑ 98Fle-551
❑ 98MetUni-152
❑ 98MetUniPMG-152
❑ 98Pac-385
❑ 98PacAur-114
❑ 98PacInv-125
❑ 98PacInvPBlue-125
❑ 98PacInvSilv-125
❑ 98PacOnl-147
❑ 98PacOnlR-147
❑ 98PacOnlWC-147
❑ 98PacPar-140
❑ 98PacParC-140
❑ 98PacParG-140
❑ 98PacParHS-140
❑ 98PacParPB-140
❑ 98PacParR-140
❑ 98PacPlaB-385
❑ 98PacRedT-385
❑ 98PacSil-385
❑ 98Revo-30
❑ 98RevoSS-30
❑ 98ScrRedB1ATI-13
❑ 98StaCluFDI-133
❑ 98StaCluI-133
❑ 98StaCluOneK-133
❑ 98StaCluPP-133
❑ 98Top-219
❑ 98TopChr-219
❑ 98TopChrR-219
❑ 98TopDevR-219
❑ 98TopDia-219
❑ 98TopMiniC-219
❑ 98TopOpeD-106
❑ 98Ult-138
❑ 98Ult-292
❑ 98UltGolM-138
❑ 98UltGolM-292
❑ 98UltMas-138
❑ 98UltMas-292
❑ 98UltPlaM-138
❑ 98UltPlaM-292
❑ 98UppDec-189
❑ 98UppDec-659
❑ 99199Fin-186
❑ 99FinGolRef-186
❑ 99FinRef-186
❑ 99Fle-185
❑ 99FleSta9-185
❑ 99FleWarT-185
❑ 99KinDis-14
❑ 99MetUni-123
❑ 99MetUniGM-123
❑ 99MetUniPMG-123
❑ 99Pac-88
❑ 99PacAur-35
❑ 99PacAurOD-35
❑ 99PacOme-50
❑ 99PacOmeC-50
❑ 99PacOmeG-50
❑ 99PacOmePB-50
❑ 99PacPar-50
❑ 99PacParC-50
❑ 99PacParG-50
❑ 99PacParHoloGold-50
❑ 99PacParHS-50
❑ 99PacParOD-50
❑ 99PacParPB-50
❑ 99PacParRed-50
❑ 99PacPlaB-88
❑ 99PacRed-88
❑ 99Rev-29
❑ 99RevPremDate-29
❑ 99RevRet-29
❑ 99RevShaSS-29
❑ 99SkyPre-43
❑ 99SkyPreR-43
❑ 99SkyThu-127
❑ 99SkyThuRant-127
❑ 99SkyThuRave-127
❑ 99StaClu-57
❑ 99StaCluFDI-57
❑ 99StaCluOoaK-57
❑ 99StaCluPP-57
❑ 99ThuSkySupR-127
❑ 99Top-23
❑ 99TopChr-23
❑ 99TopChrR-23
❑ 99TopMVPP-23
❑ 99UD Cho-69
❑ 99UD ChoPCR-69
❑ 99Ult-39
❑ 99UltGolM-39
❑ 99UltMas-39
❑ 99UltPlaM-39
❑ 99UppDec-334
❑ 99UppDecEL1-334
❑ 99UppDecEL2-334
❑ 99Vic-84

Morando, Dean
❑ 78WisRapTT-14

Moraw, Carl
❑ 86BelBreP-16
❑ 87StoPorP-21
❑ 88StoPorCLC-184
❑ 88StoPorP-746
❑ 89ElPasDGS-12
❑ 89StoPorB-5
❑ 89StoPorCLC-156
❑ 89StoPorP-378

Mordecai, Mike
❑ 88CapCodPB-17
❑ 88CapCodPPaLP-42
❑ 90CarLeaA-28
❑ 90DurBulTI-7
❑ 91DurBulC-13
❑ 91DurBulP-1557
❑ 92GreBraF-1161
❑ 92GreBraS-241
❑ 93RicBraBB-6
❑ 93RicBraF-192
❑ 93RicBraP-4
❑ 93RicBraRC-1
❑ 93RicBraRC-21
❑ 94BraLykP-24
❑ 94RicBraF-2854
❑ 94TopTra-63T
❑ 95FleUpd-92
❑ 95LinVen-109
❑ 96ColCho-456
❑ 96ColChoGS-456
❑ 96ColChoSS-456
❑ 96Don-131
❑ 96DonPreP-131
❑ 96Fle-303
❑ 96FleTif-303
❑ 96LeaSigEA-132
❑ 96MLBPin-21
❑ 97PacPriGotD-GD114
❑ 98PacInvGems-124
❑ 98PacOnl-457
❑ 98PacOnlR-457
❑ 98PacOnlWC-457

More, Billy
❑ 87SpoTeaP-20

Moreau, Guy
❑ 36GouWidPPR-D19

Morehart, Ray
❑ 75Yan192T-17
❑ 79Yan192T-21
❑ 84Yan192G-23
❑ 91ConTSN-102

Morehead, Dave
❑ 62SeaPop-8
❑ 63Top-299
❑ 64Top-376
❑ 65RedSoxTI-10
❑ 65Top-434
❑ 66OPC-135
❑ 66RedSoxTI-7
❑ 66Top-135
❑ 66TopVen-135
❑ 67Top-297
❑ 67TopRedSS-11
❑ 68DexPre-57
❑ 68Top-212
❑ 68TopVen-212
❑ 69MLBOffS-60
❑ 69OPC-29
❑ 69Top-29
❑ 69TopTeaP-7
❑ 70MLBOffS-224
❑ 70OPC-495
❑ 70RoyTeal-24
❑ 70Top-495
❑ 71MLBOffS-422
❑ 71OPC-221
❑ 71oySigST-16
❑ 71Top-221
❑ 72MilBra-243
❑ 81RedSoxBG2S-96

Morehead, Seth
❑ 59Top-253
❑ 60Lea-87
❑ 60Top-504
❑ 61Top-107

Morehouse, Richard
❑ 86QuaCitAP-24
❑ 87PalSprP-28
❑ 88PalSprACLC-91
❑ 88PalSprAP-1449
❑ 89MidAngGS-24

Morehouse, Scott
❑ 88CapCodPPaLP-162

Morel, Plinio
❑ 94SavCarC-21
❑ 94SavCarF-509

Morel, Ramon
❑ 93WelPirC-15
❑ 93WelPirF-3352
❑ 94AugGreC-13
❑ 94AugGreF-3004
❑ 95Bow-151
❑ 95Exc-258
❑ 95LynHilTI-17
❑ 96Bow-135
❑ 96BowFoi-135
❑ 96ColCho-679
❑ 96ColChoGS-679
❑ 96ColChoSS-679
❑ 96Fle-529
❑ 96FleTif-529
❑ 96Pac-169
❑ 97CalCanB-19
❑ 97Fle-434
❑ 97FleTif-434
❑ 97Pac-401
❑ 97PacLigB-401
❑ 97PacSil-401

Moreland, Keith
❑ 80PhiBul-33
❑ 80PhiBurK-3
❑ 81Don-382
❑ 81Fle-13
❑ 81Top-131
❑ 82CubRedL-6
❑ 82Don-119
❑ 82Fle-252
❑ 82Top-384
❑ 82TopTra-76T
❑ 83CubThoAV-6
❑ 83Don-309
❑ 83Fle-503
❑ 83FleSta-130
❑ 83FleSti-125
❑ 83OPC-58
❑ 83Top-619
❑ 83TopSti-222
❑ 84AllGamPI-60
❑ 84CubBriPC-2S
❑ 84CubChiT-19
❑ 84CubSev-6
❑ 84Don-483
❑ 84Fle-499
❑ 84Nes792-23
❑ 84Nes792-456
❑ 84OPC-23
❑ 84Top-23
❑ 84Top-456
❑ 84TopSti-39
❑ 84TopTif-23
❑ 84TopTif-456
❑ 85AllGamPI-152
❑ 85CubLioP-17
❑ 85CubSev-6
❑ 85Don-117
❑ 85Fle-62
❑ 85Lea-197
❑ 85OPC-197
❑ 85Top-538
❑ 85TopMin-538
❑ 85TopSti-39
❑ 85TopTif-538
❑ 86BasStaB-74
❑ 86CubGat-6
❑ 86CubUno-13
❑ 86Don-167
❑ 86Dra-9
❑ 86Fle-375
❑ 86FleLeaL-25
❑ 86FleMin-79
❑ 86FleStiC-78
❑ 86Lea-94
❑ 86MSAJayPCD-13
❑ 86OPC-266
❑ 86Spo-90
❑ 86Top-266
❑ 86TopMinL-38
❑ 86TopSti-54
❑ 86TopTat-12
❑ 86TopTif-266
❑ 87CubCan-20
❑ 87CubDavB-6
❑ 87Don-24
❑ 87Don-169
❑ 87DonOpeD-71
❑ 87DonSupD-24
❑ 87Dra-7
❑ 87Fle-569
❑ 87FleGlo-569
❑ 87FleLeaL-31
❑ 87FleMin-69
❑ 87FleStiC-79
❑ 87Lea-24
❑ 87Lea-77
❑ 87OPC-177
❑ 87SevCoi-C12
❑ 87SevCoi-M7
❑ 87Spo-122
❑ 87SpoTeaP-22
❑ 87Top-177
❑ 87TopSti-65
❑ 87TopTif-177
❑ 88Don-201
❑ 88DonBasB-266
❑ 88Fle-425A
❑ 88Fle-425B
❑ 88FleGlo-425
❑ 88FleUpd-124
❑ 88FleUpdG-124
❑ 88Lea-160
❑ 88OPC-31
❑ 88PadCok-7
❑ 88PadSmo-19
❑ 88PanSti-263
❑ 88RedFolSB-58
❑ 88Sco-71
❑ 88ScoGlo-71
❑ 88ScoRoo-9T
❑ 88ScoRooG-9T
❑ 88ScoSam-71
❑ 88Spo-164
❑ 88StaLinCu-7
❑ 88Top-416
❑ 88TopBig-207
❑ 88TopSti-58
❑ 88TopTif-416
❑ 88TopTra-72T
❑ 88TopTraT-72T
❑ 89Bow-109
❑ 89BowTif-109
❑ 89Don-111
❑ 89DonBasB-203
❑ 89Fle-313
❑ 89FleGlo-313
❑ 89OPC-293
❑ 89Sco-42
❑ 89ScoRoo-29T
❑ 89Spo-141
❑ 89TigMar-10
❑ 89Top-773
❑ 89TopSti-105
❑ 89TopTif-773
❑ 89TopTra-83T
❑ 89TopTraT-83T
❑ 89UppDec-361
❑ 90PubIntS-477
❑ 90Sco-444
❑ 90Spo-139
❑ 90UppDec-401
❑ 91OriCro-315
❑ 92TexLon-29

Moreland, Owen III
❑ 84LitFalMT-11

Morelli, Frank
❑ 89ElmPioP-10

Morelock, Charlie
❑ 83AndBraT-12
❑ 86DurBulP-19
❑ 87EdmTraP-2069

Moren, Lew
❑ 10NadE1-39
❑ 11PinT-5-401
❑ 11SpoLifCW-259
❑ 11SpoLifM-237

Morena, Jamie
❑ 87ChaRaiP-18

Moreno, Angel
❑ 82Fle-469
❑ 84EdmTraC-99
❑ 93LinVenB-306

Moreno, Armando
❑ 86JacExpT-4
❑ 87JacExpP-440
❑ 88BlaYNPRWL-109
❑ 88JacExpB-27
❑ 88JacExpP-983
❑ 88SouLeaAJ-21
❑ 89BlaYNPRWL-120
❑ 89BlaYNPRWLU-16
❑ 89IndIndC-19
❑ 89IndIndP-1222
❑ 90BufBisC-19
❑ 90BufBisP-381
❑ 90BufBisTI-17
❑ 90CMC-19
❑ 90ProAAAF-496
❑ 91BufBisLD-39
❑ 91BufBisP-548
❑ 91LinDriAAA-39
❑ 92OPC-179
❑ 92Top-179
❑ 92TopGol-179
❑ 92TopGolW-179
❑ 92TopMic-179

Moreno, Carlos
❑ 76VenLeaS-116
❑ 80VenLeaS-184
❑ 82MiaMarT-5

Moreno, Chris
❑ 89StoPorB-26

Moreno, Claudio
❑ 96SanBerSB-18

Moreno, Douglas
❑ 86MacPirP-16
❑ 86WatPirP-14
❑ 93LinVenB-257

Moreno, Erik
❑ 93IdaFalBF-4036
❑ 93IdaFalBSP-6

Moreno, Jaime
❑ 86ChaRaiP-18
❑ 88ChaRaiP-1218
❑ 89BlaYNPRWL-66
❑ 89BlaYNPRWL-67
❑ 89WatDiaP-1785
❑ 89WatDiaS-26
❑ 91ChaRaiC-26
❑ 91ChaRaiP-111
❑ 92ChaRaiC-24
❑ 92ChaRaiF-137

Moreno, Jorge A.
❑ 73CedRapAT-28
❑ 74CedRapAT-15
❑ 75DubPacT-25
❑ 91BriTigC-13
❑ 91BriTigP-3615
❑ 92BriTigF-1427
❑ 93FayGenC-16
❑ 93FayGenF-142
❑ 93NiaFalRF-3404
❑ 94FayGenC-17
❑ 94FayGenF-2156

Moreno, Jose D.
❑ 91WatIndC-15
❑ 91WatIndP-3370
❑ 93LinVenB-111
❑ 94VenLinU-117

Moreno, Jose delos
❑ 77ReaPhiT-17
❑ 79TidTidT-3
❑ 80TidTidT-2
❑ 81HawIslT-2
❑ 91MetWIZ-285

Moreno, Jose M
❑ 98WisTimRM-19

Moreno, Juan
❑ 92ColMetC-17
❑ 92ColMetF-308
❑ 92ColMetPI-10
❑ 93CapCitBC-14
❑ 93CapCitBF-471
❑ 93KinMetC-17
❑ 93KinMetF-3793
❑ 96-97LinVen-251
❑ 96WesMicWB-16
❑ 97PitMet-19
❑ 98CapCitBF5-29
❑ 98CapCitBM-29

Moreno, Julio Cesar
❑ 96FreKeyB-15
❑ 97BowBay-24
❑ 98Bes-33
❑ 98Bow-169
❑ 98BowChr-169
❑ 98BowChrGA-169
❑ 98BowChrGAR-169
❑ 98BowChrI-169
❑ 98BowChrIR-169
❑ 98BowChrR-169
❑ 98BowGolA-169
❑ 98BowInt-169

Moreno, Julio Gonzalez
❑ 53Bri-13

Moreno, Michael
❑ 83WisRapTF-24
❑ 85OrlTwiT-8

Moreno, Mikel
❑ 98WilCubM-19

Moreno, Omar
❑ 77PirPosP-16
❑ 77Top-104
❑ 78Top-283
❑ 79Hos-12
❑ 79OPC-321
❑ 79Top-4
❑ 79Top-607
❑ 80BurKinPHR-29
❑ 80OPC-372
❑ 80Top-165
❑ 80Top-204
❑ 81AllGamPI-156
❑ 81CokTeaS-115
❑ 81Don-17
❑ 81Fle-361
❑ 81FleStiC-100
❑ 81OPC-213
❑ 81Top-535
❑ 81TopScr-100
❑ 81TopSti-24
❑ 81TopSti-211
❑ 82Don-347
❑ 82Fle-487
❑ 82FleSta-79
❑ 82OPC-395
❑ 82Top-395
❑ 82TopSti-81
❑ 82TopStiV-81
❑ 83AllGamPI-154
❑ 83AstPos-18
❑ 83Don-347
❑ 83Fle-312
❑ 83FleSti-142
❑ 83OPC-332
❑ 83Top-485
❑ 83TopFol-5
❑ 83TopSti-278
❑ 83TopTra-76T
❑ 84Don-637
❑ 84Fle-133
❑ 84Nes792-16
❑ 84Nes792-714
❑ 84OPC-16
❑ 84Top-16
❑ 84Top-714
❑ 84TopSti-322
❑ 84TopTif-16
❑ 84TopTif-714
❑ 85Don-591
❑ 85Fle-136
❑ 85Top-738
❑ 85TopTif-738
❑ 85YanTCMP-37
❑ 86BraPol-18
❑ 86Fle-15
❑ 86FleUpd-78
❑ 86TopTra-75T
❑ 86TopTraT-75T
❑ 87Fle-521
❑ 87FleGlo-521
❑ 87Top-214
❑ 87TopSti-44
❑ 87TopTif-214
❑ 89PacSenL-138
❑ 89T/MSenL-80
❑ 90EliSenL-41
❑ 91PacSenL-46
❑ 92YanWIZ8-124
❑ 95MCIAmb-10
❑ 96MedHatBJTI-21
❑ 98GreFalDG-22

Moreno, Orber
❑ 97LanLugTS-17
❑ 98CarLeaAC-2
❑ 98WilBluRC-21
❑ 99Bow-348
❑ 99BowGol-348
❑ 99BowInt-348
❑ 99PacOme-118
❑ 99PacOmeC-118
❑ 99PacOmeG-118

❑ 99PacOmePB-118
❑ 99SkyPre-265
❑ 99SkyPre-265
❑ 99SkyPreR-265
❑ 99SkyPreR-265
❑ 99SPSig-91
Moreno, Ric
❑ 87DunBluJP-936
❑ 93ModA'sC-28
❑ 94ModA'sC-28
❑ 96PawRedSDD-19
❑ 97TreThuB-4
Morenz, Shea
❑ 95Bes-131
❑ 96Exc-91
❑ 96ExcFirYP-9
❑ 96GreBatB-16
❑ 96SigRooOJPP-P9
❑ 96SigRooOJPPS-P9
❑ 97TamYan-20
❑ 98NorNavQ-17
❑ 99SP TopP-91
❑ 99SP TopPPE-91
Moret, Roger (Rogelio)
❑ 71OPC-692
❑ 71Top-692
❑ 72OPC-113
❑ 72RedSoxTI-17
❑ 72Top-113
❑ 73OPC-291
❑ 73Top-291
❑ 74OPC-590
❑ 74Top-590
❑ 74TopSta-137
❑ 75OPC-8
❑ 75Top-8
❑ 75TopMin-8
❑ 76AtlBraP-20
❑ 76OPC-632
❑ 76SSP-420
❑ 76Top-632
❑ 76TopTra-632T
❑ 77Top-292
❑ 78SSP270-106
❑ 78Top-462
❑ 93RanKee-273
Moreta, Manuel
❑ 75WatRoyT-20
❑ 76WatRoyT-19
Moreta, Ramon
❑ 97GreFalDTI-18
❑ 98SanBerS-22
❑ 98SanBerSTIS-19
Morfin, Arvid
❑ 84ButCopKT-18
❑ 86BelMarCr-116
Morgan, Bill
❑ 79QuaCitCT-5
Morgan, Bob M.
❑ 50Bow-222
❑ 52Top-355
❑ 53BowC-135
❑ 53Top-85
❑ 55Bow-81
❑ 56Top-337
❑ 58Top-144
❑ 74dod195T-23
❑ 79DiaGre-323
❑ 79TCM50-193
❑ 83TopRep5-355
❑ 90DodTar-551
❑ 91TopArc1-85
❑ 95TopArcBD-26
❑ 95TopArcBD-45
Morgan, Chet
❑ 74TigTCM1AC-20
❑ 79DiaGre-381
Morgan, Chris
❑ 86FloStaLAP-36
❑ 86LakTigP-16
❑ 87GleFalTP-17
Morgan, Curt
❑ 86MiaMarP-18
Morgan, Cy (Harry)
❑ 09PhiCarE-19
❑ 09RamT20-83
❑ 10NadE1-40
❑ 11A'sFirT20-13
❑ 11D35RocB-13
❑ 11PinT-5-517
❑ 11PloCanE-48
❑ 11SpoLifCW-260
❑ 11SpoLifM-100
❑ 12T207-133
Morgan, David
❑ 93MedHatBJF-3740
❑ 93MedHatBJSP-19
❑ 95HagSunF-72
❑ 96DunBluJUTI-10
❑ 97KnoSmo-18
❑ 98DunBluJSB-19
❑ 98DunBluJTI-25
Morgan, Eddie
❑ 28StaPlaCE-49
❑ 31Exh-21
❑ 33ExhFou-11
❑ 33Gou-116
❑ 34BatR31-60
❑ 34GouCanV-2
❑ 35AlDemDCR3-71
❑ 90DodTar-552
❑ 93ConTSN-943
Morgan, Eric
❑ 97LanJet-19
Morgan, Gary
❑ 90BatCliP-3081
Morgan, Gene
❑ 86MemChiSTOS-19
❑ 86MemChiTOS-19
❑ 87MemChiB-17
❑ 87MemChiP-16
Morgan, Jim
❑ 89ChaLooLITI-18
Morgan, Joe L.
❑ 65OPC-16
❑ 65Top-16
❑ 66OPC-195
❑ 66Top-195
❑ 66TopRubI-69
❑ 66TopVen-195
❑ 67Ast-20
❑ 67AstTeal1-10
❑ 67AstTeal2-17
❑ 67CokCapA-30
❑ 67CokCapAs-12
❑ 67CokCapNLA-24
❑ 67DexPre-148
❑ 67OPCPapI-25
❑ 67Top-337
❑ 67TopPos-25
❑ 67TopTesF-16
❑ 67TopVen-308
❑ 68CokCapA-12
❑ 68DexPre-56
❑ 68OPC-144
❑ 68Top-144
❑ 68Top-364
❑ 68TopVen-144
❑ 68TopVen-364
❑ 69MilBra-195
❑ 69MLBOffS-141
❑ 69OPC-35
❑ 69Top-35
❑ 69TopSta-36
❑ 69TopSup-42
❑ 69TopTeaP-6
❑ 70AstPho-20
❑ 70AstTeal-8
❑ 70DayDaiNM-112
❑ 70Kel-72
❑ 70MLBOffS-44
❑ 70OPC-537
❑ 70Top-537
❑ 71AstCok-8
❑ 71AstTeal-16
❑ 71MLBOffS-89
❑ 71OPC-264
❑ 71Top-264
❑ 71TopCoi-117
❑ 71TopGreM-34
❑ 72MilBra-244
❑ 72OPC-132
❑ 72Top-132
❑ 72Top-752
❑ 73BooProC-21
❑ 73Kel2D-34
❑ 73LinPor-57
❑ 73OPC-230
❑ 73SevTraC-49
❑ 73Top-230
❑ 74GreHeroBP-6
❑ 74Kel-36
❑ 74OPC-85
❑ 74OPC-333
❑ 74Top-85
❑ 74Top-333
❑ 74TopSta-28
❑ 75GreHeroBP-4
❑ 75Hos-5
❑ 75HosTwi-5
❑ 75Kel-27
❑ 75OPC-180
❑ 75Top-180
❑ 75TopMin-180
❑ 76BlaDis-40
❑ 76BucDis-40
❑ 76CarDis-40
❑ 76CraDis-40
❑ 76DailsID-40
❑ 76GreHeroBP-4
❑ 76Hos-2
❑ 76HosTwi-2
❑ 76IsaDis-40
❑ 76Kel-14
❑ 76LinSup-96
❑ 76OPC-197
❑ 76OPC-420
❑ 76OrbDis-40
❑ 76RedBarD-40
❑ 76RedIceL-9
❑ 76RedKro-12
❑ 76SafDis-40
❑ 76SSP-38
❑ 76Top-197
❑ 76Top-420
❑ 76TowCluD-40
❑ 77BurCheD-207
❑ 77ChiWilD-48
❑ 77DailsID-48
❑ 77DetCaeD-48
❑ 77HolInnD-48
❑ 77Hos-2
❑ 77MSADis-48
❑ 77OPC-220
❑ 77PepGloD-46
❑ 77RCColC-45
❑ 77RedCarP-13
❑ 77SagDis-48
❑ 77sDis-48
❑ 77Spo-1805
❑ 77Spo-3419
❑ 77Top-100
❑ 77Top-411
❑ 77TopCloS-31
❑ 77WenDis-48
❑ 77ZipDis-48
❑ 78Hos-87
❑ 78OPC-160
❑ 78Pep-18
❑ 78RCColC-7
❑ 78SSP270-121
❑ 78Top-300
❑ 78WifBalD-52
❑ 79BasPat-58
❑ 79Hos-61
❑ 79OPC-5
❑ 79Top-20
❑ 80BurKinPHR-30
❑ 80OPC-342
❑ 80PerHaloFP-205
❑ 80PerHaloFPS-68
❑ 80Top-650
❑ 81Don-18
❑ 81Fle-78
❑ 81FleStiC-109
❑ 81GiaTeal-12
❑ 81Kel-22
❑ 81Top-560
❑ 81TopTra-807
❑ 82Don-312
❑ 82Fle-397
❑ 82FleSta-63
❑ 82Gia25tATI-21
❑ 82K-M-28
❑ 82K-M-30
❑ 82OPC-146
❑ 82OPC-208
❑ 82Top-754
❑ 82Top-755
❑ 83AllGamPI-104
❑ 83Don-24
❑ 83Don-438
❑ 83Don-648
❑ 83Fle-270
❑ 83FleSta-131
❑ 83FleSti-55
❑ 83Oco& SSBG-11
❑ 83OPC-81
❑ 83OPC-264
❑ 83PhiTas-21
❑ 83Top-171
❑ 83Top-603
❑ 83Top-604
❑ 83TopFol-2
❑ 83TopFol-5
❑ 83TopSti-303
❑ 83TopTra-77T
❑ 84A'sMot-3
❑ 84Don-355
❑ 84DonCha-44
❑ 84Fle-43
❑ 84Fle-636
❑ 84FleSti-100
❑ 84FleSti-120
❑ 84FleUpd-80
❑ 84FunFooP-74
❑ 84Nes792-210
❑ 84Nes792-705
❑ 84OCoandSI-37
❑ 84OCoandSI-138
❑ 84OPC-210
❑ 84Top-210
❑ 84Top-705
❑ 84TopGaloC-7
❑ 84TopSti-116
❑ 84TopTif-210
❑ 84TopTif-705
❑ 84TopTra-82T
❑ 84TopTraT-82T
❑ 85Don-584
❑ 85Fle-431
❑ 85Lea-28
❑ 85OPC-352
❑ 85Top-5
❑ 85Top-352
❑ 85TopMin-352
❑ 85TopSti-5
❑ 85TopSti-6
❑ 85TopSti-325
❑ 85TopTif-5
❑ 85TopTif-352
❑ 86AstGreT-2
❑ 86AstMot-3
❑ 86RedGreT-10
❑ 86SpoDecG-56
❑ 87AstSer1-17
❑ 87AstSer1-25
❑ 87AstSer1-29
❑ 87AstShoSO-18
❑ 87AstShoSPO-21
❑ 87AstShoSTw-22
❑ 87AstShoSTw-24
❑ 87AstShoSTw-27
❑ 89TopBasT-28
❑ 90AGFA-11
❑ 90PerGreM-89
❑ 90TopMag-13
❑ 92UppDecBH-40
❑ 92UppDecBH-41
❑ 92UppDecBH-43
❑ 92UppDecBH-44
❑ 92UppDecBH-AU5
❑ 93TedWil-30
❑ 93TedWilM-18
❑ 93UppDecS-12
❑ 93Yoo-10
❑ 94CarLeaA-DJ10
❑ 95SonGre-9
❑ 96Red76K-3
❑ 96Red76K-9
❑ 97SpollICC-7
❑ 97St.VinHHS-12
❑ 98SpollITaN-22
❑ 98SpollITaNEE-22
❑ 98TopStaRR-3
❑ 98TopStaRRA-3
❑ 99DumSet-JM
❑ 99DumSet-JM
Morgan, Joe M.
❑ 60Top-229
❑ 61Top-511
❑ 62KahAtl-15
❑ 81PawRedST-12
❑ 89Sco-660
❑ 89Top-714
❑ 89TopTif-714
❑ 90OPC-321
❑ 90Top-321
❑ 90TopTif-321
❑ 90TopTVRS-1
❑ 91OPC-21
❑ 91Top-21
❑ 91TopDesS-21
❑ 91TopMic-21
❑ 91TopTif-21
Morgan, Ken
❑ 87VisOakP-3
❑ 88VisOakCLC-146
❑ 88VisOakP-90
❑ 89OrlTwiB-17
❑ 89OrlTwiP-1341
❑ 90Bes-30
❑ 90CMC-751
❑ 90OrlSunRB-10
❑ 90OrlSunRP-1096
❑ 90OrlSunRS-12
❑ 91LinDriAAA-411
❑ 91PorBeaLD-411
❑ 91PorBeaP-1578
Morgan, Kevin
❑ 91NiaFalRC-1
❑ 91NiaFalRP-3642
❑ 92ClaFS7-104
❑ 92FayGenF-2177
❑ 93LakTigC-19
❑ 93LakTigF-1318
❑ 94St.LucMC-18
❑ 94St.LucMF-1202
❑ 95BinMetTI-15
❑ 96BinMetB-20
❑ 97BinMetB-22
Morgan, Mike (Michael)
❑ 79OgdA'sT-3
❑ 80Top-671
❑ 81NasSouTI-10
❑ 82YanPhoA-16
❑ 83Don-108
❑ 83Fle-388
❑ 83Top-203
❑ 83TopTra-78T
❑ 84Nes792-423
❑ 84OPC-6
❑ 84SyrChiT-22
❑ 84Top-423
❑ 84TopTif-423
❑ 85MarMot-25
❑ 86MarMot-25
❑ 86MarPacNB-9
❑ 86Top-152
❑ 86TopTif-152
❑ 87Don-366
❑ 87Fle-591
❑ 87FleGlo-591
❑ 87MarMot-8
❑ 87Top-546
❑ 87TopTif-546
❑ 88Don-120
❑ 88DonBasB-86
❑ 88Fle-380
❑ 88FleGlo-380
❑ 88OriFreB-12
❑ 88OriPos-21
❑ 88Sco-295
❑ 88ScoGlo-295
❑ 88Top-32
❑ 88TopBig-98
❑ 88TopTif-32
❑ 88TopTra-73T
❑ 88TopTraT-73T
❑ 89DodMot-13
❑ 89DodPol-23
❑ 89DodStaSV-8
❑ 89Don-164
❑ 89DonBasB-122
❑ 89FleUpd-91
❑ 89Top-788
❑ 89TopTif-788
❑ 89TopTra-84T
❑ 89TopTraT-84T
❑ 89UppDec-653
❑ 90DodMot-21
❑ 90DodPol-36
❑ 90DodTar-553
❑ 90Don-132
❑ 90Fle-403
❑ 90FleCan-403
❑ 90Lea-358
❑ 90OPC-367
❑ 90RedFolSB-66
❑ 90Sco-342
❑ 90Top-367
❑ 90TopTif-367
❑ 90UppDec-317
❑ 91DodMot-21
❑ 91DodPho-19
❑ 91DodPol-36
❑ 91DodSt.V-12
❑ 91Don-182
❑ 91Fle-213
❑ 91Lea-193
❑ 91OPC-631
❑ 91OriCro-316
❑ 91PanCanT1-89
❑ 91PanFreS-63
❑ 91PanSti-52
❑ 91RedFolS-67
❑ 91Sco-276
❑ 91StaClu-562
❑ 91Top-631
❑ 91TopDesS-631
❑ 91TopMic-631
❑ 91TopTif-631
❑ 91Ult-165
❑ 91UppDec-578
❑ 91USPlaCA-5C
❑ 92Bow-647
❑ 92CubMar-36
❑ 92DodStaTA-30
❑ 92Don-200
❑ 92Fle-465
❑ 92FleUpd-74
❑ 92Lea-204
❑ 92LeaBlaG-204
❑ 92OPC-289
❑ 92OPCPre-180
❑ 92Pin-414
❑ 92Sco-171
❑ 92ScoRoo-66T
❑ 92StaClu-787
❑ 92StaCluD-124
❑ 92Stu-17
❑ 92Top-289
❑ 92TopGol-289
❑ 92TopGolW-289
❑ 92TopMic-289
❑ 92TopTra-76T
❑ 92TopTraG-76T
❑ 92Ult-471
❑ 92UppDec-513
❑ 92UppDec-703
❑ 92YanWIZ8-125
❑ 93Bow-144
❑ 93CubMar-17
❑ 93CubStaC-17
❑ 93Don-394
❑ 93Fin-188
❑ 93FinRef-188
❑ 93Fla-18
❑ 93Fle-23
❑ 93FunPac-82
❑ 93Lea-123
❑ 93OPC-207
❑ 93PacSpa-59
❑ 93PanSti-201
❑ 93Pin-63
❑ 93Sco-73
❑ 93Sel-145
❑ 93SelAce-10
❑ 93SelStaL-90
❑ 93SP-86
❑ 93StaClu-285
❑ 93StaCluFDI-285
❑ 93StaCluMOP-285
❑ 93Top-373
❑ 93TopGol-373
❑ 93TopInaM-373
❑ 93TopInaR-373
❑ 93TopMic-373
❑ 93TriPla-76
❑ 93Ult-21
❑ 93UppDec-106
❑ 93UppDecGold-106
❑ 93USPlaCA-7S
❑ 94Bow-26
❑ 94ColC-212
❑ 94ColChoGS-212
❑ 94ColChoSS-212
❑ 94Don-206
❑ 94Fin-96
❑ 94FinRef-96
❑ 94Fle-391
❑ 94Lea-192
❑ 94OPC-235
❑ 94Pac-104
❑ 94Pin-113
❑ 94PinArtP-113
❑ 94PinMusC-113
❑ 94Sco-214
❑ 94ScoGolR-214
❑ 94Sel-121
❑ 94StaClu-304
❑ 94StaCluFDI-304
❑ 94StaCluGR-304
❑ 94StaCluMOP-304
❑ 94StaCluT-359
❑ 94StaCluTFDI-359
❑ 94Top-479
❑ 94TopGol-479
❑ 94TopSpa-479
❑ 94TriPla-75
❑ 94Ult-164
❑ 94UppDec-451
❑ 94UppDecED-451
❑ 95ColCho-216

❑ 95ColChoGS-216
❑ 95ColChoSS-216
❑ 95Don-385
❑ 95DonPreP-385
❑ 95StaClu-336
❑ 95StaCluMOP-336
❑ 95StaCluSTWS-336
❑ 95Top-121
❑ 96CarPol-19
❑ 96ColCho-691
❑ 96ColChoGS-691
❑ 96ColChoSS-691
❑ 96Don-282
❑ 96DonPreP-282
❑ 96Fla-364
❑ 96Fle-549
❑ 96FleTif-549
❑ 96LeaSigEA-133
❑ 96Pac-225
❑ 96StaClu-87
❑ 96StaCluMOP-87
❑ 96UppDec-181
❑ 98PacInvGems-138
❑ 98PacOnl-428
❑ 98PacOnlR-428
❑ 98PacOnlWC-428
❑ 98UppDec-694
❑ 99UppDecEM-MC2
❑ 99UppDecEMFXG-MC2
Morgan, Ray
❑ 12T207-134
❑ 14B18B-45
❑ 14FatPlaT-34
❑ 15SpoNewM-124
❑ 16BF2FP-51
❑ 16SpoNewM-126
❑ 16TanBraE-14
❑ 17ColE13-90A
❑ 17ColE13-121A
❑ 17ColE13-121B
❑ 17HolBreD-70
Morgan, Rick
❑ 80KnoBluJT-26
Morgan, Scott
❑ 91KinIndC-7
❑ 91KinIndP-319
❑ 92CanIndS-113
❑ 92KinIndF-2472
❑ 93KinIndC-20
❑ 93KinIndF-2245
❑ 93KinIndTI-20
❑ 95WatIndTI-21
❑ 96WesOahCHWB-44
Morgan, Scott A.
❑ 97CalLeaATI-38
❑ 97CarLeaTP-6
❑ 97KinIndB-16
❑ 97Top-488
❑ 98AkrAerM-28
❑ 98DonSigA-61
❑ 98DonSigAC-80
❑ 98DonSigAM-81
❑ 98SP MinPE-46
❑ 98SP SPTSC-SM
❑ 98SPMin-46
❑ 99Top-430
❑ 99TopChr-430
❑ 99TopChrR-430
Morgan, Steve
❑ 96LowSpiB-20
Morgan, Tim
❑ 66St.PetCTI-10
Morgan, Tom S.
❑ 47StaPinP2-29
❑ 52BerRos-43
❑ 52Bow-109
❑ 52Top-331
❑ 53Top-132
❑ 54NewYorJA-54
❑ 55Bow-100
❑ 56YanTeal-18
❑ 57Top-239
❑ 58Top-365
❑ 59TigGraASP-13
❑ 59Top-545
❑ 60Lea-97
❑ 60Top-33
❑ 60TopVen-33
❑ 61AngJayP-8
❑ 61Top-272
❑ 62AngJayP-7
❑ 62Top-11
❑ 62TopVen-11
❑ 63AngJayP-10
❑ 63Top-421
❑ 73OPC-421
❑ 73Top-421A
❑ 73Top-421B
❑ 74OPC-276
❑ 74Top-276
❑ 75PadDea-21
❑ 83TopRep5-331
❑ 91TopArc1-132
Morgan, Vern
❑ 55DesMoiHB-14
❑ 72TwiPos-12
❑ 72TwiTeal-8
❑ 73OPC-49
❑ 73Top-49A
❑ 73Top-49B
❑ 74OPC-447
❑ 74Top-447
❑ 75TwiPos-17
Morgan, Willis
❑ 15Zee-84
Morganna, Kissing Bandit (Entertainer)
❑ 90UtiBluSP-27
Morhardt, Greg
❑ 85OrlTwiT-9
❑ 86OrlTwiP-13
❑ 87PorBeaP-20
Morhardt, Moe
❑ 62Top-309
Mori, Dan
❑ 87SanJosBP-12
Moriarty, Edward
❑ 11SpoLifCW-261
❑ 36GouWidPPR-A76
Moriarty, George
❑ 07TigACDPP-24
❑ 09ColChiE-205
❑ 09ColChiE-206A
❑ 09ColChiE-206B
❑ 09T206-256
❑ 09TigMorBBBP-11
❑ 09TigMorPWBPP-8
❑ 09TigTaCP-12
❑ 10NadE1-41
❑ 11HelSta-34
❑ 11PinT-5-155
❑ 11PloCanE-49
❑ 11S74Sil-16
❑ 11SpoLifM-64
❑ 11T205-124
❑ 12ColRedB-205
❑ 12ColRedB-206A
❑ 12ColRedB-206B
❑ 12ColTinT-205
❑ 12ColTinT-206A
❑ 12ColTinT-206B
❑ 12HasTriFT-39
❑ 12HasTriFT-55
❑ 12HasTriFT-75B
❑ 12T207-135
❑ 14B18B-19A
❑ 14B18B-19B
❑ 14B18B-19C
❑ 14CraJacE-114
❑ 14PieStaT-78
❑ 15CraJacE-114
❑ 15SpoNewM-125
❑ 16SpoNewM-127
❑ 21Exh-111
❑ 72ClaCar-87
❑ 93UppDecTR-6
❑ 94ConTSN-1209
❑ 94ConTSNB-1209
Moriarty, Mike
❑ 96FtMyeMB-11
❑ 97NewBriRC-22
❑ 98NewBriRCM-20
Moriarty, Todd
❑ 84EveGiaC-26
Morillo, Cesar
❑ 91BasCitRC-19
❑ 91BasCitRP-1405
❑ 91Cla/Bes-60
❑ 92BasCitRC-12
❑ 92EugEmeC-20
❑ 92EugEmeF-3038
❑ 93RocRoyC-18
❑ 93RocRoyF-724
❑ 94VenLinU-6
❑ 94WilBluRC-15
❑ 94WilBluRF-309
❑ 95BakBlaTI-5
❑ 95LinVen-88
❑ 96-97LinVen-5
❑ 96WicWraB-21
❑ 97TulDriTI-19
Morillo, Donald
❑ 95ChaRivUTIS-31
❑ 95ChaRivUTIS-35
Morillo, Santiago
❑ 91SouOreAC-17
❑ 91SouOreAP-3840
Morimoto, Ken
❑ 95YakBeaTI-23
❑ 96GreFalDB-21
❑ 96GreFalDTI-25
❑ 97VerBeaD-18
Moritz, Chris
❑ 85GreHorT-7
❑ 86WinHavRSP-18
❑ 87NewBriRSP-23
❑ 88NewBriRSP-907
❑ 89NewBriRSP-603
❑ 89NewBriRSS-11
Moritz, Tom
❑ 86BirBarTI-7
Mork, Dennis
❑ 80QuaCitCT-22
Morlan, John
❑ 75OPC-651
❑ 75Top-651
❑ 75TopMin-651
Morland, Mike
❑ 91St.CatBJC-1
❑ 91St.CatBJP-3398
❑ 92MyrBeaHC-8
❑ 92MyrBeaHF-2201
❑ 93KnoSmoF-1254
❑ 94KnoSmoF-1307
Morley, Mike
❑ 80OmaRoyP-18
Morlock, Allen
❑ 83SprCarF-24
❑ 84ArkTraT-8
❑ 86ArkTraP-16
Morman, Alvin
❑ 92AshTouC-20
❑ 93JacGenF-2108
❑ 94Bow-314
❑ 94Cla-115
❑ 94ExcFS7-205
❑ 94TucTorF-759
❑ 94UppDecML-70
❑ 95TucTotTI-17
❑ 96AstMot-17
❑ 96Fin-B201
❑ 96FinRef-B201
❑ 96FleUpd-U140
❑ 96FleUpdTC-U140
❑ 97PacPriGotD-GD154
❑ 98PacOnl-225
❑ 98PacOnlR-225
❑ 98PacOnlWC-225
Morman, Russ
❑ 86BufBisP-19
❑ 86SpoRoo-33
❑ 87Don-306
❑ 87Fle-645
❑ 87FleGlo-645
❑ 87HawIsIP-22
❑ 87SpoTeaP-26
❑ 87Top-233
❑ 87TopTif-233
❑ 87WhiSoxC-23
❑ 88VanCanC-17
❑ 88VanCanP-760
❑ 89VanCanC-16
❑ 89VanCanP-590
❑ 90CMC-190
❑ 90OmaRoyC-15
❑ 90OmaRoyP-73
❑ 90ProAAAF-608
❑ 90WicStaSGD-21
❑ 91Lea-263
❑ 92NasSouF-1840
❑ 93BufBisF-524
❑ 94EdmTraF-2880
❑ 95ChaKniTI-17
❑ 96ChaKniB-20
❑ 97ChaKni-21
❑ 98DurBulTI-21
Morogiello, Dan
❑ 79RicBraT-18
❑ 80RicBraT-1
❑ 82LouRedE-20
❑ 83RocRedWT-6
❑ 84Nes792-682
❑ 84Top-682
❑ 84TopTif-682
❑ 85DomLeaS-50
❑ 85RicBraT-5
❑ 91OriCro-317
Morones, Geno
❑ 91HunCubC-15
❑ 91HunCubP-3331
❑ 92GenCubC-10
❑ 92GenCubF-1558
❑ 93PeoChiC-15
❑ 93PeoChiF-1082
❑ 95WicWraTI-32
❑ 96WilBluRB-16
Moronko, Jeff
❑ 80BatTroT-28
❑ 81ChaLooT-12
❑ 82ChaLooT-21
❑ 83BufBisT-17
❑ 84BufBisT-1
❑ 85MaiGuiT-19
❑ 85TulDriTI-22
❑ 86OklCit8P-14
❑ 87ColCliP-11
❑ 87ColCliT-17
❑ 87IntLeaAT-1
❑ 88ColCliC-18
❑ 88ColCliP-20
❑ 88ColCliP-328
❑ 89ChaLooLITI-19
❑ 92YanWIZ8-126
Morphy, Pat
❑ 90OneYanP-3379
❑ 91GreHorP-3055
❑ 92ForLauYC-17
❑ 92ForLauYTI-21
❑ 92Ft.LauYF-2609
Morreale, John
❑ 94BelBreC-18
❑ 94BelBreFI-111
❑ 96StoPorB-19
Morrell, John
❑ 87BucN28-10A
❑ 87BucN28-10B
❑ 87OldJudN-350
❑ 88AllandGN-5
❑ 88AllandGN-5
Morrell, Tim
❑ 93HolLeg-14
Morrelli, Anthony
❑ 85CloHSS-27
Morrill, Craig
❑ 93ButCopKSP-17
Morrill, John
❑ 88GandBCGCE-27
❑ 88WG1CarG-6
Morris, Aaron
❑ 91WatIndC-19
❑ 91WatIndP-3375
Morris, Angel
❑ 81BurBeeT-14
❑ 82BelBreFr-26
❑ 85Ft.MyeRT-7
❑ 86MemChiSTOS-20
❑ 86MemChiTOS-20
❑ 87Ft.MyeRP-30
❑ 88BlaYNPRWL-170
❑ 88VirGenS-16
❑ 89BlaYNPRWL-146
❑ 89MemChiB-14
❑ 89MemChiP-1203
❑ 89MemChiS-18
❑ 90MiaMirIS-19
Morris, Bobby
❑ 93HunCubC-21
❑ 93HunCubF-3245
❑ 94MidLeaAF-MDW49
❑ 94PeoChiC-1
❑ 94PeoChiF-2277
❑ 95Bes-60
❑ 95Exc-167
❑ 95SPML-33
❑ 95UppDecML-172
❑ 95UppDecMLFS-172
❑ 96Bow-274
❑ 96BowFoi-274
❑ 96Exc-141
❑ 96OrlCubB-17
❑ 96Top-426
❑ 97OrlRayB-17
Morris, Chad
❑ 96VerExpB-19
Morris, Danny W.
❑ 69OPC-99
❑ 69Top-99A
❑ 69Top-99B
Morris, Dave
❑ 81BurBeeT-1
❑ 83AndBraT-29
❑ 85DurBulT-8
❑ 85EveGiaIC-11
❑ 86CliGiaP-14
Morris, Don
❑ 80WesHavWCT-4
❑ 81WesHavAT-16
Morris, Edward
❑ 87OldJudN-351
Morris, Fred
❑ 78DayBeaAT-19
Morris, Greg
❑ 94BoiHawC-19
❑ 94BoiHawF-3365
❑ 94SigRooDP-83
❑ 94SigRooDPS-83
❑ 94StaCluDP-75
❑ 94StaCluDPFDI-75
❑ 95CedRapKTI-36
❑ 95MidLeaA-36
❑ 96LakElsSB-19
❑ 97LakElsSG-23
❑ 98LakElsSG-22
❑ 98MidAngO-17
Morris, Hal
❑ 87AlbYanP-21
❑ 88ColCliC-20
❑ 88ColCliP-21
❑ 88ColCliP-327
❑ 89ClaLigB-28
❑ 89ColCliC-16
❑ 89ColCliP-16
❑ 89ColCliP-743
❑ 89Don-545
❑ 89Fle-260
❑ 89FleGlo-260
❑ 89ScoHot1R-8
❑ 89TriAAAP-AAA20
❑ 89YanScoNW-29
❑ 90AlbDecGB-18
❑ 90Bow-57
❑ 90BowTif-57
❑ 90ClaUpd-T35
❑ 90Don-514
❑ 90FleUpd-15
❑ 90Hot50RS-32
❑ 90Lea-321
❑ 90OPC-236
❑ 90RedKah-16
❑ 90Sco-602
❑ 90Sco100RS-87
❑ 90ScoYouS2-37
❑ 90Top-236
❑ 90TopTif-236
❑ 90TopTra-76T
❑ 90TopTraT-76T
❑ 90TriAAAC-17
❑ 90UppDec-31
❑ 91Baz-13
❑ 91Bow-691
❑ 91Cla1-T98
❑ 91Cla3-T62
❑ 91ClaGam-178
❑ 91Don-141
❑ 91Fle-72
❑ 91Lea-51
❑ 91MajLeaCP-71
❑ 91OPC-642
❑ 91RedKah-23
❑ 91RedPep-12
❑ 91Sco-647
❑ 91Sco100RS-98
❑ 91ScoHotR-3
❑ 91StaClu-339
❑ 91Stu-168
❑ 91Top-642
❑ 91TopDesS-642
❑ 91TopMic-642
❑ 91TopRoo-20
❑ 91TopTif-642
❑ 91ToyRoo-20
❑ 91Ult-98
❑ 91UppDec-351
❑ 92Bow-468
❑ 92Cla1-T65
❑ 92ClaGam-137
❑ 92Don-258
❑ 92DonCraJ1-32
❑ 92DonDiaK-DK19
❑ 92DonSupD-DK19
❑ 92Fle-412
❑ 92Hig5-33
❑ 92Lea-205
❑ 92LeaBlaG-205
❑ 92OPC-773
❑ 92PanSti-262
❑ 92Pin-22
❑ 92RedKah-23
❑ 92RemUltP-P7
❑ 92RemUltP-P8
❑ 92RemUltP-P9
❑ 92Sco-125
❑ 92Sco100S-14
❑ 92ScoCokD-16
❑ 92ScoImpP-45
❑ 92SpoStaCC-34
❑ 92StaClu-63
❑ 92Stu-24
❑ 92Top-773
❑ 92TopGol-773
❑ 92TopGolW-773
❑ 92TopMic-773
❑ 92TriPla-30
❑ 92Ult-192
❑ 92UppDec-121
❑ 92YanWIZ8-127
❑ 93Don-294
❑ 93Fla-29
❑ 93Fle-37
❑ 93Lea-257
❑ 93OPC-197
❑ 93PacSpa-85
❑ 93PanSti-291
❑ 93Pin-222
❑ 93RedKah-16
❑ 93Sco-38
❑ 93Sel-45
❑ 93SP-211
❑ 93StaClu-534
❑ 93StaCluFDI-534
❑ 93StaCluMOP-534
❑ 93Top-546
❑ 93TopGol-546
❑ 93TopInaM-546
❑ 93TopInaR-546
❑ 93TopMic-546
❑ 93TriPla-223
❑ 93Ult-31
❑ 93UppDec-121
❑ 93UppDec-833
❑ 93UppDecGold-121
❑ 93UppDecGold-833
❑ 94Bow-186
❑ 94ColC-482
❑ 94ColChoGS-482
❑ 94ColChoSS-482
❑ 94Don-221
❑ 94Fin-70
❑ 94FinRef-70
❑ 94Fla-147
❑ 94Fle-417
❑ 94FleExtB-235
❑ 94Lea-433
❑ 94LeaL-97
❑ 94OPC-153
❑ 94PanSti-165
❑ 94Pin-314
❑ 94PinArtP-314
❑ 94PinMusC-314
❑ 94RedKah-20
❑ 94Sco-526
❑ 94ScoGolR-526
❑ 94Sel-158
❑ 94StaClu-363
❑ 94StaCluFDI-363
❑ 94StaCluGR-363
❑ 94StaCluMOP-363
❑ 94Stu-170
❑ 94Top-126
❑ 94TopGol-126
❑ 94TopSpa-126
❑ 94TriPla-216
❑ 94Ult-475
❑ 94UppDec-494
❑ 94UppDecED-494
❑ 95Baz-92
❑ 95Bow-346
❑ 95ColCho-424
❑ 95ColChoGS-424
❑ 95ColChoSE-201
❑ 95ColChoSEGS-201
❑ 95ColChoSESS-201
❑ 95ColChoSS-424
❑ 95Don-234
❑ 95DonDiaK-DK20
❑ 95DonPreP-234
❑ 95DonTopotO-216
❑ 95Fin-102
❑ 95FinRef-102
❑ 95Fla-121
❑ 95Fle-442
❑ 95Lea-210
❑ 95Lea300C-7
❑ 95LeaLim-75
❑ 95Pac-110
❑ 95PacPri-34

❑ 95Pin-332
❑ 95PinArtP-332
❑ 95PinMusC-332
❑ 95RedKah-19
❑ 95Sco-226
❑ 95ScoGolR-226
❑ 95ScoHaloG-HG46
❑ 95ScoPlaTS-226
❑ 95Sel-91
❑ 95SelArtP-91
❑ 95SelCer-35
❑ 95SelCerMG-35
❑ 95Spo-69
❑ 95SpoArtP-69
❑ 95StaClu-231
❑ 95StaCluCC-CC9
❑ 95StaCluFDI-231
❑ 95StaCluMO-34
❑ 95StaCluMOP-231
❑ 95StaCluMOP-CC9
❑ 95StaCluSTDW-RE231
❑ 95StaCluSTWS-231
❑ 95StaCluVR-117
❑ 95StaCluVRMO-117
❑ 95Stu-106
❑ 95Sum-51
❑ 95SumNthD-51
❑ 95Top-27
❑ 95TopCyb-22
❑ 95TopEmb-3
❑ 95TopEmbGI-3
❑ 95TopLeaL-LL29
❑ 95UC3-35
❑ 95UC3ArtP-35
❑ 95Ult-367
❑ 95UltGolM-367
❑ 95UppDec-406
❑ 95UppDecED-406
❑ 95UppDecEDG-406
❑ 95UppDecPLL-R29
❑ 95UppDecPLLE-R29
❑ 95UppDecSE-29
❑ 95UppDecSEG-29
❑ 95USPlaCMLA-5D
❑ 95Zen-42
❑ 96Baz-112
❑ 96ColCho-112
❑ 96ColChoGS-112
❑ 96ColChoSS-112
❑ 96Don-272
❑ 96DonPreP-272
❑ 96EmoXL-166
❑ 96Fin-B185
❑ 96FinRef-B185
❑ 96Fla-235
❑ 96Fle-347
❑ 96FleTif-347
❑ 96Lea-175
❑ 96LeaPre-106
❑ 96LeaPreP-106
❑ 96LeaPrePB-175
❑ 96LeaPrePG-175
❑ 96LeaPrePS-175
❑ 96MetUni-150
❑ 96MetUniP-150
❑ 96Pac-37
❑ 96PanSti-54
❑ 96Pin-119
❑ 96Pin-308
❑ 96PinAfi-49
❑ 96PinAfiAP-49
❑ 96PinAfiFPP-49
❑ 96PinArtP-193
❑ 96PinFoil-308
❑ 96PinSta-193
❑ 96Sco-330
❑ 96ScoDugC-B55
❑ 96ScoDugCAP-B55
❑ 96SelCer-89
❑ 96SelCerAP-89
❑ 96SelCerCB-89
❑ 96SelCerCR-89
❑ 96SelCerMB-89
❑ 96SelCerMG-89
❑ 96SelCerMR-89
❑ 96StaClu-97
❑ 96StaCluMOP-97
❑ 96Stu-36
❑ 96StuPrePB-36
❑ 96StuPrePG-36
❑ 96StuPrePS-36
❑ 96Sum-78
❑ 96SumAbo&B-78
❑ 96SumArtP-78
❑ 96SumFoi-78
❑ 96Top-158
❑ 96TopGal-83
❑ 96TopGalPPI-83
❑ 96TopLas-73
❑ 96Ult-463
❑ 96UltGolM-463
❑ 96UppDec-308
❑ 96Zen-51
❑ 96ZenArtP-51
❑ 96ZenMoz-10
❑ 97Bow-286
❑ 97BowChr-97
❑ 97BowChrI-97
❑ 97BowChrIR-97
❑ 97BowChrR-97
❑ 97BowInt-286
❑ 97Cir-372
❑ 97CirRav-372
❑ 97ColCho-307
❑ 97Don-117
❑ 97DonGolPP-117
❑ 97DonSilPP-117
❑ 97Fin-281
❑ 97FinEmb-281
❑ 97FinEmbR-281
❑ 97FinRef-281
❑ 97FlaShoLC-123
❑ 97FlaShoLeg0-123
❑ 97FlaShoLeg1-123
❑ 97FlaShoM-A123
❑ 97FlaShoM-B123
❑ 97FlaShoM-C123
❑ 97FlaShoR0-123
❑ 97FlaShoR1-123
❑ 97FlaShoR2-123
❑ 97Fle-298
❑ 97FleTif-298
❑ 97Lea-276
❑ 97LeaFraM-276
❑ 97LeaFraMDC-276
❑ 97MetUni-48
❑ 97Pac-272
❑ 97PacLigB-272
❑ 97PacSil-272
❑ 97Sco-49
❑ 97ScoArtPWB-49
❑ 97ScoPreS-49
❑ 97ScoShoS-49
❑ 97ScoShoSAP-49
❑ 97SP-54
❑ 97StaClu-292
❑ 97StaCluMOP-292
❑ 97Top-44
❑ 97TopChr-16
❑ 97TopChrR-16
❑ 97Ult-407
❑ 97UltGolME-407
❑ 97UltPlaME-407
❑ 97UppDec-43
❑ 98CroRoy-67
❑ 98Fle-414
❑ 98Pac-267
❑ 98PacAur-47
❑ 98PacOnl-345
❑ 98PacOnlR-345
❑ 98PacOnlWC-345
❑ 98PacPlaB-267
❑ 98PacRedT-267
❑ 98PacSil-267
❑ 98PinPlu-98
❑ 98Revo-71
❑ 98RevoSS-71
❑ 98SPxFin-283
❑ 98SPxFinR-283
❑ 98SPxFinS-283
❑ 98Top-177
❑ 98TopChr-177
❑ 98TopChrR-177
❑ 98TopDevR-177
❑ 98TopDia-177
❑ 98TopMiniC-177
❑ 98TopSta-64
❑ 98TopStaB-64
❑ 98TopStaG-64
❑ 98TopStaGR-64
❑ 98TopStaS-64
❑ 98Ult-282
❑ 98UltGolM-282
❑ 98UltMas-282
❑ 98UltPlaM-282
❑ 98UppDec-686
❑ 99Fle-482
❑ 99FleSta9-482
❑ 99FleWarT-482
❑ 99MetUni-61
❑ 99MetUniGM-61
❑ 99MetUniPMG-61
❑ 99Pac-208
❑ 99PacAur-46
❑ 99PacAurOD-46
❑ 99PacCroC-134
❑ 99PacCroCPB-134
❑ 99PacPar-64
❑ 99PacParC-64
❑ 99PacParG-64
❑ 99PacParHoloGold-64
❑ 99PacParHS-64
❑ 99PacParOD-64
❑ 99PacParPB-64
❑ 99PacParRed-64
❑ 99PacPlaB-208
❑ 99PacPri-72
❑ 99PacPriHB-72
❑ 99PacPriHG-72
❑ 99PacPriHM-72
❑ 99PacPriHP-72
❑ 99PacPriRed-72
❑ 99PacPriS-117
❑ 99PacPriS206-117
❑ 99PacPriS206R-117
❑ 99PacRed-208
❑ 99Top-349
❑ 99TopChr-349
❑ 99TopChrR-349
❑ 99TopMVPP-349
❑ 99Ult-86
❑ 99UltGolM-86
❑ 99UltMas-86
❑ 99UltPlaM-86
❑ 99UppDec-113
❑ 99UppDec-348
❑ 99UppDecEL1-113
❑ 99UppDecEL1-348
❑ 99UppDecEL2-113
❑ 99UppDecEL2-348

Morris, Jack

❑ 77EvaTriT-20
❑ 78TigBurK-8
❑ 78TigTeal-20
❑ 78Top-703
❑ 79Top-251
❑ 80Top-371
❑ 81CokTeaS-54
❑ 81Don-127
❑ 81Fle-475
❑ 81OPC-284
❑ 81PerAll-15
❑ 81TigDetN-128
❑ 81Top-572
❑ 81TopSti-80
❑ 82Don-107
❑ 82Fle-274
❑ 82FleSta-159
❑ 82Kel-5
❑ 82OPC-47
❑ 82OPC-108
❑ 82Top-165
❑ 82Top-450
❑ 82Top-556
❑ 82TopSti-10
❑ 82TopSti-139
❑ 82TopSti-183
❑ 83Don-5
❑ 83Don-107
❑ 83Fle-336
❑ 83FleSti-252
❑ 83Kel-35
❑ 83OPC-65
❑ 83TigPos-21
❑ 83Top-65
❑ 83TopSti-69
❑ 84AllGamPI-174
❑ 84Don-415
❑ 84Fle-87
❑ 84FleSti-83
❑ 84FunFooP-59
❑ 84Nes792-136
❑ 84Nes792-195
❑ 84Nes792-666
❑ 84OPC-195
❑ 84TigFarJ-10
❑ 84TigTeal-25
❑ 84TigWavP-27
❑ 84Top-136
❑ 84Top-195
❑ 84Top-666
❑ 84TopGloS-10
❑ 84TopRubD-16
❑ 84TopSti-263
❑ 84TopTif-136
❑ 84TopTif-195
❑ 84TopTif-666
❑ 85AllGamPI-81
❑ 85Don-415
❑ 85Fle-18
❑ 85Fle-643
❑ 85FleLimE-21
❑ 85FleStaS-82
❑ 85Lea-142
❑ 85OPC-382
❑ 85SevCoi-D12
❑ 85SubDis-15
❑ 85ThoMcAD-15
❑ 85TigCaiD-14
❑ 85TigWen-16
❑ 85Top-610
❑ 85Top3-D-28
❑ 85TopGloS-26
❑ 85TopMin-610
❑ 85TopRubD-14
❑ 85TopSti-9
❑ 85TopSti-15
❑ 85TopSti-256
❑ 85TopSup-43
❑ 85TopTif-610
❑ 86BasStaB-75
❑ 86Don-105
❑ 86DonAll-18
❑ 86DonHig-27
❑ 86DonPop-18
❑ 86DorChe-2
❑ 86Fle-232
❑ 86FleMin-48
❑ 86FleSlu-23
❑ 86FleStiC-79
❑ 86GenMilB-1E
❑ 86Lea-38
❑ 86OPC-270
❑ 86SevCoi-C10
❑ 86Spo-117
❑ 86Spo-141
❑ 86TigCaiD-12
❑ 86Top-270
❑ 86Top3-D-17
❑ 86TopGloA-10
❑ 86TopMinL-14
❑ 86TopSti-163
❑ 86TopSti-268
❑ 86TopSup-38
❑ 86TopTat-11
❑ 86TopTif-270
❑ 87ClaGam-90
❑ 87Don-13
❑ 87Don-173
❑ 87DonOpeD-212
❑ 87DonSupD-13
❑ 87Dra-27
❑ 87Fle-158
❑ 87FleBasA-28
❑ 87FleGlo-158
❑ 87FleLimE-28
❑ 87FleMin-70
❑ 87FleSlu-27
❑ 87FleStiC-80
❑ 87GenMilB-2F
❑ 87KayB-20
❑ 87Lea-13
❑ 87Lea-135
❑ 87MandMSL-6
❑ 87MSAJifPD-3
❑ 87OPC-376
❑ 87RedFolSB-114
❑ 87SevCoi-D8
❑ 87SmoAmeL-6
❑ 87Spo-87
❑ 87Spo-111
❑ 87SpoTeaP-15
❑ 87StuPan-19
❑ 87TigCaiD-14
❑ 87TigCok-7
❑ 87Top-778
❑ 87TopCoi-18
❑ 87TopGloS-47
❑ 87TopMinL-55
❑ 87TopSti-266
❑ 87TopTif-778
❑ 88CheBoy-3
❑ 88ClaRed-174
❑ 88Don-127
❑ 88DonAll-24
❑ 88DonBasB-181
❑ 88Dra-32
❑ 88Fle-64
❑ 88Fle-626
❑ 88FleAwaW-26
❑ 88FleBasA-26
❑ 88FleBasM-24
❑ 88FleExcS-27
❑ 88FleGlo-64
❑ 88FleGlo-626
❑ 88FleHea-3
❑ 88FleHotS-28
❑ 88FleLeaL-28
❑ 88FleMin-22
❑ 88FleRecS-26
❑ 88FleStiC-26
❑ 88FleTeaL-23
❑ 88GreBasS-67
❑ 88Lea-85
❑ 88OPC-340
❑ 88PanSti-85
❑ 88Sco-545
❑ 88ScoGlo-545
❑ 88Spo-176
❑ 88StaLinAl-18
❑ 88StaLinTi-14
❑ 88TarPla-29
❑ 88TigPep-47
❑ 88TigPol-8
❑ 88Top-340
❑ 88TopBig-170
❑ 88TopCoi-21
❑ 88TopGloS-17
❑ 88TopMinL-11
❑ 88TopRitTM-27
❑ 88TopSti-268
❑ 88TopStiB-59
❑ 88TopTif-340
❑ 88TopUKM-50
❑ 88TopUKMT-50
❑ 89Bow-93
❑ 89BowTif-93
❑ 89Don-234
❑ 89Fle-139
❑ 89FleBasM-30
❑ 89FleGlo-139
❑ 89OPC-266
❑ 89PanSti-334
❑ 89RedFolSB-82
❑ 89Sco-250
❑ 89Scomast-8
❑ 89Spo-5
❑ 89TigMar-47
❑ 89TigPol-47
❑ 89Top-645
❑ 89TopBasT-68
❑ 89TopBig-61
❑ 89TopSti-277
❑ 89TopTif-645
❑ 89TopUKM-54
❑ 89TVSpoM-71
❑ 89UppDec-352
❑ 90Don-639A
❑ 90Don-639B
❑ 90DonBesA-34
❑ 90Fle-610
❑ 90FleCan-610
❑ 90FleLeaL-27
❑ 90FleLeaLC-27
❑ 90KayB-19
❑ 90Lea-482
❑ 90M.Vpin-36
❑ 90OPC-555
❑ 90PanSti-76
❑ 90PubIntS-478
❑ 90Sco-203
❑ 90TigCok-12
❑ 90Top-555
❑ 90TopMag-78
❑ 90TopSti-276
❑ 90TopTif-555
❑ 90UppDec-573
❑ 91BluJayFS-20
❑ 91Bow-319
❑ 91Cla2-T49
❑ 91Cla3-T61
❑ 91DodPho-23
❑ 91Don-492
❑ 91Fle-343
❑ 91FleUpd-39
❑ 91Lea-294
❑ 91OPC-75
❑ 91OPCPre-84
❑ 91PanFreS-296
❑ 91Sco-114
❑ 91ScoPro-114
❑ 91ScoRoo-74T
❑ 91StaClu-447
❑ 91StaCluMO-22
❑ 91Stu-89
❑ 91Top-75
❑ 91TopDesS-75
❑ 91TopMic-75
❑ 91TopTif-75
❑ 91TopTra-82T
❑ 91TopTraT-82T
❑ 91UltUpd-39
❑ 91UppDec-45
❑ 91UppDec-336
❑ 91UppDec-736
❑ 91UppDecFE-80F
❑ 91USPlaCA-1H
❑ 92BluJayP-7
❑ 92Bow-16
❑ 92Cla1-T66
❑ 92ClaGam-199
❑ 92Don-25
❑ 92Don-216
❑ 92DonMcD-G4
❑ 92Fle-211
❑ 92FleUpd-66
❑ 92Fre-18
❑ 92KinDis-18
❑ 92Lea-425
❑ 92LeaBlaG-425
❑ 92New-18
❑ 92OPC-235
❑ 92OPCPre-79
❑ 92PanSti-122
❑ 92PanSti-279
❑ 92PepDieM-6
❑ 92Pin-483
❑ 92Pin-585
❑ 92RedFolS-122
❑ 92Sco-652
❑ 92Sco-798
❑ 92ScoRoo-15T
❑ 92SpollIFK1-81
❑ 92StaClu-640
❑ 92StaCluD-125
❑ 92StaCluD-126
❑ 92StaCluMO-7
❑ 92Stu-257
❑ 92Top-235
❑ 92TopGol-235
❑ 92TopGolW-235
❑ 92TopMic-235
❑ 92TopTra-77T
❑ 92TopTraG-77T
❑ 92TriPlaG-GS3
❑ 92Ult-452
❑ 92UltAwaW-1
❑ 92UppDec-315
❑ 92UppDec-732
❑ 93BluJayCP1-8
❑ 93BluJayD-7
❑ 93BluJayD4-20
❑ 93BluJayDM-9
❑ 93BluJayFS-21
❑ 93Bow-463
❑ 93ClaGam-68
❑ 93Don-351
❑ 93Fle-347
❑ 93Fle-697
❑ 93FunPac-59
❑ 93HumDumC-21
❑ 93Lea-113
❑ 93MSABenSPD-3
❑ 93OPC-179
❑ 93OPCWorC-11
❑ 93PacSpa-326
❑ 93PanSti-24
❑ 93Pin-57
❑ 93Pin-298
❑ 93Pin-472
❑ 93Sco-37
❑ 93Sco-508
❑ 93Sel-158
❑ 93SelAce-5
❑ 93SelStaL-85
❑ 93SP-51
❑ 93StaClu-356
❑ 93StaCluFDI-356
❑ 93StaCluMOP-356
❑ 93Top-185
❑ 93TopGol-185
❑ 93TopInaM-185
❑ 93TopInaR-185
❑ 93TopMic-185
❑ 93TriPla-160
❑ 93Ult-290
❑ 93UppDec-164
❑ 93UppDecGold-164
❑ 94ColC-542
❑ 94ColChoGS-542
❑ 94ColChoSS-542
❑ 94Fla-285
❑ 94Fle-339
❑ 94FleExtB-63
❑ 94FleUpd-33
❑ 94Lea-401

❑ 94Pac-649
❑ 94Pin-532
❑ 94PinArtP-532
❑ 94PinMusC-532
❑ 94Sco-453
❑ 94ScoGolR-453
❑ 94ScoRoo-RT21
❑ 94ScoRooGR-RT21
❑ 94Sel-289
❑ 94SpoRoo-99
❑ 94SpoRooAP-99
❑ 94StaClu-556
❑ 94StaCluFDI-556
❑ 94StaCluGR-556
❑ 94StaCluMOP-556
❑ 94TopTra-36T
❑ 94Ult-346
❑ 94UppDec-331
❑ 94UppDecED-331
❑ 95BluJayUSPC-5D
❑ 95BluJayUSPC-12S
❑ 95ColCho-433
❑ 95ColChoGS-433
❑ 95ColChoSS-433
❑ 95Ult-368
❑ 95UltGolM-368
❑ 95UppDecSE-31
❑ 95UppDecSEG-31
❑ 97BluJayS-41

Morris, Jeff
❑ 83TucTorT-6
❑ 87EveGiaC-26
❑ 88CliGiaP-717
❑ 89CliGiaP-901
❑ 90SanJosGB-26
❑ 90SanJosGCLC-54
❑ 90SanJosGP-2028
❑ 90SanJosGS-29
❑ 92PitMetC-19
❑ 92PitMetF-3312
❑ 93BluOriC-26
❑ 94AlbPolC-28
❑ 94AlbPolF-2255
❑ 96FreKeyB-25
❑ 96MauStiHWB-33
❑ 97FreKey-2

Morris, Jeremy
❑ 98TamYanM-21

Morris, Jim
❑ 87PanAmTUBI-NNO
❑ 87StoPorP-23
❑ 89SarWhiSS-15

Morris, Joe
❑ 90JamExpP-23

Morris, John Daniel
❑ 84OmaRoyT-8
❑ 85DomLeaS-136
❑ 85Don-32
❑ 85LouRedR-23
❑ 85OmaRoyT-19
❑ 86LouRedTI-20
❑ 87CarTeal-22
❑ 87Don-480
❑ 87FleUpd-83
❑ 87FleUpdG-83
❑ 87LouRedTI-20
❑ 87SpoRoo2-42
❑ 87Top-211
❑ 87TopRoo-10
❑ 87TopTif-211
❑ 88CarTeal-22
❑ 88Don-480
❑ 88Fle-43
❑ 88FleGlo-43
❑ 88LouRedBTI-35
❑ 88Sco-346
❑ 88ScoGlo-346
❑ 88Top-536
❑ 88TopTif-536
❑ 89CarSmo-14
❑ 89CarTeal-19
❑ 89Top-578
❑ 89TopTif-578
❑ 90CarSmo-15
❑ 90Don-516
❑ 90Fle-254
❑ 90FleCan-254
❑ 90OPC-383
❑ 90Sco-134
❑ 90Top-383
❑ 90TopTif-383
❑ 90TopTVCa-35
❑ 91FleUpd-109
❑ 91Lea-496
❑ 91OriCro-318
❑ 91PhiMed-29
❑ 92Bow-474
❑ 92Don-92
❑ 92StaClu-796
❑ 93LouRedF-228
❑ 94MidAngF-2456
❑ 94MidAngOHP-18
❑ 96VanCanB-3

Morris, John W.
❑ 67BalOriP-70
❑ 69OPC-111
❑ 69PilPos-27
❑ 69Top-111
❑ 69TopFou-1
❑ 70BreMcD-22
❑ 70BreMil-17
❑ 71MLBOffS-446
❑ 71OPC-721
❑ 71Top-721
❑ 75OPC-577
❑ 75Top-577
❑ 75TopMin-577
❑ 77PilPosR-27
❑ 83Pil69G-38
❑ 94BreMilB-337

Morris, Ken
❑ 88AubAstP-1957

Morris, Marc
❑ 91PocPioP-3786
❑ 91PocPioSP-12
❑ 92VisOakC-5
❑ 92VisOakF-1012

Morris, Matt
❑ 95Bes-133
❑ 95NewJerCTI-22
❑ 96ArkTraB-21
❑ 96Bow-301
❑ 96BowBes-137
❑ 96BowBesAR-137
❑ 96BowBesR-137
❑ 96BowFoi-301
❑ 96Exc-231
❑ 96ExcFirYP-10
❑ 96SigRooOJPP-P5
❑ 96SigRooOJPPS-P5
❑ 96StPetCB-3
❑ 96Top-232
❑ 96TopChr-92
❑ 96TopChrR-92
❑ 97Bes-17
❑ 97Bow-113
❑ 97BowBes-150
❑ 97BowBesAR-150
❑ 97BowBesR-150
❑ 97BowChr-132
❑ 97BowChrI-132
❑ 97BowChrIR-132
❑ 97BowChrR-132
❑ 97BowInt-113
❑ 97ColCho-471
❑ 97Don-386
❑ 97DonGolPP-386
❑ 97DonLim-143
❑ 97DonLimE-143
❑ 97DonLimENG-143
❑ 97DonSig-93
❑ 97DonSigA-73
❑ 97DonSigAC-89
❑ 97DonSigAM-89
❑ 97DonSigPPP-93
❑ 97DonSilPP-386
❑ 97DonTea-165
❑ 97DonTeaSPE-165
❑ 97Fin-316
❑ 97FinEmb-316
❑ 97FinEmbR-316
❑ 97FinRef-316
❑ 97Fle-683
❑ 97FleTif-683
❑ 97Lea-335
❑ 97LeaFraM-335
❑ 97LeaFraMDC-335
❑ 97LouRedB-24
❑ 97NewJerCB-1
❑ 97PinX-P-133
❑ 97PinX-PMoS-133
❑ 97Sel-169
❑ 97SelCom-169
❑ 97SpoIll-17
❑ 97SpoIllEE-17
❑ 97TopStaFAS-FAS13
❑ 97Ult-529
❑ 97UltGolME-529
❑ 97UltPlaME-529
❑ 98Bow-28
❑ 98BowChr-28
❑ 98BowChrGA-28
❑ 98BowChrGAR-28
❑ 98BowChrI-28
❑ 98BowChrIR-28
❑ 98BowChrR-28
❑ 98BowGolA-28
❑ 98BowInt-28
❑ 98CarScoP-15
❑ 98CirThu-254
❑ 98CirThuRav-254
❑ 98CirThuSupRav-254
❑ 98ColCho-221
❑ 98ColChoSQ-SQ7
❑ 98Don-110
❑ 98DonCol-110
❑ 98DonColE-491
❑ 98DonColL-205
❑ 98DonColP-676
❑ 98DonColS-110
❑ 98DonCruG-94
❑ 98DonCruP-94
❑ 98DonCruR-94
❑ 98DonEli-91
❑ 98DonEliA-91
❑ 98DonEliS-91
❑ 98DonGolPP-110
❑ 98DonPre-126
❑ 98DonPreSeat-126
❑ 98DonPriCD-110
❑ 98DonPriCE-491
❑ 98DonPriCL-205
❑ 98DonPriCP-676
❑ 98DonSilPP-110
❑ 98Fin-45
❑ 98FinNo--45
❑ 98FinNo-R-45
❑ 98FinRef-45
❑ 98FlaShoLeg0-80
❑ 98FlaShoLeg1-80
❑ 98FlaShoLeg2-80
❑ 98FlaShoLeg3-80
❑ 98FlaShoLegM-80
❑ 98FlaShoR0-80
❑ 98FlaShoR1-80
❑ 98FlaShoR2-80
❑ 98FlaShoR3-80
❑ 98Fle-183
❑ 98FleRooS-14
❑ 98FleVin'-51
❑ 98FleVin'C-51
❑ 98Lea-5
❑ 98LeaFraDA-5
❑ 98LeaFraF-5
❑ 98LeaFraM-5
❑ 98LeaFraM-5
❑ 98LeaFraMDC-5
❑ 98LeaFraMDC-5
❑ 98LeaFraMS-5
❑ 98LeaFraMZ2-5
❑ 98MetUni-92
❑ 98MetUniPMG-92
❑ 98Pac-417
❑ 98PacOnl-623
❑ 98PacOnlR-623
❑ 98PacOnlWC-623
❑ 98PacPlaB-417
❑ 98PacRedT-417
❑ 98PacSil-417
❑ 98Pin-76
❑ 98PinIns-78
❑ 98PinInsCE-78
❑ 98PinInsDE-78
❑ 98PinPreP-76
❑ 98PinSna-SLC14
❑ 98Sco-242
❑ 98ScoCar-15
❑ 98ScoRT-56
❑ 98ScoRTSS-PP53
❑ 98ScoRTSSAP-PP53
❑ 98ScoRTSSAP1-PP53
❑ 98SpoIllTaN-115
❑ 98SpoIllTaNEE-115
❑ 98SpoIllWSF-85
❑ 98SpoIllWSFEE-85
❑ 98SpoIllWSFFE-85
❑ 98SPxFin-12
❑ 98SPxFinR-12
❑ 98SPxFinS-12
❑ 98StaCluC-CS33
❑ 98StaCluC-CS35
❑ 98StaCluC-CS36
❑ 98StaCluFDI-353
❑ 98StaCluI-353
❑ 98StaCluOneK-353
❑ 98StaCluPP-353
❑ 98Stu-106
❑ 98StuGPP-106
❑ 98StuSPP-106
❑ 98Top-128
❑ 98TopChr-128
❑ 98TopChrR-128
❑ 98TopDevR-128
❑ 98TopDia-128
❑ 98TopGal-146
❑ 98TopGalGP-146
❑ 98TopGalOPP-146
❑ 98TopGalPPI-146
❑ 98TopGalPPIA-146
❑ 98TopMiniC-128
❑ 98TopOpeD-63
❑ 98Ult-2
❑ 98UltGolM-2
❑ 98UltMas-2
❑ 98UltPlaM-2
❑ 98UppDec-262
❑ 98UppDec-491
❑ 98UppDecBCP-BC8
❑ 98UppDecDS-DS7
❑ 98UppDecSF-145
❑ 99Fle-200
❑ 99FleSta9-200
❑ 99FleWarT-200
❑ 99MetUni-220
❑ 99MetUniGM-220
❑ 99MetUniPMG-220
❑ 99Pac-358
❑ 99PacPlaB-358
❑ 99PacRed-358
❑ 99SkyThu-177
❑ 99SkyThuRant-177
❑ 99SkyThuRave-177
❑ 99SP Aut-81
❑ 99StaClu-266
❑ 99StaCluFDI-266
❑ 99StaCluOoaK-266
❑ 99StaCluPP-266
❑ 99ThuSkySupR-177
❑ 99Top-263
❑ 99TopChr-263
❑ 99TopChrR-263
❑ 99TopMVPP-263
❑ 99UppDec-188
❑ 99UppDecEL1-188
❑ 99UppDecEL2-188
❑ 99UppDecM-173
❑ 99UppDecMGS-173
❑ 99UppDecMHFS-173
❑ 99UppDecMSS-173
❑ 99Vic-330

Morris, Rick
❑ 87DurBulP-20
❑ 88CarLeaAS-32
❑ 88DurBulS-15
❑ 89GreBraB-5
❑ 89GreBraP-1172
❑ 89GreBraS-15
❑ 89Sta-37
❑ 90GreBraB-11
❑ 90GreBraP-1136
❑ 90GreBraS-14
❑ 91GreBraC-19
❑ 91GreBraLD-213
❑ 91GreBraP-3013
❑ 91LinDriAA-213

Morris, Rod
❑ 88ButCopKSP-19
❑ 89ChaRanS-16
❑ 89Sta-8
❑ 90ChaRanS-14
❑ 91LinDriAA-588
❑ 91TulDriLD-588
❑ 91TulDriP-2786
❑ 91TulDriTI-19
❑ 92TulDriF-2708

Morris, Rossi
❑ 91PriRedC-10
❑ 91PriRedP-3528
❑ 92PriRedC-20
❑ 92PriRedF-3100

Morris, Steve
❑ 87HawRai-12
❑ 89EliTwiS-20
❑ 89KenTwiP-1060
❑ 89KenTwiS-16
❑ 89Sta-53
❑ 90Bes-185
❑ 90KenTwiB-9
❑ 90KenTwiP-2308
❑ 90KenTwiS-14

Morris, Tom
❑ 63GadFunC-78

Morris, Tom 80s
❑ 80QuaCitCT-5

Morris, Warren
❑ 98AriFalLTP-17
❑ 98BesAutSS-38
❑ 98Bow-72
❑ 98BowChr-72
❑ 98BowChrGA-72
❑ 98BowChrGAR-72
❑ 98BowChrI-72
❑ 98BowChrIR-72
❑ 98BowChrR-72
❑ 98BowGolA-72
❑ 98BowInt-72
❑ 98SP MinDTSPE-DS14
❑ 98SP MinPE-121
❑ 98SP SPTSC-WM
❑ 98SPMin-121
❑ 98SPMinDTS-DS14
❑ 98TexLeaC-14
❑ 98TexLeaTPG-25
❑ 98Top-260
❑ 98TopChr-260
❑ 98TopChrR-260
❑ 98TopDevR-260
❑ 98TopDia-260
❑ 98TopMiniC-260
❑ 98TulDriTI-1
❑ 99BowBes-139
❑ 99BowBesAR-139
❑ 99BowBesR-139
❑ 99DumSet-124
❑ 99FlaShoLeg1-42
❑ 99FlaShoLeg2-42
❑ 99FlaShoLeg3-42
❑ 99FlaShoLegM1-42
❑ 99FlaShoLegM2-42
❑ 99FlaShoLegM3-42
❑ 99FlaShoR1-42
❑ 99FlaShoR2-42
❑ 99FlaShoR3-42
❑ 99FleBri-167
❑ 99FleBri2G-167
❑ 99FleBriBlu-167
❑ 99FleBriGol-167
❑ 99FleMys-124
❑ 99FleMysM-124
❑ 99JustheS-35
❑ 99JustheSJB-35
❑ 99JustheSJN-4
❑ 99JustheSJN-7
❑ 99PacInv-115
❑ 99PacInvOD-115
❑ 99PacInvPB-115
❑ 99PacOme-191
❑ 99PacOmeC-191
❑ 99PacOmeG-191
❑ 99PacOmePB-191
❑ 99SkyPre-230
❑ 99SkyPre-230
❑ 99SkyPreR-230
❑ 99SkyPreR-230
❑ 99SP TopP-92
❑ 99SP TopPC-WM
❑ 99SP TopPDtS-D24
❑ 99SP TopPGF-GF24
❑ 99SP TopPPE-92
❑ 99UDHolo-46
❑ 99UDHoloAUsome-46
❑ 99UppDecE-96
❑ 99UppDecEFXG-96
❑ 99UppDecROSS-S27
❑ 99UppDecROSS-S27

Morrisette, James
❑ 89ColMetB-15
❑ 89ColMetGS-16
❑ 89SouAtlLAGS-20
❑ 90St.LucMS-17
❑ 91MiaMirC-25
❑ 91St.LucMC-3

Morrisey, Todd
❑ 85CloHSS-28

Morrison, Brian
❑ 87SanBerSP-17
❑ 88FloStaLAS-13
❑ 88MiaMarS-15
❑ 89KnoBluJB-17
❑ 89KnoBluJP-1146
❑ 90SalBucS-14
❑ 98HudValR-19

Morrison, Bruce
❑ 83LynMetT-9
❑ 91MelBusF-14

Morrison, Chris
❑ 96WesMicWB-17
❑ 97VisOakG-19

Morrison, Dan
❑ 88T/MUmp-47
❑ 89T/MUmp-45
❑ 89T/MUmp-60
❑ 90T/MUmp-43

Morrison, Greg
❑ 95GreFalDTI-35
❑ 96SavSanB-8
❑ 98HagSunM-19

Morrison, Jeff
❑ 87BelMarTI-13

Morrison, Jim
❑ 91WinHavRSC-23
❑ 91WinHavRSP-502
❑ 92LynRedSC-25
❑ 92LynRedSF-2921
❑ 93NewBriRSF-1234

Morrison, Jim (James Forrest)
❑ 76OklCit8TI-6
❑ 79Top-722
❑ 80OPC-272
❑ 80Top-522
❑ 81CokTeaS-34
❑ 81Don-158
❑ 81Fle-357
❑ 81Top-323
❑ 81TopSti-60
❑ 81TopSupHT-20
❑ 82Don-395
❑ 82Fle-354
❑ 82OPC-154
❑ 82Top-654
❑ 82TopTra-77T
❑ 83Don-150
❑ 83Fle-313
❑ 83Top-173
❑ 84Don-322
❑ 84Fle-257
❑ 84Nes792-44
❑ 84Pir-13
❑ 84Top-44
❑ 84TopTif-44
❑ 85Don-532
❑ 85Fle-471
❑ 85Pir-13
❑ 85Top-433
❑ 85TopTif-433
❑ 86Don-386
❑ 86ElmPioRSP-13
❑ 86Fle-614
❑ 86OPC-56
❑ 86Top-553
❑ 86TopSti-133
❑ 86TopTif-553
❑ 87Don-484
❑ 87DonOpeD-169
❑ 87Fle-614
❑ 87FleGamW-29
❑ 87FleGlo-614
❑ 87FleMin-71
❑ 87FleStiC-81
❑ 87GreHorP-22
❑ 87Lea-215
❑ 87OPC-237
❑ 87SpoTeaP-18
❑ 87StuPan-10
❑ 87Top-237
❑ 87TopSti-133
❑ 87TopTif-237
❑ 88Don-543A
❑ 88Don-543B
❑ 88Fle-65
❑ 88FleGlo-65
❑ 88OPC-288
❑ 88Sco-272
❑ 88ScoGlo-272
❑ 88StaLinTi-15
❑ 88Top-751
❑ 88TopBig-237
❑ 88TopSti-272
❑ 88TopTif-751
❑ 89ElmPioP-8
❑ 89PacSenL-137
❑ 89T/MSenL-81
❑ 89TopSenL-61
❑ 89UppDec-568
❑ 90EliSenL-42

Morrison, John
❑ 21Exh-112
❑ 21Nei-115
❑ 22E120-222
❑ 22W572-67
❑ 22W573-89
❑ 23WilChoV-108
❑ 90DodTar-554
❑ 93ConTSN-794

Morrison, Keith

❑ 90PulBraB-6
❑ 90PulBraP-3104
❑ 91MacBraC-6
❑ 91MacBraP-860
❑ 92AlbPolCB-20
❑ 92AlbPolF-2301
❑ 93PalSprAC-14
❑ 93PalSprAF-65
❑ 94MidAngF-2435
❑ 94MidAngOHP-19

Morrison, Perry
❑ 80ElPasDT-19
❑ 81HolMilT-24
❑ 82HolMilT-7

Morrison, Red (Anthony)
❑ 87OneYanP-2
❑ 88FloStaLAS-45
❑ 88Ft.LauYS-17
❑ 89Ft.LauYS-17

Morrison, Robbie
❑ 98SpoIndG-22

Morrison, Ryan
❑ 96PitMetB-15

Morrison, Scott
❑ 96YakBeaTI-21

Morriss, Guy
❑ 80PhiBul-15

Morrissey, Joe
❑ 33ButCanV-35
❑ 33Gou-97
❑ 34BabRutG-47
❑ 34ButPreR-46
❑ 34DiaMatCSB-135
❑ 72TCMthe3-86

Morrissey, Tom
❑ 87BucN28-54

Morrow, Alvin
❑ 99Bow-328
❑ 99BowGol-328
❑ 99BowInt-328

Morrow, Ben
❑ 87SalBucP-9

Morrow, Brian
❑ 90WicStaSGD-27

Morrow, Chris
❑ 88GreFalDTI-5
❑ 89BakDodCLC-204
❑ 89SalDodTI-18
❑ 90BakDodCLC-247
❑ 90CalLeaACLC-12
❑ 91FloStaLAP-FSL41
❑ 91VerBeaDC-29
❑ 91VerBeaDP-789
❑ 92SanAntMS-571
❑ 92SkyAA F-250
❑ 93AlbDukF-1476
❑ 93VerBeaDC-19

Morrow, Chuck
❑ 33WorCig(-56

Morrow, David
❑ 86JamExpP-17
❑ 87BurExpP-1083

Morrow, Nick
❑ 94BilMusF-3682
❑ 94BilMusSP-11
❑ 95Exc-178
❑ 96BesAutS-64
❑ 97St.PetDRUB-23

Morrow, Red
❑ 88CalLeaACLC-50

Morrow, Steve
❑ 82ForMyeRT-23
❑ 84MemChiT-22
❑ 86MemChiSTOS-21
❑ 86MemChiTOS-21
❑ 87MemChiB-27
❑ 87MemChiP-26
❑ 88MemChiB-4
❑ 89OmaRoyC-24
❑ 89OmaRoyP-1723

Morrow, Timmie
❑ 89ButCopKSP-26
❑ 90Bes-284
❑ 90CMC-847
❑ 90GasRanB-17
❑ 90GasRanP-2533
❑ 90GasRanS-15
❑ 91ChaRanC-23
❑ 91ChaRanP-1327
❑ 92ChaRanF-2238
❑ 92ClaFS7-68
❑ 93TulDriF-2748
❑ 93TulDriTI-20
❑ 94TulDriF-256
❑ 94TulDriTI-17
❑ 94TulDriTI-23

Morse, Harry
❑ 20Zee-148
❑ 21Zee-165

Morse, Jacob C.
❑ 90LitSunW-3

Morse, Matt
❑ 90EliTwiS-14
❑ 91KenTwiC-5
❑ 91KenTwiP-2083

Morse, Mike
❑ 81AppFoxT-20
❑ 82GleFalWST-8
❑ 83GleFalWST-7

Morse, Paul
❑ 94EliTwiC-14
❑ 94EliTwiF-3727
❑ 95ForMyeMTI-17
❑ 96FtMyeMB-12
❑ 96HarCitRCB-21
❑ 97NewBriRC-23
❑ 98SanBerS-23
❑ 98SanBerSTIS-20

Morse, Peter
❑ 09ObaT21-400
❑ 12ObaPreT-149

Morse, Randy
❑ 84ShrCapFB-13

Morse, Scott
❑ 87PorChaRP-4
❑ 89ChaRanS-17

Morseman, Robert
❑ 96FreKeyB-16
❑ 97DelSho-8
❑ 97FreKey-18

Morsler, Joseph
❑ 88KimN18-25

Mort, Roy
❑ 33Zee-32
❑ 33Zee-33
❑ 37Zee-3
❑ 37Zee-19

Mortensen, Tony
❑ 89FreStaBS-14
❑ 90SpoIndSP-4
❑ 91WatDiaC-6
❑ 91WatDiaP-1253
❑ 92HigDesMC-11

Mortillaro, John
❑ 83AndBraT-13
❑ 84DurBulT-24

Mortimer, Bob
❑ 86SalRedBP-20

Mortimer, Mark
❑ 97EugEmeB-19
❑ 98MacBraM-15

Mortimer, Mike
❑ 94HudValRC-15
❑ 94HudValRF-3381

Morton, Bubba (Wycliffe)
❑ 62Top-554
❑ 63Top-164
❑ 66SeaPop-14
❑ 67OPC-79
❑ 67Top-79
❑ 68Top-216
❑ 68TopVen-216
❑ 69MilBra-196
❑ 69Top-342

Morton, Carl
❑ 69ExpFudP-9
❑ 69Top-646
❑ 70ExpPin-11
❑ 70OPC-109
❑ 70Top-109
❑ 71ExpPS-17
❑ 71Kel-23
❑ 71MLBOffS-135
❑ 71OPC-515
❑ 71Top-515
❑ 71TopCoi-35
❑ 71TopGreM-4
❑ 71TopSup-28
❑ 71TopTat-132
❑ 72OPC-134
❑ 72ProStaP-9
❑ 72Top-134
❑ 73LinPor-6
❑ 73OPC-331
❑ 73Top-331
❑ 74OPC-244
❑ 74Top-244
❑ 74TopSta-8
❑ 75AtlBraP-23
❑ 75OPC-237
❑ 75Top-237
❑ 75TopMin-237
❑ 76AtlBraP-21
❑ 76Hos-43
❑ 76HosTwi-43
❑ 76OPC-328
❑ 76SSP-4
❑ 76Top-328
❑ 77Top-24

Morton, Guy
❑ 15SpoNewM-126
❑ 16BF2FP-24
❑ 16SpoNewM-128
❑ 17ColE13-122
❑ 20WalMaiW-34
❑ 21E121So8-64
❑ 22AmeCarE122-48
❑ 22W575-86
❑ 23W503-33
❑ 77Ind192T-13

Morton, Harry
❑ 18Zee-67

Morton, Kevin
❑ 88CapCodPB-12
❑ 88CapCodPPaLP-139
❑ 89ElmPioP-27
❑ 90Bes-211
❑ 90EasLeaAP-EL32
❑ 90NewBriRSB-14
❑ 90NewBriRSP-1316
❑ 90NewBriRSS-12
❑ 90ProAaA-5
❑ 90TopTVRS-52
❑ 91Bow-130
❑ 91Cla3-T63
❑ 91Don-37
❑ 91DonRoo-40
❑ 91LinDriAAA-361
❑ 91PawRedSDD-13
❑ 91PawRedSLD-361
❑ 91PawRedSP-36
❑ 91RedSoxP-20
❑ 91UppDecF-66F
❑ 92Don-330
❑ 92OPC-724
❑ 92OPCPre-7
❑ 92PawRedSF-919
❑ 92PinTea2-14
❑ 92ProFS7-18
❑ 92RedSoxDD-19
❑ 92Sco-420
❑ 92Sco100RS-36
❑ 92StaClu-115
❑ 92Top-724
❑ 92TopDeb91-127
❑ 92TopGol-724
❑ 92TopGolW-724
❑ 92TopMic-724
❑ 92UppDec-676
❑ 94NorTidF-2918
❑ 95IowCubTI-22
❑ 97DunDonPPS-15

Morton, Lew
❑ 52Par-13

Morton, Maurice
❑ 85SpoIndC-15

Morton, Ron
❑ 88SpoIndP-1946
❑ 89Sta-190
❑ 89WatDiaP-1782
❑ 89WatDiaS-21
❑ 90WatDiaB-12
❑ 90WatDiaP-2378

Morton, Stan
❑ 80CliGiaT-22

Morton, Sydney
❑ 86NegLeaF-36

Morvay, Joe
❑ 93EriSaiC-17
❑ 93EriSaiF-3113
❑ 94ChaRivC-14
❑ 94ChaRivF-2669
❑ 95TulDriTI-16
❑ 96TulDriTI-19
❑ 97WicWra-5

Moryn, Walt
❑ 52Par-72
❑ 53ExhCan-39
❑ 55Bow-261
❑ 57Top-16
❑ 58Top-122
❑ 59Top-147
❑ 59Top-488
❑ 59TopVen-147
❑ 60CubJayP-9
❑ 60Lea-17
❑ 60Top-74
❑ 60TopTat-37
❑ 60TopVen-74
❑ 61CarJayP-9
❑ 61Top-91
❑ 61TopMagR-32
❑ 79DiaGre-122
❑ 79TCM50-141
❑ 90DodTar-555
❑ 95TopArcBD-137

Mosby, Linvel
❑ 78AshTouT-19
❑ 79AshTouT-4
❑ 80AshTouT-20

Moscaret, Jeff
❑ 84MidCubT-11

Moscat, Frank
❑ 85LynMetT-20

Moschetti, Mike
❑ 94SouOreAC-20
❑ 94SouOreAF-3632

Moschitto, Ross
❑ 65Top-566
❑ 81TCM60I-441
❑ 92YanWIZ6-91

Moscrey, Mike
❑ 88CedRapRP-1139
❑ 89ChaLooB-19
❑ 90ChaLooGS-22

Moseby, Lloyd
❑ 80SyrChiT-16
❑ 80SyrChiTI-15
❑ 80VenLeaS-68
❑ 81Fle-421
❑ 81OPC-52
❑ 81OPCPos-24
❑ 81Top-643
❑ 82BluJayS-13
❑ 82Don-129
❑ 82Fle-621
❑ 82OPC-223
❑ 82OPCPos-4
❑ 82Top-223
❑ 82TopSti-246
❑ 82TopStiV-246
❑ 83Don-556
❑ 83Fle-435
❑ 83OPC-124
❑ 83Top-452
❑ 83TopSti-130
❑ 84AllGamPI-153
❑ 84BluJayFS-25
❑ 84Don-363
❑ 84Fle-164
❑ 84FunFooP-132
❑ 84Nes792-92
❑ 84Nes792-403
❑ 84Nes792-606
❑ 84NesDreT-7
❑ 84OPC-3
❑ 84OPC-92
❑ 84OPC-289
❑ 84Top-92
❑ 84Top-403
❑ 84Top-606
❑ 84TopRubD-3
❑ 84TopSti-191
❑ 84TopSti-365
❑ 84TopStiB-4
❑ 84TopTif-92
❑ 84TopTif-403
❑ 84TopTif-606
❑ 85AllGamPI-64
❑ 85BluJayCC-5
❑ 85BluJayFS-23
❑ 85Don-437
❑ 85DonActA-5
❑ 85Fle-115
❑ 85Fle-636
❑ 85Lea-143
❑ 85OPC-77
❑ 85OPCPos-19
❑ 85Top-545
❑ 85TopMin-545
❑ 85TopRubD-3
❑ 85TopSti-359
❑ 85TopSup-39
❑ 85TopTif-545
❑ 86BluJayAF-20
❑ 86BluJayFS-26
❑ 86Don-73
❑ 86Fle-67
❑ 86FleLeaL-26
❑ 86GenMilB-3F
❑ 86Lea-72
❑ 86OPC-360
❑ 86Top-360
❑ 86TopSti-195
❑ 86TopTat-21
❑ 86TopTif-360
❑ 87BluJayFS-23
❑ 87Don-21
❑ 87Don-74
❑ 87DonAll-59
❑ 87DonOpeD-36
❑ 87DonSupD-21
❑ 87Fle-236
❑ 87FleGlo-236
❑ 87FleLimE-29
❑ 87FleMin-72
❑ 87FleRecS-22
❑ 87GenMilB-1G
❑ 87Lea-21
❑ 87Lea-105
❑ 87OPC-210
❑ 87RedFolSB-55
❑ 87Spo-96
❑ 87SpoTeaP-5
❑ 87StuPan-28
❑ 87SyrChi1A-1
❑ 87Top-210
❑ 87TopSti-190
❑ 87TopTif-210
❑ 88BluJay5-9
❑ 88BluJayFS-23
❑ 88Don-367
❑ 88DonBasB-199
❑ 88Fle-119
❑ 88FleGlo-119
❑ 88FleStiC-75
❑ 88GreBasS-61
❑ 88Lea-140
❑ 88MSAHosD-20
❑ 88OPC-272
❑ 88PanSti-225
❑ 88Sco-109
❑ 88ScoGlo-109
❑ 88Spo-74
❑ 88StaLinBJ-15
❑ 88Top-565
❑ 88TopBig-113
❑ 88TopSti-189
❑ 88TopTif-565
❑ 88TopUKM-51
❑ 88TopUKMT-51
❑ 89BluJayFS-20
❑ 89Don-231
❑ 89Fle-241
❑ 89FleGlo-241
❑ 89OPC-113
❑ 89PanSti-473
❑ 89RedFolSB-83
❑ 89Sco-12
❑ 89Top-113
❑ 89TopBig-262
❑ 89TopSti-188
❑ 89TopTif-113
❑ 89UppDec-381
❑ 90BluJayHS-2
❑ 90Bow-362
❑ 90BowTif-362
❑ 90Don-504
❑ 90DonBesA-62
❑ 90Fle-90
❑ 90FleCan-90
❑ 90FleUpd-97
❑ 90Lea-377
❑ 90OPC-779
❑ 90PubIntS-524
❑ 90Sco-404
❑ 90ScoRoo-25T
❑ 90TigCok-13
❑ 90TigTeal-15
❑ 90Top-779
❑ 90TopBig-305
❑ 90TopTif-779
❑ 90TopTra-77T
❑ 90TopTraT-77T
❑ 90UppDec-421
❑ 90UppDec-789
❑ 91Bow-135
❑ 91Don-188
❑ 91Fle-344
❑ 91Lea-223
❑ 91OPC-632
❑ 91PanFreS-293
❑ 91PanSti-239
❑ 91Sco-133
❑ 91StaClu-364
❑ 91Stu-56
❑ 91TigCok-15
❑ 91TigPol-7
❑ 91Top-632
❑ 91TopDesS-632
❑ 91TopMic-632
❑ 91TopTif-632
❑ 91Ult-124
❑ 91UppDec-559
❑ 92Don-443
❑ 92Fle-142
❑ 92New-19
❑ 92PanSti-111
❑ 92Sco-468
❑ 92UppDec-468
❑ 96BluJayOH-20
❑ 97St.CatSB-1
❑ 98SyrSkyG-20

Moseley, Scott
❑ 90HelBreSP-8

Moser, Arnold
❑ 39WorWidGV-19

Moser, Larry
❑ 83AndBraT-30

Moser, Ricky
❑ 90EugEmeGS-20

Moser, Steve
❑ 86WatPirP-15
❑ 87SalBucP-13

Moser, Walt
❑ 09ObaT21-106

Moses, Gerry (Gerald)
❑ 65Top-573
❑ 69Top-476A
❑ 69Top-476B
❑ 70DayDaiNM-104
❑ 70OPC-104
❑ 70RedSoxCPPC-8
❑ 70Top-104
❑ 71MLBOffS-352
❑ 71OPC-205
❑ 71Top-205
❑ 71TopCoi-6
❑ 72OPC-356
❑ 72Top-356
❑ 73OPC-431
❑ 73Top-431
❑ 74OPC-19
❑ 74Top-19
❑ 75OPC-271
❑ 75Top-271
❑ 75TopMin-271
❑ 81RedSoxBG2S-97
❑ 92YanWIZ7-117

Moses, John
❑ 81WauTimT-25
❑ 83AppFoxFr-24
❑ 83SalLakCGT-19
❑ 84ChaLooT-24
❑ 84Don-74
❑ 84Nes792-517
❑ 84Top-517
❑ 84TopTif-517
❑ 85CalCanC-83
❑ 86CalCanP-16
❑ 87Don-393
❑ 87Fle-592
❑ 87FleGlo-592
❑ 87MarMot-18
❑ 87Top-284
❑ 87TopTif-284
❑ 88Don-440
❑ 88Fle-381
❑ 88FleGlo-381
❑ 88FleUpd-45
❑ 88FleUpdG-45
❑ 88PorBeaC-22
❑ 88PorBeaP-643
❑ 88Sco-309
❑ 88ScoGlo-309
❑ 88StaLinMa-10
❑ 88Top-712
❑ 88TopClo-76
❑ 88TopTif-712
❑ 89Don-626
❑ 89Fle-121A
❑ 89Fle-121B
❑ 89FleGlo-121
❑ 89Sco-432
❑ 89Top-72
❑ 89TopTif-72
❑ 89UppDec-242
❑ 90Don-590
❑ 90Fle-381
❑ 90FleCan-381
❑ 90Lea-433
❑ 90OPC-653
❑ 90PubIntS-333
❑ 90Sco-391

❑ 90Top-653
❑ 90TopTif-653
❑ 90UppDec-240
❑ 91ColSprSSP-2198
❑ 91Fle-619
❑ 91OPC-341
❑ 91Sco-429
❑ 91Top-341
❑ 91TopDesS-341
❑ 91TopMic-341
❑ 91TopTif-341
❑ 92CalCanF-3743
❑ 92CalCanS-63
❑ 93HolLeg-15
Moses, Mark
❑ 80AndBraT-13
Moses, Mike
❑ 93BilMusF-3943
❑ 93BilMusSP-20
Moses, Shane
❑ 94HelBreF-3612
❑ 94HelBreSP-9
Moses, Steve
❑ 85PorBeaC-30
❑ 86ReaPhiP-18
❑ 87WilBilP-6
Moses, Wally (Wallace)
❑ 34BatR31-98
❑ 35DiaMatCS3T1-110
❑ 36GouWidPPR-A77
❑ 36GouWidPPR-C19
❑ 36NatChiFPR-58
❑ 37ExhFou-14
❑ 37GouThuMR-5
❑ 37OPCBatUV-109
❑ 37WheBB9-13
❑ 38DixLid-5
❑ 38DixLidP-5
❑ 38ExhFou-14
❑ 38GouFliMR-5A
❑ 38GouFliMR-5B
❑ 39PlaBal-64
❑ 40PlaBal-26
❑ 41DouPlaR-125
❑ 41PlaBal-42
❑ 47RedSoxTI-15
❑ 48RedSoxTI-18
❑ 49A'sTeal-26
❑ 49PhiBul-40
❑ 50A'sTeal-21
❑ 51A'sTeal-24
❑ 51Bow-261
❑ 52A'sTeal-19
❑ 53A'sTeal-21
❑ 53BowC-95
❑ 54A'STEAI-15
❑ 55Bow-294
❑ 60Top-459
❑ 61Yan61RL-32
❑ 68TigDetFPB-15
❑ 75RedSox1T-27
❑ 77PhiFav-24
❑ 81TCM60I-481
❑ 83Yan196-NNO
❑ 85TCMPpl1-44
❑ 91ConTSN-90
Mosher, Peyton
❑ 82VerBeaDT-9
Mosier, Mark
❑ 97SalVolG-23
Moskau, Paul
❑ 77IndIndTI-9
❑ 78IndIndTI-3
❑ 78OPC-181
❑ 78Pep-19
❑ 78Top-126
❑ 79OPC-197
❑ 79Top-377
❑ 80RedEnq-31
❑ 80Top-258
❑ 81Fle-207
❑ 81OPC-358
❑ 81Top-546
❑ 82Don-355
❑ 82Fle-76
❑ 82Top-97
Moskau, Ryan
❑ 98YakBeaG-23
❑ 99TeaBesR-60
❑ 99TeaBesRFS-11
❑ 99TeaBesRG-60
❑ 99TeaBesRS-60
Moskiman, Doc
❑ 09ObaT21-330
❑ 11Zee-95
❑ 12ObaPreT-79
Mosley, Dave
❑ 87SalSpuS-8
Mosley, Reggie
❑ 83TriTriT-15
Mosley, Tim
❑ 96RocCubTI-21
Mosley, Tony
❑ 87ElmPioBC-17
❑ 87ElmPioRC-17
❑ 88ElmPio1C-2
❑ 88WinHavRSS-15
❑ 89ElmPioP-11
❑ 90WinHavRSS-19
❑ 91LynRedSC-5
❑ 91LynRedSP-1194
❑ 92NewBriRSF-429
❑ 92NewBriRSS-490
❑ 92SkyAA F-210
Mosman, Marc
❑ 95BelGiaTI-23
Mosolf, Jim
❑ 32Zee-40
Mosquea, Alberto
❑ 95MarPhiTI-17
❑ 96MarPhiB-17
Mosquera, David
❑ 94VenLinU-244
Mosquera, Julio
❑ 94MedHatBJF-3687
❑ 94MedHatBJSP-11
❑ 95HagSunF-73
❑ 96BesAutSA-47
❑ 96Exc-116
❑ 96KnoSmoB-18
❑ 96Top-432
❑ 97Bow-112
❑ 97BowCerBlaIA-CA55
❑ 97BowCerBluIA-CA55
❑ 97BowCerGolIA-CA55
❑ 97BowInt-112
❑ 97PacPriGotD-GD103
❑ 98SyrSkyG-21
Moss, Barry
❑ 77IndIndTI-23
❑ 87SalLakTTT-NNO
❑ 88SalLakCTTI-3
❑ 88SalLakCTTI-18
❑ 89SalLakTTI-15
❑ 91EriSaiC-28
❑ 91EriSaiP-4084
❑ 92SpoIndC-29
❑ 92SpoIndF-1312
❑ 93SpoIndC-29
❑ 96OrlCubB-3
❑ 97St.PauS-19
❑ 98St.PauSTI-15
Moss, Damian
❑ 93AusFut-29
❑ 94DanBraC-19
❑ 94DanBraF-3529
❑ 95AusFut-4
❑ 95Bes-55
❑ 95Bow-88
❑ 95MacBraTI-20
❑ 95MacBraUTI-5
❑ 95SPML-14
❑ 95UppDecML-72
❑ 95UppDecMLFS-72
❑ 96Bow-149
❑ 96BowBes-161
❑ 96BowBesAR-161
❑ 96BowBesR-161
❑ 96BowFoi-149
❑ 96CarLeaA1B-3
❑ 96CarLeaA2B-3
❑ 96CarLeaAIB-B2
❑ 96DurBulBIB-14
❑ 96DurBulBrB-14
❑ 96Exc-132
❑ 96GreBraB-21
❑ 96GreBraTI-10
❑ 97Bow-412
❑ 97BowInt-412
❑ 97BowIntB-BBI20
❑ 97BowIntBAR-BBI20
❑ 97BowIntBR-BBI20
❑ 97GreBraG-23
❑ 97SouLeaTP-12
❑ 97Top-200
❑ 98Don-317
❑ 98DonGolPP-317
❑ 98DonSilPP-317
❑ 98LeaRS-271
❑ 98LeaRSLHolo-271
❑ 98LeaRSLong-271
❑ 98LeaRTrue-271
Moss, Darren
❑ 87AncGlaP-36
Moss, J. Lester
❑ 47TipTop-68
❑ 50Bow-251
❑ 51Bow-210
❑ 52Top-143
❑ 54Bow-181
❑ 54OriEss-26
❑ 54OriTeal-14
❑ 55OriEss-20
❑ 57Top-213
❑ 58Top-153
❑ 59Top-453
❑ 77EvaTriT-21
❑ 79Top-66
❑ 83AstPos-19
❑ 83TopRep5-143
❑ 84AstMot-27
❑ 84AstPos-18
❑ 85TCMPla1-42
❑ 86AstPol-26
❑ 87AstMot-27
❑ 88AstMot-27
❑ 89AstLenH-14
❑ 89AstMot-27
❑ 89AstSmo-28
❑ 91OriCro-319
❑ 97BalOriP-35
Moss, Malcolm
❑ 31Zee-21
❑ 32Zee-26
Moss, Ray
❑ 90DodTar-556
Moss, Rick
❑ 97ForWayW-22
❑ 98ForMyeMTI-21
Moss, Wally
❑ 97SalAva-36
Mosser, Todd
❑ 90NebCor-19
Mossi, Don
❑ 55Bow-259
❑ 55Ind-6
❑ 55IndGolS-8
❑ 55Top-85
❑ 55TopDouH-83
❑ 55TopTesS-7
❑ 56Top-39
❑ 56TopPin-9
❑ 57IndSoh-9
❑ 57IndTeal-14
❑ 57Top-8
❑ 58IndTeal-16
❑ 58IndTeal-29
❑ 58Top-35A
❑ 58Top-35B
❑ 59Top-302
❑ 60TigJayP-10
❑ 60Top-418
❑ 60TopTat-38
❑ 61Pos-42A
❑ 61Pos-42B
❑ 61SevElev-2
❑ 61Top-14
❑ 62Jel-23
❑ 62Pos-23
❑ 62PosCan-23
❑ 62TigJayP-10
❑ 62TigPosCF-12
❑ 62Top-55
❑ 62Top-105
❑ 62TopStal-49
❑ 62TopVen-55
❑ 62TopVen-105
❑ 63Jel-56
❑ 63Pos-56
❑ 63Top-218
❑ 63Top-530
❑ 64Top-335
❑ 64TopVen-335
❑ 66OPC-74
❑ 66Top-74
❑ 66TopVen-74
❑ 75TCM195CI-22
❑ 79DiaGre-297
❑ 79TCM50-215
❑ 81TCM60I-418
❑ 81TigDetN-49
❑ 84OCoandSI-152
❑ 90PacLeg-95
Mossor, Earl
❑ 90DodTar-1041
Mostil, Johnny A.
❑ 20WalMaiW-35
❑ 21E121So1-67
❑ 21Exh-113
❑ 21Nei-45
❑ 22E120-25
❑ 22W572-68
❑ 22W573-90
❑ 23W501-40
❑ 23WilChoV-109
❑ 26SpoNewSM-6
❑ 27YorCarE-24
❑ 28W502-24
❑ 28W56PlaC-S12A
❑ 28Yue-24
❑ 61Fle-64
❑ 76WhiSoxTAG-7
❑ 80WhiSoxGT-7
❑ 93ConTSN-912
Mota, Alfonso
❑ 95BoiHawTI-24
❑ 96CedRapKTI-17
Mota, Andy (Andres)
❑ 87AubAstP-7
❑ 88AubAstP-1966
❑ 89OscAstS-12
❑ 89Sta-16
❑ 90Bes-48
❑ 90CMC-752
❑ 90ColMudB-2
❑ 90ColMudP-1354
❑ 90ColMudS-17
❑ 90StaFS7-17
❑ 91LinDriAAA-616
❑ 91TucTorLD-616
❑ 91TucTorP-2220
❑ 91UppDecFE-22F
❑ 92Don-598
❑ 92Fle-441
❑ 92OPC-214
❑ 92Pin-257
❑ 92ProFS7-222
❑ 92Sco-872
❑ 92ScoImpP-33
❑ 92ScoRoo-16
❑ 92SkyAAAF-274
❑ 92StaClu-166
❑ 92Top-214
❑ 92TopDeb91-128
❑ 92TopGol-214
❑ 92TopGolW-214
❑ 92TopMic-214
❑ 92TucTorF-497
❑ 92TucTorS-615
❑ 92UppDec-564
❑ 93ColSprSSF-3097
❑ 93PhoFirF-1529
❑ 94ColSprSSF-745
Mota, Carlos
❑ 88BurIndP-1783
❑ 89Sta-183
❑ 89WatIndS-15
❑ 90RenSilSCLC-271
❑ 91Cla/Bes-118
❑ 91KinIndC-13
❑ 91KinIndP-326
❑ 92CanIndF-693
❑ 92CanIndS-114
❑ 93CanIndF-2843
❑ 93LimRocDWB-17
Mota, Christian
❑ 96BurIndB-21
❑ 97WatIndTI-20
Mota, Daniel
❑ 97GreBatB-19
❑ 98ForWayW!-21
Mota, Domingo
❑ 89AncBucTI-16
❑ 90KisDodD-18
❑ 91BakDodCLC-10
❑ 91Bow-696
❑ 92ClaFS7-182
❑ 92MemChiF-2427
❑ 92MemChiS-439
❑ 92SkyAA F-185
❑ 93ClaGolF-127
❑ 93MemChiF-382
Mota, Gary
❑ 92AshTouC-1
❑ 92ClaFS7-384
❑ 92UppDecML-25
❑ 92UppDecML-272
❑ 92UppDecMLPotY-PY2
❑ 93AstStaC-12
❑ 93Bow-695
❑ 93ClaGolF-106
❑ 93ClaMVPF-6
❑ 93JacGenF-2122
❑ 93SouAtlLAIPI-16
❑ 93SouAtlLAPI-26
❑ 94JacGenF-230
❑ 94Top-782
❑ 94TopGol-782
❑ 94TopSpa-782
❑ 95ReaPhiTI-8
❑ 97HigDesMUG-15
Mota, Gleydel
❑ 95PitMetTI-32
Mota, Guillermo
❑ 94KinMetC-13
❑ 94KinMetF-3831
❑ 96StLucMTI-31
❑ 98JupHamQ-11
❑ 99Bow-370
❑ 99BowGol-370
❑ 99BowInt-370
❑ 99Rev-86
❑ 99RevPremDate-86
❑ 99RevRet-86
❑ 99RevShaSS-86
Mota, Henry
❑ 98Cha-7
Mota, Jose
❑ 77CocAstT-15
❑ 78DayBeaAT-20
❑ 80CedRapRT-13
Mota, Jose Manuel
❑ 86TulDriTI-27
❑ 89HunStaB-26
❑ 89WicChaR-7
❑ 89WicUpdR-11
❑ 90CMC-516
❑ 90LasVegSC-13
❑ 90LasVegSP-130
❑ 90ProAAAF-18
❑ 91FleUpd-126
❑ 91LasVegSLD-289
❑ 91LasVegSP-243
❑ 91LinDriAAA-289
❑ 91PadSmo-24
❑ 92Fle-616
❑ 92OmaRoyF-2970
❑ 92OmaRoyS-339
❑ 92Sco-742
❑ 92Sco100RS-47
❑ 92ScoRoo-19
❑ 92TopDeb91-129
❑ 93OmaRoyF-1686
❑ 94OmaRoyF-1230
❑ 96OmaRoyB-20
Mota, Manny
❑ 90AubAstB-1
❑ 90AubAstP-3398
❑ 93LimRocDWB-121
❑ 96MarPhiB-12
❑ 97DodMot-27
Mota, Manny Rafael
❑ 61TacBan-13
❑ 63Top-141
❑ 64PirKDK-20
❑ 64Top-246
❑ 64TopVen-246
❑ 65Top-463
❑ 66OPC-112
❑ 66PirEasH-15
❑ 66Top-112
❑ 66TopVen-112
❑ 67CokCapPi-8
❑ 67DexPre-149
❑ 67OPC-66
❑ 67PirTeal-14
❑ 67Top-66
❑ 67TopPirS-16
❑ 67TopVen-293
❑ 68PirKDK-15
❑ 68PirTeal-14
❑ 68Top-325
❑ 68TopVen-325
❑ 69ExpFudP-10
❑ 69MilBra-197
❑ 69MLBOffS-160
❑ 69Top-236
❑ 69TopSta-58
❑ 69TopTeaP-10
❑ 70DayDaiNM-117
❑ 70MLBOffS-53
❑ 70OPC-157
❑ 70Top-157
❑ 71Dod-9
❑ 71DodTic-11
❑ 71MLBOffS-109
❑ 71OPC-112
❑ 71Top-112
❑ 72MilBra-245
❑ 72Top-596
❑ 73OPC-412
❑ 73Top-412
❑ 74Kel-49
❑ 74OPC-368
❑ 74Top-368
❑ 75OPC-414
❑ 75Top-414
❑ 75TopMin-414
❑ 76OPC-548
❑ 76SSP-87
❑ 76Top-548
❑ 77DodPho-9
❑ 77Top-386
❑ 78SSP270-79
❑ 78Top-228
❑ 78TopZes-5
❑ 79DodBlu-9
❑ 79Top-644
❑ 80Top-3
❑ 80Top-104
❑ 81Dod-21
❑ 81DodPol-NNO
❑ 81Don-299
❑ 81Fle-141
❑ 81Gia196T-16
❑ 83DodPol-NNO
❑ 83DodPos-10
❑ 84DodPol-NNO
❑ 84DodUniO-5
❑ 85DodCokP-21
❑ 85DomLeaS-213
❑ 86DodCokP-20
❑ 87DodMot-27
❑ 87DodPol-29
❑ 87DodSmoA-24
❑ 88DodMot-28
❑ 88DodSmo-5
❑ 89DodMot-27
❑ 89DodPol-1
❑ 89DodSmoG-80
❑ 90BasWit-25
❑ 90DodMot-28
❑ 90DodPol-NNO
❑ 90DodTar-557
❑ 90PacLeg-41
❑ 90SweBasG-26
❑ 91DodMot-28
❑ 91DodPol-NNO
❑ 91DodSt.V-7
❑ 91DodUno7P-2
❑ 91LinDri-22
❑ 91SweBasG-63
❑ 92ActPacA-83
❑ 92DodMot-28
❑ 92DodPol-NNO
❑ 92DodStaTA-12
❑ 93DodMot-28
❑ 93DodPol-30
❑ 93UppDecAH-99
❑ 94CarLeaA-DJ29
❑ 94DodPol-30
❑ 94UppDecAH-139
❑ 94UppDecAH1-139
❑ 95DodMot-28
❑ 95DodPol-30
❑ 96DodMot-28
❑ 96DodPol-8
❑ 97DodPol-30
❑ 98DodMot-28
❑ 98DodPol-30
Mota, Miguel
❑ 87BakDodP-4
Mota, Pedro
❑ 98SanJosGQ-15
Mota, Santo
❑ 92JohCitCC-11
❑ 92JohCitCF-3124
❑ 94MadHatC-18
❑ 94MadHatF-143
Mota, Tony
❑ 96YakBeaTI-11
❑ 97SanBerS-27
❑ 98VerBeaDM-29
Mota, Willie
❑ 89EliTwiS-21
❑ 89Sta-151
❑ 90KenTwiB-10
❑ 90KenTwiP-2297
❑ 90KenTwiS-15
❑ 91KenTwiC-2
❑ 92ClaFS7-349
❑ 92Ft.MyeMCB-10
❑ 92Ft.MyeMF-2754
❑ 93ClaFS7-286
❑ 93ForMyeMC-16

❑ 93LinVenB-169
❑ 94VenLinU-228
❑ 95LinVen-55
Moten, Scott
❑ 92EliTwiC-4
❑ 92EliTwiF-3679
❑ 93ForWayWC-20
❑ 93ForWayWF-1967
❑ 94FloStaLAF-FSL11
❑ 94ForMyeMC-15
❑ 94ForMyeMF-1166
❑ 95HarCitRCTI-16
❑ 96IowCubB-20
❑ 97OrlRayB-18
Motes, Jeff
❑ 95PitMetTI-18
❑ 95StLucMTI-23
Mothell, Dink (Carroll Ray)
❑ 87NegLeaPD-19
Motley, Bob
❑ 96NegLeaBMKC-6
Motley, Darryl
❑ 81OmaRoyT-22
❑ 82Don-390
❑ 82Fle-417
❑ 82OmaRoyT-19
❑ 82Top-471
❑ 83EvaTriT-21
❑ 84Don-344
❑ 84FleUpd-81
❑ 84RoyPos-23
❑ 85Don-461
❑ 85Fle-208
❑ 85Lea-69
❑ 85RoyTeal-22
❑ 85Top-561
❑ 85TopSti-276
❑ 85TopTif-561
❑ 86Don-217
❑ 86Fle-16
❑ 86Lea-95
❑ 86RoyKitCD-14
❑ 86RoyNatP-24
❑ 86RoyTeal-17
❑ 86Spo-186
❑ 86Top-332
❑ 86TopSti-22
❑ 86TopTif-332
❑ 87OPC-99
❑ 87RicBraBC-15
❑ 87RicBraC-30
❑ 87RicBraT-19
❑ 87Top-99
❑ 87TopTif-99
❑ 89IndIndC-22
❑ 89IndIndP-1238
❑ 90CMC-143
❑ 90NasSouC-18
❑ 90NasSouP-248
❑ 90ProAAAF-560
❑ 98FarRedHM-19
Motley, Mel
❑ 96WatIndTI-21
Motoi, Mitsuo
❑ 79TCMJapPB-53
Mott, Anson
❑ 09ObaT21-74
Mott, Tom
❑ 94SigRooDP-74
❑ 94SigRooDPS-74
❑ 95ForWayWTI-8
❑ 95MidLeaA-37
❑ 96FtMyeMB-14
❑ 97ForMyeM-19
Motte, James
❑ 93EliTwiC-16
❑ 93EliTwiF-3421
❑ 94ForWayWC-16
❑ 94ForWayWF-2015
❑ 94MidLeaAF-MDW13
❑ 95ForMyeMTI-18
Mottola, Chad
❑ 92BilMusF-3370
❑ 92BilMusSP-2
❑ 92ClaDraP-5
❑ 92ClaDraPFB-BC5
❑ 92ClaDraPP-BB5
❑ 92FroRowDP-82
❑ 92FroRowDPG-82
❑ 92FroRowDPPC-1
❑ 92FroRowDPPC-2
❑ 92FroRowDPPS-82
❑ 92FroRowDPS-82
❑ 92UppDecML-4
❑ 93Bow-90
❑ 93CarLeaAGF-44
❑ 93ClaYouG-YG13
❑ 93ExcFS7-25
❑ 93SP-282
❑ 93StaCluM-55
❑ 93StaCluMMP-6
❑ 93Top-56
❑ 93TopGol-56
❑ 93TopInaM-56
❑ 93TopInaR-56
❑ 93TopMic-56
❑ 93UppDec-443
❑ 93UppDecGold-443
❑ 93WinSpiC-1
❑ 94ActPac-19
❑ 94Bow-214
❑ 94BowBes-B21
❑ 94BowBes-X102
❑ 94BowBesR-B21
❑ 94BowBesR-X102
❑ 94ChaLooF-1372
❑ 94Cla-152
❑ 94ClaGolF-196
❑ 94ExcFS7-179
❑ 94ExcLeaLF-15
❑ 94SigRooBS-P3
❑ 94TedWil-129
❑ 94Top-616
❑ 94TopGol-616
❑ 94TopSpa-616
❑ 94UppDecML-10
❑ 94UppDecML-265
❑ 94UppDecMLPotYF-PY22
❑ 94UppDecMLT1PJF-TP5
❑ 94UppDecMLT1PMF-5
❑ 95ChaLooTI-15
❑ 95Sel-167
❑ 95SelArtP-167
❑ 95SPML-41
❑ 95Sum-144
❑ 95SumNthD-144
❑ 95UppDecML-21
❑ 95UppDecMLFS-21
❑ 96Bow-244
❑ 96BowFoi-244
❑ 96Fin-S284
❑ 96FinRef-S284
❑ 96FleUpd-U124
❑ 96FleUpdTC-U124
❑ 96IndIndB-16
❑ 96LeaPre-113
❑ 96LeaPreP-113
❑ 96LeaSig-70
❑ 96LeaSigPPG-70
❑ 96LeaSigPPP-70
❑ 96Zen-103
❑ 96ZenArtP-103
❑ 97ChaLoo-17
❑ 97DonEli-112
❑ 97DonEliGS-112
❑ 97DonEliTotC-20
❑ 97DonEliTotCDC-20
❑ 97DonRatR-21
❑ 97Fle-299
❑ 97FleTif-299
❑ 97IndInd-16
❑ 97Lea-83
❑ 97LeaFraM-83
❑ 97LeaFraMDC-83
❑ 97PacPriGotD-GD127
❑ 97Pin-144
❑ 97PinArtP-PP144
❑ 97PinIns-141
❑ 97PinInsCE-141
❑ 97PinInsDE-141
❑ 97PinMusC-144
❑ 97PinPrePla-144
❑ 97Sco-23
❑ 97ScoArtPWB-23
❑ 97ScoPreS-23
❑ 97ScoShoS-23
❑ 97ScoShoSAP-23
❑ 97StaClu-276
❑ 97StaCluM-M33
❑ 97StaCluMOP-276
❑ 97StaCluMOP-M33
❑ 97Top-358
❑ 97Ult-178
❑ 97UltGolME-178
❑ 97UltPlaME-178
❑ 97UppDec-477
❑ 98OklRedM-10
Motton, Curt
❑ 67BalOriP-71
❑ 67BalOriP-72
❑ 68Top-549
❑ 69OPC-37
❑ 69Top-37
❑ 70BalOriP-21
❑ 70OPC-261
❑ 70Ori-8
❑ 70Top-261
❑ 71BalOriP-19
❑ 71MLBOffS-305
❑ 71OPC-684
❑ 71Top-684
❑ 72MilBra-246
❑ 72OPC-393
❑ 72Top-393
❑ 85EveGialC-12
❑ 86RocRedWP-13
❑ 87RocRedWP-13
❑ 87RocRedWT-23
❑ 88RocRedWC-25
❑ 88RocRedWGCP-29
❑ 88RocRedWP-218
❑ 88RocRedWTI-14
❑ 89BalOriP-21
❑ 91OriCro-320
❑ 94BreMilB-338
Motuzas, Jeff
❑ 92ClaFS7-386
❑ 92PriWilCC-10
❑ 92PriWilCF-152
❑ 93PriWilCC-17
❑ 93PriWilCF-659
❑ 94SanBerSC-11
❑ 94SanBerSF-2763
❑ 95TamYanYI-20
❑ 97NorNav-4
❑ 97NorNavTI-23
Motz, Frank
❑ 98CamPepP-57
Motz, Willie
❑ 91KenTwiP-2079
Moudy, M. J.
❑ 25Zee-115
❑ 26Zee-146
❑ 27Zee-119
❑ 28Zee-139
Moulder, Glen
❑ 48WhiSoxTI-20
❑ 49Bow-159
❑ 49W72HolS-11
❑ 50W720HolS-21
❑ 90DodTar-1042
Moulton, Brian
❑ 77CedRapGT-6
Moultrie, Patrick
❑ 93St.CatBJC-16
❑ 93St.CatBJF-3987
❑ 94HagSunC-16
❑ 94HagSunF-2743
❑ 96HagSunB-15
Mounce, Tony
❑ 95Bes-75
❑ 95MidLeaA-35
❑ 95QuaCitRBTI-16
❑ 96BesAutSA-48
❑ 96Bow-125
❑ 96BowFoi-125
❑ 96Exc-173
❑ 96KisCobB-18
❑ 97BesAutAS-34
❑ 97JacGen-18
❑ 97JacGenS-17
❑ 97TexLeaTP-10
❑ 98JacGenM-13
Mount, Chuck
❑ 86EugEmeC-42
❑ 87AppFoxP-1
❑ 88BirBarB-27
❑ 89BirBarB-18
❑ 89BirBarP-92
❑ 90ChaKniTI-18
❑ 91IowCubLD-212
❑ 91IowCubP-1056
❑ 91LinDriAAA-212
Mountain, Joe
❑ 92BelMarCB-12
❑ 92BelMarF-1440
Mounts, J.R.
❑ 98HicCraM-21
❑ 98HicCraUO-22
Moure, Brian
❑ 88CapCodPPaLP-12
Mouse, Bomber the
❑ 98CapCitBF5-1
❑ 98CapCitBM-1
Moushon, Dan
❑ 89SprCarB-28
Mouton, Brian
❑ 90ButCopKSP-21
Mouton, James
❑ 91AubAstC-17
❑ 91AubAstP-4282
❑ 92ClaFS7-207
❑ 92OscAstC-21
❑ 92OscAstF-2538
❑ 93AstStaC-3
❑ 93Bow-236
❑ 93ClaFS7-225
❑ 93ExcFS7-48
❑ 93TriAAAGF-12
❑ 93TucTorF-3068
❑ 94AstMot-13
❑ 94Bow-258
❑ 94Bow-339
❑ 94BowBes-R82
❑ 94BowBesR-R82
❑ 94BowPre-10
❑ 94ClaGolF-136
❑ 94ColC-664
❑ 94ColChoGS-664
❑ 94ColChoSS-664
❑ 94ExcAllF-3
❑ 94ExcFS7-206
❑ 94Fin-421
❑ 94FinJum-421
❑ 94FinRef-421
❑ 94Fla-174
❑ 94FlaWavotF-A7
❑ 94FleAllR-M9
❑ 94FleExtB-279
❑ 94FleExtBRS-14
❑ 94FleUpd-146
❑ 94LeaGolR-15
❑ 94LeaLimR-76
❑ 94OPC-97
❑ 94OPCHotP-2
❑ 94Pin-535
❑ 94PinArtP-535
❑ 94PinMusC-535
❑ 94ScoRoo-RT99
❑ 94ScoRooGR-RT99
❑ 94ScoRooSR-SU15
❑ 94Sel-184
❑ 94SelRooS-RS15
❑ 94SpoRoo-109
❑ 94SpoRooAP-109
❑ 94StaClu-668
❑ 94StaCluFDI-668
❑ 94StaCluGR-668
❑ 94StaCluMOP-668
❑ 94Top-782
❑ 94TopGol-782
❑ 94TopSpa-782
❑ 94Ult-509
❑ 94UltAllR-8
❑ 94UltAllRJ-8
❑ 94UppDec-518
❑ 94UppDecED-518
❑ 94UppDecML-154
❑ 94UppDecML-215
❑ 95AstMot-14
❑ 95Baz-122
❑ 95ColCho-112
❑ 95ColChoGS-112
❑ 95ColChoSS-112
❑ 95Don-246
❑ 95DonPreP-246
❑ 95DonTopotO-259
❑ 95Fin-27
❑ 95FinRef-27
❑ 95Fla-362
❑ 95Fle-466
❑ 95Lea-101
❑ 95Pac-191
❑ 95Pin-58
❑ 95PinArtP-58
❑ 95PinMusC-58
❑ 95Sco-125
❑ 95ScoGolR-125
❑ 95ScoPlaTS-125
❑ 95Sel-109
❑ 95SelArtP-109
❑ 95Spo-67
❑ 95SpoArtP-67
❑ 95StaClu-305
❑ 95StaCluMOP-305
❑ 95StaCluSTWS-305
❑ 95StaCluVR-161
❑ 95StaCluVRMO-161
❑ 95Sum-63
❑ 95SumNthD-63
❑ 95Top-597
❑ 95TopCyb-369
❑ 95Ult-175
❑ 95UltGolM-175
❑ 95UppDec-28
❑ 95UppDecED-28
❑ 95UppDecEDG-28
❑ 95Zen-32
❑ 96AstMot-14
❑ 96ColCho-167
❑ 96ColChoGS-167
❑ 96ColChoSS-167
❑ 96Don-233
❑ 96DonPreP-233
❑ 96Fla-283
❑ 96Fle-417
❑ 96FleTif-417
❑ 96LeaSigA-163
❑ 96LeaSigAG-163
❑ 96LeaSigAS-163
❑ 96Pac-96
❑ 96Pin-95
❑ 96Sco-80
❑ 96StaClu-384
❑ 96StaCluMOP-384
❑ 96Ult-213
❑ 96UltGolM-213
❑ 96UppDec-83
❑ 97AstMot-7
❑ 97Don-209
❑ 97DonGolPP-209
❑ 97DonSilPP-209
❑ 97Fle-352
❑ 97FleTif-352
❑ 97Pac-323
❑ 97PacLigB-323
❑ 97PacSil-323
❑ 97Sco-293
❑ 97ScoArtPWB-293
❑ 97ScoPreS-293
❑ 97ScoShoS-293
❑ 97ScoShoSAP-293
❑ 97Ult-481
❑ 97UltGolME-481
❑ 97UltPlaME-481
❑ 98PacOnl-644
❑ 98PacOnlR-644
❑ 98PacOnlWC-644
❑ 98PadMot-19
❑ 98Ult-422
❑ 98UltGolM-422
❑ 98UltMas-422
❑ 98UltPlaM-422
❑ 98UppDec-717
Mouton, Lyle
❑ 91LSUTigP-12
❑ 91LSUTigP-13
❑ 91OneYanP-4166
❑ 92PriWilCC-16
❑ 92PriWilCF-162
❑ 92ProFS7-127
❑ 92UppDecML-194
❑ 93AlbYanF-2174
❑ 93ClaFS7-81
❑ 93ClaGolF-3
❑ 93ExcFS7-212
❑ 94AlbYanF-1455
❑ 94ExcFS7-110
❑ 94UppDecML-164
❑ 95ColCliMCTI-20
❑ 95SigRooOJ-24
❑ 95SigRooOJP-24
❑ 95SigRooOJPS-24
❑ 95SigRooOJS-24
❑ 95TopTra-130T
❑ 95UppDecML-208
❑ 95UppDecMLFS-208
❑ 96ColCho-17
❑ 96ColChoGS-17
❑ 96ColChoSS-17
❑ 96Don-54
❑ 96DonPreP-54
❑ 96EmoXL-39
❑ 96Fin-S168
❑ 96FinRef-S168
❑ 96Fla-55
❑ 96Fle-74
❑ 96FleTif-74
❑ 96Lea-103
❑ 96LeaPrePB-103
❑ 96LeaPrePG-103
❑ 96LeaPrePS-103
❑ 96LeaSigA-162
❑ 96LeaSigAG-162
❑ 96LeaSigAS-162
❑ 96MetUni-39
❑ 96MetUniP-39
❑ 96Pac-282
❑ 96Sco-257
❑ 96StaClu-54
❑ 96StaCluMOP-54
❑ 96Stu-60
❑ 96StuPrePB-60
❑ 96StuPrePG-60
❑ 96StuPrePS-60
❑ 96Top-119
❑ 96TopGal-105
❑ 96TopGalPPI-105
❑ 96Ult-42
❑ 96UltGolM-42
❑ 96UppDec-39
❑ 96WhiSoxF-12
❑ 97Cir-109
❑ 97CirRav-109
❑ 97ColCho-73
❑ 97ColChoT-CW4
❑ 97DonTea-73
❑ 97DonTeaSPE-73
❑ 97Fle-66
❑ 97FleTif-66
❑ 97Pac-59
❑ 97PacLigB-59
❑ 97PacSil-59
❑ 97Sco-218
❑ 97ScoArtPWB-218
❑ 97ScoPreS-218
❑ 97ScoShoS-218
❑ 97ScoShoSAP-218
❑ 97Top-407
❑ 97UppDec-41
❑ 97WhiSoxCM-4
❑ 97WhiSoxS-10
❑ 97WhiSoxSPI-10
❑ 97WhiSoxSPr-10
❑ 97WhiSoxTI-28
❑ 98Pac-61
❑ 98PacPlaB-61
❑ 98PacRedT-61
❑ 98PacSil-61
❑ 98PriWilCASM-30
❑ 98Sco-99
❑ 98Top-74
❑ 98TopChr-74
❑ 98TopChrR-74
❑ 98TopDevR-74
❑ 98TopDia-74
❑ 98TopMiniC-74
❑ 98UppDec-56
❑ 98WhiSoxS-7
❑ 98WhiSoxSP-7
Mowell, Michael
❑ 98LowSpiM-27
Mowrey, Mike (Harry)
❑ 08RosComP-122
❑ 09T206-257
❑ 10CouT21-49
❑ 10CouT21-193
❑ 10CouT21-194
❑ 10CouT21-195
❑ 10CouT21-307
❑ 10DarChoE-24
❑ 10RedCroT-140
❑ 10RedCroT-227
❑ 10W555-50
❑ 11HelSta-174
❑ 11PinT-5-359
❑ 11PloCanE-50
❑ 11SpoLifCW-262
❑ 11SpoLifM-275
❑ 12PhiCarE-22
❑ 14B18B-80A
❑ 14B18B-80B
❑ 14TexTomE-36
❑ 16FleBreD-68
❑ 16SpoNewM-129
❑ 17ColE13-123
❑ 72ClaCar-51
Mowry, David
❑ 90HigSchPLS-21
❑ 92ChaRaiC-20
❑ 92ChaRaiF-128
❑ 92ClaFS7-55
❑ 94SprSulC-18
❑ 94SprSulF-2045
❑ 95RanCucQT-33
Mowry, Joe
❑ 33ButCanV-36
❑ 33WorCig(-61
❑ 33WorCig(-62
❑ 34BabRutG-48
❑ 34ButPreR-47
❑ 34DiaMatCSB-136
❑ 34Gou-59
Moya, Felix

❑ 90JamExpP-22
❑ 91WesPalBEC-8
❑ 91WesPalBEP-1224
❑ 92WesPalBEC-24
❑ 92WesPalBEF-2087
Moyer, Greg
❑ 81ShrCapT-22
Moyer, Jamie
❑ 86CubGat-49
❑ 86PitCubP-17
❑ 87CubCan-21
❑ 87CubDavB-49
❑ 87Don-315
❑ 87Fle-570
❑ 87FleGlo-570
❑ 87Top-227
❑ 87TopTif-227
❑ 88CubDavB-49
❑ 88Don-169
❑ 88DonBasB-228
❑ 88DonTeaBC-169
❑ 88Fle-426
❑ 88FleGlo-426
❑ 88OPC-36
❑ 88PanSti-255
❑ 88Sco-573
❑ 88ScoGlo-573
❑ 88StaLinCu-8
❑ 88Top-36
❑ 88TopSti-62
❑ 88TopTif-36
❑ 89Bow-223
❑ 89BowTif-223
❑ 89Don-157
❑ 89DonTra-39
❑ 89Fle-432
❑ 89FleGlo-432
❑ 89FleUpd-65
❑ 89OPC-171
❑ 89RanMot-17
❑ 89RanSmo-22
❑ 89Sco-263
❑ 89Top-549
❑ 89Top-717
❑ 89TopSti-53
❑ 89TopTif-549
❑ 89TopTif-717
❑ 89TopTra-85T
❑ 89TopTraT-85T
❑ 89UppDec-63
❑ 89UppDec-791
❑ 90Don-378
❑ 90Fle-307
❑ 90FleCan-307
❑ 90OPC-412
❑ 90PublntS-417
❑ 90RanMot-24
❑ 90Sco-107A
❑ 90Sco-107B
❑ 90Top-412
❑ 90TopTif-412
❑ 90UppDec-619
❑ 91Bow-391
❑ 91Fle-294
❑ 91LouRedTI-8
❑ 91OPC-138
❑ 91Sco-437
❑ 91StaClu-481
❑ 91Top-138
❑ 91TopDesS-138
❑ 91TopMic-138
❑ 91TopTif-138
❑ 91UppDec-610
❑ 92TolMudHF-1042
❑ 93BalOriP-19
❑ 93FleFinE-160
❑ 93RanKee-274
❑ 93RocRedWF-234
❑ 94BalOriP-20
❑ 94ColC-213
❑ 94ColChoGS-213
❑ 94ColChoSS-213
❑ 94Don-547
❑ 94Fla-6
❑ 94Fle-11
❑ 94Lea-215
❑ 94OriPro-69
❑ 94OriUSPC-6H
❑ 94OriUSPC-12S
❑ 94Pin-442
❑ 94PinArtP-442
❑ 94PinMusC-442
❑ 94Sco-270
❑ 94ScoGolR-270
❑ 94StaClu-284
❑ 94StaCluFDI-284
❑ 94StaCluGR-284
❑ 94StaCluMOP-284
❑ 94StaCluT-287
❑ 94StaCluTFDI-287
❑ 94Top-526
❑ 94TopGol-526
❑ 94TopSpa-526
❑ 94Ult-6
❑ 94UppDec-147
❑ 94UppDecED-147
❑ 95BalOriP-35
❑ 95ColCho-342
❑ 95ColChoGS-342
❑ 95ColChoSS-342
❑ 95Don-66
❑ 95DonPreP-66
❑ 95Fla-5
❑ 95Fle-14
❑ 95Pac-26
❑ 95Sco-114
❑ 95ScoGolR-114
❑ 95ScoPlaTS-114
❑ 95Top-318
❑ 95TopCyb-172
❑ 95Ult-256
❑ 95UltGolM-256
❑ 96ColCho-479
❑ 96ColChoGS-479
❑ 96ColChoSS-479
❑ 96Don-69
❑ 96DonPreP-69
❑ 96Fle-16
❑ 96FleTif-16
❑ 96FleUpd-U16
❑ 96FleUpdTC-U16
❑ 96LeaSigA-164
❑ 96LeaSigAG-164
❑ 96LeaSigAS-164
❑ 96Sco-210
❑ 96StaClu-415
❑ 96StaCluMOP-415
❑ 96Ult-318
❑ 96UltGolM-318
❑ 97Cir-364
❑ 97CirRav-364
❑ 97ColCho-479
❑ 97ColChoT-SM9
❑ 97Don-224
❑ 97DonGolPP-224
❑ 97DonSilPP-224
❑ 97DonTea-145
❑ 97DonTeaSPE-145
❑ 97Fle-212
❑ 97FleTif-212
❑ 97MarSco-14
❑ 97MarScoPl-14
❑ 97MarScoPr-14
❑ 97Pac-191
❑ 97PacLigB-191
❑ 97PacPriSH-SH7B
❑ 97PacSil-191
❑ 97Pin-30
❑ 97PinArtP-PP30
❑ 97PinMusC-30
❑ 97PinPrePla-30
❑ 97Sco-254
❑ 97ScoArtPWB-254
❑ 97ScoPreS-254
❑ 97ScoShoS-254
❑ 97ScoShoSAP-254
❑ 97Top-283
❑ 97Ult-507
❑ 97UltGolME-507
❑ 97UltPlaME-507
❑ 97UppDec-504
❑ 97UppDecMP-P12
❑ 98ColCho-237
❑ 98Fin-63
❑ 98FinNo--63
❑ 98FinNo-R-63
❑ 98FinRef-63
❑ 98MarSco-15
❑ 98MarScoP-15
❑ 98Pac-191
❑ 98PacAur-75
❑ 98PacOme-224
❑ 98PacOmeR-224
❑ 98PacOnl-692
❑ 98PacOnlR-692
❑ 98PacOnlWC-692
❑ 98PacPlaB-191
❑ 98PacRedT-191
❑ 98PacSil-191
❑ 98Pin-123
❑ 98PinPreP-123
❑ 98Sco-214
❑ 98SpoIll-90
❑ 98SpoIllEE-90
❑ 98SpoIllFE-90
❑ 98StaCluFDI-278
❑ 98StaCluI-278
❑ 98StaCluOneK-278
❑ 98StaCluPP-278
❑ 98Top-217
❑ 98TopChr-217
❑ 98TopChrR-217
❑ 98TopDevR-217
❑ 98TopDia-217
❑ 98TopMiniC-217
❑ 98Ult-377
❑ 98UltGolM-377
❑ 98UltMas-377
❑ 98UltPlaM-377
❑ 98UppDec-221
❑ 98UppDecSF-123
❑ 99Fle-191
❑ 99FleSta9-191
❑ 99FleWarT-191
❑ 99Pac-401
❑ 99PacCroC-266
❑ 99PacCroCPB-266
❑ 99PacOme-223
❑ 99PacOmeC-223
❑ 99PacOmeG-223
❑ 99PacOmePB-223
❑ 99PacPlaB-401
❑ 99PacRed-401
❑ 99SkyThu-53
❑ 99SkyThuRant-53
❑ 99SkyThuRave-53
❑ 99SpoIll-120
❑ 99StaClu-197
❑ 99StaCluFDI-197
❑ 99StaCluOoaK-197
❑ 99StaCluPP-197
❑ 99ThuSkySupR-53
❑ 99Top-343
❑ 99TopChr-343
❑ 99TopChrR-343
❑ 99TopMVPP-343
❑ 99Ult-13
❑ 99UltGolM-13
❑ 99UltMas-13
❑ 99UltPlaM-13
❑ 99UppDec-494
❑ 99UppDecEL1-494
❑ 99UppDecEL2-494
❑ 99Vic-381
Moyer, Jim
❑ 71MLBOffS-260
❑ 72OPC-506
❑ 72Top-506
Moyle, Michael
❑ 91PerHeaF-11
❑ 92BurIndC-20
❑ 92BurIndF-1661
❑ 93AusFut-73
❑ 93BurIndC-19
❑ 93BurIndF-3302
❑ 94ButCopKSP-17
❑ 95AusFut-18
❑ 95AusFutGP-3
❑ 96CarLeaA1B-10
❑ 96CarLeaA2B-10
❑ 96KenIndB-18
❑ 97AkrAer-18
❑ 98AkrAerM-19
Mozzali, Mo
❑ 77Car5-15
❑ 77CarTeal-15
❑ 78CarTeal-19
Mraz, Don
❑ 76QuaCitAT-23
Mrowka, Jim
❑ 92KinMetF-1540
Mrozinski, Ron
❑ 55Bow-287
Mucerino, Greg
❑ 92ChaRaiC-6
❑ 92ChaRaiF-129
Mucker, Kelcey
❑ 94ClaGolF-81
❑ 94EliTwiC-15
❑ 94EliTwiF-3743
❑ 95ForWayWTI-23
❑ 96FtMyeMB-13
❑ 97ForMyeM-20
Mud Hens, Toledo
❑ 87IntLeaAT-43
Mudcat, Muddy the
❑ 96CarMudB-29
❑ 97CarMudC-29
❑ 98CarMudM-29
Mudcats, Columbus
❑ 89ColMudP-149
Mudd, Scott
❑ 95HudValRTI-4
❑ 96ChaRivTI-9623
Muddy, Mascot
❑ 95TolMudHTI-30
❑ 97TolMudHB-33
❑ 97TolMudHB-34
❑ 97TolMudHB-35
❑ 97TolMudHB-36
Mueller, Bill
❑ 93EveGiaC-19
❑ 93EveGiaF-3776
❑ 94SanJosGC-18
❑ 94SanJosGF-2827
❑ 96PhoFirB-21
❑ 97ColCho-8
❑ 97Don-380
❑ 97DonGolPP-380
❑ 97DonSilPP-380
❑ 97Fle-485
❑ 97FleTif-485
❑ 97MetUni-246
❑ 97Pac-446
❑ 97PacLigB-446
❑ 97PacSil-446
❑ 97Top-490
❑ 97Ult-297
❑ 97UltGolME-297
❑ 97UltPlaME-297
❑ 97UppDec-270
❑ 98CirThu-32
❑ 98CirThuRav-32
❑ 98CirThuSupRav-32
❑ 98ColCho-232
❑ 98CroRoy-122
❑ 98Don-129
❑ 98DonCol-129
❑ 98DonColL-282
❑ 98DonColS-129
❑ 98DonGolPP-129
❑ 98DonPriCD-129
❑ 98DonPriCL-282
❑ 98DonSilPP-129
❑ 98Fle-114
❑ 98GiaMot-8
❑ 98Lea-83
❑ 98LeaFraDA-83
❑ 98LeaFraF-83
❑ 98LeaFraM-83
❑ 98LeaFraM-83
❑ 98LeaFraMDC-83
❑ 98LeaFraMDC-83
❑ 98LeaFraMZ2-83
❑ 98Pac-446
❑ 98PacOme-214
❑ 98PacOmeR-214
❑ 98PacOnl-667
❑ 98PacOnlR-667
❑ 98PacOnlWC-667
❑ 98PacPlaB-446
❑ 98PacRedT-446
❑ 98PacSil-446
❑ 98Revo-130
❑ 98RevoSS-130
❑ 98StaCluFDI-158
❑ 98StaCluI-158
❑ 98StaCluOneK-158
❑ 98StaCluPP-158
❑ 98Top-201
❑ 98TopChr-201
❑ 98TopChrR-201
❑ 98TopDevR-201
❑ 98TopDia-201
❑ 98TopMiniC-201
❑ 98Ult-408
❑ 98UltGolM-408
❑ 98UltMas-408
❑ 98UltPlaM-408
❑ 98UppDec-214
❑ 98UppDecSF-117
❑ 99Fle-198
❑ 99FleSta9-198
❑ 99FleWarT-198
❑ 99Pac-385
❑ 99PacAur-172
❑ 99PacAurOD-172
❑ 99PacPar-211
❑ 99PacParC-211
❑ 99PacParG-211
❑ 99PacParHoloGold-211
❑ 99PacParHS-211
❑ 99PacParOD-211
❑ 99PacParPB-211
❑ 99PacParRed-211
❑ 99PacPlaB-385
❑ 99PacPriS-118
❑ 99PacPriS206-118
❑ 99PacPriS206R-118
❑ 99PacRed-385
❑ 99SkyThu-148
❑ 99SkyThuRant-148
❑ 99SkyThuRave-148
❑ 99StaClu-8
❑ 99StaCluFDI-8
❑ 99StaCluOoaK-8
❑ 99StaCluPP-8
❑ 99ThuSkySupR-148
❑ 99Top-377
❑ 99TopChr-377
❑ 99TopChrR-377
❑ 99TopMVPP-377
❑ 99UD Cho-138
❑ 99UD ChoP-138
❑ 99UD ChoPCR-138
❑ 99Ult-195
❑ 99UltGolM-195
❑ 99UltMas-195
❑ 99UltPlaM-195
❑ 99UppDec-199
❑ 99UppDecEL1-199
❑ 99UppDecEL2-199
❑ 99Vic-355
Mueller, Bret
❑ 95NewJerCTI-21
❑ 96PeoChiB-21
Mueller, Clarence F.
❑ 23WilChoV-110
❑ 25Exh-62
❑ 26Exh-61
Mueller, Don
❑ 47Exh-163
❑ 47PM1StaP1-144
❑ 49EurSta-121
❑ 49GiaTeal-21
❑ 50Bow-221
❑ 50JJKCopP-11
❑ 51Bow-268
❑ 52BerRos-44
❑ 52Bow-18
❑ 52CokTip-6
❑ 52DixLid-13
❑ 52DixPre-13
❑ 52NatTeaL-18
❑ 52TipTop-27
❑ 52Top-52
❑ 53BowC-74
❑ 53Bri-37
❑ 53DixLid-13
❑ 53DixPre-13
❑ 54Bow-73
❑ 54NewYorJA-33
❑ 54RedMan-NL7
❑ 54StaMey-9
❑ 54Top-42
❑ 55ArmCoi-14
❑ 55GiaGolS-22
❑ 55RedMan-NL8
❑ 55RobGouS-9
❑ 55RobGouW-9
❑ 55StaMey-8
❑ 56GiaJayP-8
❑ 56Top-241
❑ 57GiaJayP-6
❑ 57Top-148
❑ 58GiaArmT-6
❑ 58Top-253
❑ 59Top-368
❑ 75Gia195T-21
❑ 79TCM50-149
❑ 81WhiSox1T-24
❑ 83TopRep5-52
❑ 85TCMPhoC-37
❑ 94TopArc1-42
❑ 94TopArc1G-42
Mueller, Heinie (Emmett)
❑ 38CloFotW-65
❑ 39PlaBal-63
❑ 40PlaBal-96
❑ 91ConTSN-179
❑ 92ConTSN-643
Mueller, Mark
❑ 72CedRapCT-26
Mueller, Pete
❑ 86OscAstP-19
Mueller, Ray
❑ 46SpoExcW-6-1B
❑ 49EurSta-122
❑ 50PirTeal-15
❑ 51Bow-313
❑ 61Fle-128
Mueller, Willard
❑ 75BurBeeT-18
❑ 76BurBeeT-23
❑ 76CliPilT-24
❑ 77BurBeeT-19
❑ 78HolMilT-16
❑ 79VanCanT-23B
❑ 80Top-668
❑ 80VanCanT-2
❑ 81VanCanT-15
❑ 82WicAerTI-10
❑ 94BreMilB-339
Muffett, Billy
❑ 58Top-143
❑ 59Top-241
❑ 61Top-16
❑ 62Top-336
❑ 71CarTeal-29
❑ 72CarTeal-13
❑ 75CalAngP-27
❑ 76SSP-614
❑ 88TigPep-NNO
❑ 89TigMar-NNO
❑ 90TigCok-28
❑ 90TigTeal-16
❑ 91TigCok-NNO
❑ 92TigTeal-25
❑ 93TigGat-28
Mugsy, Mascot
❑ 97SalAva-38
❑ 98SalAvaC-22
Muh, Steve
❑ 89KenTwiP-1079
❑ 89KenTwiS-17
❑ 90OrlSunRB-20
❑ 90OrlSunRP-1080
❑ 91LinDriAA-489
❑ 91OrlSunRLD-489
❑ 91OrlSunRP-1847
Muhammad, Bob
❑ 87HawRai-23
❑ 89BelBrelS-18
Muhlethaler, Mike
❑ 90SouOreAB-26
❑ 90SouOreAP-3448
Muir, Harry
❑ 92MedHatBJF-3206
❑ 92MedHatBJSP-10
❑ 93St.CatBJC-17
❑ 93St.CatBJF-3973
❑ 94HagSunC-17
❑ 94HagSunF-2727
Muir, Joseph
❑ 52Top-154
❑ 83TopRep5-154
Mula, Jared
❑ 92LSUTigM-16
Mulana, Frank
❑ 30Zee-108
Mulcahy, Hugh
❑ 38CloFotW-66
❑ 39ExhSal-45
❑ 39PlaBal-145
❑ 40PhiTeal-17
❑ 40PlaBal-95
❑ 41Gou-1
❑ 41PhiTeal-19
❑ 52LavPro-51
❑ 79DiaGre-309
❑ 93DiaStaES-147
❑ 95ConTSN-1346
Mulcahy, Phil
❑ 26Zee-12
❑ 28Zee-15
Mulden, Chris
❑ 78CliDodT-24
Mulder, Mark
❑ 99BasAmeTP-70
❑ 99BasAmeTPA-30
❑ 99BasAmeTPG-70
❑ 99Bow-355
❑ 99Bow200RF-ROY7
❑ 99BowBes-164
❑ 99BowBesAR-164
❑ 99BowBesR-164
❑ 99BowGol-355
❑ 99BowInt-355
❑ 99JustheSAC-18
❑ 99JustheSAD-12
❑ 99JustheSJB-36
❑ 99TeaBesR-61
❑ 99TeaBesRFS-15
❑ 99TeaBesRG-61
❑ 99TeaBesRS-61

- 99TopBlaLC1-97
- 99TopBlaLC2-97
- 99TopBlaLC3-97
- 99TopGal-144
- 99TopGalPP-144
- 99TopGalPPI-144
- 99TopGolL-97
- 99TopGolLC1-97
- 99TopGolLC2-97
- 99TopGolLOtO-97
- 99TopRedLC1-97
- 99TopRedLC2-97
- 99TopRedLC3-97
- 99TopSta-45
- 99TopSta1Foil-45
- 99TopSta2Foil-45
- 99TopStaFoil-45
- 99TopStaOS-45
- 99TopStaTS-45

Muldoon, William
- 88KimN18-26

Mulholland, Terry
- 84EveGiaC-20
- 86PhoFirP-18
- 86StaoftFT-39
- 87Don-515
- 87PhoFirP-5
- 87SpoTeaP-10
- 87Top-536
- 87TopTif-536
- 88PhoFirC-10
- 88PhoFirP-77
- 89FleUpd-111
- 89PhiTas-44
- 89PhoFirC-4
- 89PhoFirP-1480
- 89Sco-474
- 89Top-41
- 89TopTif-41
- 90ClaBlu-127
- 90Don-515
- 90Fle-568
- 90FleCan-568
- 90Lea-474
- 90OPC-657
- 90PhiTas-24
- 90Sco-542
- 90Top-657
- 90TopTif-657
- 90UppDec-474
- 91Bow-504
- 91ClaGam-78
- 91Don-541
- 91DonBonC-BC14
- 91Fle-408
- 91FleWaxBC-8
- 91Lea-46
- 91OPC-413
- 91PanFreS-359
- 91PanSti-8
- 91PhiMed-30
- 91Sco-33
- 91Sco-706
- 91StaClu-58
- 91StaCluCM-21
- 91Stu-219
- 91Top-413
- 91TopDesS-413
- 91TopMic-413
- 91TopTif-413
- 91Ult-269
- 91UppDec-426
- 92Bow-39
- 92Don-268
- 92Fle-540
- 92Hig5-79
- 92Lea-464
- 92LeaBlaG-464
- 92MooSna-16
- 92OPC-719
- 92PanSti-249
- 92PhiMed-22
- 92PhiMed-44
- 92Pin-199
- 92RedFolS-69
- 92Sco-118
- 92StaClu-98
- 92Stu-78
- 92SunSee-4
- 92Top-719
- 92TopGol-719
- 92TopGolW-719
- 92TopMic-719
- 92TriPla-11
- 92Ult-248
- 92UppDec-129
- 93Bow-484
- 93Don-172
- 93Fla-106
- 93Fle-106
- 93Lea-22
- 93LeaGolA-U1
- 93OPC-283
- 93PacSpa-240
- 93PanSti-267
- 93PhiMed-24
- 93PhiStaC-17
- 93Pin-73
- 93Sco-117
- 93Sel-127
- 93SelStaL-64
- 93SP-16
- 93StaClu-716
- 93StaCluFDI-716
- 93StaCluMOP-716
- 93Stu-10
- 93Top-555
- 93TopGol-555
- 93TopInaM-555
- 93TopInaR-555
- 93TopMic-555
- 93TriPla-170
- 93Ult-92
- 93UppDec-279
- 93UppDecGold-279
- 94Bow-81
- 94ColC-508
- 94ColChoGS-508
- 94ColChoSS-508
- 94Don-160
- 94Fin-305
- 94FinRef-305
- 94Fla-322
- 94Fle-597
- 94FleAllS-46
- 94FleExtB-134
- 94FleUpd-69
- 94Lea-373
- 94OPC-34
- 94Pac-483
- 94PhiUSPC-1D
- 94PhiUSPC-6C
- 94PhiUSPC-9C
- 94Pin-47
- 94PinArtP-47
- 94PinMusC-47
- 94Sco-184
- 94ScoGolR-184
- 94ScoRoo-RT14
- 94ScoRooGR-RT14
- 94Sel-255
- 94Spo-134
- 94SpoRoo-22
- 94SpoRooAP-22
- 94StaClu-222
- 94StaClu-700
- 94StaCluFDI-222
- 94StaCluFDI-700
- 94StaCluGR-222
- 94StaCluGR-700
- 94StaCluMOP-222
- 94StaCluMOP-700
- 94StaCluT-207
- 94StaCluTFDI-207
- 94Top-170
- 94TopGol-170
- 94TopSpa-170
- 94TopTra-50T
- 94TriPla-178
- 94Ult-251
- 94Ult-401
- 94UppDec-399
- 94UppDecED-399
- 95ColCho-554T
- 95Don-404
- 95DonPreP-404
- 95DonTopotO-353
- 95Fla-426
- 95Fle-77
- 95FleUpd-195
- 95GiaMot-6
- 95Lea-350
- 95Pac-300
- 95Top-380
- 95TopTra-53T
- 95UppDec-337
- 95UppDecED-337
- 95UppDecEDG-337
- 96Fle-592
- 96FleTif-592
- 96FleUpd-U168
- 96FleUpdTC-U168
- 96Pac-208
- 96PhiTeal-24
- 97Cir-108
- 97CirRav-108
- 97ColChoU-U7
- 97Fle-634
- 97FleTif-634
- 97PhoFirDTTI-10
- 97Ult-429
- 97UltGolME-429
- 97UltPlaME-429
- 98PacOnl-148
- 98PacOnlR-148
- 98PacOnlWC-148
- 98UppDec-218
- 99Fle-575
- 99FleSta9-575
- 99FleWarT-575
- 99Pac-89
- 99PacPlaB-89
- 99PacRed-89

Mull, Blaine
- 95SprSulTI-17
- 96LanLugB-17
- 96MidLeaAB-38
- 97WicWra-6
- 98PorSeaDQ-7

Mull, Jack
- 75PhoGiaC-6
- 75PhoGiaCK-2
- 76PheGiaCr-10
- 76PhoGiaCC-16
- 76PhoGiaVNB-18
- 77CedRapGT-11
- 78CedRapGT-18
- 81ShrCapT-1
- 83PhoGiaBHN-24
- 84PhoGiaC-24
- 85GiaMot-27
- 85GiaPos-24
- 86CliGiaP-15
- 87ShrCapP-25
- 87TexLeaAF-6
- 88ShrCapP-1279
- 88TexLeaAGS-1
- 89PhoFirC-21
- 89PhoFirP-1503
- 90CliGiaB-9
- 90CliGiaP-2565
- 91CliGiaC-26
- 91CliGiaP-851
- 93CliGiaC-26
- 93CliGiaF-2504
- 94CliLumC-26
- 94CliLumF-1997
- 96KenIndB-28

Mullan, Paul
- 92FleCle-NNO
- 93UltEck-P1

Mullane, Count (Anthony)
- 87OldJudN-353
- 94OriofB-66

Mullaney, Dominic
- 09T206-504

Mullaney, Jack
- 52LavPro-20

Mulleavy, Greg
- 30WhiSoxTI-20
- 58DodTeal-15
- 59DodTeal-18
- 60DodUniO-23
- 60Top-463

Mullee, James
- 88SFHesCreN32-20

Mullen, Adam
- 95DanBraTI-19

Mullen, Billy
- 27MidBre-35
- 90DodTar-1043

Mullen, Ford
- 43CenFlo-20

Mullen, Rebecca
- 96BatCliTI-29

Mullen, Scott
- 96SpoIndB-19
- 97LanLugTS-18
- 98CarLeaAC-3
- 98WilBluRC-19
- 99Bow-302
- 99BowGol-302
- 99BowInt-302

Mullen, Tom
- 81AppFoxT-5
- 81GleFalWST-6
- 82GleFalWST-22
- 83GleFalWST-17
- 85BufBisT-23
- 86OmaRoyP-16
- 86OmaRoyT-22
- 88OmaRoyC-8
- 88OmaRoyP-1507

Muller, Fred
- 28Zee-160
- 29Zee-164
- 30Zee-182
- 32Zee-119
- 33Zee-66
- 33Zee-159
- 34DiaMatCSB-137
- 37WheBB7-290
- 37Zee-98

Muller, Mike
- 87MemChiP-22

Muller, S.
- 88KimN18-27

Mulligan, Bill
- 86Ft.MyeRP-20
- 87Ft.MyeRP-1

Mulligan, Bob
- 80WisRapTT-3
- 82OrlTwi8SCT-21
- 82OrlTwiT-21
- 83TolMudHT-8
- 84TolMudHT-9
- 85OrlTwiT-19

Mulligan, Edward
- 21E121So1-68
- 22W575-87
- 23W501-45
- 23Zee-141
- 24Zee-97
- 25Zee-116
- 26Zee-147
- 27Zee-120
- 28Zee-140
- 29Zee-51
- 30Zee-61
- 31Zee-37
- 32Zee-41
- 33Zee-67
- 33Zee-68

Mulligan, Sean
- 92ClaFS7-132
- 92HigDesMC-17
- 92StaCluD-127
- 92WatDiaF-2144
- 93RanCucQC-21
- 94AriFalLS-13
- 94RanCucQC-21
- 94RanCucQF-1642
- 96LasVegSB-18

Mulligan, William J.
- 08BufBisFJO-10

Mullin, George
- 04FanCraAL-37
- 07TigACDPP-9
- 08RosComP-37
- 09AmeCarE90-1-82
- 09BriE97-23
- 09ColChiE-207
- 09SpoNewSM-33
- 09T206-258
- 09T206-259
- 09T206-260
- 09TigMorBBBP-12
- 09TigMorPWBPP-9
- 09TigTaCP-13
- 09WolNewDTPP-11
- 10CouT21-196
- 10CouT21-197
- 10DomDisP-89
- 10E-UOraBSC-18
- 10E98-24
- 10JuJuDE-30
- 10NadE1-42
- 10RedCroT-56
- 10RedCroT-141
- 10RedCroT-228
- 10SweCapPP-28A
- 10SweCapPP-28B
- 10W555-51
- 11DiaGumP-21
- 11HelSta-35
- 11PinT-5-162
- 11S74Sil-17
- 11SpoLifCW-263
- 11SpoLifM-65
- 11T205-125
- 11TurRedT-30
- 12ColRedB-207
- 12ColTinT-207
- 12HasTriFT-5
- 12PhiCarE-23
- 12T207-136
- 12T207-137
- 14CraJacE-24
- 14PieStaT-79
- 15CraJacE-24
- 15VicT21-21
- 67SpoHobFC-16
- 68SCFOldT-13
- 72ClaCar-60
- 81TigDetN-119
- 81TigSecNP-4
- 92ConTSN-338

Mullin, James
- 07NewEveWS-10

Mullin, Jay
- 89TenTecGE-18

Mullin, Pat
- 47TipTop-38
- 49Bow-56
- 50Bow-135
- 51Bow-106
- 52Bow-183
- 52Top-275
- 53BowBW-4
- 53TigGle-22
- 54Bow-151
- 79ExpPos-17
- 80ExpPos-17
- 81TigDetN-21
- 83TigAlKS-8
- 83TigAlKS-61
- 83TopRep5-275
- 85TCMPla1-6

Mullin, Williard
- 88WilMulP-1

Mulliniks, Rance (S. Rance)
- 75QuaCitAT-10
- 77SalLakCGC-4
- 78AngFamF-28
- 78SSP270-216
- 78Top-579
- 79SalLakCGT-11
- 81Don-504
- 81Fle-48
- 81Top-433
- 82BluJayS-14
- 82Don-630
- 82Fle-418
- 82Top-104
- 82TopTra-78T
- 83Don-432
- 83Fle-436
- 83OPC-277
- 83Top-277
- 84BluJayFS-26
- 84Don-584
- 84Fle-165
- 84Nes792-762
- 84OPC-19
- 84Top-762
- 84TopSti-374
- 84TopTif-762
- 85AllGamPI-36
- 85BluJayCC-6
- 85BluJayFS-24
- 85Don-485
- 85Fle-116
- 85Lea-153
- 85OPC-336
- 85OPCPos-17
- 85Top-336
- 85TopTif-336
- 86BluJayAF-21
- 86BluJayFS-27
- 86Don-606
- 86Fle-68
- 86GenMilB-3G
- 86OPC-74
- 86Top-74
- 86TopTif-74
- 87BluJayFS-24
- 87Don-319
- 87DonOpeD-32
- 87Fle-237
- 87FleGlo-237
- 87OPC-91
- 87Top-537
- 87TopTif-537
- 88BluJayFS-24
- 88Don-197
- 88DonBasB-328
- 88Fle-120
- 88FleGlo-120
- 88Lea-204
- 88MSAHosD-14
- 88OPC-167
- 88Sco-235
- 88ScoGlo-235
- 88StaLinBJ-16
- 88Top-167
- 88TopTif-167
- 89BluJayFS-21
- 89Bow-250
- 89BowTif-250
- 89Don-87
- 89Fle-242
- 89FleGlo-242
- 89OPC-111
- 89Sco-385
- 89Top-618
- 89TopSti-192
- 89TopTif-618
- 89UppDec-43
- 90BluJayFS-21
- 90Don-607
- 90El PasDAGTI-42
- 90Fle-91
- 90FleCan-91
- 90OPC-466
- 90PubIntS-525
- 90Sco-204
- 90Top-466
- 90TopTif-466
- 90UppDec-132
- 91BluJayFS-18
- 91BluJayFS-21
- 91BluJayS-17
- 91Don-663
- 91Fle-181
- 91OPC-229
- 91Sco-433
- 91Top-229
- 91TopDesS-229
- 91TopMic-229
- 91TopTif-229
- 91Ult-366
- 92Don-542
- 92Fle-337
- 92KnoBluJF-2999
- 92OPC-133
- 92Sco-132
- 92StaClu-202
- 92Top-133
- 92TopGol-133
- 92TopGolW-133
- 92TopMic-133
- 92Ult-149
- 93BluJayD4-26
- 97BirBarB-28

Mullino, Ray
- 87GenCubP-9
- 87PeoChiP-1
- 88ChaWheB-25
- 89WinSpiS-12
- 90ChaKniTI-15
- 90PeoChiTI-26
- 90TopTVCu-54

Mullins, Daryl
- 93HolLeg-11

Mullins, Fran
- 80GleFalWSBT-23
- 80GleFalWSCT-12
- 81EdmTraRR-20
- 81Top-112
- 82EdmTraT-9
- 84GiaPos-18
- 85PhoGiaC-180
- 85Top-283
- 85TopTif-283
- 86IndOhH-22
- 86IndTeal-28

Mullins, Gregory
- 95BelBreTI-16
- 95HelBreTI-23
- 96El PasDB-20
- 97CalLeaATI-20
- 97StoPor-8
- 98LouRedQ-17

Mullins, Ron
- 87CedRapRP-8
- 88GreHorP-1561
- 88SouAtlLAGS-9
- 89MiaMirIS-14
- 90PenPilS-13

Mullins, Sam
- 92PriRedC-7
- 92PriRedF-3086
- 93PriRedC-20
- 93PriRedF-4176

Mulroy, Emmett
❑ 19Zee-73
Mulvaney, Michael
❑ 88BilMusP-1808
❑ 89GreHorP-410
❑ 89SouAtlLAGS-33
❑ 90CedRapRB-7
❑ 90CedRapRP-2330
❑ 90MidLeaASGS-44
Mulvehill, Chase
❑ 98PitMetM-21
Mulvey, Joe (Joseph)
❑ 87AllandGN-9
❑ 87BucN28-82A
❑ 87BucN28-82B
❑ 87OldJudN-354
❑ 88WG1CarG-53
❑ 90DodTar-558
❑ 90KalBatN-41
Mulville, Duane
❑ 88BilMusP-1805
❑ 89CedRapRB-11
❑ 89CedRapRP-924
❑ 89CedRapRS-13
❑ 92ClePhiC-20
❑ 92ClePhiF-2059
Mumaw, Steve
❑ 86VenGulP-15
❑ 87DunBluJP-932
❑ 88DunBluJS-11
❑ 89ArkTraGS-14
Mummau, Rob
❑ 93St.CatBJC-18
❑ 93St.CatBJF-3982
❑ 94SouBenSHC-13
❑ 94SouBenSHF-600
❑ 95HagSunF-75
❑ 96DunBluJB-18
❑ 96DunBluJTI-21
❑ 97SyrSkyCB-16
Mumphrey, Jerry
❑ 75TulOil7-16
❑ 76SSP-289
❑ 76St.LouCP-24
❑ 77Car5-16
❑ 77CarTeal-16
❑ 77Top-136
❑ 78CarTeal-20
❑ 78Top-452
❑ 79Car5-18
❑ 79Top-32
❑ 80OPC-196
❑ 80Top-378
❑ 81Don-124
❑ 81Dra-26
❑ 81Fle-494
❑ 81OPC-196
❑ 81Squ-23
❑ 81Top-556
❑ 81TopScr-97
❑ 81TopSti-227
❑ 81TopTra-808
❑ 81YanPhoA-15
❑ 82Don-261
❑ 82Fle-43
❑ 82OPC-175
❑ 82Top-175
❑ 82Top-486
❑ 82TopSti-220
❑ 82YanPhoA-17
❑ 83AllGamPI-63
❑ 83Don-360
❑ 83Fle-389
❑ 83FleSta-132
❑ 83FleSti-41
❑ 83OPC-246
❑ 83Top-81
❑ 83Top-670
❑ 83TopSti-97
❑ 83YanPhoA-16
❑ 83YanRoyRD-6
❑ 84AllGamPI-61
❑ 84AstMot-9
❑ 84AstPos-19
❑ 84Don-426
❑ 84Fle-233
❑ 84Nes792-45
❑ 84OPC-45
❑ 84Top-45
❑ 84TopSti-70
❑ 84TopTif-45
❑ 85AllGamPI-153
❑ 85AstHouP-6
❑ 85AstMot-15
❑ 85Don-206
❑ 85Fle-354
❑ 85Lea-124
❑ 85OPC-186
❑ 85Top-736
❑ 85TopMin-736
❑ 85TopSti-60
❑ 85TopTif-736
❑ 86AstMot-27
❑ 86CubGat-22
❑ 86CubUno-14
❑ 86Don-84
❑ 86Fle-306
❑ 86FleUpd-79
❑ 86OPC-282
❑ 86SevCoi-S16
❑ 86Top-282
❑ 86TopTif-282
❑ 86TopTra-76T
❑ 86TopTraT-76T
❑ 87CubCan-22
❑ 87CubDavB-22
❑ 87Don-324
❑ 87Fle-571
❑ 87FleGlo-571
❑ 87FleMin-73
❑ 87FleStiC-82
❑ 87SpoTeaP-22
❑ 87Top-372
❑ 87TopSti-58
❑ 87TopTif-372
❑ 88CubDavB-22
❑ 88Don-447
❑ 88DonTeaBC-447
❑ 88Fle-427
❑ 88FleGlo-427
❑ 88FleMin-69
❑ 88OPC-63
❑ 88PanSti-267
❑ 88Sco-467
❑ 88ScoGlo-467
❑ 88StaLinCu-9
❑ 88Top-466
❑ 88TopBig-70
❑ 88TopTif-466
❑ 89Sco-288
❑ 92YanWIZ8-128
Muncrief, Bob
❑ 41BroW75-22
❑ 41Gou-8
❑ 46SeaSLP-45
❑ 46SpoExcW-5-8
❑ 47TipTop-69
❑ 48IndTeal-23
❑ 49Bow-221
❑ 53SanFraSTI-15
❑ 79DiaGre-186
❑ 83TCMPla1945-9
❑ 96Bro194F-12
Munda, Steve
❑ 91OneYanP-4152
❑ 92GreHorC-22
❑ 92GreHorF-776
❑ 93PriWilCC-18
❑ 93PriWilCF-653
❑ 94SanBerSC-12
❑ 94TamYanF-2380
Mundorff, Rabbit
❑ 09ObaT21-57
❑ 09ObaT21-165
❑ 09ObaT21-365
❑ 12HomRunKE-70
❑ 12ObaPreT-114
❑ 12Zee-123
❑ 12Zee-124
❑ 13Zee-118
❑ 14Zee-115
❑ 15Zee-47
Mundroig, Jorge
❑ 79CedRapGT-4
Mundy, Mike
❑ 98PorRocG-25
Mundy, Rick
❑ 88GenCubP-1640
❑ 89GenCubP-1883
❑ 89PeoChiTI-12
❑ 90PeoChiTI-6
❑ 91PeoChiC-11
❑ 91PeoChiP-1345
❑ 91PeoChiTI-15
Munger, Red (George)
❑ 46SpoExcW-8-10
❑ 47TipTop-160
❑ 49Bow-40
❑ 49EurSta-190
❑ 50Bow-89
❑ 51Bow-11
❑ 51TopBluB-14
❑ 52Bow-243
❑ 52Top-115
❑ 57SeaPop-15
❑ 83Car194T-51
❑ 83TopRep5-115
Mungin, Mike
❑ 88SouOreAP-1710
Mungo, Dave
❑ 89GenCubP-1859
Mungo, Van Lingle
❑ 33WorCig-71
❑ 34BatR31-26
❑ 34BatR31-131
❑ 34DiaMatCSB-138
❑ 34DiaStaR-19
❑ 34DiaStaR-102
❑ 35DiaMatCS2-16
❑ 35DiaMatCS3T1-112
❑ 35ExhFou-2
❑ 36DiaMatCS4-11
❑ 36ExhFou-2
❑ 36NatChiFPR-59
❑ 36R31PasP-18
❑ 36R31Pre-L9
❑ 36SandSW-42
❑ 36WheBB3-9
❑ 37ExhFou-2
❑ 37GouThuMR-6
❑ 37WheBB14-11
❑ 37WheBB7-29K
❑ 37WheBB9-14
❑ 38BasTabP-23
❑ 38CloFotW-67
❑ 38ExhFou-2
❑ 38GouFliMR-6A
❑ 38GouFliMR-6B
❑ 38GouHeaU-254
❑ 38GouHeaU-278
❑ 39GouPreR303A-33
❑ 39PlaBal-111
❑ 39WorWidGTP-33
❑ 40DodTeal-17
❑ 40PlaBal-64
❑ 73Dod194T-19
❑ 78DodTCM4-9
❑ 84OCoandSI-122
❑ 85BigLeaC3-38
❑ 89DodSmoG-45
❑ 90DodTar-559
❑ 94ConTSN-1107
❑ 94ConTSNB-1107
Munley, John
❑ 83TriTriT-7
Munninghoff, Scott
❑ 81OklCit8T-13
❑ 82ChaLooT-2
Munns, Les
❑ 33WorCig(-63
❑ 90DodTar-560
Munoz, Anthony
❑ 98SanJosGQ-30
Munoz, Billy Ray
❑ 98ColRedSM-17
Munoz, Bobby (Bob)
❑ 89BlaYNPRWL-181
❑ 90Bes-192
❑ 90GreHorB-8
❑ 90GreHorP-2660
❑ 90GreHorS-14
❑ 91FloStaLAP-FSL16
❑ 91Ft.LauYC-9
❑ 91Ft.LauYP-2422
❑ 92AlbYanF-2224
❑ 92AlbYanSk-13
❑ 92Bow-523
❑ 92ClaFS7-6
❑ 92SkyAA F-8
❑ 92UppDecML-222
❑ 93Bow-47
❑ 93ClaFS7-82
❑ 93ColCliF-1110
❑ 93ColCliP-10
❑ 93ExcFS7-213
❑ 93FlaWavotF-10
❑ 93FleFinE-249
❑ 93Lea-548
❑ 93SelRoo-32T
❑ 93TopTra-13T
❑ 93Ult-598
❑ 94Bow-56
❑ 94ColC-214
❑ 94ColC-553
❑ 94ColChoGS-214
❑ 94ColChoGS-553
❑ 94ColChoSS-214
❑ 94ColChoSS-553
❑ 94Don-174
❑ 94Fin-414
❑ 94FinRef-414
❑ 94Fla-416
❑ 94Fle-241
❑ 94FleUpd-168
❑ 94Pac-431
❑ 94PhiMed-24
❑ 94PhiMel-17
❑ 94Pin-188
❑ 94PinArtP-188
❑ 94PinMusC-188
❑ 94Sco-566
❑ 94ScoGolR-566
❑ 94SpoRoo-140
❑ 94SpoRooAP-140
❑ 94StaClu-246
❑ 94StaCluFDI-246
❑ 94StaCluGR-246
❑ 94StaCluMOP-246
❑ 94StaCluT-214
❑ 94StaCluTFDI-214
❑ 94Top-144
❑ 94TopGol-144
❑ 94TopSpa-144
❑ 94TopTra-102T
❑ 94Ult-98
❑ 94Ult-553
❑ 94UppDec-343
❑ 94UppDecED-343
❑ 95ColCho-372
❑ 95ColChoGS-372
❑ 95ColChoSE-173
❑ 95ColChoSEGS-173
❑ 95ColChoSESS-173
❑ 95ColChoSS-372
❑ 95Don-159
❑ 95DonPreP-159
❑ 95Fin-84
❑ 95FinRef-84
❑ 95Fla-182
❑ 95Fle-402
❑ 95Lea-103
❑ 95Pac-335
❑ 95Phi-22
❑ 95Pin-243
❑ 95PinArtP-243
❑ 95PinMusC-243
❑ 95StaClu-385
❑ 95StaCluMOP-385
❑ 95StaCluSTWS-385
❑ 95StaCluVR-203
❑ 95StaCluVRMO-203
❑ 95Top-458
❑ 95TopCyb-253
❑ 95TopEmb-80
❑ 95TopEmbGI-80
❑ 95Ult-208
❑ 95UltGolM-208
❑ 95UppDec-143
❑ 95UppDecED-143
❑ 95UppDecEDG-143
❑ 97PacPriGotD-GD185
❑ 97PhiTeal-35
❑ 98RocRedWQ-20
Munoz, Francisco
❑ 93LinVenB-96
❑ 94VenLinU-31
❑ 95LinVen-137
❑ 96-97LinVen-219
Munoz, J.J.
❑ 90MarPhiP-3196
❑ 90ProAaA-186
❑ 91SpaPhiC-9
❑ 91SpaPhiP-894
❑ 92ClePhiC-17
❑ 92ClePhiF-2056
❑ 93ClePhiC-17
❑ 93ClePhiF-2681
❑ 94ReaPhiF-2060
❑ 95OmaRoyTI-23
Munoz, Jose
❑ 88BakDodCLC-239
❑ 88BlaYNPRWL-46
❑ 89BlaYNPRWL-47
❑ 89VerBeaDS-18
❑ 90BakDodCLC-258
❑ 91LinDriAA-538
❑ 91SanAntMLD-538
❑ 91SanAntMP-2983
❑ 92AlbDukF-728
❑ 92AlbDukS-17
❑ 92SkyAAAF-9
❑ 93AlbDukF-1470
❑ 93LinVenB-299
❑ 94PawRedSDD-14
❑ 94PawRedSF-951
❑ 95RicBraRC-13
❑ 95RicBraTI-10
❑ 97Pac-60
❑ 97PacLigB-60
❑ 97PacSil-60
❑ 97Ult-42
❑ 97UltGolME-42
❑ 97UltPlaME-42
Munoz, Juan
❑ 96-97LinVen-36
❑ 96MidLeaAB-20
❑ 96PeoChiB-22
❑ 97PriWilC-24
❑ 98ArkTraM-21
❑ 98MemRedG-14
Munoz, Julio
❑ 90AshTouP-2744
Munoz, Lou
❑ 88ElmPioC-16
❑ 88WinHavRSS-16
❑ 89ElmPioP-12
❑ 90WinHavRSS-20
Munoz, Mario
❑ 93BenRocCB-18
❑ 93BenRocF-3278
Munoz, Michael
❑ 87BakDodP-27
❑ 88BasAmeAAB-26
❑ 88BlaYNPRWL-186
❑ 88SanAntMB-7
❑ 88TexLeaAGS-30
❑ 89AlbDukCm-8
❑ 89AlbDukP-62
❑ 90DodTar-561
❑ 90DonRoo-8
❑ 90Sco-653
❑ 90TopDeb89-85
❑ 91LinDriAAA-593
❑ 91Sco100RS-93
❑ 91TolMudHLD-593
❑ 91TolMudHP-1929
❑ 92StaClu-441
❑ 92TigKro-19
❑ 92Ult-367
❑ 93ColSprSSF-3083
❑ 93Don-627
❑ 93Fle-609
❑ 93Lea-191
❑ 93PacSpa-449
❑ 93Sco-228
❑ 93StaClu-248
❑ 93StaCluFDI-248
❑ 93StaCluMOP-248
❑ 93Top-379
❑ 93TopGol-379
❑ 93TopInaM-379
❑ 93TopInaR-379
❑ 93TopMic-379
❑ 93UppDec-601
❑ 93UppDecGold-601
❑ 94FleUpd-129
❑ 94RocPol-18
❑ 94StaClu-492
❑ 94StaCluFDI-492
❑ 94StaCluGR-492
❑ 94StaCluMOP-492
❑ 94StaCluT-102
❑ 94StaCluTFDI-102
❑ 95Fla-131
❑ 95Fle-524
❑ 95Sco-228
❑ 95ScoGolR-228
❑ 95ScoPlaTS-228
❑ 95Ult-375
❑ 95UltGolM-375
❑ 96Fle-368
❑ 96FleTif-368
❑ 96LeaSigEA-134
❑ 96RocFle-9
❑ 96RocPol-13
❑ 97PacPriGotD-GD136
❑ 98PacInvGems-147
❑ 98PacOnl-254
❑ 98PacOnlR-254
❑ 98PacOnlWC-254
❑ 99PacCroC-98
❑ 99PacCroCPB-98
Munoz, Noe
❑ 94SanAntMF-2473
Munoz, Omer
❑ 87WesPalBEP-669
❑ 88WesPalBES-19
❑ 90JacExpB-7
❑ 90JacExpP-1383
❑ 91HarSenLD-265
❑ 91HarSenP-635
❑ 91LinDriAA-265
❑ 92IndIndF-1868
❑ 92IndIndS-188
❑ 93BufBisF-525
❑ 94VenLinU-231
❑ 94VenLinU-245
❑ 95CarMudF-167
❑ 96LynHilB-29
❑ 97WisTimR-3
❑ 98WisTimRM-27
Munoz, Orlando
❑ 92PalSprAC-14
❑ 92PalSprAF-848
❑ 93LinVenB-268
❑ 93PalSprAC-15
❑ 93PalSprAF-78
❑ 94VanCanF-1870
❑ 95LinVen-46
❑ 95MidAngOHP-23
❑ 95MidAngTI-21
❑ 96-97LinVen-106
❑ 97MidAngOHP-19
Munoz, Oscar
❑ 90WatIndS-14
❑ 91Cla/Bes-149
❑ 91KinIndC-8
❑ 91KinIndP-320
❑ 92OrlSunRF-2847
❑ 92OrlSunRS-522
❑ 92UppDecML-293
❑ 93NasXprF-401
❑ 94Bow-597
❑ 94ExcFS7-96
❑ 94SalLakBF-814
❑ 94Top-771
❑ 94TopGol-771
❑ 94TopSpa-771
❑ 94UppDecML-217
❑ 96Pac-366
❑ 96RocRedWB-19
❑ 96Sco-249
❑ 96SigRooOJ-23
❑ 96SigRooOJS-23
Munoz, Pedro
❑ 87DunBluJP-948
❑ 88BlaYNPRWL-110
❑ 88DunBluJS-13
❑ 89KnoBluJB-18
❑ 89KnoBluJP-1126
❑ 89KnoBluJS-14
❑ 89Sta-122
❑ 90ProAAAF-365
❑ 90SyrChiMB-17
❑ 90SyrChiP-585
❑ 91Bow-336
❑ 91Cla3-T64
❑ 91Don-758
❑ 91DonRoo-21
❑ 91Fle-620
❑ 91Lea-186
❑ 91LinDriAAA-412
❑ 91PorBeaLD-412
❑ 91PorBeaP-1579
❑ 91Sco-332
❑ 91StaClu-318
❑ 91TopDeb90-111
❑ 91Ult-192
❑ 91UppDec-432
❑ 92Don-305
❑ 92Fle-212
❑ 92Lea-53
❑ 92LeaBlaG-53
❑ 92OPC-613
❑ 92Pin-139
❑ 92PinTea2-61
❑ 92ProFS7-91
❑ 92Sco-514
❑ 92Sco100RS-74
❑ 92StaClu-541
❑ 92Top-613
❑ 92TopGol-613
❑ 92TopGolW-613
❑ 92TopMic-613
❑ 92Ult-399
❑ 92UppDec-764
❑ 93Don-311
❑ 93Fla-240
❑ 93Fle-272
❑ 93Lea-219
❑ 93OPC-289
❑ 93PacSpa-175
❑ 93PanSti-132
❑ 93Pin-135
❑ 93Sco-130
❑ 93Sel-370

❑ 93SP-251
❑ 93StaClu-117
❑ 93StaCluFDI-117
❑ 93StaCluMOP-117
❑ 93Stu-166
❑ 93Top-119
❑ 93TopGol-119
❑ 93TopInaM-119
❑ 93TopInaR-119
❑ 93TopMic-119
❑ 93Toy-26
❑ 93Ult-235
❑ 93UppDec-341
❑ 93UppDecGold-341
❑ 94ColC-543
❑ 94ColChoGS-543
❑ 94ColChoSS-543
❑ 94Don-55
❑ 94Fin-338
❑ 94FinRef-338
❑ 94Fle-215
❑ 94Lea-360
❑ 94Pac-363
❑ 94PanSti-95
❑ 94Pin-356
❑ 94PinArtP-356
❑ 94PinMusC-356
❑ 94Sco-435
❑ 94ScoGolR-435
❑ 94Sel-301
❑ 94StaClu-22
❑ 94StaCluFDI-22
❑ 94StaCluGR-22
❑ 94StaCluMOP-22
❑ 94Top-459
❑ 94TopGol-459
❑ 94TopSpa-459
❑ 94Ult-392
❑ 94UppDec-302
❑ 94UppDecED-302
❑ 95ColCho-489
❑ 95ColChoGS-489
❑ 95ColChoSS-489
❑ 95Don-436
❑ 95DonPreP-436
❑ 95DonTopotO-112
❑ 95Fla-61
❑ 95Fle-211
❑ 95Lea-125
❑ 95Pac-254
❑ 95PacPri-81
❑ 95Pin-125
❑ 95PinArtP-125
❑ 95PinMusC-125
❑ 95Sco-331
❑ 95ScoGolR-331
❑ 95ScoPlaTS-331
❑ 95SPCha-168
❑ 95SPChaDC-168
❑ 95StaClu-471
❑ 95StaCluMOP-471
❑ 95StaCluSTWS-471
❑ 95Top-274
❑ 95TopCyb-77
❑ 95Ult-305
❑ 95UltGolM-305
❑ 95UppDec-432
❑ 95UppDecED-432
❑ 95UppDecEDG-432
❑ 95UppDecSE-84
❑ 95UppDecSEG-84
❑ 96A'sMot-12
❑ 96ColCho-202
❑ 96ColCho-646
❑ 96ColChoGS-202
❑ 96ColChoGS-646
❑ 96ColChoSS-202
❑ 96ColChoSS-646
❑ 96Don-196
❑ 96DonPreP-196
❑ 96EmoXL-105
❑ 96Fla-151
❑ 96Fle-170
❑ 96FleTif-170
❑ 96FleUpd-U74
❑ 96FleUpdTC-U74
❑ 96MetUni-79
❑ 96MetUniP-79
❑ 96Pac-357
❑ 96PacPri-P116
❑ 96PacPriG-P116
❑ 96PanSti-206
❑ 96ProSta-129
❑ 96Sco-87
❑ 96Top-384
❑ 96Ult-91
❑ 96Ult-402
❑ 96UltGolM-91
❑ 96UltGolM-402
❑ 96UppDec-129
❑ 96UppDec-414
❑ 97PacPriGotD-GD81

Munoz, Ricky (Riccardo)
❑ 92BriTigC-8
❑ 92BriTigF-1408

Munoz, Roberto
❑ 76VenLeaS-16

Munoz, Tom
❑ 75OakOak2A-24

Munro, Peter
❑ 91SydWavF-15
❑ 95Bow-208
❑ 96Bow-291
❑ 96BowFoi-291
❑ 96SarRedSB-24
❑ 97EasLeaTPB-30
❑ 97TreThuB-22
❑ 98Bow-164
❑ 98BowCerBlueAU-67
❑ 98BowCerGA-67
❑ 98BowCerSA-67
❑ 98BowChr-164
❑ 98BowChrGA-164
❑ 98BowChrGAR-164
❑ 98BowChrI-164
❑ 98BowChrIR-164
❑ 98BowChrR-164
❑ 98BowGolA-164
❑ 98BowInt-164
❑ 98PawRedSQ-22

Munsell, Emmett
❑ 13Zee-86
❑ 16Zee-84

Munson, Eric
❑ 99UppDecE-104
❑ 99UppDecEFXG-104

Munson, Jay
❑ 83CedRapRF-7
❑ 83CedRapRT-25

Munson, Joseph M.
❑ 26Exh-24

Munson, Thurman
❑ 70OPC-189
❑ 70Top-189
❑ 70YanCliDP-9
❑ 70YanPhoS-27
❑ 71MilDud-19
❑ 71MLBOffS-497
❑ 71OPC-5
❑ 71Top-5
❑ 71Top-275
❑ 71TopCoi-118
❑ 71TopGreM-1
❑ 71TopTat-83
❑ 71YanArcO-8
❑ 71YanCliDP-12
❑ 72OPC-441
❑ 72OPC-442
❑ 72Top-441
❑ 72Top-442
❑ 72YanSch-3
❑ 72YanTeal-3
❑ 73LinPor-132
❑ 73NewYorSNM-14
❑ 73OPC-142
❑ 73SevTraC-50
❑ 73SyrChiTI-19
❑ 73Top-142
❑ 73TopCanL-34
❑ 74OPC-340
❑ 74SyrChiTI-18
❑ 74Top-238
❑ 74Top-340
❑ 74TopDecE-7
❑ 74TopSta-215
❑ 75Hos-138
❑ 75OPC-20
❑ 75SSPPuzB-18
❑ 75SyrChiTI-13
❑ 75Top-20
❑ 75TopMin-20
❑ 75YanSSP-5
❑ 76BlaDis-41
❑ 76BucDis-41
❑ 76CarDis-41
❑ 76CraDis-41
❑ 76DailsID-41
❑ 76Hos-16
❑ 76HosTwi-16
❑ 76IsaDis-41
❑ 76Kel-53
❑ 76OPC-192
❑ 76OPC-650
❑ 76OrbDis-41
❑ 76RedBarD-41
❑ 76SafDis-41
❑ 76SSP-433
❑ 76Top-192
❑ 76Top-650
❑ 76TowCluD-41
❑ 77BurCheD-177
❑ 77ChiWilD-49
❑ 77DailsID-49
❑ 77DetCaeD-49
❑ 77HolInnD-49
❑ 77Hos-5
❑ 77Kel-23
❑ 77MSADis-49
❑ 77OPC-30
❑ 77PepGloD-36
❑ 77RCColC-46
❑ 77SagDis-49
❑ 77sDis-49
❑ 77Spo-2005
❑ 77Top-170
❑ 77TopCloS-32
❑ 77WenDis-49
❑ 77YanBurK-2
❑ 77YanNedC-3
❑ 77ZipDis-49
❑ 78Hos-150
❑ 78Kel-30
❑ 78OPC-200
❑ 78PapGinD-27
❑ 78RCColC-15
❑ 78SagDis-7
❑ 78SSP270-1
❑ 78TasDis-7
❑ 78Top-60
❑ 78WifBalD-53
❑ 78YanBurK-2
❑ 78YanPhoA-18
❑ 78YanSSPD-1
❑ 79BasPat-59
❑ 79Hos-26
❑ 79OPC-157
❑ 79Top-310
❑ 79YanBurK-2
❑ 79YanPicA-25
❑ 80LauFamF-13
❑ 82K-M-29
❑ 82OhiHaloF-50
❑ 83FraBroR-39
❑ 84OCoandSI-32
❑ 84OCoandSI-158
❑ 84SpoDesPW-15
❑ 85GeoSteM-7
❑ 86SpoDecG-62
❑ 86TCMSupS-31
❑ 87SpoCubG-3
❑ 88PacLegI-30
❑ 89YanScoNW-32
❑ 90RinPosM-1
❑ 90RinPosM-2
❑ 90RinPosM-3
❑ 90RinPosM-4
❑ 90RinPosM-5
❑ 90RinPosM-6
❑ 90RinPosM-7
❑ 90RinPosM-8
❑ 90RinPosM-9
❑ 90RinPosM-10
❑ 90RinPosM-11
❑ 90RinPosM-12
❑ 90YanMomPRP-3
❑ 91Col-22
❑ 91LinDri-38
❑ 91SweBasG-149
❑ 92PinRool-10
❑ 92YanWIZ6-92
❑ 92YanWIZ7-118
❑ 92YanWIZA-50
❑ 93ActPacA-161
❑ 93UppDecS-20
❑ 94TedWil-62
❑ 94Yoo-11

Mura, Steve
❑ 79PadFamF-15
❑ 79Top-725
❑ 80Top-491
❑ 81Don-362
❑ 81Fle-496
❑ 81Top-134
❑ 82Don-523
❑ 82Fle-578
❑ 82Top-641
❑ 82TopTra-79T
❑ 83Don-292
❑ 83Fle-16
❑ 83FleSta-133
❑ 83OPC-24
❑ 83Top-24
❑ 84PorBeaC-196
❑ 85TacTigC-147
❑ 86Top-281
❑ 86TopTif-281

Murakami, Les
❑ 87HawRai-1

Murakami, Masanori
❑ 65OPC-282
❑ 65Top-282
❑ 78TCM60I-182
❑ 79TCMJapPB-37

Murakami, Seiichi
❑ 90SalSpuCLC-119
❑ 90SalSpuP-2717

Muramatsu, Arihito
❑ 91SalSpuC-10

Murata, Katsuyoshi
❑ 96HonShaHWB-14

Muratti, Rafael
❑ 86MacPirP-17
❑ 87SalBucP-17
❑ 88BlaYNPRWL-138
❑ 88MiaMarS-16
❑ 89BlaYNPRWLU-7
❑ 91QuaCitAC-26
❑ 91QuaCitAP-2644

Murcer, Bobby
❑ 47PM1StaP1-145
❑ 66TolMudHTI-19
❑ 66Top-469
❑ 67CokCapYM-V12
❑ 67OPC-93
❑ 67Top-93
❑ 69Top-657
❑ 69YanPhoS-45
❑ 70Kel-60
❑ 70MLBOffS-247
❑ 70OPC-333
❑ 70Top-333
❑ 70TopBoo-9
❑ 70YanCliDP-1
❑ 70YanPhoS-28
❑ 71BazNumT-9
❑ 71BazUnn-27
❑ 71MLBOffS-498
❑ 71OPC-635
❑ 71Top-635
❑ 71TopCoi-54
❑ 71TopGreM-46
❑ 71YanArcO-9
❑ 71YanCliDP-13
❑ 72Kel-16
❑ 72MilBra-247
❑ 72OPC-86
❑ 72ProStaP-32
❑ 72SevTraC-36
❑ 72Top-86
❑ 72Top-699
❑ 72Top-700
❑ 72YanSch-4
❑ 72YanTeal-4
❑ 73Kel2D-19
❑ 73LinPor-133
❑ 73NewYorSNM-18
❑ 73OPC-240
❑ 73OPC-343
❑ 73SevTraC-51
❑ 73SyrChiTI-20
❑ 73Top-240
❑ 73Top-343
❑ 73TopCanL-35
❑ 73TopCom-12
❑ 73TopPin-12
❑ 73Yan-3
❑ 74Kel-22
❑ 74NewYorNTDiS-6
❑ 74OPC-90
❑ 74OPC-336
❑ 74SyrChiTI-19
❑ 74Top-90
❑ 74Top-336
❑ 74TopDecE-63
❑ 74TopPuz-7
❑ 74TopSta-216
❑ 75GiaTeal-12
❑ 75Hos-141
❑ 75OPC-350
❑ 75Top-350
❑ 75TopMin-350
❑ 76BlaDis-42
❑ 76BucDis-42
❑ 76CarDis-42
❑ 76CraDis-42
❑ 76CubTri-17
❑ 76DailsID-42
❑ 76Hos-123
❑ 76IsaDis-42
❑ 76Kel-38
❑ 76OPC-470
❑ 76OrbDis-42
❑ 76RedBarD-42
❑ 76SafDis-42
❑ 76SanFraGP-15
❑ 76SSP-111
❑ 76Top-470
❑ 76TowCluD-42
❑ 77BurCheD-105
❑ 77ChiWilD-50
❑ 77CubJewT-11
❑ 77DailsID-50
❑ 77DetCaeD-50
❑ 77HolInnD-50
❑ 77Hos-29
❑ 77MSADis-50
❑ 77OPC-83
❑ 77SagDis-50
❑ 77sDis-50
❑ 77Top-40
❑ 77TopCloS-33
❑ 77WenDis-50
❑ 77ZipDis-50
❑ 78Hos-90
❑ 78OPC-95
❑ 78RCColC-87
❑ 78SSP270-265
❑ 78Top-590
❑ 79BasPat-60
❑ 79Hos-6
❑ 79OPC-63
❑ 79Top-135
❑ 79YanPicA-26
❑ 80OPC-190
❑ 80Top-365
❑ 80YanPhoA-17
❑ 81Don-111
❑ 81Fle-94
❑ 81OPC-253
❑ 81Top-602
❑ 81YanPhoA-16
❑ 82Don-486
❑ 82Fle-44
❑ 82Top-208
❑ 82YanPhoA-18
❑ 83Don-261
❑ 83Fle-390
❑ 83OPC-122
❑ 83OPC-304
❑ 83Top-782
❑ 83Top-783
❑ 83TopFol-2
❑ 83YanASFY-30
❑ 84GiaMot-23
❑ 89PacLegI-196
❑ 91SweBasG-117
❑ 91UppDecS-16
❑ 92ActPacA-32
❑ 92PinRool-14
❑ 92YanWIZ6-93
❑ 92YanWIZ7-119
❑ 92YanWIZ8-129
❑ 92YanWIZA-51
❑ 93TedWil-67
❑ 93UppDecAH-100
❑ 94CarLeaA-DJ28

Murch, Simmy (Simeon)
❑ 09ColChiE-208A
❑ 09ColChiE-208B
❑ 12ColRedB-208A
❑ 12ColRedB-208B
❑ 12ColTinT-208A
❑ 12ColTinT-208B
❑ 90DodTar-562

Murchio, George
❑ 23Zee-53

Murdock, Joe
❑ 89ChaRaiP-982
❑ 90ChaRaiB-17
❑ 90ChaRaiP-2036

Murdock, Kevin
❑ 88SouBenWSGS-4
❑ 88TamTarS-18

Murelli, Don
❑ 81MiaOriT-5

Murff, Red (John)
❑ 57Top-321
❑ 80Bra195T-13

Murillo, Javier
❑ 89MiaMirIS-15

Murillo, Ray
❑ 79KnoKnoST-19
❑ 81EdmTraRR-15

Murnane, Tim
❑ 09RamT20-84

Murphy, Bill
❑ 28Zee-16
❑ 67SeaPop-12

Murphy, Bob
❑ 75OakOak2A-25
❑ 87MetColP-52
❑ 88MetColP-53
❑ 89MetColP-45
❑ 89MetRinP69-33

Murphy, Brian
❑ 76OmaRoyTT-15
❑ 88BurBraP-7
❑ 91SydWavF-2
❑ 95AusFut-23
❑ 95AusFut-96

Murphy, Brian C.
❑ 98BluOriQ-29

Murphy, Chris
❑ 92SpoIndC-10
❑ 92SpoIndF-1291
❑ 96Exc-148

Murphy, Dale
❑ 77Top-476
❑ 78BraCok-10
❑ 78Top-708
❑ 79Hos-121
❑ 79OPC-15
❑ 79Top-39
❑ 80OPC-143
❑ 80Top-274
❑ 81AllGamPI-157
❑ 81BraPol-3
❑ 81Don-437
❑ 81Fle-243
❑ 81FleStiC-119
❑ 81OPC-118
❑ 81Top-504
❑ 81TopScr-72
❑ 81TopSti-146
❑ 82BraBurKL-18
❑ 82BraPol-3
❑ 82Don-299
❑ 82Fle-443
❑ 82OPC-391
❑ 82PerAll-14
❑ 82PerAllG-14
❑ 82Top-668
❑ 82TopSti-19
❑ 83AllGamPI-155
❑ 83BraPol-3
❑ 83Don-12
❑ 83Don-47
❑ 83DonActA-45
❑ 83Dra-18
❑ 83Fle-142
❑ 83FleSta-134
❑ 83FleSti-90
❑ 83FleSti-140
❑ 83Kel-52
❑ 83OPC-21
❑ 83OPC-23
❑ 83PerAll-12
❑ 83PerAllG-12
❑ 83PerCreC-9
❑ 83PerCreCG-9
❑ 83Top-401
❑ 83Top-502
❑ 83Top-703
❑ 83Top-760
❑ 83TopGloS-16
❑ 83TopSti-160
❑ 83TopSti-206
❑ 83TopSti-211
❑ 84AllGamPI-62
❑ 84BraPol-3
❑ 84Don-66
❑ 84DonActAS-40
❑ 84DonCha-49
❑ 84Dra-22
❑ 84Fle-186
❑ 84FleSti-17
❑ 84FleSti-32
❑ 84FleSti-50
❑ 84FunFooP-103
❑ 84MilBra-17
❑ 84MLBPen-17
❑ 84Nes792-126
❑ 84Nes792-133
❑ 84Nes792-150

❑ 84Nes792-391
❑ 84NesDreT-18
❑ 84OCoandSI-11
❑ 84OCoandSI-93
❑ 84OPC-150
❑ 84OPC-391
❑ 84RalPur-12
❑ 84raPho-21
❑ 84SevCoi-C3
❑ 84SevCoi-E3
❑ 84SevCoi-W3
❑ 84Top-126
❑ 84Top-133
❑ 84Top-150
❑ 84Top-391
❑ 84TopCer-12
❑ 84TopGloA-19
❑ 84TopGloS-31
❑ 84TopRubD-29
❑ 84TopSti-27
❑ 84TopSti-180
❑ 84TopSti-199
❑ 84TopSup-2
❑ 84TopTif-126
❑ 84TopTif-133
❑ 84TopTif-150
❑ 84TopTif-391
❑ 85AllGamPI-154
❑ 85BraHos-16
❑ 85BraPol-3
❑ 85BraTBSAT-2
❑ 85Don-66
❑ 85DonActA-25
❑ 85DonHig-5
❑ 85Dra-20
❑ 85Fle-335
❑ 85FleLimE-22
❑ 85FleStaS-18
❑ 85FleStaS-33
❑ 85GenMilS-5
❑ 85Lea-222
❑ 85OPC-320
❑ 85SevCoi-S1
❑ 85SevCoi-W3
❑ 85SpoSam-1
❑ 85Top-320
❑ 85Top-716
❑ 85Top3-D-3
❑ 85TopGaloC-7
❑ 85TopGloA-7
❑ 85TopGloS-1
❑ 85TopRubD-30
❑ 85TopSti-22
❑ 85TopSti-96
❑ 85TopSti-177
❑ 85TopSup-11
❑ 85TopTif-320
❑ 85TopTif-716
❑ 86BasStaB-76
❑ 86BraPol-3
❑ 86BurKinA-11
❑ 86Don-66
❑ 86DonAll-4
❑ 86DonHig-41
❑ 86DonPop-4
❑ 86DorChe-10
❑ 86Dra-12
❑ 86Fle-522
❑ 86Fle-635
❑ 86Fle-640
❑ 86FleLeaL-27
❑ 86FleLimE-31
❑ 86FleMin-105
❑ 86FleSlu-24
❑ 86FleStiC-80
❑ 86FleStiC-132
❑ 86FleWaxBC-C4
❑ 86GenMilB-5D
❑ 86Lea-60
❑ 86MeaGolBB-10
❑ 86MeaGolM-7
❑ 86MeaGolSB-4
❑ 86MSAJifPD-16
❑ 86OPCBoxB-M
❑ 86QuaGra-8
❑ 86SevCoi-C5
❑ 86SevCoi-E5
❑ 86SevCoi-S5
❑ 86SevCoi-W5
❑ 86Spo-5
❑ 86Spo-62
❑ 86Spo-179
❑ 86Spo-183
❑ 86SpoDecG-67
❑ 86StaMur-1
❑ 86StaMur-2
❑ 86StaMur-3
❑ 86StaMur-4
❑ 86StaMur-5
❑ 86StaMur-6
❑ 86StaMur-7
❑ 86StaMur-8
❑ 86StaMur-9
❑ 86StaMur-10
❑ 86StaMur-11
❑ 86StaMur-12
❑ 86Top-456
❑ 86Top-600
❑ 86Top-705
❑ 86Top3-D-16
❑ 86TopGaloC-8
❑ 86TopGloA-18
❑ 86TopGloS-37
❑ 86TopMinL-37
❑ 86TopSti-35
❑ 86TopSti-145
❑ 86TopSti-149
❑ 86TopSup-39
❑ 86TopTat-2
❑ 86TopTif-456
❑ 86TopTif-600
❑ 86TopTif-705
❑ 86TopWaxBC-M
❑ 86TruVal-10
❑ 86Woo-23
❑ 87BoaandB-3
❑ 87BraSmo-14
❑ 87ClaGam-37
❑ 87ClaUpdY-106
❑ 87Don-3
❑ 87Don-78
❑ 87DonAll-14
❑ 87DonOpeD-40
❑ 87DonP-14
❑ 87DonSupD-3
❑ 87DonWaxBC-PC10
❑ 87Dra-13
❑ 87Fle-522
❑ 87FleAwaW-26
❑ 87FleBasA-29
❑ 87FleGamW-30
❑ 87FleGlo-522
❑ 87FleHotS-28
❑ 87FleLimE-30
❑ 87FleMin-74
❑ 87FleRecS-23
❑ 87FleSlu-28
❑ 87FleStiC-83
❑ 87FleWaxBC-C8
❑ 87GenMilB-6F
❑ 87HosSti-7
❑ 87K-M-29
❑ 87KayB-21
❑ 87KeyFooD-15
❑ 87KraFoo-2
❑ 87Lea-3
❑ 87Lea-141
❑ 87MandMSL-9
❑ 87MSAIceTD-15
❑ 87MSAJifPD-2
❑ 87OPC-359
❑ 87OurOwnTD-15
❑ 87RedFolSB-47
❑ 87SmoNatL-2A
❑ 87SmoNatL-2B
❑ 87Spo-3
❑ 87Spo-155
❑ 87Spo-159
❑ 87SpoDeaP-3
❑ 87SpoSupD-5
❑ 87SpoTeaP-24
❑ 87StuPan-2
❑ 87Top-490
❑ 87TopCoi-37
❑ 87TopGloA-7
❑ 87TopGloS-6
❑ 87TopMinL-2
❑ 87TopSti-36
❑ 87TopSti-161
❑ 87TopTif-490
❑ 87WeiMarD-15
❑ 88CheBoy-17
❑ 88ClaBlu-201
❑ 88ClaBlu-215
❑ 88ClaRed-156
❑ 88Don-78
❑ 88DonAll-46
❑ 88DonBasB-113
❑ 88DonBonM-BC14
❑ 88Dra-15
❑ 88Fle-544
❑ 88Fle-639
❑ 88FleAwaW-27
❑ 88FleBasA-27
❑ 88FleBasM-25
❑ 88FleExcS-28
❑ 88FleGlo-544
❑ 88FleGlo-639
❑ 88FleHotS-29
❑ 88FleLeaL-29
❑ 88FleMin-65
❑ 88FleRecS-27
❑ 88FleSlu-28
❑ 88FleStiC-77
❑ 88FleSup-25
❑ 88FleTeaL-24
❑ 88FleWaxBC-C6
❑ 88GreBasS-72
❑ 88K-M-18
❑ 88KayB-20
❑ 88KeyFooD-14
❑ 88KinDis-2
❑ 88Lea-83
❑ 88MSAFanSD-13
❑ 88MSAIceTD-14
❑ 88Nes-2
❑ 88OPC-90
❑ 88OurOwnTD-14
❑ 88PanSti-251
❑ 88RedFolSB-59
❑ 88Sco-450
❑ 88ScoGlo-450
❑ 88Spo-170
❑ 88StaLinAl-19
❑ 88StaLinBra-12
❑ 88TarPla-30
❑ 88TetTeaD-14
❑ 88Top-90
❑ 88Top-549
❑ 88TopBig-14
❑ 88TopClo-16
❑ 88TopCoi-48
❑ 88TopGloS-26
❑ 88TopMinL-41
❑ 88TopRitTM-1
❑ 88TopSti-45
❑ 88TopStiB-18
❑ 88TopTif-90
❑ 88TopTif-549
❑ 88TopUKM-52
❑ 88TopUKMT-52
❑ 88WeiMarD-14
❑ 89Bow-276
❑ 89BowTif-276
❑ 89BraDub-18
❑ 89ClaTraO-124
❑ 89Don-104
❑ 89DonBasB-29
❑ 89Fle-596
❑ 89FleExcS-33
❑ 89FleGlo-596
❑ 89FleLeaL-28
❑ 89KayB-22
❑ 89KeyFooD-20
❑ 89MSAIceTD-20
❑ 89OPC-210
❑ 89OurOwnTD-20
❑ 89PanSti-45
❑ 89RedFolSB-84
❑ 89Sco-30
❑ 89ScoHot1S-66
❑ 89Scomast-15
❑ 89Spo-110
❑ 89TetTeaD-20
❑ 89Top-210
❑ 89TopAme2C-21
❑ 89TopBasT-66
❑ 89TopBig-172
❑ 89TopCapC-11
❑ 89TopCoi-19
❑ 89TopHeaUT-23
❑ 89TopHilTM-21
❑ 89TopMinL-1
❑ 89TopSti-32
❑ 89TopTif-210
❑ 89TopUKM-55
❑ 89TVSpoM-58
❑ 89UppDec-357A
❑ 89UppDec-357B
❑ 89UppDec-672
❑ 89WeiMarD-20
❑ 90BasWit-38
❑ 90Bow-19
❑ 90BowTif-19
❑ 90BraDubP-20
❑ 90BraDubS-23
❑ 90ClaUpd-T36
❑ 90Don-168
❑ 90DonBesN-62
❑ 90Fle-591
❑ 90Fle-623
❑ 90FleBasM-28
❑ 90FleBasMC-28
❑ 90FleCan-591
❑ 90FleCan-623
❑ 90FleUpd-46
❑ 90Hot50PS-29
❑ 90KayB-20
❑ 90KinDis-11
❑ 90Lea-243
❑ 90M.Vpin-2
❑ 90OPC-750
❑ 90PanSti-222
❑ 90Pos-18
❑ 90PubIntS-117
❑ 90RedFolSB-67
❑ 90RicBra2ATI-17
❑ 90Sco-66
❑ 90Sco100S-64
❑ 90ScoRoo-31T
❑ 90Spo-189
❑ 90Top-750
❑ 90TopAmeA-11
❑ 90TopBig-40
❑ 90TopCoi-53
❑ 90TopHilHM-16
❑ 90TopSti-25
❑ 90TopTif-750
❑ 90UppDec-533
❑ 90Woo-15
❑ 91Bow-486
❑ 91Cla1-T96
❑ 91ClaGam-148
❑ 91Don-484
❑ 91Don-744
❑ 91Fle-409
❑ 91JimDea-3
❑ 91Lea-412
❑ 91MajLeaCP-62
❑ 91OPC-545
❑ 91OPCBoxB-J
❑ 91OPCPre-85
❑ 91PanFreS-109
❑ 91PanSti-104
❑ 91PetSta-14
❑ 91PhiMed-31
❑ 91Sco-650
❑ 91Sco100S-35
❑ 91Sev3DCN-13
❑ 91SevCoi-NE13
❑ 91StaClu-243
❑ 91Stu-220
❑ 91Top-545
❑ 91TopDesS-545
❑ 91TopMic-545
❑ 91TopTif-545
❑ 91TopTriH-N8
❑ 91TopWaxBC-J
❑ 91Ult-270
❑ 91UppDec-447
❑ 91Woo-14
❑ 92Bow-646
❑ 92ClaGam-65
❑ 92DenHol-18
❑ 92Don-146
❑ 92Fle-541
❑ 92HitTheBB-24
❑ 92Lea-527
❑ 92LeaBlaG-527
❑ 92Mr.TurS-17
❑ 92OPC-680
❑ 92PanSti-246
❑ 92PhiMed-23
❑ 92Pin-124
❑ 92Pin-284
❑ 92RedFolS-70
❑ 92Sco-80
❑ 92Sco100S-40
❑ 92StaClu-280
❑ 92Stu-79
❑ 92Top-680
❑ 92TopGol-680
❑ 92TopGolW-680
❑ 92TopMcD-30
❑ 92TopMic-680
❑ 92TriPla-158
❑ 92TriPla-260
❑ 92Ult-249
❑ 92UppDec-127
❑ 92UppDecF-33
❑ 92UppDecFG-33
❑ 93Don-646
❑ 93Fle-496
❑ 93PacSpa-432
❑ 93Pin-479
❑ 93Pin-503
❑ 93PinCoo-5
❑ 93PinCooD-5
❑ 93RedFolS-68
❑ 93RocUSPC-3C
❑ 93RocUSPC-10S
❑ 93Sco-597
❑ 93Sel-103
❑ 93StaClu-572
❑ 93StaCluFDI-572
❑ 93StaCluMOP-572
❑ 93Top-445
❑ 93TopGol-445
❑ 93TopInaM-445
❑ 93TopInaR-445
❑ 93TopMic-445
❑ 93Ult-353
❑ 93UppDec-32
❑ 93UppDec-706
❑ 93UppDecGold-32
❑ 93UppDecGold-706
❑ 99DumSet-DMU
❑ 99DumSet-DMU

Murphy, Daniel

❑ 82TulDriT-17
❑ 83TulDriT-21
❑ 84OklCit8T-23
❑ 84TulDriTl-16
❑ 85MidAngT-9

Murphy, Daniel F. P/OF

❑ 61Top-214
❑ 62Top-119
❑ 62TopVen-119
❑ 63Top-272
❑ 70OPC-146
❑ 70Top-146

Murphy, Daniel F. IF

❑ 03BreE10-108
❑ 08AmeCarE91-16
❑ 08AmeCarE91-55
❑ 08RosComP-61
❑ 09ColChiE-209
❑ 09RamT20-85
❑ 09T206-261
❑ 09T206-262
❑ 10CouT21-198
❑ 10DomDisP-90
❑ 10E101-35
❑ 10E102-19
❑ 10E12AmeCDCE125-27
❑ 10LuxCigPP-18
❑ 10MelMinE-35
❑ 10NadCarE-40
❑ 10NadE1-43
❑ 10PeoT21-42A
❑ 10PeoT21-42B
❑ 10RedCroT-57
❑ 10RedCroT-142
❑ 10RedCroT-229
❑ 10SweCapPP-48
❑ 11A'sFirT20-14
❑ 11D35RocB-14
❑ 11DiaGumP-22
❑ 11HelSta-57
❑ 11PinT-5-518
❑ 11S74Sil-33
❑ 11SpoLifCW-264
❑ 11SpoLifM-101
❑ 11T205-126
❑ 12ColRedB-209
❑ 12ColTinT-209
❑ 12HasTriFT-25C
❑ 14CraJacE-140
❑ 14PieStaT-80
❑ 15AmeCarE106-31
❑ 15CraJacE-140
❑ 16FleBreD-69
❑ 74A'sTCM1P-8

Murphy, Daniel Lee

❑ 86ElPasDP-16
❑ 87ElPasDP-22
❑ 89BlaYNPRWL-128
❑ 89BlaYNPRWLU-69
❑ 89LasVegSC-7
❑ 89LasVegSP-2
❑ 90CMC-511
❑ 90LasVegSC-8
❑ 90LasVegSP-117
❑ 90OPC-649
❑ 90ProAAAF-5
❑ 90Top-649
❑ 90TopDeb89-86
❑ 90TopTif-649

Murphy, Darren

❑ 98BluOriQ-21
❑ 98DelShoM-22

Murphy, Dennis

❑ 21Zee-166
❑ 22Zee-158
❑ 23Zee-192
❑ 24Zee-135
❑ 26Zee-54
❑ 27Zee-6

Murphy, Dwayne

❑ 79Top-711
❑ 80Top-461
❑ 81A'sGraG-21
❑ 81AllGamPI-61
❑ 81Don-359
❑ 81Fle-590
❑ 81OPC-341
❑ 81Top-341
❑ 81TopSti-119
❑ 82A'sGraG-11
❑ 82Don-239
❑ 82Fle-101
❑ 82FleSta-122
❑ 82Kel-57
❑ 82OPC-29
❑ 82Top-29
❑ 82TopSti-227
❑ 83A'sGraG-21
❑ 83AllGamPI-64
❑ 83Don-161
❑ 83Fle-528
❑ 83FleSta-135
❑ 83FleSti-189
❑ 83OPC-184
❑ 83Top-598
❑ 83TopSti-107
❑ 84A'sMot-4
❑ 84AllGamPI-154
❑ 84Don-3
❑ 84Don-3A
❑ 84Don-101
❑ 84Fle-456
❑ 84FunFooP-93
❑ 84Nes792-103
❑ 84OPC-103
❑ 84Top-103
❑ 84TopSti-332
❑ 84TopTif-103
❑ 85A'sMot-6
❑ 85AllGamPI-65
❑ 85Don-420
❑ 85Fle-432
❑ 85FleStaS-30
❑ 85GenMilS-20
❑ 85Lea-74
❑ 85Top-231
❑ 85TopSti-323
❑ 85TopTif-231
❑ 86A'sMot-6
❑ 86Don-176
❑ 86Fle-428
❑ 86FleMin-90
❑ 86OPC-8
❑ 86Top-8
❑ 86Top-216
❑ 86TopSti-171
❑ 86TopTat-20
❑ 86TopTif-8
❑ 86TopTif-216
❑ 86TruVal-27
❑ 87A'sSmoC-9
❑ 87Don-379
❑ 87DonOpeD-27
❑ 87Fle-400
❑ 87FleGlo-400
❑ 87OPC-121
❑ 87SpoTeaP-23
❑ 87Top-743
❑ 87TopSti-170
❑ 87TopTif-743
❑ 88Don-405
❑ 88Fle-287
❑ 88FleGlo-287
❑ 88OPC-334
❑ 88PanSti-176
❑ 88Sco-455
❑ 88ScoGlo-455
❑ 88Top-424
❑ 88TopTif-424
❑ 89PhiTas-23
❑ 89Sco-545
❑ 89Top-667
❑ 89TopAme2C-22
❑ 89TopTif-667
❑ 90Fle-569
❑ 90FleCan-569

❑ 97HigDesMG-16
Murphy, Eddie (John Edward)
❑ 14FatPlaT-35
❑ 15CraJacE-165
❑ 15SpoNewM-127
❑ 16BF2FP-15
❑ 16SpoNewM-130
❑ 16TanBraE-15
❑ 18WhiSoxTI-17
❑ 21E121So8-65
❑ 22AmeCarE122-49
❑ 22W575-88
❑ 75WhiSox1T-18
❑ 92Man191BSR-18
Murphy, Eddie Joseph
❑ 48SmiClo-24
Murphy, Gary
❑ 86AshTouP-21
❑ 88BenBucL-31
❑ 89MisStaB-44
❑ 89QuaCitAB-16
❑ 89QuaCitAGS-19
Murphy, Harriett
❑ 08AllLadBC-3
Murphy, Herbert
❑ 15Zee-68
❑ 16Zee-85
Murphy, Howard
❑ 09ObaT21-18
❑ 09ObaT21-88
Murphy, Isaac
❑ 88KimN18-28
Murphy, James
❑ 88GenCubP-1638
❑ 89ChaWheB-10
❑ 89ChaWheP-1745
❑ 89FayGenP-1586
❑ 90PeoChiUTI-U7
❑ 90WinSpiTI-14
Murphy, Jeff
❑ 91PriRedC-18
❑ 91PriRedP-3511
❑ 92BilMusF-3352
❑ 92BilMusSP-21
❑ 92HamRedC-25
❑ 92HamRedF-1595
❑ 93PriRedC-21
❑ 93PriRedF-4177
❑ 93SavCarC-19
❑ 93SavCarF-688
❑ 94St.PetCC-20
❑ 94St.PetCF-2588
❑ 96ArkTraB-22
Murphy, John
❑ 88KimN18-29
Murphy, John J.
❑ 80ArkTraT-21
Murphy, John Joseph
❑ 34BatR31-154
❑ 38CloFotW-68
❑ 41DouPlaR-109
❑ 43YanSta-20
❑ 47RedSoxTI-16
❑ 72TCMthe3-53
❑ 75YanAllTT-7
❑ 75YanDyn1T-34
❑ 80YanGreT-11
❑ 85BigLeaC3-81
❑ 88ConSer3-20
❑ 91ConTSN-84
❑ 92YanWIZA-52
❑ 94ConTSN-1057
❑ 94ConTSNB-1057
Murphy, John V.
❑ 87LouRedTI-21
❑ 87St.PetCP-13
❑ 88LouRedBC-16
❑ 88LouRedBP-429
❑ 88LouRedBTI-36
❑ 88SprCarB-22
Murphy, Kent
❑ 86WatIndP-17
❑ 87BufBisP-2
❑ 88WilBilP-1305
Murphy, Matt
❑ 93HelBreF-4090
❑ 93HelBreSP-15
❑ 95AusFut-59
Murphy, Micah
❑ 89GenCubP-1880
❑ 90HunCubP-3291
Murphy, Michael
❑ 86WatIndP-18
Murphy, Miguel
❑ 87KenTwiP-25
❑ 88FayGenP-1100
Murphy, Mike
❑ 77ArkTraT-6
❑ 87BufBisP-17
❑ 91AubAstC-14
❑ 91AubAstP-4278
Murphy, Mike Francis
❑ 90MarPhiP-3198
❑ 91MarPhiC-1
❑ 91MarPhiP-3470
❑ 92BatCliCB-2
❑ 92BatCliF-3278
❑ 93SouAtlLAGF-53
❑ 93SpaPhiC-20
❑ 93SpaPhiF-1069
❑ 94ClaGolF-164
❑ 94DunBluJC-21
❑ 94DunBluJF-2570
❑ 95KinIndTI-20
❑ 97TulDriTI-20
❑ 98TulDriTI-8
Murphy, Nate
❑ 96BoiHawB-20
❑ 97CedRapK-18
Murphy, Neil
❑ 93BatCliCB-22
❑ 93BatCliF-3149
Murphy, P.L.
❑ 87OldJudN-355
Murphy, Pat
❑ 89WesPalBES-25
❑ 92BurAstC-21
❑ 92BurAstF-541
❑ 93QuaCitRBC-14
❑ 93QuaCitRBF-97
❑ 94CarLeaAF-CAR3
❑ 94LynRedSC-20
❑ 94LynRedSF-1901
Murphy, Patrick J.
❑ 87OldJudN-356
❑ 89SFHaCN-12
Murphy, Pete
❑ 87MacPirP-11
❑ 87WatPirP-24
❑ 88SalBucS-14
❑ 89HarSenP-308
❑ 89HarSenS-12
❑ 90HarSenP-1190
❑ 90HarSenS-12
❑ 91CarMudLD-113
❑ 91CarMudP-1084
❑ 91LinDriAA-113
Murphy, Quinn
❑ 94BurIndC-16
❑ 94BurIndF-3803
Murphy, Red
❑ 20WalMaiW-36
Murphy, Rob
❑ 82CedRapRT-2
❑ 83CedRapRF-24
❑ 83CedRapRT-13
❑ 87ClaGam-70
❑ 87Don-452
❑ 87Fle-206
❑ 87FleGlo-206
❑ 87RedKah-46
❑ 87SpoTeaP-4
❑ 87Top-82
❑ 87TopTif-82
❑ 88Don-82
❑ 88DonBasB-230
❑ 88Fle-241
❑ 88FleGlo-241
❑ 88RedKah-46
❑ 88Sco-559
❑ 88ScoGlo-559
❑ 88StaLinRe-13
❑ 88Top-603
❑ 88TopTif-603
❑ 89Bow-22
❑ 89BowTif-22
❑ 89CedRapRAB-13
❑ 89ClaTraP-183
❑ 89Don-139
❑ 89DonBasB-196
❑ 89DonTra-15
❑ 89Fle-165
❑ 89FleGlo-165
❑ 89FleUpd-10
❑ 89OPC-182
❑ 89Sco-141
❑ 89ScoRoo-8T
❑ 89Top-446
❑ 89TopTif-446
❑ 89TopTra-86T
❑ 89TopTraT-86T
❑ 89UppDec-372
❑ 89UppDec-759
❑ 90Bow-269
❑ 90BowTif-269
❑ 90CedRapRDGB-13
❑ 90Don-186
❑ 90Fle-281
❑ 90FleCan-281
❑ 90Lea-183
❑ 90OPC-268
❑ 90PubIntS-461
❑ 90RedSoxP-13
❑ 90Sco-181
❑ 90Top-268
❑ 90TopBig-297
❑ 90TopSti-261
❑ 90TopTif-268
❑ 90TopTVRS-14
❑ 90UppDec-461
❑ 91Don-250
❑ 91Fle-104
❑ 91OPC-542
❑ 91Sco-183
❑ 91ScoRoo-33T
❑ 91Top-542
❑ 91TopDesS-542
❑ 91TopMic-542
❑ 91TopTif-542
❑ 91UppDec-683
❑ 91UppDec-707
❑ 92AstMot-21
❑ 92Don-329
❑ 92Fle-288
❑ 92OPC-706
❑ 92Sco-492
❑ 92StaClu-663
❑ 92Top-706
❑ 92TopGol-706
❑ 92TopGolW-706
❑ 92TopMic-706
❑ 92Ult-493
❑ 92UppDec-639
❑ 93CarPol-10
❑ 93CarStaC-21
❑ 93Don-588
❑ 93Fle-439
❑ 93FleFinE-128
❑ 93StaClu-250
❑ 93StaCluFDI-250
❑ 93StaCluMOP-250
❑ 94CarPol-10
❑ 94Fle-637
❑ 94StaCluT-318
❑ 94StaCluTFDI-318
Murphy, Rod
❑ 14Zee-44
❑ 17Zee-35
❑ 19Zee-25
❑ 20Zee-128
❑ 21Zee-147
❑ 22Zee-135
❑ 23Zee-193
❑ 24Zee-136
Murphy, Sean
❑ 96AshTouB-26
❑ 97SalAva-21
Murphy, Shaun
❑ 91MidLeaAP-MWL46
❑ 91RocExpC-24
❑ 91RocExpP-2059
❑ 92WesPalBEC-13
❑ 92WesPalBEF-2099
Murphy, Steve
❑ 85RedWinA-20
❑ 86RedWinA-5
❑ 91WasVia-3
❑ 93ClaFS7-226
❑ 93RocRoyC-20
❑ 93RocRoyF-728
❑ 93StaCluM-100
❑ 94WilBluRC-16
❑ 94WilBluRF-313
❑ 95WicWraTI-3
Murphy, Tim
❑ 74GasRanT-12
Murphy, Tom A.
❑ 69AngJacitB-9
❑ 69Top-474
❑ 70OPC-351
❑ 70Top-351
❑ 71OPC-401
❑ 71Top-401
❑ 71TopTat-39
❑ 72MilBra-248
❑ 72OPC-354
❑ 72Top-354
❑ 73OPC-539
❑ 73Top-539
❑ 74OPC-496
❑ 74Top-496
❑ 74TopTra-496T
❑ 75OPC-28
❑ 75Top-28
❑ 75TopMin-28
❑ 76OPC-219
❑ 76SSP-227
❑ 76Top-219
❑ 77Top-396
❑ 78BluJayP-19
❑ 78OPC-193
❑ 78Top-103
❑ 79OPC-308
❑ 79Top-588
❑ 89PacSenL-122
❑ 89TopSenL-28
❑ 94BreMilB-340
Murphy, Wayne
❑ 87WinHavRSP-18
Murphy, William E.
❑ 66Top-574
❑ 91MetWIZ-286
Murphy, Yale (William Henry)
❑ 95May-22
❑ 95NewN566-174
Murray, Bill
❑ 88SalLakCTTI-2
❑ 88SalLakCTTI-29
❑ 89SalLakTTI-29
❑ 90CarLeaA-8
❑ 91RenSilSCLC-27
❑ 93WatDiaC-30
❑ 96ButCopKB-2
❑ 98ChaRivDG-19
Murray, Brian
❑ 88SalLakCTTI-2
Murray, Calvin
❑ 92Bow-652
❑ 92TopTra-78T
❑ 92TopTraG-78T
❑ 93ClaYouG-YG14
❑ 93ShrCapF-2773
❑ 93StaCluM-34
❑ 93UppDec-421
❑ 93UppDec-432
❑ 93UppDecGold-421
❑ 93UppDecGold-432
❑ 94Cla-153
❑ 94ExcFS7-293
❑ 94ShrCapF-1620
❑ 94UppDecML-140
❑ 94UppDecML-261
❑ 94UppDecMLPotYF-PY11
❑ 97ShrCap-17
❑ 97ShrCapB-17
❑ 98FreGriG-20
❑ 99Bow-293
❑ 99BowGol-293
❑ 99BowInt-293
Murray, Dale
❑ 75ExpPos-26
❑ 75OPC-568
❑ 75Top-568
❑ 75TopMin-568
❑ 76ExpRed-23
❑ 76MonExpP-22
❑ 76OPC-18
❑ 76SSP-350
❑ 76Top-18
❑ 77Top-252
❑ 78SSP270-131
❑ 78Top-149
❑ 79OPC-198
❑ 79Top-379
❑ 80ExpPos-18
❑ 80OPC-274
❑ 80Top-559
❑ 81SyrChiT-7
❑ 81SyrChiTI-15
❑ 82BluJayS-15
❑ 83Don-381
❑ 83Fle-437
❑ 83OPC-42
❑ 83Top-42
❑ 83TopTra-79T
❑ 83YanPhoA-17
❑ 84Don-577
❑ 84Fle-134
❑ 84Nes792-697
❑ 84OPC-281
❑ 84Top-697
❑ 84TopTif-697
❑ 85Fle-137
❑ 85OklCit8T-27
❑ 85Top-481
❑ 85TopTif-481
❑ 85YanTCMP-14
❑ 86OPC-197
❑ 87SpoIllS-9
❑ 91MetWIZ-287
❑ 92YanWIZ8-130
❑ 93RanKee-275
Murray, Dan PCL
❑ 11PacCoaBD-45
❑ 17Zee-36
❑ 18Zee-32
❑ 19Zee-58
Murray, Dan Saffle
❑ 95PitMetTI-29
❑ 96HilStaHWB-38
❑ 96StLucMTI-4
❑ 97St.LucM-20
❑ 98BinMetQ-21
Murray, Dave
❑ 86SalRedBP-21
Murray, Douglas
❑ 97AubDouTI-30
❑ 98QuaCitRBG-21
Murray, Eddie
❑ 77BalOriP-15
❑ 78BalOriP-22
❑ 78Hos-31
❑ 78Kel-25
❑ 78OPC-154
❑ 78RCColC-75
❑ 78Top-36
❑ 79BalOriP-12
❑ 79Hos-115
❑ 79OPC-338
❑ 79Top-640
❑ 79TopCom-1
❑ 80BalOriP-14
❑ 80Kel-24
❑ 80OPC-88
❑ 80Top-160
❑ 80TopSup-28
❑ 81AllGamPI-8
❑ 81BalOriP-13
❑ 81Don-112
❑ 81Dra-6
❑ 81Fle-184
❑ 81FleStiC-117
❑ 81Kel-18
❑ 81MSAMinD-23
❑ 81OPC-39
❑ 81Squ-15
❑ 81Top-490
❑ 81TopScr-9
❑ 81TopSti-34
❑ 82Don-483
❑ 82Dra-25
❑ 82Fle-174
❑ 82FleSta-151
❑ 82Kel-64
❑ 82OnDecD-23
❑ 82OPC-390
❑ 82PerCreC-22
❑ 82PerCreCG-22
❑ 82SevSluC-20
❑ 82Top-162
❑ 82Top-163
❑ 82Top-390
❑ 82Top-426
❑ 82TopSti-4
❑ 82TopSti-6
❑ 82TopSti-145
❑ 83AllGamPI-5
❑ 83Don-405
❑ 83DonActA-1
❑ 83Dra-19
❑ 83Fle-67
❑ 83FleSta-136
❑ 83FleSti-202
❑ 83Kel-11
❑ 83OPC-141
❑ 83OriPos-19
❑ 83PerCreC-29
❑ 83PerCreCG-29
❑ 83Top-21
❑ 83Top-530
❑ 83TopGloS-37
❑ 83TopSti-29
❑ 84AllGamPI-96
❑ 84BalOriP-23
❑ 84Don-22
❑ 84Don-22A
❑ 84Don-47
❑ 84DonActAS-50
❑ 84DonCha-19
❑ 84Dra-23
❑ 84Fle-14
❑ 84FleSti-23
❑ 84FleSti-38
❑ 84FunFooP-119
❑ 84Nes792-240
❑ 84Nes792-397
❑ 84NesDreT-1
❑ 84OCoandSI-23
❑ 84OPC-240
❑ 84OPC-291
❑ 84OriEng-9
❑ 84RalPur-1
❑ 84SevCoi-C6
❑ 84SevCoi-E6
❑ 84SevCoi-W6
❑ 84Top-240
❑ 84Top-397
❑ 84TopCer-1
❑ 84TopGloS-4
❑ 84TopRubD-28
❑ 84TopSti-26
❑ 84TopSti-195
❑ 84TopSti-203
❑ 84TopStiB-12
❑ 84TopSup-25
❑ 84TopTif-240
❑ 84TopTif-397
❑ 85AllGamPI-7
❑ 85BalOriP-19
❑ 85Don-47
❑ 85DonActA-9
❑ 85DonHig-34
❑ 85Dra-21
❑ 85Fle-184
❑ 85FleLimE-23
❑ 85FleStaS-20
❑ 85FleStaS-62
❑ 85FleStaS-63
❑ 85FleStaS-64
❑ 85FleStaS-65
❑ 85FleStaS-66
❑ 85FleStaS-67
❑ 85GenMilS-21
❑ 85Lea-203
❑ 85OPC-221
❑ 85OriHea-13
❑ 85SevCoi-E1
❑ 85SevCoi-G4
❑ 85SevCoi-W4
❑ 85Top-700
❑ 85Top-701
❑ 85Top3-D-2
❑ 85TopGloS-28
❑ 85TopMin-700
❑ 85TopRubD-28
❑ 85TopSti-196
❑ 85TopSup-18
❑ 85TopTif-700
❑ 85TopTif-701
❑ 86BalOriHMP-13
❑ 86BalOriP-12
❑ 86BasStaB-77
❑ 86BurKinA-14
❑ 86Don-88
❑ 86DonAll-13
❑ 86DonPop-13
❑ 86DorChe-12
❑ 86Dra-25
❑ 86Fle-282
❑ 86FleLimE-32
❑ 86FleMin-58
❑ 86FleSlu-25
❑ 86FleStiC-81
❑ 86Lea-83
❑ 86MSAJifPD-10
❑ 86OPC-30
❑ 86QuaGra-27
❑ 86SevCoi-E13
❑ 86Spo-4
❑ 86Spo-73
❑ 86Spo-145
❑ 86SpoDecG-70
❑ 86SpoRoo-48
❑ 86Top-30
❑ 86Top3-D-19
❑ 86TopGloA-2
❑ 86TopGloS-33
❑ 86TopMinL-1
❑ 86TopSti-158
❑ 86TopSti-227
❑ 86TopSup-40
❑ 86TopTat-13
❑ 86TopTif-30

❑ 86TruVal-3
❑ 86Woo-24
❑ 87BalOriP-24
❑ 87BoaandB-2
❑ 87ClaGam-51
❑ 87Don-48
❑ 87DonAll-31
❑ 87DonHig-37
❑ 87DonOpeD-136
❑ 87Dra-24
❑ 87Fle-476
❑ 87Fle-636
❑ 87FleGlo-476
❑ 87FleGlo-636
❑ 87FleLeaL-32
❑ 87FleLimE-31
❑ 87FleMin-75
❑ 87FleRecS-24
❑ 87FleStiC-84
❑ 87GenMilB-2G
❑ 87HosSti-18
❑ 87K-M-30
❑ 87KayB-22
❑ 87KraFoo-1
❑ 87Lea-110
❑ 87OPC-120
❑ 87OriFreB-33
❑ 87RalPur-8
❑ 87RedFolSB-66
❑ 87SevCoi-M12
❑ 87Spo-6
❑ 87Spo-75
❑ 87Spo-159
❑ 87SpoDeaP-2
❑ 87SpoTeaP-21
❑ 87StuPan-14
❑ 87Top-120
❑ 87TopCoi-19
❑ 87TopGloS-12
❑ 87TopMinL-39
❑ 87TopSti-224
❑ 87TopTif-120
❑ 88Don-231
❑ 88DonBasB-142
❑ 88Dra-21
❑ 88Fle-567
❑ 88FleBasA-28
❑ 88FleGlo-567
❑ 88FleMin-1
❑ 88FleStiC-2
❑ 88Lea-172
❑ 88MSAJifPD-13
❑ 88OPC-4
❑ 88OriFreB-33
❑ 88OriPos-22
❑ 88PanSti-8
❑ 88PanSti-203
❑ 88PanSti-442
❑ 88Sco-18
❑ 88ScoGlo-18
❑ 88Spo-59
❑ 88StaLinAl-20
❑ 88StaLinO-10
❑ 88Top-4
❑ 88Top-4A
❑ 88Top-51
❑ 88Top-495
❑ 88TopBig-215
❑ 88TopCoi-22
❑ 88TopSti-11
❑ 88TopSti-233
❑ 88TopTif-4
❑ 88TopTif-51
❑ 88TopTif-495
❑ 88TopUKM-53
❑ 88TopUKMT-53
❑ 88Woo-5
❑ 89Bow-346
❑ 89BowTif-346
❑ 89ClaTraP-160
❑ 89DodMot-2
❑ 89DodPol-21
❑ 89DodStaSV-11
❑ 89Don-96
❑ 89DonBasB-92
❑ 89DonTra-12
❑ 89Fle-611
❑ 89FleGlo-611
❑ 89FleUpd-92
❑ 89KayB-23
❑ 89KinDis-2
❑ 89OPC-148
❑ 89PanSti-260
❑ 89RedFolSB-85
❑ 89Sco-94
❑ 89ScoHot1S-83
❑ 89ScoRoo-31T
❑ 89Spo-147
❑ 89Top-625
❑ 89TopBasT-89
❑ 89TopBatL-11
❑ 89TopBig-319
❑ 89TopCapC-15
❑ 89TopCoi-20
❑ 89TopHilTM-22
❑ 89TopMinL-44
❑ 89TopSti-238
❑ 89TopTif-625
❑ 89TopTra-87T
❑ 89TopTraT-87T
❑ 89TopUKM-56
❑ 89UppDec-275
❑ 89UppDec-763
❑ 90Bow-101
❑ 90BowTif-101
❑ 90ClaUpd-T37
❑ 90DodMot-5
❑ 90DodPol-33
❑ 90DodTar-563
❑ 90Don-77
❑ 90DonBesN-78
❑ 90Fle-404
❑ 90FleCan-404
❑ 90Hot50PS-30
❑ 90KayB-21
❑ 90Lea-181
❑ 90OPC-305
❑ 90PanSti-273
❑ 90PubIntS-14
❑ 90RedFolSB-68
❑ 90Sco-80
❑ 90SunSee-24
❑ 90Top-305
❑ 90TopAmeA-7
❑ 90TopBatL-17
❑ 90TopBig-29
❑ 90TopHilHM-13
❑ 90TopMinL-60
❑ 90TopSti-57
❑ 90TopTif-305
❑ 90UppDec-277
❑ 90Woo-16
❑ 91BasBesHRK-15
❑ 91Bow-376
❑ 91Bow-614
❑ 91Cla1-T51
❑ 91Cla3-T65
❑ 91ClaGam-112
❑ 91DenHol-15
❑ 91DodMot-5
❑ 91DodPho-20
❑ 91DodPol-33
❑ 91DodSt.V-11
❑ 91Don-405
❑ 91Don-502
❑ 91DonBonC-BC18
❑ 91DonPre-12
❑ 91Fle-214
❑ 91Lea-126
❑ 91MajLeaCP-53
❑ 91OPC-397
❑ 91OPC-590
❑ 91OPCBoxB-K
❑ 91OPCPre-86
❑ 91OriCro-321
❑ 91PanCanT1-2
❑ 91PanFreS-55
❑ 91PanSti-53
❑ 91PosCan-11
❑ 91RedFolS-68
❑ 91Sco-310
❑ 91Sco100S-52
❑ 91SevCoi-SC10
❑ 91StaClu-177
❑ 91StaCluP-27
❑ 91StaPinB-34
❑ 91Stu-185
❑ 91Top-397
❑ 91Top-590
❑ 91TopCraJ2-1
❑ 91TopDesS-397
❑ 91TopDesS-590
❑ 91TopMic-397
❑ 91TopMic-590
❑ 91TopTif-397
❑ 91TopTif-590
❑ 91TopTriH-N5
❑ 91TopWaxBC-K
❑ 91Ult-166
❑ 91UppDec-237
❑ 91UppDecSS-SS6
❑ 91USPlaCA-2S
❑ 91Woo-15
❑ 92Bow-433
❑ 92ClaGam-162
❑ 92DodStaTA-30
❑ 92Don-392
❑ 92DonUpd-U8
❑ 92Fle-466
❑ 92Hig5-54
❑ 92Lea-396
❑ 92LeaBlaG-396
❑ 92MetColP-8
❑ 92MetKah-33
❑ 92OPC-780
❑ 92OPCPre-193
❑ 92PanSti-192
❑ 92Pin-424
❑ 92RedFolS-71
❑ 92Sco-195
❑ 92Sco100S-78
❑ 92ScoRoo-11T
❑ 92SpolIIFK1-398
❑ 92SpoStaCC-35
❑ 92StaClu-795
❑ 92StaCluD-128
❑ 92StaCluMO-8
❑ 92Stu-68
❑ 92Top-780
❑ 92TopGol-780
❑ 92TopGolW-780
❑ 92TopKid-50
❑ 92TopMic-780
❑ 92TopTra-79T
❑ 92TopTraG-79T
❑ 92Ult-532
❑ 92UppDec-32
❑ 92UppDec-265
❑ 92UppDec-728
❑ 92UppDec-753
❑ 93Ble-27
❑ 93Bow-454
❑ 93ClaGam-69
❑ 93DenHol-15
❑ 93DiaMar-78
❑ 93Don-278
❑ 93DonDiaK-DK25
❑ 93DonEli-21
❑ 93DonEliS-3
❑ 93DonMVP-10
❑ 93DonPre-7
❑ 93Fin-122
❑ 93FinRef-122
❑ 93Fla-94
❑ 93Fle-91
❑ 93FleFruotL-48
❑ 93FunPac-128
❑ 93JimDea-17
❑ 93Lea-167
❑ 93LeaHeaftH-4
❑ 93MetColP-41
❑ 93MetKah-33
❑ 93OPC-280
❑ 93PacSpa-545
❑ 93PanSti-247
❑ 93Pin-18
❑ 93Pin-292
❑ 93PinCoo-27
❑ 93PinCooD-27
❑ 93PinHomRC-35
❑ 93Sco-77
❑ 93Sel-29
❑ 93SP-152
❑ 93StaClu-50
❑ 93StaCluFDI-50
❑ 93StaCluMO-17
❑ 93StaCluMOP-50
❑ 93Top-430
❑ 93TopGol-430
❑ 93TopInaM-430
❑ 93TopInaR-430
❑ 93TopMic-430
❑ 93TriPla-41
❑ 93Ult-78
❑ 93UppDec-115
❑ 93UppDec-484
❑ 93UppDecGold-115
❑ 93UppDecGold-484
❑ 93UppDecSH-HI13
❑ 93UppDecTAN-TN14
❑ 94Bow-467
❑ 94BowBes-R2
❑ 94BowBesR-R2
❑ 94ColC-595
❑ 94ColChoGS-595
❑ 94ColChoSS-595
❑ 94Don-386
❑ 94Fin-317
❑ 94FinRef-317
❑ 94Fla-286
❑ 94Fle-573
❑ 94FleExtB-64
❑ 94FleUpd-34
❑ 94FleUpdDT-8
❑ 94FUnPac-85
❑ 94Lea-313
❑ 94LeaL-29
❑ 94OPC-184
❑ 94Pac-413
❑ 94PanSti-221
❑ 94Pin-495
❑ 94PinArtP-495
❑ 94PinMusC-495
❑ 94ProMag-40
❑ 94Sco-36
❑ 94ScoGolR-36
❑ 94ScoRoo-RT5
❑ 94ScoRooGR-RT5
❑ 94ScoRooS-RT5
❑ 94Sel-329
❑ 94SP-100
❑ 94SPDieC-100
❑ 94SpoRoo-91
❑ 94SpoRooAP-91
❑ 94StaClu-542
❑ 94StaClu-674
❑ 94StaCluFDI-542
❑ 94StaCluFDI-674
❑ 94StaCluGR-542
❑ 94StaCluGR-674
❑ 94StaCluMOP-542
❑ 94StaCluMOP-674
❑ 94Stu-94
❑ 94Top-65
❑ 94TopGol-65
❑ 94TopSpa-65
❑ 94TopTra-60T
❑ 94TriPla-117
❑ 94Ult-347
❑ 94UppDec-341
❑ 94UppDecED-341
❑ 95Baz-78
❑ 95Bow-392
❑ 95BowBes-R60
❑ 95BowBesR-R60
❑ 95ClaPhoC-21
❑ 95ColCho-265
❑ 95ColCho-526
❑ 95ColChoGS-265
❑ 95ColChoGS-526
❑ 95ColChoSE-116
❑ 95ColChoSEGS-116
❑ 95ColChoSESS-116
❑ 95ColChoSS-265
❑ 95ColChoSS-526
❑ 95Don-435
❑ 95DonPreP-435
❑ 95DonTopotO-62
❑ 95Emo-36
❑ 95Fin-112
❑ 95FinRef-112
❑ 95Fla-33
❑ 95Fle-141
❑ 95Lea-265
❑ 95LeaLim-39
❑ 95LeaLimIBP-19
❑ 95Pac-125
❑ 95PanSti-96
❑ 95Pin-342
❑ 95PinArtP-342
❑ 95PinMusC-342
❑ 95Sco-257
❑ 95ScoGolR-257
❑ 95ScoHaloG-HG34
❑ 95ScoPlaTS-257
❑ 95SelCer-14
❑ 95SelCer-32
❑ 95SelCerMG-14
❑ 95SelCerMG-32
❑ 95SP-27
❑ 95SP-148
❑ 95SPCha-98
❑ 95SPCha-142
❑ 95SPCha-144
❑ 95SPChaDC-98
❑ 95SPChaDC-142
❑ 95SPChaDC-144
❑ 95SPPlaP-PP14
❑ 95SPSil-27
❑ 95SPSil-148
❑ 95StaClu-186
❑ 95StaCluFDI-186
❑ 95StaCluMOP-186
❑ 95StaCluMOP-RL6
❑ 95StaCluRL-RL6
❑ 95StaCluSTDW-I186
❑ 95StaCluSTMP-17
❑ 95StaCluSTWS-186
❑ 95StaCluVR-96
❑ 95StaCluVRMO-96
❑ 95Stu-142
❑ 95Sum-101
❑ 95SumNthD-101
❑ 95Top-370
❑ 95TopCyb-196
❑ 95TopEmb-114
❑ 95TopEmbGI-114
❑ 95Ult-39
❑ 95UltGolM-39
❑ 95UppDec-341
❑ 95UppDecED-341
❑ 95UppDecEDG-341
❑ 95UppDecSE-24
❑ 95UppDecSEG-24
❑ 95Zen-43
❑ 96Bow-69
❑ 96BowBes-42
❑ 96BowBesAR-42
❑ 96BowBesR-42
❑ 96BowFoi-69
❑ 96Cir-4
❑ 96CirRav-4
❑ 96ColCho-124
❑ 96ColCho-364
❑ 96ColCho-389T
❑ 96ColChoGS-124
❑ 96ColChoGS-364
❑ 96ColChoSS-124
❑ 96ColChoSS-364
❑ 96ColChoYMtP-28
❑ 96ColChoYMtP-28A
❑ 96ColChoYMtPGS-28
❑ 96ColChoYMtPGS-28A
❑ 96Don-105
❑ 96Don-220
❑ 96DonDiaK-29
❑ 96DonHitL-16
❑ 96DonPreP-105
❑ 96DonPreP-220
❑ 96EmoXL-53
❑ 96Fin-B21
❑ 96FinLan-4
❑ 96FinRef-B21
❑ 96Fla-71
❑ 96FlaDiaC-7
❑ 96Fle-92
❑ 96FleGolM-7
❑ 96FleTif-92
❑ 96FleUpd-7
❑ 96IndFle-9
❑ 96Lea-102
❑ 96LeaLim-67
❑ 96LeaLimG-67
❑ 96LeaPre-68
❑ 96LeaPreP-68
❑ 96LeaPrePB-102
❑ 96LeaPrePG-102
❑ 96LeaPrePS-102
❑ 96LeaSig-116
❑ 96LeaSigPPG-116
❑ 96LeaSigPPP-116
❑ 96MetMod-7
❑ 96MetUni-50
❑ 96MetUniP-50
❑ 96Pac-294
❑ 96PacMil-M8
❑ 96PacPri-P97
❑ 96PacPriFB-FB12
❑ 96PacPriG-P97
❑ 96PanSti-177
❑ 96Pin-117
❑ 96Pin-154
❑ 96Pin-280
❑ 96PinAfi-28
❑ 96PinAfiAP-28
❑ 96PinAfiFPP-28
❑ 96PinAfiSP-32
❑ 96PinArtP-46
❑ 96PinArtP-81
❑ 96PinArtP-180
❑ 96PinEssotG-17
❑ 96PinFoil-280
❑ 96PinPow-17
❑ 96PinSlu-14
❑ 96PinSta-46
❑ 96PinSta-81
❑ 96PinSta-180
❑ 96ProMagDM-11
❑ 96ProSta-58
❑ 96RedF-14
❑ 96SchDis-8
❑ 96Sco-79
❑ 96Sco-366
❑ 96ScoAll-20
❑ 96ScoBigB-19
❑ 96ScoDiaA-22
❑ 96ScoDugC-A65
❑ 96ScoDugC-B91
❑ 96ScoDugCAP-A65
❑ 96ScoDugCAP-B91
❑ 96Sel-60
❑ 96SelArtP-60
❑ 96SelCer-10
❑ 96SelCerAP-10
❑ 96SelCerCB-10
❑ 96SelCerCR-10
❑ 96SelCerMB-10
❑ 96SelCerMG-10
❑ 96SelCerMR-10
❑ 96SelClaTF-20
❑ 96SP-69
❑ 96Spo-26
❑ 96Spo-119
❑ 96SpoArtP-26
❑ 96SpoArtP-119
❑ 96SpoPowS-23
❑ 96SPSpeFX-34
❑ 96SPSpeFXDC-34
❑ 96SPx-20
❑ 96SPxGol-20
❑ 96StaClu-224
❑ 96StaClu-293
❑ 96StaCluEPB-290
❑ 96StaCluEPG-290
❑ 96StaCluEPS-290
❑ 96StaCluMO-28
❑ 96StaCluMOP-224
❑ 96StaCluMOP-293
❑ 96Stu-96
❑ 96StuPrePB-96
❑ 96StuPrePG-96
❑ 96StuPrePS-96
❑ 96Sum-53
❑ 96SumAbo&B-53
❑ 96SumArtP-53
❑ 96SumFoi-53
❑ 96Top-125
❑ 96TopChr-34
❑ 96TopChrMotG-3
❑ 96TopChrMotGR-3
❑ 96TopChrR-34
❑ 96TopGal-167
❑ 96TopGalPG-PG1
❑ 96TopGalPPI-167
❑ 96TopLas-74
❑ 96TopMasotG-3
❑ 96Ult-51
❑ 96UltCaltH-6
❑ 96UltCaltHGM-6
❑ 96UltGolM-51
❑ 96UltRes-5
❑ 96UltResGM-5
❑ 96UltThu-14
❑ 96UltThuGM-14
❑ 96UppDec-2
❑ 96UppDec-105
❑ 96UppDec-316
❑ 96UppDec-382
❑ 96UppDec-415
❑ 96UppDecDD-DD8
❑ 96UppDecDDG-DD8
❑ 96UppDecDDS-DD8
❑ 96UppDecRCJ-22
❑ 96UppDecRipC-22
❑ 96Zen-49
❑ 96ZenArtP-49
❑ 97AngMot-3
❑ 97Bow-32
❑ 97BowInt-32
❑ 97Cir-33
❑ 97CirRav-33
❑ 97CirRavR-8
❑ 97ColCho-40
❑ 97ColCho-250
❑ 97ColChoPP-PP20
❑ 97ColChoPPG-PP20
❑ 97ColChoPPJ-PP20
❑ 97ColChoTBS-8
❑ 97ColChoTBSWH-8
❑ 97Don-115
❑ 97Don-267
❑ 97Don-298
❑ 97DonEli-25
❑ 97DonEliGS-25
❑ 97DonGolPP-115
❑ 97DonGolPP-267

❑ 97DonGolPP-298
❑ 97DonLim-7
❑ 97DonLim-75
❑ 97DonLim-197
❑ 97DonLimE-7
❑ 97DonLimE-75
❑ 97DonLimE-197
❑ 97DonLimENG-7
❑ 97DonLimFotG-34
❑ 97DonPre-60
❑ 97DonPreCttC-60
❑ 97DonPrePM-12
❑ 97DonSigAC-90
❑ 97DonSigAM-90
❑ 97DonSilPP-115
❑ 97DonSilPP-267
❑ 97DonSilPP-298
❑ 97DonTea-8
❑ 97DonTeaSPE-8
❑ 97E-X2-3
❑ 97E-X2Cred-3
❑ 97E-X2EssCre-3
❑ 97E-X2Hall-3
❑ 97Fin-235
❑ 97FinRef-235
❑ 97FlaShoLC-100
❑ 97FlaShoLeg0-100
❑ 97FlaShoLeg1-100
❑ 97FlaShoM-A100
❑ 97FlaShoM-B100
❑ 97FlaShoM-C100
❑ 97FlaShoR0-100
❑ 97FlaShoR1-100
❑ 97FlaShoR2-100
❑ 97Fle-9
❑ 97Fle-550
❑ 97FleDecoE-9
❑ 97FleDecoERT-9
❑ 97FleDiaT-8
❑ 97FleGolM-6
❑ 97FleGouG-9
❑ 97FleGouGF-9
❑ 97FleHea-14
❑ 97FleTif-9
❑ 97FleTif-550
❑ 97HigMinM-80
❑ 97Lea-124
❑ 97Lea-224
❑ 97Lea-364
❑ 97LeaFraM-124
❑ 97LeaFraM-224
❑ 97LeaFraM-364
❑ 97LeaFraMDC-124
❑ 97LeaFraMDC-224
❑ 97LeaFraMDC-364
❑ 97LeaGolS-34
❑ 97MetUni-5
❑ 97NewPin-139
❑ 97NewPinAP-139
❑ 97NewPinMC-139
❑ 97NewPinPP-139
❑ 97OriSco-2
❑ 97OriScoPl-2
❑ 97OriScoPr-2
❑ 97Pac-25
❑ 97PacCar-3
❑ 97PacCarM-3
❑ 97PacFirD-3
❑ 97PacGolCD-4
❑ 97PacLigB-25
❑ 97PacPri-9
❑ 97PacPriGotD-GD12
❑ 97PacPriLB-9
❑ 97PacPriP-9
❑ 97PacSil-25
❑ 97Pin-65
❑ 97PinArtP-PP65
❑ 97PinCer-66
❑ 97PinCerMBla-66
❑ 97PinCerMBlu-66
❑ 97PinCerMG-66
❑ 97PinCerMR-66
❑ 97PinCerR-66
❑ 97PinEpixGO-E24
❑ 97PinEpixPE-E24
❑ 97PinIns-93
❑ 97PinInsCE-93
❑ 97PinInsDE-93
❑ 97PinMusC-65
❑ 97PinPrePla-65
❑ 97PinTotCPB-66
❑ 97PinTotCPG-66
❑ 97PinTotCPR-66
❑ 97PinX-P-14
❑ 97PinX-PMoS-14
❑ 97Sco-46
❑ 97Sco-328
❑ 97Sco-421
❑ 97ScoArtPWB-46
❑ 97ScoArtPWB-328
❑ 97ScoArtPWB-421
❑ 97ScoHigZ-18
❑ 97ScoPreS-46
❑ 97ScoPreS-328
❑ 97ScoResC-421
❑ 97ScoShoS-46
❑ 97ScoShoS-328
❑ 97ScoShoS-421
❑ 97ScoShoSAP-46
❑ 97ScoShoSAP-328
❑ 97ScoShoSAP-421
❑ 97SP-16
❑ 97SpoIll-48
❑ 97SpoIllEE-48
❑ 97SPSpeF-41
❑ 97SPSpxF-9
❑ 97SPSPxFA-9
❑ 97SPx-1
❑ 97SPxBro-1
❑ 97SPxCorotG-8
❑ 97SPxGol-1
❑ 97SPxGraF-1
❑ 97SPxSil-1
❑ 97SPxSte-1
❑ 97StaClu-36
❑ 97StaClul-I1
❑ 97StaCluMat-36
❑ 97StaCluMOP-36
❑ 97StaCluMOP-I1
❑ 97Stu-44
❑ 97StuPrePG-44
❑ 97StuPrePS-44
❑ 97Top-333
❑ 97Top-462
❑ 97TopChr-113
❑ 97TopChr-163
❑ 97TopChrR-113
❑ 97TopChrR-163
❑ 97TopGal-44
❑ 97TopGalPG-PG3
❑ 97TopGalPPI-44
❑ 97UD3-20
❑ 97Ult-6
❑ 97Ult-398
❑ 97UltFamGam-18
❑ 97UltGolME-6
❑ 97UltGolME-398
❑ 97UltHitM-16
❑ 97UltPlaME-6
❑ 97UltPlaME-398
❑ 97UltTop3-23
❑ 97UltTop3GM-23
❑ 97UppDec-220
❑ 97UppDec-521
❑ 97UppDecAG-AG6
❑ 98ColCho-15
❑ 98ColCho-149
❑ 98ColChoSQ-SQ58
❑ 98DonColL-224
❑ 98DonColP-577
❑ 98DonPre-27
❑ 98DonPreSeat-27
❑ 98DonPriCL-224
❑ 98DonPriCP-577
❑ 98Lea-24
❑ 98LeaFraDA-24
❑ 98LeaFraF-24
❑ 98LeaFraM-24
❑ 98LeaFraM-24
❑ 98LeaFraMDC-24
❑ 98LeaFraMDC-24
❑ 98LeaFraMZ2-24
❑ 98LeaHeaftH-15
❑ 98LeaHeaftHS-15
❑ 98PinEpixGE-E24
❑ 98PinEpixGP-E24
❑ 98PinEpixME-E24
❑ 98PinEpixMO-E24
❑ 98PinEpixMP-E24
❑ 98PinEpixPO-E24
❑ 98PinEpixPP-E24
❑ 98PinInsSG-21AB
❑ 98PinInsSG-21CD
❑ 98PinInsSGS-21AB
❑ 98PinInsSGS-21CD
❑ 98PinPreP-E24
❑ 98ScoEpix-E24
❑ 98SpoIll-180
❑ 98SpoIllEE-180
❑ 98SpoIllFE-180
❑ 98UppDec-20
❑ 98UppDec-401
❑ 98UppDec10AP-60
❑ 98UppDec1APR-60
❑ 98ZenEpi-E24
❑ 99DumSet-EMU
❑ 99SPSig-180
❑ 99UppDecAP-EM
❑ 99UppDecCLJotC-EM
❑ 99UppDecR-109
❑ 99UppDecRG-109
❑ 99UppDecRI-EM
❑ 99UppDecRIL2-EM
❑ 99UppDecRP-109

Murray, Feg
❑ 85FegMurCG-1
❑ 93Ble-26

Murray, Frank
❑ 76DalCon-8

Murray, George
❑ 36GouWidPPR-D20
❑ 37Zee-56

Murray, Glenn
❑ 90JamExpP-9
❑ 91MidLeaAP-MWL47
❑ 91RocExpC-25
❑ 91RocExpP-2060
❑ 92Bow-289
❑ 92ClaFS7-214
❑ 92ProFS7-265
❑ 92UppDecML-302
❑ 92WesPalBEC-19
❑ 92WesPalBEF-2100
❑ 93ClaGolF-139
❑ 93HarSenF-279
❑ 94Cla-118
❑ 94ExcFS7-228
❑ 94PawRedSDD-15
❑ 94PawRedSF-956
❑ 94Top-616
❑ 94TopGol-616
❑ 94TopSpa-616
❑ 94UppDecML-133
❑ 95Bow-98
❑ 95Exc-12
❑ 95PawRedSDD-20
❑ 95PawRedTI-34
❑ 95SigRoo-38
❑ 95SigRooSig-38
❑ 96ScrRedBB-20
❑ 97ChaLoo-18
❑ 98IndIndQ-31

Murray, Heath
❑ 94SigRooDP-56
❑ 94SigRooDPS-56
❑ 94SpoIndF-3323
❑ 94StaCluDP-74
❑ 94StaCluDPFDI-74
❑ 95RanCucQT-28
❑ 96Bow-310
❑ 96BowFoi-310
❑ 96DouAllB-35
❑ 96MemChiB-25
❑ 97Bow-407
❑ 97BowCerBlaIA-CA56
❑ 97BowCerBluIA-CA56
❑ 97BowCerGolIA-CA56
❑ 97BowChr-270
❑ 97BowChrI-270
❑ 97BowChrIR-270
❑ 97BowChrR-270
❑ 97BowInt-407
❑ 97ColCho-466
❑ 97LasVegS1A-24
❑ 97Top-493
❑ 98Bow-102
❑ 98BowChr-102
❑ 98BowChrGA-102
❑ 98BowChrGAR-102
❑ 98BowChrI-102
❑ 98BowChrIR-102
❑ 98BowChrR-102
❑ 98BowGolA-102
❑ 98BowInt-102
❑ 98Fle-215
❑ 98Las-17

Murray, Jack
❑ 11TurRedT-48
❑ 14PieStaT-81
❑ 15SpoNewM-128

Murray, James
❑ 08BufBisFJO-11
❑ 12ImpTobC-5

Murray, Jed
❑ 80SanJosMJitB-14
❑ 81LynSaiT-8
❑ 82LynSaiT-6
❑ 83SalLakCGT-9
❑ 84SalLakCGC-177
❑ 86CalCanP-17
❑ 87TolMudHP-13
❑ 87TolMudHT-18

Murray, Jeremiah
❑ 87OldJudN-191
❑ 87OldJudN-357

Murray, Jim
❑ 75CliPilT-11

Murray, Joseph
❑ 52Par-99

Murray, Keith
❑ 90ButCopKSP-16
❑ 91GasRanC-25
❑ 91GasRanP-2702

Murray, Larry
❑ 76SSP-449
❑ 80Top-284
❑ 92YanWIZ7-120

Murray, Matt
❑ 90Bes-285
❑ 90BurBraB-2
❑ 90BurBraP-2346
❑ 90BurBraS-19
❑ 90MidLeaASGS-45
❑ 91DurBulC-4
❑ 91DurBulP-1540
❑ 94DurBulC-12
❑ 94DurBulF-325
❑ 94DurBulTI-13
❑ 94UppDecML-28
❑ 95BowBes-B13
❑ 95BowBesR-B13
❑ 95RicBraRC-14
❑ 95RicBraTI-11
❑ 96RicBraUB-19
❑ 96ScrRedBB-21

Murray, Mike
❑ 87MyrBeaBJP-1442
❑ 88MyrBeaBJP-1179
❑ 89KinMetS-28

Murray, Pat
❑ 91JohCitCC-4
❑ 91JohCitCP-3985

Murray, Ray
❑ 50IndNumN-17
❑ 50IndTeal-19
❑ 51A'sTeal-25
❑ 52A'sTeal-20
❑ 52Bow-118
❑ 52Top-299
❑ 53A'sTeal-22
❑ 53BowBW-6
❑ 53IndPenCBP-22
❑ 53Top-234
❑ 54A'STEAI-16
❑ 54Bow-83
❑ 54OriEss-27
❑ 54OriTeal-15
❑ 54Top-49
❑ 83TopRep5-299
❑ 91OriCro-322
❑ 91TopArc1-234
❑ 94TopArc1-49
❑ 94TopArc1G-49
❑ 97BalOriP-36

Murray, Red (John Joseph)
❑ 08AmeCarE91-56
❑ 08RosComP-170
❑ 09BriE97-24
❑ 09ColChiE-210A
❑ 09ColChiE-210B
❑ 09RamT20-86
❑ 09T206-263
❑ 09T206-264
❑ 10CouT21-199
❑ 10CouT21-200
❑ 10CouT21-201
❑ 10DomDisP-91
❑ 10E12AmeCDCE125-28
❑ 10NadE1-44
❑ 10RedCroT-58
❑ 10RedCroT-143
❑ 10RedCroT-230
❑ 10SweCapPP-121
❑ 10W555-52
❑ 11E94-26
❑ 11HelSta-135
❑ 11PinT-5-257
❑ 11S74Sil-92
❑ 11SpoLifCW-265
❑ 11SpoLifM-214
❑ 11T205-127
❑ 12ColRedB-210A
❑ 12ColRedB-210B
❑ 12ColRedB-211
❑ 12ColTinT-210A
❑ 12ColTinT-210B
❑ 12ColTinT-211
❑ 12HasTriFT-48I
❑ 12PhiCarE-24
❑ 14B18B-70
❑ 14FatPlaT-36
❑ 14PolGroW-21
❑ 94ConTSN-1049
❑ 94ConTSNB-1049
❑ 97HicCraB-4

Murray, Rich
❑ 76CedRapGT-17
❑ 77CedRapGT-1
❑ 78PhoGiaC-18
❑ 79PhoGiaVNB-18
❑ 80GiaTeal-22
❑ 80PhoGiaVNB-19
❑ 81Fle-452
❑ 81PhoGiaVNB-24
❑ 81Top-195
❑ 82ChaChaT-16
❑ 83PhoGiaBHN-6
❑ 84PhoGiaC-6
❑ 85OmaRoyT-8

Murray, Richard
❑ 80VenLeaS-63
❑ 82WicAerTI-11

Murray, Scott
❑ 86St.PetCP-21
❑ 88SanJosGCLC-125
❑ 88SanJosGP-113

Murray, Steve
❑ 84BeaGolGT-7
❑ 87SalSpuS-22
❑ 88SanBerSCLC-29
❑ 89WauTimGS-20
❑ 90SanBerSB-19
❑ 90SanBerSCLC-113
❑ 90SanBerSP-2651
❑ 91SanBerSC-12
❑ 91SanBerSP-2005

Murray, Thomas
❑ 09ObaT21-296
❑ 11Zee-54
❑ 12ObaPreT-45

Murray, Venice
❑ 78CedRapGT-19

Murrell, Ivan
❑ 67Ast-21
❑ 68Top-569
❑ 69Top-333
❑ 70OPC-179
❑ 70Top-179
❑ 71MLBOffS-232
❑ 71OPC-569
❑ 71Top-569
❑ 72MilBra-249
❑ 72PadPos-19
❑ 72Top-677
❑ 73OPC-409
❑ 73PadDea-19
❑ 73Top-409
❑ 74OPC-628
❑ 74Top-628
❑ 87WilBilP-11
❑ 89PacSenL-131
❑ 89TopSenL-7

Murrell, Michael
❑ 90GeoColC-22

Murrell, Rodney
❑ 86LitFalMP-20
❑ 87ColMetP-22
❑ 88ColMetGS-17
❑ 89PenPilS-16

Murtaugh, Danny
❑ 43PhiTeal-17
❑ 47PM1StaP1-146
❑ 49Bow-124A
❑ 49Bow-124B
❑ 49EurSta-168
❑ 49Lea-142
❑ 50Bow-203
❑ 50PirTeal-16
❑ 51Bow-273
❑ 52NatTeaL-19
❑ 58PirTeal-8
❑ 59Top-17
❑ 59TopVen-17
❑ 60KeyChal-35
❑ 60PirJayP-10
❑ 60Top-223
❑ 61PirJayP-9
❑ 61Top-138
❑ 61Top-567
❑ 62Top-503
❑ 63PirIDL-15
❑ 63PirJayP-10
❑ 63Top-559
❑ 64PirKDK-21
❑ 64Top-141
❑ 64Top-268
❑ 64TopVen-141
❑ 64TopVen-268
❑ 70OPC-532
❑ 70Top-532
❑ 71OPC-437
❑ 71Top-437
❑ 74OPC-489
❑ 74Top-489
❑ 75OPC-304
❑ 75PitPirP-15
❑ 75Top-304
❑ 75TopMin-304
❑ 76OPC-504
❑ 76PirPos-13
❑ 76SSP-586
❑ 76Top-504
❑ 77PirTCM1WC-1
❑ 80PirGreT-12
❑ 81TCM60I-393
❑ 84OCoandSI-182
❑ 86PirGreT-12
❑ 95PirCocP-21

Murtaugh, Tim
❑ 75ShrCapT-12
❑ 76ShrCapT-NNO
❑ 77ColCliT-13
❑ 77ShrCapT-14

Murtha, Brian
❑ 82CliGiaF-20

Musachio, John
❑ 97HicCraB-20
❑ 97HicCraRB-25

Muscat, Scott
❑ 89HelBreSP-24
❑ 90BelBreB-10
❑ 90BelBreS-15

Muser, Tony
❑ 73OPC-238
❑ 73Top-238
❑ 74OPC-286
❑ 74Top-286
❑ 75OPC-348
❑ 75SSP18-4
❑ 75Top-348
❑ 75TopMin-348
❑ 76BalOriP-28
❑ 76OPC-537
❑ 76SSP-390
❑ 76Top-537
❑ 77Top-251
❑ 78BalOriP-23
❑ 78SpoIndC-8
❑ 78Top-418
❑ 79TCMJapPB-4
❑ 81ElPasDT-23
❑ 82ElPasDT-23
❑ 84VanCanC-27
❑ 85BrePol-NNO
❑ 86BrePol-35
❑ 87BrePol-NNO
❑ 88BrePol-NNO
❑ 88BreTeal-26
❑ 88Top-639
❑ 88TopTif-639
❑ 89BrePol-NNO
❑ 90El PasDAGTI-17
❑ 91DenZepLD-149
❑ 91DenZepP-137
❑ 91LinDriAAA-149
❑ 91OriCro-323
❑ 92DenZepF-2655
❑ 92DenZepS-149
❑ 93CubMar-19
❑ 94BreMilB-341

Musgrave, Scott
❑ 96LowSpiB-21

Musgraves, Dennis
❑ 77FriOneYW-47
❑ 81TCM60I-398
❑ 91MetWIZ-288

Musial, Stan
❑ 46SeaSLP-46
❑ 46SpoExcW-7-2
❑ 47Exh-164A
❑ 47Exh-164B
❑ 47HomBon-35
❑ 47PM1StaP1-147
❑ 47PM1StaP1-148
❑ 47PM1StaP1-149

❑ 48Bow-36
❑ 49Bow-24
❑ 49EurSta-191
❑ 49Lea-4
❑ 50RoyDes-1
❑ 51BerRos-B1
❑ 51R42SmaS-72
❑ 51Whe-4
❑ 52BerRos-45
❑ 52Bow-196
❑ 52RedMan-NL16
❑ 52RoyPre-7
❑ 52StaCalL-81E
❑ 52StaCalL-81F
❑ 52StaCalS-93A
❑ 52Whe-22A
❑ 52Whe-22B
❑ 53BowC-32
❑ 53CarHunW-16
❑ 53ExhCan-57
❑ 53RedMan-NL26
❑ 53SpoMagP-6
❑ 54CarHunW-14
❑ 54RedHeaF-23
❑ 55BigLealS-14
❑ 55CarHunW-15
❑ 55DaiQueS-14
❑ 55DonWin-34
❑ 55RawMus-1
❑ 55RawMus-1A
❑ 55RawMus-2
❑ 55RawMus-2A
❑ 55RawMus-3
❑ 55RawMus-4
❑ 56YelBasP-23
❑ 58CarJayP-13
❑ 58HarSta-6
❑ 58JayPubA-14
❑ 58JayPubS-8
❑ 58Top-476
❑ 59Top-150
❑ 59Top-470
❑ 59TopVen-150
❑ 60CarJayP-8
❑ 60KeyChal-36
❑ 60NuHi-21
❑ 60RawGloT-22
❑ 60Top-250
❑ 60TopTat-39
❑ 60TopTat-94
❑ 61CarJayP-10
❑ 61NuSco-421
❑ 61Raw-7
❑ 61SevElev-16
❑ 61Top-290
❑ 61TopDicG-11
❑ 61TopStal-92
❑ 62CarJayP-10
❑ 62ExhStaB-28
❑ 62Top-50
❑ 62Top-317
❑ 62TopBuc-63
❑ 62TopStal-189
❑ 62TopVen-50
❑ 63BasMagM-61
❑ 63Baz-23
❑ 63CarJayP-15
❑ 63ExhStaB-48
❑ 63Top-1
❑ 63Top-138
❑ 63Top-250
❑ 63TopStil-30
❑ 66CarCoi-2
❑ 67TopVen-157
❑ 69EquSpoHoF-BB14
❑ 72LauGreF-24
❑ 73HalofFPP-12
❑ 73SevTraC-52
❑ 73TCMAllG-11
❑ 74LauAllG-55
❑ 76GalBasGHoF-20
❑ 76JerJonPC-4
❑ 76RowExh-3
❑ 76ShaPiz-112
❑ 76TayBow4-2
❑ 77BobParHoF-69
❑ 77GalGloG-16
❑ 77GalGloG-237
❑ 77ShaPiz-25
❑ 77Spo-2116
❑ 78DexHaloFP-39
❑ 79BasGre-68
❑ 79DiaGre-158
❑ 79TCM50-9
❑ 80MarExh-21
❑ 80PacLeg-8
❑ 80PerHaloFP-114
❑ 80PerHaloFPS-14
❑ 80SSPHOF-114
❑ 81SanDieSC-13
❑ 82BasCarN-3
❑ 82DavHaloFB-18
❑ 82DiaCla-46
❑ 82GSGalAG-1
❑ 82TCMGreH-2
❑ 82TCMStaot5-20
❑ 83Car194T-14
❑ 83Car194T-65
❑ 83Car194T-68
❑ 83CarGreT-7
❑ 83DonHOFH-32
❑ 83MLBPin-29
❑ 83Oco& SSBG-12
❑ 83TCMPla1942-26
❑ 83TigAlKS-67
❑ 84OCoandSI-40
❑ 84OCoandSI-200
❑ 84OCoandSI-228
❑ 84SpoDesPW-11
❑ 84TCMBruS-BS5
❑ 84WilMay-30
❑ 85CirK-15
❑ 85DalNatCC-1
❑ 85DonHOFS-5
❑ 85MusTTC-1
❑ 85MusTTC-2
❑ 85MusTTC-3
❑ 85MusTTC-4
❑ 85MusTTC-5
❑ 85MusTTC-6
❑ 85MusTTC-7
❑ 85MusTTC-8
❑ 85TCMPhoC-34
❑ 85TCMPhoC-39
❑ 85Woo-27
❑ 86SpoDecG-30
❑ 86TCM-9
❑ 86TCMSupS-34
❑ 87HygAllG-34
❑ 87LeaSpeO*-H4
❑ 87NesDreT-23
❑ 87SpoRea-18
❑ 88Don-641
❑ 88GreBasS-7
❑ 88HouSho-4
❑ 88Lea-263
❑ 88PacLegI-6
❑ 88Top-665
❑ 88TopTif-665
❑ 88WilMulP-18
❑ 89HOFStiB-30
❑ 89PerCelP-33
❑ 89TopBasT-27
❑ 90BasWit-36
❑ 90HOFStiB-51
❑ 90PerGreM-11
❑ 91TopEasCN-3
❑ 91USGamSBL-8C
❑ 91USGamSBL-8D
❑ 91USGamSBL-8H
❑ 91USGamSBL-8S
❑ 92AFUMus-1
❑ 92AFUMus-2
❑ 92AFUMus-3
❑ 92AFUMus-4
❑ 92AFUMus-5
❑ 92CarMcD-22
❑ 92PinMan-24
❑ 92ScoFra-1
❑ 92ScoFra-4
❑ 92ScoFra-AU1
❑ 92ScoFra-AU4
❑ 92SpollIFK1-320
❑ 93Yoo-11
❑ 97DonSigNN-6
❑ 97DonSigSS-15
❑ 98DonSigSB-22
❑ 98DonSigSS-12
❑ 99Fle-6
❑ 99FleSta9-6
❑ 99FleStaMMM-1
❑ 99FleStaMMM-2
❑ 99FleStaMMM-3
❑ 99FleStaMMM-4
❑ 99FleStaMMM-5
❑ 99FleStaMMM-6
❑ 99FleStaMMM-7
❑ 99FleStaMMM-8
❑ 99FleStaMMM-9
❑ 99FleStaMMM-10
❑ 99FleStaMMM-NNO
❑ 99FleStaMMMA-1
❑ 99FleStaMMMA-2
❑ 99FleStaMMMA-3
❑ 99FleStaMMMA-4
❑ 99FleStaMMMA-5
❑ 99FleStaMMMA-6
❑ 99FleStaMMMA-7
❑ 99FleStaMMMA-8
❑ 99FleStaMMMA-9
❑ 99FleStaMMMA-10
❑ 99FleVin'-6
❑ 99FleWarT-6
❑ 99SP SigAuto-SM
❑ 99SpollIGotG-6
❑ 99SpollIGotGA-50
❑ 99SpollIGotGC-3
❑ 99SpollIGotGRB-2
❑ 99SpollIGotGRBG-2
❑ 99SPSig-169
❑ 99TopHaloFC-HOF3
❑ 99UppDecCL-10
❑ 99UppDecCLCC-10
❑ 99UppDecCLES-SM
❑ 99UppDecCLESC-SM

Musolino, Mike
❑ 87SalAngP-23
❑ 88PalSprACLC-105
❑ 88QuaCitAGS-30
❑ 89QuaCitAB-20
❑ 89QuaCitAGS-15
❑ 92PalSprAC-22
❑ 92PalSprAF-844

Musselman, Jeff
❑ 86VenGulP-16
❑ 87BluJayFS-25
❑ 87Don-591
❑ 87DonRoo-53
❑ 87FleUpd-84
❑ 87FleUpdG-84
❑ 87SpoRool-15
❑ 87TopTra-83T
❑ 87TopTraT-83T
❑ 88BluJayFS-25
❑ 88Don-630
❑ 88Fle-121
❑ 88FleGlo-121
❑ 88Lea-234
❑ 88OPC-229
❑ 88Sco-478
❑ 88ScoGlo-478
❑ 88ScoYouS2-30
❑ 88StaLinBJ-17
❑ 88Top-229
❑ 88TopBig-69
❑ 88TopRoo-22
❑ 88TopSti-308
❑ 88TopTif-229
❑ 88ToyRoo-20
❑ 89BluJayFS-22
❑ 89Bow-240
❑ 89BowTif-240
❑ 89Don-656
❑ 89Fle-243
❑ 89FleGlo-243
❑ 89MetKah-U3
❑ 89OPC-362
❑ 89Sco-558
❑ 89Top-591
❑ 89TopTif-591
❑ 89UppDec-41
❑ 90Don-623
❑ 90Fle-212
❑ 90FleCan-212
❑ 90MetColP-21
❑ 90MetKah-13
❑ 90OPC-382
❑ 90Sco-525
❑ 90Top-382
❑ 90TopTif-382
❑ 90TopTVM-15
❑ 90UppDec-585
❑ 91LinDriAAA-542
❑ 91MetWIZ-289
❑ 91Sco-294
❑ 91TacTigLD-542
❑ 91TacTigP-2301
❑ 92TacTigF-2498
❑ 92TacTigS-540

Musselman, Ron
❑ 80LynSaiT-23
❑ 81SpoIndT-17
❑ 82SalLakCGT-14
❑ 83OklCit8T-14
❑ 85BluJayFS-25
❑ 85FleUpd-83
❑ 86SyrChiP-20
❑ 87PorBeaP-21

Musselwhite, Darren
❑ 90KenTwiB-16
❑ 90KenTwiS-28
❑ 91VisOakC-6
❑ 91VisOakP-1740

Musselwhite, Jim
❑ 93OneYanF-3500
❑ 94Bow-27
❑ 94FloStaLAF-FSL24
❑ 94TamYanC-19
❑ 94TamYanF-2381
❑ 95Exc-100
❑ 95NorNavTI-25

Musser, Andy
❑ 84PhiTas-7
❑ 88PhiTas-39
❑ 90PhiTas-35

Musser, Paul
❑ 14Zee-19

Musset, Jose
❑ 92QuaCitRBC-12
❑ 92QuaCitRBF-806
❑ 93MidAngF-321
❑ 94Bow-221
❑ 94ColCliF-2951
❑ 94ExcFS7-28
❑ 95ColCliMCTI-6
❑ 95NorNagUTI-45
❑ 97MidAngOHP-20

Mussina, Mike
❑ 90ClaDraP-20
❑ 90RocRedWGC-12
❑ 90TopMag-83
❑ 91Bow-97
❑ 91Cla1-T17
❑ 91ClaGam-146
❑ 91LeaGolR-BC12
❑ 91LeaGolRNV-276
❑ 91LinDriAAA-462
❑ 91RocRedWLD-462
❑ 91RocRedWP-1899
❑ 91Sco-383
❑ 91UltUpd-4
❑ 91UppDec-65
❑ 92BalOriP-24
❑ 92BalOriP-25
❑ 92Bow-612
❑ 92Cla1-T67
❑ 92Cla2-T14
❑ 92Cla2-NNO
❑ 92ClaDraP-95
❑ 92ClaDraPFB-BC20
❑ 92ClaGam-148
❑ 92ColAllG-15
❑ 92ColAllP-15
❑ 92Don-632
❑ 92Fle-20
❑ 92Lea-13
❑ 92LeaBlaG-13
❑ 92OPC-242
❑ 92OPCPre-87
❑ 92Pin-204
❑ 92PinTea2-1
❑ 92ProFS7-1
❑ 92Sco-755
❑ 92ScoImpP-48
❑ 92SpollIFK1-311
❑ 92StaClu-225
❑ 92Stu-127
❑ 92TigTeal-26
❑ 92Top-242
❑ 92TopDeb91-130
❑ 92TopGol-242
❑ 92TopGolW-242
❑ 92TopMic-242
❑ 92TriPla-237
❑ 92Ult-9
❑ 92UppDec-675
❑ 93BalOriP-20
❑ 93Bow-633
❑ 93ClaGam-70
❑ 93ColAllG-17
❑ 93DiaMar-79
❑ 93Don-427
❑ 93Fin-157
❑ 93FinRef-157
❑ 93Fla-154
❑ 93Fle-172
❑ 93FunPac-134
❑ 93HumDumC-2
❑ 93JimDea-27
❑ 93Lea-343
❑ 93LeaFas-4
❑ 93MSABenSPD-13
❑ 93OPC-214
❑ 93PacSpa-21
❑ 93PanSti-69
❑ 93Pin-44
❑ 93PinTea2-3
❑ 93PinTeaP-1
❑ 93RedFolS-69
❑ 93Sco-27
❑ 93Sel-92
❑ 93SelAce-20
❑ 93SelStaL-81
❑ 93SelStaL-87
❑ 93SP-160
❑ 93StaClu-77
❑ 93StaCluFDI-77
❑ 93StaCluM-145
❑ 93StaCluMOP-77
❑ 93Stu-202
❑ 93StuSupoC-4
❑ 93Top-710
❑ 93TopComotH-2
❑ 93TopGol-710
❑ 93TopInaM-710
❑ 93TopInaR-710
❑ 93TopMic-710
❑ 93Toy-37
❑ 93TriPla-13
❑ 93Ult-144
❑ 93UltAllS-20
❑ 93UppDec-233
❑ 93UppDec-463
❑ 93UppDecGold-233
❑ 93UppDecGold-463
❑ 93USPlaCA-8S
❑ 94BalOriP-21
❑ 94Bow-627
❑ 94BowBes-R54
❑ 94BowBesR-R54
❑ 94ColC-475
❑ 94ColChoGS-475
❑ 94ColChoSS-475
❑ 94Don-331
❑ 94DonDiaK-DK26
❑ 94DonDiaKJ-DK26
❑ 94DonSpeE-331
❑ 94Fin-66
❑ 94FinPre-66P
❑ 94FinRef-66
❑ 94Fla-255
❑ 94Fle-12
❑ 94Fle-708
❑ 94FleAllS-18
❑ 94FleExtB-9
❑ 94FleExtBPD-4
❑ 94FleSmo'nH-8
❑ 94FUnPac-148
❑ 94Lea-105
❑ 94LeaL-3
❑ 94OPC-82
❑ 94OriPro-70
❑ 94OriUSPC-1D
❑ 94OriUSPC-9S
❑ 94Pac-38
❑ 94PanSti-21
❑ 94Pin-295
❑ 94PinArtP-295
❑ 94PinMusC-295
❑ 94ProMag-9
❑ 94RedFolMI-22
❑ 94Sco-9
❑ 94ScoDreT-1
❑ 94ScoGolR-9
❑ 94Sel-36
❑ 94SP-124
❑ 94SPDieC-124
❑ 94Spo-44
❑ 94SpoFanA-AS9
❑ 94StaClu-488
❑ 94StaCluFDI-488
❑ 94StaCluGR-488
❑ 94StaCluMOP-488
❑ 94StaCluT-279
❑ 94StaCluTFDI-279
❑ 94Stu-125
❑ 94StuHer-8
❑ 94Top-598
❑ 94TopGol-598
❑ 94TopSpa-598
❑ 94TriPla-157
❑ 94Ult-307
❑ 94UppDec-44
❑ 94UppDec-102
❑ 94UppDecAJ-19
❑ 94UppDecAJG-19
❑ 94UppDecED-44
❑ 94UppDecED-102
❑ 95BalOriP-36
❑ 95Baz-10
❑ 95Bow-334
❑ 95ClaPhoC-6
❑ 95ColCho-340
❑ 95ColChoGS-340
❑ 95ColChoSE-157
❑ 95ColChoSEGS-157
❑ 95ColChoSESS-157
❑ 95ColChoSS-340
❑ 95Don-9
❑ 95DonDom-1
❑ 95DonMouM-3
❑ 95DonPreP-9
❑ 95DonTopotO-13
❑ 95Emo-6
❑ 95Fin-48
❑ 95FinRef-48
❑ 95Fla-6
❑ 95FlaTodS-8
❑ 95Fle-15
❑ 95FleAllS-20
❑ 95FlePro-1
❑ 95FleTeaL-1
❑ 95Kra-9
❑ 95Lea-387
❑ 95LeaLim-70
❑ 95Pac-27
❑ 95PacPri-8
❑ 95PanSti-13
❑ 95Pin-14
❑ 95PinArtP-14
❑ 95PinMusC-14
❑ 95PinPin-2
❑ 95PinPinR-2
❑ 95PinTeaP-TP1
❑ 95RedFol-10
❑ 95Sco-415
❑ 95ScoGolR-415
❑ 95ScoHaloG-HG85
❑ 95ScoPlaTS-415
❑ 95ScoRul-SR30
❑ 95ScoRulJ-SR30
❑ 95Sel-19
❑ 95SelArtP-19
❑ 95SelCer-9
❑ 95SelCerMG-9
❑ 95SP-119
❑ 95SPCha-117
❑ 95SPChaDC-117
❑ 95Spo-60
❑ 95SpoArtP-60
❑ 95SPSil-119
❑ 95StaClu-426
❑ 95StaCluMOP-426
❑ 95StaCluSTWS-426
❑ 95StaCluVR-223
❑ 95StaCluVRMO-223
❑ 95Stu-29
❑ 95StuGolS-29
❑ 95Sum-102
❑ 95Sum-192
❑ 95SumNthD-102
❑ 95SumNthD-192
❑ 95Top-50
❑ 95TopCyb-37
❑ 95TopEmb-93
❑ 95TopEmbGI-93
❑ 95UC3-5
❑ 95UC3ArtP-5
❑ 95Ult-6
❑ 95UltGolM-6
❑ 95UppDec-130
❑ 95UppDecED-130
❑ 95UppDecEDG-130
❑ 95UppDecSE-186
❑ 95UppDecSEG-186
❑ 95USPlaCMLA-6S
❑ 95Zen-75
❑ 96BalOriP-23
❑ 96Baz-81
❑ 96Bow-93
❑ 96BowBes-54
❑ 96BowBesAR-54
❑ 96BowBesMI-9
❑ 96BowBesMIAR-9
❑ 96BowBesMIR-9
❑ 96BowBesR-54
❑ 96BowFoi-93
❑ 96Cir-5
❑ 96CirRav-5
❑ 96ColCho-6
❑ 96ColCho-465
❑ 96ColChoGS-6
❑ 96ColChoGS-465
❑ 96ColChoSS-6
❑ 96ColChoSS-465
❑ 96Don-518

❑ 96DonDiaK-28
❑ 96DonPreP-518
❑ 96DonSho-5
❑ 96EmoXL-6
❑ 96Fin-G90
❑ 96FinRef-G90
❑ 96Fla-9
❑ 96Fle-17
❑ 96FleTif-17
❑ 96Lea-191
❑ 96LeaLim-30
❑ 96LeaLimG-30
❑ 96LeaPre-36
❑ 96LeaPreP-36
❑ 96LeaPrePB-191
❑ 96LeaPrePG-191
❑ 96LeaPrePS-191
❑ 96LeaPreSG-49
❑ 96LeaPreSte-49
❑ 96LeaSig-19
❑ 96LeaSigPPG-19
❑ 96LeaSigPPP-19
❑ 96MetUni-6
❑ 96MetUniP-6
❑ 96MLBPin-22
❑ 96OriFle-11
❑ 96Pac-243
❑ 96PacPri-P75
❑ 96PacPriFT-FT2
❑ 96PacPriG-P75
❑ 96PanSti-125
❑ 96PanSti-127
❑ 96Pin-34
❑ 96PinAfi-83
❑ 96PinAfiAP-83
❑ 96PinAfiFPP-83
❑ 96PinArtP-16
❑ 96PinSta-16
❑ 96ProSta-79
❑ 96Sco-197
❑ 96Sco-301
❑ 96ScoDugC-B26
❑ 96ScoDugCAP-B26
❑ 96ScoRef-17
❑ 96Sel-30
❑ 96SelArtP-30
❑ 96SelCer-12
❑ 96SelCerAP-12
❑ 96SelCerCB-12
❑ 96SelCerCR-12
❑ 96SelCerIP-16
❑ 96SelCerMB-12
❑ 96SelCerMG-12
❑ 96SelCerMR-12
❑ 96SelTeaN-20
❑ 96SP-33
❑ 96SPMarM-MM17
❑ 96SPMarMDC-17
❑ 96Spo-74
❑ 96SpoArtP-74
❑ 96StaClu-6
❑ 96StaCluEPB-6
❑ 96StaCluEPG-6
❑ 96StaCluEPS-6
❑ 96StaCluMO-29
❑ 96StaCluMOP-6
❑ 96Stu-128
❑ 96StuPrePB-128
❑ 96StuPrePG-128
❑ 96StuPrePS-128
❑ 96Sum-119
❑ 96SumAbo&B-119
❑ 96SumArtP-119
❑ 96SumFoi-119
❑ 96Top-65
❑ 96Top-228
❑ 96TopChr-23
❑ 96TopChr-88
❑ 96TopChrR-23
❑ 96TopChrR-88
❑ 96TopClaC-CC12
❑ 96TopGal-159
❑ 96TopGalPPI-159
❑ 96TopLas-125
❑ 96Ult-9
❑ 96UltGolM-9
❑ 96UppDec-281
❑ 96UppDecPHE-H16
❑ 96UppDecPreH-H16
❑ 96Zen-52
❑ 96ZenArtP-52
❑ 96ZenMoz-8
❑ 97BalOriP-23
❑ 97Bow-44
❑ 97BowBes-54
❑ 97BowBesAR-54
❑ 97BowBesR-54
❑ 97BowChr-35
❑ 97BowChrI-35
❑ 97BowChrIR-35
❑ 97BowChrR-35
❑ 97BowInt-44
❑ 97Cir-375
❑ 97CirRav-375
❑ 97ColCho-271
❑ 97ColChoNF-NF39
❑ 97ColChoT-BO8
❑ 97Don-119
❑ 97Don-432
❑ 97DonEli-29
❑ 97DonEliGS-29
❑ 97DonGolPP-119
❑ 97DonGolPP-432
❑ 97DonLim-155
❑ 97DonLim-160
❑ 97DonLimE-155
❑ 97DonLimE-160
❑ 97DonLimENG-155
❑ 97DonPre-132
❑ 97DonPreCttC-132
❑ 97DonSig-82
❑ 97DonSigAC-91
❑ 97DonSigAM-91
❑ 97DonSigPPP-82
❑ 97DonSilPP-119
❑ 97DonSilPP-432
❑ 97DonTea-34
❑ 97DonTeaSPE-34
❑ 97E-X2-6
❑ 97E-X2Cred-6
❑ 97E-X2EssCre-6
❑ 97Fin-95
❑ 97FinRef-95
❑ 97FlaShoLC-53
❑ 97FlaShoLeg0-53
❑ 97FlaShoLeg1-53
❑ 97FlaShoM-A53
❑ 97FlaShoM-B53
❑ 97FlaShoM-C53
❑ 97FlaShoR0-53
❑ 97FlaShoR1-53
❑ 97FlaShoR2-53
❑ 97Fle-10
❑ 97FleTif-10
❑ 97Lea-146
❑ 97LeaFraM-146
❑ 97LeaFraMDC-146
❑ 97LeaGet-8
❑ 97MetUni-6
❑ 97NewPin-128
❑ 97NewPinAP-128
❑ 97NewPinMC-128
❑ 97NewPinPP-128
❑ 97OriSco-8
❑ 97OriScoPI-8
❑ 97OriScoPr-8
❑ 97OriSun-6
❑ 97Pac-26
❑ 97PacGolCD-3
❑ 97PacLigB-26
❑ 97PacPri-10
❑ 97PacPriLB-10
❑ 97PacPriP-10
❑ 97PacPriSH-SH1B
❑ 97PacSil-26
❑ 97Pin-155
❑ 97PinArtP-PP155
❑ 97PinCar-9
❑ 97PinCer-43
❑ 97PinCerLI-20
❑ 97PinCerMBla-43
❑ 97PinCerMBlu-43
❑ 97PinCerMG-43
❑ 97PinCerMR-43
❑ 97PinCerR-43
❑ 97PinIns-122
❑ 97PinInsCE-122
❑ 97PinInsDD-18
❑ 97PinInsDE-122
❑ 97PinMusC-155
❑ 97PinPrePla-155
❑ 97PinTotCPB-43
❑ 97PinTotCPG-43
❑ 97PinTotCPR-43
❑ 97PinX-P-74
❑ 97PinX-PMoS-74
❑ 97Sco-154
❑ 97Sco-519
❑ 97ScoArtPWB-154
❑ 97ScoArtPWB-519
❑ 97ScoPreS-154
❑ 97ScoResC-519
❑ 97ScoShoS-154
❑ 97ScoShoS-519
❑ 97ScoShoSAP-154
❑ 97ScoShoSAP-519
❑ 97Sel-82
❑ 97SelArtP-82
❑ 97SelCom-82
❑ 97SelRegG-82
❑ 97SelTooотT-23
❑ 97SelTooотTMB-23
❑ 97SP-31
❑ 97SpoIll-125
❑ 97SpoIllEE-125
❑ 97SPSpeF-21
❑ 97StaClu-21
❑ 97StaCluMat-21
❑ 97StaCluMOP-21
❑ 97StrAll-46
❑ 97Stu-39
❑ 97StuPrePG-39
❑ 97StuPrePS-39
❑ 97Top-375
❑ 97TopChr-128
❑ 97TopChrR-128
❑ 97TopChrSB-19
❑ 97TopChrSBR-19
❑ 97TopGal-112
❑ 97TopGalPPI-112
❑ 97TopSeaB-SB19
❑ 97TopSta-70
❑ 97TopStaAM-70
❑ 97Ult-7
❑ 97UltGolME-7
❑ 97UltPlaME-7
❑ 97UppDec-22
❑ 97UppDec-67
❑ 97UppDecHTH-HT7
❑ 97Zen-33
❑ 98Bow-9
❑ 98BowBes-63
❑ 98BowBesAR-63
❑ 98BowBesR-63
❑ 98BowChr-9
❑ 98BowChrGA-9
❑ 98BowChrGAR-9
❑ 98BowChrI-9
❑ 98BowChrIR-9
❑ 98BowChrR-9
❑ 98BowChrR-24
❑ 98BowChrRR-24
❑ 98BowGolA-9
❑ 98BowInt-9
❑ 98CirThu-35
❑ 98CirThuRav-35
❑ 98CirThuSupRav-35
❑ 98ColCho-170
❑ 98ColCho-315
❑ 98CroRoy-21
❑ 98Don-9
❑ 98Don-378
❑ 98DonCol-9
❑ 98DonColE-447
❑ 98DonColL-242
❑ 98DonColP-583
❑ 98DonColS-9
❑ 98DonCruG-11
❑ 98DonCruP-11
❑ 98DonCruR-11
❑ 98DonEli-47
❑ 98DonEliA-47
❑ 98DonEliS-47
❑ 98DonGolPP-9
❑ 98DonGolPP-378
❑ 98DonPre-33
❑ 98DonPreSeat-33
❑ 98DonPriCD-9
❑ 98DonPriCE-447
❑ 98DonPriCL-242
❑ 98DonPriCP-583
❑ 98DonSig-64
❑ 98DonSigAC-81
❑ 98DonSigAM-82
❑ 98DonSigP-64
❑ 98DonSilPP-9
❑ 98DonSilPP-378
❑ 98DonSonM9-4
❑ 98E-X2-24
❑ 98E-X2ECFut-24
❑ 98E-X2ECNow-24
❑ 98Fin-70
❑ 98FinNo--70
❑ 98FinNo-R-70
❑ 98FinRef-70
❑ 98FlaShoLeg0-84
❑ 98FlaShoLeg1-84
❑ 98FlaShoLeg2-84
❑ 98FlaShoLeg3-84
❑ 98FlaShoLegM-84
❑ 98FlaShoR0-84
❑ 98FlaShoR1-84
❑ 98FlaShoR2-84
❑ 98FlaShoR3-84
❑ 98Fle-307
❑ 98Fle-389
❑ 98FleVin'-78
❑ 98FleVin'C-78
❑ 98Lea-43
❑ 98LeaCruG-11
❑ 98LeaCruP-11
❑ 98LeaCruR-11
❑ 98LeaFraDA-43
❑ 98LeaFraF-43
❑ 98LeaFraM-43
❑ 98LeaFraM-43
❑ 98LeaFraMDC-43
❑ 98LeaFraMDC-43
❑ 98LeaFraMZ2-43
❑ 98LeaRS-6
❑ 98LeaRSLHolo-6
❑ 98LeaRSLong-6
❑ 98LeaRTrue-6
❑ 98MetUni-170
❑ 98MetUniPMG-170
❑ 98OriSco-8
❑ 98OriScoP-8
❑ 98Pac-28
❑ 98PacAur-12
❑ 98PacInv-10
❑ 98PacInvGems-12
❑ 98PacInvPBlue-10
❑ 98PacInvSilv-10
❑ 98PacInvTeam-3
❑ 98PacOme-32
❑ 98PacOmeR-32
❑ 98PacOnl-95
❑ 98PacOnlR-95
❑ 98PacOnlWC-95
❑ 98PacPar-15
❑ 98PacParC-15
❑ 98PacParG-15
❑ 98PacParHS-15
❑ 98PacParPB-15
❑ 98PacParR-15
❑ 98PacPlaB-28
❑ 98PacRedT-28
❑ 98PacSil-28
❑ 98PinIns-70
❑ 98PinInsCE-70
❑ 98PinInsDE-70
❑ 98PinPer-34
❑ 98PinPerPP-34
❑ 98PinPlu-16
❑ 98PinSna-BO5
❑ 98PreCon-14
❑ 98Revo-20
❑ 98RevoSS-20
❑ 98Sco-126
❑ 98Sco-258
❑ 98ScoRT-24
❑ 98ScoRTSS-PP24
❑ 98ScoRTSSAP-PP24
❑ 98ScoRTSSAP1-PP24
❑ 98ScoSS-PP151
❑ 98ScoSSAP-PP151
❑ 98SkyDugA-53
❑ 98SkyDugAD-D10
❑ 98SkyDugAIA-53
❑ 98SP Aut-52
❑ 98SP AutC-MM
❑ 98SpoIll-91
❑ 98SpoIllEE-91
❑ 98SpoIllFE-91
❑ 98SpoIllTaN-39
❑ 98SpoIllTaNEE-39
❑ 98SpoIllWSF-100
❑ 98SpoIllWSFEE-100
❑ 98SpoIllWSFFE-100
❑ 98SPxFin-63
❑ 98SPxFin-144
❑ 98SPxFinR-63
❑ 98SPxFinR-144
❑ 98SPxFinS-63
❑ 98SPxFinS-144
❑ 98StaCluFDI-108
❑ 98StaCluI-108
❑ 98StaCluOneK-108
❑ 98StaCluPP-108
❑ 98StaCluTIII-T9A
❑ 98StaCluTLme-T9A
❑ 98StaCluTLmo-T9A
❑ 98Stu-165
❑ 98StuGPP-165
❑ 98StuSony99-4
❑ 98StuSPP-165
❑ 98Top-165
❑ 98TopChr-165
❑ 98TopChrR-165
❑ 98TopDevR-165
❑ 98TopDia-165
❑ 98TopGal-48
❑ 98TopGalGP-48
❑ 98TopGalOPP-48
❑ 98TopGalPPI-48
❑ 98TopGalPPIA-48
❑ 98TopGolLabC1-43
❑ 98TopGolLabC1B-43
❑ 98TopGolLabC1One-43
❑ 98TopGolLabC1R-43
❑ 98TopGolLabC2-43
❑ 98TopGolLabC2B-43
❑ 98TopGolLabC2One-43
❑ 98TopGolLabC2R-43
❑ 98TopGolLabC3-43
❑ 98TopGolLabC3B-43
❑ 98TopGolLabC3One-43
❑ 98TopGolLabC3R-43
❑ 98TopMiniC-165
❑ 98TopOpeD-86
❑ 98TopSta-9
❑ 98TopStaB-9
❑ 98TopStaG-9
❑ 98TopStaGR-9
❑ 98TopStaS-9
❑ 98TopTek-80
❑ 98TopTekD-80
❑ 98UD3-86
❑ 98UD3-176
❑ 98UD3-266
❑ 98UD3DieCut-86
❑ 98UD3DieCut-176
❑ 98UD3DieCut-266
❑ 98Ult-204
❑ 98UltGolM-204
❑ 98UltMas-204
❑ 98UltPlaM-204
❑ 98UppDec-306
❑ 98UppDec-416
❑ 98UppDec-423
❑ 98UppDec10AP-2
❑ 98UppDec1APR-2
❑ 98UppDecCD-CD17
❑ 98UppDecRTC-TC1
❑ 98Zen-30
❑ 98Zen5 xx7-27
❑ 98Zen5x7GoldImp-27
❑ 98Zen5x7Imp-27
❑ 98ZenZ-G-30
❑ 98ZenZ-S-30
❑ 99199Fin-34
❑ 99Bow-60
❑ 99BowBes-29
❑ 99BowBesAR-29
❑ 99BowBesR-29
❑ 99BowChr-60
❑ 99BowChrG-60
❑ 99BowChrGR-60
❑ 99BowChrI-60
❑ 99BowChrIR-60
❑ 99BowChrR-60
❑ 99BowGol-60
❑ 99BowInt-60
❑ 99CroRoyB-21
❑ 99CroRoyL-21
❑ 99CroRoyOD-21
❑ 99E-X Cen-31
❑ 99E-X CenECFut-31
❑ 99E-X CenECNow-31
❑ 99FinGolRef-34
❑ 99FinRef-34
❑ 99FlaShoLeg1-108
❑ 99FlaShoLeg2-108
❑ 99FlaShoLeg3-108
❑ 99FlaShoLegM1-108
❑ 99FlaShoLegM2-108
❑ 99FlaShoLegM3-108
❑ 99FlaShoR1-108
❑ 99FlaShoR2-108
❑ 99FlaShoR3-108
❑ 99Fle-154
❑ 99FleBri-15
❑ 99FleBri2G-15
❑ 99FleBriBlu-15
❑ 99FleBriGol-15
❑ 99FleMys-99
❑ 99FleMysG-99
❑ 99FleMysM-99
❑ 99FleSta9-154
❑ 99FleWarT-154
❑ 99MetUni-79
❑ 99MetUniGM-79
❑ 99MetUniPMG-79
❑ 99Pac-55
❑ 99PacAur-24
❑ 99PacAurOD-24
❑ 99PacCroC-37
❑ 99PacCroCPB-37
❑ 99PacInv-21
❑ 99PacInvOD-21
❑ 99PacInvPB-21
❑ 99PacOme-36
❑ 99PacOmeC-36
❑ 99PacOmeG-36
❑ 99PacOmePB-36
❑ 99PacPar-35
❑ 99PacParC-35
❑ 99PacParG-35
❑ 99PacParHoloGold-35
❑ 99PacParHS-35
❑ 99PacParOD-35
❑ 99PacParPB-35
❑ 99PacParRed-35
❑ 99PacPlaB-55
❑ 99PacPri-19
❑ 99PacPriHB-19
❑ 99PacPriHG-19
❑ 99PacPriHM-19
❑ 99PacPriHP-19
❑ 99PacPriRed-19
❑ 99PacPriS-119
❑ 99PacPriS206-119
❑ 99PacPriS206R-119
❑ 99PacRed-55
❑ 99SkyMolM-99
❑ 99SkyMolMX-99
❑ 99SkyPre-156
❑ 99SkyPreR-156
❑ 99SkyThu-125
❑ 99SkyThuRant-125
❑ 99SkyThuRave-125
❑ 99SpoIll-147
❑ 99SPx-22
❑ 99SPxFinR-22
❑ 99SPxFinS-22
❑ 99StaClu-59
❑ 99StaCluFDI-59
❑ 99StaCluOoaK-59
❑ 99StaCluPP-59
❑ 99ThuSkySupR-125
❑ 99Top-180
❑ 99TopBlaLC1-49
❑ 99TopBlaLC2-49
❑ 99TopBlaLC3-49
❑ 99TopChr-180
❑ 99TopChrR-180
❑ 99TopGal-67
❑ 99TopGalPP-67
❑ 99TopGalPPI-67
❑ 99TopGolL-49
❑ 99TopGolLC1-49
❑ 99TopGolLC2-49
❑ 99TopGolLOtO-49
❑ 99TopMVPP-180
❑ 99TopOpeD-98
❑ 99TopRedLC1-49
❑ 99TopRedLC2-49
❑ 99TopRedLC3-49
❑ 99TopSta-123
❑ 99TopStaFoil-123
❑ 99Ult-96
❑ 99UltGolM-96
❑ 99UltMas-96
❑ 99UltPlaM-96
❑ 99UppDec-48
❑ 99UppDecBD-14
❑ 99UppDecBDD-14
❑ 99UppDecBDQ-14
❑ 99UppDecBDT-14
❑ 99UppDecE-12
❑ 99UppDecEFXG-12
❑ 99UppDecEL1-48
❑ 99UppDecEL2-48
❑ 99UppDecM-27
❑ 99UppDecMGS-27
❑ 99UppDecMHFS-27
❑ 99UppDecMP-27
❑ 99UppDecMSS-27
❑ 99UppDecO-31
❑ 99UppDecOSO-31
❑ 99Vic-50

Mustad, Eric

❑ 80HawIsIT-5
❑ 81TacTigT-4
❑ 82TacTigT-7
❑ 83WicAerDS-14

❑ 84IndIndTI-11
❑ 84IndIndTI-18
Mustaikis, Alex
❑ 79RedSoxEF-6
Mustari, Frank
❑ 88VerBeaDS-16
Muth, Bill
❑ 77WauMetT-12
Mutis, Jeff
❑ 87PanAmTUBI-8
❑ 87PanAmTURB-16
❑ 88BurIndP-1792
❑ 89KinIndS-13
❑ 90Bes-290
❑ 90CanIndB-22
❑ 90CanIndP-1291
❑ 90CanIndS-13
❑ 90CMC-834
❑ 91CanIndLD-90
❑ 91CanIndP-979
❑ 91Cla/Bes-24
❑ 91LinDriAA-90
❑ 92ColSprSSF-749
❑ 92ColSprSSS-92
❑ 92Don-411
❑ 92ProFS7-52
❑ 92SkyAA F-296
❑ 92SkyAAAF-40
❑ 92TopDeb91-131
❑ 93Bow-586
❑ 93IndWUA-21
❑ 93OPCPre-122
❑ 93Ult-543
❑ 94Fle-114
❑ 94Pac-178
❑ 94StaCluT-88
❑ 94StaCluTFDI-88
❑ 95ChaKniTI-18
❑ 96LouRedB-23
Mutrie, James
❑ 86OldJudN-10
❑ 87FouBasHN-8
❑ 87OldJudN-358
❑ 88GandBCGCE-28
❑ 89SFHaCN-13
Mutz, Frank
❑ 87SalAngP-16
❑ 88QuaCitAGS-12
❑ 88RenSilSCLC-276
❑ 89QuaCitAB-13
❑ 89QuaCitAGS-22
Mutz, Tommy
❑ 77IndIndTI-16
❑ 78IndIndTI-10
❑ 79IndIndTI-8
❑ 80OmaRoyP-19
Myaer, Jeff
❑ 86BenPhiC-153
Myatt, George
❑ 35GouPuzR-5B
❑ 35GouPuzR-6B
❑ 35GouPuzR-11K
❑ 35GouPuzR-13B
❑ 60BraLaktL-17
❑ 60BraSpiaS-15
❑ 60Top-464
❑ 62TigPosCF-13
❑ 72TCMthe1-193
❑ 79DiaGre-69
Myatt, Glenn
❑ 25Exh-84
❑ 26Exh-83
❑ 27Exh-43
❑ 28Exh-42
❑ 32R33So2-417
❑ 33Gou-10
❑ 33GouCanV-10
❑ 34DiaMatCSB-139
❑ 34DiaStaR-58
❑ 35DiaMatCS3T1-113
❑ 36GouWidPPR-D21
❑ 36WorWidGV-26
❑ 91ConTSN-187
Myer, Buddy (Charles M.)
❑ 28W56PlaC-C6A
❑ 29ExhFou-32
❑ 31Exh-32
❑ 31SenTealPW-25
❑ 33Gou-153
❑ 33GouCanV-78
❑ 34BatR31-19
❑ 34BatR31-133
❑ 34DiaStaR-4
❑ 35AlDemDCR3-66
❑ 35ExhFou-16
❑ 35GouPuzR-8H
❑ 35GouPuzR-9H
❑ 36ExhFou-16
❑ 36GouWidPPR-A78
❑ 36NatChiFPR-57
❑ 36NatChiFPR-95
❑ 36WorWidGV-132
❑ 37ExhFou-16
❑ 37KelPepS-BB11
❑ 37OPCBatUV-114
❑ 38CloFotW-61
❑ 38ExhFou-16
❑ 39PlaBal-100
❑ 40PlaBal-17
❑ 41DouPlaR-73
❑ 60SenUniMC-14
❑ 68SCFOldT-14
❑ 72TCMthe1-177
❑ 75SenTCM1-23
❑ 85BigLeaC3-37
❑ 92ConTSN-503
Myerchin, Mike
❑ 82BelBreFr-12
Myers, Aaron
❑ 96PorRocB-24
❑ 97AshTou-19
Myers, Adrian
❑ 96HudValRB-11
❑ 98Cha-21
Myers, Al
❑ 87BucN28-115
❑ 87OldJudN-360
❑ 88WG1CarG-68
❑ 89EdgR.WG-16
Myers, Brad
❑ 88CapCodPPaLP-135
Myers, Chris
❑ 88HagSunS-13
❑ 89FreKeyS-19
❑ 90Bes-34
❑ 90Bow-250
❑ 90BowTif-250
❑ 90CMC-792
❑ 90HagSunB-18
❑ 90HagSunDGB-18
❑ 90HagSunP-1412
❑ 90HagSunS-19
❑ 91LinDriAAA-463
❑ 91RocRedWLD-463
❑ 91RocRedWP-1900
❑ 92HarSenF-459
Myers, Dave
❑ 77CedRapGT-15
❑ 83WauTimF-12
❑ 86ChaLooP-21
❑ 87ChaLooB-20
❑ 87SouLeaAJ-11
❑ 88VerMarP-952
❑ 91BelMarCB-27
❑ 91BelMarP-3683
❑ 92BelMarF-1461
❑ 93RivPilCLC-28
❑ 94RivPilCLC-29
❑ 95PorCitRTI-15
❑ 96TacRaiB-1
❑ 97TacRai-1
❑ 98TacRaiQ-1
Myers, Ed
❑ 84AlbA'sT-18
❑ 86VanCanP-18
Myers, Elmer
❑ 17ColE13-124
❑ 22E120-8
❑ 22W573-91
❑ 24Zee-14
Myers, Eric
❑ 90SouOreAB-27
❑ 90SouOreAP-3444
❑ 91MadMusC-12
❑ 91MadMusP-2129
Myers, Gene
❑ 98BluOriQ-22
Myers, George
❑ 87OldJudN-359
Myers, George I.
❑ 40WheM4-8A
❑ 40WheM4-8B
❑ 41WheM5-21
Myers, Glen
❑ 87VisOakP-2
Myers, Greg
❑ 86VenGulP-17
❑ 87SyrChiP-1931
❑ 87SyrChiT-10
❑ 88Don-624
❑ 88Fle-644
❑ 88FleGlo-644
❑ 88SyrChiC-18
❑ 88SyrChiP-821
❑ 89BluJayFS-23
❑ 90BluJayFS-22
❑ 90Bow-520
❑ 90BowTif-520
❑ 90Don-706
❑ 90Lea-527
❑ 90OPC-438
❑ 90Top-438
❑ 90TopTif-438
❑ 90UppDec-718
❑ 91BluJayFS-19
❑ 91BluJayFS-22
❑ 91BluJayS-12
❑ 91Don-494
❑ 91Fle-182
❑ 91Lea-256
❑ 91OPC-599
❑ 91PanFreS-346
❑ 91Sco-88
❑ 91Sco100RS-75
❑ 91StaClu-289
❑ 91Top-599A
❑ 91Top-599B
❑ 91TopDesS-599
❑ 91TopMic-599
❑ 91TopTif-599
❑ 91UltUpd-62
❑ 91UppDec-259
❑ 92Don-342
❑ 92Fle-338
❑ 92Lea-192
❑ 92LeaBlaG-192
❑ 92OPC-203
❑ 92Pin-324
❑ 92Sco-471
❑ 92StaClu-468
❑ 92Top-203
❑ 92TopGol-203
❑ 92TopGolW-203
❑ 92TopMic-203
❑ 92Ult-150
❑ 92UppDec-407
❑ 93AngMot-16
❑ 93AngPol-18
❑ 93AngStaCl-11
❑ 93BluJayD4-42
❑ 93Don-269
❑ 93FleFinE-185
❑ 93Lea-318
❑ 93OPC-241
❑ 93PacSpa-370
❑ 93Sco-468
❑ 93StaClu-490
❑ 93StaCluFDI-490
❑ 93StaCluMOP-490
❑ 93Top-637
❑ 93TopGol-637
❑ 93TopInaM-637
❑ 93TopInaR-637
❑ 93TopMic-637
❑ 93UppDec-789
❑ 93UppDecGold-789
❑ 94AngAdoF-4
❑ 94AngLAT-19
❑ 94AngMot-23
❑ 94ColC-461
❑ 94ColChoGS-461
❑ 94ColChoSS-461
❑ 94Don-198
❑ 94Fla-25
❑ 94Fle-65
❑ 94Lea-33
❑ 94Pac-85
❑ 94PanSti-40
❑ 94Pin-156
❑ 94PinArtP-156
❑ 94PinMusC-156
❑ 94Sco-121
❑ 94ScoGolR-121
❑ 94StaClu-468
❑ 94StaCluFDI-468
❑ 94StaCluGR-468
❑ 94StaCluMOP-468
❑ 94Top-171
❑ 94TopGol-171
❑ 94TopSpa-171
❑ 94UppDec-334
❑ 94UppDecED-334
❑ 95AngCHP-11
❑ 95AngMot-11
❑ 95Don-426
❑ 95DonPreP-426
❑ 95DonTopotO-38
❑ 95Sco-184
❑ 95ScoGolR-184
❑ 95ScoPlaTS-184
❑ 96Don-96
❑ 96DonPreP-96
❑ 96Fle-52
❑ 96FleTif-52
❑ 96LeaSigEA-135
❑ 96StaClu-206
❑ 96StaCluMOP-206
❑ 97Don-148
❑ 97DonGolPP-148
❑ 97DonSilPP-148
❑ 97Fle-152
❑ 97FleTif-152
❑ 97Pac-143
❑ 97PacLigB-143
❑ 97PacSil-143
❑ 97Pin-5
❑ 97PinArtP-PP5
❑ 97PinMusC-5
❑ 97PinPrePla-5
❑ 97Top-97
❑ 97Ult-91
❑ 97UltGolME-91
❑ 97UltPlaME-91
❑ 98PacOnl-645
❑ 98PacOnlR-645
❑ 98PacOnlWC-645
❑ 98PadMot-15
❑ 98UppDec-719
Myers, Hy (Henry)
❑ 10CouT21-50
❑ 10CouT21-51
❑ 10CouT21-308
❑ 10CouT21-309
❑ 11PinT-5-264
❑ 15SpoNewM-129
❑ 16SpoNewM-131
❑ 17ColE13-125
❑ 17HolBreD-72
❑ 21E121So1-69A
❑ 21E121So1-69B
❑ 21E121So8-66
❑ 21Exh-115
❑ 22AmeCarE122-50
❑ 22E120-145
❑ 22W575-89
❑ 90DodTar-564
Myers, Jason
❑ 94Bow-163
❑ 94Bow-352
❑ 94CliLumC-17
❑ 94CliLumF-1978
❑ 94Top-754
❑ 94TopGol-754
❑ 94TopSpa-754
❑ 95BurBeeTI-14
❑ 96SanJosGB-20
❑ 96WesOahCHWB-43
Myers, Jeff
❑ 92EveGiaC-12
❑ 92EveGiaF-1685
❑ 93CliGiaF-2487
Myers, Jim
❑ 87PocGiaTB-16
❑ 88PocGiaP-2076
❑ 89CliGiaP-886
❑ 90Bes-223
❑ 90ProAaA-146
❑ 90SanJosGB-15
❑ 90SanJosGCLC-49
❑ 90SanJosGP-2008
❑ 90SanJosGS-16
❑ 91LinDriAA-314
❑ 91ShrCapLD-314
❑ 91ShrCapP-1819
❑ 92PhoFirS-390
❑ 92SkyAAAF-178
❑ 93PhoFirF-1514
❑ 93ShrCapF-2756
❑ 94MemChiF-355
❑ 95RocRedWTI-26
❑ 96FleUpd-U6
❑ 96FleUpdTC-U6
❑ 96LeaSigEA-136
❑ 96RocRedWB-20
❑ 97Ult-8
❑ 97UltGolME-8
❑ 97UltPlaME-8
Myers, Jimmy
❑ 97NorTid-23
❑ 97NorTidB-23
Myers, L.E.
❑ 88KimN18-30
Myers, Linwood
❑ 39PlaBal-133
Myers, Matt
❑ 93BoiHawC-20
❑ 93BoiHawF-3913
Myers, Michael Stanley
❑ 88CapCodPPaLP-158
❑ 89CedRapRB-5
Myers, Mike (Michael R.)
❑ 87SpoIndP-24
❑ 88ChaRaiP-1199
❑ 89CedRapRP-918
❑ 89CedRapRS-14
❑ 90EveGiaB-9
❑ 90EveGiaP-3125
❑ 91Cla/Bes-323
❑ 91CliGiaP-831
❑ 91MidLeaAP-MWL5
❑ 93Bow-150
❑ 93MarlStaClu-22
❑ 93StaClu-437
❑ 93StaCluFDI-437
❑ 93StaCluMOP-437
❑ 94Bow-488
❑ 95ChaKniTI-19
❑ 96LeaSigEA-137
❑ 96TigHebN-12
❑ 97DelSho-22
❑ 97PacPriGotD-GD43
❑ 98DelShoM-5
❑ 98PacInvGems-48
❑ 98PacOnl-407
❑ 98PacOnlR-407
❑ 98PacOnlWC-407
❑ 99KinDis-21
❑ 99Pac-239
❑ 99PacPlaB-239
❑ 99PacRed-239
Myers, Randy
❑ 86MetColP-22
❑ 86MetTCM-9
❑ 86MetWorSC-20
❑ 86TidTidP-22
❑ 87Don-29
❑ 87FleUpd-85
❑ 87FleUpdG-85
❑ 87Lea-29
❑ 87MetColP-18
❑ 87SpoTeaP-2
❑ 87Top-213
❑ 87TopTif-213
❑ 88Don-620
❑ 88DonBasB-265
❑ 88DonTeaBM-620
❑ 88Fle-146
❑ 88FleGlo-146
❑ 88MetColP-8
❑ 88MetFanC-48
❑ 88MetKah-48
❑ 88Sco-336
❑ 88ScoGlo-336
❑ 88Top-412
❑ 88TopRoo-12
❑ 88TopTif-412
❑ 88ToyRoo-21
❑ 89Bow-374
❑ 89BowTif-374
❑ 89ClaTraP-197
❑ 89Don-336
❑ 89DonBasB-153
❑ 89Fle-46
❑ 89FleGlo-46
❑ 89MetColP-15
❑ 89MetKah-19
❑ 89OPC-104
❑ 89PanSti-135
❑ 89Sco-306
❑ 89ScoYouSI-41
❑ 89Top-610
❑ 89TopBasT-121
❑ 89TopDouM-9
❑ 89TopSti-97
❑ 89TopStiB-66
❑ 89TopTif-610
❑ 89TVSpoM-7
❑ 89UppDec-634
❑ 90Bow-47
❑ 90BowTif-47
❑ 90ClaBlu-107
❑ 90ClaYel-T18
❑ 90Don-336
❑ 90DonBesN-88
❑ 90Fle-213
❑ 90FleCan-213
❑ 90Lea-149
❑ 90OPC-105
❑ 90PanSti-307
❑ 90PubIntS-142
❑ 90RedFolSB-63
❑ 90RedKah-17
❑ 90Sco-351
❑ 90ScoRoo-16T
❑ 90Top-105
❑ 90TopSti-100
❑ 90TopTif-105
❑ 90TopTra-78T
❑ 90TopTraT-78T
❑ 90UppDec-581
❑ 90UppDec-797
❑ 90USPlaCA-WCO
❑ 91BasBesAotM-12
❑ 91Bow-666
❑ 91Cla2-T32
❑ 91ClaGam-114
❑ 91Don-209
❑ 91Fle-73
❑ 91Lea-504
❑ 91MajLeaCP-73
❑ 91MetWIZ-290
❑ 91MSAHoID-8
❑ 91OPC-780
❑ 91PanCanT1-82
❑ 91PanFreS-135
❑ 91PanSti-121
❑ 91RedKah-28
❑ 91RedPep-13
❑ 91Sco-501
❑ 91Sco-662
❑ 91Sco-885
❑ 91Sco100S-79
❑ 91StaClu-275
❑ 91Top-780A
❑ 91Top-780B
❑ 91TopDesS-780
❑ 91TopMic-780
❑ 91TopTif-780
❑ 91Ult-97
❑ 91UppDec-371
❑ 91Woo-23
❑ 92Bow-154
❑ 92Don-624
❑ 92Fle-413
❑ 92FleUpd-123
❑ 92OPC-24
❑ 92OPCPre-104
❑ 92PadCarJ-15
❑ 92PadMot-11
❑ 92PadSmo-21
❑ 92Sco-155
❑ 92ScoRoo-12T
❑ 92StaClu-805
❑ 92StaCluNC-805
❑ 92Top-24
❑ 92TopGol-24
❑ 92TopGolW-24
❑ 92TopMic-24
❑ 92TopTra-80T
❑ 92TopTraG-80T
❑ 92Ult-579
❑ 92UppDec-278
❑ 92UppDec-741
❑ 93Bow-32
❑ 93CubMar-18
❑ 93CubRol-1
❑ 93CubStaC-16
❑ 93DiaMar-80
❑ 93Fin-182
❑ 93FinRef-182
❑ 93Fla-19
❑ 93Fle-522
❑ 93FleFinE-10
❑ 93FunPac-83
❑ 93Lea-358
❑ 93MSABenSPD-9
❑ 93OPC-215
❑ 93OPCPre-33
❑ 93Pin-549
❑ 93Sco-607
❑ 93Sel-215
❑ 93SelRoo-25T
❑ 93SelStaL-71
❑ 93SP-87
❑ 93StaClu-44
❑ 93StaClu-667
❑ 93StaCluFDI-44
❑ 93StaCluFDI-667
❑ 93StaCluMOP-44
❑ 93StaCluMOP-667
❑ 93Top-302
❑ 93TopGol-302
❑ 93TopInaM-302

❑ 93TopInaR-302
❑ 93TopMic-302
❑ 93TopTra-65T
❑ 93TriPla-142
❑ 93Ult-317
❑ 93UppDec-283
❑ 93UppDec-483
❑ 93UppDec-667
❑ 93UppDecGold-283
❑ 93UppDecGold-483
❑ 93UppDecGold-667
❑ 94Bow-194
❑ 94BowBes-R58
❑ 94BowBesR-R58
❑ 94ColC-308
❑ 94ColC-460
❑ 94ColChoGS-308
❑ 94ColChoGS-460
❑ 94ColChoSS-308
❑ 94ColChoSS-460
❑ 94Don-399
❑ 94Fin-357
❑ 94FinRef-357
❑ 94Fla-139
❑ 94Fle-392
❑ 94FleExtB-221
❑ 94FUnPac-28
❑ 94Lea-396
❑ 94OPC-119
❑ 94Pac-105
❑ 94PanSti-16
❑ 94PanSti-155
❑ 94Pin-271
❑ 94PinArtP-271
❑ 94PinMusC-271
❑ 94RedFolMI-11
❑ 94Sco-534
❑ 94ScoGolR-534
❑ 94Sel-22
❑ 94SP-70
❑ 94SPDieC-70
❑ 94StaClu-162
❑ 94StaCluFDI-162
❑ 94StaCluGR-162
❑ 94StaCluMO-36
❑ 94StaCluMOP-162
❑ 94StaCluT-350
❑ 94StaCluTFDI-350
❑ 94Top-394
❑ 94Top-575
❑ 94TopBlaG-40
❑ 94TopGol-394
❑ 94TopGol-575
❑ 94TopSpa-394
❑ 94TopSpa-575
❑ 94TriPla-76
❑ 94Ult-462
❑ 94UltFir-6
❑ 94UppDec-257
❑ 94UppDecED-257
❑ 95Baz-14
❑ 95Bow-295
❑ 95ColCho-215
❑ 95ColChoGS-215
❑ 95ColChoSE-81
❑ 95ColChoSEGS-81
❑ 95ColChoSESS-81
❑ 95ColChoSS-215
❑ 95Don-429
❑ 95DonPreP-429
❑ 95DonTopotO-201
❑ 95Emo-112
❑ 95Fin-162
❑ 95FinRef-162
❑ 95Fla-114
❑ 95Fle-420
❑ 95FleAllS-24
❑ 95Lea-151
❑ 95LeaLim-101
❑ 95Pac-75
❑ 95PacPri-24
❑ 95Pin-255
❑ 95PinArtP-255
❑ 95PinMusC-255
❑ 95RedFol-13
❑ 95Sco-11
❑ 95ScoGolR-11
❑ 95ScoPlaTS-11
❑ 95SP-37
❑ 95SPCha-28
❑ 95SPChaDC-28
❑ 95SPSil-37
❑ 95StaClu-235
❑ 95StaCluFDI-235
❑ 95StaCluMOP-235
❑ 95StaCluSTWS-235
❑ 95StaCluVR-119
❑ 95StaCluVRMO-119
❑ 95Top-330
❑ 95TopCyb-180
❑ 95Ult-361
❑ 95UltGolM-361
❑ 95UppDec-66
❑ 95UppDecED-66
❑ 95UppDecEDG-66
❑ 95UppDecSE-259
❑ 95UppDecSEG-259
❑ 96BalOriP-24
❑ 96Baz-123
❑ 96Cir-6
❑ 96CirRav-6
❑ 96ColCho-9
❑ 96ColCho-85
❑ 96ColChoGS-9
❑ 96ColChoGS-85
❑ 96ColChoSS-9
❑ 96ColChoSS-85
❑ 96Don-99
❑ 96DonPreP-99
❑ 96EmoXL-7
❑ 96Fin-B204
❑ 96FinRef-B204
❑ 96Fla-10
❑ 96Fle-323
❑ 96FleTif-323
❑ 96FleUpd-U7
❑ 96FleUpdTC-U7
❑ 96MetUni-7
❑ 96MetUniP-7
❑ 96MLBPin-23
❑ 96OriFle-12
❑ 96Pac-19
❑ 96PanSti-43
❑ 96PanSti-119
❑ 96Sco-161
❑ 96ScoDugC-A94
❑ 96ScoDugCAP-A94
❑ 96SP-34
❑ 96StaClu-15
❑ 96StaClu-265
❑ 96StaCluEPB-15
❑ 96StaCluEPG-15
❑ 96StaCluEPS-15
❑ 96StaCluMO-30
❑ 96StaCluMOP-15
❑ 96StaCluMOP-265
❑ 96Top-198
❑ 96TopChr-66
❑ 96TopChrR-66
❑ 96TopGal-62
❑ 96TopGalPPI-62
❑ 96TopLas-126
❑ 96Ult-308
❑ 96UltGolM-308
❑ 96UppDec-481U
❑ 97BalOriP-24
❑ 97Cir-92
❑ 97CirRav-92
❑ 97ColCho-42
❑ 97ColChoT-BO6
❑ 97Don-207
❑ 97Don-299
❑ 97DonGolPP-207
❑ 97DonGolPP-299
❑ 97DonSilPP-207
❑ 97DonSilPP-299
❑ 97DonTea-37
❑ 97DonTeaSPE-37
❑ 97Fin-91
❑ 97FinRef-91
❑ 97Fle-11
❑ 97FleTif-11
❑ 97OriSco-10
❑ 97OriScoPl-10
❑ 97OriScoPr-10
❑ 97Pac-27
❑ 97PacLigB-27
❑ 97PacSil-27
❑ 97Sco-190
❑ 97ScoArtPWB-190
❑ 97ScoPreS-190
❑ 97ScoShoS-190
❑ 97ScoShoSAP-190
❑ 97StaClu-272
❑ 97StaCluMOP-272
❑ 97StrAll-47
❑ 97Top-133
❑ 97TopSta-80
❑ 97TopStaAM-80
❑ 97Ult-9
❑ 97UltGolME-9
❑ 97UltPlaME-9
❑ 97UppDec-18
❑ 98CirThu-103
❑ 98CirThuRav-103
❑ 98CirThuSupRav-103
❑ 98ColCho-260
❑ 98ColCho-524
❑ 98Fle-117
❑ 98Fle-496
❑ 98FleVin'-126
❑ 98FleVin'C-126
❑ 98OriSco-9
❑ 98OriScoP-9
❑ 98Pac-29
❑ 98PacOnl-769
❑ 98PacOnlR-769
❑ 98PacOnlWC-769
❑ 98PacPlaB-29
❑ 98PacRedT-29
❑ 98PacSil-29
❑ 98PinPlu-20
❑ 98Sco-153
❑ 98ScoSS-PP160
❑ 98ScoSSAP-PP160
❑ 98SP Aut-197
❑ 98SPxFin-329
❑ 98SPxFinR-329
❑ 98SPxFinS-329
❑ 98Ult-444
❑ 98UltGolM-444
❑ 98UltMas-444
❑ 98UltPlaM-444
❑ 98UppDec-37
❑ 98UppDec-744
❑ 98UppDec10AP-13
❑ 98UppDec1APR-13
❑ 99UppDec10AT-X22
❑ 99UppDec10ATD-X22
❑ 99UppDec10ATHR-X22
❑ 99UppDec10ATT-X22

Myers, Richard
❑ 52MotCoo-58
❑ 53MotCoo-15

Myers, Rob
❑ 97HelBreB-23
❑ 98HelBreM-25

Myers, Rod (Rodney)
❑ 91AppFoxP-1713
❑ 92LetMouSP-23
❑ 93MidLeaAGF-19
❑ 93RocRoyC-19
❑ 93RocRoyF-714
❑ 94WilBluRC-18
❑ 94WilBluRF-297
❑ 94WilBluRF-314
❑ 95OmaRoyTI-24
❑ 95WicWraTI-7
❑ 96FleUpd-U115
❑ 96FleUpdTC-U115
❑ 96LeaSigA-165
❑ 96LeaSigAG-165
❑ 96LeaSigAS-165
❑ 96Ult-455
❑ 96UltGolM-455
❑ 97Bow-348
❑ 97BowInt-348
❑ 97ColCho-128
❑ 97NewPin-166
❑ 97NewPinAP-166
❑ 97NewPinMC-166
❑ 97NewPinPP-166
❑ 97PinCer-126
❑ 97PinCerMBla-126
❑ 97PinCerMBlu-126
❑ 97PinCerMG-126
❑ 97PinCerMR-126
❑ 97PinCerR-126
❑ 97PinTotCPB-126
❑ 97PinTotCPG-126
❑ 97PinTotCPR-126
❑ 97Sco-479
❑ 97ScoArtPWB-479
❑ 97ScoResC-479
❑ 97ScoShoS-479
❑ 97ScoShoSAP-479
❑ 97Sel-114
❑ 97SelArtP-114
❑ 97SelCom-114
❑ 97SelRegG-114
❑ 97UppDec-277
❑ 98Bes-34
❑ 98SkyDugA-99
❑ 98SkyDugAIA-99
❑ 98Ult-420
❑ 98UltGolM-420
❑ 98UltMas-420
❑ 98UltPlaM-420
❑ 98UltRoctS-13

Myers, Rodney (Roderick)
❑ 93RocRoyC-21
❑ 93RocRoyF-729
❑ 94WilBluRC-17
❑ 97IowCub-19
❑ 98CirThu-30
❑ 98CirThuRav-30
❑ 98CirThuSupRav-30
❑ 98IowCubQ-18

Myers, Ron
❑ 89AncBucTI-24

Myers, Taylor
❑ 97LanLugTS-19
❑ 97MidLeaTP-14
❑ 98LanLugQ-10

Myers, Thomas
❑ 92MadMusC-21
❑ 92MadMusF-1231
❑ 92RenSilSCLC-50
❑ 93ModA'sC-14
❑ 93ModA'sF-796
❑ 94FreKeyF-2611

Myers, Tootie
❑ 98VerExpO-26

Myers, William
❑ 35GouPuzR-8D
❑ 35GouPuzR-9D
❑ 38RedOraW-21
❑ 39OrcPhoAP-17
❑ 39PlaBal-38
❑ 39RedTeal-17
❑ 40PlaBal-80
❑ 41CubTeal-14
❑ 41HarHarW-18
❑ 76RedParC-18
❑ 77CinRedT-33

Myette, Aaron
❑ 97AppLeaTPB-26
❑ 97BriWhiSB-8
❑ 98HicCraUO-23
❑ 99Bow-315
❑ 99BowGol-315
❑ 99BowInt-315

Myles, Rick
❑ 81CedRapRT-4
❑ 82LynMetT-17
❑ 84JacMetT-2

Myllykangas, Lauri
❑ 36GouWidPPR-D22
❑ 36WorWidGV-82

Myres, Doug
❑ 88St.LucMS-17

Myrick, Robert
❑ 77MetDaiPA-18
❑ 77Top-627
❑ 78MetDaiPA-19
❑ 78TidTidT-15
❑ 78Top-676
❑ 79TucTorT-21
❑ 80VenLeaS-163
❑ 91MetWIZ-291

Myrow, John
❑ 94CenValRC-13
❑ 94CenValRF-3216
❑ 95NewHavRTI-8
❑ 96NewHavRB-18

Mysel, David
❑ 92FroRowDP-32
❑ 92FroRowDPG-32
❑ 92FroRowDPS-32
❑ 92NiaFalRC-12
❑ 92NiaFalRF-3321
❑ 93FayGenC-17
❑ 93FayGenF-127
❑ 93StaCluM-48
❑ 94Bow-537
❑ 94TreThuF-2119
❑ 94UppDecML-188
❑ 95SigRooOJ-25
❑ 95SigRooOJP-25
❑ 95SigRooOJS-25
❑ 95SigRooOJSS-25

Na'te, Nikko (Jeff)
❑ 90BelBreB-21
❑ 90BelBreS-26

Na, Jim
❑ 98VerExpO-29

Nabekawa, Tom
❑ 87SanJosBP-13

Naber, Bob
❑ 83CliGiaF-13

Nabholz, Chris
❑ 89RocExpLC-19
❑ 90Bes-300
❑ 90FleUpd-30
❑ 90JacExpB-21
❑ 90JacExpP-1371
❑ 90ProAaA-37
❑ 91Bow-459
❑ 91ClaGam-74
❑ 91Don-667
❑ 91ExpPos-15
❑ 91Fle-240
❑ 91Lea-416
❑ 91OPC-197
❑ 91OPCPre-87
❑ 91Sco-804
❑ 91StaClu-326
❑ 91Top-197
❑ 91TopDeb90-112
❑ 91TopDesS-197
❑ 91TopMic-197
❑ 91TopRoo-21
❑ 91TopTif-197
❑ 91ToyRoo-21
❑ 91UppDec-538
❑ 92Don-170
❑ 92ExpDonD-13
❑ 92ExpPos-23
❑ 92Fle-487
❑ 92Lea-327
❑ 92LeaBlaG-327
❑ 92OPC-32
❑ 92OPCPre-26
❑ 92Pin-360
❑ 92Sco-140
❑ 92StaClu-318
❑ 92Top-32
❑ 92TopGol-32
❑ 92TopGolW-32
❑ 92TopMic-32
❑ 92Ult-521
❑ 92UppDec-579
❑ 93Don-114
❑ 93ExpPosN-17
❑ 93Fle-78
❑ 93HumDumC-40
❑ 93Lea-73
❑ 93OPC-315
❑ 93PacSpa-536
❑ 93Pin-373
❑ 93Sco-477
❑ 93StaClu-469
❑ 93StaCluFDI-469
❑ 93StaCluMOP-469
❑ 93Top-278
❑ 93TopGol-278
❑ 93TopInaM-278
❑ 93TopInaR-278
❑ 93TopMic-278
❑ 93Ult-69
❑ 93UppDec-404
❑ 93UppDecGold-404
❑ 94ColC-527
❑ 94ColChoGS-527
❑ 94ColChoSS-527
❑ 94Don-589
❑ 94Fin-420
❑ 94FinRef-420
❑ 94Fle-546
❑ 94Pin-60
❑ 94PinArtP-60
❑ 94PinMusC-60
❑ 94StaClu-31
❑ 94StaClu-619
❑ 94StaCluFDI-31
❑ 94StaCluFDI-619
❑ 94StaCluGR-31
❑ 94StaCluGR-619
❑ 94StaCluMOP-31
❑ 94StaCluMOP-619
❑ 94Top-656
❑ 94TopGol-656
❑ 94TopSpa-656
❑ 94Ult-348
❑ 95Fle-34

Naccarato, Stan
❑ 81TacTigT-30
❑ 82TacTigT-22
❑ 83TacTigT-19
❑ 88TacTigP-620
❑ 89TacTigP-1566

Nace, Todd
❑ 88MisStaB-23
❑ 91PitMetC-5
❑ 91PitMetP-3435

Nadeau, Michael
❑ 94BluOriC-15
❑ 94BluOriF-3569

Nader, John
❑ 93OneYanC-30

Naehring, Mark
❑ 78KnoKnoST-15
❑ 79KnoKnoST-1

Naehring, Tim
❑ 88ElmPioC-17
❑ 89LynRedSS-15
❑ 90CMC-268
❑ 90FleUpd-73
❑ 90PawRedSC-17
❑ 90PawRedSDD-16
❑ 90PawRedSP-469
❑ 90ProAAAF-441
❑ 90ScoRoo-87T
❑ 90TopTra-79T
❑ 90TopTraT-79T
❑ 90TopTVRS-54
❑ 90TriAAAC-30
❑ 90TriAllGP-AAA16
❑ 91Bow-127
❑ 91Cla1-T20
❑ 91Don-367
❑ 91Fle-105
❑ 91Lea-150
❑ 91OPC-702
❑ 91OPCPre-88
❑ 91RedSoxP-13
❑ 91RedSoxP-21
❑ 91Sco-356
❑ 91Sco100RS-77
❑ 91ScoAllF-5
❑ 91ScoRoo-30
❑ 91StaClu-83
❑ 91Stu-16
❑ 91Top-702
❑ 91TopDeb90-113
❑ 91TopDesS-702
❑ 91TopMic-702
❑ 91TopRoo-22
❑ 91TopTif-702
❑ 91ToyRoo-22
❑ 91Ult-36
❑ 91UppDec-527
❑ 92Bow-416
❑ 92Don-742
❑ 92Lea-235
❑ 92LeaBlaG-235
❑ 92OPC-758
❑ 92OPCPre-37
❑ 92Pin-242
❑ 92PinTea2-15
❑ 92RedSoxDD-20
❑ 92Sco-259
❑ 92StaClu-854
❑ 92Stu-134
❑ 92Top-758
❑ 92TopGol-758
❑ 92TopGolW-758
❑ 92TopMic-758
❑ 92Ult-317
❑ 92UppDec-523
❑ 93Don-399
❑ 93OPC-304
❑ 93Pin-382
❑ 93RedSoxP-23
❑ 93RedSoxWHP-19
❑ 93Sco-452
❑ 93Top-24
❑ 93TopGol-24
❑ 93TopInaM-24
❑ 93TopInaR-24
❑ 93TopMic-24
❑ 93Toy-50
❑ 93Ult-153
❑ 93UppDec-583
❑ 93UppDecGold-583
❑ 94ColC-452
❑ 94ColChoGS-452
❑ 94ColChoSS-452
❑ 94Fla-264
❑ 94FleExtB-21
❑ 94FleUpd-13
❑ 94Lea-201
❑ 94Pac-60
❑ 94Pin-65
❑ 94PinArtP-65
❑ 94PinMusC-65
❑ 94Sco-429
❑ 94ScoGolR-429
❑ 94Sel-151
❑ 94StaClu-131
❑ 94StaCluFDI-131
❑ 94StaCluGR-131
❑ 94StaCluMOP-131
❑ 94Top-474
❑ 94TopGol-474

❑ 94TopSpa-474
❑ 94Ult-315
❑ 94UppDec-337
❑ 94UppDecED-337
❑ 95ColCho-418
❑ 95ColChoGS-418
❑ 95ColChoSS-418
❑ 95Don-188
❑ 95DonPreP-188
❑ 95DonTopotO-23
❑ 95Emo-14
❑ 95Fin-184
❑ 95FinRef-184
❑ 95Fla-229
❑ 95Fle-35
❑ 95Lea-186
❑ 95LeaLim-125
❑ 95Pac-42
❑ 95Pin-105
❑ 95PinArtP-105
❑ 95PinMusC-105
❑ 95Sco-355
❑ 95ScoGolR-355
❑ 95ScoPlaTS-355
❑ 95SP-124
❑ 95SPCha-123
❑ 95SPChaDC-123
❑ 95SPSil-124
❑ 95StaClu-395
❑ 95StaCluMOP-395
❑ 95StaCluSTDW-RS395
❑ 95StaCluSTWS-395
❑ 95Sum-138
❑ 95SumNthD-138
❑ 95Top-329
❑ 95TopCyb-179
❑ 95Ult-12
❑ 95UltGolM-12
❑ 95UppDec-398
❑ 95UppDecED-398
❑ 95UppDecEDG-398
❑ 95Zen-101
❑ 96Cir-12
❑ 96CirRav-12
❑ 96ColCho-66
❑ 96ColChoGS-66
❑ 96ColChoSS-66
❑ 96Don-217
❑ 96DonPreP-217
❑ 96EmoXL-16
❑ 96Fin-B19
❑ 96FinRef-B19
❑ 96Fla-22
❑ 96Fle-31
❑ 96FleRedS-10
❑ 96FleTif-31
❑ 96Lea-7
❑ 96LeaPrePB-7
❑ 96LeaPrePG-7
❑ 96LeaPrePS-7
❑ 96MetUni-17
❑ 96MetUniP-17
❑ 96Pac-249
❑ 96PanSti-142
❑ 96Pin-100
❑ 96Sco-90
❑ 96ScoDugC-A70
❑ 96ScoDugCAP-A70
❑ 96SP-37
❑ 96StaClu-144
❑ 96StaCluEPB-144
❑ 96StaCluEPG-144
❑ 96StaCluEPS-144
❑ 96StaCluMOP-144
❑ 96Top-63
❑ 96Ult-19
❑ 96UltGolM-19
❑ 96UppDec-21
❑ 97Cir-127
❑ 97CirRav-127
❑ 97ColCho-279
❑ 97Don-179
❑ 97DonGolPP-179
❑ 97DonSilPP-179
❑ 97DonTea-50
❑ 97DonTeaSPE-50
❑ 97Fin-267
❑ 97FinRef-267
❑ 97FlaShoLC-59
❑ 97FlaShoLeg0-59
❑ 97FlaShoLeg1-59
❑ 97FlaShoM-A59
❑ 97FlaShoM-B59
❑ 97FlaShoM-C59
❑ 97FlaShoR0-59
❑ 97FlaShoR1-59
❑ 97FlaShoR2-59
❑ 97Fle-27
❑ 97FleTif-27
❑ 97Lea-39
❑ 97LeaFraM-39
❑ 97LeaFraMDC-39
❑ 97MetUni-23
❑ 97NewPin-56
❑ 97NewPinAP-56
❑ 97NewPinMC-56
❑ 97NewPinPP-56
❑ 97Pac-43
❑ 97PacLigB-43
❑ 97PacSil-43
❑ 97PinX-PSfF-43
❑ 97PinX-PSfFU-43
❑ 97RedSoxS-14
❑ 97RedSoxSPl-14
❑ 97RedSoxSPr-14
❑ 97Sco-196
❑ 97ScoArtPWB-196
❑ 97ScoPreS-196
❑ 97ScoShoS-196
❑ 97ScoShoSAP-196
❑ 97SP-38
❑ 97Spolll-140
❑ 97SpollIEE-140
❑ 97StaClu-269
❑ 97StaCluMOP-269
❑ 97Top-230
❑ 97Ult-16
❑ 97UltGolME-16
❑ 97UltPlaME-16
❑ 97UppDec-27
❑ 98ColCho-323
❑ 98Fin-247
❑ 98FinNo--247
❑ 98FinNo-R-247
❑ 98FinRef-247
❑ 98KinDis-8
❑ 98MetUni-123
❑ 98MetUniPMG-123
❑ 98Pac-45
❑ 98PacPar-23
❑ 98PacParC-23
❑ 98PacParG-23
❑ 98PacParHS-23
❑ 98PacParPB-23
❑ 98PacParR-23
❑ 98PacPlaB-45
❑ 98PacRedT-45
❑ 98PacSil-45
❑ 98PinSna-BRS1
❑ 98PinSna-BRS12
❑ 98RedSoxS-8
❑ 98RedSoxSP-8
❑ 98Sco-133
❑ 98ScoRT-107
❑ 98ScoSS-PP56
❑ 98ScoSSAP-PP56
❑ 98Spolll-92
❑ 98SpollIEE-92
❑ 98SpollIFE-92
❑ 98SPxFin-66
❑ 98SPxFinR-66
❑ 98SPxFinS-66
❑ 98StaCluFDI-98
❑ 98StaClul-98
❑ 98StaCluOneK-98
❑ 98StaCluPP-98
❑ 98Top-205
❑ 98TopChr-205
❑ 98TopChrR-205
❑ 98TopDevR-205
❑ 98TopDia-205
❑ 98TopMiniC-205
❑ 98TopOpeD-102
❑ 98Ult-196
❑ 98UltGolM-196
❑ 98UltMas-196
❑ 98UltPlaM-196
❑ 98UppDec-44
❑ 98UppDecSF-26

Naff, Todd
❑ 97IdaFalBTI-11
❑ 98CliLumG-14

Nagano, Cary
❑ 87HawRai-4

Nagano, Tetsuya
❑ 90IBAWorA-28

Nagasaki, Keiichi
❑ 79TCMJapPB-57

Nagashima, Kazushige
❑ 92VerBeaDC-28

Nagashima, Shigeo
❑ 79TCMJapPB-55

Nagel, Bill (William T.)
❑ 41DouPlaR-49

Nagelson, Rusty (Russell C.)
❑ 70OPC-7
❑ 70Top-7
❑ 71OPC-708
❑ 71Top-708

Nagle, Mike
❑ 77St.PetCT-NNO

Nagle, Tom (Thomas E.)
❑ 87OldJudN-361

Nagle, Walter
❑ 09ObaT21-5
❑ 09ObaT21-89
❑ 12HomRunKE-13
❑ 12Zee-17

Nago, Garrett
❑ 83ElPasDT-12
❑ 84ElPasDT-25
❑ 85VanCanC-223
❑ 86ElPasDP-17
❑ 87ElPasDP-5
❑ 88IndIndC-22
❑ 88IndIndP-515
❑ 89ColMudB-3
❑ 89ColMudP-146
❑ 89ColMudS-18

Nagurski, Bronko
❑ 74NewYorNTDiS-35

Nagy, Charles
❑ 88TopTra-74T
❑ 88TopTraT-74T
❑ 89Bow-73
❑ 89BowTif-73
❑ 89KinIndS-14
❑ 89Sta-77
❑ 89Sta-178
❑ 89TopBig-217
❑ 90Bes-244
❑ 90Bes-323
❑ 90CanIndB-27
❑ 90CanIndP-1292
❑ 90CanIndS-14
❑ 90CMC-833
❑ 90EasLeaAP-EL37
❑ 90ProAaA-9
❑ 90Sco-611
❑ 91Bow-65
❑ 91Don-592
❑ 91DonRoo-18
❑ 91FleUpd-20
❑ 91IndFanC-20
❑ 91OPC-466
❑ 91Sco-75
❑ 91Sco100RS-47
❑ 91ScoAllF-8
❑ 91StaClu-472
❑ 91Top-466
❑ 91TopDeb90-114
❑ 91TopDesS-466
❑ 91TopMic-466
❑ 91TopTif-466
❑ 91UltUpd-20
❑ 91UppDec-19
❑ 92Bow-203
❑ 92Bow-566
❑ 92ClaGam-138
❑ 92Don-315
❑ 92Fle-118
❑ 92Hig5-45
❑ 92IndFanC-18
❑ 92Lea-115
❑ 92LeaBlaG-115
❑ 92OPC-299
❑ 92OPCPre-138
❑ 92Pin-383
❑ 92Pin-609
❑ 92PinTea2-19
❑ 92Sco-330
❑ 92Sco100RS-26
❑ 92ScoImpP-19
❑ 92StaClu-389
❑ 92Top-299
❑ 92TopDaiQTU-12
❑ 92TopGol-299
❑ 92TopGolW-299
❑ 92TopMic-299
❑ 92Ult-351
❑ 92UppDec-178
❑ 92UppDecTMH-37
❑ 93Bow-149
❑ 93Don-141
❑ 93DurPowP2-11
❑ 93Fin-58
❑ 93FinRef-58
❑ 93Fle-219
❑ 93FleFruotL-49
❑ 93FunPac-110
❑ 93IndWUA-22
❑ 93Lea-171
❑ 93OPC-278
❑ 93PacSpa-415
❑ 93PanSti-46
❑ 93Pin-65
❑ 93PinTea2-22
❑ 93RedFolS-70
❑ 93Sco-29
❑ 93Sco-538
❑ 93ScoGolDT-7
❑ 93Sel-70
❑ 93SelAce-12
❑ 93SelStaL-63
❑ 93SP-125
❑ 93StaClu-551
❑ 93StaCluFDI-551
❑ 93StaCluM-88
❑ 93StaCluMOP-551
❑ 93Stu-203
❑ 93Top-730
❑ 93TopComotH-6
❑ 93TopGol-730
❑ 93TopInaM-730
❑ 93TopInaR-730
❑ 93TopMic-730
❑ 93TriPla-49
❑ 93Ult-189
❑ 93UppDec-243
❑ 93UppDecGold-243
❑ 94Bow-251
❑ 94ColC-578
❑ 94ColChoGS-578
❑ 94ColChoSS-578
❑ 94Don-239
❑ 94Fin-104
❑ 94FinRef-104
❑ 94Fla-42
❑ 94Fle-115
❑ 94FleExtB-65
❑ 94Lea-297
❑ 94OPC-254
❑ 94Pac-179
❑ 94PanSti-59
❑ 94Pin-385
❑ 94PinArtP-385
❑ 94PinMusC-385
❑ 94Sco-333
❑ 94ScoGolR-333
❑ 94Sel-264
❑ 94Spo-130
❑ 94StaClu-478
❑ 94StaCluFDI-478
❑ 94StaCluGR-478
❑ 94StaCluMOP-478
❑ 94Top-330
❑ 94TopGol-330
❑ 94TopSpa-330
❑ 94TriPla-118
❑ 94Ult-349
❑ 94UppDec-394
❑ 94UppDecED-394
❑ 95ColCho-277
❑ 95ColChoGS-277
❑ 95ColChoSS-277
❑ 95Don-134
❑ 95DonPreP-134
❑ 95DonTopotO-63
❑ 95Fin-211
❑ 95FinRef-211
❑ 95Fla-34
❑ 95Fle-142
❑ 95Lea-311
❑ 95Pac-126
❑ 95Pin-89
❑ 95PinArtP-89
❑ 95PinMusC-89
❑ 95Sco-371
❑ 95ScoGolR-371
❑ 95ScoPlaTS-371
❑ 95Sel-64
❑ 95SelArtP-64
❑ 95StaClu-14
❑ 95StaCluFDI-14
❑ 95StaCluMOP-14
❑ 95StaCluSTWS-14
❑ 95StaCluVR-9
❑ 95StaCluVRMO-9
❑ 95Top-76
❑ 95TopCyb-53
❑ 95TopEmb-67
❑ 95TopEmbGI-67
❑ 95Ult-281
❑ 95UltGolM-281
❑ 95UppDec-91
❑ 95UppDecED-91
❑ 95UppDecEDG-91
❑ 96Cir-36
❑ 96CirRav-36
❑ 96ColCho-531
❑ 96ColChoGS-531
❑ 96ColChoSS-531
❑ 96Don-182
❑ 96DonPreP-182
❑ 96EmoXL-54
❑ 96Fla-72
❑ 96Fle-93
❑ 96FleTif-93
❑ 96IndFle-10
❑ 96LeaPre-102
❑ 96LeaPreP-102
❑ 96LeaSig-91
❑ 96LeaSigPPG-91
❑ 96LeaSigPPP-91
❑ 96MetUni-51
❑ 96MetUniP-51
❑ 96Pin-18
❑ 96ProSta-60
❑ 96SchDis-4
❑ 96Sco-350
❑ 96ScoDugC-B75
❑ 96ScoDugCAP-B75
❑ 96Top-326
❑ 96Ult-343
❑ 96UltGolM-343
❑ 96UppDec-317
❑ 96UppDecA-13
❑ 97Cir-357
❑ 97CirRav-357
❑ 97ColCho-89
❑ 97ColChoT-CI5
❑ 97Don-242
❑ 97DonEli-133
❑ 97DonEliGS-133
❑ 97DonGolPP-242
❑ 97DonLim-43
❑ 97DonLimE-43
❑ 97DonLimENG-43
❑ 97DonPre-11
❑ 97DonPreCttC-11
❑ 97DonSilPP-242
❑ 97DonTea-82
❑ 97DonTeaSPE-82
❑ 97Fin-7
❑ 97FinRef-7
❑ 97FlaShoLC-141
❑ 97FlaShoLeg0-141
❑ 97FlaShoLeg1-141
❑ 97FlaShoM-A141
❑ 97FlaShoM-B141
❑ 97FlaShoM-C141
❑ 97FlaShoR0-141
❑ 97FlaShoR1-141
❑ 97FlaShoR2-141
❑ 97Fle-84
❑ 97FleTif-84
❑ 97IndSco-10
❑ 97IndScoPl-10
❑ 97IndScoPr-10
❑ 97IndScoU-10
❑ 97IndScoUTC-10
❑ 97Lea-56
❑ 97LeaFraM-56
❑ 97LeaFraMDC-56
❑ 97MetUni-85
❑ 97NewPin-136
❑ 97NewPinAP-136
❑ 97NewPinMC-136
❑ 97NewPinPP-136
❑ 97Pac-77
❑ 97PacLigB-77
❑ 97PacSil-77
❑ 97Pin-3
❑ 97PinArtP-PP3
❑ 97PinCar-20
❑ 97PinCer-29
❑ 97PinCerMBla-29
❑ 97PinCerMBlu-29
❑ 97PinCerMG-29
❑ 97PinCerMR-29
❑ 97PinCerR-29
❑ 97PinIns-105
❑ 97PinInsCE-105
❑ 97PinInsDE-105
❑ 97PinMusC-3
❑ 97PinPrePla-3
❑ 97PinTotCPB-29
❑ 97PinTotCPG-29
❑ 97PinTotCPR-29
❑ 97PinX-P-41
❑ 97PinX-PMoS-41
❑ 97Sco-177
❑ 97Sco-526
❑ 97ScoArtPWB-177
❑ 97ScoArtPWB-526
❑ 97ScoPreS-177
❑ 97ScoResC-526
❑ 97ScoShoS-177
❑ 97ScoShoS-526
❑ 97ScoShoSAP-177
❑ 97ScoShoSAP-526
❑ 97Sel-85
❑ 97SelArtP-85
❑ 97SelCom-85
❑ 97SelRegG-85
❑ 97SP-59
❑ 97Spolll-49
❑ 97SpollIEE-49
❑ 97StaClu-6
❑ 97StaCluMat-6
❑ 97StaCluMOP-6
❑ 97Stu-136
❑ 97StuPrePG-136
❑ 97StuPrePS-136
❑ 97Top-88
❑ 97TopChr-34
❑ 97TopChrR-34
❑ 97TopSta-81
❑ 97TopStaAM-81
❑ 97Ult-53
❑ 97UltGolME-53
❑ 97UltPlaME-53
❑ 97UppDec-49
❑ 98CirThu-263
❑ 98CirThuRav-263
❑ 98CirThuSupRav-263
❑ 98ColCho-357
❑ 98Don-190
❑ 98DonGolPP-190
❑ 98DonSilPP-190
❑ 98Fin-77
❑ 98FinNo--77
❑ 98FinNo-R-77
❑ 98FinRef-77
❑ 98Fle-292
❑ 98IndSco-7
❑ 98IndScoP-7
❑ 98MetUni-104
❑ 98MetUniPMG-104
❑ 98Pac-76
❑ 98PacOme-73
❑ 98PacOmeR-73
❑ 98PacOnl-226
❑ 98PacOnlR-226
❑ 98PacOnlWC-226
❑ 98PacPar-39
❑ 98PacParC-39
❑ 98PacParG-39
❑ 98PacParHS-39
❑ 98PacParPB-39
❑ 98PacParR-39
❑ 98PacPlaB-76
❑ 98PacRedT-76
❑ 98PacSil-76
❑ 98Pin-119
❑ 98PinPreP-119
❑ 98PinSna-Cl17
❑ 98Sco-79
❑ 98ScoRT-54
❑ 98ScoSS-PP36
❑ 98ScoSSAP-PP36
❑ 98Spolll-93
❑ 98SpollIEE-93
❑ 98SpollIFE-93
❑ 98SpollITaN-116
❑ 98SpollITaNEE-116
❑ 98SPxFin-267
❑ 98SPxFinR-267
❑ 98SPxFinS-267
❑ 98StaCluFDI-160
❑ 98StaClul-160
❑ 98StaCluOneK-160
❑ 98StaCluPP-160
❑ 98Top-85
❑ 98TopChr-85
❑ 98TopChrR-85
❑ 98TopDevR-85
❑ 98TopDia-85
❑ 98TopGal-64
❑ 98TopGalGP-64
❑ 98TopGalOPP-64
❑ 98TopGalPPI-64

❑ 98TopGalPPIA-64
❑ 98TopMiniC-85
❑ 98TopOpeD-41
❑ 98TopSta-45
❑ 98TopStaB-45
❑ 98TopStaG-45
❑ 98TopStaGR-45
❑ 98TopStaS-45
❑ 98Ult-102
❑ 98UltGolM-102
❑ 98UltMas-102
❑ 98UltPlaM-102
❑ 98UppDec-347
❑ 99Fle-488
❑ 99FleBri-82
❑ 99FleBri2G-82
❑ 99FleBriBlu-82
❑ 99FleBriGol-82
❑ 99FleSta9-488
❑ 99FleWarT-488
❑ 99Pac-132
❑ 99PacPlaB-132
❑ 99PacRed-132
❑ 99StaClu-289
❑ 99StaCluFDI-289
❑ 99StaCluOoaK-289
❑ 99StaCluPP-289
❑ 99Top-389
❑ 99TopChr-389
❑ 99TopChrR-389
❑ 99TopMVPP-389
❑ 99UppDec-85
❑ 99UppDec-356
❑ 99UppDecEL1-85
❑ 99UppDecEL1-356
❑ 99UppDecEL2-85
❑ 99UppDecEL2-356

Nagy, Jeff
❑ 92BilMusF-3371
❑ 92BilMusSP-25
❑ 93WesVirWC-20
❑ 93WesVirWF-2879

Nagy, Mike
❑ 70OPC-39
❑ 70RedSoxCPPC-9
❑ 70Top-39
❑ 71MLBOffS-325
❑ 71OPC-363
❑ 71Top-363
❑ 72OPC-488
❑ 72Top-488
❑ 81RedSoxBG2S-98

Nagy, Steve
❑ 49SomandK-7
❑ 54SeaPop-19

Nahem, Sam
❑ 41CarW75-20
❑ 77TCMTheWY-19
❑ 90DodTar-565

Nahorodny, Bill (William G.)
❑ 76OklCit8TI-19
❑ 78SSP270-156
❑ 78Top-702
❑ 79Top-169
❑ 80OPC-286
❑ 80Top-552
❑ 81BraPol-15
❑ 81Fle-254
❑ 81Top-296
❑ 82ChaChaT-11
❑ 82Ind-26
❑ 83Fle-416
❑ 83Top-616
❑ 84SalLakCGC-181
❑ 85PorBeaC-39

Nail, Charlie
❑ 82BirBarT-21
❑ 83EvaTriT-6
❑ 84WicAerRD-6

Naismith, James
❑ 87SpoCubG-1

Najera, Noe
❑ 92WatIndC-12
❑ 92WatIndF-3230
❑ 94WatIndC-21
❑ 94WatIndF-3934
❑ 96CarLeaA1B-6
❑ 96CarLeaA2B-6
❑ 96KenIndB-19
❑ 97AkrAer-19

Naka, Toshio
❑ 79TCMJapPB-79

Nakabayashi, Debbie
❑ 91HawWomS-9
❑ 91HawWomS-10

Nakagawa, Shinya
❑ 93BriTigF-3646

Nakamoto, Brian
❑ 75LynRanT-17
❑ 76SanAntBTI-15

Nakamura, Hector
❑ 87SanJosBP-2

Nakamura, Katsuhiro
❑ 79TCMJapPB-84

Nakamura, Michael
❑ 98ForWayW!-22

Nakanose, Yukiyasu
❑ 96HilStaHWB-15

Nakashima, Toni
❑ 95GreFalDTI-6
❑ 96SavSanB-22

Nakashima, Yoshi
❑ 86SanJosBP-14

Nakatsuka, Masayuki
❑ 79TCMJapPB-6

Naktenis, Pete
❑ 77CinRedT-27

Nalepka, Keith
❑ 91GulCoaRSP-3
❑ 92ButCopKSP-27

Nalley, Jerry
❑ 81BatTroT-14
❑ 82WatIndF-6
❑ 82WatIndT-21

Nallin, Dick
❑ 94ConTSN-1199
❑ 94ConTSNB-1199

Nalls, Gary
❑ 86QuaCitAP-25
❑ 87PalSprP-32
❑ 88PalSprACLC-106
❑ 88PalSprAP-1454
❑ 89CalLeaA-36
❑ 89RenSilSCLC-250
❑ 90RenSilSCLC-274

Nalls, Kevin
❑ 92IdaFalGF-3518
❑ 92IdaFalGSP-3

Nance, Clyde
❑ 28Zee-161
❑ 29Zee-52

Nandin, Bob
❑ 81BirBarT-14
❑ 83SyrChiT-18
❑ 84SyrChiT-13
❑ 86ElPasDP-18

Nanni, Tito
❑ 80SanJosMJitB-15
❑ 81LynSaiT-23
❑ 82LynSaiT-15
❑ 83SalLakCGT-13
❑ 84SalLakCGC-174
❑ 85MidAngT-1

Nannini, Mike
❑ 99Bow-84
❑ 99BowBes-163
❑ 99BowBesAR-163
❑ 99BowBesR-163
❑ 99BowChr-84
❑ 99BowChrG-84
❑ 99BowChrGR-84
❑ 99BowChrI-84
❑ 99BowChrIR-84
❑ 99BowChrR-84
❑ 99BowGol-84
❑ 99BowInt-84
❑ 99StaClu-157
❑ 99StaCluFDI-157
❑ 99StaCluOoaK-157
❑ 99StaCluPP-157
❑ 99Top-441
❑ 99TopChr-441
❑ 99TopChrR-441
❑ 99TopMVPP-441

Nantel, Pierre
❑ 52LavPro-97

Nape, John
❑ 94LetMouF-3877
❑ 94LetMouSP-15

Napier, Jim
❑ 61UniOil-SD7
❑ 79QuaCitCT-22
❑ 80QuaCitCT-30
❑ 82IowCubT-25
❑ 83IowCubT-26
❑ 84IowCubT-11
❑ 86MaiGuiP-12

Naples, Brandon
❑ 96PitMetB-16

Napoleon, Danny (Daniel)
❑ 65Top-533
❑ 66OPC-87
❑ 66Top-87
❑ 66TopVen-87
❑ 81TCM60I-472
❑ 91MetWIZ-292

Napoleon, Ed
❑ 77ForLauYS-31
❑ 78TacYanC-8
❑ 79WesHavYT-2
❑ 80NasSouTI-16
❑ 83IndPos-24
❑ 83IndWhe-23
❑ 84Ind-22
❑ 84IndWhe-NNO
❑ 85Ind-22
❑ 85IndPol-NNO
❑ 88RoySmo-2
❑ 88RoyTeal-21
❑ 89AstLenH-14
❑ 89AstMot-27
❑ 89AstSmo-29
❑ 90AstMot-27
❑ 94RocRedWF-1015
❑ 95RanCra-19
❑ 96RanDr P-20
❑ 96RanMot-28
❑ 97RanDr P-18

Napp, Larry
❑ 55Bow-250

Naragon, Hal (Harold R.)
❑ 55Bow-129
❑ 55IndGolS-19
❑ 56Top-311
❑ 57IndTeal-15
❑ 57Top-347
❑ 58Top-22
❑ 59Ind-13
❑ 59SenTealW-11
❑ 59Top-376
❑ 60Top-231
❑ 61Top-92
❑ 61TwiCloD-19
❑ 61TwiPetM-8
❑ 62Top-164
❑ 62TopVen-164
❑ 75TCM195CI-23

Naranjo, Cholly
❑ 57JetPos-13
❑ 58JetPos-12

Narcisse, Ron
❑ 85LitFalMT-14
❑ 86LitFalMP-21

Narcisse, Tyrone
❑ 93AshTouC-15
❑ 93AshTouF-2274
❑ 94OscAstC-18
❑ 94OscAstF-1137
❑ 95JacGenTI-7
❑ 96JacGenB-21
❑ 97RanCucQG-20
❑ 98NorNavQ-18

Narleski, Bill
❑ 88WatIndP-674

Narleski, Ray
❑ 55Bow-96
❑ 55IndGolS-9
❑ 55Top-160
❑ 56Top-133
❑ 57IndSoh-10
❑ 57IndTeal-16
❑ 57Top-144
❑ 58Hir-22
❑ 58IndTeal-17
❑ 58Top-439
❑ 59Top-442
❑ 60TigJayP-11
❑ 60Top-161
❑ 60TopVen-161
❑ 75TCM195CI-24
❑ 75TCM195CI-39
❑ 86IndGreT-11

Narleski, Steve
❑ 76BatTroTI-15
❑ 77WatIndT-15
❑ 81ChaLooT-5
❑ 82ChaLooT-19

Narron, Jerry (Jerry A.)
❑ 75ForLauYS-30
❑ 76ForLauYS-3
❑ 77WesHavYT-17
❑ 78TacYanC-38
❑ 79YanPicA-27
❑ 80Top-16
❑ 81Don-405
❑ 81MarPol-12
❑ 81MarPos-22
❑ 81OPC-249
❑ 81Top-637
❑ 82Don-433
❑ 82Fle-513
❑ 82SpoIndT-12
❑ 82Top-719
❑ 84AngSmo-20
❑ 85AngSmo-10
❑ 85Don-643
❑ 85Top-234
❑ 85TopTif-234
❑ 86AngSmo-10
❑ 86Don-451
❑ 86Top-543
❑ 86TopTif-543
❑ 87CalCanP-2329
❑ 87Don-603
❑ 87Top-474
❑ 87TopTif-474
❑ 88RocRedWC-14
❑ 88RocRedWGCP-17
❑ 88RocRedWP-216
❑ 88RocRedWTI-15
❑ 89FreKeyS-25
❑ 90HagSunB-29
❑ 90HagSunP-1431
❑ 90HagSunS-26
❑ 91HagSunLD-249
❑ 91HagSunP-2471
❑ 91LinDriAA-249
❑ 92RocRedWF-1955
❑ 92RocRedWS-474
❑ 92YanWIZ7-121
❑ 93BalOriP-21
❑ 94BalOriP-22
❑ 95RanCra-20
❑ 96RanDr P-21
❑ 96RanMot-28
❑ 97RanDr P-19

Narron, Johnny
❑ 75AppFoxT-19

Narron, Sam
❑ 49EurSta-44
❑ 60Top-467
❑ 63PirIDL-16
❑ 77PirTCM1WC-41
❑ 77TCMTheWY-1
❑ 83Car194T-5

Narum, Buster (L.F.)
❑ 63BalOriP-22
❑ 64Top-418
❑ 65OPC-86
❑ 65Top-86
❑ 66Top-274
❑ 66TopVen-274
❑ 78TCM60I-44
❑ 91OriCro-324

Nash, Billy (William M.)
❑ 87OldJudN-362
❑ 88AugBecN-25
❑ 88WG1CarG-7
❑ 89N526N7C-10
❑ 94DukCabN-3
❑ 95May-23

Nash, Cotton (Charles F.)
❑ 66SeaPop-15
❑ 71OPC-391
❑ 71Top-391
❑ 78QuaCitAT-15

Nash, Dave
❑ 86EveGiaC-184
❑ 86EveGiaPC-18
❑ 88FreSunCLC-13
❑ 88FreSunP-1228

Nash, Jim
❑ 67CokCapA-7
❑ 67CokCapAAm-30
❑ 67CokCapAt-1
❑ 67DexPre-150
❑ 67OPC-90
❑ 67Top-90
❑ 67TopVen-263
❑ 68Top-324
❑ 68TopVen-324
❑ 69AtlBraBPPS-17
❑ 69MilBra-198
❑ 69MLBOffS-89
❑ 69Top-546
❑ 69TopSta-219
❑ 69TopTeaP-21
❑ 70MLBOffS-9
❑ 70OPC-171
❑ 70Top-171
❑ 71MLBOffS-18
❑ 71OPC-306
❑ 71Top-306
❑ 72MilBra-250
❑ 72OPC-401
❑ 72Top-401
❑ 73OPC-509
❑ 73Top-509

Nash, Rob
❑ 91BatCliCB-1
❑ 91BatCliP-3498

Nastu, Phil
❑ 77CedRapGT-7
❑ 78PhoGiaC-19
❑ 79PhoGiaVNB-6
❑ 80PhoGiaVNB-7
❑ 80Top-686
❑ 80VenLeaS-75

Natal, Rob (Bob)
❑ 87JamExpP-2555
❑ 88FloStaLAS-14
❑ 88WesPalBES-20
❑ 89JacExpB-17
❑ 89JacExpP-176
❑ 90JacExpB-2
❑ 90JacExpP-1378
❑ 91HarSenLD-266
❑ 91HarSenP-630
❑ 91LinDriAA-266
❑ 92DonRoo-84
❑ 92IndIndF-1863
❑ 92IndIndS-189
❑ 92ProFS7-261
❑ 92SkyAAAF-93
❑ 92TriA AAS-189
❑ 93Bow-558
❑ 93Don-744
❑ 93EdmTraF-1141
❑ 93Fle-428
❑ 93FleFinE-67
❑ 93LinVenB-130
❑ 93LinVenB-277
❑ 93LinVenB-288
❑ 93MarPub-17
❑ 93MarUSPC-10S
❑ 93PacSpa-468
❑ 93StaClu-737
❑ 93StaCluFDI-737
❑ 93StaCluMOP-737
❑ 93TopTra-108T
❑ 94EdmTraF-2878
❑ 94Fle-472
❑ 94MarTeal-11
❑ 94Pac-248
❑ 94Pin-173
❑ 94PinArtP-173
❑ 94PinMusC-173
❑ 94StaClu-291
❑ 94StaCluFDI-291
❑ 94StaCluGR-291
❑ 94StaCluMOP-291
❑ 94StaCluT-75
❑ 94StaCluTFDI-75
❑ 94Top-437
❑ 94TopGol-437
❑ 94TopSpa-437
❑ 94Ult-198
❑ 95ChaKniTI-20
❑ 95Top-192
❑ 96LeaSigEA-138
❑ 97PacPriGotD-GD146
❑ 98DurBulTI-22

Nate, Scott
❑ 95BelBreTI-22

Natera, Luis
❑ 85LitFalMT-20
❑ 86LitFalMP-22
❑ 87ColMetP-14

Nathan, Joseph
❑ 95BelGiaTI-11
❑ 97SalVolG-24
❑ 98SanJosGQ-10
❑ 99Bow-388
❑ 99BowGol-388
❑ 99BowInt-388
❑ 99Rev-128
❑ 99RevPremDate-128
❑ 99RevRet-128
❑ 99RevShaSS-128

Nation, Carrie
❑ 08AllLadBC-4

Nationals, New York
❑ 94OriofB-91

Nations, Joel
❑ 95SpoIndTI-15
❑ 98MacBraM-10

Nattile, Sam
❑ 85PawRedST-10
❑ 86NewBriRSP-19

Nattress, Natty (William W.)
❑ 08BufBisFJO-12
❑ 09ColChiE-212
❑ 09T206-450
❑ 12ColRedB-212
❑ 12ColTinT-212
❑ 12ImpTobC-8

Natupsky, Hal
❑ 79ElmPioRST-20

Naughton, Danny
❑ 87ColMetP-19
❑ 87LitFalMP-2405
❑ 88ColMetGS-23
❑ 89St.LucMS-18

Naulty, Dan
❑ 89AlaGol-2
❑ 92KenTwiF-600
❑ 93ForMyeMC-17
❑ 93ForMyeMF-2651
❑ 94ForMyeMC-16
❑ 94ForMyeMF-1167
❑ 96Fin-B358
❑ 96FinRef-B358
❑ 96FleUpd-U57
❑ 96FleUpdTC-U57
❑ 96LeaSigEA-139
❑ 96Ult-378
❑ 96UltGolM-378
❑ 97Cir-26
❑ 97CirRav-26
❑ 97ColCho-382
❑ 97Fle-153
❑ 97FleTif-153
❑ 97Ult-92
❑ 97UltGolME-92
❑ 97UltPlaME-92
❑ 97UppDec-106
❑ 98PacOnl-429
❑ 98PacOnlR-429
❑ 98PacOnlWC-429

Naumann, Rick
❑ 80AppFoxT-5
❑ 81AppFoxT-6

Nava, Lipso
❑ 91SanBerSC-19
❑ 91SanBerSP-1996
❑ 92PenPilC-4
❑ 92PenPilF-2940
❑ 93JacSunF-2717
❑ 93LinVenB-123
❑ 94VenLinU-204
❑ 95LinVen-39
❑ 96-97LinVen-105
❑ 97IowCub-20

Nava, Marlon
❑ 92EliTwiC-11
❑ 92EliTwiF-3687
❑ 92KenTwiC-13
❑ 93ForWayWC-21
❑ 93ForWayWF-1975
❑ 93LinVenB-78
❑ 94VenLinU-264
❑ 95ForMyeMTI-20
❑ 95LinVen-205
❑ 96-97LinVen-68

Navarette, Juan
❑ 98ModA'sG-22

Navarro, Emilio
❑ 95NegLeaL2-27

Navarro, Jaime
❑ 88BlaYNPRWL-171
❑ 88StoPorCLC-182
❑ 88StoPorP-736
❑ 89BlaYNPRWL-147
❑ 89ElPasDGS-13
❑ 89FleUpd-39
❑ 90Bow-388
❑ 90BowTif-388
❑ 90BreMilB-16
❑ 90BrePol-31
❑ 90ClaUpd-T38
❑ 90Don-640
❑ 90El PasDAGTI-23
❑ 90Fle-331
❑ 90FleCan-331
❑ 90Lea-85
❑ 90Sco-569
❑ 90TopDeb89-87
❑ 90UppDec-646
❑ 91Bow-42

❑ 91BreMilB-18
❑ 91BrePol-16
❑ 91Don-216
❑ 91Fle-592
❑ 91Lea-409
❑ 91OPC-548
❑ 91Sco-102
❑ 91StaClu-436
❑ 91Top-548
❑ 91TopDesS-548
❑ 91TopMic-548
❑ 91TopTif-548
❑ 91UltUpd-31
❑ 91UppDec-476
❑ 92Bow-167
❑ 92BrePol-16
❑ 92Don-705
❑ 92Fle-183
❑ 92Lea-144
❑ 92LeaBlaG-144
❑ 92OPC-222
❑ 92Pin-212
❑ 92Sco-231
❑ 92StaClu-87
❑ 92Stu-195
❑ 92Top-222
❑ 92TopGol-222
❑ 92TopGolW-222
❑ 92TopMic-222
❑ 92TriPla-188
❑ 92Ult-82
❑ 92UppDec-633
❑ 93Bow-647
❑ 93BrePol-18
❑ 93Don-281
❑ 93Fle-255
❑ 93Lea-296
❑ 93OPC-247
❑ 93PacBeiA-9
❑ 93PacSpa-161
❑ 93PanSti-35
❑ 93Pin-343
❑ 93Sco-218
❑ 93Sel-260
❑ 93SP-68
❑ 93StaClu-621
❑ 93StaCluFDI-621
❑ 93StaCluMOP-621
❑ 93Top-369
❑ 93TopGol-369
❑ 93TopInaM-369
❑ 93TopInaR-369
❑ 93TopMic-369
❑ 93TriPla-233
❑ 93UppDec-237
❑ 93UppDecGold-237
❑ 94Bow-121
❑ 94BreMilB-57
❑ 94BrePol-19
❑ 94BreTeal-18
❑ 94ColC-531
❑ 94ColChoGS-531
❑ 94ColChoSS-531
❑ 94Don-621
❑ 94Fin-129
❑ 94FinRef-129
❑ 94Fle-185
❑ 94Lea-439
❑ 94OPC-14
❑ 94Pac-336
❑ 94Sco-145
❑ 94ScoGolR-145
❑ 94StaClu-592
❑ 94StaCluFDI-592
❑ 94StaCluGR-592
❑ 94StaCluMOP-592
❑ 94Top-679
❑ 94TopGol-679
❑ 94TopSpa-679
❑ 94TriPla-56
❑ 94UppDec-426
❑ 94UppDecED-426
❑ 95ColCho-544T
❑ 95DonTopotO-202
❑ 95Fin-242
❑ 95FinRef-242
❑ 95FleUpd-127
❑ 95Pac-237
❑ 95SP-36
❑ 95SPSil-36
❑ 95StaClu-343
❑ 95StaClu-537
❑ 95StaCluMOP-343
❑ 95StaCluMOP-537
❑ 95StaCluSTWS-343
❑ 95StaCluSTWS-537
❑ 95Top-93
❑ 95TopTra-80T
❑ 95UppDec-459
❑ 96ColCho-86
❑ 96ColChoGS-86
❑ 96ColChoSS-86
❑ 96CubFle-13
❑ 96Don-441
❑ 96DonPreP-441
❑ 96EmoXL-157
❑ 96Fla-221
❑ 96Fle-324
❑ 96FleTif-324
❑ 96MetUni-143
❑ 96MetUniP-143
❑ 96Pac-29
❑ 96PacEstL-EL22
❑ 96PacPri-P12
❑ 96PacPriG-P12
❑ 96PanSti-46
❑ 96Pin-22
❑ 96ProSta-39
❑ 96Sco-39
❑ 96SP-55
❑ 96StaClu-37
❑ 96StaClu-254
❑ 96StaCluMOP-37
❑ 96StaCluMOP-254
❑ 96Top-381
❑ 96Ult-456
❑ 96UltGolM-456
❑ 96UppDec-298
❑ 97Cir-388
❑ 97CirRav-388
❑ 97ColCho-294
❑ 97ColChoT-CW13
❑ 97ColChoU-U5
❑ 97Don-254
❑ 97Don-297
❑ 97DonGolPP-254
❑ 97DonGolPP-297
❑ 97DonSilPP-254
❑ 97DonSilPP-297
❑ 97DonTea-71
❑ 97DonTeaSPE-71
❑ 97Fin-259
❑ 97FinRef-259
❑ 97Fle-281
❑ 97Fle-572
❑ 97FleTif-281
❑ 97FleTif-572
❑ 97Lea-52
❑ 97LeaFraM-52
❑ 97LeaFraMDC-52
❑ 97MetUni-13
❑ 97Pac-254
❑ 97PacLigB-254
❑ 97PacPri-87
❑ 97PacPriLB-87
❑ 97PacPriP-87
❑ 97PacSil-254
❑ 97Pin-60
❑ 97PinArtP-PP60
❑ 97PinMusC-60
❑ 97PinPrePla-60
❑ 97Sco-15
❑ 97Sco-348
❑ 97ScoArtPWB-15
❑ 97ScoArtPWB-348
❑ 97ScoPreS-15
❑ 97ScoResC-348
❑ 97ScoShoS-15
❑ 97ScoShoS-348
❑ 97ScoShoSAP-15
❑ 97ScoShoSAP-348
❑ 97StaClu-258
❑ 97StaCluMOP-258
❑ 97Top-21
❑ 97Ult-420
❑ 97UltGolME-420
❑ 97UltPlaME-420
❑ 97WhiSoxTI-38
❑ 98ColCho-336
❑ 98Fle-96
❑ 98Fle-556
❑ 98Pac-62
❑ 98PacOme-57
❑ 98PacOmeR-57
❑ 98PacOnl-174
❑ 98PacOnlR-174
❑ 98PacOnlWC-174
❑ 98PacPar-30
❑ 98PacParC-30
❑ 98PacParG-30
❑ 98PacParHS-30
❑ 98PacParPB-30
❑ 98PacParR-30
❑ 98PacPlaB-62
❑ 98PacRedT-62
❑ 98PacSil-62
❑ 98Pin-153
❑ 98PinPreP-153
❑ 98Sco-89
❑ 98SPxFin-259
❑ 98SPxFinR-259
❑ 98SPxFinS-259
❑ 98StaCluFDI-197
❑ 98StaCluI-197
❑ 98StaCluOneK-197
❑ 98StaCluPP-197
❑ 98Top-141
❑ 98TopChr-141
❑ 98TopChrR-141
❑ 98TopDevR-141
❑ 98TopDia-141
❑ 98TopMiniC-141
❑ 98Ult-154
❑ 98UltGolM-154
❑ 98UltMas-154
❑ 98UltPlaM-154
❑ 98UppDec-58
❑ 98UppDecSF-37
❑ 98WhiSoxS-5
❑ 98WhiSoxSP-5
❑ 99Pac-102
❑ 99PacCroC-68
❑ 99PacCroCPB-68
❑ 99PacPar-57
❑ 99PacParC-57
❑ 99PacParG-57
❑ 99PacParHoloGold-57
❑ 99PacParHS-57
❑ 99PacParOD-57
❑ 99PacParPB-57
❑ 99PacParRed-57
❑ 99PacPlaB-102
❑ 99PacRed-102
❑ 99UppDec-67
❑ 99UppDec-339
❑ 99UppDecEL1-67
❑ 99UppDecEL1-339
❑ 99UppDecEL2-67
❑ 99UppDecEL2-339
❑ 99Vic-101

Navarro, Jason
❑ 97NewJerCB-21
❑ 98CarLeaTPQ-4
❑ 98PriWilCQ-11

Navarro, Julio
❑ 60Top-140
❑ 60TopVen-140
❑ 63Top-169
❑ 64Top-489
❑ 65Top-563
❑ 66Top-527

Navarro, Norberto
❑ 89PitMetS-18

Navarro, Rick
❑ 89SanDieSAS-19
❑ 92FroRowDP-48
❑ 92FroRowDPG-48
❑ 92FroRowDPS-48
❑ 92NiaFalRC-8
❑ 93FayGenC-18
❑ 93FayGenF-128
❑ 94LakTigC-17
❑ 94LakTigF-3034

Navarro, Tito
❑ 90ColMetGS-13
❑ 90ColMetPPI-6
❑ 90SouAtlLAS-37
❑ 90StaFS7-100
❑ 91ColMetPI-32
❑ 91LinDriAA-639
❑ 91WilBilLD-639
❑ 91WilBilP-302
❑ 92Bow-139
❑ 92ProFS7-281
❑ 92UppDecML-91
❑ 93NorTidF-2576
❑ 94Pac-414
❑ 94St.LucMF-1203
❑ 94StaClu-473
❑ 94StaCluFDI-473
❑ 94StaCluGR-473
❑ 94StaCluMOP-473

Navas, Francisco
❑ 76VenLeaS-64

Navas, Silverio
❑ 93LinVenB-88
❑ 93OneYanC-16
❑ 93OneYanF-3512
❑ 94VenLinU-193
❑ 95LinVen-104
❑ 96-97LinVen-66

Naveda, Edgar
❑ 86KenTwiP-17
❑ 87KenTwiP-5
❑ 88VisOakCLC-156
❑ 88VisOakP-103
❑ 89OrlTwiB-18
❑ 89OrlTwiP-1347
❑ 90CMC-567
❑ 90OrlSunRB-5
❑ 90PorBeaC-15
❑ 90PorBeaP-187
❑ 90ProAAAF-257
❑ 91LinDriAAA-413
❑ 91PorBeaLD-413
❑ 91PorBeaP-1580
❑ 92PorBeaF-2680
❑ 92PorBeaS-414
❑ 92SkyAAAF-189
❑ 93LinVenB-25
❑ 93LinVenB-318
❑ 94VenLinU-8
❑ 95LinVen-74
❑ 96-97LinVen-70

Naveda, Yonni
❑ 93LinVenB-19

Navilliat, James
❑ 86SpoIndC-157
❑ 87ChaRaiP-11

Navratilova, Martina
❑ 82MonNew-10

Naworski, Andy
❑ 86BakDodP-21
❑ 86TriTriC-187
❑ 87Ft.MyeRP-9

Naylor, Arthur
❑ 11Zee-96

Naylor, Earl
❑ 90DodTar-566

Naylor, Roleine C.
❑ 21Exh-116
❑ 22E120-86
❑ 22W572-69
❑ 22W573-92

Nazabal, Robert
❑ 85BenPhiC-17

Nazario, Victor Horatio
❑ 85DomLeaS-178

Ndungidi, Ntema
❑ 98BluOriQ-10
❑ 98Bow-151
❑ 98BowChr-151
❑ 98BowChrGA-151
❑ 98BowChrGAR-151
❑ 98BowChrI-151
❑ 98BowChrIR-151
❑ 98BowChrR-151
❑ 98BowGolA-151
❑ 98BowInt-151
❑ 98Top-490
❑ 98TopChr-490
❑ 98TopChrR-490
❑ 98TopDevR-490
❑ 98TopDia-490
❑ 98TopMiniC-490
❑ 99Bow-129
❑ 99BowChr-129
❑ 99BowChrG-129
❑ 99BowChrGR-129
❑ 99BowChrI-129
❑ 99BowChrIR-129
❑ 99BowChrR-129
❑ 99BowGol-129
❑ 99BowInt-129

Neagle, Denny (Dennis)
❑ 88CapCodPPaLP-53
❑ 89EliTwiS-22
❑ 90CalLeaACLC-24
❑ 90CMC-862
❑ 90OrlSunRS-13
❑ 90ProAaA-142
❑ 90VisOakP-2150
❑ 91Bow-323
❑ 91Lea-466
❑ 91LinDriAAA-414
❑ 91PorBeaLD-414
❑ 91PorBeaP-1563
❑ 91TriA AAGP-AAA36
❑ 91Ult-383
❑ 91UppDecFE-34F
❑ 92Bow-485
❑ 92Cla1-T68
❑ 92Cla2-T66
❑ 92Don-605
❑ 92Fle-213
❑ 92LeaGolR-BC22
❑ 92OPC-592
❑ 92OPCPre-165
❑ 92Pin-556
❑ 92PinRoo-19
❑ 92PirNatl-17
❑ 92ProFS7-89
❑ 92ScoRoo-89T
❑ 92SpollIFK1-693
❑ 92StaClu-724
❑ 92Stu-87
❑ 92Top-592
❑ 92TopDeb91-132
❑ 92TopGol-592
❑ 92TopGolW-592
❑ 92TopMic-592
❑ 92TopTra-81T
❑ 92TopTraG-81T
❑ 92Ult-556
❑ 92UppDec-426
❑ 92UppDec-748
❑ 92UppDecSR-SR17
❑ 93Don-226
❑ 93Fle-503
❑ 93Lea-42
❑ 93PacSpa-590
❑ 93PirHil-10
❑ 93PirNatl-22
❑ 93Sco-350
❑ 93Sel-299
❑ 93StaClu-241
❑ 93StaCluFDI-241
❑ 93StaCluMOP-241
❑ 93Top-244
❑ 93TopGol-244
❑ 93TopInaM-244
❑ 93TopInaR-244
❑ 93TopMic-244
❑ 93Ult-454
❑ 93UppDec-415
❑ 93UppDecGold-415
❑ 94ColC-562
❑ 94ColChoGS-562
❑ 94ColChoSS-562
❑ 94Fin-195
❑ 94FinRef-195
❑ 94Fla-425
❑ 94Fle-616
❑ 94FleExtB-350
❑ 94Pac-504
❑ 94PirQui-19
❑ 94StaClu-232
❑ 94StaCluFDI-232
❑ 94StaCluGR-232
❑ 94StaCluMOP-232
❑ 94Top-129
❑ 94TopGol-129
❑ 94TopSpa-129
❑ 95BowBes-R7
❑ 95BowBesR-R7
❑ 95ClaPhoC-45
❑ 95ColCho-388
❑ 95ColChoGS-388
❑ 95ColChoSS-388
❑ 95Don-111
❑ 95DonPreP-111
❑ 95DonTopotO-322
❑ 95Emo-178
❑ 95Fla-188
❑ 95Fle-486
❑ 95Lea-400
❑ 95Pac-349
❑ 95PirFil-23
❑ 95Sco-513
❑ 95ScoGolR-513
❑ 95ScoPlaTS-513
❑ 95SP-94
❑ 95SPCha-80
❑ 95SPChaDC-80
❑ 95SPSil-94
❑ 95StaClu-474
❑ 95StaCluMOP-474
❑ 95StaCluSTWS-474
❑ 95StaCluVR-260
❑ 95StaCluVRMO-260
❑ 95Top-445
❑ 95TopCyb-241
❑ 95Ult-425
❑ 95UltGolM-425
❑ 95UppDec-386
❑ 95UppDecED-386
❑ 95UppDecEDG-386
❑ 96Baz-29
❑ 96ColCho-266
❑ 96ColChoGS-266
❑ 96ColChoSS-266
❑ 96Don-501
❑ 96DonPreP-501
❑ 96EmoXL-260
❑ 96Fin-B63
❑ 96FinRef-B63
❑ 96Fla-353
❑ 96Fle-530
❑ 96FleTif-530
❑ 96Lea-96
❑ 96LeaPrePB-96
❑ 96LeaPrePG-96
❑ 96LeaPrePS-96
❑ 96LeaSigA-166
❑ 96LeaSigAG-166
❑ 96LeaSigAS-166
❑ 96MetUni-220
❑ 96MetUniP-220
❑ 96Pac-178
❑ 96PanSti-72
❑ 96Pin-220
❑ 96PinAfi-130
❑ 96PinAfiAP-130
❑ 96PinArtP-120
❑ 96PinFoil-220
❑ 96PinSta-120
❑ 96ProSta-95
❑ 96Sco-168
❑ 96Sel-99
❑ 96SelArtP-99
❑ 96SelTeaN-3
❑ 96SP-146
❑ 96StaClu-242
❑ 96StaCluMOP-242
❑ 96Stu-119
❑ 96StuPrePB-119
❑ 96StuPrePG-119
❑ 96StuPrePS-119
❑ 96TeaOut-58
❑ 96Top-421
❑ 96TopGal-42
❑ 96TopGalPPI-42
❑ 96Ult-269
❑ 96UltGolM-269
❑ 96UppDec-177
❑ 97Cir-304
❑ 97CirRav-304
❑ 97ColCho-36
❑ 97ColChoT-AB9
❑ 97Don-20
❑ 97DonGolPP-20
❑ 97DonLim-34
❑ 97DonLimE-34
❑ 97DonLimENG-34
❑ 97DonSilPP-20
❑ 97DonTea-17
❑ 97DonTeaSPE-17
❑ 97Fin-80
❑ 97FinRef-80
❑ 97FlaShoLC-132
❑ 97FlaShoLeg0-132
❑ 97FlaShoLeg1-132
❑ 97FlaShoM-A132
❑ 97FlaShoM-B132
❑ 97FlaShoM-C132
❑ 97FlaShoR0-132
❑ 97FlaShoR1-132
❑ 97FlaShoR2-132
❑ 97Fle-266
❑ 97FleTif-266
❑ 97Lea-282
❑ 97LeaFraM-282
❑ 97LeaFraMDC-282
❑ 97NewPin-83
❑ 97NewPin-187
❑ 97NewPinAP-83
❑ 97NewPinAP-187
❑ 97NewPinMC-83
❑ 97NewPinMC-187
❑ 97NewPinPP-83
❑ 97NewPinPP-187
❑ 97Pac-242
❑ 97PacLigB-242
❑ 97PacSil-242
❑ 97Sco-397
❑ 97ScoArtPWB-397
❑ 97ScoResC-397
❑ 97ScoShoS-397
❑ 97ScoShoSAP-397
❑ 97Sel-191
❑ 97SelCom-191
❑ 97StaClu-246
❑ 97StaCluMat-246
❑ 97StaCluMOP-246

❑ 97StrAll-48
❑ 97Top-445
❑ 97TopChr-157
❑ 97TopChrR-157
❑ 97TopSta-98
❑ 97TopStaAM-98
❑ 97Ult-265
❑ 97Ult-319
❑ 97UltGolME-265
❑ 97UltGolME-319
❑ 97UltPlaME-265
❑ 97UltPlaME-319
❑ 97UppDec-303
❑ 98Bow-265
❑ 98BowBes-96
❑ 98BowBesAR-96
❑ 98BowBesR-96
❑ 98BowChr-265
❑ 98BowChrGA-265
❑ 98BowChrGAR-265
❑ 98BowChrI-265
❑ 98BowChrIR-265
❑ 98BowChrR-265
❑ 98BowGolA-265
❑ 98BowInt-265
❑ 98BraSco-4
❑ 98BraScoP-4
❑ 98CirThu-251
❑ 98CirThuRav-251
❑ 98CirThuSupRav-251
❑ 98ColCho-36
❑ 98ColCho-257
❑ 98ColChoSQ-SQ22
❑ 98Don-30
❑ 98DonCol-30
❑ 98DonColL-268
❑ 98DonColP-628
❑ 98DonColS-30
❑ 98DonGolPP-30
❑ 98DonPre-78
❑ 98DonPreSeat-78
❑ 98DonPriCD-30
❑ 98DonPriCL-268
❑ 98DonPriCP-628
❑ 98DonSilPP-30
❑ 98Fin-95
❑ 98FinNo--95
❑ 98FinNo-R-95
❑ 98FinRef-95
❑ 98Fle-490
❑ 98FleVin'-74
❑ 98FleVin'C-74
❑ 98Lea-69
❑ 98LeaFraDA-69
❑ 98LeaFraF-69
❑ 98LeaFraM-69
❑ 98LeaFraM-69
❑ 98LeaFraMDC-69
❑ 98LeaFraMDC-69
❑ 98LeaFraMZ2-69
❑ 98LeaRS-80
❑ 98LeaRSLHolo-80
❑ 98LeaRSLong-80
❑ 98LeaRTrue-80
❑ 98Pac-242
❑ 98PacGolCDC-3
❑ 98PacOme-25
❑ 98PacOmeR-25
❑ 98PacOnl-70
❑ 98PacOnlR-70
❑ 98PacOnlWC-70
❑ 98PacPar-134
❑ 98PacParC-134
❑ 98PacParG-134
❑ 98PacParHS-134
❑ 98PacParPB-134
❑ 98PacParR-134
❑ 98PacPlaB-242
❑ 98PacRedT-242
❑ 98PacSil-242
❑ 98Pin-26
❑ 98PinArtP-PP26
❑ 98PinMusC-PP26
❑ 98PinPer-79
❑ 98PinPerPP-79
❑ 98PinPreP-26
❑ 98PinSna-AB16
❑ 98Sco-27
❑ 98Sco-263
❑ 98ScoRT-91
❑ 98ScoSS-PP121
❑ 98ScoSSAP-PP121
❑ 98SpoIll-94
❑ 98SpoIllEE-94
❑ 98SpoIllFE-94
❑ 98SpoIllTaN-117
❑ 98SpoIllTaNEE-117
❑ 98SpoIllWSF-98
❑ 98SpoIllWSFEE-98
❑ 98SpoIllWSFFE-98
❑ 98SPxFin-58
❑ 98SPxFinR-58
❑ 98SPxFinS-58
❑ 98StaCluFDI-14
❑ 98StaCluI-14
❑ 98StaCluOneK-14
❑ 98StaCluPP-14
❑ 98Stu-76
❑ 98StuGPP-76
❑ 98StuSPP-76
❑ 98Top-4
❑ 98Top-272
❑ 98TopChr-4
❑ 98TopChr-272
❑ 98TopChrR-4
❑ 98TopChrR-272
❑ 98TopDevR-4
❑ 98TopDevR-272
❑ 98TopDia-4
❑ 98TopDia-272
❑ 98TopGal-68
❑ 98TopGalGP-68
❑ 98TopGalOPP-68
❑ 98TopGalPPI-68
❑ 98TopGalPPIA-68
❑ 98TopMiniC-4
❑ 98TopMiniC-272
❑ 98TopOpeD-4
❑ 98TopSta-99
❑ 98TopStaB-99
❑ 98TopStaG-99
❑ 98TopStaGR-99
❑ 98TopStaS-99
❑ 98Ult-350
❑ 98UltGolM-350
❑ 98UltMas-350
❑ 98UltPlaM-350
❑ 98UppDec-304
❑ 98UppDec-419
❑ 99199Fin-206
❑ 99Bow-276
❑ 99BowGol-276
❑ 99BowInt-276
❑ 99FinGolRef-206
❑ 99FinRef-206
❑ 99FlaShoLeg1-105
❑ 99FlaShoLeg2-105
❑ 99FlaShoLeg3-105
❑ 99FlaShoLegM1-105
❑ 99FlaShoLegM2-105
❑ 99FlaShoLegM3-105
❑ 99FlaShoR1-105
❑ 99FlaShoR2-105
❑ 99FlaShoR3-105
❑ 99Fle-237
❑ 99FleBri-118
❑ 99FleBri2G-118
❑ 99FleBriBlu-118
❑ 99FleBriGol-118
❑ 99FleSta9-237
❑ 99FleWarT-237
❑ 99Pac-41
❑ 99PacAur-47
❑ 99PacAurOD-47
❑ 99PacPlaB-41
❑ 99PacRed-41
❑ 99SkyMolM-8
❑ 99SkyMolMOA-21
❑ 99SkyMolMX-8
❑ 99SkyThu-129
❑ 99SkyThuRant-129
❑ 99SkyThuRave-129
❑ 99SpoIll-128
❑ 99SPSig-137
❑ 99ThuSkySupR-129
❑ 99Top-185
❑ 99TopChr-185
❑ 99TopChrR-185
❑ 99TopGal-97
❑ 99TopGalPP-97
❑ 99TopGalPPI-97
❑ 99TopMVPP-185
❑ 99TopOpeD-99
❑ 99TopSta-115
❑ 99TopStaFoil-115
❑ 99Ult-203
❑ 99UltGolM-203
❑ 99UltMas-203
❑ 99UltPlaM-203
❑ 99UppDec-37
❑ 99UppDec-350
❑ 99UppDecCLM-C21
❑ 99UppDecEL1-37
❑ 99UppDecEL1-350
❑ 99UppDecEL2-37
❑ 99UppDecEL2-350
❑ 99UppDecM-52
❑ 99UppDecMGS-52
❑ 99UppDecMHFS-52
❑ 99UppDecMSS-52
❑ 99Vic-103

Neal, Billy
❑ 96VerBeaDB-21
❑ 97SanAntMB-7
❑ 98SanAntMG-18
❑ 98SanAntMM-7

Neal, Bob
❑ 80PenPilBT-25
❑ 80PenPilCT-9
❑ 88AubAstP-1964
❑ 89AubAstP-2178

Neal, Bryan
❑ 82DurBulT-6
❑ 83DurBulT-10

Neal, Charlie (Charles Lenard)
❑ 47Exh-165
❑ 55Bow-278
❑ 56Dod-19
❑ 56Top-299
❑ 57Top-242
❑ 58DodJayP-8
❑ 58DodTeal-16
❑ 58Hir-54
❑ 58Top-16
❑ 59DodMor-8
❑ 59DodPos-9
❑ 59DodTeal-19
❑ 59Top-427
❑ 60DodJayP-10
❑ 60DodMor-8
❑ 60DodPos-8
❑ 60DodTeal-13
❑ 60DodUniO-13
❑ 60Top-155
❑ 60Top-385
❑ 60Top-386
❑ 60Top-556
❑ 60TopTat-40
❑ 60TopVen-155
❑ 61DodBelB-43
❑ 61DodJayP-7
❑ 61DodUniO-14
❑ 61Pos-157A
❑ 61Pos-157B
❑ 61Top-423
❑ 62Jel-102
❑ 62MetJayP-9
❑ 62Pos-102
❑ 62PosCan-102
❑ 62SalPlaC-102A
❑ 62SalPlaC-102B
❑ 62ShiPlaC-102
❑ 62Top-365
❑ 63BasMagM-62
❑ 63ExhStaB-49
❑ 63Jel-195
❑ 63MetJayP-8
❑ 63Pos-195
❑ 63Top-511
❑ 64Top-436
❑ 74MetOriEB-12
❑ 81TCM60I-482
❑ 82MetGal62-3
❑ 89DodSmoG-66
❑ 90DodTar-567
❑ 91DodRinP4-4
❑ 91MetWIZ-293
❑ 94UppDecAH-64
❑ 94UppDecAH1-64
❑ 95TopArcBD-139
❑ 95TopArcBD-163

Neal, Dave
❑ 88BenBucL-19
❑ 89PalSprACLC-49
❑ 89PalSprAP-474
❑ 90QuaCitAGS-5

Neal, Edwin
❑ 80ChaO'sP-13
❑ 80ChaO'sW-14

Neal, Len
❑ 75OakOak2A-26

Neal, Mike
❑ 92LSUTigM-7
❑ 93LSUTigM-8
❑ 93WatIndC-19
❑ 93WatIndF-3570
❑ 94ExcFirYPF-5
❑ 94ExcFS7-46
❑ 94KinIndC-14
❑ 94KinIndF-2652
❑ 94LSUTigMP-11
❑ 94Top-158
❑ 94TopGol-158
❑ 94TopSpa-158
❑ 96CanIndB-19
❑ 97AkrAer-20
❑ 97TexAllM-23
❑ 98JacGenM-14

Neal, Rob
❑ 96BoiHawB-21

Neal, Scott
❑ 85PriWilPT-2
❑ 86HawIsIP-18
❑ 87HarSenP-9

Neal, Willie
❑ 81ChaRoyT-25
❑ 82ChaRoyT-22

Neale, Greasy (Alfred Earle)
❑ 17ColE13-126
❑ 17HolBreD-73
❑ 19W514-6
❑ 20NatCarE-66
❑ 20RedWorCP-14
❑ 21E121So1-70
❑ 21Exh-117
❑ 22E120-176
❑ 22W575-90
❑ 23W501-51
❑ 23WilChoV-111
❑ 81ConTSN-29
❑ 88ConSer4-20
❑ 88PacEigMO-88
❑ 92ConTSN-401
❑ 94ConTSN-1028
❑ 94ConTSNB-1028

Nealeigh, Rod
❑ 83MemChiT-13

Nebinger, Richard
❑ 11BigEatEU-14
❑ 11Zee-74

Nebraska, David
❑ 89BurIndS-18

Necciai, Ron
❑ 77FriOneYW-9
❑ 93UppDecAH-101
❑ 94UppDecAH-203
❑ 94UppDecAH1-203

Nedeau, John
❑ 93BoiHawC-21
❑ 93BoiHawF-3914

Nedin, Tim
❑ 89EliTwiS-23
❑ 89Sta-152
❑ 90Bes-306
❑ 90KenTwiB-22
❑ 90KenTwiP-2291
❑ 90KenTwiS-16
❑ 91Cla/Bes-185
❑ 91VisOakC-7
❑ 92Ft.MyeMCB-14

Nee, John
❑ 11T205-195

Needham, Kevin
❑ 96BilMusTI-23
❑ 98BurBeeM-15

Needham, Tom (Thomas J.)
❑ 09MaxPubP-20
❑ 09T206-265
❑ 10CouT21-202
❑ 10DomDisP-92
❑ 10JuJuDE-31
❑ 10SweCapPP-85
❑ 11BasBatEU-30
❑ 11HelSta-99
❑ 11PinT-5-219
❑ 11S74Sil-65
❑ 11SpoLifCW-267
❑ 11SpoLifM-175
❑ 11T205-128
❑ 12HasTriFT-53
❑ 12T207-138
❑ 14PieStaT-82
❑ 15VicT21-22
❑ 72ClaCar-104

Needle, Chad
❑ 96StCatSB-21

Neel, Troy
❑ 88MidLeaAGS-21
❑ 88WatIndP-681
❑ 89CanIndB-25
❑ 89CanIndP-1324
❑ 89CanIndS-17
❑ 89EasLeaAP-7
❑ 89EasLeaDDP-DD37
❑ 89Sta-155
❑ 90CMC-469
❑ 90ColSprSSC-17
❑ 90ColSprSSP-45
❑ 90ProAAAF-226
❑ 91HunStaTI-14
❑ 91LinDriAAA-543
❑ 91TacTigLD-543
❑ 91TacTigP-2318
❑ 92DonRoo-85
❑ 92FleUpd-50
❑ 92SkyAAAF-241
❑ 92TacTigF-2517
❑ 92TacTigS-541
❑ 93AthMot-15
❑ 93AthStaC-28
❑ 93Bow-541
❑ 93Don-308
❑ 93FleFinE-259
❑ 93FleMajLP-A18
❑ 93LeaGolR-R9
❑ 93LeaGolRJ-R9
❑ 93OPCPre-85
❑ 93PacSpa-571
❑ 93Pin-246
❑ 93Sco-326
❑ 93ScoBoyoS-6
❑ 93SelRoo-68T
❑ 93StaClu-429
❑ 93StaCluFDI-429
❑ 93StaCluMOP-429
❑ 93TacTigF-3048
❑ 93Top-807
❑ 93TopGol-807
❑ 93TopInaM-807
❑ 93TopInaR-807
❑ 93TopMic-807
❑ 93Ult-260
❑ 93UppDec-767
❑ 93UppDecGold-767
❑ 94A'sMot-15
❑ 94Bow-464
❑ 94ColC-215
❑ 94ColChoGS-215
❑ 94ColChoSS-215
❑ 94Don-520
❑ 94Fin-13
❑ 94FinJum-13
❑ 94FinRef-13
❑ 94Fla-95
❑ 94Fle-270
❑ 94FleExtB-154
❑ 94FleExtBSYS-14
❑ 94FleRooS-13
❑ 94Lea-6
❑ 94LeaL-62
❑ 94OPC-249
❑ 94Pac-459
❑ 94PanSti-111
❑ 94Pin-150
❑ 94PinArtP-150
❑ 94PinMusC-150
❑ 94Sco-248
❑ 94ScoGolR-248
❑ 94Sel-68
❑ 94StaClu-40
❑ 94StaCluFDI-40
❑ 94StaCluGR-40
❑ 94StaCluMOP-40
❑ 94Stu-5
❑ 94Top-493
❑ 94TopGol-493
❑ 94TopSpa-493
❑ 94TriPla-6
❑ 94Ult-112
❑ 94UppDec-391
❑ 94UppDecED-391
❑ 94USPlaCR-11H
❑ 94USPlaCR-12C
❑ 95Baz-29
❑ 95ColCho-123
❑ 95Don-112
❑ 95DonPreP-112
❑ 95Fle-250
❑ 95Lea-106
❑ 95Pac-317
❑ 95Pin-81
❑ 95PinArtP-81
❑ 95PinMusC-81
❑ 95Sco-469
❑ 95ScoGolR-469
❑ 95ScoPlaTS-469
❑ 95StaClu-277
❑ 95StaCluMOP-277
❑ 95StaCluSTWS-277
❑ 95StaCluVR-141
❑ 95StaCluVRMO-141
❑ 95Top-157
❑ 95TopCyb-94
❑ 95Ult-95
❑ 95UltGolM-95

Neely, Jeff
❑ 89AugPirP-495
❑ 89SouAtlLAGS-7
❑ 91BufBisLD-40
❑ 91BufBisP-539
❑ 91LinDriAAA-40

Neeman, Cal (Calvin A.)
❑ 57Top-353
❑ 58Top-33A
❑ 58Top-33B
❑ 59Top-367
❑ 60Top-337
❑ 79TCM50-142

Neese, Joshua
❑ 93NiaFalRF-3384
❑ 94ExcFirYPF-10
❑ 94ExcFS7-58

Neff, Marty
❑ 91WelPirC-16
❑ 91WelPirP-3588
❑ 92AugPirC-16
❑ 92AugPirF-253
❑ 93Bow-274
❑ 93ClaFS7-287
❑ 93ClaGolF-179
❑ 93SalBucC-18
❑ 93SalBucF-446
❑ 93SouAtlLAPI-27

Neff, Paul
❑ 85FreGiaSB-28

Nega, Chris
❑ 93DunBluJC-30

Negray, Ron
❑ 56Top-7
❑ 56TopPin-20
❑ 57Top-254
❑ 60MapLeaSF-15
❑ 61MapLeaBH-15
❑ 74dod195T-24
❑ 90DodTar-568

Negrette, Richard
❑ 95LinVen-140
❑ 95WatIndTI-22
❑ 96-97LinVen-218
❑ 96BurIndB-8
❑ 97WatIndTI-21
❑ 98ColRedSM-8

Negron, Miguel
❑ 80LynSaiT-10
❑ 83ChaLooT-10

Nehf, Art N.
❑ 16FleBreD-70
❑ 17ColE13-127
❑ 17HolBreD-74
❑ 20GasAmeMBD-30
❑ 20NatCarE-67
❑ 20W516-17
❑ 21E121So1-71
❑ 21E121So8-67
❑ 21Exh-118
❑ 21KoBreWSI-17
❑ 21Nei-93
❑ 22E120-189
❑ 22W572-70
❑ 22W575-91
❑ 22WilPatV-41
❑ 23W501-70
❑ 23W501-119
❑ 23W503-12
❑ 23W515-22
❑ 25Exh-37
❑ 27AmeCarE126-59
❑ 28W502-43
❑ 28Yue-43
❑ 61Fle-65
❑ 75FlePio-28
❑ 76ISCHooHA-11
❑ 92ConTSN-492
❑ 94ConTSN-1246
❑ 94ConTSNB-1246

Nehf, Robert
❑ 20NatCarE-67

Neibauer, Gary
❑ 69Top-611
❑ 70OPC-384
❑ 70Top-384
❑ 71OPC-668

❑ 71RicBraTI-15
❑ 71Top-668
❑ 72OPC-149
❑ 72Top-149
Neidinger, Joe
❑ 89BriTigS-18
❑ 91FayGenC-6
❑ 91FayGenP-1166
Neidlinger, Jim
❑ 85PriWilPT-10
❑ 86NasPirP-19
❑ 87HarSenP-20
❑ 88HarSenP-842
❑ 89AlbDukCm-9
❑ 89AlbDukP-71
❑ 90AlbDukCm-10
❑ 90AlbDukP-343
❑ 90AlbDukTr-23
❑ 90CMC-412
❑ 90DodPol-39
❑ 90ProAAAF-64
❑ 91AlbDukLD-16
❑ 91AlbDukP-1139
❑ 91Cla1-T53
❑ 91DodPol-31
❑ 91Don-713
❑ 91Fle-215
❑ 91LinDriAAA-16
❑ 91OPC-39
❑ 91Sco-794
❑ 91Top-39
❑ 91TopDeb90-115
❑ 91TopDesS-39
❑ 91TopMic-39
❑ 91TopTif-39
❑ 91UppDec-632
❑ 92AlbDukF-718
❑ 92AlbDukS-18
❑ 93PorBeaF-2382
❑ 94LouRedF-2980
Neier, Chris
❑ 93BenRocCB-19
❑ 93BenRocF-3266
❑ 94AshTouC-18
❑ 94AshTouF-1778
❑ 95NewHavRTI-28
❑ 96NewHavRB-19
Neiger, Al
❑ 61Top-202
❑ 89ChaLooLITI-20
Neighbors, Bob
❑ 95ConTSN-1345
Neill, Mike
❑ 91Cla/Bes-415
❑ 91FroRowDP-9
❑ 91FroRowDPG-9
❑ 91FroRowDPP-2
❑ 91FroRowDPS-9
❑ 91SouOreAC-15
❑ 91SouOreAP-3864
❑ 92Bow-266
❑ 92CalLeaACL-4
❑ 92ProFS7-135
❑ 92RenSilSCLC-35
❑ 92StaCluD-129
❑ 92UppDecML-26
❑ 92UppDecML-52
❑ 92UppDecML-273
❑ 93AthStaC-30
❑ 93Bow-217
❑ 93ClaFS7-227
❑ 93UppDec-424
❑ 93UppDecGold-424
❑ 94SigRoo-20
❑ 94SigRooS-20
❑ 95ModA'sTI-20
❑ 96ModA'sB-23
❑ 97HunStaTI-19
❑ 99SpoIII-44
Neill, Scott
❑ 89WatIndS-16
❑ 90KinIndTI-24
❑ 91CarLeaAP-CAR18
❑ 91KinIndC-9
❑ 91KinIndP-321
Neilson, Mike
❑ 92WatIndC-11
❑ 92WatIndF-3231
❑ 93WatIndC-20
❑ 93WatIndF-3559
Neiper, Jim
❑ 80VenLeaS-167
Neis, Bernie (Bernard E.)
❑ 20NatCarE-68
❑ 26Exh-6
❑ 27Exh-44
❑ 90DodTar-569
Neisen, Gertrude
❑ 48BabRutS-7
Neitzel, R.A.
❑ 90BatCliP-3073
❑ 91ClePhiC-19
❑ 91ClePhiP-1630
❑ 92ReaPhiF-581
❑ 92ReaPhiS-536
Nelloms, Skip
❑ 88OneYanP-2048
❑ 89Ft.LauYS-18
❑ 90Ft.LauYS-13
Nelson, Andre
❑ 92HunCubC-5
❑ 92HunCubF-3163
Nelson, Barry
❑ 98FarRedHM-20
Nelson, Bob (Robert S.)
❑ 56BalOriP-3
❑ 56Top-169
❑ 91OriCro-325
❑ 97BalOriP-37
Nelson, Brian
❑ 90NiaFalRP-22
❑ 91BriTigC-22
❑ 91BriTigP-3600
❑ 96EveAquB-16
❑ 97EveAquG-20
Nelson, Bryant
❑ 94AubAstC-8
❑ 94AubAstF-3766
❑ 94QuaCitRBC-14
❑ 94QuaCitRBF-543
❑ 96BesAutS-65
❑ 96Bow-279
❑ 96BowFoi-279
❑ 96KisCobB-19
❑ 97OrlRayB-19
Nelson, Byron
❑ 40WheM4-7A
❑ 40WheM4-7B
❑ 40WheM4-7C
❑ 41WheM5-17
❑ 74NewYorNTDiS-2
Nelson, Charles O.
❑ 98SanAntMG-19
Nelson, Charlie
❑ 92Min-15
❑ 93BazTeaU-5
❑ 93TopTra-57T
❑ 94YakBeaC-10
❑ 94YakBeaF-3863
❑ 95VerBeaDTI-17
❑ 97VerBeaD-19
Nelson, Chester
❑ 77NewCoPT-24
Nelson, Chris
❑ 96MidLeaAB-58
❑ 96WesMicWB-18
❑ 97HunStaTI-20
❑ 97ModA'sG-19
❑ 98HunStaTI-25
Nelson, Darren
❑ 87EriCarP-25
❑ 88St.PetCS-19
Nelson, Dave (David Earl)
❑ 69MilBra-199
❑ 69Top-579
❑ 70OPC-112
❑ 70Top-112
❑ 71MLBOffS-547
❑ 71OPC-241
❑ 71SenTealW-18
❑ 71Top-241
❑ 72RanTeal-20
❑ 72Top-529
❑ 73LinPor-179
❑ 73OPC-111
❑ 73RanTeal-18
❑ 73Top-111
❑ 74GreHeroBP-5
❑ 74OPC-355
❑ 74Top-355
❑ 74TopDecE-4
❑ 74TopSta-238
❑ 75OPC-435
❑ 75RanPos-24
❑ 75RanPos-25
❑ 75ShrCapT-13
❑ 75SSP42-18
❑ 75Top-435
❑ 75TopMin-435
❑ 76KanCitRP-21
❑ 76OPC-535
❑ 76ShrCapT-10
❑ 76SSP-273
❑ 76Top-535
❑ 78Roy-15
❑ 84WhiSoxTV-8
❑ 92IndFanC-30
❑ 93IndWUA-33
❑ 93RanKee-30
❑ 94RanAllP-1
Nelson, Doug
❑ 75ShrCapT-14
❑ 76ShrCapT-4
❑ 77ColCliT-14
❑ 77ShrCapT-15
Nelson, Doug P.
❑ 87EugEmeP-2657
❑ 88AppFoxP-141
❑ 89BasCitRS-19
❑ 90MemChiB-24
❑ 90MemChiP-1004
❑ 90MemChiS-21
Nelson, Earl
❑ 93IdaFalBF-4027
❑ 93IdaFalBSP-5
Nelson, Eric
❑ 89WelPirP-19
Nelson, Erick
❑ 97DurBulTI-12
❑ 98DanQ-C-26
Nelson, Frank
❑ 47SunBre-13
❑ 49RemBre-19
❑ 50RemBre-18
Nelson, Gene
❑ 79AshTouT-28
❑ 81TopTra-809
❑ 81YanPhoA-17
❑ 82Don-513
❑ 82Fle-45
❑ 82MarPos-23
❑ 82Top-373
❑ 82TopTra-80T
❑ 83Don-55
❑ 83Top-106
❑ 85Don-615
❑ 85Fle-522
❑ 85TopTifT-86T
❑ 85TopTra-86T
❑ 85WhiSoxC-30
❑ 86Don-501
❑ 86Fle-213
❑ 86Lea-245
❑ 86Top-493
❑ 86TopTif-493
❑ 86WhiSoxC-30
❑ 87Don-580
❑ 87Fle-504
❑ 87FleGlo-504
❑ 87FleUpd-86
❑ 87FleUpdG-86
❑ 87Top-273
❑ 87TopTif-273
❑ 87TopTra-84T
❑ 87TopTraT-84T
❑ 88A'sMot-25
❑ 88Don-133
❑ 88DonTeaBA-133
❑ 88Fle-288
❑ 88FleGlo-288
❑ 88Sco-588
❑ 88ScoGlo-588
❑ 88Top-621
❑ 88TopTif-621
❑ 89A'sMot-26
❑ 89Bow-185
❑ 89BowTif-185
❑ 89Don-540
❑ 89Fle-18
❑ 89FleGlo-18
❑ 89OPC-318
❑ 89Sco-434
❑ 89Top-581
❑ 89TopTif-581
❑ 89UppDec-643
❑ 89Woo-16
❑ 90A'sMot-22
❑ 90Don-540
❑ 90Fle-17
❑ 90FleCan-17
❑ 90Lea-477
❑ 90OPC-726
❑ 90Sco-441
❑ 90Top-726
❑ 90TopTif-726
❑ 90UppDec-80
❑ 91A'sMot-22
❑ 91A'sSFE-10
❑ 91Don-385
❑ 91Fle-19
❑ 91Lea-328
❑ 91OPC-316
❑ 91Sco-478
❑ 91StaClu-359
❑ 91Top-316
❑ 91TopDesS-316
❑ 91TopMic-316
❑ 91TopTif-316
❑ 91UppDec-403
❑ 92AthMot-22
❑ 92Don-696
❑ 92Fle-264
❑ 92OPC-62
❑ 92Pin-443
❑ 92Sco-383
❑ 92StaClu-414
❑ 92Top-62
❑ 92TopGol-62
❑ 92TopGolW-62
❑ 92TopMic-62
❑ 92Ult-426
❑ 92UppDec-508
❑ 92YanWIZ8-131
❑ 93AngMot-17
❑ 93AngStaCl-22
❑ 93FleFinE-186
❑ 93RanKee-416
❑ 94Sco-274
❑ 94ScoGolR-274
Nelson, Harry
❑ 09ObaT21-19
❑ 09ObaT21-107
Nelson, Jackson
❑ 87BucN28-61
❑ 87OldJudN-363
❑ 90KalBatN-42
Nelson, Jamie
❑ 83SalLakCGT-16
❑ 84Nes792-166
❑ 84Top-166
❑ 84TopTif-166
❑ 84VanCanC-43
❑ 85VanCanC-221
❑ 87MemChiB-26
❑ 87MemChiP-8
❑ 88ColCliC-12
❑ 88ColCliP-23
❑ 88ColCliP-305
❑ 89EdmTraC-19
❑ 89EdmTraP-569
❑ 90CMC-565
❑ 90PorBeaC-13
❑ 90PorBeaP-180
❑ 90ProAAAF-250
Nelson, Jeff
❑ 86BakDodP-22
❑ 87SalSpuS-27
❑ 88SanBerSB-23
❑ 88SanBerSCLC-48
❑ 89WilBilP-637
❑ 89WilBilS-15
❑ 90WilBilB-17
❑ 90WilBilP-1056
❑ 90WilBilS-18
❑ 91JacSunLD-339
❑ 91JacSunP-147
❑ 91LinDriAA-339
❑ 92Don-408
❑ 92FleUpd-57
❑ 92MarMot-19
❑ 93Don-685
❑ 93Fle-311
❑ 93MarMot-19
❑ 93Sco-272
❑ 93StaClu-467
❑ 93StaCluFDI-467
❑ 93StaCluMOP-467
❑ 93Top-493
❑ 93TopGol-493
❑ 93TopInaM-493
❑ 93TopInaR-493
❑ 93TopMic-493
❑ 94ColC-609
❑ 94ColChoGS-609
❑ 94ColChoSS-609
❑ 94Don-492
❑ 94Fle-296
❑ 94HelBreSP-29
❑ 94MarMot-25
❑ 94Pac-578
❑ 94Sco-302
❑ 94ScoGolR-302
❑ 94Top-24
❑ 94TopGol-24
❑ 94TopSpa-24
❑ 95Don-438
❑ 95DonPreP-438
❑ 95Fla-84
❑ 95FleUpd-76
❑ 95MarMot-25
❑ 95MarPac-37
❑ 95Top-564
❑ 95TopCyb-340
❑ 96BelSnaTI-24
❑ 96Don-108
❑ 96DonPreP-108
❑ 96Fle-191
❑ 96FleTif-191
❑ 96FleUpd-U65
❑ 96FleUpdTC-U65
❑ 96LeaSigEA-140
❑ 96Ult-391
❑ 96UltGolM-391
❑ 97Fle-173
❑ 97FleTif-173
❑ 97PacPriGotD-GD75
❑ 98PacInvGems-77
❑ 98PacOnl-510
❑ 98PacOnlR-510
❑ 98PacOnlWC-510
❑ 99YanFle-15
Nelson, Jerome
❑ 86ModA'sC-16
❑ 86ModA'sP-20
❑ 87ModA'sC-12
❑ 87ModA'sP-5
❑ 88HunStaTI-13
❑ 89ChaLooB-23
❑ 89ChaLooGS-19
❑ 90ChaLooGS-23
❑ 91RicBraBC-31
❑ 92HarSenF-472
Nelson, Jim
❑ 81LynSaiT-13
❑ 82LynSaiT-9
Nelson, Jim (James Lorin)
❑ 71OPC-298
❑ 71Top-298
Nelson, Joe
❑ 96EugEmeB-16
❑ 97DurBulTI-13
❑ 98GreBraG-16
Nelson, Kim
❑ 79WisRapTT-11
Nelson, Lindsey
❑ 89MetRinP69-34
❑ 95TenVolW-14
Nelson, Lynn (Lynn B.)
❑ 33Zee-48
❑ 34DiaMatCSB-140
❑ 34Gou-60
❑ 38CloFotW-69
❑ 39PlaBal-118
❑ 40PlaBal-135
Nelson, Mel
❑ 60DarFar-11
❑ 61UniOil-P10
❑ 63Top-522
❑ 64Top-273
❑ 64TopVen-273
❑ 65Top-564
❑ 66Top-367
❑ 66TopVen-367
❑ 69OPC-181
❑ 69Top-181
❑ 69TopFou-11
❑ 81TCM60I-346
Nelson, Merton
❑ 28Zee-56
❑ 29Zee-53
❑ 30Zee-62
Nelson, Michael
❑ 89PeoChiTI-34
❑ 90PeoChiTI-3
❑ 91PeoChiTI-30
Nelson, Pat
❑ 78AshTouT-20
❑ 79AshTouT-19
Nelson, Red (Albert)
❑ 09ColChiE-213A
❑ 09ColChiE-213B
❑ 11PinT-5-1057
❑ 12ColRedB-213A
❑ 12ColRedB-213B
❑ 12ColTinT-213A
❑ 12ColTinT-213B
❑ 12T207-139
Nelson, Rick
❑ 84Don-636
❑ 84Fle-615
❑ 84Nes792-672
❑ 84Top-672
❑ 84TopSti-347
❑ 84TopTif-672
❑ 85CalCanC-91
❑ 85EveGiaC-11A
❑ 85EveGiaC-11B
❑ 85Top-296
❑ 85TopTif-296
❑ 86CalCanP-18
❑ 86CliGiaP-16
❑ 87TidTidP-16
❑ 88ShrCapP-1294
❑ 90ShrCapP-1455
❑ 90ShrCapS-16
Nelson, Rob
❑ 83IdaFalAT-22
❑ 84MadMusP-11
❑ 85HunStaJ-41
❑ 86TacTigP-15
❑ 87Don-595
❑ 87DonOpeD-25
❑ 87Fle-653
❑ 87FleGlo-653
❑ 87SpoTeaP-23
❑ 88Don-574
❑ 88LasVegSC-16
❑ 88LasVegSP-237
❑ 89LasVegSC-16
❑ 89LasVegSP-24
❑ 89PadPos-20
❑ 90Bow-213
❑ 90BowTif-213
❑ 90UppDec-51
❑ 91LinDriAAA-642
❑ 91VanCanLD-642
❑ 91VanCanP-1604
❑ 92PorBeaS-415
Nelson, Rocky (Glenn Richard)
❑ 52Par-61
❑ 52Top-390
❑ 53ExhCan-49
❑ 54Top-199
❑ 59Top-446
❑ 60KeyChal-37
❑ 60Lea-127
❑ 60Top-157
❑ 60TopVen-157
❑ 61Kah-29
❑ 61Pos-137
❑ 61Raw-8
❑ 61Top-304
❑ 61TopStal-68
❑ 74dod195T-25
❑ 75TCM195Cl-25
❑ 77PirTCM1WC-11
❑ 82OhiHaloF-59
❑ 83TopRep5-390
❑ 90DodTar-570
❑ 94TopArc1-199
❑ 94TopArc1G-199
❑ 95TopArcBD-30
Nelson, Rod
❑ 79CliDodT-20
Nelson, Rodney
❑ 95SprSulTI-18
Nelson, Roger
❑ 67BalOriP-73
❑ 68Top-549
❑ 69MLBOffS-61
❑ 69RoySol-11
❑ 69RoyTeal-9
❑ 69Top-279
❑ 69TopSta-186
❑ 69TopSup-23
❑ 69TopTeaP-7
❑ 70MLBOffS-225
❑ 70Top-633
❑ 71OPC-581
❑ 71Top-581
❑ 72oyTeal-16
❑ 73OPC-251
❑ 73Top-251
❑ 74OPC-491
❑ 74Top-491
❑ 75OPC-572
❑ 75Top-572
❑ 75TopMin-572
❑ 75TucTorC-20
❑ 75TucTorTI-13

❑ 76OmaRoyTT-16
❑ 78ColCliT-17
❑ 81TCM60I-396
❑ 91OriCro-326

Nelson, Ron

❑ 87SpaPhiP-12

Nelson, Scott

❑ 88CliGiaP-698
❑ 89SalSpuCLC-127
❑ 89SalSpuP-1824

Nelson, Spike

❑ 49EurSta-192

Nelson, Tom (Thomas C.)

❑ 47SunBre-14

Nelson, Tracie

❑ 96BelSnaTI-25

Nelson, Travion

❑ 92GulCoaYF-3704

Nelson, Tray

❑ 92HigSchPLS-21
❑ 94OneYanC-16
❑ 94OneYanF-3804

Nemeth, Carey

❑ 86EriCarP-20
❑ 87SavCarP-16

Nemeth, Joe

❑ 79WauTimT-9
❑ 80AshTouT-12
❑ 81TulDriT-11
❑ 82ReaPhiT-17
❑ 82TulDriT-24
❑ 83TulDriT-19

Nen, Dick (Richard LeRoy)

❑ 64Top-14
❑ 64TopVen-14
❑ 65Top-466
❑ 66OPC-149
❑ 66Top-149
❑ 66TopVen-149
❑ 67CokCapS-11
❑ 67DexPre-151
❑ 67SenPos-16
❑ 67Top-403
❑ 68Top-591
❑ 69MilBra-200
❑ 90DodTar-571

Nen, Robb

❑ 88ButCopKSP-5
❑ 88GasRanP-1003
❑ 89GasRanP-1003
❑ 89GasRanS-16
❑ 89Sta-139
❑ 90Bow-487
❑ 90BowTif-487
❑ 90ChaRanS-15
❑ 91Bow-270
❑ 91Cla/Bes-240
❑ 91LinDriAA-589
❑ 91TulDriLD-589
❑ 91TulDriP-2769
❑ 91TulDriTI-20
❑ 92ClaFS7-288
❑ 92SkyAA F-271
❑ 92TulDriF-2692
❑ 92TulDriS-612
❑ 92UppDecML-84
❑ 93FleFinE-281
❑ 93MarPub-18
❑ 93PacSpa-643
❑ 93Pin-586
❑ 93RanKee-417
❑ 93RanStaC-24
❑ 93Ult-633
❑ 93UppDec-687
❑ 93UppDecGold-687
❑ 94ColC-604
❑ 94ColChoGS-604
❑ 94ColChoSS-604
❑ 94Don-625
❑ 94FleUpd-138
❑ 94Lea-212
❑ 94MarTeal-12
❑ 94Pin-279
❑ 94PinArtP-279
❑ 94PinMusC-279
❑ 94StaClu-45
❑ 94StaCluFDI-45
❑ 94StaCluGR-45
❑ 94StaCluMOP-45
❑ 94StaCluT-80
❑ 94StaCluTFDI-80
❑ 94Top-284
❑ 94TopGol-284
❑ 94TopSpa-284
❑ 95ColCho-308
❑ 95ColChoGS-308
❑ 95ColChoSS-308
❑ 95Don-149
❑ 95DonPreP-149
❑ 95DonTopotO-245
❑ 95Fin-206
❑ 95FinRef-206
❑ 95Fla-140
❑ 95Fle-338
❑ 95FleTeaL-19
❑ 95Lea-170
❑ 95Pac-174
❑ 95Pin-439
❑ 95PinArtP-439
❑ 95PinMusC-439
❑ 95Sco-187
❑ 95ScoGolR-187
❑ 95ScoPlaTS-187
❑ 95StaClu-159
❑ 95StaCluFDI-159
❑ 95StaCluMOP-159
❑ 95StaCluSTWS-159
❑ 95StaCluVR-84
❑ 95StaCluVRMO-84
❑ 95Top-528
❑ 95TopCyb-313
❑ 95Ult-382
❑ 95UltGolM-382
❑ 95UppDec-114
❑ 95UppDecED-114
❑ 95UppDecEDG-114
❑ 96ColCho-151
❑ 96ColChoGS-151
❑ 96ColChoSS-151
❑ 96Don-159
❑ 96DonPreP-159
❑ 96Fla-265
❑ 96Fle-390
❑ 96FleTif-390
❑ 96LeaSigA-167
❑ 96LeaSigAG-167
❑ 96LeaSigAS-167
❑ 96Pac-68
❑ 96Sco-486
❑ 96StaClu-161
❑ 96StaCluEPB-161
❑ 96StaCluEPG-161
❑ 96StaCluEPS-161
❑ 96StaCluMOP-161
❑ 96Top-69
❑ 96Ult-202
❑ 96UltGolM-202
❑ 96UppDec-337
❑ 97Bow-17
❑ 97BowChr-13
❑ 97BowChrI-13
❑ 97BowChrIR-13
❑ 97BowChrR-13
❑ 97BowInt-17
❑ 97Cir-151
❑ 97CirRav-151
❑ 97ColCho-117
❑ 97ColChoT-FM7
❑ 97Don-307
❑ 97DonGolPP-307
❑ 97DonSilPP-307
❑ 97Fin-242
❑ 97FinRef-242
❑ 97Fle-333
❑ 97FleTif-333
❑ 97Lea-258
❑ 97LeaFraM-258
❑ 97LeaFraMDC-258
❑ 97MarPac-17
❑ 97MetUni-177
❑ 97NewPin-26
❑ 97NewPinAP-26
❑ 97NewPinMC-26
❑ 97NewPinPP-26
❑ 97Pac-303
❑ 97PacLigB-303
❑ 97PacSil-303
❑ 97PinCer-60
❑ 97PinCerMBla-60
❑ 97PinCerMBlu-60
❑ 97PinCerMG-60
❑ 97PinCerMR-60
❑ 97PinCerR-60
❑ 97PinTotCPB-60
❑ 97PinTotCPG-60
❑ 97PinTotCPR-60
❑ 97Sco-266
❑ 97ScoArtPWB-266
❑ 97ScoPreS-266
❑ 97ScoShoS-266
❑ 97ScoShoSAP-266
❑ 97StaClu-321
❑ 97StaCluMOP-321
❑ 97Top-79
❑ 97TopChr-29
❑ 97TopChrR-29
❑ 97TopGal-120
❑ 97TopGalPPI-120
❑ 97Ult-200
❑ 97UltGolME-200
❑ 97UltPlaME-200
❑ 97UppDec-361
❑ 98CirThu-166
❑ 98CirThuRav-166
❑ 98CirThuSupRav-166
❑ 98ColCho-128
❑ 98ColCho-491
❑ 98CroRoy-123
❑ 98Fle-166
❑ 98Fle-530
❑ 98GiaMot-14
❑ 98Pac-306
❑ 98PacAur-199
❑ 98PacOme-215
❑ 98PacOmeR-215
❑ 98PacOnl-668
❑ 98PacOnlR-668
❑ 98PacOnlWC-668
❑ 98PacPar-249
❑ 98PacParC-249
❑ 98PacParG-249
❑ 98PacParHS-249
❑ 98PacParPB-249
❑ 98PacParR-249
❑ 98PacPlaB-306
❑ 98PacRedT-306
❑ 98PacSil-306
❑ 98Pin-102
❑ 98PinPlu-48
❑ 98PinPreP-102
❑ 98Sco-163
❑ 98ScoRT-202
❑ 98ScoSS-PP69
❑ 98ScoSSAP-PP69
❑ 98SP Aut-174
❑ 98SPxFin-317
❑ 98SPxFinR-317
❑ 98SPxFinS-317
❑ 98StaCluFDI-390
❑ 98StaCluI-390
❑ 98StaCluOneK-390
❑ 98StaCluPP-390
❑ 98Top-398
❑ 98TopChr-398
❑ 98TopChrR-398
❑ 98TopDevR-398
❑ 98TopDia-398
❑ 98TopMiniC-398
❑ 98Ult-352
❑ 98UltGolM-352
❑ 98UltMas-352
❑ 98UltPlaM-352
❑ 98UppDec-98
❑ 98UppDec-722
❑ 99199Fin-39
❑ 99FinGolRef-39
❑ 99FinRef-39
❑ 99Fle-184
❑ 99FleSta9-184
❑ 99FleWarT-184
❑ 99MetUni-132
❑ 99MetUniGM-132
❑ 99MetUniPMG-132
❑ 99Pac-386
❑ 99PacOme-214
❑ 99PacOmeC-214
❑ 99PacOmeG-214
❑ 99PacOmePB-214
❑ 99PacPar-212
❑ 99PacParC-212
❑ 99PacParG-212
❑ 99PacParHoloGold-212
❑ 99PacParHS-212
❑ 99PacParOD-212
❑ 99PacParPB-212
❑ 99PacParRed-212
❑ 99PacPlaB-386
❑ 99PacPri-130
❑ 99PacPriHB-130
❑ 99PacPriHG-130
❑ 99PacPriHM-130
❑ 99PacPriHP-130
❑ 99PacPriRed-130
❑ 99PacRed-386
❑ 99SkyPre-22
❑ 99SkyPreR-22
❑ 99SkyThu-144
❑ 99SkyThuRant-144
❑ 99SkyThuRave-144
❑ 99SP SigAuto-RN
❑ 99SPSig-156
❑ 99StaClu-33
❑ 99StaCluFDI-33
❑ 99StaCluOoaK-33
❑ 99StaCluPP-33
❑ 99ThuSkySupR-144
❑ 99Top-160
❑ 99TopChr-160
❑ 99TopChrR-160
❑ 99TopMVPP-160
❑ 99UD Cho-141
❑ 99UD ChoPCR-141
❑ 99Ult-194
❑ 99UltGolM-194
❑ 99UltMas-194
❑ 99UltPlaM-194
❑ 99UppDec-200
❑ 99UppDecCLM-C85
❑ 99UppDecE-79
❑ 99UppDecEFXG-79
❑ 99UppDecEL1-200
❑ 99UppDecEL2-200
❑ 99UppDecM-189
❑ 99UppDecMGS-189
❑ 99UppDecMHFS-189
❑ 99UppDecMSS-189
❑ 99UppDecR-75
❑ 99UppDecRG-75
❑ 99UppDecRP-75
❑ 99Vic-354

Nenad, David

❑ 82CliGiaF-9

Neneviller, Tom

❑ 93ClaFS7-230

Nerat, Dan

❑ 91SouOreAC-27
❑ 91SouOreAP-3841
❑ 92ModA'sF-3897

Neri, Frank

❑ 52LavPro-4

Nerone, Phil

❑ 75AppFoxT-20
❑ 76AppFoxT-16

Nesmoe, Davey

❑ 80QuaCitCT-31

Ness, John

❑ 13Zee-42
❑ 14Zee-45
❑ 15Zee-48

Nestor, Don

❑ 94BoiHawC-20
❑ 94BoiHawF-3352

Nestor, Joe

❑ 97PriWilC-25

Nettles, Dru

❑ 93Sou-14

Nettles, Graig

❑ 69OPC-99
❑ 69Top-99A
❑ 69Top-99B
❑ 70Ind-9
❑ 70OPC-491
❑ 70Top-491
❑ 71MLBOffS-380
❑ 71OPC-324
❑ 71Top-324
❑ 72Top-590
❑ 73LinPor-134
❑ 73NewYorSNM-12
❑ 73OPC-498
❑ 73SyrChiTI-21
❑ 73Top-498
❑ 73Yan-4
❑ 74OPC-251
❑ 74SyrChiTI-20
❑ 74Top-251
❑ 74TopSta-217
❑ 75Hos-24
❑ 75HosTwi-24
❑ 75OPC-160
❑ 75SyrChiTI-14
❑ 75Top-160
❑ 75TopMin-160
❑ 75YanSSP-20
❑ 76Hos-81
❑ 76OPC-169
❑ 76SSP-437
❑ 76Top-169
❑ 77BurCheD-174
❑ 77Hos-116
❑ 77OPC-2
❑ 77OPC-217
❑ 77Top-2
❑ 77Top-20
❑ 77YanBurK-15
❑ 78Hos-132
❑ 78OPC-10
❑ 78RCColC-88
❑ 78SSP270-25
❑ 78Top-250
❑ 78WifBalD-54
❑ 78YanBurK-14
❑ 78YanPhoA-19
❑ 78YanSSPD-25
❑ 79BasPat-61
❑ 79Hos-110
❑ 79OPC-240
❑ 79Top-460
❑ 79YanBurK-15
❑ 79YanPicA-28
❑ 80Kel-18
❑ 80OPC-359
❑ 80Top-710
❑ 80TopSup-21
❑ 80YanPhoA-18
❑ 81AllGamPI-36
❑ 81Don-105
❑ 81Fle-87A
❑ 81Fle-87B
❑ 81FleStiC-72
❑ 81OPC-365
❑ 81Top-365
❑ 81TopSupHT-69
❑ 81YanPhoA-18
❑ 82Don-335
❑ 82Dra-26
❑ 82Fle-46
❑ 82FleSta-119
❑ 82FleSta-238
❑ 82LouSlu-4
❑ 82OPC-21
❑ 82OPC-62
❑ 82Top-505
❑ 82Top-506
❑ 82TopSti-215
❑ 82TopStiV-215
❑ 82YanPhoA-19
❑ 83AllGamPI-36
❑ 83Don-83
❑ 83Fle-391
❑ 83FleSta-137
❑ 83FleSti-38
❑ 83OPC-207
❑ 83OPC-293
❑ 83Top-635
❑ 83Top-636
❑ 83TopFol-2
❑ 83TopSti-13
❑ 83YanPhoA-18
❑ 83YanRoyRD-7
❑ 84AllGamPI-33
❑ 84Don-518
❑ 84DonCha-12
❑ 84Fle-135
❑ 84FleUpd-82
❑ 84FunFooP-66
❑ 84Nes792-175
❑ 84Nes792-712
❑ 84Nes792-713
❑ 84OCoandSI-196
❑ 84OPC-175
❑ 84PadMot-22
❑ 84Top-175
❑ 84Top-712
❑ 84Top-713
❑ 84TopSti-326
❑ 84TopTif-175
❑ 84TopTif-712
❑ 84TopTif-713
❑ 84TopTra-83T
❑ 84TopTraT-83T
❑ 85AllGamPI-123
❑ 85Don-234
❑ 85Fle-42
❑ 85Lea-177
❑ 85OPC-35
❑ 85PadMot-4
❑ 85Top-35
❑ 85TopSti-155
❑ 85TopTif-35
❑ 86Don-478
❑ 86DonAll-6
❑ 86DonPop-6
❑ 86Fle-332
❑ 86GenMilB-5E
❑ 86OPC-151
❑ 86SevCoi-W11
❑ 86Spo-91
❑ 86Top-450
❑ 86TopGloA-15
❑ 86TopSti-106
❑ 86TopSti-151
❑ 86TopTat-7
❑ 86TopTif-450
❑ 87BraSmo-15
❑ 87Fle-426
❑ 87FleGlo-426
❑ 87OPC-205
❑ 87RedFolSB-87
❑ 87Top-205
❑ 87TopTif-205
❑ 87TopTra-85T
❑ 87TopTraT-85T
❑ 88AlaGolAA60TI-4
❑ 88ExpPos-23
❑ 88SanDieS-14
❑ 88SanDieSAAG-13
❑ 88Sco-440
❑ 88ScoGlo-440
❑ 88ScoRoo-25T
❑ 88ScoRooG-25T
❑ 88Top-574
❑ 88TopTif-574
❑ 89PacSenL-115
❑ 89PacSenL-132
❑ 89PacSenL-158
❑ 89SanDieSAG-12
❑ 89Sco-277
❑ 89T/MSenL-82
❑ 89TopSenL-25
❑ 90EliSenL-43
❑ 91FouBal-25
❑ 91LinDri-26
❑ 91SweBasG-67
❑ 92KodCelD-3
❑ 92MCIAmb-6
❑ 92MVP-7
❑ 92MVP2H-19
❑ 92YanWIZ7-122
❑ 92YanWIZA-53
❑ 93ActPacA-162
❑ 93MCIAmb-13
❑ 93TedWil-68
❑ 93UppDecS-11
❑ 93UppDecS-13
❑ 93Yoo-13
❑ 94UppDecAH-148
❑ 94UppDecAH1-148
❑ 95PadMot-28
❑ 95SonGre-10
❑ 99SpollIGotG-90
❑ 99SpollIGotGA-51
❑ 99SpollIGotGC-42

Nettles, Jim (James W.)

❑ 71OPC-74
❑ 71Top-74
❑ 72OPC-131
❑ 72Top-131
❑ 72TwiPos-13
❑ 73OPC-358
❑ 73TacTwiC-16
❑ 73Top-358
❑ 75OPC-497
❑ 75Top-497
❑ 75TopMin-497
❑ 77ColCliT-15
❑ 80ColCliP-28
❑ 80ColCliT-12
❑ 81TacTigT-12
❑ 82TacTigT-17
❑ 83IdaFalAT-30
❑ 83TacTigT-20
❑ 84IdaFalATI-18
❑ 85MadMusP-20
❑ 85MadMusT-23
❑ 86MadMusP-24
❑ 86MadMusP-15
❑ 87MadMusP-22
❑ 87MadMusP-4
❑ 88MadMusP-16
❑ 88SanDieS-13
❑ 88SanDieSAAG-14
❑ 89MadMusS-17
❑ 89PacSenL-126A
❑ 89PacSenL-126B
❑ 89SanDieSAG-13
❑ 90EliSenL-44
❑ 90PenPilS-25
❑ 91JacSunLD-349
❑ 91JacSunP-166
❑ 91LinDriAA-349
❑ 92MedHatBJF-3222
❑ 92MedHatBJSP-29

❑ 93HagSunC-25
❑ 93HagSunF-1895
❑ 94DunBluJC-27
❑ 94DunBluJF-2572
❑ 95DunBluJTI-16
Nettles, Morris
❑ 74SalLakCAC-95
❑ 75CalAngP-28
❑ 75OPC-632
❑ 75Top-632
❑ 75TopMin-632
❑ 76OPC-434
❑ 76SSP-202
❑ 76Top-434
❑ 76TopTra-434T
Nettles, Robert
❑ 86EriCarP-21
Nettnin, Rodney
❑ 91MiaMirC-3
Netzel, Milo
❑ 09ObaT21-122
❑ 09ObaT21-388
❑ 12ObaPreT-137
Neubart, Garrett
❑ 96AshTouB-27
❑ 97Bow-361
❑ 97BowInt-361
❑ 97SalAva-22
❑ 98BinMetQ-22
Neuberger, Scott
❑ 98ChaRivDG-20
Neuendorff, Tony
❑ 83DurBulT-11
❑ 84DurBulT-16
Neuenschwander, Doug
❑ 80WatRedT-4
❑ 81WatRedT-5
Neufang, Gerry
❑ 82TulDriT-20
❑ 83TulDriT-23
Neun, Johnny
❑ 76TayBow4-75
❑ 91ConTSN-204
Neuzil, Jeff
❑ 84MemChiT-10
Nevala, Adam
❑ 98ButCopKG-21
Nevers, Ernie
❑ 27MidBre-36
❑ 29Zee-54
❑ 30Zee-63
❑ 92ConTSN-394
Nevers, Tom
❑ 90AshTouC-16
❑ 90ClaDraP-21
❑ 91AshTouP-577
❑ 91Bow-542
❑ 91Cla/Bes-201
❑ 91Sco-387
❑ 91SouAtlLAGP-SAL2
❑ 92Bow-226
❑ 92ClaFS7-208
❑ 92OscAstC-1
❑ 92OscAstF-2539
❑ 92ProFS7-234
❑ 92UppDec-53
❑ 92UppDecML-250
❑ 93Bow-68
❑ 93ClaFS7-228
❑ 93ClaGolF-67
❑ 93ExcFS7-49
❑ 93JacGenF-2116
❑ 94JacGenF-225
❑ 95JacGenTI-24
❑ 96HarCitRCB-22
❑ 97LouRedB-25
Nevill, Glenn
❑ 91BatCliCB-19
❑ 91BatCliP-3482
❑ 92BatCliCB-14
❑ 92BatCliF-3262
Neville, Dan
❑ 65Top-398
Neville, David
❑ 89BenBucL-13
Neville, Eddie
❑ 94CarLeaA-DJ31
Neville, Frank
❑ 92BluOriC-25
❑ 93BluOriC-27
Nevin, Phil
❑ 91TopGolS-3
❑ 91TopTra-83T
❑ 91TopTraT-83T
❑ 92Bow-670
❑ 92ClaDraP-1
❑ 92ClaDraPFB-BC1
❑ 92ClaDraPP-BB1
❑ 92ClaDraPP-2
❑ 92StaCluD-130
❑ 92StaCluFDP-3
❑ 92TopTra-82T
❑ 92TopTraG-82T
❑ 93ClaInsC-6
❑ 93ClaYouG-YG15
❑ 93StaCluM-83
❑ 93TucTorF-3069
❑ 94ActPac-14
❑ 94ActPac-61
❑ 94ActPac2G-7G
❑ 94ActPac2GD-7G
❑ 94Cla-90
❑ 94ClaCreotC-C20
❑ 94ClaGolA-SH4
❑ 94ClaGolF-16
❑ 94ClaGolP-2
❑ 94ExcFS7-207
❑ 94SigRoo-37
❑ 94SigRooFCS-AU9
❑ 94SigRooHP-S8
❑ 94SigRooHPS-S8
❑ 94SigRooP-2
❑ 94SigRooS-37
❑ 94TucTorF-771
❑ 94UppDecML-156
❑ 94UppDecML-230
❑ 94UppDecMLT1PJF-TP6
❑ 94UppDecMLT1PMF-6
❑ 95ActPacF-14
❑ 95AstMot-13
❑ 95ColCho-9
❑ 95ColChoGS-9
❑ 95ColChoSS-9
❑ 95Fin-295
❑ 95FinRef-295
❑ 95SP-62
❑ 95SPCha-51
❑ 95SPChaDC-51
❑ 95SPSil-62
❑ 95StaCluCB-CB4
❑ 95StaCluMOP-CB4
❑ 95TucTotTI-18
❑ 95UppDecML-22
❑ 95UppDecMLFS-22
❑ 96ColCho-548
❑ 96ColChoGS-548
❑ 96ColChoSS-548
❑ 96Don-506
❑ 96DonPreP-506
❑ 96Fin-B138
❑ 96FinRef-B138
❑ 96JacSunB-22
❑ 96Pac-311
❑ 96Pin-172
❑ 96PinAfi-119
❑ 96PinAfiAP-119
❑ 96PinArtP-98
❑ 96PinSta-98
❑ 96ProSta-122
❑ 96Sco-465
❑ 96SelTeaN-13
❑ 96Spo-50
❑ 96SpoArtP-50
❑ 96StaClu-60
❑ 96StaCluMOP-60
❑ 96Top-348
❑ 96UppDec-69
❑ 97Cir-289
❑ 97CirRav-289
❑ 97ColCho-103
❑ 97Fle-102
❑ 97FleTif-102
❑ 97Pac-92
❑ 97PacLigB-92
❑ 97PacSil-92
❑ 97Sco-407
❑ 97ScoArtPWB-407
❑ 97ScoResC-407
❑ 97ScoShoS-407
❑ 97ScoShoSAP-407
❑ 97Top-369
❑ 97Ult-547
❑ 97UltGolME-547
❑ 97UltPlaME-547
❑ 98Fle-518
❑ 98PacInvGems-49
❑ 98PacOnl-18
❑ 98PacOnlR-18
❑ 98PacOnlWC-18
❑ 99Pac-10
❑ 99PacPlaB-10
❑ 99PacRed-10
❑ 99StaClu-292
❑ 99StaCluFDI-292
❑ 99StaCluOoaK-292
❑ 99StaCluPP-292
Newberg, Tom
❑ 87SalSpuS-24
❑ 88VerMarP-955
❑ 90MarMot-28
Newby, Mike
❑ 90HamRedB-11
❑ 90HamRedS-17
Newcomb, Chris
❑ 92ButCopKSP-14
Newcomb, Joe Dean
❑ 89KnoBluJB-19
❑ 89KnoBluJP-1135
❑ 89KnoBluJS-15
Newcombe, Don (Donald)
❑ 47Exh-166A
❑ 47Exh-166B
❑ 47Exh-166C
❑ 47PM1StaP1-150
❑ 47PM1StaP1-151
❑ 47PM1StaP1-152
❑ 47PM1StaP1-153
❑ 47StaPinP2-30
❑ 49EurSta-45
❑ 50Bow-23
❑ 51Bow-6
❑ 51R42SmaS-74
❑ 52BerRos-46
❑ 52Bow-128
❑ 52StaCalL-79D
❑ 53Bri-38
❑ 53ExhCan-16
❑ 54Bow-154
❑ 54NewYorJA-12
❑ 54StaMey-10
❑ 55Bow-143
❑ 55DodGolS-2
❑ 55RobGouS-21
❑ 55RobGouW-21
❑ 55StaMey-9
❑ 56Dod-20
❑ 56Dod-21
❑ 56Top-235
❑ 56YelBasP-24
❑ 57Top-130
❑ 58DodJayP-9
❑ 58DodTeal-17
❑ 58DodVol-9
❑ 58Hir-13
❑ 58Top-340
❑ 59DodVol-10
❑ 59RedEnq-15
❑ 59RedShiBS-14
❑ 59Top-312
❑ 60Kah-28
❑ 60Lea-19
❑ 60RawGloT-23
❑ 60RedJayP-6
❑ 60Top-345
❑ 60TopTat-41
❑ 61Top-483
❑ 70Houof J-20
❑ 75OPC-194
❑ 75TCMHouoJ-22
❑ 75Top-194
❑ 75TopMin-194
❑ 77GalGloG-17
❑ 79TCM50-182
❑ 82TCMGreP-10
❑ 86SpoDecG-39
❑ 87Dod195T-7
❑ 88DodRinP1-3A
❑ 88PacLegI-33
❑ 89DodSmoG-55
❑ 89SweBasG-122
❑ 90DodTar-572
❑ 90PacLeg-42
❑ 90SweBasG-76
❑ 91SweBasG-68
❑ 91TopArc1-320
❑ 92ActPacA-51
❑ 92BazQua5A-2
❑ 93MetIma-14
❑ 93TedWil-15
❑ 93TedWil-139
❑ 94UppDecAH-72
❑ 94UppDecAH1-72
❑ 95DodROY-2
❑ 95TopArcBD-36
❑ 95TopArcBD-62
❑ 95TopArcBD-88
❑ 95TopArcBD-129
❑ 95TopArcBD-158
❑ 97NegLeaPC-10S
❑ 98BowChrR-3
❑ 98BowChrRR-3
Newcomer, Breen
❑ 77BriRedST-13
Newell, Brandon
❑ 93PitMetC-15
❑ 93PitMetF-3707
❑ 94CapCitBC-15
❑ 94CapCitBF-1749
❑ 95StLucMTI-24
Newell, Brett
❑ 94DanBraC-20
❑ 94DanBraF-3542
❑ 95MacBraTI-21
❑ 96GreBraB-22
❑ 96GreBraTI-15
❑ 97EugEmeB-10
❑ 98WilBluRC-22
Newell, Paul
❑ 93MisStaB-33
Newell, Tom
❑ 86ClePhiP-18
❑ 87MaiGuiP-20
❑ 87MaiGuiT-6
❑ 87PhiTas-50
❑ 88Don-604
❑ 88Fle-648
❑ 88FleGlo-648
❑ 88MaiPhiC-8
❑ 88MaiPhiP-293
❑ 90AlbYanB-4
❑ 90Ft.LauYS-14
❑ 91AlbYanLD-16
❑ 91AlbYanP-1005
❑ 91LinDriAA-16
❑ 96BurBeeTI-29
Newfield, Marc
❑ 90ClaDraP-6
❑ 90ClaYel-T89
❑ 91Bow-698
❑ 91CalLeLA-1
❑ 91Cla/Bes-4
❑ 91ClaGam-62
❑ 91ClaGolB-BC2
❑ 91ClaPro-1
❑ 91OPC-529
❑ 91SanBerSC-23
❑ 91SanBerSP-2000
❑ 91Sco-391
❑ 91Top-529
❑ 91TopDesS-529
❑ 91TopMic-529
❑ 91TopTif-529
❑ 91UppDecFE-18F
❑ 92Bow-406
❑ 92ClaFS7-142
❑ 92JacSunF-3722
❑ 92JacSunS-365
❑ 92ProFS7-144
❑ 92SkyAA F-157
❑ 92UppDec-51
❑ 92UppDec-64
❑ 92UppDecML-36
❑ 92UppDecML-263
❑ 93Bow-51
❑ 93Bow-372
❑ 93ClaFisN-7
❑ 93ClaYouG-YG16
❑ 93ExcFS7-229
❑ 93JacSunF-2722
❑ 93Lea-490
❑ 93MariStaClu-19
❑ 93SP-283
❑ 93UppDec-434
❑ 93UppDecGold-434
❑ 94ActPac-30
❑ 94Bow-417
❑ 94CalCanF-802
❑ 94Cla-95
❑ 94ColC-14
❑ 94ColChoGS-14
❑ 94ColChoSS-14
❑ 94Don-574
❑ 94FleMajLP-26
❑ 94FUnPac-173
❑ 94LeaLimR-67
❑ 94Pac-579
❑ 94Pin-250
❑ 94PinArtP-250
❑ 94PinMusC-250
❑ 94PinRooTP-8
❑ 94Sco-584
❑ 94ScoBoyoS-46
❑ 94ScoGolR-584
❑ 94ScoRoo-RT155
❑ 94ScoRooGR-RT155
❑ 94ScoRooSR-SU10
❑ 94Sel-377
❑ 94Spo-165
❑ 94StaClu-357
❑ 94StaCluFDI-357
❑ 94StaCluGR-357
❑ 94StaCluMOP-357
❑ 94Top-262
❑ 94TopGol-262
❑ 94TopSpa-262
❑ 94TriPla-295
❑ 94Ult-122
❑ 94UppDec-22
❑ 94UppDecED-22
❑ 95ActPac2G-2G
❑ 95ActPacF-15
❑ 95ActPacF-63
❑ 95Bow-259
❑ 95BowBes-B80
❑ 95BowBesR-B80
❑ 95BowGolF-259
❑ 95ColCho-282
❑ 95ColChoGS-282
❑ 95ColChoSS-282
❑ 95Don-478
❑ 95DonPreP-478
❑ 95Emo-81
❑ 95Fin-320
❑ 95FinRef-320
❑ 95Pin-197
❑ 95PinArtP-197
❑ 95PinMusC-197
❑ 95Sco-587
❑ 95ScoAi-AM3
❑ 95ScoGolR-587
❑ 95ScoPlaTS-587
❑ 95Sel-45
❑ 95SelArtP-45
❑ 95SigRooOJ-26
❑ 95SigRooOJP-26
❑ 95SigRooOJPS-26
❑ 95SigRooOJS-26
❑ 95Spo-155
❑ 95SpoArtP-155
❑ 95StaClu-180
❑ 95StaCluFDI-180
❑ 95StaCluMOP-180
❑ 95StaCluSTWS-180
❑ 95TacRaiTI-13
❑ 95Ult-329
❑ 95UltGolM-329
❑ 95UppDec-113
❑ 95UppDecED-113
❑ 95UppDecEDG-113
❑ 96Cir-51
❑ 96CirRav-51
❑ 96ColCho-697
❑ 96ColChoGS-697
❑ 96ColChoSS-697
❑ 96Don-364
❑ 96DonPreP-364
❑ 96Fla-379
❑ 96Fle-574
❑ 96FleTif-574
❑ 96LeaLim-14
❑ 96LeaLimG-14
❑ 96LeaPre-9
❑ 96LeaPreP-9
❑ 96LeaSig-4
❑ 96LeaSigA-168
❑ 96LeaSigAG-168
❑ 96LeaSigAS-168
❑ 96LeaSigPPG-4
❑ 96LeaSigPPP-4
❑ 96Pac-191
❑ 96PadMot-14
❑ 96Pin-51
❑ 96PinAfi-131
❑ 96PinAfiAP-131
❑ 96Sco-349
❑ 96ScoDugC-B74
❑ 96ScoDugCAP-B74
❑ 96ScoFutF-14
❑ 96Sel-33
❑ 96SelArtP-33
❑ 96SelCer-15
❑ 96SelCerAP-15
❑ 96SelCerCB-15
❑ 96SelCerCR-15
❑ 96SelCerMB-15
❑ 96SelCerMG-15
❑ 96SelCerMR-15
❑ 96SelTeaN-22
❑ 96Spo-33
❑ 96SpoArtP-33
❑ 96StaClu-115
❑ 96StaCluMOP-115
❑ 96Sum-116
❑ 96SumAbo&B-116
❑ 96SumArtP-116
❑ 96SumFoi-116
❑ 96Ult-561
❑ 96UltGolM-561
❑ 96Zen-8
❑ 96ZenArtP-8
❑ 97BrePol-21
❑ 97Cir-318
❑ 97CirRav-318
❑ 97ColCho-373
❑ 97Don-13
❑ 97DonEli-92
❑ 97DonEliGS-92
❑ 97DonGolPP-13
❑ 97DonSilPP-13
❑ 97Fle-136
❑ 97FleTif-136
❑ 97Lea-95
❑ 97LeaFraM-95
❑ 97LeaFraMDC-95
❑ 97MetUni-68
❑ 97NewPin-86
❑ 97NewPinAP-86
❑ 97NewPinMC-86
❑ 97NewPinPP-86
❑ 97PacPriGotD-GD56
❑ 97Pin-22
❑ 97PinArtP-PP22
❑ 97PinIns-7
❑ 97PinInsCE-7
❑ 97PinInsDE-7
❑ 97PinMusC-22
❑ 97PinPrePla-22
❑ 97Sco-65
❑ 97ScoArtPWB-65
❑ 97ScoPreS-65
❑ 97ScoShoS-65
❑ 97ScoShoSAP-65
❑ 97Sel-45
❑ 97SelArtP-45
❑ 97SelCom-45
❑ 97SelRegG-45
❑ 97Stu-142
❑ 97StuPrePG-142
❑ 97StuPrePS-142
❑ 97Top-436
❑ 97Ult-81
❑ 97UltGolME-81
❑ 97UltPlaME-81
❑ 97UppDec-407
❑ 98PacOnl-408
❑ 98PacOnlR-408
❑ 98PacOnlWC-408
❑ 99Fle-531
❑ 99FleSta9-531
❑ 99FleWarT-531
Newhan, Dave
❑ 96ModA'sB-17
❑ 97VisOakG-20
❑ 98MobBayBTI-18
Newhart, Billy
❑ 88SFHesCreN32-21
Newhauser, Don
❑ 74OPC-33
❑ 74Top-33
Newhouse, Andre
❑ 92AppFoxCB-3
❑ 92AppFoxFI-998
❑ 93RocRoyC-22
❑ 93RocRoyF-730
❑ 94SouBenSHC-14
❑ 94SouBenSHF-609
❑ 95PriWilCTI-3
Newhouser, Hal
❑ 39ExhSal-46
❑ 46SpoExcW-7-1B
❑ 47Exh-167
❑ 49Lea-98
❑ 51R42SmaS-73
❑ 52StaCalL-72B
❑ 52StaCalS-86A
❑ 53ExhCan-12
❑ 53Top-228
❑ 55Top-24
❑ 55TopDouH-109
❑ 60Fle-68
❑ 61Fle-66
❑ 61NuSco-446
❑ 72TopTes5-5
❑ 75TCM195CI-26

❑ 76TayBow4-33
❑ 77TCMTheWY-30
❑ 79DiaGre-395
❑ 80PerHaloFP-214
❑ 80PerHaloFPS-74
❑ 80TigGreT-8
❑ 81TigDetN-116
❑ 81TigSecNP-20
❑ 82DiaCla-87
❑ 82TCMGreP-22
❑ 83TCMPla1944-6
❑ 83TigAlKS-31
❑ 83TigAlKS-39
❑ 86SpoDecG-19
❑ 86TigSpoD-9
❑ 90HOFStiB-42
❑ 90PerGreM-81
❑ 91TopArc1-228
❑ 92BazQua5A-8
❑ 92ConTSN-445
❑ 92PhoFilHoF-2
❑ 93ActPacA-111
❑ 93ActPacA2-45G
❑ 93FroRowN-1
❑ 93FroRowN-2
❑ 93FroRowN-3
❑ 93FroRowN-4
❑ 93FroRowN-5
❑ 94ConTSN-1009
❑ 94ConTSNB-1009
❑ 94ConTSNCI-24
❑ 97TopStaHRR-10
❑ 97TopStaRRAU-10

Newkirk, Craig
❑ 90Bes-234
❑ 90GasRanB-22
❑ 90GasRanP-2529
❑ 90GasRanS-16
❑ 91ChaRanC-19
❑ 91ChaRanP-1323
❑ 92ChaRanC-6
❑ 92ChaRanF-2234

Newkirk, Floyd
❑ 33WorCig(-64
❑ 33Zee-134

Newkirk, J.J.
❑ 97BriWhiSB-22
❑ 98HicCraM-22

Newlin, Jim
❑ 90Bes-259
❑ 90CalLeaACLC-23
❑ 90SanBerSB-23
❑ 90SanBerSCLC-89
❑ 90SanBerSP-2630
❑ 91JacSunLD-340
❑ 91JacSunP-148
❑ 91LinDriAA-340
❑ 92CalCanF-3728
❑ 92CalCanS-72
❑ 92SkyAAAF-29
❑ 93JacSunF-2709
❑ 93LinVenB-216
❑ 94PorSeaDF-675
❑ 94PorSeaDTI-23
❑ 95BowBayTI-34

Newman, Al
❑ 84BeaGolGT-4
❑ 85ExpPos-13
❑ 85IndIndTI-14
❑ 86DonRoo-9
❑ 86ExpPos-9
❑ 86ExpProPa-18
❑ 86FleUpd-80
❑ 87Don-426
❑ 87Fle-327
❑ 87FleGlo-327
❑ 87OPC-323
❑ 87Top-323
❑ 87TopTif-323
❑ 87TopTra-86T
❑ 87TopTraT-86T
❑ 87TwiPos-16
❑ 87TwiTeal-17
❑ 88BlaYNPRWL-94
❑ 88Don-645
❑ 88Fle-17
❑ 88FleGlo-17
❑ 88SanDieS-15
❑ 88SanDieS-16
❑ 88SanDieSAAG-15
❑ 88SanDieSAAG-16
❑ 88Sco-252
❑ 88ScoGlo-252
❑ 88StaLinTw-14
❑ 88Top-648
❑ 88TopTif-648
❑ 88TwiSmoC-11
❑ 89Bow-156
❑ 89BowTif-156
❑ 89Don-436
❑ 89Fle-122
❑ 89FleGlo-122
❑ 89SanDieSAG-14
❑ 89SanDieSAG-15
❑ 89Sco-493
❑ 89Top-503
❑ 89TopTif-503
❑ 89UppDec-197
❑ 90Bow-419
❑ 90BowTif-419
❑ 90Don-506
❑ 90Fle-382
❑ 90FleCan-382
❑ 90Lea-347
❑ 90OPC-19
❑ 90PanSti-110
❑ 90PubIntS-334
❑ 90Sco-128
❑ 90Top-19
❑ 90TopBig-53
❑ 90TopSti-293
❑ 90TopTif-19
❑ 90UppDec-199
❑ 91DodPho-21
❑ 91Don-208
❑ 91Fle-621
❑ 91Lea-446
❑ 91OPC-748
❑ 91PanFreS-301
❑ 91Sco-424
❑ 91StaClu-146
❑ 91Top-748
❑ 91TopDesS-748
❑ 91TopMic-748
❑ 91TopTif-748
❑ 91Ult-193
❑ 91UppDec-413
❑ 91VisOakC-8
❑ 92Don-339
❑ 92Fle-214
❑ 92Lea-511
❑ 92LeaBlaG-511
❑ 92OPC-146
❑ 92RanMot-25
❑ 92RanTeal-13
❑ 92Sco-357
❑ 92ScoRoo-49T
❑ 92StaClu-821
❑ 92Top-146
❑ 92TopGol-146
❑ 92TopGolW-146
❑ 92TopMic-146
❑ 92UppDec-293
❑ 93Fle-685
❑ 93RanKee-276
❑ 95ForMyeMTI-30
❑ 96HarCitRCB-2
❑ 97NewBriRC-27
❑ 98Las-18
❑ 98SalLakBO-3

Newman, Alan
❑ 90Bes-39
❑ 90KenTwiB-23
❑ 90KenTwiP-2292
❑ 90KenTwiS-17
❑ 90MidLeaASGS-17
❑ 90ProAaA-112
❑ 90StaFS7-56
❑ 91CalLeLA-13
❑ 92Bow-221
❑ 92ClaFS7-202
❑ 92OrlSunRS-514
❑ 92SkyAA F-222
❑ 92UppDecML-240
❑ 93Bow-129
❑ 93ClaFS7-229
❑ 93NasXprF-402
❑ 97BirBarB-25

Newman, Bruce
❑ 93IdaFalBF-4046
❑ 93IdaFalBSP-19
❑ 94DanBraC-21
❑ 94DanBraF-3546

Newman, Damon
❑ 94SouOreAC-21
❑ 95WesMicWTI-19

Newman, Danny
❑ 88AshTouP-1071

Newman, Doug
❑ 91MisStaB-33
❑ 92MisStaB-30

Newman, Eric
❑ 95IdaFalBTI-30
❑ 96CliLumKTI-20
❑ 97RanCucQG-21
❑ 98MobBayBTI-19

Newman, Fred
❑ 63Top-496
❑ 64Top-569
❑ 65OPC-101
❑ 65Top-101
❑ 66AngDexP-9
❑ 66Top-213
❑ 66TopRubI-70
❑ 66TopVen-213
❑ 67CokCapDA-24
❑ 67Top-451
❑ 69Top-543
❑ 81TCM60I-374

Newman, Jeff
❑ 76TucTorCa-19
❑ 76TusTorCr-12
❑ 76VenLeaS-20
❑ 77Top-204
❑ 78Top-458
❑ 79OPC-319
❑ 79Top-604
❑ 80Kel-7
❑ 80OPC-18
❑ 80Top-34
❑ 81A'sGraG-5
❑ 81Don-477
❑ 81Fle-577
❑ 81Top-587
❑ 81TopSti-120
❑ 82A'sGraG-12
❑ 82Don-517
❑ 82Fle-102
❑ 82Top-187
❑ 83Don-635
❑ 83Fle-529
❑ 83Top-784
❑ 83TopTra-80T
❑ 84Don-249
❑ 84Fle-404
❑ 84Nes792-296
❑ 84Top-296
❑ 84TopTif-296
❑ 85Top-376
❑ 85TopTif-376
❑ 86A'sMot-27
❑ 87A'sMot-19
❑ 88ModA'sCLC-81
❑ 88ModA'sTI-1
❑ 89HunStaB-20
❑ 89SouLeaAJ-25
❑ 90HunStaB-24
❑ 91LinDriAAA-549
❑ 91TacTigLD-549
❑ 91TacTigP-2321
❑ 92IndFanC-30
❑ 93IndWUA-33

Newman, Mark
❑ 82ForMyeRT-20

Newman, Pat
❑ 11PinT-5-114

Newman, Randy
❑ 83WauTimF-25
❑ 86CalCanP-19

Newman, Ray
❑ 72Top-667
❑ 73OPC-568
❑ 73Top-568
❑ 94BreMilB-58

Newman, Rob
❑ 92IdaFalGF-3519
❑ 92IdaFalGSP-17

Newman, Todd
❑ 87AubAstP-17
❑ 87BriYouC-2

Newman, Tom
❑ 89IdaFalBP-2036
❑ 90IdaFalBP-3243
❑ 90SumBraB-14

Newsom, Bobo (Louis Norman)
❑ 33ButCanV-37
❑ 35ExhFou-15
❑ 36ExhFou-16
❑ 36GouBWR-22
❑ 36GouWidPPR-A79
❑ 36GouWidPPR-C20
❑ 36NatChiFPR-61
❑ 36WheBB3-10
❑ 37ExhFou-16
❑ 37OPCBatUV-139
❑ 38ExhFou-15
❑ 39ExhSal-47
❑ 39ExhSal-48
❑ 39GouPreR303A-34
❑ 39TigSpo-7
❑ 39WorWidGTP-34
❑ 41DouPlaR-51
❑ 43DodTeal-19
❑ 45A'sTeal-23
❑ 48GiaTeal-19
❑ 52A'sTeal-21
❑ 53A'sTeal-23
❑ 53Top-15
❑ 54OriEss-28
❑ 55OriEss-21
❑ 60Fle-70
❑ 61Fle-67
❑ 70SpoCarfCOP-24
❑ 81TigDetN-64
❑ 82DiaCla-71
❑ 83TCMPla1942-21
❑ 85TCMPhoC-10
❑ 88ChaLooLTI-24
❑ 90DodTar-573
❑ 91ConTSN-230
❑ 91TopArc1-15
❑ 92BazQua5A-10
❑ 92ConTSN-364
❑ 93ConTSN-760
❑ 93DiaStaES-148

Newsom, Gary
❑ 83VerBeaDT-19
❑ 85VerBeaDT-4
❑ 86AlbDukP-18
❑ 87DurBulP-9

Newsome, Dick
❑ 42RedSoxTI-17
❑ 43RedSoxTI-17

Newsome, H. H.
❑ 37Zee-57

Newsome, Skeeter (Lamar A.)
❑ 36NatChiFPR-60
❑ 39PlaBal-84
❑ 42RedSoxTI-18
❑ 43RedSoxTI-18
❑ 76TayBow4-60
❑ 83TCMPla1945-18

Newson, Warren
❑ 86SpoIndC-174
❑ 88CalLeaACLC-45
❑ 88RivRedWCLC-225
❑ 88RivRedWP-1416
❑ 89TexLeaAGS-8
❑ 89WicChaR-2
❑ 89WicChaR-8
❑ 89WicChaR-12
❑ 89WicChaR-13
❑ 89WicStaR-2
❑ 89WicUpdR-7
❑ 89WicUpdR-17
❑ 89WicWraR-24
❑ 90CMC-518
❑ 90LasVegSC-15
❑ 90LasVegSP-136
❑ 90ProAAAF-24
❑ 91DonRoo-15
❑ 91FleUpd-14
❑ 91LinDriAAA-643
❑ 91UltUpd-17
❑ 91VanCanLD-643
❑ 91VanCanP-1608
❑ 92Don-668
❑ 92Fle-91
❑ 92OPC-355
❑ 92OPCPre-76
❑ 92Sco-398
❑ 92StaClu-512
❑ 92Top-355
❑ 92TopDeb91-133
❑ 92TopGol-355
❑ 92TopGolW-355
❑ 92TopMic-355
❑ 92UppDec-621
❑ 92WhiSoxK-24
❑ 93Don-463
❑ 93WhiSoxSC-7
❑ 94Fle-90
❑ 94StaCluT-138
❑ 94StaCluTFDI-138
❑ 94WhiSoxK-23
❑ 95ColCho-501
❑ 95ColChoGS-501
❑ 95ColChoSS-501
❑ 95MarPac-38
❑ 95Sco-547
❑ 95ScoGolR-547
❑ 95ScoPlaTS-547
❑ 95WhiSoxK-22
❑ 96LeaSigEA-141
❑ 96RanDr P-22
❑ 96RanMot-15
❑ 97RanDr P-20
❑ 97RanMot-15
❑ 97RanSco-15
❑ 97RanScoPl-15
❑ 97RanScoPr-15
❑ 97Sco-252
❑ 97ScoArtPWB-252
❑ 97ScoPreS-252
❑ 97ScoShoS-252
❑ 97ScoShoSAP-252
❑ 98OklRedM-18

Newstrom, Doug
❑ 93YakBeaC-18
❑ 93YakBeaF-3889
❑ 94ExcFirYPF-4
❑ 94ExcFS7-219
❑ 94FloStaLAF-FSL48
❑ 94VerBeaDC-12
❑ 94VerBeaDF-80
❑ 95SanBerSTI-13
❑ 96HigDesMB-21
❑ 97NewHavRB-12
❑ 98NewHavRM-20
❑ 98NewHavRMA-20

Newton, Chris
❑ 94JamJamC-18
❑ 94JamJamF-3961

Newton, Doc (Eustace)
❑ 08RosComP-51
❑ 09RamT20-87
❑ 11SpoLifCW-268
❑ 72ClaCar-28
❑ 90DodTar-574

Newton, Geronimo
❑ 94BelMarC-20
❑ 94BelMarF-3230
❑ 96PorCitRB-21
❑ 98OrlRayM-13

Newton, Kimani
❑ 96YakBeaTI-26
❑ 97YakBeaG-20
❑ 98YakBeaG-24

Newton, Marty
❑ 86EveGiaC-15
❑ 86EveGiaPC-19

Newton, Newt (Warren)
❑ 87ChaRaiP-16

Newton, Steve
❑ 87LitFalMP-2390
❑ 88LitFalMP-18
❑ 89ColMetB-18
❑ 89ColMetGS-17
❑ 90St.LucMS-18
❑ 91ChaRaiC-9

Nezelek, Andy
❑ 88GreBraB-19
❑ 89BlaYNPRWL-62
❑ 89Don-616
❑ 89RicBraBC-19
❑ 89RicBraC-6
❑ 89RicBraP-839
❑ 89RicBraTI-17
❑ 90Bow-3
❑ 90BowTif-3
❑ 90CMC-281
❑ 90Don-523A
❑ 90Don-523B
❑ 90ProAAAF-401
❑ 90RicBraBC-13
❑ 90RicBraC-5
❑ 90RicBraP-256
❑ 90RicBraTI-24
❑ 91RicBraBC-11
❑ 92GreBraS-242
❑ 93ClaGolF-19

Niarhos, Gus (Constantine)
❑ 48BluTin-25
❑ 48YanTeal-19
❑ 49Bow-181
❑ 49YanTeal-14
❑ 50Bow-154
❑ 51Bow-124
❑ 52Bow-129
❑ 52Top-121
❑ 53RedSoxTI-21
❑ 53Top-63
❑ 83TopRep5-121
❑ 91TopArc1-63

Nicastro, Steve
❑ 79NewCoPT-2

Nice, Bill
❑ 80AndBraT-14

Nicely, Roy M.
❑ 48SomandK-24
❑ 49SomandK-13

Nicely, Tony
❑ 78ChaPirT-16

Nichioka, Tsuyoshi
❑ 91SalSpuC-18

Nicholas, Darrell
❑ 94HelBreF-3626
❑ 94HelBreSP-18
❑ 94SigRooDPBSDP-7
❑ 94StaCluDPFDI-49
❑ 96El PasDB-21
❑ 97El PasDB-10
❑ 98LouRedQ-10

Nicholas, Franci
❑ 36GouWidPPR-D23

Nicholas, Otho
❑ 33Zee-34

Nicholls, Simon B.
❑ 08AmeCarE91-17
❑ 08RosComP-62
❑ 09BriE97-25
❑ 09RamT20-88
❑ 09T206-266
❑ 09T206-267
❑ 10NadE1-45
❑ 10W555-53

Nichols, Brian
❑ 88BilMusP-1819
❑ 89BilMusP-2043
❑ 90BilMusP-3224
❑ 90CedRapRP-2326
❑ 90ChaWheB-13

Nichols, Carl
❑ 83SanJosBC-20
❑ 85ChaO'sT-9
❑ 86ChaOriW-18
❑ 87RocRedWP-11
❑ 87RocRedWT-10
❑ 88Don-477
❑ 88DonRoo-39
❑ 88RocRedWGCP-18
❑ 89Fle-612
❑ 89FleGlo-612
❑ 89TriAAAP-AAA45
❑ 89TucTorC-15
❑ 89TucTorJP-18
❑ 89TucTorP-185
❑ 90CMC-613
❑ 90ProAAAF-195
❑ 90TucTorC-11
❑ 90TucTorP-205
❑ 91AstMot-22
❑ 91Lea-217
❑ 91OPC-119
❑ 91OriCro-327
❑ 91StaClu-440
❑ 91Top-119
❑ 91TopDesS-119
❑ 91TopMic-119
❑ 91TopTif-119

Nichols, Chet
❑ 52Bow-120
❑ 52Top-288
❑ 53BraSpiaS7-9
❑ 54BraJohC-16
❑ 54BraSpiaSP-14
❑ 55Bow-72
❑ 55BraGolS-5
❑ 55BraJohC-17
❑ 55BraSpiaSD-13
❑ 56Top-278
❑ 61Top-301
❑ 62Top-403
❑ 63Top-307
❑ 81RedSoxBG2S-40
❑ 83TopRep5-288
❑ 89BluOriS-30
❑ 90WauTimP-2144
❑ 90WauTimS-28

Nichols, Dolan
❑ 59Top-362A
❑ 59Top-362B

Nichols, Fred
❑ 74GasRanT-13

Nichols, Gary
❑ 88SprCarB-23
❑ 90CMC-125
❑ 90LouRedBC-25

Nichols, Howard
❑ 86ReaPhiP-19
❑ 87ReaPhiP-14

❑ 88PhiTas-27
❑ 88ReaPhiP-879
❑ 89IowCubC-18
❑ 89IowCubP-1712
Nichols, James
❑ 96AppLeaAB-7
❑ 96BriWhiSB-26
❑ 97HicCraB-21
❑ 97HicCraRB-26
❑ 98HicCraM-23
❑ 98WinWar-18
Nichols, Kevin
❑ 96MarPhiB-18
❑ 97PieBolWB-22
Nichols, Kid (Charles A.)
❑ 06FanCraNL-33
❑ 39PC7AlbHoF-58
❑ 50CalHOFW-56
❑ 53ArtHaloFP-64
❑ 61Fle-129
❑ 76ShaPiz-58
❑ 80PerHaloFP-58
❑ 80SSPHOF-58
❑ 86BraGreT-10
❑ 87OldJudN-364
❑ 94ConTSN-1012
❑ 94ConTSNB-1012
❑ 94OriofB-78
❑ 95May-24
❑ 98CamPepP-58
Nichols, Lance
❑ 82RocRedWT-20
❑ 83RocRedWT-1
Nichols, Reid (Thomas Reid)
❑ 81Top-689
❑ 82Don-632
❑ 82Fle-300
❑ 82RedSoxC-12
❑ 82Top-124
❑ 83Don-460
❑ 83Fle-189
❑ 83Top-446
❑ 84Don-614
❑ 84Fle-405
❑ 84Nes792-238
❑ 84Top-238
❑ 84TopTif-238
❑ 85Don-636
❑ 85Fle-164
❑ 85Top-37
❑ 85TopTif-37
❑ 86Don-574
❑ 86Fle-214
❑ 86Lea-224
❑ 86Top-364
❑ 86TopTif-364
❑ 86WhiSoxC-20
❑ 87DonOpeD-87
❑ 87ExpPos-18
❑ 87FleUpd-89
❑ 87FleUpdG-89
❑ 87Top-539
❑ 87TopTif-539
❑ 87TopTra-87T
❑ 87TopTraT-87T
❑ 88Fle-191
❑ 88FleGlo-191
❑ 88OPC-261
❑ 88Top-748
❑ 88TopTif-748
Nichols, Rod
❑ 86WatIndP-20
❑ 87KinIndP-24
❑ 89Don-649
❑ 89IndTeal-20
❑ 89Top-443
❑ 89TopTif-443
❑ 90Don-546
❑ 90Fle-497
❑ 90FleCan-497
❑ 90IndTeal-29
❑ 90OPC-108
❑ 90Top-108
❑ 90TopTif-108
❑ 90UppDec-572
❑ 91IndFanC-21
❑ 92Don-194
❑ 92Fle-119
❑ 92IndFanC-19
❑ 92OPC-586
❑ 92Pin-525
❑ 92Sco-559
❑ 92StaClu-534
❑ 92Top-586
❑ 92TopGol-586
❑ 92TopGolW-586
❑ 92TopMic-586
❑ 92Ult-352
❑ 92UppDec-212
❑ 93AlbDukF-1457
❑ 93Don-521
❑ 93Fle-597
❑ 93PacSpa-99
❑ 93Top-372
❑ 93TopGol-372
❑ 93TopInaM-372
❑ 93TopInaR-372
❑ 93TopMic-372
❑ 95RicBraTI-12
❑ 96RicBraB-22
❑ 96RicBraRC-16
❑ 96RicBraUB-20
❑ 97ColSprSATTI-12
Nichols, Samuel
❑ 87OldJudN-365
Nichols, Scott
❑ 87SavCarP-6
❑ 89St.PetCS-21
❑ 90LouRedBLBC-28
❑ 90LouRedBP-404
❑ 90ProAAAF-518
❑ 91LouRedP-2917
❑ 91LouRedTI-29
Nichols, Todd
❑ 95AusFut-48
Nichols, Ty
❑ 85NewOriT-3
❑ 86HagSunP-13
❑ 88ChaKniTI-22
❑ 89HagSunB-28
❑ 89HagSunP-279
❑ 89HagSunS-13
❑ 90HagSunB-8
❑ 90HagSunP-1425
❑ 90HagSunS-20
Nicholson, Bill (William B.)
❑ 41CubTeal-15
❑ 42CubTeal-15
❑ 43CubTeal-17
❑ 44CubTeal-17
❑ 48BluTin-11
❑ 49Bow-76
❑ 49EurSta-142
❑ 49PhiBul-41
❑ 49PhiLumPB-7
❑ 50Bow-228
❑ 50PhiPhil-17
❑ 51Bow-113
❑ 52Top-185
❑ 53BowBW-14
❑ 75Phi195T-21
❑ 76ChiGre-14
❑ 76TayBow4-89
❑ 77TCMTheWY-39
❑ 79DiaGre-111
❑ 80Phi195T-21
❑ 82DiaCla-76
❑ 83TCMPla1943-36
❑ 83TopRep5-185
❑ 84CubBriPC-13C
Nicholson, Carl
❑ 78WatIndT-15
❑ 79TacTugT-18
Nicholson, Dave (David L.)
❑ 56BalOriP-37
❑ 61Top-182
❑ 62BalOriP-18
❑ 62Top-577
❑ 63Top-234
❑ 63WhiSoxJP-9
❑ 63WhiSoxTS-20
❑ 64Top-31
❑ 64TopCoi-32
❑ 64TopSta-26
❑ 64TopTatI-57
❑ 64TopVen-31
❑ 64WhiSoxI-20
❑ 64WhiSoxTS-17
❑ 65OPC-183
❑ 65Top-183
❑ 65WhiSoxJP-5
❑ 66Top-576
❑ 67OPC-113
❑ 67Top-113
❑ 69Top-298
❑ 69TopTeaP-7
❑ 78TCM60I-99
❑ 87AstShoSTw-11
❑ 91OriCro-328
Nicholson, Derek
❑ 98AubDouTI-17
Nicholson, J.W.
❑ 87OldJudN-366
Nicholson, John
❑ 97AshTou-20
❑ 97SouAtlTPB-1
❑ 97Top-482
❑ 98BesPreA-28
❑ 98Bow-336
❑ 98BowChr-336
❑ 98BowChrGA-336
❑ 98BowChrGAR-336
❑ 98BowChrI-336
❑ 98BowChrIR-336
❑ 98BowChrR-336
❑ 98BowGolA-336
❑ 98BowInt-336
❑ 98JupHamQ-12
❑ 99Top-437
❑ 99TopChr-437
❑ 99TopChrR-437
Nicholson, Keith
❑ 87LakTigP-2
❑ 88FayGenP-1079
Nicholson, Kevin
❑ 97BesAutSBPP-31
❑ 98BesNumOP-34
❑ 98Bow-338
❑ 98BowChr-338
❑ 98BowChrGA-338
❑ 98BowChrGAR-338
❑ 98BowChrI-338
❑ 98BowChrIR-338
❑ 98BowChrR-338
❑ 98BowGolA-338
❑ 98BowInt-338
❑ 98MobBayBTI-20
❑ 98SouLeaTPG-19
❑ 98SP MinPE-108
❑ 98SPMin-108
Nicholson, Larry
❑ 80BufBisT-14
Nicholson, Rick
❑ 77NewCoPT-25
❑ 78HolMilT-17
Nicholson, Thomas
❑ 87OldJudN-367
Nichting, Chris
❑ 87PanAmTUBI-27
❑ 87PanAmTURB-8
❑ 88FloStaLAS-15
❑ 88VerBeaDS-18A
❑ 89SanAntMB-22
❑ 92AlbDukF-719
❑ 92SanAntMS-572
❑ 94SanAntMF-2464
❑ 95RanCra-21
❑ 96LeaSigEA-142
❑ 98BufBisG-22
Nickell, Jackie
❑ 92BelMarCB-16
❑ 92BelMarF-1441
❑ 93AppFoxCB-18
❑ 93AppFoxFI-2458
❑ 93ClaFS7-246
❑ 94ExcFS7-126
❑ 94RivPilCLC-19
❑ 95PorCitRTI-16
Nickerson, Drew
❑ 74GasRanT-14
❑ 75AndRanT-57
❑ 77CedRapGT-12
Nickerson, Jim
❑ 77SpaPhiT-4
Nickle, Doug
❑ 97BoiHawG-21
❑ 98CedRapKTI-21
Nicol, Hugh (Hugh N.)
❑ 87BucN28-101
❑ 87LonJacN-9
❑ 87OldJudN-368
❑ 87OldJudN-369
❑ 87OldJudN-370
Nicolas, Darrell
❑ 94StaCluDP-49
Nicolas, Jose
❑ 98AugGreM-4
❑ 98EriSeaWM-19
Nicolau, Travis
❑ 91DaiDolF-16
Nicolet, Don
❑ 80WatIndT-22
Nicoll, Sam
❑ 88GandBCGCE-29
Nicolosi, Chris
❑ 59DarFar-13
❑ 60DarFar-1
Nicolosi, Sal
❑ 85VisOakT-5
❑ 86VisOakP-13
Nicometi, Tony
❑ 86JacExpT-1
Nicosia, Steve (Steven R.)
❑ 75ShrCapT-15
❑ 76VenLeaS-162
❑ 77ColCliT-16
❑ 78ColCliT-18
❑ 80Top-519
❑ 81Don-373
❑ 81Fle-371
❑ 81OPC-212
❑ 81Top-212
❑ 82Don-45
❑ 82Fle-488
❑ 82Top-652
❑ 83Don-528
❑ 83Fle-314
❑ 83Top-462
❑ 84GiaPos-19
❑ 84Nes792-98
❑ 84Top-98
❑ 84TopTif-98
❑ 85ExpPos-14
❑ 85Fle-618
❑ 85Top-191
❑ 85TopTif-191
❑ 85TopTifT-87T
❑ 85TopTra-87T
❑ 89EriOriS-15
Niebla, Ruben
❑ 98JupHamQ-13
Niebrugge, Kenn
❑ 94DavLipB-21
❑ 94DavLipB-24
Nieckula, Aaron
❑ 98SouOreTG-20
Nied, David
❑ 88SumBraP-413
❑ 89DurBullS-16
❑ 89DurBullS-16
❑ 89DurBulTI-16
❑ 90DurBulTI-17
❑ 91DurBulC-3
❑ 91DurBulP-1541
❑ 92Bow-504
❑ 92DonRoo-86
❑ 92FleUpd-68
❑ 92LeaGolR-BC10
❑ 92ProFS7-188
❑ 92RicBraBB-22
❑ 92RicBraF-373
❑ 92RicBraRC-13
❑ 92RicBraS-435
❑ 92SkyAAAF-200
❑ 92TriA AAS-435
❑ 93Bow-148
❑ 93Don-792
❑ 93DonDiaK-DK28
❑ 93Fin-198
❑ 93FinRef-198
❑ 93Fla-43
❑ 93Fle-9
❑ 93FleFinE-36
❑ 93FunPac-178
❑ 93HumDumC-30
❑ 93JimDeaR-7
❑ 93Lea-390
❑ 93OPC-49
❑ 93OPCPre-107
❑ 93PacSpa-433
❑ 93Pin-238
❑ 93PinExpOD-1
❑ 93RocStaC-1
❑ 93RocUSPC-1S
❑ 93RocUSPC-2D
❑ 93Sco-553
❑ 93ScoBoyoS-23
❑ 93ScoFra-28
❑ 93ScoProaG-10
❑ 93SelRoo-78T
❑ 93StaClu-718
❑ 93StaCluFDI-718
❑ 93StaCluI-A3
❑ 93StaCluI-C1
❑ 93StaCluMOP-718
❑ 93StaCluMOP-MA3
❑ 93StaCluMOP-MC1
❑ 93StaCluMP-28
❑ 93Stu-74
❑ 93Top-444
❑ 93TopGol-444
❑ 93TopInaM-444
❑ 93TopInaR-444
❑ 93TopMic-444
❑ 93TopMic-P444
❑ 93TriPla-105
❑ 93TriPlaG-GS10
❑ 93Ult-354
❑ 93UltAllR-6
❑ 93UltPer-7
❑ 93UppDec-27
❑ 93UppDec-478
❑ 93UppDec-834
❑ 93UppDecDG-23
❑ 93UppDecGold-27
❑ 93UppDecGold-478
❑ 93UppDecGold-834
❑ 93UppDecSH-HI14
❑ 93USPlaCR-6S
❑ 94Bow-470
❑ 94ColC-576
❑ 94ColChoGS-576
❑ 94ColChoSS-576
❑ 94Don-106
❑ 94Fin-282
❑ 94FinRef-282
❑ 94Fla-376
❑ 94Fle-447
❑ 94FleExtB-251
❑ 94FleExtBSYS-15
❑ 94Lea-312
❑ 94OPC-208
❑ 94Pac-202
❑ 94Pin-43
❑ 94PinArtP-43
❑ 94PinMusC-43
❑ 94ProMag-45
❑ 94RocPol-19
❑ 94Sco-528
❑ 94ScoBoyoS-15
❑ 94ScoGolR-528
❑ 94Sel-113
❑ 94SP-168
❑ 94SPDieC-168
❑ 94StaClu-153
❑ 94StaCluFDI-153
❑ 94StaCluGR-153
❑ 94StaCluMOP-153
❑ 94StaCluT-111
❑ 94StaCluTFDI-111
❑ 94Top-135
❑ 94TopGol-135
❑ 94TopSpa-135
❑ 94TriPla-229
❑ 94Ult-486
❑ 94UppDec-70
❑ 94UppDecED-70
❑ 95Bow-396
❑ 95ColCho-438
❑ 95ColChoGS-438
❑ 95ColChoSE-208
❑ 95ColChoSEGS-208
❑ 95ColChoSESS-208
❑ 95ColChoSS-438
❑ 95Don-120
❑ 95DonPreP-120
❑ 95Fin-77
❑ 95FinRef-77
❑ 95Fla-132
❑ 95Fle-525
❑ 95Lea-192
❑ 95Pac-142
❑ 95Pin-95
❑ 95PinArtP-95
❑ 95PinMusC-95
❑ 95Sco-139
❑ 95ScoGolR-139
❑ 95ScoPlaTS-139
❑ 95Spo-10
❑ 95SpoArtP-10
❑ 95StaClu-428
❑ 95StaCluMOP-428
❑ 95StaCluSTWS-428
❑ 95StaCluVR-224
❑ 95StaCluVRMO-224
❑ 95Top-594
❑ 95TopCyb-366
❑ 95TopEmb-35
❑ 95TopEmbGI-35
❑ 95Ult-376
❑ 95UltGolM-376
❑ 95UppDec-173
❑ 95UppDecED-173
❑ 95UppDecEDG-173
❑ 95UppDecSE-241
❑ 95UppDecSEG-241
❑ 96ColCho-134
❑ 96ColChoGS-134
❑ 96ColChoSS-134
❑ 96ColSprSSTI-24
❑ 96Fle-369
❑ 96FleTif-369
❑ 97RicBraBC-7
Niedenfuer, Tom
❑ 82AlbDukTc-7
❑ 82DodPol-49
❑ 82DodPos-6
❑ 82DodUniOV-14
❑ 82Fle-16
❑ 83DodPol-49
❑ 83DodPos-11
❑ 83Don-536
❑ 83Fle-214
❑ 83Top-477
❑ 84DodPol-49
❑ 84DodSmo-2
❑ 84Don-128
❑ 84Fle-108
❑ 84Nes792-112
❑ 84Top-112
❑ 84TopTif-112
❑ 85DodCokP-22
❑ 85Don-153
❑ 85Fle-378
❑ 85OPC-281
❑ 85Top-782
❑ 85TopMin-782
❑ 85TopSti-80
❑ 85TopTif-782
❑ 86DodCokP-21
❑ 86DodPol-49
❑ 86DodUniOP-14
❑ 86Don-397
❑ 86Fle-139
❑ 86Lea-186
❑ 86Top-56
❑ 86TopTif-56
❑ 87BalOriP-25
❑ 87DodMot-14
❑ 87DodPol-26
❑ 87Don-218
❑ 87Fle-448
❑ 87FleGlo-448
❑ 87Lea-204
❑ 87OPC-43
❑ 87OriFreB-49
❑ 87Top-538
❑ 87TopTif-538
❑ 87TopTra-88T
❑ 87TopTraT-88T
❑ 88Don-294
❑ 88DonBasB-321
❑ 88Fle-568
❑ 88FleGlo-568
❑ 88OPC-242
❑ 88OriFreB-49
❑ 88OriPos-21
❑ 88Sco-261A
❑ 88Sco-261B
❑ 88ScoGlo-261A
❑ 88ScoGlo-261B
❑ 88StaLinO-11
❑ 88Top-242
❑ 88TopSti-232
❑ 88TopTif-242
❑ 89Bow-204
❑ 89BowTif-204
❑ 89Don-282
❑ 89DonTra-54
❑ 89Fle-613
❑ 89FleGlo-613
❑ 89MarMot-12
❑ 89OPC-14
❑ 89PanSti-254
❑ 89Sco-252
❑ 89Top-651
❑ 89TopSti-236
❑ 89TopTif-651
❑ 89UppDec-488
❑ 90CarSmo-16
❑ 90DodTar-575
❑ 90LouRedBLBC-29
❑ 90OPC-306
❑ 90PubIntS-438
❑ 90Top-306
❑ 90TopTif-306
❑ 91Fle-639
❑ 91OriCro-329
❑ 91Sco-217
Niedermaier, Brad
❑ 96ForWayWB-17

❑ 97ForMyeM-21
Niehaus, Dave
❑ 95MarPac-17
Niehaus, Dick
❑ 21Zee-76
❑ 22Zee-65
Niehaus, Troy
❑ 98LetBlaDG-23
Niehoff, Bert (John Albert)
❑ 14CraJacE-125
❑ 15CraJacE-125
❑ 15SpoNewM-130
❑ 16SpoNewM-132
❑ 17ColE13-128
❑ 19Zee-12
❑ 19Zee-118
❑ 20Zee-15
❑ 21Zee-16
❑ 91ConTSN-151
Niekro, Joe
❑ 67Top-536
❑ 68Top-475
❑ 69OPC-43
❑ 69Top-43
❑ 70OPC-508
❑ 70Top-508
❑ 71MLBOffS-400
❑ 71OPC-695
❑ 71Top-695
❑ 72MilBra-251
❑ 72OPC-216
❑ 72Top-216
❑ 73OPC-585
❑ 73TigJew-14
❑ 73Top-585
❑ 74OPC-504
❑ 74Top-504
❑ 75IowOakT-12
❑ 75OPC-595
❑ 75Top-595
❑ 75TopMin-595
❑ 76HouAstP-23
❑ 76OPC-273
❑ 76SSP-50
❑ 76Top-273
❑ 77AstPho-9
❑ 77Spo-8321
❑ 77Top-116
❑ 78AstBurK-5
❑ 78AstPos-20
❑ 78Top-306
❑ 79AstPos-15
❑ 79AstTeal-9
❑ 79Top-68
❑ 80OPC-226
❑ 80Top-205
❑ 80Top-437
❑ 81AllGamPI-171
❑ 81AstPos-13
❑ 81CokTeaS-66
❑ 81Don-380
❑ 81Fle-54
❑ 81OPC-102
❑ 81Top-722
❑ 81TopSti-26
❑ 81TopSti-174
❑ 82AstAstI-8
❑ 82AstPos-16
❑ 82Don-167
❑ 82Fle-221
❑ 82FleSta-45
❑ 82OPC-74
❑ 82Top-611
❑ 83AstPos-20
❑ 83Don-10
❑ 83Don-470
❑ 83Don-613
❑ 83DonActA-51
❑ 83Fle-457
❑ 83FleSta-138
❑ 83FleSti-210
❑ 83OPC-221
❑ 83Top-221
❑ 83Top-441
❑ 83TopFol-1
❑ 83TopSti-240
❑ 84AstMot-2
❑ 84AstPos-20
❑ 84Don-110
❑ 84Fle-234
❑ 84FunFooP-128
❑ 84Nes792-586
❑ 84OPC-384
❑ 84Top-586
❑ 84TopSti-69
❑ 84TopTif-586
❑ 85AstHouP-11
❑ 85AstMot-6
❑ 85Don-182
❑ 85Fle-355
❑ 85FleStaS-88
❑ 85Lea-189
❑ 85OPC-295
❑ 85Top-295
❑ 85TopSti-69
❑ 85TopTif-295
❑ 86AstMot-17
❑ 86Don-601
❑ 86Don-645
❑ 86Lea-243
❑ 86OPC-135
❑ 86Top-135
❑ 86TopTif-135
❑ 86YanTCM-10
❑ 87AstShoSPO-22
❑ 87AstShoSPT-10
❑ 87AstShoSPT-20
❑ 87ClaUpdY-120
❑ 87Don-217
❑ 87Fle-106
❑ 87FleGlo-106
❑ 87FleUpd-87
❑ 87FleUpdG-87
❑ 87Top-344A
❑ 87Top-344B
❑ 87TopTif-344A
❑ 87TopTif-344B
❑ 87TopTra-89T
❑ 87TopTraT-89T
❑ 87TwiTeal-24
❑ 88Fle-18
❑ 88FleGlo-18
❑ 88OPC-233
❑ 88Sco-237
❑ 88ScoGlo-237
❑ 88Top-5
❑ 88Top-473
❑ 88TopTif-5
❑ 88TopTif-473
❑ 92BenRocCB-25
❑ 92BenRocF-1490
❑ 92UppDecS-8
❑ 92YanWIZ8-132
❑ 95ColSilB-21
❑ 99SpoIllGotG-84
❑ 99SpoIllGotGA-52
Niekro, John
❑ 95ColSilB-22
❑ 96ColSilB-21
Niekro, Phil
❑ 64Top-541
❑ 65Top-461
❑ 66OPC-28
❑ 66Top-28
❑ 66TopVen-28
❑ 67BraPho-23
❑ 67Top-456
❑ 68BraPos-23
❑ 68DexPre-58
❑ 68OPC-7
❑ 68Top-7
❑ 68Top-257
❑ 68TopVen-7
❑ 68TopVen-257
❑ 69AtlBraBPPS-18
❑ 69MilBra-201
❑ 69MLBOffS-116
❑ 69Top-355
❑ 69TopTeaP-2
❑ 70MilBra-20
❑ 70MLBOffS-10
❑ 70OPC-69
❑ 70OPC-160
❑ 70Top-69
❑ 70Top-160
❑ 70TopPos-2
❑ 70TopSup-15
❑ 71MLBOffS-19
❑ 71OPC-30
❑ 71Top-30
❑ 71TopCoi-37
❑ 72MilBra-252
❑ 72Top-620
❑ 73Kel2D-29
❑ 73OPC-503
❑ 73Top-503
❑ 74BraPhoC-5
❑ 74OPC-29
❑ 74Top-29
❑ 74TopSta-9
❑ 75AtlBraP-24
❑ 75Hos-99
❑ 75OPC-130
❑ 75OPC-310
❑ 75Top-130
❑ 75Top-310
❑ 75TopMin-130
❑ 75TopMin-310
❑ 76AtlBraP-22
❑ 76Hos-3
❑ 76HosTwi-3
❑ 76OPC-435
❑ 76SSP-5
❑ 76Top-435
❑ 77BurCheD-209
❑ 77Hos-111
❑ 77OPC-43
❑ 77Spo-7410
❑ 77Spo-8321
❑ 77Top-615
❑ 78BraCok-11
❑ 78Hos-122
❑ 78OPC-6
❑ 78OPC-155
❑ 78RCColC-89
❑ 78Top-10
❑ 78Top-206
❑ 79BasPat-62
❑ 79Hos-62
❑ 79Kel-28
❑ 79OPC-313
❑ 79Top-595
❑ 79TopCom-19
❑ 80BurKinPHR-6
❑ 80Kel-51
❑ 80OPC-130
❑ 80Top-205
❑ 80Top-245
❑ 80TopSup-46
❑ 81BraPol-35
❑ 81Don-328
❑ 81Fle-242
❑ 81FleStiC-23
❑ 81Kel-12
❑ 81OPC-201
❑ 81Top-387
❑ 81TopSti-148
❑ 82BraBurKL-19
❑ 82BraPol-35
❑ 82Don-10
❑ 82Don-475
❑ 82Fle-444
❑ 82FleSta-68
❑ 82Kel-36
❑ 82OPC-185
❑ 82Top-185
❑ 82TopSti-20
❑ 83BraPol-35
❑ 83Don-97
❑ 83Don-613
❑ 83DonActA-12
❑ 83Fle-143
❑ 83FleSta-139
❑ 83FleSti-91
❑ 83OPC-205
❑ 83OPC-316
❑ 83Top-410
❑ 83Top-411
❑ 83Top-502
❑ 83TopFol-1
❑ 83TopSti-218
❑ 84Don-188
❑ 84DonCha-34
❑ 84Fle-187
❑ 84FleUpd-83
❑ 84FunFooP-115
❑ 84Nes792-650
❑ 84OCoandSI-234
❑ 84OPC-29
❑ 84Top-650
❑ 84TopSti-31
❑ 84TopTif-650
❑ 84TopTra-84T
❑ 84TopTraT-84T
❑ 85Don-458
❑ 85DonActA-49
❑ 85DonHig-50
❑ 85Fle-138
❑ 85FleStaS-93
❑ 85Lea-138
❑ 85OPC-40
❑ 85PolMet-Y2
❑ 85SevCoi-S11
❑ 85Top-40
❑ 85TopGloS-32
❑ 85TopSti-309
❑ 85TopTif-40
❑ 85YanTCMP-15
❑ 86Don-580
❑ 86Don-645
❑ 86Fle-112
❑ 86Fle-630
❑ 86FleLeaL-28
❑ 86FleStiC-82
❑ 86FleUpd-81
❑ 86IndOhH-35
❑ 86IndTeal-29
❑ 86Lea-243
❑ 86OPC-246
❑ 86QuaGra-28
❑ 86Spo-53
❑ 86Spo-135
❑ 86Spo-163
❑ 86Spo-182
❑ 86Top-204
❑ 86Top-790
❑ 86TopSti-7
❑ 86TopTat-8
❑ 86TopTif-204
❑ 86TopTif-790
❑ 86TopTra-77T
❑ 86TopTraT-77T
❑ 87AstShoSPO-23
❑ 87Don-465
❑ 87Fle-254
❑ 87Fle-626
❑ 87FleGlo-254
❑ 87FleGlo-626
❑ 87FleRecS-25
❑ 87IndGat-35
❑ 87Lea-181
❑ 87OPC-6
❑ 87Spo-147
❑ 87SpoRea-22
❑ 87SpoTeaP-3
❑ 87Top-694
❑ 87TopTif-694
❑ 88ClaRed-198
❑ 88ClaRed-199
❑ 88ClaRed-200
❑ 88Sco-555
❑ 88ScoGlo-555
❑ 88Top-5
❑ 88TopTif-5
❑ 89PacLegI-212
❑ 89SweBasG-22
❑ 90BraDubS-24
❑ 90PacLeg-96
❑ 90PerGreM-106
❑ 91LinDriAAA-449
❑ 91RicBraBC-38
❑ 91RicBraLD-449
❑ 91RicBraP-2583
❑ 91RicBraTI-4
❑ 92KelAll-6
❑ 92YanWIZ8-133
❑ 92YanWIZA-54
❑ 93MCIAmb-4
❑ 93NabAllA-4
❑ 94ColSilBC-6
❑ 95ColSilB-23
❑ 95ColSilB9-1
❑ 96ColSilB-22
Nielsen, Dan
❑ 88WatPirP-9
Nielsen, Jerry (Gerald)
❑ 88OneYanP-2062
❑ 89PriWilCS-14
❑ 89Sta-91
❑ 90PriWilCTI-16
❑ 91Ft.LauYC-10
❑ 91Ft.LauYP-2423
❑ 92AlbYanF-2225
❑ 92AlbYanSk-14
❑ 92DonRoo-87
❑ 93AngStaCl-28
❑ 93Don-359
❑ 93Fle-654
❑ 93Sco-268
❑ 93Top-594
❑ 93TopGol-594
❑ 93TopInaM-594
❑ 93TopInaR-594
❑ 93TopMic-594
❑ 93VanCanF-2593
❑ 94MidAngF-2436
❑ 94MidAngOHP-20
Nielsen, Kevin
❑ 89SanDieSAS-20
❑ 90SanDieSA3-6
❑ 91SprCarC-19
❑ 91SprCarP-740
❑ 92St.PetCC-13
❑ 92St.PetCF-2026
Nielsen, Scott
❑ 84NasSouTI-15
❑ 85AlbYanT-9
❑ 87Don-597
❑ 87HawIslP-15
❑ 87Top-57
❑ 87TopTif-57
❑ 88ColCliC-3
❑ 88ColCliP-6
❑ 88ColCliP-310
❑ 88TriAAAP-11
❑ 89ColCliC-2
❑ 89ColCliP-7
❑ 89ColCliP-754
❑ 89Fle-261
❑ 89FleGlo-261
❑ 90AlbDecGB-9
❑ 90CMC-359
❑ 90ProAAAF-272
❑ 90TidTidC-8
❑ 90TidTidP-541
❑ 90TopTVM-52
❑ 92YanWIZ8-134
Nielsen, Steve
❑ 78AshTouT-21
❑ 79TulDriT-9
❑ 80TulDriT-19
❑ 81TulDriT-9
❑ 82BurRanF-30
❑ 82BurRanT-26
❑ 83TulDriT-18
❑ 85BurRanT-11
Nielsen, Thomas
❑ 98SalVol-26
Nielson, Thomas
❑ 97SalVolG-25
Nieman, Bob (Robert C.)
❑ 53TigGle-23
❑ 55Bow-145
❑ 56BalOriP-30
❑ 56BalOriP-38
❑ 56BalOriP-39
❑ 56Top-267
❑ 57Top-14
❑ 58Hir-26
❑ 58OriJayP-7
❑ 58Top-165
❑ 59OriJayP-4
❑ 59Top-375
❑ 60CarJayP-9
❑ 60Top-149
❑ 60TopVen-149
❑ 61Top-178
❑ 62IndJayP-9
❑ 62Top-182
❑ 62TopVen-182
❑ 79TCM50-211
❑ 81Gia196T-35
❑ 91OriCro-330
Niemann, Art
❑ 82AppFoxFr-23
Niemann, Randy
❑ 76ForLauYS-28
❑ 79AstPos-16
❑ 80Top-469
❑ 81Don-143
❑ 81Fle-77
❑ 81Top-148
❑ 82Don-473
❑ 82PorBeaT-6
❑ 83Top-329
❑ 85TidTidT-7
❑ 86FleUpd-82
❑ 86MetTCM-31
❑ 86MetWorSC-26
❑ 86TopTra-78T
❑ 86TopTraT-78T
❑ 87AstShoSPT-21
❑ 87Fle-18
❑ 87FleGlo-18
❑ 87PorBeaP-3
❑ 87Top-147
❑ 87TopTif-147
❑ 88TidTidCa-24
❑ 88TidTidCM-10
❑ 89PacSenL-127
❑ 90PitMetP-26
❑ 91MetWIZ-294
❑ 91St.LucMC-28
❑ 91St.LucMP-729
❑ 92BinMetF-534
❑ 92BinMetS-75
❑ 93BinMetF-2350
❑ 94BinMetF-722
❑ 95StLucMTI-2
Niemann, Tom
❑ 83ButCopKT-14
❑ 85Ft.MyeRT-6
Niemeier, Todd
❑ 95EveAqaTI-14
❑ 96LanJetB-21
Nieporte, Jay
❑ 85SpoIndC-16
Nieson, Chuck
❑ 77FriOneYW-26
Niethammer, Darren
❑ 88ChaRanS-17
❑ 90ChaRanS-16
❑ 91ChaRanC-13
❑ 91ChaRanP-1317
❑ 91FloStaLAP-FSL5
❑ 92TulDriF-2698
❑ 92TulDriS-613
Niethammer, Marc
❑ 94BurBeeC-17
❑ 94BurBeeF-1090
❑ 96HudValRB-14
Nieto, Andy
❑ 87DayBeaAP-23
Nieto, Rene
❑ 80VenLeaS-149
Nieto, Roy
❑ 92AshTouC-11
❑ 93OscAstC-17
❑ 93OscAstF-625
Nieto, Tom (Thomas Andrew)
❑ 82ArkTraT-12
❑ 83LouRedR-9
❑ 84Car5x7-19
❑ 84LouRedR-8
❑ 85CarTeal-25
❑ 85Don-596
❑ 85Fle-235
❑ 85OPC-294
❑ 85Top-294
❑ 85TopTif-294
❑ 86CarKASD-12
❑ 86CarTeal-31
❑ 86Don-327
❑ 86ExpPos-10
❑ 86Fle-43
❑ 86IndIndTI-30
❑ 86Top-88
❑ 86TopTif-88
❑ 87DonOpeD-220
❑ 87FleUpd-88
❑ 87FleUpdG-88
❑ 87OPC-124
❑ 87Top-416
❑ 87TopTif-416
❑ 87TopTra-90T
❑ 87TopTraT-90T
❑ 87TwiPos-17
❑ 88Don-612
❑ 88Top-317
❑ 88TopClo-77
❑ 88TopTif-317
❑ 89PhiTas-24
❑ 90ProAAAF-305
❑ 90ScrRedBP-603
❑ 92ChaLooF-3835
❑ 92ChaLooS-200
❑ 93WesVirWC-25
❑ 94ChaWheF-2718
❑ 95NorNavTI-50
❑ 96GreBatB-2
❑ 97GreBatB-1
❑ 98GreBatM-26
Nieto, Tony
❑ 94BilMusF-3666
❑ 94BilMusSP-18
Nieves, Adelberto
❑ 81BatTroT-10
❑ 81WatIndT-30
Nieves, Ernie (Ernesto)
❑ 90BilMusP-3219
❑ 90ChaWheB-5
❑ 90ChaWheP-2237
❑ 91ChaWheC-7
❑ 91ChaWheP-2884
❑ 92ChaWheF-8
❑ 92ChaWVWC-5
❑ 93SouAtlLAPI-28
❑ 95MidAngOHP-24
❑ 98BriBluM-20
Nieves, Fionel
❑ 90AshTouC-7

❑ 91AshTouP-565
Nieves, Jose
❑ 96RocCubTI-22
❑ 98SouLeaTPG-11
❑ 98WesTenDJM-20
❑ 99SpoIll-49
Nieves, Juan
❑ 86BrePol-20
❑ 86Don-40
❑ 86DonRoo-12
❑ 86FleUpd-83
❑ 86SpoRoo-5
❑ 86TopTra-79T
❑ 86TopTraT-79T
❑ 87BrePol-20
❑ 87BreTeal-9
❑ 87ClaUpdY-136
❑ 87Don-90
❑ 87DonHig-1
❑ 87Fle-352
❑ 87FleGlo-352
❑ 87OPC-79
❑ 87SpoTeaP-19
❑ 87Top-79
❑ 87TopRoo-11
❑ 87TopTif-79
❑ 88BrePol-20
❑ 88BreTeal-27
❑ 88Don-126
❑ 88Fle-170
❑ 88FleGlo-170
❑ 88OPC-104
❑ 88PanSti-117
❑ 88PanSti-431
❑ 88RedFolSB-60
❑ 88Sco-513
❑ 88Sco-655
❑ 88ScoGlo-513
❑ 88ScoGlo-655
❑ 88ScoYouS2-33
❑ 88Spo-180
❑ 88Spo-211
❑ 88StaLinBre-12
❑ 88Top-515
❑ 88TopBig-190
❑ 88TopTif-515
❑ 89BimBreD-10
❑ 89Bow-131
❑ 89BowTif-131
❑ 89BreGar-10
❑ 89BrePol-20
❑ 89BreYea-20
❑ 89Don-575
❑ 89Sco-410
❑ 89Top-287
❑ 89TopTif-287
❑ 89UppDec-646
❑ 90BrePol-20
❑ 90OPC-467
❑ 90PubIntS-501
❑ 90Top-467
❑ 90TopTif-467
❑ 90UppDec-648
❑ 92BreUSO-3
❑ 93BreSen-2
❑ 93OneYanC-29
❑ 93OneYanF-3522
❑ 94BreMilB-59
❑ 94BreSen-6
❑ 94BreUSO-3
❑ 94GreBatF-493
❑ 95NorNavTI-49
❑ 96GreBatB-3
❑ 97GreBatC-28
❑ 97St.CatSB-24
❑ 98St.CatSM-29
Nieves, Mel (Melvin)
❑ 89BlaYNPRWL-81
❑ 89PulBraP-1893
❑ 90Bes-219
❑ 90ProAaA-105
❑ 90SumBraB-15
❑ 90SumBraP-2447
❑ 91DurBulP-1560
❑ 92Bow-143
❑ 92ClaFS7-94
❑ 92DurBulC-22
❑ 92DurBulTI-21
❑ 92GreBraF-1165
❑ 93Bow-662
❑ 93BraStaC-28
❑ 93ClaFS7-56
❑ 93Don-320
❑ 93FleMajLP-A1
❑ 93OPC-246
❑ 93PacSpa-10
❑ 93Pin-248
❑ 93PinRooTP-10
❑ 93PinTea2-5
❑ 93RicBraBB-5
❑ 93RicBraF-199
❑ 93RicBraP-21
❑ 93RicBraRC-16
❑ 93RicBraRC-22
❑ 93Sco-248
❑ 93ScoBoyoS-7
❑ 93ScoProaG-4
❑ 93StaClu-89
❑ 93StaCluFDI-89
❑ 93StaCluMOP-89
❑ 93Top-658
❑ 93TopGol-658
❑ 93TopInaM-658
❑ 93TopInaR-658
❑ 93TopMic-658
❑ 93Toy-20
❑ 93UppDec-21
❑ 93UppDecGold-21
❑ 94Bow-176
❑ 94Bow-365
❑ 94BowBes-X105
❑ 94BowBesR-X105
❑ 94Cla-154
❑ 94Fin-432
❑ 94FinJum-432
❑ 94FinRef-432
❑ 94Fle-671
❑ 94LasVegSF-881
❑ 94LeaLimR-3
❑ 94Pac-531
❑ 94Pin-478
❑ 94PinArtP-478
❑ 94PinMusC-478
❑ 94ScoBoyoS-40
❑ 94ScoRoo-RT150
❑ 94ScoRooGR-RT150
❑ 94Sel-415
❑ 94SpoRoo-40
❑ 94SpoRooAP-40
❑ 94StaClu-567
❑ 94StaCluFDI-567
❑ 94StaCluGR-567
❑ 94StaCluMOP-567
❑ 94Top-307
❑ 94TopGol-307
❑ 94TopSpa-307
❑ 94UppDec-256
❑ 94UppDecED-256
❑ 95Baz-130
❑ 95Bow-79
❑ 95ColCho-356
❑ 95ColChoGS-356
❑ 95ColChoSS-356
❑ 95Don-482
❑ 95DonPreP-482
❑ 95Emo-189
❑ 95Fla-421
❑ 95FleUpd-187
❑ 95Lea-15
❑ 95PadMot-26
❑ 95Pin-376
❑ 95PinArtP-376
❑ 95PinMusC-376
❑ 95PinUps-US14
❑ 95Sco-579
❑ 95ScoAi-AM13
❑ 95ScoGolR-579
❑ 95ScoPlaTS-579
❑ 95SPSpeF-47
❑ 95StaClu-438
❑ 95StaCluMOP-438
❑ 95StaCluSTWS-438
❑ 95Top-243
❑ 95TopCyb-137
❑ 95Ult-440
❑ 95UltGolM-440
❑ 95UppDec-372
❑ 95UppDecED-372
❑ 95UppDecEDG-372
❑ 95UppDecSE-132
❑ 95UppDecSEG-132
❑ 96Cir-41
❑ 96CirRav-41
❑ 96Don-152
❑ 96DonPreP-152
❑ 96Fle-575
❑ 96FleTif-575
❑ 96FleUpd-U35
❑ 96FleUpdTC-U35
❑ 96LeaPre-110
❑ 96LeaPreP-110
❑ 96LeaSigEA-143
❑ 96Pac-186
❑ 96PacPri-P62
❑ 96PacPriG-P62
❑ 96Sco-149
❑ 96SelCer-92
❑ 96SelCerAP-92
❑ 96SelCerCB-92
❑ 96SelCerCR-92
❑ 96SelCerMB-92
❑ 96SelCerMG-92
❑ 96SelCerMR-92
❑ 96SP-82
❑ 96Sum-121
❑ 96SumAbo&B-121
❑ 96SumArtP-121
❑ 96SumFoi-121
❑ 96TigHebN-13
❑ 96Ult-349
❑ 96UltGolM-349
❑ 96UppDec-189
❑ 96Zen-59
❑ 96ZenArtP-59
❑ 97Cir-214
❑ 97CirRav-214
❑ 97ColCho-340
❑ 97Don-53
❑ 97DonGolPP-53
❑ 97DonSilPP-53
❑ 97DurBulATI-7
❑ 97FlaShoLC-36
❑ 97FlaShoLeg0-36
❑ 97FlaShoLeg1-36
❑ 97FlaShoM-A36
❑ 97FlaShoM-B36
❑ 97FlaShoM-C36
❑ 97FlaShoR0-36
❑ 97FlaShoR1-36
❑ 97FlaShoR2-36
❑ 97Fle-103
❑ 97FleTif-103
❑ 97Lea-232
❑ 97LeaFraM-232
❑ 97LeaFraMDC-232
❑ 97MetUni-112
❑ 97Pac-93
❑ 97PacLigB-93
❑ 97PacPri-33
❑ 97PacPriLB-33
❑ 97PacPriP-33
❑ 97PacSil-93
❑ 97Sco-383
❑ 97ScoArtPWB-383
❑ 97ScoResC-383
❑ 97ScoShoS-383
❑ 97ScoShoSAP-383
❑ 97SP-73
❑ 97StaClu-169
❑ 97StaCluMOP-169
❑ 97Top-304
❑ 97Ult-61
❑ 97UltGolME-61
❑ 97UltPlaME-61
❑ 97UppDec-356
❑ 98Pac-94
❑ 98PacPlaB-94
❑ 98PacRedT-94
❑ 98PacSil-94
❑ 98Sco-69
❑ 98Top-121
❑ 98TopChr-121
❑ 98TopChrR-121
❑ 98TopDevR-121
❑ 98TopDia-121
❑ 98TopMiniC-121
❑ 98Ult-381
❑ 98UltGolM-381
❑ 98UltMas-381
❑ 98UltPlaM-381
❑ 99PacCroC-76
❑ 99PacCroCPB-76
Nieves, Miguel
❑ 96-97LinVen-205
Nieves, Raul
❑ 76DubPacT-24
Nieves, Wilbert
❑ 98CliLumG-15
Niggeling, Johnny
❑ 41BroW75-23
❑ 77CinRedT-30
❑ 93ConTSN-954
Niles, Harry (Harry Clyde)
❑ 08AmeCarE91-88
❑ 08RosComP-52
❑ 09RamT20-89
❑ 09T206-268
❑ 10E12AmeCDCE125-29
❑ 11SpoLifCW-269
❑ 11SpoLifM-49
❑ 11TurRedT-111
Niles, Randy
❑ 98VisOakG-20
Niles, Thomas
❑ 91WinHavRSP-485
❑ 92ElmPioC-10
❑ 92ElmPioF-1383
❑ 93LynRedSC-21
❑ 93LynRedSF-2517
Nill, George
❑ 08AmeLeaPC-13
❑ 11SpoLifCW-270
Nilsson, Anna Q.
❑ 28BabRCCE-4
Nilsson, Bob
❑ 91Cla/Bes-146
❑ 91DaiDolF-1
❑ 91DaiDolF-10
Nilsson, Dave
❑ 88BelBreGS-19
❑ 89StoPorB-1
❑ 89StoPorCLC-162
❑ 89StoPorP-374
❑ 89StoPorS-21
❑ 90ProAaA-151
❑ 90StoPorB-2
❑ 90StoPorCLC-187
❑ 90StoPorP-2186
❑ 91Cla/Bes-227
❑ 91ClaGolB-BC11
❑ 91DaiDolF-1
❑ 91DaiDolF-19
❑ 91ElPasDLD-194
❑ 91ElPasDP-2751
❑ 91LinDriAA-194
❑ 91UppDecFE-25F
❑ 92Bow-653
❑ 92DenZepS-142
❑ 92Don-4
❑ 92FleUpd-37
❑ 92OPC-58
❑ 92Pin-568
❑ 92PinRoo-27
❑ 92ProFS7-83
❑ 92ScoRoo-94T
❑ 92SkyAAAF-69
❑ 92Top-58
❑ 92TopGol-58
❑ 92TopGolW-58
❑ 92TopMic-58
❑ 92TopTra-83T
❑ 92TopTraG-83T
❑ 92UppDec-57
❑ 92UppDecSR-SR18
❑ 93AusFut-13
❑ 93AusFut-111
❑ 93AusFut-130
❑ 93Bow-591
❑ 93BrePol-19
❑ 93Don-235
❑ 93Fle-631
❑ 93Lea-327
❑ 93OPC-272
❑ 93PacSpa-162
❑ 93Pin-61
❑ 93Sco-344
❑ 93Sel-283
❑ 93StaClu-709
❑ 93StaCluFDI-709
❑ 93StaCluMOP-709
❑ 93Top-316
❑ 93TopGol-316
❑ 93TopInaM-316
❑ 93TopInaR-316
❑ 93TopMic-316
❑ 93Toy-31
❑ 93Ult-222
❑ 93UppDec-795
❑ 93UppDecGold-795
❑ 94BreMilB-60
❑ 94BrePol-20
❑ 94BreTeal-19
❑ 94ColC-216
❑ 94ColChoGS-216
❑ 94ColChoSS-216
❑ 94Don-204
❑ 94Fin-268
❑ 94FinRef-268
❑ 94Fla-307
❑ 94Fle-186
❑ 94FleExtB-106
❑ 94Lea-302
❑ 94LeaL-46
❑ 94Pac-337
❑ 94PanSti-84
❑ 94Pin-210
❑ 94PinArtP-210
❑ 94PinMusC-210
❑ 94Sco-533
❑ 94ScoGolR-533
❑ 94Sel-339
❑ 94StaClu-376
❑ 94StaCluFDI-376
❑ 94StaCluGR-376
❑ 94StaCluMOP-376
❑ 94Stu-46
❑ 94Top-548
❑ 94TopGol-548
❑ 94TopSpa-548
❑ 94TriPla-57
❑ 94Ult-80
❑ 94UppDec-359
❑ 94UppDecED-359
❑ 95AusFut-1
❑ 95AusFut-90
❑ 95AusFut-98
❑ 95Baz-79
❑ 95Bow-296
❑ 95ColCho-182
❑ 95ColChoGS-182
❑ 95ColChoSE-71
❑ 95ColChoSEGS-71
❑ 95ColChoSESS-71
❑ 95ColChoSS-182
❑ 95Don-288
❑ 95DonPreP-288
❑ 95DonTopotO-100
❑ 95Fin-183
❑ 95FinRef-183
❑ 95Fla-54
❑ 95Fle-186
❑ 95Lea-73
❑ 95LeaLim-110
❑ 95Pac-238
❑ 95PacPri-76
❑ 95PanSti-30
❑ 95Pin-320
❑ 95PinArtP-320
❑ 95PinMusC-320
❑ 95RedFol-23
❑ 95Sco-120
❑ 95ScoGolR-120
❑ 95ScoHaloG-HG37
❑ 95ScoPlaTS-120
❑ 95Sel-69
❑ 95SelArtP-69
❑ 95Spo-22
❑ 95SpoArtP-22
❑ 95StaClu-140
❑ 95StaCluFDI-140
❑ 95StaCluMOP-140
❑ 95StaCluSTWS-140
❑ 95StaCluVR-72
❑ 95StaCluVRMO-72
❑ 95Stu-102
❑ 95Sum-128
❑ 95SumNthD-128
❑ 95Top-17
❑ 95TopCyb-15
❑ 95TopD3-49
❑ 95TopEmb-33
❑ 95TopEmbGI-33
❑ 95Ult-298
❑ 95UltGolM-298
❑ 95UppDec-301
❑ 95UppDecED-301
❑ 95UppDecEDG-301
❑ 95UppDecSE-234
❑ 95UppDecSEG-234
❑ 96BrePol-20
❑ 96Cir-52
❑ 96CirBos-11
❑ 96CirRav-52
❑ 96ColCho-325
❑ 96ColCho-594
❑ 96ColChoGS-325
❑ 96ColChoGS-594
❑ 96ColChoSS-325
❑ 96ColChoSS-594
❑ 96Don-356
❑ 96DonPreP-356
❑ 96EmoXL-76
❑ 96Fin-B110
❑ 96FinRef-B110
❑ 96Fla-105
❑ 96Fle-154
❑ 96FleTif-154
❑ 96Lea-209
❑ 96LeaPrePB-209
❑ 96LeaPrePG-209
❑ 96LeaPrePS-209
❑ 96LeaSigA-169
❑ 96LeaSigAG-169
❑ 96LeaSigAS-169
❑ 96MetUni-71
❑ 96MetUniP-71
❑ 96Pac-343
❑ 96PanSti-194
❑ 96Pin-94
❑ 96PinAfi-135
❑ 96PinAfi-155
❑ 96PinAfiAP-135
❑ 96PinAfiAP-155
❑ 96Sco-297
❑ 96ScoDugC-B22
❑ 96ScoDugCAP-B22
❑ 96Sel-134
❑ 96SelArtP-134
❑ 96StaClu-372
❑ 96StaCluMOP-372
❑ 96Stu-134
❑ 96StuPrePB-134
❑ 96StuPrePG-134
❑ 96StuPrePS-134
❑ 96Sum-135
❑ 96SumAbo&B-135
❑ 96SumArtP-135
❑ 96SumFoi-135
❑ 96Top-302
❑ 96TopGal-74
❑ 96TopGalPPI-74
❑ 96Ult-82
❑ 96UltGolM-82
❑ 96UppDec-119
❑ 97BrePol-22
❑ 97Cir-130
❑ 97CirRav-130
❑ 97ColCho-150
❑ 97Don-331
❑ 97DonEli-113
❑ 97DonEliGS-113
❑ 97DonGolPP-331
❑ 97DonLim-38
❑ 97DonLimE-38
❑ 97DonLimENG-38
❑ 97DonPre-68
❑ 97DonPreCttC-68
❑ 97DonSilPP-331
❑ 97Fin-24
❑ 97FinRef-24
❑ 97FlaShoLC-164
❑ 97FlaShoLeg0-164
❑ 97FlaShoLeg1-164
❑ 97FlaShoM-A164
❑ 97FlaShoM-B164
❑ 97FlaShoM-C164
❑ 97FlaShoR0-164
❑ 97FlaShoR1-164
❑ 97FlaShoR2-164
❑ 97Fle-137
❑ 97FleTif-137
❑ 97Lea-316
❑ 97LeaFraM-316
❑ 97LeaFraMDC-316
❑ 97MetUni-69
❑ 97Pac-127
❑ 97PacLigB-127
❑ 97PacPri-41
❑ 97PacPriLB-41
❑ 97PacPriP-41
❑ 97PacSil-127
❑ 97PinIns-84
❑ 97PinInsCE-84
❑ 97PinInsDE-84
❑ 97PinX-P-70
❑ 97PinX-PMoS-70
❑ 97PinX-PMP-13
❑ 97PinX-PreMPS-13
❑ 97PinX-PSfF-44
❑ 97PinX-PSfFU-44
❑ 97Sco-122
❑ 97ScoArtPWB-122
❑ 97ScoPreS-122
❑ 97ScoShoS-122
❑ 97ScoShoSAP-122
❑ 97Sel-179
❑ 97SelCom-179
❑ 97SP-99
❑ 97SpoIll-50
❑ 97SpoIllEE-50
❑ 97StaClu-153
❑ 97StaCluMOP-153
❑ 97Top-183
❑ 97TopGal-97
❑ 97TopGalPPI-97

❑ 97Ult-82
❑ 97UltGolME-82
❑ 97UltPlaME-82
❑ 97UppDec-181
❑ 97UppDec-404
❑ 98CirThu-183
❑ 98CirThuRav-183
❑ 98CirThuSupRav-183
❑ 98ColCho-153
❑ 98Don-135
❑ 98DonCol-135
❑ 98DonColL-311
❑ 98DonColS-135
❑ 98DonGolPP-135
❑ 98DonPriCD-135
❑ 98DonPriCL-311
❑ 98DonSilPP-135
❑ 98Fin-55
❑ 98FinNo--55
❑ 98FinNo-R-55
❑ 98FinRef-55
❑ 98Fle-248
❑ 98Lea-112
❑ 98LeaFraDA-112
❑ 98LeaFraF-112
❑ 98LeaFraM-112
❑ 98LeaFraM-112
❑ 98LeaFraMDC-112
❑ 98LeaFraMDC-112
❑ 98LeaFraMZ2-112
❑ 98MetUni-35
❑ 98MetUniPMG-35
❑ 98Pac-124
❑ 98PacAur-154
❑ 98PacInv-42
❑ 98PacInvPBlue-42
❑ 98PacInvSilv-42
❑ 98PacInvTeam-15
❑ 98PacOme-136
❑ 98PacOmeR-136
❑ 98PacOnl-409
❑ 98PacOnlR-409
❑ 98PacOnlWC-409
❑ 98PacPar-189
❑ 98PacParC-189
❑ 98PacParG-189
❑ 98PacParHS-189
❑ 98PacParPB-189
❑ 98PacParR-189
❑ 98PacPlaB-124
❑ 98PacRedT-124
❑ 98PacSil-124
❑ 98PacTeaC-8
❑ 98Pin-100
❑ 98PinPlu-154
❑ 98PinPreP-100
❑ 98Revo-80
❑ 98RevoSS-80
❑ 98ScoRT-138
❑ 98SP Aut-121
❑ 98SpoIll-95
❑ 98SpoIllEE-95
❑ 98SpoIllFE-95
❑ 98StaCluFDI-118
❑ 98StaCluI-118
❑ 98StaCluOneK-118
❑ 98StaCluPP-118
❑ 98Stu-151
❑ 98StuGPP-151
❑ 98StuSPP-151
❑ 98Top-355
❑ 98TopChr-355
❑ 98TopChrR-355
❑ 98TopDevR-355
❑ 98TopDia-355
❑ 98TopMiniC-355
❑ 98Ult-123
❑ 98UltGolM-123
❑ 98UltMas-123
❑ 98UltPlaM-123
❑ 98UppDec-125
❑ 98UppDecNP-NP1
❑ 98UppDecSF-77
❑ 99Fle-562
❑ 99FleSta9-562
❑ 99FleWarT-562
❑ 99MetUni-80
❑ 99MetUniGM-80
❑ 99MetUniPMG-80
❑ 99Pac-240
❑ 99PacAur-101
❑ 99PacAurOD-101
❑ 99PacCroC-152
❑ 99PacCroCPB-152
❑ 99PacOme-133
❑ 99PacOmeC-133
❑ 99PacOmeG-133
❑ 99PacOmePB-133
❑ 99PacPar-128
❑ 99PacParC-128
❑ 99PacParG-128
❑ 99PacParHoloGold-128
❑ 99PacParHS-128
❑ 99PacParOD-128
❑ 99PacParPB-128
❑ 99PacParRed-128
❑ 99PacPlaB-240
❑ 99PacPriS-120
❑ 99PacPriS206-120
❑ 99PacPriS206R-120
❑ 99PacRed-240
❑ 99SkyPre-216
❑ 99SkyPreR-216
❑ 99StaClu-68
❑ 99StaCluFDI-68
❑ 99StaCluOoaK-68
❑ 99StaCluPP-68
❑ 99Top-141
❑ 99TopChr-141
❑ 99TopChrR-141
❑ 99TopMVPP-141
❑ 99UppDec-407
❑ 99UppDecEL1-407
❑ 99UppDecEL2-407
❑ 99Vic-218

Nilsson, Gary
❑ 91DaiDolF-1
❑ 91DaiDolF-7
❑ 93AusFut-22

Nimura, Kaoru
❑ 96HonShaHWB-33

Nina, Elvin
❑ 97SouOreTB-26
❑ 98VisOakG-21

Nina, Robin
❑ 89SalDodTI-19
❑ 90VerBeaDS-20

Nipp, Mark
❑ 80AlbDukTc-21

Nipper, Al
❑ 85Don-614
❑ 85Fle-165
❑ 85Top-424
❑ 85TopTif-424
❑ 86Don-538
❑ 86Fle-356
❑ 86Top-181
❑ 86TopTif-181
❑ 87Don-297
❑ 87Fle-39
❑ 87FleGlo-39
❑ 87OPC-64
❑ 87RedSoxP-14
❑ 87Top-617
❑ 87TopTif-617
❑ 88CubDavB-45
❑ 88Don-523
❑ 88DonBasB-250
❑ 88DonTeaBC-NEW
❑ 88Fle-358
❑ 88FleGlo-358
❑ 88Sco-527
❑ 88ScoGlo-527
❑ 88Top-313
❑ 88TopTif-326
❑ 88TopTra-75T
❑ 88TopTraT-75T
❑ 89Don-394
❑ 89Fle-433
❑ 89FleGlo-433
❑ 89Sco-532
❑ 89Top-86
❑ 89TopTif-86
❑ 89UppDec-494
❑ 90IndTeal-30
❑ 91LinDriAAA-241
❑ 91LouRedLD-241
❑ 91LouRedP-2911
❑ 94SarRedSC-30
❑ 95TreThuTI-2
❑ 97TexAllM-4
❑ 97TreThuB-3

Nipper, Mike
❑ 85DurBulT-28
❑ 86DurBulP-20

Nipper, Ronald
❑ 87GreBraB-6

Nippert, Merlin
❑ 64SeaPop-12
❑ 77FriOneYW-93

Nischwitz, Ron
❑ 62TigPosCF-14
❑ 62Top-591
❑ 63Top-152
❑ 66OPC-38
❑ 66Top-38
❑ 66TopVen-38
❑ 81TCM60I-380

Nishi, Masafumi
❑ 90IBAWorA-26

Nishijima, Takayuki
❑ 92SalSpuC-7
❑ 92SalSpuF-3771

Nishimura, Hioetsugu
❑ 88VerBeaDS-19

Nishioka, Tsuyoshi
❑ 91SalSpuP-2241

Nista, Brett
❑ 97UCLBruTI-13

Nitcholas, Otho
❑ 33Zee-35
❑ 37Zee-20
❑ 90DodTar-576

Nitkowski, C.J.
❑ 94ClaUpdCotC-CC8
❑ 94SigRooDP-9
❑ 94SigRooDPS-9
❑ 94StaCluDP-2
❑ 94StaCluDPFDI-2
❑ 95ActPacF-61
❑ 95Bow-53
❑ 95BowBes-B71
❑ 95BowBesR-B71
❑ 95ColCho-43
❑ 95ColChoGS-43
❑ 95ColChoSS-43
❑ 95Exc-179
❑ 95Fin-301
❑ 95FinRef-301
❑ 95Pin-168
❑ 95PinArtP-168
❑ 95PinMusC-168
❑ 95RedKah-20
❑ 95ScoDraP-DP4
❑ 95SP-24
❑ 95SPChaDC-6
❑ 95SPSil-24
❑ 95StaClu-114
❑ 95StaCluFDI-114
❑ 95StaCluMOP-114
❑ 95StaCluSTWS-114
❑ 95Top-84
❑ 95UppDecML-192
❑ 95UppDecMLFS-192
❑ 95UppDecMLOP-OP7
❑ 96ColCho-545
❑ 96ColChoGS-545
❑ 96ColChoSS-545
❑ 96Don-467
❑ 96DonPreP-467
❑ 96Fin-S127
❑ 96FinRef-S127
❑ 96Fle-118
❑ 96FleTif-118
❑ 96Pin-174
❑ 96Sco-506
❑ 96TolMudHB-21
❑ 96Top-398
❑ 96UppDec-331
❑ 97Top-313
❑ 98PacOnl-330
❑ 98PacOnlR-330
❑ 98PacOnlWC-330

Nitschke, Bear
❑ 94MarPhiC-14
❑ 94MarPhiF-3296

Nitschke, Buzz (David)
❑ 75IntLeaASB-19
❑ 75PacCoaLAB-19
❑ 75TucTorC-5
❑ 75TucTorTI-14

Nittoli, Mike
❑ 86SanJosBP-15

Nitz, Rick
❑ 74AlbDukTI-11
❑ 75AlbDukCa-16
❑ 75IntLeaASB-20
❑ 75PacCoaLAB-20

Niura, Hisao
❑ 79TCMJapPB-64

Nivens, Toby
❑ 87OrlTwiP-12
❑ 88OrlTwiB-6
❑ 89JacMetGS-6
❑ 90JacMetGS-17
❑ 91LinDriAA-640
❑ 91WilBilLD-640
❑ 91WilBilP-289

Nix, Dave
❑ 81AppFoxT-21
❑ 82AppFoxFr-15
❑ 83GleFalWST-8
❑ 86HunStaDJ-12
❑ 86MadMusP-15
❑ 86MadMusP-16

Nix, James
❑ 92PriRedC-16
❑ 92PriRedF-3087
❑ 93WesVirWC-21
❑ 93WesVirWF-2865
❑ 94WinSpiC-18
❑ 94WinSpiF-268
❑ 95ChaLooTI-16
❑ 96ChaLooB-22
❑ 97ChaLoo-19
❑ 98LouRedQ-16

Nix, John
❑ 75CedRapGT-11

Nix, Wayne
❑ 98SouOreTG-21

Nixon, Al
❑ 90DodTar-577

Nixon, Donell
❑ 81WauTimT-17
❑ 82WauTimF-9
❑ 84ChaLooT-10
❑ 87CalCanP-2327
❑ 87DonOpeD-114
❑ 87MarMot-19
❑ 87SpoTeaP-25
❑ 88CalCanC-11
❑ 88Fle-382
❑ 88FleGlo-382
❑ 88FleUpd-129
❑ 88FleUpdG-129
❑ 88Sco-436
❑ 88ScoGlo-436
❑ 88Top-146
❑ 88TopTif-146
❑ 89Bow-477
❑ 89BowTif-477
❑ 89Fle-337
❑ 89FleGlo-337
❑ 89GiaMot-25
❑ 89Sco-481
❑ 89Top-447
❑ 89TopBig-214
❑ 89TopTif-447
❑ 90CMC-314
❑ 90Don-571
❑ 90Fle-66
❑ 90FleCan-66
❑ 90MLBBasB-25
❑ 90OPC-658
❑ 90ProAAAF-472
❑ 90PubIntS-78
❑ 90RocRedWC-11
❑ 90RocRedWGC-8
❑ 90RocRedWP-715
❑ 90Sco-538
❑ 90Top-658
❑ 90TopTif-658
❑ 91OriCro-331
❑ 92ColSprSSF-765
❑ 92ColSprSSS-93
❑ 94ChaKniF-911

Nixon, Jason
❑ 90AugPirP-2467

Nixon, Otis
❑ 81NasSouTI-11
❑ 83ColCliT-25
❑ 84Ind-23
❑ 85Ind-23
❑ 85IndPol-20
❑ 86Fle-591
❑ 86IndOhH-20
❑ 86IndTeal-30
❑ 86TopTra-80T
❑ 86TopTraT-80T
❑ 87Fle-255
❑ 87FleGlo-255
❑ 87IndGat-20
❑ 87Top-486
❑ 87TopTif-486
❑ 88BlaYNPRWLU-19
❑ 88ExpPos-24
❑ 88IndIndC-14
❑ 88IndIndP-518
❑ 88StaLinMa-11
❑ 89Bow-366
❑ 89BowTif-366
❑ 89Fle-387
❑ 89FleGlo-387
❑ 89OPC-54
❑ 89Sco-451
❑ 89Top-674
❑ 89TopBig-234
❑ 89TopMinL-23
❑ 89TopTif-674
❑ 89UppDec-480
❑ 90Don-456
❑ 90ExpPos-25
❑ 90Fle-356
❑ 90FleCan-356
❑ 90OPC-252
❑ 90PubIntS-183
❑ 90Sco-241
❑ 90Top-252
❑ 90TopBig-279
❑ 90TopMag-89
❑ 90TopTif-252
❑ 90UppDec-379
❑ 91Bow-571
❑ 91BraDubP-20
❑ 91BraSubS-27
❑ 91Don-626
❑ 91Fle-241
❑ 91FleUpd-75
❑ 91Lea-395
❑ 91OPC-558
❑ 91OPCPre-89
❑ 91PanFreS-152
❑ 91Sco-431
❑ 91ScoRoo-29T
❑ 91StaClu-174
❑ 91StaClu-392
❑ 91Top-558
❑ 91TopDesS-558
❑ 91TopMic-558
❑ 91TopTif-558
❑ 91TopTra-84T
❑ 91TopTraT-84T
❑ 91UltUpd-69
❑ 91UppDec-520
❑ 91UppDecFE-58F
❑ 92Bow-669
❑ 92BraLykP-20
❑ 92BraLykS-24
❑ 92Don-33
❑ 92Don-41
❑ 92FleUpd-69
❑ 92Lea-358
❑ 92LeaBlaG-358
❑ 92OPC-340
❑ 92Pin-519
❑ 92Sco-429
❑ 92Sco-443
❑ 92Sco100S-73
❑ 92StaClu-882
❑ 92StaCluNC-882
❑ 92Top-340
❑ 92TopGol-340
❑ 92TopGolW-340
❑ 92TopKid-35
❑ 92TopMic-340
❑ 92TopPreS-174
❑ 92Ult-461
❑ 92UppDec-451
❑ 92YanWIZ8-135
❑ 93BluJayDM-22
❑ 93Bow-310
❑ 93BraLykP-21
❑ 93BraLykS-26
❑ 93BraStaC-16
❑ 93ClaGam-71
❑ 93Don-262
❑ 93Fin-181
❑ 93FinRef-181
❑ 93Fle-10
❑ 93Lea-180
❑ 93OPC-271
❑ 93PacSpa-337
❑ 93PanSti-186
❑ 93Pin-35
❑ 93Sco-87
❑ 93Sel-159
❑ 93StaClu-678
❑ 93StaCluFDI-678
❑ 93StaCluM-92
❑ 93StaCluMOP-678
❑ 93Stu-216
❑ 93Top-333
❑ 93TopGol-333
❑ 93TopInaM-333
❑ 93TopInaR-333
❑ 93TopMic-333
❑ 93Ult-310
❑ 93UppDec-292
❑ 93UppDecGold-292
❑ 94Bow-91
❑ 94ColC-579
❑ 94ColChoGS-579
❑ 94ColChoSS-579
❑ 94Don-232
❑ 94Fin-274
❑ 94FinRef-274
❑ 94Fla-265
❑ 94Fle-369
❑ 94FleExtB-22
❑ 94FleUpd-14
❑ 94Lea-375
❑ 94OPC-188
❑ 94Pac-19
❑ 94Pin-498
❑ 94PinArtP-498
❑ 94PinMusC-498
❑ 94ProMag-15
❑ 94Sco-106
❑ 94ScoGolR-106
❑ 94ScoRoo-RT26
❑ 94ScoRooCP-CP5
❑ 94ScoRooGR-RT26
❑ 94Sel-228
❑ 94SpoRoo-36
❑ 94SpoRooAP-36
❑ 94StaClu-106
❑ 94StaClu-597
❑ 94StaCluFDI-106
❑ 94StaCluFDI-597
❑ 94StaCluGR-106
❑ 94StaCluGR-597
❑ 94StaCluMOP-106
❑ 94StaCluMOP-597
❑ 94Stu-163
❑ 94Top-52
❑ 94TopGol-52
❑ 94TopSpa-52
❑ 94TopTra-40T
❑ 94Ult-316
❑ 94UppDec-497
❑ 94UppDecED-497
❑ 94USPlaCA-7H
❑ 95ColCho-396
❑ 95ColChoGS-396
❑ 95ColChoSS-396
❑ 95Don-213
❑ 95DonPreP-213
❑ 95DonTopotO-163
❑ 95Fin-186
❑ 95FinRef-186
❑ 95Fla-308
❑ 95Fle-36
❑ 95FleUpd-85
❑ 95Lea-376
❑ 95Pac-43
❑ 95Pin-106
❑ 95PinArtP-106
❑ 95PinMusC-106
❑ 95RanCra-22
❑ 95StaClu-262
❑ 95StaClu-552
❑ 95StaCluFDI-262
❑ 95StaCluMOP-262
❑ 95StaCluMOP-552
❑ 95StaCluSTWS-262
❑ 95StaCluSTWS-552
❑ 95StaCluVR-130
❑ 95StaCluVRMO-130
❑ 95Top-148
❑ 95TopCyb-91
❑ 95TopLeaL-LL17
❑ 95TopTra-101T
❑ 95Ult-13
❑ 95UltGolM-13
❑ 95UppDec-155
❑ 95UppDecED-155
❑ 95UppDecEDG-155
❑ 95USPlaCMLA-12H
❑ 96BluJayB-3
❑ 96BluJayOH-21
❑ 96ColCho-343
❑ 96ColCho-746
❑ 96ColChoGS-343
❑ 96ColChoGS-746
❑ 96ColChoSS-343
❑ 96ColChoSS-746
❑ 96Don-402
❑ 96DonPreP-402
❑ 96EmoXL-135
❑ 96Fin-B269
❑ 96FinRef-B269
❑ 96Fla-189
❑ 96Fle-255
❑ 96FleTif-255
❑ 96FleUpd-U98
❑ 96FleUpdTC-U98

❑ 96MetUni-124
❑ 96MetUniP-124
❑ 96Pac-434
❑ 96PanSti-238
❑ 96Sco-113
❑ 96StaClu-113
❑ 96StaCluMOP-113
❑ 96Top-178
❑ 96Ult-433
❑ 96UltGolM-433
❑ 96UppDec-472
❑ 97BluJayB-9
❑ 97BluJayOH-20
❑ 97BluJayS-16
❑ 97BluJayS-7
❑ 97Cir-320
❑ 97CirRav-320
❑ 97ColCho-502
❑ 97Don-318
❑ 97DonGolPP-318
❑ 97DonSilPP-318
❑ 97Fin-8
❑ 97FinRef-8
❑ 97Fle-245
❑ 97FleTif-245
❑ 97Lea-290
❑ 97LeaFraM-290
❑ 97LeaFraMDC-290
❑ 97PacPriGotD-GD104
❑ 97Sco-408
❑ 97ScoArtPWB-408
❑ 97ScoResC-408
❑ 97ScoShoS-408
❑ 97ScoShoSAP-408
❑ 97StaClu-163
❑ 97StaCluMOP-163
❑ 97Top-170
❑ 97TopChrSB-23
❑ 97TopChrSBR-23
❑ 97TopSeaB-SB23
❑ 97Ult-147
❑ 97UltGolME-147
❑ 97UltPlaME-147
❑ 97UppDec-212
❑ 98ColCho-413
❑ 98Pac-335
❑ 98PacAur-53
❑ 98PacOnl-430
❑ 98PacOnlR-430
❑ 98PacOnlWC-430
❑ 98PacPar-64
❑ 98PacParC-64
❑ 98PacParG-64
❑ 98PacParHS-64
❑ 98PacParPB-64
❑ 98PacParR-64
❑ 98PacPlaB-335
❑ 98PacRedT-335
❑ 98PacSil-335
❑ 98PinPlu-80
❑ 98Top-392
❑ 98TopChr-392
❑ 98TopChrR-392
❑ 98TopDevR-392
❑ 98TopDia-392
❑ 98TopMiniC-392
❑ 98Ult-38
❑ 98Ult-356
❑ 98UltGolM-38
❑ 98UltGolM-356
❑ 98UltMas-38
❑ 98UltMas-356
❑ 98UltPlaM-38
❑ 98UltPlaM-356
❑ 98UppDec-698
❑ 99Fle-453
❑ 99FleSta9-453
❑ 99FleWarT-453
❑ 99Pac-251
❑ 99PacCroC-162
❑ 99PacCroCPB-162
❑ 99PacPlaB-251
❑ 99PacPri-84
❑ 99PacPriHB-84
❑ 99PacPriHG-84
❑ 99PacPriHM-84
❑ 99PacPriHP-84
❑ 99PacPriRed-84
❑ 99PacPriS-121
❑ 99PacPriS206-121
❑ 99PacPriS206R-121
❑ 99PacRed-251
❑ 99SkyMolMOA-4
❑ 99Ult-44
❑ 99UltGolM-44
❑ 99UltMas-44
❑ 99UltPlaM-44

Nixon, Robert
❑ 20Zee-129

Nixon, Russ (Russell E.)
❑ 57IndSoh-11
❑ 57IndTeal-17
❑ 58IndTeal-18
❑ 58Top-133
❑ 59Ind-14
❑ 59Kah-25
❑ 59Top-344
❑ 60IndJayP-6
❑ 60Kah-29
❑ 60MacSta-17
❑ 60Top-36
❑ 60TopVen-36
❑ 61Pos-52A
❑ 61Pos-52B
❑ 61Top-53
❑ 61TopStal-115
❑ 62RedSoxJP-7
❑ 62Top-523
❑ 62TopStal-16
❑ 63Top-168
❑ 64Top-329
❑ 64TopVen-329
❑ 65OPC-162
❑ 65Top-162
❑ 66Top-227
❑ 66TopVen-227
❑ 67Top-446
❑ 68DexPre-59
❑ 68Top-515
❑ 69Top-363
❑ 80RedEnq-2
❑ 81RedSoxBG2S-99
❑ 83RedYea-7
❑ 83Top-756
❑ 84ExpPos-20
❑ 84ExpStu-5
❑ 84ExpStu-38
❑ 84Nes792-351
❑ 84Top-351
❑ 84TopTif-351
❑ 86BraPol-2
❑ 88TopTra-76T
❑ 88TopTraT-76T
❑ 89BraDub-19
❑ 89Top-564
❑ 89TopTif-564
❑ 90BraDubP-21
❑ 90OPC-171
❑ 90Top-171
❑ 90TopTif-171
❑ 91LinDriAAA-424
❑ 91PorBeaLD-424
❑ 91PorBeaP-1581
❑ 92MarMot-27
❑ 93LasVegSF-960
❑ 94LasVegSF-883
❑ 98BilMusTI-25
❑ 98IndIndQ-4

Nixon, Trot
❑ 94ActPac-2
❑ 94ActPac-65
❑ 94ActPac2G-11G
❑ 94ActPac2GD-11G
❑ 94ActPacP-1
❑ 94CarLeaAF-CAR4
❑ 94Cla-10
❑ 94ClaBonB-BB1
❑ 94ClaCreotC-C1
❑ 94ClaGolF-3
❑ 94ClaGolN1PLF-LP9
❑ 94ClaGolREF-RE9
❑ 94ClaTriF-T7
❑ 94ColC-25
❑ 94ColChoGS-25
❑ 94ColChoSS-25
❑ 94LynRedSC-1
❑ 94LynRedSF-1907
❑ 94Pin-270
❑ 94PinArtP-270
❑ 94PinMusC-270
❑ 94Sco-486
❑ 94ScoGolR-486
❑ 94SP-11
❑ 94SPDieC-11
❑ 94SPHol-28
❑ 94SPHolDC-28
❑ 94UppDec-543
❑ 94UppDecAHNIL-9
❑ 94UppDecED-543
❑ 94UppDecML-4
❑ 94UppDecML-270
❑ 95ActPacF-2
❑ 95Bes-6
❑ 95Bow-152
❑ 95BowBes-B39
❑ 95BowBesR-B39
❑ 95Exc-13
❑ 95SPML-21
❑ 95UppDecML-17
❑ 95UppDecMLFS-17
❑ 96Bow-211
❑ 96BowFoi-211
❑ 96Exc-15
❑ 96TreThuB-28
❑ 97BesAutSBPP-30
❑ 97Cir-204
❑ 97CirRav-204
❑ 97Lea-178
❑ 97LeaFraM-178
❑ 97LeaFraMDC-178
❑ 97PawRedS-18
❑ 97SarRedS-17
❑ 97UppDec-282
❑ 98Bow-165
❑ 98BowChr-165
❑ 98BowChrGA-165
❑ 98BowChrGAR-165
❑ 98BowChrI-165
❑ 98BowChrIR-165
❑ 98BowChrR-165
❑ 98BowGolA-165
❑ 98BowInt-165
❑ 98PawRedSQ-1
❑ 99BasAmeTPA-31
❑ 99Bow-174
❑ 99BowChr-174
❑ 99BowChrG-174
❑ 99BowChrGR-174
❑ 99BowChrI-174
❑ 99BowChrIR-174
❑ 99BowChrR-174
❑ 99BowGol-174
❑ 99BowInt-174
❑ 99DumSet-112
❑ 99E-X Cen-100
❑ 99E-X CenECFut-100
❑ 99E-X CenECNow-100
❑ 99Fle-148
❑ 99FleBri-157
❑ 99FleBri2G-157
❑ 99FleBriBlu-157
❑ 99FleBriGol-157
❑ 99FleMys-112
❑ 99FleMysM-112
❑ 99FleSta9-148
❑ 99FleWarT-148
❑ 99PacInv-25
❑ 99PacInvOD-25
❑ 99PacInvPB-25
❑ 99SkyThu-95
❑ 99SkyThuRant-95
❑ 99SkyThuRave-95
❑ 99TeaBesR-8
❑ 99TeaBesRA-16
❑ 99ThuSkySupR-95
❑ 99UppDec-329
❑ 99UppDecE-17
❑ 99UppDecEFXG-17
❑ 99UppDecEL1-329
❑ 99UppDecEL2-329
❑ 99Vic-58

Nixon, Willard
❑ 50RedSoxTI-15
❑ 51Bow-270
❑ 52Top-269
❑ 53BowBW-2
❑ 53RedSoxTI-22
❑ 53Top-30
❑ 54Bow-114
❑ 55Bow-177
❑ 56Top-122
❑ 57Top-189
❑ 58Hir-47
❑ 58Top-395
❑ 59Top-361
❑ 79DiaGre-247
❑ 81RedSoxBG2S-41
❑ 83TopRep5-269
❑ 91TopArc1-30

Nixon, William
❑ 16Zee-60

Nizov, Alexander
❑ 97ButCopKB-16
❑ 97ButCopKK-16
❑ 98ButCopKG-22

Noack, Gus
❑ 23Zee-142

Nobis, Tommy
❑ 78AtlCon-19

Noble, Jeff
❑ 85CloHSS-29

Noble, Ray
❑ 85UtiBluST-20
❑ 86TucTorP-17

Noble, Ray (Rafael Miguel)
❑ 50RemBre-19
❑ 51Bow-269
❑ 52BerRos-47
❑ 75Gia195T-22
❑ 95NegLeaL2-14

Nobles, Jim
❑ 79LodDodT-10

Noboa, Junior (Milicades A.)
❑ 81BatTroT-15
❑ 82WatIndF-28
❑ 82WatIndT-18
❑ 83WatIndF-8
❑ 84BufBisT-4
❑ 85DomLeaS-186
❑ 85MaiGuiT-20
❑ 86IndTeal-31
❑ 86MaiGuiP-13
❑ 87BufBisP-8
❑ 87IndGat-17
❑ 88EdmTraP-564
❑ 88StaLinI-16
❑ 88Top-503
❑ 88TopTif-503
❑ 89IndIndC-20
❑ 89IndIndP-1235
❑ 89TriAAAP-AAA8
❑ 90ExpPos-26
❑ 90TopTra-80T
❑ 90TopTraT-80T
❑ 90TriAAAC-3
❑ 91Don-726
❑ 91ExpPos-16
❑ 91Fle-242
❑ 91Lea-255
❑ 91OPC-182
❑ 91Sco-423
❑ 91Top-182
❑ 91TopDesS-182
❑ 91TopMic-182
❑ 91TopTif-182
❑ 91Ult-207
❑ 92Don-765
❑ 92Lea-403
❑ 92LeaBlaG-403
❑ 92MetColP-25
❑ 92MetKah-3
❑ 92OPCPre-187
❑ 92StaClu-709
❑ 92StaCluNC-709
❑ 92Ult-533
❑ 93LimRocDWB-22
❑ 95RocRedWTI-27

Nocas, Luke
❑ 87AppFoxP-25
❑ 89AppFoxP-877

Nocciolo, Mark
❑ 80SalLakCGT-5
❑ 81HolMilT-18

Nocé, Doug
❑ 90GatCitPP-3356
❑ 90GatCitPSP-18
❑ 91SumFlyC-14
❑ 91SumFlyP-2337

Noce, John
❑ 93GenCubC-30
❑ 94HunCubC-30
❑ 94HunCubF-3571

Noce, Paul
❑ 83MiaMarT-17
❑ 84MidCubT-21
❑ 85IowCubT-5
❑ 86IowCubP-20
❑ 87DonRoo-51
❑ 87IowCubTI-11
❑ 88Don-315
❑ 88DonTeaBC-315
❑ 88Fle-428
❑ 88FleGlo-428
❑ 88IowCubC-16
❑ 88IowCubP-538
❑ 88RedFolSB-61
❑ 88Sco-329
❑ 88ScoGlo-329
❑ 88Top-542
❑ 88TopTif-542
❑ 89CalCanC-16
❑ 89CalCanP-539
❑ 90CMC-139
❑ 90NasSouC-14
❑ 90NasSouP-241
❑ 90ProAAAF-553
❑ 91PhoFirP-72

Noch, Douglas
❑ 88VerBeaDS-20
❑ 89VerBeaDS-19

Nodell, Ray
❑ 83MiaMarT-12

Nodine, Rob
❑ 96LanJetB-4

Nodine, Robert
❑ 93RivPilCLC-31
❑ 94RivPilCLC-32

Noe, Matt
❑ 97EveAquG-21

Noel, Jay
❑ 92PulBraC-3
❑ 92PulBraF-3192
❑ 93MacBraC-16
❑ 93MacBraF-1414

Noel, Mike
❑ 89FreStaBS-15
❑ 90FreStaS-10
❑ 91FreStaBS-8

Noel, Todd
❑ 96BesAutS1RP-FR7
❑ 97Bow-383
❑ 97BowInt-383
❑ 97Top-269
❑ 98BesPreA-29
❑ 98Bow-191
❑ 98BowChr-191
❑ 98BowChrGA-191
❑ 98BowChrGAR-191
❑ 98BowChrI-191
❑ 98BowChrIR-191
❑ 98BowChrR-191
❑ 98BowGolA-191
❑ 98BowInt-191
❑ 98MidLeaPM-21
❑ 98RocCubM-22
❑ 98RocCubTI-23
❑ 99BasAmeTPA-32
❑ 99SP TopP-94
❑ 99SP TopPPE-94
❑ 99TeaBesRA-17

Noelke, Michael
❑ 88LitFalMP-7
❑ 89ColMetB-9
❑ 89ColMetGS-18

Noffke, Andy
❑ 96MicBatCB-17

Nofziger, J. F.
❑ 21Zee-56

Noggle, Anne
❑ 75TopPho-85

Nogowski, Brandon
❑ 96EveAquB-17
❑ 97EveAquG-22
❑ 98SouOreTG-22

Noguchi, Shigeki
❑ 94CenValRC-14
❑ 94CenValRF-3200

Nokes, David
❑ 91WasVia-4

Nokes, Matt
❑ 82CliGiaF-4
❑ 84ShrCapFB-14
❑ 86NasSouTI-18
❑ 87ClaUpdY-129
❑ 87DonRoo-12
❑ 87FleUpd-90
❑ 87FleUpdG-90
❑ 87SpoRooI-16
❑ 87TopTra-91T
❑ 87TopTraT-91T
❑ 88ClaBlu-207
❑ 88ClaRed-166
❑ 88Don-152
❑ 88DonAll-16
❑ 88DonBasB-237
❑ 88Fle-66
❑ 88Fle-638
❑ 88FleAll-1
❑ 88FleBasA-29
❑ 88FleExcS-29
❑ 88FleGlo-66
❑ 88FleGlo-638
❑ 88FleMin-23
❑ 88FleStiC-27
❑ 88FleSup-26
❑ 88KeyFooD-5
❑ 88Lea-60
❑ 88MSAIceTD-5
❑ 88Nes-41
❑ 88OPC-266
❑ 88OurOwnTD-5
❑ 88PanSti-88
❑ 88RedFolSB-62
❑ 88Sco-15
❑ 88Sco-648
❑ 88ScoGlo-15
❑ 88ScoGlo-648
❑ 88ScoYouSI-5
❑ 88Spo-6
❑ 88SpoGam-18
❑ 88StaLinTi-16
❑ 88StaNok-1
❑ 88StaNok-2
❑ 88StaNok-3
❑ 88StaNok-4
❑ 88StaNok-5
❑ 88StaNok-6
❑ 88StaNok-7
❑ 88StaNok-8
❑ 88StaNok-9
❑ 88StaNok-10
❑ 88StaNok-11
❑ 88TetTeaD-5
❑ 88TigPep-33
❑ 88TigPol-9
❑ 88Top-393
❑ 88Top-645
❑ 88TopBig-185
❑ 88TopClo-78
❑ 88TopGloS-59
❑ 88TopRoo-8
❑ 88TopSti-269
❑ 88TopSti-311
❑ 88TopStiB-56
❑ 88TopTif-393
❑ 88TopTif-645
❑ 88TopUKM-54
❑ 88TopUKMT-54
❑ 88ToyRoo-22
❑ 88WeiMarD-5
❑ 89Bow-101
❑ 89BowTif-101
❑ 89ClaTraO-113
❑ 89Don-116
❑ 89DonBasB-181
❑ 89Fle-140
❑ 89FleGlo-140
❑ 89MSAHolD-13
❑ 89Nis-13
❑ 89OPC-116
❑ 89PanSti-339
❑ 89RedFolSB-86
❑ 89Sco-23
❑ 89Spo-203
❑ 89TigMar-33
❑ 89TigPol-33
❑ 89Top-445
❑ 89TopBig-303
❑ 89TopSti-280
❑ 89TopTif-445
❑ 89TVSpoM-70
❑ 89UppDec-150
❑ 90ClaBlu-141
❑ 90ClaYel-T15
❑ 90Don-178
❑ 90DonBesA-11
❑ 90Fle-611
❑ 90FleCan-611
❑ 90FleUpd-115
❑ 90Lea-192
❑ 90Lea-314
❑ 90MLBBasB-86
❑ 90OPC-131
❑ 90PubIntS-479
❑ 90RedFolSB-69
❑ 90Sco-55
❑ 90ScoRoo-38T
❑ 90TigCok-14
❑ 90Top-131
❑ 90TopTif-131
❑ 90TopTra-81T
❑ 90TopTraT-81T
❑ 90UppDec-226
❑ 90UppDec-744
❑ 90YanScoNW-24
❑ 91Bow-164
❑ 91ClaGam-32
❑ 91Don-170
❑ 91Fle-674
❑ 91Lea-89
❑ 91OPC-336
❑ 91Sco-551
❑ 91StaClu-64

❑ 91StaCluP-28
❑ 91Top-336
❑ 91TopDesS-336
❑ 91TopMic-336
❑ 91TopTif-336
❑ 91UltUpd-42
❑ 91UppDec-673
❑ 92Bow-540
❑ 92DenHol-21
❑ 92Don-126
❑ 92DonCraJ2-34
❑ 92Fle-239
❑ 92Lea-102
❑ 92LeaBlaG-102
❑ 92OPC-748
❑ 92PanSti-134
❑ 92Pin-72
❑ 92Sco-573
❑ 92StaClu-111
❑ 92Stu-217
❑ 92Top-404
❑ 92Top-748
❑ 92TopGol-404
❑ 92TopGol-748
❑ 92TopGolW-404
❑ 92TopGolW-748
❑ 92TopMic-404
❑ 92TopMic-748
❑ 92TriPla-178
❑ 92Ult-107
❑ 92UppDec-295
❑ 92UppDecHRH-HR22
❑ 92UppDecS-1
❑ 93Bow-334
❑ 93Don-239
❑ 93Fla-250
❑ 93Fle-283
❑ 93Lea-352
❑ 93OPC-177
❑ 93PacSpa-209
❑ 93PanSti-146
❑ 93Pin-82
❑ 93Sco-192
❑ 93Sel-368
❑ 93StaClu-189
❑ 93StaCluFDI-189
❑ 93StaCluMOP-189
❑ 93Top-561
❑ 93TopGol-561
❑ 93TopInaM-561
❑ 93TopInaR-561
❑ 93TopMic-561
❑ 93Ult-247
❑ 93UppDec-116
❑ 93UppDecGold-116
❑ 93YanStaC-3
❑ 94Don-564
❑ 94Fla-85
❑ 94Fle-242
❑ 94FleExtB-135
❑ 94Pac-432
❑ 94Sco-196
❑ 94ScoGolR-196
❑ 94StaClu-23
❑ 94StaCluFDI-23
❑ 94StaCluGR-23
❑ 94StaCluMOP-23
❑ 94StaCluT-206
❑ 94StaCluTFDI-206
❑ 94Top-59
❑ 94TopGol-59
❑ 94TopSpa-59
❑ 94Ult-402
❑ 95Pin-417
❑ 95PinArtP-417
❑ 95PinMusC-417
❑ 95Top-238
❑ 98St.PauSTI-18

Nokes, Wesley
❑ 89CarNewE-1

Nolan, Bob
❑ 75PhoGiaCK-4
❑ 77SalLakCGC-15

Nolan, Darin
❑ 91St.CatBJC-22
❑ 91St.CatBJP-3393
❑ 92MyrBeaHC-17

Nolan, Gary
❑ 68OPC-196
❑ 68Top-196
❑ 68TopVen-196
❑ 69MLBOffS-133
❑ 69Top-581
❑ 69TopTeaP-20
❑ 70DayDaiNM-14
❑ 70Kel-53
❑ 70MLBOffS-33
❑ 70OPC-484
❑ 70Top-484
❑ 71Kel-36A
❑ 71Kel-36B
❑ 71Kel-36C
❑ 71MLBOffS-66
❑ 71OPC-75
❑ 71Top-75
❑ 71TopTat-31
❑ 72MilBra-253
❑ 72OPC-475
❑ 72Top-475
❑ 73Kel2D-30
❑ 73OPC-260
❑ 73SevTraC-53
❑ 73Top-260
❑ 73TopCanL-36
❑ 74OPC-277
❑ 74Top-277
❑ 75OPC-562
❑ 75Top-562
❑ 75TopMin-562
❑ 76OPC-444
❑ 76RedIceL-10
❑ 76RedKro-13
❑ 76RedParC-19
❑ 76SSP-29
❑ 76Top-444
❑ 77BurCheD-203
❑ 77Hos-113
❑ 77OPC-70
❑ 77PepGloD-51
❑ 77Top-121
❑ 78Top-115
❑ 92UppDecS-14

Nolan, Joseph W. Jr.
❑ 78Top-617
❑ 79Top-464
❑ 80Top-64
❑ 81Don-302
❑ 81Fle-212
❑ 81OPC-149
❑ 81Top-149
❑ 81TopSupHT-39
❑ 82Don-62
❑ 82Fle-77
❑ 82Top-327
❑ 82TopTra-81T
❑ 83Don-79
❑ 83Fle-68
❑ 83OriPos-20
❑ 83Top-242
❑ 84BalOriP-24
❑ 84Don-489
❑ 84Fle-15
❑ 84Nes792-553
❑ 84Top-553
❑ 84TopTif-553
❑ 85BalOriP-20
❑ 85Don-594
❑ 85Fle-185
❑ 85Top-652
❑ 85TopTif-652
❑ 86Top-781
❑ 86TopTif-781
❑ 91MetWIZ-295
❑ 91OriCro-332

Noland, J.D. (James D.)
❑ 89WatDiaP-1778
❑ 89WatDiaS-22
❑ 90Bes-238
❑ 90CMC-700
❑ 90MidLeaASGS-46
❑ 90WatDiaB-13
❑ 90WatDiaP-2390
❑ 91CalLeLA-18
❑ 91HigDesMC-27
❑ 91HigDesMP-2410
❑ 92ClaFS7-311
❑ 92ProFS7-337
❑ 92SkyAA F-284
❑ 92WicWraS-642
❑ 94NewHavRF-1563
❑ 95LinVen-271
❑ 95TacRaiTI-14

Nolasco, Jose
❑ 98ButCopKG-23

Nolasco, Regino
❑ 98BluOriQ-24

Nold, Dick
❑ 68OPC-96
❑ 68Top-96
❑ 68TopVen-96

Noles, Dickie
❑ 80Top-682
❑ 81Don-568
❑ 81Fle-12
❑ 81OklCit8T-14
❑ 81Top-406
❑ 82CubRedL-48
❑ 82Fle-253
❑ 82Top-530
❑ 82TopTra-82T
❑ 83CubThoAV-48
❑ 83Don-426
❑ 83Fle-504
❑ 83OPC-99
❑ 83Top-99
❑ 84Don-266
❑ 84Fle-500
❑ 84Nes792-618
❑ 84RanJarP-36
❑ 84Top-618
❑ 84TopTif-618
❑ 85AllGamPI-82
❑ 85OPC-149
❑ 85RanPer-36
❑ 85Top-149
❑ 85TopTif-149
❑ 86Don-587
❑ 86Fle-567
❑ 86IndOhH-48
❑ 86IndTeaI-32
❑ 86Top-388
❑ 86TopTif-388
❑ 87CubCan-23
❑ 87CubDavB-47
❑ 87Fle-256
❑ 87FleGlo-256
❑ 87FleUpd-91
❑ 87FleUpdG-91
❑ 87Top-244
❑ 87TopTif-244
❑ 87TopTra-92T
❑ 87TopTraT-92T
❑ 88RocRedWC-8
❑ 88RocRedWGCP-19
❑ 88RocRedWP-219
❑ 88RocRedWTI-16
❑ 88Top-768
❑ 88TopTif-768
❑ 89ColCliC-3
❑ 89ColCliP-8
❑ 89ColCliP-749
❑ 90CMC-231
❑ 90ScrRedBC-5
❑ 91OriCro-333
❑ 93RanKee-277

Nolte, Bruce
❑ 96PitMetB-30
❑ 97PitMet-20

Nolte, Eric
❑ 85SpoIndC-17
❑ 86ChaRaiP-19
❑ 87WicPilRD-12
❑ 88Don-534
❑ 88Fle-593
❑ 88FleGlo-593
❑ 88PadSmo-20
❑ 88Sco-568
❑ 88ScoGlo-568
❑ 88Top-694
❑ 88TopTif-694
❑ 89LasVegSC-8
❑ 89LasVegSP-12
❑ 90CMC-508
❑ 90LasVegSC-5
❑ 90LasVegSP-118
❑ 90ProAAAF-6
❑ 92DenZepF-2639
❑ 92DenZepS-143
❑ 93NewOrlZF-970
❑ 93RanKee-278
❑ 94SanBerSC-13
❑ 94SanBerSF-2753

Nomo, Hideo
❑ 92SpollIFK1-470
❑ 95BakBlaTI-4
❑ 95BakBlaTI-29
❑ 95Bow-238
❑ 95BowBes-R83
❑ 95BowBesJR-5
❑ 95BowBesR-R83
❑ 95BowGolF-238
❑ 95ClaPhoC-32
❑ 95ColCho-547T
❑ 95DodMot-13
❑ 95DodPol-16
❑ 95DonTopotO-269
❑ 95Emo-144
❑ 95EmoRoo-9
❑ 95Fin-228
❑ 95FinRef-228
❑ 95Fla-368
❑ 95FlaWavotF-10
❑ 95FleUpd-175
❑ 95FleUpdRU-7
❑ 95Lea-267
❑ 95LeaLim-64
❑ 95NatPac2-6
❑ 95Sel-251S
❑ 95SelArtP-251S
❑ 95SelCer-98
❑ 95SelCerF-3
❑ 95SelCerMG-98
❑ 95SelCerPU-10
❑ 95SelCerPU9-10
❑ 95SP-14
❑ 95SPCha-1
❑ 95SPChaDC-1
❑ 95SPChaDFC-6
❑ 95SPChaFCDC-6
❑ 95SPSil-14
❑ 95StaClu-556
❑ 95StaCluMOP-556
❑ 95StaCluSTDW-D556
❑ 95StaCluSTWS-556
❑ 95Sum-141
❑ 95SumNthD-141
❑ 95TopTra-40T
❑ 95TopTra-124T
❑ 95TopTra-164T
❑ 95UC3-97
❑ 95UC3ArtP-97
❑ 95UC3CleS-CS3
❑ 95UDAUnsBC-NNO
❑ 95UltGolMR-M17
❑ 95UppDec-226
❑ 95UppDecED-226
❑ 95UppDecEDG-226
❑ 95UppDecPAW-H38
❑ 95UppDecPAWE-H38
❑ 95UppDecSE-168
❑ 95UppDecSEG-168
❑ 95Zen-48
❑ 95Zen-149
❑ 95ZenAllS-7
❑ 95ZenRooRC-7
❑ 95ZenSam-R7
❑ 96Baz-98
❑ 96Bow-5
❑ 96BowBes-1
❑ 96BowBesAR-1
❑ 96BowBesC-8
❑ 96BowBesCAR-8
❑ 96BowBesCR-8
❑ 96BowBesP-BBP26
❑ 96BowBesPAR-BBP26
❑ 96BowBesPR-BBP26
❑ 96BowBesR-1
❑ 96BowFoi-5
❑ 96Cir-144
❑ 96CirAcc-20
❑ 96CirBos-38
❑ 96CirRav-144
❑ 96Cla7/1PC-3
❑ 96ColCho-7
❑ 96ColCho-180
❑ 96ColCho-270
❑ 96ColCho-332
❑ 96ColCho-359
❑ 96ColCho-705
❑ 96ColChoGS-7
❑ 96ColChoGS-180
❑ 96ColChoGS-270
❑ 96ColChoGS-332
❑ 96ColChoGS-359
❑ 96ColChoGS-705
❑ 96ColChoNS-1
❑ 96ColChoNS-2
❑ 96ColChoNS-3
❑ 96ColChoNS-4
❑ 96ColChoNS-5
❑ 96ColChoSS-7
❑ 96ColChoSS-180
❑ 96ColChoSS-270
❑ 96ColChoSS-332
❑ 96ColChoSS-359
❑ 96ColChoSS-705
❑ 96ColChoYMtP-29
❑ 96ColChoYMtP-29A
❑ 96ColChoYMtPGS-29
❑ 96ColChoYMtPGS-29A
❑ 96DenHol-10
❑ 96DodFle-13
❑ 96DodMot-3
❑ 96DodPol-25
❑ 96Don-390
❑ 96DonDiaK-27
❑ 96DonEli-62
❑ 96DonFreF-4
❑ 96DonPreP-390
❑ 96DonSam-3
❑ 96DonSho-1
❑ 96EmoRarB-8
❑ 96EmoXL-213
❑ 96Fin-G33
❑ 96Fin-G232
❑ 96Fin-S59
❑ 96FinRef-G33
❑ 96FinRef-G232
❑ 96FinRef-S59
❑ 96Fla-297
❑ 96Fle-442
❑ 96FleRooS-12
❑ 96FleSmo'H-8
❑ 96FleTif-442
❑ 96FleTomL-8
❑ 96FleUpd-U234
❑ 96FleUpdH-14
❑ 96FleUpdTC-U234
❑ 96Kin-19
❑ 96Lea-148
❑ 96LeaGolS-7
❑ 96LeaHatO-6
❑ 96LeaLim-65
❑ 96LeaLimG-65
❑ 96LeaPre-64
❑ 96LeaPreP-64
❑ 96LeaPrePB-148
❑ 96LeaPrePG-148
❑ 96LeaPrePS-148
❑ 96LeaPreSG-11
❑ 96LeaPreSte-11
❑ 96LeaSig-51
❑ 96LeaSigPPG-51
❑ 96LeaSigPPP-51
❑ 96LeaStaS-5
❑ 96MetUni-186
❑ 96MetUniMFG-9
❑ 96MetUniP-186
❑ 96MetUniPP-7
❑ 96Pac-100
❑ 96Pac-117
❑ 96PacGolCD-DC19
❑ 96PacHom-HP19
❑ 96PacOctM-OM16
❑ 96PacPri-P37
❑ 96PacPriFT-FT5
❑ 96PacPriG-P37
❑ 96PanSti-92
❑ 96PanSti-117
❑ 96PanSti-239
❑ 96Pin-131
❑ 96Pin-132
❑ 96Pin-256
❑ 96PinAfi-132
❑ 96PinAfi-151
❑ 96PinAfiAP-132
❑ 96PinAfiAP-151
❑ 96PinAfiSP-11
❑ 96PinArtP-54
❑ 96PinArtP-156
❑ 96PinEssotG-9
❑ 96PinFan-6
❑ 96PinFoil-256
❑ 96PinSky-12
❑ 96PinSta-54
❑ 96PinSta-156
❑ 96PinTeaT-5
❑ 96ProMagA-11
❑ 96ProMagDM-15
❑ 96ProSta-45
❑ 96Sco-195
❑ 96Sco-320
❑ 96ScoAll-12
❑ 96ScoDiaA-1
❑ 96ScoDugC-B45
❑ 96ScoDugCAP-B45
❑ 96ScoFutF-13
❑ 96ScoGolS-24
❑ 96ScoNumG-10
❑ 96ScoRef-18
❑ 96Sel-73
❑ 96SelArtP-73
❑ 96SelCer-13
❑ 96SelCer-143
❑ 96SelCerAP-13
❑ 96SelCerAP-143
❑ 96SelCerCB-13
❑ 96SelCerCB-143
❑ 96SelCerCR-13
❑ 96SelCerCR-143
❑ 96SelCerIP-1
❑ 96SelCerMB-13
❑ 96SelCerMB-143
❑ 96SelCerMG-13
❑ 96SelCerMG-143
❑ 96SelCerMR-13
❑ 96SelCerMR-143
❑ 96SelCerSF-12
❑ 96SelClaTF-10
❑ 96SelEnF-25
❑ 96SelTeaN-11
❑ 96SP-106
❑ 96SP-186
❑ 96SPBasH-86
❑ 96SPMarM-MM2
❑ 96SPMarMDC-2
❑ 96Spo-48
❑ 96SpoArtP-48
❑ 96SpoDouT-5
❑ 96SpoPro-9
❑ 96SPSpeFX-5
❑ 96SPSpeFXDC-5
❑ 96SPx-35
❑ 96SPxGol-35
❑ 96StaClu-1
❑ 96StaClu-247
❑ 96StaCluEPB-1
❑ 96StaCluEPG-1
❑ 96StaCluEPS-1
❑ 96StaCluMeg-MH3
❑ 96StaCluMM-MM1
❑ 96StaCluMO-31
❑ 96StaCluMO-46
❑ 96StaCluMOP-1
❑ 96StaCluMOP-247
❑ 96StaCluMOP-MH3
❑ 96StaCluMOP-MM1
❑ 96StaCluMOP-PS2
❑ 96StaCluMOP-TSCA6
❑ 96StaCluPS-PS2
❑ 96StaCluTA-6
❑ 96Stu-55
❑ 96StuPrePB-55
❑ 96StuPrePB-63
❑ 96StuPrePG-55
❑ 96StuPrePG-63
❑ 96StuPrePS-55
❑ 96StuPrePS-63
❑ 96StuStaGS-9
❑ 96Sum-40
❑ 96SumAbo&B-40
❑ 96SumArtP-40
❑ 96SumFoi-40
❑ 96SumPos-6
❑ 96TeaOut-59
❑ 96Top-136
❑ 96TopBigC-6
❑ 96TopBroLL-3
❑ 96TopChr-37
❑ 96TopChrR-37
❑ 96TopGal-92
❑ 96TopGalE-7
❑ 96TopGalPPI-92
❑ 96TopLas-60
❑ 96TopLasBS-15
❑ 96TopMysF-M1
❑ 96TopMysF-M22
❑ 96TopMysFR-M1
❑ 96TopMysFR-M22
❑ 96TopPro-NL18
❑ 96Ult-223
❑ 96UltDiaP-6
❑ 96UltDiaPGM-6
❑ 96UltFreF-8
❑ 96UltFreFGM-8
❑ 96UltGolM-223
❑ 96UltRisS-8
❑ 96UltRisSGM-8
❑ 96UltSeaC-7
❑ 96UltSeaCGM-7
❑ 96UppDec-95
❑ 96UppDec-150
❑ 96UppDecBCP-BC1
❑ 96UppDecDD-DD22
❑ 96UppDecDDG-DD22
❑ 96UppDecDDS-DD22
❑ 96UppDecG-GF9
❑ 96UppDecHC-HC2
❑ 96UppDecNCJ-1
❑ 96UppDecNCJ-2
❑ 96UppDecNCJ-3
❑ 96UppDecNCJ-4
❑ 96UppDecNCJ-5
❑ 96UppDecNCJ-6
❑ 96UppDecNCJ-7

❑ 96UppDecNCJ-8
❑ 96UppDecNCJ-9
❑ 96UppDecNCJ-10
❑ 96UppDecNCJ-11
❑ 96UppDecNCJ-12
❑ 96UppDecNCJ-13
❑ 96UppDecNCJ-14
❑ 96UppDecNCJ-15
❑ 96UppDecNCJ-16
❑ 96UppDecNomH-1
❑ 96UppDecNomH-2
❑ 96UppDecNomH-3
❑ 96UppDecNomH-4
❑ 96UppDecNomH-5
❑ 96UppDecNRJ-1
❑ 96UppDecPHE-H46
❑ 96UppDecPreH-H46
❑ 96UppDecVJLS-VJ2
❑ 96Zen-84
❑ 96Zen-140
❑ 96ZenArtP-84
❑ 96ZenArtP-140
❑ 96ZenMoz-13
❑ 96ZenZ-10
❑ 97Bow-4
❑ 97BowBes-78
❑ 97BowBesAR-78
❑ 97BowBesR-78
❑ 97BowChr-3
❑ 97BowChrI-3
❑ 97BowChrIR-3
❑ 97BowChrR-3
❑ 97BowInt-4
❑ 97BowIntB-BBI5
❑ 97BowIntBAR-BBI5
❑ 97BowIntBR-BBI5
❑ 97Cir-15
❑ 97CirRav-15
❑ 97ColCho-141
❑ 97ColChoAC-45
❑ 97ColChoNF-NF4
❑ 97ColChoT-LA5
❑ 97ColChoTBS-27
❑ 97ColChoTBSWH-27
❑ 97DodDWPM-4
❑ 97DodMot-5
❑ 97DodPol-20
❑ 97DodSco-15
❑ 97DodScoPl-15
❑ 97DodScoPr-15
❑ 97Don-36
❑ 97Don-427
❑ 97DonDom-10
❑ 97DonEli-32
❑ 97DonEli-150
❑ 97DonEliGS-32
❑ 97DonEliGS-150
❑ 97DonGolPP-36
❑ 97DonGolPP-427
❑ 97DonLim-43
❑ 97DonLim-53
❑ 97DonLim-137
❑ 97DonLimE-43
❑ 97DonLimE-53
❑ 97DonLimE-137
❑ 97DonLimENG-43
❑ 97DonPre-28
❑ 97DonPre-194
❑ 97DonPreCttC-28
❑ 97DonPreCttC-194
❑ 97DonPreS-16
❑ 97DonPreSS-16
❑ 97DonPreTB-14
❑ 97DonPreTBG-14
❑ 97DonPreTF-14
❑ 97DonPreTP-14
❑ 97DonPreTPG-14
❑ 97DonSig-84
❑ 97DonSigPPP-84
❑ 97DonSilPP-36
❑ 97DonSilPP-427
❑ 97DonTea-107
❑ 97DonTeaSPE-107
❑ 97DonVxP1-44
❑ 97E-X2-81
❑ 97E-X2Cred-81
❑ 97E-X2EssCre-81
❑ 97Fin-143
❑ 97Fin-345
❑ 97FinEmb-143
❑ 97FinEmb-345
❑ 97FinEmbR-143
❑ 97FinEmbR-345
❑ 97FinPro-143
❑ 97FinRef-143
❑ 97FinRef-345
❑ 97FlaShoLC-16
❑ 97FlaShoLeg0-16
❑ 97FlaShoLeg1-16
❑ 97FlaShoM-A16
❑ 97FlaShoM-B16
❑ 97FlaShoM-C16
❑ 97FlaShoR0-16
❑ 97FlaShoR1-16
❑ 97FlaShoR2-16
❑ 97Fle-368
❑ 97Fle-710
❑ 97FleGolM-7
❑ 97FleMilDM-16
❑ 97FleMilDMR-16
❑ 97FleTif-368
❑ 97FleTif-710
❑ 97HigMinM-85
❑ 97HigMinM-86
❑ 97Lea-99
❑ 97Lea-360
❑ 97LeaFraM-99
❑ 97LeaFraM-360
❑ 97LeaFraMDC-99
❑ 97LeaFraMDC-360
❑ 97LeaGet-9
❑ 97LeaGolS-14
❑ 97MetUni-104
❑ 97NewPin-29
❑ 97NewPinAP-29
❑ 97NewPinIE-8
❑ 97NewPinKtP-16
❑ 97NewPinMC-29
❑ 97NewPinPP-29
❑ 97NewPinPP-I8B
❑ 97NewPinPP-K16
❑ 97Pac-336
❑ 97PacCar-30
❑ 97PacCarM-30
❑ 97PacCerCGT-18
❑ 97PacFirD-16
❑ 97PacGolCD-30
❑ 97PacLigB-336
❑ 97PacPri-114
❑ 97PacPriGA-GA25
❑ 97PacPriGotD-GD160
❑ 97PacPriLB-114
❑ 97PacPriP-114
❑ 97PacPriSH-SH11B
❑ 97PacSil-336
❑ 97Pin-192
❑ 97PinAllFP-4
❑ 97PinArtP-PP192
❑ 97PinCar-7
❑ 97PinCer-63
❑ 97PinCer-149
❑ 97PinCerCMGT-18
❑ 97PinCerCT-18
❑ 97PinCerCT-G18
❑ 97PinCerMBla-63
❑ 97PinCerMBla-149
❑ 97PinCerMBlu-63
❑ 97PinCerMBlu-149
❑ 97PinCerMG-63
❑ 97PinCerMG-149
❑ 97PinCerMR-63
❑ 97PinCerMR-149
❑ 97PinCerR-63
❑ 97PinCerR-149
❑ 97PinFan-FF18
❑ 97PinIns-5
❑ 97PinInsC-20
❑ 97PinInsCE-5
❑ 97PinInsDD-18
❑ 97PinInsDE-5
❑ 97PinMin-12
❑ 97PinMinB-12
❑ 97PinMinCB-12
❑ 97PinMinCG-12
❑ 97PinMinCGR-12
❑ 97PinMinCN-12
❑ 97PinMinCSS-12
❑ 97PinMinG-12
❑ 97PinMinS-12
❑ 97PinMusC-192
❑ 97PinPasttM-21
❑ 97PinPrePla-192
❑ 97PinTotCPB-63
❑ 97PinTotCPB-149
❑ 97PinTotCPG-63
❑ 97PinTotCPG-149
❑ 97PinTotCPR-63
❑ 97PinTotCPR-149
❑ 97PinX-P-10
❑ 97PinX-P-150
❑ 97PinX-PMoS-10
❑ 97PinX-PMoS-150
❑ 97PinX-PMP-11
❑ 97PinX-PreMPS-11
❑ 97Sco-159
❑ 97Sco-522
❑ 97ScoArtPWB-159
❑ 97ScoArtPWB-522
❑ 97ScoPreS-159
❑ 97ScoResC-522
❑ 97ScoShoS-159
❑ 97ScoShoS-522
❑ 97ScoShoSAP-159
❑ 97ScoShoSAP-522
❑ 97ScoStaaD-14
❑ 97Sel-29
❑ 97SelArtP-29
❑ 97SelCom-29
❑ 97SelRegG-29
❑ 97SP-92
❑ 97SpoIll-64
❑ 97SpoIll-116
❑ 97SpoIll-176
❑ 97SpoIllEE-64
❑ 97SpoIllEE-116
❑ 97SpoIllEE-176
❑ 97SPSpeF-27
❑ 97SPSpxF-7
❑ 97SPSPxFA-7
❑ 97SPx-29
❑ 97SPxBro-29
❑ 97SPxGol-29
❑ 97SPxGraF-29
❑ 97SPxSil-29
❑ 97SPxSte-29
❑ 97StaClu-212
❑ 97StaClul-I10
❑ 97StaCluMat-212
❑ 97StaCluMOP-212
❑ 97StaCluMOP-I10
❑ 97Stu-73
❑ 97StuMasS-18
❑ 97StuMasS8-18
❑ 97StuPor8-19
❑ 97StuPrePG-73
❑ 97StuPrePS-73
❑ 97Top-440
❑ 97Top-464
❑ 97TopChr-156
❑ 97TopChrDD-DD8
❑ 97TopChrDDR-DD8
❑ 97TopChrR-156
❑ 97TopDodRotY-5
❑ 97TopGal-139
❑ 97TopGalPPI-139
❑ 97TopMemO5-36
❑ 97TopScr-16
❑ 97TopScrT-16
❑ 97TopSta-71
❑ 97TopStaAM-71
❑ 97TopStaASM-ASM8
❑ 97UD3-27
❑ 97Ult-221
❑ 97UltDouT-15
❑ 97UltGolME-221
❑ 97UltPlaME-221
❑ 97UltTop3-21
❑ 97UltTop3GM-21
❑ 97UppDec-70
❑ 97UppDec-94
❑ 97UppDec-192
❑ 97UppDec-321
❑ 97UppDecHC-HC18
❑ 97UppDecHTH-HT4
❑ 97UppDecP-17
❑ 97UppDecPE-17
❑ 97Zen-18
❑ 97Zen8x10-18
❑ 97Zen8x1D-18
❑ 98Bow-289
❑ 98Bow-NNO
❑ 98BowChr-289
❑ 98BowChrGA-289
❑ 98BowChrGAR-289
❑ 98BowChrI-289
❑ 98BowChrIR-289
❑ 98BowChrR-289
❑ 98BowChrR-47
❑ 98BowChrRR-47
❑ 98BowGolA-289
❑ 98BowInt-289
❑ 98CirThu-16
❑ 98CirThuRav-16
❑ 98CirThuSupRav-16
❑ 98ColCho-400
❑ 98CroRoy-87
❑ 98CroRoyFoB-13
❑ 98CroRoyFoBA-13
❑ 98DodPol-19
❑ 98DodSco-1
❑ 98DodScoP-1
❑ 98Don-103
❑ 98Don-381
❑ 98Don-413
❑ 98DonCol-103
❑ 98DonColE-435
❑ 98DonColL-375
❑ 98DonColP-564
❑ 98DonColP-731
❑ 98DonColS-103
❑ 98DonCruG-81
❑ 98DonCruP-81
❑ 98DonCruR-81
❑ 98DonDiaK-11
❑ 98DonDiaKC-11
❑ 98DonDom-15
❑ 98DonEli-35
❑ 98DonEliA-35
❑ 98DonEliI-9
❑ 98DonEliS-35
❑ 98DonGolPP-103
❑ 98DonGolPP-381
❑ 98DonGolPP-413
❑ 98DonPre-14
❑ 98DonPre-181
❑ 98DonPreGB-13
❑ 98DonPreGES-14
❑ 98DonPreGoB-13
❑ 98DonPreGX-14
❑ 98DonPreGXDC-14
❑ 98DonPrePM-14
❑ 98DonPreSeat-14
❑ 98DonPreSeat-181
❑ 98DonPreTP-13
❑ 98DonPreTPD-7
❑ 98DonPreTPG-13
❑ 98DonPreTPS-13
❑ 98DonPreTW-19
❑ 98DonPriCD-103
❑ 98DonPriCE-435
❑ 98DonPriCL-375
❑ 98DonPriCP-564
❑ 98DonPriCP-731
❑ 98DonSig-38
❑ 98DonSigP-38
❑ 98DonSilPP-103
❑ 98DonSilPP-381
❑ 98DonSilPP-413
❑ 98E-X2-12
❑ 98E-X2DesCoop-14
❑ 98E-X2ECFut-12
❑ 98E-X2ECNow-12
❑ 98Fin-240
❑ 98FinNo--240
❑ 98FinNo-R-240
❑ 98FinRef-240
❑ 98FlaShoLeg0-59
❑ 98FlaShoLeg1-59
❑ 98FlaShoLeg2-59
❑ 98FlaShoLeg3-59
❑ 98FlaShoLegM-59
❑ 98FlaShoR0-59
❑ 98FlaShoR1-59
❑ 98FlaShoR2-59
❑ 98FlaShoR3-59
❑ 98Fle-504
❑ 98FleUpd-U88
❑ 98FleVin'-100
❑ 98FleVin'C-100
❑ 98Lea-176
❑ 98LeaFraDA-176
❑ 98LeaFraF-176
❑ 98LeaFraM-176
❑ 98LeaFraM-176
❑ 98LeaFraMDC-176
❑ 98LeaFraMDC-176
❑ 98LeaFraMS-176
❑ 98LeaFraMZ2-176
❑ 98LeaRS-39
❑ 98LeaRS-157
❑ 98LeaRSGAHSamp-11
❑ 98LeaRSGreAH-11
❑ 98LeaRSLHolo-39
❑ 98LeaRSLHolo-157
❑ 98LeaRSLong-39
❑ 98LeaRSLong-157
❑ 98LeaRTrue-39
❑ 98LeaRTrue-157
❑ 98MetUni-83
❑ 98MetUni-211
❑ 98MetUniPMG-83
❑ 98MetUniPMG-211
❑ 98MetUniUL-17
❑ 98Pac-336
❑ 98PacAur-147
❑ 98PacAurCube-9
❑ 98PacAurHC-9
❑ 98PacAurODLC-9
❑ 98PacAurPF-30
❑ 98PacAurPFC-30
❑ 98PacAurPFPB-30
❑ 98PacAurPFR-30
❑ 98PacAurPFS-30
❑ 98PacGolCDC-20
❑ 98PacInv-110
❑ 98PacInvGems-171
❑ 98PacInvInt-7N
❑ 98PacInvMiT-9
❑ 98PacInvPBlue-110
❑ 98PacInvPhoto-7
❑ 98PacInvSilv-110
❑ 98PacInvTeam-14
❑ 98PacOme-127
❑ 98PacOmeFTF-9
❑ 98PacOmeOnIns-31
❑ 98PacOmeP-17
❑ 98PacOmeR-127
❑ 98PacOnl-380
❑ 98PacOnlR-380
❑ 98PacOnlWC-380
❑ 98PacPar-179
❑ 98PacParC-179
❑ 98PacParFC-9
❑ 98PacParG-179
❑ 98PacParHS-179
❑ 98PacParI-18
❑ 98PacParPB-179
❑ 98PacParR-179
❑ 98PacParSD-10
❑ 98PacPlaB-336
❑ 98PacRedT-336
❑ 98PacSil-336
❑ 98PacTeaC-21
❑ 98Pin-44
❑ 98PinArtP-PP41
❑ 98PinIns-52
❑ 98PinInsBtN-19
❑ 98PinInsC-14
❑ 98PinInsCE-52
❑ 98PinInsCG-14
❑ 98PinInsDE-52
❑ 98PinInsSG-12AB
❑ 98PinInsSG-12CD
❑ 98PinInsSG-17AB
❑ 98PinInsSG-17CD
❑ 98PinInsSGS-12AB
❑ 98PinInsSGS-12CD
❑ 98PinInsSGS-17AB
❑ 98PinInsSGS-17CD
❑ 98PinMinB-15
❑ 98PinMinCB-15
❑ 98PinMinCBAP-15
❑ 98PinMinCGP-15
❑ 98PinMinCGPAP-15
❑ 98PinMinCN-15
❑ 98PinMinCNAP-15
❑ 98PinMinCSGR-15
❑ 98PinMinDC-15
❑ 98PinMinG-15
❑ 98PinMinMCSS-15
❑ 98PinMinS-15
❑ 98PinMusC-PP41
❑ 98PinPer-14
❑ 98PinPerPP-14
❑ 98PinPlu-188
❑ 98PinPlu-199
❑ 98PinPluAE-24
❑ 98PinPluAEE-24
❑ 98PinPluAEP-24
❑ 98PinPluLM-4
❑ 98PinPluTP-13
❑ 98PinPluTPG-13
❑ 98PinPluTPM-13
❑ 98PinPreP-44
❑ 98PinSna-LAD11
❑ 98Revo-93
❑ 98RevoSS-93
❑ 98Sco-3
❑ 98ScoFirP-14
❑ 98ScoRT-26
❑ 98ScoRTComPla-10A
❑ 98ScoRTComPla-10B
❑ 98ScoRTComPla-10C
❑ 98ScoRTCPSamp-10A
❑ 98ScoRTCPSamp-10B
❑ 98ScoRTCPSamp-10C
❑ 98ScoRTSS-PP26
❑ 98ScoRTSSAP-PP26
❑ 98ScoRTSSAP1-PP26
❑ 98ScoSS-PP3
❑ 98ScoSSAP-PP3
❑ 98SkyDugA-23
❑ 98SkyDugAIA-23
❑ 98SkyDugAS-SH6
❑ 98SP Aut-108
❑ 98SpoIll-96
❑ 98SpoIllEE-96
❑ 98SpoIllFE-96
❑ 98SpoIllTaN-118
❑ 98SpoIllTaNEE-118
❑ 98SpoIllWSF-94
❑ 98SpoIllWSFEE-94
❑ 98SpoIllWSFFE-94
❑ 98SPxFin-93
❑ 98SPxFinR-93
❑ 98SPxFinS-93
❑ 98StaCluFDI-84
❑ 98StaCluI-84
❑ 98StaCluOneK-84
❑ 98StaCluPP-84
❑ 98Stu-43
❑ 98StuGPP-43
❑ 98StuMast-7
❑ 98StuPor8x10-16
❑ 98StuPor8x10GP-16
❑ 98StuSPP-43
❑ 98Top-167
❑ 98TopChr-167
❑ 98TopChrR-167
❑ 98TopDevR-167
❑ 98TopDia-167
❑ 98TopEtc-ES5
❑ 98TopGal-63
❑ 98TopGalGoH-GH14
❑ 98TopGalGoHJ-GH14
❑ 98TopGalGP-63
❑ 98TopGalOPP-63
❑ 98TopGalPPI-63
❑ 98TopGalPPIA-63
❑ 98TopMiniC-167
❑ 98TopOpeD-88
❑ 98TopSta-57
❑ 98TopStaB-57
❑ 98TopStaG-57
❑ 98TopStaGR-57
❑ 98TopStaS-57
❑ 98TopSup-15
❑ 98TopSup-15
❑ 98UD3-62
❑ 98UD3-152
❑ 98UD3-242
❑ 98UD3DieCut-62
❑ 98UD3DieCut-152
❑ 98UD3DieCut-242
❑ 98Ult-30
❑ 98Ult-489
❑ 98UltDouT-8
❑ 98UltGolM-30
❑ 98UltGolM-489
❑ 98UltMas-30
❑ 98UltMas-489
❑ 98UltPlaM-30
❑ 98UltPlaM-489
❑ 98UltTop3-12
❑ 98UltWinN-9
❑ 98UppDec-7
❑ 98UppDec-118
❑ 98UppDec10AP-4
❑ 98UppDec1APR-4
❑ 98UppDecAC-AS7
❑ 98UppDecNP-NP16
❑ 98UppDecR-62
❑ 98UppDecSF-71
❑ 98UppDecU-6
❑ 98Zen-70
❑ 98Zen5 xx7-30
❑ 98Zen5x7GoldImp-30
❑ 98Zen5x7Imp-30
❑ 98ZenRaitB-9
❑ 98ZenZ-G-70
❑ 98ZenZ-S-70
❑ 99Fle-168
❑ 99FleSta9-168
❑ 99FleWarT-168
❑ 99MetUni-186
❑ 99MetUniGM-186
❑ 99MetUniPMG-186
❑ 99Pac-283
❑ 99PacAur-120
❑ 99PacAurOD-120
❑ 99PacCroC-181
❑ 99PacCroCPB-181
❑ 99PacDynaD-15
❑ 99PacDynaDT-15
❑ 99PacOme-134
❑ 99PacOmeC-134

❑ 99PacOmeG-134
❑ 99PacOmePB-134
❑ 99PacPar-152
❑ 99PacParC-152
❑ 99PacParG-152
❑ 99PacParHoloGold-152
❑ 99PacParHS-152
❑ 99PacParOD-152
❑ 99PacParPB-20
❑ 99PacParPB-152
❑ 99PacParRed-152
❑ 99PacPlaB-283
❑ 99PacPri-93
❑ 99PacPriHB-93
❑ 99PacPriHG-93
❑ 99PacPriHM-93
❑ 99PacPriHP-93
❑ 99PacPriRed-93
❑ 99PacPriS-122
❑ 99PacPriS206-122
❑ 99PacPriS206R-122
❑ 99PacRed-283
❑ 99SkyThu-141
❑ 99SkyThuRant-141
❑ 99SkyThuRave-141
❑ 99StaClu-247
❑ 99StaCluFDI-247
❑ 99StaCluOoaK-247
❑ 99StaCluPP-247
❑ 99ThuSkySupR-141
❑ 99Top-302
❑ 99TopChr-302
❑ 99TopChrR-302
❑ 99TopMVPP-302
❑ 99UD Ion-40
❑ 99UD IonR-40
❑ 99Ult-208
❑ 99UltGolM-208
❑ 99UltMas-208
❑ 99UltPlaM-208
❑ 99UppDec-152
❑ 99UppDecBD-53
❑ 99UppDecBDD-53
❑ 99UppDecBDQ-53
❑ 99UppDecBDT-53
❑ 99UppDecEL1-152
❑ 99UppDecEL2-152
❑ 99UppDecIP-I17
❑ 99UppDecIPD-I17
❑ 99UppDecIPHR-I17
❑ 99UppDecIPT-I17
❑ 99UppDecM-135
❑ 99UppDecMGS-135
❑ 99UppDecMHFS-135
❑ 99UppDecMP-135
❑ 99UppDecMSS-135
Nomura, Katsuya
❑ 79TCMJapPB-13
Nonnenkamp, Red (Leo W.)
❑ 40PlaBal-196
Noonan, Dennis
❑ 90CarLeaA-33
❑ 90KinIndTI-29
Noonan, Jim
❑ 78WauMetT-20
Noonan, Joseph
❑ 88SFHesCreN32-22
Noonan, Pete
❑ 11SpoLifCW-271
Noonan, Todd
❑ 87SalLakTTT-10
Noore, Daryl
❑ 89BluOriS-27
Nops, Jerry
❑ 90DodTar-578
Norbert, Ted
❑ 33Zee-135
❑ 45CenFlo-18
Nordbrook, Tim (Timothy C.)
❑ 75BalOriP-21
❑ 76BalOriP-29
❑ 76OPC-252
❑ 76SSP-391
❑ 76Top-252
❑ 77WhiSoxT-19
❑ 78OPC-139
❑ 78Top-369
❑ 79VanCanT-6
❑ 80VanCanT-10
❑ 83BelBreFr-16
❑ 91OriCro-334
❑ 94BreMilB-157
Nordhagen, Wayne O.
❑ 76OklCit8TI-22
❑ 77WhiSoxT-20
❑ 78SSP270-162
❑ 78Top-231
❑ 79Kel-4
❑ 79Top-351
❑ 80OPC-253
❑ 80Top-487
❑ 81CokTeaS-35
❑ 81Don-401
❑ 81Fle-348
❑ 81Top-186
❑ 81TopSti-59
❑ 81TopSupHT-21
❑ 82Don-67
❑ 82Fle-355
❑ 82OPC-139
❑ 82Top-597
❑ 83Fle-438
❑ 83OPC-47
❑ 83Top-714
❑ 89PacSenL-154
❑ 89TopSenL-47
❑ 90EliSenL-45
Nordstrom, Burt
❑ 72CedRapCT-18
Nordstrom, Carl
❑ 88BilMusP-1831
❑ 88CedRapRP-1158
❑ 89GreHorP-429
Nordyke, Louis
❑ 09ObaT21-217
❑ 09ObaT21-389
❑ 12ObaPreT-138
Nored, Mike
❑ 76AppFoxT-17
Noren, Irv (Irving Arnold)
❑ 47StaPinP2-31
❑ 49W72HolS-12
❑ 50Bow-247
❑ 51Bow-241
❑ 51FisBakL-20
❑ 51TopBluB-38
❑ 52Bow-63
❑ 52Top-40
❑ 53BowBW-45
❑ 53Dor-132
❑ 53Top-35
❑ 54NewYorJA-55
❑ 55Bow-63
❑ 55RedMan-AL9
❑ 56Top-253
❑ 56YanTeal-19
❑ 57Top-298
❑ 58Top-114
❑ 59Top-59
❑ 59TopVen-59
❑ 60Lea-101
❑ 60Top-433
❑ 73OPC-179
❑ 73Top-179A
❑ 73Top-179B
❑ 83TopRep5-40
❑ 83YanASFY-31
❑ 89SweBasG-102
❑ 90DodTar-579
❑ 91TopArc1-35
❑ 92YanWIZA-55
Noriega, Kevin
❑ 93LinVenB-148
❑ 95LinVen-115
❑ 96-97LinVen-171
❑ 96BelSnaTI-26
Noriega, Ray
❑ 96SouOreTI-11
❑ 97ModA'sG-20
❑ 98VisOakG-22
Noriega, Rey
❑ 90Ft.LauYS-15
❑ 91FloStaLAP-FSL17
❑ 91Ft.LauYC-22
❑ 91Ft.LauYP-2435
❑ 92AlbYanSk-15
❑ 92Ft.LauYF-2628
❑ 92ProFS7-118
❑ 92SkyAA F-9
Norko, Tom
❑ 80UtiBluJT-7
Norman, Bill (H. Willis)
❑ 53Top-245
❑ 91TopArc1-245
Norman, Bull
❑ 83TamTarT-30
Norman, Dan (Daniel E.)
❑ 77IndIndTI-10
❑ 78TidTidT-16
❑ 79TidTidT-11
❑ 79Top-721
❑ 80Top-681
❑ 81Fle-337
❑ 81TidTidT-28
❑ 82ExpHygM-14
❑ 82ExpPos-24
❑ 83Fle-289
❑ 83OPC-237
❑ 83Top-237
❑ 84MidCubT-17
❑ 89KinMetS-27
❑ 90KinMetB-27
❑ 91MetWIZ-296
❑ 91PacSenL-64
❑ 92ColRedC-28
❑ 93CarLeaAGF-33
❑ 93KinIndC-28
❑ 93KinIndF-2265
❑ 93KinIndTI-28
❑ 94KinIndC-25
❑ 96RanCucQB-3
❑ 98EugEme-19
Norman, Fred
❑ 64Top-469
❑ 65Top-386
❑ 70OPC-427
❑ 70Top-427
❑ 71MLBOffS-280
❑ 71OPC-348
❑ 71Top-348
❑ 72OPC-194
❑ 72PadPos-20
❑ 72Top-194
❑ 73OPC-32
❑ 73PadDea-20
❑ 73Top-32
❑ 74OPC-581
❑ 74Top-581
❑ 75OPC-396
❑ 75Top-396
❑ 75TopMin-396
❑ 76OPC-609
❑ 76RedKro-14
❑ 76RedParC-20
❑ 76SSP-30
❑ 76Top-609
❑ 77Kel-8
❑ 77OPC-181
❑ 77PadSchC-42A
❑ 77PadSchC-42B
❑ 77PepGloD-56
❑ 77Top-139
❑ 78Pep-20
❑ 78SSP270-109
❑ 78Top-273
❑ 79OPC-20
❑ 79Top-47
❑ 80ExpPos-19
❑ 80OPC-362
❑ 80Top-714
❑ 81Don-92
❑ 81Fle-158
❑ 81OPC-183
❑ 81Top-497
❑ 90DodTar-580
Norman, Greg
❑ 83BirBarT-13
Norman, Kenny
❑ 91EliTwiP-4313
❑ 92EliTwiC-17
❑ 92EliTwiF-3696
❑ 92KenTwiC-15
❑ 93ForMyeMC-18
❑ 93ForMyeMF-2670
❑ 94ForMyeMC-17
Norman, Les
❑ 91EugEmeC-13
❑ 91EugEmeP-3739
❑ 92AppFoxCB-14
❑ 92AppFoxFI-999
❑ 92MemChiF-2432
❑ 92UppDecML-100
❑ 93Bow-673
❑ 93ExcFS7-176
❑ 93MemChiF-390
❑ 94ClaGolF-121
❑ 94ExcFS7-69
❑ 94ForMyeMF-1181
❑ 94OmaRoyF-1236
❑ 94UppDecML-34
❑ 96ColCho-576
❑ 96ColChoGS-576
❑ 96ColChoSS-576
❑ 96Don-537
❑ 96DonPreP-537
❑ 96RoyPol-19
❑ 96Sco-262
❑ 96SigRooOJ-24
❑ 96SigRooOJS-24
❑ 97BufBis-22
❑ 97PacPriGotD-GD48
❑ 98OklRedM-19
Norman, Nelson A.
❑ 77ShrCapT-16
❑ 78TucTorC-4
❑ 80ChaChaT-4
❑ 80OPC-270
❑ 80Top-518
❑ 81Don-509
❑ 82PorBeaT-16
❑ 83LynPirT-15
❑ 84HawIslC-133
❑ 85DomLeaS-187
❑ 85RocRedWT-7
❑ 86JacExpT-22
❑ 87IndIndTI-29
❑ 88IndIndP-517
❑ 89IndIndP-1227
❑ 93RanKee-279
❑ 95MacBraTI-22
❑ 96DanBraB-3
Norman, Rob
❑ 88MisStaB-24
❑ 89MisStaB-28
❑ 90MisStaB-28
❑ 91MisStaB-34
Norman, Ron
❑ 75SpoIndC-21
❑ 76SanAntBTI-16
Norman, Scott
❑ 83CliGiaF-3
❑ 87SprCarB-28
❑ 89TenTecGE-19
❑ 93BriTigC-16
❑ 94FayGenC-18
❑ 94FayGenF-2142
❑ 96JacSunB-23
❑ 97NewHavRB-20
❑ 97SalAva-U8
Norman, Terry
❑ 80BatTroT-2
Normand, Guy
❑ 85AncGlaPTI-21
❑ 86AubAstP-17
❑ 87AshTouP-13
❑ 88OscAstS-18
❑ 89OscAstS-13
Norrell, Troy
❑ 97AppLeaTPB-13
❑ 98MarPhiG-23
Norrid, Tim
❑ 76WilTomT-16
❑ 79TacTugT-22
❑ 79Top-705
❑ 80TacTigT-2
❑ 81ChaChaT-9
❑ 82ChaChaT-12
❑ 83ChaChaT-14
Norris, Allen
❑ 59DarFar-14
❑ 60DarFar-23
Norris, Ben
❑ 97LetBlaDB-26
❑ 97SouBenSH-21
❑ 98SouBenSHM-20
Norris, Bill
❑ 91CarLeaAP-CAR25
❑ 91LynRedSC-17
❑ 91LynRedSP-1207
❑ 92NewBriRSF-442
❑ 92NewBriRSS-491
❑ 92SkyAA F-211
❑ 93NewBriRSF-1229
❑ 94NewBriRSF-659
Norris, David
❑ 90JohCitCS-19
❑ 91SprCarC-20
❑ 91SprCarP-741
Norris, Dax
❑ 96EugEmeB-17
❑ 97DurBulTI-19
❑ 98DanQ-C-8
❑ 98GreBraG-17
Norris, Jim (James Frances)
❑ 75OklCit8TI-17
❑ 76VenLeaS-45
❑ 77IndTeal-19
❑ 78IndTeal-22
❑ 78Top-484
❑ 79Top-611
❑ 80Top-333
❑ 81Don-388
❑ 81Fle-634
❑ 81Top-264
❑ 93RanKee-280
Norris, Joe
❑ 91SumFlyC-9
❑ 91SumFlyP-2332
❑ 92RocExpC-22
❑ 92RocExpF-2113
❑ 93WesPalBEC-16
❑ 93WesPalBEF-1337
❑ 94NasXprF-383
❑ 95HarCitRCTI-17
❑ 97PorSeaD-22
❑ 98El PasDG-20
Norris, Leo
❑ 33WorCig(-65
Norris, MacKenzie
❑ 96HelBreTI-16
Norris, Mike
❑ 76OPC-653
❑ 76SSP-487
❑ 76Top-653
❑ 77BurCheD-113
❑ 77Top-284
❑ 78Top-434
❑ 79Top-191
❑ 80Top-599
❑ 81A'sGraG-17
❑ 81AllGamPI-88
❑ 81Don-118
❑ 81Fle-573
❑ 81FleStiC-6
❑ 81MSAMinD-24
❑ 81OPC-55
❑ 81Top-55
❑ 81TopScr-53
❑ 81TopSti-2
❑ 81TopSti-4
❑ 81TopSti-6
❑ 81TopSti-122
❑ 82A'sGraG-13
❑ 82Don-19
❑ 82Don-197
❑ 82Fle-103
❑ 82FleSta-125
❑ 82Kel-59
❑ 82OnDecD-24
❑ 82OPC-370
❑ 82Top-370
❑ 82TopSti-222
❑ 83A'sGraG-17
❑ 83AllGamPI-82
❑ 83Don-139
❑ 83Fle-530
❑ 83OPC-276
❑ 83Top-620
❑ 84Fle-457
❑ 84Nes792-493
❑ 84OPC-49
❑ 84Top-493
❑ 84TopTif-493
❑ 85Top-246
❑ 85TopTif-246
❑ 87A'sMot-22
❑ 90A'sMot-19
❑ 90HelBreSP-26
❑ 91PacSenL-107
❑ 91RenSilSCLC-15
Norris, Niles
❑ 93MisStaB-34
Norris, Scott
❑ 75ForLauYS-1
Norris, Steve
❑ 96JohCitCTI-24
❑ 97JohCitCTI-25
❑ 98PeoChiM-16
Norris, Wade
❑ 92MedHatBJF-3216
❑ 92MedHatBJSP-13
Norse, Chester
❑ 19Zee-26
Norsetter, Howard
❑ 91MelBusF-16
North, Billy (William Alex)
❑ 73OPC-234
❑ 73Top-234
❑ 74GreHeroBP-1
❑ 74GreHeroBP-5
❑ 74OPC-345
❑ 74Top-345
❑ 74TopSta-228
❑ 75A'sPos-65
❑ 75GreHeroBP-5
❑ 75Kel-23
❑ 75OPC-121
❑ 75OPC-309
❑ 75Top-121
❑ 75Top-309
❑ 75TopMin-121
❑ 75TopMin-309
❑ 76GreHeroBP-1
❑ 76GreHeroBP-5
❑ 76OPC-33
❑ 76SSP-491
❑ 76Top-33
❑ 77BurCheD-116
❑ 77ChiWilD-51
❑ 77DailsID-51
❑ 77DetCaeD-51
❑ 77HolInnD-51
❑ 77Hos-33
❑ 77Kel-22
❑ 77MSADis-51
❑ 77OPC-4
❑ 77OPC-106
❑ 77SagDis-51
❑ 77sDis-51
❑ 77Top-4
❑ 77Top-551
❑ 77WenDis-51
❑ 77ZipDis-51
❑ 78Hos-76
❑ 78SagDis-13
❑ 78TasDis-13
❑ 78Top-163
❑ 79GiaPol-36
❑ 79OPC-351
❑ 79Top-668
❑ 80BurKinPHR-31
❑ 80GiaEurFS-7
❑ 80GiaPol-36
❑ 80GiaTeal-23
❑ 80OPC-213
❑ 80Top-408
❑ 81Don-76
❑ 81Fle-441
❑ 81GiaTeal-13
❑ 81OPC-47
❑ 81Top-713
❑ 86A'sGreT-7
❑ 90DodTar-581
❑ 94MCIAmb-11
North, Jay
❑ 85SprCarT-21
❑ 86St.PetCP-22
❑ 87St.PetCP-25
❑ 88St.PetCS-20
❑ 89SavCarP-343
❑ 90St.PetCS-26
❑ 91St.PetCC-11
❑ 91St.PetCP-2293
North, Mark
❑ 87GenCubP-3
❑ 88PeoChiTI-22
❑ 89KenTwiP-1061
❑ 89KenTwiS-18
North, Roy
❑ 80AndBraT-18
❑ 81DurBulT-21
North, Tim
❑ 92EriSaiC-6
❑ 92EriSaiF-1632
❑ 93HigDesMC-14
❑ 93HigDesMF-50
Northam, J.J.
❑ 90AriWilP-14
Northeimer, James
❑ 94BatCliC-15
❑ 94BatCliF-3450
❑ 95PiePhiF-189
❑ 95TenVolW-8
❑ 97ReaPhi-22
Northern, Hubbard
❑ 12T207-140
❑ 90DodTar-1144
Northey, Ron (Ronald J.)
❑ 43PhiTeal-18
❑ 47Exh-168
❑ 49Bow-79
❑ 50Bow-81
❑ 51Bow-70
❑ 52Top-204
❑ 57Top-31
❑ 63PirIDL-17
❑ 76TayBow4-77
❑ 77TCMTheWY-40

❑ 83TCMPla1942-44
❑ 83TopRep5-204
Northey, Scott (Scott R.)
❑ 70OPC-241
❑ 70Top-241
❑ 71OPC-633
❑ 71Top-633
Northrup, George
❑ 09ColChiE-214
❑ 12ColTinT-214
Northrup, Jim (James T.)
❑ 65OPC-259
❑ 65Top-259
❑ 66Top-554
❑ 67CokCapTi-8
❑ 67Top-408
❑ 68CokCapT-8
❑ 68OPC-78
❑ 68TigDetFPB-16
❑ 68Top-78
❑ 68TopVen-78
❑ 69MilBra-202
❑ 69MLBOffS-53
❑ 69OPC-3
❑ 69OPC-167
❑ 69TigFarJ-1
❑ 69TigTeal-9
❑ 69TigTealC-13
❑ 69Top-3
❑ 69Top-167
❑ 69Top-580
❑ 69TopSta-178
❑ 69TopTeaP-1
❑ 70DayDaiNM-126
❑ 70MLBOffS-213
❑ 70OPC-177
❑ 70Top-177
❑ 71Kel-63
❑ 71MLBOffS-401
❑ 71OPC-265
❑ 71Top-265
❑ 71TopCoi-82
❑ 71TopGreM-21
❑ 71TopSup-55
❑ 72MilBra-254
❑ 72OPC-408
❑ 72Top-408
❑ 73LinPor-75
❑ 73OPC-168
❑ 73TigJew-15
❑ 73Top-168
❑ 74OPC-266
❑ 74Tig-8
❑ 74Top-266
❑ 75BalOriP-22
❑ 75OPC-641
❑ 75Top-641
❑ 75TopMin-641
❑ 76SSP-399
❑ 78TigDeaCS-18
❑ 81TigDetN-52
❑ 83TigAlKS-52
❑ 86TigSpoD-16
❑ 88TigDom-17
❑ 90SweBasG-78
❑ 91OriCro-335
❑ 93UppDecS-26
Northrup, Kevin
❑ 92JamExpC-24
❑ 92JamExpF-1514
❑ 93WesPalBEC-17
❑ 93WesPalBEF-1355
❑ 94HarSenF-2106
❑ 95Exc-223
❑ 95MetColP-23
❑ 96ColCliB-23
Norton, Andy
❑ 95BelGiaTI-25
Norton, Chris
❑ 94SavCarC-22
❑ 94SavCarF-510
❑ 98MidAngG-22
❑ 98VanCanG-19
Norton, Doug
❑ 83BelBreFr-11
❑ 86StoPorP-19
Norton, Greg
❑ 94SouBenSHC-15
❑ 94SouBenSHF-601
❑ 94Top-758
❑ 94TopGol-758
❑ 94TopSpa-758
❑ 96BirBarB-7
❑ 96Bow-234
❑ 96BowFoi-234
❑ 97Fle-67
❑ 97FleTif-67
❑ 97PacPriGotD-GD31
❑ 97Sel-135
❑ 97SelArtP-135
❑ 97SelCom-135
❑ 97SelRegG-135
❑ 97UppDec-280
❑ 98Don-287
❑ 98DonGolPP-287
❑ 98DonSilPP-287
❑ 98LeaRS-288
❑ 98LeaRSLHolo-288
❑ 98LeaRSLong-288
❑ 98LeaRTrue-288
❑ 98PacInvGems-32
❑ 98PacOme-58
❑ 98PacOmeR-58
❑ 98PacOmeRS-24
❑ 98PacOmeRST5-24
❑ 98PacOnl-175
❑ 98PacOnlR-175
❑ 98PacOnlWC-175
❑ 98SkyDugA-115
❑ 98SkyDugAIA-115
❑ 99Fle-504
❑ 99FleSta9-504
❑ 99FleWarT-504
❑ 99Pac-103
❑ 99PacPar-58
❑ 99PacParC-58
❑ 99PacParG-58
❑ 99PacParHoloGold-58
❑ 99PacParHS-58
❑ 99PacParOD-58
❑ 99PacParPB-58
❑ 99PacParRed-58
❑ 99PacPlaB-103
❑ 99PacRed-103
❑ 99StaClu-238
❑ 99StaCluFDI-238
❑ 99StaCluOoaK-238
❑ 99StaCluPP-238
Norton, Jason
❑ 98LowSpiM-28
Norton, Phil
❑ 97RocCub-23
❑ 99Bow-136
❑ 99BowBes-182
❑ 99BowBesAR-182
❑ 99BowBesR-182
❑ 99BowChr-136
❑ 99BowChrG-136
❑ 99BowChrGR-136
❑ 99BowChrI-136
❑ 99BowChrIR-136
❑ 99BowChrR-136
❑ 99BowGol-136
❑ 99BowInt-136
❑ 99Top-428
❑ 99TopChr-428
❑ 99TopChrR-428
❑ 99TopMVPP-428
Norton, Rick
❑ 91SouOreAC-8
❑ 91SouOreAP-3856
❑ 92SouOreAF-3421
❑ 93ModA'sC-15
❑ 93ModA'sF-803
Norton, Tom
❑ 72TwiPos-14
❑ 72TwiTeal-9
❑ 73TacTwiC-17
Norton, Wayne
❑ 67VanMouSO-17
Norwood, Aaron
❑ 89BluOriS-19
Norwood, Steve
❑ 78NewWayCT-31
❑ 79BurBeeT-24
❑ 80BurBeeT-15
❑ 81BurBeeT-4
Norwood, Willie
❑ 76TacTwiDQ-14
❑ 76VenLeaS-23
❑ 77TacTwiDQ-8B
❑ 78Top-705
❑ 78TwiFriP-13
❑ 79Top-274
❑ 79TwiFriP-19
❑ 80TolMudHT-10
❑ 80Top-432
❑ 80TwiPos-21
❑ 81Don-516A
❑ 81Don-516B
Nosek, Randy
❑ 88LakTigS-18
❑ 89LonTigP-1377
❑ 90CMC-383
❑ 90ProAAAF-375
❑ 90Sco-607
❑ 90TolMudHC-6
❑ 90TolMudHP-145
❑ 90TopDeb89-88
❑ 90UppDec-2
❑ 91LinDriAAA-594
❑ 91TolMudHLD-594
❑ 91TolMudHP-1930
Nossek, Joe (Joseph R.)
❑ 64Top-532
❑ 65Top-597
❑ 66OPC-22
❑ 66Top-22
❑ 66TopVen-22
❑ 67CokCapAt-12
❑ 67DexPre-152
❑ 67Top-209
❑ 69OPC-143
❑ 69Top-143
❑ 69TopFou-25
❑ 73OPC-646
❑ 73Top-646
❑ 74Top-99
❑ 77IndTeal-20
❑ 78IndTeal-23
❑ 78TwiFri-39
❑ 80IndTeal-21
❑ 83RoyPos-20
❑ 84WhiSoxTV-8
❑ 90WhiSoxC-30
❑ 91WhiSoxK-NNO
❑ 92WhiSoxK-NNO
❑ 93WhiSoxK-30
❑ 94WhiSoxK-30
❑ 95WhiSoxK-31
Nossek, Scott
❑ 84AriWilP-14
Nottebart, Don
❑ 60Top-351
❑ 61SevElev-29
❑ 61Top-29
❑ 62Top-541
❑ 63Top-204
❑ 64Top-434
❑ 64TopCoi-119
❑ 65Top-469
❑ 66OPC-21
❑ 66Top-21
❑ 66TopVen-21
❑ 67AstTeal2-18
❑ 67Top-269
❑ 68OPC-171
❑ 68Top-171
❑ 68TopVen-171
❑ 69Top-593
❑ 78TCM60I-72
❑ 87AstSer1-18
❑ 92YanWIZ6-94
Nottle, Ed
❑ 74GasRanT-15
❑ 75AndRanT-NNO
❑ 76SacSolC-14
❑ 77TucTorC-27
❑ 79WatA'sT-9
❑ 80WesHavWCT-20A
❑ 81TacTigT-6
❑ 82TacTigT-19
❑ 84TacTigC-90
❑ 86PawRedSP-16
❑ 87IntLeaAT-9
❑ 87PawRedSP-72
❑ 87PawRedST-21
❑ 88PawRedSC-24
❑ 88PawRedSP-469
❑ 88TriAAAP-52
❑ 89PacSenL-51
❑ 89PawRedSC-25
❑ 89PawRedSP-677
❑ 89PawRedSP-678
❑ 89PawRedSTI-18
❑ 90CMC-261
❑ 90PawRedSC-10
❑ 90PawRedSDD-17
❑ 90PawRedSP-477
❑ 90ProAAAF-449
❑ 90TopTVRS-34
Nourse, Chester
❑ 09ObaT21-145
❑ 10BisCoaLE99-23
❑ 11PacCoaBD-46
❑ 11Zee-75
Nova, Fernando
❑ 97BriWhiSB-23
Nova, Pascual
❑ 96IdaFalB-18
Novak, Dave
❑ 92HamRedF-1609
Novak, Tom
❑ 87TamTarP-11
Novak, Troy
❑ 95OdgRapTI-20
Novick, Walter
❑ 52Par-77
Novikoff, Lou
❑ 41CubTeal-16
❑ 42CubTeal-16
❑ 43CubTeal-18
❑ 43MPR302-1-18
❑ 44CubTeal-18
❑ 47CenFlo-16
❑ 47SigOil-82
❑ 83TCMPla1942-41
Novits, Carey
❑ 98WatIndTI-21
Novoa, Rafael
❑ 88CapCodPPaLP-36
❑ 89BlaYNPRWLU-8
❑ 90Bes-89
❑ 90CliGiaB-24
❑ 90CliGiaP-2541
❑ 90CMC-843
❑ 90MidLeaASGS-57
❑ 90ProAaA-116
❑ 91Cla1-T9
❑ 91LinDriAAA-386
❑ 91PhoFirLD-386
❑ 91PhoFirP-62
❑ 91Sco-366
❑ 91TopDeb90-116
❑ 91UppDec-674
❑ 92ElPasDF-3918
❑ 93NewOrlZF-971
❑ 94BreMilB-257
❑ 94IowCubF-1274
❑ 94Pac-338
❑ 94StaCluT-343
❑ 94StaCluTFDI-343
❑ 94Top-623
❑ 94TopGol-623
❑ 94TopSpa-623
Novosel, Frank
❑ 52LavPro-102
Novotney, Rube
❑ 48AngTeal-21
❑ 49AngTeal-28
❑ 49EurSta-65
❑ 49W725AngTI-22
Nowak, Matt
❑ 88HagSunS-14
Nowak, Rick
❑ 90MyrBeaBJP-2774
Nowak, Steve
❑ 93BriTigF-3647
❑ 94FayGenF-2143
❑ 94JamJamF-3962
Nowlan, Bill
❑ 81BurBeeT-28
❑ 82BelBreFr-25
❑ 83BelBreFr-13
Nowlin, Jim (James)
❑ 87SumBraP-25
❑ 88BurBraP-15
Noworyta, Steve
❑ 83AppFoxFr-9
Noyes, Winfield
❑ 11Zee-97
❑ 12HomRunKE-71
❑ 12Zee-125
❑ 16Zee-61
Nozling, Paul
❑ 88BriTigP-1890
❑ 89FayGenP-1591
Nueberger, Scott
❑ 97PriDevR-7
Nugent, Barney
❑ 86ReaPhiP-20
❑ 87MaiGuiP-10
❑ 88MaiPhiC-3
❑ 88MaiPhiP-299
❑ 89ScrRedBC-2
❑ 89ScrRedBP-712
❑ 90CMC-251
❑ 90ScrRedBC-25
Nuismer, Jack
❑ 80WatIndT-8
❑ 81ChaLooT-7
❑ 82ChaChaT-8
Nunamaker, Les (Leslie G.)
❑ 12T207-141
❑ 14CraJacE-132
❑ 15CraJacE-132
❑ 15SpoNewM-131
❑ 19W514-7
❑ 20W52-20
❑ 21E121So1-72
❑ 22E120-38
❑ 22W573-93
❑ 23W501-116
❑ 77Ind192T-14
❑ 95ConTSN-1361
Nuneviller, Tom
❑ 90BatCliP-3082
❑ 91ClePhiC-22
❑ 91ClePhiP-1633
❑ 92ClaFS7-233
❑ 92ReaPhiF-589
❑ 92ReaPhiS-537
❑ 92SkyAA F-233
❑ 92UppDecML-112
❑ 93ExcFS7-87
❑ 94ReaPhiF-2076
Nunex, Nelson
❑ 87WytCubP-11
Nunez, Abraham
❑ 96StCatSB-22
❑ 97Bes-86
❑ 97BesLimA-26
❑ 97Bow-362
❑ 97BowBes-164
❑ 97BowBesAR-164
❑ 97BowBesR-164
❑ 97BowChr-242
❑ 97BowChrI-242
❑ 97BowChrIR-242
❑ 97BowChrR-242
❑ 97BowInt-362
❑ 97CarLeaTP-3
❑ 97LynHil-15
❑ 98Bes-35
❑ 98Bes-81
❑ 98BesFulCA-14
❑ 98BesPreA-30
❑ 98Bow-82
❑ 98BowBes-175
❑ 98BowBesAR-175
❑ 98BowBesR-175
❑ 98BowChr-82
❑ 98BowChrGA-82
❑ 98BowChrGAR-82
❑ 98BowChrI-82
❑ 98BowChrIR-82
❑ 98BowChrR-82
❑ 98BowGolA-82
❑ 98BowInt-82
❑ 98BowScoC-SC13
❑ 98CirThu-267
❑ 98CirThuRav-267
❑ 98CirThuSupRav-267
❑ 98Don-282
❑ 98DonColL-259
❑ 98DonColP-710
❑ 98DonGolPP-282
❑ 98DonPre-160
❑ 98DonPreSeat-160
❑ 98DonPriCL-259
❑ 98DonPriCP-710
❑ 98DonSigA-62
❑ 98DonSigAC-82
❑ 98DonSigAM-83
❑ 98DonSigSB-23
❑ 98DonSilPP-282
❑ 98E-X2SD2001-8
❑ 98Fle-140
❑ 98Lea-60
❑ 98LeaFraDA-60
❑ 98LeaFraF-60
❑ 98LeaFraM-60
❑ 98LeaFraM-60
❑ 98LeaFraMDC-60
❑ 98LeaFraMDC-60
❑ 98LeaFraMZ2-60
❑ 98LeaRCrusUP-119
❑ 98LeaRS-260
❑ 98LeaRSCrusUG-119
❑ 98LeaRSCrusUR-119
❑ 98LeaRSLHolo-260
❑ 98LeaRSLong-260
❑ 98LeaRTrue-260
❑ 98NasSouTI-24
❑ 98NasSouTISS-23
❑ 98PacPar-223
❑ 98PacParC-223
❑ 98PacParG-223
❑ 98PacParHS-223
❑ 98PacParPB-223
❑ 98PacParR-223
❑ 98Pin-161
❑ 98PinIns-122
❑ 98PinInsCE-122
❑ 98PinInsDE-122
❑ 98PinPer-132
❑ 98PinPerPP-132
❑ 98PinPreP-161
❑ 98ScoRT-248
❑ 98ScoRTSS-PP141
❑ 98ScoRTSSAP-PP141
❑ 98ScoRTSSAP1-PP141
❑ 98SouBenSHM-12
❑ 98StaCluFDI-334
❑ 98StaCluI-334
❑ 98StaCluOneK-334
❑ 98StaCluPP-334
❑ 98Stu-141
❑ 98StuGPP-141
❑ 98StuSPP-141
❑ 98Ult-442
❑ 98UltGolM-442
❑ 98UltMas-442
❑ 98UltPlaM-442
❑ 98Zen-84
❑ 98Zen5 xx7-74
❑ 98Zen5x7GoldImp-74
❑ 98Zen5x7Imp-74
❑ 98ZenRooT-8
❑ 98ZenZ-G-84
❑ 98ZenZ-S-84
❑ 99BowGol-394
❑ 99BowInt-394
❑ 99Fle-493
❑ 99FleSta9-493
❑ 99FleWarT-493
❑ 99Pac-343
❑ 99PacCroC-223
❑ 99PacCroCPB-223
❑ 99PacPlaB-343
❑ 99PacRed-343
❑ 99SP SigAuto-AN
❑ 99SpoIll-62
❑ 99SPSig-120
❑ 99SPx-112
❑ 99SPxFinR-112
❑ 99SPxFinS-112
❑ 99StaClu-236
❑ 99StaCluFDI-236
❑ 99StaCluOoaK-236
❑ 99StaCluPP-236
❑ 99UppDec-457
❑ 99UppDecEL1-457
❑ 99UppDecEL2-457
❑ 99UppDecMP-AN
Nunez, Abraham OF
❑ 99Bow-394
Nunez, Alex
❑ 90KenTwiB-11
❑ 90KenTwiP-2303
❑ 90KenTwiS-18
❑ 91VisOakC-18
❑ 91VisOakP-1750
Nunez, Bernie (Bernardino)
❑ 88MyrBeaBJP-1169
❑ 89DunBluJS-12
❑ 90CMC-772
❑ 90KnoBluJB-14
❑ 90KnoBluJP-1256
❑ 90KnoBluJS-13
❑ 91KnoBluJLD-363
❑ 91KnoBluJP-1781
❑ 91LinDriAA-363
❑ 93DayCubC-14
❑ 93DayCubF-870
❑ 93FloStaLAF-32
❑ 94ClaGolF-51
Nunez, Clemente
❑ 92Bow-417
❑ 92UppDec-701
❑ 93ElmPioC-1
❑ 93ElmPioF-3821
❑ 93Top-599
❑ 93TopGol-599
❑ 93TopInaM-599
❑ 93TopInaR-599
❑ 93TopMic-599
❑ 94BreCouMC-10
❑ 95Bes-72
❑ 95BreCouMF-244
❑ 95SPML-58

- 96Exc-165
- 96PorSeaDB-20

Nunez, Dario
- 86PalSprAP-24
- 86PalSprAS-25
- 87PalSprP-22
- 88PalSprAP-1448

Nunez, Edwin
- 80WauTimT-6
- 81WauTimT-4
- 83SalLakCGT-1
- 84Don-435
- 84SalLakCGC-183
- 85Don-484
- 85Fle-496
- 85MarMot-24
- 85Top-34
- 85TopTif-34
- 86Don-145
- 86Fle-470
- 86Lea-66
- 86MarMot-24
- 86OPC-364
- 86SevCoi-W15
- 86Top-511
- 86TopSti-223
- 86TopTat-8
- 86TopTif-511
- 87Don-243
- 87FleUpd-92
- 87FleUpdG-92
- 87MarMot-11
- 87Top-427
- 87TopTif-427
- 88Don-445
- 88DonRoo-36
- 88Fle-383
- 88FleGlo-383
- 88MarMot-11
- 88OPC-258
- 88PanSti-182
- 88StaLinMa-12
- 88Top-258
- 88TopSti-216
- 88TopTif-258
- 89BlaYNPRWL-121
- 89BlaYNPRWLU-67
- 89MetColP-46
- 89TolMudHP-773
- 90Don-563
- 90FleUpd-98
- 90Lea-397
- 90OPC-586
- 90TigCok-15
- 90Top-586
- 90TopTif-586
- 91Bow-40
- 91BreMilB-19
- 91BrePol-17
- 91Don-620
- 91Fle-345
- 91FleUpd-32
- 91Lea-352
- 91MetWIZ-297
- 91OPC-106
- 91StaClu-595
- 91Top-106
- 91TopDesS-106
- 91TopMic-106
- 91TopTif-106
- 92BrePol-17
- 92Don-541
- 92Fle-184
- 92OPC-352
- 92RanTeal-14
- 92Sco-676
- 92StaClu-776
- 92StaCluECN-776
- 92Top-352
- 92TopGol-352
- 92TopGolW-352
- 92TopMic-352
- 92Ult-387
- 93AthMot-24
- 93Fle-686
- 93FleFinE-260
- 93RanKee-281
- 93Top-19
- 93TopGol-19
- 93TopInaM-19
- 93TopInaR-19
- 93TopMic-19
- 93Ult-611
- 94BreMilB-342
- 94Fle-271
- 94Pac-460
- 94Sco-296
- 94ScoGolR-296

Nunez, Isaias
- 94JohCitCC-23
- 94JohCitCF-3711
- 95PeoChiTI-33
- 96PeoChiB-23

Nunez, Jose
- 96AriBlaDB-23
- 97SouBenSH-22
- 98JupHamQ-20
- 98NewJerCM-22
- 98PorRocG-26

Nunez, Jose Jiminez
- 85Ft.MyeRT-13
- 87BluJayFS-26
- 87FleUpd-93
- 87FleUpdG-93
- 88Don-611
- 88Fle-122
- 88FleGlo-122
- 88OPC-28
- 88Sco-312
- 88ScoGlo-312
- 88SyrChiC-4
- 88SyrChiP-820
- 88Top-28
- 88TopTif-28
- 89BluJayFS-24
- 89SyrChiC-2
- 89SyrChiMB-16
- 89SyrChiP-806
- 90Don-467
- 90TopTVCu-13
- 90UppDec-716
- 91IowCubP-1057
- 92CalCanS-65
- 92SkyAAAF-30
- 93LimRocDWB-11

Nunez, Juan
- 96ChaRivTI-9624

Nunez, Mauricio
- 86St.PetCP-23
- 87St.PetCP-6
- 88ArkTraGS-10
- 89SavCarP-357
- 89SouAtlLAGS-38
- 90CMC-669
- 90LouRedBC-26
- 90LouRedBLBC-30
- 90LouRedBP-417
- 90ProAAAF-531
- 90TopTVCa-57
- 91St.PetCC-28
- 93GleFalRC-30
- 93LimRocDWB-37

Nunez, Maximo
- 95HagSunF-66
- 96HicCraB-12
- 98DurBulTI-23
- 98OrlRayM-14

Nunez, Primivito
- 94AugGreC-14

Nunez, Ramon
- 84IdaFalATI-19
- 94DurBulC-13
- 94DurBulF-335
- 97TexAllM-47

Nunez, Raymond
- 92PulBraC-8
- 92PulBraF-3185
- 93MacBraC-17
- 93MacBraF-1410
- 93SouAtlLAGF-41
- 94DurBulTI-14
- 95BreBtaTI-8
- 95DurBulTI-23
- 96DurBulBrB-15
- 97OrlRayB-20
- 98WesTenDJM-21

Nunez, Rogelio
- 90UtiBluSP-4
- 91Cla/Bes-277
- 91MidLeaAP-MWL11
- 91SouBenWSC-22
- 91SouBenWSP-2859
- 92ClaFS7-150
- 92ProFS7-46
- 92SarWhiSCB-3
- 92SarWhiSF-208
- 93BirBarF-1196
- 94BirBarC-17
- 94BirBarF-624
- 95TulDriTI-17

Nunez, Sergio
- 95Bow-235
- 95BowBes-B35
- 95BowBesR-B35
- 95BowGolF-235
- 95SPML-72
- 95UppDecML-185
- 95UppDecMLFS-185
- 95WilBluRTI-35
- 96BesAutS-66
- 96BesAutSA-49
- 96ColCho-436
- 96ColChoGS-436
- 96ColChoSS-436
- 96Exc-65
- 96UppDec-263
- 96WilBluRB-10
- 97BesAutAS-35
- 97TexLeaTP-29
- 97WicWra-1
- 98BirBarG-20

Nunez, Vladimir
- 96AriBlaDB-24
- 97Bow-154
- 97BowChr-154
- 97BowChrI-154
- 97BowChrIR-154
- 97BowChrR-154
- 97BowInt-154
- 97CalLeaTP-5
- 97HigDesMG-17
- 97Top-250
- 98AriFalLTP-7
- 98Bes-36
- 98Bow-331
- 98BowChr-331
- 98BowChrGA-331
- 98BowChrGAR-331
- 98BowChrI-331
- 98BowChrIR-331
- 98BowChrR-331
- 98BowGolA-331
- 98BowInt-331
- 98SP MinPE-18
- 98SPMin-18
- 98Top-498
- 98TopChr-498
- 98TopChrR-498
- 98TopDevR-498
- 98TopDia-498
- 98TopMiniC-498
- 99BasAmeTP-71
- 99BasAmeTPG-71
- 99Fle-465
- 99FleSta9-465
- 99FleWarT-465
- 99SPx-82
- 99SPxFinR-82
- 99SPxFinS-82

Nunley, Angelo
- 85SprCarT-22
- 86TamTarP-14
- 87VerRedP-13
- 88ChaLooB-25
- 88ChaLooB-26

Nunley, Jay
- 97BoiHawG-22

Nunn, Howard
- 59Top-549
- 61Top-346
- 62Top-524
- 80Red196T-37

Nunn, Wally
- 77SpaPhiT-6

Nunnally, Jon (Jonathan)
- 92ClaDraP-51
- 92FroRowDP-15
- 92FroRowDPG-15
- 92FroRowDPS-15
- 92WatIndC-17
- 92WatIndF-3248
- 93ClaFS7-231
- 93ColRedC-17
- 93ColRedF-606
- 93ExcFS7-161
- 93SouAtlLAGF-14
- 93StaCluM-7
- 94CarLeaAF-CAR35
- 94KinIndC-15
- 94KinIndF-2658
- 95ARuFalLS-15
- 95Bow-176
- 95BowBes-R79
- 95BowBesR-R79
- 95Emo-51
- 95Fin-260
- 95FinRef-260
- 95Fla-266
- 95FleUpd-47
- 95FleUpdRU-8
- 95SelCer-111
- 95SelCerF-9
- 95SelCerMG-111
- 95SP-158
- 95SPCha-4
- 95SPChaDC-4
- 95SPSil-158
- 95StaClu-587
- 95StaCluMOP-587
- 95StaCluSTWS-587
- 95Sum-121
- 95SumNthD-121
- 95TopTra-15T
- 95TopTra-133T
- 95UltGolMR-M18
- 95UppDec-258
- 95UppDecED-258
- 95UppDecEDG-258
- 95Zen-145
- 96ColCho-175
- 96ColCho-657
- 96ColChoGS-175
- 96ColChoGS-657
- 96ColChoSS-175
- 96ColChoSS-657
- 96ColChoYMtP-30
- 96ColChoYMtP-30A
- 96ColChoYMtPGS-30
- 96ColChoYMtPGS-30A
- 96Don-269
- 96DonPreP-269
- 96EmoXL-69
- 96Fla-93
- 96Fle-136
- 96FleTif-136
- 96Lea-106
- 96LeaPrePB-106
- 96LeaPrePG-106
- 96LeaPrePS-106
- 96LeaSigA-170
- 96LeaSigAG-170
- 96LeaSigAS-170
- 96MetUni-67
- 96MetUniP-67
- 96MetUniProS-67
- 96MetUniProS-XX
- 96OmaRoyB-21
- 96Pac-331
- 96PanSti-186
- 96ProSta-119
- 96RoyPol-20
- 96Sco-17
- 96ScoDugC-A16
- 96ScoDugCAP-A16
- 96StaClu-229
- 96StaCluMOP-229
- 96Top-137
- 96TopGal-103
- 96TopGalPPI-103
- 96Ult-75
- 96UltGolM-75
- 96UppDec-91
- 97OmaRoyB-24
- 97PacPriGotD-GD49
- 98CirThu-211
- 98CirThuRav-211
- 98CirThuSupRav-211
- 98ColCho-67
- 98DonColL-227
- 98DonPriCL-227
- 98E-X2-84
- 98E-X2ECFut-84
- 98E-X2ECNow-84
- 98Fin-178
- 98FinNo--178
- 98FinNo-R-178
- 98FinRef-178
- 98Fle-567
- 98Lea-27
- 98LeaFraDA-27
- 98LeaFraF-27
- 98LeaFraM-27
- 98LeaFraM-27
- 98LeaFraMDC-27
- 98LeaFraMDC-27
- 98LeaFraMZ2-27
- 98PacOme-65
- 98PacOmeR-65
- 98StaCluFDI-307
- 98StaCluI-307
- 98StaCluOneK-307
- 98StaCluPP-307
- 98Ult-419
- 98UltGolM-419
- 98UltMas-419
- 98UltPlaM-419
- 98UppDec-337
- 99UppDec-72
- 99UppDecEL1-72
- 99UppDecEL2-72

Nunnari, Talmadge
- 97VerExpB-21
- 98CapFeaCM-14

Nurre, Peter
- 90KisDodD-19

Nussbeck, Mark
- 96NewJerCB-20
- 97PeoChi-19
- 98PriWilCQ-12

Nutt, John
- 15Zee-85
- 16Zee-86

Nutt, Steven
- 92MarPhiC-28
- 92MarPhiF-3055
- 93SpaPhiC-21
- 93SpaPhiF-1055
- 94SpaPhiF-1719
- 94SparPhiC-16

Nuttall, Todd
- 94OgdRapSP-28

Nutting, Robert
- 92Bow-85
- 92HunCubC-2
- 92HunCubF-3154

Nuttle, Jamison
- 93WelPirC-16
- 93WelPirF-3353

Nuxhall, Joe
- 52Top-406
- 53BowC-90
- 53Top-105
- 54Bow-76
- 55Bow-194
- 55Kah-4
- 56Kah-12
- 56RedBurB-15
- 56Top-218
- 57Kah-23
- 57RedSoh-15
- 57Top-103
- 58Kah-21
- 58RedEnq-27
- 58Top-63
- 59Kah-26
- 59RedBurBP-11
- 59RedEnq-16
- 59RedShiBS-15
- 59Top-389
- 60Kah-30
- 60RawGloT-24
- 60RedJayP-7
- 60Top-282
- 61A'sTeal-14
- 61AthJayP-14
- 61Top-444
- 63GadFunC-10
- 63Kah-22
- 63RedEnq-21
- 63RedFreBC-14
- 63Top-194
- 64Kah-19
- 64RedJayP-7
- 64Top-106
- 64TopVen-106
- 65Kah-31
- 65RedEnq-19
- 65Top-312
- 66Kah-23
- 66RedVolC-9
- 66Top-483
- 67CokCapR-15
- 67OPC-44
- 67Top-44
- 70HouofJ-21
- 75TCMHouoJ-23
- 77RedCarP-6
- 78TCM60I-65
- 79DiaGre-274
- 82OhiHaloF-63
- 83TopRep5-406
- 89PacLegI-161
- 89SweBasG-53
- 90BasWit-105
- 91TopArc1-105
- 91UppDecS-9
- 93RedKah-4
- 97FleMilDM-15
- 97FleMilDMR-15

Nyari, Pete
- 94BatCliC-16
- 94BatCliF-3442
- 95PiePhiF-186
- 97ClePhi-14
- 98ReaPhiM-18
- 98ReaPhiUM-16

Nybo, Tim
- 86RedWinA-17

Nyce, Frederick
- 87OldJudN-371

Nye, Rich
- 67Top-608
- 68Top-339
- 68TopVen-339
- 69CubJewT-11
- 69MilBra-203
- 69OPC-88
- 69Top-88
- 70OPC-139
- 70Top-139
- 71ExpLaPR-7
- 72MilBra-255
- 78TCM60I-281

Nye, Ryan
- 94BatCliC-17
- 94BatCliF-3443
- 94SigRooDP-49
- 94SigRooDPS-49
- 94StaCluDP-29
- 94StaCluDPFDI-29
- 95Bow-95
- 95ClePhiF-216
- 95Exc-244
- 95Top-421
- 96Bow-243
- 96BowFoi-243
- 96Exc-211
- 96ReaPhiB-10
- 97Bow-358
- 97BowCerBlaIA-CA57
- 97BowCerBluIA-CA57
- 97BowCerGolIA-CA57
- 97BowInt-358
- 97ScrRedB-3
- 98ScrRedBQ-22

Nykoluk, Kevin
- 98PeoChiM-17

Nyman, Chris (Christopher C.)
- 78KnoKnoST-16
- 79IowOakP-12
- 80IowOakP-9
- 81EdmTraRR-7
- 82EdmTraT-5
- 84Nes792-382
- 84Top-382
- 84TopTif-382
- 86BufBisP-20
- 86NasSouTI-19

Nyman, Gerald
- 69OPC-173
- 69Top-173
- 69TopFou-21
- 70Top-644
- 71MLBOffS-233
- 71OPC-656
- 71Top-656
- 89SalSpuCLC-147
- 89SalSpuP-1820
- 90JamExpP-10
- 90WelPirP-33
- 91WelPirP-3592
- 94DanBraF-3549
- 95EugEmeTI-30
- 96EugEmeB-27

Nyman, Jerry
- 97EugEmeB-2
- 98EugEme-20

Nyman, Nyls (Nyls W.)
- 75OPC-619
- 75Top-619
- 75TopMin-619
- 76OPC-258
- 76SSP-149
- 76Top-258
- 78SprRedWK-6

Nyquist, Mike
- 89SalLakTTI-5

Nyssen, Dan
- 87AubAstP-13
- 87HawRai-14
- 88OscAstS-19
- 89OscAstS-14
- 90OscAstS-21

O'Berry, Mike (Preston M.)
❑ 77BriRedST-14
❑ 80Top-662
❑ 82Don-538
❑ 82Fle-78
❑ 82RedCok-15
❑ 82Top-562
❑ 84ColCliP-16
❑ 84ColCliT-20
❑ 84Nes792-184
❑ 84Top-184
❑ 84TopTif-184
❑ 84TopTra-86T
❑ 84TopTraT-86T
❑ 85ColCliT-12
❑ 92BluOriC-23
❑ 92YanWIZ8-137
❑ 93AlbPolCB-23
❑ 93AlbPolF-2042
❑ 94FreKeyC-25
❑ 94FreKeyF-2630

O'Bradovich, Jim (James T.)
❑ 78ChaChaT-10

O'Brien, Billy (William S.)
❑ 36GouWidPPR-D24

O'Brien, Brian
❑ 93EliTwiC-17
❑ 93EliTwiF-3415
❑ 94ForWayWC-17
❑ 94ForWayWF-2008
❑ 95ForMyeMTI-21

O'Brien, Buck (Thomas Joseph)
❑ 12T207-143

O'Brien, Charlie
❑ 83AlbA'sT-10
❑ 86VanCanP-19
❑ 87DenZepP-24
❑ 88BrePol-11
❑ 88BreTeal-28
❑ 88DenZepC-15
❑ 88DenZepP-1268
❑ 88Top-566
❑ 88TopClo-79
❑ 88TopTif-566
❑ 89BrePol-22
❑ 89Fle-194
❑ 89FleGlo-194
❑ 89Sco-606
❑ 89Top-214
❑ 89TopTif-214
❑ 90BreMilB-17
❑ 90BrePol-22
❑ 90Don-410
❑ 90El PasDAGTI-30
❑ 90Fle-332
❑ 90FleCan-332
❑ 90Lea-375
❑ 90OPC-106
❑ 90PubIntS-502
❑ 90Top-106
❑ 90TopTif-106
❑ 90UppDec-650
❑ 90WicStaSGD-28
❑ 91Bow-473
❑ 91Don-623
❑ 91Lea-122
❑ 91MetColP-41
❑ 91MetKah-5
❑ 91MetPerPA-24
❑ 91MetWIZ-298
❑ 91OPC-442
❑ 91Sco-829
❑ 91SouOreAAP-SOA33
❑ 91StaClu-157
❑ 91Top-442
❑ 91TopDesS-442
❑ 91TopMic-442
❑ 91TopTif-442
❑ 91UppDec-420
❑ 92Don-777
❑ 92Fle-514
❑ 92MetColP-17
❑ 92MetKah-22
❑ 92OPC-56
❑ 92Pin-488
❑ 92Sco-621
❑ 92StaClu-154
❑ 92Top-56
❑ 92TopGol-56
❑ 92TopGolW-56
❑ 92TopMic-56
❑ 92Ult-534
❑ 92UppDec-381
❑ 93Don-698
❑ 93Fle-478
❑ 93MetColP-42
❑ 93MetKah-22
❑ 93PacSpa-546
❑ 93StaClu-128
❑ 93StaCluFDI-128
❑ 93StaCluMOP-128
❑ 93Top-242
❑ 93TopGol-242
❑ 93TopInaM-242
❑ 93TopInaR-242
❑ 93TopMic-242
❑ 93Ult-431
❑ 93UppDec-209
❑ 93UppDecGold-209
❑ 94BraLykP-25
❑ 94BraLykS-24
❑ 94BraUSPC-5S
❑ 94BreMilB-61
❑ 94Don-242
❑ 94Fle-574
❑ 94FleUpd-103
❑ 94Sco-195
❑ 94ScoGolR-195
❑ 94StaCluT-34
❑ 94StaCluTFDI-34
❑ 94Top-671
❑ 94TopGol-671
❑ 94TopSpa-671
❑ 94TopTra-92T
❑ 94Ult-448
❑ 95Don-437
❑ 95DonPreP-437
❑ 95Fle-315
❑ 95Sco-537
❑ 95ScoGolR-537
❑ 95ScoPlaTS-537
❑ 95StaClu-258
❑ 95StaCluFDI-258
❑ 95StaCluMOP-258
❑ 95StaCluSTWS-258
❑ 95Top-379
❑ 95Ult-132
❑ 95UltGolM-132
❑ 96BluJayOH-22
❑ 96ColCho-378T
❑ 96Fle-304
❑ 96FleTif-304
❑ 96FleUpd-U99
❑ 96FleUpdTC-U99
❑ 96LeaSigEA-144
❑ 97BluJayB-10
❑ 97BluJayOH-21
❑ 97BluJayS-15
❑ 97BluJayS-8
❑ 97ColCho-504
❑ 97Fle-246
❑ 97FleTif-246
❑ 97Pac-223
❑ 97PacLigB-223
❑ 97PacSil-223
❑ 97Top-353
❑ 97Ult-148
❑ 97UltGolME-148
❑ 97UltPlaME-148
❑ 97UppDec-517
❑ 98ColCho-20
❑ 98ColCho-181
❑ 98ColCho-262
❑ 98PacOnl-176
❑ 98PacOnlR-176
❑ 98PacOnlWC-176
❑ 99SkyMolMOA-19

O'Brien, Dan
❑ 77St.PetCT-11
❑ 78ArkTraT-18
❑ 80RicBraT-10
❑ 80Top-684
❑ 81RicBraT-18

O'Brien, Darby (William D.)
❑ 74BroClu-12
❑ 87OldJudN-376
❑ 90DodTar-1104

O'Brien, Eddie (Edward J.)
❑ 53Top-249
❑ 54Top-139
❑ 56Top-116
❑ 57JetPos-14
❑ 57Top-259
❑ 69PilPos-34
❑ 77PilPosR-34
❑ 91TopArc1-249
❑ 94TopArc1-139
❑ 94TopArc1G-139

O'Brien, FB QB (Davey)
❑ 40WheM4-6A
❑ 40WheM4-6C

O'Brien, Frank
❑ 16Zee-114
❑ 17Zee-53

O'Brien, Jack (John Joseph)
❑ 11SpoLifCW-272
❑ 90DodTar-584

O'Brien, Jack (John K.)
❑ 87OldJudN-373
❑ 87OldJudN-377

O'Brien, Joe
❑ 94BatCliC-18
❑ 94BatCliF-3456
❑ 95PiePhiF-194

O'Brien, John
❑ 91HamRedC-18
❑ 91HamRedP-4047
❑ 92SprCarC-21
❑ 92SprCarF-875
❑ 93SavCarC-20
❑ 93SavCarF-693
❑ 93SouAtlLAGF-49
❑ 94ClaGolF-159

O'Brien, Johnny (John Thomas)
❑ 53Top-223
❑ 54Top-139
❑ 55Top-135
❑ 56PirTeal-18
❑ 56Top-65
❑ 56TopPin-44
❑ 57PirTeal-7
❑ 58Top-426
❑ 59Top-499
❑ 60HenHouW-4
❑ 60SeaPop-9
❑ 91TopArc1-223
❑ 94TopArc1-139
❑ 94TopArc1G-139

O'Brien, Kelly
❑ 91SalLakTSP-29

O'Brien, Mark
❑ 91GulCoaRSP-8
❑ 92ButCopKSP-19
❑ 92StaCluD-131
❑ 93EriSaiC-18
❑ 93EriSaiF-3114
❑ 94HudValRC-16
❑ 94HudValRF-3382

O'Brien, Perry
❑ 23Zee-194
❑ 27Zee-75

O'Brien, Pete (Peter James)
❑ 09T206-452
❑ 11SpoLifCW-273

O'Brien, Pete (Peter M.)
❑ 80AshTouT-13
❑ 81TulDriT-16B
❑ 83RanAffF-9
❑ 83TopTra-81T
❑ 84AllGamPI-184
❑ 84Don-281
❑ 84Fle-423
❑ 84Nes792-534
❑ 84OPC-71
❑ 84RanJarP-9
❑ 84Top-534
❑ 84TopSti-357
❑ 84TopTif-534
❑ 85AllGamPI-8
❑ 85Don-178
❑ 85Fle-563
❑ 85Lea-201
❑ 85OPC-196
❑ 85RanPer-9
❑ 85Top-196
❑ 85TopSti-344
❑ 85TopTif-196
❑ 86BasStaB-78
❑ 86Don-99
❑ 86Fle-568
❑ 86FleMin-112
❑ 86OPC-328
❑ 86RanPer-9
❑ 86Top-328
❑ 86TopSti-236
❑ 86TopTat-19
❑ 86TopTif-328
❑ 87ClaUpdY-138
❑ 87Don-259
❑ 87DonOpeD-174
❑ 87Fle-132
❑ 87FleGamW-31
❑ 87FleGlo-132
❑ 87FleMin-76
❑ 87HosSti-30
❑ 87Lea-186
❑ 87OPC-17
❑ 87RanMot-9
❑ 87RanSmo-12
❑ 87Spo-52
❑ 87SpoTeaP-1
❑ 87StuPan-26
❑ 87Top-17
❑ 87TopMinL-72
❑ 87TopSti-239
❑ 87TopTif-17
❑ 88Don-284
❑ 88DonBasB-167
❑ 88Fle-475
❑ 88FleGlo-475
❑ 88FleStiC-67
❑ 88GreBasS-6
❑ 88Lea-132
❑ 88OPC-381
❑ 88PanSti-200
❑ 88RanMot-9
❑ 88RanSmo-2
❑ 88RedFolSB-63
❑ 88Sco-29
❑ 88ScoGlo-29
❑ 88Spo-145
❑ 88StaLinRa-10
❑ 88Top-201
❑ 88Top-721
❑ 88TopBig-227
❑ 88TopSti-240
❑ 88TopTif-201
❑ 88TopTif-721
❑ 89Bow-84
❑ 89BowTif-84
❑ 89ClaTraP-184
❑ 89Don-107
❑ 89DonBasB-5
❑ 89DonTra-16
❑ 89Fle-529
❑ 89FleGlo-529
❑ 89FleUpd-29
❑ 89IndTeal-21
❑ 89OPC-314
❑ 89PanSti-452
❑ 89RedFolSB-87
❑ 89Sco-22
❑ 89ScoRoo-6T
❑ 89Spo-8
❑ 89Top-629
❑ 89TopBig-115
❑ 89TopSti-248
❑ 89TopTif-629
❑ 89TopTra-88T
❑ 89TopTraT-88T
❑ 89TopUKM-57
❑ 89UppDec-54
❑ 89UppDec-800
❑ 90Bow-475
❑ 90BowTif-475
❑ 90ClaYel-T38
❑ 90Don-24
❑ 90Don-202
❑ 90DonBesA-98
❑ 90DonSupD-24
❑ 90Fle-498
❑ 90FleCan-498
❑ 90Lea-9
❑ 90MarMot-17
❑ 90OPC-265
❑ 90PanSti-55
❑ 90PubIntS-565
❑ 90Sco-175
❑ 90ScoRoo-23T
❑ 90Spo-92
❑ 90Top-265
❑ 90TopSti-218
❑ 90TopTif-265
❑ 90TopTra-82T
❑ 90TopTraT-82T
❑ 90TulDriDGB-4
❑ 90UppDec-110
❑ 90UppDec-719
❑ 91Bow-259
❑ 91Don-119
❑ 91Fle-459
❑ 91Lea-244
❑ 91MarCouH-8
❑ 91OPC-585
❑ 91PanFreS-228
❑ 91Sco-509
❑ 91StaClu-285
❑ 91Top-585
❑ 91TopDesS-585
❑ 91TopMic-585
❑ 91TopTif-585
❑ 91Ult-342
❑ 91UppDec-459
❑ 92Bow-313
❑ 92Don-86
❑ 92Fle-289
❑ 92Lea-260
❑ 92LeaBlaG-260
❑ 92MarMot-8
❑ 92OPC-455
❑ 92PanSti-55
❑ 92Pin-125
❑ 92Sco-141
❑ 92StaClu-192
❑ 92Stu-238
❑ 92Top-455
❑ 92TopGol-455
❑ 92TopGolW-455
❑ 92TopMic-455
❑ 92Ult-128
❑ 92UppDec-388
❑ 93DiaMar-81
❑ 93Don-613
❑ 93Fle-678
❑ 93Lea-412
❑ 93MariStaClu-26
❑ 93MarMot-3
❑ 93PacSpa-625
❑ 93PanSti-59
❑ 93Pin-151
❑ 93RanKee-282
❑ 93Sco-460
❑ 93StaClu-378
❑ 93StaCluFDI-378
❑ 93StaCluMOP-378
❑ 93Top-125
❑ 93TopGol-125
❑ 93TopInaM-125
❑ 93TopInaR-125
❑ 93TopMic-125
❑ 93UppDec-627
❑ 93UppDecGold-627

O'Brien, Robert
❑ 72OPC-198
❑ 72Top-198
❑ 90DodTar-583

O'Brien, Sid (Sydney L.)
❑ 69RedSoxAO-8
❑ 69Top-628
❑ 70OPC-163
❑ 70Top-163
❑ 71MLBOffS-353
❑ 71OPC-561
❑ 71Top-561
❑ 72OPC-289
❑ 72Top-289
❑ 72TopCloT-25
❑ 94BreMilB-62

O'Brien, Tommy (Thomas Edward)
❑ 49RedSoxTI-16

O'Brien, William Smith
❑ 87BucN28-116
❑ 87OldJudN-374
❑ 87OldJudN-375
❑ 88WG1CarG-69

O'Connell, Danny (Daniel F.)
❑ 47PM1StaP1-154
❑ 50JJKCopP-12
❑ 51Bow-93
❑ 53BraSpiaS3-18
❑ 53BraSpiaS7-10
❑ 53Top-107
❑ 54Bow-160
❑ 54BraJohC-4
❑ 54BraMer-7
❑ 54BraSpiaSP-15
❑ 54DixLid-11
❑ 55Bow-44
❑ 55BraGolS-24
❑ 55BraJohC-4
❑ 55BraSpiaSD-14
❑ 56Top-272
❑ 57Bra8x1-8
❑ 57BraSpiaS4-15
❑ 57Top-271
❑ 58GiaArmT-7
❑ 58GiaJayP-8
❑ 58GiaSFCB-18
❑ 58Hir-19
❑ 58Top-166
❑ 59Top-87
❑ 59TopVen-87
❑ 60TacBan-11
❑ 60Top-192
❑ 60TopVen-192
❑ 61SenJayP-7
❑ 61Top-318
❑ 62SalPlaC-221
❑ 62ShiPlaC-221
❑ 62Top-411
❑ 62TopBuc-64
❑ 62TopStal-99
❑ 80Bra195T-37
❑ 91TopArc1-107

O'Connell, Jimmy (James J.)
❑ 20WalMaiW-37
❑ 21Zee-128
❑ 22Zee-106
❑ 23W503-8
❑ 23W515-13

O'Connell, Mark
❑ 81CliGiaT-11

O'Connell, P.J.
❑ 87OldJudN-378

O'Connell, Shawn
❑ 91BluOriC-23
❑ 91BluOriP-4126
❑ 92KanCouCC-19
❑ 92KanCouCF-91

O'Conner, Tim
❑ 86KenTwiP-18
❑ 87VisOakP-17
❑ 88OrlTwiB-2

O'Connor, Ben
❑ 90YakBeaTI-16
❑ 91YakBeaC-15
❑ 91YakBeaP-4246

O'Connor, Bill
❑ 85VisOakT-4
❑ 86VisOakP-14

O'Connor, Bob
❑ 82CliGiaF-25
❑ 84ShrCapFB-15

O'Connor, Brian
❑ 93MarPhiC-20
❑ 93MarPhiF-3471
❑ 96AugGreB-20
❑ 96EriSeaB-17
❑ 97AugGre-14
❑ 98LynHilQ-11

O'Connor, Jack (John J.)
❑ 03BreE10-109
❑ 11PinT-5-105
❑ 11SpoLifM-113
❑ 87OldJudN-379
❑ 93JusSo-8
❑ 98CamPepP-59

O'Connor, Jack William
❑ 81TwiPos-20
❑ 82Don-539
❑ 82Fle-557
❑ 82TolMudHT-5
❑ 82Top-353
❑ 82TwiPos-22
❑ 83Don-51
❑ 83Fle-621
❑ 83FleSti-134
❑ 83TolMudHT-29
❑ 83Top-33
❑ 83TwiTeal-22
❑ 84Nes792-268
❑ 84TolMudHT-15
❑ 84Top-268
❑ 84TopTif-268
❑ 85ExpPos-15
❑ 85IndIndTI-22
❑ 86CalCanP-20
❑ 87BalOriP-26
❑ 87RocRedWP-20
❑ 87RocRedWT-7
❑ 88Sco-434
❑ 88ScoGlo-434
❑ 88SyrChiC-10
❑ 88SyrChiP-805
❑ 89SyrChiC-3
❑ 89SyrChiMB-17
❑ 89SyrChiP-812

❑ 91OriCro-336
O'Connor, James
❑ 91St.CatBJC-14
❑ 91St.CatBJP-3394
O'Connor, Kevin
❑ 90IdaFalBP-3257
❑ 91MacBraC-25
❑ 91MacBraP-878
❑ 92DurBulC-14
❑ 92DurBulTI-12
❑ 93GreBraF-363
❑ 94GreBraF-425
❑ 94GreBraTI-17
❑ 95AusFut-35
❑ 95RicBraRC-15
❑ 95RicBraTI-13
O'Connor, Nick
❑ 81BirBarT-18
O'Connor, Paddy (Patrick F.)
❑ 09AmeCarE90-1-84
❑ 10PirTipTD-21
❑ 11PinT-5-867
❑ 11SpoLifM-257
O'Connor, Richard
❑ 95MarPhiTI-18
❑ 96PieBolWB-18
O'Day, Hank (Henry Francis)
❑ 87OldJudN-380
❑ 88SpoTimM-7
❑ 94ConTSN-1201
❑ 94ConTSNB-1201
O'Day, Harry
❑ 88SFHesCreN32-23
O'Dea, Ken (James Kenneth)
❑ 35DiaMatCS3T1-114
❑ 36CubTeal-24
❑ 36DiaMatCS3T2-18
❑ 36SandSW-43
❑ 40PlaBal-214
❑ 46SeaSLP-47
❑ 72TCMthe3-54
❑ 77TCMTheWY-24
❑ 83Car194T-8
❑ 83TCMPla1945-27
❑ 92ConTSN-497
O'Dell, Bill
❑ 47Exh-169
❑ 54OriTeal-16
❑ 55Top-57
❑ 55TopDouH-7
❑ 56BalOriP-40
❑ 56BalOriP-41
❑ 57Top-316
❑ 58OriJayP-8
❑ 58Top-84
❑ 59OriJayP-5
❑ 59Top-250
❑ 60Top-303
❑ 61Pos-155
❑ 61Top-96
❑ 61Top-383
❑ 61TopStal-83
❑ 62Top-429
❑ 63ExhStaB-50
❑ 63Fle-66
❑ 63GiaJayP-9
❑ 63Jel-111
❑ 63Pos-111
❑ 63Top-7
❑ 63Top-9
❑ 63Top-235
❑ 64GiaJayP-9
❑ 64Top-18
❑ 64TopCoi-115
❑ 64TopVen-18
❑ 65BraTeal-8
❑ 65Top-476
❑ 66Top-237
❑ 66TopVen-237
❑ 67OPC-162
❑ 67Top-162
❑ 67TopPirS-17
❑ 81Gia196T-30
❑ 91OriCro-337
❑ 97BalOriP-38
O'Dell, Jake
❑ 96SouOreTI-23
❑ 97VisOakG-21
❑ 98HunStaTI-18
O'Dell, Jim (James Wesley)
❑ 85OscAstTI-20
❑ 86ColAstP-20
❑ 87BirBarB-4
❑ 88ChaKniTI-7
O'Dette, Rick
❑ 98LowSpiM-14
O'Donnell, Erik
❑ 91BelMarCB-10
❑ 91BelMarP-3659
❑ 92PenPilC-5
❑ 92PenPilF-2929
❑ 93AppFoxCB-19
❑ 94CenValRC-15
❑ 94CenValRF-3201
O'Donnell, George
❑ 58JetPos-13
❑ 60DarFar-15
O'Donnell, Glen
❑ 86ElmPioRSP-14
O'Donnell, Stephen P.
❑ 88CapCodPB-18
❑ 88CapCodPPaLP-41
❑ 89GreFalDSP-25
❑ 90BakDodCLC-248
❑ 91VerBeaDC-23
❑ 91VerBeaDP-784
❑ 92VerBeaDC-19
❑ 92VerBeaDF-2886
O'Donnell, T.J.
❑ 93UtiBluSC-17
❑ 93UtiBluSF-3542
❑ 94SarRedSC-20
❑ 94SarRedSF-1960
O'Donoghue, John
❑ 90LSUTigP-15
❑ 91FreKeyC-6
❑ 91FreKeyP-2361
❑ 92FreKeyF-1824
❑ 92HagSunF-2552
❑ 92HagSunS-267
❑ 92SkyAA F-111
❑ 93Bow-197
❑ 93FleFinE-162
❑ 93RocRedWF-235
❑ 93TriAAAGF-29
❑ 94ColC-217
❑ 94ColChoGS-217
❑ 94ColChoSS-217
❑ 94OriPro-73
❑ 94OriUSPC-3H
❑ 94Pin-253
❑ 94PinArtP-253
❑ 94PinMusC-253
❑ 94RocRedWF-996
❑ 94RocRedWTI-17
❑ 94Sco-593
❑ 94ScoGolR-593
❑ 94StaClu-86
❑ 94StaCluFDI-86
❑ 94StaCluGR-86
❑ 94StaCluMOP-86
❑ 94StaCluT-297
❑ 94StaCluTFDI-297
❑ 94Top-763
❑ 94TopGol-763
❑ 94TopSpa-763
❑ 96BowBayB-22
❑ 96TulDriTI-20
O'Donoghue, John Sr.
❑ 64Top-388
❑ 65OPC-71
❑ 65Top-71
❑ 66Top-501
❑ 66TopRubl-71
❑ 67BalOriP-74
❑ 67CokCapl-5
❑ 67OPC-127
❑ 67Top-127
❑ 68CokCapO-6
❑ 68Top-456
❑ 70BreMcD-23
❑ 70BreMil-18
❑ 70OPC-441
❑ 70Top-441
❑ 71ExpLaPR-8
❑ 71ExpPS-18
❑ 71MLBOffS-136
❑ 71OPC-743
❑ 71Top-743
❑ 72MilBra-257
❑ 81TCM60I-377
❑ 83Pil69G-13
❑ 91FreKeyC-27
❑ 91OriCro-338
❑ 93BowBayF-2204
❑ 94BowBayF-2428
❑ 94BreMilB-63
O'Dougherty, Pat
❑ 43YanSta-21
O'Doul, Lefty (Francis J.)
❑ 18Zee-88
❑ 21Zee-129
❑ 25Zee-96
❑ 26Zee-13
❑ 27Zee-121
❑ 28PorandAR-A26
❑ 28PorandAR-B26
❑ 29ExhFou-11
❑ 29PorandAR-66
❑ 30W554-11
❑ 31Exh-3
❑ 31W517-33
❑ 32OrbPinNP-31A
❑ 32OrbPinNP-31B
❑ 32OrbPinUP-48
❑ 32USCar*-24
❑ 33DelR33-10
❑ 33DouDisP-33
❑ 33ExhFou-2
❑ 33GeoCMil-23
❑ 33Gou-58
❑ 33Gou-232
❑ 33GouCanV-58
❑ 33NatLeaAC-6
❑ 33RitCE-3C
❑ 33TatOrb-48
❑ 33WorCig-72
❑ 33WorCig-73
❑ 33Zee-136
❑ 33Zee-137
❑ 34DiaMatCSB-142
❑ 35PebBea-5
❑ 46SpoExcW-5-5
❑ 48SomandK-1
❑ 49SomandK-1
❑ 51R42SmaS-75
❑ 52MotCoo-25
❑ 53MotCoo-9
❑ 57HygMea-9
❑ 57SeaPop-16
❑ 60Fle-37
❑ 61Fle-130
❑ 72FleFamF-34
❑ 73BooProC-10
❑ 74Bra193NLA-6
❑ 75OakOak2A-27
❑ 75ShaPiz-17
❑ 77GalGloG-47
❑ 77GalGloG-219
❑ 80LauFamF-31
❑ 80PacLeg-29
❑ 82DiaCla-52
❑ 82TCMGreH-41
❑ 83BigLeaCOA-26
❑ 88ConSer5-23
❑ 90DodTar-585
❑ 91ConTSN-165
❑ 92ConTSN-447
❑ 93ConTSN-681
O'Dowd, ,Tom
❑ 80UtiBluJT-22
O'Farrell, Bob (Robert A.)
❑ 20NatCarE-70
❑ 21Nei-76
❑ 22E120-164
❑ 22W572-72
❑ 22W573-94
❑ 23WilChoV-113
❑ 26Exh-62
❑ 27Exh-31
❑ 27YorCarE-12A
❑ 27YorCarE-12B
❑ 28PorandAR-A27
❑ 28PorandAR-B27
❑ 28W502-12
❑ 28Yue-12
❑ 31Exh-10
❑ 33ButCre-19
❑ 33ExhFou-5
❑ 33Gou-34
❑ 33GouCanV-34
❑ 33WorCig-74
❑ 34BabRutG-49
❑ 34ButPreR-48
❑ 34DiaMatCSB-143
❑ 34TarThoBD-22
❑ 35GouPuzR-4F
❑ 35GouPuzR-7F
❑ 35GouPuzR-12F
❑ 36WorWidGV-115
❑ 61Fle-131
❑ 72TCMthe3-55
❑ 76GrePlaG-29
❑ 91ConTSN-175
❑ 91ConTSN-316
❑ 92CarMcD-13
❑ 92ConTSN-621
❑ 93ConTSN-862
O'Flynn, Gardner
❑ 94HudValRC-17
❑ 94HudValRF-3383
❑ 95ChaRivTI-12
O'Halloran, Greg
❑ 89St.CatBJP-2079
❑ 90DunBluJS-14
❑ 90FloStaLAS-38
❑ 90StaFS7-66
❑ 91Cla/Bes-30
❑ 91DunBluJC-14
❑ 91DunBluJP-211
❑ 92ClaFS7-157
❑ 92KnoBluJF-2993
❑ 92KnoBluJS-389
❑ 92SkyAA F-164
❑ 93LinVenB-236
❑ 93LinVenB-288
❑ 93SyrChiF-1001
❑ 94PorSeaDF-682
❑ 94PorSeaDTI-24
❑ 94SpoRoo-52
❑ 94SpoRooAP-52
❑ 95Sco-293
❑ 95ScoGolR-293
❑ 95ScoPlaTS-293
❑ 98PorSeaD5AQ-16
O'Halloran, Mike
❑ 91MedHatBJP-4098
❑ 91MedHatBJSP-23
❑ 92MedHatBJF-3207
❑ 92MedHatBJSP-20
O'Hara, Duane
❑ 88CapCodPPaLP-73
O'Hara, Pat
❑ 82MadMusF-27
O'Hara, William A.
❑ 09RamT20-90
❑ 09T206-270
❑ 09T206-271
❑ 10E101-36
❑ 10MelMinE-36
❑ 10NadCarE-42
❑ 10PeoT21-44
❑ 11SpoLifM-286
❑ 12ImpTobC-1
❑ 72ClaCar-58
O'Hearn, Bob
❑ 85BurRanT-16
❑ 86SalRedBP-22
O'Hearn, Brandon
❑ 98ChaAllCM-23
O'Hearn, Paul
❑ 94OgdRapF-3736
❑ 94OgdRapSP-23
❑ 95OdgRapTI-21
O'Keeffe, Richard
❑ 76BurBeeT-24
❑ 80VenLeaS-253
❑ 80WatRedT-11
❑ 81WatRedT-6
❑ 82SyrChiT-27B
❑ 82SyrChiTI-17
O'Laughlin, Chad
❑ 92BelBreCB-11
❑ 94SanBerSF-2754
O'Laughlin, Silk (Francis H)
❑ 09SpoNewSM-38
❑ 94ConTSN-1187
❑ 94ConTSNB-1187
O'Leary, Bill
❑ 84ButCopKT-20
O'Leary, Charley (Charles T.)
❑ 07TigACDPP-10
❑ 08RosComP-38
❑ 09AmeCarE90-1-85
❑ 09RamT20-91
❑ 09T206-274
❑ 09T206-275
❑ 09TigTaCP-14
❑ 09WolNewDTPP-12
❑ 09WolNewDTPP-16
❑ 10NadE1-46
❑ 10RedCroT-60
❑ 10RedCroT-146
❑ 10RedCroT-233
❑ 10SweCapPP-29
❑ 11PinT-5-164
❑ 11SpoLifCW-275
❑ 11SpoLifM-66
❑ 11T205-131
❑ 12HasTriFT-2
❑ 12HasTriFT-37
❑ 14Zee-116
❑ 21E121So1-74
❑ 21KoBreWSI-43
❑ 22W575-93
❑ 32CubTeal-19
❑ 72TCMthe3-109
❑ 79Yan192T-22
❑ 84Yan192G-22
❑ 91ConTSN-116
❑ 93UppDecTR-7
❑ 93UppDecTR-8
O'Leary, Daniel
❑ 88KimN18-32
O'Leary, Mike
❑ 92BluOriF-2375
O'Leary, Troy
❑ 89HelBrelS-19
❑ 89HelBreSP-11
❑ 89Sta-6
❑ 90BelBreB-5
❑ 90BelBreS-16
❑ 90Bes-98
❑ 91CalLeLA-36
❑ 91Cla/Bes-160
❑ 91DaiDolF-17
❑ 91StoPorC-17
❑ 91StoPorP-3046
❑ 92ClaFS7-98
❑ 92ElPasDF-3936
❑ 92ElPasDS-220
❑ 92SkyAA F-96
❑ 92UppDecML-268
❑ 92UppDecMLPotY-PY6
❑ 93Bow-344
❑ 93ClaGolF-215
❑ 93ClaMVPF-4
❑ 93ExcFS7-193
❑ 93ExcLeaLF-17
❑ 93FleFinE-231
❑ 93LinVenB-204
❑ 93NewOrlZF-985
❑ 93TopTra-59T
❑ 93TriAAAGF-45
❑ 94BreMilB-159
❑ 94Don-459
❑ 94Fle-187
❑ 94LeaLimR-21
❑ 94NewOrlZF-1482
❑ 94Pac-339
❑ 94Pin-424
❑ 94PinArtP-424
❑ 94PinMusC-424
❑ 94ScoRoo-RT114
❑ 94ScoRooGR-RT114
❑ 94SpoRoo-133
❑ 94SpoRooAP-133
❑ 94StaClu-347
❑ 94StaCluFDI-347
❑ 94StaCluGR-347
❑ 94StaCluMOP-347
❑ 94Top-770
❑ 94TopGol-770
❑ 94TopSpa-770
❑ 94Ult-81
❑ 95ColCho-169
❑ 95ColChoGS-169
❑ 95ColChoSS-169
❑ 95Don-273
❑ 95DonPreP-273
❑ 95DonTopotO-24
❑ 95FleUpd-12
❑ 95Sco-593
❑ 95ScoGolR-593
❑ 95ScoPlaTS-593
❑ 95SigRoo-39
❑ 95SigRooSig-39
❑ 95StaClu-600
❑ 95StaCluMOP-600
❑ 95StaCluSTDW-RS600
❑ 95StaCluSTWS-600
❑ 95Top-496
❑ 95TopCyb-286
❑ 95UppDec-51
❑ 95UppDec-485
❑ 95UppDecED-51
❑ 95UppDecEDG-51
❑ 96ColCho-68
❑ 96ColChoGS-68
❑ 96ColChoSS-68
❑ 96Don-246
❑ 96DonPreP-246
❑ 96EmoXL-17
❑ 96Fla-23
❑ 96Fle-32
❑ 96FleRedS-11
❑ 96FleTif-32
❑ 96LeaSigA-172
❑ 96LeaSigAG-172
❑ 96LeaSigAS-172
❑ 96MetUni-18
❑ 96MetUniP-18
❑ 96Pac-252
❑ 96Sco-134
❑ 96ScoDugC-A85
❑ 96ScoDugCAP-A85
❑ 96StaClu-92
❑ 96StaCluMOP-92
❑ 96Top-91
❑ 96Ult-20
❑ 96UltGolM-20
❑ 96UppDec-22
❑ 97Cir-384
❑ 97CirRav-384
❑ 97ColCho-281
❑ 97Don-321
❑ 97DonGolPP-321
❑ 97DonSilPP-321
❑ 97DonTea-58
❑ 97DonTeaSPE-58
❑ 97Fle-28
❑ 97FleTif-28
❑ 97Pac-44
❑ 97PacLigB-44
❑ 97PacSil-44
❑ 97RedSoxS-15
❑ 97RedSoxSPl-15
❑ 97RedSoxSPr-15
❑ 97Sco-251
❑ 97ScoArtPWB-251
❑ 97ScoPreS-251
❑ 97ScoShoS-251
❑ 97ScoShoSAP-251
❑ 97SP-39
❑ 97StaClu-168
❑ 97StaCluMOP-168
❑ 97Top-54
❑ 97Ult-17
❑ 97UltGolME-17
❑ 97UltPlaME-17
❑ 97UppDec-315
❑ 98CirThu-78
❑ 98CirThuRav-78
❑ 98CirThuSupRav-78
❑ 98ColCho-324
❑ 98CroRoy-26
❑ 98Fin-134
❑ 98FinNo--134
❑ 98FinNo-R-134
❑ 98FinRef-134
❑ 98Fle-99
❑ 98Pac-46
❑ 98PacOnl-123
❑ 98PacOnlR-123
❑ 98PacOnlWC-123
❑ 98PacPlaB-46
❑ 98PacRedT-46
❑ 98PacSil-46
❑ 98Pin-140
❑ 98PinPreP-140
❑ 98PinSna-BRS7
❑ 98PinSna-BRS17
❑ 98RedSoxS-13
❑ 98RedSoxSP-13
❑ 98Revo-27
❑ 98RevoSS-27
❑ 98Sco-216
❑ 98StaCluFDI-280
❑ 98StaClul-280
❑ 98StaCluOneK-280
❑ 98StaCluPP-280
❑ 98Top-80
❑ 98TopChr-80
❑ 98TopChrR-80
❑ 98TopDevR-80
❑ 98TopDia-80
❑ 98TopMiniC-80
❑ 98UppDec-47
❑ 98UppDecSF-28
❑ 99Fle-183
❑ 99FleBri-18
❑ 99FleBri2G-18
❑ 99FleBriBlu-18
❑ 99FleBriGol-18
❑ 99FleSta9-183
❑ 99FleWarT-183
❑ 99Pac-72
❑ 99PacCroC-48

❑ 99PacCroCPB-48
❑ 99PacOme-43
❑ 99PacOmeC-43
❑ 99PacOmeG-43
❑ 99PacOmePB-43
❑ 99PacPar-42
❑ 99PacParC-42
❑ 99PacParG-42
❑ 99PacParHoloGold-42
❑ 99PacParHS-42
❑ 99PacParOD-42
❑ 99PacParPB-42
❑ 99PacParRed-42
❑ 99PacPlaB-72
❑ 99PacRed-72
❑ 99Rev-26
❑ 99RevPremDate-26
❑ 99RevRet-26
❑ 99RevShaSS-26
❑ 99SkyThu-157
❑ 99SkyThuRant-157
❑ 99SkyThuRave-157
❑ 99StaClu-281
❑ 99StaCluFDI-281
❑ 99StaCluOoaK-281
❑ 99StaCluPP-281
❑ 99ThuSkySupR-157
❑ 99Top-288
❑ 99TopChr-288
❑ 99TopChrR-288
❑ 99TopMVPP-288
❑ 99UD Cho-63
❑ 99UD ChoPCR-63
❑ 99Ult-6
❑ 99UltGolM-6
❑ 99UltMas-6
❑ 99UltPlaM-6
❑ 99UppDec-54
❑ 99UppDecEL1-54
❑ 99UppDecEL2-54
❑ 99UppDecM-34
❑ 99UppDecMGS-34
❑ 99UppDecMHFS-34
❑ 99UppDecMP-34
❑ 99UppDecMSS-34
❑ 99Vic-67

O'Malley, Mike
❑ 81VerBeaDT-13

O'Malley, Pat
❑ 97OmaRoyB-28
❑ 98OmaRoyM-28

O'Malley, Paul
❑ 94AubAstC-9
❑ 94AubAstF-3754
❑ 94SigRooDPBSDP-8
❑ 94StaCluDP-51
❑ 94StaCluDPFDI-51
❑ 96QuaCitRB-21
❑ 97JacGen-19
❑ 97JacGenS-18
❑ 98JacGenM-15

O'Malley, Tom (Thomas P.)
❑ 81ShrCapT-4
❑ 82Gia25tATI-22
❑ 82PhoGiaVNB-23
❑ 83Don-96
❑ 83Fle-271
❑ 83GiaMot-10
❑ 83GiaPos-22
❑ 83Top-663
❑ 84Don-601
❑ 84Fle-384
❑ 84Nes792-469
❑ 84PhoGiaC-11
❑ 84Top-469
❑ 84TopSti-170
❑ 84TopTif-469
❑ 86BalOriP-13
❑ 86RocRedWP-14
❑ 87Fle-477
❑ 87FleGlo-477
❑ 87OklCit8P-20
❑ 87Top-154
❑ 87TopTif-154
❑ 88OklCit8C-19
❑ 88OklCit8P-48
❑ 88RanSmo-1
❑ 88Sco-534
❑ 88ScoGlo-534
❑ 88StaLinRa-11
❑ 88Top-77
❑ 88TopTif-77
❑ 88TriAAAP-28
❑ 88TriAAC-4
❑ 89TidTidC-15
❑ 89TidTidP-1965
❑ 89TriAAAP-AAA13
❑ 90MetColP-43
❑ 90MetKah-27
❑ 90OPC-504
❑ 90Top-504
❑ 90TopTif-504
❑ 90TopTVM-28
❑ 90TriAAAC-20
❑ 91Fle-157
❑ 91MetWIZ-299
❑ 91OPC-257
❑ 91OriCro-339
❑ 91Sco-439
❑ 91Top-257
❑ 91TopDesS-257
❑ 91TopMic-257
❑ 91TopTif-257
❑ 93GolCar-2
❑ 93RanKee-284

O'Malley, Walter
❑ 88DodRinP1-10B

O'Mara, Ollie (Oliver E.)
❑ 15SpoNewM-133
❑ 16FleBreD-72
❑ 16SpoNewM-134
❑ 17Zee-37

O'Neal, Doug
❑ 92AlbPolF-2318
❑ 93BurBeeC-14
❑ 93BurBeeF-171

O'Neal, Kelley
❑ 89BriTigS-19
❑ 90NiaFalRP-8
❑ 91FayGenC-21
❑ 91FayGenP-1180
❑ 91SouAtlLAGP-SAL20
❑ 92ClaFS7-167
❑ 92LakTigC-7
❑ 92LakTigF-2287
❑ 93LakTigC-20
❑ 93LakTigF-1319
❑ 94TreThuF-2128

O'Neal, Mark
❑ 90SavCarP-2084
❑ 95LouRedF-294
❑ 96LouRedB-4
❑ 97LouRedB-5

O'Neal, Randy
❑ 82BirBarT-8
❑ 83EvaTriT-7
❑ 84EvaTriT-17
❑ 85Fle-645
❑ 86Don-394
❑ 86Fle-233
❑ 86TigCaiD-13
❑ 86Top-73
❑ 86TopTif-73
❑ 87BraSmo-3
❑ 87Don-584
❑ 87Fle-159
❑ 87FleGlo-159
❑ 87Top-196
❑ 87TopTif-196
❑ 88CarTeal-23
❑ 88LouRedBC-4
❑ 88LouRedBP-430
❑ 88LouRedBTI-37
❑ 89PhiTas-25
❑ 89ScrRedBC-10
❑ 89ScrRedBP-726
❑ 90GiaMot-23
❑ 91Fle-268

O'Neal, Troy
❑ 96BelSnaTI-27
❑ 98El PasDG-21

O'Neil, Buck (John Jordan)
❑ 49W72HolS-14
❑ 50W720HolS-22
❑ 86NegLeaF-45
❑ 87NegLeaPD-20
❑ 92NegLeaRLI-45
❑ 93NegLeaRL2-48
❑ 93UppDecS-17
❑ 94TedWil-109
❑ 94UppDecTAE-61
❑ 94UppDecTAELD-LD11
❑ 95NegLeaL2-31
❑ 96NegLeaBMKC-7
❑ 97NegLeaPC-3H
❑ 99SpoIllGotG-59
❑ 99SpoIllGotGA-53

O'Neil, Johnny
❑ 25Zee-97
❑ 47CenFlo-17

O'Neil, Mickey (George M.)
❑ 21Exh-121
❑ 22E120-132
❑ 23WilChoV-116
❑ 25Exh-8
❑ 26Exh-14
❑ 90DodTar-591

O'Neil, Richard
❑ 91IdaFalBSP-7

O'Neil, William John
❑ 04RedSoxUP-10
❑ 09T206-453

O'Neill, Dan
❑ 87FayGenP-3
❑ 88LakTigS-19
❑ 89LakTigS-16
❑ 90NewBriRSP-1317
❑ 90ProAaA-6
❑ 91LinDriAAA-362
❑ 91PawRedSDD-14
❑ 91PawRedSLD-362
❑ 91PawRedSP-37

O'Neill, Douglas
❑ 91JamExpC-11
❑ 91JamExpP-3559
❑ 92RocExpC-12
❑ 94OgdRapF-3748
❑ 94OgdRapSP-17
❑ 96PorSeaDB-21
❑ 97OklCit8-20
❑ 97TulDriTI-30

O'Neill, Emmett (Robert Emmett)
❑ 77TCMTheWY-36

O'Neill, J.F.
❑ 21Exh-123
❑ 26Zee-14

O'Neill, Jack (John Joseph)
❑ 11SpoLifCW-276

O'Neill, John (John J.)
❑ 47SigOil-83

O'Neill, Mike
❑ 06FanCraNL-34
❑ 11SpoLifCW-277

O'Neill, Paul Andrew
❑ 82CedRapRT-21
❑ 83TamTarT-19
❑ 86Don-37
❑ 86Fle-646
❑ 87FleUpd-94
❑ 87FleUpdG-94
❑ 87RedKah-21
❑ 87SpoRool-17
❑ 87SpoTeaP-4
❑ 88Don-433
❑ 88FleUpd-85
❑ 88FleUpdG-85
❑ 88RedFolSB-64
❑ 88RedKah-21
❑ 88Sco-304
❑ 88ScoGlo-304
❑ 88StaLinRe-14
❑ 88Top-204
❑ 88TopClo-80
❑ 88TopTif-204
❑ 89Bow-313
❑ 89BowTif-313
❑ 89CedRapRAB-5
❑ 89Don-360
❑ 89DonBasB-230
❑ 89Fle-166
❑ 89FleGlo-166
❑ 89OPC-187
❑ 89PanSti-77
❑ 89RedKah-21
❑ 89Sco-206
❑ 89ScoYouS2-5
❑ 89Top-604
❑ 89TopBig-39
❑ 89TopTif-604
❑ 89TVSpoM-44
❑ 89UppDec-428
❑ 90Bow-49
❑ 90BowTif-49
❑ 90CedRapRDGB-5
❑ 90ClaBlu-117
❑ 90Don-198
❑ 90DonBesN-39
❑ 90Fle-427
❑ 90FleCan-427
❑ 90Lea-70
❑ 90OPC-332
❑ 90PanSti-245
❑ 90PubIntS-36
❑ 90RedFolSB-71
❑ 90RedKah-20
❑ 90Sco-295
❑ 90Sco100S-17
❑ 90Spo-4
❑ 90Top-332
❑ 90TopBig-30
❑ 90TopSti-141
❑ 90TopTif-332
❑ 90UppDec-161
❑ 91Bow-685
❑ 91Don-583
❑ 91Fle-76
❑ 91Lea-219
❑ 91OPC-122
❑ 91PanFreS-133
❑ 91PanSti-120
❑ 91RedKah-21
❑ 91RedPep-15
❑ 91Sco-227
❑ 91StaClu-218
❑ 91Stu-169
❑ 91Top-122
❑ 91TopDesS-122
❑ 91TopMic-122
❑ 91TopTif-122
❑ 91Ult-100
❑ 91UppDec-133
❑ 91USPlaCA-2C
❑ 92Bow-267
❑ 92DenHol-11
❑ 92Don-63
❑ 92Fle-415
❑ 92Lea-99
❑ 92LeaBlaG-99
❑ 92OPC-61
❑ 92PanSti-266
❑ 92Pin-154
❑ 92RedKah-21
❑ 92Sco-57
❑ 92Sco100S-58
❑ 92ScoImpP-66
❑ 92SpoIllFK1-391
❑ 92StaClu-175
❑ 92StaCluD-135
❑ 92Stu-25
❑ 92Top-61
❑ 92TopGol-61
❑ 92TopGolW-61
❑ 92TopKid-41
❑ 92TopMic-61
❑ 92TriPla-162
❑ 92Ult-194
❑ 92UppDec-464
❑ 92UppDecHRH-HR15
❑ 93Bow-75
❑ 93Don-696
❑ 93Fin-170
❑ 93FinRef-170
❑ 93Fla-251
❑ 93Fle-39
❑ 93FleFinE-250
❑ 93Lea-379
❑ 93OPC-218
❑ 93OPCPre-14
❑ 93PacSpa-560
❑ 93PanSti-151
❑ 93Pin-446
❑ 93Sco-439
❑ 93Sel-86
❑ 93SelRoo-21T
❑ 93SP-266
❑ 93StaClu-717
❑ 93StaCluFDI-717
❑ 93StaCluMOP-717
❑ 93Stu-140
❑ 93Top-276
❑ 93TopGol-276
❑ 93TopInaM-276
❑ 93TopInaR-276
❑ 93TopMic-276
❑ 93TopTra-84T
❑ 93Ult-599
❑ 93UppDec-796
❑ 93UppDecGold-796
❑ 93UppDecHRH-HR27
❑ 93YanStaC-14
❑ 94Bow-249
❑ 94BowBes-R31
❑ 94BowBesR-R31
❑ 94ColC-218
❑ 94ColChoGS-218
❑ 94ColChoSS-218
❑ 94Don-50
❑ 94DonSpeE-50
❑ 94Fin-69
❑ 94FinRef-69
❑ 94Fla-86
❑ 94Fle-243
❑ 94FleExtB-136
❑ 94FUnPac-67
❑ 94Lea-108
❑ 94LeaL-57
❑ 94OPC-229
❑ 94Pac-433
❑ 94PanSti-103
❑ 94Pin-280
❑ 94PinArtP-280
❑ 94PinMusC-280
❑ 94Sco-15
❑ 94ScoGolR-15
❑ 94Sel-8
❑ 94SP-199
❑ 94SPDieC-199
❑ 94Spo-147
❑ 94StaClu-74
❑ 94StaCluFDI-74
❑ 94StaCluGR-74
❑ 94StaCluMOP-74
❑ 94StaCluT-199
❑ 94StaCluTFDI-199
❑ 94Stu-216
❑ 94StuEdiC-7
❑ 94Top-546
❑ 94TopGol-546
❑ 94TopSpa-546
❑ 94TriPla-277
❑ 94Ult-99
❑ 94UppDec-186
❑ 94UppDecED-186
❑ 95Baz-45
❑ 95BazRedH-RH10
❑ 95Bow-356
❑ 95BowBes-R66
❑ 95BowBesR-R66
❑ 95ClaPhoC-39
❑ 95ColCho-72
❑ 95ColChoGS-72
❑ 95ColChoSE-243
❑ 95ColChoSEGS-243
❑ 95ColChoSESS-243
❑ 95ColChoSS-72
❑ 95Don-284
❑ 95DonDiaK-DK7
❑ 95DonDom-9
❑ 95DonEli-50
❑ 95DonPreP-284
❑ 95DonTopotO-122
❑ 95Emo-64
❑ 95Fin-181
❑ 95FinRef-181
❑ 95Fla-67
❑ 95Fle-78
❑ 95FleAllS-18
❑ 95FleLeaL-1
❑ 95Kra-10
❑ 95Lea-80
❑ 95LeaChe-4
❑ 95LeaLim-76
❑ 95Pac-301
❑ 95PacPri-98
❑ 95PanSti-89
❑ 95PanSti-122
❑ 95Pin-245
❑ 95PinArtP-245
❑ 95PinMusC-245
❑ 95PinPer-PP17
❑ 95PosCan-7
❑ 95Sco-41
❑ 95ScoGolR-41
❑ 95ScoHaloG-HG26
❑ 95ScoPlaTS-41
❑ 95ScoRul-SR21
❑ 95ScoRulJ-SR21
❑ 95Sel-131
❑ 95SelArtP-131
❑ 95SelCer-65
❑ 95SelCerMG-65
❑ 95SP-178
❑ 95SPCha-173
❑ 95SPChaDC-173
❑ 95Spo-58
❑ 95SpoArtP-58
❑ 95SPSil-178
❑ 95StaClu-124
❑ 95StaClu-519
❑ 95StaCluCC-CC22
❑ 95StaCluFDI-124
❑ 95StaCluMO-35
❑ 95StaCluMOP-124
❑ 95StaCluMOP-519
❑ 95StaCluMOP-CC22
❑ 95StaCluMOP-RL20
❑ 95StaCluMOP-SS13
❑ 95StaCluRL-RL20
❑ 95StaCluSS-SS13
❑ 95StaCluSTWS-124
❑ 95StaCluSTWS-519
❑ 95StaCluVR-63
❑ 95StaCluVRMO-63
❑ 95Stu-162
❑ 95Sum-77
❑ 95SumNthD-77
❑ 95Top-426
❑ 95TopCyb-224
❑ 95TopD3-26
❑ 95TopEmb-72
❑ 95TopEmbGI-72
❑ 95TopLeaL-LL26
❑ 95UC3-68
❑ 95UC3ArtP-68
❑ 95Ult-84
❑ 95UltAllS-14
❑ 95UltAllSGM-14
❑ 95UltGolM-84
❑ 95UltLeaL-1
❑ 95UltLeaLGM-1
❑ 95UltOnBL-9
❑ 95UltOnBLGM-9
❑ 95UppDec-208
❑ 95UppDecED-208
❑ 95UppDecEDG-208
❑ 95UppDecPLL-R24
❑ 95UppDecPLLE-R24
❑ 95UppDecSE-141
❑ 95UppDecSEG-141
❑ 95USPlaCMLA-12D
❑ 95Zen-80
❑ 96Baz-128
❑ 96Bow-34
❑ 96BowBes-37
❑ 96BowBesAR-37
❑ 96BowBesR-37
❑ 96BowFoi-34
❑ 96Cir-67
❑ 96CirAcc-10
❑ 96CirBos-17
❑ 96CirRav-67
❑ 96ColCho-635
❑ 96ColChoGS-635
❑ 96ColChoSS-635
❑ 96Don-404
❑ 96DonPreP-404
❑ 96EmoXL-92
❑ 96Fin-B93
❑ 96Fin-S182
❑ 96Fin-S242
❑ 96FinBro-5
❑ 96FinRef-B93
❑ 96FinRef-S182
❑ 96FinRef-S242
❑ 96Fla-133
❑ 96Fle-192
❑ 96FleTif-192
❑ 96Lea-13
❑ 96LeaLim-44
❑ 96LeaLimG-44
❑ 96LeaPre-50
❑ 96LeaPreP-50
❑ 96LeaPrePB-13
❑ 96LeaPrePG-13
❑ 96LeaPrePS-13
❑ 96LeaSig-31
❑ 96LeaSigPPG-31
❑ 96LeaSigPPP-31
❑ 96LibSpo-2
❑ 96MetUni-91
❑ 96MetUniP-91
❑ 96MLBPin-24
❑ 96Pac-384
❑ 96PacPri-P121
❑ 96PacPriG-P121
❑ 96PanSti-154
❑ 96Pin-237
❑ 96PinAfi-17
❑ 96PinAfiAP-17
❑ 96PinAfiFPP-17
❑ 96PinArtP-137
❑ 96PinFoil-237
❑ 96PinSta-137
❑ 96ProSta-138
❑ 96RedF-3
❑ 96Sco-296
❑ 96ScoDugC-B21
❑ 96ScoDugCAP-B21
❑ 96Sel-92
❑ 96SelArtP-92

❑ 96SelCer-49
❑ 96SelCerAP-49
❑ 96SelCerCB-49
❑ 96SelCerCR-49
❑ 96SelCerIP-21
❑ 96SelCerMB-49
❑ 96SelCerMG-49
❑ 96SelCerMR-49
❑ 96SP-132
❑ 96Spo-81
❑ 96SpoArtP-81
❑ 96StaClu-212
❑ 96StaClu-272
❑ 96StaCluEPB-272
❑ 96StaCluEPG-272
❑ 96StaCluEPS-272
❑ 96StaCluMOP-212
❑ 96StaCluMOP-272
❑ 96Stu-110
❑ 96StuPrePB-110
❑ 96StuPrePG-110
❑ 96StuPrePS-110
❑ 96Sum-104
❑ 96SumAbo&B-104
❑ 96SumArtP-104
❑ 96SumFoi-104
❑ 96Top-284
❑ 96TopChr-114
❑ 96TopChrR-114
❑ 96TopGal-153
❑ 96TopGalPPI-153
❑ 96TopLas-75
❑ 96TopPro-AL7
❑ 96Ult-103
❑ 96UltGolM-103
❑ 96UppDec-155
❑ 96Zen-45
❑ 96ZenArtP-45
❑ 96ZenMoz-22
❑ 97Bow-260
❑ 97BowChr-82
❑ 97BowChrI-82
❑ 97BowChrIR-82
❑ 97BowChrR-82
❑ 97BowInt-260
❑ 97Cir-359
❑ 97CirRav-359
❑ 97ColCho-401
❑ 97ColChoT-NY12
❑ 97Don-35
❑ 97DonGolPP-35
❑ 97DonLim-125
❑ 97DonLim-182
❑ 97DonLimE-125
❑ 97DonLimE-182
❑ 97DonLimENG-182
❑ 97DonPre-64
❑ 97DonPreCttC-64
❑ 97DonSigA-74
❑ 97DonSigAC-92
❑ 97DonSigAM-92
❑ 97DonSilPP-35
❑ 97DonTea-122
❑ 97DonTeaSPE-122
❑ 97Fin-87
❑ 97FinRef-87
❑ 97FlaShoLC-121
❑ 97FlaShoLeg0-121
❑ 97FlaShoLeg1-121
❑ 97FlaShoM-A121
❑ 97FlaShoM-B121
❑ 97FlaShoM-C121
❑ 97FlaShoR0-121
❑ 97FlaShoR1-121
❑ 97FlaShoR2-121
❑ 97Fle-174
❑ 97FleTif-174
❑ 97Lea-92
❑ 97LeaFraM-92
❑ 97LeaFraMDC-92
❑ 97MetUni-120
❑ 97NewPin-8
❑ 97NewPinAP-8
❑ 97NewPinMC-8
❑ 97NewPinPP-8
❑ 97Pac-155
❑ 97PacLigB-155
❑ 97PacSil-155
❑ 97PinX-P-43
❑ 97PinX-PMoS-43
❑ 97Sco-150
❑ 97ScoArtPWB-150
❑ 97ScoPreS-150
❑ 97ScoShoS-150
❑ 97ScoShoSAP-150
❑ 97StaClu-32
❑ 97StaCluMat-32
❑ 97StaCluMOP-32
❑ 97StrAll-49
❑ 97Stu-117
❑ 97StuPrePG-117
❑ 97StuPrePS-117
❑ 97Top-247
❑ 97TopChr-88
❑ 97TopChrR-88
❑ 97TopGal-45
❑ 97TopGalPPI-45
❑ 97TopSta-83
❑ 97TopSta97AS-AS18
❑ 97TopStaAM-83
❑ 97Ult-339
❑ 97UltGolME-339
❑ 97UltPlaME-339
❑ 97UppDec-126
❑ 97YanSco-9
❑ 97YanScoPI-9
❑ 97YanScoPr-9
❑ 98Bow-241
❑ 98BowBes-55
❑ 98BowBesAR-55
❑ 98BowBesR-55
❑ 98BowChr-241
❑ 98BowChrGA-241
❑ 98BowChrGAR-241
❑ 98BowChrI-241
❑ 98BowChrIR-241
❑ 98BowChrR-241
❑ 98BowGolA-241
❑ 98BowInt-241
❑ 98CirThu-115
❑ 98CirThuRav-115
❑ 98CirThuSupRav-115
❑ 98ColCho-444
❑ 98CroRoy-98
❑ 98Don-78
❑ 98DonCol-78
❑ 98DonColL-317
❑ 98DonColP-642
❑ 98DonColS-78
❑ 98DonGolPP-78
❑ 98DonPre-92
❑ 98DonPreSeat-92
❑ 98DonPriCD-78
❑ 98DonPriCL-317
❑ 98DonPriCP-642
❑ 98DonSigA-63
❑ 98DonSigAC-83
❑ 98DonSigAM-84
❑ 98DonSilPP-78
❑ 98Fin-62
❑ 98FinNo--62
❑ 98FinNo-R-62
❑ 98FinRef-62
❑ 98Fle-167
❑ 98FleDecERT-11
❑ 98FleDecoE-11
❑ 98FleVin'-40
❑ 98FleVin'C-40
❑ 98Lea-118
❑ 98LeaFraDA-118
❑ 98LeaFraF-118
❑ 98LeaFraM-118
❑ 98LeaFraM-118
❑ 98LeaFraMDC-118
❑ 98LeaFraMDC-118
❑ 98LeaFraMZ2-118
❑ 98LeaRS-92
❑ 98LeaRSLHolo-92
❑ 98LeaRSLong-92
❑ 98LeaRTrue-92
❑ 98MetUni-144
❑ 98MetUniPMG-144
❑ 98Pac-154
❑ 98PacAur-61
❑ 98PacOme-168
❑ 98PacOmeR-168
❑ 98PacOnl-511
❑ 98PacOnlR-511
❑ 98PacOnlWC-511
❑ 98PacPar-72
❑ 98PacParC-72
❑ 98PacParG-72
❑ 98PacParHS-72
❑ 98PacParPB-72
❑ 98PacParR-72
❑ 98PacPlaB-154
❑ 98PacRedT-154
❑ 98PacSil-154
❑ 98PinPlu-104
❑ 98PinSna-NYY17
❑ 98Revo-102
❑ 98RevoSS-102
❑ 98Sco-116
❑ 98ScoRT-164
❑ 98ScoRTSS-PP93
❑ 98ScoRTSSAP-PP93
❑ 98ScoRTSSAP1-PP93
❑ 98ScoSS-PP47
❑ 98ScoSSAP-PP47
❑ 98SP Aut-146
❑ 98SpoIllWSF-104
❑ 98SpoIllWSFEE-104
❑ 98SpoIllWSFFE-104
❑ 98SpoIllWSFRJP-1
❑ 98SPxFin-107
❑ 98SPxFinR-107
❑ 98SPxFinS-107
❑ 98StaCluFDI-104
❑ 98StaCluI-104
❑ 98StaCluOneK-104
❑ 98StaCluPP-104
❑ 98Stu-130
❑ 98StuGPP-130
❑ 98StuSPP-130
❑ 98Top-322
❑ 98TopChr-322
❑ 98TopChrR-322
❑ 98TopDevR-322
❑ 98TopDia-322
❑ 98TopGal-149
❑ 98TopGalGP-149
❑ 98TopGalOPP-149
❑ 98TopGalPPI-149
❑ 98TopGalPPIA-149
❑ 98TopGolLabC1-33
❑ 98TopGolLabC1B-33
❑ 98TopGolLabC1One-33
❑ 98TopGolLabC1R-33
❑ 98TopGolLabC2-33
❑ 98TopGolLabC2B-33
❑ 98TopGolLabC2One-33
❑ 98TopGolLabC2R-33
❑ 98TopGolLabC3-33
❑ 98TopGolLabC3B-33
❑ 98TopGolLabC3One-33
❑ 98TopGolLabC3R-33
❑ 98TopMiniC-322
❑ 98TopOpeD-148
❑ 98TopSta-18
❑ 98TopStaB-18
❑ 98TopStaG-18
❑ 98TopStaGR-18
❑ 98TopStaS-18
❑ 98TopTek-37
❑ 98TopTekD-37
❑ 98Ult-47
❑ 98UltGolM-47
❑ 98UltMas-47
❑ 98UltPlaM-47
❑ 98UppDec-172
❑ 98UppDecR-69
❑ 98UppDecSF-93
❑ 98YanSco-10
❑ 98YanScoP-10
❑ 98YanUppD-172
❑ 98YanUppDWSC-1
❑ 99199Fin-51
❑ 99Bow-20
❑ 99BowBes-36
❑ 99BowBesAR-36
❑ 99BowBesR-36
❑ 99BowChr-20
❑ 99BowChrG-20
❑ 99BowChrGR-20
❑ 99BowChrI-20
❑ 99BowChrIR-20
❑ 99BowChrR-20
❑ 99BowGol-20
❑ 99BowInt-20
❑ 99E-X Cen-77
❑ 99E-X CenECFut-77
❑ 99E-X CenECNow-77
❑ 99FinGolRef-51
❑ 99FinRef-51
❑ 99FlaShoLeg1-130
❑ 99FlaShoLeg2-130
❑ 99FlaShoLeg3-130
❑ 99FlaShoLegM1-130
❑ 99FlaShoLegM2-130
❑ 99FlaShoLegM3-130
❑ 99FlaShoR1-130
❑ 99FlaShoR2-130
❑ 99FlaShoR3-130
❑ 99Fle-286
❑ 99FleBri-81
❑ 99FleBriBlu-81
❑ 99FleBriGol-81
❑ 99FleMys-34
❑ 99FleMysG-34
❑ 99FleMysM-34
❑ 99FleSta9-286
❑ 99FleWarT-286
❑ 99MetUni-230
❑ 99MetUniGM-230
❑ 99MetUniPMG-230
❑ 99Pac-299
❑ 99PacCroC-194
❑ 99PacCroCPB-194
❑ 99PacInv-103
❑ 99PacInvOD-103
❑ 99PacInvPB-103
❑ 99PacOme-166
❑ 99PacOmeC-166
❑ 99PacOmeG-166
❑ 99PacOmePB-166
❑ 99PacPar-165
❑ 99PacParC-165
❑ 99PacParG-165
❑ 99PacParHoloGold-165
❑ 99PacParHS-165
❑ 99PacParOD-165
❑ 99PacParPB-165
❑ 99PacParRed-165
❑ 99PacPlaB-299
❑ 99PacPriS-123
❑ 99PacPriS206-123
❑ 99PacPriS206R-123
❑ 99PacRed-299
❑ 99Rev-98
❑ 99RevPremDate-98
❑ 99RevRet-98
❑ 99RevShaSS-98
❑ 99SkyMolM-10
❑ 99SkyMolMX-10
❑ 99SkyPre-17
❑ 99SkyPreR-17
❑ 99SkyThu-200
❑ 99SkyThuRant-200
❑ 99SkyThuRave-200
❑ 99SP SigAuto-PO
❑ 99SP SigAutoG-PO
❑ 99SPSig-47
❑ 99StaClu-19
❑ 99StaCluFDI-19
❑ 99StaCluOoaK-19
❑ 99StaCluPP-19
❑ 99ThuSkySupR-200
❑ 99Top-416
❑ 99TopBlaLC1-73
❑ 99TopBlaLC2-73
❑ 99TopBlaLC3-73
❑ 99TopChr-416
❑ 99TopChrR-416
❑ 99TopGal-41
❑ 99TopGalPP-41
❑ 99TopGalPPI-41
❑ 99TopGolL-73
❑ 99TopGolLC1-73
❑ 99TopGolLC2-73
❑ 99TopGolLOtO-73
❑ 99TopMVPP-416
❑ 99TopOpeD-133
❑ 99TopRedLC1-73
❑ 99TopRedLC2-73
❑ 99TopRedLC3-73
❑ 99TopSta-114
❑ 99TopSta'S-25
❑ 99TopSta'SG-25
❑ 99TopSta'SGDH-25
❑ 99TopStaFoil-114
❑ 99TopStaPre-PP1
❑ 99UD Cho-118
❑ 99UD ChoP-118
❑ 99UD ChoPCR-118
❑ 99UltRBIK-25
❑ 99UppDec-156
❑ 99UppDecCLM-C63
❑ 99UppDecE-60
❑ 99UppDecEFXG-60
❑ 99UppDecEL1-156
❑ 99UppDecEL2-156
❑ 99UppDecM-141
❑ 99UppDecMGS-141
❑ 99UppDecMHFS-141
❑ 99UppDecMP-141
❑ 99UppDecMSS-141
❑ 99UppDecRI-PO
❑ 99UppDecRIL2-PO
❑ 99Vic-271
❑ 99YanFle-2

O'Neill, Paul Minors
❑ 80IndIndTI-12

O'Neill, Steve F.
❑ 09ColChiE-218
❑ 12ColRedB-218
❑ 12ColTinT-218
❑ 14B18B-8A
❑ 14B18B-8B
❑ 15CraJacE-48
❑ 15SpoNewM-134
❑ 16SpoNewM-135
❑ 17ColE13-129
❑ 17HolBreD-75
❑ 19W514-26
❑ 20NatCarE-72
❑ 20WalMaiW-39
❑ 21E121So1-75
❑ 21E121So8-68
❑ 21Exh-122
❑ 21Nei-22
❑ 22AmeCarE122-51
❑ 22E120-39
❑ 22W572-73
❑ 22W573-95
❑ 22W575-94
❑ 23W501-117
❑ 23WilChoV-117
❑ 27MidBre-37
❑ 34BatR31-160
❑ 34DiaStaR-87
❑ 36GouWidPPR-A119
❑ 36GouWidPPR-B17
❑ 36NatChiFPR-62
❑ 36R31Pre-L10
❑ 36WorWidGV-67
❑ 46SpoExcW-6-5
❑ 49IndTeal-29
❑ 50RedSoxTI-16
❑ 51Bow-201
❑ 54Top-127
❑ 77Ind192T-15
❑ 80TigGreT-9
❑ 81TigDetN-11
❑ 88ConSer3-21
❑ 91ConTSN-186
❑ 91TopArc1-307
❑ 93ConTSN-826
❑ 93ConTSN-876
❑ 94TopArc1-127
❑ 94TopArc1G-127
❑ 95ConTSN-1356

O'Neill, Ted
❑ 76WauMetT-21
❑ 77LynMetT-21

O'Neill, Tip (James E.)
❑ 76SSP188WS-7
❑ 87BucN28-102
❑ 87LonJacN-10
❑ 87OldJudN-382
❑ 87OldJudN-383
❑ 87ScrDC-7
❑ 88GandBCGCE-30
❑ 88KimN18-33
❑ 90HOFStiB-7

O'Neill, Tip (Norris)
❑ 87OldJudN-384

O'Neill, Tom
❑ 92CliGiaF-3605
❑ 92EveGiaC-19
❑ 92EveGiaF-1698
❑ 93CliGiaC-17
❑ 93CliGiaF-2496

O'Quinn, James
❑ 95BoiHawTI-25
❑ 96CedRapKTI-18
❑ 97CedRapK-22

O'Quinn, Steven
❑ 87ChaWheP-21

O'Rear, John
❑ 77RocRedWM-14
❑ 79AlbDukTc-12
❑ 80AlbDukTc-7

O'Regan, Dan
❑ 82OneYanT-5

O'Reilly, Jim
❑ 89ChaWheB-26
❑ 89ChaWheP-1746
❑ 90PeoChiTI-33
❑ 91PeoChiC-24
❑ 91PeoChiTI-3
❑ 92PeoChiC-30
❑ 92PeoChiTI-18
❑ 93PeoChiC-26
❑ 93PeoChiTI-18
❑ 96DayCubB-29
❑ 97RocCub-4
❑ 98WesTenDJM-29

O'Reilly, John
❑ 96OgdRapTI-46
❑ 97BelSnaB-21
❑ 98StoPorG-21

O'Reilly, Tom
❑ 90JamExpP-31
❑ 91JamExpC-29

O'Riley, Don
❑ 70Top-552
❑ 71OPC-679
❑ 71Top-679

O'Rourke, Frank (Francis J.)
❑ 25Exh-93
❑ 26Exh-94
❑ 29ExhFou-30
❑ 31Exh-29
❑ 33Gou-87
❑ 34GouCanV-43
❑ 79DiaGre-376
❑ 90DodTar-594
❑ 92ConTSN-604

O'Rourke, James
❑ 11PinT-5-1060
❑ 39PC7AlbHoF-37
❑ 50CalHOFW-57
❑ 53ArtHaloFP-65
❑ 73FleWilD-24
❑ 76ShaPiz-37
❑ 77BobParHoF-97
❑ 80PerHaloFP-37
❑ 80SSPHOF-37
❑ 84GalHaloFRL-37
❑ 86OldJudN-11
❑ 87BucN28-71A
❑ 87BucN28-71B
❑ 87OldJudN-385
❑ 88AugBecN-26A
❑ 88AugBecN-26B
❑ 88GandBCGCE-31
❑ 88WG1CarG-42
❑ 90BasWit-58
❑ 90KalBatN-43
❑ 94OriofB-29

O'Rourke, Patsy (Joseph Leo) Sr.
❑ 08RosComP-171
❑ 09ObaT21-315
❑ 11BigEatEU-15
❑ 11Zee-76
❑ 12HomRunKE-52
❑ 12ObaPreT-64
❑ 12Zee-89
❑ 13Zee-145

O'Rourke, Tom (Thomas J.)
❑ 87OldJudN-386

O's, Charlotte
❑ 80ChaO'sW-27

O'Shaughnessy, Elmer
❑ 20Zee-91

O'Shaughnessy, Jay
❑ 96YakBeaTI-31
❑ 98VerBeaDM-14

O'Toole, Bobby
❑ 96BluOriB-21
❑ 98FreKeyM-19

O'Toole, Dennis
❑ 73OPC-604
❑ 73Top-604

O'Toole, Jack
❑ 85AncGlaPTI-24
❑ 86AncGlaPTI-27
❑ 87AncGlaP-23
❑ 89AncGlaP-18

O'Toole, Jim
❑ 56RedBurB-16
❑ 58RedEnq-28
❑ 59RedBurBP-12
❑ 59RedBurBP-13
❑ 59RedShiBS-16
❑ 59Top-136
❑ 59TopVen-136
❑ 60Kah-31
❑ 60RedJayP-8
❑ 60Top-32
❑ 60Top-325
❑ 60TopVen-32
❑ 61Kah-30
❑ 61Pos-189A
❑ 61Pos-189B
❑ 61Top-328
❑ 61TopStaI-21
❑ 62Jel-126
❑ 62Kah-28
❑ 62Pos-126
❑ 62PosCan-126
❑ 62RedEnq-24

❑ 62RedJayP-9
❑ 62Top-56
❑ 62Top-58
❑ 62Top-60
❑ 62Top-450
❑ 62TopBuc-65
❑ 62TopStal-118
❑ 62TopVen-56
❑ 62TopVen-58
❑ 62TopVen-60
❑ 63Jel-136
❑ 63Kah-23
❑ 63Pos-136
❑ 63RedEnq-22
❑ 63RedFreBC-16
❑ 63RedJayP-8
❑ 63Top-70
❑ 64ChatheY-39
❑ 64RedJayP-8
❑ 64Top-185
❑ 64TopCoi-85
❑ 64TopSta-55
❑ 64TopStaU-53
❑ 64TopVen-185
❑ 64WheSta-32
❑ 65Baz-6
❑ 65ChaTheY-40
❑ 65Kah-33
❑ 65OPC-60
❑ 65RedEnq-20
❑ 65Top-60
❑ 65TopTral-22
❑ 66RedVolC-10
❑ 66Top-389
❑ 67CokCapWS-12
❑ 67DexPre-157
❑ 67Top-467
❑ 76RedParC-21
❑ 78TCM60I-92
❑ 80Red196T-28
❑ 89PacLegI-147

O'Toole, Martin J.
❑ 09MaxPubP-9
❑ 09SpoNewSM-70
❑ 11HelSta-164
❑ 11L1L-112
❑ 11PloCanE-53
❑ 11S81LarS-87
❑ 12T207-146
❑ 13NatGamW-33
❑ 13TomBarW-31
❑ 14B18B-81A
❑ 14B18B-81B
❑ 14CraJacE-54
❑ 14TexTomE-37
❑ 15CraJacE-54

O'Toole, Ryan
❑ 97UCLBruTI-15

Oakes, Rebel (Ennis T.)
❑ 09AmeCarE90-1-83
❑ 09ColChiE-215
❑ 09PC7HHB-32
❑ 09T206-269
❑ 10CouT21-203
❑ 10DomDisP-93
❑ 10NadCarE-41
❑ 10NadCarE-54
❑ 10PeoT21-43
❑ 10RedCroT-59
❑ 10RedCroT-144
❑ 10RedCroT-231
❑ 10SweCapPP-151A
❑ 10SweCapPP-151B
❑ 11HelSta-175
❑ 11PinT-5-362
❑ 11S74Sil-122
❑ 11SpoLifM-276
❑ 11T205-129
❑ 12ColRedB-215
❑ 12ColTinT-215
❑ 12HasTriFT-11
❑ 12T207-142
❑ 14CraJacE-139
❑ 14PieStaT-83
❑ 15AmeCarE106-32
❑ 15CraJacE-139
❑ 15VicT21-23

Oakes, Todd
❑ 85FreGiaSB-26
❑ 87CliGiaP-18
❑ 88SanJosGCLC-143
❑ 88SanJosGP-122
❑ 89CalLeaA-50
❑ 89SanJosGB-29
❑ 89SanJosGCLC-236
❑ 89SanJosGP-455
❑ 89SanJosGS-26
❑ 90ShrCapP-1460
❑ 90ShrCapS-26
❑ 91LinDriAA-325
❑ 91ShrCapP-1839
❑ 92PhoFirF-2838
❑ 93SanJosGC-28
❑ 93SanJosGF-29
❑ 94SanJosGC-28
❑ 94SanJosGF-2835
❑ 98ShrCapM-5
❑ 98ShrCapWS-5

Oakland, Mike
❑ 92BenRocCB-19
❑ 93CenValRC-20
❑ 93CenValRF-2900
❑ 94CenValRC-16
❑ 94CenValRF-3211

Oakley, Annie
❑ 88KimN18-31

Oakley, Matt
❑ 97LakTigB-24

Oana, Prince (Henry)
❑ 29Zee-138
❑ 32Zee-106
❑ 34DiaMatCSB-141
❑ 35AlDemDCR3-117

Oates, Johnny (Johnny Lane)
❑ 72OPC-474
❑ 72OriPos-22
❑ 72Top-474
❑ 73BalOriP-30
❑ 73OPC-9
❑ 73Top-9
❑ 74BraPhoC-6
❑ 74OPC-183
❑ 74Top-183
❑ 74TopSta-10
❑ 75AtlBraP-25
❑ 75OPC-319
❑ 75Top-319
❑ 75TopMin-319
❑ 76OPC-62
❑ 76PhiPhiP-21
❑ 76SSP-468
❑ 76Top-62
❑ 77DodPho-10
❑ 77Top-619
❑ 78SSP270-72
❑ 78Top-508
❑ 79Top-104
❑ 80DodPol-5
❑ 80Top-228
❑ 81Fle-99
❑ 81Top-303
❑ 82Fle-47
❑ 82NasSouTI-28
❑ 83ColCliT-1
❑ 84CubChiT-20
❑ 84CubSev-NNO
❑ 85CubSev-NNO
❑ 86CubGat-NNO
❑ 87CubCan-24
❑ 87CubDavB-NNO
❑ 88OriPos-23
❑ 88RocRedWC-24
❑ 88RocRedWGCP-30
❑ 88RocRedWP-211
❑ 88RocRedWTI-17
❑ 89BalOriP-22
❑ 89OriFreB-46
❑ 90DodTar-582
❑ 91OriCro-340
❑ 91TopTra-85T
❑ 91TopTraT-85T
❑ 92BalOriP-26
❑ 92OPC-579
❑ 92Top-579
❑ 92TopGol-579
❑ 92TopGolW-579
❑ 92TopMic-579
❑ 92YanWIZ8-136
❑ 93BalOriP-22
❑ 93Top-501
❑ 93TopGol-501
❑ 93TopInaM-501
❑ 93TopInaR-501
❑ 93TopMic-501
❑ 94BalOriP-23
❑ 95RanCra-23
❑ 96RanDr P-23
❑ 96RanMot-1
❑ 97RanDr P-21
❑ 97RanMinM-5
❑ 97RanMot-1

Obal, Dave
❑ 76BatRouCT-16

Obando, Omar
❑ 97GreBatB-20
❑ 98GreBatM-13

Obando, Sherman
❑ 89OneYanP-2102
❑ 90PriWilCTI-17
❑ 91Cla/Bes-116
❑ 91PriWilCC-28
❑ 91PriWilCP-1438
❑ 92AlbYanF-2232
❑ 92AlbYanSk-1
❑ 92SkyAA F-10
❑ 93BalOriP-23
❑ 93Bow-29
❑ 93FleFinE-161
❑ 93Lea-446
❑ 93LinVenB-157
❑ 93OPCPre-63
❑ 93PacJugC-11
❑ 93PacSpa-347
❑ 93SelRoo-70T
❑ 93StaClu-715
❑ 93StaCluFDI-715
❑ 93StaCluMOP-715
❑ 93TopTra-23T
❑ 93Ult-497
❑ 94OriPro-71
❑ 94OriUSPC-10S
❑ 94Pac-39
❑ 94RocRedWF-1010
❑ 94RocRedWTI-16
❑ 94Sco-597
❑ 94ScoGolR-597
❑ 94StaCluT-274
❑ 94StaCluTFDI-274
❑ 94TriAAF-AAA14
❑ 95FleUpd-6
❑ 96FleUpd-U149
❑ 96FleUpdTC-U149
❑ 96Ult-506
❑ 96UltGolM-506
❑ 97Fle-573
❑ 97FleTif-573
❑ 97Pac-348
❑ 97PacLigB-348
❑ 97PacSil-348
❑ 98ColSprSS-27
❑ 98PacInvGems-179

Obardovich, Jim
❑ 74TacTwiC-1

Oberdank, Jeff
❑ 88BenBucL-4
❑ 89QuaCitAB-5
❑ 89QuaCitAGS-20
❑ 90PalSprACLC-206
❑ 90PalSprAP-2585
❑ 91MelBusF-5
❑ 91QuaCitAC-20
❑ 91QuaCitAP-2639

Oberkfell, Ken (Kenneth R.)
❑ 76ArkTraT-7
❑ 78CarTeal-21
❑ 78SprRedWK-1
❑ 79Car5-19
❑ 80Top-701
❑ 81AllGamPI-123
❑ 81Car5x7-18
❑ 81Car5x7-19
❑ 81CokTeaS-126
❑ 81Don-583
❑ 81Fle-532
❑ 81OPC-32
❑ 81Top-32
❑ 81TopSti-222
❑ 82Don-404
❑ 82Fle-123
❑ 82FleSta-21
❑ 82OPC-121
❑ 82Top-474
❑ 82TopSti-89
❑ 82TopStiV-89
❑ 83AllGamPI-124
❑ 83Car-20
❑ 83CarPanP-5
❑ 83Don-246
❑ 83Fle-17
❑ 83FleSta-140
❑ 83FleSti-8
❑ 83OPC-206
❑ 83Top-206
❑ 83TopSti-287
❑ 84AllGamPI-34
❑ 84Don-504
❑ 84Fle-330
❑ 84FleUpd-84
❑ 84Nes792-102
❑ 84OPC-102
❑ 84raPho-22
❑ 84Top-102
❑ 84TopSti-148
❑ 84TopStiB-2
❑ 84TopTif-102
❑ 84TopTra-85T
❑ 84TopTraT-85T
❑ 85BraHos-17
❑ 85BraPol-24
❑ 85Don-432
❑ 85Fle-336
❑ 85Lea-141
❑ 85OPC-307
❑ 85Top-569
❑ 85TopMin-569
❑ 85TopSti-32
❑ 85TopTif-569
❑ 86BraPol-24
❑ 86Don-531
❑ 86Fle-523
❑ 86OPC-334
❑ 86Top-334
❑ 86TopSti-38
❑ 86TopTif-334
❑ 87BraSmo-16
❑ 87Don-437
❑ 87DonOpeD-46
❑ 87Fle-523
❑ 87FleGlo-523
❑ 87Lea-171
❑ 87OPC-132
❑ 87RedFolSB-99
❑ 87SpoTeaP-24
❑ 87Top-627
❑ 87TopSti-38
❑ 87TopTif-627
❑ 88Don-67
❑ 88DonBasB-226
❑ 88Fle-545
❑ 88FleGlo-545
❑ 88OPC-67
❑ 88PanSti-244
❑ 88Sco-245
❑ 88ScoGlo-245
❑ 88Spo-165
❑ 88StaLinBra-13
❑ 88Top-67
❑ 88TopSti-37
❑ 88TopTif-67
❑ 89Bow-418
❑ 89BowTif-418
❑ 89Don-506
❑ 89OPC-97
❑ 89PirVerFJ-14
❑ 89Sco-139
❑ 89Top-751
❑ 89TopTif-751
❑ 89UppDec-313
❑ 90AstMot-16
❑ 90Bow-74
❑ 90BowTif-74
❑ 90Don-494
❑ 90Fle-67
❑ 90FleCan-67
❑ 90Lea-294
❑ 90OPC-488
❑ 90Sco-422
❑ 90ScoRoo-58T
❑ 90Top-488
❑ 90TopTif-488
❑ 90UppDec-360
❑ 91AstMot-16
❑ 91Don-109
❑ 91Fle-511
❑ 91OPC-286
❑ 91Sco-214
❑ 91StaClu-414
❑ 91Top-286
❑ 91TopDesS-286
❑ 91TopMic-286
❑ 91TopTif-286
❑ 92EdmTraF-3547
❑ 97PieBolWB-1
❑ 98PieBolWM-1

Oberlander, Hartman
❑ 87OldJudN-372

Oberlin, Frank
❑ 09T206-451
❑ 10SenWasT-4

Oblesbee, Mike
❑ 86EugEmeC-29

Obregon, Francisco
❑ 60HenHouW-3
❑ 60SeaPop-8
❑ 60UniOil-4

Obregon, T.
❑ 76VenLeaS-182

Ocasio, Fredy
❑ 92OklStaC-22
❑ 95AshTouUTI-18

Ocasio, Javier
❑ 88BlaYNPRWL-75
❑ 88SouBenWSGS-3
❑ 89BlaYNPRWL-82
❑ 89SarWhiSS-16
❑ 90FloStaLAS-37
❑ 90SarWhiSS-17
❑ 91BirBarLD-69
❑ 91BirBarP-1463
❑ 91Cla/Bes-234
❑ 91LinDriAA-69

Oceak, Frank
❑ 57JetPos-15
❑ 60Top-467
❑ 63PirIDL-18

Ochiai, Hiro
❑ 87JapPlaB-13

Ochoa, Alex
❑ 91FroRowDP-29
❑ 91FroRowDPG-29
❑ 91FroRowDPS-29
❑ 92Bow-250
❑ 92KanCouCC-13
❑ 92KanCouCF-106
❑ 92KanCouCTI-23
❑ 92MidLeaATI-30
❑ 92StaCluD-132
❑ 92UppDecML-59
❑ 92UppDecML-254
❑ 93Bow-521
❑ 93BurBeeC-29
❑ 93CarLeaAGF-4
❑ 93ClaFS7-83
❑ 93ClaGolF-73
❑ 93ExcFS7-125
❑ 93FreKeyC-18
❑ 93FreKeyF-1040
❑ 94ActPac-11
❑ 94ActPac-59
❑ 94ActPac2G-5G
❑ 94ActPac2GD-5G
❑ 94AriFalLS-14
❑ 94Bow-103
❑ 94Bow-367
❑ 94BowBayF-2425
❑ 94BowBes-B52
❑ 94BowBesR-B52
❑ 94Cla-120
❑ 94ColC-646
❑ 94ColChoGS-646
❑ 94ColChoSS-646
❑ 94ExcFS7-13
❑ 94OriPro-72
❑ 94SigRoo-19
❑ 94SigRooHP-S9
❑ 94SigRooHPS-S9
❑ 94SigRooS-19
❑ 94SP-12
❑ 94SPDieC-12
❑ 94StaCluT-296
❑ 94StaCluTFDI-296
❑ 94UppDec-538
❑ 94UppDecAHNIL-10
❑ 94UppDecED-538
❑ 94UppDecML-20
❑ 94UppDecML-258
❑ 94UppDecMLPotYF-PY16
❑ 94UppDecMLT1PJF-TP7
❑ 94UppDecMLT1PMF-7
❑ 94WesPalBEC-30
❑ 95ActPacF-29
❑ 95Bow-248
❑ 95BowBes-B63
❑ 95BowBesR-B63
❑ 95BowGolF-248
❑ 95ColChoSE-8
❑ 95ColChoSEGS-8
❑ 95ColChoSESS-8
❑ 95Exc-8
❑ 95HarSenTI-NNO
❑ 95PinETA-2
❑ 95RocRedWTI-28
❑ 95Sum-132
❑ 95SumNthD-132
❑ 95UppDecML-3
❑ 95UppDecML-102
❑ 95UppDecMLFS-3
❑ 95UppDecMLFS-102
❑ 95UppDecMLMLA-8
❑ 95UppDecMLOP-OP2
❑ 96Bow-169
❑ 96BowBes-93
❑ 96BowBesAR-93
❑ 96BowBesR-93
❑ 96BowFoi-169
❑ 96BowMinLP-9
❑ 96Cir-160
❑ 96CirRav-160
❑ 96ColCho-618
❑ 96ColChoGS-618
❑ 96ColChoSS-618
❑ 96Don-451
❑ 96DonPreP-451
❑ 96FlePro-7
❑ 96HarSenB-3
❑ 96Lea-214
❑ 96LeaLimR-1
❑ 96LeaLimRG-1
❑ 96LeaPrePB-214
❑ 96LeaPrePG-214
❑ 96LeaPrePS-214
❑ 96LeaSig-102
❑ 96LeaSigEA-145
❑ 96LeaSigEACM-21
❑ 96LeaSigPPG-102
❑ 96LeaSigPPP-102
❑ 96MetKah-24
❑ 96MetUniMFG-10
❑ 96NorTidB-21
❑ 96Pac-148
❑ 96Pin-164
❑ 96PinArtP-91
❑ 96PinSta-91
❑ 96Sco-494
❑ 96ScoFutF-5
❑ 96SelCer-129
❑ 96SelCerAP-129
❑ 96SelCerCB-129
❑ 96SelCerCR-129
❑ 96SelCerMB-129
❑ 96SelCerMG-129
❑ 96SelCerMR-129
❑ 96Spo-130
❑ 96SpoArtP-130
❑ 96SpoRooJ-5
❑ 96StaClu-381
❑ 96StaCluMOP-381
❑ 96Top-339
❑ 96TopChr-133
❑ 96TopChrR-133
❑ 96TopGal-136
❑ 96TopGalPPI-136
❑ 96UppDec-232
❑ 96UppDecFSP-FS10
❑ 96Zen-123
❑ 96ZenArtP-123
❑ 97Cir-308
❑ 97CirEmeA-308
❑ 97CirEmeAR-AU3
❑ 97CirRav-308
❑ 97ColCho-398
❑ 97Don-345
❑ 97DonEli-56
❑ 97DonEliGS-56
❑ 97DonEliTotC-15
❑ 97DonEliTotCDC-15
❑ 97DonGolPP-345
❑ 97DonPre-136
❑ 97DonPreCttC-136
❑ 97DonSilPP-345
❑ 97E-X2-87
❑ 97E-X2Cred-87
❑ 97E-X2EmeAuto-86
❑ 97E-X2EmeAutoR-AU3
❑ 97E-X2EssCre-87
❑ 97Fin-200
❑ 97FinRef-200
❑ 97FlaShoLC-66
❑ 97FlaShoLeg0-66
❑ 97FlaShoLeg1-66
❑ 97FlaShoM-A66
❑ 97FlaShoM-B66
❑ 97FlaShoM-C66
❑ 97FlaShoR0-66
❑ 97FlaShoR1-66
❑ 97FlaShoR2-66
❑ 97Fle-402
❑ 97FleRooS-9
❑ 97FleTif-402
❑ 97Lea-9
❑ 97LeaFraM-9
❑ 97LeaFraMDC-9

❑ 97MetUni-197
❑ 97MetUniEA-AU3
❑ 97MetUniEAR-AU3
❑ 97NewPin-148
❑ 97NewPinAP-148
❑ 97NewPinMC-148
❑ 97NewPinPP-148
❑ 97Pac-371
❑ 97PacLigB-371
❑ 97PacPri-126
❑ 97PacPriLB-126
❑ 97PacPriP-126
❑ 97PacSil-371
❑ 97Pin-184
❑ 97PinArtP-PP184
❑ 97PinCer-72
❑ 97PinCerMBla-72
❑ 97PinCerMBlu-72
❑ 97PinCerMG-72
❑ 97PinCerMR-72
❑ 97PinCerR-72
❑ 97PinIns-94
❑ 97PinInsCE-94
❑ 97PinInsDE-94
❑ 97PinMusC-184
❑ 97PinPrePla-184
❑ 97PinTotCPB-72
❑ 97PinTotCPG-72
❑ 97PinTotCPR-72
❑ 97PinX-P-106
❑ 97PinX-PMoS-106
❑ 97Sco-120
❑ 97ScoArtPWB-120
❑ 97ScoPreS-120
❑ 97ScoShoS-120
❑ 97ScoShoSAP-120
❑ 97Sel-22
❑ 97SelArtP-22
❑ 97SelCom-22
❑ 97SelRegG-22
❑ 97SelRooR-9
❑ 97SelToootT-9
❑ 97SelToootTMB-9
❑ 97StaClu-198
❑ 97StaCluM-M23
❑ 97StaCluMat-198
❑ 97StaCluMOP-198
❑ 97StaCluMOP-M23
❑ 97Stu-107
❑ 97StuPrePG-107
❑ 97StuPrePS-107
❑ 97Top-103
❑ 97Top-298
❑ 97TopAwel-AI12
❑ 97TopGal-171
❑ 97TopGalPPI-171
❑ 97Ult-244
❑ 97UltAutE-1
❑ 97UltDouT-17
❑ 97UltGolME-244
❑ 97UltPlaME-244
❑ 97UltRooR-7
❑ 97UppDec-118
❑ 97UppDecRSF-RS14
❑ 97UppDecTTS-TS4
❑ 98Pac-372
❑ 98PacOnl-431
❑ 98PacOnlR-431
❑ 98PacOnlWC-431
❑ 98PacPlaB-372
❑ 98PacRedT-372
❑ 98PacSil-372
❑ 98SkyDugAAR-10
❑ 98Ult-320
❑ 98UltGolM-320
❑ 98UltMas-320
❑ 98UltPlaM-320
❑ 98UppDec-693
❑ 99Pac-252
❑ 99PacCroC-163
❑ 99PacCroCPB-163
❑ 99PacPlaB-252
❑ 99PacRed-252
❑ 99UppDecM-111
❑ 99UppDecMGS-111
❑ 99UppDecMHFS-111
❑ 99UppDecMSS-111
Ochoa, Levy
❑ 76VenLeaS-206
❑ 80VenLeaS-105
Ochoa, Rafael
❑ 90UtiBluSP-5
❑ 91UtiBluSC-29
❑ 91UtiBluSP-3254
❑ 92SouBenWSF-190
Ochs, Kevin
❑ 84ButCopKT-19
Ochs, Tony
❑ 89JohCitCS-16
❑ 90CMC-841
❑ 90SavCarP-2070
❑ 91St.PetCC-22
❑ 91St.PetCP-2285
Ochsenfeld, Chris
❑ 95GreFalDTI-15
❑ 96SavSanB-14
❑ 97YakBeaG-21
❑ 98WinWar-19
Oda, Yoshito
❑ 79TCMJapPB-66
Oddo, Ron
❑ 80ElmPioRST-23
Odekirk, Rick
❑ 88OklCit8C-10
❑ 88OklCit8P-29
❑ 91RenSilSCLC-8
Odell, Ray
❑ 30Zee-109
Odgers, Steve
❑ 95WhiSoxK-24
Odierno, Scott
❑ 88CapCodPPaLP-60
Odle, Page
❑ 86PriWilPP-18
Odman, Matt
❑ 86RedWinA-15
Odom, Blue Moon (John)
❑ 65Top-526
❑ 67CokCapAt-5
❑ 67Top-282
❑ 68Top-501
❑ 69A'sJacitB-11
❑ 69MilBra-204
❑ 69MLBOffS-90
❑ 69OPC-195
❑ 69Top-195
❑ 69TopFou-12
❑ 69TopSta-220
❑ 69TopTeaP-21
❑ 69TraSta-8
❑ 70DayDaiNM-113
❑ 70Kel-38
❑ 70MLBOffS-263
❑ 70OPC-55
❑ 70Top-55
❑ 70TraSta-15A
❑ 71MLBOffS-523
❑ 71OPC-523
❑ 71Top-523
❑ 72'sA'sPos-13
❑ 72MilBra-256
❑ 72Top-557
❑ 72Top-558
❑ 73A'sPos-27
❑ 73OPC-207
❑ 73OPC-315
❑ 73Top-207
❑ 73Top-315
❑ 74OPC-461
❑ 74Top-461
❑ 75AtlBraP-26
❑ 75OPC-69
❑ 75Top-69
❑ 75TopMin-69
❑ 76OPC-651
❑ 76Top-651
❑ 77SanJosMC-3
❑ 78TCM60I-68
❑ 87A'sMot-3
Odom, Clark
❑ 98TenKry-15
Odom, Joe
❑ 84MadMusP-6
❑ 85ModA'sC-25
Odom, Tim
❑ 87Ft.MyeRP-10
❑ 88AppFoxP-150
❑ 89AugPirP-493
Odor, Rouglas
❑ 88BurIndP-1780
❑ 89KinIndS-15
❑ 89WatIndS-17
❑ 90CarLeaA-41
❑ 90KinIndTI-3
❑ 91CanIndLD-91
❑ 91CanIndP-988
❑ 91LinDriAA-91
❑ 92KinIndC-9
❑ 92KinIndF-2485
❑ 93CanIndF-2847
❑ 93LinVenB-181
❑ 94CanIndF-3125
❑ 94VenLinU-259
❑ 95LinVen-203
❑ 96-97LinVen-237
Odwell, Fred (Frederick W.)
❑ 09ColChiE-216
❑ 11MecDFT-37
❑ 11PinT-5-1053
❑ 12ColRedB-216
❑ 12ColTinT-216
Oedewaldt, Larry
❑ 89StoPorB-15
❑ 89StoPorCLC-167
❑ 89StoPorP-375
❑ 89StoPorS-2
Oehrlein, David
❑ 92HamRedF-1590
❑ 93ExcFS7-104
❑ 93SprCarC-20
❑ 93SprCarF-1849
❑ 94SavCarC-23
❑ 94SavCarF-504
❑ 94SouAtlLAF-SAL53
❑ 95ArkTraTI-22
Oelkers, Bryan
❑ 83TolMudHT-28
❑ 83TwiTeal-12
❑ 84Don-486
❑ 86IndTeal-33
❑ 86MaiGuiP-14
❑ 87BufBisP-18
❑ 87Don-596
❑ 87Fle-257
❑ 87FleGlo-257
❑ 87Top-77
❑ 87TopTif-77
❑ 89LouRedBP-1244
❑ 89LouRedBTI-29
Oelschlager, Ron
❑ 92AriWilP-11
Oertel, Chuck
❑ 91OriCro-341
Oertli, Chuck
❑ 86GenCubP-20
Oeschger, Joe
❑ 20NatCarE-69
❑ 20WalMaiW-38
❑ 21E121So1-73
❑ 21Exh-119
❑ 21Nei-98
❑ 22E120-131
❑ 22W572-71
❑ 22W575-92
❑ 22WilPatV-6
❑ 23W501-93
❑ 23W503-40
❑ 23WilChoV-112
❑ 26Zee-55
❑ 61Top-403
❑ 72FleFamF-19
❑ 72LauGreF-37
❑ 90DodTar-586
Oester, Ron (Ronald John)
❑ 77IndIndTI-6
❑ 78IndIndTI-6
❑ 79IndIndTI-3
❑ 79Top-717
❑ 80RedEnq-16
❑ 81AllGamPI-105
❑ 81CokTeaS-45
❑ 81Don-423
❑ 81Fle-218
❑ 81OPC-21
❑ 81Top-21
❑ 81TopSupHT-40
❑ 82Don-500
❑ 82Fle-79
❑ 82FleSta-20
❑ 82RedCok-16
❑ 82Top-427
❑ 82TopSti-34
❑ 83AllGamPI-105
❑ 83Don-526
❑ 83Fle-598
❑ 83OPC-269
❑ 83RedYea-16
❑ 83Top-269
❑ 83TopSti-230
❑ 84AllGamPI-13
❑ 84Don-62
❑ 84DonActAS-46
❑ 84Fle-475
❑ 84Nes792-526
❑ 84Nes792-756
❑ 84OPC-99
❑ 84RedBor-16
❑ 84RedEnq-3
❑ 84Top-526
❑ 84Top-756
❑ 84TopSti-53
❑ 84TopTif-526
❑ 84TopTif-756
❑ 85Don-81
❑ 85Fle-542
❑ 85IndIndTI-30
❑ 85OPC-314
❑ 85RedYea-10
❑ 85Top-314
❑ 85TopSti-54
❑ 85TopTif-314
❑ 86BasStaB-79
❑ 86Don-81
❑ 86Fle-183
❑ 86Lea-78
❑ 86OPC-264
❑ 86RedTexG-16
❑ 86SevCoi-S14
❑ 86Top-627
❑ 86TopSti-138
❑ 86TopTif-627
❑ 87Don-206
❑ 87DonOpeD-195
❑ 87Fle-207
❑ 87FleGlo-207
❑ 87OPC-172
❑ 87RedKah-16
❑ 87Top-172
❑ 87TopSti-141
❑ 87TopTif-172
❑ 88Don-246
❑ 88Fle-242
❑ 88FleGlo-242
❑ 88OPC-17
❑ 88Sco-183
❑ 88ScoGlo-183
❑ 88Top-17
❑ 88TopSti-144
❑ 88TopTif-17
❑ 89Bow-310
❑ 89BowTif-310
❑ 89Don-553
❑ 89RedKah-16
❑ 89Sco-615
❑ 89Top-772
❑ 89TopBig-229
❑ 89TopTif-772
❑ 89UppDec-287
❑ 90Don-317
❑ 90OPC-492
❑ 90PubIntS-35
❑ 90RedKah-18
❑ 90Sco-59
❑ 90Top-492
❑ 90TopBig-55
❑ 90TopTif-492
❑ 90UppDec-118
❑ 91Don-628
❑ 91Fle-74
❑ 91Sco-651
❑ 91UppDec-611
❑ 92ChaLooF-3833
Oestreich, Mark
❑ 89BurIndS-28
Offerman, Jose
❑ 88GreFalDTI-22
❑ 89BakDodCLC-194
❑ 89BasAmeAPB-AA25
❑ 89CalLeaA-1
❑ 89SanAntMB-27
❑ 90AlbDukCm-19
❑ 90AlbDukP-354
❑ 90AlbDukTr-24
❑ 90Bow-92
❑ 90BowTif-92
❑ 90ClaBlu-45
❑ 90CMC-421
❑ 90FleUpd-24
❑ 90Lea-464
❑ 90ProAAAF-75
❑ 90TopMag-39
❑ 90TriAllGP-AAA31
❑ 90UppDec-46
❑ 91AlbDukLD-17
❑ 91AlbDukP-1149
❑ 91Baz-6
❑ 91Bow-182
❑ 91Cla2-T37
❑ 91ClaGam-145
❑ 91DodPho-21
❑ 91DodPol-30
❑ 91DodSt.V-10
❑ 91Don-33
❑ 91Fle-216
❑ 91LinDriAAA-17
❑ 91MajLeaCP-51
❑ 91OPC-587
❑ 91OPCPre-90
❑ 91RedFolS-110
❑ 91Sco-343
❑ 91Sco100RS-99
❑ 91ScoHotR-10
❑ 91ScoRoo-26
❑ 91SevCoi-F12
❑ 91SevCoi-SC11
❑ 91StaClu-340
❑ 91StaCluCM-22
❑ 91Stu-186
❑ 91Top-587
❑ 91TopDeb90-117
❑ 91TopDesS-587
❑ 91TopMic-587
❑ 91TopRoo-23
❑ 91TopTif-587
❑ 91ToyRoo-23
❑ 91Ult-167
❑ 91UppDec-356
❑ 92Bow-304
❑ 92ClaGam-36
❑ 92DodMot-8
❑ 92DodPol-30
❑ 92DodSmo-10292
❑ 92Don-721
❑ 92Fle-467
❑ 92Lea-322
❑ 92LeaBlaG-322
❑ 92OPC-493
❑ 92OPCPre-123
❑ 92Pin-153
❑ 92PinTea2-25
❑ 92ProFS7-237
❑ 92Sco-699
❑ 92Sco100RS-31
❑ 92StaClu-378
❑ 92Stu-47
❑ 92Top-493
❑ 92TopGol-493
❑ 92TopGolW-493
❑ 92TopMic-493
❑ 92TriPla-153
❑ 92Ult-215
❑ 92UppDec-532
❑ 93Bow-294
❑ 93DodMot-5
❑ 93DodPol-18
❑ 93DodStaC-17
❑ 93Don-376
❑ 93Fle-66
❑ 93FunPac-91
❑ 93Lea-17
❑ 93LimRocDP-P1
❑ 93LimRocDWB-77
❑ 93OPC-299
❑ 93PacSpa-153
❑ 93PanSti-216
❑ 93Pin-345
❑ 93Sco-129
❑ 93Sel-197
❑ 93SP-97
❑ 93StaClu-129
❑ 93StaCluFDI-129
❑ 93StaCluMOP-129
❑ 93Stu-182
❑ 93Top-776
❑ 93TopGol-776
❑ 93TopInaM-776
❑ 93TopInaR-776
❑ 93TopMic-776
❑ 93Ult-59
❑ 93UppDec-225
❑ 93UppDec-464
❑ 93UppDecGold-225
❑ 93UppDecGold-464
❑ 94Bow-182
❑ 94ColC-219
❑ 94ColChoGS-219
❑ 94ColChoSS-219
❑ 94DodMot-5
❑ 94DodPol-20
❑ 94Don-623
❑ 94Fin-23
❑ 94FinPre-23P
❑ 94FinRef-23
❑ 94Fla-180
❑ 94Fle-519
❑ 94FleExtB-292
❑ 94Lea-123
❑ 94OPC-104
❑ 94Pac-317
❑ 94PacAll-5
❑ 94PanSti-202
❑ 94Pin-190
❑ 94PinArtP-190
❑ 94PinMusC-190
❑ 94Sco-340
❑ 94ScoGolR-340
❑ 94Sel-246
❑ 94StaClu-282
❑ 94StaCluFDI-282
❑ 94StaCluGR-282
❑ 94StaCluMOP-282
❑ 94Stu-71
❑ 94Top-241
❑ 94TopGol-241
❑ 94TopSpa-241
❑ 94TriPla-87
❑ 94Ult-217
❑ 94UppDec-236
❑ 94UppDecED-236
❑ 95ColCho-221
❑ 95ColChoGS-221
❑ 95ColChoSS-221
❑ 95DodMot-8
❑ 95DodPol-17
❑ 95Don-77
❑ 95DonPreP-77
❑ 95DonTopotO-270
❑ 95Fin-281
❑ 95FinRef-281
❑ 95Fla-369
❑ 95FleUpd-176
❑ 95Lea-260
❑ 95LeaLim-108
❑ 95LinVen-316
❑ 95Pac-223
❑ 95Pin-312
❑ 95PinArtP-312
❑ 95PinMusC-312
❑ 95StaClu-595
❑ 95StaCluMOP-595
❑ 95StaCluSTWS-595
❑ 95Top-152
❑ 95Zen-58
❑ 96ColCho-775
❑ 96Don-546
❑ 96DonPreP-546
❑ 96FleUpd-U42
❑ 96FleUpdTC-U42
❑ 96Pac-109
❑ 96RoyPol-21
❑ 96Sco-172
❑ 96Top-89
❑ 96Ult-359
❑ 96UltGolM-359
❑ 97Cir-136
❑ 97CirRav-136
❑ 97ColCho-359
❑ 97Don-189
❑ 97DonGolPP-189
❑ 97DonSilPP-189
❑ 97Fle-118
❑ 97FleTif-118
❑ 97Lea-142
❑ 97LeaFraM-142
❑ 97LeaFraMDC-142
❑ 97Pac-107
❑ 97PacLigB-107
❑ 97PacPri-38
❑ 97PacPriLB-38
❑ 97PacPriP-38
❑ 97PacSil-107
❑ 97Pin-37
❑ 97PinArtP-PP37
❑ 97PinMusC-37
❑ 97PinPrePla-37
❑ 97RoyPol-16
❑ 97Sco-302
❑ 97ScoArtPWB-302
❑ 97ScoPreS-302
❑ 97ScoShoS-302
❑ 97ScoShoSAP-302
❑ 97StaClu-309
❑ 97StaCluMOP-309
❑ 97Top-164
❑ 97Ult-69
❑ 97UltGolME-69
❑ 97UltPlaME-69
❑ 97UppDec-391
❑ 98ColCho-140
❑ 98Fin-141
❑ 98FinNo--141
❑ 98FinNo-R-141
❑ 98FinRef-141

❑ 98Fle-557
❑ 98Pac-109
❑ 98PacOnl-346
❑ 98PacOnlR-346
❑ 98PacOnlWC-346
❑ 98PacPlaB-109
❑ 98PacRedT-109
❑ 98PacSil-109
❑ 98Pin-105
❑ 98PinPreP-105
❑ 98StaCluFDI-243
❑ 98StaCluFDI-282
❑ 98StaCluI-243
❑ 98StaCluI-282
❑ 98StaCluOneK-243
❑ 98StaCluOneK-282
❑ 98StaCluPP-243
❑ 98StaCluPP-282
❑ 98Top-222
❑ 98TopChr-222
❑ 98TopChrR-222
❑ 98TopDevR-222
❑ 98TopDia-222
❑ 98TopMiniC-222
❑ 98Ult-363
❑ 98UltGolM-363
❑ 98UltMas-363
❑ 98UltPlaM-363
❑ 98UppDec-389
❑ 99199Fin-207
❑ 99Bow-231
❑ 99BowGol-231
❑ 99BowInt-231
❑ 99CroRoyB-25
❑ 99CroRoyL-25
❑ 99CroRoyOD-25
❑ 99FinGolRef-207
❑ 99FinRef-207
❑ 99Fle-302
❑ 99FleBri-59
❑ 99FleBri2G-59
❑ 99FleBriBlu-59
❑ 99FleBriGol-59
❑ 99FleMys-65
❑ 99FleMysG-65
❑ 99FleMysM-65
❑ 99FleSta9-302
❑ 99FleWarT-302
❑ 99MetUni-48
❑ 99MetUniGM-48
❑ 99MetUniPMG-48
❑ 99Pac-209
❑ 99PacCroC-135
❑ 99PacCroCPB-135
❑ 99PacInv-26
❑ 99PacInvOD-26
❑ 99PacInvPB-26
❑ 99PacOme-42
❑ 99PacOmeC-42
❑ 99PacOmeG-42
❑ 99PacOmePB-42
❑ 99PacPar-43
❑ 99PacParC-43
❑ 99PacParG-43
❑ 99PacParHoloGold-43
❑ 99PacParHS-43
❑ 99PacParOD-43
❑ 99PacParPB-43
❑ 99PacParRed-43
❑ 99PacPlaB-209
❑ 99PacPriS-124
❑ 99PacPriS206-124
❑ 99PacPriS206R-124
❑ 99PacRed-209
❑ 99Rev-27
❑ 99RevPremDate-27
❑ 99RevRet-27
❑ 99RevShaSS-27
❑ 99SkyPre-138
❑ 99SkyPreR-138
❑ 99SkyThu-126
❑ 99SkyThuRant-126
❑ 99SkyThuRave-126
❑ 99StaClu-321
❑ 99StaCluFDI-321
❑ 99StaCluOoaK-321
❑ 99StaCluPP-321
❑ 99ThuSkySupR-126
❑ 99Top-403
❑ 99TopChr-403
❑ 99TopChrR-403
❑ 99TopMVPP-403
❑ 99TopSta-134
❑ 99TopStaFoil-134
❑ 99Ult-66
❑ 99UltGolM-66
❑ 99UltMas-66
❑ 99UltPlaM-66
❑ 99UppDec-327
❑ 99UppDecE-15
❑ 99UppDecEFXG-15
❑ 99UppDecEL1-327
❑ 99UppDecEL2-327
❑ 99Vic-64

Office, Rowland J.
❑ 75AtlBraP-27
❑ 75OPC-262
❑ 75Top-262
❑ 75TopMin-262
❑ 76AtlBraP-23
❑ 76OPC-256
❑ 76SSP-20
❑ 76Top-256
❑ 77Top-524
❑ 78BraCok-12
❑ 78Top-632
❑ 79OPC-62
❑ 79Top-132
❑ 80ExpPos-20
❑ 80Top-39
❑ 81Don-213
❑ 81Fle-147
❑ 81OPC-319
❑ 81Top-319
❑ 82ExpPos-28
❑ 82Fle-198
❑ 82OklCit8T-2
❑ 82OPC-165
❑ 82Top-479
❑ 83ColCliT-27
❑ 92YanWIZ8-138

Officer, Jim
❑ 76QuaCitAT-25

Ofstun, John
❑ 90NebCor-20

Ogawa, Kuni
❑ 79VanCanT-15
❑ 80HolMilT-8

Ogawa, Toru
❑ 79TCMJapPB-46

Ogden, Charles
❑ 88CarLeaAS-33
❑ 88KinIndS-18
❑ 89CanIndB-27

Ogden, Curly (Warren)
❑ 33Gou-174
❑ 75SenTCM1-24

Ogden, Jamie
❑ 92ClaFS7-149
❑ 92KenTwiC-1
❑ 92KenTwiF-619
❑ 92UtiBluSC-8
❑ 93ForMyeMC-19
❑ 93ForMyeMF-2671
❑ 94ForMyeMC-18
❑ 94ForMyeMF-1182
❑ 95HarCitRCTI-18
❑ 97SalLakB-18
❑ 98SalLakBO-19

Ogden, Jason
❑ 93SarWhiSC-20
❑ 94SouBenSHC-16
❑ 94SouBenSHF-591

Ogden, John M.
❑ 28Exh-58
❑ 33Gou-176

Ogden, Todd
❑ 89CanIndP-1322
❑ 89CanIndS-18

Ogea, Chad
❑ 90LSUTigA-6
❑ 90LSUTigP-8
❑ 91LSUTigP-15
❑ 92ClaFS7-154
❑ 92KinIndC-25
❑ 92KinIndF-2473
❑ 92StaCluD-133
❑ 92UppDecML-296
❑ 92UppDecMLPotY-PY12
❑ 93Bow-289
❑ 93ChaKniF-540
❑ 93ClaFS7-232
❑ 93ClaGolF-21
❑ 93ExcFS7-162
❑ 93ExcLeaLF-16
❑ 94Bow-607
❑ 94BowBes-B72
❑ 94BowBesR-B72
❑ 94ChaKniF-894
❑ 94Cla-124
❑ 94ExcFS7-47
❑ 94Fla-287
❑ 94FleUpd-35
❑ 94Top-316
❑ 94TopGol-316
❑ 94TopSpa-316
❑ 94Ult-350
❑ 94UppDecML-202
❑ 95BowBes-B6
❑ 95BowBesR-B6
❑ 95ColCho-7
❑ 95ColChoGS-7
❑ 95ColChoSS-7
❑ 95Fin-293
❑ 95FinRef-293
❑ 95Pin-412
❑ 95PinArtP-412
❑ 95PinMusC-412
❑ 95Sel-186
❑ 95SelArtP-186
❑ 95StaClu-479
❑ 95StaCluMOP-479
❑ 95StaCluSTWS-479
❑ 95Top-47
❑ 95UppDec-343
❑ 95UppDecED-343
❑ 95UppDecEDG-343
❑ 96ColCho-524
❑ 96ColChoGS-524
❑ 96ColChoSS-524
❑ 96Don-545
❑ 96DonPreP-545
❑ 96Fle-94
❑ 96FleTif-94
❑ 96LeaSigA-171
❑ 96LeaSigAG-171
❑ 96LeaSigAS-171
❑ 96Sco-407
❑ 96StaClu-27
❑ 96StaCluMOP-27
❑ 96Top-358
❑ 96Ult-52
❑ 96UltGolM-52
❑ 96UppDec-318
❑ 97Cir-39
❑ 97CirRav-39
❑ 97ColCho-311
❑ 97ColChoT-CI12
❑ 97Fle-85
❑ 97FleTif-85
❑ 97IndScoU-4
❑ 97IndScoUTC-4
❑ 97PacPriGotD-GD37
❑ 97Sco-403
❑ 97ScoArtPWB-403
❑ 97ScoResC-403
❑ 97ScoShoS-403
❑ 97ScoShoSAP-403
❑ 97Top-367
❑ 97Ult-477
❑ 97UltGolME-477
❑ 97UltPlaME-477
❑ 97UppDec-346
❑ 98ColCho-358
❑ 98Fin-7
❑ 98FinNo--7
❑ 98FinNo-R-7
❑ 98FinRef-7
❑ 98Fle-472
❑ 98Pac-77
❑ 98PacOnl-227
❑ 98PacOnlR-227
❑ 98PacOnlWC-227
❑ 98PacPlaB-77
❑ 98PacRedT-77
❑ 98PacSil-77
❑ 98PinSna-CI16
❑ 98Top-282
❑ 98TopChr-282
❑ 98TopChrR-282
❑ 98TopDevR-282
❑ 98TopDia-282
❑ 98TopMiniC-282
❑ 98UppDec-343
❑ 98UppDec-431
❑ 99Pac-133
❑ 99PacPlaB-133
❑ 99PacRed-133
❑ 99UppDec-456
❑ 99UppDecEL1-456
❑ 99UppDecEL2-456
❑ 99Vic-301

Ogier, Moe
❑ 68Top-589

Ogiwara, Mitsuru
❑ 88MiaMarS-17

Oglesbee, Mike
❑ 85AncGlaPTI-22
❑ 87AshTouP-22

Oglesby, Jim
❑ 33Zee-9

Oglesby, Luke
❑ 93EugEmeC-20
❑ 93EugEmeF-3870
❑ 94RocRoyC-17
❑ 94RocRoyF-577
❑ 95WilBluRTI-1

Oglesby, Ron
❑ 88RivRedWCLC-232
❑ 88RivRedWP-1407
❑ 89ChaRaiP-978
❑ 90WatDiaB-20
❑ 90WatDiaP-2394

Ogliaruso, Mike
❑ 89MyrBeaBJP-1464
❑ 90MyrBeaBJP-2775
❑ 90ProAaA-90
❑ 90SouAtlLAS-38
❑ 91Cla/Bes-133
❑ 91DunBluJC-9
❑ 91DunBluJP-205
❑ 92DunBluJF-1998
❑ 92KnoBluJF-2989
❑ 92KnoBluJS-388

Oglivie, Ben (Benjamin A.)
❑ 72RedSoxTI-18
❑ 72Top-761
❑ 73LinPor-76
❑ 73OPC-388
❑ 73Top-388
❑ 74Tig-9
❑ 75DetTigP-23
❑ 75OPC-344
❑ 75Top-344
❑ 75TopMin-344
❑ 76DetTigP-22
❑ 76OPC-659
❑ 76SSP-359
❑ 76Top-659
❑ 77BurCheD-91
❑ 77OPC-236
❑ 77Top-122
❑ 78Top-286
❑ 79Top-519
❑ 80BreTeal-19
❑ 80Top-53
❑ 81AllGamPI-62
❑ 81Don-446
❑ 81Fle-508
❑ 81FleStiC-14
❑ 81Kel-20
❑ 81OPC-340
❑ 81PerCreC-30
❑ 81Squ-3
❑ 81Top-2
❑ 81Top-415
❑ 81TopScr-7
❑ 81TopSti-13
❑ 81TopSti-14
❑ 81TopSti-92
❑ 82BrePol-24
❑ 82Don-484
❑ 82Fle-151
❑ 82FleSta-138
❑ 82OPC-280
❑ 82Top-280
❑ 82TopSti-197
❑ 83AllGamPI-65
❑ 83BreGar-14
❑ 83BrePlaM-3
❑ 83BrePol-24
❑ 83Don-384
❑ 83Dra-20
❑ 83Fle-43
❑ 83Fle-640
❑ 83FleSta-141
❑ 83FleSti-15
❑ 83FleSti-146
❑ 83OPC-91
❑ 83Top-750
❑ 83TopSti-82
❑ 84AllGamPI-156
❑ 84BreGar-15
❑ 84BrePol-24
❑ 84Don-229
❑ 84DonCha-6
❑ 84Fle-210
❑ 84FunFooP-67
❑ 84Nes792-190
❑ 84OPC-190
❑ 84Top-190
❑ 84TopRubD-31
❑ 84TopSti-296
❑ 84TopTif-190
❑ 85AllGamPI-66
❑ 85BreGar-15
❑ 85BrePol-24
❑ 85Don-333
❑ 85Fle-590
❑ 85Lea-123
❑ 85OPC-332
❑ 85Top-681
❑ 85TopRubD-29
❑ 85TopSti-292
❑ 85TopTif-681
❑ 86BrePol-24
❑ 86Don-333
❑ 86Fle-497
❑ 86Lea-199
❑ 86OPC-372
❑ 86Top-372
❑ 86TopSti-200
❑ 86TopTat-24
❑ 86TopTif-372
❑ 86Woo-25
❑ 87Don-419
❑ 87Fle-353
❑ 87FleGlo-353
❑ 87FleRecS-26
❑ 87FleStiC-85
❑ 87JapPlaB-19
❑ 87RedFolSB-100
❑ 87Top-586
❑ 87TopTif-586
❑ 91UppDecS-10
❑ 92BreCarT-18
❑ 92UppDecS-9
❑ 93El PasDF-2968
❑ 94BreMilB-158
❑ 94BreMilB-343
❑ 94TedWil-44
❑ 97CalCanB-2

Ogrodowski, Bruce
❑ 40SolHug-15
❑ 48SomandK-21

Oh, Sadaharu
❑ 79TCMJapPB-1
❑ 87JapPlaB-2
❑ 93UppDecS-22

Ohba, Toyokazu
❑ 96HonShaHWB-3

Ohishi, Tomoyoshi
❑ 94CenValRC-28
❑ 94CenValRF-3221

Ohlms, Mark
❑ 89PriWilCS-15
❑ 89Sta-92
❑ 90Ft.LauYS-16
❑ 91CarLeaAP-CAR35
❑ 91PriWilCC-8
❑ 91PriWilCP-1424
❑ 92KnoBluJF-2990
❑ 92KnoBluJS-390
❑ 92SkyAA F-165
❑ 93LinVenB-57
❑ 93SyrChiF-998
❑ 94KnoSmoF-1302

Ohman, Ed
❑ 89ChaRanS-18
❑ 89Sta-9

Ohman, Shawn
❑ 93LetMouF-4148
❑ 93LetMouSP-15

Ohman, Will
❑ 99TeaBesR-62
❑ 99TeaBesRG-62
❑ 99TeaBesRS-62

Ohme, Kevin
❑ 95HarCitRCTI-19
❑ 96HarCitRCB-23
❑ 97SalLakB-19
❑ 98SalLakBO-20

Ohnoutka, Brian
❑ 85EveGialC-13
❑ 86ShrCapP-20
❑ 87ShrCapP-12
❑ 88PhoFirC-7
❑ 88PhoFirP-79
❑ 90CMC-524
❑ 90LasVegSC-21
❑ 90LasVegSP-119
❑ 90ProAAAF-7

Ohsubo, Kukio
❑ 91SalSpuC-16

Ohta, Katsumasa
❑ 91SalSpuC-14
❑ 91SalSpuP-2242

Ohtsubo, Yukio
❑ 91SalSpuP-2243

Ohtsuka, Ken (Kenichi)
❑ 90SalSpuP-2716

Ohtsuka, Yoshiki
❑ 90SalSpuP-2722

Oiler, David
❑ 93EliTwiC-18
❑ 93EliTwiF-3416

Oiseth, John
❑ 97IdaFalBTI-12
❑ 98CliLumG-16

Ojala, Kirt
❑ 90OneYanP-3380
❑ 90ProAaA-178
❑ 91PriWilCC-9
❑ 91PriWilCP-1425
❑ 92AlbYanF-2226
❑ 93ColCliF-1111
❑ 93ColCliP-6
❑ 94ColCliF-2952
❑ 94ColCliP-21
❑ 94TriAAF-AAA4
❑ 95ColCliMCTI-10
❑ 95ColCliP-19
❑ 95ColCliTI-19
❑ 96IndIndB-17
❑ 97ChaKni-22

Ojea, Alex
❑ 87SprCarB-3
❑ 88SprCarB-17

Ojeda, Augie
❑ 97FreKey-19

Ojeda, Bob
❑ 81PawRedST-5
❑ 82Don-540
❑ 82Fle-301
❑ 82RedSoxC-13
❑ 82Top-274
❑ 83Don-260
❑ 83Fle-190
❑ 83Top-654
❑ 84Don-538
❑ 84Fle-406
❑ 84Nes792-162
❑ 84Nes792-786
❑ 84OPC-162
❑ 84Top-162
❑ 84Top-786
❑ 84TopTif-162
❑ 84TopTif-786
❑ 85Don-371
❑ 85Fle-166
❑ 85OPC-329
❑ 85Top-477
❑ 85TopTif-477
❑ 86BasStaB-80
❑ 86Don-636
❑ 86Fle-357
❑ 86FleUpd-84
❑ 86MetColP-25
❑ 86MetTCM-10
❑ 86MetWorSC-16
❑ 86OPC-11
❑ 86Top-11
❑ 86TopTif-11
❑ 86TopTra-81T
❑ 86TopTraT-81T
❑ 87ClaGam-73
❑ 87Don-364
❑ 87DonOpeD-127
❑ 87Fle-19
❑ 87FleBasA-30
❑ 87FleGamW-32
❑ 87FleGlo-19
❑ 87FleMin-77
❑ 87FleStiC-86
❑ 87Lea-94
❑ 87MetColP-14
❑ 87MetFanC-6
❑ 87OPC-83
❑ 87Spo-36
❑ 87SpoTeaP-2
❑ 87Top-746
❑ 87TopGloS-36
❑ 87TopMinL-25
❑ 87TopSti-99
❑ 87TopTif-746
❑ 87Woo-24
❑ 88Don-632
❑ 88DonBasB-238
❑ 88DonTeaBM-632
❑ 88Fle-147
❑ 88FleGlo-147
❑ 88MetColP-41
❑ 88MetKah-19
❑ 88Sco-563

❑ 88ScoGlo-563
❑ 88Top-558
❑ 88TopBig-234
❑ 88TopTif-558
❑ 89Bow-371
❑ 89BowTif-371
❑ 89Don-218
❑ 89DonBasB-209
❑ 89Fle-47
❑ 89FleGlo-47
❑ 89MetColP-16
❑ 89MetKah-20
❑ 89OPC-333
❑ 89Sco-116
❑ 89Top-333
❑ 89TopTif-333
❑ 89UppDec-386
❑ 90Don-117
❑ 90Fle-214
❑ 90FleCan-214
❑ 90MetColP-22
❑ 90MetColP-5
❑ 90MetKah-19
❑ 90OPC-207
❑ 90PubIntS-143
❑ 90Sco-53
❑ 90Top-207
❑ 90TopBig-131
❑ 90TopTif-207
❑ 90TopTVM-16
❑ 90UppDec-204
❑ 91Bow-591
❑ 91DodMot-13
❑ 91DodPho-22
❑ 91DodPol-17
❑ 91DodSt.V-4
❑ 91Don-584
❑ 91Fle-156
❑ 91FleUpd-95
❑ 91Lea-476
❑ 91MetWIZ-300
❑ 91OPC-601
❑ 91OPCPre-91
❑ 91Sco-321
❑ 91ScoRoo-79T
❑ 91SimandSMLBL-31
❑ 91StaClu-449
❑ 91Stu-187
❑ 91Top-601
❑ 91TopDesS-601
❑ 91TopMic-601
❑ 91TopTif-601
❑ 91TopTra-86T
❑ 91TopTraT-86T
❑ 91UltUpd-89
❑ 91UppDec-179
❑ 91UppDec-715
❑ 92Bow-379
❑ 92DodMot-23
❑ 92DodPol-17
❑ 92DodSmo-10392
❑ 92Don-157
❑ 92Fle-468
❑ 92Lea-345
❑ 92LeaBlaG-345
❑ 92OPC-123
❑ 92Pin-512
❑ 92Sco-527
❑ 92StaClu-537
❑ 92Top-123
❑ 92TopGol-123
❑ 92TopGolW-123
❑ 92TopMic-123
❑ 92TriPla-21
❑ 92Ult-509
❑ 92UppDec-666
❑ 93Don-614
❑ 93Fle-452
❑ 93IndWUA-23
❑ 93Pin-537
❑ 93Sco-589
❑ 93Sel-263
❑ 93SelRoo-121T
❑ 93Top-338
❑ 93TopGol-338
❑ 93TopInaM-338
❑ 93TopInaR-338
❑ 93TopMic-338
❑ 93UppDec-808
❑ 93UppDecGold-808
❑ 94Fle-116
❑ 94Pac-180
❑ 94Pin-507
❑ 94PinArtP-507
❑ 94PinMusC-507
❑ 94Top-93
❑ 94TopGol-93
❑ 94TopSpa-93

Ojeda, Erick
❑ 94VenLinU-4
❑ 95LinVen-98
❑ 96-97LinVen-23

Ojeda, Jorge
❑ 89BlaYNPRWL-148

Ojeda, Joseph
❑ 98SalVol-27

Ojeda, Luis
❑ 82ArkTraT-16
❑ 83ArkTraT-16
❑ 86MiaMarP-19
❑ 87MiaMarP-26
❑ 88BlaYNPRWLU-20

Ojeda, Miguel
❑ 94WelPirC-21
❑ 94WelPirF-3499
❑ 98CarMudM-10

Ojeda, Ray
❑ 86BelBreP-17
❑ 87BelBreP-22
❑ 88BlaYNPRWL-172

Ojeta, Erick
❑ 93LinVenB-4

Oka, Yukitoshi
❑ 91SalSpuC-15
❑ 91SalSpuP-2244

Okajima, Hideki
❑ 96HonShaHWB-8

Okamoto, Yoshi
❑ 90SalSpuCLC-147

Okerlund, Ron
❑ 85AncGlaPTI-39

Okubo, Dave
❑ 86SanJosBP-16

Olah, Bob
❑ 87LitFalMP-2401
❑ 89ColMetB-7
❑ 89ColMetGS-19
❑ 89SouAtlLAGS-18
❑ 90St.LucMS-19

Olander, Jim
❑ 85PorBeaC-36
❑ 86ReaPhiP-21
❑ 87MaiGuiP-1
❑ 87MaiGuiT-18
❑ 87PhiTas-38
❑ 88MaiPhiC-21
❑ 88MaiPhiP-277
❑ 89ScrRedBC-15
❑ 89ScrRedBP-723
❑ 90CMC-619
❑ 90ProAAAF-206
❑ 90TucTorC-17
❑ 90TucTorP-216
❑ 91DenZepLD-147
❑ 91DenZepP-135
❑ 91LinDriAAA-147
❑ 91TriA AAGP-AAA11
❑ 92Bow-575
❑ 92DenZepS-144
❑ 92Don-766
❑ 92OPC-7
❑ 92Sco-839
❑ 92SkyAAAF-70
❑ 92SkyAAAF-293
❑ 92StaClu-274
❑ 92Top-7
❑ 92TopDeb91-134
❑ 92TopGol-7
❑ 92TopGolW-7
❑ 92TopMic-7
❑ 93ColSprSSF-3099
❑ 94BreMilB-160
❑ 94IndIndF-1822

Olden, Paul
❑ 82SpoIndT-6

Oldham, J.C.
❑ 16Zee-115
❑ 17Zee-94
❑ 19Zee-40
❑ 23WilChoV-114
❑ 55SeaPop-16

Oldham, Robert
❑ 94BurIndC-17
❑ 94BurIndF-3790

Oldis, Bob (Robert Carl)
❑ 53Bri-14
❑ 53Top-262
❑ 54Top-91
❑ 55Top-169
❑ 60KeyChal-38
❑ 60Top-361
❑ 61Top-149
❑ 62Top-269
❑ 63Top-404
❑ 77PirTCM1WC-16
❑ 89ChaLooLITI-22
❑ 91TopArc1-262
❑ 94TopArc1-91
❑ 94TopArc1G-91

Oldring, Rube (Reuben Henry)
❑ 08AmeCarE91-18
❑ 08RosComP-63
❑ 09ColChiE-217
❑ 09T206-272
❑ 09T206-273
❑ 10CouT21-204
❑ 10CouT21-205
❑ 10DomDisP-94
❑ 10E12AmeCDCE125-30
❑ 10JuJuDE-32
❑ 10NadE1-47
❑ 10RedCroT-145
❑ 10RedCroT-232
❑ 10SweCapPP-49
❑ 11A'sFirT20-15
❑ 11BasBatEU-31
❑ 11D35RocB-15
❑ 11HelSta-58
❑ 11MecDFT-38
❑ 11PinT-5-510
❑ 11PloCanE-52
❑ 11S74Sil-34
❑ 11SpoLifCW-274
❑ 11SpoLifM-102
❑ 11T205-130
❑ 12ColRedB-217
❑ 12ColTinT-217
❑ 12HasTriFT-57
❑ 12HasTriFT-60
❑ 12T207-144
❑ 14CraJacE-8
❑ 14FatPlaT-37
❑ 14PieStaT-84
❑ 15CraJacE-8
❑ 15SpoNewM-132
❑ 16BF2FP-40
❑ 16FleBreD-71
❑ 16SpoNewM-133
❑ 21Zee-148
❑ 74A'sTCM1P-9
❑ 93ConTSN-788

Olds, Floyd
❑ 37Zee-27

Oleksak, Mike
❑ 79NewCoPT-8

Oleksik, George
❑ 96AriBlaDB-25
❑ 97HigDesMG-18
❑ 98HigDesMG-17

Olerud, John Garrett
❑ 90BluJayFS-23
❑ 90Bow-510
❑ 90BowTif-510
❑ 90ClaBlu-35
❑ 90ClaYel-T96
❑ 90Don-711
❑ 90DonBesA-100
❑ 90DonRoo-2
❑ 90FleUpd-128
❑ 90Lea-237
❑ 90Sco-589
❑ 90Sco100RS-39
❑ 90ScoMcD-17
❑ 90ScoYouS2-5
❑ 90TopBig-199
❑ 90TopDeb89-89
❑ 90TopMag-16
❑ 90TopTra-83T
❑ 90TopTraT-83T
❑ 90UppDec-56
❑ 91BluJayFS-20
❑ 91BluJayFS-23
❑ 91BluJayS-18
❑ 91Bow-7
❑ 91Cla1-T1
❑ 91Cla2-T24
❑ 91ClaGam-116
❑ 91Don-530
❑ 91Fle-183
❑ 91KinDis-7
❑ 91Lea-125
❑ 91MajLeaCP-27
❑ 91OPC-168
❑ 91OPCPre-92
❑ 91PanFreS-348
❑ 91PanSti-159
❑ 91PosCan-17
❑ 91Sco-625
❑ 91Sco-860
❑ 91Sco100RS-100
❑ 91StaClu-482
❑ 91Stu-136
❑ 91Top-168
❑ 91TopDesS-168
❑ 91TopMic-168
❑ 91TopRoo-24
❑ 91TopTif-168
❑ 91ToyRoo-24
❑ 91Ult-367
❑ 91UppDec-145
❑ 92BluJayP-8
❑ 92Bow-644
❑ 92Don-98
❑ 92Fle-339
❑ 92Hig5-119
❑ 92Lea-60
❑ 92LeaBlaG-60
❑ 92OPC-777
❑ 92PanSti-25
❑ 92Pin-78
❑ 92PinTea2-65
❑ 92RedFolS-72
❑ 92Sco-345
❑ 92Sco100S-71
❑ 92ScoImpP-41
❑ 92ScoProP-16
❑ 92SpollIFK1-281
❑ 92StaClu-531
❑ 92Stu-258
❑ 92Top-777
❑ 92TopGol-777
❑ 92TopGolW-777
❑ 92TopMic-777
❑ 92TriPla-110
❑ 92Ult-151
❑ 92UppDec-375
❑ 93BluJayCP1-9
❑ 93BluJayD-10
❑ 93BluJayD4-10
❑ 93BluJayDM-27
❑ 93BluJayDWS-6
❑ 93BluJayFS-22
❑ 93Bow-659
❑ 93ColAllG-13
❑ 93DiaMar-82
❑ 93DiaMarA-5
❑ 93Don-483
❑ 93DonEliD-9
❑ 93Fin-13
❑ 93FinRef-13
❑ 93Fla-293
❑ 93Fle-339
❑ 93FunPac-60
❑ 93HumDumC-19
❑ 93Lea-47
❑ 93LeaGolA-U3
❑ 93OPC-188
❑ 93OPCPre-52
❑ 93OPCWorC-12
❑ 93PacJugC-12
❑ 93PacSpa-327
❑ 93PanSti-26
❑ 93Pin-86
❑ 93PinHomRC-29
❑ 93Sco-68
❑ 93Sel-124
❑ 93SP-6
❑ 93StaClu-649
❑ 93StaCluFDI-649
❑ 93StaCluMOP-649
❑ 93Stu-195
❑ 93Top-240
❑ 93TopFulS-10
❑ 93TopGol-240
❑ 93TopInaM-240
❑ 93TopInaR-240
❑ 93TopMic-240
❑ 93TriPla-222
❑ 93Ult-291
❑ 93UppDec-344
❑ 93UppDecGold-344
❑ 94BluJayP-7
❑ 94BluJayUSPC-1C
❑ 94BluJayUSPC-6H
❑ 94BluJayUSPC-7D
❑ 94Bow-169
❑ 94BowBes-R62
❑ 94BowBes-X110
❑ 94BowBesR-R62
❑ 94BowBesR-X110
❑ 94ColC-600
❑ 94ColChoGS-600
❑ 94ColChoSS-600
❑ 94Don-354
❑ 94DonDiaK-DK24
❑ 94DonDiaKJ-DK24
❑ 94DonEli-43
❑ 94DonMVP-28
❑ 94DonPro-3
❑ 94DonSpeE-354
❑ 94DonSpiotG-1
❑ 94DonSpiotGJ-1
❑ 94Fin-221
❑ 94FinJum-221
❑ 94FinRef-221
❑ 94Fla-120
❑ 94FlaHotN-6
❑ 94Fle-340
❑ 94Fle-707
❑ 94FleAllS-19
❑ 94FleExtB-193
❑ 94FleExtBGB-21
❑ 94FleLeaL-1
❑ 94FlePro-2
❑ 94FleSun-19
❑ 94FUnPac-99
❑ 94KinDis-13
❑ 94Lea-378
❑ 94LeaGolS-12
❑ 94LeaL-79
❑ 94O-PJumAF-16
❑ 94OPC-130
❑ 94OPCAllR-16
❑ 94OPCJumA-16
❑ 94OPCWorC-5
❑ 94Pac-650
❑ 94PacSilP-6
❑ 94PacSilPC-6
❑ 94PanSti-5
❑ 94PanSti-141
❑ 94Pin-5
❑ 94PinArtP-5
❑ 94PinMusC-5
❑ 94PinRunC-RC1
❑ 94PinSam-5
❑ 94PinTheN-24
❑ 94Pos-24
❑ 94PosCan-4
❑ 94ProMag-140
❑ 94RedFolMI-1
❑ 94Sco-2
❑ 94ScoCyc-TC6
❑ 94ScoGolR-2
❑ 94ScoGolS-37
❑ 94ScoSam-2
❑ 94ScoSam-2GR
❑ 94Sel-239
❑ 94SelCroC-CC8
❑ 94SP-45
❑ 94SPDieC-45
❑ 94Spo-75
❑ 94StaClu-110
❑ 94StaClu-228
❑ 94StaCluFDI-110
❑ 94StaCluFDI-228
❑ 94StaCluGR-110
❑ 94StaCluGR-228
❑ 94StaCluMO-9
❑ 94StaCluMOP-110
❑ 94StaCluMOP-228
❑ 94StaCluMOP-ST28
❑ 94StaCluST-ST28
❑ 94StaCluT-172
❑ 94StaCluTFDI-172
❑ 94Stu-30
❑ 94TomPiz-24
❑ 94Top-10
❑ 94TopBlaG-15
❑ 94TopGol-10
❑ 94TopSpa-10
❑ 94TopSupS-32
❑ 94TriPla-36
❑ 94TriPlaM-3
❑ 94TriPlaN-5
❑ 94Ult-141
❑ 94UltAllS-9
❑ 94UltHitM-8
❑ 94UltLeaL-1
❑ 94UltOnBL-10
❑ 94UltRisS-8
❑ 94UppDec-48
❑ 94UppDec-99
❑ 94UppDecAJ-24
❑ 94UppDecAJG-24
❑ 94UppDecED-48
❑ 94UppDecED-99
❑ 94USPlaCA-13D
❑ 95Baz-41
❑ 95BluJayB-4
❑ 95BluJayOH-27
❑ 95BluJayP-5
❑ 95BluJayUSPC-1C
❑ 95BluJayUSPC-7D
❑ 95Bow-359
❑ 95ColCho-139
❑ 95ColChoGS-139
❑ 95ColChoSE-57
❑ 95ColChoSEGS-57
❑ 95ColChoSESS-57
❑ 95ColChoSS-139
❑ 95Don-433
❑ 95DonPreP-433
❑ 95DonTopotO-176
❑ 95Emo-97
❑ 95Fin-59
❑ 95FinRef-59
❑ 95Fla-100
❑ 95Fle-102
❑ 95Lea-41
❑ 95LeaLim-179
❑ 95Pac-448
❑ 95PacPri-144
❑ 95Pin-94
❑ 95PinArtP-94
❑ 95PinMusC-94
❑ 95RedFol-36
❑ 95Sco-60
❑ 95ScoGolR-60
❑ 95ScoHaloG-HG29
❑ 95ScoPlaTS-60
❑ 95Sel-84
❑ 95SelArtP-84
❑ 95SelCer-7
❑ 95SelCerMG-7
❑ 95Spo-61
❑ 95SpoArtP-61
❑ 95StaClu-448
❑ 95StaCluMOP-448
❑ 95StaCluMOP-RL28
❑ 95StaCluRL-RL28
❑ 95StaCluSTWS-448
❑ 95StaCluVR-239
❑ 95StaCluVRMO-239
❑ 95Stu-195
❑ 95Sum-55
❑ 95SumNthD-55
❑ 95Top-499
❑ 95TopCyb-289
❑ 95TopEmb-52
❑ 95TopEmbGI-52
❑ 95UC3-3
❑ 95UC3ArtP-3
❑ 95Ult-342
❑ 95UltGolM-342
❑ 95UppDec-41
❑ 95UppDecED-41
❑ 95UppDecEDG-41
❑ 95UppDecPLL-R54
❑ 95UppDecPLLE-R54
❑ 95Zen-55
❑ 96Baz-78
❑ 96BluJayB-4
❑ 96BluJayOH-23
❑ 96Bow-70
❑ 96BowFoi-70
❑ 96Cir-96
❑ 96CirRav-96
❑ 96ColCho-750
❑ 96ColChoGS-750
❑ 96ColChoSS-750
❑ 96Don-382
❑ 96DonPreP-382
❑ 96EmoXL-136
❑ 96Fin-B98
❑ 96FinRef-B98
❑ 96Fla-190
❑ 96Fle-280
❑ 96FleTif-280
❑ 96Lea-181
❑ 96LeaPrePB-181
❑ 96LeaPrePG-181
❑ 96LeaPrePS-181
❑ 96MetUni-125
❑ 96MetUniP-125
❑ 96Pac-442
❑ 96PanSti-166
❑ 96Pin-50
❑ 96Pin-225
❑ 96PinAfi-82
❑ 96PinAfiAP-82
❑ 96PinAfiFPP-82
❑ 96PinArtP-125
❑ 96PinFoil-225
❑ 96PinSta-125

❑ 96ProSta-19
❑ 96Sco-413
❑ 96Sel-57
❑ 96SelArtP-57
❑ 96StaClu-277
❑ 96StaCluEPB-277
❑ 96StaCluEPG-277
❑ 96StaCluEPS-277
❑ 96StaCluMOP-277
❑ 96Sum-138
❑ 96SumAbo&B-138
❑ 96SumArtP-138
❑ 96SumFoi-138
❑ 96TeaOut-60
❑ 96Top-264
❑ 96TopChr-106
❑ 96TopChrR-106
❑ 96TopGal-87
❑ 96TopGalPPI-87
❑ 96TopLas-87
❑ 96Ult-150
❑ 96UltGolM-150
❑ 96UppDec-475
❑ 97BluJayS-48
❑ 97Bow-240
❑ 97BowBes-31
❑ 97BowBesAR-31
❑ 97BowBesR-31
❑ 97BowChr-66
❑ 97BowChrI-66
❑ 97BowChrIR-66
❑ 97BowChrR-66
❑ 97BowInt-240
❑ 97Cir-9
❑ 97CirRav-9
❑ 97ColCho-392
❑ 97Don-69
❑ 97Don-350
❑ 97DonGolPP-69
❑ 97DonGolPP-350
❑ 97DonLim-20
❑ 97DonLimE-20
❑ 97DonLimENG-20
❑ 97DonSilPP-69
❑ 97DonSilPP-350
❑ 97Fin-84
❑ 97FinRef-84
❑ 97FlaShoLC-149
❑ 97FlaShoLeg0-149
❑ 97FlaShoLeg1-149
❑ 97FlaShoM-A149
❑ 97FlaShoM-B149
❑ 97FlaShoM-C149
❑ 97FlaShoR0-149
❑ 97FlaShoR1-149
❑ 97FlaShoR2-149
❑ 97Fle-247
❑ 97Fle-651
❑ 97FleTif-247
❑ 97FleTif-651
❑ 97Lea-278
❑ 97LeaFraM-278
❑ 97LeaFraMDC-278
❑ 97MetUni-188
❑ 97Pac-224
❑ 97PacLigB-224
❑ 97PacSil-224
❑ 97Sco-76
❑ 97Sco-336
❑ 97ScoArtPWB-76
❑ 97ScoArtPWB-336
❑ 97ScoPreS-76
❑ 97ScoResC-336
❑ 97ScoShoS-76
❑ 97ScoShoS-336
❑ 97ScoShoSAP-76
❑ 97ScoShoSAP-336
❑ 97Sel-158
❑ 97SelCom-158
❑ 97StaClu-301
❑ 97StaCluMOP-301
❑ 97Top-426
❑ 97TopChr-151
❑ 97TopChrR-151
❑ 97TopGal-88
❑ 97TopGalPPI-88
❑ 97TopSta-36
❑ 97TopStaAM-36
❑ 97Ult-149
❑ 97Ult-436
❑ 97UltGolME-149
❑ 97UltGolME-436
❑ 97UltPlaME-149
❑ 97UltPlaME-436
❑ 97UppDec-541
❑ 98Bow-67
❑ 98BowBes-22
❑ 98BowBesAR-22
❑ 98BowBesR-22
❑ 98BowChr-67
❑ 98BowChrGA-67
❑ 98BowChrGAR-67
❑ 98BowChrI-67
❑ 98BowChrIR-67
❑ 98BowChrR-67
❑ 98BowGolA-67
❑ 98BowInt-67
❑ 98CirThu-206
❑ 98CirThuRav-206
❑ 98CirThuSupRav-206
❑ 98ColCho-443
❑ 98CroRoy-88
❑ 98Don-199
❑ 98DonColL-312
❑ 98DonColP-633
❑ 98DonGolPP-199
❑ 98DonPre-83
❑ 98DonPreSeat-83
❑ 98DonPriCL-312
❑ 98DonPriCP-633
❑ 98DonSig-111
❑ 98DonSigP-111
❑ 98DonSilPP-199
❑ 98E-X2-48
❑ 98E-X2ECFut-48
❑ 98E-X2ECNow-48
❑ 98Fin-162
❑ 98FinNo--162
❑ 98FinNo-R-162
❑ 98FinRef-162
❑ 98FlaShoLeg0-99
❑ 98FlaShoLeg1-99
❑ 98FlaShoLeg2-99
❑ 98FlaShoLeg3-99
❑ 98FlaShoLegM-99
❑ 98FlaShoR0-99
❑ 98FlaShoR1-99
❑ 98FlaShoR2-99
❑ 98FlaShoR3-99
❑ 98Fle-214
❑ 98Lea-113
❑ 98LeaFraDA-113
❑ 98LeaFraF-113
❑ 98LeaFraM-113
❑ 98LeaFraM-113
❑ 98LeaFraMDC-113
❑ 98LeaFraMDC-113
❑ 98LeaFraMZ2-113
❑ 98LeaRS-84
❑ 98LeaRSLHolo-84
❑ 98LeaRSLong-84
❑ 98LeaRTrue-84
❑ 98MetUni-66
❑ 98MetUniPMG-66
❑ 98Pac-373
❑ 98PacAur-166
❑ 98PacInv-121
❑ 98PacInvPBlue-121
❑ 98PacInvSilv-121
❑ 98PacInvTeam-18
❑ 98PacOme-160
❑ 98PacOmeR-160
❑ 98PacOnl-485
❑ 98PacOnlR-485
❑ 98PacOnlWC-485
❑ 98PacPar-208
❑ 98PacParC-208
❑ 98PacParG-208
❑ 98PacParHS-208
❑ 98PacParPB-208
❑ 98PacParR-208
❑ 98PacPlaB-373
❑ 98PacRedT-373
❑ 98PacSil-373
❑ 98Pin-36
❑ 98PinArtP-PP35
❑ 98PinMusC-PP35
❑ 98PinPreP-36
❑ 98PinSna-NYM15
❑ 98Revo-94
❑ 98RevoSS-94
❑ 98ScoRT-125
❑ 98SP Aut-138
❑ 98SPxFin-104
❑ 98SPxFinR-104
❑ 98SPxFinS-104
❑ 98StaCluFDI-122
❑ 98StaCluI-122
❑ 98StaCluOneK-122
❑ 98StaCluPP-122
❑ 98Stu-133
❑ 98StuGPP-133
❑ 98StuSPP-133
❑ 98Top-324
❑ 98Top-477
❑ 98TopChr-324
❑ 98TopChr-477
❑ 98TopChrR-324
❑ 98TopChrR-477
❑ 98TopDevR-324
❑ 98TopDevR-477
❑ 98TopDia-324
❑ 98TopDia-477
❑ 98TopGal-99
❑ 98TopGalGP-99
❑ 98TopGalOPP-99
❑ 98TopGalPPI-99
❑ 98TopGalPPIA-99
❑ 98TopGolLabC1-56
❑ 98TopGolLabC1B-56
❑ 98TopGolLabC1One-56
❑ 98TopGolLabC1R-56
❑ 98TopGolLabC2-56
❑ 98TopGolLabC2B-56
❑ 98TopGolLabC2One-56
❑ 98TopGolLabC2R-56
❑ 98TopGolLabC3-56
❑ 98TopGolLabC3B-56
❑ 98TopGolLabC3One-56
❑ 98TopGolLabC3R-56
❑ 98TopMiniC-324
❑ 98TopMiniC-477
❑ 98TopMysF-ILM7
❑ 98TopMysFR-ILM7
❑ 98TopOpeD-150
❑ 98TopSta-122
❑ 98TopStaB-122
❑ 98TopStaG-122
❑ 98TopStaGR-122
❑ 98TopStaS-122
❑ 98TopTek-4
❑ 98TopTekD-4
❑ 98Ult-158
❑ 98UltGolM-158
❑ 98UltMas-158
❑ 98UltPlaM-158
❑ 98UppDec-168
❑ 98UppDecSF-89
❑ 99199Fin-54
❑ 99AllMysFR-M4
❑ 99Bow-29
❑ 99BowBes-40
❑ 99BowBesAR-40
❑ 99BowBesR-40
❑ 99BowChr-29
❑ 99BowChrG-29
❑ 99BowChrGR-29
❑ 99BowChrI-29
❑ 99BowChrIR-29
❑ 99BowChrR-29
❑ 99BowGol-29
❑ 99BowInt-29
❑ 99E-X Cen-54
❑ 99E-X CenECFut-54
❑ 99E-X CenECNow-54
❑ 99FinGolRef-54
❑ 99FinProF-PF25
❑ 99FinRef-54
❑ 99Fle-21
❑ 99FleBri-65
❑ 99FleBri2G-65
❑ 99FleBriBlu-65
❑ 99FleBriGol-65
❑ 99FleMys-83
❑ 99FleMysG-83
❑ 99FleMysM-83
❑ 99FleSta9-21
❑ 99FleVin'-21
❑ 99FleWarT-21
❑ 99MetUni-221
❑ 99MetUniGM-221
❑ 99MetUniPMG-221
❑ 99Pac-284
❑ 99PacAur-121
❑ 99PacAurOD-121
❑ 99PacCroC-182
❑ 99PacCroCPB-182
❑ 99PacOme-154
❑ 99PacOmeC-154
❑ 99PacOmeG-154
❑ 99PacOmePB-154
❑ 99PacPar-153
❑ 99PacParC-153
❑ 99PacParG-153
❑ 99PacParHoloGold-153
❑ 99PacParHS-153
❑ 99PacParOD-153
❑ 99PacParPB-153
❑ 99PacParRed-153
❑ 99PacPlaB-284
❑ 99PacPri-94
❑ 99PacPriHB-94
❑ 99PacPriHG-94
❑ 99PacPriHM-94
❑ 99PacPriHP-94
❑ 99PacPriRed-94
❑ 99PacPriS-125
❑ 99PacPriS206-125
❑ 99PacPriS206R-125
❑ 99PacRed-284
❑ 99Rev-90
❑ 99RevPremDate-90
❑ 99RevRet-90
❑ 99RevShaSS-90
❑ 99SkyMolM-86
❑ 99SkyMolMX-86
❑ 99SkyPre-116
❑ 99SkyPreR-116
❑ 99SkyThu-171
❑ 99SkyThuRant-171
❑ 99SkyThuRave-171
❑ 99SP Aut-56
❑ 99SP SigAuto-JO
❑ 99SpoIll-90
❑ 99SPSig-121
❑ 99StaClu-122
❑ 99StaCluFDI-122
❑ 99StaCluOoaK-122
❑ 99StaCluPP-122
❑ 99ThuSkySupR-171
❑ 99Top-32
❑ 99Top-451
❑ 99TopAllMF-M4
❑ 99TopBlaLC1-77
❑ 99TopBlaLC2-77
❑ 99TopBlaLC3-77
❑ 99TopChr-32
❑ 99TopChr-451
❑ 99TopChrR-32
❑ 99TopChrR-451
❑ 99TopGal-52
❑ 99TopGalPP-52
❑ 99TopGalPPI-52
❑ 99TopGolL-77
❑ 99TopGolLC1-77
❑ 99TopGolLC2-77
❑ 99TopGolLOtO-77
❑ 99TopMVPP-32
❑ 99TopMVPP-451
❑ 99TopOpeD-20
❑ 99TopRedLC1-77
❑ 99TopRedLC2-77
❑ 99TopRedLC3-77
❑ 99TopSta-100
❑ 99TopSta1Foil-100
❑ 99TopStaFoil-100
❑ 99TopStaOS-100
❑ 99UD Cho-113
❑ 99UD ChoPCR-113
❑ 99Ult-85
❑ 99UltGolM-85
❑ 99UltMas-85
❑ 99UltPlaM-85
❑ 99UppDec-149
❑ 99UppDecBD-55
❑ 99UppDecBDD-55
❑ 99UppDecBDQ-55
❑ 99UppDecBDT-55
❑ 99UppDecCL-94
❑ 99UppDecCLCC-94
❑ 99UppDecEL1-149
❑ 99UppDecEL2-149
❑ 99UppDecM-133
❑ 99UppDecMGS-133
❑ 99UppDecMHFS-133
❑ 99UppDecMP-133
❑ 99UppDecMSS-133
❑ 99UppDecO-8
❑ 99UppDecOSO-8
❑ 99Vic-261

Olerud, John Sr

❑ 66SeaPop-16

Olexa, Mike

❑ 93HelBreF-4104
❑ 93HelBreSP-11

Olin, Steve

❑ 88MidLeaAGS-30
❑ 88WatIndP-688
❑ 89ColSprSSP-252
❑ 89TriAAAP-AAA34
❑ 90Bow-326
❑ 90BowTif-326
❑ 90Don-438
❑ 90Fle-499
❑ 90FleCan-499
❑ 90IndTeal-31
❑ 90OPC-433
❑ 90PanSti-375
❑ 90Sco-590
❑ 90ScoYouS2-23
❑ 90Spo-178
❑ 90Top-433
❑ 90TopDeb89-90
❑ 90TopTif-433
❑ 90TriAAAC-42
❑ 90UppDec-553
❑ 91Don-339
❑ 91Fle-374
❑ 91IndFanC-22
❑ 91Lea-94
❑ 91OPC-696
❑ 91Sco-496
❑ 91Sco100RS-86
❑ 91StaClu-336
❑ 91Top-696
❑ 91TopDesS-696
❑ 91TopMic-696
❑ 91TopTif-696
❑ 91Ult-116
❑ 91UppDec-118
❑ 92Bow-236
❑ 92Don-151
❑ 92Fle-120
❑ 92IndFanC-20
❑ 92Lea-141
❑ 92LeaBlaG-141
❑ 92OPC-559
❑ 92Pin-120
❑ 92Sco-644
❑ 92StaClu-169
❑ 92Top-559
❑ 92TopGol-559
❑ 92TopGolW-559
❑ 92TopMic-559
❑ 92TriPla-156
❑ 92Ult-53
❑ 92UppDec-215
❑ 93Don-567
❑ 93Fle-220
❑ 93OPC-349
❑ 93Pin-410
❑ 93Sco-388
❑ 93Sel-377
❑ 93Top-167
❑ 93TopGol-167
❑ 93TopInaM-167
❑ 93TopInaR-167
❑ 93TopMic-167
❑ 93TriPla-204
❑ 93UppDec-206
❑ 93UppDecGold-206
❑ 97ColSprSATTI-20

Olinde, Chad

❑ 94WilCubC-17
❑ 94WilCubF-3772
❑ 95RocCubTI-14

Oliphant, John

❑ 87NewOriP-5

Oliva, Jose

❑ 89ButCopKSP-12
❑ 90GasRanB-21
❑ 90GasRanP-2530
❑ 90GasRanS-17
❑ 91ChaRanC-20
❑ 91ChaRanP-1324
❑ 92Bow-55
❑ 92ClaFS7-289
❑ 92SkyAA F-272
❑ 92TulDriF-2703
❑ 92TulDriS-614
❑ 92UppDecML-283
❑ 93Bow-282
❑ 93ExcFS7-235
❑ 93LimRocDWB-25
❑ 93LimRocDWB-146
❑ 93RicBraBB-16
❑ 93RicBraF-193
❑ 93RicBraP-7
❑ 93RicBraRC-7
❑ 93RicBraRC-23
❑ 93UppDec-426
❑ 93UppDecGold-426
❑ 94BraLykP-26
❑ 94FleUpd-104
❑ 94LeaLimR-48
❑ 94RicBraF-2855
❑ 94SpoRoo-144
❑ 94SpoRooAP-144
❑ 94StaCluT-48
❑ 94StaCluTFDI-48
❑ 95ActPac2G-7G
❑ 95ActPacF-30
❑ 95ActPacF-68
❑ 95Baz-131
❑ 95Bow-438
❑ 95ColCho-166
❑ 95ColChoGS-166
❑ 95ColChoSE-64
❑ 95ColChoSEGS-64
❑ 95ColChoSESS-64
❑ 95ColChoSS-166
❑ 95Don-124
❑ 95DonPreP-124
❑ 95Fin-22
❑ 95FinRef-22
❑ 95Fla-107
❑ 95Fle-316
❑ 95Lea-349
❑ 95LeaGolR-7
❑ 95Pac-14
❑ 95PacLatD-25
❑ 95Pin-140
❑ 95PinArtP-140
❑ 95PinMusC-140
❑ 95Sco-295
❑ 95ScoAi-AM4
❑ 95ScoGolR-295
❑ 95ScoPlaTS-295
❑ 95ScoRooDT-RDT4
❑ 95Sel-181
❑ 95SelArtP-181
❑ 95SelCer-109
❑ 95SelCerMG-109
❑ 95Spo-147
❑ 95SpoArtP-147
❑ 95StaClu-332
❑ 95StaCluMOP-332
❑ 95StaCluSTWS-332
❑ 95StaCluVR-172
❑ 95StaCluVRMO-172
❑ 95Sum-119
❑ 95SumNthD-119
❑ 95Top-451
❑ 95TopCyb-247
❑ 95UC3-113
❑ 95UC3ArtP-113
❑ 95Ult-352
❑ 95UltGolM-352
❑ 95UppDec-214
❑ 95UppDecED-214
❑ 95UppDecEDG-214
❑ 95UppDecPAW-H19
❑ 95UppDecPAWE-H19
❑ 95UppDecSE-17
❑ 95UppDecSEG-17
❑ 95UppDecSoaD-SD4
❑ 96ColCho-689
❑ 96ColChoGS-689
❑ 96ColChoSS-689
❑ 96Don-417
❑ 96DonPreP-417
❑ 96Fle-550
❑ 96FleTif-550
❑ 96LouRedB-24
❑ 96Sco-138

Oliva, Steve

❑ 77QuaCitAT-22
❑ 78QuaCitAT-16

Oliva, Tony (Antonio Pedro)

❑ 63Top-228
❑ 64Top-116
❑ 64TopGia-44
❑ 64TopRooAB-27
❑ 64TopVen-116
❑ 64TwiJayP-8
❑ 65Baz-4
❑ 65MacSta-7
❑ 65OPC-1
❑ 65Top-1
❑ 65Top-340
❑ 65TopTral-60
❑ 65TwiPos-7
❑ 66Baz-41
❑ 66Top-216
❑ 66Top-220
❑ 66Top-450
❑ 66TopRubI-72
❑ 66TopVen-216
❑ 66TopVen-220
❑ 66TwiFaiG-10
❑ 67Baz-41
❑ 67CokCapA-12
❑ 67CokCapAAm-27
❑ 67CokCapTw-17
❑ 67DexPre-153

❑ 67OPC-50
❑ 67OPCPapI-18
❑ 67Top-50
❑ 67Top-239
❑ 67TopPos-18
❑ 67TopTesF-17
❑ 67TopVen-230
❑ 67TwiTeal-12
❑ 67TwiTeal-13
❑ 68AtlOilPBCC-31
❑ 68Baz-9
❑ 68DexPre-60
❑ 68OPC-165
❑ 68Top-165
❑ 68Top-371
❑ 68Top-480
❑ 68TopActS-11A
❑ 68TopVen-165
❑ 69MilBra-205
❑ 69MLBOffS-69
❑ 69MLBPin-20
❑ 69NabTeaF-17
❑ 69OPC-1
❑ 69Top-1
❑ 69Top-427
❑ 69Top-582A
❑ 69Top-582B
❑ 69Top-600
❑ 69TopDecl-32
❑ 69TopSta-196
❑ 69TopSup-20
❑ 69TopTeaP-15
❑ 69TraSta-7
❑ 69TwiTealC-8
❑ 70DayDaiNM-30
❑ 70Kel-63
❑ 70MLBOffS-235
❑ 70OPC-62
❑ 70OPC-510
❑ 70Top-62
❑ 70Top-510
❑ 70TopBoo-8
❑ 70TopSup-26
❑ 70TraSta-13B
❑ 70TwiSupV-7
❑ 71BazNumT-36
❑ 71Kel-12
❑ 71MatMin-11
❑ 71MatMin-12
❑ 71MilDud-20
❑ 71MLBOffS-468
❑ 71OPC-61
❑ 71OPC-290
❑ 71Top-61
❑ 71Top-290
❑ 71TopCoi-128
❑ 71TopGreM-11
❑ 71TopSup-11
❑ 71TopTat-133
❑ 72EssCoi-10
❑ 72Kel-25
❑ 72MilBra-258
❑ 72OPC-86
❑ 72OPC-400
❑ 72SevTraC-37
❑ 72Top-86
❑ 72Top-400
❑ 72TopPos-7
❑ 72TwiPos-15
❑ 73Kel2D-4
❑ 73OPC-80
❑ 73SevTraC-54
❑ 73Top-80
❑ 74OPC-190
❑ 74Top-190
❑ 74TopDecE-62
❑ 74TopSta-210
❑ 75Hos-20
❑ 75HosTwi-20
❑ 75OPC-325
❑ 75SSP42-20
❑ 75Top-325
❑ 75TopMin-325
❑ 75TwiPos-18
❑ 75TwiTeal-21
❑ 76Hos-10
❑ 76HosTwi-10
❑ 76OPC-35
❑ 76SSP-217
❑ 76Top-35
❑ 77GalGloG-257
❑ 78TCM60I-71
❑ 78TwiFri-15
❑ 80WisRapTT-27
❑ 82CraJac-7
❑ 82TCMGreH-10
❑ 83FraBroR-27
❑ 83MLBPin-13
❑ 84OCoandSI-35
❑ 84OCoandSI-167
❑ 84SpoDesPW-41
❑ 85TwiPos-19
❑ 85TwiTeal-3
❑ 85TwiTeal-17
❑ 86SpoDecG-51
❑ 86TwiGreT-7
❑ 86TwiTeal-4
❑ 87TwiPos-18
❑ 87TwiTeal-3
❑ 88PacLegI-59
❑ 89SweBasG-12
❑ 89Top-665A
❑ 89Top-665B
❑ 89TopTif-665
❑ 91DodPho-5
❑ 92ActPacA-60
❑ 92UppDecS-8
❑ 92UppDecS-29
❑ 93TedWil-50
❑ 93UppDecS-15
❑ 94UppDecAH-85
❑ 94UppDecAH-209
❑ 94UppDecAH1-85
❑ 94UppDecAH1-209

Olivares, Ed (Edward B.)
❑ 62Col45'HC-12
❑ 62Top-598

Olivares, Jose
❑ 89MyrBeaBJP-1473
❑ 90MyrBeaBJP-2776

Olivares, Mako
❑ 93LinVenB-316

Olivares, O.
❑ 76VenLeaS-163
❑ 78ColCliT-19
❑ 79PorBeaT-2
❑ 93LinVenB-125

Olivares, Omar
❑ 87ChaRaiP-13
❑ 88BlaYNPRWL-47
❑ 88ChaRaiP-1210
❑ 88SouAtlLAGS-10
❑ 89BlaYNPRWL-48
❑ 89TexLeaAGS-11
❑ 89WicChaR-18
❑ 89WicStaR-11
❑ 89WicUpdR-4
❑ 89WicWraR-26
❑ 90CMC-120
❑ 90LouRedBC-20
❑ 90LouRedBLBC-31
❑ 90LouRedBP-400
❑ 90ProAAAF-514
❑ 90TopTVCa-58
❑ 91Don-503
❑ 91LinDriAAA-237
❑ 91LouRedLD-237
❑ 91LouRedP-2912
❑ 91LouRedTI-3
❑ 91OPC-271
❑ 91Sco-748
❑ 91ScoRoo-5
❑ 91Top-271
❑ 91TopDeb90-118
❑ 91TopDesS-271
❑ 91TopMic-271
❑ 91TopTif-271
❑ 91UltUpd-108
❑ 91UppDec-463
❑ 92Bow-420
❑ 92CarPol-12
❑ 92ClaGam-22
❑ 92Don-481
❑ 92Fle-584
❑ 92Lea-282
❑ 92LeaBlaG-282
❑ 92OPC-193
❑ 92OPCPre-38
❑ 92Pin-186
❑ 92ProFS7-316
❑ 92Sco-334
❑ 92StaClu-386
❑ 92Top-193
❑ 92TopGol-193
❑ 92TopGolW-193
❑ 92TopMic-193
❑ 92Ult-266
❑ 92UppDec-478
❑ 93Bow-432
❑ 93CarPol-11
❑ 93CarStaC-24
❑ 93Don-388
❑ 93Fle-512
❑ 93Lea-438
❑ 93OPC-206
❑ 93PacSpa-297
❑ 93Pin-394
❑ 93StaClu-489
❑ 93StaCluFDI-489
❑ 93StaCluMOP-489
❑ 93Top-490
❑ 93TopGol-490
❑ 93TopInaM-490
❑ 93TopInaR-490
❑ 93TopMic-490
❑ 93Ult-465
❑ 93UppDec-194
❑ 93UppDecGold-194
❑ 94CarPol-11
❑ 94Don-120
❑ 94Fle-638
❑ 94LouRedF-2981
❑ 94Pac-595
❑ 94StaClu-425
❑ 94StaCluFDI-425
❑ 94StaCluGR-425
❑ 94StaCluMOP-425
❑ 94StaCluT-302
❑ 94StaCluTFDI-302
❑ 94Top-689
❑ 94TopGol-689
❑ 94TopSpa-689
❑ 95Pac-410
❑ 96LeaSigEA-146
❑ 96TigHebN-21
❑ 97ColCho-337
❑ 97UppDec-354
❑ 98Pac-192
❑ 98PacOnl-19
❑ 98PacOnlR-19
❑ 98PacOnlWC-19
❑ 98PacPlaB-192
❑ 98PacRedT-192
❑ 98PacSil-192
❑ 99Fle-436
❑ 99FleSta9-436
❑ 99FleWarT-436
❑ 99PacCroC-7
❑ 99PacCroCPB-7

Olivares, Teuris
❑ 98OneYanG-20

Olivaros, Ed
❑ 77ReaPhiT-18

Olivas, Rich
❑ 86AncGlaPTI-25

Oliver, Al (Albert)
❑ 69OPC-82
❑ 69PirJacitB-7
❑ 69PirTeal-17
❑ 69Top-82
❑ 70MLBOffS-105
❑ 70OPC-166
❑ 70PirTeal-13
❑ 70Top-166
❑ 71MLBOffS-210
❑ 71OPC-388
❑ 71PirActP-21
❑ 71PirArc-8
❑ 71Top-388
❑ 72PirTeal-5
❑ 72Top-575
❑ 73LinPor-151
❑ 73OPC-225
❑ 73SevTraC-55
❑ 73Top-225
❑ 74OPC-52
❑ 74Top-52
❑ 74TopSta-85
❑ 75Hos-81
❑ 75Kel-15
❑ 75OPC-555
❑ 75PitPirP-16
❑ 75Top-555
❑ 75TopMin-555
❑ 76BlaDis-43
❑ 76BucDis-43
❑ 76CarDis-43
❑ 76CraDis-43
❑ 76DailsID-43
❑ 76Hos-112
❑ 76IsaDis-43
❑ 76OPC-620
❑ 76OrbDis-43
❑ 76PirPos-14
❑ 76RedBarD-43
❑ 76SafDis-43
❑ 76SSP-576
❑ 76Top-620
❑ 76TowCluD-43
❑ 77BurCheD-189
❑ 77Hos-45
❑ 77Kel-46
❑ 77OPC-203
❑ 77PirPosP-17
❑ 77RCColC-47
❑ 77Top-130
❑ 77TopCloS-34
❑ 78OPC-97
❑ 78RanBurK-17
❑ 78RCColC-30
❑ 78SSP270-108
❑ 78Top-430
❑ 78WifBalD-55
❑ 79BasPat-63
❑ 79Hos-80
❑ 79OPC-204
❑ 79Top-391
❑ 79TopCom-16
❑ 80OPC-136
❑ 80Top-260
❑ 80TopSup-35
❑ 81AllGamPI-63
❑ 81Don-387
❑ 81Dra-24
❑ 81Fle-626
❑ 81FleStiC-64
❑ 81Kel-4
❑ 81OPC-70
❑ 81Squ-22
❑ 81Top-70
❑ 81TopScr-4
❑ 81TopSti-131
❑ 81TopSti-246
❑ 81TopSupHT-93
❑ 82Don-116
❑ 82ExpHygM-15
❑ 82ExpPos-25
❑ 82ExpPos-26
❑ 82ExpPos-27
❑ 82FBIDis-15
❑ 82Fle-326
❑ 82FleSta-178
❑ 82Kel-61
❑ 82OPC-22
❑ 82OPC-326
❑ 82Top-36
❑ 82Top-590
❑ 82Top-591
❑ 82TopSti-239
❑ 82TopTra-83T
❑ 83AllGamPI-97
❑ 83Don-140
❑ 83DonActA-6
❑ 83Dra-21
❑ 83ExpPos-20
❑ 83ExpStu-6
❑ 83Fle-290
❑ 83FleSta-142
❑ 83FleSti-143
❑ 83FleSti-268
❑ 83OPC-5
❑ 83OPC-111
❑ 83OPC-311
❑ 83PerAll-13
❑ 83PerAllG-13
❑ 83PerCreC-10
❑ 83PerCreCG-10
❑ 83Top-111
❑ 83Top-420
❑ 83Top-421
❑ 83Top-701
❑ 83Top-703
❑ 83TopFol-2
❑ 83TopFol-3
❑ 83TopGloS-30
❑ 83TopSti-174
❑ 83TopSti-205
❑ 83TopSti-206
❑ 83TopSti-251
❑ 84AllGamPI-8
❑ 84Don-9
❑ 84Don-9A
❑ 84Don-177
❑ 84DonCha-30
❑ 84Dra-24
❑ 84Fle-280
❑ 84Fle-632
❑ 84FleSti-27
❑ 84FleUpd-85
❑ 84GiaPos-20
❑ 84MilBra-18
❑ 84Nes792-516
❑ 84Nes792-620
❑ 84Nes792-704
❑ 84OPC-307
❑ 84OPC-332
❑ 84Top-516
❑ 84Top-620
❑ 84Top-704
❑ 84TopGloA-13
❑ 84TopGloS-21
❑ 84TopSti-87
❑ 84TopStiB-1
❑ 84TopTif-516
❑ 84TopTif-620
❑ 84TopTif-704
❑ 84TopTra-87T
❑ 84TopTraT-87T
❑ 85DodCokP-23
❑ 85Don-598
❑ 85Fle-262
❑ 85FleUpd-84
❑ 85Lea-67
❑ 85OPC-130
❑ 85Top-130
❑ 85TopSti-118
❑ 85TopTif-130
❑ 85TopTifT-88T
❑ 85TopTra-88T
❑ 86Don-485
❑ 86Fle-69
❑ 86OPC-114
❑ 86RanGreT-9
❑ 86Spo-126
❑ 86Spo-140
❑ 86Spo-164
❑ 86Top-775
❑ 86TopSti-14
❑ 86TopTif-775
❑ 86Woo-26
❑ 89PacSenL-142
❑ 89T/MSenL-83
❑ 89TopSenL-36
❑ 90DodTar-587
❑ 90EliSenL-46
❑ 91UppDecS-13
❑ 92ActPacA-68
❑ 92Nab-21
❑ 92UppDecS-12
❑ 92UppDecS-30
❑ 93ExpDonM-16
❑ 93MCIAmb-11
❑ 93RanKee-283
❑ 93TedWil-79
❑ 93TedWilM-12
❑ 93UppDecAH-102
❑ 94RanAllP-8
❑ 94RanAllP-9
❑ 94UppDecAH-82
❑ 94UppDecAH1-82
❑ 99SpoIllGotG-37
❑ 99SpoIllGotGA-54

Oliver, Bob (Robert Lee)
❑ 69RoySol-12
❑ 69RoyTeal-10
❑ 69Top-662
❑ 69TopSta-187
❑ 70MLBOffS-226
❑ 70RoyTeal-25
❑ 70Top-567
❑ 71MLBOffS-423
❑ 71OPC-470
❑ 71oySigST-17
❑ 71Top-470
❑ 71TopCoi-48
❑ 71TopTat-91
❑ 72MilBra-259
❑ 72OPC-57
❑ 72Top-57
❑ 73LinPor-33
❑ 73OPC-289
❑ 73Top-289
❑ 74OPC-243
❑ 74Top-243
❑ 74TopSta-143
❑ 75OPC-657
❑ 75SSP18-16
❑ 75Top-657
❑ 75TopMin-657
❑ 76OklCit8TI-30
❑ 76VenLeaS-53
❑ 77ColCliT-17
❑ 79QuaCitCT-26
❑ 91OriCro-342
❑ 92YanWIZ7-123
❑ 93UppDecS-4

Oliver, Brent
❑ 92DavLipB-20

Oliver, Bruce
❑ 79CedRapGT-11
❑ 81CliGiaT-5

Oliver, Darren
❑ 89GasRanP-1021
❑ 89GasRanS-17
❑ 89SouAtlLAGS-24
❑ 90ChaRanS-17
❑ 91ChaRanC-7
❑ 91ChaRanP-1311
❑ 92ChaRanC-19
❑ 92UppDecML-308
❑ 93RanKee-418
❑ 93TulDriF-2733
❑ 93TulDriTI-21
❑ 94Bow-513
❑ 94FleMajLP-27
❑ 94Pin-233
❑ 94PinArtP-233
❑ 94PinMusC-233
❑ 94RanMagM-26
❑ 94ScoRoo-RT113
❑ 94ScoRooGR-RT113
❑ 94Sel-203
❑ 95ColCho-399
❑ 95ColChoGS-399
❑ 95ColChoSS-399
❑ 95Fla-90
❑ 95Lea-185
❑ 95Pin-262
❑ 95PinArtP-262
❑ 95PinMusC-262
❑ 95RanCra-24
❑ 95Sel-57
❑ 95SelArtP-57
❑ 95Top-403
❑ 95TopCyb-204
❑ 95UppDec-153
❑ 95UppDecED-153
❑ 95UppDecEDG-153
❑ 96ColCho-734
❑ 96ColChoGS-734
❑ 96ColChoSS-734
❑ 96RanDr P-24
❑ 96RanMot-27
❑ 97Cir-302
❑ 97CirRav-302
❑ 97ColCho-237
❑ 97ColChoT-TR2
❑ 97Don-107
❑ 97DonGolPP-107
❑ 97DonSilPP-107
❑ 97Fle-228
❑ 97FleTif-228
❑ 97Lea-160
❑ 97LeaFraM-160
❑ 97LeaFraMDC-160
❑ 97Pac-206
❑ 97PacLigB-206
❑ 97PacSil-206
❑ 97Pin-131
❑ 97PinArtP-PP131
❑ 97PinMusC-131
❑ 97PinPrePla-131
❑ 97RanDr P-22
❑ 97RanMot-22
❑ 97RanSco-6
❑ 97RanScoPl-6
❑ 97RanScoPr-6
❑ 97Sco-129
❑ 97ScoArtPWB-129
❑ 97ScoPreS-129
❑ 97ScoShoS-129
❑ 97ScoShoSAP-129
❑ 97Top-303
❑ 97Ult-305
❑ 97UltGolME-305
❑ 97UltPlaME-305
❑ 97UppDec-209
❑ 98ColCho-247
❑ 98Fle-109
❑ 98Pac-206
❑ 98PacOnl-740
❑ 98PacOnlR-740
❑ 98PacOnlWC-740
❑ 98PacPlaB-206
❑ 98PacRedT-206
❑ 98PacSil-206
❑ 98PinSna-TR7
❑ 98StaCluFDI-81
❑ 98StaCluI-81
❑ 98StaCluOneK-81
❑ 98StaCluPP-81
❑ 98Top-418
❑ 98TopChr-418
❑ 98TopChrR-418

❑ 98TopDevR-418
❑ 98TopDia-418
❑ 98TopMiniC-418
❑ 98Ult-289
❑ 98UltGolM-289
❑ 98UltMas-289
❑ 98UltPlaM-289
❑ 98UppDec-523
❑ 99StaClu-21
❑ 99StaCluFDI-21
❑ 99StaCluOoaK-21
❑ 99StaCluPP-21

Oliver, Dave (David Jacob)
❑ 78Top-704
❑ 79TacTugT-12
❑ 79Top-705
❑ 80TacTigT-15
❑ 81BatTroT-27
❑ 83TriTriT-26
❑ 85OklCit8T-15
❑ 86OklCit8P-15
❑ 87RanMot-28
❑ 87RanSmo-30
❑ 88RanMot-27
❑ 89RanMot-27
❑ 89RanSmo-23
❑ 90RanMot-27
❑ 91RanMot-28
❑ 92RanMot-28
❑ 93RanKee-439
❑ 94RanMagM-27

Oliver, Edward
❑ 49W72HolS-13

Oliver, Gene (Eugene George)
❑ 59Top-135
❑ 59TopVen-135
❑ 60Top-307
❑ 61Top-487
❑ 62CarJayP-11
❑ 62Top-561
❑ 63Fle-62
❑ 63Jel-164
❑ 63Pos-164
❑ 63Top-172
❑ 64Top-316
❑ 64TopVen-316
❑ 65Kah-32
❑ 65OPC-106
❑ 65Top-106
❑ 66BraPos-20
❑ 66Top-541
❑ 67BraPho-24
❑ 67CokCapB-4
❑ 67DexPre-154
❑ 67OPC-18
❑ 67Top-18
❑ 68CokCapRS-9
❑ 68Top-449
❑ 69MilBra-206
❑ 69Top-247
❑ 78AtlCon-20
❑ 81QuaCitCT-31
❑ 81RedSoxBG2S-100

Oliver, Harry
❑ 82RedPioT-19

Oliver, Harry PCL
❑ 21Zee-105

Oliver, Joe
❑ 84CedRapRT-14
❑ 87VerRedP-19
❑ 88NasSouC-17
❑ 88NasSouP-483
❑ 89CedRapRAB-8
❑ 89NasSouC-12
❑ 89NasSouP-1283
❑ 89NasSouTI-17
❑ 89ScoRoo-104T
❑ 90Bow-54
❑ 90BowTif-54
❑ 90CedRapRDGB-8
❑ 90ClaYel-T98
❑ 90Don-586
❑ 90DonBesN-15
❑ 90Fle-426
❑ 90FleCan-426
❑ 90Hot50RS-33
❑ 90Lea-453
❑ 90OPC-668
❑ 90PanSti-378
❑ 90RedKah-19
❑ 90Sco-576
❑ 90Sco100RS-26
❑ 90ScoYouSI-10
❑ 90Spo-71
❑ 90Top-668
❑ 90TopBig-281
❑ 90TopDeb89-91
❑ 90TopTif-668
❑ 90UppDec-568
❑ 91Bow-671
❑ 91Don-381
❑ 91Fle-75
❑ 91Lea-73
❑ 91OPC-517
❑ 91PanFreS-126
❑ 91RedKah-9
❑ 91RedPep-14
❑ 91Sco-620
❑ 91StaClu-68
❑ 91Top-517
❑ 91TopDesS-517
❑ 91TopMic-517
❑ 91TopTif-517
❑ 91Ult-99
❑ 91UppDec-279
❑ 91Woo-28
❑ 92Bow-594
❑ 92Don-261
❑ 92Fle-414
❑ 92Lea-7
❑ 92LeaBlaG-7
❑ 92OPC-304
❑ 92PanSti-261
❑ 92Pin-331
❑ 92RedKah-9
❑ 92Sco-370
❑ 92StaClu-306
❑ 92Top-304
❑ 92TopGol-304
❑ 92TopGolW-304
❑ 92TopMic-304
❑ 92Ult-193
❑ 92UppDec-101
❑ 93Bow-6
❑ 93CadDis-43
❑ 93DenHol-22
❑ 93Don-586
❑ 93Fla-30
❑ 93Fle-38
❑ 93Lea-263
❑ 93OPC-260
❑ 93PacSpa-86
❑ 93PanSti-290
❑ 93Pin-190
❑ 93RedKah-17
❑ 93Sco-125
❑ 93Sel-235
❑ 93SP-212
❑ 93StaClu-96
❑ 93StaCluFDI-96
❑ 93StaCluMOP-96
❑ 93StaCluMP-5
❑ 93Stu-187
❑ 93Top-138
❑ 93TOPBLAG-14
❑ 93TopGol-138
❑ 93TopInaM-138
❑ 93TopInaR-138
❑ 93TopMic-138
❑ 93TriPla-220
❑ 93Ult-32
❑ 93UppDec-234
❑ 93UppDecGold-234
❑ 94Bow-298
❑ 94ColC-220
❑ 94ColChoGS-220
❑ 94ColChoSS-220
❑ 94Don-249
❑ 94Fin-37
❑ 94FinRef-37
❑ 94Fle-418
❑ 94FleExtB-236
❑ 94Lea-146
❑ 94OPC-189
❑ 94Pac-153
❑ 94PanSti-166
❑ 94Pin-402
❑ 94PinArtP-402
❑ 94PinMusC-402
❑ 94RedKah-21
❑ 94Sco-444
❑ 94ScoGolR-444
❑ 94Sel-149
❑ 94StaClu-7
❑ 94StaCluFDI-7
❑ 94StaCluGR-7
❑ 94StaCluMOP-7
❑ 94Top-485
❑ 94TopGol-485
❑ 94TopSpa-485
❑ 94TriPla-217
❑ 94Ult-174
❑ 94UppDec-134
❑ 94UppDecED-134
❑ 95ColCho-539T
❑ 95DonTopotO-101
❑ 95Emo-54
❑ 95Fin-328
❑ 95FinRef-328
❑ 95Fla-274
❑ 95FleUpd-55
❑ 95LinVen-155
❑ 95Sco-418
❑ 95ScoGolR-418
❑ 95ScoPlaTS-418
❑ 95SP-168
❑ 95SPSil-168
❑ 95StaClu-549
❑ 95StaCluMOP-549
❑ 95StaCluSTWS-549
❑ 95TopTra-23T
❑ 95UppDec-297
❑ 95UppDecED-297
❑ 95UppDecEDG-297
❑ 96ColCho-194
❑ 96ColChoGS-194
❑ 96ColChoSS-194
❑ 96Don-299
❑ 96DonPreP-299
❑ 96Fle-155
❑ 96FleTif-155
❑ 96LeaSigEA-147
❑ 96MetUni-72
❑ 96MetUniP-72
❑ 96Pac-339
❑ 96PanSti-198
❑ 96Sco-477
❑ 96StaClu-387
❑ 96StaCluMOP-387
❑ 96Top-108
❑ 97Fle-300
❑ 97FleTif-300
❑ 97Pac-273
❑ 97PacLigB-273
❑ 97PacSil-273
❑ 98Pac-268
❑ 98PacOnl-280
❑ 98PacOnlR-280
❑ 98PacOnlWC-280
❑ 98PacPlaB-268
❑ 98PacRedT-268
❑ 98PacSil-268
❑ 98Top-194
❑ 98TopChr-194
❑ 98TopChrR-194
❑ 98TopDevR-194
❑ 98TopDia-194
❑ 98TopMiniC-194
❑ 98UppDec-370

Oliver, John
❑ 96AppLeaAB-30
❑ 96BesAutS1RP-FR11
❑ 97BesLimA-27
❑ 97Top-269
❑ 98ChaAllCM-24

Oliver, Nate (Nathaniel)
❑ 63Top-466
❑ 65DodTeal-12
❑ 65OPC-59
❑ 65Top-59
❑ 66Top-364
❑ 66TopVen-364
❑ 68OPC-124
❑ 68Top-124
❑ 68TopVen-124
❑ 69Top-354
❑ 70OPC-223
❑ 70Top-223
❑ 81TCM60I-389
❑ 88RenSilSCLC-291
❑ 89MidAngGS-2
❑ 90DodTar-588
❑ 90PalSprACLC-228
❑ 90PalSprAP-2594
❑ 91PalSprAP-2033
❑ 92MidAngF-4041
❑ 92MidAngOHP-17
❑ 92MidAngS-475
❑ 92YanWIZ6-95
❑ 93MidAngF-338
❑ 94AlbDukF-860
❑ 97MidAngOHP-21

Oliver, Rick
❑ 76WilTomT-17
❑ 80SalLakCGT-10

Oliver, Scott
❑ 82DanSunF-16
❑ 83RedPioT-20
❑ 85EdmTraC-5

Oliver, Thomas
❑ 26Zee-56
❑ 27Zee-32
❑ 36GouWidPPR-D25
❑ 36WorWidGV-119
❑ 51A'sTeal-26
❑ 53A'sTeal-24
❑ 54OriEss-29
❑ 54Top-207
❑ 79RedSoxEF-3
❑ 79RedSoxEF-23
❑ 94TopArc1-207
❑ 94TopArc1G-207

Oliver, Warren
❑ 82ForMyeRT-5

Oliveras, David
❑ 88BlaYNPRWLU-51
❑ 88BurIndP-1789
❑ 89KinIndS-16
❑ 90KinIndTI-17

Oliveras, Francisco
❑ 81MiaOriT-10
❑ 85ChaO'sT-15
❑ 86ChaOriW-20
❑ 87ChaO'sW-12
❑ 88BlaYNPRWL-48
❑ 88OrlTwiB-24
❑ 89BlaYNPRWL-49
❑ 89DonRoo-9
❑ 89PorBeaC-9
❑ 89PorBeaP-229
❑ 90CMC-560
❑ 90Lea-515
❑ 90PorBeaC-8
❑ 90PorBeaP-176
❑ 90ProAAAF-246
❑ 90TopDeb89-92
❑ 91Don-469
❑ 91GiaPacGaE-24
❑ 91GiaPos-2
❑ 91LinDriAAA-387
❑ 91OPC-52
❑ 91PhoFirLD-387
❑ 91PhoFirP-63
❑ 91Sco-635
❑ 91Top-52
❑ 91TopDesS-52
❑ 91TopMic-52
❑ 91TopTif-52
❑ 92Don-702
❑ 92Fle-645
❑ 92PhoFirS-391
❑ 92Sco-295
❑ 92StaClu-347
❑ 92UppDec-49
❑ 93Fle-534
❑ 93OklCit8F-1624
❑ 93PacSpa-276

Oliveras, Herbie
❑ 84ChaO'sT-27

Oliveras, Mako
❑ 89BlaYNPRWL-2
❑ 98KinIndQ-26

Oliveras, Max
❑ 75ShrCapT-16
❑ 86FloStaLAP-37
❑ 87MidAngP-15
❑ 88BlaYNPRWL-129
❑ 88MidAngGS-1
❑ 89MidAngGS-1
❑ 90CMC-502
❑ 90EdmTraC-2
❑ 90EdmTraP-531
❑ 90ProAAAF-107
❑ 91EdmTraLD-174
❑ 91EdmTraP-1531
❑ 91LinDriAAA-174
❑ 91TriA AAGP-AAA14
❑ 92EdmTraF-3553
❑ 92EdmTraS-174
❑ 93VanCanF-2613
❑ 94AngMot-28

Oliveras, Ossie
❑ 77SalPirT-16A
❑ 77SalPirT-16B
❑ 80VenLeaS-146

Oliverio, Steve
❑ 85CedRapRT-10
❑ 86VerRedP-14
❑ 87VerRedP-14
❑ 88NasSouC-9
❑ 88NasSouP-482
❑ 88NasSouTI-18
❑ 89CalCanC-4
❑ 89CalCanP-543
❑ 89ColMudB-24
❑ 94BilMusF-3686
❑ 94BilMusSP-24
❑ 95BilMusTI-28
❑ 96BilMusTI-24

Oliveros, Leonardo
❑ 94MarPhiC-15
❑ 94MarPhiF-3297
❑ 95MarPhiTI-19
❑ 96BatCliTI-15
❑ 97PieBolWB-23

Olivier, Richard
❑ 96GreBatB-17
❑ 97GreBatB-21

Olivo, Chi-Chi (Frederico)
❑ 65BraTeal-9
❑ 66Top-578
❑ 81TCM60I-349
❑ 84OCoandSI-127

Olivo, Diomedes
❑ 77PirTCM1WC-32

Olivo, Gary
❑ 97SalVolG-26

Olivo, Mike
❑ 70OPC-381
❑ 70Top-381

Olker, Joe
❑ 84EveGiaC-4
❑ 86FreGiaSB-12
❑ 88ShrCapP-1282
❑ 88TexLeaAGS-8
❑ 89PhoFirC-8
❑ 89PhoFirP-1497
❑ 91RenSilSCLC-25

Ollar, Rick
❑ 78CliDodT-25

Oller, Jeff
❑ 86JamExpP-18
❑ 87BurExpP-1074
❑ 88WesPalBES-21
❑ 90ChaRanS-18

Ollison, Ron
❑ 92ClePhiF-2064
❑ 94ClePhiC-21
❑ 94ClePhiF-2536

Ollison, Scott
❑ 91BenBucCB-20
❑ 91BenBucP-3702

Ollom, James
❑ 67OPC-137
❑ 67Top-137
❑ 67TwiTeal-14
❑ 68OPC-91
❑ 68Top-91
❑ 68TopVen-91
❑ 81TCM60I-378

Ollom, Mike
❑ 84AriWilP-15
❑ 87PenWhiSP-9
❑ 88TamTarS-19
❑ 89BirBarB-2
❑ 89BirBarP-95

Olmeda, Jose
❑ 89IdaFalBP-2015
❑ 90Bes-183
❑ 90SumBraB-16
❑ 90SumBraP-2444
❑ 91MacBraP-874
❑ 91SouAtlLAGP-SAL35
❑ 92ClaFS7-95
❑ 92DurBulTI-13
❑ 92GreBraF-1162
❑ 93GreBraF-358
❑ 94RicBraF-2856
❑ 95RicBraRC-16
❑ 95RicBraTI-14
❑ 95TopTra-146T
❑ 96ChaKniB-21
❑ 97ChaKni-23
❑ 97LowSpiB-15
❑ 97MicBatC-21
❑ 98RicBraQ-22

Olmo, Luis
❑ 77TCMTheWY-35
❑ 90DodTar-589
❑ 91DodRinP4-10

Olmstead, Fred
❑ 11PinT-5-769
❑ 11T205-132

Olmstead, Henry
❑ 12HomRunKE-26
❑ 12Zee-41

Olmstead, Nate
❑ 94ButCopKSP-4
❑ 95CedRapKTI-30

Olmstead, Reed
❑ 87EriCarP-4
❑ 87SavCarP-17
❑ 88SavCarP-346
❑ 89SpaPhiP-1048
❑ 89SpaPhiS-19
❑ 90Bes-257
❑ 90CMC-754
❑ 90OrlSunRB-7
❑ 90OrlSunRP-1092
❑ 90OrlSunRS-14
❑ 90StaFS7-46
❑ 91LinDriAA-490
❑ 91OrlSunRLD-490
❑ 91OrlSunRP-1860

Olmsted, Alan
❑ 80ArkTraT-11
❑ 81HawIslT-13
❑ 81Top-244
❑ 82LouRedE-21

Olney, Walter
❑ 29Zee-165
❑ 30Zee-183

Olsen, Al
❑ 51IndHag-5
❑ 86VenGulP-18
❑ 87MidAngP-9
❑ 88EdmTraP-584
❑ 89PalSprACLC-61
❑ 89PalSprAP-480

Olsen, Christopher
❑ 94SpaPhiF-1720

Olsen, D.C.
❑ 96DelShoB-24

Olsen, Jason
❑ 96MidLeaAB-54
❑ 96SouBenSHS-21
❑ 97BirBarB-24
❑ 98BirBarG-21
❑ 98SouLeaTPG-24

Olsen, John
❑ 47PadTeal-15
❑ 52LavPro-113

Olsen, Lefty
❑ 52MotCoo-23

Olsen, Lew
❑ 75WatRoyT-21
❑ 76OmaRoyTT-17
❑ 77JacSunT-16

Olsen, Rick
❑ 78NewWayCT-32
❑ 79HolMilT-9
❑ 80VanCanT-22
❑ 81VanCanT-13
❑ 82VanCanT-15

Olsen, Steve
❑ 92SarWhiSCB-21
❑ 92SarWhiSF-202
❑ 92UppDecML-208
❑ 93BirBarF-1190
❑ 93Bow-691
❑ 93ClaFS7-84
❑ 93ClaGolF-77
❑ 93ExcFS7-153
❑ 94BirBarC-18
❑ 94BirBarF-621
❑ 96WicWraB-20
❑ 97OmaRoyB-11

Olsen, Vern
❑ 41CubTeal-17
❑ 42CubTeal-17
❑ 79DiaGre-112

Olsen, Walter
❑ 49W72HolS-15

Olsen, Zoe Ann
❑ 63GadFunC-79

Olson, Brad
❑ 93EliTwiC-24

Olson, Cassidy
❑ 97UCLBruTI-14

Olson, Dan
❑ 89BoiHawP-1995
❑ 96HicCraB-13
❑ 97HicCraB-22
❑ 97HicCraRB-27
❑ 98CarLeaAC-36
❑ 98WinWar-20

Olson, Dean
❑ 77VisOakT-9

Olson, Greg
❑ 83LynMetT-8
❑ 84JacMetT-NNO
❑ 86JacMetT-12

❑ 87MetColP-42
❑ 87TidTidP-19
❑ 87TidTidT-11
❑ 88TidTidCa-6
❑ 88TidTidCM-13
❑ 88TidTidP-1597
❑ 89PorBeaC-13
❑ 89PorBeaP-225
❑ 90BraDubP-22
❑ 90BraDubS-25
❑ 90ClaYel-T19
❑ 90DonBesN-25
❑ 90DonRoo-46
❑ 90FleUpd-5
❑ 90Lea-323
❑ 90RedFolSB-70
❑ 90ScoRoo-69T
❑ 90TopBig-241
❑ 90TopTra-84T
❑ 90TopTraT-84T
❑ 90USPlaCA-2D
❑ 91Bow-577
❑ 91BraDubP-21
❑ 91BraSubS-28
❑ 91Don-285
❑ 91Fle-698
❑ 91Lea-158
❑ 91OPC-673
❑ 91PanFreS-18
❑ 91PanSti-25
❑ 91PetSta-2
❑ 91Sco-56
❑ 91Sco100RS-15
❑ 91StaClu-288
❑ 91StaCluP-29
❑ 91Top-673
❑ 91TopDesS-673
❑ 91TopMic-673
❑ 91TopTif-673
❑ 91Ult-9
❑ 91UppDec-303
❑ 92BraLykP-21
❑ 92BraLykS-25
❑ 92Don-386
❑ 92Fle-365
❑ 92Lea-226
❑ 92LeaBlaG-226
❑ 92OPC-39
❑ 92PanSti-161
❑ 92Pin-149
❑ 92Sco-474
❑ 92ScoProP-18
❑ 92StaClu-675
❑ 92StaCluD-134
❑ 92StaCluNC-675
❑ 92Stu-7
❑ 92Top-39
❑ 92TopGol-39
❑ 92TopGolW-39
❑ 92TopMic-39
❑ 92TriPla-54
❑ 92Ult-166
❑ 92UppDec-189
❑ 93BraFloA-7
❑ 93BraLykP-22
❑ 93BraLykS-27
❑ 93BraStaC-7
❑ 93Don-530
❑ 93Fle-11
❑ 93Lea-357
❑ 93OPC-296
❑ 93PacSpa-338
❑ 93PanSti-180
❑ 93Pin-173
❑ 93Sco-209
❑ 93Sel-46
❑ 93Sel-233
❑ 93StaClu-450
❑ 93StaCluFDI-450
❑ 93StaCluMOP-450
❑ 93Top-708
❑ 93TopGol-708
❑ 93TopInaM-708
❑ 93TopInaR-708
❑ 93TopMic-708
❑ 93Ult-10
❑ 93UppDec-187
❑ 93UppDecGold-187
❑ 94ColC-221
❑ 94ColChoGS-221
❑ 94ColChoSS-221
❑ 94Don-382
❑ 94Fle-370
❑ 94MetShuST-7
❑ 94Sco-442
❑ 94ScoGolR-442
❑ 94Top-346
❑ 94TopGol-346
❑ 94TopSpa-346

Olson, Gregg
❑ 87PanAmTUBI-31
❑ 87PanAmTURB-12
❑ 89BalOriP-23
❑ 89Bow-6
❑ 89BowTif-6
❑ 89ClaTraO-132
❑ 89Don-46
❑ 89DonBasB-322
❑ 89DonRoo-35
❑ 89OriFreB-30
❑ 89ScoRoo-96T
❑ 89StaWal/O-1
❑ 89StaWal/O-3
❑ 89StaWal/O-5
❑ 89StaWal/O-7
❑ 89StaWal/O-9
❑ 89StaWal/O-11
❑ 89Top-161
❑ 89TopAwaW-3
❑ 89TopTif-161
❑ 89TopTra-89T
❑ 89TopTraT-89T
❑ 89UppDec-723
❑ 90Baz-11
❑ 90Bow-249
❑ 90BowIns-7
❑ 90BowInsL-7
❑ 90BowInsT-7
❑ 90BowTif-249
❑ 90BowTif-A7
❑ 90ClaBlu-3
❑ 90Col-32
❑ 90Don-377
❑ 90DonBesA-43
❑ 90DonLeaS-27
❑ 90Fle-184
❑ 90FleAwaW-24
❑ 90FleCan-184
❑ 90FleLeaL-28
❑ 90FleLeaLC-28
❑ 90GooHumICBLS-14
❑ 90HagSunDGB-19
❑ 90Hot50RS-34
❑ 90KinDis-23
❑ 90Lea-7
❑ 90M.Vpin-5
❑ 90MLBBasB-114
❑ 90MSAHolD-20
❑ 90OPC-655
❑ 90PanSti-2
❑ 90PubIntS-581
❑ 90Sco-63
❑ 90Sco100RS-32
❑ 90ScoYouSI-4
❑ 90Spo-215
❑ 90Top-655
❑ 90TopCoi-3
❑ 90TopDeb89-93
❑ 90TopDou-48
❑ 90TopGaloC-6
❑ 90TopGloS-29
❑ 90TopHeaU-10
❑ 90TopRoo-22
❑ 90TopSti-10
❑ 90TopSti-238
❑ 90TopStiB-65
❑ 90TopTif-655
❑ 90TopTVA-30
❑ 90ToyRoo-21
❑ 90UppDec-604
❑ 90UppDecS-4
❑ 90USPlaCA-4C
❑ 90Woo-5
❑ 91BalOriP-22
❑ 91BasBesAotM-13
❑ 91Bow-92
❑ 91Cla3-T70
❑ 91Don-23
❑ 91Don-111
❑ 91Don-393
❑ 91DonSupD-23
❑ 91Fle-486
❑ 91Lea-519
❑ 91OPC-10
❑ 91OPCPre-343
❑ 91OriCro-343
❑ 91PanCanT1-88
❑ 91PanFreS-248
❑ 91PanSti-193
❑ 91RedFolS-69
❑ 91Sco-490
❑ 91Sco100S-27
❑ 91SevCoi-A10
❑ 91SimandSMLBL-32
❑ 91StaClu-156
❑ 91StaCluMO-10
❑ 91StaCluP-30
❑ 91Stu-8
❑ 91Top-10
❑ 91TopCraJ2-22
❑ 91TopDesS-10
❑ 91TopMic-10
❑ 91TopTif-10
❑ 91TopTriH-A1
❑ 91Ult-21
❑ 91UppDec-47
❑ 91UppDec-326
❑ 92BalOriP-27
❑ 92Bow-577
❑ 92Bow-629
❑ 92Bow-677
❑ 92Don-110
❑ 92DonCraJ2-25
❑ 92Fle-21
❑ 92Fle-701
❑ 92Hig5-3
❑ 92Lea-277
❑ 92LeaBlaG-277
❑ 92OPC-350
❑ 92OPCPre-101
❑ 92PanSti-72
❑ 92Pin-61
❑ 92PinTea2-13
❑ 92Sco-71
❑ 92Sco-427
❑ 92Sco100S-91
❑ 92ScoImpP-87
❑ 92StaClu-293
❑ 92Stu-128
❑ 92Top-350
❑ 92TopGol-350
❑ 92TopGolW-350
❑ 92TopKid-66
❑ 92TopMic-350
❑ 92TriPla-13
❑ 92Ult-307
❑ 92UppDec-227
❑ 92UppDecTMH-38
❑ 93BalOriP-24
❑ 93Bow-465
❑ 93Don-117
❑ 93Fin-121
❑ 93FinRef-121
❑ 93Fla-155
❑ 93Fle-173
❑ 93Lea-23
❑ 93MSABenSPD-17
❑ 93OPC-281
❑ 93PacSpa-22
❑ 93Pin-97
❑ 93RedFolS-71
❑ 93Sco-80
❑ 93SP-161
❑ 93StaClu-418
❑ 93StaCluFDI-418
❑ 93StaCluMOP-418
❑ 93Top-246
❑ 93TopGol-246
❑ 93TopInaM-246
❑ 93TopInaR-246
❑ 93TopMic-246
❑ 93TriPla-135
❑ 93Ult-145
❑ 93UppDec-674
❑ 93UppDecGold-674
❑ 94Bow-461
❑ 94BraLykP-27
❑ 94BraLykS-25
❑ 94ColC-368
❑ 94ColChoGS-368
❑ 94ColChoSS-368
❑ 94Don-8
❑ 94DonSpeE-8
❑ 94Fin-246
❑ 94FinRef-246
❑ 94Fle-13
❑ 94FleUpd-105
❑ 94Pac-40
❑ 94Pin-277
❑ 94PinArtP-277
❑ 94PinMusC-277
❑ 94Sco-525
❑ 94ScoGolR-525
❑ 94SpoRoo-29
❑ 94SpoRooAP-29
❑ 94StaClu-196
❑ 94StaClu-602
❑ 94StaCluFDI-196
❑ 94StaCluFDI-602
❑ 94StaCluGR-196
❑ 94StaCluGR-602
❑ 94StaCluMOP-196
❑ 94StaCluMOP-602
❑ 94Top-723
❑ 94TopGol-723
❑ 94TopSpa-723
❑ 94TopTra-118T
❑ 94UppDec-393
❑ 94UppDecED-393
❑ 96TigHebN-22
❑ 98DiaBacP-8
❑ 98DiaMcD-16
❑ 98PacOnl-43
❑ 98PacOnlR-43
❑ 98PacOnlWC-43
❑ 99Fle-498
❑ 99FleSta9-498
❑ 99FleWarT-498
❑ 99MetUni-88
❑ 99MetUniGM-88
❑ 99MetUniPMG-88
❑ 99SkyPre-157
❑ 99SkyPreR-157
❑ 99StaClu-233
❑ 99StaCluFDI-233
❑ 99StaCluOoaK-233
❑ 99StaCluPP-233
❑ 99Top-261
❑ 99TopChr-261
❑ 99TopChrR-261
❑ 99TopMVPP-261

Olson, James Vincent
❑ 87BurExpP-1068

Olson, Jimmy
❑ 86AubAstP-18
❑ 87AshTouP-9

Olson, Karl (Karl Arthur)
❑ 52Top-72
❑ 54Top-186
❑ 55Top-72
❑ 55TopDouH-35
❑ 56Top-322
❑ 57Top-153
❑ 83TopRep5-72
❑ 94TopArc1-186
❑ 94TopArc1G-186

Olson, Ken
❑ 91SalSpuP-2240

Olson, Kurt
❑ 88CapCodPPaLP-47
❑ 90YakBeaTI-6

Olson, Mike
❑ 81ChaRoyT-4

Olson, Mitch
❑ 80AppFoxT-18

Olson, Ollie (Ivan M.)
❑ 09ObaT21-30
❑ 09ObaT21-123
❑ 10BisCoaLE99-24
❑ 12T207-145
❑ 14B18B-7A
❑ 14B18B-7B
❑ 19W514-70
❑ 20NatCarE-71
❑ 21Exh-120
❑ 22E120-146
❑ 23WilChoV-115
❑ 90DodTar-590

Olson, Phil
❑ 96StLucMTI-9
❑ 97St.LucM-21

Olson, Terry
❑ 75AndRanT-17

Olson, Warren
❑ 86BelBreP-18
❑ 88WinHavRSS-17

Olsson, Dan
❑ 86TulDriTI-19

Olszewski, Eric
❑ 94IdaFalBF-3582
❑ 94IdaFalBSP-20
❑ 95MacBraTI-23
❑ 96DurBulBIB-5
❑ 96DurBulBrB-6

Olszewski, Tim
❑ 96HigDesMB-22
❑ 97FreKey-20
❑ 98FreKeyM-12

Olszta, Ed
❑ 75AppFoxT-21
❑ 76AppFoxT-18
❑ 77AppFoxT-17

Olwine, Ed
❑ 83NasSouTI-13
❑ 84TidTidT-11
❑ 85TidTidT-12
❑ 86RicBraP-14
❑ 87BraSmo-6
❑ 87Don-560
❑ 87Fle-524
❑ 87FleGlo-524
❑ 87RicBraBC-16
❑ 87Top-159
❑ 87TopTif-159
❑ 88BlaYNPRWLU-41
❑ 88Sco-379
❑ 88ScoGlo-379
❑ 88Top-353
❑ 88TopClo-81
❑ 88TopTif-353
❑ 89OmaRoyC-8
❑ 89OmaRoyP-1725
❑ 89UppDec-435
❑ 90CMC-282
❑ 90ProAAAF-402
❑ 90RicBraBC-1
❑ 90RicBraC-6
❑ 90RicBraP-257
❑ 90RicBraTI-25

Omachi, George
❑ 88FreSunP-1246

Omo, Bob
❑ 78CedRapGT-20

Oms, Alejandro
❑ 91PomBlaBPB-9

Ongarato, Mike
❑ 81PawRedST-21

Onichuk, Sergei
❑ 89EasLeaDDP-DD11

Onis, Curly
❑ 72TCMthe3-56
❑ 90DodTar-1045

Onley, Shawn
❑ 96AppLeaAB-13
❑ 96DanBraB-15
❑ 97DurBulTI-14
❑ 98DanQ-C-17

Onofrei, Tim
❑ 96JohCitCTI-25
❑ 97PeoChi-20

Onslow, Eddie
❑ 82OhiHaloF-28

Onslow, Jack
❑ 23Zee-73

Ontiveros, Art
❑ 94LetMouF-3878
❑ 94LetMouSP-16

Ontiveros, Steve
❑ 83AlbA'sT-7
❑ 84TacTigC-83
❑ 85TacTigC-142
❑ 86A'sMot-22
❑ 86Don-589
❑ 86Fle-429
❑ 86SevCoi-W16
❑ 86Top-507
❑ 86TopTif-507
❑ 87Don-221
❑ 87DonHig-15
❑ 87Fle-401
❑ 87FleGlo-401
❑ 87Top-161
❑ 87TopTif-161
❑ 88A'sMot-13
❑ 88Don-467
❑ 88DonTeaBA-467
❑ 88Fle-289
❑ 88FleGlo-289
❑ 88Sco-511
❑ 88ScoGlo-511
❑ 88StaLinAs-11
❑ 88Top-272
❑ 88TopClo-82
❑ 88TopTif-272
❑ 89Don-596
❑ 89DonTra-11
❑ 89PhiTas-26
❑ 89Sco-337
❑ 89Top-692
❑ 89TopTif-692
❑ 89TopTra-90T
❑ 89TopTraT-90T
❑ 90AlbDecGB-7
❑ 90Bow-145
❑ 90BowTif-145
❑ 91Sco-832
❑ 94A'sMot-18
❑ 95AthMot-18
❑ 95ColCho-122
❑ 95ColChoGS-122
❑ 95ColChoSS-122
❑ 95Don-177
❑ 95DonPreP-177
❑ 95DonTopotO-140
❑ 95Emo-73
❑ 95Fla-294
❑ 95Fle-251
❑ 95Lea-389
❑ 95Pac-318
❑ 95Sco-38
❑ 95ScoGolR-38
❑ 95ScoPlaTS-38
❑ 95SelCer-19
❑ 95SelCerMG-19
❑ 95Top-593
❑ 95TopCyb-365
❑ 95Ult-320
❑ 95UltGolM-320
❑ 95UppDec-32
❑ 95UppDecED-32
❑ 95UppDecEDG-32
❑ 95USPlaCMLA-13S
❑ 95Zen-100
❑ 96ColCho-244
❑ 96ColChoGS-244
❑ 96ColChoSS-244
❑ 96Don-329
❑ 96DonPreP-329
❑ 96Fle-214
❑ 96FleTif-214
❑ 96MetUni-102
❑ 96MetUniP-102
❑ 96Pac-398
❑ 96Pin-75
❑ 96Sco-178
❑ 96StaClu-388
❑ 96StaCluEPB-388
❑ 96StaCluEPG-388
❑ 96StaCluEPS-388
❑ 96StaCluMOP-388
❑ 96Top-176
❑ 96UppDec-161
❑ 98RocRedWQ-21

Ontiveros, Steve (Steven Robert)
❑ 74OPC-598
❑ 74Top-598
❑ 75Gia-7
❑ 75GiaTeal-13
❑ 75OPC-483
❑ 75Top-483
❑ 75TopMin-483
❑ 76CubTri-18
❑ 76OPC-284
❑ 76SanFraGP-16
❑ 76SSP-104
❑ 76Top-284
❑ 77CubJewT-12
❑ 78Kel-44
❑ 78SSP270-250
❑ 78Top-76
❑ 79OPC-150
❑ 79Top-299
❑ 80OPC-268
❑ 80Top-514
❑ 89TopSenL-79
❑ 90EliSenL-117

Ootsuka, Kenichi
❑ 90SalSpuCLC-120

Ootsuka, Yoshiki
❑ 90SalSpuCLC-141

Opatkiewicz, Ryan
❑ 94HunCubC-21
❑ 94HunCubF-3562

Opdyke, Paul
❑ 88IdaFalBP-1854

Opie, James
❑ 83AleDukT-6
❑ 85HawIslC-226
❑ 86NasPirP-20
❑ 87JacExpP-441

Opipari, Mario
❑ 97ForWayW-23
❑ 98ForMyeMTI-22

Oppenheimer, Jose
❑ 77BurBeeT-20

Oppenheimer, Juan
❑ 78CedRapGT-21
❑ 79CedRapGT-26

Opperman, Dan
❑ 88GreFalDTI-10
❑ 89VorBeaDS-20
❑ 90SanAntMGS-19
❑ 91AlbDukP-1140
❑ 91Bow-606

- 91Cla2-T83
- 91DodSt.V-9
- 91Ult-384
- 92AlbDukF-720

Oquendo, Ismael
- 84RocRedWT-8

Oquendo, Jorge
- 82IdaFalAT-27

Oquendo, Jose (Jose Manuel)
- 82TidTidT-15
- 83TidTidT-29
- 84Don-643
- 84Fle-592
- 84Nes792-208
- 84OPC-208
- 84Top-208
- 84TopSti-112
- 84TopTif-208
- 85Fle-88
- 85LouRedR-15
- 85Top-598
- 85TopTif-598
- 86CarSchM-17
- 86CarTeal-32
- 86TopTra-82T
- 86TopTraT-82T
- 87CarSmo-18
- 87CarTeal-23
- 87Don-510
- 87Fle-305
- 87FleGlo-305
- 87Top-133
- 87TopTif-133
- 88CarSmo-16
- 88CarTeal-24
- 88Don-234
- 88DonBasB-313
- 88Fle-44
- 88FleGlo-44
- 88Sco-248
- 88ScoGlo-248
- 88StaLinCa-15
- 88Top-83
- 88TopSti-18
- 88TopTif-83
- 89BimBreD-5
- 89Bow-438
- 89BowTif-438
- 89CarSmo-15
- 89CarTeal-20
- 89Don-319
- 89DonBasB-100
- 89Fle-459
- 89FleGlo-459
- 89KeyFooD-19
- 89MSAIceTD-19
- 89OPC-69
- 89OurOwnTD-19
- 89PanSti-184
- 89Sco-529
- 89ScoYouS2-16
- 89TetTeaD-19
- 89Top-442
- 89TopBig-77
- 89TopSti-45
- 89TopTif-442
- 89UppDec-514
- 89WeiMarD-19
- 90Bow-200
- 90BowTif-200
- 90CarSmo-17
- 90Don-161
- 90DonBesN-108
- 90Fle-255
- 90FleCan-255
- 90Lea-129
- 90MLBBasB-59
- 90OPC-645
- 90PanSti-341
- 90PubIntS-223
- 90Sco-68
- 90Spo-85
- 90Top-645
- 90TopBig-65
- 90TopSti-44
- 90TopTif-645
- 90TopTVCa-27
- 90UppDec-319
- 91Bow-395
- 91CarPol-11
- 91Don-281
- 91Fle-640
- 91Lea-58
- 91MetWIZ-301
- 91OPC-343
- 91PanFreS-32
- 91PanSti-30
- 91Sco-622
- 91StaClu-190
- 91StaCluP-31
- 91Stu-236
- 91Top-343
- 91TopDesS-343
- 91TopMic-343
- 91TopTif-343
- 91Ult-292
- 91UppDec-193
- 92CarPol-13
- 92Don-280
- 92Fle-585
- 92Lea-289
- 92LeaBlaG-289
- 92OPC-723
- 92PanSti-173
- 92Pin-239
- 92Sco-305
- 92StaClu-571
- 92Top-723
- 92TopGol-723
- 92TopGolW-723
- 92TopMic-723
- 92TriPla-118
- 92Ult-267
- 92UppDec-283
- 93CarPol-12
- 93CarStaC-4
- 93Don-46
- 93Fle-513
- 93Lea-26
- 93PacBeiA-28
- 93PacSpa-298
- 93PacSpaGE-7
- 93Pin-316
- 93Sco-163
- 93Top-535
- 93TopGol-535
- 93TopInaM-535
- 93TopInaR-535
- 93TopMic-535
- 93TriPla-228
- 93UppDec-84
- 93UppDecGold-84
- 94CarPol-12
- 94Fle-639
- 94Pac-596
- 94StaCluT-313
- 94StaCluTFDI-313
- 94Top-406
- 94TopGol-406
- 94TopSpa-406
- 94Ult-268
- 95DonTopotO-333
- 95Fla-193
- 95Pac-411
- 95Sco-218
- 95ScoGolR-218
- 95ScoPlaTS-218
- 95Top-291
- 96Don-234
- 96DonPreP-234
- 96Fle-551
- 96FleTif-551
- 96Pac-228
- 96Sco-143
- 98NewJerCM-33

Oquendo, Nelwin
- 97SalVolG-27

Oquist, Mike
- 89EriOriS-16
- 90CarLeaA-2
- 90FreKeyTI-22
- 91Cla/Bes-188
- 91HagSunLD-241
- 91HagSunP-2455
- 91LinDriAA-241
- 92RocRedWF-1938
- 92RocRedWS-461
- 92SkyAAAF-210
- 93Bow-74
- 93RocRedWF-236
- 94BalOriP-24
- 94Fla-256
- 94FleExtB-10
- 94FleUpd-4
- 94OriPro-74
- 94OriUSPC-2D
- 94Pin-224
- 94PinArtP-224
- 94PinMusC-224
- 94ScoRoo-RT129
- 94ScoRooGR-RT129
- 94SpoRoo-66
- 94SpoRooAP-66
- 94StaCluT-276
- 94StaCluTFDI-276
- 94Top-763
- 94TopGol-763
- 94TopSpa-763
- 95BalOriP-37
- 95ColCho-343
- 95ColChoGS-343
- 95ColChoSS-343
- 95Fla-7
- 95Fle-16
- 95Sco-200
- 95ScoGolR-200
- 95ScoPlaTS-200
- 95UppDecSE-47
- 95UppDecSEG-47
- 96LasVegSB-19
- 98A'sMot-17
- 98PacOnl-541
- 98PacOnlR-541
- 98PacOnlWC-541

Oram, Jon
- 93WatIndC-21
- 93WatIndF-3571
- 94WatIndC-22
- 94WatIndF-3946

Oramas, Victor
- 94VenLinU-162
- 96-97LinVen-202

Oravetz, Ernie (Ernest E.)
- 56Top-51
- 57Top-179
- 89ChaLooLITI-23

Orbit, Mascot
- 94MasMan-9

Ordaz, Luis
- 93PriRedC-22
- 93PriRedF-4188
- 94ChaWheC-18
- 94ChaWheF-2713
- 94PriRedC-19
- 94PriRedF-3270
- 95LinVen-199
- 96-97LinVen-176
- 96StPetCB-22
- 97ArkTraB-16
- 97Bow-215
- 97BowInt-215
- 97TexLeaTP-1
- 98Bow-220
- 98BowCerBlueAU-47
- 98BowCerGA-47
- 98BowCerSA-47
- 98BowChr-220
- 98BowChrGA-220
- 98BowChrGAR-220
- 98BowChrI-220
- 98BowChrIR-220
- 98BowChrR-220
- 98BowGolA-220
- 98BowInt-220
- 98DonColL-392
- 98DonPriCL-392
- 98DonSigA-64
- 98DonSigAC-84
- 98DonSigAM-85
- 98DonSigSB-24
- 98Fle-65
- 98Lea-193
- 98LeaFraDA-193
- 98LeaFraF-193
- 98LeaFraM-193
- 98LeaFraM-193
- 98LeaFraMDC-193
- 98LeaFraMDC-193
- 98LeaFraMZ2-193
- 98Pac-418
- 98PacPlaB-418
- 98PacRedT-418
- 98PacSil-418
- 98PinSna-SLC16
- 99MetUni-267
- 99MetUniGM-267
- 99MetUniPMG-267
- 99Pac-359
- 99PacAur-157
- 99PacAurOD-157
- 99PacCroC-234
- 99PacCroCPB-234
- 99PacPlaB-359
- 99PacRed-359
- 99Ult-246
- 99UltGolM-246
- 99UltMas-246
- 99UltPlaM-246

Ordonez, Magglio
- 93HicCraC-17
- 93HicCraF-1292
- 94HicCraC-17
- 94HicCraF-2189
- 94SouAtlLAF-SAL25
- 94VenLinU-149
- 95LinVen-151
- 95PriWilCTI-4
- 96-97LinVen-201
- 96BirBarB-5
- 97Bes-60
- 97BesAutSBPP-48
- 98Bow-185
- 98BowBes-178
- 98BowBesAR-178
- 98BowBesR-178
- 98BowChr-185
- 98BowChrGA-185
- 98BowChrGAR-185
- 98BowChrI-185
- 98BowChrIR-185
- 98BowChrR-185
- 98BowGolA-185
- 98BowInt-185
- 98CirThu-175
- 98CirThuRav-175
- 98CirThuSupRav-175
- 98ColCho-102
- 98Don-305
- 98DonGolPP-305
- 98DonSig-90
- 98DonSigA-65
- 98DonSigAC-85
- 98DonSigAM-86
- 98DonSigP-90
- 98DonSigSB-25
- 98DonSigSP-19
- 98DonSilPP-305
- 98E-X2SD2001-5
- 98FlaShoLeg0-32
- 98FlaShoLeg1-32
- 98FlaShoLeg2-32
- 98FlaShoLeg3-32
- 98FlaShoLegM-32
- 98FlaShoR0-32
- 98FlaShoR1-32
- 98FlaShoR2-32
- 98FlaShoR3-32
- 98FlaShoWotF-10
- 98Fle-235
- 98FleProF-PF14
- 98FleRooS-15
- 98LeaRCrusUP-130
- 98LeaRS-211
- 98LeaRSCrusUG-130
- 98LeaRSCrusUR-130
- 98LeaRSFOSamp-17
- 98LeaRSFresh-17
- 98LeaRSLHolo-211
- 98LeaRSLong-211
- 98LeaRTrue-211
- 98PacAur-24
- 98PacInvGems-33
- 98PacOme-59
- 98PacOmeR-59
- 98PacOmeRS-24
- 98PacOmeRST5-24
- 98PacOnl-177
- 98PacOnlR-177
- 98PacOnlWC-177
- 98PacPar-31
- 98PacParC-31
- 98PacParG-31
- 98PacParHS-31
- 98PacParPB-31
- 98PacParR-31
- 98PinPlu-62
- 98PriWilCASM-14
- 98Revo-36
- 98RevoRooHH-5
- 98RevoRooHH6-5
- 98RevoSS-36
- 98ScoRT-244
- 98ScoRTSS-PP137
- 98ScoRTSSAP-PP137
- 98ScoRTSSAP1-PP137
- 98SkyDugA-103
- 98SkyDugAIA-103
- 98SP Aut-5
- 98SpoIll-155
- 98SpoIllEE-155
- 98SpoIllFE-155
- 98SpoIllTaN-149
- 98SpoIllTaNEE-149
- 98SpoIllWSF-131
- 98SpoIllWSFEE-131
- 98SpoIllWSFFE-131
- 98SPxFin-203
- 98SPxFinR-203
- 98SPxFinS-203
- 98StaCluFDI-137
- 98StaCluI-137
- 98StaCluOneK-137
- 98StaCluPP-137
- 98Stu-92
- 98StuGPP-92
- 98StuSPP-92
- 98UD3-9
- 98UD3-99
- 98UD3-189
- 98UD3DieCut-9
- 98UD3DieCut-99
- 98UD3DieCut-189
- 98Ult-380
- 98UltGolM-380
- 98UltMas-380
- 98UltPlaM-380
- 98UltRoctS-2
- 98UppDec-570
- 98UppDecDS-DS16
- 99CroRoyB-34
- 99CroRoyL-34
- 99CroRoyOD-34
- 99E-X Cen-29
- 99E-X CenECFut-29
- 99E-X CenECNow-29
- 99E-X CenEQ-14
- 99Fle-119
- 99FleSta9-119
- 99FleWarT-119
- 99MetUni-231
- 99MetUniGM-231
- 99MetUniPMG-231
- 99Pac-104
- 99PacAur-41
- 99PacAurOD-41
- 99PacCroC-69
- 99PacCroC-5
- 99PacCroCPB-69
- 99PacOme-58
- 99PacOmeC-58
- 99PacOmeG-58
- 99PacOmePB-58
- 99PacPar-59
- 99PacParC-59
- 99PacParG-59
- 99PacParHoloGold-59
- 99PacParHS-59
- 99PacParOD-59
- 99PacParPB-59
- 99PacParRed-59
- 99PacPlaB-104
- 99PacPri-34
- 99PacPriHB-34
- 99PacPriHG-34
- 99PacPriHM-34
- 99PacPriHP-34
- 99PacPriRed-34
- 99PacRed-104
- 99Rev-35
- 99RevPremDate-35
- 99RevRet-35
- 99RevShaSS-35
- 99SkyPre-175
- 99SkyPreR-175
- 99SkyThu-159
- 99SkyThuRant-159
- 99SkyThuRave-159
- 99StaClu-226
- 99StaCluFDI-226
- 99StaCluOoaK-226
- 99StaCluPP-226
- 99ThuSkySupR-159
- 99Top-155
- 99TopChr-155
- 99TopChrR-155
- 99TopMVPP-155
- 99TopOpeD-89
- 99Ult-84
- 99UltGolM-84
- 99UltMas-84
- 99UltPlaM-84
- 99UppDec-68
- 99UppDec-246
- 99UppDecBD-21
- 99UppDecBDD-21
- 99UppDecBDQ-21
- 99UppDecBDT-21
- 99UppDecEL1-68
- 99UppDecEL1-246
- 99UppDecEL2-68
- 99UppDecEL2-246
- 99UppDecM-47
- 99UppDecMGS-47
- 99UppDecMHFS-47
- 99UppDecMP-47
- 99UppDecMSS-47
- 99Vic-97

Ordonez, Rey
- 92SpoIllFK1-513
- 94Cla-199
- 94FloStaLAF-FSL40
- 94St.LucMC-1
- 94St.LucMF-1204
- 95Bes-85
- 95Bow-140
- 95BowBes-B33
- 95BowBesR-B33
- 95Exc-233
- 95ExcFirYP-5
- 95NorTidTI-19
- 95SPML-96
- 95SPMLA-19
- 95Top-571
- 95UppDecML-19
- 95UppDecML-110
- 95UppDecMLFS-19
- 95UppDecMLFS-110
- 96Bow-349
- 96BowBes-17
- 96BowBesAR-17
- 96BowBesP-BBP5
- 96BowBesPAR-BBP5
- 96BowBesPR-BBP5
- 96BowBesR-17
- 96BowFoi-349
- 96Cir-161
- 96CirAcc-24
- 96CirBos-42
- 96CirRav-161
- 96ColCho-429
- 96ColChoGS-429
- 96ColChoSS-429
- 96EmoXL-237
- 96Fin-B276
- 96Fin-G338
- 96FinRef-B276
- 96FinRef-G338
- 96Fla-325
- 96FlaWavotF-18
- 96FleUpd-U160
- 96FleUpd-U248
- 96FleUpdNH-19
- 96FleUpdSL-8
- 96FleUpdTC-U160
- 96FleUpdTC-U248
- 96LeaLimR-9
- 96LeaLimRG-9
- 96LeaPre-117
- 96LeaPreP-117
- 96LeaSig-58
- 96LeaSigA-173
- 96LeaSigAG-173
- 96LeaSigAS-173
- 96LeaSigPPG-58
- 96LeaSigPPP-58
- 96MetKah-25
- 96Pin-380
- 96PinAfi-159
- 96PinAfi-191
- 96PinAfiAP-159
- 96PinAfiAP-191
- 96PinFoil-380
- 96Sel-173
- 96SelArtP-173
- 96SelCer-112
- 96SelCerAP-112
- 96SelCerCB-112
- 96SelCerCR-112
- 96SelCerIP-6
- 96SelCerMB-112
- 96SelCerMG-112
- 96SelCerMR-112
- 96SP-1
- 96SPMarM-MM4
- 96SPMarMDC-3
- 96SPSpeFX-46
- 96SPSpeFXDC-46
- 96SPx-42
- 96SPxGol-42
- 96Stu-14
- 96StuPrePB-14
- 96StuPrePG-14
- 96StuPrePS-14
- 96Sum-153

❑ 96Sum-162
❑ 96SumAbo&B-153
❑ 96SumAbo&B-162
❑ 96SumArtP-153
❑ 96SumArtP-162
❑ 96SumFoi-153
❑ 96SumFoi-162
❑ 96TeaOut-61
❑ 96Top-427
❑ 96TopGal-140
❑ 96TopGalPPI-140
❑ 96TopLas-76
❑ 96TopLasBS-5
❑ 96Ult-514
❑ 96UltGolM-514
❑ 96UppDec-245
❑ 96UppDecDD-DD29
❑ 96UppDecDDG-DD29
❑ 96UppDecDDS-DD29
❑ 96UppDecPHE-H59
❑ 96UppDecPreH-H59
❑ 96Zen-118
❑ 96ZenArtP-118
❑ 97Bow-42
❑ 97BowInt-42
❑ 97Cir-253
❑ 97CirRav-253
❑ 97ColCho-167
❑ 97ColChoTBS-32
❑ 97ColChoTBSWH-32
❑ 97Don-232
❑ 97DonEli-59
❑ 97DonEliGS-59
❑ 97DonGolPP-232
❑ 97DonLim-10
❑ 97DonLimE-10
❑ 97DonLimENG-10
❑ 97DonPre-108
❑ 97DonPreCttC-108
❑ 97DonSilPP-232
❑ 97E-X2-86
❑ 97E-X2Cred-86
❑ 97E-X2EssCre-86
❑ 97Fin-22
❑ 97FinRef-22
❑ 97FlaShoLC-50
❑ 97FlaShoLeg0-50
❑ 97FlaShoLeg1-50
❑ 97FlaShoM-A50
❑ 97FlaShoM-B50
❑ 97FlaShoM-C50
❑ 97FlaShoR0-50
❑ 97FlaShoR1-50
❑ 97FlaShoR2-50
❑ 97Fle-403
❑ 97FleRooS-10
❑ 97FleTif-403
❑ 97KinB-4
❑ 97Lea-41
❑ 97LeaFraM-41
❑ 97LeaFraMDC-41
❑ 97MetUni-198
❑ 97MetUniPP-7
❑ 97Pac-372
❑ 97PacBaeS-8
❑ 97PacLatotML-34
❑ 97PacLigB-372
❑ 97PacPri-127
❑ 97PacPriGotD-GD175
❑ 97PacPriLB-127
❑ 97PacPriP-127
❑ 97PacSil-372
❑ 97Pin-105
❑ 97PinArtP-PP105
❑ 97PinCer-32
❑ 97PinCerMBla-32
❑ 97PinCerMBlu-32
❑ 97PinCerMG-32
❑ 97PinCerMR-32
❑ 97PinCerR-32
❑ 97PinIns-133
❑ 97PinInsCE-133
❑ 97PinInsDE-133
❑ 97PinMusC-105
❑ 97PinPasttM-20
❑ 97PinPrePla-105
❑ 97PinTotCPB-32
❑ 97PinTotCPG-32
❑ 97PinTotCPR-32
❑ 97PinX-P-24
❑ 97PinX-PMoS-24
❑ 97PinX-PMP-20
❑ 97PinX-PreMPS-20
❑ 97Sco-100
❑ 97Sco-543
❑ 97ScoArtPWB-100
❑ 97ScoArtPWB-543
❑ 97ScoPreS-100
❑ 97ScoResC-543
❑ 97ScoShoS-100
❑ 97ScoShoS-543
❑ 97ScoShoSAP-100
❑ 97ScoShoSAP-543
❑ 97SelRooR-6
❑ 97SelToootT-24
❑ 97SelToootTMB-24
❑ 97SP-116
❑ 97SpolII-65
❑ 97SpolIIEE-65
❑ 97SPSpxF-6
❑ 97SPVinAu-22
❑ 97SPVinAu-23
❑ 97StaClu-48
❑ 97StaCluC-CO8
❑ 97StaCluM-M12
❑ 97StaCluMat-48
❑ 97StaCluMOP-48
❑ 97StaCluMOP-M12
❑ 97StaCluMOP-PL11
❑ 97StaCluPL-PL11
❑ 97Stu-92
❑ 97StuPrePG-92
❑ 97StuPrePS-92
❑ 97Top-180
❑ 97TopAwel-AI13
❑ 97TopChr-70
❑ 97TopChrR-70
❑ 97TopGal-141
❑ 97TopGalPPI-141
❑ 97UD3-49
❑ 97UD3GenNex-GN4
❑ 97Ult-245
❑ 97UltDouT-17
❑ 97UltFieC-14
❑ 97UltGolME-245
❑ 97UltPlaME-245
❑ 97UltRooR-8
❑ 97UppDec-114
❑ 97UppDec-149
❑ 97UppDec-184
❑ 97UppDecGJ-GJ3
❑ 97UppDecRSF-RS2
❑ 97UppDecTTS-TS3
❑ 98Bow-230
❑ 98BowChr-230
❑ 98BowChrGA-230
❑ 98BowChrGAR-230
❑ 98BowChrI-230
❑ 98BowChrIR-230
❑ 98BowChrR-230
❑ 98BowGolA-230
❑ 98BowInt-230
❑ 98CirThu-54
❑ 98CirThuRav-54
❑ 98CirThuSupRav-54
❑ 98ColCho-176
❑ 98CroRoy-89
❑ 98Don-217
❑ 98DonGolPP-217
❑ 98DonSilPP-217
❑ 98Fin-175
❑ 98FinNo--175
❑ 98FinNo-R-175
❑ 98FinRef-175
❑ 98FlaShoLeg0-54
❑ 98FlaShoLeg1-54
❑ 98FlaShoLeg2-54
❑ 98FlaShoLeg3-54
❑ 98FlaShoLegM-54
❑ 98FlaShoR0-54
❑ 98FlaShoR1-54
❑ 98FlaShoR2-54
❑ 98FlaShoR3-54
❑ 98Fle-369
❑ 98FleVin'-106
❑ 98FleVin'C-106
❑ 98KinDis-4
❑ 98MetUni-105
❑ 98MetUniPMG-105
❑ 98Pac-374
❑ 98PacAur-167
❑ 98PacInv-122
❑ 98PacInvInt-8N
❑ 98PacInvPBlue-122
❑ 98PacInvSilv-122
❑ 98PacInvTeam-18
❑ 98PacLatotML-25
❑ 98PacOme-161
❑ 98PacOmeR-161
❑ 98PacOnl-486
❑ 98PacOnlR-486
❑ 98PacOnlWC-486
❑ 98PacPar-209
❑ 98PacParC-209
❑ 98PacParG-209
❑ 98PacParHS-209
❑ 98PacParPB-209
❑ 98PacParR-209
❑ 98PacPlaB-374
❑ 98PacRedT-374
❑ 98PacSil-374
❑ 98PacTeaC-23
❑ 98PinSna-NYM1
❑ 98PinSna-NYM6
❑ 98Revo-95
❑ 98RevoSS-95
❑ 98Sco-185
❑ 98ScoRT-83
❑ 98ScoSS-PP85
❑ 98ScoSSAP-PP85
❑ 98SkyDugA-32
❑ 98SkyDugAIA-32
❑ 98SP Aut-134
❑ 98SpolII-97
❑ 98SpolIIEE-97
❑ 98SpolIIFE-97
❑ 98SpolIIODMP-OD19
❑ 98SpolIIWSF-105
❑ 98SpolIIWSFEE-105
❑ 98SpolIIWSFFE-105
❑ 98SPxFin-300
❑ 98SPxFinR-300
❑ 98SPxFinS-300
❑ 98StaCluFDI-87
❑ 98StaCluI-87
❑ 98StaCluOneK-87
❑ 98StaCluPP-87
❑ 98Top-103
❑ 98TopChr-103
❑ 98TopChrR-103
❑ 98TopDevR-103
❑ 98TopDia-103
❑ 98TopGal-62
❑ 98TopGalGP-62
❑ 98TopGalOPP-62
❑ 98TopGalPPI-62
❑ 98TopGalPPIA-62
❑ 98TopMiniC-103
❑ 98TopOpeD-51
❑ 98TopSta-32
❑ 98TopStaB-32
❑ 98TopStaG-32
❑ 98TopStaGR-32
❑ 98TopStaS-32
❑ 98Ult-84
❑ 98UltGolM-84
❑ 98UltKidG-11
❑ 98UltMas-84
❑ 98UltPlaM-84
❑ 98UppDec-166
❑ 98UppDecNP-NP5
❑ 98UppDecRGKoG-G23
❑ 99199Fin-199
❑ 99CroRoyB-92
❑ 99CroRoyL-92
❑ 99CroRoyOD-92
❑ 99FinGolRef-199
❑ 99FinRef-199
❑ 99Fle-224
❑ 99FleSta9-224
❑ 99FleWarT-224
❑ 99Pac-285
❑ 99PacAur-122
❑ 99PacAurOD-122
❑ 99PacCroC-183
❑ 99PacCroC-36
❑ 99PacCroCPB-183
❑ 99PacInv-96
❑ 99PacInvOD-96
❑ 99PacInvPB-96
❑ 99PacOme-155
❑ 99PacOmeC-155
❑ 99PacOmeG-155
❑ 99PacOmePB-155
❑ 99PacPar-154
❑ 99PacParC-154
❑ 99PacParG-154
❑ 99PacParHoloGold-154
❑ 99PacParHS-154
❑ 99PacParOD-154
❑ 99PacParPB-154
❑ 99PacParRed-154
❑ 99PacPlaB-285
❑ 99PacPri-95
❑ 99PacPriHB-95
❑ 99PacPriHG-95
❑ 99PacPriHM-95
❑ 99PacPriHP-95
❑ 99PacPriRed-95
❑ 99PacPriS-126
❑ 99PacPriS206-126
❑ 99PacPriS206R-126
❑ 99PacRed-285
❑ 99SkyThu-199
❑ 99SkyThuRant-199
❑ 99SkyThuRave-199
❑ 99StaClu-55
❑ 99StaCluFDI-55
❑ 99StaCluOoaK-55
❑ 99StaCluPP-55
❑ 99ThuSkySupR-199
❑ 99Top-194
❑ 99TopChr-194
❑ 99TopChrR-194
❑ 99TopMVPP-194
❑ 99TopOpeD-103
❑ 99UD Cho-114
❑ 99UD ChoP-114
❑ 99UD ChoPCR-114
❑ 99UppDec-150
❑ 99UppDecCLM-C60
❑ 99UppDecEL1-150
❑ 99UppDecEL2-150
❑ 99UppDecM-132
❑ 99UppDecMGS-132
❑ 99UppDecMHFS-132
❑ 99UppDecMP-132
❑ 99UppDecMSS-132
❑ 99Vic-258

Ordway, Jeff
❑ 90SpoIndSP-2

Ordway, Kirk
❑ 93NiaFalRF-3398

Orellano, Rafael
❑ 93UtiBluSC-18
❑ 93UtiBluSF-3531
❑ 94SarRedSC-21
❑ 94SarRedSF-1947
❑ 95Bes-2
❑ 95Bow-89
❑ 95SPML-24
❑ 95TreThuTI-12
❑ 96Bow-167
❑ 96BowFoi-167
❑ 96ColCho-442
❑ 96ColChoGS-442
❑ 96ColChoSS-442
❑ 96Exc-16
❑ 96PawRedSDD-20
❑ 96Top-428
❑ 96UppDec-268
❑ 97PawRedS-19

Orendorff, Jess
❑ 09ObaT21-6

Orengo, Joe (Joseph C.)
❑ 37Zee-58
❑ 41DouPlaR-29
❑ 47SunBre-15
❑ 79DiaGre-163
❑ 90DodTar-592

Orensky, Herb
❑ 80PenPilBT-23
❑ 81ReaPhiT-11
❑ 82OklCit8T-20

Orhan, Hugh
❑ 47SunBre-16

Orie, Kevin
❑ 93PeoChiTI-19
❑ 94Bow-166
❑ 94BowBes-B71
❑ 94BowBes-X94
❑ 94BowBesR-B71
❑ 94BowBesR-X94
❑ 94DayCubC-18
❑ 94DayCubF-2361
❑ 94Top-762
❑ 94TopGol-762
❑ 94TopSpa-762
❑ 95Bow-94
❑ 95Top-571
❑ 96BowBes-180
❑ 96BowBesAR-180
❑ 96BowBesR-180
❑ 96DouAllB-42
❑ 96OrlCubB-18
❑ 97Bow-146
❑ 97BowBes-195
❑ 97BowBesAR-195
❑ 97BowBesR-195
❑ 97BowCerBlaIA-CA58
❑ 97BowCerBluIA-CA58
❑ 97BowCerGolIA-CA58
❑ 97BowChr-151
❑ 97BowChrI-151
❑ 97BowChrIR-151
❑ 97BowChrR-151
❑ 97BowChrSHR-SHR5
❑ 97BowChrSHRR-SHR5
❑ 97BowInt-146
❑ 97BowScoHR-5
❑ 97ColCho-460
❑ 97ColChoNF-NF24
❑ 97Don-365
❑ 97DonGolPP-365
❑ 97DonLim-5
❑ 97DonLimE-5
❑ 97DonLimENG-5
❑ 97DonPre-159
❑ 97DonPreCttC-159
❑ 97DonSig-90
❑ 97DonSigA-75
❑ 97DonSigAC-93
❑ 97DonSigAM-93
❑ 97DonSigPPP-90
❑ 97DonSilPP-365
❑ 97Fin-307
❑ 97FinEmb-307
❑ 97FinEmbR-307
❑ 97FinRef-307
❑ 97FlaShoLC-15
❑ 97FlaShoLeg0-15
❑ 97FlaShoLeg1-15
❑ 97FlaShoM-A15
❑ 97FlaShoM-B15
❑ 97FlaShoM-C15
❑ 97FlaShoR0-15
❑ 97FlaShoR1-15
❑ 97FlaShoR2-15
❑ 97Fle-523
❑ 97FleNewH-10
❑ 97FleTif-523
❑ 97Lea-320
❑ 97LeaFraM-320
❑ 97LeaFraMDC-320
❑ 97NewPin-159
❑ 97NewPinAP-159
❑ 97NewPinMC-159
❑ 97NewPinPP-159
❑ 97PinCer-108
❑ 97PinCerMBla-108
❑ 97PinCerMBlu-108
❑ 97PinCerMG-108
❑ 97PinCerMR-108
❑ 97PinCerR-108
❑ 97PinTotCPB-108
❑ 97PinTotCPG-108
❑ 97PinTotCPR-108
❑ 97PinX-P-125
❑ 97PinX-PMoS-125
❑ 97Sco-492
❑ 97ScoArtPWB-492
❑ 97ScoResC-492
❑ 97ScoShoS-492
❑ 97ScoShoSAP-492
❑ 97Sel-131
❑ 97SelArtP-131
❑ 97SelCom-131
❑ 97SelRegG-131
❑ 97SP-2
❑ 97SpolII-18
❑ 97SpolIIEE-18
❑ 97Top-204
❑ 97TopStaFAS-FAS10
❑ 97Ult-455
❑ 97UltGolME-455
❑ 97UltGolP-5
❑ 97UltPlaME-455
❑ 97UppDec-274
❑ 98BowBes-42
❑ 98BowBesAR-42
❑ 98BowBesR-42
❑ 98CirThu-271
❑ 98CirThuRav-271
❑ 98CirThuSupRav-271
❑ 98ColCho-53
❑ 98ColChoSQ-SQ5
❑ 98Don-133
❑ 98DonCol-133
❑ 98DonCol-183
❑ 98DonColE-506
❑ 98DonColL-265
❑ 98DonColP-681
❑ 98DonColS-133
❑ 98DonColS-178
❑ 98DonCruG-62
❑ 98DonCruP-62
❑ 98DonCruR-62
❑ 98DonEli-106
❑ 98DonEliA-106
❑ 98DonEliS-106
❑ 98DonGolPP-133
❑ 98DonPre-131
❑ 98DonPreSeat-131
❑ 98DonPriCD-133
❑ 98DonPriCD-183
❑ 98DonPriCE-506
❑ 98DonPriCL-265
❑ 98DonPriCP-681
❑ 98DonRatR-8
❑ 98DonRatRM-8
❑ 98DonSigA-66
❑ 98DonSigAC-86
❑ 98DonSigAM-87
❑ 98DonSilPP-133
❑ 98E-X2-83
❑ 98E-X2ECFut-83
❑ 98E-X2ECNow-83
❑ 98Fin-33
❑ 98FinNo--33
❑ 98FinNo-R-33
❑ 98FinRef-33
❑ 98Fle-163
❑ 98Lea-66
❑ 98LeaFraDA-66
❑ 98LeaFraF-66
❑ 98LeaFraM-66
❑ 98LeaFraM-66
❑ 98LeaFraMDC-66
❑ 98LeaFraMDC-66
❑ 98LeaFraMS-66
❑ 98LeaFraMZ2-66
❑ 98LeaRS-116
❑ 98LeaRSLHolo-116
❑ 98LeaRSLong-116
❑ 98LeaRTrue-116
❑ 98MetUni-77
❑ 98MetUniPMG-77
❑ 98Pac-255
❑ 98PacInv-84
❑ 98PacInvGems-133
❑ 98PacInvPBlue-84
❑ 98PacInvSilv-84
❑ 98PacOme-49
❑ 98PacOmeR-49
❑ 98PacOnl-149
❑ 98PacOnlR-149
❑ 98PacOnlWC-149
❑ 98PacPar-141
❑ 98PacParC-141
❑ 98PacParG-141
❑ 98PacParHS-141
❑ 98PacParPB-141
❑ 98PacParR-141
❑ 98PacPlaB-255
❑ 98PacRedT-255
❑ 98PacSil-255
❑ 98Pin-71
❑ 98PinIns-71
❑ 98PinInsCE-71
❑ 98PinInsDE-71
❑ 98PinPer-107
❑ 98PinPerPP-107
❑ 98PinPreP-71
❑ 98PinSna-CC15
❑ 98ScoRT-92
❑ 98ScoRTSS-PP66
❑ 98ScoRTSSAP-PP66
❑ 98ScoRTSSAP1-PP66
❑ 98SP Aut-63
❑ 98SPxFin-69
❑ 98SPxFinR-69
❑ 98SPxFinS-69
❑ 98StaCluFDI-345
❑ 98StaCluI-345
❑ 98StaCluOneK-345
❑ 98StaCluPP-345
❑ 98Stu-105
❑ 98StuGPP-105
❑ 98StuSPP-105
❑ 98Top-108
❑ 98TopChr-108
❑ 98TopChrR-108
❑ 98TopDevR-108
❑ 98TopDia-108
❑ 98TopGal-128
❑ 98TopGalGP-128
❑ 98TopGalOPP-128
❑ 98TopGalPPI-128
❑ 98TopGalPPIA-128
❑ 98TopMiniC-108
❑ 98TopOpeD-55
❑ 98Ult-155
❑ 98UltGolM-155
❑ 98UltMas-155
❑ 98UltPlaM-155

❑ 98UppDec-55
❑ 98UppDecBCP-BC21
❑ 98UppDecSF-34
❑ 99Fle-301
❑ 99FleSta9-301
❑ 99FleWarT-301
❑ 99PacPar-99
❑ 99PacParC-99
❑ 99PacParG-99
❑ 99PacParHoloGold-99
❑ 99PacParHS-99
❑ 99PacParOD-99
❑ 99PacParPB-99
❑ 99PacParRed-99
❑ 99Rev-59
❑ 99RevPremDate-59
❑ 99RevRet-59
❑ 99RevShaSS-59
❑ 99Vic-163

Orioles, 19th C. (Baltimore)
❑ 86JosHalC-1
❑ 90KalTeaN-2

Orioles, Baltimore
❑ 56BalOriP-60
❑ 56Top-100A
❑ 56Top-100B
❑ 56Top-100C
❑ 57Top-251
❑ 58Top-408A
❑ 58Top-408B
❑ 59Top-48
❑ 59TopVen-48
❑ 60Top-494
❑ 60TopTat-64
❑ 61Top-159
❑ 61TopMagR-8
❑ 62GuyPotCP-1
❑ 62Top-476
❑ 63Top-377
❑ 64Top-473
❑ 64TopTatI-1
❑ 65Top-572
❑ 66Top-348
❑ 66TopRubI-101
❑ 66TopVen-348
❑ 67Top-302
❑ 68LauWorS-63
❑ 68Top-334
❑ 68TopVen-334
❑ 69FleCloS-2
❑ 69FleCloS-36
❑ 69TopStaA-2
❑ 70FleWorS-63
❑ 70FleWorS-66
❑ 70OPC-387
❑ 70Top-387
❑ 71FleWorS-64
❑ 71FleWorS-67
❑ 71FleWorS-68
❑ 71OPC-1
❑ 71Top-1
❑ 71TopTat-86
❑ 72Top-731
❑ 73OPC-278
❑ 73OPCBTC-2
❑ 73Top-278
❑ 73TopBluTC-2
❑ 74OPC-16
❑ 74OPCTC-2
❑ 74Top-16
❑ 74TopStaA-2
❑ 74TopTeaC-2
❑ 78Top-96
❑ 81Ori6F-2
❑ 83FleSta-226
❑ 83FleSti-NNO
❑ 83FleSti-NNO
❑ 87SpoTeaL-21
❑ 87Top-506
❑ 87TopTif-506
❑ 88PanSti-455
❑ 88RedFolSB-109
❑ 90FleWaxBC-C24
❑ 90PubIntS-648
❑ 90RedFolSB-108
❑ 93TedWilPC-3
❑ 94ImpProP-1
❑ 94Sco-317
❑ 94ScoGolR-317
❑ 95PacPriTL-1
❑ 95PanSti-147
❑ 96OriFle-19
❑ 96PanSti-131
❑ 97ColChoT-BO
❑ 99Vic-41

Orman, Richard
❑ 90MedHatBJB-7

Ormonde, Troy
❑ 94HunCubC-22
❑ 94HunCubF-3550
❑ 95RocCubTI-35

Ormsby, Red
❑ 94ConTSN-1207
❑ 94ConTSNB-1207

Orndorff, Dave
❑ 98ForWayW!-7

Ornsdorff, Jesse
❑ 09ObaT21-90

Oropesa, Eddie
❑ 95SanAntMTI-54
❑ 96SanBerSB-19
❑ 97ShrCap-18
❑ 97ShrCapB-18
❑ 98ShrCapM-26
❑ 98ShrCapWS-26

Oropeza, Clemente
❑ 82IdaFalAT-20

Oropeza, Dave
❑ 89RocExpLC-20

Oropeza, Igor
❑ 94VenLinU-73
❑ 94WatIndC-23
❑ 94WatIndF-3935
❑ 95KinIndTI-21
❑ 95LinVen-248
❑ 96-97LinVen-249

Oropeza, Willie
❑ 95LinVen-221
❑ 96-97LinVen-228
❑ 96VerExpB-20
❑ 98CapFeaCM-15

Orosco, Jesse
❑ 79TidTidT-23
❑ 80Top-681
❑ 80VenLeaS-210
❑ 81TidTidT-20
❑ 82Don-646
❑ 82MetPhoA-16
❑ 83Don-434
❑ 83Fle-550
❑ 83Top-369
❑ 84AllGamPI-84
❑ 84Don-197
❑ 84Fle-593
❑ 84FleSti-60
❑ 84JacMetF-9
❑ 84MetFanC-5
❑ 84Nes792-54
❑ 84Nes792-396
❑ 84OPC-54
❑ 84OPC-396
❑ 84Top-54
❑ 84Top-396
❑ 84TopGloS-33
❑ 84TopRubD-15
❑ 84TopSti-104
❑ 84TopTif-54
❑ 84TopTif-396
❑ 85AllGamPI-173
❑ 85Don-22
❑ 85Don-75
❑ 85DonSupD-22
❑ 85Fle-89
❑ 85FleStaS-106
❑ 85Lea-22
❑ 85MetColP-21
❑ 85MetTCM-15
❑ 85OPC-250
❑ 85SubDis-37
❑ 85ThoMcAD-37
❑ 85Top-250
❑ 85TopGloS-2
❑ 85TopMin-250
❑ 85TopRubD-13
❑ 85TopSti-101
❑ 85TopSup-54
❑ 85TopTif-250
❑ 86BasStaB-81
❑ 86Don-646
❑ 86Fle-90
❑ 86MetColP-8
❑ 86MetTCM-11
❑ 86MetWorSC-27
❑ 86OPC-182
❑ 86Top-465
❑ 86TopTat-5
❑ 86TopTif-465
❑ 87ClaGam-75
❑ 87Don-439
❑ 87Fle-20
❑ 87FleGlo-20
❑ 87FleMin-78
❑ 87FleRecS-27
❑ 87FleStiC-87
❑ 87Lea-175
❑ 87MetColP-19
❑ 87OPC-148
❑ 87RedFolSB-84
❑ 87Spo-76A
❑ 87Spo-76B
❑ 87Top-704
❑ 87TopTif-704
❑ 88DodMot-13
❑ 88DodPol-47
❑ 88Don-192
❑ 88DonBasB-234
❑ 88Fle-148
❑ 88FleGlo-148
❑ 88FleUpd-96
❑ 88FleUpdG-96
❑ 88Sco-495
❑ 88ScoGlo-495
❑ 88ScoRoo-64T
❑ 88ScoRooG-64T
❑ 88Spo-89
❑ 88StaLinD-12
❑ 88StaLinMe-16
❑ 88Top-105
❑ 88TopTif-105
❑ 88TopTra-77T
❑ 88TopTraT-77T
❑ 89Bow-81
❑ 89BowTif-81
❑ 89Don-228
❑ 89DonTra-26
❑ 89Fle-68
❑ 89FleGlo-68
❑ 89IndTeal-22
❑ 89Sco-356
❑ 89Top-513
❑ 89TopTif-513
❑ 89TopTra-91T
❑ 89TopTraT-91T
❑ 89UppDec-87
❑ 90DodTar-593
❑ 90Don-154
❑ 90Fle-500
❑ 90FleCan-500
❑ 90IndTeal-32
❑ 90Lea-101
❑ 90OPC-636
❑ 90PubIntS-566
❑ 90Sco-353
❑ 90Top-636
❑ 90TopTif-636
❑ 90UppDec-588
❑ 91Bow-72
❑ 91Don-171
❑ 91Fle-375
❑ 91IndFanC-23
❑ 91MetWIZ-302
❑ 91OPC-346
❑ 91Sco-578
❑ 91StaClu-322
❑ 91Top-346
❑ 91TopDesS-346
❑ 91TopMic-346
❑ 91TopTif-346
❑ 91UppDec-240
❑ 92BrePol-18
❑ 92Don-473
❑ 92Fle-121
❑ 92Lea-524
❑ 92LeaBlaG-524
❑ 92OPC-79
❑ 92Sco-547
❑ 92Top-79
❑ 92TopGol-79
❑ 92TopGolW-79
❑ 92TopMic-79
❑ 92UppDec-580
❑ 93BrePol-20
❑ 93Fle-632
❑ 93PacBeiA-10
❑ 93PacSpa-163
❑ 93StaClu-37
❑ 93StaCluFDI-37
❑ 93StaCluMOP-37
❑ 93Top-289
❑ 93TopGol-289
❑ 93TopInaM-289
❑ 93TopInaR-289
❑ 93TopMic-289
❑ 93Ult-223
❑ 94BreMilB-258
❑ 94BrePol-21
❑ 94BreTeal-20
❑ 94ColC-616
❑ 94ColChoGS-616
❑ 94ColChoSS-616
❑ 94Fle-188
❑ 94Pac-340
❑ 94Pin-473
❑ 94PinArtP-473
❑ 94PinMusC-473
❑ 94Sco-299
❑ 94ScoGolR-299
❑ 94Top-492
❑ 94TopGol-492
❑ 94TopSpa-492
❑ 95BalOriP-38
❑ 95Pac-239
❑ 96BalOriP-25
❑ 96Fle-18
❑ 96FleTif-18
❑ 96OriFle-13
❑ 96Pac-234
❑ 97BalOriP-25
❑ 97PacPriGotD-GD13
❑ 98Pac-30
❑ 98PacOnl-96
❑ 98PacOnlR-96
❑ 98PacOnlWC-96
❑ 98PacPlaB-30
❑ 98PacRedT-30
❑ 98PacSil-30
❑ 99Pac-56
❑ 99PacCroC-38
❑ 99PacCroCPB-38
❑ 99PacPlaB-56
❑ 99PacRed-56

Oroz, Felix Andres
❑ 83LasVegSBHN-16
❑ 84LasVegSC-233

Orphal, John
❑ 47CenFlo-18

Orr, Bobby
❑ 74NewYorNTDiS-34

Orr, David L.
❑ 87BucN28-62
❑ 87OldJudN-387
❑ 87OldJudN-388
❑ 89EdgR.WG-10
❑ 89SFHaCN-14
❑ 90KalBatN-44

Orr, Geoff
❑ 90IdaFalBP-3252
❑ 91MacBraC-22
❑ 91MacBraP-875

Orr, Jimmy
❑ 52LavPro-42

Orr, Johnny
❑ 89TenTecGE-20

Orr, Russell
❑ 98TamYanM-5

Orr, William
❑ 12Zee-90
❑ 14FatPlaT-38
❑ 14Zee-90
❑ 15Zee-86
❑ 16Zee-87
❑ 17Zee-72
❑ 18Zee-68
❑ 19Zee-59
❑ 20Zee-71
❑ 21Zee-77
❑ 22Zee-66
❑ 23Zee-166

Orsag, Jim
❑ 86GreHorP-15
❑ 87WinHavRSP-28
❑ 88CarLeaAS-13
❑ 88LynRedSS-16
❑ 89NewBriRSP-610
❑ 89NewBriRSS-12
❑ 89Sta-128
❑ 90Bes-269
❑ 90CanIndB-9

Orsatti, Ernie (Ernesto R.)
❑ 31CarMet-22
❑ 33ButCanV-38
❑ 33Gou-201
❑ 33WorCig-75
❑ 33WorCig-76
❑ 34DiaMatCSB-144
❑ 35AlDemDCR3-130
❑ 35DiaMatCS3T1-115
❑ 35GouPuzR-1A
❑ 35GouPuzR-2A
❑ 35GouPuzR-16A
❑ 35GouPuzR-17A
❑ 74Car193T-20
❑ 92ConTSN-650

Orsino, Johnny (John Joseph)
❑ 61TacBan-14
❑ 61UniOil-T25
❑ 62Top-377
❑ 63BalOriP-23
❑ 63BalOriP-24
❑ 63Top-418
❑ 64BalOriP-26
❑ 64OriJayP-7
❑ 64Top-63
❑ 64TopCoi-3
❑ 64TopVen-63
❑ 65BalOriP-24
❑ 65Top-303
❑ 65TopEmbl-51
❑ 66OPC-77
❑ 66Top-77
❑ 66TopRubI-73
❑ 66TopVen-77
❑ 67Top-207
❑ 81Gia196T-19
❑ 81TCM60I-375
❑ 91OriCro-344

Orsulak, Joe
❑ 82AleDukT-22
❑ 85FleUpd-85
❑ 85TopTifT-89T
❑ 85TopTra-89T
❑ 86Don-444
❑ 86Fle-615
❑ 86FleLeaL-29
❑ 86FleMin-118
❑ 86FleStiC-83
❑ 86Lea-218
❑ 86Spo-177
❑ 86Top-102
❑ 86TopSti-132
❑ 86TopTif-102
❑ 87Don-291
❑ 87Fle-615
❑ 87FleGlo-615
❑ 87FleRecS-28
❑ 87SpoTeaP-18
❑ 87Top-414
❑ 87TopSti-132
❑ 87TopTif-414
❑ 88DonBasB-310
❑ 88FleUpd-2
❑ 88FleUpdG-2
❑ 88OriFreB-6
❑ 88OriPos-24
❑ 88ScoRoo-41T
❑ 88ScoRooG-41T
❑ 88TopTra-78T
❑ 88TopTraT-78T
❑ 89BalOriP-24
❑ 89Don-287
❑ 89DonBasB-310
❑ 89Fle-614
❑ 89FleGlo-614
❑ 89OriFreB-6
❑ 89PanSti-263
❑ 89Sco-247
❑ 89Top-727
❑ 89TopBig-181
❑ 89TopTif-727
❑ 89UppDec-429
❑ 90Bow-252
❑ 90BowTif-252
❑ 90ClaYel-T50
❑ 90Don-287
❑ 90DonBesA-129
❑ 90Fle-185
❑ 90FleCan-185
❑ 90Lea-355
❑ 90OPC-212
❑ 90PanSti-5
❑ 90PubIntS-582
❑ 90Sco-41
❑ 90Spo-38
❑ 90Top-212
❑ 90TopBig-318
❑ 90TopSti-234
❑ 90TopTif-212
❑ 90UppDec-270
❑ 91BalOriP-23
❑ 91Bow-84
❑ 91Don-654
❑ 91Fle-487
❑ 91Lea-152
❑ 91OPC-521
❑ 91OriCro-345
❑ 91PanFreS-246
❑ 91PanSti-200
❑ 91RedFolS-70
❑ 91Sco-508
❑ 91Sco100S-8
❑ 91StaClu-191
❑ 91Top-521
❑ 91TopDesS-521
❑ 91TopMic-521
❑ 91TopTif-521
❑ 91Ult-22
❑ 91UppDec-506
❑ 92BalOriP-28
❑ 92Bow-432
❑ 92Don-475
❑ 92Fle-22
❑ 92Hig5-4
❑ 92Lea-36
❑ 92LeaBlaG-36
❑ 92OPC-325
❑ 92PanSti-71
❑ 92Pin-362
❑ 92Sco-551
❑ 92StaClu-135
❑ 92Top-325
❑ 92TopGol-325
❑ 92TopGolW-325
❑ 92TopMic-325
❑ 92UppDec-207
❑ 93Don-751
❑ 93Fla-95
❑ 93Fle-549
❑ 93FleFinE-104
❑ 93Lea-337
❑ 93MetColP-43
❑ 93MetKah-6
❑ 93OPC-303
❑ 93OPCPre-55
❑ 93PacSpa-23
❑ 93PanSti-77
❑ 93Pin-501
❑ 93Sco-590
❑ 93Sel-234
❑ 93SelRoo-131T
❑ 93StaClu-92
❑ 93StaCluFDI-92
❑ 93StaCluMOP-92
❑ 93Top-28
❑ 93TopGol-28
❑ 93TopInaM-28
❑ 93TopInaR-28
❑ 93TopMic-28
❑ 93Ult-432
❑ 93UppDec-260
❑ 93UppDec-712
❑ 93UppDecGold-260
❑ 93UppDecGold-712
❑ 94Bow-72
❑ 94ColC-419
❑ 94ColChoGS-419
❑ 94ColChoSS-419
❑ 94Don-270
❑ 94Fin-45
❑ 94FinRef-45
❑ 94Fle-575
❑ 94Lea-124
❑ 94MetColP-20
❑ 94MetShuST-2
❑ 94Pac-415
❑ 94Pin-92
❑ 94PinArtP-92
❑ 94PinMusC-92
❑ 94Sco-398
❑ 94ScoGolR-398
❑ 94Sel-94
❑ 94StaClu-384
❑ 94StaCluFDI-384
❑ 94StaCluGR-384
❑ 94StaCluMOP-384
❑ 94Top-643
❑ 94TopGol-643
❑ 94TopSpa-643
❑ 94TriPla-147
❑ 94Ult-240
❑ 95ColCho-321
❑ 95ColChoGS-321
❑ 95ColChoSS-321
❑ 95Don-266
❑ 95DonPreP-266
❑ 95DonTopotO-296
❑ 95Fla-174
❑ 95Fle-378
❑ 95Lea-96
❑ 95MetColP-24
❑ 95Pac-285
❑ 95Sco-129
❑ 95ScoGolR-129
❑ 95ScoPlaTS-129

- ❑ 95StaClu-351
- ❑ 95StaCluMOP-351
- ❑ 95StaCluSTWS-351
- ❑ 95Top-128
- ❑ 95Ult-414
- ❑ 95UltGolM-414
- ❑ 96Don-322
- ❑ 96DonPreP-322
- ❑ 96Fle-391
- ❑ 96FleTif-391
- ❑ 96MetKah-24
- ❑ 96Pac-143
- ❑ 97Pac-304
- ❑ 97PacLigB-304
- ❑ 97PacSil-304

Ort, George

- ❑ 09ObaT21-124

Orta, Jorge (Jorge Nunez)

- ❑ 09ObaT21-31
- ❑ 72WhiSox-10
- ❑ 72WhiSoxTI1-12
- ❑ 73LinPor-51
- ❑ 73OPC-194
- ❑ 73Top-194
- ❑ 74OPC-376
- ❑ 74Top-376
- ❑ 74TopSta-159
- ❑ 75Hos-122
- ❑ 75HosTwi-122
- ❑ 75Kel-14
- ❑ 75OPC-184
- ❑ 75Top-184
- ❑ 75TopMin-184
- ❑ 76Hos-57
- ❑ 76HosTwi-57
- ❑ 76Kel-45A
- ❑ 76Kel-45B
- ❑ 76OPC-560
- ❑ 76SSP-144
- ❑ 76Top-560
- ❑ 77BurCheD-74
- ❑ 77Top-109
- ❑ 77WhiSoxJT-11
- ❑ 77WhiSoxT-21
- ❑ 78Hos-105
- ❑ 78OPC-77
- ❑ 78SSP270-142
- ❑ 78Top-42
- ❑ 78WifBalD-56
- ❑ 79Hos-126
- ❑ 79OPC-333
- ❑ 79Top-631
- ❑ 80IndTeal-22
- ❑ 80Top-442
- ❑ 81AllGamPI-64
- ❑ 81Don-439
- ❑ 81Fle-388
- ❑ 81OPC-222
- ❑ 81Top-222
- ❑ 82DodPol-31
- ❑ 82DodUniOV-15
- ❑ 82Don-211
- ❑ 82Fle-376
- ❑ 82OPC-26
- ❑ 82Top-26
- ❑ 82TopSti-175
- ❑ 82TopTra-84T
- ❑ 83Don-388
- ❑ 83Fle-215
- ❑ 83Top-722
- ❑ 83TopTra-82T
- ❑ 84Don-317
- ❑ 84Fle-166
- ❑ 84FleUpd-86
- ❑ 84Nes792-312
- ❑ 84OPC-312
- ❑ 84RoyPos-24
- ❑ 84Top-312
- ❑ 84TopTif-312
- ❑ 84TopTra-88T
- ❑ 84TopTraT-88T
- ❑ 85Don-130
- ❑ 85Fle-209
- ❑ 85Lea-226
- ❑ 85RoyTeal-23
- ❑ 85Top-164
- ❑ 85TopSti-273
- ❑ 85TopTif-164
- ❑ 86Don-339
- ❑ 86Fle-17
- ❑ 86Lea-205
- ❑ 86OPC-44
- ❑ 86RoyKitCD-6
- ❑ 86RoyNatP-3
- ❑ 86RoyTeal-18
- ❑ 86Top-541
- ❑ 86TopTif-541
- ❑ 87Don-348
- ❑ 87Fle-376
- ❑ 87FleGlo-376
- ❑ 87OPC-63
- ❑ 87Top-738
- ❑ 87TopTif-738
- ❑ 90DodTar-595
- ❑ 97QuaCitRBB-20
- ❑ 98JacGenM-26

Ortega, Dan

- ❑ 80AppFoxT-14
- ❑ 81AppFoxT-7

Ortega, Eduardo

- ❑ 89BatCliP-1939
- ❑ 90SpaPhiB-17
- ❑ 90SpaPhiP-2499
- ❑ 90SpaPhiS-16
- ❑ 91SalLakTP-3219
- ❑ 91SalLakTSP-18
- ❑ 92SalLakTSP-19

Ortega, Franklin

- ❑ 97JohCitCTI-26
- ❑ 98NewJerCM-23

Ortega, Hector

- ❑ 90GatCitPP-3341
- ❑ 91SumFlyC-17
- ❑ 91SumFlyP-2342
- ❑ 92RocExpC-16
- ❑ 92RocExpF-2126
- ❑ 93LinVenB-217
- ❑ 94VenLinU-84
- ❑ 95LinVen-226
- ❑ 96-97LinVen-239
- ❑ 96BesAutS-67
- ❑ 96El PasDB-22

Ortega, Jose

- ❑ 98JohCCTI-26

Ortega, Kirk

- ❑ 81CliGiaT-16

Ortega, Pablo

- ❑ 97Bes-90
- ❑ 97Bow-183
- ❑ 97BowInt-183
- ❑ 97ChaRivDG-20
- ❑ 97Top-253
- ❑ 98Bow-180
- ❑ 98BowChr-180
- ❑ 98BowChrGA-180
- ❑ 98BowChrGAR-180
- ❑ 98BowChrI-180
- ❑ 98BowChrIR-180
- ❑ 98BowChrR-180
- ❑ 98BowGolA-180
- ❑ 98BowInt-180
- ❑ 98St.PetDRM-13
- ❑ 98Top-251
- ❑ 98TopChr-251
- ❑ 98TopChrR-251
- ❑ 98TopDevR-251
- ❑ 98TopDia-251
- ❑ 98TopMiniC-251

Ortega, Phil

- ❑ 59DarFar-15
- ❑ 62Top-69
- ❑ 62TopVen-69
- ❑ 63Top-467
- ❑ 64Top-291
- ❑ 64TopVen-291
- ❑ 65OPC-152
- ❑ 65Top-152
- ❑ 66SenTeal-10
- ❑ 66Top-416
- ❑ 66TopRubI-74
- ❑ 67CokCapS-16
- ❑ 67DexPre-155
- ❑ 67SenPos-17
- ❑ 67SenTeal-9
- ❑ 67Top-493
- ❑ 68SenTeal-9
- ❑ 68Top-595
- ❑ 69MilBra-207
- ❑ 69SenTeal8-15
- ❑ 69Top-406
- ❑ 81TCM60I-390
- ❑ 90DodTar-596

Ortega, Randy

- ❑ 94WesMicWC-19
- ❑ 94WesMicWF-2301
- ❑ 95ModA'sTI-21
- ❑ 96WesMicWB-19

Ortega, Raul

- ❑ 76VenLeaS-4
- ❑ 80VenLeaS-4

Ortega, Roberto

- ❑ 92BriTigC-19
- ❑ 92BriTigF-1420

Ortega, Wilbert

- ❑ 98CliLumG-17

Ortega, William

- ❑ 97PriWilC-26

Ortegon, Ronnie

- ❑ 89PalSprACLC-35
- ❑ 89PalSprAP-478
- ❑ 90QuaCitAGS-22

Orteig, Ray

- ❑ 48SomandK-25
- ❑ 52MotCoo-50
- ❑ 53MotCoo-31
- ❑ 54SeaPop-20
- ❑ 56SeaPop-13
- ❑ 57HygMea-10
- ❑ 57SeaPop-17
- ❑ 58SeaRalT-12

Ortenzio, Frank

- ❑ 75OmaRoyTI-12
- ❑ 76OmaRoyTT-18
- ❑ 79TCMJapPB-69

Orth, Al (Albert Lewis)

- ❑ 03BreE10-110
- ❑ 08RosComP-53
- ❑ 09ColChiE-220A
- ❑ 09ColChiE-220B
- ❑ 09T206-505
- ❑ 11SpoLifCW-278
- ❑ 12ColRedB-220A
- ❑ 12ColRedB-220B
- ❑ 12ColTinT-220A
- ❑ 12ColTinT-220B
- ❑ 74CapPub-74
- ❑ 94ConTSN-1192
- ❑ 94ConTSNB-1192

Ortiz, Alfredo

- ❑ 76VenLeaS-11
- ❑ 86VenGulP-19
- ❑ 89JohCitCS-25
- ❑ 93LinVenB-62
- ❑ 95LinVen-130
- ❑ 96-97LinVen-96

Ortiz, Andy

- ❑ 83WatIndF-5
- ❑ 84BufBisT-15

Ortiz, Angel

- ❑ 88BlaYNPRWLU-35
- ❑ 88WatIndP-667
- ❑ 89KinIndS-17
- ❑ 92CliGiaC-3
- ❑ 92CliGiaF-3596

Ortiz, Asbel

- ❑ 96ChaRivTI-9625
- ❑ 98BriBluM-21

Ortiz, Bo (Basilio)

- ❑ 91BluOriC-9
- ❑ 91BluOriP-4140
- ❑ 92FreKeyC-16
- ❑ 92FreKeyF-1820
- ❑ 93FreKeyC-19
- ❑ 93FreKeyF-1041
- ❑ 94BowBayF-2426
- ❑ 94OriPro-75
- ❑ 95MidAngOHP-25
- ❑ 95MidAngTI-22
- ❑ 96DouAllB-44
- ❑ 96MidAngB-25
- ❑ 96MidAngOHP-21
- ❑ 96TexLeaAB-34
- ❑ 97HarSen-19

Ortiz, Danny

- ❑ 93HunCubC-22
- ❑ 93HunCubF-3235

Ortiz, Darrell

- ❑ 80TulDriT-23

Ortiz, David Arias

- ❑ 96MidLeaAB-2
- ❑ 96WisTimRB-6
- ❑ 97Bes-74
- ❑ 97BesAutSBPP-24
- ❑ 97BesDiaB-19
- ❑ 97DonSigA-76
- ❑ 97DonSigAC-94
- ❑ 97DonSigAM-94
- ❑ 97FlaShoWotF-11
- ❑ 97Fle-512
- ❑ 97FleTif-512
- ❑ 97FloStaLTPB-12
- ❑ 97ForMyeM-22
- ❑ 97Ult-518
- ❑ 97UltGolME-518
- ❑ 97UltPlaME-518
- ❑ 98Bow-71
- ❑ 98BowBes-173
- ❑ 98BowBesAR-173
- ❑ 98BowBesMIF-MI1
- ❑ 98BowBesMIFAR-MI1
- ❑ 98BowBesMIFR-MI1
- ❑ 98BowBesR-173
- ❑ 98BowCerBlueAU-4
- ❑ 98BowCerGA-4
- ❑ 98BowCerSA-4
- ❑ 98BowChr-71
- ❑ 98BowChrGA-71
- ❑ 98BowChrGAR-71
- ❑ 98BowChrI-71
- ❑ 98BowChrIR-71
- ❑ 98BowChrR-71
- ❑ 98BowGolA-71
- ❑ 98BowInt-71
- ❑ 98CirThu-173
- ❑ 98CirThuRav-173
- ❑ 98CirThuSupRav-173
- ❑ 98Don-299
- ❑ 98DonColE-499
- ❑ 98DonColL-382
- ❑ 98DonColP-697
- ❑ 98DonEli-99
- ❑ 98DonEliA-99
- ❑ 98DonEliBttF-6
- ❑ 98DonEliS-99
- ❑ 98DonGolPP-299
- ❑ 98DonPre-147
- ❑ 98DonPreGES-10
- ❑ 98DonPreGX-10
- ❑ 98DonPreGXDC-10
- ❑ 98DonPreSeat-147
- ❑ 98DonPriCE-499
- ❑ 98DonPriCL-382
- ❑ 98DonPriCP-697
- ❑ 98DonSig-100
- ❑ 98DonSigA-67
- ❑ 98DonSigAC-87
- ❑ 98DonSigAM-88
- ❑ 98DonSigP-100
- ❑ 98DonSigSP-20
- ❑ 98DonSilPP-299
- ❑ 98E-X2Sig2001-13
- ❑ 98Fle-285
- ❑ 98FleProF-PF15
- ❑ 98Lea-183
- ❑ 98LeaFraDA-183
- ❑ 98LeaFraF-183
- ❑ 98LeaFraM-183
- ❑ 98LeaFraM-183
- ❑ 98LeaFraMDC-183
- ❑ 98LeaFraMDC-183
- ❑ 98LeaFraMZ2-183
- ❑ 98LeaRCrusUP-110
- ❑ 98LeaRS-196
- ❑ 98LeaRSCrusUG-110
- ❑ 98LeaRSCrusUR-110
- ❑ 98LeaRSFOSamp-12
- ❑ 98LeaRSFresh-12
- ❑ 98LeaRSLHolo-196
- ❑ 98LeaRSLong-196
- ❑ 98LeaRTrue-196
- ❑ 98Pac-139
- ❑ 98PacOme-143
- ❑ 98PacOmeR-143
- ❑ 98PacOmeRS-23
- ❑ 98PacOmeRST2-23
- ❑ 98PacOnl-432
- ❑ 98PacOnlR-432
- ❑ 98PacOnlWC-432
- ❑ 98PacPlaB-139
- ❑ 98PacRedT-139
- ❑ 98PacSil-139
- ❑ 98PinPer-125
- ❑ 98PinPerPP-125
- ❑ 98RevoRooHH-10
- ❑ 98RevoRooHHG-10
- ❑ 98ScoRT-74
- ❑ 98ScoRTSS-PP58
- ❑ 98ScoRTSSAP-PP58
- ❑ 98ScoRTSSAP1-PP58
- ❑ 98SP Aut-21
- ❑ 98SP MinPE-75
- ❑ 98SPMin-75
- ❑ 98SPxFin-182
- ❑ 98SPxFinR-182
- ❑ 98SPxFinS-182
- ❑ 98StaCluFDI-344
- ❑ 98StaCluI-344
- ❑ 98StaCluITW-W12
- ❑ 98StaCluOneK-344
- ❑ 98StaCluPP-344
- ❑ 98Stu-64
- ❑ 98StuGPP-64
- ❑ 98StuSPP-64
- ❑ 98Top-257
- ❑ 98TopChr-257
- ❑ 98TopChrR-257
- ❑ 98TopDevR-257
- ❑ 98TopDia-257
- ❑ 98TopMiniC-257
- ❑ 98TopSta-6
- ❑ 98TopStaB-6
- ❑ 98TopStaG-6
- ❑ 98TopStaGR-6
- ❑ 98TopStaS-6
- ❑ 98TopStaSB-S6
- ❑ 98TopStaSG-S6
- ❑ 98TopStaSGR-S6
- ❑ 98TopStaSS-S6
- ❑ 98Ult-405
- ❑ 98UltGolM-405
- ❑ 98UltMas-405
- ❑ 98UltPlaM-405
- ❑ 98UppDec-696
- ❑ 99199Fin-166
- ❑ 99FinGolRef-166
- ❑ 99FinRef-166
- ❑ 99Fle-248
- ❑ 99FleSta9-248
- ❑ 99FleWarT-248
- ❑ 99MetUni-21
- ❑ 99MetUniGM-21
- ❑ 99MetUniPMG-21
- ❑ 99Pac-253
- ❑ 99PacAur-106
- ❑ 99PacAurOD-106
- ❑ 99PacCroC-164
- ❑ 99PacCroC-11
- ❑ 99PacCroCPB-164
- ❑ 99PacCroCTC-17
- ❑ 99PacPar-135
- ❑ 99PacParC-135
- ❑ 99PacParG-135
- ❑ 99PacParHoloGold-135
- ❑ 99PacParHS-135
- ❑ 99PacParOD-135
- ❑ 99PacParPB-135
- ❑ 99PacParRed-135
- ❑ 99PacPlaB-253
- ❑ 99PacPri-85
- ❑ 99PacPriHB-85
- ❑ 99PacPriHG-85
- ❑ 99PacPriHM-85
- ❑ 99PacPriHP-85
- ❑ 99PacPriRed-85
- ❑ 99PacPriS-127
- ❑ 99PacPriS206-127
- ❑ 99PacPriS206R-127
- ❑ 99PacRed-253
- ❑ 99SkyThu-197
- ❑ 99SkyThuRant-197
- ❑ 99SkyThuRave-197
- ❑ 99SP Aut-49
- ❑ 99SP SigAuto-DO
- ❑ 99SPSig-151
- ❑ 99SPx-51
- ❑ 99SPxFinR-51
- ❑ 99SPxFinS-51
- ❑ 99StaClu-228
- ❑ 99StaCluFDI-228
- ❑ 99StaCluOoaK-228
- ❑ 99StaCluPP-228
- ❑ 99ThuSkySupR-197
- ❑ 99Top-291
- ❑ 99TopChr-291
- ❑ 99TopChrR-291
- ❑ 99TopMVPP-291
- ❑ 99TopSta-85
- ❑ 99TopSta1Foil-85
- ❑ 99TopStaFoil-85
- ❑ 99TopStaOS-85
- ❑ 99UD Cho-106
- ❑ 99UD ChoP-106
- ❑ 99UD ChoPCR-106
- ❑ 99Ult-24
- ❑ 99UltGolM-24
- ❑ 99UltMas-24
- ❑ 99UltPlaM-24
- ❑ 99UppDec-138
- ❑ 99UppDecEL1-138
- ❑ 99UppDecEL2-138
- ❑ 99UppDecM-121
- ❑ 99UppDecMGS-121
- ❑ 99UppDecMHFS-121
- ❑ 99UppDecMP-121
- ❑ 99UppDecMSS-121
- ❑ 99Vic-224

Ortiz, Hector

- ❑ 89SalDodTI-20
- ❑ 89VerBeaDS-21
- ❑ 90YakBeaTI-11
- ❑ 91VerBeaDC-16
- ❑ 91VerBeaDP-777
- ❑ 92BakDodCLC-18
- ❑ 92CalLeaACL-44
- ❑ 93SanAntMF-3008
- ❑ 94AlbDukF-845
- ❑ 95OrlCubF-14
- ❑ 96OrlCubB-19
- ❑ 97OmaRoyB-8
- ❑ 98OmaRoyM-17

Ortiz, Javier

- ❑ 84TulDriTI-31
- ❑ 85TulDriTI-31
- ❑ 86TulDriTI-17
- ❑ 87OklCit8P-15
- ❑ 88BlaYNPRWL-187
- ❑ 88SanAntMB-22
- ❑ 89AlbDukCm-25
- ❑ 89AlbDukP-84
- ❑ 89TriAAAP-AAA46
- ❑ 90CMC-617
- ❑ 90FleUpd-16
- ❑ 90ProAAAF-207
- ❑ 90TucTorC-15
- ❑ 90TucTorP-217
- ❑ 91Bow-562
- ❑ 91Don-643
- ❑ 91LinDriAAA-617
- ❑ 91TopDeb90-119
- ❑ 91TucTorLD-617
- ❑ 91TucTorP-2226
- ❑ 92Don-551
- ❑ 92OPC-362
- ❑ 92Sco-403
- ❑ 92Top-362
- ❑ 92TopGol-362
- ❑ 92TopGolW-362
- ❑ 92TopMic-362
- ❑ 92UppDec-657
- ❑ 94NasSouF-1262

Ortiz, Joe

- ❑ 86AncGlaPTI-26
- ❑ 88AshTouP-1066
- ❑ 88CalLeaACLC-22
- ❑ 88RenSilSCLC-285
- ❑ 89BelBrelS-20
- ❑ 89OscAstS-15
- ❑ 90ColMudS-18
- ❑ 90ModA'sCLC-158
- ❑ 90ModA'sP-2216

Ortiz, Jorge

- ❑ 81WisRapTT-7

Ortiz, Jose Daniel

- ❑ 97CalLeaATI-21
- ❑ 97CalLeaTP-15
- ❑ 97ModA'sG-21
- ❑ 98HunStaTI-11

Ortiz, Jose Minors

- ❑ 73WicAerJPKB-11

Ortiz, Junior (Adalberto)

- ❑ 77ChaPatT-10
- ❑ 77ShrCapT-17
- ❑ 78ChaPirT-17
- ❑ 79AshTouT-14
- ❑ 80BufBisT-9
- ❑ 81PorBeaT-19
- ❑ 82PorBeaT-11
- ❑ 84Don-319
- ❑ 84Fle-594
- ❑ 84Nes792-161
- ❑ 84Top-161
- ❑ 84TopSti-114
- ❑ 84TopTif-161
- ❑ 85Pir-14
- ❑ 85SubDis-38
- ❑ 85ThoMcAD-38
- ❑ 85Top-439
- ❑ 85TopTif-439
- ❑ 86Don-508
- ❑ 86Top-682
- ❑ 86TopTif-682
- ❑ 87Don-449
- ❑ 87DonOpeD-164
- ❑ 87Fle-616
- ❑ 87FleGlo-616
- ❑ 87Top-583
- ❑ 87TopTif-583
- ❑ 88BlaYNPRWL-111
- ❑ 88Don-168
- ❑ 88Fle-335
- ❑ 88FleGlo-335
- ❑ 88PanSti-341
- ❑ 88PirTeal-24
- ❑ 88Sco-404

❑ 88ScoGlo-404
❑ 88StaLinPi-15
❑ 88Top-274
❑ 88TopTif-274
❑ 89BlaYNPRWL-11
❑ 89Don-387
❑ 89DonBasB-269
❑ 89Fle-215
❑ 89FleGlo-215
❑ 89PirVerFJ-0
❑ 89Sco-402
❑ 89Top-769
❑ 89TopBig-66
❑ 89TopTif-769
❑ 89UppDec-86
❑ 90Fle-475
❑ 90FleCan-475
❑ 90FleUpd-108
❑ 90OPC-322
❑ 90PubIntS-160
❑ 90Sco-143
❑ 90ScoRoo-66T
❑ 90Top-322
❑ 90TopTif-322
❑ 90TopTra-85T
❑ 90TopTraT-85T
❑ 90UppDec-389
❑ 91Bow-328
❑ 91DodPho-25
❑ 91Don-659
❑ 91Fle-622
❑ 91Lea-498
❑ 91MetWIZ-303
❑ 91OPC-72
❑ 91Sco-438
❑ 91StaClu-13
❑ 91Top-72
❑ 91TopDesS-72
❑ 91TopMic-72
❑ 91TopTif-72
❑ 91Ult-194
❑ 91UppDec-170
❑ 92Don-684
❑ 92Fle-215
❑ 92IndFanC-21
❑ 92OPC-617
❑ 92Sco-473
❑ 92StaClu-727
❑ 92StaCluNC-727
❑ 92Top-617
❑ 92TopGol-617
❑ 92TopGolW-617
❑ 92TopMic-617
❑ 92TopTra-84T
❑ 92TopTraG-84T
❑ 92Ult-353
❑ 92UppDec-109
❑ 93Don-699
❑ 93Fle-598
❑ 93IndWUA-24
❑ 93LinVenB-310
❑ 93PacBeiA-6
❑ 93PacSpa-416
❑ 93Top-199
❑ 93TopGol-199
❑ 93TopInaM-199
❑ 93TopInaR-199
❑ 93TopMic-199
❑ 93Ult-544
❑ 93Ult-650
❑ 93UppDec-603
❑ 93UppDecGold-603
❑ 94Don-425
❑ 94Fle-117
❑ 94Pac-181
❑ 94RanMagM-28
❑ 94Sco-262
❑ 94ScoGolR-262
❑ 94StaClu-15
❑ 94StaCluFDI-15
❑ 94StaCluGR-15
❑ 94StaCluMOP-15
❑ 94StaCluP-15
❑ 94Top-423
❑ 94TopGol-423
❑ 94TopSpa-423
❑ 95NasSouTI-15
❑ 95Pac-431
❑ 95Sco-64
❑ 95ScoGolR-64
❑ 95ScoPlaTS-64

Ortiz, Leo
❑ 85DomLeaS-188

Ortiz, Lou
❑ 55Top-114
❑ 55TopDouH-91

Ortiz, Luis
❑ 92Bow-306
❑ 92LynRedSC-11
❑ 92LynRedSF-2916
❑ 92UppDecML-114
❑ 93Bow-523
❑ 93ClaFS7-57
❑ 93ExcFS7-135
❑ 93LimRocDWB-35
❑ 93LimRocDWB-144
❑ 93PawRedSDD-20
❑ 93PawRedSF-2416
❑ 93PawRedSTI-18
❑ 94Bow-119
❑ 94Cla-155
❑ 94ColC-15
❑ 94ColChoGS-15
❑ 94ColChoSS-15
❑ 94FleMajLP-28
❑ 94PawRedSDD-16
❑ 94PawRedSF-952
❑ 94Pin-243
❑ 94PinArtP-243
❑ 94PinMusC-243
❑ 94PinRooTP-4
❑ 94Sco-602
❑ 94ScoGolR-602
❑ 94Top-369
❑ 94TopGol-369
❑ 94TopSpa-369
❑ 94TriAAF-AAA12
❑ 94UppDec-109
❑ 94UppDecED-109
❑ 95BowBes-B16
❑ 95BowBesR-B16
❑ 95Fin-324
❑ 95FinRef-324
❑ 95Pin-19
❑ 95PinArtP-19
❑ 95PinMusC-19
❑ 95Sco-276
❑ 95ScoGolR-276
❑ 95ScoPlaTS-276
❑ 95Sel-217
❑ 95SelArtP-217
❑ 96ColCho-737
❑ 96ColChoGS-737
❑ 96ColChoSS-737
❑ 96Don-191
❑ 96DonPreP-191
❑ 96Fle-256
❑ 96FleTif-256
❑ 96OklCit8B-14
❑ 97PacPriGotD-GD98
❑ 98OmaRoyM-18

Ortiz, Miguel
❑ 80UtiBluJT-21

Ortiz, Nick
❑ 93ForLauRSC-19
❑ 93ForLauRSFP-1606
❑ 93UtiBluSC-19
❑ 93UtiBluSF-3543
❑ 96MicBatCB-18
❑ 97TreThuB-23

Ortiz, Omar
❑ 99Bow-437
❑ 99BowGol-437
❑ 99BowInt-437

Ortiz, Ramon
❑ 89BurIndS-19
❑ 90BurIndP-3022
❑ 92SavCarC-24
❑ 92SavCarF-680
❑ 93SavCarC-27
❑ 94SavCarC-30
❑ 94SavCarF-524
❑ 97CedRapK-20
❑ 97GreBatB-3
❑ 98Bes-37
❑ 98Bow-178
❑ 98BowChr-178
❑ 98BowChrGA-178
❑ 98BowChrGAR-178
❑ 98BowChrI-178
❑ 98BowChrIR-178
❑ 98BowChrR-178
❑ 98BowGolA-178
❑ 98BowInt-178
❑ 98MidAngG-23
❑ 98TexLeaTPG-26

Ortiz, Ray
❑ 90CMC-864
❑ 90ProAaA-153
❑ 90VisOakCLC-70
❑ 90VisOakP-2169
❑ 91LinDriAA-491
❑ 91OrlSunRLD-491
❑ 91OrlSunRP-1863
❑ 92OrlSunRF-2861
❑ 92OrlSunRS-515
❑ 93ClaFS7-233
❑ 93PorBeaF-2395
❑ 94PhoFirF-1527
❑ 95PhoFirTI-29

Ortiz, Russ
❑ 95BelGiaTI-20
❑ 96BesAutS-68
❑ 96BesAutSA-50
❑ 96Bow-360
❑ 96BowFoi-360
❑ 96SanJosGB-13
❑ 96WesOahCHWB-36
❑ 97BesAutAS-36
❑ 97BesLimA-28
❑ 97Bow-373
❑ 97BowCerBlaIA-CA59
❑ 97BowCerBluIA-CA59
❑ 97BowCerGolIA-CA59
❑ 97BowInt-373
❑ 97ShrCap-19
❑ 97ShrCapB-19
❑ 97TexLeaTP-21
❑ 98BesPreA-31
❑ 98Bow-100
❑ 98BowChr-100
❑ 98BowChrGA-100
❑ 98BowChrGAR-100
❑ 98BowChrI-100
❑ 98BowChrIR-100
❑ 98BowChrR-100
❑ 98BowGolA-100
❑ 98BowInt-100
❑ 98Fle-442
❑ 98FreGriG-21
❑ 99Fle-118
❑ 99FleSta9-118
❑ 99FleWarT-118
❑ 99SkyPreA-42
❑ 99SkyPreABlue-42
❑ 99SkyThu-205
❑ 99SkyThuRant-205
❑ 99SkyThuRave-205
❑ 99ThuSkySupR-205

Ortiz, Steve
❑ 94BurIndC-18
❑ 94BurIndF-3791

Ortman, Benjamin
❑ 93BenRocCB-20
❑ 93BenRocF-3282
❑ 94CenValRC-17
❑ 94CenValRF-3217

Ortman, Doug
❑ 87MadMusP-13
❑ 87MadMusP-9

Ortman, Fred
❑ 25Zee-49
❑ 26Zee-99
❑ 29Zee-95
❑ 31Zee-48

Orton, John
❑ 85AncGlaPTI-23
❑ 87SalAngP-6
❑ 88PalSprACLC-107
❑ 88PalSprAP-1433
❑ 89MidAngGS-25
❑ 90Bow-298
❑ 90BowTif-298
❑ 90ClaYel-T61
❑ 90DonRoo-54
❑ 90Fle-647
❑ 90FleCan-647
❑ 90FleUpd-79
❑ 90Lea-511
❑ 90Sco-582
❑ 90Sco100RS-64
❑ 90ScoYouS2-30
❑ 90Spo-132
❑ 90TopDeb89-94
❑ 90UppDec-672
❑ 91AngSmo-20
❑ 91Don-714
❑ 91Fle-320
❑ 91Lea-191
❑ 91OPC-176
❑ 91Sco-467
❑ 91StaClu-591
❑ 91Top-176
❑ 91TopDesS-176
❑ 91TopMic-176
❑ 91TopTif-176
❑ 92EdmTraS-155
❑ 92Fle-65
❑ 92OPC-398
❑ 92Sco-712
❑ 92StaClu-263
❑ 93AngMot-10
❑ 93AngPol-16
❑ 93AngStaCl-17
❑ 93Don-431
❑ 93Fle-195
❑ 93Lea-385
❑ 93PacSpa-371
❑ 93Pin-197
❑ 93Sco-453
❑ 93StaClu-459
❑ 93StaCluFDI-459
❑ 93StaCluMOP-459
❑ 93TriPla-131
❑ 93Ult-167
❑ 93UppDec-317
❑ 93UppDecGold-317
❑ 94RicBraF-2949
❑ 95NorTidTI-20

Oruna, Roland
❑ 83ChaRoyT-11

Orwall, Oswald
❑ 31Zee-71

Osaka, Rocky
❑ 87SanJosBP-7

Osborn, Bob
❑ 30CubTeal-13
❑ 93ConTSN-947

Osborn, Dan
❑ 76OPC-282
❑ 76SSP-135
❑ 76Top-282

Osborn, Don
❑ 47SigOil-31
❑ 74OPC-489
❑ 74Top-489
❑ 75PitPirP-17

Osborn, Pat
❑ 75SacSolC-21
❑ 94BreMilB-344

Osborn, Wilfred
❑ 08RosComP-145
❑ 09ColChiE-221
❑ 12ColRedB-221
❑ 12ColTinT-221

Osborne, Bob
❑ 28Zee-36

Osborne, Bobo (Lawrence S.)
❑ 59Top-524
❑ 60Top-201
❑ 61Top-208
❑ 62TigPosCF-15
❑ 62Top-583
❑ 63Top-514
❑ 81TCM60I-463

Osborne, Donovan
❑ 90ClaDraP-13
❑ 90HamRedB-1
❑ 91ArkTraLD-40
❑ 91ArkTraP-1283
❑ 91Bow-406
❑ 91Cla/Bes-27
❑ 91LinDriAA-40
❑ 91Sco-677
❑ 92Bow-96
❑ 92Cla2-T94
❑ 92DonRoo-88
❑ 92FleUpd-120
❑ 92JimDeaRS-7
❑ 92LeaGolR-BC19
❑ 92Pin-541
❑ 92PinRoo-20
❑ 92ProFS7-317
❑ 92ScoRoo-90T
❑ 92Stu-95
❑ 92TopTra-85T
❑ 92TopTraG-85T
❑ 92Ult-570
❑ 92UltAllR-10
❑ 92UppDec-702
❑ 92UppDec-770
❑ 92UppDec-777
❑ 92UppDecSR-SR19
❑ 93Bow-376
❑ 93CarPol-13
❑ 93CarStaC-16
❑ 93ClaGam-72
❑ 93Don-178
❑ 93Fla-123
❑ 93Fle-129
❑ 93FleRooS-RSA10
❑ 93Lea-62
❑ 93OPC-248
❑ 93PacSpa-634
❑ 93PanSti-199
❑ 93Pin-370
❑ 93Sco-349
❑ 93Sel-276
❑ 93SelChaR-7
❑ 93StaClu-586
❑ 93StaCluFDI-586
❑ 93StaCluMOP-586
❑ 93Top-662
❑ 93TopGol-662
❑ 93TopInaM-662
❑ 93TopInaR-662
❑ 93TopMic-662
❑ 93Toy-41
❑ 93Ult-109
❑ 93UppDec-347
❑ 93UppDecGold-347
❑ 93USPlaCR-11H
❑ 94ColC-222
❑ 94ColChoGS-222
❑ 94ColChoSS-222
❑ 94Don-149
❑ 94Fle-640
❑ 94Pac-597
❑ 94Pin-209
❑ 94PinArtP-209
❑ 94PinMusC-209
❑ 94Sco-63
❑ 94ScoGolR-63
❑ 94StaCluT-304
❑ 94StaCluTFDI-304
❑ 94Top-501
❑ 94TopGol-501
❑ 94TopSpa-501
❑ 94Ult-269
❑ 95FleUpd-162
❑ 95TopTra-42T
❑ 96CarPol-20
❑ 96Fla-365
❑ 96Fle-552
❑ 96FleTif-552
❑ 96Pac-218
❑ 96Sco-115
❑ 97CarPol-20
❑ 97Cir-288
❑ 97CirRav-288
❑ 97ColCho-441
❑ 97Don-147
❑ 97DonGolPP-147
❑ 97DonSilPP-147
❑ 97Fle-450
❑ 97FleTif-450
❑ 97PacPriGotD-GD202
❑ 97Sco-144
❑ 97ScoArtPWB-144
❑ 97ScoPreS-144
❑ 97ScoShoS-144
❑ 97ScoShoSAP-144
❑ 97StaClu-91
❑ 97StaCluMOP-91
❑ 97Top-451
❑ 97UppDec-487
❑ 98PacOnl-624
❑ 98PacOnlR-624
❑ 98PacOnlWC-624
❑ 98PinSna-SLC3
❑ 98Top-370
❑ 98TopChr-370
❑ 98TopChrR-370
❑ 98TopDevR-370
❑ 98TopDia-370
❑ 98TopMiniC-370
❑ 98Ult-367
❑ 98UltGolM-367
❑ 98UltMas-367
❑ 98UltPlaM-367
❑ 99Fle-405
❑ 99Pac-360
❑ 99PacPlaB-360
❑ 99PacRed-360
❑ 99UppDec-468
❑ 99UppDecEL1-468
❑ 99UppDecEL2-468

Osborne, Frank
❑ 24Zee-118
❑ 26Zee-123
❑ 27Zee-99
❑ 28Zee-116
❑ 29Zee-118
❑ 30Zee-128
❑ 32Zee-87

Osborne, Jeff
❑ 89AugPirP-494
❑ 89SouAtlLAGS-46
❑ 90CMC-786
❑ 90HarSenP-1200
❑ 90HarSenS-13

Osborne, Mark
❑ 97SouBenSH-23
❑ 98Bow-355
❑ 98BowChr-355
❑ 98BowChrGA-355
❑ 98BowChrGAR-355
❑ 98BowChrI-355
❑ 98BowChrIR-355
❑ 98BowChrR-355
❑ 98BowGolA-355
❑ 98BowInt-355
❑ 98MidLeaPM-24
❑ 98SouBenSHM-1
❑ 98Top-487
❑ 98TopChr-487
❑ 98TopChrR-487
❑ 98TopDevR-487
❑ 98TopDia-487
❑ 98TopMiniC-487
❑ 99Bow-135
❑ 99BowChr-135
❑ 99BowChrG-135
❑ 99BowChrGR-135
❑ 99BowChrI-135
❑ 99BowChrIR-135
❑ 99BowChrR-135
❑ 99BowGol-135
❑ 99BowInt-135

Osborne, Tiny
❑ 90DodTar-1046

Osborne, Wayne
❑ 33Zee-17
❑ 37Zee-21

Osentowski, Jared
❑ 92KinMetC-3
❑ 92StaCluD-136
❑ 93CapCitBC-15
❑ 93CapCitBF-469
❑ 94CapCitBC-16
❑ 94CapCitBF-1757
❑ 94PitMetC-16
❑ 94PitMetF-3530

Osentowski, Ozzie
❑ 92KinMetF-1541

Oshima, Yasuroni
❑ 79TCMJapPB-75

Osik, Keith
❑ 90LSUTigA-4
❑ 90LSUTigP-5
❑ 91SalBucC-2
❑ 91SalBucP-956
❑ 92CarMudF-1184
❑ 92CarMudS-138
❑ 93CarMudF-2058
❑ 93CarMudTI-2
❑ 94BufBisF-1840
❑ 97PirPos-26

Osilka, Garrett
❑ 96HelBreTI-17
❑ 98BelSnaM-20

Osinski, Dan
❑ 63AngJayP-11
❑ 63Top-114
❑ 64Top-537
❑ 65BraTeal-10
❑ 65OPC-223
❑ 65Top-223
❑ 66OPC-168
❑ 66RedSoxTI-8
❑ 66Top-168
❑ 66TopVen-168
❑ 67Top-594
❑ 68Top-331
❑ 68TopVen-331
❑ 69Top-622
❑ 81RedSoxBG2S-101

Osinski, Glenn
❑ 90MadMusB-8
❑ 90SouOreAB-28
❑ 91ModA'sC-10
❑ 91ModA'sP-3098

Osmon, Scott
❑ 89IdaFalBP-2032

Osofsky, Aaron
❑ 52LavPro-86

Osofsky, Alvin
❑ 75DubPacT-32

Osorio, Sam
❑ 93PriRedC-23
❑ 93PriRedF-4196

Osowski, Tom
❑ 83ButCopKT-33
❑ 84ButCopKT-6
❑ 85EveGiaC-12

❑ 86PalSprAS-1
Ostdiek, Henry
❑ 09ObaT21-218
❑ 09ObaT21-390
❑ 12ObaPreT-139
Osteen, Claude
❑ 55DonWin-35
❑ 59RedEnq-17
❑ 59SeaPop-8
❑ 59Top-224
❑ 60Top-206
❑ 61RedJayP-10
❑ 62Top-501
❑ 63Jel-100
❑ 63Pos-100
❑ 63Top-374
❑ 64Top-28
❑ 64TopCoi-13
❑ 64TopSta-74
❑ 64TopStaU-52
❑ 64TopTatI-58
❑ 64TopVen-28
❑ 65DodJayP-9
❑ 65DodTeal-13
❑ 65MacSta-8
❑ 65Top-570
❑ 66DodVolT-5
❑ 66Top-270
❑ 66TopVen-270
❑ 67CokCapA-16
❑ 67CokCapD-15
❑ 67CokCapDA-15
❑ 67CokCapNLA-22
❑ 67DexPre-156
❑ 67Top-330
❑ 67TopVen-302
❑ 68AtlOilPBCC-32
❑ 68OPC-9
❑ 68Top-9
❑ 68Top-440
❑ 68TopActS-1C
❑ 68TopActS-16C
❑ 68TopGamI-12
❑ 69MilBra-208
❑ 69MLBOffS-150
❑ 69Top-528
❑ 69TopSta-47
❑ 69TopTeaP-22
❑ 70DayDaiNM-20
❑ 70MLBOffS-54
❑ 70OPC-260
❑ 70Top-260
❑ 70TopScr-15
❑ 70TopSup-1
❑ 71BazNumT-39
❑ 71BazUnn-12
❑ 71DodTic-12
❑ 71Kel-70A
❑ 71Kel-70B
❑ 71Kel-70C
❑ 71MilDud-56
❑ 71MLBOffS-110
❑ 71OPC-10
❑ 71Top-10
❑ 71TopCoi-45
❑ 71TopSup-27
❑ 72Kel-34A
❑ 72Kel-34B
❑ 72MilBra-260
❑ 72OPC-297
❑ 72OPC-298
❑ 72Top-297
❑ 72Top-298
❑ 73Kel2D-49
❑ 73OPC-490
❑ 73SevTraC-56
❑ 73Top-490
❑ 74AstFouTIP-2
❑ 74OPC-42
❑ 74Top-42
❑ 74TopDecE-38
❑ 74TopSta-48
❑ 74TopTra-42T
❑ 75OPC-453
❑ 75Top-453
❑ 75TopMin-453
❑ 76OPC-488
❑ 76SSP-137
❑ 76Top-488
❑ 77Car5-17
❑ 77CarTeal-17
❑ 78CarTeal-22
❑ 78TCM60I-273
❑ 79Car5-20
❑ 80Red196T-40
❑ 84PhiTas-12
❑ 85PhiTas-5
❑ 85PhiTas-8
❑ 86PhiTas-3
❑ 87AstShoSTw-12
❑ 87DodSmoA-25
❑ 87PhiTas-xx0
❑ 88PhiTas-29
❑ 89DodSmoG-73
❑ 89PacLegI-132
❑ 89SanAntMB-26
❑ 89SweBasG-17
❑ 90AlbDukCm-28
❑ 90AlbDukP-363
❑ 90AlbDukTr-25
❑ 90CMC-658
❑ 90DodTar-597
❑ 90ProAAAF-83
❑ 91AlbDukP-1159
❑ 91LinDriAAA-25
❑ 92AlbDukF-740
❑ 92DodStaTA-9
❑ 93RanKee-440
❑ 94RanMagM-29
❑ 95RocRedWTI-42
❑ 96SanAntMB-29
❑ 97AlbDukGS-22
❑ 98AlbDukG-19
Osteen, Dave
❑ 87St.PetCP-1
❑ 88ArkTraGS-23
❑ 89ArkTraGS-15
❑ 89TexLeaAGS-23
❑ 90ArkTraGS-22
❑ 90CMC-107
❑ 90LouRedBC-7
❑ 90LouRedBLBC-32
❑ 90LouRedBP-401
❑ 90ProAAAF-515
❑ 90TexLeaAGS-34
❑ 91LinDriAAA-242
❑ 91LouRedLD-242
❑ 91LouRedP-2913
❑ 96YakBeaTI-NNO
❑ 97AubBeaG-22
❑ 98BriBluM-3
Osteen, Gavin
❑ 89MedAthB-29
❑ 90CMC-692
❑ 90MadMusB-21
❑ 90MadMusP-2268
❑ 91HunStaC-16
❑ 91HunStaLD-290
❑ 91HunStaP-1792
❑ 91HunStaTI-15
❑ 91LinDriAA-290
❑ 92HunStaF-3947
❑ 92SkyAAAF-242
❑ 92TacTigS-542
❑ 93HunStaF-2081
❑ 94TacTigF-3171
❑ 98RocRedWQ-22
Osteen, M. Darrell
❑ 66Top-424
❑ 67Top-222
❑ 68Top-199
❑ 68TopVen-199
Ostenberg, Leo
❑ 29Zee-9
❑ 33Zee-93
Oster, Dave
❑ 88GenCubP-1659
Oster, Mike
❑ 92Min-21
Oster, Paul
❑ 88OklSoo-18
❑ 89OklSoo-21
❑ 89OneYanP-2127
❑ 90PriWilCTI-18
❑ 91PriWilCC-21
❑ 91PriWilCP-1439
❑ 93AlbYanF-2175
Osterkamp, Ken
❑ 93ForLauRSC-20
❑ 93ForLauRSFP-1596
Ostermeyer, Bill
❑ 90SpoIndSP-6
❑ 91ChaRaiP-105
❑ 91Cla/Bes-196
❑ 91SouAtlLAGP-SAL5
❑ 92ChaRaiF-130
❑ 92HigDesMC-19
Ostermueller, Fritz (Fred)
❑ 34DiaMatCSB-145
❑ 34DiaStaR-73
❑ 34Gou-93
❑ 35DiaMatCS3T1-116
❑ 35GouPuzR-8G
❑ 35GouPuzR-9G
❑ 36GouWidPPR-A80
❑ 39PlaBal-27
❑ 40PlaBal-33
❑ 41BroW75-24
❑ 41Gou-12
❑ 47TipTop-144
❑ 49Bow-227
❑ 76TayBow4-57
❑ 79RedSoxEF-4
❑ 90DodTar-598
❑ 91ConTSN-99
Osting, Jimmy
❑ 95DanBraTI-20
❑ 96EugEmeB-18
❑ 97Bow-318
❑ 97BowInt-318
❑ 97MacBra-3
Ostopowicz, Rich
❑ 89KinMetS-18
Ostrosser, Brian (Brian L.)
❑ 75OklCit8TI-14
❑ 91MetWIZ-304
Ostrowski, Joe P.
❑ 52BerRos-48
❑ 52Top-206
❑ 53MotCoo-2
❑ 83TopRep5-206
Ostrowski, John (John T.)
❑ 47SigOil-32
❑ 48AngTeal-22
❑ 49AngTeal-29
❑ 49W725AngTI-23
❑ 50RoyDes-20
Osugi, Katsuo
❑ 79TCMJapPB-19
Osuna, Adrian
❑ 98ButCopKG-24
Osuna, Al
❑ 87AubAstP-22
❑ 88OscAstS-20
❑ 89OscAstS-16
❑ 90Bes-312
❑ 90ColMudB-19
❑ 90ColMudP-1344
❑ 90ColMudS-19
❑ 90ProAaA-43
❑ 91AstMot-20
❑ 91DonRoo-52
❑ 91Lea-492
❑ 91OPC-149
❑ 91ScoRoo-89T
❑ 91Top-149
❑ 91TopDeb90-120
❑ 91TopDesS-149
❑ 91TopMic-149
❑ 91TopTif-149
❑ 91UppDec-752
❑ 92AstMot-20
❑ 92Bow-639
❑ 92Don-318
❑ 92Fle-442
❑ 92Lea-209
❑ 92LeaBlaG-209
❑ 92OPC-614
❑ 92OPCPre-121
❑ 92Pin-347
❑ 92Sco-452
❑ 92Sco100RS-83
❑ 92StaClu-68
❑ 92Top-614
❑ 92TopGol-614
❑ 92TopGolW-614
❑ 92TopMic-614
❑ 92Ult-207
❑ 92UppDec-259
❑ 93AstStaC-11
❑ 93Don-216
❑ 93Fle-440
❑ 93LinVenB-76
❑ 93Sco-475
❑ 93StaClu-236
❑ 93StaCluFDI-236
❑ 93StaCluMOP-236
❑ 93Top-63
❑ 93TopGol-63
❑ 93TopInaM-63
❑ 93TopInaR-63
❑ 93TopMic-63
❑ 93Ult-45
❑ 94AlbDukF-840
❑ 94DodMot-23
❑ 94Don-541
❑ 94Fle-497
❑ 94Pac-271
❑ 94StaClu-293
❑ 94StaCluFDI-293
❑ 94StaCluGR-293
❑ 94StaCluMOP-293
❑ 94Top-277
❑ 94TopGol-277
❑ 94TopSpa-277
❑ 94VenLinU-23
❑ 95DodPol-18
❑ 95NorTidTI-21
Osuna, Antonio
❑ 91KisDodP-4181
❑ 94Bow-678
❑ 95Bow-18
❑ 95DodMot-22
❑ 95DodPol-19
❑ 95Exc-215
❑ 95Fla-370
❑ 95FleUpd-177
❑ 95SelCer-133
❑ 95SelCerMG-133
❑ 95SP-6
❑ 95SPSil-6
❑ 95StaClu-524
❑ 95StaCluMOP-524
❑ 95StaCluSTWS-524
❑ 95Sum-161
❑ 95SumNthD-161
❑ 95TopTra-111T
❑ 95UppDec-232
❑ 95UppDecED-232
❑ 95UppDecEDG-232
❑ 95Zen-142
❑ 96ColCho-583
❑ 96ColChoGS-583
❑ 96ColChoSS-583
❑ 96DodFle-14
❑ 96DodMot-19
❑ 96DodPol-26
❑ 96Don-293
❑ 96DonPreP-293
❑ 96Fle-443
❑ 96FleTif-443
❑ 96Pac-116
❑ 96Sco-221
❑ 96StaClu-419
❑ 96StaCluMOP-419
❑ 97AlbDukGS-23
❑ 97DodPol-21
❑ 97Fle-369
❑ 97FleTif-369
❑ 97Lea-126
❑ 97LeaFraM-126
❑ 97LeaFraMDC-126
❑ 97Pac-337
❑ 97PacLigB-337
❑ 97PacSil-337
❑ 97StaClu-329
❑ 97StaCluMOP-329
❑ 97Top-240
❑ 98DodMot-15
❑ 98DodPol-20
❑ 98Fle-548
❑ 98Pac-337
❑ 98PacOnl-381
❑ 98PacOnlR-381
❑ 98PacOnlWC-381
❑ 98PacPlaB-337
❑ 98PacRedT-337
❑ 98PacSil-337
❑ 98Ult-425
❑ 98UltGolM-425
❑ 98UltMas-425
❑ 98UltPlaM-425
❑ 99DodPol-18
❑ 99Fle-323
❑ 99FleSta9-323
❑ 99FleWarT-323
❑ 99PacCroC-143
❑ 99PacCroCPB-143
❑ 99Ult-38
❑ 99UltGolM-38
❑ 99UltMas-38
❑ 99UltPlaM-38
Osuna, Pedro
❑ 92ProFS7-252
❑ 94SanAntMF-2465
Oswald, Steve
❑ 86BirBarTI-1
Oswalt, Roy
❑ 97AubDouTI-31
❑ 98AubDouTI-18
Otanez, Willis
❑ 91GreFalDSP-14
❑ 92ClaFS7-356
❑ 92UppDecML-102
❑ 92VerBeaDC-8
❑ 92VerBeaDF-2887
❑ 93BakDodCLC-21
❑ 93LimRocDWB-76
❑ 94FloStaLAF-FSL49
❑ 94VerBeaDC-13
❑ 94VerBeaDF-81
❑ 95Bow-11
❑ 95Exc-216
❑ 95UppDecML-212
❑ 95UppDecMLFS-212
❑ 95VerBeaDTI-18
❑ 96BowBayB-23
❑ 97RocRedW-19
❑ 98RocRedWQ-23
❑ 99Fle-500
❑ 99FleBri-163
❑ 99FleBri2G-163
❑ 99FleBriBlu-163
❑ 99FleBriGol-163
❑ 99FleSta9-500
❑ 99FleWarT-500
❑ 99Rev-21
❑ 99RevPremDate-21
❑ 99RevRet-21
❑ 99RevShaSS-21
❑ 99SpoIll-59
Otero, Oscar
❑ 97WilCubB-15
Otero, Reggie (Regino J.)
❑ 47SigOil-33
❑ 60Top-459
❑ 63RedFreBC-15
❑ 80Red196T-6
Otero, Ricky
❑ 91KinMetC-8
❑ 91KinMetP-3826
❑ 92ColMetC-12
❑ 92ColMetF-309
❑ 92ColMetPI-24
❑ 92ColMetPIISPI-6
❑ 92ProFS7-288
❑ 92UppDecML-236
❑ 93BinMetF-2347
❑ 93ClaGolF-158
❑ 93ExcFS7-77
❑ 93SouAtlLAIPI-9
❑ 93SouAtlLAPI-29
❑ 94BinMetF-718
❑ 95Bow-40
❑ 95Exc-234
❑ 95FleUpd-117
❑ 95MetColP-25
❑ 95NorTidTI-22
❑ 95Sum-155
❑ 95SumNthD-155
❑ 96Cir-168
❑ 96CirBos-43
❑ 96CirRav-168
❑ 96MetKah-25
❑ 96Sco-235
❑ 96ScrRedBB-22
❑ 97Cir-219
❑ 97CirRav-219
❑ 97Don-233
❑ 97DonGolPP-233
❑ 97DonSilPP-233
❑ 97Fle-417
❑ 97FleTif-417
❑ 97Lea-36
❑ 97LeaFraM-36
❑ 97LeaFraMDC-36
❑ 97MetUni-204
❑ 97Pac-383
❑ 97PacLigB-383
❑ 97PacPri-130
❑ 97PacPriLB-130
❑ 97PacPriP-130
❑ 97PacSil-383
❑ 97PhiCopQ-20
❑ 97ScrRedB-13
❑ 97StaClu-328
❑ 97StaCluMOP-328
❑ 97Top-106
❑ 97Ult-254
❑ 97UltGolME-254
❑ 97UltPlaME-254
❑ 97UppDec-134
❑ 98RocRedWQ-24
Otero, Will
❑ 97SalVolG-28
Otey, William
❑ 09T206-506
Otis, Amos (Amos Joseph)
❑ 69OPC-31
❑ 69Top-31
❑ 70DayDaiNM-114
❑ 70OPC-354
❑ 70RoyTeal-26
❑ 70Top-354
❑ 71BazNumT-42
❑ 71BazUnn-36
❑ 71Kel-38
❑ 71MLBOffS-424
❑ 71OPC-610
❑ 71oySigST-18
❑ 71Top-610
❑ 71TopCoi-96
❑ 71TopSup-45
❑ 71TopTat-32
❑ 72Kel-2
❑ 72OPC-10
❑ 72oyTeal-17
❑ 72SevTraC-38
❑ 72Top-10
❑ 72TopPos-6
❑ 73Kel2D-1
❑ 73LinPor-88
❑ 73OPC-510
❑ 73Top-510
❑ 73TopCanL-37
❑ 74GreHeroBP-5
❑ 74Kel-17
❑ 74OPC-65
❑ 74OPC-337
❑ 74RoyPos-21
❑ 74Top-65
❑ 74Top-337
❑ 74TopDecE-1
❑ 74TopSta-185
❑ 75Hos-50
❑ 75OPC-520
❑ 75RoyPos-23
❑ 75SSP42-22
❑ 75Top-520
❑ 75TopMin-520
❑ 76Hos-51
❑ 76HosTwi-51
❑ 76KanCitRP-22
❑ 76OPC-198
❑ 76OPC-510
❑ 76RoyAaP-10
❑ 76SSP-177
❑ 76Top-198
❑ 76Top-510
❑ 77BurCheD-65
❑ 77Hos-92
❑ 77OPC-141
❑ 77PepGloD-33
❑ 77RCColC-48
❑ 77Top-290
❑ 78OPC-16
❑ 78RCColC-55
❑ 78Roy-16
❑ 78SSP270-227
❑ 78Top-490
❑ 79BasPat-64
❑ 79Hos-132
❑ 79OPC-185
❑ 79RoyTeal-7
❑ 79Top-360
❑ 80OPC-72
❑ 80Top-130
❑ 80TopSup-50
❑ 81AllGamPI-65
❑ 81CokTeaS-78
❑ 81Don-104
❑ 81Fle-32A
❑ 81Fle-32B
❑ 81Fle-483A
❑ 81Fle-483B
❑ 81FleStiC-28
❑ 81OPC-288
❑ 81RoyPol-7
❑ 81RoyProPS-13
❑ 81Top-585
❑ 82Don-70
❑ 82Fle-419
❑ 82FleSta-211
❑ 82OPC-162
❑ 82OPC-350
❑ 82Roy-14
❑ 82Top-725
❑ 82Top-726
❑ 82TopSti-194
❑ 83AllGamPI-66
❑ 83Don-364

❑ 83Fle-120
❑ 83FleSta-143
❑ 83FleSti-99
❑ 83OPC-75
❑ 83RoyPol-5
❑ 83RoyPos-21
❑ 83Top-75
❑ 83TopFol-5
❑ 83TopSti-72
❑ 84AllGamPI-63
❑ 84Fle-351
❑ 84FleUpd-87
❑ 84Nes792-655
❑ 84OPC-53
❑ 84Pir-14
❑ 84Top-655
❑ 84TopTif-655
❑ 84TopTra-89T
❑ 84TopTraT-89T
❑ 86RoyGreT-6
❑ 88PadSmo-21
❑ 89PacSenL-83
❑ 89PadPos-21
❑ 89T/MSenL-84
❑ 89TidTidC-4
❑ 89TopSenL-81
❑ 90EliSenL-74
❑ 90PadMag-22
❑ 91MetWIZ-305
❑ 91PacSenL-26
❑ 93RoySta2-8
❑ 94ColSprSSF-750
❑ 94TedWil-38

Otis, David
❑ 86MadMusP-17

Ott, Ed (Nathan Edward)
❑ 76OPC-594
❑ 76PirPos-15
❑ 76Top-594
❑ 77PirPosP-18
❑ 77Top-197
❑ 78OPC-161
❑ 78Top-28
❑ 79Hos-31
❑ 79OPC-289
❑ 79Top-561
❑ 80OPC-200
❑ 80Top-383
❑ 81CokTeaS-116
❑ 81Don-133
❑ 81Fle-365
❑ 81LonBeaPT-18A
❑ 81OPC-246
❑ 81Top-246
❑ 81TopSti-214
❑ 81TopTra-810
❑ 82Don-192
❑ 82Fle-470
❑ 82OPC-225
❑ 82Top-469
❑ 83Fle-98
❑ 83Top-131
❑ 84EdmTraC-120
❑ 85PriWilPT-23
❑ 86WatPirP-16
❑ 89AstLenH-14
❑ 89AstMot-27
❑ 89AstSmo-30
❑ 91AstMot-28
❑ 92AstMot-27
❑ 93AstMot-28

Ott, Mel (Melvin Thomas)
❑ 29ExhFou-9
❑ 29PorandAR-67
❑ 30W554-12
❑ 31Exh-10
❑ 31W517-30
❑ 33GeoCMil-24
❑ 33Gou-127
❑ 33Gou-207
❑ 33RitCE-4C
❑ 33WorCig-77
❑ 34BabRutG-50
❑ 34BatR31-27
❑ 34ButPreR-49
❑ 34DiaMatCSB-146
❑ 34DiaStaR-50
❑ 34ExhFou-5
❑ 35DiaMatCS2-17
❑ 35DiaMatCS3T1-117
❑ 35ExhFou-5
❑ 35GouPreR-14
❑ 35GouPuzR-4A
❑ 35GouPuzR-7A
❑ 35GouPuzR-12A
❑ 35WheBB1-22
❑ 36DiaMatCS4-12
❑ 36ExhFou-5
❑ 36SandSW-44
❑ 36WheBB4-8
❑ 36WheBB5-7A
❑ 36WheBB5-7B
❑ 37ExhFou-5
❑ 37GouThuMR-3
❑ 37WheBB14-12
❑ 38CloFotW-70
❑ 38ExhFou-5
❑ 38GouFliMR-3A
❑ 38GouFliMR-3B
❑ 38OurNatGPP-22
❑ 39ExhSal-49A
❑ 39ExhSal-49B
❑ 39GouPreR303A-35
❑ 39GouPreR303B-20
❑ 39PC7AlbHoF-60
❑ 39PlaBal-51
❑ 39WheBB12-8
❑ 39WorWidGTP-35
❑ 40PlaBal-88
❑ 40WheM4-2B
❑ 41DouPlaR-31
❑ 41DouPlaR-89
❑ 41Gou-33
❑ 41PlaBal-8
❑ 43MPR302-1-19
❑ 48BluTin-18A
❑ 48BluTin-18B
❑ 48GiaTeal-20
❑ 50CalHOFW-58
❑ 51R42SmaS-76
❑ 52MotCoo-32
❑ 53ArtHaloFP-66
❑ 60ExhWriH-18
❑ 60Fle-36
❑ 60NuHi-58
❑ 61Fle-68
❑ 61GolPre-1
❑ 61NuSco-458
❑ 61SevElev-28
❑ 63BasMagM-63
❑ 63BazA-36
❑ 67TopVen-149
❑ 68LauWorS-30
❑ 69Baz-8
❑ 69Baz-11
❑ 70FleWorS-30
❑ 70SpoCarfCOP-23
❑ 72FleFamF-25
❑ 72TCMthe1-202
❑ 73FleWilD-17
❑ 73TCMAllG-14
❑ 75GiaAllT-8
❑ 75GiaAllT-9
❑ 75SpoHobBG-6
❑ 76GalBasGHoF-21
❑ 76JerJonPC-2
❑ 76RowExh-12
❑ 76ShaPiz-60
❑ 76TayBow4-43
❑ 77BobParHoF-70
❑ 77GalGloG-59
❑ 77GalGloG-256
❑ 77TCMTheWY-17
❑ 79Pew-13
❑ 80GiaGreT-9
❑ 80Lau300-12
❑ 80LauFamF-14
❑ 80PacLeg-35
❑ 80PerHaloFP-60
❑ 80SSPHOF-60
❑ 81ConTSN-85
❑ 82DiaCla-50
❑ 82TCMGreS-32
❑ 83DonHOFH-40
❑ 83TCMPla1942-32
❑ 85BigLeaC3-46
❑ 85CirK-12
❑ 85FegMurCG-14
❑ 86BigLeaC-11
❑ 86ConSer1-36
❑ 86SpoDecG-8
❑ 86SpoDecGS-2
❑ 87HygAllG-35
❑ 88ConSer4-21
❑ 88GreBasS-58
❑ 89HOFStiB-49
❑ 89PacLegI-189
❑ 90SweBasG-55
❑ 91ConTSN-7
❑ 91ConTSN-225
❑ 91SweBasG-144
❑ 92ConTSNCI-11
❑ 92St.VinHHS-7
❑ 92TVSpoMF5HRC-10
❑ 93ActPacA-102
❑ 93ActPacA2-36G
❑ 93ConTSN-834
❑ 93UppDecAH-103
❑ 93UppDecAH-136
❑ 94ConTSN-1097
❑ 94ConTSN-1254
❑ 94ConTSNB-1097
❑ 94ConTSNB-1254
❑ 94TedWil-55
❑ 94UppDecAH-45
❑ 94UppDecAH-171
❑ 94UppDecAH1-45
❑ 94UppDecAH1-171
❑ 95ConTSNGJ-5
❑ 99SP SigLC-MEL1
❑ 99SP SigLC-MEL2
❑ 99SpoIllGotG-5
❑ 99UppDecAP-MO
❑ 99UppDecCL-42
❑ 99UppDecCLCC-42
❑ 99UppDecCLLC-SP

Ott, William
❑ 65Top-354

Ottavinia, Paul
❑ 94SigRooDP-69
❑ 94SigRooDPS-69
❑ 94StaCluDP-41
❑ 94StaCluDPFDI-41
❑ 96WesPalBEB-30
❑ 98TamYanM-22

Otten, Brian
❑ 86GenCubP-21
❑ 87PeoChiP-15
❑ 88WinSpiS-13

Otten, Jim
❑ 75OPC-624
❑ 75Top-624
❑ 75TopMin-624
❑ 77Top-493
❑ 81Car5x7-20

Ottmers, Marc
❑ 93GleFalRC-22
❑ 93GleFalRF-4001
❑ 94MadHatC-19
❑ 94MadHatF-129

Otto, Dave
❑ 86MadMusP-16
❑ 87MadMusP-14
❑ 88Fle-652
❑ 88FleGlo-652
❑ 89ScoHot1R-60
❑ 89TacTigC-10
❑ 89TacTigP-1547
❑ 89Top-131
❑ 89TopTif-131
❑ 89UppDec-4
❑ 90Bow-448
❑ 90BowTif-448
❑ 90CMC-584
❑ 90ProAAAF-136
❑ 90ScoRoo-101T
❑ 90TacTigC-7
❑ 90TacTigP-89
❑ 91ColSprSSLD-93
❑ 91ColSprSSP-2180
❑ 91Fle-20
❑ 91IndFanC-24
❑ 91LinDriAAA-93
❑ 91SouOreAAP-SOA21
❑ 92Bow-619
❑ 92Don-730
❑ 92IndFanC-22
❑ 92Lea-218
❑ 92LeaBlaG-218
❑ 92OPC-499
❑ 92Pin-316
❑ 92StaClu-461
❑ 92Top-499
❑ 92TopGol-499
❑ 92TopGolW-499
❑ 92TopMic-499
❑ 92Ult-354
❑ 92UppDec-698
❑ 93PirNatI-23

Otto, Mascot
❑ 95SpoIndTI-16
❑ 97SpoIndG-20
❑ 98SpoIndG-23

Otto, Steve
❑ 88EugEmeB-4
❑ 89AppFoxP-876
❑ 90BasCitRS-17

Ouellette, Phil
❑ 82CliGiaF-5
❑ 84PhoGiaC-1
❑ 85PhoGiaC-182
❑ 86PhoFirP-19
❑ 88CalCanC-12
❑ 88CalCanP-801
❑ 88TriAAAP-7
❑ 90CMC-390
❑ 90ProAAAF-383
❑ 90TolMudHC-13
❑ 90TolMudHP-153

Outen, Chink
❑ 33Zee-36
❑ 33Zee-37
❑ 37Zee-4
❑ 37Zee-22
❑ 37Zee-23
❑ 90DodTar-1049

Outlaw, Jimmy (James Paulus)
❑ 39PlaBal-155
❑ 46SpoExcW-2-6
❑ 47TipTop-39
❑ 79DiaGre-253
❑ 83TCMPla1944-4

Ovalles, Evilio
❑ 95LinVen-251

Overall, Orval
❑ 06FanCraNL-35
❑ 07CubA.CDPP-8
❑ 07CubGFGCP-8
❑ 08AmeCarE91-19
❑ 08AmeCarE91-57
❑ 08RosComP-106
❑ 09AmeCarE90-1-86
❑ 09ColChiE-222
❑ 09SpoNewSM-30
❑ 09T206-276
❑ 09T206-277
❑ 09T206-278
❑ 10ChiE-7
❑ 10SepAnoP-20
❑ 10SweCapPP-86
❑ 11DiaGumP-23
❑ 11PinT-5-209
❑ 11S74Sil-66
❑ 11SpoLifCW-279
❑ 11SpoLifM-176
❑ 11T205-133
❑ 11TurRedT-32
❑ 12ColRedB-222
❑ 12ColTinT-222
❑ 12HasTriFT-13C
❑ 12HasTriFT-36C
❑ 13Zee-119
❑ 72ClaCar-54
❑ 87Cub190T-5

Overeem, Steve
❑ 88JamExpP-1914

Overholser, Drew
❑ 91SpoIndC-14
❑ 91SpoIndP-3947

Overman, Dan
❑ 93PocPosSP-26
❑ 94OgdRapSP-26
❑ 95ForWayWTI-29

Overmire, Stubby (Frank)
❑ 47TipTop-40
❑ 49Lea-17
❑ 51Bow-280
❑ 52Top-155
❑ 83TopRep5-155

Overton, Jeff
❑ 82AppFoxFr-2

Overton, Joe
❑ 68SeaPop-11

Overton, Mike
❑ 79NewCoPT-5

Overy, Mike
❑ 76SalLakCGC-3
❑ 77SalLakCGC-24
❑ 77Top-489
❑ 78SalLakCGC-24
❑ 79SalLakCGT-9
❑ 80SalLakCGT-26

Oviedo, Alex
❑ 96-97LinVen-250

Oviedo, Gelso
❑ 52LavPro-104

Oviedo, Igor
❑ 93LinVenB-241

Owchinko, Bob
❑ 77PadFamF-4
❑ 77PadSchC-43
❑ 78PadFamF-20
❑ 78Top-164
❑ 79OPC-257
❑ 79PadFamF-7
❑ 79Top-488
❑ 80IndTeal-23
❑ 80OPC-44
❑ 80Top-79
❑ 81Don-563A
❑ 81Don-563B
❑ 81Top-536
❑ 81TopTra-811
❑ 82Don-287
❑ 82Fle-104
❑ 82Top-243
❑ 83Don-265
❑ 83Fle-531
❑ 83Top-338
❑ 84FleUpd-88
❑ 84RedEnq-21
❑ 85Don-506
❑ 85Fle-543
❑ 85TacTigC-144
❑ 85Top-752
❑ 85TopTif-752
❑ 86IndIndTI-9
❑ 91PacSenL-83

Owen, Andy
❑ 95YakBeaTI-24
❑ 96VerBeaDB-22
❑ 97SanBerS-28

Owen, Billy
❑ 04FanCraAL-38

Owen, Dave
❑ 83IowCubT-18
❑ 84CubChiT-21
❑ 84CubSev-19
❑ 84IowCubT-18
❑ 85Don-483
❑ 85IowCubT-6
❑ 85Top-642
❑ 85TopTif-642
❑ 86OklCit8P-16
❑ 87OklCit8P-3
❑ 88OmaRoyC-16
❑ 88OmaRoyP-1510
❑ 89IowCubC-19
❑ 89IowCubP-1694
❑ 89LynRedSS-16
❑ 90NewBriRSB-18
❑ 90NewBriRSP-1318
❑ 90NewBriRSS-13
❑ 90ProAaA-7
❑ 91Bow-110
❑ 92WinHavRSF-1774

Owen, Frank Malcomb
❑ 09T206-279

Owen, Larry (Lawrence T.)
❑ 79RicBraT-5
❑ 82RicBraT-11
❑ 82Top-502
❑ 83BraPol-24
❑ 84RicBraT-8
❑ 85IntLeaAT-9
❑ 85RicBraT-12
❑ 86RicBraP-15
❑ 88OmaRoyC-18
❑ 88OmaRoyP-1516
❑ 88RoyTeal-22
❑ 88Sco-230
❑ 88ScoGlo-230
❑ 88StaLinRo-10
❑ 89Top-87
❑ 89TopTif-87
❑ 89UppDec-528
❑ 90RicBra2ATI-18

Owen, Lem
❑ 22Zee-85

Owen, Marv (Marvin James)
❑ 34BatR31-168
❑ 34DiaStaR-67
❑ 34TigTeal-13
❑ 36GouWidPPR-A81
❑ 36GouWidPPR-B18
❑ 36WorWidGV-69
❑ 38GouHeaU-263
❑ 38GouHeaU-287
❑ 39GouPreR303A-36
❑ 39WorWidGTP-36
❑ 74TigTCM1AC-21
❑ 76TigOldTS-16
❑ 81TigSecNP-24
❑ 93ConTSN-941

Owen, Mickey (Arnold Malcolm)
❑ 35AlDemDCR3-28
❑ 39PlaBal-135
❑ 40PlaBal-111
❑ 41DouPlaR-15
❑ 42DodTeal-15
❑ 43DodTeal-20
❑ 50Bow-78
❑ 51Bow-174
❑ 60NuHi-15
❑ 61NuSco-475
❑ 68LauWorS-38
❑ 73Dod194T-21
❑ 77TCMTheWY-3
❑ 78DodTCM4-1
❑ 83TCMPla1944-43
❑ 88DodRinP1-8C
❑ 89DodSmoG-44
❑ 90DodTar-599
❑ 91UppDecS-4

Owen, Spike D.
❑ 83SalLakCGT-23
❑ 84Don-313
❑ 84Fle-616
❑ 84MarMot-6
❑ 84Nes792-413
❑ 84Top-413
❑ 84TopSti-349
❑ 84TopTif-413
❑ 85AllGamPI-24
❑ 85Don-435
❑ 85DonActA-4
❑ 85Fle-497
❑ 85Lea-167
❑ 85MarMot-7
❑ 85Top-84
❑ 85TopSti-339
❑ 85TopTif-84
❑ 86Don-362
❑ 86Fle-471
❑ 86MarMot-20
❑ 86OPC-248
❑ 86Top-248
❑ 86TopSti-224
❑ 86TopTif-248
❑ 87Don-633
❑ 87DonOpeD-185
❑ 87Fle-40
❑ 87FleGlo-40
❑ 87Lea-87
❑ 87RedSoxP-15
❑ 87RedSoxSAP-9
❑ 87Top-591
❑ 87TopTif-591
❑ 88Don-544
❑ 88DonTeaBRS-544
❑ 88Fle-359
❑ 88FleGlo-359
❑ 88OPC-188
❑ 88PanSti-30
❑ 88Sco-372
❑ 88ScoGlo-372
❑ 88StaLinRS-14
❑ 88Top-21
❑ 88Top-733
❑ 88TopTif-21
❑ 88TopTif-733
❑ 89Bow-363
❑ 89BowTif-363
❑ 89Don-593
❑ 89DonBasB-236
❑ 89DonTra-14
❑ 89ExpPos-23
❑ 89Fle-93
❑ 89FleGlo-93
❑ 89FleUpd-98
❑ 89Sco-218
❑ 89ScoRoo-13T
❑ 89Top-123
❑ 89TopBig-221
❑ 89TopTif-123
❑ 89TopTra-92T
❑ 89TopTraT-92T
❑ 89UppDec-161
❑ 89UppDec-717
❑ 90Bow-116
❑ 90BowTif-116
❑ 90Don-102
❑ 90DonBesN-6
❑ 90ExpPos-27
❑ 90Fle-357
❑ 90FleCan-357
❑ 90Lea-186
❑ 90OPC-674
❑ 90PanSti-285

❑ 90PubIntS-184
❑ 90Sco-247
❑ 90Top-674
❑ 90TopBig-25
❑ 90TopSti-73
❑ 90TopTif-674
❑ 90UppDec-291
❑ 91Bow-454
❑ 91Don-251
❑ 91Fle-243
❑ 91Lea-36
❑ 91OPC-372
❑ 91PanFreS-142
❑ 91PanSti-62
❑ 91Sco-452
❑ 91StaClu-236
❑ 91Top-372
❑ 91TopDesS-372
❑ 91TopMic-372
❑ 91TopTif-372
❑ 91Ult-208
❑ 91UppDec-189
❑ 92Bow-121
❑ 92Don-518
❑ 92ExpDonD-14
❑ 92ExpPos-24
❑ 92Fle-488
❑ 92Lea-455
❑ 92LeaBlaG-455
❑ 92OPC-443
❑ 92PanSti-205
❑ 92Pin-234
❑ 92Sco-323
❑ 92StaClu-221
❑ 92Stu-58
❑ 92TexLon-30
❑ 92Top-443
❑ 92TopGol-443
❑ 92TopGolW-443
❑ 92TopMic-443
❑ 92Ult-224
❑ 92UppDec-206
❑ 93Bow-483
❑ 93Don-732
❑ 93Fle-463
❑ 93FleFinE-251
❑ 93Lea-405
❑ 93OPC-327
❑ 93OPCPre-8
❑ 93PacSpa-561
❑ 93Pin-499
❑ 93Sco-554
❑ 93Sel-239
❑ 93SelRoo-109T
❑ 93StaClu-677
❑ 93StaCluFDI-677
❑ 93StaCluMOP-677
❑ 93Stu-79
❑ 93Top-42
❑ 93TopGol-42
❑ 93TopInaM-42
❑ 93TopInaR-42
❑ 93TopMic-42
❑ 93TopPreS-8
❑ 93Ult-600
❑ 93UppDec-548
❑ 93UppDecGold-548
❑ 93YanStaC-15
❑ 94AngLAT-24
❑ 94AngMot-11
❑ 94ColC-591
❑ 94ColChoGS-591
❑ 94ColChoSS-591
❑ 94Don-80
❑ 94Fin-264
❑ 94FinRef-264
❑ 94Fle-244
❑ 94FleUpd-20
❑ 94Pac-434
❑ 94Pin-492
❑ 94PinArtP-492
❑ 94PinMusC-492
❑ 94Sco-507
❑ 94ScoGolR-507
❑ 94ScoRoo-RT66
❑ 94ScoRooGR-RT66
❑ 94Sel-325
❑ 94Top-297
❑ 94TopGol-297
❑ 94TopSpa-297
❑ 95AngCHP-6
❑ 95AngMot-12
❑ 95ColChoGS-93
❑ 95ColChoSS-93
❑ 95Don-32
❑ 95DonPreP-32
❑ 95DonTopotO-39
❑ 95Fla-20
❑ 95Fle-231
❑ 95Sco-88
❑ 95ScoGolR-88
❑ 95ScoPlaTS-88
❑ 95Top-520
❑ 95TopCyb-307
❑ 95Ult-271
❑ 95UltGolM-271
❑ 96ColCho-74
❑ 96ColChoGS-74
❑ 96ColChoSS-74
❑ 96Don-321
❑ 96DonPreP-321

Owen, Tim
❑ 85BurRanT-14
❑ 86DayBealP-20

Owen, Tommy
❑ 90IdaFalBP-3248
❑ 91JamExpC-13
❑ 91JamExpP-3549
❑ 96BreCouMB-23

Owens, Bill (William John)
❑ 95NegLeaL2-7

Owens, Billy
❑ 90AriWilP-15
❑ 92AriWilP-12
❑ 92ClaDraP-53
❑ 92FroRowDP-2
❑ 92FroRowDPG-2
❑ 92FroRowDPS-2
❑ 92KanCouCTI-24
❑ 93AlbPolCB-1
❑ 93AlbPolF-2034
❑ 93ClaFS7-85
❑ 93SouAtlLAGF-4
❑ 93StaCluM-146
❑ 94ClaGolF-7
❑ 94FreKeyF-2624
❑ 94OriPro-76
❑ 95BowBayTI-26
❑ 95RocRedWTI-29
❑ 96Exc-6
❑ 96RocRedWB-21
❑ 96Top-425
❑ 98JacGenM-16

Owens, Brad
❑ 92HamRedC-28
❑ 92HamRedF-1602

Owens, Brick
❑ 94ConTSN-1211
❑ 94ConTSNB-1211

Owens, Eric
❑ 92BilMusF-3366
❑ 92BilMusSP-16
❑ 92ClaDraP-121
❑ 92FroRowDP-88
❑ 92FroRowDPG-88
❑ 92FroRowDPS-88
❑ 93ClaFS7-288
❑ 93StaCluM-109
❑ 93WinSpiC-16
❑ 93WinSpiF-1577
❑ 94ChaLooF-1365
❑ 94ExcFS7-180
❑ 94UppDecML-162
❑ 95Bow-219
❑ 95IndIndF-102
❑ 95SigRoo-40
❑ 95SigRooSig-40
❑ 96BesAutS-69
❑ 96Bow-373
❑ 96BowFoi-373
❑ 96ColCho-519
❑ 96ColChoGS-519
❑ 96ColChoSS-519
❑ 96Fin-B227
❑ 96FinRef-B227
❑ 96Fle-348
❑ 96FleTif-348
❑ 96IndIndB-18
❑ 96LeaPre-134
❑ 96LeaPreP-134
❑ 96Pin-384
❑ 96PinFoil-384
❑ 96SelCer-119
❑ 96SelCerAP-119
❑ 96SelCerCB-119
❑ 96SelCerCR-119
❑ 96SelCerMB-119
❑ 96SelCerMG-119
❑ 96SelCerMR-119
❑ 96Sum-181
❑ 96SumAbo&B-181
❑ 96SumArtP-181
❑ 96SumFoi-181
❑ 96Top-103
❑ 96Top-104
❑ 96TopGal-129
❑ 96TopGalPPI-129
❑ 96Ult-464
❑ 96UltGolM-464
❑ 96Zen-126
❑ 96ZenArtP-126
❑ 97Don-348
❑ 97DonGolPP-348
❑ 97DonLim-113
❑ 97DonLimE-113
❑ 97DonLimENG-113
❑ 97DonSilPP-348
❑ 97IndInd-17
❑ 97Pac-274
❑ 97PacLigB-274
❑ 97PacSil-274
❑ 97StaClu-103
❑ 97StaCluMOP-103
❑ 97Top-266
❑ 98LouRedQ-19

Owens, Farrell
❑ 79NaSouTI-18

Owens, Frank (Frank Walter)
❑ 07WhiSoxGWH-8
❑ 09ColChiE-223
❑ 11SpoLifCW-280
❑ 12ColRedB-223
❑ 12ColTinT-223
❑ 14CraJacE-74
❑ 15CraJacE-74

Owens, J. (Jayhawk)
❑ 90Bes-224
❑ 92OrlSunRF-2849
❑ 92OrlSunRS-516
❑ 92SkyAA F-223
❑ 93FleFinE-37
❑ 93Lea-505
❑ 93Top-606
❑ 93TopGol-606
❑ 93TopInaM-606
❑ 93TopInaR-606
❑ 93TopMic-606
❑ 94ColC-223
❑ 94ColChoGS-223
❑ 94ColChoSS-223
❑ 94ColSprSSF-737
❑ 94Don-278
❑ 94Fle-448
❑ 94Pac-203
❑ 94Pin-418
❑ 94PinArtP-418
❑ 94PinMusC-418
❑ 94StaClu-512
❑ 94StaCluFDI-512
❑ 94StaCluGR-512
❑ 94StaCluMOP-512
❑ 94StaCluT-100
❑ 94StaCluTFDI-100
❑ 95Sco-588
❑ 95ScoGolR-588
❑ 95ScoPlaTS-588
❑ 96FleUpd-U129
❑ 96FleUpdTC-U129
❑ 96LeaSigA-174
❑ 96LeaSigAG-174
❑ 96LeaSigAS-174
❑ 96RocFle-10
❑ 96RocPol-14
❑ 96SigRooOJ-25
❑ 96SigRooOJS-25
❑ 96Ult-471
❑ 96UltGolM-471
❑ 97ColSprSATTI-19
❑ 97ColSprSTI-17
❑ 97Pac-284
❑ 97PacLigB-284
❑ 97PacSil-284
❑ 97RocSco-12
❑ 97RocScoPl-12
❑ 97RocScoPr-12
❑ 97Sco-224
❑ 97ScoArtPWB-224
❑ 97ScoPreS-224
❑ 97ScoShoS-224
❑ 97ScoShoSAP-224
❑ 98SalLakBO-21

Owens, Jesse
❑ 62PC7HFGSS-5

Owens, Jim
❑ 55Top-202
❑ 55TopDouH-121
❑ 56Top-114
❑ 59Top-503
❑ 60Lea-39
❑ 60PhiJayP-9
❑ 60Top-185
❑ 60TopVen-185
❑ 61Pos-116A
❑ 61Pos-116B
❑ 61Top-341
❑ 62Top-212
❑ 63RedEnq-23
❑ 63RedFreBC-17
❑ 63Top-483
❑ 64Top-241
❑ 64TopVen-241
❑ 65Top-451
❑ 66Top-297
❑ 66TopVen-297
❑ 67Ast-22
❑ 67AstTeal2-19
❑ 67Top-582
❑ 67TopVen-304
❑ 71AstTeal-17
❑ 72AstTeal-18
❑ 73OPC-624
❑ 73Top-624
❑ 87AstSer1-27
❑ 87AstShowSTh-17
❑ 87AstShowSTh-26

Owens, Larry
❑ 88CapCodPPaLP-52
❑ 90PulBraB-7
❑ 90PulBraP-3102

Owens, Mark (Markus)
❑ 87EveGiaC-30
❑ 87HawRai-19
❑ 88CliGiaP-704
❑ 88MidLeaAGS-1
❑ 89ShrCapP-1849
❑ 90ShrCapP-1446
❑ 90ShrCapS-17

Owens, Marty
❑ 88GenCubP-1658

Owens, Michael
❑ 88BatCliP-1675
❑ 89BatCliP-1930
❑ 90BatCliP-3074
❑ 91SpaPhiC-10
❑ 91SpaPhiP-895

Owens, Paul
❑ 84Fle-643
❑ 84Fle-648
❑ 84FleSti-123
❑ 84Nes792-229
❑ 84PhiTas-8
❑ 84Top-229
❑ 84TopTif-229
❑ 85Top-92
❑ 85TopGloA-1
❑ 85TopTif-92

Owens, Steve
❑ 87GenCubP-26
❑ 88ChaWheB-8

Owens, Tom
❑ 79WauTimT-25
❑ 81WatIndT-12
❑ 82ChaLooT-9
❑ 83BufBisT-6

Owens, Walter
❑ 94BurIndC-19
❑ 94BurIndF-3811
❑ 95WatIndTI-23

Owens-Bragg, Luke
❑ 96HudValRB-15
❑ 96WesOahCHWB-2
❑ 97ChaRivDG-21
❑ 98St.PetDRM-23

Ownbey, Rick
❑ 82MetPhoA-27
❑ 82TidTidT-1
❑ 83Fle-551
❑ 83Top-739
❑ 84LouRedR-23
❑ 85LouRedR-26
❑ 86CarSchM-18
❑ 86CarTeal-33
❑ 86FleUpd-85
❑ 91MetWIZ-306

Oxner, Stan
❑ 83ButCopKT-15

Oyama, Randy
❑ 87HawRai-26

Oyas, Danny
❑ 92PriRedC-26
❑ 92PriRedF-3101
❑ 93BilMusF-3959
❑ 93BilMusSP-8
❑ 94ChaWheC-19
❑ 94ChaWheF-2716
❑ 94SouAtlLAF-SAL42

Oyler, Ray (Raymond F.)
❑ 65OPC-259
❑ 65Top-259
❑ 66OPC-81
❑ 66Top-81
❑ 66TopVen-81
❑ 67Top-352
❑ 68CokCapT-1
❑ 68TigDetFPB-17
❑ 68Top-399
❑ 69MilBra-209
❑ 69MLBOffS-97
❑ 69OPC-178
❑ 69PilPos-3
❑ 69PilWhe-6
❑ 69Top-178
❑ 69TopFou-13
❑ 69TopSta-228
❑ 69TopTeaP-9
❑ 70MLBOffS-264
❑ 70Top-603
❑ 72MilBra-261
❑ 77PilPosR-3
❑ 81TCM60I-379
❑ 81TigDetN-30
❑ 83Pil69G-29
❑ 88TigDom-18

Oyler, Scott
❑ 98SouOreTG-23

Oyster, Jeff
❑ 87ArkTraP-18
❑ 88ArkTraGS-24
❑ 88LouRedBTI-38
❑ 89ArkTraGS-16
❑ 90SprCarDGB-11

Ozario, Claudio
❑ 91SumFlyC-18
❑ 91SumFlyP-2343
❑ 92AlbPolCB-4
❑ 92AlbPolF-2319
❑ 93WesPalBEC-18
❑ 93WesPalBEF-1356

Ozario, Yudith
❑ 94PitMetF-3535
❑ 98BesPreA-32

Ozark, Danny
❑ 71Dod-10
❑ 73OPC-486
❑ 73PhiTeal-25
❑ 73Top-486A
❑ 73Top-486B
❑ 74OPC-119
❑ 74Top-119
❑ 75OPC-46
❑ 75PhiPhiP-24
❑ 75PhiProPS-12
❑ 75Top-46
❑ 75TopMin-46
❑ 76OPC-384
❑ 76PhiPhiP-22
❑ 76SSP-476
❑ 76Top-384
❑ 77Top-467
❑ 78SSP270-50
❑ 78Top-631
❑ 79PhiBurK-1
❑ 79Top-112
❑ 81Dod-22
❑ 81DodPol-NNO
❑ 83GiaPos-8
❑ 84GiaPos-21
❑ 85Top-365
❑ 85TopTif-365
❑ 86PhiGreT-8

Ozarowski, Rich
❑ 98WesMicWM-15

Ozawa, Kouichi
❑ 89VisOakCLC-114
❑ 89VisOakP-1422

Ozias, Todd
❑ 98SalVol-28
❑ 99TeaBesR-63
❑ 99TeaBesRG-63
❑ 99TeaBesRS-63

Oziomiela, Rich
❑ 77ModA'sC-16

Ozorio, Claudio
❑ 94WesPalBEC-18
❑ 94WesPalBEF-57

Ozorio, Yudith
❑ 94PitMetC-28
❑ 96StPetCB-23
❑ 97ArkTraB-23

Ozuna, Gabriel
❑ 89SavCarP-345
❑ 89SouAtlLAGS-37
❑ 90ArkTraGS-23
❑ 91ArkTraLD-41
❑ 91ArkTraP-1284
❑ 91LinDriAA-41
❑ 92ArkTraF-1127
❑ 92ArkTraS-40
❑ 92SkyAA F-17
❑ 93LimRocDWB-63
❑ 93LouRedF-212
❑ 94ArkTraF-3088

Ozuna, Mateo
❑ 89SavCarP-359
❑ 90SavCarP-2077
❑ 91Cla/Bes-244
❑ 91SprCarC-21
❑ 91SprCarP-749
❑ 92ClaFS7-281
❑ 92St.PetCC-18
❑ 92St.PetCF-2036
❑ 93LimRocDWB-85
❑ 93WinSpiC-17
❑ 93WinSpiF-1578

Ozuna, Pablo
❑ 97AppLeaTPB-22
❑ 97JohCitCTI-27
❑ 98Bes-82
❑ 98BesAutSS-39
❑ 98Bow-430
❑ 98BowChr-430
❑ 98BowChrGA-430
❑ 98BowChrGAR-430
❑ 98BowChrI-430
❑ 98BowChrIR-430
❑ 98BowChrR-430
❑ 98BowGolA-430
❑ 98BowInt-430
❑ 98MidLeaPM-18
❑ 98PeoChiM-18
❑ 99BasAmeTP-72
❑ 99BasAmeTPA-33
❑ 99BasAmeTPG-72
❑ 99BasAmeTPLM-8
❑ 99BasAmeTPSC-9
❑ 99Bow-351
❑ 99Bow200RF-ROY6
❑ 99BowBes-129
❑ 99BowBesAR-129
❑ 99BowBesMI-M9
❑ 99BowBesMIAR-M9
❑ 99BowBesMIR-M9
❑ 99BowBesR-129
❑ 99BowGol-351
❑ 99BowInt-351
❑ 99JustheS-37
❑ 99JustheSJB-37
❑ 99JustheSJN-8
❑ 99SP TopP-95
❑ 99SP TopPDtS-D29
❑ 99SP TopPPE-95
❑ 99TeaBesRA-18
❑ 99TeaBesRBW-5
❑ 99TeaBesRFS-18

Ozuna, Rafael
❑ 95GreFalDTI-28
❑ 96SavSanB-28
❑ 96VerBeaDB-23

Ozzie, Mascot
❑ 91KanCouCTI-27
❑ 92KanCouCTI-25
❑ 94KanCouCTI-20
❑ 95KanCouCTI-NNO
❑ 96KanCouCTI-19

Paasch, Steve
❑ 94BatCliC-19
❑ 94BatCliF-3444

Paccito, Fred
❑ 52LavPro-85

Pace, Jim
❑ 88RenSilSCLC-288

Pace, Scott
❑ 94ElmPioC-14
❑ 94ElmPioF-3470
❑ 95HagSunF-67
❑ 96DunBluJB-19
❑ 96DunBluJTI-22
❑ 97El PasDB-18

Pace, Tubby
❑ 85CedRapRT-23

Pacella, John
❑ 78TidTidT-17

❑ 79TidTidT-2
❑ 81ColCliP-30
❑ 81ColCliT-22
❑ 81Top-414
❑ 82ColCliP-17
❑ 82ColCliT-1
❑ 83Don-130
❑ 83Fle-622
❑ 83Top-166
❑ 85NasSouTI-17
❑ 87TolMudHP-8
❑ 87TolMudHT-14
❑ 91MetWIZ-307
❑ 91OriCro-346
❑ 92YanWIZ8-139
Pacheco, Al
❑ 89JohCitCS-17
❑ 90CMC-706
❑ 90SavCarP-2067
Pacheco, Alex
❑ 90WelPirP-24
❑ 92JamExpC-5
❑ 92JamExpF-1499
❑ 93JamExpC-15
❑ 93JamExpF-3323
❑ 94BurBeeC-18
❑ 94BurBeeF-1080
❑ 95HarSenTI-16
Pacheco, Antonio
❑ 90IBAWorA-10
❑ 90IBAWorA-48
Pacheco, Delvis
❑ 96DanBraB-16
❑ 97MacBra-6
❑ 98MacBraM-12
Pacheco, Domingo
❑ 98EveAquG-18
Pacheco, Melcher
❑ 94VenLinU-19
❑ 95LinVen-94
❑ 96-97LinVen-20
Pacheco, Tony
❑ 73IndTeal-20
❑ 74OPC-521
❑ 74Top-521
❑ 76HouAstP-24
❑ 77AstPho-10
❑ 78AstPos-17
Pacheco, Yogi
❑ 92PeoChiC-15
Pacheo, Jose
❑ 91HunCubC-16
❑ 91HunCubP-3332
❑ 92HunCubC-15
❑ 92HunCubF-3147
Pacho, Juan
❑ 81WatIndT-24
❑ 83ChaChaT-11
❑ 89GreBraB-8
❑ 89GreBraP-1155
❑ 89GreBraS-16
Pacholec, Joe
❑ 87WatPirP-23
❑ 88AugPirP-373
❑ 89SalBucS-16
Pachot, John
❑ 94BurBeeC-19
❑ 94BurBeeF-1085
❑ 94MidLeaAF-MDW33
❑ 96WesPalBEB-20
❑ 97HarSen-20
Pacillo, Pat
❑ 85Top-402
❑ 85TopTif-402
❑ 87NasSouTI-16
❑ 87RedKah-35
❑ 87TopTra-93T
❑ 87TopTraT-93T
❑ 88Don-536
❑ 88NasSouC-10
❑ 88NasSouP-472
❑ 88Top-288
❑ 88TopClo-83
❑ 88TopTif-288
❑ 89IndIndC-4
❑ 89IndIndP-1236
❑ 90CalCanC-1
❑ 90CalCanP-649
❑ 90CMC-428
❑ 90ProAAAF-114
Paciorek, Jim
❑ 83ElPasDT-4
❑ 85VanCanC-213
❑ 86VanCanP-20
❑ 87BrePol-14
❑ 87FleUpd-95
❑ 87FleUpdG-95
❑ 90El PasDAGTI-11
❑ 93GolCar-4
❑ 94BreMilB-64
Paciorek, John
❑ 77FriOneYW-95
Paciorek, Peter S.
❑ 96IdaFalB-19
❑ 97CliLumG-19
❑ 98RanCucQG-22
❑ 98RanCucQG-22
Paciorek, Tom (Thomas M.)
❑ 71OPC-709
❑ 71Top-709
❑ 73OPC-606
❑ 73Top-606
❑ 74OPC-127
❑ 74Top-127
❑ 75OPC-523
❑ 75Top-523
❑ 75TopMin-523
❑ 76OPC-641
❑ 76SSP-88
❑ 76Top-641
❑ 77BurCheD-215
❑ 77Top-48
❑ 78Top-322
❑ 79OPC-65
❑ 79Top-141
❑ 80Top-481
❑ 81Don-408
❑ 81Fle-614
❑ 81MarPol-11
❑ 81MarPos-23
❑ 81OPC-228
❑ 81Top-228
❑ 81TopScr-23
❑ 81TopSti-124
❑ 82Don-253
❑ 82Fle-514
❑ 82FleSta-224
❑ 82OPC-371
❑ 82Top-336
❑ 82Top-678
❑ 82TopSti-236
❑ 82TopStiV-236
❑ 82TopTra-85T
❑ 83AllGamPI-6
❑ 83Don-243
❑ 83Fle-248
❑ 83FleSta-144
❑ 83FleSti-157
❑ 83OPC-72
❑ 83Top-72
❑ 83TopSti-47
❑ 83WhiSoxTV-44
❑ 84AllGamPI-97
❑ 84AllGamPI-185
❑ 84Don-282
❑ 84Fle-70
❑ 84Nes792-777
❑ 84OPC-132
❑ 84Top-777
❑ 84TopSti-246
❑ 84TopTif-777
❑ 84WhiSoxTV-25
❑ 85Don-488
❑ 85Fle-523
❑ 85OPC-381
❑ 85SpoIndGC-15
❑ 85Top-572
❑ 85TopTif-572
❑ 85WhiSoxC-44
❑ 86BasStaB-82
❑ 86Fle-91
❑ 86FleUpd-86
❑ 86RanPer-44
❑ 86Top-362
❑ 86TopTif-362
❑ 86TopTra-83T
❑ 86TopTraT-83T
❑ 87Fle-133
❑ 87FleGlo-133
❑ 87OPC-21
❑ 87RanMot-8
❑ 87RanSmo-14
❑ 87Top-729
❑ 87TopTif-729
❑ 88Sco-531
❑ 88ScoGlo-531
❑ 89PacSenL-204
❑ 89T/MSenL-85
❑ 89TopSenL-107
❑ 90DodTar-600
❑ 90EliSenL-60
❑ 90PacLeg-97
❑ 91MetWIZ-308
❑ 93RanKee-285
❑ 93UppDecS-14
❑ 98PitMetM-22
Pack, Steve
❑ 94KinMetC-14
❑ 94KinMetF-3820
❑ 96StLucMTI-14
Packard, Bob
❑ 94SprSulC-30
Packard, Eugene
❑ 11PinT-5-1055
❑ 14CraJacE-142
❑ 15CraJacE-142
Packel, Steve
❑ 89AncBucTI-27
Packer, Bill
❑ 83EriCarT-6
❑ 84SavCarT-17
Pactwa, Joe
❑ 76OPC-589
❑ 76Top-589
❑ 81TCM60I-376
Padden, Dick (Richard J.)
❑ 03BreE10-111
Padden, Tom (Thomas F.)
❑ 35GouPuzR-8K
❑ 35GouPuzR-9K
❑ 36GouWidPPR-A82
❑ 36NatChiFPR-63
❑ 43PhiTeal-19
❑ 92ConTSN-607
Paddy, Marco
❑ 88IdaFalBP-1835
Padget, Chris
❑ 86ChaOriW-21
❑ 86SouLeaAJ-7
❑ 87IntLeaAT-31
❑ 87RocRedWP-6
❑ 87RocRedWT-12
❑ 88RocRedWC-13
❑ 88RocRedWGCP-20
❑ 88RocRedWP-204
❑ 88RocRedWTI-18
❑ 89RocRedWC-14
❑ 89RocRedWP-1644
❑ 90CMC-317
❑ 90ProAAAF-473
❑ 90RocRedWC-17
❑ 90RocRedWGC-21
❑ 90RocRedWP-716
Padgett, Don (Don W.)
❑ 39PlaBal-157
❑ 40PlaBal-109
❑ 41CarW75-21
❑ 49RemBre-20
❑ 50RemBre-20
❑ 90DodTar-601
❑ 93ConTSN-716
Padgett, Ernie (Ernest)
❑ 21Exh-124
❑ 91ConTSN-206
Padgett, Matt
❑ 99TeaBesR-64
❑ 99TeaBesRG-64
❑ 99TeaBesRS-64
Padia, Steve
❑ 83CedRapRF-25
❑ 83CedRapRT-12
❑ 86OrlTwiP-14
Padilla, Charly
❑ 97ButCopKB-17
❑ 97ButCopKK-17
❑ 98ButCopKG-25
Padilla, Freddy
❑ 88BriTigP-1873
❑ 89FayGenP-1595
Padilla, Livio
❑ 87WinHavRSP-3
❑ 88FloStaLAS-46
❑ 88WinHavRSS-18
❑ 89NewBriRSP-620
❑ 89NewBriRSS-13
Padilla, Paul
❑ 79AlbDukTc-23
❑ 80AlbDukTc-24
Padilla, Roy
❑ 95ButCopKtI-16
❑ 96MicBatCB-19
❑ 96MidLeaAB-45
❑ 97SarRedS-18
Padres, San Diego
❑ 69TopStaA-21
❑ 70Top-657
❑ 71OPC-482
❑ 71Top-482
❑ 71TopTat-70
❑ 72OPC-262
❑ 72Top-262
❑ 73OPC-316
❑ 73OPCBTC-21
❑ 73Top-316
❑ 73TopBluTC-21
❑ 74OPC-226
❑ 74OPCTC-21
❑ 74Top-226A
❑ 74Top-226B
❑ 74TopStaA-21
❑ 74TopTeaC-21
❑ 78Top-192
❑ 83FleSta-246
❑ 83FleSti-NNO
❑ 83FleSti-NNO
❑ 87SpoTeaL-16
❑ 88PanSti-479
❑ 88RedFolSB-107
❑ 90PubIntS-625
❑ 90RedFolSB-119
❑ 94ImpProP-27
❑ 94Sco-659
❑ 94ScoGolR-659
❑ 95PacPriTL-27
❑ 95PanSti-134
❑ 96PanSti-101
❑ 99Vic-333
Padron, Jesus
❑ 76VenLeaS-9
Padron, Oscar
❑ 95LinVen-91
Padua, Geraldo
❑ 98OneYanG-21
Padula, Jim
❑ 78NewWayCT-33
❑ 79BurBeeT-23
Paepke, Dennis (Dennis Rae)
❑ 70Top-552
❑ 71oySigST-19
Paepke, Jack
❑ 49W72HolS-16
❑ 50W720HolS-23
Paez, Israel
❑ 95ForWayWTI-19
❑ 96ForWayWB-18
❑ 97ForMyeM-23
❑ 98NewBriRCM-21
Paez, Raul
❑ 93WelPirC-17
❑ 93WelPirF-3368
❑ 94SalBucF-2329
Pafko, Andy (Andrew)
❑ 39ExhSal-50A
❑ 39ExhSal-50B
❑ 39ExhSal-50C
❑ 44CubTeal-19
❑ 46SpoExcW-3-6
❑ 47HomBon-36
❑ 47PM1StaP1-155
❑ 47TipTop-114
❑ 49Bow-63
❑ 49EurSta-66
❑ 49Lea-125
❑ 49MPR302-2-108
❑ 50Bow-60
❑ 50RoyDes-6A
❑ 50RoyDes-6B
❑ 51Bow-103
❑ 51FisBakL-21
❑ 51R42SmaS-82
❑ 51TopBluB-27
❑ 52Bow-204
❑ 52RoyPre-8
❑ 52TipTop-28
❑ 52Top-1
❑ 53BowBW-57
❑ 53BraJohC-24
❑ 53BraMer-13
❑ 53BraSpiaS3-19
❑ 53BraSpiaS7-11
❑ 53RedMan-NL9
❑ 54Bow-112
❑ 54BraJohC-48
❑ 54BraMer-8
❑ 54BraSpiaSP-16
❑ 54RedMan-NL8
❑ 54Top-79
❑ 54Wil-13
❑ 55Bow-12
❑ 55BraGolS-20
❑ 55BraJohC-48
❑ 55BraSpiaSD-15
❑ 56Top-312
❑ 57Bra8x1-9
❑ 57BraSpiaS4-16
❑ 57Top-143
❑ 58BraJayP-10
❑ 58Top-223
❑ 59Top-27
❑ 59TopVen-27
❑ 60BraLaktL-18
❑ 60BraSpiaS-16
❑ 60Top-464
❑ 74dod195T-29
❑ 76TayBow4-5
❑ 78BraTCC-10
❑ 79DiaGre-97
❑ 79TCM50-181
❑ 80Bra195T-24
❑ 83Bra53F-48
❑ 83TopRep5-1
❑ 84CubBriPC-9C
❑ 85TCMPla1-9
❑ 88DodRinP1-4B
❑ 89PacLegI-123
❑ 89SweBasG-74
❑ 90DodTar-602
❑ 92CubOldS-18
❑ 94TopArc1-79
❑ 94TopArc1G-79
❑ 95TopArcBD-1
Pagan, Angel
❑ 94AlbPolC-18
❑ 94AlbPolF-2244
❑ 94BluOriC-16
❑ 94BluOriF-3570
Pagan, Carlos
❑ 97SpoIndG-21
❑ 98WilBluRC-23
Pagan, Dave
❑ 74SyrChiTI-21
❑ 75IntLeaAT-9
❑ 75OPC-648
❑ 75SyrChiTI-15
❑ 75Top-648
❑ 75TopMin-648
❑ 76BalOriP-30
❑ 76SSP-432
❑ 77Hos-133
❑ 77OPC-151
❑ 77Top-508
❑ 77TopCloS-35
❑ 78ColCliT-20
❑ 91OriCro-347
❑ 92YanWIZ7-124
Pagan, Felix
❑ 83IdaFalAT-23
❑ 98ForWayW!-8
Pagan, Jose (Jose Antonio)
❑ 60TacBan-12
❑ 60Top-67
❑ 60TopVen-67
❑ 61Top-279
❑ 62Jel-132
❑ 62Pos-132
❑ 62PosCan-132
❑ 62SalPlaC-200
❑ 62ShiPlaC-200
❑ 62Top-565
❑ 63GiaJayP-10
❑ 63Jel-103
❑ 63Pos-103
❑ 63Top-545
❑ 64GiaJayP-10
❑ 64Top-123
❑ 64TopVen-123
❑ 65Top-575
❑ 66OPC-54
❑ 66PirEasH-11
❑ 66Top-54
❑ 66TopVen-54
❑ 67CokCapPi-11
❑ 67PirTeal-15
❑ 67Top-322
❑ 67TopPirS-18
❑ 68PirKDK-11
❑ 68PirTeal-15
❑ 68Top-482
❑ 69MilBra-210
❑ 69OPC-192
❑ 69PirJacitB-8
❑ 69PirTeal-18
❑ 69Top-192
❑ 69TopFou-18
❑ 70PirTeal-14
❑ 70Top-643
❑ 71MLBOffS-211
❑ 71OPC-282
❑ 71PirActP-9
❑ 71Top-282
❑ 72MilBra-262
❑ 72Top-701
❑ 72Top-702
❑ 73OPC-659
❑ 73PhiTeal-14
❑ 73Top-659
❑ 75PitPirP-18
❑ 77PirPosP-19
❑ 78TCM60I-102
❑ 79OgdA'sT-6
❑ 80OgdA'sT-23
❑ 81Gia196T-12
Pagano, Scott
❑ 92NiaFalRC-3
❑ 92NiaFalRF-3341
❑ 95DurBulTI-24
❑ 96BinMetB-21
❑ 97ReaPhi-23
Page, Dave
❑ 98TusSidM-5
Page, Greg
❑ 90SalSpuCLC-126
❑ 90SalSpuP-2714
Page, Joe
❑ 46SpoExcW-7-8
❑ 47Exh-170
❑ 47PM1StaP1-156
❑ 47TipTop-54
❑ 47YanTeaT-19
❑ 48Bow-29
❑ 48YanTeal-21
❑ 49Bow-82
❑ 49YanTeal-15
❑ 50Bow-12
❑ 50Dra-27
❑ 50YanTeal-15
❑ 51BerRos-C5
❑ 51Bow-217
❑ 51FisBakL-22
❑ 51TopBluB-10
❑ 52Top-48A
❑ 52Top-48B
❑ 79TCM50-197
❑ 82TCMGreP-4
❑ 83TopRep5-48
❑ 85TCMPla1-7
❑ 92YanWIZA-56
Page, Kelvin
❑ 85LitFalMT-7
Page, Ken
❑ 81SpoIndT-21
Page, Marc J.
❑ 82WisRapTF-24
Page, Mike
❑ 68BraPos-24
❑ 77FriOneYW-75
❑ 85BurRanT-2
Page, Mitchell (Mitchell Otis)
❑ 75ShrCapT-17
❑ 76VenLeaS-152
❑ 78Hos-38
❑ 78Kel-47
❑ 78OPC-75
❑ 78PapGinD-39
❑ 78Top-55
❑ 79Hos-17
❑ 79OPC-147
❑ 79Top-295
❑ 79TopCom-14
❑ 80OPC-307
❑ 80Top-586
❑ 81A'sGraG-6
❑ 81Don-480
❑ 81Fle-580
❑ 81Top-35
❑ 82Fle-105
❑ 82OPC-178
❑ 82TacTigT-36
❑ 82Top-633
❑ 83Top-737
❑ 84Nes792-414
❑ 84Top-414
❑ 84TopTif-414
❑ 85HawIslC-234
❑ 92TacTigF-2519
❑ 92TacTigS-550
❑ 93TacTigF-3049
❑ 98MemRedG-15
Page, Phil

❑ 33Zee-160
❑ 49EurSta-91

Page, Phillip
❑ 92MisStaB-50

Page, Sean
❑ 90JohCitCS-20
❑ 91SavCarC-20
❑ 91SavCarP-1661

Page, Ted
❑ 78LauLonABS-16
❑ 86NegLeaF-2
❑ 86NegLeaF-4
❑ 88NegLeaD-15

Page, Thane
❑ 91MarPhiC-19
❑ 91MarPhiP-3452
❑ 92BatCliCB-21
❑ 92BatCliF-3263

Page, Vance
❑ 30Zee-13
❑ 32Zee-12
❑ 33Zee-6
❑ 39CubTeal-18
❑ 41CubTeal-18
❑ 41DouPlaR-1

Page, William Byrd
❑ 12HomRunKE-14
❑ 12Zee-18
❑ 13Zee-17
❑ 14Zee-20
❑ 88KimN18-34

Pagee, Shawn
❑ 94JamJamC-19
❑ 94JamJamF-3969
❑ 96FayGenB-3

Pagel, Dave
❑ 81QuaCitCT-1

Pagel, Karl (Karl Douglas)
❑ 79Top-716
❑ 80Top-676
❑ 80WicAerT-1
❑ 81ChaChaT-18
❑ 82ChaChaT-21
❑ 82Ind-27
❑ 83ChaChaT-12
❑ 83IndPos-25
❑ 84MaiGuiT-16

Pageler, Michael
❑ 96BelGiaTI-22
❑ 97BakBlaB-5
❑ 97BakBlaTI-5
❑ 98PorSeaDQ-8

Pages, Javier
❑ 92AlbPolCB-11
❑ 92AlbPolF-2310
❑ 93BurBeeC-15
❑ 93BurBeeF-162
❑ 93MidLeaAGF-31
❑ 94WesPalBEC-19
❑ 94WesPalBEF-44

Pagliari, Armando
❑ 88St.CatBJP-2005
❑ 89St.CatBJP-2092
❑ 91MyrBeaHC-30

Pagliaroni, Jim (James V.)
❑ 60DarFar-2
❑ 61Top-519
❑ 62Jel-63
❑ 62Pos-63
❑ 62PosCan-63
❑ 62SalPlaC-81
❑ 62ShiPlaC-81
❑ 62Top-81
❑ 62TopVen-81
❑ 63PirIDL-19
❑ 63Top-159
❑ 64Kah-20
❑ 64PirKDK-22
❑ 64Top-392
❑ 64TopCoi-62
❑ 65Kah-34
❑ 65OPC-265
❑ 65Top-265
❑ 66Kah-24
❑ 66OPC-33
❑ 66PirEasH-10
❑ 66Top-33
❑ 66TopVen-33
❑ 67CokCapPi-9
❑ 67DexPre-158
❑ 67Kah-27
❑ 67OPC-183
❑ 67PirTeal-16
❑ 67Top-183
❑ 67TopPirS-19
❑ 68Top-586
❑ 69MilBra-211
❑ 69Top-302
❑ 69TopTeaP-21
❑ 78TCM60I-91
❑ 81RedSoxBG2S-42
❑ 83Pil69G-35

Pagliarulo, Mike
❑ 83NasSouTI-14
❑ 84ColCliP-17
❑ 84ColCliT-1
❑ 85DomLeaS-184
❑ 85Don-539
❑ 85Fle-139
❑ 85Top-638
❑ 85TopSti-317
❑ 85TopTif-638
❑ 85YanTCMP-29
❑ 86Don-152
❑ 86Fle-113
❑ 86Lea-80
❑ 86OPC-327
❑ 86Spo-177
❑ 86Top-327
❑ 86TopTif-327
❑ 86YanTCM-26
❑ 87ClaGam-22
❑ 87Don-298
❑ 87DonOpeD-239
❑ 87Fle-107
❑ 87FleGlo-107
❑ 87FleLeaL-33
❑ 87Lea-189
❑ 87OPC-195
❑ 87SevCoi-E6
❑ 87SmoAmeL-9
❑ 87Spo-55
❑ 87SpoTeaP-7
❑ 87Top-195
❑ 87TopGloS-56
❑ 87TopSti-300
❑ 87TopTif-195
❑ 88Don-105
❑ 88DonBasB-105
❑ 88DonReaBY-105
❑ 88Fle-216
❑ 88FleGlo-216
❑ 88FleStiC-49
❑ 88OPC-109
❑ 88PanSti-156
❑ 88Sco-170
❑ 88ScoGlo-170
❑ 88Spo-121
❑ 88SpoGam-23
❑ 88StaLinY-10
❑ 88Top-435
❑ 88TopBig-138
❑ 88TopSti-295
❑ 88TopTif-435
❑ 89Bow-175
❑ 89BowTif-175
❑ 89Don-127
❑ 89Fle-262
❑ 89FleGlo-262
❑ 89OPC-211
❑ 89PadPos-22
❑ 89PanSti-406
❑ 89Sco-189
❑ 89ScoRoo-11T
❑ 89Spo-153
❑ 89Top-211
❑ 89TopBig-28
❑ 89TopDouM-20
❑ 89TopSti-311
❑ 89TopTif-211
❑ 89UppDec-569
❑ 89YanScoNW-13
❑ 90Bow-219
❑ 90BowTif-219
❑ 90Don-364
❑ 90DonBesN-137
❑ 90Fle-163
❑ 90FleCan-163
❑ 90Lea-320
❑ 90OPC-63
❑ 90PadCok-12
❑ 90PadMag-3
❑ 90PubIntS-542
❑ 90Sco-494
❑ 90Top-63
❑ 90TopBig-226
❑ 90TopSti-106
❑ 90TopTif-63
❑ 90UppDec-329
❑ 91Bow-339
❑ 91Don-140
❑ 91Fle-537
❑ 91FleUpd-40
❑ 91Lea-339
❑ 91OPC-547
❑ 91PanFreS-93
❑ 91Sco-199
❑ 91ScoRoo-42T
❑ 91StaClu-522
❑ 91Top-547
❑ 91TopDesS-547
❑ 91TopMic-547
❑ 91TopTif-547
❑ 91TopTra-87T
❑ 91TopTraT-87T
❑ 91UppDec-206
❑ 91UppDec-709
❑ 92Bow-685
❑ 92Don-62
❑ 92Fle-216
❑ 92Lea-346
❑ 92LeaBlaG-346
❑ 92OPC-721
❑ 92PanSti-117
❑ 92Pin-246
❑ 92Sco-173
❑ 92StaClu-152
❑ 92StaCluD-137
❑ 92Top-721
❑ 92TopGol-721
❑ 92TopGolW-721
❑ 92TopMic-721
❑ 92Ult-96
❑ 92UppDec-509
❑ 92YanWIZ8-140
❑ 93Don-707
❑ 93Fla-241
❑ 93Fle-641
❑ 93Lea-474
❑ 93PacSpa-176
❑ 93Pin-508
❑ 93SelRoo-115T
❑ 93Stu-191
❑ 93Top-336
❑ 93TopGol-336
❑ 93TopInaM-336
❑ 93TopInaR-336
❑ 93TopMic-336
❑ 93Ult-587
❑ 93UppDec-306
❑ 93UppDecGold-306
❑ 94ColC-224
❑ 94ColChoGS-224
❑ 94ColChoSS-224
❑ 94Don-243
❑ 94Fle-14
❑ 94Pac-41
❑ 94Sco-489
❑ 94ScoGolR-489
❑ 95RanCra-25
❑ 96Fle-257
❑ 96FleTif-257

Paglino, Joseph J.
❑ 82AppFoxFr-16

Pagnozzi, Tom
❑ 83EriCarT-20
❑ 86LouRedTI-21
❑ 87CarSmo-12
❑ 87LouRedTI-22
❑ 88BlaYNPRWLU-27
❑ 88CarSmo-12
❑ 88CarTeal-25
❑ 88Don-577
❑ 88Sco-358
❑ 88ScoGlo-358
❑ 88Top-689
❑ 88TopClo-84
❑ 88TopTif-689
❑ 89BlaYNPRWL-96
❑ 89CarSmo-16
❑ 89CarTeal-21
❑ 89Don-399
❑ 89Sco-483
❑ 89Top-208
❑ 89TopTif-208
❑ 89UppDec-602
❑ 90CarSmo-18
❑ 90Don-591
❑ 90Lea-498
❑ 90OPC-509
❑ 90PubIntS-224
❑ 90SprCarDGB-35
❑ 90Top-509
❑ 90TopTif 509
❑ 90TopTVCa-23
❑ 91Bow-389
❑ 91CarPol-19
❑ 91Don-337
❑ 91Fle-641
❑ 91Lea-72
❑ 91OPC-308
❑ 91PanFreS-30
❑ 91Sco-797
❑ 91StaClu-223
❑ 91Top-308
❑ 91TopDesS-308
❑ 91TopMic-308
❑ 91TopTif-308
❑ 91Ult-293
❑ 91UppDec-91
❑ 92Bow-241
❑ 92CarPol-14
❑ 92Cla1-T69
❑ 92Don-254
❑ 92Fle-586
❑ 92Fre-9
❑ 92Lea-359
❑ 92LeaBlaG-359
❑ 92OPC-448
❑ 92PanSti-171
❑ 92Pin-69
❑ 92Sco-136
❑ 92StaClu-162
❑ 92Stu-96
❑ 92Top-448
❑ 92TopGol-448
❑ 92TopGolW-448
❑ 92TopMic-448
❑ 92Ult-268
❑ 92UltAllS-15
❑ 92UltAwaW-8
❑ 92UppDec-379
❑ 93Bow-220
❑ 93CarPol-14
❑ 93CarStaC-6
❑ 93DiaMar-83
❑ 93Don-360
❑ 93Fla-124
❑ 93Fle-130
❑ 93FleFruotL-50
❑ 93Lea-136
❑ 93OPC-273
❑ 93PacSpa-299
❑ 93PanSti-191
❑ 93Pin-62
❑ 93Sco-135
❑ 93Sel-37
❑ 93SP-77
❑ 93StaClu-399
❑ 93StaCluFDI-399
❑ 93StaCluM-72
❑ 93StaCluMOP-399
❑ 93Stu-198
❑ 93Top-92
❑ 93TopGol-92
❑ 93TopInaM-92
❑ 93TopInaR-92
❑ 93TopMic-92
❑ 93TriPla-194
❑ 93Ult-110
❑ 93UltAwaW-2
❑ 93UppDec-405
❑ 93UppDecGold-405
❑ 94Bow-320
❑ 94CarMagG-6
❑ 94CarPol-13
❑ 94ColC-464
❑ 94ColChoGS-464
❑ 94ColChoSS-464
❑ 94Don-177
❑ 94Fin-384
❑ 94FinRef-384
❑ 94Fla-430
❑ 94Fle-641
❑ 94FleExtB-361
❑ 94Lea-7
❑ 94OPC-103
❑ 94Pac-598
❑ 94PanSti-246
❑ 94Pin-439
❑ 94PinArtP-439
❑ 94PinMusC-439
❑ 94Sco-466
❑ 94ScoGolR-466
❑ 94Sel-98
❑ 94StaClu-122
❑ 94StaCluFDI-122
❑ 94StaCluGR-122
❑ 94StaCluMOP-122
❑ 94StaCluP-122
❑ 94StaCluT-319
❑ 94StaCluTFDI-319
❑ 94Stu-53
❑ 94Top-719
❑ 94TopGol-719
❑ 94TopSpa-719
❑ 94TriPla-65
❑ 94Ult-567
❑ 94UppDec-106
❑ 94UppDecED-106
❑ 95Bow-338
❑ 95ColCho-193
❑ 95ColChoGS-193
❑ 95ColChoSS-193
❑ 95Don-102
❑ 95DonPreP-102
❑ 95DonTopotO-334
❑ 95Fin-143
❑ 95FinRef-143
❑ 95Fla-194
❑ 95Fle-504
❑ 95Lea-31
❑ 95PanSti-23
❑ 95Pin-37
❑ 95PinArtP-37
❑ 95PinMusC-37
❑ 95Sco-69
❑ 95ScoGolR-69
❑ 95ScoPlaTS-69
❑ 95StaClu-69
❑ 95StaClu-316
❑ 95StaCluFDI-69
❑ 95StaCluMOP-69
❑ 95StaCluMOP-316
❑ 95StaCluSTWS-69
❑ 95StaCluSTWS-316
❑ 95Top-111
❑ 95TopCyb-72
❑ 95TopEmb-56
❑ 95TopEmbGI-56
❑ 95Ult-224
❑ 95UltAwaW-10
❑ 95UltAwaWGM-10
❑ 95UltGolM-224
❑ 95UppDec-306
❑ 95UppDecED-306
❑ 95UppDecEDG-306
❑ 96CarPol-21
❑ 96ColCho-686
❑ 96ColChoGS-686
❑ 96ColChoSS-686
❑ 96Don-278
❑ 96DonPreP-278
❑ 96EmoXL-270
❑ 96Fin-B53
❑ 96FinRef-B53
❑ 96Fla-366
❑ 96Fle-553
❑ 96FleTif-553
❑ 96LeaSigA-175
❑ 96LeaSigAG-175
❑ 96LeaSigAS-175
❑ 96MLBPin-25
❑ 96Pac-221
❑ 96Pin-65
❑ 96ProSta-33
❑ 96Sco-403
❑ 96StaClu-403
❑ 96StaCluEPB-403
❑ 96StaCluEPG-403
❑ 96StaCluEPS-403
❑ 96StaCluMOP-403
❑ 96Top-131
❑ 96Ult-277
❑ 96UltGolM-277
❑ 96UppDec-439
❑ 97CarPol-21
❑ 97Cir-205
❑ 97CirRav-205
❑ 97ColCho-443
❑ 97Don-118
❑ 97DonGolPP-118
❑ 97DonSilPP-118
❑ 97DonTea-155
❑ 97DonTeaSPE-155
❑ 97Fle-451
❑ 97FleTif-451
❑ 97MetUni-234
❑ 97Pac-415
❑ 97PacLigB-415
❑ 97PacSil-415
❑ 97ScoPreS-273
❑ 97StaClu-374
❑ 97StaCluMOP-374
❑ 97Top-2
❑ 97UppDec-484
❑ 98PacOnl-625
❑ 98PacOnlR-625
❑ 98PacOnlWC-625
❑ 98PinSna-SLC7
❑ 98Top-431
❑ 98TopChr-431
❑ 98TopChrR-431
❑ 98TopDevR-431
❑ 98TopDia-431
❑ 98TopMiniC-431

Paiement, Wilfred
❑ 82MonNew-11

Paige, Carey
❑ 92ClaDraP-67
❑ 92FroRowDP-20
❑ 92FroRowDPG-20
❑ 92FroRowDPS-20
❑ 92HigSchPLS-9
❑ 93DanBraC-17
❑ 93DanBraF-3616
❑ 94MacBraC-16
❑ 94MacBraF-2201
❑ 94SouAtlLAF-SAL45
❑ 95DurBulTI-25
❑ 95Top-429
❑ 96BesAutSA-51
❑ 97BesAutAS-37
❑ 97DunBluJTI-21
❑ 98BriBluM-22

Paige, Pat (George L.)
❑ 09T206-507

Paige, Satchel (LeRoy)
❑ 47Exh-171
❑ 47PM1StaP1-157
❑ 48IndTeal-24
❑ 49Bow-224
❑ 49IndTeal-19
❑ 49IndVisEl-13
❑ 49Lea-8
❑ 52BroPenCB-2
❑ 53Top-220
❑ 60RawGloT-25
❑ 67TopVen-177
❑ 70Houof J-22
❑ 72TopTes5-1
❑ 73HalofFPP-13
❑ 73TCMAllG-15
❑ 74LauOldTBS-15
❑ 75TCMHouoJ-24
❑ 76GalBasGHoF-22
❑ 76LauIndC-21
❑ 76ShaPiz-125
❑ 76TulOilGP-23
❑ 77BobParHoF-71
❑ 77GalGloG-22
❑ 77GalGloG-258
❑ 77SerSta-18
❑ 79BasGre-76
❑ 80PacLeg-60
❑ 80PerHaloFP-125
❑ 80SSPHOF-125
❑ 82BasCarN-19
❑ 82DiaCla-31
❑ 82OhiHaloF-33
❑ 82TCMGreP-31
❑ 83ConMar-52
❑ 83DonHOFH-11
❑ 83MLBPin-14
❑ 84OCoandSI-91
❑ 84SpoDesPW-37
❑ 86NegLeaF-10
❑ 86NegLeaF-21
❑ 87NegLeaPD-21
❑ 88ConNegA-10
❑ 88NegLeaD-11
❑ 89BowInsT-8
❑ 89BowRepl-8
❑ 89BowTif-R8
❑ 90BasWit-64
❑ 90NegLeaS-20
❑ 90PerGreM-20
❑ 90SweBasG-115
❑ 91HomCooC-2
❑ 91LinDri-47
❑ 91PomBlaBPB-8
❑ 91SweBasG-133
❑ 91TopArc1-220
❑ 91USGamSBL-5C
❑ 91USGamSBL-5D
❑ 91USGamSBL-5H
❑ 91USGamSBL-5S
❑ 92BazQua5A-18
❑ 92Sco-882
❑ 92St.VinHHS-8
❑ 93ActPacA-115
❑ 93ActPacA2-49G
❑ 93DiaStaES-N3

❑ 93Hoy-5
❑ 93LegFoi-8
❑ 93LegFoiP-1
❑ 93SpeHOFI-3
❑ 93TedWil-112
❑ 93TedWil-131
❑ 93TedWilLC-5
❑ 93TedWilP-115
❑ 94UppDecTAE-40
❑ 94UppDecTAEGM-6
❑ 95S.FExaNLT-12
❑ 95UppDecSHoB-20
❑ 96NoiSatP-1
❑ 96NoiSatP-2
❑ 96NoiSatP-3
❑ 96NoiSatP-4
❑ 96NoiSatP-5
❑ 96NoiSatP-6
❑ 96NoiSatP-7
❑ 96NoiSatP-8
❑ 96NoiSatP-9
❑ 96NoiSatP-10
❑ 96NoiSatP-11
❑ 96NoiSatP-12
❑ 97NegLeaPC-1S
❑ 97St.VinHHS-13
❑ 98BowChrR-4
❑ 98BowChrRR-4
❑ 99UppDecCL-19
❑ 99UppDecCL-121
❑ 99UppDecCLA-1930
❑ 99UppDecCLCC-19
❑ 99UppDecCLCC-121
❑ 99UppDecCLLC-LG

Pailthorpe, Bob
❑ 95ElmPioTI-21
❑ 95ElmPioUTI-21
❑ 96KanCouCTI-20
❑ 97BreCouMB-25

Paine, Phil
❑ 54BraJohC-11
❑ 55BraJohC-11
❑ 58Top-442
❑ 59DarFar-16
❑ 80Bra195T-3

Painich, Joey
❑ 98MadBlaW-12

Painter, Chris
❑ 89GeoColC-21

Painter, Gary
❑ 91Cla/Bes-129
❑ 91FloStaLAP-FSL45
❑ 91WinHavRSC-6
❑ 91WinHavRSP-486
❑ 92NewBriRSF-430
❑ 92NewBriRSS-492
❑ 93NewBriRSF-1216
❑ 94SarRedSC-22
❑ 94SarRedSF-1948

Painter, Lance
❑ 90SpoIndSP-21
❑ 91Cla/Bes-352
❑ 91WatDiaC-7
❑ 91WatDiaP-1254
❑ 92ClaFS7-313
❑ 92ProFS7-339
❑ 92SkyAA F-285
❑ 92WicWraF-3657
❑ 92WicWraS-643
❑ 93Bow-89
❑ 93ColSprSSF-3084
❑ 93FleFinE-38
❑ 93SelRoo-48T
❑ 93Top-738
❑ 93TopGol-738
❑ 93TopInaM-738
❑ 93TopInaR-738
❑ 93TopMic-738
❑ 93TriAAAGF-10
❑ 94ColSprSSF-731
❑ 94Don-474
❑ 94ScoBoyoS-29
❑ 94SpoRoo-135
❑ 94SpoRooAP-135
❑ 94StaClu-77
❑ 94StaCluFDI-77
❑ 94StaCluGR-77
❑ 94StaCluMOP-77
❑ 94StaCluT-119
❑ 94StaCluTFDI-119
❑ 94Top-229
❑ 94TopGol-229
❑ 94TopSpa-229
❑ 95ColCho-449
❑ 95ColChoGS-449
❑ 95ColChoSS-449
❑ 95UppDec-408
❑ 95UppDecED-408
❑ 95UppDecEDG-408
❑ 95UppDecSE-103
❑ 95UppDecSEG-103
❑ 96LeaSigEA-148
❑ 96RocPol-15
❑ 98PacOnl-626
❑ 98PacOnlR-626
❑ 98PacOnlWC-626

Painton, Tim
❑ 80CliGiaT-15
❑ 89FreStaBS-16
❑ 91FreStaBS-16

Paiva, Nelson
❑ 76VenLeaS-167

Paixao, Paulino
❑ 85UtiBluST-4

Pakele, Louis
❑ 90BoiHawP-3309
❑ 91PalSprAP-2010

Palacios, Peter
❑ 85CloHSS-30

Palacios, Rey
❑ 86GleFalTP-17
❑ 87IntLeaAT-11
❑ 87TolMudHP-15
❑ 87TolMudHT-1
❑ 88BlaYNPRWLU-28
❑ 88TolMudHC-18
❑ 88TolMudHP-605
❑ 88TriAAAP-43
❑ 89BlaYNPRWL-83
❑ 89Fle-648
❑ 89FleGlo-648
❑ 89UppDec-21
❑ 90Bow-381
❑ 90BowTif-381
❑ 90RoyPos-18
❑ 91OPC-148
❑ 91Top-148
❑ 91TopDesS-148
❑ 91TopMic-148
❑ 91TopTif-148
❑ 93RocRedWF-243

Palacios, Vicente
❑ 87VanCanP-1619
❑ 88ClaRed-191
❑ 88Don-45
❑ 88Fle-336
❑ 88FleGlo-336
❑ 88Lea-45
❑ 88Sco-643
❑ 88ScoGlo-643
❑ 88Spo-224
❑ 88Top-322
❑ 88TopTif-322
❑ 89Fle-216
❑ 89FleGlo-216
❑ 89ScoHot1R-2
❑ 90BufBisC-7
❑ 90BufBisP-370
❑ 90BufBisTI-18
❑ 90CMC-7
❑ 90ProAAAF-485
❑ 91Don-732
❑ 91FleUpd-113
❑ 91Lea-442
❑ 91OPC-438
❑ 91StaClu-443
❑ 91Top-438
❑ 91TopDesS-438
❑ 91TopMic-438
❑ 91TopTif-438
❑ 91UppDecFE-71F
❑ 92Don-365
❑ 92OPC-582
❑ 92Pin-386
❑ 92Sco-109
❑ 92StaClu-486
❑ 92Top-582
❑ 92TopGol-582
❑ 92TopGolW-582
❑ 92TopMic-582
❑ 92Ult-557
❑ 93Pin-130
❑ 94FleUpd-181
❑ 95Don-254
❑ 95DonPreP-254
❑ 95Fle-505
❑ 95Pac-412
❑ 95Ult-225
❑ 95UltGolM-225

Palafox, Juan
❑ 85MexCitTT-12

Palat, Ed
❑ 74TacTwiC-26
❑ 75TacTwiK-20

Palermo, Pete
❑ 86HagSunP-14
❑ 87HagSunP-17
❑ 88HagSunS-16

Palermo, Steve
❑ 88T/MUmp-29
❑ 89T/MUmp-27
❑ 90T/MUmp-26

Palica, Alex
❑ 45CenFlo-19

Palica, Ambrose
❑ 46RemBre-22
❑ 47RemBre-10
❑ 47SmiClo-12

Palica, Erv
❑ 51Bow-189
❑ 52Top-273
❑ 54NewYorJA-13
❑ 55Bow-195A
❑ 55Bow-195B
❑ 56BalOriP-8
❑ 56Top-206
❑ 60HenHouW-21
❑ 61SeaPop-14
❑ 61SeaPop-15
❑ 61UniOil-S7
❑ 79TCM50-233
❑ 83TopRep5-273
❑ 90DodTar-603
❑ 91DodRinP2-8
❑ 91OriCro-348
❑ 95TopArcBD-16
❑ 95TopArcBD-134
❑ 97BalOriP-40

Palica, John
❑ 81WisRapTT-22
❑ 83OrlTwiT-8

Palki, Jeromy
❑ 97WisTimR-20
❑ 98ForMyeMTI-23

Pall, Donn Steven
❑ 86AppFoxP-17
❑ 87BirBarB-15
❑ 88BlaYNPRWL-27
❑ 88TriAAAP-45
❑ 88VanCanC-9
❑ 88VanCanP-759
❑ 89BirBarADB-26
❑ 89DonRoo-7
❑ 89Fle-505
❑ 89FleGlo-505
❑ 89ScoRoo-102T
❑ 89Top-458
❑ 89TopTif-458
❑ 89WhiSoxC-18
❑ 90BirBarADB-26
❑ 90Don-606
❑ 90Fle-543
❑ 90FleCan-543
❑ 90Lea-392
❑ 90OPC-219
❑ 90PubIntS-397
❑ 90Sco-304
❑ 90Sco100RS-7
❑ 90Top-219
❑ 90TopRoo-23
❑ 90TopTif-219
❑ 90UppDec-386
❑ 90WhiSoxC-18
❑ 91Don-215
❑ 91Fle-130
❑ 91Lea-468
❑ 91OPC-768
❑ 91Sco-132
❑ 91Top-768
❑ 91TopDesS-768
❑ 91TopMic-768
❑ 91TopTif-768
❑ 91UppDec-603
❑ 91WhiSoxK-22
❑ 92Bow-380
❑ 92Don-56
❑ 92Fle-92
❑ 92OPC-57
❑ 92Sco-484
❑ 92StaClu-184
❑ 92Top-57
❑ 92TopGol-57
❑ 92TopGolW-57
❑ 92TopMic-57
❑ 92Ult-41
❑ 92UppDec-592
❑ 92WhiSoxK-22
❑ 93Don-667
❑ 93Fle-586
❑ 93PacSpa-393
❑ 93StaClu-240
❑ 93StaCluFDI-240
❑ 93StaCluMOP-240
❑ 93Top-707
❑ 93TopGol-707
❑ 93TopInaM-707
❑ 93TopInaR-707
❑ 93TopMic-707
❑ 93WhiSoxK-21
❑ 93WhiSoxSC-21
❑ 94StaCluT-200
❑ 94StaCluTFDI-200
❑ 94Top-328
❑ 94TopGol-328
❑ 94TopSpa-328
❑ 95NasSouTI-16
❑ 97ChaKni-24
❑ 98ChaKniQ-23

Pallas, Ted
❑ 82BelBreFr-27

Pallino, John
❑ 94LetMouF-3891
❑ 94LetMouSP-3

Pallone, Dave
❑ 88T/MUmp-37
❑ 89T/MUmp-35
❑ 91FouBal-18

Palma, Brian
❑ 89RenSilSCLC-258
❑ 91SalSpuC-12
❑ 91SalSpuP-2258

Palma, Jay
❑ 83AndBraT-22

Palma, Ricardo
❑ 97WilCubB-16
❑ 98RocCubM-23
❑ 98RocCubTI-24

Palmeiro, Orlando
❑ 91BoiHawC-9
❑ 91BoiHawP-3895
❑ 92MidLeaATI-31
❑ 92QuaCitRBC-3
❑ 92QuaCitRBF-823
❑ 93Bow-637
❑ 93ClaFS7-234
❑ 93ExcFS7-145
❑ 93MidAngF-333
❑ 94ExcFS7-29
❑ 94VanCanF-1876
❑ 95SigRoo-41
❑ 95SigRooSig-41
❑ 96ColCho-37
❑ 96Don-361
❑ 96DonPreP-361
❑ 96Fle-53
❑ 96FleTif-53
❑ 96Pac-266
❑ 96UppDec-32
❑ 96VanCanB-20
❑ 97AngMot-22
❑ 97MidAngOHP-22
❑ 97Pac-11
❑ 97PacLigB-11
❑ 97PacPri-4
❑ 97PacPriLB-4
❑ 97PacPriP-4
❑ 97PacSil-11
❑ 98Pac-12
❑ 98PacPlaB-12
❑ 98PacRedT-12
❑ 98PacSil-12
❑ 98VanCanG-20
❑ 99PacCroC-8
❑ 99PacCroCPB-8
❑ 99SP SigAuto-OP
❑ 99SPSig-95

Palmeiro, Rafael
❑ 86PitCubP-18
❑ 87Don-43
❑ 87DonRoo-47
❑ 87IowCubTI-24
❑ 87Lea-43
❑ 87Spo-158
❑ 87SpoRoo2-32
❑ 87SpoRooP-2
❑ 87SpoTeaP-22
❑ 87Top-634
❑ 87TopRoo-12
❑ 87TopTif-634
❑ 88CubDavB-25
❑ 88Don-324
❑ 88DonBasB-93
❑ 88DonTeaBC-324
❑ 88Fle-429
❑ 88FleGlo-429
❑ 88FleSluBC-C4
❑ 88OPC-186
❑ 88PanSti-268
❑ 88PeoChiTI-23
❑ 88Sco-186
❑ 88ScoGlo-186
❑ 88Top-186
❑ 88TopTif-186
❑ 89Bow-237
❑ 89BowTif-237
❑ 89ClaTraP-163
❑ 89Don-49
❑ 89DonAll-53
❑ 89DonBasB-88
❑ 89DonTra-6
❑ 89Fle-434
❑ 89Fle-631
❑ 89FleGlo-434
❑ 89FleGlo-631
❑ 89FleUpd-66
❑ 89OPC-310
❑ 89PanSti-60
❑ 89RanMot-5
❑ 89RanSmo-24
❑ 89RedFolSB-88
❑ 89Sco-199
❑ 89ScoHot1S-56
❑ 89ScoRoo-1T
❑ 89ScoYouSI-35
❑ 89Spo-30
❑ 89SpoIllFKI-268
❑ 89Top-310
❑ 89TopBig-257
❑ 89TopCoi-47
❑ 89TopMinL-5
❑ 89TopSti-47
❑ 89TopStiB-52
❑ 89TopTif-310
❑ 89TopTra-93T
❑ 89TopTraT-93T
❑ 89TopUKM-58
❑ 89UppDec-235
❑ 89UppDec-772
❑ 90Bow-496
❑ 90BowTif-496
❑ 90ClaBlu-74
❑ 90Don-225
❑ 90DonBesA-41
❑ 90Fle-308
❑ 90FleCan-308
❑ 90Lea-100
❑ 90OPC-755
❑ 90PanSti-164
❑ 90PubIntS-418
❑ 90RanMot-9
❑ 90RedFolSB-72
❑ 90Sco-405
❑ 90Sco100S-58
❑ 90Spo-9
❑ 90Top-755
❑ 90TopBig-127
❑ 90TopHeaU-12
❑ 90TopSti-250
❑ 90TopTif-755
❑ 90UppDec-335
❑ 91Bow-286
❑ 91Cla1-T85
❑ 91Cla3-T71
❑ 91ClaGam-115
❑ 91Don-19
❑ 91Don-394
❑ 91Don-521
❑ 91DonSupD-19
❑ 91Fle-295
❑ 91Lea-347
❑ 91MisStaB-35
❑ 91OPC-295
❑ 91PanCanT1-7
❑ 91PanCanT1-29
❑ 91PanFreS-252
❑ 91PanSti-211
❑ 91PepSup-14
❑ 91RanMot-9
❑ 91Sco-216
❑ 91Sco100S-56
❑ 91SevCoi-T10
❑ 91StaClu-502
❑ 91Stu-127
❑ 91Top-295
❑ 91TopDesS-295
❑ 91TopMic-295
❑ 91TopTif-295
❑ 91Ult-350
❑ 91UppDec-30
❑ 91UppDec-474
❑ 91USPlaCA-6D
❑ 92Bow-610
❑ 92Cla2-T62
❑ 92ClaGam-69
❑ 92Don-46
❑ 92Fle-311
❑ 92FleAll-17
❑ 92FleTeaL-12
❑ 92Hig5-113
❑ 92Lea-296
❑ 92LeaBlaG-296
❑ 92OPC-55
❑ 92PanSti-75
❑ 92Pin-35
❑ 92RanMot-9
❑ 92RanTeal-15
❑ 92RedFolS-73
❑ 92Sco-55
❑ 92Sco100S-27
❑ 92ScoCokD-17
❑ 92ScoImpP-68
❑ 92ScoProP-14
❑ 92StaClu-516
❑ 92StaCluD-138
❑ 92Stu-244
❑ 92Top-55
❑ 92TopGol-55
❑ 92TopGolW-55
❑ 92TopKid-130
❑ 92TopMic-55
❑ 92TriPla-183
❑ 92Ult-136
❑ 92UppDec-223
❑ 92UppDecF-34
❑ 92UppDecFG-34
❑ 93Bow-137
❑ 93Don-365
❑ 93Fin-52
❑ 93FinRef-52
❑ 93Fla-283
❑ 93Fle-687
❑ 93FunPac-157
❑ 93KinDis-20
❑ 93Lea-49
❑ 93MilBonSS-8
❑ 93OPC-171
❑ 93PacBeiA-14
❑ 93PacSpa-314
❑ 93PacSpaGE-17
❑ 93PanSti-81
❑ 93Pin-220
❑ 93RanKee-419
❑ 93RanStaC-26
❑ 93RedFolS-72
❑ 93Sco-74
❑ 93Sel-162
❑ 93SP-196
❑ 93StaClu-115
❑ 93StaCluFDI-115
❑ 93StaCluMOP-115
❑ 93Stu-185
❑ 93Top-305
❑ 93TopGol-305
❑ 93TopInaM-305
❑ 93TopInaR-305
❑ 93TopMic-305
❑ 93TriPla-71
❑ 93Ult-281
❑ 93UppDec-52
❑ 93UppDec-574
❑ 93UppDecGold-52
❑ 93UppDecGold-574
❑ 94BalOriP-25
❑ 94Bow-515
❑ 94BowBes-R51
❑ 94BowBesR-R51
❑ 94ColC-605
❑ 94ColChoGS-605
❑ 94ColChoSS-605
❑ 94Don-26
❑ 94DonSpeE-26
❑ 94Fin-227
❑ 94FinJum-227
❑ 94FinRef-227
❑ 94Fla-257
❑ 94FlaInfP-6
❑ 94Fle-313
❑ 94Fle-710
❑ 94FleExtB-11
❑ 94FleLeaL-3
❑ 94FleLumC-8
❑ 94FleUpd-5
❑ 94FUnPac-154
❑ 94Lea-289
❑ 94LeaL-4
❑ 94LeaMVPC-A10

❑ 94LeaMVPCG-A10
❑ 94OPC-25
❑ 94OriPro-77
❑ 94OriUSPC-7D
❑ 94OriUSPC-13C
❑ 94Pac-622
❑ 94PacAll-16
❑ 94PacGolP-5
❑ 94PacSilP-3
❑ 94PacSilPC-3
❑ 94PanSti-130
❑ 94Pin-493
❑ 94PinArtP-493
❑ 94PinMusC-493
❑ 94PinRunC-RC5
❑ 94RanAllP-19
❑ 94Sco-495
❑ 94ScoGolR-495
❑ 94ScoGolS-59
❑ 94ScoRoo-RT8
❑ 94ScoRooCP-CP2
❑ 94ScoRooGR-RT8
❑ 94ScoRooS-CP2
❑ 94Sel-317
❑ 94SP-125
❑ 94SPDieC-125
❑ 94Spo-144
❑ 94SpoRoo-26
❑ 94SpoRooAP-26
❑ 94StaClu-112
❑ 94StaClu-208
❑ 94StaClu-265
❑ 94StaClu-557
❑ 94StaCluFDI-112
❑ 94StaCluFDI-208
❑ 94StaCluFDI-265
❑ 94StaCluFDI-557
❑ 94StaCluGR-112
❑ 94StaCluGR-208
❑ 94StaCluGR-265
❑ 94StaCluGR-557
❑ 94StaCluMO-6
❑ 94StaCluMOP-112
❑ 94StaCluMOP-208
❑ 94StaCluMOP-265
❑ 94StaCluMOP-557
❑ 94StaCluT-295
❑ 94StaCluTFDI-295
❑ 94Stu-126
❑ 94Top-470
❑ 94TopBlaG-16
❑ 94TopGol-470
❑ 94TopSpa-470
❑ 94TopSupS-33
❑ 94TopTra-76T
❑ 94TriPla-158
❑ 94TriPlaM-3
❑ 94Ult-308
❑ 94UltHomRK-5
❑ 94UltLeaL-2
❑ 94UppDec-34
❑ 94UppDec-340
❑ 94UppDecED-34
❑ 94UppDecED-340
❑ 94USPlaCA-6C
❑ 95BalOriP-40
❑ 95Baz-23
❑ 95Bow-385
❑ 95BowBes-R39
❑ 95BowBesR-R39
❑ 95ColCho-330
❑ 95ColChoGS-330
❑ 95ColChoSE-153
❑ 95ColChoSEGS-153
❑ 95ColChoSESS-153
❑ 95ColChoSS-330
❑ 95DenHol-19
❑ 95Don-357
❑ 95DonDiaK-DK23
❑ 95DonPreP-357
❑ 95DonTopotO-14
❑ 95Emo-7
❑ 95Fin-177
❑ 95FinRef-177
❑ 95Fla-224
❑ 95FlaInfP-6
❑ 95Fle-17
❑ 95Lea-129
❑ 95LeaLim-86
❑ 95LeaLimIBP-14
❑ 95Pac-28
❑ 95PacGolCDC-3
❑ 95PacGolP-18
❑ 95PacLatD-26
❑ 95PacPri-9
❑ 95Pin-293
❑ 95Pin-398
❑ 95PinArtP-293
❑ 95PinArtP-398
❑ 95PinMusC-293
❑ 95PinMusC-398
❑ 95PinPer-PP16
❑ 95RedFol-10
❑ 95Sco-419
❑ 95ScoGolR-419
❑ 95ScoHaloG-HG89
❑ 95ScoPlaTS-419
❑ 95Sel-121
❑ 95SelArtP-121
❑ 95SelCer-26
❑ 95SelCerMG-26
❑ 95SP-120
❑ 95SPCha-118
❑ 95SPChaDC-118
❑ 95Spo-84
❑ 95SpoArtP-84
❑ 95SPSil-120
❑ 95StaClu-30
❑ 95StaCluCC-CC6
❑ 95StaCluCT-17
❑ 95StaCluFDI-30
❑ 95StaCluMO-36
❑ 95StaCluMOP-30
❑ 95StaCluMOP-CC6
❑ 95StaCluMOP-PZ10
❑ 95StaCluPZ-PZ10
❑ 95StaCluSTWS-30
❑ 95StaCluVR-20
❑ 95StaCluVRMO-20
❑ 95Stu-49
❑ 95StuGolS-49
❑ 95Sum-5
❑ 95SumBigB-BB16
❑ 95SumNthD-5
❑ 95Top-80
❑ 95TopCyb-56
❑ 95TopD3-45
❑ 95TopEmb-126
❑ 95TopEmbGI-126
❑ 95TopFinIns-11
❑ 95UC3-25
❑ 95UC3-147
❑ 95UC3ArtP-25
❑ 95UC3ArtP-147
❑ 95UC3CycS-CS16
❑ 95Ult-7
❑ 95UltGolM-7
❑ 95UppDec-366
❑ 95UppDecED-366
❑ 95UppDecEDG-366
❑ 95UppDecPLL-R33
❑ 95UppDecPLL-R44
❑ 95UppDecPLLE-R33
❑ 95UppDecPLLE-R44
❑ 95UppDecSE-50
❑ 95UppDecSEG-50
❑ 95Zen-82
❑ 95ZenZ-10
❑ 96BalOriP-26
❑ 96Baz-102
❑ 96Bow-30
❑ 96BowBes-32
❑ 96BowBesAR-32
❑ 96BowBesR-32
❑ 96BowFoi-30
❑ 96Cir-7
❑ 96CirRav-7
❑ 96ColCho-470
❑ 96ColChoCtG-CG3
❑ 96ColChoCtG-CG3B
❑ 96ColChoCtG-CG3C
❑ 96ColChoCtGE-CR3
❑ 96ColChoCtGG-CG3
❑ 96ColChoCtGG-CG3B
❑ 96ColChoCtGG-CG3C
❑ 96ColChoCtGGE-CR3
❑ 96ColChoGS-470
❑ 96ColChoSS-470
❑ 96Don-357
❑ 96DonPreP-357
❑ 96EmoXL-8
❑ 96Fin-B287
❑ 96Fin-S68
❑ 96FinRef-B287
❑ 96FinRef-S68
❑ 96Fla-11
❑ 96Fle-19
❑ 96FleTif-19
❑ 96Lea-174
❑ 96LeaLim-84
❑ 96LeaLimG-84
❑ 96LeaPre-47
❑ 96LeaPreP-47
❑ 96LeaPrePB-174
❑ 96LeaPrePG-174
❑ 96LeaPrePS-174
❑ 96LeaPreSG-15
❑ 96LeaPreSte-15
❑ 96LeaSig-75
❑ 96LeaSigEA-149
❑ 96LeaSigEACM-22
❑ 96LeaSigPPG-75
❑ 96LeaSigPPP-75
❑ 96LeaTotB-3
❑ 96MetUni-8
❑ 96MetUniML-6
❑ 96MetUniP-8
❑ 96MLBPin-26
❑ 96OriFle-14
❑ 96Pac-239
❑ 96PacEstL-EL23
❑ 96PacPri-P76
❑ 96PacPriG-P76
❑ 96PanSti-129
❑ 96Pin-146
❑ 96Pin-250
❑ 96PinAfi-3
❑ 96PinAfiAP-3
❑ 96PinAfiFPP-3
❑ 96PinArtP-73
❑ 96PinArtP-150
❑ 96PinFoil-250
❑ 96PinSlu-17
❑ 96PinSta-73
❑ 96PinSta-150
❑ 96ProSta-80
❑ 96RedF-18
❑ 96Sco-31
❑ 96Sco-363
❑ 96ScoDugC-A30
❑ 96ScoDugC-B88
❑ 96ScoDugCAP-A30
❑ 96ScoDugCAP-B88
❑ 96ScoGolS-26
❑ 96ScoNumG-29
❑ 96ScoPowP-10
❑ 96ScoTitT-10
❑ 96Sel-58
❑ 96SelArtP-58
❑ 96SP-35
❑ 96Spo-29
❑ 96Spo-110
❑ 96SpoArtP-29
❑ 96SpoArtP-110
❑ 96SpoPowS-14
❑ 96SPSpeFX-28
❑ 96SPSpeFXDC-28
❑ 96SPx-7
❑ 96SPxGol-7
❑ 96StaClu-343
❑ 96StaCluEPB-343
❑ 96StaCluEPG-343
❑ 96StaCluEPS-343
❑ 96StaCluMO-32
❑ 96StaCluMOP-343
❑ 96StaCluMOP-PC6
❑ 96StaCluMOP-PS8
❑ 96StaCluPC-PC6
❑ 96StaCluPS-PS8
❑ 96Stu-9
❑ 96StuPrePB-9
❑ 96StuPrePG-9
❑ 96StuPrePS-9
❑ 96Sum-123
❑ 96SumAbo&B-123
❑ 96SumArtP-123
❑ 96SumFoi-123
❑ 96Top-395
❑ 96TopChr-158
❑ 96TopChrR-158
❑ 96TopGal-89
❑ 96TopGalPPI-89
❑ 96TopLas-88
❑ 96TopPro-AL19
❑ 96Ult-10
❑ 96UltGolM-10
❑ 96UltHitM-6
❑ 96UltHitMGM-6
❑ 96UltPowP-5
❑ 96UltPowPGM-5
❑ 96UltThu-15
❑ 96UltThuGM-15
❑ 96UppDec-15
❑ 96UppDecPD-PD11
❑ 96UppDecPHE-H3
❑ 96UppDecPRE-R6
❑ 96UppDecPreH-H3
❑ 96UppDecPreR-R6
❑ 96UppDecRunP-RP13
❑ 97BalOriP-26
❑ 97Bow-239
❑ 97BowBes-85
❑ 97BowBesAR-85
❑ 97BowBesMI-MI7
❑ 97BowBesMIAR-MI7
❑ 97BowBesMIARI-MI7
❑ 97BowBesMII-MI7
❑ 97BowBesMIR-MI7
❑ 97BowBesMIRI-MI7
❑ 97BowBesR-85
❑ 97BowChr-65
❑ 97BowChrI-65
❑ 97BowChrIR-65
❑ 97BowChrR-65
❑ 97BowInt-239
❑ 97BowIntB-BBI10
❑ 97BowIntBAR-BBI10
❑ 97BowIntBR-BBI10
❑ 97Cir-198
❑ 97CirRav-198
❑ 97ColCho-272
❑ 97ColChoCtG-5A
❑ 97ColChoCtG-5B
❑ 97ColChoCtG-5C
❑ 97ColChoCtGE-CG5
❑ 97ColChoCtGIW-CG5
❑ 97ColChoPP-PP17
❑ 97ColChoPPG-PP17
❑ 97ColChoPPJ-PP17
❑ 97ColChoT-BO9
❑ 97ColChoTBS-7
❑ 97ColChoTBSWH-7
❑ 97DenHol-2
❑ 97Don-56
❑ 97Don-440
❑ 97DonDom-18
❑ 97DonEli-35
❑ 97DonEliGS-35
❑ 97DonGolPP-56
❑ 97DonGolPP-440
❑ 97DonLim-130
❑ 97DonLimE-130
❑ 97DonLimFotG-19
❑ 97DonPre-47
❑ 97DonPreCttC-47
❑ 97DonSig-26
❑ 97DonSigA-77
❑ 97DonSigAC-95
❑ 97DonSigAM-95
❑ 97DonSigPPP-26
❑ 97DonSilPP-56
❑ 97DonSilPP-440
❑ 97DonTea-33
❑ 97DonTeaSPE-33
❑ 97DonVxP1-16
❑ 97E-X2-7
❑ 97E-X2Cred-7
❑ 97E-X2EssCre-7
❑ 97Fin-60
❑ 97Fin-156
❑ 97Fin-278
❑ 97FinEmb-156
❑ 97FinEmb-278
❑ 97FinEmbR-156
❑ 97FinEmbR-278
❑ 97FinRef-60
❑ 97FinRef-156
❑ 97FinRef-278
❑ 97FlaShoLC-71
❑ 97FlaShoLeg0-71
❑ 97FlaShoLeg1-71
❑ 97FlaShoM-A71
❑ 97FlaShoM-B71
❑ 97FlaShoM-C71
❑ 97FlaShoR0-71
❑ 97FlaShoR1-71
❑ 97FlaShoR2-71
❑ 97Fle-12
❑ 97FleTif-12
❑ 97Lea-43
❑ 97Lea-388
❑ 97LeaFraM-43
❑ 97LeaFraM-388
❑ 97LeaFraMDC-43
❑ 97LeaFraMDC-388
❑ 97LeaGolS-35
❑ 97MetUni-7
❑ 97NewPin-84
❑ 97NewPinAP-84
❑ 97NewPinMC-84
❑ 97NewPinPP-84
❑ 97OriSco-1
❑ 97OriScoPI-1
❑ 97OriScoPr-1
❑ 97Pac-28
❑ 97PacLatotML-3
❑ 97PacLigB-28
❑ 97PacPri-11
❑ 97PacPriLB-11
❑ 97PacPriP-11
❑ 97PacPriSL-SL1B
❑ 97PacSil-28
❑ 97PacTriCD-2
❑ 97Pin-43
❑ 97PinArtP-PP43
❑ 97PinCer-61
❑ 97PinCerMBla-61
❑ 97PinCerMBlu-61
❑ 97PinCerMG-61
❑ 97PinCerMR-61
❑ 97PinCerR-61
❑ 97PinIns-17
❑ 97PinInsCE-17
❑ 97PinInsDD-14
❑ 97PinInsDE-17
❑ 97PinMusC-43
❑ 97PinPasttM-19
❑ 97PinPrePla-43
❑ 97PinTotCPB-61
❑ 97PinTotCPG-61
❑ 97PinTotCPR-61
❑ 97PinX-P-20
❑ 97PinX-PMoS-20
❑ 97PinX-PMP-12
❑ 97PinX-PreMPS-12
❑ 97PinX-PSfF-45
❑ 97PinX-PSfFU-45
❑ 97Sco-45
❑ 97Sco-497
❑ 97ScoArtPWB-45
❑ 97ScoArtPWB-497
❑ 97ScoHeatO-10
❑ 97ScoPreS-45
❑ 97ScoResC-497
❑ 97ScoShoS-45
❑ 97ScoShoS-497
❑ 97ScoShoSAP-45
❑ 97ScoShoSAP-497
❑ 97Sel-31
❑ 97SelArtP-31
❑ 97SelCom-31
❑ 97SelRegG-31
❑ 97SP-30
❑ 97SPx-10
❑ 97SPxBro-10
❑ 97SPxGol-10
❑ 97SPxGraF-10
❑ 97SPxSil-10
❑ 97SPxSte-10
❑ 97StaClu-56
❑ 97StaCluMat-56
❑ 97StaCluMOP-56
❑ 97Stu-128
❑ 97StuPrePG-128
❑ 97StuPrePS-128
❑ 97Top-140
❑ 97TopChr-54
❑ 97TopChrR-54
❑ 97TopChrSB-15
❑ 97TopChrSBR-15
❑ 97TopGal-36
❑ 97TopGalPPI-36
❑ 97TopMem05-37
❑ 97TopSeaB-SB15
❑ 97TopSta-20
❑ 97TopStaAM-20
❑ 97TopSweS-SS11
❑ 97TopTeaT-TT8
❑ 97UD3-17
❑ 97UppDec-21
❑ 97UppDec-185
❑ 97UppDecLDC-LD14
❑ 97UppDecPP-PP3
❑ 97UppDecPPJ-PP3
❑ 97UppDecRP-RP9
❑ 98Bow-26
❑ 98BowBes-35
❑ 98BowBesAR-35
❑ 98BowBesR-35
❑ 98BowChr-26
❑ 98BowChrGA-26
❑ 98BowChrGAR-26
❑ 98BowChrI-26
❑ 98BowChrIR-26
❑ 98BowChrR-26
❑ 98BowGolA-26
❑ 98BowInt-26
❑ 98CirThu-249
❑ 98CirThuRav-249
❑ 98CirThuSupRav-249
❑ 98ColCho-314
❑ 98ColChoRJ-SQ68
❑ 98ColChoSQ-SQ68
❑ 98CroRoy-22
❑ 98Don-80
❑ 98DonCol-80
❑ 98DonColE-446
❑ 98DonColP-631
❑ 98DonColS-80
❑ 98DonCruG-9
❑ 98DonCruP-9
❑ 98DonCruR-9
❑ 98DonEli-46
❑ 98DonEliA-46
❑ 98DonEliS-46
❑ 98DonGolPP-80
❑ 98DonPre-81
❑ 98DonPreSeat-81
❑ 98DonPriCD-80
❑ 98DonPriCE-446
❑ 98DonPriCP-631
❑ 98DonSig-44
❑ 98DonSigA-68
❑ 98DonSigAC-88
❑ 98DonSigAM-89
❑ 98DonSigP-44
❑ 98DonSigSP-21
❑ 98DonSilPP-80
❑ 98E-X2-36
❑ 98E-X2ECFut-36
❑ 98E-X2ECNow-36
❑ 98Fin-179
❑ 98FinNo--179
❑ 98FinNo-R-179
❑ 98FinPowZ-P11
❑ 98FinRef-179
❑ 98FlaShoLeg0-88
❑ 98FlaShoLeg1-88
❑ 98FlaShoLeg2-88
❑ 98FlaShoLeg3-88
❑ 98FlaShoLegM-88
❑ 98FlaShoR0-88
❑ 98FlaShoR1-88
❑ 98FlaShoR2-88
❑ 98FlaShoR3-88
❑ 98Fle-266
❑ 98Fle-333
❑ 98FleVin'-7
❑ 98FleVin'C-7
❑ 98HamHel-2
❑ 98LeaRS-56
❑ 98LeaRSLHolo-56
❑ 98LeaRSLong-56
❑ 98LeaRTrue-56
❑ 98MetUni-3
❑ 98MetUniPMG-3
❑ 98OriSco-7
❑ 98OriScoP-7
❑ 98Pac-31
❑ 98PacAur-13
❑ 98PacAurPF-43
❑ 98PacAurPFC-43
❑ 98PacAurPFPB-43
❑ 98PacAurPFR-43
❑ 98PacAurPFS-43
❑ 98PacGolCDC-5
❑ 98PacHomRH-1
❑ 98PacInv-11
❑ 98PacInvGems-13
❑ 98PacInvPBlue-11
❑ 98PacInvSilv-11
❑ 98PacInvTeam-3
❑ 98PacLatotML-5
❑ 98PacOme-33
❑ 98PacOmeR-33
❑ 98PacOnl-97
❑ 98PacOnlR-97
❑ 98PacOnlWC-97
❑ 98PacPar-16
❑ 98PacParC-16
❑ 98PacParG-16
❑ 98PacParHS-16
❑ 98PacParI-38
❑ 98PacParPB-16
❑ 98PacParR-16
❑ 98PacPlaB-31
❑ 98PacRedT-31
❑ 98PacSil-31
❑ 98Pin-61
❑ 98PinArtP-PP54
❑ 98PinIns-44
❑ 98PinInsCE-44
❑ 98PinInsDE-44
❑ 98PinInsSG-15AB
❑ 98PinInsSG-15CD
❑ 98PinInsSGS-15AB

❑ 98PinInsSGS-15CD
❑ 98PinMusC-PP54
❑ 98PinPer-89
❑ 98PinPerPP-89
❑ 98PinPerSftF-17
❑ 98PinPreP-61
❑ 98PinSna-BO7
❑ 98PinSna-BO17
❑ 98Revo-21
❑ 98RevoSS-21
❑ 98Sco-92
❑ 98ScoRT-204
❑ 98ScoRTSS-PP112
❑ 98ScoRTSSAP-PP112
❑ 98ScoRTSSAP1-PP112
❑ 98ScoSS-PP40
❑ 98ScoSSAP-PP40
❑ 98SkyDugA-145
❑ 98SkyDugAIA-145
❑ 98SP Aut-51
❑ 98SpoIll-99
❑ 98SpoIll-177
❑ 98SpoIllEE-99
❑ 98SpoIllEE-177
❑ 98SpoIllFE-99
❑ 98SpoIllFE-177
❑ 98SpoIllWSF-107
❑ 98SpoIllWSFEE-107
❑ 98SpoIllWSFFE-107
❑ 98SPxFin-62
❑ 98SPxFin-143
❑ 98SPxFin-238
❑ 98SPxFinR-62
❑ 98SPxFinR-143
❑ 98SPxFinR-238
❑ 98SPxFinS-62
❑ 98SPxFinS-143
❑ 98SPxFinS-238
❑ 98StaCluFDI-134
❑ 98StaCluI-134
❑ 98StaCluOneK-134
❑ 98StaCluPP-134
❑ 98StaCluTIII-T5C
❑ 98StaCluTLme-T5C
❑ 98StaCluTLmo-T5C
❑ 98Stu-166
❑ 98StuGPP-166
❑ 98StuSPP-166
❑ 98Top-50
❑ 98TopChr-50
❑ 98TopChrR-50
❑ 98TopDevR-50
❑ 98TopDia-50
❑ 98TopGal-133
❑ 98TopGalGP-133
❑ 98TopGalOPP-133
❑ 98TopGalPPI-133
❑ 98TopGalPPIA-133
❑ 98TopGolLabC1-24
❑ 98TopGolLabC1B-24
❑ 98TopGolLabC1One-24
❑ 98TopGolLabC1R-24
❑ 98TopGolLabC2-24
❑ 98TopGolLabC2B-24
❑ 98TopGolLabC2One-24
❑ 98TopGolLabC2R-24
❑ 98TopGolLabC3-24
❑ 98TopGolLabC3B-24
❑ 98TopGolLabC3One-24
❑ 98TopGolLabC3R-24
❑ 98TopMiniC-50
❑ 98TopMysF-ILM4
❑ 98TopMysFR-ILM4
❑ 98TopOpeD-30
❑ 98TopSta-117
❑ 98TopSta'S-31
❑ 98TopSta'SGH-31
❑ 98TopStaB-117
❑ 98TopStaG-117
❑ 98TopStaGR-117
❑ 98TopStaS-117
❑ 98TopStaSteG-31
❑ 98TopTek-40
❑ 98TopTekD-40
❑ 98UD3-72
❑ 98UD3-162
❑ 98UD3-252
❑ 98UD3DieCut-72
❑ 98UD3DieCut-162
❑ 98UD3DieCut-252
❑ 98Ult-141
❑ 98UltGolM-141
❑ 98UltMas-141
❑ 98UltPlaM-141
❑ 98UppDec-40
❑ 98UppDec10AP-19
❑ 98UppDec1APR-19
❑ 98UppDec5x7-40
❑ 98UppDecNP-NP6
❑ 98UppDecR-10
❑ 98UppDecR-14
❑ 98UppDecRBBop-BB2
❑ 98UppDecRTC-TC2
❑ 98UppDecSF-25
❑ 98UppDecTMT-6
❑ 98UppDecTMTG-6
❑ 98Zen-8
❑ 98Zen5 xx7-6
❑ 98Zen5x7GoldImp-6
❑ 98Zen5x7Imp-6
❑ 98ZenZ-G-8
❑ 98ZenZ-S-8
❑ 99199Fin-235
❑ 99Bow-275
❑ 99BowBes-54
❑ 99BowBesAR-54
❑ 99BowBesR-54
❑ 99BowGol-275
❑ 99BowInt-275
❑ 99CroRoyB-139
❑ 99CroRoyL-139
❑ 99CroRoyOD-139
❑ 99E-X Cen-39
❑ 99E-X CenECFut-39
❑ 99E-X CenECNow-39
❑ 99FinGolRef-235
❑ 99FinRef-235
❑ 99FlaShoLeg1-64
❑ 99FlaShoLeg2-64
❑ 99FlaShoLeg3-64
❑ 99FlaShoLegM1-64
❑ 99FlaShoLegM2-64
❑ 99FlaShoLegM3-64
❑ 99FlaShoR1-64
❑ 99FlaShoR2-64
❑ 99FlaShoR3-64
❑ 99Fle-18
❑ 99FleBri-101
❑ 99FleBri2G-101
❑ 99FleBriBlu-101
❑ 99FleBriGol-101
❑ 99FleGoiYar-10
❑ 99FleMys-36
❑ 99FleMysG-36
❑ 99FleMysM-36
❑ 99FleSta9-18
❑ 99FleVin'-18
❑ 99FleWarT-18
❑ 99MetUni-62
❑ 99MetUniGM-62
❑ 99MetUniPMG-62
❑ 99Pac-57
❑ 99Pac-57A
❑ 99PacAur-193
❑ 99PacAurOD-193
❑ 99PacCroC-39
❑ 99PacCroC-2
❑ 99PacCroCPB-39
❑ 99PacOme-238
❑ 99PacOmeC-238
❑ 99PacOmeG-238
❑ 99PacOmePB-238
❑ 99PacPar-237
❑ 99PacParC-237
❑ 99PacParG-237
❑ 99PacParHoloGold-237
❑ 99PacParHS-237
❑ 99PacParOD-237
❑ 99PacParPB-237
❑ 99PacParRed-237
❑ 99PacPlaB-57
❑ 99PacPlaB-57A
❑ 99PacPri-20
❑ 99PacPriHB-20
❑ 99PacPriHG-20
❑ 99PacPriHM-20
❑ 99PacPriHP-20
❑ 99PacPriRed-20
❑ 99PacPriS-43
❑ 99PacPriS206-43
❑ 99PacPriS206R-43
❑ 99PacPriSP-43
❑ 99PacPriSV-43
❑ 99PacRed-57
❑ 99PacRed-57A
❑ 99Rev-142
❑ 99RevPremDate-142
❑ 99RevRet-142
❑ 99RevShaSS-142
❑ 99SkyMolM-4
❑ 99SkyMolMX-4
❑ 99SkyPre-60
❑ 99SkyPreR-60
❑ 99SkyThu-252
❑ 99SkyThuRant-252
❑ 99SkyThuRave-252
❑ 99SP AutHRC-HR10
❑ 99SPAutHRCDC-HR10
❑ 99SpoIll-74
❑ 99SpoIllF4-11
❑ 99SpoIllF4E-11
❑ 99SPx-78
❑ 99SPxFinR-78
❑ 99SPxFinS-78
❑ 99StaClu-330
❑ 99StaCluFDI-330
❑ 99StaCluOoaK-330
❑ 99StaCluPP-330
❑ 99ThuSkySupR-252
❑ 99Top-315
❑ 99TopAll-AM11
❑ 99TopChr-315
❑ 99TopChrA-AE11
❑ 99TopChrAR-AE11
❑ 99TopChrR-315
❑ 99TopMVPP-315
❑ 99TopOpeD-137
❑ 99TopSta-64
❑ 99TopSta1Foil-64
❑ 99TopStaFoil-64
❑ 99TopStaOS-64
❑ 99UD Cho-60
❑ 99UD ChoP-60
❑ 99UD ChoPCR-60
❑ 99UD ChoYW-Y3
❑ 99UDHolo-58
❑ 99UDHoloAUsome-58
❑ 99Ult-143
❑ 99UltGolM-143
❑ 99UltMas-143
❑ 99UltPlaM-143
❑ 99UltRBIK-1
❑ 99UppDec-503
❑ 99UppDecBD-12
❑ 99UppDecBDD-12
❑ 99UppDecBDQ-12
❑ 99UppDecBDT-12
❑ 99UppDecCf7-11
❑ 99UppDecCf7-54
❑ 99UppDecCf7-C11
❑ 99UppDecCf7Cf7P-C11
❑ 99UppDecCf7LL-L18
❑ 99UppDecCL-88
❑ 99UppDecCLCC-88
❑ 99UppDecCLM-C96
❑ 99UppDecCo7CE-11
❑ 99UppDecCo7CE-54
❑ 99UppDecE-88
❑ 99UppDecEFXG-88
❑ 99UppDecEL1-503
❑ 99UppDecEL2-503
❑ 99UppDecM-206
❑ 99UppDecMGS-206
❑ 99UppDecMHFS-206
❑ 99UppDecMSS-206
❑ 99UppDecR-84
❑ 99UppDecRG-84
❑ 99UppDecRP-84
❑ 99Vic-400

Palmer, Arnold

❑ 80PhiBul-34

Palmer, Bob

❑ 75AppFoxT-22
❑ 82HolMilT-11

Palmer, Brett

❑ 93BurIndC-20
❑ 93BurIndF-3296
❑ 94BurIndC-20

Palmer, David

❑ 79ExpPos-18
❑ 80ExpPos-21
❑ 80OPC-21
❑ 80Top-42
❑ 81Don-451
❑ 81Fle-160
❑ 81OPC-243
❑ 81Top-607
❑ 82ExpPos-29
❑ 82Fle-199
❑ 82OPC-292
❑ 82Top-292
❑ 83Don-68
❑ 83ExpPos-21
❑ 83Fle-291
❑ 83OPC-164
❑ 83Top-164
❑ 84ExpPos-21
❑ 84ExpStu-23
❑ 85Don-341
❑ 85ExpPos-16
❑ 85Fle-404
❑ 85Fle-643
❑ 85Lea-105
❑ 85OPC-211
❑ 85OPCPos-3
❑ 85Top-526
❑ 85TopMin-526
❑ 85TopTif-526
❑ 86BraPol-46
❑ 86Don-254A
❑ 86Don-254B
❑ 86Fle-255
❑ 86FleUpd-87
❑ 86OPC-143
❑ 86Top-421
❑ 86TopTif-421
❑ 86TopTra-84T
❑ 86TopTraT-84T
❑ 87BraSmo-4
❑ 87Don-325
❑ 87Fle-525
❑ 87FleGlo-525
❑ 87SpoTeaP-24
❑ 87Top-324
❑ 87TopSti-45
❑ 87TopTif-324
❑ 88Don-266
❑ 88Fle-546
❑ 88FleGlo-546
❑ 88FleUpd-111
❑ 88FleUpdG-111
❑ 88PhiTas-17
❑ 88Sco-457
❑ 88ScoGlo-457
❑ 88Top-732
❑ 88TopTif-732
❑ 88TopTra-79T
❑ 88TopTraT-79T
❑ 89Don-133
❑ 89Fle-577
❑ 89FleGlo-577
❑ 89OPC-67
❑ 89Sco-544
❑ 89TolMudHC-4
❑ 89TolMudHP-789
❑ 89Top-67
❑ 89TopTif-67
❑ 89UppDec-515

Palmer, Dean

❑ 87GasRanP-8
❑ 88ChaRanS-18
❑ 88FloStaLAS-47
❑ 89BasAmeAPB-AA27
❑ 89TexLeaAGS-32
❑ 89TulDriGS-19
❑ 89TulDriTI-17
❑ 90ClaUpd-T39
❑ 90Don-529
❑ 90Hot50RS-35
❑ 90OklCit8P-441
❑ 90ProAAAF-687
❑ 90Sco-594
❑ 90Sco100RS-38
❑ 90Spo-225
❑ 90TopDeb89-95
❑ 90TulDriDGB-5
❑ 90TulDriP-1170
❑ 90UppDec-74
❑ 91Bow-288
❑ 91Cla3-T72
❑ 91DonRoo-48
❑ 91FleUpd-61
❑ 91LinDriAAA-314
❑ 91OklCit8LD-314
❑ 91OklCit8P-187
❑ 91Sco100RS-28
❑ 91TopTra-88T
❑ 91TopTraT-88T
❑ 91UltUpd-56
❑ 91UppDecFE-74F
❑ 92Bow-107
❑ 92Don-177
❑ 92Fle-312
❑ 92Lea-225
❑ 92LeaBlaG-225
❑ 92LeaGolP-28
❑ 92OPC-567
❑ 92OPCPre-112
❑ 92PanSti-77
❑ 92Pin-351
❑ 92PinTea2-64
❑ 92ProFS7-148
❑ 92RanMot-26
❑ 92RanTeal-16
❑ 92Sco-392
❑ 92Sco100RS-60
❑ 92StaClu-211
❑ 92StaPal-1
❑ 92StaPal-2
❑ 92StaPal-3
❑ 92StaPal-4
❑ 92StaPal-5
❑ 92StaPal-6
❑ 92StaPal-7
❑ 92StaPal-8
❑ 92StaPal-9
❑ 92StaPal-10
❑ 92StaPal-11
❑ 92Stu-245
❑ 92Top-567
❑ 92TopGol-567
❑ 92TopGolW-567
❑ 92TopMic-567
❑ 92Ult-137
❑ 92UppDec-465
❑ 93Bow-81
❑ 93Don-339
❑ 93Fin-159
❑ 93FinRef-159
❑ 93Fla-284
❑ 93Fle-325
❑ 93FunPac-158
❑ 93FunPac-217
❑ 93Lea-159
❑ 93OPC-258
❑ 93PacSpa-315
❑ 93PanSti-84
❑ 93Pin-161
❑ 93PinHomRC-25
❑ 93PinTea2-28
❑ 93RanKee-420
❑ 93RanStaC-11
❑ 93RedFolS-73
❑ 93Sco-138
❑ 93Sel-248
❑ 93SP-197
❑ 93SPPlaP-PP14
❑ 93StaClu-22
❑ 93StaCluFDI-22
❑ 93StaCluMOP-22
❑ 93Stu-210
❑ 93Top-545
❑ 93TopGol-545
❑ 93TopInaM-545
❑ 93TopInaR-545
❑ 93TopMic-545
❑ 93TriPla-111
❑ 93Ult-282
❑ 93UppDec-241
❑ 93UppDec-465
❑ 93UppDecGold-241
❑ 93UppDecGold-465
❑ 94Bow-213
❑ 94ColC-580
❑ 94ColChoGS-580
❑ 94ColChoSS-580
❑ 94Don-355
❑ 94DonLonBL-2
❑ 94DonSpeE-355
❑ 94Fin-177
❑ 94FinPre-177P
❑ 94FinRef-177
❑ 94Fla-345
❑ 94Fle-314
❑ 94FleExtB-183
❑ 94FUnPac-71
❑ 94Lea-311
❑ 94LeaL-73
❑ 94OPC-152
❑ 94Pac-623
❑ 94PacGolP-7
❑ 94PanSti-131
❑ 94Pin-101
❑ 94PinArtP-101
❑ 94PinMusC-101
❑ 94PinPowS-PS25
❑ 94PinTeaP-3
❑ 94PinTheN-20
❑ 94RanMagM-30
❑ 94Sco-389
❑ 94ScoGolR-389
❑ 94Sel-223
❑ 94SP-150
❑ 94SPDieC-150
❑ 94Spo-85
❑ 94SpoSha-SH8
❑ 94StaClu-112
❑ 94StaClu-336
❑ 94StaCluFDI-112
❑ 94StaCluFDI-336
❑ 94StaCluGR-112
❑ 94StaCluGR-336
❑ 94StaCluMOP-112
❑ 94StaCluMOP-336
❑ 94StaCluMOP-ST27
❑ 94StaCluST-ST27
❑ 94StaCluT-269
❑ 94StaCluTFDI-269
❑ 94Stu-156
❑ 94Top-136
❑ 94TopGol-136
❑ 94TopSpa-136
❑ 94TriPla-197
❑ 94Ult-130
❑ 94UppDec-180
❑ 94UppDecAJ-22
❑ 94UppDecAJG-22
❑ 94UppDecED-180
❑ 94UppDecMLS-MM14
❑ 94UppDecMLSED-MM14
❑ 95Baz-75
❑ 95Bow-380
❑ 95ColCho-395
❑ 95ColChoGS-395
❑ 95ColChoSE-187
❑ 95ColChoSEGS-187
❑ 95ColChoSESS-187
❑ 95ColChoSS-395
❑ 95Don-19
❑ 95DonPreP-19
❑ 95DonTopotO-164
❑ 95Emo-87
❑ 95Fin-91
❑ 95FinRef-91
❑ 95Fla-91
❑ 95Fle-292
❑ 95Lea-21
❑ 95LeaCor-5
❑ 95LeaLim-127
❑ 95Pac-432
❑ 95PanSti-60
❑ 95Pin-192
❑ 95PinArtP-192
❑ 95PinMusC-192
❑ 95RanCra-26
❑ 95Sco-245
❑ 95ScoGolR-245
❑ 95ScoPlaTS-245
❑ 95Sel-88
❑ 95SelArtP-88
❑ 95SelCer-44
❑ 95SelCerMG-44
❑ 95SP-197
❑ 95Spo-92
❑ 95SpoArtP-92
❑ 95SPSil-197
❑ 95StaClu-31
❑ 95StaCluFDI-31
❑ 95StaCluMOP-31
❑ 95StaCluSTWS-31
❑ 95StaCluVR-21
❑ 95StaCluVRMO-21
❑ 95Stu-59
❑ 95Sum-83
❑ 95SumNthD-83
❑ 95Top-365
❑ 95TopCyb-193
❑ 95TopD3-46
❑ 95TopEmb-41
❑ 95TopEmbGI-41
❑ 95Ult-336
❑ 95UltGolM-336
❑ 95UppDec-154
❑ 95UppDecED-154
❑ 95UppDecEDG-154
❑ 95UppDecSE-176
❑ 95UppDecSEG-176
❑ 95Zen-25
❑ 96Baz-94
❑ 96Bow-13
❑ 96BowFoi-13
❑ 96Cir-90
❑ 96CirRav-90
❑ 96ColCho-735
❑ 96ColChoGS-735
❑ 96ColChoSS-735
❑ 96Don-45
❑ 96DonPreP-45
❑ 96EmoXL-125
❑ 96Fin-B173
❑ 96FinRef-B173
❑ 96Fla-176
❑ 96Fle-258
❑ 96FleTif-258
❑ 96Lea-188

❑ 96LeaLim-82
❑ 96LeaLimG-82
❑ 96LeaPre-96
❑ 96LeaPreP-96
❑ 96LeaPrePB-188
❑ 96LeaPrePG-188
❑ 96LeaPrePS-188
❑ 96LeaSig-83
❑ 96LeaSigA-176
❑ 96LeaSigAG-176
❑ 96LeaSigAS-176
❑ 96LeaSigPPG-83
❑ 96LeaSigPPP-83
❑ 96MetUni-115
❑ 96MetUniP-115
❑ 96Pac-426
❑ 96PacPri-P137
❑ 96PacPriG-P137
❑ 96PanSti-237
❑ 96Pin-159
❑ 96Pin-227
❑ 96PinAfi-88
❑ 96PinAfiAP-88
❑ 96PinAfiFPP-88
❑ 96PinArtP-86
❑ 96PinArtP-127
❑ 96PinFoil-227
❑ 96PinSlu-16
❑ 96PinSta-86
❑ 96PinSta-127
❑ 96ProSta-100
❑ 96RanDr P-25
❑ 96RanFle-12
❑ 96RanMot-6
❑ 96Sco-179
❑ 96ScoDugC-A100
❑ 96ScoDugCAP-A100
❑ 96ScoRef-19
❑ 96Sel-146
❑ 96SelArtP-146
❑ 96SelCer-80
❑ 96SelCerAP-80
❑ 96SelCerCB-80
❑ 96SelCerCR-80
❑ 96SelCerMB-80
❑ 96SelCerMG-80
❑ 96SelCerMR-80
❑ 96SP-179
❑ 96StaClu-40
❑ 96StaCluEPB-40
❑ 96StaCluEPG-40
❑ 96StaCluEPS-40
❑ 96StaCluMOP-40
❑ 96Sum-144
❑ 96SumAbo&B-144
❑ 96SumArtP-144
❑ 96SumFoi-144
❑ 96Top-379
❑ 96TopChr-152
❑ 96TopChrR-152
❑ 96TopGal-81
❑ 96TopGalPPI-81
❑ 96TopLas-28
❑ 96Ult-423
❑ 96UltGolM-423
❑ 96UppDec-469
❑ 96Zen-32
❑ 96ZenArtP-32
❑ 97Bow-228
❑ 97BowBes-42
❑ 97BowBesAR-42
❑ 97BowBesR-42
❑ 97BowInt-228
❑ 97Cir-184
❑ 97CirRav-184
❑ 97ColCho-242
❑ 97ColChoBS-11
❑ 97ColChoBSGS-11
❑ 97ColChoT-TR6
❑ 97Don-62
❑ 97DonEli-74
❑ 97DonEliGS-74
❑ 97DonGolPP-62
❑ 97DonLim-194
❑ 97DonLimE-194
❑ 97DonPre-100
❑ 97DonPreCttC-100
❑ 97DonSilPP-62
❑ 97Fin-105
❑ 97Fin-270
❑ 97FinEmb-105
❑ 97FinEmbR-105
❑ 97FinRef-105
❑ 97FinRef-270
❑ 97FlaShoLC-61
❑ 97FlaShoLeg0-61
❑ 97FlaShoLeg1-61
❑ 97FlaShoM-A61
❑ 97FlaShoM-B61
❑ 97FlaShoM-C61
❑ 97FlaShoR0-61
❑ 97FlaShoR1-61
❑ 97FlaShoR2-61
❑ 97Fle-229
❑ 97FleTif-229
❑ 97FleZon-12
❑ 97Lea-257
❑ 97LeaFraM-257
❑ 97LeaFraMDC-257
❑ 97MetUni-166
❑ 97NewPin-93
❑ 97NewPinAP-93
❑ 97NewPinMC-93
❑ 97NewPinPP-93
❑ 97Pac-207
❑ 97PacLigB-207
❑ 97PacPri-70
❑ 97PacPriLB-70
❑ 97PacPriP-70
❑ 97PacPriSL-SL7B
❑ 97PacSil-207
❑ 97PinCer-19
❑ 97PinCerMBla-19
❑ 97PinCerMBlu-19
❑ 97PinCerMG-19
❑ 97PinCerMR-19
❑ 97PinCerR-19
❑ 97PinIns-50
❑ 97PinInsCE-50
❑ 97PinInsDE-50
❑ 97PinTotCPB-19
❑ 97PinTotCPG-19
❑ 97PinTotCPR-19
❑ 97PinX-P-72
❑ 97PinX-PMoS-72
❑ 97PinX-PSfF-46
❑ 97PinX-PSfFU-46
❑ 97RanDr P-23
❑ 97RanMot-7
❑ 97RanSco-9
❑ 97RanScoPl-9
❑ 97RanScoPr-9
❑ 97Sco-175
❑ 97Sco-516
❑ 97ScoArtPWB-175
❑ 97ScoArtPWB-516
❑ 97ScoPreS-175
❑ 97ScoResC-516
❑ 97ScoShoS-175
❑ 97ScoShoS-516
❑ 97ScoShoSAP-175
❑ 97ScoShoSAP-516
❑ 97Sel-41
❑ 97SelArtP-41
❑ 97SelCom-41
❑ 97SelRegG-41
❑ 97SP-173
❑ 97SpoIll-162
❑ 97SpoIllEE-162
❑ 97StaClu-225
❑ 97StaCluMat-225
❑ 97StaCluMOP-225
❑ 97Stu-24
❑ 97StuPrePG-24
❑ 97StuPrePS-24
❑ 97Top-393
❑ 97TopChr-136
❑ 97TopChrR-136
❑ 97TopGal-63
❑ 97TopGalPPI-63
❑ 97Ult-138
❑ 97UltGolME-138
❑ 97UltPlaME-138
❑ 97UppDec-210
❑ 97UppDecP-29
❑ 97UppDecPE-29
❑ 98Bow-270
❑ 98BowBes-91
❑ 98BowBesAR-91
❑ 98BowBesR-91
❑ 98BowChr-270
❑ 98BowChrGA-270
❑ 98BowChrGAR-270
❑ 98BowChrI-270
❑ 98BowChrIR-270
❑ 98BowChrR-270
❑ 98BowGolA-270
❑ 98BowInt-270
❑ 98CirThu-252
❑ 98CirThuRav-252
❑ 98CirThuSupRav-252
❑ 98ColCho-390
❑ 98CroRoy-68
❑ 98Don-246
❑ 98DonGolPP-246
❑ 98DonSilPP-246
❑ 98E-X2-42
❑ 98E-X2ECFut-42
❑ 98E-X2ECNow-42
❑ 98Fin-204
❑ 98FinNo--204
❑ 98FinNo-R-204
❑ 98FinRef-204
❑ 98FlaShoLeg0-118
❑ 98FlaShoLeg1-118
❑ 98FlaShoLeg2-118
❑ 98FlaShoLeg3-118
❑ 98FlaShoLegM-118
❑ 98FlaShoR0-118
❑ 98FlaShoR1-118
❑ 98FlaShoR2-118
❑ 98FlaShoR3-118
❑ 98Fle-73
❑ 98MetUni-171
❑ 98MetUniPMG-171
❑ 98Pac-110
❑ 98PacAur-48
❑ 98PacOme-117
❑ 98PacOmeR-117
❑ 98PacOnl-347
❑ 98PacOnlR-347
❑ 98PacOnlWC-347
❑ 98PacPar-57
❑ 98PacParC-57
❑ 98PacParG-57
❑ 98PacParHS-57
❑ 98PacParPB-57
❑ 98PacParR-57
❑ 98PacParTC-7
❑ 98PacPlaB-110
❑ 98PacRedT-110
❑ 98PacSil-110
❑ 98Pin-98
❑ 98PinPreP-98
❑ 98Revo-72
❑ 98RevoSS-72
❑ 98ScoRT-114
❑ 98SkyDugA-67
❑ 98SkyDugAIA-67
❑ 98SP Aut-103
❑ 98SpoIll-98
❑ 98SpoIllEE-98
❑ 98SpoIllFE-98
❑ 98SpoIllTaN-119
❑ 98SpoIllTaNEE-119
❑ 98SpoIllWSF-93
❑ 98SpoIllWSFEE-93
❑ 98SpoIllWSFFE-93
❑ 98SPxFin-285
❑ 98SPxFinR-285
❑ 98SPxFinS-285
❑ 98StaCluFDI-73
❑ 98StaCluI-73
❑ 98StaCluOneK-73
❑ 98StaCluPP-73
❑ 98Top-328
❑ 98TopChr-328
❑ 98TopChrR-328
❑ 98TopDevR-328
❑ 98TopDia-328
❑ 98TopGal-124
❑ 98TopGalGP-124
❑ 98TopGalOPP-124
❑ 98TopGalPPI-124
❑ 98TopGalPPIA-124
❑ 98TopGolLabC1-52
❑ 98TopGolLabC1B-52
❑ 98TopGolLabC1One-52
❑ 98TopGolLabC1R-52
❑ 98TopGolLabC2-52
❑ 98TopGolLabC2B-52
❑ 98TopGolLabC2One-52
❑ 98TopGolLabC2R-52
❑ 98TopGolLabC3-52
❑ 98TopGolLabC3B-52
❑ 98TopGolLabC3One-52
❑ 98TopGolLabC3R-52
❑ 98TopMiniC-328
❑ 98TopOpeD-154
❑ 98TopSta-124
❑ 98TopStaB-124
❑ 98TopStaG-124
❑ 98TopStaGR-124
❑ 98TopStaS-124
❑ 98Ult-62
❑ 98UltGolM-62
❑ 98UltMas-62
❑ 98UltPlaM-62
❑ 98UppDec-108
❑ 98UppDec10AP-35
❑ 98UppDec1APR-35
❑ 98UppDecR-43
❑ 98UppDecSF-65
❑ 99199Fin-167
❑ 99Bow-258
❑ 99BowGol-258
❑ 99BowInt-258
❑ 99FinGolRef-167
❑ 99FinRef-167
❑ 99FlaShoLeg1-120
❑ 99FlaShoLeg2-120
❑ 99FlaShoLeg3-120
❑ 99FlaShoLegM1-120
❑ 99FlaShoLegM2-120
❑ 99FlaShoLegM3-120
❑ 99FlaShoR1-120
❑ 99FlaShoR2-120
❑ 99FlaShoR3-120
❑ 99Fle-218
❑ 99FleBri-120
❑ 99FleBri2G-120
❑ 99FleBriBlu-120
❑ 99FleBriGol-120
❑ 99FleMys-91
❑ 99FleMysG-91
❑ 99FleMysM-91
❑ 99FleSta9-218
❑ 99FleWarT-218
❑ 99MetUni-31
❑ 99MetUniGM-31
❑ 99MetUniPMG-31
❑ 99Pac-210
❑ 99PacAur-69
❑ 99PacAurOD-69
❑ 99PacOme-92
❑ 99PacOmeC-92
❑ 99PacOmeG-92
❑ 99PacOmePB-92
❑ 99PacPar-91
❑ 99PacParC-91
❑ 99PacParG-91
❑ 99PacParHoloGold-91
❑ 99PacParHS-91
❑ 99PacParOD-91
❑ 99PacParPB-91
❑ 99PacParRed-91
❑ 99PacPlaB-210
❑ 99PacPri-73
❑ 99PacPriHB-73
❑ 99PacPriHG-73
❑ 99PacPriHM-73
❑ 99PacPriHP-73
❑ 99PacPriRed-73
❑ 99PacPriS-128
❑ 99PacPriS206-128
❑ 99PacPriS206R-128
❑ 99PacRed-210
❑ 99SkyPre-89
❑ 99SkyPreR-89
❑ 99SkyThu-176
❑ 99SkyThuRant-176
❑ 99SkyThuRave-176
❑ 99SP Aut-34
❑ 99SpoIll-177
❑ 99StaClu-333
❑ 99StaCluFDI-333
❑ 99StaCluOoaK-333
❑ 99StaCluPP-333
❑ 99ThuSkySupR-176
❑ 99Top-103
❑ 99TopChr-103
❑ 99TopChrR-103
❑ 99TopGal-90
❑ 99TopGalPP-90
❑ 99TopGalPPI-90
❑ 99TopMVPP-103
❑ 99TopOpeD-60
❑ 99TopSta-136
❑ 99TopStaFoil-136
❑ 99UD Cho-95
❑ 99UD ChoPCR-95
❑ 99UD ChoYW-Y16
❑ 99Ult-56
❑ 99UltGolM-56
❑ 99UltMas-56
❑ 99UltPlaM-56
❑ 99UppDec-370
❑ 99UppDecBD-40
❑ 99UppDecBDD-40
❑ 99UppDecBDQ-40
❑ 99UppDecBDT-40
❑ 99UppDecCLM-C34
❑ 99UppDecE-36
❑ 99UppDecEBPC-C-DP
❑ 99UppDecEFXG-36
❑ 99UppDecEL1-370
❑ 99UppDecEL2-370
❑ 99UppDecM-76
❑ 99UppDecMGS-76
❑ 99UppDecMHFS-76
❑ 99UppDecMSS-76
❑ 99UppDecO-38
❑ 99UppDecOSO-38
❑ 99UppDecR-33
❑ 99UppDecRG-33
❑ 99UppDecRP-33
❑ 99Vic-146

Palmer, Denzil

❑ 76CliPilT-25

Palmer, Donald

❑ 87BufBisP-28

Palmer, Doug

❑ 85VisOakT-2
❑ 86OrlTwiP-15
❑ 87OrlTwiP-17
❑ 88NewBriRSP-892

Palmer, Jim

❑ 65BalOriP-25
❑ 66BalOriP-26
❑ 66OPC-126
❑ 66Top-126
❑ 66TopVen-126
❑ 67BalOriP-75
❑ 67BalOriP-76
❑ 67BalOriP-77
❑ 67CokCapO-5
❑ 67DexPre-159
❑ 67OPC-152
❑ 67Top-152
❑ 67Top-475
❑ 68CokCapO-5
❑ 68Top-575
❑ 69Top-573
❑ 70BalOriP-22
❑ 70DayDaiNM-82
❑ 70OPC-68
❑ 70OPC-449
❑ 70Ori-9
❑ 70Top-68
❑ 70Top-449
❑ 71BalOriP-20
❑ 71Kel-60
❑ 71MilDud-21
❑ 71MLBOffS-306
❑ 71OPC-67
❑ 71OPC-197
❑ 71OPC-570
❑ 71OriCha-11
❑ 71Top-67
❑ 71Top-197
❑ 71Top-570
❑ 71TopCoi-90
❑ 71TopTat-23
❑ 72Kel-13A
❑ 72Kel-13B
❑ 72MilBra-263
❑ 72OPC-92
❑ 72OPC-270
❑ 72OriPos-23
❑ 72SevTraC-39
❑ 72Top-92
❑ 72Top-270
❑ 73BalOriP-31
❑ 73BalOriP-32
❑ 73Kel2D-17
❑ 73LinPor-12
❑ 73OPC-160
❑ 73OPC-341
❑ 73OriJohP-22A
❑ 73OriJohP-22B
❑ 73OriTeal-22
❑ 73SevTraC-57
❑ 73Top-160
❑ 73Top-341
❑ 73TopCanL-38
❑ 73TopCom-13
❑ 73TopPin-13
❑ 74Kel-6
❑ 74OPC-40
❑ 74OPC-206
❑ 74Top-40
❑ 74Top-206
❑ 74TopDecE-45
❑ 74TopPuz-8
❑ 74TopSta-128
❑ 75BalOriP-23
❑ 75Hos-126
❑ 75OPC-335
❑ 75SSP42-5
❑ 75SSPPuzB-19
❑ 75Top-335
❑ 75TopMin-335
❑ 76BalOriP-31
❑ 76BlaDis-44
❑ 76BucDis-44
❑ 76CarDis-44
❑ 76CraDis-44
❑ 76DailsID-44
❑ 76Hos-56
❑ 76HosTwi-56
❑ 76IsaDis-44
❑ 76Kel-37
❑ 76OPC-200
❑ 76OPC-202
❑ 76OPC-450
❑ 76OrbDis-44
❑ 76OriEngCL-3
❑ 76RedBarD-44
❑ 76SafDis-44
❑ 76SSP-380
❑ 76Top-200
❑ 76Top-202
❑ 76Top-450
❑ 76TowCluD-44
❑ 77BurCheD-42
❑ 77ChiWilD-52
❑ 77DailsID-52
❑ 77DetCaeD-52
❑ 77HolInnD-52
❑ 77Hos-1
❑ 77MSADis-52
❑ 77OPC-5
❑ 77OPC-80
❑ 77PepGloD-20
❑ 77RCColC-49
❑ 77SagDis-52
❑ 77sDis-52
❑ 77Spo-2615
❑ 77Top-5
❑ 77Top-600
❑ 77TopCloS-36
❑ 77WenDis-52
❑ 77ZipDis-52
❑ 78BalOriP-24
❑ 78Hos-116
❑ 78OPC-5
❑ 78OPC-179
❑ 78PapGinD-31
❑ 78Pep-36
❑ 78RCColC-45
❑ 78SagDis-2
❑ 78TasDis-2
❑ 78Top-160
❑ 78Top-205
❑ 78WifBalD-57
❑ 79BalOriP-13
❑ 79BasPat-65
❑ 79Hos-11
❑ 79Kel-5
❑ 79OPC-174
❑ 79Top-340
❑ 80BalOriP-15
❑ 80BurKinPHR-7
❑ 80Kel-15
❑ 80OPC-310
❑ 80PerHaloFP-206
❑ 80PerHaloFPS-69
❑ 80Top-590
❑ 80TopSup-4
❑ 81BalOriP-14
❑ 81Don-353
❑ 81Don-473
❑ 81Fle-169
❑ 81FleStiC-124
❑ 81Kel-2
❑ 81OPC-210
❑ 81Ori6F-25
❑ 81PerCreC-28
❑ 81Top-210
❑ 81TopScr-50
❑ 81TopSti-39
❑ 81TopSupN-9
❑ 82Don-231
❑ 82Fle-175
❑ 82FleSta-143
❑ 82Kel-42
❑ 82OPC-80
❑ 82OPC-81
❑ 82Top-80
❑ 82Top-81
❑ 82TopSti-146
❑ 83Don-4
❑ 83Don-77
❑ 83Fle-69
❑ 83FleSta-145
❑ 83FleSti-200

❑ 83Kel-39
❑ 83OPC-299
❑ 83OPC-328
❑ 83OriPos-21
❑ 83Top-21
❑ 83Top-490
❑ 83Top-491
❑ 83TopFol-1
❑ 83TopGloS-19
❑ 83TopSti-23
❑ 83TopSti-175
❑ 83TopStiB-5
❑ 84BalOriP-25
❑ 84Don-576
❑ 84DonCha-35
❑ 84Fle-16
❑ 84FleSti-102
❑ 84Nes792-715
❑ 84Nes792-717
❑ 84Nes792-750
❑ 84OCoandSI-157
❑ 84OPC-194
❑ 84OriEng-10
❑ 84RalPur-23
❑ 84Top-715
❑ 84Top-717
❑ 84Top-750
❑ 84TopCer-23
❑ 84TopGaloC-8
❑ 84TopRubD-31
❑ 84TopSti-21
❑ 84TopSti-211
❑ 84TopTif-715
❑ 84TopTif-717
❑ 84TopTif-750
❑ 86OriGreT-3
❑ 86SpoDecG-58
❑ 86TCMSupS-33
❑ 87K-M-17
❑ 89SweBasG-105
❑ 90AGFA-17
❑ 90BasWit-33
❑ 90PerGreM-85
❑ 90TopMag-14
❑ 91OriCro-349
❑ 92KelAll-3
❑ 93ActPacA-127
❑ 93ActPacA2-61G
❑ 93BalOriP-25
❑ 93FroRowP-1
❑ 93FroRowP-2
❑ 93FroRowP-3
❑ 93FroRowP-4
❑ 93FroRowP-5
❑ 93OriCroASU-2
❑ 93UppDecS-18
❑ 94NabAllA-2
❑ 95BalOriP-39
❑ 97DonSigSS-16
❑ 99DumSet-JP
❑ 99DumSet-JP
Palmer, Ken
❑ 76BatRouCT-17
Palmer, Lowell
❑ 70OPC-252
❑ 70Top-252
❑ 71OPC-554
❑ 71Top-554
❑ 72Top-746
❑ 77ColCliT-18A
❑ 77ColCliT-18B
❑ 89PacSenL-174
❑ 89T/MSenL-86
Palmer, Mickey
❑ 82ForMyeRT-8
Palmer, Mike
❑ 81QuaCitCT-33
Palmieri, John
❑ 82ReaPhiT-5
Palmisano, Joseph
❑ 30Zee-110
❑ 33Zee-82
Palmquist, Ed
❑ 60DarFar-7
❑ 90DodTar-604
Paluk, Brian
❑ 96YakBeaTI-47
❑ 98VerBeaDM-15
Paluk, Jeff
❑ 94YakBeaC-11
❑ 94YakBeaF-3843
❑ 95SanBerSTI-14
❑ 96SanBerSB-20
❑ 97SanBerS-11
Palumbo, Richard
❑ 92SalLakTSP-21
Palva, Nelson
❑ 80VenLeaS-150
Palyan, Vince
❑ 89EveGiaS-23
❑ 90CliGiaB-26
❑ 90CliGiaP-2564
Palys, Stan (Stanley F.)
❑ 58RedEnq-29
❑ 58Top-126
Pamus, Javier
❑ 98SpolndG-24
Panaro, Carmen
❑ 97HigDesMG-20
Pancoski, Tracey
❑ 88FreSunCLC-7
❑ 88FreSunP-1240
Pandolfini, Ryan
❑ 97HudValRB-3
Panetta, Mario
❑ 83QuaCitCT-4
Paniagua, Jose
❑ 94Bow-32
❑ 94Cla-169
❑ 94ClaTriF-T49
❑ 94WesPalBEC-20
❑ 94WesPalBEF-35
❑ 96Bow-152
❑ 96BowFoi-152
❑ 96FleUpd-U150
❑ 96FleUpdTC-U150
❑ 96HarSenB-21
❑ 96Ult-507
❑ 96UltGolM-507
❑ 97ColCho-19
❑ 97Don-165
❑ 97DonGolPP-165
❑ 97DonSilPP-165
❑ 97Pac-349
❑ 97PacLigB-349
❑ 97PacSil-349
❑ 97Pin-173
❑ 97PinArtP-PP173
❑ 97PinMusC-173
❑ 97PinPrePla-173
❑ 97StaClu-296
❑ 97StaCluMOP-296
❑ 97UppDec-239
❑ 98Pac-351
❑ 98PacPlaB-351
❑ 98PacRedT-351
❑ 98PacSil-351
❑ 98TacRaiQ-23
❑ 99Fle-496
❑ 99FleSta9-496
❑ 99FleWarT-496
Panick, Frank
❑ 77SalLakCGC-19
Pankovits, Jim (James F.)
❑ 77CocAstT-16
❑ 80TucTorT-19
❑ 81TucTorT-17
❑ 82HawIslT-4
❑ 83TucTorT-16
❑ 84TucTorC-61
❑ 85AstHouP-14
❑ 85AstMot-25
❑ 85Don-502
❑ 86AstMilL-15
❑ 86AstPol-1
❑ 86Don-450
❑ 86Fle-307
❑ 86Top-618
❑ 86TopTif-618
❑ 87AstMot-22
❑ 87AstPol-25
❑ 87Don-605
❑ 87Fle-64
❑ 87FleGlo-64
❑ 87Top-249
❑ 87TopTif-249
❑ 88AstMot-22
❑ 88AstPol-16
❑ 88StaLinAst-11
❑ 88Top-487
❑ 88TopBig-109
❑ 88TopClo-85
❑ 88TopTif-487
❑ 89BufBisC-18
❑ 89BufBisP-1664
❑ 89Fle-363
❑ 89FleGlo-363
❑ 89Sco-192
❑ 89Top-153
❑ 89TopTif-153
❑ 89UppDec-100
❑ 90CMC-269
❑ 90PawRedSC-18
❑ 90PawRedSDD-18
❑ 90PawRedSP-470
❑ 90ProAAAF-442
❑ 90TopTVRS-55
❑ 91LinDriAAA-363
❑ 91PacSenL-89
❑ 91PawRedSDD-15
❑ 91PawRedSLD-363
❑ 91PawRedSP-48
❑ 92NewBriRSF-449
❑ 92NewBriRSS-499
❑ 93NewBriRSF-1237
❑ 94NewBriRSF-665
❑ 95QuaCitRBTI-17
❑ 96QuaCitRB-1
❑ 98JacGenM-24
Panther, Jim
❑ 72RanTeal-21
❑ 93RanKee-31
Pantoja, Jhonny
❑ 94AlbYanF-1437
❑ 95NorNavTI-27
Papa, John
❑ 77FriOneYW-77
❑ 91OriCro-350
Papagellin, Donna
❑ 93TulDriTI-22
❑ 94TulDriTI-29
Papageorge, Greg
❑ 88VirGenS-17
❑ 89PenPilS-17
Papai, Al
❑ 50Bow-245
❑ 50RedSoxTI-17
Papajohn, Mike
❑ 87LSUTigP-7
Papangellin, Donna
❑ 97PhoFirTI-17
❑ 98FreGriG-22
Paparella, Joe (Joseph J.)
❑ 55Bow-235
Paparesta, Nick
❑ 96WatIndTI-22
❑ 98WatIndTI-22
Pape, Ken (Kenneth Wayne)
❑ 75SpoIndC-7
❑ 77TucTorC-5
❑ 78SyrChiT-15
❑ 79SpoIndT-8
❑ 92TexLon-31
❑ 93RanKee-286
Pape, Lawrence
❑ 09ColChiE-224
❑ 12ColRedB-224
❑ 12ColTinT-224
❑ 14Zee-69
Papi, Stan (Stanley Gerard)
❑ 78ExpPos-9
❑ 79OPC-344
❑ 79RedSoxTI-3
❑ 79Top-652
❑ 81Don-246
❑ 81Fle-480A
❑ 81Fle-480B
❑ 81Top-273
❑ 82Don-333
❑ 82Fle-280
❑ 82Top-423
Papish, Frank
❑ 48WhiSoxTI-21
❑ 49IndTeal-20
Pappageorgas, Bob
❑ 77WauMetT-13
Pappalau, John
❑ 98CamPepP-60
Pappas, Erik
❑ 86PalSprAP-25
❑ 86PalSprAS-6
❑ 87PalSprP-23
❑ 88MidAngGS-14
❑ 89ChaKniTI-12
❑ 90CMC-92
❑ 90IowCubC-17
❑ 90IowCubP-321
❑ 90ProAAAF-628
❑ 90TopTVCu-55
❑ 90TriAllGP-AAA34
❑ 91Bow-432
❑ 91CubVinL-20
❑ 91ScoRoo-95T
❑ 92OmaRoyF-2964
❑ 92OmaRoyS-340
❑ 92StaClu-442
❑ 92TopDeb91-135
❑ 93Fla-125
❑ 93FleFinE-129
❑ 93Lea-535
❑ 93LouRedF-219
❑ 93TopTra-5T
❑ 94CarPol-14
❑ 94ColC-593
❑ 94ColChoGS-593
❑ 94ColChoSS-593
❑ 94Don-205
❑ 94Fin-287
❑ 94FinRef-287
❑ 94Fle-642
❑ 94Pac-599
❑ 94Sco-188
❑ 94ScoBoyoS-30
❑ 94ScoGolR-188
❑ 94StaClu-448
❑ 94StaCluFDI-448
❑ 94StaCluGR-448
❑ 94StaCluMOP-448
❑ 94StaCluT-323
❑ 94StaCluTFDI-323
❑ 94Top-234
❑ 94TopGol-234
❑ 94TopSpa-234
❑ 94Ult-270
❑ 94USPlaCR-4H
❑ 95ChaKniTI-21
❑ 96OklCit8B-15
Pappas, Milt
❑ 47Exh-172
❑ 56BalOriP-42
❑ 56BalOriP-43
❑ 58BalOriP-11
❑ 58BalOriP-12
❑ 58Top-457
❑ 59OriJayP-6
❑ 59Top-391
❑ 60Baz-5
❑ 60Lea-57
❑ 60OriJayP-5
❑ 60Top-12
❑ 60Top-399
❑ 60TopTat-42
❑ 60TopVen-12
❑ 61BalOriP-14
❑ 61Pos-71A
❑ 61Pos-71B
❑ 61Top-48
❑ 61Top-295
❑ 61TopStal-103
❑ 62BalOriP-19
❑ 62Baz-28
❑ 62ExhStaB-29
❑ 62Jel-34
❑ 62Pos-34
❑ 62PosCan-34
❑ 62SalPlaC-98
❑ 62ShiPlaC-98
❑ 62Top-55
❑ 62Top-75
❑ 62TopStal-7
❑ 62TopVen-55
❑ 62TopVen-75
❑ 63BalOriP-25
❑ 63ExhStaB-51
❑ 63Fle-3
❑ 63Jel-65
❑ 63Pos-65
❑ 63SalMetC-43
❑ 63Top-358
❑ 64BalOriP-27
❑ 64ChatheY-40
❑ 64OriJayP-8
❑ 64Top-45
❑ 64TopCoi-70
❑ 64TopGia-5
❑ 64TopSta-4
❑ 64TopTatl-59
❑ 64TopVen-45
❑ 65BalOriP-26
❑ 65ChaTheY-41
❑ 65OPC-270
❑ 65Top-270
❑ 65TopEmbl-20
❑ 65TopTral-61
❑ 66Baz-29
❑ 66Kah-25
❑ 66OPC-105
❑ 66Top-105
❑ 66TopRubl-75
❑ 66TopVen-105
❑ 67CokCapR-1
❑ 67DexPre-160
❑ 67Top-254
❑ 68AtlOilPBCC-33
❑ 68BraPos-25
❑ 68OPC-74
❑ 68Top-74
❑ 68TopVen-74
❑ 69AtlBraBPPS-19
❑ 69MilBra-212
❑ 69MLBOffS-117
❑ 69OPC-79
❑ 69Top-79
❑ 69TopSta-8
❑ 69TopTeaP-2
❑ 70DayDaiNM-123
❑ 70MLBOffS-11
❑ 70Top-576
❑ 71MilDud-57
❑ 71MLBOffS-39
❑ 71OPC-441
❑ 71Top-441
❑ 72CubChi-5
❑ 72CubTeal-9
❑ 72MilBra-264
❑ 72OPC-208
❑ 72Top-208
❑ 73OPC-70
❑ 73Top-70
❑ 74OPC-640
❑ 74Top-640
❑ 78TCM60I-56
❑ 84CubBriPC-13S
❑ 89PacLegI-204
❑ 89SweBasG-113
❑ 90SweBasG-107
❑ 91OriCro-351
❑ 91SweBasG-69
❑ 92UppDecS-26
Paquette, Craig
❑ 89MedAthB-22
❑ 90CMC-846
❑ 90ModA'sC-22
❑ 90ModA'sP-2222
❑ 91Bow-236
❑ 91HunStaTI-16
❑ 91SouOreAAP-SOA29
❑ 92Bow-94
❑ 92ClaFS7-138
❑ 92HunStaF-3957
❑ 92HunStaS-316
❑ 92OPC-473
❑ 92SkyAA F-135
❑ 92Top-473
❑ 92TopGol-473
❑ 92TopGolW-473
❑ 92TopMic-473
❑ 92UppDecML-122
❑ 93Bow-329
❑ 93ClaFS7-235
❑ 93FleFinE-261
❑ 93Lea-506
❑ 93SelRoo-57T
❑ 93SP-42
❑ 93TopTra-38T
❑ 94ColC-225
❑ 94ColChoGS-225
❑ 94ColChoSS-225
❑ 94Don-532
❑ 94Fle-272
❑ 94Pac-461
❑ 94Pin-328
❑ 94PinArtP-328
❑ 94PinMusC-328
❑ 94Sco-567
❑ 94ScoGolR-567
❑ 94StaClu-328
❑ 94StaCluFDI-328
❑ 94StaCluGR-328
❑ 94StaCluMOP-328
❑ 94TacTigF-3184
❑ 94Top-46
❑ 94TopGol-46
❑ 94TopSpa-46
❑ 94TriPla-7
❑ 94Ult-113
❑ 94UppDec-262
❑ 94UppDecED-262
❑ 94USPlaCR-5C
❑ 95AthMot-22
❑ 96ColCho-644
❑ 96ColChoGS-644
❑ 96ColChoSS-644
❑ 96Don-530
❑ 96DonPreP-530
❑ 96Fle-215
❑ 96FleTif-215
❑ 96OmaRoyB-22
❑ 96Pac-390
❑ 97Cir-191
❑ 97CirRav-191
❑ 97ColCho-132
❑ 97Don-253
❑ 97DonGolPP-253
❑ 97DonSilPP-253
❑ 97Fle-119
❑ 97FleTif-119
❑ 97MetUni-96
❑ 97PacPriGotD-GD50
❑ 97Pin-58
❑ 97PinArtP-PP58
❑ 97PinMusC-58
❑ 97PinPrePla-58
❑ 97RoyPol-17
❑ 97Top-417
❑ 97UppDec-393
❑ 98NorTidP-19
❑ 98PacOnl-487
❑ 98PacOnlR-487
❑ 98PacOnlWC-487
Paquette, Darryl
❑ 78WauMetT-21
Paradis, Mike
❑ 99Bow-434
❑ 99BowGol-434
❑ 99BowInt-434
Paragin, Billy
❑ 92PulBraC-22
❑ 92PulBraF-3181
❑ 93DanBraC-18
❑ 93DanBraF-3621
Paramo, Paul
❑ 91GulCoaRSP-9
Parascand, Steve
❑ 87FayGenP-4
❑ 88FayGenP-1088
Pardee, Al
❑ 07NewEveWS-11
Pardo, Al
❑ 81MiaOriT-2
❑ 83RocRedWT-12
❑ 84ChaO'sT-7
❑ 85BalOriP-21
❑ 85RocRedWT-2
❑ 86Don-489
❑ 86RocRedWP-15
❑ 86Top-279
❑ 86TopTif-279
❑ 88TidTidP-1594
❑ 89ScrRedBC-21
❑ 89ScrRedBP-711
❑ 90HagSunDGB-20
❑ 91OriCro-352
Pardo, Bed
❑ 89EugEmeB-8
Pardo, Larry
❑ 86DayBealP-21
❑ 87QuaCitAP-6
❑ 88QuaCitAGS-6
❑ 89QuaCitAB-12
❑ 89QuaCitAGS-24
❑ 90CMC-710
❑ 90PalSprAP-2575
Pardue, Roy
❑ 93DavLipB-23
❑ 94DavLipB-20
❑ 95DavLipB-18
Paredes, Carlos
❑ 96LanLugB-18
❑ 97WilBluR-21
❑ 98WilBluRC-24
Paredes, German
❑ 91KanCouCC-24
❑ 91KanCouCP-2672
Paredes, Jesus
❑ 87JamExpP-2543
❑ 88RocExpLC-26
❑ 89RocExpLC-21
❑ 90CMC-71
❑ 90IndIndC-21
Paredes, Johnny
❑ 86JacExpT-2
❑ 87IndIndTI-20
❑ 88DonRoo-29
❑ 88IndIndC-11
❑ 88IndIndP-516
❑ 88TriAAC-3
❑ 89Don-570
❑ 89Fle-388
❑ 89FleGlo-388
❑ 89OPC-367

❑ 89ScoHot1R-27
❑ 89Top-367
❑ 89TopTif-367
❑ 89UppDec-477
❑ 90IndIndP-303
❑ 90ProAAAF-586
❑ 91LinDriAAA-595
❑ 91TolMudHLD-595
❑ 91TolMudHP-1941
❑ 92TolMudHF-1056
❑ 93LinVenB-190
❑ 93LinVenB-313
❑ 93TolMudHF-1660
❑ 94VenLinU-150
❑ 95LinVen-227
❑ 96-97LinVen-113

Paredes, Roberto

❑ 96HelBreTI-18
❑ 97BelSnaB-23
❑ 98StoPorG-22

Parent, Eric

❑ 82WauTimF-11
❑ 83WauTimF-10
❑ 84GreHorT-16

Parent, Freddy (Frederick A.)

❑ 03BreE10-112
❑ 04FanCraAL-39
❑ 04RedSoxUP-11
❑ 08RosComP-16
❑ 09ColChiE-225A
❑ 09ColChiE-225B
❑ 09T206-280
❑ 10DomDisP-95
❑ 10SweCapPP-13
❑ 11HelSta-14
❑ 11PinT-5-754
❑ 11S74Sil-7
❑ 11SpoLifCW-281
❑ 11SpoLifM-26
❑ 11T205-134
❑ 12ColRedB-225A
❑ 12ColRedB-225B
❑ 12ColTinT-225A
❑ 12ColTinT-225B
❑ 12ImpTobC-44
❑ 14PieStaT-85

Parent, Gerald

❑ 95HelBreTI-30
❑ 96BelSnaTI-28
❑ 96Exc-73
❑ 96OgdRapTI-27
❑ 97CliLumG-20
❑ 98CliLumG-18

Parent, Mark

❑ 82AmaGolST-10
❑ 83BeaGolGT-13
❑ 84BeaGolGT-8
❑ 85LasVegSC-105
❑ 86LasVegSP-12
❑ 88DonRoo-8
❑ 88FleUpd-125
❑ 88FleUpdG-125
❑ 88PadCok-27
❑ 88PadSmo-22
❑ 88TopTra-80T
❑ 88TopTraT-80T
❑ 89Don-420
❑ 89FleUpd-125
❑ 89PadCok-11
❑ 89PadPos-23
❑ 89Sco-576
❑ 89Top-617
❑ 89TopTif-617
❑ 89UppDec-492
❑ 90Don-229
❑ 90Fle-164
❑ 90FleCan-164
❑ 90Lea-497
❑ 90OPC-749
❑ 90PadCok-13
❑ 90PadMag-7
❑ 90PubIntS-55
❑ 90Sco-119
❑ 90Top-749
❑ 90TopTif-749
❑ 90UppDec-569
❑ 91Don-506
❑ 91Fle-538
❑ 91OPC-358
❑ 91Sco-213
❑ 91Top-358
❑ 91TopDesS-358
❑ 91TopMic-358
❑ 91TopTif-358
❑ 91UppDec-470
❑ 92RocRedWF-1942
❑ 92RocRedWS-462
❑ 92StaClu-623
❑ 92StaCluECN-623
❑ 92TriA AAS-462
❑ 93RanKee-287
❑ 93RocRedWF-244
❑ 94StaCluT-349
❑ 94StaCluTFDI-349
❑ 95DonTopotO-323
❑ 95PirFil-24
❑ 96Fle-325
❑ 96FleTif-325
❑ 96FleUpd-U36
❑ 96FleUpdTC-U36
❑ 96LeaSigEA-150
❑ 96Sco-173
❑ 96TigHebN-19
❑ 96Ult-350
❑ 96UltGolM-350
❑ 96UppDec-329
❑ 97PhiCopQ-19
❑ 97PhiTeal-8
❑ 97Ult-465
❑ 97UltGolME-465
❑ 97UltPlaME-465
❑ 98PacOnl-568
❑ 98PacOnlR-568
❑ 98PacOnlWC-568
❑ 98PhiTeal-26

Parese, Billy

❑ 89St.CatBJP-2082
❑ 90MyrBeaBJP-2786
❑ 91DunBluJC-18
❑ 91DunBluJP-216

Parfrey, Brian

❑ 82RedPioT-26

Parham, Bill

❑ 89BakDodCLC-191

Paris, Juan

❑ 85SpoIndC-18
❑ 86ChaRaiP-20
❑ 87GreHorP-12
❑ 88WinHavRSS-19
❑ 89LynRedSS-17
❑ 90NewBriRSB-17
❑ 90NewBriRSP-1331
❑ 90NewBriRSS-14
❑ 91LinDriAA-467
❑ 91NewBriRSLD-467
❑ 91NewBriRSP-366
❑ 92PawRedSF-936
❑ 92PawRedSS-361
❑ 97DunDonPPS-16

Paris, Kelly (Kelly Jay)

❑ 77St.PetCT-1
❑ 78St.PetCT-19
❑ 80ArkTraT-22
❑ 82LouRedE-22
❑ 84Don-384
❑ 84Fle-476
❑ 84HawIslC-123
❑ 84Nes792-113
❑ 84Top-113
❑ 84TopTif-113
❑ 85IntLeaAT-28
❑ 85RocRedWT-8
❑ 86RocRedWP-16
❑ 88VanCanC-12
❑ 89Fle-506
❑ 89FleGlo-506
❑ 89UppDec-192
❑ 89VanCanC-11
❑ 89VanCanP-594
❑ 91OriCro-353

Paris, Porfino

❑ 85DomLeaS-93

Paris, Zacarias

❑ 82TucTorT-14
❑ 83ColAstT-17
❑ 86VenGulP-20

Parish, Jack

❑ 76CliPilT-26

Parisi, Michael

❑ 94ElmPioC-15
❑ 94ElmPioF-3471
❑ 95KanCouCTI-18
❑ 96BreCouMB-24
❑ 97PorSeaD-23

Parisotto, Barry

❑ 89GreFalDSP-20
❑ 90BakDodCLC-242
❑ 92SalLakTSP-5
❑ 93HigDesMC-15
❑ 93HigDesMF-38

Parisse, Tony (Louis Peter)

❑ 77TCMTheWY-25

Park, Chan Ho

❑ 94ActPac-3
❑ 94ActPac-56
❑ 94ActPac2G-2G
❑ 94ActPac2GD-2G
❑ 94Bow-98
❑ 94BowBes-B25
❑ 94BowBesR-B25
❑ 94Cla-20
❑ 94ClaCreotC-C16
❑ 94DodPol-14
❑ 94Fin-426
❑ 94FinJum-426
❑ 94FinRef-426
❑ 94Fla-181
❑ 94FlaWavotF-A8
❑ 94FleExtB-293
❑ 94FleExtBRS-15
❑ 94FleUpd-151
❑ 94LeaLimR-78
❑ 94Pin-527
❑ 94PinArtP-527
❑ 94PinMusC-527
❑ 94SanAntMF-2466
❑ 94ScoRoo-RT136
❑ 94ScoRooGR-RT136
❑ 94Sel-177
❑ 94SelRooS-RS13
❑ 94SP-13
❑ 94SPDieC-13
❑ 94SpoRoo-122
❑ 94SpoRooAP-122
❑ 94SpoRooRS-TR13
❑ 94StaClu-521
❑ 94StaCluFDI-521
❑ 94StaCluGR-521
❑ 94StaCluMOP-521
❑ 94TopTra-70T
❑ 94Ult-520
❑ 94UltAllR-9
❑ 94UltAllRJ-9
❑ 94UppDec-520
❑ 94UppDecED-520
❑ 95ActPacF-4
❑ 95ARuFalLS-11
❑ 95Bow-432
❑ 95BowBes-B4
❑ 95BowBesR-B4
❑ 95ColCho-232
❑ 95ColChoGS-232
❑ 95ColChoSE-25
❑ 95ColChoSEGS-25
❑ 95ColChoSESS-25
❑ 95ColChoSS-232
❑ 95DodPol-20
❑ 95Don-175
❑ 95DonPreP-175
❑ 95Fle-546
❑ 95LeaGolR-12
❑ 95PacGolCDC-11
❑ 95Sco-582
❑ 95ScoGolR-582
❑ 95ScoPlaTS-582
❑ 95Sel-6
❑ 95SelArtP-6
❑ 95Spo-146
❑ 95SpoArtP-146
❑ 95Stu-152
❑ 95Sum21C-TC6
❑ 95Ult-398
❑ 95UltGolM-398
❑ 95UppDecSE-36
❑ 95UppDecSEG-36
❑ 96Bow-136
❑ 96BowBes-74
❑ 96BowBesAR-74
❑ 96BowBesR-74
❑ 96BowFoi-136
❑ 96Cir-145
❑ 96CirRav-145
❑ 96ColCho-29
❑ 96ColCho-658
❑ 96ColChoGS-658
❑ 96ColChoSS-658
❑ 96DodFle-15
❑ 96DodMot-18
❑ 96Don-481
❑ 96DonPreP-481
❑ 96EmoXL-214
❑ 96Fin-S296
❑ 96FinRef-S296
❑ 96Fle-444
❑ 96FleTif-444
❑ 96Lea-18
❑ 96LeaPre-135
❑ 96LeaPreP-135
❑ 96LeaPrePB-18
❑ 96LeaPrePG-18
❑ 96LeaPrePS-18
❑ 96LeaSig-118
❑ 96LeaSigPPG-118
❑ 96LeaSigPPP-118
❑ 96Pin-386
❑ 96PinAfi-156
❑ 96PinAfi-188
❑ 96PinAfiAP-156
❑ 96PinAfiAP-188
❑ 96PinFoil-386
❑ 96Sco-514
❑ 96Sel-179
❑ 96SelArtP-179
❑ 96SelCer-120
❑ 96SelCerAP-120
❑ 96SelCerCB-120
❑ 96SelCerCR-120
❑ 96SelCerMB-120
❑ 96SelCerMG-120
❑ 96SelCerMR-120
❑ 96SP-107
❑ 96Spo-128
❑ 96SpoArtP-128
❑ 96StaClu-416
❑ 96StaCluMOP-416
❑ 96Stu-15
❑ 96StuPrePB-15
❑ 96StuPrePG-15
❑ 96StuPrePS-15
❑ 96Sum-176
❑ 96SumAbo&B-176
❑ 96SumArtP-176
❑ 96SumFoi-176
❑ 96Ult-499
❑ 96UltGolM-499
❑ 96UppDec-94
❑ 96UppDecFSP-FS16
❑ 96Zen-124
❑ 96ZenArtP-124
❑ 97Cir-278
❑ 97CirRav-278
❑ 97ColCho-367
❑ 97ColChoT-LA11
❑ 97DodMot-15
❑ 97DodPol-22
❑ 97DodSco-5
❑ 97DodScoPl-5
❑ 97DodScoPr-5
❑ 97Don-194
❑ 97DonEli-115
❑ 97DonEliGS-115
❑ 97DonEliTotC-19
❑ 97DonEliTotCDC-19
❑ 97DonGolPP-194
❑ 97DonLim-53
❑ 97DonLimE-53
❑ 97DonPre-33
❑ 97DonPreCttC-33
❑ 97DonSilPP-194
❑ 97DonTea-113
❑ 97DonTeaSPE-113
❑ 97FlaShoLC-161
❑ 97FlaShoLeg0-161
❑ 97FlaShoLeg1-161
❑ 97FlaShoM-A161
❑ 97FlaShoM-B161
❑ 97FlaShoM-C161
❑ 97FlaShoR0-161
❑ 97FlaShoR1-161
❑ 97FlaShoR2-161
❑ 97Fle-370
❑ 97FleTif-370
❑ 97Lea-48
❑ 97LeaFraM-48
❑ 97LeaFraMDC-48
❑ 97Pac-338
❑ 97PacLigB-338
❑ 97PacSil-338
❑ 97Pin-31
❑ 97PinArtP-PP31
❑ 97PinIns-92
❑ 97PinInsCE-92
❑ 97PinInsDE-92
❑ 97PinMusC-31
❑ 97PinPasttM-23
❑ 97PinPrePla-31
❑ 97Sco-148
❑ 97ScoArtPWB-148
❑ 97ScoPreS-148
❑ 97ScoShoS-148
❑ 97ScoShoSAP-148
❑ 97Sel-7
❑ 97SelArtP-7
❑ 97SelCom-7
❑ 97SelRegG-7
❑ 97StaClu-69
❑ 97StaCluMOP-69
❑ 97Stu-64
❑ 97StuPrePG-64
❑ 97StuPrePS-64
❑ 97Top-338
❑ 97Ult-222
❑ 97UltGolME-222
❑ 97UltPlaME-222
❑ 97UppDec-194
❑ 97UppDec-397
❑ 98Bow-248
❑ 98BowBes-43
❑ 98BowBesAR-43
❑ 98BowBesR-43
❑ 98BowChr-248
❑ 98BowChrGA-248
❑ 98BowChrGAR-248
❑ 98BowChrI-248
❑ 98BowChrIR-248
❑ 98BowChrR-248
❑ 98BowGolA-248
❑ 98BowInt-248
❑ 98CirThu-247
❑ 98CirThuRav-247
❑ 98CirThuSupRav-247
❑ 98ColCho-397
❑ 98DodMot-13
❑ 98DodPol-21
❑ 98DodSco-8
❑ 98DodScoP-8
❑ 98Don-116
❑ 98Don-377
❑ 98DonCol-116
❑ 98DonColE-484
❑ 98DonColL-244
❑ 98DonColP-609
❑ 98DonColS-116
❑ 98DonEli-84
❑ 98DonEliA-84
❑ 98DonEliS-84
❑ 98DonGolPP-116
❑ 98DonGolPP-377
❑ 98DonPre-59
❑ 98DonPreSeat-59
❑ 98DonPriCD-116
❑ 98DonPriCE-484
❑ 98DonPriCL-244
❑ 98DonPriCP-609
❑ 98DonSig-62
❑ 98DonSigP-62
❑ 98DonSilPP-116
❑ 98DonSilPP-377
❑ 98Fin-146
❑ 98FinNo--146
❑ 98FinNo-R-146
❑ 98FinRef-146
❑ 98Fle-47
❑ 98Lea-45
❑ 98LeaFraDA-45
❑ 98LeaFraF-45
❑ 98LeaFraM-45
❑ 98LeaFraM-45
❑ 98LeaFraMDC-45
❑ 98LeaFraMDC-45
❑ 98LeaFraMZ2-45
❑ 98LeaRS-18
❑ 98LeaRSLHolo-18
❑ 98LeaRSLong-18
❑ 98LeaRTrue-18
❑ 98Pac-338
❑ 98PacAur-148
❑ 98PacInv-111
❑ 98PacInvPBlue-111
❑ 98PacInvSilv-111
❑ 98PacOnl-382
❑ 98PacOnlR-382
❑ 98PacOnlWC-382
❑ 98PacPar-180
❑ 98PacParC-180
❑ 98PacParG-180
❑ 98PacParHS-180
❑ 98PacParPB-180
❑ 98PacParR-180
❑ 98PacPlaB-338
❑ 98PacRedT-338
❑ 98PacSil-338
❑ 98Pin-55
❑ 98PinIns-89
❑ 98PinInsCE-89
❑ 98PinInsDE-89
❑ 98PinPer-60
❑ 98PinPerPP-60
❑ 98PinPreP-55
❑ 98PinSna-LAD13
❑ 98Sco-103
❑ 98ScoRT-228
❑ 98ScoRTSS-PP125
❑ 98ScoRTSSAP-PP125
❑ 98ScoRTSSAP1-PP125
❑ 98SP Aut-112
❑ 98SpoIllWSF-61
❑ 98SpoIllWSFEE-61
❑ 98SpoIllWSFFE-61
❑ 98SPxFin-290
❑ 98SPxFinR-290
❑ 98SPxFinS-290
❑ 98StaCluFDI-45
❑ 98StaCluI-45
❑ 98StaCluOneK-45
❑ 98StaCluPP-45
❑ 98Stu-56
❑ 98StuGPP-56
❑ 98StuSPP-56
❑ 98Top-17
❑ 98TopChr-17
❑ 98TopChrR-17
❑ 98TopDevR-17
❑ 98TopDia-17
❑ 98TopGal-92
❑ 98TopGalGP-92
❑ 98TopGalOPP-92
❑ 98TopGalPPI-92
❑ 98TopGalPPIA-92
❑ 98TopMiniC-17
❑ 98TopOpeD-13
❑ 98TopSta-112
❑ 98TopStaB-112
❑ 98TopStaG-112
❑ 98TopStaGR-112
❑ 98TopStaS-112
❑ 98Ult-275
❑ 98UltGolM-275
❑ 98UltMas-275
❑ 98UltPlaM-275
❑ 98UppDec-114
❑ 98UppDecNP-NP20
❑ 98UppDecSF-69
❑ 98Zen-45
❑ 98ZenZ-G-45
❑ 98ZenZ-S-45
❑ 99199Fin-14
❑ 99DodPol-19
❑ 99FinGolRef-14
❑ 99FinRef-14
❑ 99FlaShoLeg1-131
❑ 99FlaShoLeg2-131
❑ 99FlaShoLeg3-131
❑ 99FlaShoLegM1-131
❑ 99FlaShoLegM2-131
❑ 99FlaShoLegM3-131
❑ 99FlaShoR1-131
❑ 99FlaShoR2-131
❑ 99FlaShoR3-131
❑ 99Fle-219
❑ 99FleBri-51
❑ 99FleBri2G-51
❑ 99FleBriBlu-51
❑ 99FleBriGol-51
❑ 99FleSta9-219
❑ 99FleWarT-219
❑ 99MetUni-222
❑ 99MetUniGM-222
❑ 99MetUniPMG-222
❑ 99Pac-226
❑ 99PacAur-95
❑ 99PacAurOD-95
❑ 99PacCroC-144
❑ 99PacCroCPB-144
❑ 99PacOme-123
❑ 99PacOmeC-123
❑ 99PacOmeG-123
❑ 99PacOmePB-123
❑ 99PacPar-120
❑ 99PacParC-120
❑ 99PacParG-120
❑ 99PacParHoloGold-120
❑ 99PacParHS-120
❑ 99PacParOD-120
❑ 99PacParPB-120
❑ 99PacParRed-120
❑ 99PacPlaB-226
❑ 99PacPri-76
❑ 99PacPriHB-76
❑ 99PacPriHG-76
❑ 99PacPriHM-76
❑ 99PacPriHP-76
❑ 99PacPriRed-76

❑ 99PacPriS-129
❑ 99PacPriS206-129
❑ 99PacPriS206R-129
❑ 99PacRed-226
❑ 99SkyMolM-85
❑ 99SkyMolMX-85
❑ 99SkyPre-90
❑ 99SkyPreR-90
❑ 99SkyThu-195
❑ 99SkyThuRant-195
❑ 99SkyThuRave-195
❑ 99SpoIll-164
❑ 99SPSig-122
❑ 99StaClu-112
❑ 99StaCluFDI-112
❑ 99StaCluOoaK-112
❑ 99StaCluPP-112
❑ 99ThuSkySupR-195
❑ 99Top-166
❑ 99TopChr-166
❑ 99TopChrR-166
❑ 99TopMVPP-166
❑ 99TopOpeD-92
❑ 99Ult-165
❑ 99UltGolM-165
❑ 99UltMas-165
❑ 99UltPlaM-165
❑ 99UppDec-400
❑ 99UppDecBD-42
❑ 99UppDecBDD-42
❑ 99UppDecBDQ-42
❑ 99UppDecBDT-42
❑ 99UppDecCLM-C48
❑ 99UppDecEL1-400
❑ 99UppDecEL2-400
❑ 99UppDecM-104
❑ 99UppDecMGS-104
❑ 99UppDecMHFS-104
❑ 99UppDecMP-104
❑ 99UppDecMSS-104
❑ 99Vic-200

Park, Ji Chol
❑ 96WesOahCHWB-39

Parke, Jim
❑ 77ChaPatT-11

Parker, Ace (Clarence McKay)
❑ 79DiaGre-327

Parker, Allan
❑ 95TenVolW-9
❑ 96LakElsSB-20

Parker, Arthur
❑ 27Zee-76
❑ 30Zee-36
❑ 31Zee-22
❑ 33Zee-38

Parker, Beau
❑ 97YakBeaG-23
❑ 98GreFalDG-23

Parker, Billy (William David)
❑ 72OPC-213
❑ 72Top-213
❑ 73OPC-354
❑ 73Top-354
❑ 75SyrChiTI-16

Parker, Billy Ray
❑ 76CedRapGT-18

Parker, Bob
❑ 85OscAstTI-21
❑ 86ColAstP-21

Parker, Brad
❑ 89AncBucTI-12
❑ 92ClaFS7-178
❑ 92MadMusC-17
❑ 92MadMusF-1245

Parker, Brandon
❑ 98WisTimRM-7

Parker, Carrol
❑ 86EriCarP-22
❑ 87SavCarP-14

Parker, Christian
❑ 96VerExpB-21
❑ 97SouAtlTPB-5
❑ 98arSenW1-16
❑ 98HarSenM-16

Parker, Clay
❑ 86WauTimP-18
❑ 88ColCliC-2
❑ 88ColCliP-7
❑ 88ColCliP-309
❑ 88Fle-649
❑ 88FleGlo-649
❑ 89ColCliC-4
❑ 89ColCliP-9
❑ 89ColCliP-751
❑ 89DonBasB-164
❑ 89DonRoo-52
❑ 89ScoRoo-94T
❑ 89TopTra-94T
❑ 89TopTraT-94T
❑ 89YanScoNW-30
❑ 90Don-363
❑ 90Fle-451
❑ 90FleCan-451
❑ 90LSUTigGM-11
❑ 90OPC-511
❑ 90PubIntS-543
❑ 90Sco-316
❑ 90Sco100RS-17
❑ 90ScoYouSI-8
❑ 90Top-511
❑ 90TopTif-511
❑ 90TopTVY-15
❑ 91Don-605
❑ 91Fle-346
❑ 91OPC-183
❑ 91TacTigP-2302
❑ 91Top-183
❑ 91TopDesS-183
❑ 91TopMic-183
❑ 91TopTif-183
❑ 92Bow-366
❑ 92CalCanS-67
❑ 92MarMot-25
❑ 92StaClu-631
❑ 92StaCluECN-631
❑ 92Ult-435
❑ 92YanWIZ8-141
❑ 93StaClu-45
❑ 93StaCluFDI-45
❑ 93StaCluMOP-45

Parker, Corey
❑ 92NiaFalRC-13
❑ 92NiaFalRF-3334
❑ 93FayGenC-19
❑ 93FayGenF-137
❑ 94FayGenC-19
❑ 94FayGenF-2157

Parker, Darrell
❑ 75WatRoyT-22
❑ 76WatRoyT-20
❑ 77JacSunT-17

Parker, Dave (David Gene)
❑ 74OPC-252
❑ 74Top-252
❑ 74TopSta-86
❑ 75OPC-29
❑ 75PitPirP-19
❑ 75SSPPuzB-20
❑ 75Top-29
❑ 75TopMin-29
❑ 76BlaDis-45
❑ 76BucDis-45
❑ 76CarDis-45
❑ 76CraDis-45
❑ 76DailsID-45
❑ 76Hos-133
❑ 76IsaDis-45
❑ 76Kel-15
❑ 76OPC-185
❑ 76OrbDis-45
❑ 76PirPos-16
❑ 76RedBarD-45
❑ 76SafDis-45
❑ 76SSP-572
❑ 76Top-185
❑ 76TowCluD-45
❑ 76VenLeaS-180
❑ 77BurCheD-187
❑ 77Kel-19
❑ 77OPC-242
❑ 77PirPosP-20
❑ 77RCColC-50
❑ 77Spo-4208
❑ 77Top-270
❑ 78Hos-135
❑ 78Kel-52
❑ 78OPC-1
❑ 78OPC-60
❑ 78RCColC-35
❑ 78Top-201
❑ 78Top-560
❑ 78WifBalD-58
❑ 79BasPat-66
❑ 79Hos-53
❑ 79Kel-21
❑ 79OPC-223
❑ 79Top-1
❑ 79Top-430
❑ 79TopCom-29
❑ 80BurKinPHR-19
❑ 80Kel-23
❑ 80OPC-163
❑ 80Top-310
❑ 80TopSup-17
❑ 81AllGamPI-158
❑ 81CokTeaS-117
❑ 81Don-136
❑ 81Dra-4
❑ 81Fle-360
❑ 81FleStiC-26
❑ 81Kel-13
❑ 81MSAMinD-25
❑ 81OPC-178
❑ 81PerAll-6
❑ 81PerCreC-13
❑ 81Squ-10
❑ 81Top-640
❑ 81TopScr-59
❑ 81TopSti-210
❑ 81TopSti-257
❑ 81TopSupN-10
❑ 82Don-12
❑ 82Don-95
❑ 82FBIDis-16
❑ 82Fle-489
❑ 82Fle-638
❑ 82FleSta-71
❑ 82FleSta-241
❑ 82K-M-34
❑ 82Kel-48
❑ 82OnDecD-25
❑ 82OPC-40
❑ 82OPC-41
❑ 82OPC-343
❑ 82Top-40
❑ 82Top-41
❑ 82Top-343
❑ 82TopSti-87
❑ 82TopSti-127
❑ 83AllGamPI-156
❑ 83Don-473
❑ 83Fle-315
❑ 83FleSta-146
❑ 83FleSti-72
❑ 83OPC-205
❑ 83PerCreC-11
❑ 83PerCreCG-11
❑ 83Top-205
❑ 83TopFol-3
❑ 83TopSti-280
❑ 84AllGamPI-64
❑ 84Don-288
❑ 84DonCha-57
❑ 84Fle-258
❑ 84FleUpd-89
❑ 84FunFooP-80
❑ 84Nes792-701
❑ 84Nes792-775
❑ 84OPC-31
❑ 84RedBor-39
❑ 84RedEnq-12
❑ 84Top-701
❑ 84Top-775
❑ 84TopSti-130
❑ 84TopTif-701
❑ 84TopTif-775
❑ 84TopTra-90T
❑ 84TopTraT-90T
❑ 85AllGamPI-155
❑ 85Don-62
❑ 85DonActA-35
❑ 85DonHig-13
❑ 85Dra-22
❑ 85Fle-544
❑ 85Lea-169
❑ 85OPC-175
❑ 85RedYea-11
❑ 85Top-175
❑ 85TopSti-47
❑ 85TopSup-42
❑ 85TopTif-175
❑ 86BasStaB-83
❑ 86Don-203
❑ 86DonAll-24
❑ 86Dra-4
❑ 86Fle-184
❑ 86Fle-640
❑ 86FleAll-6
❑ 86FleLeaL-30
❑ 86FleLimE-33
❑ 86FleMin-39
❑ 86FleStiC-84
❑ 86GenMilB-5F
❑ 86Lea-135
❑ 86OPC-287
❑ 86QuaGra-9
❑ 86RedTexG-39
❑ 86SevCoi-C4
❑ 86SevCoi-E4
❑ 86SevCoi-S4
❑ 86SevCoi-W4
❑ 86Spo-23
❑ 86Spo-58
❑ 86Spo-181
❑ 86Spo-183
❑ 86Top-595
❑ 86Top3-D-18
❑ 86TopGloS-13
❑ 86TopMinL-41
❑ 86TopSti-135
❑ 86TopSup-41
❑ 86TopTat-9
❑ 86TopTif-595
❑ 86Woo-27
❑ 87BoaandB-20
❑ 87ClaGam-33
❑ 87Don-388
❑ 87DonAll-34
❑ 87DonOpeD-198
❑ 87Dra-18
❑ 87Fle-208
❑ 87Fle-639
❑ 87FleAwaW-27
❑ 87FleGlo-208
❑ 87FleGlo-639
❑ 87FleMin-80
❑ 87FleSlu-29
❑ 87FleStiC-88
❑ 87FleWaxBC-C10
❑ 87GenMilB-6G
❑ 87KayB-23
❑ 87Lea-79
❑ 87OPC-352
❑ 87RalPur-7
❑ 87RedFolSB-90
❑ 87RedKah-39
❑ 87Spo-35
❑ 87Spo-117
❑ 87SpoTeaP-4
❑ 87StuPan-4
❑ 87Top-600
❑ 87Top-691
❑ 87TopCoi-38
❑ 87TopGloS-17
❑ 87TopMinL-6
❑ 87TopSti-145
❑ 87TopTif-600
❑ 87TopTif-691
❑ 88A'sMot-5
❑ 88Don-388
❑ 88DonBasB-190
❑ 88DonTeaBA-NEW
❑ 88Fle-243
❑ 88FleGlo-243
❑ 88FleMin-47
❑ 88FleUpd-55
❑ 88FleUpdG-55
❑ 88KayB-21
❑ 88OPC-315
❑ 88PanSti-277
❑ 88PanSti-278
❑ 88PanSti-284
❑ 88Sco-17
❑ 88ScoGlo-17
❑ 88ScoRoo-50T
❑ 88ScoRooG-50T
❑ 88Spo-101
❑ 88StaLinAs-12
❑ 88StaLinRe-15
❑ 88Top-315
❑ 88TopBig-242
❑ 88TopGloS-34
❑ 88TopMinL-48
❑ 88TopSti-136
❑ 88TopStiB-19
❑ 88TopTif-315
❑ 88TopTra-81T
❑ 88TopTraT-81T
❑ 88TopUKM-55
❑ 88TopUKMT-55
❑ 89A'sMot-4
❑ 89Bow-202
❑ 89BowTif-202
❑ 89Don-150
❑ 89DonBasB-336
❑ 89Fle-19
❑ 89FleGlo-19
❑ 89OPC-199
❑ 89PanSti-424
❑ 89Sco-108
❑ 89Spo-49
❑ 89Top-475
❑ 89TopAme2C-23
❑ 89TopBasT-116
❑ 89TopBatL-13
❑ 89TopBig-144
❑ 89TopSti-169
❑ 89TopTif-475
❑ 89UppDec-605
❑ 90Bow-398
❑ 90BowTif-398
❑ 90BreMilB-18
❑ 90BrePol-39
❑ 90ClaBlu-95
❑ 90ClaYel-T10
❑ 90Don-328
❑ 90DonBesA-51
❑ 90DonLeaS-33
❑ 90Fle-18
❑ 90FleCan-18
❑ 90FleUpd-106
❑ 90FleWorS-9
❑ 90FleWorS-10
❑ 90KayB-22
❑ 90Lea-190
❑ 90OPC-45
❑ 90OPCBoxB-J
❑ 90PubIntS-312
❑ 90Sco-135
❑ 90ScoRoo-12T
❑ 90Top-45
❑ 90TopAmeA-6
❑ 90TopBatL-13
❑ 90TopBig-227
❑ 90TopHilHM-21
❑ 90TopSti-179
❑ 90TopTif-45
❑ 90TopTra-86T
❑ 90TopTraT-86T
❑ 90TopWaxBC-J
❑ 90UppDec-192
❑ 90UppDec-766
❑ 90USPlaCA-12S
❑ 90WinDis-1
❑ 91AngSmo-4
❑ 91Bow-199
❑ 91Bow-375
❑ 91ClaGam-34
❑ 91DenHol-5
❑ 91Don-6
❑ 91Don-142
❑ 91Don-390
❑ 91DonSupD-6
❑ 91Fle-593
❑ 91FleUpd-10
❑ 91Lea-334
❑ 91OPC-235
❑ 91OPCBoxB-L
❑ 91OPCPre-94
❑ 91PanFreS-210
❑ 91PanSti-171
❑ 91Sco-484
❑ 91Sco100S-44
❑ 91StaClu-75
❑ 91StaPinB-35
❑ 91StuPre-3
❑ 91Top-235
❑ 91TopCraJI-11
❑ 91TopDesS-235
❑ 91TopMic-235
❑ 91TopTif-235
❑ 91TopTra-89T
❑ 91TopTraT-89T
❑ 91TopWaxBC-L
❑ 91UltUpd-10
❑ 91UppDec-48
❑ 91UppDec-274
❑ 91UppDec-733
❑ 91UppDecSS-SS14
❑ 91Woo-16
❑ 92UppDec-522
❑ 93ActPacA-165
❑ 94BreMilB-65
❑ 94CarLeaA-DJ25
❑ 95MCIAmb-13
❑ 99SpoIllGotG-39
❑ 99SpoIllGotGA-55
❑ 99SpoIllGotGC-34

Parker, Don
❑ 92AriWilP-13
❑ 92KinMetF-1543

Parker, Eric
❑ 97LowSpiB-22

Parker, Harry
❑ 66St.PetCTI-11
❑ 73LinPor-121
❑ 74OPC-106
❑ 74Top-106
❑ 75OPC-214
❑ 75SSP18-1
❑ 75Top-214
❑ 75TopMin-214
❑ 91MetWIZ-309

Parker, James
❑ 87ChaLooB-4
❑ 89GeoColC-22
❑ 90GeoColC-23

Parker, Jarrod
❑ 89PulBraP-1906
❑ 90ColMetGS-4
❑ 90ColMetPPI-2
❑ 90PitMetP-7

Parker, Joel
❑ 81BurBeeT-27

Parker, Mark
❑ 80WicAerT-4
❑ 82IowCubT-21

Parker, Michael
❑ 95PitMetTI-33

Parker, Mike
❑ 89IdaFalBP-2035

Parker, Olen
❑ 87ClePhiP-5

Parker, Richard
❑ 85BenPhiC-18
❑ 87ClePhiP-1
❑ 88ReaPhiP-878
❑ 89BenBucL-14
❑ 89EasLeaAP-25
❑ 89ReaPhiB-9
❑ 89ReaPhiP-660
❑ 89ReaPhiS-19
❑ 90ClaYel-T72
❑ 90FleUpd-63
❑ 90Lea-398
❑ 90PalSprACLC-210
❑ 90PalSprAP-2581
❑ 90PhoFirP-26
❑ 90ProAAAF-52
❑ 90ScoRoo-77T
❑ 90TopTra-87T
❑ 90TopTraT-87T
❑ 90UppDec-732
❑ 91Fle-269
❑ 91GiaPacGaE-26
❑ 91OPC-218
❑ 91PhoFirP-73
❑ 91Sco-58
❑ 91Sco100RS-11
❑ 91Top-218
❑ 91TopDeb90-121
❑ 91TopDesS-218
❑ 91TopMic-218
❑ 91TopTif-218
❑ 92Sco-601
❑ 92StaClu-769
❑ 92StaCluECN-769
❑ 92TucTorF-500
❑ 92TucTorS-616
❑ 93AstMot-13
❑ 93AstStaC-27
❑ 93TucTorF-3075
❑ 94NorTidF-2934
❑ 94Pac-272
❑ 95DodMot-27
❑ 97AlbDukGS-24
❑ 98NorTidP-18
❑ 98NorTidQ-18

Parker, Rob
❑ 87ColAstP-10

Parker, Roy
❑ 28Zee-162

Parker, S. R.
❑ 27Zee-33
❑ 27Zee-34

Parker, Salty (Francis James)
❑ 60Top-469
❑ 67Ast-23
❑ 71AstTeal-18
❑ 72AstTeal-19
❑ 73OPC-421
❑ 73Top-421A
❑ 73Top-421B
❑ 74OPC-276
❑ 74Top-276
❑ 76CedRapGT-19
❑ 87BelMarTI-28

Parker, Stacy
❑ 89ButCopKSP-1
❑ 91BenBucCB-21
❑ 91BenBucP-3706
❑ 91ClePhiC-23

❑ 91ClePhiP-1634
Parker, Steve
❑ 87PeoChiP-24
❑ 88PitCubP-1369
❑ 89WinSpiS-13
❑ 90CMC-80
❑ 90IowCubC-5
❑ 90IowCubP-316
❑ 90ProAAAF-623
❑ 90TopTVCu-56
Parker, Tim
❑ 90GenCubP-3049
❑ 90GenCubS-18
❑ 90ProAaA-174
❑ 91ChaKniLD-137
❑ 91ChaKniP-1686
❑ 91LinDriAA-137
❑ 92ChaKniS-163
❑ 92ClaFS7-62
❑ 92SkyAA F-75
Parker, Tre
❑ 98EveAquG-19
Parker, Wes (Maurice W.)
❑ 64Top-456
❑ 65DodJayP-10
❑ 65DodTeal-14
❑ 65Top-344
❑ 66DodVolT-7
❑ 66OPC-134
❑ 66Top-134
❑ 66TopVen-134
❑ 67CokCapD-13
❑ 67CokCapDA-13
❑ 67DexPre-161
❑ 67Top-218
❑ 68Top-533
❑ 69MilBra-213
❑ 69MLBOffS-151
❑ 69Top-493A
❑ 69Top-493B
❑ 70DayDaiNM-127
❑ 70MLBOffS-55
❑ 70OPC-5
❑ 70Top-5
❑ 71DodTic-13
❑ 71MLBOffS-111
❑ 71OPC-430
❑ 71Top-430
❑ 71TopCoi-121
❑ 71TopGreM-30
❑ 71TopSup-14
❑ 71TopTat-66
❑ 72Kel-17
❑ 72MilBra-265
❑ 72OPC-265
❑ 72Top-265
❑ 73OPC-151
❑ 73Top-151
❑ 81TCM60I-365
❑ 84OCoandSI-189
❑ 88DodSmo-10
❑ 90DodTar-605
Parkins, Rob
❑ 86WinHavRSP-19
❑ 93CalCanF-1164
❑ 94SanBerSC-14
❑ 94SanBerSF-2755
Parkins, Roy
❑ 12HomRunKE-27
❑ 12PCLPin-17
❑ 12Zee-42
❑ 13Zee-43
❑ 14Zee-117
Parkinson, Eric
❑ 89PriPirS-14
❑ 90AugPirP-2460
❑ 90CMC-726
❑ 91SalBucC-17
❑ 91SalBucP-947
❑ 92SalBucC-4
❑ 92SalBucF-62
❑ 93CarMudF-2052
❑ 93CarMudTI-8
Parkinson, Frank J.
❑ 22E120-203
❑ 22W572-74
❑ 23WilChoV-118
Parks, Art
❑ 90DodTar-1048
Parks, Danny
❑ 81PawRedST-6
Parks, Derek
❑ 87KenTwiP-19
❑ 88BasAmeAAB-12
❑ 88OrlTwiB-1
❑ 88SouLeaAJ-12
❑ 89OrlTwiB-19
❑ 89OrlTwiP-1350
❑ 90Bow-422
❑ 90BowTif-422
❑ 90ClaUpd-T40
❑ 90CMC-566
❑ 90PorBeaC-14
❑ 90PorBeaP-181
❑ 90ProAAAF-251
❑ 91Cla/Bes-159
❑ 91LinDriAA-492
❑ 91OrlSunRLD-492
❑ 91OrlSunRP-1852
❑ 92PorBeaF-2670
❑ 92PorBeaS-416
❑ 92SkyAAAF-190
❑ 93Don-237
❑ 93Pin-267
❑ 93PorBeaF-2386
❑ 93Sco-245
❑ 93StaClu-74
❑ 93StaCluFDI-74
❑ 93StaCluMOP-74
❑ 93TriAAAGF-47
❑ 94ColC-378
❑ 94ColChoGS-378
❑ 94ColChoSS-378
❑ 94Don-477
❑ 94Fle-216
❑ 94Pac-364
❑ 94ScoRoo-RT97
❑ 94ScoRooGR-RT97
❑ 94SpoRoo-79
❑ 94SpoRooAP-79
❑ 94Top-649
❑ 94TopGol-649
❑ 94TopSpa-649
❑ 94Ult-393
❑ 95Sco-375
❑ 95ScoGolR-375
❑ 95ScoPlaTS-375
❑ 95Top-151
Parks, Jack
❑ 55Top-23
❑ 55TopDouH-67
Parks, Jeff
❑ 85SpoIndC-19
Parmelee, Roy (LeRoy Earl)
❑ 28LaPre-28
❑ 33Gou-239
❑ 34BatR31-94
❑ 34DiaMatCSB-147
❑ 35DiaMatCS3T1-118
❑ 36DiaMatCS3T2-19
❑ 36R31PasP-19
❑ 36WorWidGV-20
❑ 91ConTSN-85
❑ 94ConTSN-1062
❑ 94ConTSNB-1062
Parmenter, Gary
❑ 86IowCubP-21
❑ 87IowCubTI-7
❑ 88PitCubP-1378
Parmenter, Ross
❑ 96OgdRapTI-9
Parnell, Mark
❑ 89AppFoxP-875
❑ 90BasCitRS-18
❑ 90StaFS7-44
❑ 91Cla/Bes-301
❑ 91LinDriAA-410
❑ 91MemChiLD-410
❑ 91MemChiP-648
❑ 92MemChiF-2416
❑ 92MemChiS-440
❑ 92SkyAA F-186
Parnell, Mel
❑ 47PM1StaP1-158
❑ 47RedSoxTI-17
❑ 48RedSoxTI-19
❑ 49RedSoxTI-17
❑ 50Bow-1
❑ 50RedSoxTI-18
❑ 51FisBakL-23
❑ 51R42SmaS-77
❑ 51TopRedB-10
❑ 52BerRos-49
❑ 52Bow-241
❑ 52DixLid-14
❑ 52DixPre-14
❑ 52StaCalL-71A
❑ 52StaCalS-85B
❑ 52Top-30
❑ 53BowC-66
❑ 53DixLid-14
❑ 53DixPre-14
❑ 53NorBreL-20
❑ 53RedMan-AL25
❑ 53RedSoxFNSMS-3
❑ 53RedSoxTI-23
❑ 53Top-19
❑ 54DixLid-12
❑ 54RedMan-AL8
❑ 54Top-40
❑ 55RobGouS-28
❑ 55RobGouW-28
❑ 55Top-140
❑ 55TopDouH-119
❑ 56TopHocF-A18
❑ 57Top-313
❑ 63MilSau-5
❑ 63SeaPop-7
❑ 79DiaGre-242
❑ 79TCM50-58
❑ 81RedSoxBG2S-43
❑ 82GSGalAG-21
❑ 83TopRep5-30
❑ 83YanYealT-6
❑ 85TCMPla1-25
❑ 90PacLeg-98
❑ 91SweBasG-118
❑ 91TopArc1-19
❑ 92ActPacA-21
❑ 92BazQua5A-14
❑ 93TedWil-4
❑ 93UppDecAH-104
❑ 94TopArc1-40
❑ 94TopArc1G-40
Paronto, Chad
❑ 96BluOriB-22
❑ 97DelSho-26
❑ 98CarLeaTPQ-32
❑ 98FreKeyM-14
Parotte, Frisco
❑ 95GreBatTI-19
❑ 96GreBatB-18
Parque, Jim
❑ 97UCLBruTI-16
❑ 98Bow-351
❑ 98BowBes-187
❑ 98BowBesAR-187
❑ 98BowBesR-187
❑ 98BowChr-351
❑ 98BowChrGA-351
❑ 98BowChrGAR-351
❑ 98BowChrI-351
❑ 98BowChrIR-351
❑ 98BowChrR-351
❑ 98BowGolA-351
❑ 98BowInt-351
❑ 98DonSig-133
❑ 98DonSigP-133
❑ 98FleUpd-U24
❑ 98LeaRS-307
❑ 98LeaRSLHolo-307
❑ 98LeaRSLong-307
❑ 98LeaRTrue-307
❑ 98UppDecR-107
❑ 98UppDecRNF-NF6
❑ 99DumSet-JP
❑ 99Fle-526
❑ 99FleSta9-526
❑ 99FleWarT-526
❑ 99SkyPreA-43
❑ 99SkyPreABlue-43
❑ 99SP SigAuto-JP
❑ 99SPSig-164
❑ 99Top-413
❑ 99TopChr-413
❑ 99TopChrR-413
❑ 99TopMVPP-413
❑ 99UppDec-14
❑ 99UppDecBD-96
❑ 99UppDecBDD-96
❑ 99UppDecBDQ-96
❑ 99UppDecBDT-96
❑ 99UppDecEL1-14
❑ 99UppDecEL2-14
❑ 99UppDecEM-MC7
❑ 99UppDecEMFXG-MC7
❑ 99UppDecM-50
❑ 99UppDecMGS-50
❑ 99UppDecMHFS-50
❑ 99UppDecMP-50
❑ 99UppDecMP-JP
❑ 99UppDecMSS-50
❑ 99Vic-93
Parra, Franklin
❑ 91ButCopKSP-20
❑ 92ButCopKSP-13
❑ 92GasRanC-17
❑ 93ChaRaiF-1922
❑ 94ChaRanF-2505
❑ 95TulDriTI-18
Parra, Jose
❑ 90KisDodD-20
❑ 91GreFalDSP-6
❑ 92BakDodCLC-19
❑ 93LimRocDWB-56
❑ 93SanAntMF-3002
❑ 94AlbDukF-841
❑ 94Bow-42
❑ 95Sum-170
❑ 95SumNthD-170
❑ 95TopTra-58T
❑ 96ChaRivTI-9626
❑ 96Don-380
❑ 96DonPreP-380
❑ 96Fle-171
❑ 96FleTif-171
❑ 97SalLakB-20
Parra, Julio
❑ 95VerBeaDTI-19
Parra, Luis
❑ 92GulCoaYF-3790
Parrett, Jeff
❑ 86ExpPos-11
❑ 86ExpProPa-25
❑ 86FleUpd-88
❑ 87ExpPos-19
❑ 87IndIndTI-17
❑ 88Don-406
❑ 88ExpPos-25
❑ 88FleUpd-102
❑ 88FleUpdG-102
❑ 88OPC-144
❑ 88Top-588
❑ 88TopTif-588
❑ 89Bow-390
❑ 89BowTif-390
❑ 89Don-334
❑ 89DonBasB-296
❑ 89DonTra-55
❑ 89Fle-389
❑ 89FleGlo-389
❑ 89FleUpd-112
❑ 89OPC-176
❑ 89PhiTas-27
❑ 89Sco-377
❑ 89ScoRoo-33T
❑ 89ScoYouSI-18
❑ 89Top-176
❑ 89TopSti-73
❑ 89TopTif-176
❑ 89TopTra-95T
❑ 89TopTraT-95T
❑ 89UppDec-398
❑ 89UppDec-741
❑ 90Bow-149
❑ 90BowTif-149
❑ 90Don-369
❑ 90Fle-570
❑ 90FleCan-570
❑ 90Lea-210
❑ 90OPC-439
❑ 90PanSti-312
❑ 90PhiTas-25
❑ 90PubIntS-248
❑ 90Top-439
❑ 90TopSti-119
❑ 90TopTif-439
❑ 90UppDec-92
❑ 91BraDubP-22
❑ 91BraSubS-29
❑ 91Don-660
❑ 91Fle-699
❑ 91OPC-56
❑ 91RicBraBC-32
❑ 91Sco-565
❑ 91StaClu-544
❑ 91Top-56
❑ 91TopDesS-56
❑ 91TopMic-56
❑ 91TopTif-56
❑ 91UppDec-417
❑ 92AthMot-16
❑ 92Lea-520
❑ 92LeaBlaG-520
❑ 92StaClu-834
❑ 93Don-241
❑ 93Fle-297
❑ 93FleFinE-39
❑ 93PacSpa-434
❑ 93Pin-431
❑ 93RocStaC-9
❑ 93RocUSPC-7S
❑ 93RocUSPC-12D
❑ 93Sco-180
❑ 93Sel-396
❑ 93StaClu-99
❑ 93StaClu-414
❑ 93StaCluFDI-99
❑ 93StaCluFDI-414
❑ 93StaCluMOP-99
❑ 93StaCluMOP-414
❑ 93Top-209
❑ 93TopGol-209
❑ 93TopInaM-209
❑ 93TopInaR-209
❑ 93TopMic-209
❑ 93TopTra-46T
❑ 93Ult-261
❑ 93Ult-355
❑ 93UppDec-311
❑ 93UppDec-529
❑ 93UppDecGold-311
❑ 93UppDecGold-529
❑ 94Fle-449
❑ 96Don-542
❑ 96DonPreP-542
❑ 96FleUpd-U193
❑ 96FleUpdTC-U193
Parrill, Marty
❑ 78RocRedWT-13
Parris, Clyde
❑ 58MonRoyF-16
❑ 59O'KAleMR-15
Parris, Steve
❑ 88CapCodPPaLP-43
❑ 89BatCliP-1923
❑ 90BatCliP-3065
❑ 91ClePhiC-7
❑ 91ClePhiP-1618
❑ 92ReaPhiF-572
❑ 92ReaPhiS-538
❑ 93ScrRedBTI-20
❑ 95CarMudF-152
❑ 96ColCho-267
❑ 96ColChoGS-267
❑ 96ColChoSS-267
❑ 96Don-59
❑ 96DonPreP-59
❑ 96Fle-531
❑ 96FleTif-531
❑ 96LeaSigEA-151
❑ 96StaClu-76
❑ 96StaCluMOP-76
❑ 97ChaLoo-20
❑ 98IndIndQ-14
❑ 99Fle-383
❑ 99FleSta9-383
❑ 99FleWarT-383
Parrish, John
❑ 98FreKeyM-13
Parrish, Lance M.
❑ 77EvaTriT-22
❑ 78TigTeal-21
❑ 78Top-708
❑ 79Top-469
❑ 80Kel-54
❑ 80OPC-110
❑ 80Top-196
❑ 81AllGamPI-42
❑ 81CokTeaS-55
❑ 81Don-366
❑ 81Fle-467
❑ 81OPC-8
❑ 81TigDetN-90
❑ 81Top-392
❑ 81TopScr-14
❑ 81TopSti-73
❑ 82Don-281
❑ 82Fle-276
❑ 82FleSta-152
❑ 82OPC-214
❑ 82Top-535
❑ 82TopSti-188
❑ 83AllGamPI-42
❑ 83Don-407
❑ 83DonActA-50
❑ 83Fle-337
❑ 83FleSta-147
❑ 83FleSti-255
❑ 83Kel-40
❑ 83OPC-285
❑ 83PerCreC-30
❑ 83PerCreCG-30
❑ 83TigPos-22
❑ 83Top-4
❑ 83Top-285
❑ 83TopGloS-27
❑ 83TopSti-63
❑ 83TopSti-193
❑ 83TopSti-194
❑ 84AllGamPI-131
❑ 84Don-15
❑ 84Don-15A
❑ 84Don-49
❑ 84DonActAS-34
❑ 84Fle-88
❑ 84Fle-637
❑ 84FunFooP-2
❑ 84Nes792-640
❑ 84NesDreT-8
❑ 84OPC-158
❑ 84TigFarJ-11
❑ 84TigTeal-26
❑ 84TigWavP-28
❑ 84Top-640
❑ 84TopGloS-2
❑ 84TopRubD-14
❑ 84TopSti-265
❑ 84TopTif-640
❑ 85AllGamPI-42
❑ 85Don-49
❑ 85DonActA-53
❑ 85Dra-23
❑ 85Fle-19
❑ 85FleStaS-31
❑ 85Lea-41
❑ 85OPC-160
❑ 85SevCoi-C13
❑ 85SevCoi-D14
❑ 85TigCaiD-15
❑ 85TigWen-17
❑ 85Top-160
❑ 85Top-708
❑ 85TopGloA-20
❑ 85TopMin-160
❑ 85TopRubD-12
❑ 85TopSti-189
❑ 85TopSti-259
❑ 85TopSup-55
❑ 85TopTif-160
❑ 85TopTif-708
❑ 86Don-334
❑ 86Fle-234
❑ 86FleLeaL-31
❑ 86FleMin-49
❑ 86FleStiC-85
❑ 86GenMilB-1F
❑ 86Lea-201
❑ 86MSAJifPD-3
❑ 86OPC-147
❑ 86SevCoi-C12
❑ 86Spo-92
❑ 86SpoDecG-72
❑ 86TigCaiD-14
❑ 86Top-36
❑ 86Top-740
❑ 86TopGloS-8
❑ 86TopMinL-15
❑ 86TopSti-273
❑ 86TopTat-22
❑ 86TopTif-36
❑ 86TopTif-740
❑ 87BoaandB-19
❑ 87ClaGam-50
❑ 87Don-91
❑ 87DonAll-9
❑ 87DonOpeD-153
❑ 87DonP-9
❑ 87Fle-160
❑ 87FleAwaW-28
❑ 87FleGlo-160
❑ 87FleUpd-96
❑ 87FleUpdG-96
❑ 87KeyFooD-19
❑ 87Lea-107
❑ 87MSAIceTD-19
❑ 87MSAJifPD-13
❑ 87OPC-374
❑ 87OurOwnTD-19
❑ 87PhiTas-13
❑ 87RedFolSB-36
❑ 87Spo-101
❑ 87Spo-154
❑ 87Top-613
❑ 87Top-791
❑ 87TopGloA-20
❑ 87TopGloS-58
❑ 87TopSti-149
❑ 87TopSti-269
❑ 87TopTif-613
❑ 87TopTif-791
❑ 87TopTra-94T
❑ 87TopTraT-94T
❑ 87WeiMarD-19

❑ 88Don-359
❑ 88DonBasB-184
❑ 88Fle-310
❑ 88FleGlo-310
❑ 88KayB-22
❑ 88Lea-130
❑ 88OPC-95
❑ 88PanSti-355
❑ 88PhiTas-18
❑ 88RedFolSB-65
❑ 88Sco-131
❑ 88ScoGlo-131
❑ 88Spo-143
❑ 88StaLinPh-12
❑ 88Top-95
❑ 88Top-669
❑ 88TopBig-45
❑ 88TopSti-123
❑ 88TopTif-95
❑ 88TopTif-669
❑ 89Bow-45
❑ 89BowTif-45
❑ 89Don-278
❑ 89DonAll-55
❑ 89DonBasB-59
❑ 89Fle-578
❑ 89FleGlo-578
❑ 89FleUpd-15
❑ 89OPC-114
❑ 89Sco-95
❑ 89ScoRoo-36T
❑ 89Spo-59
❑ 89Top-470
❑ 89TopBig-250
❑ 89TopTif-470
❑ 89TopTra-96T
❑ 89TopTraT-96T
❑ 89UppDec-240
❑ 89UppDec-775
❑ 90AngSmo-13
❑ 90Bow-295
❑ 90BowTif-295
❑ 90Don-213
❑ 90DonBesA-59
❑ 90DonLeaS-41
❑ 90Fle-141
❑ 90FleCan-141
❑ 90Lea-195
❑ 90MLBBasB-94
❑ 90OPC-575
❑ 90PanSti-38
❑ 90PublntS-376
❑ 90RedFolSB-73
❑ 90Sco-35
❑ 90Top-575
❑ 90TopBig-323
❑ 90TopSti-170
❑ 90TopTif-575
❑ 90UppDec-674
❑ 90USPlaCA-2C
❑ 91AngSmo-5
❑ 91Bow-188
❑ 91Bow-374
❑ 91CadEllD-40
❑ 91Don-135
❑ 91Don-388
❑ 91Fle-321
❑ 91Lea-368
❑ 91MooSna-20
❑ 91OPC-210
❑ 91PanFreS-179
❑ 91PanSti-133
❑ 91Sco-37
❑ 91StaClu-166
❑ 91Stu-29
❑ 91Top-210
❑ 91TopDesS-210
❑ 91TopMic-210
❑ 91TopTif-210
❑ 91Ult-51
❑ 91UppDec-552
❑ 91UppDecSS-SS11
❑ 92Don-166
❑ 92Fle-66
❑ 92Lea-269
❑ 92LeaBlaG-269
❑ 92OPC-360
❑ 92PanSti-4
❑ 92Pin-105
❑ 92Sco-298
❑ 92StaClu-94
❑ 92Stu-149
❑ 92Top-360
❑ 92TopGol-360
❑ 92TopGolW-360
❑ 92TopMic-360
❑ 92TriPla-169
❑ 92TriPla-234
❑ 92Ult-28
❑ 92UppDec-431
❑ 93AlbDukF-1464
❑ 93DodPol-19
❑ 93Don-85
❑ 93Fle-679
❑ 93Sco-587
❑ 93Sel-388
❑ 93StaClu-252
❑ 93StaCluFDI-252
❑ 93StaCluMOP-252
❑ 93Top-609
❑ 93TopGol-609
❑ 93ToplnaM-609
❑ 93ToplnaR-609
❑ 93TopMic-609
❑ 93UppDec-117
❑ 93UppDecGold-117
❑ 95ColCho-377
❑ 95ColChoGS-377
❑ 95ColChoSS-377
❑ 95DonTopotO-177
❑ 95Fle-487
❑ 95Sco-550
❑ 95ScoGolR-550
❑ 95ScoPlaTS-550
❑ 95StaClu-604
❑ 95StaCluMOP-604
❑ 95StaCluSTWS-604
❑ 96ColCho-349
❑ 96ColChoGS-349
❑ 96ColChoSS-349
❑ 96UppDec-104
❑ 97SanAntMB-28
❑ 97TexAllM-33
❑ 98SanAntMG-20
❑ 98SanAntMM-28

Parrish, Larry A.
❑ 75ExpPos-27
❑ 76ExpRed-24
❑ 76Hos-126
❑ 76MonExpP-23
❑ 76OPC-141
❑ 76SSP-326
❑ 76Top-141
❑ 77BurCheD-161
❑ 77ExpPos-24
❑ 77OPC-72
❑ 77Top-526
❑ 78ExpPos-10
❑ 78OPC-153
❑ 78Top-294
❑ 79OPC-357
❑ 79Top-677
❑ 80ExpPos-22
❑ 80OPC-182
❑ 80Top-345
❑ 80TopSup-53
❑ 81AllGamPI-124
❑ 81Don-89
❑ 81Fle-146
❑ 81FleStiC-69
❑ 81OPC-15
❑ 81OPCPos-4
❑ 81Top-15
❑ 81TopScr-89
❑ 81TopSti-183
❑ 82Don-466
❑ 82Fle-200
❑ 82FleSta-34
❑ 82OPC-353
❑ 82OPCPos-15
❑ 82Top-445
❑ 82TopSti-64
❑ 82TopTra-86T
❑ 83Don-467
❑ 83Fle-574
❑ 83FleSta-148
❑ 83FleSti-168
❑ 83OPC-2
❑ 83RanAffF-15
❑ 83Top-776
❑ 83TopSti-120
❑ 84AllGamPI-155
❑ 84Don-21
❑ 84Don-21A
❑ 84Don-422
❑ 84DonActAS-42
❑ 84Fle-424
❑ 84Nes792-169
❑ 84OPC-169
❑ 84RanJarP-15
❑ 84Top-169
❑ 84TopRubD-26
❑ 84TopSti-354
❑ 84TopTif-169
❑ 85AllGamPI-67
❑ 85Don-300
❑ 85DonActA-29
❑ 85Fle-564
❑ 85FleStaS-38
❑ 85Lea-96
❑ 85OPC-203
❑ 85RanPer-15
❑ 85Top-548
❑ 85TopRubD-26
❑ 85TopSti-346
❑ 85TopTif-548
❑ 86Don-178
❑ 86Fle-569
❑ 86FleStiC-86
❑ 86Lea-110
❑ 86OPC-238
❑ 86RanLit-4
❑ 86RanPer-15
❑ 86Top-238
❑ 86TopSti-240
❑ 86TopTat-19
❑ 86TopTif-238
❑ 87ClaGam-25
❑ 87Don-469
❑ 87DonHig-10
❑ 87DonOpeD-173
❑ 87Fle-134
❑ 87FleGamW-33
❑ 87FleGlo-134
❑ 87FleLeaL-34
❑ 87FleMin-81
❑ 87FleRecS-29
❑ 87FleStiC-89
❑ 87GenMilB-3H
❑ 87Lea-209
❑ 87RanMot-5
❑ 87RanSmo-18
❑ 87RedFolSB-104
❑ 87Spo-174
❑ 87SpoTeaP-1
❑ 87StuPan-26
❑ 87Top-629
❑ 87TopSti-234
❑ 87TopTif-629
❑ 88CheBoy-9
❑ 88Don-347
❑ 88DonAll-21
❑ 88DonBasB-334
❑ 88Fle-476
❑ 88FleGlo-476
❑ 88FleMin-57
❑ 88FleRecS-28
❑ 88FleStiC-68
❑ 88FleTeaL-25
❑ 88FleUpd-7
❑ 88FleUpdG-7
❑ 88KinDis-21
❑ 88Lea-119
❑ 88OPC-226
❑ 88PanSti-205
❑ 88RanMot-5
❑ 88RanSmo-14
❑ 88RedFolSB-66
❑ 88Sco-191
❑ 88ScoGlo-191
❑ 88ScoRoo-65T
❑ 88ScoRooG-65T
❑ 88Spo-49
❑ 88StaLinRa-12
❑ 88Top-490
❑ 88TopSti-243
❑ 88TopTif-490
❑ 88TopUKM-56
❑ 88TopUKMT-56
❑ 89Fle-94
❑ 89FleGlo-94
❑ 89Sco-495
❑ 89Top-354
❑ 89TopTif-354
❑ 89UppDec-36
❑ 91UppDecS-23
❑ 92Nab-17
❑ 92NiaFalRC-27
❑ 92NiaFalRF-3342
❑ 93ExpDonM-17
❑ 93NiaFalRF-3406
❑ 93RanKee-288
❑ 94RanAllP-15

Parrot, Pirate
❑ 88PirTeal-26
❑ 93FunPacM-2
❑ 93PirNatl-24
❑ 93TriPla-164
❑ 94MasMan-12
❑ 94PirQui-20

Parrot, Steve
❑ 83ElPasDT-16

Parrott, Mike
❑ 77MarPos-14
❑ 77RocRedWM-4
❑ 79OPC-300
❑ 79Top-576
❑ 80MarPos-17
❑ 80Top-443
❑ 81MarPol-10
❑ 81MarPos-24
❑ 81Top-187
❑ 82Don-226
❑ 82Top-358
❑ 83OmaRoyT-7
❑ 84OmaRoyT-11
❑ 85OklCit8T-12
❑ 86OklCit8P-17
❑ 88RocExpLC-27
❑ 89RocExpLC-22
❑ 91OriCro-354
❑ 91WesPalBEP-1246
❑ 92HarSenF-476
❑ 92HarSenS-300
❑ 95ChaKniTI-3
❑ 96ChaKniB-3
❑ 97LetBlaDB-2
❑ 98SouBenSHM-25

Parrott, Ralph
❑ 08BufBisFJO-13

Parrotte, Brian
❑ 89BilMusP-2050

Parry, Bob
❑ 86AncGlaPTI-28
❑ 88MadMusP-17
❑ 89ModA'sC-31
❑ 89ModA'sCLC-286
❑ 90ModA'sC-23
❑ 90ModA'sP-2228

Parsons, Bill
❑ 59DarFar-17
❑ 71BreTeal-10
❑ 72Kel-5
❑ 72OPC-281
❑ 72Top-281
❑ 73OPC-231
❑ 73Top-231
❑ 74OPC-574
❑ 74Top-574
❑ 75OPC-613
❑ 75Top-613
❑ 75TopMin-613
❑ 94BreMilB-66

Parsons, Bob
❑ 78SalPirT-11

Parsons, Casey (Casey R.)
❑ 78PhoGiaC-20
❑ 79PhoGiaVNB-17
❑ 80PhoGiaVNB-13
❑ 81SpolndT-26
❑ 82Fle-515
❑ 82SalLakCGT-15
❑ 85DomLeaS-91
❑ 85LouRedR-27
❑ 86LouRedTI-22
❑ 87BufBisP-9
❑ 88MemChiB-9
❑ 90MadMusB-25
❑ 90MadMusP-2283
❑ 90MidLeaASGS-26
❑ 91HunStaC-22
❑ 91HunStaLD-299
❑ 91HunStaP-1811
❑ 91HunStaTI-25
❑ 91LinDriAA-299
❑ 92HunStaF-3964
❑ 92HunStaS-324
❑ 93HunStaF-2097
❑ 94TacTigF-3190

Parsons, Jason
❑ 95BilMusTI-14

Parsons, Jeff
❑ 95PitMetTI-9
❑ 96PitMetB-17
❑ 97CapCitB-17

Parsons, Scott
❑ 87LasVegSP-5

Parsons, Thomas
❑ 62Top-326
❑ 65Top-308
❑ 91MetWIZ-310

Parsons, William Raymond
❑ 75TulOil7-10

Partee, Roy (Roy Robert)
❑ 43RedSoxTI-19
❑ 46RedSoxTI-17
❑ 47RedSoxTI-18
❑ 47TipTop-10
❑ 49Bow-149
❑ 49SomandK-10
❑ 60RawGloT-26
❑ 70Houof J-23
❑ 75RedSox1T-28
❑ 75TCMHouoJ-25
❑ 77TCMTheWY-21
❑ 79DiaGre-231
❑ 83TCMPla1943-20

Partenheimer, Brian
❑ 97LowSpiB-28
❑ 98MicBatCM-25

Partin, Billy
❑ 89SumBraP-1089

Partley, Calvin
❑ 74CedRapAT-9

Partlow, Roy
❑ 87NegLeaPD-18

Partrick, Dave
❑ 88BenBucL-11
❑ 89QuaCitAB-24
❑ 89QuaCitAGS-9
❑ 90BoiHawP-3327
❑ 90PalSprACLC-212
❑ 90PalSprAP-2591
❑ 91PalSprAP-2030
❑ 92BoiHawC-6
❑ 92BoiHawF-3621

Partridge, Glenn
❑ 77BurBeeT-21

Partridge, Jay
❑ 90DodTar-606

Pascarella, Andy
❑ 79NewCoPT-24

Pascarella, Josh
❑ 98AubDouTI-19

Paschal, Ben
❑ 33WorCig(-66
❑ 75Yan192T-18
❑ 79Yan192T-23
❑ 84Yan192G-8
❑ 91ConTSN-107

Paschall, Bill
❑ 77JacSunT-18
❑ 80OmaRoyP-20
❑ 80Top-667
❑ 81OmaRoyT-11

Pascual, Camilo
❑ 83IdaFalAT-10

Pascual, Camilo Alberto
❑ 47Exh-173
❑ 55Top-84
❑ 55TopDouH-103
❑ 56Top-98
❑ 57Top-211
❑ 58SeaTeal-20
❑ 58SenJayP-7
❑ 58Top-219
❑ 59SenTealW-12
❑ 59Top-291
❑ 59Top-316A
❑ 59Top-316B
❑ 59Top-413
❑ 60Baz-14
❑ 60Lea-4
❑ 60SenJayP-11
❑ 60Top-483
❑ 60Top-569
❑ 60TopTat-43
❑ 61NuSco-411
❑ 61Pos-99A
❑ 61Pos-99B
❑ 61Top-235
❑ 61TopDicG-12
❑ 61TopStal-183
❑ 61TwiCloD-20
❑ 61TwiJayP-10
❑ 61TwiPetM-23
❑ 61TwiUniMC-11
❑ 62Jel-91
❑ 62Pos-91
❑ 62PosCan-91
❑ 62SalPlaC-78
❑ 62ShiPlaC-78
❑ 62Top-59
❑ 62Top-230
❑ 62TopBuc-66
❑ 62TopStal-78
❑ 62TopVen-59
❑ 63BasMagM-64
❑ 63Baz-13
❑ 63ExhStaB-52
❑ 63Jel-9
❑ 63Pos-9
❑ 63SalMetC-36
❑ 63Top-8
❑ 63Top-10
❑ 63Top-220
❑ 63TopStil-31
❑ 63TwiJayP-8
❑ 63TwiVol-15
❑ 64Baz-13
❑ 64Top-2
❑ 64Top-4
❑ 64Top-6
❑ 64Top-500
❑ 64TopCoi-76
❑ 64TopCoi-137
❑ 64TopGia-32
❑ 64TopSta-92
❑ 64TopStaU-54
❑ 64TopTatl-60
❑ 64TopVen-2
❑ 64TopVen-4
❑ 64TopVen-6
❑ 64TwiJayP-9
❑ 65OPC-11
❑ 65OPC-255
❑ 65Top-11
❑ 65Top-255
❑ 65TopTral-23
❑ 65TwiPos-8
❑ 66Top-305
❑ 66TopVen-305
❑ 66TwiFaiG-11
❑ 67CokCapS-5
❑ 67OPC-71
❑ 67SenPos-18
❑ 67SenTeal-10
❑ 67Top-71
❑ 67TopVen-243
❑ 68SenTeal-10
❑ 68Top-395
❑ 69MilBra-214
❑ 69MLBOffS-107
❑ 69SenTeal-12
❑ 69SenTeal8-16
❑ 69Top-513
❑ 69TopDecl-33
❑ 69TopSta-240
❑ 69TopSup-31
❑ 69TopTeaP-23
❑ 69TraSta-27
❑ 70OPC-254
❑ 70Top-254
❑ 76VenLeaS-76
❑ 78TCM60I-32
❑ 78TwiFri-16
❑ 79TwiFriP-20
❑ 80TwiPos-22
❑ 80VenLeaS-2
❑ 90DodTar-607
❑ 94TopArc1-255
❑ 94TopArc1G-255

Pascual, Carlos
❑ 80VenLeaS-1

Pascual, Jorge
❑ 76VenLeaS-2
❑ 89SalDodTI-21
❑ 90MarPhiP-3203
❑ 90MiaMirIS-19
❑ 90MiaMirIS-20

Pasculli, Jason
❑ 97AubDouTI-4

Pashnick, Larry
❑ 81EvaTriT-5
❑ 83Don-233
❑ 83EvaTriT-8
❑ 83Fle-338
❑ 83TigPos-23
❑ 84Don-394
❑ 84MinTwiP-22
❑ 84TwiTeal-14

Pasillas, Andy
❑ 77AppFoxT-18
❑ 78KnoKnoST-17
❑ 79KnoKnoST-20
❑ 80GleFalWSBT-15
❑ 80GleFalWSCT-6
❑ 81GleFalWST-10

Paskert, Dode (George H.)
❑ 08RosComP-123
❑ 09ColChiE-226A

❑ 09ColChiE-226B
❑ 09RamT20-92
❑ 09T206-281
❑ 10CouT21-52
❑ 10CouT21-206
❑ 10CouT21-207
❑ 10CouT21-310
❑ 10DomDisP-96
❑ 10RedCroT-61
❑ 10RedCroT-147
❑ 10RedCroT-234
❑ 10SweCapPP-130A
❑ 10SweCapPP-130B
❑ 11HelSta-150
❑ 11PinT-5-414
❑ 11S74Sil-103
❑ 11SpoLifCW-282
❑ 11SpoLifM-238
❑ 11T205-135
❑ 11TurRedT-112
❑ 12ColRedB-226A
❑ 12ColRedB-226B
❑ 12ColTinT-226A
❑ 12ColTinT-226B
❑ 12HasTriFT-17
❑ 12T207-147
❑ 14PieStaT-86
❑ 15SpoNewM-135
❑ 16BF2FP-92
❑ 16FleBreD-73
❑ 16SpoNewM-136
❑ 17ColE13-130
❑ 17HolBreD-76
❑ 19W514-55
❑ 20NatCarE-73
❑ 23WilChoV-119
❑ 93ConTSN-922

Paskievitch, Tom
❑ 91EriSaiC-21
❑ 91EriSaiP-4067
❑ 92WatDiaC-13
❑ 92WatDiaF-2141
❑ 93RanCucQC-22
❑ 93RanCucQF-832
❑ 94KanCouCF-159
❑ 94KanCouCTI-21
❑ 94PorSeaDTI-25

Pasley, Kevin (Kevin P.)
❑ 74AlbDukCa-69
❑ 74AlbDukTI-12
❑ 75IntLeaASB-21
❑ 75PacCoaLAB-21
❑ 77Top-476
❑ 78Top-702
❑ 80SyrChiT-3
❑ 80SyrChiTI-16
❑ 81SyrChiT-8
❑ 82BirBarT-17
❑ 90DodTar-608

Pasqua, Dan
❑ 84NasSouTI-16
❑ 85ColCliP-17
❑ 85ColCliT-21
❑ 85Don-637
❑ 85FleUpd-86
❑ 85YanTCMP-38
❑ 86ColCliP-15
❑ 86ColCliP-17
❑ 86Don-417
❑ 86Fle-114
❑ 86KayB-22
❑ 86Lea-195
❑ 86Top-259
❑ 86TopGloS-20
❑ 86TopTif-259
❑ 86YanTCM-35
❑ 87ClaGam-13
❑ 87Don-474
❑ 87DonOpeD-244
❑ 87Fle-108
❑ 87FleGlo-108
❑ 87FleMin-79
❑ 87OPC-74
❑ 87Spo-143
❑ 87SpoTeaP-7
❑ 87Top-74
❑ 87TopSti-297
❑ 87TopTif-74
❑ 88Don-463
❑ 88DonBasB-137
❑ 88Fle-217
❑ 88FleGlo-217
❑ 88FleUpd-18
❑ 88FleUpdG-18
❑ 88OPC-207
❑ 88PanSti-159
❑ 88Sco-196
❑ 88ScoGlo-196
❑ 88ScoRoo-56T
❑ 88ScoRooG-56T
❑ 88StaLinWS-14
❑ 88Top-691
❑ 88TopBig-164
❑ 88TopTif-691
❑ 88TopTra-82T
❑ 88TopTraT-82T
❑ 88WhiSoxC-19
❑ 89Bow-67
❑ 89BowTif-67
❑ 89Don-294
❑ 89DonBasB-123
❑ 89Fle-507
❑ 89FleGlo-507
❑ 89OPC-31
❑ 89PanSti-313
❑ 89Sco-338
❑ 89Top-558
❑ 89TopBig-44
❑ 89TopSti-301
❑ 89TopTif-558
❑ 89TVSpoM-116
❑ 89UppDec-204
❑ 89WhiSoxC-19
❑ 90Bow-313
❑ 90BowTif-313
❑ 90Don-176
❑ 90Fle-544
❑ 90FleCan-544
❑ 90Lea-274
❑ 90OPC-446
❑ 90PubIntS-398
❑ 90Sco-306
❑ 90Top-446
❑ 90TopBig-144
❑ 90TopSti-306
❑ 90TopSti-309
❑ 90TopTif-446
❑ 90UppDec-286
❑ 90WhiSoxC-19
❑ 91Bow-361
❑ 91Don-103
❑ 91Fle-131
❑ 91Lea-428
❑ 91OPC-364
❑ 91Sco-85
❑ 91StaClu-214
❑ 91Top-364
❑ 91TopDesS-364
❑ 91TopMic-364
❑ 91TopTif-364
❑ 91Ult-79
❑ 91UppDec-605
❑ 91WhiSoxK-44
❑ 92Don-142
❑ 92Fle-93
❑ 92Lea-369
❑ 92LeaBlaG-369
❑ 92OPC-107
❑ 92Pin-227
❑ 92Sco-237
❑ 92StaClu-794
❑ 92StaCluNC-794
❑ 92Top-107
❑ 92TopGol-107
❑ 92TopGolW-107
❑ 92TopMic-107
❑ 92Ult-339
❑ 92UppDec-281
❑ 92WhiSoxK-44
❑ 92YanWIZ8-142
❑ 93Don-491
❑ 93Fle-587
❑ 93Lea-20
❑ 93PacSpa-394
❑ 93Pin-354
❑ 93Sco-210
❑ 93StaClu-94
❑ 93StaCluFDI-94
❑ 93StaCluMOP-94
❑ 93Top-204
❑ 93TopGol-204
❑ 93TopInaM-204
❑ 93TopInaR-204
❑ 93TopMic-204
❑ 93UppDec-649
❑ 93UppDecGold-649
❑ 93WhiSoxK-22
❑ 93WhiSoxSC-11
❑ 94ColC-617
❑ 94ColChoGS-617
❑ 94ColChoSS-617
❑ 94Fle-91
❑ 94Pac-139
❑ 94StaClu-375
❑ 94StaCluFDI-375
❑ 94StaCluGR-375
❑ 94StaCluMOP-375
❑ 94StaCluT-149
❑ 94StaCluTFDI-149
❑ 94TopGol-792
❑ 94WhiSoxK-24
❑ 95Sco-188
❑ 95ScoGolR-188
❑ 95ScoPlaTS-188

Pasquale, Jeff
❑ 91HamRedC-8
❑ 91HamRedP-4037

Pasquali, Jeff
❑ 83EriCarT-13

Pasqualicchio, Mike
❑ 95HelBreTI-31
❑ 96StoPorB-4
❑ 98El PasDG-22

Passalacqua, Ricky
❑ 76WatRoyT-21

Passeau, Claude W.
❑ 39CubTeal-19
❑ 39ExhSal-51
❑ 41CubTeal-19
❑ 42CubTeal-18
❑ 43CubTeal-19
❑ 76ChiGre-15
❑ 93ConTSN-720
❑ 95ConTSN-1407
❑ 95ConTSN-1418

Passero, Joe
❑ 45CenFlo-20

Passini, Brian
❑ 96HelBreTI-19
❑ 97BelSnaB-22
❑ 98BesAutSS-40
❑ 98StoPorG-23

Passmore, Jay
❑ 76BurBeeT-25
❑ 77BurBeeT-22

Pastore, Frank
❑ 78IndIndTI-23
❑ 80RedEnq-35
❑ 80Top-677
❑ 81Fle-204
❑ 81OPC-1
❑ 81Top-499
❑ 82Don-122
❑ 82Fle-80
❑ 82FleSta-13
❑ 82RedCok-17
❑ 82Top-128
❑ 83Don-62
❑ 83Fle-599
❑ 83OPC-119
❑ 83RedYea-35
❑ 83Top-658
❑ 84Don-164
❑ 84Fle-477
❑ 84Nes792-87
❑ 84OPC-87
❑ 84RedEnq-23
❑ 84Top-87
❑ 84TopTif-87
❑ 85Don-550
❑ 85Fle-545
❑ 85OPC-292
❑ 85Top-727
❑ 85TopTif-727
❑ 86Fle-185
❑ 86Top-314
❑ 86TopTif-314
❑ 86TopTra-85T
❑ 86TopTraT-85T
❑ 87OklCit8P-4
❑ 87Top-576
❑ 87TopTif-576
❑ 89PAORelT-4

Pastorius, James
❑ 03WilCarE-25
❑ 09AmeCarE90-1-87
❑ 09T206-282
❑ 10StaCarE-23
❑ 10W555-54
❑ 11SpoLifCW-283
❑ 72ClaCar-87
❑ 90DodTar-1047

Pastornicky, Cliff
❑ 81ChaRoyT-16
❑ 82ChaRoyT-21
❑ 83OmaRoyT-17
❑ 84OmaRoyT-21
❑ 94RocRoyC-30
❑ 94RocRoyF-583

Pastors, Greg
❑ 82BufBisT-5
❑ 83LynPirT-16

Pastrovich, Steve
❑ 80AppFoxT-13
❑ 80GleFalWSBT-1
❑ 80GleFalWSCT-16
❑ 81AppFoxT-8
❑ 82AppFoxFr-11
❑ 83GleFalWST-18

Paszek, John
❑ 52LavPro-31

Patchett, Hal
❑ 45CenFlo-21

Patchin, Steve
❑ 75WatDodT-15
❑ 76OmaRoyTT-19
❑ 76VenLeaS-130
❑ 80EvaTriT-22

Pate, Bobby (Robert Wayne)
❑ 81Don-545
❑ 81OPC-136
❑ 81Top-479
❑ 83TucTorT-21
❑ 87BurExpP-1089

Patek, Freddie Joe
❑ 69PirJacitB-9
❑ 69PirTeal-19
❑ 69Top-219
❑ 70OPC-94
❑ 70PirTeal-15
❑ 70Top-94
❑ 71MLBOffS-425
❑ 71OPC-626
❑ 71oySigST-20
❑ 71Top-626
❑ 72MilBra-266
❑ 72oyTeal-18
❑ 72Top-531
❑ 73LinPor-89
❑ 73OPC-334
❑ 73Top-334
❑ 74GreHeroBP-5
❑ 74OPC-88
❑ 74RoyPos-22
❑ 74Top-88
❑ 74TopSta-186
❑ 75Hos-32
❑ 75HosTwi-32
❑ 75OPC-48
❑ 75RoyPos-24
❑ 75Top-48
❑ 75TopMin-48
❑ 76KanCitRP-23
❑ 76OPC-167
❑ 76RoyAaP-11
❑ 76SSP-170
❑ 76Top-167
❑ 77BurCheD-67
❑ 77Hos-109
❑ 77Kel-36
❑ 77OPC-244
❑ 77RCColC-51
❑ 77Spo-5409
❑ 77Top-422
❑ 78Hos-48
❑ 78OPC-4
❑ 78OPC-91
❑ 78RCColC-63
❑ 78Roy-17
❑ 78SSP270-234
❑ 78Top-204
❑ 78Top-274
❑ 79BasPat-67
❑ 79Hos-46
❑ 79Kel-36
❑ 79OPC-273
❑ 79Top-525
❑ 80OPC-356
❑ 80Top-705
❑ 81Don-170
❑ 81Fle-283
❑ 81LonBeaPT-21
❑ 81Top-311
❑ 82Don-241
❑ 82Fle-471
❑ 82Top-602
❑ 86RoyGreT-3
❑ 92UppDecS-20
❑ 93RoySta2-9
❑ 94StoPorC-29
❑ 94StoPorF-1710

Patel, Manish
❑ 93BelMarCB-21
❑ 93BelMarF-3220
❑ 94AppFoxC-15
❑ 94AppFoxFI-1062
❑ 96PorCitRB-22
❑ 97St.PetDR-23
❑ 97St.PetDRUB-24

Patellis, Anthony
❑ 96BilMusTI-25

Patenaude, Alain
❑ 85MiaHur-11

Paterson, Jeff
❑ 92CalLeaACL-27

Paterson, Joe
❑ 97YakBeaG-24
❑ 98YakBeaG-25

Paterson, Pat
❑ 86NegLeaF-106

Patino, Benny
❑ 85CloHSS-31

Patino, Leonardo
❑ 96BoiHawB-22
❑ 97LakTigB-25

Patino, Victor
❑ 76VenLeaS-63

Patkin, Max
❑ 76OmaRoyTT-20
❑ 89BulDurOS-4
❑ 95ActPacF-80
❑ 95ActPacF-81
❑ 95ActPacF-82

Paton, Hazen
❑ 21Zee-58

Patornicky, Cliff
❑ 86WatIndP-19

Patrick, Bronswell
❑ 89MadMusS-18
❑ 90CMC-666
❑ 90MadMusB-22
❑ 90ModA'sC-24
❑ 90ModA'sCLC-155
❑ 90ModA'sP-2211
❑ 91ModA'sC-11
❑ 91ModA'sP-3085
❑ 92HunStaF-3948
❑ 92HunStaS-317
❑ 93TacTigF-3027
❑ 94HunStaF-1327
❑ 94TacTigF-3172
❑ 95TucTotTI-19
❑ 96TusTorB-19
❑ 98LouRedQ-1

Patrick, Dan
❑ 96SelEnF-16

Patrick, Hisel
❑ 59DarFar-18

Patrick, James
❑ 49W725AngTI-24
❑ 85CloHSS-32

Patrick, Lynn
❑ 40WheM4-1A
❑ 40WheM4-1B

Patrick, Otis
❑ 87BelMarL-27
❑ 87BelMarTI-17

Patrick, Ron
❑ 77AshTouT-16

Patrick, Tim
❑ 90VerBeaDS-21
❑ 90YakBeaTI-14
❑ 91VerBeaDC-10
❑ 91VerBeaDP-771

Patrizi, Mike
❑ 91KinMetC-4
❑ 91KinMetP-3816
❑ 92ColMetC-4
❑ 92ColMetF-300
❑ 92ColMetPI-23
❑ 93CapCitBC-16
❑ 93CapCitBF-463

Pattee, Harry (Harry Ernest)
❑ 09T206-283

Patten, Bill
❑ 75AndRanT-39

Patten, Case
❑ 04FanCraAL-40
❑ 08RosComP-83

Patten, Chris
❑ 97HelBreB-24
❑ 98HelBreM-26

Patten, Eric
❑ 90HelBreSP-18

Patterson, Bob
❑ 83BeaGolGT-7
❑ 84LasVegSC-221
❑ 85LasVegSC-117
❑ 86HawIsIP-19
❑ 87DonOpeD-166
❑ 87SpoTeaP-18
❑ 88BufBisC-7
❑ 88BufBisP-1467
❑ 88Fle-337
❑ 88FleGlo-337
❑ 88Top-522
❑ 88TopTif-522
❑ 89BlaYNPRWLU-30
❑ 89BufBisP-1684
❑ 90Bow-168
❑ 90BowTif-168
❑ 90FleUpd-49
❑ 90TopTra-88T
❑ 90TopTraT-88T
❑ 91Don-345
❑ 91Fle-45
❑ 91OPC-479
❑ 91Sco-636
❑ 91StaClu-594
❑ 91Top-479
❑ 91TopDesS-479
❑ 91TopMic-479
❑ 91TopTif-479
❑ 92Don-590
❑ 92Fle-562
❑ 92OPC-263
❑ 92PirNatI-18
❑ 92Sco-548
❑ 92StaClu-876
❑ 92StaCluECN-876
❑ 92Top-263
❑ 92TopGol-263
❑ 92TopGolW-263
❑ 92TopMic-263
❑ 92Ult-558
❑ 93Don-174
❑ 93Fle-118
❑ 93RanKee-421
❑ 93SelRoo-120T
❑ 93Top-299
❑ 93TopGol-299
❑ 93TopInaM-299
❑ 93TopInaR-299
❑ 93TopMic-299
❑ 93UppDec-412
❑ 93UppDecGold-412
❑ 94AngLAT-23
❑ 94AngMot-15
❑ 94Don-218
❑ 94Pac-624
❑ 94Sco-292
❑ 94ScoGolR-292
❑ 95AngMot-15
❑ 95Fle-232
❑ 96Fle-54
❑ 96FleTif-54
❑ 96LeaSigEA-152
❑ 98PacOnl-150
❑ 98PacOnlR-150
❑ 98PacOnlWC-150

Patterson, Casey
❑ 95PitMetTI-30
❑ 96PitMetB-18

Patterson, Corey
❑ 99199Fin-285
❑ 99BasAmeTP-73
❑ 99BasAmeTPG-73
❑ 99Bow-352
❑ 99Bow200RF-ROY8
❑ 99BowBes-159
❑ 99BowBesAR-159
❑ 99BowBesMI-M4
❑ 99BowBesMIAR-M4
❑ 99BowBesMIR-M4
❑ 99BowBesR-159
❑ 99BowGol-352
❑ 99BowInt-352
❑ 99FinGolRef-285
❑ 99FinRef-285
❑ 99TeaBesR-65
❑ 99TeaBesRFS-7
❑ 99TeaBesRG-65
❑ 99TeaBesRS-65

Patterson, Danny
❑ 91GulCoaRSP-11
❑ 92GasRanC-24
❑ 92GasRanF-2253
❑ 93ChaRanC-18
❑ 93ChaRanF-1939
❑ 94TulDriTI-18
❑ 95TulDriTI-19
❑ 96OklCit8B-16
❑ 97Bow-213

❑ 97BowInt-213
❑ 97Fle-504
❑ 97FleTif-504
❑ 97NewPin-174
❑ 97NewPinAP-174
❑ 97NewPinMC-174
❑ 97NewPinPP-174
❑ 97PinCer-110
❑ 97PinCerMBla-110
❑ 97PinCerMBlu-110
❑ 97PinCerMG-110
❑ 97PinCerMR-110
❑ 97PinCerR-110
❑ 97PinTotCPB-110
❑ 97PinTotCPG-110
❑ 97PinTotCPR-110
❑ 97RanDr P-24
❑ 97RanMot-27
❑ 97Sco-320
❑ 97ScoPreS-320
❑ 97ScoShoS-320
❑ 97Sel-107
❑ 97SelArtP-107
❑ 97SelCom-107
❑ 97SelRegG-107
❑ 98PacInvGems-105
❑ 98PacOnl-741
❑ 98PacOnlR-741
❑ 98PacOnlWC-741
❑ 98Pin-120
❑ 98PinPreP-120
❑ 98PinSna-TR3
❑ 98Top-48
❑ 98TopChr-48
❑ 98TopChrR-48
❑ 98TopDevR-48
❑ 98TopDia-48
❑ 98TopMiniC-48
❑ 98UppDec-741

Patterson, Daryl
❑ 68OPC-113
❑ 68TigDetFPB-19
❑ 68Top-113
❑ 68TopVen-113
❑ 69OPC-101
❑ 69Top-101
❑ 70Top-592
❑ 71MLBOffS-402
❑ 71OPC-481
❑ 71Top-481
❑ 88TigDom-19

Patterson, Dave
❑ 86EveGiaPC-20
❑ 87CliGiaP-3
❑ 88CalLeaACLC-1
❑ 88SanJosGCLC-126
❑ 88SanJosGP-111
❑ 90ProAaA-73
❑ 90ShrCapP-1453
❑ 90ShrCapS-18
❑ 90TexLeaAGS-22
❑ 91Cla/Bes-253
❑ 91LinDriAA-315
❑ 91ShrCapLD-315
❑ 91ShrCapP-1831
❑ 92PhoFirF-2829
❑ 92PhoFirS-392

Patterson, Dave (David Glenn)
❑ 77LodDodT-11
❑ 79AlbDukTc-6
❑ 80AlbDukTc-10
❑ 80Top-679
❑ 81AlbDukTc-2
❑ 82TacTigT-8
❑ 86EveGiaC-12
❑ 89ShrCapP-1843
❑ 90DodTar-609

Patterson, Gil
❑ 76VenLeaS-57
❑ 77Top-472
❑ 92MadMusC-27
❑ 92MadMusF-1253
❑ 92YanWIZ7-125
❑ 93MadMusC-28
❑ 93MadMusF-1839
❑ 94WesMicWC-27
❑ 94WesMicWF-2313

Patterson, Glenn
❑ 87GasRanP-2
❑ 88GasRanP-1021

Patterson, Greg
❑ 87LSUTigP-8
❑ 88WinSpiS-14
❑ 89GenCubP-1882
❑ 90LSUTigGM-14

Patterson, Ham
❑ 09ObaT21-352
❑ 09PC7HHB-33
❑ 11PacCoaBD-47
❑ 11Zee-119
❑ 12HomRunKE-89
❑ 12ObaPreT-101
❑ 12Zee-152
❑ 13Zee-146
❑ 16Zee-139

Patterson, Jake
❑ 94EliTwiC-16
❑ 94EliTwiF-3741
❑ 95Exc-87
❑ 95ForWayWTI-20
❑ 95MidLeaA-38
❑ 96Exc-79
❑ 97ForWayW-24

Patterson, Jarrod
❑ 94KinMetC-15
❑ 94KinMetF-3832
❑ 96Bow-326
❑ 96BowFoi-326
❑ 96Exc-190
❑ 96StLucMTI-20
❑ 98HigDesMG-18

Patterson, Jeff
❑ 89MarPhiS-23
❑ 90ClePhiS-17
❑ 91SpaPhiC-11
❑ 91SpaPhiP-896
❑ 92ClePhiC-7
❑ 92ReaPhiF-573
❑ 93ScrRedBF-2544
❑ 93ScrRedBTI-21
❑ 94ScrRedBF-921
❑ 95ColCliP-20
❑ 95ColCliTI-20

Patterson, Jim
❑ 91FreStaBS-9
❑ 92EriSaiC-28
❑ 92EriSaiF-1619
❑ 93HigDesMC-16
❑ 93HigDesMF-39
❑ 94SanBerSC-15
❑ 94SanBerSF-2756

Patterson, Jimmy
❑ 52Whe-23A
❑ 52Whe-23B

Patterson, John
❑ 97Bes-28
❑ 97BesLimA-29
❑ 97Bow-297
❑ 97BowChr-205
❑ 97BowChrI-205
❑ 97BowChrIR-205
❑ 97BowChrR-205
❑ 97BowInt-297
❑ 97MidLeaTP-25
❑ 97SouBenSH-1
❑ 97Top-477
❑ 98Bes-83
❑ 98BesAutPOY-12
❑ 98BesFulCA-15
❑ 98BesNumOP-35
❑ 98BesPreA-33
❑ 98Bow-207
❑ 98BowBes-167
❑ 98BowBesAR-167
❑ 98BowBesR-167
❑ 98BowCerBlueAU-66
❑ 98BowCerGA-66
❑ 98BowCerSA-66
❑ 98BowChr-207
❑ 98BowChrGA-207
❑ 98BowChrGAR-207
❑ 98BowChrI-207
❑ 98BowChrIR-207
❑ 98BowChrR-207
❑ 98BowGolA-207
❑ 98BowInt-207
❑ 98HigDesMG-19
❑ 98SP MinSTHPE-H11
❑ 98SPMinSTH-H11
❑ 98Top-253
❑ 98TopChr-253
❑ 98TopChrR-253
❑ 98TopDevR-253
❑ 98TopDia-253
❑ 98TopMiniC-253
❑ 99BasAmeTP-74
❑ 99BasAmeTPBP-4
❑ 99BasAmeTPG-74
❑ 99Bow-331
❑ 99BowAut-BA55
❑ 99BowBes-118
❑ 99BowBesAR-118
❑ 99BowBesR-118
❑ 99BowChrSC-SC19
❑ 99BowChrSCR-SC19
❑ 99BowGol-331
❑ 99BowInt-331
❑ 99BowScoC-SC19
❑ 99SP TopP-96
❑ 99SP TopPC-JP
❑ 99SP TopPGF-GF25
❑ 99SP TopPPE-96
❑ 99TeaBesRBG-7

Patterson, John Allen
❑ 90Bes-202
❑ 90ProAaA-155
❑ 90SanJosGB-9
❑ 90SanJosGCLC-33
❑ 90SanJosGP-2017
❑ 90SanJosGS-17
❑ 91Cla/Bes-314
❑ 91LinDriAA-316
❑ 91ShrCapLD-316
❑ 91ShrCapP-1832
❑ 92Bow-67
❑ 92DonRoo-89
❑ 92PhoFirF-2830
❑ 92PhoFirS-379
❑ 92Pin-532
❑ 92ProFS7-345
❑ 92Ult-593
❑ 92UppDec-778
❑ 93Don-193
❑ 93Fle-535
❑ 93Lea-160
❑ 93Pin-413
❑ 93PinRooTP-5
❑ 93Sco-279
❑ 93ScoBoyoS-13
❑ 93Top-573
❑ 93TopGol-573
❑ 93TopInaM-573
❑ 93TopInaR-573
❑ 93TopMic-573
❑ 93Toy-32
❑ 93USPlaCR-4C
❑ 94Fle-697
❑ 94GiaAMC-16
❑ 94GiaMot-11
❑ 94GiaTarBC-19
❑ 94GiaUSPC-2C
❑ 94GiaUSPC-8H
❑ 94ScoRoo-RT96
❑ 94ScoRooGR-RT96
❑ 94Sel-189
❑ 94SpoRoo-118
❑ 94SpoRooAP-118
❑ 94StaClu-381
❑ 94StaCluFDI-381
❑ 94StaCluGR-381
❑ 94StaCluMOP-381
❑ 94StaCluT-18
❑ 94StaCluTFDI-18
❑ 94Ult-590
❑ 95ColCho-252
❑ 95ColChoGS-252
❑ 95ColChoSS-252
❑ 95Don-319
❑ 95DonPreP-319
❑ 95DonTopotO-354
❑ 95Fle-585
❑ 95GiaMot-9
❑ 95Lea-165
❑ 95Pac-382
❑ 95Sco-151
❑ 95ScoGolR-151
❑ 95ScoPlaTS-151
❑ 95StaClu-42
❑ 95StaCluFDI-42
❑ 95StaCluMOP-42
❑ 95StaCluSTWS-42
❑ 95Top-574
❑ 95TopCyb-348
❑ 95Ult-445
❑ 95UltGolM-445
❑ 96ColCho-721
❑ 96ColChoGS-721
❑ 96ColChoSS-721
❑ 96Fle-593
❑ 96FleTif-593

Patterson, Ken
❑ 82ChaRoyT-16
❑ 84IdaFalATI-20
❑ 86Ft.LauYP-17
❑ 87Ft.LauYP-30
❑ 88VanCanC-6
❑ 88VanCanP-757
❑ 89DonRoo-37
❑ 89Fle-508
❑ 89FleGlo-508
❑ 89ScoHot1R-61
❑ 89ScoRoo-97T
❑ 89Top-434
❑ 89TopTif-434
❑ 89WhiSoxC-20
❑ 90Don-371
❑ 90Fle-545
❑ 90FleCan-545
❑ 90OPC-156
❑ 90Sco-207
❑ 90Sco100RS-89
❑ 90ScoYouSI-27
❑ 90Top-156
❑ 90TopTif-156
❑ 90WhiSoxC-20
❑ 91Don-522
❑ 91Fle-132
❑ 91OPC-326
❑ 91Top-326
❑ 91TopDesS-326
❑ 91TopMic-326
❑ 91TopTif-326
❑ 91UppDec-283
❑ 91WhiSoxK-34
❑ 92CubMar-34
❑ 92Don-457
❑ 92Fle-94
❑ 92Lea-509
❑ 92LeaBlaG-509
❑ 92OPC-784
❑ 92PeoChiTI-19
❑ 92Sco-347
❑ 92StaClu-289
❑ 92Top-784
❑ 92TopGol-784
❑ 92TopGolW-784
❑ 92TopMic-784
❑ 92Ult-472
❑ 92UppDec-440
❑ 93AngMot-24
❑ 93Don-742
❑ 93Fle-381
❑ 93StaClu-162
❑ 93StaCluFDI-162
❑ 93StaCluMOP-162
❑ 94Fle-66
❑ 94Ult-25
❑ 97OmaRoyB-12

Patterson, Larry
❑ 80LynSaiT-2
❑ 81SpoIndT-23
❑ 82HolMilT-12
❑ 83NasAngT-11

Patterson, Lorenzo
❑ 11Zee-36
❑ 12HomRunKE-28
❑ 12Zee-43

Patterson, Marty
❑ 97HelBreB-25

Patterson, Michael L.
❑ 77ModA'sC-11
❑ 79OgdA'sT-24
❑ 79WatA'sT-14
❑ 80WesHavWCT-15
❑ 82ColCliP-14
❑ 82ColCliT-20
❑ 83ColCliT-22
❑ 92YanWIZ8-143

Patterson, Pat
❑ 78LauLonABS-18

Patterson, Reggie
❑ 80GleFalWSBT-9
❑ 80GleFalWSCT-18
❑ 81EdmTraRR-22
❑ 82EdmTraT-15
❑ 82Top-599
❑ 83IowCubT-7
❑ 84IowCubT-31
❑ 86Fle-376

Patterson, Rick
❑ 77WauMetT-14
❑ 88UtiBluSP-26
❑ 89SouBenWSGS-2
❑ 90SouBenWSB-24
❑ 90SouBenWSGS-27
❑ 91SarWhiSC-27
❑ 91SarWhiSP-1129
❑ 92SarWhiSCB-27
❑ 92SarWhiSF-224
❑ 94IowCubF-1290

Patterson, Rob
❑ 92MedHatBJSP-25
❑ 93MedHatBJF-3733
❑ 93MedHatBJSP-21

Patterson, Rod
❑ 77ModA'sC-13

Patterson, Roy
❑ 03BreE10-113
❑ 07WhiSoxGWH-9
❑ 11SpoLifCW-284

Patterson, Scott
❑ 80AndBraT-9
❑ 81DurBulT-22
❑ 82ColCliP-11
❑ 82ColCliT-19
❑ 83NasSouTI-15
❑ 84ColCliP-18
❑ 84ColCliT-14
❑ 85AlbYanT-10
❑ 86ColCliP-16
❑ 86ColCliP-18

Patterson, Shane
❑ 90ButCopKSP-14

Patterson, Steve
❑ 91PocPioP-3779
❑ 91PocPioSP-15

Patterson, Tony
❑ 89CarNewE-14

Pattin, Jon
❑ 90CliGiaB-28
❑ 90CliGiaP-2552
❑ 91SanJosGC-3
❑ 91SanJosGP-14

Pattin, Marty
❑ 66SeaPop-17
❑ 67SeaPop-13
❑ 68SeaPop-12
❑ 69PilPos-18
❑ 69PilWhe-7
❑ 69Top-563
❑ 70BreMcD-24
❑ 70BreMil-19
❑ 70OPC-31
❑ 70SunPin-14
❑ 70Top-31
❑ 71BreTeal-11
❑ 71MLBOffS-447
❑ 71OPC-579
❑ 71Top-579
❑ 72OPC-144
❑ 72RedSoxTI-19
❑ 72Top-144
❑ 73LinPor-28
❑ 73OPC-415
❑ 73Top-415
❑ 74OPC-583
❑ 74RoyPos-23
❑ 74Top-583
❑ 74TopSta-187
❑ 75OPC-413
❑ 75RoyPos-25
❑ 75Top-413
❑ 75TopMin-413
❑ 76KanCitRP-24
❑ 76OPC-492
❑ 76SSP-162
❑ 76Top-492
❑ 77PilPosR-18
❑ 77Top-658
❑ 78Roy-18
❑ 78SSP270-231
❑ 78Top-218
❑ 79Top-129
❑ 80Top-26
❑ 81Don-343
❑ 81Fle-37
❑ 81Top-389
❑ 83Pil69G-28
❑ 94BreMilB-67

Pattison, James
❑ 36GouWidPPR-D26
❑ 90DodTar-1050

Patton, Barry
❑ 98WatIndTI-23

Patton, Cory
❑ 97PitMet-21

Patton, Eric
❑ 89HelBreSP-20

Patton, Greg
❑ 95MicBatCTI-18
❑ 96SarRedSB-25

Patton, Jack
❑ 88BakDodCLC-266
❑ 89RenSilSCLC-263
❑ 90RenSilSCLC-292

Patton, Jeff
❑ 84PriWilPT-17

Patton, Owen
❑ 87OldJudN-390

Patton, Scott
❑ 92FroRowDP-16
❑ 92FroRowDPG-16
❑ 92FroRowDPS-16
❑ 92HigSchPLS-12
❑ 93HicCraC-18
❑ 93HicCraF-1293
❑ 93StaCluM-16

Patton, Tom
❑ 91OriCro-355

Patzke, Jeff
❑ 92HigSchPLS-26
❑ 92MedHatBJSP-23
❑ 93MedHatBJF-3746
❑ 93MedHatBJSP-12
❑ 93StaCluM-104
❑ 93Top-529
❑ 93TopGol-529
❑ 93TopInaM-529
❑ 93TopInaR-529
❑ 93TopMic-529
❑ 94HagSunC-18
❑ 94HagSunF-2740
❑ 95DunBluJTI-17
❑ 96Exc-117
❑ 96KnoSmoB-19
❑ 97SyrSkyCB-17

Paugh, Rick
❑ 94WelPirC-15
❑ 94WelPirF-3492
❑ 96LynHilB-17

Paul VI, Pope
❑ 90YanMomPRP-9

Paul, Andy
❑ 93AusFut-15
❑ 94StoPorC-18
❑ 94StoPorF-1692
❑ 96El PasDB-23
❑ 97St.PauS-20
❑ 98ChaLooG-20

Paul, Corey
❑ 87BelMarTI-31
❑ 89BelMarL-27
❑ 90SalSpuP-2733

Paul, Gabe
❑ 82OhiHaloF-51

Paul, Josh
❑ 96HicCraB-14
❑ 97Bes-45
❑ 97BesAll-3
❑ 97BirBarB-2
❑ 97Bow-97
❑ 97BowInt-97
❑ 97SouLeaTP-2
❑ 98Bes-84
❑ 98CarLeaTPQ-20
❑ 98WinWar-21
❑ 99BasAmeTP-75
❑ 99BasAmeTPG-75
❑ 99SP TopP-97
❑ 99SP TopPPE-97

Paul, Kortney
❑ 94EugEmeC-15
❑ 94EugEmeF-3716

Paul, Mike
❑ 69Top-537
❑ 70Top-582
❑ 71MLBOffS-381
❑ 71OPC-454
❑ 71Top-454
❑ 72MilBra-267
❑ 72Top-577
❑ 73OPC-58
❑ 73RanTeal-19
❑ 73Top-58
❑ 74OPC-399
❑ 74Top-399
❑ 85VanCanC-208
❑ 86VanCanP-21
❑ 88A'sMot-27
❑ 89MarMot-27
❑ 90MarMot-27
❑ 93RanKee-32

Paul, Ron
❑ 81TCM60I-381

Paul, Stu
❑ 93SalBucC-30

Paula, Carlos (Carlos C.)
❑ 55Top-97
❑ 56Top-4
❑ 56TopPin-58
❑ 58UniOil-6
❑ 79TCM50-205

Paulin, Randy
❑ 95SpoIndTI-17

Paulino, Arturo
❑ 96WesMicWB-20
❑ 97ModA'sG-22
Paulino, Dario
❑ 91IdaFalBP-4338
❑ 91IdaFalBSP-23
❑ 92MacBraC-6
❑ 92ProFS7-198
Paulino, Elvin
❑ 87PeoChiP-17
❑ 87WytCubP-10
❑ 88PeoChiTI-24
❑ 89PeoChiTI-24
❑ 90CarLeaA-48
❑ 90WinSpiTI-24
❑ 91ChaKniLD-138
❑ 91ChaKniP-1697
❑ 91LinDriAA-138
❑ 92Bow-95
❑ 92IowCubS-214
❑ 92ProFS7-201
❑ 92SkyAAAF-103
❑ 93LimRocDWB-90
Paulino, Jose
❑ 77ForLauYS-12
Paulino, Jose Luis
❑ 96SouOreTI-24
❑ 97VisOakG-22
❑ 98ModA'sG-23
Paulino, Luis
❑ 87HagSunP-14
❑ 88HagSunS-15
❑ 89FreKeyS-20
Paulino, Nelson
❑ 92PulBraC-26
❑ 92PulBraF-3186
❑ 93MacBraC-18
❑ 93MacBraF-1411
❑ 94DurBulC-14
❑ 94DurBulF-336
❑ 94DurBulTI-15
Paulino, Richard
❑ 92MacBraF-281
Paulino, Victor
❑ 84SavCarT-19
Paulis, George
❑ 89WatDiaS-28
Paull, William
❑ 20Zee-32
Pauls, Matt
❑ 95ChaRivTI-3
Paulsen, Axel
❑ 88KimN18-35
Paulsen, Troy
❑ 88AlaGolTI-13
❑ 91ClePhiC-20
❑ 91ClePhiP-1631
❑ 91FloStaLAP-FSL8
❑ 92ProFS7-300
❑ 92ReaPhiF-582
❑ 92ReaPhiS-539
❑ 92SkyAA F-234
Paustian, Mike
❑ 85CloHSS-33
Pautt, Juan
❑ 83PawRedST-23
❑ 84PawRedST-12
Pavano, Carl
❑ 95MicBatCTI-19
❑ 95MidLeaA-39
❑ 96Bow-259
❑ 96BowFoi-259
❑ 96DouAllB-9
❑ 96TreThuB-12
❑ 97Bes-10
❑ 97BesAutSBPP-36
❑ 97BesGun-6
❑ 97BesLimA-30
❑ 97Bow-161
❑ 97BowBes-120
❑ 97BowBesAR-120
❑ 97BowBesR-120
❑ 97BowCerBlaIA-CA60
❑ 97BowCerBluIA-CA60
❑ 97BowCerGolIA-CA60
❑ 97BowChr-159
❑ 97BowChrI-159
❑ 97BowChrIR-159
❑ 97BowChrR-159
❑ 97BowInt-161
❑ 97PawRedS-20
❑ 97Top-493
❑ 97TopSta-109
❑ 97TopStaAM-109
❑ 98BesAutPOY-13
❑ 98BesCon-8
❑ 98BesDiaB-6
❑ 98BesFulCA-16
❑ 98BesPreA-34
❑ 98BesYouG-8
❑ 98Bow-437
❑ 98BowBes-111
❑ 98BowBesAR-111
❑ 98BowBesR-111
❑ 98BowCerBlueAU-14
❑ 98BowCerGA-14
❑ 98BowCerSA-14
❑ 98BowChr-437
❑ 98BowChrGA-437
❑ 98BowChrGAR-437
❑ 98BowChrI-437
❑ 98BowChrIR-437
❑ 98BowChrR-437
❑ 98BowGolA-437
❑ 98BowInt-437
❑ 98ColCho-415
❑ 98ColChoPCR-415
❑ 98CroRoy-84
❑ 98Don-345
❑ 98DonColP-712
❑ 98DonGolPP-345
❑ 98DonPre-162
❑ 98DonPreSeat-162
❑ 98DonPriCP-712
❑ 98DonSig-101
❑ 98DonSigA-69
❑ 98DonSigAC-89
❑ 98DonSigAM-90
❑ 98DonSigP-101
❑ 98DonSilPP-345
❑ 98FleUpd-U56
❑ 98LeaRCrusUP-121
❑ 98LeaRS-262
❑ 98LeaRSCrusUG-121
❑ 98LeaRSCrusUR-121
❑ 98LeaRSFOSamp-8
❑ 98LeaRSFresh-8
❑ 98LeaRSLHolo-262
❑ 98LeaRSLong-262
❑ 98LeaRTrue-262
❑ 98PacOnl-458
❑ 98PacOnlR-458
❑ 98PacOnlWC-458
❑ 98PinPer-134
❑ 98PinPerPP-134
❑ 98PinPlu-34
❑ 98Revo-90
❑ 98RevoSS-90
❑ 98ScoRT-238
❑ 98ScoRTSS-PP131
❑ 98ScoRTSSAP-PP131
❑ 98ScoRTSSAP1-PP131
❑ 98SP Aut-7
❑ 98SP MinDTSPE-DS24
❑ 98SP MinPE-30
❑ 98SP MinSTHPE-H25
❑ 98SPMin-30
❑ 98SPMinDTS-DS24
❑ 98SPMinSTH-H25
❑ 98SpoIllWSF-110
❑ 98SpoIllWSFEE-110
❑ 98SpoIllWSFFE-110
❑ 98SPxFin-186
❑ 98SPxFinR-186
❑ 98SPxFinS-186
❑ 98StaCluFDI-354
❑ 98StaCluI-354
❑ 98StaCluOneK-354
❑ 98StaCluPP-354
❑ 98Stu-89
❑ 98StuGPP-89
❑ 98StuSPP-89
❑ 98Top-256
❑ 98Top-458
❑ 98TopChr-256
❑ 98TopChr-458
❑ 98TopChrR-256
❑ 98TopChrR-458
❑ 98TopDevR-256
❑ 98TopDevR-458
❑ 98TopDia-256
❑ 98TopDia-458
❑ 98TopMiniC-256
❑ 98TopMiniC-458
❑ 98UppDec-541
❑ 98UppDecDS-DS55
❑ 98UppDecR-123
❑ 98UppDecRNF-NF23
❑ 99Fle-178
❑ 99FleSta9-178
❑ 99FleWarT-178
❑ 99MetUni-26
❑ 99MetUniGM-26
❑ 99MetUniPMG-26
❑ 99Pac-268
❑ 99PacAur-114
❑ 99PacAurOD-114
❑ 99PacCroC-171
❑ 99PacCroCPB-171
❑ 99PacPar-144
❑ 99PacParC-144
❑ 99PacParG-144
❑ 99PacParHoloGold-144
❑ 99PacParHS-144
❑ 99PacParOD-144
❑ 99PacParPB-144
❑ 99PacParRed-144
❑ 99PacPlaB-268
❑ 99PacPri-88
❑ 99PacPriHB-88
❑ 99PacPriHG-88
❑ 99PacPriHM-88
❑ 99PacPriHP-88
❑ 99PacPriRed-88
❑ 99PacRed-268
❑ 99SkyMolM-76
❑ 99SkyMolMX-76
❑ 99SkyPre-61
❑ 99SkyPreR-61
❑ 99SkyThu-109
❑ 99SkyThuRant-109
❑ 99SkyThuRave-109
❑ 99ThuSkySupR-109
❑ 99Top-264
❑ 99TopChr-264
❑ 99TopChrR-264
❑ 99TopMVPP-264
❑ 99UppDec-422
❑ 99UppDecBD-108
❑ 99UppDecBDD-108
❑ 99UppDecBDQ-108
❑ 99UppDecBDT-108
❑ 99UppDecEL1-422
❑ 99UppDecEL2-422
❑ 99UppDecEM-MC1
❑ 99UppDecEMFXG-MC1
❑ 99Vic-245
Paveloff, David
❑ 91KanCouCC-8
❑ 91KanCouCP-2656
❑ 91KanCouCTI-15
❑ 92FreKeyC-3
❑ 92FreKeyF-1802
❑ 93FreKeyC-20
❑ 93FreKeyF-1025
❑ 94BowBayF-2412
❑ 94OriPro-78
Pavicich, Paul
❑ 94EliTwiC-17
❑ 94EliTwiF-3728
❑ 95ForWayWTI-9
❑ 96FtMyeMB-15
Pavlas, Dave
❑ 86WinSpiP-18
❑ 87PitCubP-15
❑ 88TexLeaAGS-21
❑ 88TulDriTI-23
❑ 89OklCit8C-8
❑ 89OklCit8P-1529
❑ 90CMC-608
❑ 90IowCubC-6
❑ 90IowCubP-317
❑ 90ProAAAF-624
❑ 90TopTVCu-57
❑ 91IowCubLD-213
❑ 91IowCubP-1058
❑ 91LinDriAAA-213
❑ 91Sco-378
❑ 91TopDeb90-122
❑ 93LinVenB-55
❑ 95ColCliP-21
❑ 95ColCliTI-21
❑ 96ColCliB-24
❑ 97ColCliB-20
❑ 97ColCliD-17
❑ 98TusSidM-13
Pavletich, Don (Donald S.)
❑ 59RedEnq-18
❑ 59Top-494
❑ 62RedEnq-25
❑ 62Top-594
❑ 63RedEnq-24
❑ 63RedFreBC-18
❑ 63RedJayP-9
❑ 65RedEnq-21
❑ 65Top-472
❑ 66OPC-196
❑ 66Top-196
❑ 66TopVen-196
❑ 67CokCapR-9
❑ 67Kah-28
❑ 67Top-292
❑ 68OPC-108
❑ 68Top-108
❑ 68TopVen-108
❑ 69MilBra-215
❑ 69OPC-179
❑ 69Top-179
❑ 69TopFou-4
❑ 70OPC-504
❑ 70Top-504
❑ 71MLBOffS-326
❑ 71OPC-409
❑ 71Top-409
❑ 72OPC-359
❑ 72RedSoxTI-20
❑ 72Top-359
❑ 81TCM60I-333
Pavlick, Greg
❑ 78TidTidT-18
❑ 79TidTidT-20
❑ 84JacMetT-10
❑ 86MetTCM-40
❑ 88MetColP-42
❑ 88MetKah-52
❑ 89MetColP-47
❑ 89MetKah-21
❑ 90MetColP-44
❑ 90MetKah-52
❑ 90TopTVM-5
❑ 91MetColP-42
❑ 91MetKah-52
❑ 91MetPerPA-4
❑ 96MetKah-26
❑ 96MetKah-26
Pavlik, John
❑ 84PriWilPT-9
Pavlik, Roger
❑ 87GasRanP-15
❑ 88GasRanP-1020
❑ 89ChaRanS-19
❑ 90ChaRanS-19
❑ 90TulDriTI-18
❑ 91LinDriAAA-315
❑ 91OklCit8LD-315
❑ 91OklCit8P-174
❑ 92DonRoo-90
❑ 92FleUpd-62
❑ 92OklCit8F-1914
❑ 92OklCit8S-317
❑ 93Don-113
❑ 93Fle-688
❑ 93Lea-550
❑ 93OklCit8F-1625
❑ 93RanKee-422
❑ 93RanStaC-5
❑ 93Sco-325
❑ 93StaClu-193
❑ 93StaCluFDI-193
❑ 93StaCluMOP-193
❑ 93Top-223
❑ 93TopGol-223
❑ 93TopInaM-223
❑ 93TopInaR-223
❑ 93TopMic-223
❑ 93Ult-283
❑ 94ColC-226
❑ 94ColChoGS-226
❑ 94ColChoSS-226
❑ 94Don-527
❑ 94Fin-155
❑ 94FinRef-155
❑ 94Fle-315
❑ 94Pac-625
❑ 94Pin-469
❑ 94PinArtP-469
❑ 94PinMusC-469
❑ 94RanMagM-12
❑ 94RanMagM-31
❑ 94Sco-365
❑ 94ScoGolR-365
❑ 94Sel-333
❑ 94StaClu-178
❑ 94StaCluFDI-178
❑ 94StaCluGR-178
❑ 94StaCluMOP-178
❑ 94StaCluT-263
❑ 94StaCluTFDI-263
❑ 94Top-22
❑ 94TopGol-22
❑ 94TopSpa-22
❑ 94TriPla-198
❑ 94Ult-131
❑ 94UppDec-418
❑ 94UppDecED-418
❑ 95Don-375
❑ 95DonPreP-375
❑ 95Fle-293
❑ 95Lea-20
❑ 95RanCra-27
❑ 95StaClu-120
❑ 95StaCluFDI-120
❑ 95StaCluMOP-120
❑ 95StaCluSTWS-120
❑ 95Top-436
❑ 95TopCyb-233
❑ 95Ult-112
❑ 95UltGolM-112
❑ 96Cir-91
❑ 96CirRav-91
❑ 96ColCho-738
❑ 96ColChoGS-738
❑ 96ColChoSS-738
❑ 96Don-143
❑ 96DonPreP-143
❑ 96EmoXL-126
❑ 96Fla-177
❑ 96Fle-259
❑ 96FleTif-259
❑ 96LeaSigA-177
❑ 96LeaSigAG-177
❑ 96LeaSigAS-177
❑ 96Pac-432
❑ 96RanDr P-26
❑ 96RanFle-13
❑ 96RanMot-19
❑ 96Sco-461
❑ 96StaClu-306
❑ 96StaCluMOP-306
❑ 96Top-79
❑ 96Ult-138
❑ 96UltGolM-138
❑ 96UppDec-209
❑ 97Cir-18
❑ 97CirRav-18
❑ 97ColCho-486
❑ 97Don-109
❑ 97DonGolPP-109
❑ 97DonSilPP-109
❑ 97Fin-81
❑ 97FinRef-81
❑ 97Fle-230
❑ 97FleTif-230
❑ 97Lea-309
❑ 97LeaFraM-309
❑ 97LeaFraMDC-309
❑ 97MetUni-167
❑ 97Pac-208
❑ 97PacLigB-208
❑ 97PacSil-208
❑ 97RanDr P-25
❑ 97RanMot-19
❑ 97RanSco-8
❑ 97RanScoPl-8
❑ 97RanScoPr-8
❑ 97Sco-161
❑ 97ScoArtPWB-161
❑ 97ScoPreS-161
❑ 97ScoShoS-161
❑ 97ScoShoSAP-161
❑ 97SP-171
❑ 97StaClu-133
❑ 97StaCluMOP-133
❑ 97Top-43
❑ 97Ult-139
❑ 97UltGolME-139
❑ 97UltPlaME-139
❑ 97UppDec-208
❑ 98PacOnl-742
❑ 98PacOnlR-742
❑ 98PacOnlWC-742
❑ 98PinSna-TR18
❑ 98Top-161
❑ 98TopChr-161
❑ 98TopChrR-161
❑ 98TopDevR-161
❑ 98TopDia-161
❑ 98TopMiniC-161
❑ 98UppDec-524
Pavlovich, Tony
❑ 96BelSnaTI-29
Pawling, Eric
❑ 86CliGiaP-17
❑ 86TriTriC-193
Pawlowski, John
❑ 86PenWhiSP-19
❑ 87BirBarB-17
❑ 88BlaYNPRWL-123
❑ 88Don-457
❑ 88WhiSoxC-20
❑ 89VanCanC-7
❑ 89VanCanP-595
❑ 90CMC-637
❑ 90ProAAAF-165
❑ 90Sco-617
❑ 90VanCanC-10
❑ 90VanCanP-487
❑ 92EdmTraF-3538
❑ 92EdmTraS-164
Paws, Mascot
❑ 96TigHebN-27
Paxson, Jeff
❑ 94BelBreC-30
❑ 95BelBreTI-27
❑ 97BelSnaB-5
Paxson, Jeffrey
❑ 96BelSnaTI-30
Paxton, Chris
❑ 98DelShoM-23
Paxton, Darrin
❑ 90WicStaSGD-29
❑ 92AlbPolCB-3
❑ 92AlbPolF-2302
❑ 93BurBeeC-16
❑ 93BurBeeF-153
❑ 94HigDesMC-1
❑ 94HigDesMF-2786
❑ 95HarSenTI-28
Paxton, Greg
❑ 90RenSilSCLC-282
Paxton, Mike
❑ 78IndTeal-24
❑ 78Top-216
❑ 79OPC-54
❑ 79Top-122
❑ 80TacTigT-27
❑ 80Top-388
❑ 81ChaChaT-5
❑ 81Fle-401
Payment, Craig
❑ 97PriDevR-4
Payne, Chad
❑ 90GeoColC-24
Payne, Fred (Frederick T.)
❑ 07TigACDPP-11
❑ 09T206-284
❑ 09WolNewDTPP-13
❑ 10ChiE-16
❑ 11MecDFT-39
❑ 11PinT-5-765
❑ 11S74Sil-8
❑ 11SpoLifCW-285
❑ 11SpoLifM-27
❑ 11T205-136
❑ 12HasTriFT-22A
❑ 12HasTriFT-22B
Payne, Harley
❑ 90DodTar-610
Payne, Jeff
❑ 90HamRedB-25
Payne, Jim
❑ 79WauTimT-24
❑ 80QuaCitCT-18
❑ 81WisRapTT-17
Payne, Joe
❑ 50WorWidGV-15
Payne, Larry
❑ 76IndIndTI-2
❑ 77IndIndTI-7
❑ 78IndIndTI-13
Payne, Mike
❑ 80AndBraT-15
❑ 81DurBulT-23
❑ 82DurBulT-19
❑ 85RicBraT-6
❑ 87JacExpP-444
Payne, Ron
❑ 98WilCubM-20
Payne, Stan
❑ 92SouOreAC-25
❑ 92SouOreAF-3415
Paynter, Billy
❑ 88WytCubP-1983
❑ 89PeoChiTI-13
❑ 90GenCubP-3040
❑ 90GenCubS-19
❑ 90PeoChiTI-5
Paynter, Norb
❑ 24Zee-98
❑ 25Zee-117
❑ 26Zee-148
Payton, Dave
❑ 87EriCarP-21
❑ 88SprCarB-15

❑ 89SprCarB-15
Payton, Jay
❑ 94PitMetC-1
❑ 94PitMetF-3536
❑ 94SigRooDP-28
❑ 94SigRooDPS-28
❑ 94StaCluDP-17
❑ 94StaCluDPFDI-17
❑ 95Bes-84
❑ 95Bes-107
❑ 95Bes-AU3
❑ 95BinMetTI-24
❑ 95Bow-240
❑ 95BowBes-B62
❑ 95BowBesR-B62
❑ 95BowGolF-240
❑ 95Exc-235
❑ 95ExcFirYP-8
❑ 95SPML-9
❑ 95SPML-95
❑ 95SPMLA-20
❑ 95SPMLDtS-DS20
❑ 95Top-443
❑ 95UppDecML-195
❑ 95UppDecMLFS-195
❑ 96BesAutSA-52
❑ 96Bow-241
❑ 96BowBes-111
❑ 96BowBesAR-111
❑ 96BowBesR-111
❑ 96BowFoi-241
❑ 96Exc-191
❑ 96ExcAll-8
❑ 96ExcCli-7
❑ 96NorTidB-22
❑ 96Top-350
❑ 96TopChr-141
❑ 96TopChrR-141
❑ 97BesAutAS-38
❑ 97BesAutP-R9
❑ 97Bow-151
❑ 97BowCerBlaIA-CA61
❑ 97BowCerBluIA-CA61
❑ 97BowCerGolIA-CA61
❑ 97BowInt-151
❑ 97ColCho-475
❑ 97DonSigA-78
❑ 97DonSigAC-96
❑ 97DonSigAM-96
❑ 97Sel-137
❑ 97SelArtP-137
❑ 97SelCom-137
❑ 97SelRegG-137
❑ 97Top-342
❑ 98DonColE-509
❑ 98DonEli-109
❑ 98DonEliA-109
❑ 98DonEliS-109
❑ 98DonPriCE-509
❑ 98FleUpd-U20
❑ 98NorTidP-20
❑ 98NorTidQ-19
❑ 98PinSna-NYM17
❑ 99Fle-253
❑ 99FleSta9-253
❑ 99FleWarT-253
❑ 99SkyThu-229
❑ 99SkyThuRant-229
❑ 99SkyThuRave-229
❑ 99SpoIll-58
❑ 99ThuSkySupR-229
Payton, Ray
❑ 88MidLeaAGS-49
❑ 88SouBenWSGS-6
❑ 89SarWhiSS-17
❑ 90SarWhiSS-18
Paz, Richard
❑ 96BluOriB-23
❑ 97DelSho-19
❑ 98DelShoM-24
Pazik, Mike
❑ 73SyrChiTI-22
❑ 74TacTwiC-8
❑ 75TacTwiK-14
❑ 76OPC-597
❑ 76SSP-212
❑ 76TacTwiDQ-15
❑ 76Top-597
❑ 77Top-643
❑ 80GleFalWSBT-24
❑ 80GleFalWSCT-21
❑ 82AppFoxFr-30
❑ 88ChaKniTI-14
❑ 89FreKeyS-26
❑ 90FreKeyTI-2
Peacock, Johnny (John Gaston)
❑ 39PlaBal-16
❑ 40PlaBal-34
❑ 42RedSoxTI-19
❑ 43RedSoxTI-20
❑ 79DiaGre-304
❑ 90DodTar-611
Peanut, (Mascot)
❑ 97ModA'sG-23
❑ 98ModA'sG-24
Pearce, Chris
❑ 94LSUTig-13
Pearce, Ducky (William C.)
❑ 09ObaT21-280
❑ 11Zee-37
❑ 12ObaPreT-29
❑ 13Zee-44
❑ 72ClaCar-105
Pearce, Jeff
❑ 90SpoIndSP-17
❑ 91ChaRaiC-23
❑ 91ChaRaiP-109
❑ 92WatDiaC-23
❑ 92WatDiaF-2153
❑ 93RanCucQC-23
❑ 93RanCucQF-844
❑ 96LanJetB-22
Pearce, Jim
❑ 55Top-170
Pearce, Steve
❑ 77CedRapGT-24
Pearce, Walt
❑ 22Zee-67
❑ 23Zee-113
Pearlman, David
❑ 93St.CatBJC-19
❑ 93St.CatBJF-3974
Pearn, Joe
❑ 87PorChaRP-27
❑ 88GasRanP-1006
Pearsall, J.J.
❑ 95YakBeaTI-25
❑ 96SavSanB-17
❑ 97SanBerS-12
❑ 98SanAntMG-21
Pearse, Steve
❑ 88RocExpLC-28
Pearsey, Les
❑ 81HolMilT-19
❑ 82SpoIndT-18
Pearson, Albie (Albert G.)
❑ 47Exh-174
❑ 56BalOriP-44
❑ 58SeaTeal-21
❑ 58SenJayP-8
❑ 58Top-317
❑ 59Top-4
❑ 59TopVen-4
❑ 60Top-241
❑ 61AngJayP-9
❑ 61Top-288
❑ 62AngJayP-8
❑ 62Jel-78
❑ 62Pos-78
❑ 62PosCan-78
❑ 62SalPlaC-63A
❑ 62SalPlaC-63B
❑ 62ShiPlaC-63
❑ 62Top-343
❑ 62TopStal-67
❑ 63AngJayP-12
❑ 63AngJayP-13
❑ 63BasMagM-65
❑ 63Fle-19
❑ 63Jel-29
❑ 63Pos-29
❑ 63Top-182
❑ 64Top-110
❑ 64TopCoi-111
❑ 64TopCoi-132
❑ 64TopGia-23
❑ 64TopSta-42
❑ 64TopStaU-55
❑ 64TopTatI-61
❑ 64TopVen-110
❑ 64WheSta-33
❑ 65Top-358
❑ 66AngDexP-10
❑ 66OPC-83
❑ 66Top-83
❑ 66TopVen-83
❑ 78TCM60I-16
❑ 79DiaGre-73
❑ 85AngStrH-10
❑ 86AngGreT-6
❑ 91OriCro-356
Pearson, Cory
❑ 92ClaDraP-82
❑ 92GulCoaRSP-22
❑ 93EriSaiC-19
❑ 93EriSaiF-3129
❑ 94ChaRivC-15
❑ 94ChaRivF-2686
❑ 95ChaRivUTIS-34
Pearson, Darren
❑ 85EveGiaC-13A
❑ 85EveGiaC-13B
❑ 86CliGiaP-18
Pearson, Don
❑ 77WauMetT-15
❑ 78WauMetT-22
Pearson, Donna
❑ 88OklSoo-19
Pearson, Eddie
❑ 92ClaFS7-409
❑ 92UppDecML-15
❑ 93ClaFS7-86
❑ 93ClaGolF-200
❑ 93HicCraC-1
❑ 93HicCraF-1286
❑ 94Bow-427
❑ 94BowBes-B14
❑ 94BowBesR-B14
❑ 94CarLeaAF-CAR10
❑ 94Cla-129
❑ 94ClaGolF-93
❑ 94ClaTriF-T16
❑ 94PriWilCC-18
❑ 94PriWilCF-1930
❑ 94UppDec-549
❑ 94UppDecED-549
❑ 94UppDecML-128
❑ 95Bow-141
❑ 96BirBarB-1
❑ 96BowBes-158
❑ 96BowBesAR-158
❑ 96BowBesR-158
❑ 97BirBarB-10
Pearson, Frank
❑ 92NegLeaRLI-46
Pearson, George
❑ 89GeoColC-23
Pearson, Ike
❑ 40PhiTeal-18
❑ 41PhiTeal-20
❑ 47CenFlo-19
❑ 48WhiSoxTI-22
❑ 79DiaGre-303
Pearson, Joe
❑ 55DesMoiHB-15
Pearson, Kevin
❑ 87TamTarP-6
❑ 88GreHorP-1560
❑ 89ChaLooB-18
❑ 89ChaLooGS-20
❑ 89NasSouTI-18
❑ 90CMC-142
❑ 90NasSouC-17
❑ 90NasSouP-242
❑ 90ProAAAF-554
❑ 91LinDriAAA-269
❑ 91NasSouLD-269
❑ 91NasSouP-2167
❑ 92FroRowDP-31
❑ 92FroRowDPG-31
❑ 92FroRowDPS-31
❑ 93StaCluM-25
❑ 94EliTwiC-18
❑ 94EliTwiF-3744
❑ 95ForWayWTI-24
Pearson, Lennie
❑ 91PomBlaBPB-19
Pearson, Monte
❑ 30Zee-91
❑ 34BabRutG-51
❑ 34ButPreR-50
❑ 35DiaMatCS3T1-119
❑ 36WorWidGV-114
❑ 37OPCBatUV-131
❑ 38CloFotW-71
❑ 39PlaBal-71
❑ 40PlaBal-5
❑ 72TCMthe3-57
❑ 75YanDyn1T-35
❑ 85BigLeaC3-3
❑ 92ConTSN-369
❑ 92YanWIZA-57
❑ 93ConTSN-748
Pearson, Ryan
❑ 97HelBreB-26
Pearson, Steve
❑ 87SalLakTTT-14
❑ 88SalLakCTTI-16
Pecci, Jay
❑ 98SouOreTG-24
Pechek, Wayne
❑ 76CedRapGT-20
❑ 81PhoGiaVNB-19
Peck, Hal
❑ 45A'sTeal-25
❑ 47IndTeal-21
❑ 47IndVanPP-20
❑ 48IndTeal-25
❑ 49Bow-182
❑ 49IndTeal-21
❑ 83TCMPla1945-21
❑ 90DodTar-612
Peck, Steve
❑ 90MadMusP-2269
❑ 90ModA'sC-25
❑ 91PalSprAP-2011
❑ 92MidAngF-4026
❑ 92MidAngOHP-18
❑ 92MidAngS-467
❑ 93VanCanF-2594
❑ 94ElPasDF-3143
❑ 98WisTimRM-28
Peck, Tom
❑ 96HagSunB-16
❑ 97DunBluJTI-22
Peckham, Chris
❑ 98ButCopKG-26
Peckinpaugh, Roger
❑ 09ObaT21-297
❑ 11PacCoaBD-49
❑ 11Zee-55
❑ 12ObaPreT-46
❑ 14B18B-26
❑ 14CraJacE-91
❑ 15CraJacE-91
❑ 15SpoNewM-136
❑ 16SpoNewM-137
❑ 17ColE13-131
❑ 17HolBreD-77
❑ 19W514-44
❑ 20NatCarE-74
❑ 20W516-20
❑ 20WalMaiW-40
❑ 21E121So8-69A
❑ 21E121So8-69B
❑ 21Exh-125
❑ 21Exh-126
❑ 21KoBreWSI-44
❑ 22AmeCarE122-52
❑ 22E120-114
❑ 22W575-95
❑ 23MapCriV-23
❑ 23WilChoV-120
❑ 27YorCarE-56
❑ 28W502-56
❑ 28Yue-56
❑ 60SenUniMC-15
❑ 61Fle-132
❑ 68SCFOldT-21
❑ 75SenTCM1-25
❑ 77GalGloG-163
❑ 82OhiHaloF-20
❑ 86ConSer1-37
❑ 91ConTSN-308
❑ 94ConTSN-1258
❑ 94ConTSNB-1258
Pecora, Tony
❑ 98BatMucTI-20
Pecorilli, Aldo
❑ 92JohCitCC-10
❑ 92JohCitCF-3119
❑ 93SavCarC-1
❑ 93SavCarF-689
❑ 93SouAtlLAGF-50
❑ 94ClaGolF-172
❑ 94ExcFS7-272
❑ 94St.PetCC-21
❑ 94St.PetCF-2595
❑ 95Bes-53
❑ 95BreBtaTI-15
❑ 95RicBraRC-17
❑ 96RicBraB-23
❑ 96RicBraRC-2
❑ 96RicBraUB-21
❑ 97ArkTraB-13
Pecota, Bill
❑ 82ForMyeRT-21
❑ 84MemChiT-24
❑ 85OmaRoyT-29
❑ 86OmaRoyP-17
❑ 86OmaRoyT-12
❑ 87FleUpd-97
❑ 87FleUpdG-97
❑ 88Don-466
❑ 88Fle-264
❑ 88FleGlo-264
❑ 88RoySmo-22
❑ 88RoyTeal-23
❑ 88Sco-377
❑ 88ScoGlo-377
❑ 88StaLinRo-11
❑ 88Top-433
❑ 88TopClo-86
❑ 88TopTif-433
❑ 89Fle-289
❑ 89FleGlo-289
❑ 89OmaRoyC-15
❑ 89Sco-339
❑ 89Top-148
❑ 89TopBig-292
❑ 89TopTif-148
❑ 89UppDec-507
❑ 90Bow-377
❑ 90BowTif-377
❑ 90CMC-191
❑ 90OmaRoyC-16
❑ 90RoyPos-19
❑ 91Don-672
❑ 91Fle-565
❑ 91OPC-754
❑ 91PanFreS-277
❑ 91RoyPol-17
❑ 91Sco-513
❑ 91Top-754
❑ 91TopDesS-754
❑ 91TopMic-754
❑ 91TopTif-754
❑ 91UltUpd-28
❑ 92Don-361
❑ 92Fle-165
❑ 92Lea-244
❑ 92LeaBlaG-244
❑ 92MetColP-26
❑ 92MetKah-32
❑ 92OPC-236
❑ 92OPCPre-149
❑ 92PanSti-96
❑ 92Pin-319
❑ 92Sco-252
❑ 92ScoRoo-52T
❑ 92StaClu-811
❑ 92Top-236
❑ 92TopGol-236
❑ 92TopGolW-236
❑ 92TopMic-236
❑ 92TopTra-86T
❑ 92TopTraG-86T
❑ 92Ult-535
❑ 92UppDec-240
❑ 92UppDec-793
❑ 93BraLykP-23
❑ 93BraLykS-28
❑ 93BraStaC-2
❑ 93Don-248
❑ 93Fle-92
❑ 93PacSpa-339
❑ 93Sco-365
❑ 93StaClu-148
❑ 93StaCluFDI-148
❑ 93StaCluMOP-148
❑ 93Top-517
❑ 93TopGol-517
❑ 93TopInaM-517
❑ 93TopInaR-517
❑ 93TopMic-517
❑ 94BraLykP-28
❑ 94BraLykS-26
❑ 94BraUSPC-5H
❑ 94BraUSPC-11D
❑ 94Fle-371
❑ 94Sco-144
❑ 94ScoGolR-144
❑ 94StaClu-486
❑ 94StaCluFDI-486
❑ 94StaCluGR-486
❑ 94StaCluMOP-486
❑ 94StaCluT-57
❑ 94StaCluTFDI-57
❑ 94Top-414
❑ 94TopGol-414
❑ 94TopSpa-414
❑ 95Sco-215
❑ 95ScoGolR-215
❑ 95ScoPlaTS-215
Peden, Les
❑ 53Top-256
❑ 91TopArc1-256
Pedersen, Don
❑ 89NiaFalRP-1
❑ 90FayGenP-2414
Pedersen, Justin
❑ 97SpoIndG-22
Pedersen, Mark
❑ 81WauTimT-6
Pederson, Justin
❑ 98LanLugQ-11
Pederson, Stu
❑ 82VerBeaDT-24
❑ 85AlbDukCr-167
❑ 86AlbDukP-19
❑ 86StaoftFT-16
❑ 87AlbDukD-29
❑ 88BlaYNPRWLU-42
❑ 89SyrChiC-16
❑ 89SyrChiMB-18
❑ 89SyrChiP-798
❑ 90CMC-349
❑ 90DodTar-613
❑ 90ProAAAF-366
❑ 90SyrChiC-23
❑ 90SyrChiMB-18
❑ 90SyrChiP-586
❑ 91LinDriAAA-512
❑ 91SyrChiLD-512
❑ 91SyrChiMB-17
❑ 91SyrChiP-2495
❑ 92SyrChiF-1983
❑ 92SyrChiMB-15
❑ 92SyrChiS-513
Pedraza, Nelson
❑ 83WatIndF-7
❑ 85WatIndT-1
Pedraza, Rodney
❑ 91Cla/Bes-425
❑ 91FroRowDP-16
❑ 91FroRowDPG-16
❑ 91FroRowDPS-16
❑ 91JamExpC-27
❑ 91JamExpP-3543
❑ 92AlbPolCB-6
❑ 92AlbPolF-2303
❑ 92StaCluD-139
❑ 93SanBerSC-1
❑ 93SanBerSF-767
❑ 94Cla-53
❑ 94NewHavRF-1546
❑ 95Top-648
❑ 96NewHavRB-20
❑ 96NewHavRUSTI-19
❑ 98Cha-8
Pedrazzini, Joe
❑ 63SeaPop-8
Pedre, Jorge
❑ 87EugEmeP-2668
❑ 88AppFoxP-137
❑ 88MidLeaAGS-37
❑ 89BasCitRS-20
❑ 90Bes-139
❑ 90MemChiB-2
❑ 90MemChiP-1013
❑ 90MemChiS-22
❑ 90StaFS7-87
❑ 91LinDriAA-411
❑ 91MemChiLD-411
❑ 91MemChiP-658
❑ 92IowCubF-4054
❑ 92IowCubS-215
❑ 92Sco-844
❑ 92TopDeb91-136
❑ 93IowCubF-2137
❑ 94PawRedSDD-17
Pedrique, Al (Alfredo)
❑ 80VenLeaS-207
❑ 82JacMetT-16
❑ 84JacMetT-23
❑ 85IntLeaAT-14
❑ 86TidTidT-24
❑ 86TidTidP-24
❑ 87MetColP-43
❑ 88Don-361
❑ 88Fle-338
❑ 88FleGlo-338
❑ 88PanSti-375
❑ 88PirTeal-25
❑ 88Sco-301
❑ 88ScoGlo-301
❑ 88StaLinPi-16
❑ 88Top-294
❑ 88TopRoo-17
❑ 88TopSti-128
❑ 88TopSti-304
❑ 88TopTif-294
❑ 88ToyRoo-23

- 89Bow-104
- 89BowTif-104
- 89Sco-614
- 89TigMar-17
- 89Top-566
- 89Top-699
- 89TopTif-566
- 90CMC-596
- 90ProAAAF-149
- 90TacTigC-19
- 90TacTigP-102
- 91LinDriAAA-565
- 91MetWIZ-311
- 91TidTidLD-565
- 91TidTidP-2519
- 92OmaRoyF-2971
- 92OmaRoyS-341
- 93EdmTraF-1144
- 93LinVenB-275
- 94EdmTraF-2881
- 94VenLinU-170
- 95SpoIndTI-18

Pedro, Blanco
- 92EliTwiC-13

Pedrosa, Alex
- 96BluOriB-24

Peek, Timothy
- 87UtiBluSP-24
- 88SpaPhiP-1027
- 88SpaPhiS-15
- 90MadMusB-23
- 91HunStaC-18
- 91HunStaLD-291
- 91HunStaP-1793
- 91HunStaTI-17
- 91LinDriAA-291
- 92ProFS7-130
- 92SkyAAAF-243
- 92TacTigF-2499
- 92TacTigS-543
- 93TacTigF-3028
- 94MemChiF-356

Peel, Homer
- 33WorCig-78
- 34Gou-88

Peel, Jack
- 87ChaWheP-24
- 88TamTarS-20
- 89SarWhiSS-18
- 90ChaRanS-20

Peeples, James
- 87OldJudN-391
- 87OldJudN-392

Peeples, Mike
- 96Exc-118
- 96HagSunB-17
- 97DunBluJTI-23
- 98KnoSG-17
- 98SouLeaTPG-29

Peer, Jeff
- 94VerExpC-25
- 94VerExpF-3918

Peery, George
- 25Zee-98

Peet, Harold
- 14Zee-70

Peever, Lloyd
- 92FroRowDP-37
- 92FroRowDPG-37
- 92FroRowDPS-37
- 92LSUTigM-8
- 93StaCluM-171
- 94NewHavRF-1547
- 95Exc-190
- 97NewHavRB-24
- 97SalAva-23

Peguero, Americo
- 96BluOriB-25
- 97DelSho-16

Peguero, Darwin
- 98AubDouTI-20

Peguero, Jerry
- 87ModA'sP-17
- 88HunStaTI-14
- 90SalSpuCLC-135

Peguero, Jose
- 86ModA'sC-17
- 87ModA'sC-13
- 89BelBreIS-21
- 90SalSpuP-2726
- 94SanBerSC-16
- 94SanBerSF-2768
- 95StCatSTI-11

Peguero, Julio
- 87MacPirP-16
- 88CarLeaAS-14
- 88SalBucS-15
- 89HarSenP-294
- 89HarSenS-13
- 90CMC-763
- 90EasLeaAP-EL24
- 90HarSenP-1206
- 90HarSenS-14
- 91LinDriAAA-492
- 91ScrRedBLD-492
- 91ScrRedBP-2553
- 92ScrRedBF-2460
- 92ScrRedBS-498
- 92Ult-547
- 93LimRocDWB-26
- 95PorCitRTI-17
- 96TacRaiB-19

Peguero, Pablo
- 75AlbDukCa-15
- 77LodDodT-12
- 79AlbDukTc-1
- 80AlbDukTc-3
- 85DomLeaS-88

Pegues, Steve
- 88FayGenP-1081
- 89FayGenP-1594
- 90CMC-836
- 90LonTigP-1282
- 91Cla/Bes-126
- 91LinDriAA-393
- 91LonTigLD-393
- 91LonTigP-1891
- 92LasVegSF-2806
- 92LasVegSS-236
- 92SkyAAAF-115
- 93Bow-166
- 93LasVegSF-958
- 93LinVenB-226
- 93TriAAAGF-25
- 94IndIndF-1823
- 94VenLinU-74
- 95PirFil-25
- 95Top-655
- 96RicBraRC-22
- 96RicBraUB-22

Peitz, Henry
- 03BreE10-114
- 09ColChiE-227
- 12ColRedB-227
- 12ColTinT-227
- 95ConTSN-1352
- 98CamPepP-61

Pelatowski, Keith
- 94WilCubC-18
- 94WilCubF-3762

Pelka, Brian
- 93WelPirC-18
- 93WelPirF-3354
- 94WelPirC-16
- 94WelPirF-3493

Pellagrini, Ed
- 46RedSoxTI-18
- 47RedSoxTI-19
- 49Bow-172
- 51Bow-292
- 52Top-405
- 53Top-28
- 75RedSox1T-29
- 79DiaGre-239
- 83TopRep5-405
- 91TopArc1-28

Pellant, Gary
- 80LynSaiT-14
- 82WauTimF-23
- 83WauTimF-3

Pellegrino, Tony
- 86SpoIndC-172
- 88ChaRaiP-1194
- 89WicStaR-3
- 89WicWraR-12

Pellot, Victor
- 93JohCitCC-15
- 93JohCitCF-3696

Pellow, Kit
- 96SpoIndB-20
- 97LanLugTS-20
- 98WicWraM-16
- 99Bow-106
- 99BowBes-174
- 99BowBesAR-174
- 99BowBesR-174
- 99BowChr-106
- 99BowChrG-106
- 99BowChrGR-106
- 99BowChrI-106
- 99BowChrIR-106
- 99BowChrR-106
- 99BowGol-106
- 99BowInt-106
- 99StaClu-146
- 99StaCluFDI-146
- 99StaCluOoaK-146
- 99StaCluPP-146
- 99Top-425
- 99TopChr-425
- 99TopChrR-425

Pells, Harry
- 76QuaCitAT-24
- 76QuaCitAT-26
- 77QuaCitAT-23
- 78QuaCitAT-17

Pelmmons, Scott
- 90ChaWheB-6

Peltier, Dan
- 89ButCopKSP-27
- 90CMC-804
- 90ProAaA-71
- 90TopMag-2
- 90TulDriP-1168
- 90TulDriTI-19
- 91Bow-266
- 91Bow-288
- 91Cla2-T23
- 91ClaGam-176
- 91LinDriAAA-316
- 91OklCit8LD-316
- 91OklCit8P-192
- 91UppDec-69
- 92DonRoo-91
- 92OklCit8F-1927
- 92OklCit8S-318
- 92OPC-618
- 92SkyAAAF-146
- 92Top-618
- 92TopGol-618
- 92TopGolW-618
- 92TopMic-618
- 93Don-473
- 93Lea-443
- 93OklCit8F-1638
- 93PacSpa-644
- 93Pin-605
- 93RanKee-423
- 93RanStaC-30
- 93Sco-240
- 93SelRoo-147T
- 93StaClu-242
- 93StaCluFDI-242
- 93StaCluMOP-242
- 94Don-515
- 94Fle-316
- 94OklCit8F-1507
- 94Sco-569
- 94ScoGolR-569
- 94StaClu-457
- 94StaCluFDI-457
- 94StaCluGR-457
- 94StaCluMOP-457
- 94StaCluT-254
- 94StaCluTFDI-254
- 94Top-441
- 94TopGol-441
- 94TopSpa-441
- 96PhoFirB-22

Pelton, Brad
- 96BurIndB-13
- 97WatIndTI-22

Pelty, Barney
- 09PC7HHB-34
- 09RamT20-93
- 09T206-285
- 09T206-286
- 10DomDisP-97
- 10JuJuDE-33
- 10RedCroT-62
- 10RedCroT-148
- 10RedCroT-235
- 10SweCapPP-54
- 11HelSta-63
- 11PinT-5-122
- 11S74Sil-35
- 11SpoLifCW-286
- 11SpoLifM-114
- 11T205-137
- 12HasTriFT-1B
- 12T207-148

Peltz, Peter
- 79WatIndT-25
- 81GleFalWST-14
- 82GleFalWST-9

Peltzer, Kurt
- 90EveGiaB-10
- 90EveGiaP-3126
- 91CliGiaC-7
- 91CliGiaP-832
- 92CliGiaC-12
- 93SanJosGC-19
- 93SanJosGF-5
- 94Bow-107
- 94ShrCapF-1602

Pemberton, Brock
- 75TidTidTI-17
- 91MetWIZ-312

Pemberton, Jose
- 87ElmPioBC-26
- 87ElmPioRC-26

Pemberton, Rudy
- 89BriTigS-20
- 90FayGenP-2421
- 90SouAtlLAS-17
- 91Cla/Bes-181
- 91LakTigC-26
- 91LakTigP-280
- 92ClaFS7-168
- 92LakTigC-26
- 92LakTigF-2292
- 92OPC-656
- 92Top-656
- 92TopGol-656
- 92TopGolW-656
- 92TopMic-656
- 93ClaGolF-164
- 93LonTigF-2321
- 95Fla-260
- 95FleAllR-M8
- 95Sum-153
- 95SumNthD-153
- 95TolMudHTI-22
- 95UppDec-249
- 95UppDecED-249
- 95UppDecEDG-249
- 96PawRedSDD-21
- 96Sco-260
- 97Don-347
- 97DonGolPP-347
- 97DonSilPP-347
- 97DonTea-59
- 97DonTeaSPE-59
- 97FlaShoLC-75
- 97FlaShoLeg0-75
- 97FlaShoLeg1-75
- 97FlaShoM-A75
- 97FlaShoM-B75
- 97FlaShoM-C75
- 97FlaShoR0-75
- 97FlaShoR1-75
- 97FlaShoR2-75
- 97Fle-547
- 97FleTif-547
- 97Lea-346
- 97LeaFraM-346
- 97LeaFraMDC-346
- 97Sco-471
- 97ScoArtPWB-471
- 97ScoResC-471
- 97ScoShoS-471
- 97ScoShoSAP-471
- 97Ult-520
- 97UltGolME-520
- 97UltPlaME-520

Pena, Abelino
- 75BurBeeT-19
- 76BurBeeT-26

Pena, Adelis
- 96EriSeaB-18

Pena, Adriano
- 81WisRapTT-8
- 85DomLeaS-163

Pena, Alejandro
- 79CliDodT-9
- 81AlbDukTc-4
- 82DodPol-26
- 83AllGamPI-171
- 83DodPol-26
- 83TopTra-83T
- 84AllGamPI-85
- 84DodPol-26
- 84Don-250
- 84Fle-109
- 84Nes792-324
- 84Top-324
- 84TopSti-82
- 84TopTif-324
- 85DodCokP-24
- 85Don-337
- 85Fle-379
- 85FleStaS-94
- 85Lea-64
- 85OPC-110
- 85SevCoi-W15
- 85Top-110
- 85TopGloS-33
- 85TopSti-73
- 85TopSup-17
- 85TopTif-110
- 86DodCokP-22
- 86DodPol-26
- 86Fle-140
- 86Top-665
- 86TopTif-665
- 87DodMot-18
- 87DodPho-11
- 87DodPol-13
- 87Fle-449
- 87FleGlo-449
- 87OPC-363
- 87Top-787
- 87TopTif-787
- 88DodMot-18
- 88DodPol-26
- 88Don-598
- 88FleUpd-97
- 88FleUpdG-97
- 88StaLinD-13
- 88Top-277
- 88TopTif-277
- 89DodMot-18
- 89DodPol-16
- 89DodStaSV-9
- 89Don-557
- 89Fle-69
- 89FleGlo-69
- 89Sco-389
- 89Top-57
- 89TopTif-57
- 89UppDec-137
- 90Bow-124
- 90BowTif-124
- 90DodTar-614
- 90Don-664
- 90Fle-405
- 90FleCan-405
- 90FleUpd-38
- 90Lea-403
- 90MetColP-23
- 90MetKah-26
- 90OPC-483
- 90PubIntS-15
- 90Sco-39
- 90ScoRoo-32T
- 90Top-483
- 90TopTif-483
- 90TopTra-89T
- 90TopTraT-89T
- 90TopTVM-17
- 90UppDec-279
- 90UppDec-703
- 91Don-566
- 91Fle-158
- 91Lea-70
- 91MetColP-43
- 91MetKah-26
- 91MetWIZ-313
- 91OPC-544
- 91Sco-204
- 91StaClu-583
- 91StaCluMO-30
- 91Top-544
- 91TopDesS-544
- 91TopMic-544
- 91TopTif-544
- 91UppDec-388
- 92BraLykP-22
- 92BraLykS-26
- 92Cla1-T18
- 92Don-616
- 92Don-772
- 92Fle-700
- 92FleUpd-70
- 92Lea-489
- 92LeaBlaG-489
- 92OPC-337
- 92Pin-528
- 92Sco-691
- 92Sco-787
- 92StaClu-833
- 92Top-337
- 92TopGol-337
- 92TopGolW-337
- 92TopMic-337
- 92Ult-462
- 92UppDec-694
- 93Fle-369
- 93OPC-311
- 93Sco-625
- 93StaClu-205
- 93StaCluFDI-205
- 93StaCluMOP-205
- 93Top-198
- 93TopGol-198
- 93TopInaM-198
- 93TopInaR-198
- 93TopMic-198
- 94ColC-458
- 94ColChoGS-458
- 94ColChoSS-458
- 95Pac-350

Pena, Alex
- 94BluOriC-17
- 94BluOriF-3561
- 96AugGreB-21
- 97AugGre-29
- 97HigDesMG-19
- 98AugGreM-23

Pena, Angel
- 95GreFalDTI-18
- 97CalLeaTP-21
- 97SanBerS-17
- 98FleUpd-U11
- 98SanAntMG-22
- 98TexLeaTPG-27
- 99BasAmeTP-76
- 99BasAmeTPG-76
- 99Bow-356
- 99BowGol-356
- 99BowInt-356
- 99DodPol-20
- 99Fle-246
- 99FleBri-154
- 99FleBri2G-154
- 99FleBriBlu-154
- 99FleBriGol-154
- 99FleSta9-246
- 99FleWarT-246
- 99PacOme-124
- 99PacOmeC-124
- 99PacOmeG-124
- 99PacOmePB-124
- 99SkyThu-225
- 99SkyThuRant-225
- 99SkyThuRave-225
- 99SP Aut-105
- 99SP SigAuto-AP
- 99SP SigAutoG-AP
- 99SP TopP-98
- 99SP TopPPE-98
- 99SpoIll-52
- 99SPSig-28
- 99SPx-101
- 99SPxFinR-101
- 99SPxFinS-101
- 99StaClu-143
- 99StaCluFDI-143
- 99StaCluOoaK-143
- 99StaCluPP-143
- 99ThuSkySupR-225
- 99UppDec-272
- 99UppDecE-115
- 99UppDecEFXG-115
- 99UppDecEL1-272
- 99UppDecEL2-272
- 99UppDecRI-AP
- 99UppDecRIL2-AP
- 99Vic-196

Pena, Antonio
- 91SanBerSC-10
- 91SanBerSP-1986

Pena, Arturo
- 85DomLeaS-69
- 93LimRocDWB-88

Pena, Bert
- 80ColAstT-8
- 81TucTorT-7
- 82AstAstI-3
- 82TucTorT-1
- 83TucTorT-17
- 84TucTorC-67
- 86TucTorP-18
- 87AstMot-24
- 87TucTorP-16
- 88BlaYNPRWL-11
- 88ColCliC-13
- 88ColCliP-16
- 88ColCliP-322
- 89BlaYNPRWL-182

Pena, Carlos
- 99199Fin-284
- 99BasAmeTP-77
- 99BasAmeTPG-77
- 99Bow-321
- 99BowBes-154

❑ 99BowBesAR-154
❑ 99BowBesR-154
❑ 99BowGol-321
❑ 99BowInt-321
❑ 99FinGolRef-284
❑ 99FinRef-284
❑ 99TopBlaLC1-90
❑ 99TopBlaLC2-90
❑ 99TopBlaLC3-90
❑ 99TopGal-133
❑ 99TopGalPP-133
❑ 99TopGalPPI-133
❑ 99TopGolL-90
❑ 99TopGolLC1-90
❑ 99TopGolLC2-90
❑ 99TopGolLOtO-90
❑ 99TopRedLC1-90
❑ 99TopRedLC2-90
❑ 99TopRedLC3-90

Pena, Dan
❑ 87VerBeaDP-4
❑ 88BakDodCLC-257

Pena, Elvis
❑ 95AshTouTI-2
❑ 96SalAvaB-21
❑ 97BesLimA-31
❑ 97SalAva-24
❑ 98AshTouM-15
❑ 98BesPreA-35

Pena, Frankie
❑ 98ForWayW!-9

Pena, George
❑ 73OPC-601
❑ 73Top-601
❑ 74TacTwiC-16
❑ 75IowOakT-13

Pena, Geronimo
❑ 87SavCarP-4
❑ 88FloStaLAS-16
❑ 88St.PetCS-21
❑ 90CMC-119
❑ 90FleUpd-52
❑ 90LouRedBC-19
❑ 90LouRedBLBC-33
❑ 90LouRedBP-412
❑ 90ProAAAF-526
❑ 90TopTVCa-59
❑ 91CarPol-7
❑ 91Don-712
❑ 91FleUpd-118
❑ 91OPC-636
❑ 91Sco-717
❑ 91ScoRoo-17
❑ 91Top-636
❑ 91TopDeb90-123
❑ 91TopDesS-636
❑ 91TopMic-636
❑ 91TopTif-636
❑ 91UppDec-20
❑ 92CarPol-15
❑ 92Don-533
❑ 92Fle-587
❑ 92OPC-166
❑ 92Pin-487
❑ 92Sco-516
❑ 92Sco100RS-12
❑ 92StaClu-466
❑ 92Top-166
❑ 92TopGol-166
❑ 92TopGolW-166
❑ 92TopMic-166
❑ 92UppDec-596
❑ 93Bow-604
❑ 93CarPol-15
❑ 93CarStaC-20
❑ 93Don-310
❑ 93Fla-126
❑ 93Fle-131
❑ 93Lea-118
❑ 93LimRocDWB-78
❑ 93OPC-238
❑ 93PacBeiA-30
❑ 93PacSpa-300
❑ 93PacSpaGE-8
❑ 93PanSti-193
❑ 93Pin-174
❑ 93Sco-161
❑ 93Sel-372
❑ 93StaClu-215
❑ 93StaCluFDI-215
❑ 93StaCluMOP-215
❑ 93Top-312
❑ 93TopGol-312
❑ 93TopInaM-312
❑ 93TopInaR-312
❑ 93TopMic-312
❑ 93Ult-466
❑ 93UppDec-331
❑ 93UppDec-466
❑ 93UppDec-482
❑ 93UppDecGold-331
❑ 93UppDecGold-466
❑ 93UppDecGold-482
❑ 94CarPol-15
❑ 94ColC-457
❑ 94ColChoGS-457
❑ 94ColChoSS-457
❑ 94Don-234
❑ 94Fin-315
❑ 94FinRef-315
❑ 94Fle-643
❑ 94Lea-172
❑ 94Pac-600
❑ 94Pin-214
❑ 94PinArtP-214
❑ 94PinMusC-214
❑ 94Sel-148
❑ 94StaClu-523
❑ 94StaCluFDI-523
❑ 94StaCluGR-523
❑ 94StaCluMOP-523
❑ 94StaCluT-307
❑ 94StaCluTFDI-307
❑ 94Top-444
❑ 94TopGol-444
❑ 94TopSpa-444
❑ 95ColCho-186
❑ 95ColChoGS-186
❑ 95ColChoSS-186
❑ 95Don-422
❑ 95DonPreP-422
❑ 95Fin-218
❑ 95FinRef-218
❑ 95Fle-506
❑ 95Lea-263
❑ 95LeaLim-119
❑ 95Pac-413
❑ 95Pin-348
❑ 95PinArtP-348
❑ 95PinMusC-348
❑ 95Sco-463
❑ 95ScoGolR-463
❑ 95ScoPlaTS-463
❑ 95Sel-100
❑ 95SelArtP-100
❑ 95StaClu-427
❑ 95StaCluMOP-427
❑ 95StaCluSTWS-427
❑ 95Ult-226
❑ 95UltGolM-226
❑ 95UppDec-61
❑ 95UppDecED-61
❑ 95UppDecEDG-61
❑ 96SP-136

Pena, Hipolito
❑ 85DomLeaS-39
❑ 86NasPirP-21
❑ 87VanCanP-1615
❑ 88ColCliC-7
❑ 88ColCliP-8
❑ 88ColCliP-315
❑ 89ColCliC-5
❑ 89ColCliP-10
❑ 89ColCliP-744
❑ 89Don-598
❑ 89Fle-263
❑ 89FleGlo-263
❑ 89Top-109
❑ 89TopTif-109
❑ 90CMC-206
❑ 90ColCliC-6
❑ 91ColCliLD-114
❑ 91ColCliP-597
❑ 91LinDriAAA-114
❑ 92YanWIZ8-144
❑ 93LimRocDWB-64

Pena, Jaime
❑ 89EriOriS-17

Pena, James
❑ 86EveGiaC-14
❑ 86EveGiaPC-21
❑ 87CliGiaP-19
❑ 89SanJosGB-16
❑ 89SanJosGCLC-216
❑ 89SanJosGP-445
❑ 89SanJosGS-21
❑ 90ShrCapP-1442
❑ 90ShrCapS-19
❑ 90TexLeaAGS-35
❑ 91LinDriAA-317
❑ 91ShrCapLD-317
❑ 91ShrCapP-1820
❑ 92DonRoo-92
❑ 92FleUpd-129
❑ 92PhoFirF-2819
❑ 92PhoFirS-393
❑ 93Bow-54
❑ 93Don-628
❑ 93Fle-536
❑ 93LasVegSF-942
❑ 93Sco-288
❑ 94SanBerSC-17
❑ 94SanBerSF-2757

Pena, Jesus
❑ 96EriSeaB-19
❑ 97HicCraB-23
❑ 97HicCraRB-28
❑ 98WinWar-22

Pena, Jose
❑ 85DomLeaS-79
❑ 86CliGiaP-19
❑ 88ShrCapP-1292
❑ 88UtiBluSP-23
❑ 89ShrCapP-1848

Pena, Jose G.
❑ 69Top-339
❑ 70OPC-523
❑ 70Top-523
❑ 71Dod-11
❑ 71MLBOffS-112
❑ 71OPC-693
❑ 71Top-693
❑ 72OPC-322
❑ 72Top-322
❑ 90DodTar-615

Pena, Jose R.
❑ 98SavSanGM-20

Pena, Juan
❑ 96MicBatCB-20
❑ 96MidLeaAB-46
❑ 97FloStaLTPB-22
❑ 97SarRedS-19
❑ 98PawRedSQ-23
❑ 98SouOreTG-25
❑ 99BasAmeTP-78
❑ 99BasAmeTPG-78
❑ 99Bow-384
❑ 99BowGol-384
❑ 99BowInt-384
❑ 99PacOme-46
❑ 99PacOmeC-46
❑ 99PacOmeG-46
❑ 99PacOmePB-46
❑ 99SP TopP-99
❑ 99SP TopPPE-99
❑ 99SPSig-98

Pena, Luis
❑ 86MacPirP-18
❑ 87NewOriP-29

Pena, Manny
❑ 83OrlTwiT-13

Pena, Orlando
❑ 59RedEnq-19
❑ 59Top-271
❑ 60RedJayP-9
❑ 63Top-214
❑ 64AthJayP-10
❑ 64Top-124
❑ 64TopVen-124
❑ 65Top-311
❑ 66Top-239
❑ 66TopVen-239
❑ 67Top-449
❑ 67TopVen-232
❑ 68Top-471
❑ 69TopSta-97
❑ 73BalOriP-33
❑ 73OriJohP-27
❑ 73OriTeal-23
❑ 74OPC-393
❑ 74Top-393
❑ 75CalAngP-29
❑ 75OPC-573
❑ 75Top-573
❑ 75TopMin-573
❑ 75TucTorTI-15
❑ 76ForLauYS-18
❑ 76VenLeaS-184
❑ 76VenLeaS-190
❑ 91OriCro-357

Pena, Pedro
❑ 89MedAthB-11
❑ 90MadMusP-2270
❑ 90MidLeaASGS-56
❑ 90ModA'sC-26
❑ 91SanJosGC-19
❑ 91SanJosGP-8

Pena, Porfirio
❑ 90BatCliP-3068
❑ 91MarPhiC-15
❑ 91MarPhiP-3456

Pena, R. Roberto
❑ 65Top-549
❑ 66Top-559
❑ 69OPC-184
❑ 69Top-184
❑ 69TopFou-15
❑ 69TopTeaP-12
❑ 70OPC-44
❑ 70Top-44
❑ 71BreTeal-12
❑ 71MLBOffS-448
❑ 71OPC-334
❑ 71Top-334
❑ 94BreMilB-161

Pena, Ramon
❑ 86GleFalTP-18
❑ 87GleFalTP-20
❑ 88TolMudHC-6
❑ 88TolMudHP-610
❑ 89TigMar-18
❑ 89TolMudHC-2
❑ 89TolMudHP-779
❑ 90TopDeb89-96

Pena, Tony
❑ 77SalPirT-17
❑ 79BufBisT-5
❑ 80PorBeaT-24
❑ 81Top-551
❑ 82Don-124
❑ 82Fle-490
❑ 82FleSta-72
❑ 82Top-138
❑ 83AllGamPI-133
❑ 83Don-59
❑ 83DonActA-35
❑ 83Fle-316
❑ 83FleSta-149
❑ 83FleSti-74
❑ 83OPC-133
❑ 83Top-590
❑ 83TopSti-281
❑ 84AllGamPI-43
❑ 84Don-186
❑ 84DonActAS-3
❑ 84Fle-259
❑ 84FunFooP-88
❑ 84Nes792-645
❑ 84NesDreT-19
❑ 84OPC-152
❑ 84Pir-15
❑ 84SevCoi-E18
❑ 84Top-645
❑ 84TopRubD-32
❑ 84TopSti-129
❑ 84TopTif-645
❑ 85AllGamPI-132
❑ 85Don-24
❑ 85Don-64
❑ 85DonActA-10
❑ 85DonSupD-24
❑ 85Fle-472
❑ 85FleLimE-24
❑ 85Lea-24
❑ 85OPC-358
❑ 85Pir-15
❑ 85Top-358
❑ 85TopMin-358
❑ 85TopRubD-32
❑ 85TopSti-124
❑ 85TopTif-358
❑ 86BurKinA-1
❑ 86Don-64
❑ 86DonAll-22
❑ 86Fle-616
❑ 86FleLimE-34
❑ 86FleMin-119
❑ 86FleStiC-87
❑ 86Lea-58
❑ 86OPC-260
❑ 86SevCoi-C12
❑ 86Spo-165
❑ 86SpoDecG-72
❑ 86Top-260
❑ 86TopSti-125
❑ 86TopTat-5
❑ 86TopTif-260
❑ 87BurKinA-15
❑ 87CarSmo-11
❑ 87CarTeal-24
❑ 87ClaGam-34
❑ 87Don-115
❑ 87DonAll-46
❑ 87DonOpeD-64
❑ 87Fle-617
❑ 87FleBasA-31
❑ 87FleGlo-617
❑ 87FleLeaL-35
❑ 87FleLimE-32
❑ 87FleStiC-90
❑ 87FleUpd-98
❑ 87FleUpdG-98
❑ 87HosSti-14
❑ 87KeyFooD-5
❑ 87KraFoo-12
❑ 87Lea-256
❑ 87MandMSL-2
❑ 87MSAIceTD-5
❑ 87OPC-60
❑ 87OurOwnTD-5
❑ 87RedFolSB-25
❑ 87Spo-93
❑ 87Spo-151
❑ 87SpoTeaP-18
❑ 87Top-60
❑ 87Top-131
❑ 87TopCoi-39
❑ 87TopSti-129
❑ 87TopTif-60
❑ 87TopTif-131
❑ 87TopTra-95T
❑ 87TopTraT-95T
❑ 87WeiMarD-5
❑ 88CarSmo-13
❑ 88CarTeal-26
❑ 88Don-170
❑ 88DonBasB-156
❑ 88Fle-45
❑ 88FleGlo-45
❑ 88FleWorS-5
❑ 88Lea-95
❑ 88OPC-117
❑ 88PanSti-387
❑ 88PanSti-447
❑ 88PanSti-449
❑ 88RedFolSB-67
❑ 88Sco-48
❑ 88ScoGlo-48
❑ 88ScoSam-48
❑ 88Spo-142
❑ 88StaLinCa-16
❑ 88Top-351
❑ 88Top-410
❑ 88TopSti-52
❑ 88TopTif-351
❑ 88TopTif-410
❑ 89Bow-435
❑ 89BowTif-435
❑ 89CadEllD-38
❑ 89CarSmo-17
❑ 89CarTeal-22
❑ 89Don-163
❑ 89DonBasB-299
❑ 89Fle-460
❑ 89FleGlo-460
❑ 89K-M-30
❑ 89OPC-94
❑ 89PanSti-180
❑ 89Sco-36
❑ 89Top-715
❑ 89TopSti-38
❑ 89TopTif-715
❑ 89UppDec-330
❑ 90Bow-271
❑ 90BowTif-271
❑ 90ClaYel-T67
❑ 90Don-181
❑ 90DonBesA-44
❑ 90Fle-256
❑ 90FleCan-256
❑ 90FleUpd-74
❑ 90Lea-104
❑ 90MLBBasB-34
❑ 90OPC-115
❑ 90PubIntS-225
❑ 90PubIntS-269
❑ 90RedSoxP-14
❑ 90Sco-122
❑ 90ScoRoo-7T
❑ 90Top-115
❑ 90TopBig-290
❑ 90TopTif-115
❑ 90TopTra-90T
❑ 90TopTraT-90T
❑ 90TopTVRS-20
❑ 90UppDec-276
❑ 90UppDec-748
❑ 91Bow-124
❑ 91CadEllD-41
❑ 91Don-456
❑ 91Fle-106
❑ 91Lea-33
❑ 91OPC-375
❑ 91PanFreS-263
❑ 91PanSti-219
❑ 91RedSoxP-14
❑ 91RedSoxP-23
❑ 91Sco-790
❑ 91StaClu-505
❑ 91Stu-17
❑ 91Top-375
❑ 91TopDesS-375
❑ 91TopMic-375
❑ 91TopTif-375
❑ 91Ult-37
❑ 91UppDec-652
❑ 92Bow-364
❑ 92Don-208
❑ 92Fle-43
❑ 92Fre-9
❑ 92HitTheBB-25
❑ 92Lea-323
❑ 92LeaBlaG-323
❑ 92OPC-569
❑ 92PanSti-84
❑ 92Pin-33
❑ 92RedSoxDD-21
❑ 92Sco-446
❑ 92StaClu-706
❑ 92StaCluNC-706
❑ 92Stu-135
❑ 92Top-569
❑ 92TopGol-569
❑ 92TopGolW-569
❑ 92TopMic-569
❑ 92TriPla-48
❑ 92Ult-18
❑ 92UltAwaW-17
❑ 92UppDec-252
❑ 93Bow-439
❑ 93CadDis-44
❑ 93Don-297
❑ 93Fle-563
❑ 93FunPac-165
❑ 93Lea-43
❑ 93LimRocDWB-105
❑ 93LinVenB-298
❑ 93LinVenB-317
❑ 93OPC-316
❑ 93PacSpa-34
❑ 93PanSti-91
❑ 93Pin-506
❑ 93RedSoxP-24
❑ 93RedSoxWHP-23
❑ 93Sco-261
❑ 93Sel-148
❑ 93StaClu-164
❑ 93StaCluFDI-164
❑ 93StaCluMOP-164
❑ 93Top-618
❑ 93TopGol-618
❑ 93TopInaM-618
❑ 93TopInaR-618
❑ 93TopMic-618
❑ 93TriPla-85
❑ 93Ult-154
❑ 93UppDec-33
❑ 93UppDec-185
❑ 93UppDecGold-33
❑ 93UppDecGold-185
❑ 94Don-191
❑ 94Fle-37
❑ 94FleUpd-36
❑ 94Pac-61
❑ 94PanSti-32
❑ 94Sco-363
❑ 94ScoGolR-363
❑ 94ScoRoo-RT59
❑ 94ScoRooGR-RT59
❑ 94StaClu-71
❑ 94StaCluFDI-71
❑ 94StaCluGR-71
❑ 94StaCluMOP-71
❑ 94Top-85
❑ 94TopGol-85
❑ 94TopSpa-85
❑ 94TopTra-119T
❑ 95Don-454
❑ 95DonPreP-454
❑ 95DonTopotO-64
❑ 95Fle-143
❑ 95Pac-127
❑ 95Sco-495
❑ 95ScoGolR-495
❑ 95ScoPlaTS-495
❑ 95Top-284

❑ 96ColCho-366T
❑ 96ColCho-527
❑ 96ColChoGS-527
❑ 96ColChoSS-527
❑ 96Don-370
❑ 96DonPreP-370
❑ 96Fla-73
❑ 96Fle-95
❑ 96FleTif-95
❑ 96IndFle-11
❑ 96LeaSigEA-153
❑ 96Pac-304
❑ 96Sco-460
❑ 96UppDec-218
❑ 97PacPriGotD-GD38
❑ 97WhiSoxTI-29
❑ 98ColCho-129
Pena, Willie Mo
❑ 99Bow-401
❑ 99BowGol-401
❑ 99BowInt-401
Penafeather, Pat
❑ 88AubAstP-1952
Penalver, Luis
❑ 80VenLeaS-97
Pencavitch, Kevin
❑ 93VerBeaDF-2216
Pender, Shawn
❑ 92WatIndC-26
❑ 92WatIndF-3250
Pendergast, Steve
❑ 19W514-117
Pendergrass, Tyrone
❑ 96DanBraB-17
❑ 97MacBra-16
❑ 98CarLeaAC-39
❑ 98DanQ-C-9
Pendleton, Jim
❑ 52Par-69
❑ 53BraJohC-25
❑ 53BraMer-14
❑ 53BraSpiaS3-20
❑ 53Top-185
❑ 54BraJohC-3
❑ 54Top-165
❑ 55BraGolS-26
❑ 55BraJohC-3
❑ 55Top-15
❑ 55TopDouH-33
❑ 55TopTesS-8
❑ 57Bra8x1-10
❑ 57Top-327
❑ 58Top-104
❑ 59RedEnq-20
❑ 59Top-174
❑ 59TopVen-174
❑ 62Col.45B-15
❑ 62Col45'HC-13
❑ 62Top-432
❑ 63Col45'JP-7
❑ 83Bra53F-53
❑ 89AstCol4S-25
❑ 91TopArc1-185
❑ 94TopArc1-165
❑ 94TopArc1G-165
Pendleton, Terry
❑ 83ArkTraT-15
❑ 84Car5x7-20
❑ 84LouRedR-15
❑ 84OCoandSI-219
❑ 85AllGamPI-124
❑ 85CarTeal-26
❑ 85Don-534A
❑ 85Don-534B
❑ 85Fle-236
❑ 85OPC-346
❑ 85Top-346
❑ 85TopTif-346
❑ 86CarIGAS-10
❑ 86CarKASD-14
❑ 86CarSchM-19
❑ 86CarTeal-34
❑ 86Don-205
❑ 86Fle-44
❑ 86KayB-23
❑ 86Lea-137
❑ 86OPC-321
❑ 86Top-528
❑ 86TopSti-53
❑ 86TopTat-17
❑ 86TopTif-528
❑ 87CarSmo-16
❑ 87CarTeal-25
❑ 87Don-183
❑ 87DonOpeD-62
❑ 87Fle-306
❑ 87FleGlo-306
❑ 87Lea-124
❑ 87OPC-8
❑ 87SpoTeaP-12
❑ 87Top-8
❑ 87TopSti-54
❑ 87TopTif-8
❑ 88CarSmo-17
❑ 88CarTeal-27
❑ 88Don-454
❑ 88DonBasB-187
❑ 88Fle-46
❑ 88FleAwaW-28
❑ 88FleGlo-46
❑ 88FleStiC-119
❑ 88FleSup-27
❑ 88Lea-246
❑ 88OPC-105
❑ 88PanSti-392
❑ 88RedFolSB-68
❑ 88Sco-190
❑ 88ScoGlo-190
❑ 88Spo-159
❑ 88StaLinCa-17
❑ 88Top-635
❑ 88TopBig-53
❑ 88TopSti-49
❑ 88TopStiB-7
❑ 88TopTif-635
❑ 89Bow-437
❑ 89BowTif-437
❑ 89CarSmo-18
❑ 89CarTeal-23
❑ 89Don-230
❑ 89DonBasB-156
❑ 89Fle-461
❑ 89FleGlo-461
❑ 89OPC-375
❑ 89PanSti-185
❑ 89Sco-137
❑ 89Spo-99
❑ 89Top-375
❑ 89TopBig-151
❑ 89TopSti-42
❑ 89TopTif-375
❑ 89UppDec-131
❑ 90Bow-197
❑ 90BowTif-197
❑ 90CarSmo-19
❑ 90Don-299
❑ 90DonBesN-34
❑ 90Fle-257
❑ 90FleCan-257
❑ 90Lea-260
❑ 90OPC-725
❑ 90PanSti-337
❑ 90PubIntS-226
❑ 90Sco-208
❑ 90Spo-174
❑ 90Top-725
❑ 90TopBig-135
❑ 90TopMag-69
❑ 90TopSti-40
❑ 90TopTif-725
❑ 90TopTVCa-28
❑ 90UppDec-469
❑ 91Bow-570
❑ 91BraDubP-23
❑ 91BraSubS-30
❑ 91Don-446
❑ 91Fle-642
❑ 91FleUpd-76
❑ 91Lea-304
❑ 91OPC-725
❑ 91OPCPre-95
❑ 91Sco-230
❑ 91ScoRoo-50T
❑ 91SimandSMLBL-33
❑ 91StaClu-327
❑ 91StaCluMO-23
❑ 91StaCluMO-24
❑ 91Stu-148
❑ 91Top-485
❑ 91TopDesS-485
❑ 91TopMic-485
❑ 91TopTif-485
❑ 91TopTra-90T
❑ 91TopTraT-90T
❑ 91Ult-10
❑ 91UppDec-484
❑ 91UppDec-708
❑ 92Bow-254
❑ 92BraLykP-23
❑ 92BraLykS-27
❑ 92CarMcD-40
❑ 92Cla1-T70
❑ 92ClaGam-182
❑ 92ColAllG-8
❑ 92ColAllP-8
❑ 92Don-237
❑ 92DonBonC-BC2
❑ 92DonCraJ1-26
❑ 92DonEli-16
❑ 92Fle-366
❑ 92Fle-691
❑ 92FleAll-15
❑ 92FleCitTP-15
❑ 92Fre-3
❑ 92Hig5-25
❑ 92KinDis-1
❑ 92Lea-245
❑ 92LeaBlaG-245
❑ 92MSABenSHD-14
❑ 92New-20
❑ 92OPC-115
❑ 92OPCPre-195
❑ 92PanSti-148
❑ 92PanSti-164
❑ 92Pin-18
❑ 92Pos-22
❑ 92RedFolS-74
❑ 92Sco-18
❑ 92Sco-789
❑ 92Sco100S-45
❑ 92ScoCokD-18
❑ 92ScoProaG-13
❑ 92ScoProP-1
❑ 92SpollIFK1-24
❑ 92StaClu-510
❑ 92Stu-8
❑ 92SunSee-7
❑ 92Top-115
❑ 92TopGol-115
❑ 92TopGolW-115
❑ 92TopKid-33
❑ 92TopMcD-7
❑ 92TopMic-115
❑ 92TriPla-139
❑ 92Ult-167
❑ 92UltAwaW-4
❑ 92UppDec-229
❑ 92UppDecTMH-2
❑ 92UppDecTMH-39
❑ 93Bow-254
❑ 93BraFloA-8
❑ 93BraLykP-24
❑ 93BraLykS-29
❑ 93BraStaC-21
❑ 93ClaGam-73
❑ 93DenHol-5
❑ 93DiaMar-84
❑ 93Don-234
❑ 93DonMVP-7
❑ 93DurPowP1-8
❑ 93Fin-101
❑ 93FinJum-101
❑ 93FinRef-101
❑ 93Fla-9
❑ 93Fle-12
❑ 93FleAtl-17
❑ 93FleFruotL-51
❑ 93FleTeaL-NL2
❑ 93FunPac-66
❑ 93FunPacA-AS5
❑ 93Hos-9
❑ 93Kra-26
❑ 93Lea-387
❑ 93LeaGolA-R6
❑ 93MetBak-34
❑ 93OPC-322
❑ 93PacSpa-340
❑ 93PanSti-184
❑ 93Pin-60
❑ 93Pin-473
❑ 93Pos-17
❑ 93PosCan-18
❑ 93Sco-36
❑ 93ScoFra-15
❑ 93Sel-17
❑ 93SelStaL-10
❑ 93SelStaL-18
❑ 93SelStaL-35
❑ 93SP-61
❑ 93StaClu-338
❑ 93StaCluFDI-338
❑ 93StaCluM-102
❑ 93StaCluMOP-338
❑ 93Stu-117
❑ 93Top-650
❑ 93TOPBLAG-15
❑ 93TopGol-650
❑ 93TopInaM-650
❑ 93TopInaR-650
❑ 93TopMic-650
❑ 93TriPla-147
❑ 93Ult-11
❑ 93UltAwaW-5
❑ 93UppDec-163
❑ 93UppDecCP-R16
❑ 93UppDecDG-5
❑ 93UppDecGold-163
❑ 93UppDecHRH-HR18
❑ 93USPlaCA-3D
❑ 94Bow-573
❑ 94BraLykP-29
❑ 94BraLykS-27
❑ 94BraUSPC-3C
❑ 94BraUSPC-10H
❑ 94BraUSPC-13D
❑ 94ColC-372
❑ 94ColChoGS-372
❑ 94ColChoSS-372
❑ 94Don-556
❑ 94Fin-118
❑ 94FinRef-118
❑ 94Fla-356
❑ 94Fle-372
❑ 94FleExtB-212
❑ 94Lea-189
❑ 94OPC-38
❑ 94Pac-20
❑ 94PanSti-149
❑ 94Pin-371
❑ 94PinArtP-371
❑ 94PinMusC-371
❑ 94ProMag-1
❑ 94Sco-72
❑ 94ScoGolR-72
❑ 94Sel-34
❑ 94StaClu-313
❑ 94StaCluFDI-313
❑ 94StaCluGR-313
❑ 94StaCluMOP-313
❑ 94StaCluMOP-ST1
❑ 94StaCluST-ST1
❑ 94StaCluT-40
❑ 94StaCluTFDI-40
❑ 94Stu-41
❑ 94SucSav-3
❑ 94Top-735
❑ 94TopGol-735
❑ 94TopSpa-735
❑ 94TriPla-48
❑ 94TriPlaM-10
❑ 94Ult-449
❑ 94UppDec-95
❑ 94UppDecAJ-33
❑ 94UppDecAJG-33
❑ 94UppDecED-95
❑ 95Bow-371
❑ 95ColCho-559T
❑ 95ColCho-TC4
❑ 95Don-394
❑ 95DonPreP-394
❑ 95DonTopotO-246
❑ 95Fin-239
❑ 95FinRef-239
❑ 95Fla-355
❑ 95Fle-317
❑ 95FleUpd-98
❑ 95Lea-338
❑ 95LeaLim-85
❑ 95Pin-404
❑ 95PinArtP-404
❑ 95PinMusC-404
❑ 95Sco-339
❑ 95ScoGolR-339
❑ 95ScoPlaTS-339
❑ 95ScoYouTE-339T
❑ 95Sel-177
❑ 95SelArtP-177
❑ 95SP-57
❑ 95SPSil-57
❑ 95StaClu-66
❑ 95StaClu-613
❑ 95StaCluFDI-66
❑ 95StaCluMOP-66
❑ 95StaCluMOP-613
❑ 95StaCluMOP-RL34
❑ 95StaCluRL-RL34
❑ 95StaCluSTDW-B1T
❑ 95StaCluSTWS-66
❑ 95StaCluSTWS-613
❑ 95StaCluVR-40
❑ 95StaCluVRMO-40
❑ 95Stu-125
❑ 95Top-242
❑ 95TopCyb-134
❑ 95TopTra-105T
❑ 95Ult-353
❑ 95UltGolM-353
❑ 95UppDec-469
❑ 95UppDec-TC2
❑ 95UppDecSE-249
❑ 95UppDecSEG-249
❑ 95UppDecT-TC2
❑ 96ColCho-156
❑ 96ColChoGS-156
❑ 96ColChoSS-156
❑ 96Don-345
❑ 96DonPreP-345
❑ 96EmoXL-188
❑ 96Fin-B8
❑ 96FinRef-B8
❑ 96Fla-266
❑ 96Fle-392
❑ 96FleTif-392
❑ 96Lea-57
❑ 96LeaPrePB-57
❑ 96LeaPrePG-57
❑ 96LeaPrePS-57
❑ 96Pac-78
❑ 96Pin-240
❑ 96PinArtP-140
❑ 96PinFoil-240
❑ 96PinSta-140
❑ 96ProSta-68
❑ 96Sco-49
❑ 96ScoDugC-A42
❑ 96ScoDugCAP-A42
❑ 96StaClu-119
❑ 96StaCluEPB-119
❑ 96StaCluEPG-119
❑ 96StaCluEPS-119
❑ 96StaCluMOP-119
❑ 96Top-170
❑ 96TopGal-71
❑ 96TopGalPPI-71
❑ 96Ult-203
❑ 96UltGolM-203
❑ 96UppDec-78
❑ 97BraSco-3
❑ 97BraScoPl-3
❑ 97BraScoPr-3
❑ 97Don-63
❑ 97DonGolPP-63
❑ 97DonSilPP-63
❑ 97Fle-267
❑ 97FleTif-267
❑ 97Pin-138
❑ 97PinArtP-PP138
❑ 97PinMusC-138
❑ 97PinPrePla-138
❑ 97Sco-62
❑ 97ScoArtPWB-62
❑ 97ScoPreS-62
❑ 97ScoShoS-62
❑ 97ScoShoSAP-62
❑ 97Top-319
❑ 97Ult-535
❑ 97UltGolME-535
❑ 97UltPlaME-535
❑ 98PacAur-49
❑ 98PacOme-118
❑ 98PacOmeR-118
❑ 98PacOnl-348
❑ 98PacOnlR-348
❑ 98PacOnlWC-348
❑ 98Ult-326
❑ 98UltGolM-326
❑ 98UltMas-326
❑ 98UltPlaM-326
❑ 98UppDec-64
❑ 99SkyMolMOA-20
Penebskey, Adolph
❑ 30Zee-151
❑ 31Zee-110
❑ 32Zee-107
Penigar, C.L.
❑ 86CliGiaP-20
❑ 88MidAngGS-17
❑ 89BirBarB-23
❑ 89BirBarP-115
❑ 90CMC-636
❑ 90ProAAAF-180
❑ 90VanCanC-9
❑ 90VanCanP-502
Penix, Troy
❑ 92ClaFS7-441
❑ 92FroRowDP-68
❑ 92FroRowDPG-68
❑ 92FroRowDPS-68
❑ 92SouOreAC-1
❑ 92SouOreAF-3427
❑ 93MadMusC-21
❑ 93MadMusF-1830
❑ 93MidLeaAGF-14
❑ 97ModA'sG-24
Penland, Ken
❑ 88ButCopKSP-6
Penn, Shannon
❑ 90ButCopKSP-24
❑ 91GasRanC-21
❑ 91GasRanP-2698
❑ 92NiaFalRC-16
❑ 92NiaFalRF-3335
❑ 93LonTigF-2316
❑ 94ExcFS7-59
❑ 94TolMudHF-1033
❑ 95Exc-51
❑ 95FleUpd-22
❑ 95Sum-160
❑ 95SumNthD-160
❑ 95TolMudHTI-23
❑ 95Top-636
❑ 96Sco-247
❑ 96TolMudHB-22
Penn, Trevor
❑ 88RocExpLC-29
❑ 89WesPalBES-21
❑ 90JacExpB-11
❑ 90JacExpP-1386
Penner, Ira
❑ 94DayCubC-30
Penner, Kenneth
❑ 17Zee-55
❑ 19Zee-41
❑ 20Zee-72
❑ 21Zee-78
❑ 23Zee-92
❑ 24Zee-137
❑ 25Zee-159
Penniall, David
❑ 77St.PetCT-23
❑ 78ArkTraT-19
❑ 80ArkTraT-10
Pennington, Art
❑ 86NegLeaF-53
❑ 92NegLeaRLI-47
❑ 95NegLeaL2-24
❑ 97NegLeaPC-7D
Pennington, Brad
❑ 89BluOriS-18
❑ 90Bes-65
❑ 90WauTimB-8
❑ 90WauTimP-2121
❑ 90WauTimS-18
❑ 91Cla/Bes-390
❑ 91KanCouCC-9
❑ 91KanCouCP-2657
❑ 92Bow-136
❑ 92ClaFS7-108
❑ 92FreKeyC-20
❑ 92UppDecML-198
❑ 93BalOriP-26
❑ 93Bow-361
❑ 93Bow-661
❑ 93ExcFS7-126
❑ 93FlaWavotF-11
❑ 93FleFinE-163
❑ 93Lea-526
❑ 93RocRedWF-237
❑ 93SelRoo-75T
❑ 93Top-797
❑ 93TopGol-797
❑ 93TopInaM-797
❑ 93TopInaR-797
❑ 93TopMic-797
❑ 93Ult-498
❑ 93UppDec-437
❑ 93UppDecGold-437
❑ 94Bow-243
❑ 94ColC-227
❑ 94ColChoGS-227
❑ 94ColChoSS-227
❑ 94Don-317
❑ 94Fle-15
❑ 94Lea-177
❑ 94OriPro-79
❑ 94OriUSPC-3D
❑ 94OriUSPC-10C
❑ 94RocRedWF-997
❑ 94RocRedWTI-18
❑ 94Sco-258
❑ 94ScoGolR-258
❑ 94StaClu-17
❑ 94StaCluFDI-17
❑ 94StaCluGR-17
❑ 94StaCluMOP-17
❑ 94StaCluT-286

❑ 94StaCluTFDI-286
❑ 94Top-271
❑ 94TopGol-271
❑ 94TopSpa-271
❑ 94Ult-7
❑ 94UppDec-227
❑ 94UppDecED-227
❑ 95RedKah-21
❑ 96VanCanB-21
❑ 98DurBulTI-24

Pennington, George
❑ 09ObaT21-199
❑ 19Zee-42

Pennington, Ken
❑ 87SumBraP-23
❑ 88DurBulS-16
❑ 89DurBullS-17
❑ 89DurBullS-17
❑ 89DurBulTI-17
❑ 89Sta-72
❑ 90Bes-177
❑ 90CMC-757
❑ 90EasLeaAP-EL16
❑ 90WilBilB-18
❑ 90WilBilP-1065
❑ 90WilBilS-19
❑ 91JacSunLD-341
❑ 91JacSunP-159
❑ 91LinDriAA-341
❑ 92SanBerSF-970

Pennock, Herb
❑ 20NatCarE-75
❑ 22E120-9
❑ 22W573-96
❑ 22WilPatV-50
❑ 23MapCriV-27
❑ 23W503-51
❑ 23WilChoV-121
❑ 27YorCarE-8
❑ 28PorandAR-A28
❑ 28PorandAR-B28
❑ 28StaPlaCE-50
❑ 28W502-8
❑ 28W513-68
❑ 28W56PlaC-JOK
❑ 28Yue-8
❑ 29PorandAR-68
❑ 30UncJac-23
❑ 30W554-13
❑ 31Exh-25
❑ 33ExhFou-13
❑ 33Gou-138
❑ 34GouCanV-16
❑ 39PC7AlbHoF-54
❑ 46SpoExcW-7-5
❑ 50CalHOFW-59
❑ 51R42SmaS-84
❑ 53ArtHaloFP-67
❑ 60ExhWriH-19
❑ 60Fle-35
❑ 61Fle-133
❑ 63BazA-5
❑ 71FleWorS-21
❑ 74CapPub-30
❑ 75Yan192T-19
❑ 76RowExh-16
❑ 76ShaPiz-54
❑ 77GalGloG-106
❑ 78DexHaloFP-40
❑ 79RedSoxEF-15
❑ 79RedSoxEF-24
❑ 79Yan192T-24
❑ 80LauFamF-2
❑ 80PacLeg-111
❑ 80PerHaloFP-54
❑ 80SSPHOF-54
❑ 82TCMGreP-30
❑ 84Yan192G-11
❑ 86ConSer1-51
❑ 87Yan192T-2
❑ 89HOFStiB-67
❑ 90PerGreM-54
❑ 91ConTSN-120
❑ 91ConTSN-143
❑ 92ConTSN-465
❑ 92ConTSN-594
❑ 92MegRut-123
❑ 92YanWIZH-25
❑ 95ConTSN-1331

Penny, Brad
❑ 97Bow-199
❑ 97BowInt-199
❑ 97SouBenSH-24
❑ 98Bow-130
❑ 98BowChr-130
❑ 98BowChrGA-130
❑ 98BowChrGAR-130
❑ 98BowChrI-130
❑ 98BowChrIR-130
❑ 98BowChrR-130
❑ 98BowGolA-130
❑ 98BowInt-130
❑ 98HigDesMG-20
❑ 98Top-499
❑ 98TopChr-499
❑ 98TopChrR-499
❑ 98TopDevR-499
❑ 98TopDia-499
❑ 98TopMiniC-499
❑ 99BasAmeTP-79
❑ 99BasAmeTPA-34
❑ 99BasAmeTPBP-5
❑ 99BasAmeTPG-79
❑ 99BasAmeTPLM-9
❑ 99Bow-140
❑ 99BowAut-BA56
❑ 99BowBes-114
❑ 99BowBesAR-114
❑ 99BowBesFFMI-FF8
❑ 99BowBesFFMI-FF8
❑ 99BowBesFFMII-FF8
❑ 99BowBesR-114
❑ 99BowChr-140
❑ 99BowChrG-140
❑ 99BowChrGR-140
❑ 99BowChrI-140
❑ 99BowChrIR-140
❑ 99BowChrR-140
❑ 99BowGol-140
❑ 99BowInt-140
❑ 99TeaBesRA-19
❑ 99Top-211
❑ 99TopChr-211
❑ 99TopChrR-211

Penny, Mike
❑ 98HelBreM-27

Penny, Tony
❑ 98SpoIndG-25

Pennye, Darwin
❑ 88WatPirP-23
❑ 89AugPirP-504
❑ 90CarLeaA-24
❑ 90SalBucS-15
❑ 91CarMudLD-114
❑ 91CarMudP-1098
❑ 91LinDriAA-114
❑ 92HarSenF-473
❑ 92HarSenS-294
❑ 92SkyAA F-124
❑ 98AubDouTI-21

Pennyfeather, William
❑ 89WelPirP-1
❑ 90AugPirP-2477
❑ 90SouAtlLAS-39
❑ 91Bow-517
❑ 91Cla/Bes-158
❑ 91SalBucC-11
❑ 91SalBucP-965
❑ 92Bow-17
❑ 92BufBisF-334
❑ 92BufBisS-37
❑ 92DonRoo-93
❑ 92SkyAAAF-16
❑ 93BufBisF-530
❑ 93ClaFS7-143
❑ 93Don-702
❑ 93FleFinE-116
❑ 93LinVenB-227
❑ 93Sco-301
❑ 93StaClu-447
❑ 93StaCluFDI-447
❑ 93StaCluMOP-447
❑ 93Top-819
❑ 93TopGol-819
❑ 93TopInaM-819
❑ 93TopInaR-819
❑ 93TopMic-819
❑ 94Don-485
❑ 94Ult-558
❑ 96VanCanB-22
❑ 97AlbDukGS-25

Penrod, Jack
❑ 88PocGiaP-2102

Pensiero, Russ
❑ 80ChaO'sP-14
❑ 80ChaO'sW-15

Penson, Paul
❑ 54Top-236
❑ 94TopArc1-236
❑ 94TopArc1G-236

Pentland, Jeff
❑ 89AriStaB-21
❑ 93ElmPioF-3841
❑ 95PorSeaDTI-19
❑ 96ChaKniB-2

Penton, Jack
❑ 28ExhPCL-6

Pentz, Gene
❑ 75DetTigP-24
❑ 76HouAstP-25
❑ 77Top-308
❑ 78AstBurK-11
❑ 78Top-64
❑ 79PorBeaT-12
❑ 80PorBeaT-25
❑ 81PhoGiaVNB-20

Penvose, Randy
❑ 86GenCubP-22

Peoples, Danny
❑ 96BesAutS1RP-FR14
❑ 96WatIndTI-23
❑ 97BesLimA-32
❑ 97Bow-410
❑ 97BowChr-272
❑ 97BowChrI-272
❑ 97BowChrIR-272
❑ 97BowChrR-272
❑ 97BowInt-410
❑ 97CalLeaATI-40
❑ 97CarLeaTP-7
❑ 97KinIndB-17
❑ 97Top-478
❑ 98AkrAerM-29
❑ 98BesAutPOY-14
❑ 98BesNumOP-36
❑ 98BesPreA-36
❑ 98Bow-140
❑ 98BowChr-140
❑ 98BowChrGA-140
❑ 98BowChrGAR-140
❑ 98BowChrI-140
❑ 98BowChrIR-140
❑ 98BowChrR-140
❑ 98BowGolA-140
❑ 98BowInt-140
❑ 98SP MinPE-44
❑ 98SP SPTSC-DP
❑ 98SPMin-44
❑ 99SP TopP-100
❑ 99SP TopPPE-100

Peoples, Derrick
❑ 97YakBeaG-26

Peoples, James
❑ 87BucN28-15

Peoples, Nathaniel
❑ 92NegLeaRLI-48

Peopping, Mike
❑ 76TacTwiDQ-16

Pepe, Joseph
❑ 18Zee-12

Pepitone, Joe
❑ 47PM1StaP1-159
❑ 62Top-596
❑ 63ReqKP-12
❑ 63Top-183
❑ 63YanJayP-9
❑ 64ChatheY-19
❑ 64Top-360
❑ 64TopCoi-121
❑ 64TopSta-22
❑ 64TopVen-360
❑ 64WheSta-34
❑ 64YanJayP-9
❑ 65ChaTheY-17
❑ 65OPC-245
❑ 65Top-245
❑ 66OPC-79
❑ 66Top-79
❑ 66TopVen-79
❑ 66YanTeal-9
❑ 67CokCapA-13
❑ 67CokCapAAm-28
❑ 67CokCapYM-V13
❑ 67DexPre-162
❑ 67DexPre-163
❑ 67OPCPapI-22
❑ 67Top-340
❑ 67TopPos-22
❑ 67TopVen-209
❑ 68AtlOilPBCC-34
❑ 68Baz-5
❑ 68OPC-195
❑ 68Top-195
❑ 68TopActS-3A
❑ 68TopActS-16A
❑ 68TopVen-195
❑ 68YanPhoS-73
❑ 69MilBra-216
❑ 69MLBOffS-76
❑ 69MLBPin-21
❑ 69Top-589
❑ 69TopSta-206
❑ 69TopTeaP-19
❑ 69YanMal-6
❑ 69YanPhoS-46
❑ 70AstTeal-9
❑ 70DayDaiNM-124
❑ 70Kel-59
❑ 70MLBOffS-45
❑ 70SunPin-7
❑ 70Top-598
❑ 71MLBOffS-40
❑ 71OPC-90
❑ 71Top-90
❑ 71TopGreM-53
❑ 72CubChi-6
❑ 72CubTeal-10
❑ 72MilBra-268
❑ 72OPC-303
❑ 72OPC-304
❑ 72SevTraC-40
❑ 72Top-303
❑ 72Top-304
❑ 73OPC-580
❑ 73Top-580
❑ 76HawIslC-11
❑ 78TCM60I-6
❑ 81TCM60I-477
❑ 82YanPhoA-2
❑ 83YanASFY-32
❑ 86TCMSupS-36
❑ 87AstShowSTh-18
❑ 91UppDecS-16
❑ 91UppDecS-19
❑ 92YanWIZ6-96
❑ 92YanWIZA-58

Pepper, (Mascot)
❑ 93AlbPolCB-30

Pepper, Laurin (Hugh)
❑ 55Top-147
❑ 56Top-108
❑ 58JetPos-15

Pepper, Ray
❑ 35AlDemDCR3-45
❑ 35DiaMatCS3T1-120
❑ 36GouWidPPR-A83

Pepper, Stu
❑ 91PacSenL-73

Pepper, Tony
❑ 75IntLeaASB-22
❑ 75PacCoaLAB-22
❑ 75PhoGiaC-4
❑ 75PhoGiaCK-18

Peppers, Devin
❑ 90EliTwiS-15

Pequignot, Jon
❑ 86VerBeaDP-19
❑ 87SanAntDTI-19

Peralta, Amado
❑ 85MexCitTT-21

Peralta, Martin
❑ 88SalLakCTTI-22

Peraza, Luis
❑ 86AppFoxP-18

Peraza, Oswald
❑ 86KnoBluJP-18
❑ 87KnoBluJP-1511
❑ 88OriFreB-23
❑ 88OriPos-25
❑ 88ScoRoo-77T
❑ 88ScoRooG-77T
❑ 89Bow-1
❑ 89BowTif-1
❑ 89Don-524
❑ 89Fle-615
❑ 89FleGlo-615
❑ 89Sco-571
❑ 89Top-297
❑ 89TopBig-219
❑ 89TopTif-297
❑ 89UppDec-651
❑ 90HagSunB-27
❑ 91HagSunLD-242
❑ 91HagSunP-2456
❑ 91LinDriAA-242
❑ 91OriCro-358
❑ 93LinVenB-66
❑ 94VenLinU-112

Percell, Brody
❑ 98WatIndTI-24

Percibal, Bill
❑ 93BluOriC-19
❑ 93BluOriF-4122
❑ 94AlbPolC-19
❑ 94AlbPolF-2235
❑ 94OriPro-80
❑ 95SPML-17
❑ 96BesAutS-70
❑ 96Exc-7

Percival, Troy
❑ 90BoiHawP-3335
❑ 91BoiHawC-23
❑ 91BoiHawP-3875
❑ 92Bow-290
❑ 92MidAngOHP-19
❑ 92ProFS7-38
❑ 92UppDecML-134
❑ 93AngStaCl-9
❑ 93Bow-363
❑ 93Bow-609
❑ 93ClaFS7-236
❑ 93FleFinE-187
❑ 93StaClu-681
❑ 93StaCluFDI-681
❑ 93StaCluMOP-681
❑ 93Ult-522
❑ 93UppDec-507
❑ 93UppDecGold-507
❑ 93VanCanF-2595
❑ 94UppDecML-227
❑ 94VanCanF-1864
❑ 95AngCHP-7
❑ 95AngMot-25
❑ 95Bow-69
❑ 95BowBes-B52
❑ 95BowBesR-B52
❑ 95DonTopotO-40
❑ 95Exc-23
❑ 95Fla-237
❑ 95Fle-233
❑ 95Pin-423
❑ 95PinArtP-423
❑ 95PinMusC-423
❑ 95Sel-219
❑ 95SelArtP-219
❑ 95Top-633
❑ 96AngMot-13
❑ 96Bow-6
❑ 96BowFoi-6
❑ 96Cir-21
❑ 96CirRav-21
❑ 96ColCho-72
❑ 96ColChoGS-72
❑ 96ColChoSS-72
❑ 96Don-524
❑ 96DonPreP-524
❑ 96EmoXL-29
❑ 96Fin-B156
❑ 96FinRef-B156
❑ 96Fla-40
❑ 96Fle-55
❑ 96FleRooS-13
❑ 96FleTif-55
❑ 96Lea-76
❑ 96LeaPrePB-76
❑ 96LeaPrePG-76
❑ 96LeaPrePS-76
❑ 96LeaSigA-178
❑ 96LeaSigAG-178
❑ 96LeaSigAS-178
❑ 96MetUni-30
❑ 96MetUniP-30
❑ 96Pin-298
❑ 96PinFoil-298
❑ 96Sco-169
❑ 96StaClu-328
❑ 96StaCluEPB-328
❑ 96StaCluEPG-328
❑ 96StaCluEPS-328
❑ 96StaCluMOP-328
❑ 96Stu-37
❑ 96StuPrePB-37
❑ 96StuPrePG-37
❑ 96StuPrePS-37
❑ 96TeaOut-62
❑ 96Top-43
❑ 96TopChr-16
❑ 96TopChrR-16
❑ 96TopGal-99
❑ 96TopGalPPI-99
❑ 96Ult-32
❑ 96UltGolM-32
❑ 96UppDec-289
❑ 97AngMot-14
❑ 97Cir-222
❑ 97CirRav-222
❑ 97ColCho-251
❑ 97Don-212
❑ 97DonEli-131
❑ 97DonEliGS-131
❑ 97DonGolPP-212
❑ 97DonPre-120
❑ 97DonPreCttC-120
❑ 97DonSilPP-212
❑ 97DonTea-5
❑ 97DonTeaSPE-5
❑ 97Fin-65
❑ 97FinRef-65
❑ 97FlaShoLC-162
❑ 97FlaShoLeg0-162
❑ 97FlaShoLeg1-162
❑ 97FlaShoM-A162
❑ 97FlaShoM-B162
❑ 97FlaShoM-C162
❑ 97FlaShoR0-162
❑ 97FlaShoR1-162
❑ 97FlaShoR2-162
❑ 97Fle-49
❑ 97FleTif-49
❑ 97Lea-240
❑ 97LeaFraM-240
❑ 97LeaFraMDC-240
❑ 97LeaGet-10
❑ 97MetUni-42
❑ 97NewPin-80
❑ 97NewPinAP-80
❑ 97NewPinKtP-13
❑ 97NewPinMC-80
❑ 97NewPinPP-80
❑ 97NewPinPP-K13
❑ 97Pac-12
❑ 97PacLigB-12
❑ 97PacSil-12
❑ 97Pin-119
❑ 97PinArtP-PP119
❑ 97PinCer-50
❑ 97PinCerMBla-50
❑ 97PinCerMBlu-50
❑ 97PinCerMG-50
❑ 97PinCerMR-50
❑ 97PinCerR-50
❑ 97PinIns-102
❑ 97PinInsCE-102
❑ 97PinInsDE-102
❑ 97PinMusC-119
❑ 97PinPrePla-119
❑ 97PinTotCPB-50
❑ 97PinTotCPG-50
❑ 97PinTotCPR-50
❑ 97PinX-P-113
❑ 97PinX-PMoS-113
❑ 97Sco-253
❑ 97Sco-523
❑ 97ScoArtPWB-253
❑ 97ScoArtPWB-523
❑ 97ScoPreS-253
❑ 97ScoResC-523
❑ 97ScoShoS-253
❑ 97ScoShoS-523
❑ 97ScoShoSAP-253
❑ 97ScoShoSAP-523
❑ 97Sel-79
❑ 97SelArtP-79
❑ 97SelCom-79
❑ 97SelRegG-79
❑ 97SelToootT-22
❑ 97SelToootTMB-22
❑ 97StaClu-232
❑ 97StaCluMat-232
❑ 97StaCluMOP-232
❑ 97Stu-7
❑ 97StuPrePG-7
❑ 97StuPrePS-7
❑ 97Top-156
❑ 97TopChr-60
❑ 97TopChrR-60
❑ 97TopGal-140
❑ 97TopGalPPI-140
❑ 97Ult-29
❑ 97UltBasR-7
❑ 97UltGolME-29
❑ 97UltPlaME-29
❑ 97UppDec-29
❑ 98AngSco-12
❑ 98AngScoP-12
❑ 98CirThu-40
❑ 98CirThuRav-40
❑ 98CirThuSupRav-40
❑ 98ColCho-284
❑ 98Fin-66
❑ 98FinNo--66
❑ 98FinNo-R-66
❑ 98FinRef-66
❑ 98Fle-263
❑ 98Pac-13
❑ 98PacOnl-20

❑ 98PacOnlR-20
❑ 98PacOnlWC-20
❑ 98PacPlaB-13
❑ 98PacRedT-13
❑ 98PacSil-13
❑ 98Pin-94
❑ 98PinPreP-94
❑ 98PinSna-AA12
❑ 98Sco-196
❑ 98ScoSS-PP92
❑ 98ScoSSAP-PP92
❑ 98StaCluFDI-76
❑ 98StaClul-76
❑ 98StaCluOneK-76
❑ 98StaCluPP-76
❑ 98Top-308
❑ 98TopChr-308
❑ 98TopChrR-308
❑ 98TopDevR-308
❑ 98TopDia-308
❑ 98TopGal-103
❑ 98TopGalGP-103
❑ 98TopGalOPP-103
❑ 98TopGalPPI-103
❑ 98TopGalPPIA-103
❑ 98TopMiniC-308
❑ 98Ult-368
❑ 98UltGolM-368
❑ 98UltMas-368
❑ 98UltPlaM-368
❑ 98UppDec-291
❑ 99Fle-204
❑ 99FleBri-19
❑ 99FleBri2G-19
❑ 99FleBriBlu-19
❑ 99FleBriGol-19
❑ 99FleSta9-204
❑ 99FleWarT-204
❑ 99MetUni-63
❑ 99MetUniGM-63
❑ 99MetUniPMG-63
❑ 99Pac-11
❑ 99PacOme-6
❑ 99PacOmeC-6
❑ 99PacOmeG-6
❑ 99PacOmePB-6
❑ 99PacPar-7
❑ 99PacParC-7
❑ 99PacParG-7
❑ 99PacParHoloGold-7
❑ 99PacParHS-7
❑ 99PacParOD-7
❑ 99PacParPB-7
❑ 99PacParRed-7
❑ 99PacPlaB-11
❑ 99PacRed-11
❑ 99SkyPre-139
❑ 99SkyPreR-139
❑ 99SkyThu-181
❑ 99SkyThuRant-181
❑ 99SkyThuRave-181
❑ 99ThuSkySupR-181
❑ 99Top-67
❑ 99TopChr-67
❑ 99TopChrR-67
❑ 99TopMVPP-67
❑ 99Ult-193
❑ 99UltGolM-193
❑ 99UltMas-193
❑ 99UltPlaM-193
❑ 99UppDec-24
❑ 99UppDecEL1-24
❑ 99UppDecEL2-24
❑ 99Vic-11

Perconte, Jack
❑ 77LodDodT-13
❑ 79AlbDukTc-13
❑ 80AlbDukTc-16
❑ 80VenLeaS-22
❑ 81AlbDukTc-17
❑ 81Top-302
❑ 82Ind-28
❑ 82IndWhe-27
❑ 82TopTra-87T
❑ 83ChaChaT-13
❑ 83Don-463
❑ 83Fle-417
❑ 83IndPos-26
❑ 83Top-569
❑ 84FleUpd-90
❑ 84MarMot-15
❑ 85Don-74A
❑ 85Don-74B
❑ 85Fle-498
❑ 85Lea-221
❑ 85MarMot-11
❑ 85Top-172
❑ 85TopSti-341
❑ 85TopTif-172
❑ 86Fle-472
❑ 86Top-146
❑ 86TopTat-1
❑ 86TopTif-146
❑ 87AlbDukD-20
❑ 90DodTar-616

Perdew, J.R.
❑ 97BriWhiSB-27
❑ 98BriWhiSQ-3

Perdomo, Felix
❑ 83GreHorT-21
❑ 86ColMetP-19
❑ 87LynMetP-12
❑ 88JacMetGS-24

Perdue, Alphie
❑ 77SalPirT-18

Perdue, Doran
❑ 81ShrCapT-15

Perdue, Hub (Herbert R.)
❑ 09T206-508
❑ 10CouT21-53
❑ 12RedSoxBASP-2
❑ 12T207-149
❑ 14B18B-53A
❑ 14B18B-53B
❑ 14CraJacE-121
❑ 14FatPlaT-39
❑ 15CraJacE-121
❑ 80BraTCM1-8

Pereira, Ray
❑ 84LitFalMT-8

Perez, Alex
❑ 88KenTwiP-1385

Perez, Angelo
❑ 98St.CatSM-30

Perez, Beban
❑ 89QuaCitAB-28
❑ 89QuaCitAGS-23
❑ 90PalSprACLC-213
❑ 90PalSprAP-2592
❑ 91PalSprAP-2031
❑ 92BoiHawF-3622
❑ 92QuaCitRBC-8
❑ 92QuaCitRBF-807
❑ 93PalSprAC-16
❑ 93PalSprAF-66

Perez, Benny
❑ 75ForLauYS-3
❑ 76ForLauYS-24
❑ 78DunBluJT-17

Perez, Carlos Gross
❑ 91Cla/Bes-92
❑ 91SumFlyP-2333
❑ 92RocExpC-15
❑ 93BurBeeC-17
❑ 93BurBeeF-154
❑ 93LimRocDWB-57
❑ 94HarSenF-2088
❑ 95Bow-113
❑ 95BowBes-R72
❑ 95BowBesR-R72
❑ 95ClaPhoC-36
❑ 95ColCho-550T
❑ 95DonTopotO-283
❑ 95Emo-154
❑ 95Exc-224
❑ 95Fin-296
❑ 95FinRef-296
❑ 95Fla-377
❑ 95FleUpd-108
❑ 95LeaLim-103
❑ 95SelCer-92
❑ 95SelCerMG-92
❑ 95SP-19
❑ 95SPCha-15
❑ 95SPChaDC-15
❑ 95SPSil-19
❑ 95StaClu-542
❑ 95StaCluMOP-542
❑ 95StaCluSTWS-542
❑ 95Sum-114
❑ 95SumNthD-114
❑ 95Top-652
❑ 95TopTra-150T
❑ 95UltGolMR-M19
❑ 95UppDec-244
❑ 95UppDecED-244
❑ 95UppDecEDG-244
❑ 95Zen-124
❑ 95ZenRooRC-16
❑ 96Baz-84
❑ 96ColCho-212
❑ 96ColChoGS-212
❑ 96ColChoSS-212
❑ 96Don-317
❑ 96DonPreP-317
❑ 96DonSho-8
❑ 96EmoXL-224
❑ 96ExpDis-14
❑ 96Fin-S109
❑ 96FinRef-S109
❑ 96Fla-311
❑ 96Fle-463
❑ 96FleTif-463
❑ 96Lea-8
❑ 96LeaPrePB-8
❑ 96LeaPrePG-8
❑ 96LeaPrePS-8
❑ 96LeaSigA-179
❑ 96LeaSigAG-179
❑ 96LeaSigAS-179
❑ 96MetUni-193
❑ 96MetUniP-193
❑ 96MetUniPP-8
❑ 96Pac-130
❑ 96PacEstL-EL24
❑ 96PanSti-22
❑ 96Pin-319
❑ 96PinFoil-319
❑ 96Sco-132
❑ 96ScoDugC-A83
❑ 96ScoDugCAP-A83
❑ 96StaClu-278
❑ 96StaCluMOP-278
❑ 96Top-174
❑ 96TopGal-98
❑ 96TopGalPPI-98
❑ 96Ult-234
❑ 96UltGolM-234
❑ 96UppDec-396
❑ 97ColCho-386
❑ 97Fle-502
❑ 97FleTif-502
❑ 97Lea-260
❑ 97LeaFraM-260
❑ 97LeaFraMDC-260
❑ 97Sco-381
❑ 97ScoArtPWB-381
❑ 97ScoResC-381
❑ 97ScoShoS-381
❑ 97ScoShoSAP-381
❑ 97Ult-357
❑ 97UltGolME-357
❑ 97UltPlaME-357
❑ 98CirThu-184
❑ 98CirThuRav-184
❑ 98CirThuSupRav-184
❑ 98ColCho-435
❑ 98Fin-76
❑ 98FinNo--76
❑ 98FinNo-R-76
❑ 98FinRef-76
❑ 98Fle-546
❑ 98FleUpd-U47
❑ 98Pac-352
❑ 98PacOnl-459
❑ 98PacOnlR-459
❑ 98PacOnlWC-459
❑ 98PacPar-196
❑ 98PacParC-196
❑ 98PacParG-196
❑ 98PacParHS-196
❑ 98PacParPB-196
❑ 98PacParR-196
❑ 98PacPlaB-352
❑ 98PacRedT-352
❑ 98PacSil-352
❑ 98PinPlu-170
❑ 98SP Aut-129
❑ 98SPxFin-99
❑ 98SPxFinR-99
❑ 98SPxFinS-99
❑ 98StaCluFDI-155
❑ 98StaClul-155
❑ 98StaCluOneK-155
❑ 98StaCluPP-155
❑ 98Top-358
❑ 98TopChr-358
❑ 98TopChrR-358
❑ 98TopDevR-358
❑ 98TopDia-358
❑ 98TopMiniC-358
❑ 98Ult-251
❑ 98UltGolM-251
❑ 98UltMas-251
❑ 98UltPlaM-251
❑ 98UppDec-156
❑ 98UppDecSF-83
❑ 99DodPol-21
❑ 99Fle-373
❑ 99FleSta9-373
❑ 99FleWarT-373
❑ 99MetUni-194
❑ 99MetUniGM-194
❑ 99MetUniPMG-194
❑ 99SkyPre-217
❑ 99SkyPreR-217
❑ 99Top-394
❑ 99TopChr-394
❑ 99TopChrR-394
❑ 99TopMVPP-394
❑ 99TopOpeD-131
❑ 99Ult-11
❑ 99UltGolM-11
❑ 99UltMas-11
❑ 99UltPlaM-11

Perez, Carlos Julio
❑ 75QuaCitAT-16
❑ 78SalLakCGC-26
❑ 79SalLakCGT-18A
❑ 80SalLakCGT-13
❑ 85DomLeaS-158

Perez, Cesar
❑ 90GreHorB-9
❑ 90GreHorP-2661
❑ 90GreHorS-15
❑ 90OneYanP-3369
❑ 91GreHorP-3056
❑ 92ForLauYC-7
❑ 92ForLauYTI-22
❑ 92Ft.LauYF-2613
❑ 93KinIndC-21
❑ 93KinIndF-2246
❑ 93KinIndTI-21
❑ 94CanIndF-3119
❑ 94ExcFS7-48

Perez, Danny
❑ 91OklStaC-18
❑ 92HelBreF-1729
❑ 92HelBreSP-23
❑ 93BelBreCB-17
❑ 93BelBreFI-1723
❑ 93MidLeaAGF-3
❑ 94ElPasDF-3159
❑ 94StoPorC-19
❑ 95Exc-73

Perez, Dario
❑ 91AppFoxCB-8
❑ 91AppFoxP-1714
❑ 92BasCitRC-17
❑ 92BasCitRF-3844
❑ 93LimRocDWB-125
❑ 93WilBluRC-19
❑ 93WilBluRF-1996
❑ 94Bow-87
❑ 94WilBluRC-19
❑ 94WilBluRF-298

Perez, David
❑ 89ButCopKSP-2
❑ 90ChaRanS-21
❑ 90FloStaLAS-39
❑ 90StaFS7-25
❑ 91LinDriAA-590
❑ 91TulDriLD-590
❑ 91TulDriP-2770
❑ 91TulDriTI-21
❑ 92ChaRanF-2224
❑ 92TulDriS-615
❑ 93TulDriTI-23
❑ 94OklCit8F-1495
❑ 98ForWayW!-28

Perez, Dick
❑ 83Don-654A
❑ 83Don-654B
❑ 85DonSupD-NNO
❑ 92DonDiaK-DK27
❑ 92DonSupD-DK27

Perez, Eddie
❑ 91DurBulC-12
❑ 91DurBulP-1548
❑ 93GreBraF-353
❑ 93IdaFalBF-4047
❑ 93IdaFalBSP-2
❑ 94RicBraF-2850
❑ 95RicBraRC-18
❑ 95RicBraTI-15
❑ 95Top-480
❑ 96BraFle-14
❑ 96BurIndB-22
❑ 96LeaSigEA-154
❑ 96Ult-444
❑ 96UltGolM-444
❑ 97Fle-268
❑ 97FleTif-268
❑ 97Pac-243
❑ 97PacLigB-243
❑ 97PacSil-243
❑ 98PacInvGems-125
❑ 98PacOnl-71
❑ 98PacOnlR-71
❑ 98PacOnlWC-71

Perez, Eduardo
❑ 88BurBraP-23
❑ 89SumBraP-1112
❑ 90SumBraB-17
❑ 90SumBraP-2438
❑ 91BoiHawC-8
❑ 91BoiHawP-3896
❑ 91Cla/Bes-424
❑ 91ClaDraP-13
❑ 91ClaGolB-BC20
❑ 92CalLeaACL-48
❑ 92ClaFS7-211
❑ 92GreBraF-1157
❑ 92GreBraS-243
❑ 92MidAngOHP-20
❑ 92PalSprAC-1
❑ 92PalSprAF-849
❑ 92ProFS7-39
❑ 92UppDec-52
❑ 92UppDecML-24
❑ 92UppDecML-271
❑ 93AngStaCl-6
❑ 93Bow-441
❑ 93ClaFisN-10
❑ 93ClaGolF-32
❑ 93ClaYouG-YG17
❑ 93ExcFS7-146
❑ 93Lea-483
❑ 93LinVenB-184
❑ 93SelRoo-50T
❑ 93SP-284
❑ 93Top-494
❑ 93TopGol-494
❑ 93TopInaM-494
❑ 93TopInaR-494
❑ 93TopMic-494
❑ 93TriAAAGF-32
❑ 93UppDec-467
❑ 93UppDecGold-467
❑ 93VanCanF-2605
❑ 94AngLAT-25
❑ 94Bow-291
❑ 94Cla-188
❑ 94ColC-228
❑ 94ColChoGS-228
❑ 94ColChoSS-228
❑ 94Don-227
❑ 94Fin-73
❑ 94FinRef-73
❑ 94Fla-26
❑ 94Fle-67
❑ 94FUnPac-121
❑ 94Lea-341
❑ 94OPC-36
❑ 94Pac-86
❑ 94PacAll-18
❑ 94Pin-202
❑ 94PinArtP-202
❑ 94PinMusC-202
❑ 94ProMag-20
❑ 94Sco-307
❑ 94ScoBoyoS-12
❑ 94ScoGolR-307
❑ 94Sel-360
❑ 94Spo-61
❑ 94StaClu-189
❑ 94StaCluFDI-189
❑ 94StaCluGR-189
❑ 94StaCluMOP-189
❑ 94Stu-14
❑ 94Top-721
❑ 94TopGol-721
❑ 94TopSpa-721
❑ 94TriPla-18
❑ 94Ult-26
❑ 94UppDec-124
❑ 94UppDecAJ-10
❑ 94UppDecAJG-10
❑ 94UppDecED-124
❑ 94VenLinU-194
❑ 95ActPacF-33
❑ 95AngMot-14
❑ 95ColCho-94
❑ 95ColChoGS-94
❑ 95ColChoSS-94
❑ 95Don-214
❑ 95DonPreP-214
❑ 95Fin-202
❑ 95FinRef-202
❑ 95Fle-234
❑ 95Lea-145
❑ 95LinVen-118
❑ 95LinVen-269
❑ 95LinVen-281
❑ 95LinVen-286
❑ 95Pac-63
❑ 95Pin-258
❑ 95PinArtP-258
❑ 95PinMusC-258
❑ 95Sel-65
❑ 95SelArtP-65
❑ 95SelCer-4
❑ 95SelCerMG-4
❑ 95StaClu-195
❑ 95StaCluFDI-195
❑ 95StaCluMOP-195
❑ 95StaCluSTWS-195
❑ 95Sum-93
❑ 95SumNthD-93
❑ 95Top-126
❑ 95TopCyb-79
❑ 95UppDec-266
❑ 95UppDecED-266
❑ 95UppDecEDG-266
❑ 95UppDecSE-125
❑ 95UppDecSEG-125
❑ 96-97LinVen-71
❑ 96ColCho-487
❑ 96ColChoGS-487
❑ 96ColChoSS-487
❑ 96Fle-305
❑ 96FleTif-305
❑ 96IndIndB-19
❑ 96MLBPin-27
❑ 96Pac-269
❑ 97Don-221
❑ 97DonGolPP-221
❑ 97DonSilPP-221
❑ 98ColCho-72
❑ 98Fle-203
❑ 98Pac-269
❑ 98PacOme-66
❑ 98PacOmeR-66
❑ 98PacOnl-196
❑ 98PacOnlR-196
❑ 98PacOnlWC-196
❑ 98PacPlaB-269
❑ 98PacRedT-269
❑ 98PacSil-269
❑ 98Sco-118
❑ 98ScoRT-129
❑ 98StaCluFDI-273
❑ 98StaClul-273
❑ 98StaCluOneK-273
❑ 98StaCluPP-273
❑ 98UppDec-339
❑ 99Pac-115
❑ 99PacCroC-77
❑ 99PacCroCPB-77
❑ 99PacPlaB-115
❑ 99PacRed-115

Perez, Elvis
❑ 98HicCraM-24

Perez, Erick
❑ 95LinVen-180
❑ 96-97LinVen-53

Perez, Eulogio
❑ 88MarPhiS-27
❑ 89MarPhiS-24
❑ 90BatCliP-3075
❑ 90SpaPhiP-2500
❑ 90SpaPhiS-17
❑ 91SpaPhiC-17
❑ 91SpaPhiP-901

Perez, Felix
❑ 93LinVenB-77
❑ 94VenLinU-159

Perez, Francisco
❑ 86EriCarP-23
❑ 89AshTouP-963
❑ 89AubAstP-2174
❑ 90AshTouP-2745

Perez, Fred
❑ 85UtiBluST-21

Perez, George
❑ 93GreFalDSP-13

Perez, Gil
❑ 92WelPirC-19
❑ 92WelPirF-1321
❑ 93WelPirC-19
❑ 93WelPirF-3355
❑ 94WelPirC-17
❑ 94WelPirF-3494

Perez, Gorky
❑ 87AshTouP-26

❑ 87AubAstP-15
❑ 88AshTouP-1062
❑ 89OscAstS-17
Perez, Hector
❑ 82MadMusF-32
❑ 83MadMusF-29
❑ 84LitFalMT-17
❑ 86LynMetP-16
❑ 87LynMetP-10
❑ 88St.LucMS-18
❑ 89PenPilS-18
❑ 93ForLauRSFP-1597
Perez, Hilario
❑ 93ForLauRSC-21
❑ 93UtiBluSC-20
❑ 93UtiBluSF-3532
❑ 94UtiBluSC-22
❑ 94UtiBluSF-3819
Perez, Jayson
❑ 92GulCoaDF-3564
❑ 93YakBeaF-3882
Perez, Jerson
❑ 97AppLeaTPB-18
❑ 98CapCitBF5-24
❑ 98CapCitBM-24
Perez, Jesse
❑ 96OgdRapTI-30
Perez, Jhonny
❑ 95SPML-68
❑ 96KisCobB-20
❑ 97KisCob-18
❑ 98JacGenM-17
Perez, Joe
❑ 90WatIndS-15
❑ 91CollndC-3
❑ 91CollndP-1501
❑ 95ChaRivTI-7
Perez, Joel
❑ 77AppFoxT-19
❑ 79KnoKnoST-16
Perez, Jose
❑ 89SalDodTI-22
❑ 90KisDodD-21
❑ 90YakBeaTI-34
Perez, Juan
❑ 95WesMicWTI-11
❑ 96ModA'sB-26
❑ 97VisOakG-23
Perez, Juan Carlos
❑ 96BluOriB-27
Perez, Julian
❑ 89BlaYNPRWL-122
Perez, Julio
❑ 75WesPalBES-1
❑ 78MemChiBC-7
❑ 79MemChiT-4
❑ 80GleFalWSBT-16
❑ 80GleFalWSCT-10
❑ 81EdmTraRR-17
❑ 83ReaPhiT-16
❑ 86MacPirP-19
❑ 87MacPirP-14
❑ 88MiaMarS-18
❑ 89HarSenP-307
❑ 89HarSenS-14
❑ 90HarSenP-1201
❑ 90HarSenS-15
Perez, Julio Cesar
❑ 94BurIndF-3792
❑ 96KenIndB-20
❑ 97KinIndB-18
❑ 98VerExpO-15
Perez, Junior
❑ 88BlaYNPRWL-112
❑ 90GreFalDSP-16
Perez, Leo
❑ 89StoPorB-13
❑ 89StoPorCLC-158
❑ 89StoPorP-373
❑ 89WytCubS-23
❑ 90CMC-865
❑ 90StoPorB-24
❑ 90StoPorCLC-186
❑ 90StoPorP-2185
❑ 91GenCubC-14
❑ 91GenCubP-4211
❑ 91WinSpiC-8
❑ 91WinSpiP-2827
❑ 92GulCoaRSP-10
Perez, Leonardo
❑ 88BelBreGS-18
Perez, Luis
❑ 92GulCoaRSP-5
❑ 94HudValRC-18
❑ 94HudValRF-3384
Perez, Manuel R.
❑ 48SomandK-17
❑ 49SomandK-8
Perez, Mario
❑ 85BenPhiC-19
❑ 87UtiBluSP-1
Perez, Martin
❑ 76DubPacT-25
Perez, Marty
❑ 71OPC-529
❑ 71Top-529
❑ 72OPC-119
❑ 72Top-119
❑ 73OPC-144
❑ 73Top-144
❑ 74OPC-374
❑ 74Top-374
❑ 75AtlBraP-28
❑ 75OPC-499
❑ 75Top-499
❑ 75TopMin-499
❑ 76AtlBraP-24
❑ 76Hos-65
❑ 76Kel-26
❑ 76OPC-177
❑ 76Top-177
❑ 77BurCheD-100
❑ 77Gia-18
❑ 77OPC-183
❑ 77RCColC-53
❑ 77Top-438
❑ 78RCColC-53
❑ 78TidTidT-19
❑ 78Top-613
❑ 92YanWIZ7-126
Perez, Melido
❑ 86BurExpP-17
❑ 88Don-589
❑ 88DonBasB-179
❑ 88DonRoo-21
❑ 88Fle-265
❑ 88FleGlo-265
❑ 88FleUpd-19
❑ 88FleUpdG-19
❑ 88ScoRoo-108T
❑ 88ScoRooG-108T
❑ 88TopTra-83T
❑ 88TopTraT-83T
❑ 88WhiSoxC-21
❑ 89Bow-59
❑ 89BowTif-59
❑ 89ClaLigB-88
❑ 89Don-58
❑ 89DonBasB-179
❑ 89Fle-509
❑ 89FleGlo-509
❑ 89OPC-88
❑ 89PanSti-300
❑ 89RedFolSB-89
❑ 89Sco-386
❑ 89ScoHot1R-79
❑ 89ScoYouSI-7
❑ 89Spo-118
❑ 89Top-786
❑ 89TopBig-235
❑ 89TopRoo-16
❑ 89TopSti-296
❑ 89TopTif-786
❑ 89ToyRoo-21
❑ 89UppDec-243
❑ 89WhiSoxC-21
❑ 90Bow-310
❑ 90BowTif-310
❑ 90Don-101
❑ 90DonBesA-18
❑ 90Fle-546
❑ 90FleCan-546
❑ 90Lea-36
❑ 90OPC-621
❑ 90PanSti-42
❑ 90PubIntS-399
❑ 90PubIntS-602
❑ 90Sco-311
❑ 90Top-621
❑ 90TopBig-195
❑ 90TopSti-304
❑ 90TopTif-621
❑ 90UppDec-525
❑ 90WhiSoxC-21
❑ 90WhiSoxK-2
❑ 91Bow-344
❑ 91Don-164
❑ 91DonBonC-BC13
❑ 91Fle-133
❑ 91FleWaxBC-7
❑ 91OPC-499
❑ 91PanCanT1-96
❑ 91PanFreS-358
❑ 91PanSti-7
❑ 91Sco-179
❑ 91Sco-705
❑ 91StaClu-232
❑ 91StaCluCM-23
❑ 91Top-499
❑ 91TopDesS-499
❑ 91TopMic-499
❑ 91TopTif-499
❑ 91Ult-80
❑ 91UppDec-623
❑ 91WhiSoxK-33
❑ 92Bow-365
❑ 92Don-509
❑ 92Fle-95
❑ 92Lea-479
❑ 92LeaBlaG-479
❑ 92OPC-129
❑ 92OPCPre-10
❑ 92Pin-322
❑ 92Sco-29
❑ 92ScoProP-10
❑ 92ScoRoo-36T
❑ 92StaClu-869
❑ 92StaCluNC-869
❑ 92Stu-218
❑ 92Top-129
❑ 92TopGol-129
❑ 92TopGolW-129
❑ 92TopMic-129
❑ 92TopTra-87T
❑ 92TopTraG-87T
❑ 92Ult-42
❑ 92Ult-413
❑ 92UppDec-190
❑ 92UppDec-799
❑ 93Bow-19
❑ 93Don-709
❑ 93DurPowP2-2
❑ 93Fle-284
❑ 93Lea-74
❑ 93LimRocDWB-127
❑ 93OPC-231
❑ 93PacSpa-210
❑ 93Pin-109
❑ 93Sco-86
❑ 93Sel-116
❑ 93SelAce-22
❑ 93SelStaL-63
❑ 93SelStaL-74
❑ 93StaClu-465
❑ 93StaCluFDI-465
❑ 93StaCluMOP-465
❑ 93Top-304
❑ 93TopComotH-11
❑ 93TopGol-304
❑ 93TopInaM-304
❑ 93TopInaR-304
❑ 93TopMic-304
❑ 93Ult-248
❑ 93UppDec-326
❑ 93UppDecGold-326
❑ 93YanStaC-6
❑ 94Bow-605
❑ 94ColC-432
❑ 94ColChoGS-432
❑ 94ColChoSS-432
❑ 94Don-476
❑ 94Fla-87
❑ 94Fle-245
❑ 94FleExtB-137
❑ 94Lea-190
❑ 94Pac-435
❑ 94Pin-168
❑ 94PinArtP-168
❑ 94PinMusC-168
❑ 94Sco-479
❑ 94ScoGolR-479
❑ 94StaClu-554
❑ 94StaCluFDI-554
❑ 94StaCluGR-554
❑ 94StaCluMOP-554
❑ 94StaCluT-188
❑ 94StaCluTFDI-188
❑ 94Top-31
❑ 94TopGol-31
❑ 94TopSpa-31
❑ 94Ult-100
❑ 94UppDec-471
❑ 94UppDecED-471
❑ 95ColCho-511
❑ 95ColChoGS-511
❑ 95ColChoSE-244
❑ 95ColChoSEGS-244
❑ 95ColChoSESS-244
❑ 95ColChoSS-511
❑ 95Don-397
❑ 95DonPreP-397
❑ 95DonTopotO-123
❑ 95Fla-68
❑ 95Fle-79
❑ 95Pin-23
❑ 95PinArtP-23
❑ 95PinMusC-23
❑ 95Sco-144
❑ 95ScoGolR-144
❑ 95ScoPlaTS-144
❑ 95StaClu-303
❑ 95StaCluMOP-303
❑ 95StaCluSTWS-303
❑ 95StaCluVR-159
❑ 95StaCluVRMO-159
❑ 95Top-511
❑ 95TopCyb-299
❑ 95Ult-313
❑ 95UltGolM-313
❑ 95UppDec-440
❑ 95UppDecED-440
❑ 95UppDecEDG-440
❑ 95UppDecSE-7
❑ 95UppDecSEG-7
❑ 96ColCho-634
❑ 96ColChoGS-634
❑ 96ColChoSS-634
❑ 96Fle-193
❑ 96FleTif-193
❑ 96Pac-377
❑ 96Sco-488
❑ 96Ult-392
❑ 96UltGolM-392
❑ 97PacPriGotD-GD76
Perez, Mike (Michael Irvin)
❑ 87SprCarB-15
❑ 88ArkTraGS-21
❑ 88BlaYNPRWL-173
❑ 89ArkTraGS-17
❑ 89BlaYNPRWL-149
❑ 89TexLeaAGS-24
❑ 90CMC-108
❑ 90LouRedBC-8
❑ 90LouRedBLBC-34
❑ 90LouRedBP-402
❑ 90ProAAAF-516
❑ 90SprCarDGB-25
❑ 90TopTVCa-60
❑ 90TriAllGP-AAA29
❑ 91Don-615
❑ 91Fle-643
❑ 91LouRedTI-12
❑ 91OPC-205
❑ 91Sco-758
❑ 91Top-205
❑ 91TopDeb90-124
❑ 91TopDesS-205
❑ 91TopMic-205
❑ 91TopTif-205
❑ 91UppDec-728
❑ 92DonRoo-94
❑ 92Fle-588
❑ 92Pin-565
❑ 92ScoRoo-95T
❑ 92StaClu-798
❑ 92StaCluNC-798
❑ 92TopTra-88T
❑ 92TopTraG-88T
❑ 92Ult-571
❑ 93CarPol-16
❑ 93CarStaC-5
❑ 93Don-256
❑ 93Fle-132
❑ 93FleRooS-RSA9
❑ 93OPC-298
❑ 93PacSpa-635
❑ 93Pin-162
❑ 93Sco-345
❑ 93Sel-319
❑ 93StaClu-202
❑ 93StaCluFDI-202
❑ 93StaCluMOP-202
❑ 93Top-229
❑ 93TopGol-229
❑ 93TopInaM-229
❑ 93TopInaR-229
❑ 93TopMic-229
❑ 93Toy-15
❑ 93Ult-111
❑ 93UppDec-204
❑ 93UppDecGold-204
❑ 94CarPol-16
❑ 94ColC-229
❑ 94ColChoGS-229
❑ 94ColChoSS-229
❑ 94Don-599
❑ 94Fin-124
❑ 94FinRef-124
❑ 94Fla-227
❑ 94Fle-644
❑ 94FleExtB-362
❑ 94Lea-130
❑ 94Pac-601
❑ 94PanSti-247
❑ 94Pin-182
❑ 94PinArtP-182
❑ 94PinMusC-182
❑ 94Sco-84
❑ 94ScoGolR-84
❑ 94Sel-108
❑ 94StaClu-175
❑ 94StaCluFDI-175
❑ 94StaCluGR-175
❑ 94StaCluMOP-175
❑ 94StaCluT-320
❑ 94StaCluTFDI-320
❑ 94Top-567
❑ 94TopGol-567
❑ 94TopSpa-567
❑ 94Ult-271
❑ 94UppDec-357
❑ 94UppDecED-357
❑ 95ColCho-199
❑ 95ColChoGS-199
❑ 95ColChoSS-199
❑ 95FleUpd-128
❑ 95Pac-414
❑ 95PacPri-132
❑ 95StaClu-150
❑ 95StaClu-558
❑ 95StaCluFDI-150
❑ 95StaCluMOP-150
❑ 95StaCluMOP-558
❑ 95StaCluSTWS-150
❑ 95StaCluSTWS-558
❑ 95TopTra-52T
❑ 96Don-254
❑ 96DonPreP-254
❑ 96Fle-326
❑ 96FleTif-326
❑ 96Pac-25
❑ 97Pac-255
❑ 97PacLigB-255
❑ 97PacSil-255
Perez, Neifi
❑ 93BenRocCB-21
❑ 93BenRocF-3279
❑ 94Bow-282
❑ 94CenValRC-18
❑ 94CenValRF-3212
❑ 94Cla-63
❑ 94ExcFS7-186
❑ 94UppDec-545
❑ 94UppDecED-545
❑ 94UppDecML-196
❑ 95Bow-102
❑ 95NewHavRTI-3
❑ 95SPML-51
❑ 95UppDecML-101
❑ 95UppDecML-117
❑ 95UppDecMLFS-101
❑ 95UppDecMLFS-117
❑ 96Bow-323
❑ 96BowBes-168
❑ 96BowBesAR-168
❑ 96BowBesMI-4
❑ 96BowBesMIAR-4
❑ 96BowBesMIR-4
❑ 96BowBesR-168
❑ 96BowFoi-323
❑ 96ColSprSSTI-25
❑ 96Top-427
❑ 97BesLimA-33
❑ 97Bow-220
❑ 97BowBes-118
❑ 97BowBesAR-118
❑ 97BowBesR-118
❑ 97BowCerBlaIA-CA62
❑ 97BowCerBluIA-CA62
❑ 97BowCerGolIA-CA62
❑ 97BowChr-197
❑ 97BowChrI-197
❑ 97BowChrIR-197
❑ 97BowChrR-197
❑ 97BowInt-220
❑ 97Cir-7
❑ 97CirRav-7
❑ 97ColCho-17
❑ 97ColSprSATTI-3
❑ 97ColSprSTI-18
❑ 97Don-264
❑ 97DonGolPP-264
❑ 97DonLim-131
❑ 97DonLimE-131
❑ 97DonSig-79
❑ 97DonSigA-79
❑ 97DonSigAC-97
❑ 97DonSigAM-97
❑ 97DonSigPPP-79
❑ 97DonSilPP-264
❑ 97DonTea-98
❑ 97DonTeaSPE-98
❑ 97E-X2SD2000-10
❑ 97Fin-58
❑ 97FinRef-58
❑ 97Fle-313
❑ 97FleRooS-17
❑ 97FleTif-313
❑ 97Lea-334
❑ 97LeaFraM-334
❑ 97LeaFraMDC-334
❑ 97MetUniMfG-8
❑ 97Pin-178
❑ 97PinArtP-PP178
❑ 97PinIns-147
❑ 97PinInsCE-147
❑ 97PinInsDE-147
❑ 97PinMusC-178
❑ 97PinPrePla-178
❑ 97Sel-127
❑ 97SelArtP-127
❑ 97SelCom-127
❑ 97SelRegG-127
❑ 97StaClu-174
❑ 97StaCluM-M40
❑ 97StaCluMOP-174
❑ 97StaCluMOP-M40
❑ 97Top-474
❑ 97TopAwel-AI14
❑ 97TopGal-162
❑ 97TopGalPPI-162
❑ 97UppDec-269
❑ 98BesPreA-37
❑ 98Bow-53
❑ 98BowBes-83
❑ 98BowBesAR-83
❑ 98BowBesR-83
❑ 98BowChr-53
❑ 98BowChrGA-53
❑ 98BowChrGAR-53
❑ 98BowChrI-53
❑ 98BowChrIR-53
❑ 98BowChrR-53
❑ 98BowGolA-53
❑ 98BowInt-53
❑ 98CirThu-226
❑ 98CirThuFT-8
❑ 98CirThuRav-226
❑ 98CirThuSupRav-226
❑ 98ColCho-84
❑ 98Don-102
❑ 98DonCol-102
❑ 98DonCol-177
❑ 98DonColE-488
❑ 98DonColL-337
❑ 98DonColP-666
❑ 98DonColS-102
❑ 98DonColS-172
❑ 98DonCruG-69
❑ 98DonCruP-69
❑ 98DonCruR-69
❑ 98DonEli-88
❑ 98DonEliA-88
❑ 98DonEliS-88
❑ 98DonGolPP-102
❑ 98DonPre-116
❑ 98DonPreSeat-116
❑ 98DonPriCD-102
❑ 98DonPriCD-177
❑ 98DonPriCE-488
❑ 98DonPriCL-337
❑ 98DonPriCP-666
❑ 98DonRatR-2
❑ 98DonRatRM-2
❑ 98DonSigA-70
❑ 98DonSigAC-90
❑ 98DonSigAM-91
❑ 98DonSilPP-102
❑ 98Fin-36
❑ 98FinNo--36
❑ 98FinNo-R-36
❑ 98FinRef-36
❑ 98Fle-124
❑ 98FleRooS-16
❑ 98Lea-138

❑ 98LeaFraDA-138
❑ 98LeaFraF-138
❑ 98LeaFraM-138
❑ 98LeaFraM-138
❑ 98LeaFraMDC-138
❑ 98LeaFraMDC-138
❑ 98LeaFraMS-138
❑ 98LeaFraMZ2-138
❑ 98LeaRS-106
❑ 98LeaRSLHolo-106
❑ 98LeaRSLong-106
❑ 98LeaRTrue-106
❑ 98MetUni-153
❑ 98MetUniPMG-153
❑ 98Pac-287
❑ 98PacInv-93
❑ 98PacInvPBlue-93
❑ 98PacInvSilv-93
❑ 98PacOme-85
❑ 98PacOmeR-85
❑ 98PacOnl-255
❑ 98PacOnlR-255
❑ 98PacOnlWC-255
❑ 98PacPlaB-287
❑ 98PacRedT-287
❑ 98PacSil-287
❑ 98Pin-134
❑ 98PinIns-48
❑ 98PinInsCE-48
❑ 98PinInsDE-48
❑ 98PinInsSG-10AB
❑ 98PinInsSG-10CD
❑ 98PinInsSGS-10AB
❑ 98PinInsSGS-10CD
❑ 98PinPer-95
❑ 98PinPerPP-95
❑ 98PinPlu-166
❑ 98PinPluAP-PP54
❑ 98PinPluGAP-PP54
❑ 98PinPluMAP-PP54
❑ 98PinPreP-134
❑ 98PinSna-CR8
❑ 98PinSna-CR11
❑ 98Sco-16
❑ 98ScoRT-80
❑ 98ScoRTSS-PP61
❑ 98ScoRTSSAP-PP61
❑ 98ScoRTSSAP1-PP61
❑ 98ScoSS-PP4
❑ 98ScoSSAP-PP4
❑ 98SP Aut-82
❑ 98SPxFin-9
❑ 98SPxFinR-9
❑ 98SPxFinS-9
❑ 98StaCluFDI-209
❑ 98StaCluI-209
❑ 98StaCluOneK-209
❑ 98StaCluPP-209
❑ 98Stu-48
❑ 98StuGPP-48
❑ 98StuSPP-48
❑ 98Top-372
❑ 98TopChr-372
❑ 98TopChrR-372
❑ 98TopDevR-372
❑ 98TopDia-372
❑ 98TopGal-123
❑ 98TopGalGP-123
❑ 98TopGalOPP-123
❑ 98TopGalPPI-123
❑ 98TopGalPPIA-123
❑ 98TopMiniC-372
❑ 98TopSta-47
❑ 98TopStaB-47
❑ 98TopStaG-47
❑ 98TopStaGR-47
❑ 98TopStaS-47
❑ 98Ult-77
❑ 98UltGolM-77
❑ 98UltMas-77
❑ 98UltPlaM-77
❑ 98UppDec-77
❑ 98UppDecSF-48
❑ 98Zen-68
❑ 98ZenZ-G-68
❑ 98ZenZ-S-68
❑ 99199Fin-36
❑ 99Bow-277
❑ 99BowGol-277
❑ 99BowInt-277
❑ 99FinGolRef-36
❑ 99FinRef-36
❑ 99Fle-155
❑ 99FleSta9-155
❑ 99FleWarT-155
❑ 99MetUni-41
❑ 99MetUniGM-41
❑ 99MetUniPMG-41
❑ 99Pac-151
❑ 99PacCroC-99
❑ 99PacCroCPB-99
❑ 99PacInv-52
❑ 99PacInvOD-52
❑ 99PacInvPB-52
❑ 99PacOme-85
❑ 99PacOmeC-85
❑ 99PacOmeG-85
❑ 99PacOmePB-85
❑ 99PacPar-85
❑ 99PacParC-85
❑ 99PacParG-85
❑ 99PacParHoloGold-85
❑ 99PacParHS-85
❑ 99PacParOD-85
❑ 99PacParPB-85
❑ 99PacParRed-85
❑ 99PacPlaB-151
❑ 99PacRed-151
❑ 99SkyMolM-98
❑ 99SkyMolMX-98
❑ 99SkyPre-188
❑ 99SkyPreR-188
❑ 99SkyThu-38
❑ 99SkyThuRant-38
❑ 99SkyThuRave-38
❑ 99StaClu-91
❑ 99StaCluFDI-91
❑ 99StaCluOoaK-91
❑ 99StaCluPP-91
❑ 99ThuSkySupR-38
❑ 99Top-97
❑ 99TopChr-97
❑ 99TopChrR-97
❑ 99TopMVPP-97
❑ 99TopOpeD-56
❑ 99TopSta-96
❑ 99TopSta1Foil-96
❑ 99TopStaFoil-96
❑ 99TopStaOS-96
❑ 99Ult-137
❑ 99UltGolM-137
❑ 99UltMas-137
❑ 99UltPlaM-137
❑ 99UppDec-90
❑ 99UppDecEL1-90
❑ 99UppDecEL2-90
❑ 99Vic-133

Perez, Nelson
❑ 95ButCopKtl-17

Perez, Nestor
❑ 98ChaRivDG-21

Perez, Norberto
❑ 98DelShoM-25

Perez, Odalis
❑ 96EugEmeB-19
❑ 97MacBra-13
❑ 98Bow-356
❑ 98BowBes-131
❑ 98BowBesAR-131
❑ 98BowBesR-131
❑ 98BowChr-356
❑ 98BowChrGA-356
❑ 98BowChrGAR-356
❑ 98BowChrI-356
❑ 98BowChrIR-356
❑ 98BowChrR-356
❑ 98BowGolA-356
❑ 98BowInt-356
❑ 98DonSig-139
❑ 98DonSigP-139
❑ 98FleUpd-U25
❑ 98GreBraG-18
❑ 98LeaRS-333
❑ 98LeaRSLHolo-333
❑ 98LeaRSLong-333
❑ 98LeaRTrue-333
❑ 98SouLeaTPG-23
❑ 99Bow-152
❑ 99BowChr-152
❑ 99BowChrG-152
❑ 99BowChrGR-152
❑ 99BowChrI-152
❑ 99BowChrIR-152
❑ 99BowChrR-152
❑ 99BowGol-152
❑ 99BowInt-152
❑ 99Fle-261
❑ 99FleSta9-261
❑ 99FleWarT-261
❑ 99PacCroC-30
❑ 99PacCroCPB-30
❑ 99PacOme-28
❑ 99PacOmeC-28
❑ 99PacOmeG-28
❑ 99PacOmePB-28
❑ 99SkyMolMX-29
❑ 99SkyThu-11
❑ 99SkyThuRant-11
❑ 99SkyThuRave-11
❑ 99ThuSkySupR-11

Perez, Onesimo
❑ 80VenLeaS-67

Perez, Ozzie
❑ 90HamRedB-18
❑ 90HamRedS-18
❑ 91SavCarC-21
❑ 91SavCarP-1662

Perez, Paco
❑ 77LynMetT-22
❑ 79JacMetT-1

Perez, Pascual
❑ 77ChaPatT-12
❑ 79PorBeaT-20
❑ 80PorBeaT-7
❑ 81PorBeaT-20
❑ 81Top-551
❑ 82Fle-491
❑ 82PorBeaT-7
❑ 82Top-383A
❑ 82Top-383B
❑ 83AllGamPI-172
❑ 83BraPol-27
❑ 83Don-557A
❑ 83Don-557B
❑ 83Fle-144
❑ 83TopTra-84T
❑ 84BraPol-27
❑ 84Don-507
❑ 84Fle-188
❑ 84FleSti-59
❑ 84Nes792-675
❑ 84OPC-1
❑ 84raPho-23
❑ 84Top-675
❑ 84TopSti-36
❑ 84TopTif-675
❑ 85BraHos-18
❑ 85BraPol-27
❑ 85Don-507
❑ 85DonActA-18
❑ 85Fle-337
❑ 85Lea-55
❑ 85OPC-106
❑ 85Top-106
❑ 85TopTif-106
❑ 86Fle-524
❑ 86Top-491
❑ 86TopTif-491
❑ 87DonHig-50
❑ 87IndIndTI-26
❑ 88Don-591
❑ 88DonBasB-236
❑ 88ExpPos-26
❑ 88Fle-192
❑ 88FleGlo-192
❑ 88Lea-248
❑ 88OPC-237
❑ 88Sco-459
❑ 88ScoGlo-459
❑ 88Top-647
❑ 88TopBig-196
❑ 88TopTif-647
❑ 89Bow-354
❑ 89BowTif-354
❑ 89ClaLigB-85
❑ 89Don-248
❑ 89DonBasB-302
❑ 89Fle-390
❑ 89FleGlo-390
❑ 89OPC-73
❑ 89PanSti-115
❑ 89Sco-299
❑ 89Top-73
❑ 89TopSti-71
❑ 89TopTif-73
❑ 89UppDec-498
❑ 90Bow-430
❑ 90BowTif-430
❑ 90Don-342
❑ 90DonBesA-80
❑ 90Fle-358
❑ 90FleCan-358
❑ 90FleUpd-116
❑ 90OPC-278
❑ 90PanSti-282
❑ 90PubIntS-185
❑ 90Sco-486
❑ 90ScoRoo-5T
❑ 90Top-278
❑ 90TopBig-291
❑ 90TopTif-278
❑ 90TopTra-91T
❑ 90TopTraT-91T
❑ 90TopTVY-16
❑ 90UppDec-487
❑ 90UppDec-769
❑ 90YanScoNW-11
❑ 91Fle-675
❑ 91FouBal-28
❑ 91Lea-293
❑ 91OPC-701
❑ 91StaClu-485
❑ 91Top-701
❑ 91TopDesS-701
❑ 91TopMic-701
❑ 91TopTif-701
❑ 91UppDec-671
❑ 92Don-695
❑ 92Fle-240
❑ 92OPC-503
❑ 92Pin-182
❑ 92Sco-88
❑ 92Top-503
❑ 92TopGol-503
❑ 92TopGolW-503
❑ 92TopMic-503

Perez, Pastor
❑ 74CedRapAT-21
❑ 76VenLeaS-137

Perez, Paulino
❑ 93ChaRaiC-15
❑ 93ChaRaiF-1908

Perez, Pedro
❑ 89SalDodTI-23
❑ 90VerBeaDS-22
❑ 91GenCubC-15
❑ 91GenCubP-4212
❑ 91PeoChiP-1340
❑ 92WinSpiF-1206

Perez, Pedro Julio
❑ 90YakBeaTI-36

Perez, Ralph
❑ 92SpoIndC-24
❑ 92SpoIndF-1307

Perez, Ramon
❑ 73CedRapAT-2
❑ 75IowOakT-14
❑ 78ChaChaT-11
❑ 79ChaChaT-9

Perez, Raul
❑ 80VenLeaS-197
❑ 94VenLinU-80
❑ 96-97LinVen-43

Perez, Richard
❑ 91HunCubC-17
❑ 91HunCubP-3342
❑ 92HunCubC-6
❑ 92HunCubF-3155
❑ 93PeoChiC-16
❑ 93PeoChiF-1093
❑ 93PeoChiTI-20
❑ 94DayCubC-19
❑ 94DayCubF-2362
❑ 94VenLinU-235
❑ 95LinVen-56
❑ 96OrlCubB-20
❑ 96RocCubTI-23
❑ 98El PasDG-23

Perez, Robert
❑ 90St.CatBJP-3456
❑ 91DunBluJC-22
❑ 91DunBluJP-220
❑ 92ClaFS7-161
❑ 92KnoBluJF-3003
❑ 92KnoBluJS-391
❑ 92ProFS7-168
❑ 92SkyAA F-166
❑ 93LinVenB-262
❑ 93LinVenB-320
❑ 93SyrChiF-1011
❑ 94ExcFS7-147
❑ 94LeaLimR-77
❑ 94SyrChiF-985
❑ 94SyrChiTI-19
❑ 94TriAAF-AAA19
❑ 94VenLinU-125
❑ 95LinVen-168
❑ 95LinVen-272
❑ 95Pac-449
❑ 95Sco-578
❑ 95ScoGolR-578
❑ 95ScoPlaTS-578
❑ 95SyrChiTI-19
❑ 96-97LinVen-39
❑ 96-97LinVen-286
❑ 96BluJayOH-24
❑ 96ColCho-747
❑ 96ColChoGS-747
❑ 96ColChoSS-747
❑ 96FleUpd-U100
❑ 96FleUpdTC-U100
❑ 96LeaSigA-180
❑ 96LeaSigAG-180
❑ 96LeaSigAS-180
❑ 96Pac-446
❑ 96Pin-173
❑ 96PinArtP-99
❑ 96PinSta-99
❑ 96Sco-491
❑ 96Sel-180
❑ 96SelArtP-180
❑ 96Ult-434
❑ 96UltGolM-434
❑ 97BluJayOH-22
❑ 97Fle-248
❑ 97FleTif-248
❑ 97Lea-158
❑ 97LeaFraM-158
❑ 97LeaFraMDC-158
❑ 97MetUni-189
❑ 97Pac-225
❑ 97PacLigB-225
❑ 97PacSil-225
❑ 97Sco-229
❑ 97ScoArtPWB-229
❑ 97ScoPreS-229
❑ 97ScoShoS-229
❑ 97ScoShoSAP-229
❑ 97Top-72
❑ 97Ult-150
❑ 97UltGolME-150
❑ 97UltPlaME-150
❑ 98PacInvGems-113
❑ 99PacCroC-172
❑ 99PacCroCPB-172

Perez, Sammie
❑ 97BurIndG-20

Perez, Santiago
❑ 95FayGenTI-19
❑ 96LakTigB-18
❑ 97LakTigB-26
❑ 98BesAutSS-41
❑ 98El PasDG-24
❑ 98TexLeaTPG-28
❑ 99SP TopP-101
❑ 99SP TopPPE-101

Perez, Segio
❑ 85DomLeaS-125
❑ 86ClePhiP-19

Perez, Tomas
❑ 94BurBeeC-20
❑ 94BurBeeF-1091
❑ 94MidLeaAF-MDW34
❑ 95BluJayOH-28
❑ 95LinVen-200
❑ 95StaClu-588
❑ 95StaCluMOP-588
❑ 95StaCluSTWS-588
❑ 95TopTra-24T
❑ 95UppDec-253
❑ 95UppDecED-253
❑ 95UppDecEDG-253
❑ 96-97LinVen-169
❑ 96-97LinVen-285
❑ 96ColCho-744
❑ 96ColChoGS-744
❑ 96ColChoSS-744
❑ 96Don-169
❑ 96DonPreP-169
❑ 96Pac-441
❑ 96Top-106
❑ 96UppDec-213
❑ 97BluJayS-56
❑ 97Don-161
❑ 97DonGolPP-161
❑ 97DonSilPP-161
❑ 97Lea-128
❑ 97LeaFraM-128
❑ 97LeaFraMDC-128
❑ 97Pac-226
❑ 97PacLigB-226
❑ 97PacSil-226
❑ 97SyrSkyCB-18
❑ 98Pac-225
❑ 98PacPlaB-225
❑ 98PacRedT-225
❑ 98PacSil-225
❑ 98SyrSkyG-22
❑ 99PacCroC-299
❑ 99PacCroCPB-299

Perez, Tony
❑ 65RedEnq-22
❑ 65Top-581
❑ 66OPC-72
❑ 66Top-72
❑ 66TopVen-72
❑ 67CokCapR-8
❑ 67Kah-29
❑ 67Top-476
❑ 67TopVen-327
❑ 68Baz-12
❑ 68Kah-B27
❑ 68OPC-130
❑ 68Top-130
❑ 68Top3-D-7
❑ 68TopActS-12C
❑ 68TopVen-130
❑ 69Kah-A3
❑ 69Kah-B16
❑ 69MilBra-217
❑ 69MLBOffS-134
❑ 69Top-295
❑ 69TopSta-28
❑ 69TopTeaP-20
❑ 69TraSta-50
❑ 70DayDaiNM-11
❑ 70MLBOffS-34
❑ 70OPC-63
❑ 70OPC-380
❑ 70Top-63
❑ 70Top-380
❑ 70TopScr-16
❑ 71Kel-58
❑ 71MilDud-58
❑ 71MLBOffS-67
❑ 71OPC-64
❑ 71OPC-66
❑ 71OPC-580
❑ 71Top-64
❑ 71Top-66
❑ 71Top-580
❑ 71TopCoi-105
❑ 71TopGreM-14
❑ 71TopSup-6
❑ 71TopTat-76
❑ 72Dia-37
❑ 72EssCoi-11
❑ 72MilBra-269
❑ 72OPC-80
❑ 72Top-80
❑ 73LinPor-58
❑ 73OPC-205
❑ 73OPC-275
❑ 73Top-205
❑ 73Top-275
❑ 74OPC-230
❑ 74Top-230
❑ 74TopDecE-54
❑ 74TopSta-29
❑ 75Hos-127
❑ 75OPC-560
❑ 75Top-560
❑ 75TopMin-560
❑ 76BlaDis-46
❑ 76BucDis-46
❑ 76CarDis-46
❑ 76CraDis-46
❑ 76DailsID-46
❑ 76Hos-86
❑ 76IsaDis-46
❑ 76LinSup-92
❑ 76OPC-195
❑ 76OPC-325
❑ 76OrbDis-46
❑ 76RedBarD-46
❑ 76RedIceL-11
❑ 76RedKro-15
❑ 76SafDis-46
❑ 76SSP-39
❑ 76Top-195
❑ 76Top-325
❑ 76TowCluD-46
❑ 77BobParMBC-16
❑ 77BurCheD-160
❑ 77ChiWilD-53
❑ 77DailsID-53
❑ 77DetCaeD-53
❑ 77ExpPos-25
❑ 77HolInnD-53
❑ 77MSADis-53
❑ 77OPC-135
❑ 77RCColC-54
❑ 77SagDis-53
❑ 77sDis-53
❑ 77Top-655
❑ 77TopCloS-37

❑ 77WenDis-53
❑ 77ZipDis-53
❑ 78Hos-4
❑ 78OPC-90
❑ 78RCColC-14
❑ 78Top-15
❑ 78WifBalD-59
❑ 79BasPat-68
❑ 79ExpPos-19
❑ 79OPC-261
❑ 79Top-495
❑ 80OPC-69
❑ 80Top-125
❑ 81AllGamPl-6
❑ 81CokTeaS-8
❑ 81Don-334
❑ 81Fle-241
❑ 81FleStiC-66
❑ 81Kel-17
❑ 81OPC-231
❑ 81Top-575
❑ 81TopScr-8
❑ 81TopSti-44
❑ 81TopSupHT-7
❑ 82Don-408
❑ 82Fle-302
❑ 82FleSta-170
❑ 82OPC-255
❑ 82OPC-256
❑ 82RedSoxC-14
❑ 82Top-255
❑ 82Top-256
❑ 82TopSti-152
❑ 83Don-578
❑ 83Fle-191
❑ 83OPC-74
❑ 83OPC-355
❑ 83PhiTas-22
❑ 83Top-715
❑ 83Top-716
❑ 83TopFol-2
❑ 83TopSti-8
❑ 83TopTra-85T
❑ 84Don-503
❑ 84DonCha-29
❑ 84Fle-44
❑ 84Fle-636
❑ 84FleUpd-91
❑ 84FunFooP-99
❑ 84Nes792-385
❑ 84Nes792-702
❑ 84Nes792-703
❑ 84Nes792-704
❑ 84OPC-385
❑ 84RedBor-24
❑ 84RedEnq-1
❑ 84Top-385
❑ 84Top-702
❑ 84Top-703
❑ 84Top-704
❑ 84TopSti-126
❑ 84TopTif-385
❑ 84TopTif-702
❑ 84TopTif-703
❑ 84TopTif-704
❑ 84TopTra-91T
❑ 84TopTraT-91T
❑ 85CirK-28
❑ 85DonHig-9
❑ 85Fle-546
❑ 85OPC-212
❑ 85Top-675
❑ 85TopTif-675
❑ 86Don-15
❑ 86Don-428
❑ 86DonSupD-15
❑ 86Fle-186
❑ 86GenMilB-5G
❑ 86Lea-15
❑ 86OPC-85
❑ 86RedTexG-24
❑ 86Spo-138
❑ 86Top-85
❑ 86Top-205
❑ 86TopSti-8
❑ 86TopSti-143
❑ 86TopTat-16
❑ 86TopTif-85
❑ 86TopTif-205
❑ 87Fle-209
❑ 87FleGlo-209
❑ 87RedKah-NNO
❑ 88RedKah-NNO
❑ 89RedKah-xx
❑ 90RedKah-27
❑ 91RedKah-NNO
❑ 91UppDecS-9
❑ 92KelAll-2
❑ 92Nab-7
❑ 92RedKah-NNO
❑ 93TedWilM-19
❑ 93Top-503
❑ 93TopGol-503
❑ 93TopInaM-503
❑ 93TopInaR-503
❑ 93TopMic-503
❑ 93UppDecS-28
❑ 96Red76K-3
❑ 96Red76K-10
❑ 97OhiLot-4
❑ 98UppDecR-27
❑ 98UppDecRSotT-TP

Perez, Victor
❑ 90BilMusP-3236

Perez, Vladimir
❑ 87SpaPhiP-23
❑ 88LitFalMP-19
❑ 89ColMetB-2
❑ 89ColMetGS-20
❑ 90St.LucMS-20
❑ 92BasCitRC-20
❑ 92MemChiF-2417
❑ 93LimRocDWB-65
❑ 93MemChiF-373
❑ 94MemChiF-357

Perez, William
❑ 89ModA'sC-14

Perez, Yorkis
❑ 86KenTwiP-19
❑ 87WesPalBEP-667
❑ 88JacExpB-11
❑ 88JacExpP-973
❑ 89WesPalBES-17
❑ 90JacExpB-22
❑ 90JacExpP-1372
❑ 91LinDriAAA-436
❑ 91RicBraBC-12
❑ 91RicBraLD-436
❑ 91RicBraP-2564
❑ 91RicBraTI-16
❑ 92Don-754
❑ 92TopDeb91-137
❑ 93HarSenF-268
❑ 93LimRocDP-P4
❑ 93LimRocDWB-68
❑ 94Bow-439
❑ 94SpoRoo-63
❑ 94SpoRooAP-63
❑ 94Ult-495
❑ 95ColCho-297
❑ 95ColChoGS-297
❑ 95ColChoSS-297
❑ 95Fle-339
❑ 95Pac-175
❑ 95PacLatD-27
❑ 95Top-600
❑ 95TopCyb-371
❑ 95Ult-165
❑ 95UltGolM-165
❑ 96ChaKniB-22
❑ 96Don-154
❑ 96DonPreP-154
❑ 96LeaSigEA-155
❑ 96Pac-81
❑ 97Fle-588
❑ 97FleTif-588
❑ 97NorTid-24
❑ 97NorTidB-24
❑ 97Pac-305
❑ 97PacLigB-305
❑ 97PacSil-305
❑ 98PacOnl-569
❑ 98PacOnlR-569
❑ 98PacOnlWC-569
❑ 99Fle-567
❑ 99FleSta9-567
❑ 99FleWarT-567

Perezchica, Tony
❑ 84EveGiaC-30B
❑ 86FreGiaSB-20
❑ 87ShrCapP-6
❑ 88PhoFirC-16
❑ 88PhoFirP-75
❑ 88TriAAAP-32
❑ 89Fle-338
❑ 89FleGlo-338
❑ 89PhoFirC-14
❑ 89PhoFirP-1502
❑ 89ScoHot1R-50
❑ 90Bow-235
❑ 90BowTif-235
❑ 90CMC-547
❑ 90PhoFirC-20
❑ 91DonRoo-10
❑ 91GiaPacGaE-30
❑ 91LinDriAAA-388
❑ 91PhoFirLD-388
❑ 91PhoFirP-74
❑ 91Sco-735
❑ 92ColSprSSF-759
❑ 92IndFanC-23
❑ 92Sco-702
❑ 92StaClu-454
❑ 92TopGol-366
❑ 92TopGolW-366
❑ 92Ult-355
❑ 94AlbYanF-1450
❑ 95ColCliMCTI-16
❑ 95ColCliP-22
❑ 95ColCliTI-22
❑ 97NorNav-3
❑ 97NorNavTI-24

Perigny, Don
❑ 91SouBenWSC-19
❑ 91SouBenWSP-2855
❑ 92SarWhiSCB-12
❑ 92SarWhiSF-203
❑ 93BirBarF-1191
❑ 94PorSeaDF-676
❑ 94PorSeaDTI-26

Perisho, Matt
❑ 94Bow-419
❑ 94CedRapKC-19
❑ 94CedRapKF-1107
❑ 96LakElsSB-9
❑ 97ColChoU-U2
❑ 97MidAng-21
❑ 97TexLeaTP-13
❑ 98Fle-142
❑ 98MetUni-93
❑ 98MetUniPMG-93
❑ 98OklRedM-23
❑ 98RevoRooHH-20
❑ 98RevoRooHHG-20
❑ 98Ult-221
❑ 98UltGolM-221
❑ 98UltMas-221
❑ 98UltPlaM-221

Perkins, Bill
❑ 86NegLeaF-94

Perkins, Broderick
❑ 78PadFamF-21
❑ 79PadFamF-22
❑ 79Top-725
❑ 80HawIsIT-22
❑ 81Don-525
❑ 81Fle-498
❑ 81Top-393
❑ 81TopSti-226
❑ 82Don-397
❑ 82Fle-579
❑ 82FleSta-103
❑ 82OPC-192
❑ 82Top-192
❑ 82TopSti-98
❑ 83Don-121
❑ 83Fle-368
❑ 83IndPos-27
❑ 83IndWhe-24
❑ 83Top-593
❑ 83TopSti-292
❑ 83TopTra-86T
❑ 84Don-276
❑ 84Fle-548
❑ 84Ind-24
❑ 84IndWhe-15
❑ 84Nes792-212
❑ 84Top-212
❑ 84TopTif-212
❑ 85Top-609
❑ 85TopTif-609

Perkins, Cecil
❑ 81TCM60I-471
❑ 92YanWIZ6-97

Perkins, Charlie
❑ 90DodTar-617

Perkins, Craig
❑ 75OmaRoyTI-13
❑ 76OmaRoyTT-21

Perkins, Cy (Ralph)
❑ 20NatCarE-76
❑ 21Exh-127
❑ 21Nei-11
❑ 21OxfConE-12
❑ 22E120-87
❑ 22W572-75
❑ 22W573-97
❑ 23WilChoV-122
❑ 25Exh-110
❑ 26Exh-110
❑ 27YorCarE-29
❑ 34DiaMatCSB-148
❑ 34TigTeal-14
❑ 36WorWidGV-24
❑ 49PhiBul-42
❑ 74TigTCM1AC-22
❑ 75Phi195T-22
❑ 76TigOldTS-17
❑ 80Phi195T-22
❑ 91ConTSN-185
❑ 94ConTSN-1157
❑ 94ConTSNB-1157
❑ 96NoiSatP-1

Perkins, Dan
❑ 93EliTwiC-1
❑ 93EliTwiF-3417
❑ 94EliTwiC-19
❑ 94EliTwiF-3729
❑ 94ExcFS7-97
❑ 94ForWayWC-18
❑ 94ForWayWF-2009
❑ 95ForWayWTI-10
❑ 96FtMyeMB-6
❑ 97EasLeaTPB-14
❑ 97NewBriRC-24
❑ 98NewBriRCM-22
❑ 99SkyPre-229
❑ 99SkyPre-229
❑ 99SkyPreR-229
❑ 99SkyPreR-229

Perkins, David
❑ 90MisStaB-29
❑ 91MisStaB-36
❑ 92MisStaB-31
❑ 93MisStaB-30

Perkins, Floyd
❑ 14Zee-71A
❑ 14Zee-71B

Perkins, Harold
❑ 82VerBeaDT-19
❑ 83VerBeaDT-20
❑ 89RocRedWC-18
❑ 89RocRedWP-1643

Perkins, Paul
❑ 91PenPilC-9
❑ 91PenPilP-375
❑ 92SanBerC-24
❑ 92SanBerSF-951
❑ 93JacSunF-2710
❑ 94Bow-33
❑ 95LynHilTI-18

Perkins, Ray
❑ 82AubAstT-5
❑ 86FloStaLAP-38
❑ 86MiaMarP-20

Perkins, Scott
❑ 94HelBreF-3613
❑ 94HelBreSP-11

Perkins, Tom
❑ 75CliPilT-22

Perkowski, Harry
❑ 52Bow-202
❑ 52Top-142
❑ 53BowC-87
❑ 53Top-236
❑ 54Bow-44
❑ 54Top-125
❑ 55Top-184
❑ 83TopRep5-142
❑ 91TopArc1-236
❑ 94TopArc1-125
❑ 94TopArc1G-125

Perlman, Jon
❑ 83IowCubT-8
❑ 84IowCubT-6
❑ 85IowCubT-19
❑ 86PhoFirP-20
❑ 87GiaPos-26
❑ 87PhoFirP-13
❑ 88ColSprSSC-6
❑ 88ColSprSSP-1542
❑ 88Fle-93
❑ 88FleGlo-93
❑ 88FleUpd-22
❑ 88FleUpdG-22
❑ 88IndTeal-27
❑ 89Sco-591
❑ 89Top-476
❑ 89TopTif-476

Perlozzo, Sam
❑ 77TacTwiDQ-4
❑ 78Top-704
❑ 79HawIsIC-5
❑ 79HawIsIT-11
❑ 79Top-709
❑ 81TidTidT-22
❑ 83LynMetT-11
❑ 84JacMetT-16
❑ 86TidTidP-23
❑ 87MetColP-44
❑ 88MetColP-43
❑ 88MetKah-34
❑ 89MetColP-48
❑ 89MetKah-22
❑ 90RedKah-27
❑ 91RedKah-NNO
❑ 92RedKah-NNO
❑ 93MarMot-28
❑ 94MarMot-28
❑ 95MarMot-28
❑ 96BalOriP-27

Perna, Bobby
❑ 90BilMusP-3230
❑ 91ChaWheC-18
❑ 91ChaWheP-2895
❑ 91SouAtlLAGP-SAL9
❑ 92ChaWheF-16
❑ 92ChaWVWC-21
❑ 92ClaFS7-56
❑ 93ClaFS7-237
❑ 93ExcFS7-26
❑ 93SouAtlLAPI-30
❑ 93WinSpiC-18
❑ 93WinSpiF-1579
❑ 94ChaLooF-1366

Pernalete, Marco
❑ 97BakBlaB-14
❑ 97BakBlaTI-14

Pernell, Brandon
❑ 98RanCucQG-23
❑ 98RanCucQG-23

Perno, Donn
❑ 87EveGiaC-23

Pernoll, H. Hub
❑ 09ObaT21-281
❑ 11PacCoaBD-50
❑ 11SpoLifM-67
❑ 11Zee-38
❑ 12HomRunKE-29
❑ 12ObaPreT-30
❑ 12Zee-44
❑ 13Zee-45
❑ 14Zee-118
❑ 15Zee-113

Perodin, Ron
❑ 80CliGiaT-21

Perona, Joe
❑ 92Bow-246
❑ 92ClaFS7-169
❑ 92LakTigC-5
❑ 92LakTigF-2282
❑ 92UppDecML-90
❑ 93LonTigF-2310
❑ 94Bow-453
❑ 94TreThuF-2123

Perozo, Danny
❑ 88BilMusP-1813
❑ 89BilMusP-2058
❑ 89GreHorP-409
❑ 90ChaWheB-23
❑ 90ChaWheP-2254
❑ 91CedRapRC-23
❑ 91CedRapRP-2733

Perozo, Ed
❑ 89ElmPioP-13
❑ 90LynRedSTI-3
❑ 91ColMetPI-6
❑ 91ColMetPPI-4
❑ 92ColMetC-15
❑ 92ColMetF-310
❑ 92ColMetPI-9
❑ 93ForLauRSC-22
❑ 93ForLauRSFP-1607
❑ 93LinVenB-266
❑ 94VenLinU-217
❑ 95LinVen-54
❑ 96-97LinVen-178

Perozo, Felix
❑ 97ButCopKB-18
❑ 97ButCopKK-18
❑ 98CedRapKTI-22

Perpetuo, Nelson
❑ 91BriTigC-28
❑ 91BriTigP-3601
❑ 95ChaRivTI-19

Perranoski, Ron
❑ 61DodUniO-15
❑ 61Top-525
❑ 62DodBelB-16
❑ 62DodVol-15
❑ 62Top-297
❑ 63Top-403
❑ 64ChatheY-41
❑ 64DodHea-8
❑ 64Top-30
❑ 64TopCoi-64
❑ 64TopSta-46
❑ 64TopTatI-62
❑ 64TopVen-30
❑ 64WheSta-35
❑ 65ChaTheY-42
❑ 65DodTeal-15
❑ 65Top-484
❑ 66DodVolT-8
❑ 66Top-555
❑ 67CokCapD-16
❑ 67CokCapDA-16
❑ 67DexPre-164
❑ 67Top-197
❑ 68Top-435
❑ 69OPC-77
❑ 69Top-77A
❑ 69Top-77B
❑ 69TopSta-197
❑ 70DayDaiNM-116
❑ 70MLBOffS-237
❑ 70OPC-226
❑ 70Top-226
❑ 70TwiSupV-8
❑ 71MLBOffS-469
❑ 71OPC-475
❑ 71Top-475
❑ 71TopCoi-104
❑ 72OPC-367
❑ 72Top-367
❑ 78TwiFri-40
❑ 81Dod-23
❑ 81DodPol-NNO
❑ 83DodPol-NNO
❑ 84DodPol-NNO
❑ 85DodCokP-25
❑ 86DodCokP-23
❑ 86DodPol-NNO
❑ 87DodMot-27
❑ 87DodPol-29
❑ 88DodMot-28
❑ 89DodMot-27
❑ 89DodPol-1
❑ 90DodMot-28
❑ 90DodPol-NNO
❑ 90DodTar-618
❑ 91DodMot-28
❑ 91DodPho-5
❑ 91DodPol-NNO
❑ 91DodSt.V-7
❑ 92DodMot-28
❑ 92DodPol-NNO
❑ 93DodMot-28
❑ 93DodPol-30
❑ 94DodMot-28
❑ 94DodPol-30
❑ 98GiaMot-28

Perrier, Hip
❑ 87OldJudN-393
❑ 88SFHesCreN32-24

Perrin, Bill
❑ 33WorCig(-67

Perring, George
❑ 08AmeLeaPC-14
❑ 09T206-287
❑ 11PinT-5-1058
❑ 11SpoLifM-287
❑ 14CraJacE-119
❑ 15CraJacE-119
❑ 72ClaCar-53

Perritt, Madison
❑ 13Zee-18
❑ 14Zee-21
❑ 15Zee-17
❑ 16Zee-116

Perritt, Pol (William D.)
❑ 17ColE13-132
❑ 17HolBreD-78
❑ 20W52-16
❑ 92ConTSN-488

Perry, Alonzo
❑ 49RemBre-21

Perry, Bob
❑ 86KenTwiP-20

Perry, Bob (Melvin)
❑ 60TacBan-13
❑ 61TacBan-16
❑ 64Top-48
❑ 64TopVen-48

Perry, Chan

- 94BurIndC-21
- 94BurIndF-3804
- 96KenIndB-21
- 97AkrAer-21
- 97BesAutSBPP-40
- 98Bes-38
- 98BufBisG-23

Perry, Clyde
- 30Zee-152

Perry, David
- 89BoiHawP-1981

Perry, Eric
- 87WytCubP-9
- 88ChaWheB-7
- 88GenCubP-1633
- 89PeoChiTI-19

Perry, Gaylord
- 47PM1StaP1-160
- 61TacBan-15
- 61UniOil-T29
- 62Top-199
- 63Top-169
- 64Top-468
- 65GiaTeal-9
- 65OPC-193
- 65Top-193
- 66Top-598
- 67CokCapA-26
- 67CokCapG-15
- 67CokCapNLA-31
- 67DexPre-165
- 67Top-236
- 67Top-320
- 67TopVen-312
- 68DexPre-61
- 68OPC-11
- 68OPC-85
- 68Top-11
- 68Top-85
- 68TopVen-11
- 68TopVen-85
- 69MilBra-218
- 69MLBOffS-207
- 69Top-485A
- 69Top-485B
- 69TopSta-110
- 69TopTeaP-14
- 70Gia-11
- 70Kel-20
- 70MLBOffS-132
- 70Top-560
- 71GiaTic-10
- 71Kel-6
- 71MilDud-59
- 71MLBOffS-261
- 71OPC-70
- 71OPC-140
- 71Top-70
- 71Top-140
- 71TopCoi-73
- 71TopSup-2
- 72MilBra-270
- 72OPC-285
- 72Top-285
- 73IndArtTC-5
- 73IndTeal-21
- 73Kel2D-38
- 73LinPor-65
- 73OPC-66
- 73OPC-346
- 73OPC-400
- 73SevTraC-58
- 73Top-66
- 73Top-346
- 73Top-400
- 73TopCanL-39
- 73TopCom-14
- 73TopPin-14
- 74OPC-35
- 74Top-35
- 74TopSta-168
- 75CleIndP-19
- 75Hos-84
- 75Kel-45
- 75OPC-530
- 75RanPos-26
- 75SSP18-9
- 75SSP42-30
- 75Top-530
- 75TopMin-530
- 76Hos-4
- 76HosTwi-4
- 76OPC-55
- 76OPC-204
- 76Top-55
- 76Top-204
- 77BurCheD-20
- 77Hos-73
- 77OPC-149
- 77RCColC-52
- 77Spo-1920
- 77Top-152
- 78Hos-139
- 78PadFamF-22
- 78Top-686
- 78WifBalD-60
- 79Hos-83
- 79Kel-49
- 79OPC-161
- 79PadFamF-18
- 79Top-5
- 79Top-321
- 80OPC-148
- 80PerHaloFP-210
- 80PerHaloFPS-72
- 80Top-280
- 81BraPol-46
- 81Don-471
- 81Fle-91
- 81Gia196T-21
- 81Top-582
- 81TopTra-812
- 82Don-543
- 82Fle-445
- 82FleSta-67
- 82MarPos-24
- 82OPC-115
- 82Top-115
- 82TopTra-88T
- 83Don-307
- 83DonActA-28
- 83Fle-483
- 83Fle-630
- 83FleSta-150
- 83FleSti-181
- 83MarNal-4
- 83OPC-96
- 83OPC-159
- 83Top-463
- 83Top-464
- 83TopFol-1
- 83TopGayP-1
- 83TopGayP-2
- 83TopGayP-3
- 83TopGayP-4
- 83TopGayP-5
- 83TopGayP-6
- 83TopSti-114
- 84Don-A
- 84DonCha-32
- 84Fle-352
- 84Fle-638
- 84Fle-641
- 84FleSti-98
- 84GiaMot-4
- 84Nes792-4
- 84Nes792-6
- 84OCoandSI-214
- 84Top-4
- 84Top-6
- 84TopTif-4
- 84TopTif-6
- 86PadGreT-9
- 86RanGreT-1
- 88GreBasS-39
- 88HouSho-3
- 89PacLegI-152
- 89PadMag-24
- 89TopBasT-18
- 90BasWit-40
- 90PacLeg-43
- 90PerGreM-79
- 90SweBasG-66
- 91FouBal-20
- 91Kel3D-1
- 91PadMag-25
- 91SweBasG-70
- 91UppDecHoB-H2
- 91UppDecHoB-AU2
- 91UppDecS-5
- 91UppDecS-15
- 91UppDecS-18
- 91UppDecS-20
- 92GiaCheHoFP-3
- 92MVP-8
- 92MVP2H-9
- 92UppDecF-49
- 92UppDecFG-49
- 92UppDecHH-HI6
- 92UppDecS-34
- 92YanWIZ8-145
- 92YanWIZH-26
- 93ActPacA-125
- 93ActPacA2-59G
- 93ActPacAC-9
- 93MetIma-15
- 93RanKee-289
- 93TedWil-94
- 93Yoo-12
- 96AriLot-2
- 97CalLot-5
- 97OhiLot-5
- 97TopStaHRR-11
- 97TopStaRRAU-11
- 98SpollITaN-23
- 98SpollITaNEE-23
- 98UppDecR-46
- 98UppDecRSotT-GP
- 99SpollIGotG-67
- 99SpollIGotGA-56
- 99SpollIGotGC-43

Perry, Gerald
- 82ArkTraT-6
- 82RicBraT-14
- 83RicBraT-14
- 84BraPol-28
- 84Don-263
- 84FleUpd-92
- 84raPho-24
- 84TopTra-92T
- 84TopTraT-92T
- 85BraHos-19
- 85BraPol-28
- 85Don-443
- 85Fle-338
- 85Top-219
- 85TopTif-219
- 86Don-165
- 86Fle-525
- 86RicBraP-16
- 86Top-557
- 86TopTif-557
- 87BraSmo-17
- 87Top-639
- 87TopTif-639
- 88Don-437
- 88DonBasB-58
- 88Fle-547
- 88FleGlo-547
- 88Lea-216
- 88PanSti-242
- 88Sco-136
- 88ScoGlo-136
- 88StaLinBra-14
- 88Top-39
- 88TopBig-40
- 88TopTif-39
- 89Bow-273
- 89BowTif-273
- 89BraDub-20
- 89CadEIID-39
- 89ClaTraO-118
- 89Don-22
- 89Don-239
- 89DonAll-57
- 89DonBasB-291
- 89DonBonM-BC24
- 89DonSupD-22
- 89Fle-597
- 89Fle-638
- 89FleBasA-31
- 89FleBasM-31
- 89FleGlo-597
- 89FleHeroB-30
- 89OPC-130
- 89PanSti-40
- 89RedFolSB-90
- 89Sco-101
- 89ScoHot1S-20
- 89Spo-164
- 89Top-130
- 89TopBasT-150
- 89TopBig-279
- 89TopCoi-21
- 89TopMinL-2
- 89TopSti-33
- 89TopTif-130
- 89TopUKM-59
- 89TVSpoM-57
- 89UppDec-431
- 90Bow-383
- 90BowTif-383
- 90ClaYel-T48
- 90Don-153
- 90Fle-592
- 90FleCan-592
- 90FleUpd-103
- 90Lea-441
- 90OPC-792
- 90PublntS-118
- 90RicBra2ATI-19
- 90RoyPos-20
- 90Sco-249
- 90ScoRoo-28T
- 90Top-792
- 90TopSti-27
- 90TopTif-792
- 90TopTra-92T
- 90TopTraT-92T
- 90UppDec-101
- 90UppDec-707
- 91Bow-405
- 91CarPol-21
- 91Don-130
- 91Fle-566
- 91FleUpd-119
- 91Lea-272
- 91OPC-384
- 91PanSti-230
- 91Sco-286
- 91ScoRoo-63T
- 91StaClu-379
- 91Top-384
- 91TopDesS-384
- 91TopMic-384
- 91TopTif-384
- 91UltUpd-109
- 91UppDec-219
- 92CarPol-16
- 92Don-634
- 92Fle-589
- 92Lea-122
- 92LeaBlaG-122
- 92OPC-498
- 92Sco-491
- 92StaClu-338
- 92Top-498
- 92TopGol-498
- 92TopGolW-498
- 92TopMic-498
- 92Ult-572
- 92UppDec-690
- 93CarPol-17
- 93Don-468
- 93Fle-514
- 93PacSpa-301
- 93Top-597
- 93TopGol-597
- 93TopInaM-597
- 93TopInaR-597
- 93TopMic-597
- 94CarPol-17
- 94Fle-645
- 94Pac-602
- 94Sco-120
- 94ScoGolR-120
- 94StaCluT-329
- 94StaCluTFDI-329
- 94Top-263
- 94TopGol-263
- 94TopSpa-263
- 95Fle-507
- 95Pac-415
- 95Sco-111
- 95ScoGolR-111
- 95ScoPlaTS-111
- 97MicBatC-3
- 98PawRedSQ-4

Perry, Hank
- 09ObaT21-146

Perry, Herb Edward Jr
- 91Cla/Bes-428
- 91FroRowDP-51
- 91FroRowDPG-51
- 91FroRowDPS-51
- 91WatIndC-21
- 91WatIndP-3376
- 92KinIndC-23
- 92KinIndF-2486
- 92UppDecML-190
- 93ExcFS7-163
- 94Bow-551
- 94BowBes-B76
- 94BowBesR-B76
- 94ChaKniF-904
- 94SigRoo-18
- 94SigRooS-18
- 94TriAAF-AAA2
- 94UppDec-519
- 94UppDecED-519
- 94UppDecML-12
- 95ColCho-272
- 95ColChoGS-272
- 95ColChoSE-15
- 95ColChoSEGS-15
- 95ColChoSESS-15
- 95ColChoSS-272
- 95Top-635
- 96BufBisB-16
- 96ColCho-532
- 96ColChoGS-532
- 96ColChoSS-532
- 96Don-124
- 96DonPreP-124
- 96Fle-96
- 96FleTif-96
- 96IndFle-12
- 96Sco-469
- 96Top-355
- 97Top-141

Perry, Herb Scott
- 12ColRedB-228
- 12ColTinT-228
- 20NatCarE-77

Perry, Jason
- 92SpoIndC-30

Perry, Jeff
- 84SavCarT-14
- 87VisOakP-7

Perry, Jim
- 59Ind-15
- 59Kah-27
- 59Top-542
- 60Kah-32
- 60Lea-49
- 60Top-324
- 61Baz-22
- 61Kah-31
- 61Pos-59A
- 61Pos-59B
- 61Top-48
- 61Top-385
- 61Top-584
- 61TopStal-138
- 62Jel-43
- 62Kah-29
- 62Pos-43
- 62PosCan-43
- 62SalPlaC-32
- 62ShiPlaC-32
- 62Top-37
- 62Top-405
- 62TopBuc-67
- 62TopStal-37
- 62TopVen-37
- 63Top-535
- 63TwiVol-14
- 64Top-34
- 64TopVen-34
- 65Top-351
- 66Top-283
- 66TopVen-283
- 66TwiFaiG-12
- 67CokCapTw-5
- 67Top-246
- 67TopVen-247
- 67TwiTeal-15
- 68Top-393
- 69MilBra-219
- 69OPC-146
- 69Top-146
- 69TopFou-14
- 69TopTeaP-15
- 70DayDaiNM-45
- 70Kel-64
- 70MLBOffS-236
- 70OPC-70
- 70Top-70
- 70Top-620
- 70TwiSupV-9
- 71Kel-3
- 71MilDud-22
- 71MLBOffS-470
- 71OPC-69
- 71OPC-500
- 71Top-69
- 71Top-500
- 71TopCoi-12
- 71TopGreM-10
- 71TopSup-24
- 71TopTat-112
- 72MilBra-271
- 72OPC-220
- 72OPC-497
- 72SevTraC-41
- 72Top-220
- 72Top-497
- 72TwiPos-16
- 72TwiTeal-10
- 73LinPor-66
- 73OPC-385
- 73Top-385
- 74OPC-316
- 74Top-316
- 75CleIndP-20
- 75OPC-263
- 75Top-263
- 75TopMin-263
- 78TCM60I-105
- 78TigDeaCS-10
- 78TwiFri-17
- 81TacTigT-31
- 86TwiGreT-9
- 88PacLegI-18
- 89SweBasG-37
- 90BasWit-44

Perry, Master (Ray)
- 88KimN18-36

Perry, Parnell
- 86GenCubP-23
- 87PeoChiP-22

Perry, Pat
- 83ColAstT-18
- 84ArkTraT-18
- 85LouRedR-18
- 86CarSchM-20
- 86CarTeal-35
- 86Don-596
- 86FleUpd-89
- 87CarSmo-4
- 87CarTeal-26
- 87Don-430
- 87Fle-307
- 87FleGlo-307
- 87Top-417
- 87TopTif-417
- 88CubDavB-37
- 88Don-626
- 88Fle-244
- 88FleGlo-244
- 88Sco-557
- 88ScoGlo-557
- 88Top-282
- 88TopTif-282
- 89Don-404
- 89Fle-435
- 89FleGlo-435
- 89Sco-364
- 89Top-186
- 89TopBig-329
- 89TopTif-186
- 89UppDec-345
- 90OPC-541
- 90PublntS-199
- 90Sco-436
- 90SprCarDGB-17
- 90Top-541
- 90TopTif-541
- 91Sco-527

Perry, Ron
- 80GleFalWSBT-17
- 80GleFalWSCT-1
- 81GleFalWST-15

Perry, Shawn
- 83TacTigT-33

Perry, Steve
- 79LodDodT-8
- 81VerBeaDT-14
- 83AlbDukTc-9
- 84AlbDukCr-154
- 90OneYanP-3370

Perry, Tim
- 97CliLumG-21
- 97IdaFalBTI-13
- 98CliLumG-19

Persails, Mark
- 98WesMicWM-16

Perschke, Greg
- 89UtiBluSP-17
- 90SarWhiSS-19
- 90StaFS7-59
- 91LinDriAAA-644
- 91VanCanLD-644
- 91VanCanP-1593
- 92Bow-282
- 92SkyAAAF-288
- 92VanCanF-2720
- 92VanCanS-645
- 93AlbDukF-1458
- 94OriCubF-1382

Persing, Tim
- 90EliTwiS-16
- 91Cla/Bes-371
- 91KenTwiC-8
- 91KenTwiP-2070
- 91MidLeaAP-MWL38

❑ 92Ft.MyeMF-2743
❑ 92VisOakC-7
❑ 92VisOakF-1013

Person, Carl
❑ 75QuaCitAT-9

Person, Robert
❑ 90KinIndTI-23
❑ 91BenBucCB-9
❑ 91BenBucP-3694
❑ 91KinIndC-10
❑ 91KinIndP-322
❑ 92SarWhiSF-204
❑ 93HigDesMC-17
❑ 93HigDesMF-40
❑ 94BinMetF-702
❑ 95BinMetTI-16
❑ 95Bow-24
❑ 95UppDec-263
❑ 95UppDecED-263
❑ 95UppDecEDG-263
❑ 96Bow-317
❑ 96BowFoi-317
❑ 96ColCho-39
❑ 96Fle-486
❑ 96FleTif-486
❑ 96LeaSigEA-156
❑ 96MetKah-27
❑ 96NorTidB-23
❑ 96Ult-515
❑ 96UltGolM-515
❑ 97BluJayOH-23
❑ 97Cir-180
❑ 97CirRav-180
❑ 97ColCho-168
❑ 97Fle-404
❑ 97Fle-511
❑ 97FleTif-404
❑ 97FleTif-511
❑ 97Top-116
❑ 97Ult-533
❑ 97UltGolME-533
❑ 97UltPlaME-533
❑ 98ColCho-264
❑ 98PacOnl-770
❑ 98PacOnlR-770
❑ 98PacOnlWC-770
❑ 98SyrSkyG-23
❑ 98Top-233
❑ 98TopChr-233
❑ 98TopChrR-233
❑ 98TopDevR-233
❑ 98TopDia-233
❑ 98TopMiniC-233
❑ 98UppDec-528
❑ 99Fle-530
❑ 99FleSta9-530
❑ 99FleWarT-530
❑ 99SkyPreA-44
❑ 99SkyPreABlue-44

Person, Wilton
❑ 94IdaFalBF-3600
❑ 94IdaFalBSP-4
❑ 95EugEmeTI-13

Persons, Archie
❑ 09T206-509
❑ 10CouT21-54

Pertica, William
❑ 18Zee-13
❑ 20Zee-16
❑ 22E120-235
❑ 23W503-60

Perusek, Bill
❑ 96FayGenB-24

Perzanowski, Stan
❑ 75IntLeaASB-23
❑ 75PacCoaLAB-23
❑ 76OPC-388
❑ 76Top-388
❑ 77SalLakCGC-17
❑ 93RanKee-290

Pesavento, Mike
❑ 85VerBeaDT-22

Pesavento, Patrick
❑ 90FayGenP-2415
❑ 90SouAtlLAS-18

Pesky, Johnny
❑ 42RedSoxTI-20
❑ 46RedSoxTI-19
❑ 46SpoExcW-7-3
❑ 47Exh-175
❑ 47HomBon-37
❑ 47PM1StaP1-161
❑ 47RedSoxTI-20
❑ 47TipTop-11
❑ 48RedSoxTI-20
❑ 49Bow-86
❑ 49Lea-121
❑ 49MPR302-2-121
❑ 49RedSoxTI-18
❑ 50AmeNut&CCP-13
❑ 50Bow-137
❑ 50Dra-32
❑ 50RedSoxCL-4
❑ 50RedSoxTI-19
❑ 51Bow-15
❑ 51TopBluB-5
❑ 52Bow-45
❑ 52Top-15
❑ 53BowC-134
❑ 53TigGle-24
❑ 54Bow-135
❑ 54Top-63
❑ 55Bow-241
❑ 61SeaPop-16
❑ 61SeaPop-17
❑ 61UniOil-S8
❑ 62SeaPop-9
❑ 63Top-343
❑ 64RedSoxTI-5
❑ 64Top-248
❑ 64TopVen-248
❑ 67TopPirS-20
❑ 75RedSox1T-30
❑ 76SSP-625
❑ 76TayBow4-6
❑ 81RedSoxBG2S-44
❑ 83TopRep5-15
❑ 84TCMPla1-3
❑ 87RedSox1T-4
❑ 91TopArc1-315
❑ 91UppDecS-4
❑ 92BazQua5A-13
❑ 94TedWil-5
❑ 94TopArc1-63
❑ 94TopArc1G-63

Pesut, Nick
❑ 47SunBre-17

Petagine, Roberto
❑ 91BurAstC-17
❑ 91BurAstP-2811
❑ 92Bow-31
❑ 92ClaFS7-205
❑ 92JacGenF-4008
❑ 92OscAstC-23
❑ 92OscAstF-2540
❑ 92UppDecML-313
❑ 93Bow-644
❑ 93JacGenF-2117
❑ 93LinVenB-234
❑ 94Bow-342
❑ 94Bow-530
❑ 94BowBes-B42
❑ 94BowBesR-B42
❑ 94Cla-184
❑ 94ClaGolF-100
❑ 94ColC-581
❑ 94ColChoGS-581
❑ 94ColChoSS-581
❑ 94ExcAllF-2
❑ 94ExcFS7-208
❑ 94Lea-365
❑ 94Sel-406
❑ 94SpoRoo-113
❑ 94SpoRooAP-113
❑ 94Top-448
❑ 94TopGol-448
❑ 94TopSpa-448
❑ 94TucTorF-772
❑ 94Ult-510
❑ 94UppDecML-9
❑ 94UppDecML-268
❑ 94UppDecMLPotYF-PY2
❑ 94VenLinU-50
❑ 95Don-230
❑ 95DonPreP-230
❑ 95Fin-226
❑ 95FinRef-226
❑ 95Fla-422
❑ 95FleUpd-188
❑ 95LinVen-27
❑ 95LinVen-265
❑ 95LinVen-307
❑ 95LinVen-314
❑ 95Pac-192
❑ 95PadCHP-8
❑ 95PadMot-9
❑ 95Pin-145
❑ 95PinArtP-145
❑ 95PinMusC-145
❑ 95Sco-305
❑ 95ScoGolR-305
❑ 95ScoPlaTS-305
❑ 95Sel-152
❑ 95SelArtP-152
❑ 95SelCer-132
❑ 95SelCerMG-132
❑ 95Spo-165
❑ 95SpoArtP-165
❑ 95StaClu-591
❑ 95StaCluMOP-591
❑ 95StaCluSTWS-591
❑ 95Sum-158
❑ 95SumNthD-158
❑ 95Top-650
❑ 95TopTra-147T
❑ 95UC3-100
❑ 95UC3ArtP-100
❑ 95Zen-138
❑ 96-97LinVen-134
❑ 96ColCho-297
❑ 96ColCho-358
❑ 96ColChoGS-297
❑ 96ColChoGS-358
❑ 96ColChoSS-297
❑ 96ColChoSS-358
❑ 96Don-63
❑ 96DonPreP-63
❑ 96NorTidB-24
❑ 96Pac-183
❑ 96Sco-352
❑ 96ScoDugC-B77
❑ 96ScoDugCAP-B77
❑ 97NorTid-25
❑ 97NorTidB-25
❑ 97PacPriGotD-GD176
❑ 98IndIndQ-26
❑ 98PacInvGems-184
❑ 99PacCroC-78
❑ 99PacCroCPB-78

Petcka, Joe
❑ 92FroRowDP-91
❑ 92FroRowDPG-91
❑ 92FroRowDPS-91
❑ 92PitMetF-3291
❑ 93CapCitBC-17
❑ 93CapCitBF-458
❑ 93StaCluM-59
❑ 94St.LucMF-1193
❑ 95StLucMTI-25

Pete, Pioneer
❑ 83RedPioT-32

Peterek, Jeff
❑ 86StoPorP-20
❑ 87ElPasDP-23
❑ 88ElPasDB-21
❑ 89DenZepC-8
❑ 89DenZepP-46
❑ 90CMC-26
❑ 90DenZepC-1
❑ 90DenZepP-623
❑ 90Don-530
❑ 90Fle-333
❑ 90FleCan-333
❑ 90ProAAAF-648
❑ 90TopDeb89-97
❑ 94BreMilB-162

Peterman, Ernie
❑ 95StCatSTI-13
❑ 97St.PauS-21

Peterman, Tommy
❑ 97ForWayW-25
❑ 98Bow-387
❑ 98BowChr-387
❑ 98BowChrGA-387
❑ 98BowChrGAR-387
❑ 98BowChrI-387
❑ 98BowChrIR-387
❑ 98BowChrR-387
❑ 98BowGolA-387
❑ 98BowInt-387
❑ 98ForMyeMTI-24
❑ 99SP TopP-102
❑ 99SP TopPPE-102

Peters, Anthony
❑ 96BelSnaTI-31
❑ 97BelSnaB-24
❑ 98HagSunM-20

Peters, Brannon
❑ 95ForWayWTI-11

Peters, Chris
❑ 93WelPirC-20
❑ 93WelPirF-3356
❑ 94AugGreC-15
❑ 94AugGreF-3005
❑ 95LynHilTI-19
❑ 96CarMudB-6
❑ 96Exc-221
❑ 97PacPriGotD-GD194
❑ 97PirPos-27
❑ 98PacOnl-590
❑ 98PacOnlR-590
❑ 98PacOnlWC-590
❑ 99Fle-519
❑ 99FleSta9-519
❑ 99FleWarT-519
❑ 99StaClu-296
❑ 99StaCluFDI-296
❑ 99StaCluOoaK-296
❑ 99StaCluPP-296

Peters, Dan
❑ 88BelBreGS-20

Peters, Donald
❑ 90ClaDraP-26
❑ 90ClaYel-T83
❑ 90ProAaA-161
❑ 90SouOreAB-25
❑ 90SouOreAP-3424
❑ 91Bow-224
❑ 91Cla/Bes-288
❑ 91Cla1-T77
❑ 91HunStaC-19
❑ 91HunStaLD-292
❑ 91HunStaP-1794
❑ 91HunStaTI-18
❑ 91LinDriAA-292
❑ 91Sco-381
❑ 92Bow-244
❑ 97HigDesMUG-10
❑ 98TusSidM-14

Peters, Doug
❑ 90EugEmeGS-22
❑ 91LinDriAA-412
❑ 91MemChiLD-412
❑ 91MemChiP-649

Peters, Francis
❑ 68Top-409
❑ 81TCM60I-400

Peters, Gary
❑ 47Exh-176
❑ 60Top-346
❑ 60Top-407
❑ 61Top-303
❑ 62WhiSoxTS-15
❑ 63Top-522
❑ 63WhiSoxJP-10
❑ 64Baz-27
❑ 64Top-2
❑ 64Top-130
❑ 64TopCoi-71
❑ 64TopCoi-140
❑ 64TopGia-1
❑ 64TopSta-56
❑ 64TopStaU-56
❑ 64TopTatI-63
❑ 64TopVen-2
❑ 64TopVen-130
❑ 64WhiSoxI-21
❑ 64WhiSoxTS-18
❑ 65Baz-27
❑ 65OldLonC-32
❑ 65OPC-9
❑ 65Top-9
❑ 65Top-430
❑ 65TopEmbI-18
❑ 65TopTral-62
❑ 65WhiSoxJP-6
❑ 66OPC-111
❑ 66Top-111
❑ 66TopVen-111
❑ 66WhiSoxTI-10
❑ 67Baz-9
❑ 67CokCapWS-1
❑ 67ProPizC-12
❑ 67Top-233
❑ 67Top-310
❑ 67TopGiaSU-2
❑ 67TopVen-196
❑ 68Baz-14
❑ 68Kah-B28
❑ 68OPC-8
❑ 68Top-8
❑ 68Top-210
❑ 68Top-379
❑ 68TopActS-10C
❑ 68TopGamI-13
❑ 68TopPla-10
❑ 68TopPos-13
❑ 68TopVen-8
❑ 68TopVen-210
❑ 69Kah-B17
❑ 69MilBra-220
❑ 69MLBOffS-34
❑ 69OPC-34
❑ 69Top-34
❑ 69TopSta-157
❑ 69WhiSoxTI-11
❑ 70DayDaiNM-134
❑ 70MLBOffS-161
❑ 70OPC-540
❑ 70RedSoxCPPC-10
❑ 70Top-540
❑ 71MLBOffS-327
❑ 71OPC-225
❑ 71RedSoxA-7
❑ 71RedSoxTI-7
❑ 71Top-225
❑ 71TopTat-84
❑ 72MilBra-272
❑ 72OPC-503
❑ 72Top-503
❑ 78TCM60I-125B
❑ 81WhiSox1T-40
❑ 85WhiSoxC-40
❑ 89PacLegI-159

Peters, Harlan
❑ 24Zee-66

Peters, Jack (John)
❑ 21Nei-63
❑ 22E120-204

Peters, Jay
❑ 79SalLakCGT-20A
❑ 80SalLakCGT-11

Peters, John
❑ 23Zee-114
❑ 24Zee-82
❑ 26Zee-15
❑ 94EliTwiC-20
❑ 94EliTwiF-3730

Peters, Ken
❑ 76SeaRaiC-11

Peters, Oscar
❑ 12T207-150

Peters, Ray
❑ 94BreMilB-163

Peters, Reed
❑ 87SalAngP-13
❑ 88PalSprACLC-108
❑ 88PalSprAP-1439
❑ 89MidAngGS-26
❑ 90CMC-494
❑ 90EdmTraC-17
❑ 90EdmTraP-529
❑ 90ProAAAF-105
❑ 91EdmTraLD-168
❑ 91EdmTraP-1529
❑ 91LinDriAAA-168
❑ 92PhoFirF-2834
❑ 92ShrCapF-3883
❑ 92ShrCapS-588
❑ 93PhoFirF-1530

Peters, Rex
❑ 89SalDodTI-24
❑ 90VerBeaDS-23
❑ 91BakDodCLC-6
❑ 91CalLeLA-19

Peters, Ricky (Richard D.)
❑ 81Don-10
❑ 81Fle-470
❑ 81Top-177
❑ 81TopSti-77
❑ 82Don-155
❑ 82Fle-277
❑ 82OPC-269
❑ 82Top-504
❑ 83TacTigT-29A
❑ 84Fle-458
❑ 84Nes792-436
❑ 84Top-436
❑ 84TopTif-436
❑ 85TacTigC-130
❑ 86A'sMot-24
❑ 89AriStaB-5
❑ 90AubAstP-3417
❑ 91PacSenL-117
❑ 92BurAstC-28

Peters, Rusty
❑ 94ConTSN-1296
❑ 94ConTSNB-1296

Peters, Samone
❑ 98BilMusTI-26

Peters, Steve
❑ 77ForLauYS-20
❑ 87ArkTraP-9
❑ 87TexLeaAF-19
❑ 88CarSmo-23
❑ 88CarTeal-28
❑ 88DonRoo-22
❑ 88LouRedBTI-39
❑ 88TopTra-84T
❑ 88TopTraT-84T
❑ 89Fle-462
❑ 89FleGlo-462
❑ 89LouRedBC-9
❑ 89LouRedBP-1247
❑ 89LouRedBTI-30
❑ 89Top-482
❑ 89TopTif-482
❑ 89UppDec-771
❑ 90CMC-504
❑ 90LasVegSC-2
❑ 90LasVegSP-120
❑ 90ProAAAF-8
❑ 90SprCarDGB-20
❑ 91LinDriAAA-317
❑ 91OklCit8LD-317
❑ 91OklCit8P-175

Peters, Tim
❑ 86AncGlaPTI-29
❑ 87SalLakTTT-25
❑ 88MidLeaAGS-47
❑ 89JacExpB-13
❑ 89JacExpP-154
❑ 90JacExpP-1373
❑ 96ForWayWB-19

Peters, Tom
❑ 87BelMarTI-10
❑ 91BakDodCLC-28

Peters, Wilber
❑ 27Zee-142
❑ 28Zee-37
❑ 29Zee-26
❑ 30Zee-37

Petersen, Andy
❑ 89SanDieSAS-21

Petersen, Chris
❑ 92FroRowDP-58
❑ 92FroRowDPG-58
❑ 92FroRowDPS-58
❑ 92GenCubF-1568
❑ 93DayCubC-15
❑ 95OrlCubF-20
❑ 96OrlCubB-21
❑ 97IowCub-21
❑ 98IowCubQ-19

Petersen, James
❑ 33Zee-26

Petersen, Matt
❑ 92EriSaiF-1620
❑ 93KanCouCC-14
❑ 93KanCouCF-914
❑ 93Top-497
❑ 93TopGol-497
❑ 93TopInaM-497
❑ 93TopInaR-497
❑ 93TopMic-497
❑ 94BreCouMC-11
❑ 94BreCouMF-8
❑ 94FloStaLAF-FSL28
❑ 95OrlCubF-7

Peterson, Adam C.
❑ 86PenWhiSP-20
❑ 87BirBarB-13
❑ 87SouLeaAJ-20
❑ 88Fle-646
❑ 88FleGlo-646
❑ 88VanCanC-7
❑ 88VanCanP-776
❑ 89BirBarADB-27
❑ 89Don-619
❑ 89VanCanC-2
❑ 89VanCanP-589
❑ 90BirBarADB-27
❑ 90Bow-307
❑ 90BowTif-307
❑ 90CMC-629
❑ 90OPC-299
❑ 90ProAAAF-166
❑ 90Top-299
❑ 90TopTif-299
❑ 90TriAAAC-45
❑ 90VanCanC-2
❑ 90VanCanP-488
❑ 91Fle-134
❑ 91LasVegSLD-290
❑ 91LasVegSP-233
❑ 91LinDriAAA-290
❑ 91OPC-559
❑ 91PadSmo-25
❑ 91Sco-604
❑ 91Sco100RS-94
❑ 91Top-559
❑ 91TopDesS-559
❑ 91TopMic-559
❑ 91TopTif-559
❑ 92LasVegSF-2794

❑ 92LasVegSS-237
❑ 92UppDec-602
Peterson, Art
❑ 76SeaRaiC-12
Peterson, Bart
❑ 91KenTwiC-14
❑ 91KenTwiP-2071
❑ 92Ft.MyeMCB-17
❑ 92Ft.MyeMF-2744
Peterson, Brian
❑ 90MemChiB-28
❑ 90MemChiP-1027
❑ 91LinDriAA-425
❑ 91MemChiLD-425
❑ 91MemChiP-671
❑ 92SalLakTSP-29
❑ 93KanCouCC-28
❑ 93KanCouCF-933
❑ 93KanCouCTI-14
❑ 94KanCouCC-28
❑ 94KanCouCF-180
❑ 94KanCouCTI-22
❑ 95KanCouCTI-19
❑ 96KanCouCTI-21
❑ 98PorSeaDQ-28
Peterson, Buddy (Carl)
❑ 52MotCoo-29
❑ 53MotCoo-8
❑ 91OriCro-359
Peterson, Cap (Charles Andrew)
❑ 64Top-568
❑ 65Top-512
❑ 66Top-349
❑ 66TopVen-349
❑ 67SenPos-19
❑ 67Top-387
❑ 68OPC-188
❑ 68SenTeal-11
❑ 68Top-188
❑ 68TopVen-188
❑ 69SenTeal8-17
❑ 69Top-571
❑ 70WicAerM-12
❑ 81Gia196T-34
Peterson, Charles
❑ 94AugGreC-16
❑ 94AugGreF-3021
❑ 94Bow-658
❑ 94ClaGolF-75
❑ 94ClaGolN1PLF-LP10
❑ 94ClaGolREF-RE10
❑ 94Top-207
❑ 94TopGol-207
❑ 94TopSpa-207
❑ 94UppDecML-211
❑ 95LynHilTI-20
❑ 95SPML-133
❑ 96BesAutS-71
❑ 96BesAutSA-53
❑ 96Bow-277
❑ 96BowFoi-277
❑ 96CarMudB-24
❑ 96Exc-222
❑ 96Top-438
❑ 97CarMudC-23
❑ 98CarMudM-22
Peterson, Chris
❑ 92GenCubC-9
❑ 93DayCubF-865
❑ 94OrlCubF-1392
Peterson, D. Scott
❑ 77AshTouT-17
❑ 78AshTouT-22
Peterson, Dave
❑ 85GreHorT-19
❑ 86NewBriRSP-20
Peterson, Dean
❑ 95TreThuTI-13
❑ 96SarRedSB-26
❑ 97TreThuB-24
Peterson, Dennis
❑ 76SeaRaiC-13
Peterson, Doug
❑ 76SeaRaiC-14
Peterson, Erik
❑ 80WatIndT-19
❑ 81NasSouTI-12
❑ 82NasSouTI-17
❑ 83NasSouTI-16
❑ 84NasSouTI-17
Peterson, Fritz
❑ 63ReqKP-11
❑ 66Top-584
❑ 67CokCapYM-V16
❑ 67DexPre-166
❑ 67Top-495
❑ 68Top-246
❑ 68TopVen-246
❑ 68YanPhoS-74
❑ 68YanPhoS-75
❑ 69MLBOffS-77
❑ 69OPC-46
❑ 69Top-46
❑ 69TopTeaP-19
❑ 69YanPhoS-47
❑ 70DayDaiNM-128
❑ 70MLBOffS-248
❑ 70OPC-142
❑ 70Top-142
❑ 70YanCliDP-4
❑ 70YanPhoS-29
❑ 71MilDud-23
❑ 71MLBOffS-499
❑ 71OPC-460
❑ 71Top-460
❑ 71TopCoi-138
❑ 71TopGreM-44
❑ 71TopSup-13
❑ 71YanArcO-10
❑ 71YanCliDP-14
❑ 72ProStaP-33
❑ 72Top-573
❑ 72Top-574
❑ 72YanTeal-5
❑ 73OPC-82
❑ 73SyrChiTI-23
❑ 73Top-82
❑ 73Yan-5
❑ 74OPC-229
❑ 74SyrChiTI-22
❑ 74Top-229
❑ 75CleIndP-21
❑ 75OPC-62
❑ 75Top-62
❑ 75TopMin-62
❑ 76Hos-32
❑ 76HosTwi-32
❑ 76OPC-255
❑ 76SSP-511
❑ 76Top-255
❑ 81TCM60I-450
❑ 83YanASFY-33
❑ 90SweBasG-79
❑ 92YanWIZ6-98
❑ 92YanWIZ7-127
❑ 92YanWIZA-59
❑ 93RanKee-291
Peterson, Geoff
❑ 86Ft.MyeRP-21
Peterson, Harding
❑ 57JetPos-16
❑ 58Top-322
Peterson, Jayson
❑ 94ClaUpdCotC-CC13
❑ 94HunCubC-1
❑ 94HunCubF-3551
❑ 94SigRooDP-15
❑ 94SigRooDPS-15
❑ 94StaCluDP-11
❑ 94StaCluDPFDI-11
❑ 95Bow-44
❑ 95Exc-168
❑ 95Pin-176
❑ 95PinArtP-176
❑ 95PinMusC-176
❑ 95ScoDraP-DP14
❑ 95StaClu-112
❑ 95StaCluFDI-112
❑ 95StaCluMOP-112
❑ 95StaCluSTWS-112
❑ 95Top-437
❑ 95UppDecML-196
❑ 95UppDecMLFS-196
❑ 96RocCubTI-24
❑ 97BurBeeB-16
Peterson, Jerry
❑ 75WatRoyT-23
❑ 76WatRoyT-22
Peterson, Jim Lyndon
❑ 77CliDodT-19
Peterson, Jim Niels
❑ 74A's192T-28
❑ 90DodTar-619
Peterson, Kent
❑ 49EurSta-92
❑ 49Lea-42
❑ 51Bow-215
Peterson, Kyle
❑ 98BowChr-386
❑ 98BowChrGA-386
❑ 98BowChrGAR-386
❑ 98BowChrI-386
❑ 98BowChrIR-386
❑ 98BowChrR-386
❑ 98StoPorG-24
❑ 98StoPorG-25
❑ 99BasAmeTP-80
❑ 99BasAmeTPG-80
❑ 99Bow-216
❑ 99BowChr-216
❑ 99BowChrG-216
❑ 99BowChrGR-216
❑ 99BowChrI-216
❑ 99BowChrIR-216
❑ 99BowChrR-216
❑ 99BowGol-216
❑ 99BowInt-216
Peterson, Mark
❑ 92EveGiaC-15
❑ 92EveGiaF-1686
❑ 93SanJosGC-20
❑ 93SanJosGF-6
❑ 94SanJosGC-19
❑ 94SanJosGF-2814
❑ 97JacGen-20
Peterson, Matt
❑ 92EriSaiC-2
❑ 93KanCouCTI-15
Peterson, Mike
❑ 97PorRocG-18
Peterson, Nate
❑ 93AubAstC-18
❑ 93AubAstF-3448
❑ 93AusFut-63
❑ 94QuaCitRBC-15
❑ 94QuaCitRBF-537
❑ 96JacGenB-22
❑ 97JacGen-21
❑ 97JacGenS-19
Peterson, Pat
❑ 75ForLauYS-11
Peterson, Rick
❑ 78SalPirT-12
❑ 82BufBisT-17
❑ 88ColSprSSP-1530
❑ 89BirBarB-28
❑ 89BirBarP-99
❑ 89PacSenL-153
❑ 89TopSenL-104
❑ 90BirBarB-25
❑ 91BirBarLD-75
❑ 91BirBarP-1471
❑ 91LinDriAA-75
❑ 91PacSenL-49
❑ 93NasSouF-586
❑ 94NasSouF-1267
❑ 94WhiSoxK-30
❑ 98A'sMot-28
Peterson, Ricky (Eric)
❑ 77ChaPatT-13
Peterson, Rob
❑ 89WelPirP-20
❑ 90WelPirP-18
Peterson, Robert A.
❑ 09ColChiE-229
❑ 12ColRedB-229
❑ 12ColTinT-229
Peterson, Tim
❑ 76CedRapGT-21
Petestio, Doug
❑ 84MidCubT-12
Petillo, Bruce
❑ 93BatCliCB-23
❑ 93BatCliF-3150
Petit, Doug
❑ 92EriSaiF-1621
Petit, Ricardo
❑ 91IdaFalBP-4326
❑ 91PulBraC-25
❑ 91PulBraP-4002
Petitt, Steven
❑ 86St.PetCP-24
Petke, Jonathan
❑ 96WatIndTI-24
❑ 97KinIndB-19
Petkovsek, Mark
❑ 88ChaRanS-19
❑ 89TexLeaAGS-36
❑ 89TulDriGS-20
❑ 89TulDriTI-18
❑ 90CMC-155
❑ 90OklCit8C-5
❑ 90OklCit8P-432
❑ 90ProAAAF-678
❑ 91LinDriAAA-318
❑ 91OklCit8LD-318
❑ 91OklCit8P-177
❑ 92BufBisBS-14
❑ 92BufBisF-321
❑ 92BufBisS-38
❑ 92SkyAAAF-17
❑ 92TexLon-32
❑ 92TopDeb91-138
❑ 93BufBisF-514
❑ 93RanKee-292
❑ 94Fle-617
❑ 94TucTorF-760
❑ 96CarPol-22
❑ 96ColCho-694
❑ 96ColChoGS-694
❑ 96ColChoSS-694
❑ 96Don-483
❑ 96DonPreP-483
❑ 96Fle-554
❑ 96FleTif-554
❑ 96LeaSigEA-157
❑ 96Pac-224
❑ 96Sco-448
❑ 96SigRooOJ-26
❑ 96SigRooOJS-26
❑ 96Ult-278
❑ 96UltGolM-278
❑ 96UppDec-182
❑ 97CarPol-22
❑ 97Fle-533
❑ 97FleTif-533
❑ 98PacOnl-627
❑ 98PacOnlR-627
❑ 98PacOnlWC-627
Petralli, Geno (Eugene J.)
❑ 20Zee-33
❑ 80KnoBluJT-2
❑ 81SyrChiT-9
❑ 81SyrChiTI-16
❑ 82SyrChiT-13
❑ 82SyrChiTI-18
❑ 83Don-623
❑ 83Fle-439
❑ 83SyrChiT-15
❑ 85Ind-24
❑ 85MaiGuiT-16
❑ 85OklCit8T-5
❑ 86RanPer-12
❑ 86Top-296
❑ 86TopTif-296
❑ 87Don-619
❑ 87Fle-135
❑ 87FleGlo-135
❑ 87RanMot-20
❑ 87RanSmo-8
❑ 87Top-388
❑ 87TopTif-388
❑ 88Don-506
❑ 88Fle-477
❑ 88FleGlo-477
❑ 88Lea-241
❑ 88RanMot-20
❑ 88RanSmo-3
❑ 88Sco-373
❑ 88ScoGlo-373
❑ 88StaLinRa-13
❑ 88Top-589
❑ 88TopClo-87
❑ 88TopTif-589
❑ 89Don-343
❑ 89DonBasB-312
❑ 89Fle-530
❑ 89FleGlo-530
❑ 89OPC-137
❑ 89PanSti-451
❑ 89RanMot-11
❑ 89RanSmo-25
❑ 89Sco-526
❑ 89Top-137
❑ 89TopBig-12
❑ 89TopStiB-24
❑ 89TopTif-137
❑ 89UppDec-482
❑ 90Bow-495
❑ 90BowTif-495
❑ 90Don-56
❑ 90DonBesA-27
❑ 90Fle-309
❑ 90FleCan-309
❑ 90Lea-73
❑ 90OPC-706
❑ 90PanSti-161
❑ 90PubIntS-419
❑ 90RanMot-7
❑ 90Sco-153
❑ 90Top-706
❑ 90TopTif-706
❑ 90UppDec-633
❑ 91Bow-284
❑ 91Don-137
❑ 91Fle-296
❑ 91Lea-148
❑ 91OPC-78
❑ 91PacRyaTEI-68
❑ 91PanFreS-251
❑ 91RanMot-7
❑ 91Sco-191
❑ 91StaClu-10
❑ 91Top-78
❑ 91TopDesS-78
❑ 91TopMic-78
❑ 91TopTif-78
❑ 91Ult-351
❑ 91UppDec-492
❑ 92Don-550
❑ 92Fle-313
❑ 92Lea-357
❑ 92LeaBlaG-357
❑ 92OPC-409
❑ 92RanMot-7
❑ 92RanTeal-17
❑ 92Sco-283
❑ 92StaClu-3
❑ 92Top-409
❑ 92TopGol-409
❑ 92TopGolW-409
❑ 92TopMic-409
❑ 92Ult-138
❑ 92UppDec-599
❑ 93Don-319
❑ 93Fle-689
❑ 93RanKee-424
❑ 93RanStaC-22
❑ 93StaClu-232
❑ 93StaCluFDI-232
❑ 93StaCluMOP-232
❑ 93Top-332
❑ 93TopGol-332
❑ 93TopInaM-332
❑ 93TopInaR-332
❑ 93TopMic-332
❑ 93UppDec-83
❑ 93UppDecGold-83
❑ 94Don-247
❑ 94Fle-317
❑ 94Sco-137
❑ 94ScoGolR-137
Petrick, Ben
❑ 96AshTouB-28
❑ 96Bow-252
❑ 96BowFoi-252
❑ 96MauStiHWB-6
❑ 97Bes-44
❑ 97BesAll-13
❑ 97BesAutAS-39
❑ 97BesAutP-H7
❑ 97Bow-206
❑ 97BowInt-206
❑ 97CalLeaATI-39
❑ 97CarLeaTP-28
❑ 97SalAva-25
❑ 97SalAva-U10
❑ 98Bes-39
❑ 98Bes-85
❑ 98Bow-83
❑ 98BowBes-164
❑ 98BowBesAR-164
❑ 98BowBesMIF-MI20
❑ 98BowBesMIFAR-MI20
❑ 98BowBesMIFR-MI20
❑ 98BowBesR-164
❑ 98BowChr-83
❑ 98BowChrGA-83
❑ 98BowChrGAR-83
❑ 98BowChrI-83
❑ 98BowChrIR-83
❑ 98BowChrR-83
❑ 98BowGolA-83
❑ 98BowInt-83
❑ 98EasLeaTPM-20
❑ 98NewHavRM-21
❑ 98NewHavRMA-21
❑ 98SP MinPE-51
❑ 98SPMin-51
❑ 99BasAmeTP-81
❑ 99BasAmeTPG-81
❑ 99Bow-194
❑ 99BowAut-BA50
❑ 99BowBes-138
❑ 99BowBesAR-138
❑ 99BowBesR-138
❑ 99BowChr-194
❑ 99BowChrG-194
❑ 99BowChrGR-194
❑ 99BowChrI-194
❑ 99BowChrIR-194
❑ 99BowChrR-194
❑ 99BowGol-194
❑ 99BowInt-194
❑ 99JustheS-38
❑ 99JustheSJB-38
❑ 99JustheSJN-9
❑ 99SP TopP-103
❑ 99SP TopPC-BP
❑ 99SP TopPGF-GF26
❑ 99SP TopPPE-103
Petrizzo, Tom
❑ 86DayBealP-22
Petrocella, Chris
❑ 92HelBreF-1713
❑ 92HelBreSP-14
Petrocelli, Rico
❑ 47PM1StaP1-162
❑ 64SeaPop-13
❑ 65OPC-74
❑ 65Top-74
❑ 66RedSoxTI-9
❑ 66Top-298
❑ 66TopVen-298
❑ 67CokCapRS-11
❑ 67DexPre-167
❑ 67Top-528
❑ 67TopRedSS-13
❑ 67TopVen-204
❑ 68Baz-5
❑ 68CokCapRS-11
❑ 68DexPre-62
❑ 68OPC-156
❑ 68RedSoxTI-6
❑ 68Top-156
❑ 68Top-430
❑ 68TopVen-156
❑ 69CitMetC-8
❑ 69MilBra-221
❑ 69MLBOffS-15
❑ 69OPC-215
❑ 69RedSoxAO-9
❑ 69RedSoxTI-8
❑ 69RedSoxTI-6
❑ 69Top-215
❑ 69TopFou-25
❑ 69TopSta-136
❑ 69TopTeaP-3
❑ 69TraSta-21
❑ 70DayDaiNM-10
❑ 70Kel-54
❑ 70MilBra-21
❑ 70MLBOffS-162
❑ 70OPC-457
❑ 70RedSoxCPPC-11
❑ 70Top-457
❑ 70Top-680
❑ 70TopBoo-2
❑ 70TopSup-14
❑ 70TraSta-15C
❑ 71BazNumT-10
❑ 71BazUnn-28
❑ 71MilDud-24
❑ 71MLBOffS-328
❑ 71OPC-340
❑ 71RedSoxTI-8
❑ 71Top-340
❑ 71TopCoi-30
❑ 71TopGreM-39
❑ 71TopSup-19
❑ 71TopTat-92
❑ 72MilBra-273
❑ 72OPC-30
❑ 72Top-30
❑ 73LinPor-29
❑ 73OPC-365
❑ 73Top-365
❑ 74OPC-609
❑ 74Top-609
❑ 75Hos-132
❑ 75OPC-356
❑ 75Top-356
❑ 75TopMin-356
❑ 76LinSup-106
❑ 76OPC-445
❑ 76RedSox-6
❑ 76RedSoxSM-12
❑ 76SSP-413
❑ 76Top-445
❑ 77Top-111
❑ 79DiaGre-250
❑ 81RedSoxBG2S-102
❑ 81TCM60I-335

❑ 87BirBarB-1
❑ 87SouLeaAJ-23
❑ 88BirBarB-8
❑ 88SouLeaAJ-38
❑ 89BirBarADB-28
❑ 89SweBasG-123
❑ 90BirBarADB-28
❑ 90PacLeg-64
❑ 90SweBasG-56
❑ 91LinDri-31
❑ 91SweBasG-71
❑ 92PawRedSF-939
❑ 92PawRedSS-374
❑ 94CarLeaA-DJ26
❑ 94TedWil-6
❑ 94TedWilM-M35
❑ 94UppDecAH-42
❑ 94UppDecAH1-42
❑ 95TreThuTI-3
❑ 96PawRedSDD-22
❑ 97DunDonPPS-17
❑ 97PawRedS-4
❑ 99SpollIGotG-38
❑ 99SpollIGotGA-57

Petroff, Dan
❑ 94BoiHawC-21
❑ 94BoiHawF-3353
❑ 95CedRapKTI-39
❑ 96CedRapKTI-19

Petrosian, Ara
❑ 97PorRocG-19
❑ 98AshTouM-16
❑ 98SouOreTG-26
❑ 98VisOakG-23

Petru, Rich
❑ 97SpoIndG-23

Petrulis, Paul
❑ 91MisStaB-37
❑ 92MisStaB-32
❑ 93MisStaB-35
❑ 93PitMetC-16
❑ 93PitMetF-3718
❑ 94CapCitBC-17
❑ 94CapCitBF-1758
❑ 95StLucMTI-26

Petry, Dan
❑ 80Top-373
❑ 81Don-128
❑ 81Fle-468
❑ 81Top-59
❑ 82Don-133
❑ 82Fle-278
❑ 82Top-211
❑ 82Top-666
❑ 83AllGamPI-83
❑ 83Don-359
❑ 83Fle-339
❑ 83OPC-79
❑ 83TigPos-24
❑ 83Top-261
❑ 83Top-638
❑ 83TopSti-70
❑ 84AllGamPI-175
❑ 84Don-105
❑ 84Fle-89
❑ 84FunFooP-60
❑ 84Nes792-147
❑ 84OPC-147
❑ 84TigFarJ-12
❑ 84TigTeal-27
❑ 84TigWavP-29
❑ 84Top-147
❑ 84TopSti-269
❑ 84TopTif-147
❑ 85AllGamPI-83
❑ 85Don-334
❑ 85Fle-20
❑ 85FleStaS-83
❑ 85Lea-188
❑ 85OPC-392
❑ 85SevCoi-D7
❑ 85TigCaiD-16
❑ 85TigWen-18
❑ 85Top-435
❑ 85TopGloS-25
❑ 85TopSti-264
❑ 85TopTif-435
❑ 86Don-212
❑ 86DonAll-42
❑ 86Fle-235
❑ 86Lea-144
❑ 86OPC-216
❑ 86TigCaiD-15
❑ 86Top-540
❑ 86TopSti-270
❑ 86TopTif-540
❑ 87Don-373
❑ 87Fle-161
❑ 87FleGlo-161
❑ 87Lea-228
❑ 87OPC-27
❑ 87SevCoi-D9
❑ 87SpoTeaP-15
❑ 87TigCaiD-15
❑ 87TigCok-12
❑ 87Top-752
❑ 87TopTif-752
❑ 88AngSmo-8
❑ 88Don-476
❑ 88DonBasB-139
❑ 88Fle-67
❑ 88FleGlo-67
❑ 88Sco-461
❑ 88ScoGlo-461
❑ 88ScoRoo-26T
❑ 88ScoRooG-26T
❑ 88Top-78
❑ 88TopTif-78
❑ 88TopTra-85T
❑ 88TopTraT-85T
❑ 89Don-344
❑ 89Fle-486
❑ 89FleGlo-486
❑ 89Sco-122
❑ 89TopBig-178
❑ 89UppDec-552
❑ 90Fle-142
❑ 90FleCan-142
❑ 90Lea-508
❑ 90OPC-363
❑ 90PubIntS-377
❑ 90Sco-211
❑ 90ScoRoo-39T
❑ 90TigCok-16
❑ 90Top-363
❑ 90TopTif-363
❑ 90TopTra-93T
❑ 90TopTraT-93T
❑ 90UppDec-690
❑ 91Bow-146
❑ 91Don-675
❑ 91Fle-347
❑ 91PanFreS-295
❑ 91PanSti-240
❑ 91RedFolS-71
❑ 91Sco-434
❑ 91TigCok-46
❑ 91TigPol-8
❑ 91Ult-125
❑ 91UppDec-316
❑ 92Sco-705

Pett, Jose
❑ 93Bow-139
❑ 94SyrChiTI-20
❑ 95Bes-48
❑ 95Exc-140
❑ 95KnoSmoF-41
❑ 95SPML-165
❑ 95UppDecML-111
❑ 95UppDecMLFS-111
❑ 96KnoSmoB-20
❑ 96SyrChiTI-22
❑ 97CarMudC-7

Pettaway, Ike
❑ 78GreBraT-18
❑ 83DurBulT-22

Pettee, Patrick E.
❑ 87OldJudN-394
❑ 87OldJudN-395

Pettengill, Tim
❑ 88NebCor-9
❑ 89SavCarP-352

Pettersen, Andy
❑ 90SanDieSA3-7

Petterson, Kyle
❑ 98Bow-386
❑ 98BowGolA-386
❑ 98BowInt-386

Petterson, Mel
❑ 30Zee-153

Pettibone, Jay
❑ 80AshTouT-17
❑ 82OrlTwiT-22
❑ 83OrlTwiT-14
❑ 84TolMudHT-24

Pettibone, Jim
❑ 82CedRapRT-10
❑ 83WatRedT-6
❑ 84CedRapRT-3
❑ 85CedRapRT-11

Pettiford, Cecil
❑ 89BurIndS-20
❑ 90CalLeaACLC-55
❑ 90RenSilSCLC-279
❑ 91KinIndC-11
❑ 91KinIndP-323
❑ 92SalLakTSP-15
❑ 93LakTigC-21
❑ 93LakTigF-1307
❑ 94TreThuF-2120

Pettiford, Torrey
❑ 94BatCliC-20
❑ 95BatCliTI-25
❑ 96PieBolWB-19

Pettini, Joe
❑ 78MemChiBC-8
❑ 80PhoGiaVNB-20
❑ 81Fle-453
❑ 81GiaTeal-14
❑ 81PhoGiaVNB-21
❑ 81Top-62
❑ 82Fle-398
❑ 82Top-568
❑ 83GiaPos-23
❑ 83Top-143
❑ 84Nes792-449
❑ 84PhoGiaC-13
❑ 84Top-449
❑ 84TopTif-449
❑ 85LouRedR-12
❑ 86LouRedTI-23
❑ 87LouRedTI-2
❑ 88LouRedBC-24
❑ 88LouRedBP-435
❑ 88LouRedBTI-2
❑ 89HamRedS-27
❑ 90St.PetCS-26
❑ 91ArkTraLD-49
❑ 91ArkTraP-1302
❑ 91LinDriAA-49
❑ 92ArkTraF-1144
❑ 92ArkTraS-49
❑ 93ArkTraF-2827
❑ 94LouRedF-2996
❑ 95LouRedF-291
❑ 96LouRedB-1

Pettipiece, Paul
❑ 95StCatSTI-32

Pettis, Gary
❑ 81HolMilT-20
❑ 82SpoIndT-23
❑ 84AngSmo-21
❑ 84Don-647
❑ 84Fle-526
❑ 84TopTra-93T
❑ 84TopTraT-93T
❑ 85AngSmo-9
❑ 85Don-499
❑ 85Fle-308
❑ 85FleStaS-57
❑ 85OPC-39
❑ 85Top-497
❑ 85TopSti-226
❑ 85TopTif-497
❑ 86AngSmo-9
❑ 86Don-158
❑ 86Fle-165
❑ 86FleMin-33
❑ 86FleStiC-88
❑ 86Lea-84
❑ 86OPC-323
❑ 86Top-604
❑ 86TopMinL-7
❑ 86TopTif-604
❑ 87AngSmo-20
❑ 87CalAngPPS-29
❑ 87ClaUpdY-134
❑ 87Don-160
❑ 87DonOpeD-10
❑ 87Fle-90
❑ 87FleAwaW-29
❑ 87FleGlo-90
❑ 87Lea-152
❑ 87OPC-278
❑ 87SevCoi-W7
❑ 87Spo-157
❑ 87SpoTeaP-11
❑ 87Top-278
❑ 87TopMinL-47
❑ 87TopSti-16
❑ 87TopSti-175
❑ 87TopTif-278
❑ 88Don-210
❑ 88DonBasB-203
❑ 88FleUpd-29
❑ 88FleUpdG-29
❑ 88OPC-71
❑ 88PanSti-48
❑ 88Sco-255
❑ 88ScoGlo-255
❑ 88ScoRoo-38T
❑ 88ScoRooG-38T
❑ 88StaLinAn-16
❑ 88TigPep-24
❑ 88Top-71
❑ 88TopSti-178
❑ 88TopTif-71
❑ 88TopTra-86T
❑ 88TopTraT-86T
❑ 89Don-60
❑ 89Fle-141
❑ 89FleGlo-141
❑ 89OPC-146
❑ 89PanSti-345
❑ 89Sco-26
❑ 89TigMar-24
❑ 89Top-146
❑ 89TopMinL-53
❑ 89TopSti-279
❑ 89TopTif-146
❑ 89UppDec-117
❑ 90Bow-498
❑ 90BowTif-498
❑ 90Don-661
❑ 90DonBesA-126
❑ 90Fle-612
❑ 90FleAwaW-25
❑ 90FleCan-612
❑ 90Lea-469
❑ 90OPC-512
❑ 90PanSti-78
❑ 90PubIntS-480
❑ 90RanMot-12
❑ 90Sco-136
❑ 90ScoRoo-6T
❑ 90Spo-202
❑ 90Top-512
❑ 90TopBig-311
❑ 90TopMinL-14
❑ 90TopSti-283
❑ 90TopTif-512
❑ 90TopTra-94T
❑ 90TopTraT-94T
❑ 90UppDec-385
❑ 90UppDec-770
❑ 91Bow-276
❑ 91Don-512
❑ 91Fle-297
❑ 91OPC-314
❑ 91PanCanT1-115
❑ 91PanFreS-256
❑ 91RanMot-12
❑ 91Sco-182
❑ 91StaClu-141
❑ 91StuPre-9
❑ 91Top-314
❑ 91TopDesS-314
❑ 91TopMic-314
❑ 91TopTif-314
❑ 91Ult-352
❑ 91UppDec-229
❑ 92Fle-314
❑ 92Lea-466
❑ 92LeaBlaG-466
❑ 92OPC-756
❑ 92PadSmo-22
❑ 92PanSti-80
❑ 92Sco-308
❑ 92StaClu-548
❑ 92TigKro-20
❑ 92Top-756
❑ 92TopGol-756
❑ 92TopGolW-756
❑ 92TopMic-756
❑ 92Ult-580
❑ 92UppDec-179
❑ 93RanKee-293
❑ 93Sco-442

Pettis, Lynn
❑ 85OPC-39
❑ 85Top-497
❑ 85TopTif-497

Pettis, Stacey
❑ 84PriWilPT-34
❑ 86PalSprAP-26

Pettit, Bob
❑ 88WG1CarG-13

Pettit, Doug
❑ 92EriSaiC-19
❑ 93KanCouCC-15
❑ 93KanCouCF-915
❑ 93KanCouCTI-16
❑ 94BreCouMC-12
❑ 94BreCouMF-9
❑ 94FloStaLAF-FSL29
❑ 95PorSeaDTI-20

Pettit, Paul
❑ 59SeaPop-30
❑ 60HenHouW-15
❑ 60SeaPop-10
❑ 77FriOneYW-13

Pettitte, Andy
❑ 92ClaFS7-286
❑ 92GreHorC-1
❑ 92GreHorF-777
❑ 92SpollIFK1-561
❑ 93Bow-103
❑ 93ClaGolF-117
❑ 93ExcFS7-214
❑ 93PriWilCC-19
❑ 93SouAtlLAPI-31
❑ 94AlbYanF-1438
❑ 94Bow-493
❑ 94Cla-28
❑ 94ExcFS7-111
❑ 95Bow-257
❑ 95BowBes-B50
❑ 95BowBesR-B50
❑ 95BowGolF-257
❑ 95ColCliMCTI-12
❑ 95ColCliP-23
❑ 95ColCliTI-23
❑ 95Emo-65
❑ 95Exc-101
❑ 95Fla-287
❑ 95FleUpd-27
❑ 95Sel-163
❑ 95SelArtP-163
❑ 95SelCer-96
❑ 95SelCerMG-96
❑ 95StaClu-565
❑ 95StaCluMOP-565
❑ 95StaCluSTWS-565
❑ 95Sum-168
❑ 95SumNthD-168
❑ 95Top-640
❑ 95UppDec-493
❑ 95UppDecML-176
❑ 95UppDecMLFS-176
❑ 96BowBes-24
❑ 96BowBesAR-24
❑ 96BowBesR-24
❑ 96Cir-68
❑ 96CirRav-68
❑ 96ColCho-234
❑ 96ColChoGS-234
❑ 96ColChoSS-234
❑ 96Don-74
❑ 96DonPreP-74
❑ 96EmoXL-93
❑ 96Fin-B122
❑ 96FinRef-B122
❑ 96Fla-134
❑ 96Fle-194
❑ 96FleRooS-14
❑ 96FleTif-194
❑ 96Lea-185
❑ 96LeaLim-81
❑ 96LeaLimG-81
❑ 96LeaPre-72
❑ 96LeaPreP-72
❑ 96LeaPrePB-185
❑ 96LeaPrePG-185
❑ 96LeaPrePS-185
❑ 96LeaSig-54
❑ 96LeaSigA-181
❑ 96LeaSigAG-181
❑ 96LeaSigAS-181
❑ 96LeaSigEA-158
❑ 96LeaSigEACM-23
❑ 96LeaSigPPG-54
❑ 96LeaSigPPP-54
❑ 96MetUni-92
❑ 96MetUniMFG-11
❑ 96MetUniP-92
❑ 96Pac-371
❑ 96PanSti-152
❑ 96PanSti-242
❑ 96Pin-103
❑ 96Pin-291
❑ 96PinFoil-291
❑ 96Sco-396
❑ 96Sel-103
❑ 96SelArtP-103
❑ 96SelCer-91
❑ 96SelCerAP-91
❑ 96SelCerCB-91
❑ 96SelCerCR-91
❑ 96SelCerMB-91
❑ 96SelCerMG-91
❑ 96SelCerMR-91
❑ 96SP-130
❑ 96StaClu-436
❑ 96StaCluEPB-436
❑ 96StaCluEPG-436
❑ 96StaCluEPS-436
❑ 96StaCluMO-50
❑ 96StaCluMOP-436
❑ 96TeaOut-63
❑ 96Top-378
❑ 96TopGal-104
❑ 96TopGalPPI-104
❑ 96Ult-104
❑ 96UltGolM-104
❑ 96UppDec-144
❑ 96Zen-88
❑ 96ZenArtP-88
❑ 97Bow-248
❑ 97BowBes-21
❑ 97BowBesAR-21
❑ 97BowBesR-21
❑ 97BowChr-72
❑ 97BowChrI-72
❑ 97BowChrIR-72
❑ 97BowChrR-72
❑ 97BowInt-248
❑ 97Cir-149
❑ 97CirFasT-6
❑ 97CirRav-149
❑ 97ColCho-60
❑ 97ColCho-404
❑ 97ColChoAC-18
❑ 97ColChoT-NY10
❑ 97ColChoTBS-35
❑ 97ColChoTBSWH-35
❑ 97ColChoTotT-T20
❑ 97CraJac-16
❑ 97Don-82
❑ 97Don-424
❑ 97DonEli-14
❑ 97DonEliGS-14
❑ 97DonGolPP-82
❑ 97DonGolPP-424
❑ 97DonLim-34
❑ 97DonLim-135
❑ 97DonLim-177
❑ 97DonLimE-34
❑ 97DonLimE-135
❑ 97DonLimE-177
❑ 97DonLimENG-34
❑ 97DonPre-20
❑ 97DonPreCttC-20
❑ 97DonSig-74
❑ 97DonSigAC-98
❑ 97DonSigAM-98
❑ 97DonSigPPP-74
❑ 97DonSilPP-82
❑ 97DonSilPP-424
❑ 97DonTea-126
❑ 97DonTeaSPE-126
❑ 97DonVxP1-37
❑ 97E-X2-34
❑ 97E-X2Cred-34
❑ 97E-X2EssCre-34
❑ 97E-X2SD2000-3
❑ 97Fin-287
❑ 97FinEmb-287
❑ 97FinEmbR-287
❑ 97FinRef-287
❑ 97FlaShoLC-46
❑ 97FlaShoLeg0-46
❑ 97FlaShoLeg1-46
❑ 97FlaShoM-A46
❑ 97FlaShoM-B46
❑ 97FlaShoM-C46
❑ 97FlaShoR0-46
❑ 97FlaShoR1-46
❑ 97FlaShoR2-46
❑ 97Fle-175
❑ 97Fle-711
❑ 97FleMilDM-48
❑ 97FleMilDMR-48
❑ 97FleTeaL-10
❑ 97FleTif-175
❑ 97FleTif-711
❑ 97FleZon-13
❑ 97Lea-136
❑ 97Lea-198
❑ 97LeaFraM-136
❑ 97LeaFraM-198
❑ 97LeaFraMDC-136
❑ 97LeaFraMDC-198
❑ 97LeaGet-3
❑ 97LeaGolS-12
❑ 97MetUni-121
❑ 97MetUniPP-8

❑ 97NewPin-24
❑ 97NewPinAP-24
❑ 97NewPinKtP-15
❑ 97NewPinMC-24
❑ 97NewPinPP-24
❑ 97NewPinPP-K15
❑ 97Pac-156
❑ 97PacCar-14
❑ 97PacCarM-14
❑ 97PacCerCGT-17
❑ 97PacCraC-4
❑ 97PacFirD-8
❑ 97PacGolCD-12
❑ 97PacLigB-156
❑ 97PacPri-53
❑ 97PacPriGA-GA10
❑ 97PacPriLB-53
❑ 97PacPriP-53
❑ 97PacPriSH-SH5B
❑ 97PacSil-156
❑ 97Pin-14
❑ 97PinAllFP-5
❑ 97PinArtP-PP14
❑ 97PinCar-5
❑ 97PinCer-92
❑ 97PinCerCMGT-17
❑ 97PinCerCT-17
❑ 97PinCerMBla-92
❑ 97PinCerMBlu-92
❑ 97PinCerMG-92
❑ 97PinCerMR-92
❑ 97PinCerR-92
❑ 97PinFan-FF17
❑ 97PinIns-52
❑ 97PinInsC-12
❑ 97PinInsCE-52
❑ 97PinInsDD-16
❑ 97PinInsDE-52
❑ 97PinMusC-14
❑ 97PinPrePla-14
❑ 97PinTeaP-9
❑ 97PinTeaP-10
❑ 97PinTotCPB-92
❑ 97PinTotCPG-92
❑ 97PinTotCPR-92
❑ 97PinX-P-2
❑ 97PinX-PMoS-2
❑ 97PinX-PMW-17
❑ 97PinX-PMWG-17
❑ 97PinX-PMWS-17
❑ 97Sco-82
❑ 97Sco-518
❑ 97ScoAllF-17
❑ 97ScoArtPWB-82
❑ 97ScoArtPWB-518
❑ 97ScoPreS-82
❑ 97ScoResC-518
❑ 97ScoShoS-82
❑ 97ScoShoS-518
❑ 97ScoShoSAP-82
❑ 97ScoShoSAP-518
❑ 97ScoStaaD-10
❑ 97Sel-58
❑ 97SelArtP-58
❑ 97SelCom-58
❑ 97SelRegG-58
❑ 97SelToootT-2
❑ 97SelToootTMB-2
❑ 97SP-128
❑ 97SpoIll-66
❑ 97SpoIll-130
❑ 97SpoIllEE-66
❑ 97SpoIllEE-130
❑ 97SPSpeF-34
❑ 97SPx-35
❑ 97SPxBro-35
❑ 97SPxGol-35
❑ 97SPxGraF-35
❑ 97SPxSil-35
❑ 97SPxSte-35
❑ 97StaClu-46
❑ 97StaCluC-CO1
❑ 97StaClul-I13
❑ 97StaCluMat-46
❑ 97StaCluMOP-46
❑ 97StaCluMOP-I13
❑ 97Stu-5
❑ 97StuMasS-6
❑ 97StuMasS8-6
❑ 97StuPrePG-5
❑ 97StuPrePS-5
❑ 97Top-60
❑ 97TopAll-AS17
❑ 97TopChr-20
❑ 97TopChrAS-AS17
❑ 97TopChrR-20
❑ 97TopChrSAR-AS17
❑ 97TopChrSB-17
❑ 97TopChrSBR-17
❑ 97TopGal-160
❑ 97TopGalPG-PG14
❑ 97TopGalPPI-160
❑ 97TopSeaB-SB17
❑ 97UD3-54
❑ 97UD3GenNex-GN12
❑ 97Ult-102
❑ 97UltDouT-7
❑ 97UltFamGam-13
❑ 97UltGolME-102
❑ 97UltPlaME-102
❑ 97UltSeaC-7
❑ 97UltTop3-15
❑ 97UltTop3GM-15
❑ 97UppDec-68
❑ 97UppDec-122
❑ 97UppDec-254
❑ 97UppDec-266
❑ 97UppDec-380
❑ 97UppDecAWJ-9
❑ 97UppDecBCP-BC17
❑ 97UppDecRSF-RS9
❑ 97YanMcDP-3
❑ 97YanSco-5
❑ 97YanScoPl-5
❑ 97YanScoPr-5
❑ 97Zen-21
❑ 98Bow-3
❑ 98BowBes-39
❑ 98BowBesAR-39
❑ 98BowBesR-39
❑ 98BowChr-3
❑ 98BowChrGA-3
❑ 98BowChrGAR-3
❑ 98BowChrI-3
❑ 98BowChrIR-3
❑ 98BowChrR-3
❑ 98BowChrR-37
❑ 98BowChrRR-37
❑ 98BowGolA-3
❑ 98BowInt-3
❑ 98CirThu-276
❑ 98CirThuRav-276
❑ 98CirThuSupRav-276
❑ 98ColCho-445
❑ 98ColChoSQ-SQ32
❑ 98Don-91
❑ 98Don-379
❑ 98DonCol-91
❑ 98DonColE-424
❑ 98DonColL-331
❑ 98DonColP-578
❑ 98DonColP-740
❑ 98DonColS-91
❑ 98DonCruG-34
❑ 98DonCruP-34
❑ 98DonCruR-34
❑ 98DonDiaK-7
❑ 98DonDiaKC-7
❑ 98DonEli-24
❑ 98DonEliA-24
❑ 98DonEliS-24
❑ 98DonGolPP-91
❑ 98DonGolPP-379
❑ 98DonPre-28
❑ 98DonPre-190
❑ 98DonPreSeat-28
❑ 98DonPreSeat-190
❑ 98DonPreTW-14
❑ 98DonPriCD-91
❑ 98DonPriCE-424
❑ 98DonPriCL-331
❑ 98DonPriCP-578
❑ 98DonPriCP-740
❑ 98DonSig-72
❑ 98DonSigAC-91
❑ 98DonSigAM-92
❑ 98DonSigP-72
❑ 98DonSilPP-91
❑ 98DonSilPP-379
❑ 98E-X2-28
❑ 98E-X2ECFut-28
❑ 98E-X2ECNow-28
❑ 98Fin-270
❑ 98FinNo--270
❑ 98FinNo-R-270
❑ 98FinRef-270
❑ 98FlaShoLeg0-43
❑ 98FlaShoLeg1-43
❑ 98FlaShoLeg2-43
❑ 98FlaShoLeg3-43
❑ 98FlaShoLegM-43
❑ 98FlaShoR0-43
❑ 98FlaShoR1-43
❑ 98FlaShoR2-43
❑ 98FlaShoR3-43
❑ 98Fle-144
❑ 98Fle-308
❑ 98Fle-592
❑ 98FleVin'-41
❑ 98FleVin'C-41
❑ 98Lea-132
❑ 98LeaCruG-34
❑ 98LeaCruP-34
❑ 98LeaCruR-34
❑ 98LeaFraDA-132
❑ 98LeaFraF-132
❑ 98LeaFraM-132
❑ 98LeaFraM-132
❑ 98LeaFraMDC-132
❑ 98LeaFraMDC-132
❑ 98LeaFraMZ2-132
❑ 98LeaRS-1
❑ 98LeaRS-190
❑ 98LeaRSLHolo-1
❑ 98LeaRSLHolo-190
❑ 98LeaRSLong-1
❑ 98LeaRSLong-190
❑ 98LeaRSTicMas-6
❑ 98LeaRSTicMasDC-6
❑ 98LeaRTrue-1
❑ 98LeaRTrue-190
❑ 98LeaStaRep-25
❑ 98LeaStaS-17
❑ 98LeaStaSDC-17
❑ 98MetUni-192
❑ 98MetUniPMG-192
❑ 98Pac-155
❑ 98PacAur-62
❑ 98PacInv-54
❑ 98PacInvPBlue-54
❑ 98PacInvSilv-54
❑ 98PacInvTeam-19
❑ 98PacOme-169
❑ 98PacOmeR-169
❑ 98PacOnl-512
❑ 98PacOnlR-512
❑ 98PacOnlWC-512
❑ 98PacPar-73
❑ 98PacParC-73
❑ 98PacParG-73
❑ 98PacParHS-73
❑ 98PacParPB-73
❑ 98PacParR-73
❑ 98PacPlaB-155
❑ 98PacRedT-155
❑ 98PacSil-155
❑ 98Pin-29
❑ 98PinArtP-PP29
❑ 98PinIns-32
❑ 98PinInsCE-32
❑ 98PinInsDE-32
❑ 98PinInsSG-19AB
❑ 98PinInsSG-19CD
❑ 98PinInsSGS-19AB
❑ 98PinInsSGS-19CD
❑ 98PinMinB-16
❑ 98PinMinCB-16
❑ 98PinMinCBAP-16
❑ 98PinMinCGP-16
❑ 98PinMinCGPAP-16
❑ 98PinMinCN-16
❑ 98PinMinCNAP-16
❑ 98PinMinCSGR-16
❑ 98PinMinDC-16
❑ 98PinMinG-16
❑ 98PinMinMCSS-16
❑ 98PinMinS-16
❑ 98PinMusC-PP29
❑ 98PinPer-29
❑ 98PinPerPP-29
❑ 98PinPreP-29
❑ 98PinSna-NYY1
❑ 98PinSna-NYY5
❑ 98PreCon-20
❑ 98PriWilCASM-23
❑ 98Sco-57
❑ 98ScoRT-23
❑ 98ScoRTSS-PP23
❑ 98ScoRTSSAP-PP23
❑ 98ScoRTSSAP1-PP23
❑ 98ScoSS-PP20
❑ 98ScoSSAP-PP20
❑ 98SkyDugA-75
❑ 98SkyDugAD-D9
❑ 98SkyDugAIA-75
❑ 98SP Aut-141
❑ 98SpoIll-100
❑ 98SpoIll-143
❑ 98SpoIllEE-100
❑ 98SpoIllEE-143
❑ 98SpoIllFE-100
❑ 98SpoIllFE-143
❑ 98SpoIllTaN-120
❑ 98SpoIllTaNEE-120
❑ 98SpoIllWSF-109
❑ 98SpoIllWSFEE-109
❑ 98SpoIllWSFFE-109
❑ 98SPxFin-108
❑ 98SPxFinR-108
❑ 98SPxFinS-108
❑ 98StaCluC-CS20
❑ 98StaCluC-CS22
❑ 98StaCluC-CS24
❑ 98StaCluFDI-117
❑ 98StaCluI-117
❑ 98StaCluOneK-117
❑ 98StaCluPP-117
❑ 98Stu-41
❑ 98StuGPP-41
❑ 98StuPor8x10-29
❑ 98StuPor8x10GP-29
❑ 98StuSPP-41
❑ 98Top-337
❑ 98TopBabB-BB13
❑ 98TopChr-337
❑ 98TopChrBB-BB13
❑ 98TopChrBBR-BB13
❑ 98TopChrR-337
❑ 98TopDevR-337
❑ 98TopDia-337
❑ 98TopGal-129
❑ 98TopGalGP-129
❑ 98TopGalOPP-129
❑ 98TopGalPPI-129
❑ 98TopGalPPIA-129
❑ 98TopMiniC-337
❑ 98TopOpeD-164
❑ 98TopSta-76
❑ 98TopStaB-76
❑ 98TopStaG-76
❑ 98TopStaGR-76
❑ 98TopStaS-76
❑ 98TopSup-35
❑ 98TopSup-35
❑ 98Ult-175
❑ 98UltDouT-15
❑ 98UltGolM-175
❑ 98UltMas-175
❑ 98UltPlaM-175
❑ 98UppDec-170
❑ 98UppDec10AP-7
❑ 98UppDec1APR-7
❑ 98UppDecAG-AG16
❑ 98UppDecAGDC-AG16
❑ 98UppDecBCP-BC12
❑ 98UppDecR-70
❑ 98UppDecSF-92
❑ 98YanSco-5
❑ 98YanScoP-5
❑ 98YanUppD-170
❑ 98Zen-27
❑ 98Zen5 xx7-24
❑ 98Zen5x7GoldImp-24
❑ 98Zen5x7Imp-24
❑ 98ZenZ-G-27
❑ 98ZenZ-S-27
❑ 99199Fin-208
❑ 99Bow-238
❑ 99BowGol-238
❑ 99BowInt-238
❑ 99BowLatB-LB5
❑ 99FinGolRef-208
❑ 99FinRef-208
❑ 99FlaShoLeg1-112
❑ 99FlaShoLeg2-112
❑ 99FlaShoLeg3-112
❑ 99FlaShoLegM1-112
❑ 99FlaShoLegM2-112
❑ 99FlaShoLegM3-112
❑ 99FlaShoR1-112
❑ 99FlaShoR2-112
❑ 99FlaShoR3-112
❑ 99Fle-275
❑ 99FleBri-106
❑ 99FleBri2G-106
❑ 99FleBriBlu-106
❑ 99FleBriGol-106
❑ 99FleMys-17
❑ 99FleMysG-17
❑ 99FleMysM-17
❑ 99FleSta9-275
❑ 99FleWarT-275
❑ 99MetUni-217
❑ 99MetUniGM-217
❑ 99MetUniPMG-217
❑ 99Pac-300
❑ 99PacOmeDD-2
❑ 99PacPlaB-300
❑ 99PacRed-300
❑ 99SkyMolM-50
❑ 99SkyMolMX-50
❑ 99SkyPre-23
❑ 99SkyPreR-23
❑ 99SkyThu-172
❑ 99SkyThuRant-172
❑ 99SkyThuRave-172
❑ 99SpoIll-86
❑ 99StaClu-227
❑ 99StaCluFDI-227
❑ 99StaCluOoaK-227
❑ 99StaCluPP-227
❑ 99ThuSkySupR-172
❑ 99Top-74
❑ 99Top-239
❑ 99TopChr-74
❑ 99TopChr-239
❑ 99TopChrR-74
❑ 99TopChrR-239
❑ 99TopMVPP-74
❑ 99TopOpeD-42
❑ 99TopSta-138
❑ 99TopStaFoil-138
❑ 99UppDec-157
❑ 99UppDecEL1-157
❑ 99UppDecEL2-157
❑ 99YanFle-12

Petty, Brian
❑ 85EveGiaC-14

Petty, Jesse
❑ 30CubTeal-14
❑ 33Gou-90
❑ 33WorCig(-68
❑ 33WorCig(-69
❑ 34GouCanV-42
❑ 90DodTar-620

Pettyjohn, Adam
❑ 99TeaBesR-66
❑ 99TeaBesRG-66
❑ 99TeaBesRS-66

Petway, Bruce
❑ 78LauLonABS-7
❑ 90NegLeaS-31

Pevey, Marty
❑ 86LouRedTI-24
❑ 89IndIndC-15
❑ 89IndIndP-1217
❑ 90OPC-137
❑ 90Top-137
❑ 90TopDeb89-98
❑ 90TopTif-137
❑ 90UppDec-628
❑ 91LinDriAAA-513
❑ 91SyrChiLD-513
❑ 91SyrChiMB-18
❑ 91SyrChiP-2483
❑ 92TolMudHF-1046
❑ 94SyrChiF-973
❑ 94SyrChiTI-21
❑ 96MedHatBJTI-22
❑ 98HagSunM-1

Peyton, Byron
❑ 82CedRapRT-17

Peyton, Eric
❑ 82ElPasDT-1
❑ 83ElPasDT-2
❑ 84VanCanC-41

Peyton, Mickey
❑ 88AugPirP-362

Pezzoni, Ron
❑ 90PenPilS-14
❑ 91CarLeaAP-CAR29
❑ 91PenPilC-20
❑ 91PenPilP-390
❑ 92ClaFS7-247
❑ 92SanBerC-2
❑ 92SanBerSF-971
❑ 93SanJosGC-21
❑ 93SanJosGF-26
❑ 94Bow-219
❑ 94ShrCapF-1621

Pfaff, Bob
❑ 86SumBraP-21
❑ 87DurBulP-4
❑ 89BurBraP-1606
❑ 89BurBraS-16

Pfaff, Jason
❑ 92LakTigC-18
❑ 92LakTigF-2276
❑ 93Bow-503
❑ 93LonTigF-2305
❑ 95LynHilTI-21

Pfaff, Rich
❑ 89BelBre2S-23
❑ 89BelBrelS-22

Pfahler, Fred
❑ 26Zee-124

Pfeffer, Big Jeff (Francis)
❑ 11SpoLifCW-287
❑ 11SpoLifM-177

Pfeffer, Jeff (Edward)
❑ 09T206-288
❑ 15SpoNewM-137
❑ 17ColE13-133
❑ 17HolBreD-79
❑ 19W514-58
❑ 20GasAmeMBD-36
❑ 20NatCarE-78
❑ 21E121So8-70
❑ 21E121So8-71
❑ 22AmeCarE122-53
❑ 22W575-97
❑ 22W575-98
❑ 23WilChoV-123
❑ 25Zee-118
❑ 90DodTar-621

Pfeffer, Kurt
❑ 90EliTwiS-17
❑ 91KenTwiC-11
❑ 91KenTwiP-2090

Pfeffer, Nathaniel F.
❑ 06FanCraNL-36
❑ 87BucN28-22
❑ 87OldJudN-396
❑ 88SpoTimM-19
❑ 88WG1CarG-14
❑ 89EdgR.WG-17
❑ 95May-25A
❑ 95May-25B

Pfeil, Bobby
❑ 70OPC-99
❑ 70Top-99
❑ 72Top-681
❑ 89MetRinP69-23
❑ 91MetWIZ-314
❑ 94Met69CCPP-26
❑ 94Met69CS-25
❑ 94Met69T-27

Pfiester, John
❑ 07CubA.CDPP-9
❑ 07CubGFGCP-9
❑ 09ColChiE-230
❑ 09RamT20-94
❑ 09T206-289
❑ 09T206-290
❑ 10SweCapPP-87
❑ 11PinT-5-217
❑ 11SpoLifCW-288
❑ 11SpoLifM-178
❑ 11T205-138
❑ 11TurRedT-33
❑ 12ColRedB-230
❑ 12ColTinT-230
❑ 12PhiCarE-25
❑ 72ClaCar-9

Pfirman, Charles
❑ 94ConTSN-1204
❑ 94ConTSNB-1204

Pfister, Dan
❑ 62Top-592
❑ 63Top-521
❑ 64Top-302
❑ 64TopVen-302

Pfister, George
❑ 78DodTCM4-42

Pfyl, Monte
❑ 09ObaT21-282
❑ 11PacCoaBD-51
❑ 11Zee-39
❑ 12ObaPreT-31

Phair, Kelly
❑ 95OdgRapTI-22
❑ 96OgdRapTI-7
❑ 97CalLeaATI-22
❑ 97StoPor-14

Phanatic, Phillie
❑ 73PicCle-XX
❑ 83PhiTas-30
❑ 84PhiTas-3
❑ 87PhiTas-xx
❑ 88PhiTas-30
❑ 90PhiTas-33
❑ 92PhiMed-33
❑ 92TriPla-133
❑ 93FunPacM-1
❑ 93PhiMed-25

❑ 94MasMan-11
❑ 96PhiTeal-25
❑ 96PinFan-PP1
❑ 97PhiCopQ-21
❑ 97PhiTeal-NNO
❑ 98PhiTeal-36
Phebus, Raymond
❑ 33Zee-69
Phelan, Art
❑ 11PinT-5-413
❑ 11SpoLifM-200
❑ 12ImpTobC-35
❑ 12T207-151
❑ 14FatPlaT-40
Phelan, James D.
❑ 87OldJudN-397
Phelan, James F.
❑ 09T206-454
❑ 11T205-197
Phelan, John
❑ 89SpoIndSP-6
Phelps, Babe (Ernest Gordon)
❑ 36NatChiFPR-64
❑ 37ExhFou-2
❑ 38ExhFou-2
❑ 39PlaBal-96
❑ 40DodTeal-18
❑ 40PlaBal-66
❑ 41DodTeal-5
❑ 73Dod194T-22
❑ 78DodTCM4-18
❑ 89DodSmoG-41
❑ 90DodTar-622
❑ 94ConTSN-1125
❑ 94ConTSNB-1125
Phelps, Edward
❑ 09AmeCarE90-1-88
❑ 09PC7HHB-35
❑ 09T206-291
❑ 10DomDisP-98
❑ 10NadCarE-43
❑ 10SweCapPP-152
❑ 11HelSta-176
❑ 11PinT-5-364
❑ 11SpoLifCW-289
❑ 11SpoLifM-277
❑ 11T205-139
❑ 12ImpTobC-36
Phelps, Joshua
❑ 96MedHatBJTI-23
❑ 97HagSunB-17
❑ 98HagSunM-21
Phelps, Ken
❑ 76WatRoyT-23
❑ 77DayBealT-15
❑ 77JacSunT-19
❑ 80OmaRoyP-21
❑ 82Fle-420
❑ 82WicAerTI-12
❑ 85Don-318
❑ 85Fle-499
❑ 85Lea-129
❑ 85MarMot-18
❑ 85OPC-322
❑ 85Top-582
❑ 85TopTif-582
❑ 86MarMot-18
❑ 86MarPacNB-10
❑ 86Top-34
❑ 86TopTif-34
❑ 87Don-317
❑ 87DonOpeD-118
❑ 87Fle-593
❑ 87FleGamW-34
❑ 87FleGlo-593
❑ 87FleSlu-30
❑ 87MarMot-7
❑ 87SpoTeaP-25
❑ 87Top-333
❑ 87TopSti-222
❑ 87TopTif-333
❑ 88Don-489
❑ 88DonBasB-248
❑ 88Fle-384
❑ 88FleGlo-384
❑ 88FleSlu-29
❑ 88FleStiC-61
❑ 88MarMot-7
❑ 88OPC-182
❑ 88RedFolSB-69
❑ 88Sco-256
❑ 88ScoGlo-256
❑ 88StaLinMa-13
❑ 88Top-182
❑ 88TopBig-189
❑ 88TopTif-182
❑ 89Bow-177
❑ 89BowTif-177
❑ 89Don-363
❑ 89DonBasB-276
❑ 89Fle-264
❑ 89FleGlo-264
❑ 89Sco-242
❑ 89Top-741
❑ 89TopBig-293
❑ 89TopDouM-24
❑ 89TopTif-741
❑ 89UppDec-167
❑ 89YanScoNW-10
❑ 90A'sMot-14
❑ 90Bow-462
❑ 90BowTif-462
❑ 90Don-675
❑ 90OPC-411
❑ 90PublntS-544
❑ 90Top-411
❑ 90TopTif-411
❑ 91PhoFirP-75
❑ 92YanWIZ8-146
Phelps, Ray
❑ 35DiaMatCS3T1-121
Phelps, Tom
❑ 93BurBeeC-18
❑ 93BurBeeF-155
❑ 94BurBeeC-21
❑ 96BesAutSA-54
❑ 96Bow-339
❑ 96BowFoi-339
❑ 97HarSen-21
Phelps, Tommy
❑ 93JamExpC-16
❑ 93JamExpF-3324
❑ 96WesPalBEB-12
❑ 97BesAutAS-40
Phelps, Travis
❑ 97PriDevR-26
Phifer, Phil
❑ 91DodRinP2-12
Philley, Dave
❑ 47Exh-177
❑ 48WhiSoxTI-23
❑ 49Bow-44
❑ 49Lea-85
❑ 50Bow-127
❑ 51A'sTeal-27
❑ 51Bow-297
❑ 51R42SmaS-80
❑ 52A'sTeal-22
❑ 52NatTeaL-20
❑ 52Top-226
❑ 53A'sTeal-25
❑ 53Top-64
❑ 54A'STEAI-17
❑ 54Bow-163A
❑ 54Bow-163B
❑ 54RedMan-AL9A
❑ 54RedMan-AL9B
❑ 54Top-159
❑ 55IndGolS-25
❑ 56BalOriP-7
❑ 56Top-222
❑ 57Top-124
❑ 58Hir-12
❑ 58Top-116
❑ 59Top-92
❑ 59TopVen-92
❑ 60BalOriP-8
❑ 60Top-52
❑ 60TopVen-52
❑ 61BalOriP-15
❑ 61Top-369
❑ 62Top-542
❑ 72LauGreF-46
❑ 75TCM195CI-27
❑ 79DiaGre-347
❑ 79TCM50-192
❑ 83TopRep5-226
❑ 85TCMPla1-13
❑ 90HOFStiB-55
❑ 91OriCro-360
❑ 91TopArc1-64
❑ 94TopArc1-159
❑ 94TopArc1G-159
❑ 97BalOriP-39
Phillies, Philadelphia
❑ 13FatT20-14
❑ 38BasTabP-40
❑ 48ExhTea-5
❑ 51TopTea-7
❑ 56Top-72A
❑ 56Top-72B
❑ 56Top-72C
❑ 57Top-214
❑ 58Top-134
❑ 59Top-8
❑ 59TopVen-8
❑ 60Top-302
❑ 60TopTat-60
❑ 61Top-491
❑ 61TopMagR-14
❑ 62GuyPotCP-15
❑ 62Top-294
❑ 63Top-13
❑ 64Top-293
❑ 64TopTatl-16
❑ 64TopVen-293
❑ 65Top-338
❑ 66Top-463
❑ 66TopRubl-116
❑ 67OPC-102
❑ 67Top-102
❑ 68LauWorS-47
❑ 68Top-477
❑ 69FleCloS-18
❑ 69FleCloS-37
❑ 69TopStaA-18
❑ 70FleWorS-47
❑ 70OPC-436
❑ 70Top-436
❑ 71OPC-268
❑ 71Top-268
❑ 71TopTat-24
❑ 72OPC-397
❑ 72Top-397
❑ 73FleWilD-1
❑ 73OPC-536
❑ 73OPCBTC-19
❑ 73Top-536
❑ 73TopBluTC-19
❑ 74OPC-383
❑ 74OPCTC-19
❑ 74Top-383
❑ 74TopStaA-19
❑ 74TopTeaC-19
❑ 78Top-381
❑ 83FleSta-243
❑ 83FleSti-NNO
❑ 83FleSti-NNO
❑ 84PhiTas-2
❑ 85PhiTas-47
❑ 87FleStiWBC-S6
❑ 87PhiTas-xx
❑ 87SpoTeaL-6
❑ 88PanSti-476
❑ 88PhiTas-28
❑ 88RedFolSB-106
❑ 90KalTeaN-5
❑ 90PublntS-634
❑ 90RedFolSB-129
❑ 91PanCanT1-127
❑ 92PhiMed-34
❑ 94ImpProP-24
❑ 94PhiMel-26
❑ 94Sco-656
❑ 94ScoGolR-656
❑ 94SparPhiC-29
❑ 95PacPriTL-24
❑ 95PanSti-138
❑ 95Phi-36
❑ 96PanSti-37
❑ 99Vic-290
Phillies, Reading
❑ 95ReaPhiELC-NNO
Phillip, Jim
❑ 86WinSpiP-19
Phillippe, Deacon (Charles)
❑ 03BreE10-115
❑ 06FanCraNL-37
❑ 08AmeCarE91-89
❑ 08RosComP-155
❑ 09ColChiE-231
❑ 09T206-292
❑ 10DomDisP-99
❑ 10NadE1-48
❑ 10PirAmeCE-9
❑ 10PirTipTD-12
❑ 10StaCarE-24
❑ 10SweCapPP-143
❑ 10W555-55
❑ 11PinT-5-864
❑ 11S74Sil-114
❑ 11SpoLifCW-290
❑ 11SpoLifM-258
❑ 11T205-140
❑ 12ColRedB-231
❑ 12ColTinT-231
❑ 12HasTriFT-14C
❑ 12HasTriFT-30E
❑ 68LauWorS-1
❑ 72FleFamF-37
❑ 80PirGreT-9
Phillips, Adolfo
❑ 66OPC-32
❑ 66Top-32
❑ 66TopVen-32
❑ 67CokCapC-8
❑ 67CubProPS-10
❑ 67DexPre-168
❑ 67OPC-148
❑ 67Top-148
❑ 68Top-202
❑ 68TopVen-202
❑ 69MilBra-222
❑ 69Top-372
❑ 69TopSta-17
❑ 69TopTeaP-4
❑ 70Top-666
❑ 71ExpLaPR-9
❑ 71ExpPS-19
❑ 71MLBOffS-137
❑ 71OPC-418
❑ 71Top-418
Phillips, Andrew
❑ 18Zee-89
Phillips, Anthony
❑ 92SanBerSF-952
Phillips, Ben
❑ 97TamYan-21
❑ 98TamYanM-23
Phillips, Bill
❑ 83ChaRoyT-8
❑ 86PeoChiP-19
Phillips, Bill (William B.)
❑ 87BucN28-16
❑ 87OldJudN-398
Phillips, Bill (William Corcoran)
❑ 11SpoLifCW-291
❑ 63GadFunC-56
Phillips, Bubba (John)
❑ 55Bow-228
❑ 57Top-395
❑ 58Top-212
❑ 59Top-187
❑ 59TopVen-187
❑ 60IndJayP-7
❑ 60Top-243
❑ 61Kah-32
❑ 61Top-101
❑ 61TopStal-140
❑ 62IndJayP-10
❑ 62Jel-39
❑ 62Kah-30
❑ 62Pos-39
❑ 62PosCan-39
❑ 62SalPlaC-74
❑ 62ShiPlaC-74
❑ 62Top-511
❑ 62TopStal-38
❑ 63Jel-70
❑ 63Pos-70
❑ 63Top-177
❑ 64TigLid-11
❑ 64Top-143
❑ 64TopVen-143
❑ 65Top-306
❑ 78TCM60I-192
❑ 81WhiSox1T-4
❑ 97UCLBruTI-17
Phillips, Charlie
❑ 77LodDodT-14
❑ 80ElPasDT-24
❑ 80SalLakCGT-8
❑ 88BenBucL-35
Phillips, Chris
❑ 83KnoBluJT-6
❑ 93SanBerSC-24
❑ 94ForMyeMC-19
❑ 94ForMyeMF-1174
Phillips, Crystal
❑ 94SanBerSC-28
Phillips, Damon
❑ 77TCMTheWY-45
Phillips, Dave
❑ 88T/MUmp-9
❑ 89T/MUmp-7
❑ 90T/MUmp-7
Phillips, Dick (Richard E.)
❑ 60TacBan-14
❑ 61TacBan-17
❑ 61UniOil-T12
❑ 63Top-544
❑ 64Top-559
❑ 78TCM60I-179
❑ 79HawIslC-24
❑ 79HawIslT-6
❑ 81Gia196T-33
Phillips, Eddie
❑ 93ConTSN-980
Phillips, Elmer
❑ 25Zee-10
Phillips, Gary
❑ 93EveGiaC-20
❑ 93EveGiaF-3777
❑ 94CliLumC-18
❑ 94CliLumF-1988
❑ 94MidLeaAF-MDW40
Phillips, J.R.
❑ 89QuaCitAB-22
❑ 89QuaCitAGS-7
❑ 90BoiHawP-3319
❑ 90PalSprACLC-207
❑ 90PalSprAP-2586
❑ 91PalSprAP-2025
❑ 92Bow-59
❑ 92ClaFS7-342
❑ 92MidAngOHP-21
❑ 92MidAngS-468
❑ 92SkyAA F-199
❑ 92UppDecML-228
❑ 93GiaStaC-7
❑ 93PhoFirF-1524
❑ 93TriAAAGF-27
❑ 94ActPac-15
❑ 94Bow-247
❑ 94Cla-166
❑ 94ClaCreotC-C9
❑ 94Don-588
❑ 94Fin-429
❑ 94FinJum-429
❑ 94FinRef-429
❑ 94GiaUSPC-9H
❑ 94LeaLimR-9
❑ 94OPC-148
❑ 94PhoFirF-1528
❑ 94Pin-419
❑ 94PinArtP-419
❑ 94PinMusC-419
❑ 94PinNewG-NG13
❑ 94PinRooTP-2
❑ 94ScoRoo-RT118
❑ 94ScoRooGR-RT118
❑ 94Sel-396
❑ 94SigRooBS-P4
❑ 94Spo-164
❑ 94StaClu-158
❑ 94StaCluFDI-158
❑ 94StaCluGR-158
❑ 94StaCluMOP-158
❑ 94StaCluT-4
❑ 94StaCluTFDI-4
❑ 94Top-790
❑ 94TopGol-790
❑ 94TopSpa-790
❑ 94TriPla-294
❑ 94UppDec-116
❑ 94UppDecED-116
❑ 95Baz-132
❑ 95Bow-247
❑ 95BowGolF-247
❑ 95ColCho-27
❑ 95ColChoGS-27
❑ 95ColChoSS-27
❑ 95Don-138
❑ 95DonPreP-138
❑ 95DonTopotO-355
❑ 95Fin-93
❑ 95FinRef-93
❑ 95Fla-427
❑ 95Fle-586
❑ 95GiaMot-20
❑ 95Lea-380
❑ 95LeaCor-6
❑ 95Pin-63
❑ 95PinArtP-63
❑ 95PinMusC-63
❑ 95PinNewB-NB9
❑ 95Sco-303
❑ 95ScoAi-AM10
❑ 95ScoGolR-303
❑ 95ScoPlaTS-303
❑ 95ScoRooDT-RDT1
❑ 95Sel-82
❑ 95Sel-234
❑ 95SelArtP-82
❑ 95SelArtP-234
❑ 95Spo-149
❑ 95SpoArtP-149
❑ 95StaClu-337
❑ 95StaCluMOP-337
❑ 95StaCluSTWS-337
❑ 95Stu-112
❑ 95Sum-16
❑ 95SumNthD-16
❑ 95Top-590
❑ 95UC3-99
❑ 95UC3ArtP-99
❑ 95UC3CleS-CS11
❑ 95Ult-446
❑ 95UltGolM-446
❑ 95UppDec-334
❑ 95UppDecED-334
❑ 95UppDecEDG-334
❑ 95UppDecSE-203
❑ 95UppDecSEG-203
❑ 96ColCho-714
❑ 96ColChoGS-714
❑ 96ColChoSS-714
❑ 96Don-276
❑ 96DonPreP-276
❑ 96Fle-594
❑ 96FleTif-594
❑ 96GiaMot-10
❑ 96LeaSigEA-159
❑ 96Pac-211
❑ 96PacPri-P66
❑ 96PacPriG-P66
❑ 96Sco-119
❑ 96Ult-297
❑ 96UltGolM-297
❑ 98NewOrlZM-17
Phillips, Jack Dorn
❑ 50PirTeal-17
❑ 52Top-240
❑ 53MotCoo-57
❑ 57Top-307
❑ 83TopRep5-240
Phillips, Jason
❑ 93WelPirC-21
❑ 93WelPirF-3357
❑ 94AugGreC-17
❑ 94AugGreF-3006
❑ 96AugGreB-22
❑ 97LynHil-16
❑ 97PitMet-22
❑ 98CapCitBF5-17
❑ 98CapCitBM-17
❑ 98CarMudM-6
❑ 99Bow-308
❑ 99BowGol-308
❑ 99BowInt-308
❑ 99DumSet-144
❑ 99FleMys-144
❑ 99FleMysM-144
❑ 99SkyPre-233
❑ 99SkyPre-233
❑ 99SkyPreR-233
❑ 99SkyPreR-233
Phillips, Jim
❑ 87PitCubP-12
❑ 89MarPhiS-25
Phillips, Jon
❑ 94AubAstC-10
❑ 94AubAstF-3755
❑ 95AubAstTI-19
❑ 97BurBeeB-17
Phillips, Lanny
❑ 77HolMilT-19
❑ 78SpoIndC-6
Phillips, Lefty
❑ 70OPC-376
❑ 70Top-376
❑ 71AngJacitB-8
❑ 71OPC-279
❑ 71Top-279
Phillips, Lonnie
❑ 87EveGiaC-5
❑ 88CliGiaP-720
❑ 89SanJosGB-5
❑ 89SanJosGCLC-217
❑ 89SanJosGP-452
❑ 91RenSilSCLC-3
Phillips, Marc
❑ 94EugEmeC-16
❑ 94EugEmeF-3709
❑ 95SprSulTI-19
❑ 96WilBluRB-25
❑ 97WilBluR-22
Phillips, Matt
❑ 98LowSpiM-29
Phillips, Mike
❑ 72GiaTeal-15

❑ 74MetTeal-17
❑ 74OPC-533
❑ 74Top-533
❑ 75MetSSP-18
❑ 75OPC-642
❑ 75Top-642
❑ 75TopMin-642
❑ 76OPC-93
❑ 76SSP-540
❑ 76Top-93
❑ 77Car5-18
❑ 77MetDaiPA-19
❑ 77Top-352
❑ 78CarTeal-23
❑ 78Top-88
❑ 79Car5-21
❑ 79Top-258
❑ 80Top-439
❑ 81Don-188
❑ 81ExpPos-8
❑ 81Fle-538
❑ 81Top-113
❑ 81TopTra-813
❑ 82ExpPos-30
❑ 82Fle-201
❑ 82OPC-263
❑ 82Top-762
❑ 83ExpPos-22
❑ 91MetWIZ-315
Phillips, Montie
❑ 87EugEmeP-2670
❑ 88CalLeaACLC-8
❑ 89SanJosGB-12
❑ 89SanJosGP-433
❑ 89SanJosGS-22
❑ 91FloStaLAP-FSL26
❑ 91OscAstC-8
❑ 91OscAstP-680
Phillips, Paul
❑ 98SpoIndG-26
Phillips, Randy
❑ 90PulBraB-27
❑ 90PulBraP-3113
❑ 92MedHatBJF-3208
❑ 92MedHatBJSP-11
❑ 93DunBluJF-1794
❑ 93FloStaLAF-9
❑ 94ClaGolF-56
❑ 94KnoSmoF-1303
❑ 95PhoFirTI-26
❑ 97HagSunB-29
❑ 97ShrCap-20
❑ 97ShrCapB-20
❑ 98DanBraQ-26
❑ 98ShrCapM-27
❑ 98ShrCapWS-27
Phillips, Red
❑ 74TigTCM1AC-23
Phillips, Robbie
❑ 84CedRapRT-1
Phillips, Steve
❑ 85LynMetT-16
❑ 86LynMetP-17
❑ 87JacMetF-18
❑ 91OneYanP-4167
❑ 92GreHorC-12
❑ 92GreHorF-794
❑ 94SanBerSC-18
❑ 94SanBerSF-2771
❑ 95NorNavTI-28
❑ 98JupHamQ-3
Phillips, Thomas G.
❑ 22E120-115
❑ 22W573-98
Phillips, Tony
❑ 91Cla3-T73
❑ 91TopTra-91T
❑ 91TopTraT-91T
❑ 92StaCluD-140
❑ 92TopDaiQTU-29
❑ 93RivPilCLC-13
❑ 94CalCanF-786
❑ 94Cla-158
❑ 95TacRaiTI-15
❑ 96TacRaiB-20
❑ 98CliLumG-28
❑ 98Sco-213
❑ 98ScoSS-PP103
❑ 98ScoSSAP-PP103
❑ 99Fle-512
❑ 99FleSta9-512
❑ 99FleWarT-512
❑ 99PacOme-172
❑ 99PacOmeC-172
❑ 99PacOmeG-172
❑ 99PacOmePB-172
Phillips, Tony (Keith Anthony)
❑ 80MemChiT-16
❑ 81WesHavAT-14
❑ 82TacTigT-32
❑ 83TopTra-87T
❑ 84A'sMot-23
❑ 84Don-278
❑ 84Fle-459
❑ 84Nes792-309
❑ 84Top-309
❑ 84TopTif-309
❑ 85Don-101
❑ 85Fle-433
❑ 85Top-444
❑ 85TopSti-329
❑ 85TopTif-444
❑ 86A'sMot-19
❑ 86Don-542
❑ 86Fle-430
❑ 86Top-29
❑ 86TopTif-29
❑ 87A'sSmoC-10
❑ 87Don-103
❑ 87DonOpeD-26
❑ 87Fle-402
❑ 87FleGlo-402
❑ 87SpoTeaP-23
❑ 87Top-188
❑ 87TopTif-188
❑ 88A'sMot-12
❑ 88Don-221
❑ 88DonTeaBA-221
❑ 88Fle-290
❑ 88FleGlo-290
❑ 88OPC-12
❑ 88PanSti-168
❑ 88Sco-294
❑ 88ScoGlo-294
❑ 88StaLinAs-13
❑ 88Top-673
❑ 88TopSti-165
❑ 88TopTif-673
❑ 89A'sMot-11
❑ 89DonBasB-211
❑ 89FleUpd-56
❑ 89Sco-156
❑ 89Top-248
❑ 89TopTif-248
❑ 89UppDec-267
❑ 90Bow-359
❑ 90BowTif-359
❑ 90ClaYel-T79
❑ 90Don-91
❑ 90DonBesA-20
❑ 90Fle-19
❑ 90FleCan-19
❑ 90FleUpd-99
❑ 90Lea-324
❑ 90OPC-702
❑ 90Sco-84
❑ 90ScoRoo-14T
❑ 90TigCok-17
❑ 90TigTeal-17
❑ 90Top-702
❑ 90TopBig-239
❑ 90TopTif-702
❑ 90TopTra-95T
❑ 90TopTraT-95T
❑ 90UppDec-154
❑ 90UppDec-768
❑ 91Bow-137
❑ 91Don-286
❑ 91Fle-348
❑ 91Lea-4
❑ 91OPC-583
❑ 91PanFreS-290
❑ 91Sco-38
❑ 91StaClu-41
❑ 91StaCluP-32
❑ 91TigCok-4
❑ 91TigPol-9
❑ 91Top-583
❑ 91TopDesS-583
❑ 91TopMic-583
❑ 91TopTif-583
❑ 91TopTriH-A6
❑ 91Ult-126
❑ 91UppDec-131
❑ 92Bow-272
❑ 92Don-328
❑ 92DonDiaK-DK25
❑ 92DonSupD-DK25
❑ 92Fle-143
❑ 92Hig5-48
❑ 92Lea-40
❑ 92LeaBlaG-40
❑ 92OPC-319
❑ 92Pin-243
❑ 92Sco-453
❑ 92StaClu-488
❑ 92Stu-176
❑ 92TigKro-21
❑ 92Top-319
❑ 92TopGol-319
❑ 92TopGolW-319
❑ 92TopKid-79
❑ 92TopMic-319
❑ 92TriPla-99
❑ 92TriPla-218
❑ 92Ult-62
❑ 92UppDec-184
❑ 93Bow-419
❑ 93DiaMar-85
❑ 93Don-701
❑ 93Fin-75
❑ 93FinRef-75
❑ 93Fla-207
❑ 93Fle-233
❑ 93FunPac-188
❑ 93Lea-126
❑ 93OPC-262
❑ 93PacSpa-113
❑ 93PanSti-115
❑ 93Pin-406
❑ 93Sco-614
❑ 93Sel-218
❑ 93SelStaL-37
❑ 93SP-239
❑ 93StaClu-5
❑ 93StaCluFDI-5
❑ 93StaCluMOP-5
❑ 93Stu-213
❑ 93TigGat-22
❑ 93Top-189
❑ 93TopGol-189
❑ 93TopInaM-189
❑ 93TopInaR-189
❑ 93TopMic-189
❑ 93TriPla-176
❑ 93Ult-203
❑ 93UppDec-195
❑ 93UppDecGold-195
❑ 94Bow-397
❑ 94ColC-230
❑ 94ColChoGS-230
❑ 94ColChoSS-230
❑ 94Don-445
❑ 94Fin-178
❑ 94FinRef-178
❑ 94Fla-52
❑ 94Fle-142
❑ 94FleExtB-79
❑ 94FUnPac-64
❑ 94Lea-160
❑ 94OPC-192
❑ 94Pac-227
❑ 94PanSti-67
❑ 94Pin-330
❑ 94PinArtP-330
❑ 94PinMusC-330
❑ 94PinRunC-RC11
❑ 94Sco-103
❑ 94ScoCyc-TC5
❑ 94ScoGolR-103
❑ 94ScoGolS-54
❑ 94Sel-215
❑ 94SP-179
❑ 94SPDieC-179
❑ 94Spo-56
❑ 94StaClu-553
❑ 94StaCluFDI-553
❑ 94StaCluGR-553
❑ 94StaCluMO-37
❑ 94StaCluMOP-553
❑ 94StaCluMOP-ST20
❑ 94StaCluST-ST20
❑ 94Stu-192
❑ 94Top-48
❑ 94TopGol-48
❑ 94TopSpa-48
❑ 94TriPla-247
❑ 94Ult-59
❑ 94UltOnBL-11
❑ 94UppDec-56
❑ 94UppDecED-56
❑ 95AngCHP-14
❑ 95AngMot-7
❑ 95Bow-422
❑ 95ColCho-473
❑ 95ColCho-531T
❑ 95ColChoGS-473
❑ 95ColChoSE-223
❑ 95ColChoSEGS-223
❑ 95ColChoSESS-223
❑ 95ColChoSS-473
❑ 95Don-407
❑ 95DonPreP-407
❑ 95DonTopotO-41
❑ 95Fin-212
❑ 95Fin-223
❑ 95FinRef-212
❑ 95FinRef-223
❑ 95Fla-41
❑ 95Fla-238
❑ 95Fle-59
❑ 95FleUpd-67
❑ 95Lea-331
❑ 95LeaLim-3
❑ 95Pac-158
❑ 95PacPri-50
❑ 95Pin-209
❑ 95PinArtP-209
❑ 95PinMusC-209
❑ 95Sco-49
❑ 95ScoGolR-49
❑ 95ScoHaloG-HG50
❑ 95ScoPlaTS-49
❑ 95SP-136
❑ 95Spo-97
❑ 95SpoArtP-97
❑ 95SPSil-136
❑ 95StaClu-208
❑ 95StaClu-607
❑ 95StaCluFDI-208
❑ 95StaCluMO-37
❑ 95StaCluMOP-208
❑ 95StaCluMOP-607
❑ 95StaCluSTWS-208
❑ 95StaCluSTWS-607
❑ 95StaCluVR-109
❑ 95StaCluVRMO-109
❑ 95Stu-175
❑ 95Top-541
❑ 95TopCyb-322
❑ 95TopEmb-79
❑ 95TopEmbGI-79
❑ 95TopTra-44T
❑ 95Ult-50
❑ 95UltGolM-50
❑ 95UppDec-267
❑ 95UppDecED-267
❑ 95UppDecEDG-267
❑ 95UppDecSE-97
❑ 95UppDecSEG-97
❑ 96Cir-28
❑ 96CirRav-28
❑ 96Don-232
❑ 96DonPreP-232
❑ 96EmoXL-40
❑ 96Fin-B225
❑ 96FinRef-B225
❑ 96Fla-56
❑ 96Fle-56
❑ 96FleTif-56
❑ 96FleUpd-U26
❑ 96FleUpdTC-U26
❑ 96MetUni-31
❑ 96MetUniP-31
❑ 96Pac-273
❑ 96Sco-165
❑ 96SP-58
❑ 96StaClu-195
❑ 96StaClu-434
❑ 96StaCluEPB-434
❑ 96StaCluEPG-434
❑ 96StaCluEPS-434
❑ 96StaCluMO-33
❑ 96StaCluMOP-195
❑ 96StaCluMOP-434
❑ 96Top-199
❑ 96TopLas-12
❑ 96Ult-334
❑ 96UltGolM-334
❑ 96UppDec-305
❑ 96WhiSoxF-13
❑ 97AngMot-6
❑ 97Cir-215
❑ 97CirRav-215
❑ 97ColCho-72
❑ 97ColChoT-CW3
❑ 97Don-218
❑ 97DonGolPP-218
❑ 97DonSilPP-218
❑ 97DonTea-3
❑ 97DonTeaSPE-3
❑ 97Fin-215
❑ 97FinRef-215
❑ 97Fle-68
❑ 97FleTif-68
❑ 97Lea-227
❑ 97LeaFraM-227
❑ 97LeaFraMDC-227
❑ 97MetUni-60
❑ 97Pac-61
❑ 97PacLigB-61
❑ 97PacSil-61
❑ 97Sco-214
❑ 97ScoArtPWB-214
❑ 97ScoPreS-214
❑ 97ScoShoS-214
❑ 97ScoShoSAP-214
❑ 97StaClu-27
❑ 97StaCluMat-27
❑ 97StaCluMOP-27
❑ 97Stu-114
❑ 97StuPrePG-114
❑ 97StuPrePS-114
❑ 97Top-165
❑ 97TopChr-66
❑ 97TopChrR-66
❑ 97TopGal-25
❑ 97TopGalPPI-25
❑ 97Ult-43
❑ 97UltGolME-43
❑ 97UltPlaME-43
❑ 97UppDec-38
❑ 97WhiSoxS-14
❑ 97WhiSoxSPl-14
❑ 97WhiSoxSPr-14
❑ 98AngSco-14
❑ 98AngScoP-14
❑ 98FleUpd-U29
❑ 98Pac-14
❑ 98PacPlaB-14
❑ 98PacRedT-14
❑ 98PacSil-14
❑ 98Ult-107
❑ 98UltGolM-107
❑ 98UltMas-107
❑ 98UltPlaM-107
❑ 99PacPar-172
❑ 99PacParC-172
❑ 99PacParG-172
❑ 99PacParHoloGold-172
❑ 99PacParHS-172
❑ 99PacParOD-172
❑ 99PacParPB-172
❑ 99PacParRed-172
❑ 99UppDec-445
❑ 99UppDecEL1-445
❑ 99UppDecEL2-445
Phillips, Vince
❑ 89PriWilCS-16
❑ 90AlbYanB-22
❑ 90AlbYanP-1046
❑ 90AlbYanSt-12
❑ 90CMC-782
❑ 90TopTVY-57
❑ 91AlbYanLD-12
❑ 91AlbYanP-1021
❑ 91LinDriAA-12
Phillips, W. Taylor
❑ 57Top-343
❑ 58Top-159
❑ 59Top-113
❑ 59TopVen-113
❑ 60Top-211
❑ 80Bra195T-9
Phillips, Wade
❑ 87FayGenP-9
❑ 87LakTigP-15
❑ 88LakTigS-20
Philyaw, Dino
❑ 91PocPioP-3798
❑ 91PocPioSP-25
Philyaw, Thad
❑ 75WatDodT-16
Phipps, Brian
❑ 93HunCubC-30
Phipps, Chris
❑ 93MarPhiC-21
❑ 93MarPhiF-3472
❑ 94MarPhiC-16
❑ 94MarPhiF-3290
Phipps, Ron
❑ 83PeoSunF-26
Phoebus, Tom
❑ 67BalOriP-78
❑ 67BalOriP-79
❑ 67BalOriP-80
❑ 67CokCapO-18
❑ 67Top-204
❑ 68BalOriDPCP-9
❑ 68CokCapO-18
❑ 68DexPre-63
❑ 68OPC-97
❑ 68Top-97
❑ 68TopActS-2C
❑ 68TopActS-13C
❑ 68TopVen-97
❑ 69MilBra-223
❑ 69MLBOffS-6
❑ 69OPC-185
❑ 69Top-185
❑ 69Top-532
❑ 69TopFou-18
❑ 69TopSta-127
❑ 69TopTeaP-5
❑ 70BalOriP-23
❑ 70MLBOffS-152
❑ 70Top-717
❑ 71MLBOffS-234
❑ 71OPC-611
❑ 71Top-611
❑ 72MilBra-274
❑ 72OPC-477
❑ 72Top-477
❑ 91OriCro-361
Phoenix, Steve
❑ 91ModA'sP-3086
❑ 92HunStaF-3949
❑ 92HunStaS-318
❑ 93TacTigF-3029
❑ 94HunStaF-1328
❑ 95EdmTraTI-18
❑ 95Top-369
❑ 96CarMudB-7
❑ 97HunStaTI-21
Phoenix, Wynter
❑ 97YakBeaG-25
❑ 98SanBerS-24
❑ 98SanBerSTIS-21
Phox, Phil E.
❑ 97ClePhi-30
Pi-Gonzalez, Amaury
❑ 98GiaMot-27
Piatt, Adam
❑ 98ModA'sG-25
❑ 99Bow-413
❑ 99BowGol-413
❑ 99BowInt-413
Piatt, Bruce
❑ 83ButCopKT-32
Piatt, Doug
❑ 88BurIndP-1790
❑ 89KinIndS-18
❑ 89Sta-184
❑ 89WatIndS-18
❑ 90WesPalBES-17
❑ 91IndIndLD-191
❑ 91IndIndP-459
❑ 91LinDriAAA-191
❑ 91TopTra-92T
❑ 91TopTraT-92T
❑ 92ClaFS7-118
❑ 92Don-640
❑ 92HarSenF-460
❑ 92HarSenS-295
❑ 92OPC-526
❑ 92ProFS7-253
❑ 92Sco-422
❑ 92SkyAA F-125
❑ 92StaClu-408
❑ 92Top-526
❑ 92TopDeb91-139
❑ 92TopGol-526
❑ 92TopGolW-526
❑ 92TopMic-526
❑ 93MemChiF-374
Piatt, Wiley
❑ 03BreE10-116
Piazza, Anthony
❑ 87EveGiaC-4
Piazza, Mike
❑ 89SalDodTI-25
❑ 90TopMag-107
❑ 90VerBeaDS-24
❑ 91BakDodCLC-7
❑ 91CalLeLA-6
❑ 92AlbDukF-723
❑ 92Bow-461
❑ 92ClaBluBF-BC16
❑ 92ClaFS7-345
❑ 92ClaRedB-BC16
❑ 92DonRooP-BC9
❑ 92FleUpd-92
❑ 92SanAntMS-573
❑ 92SkyAA F-251
❑ 92SpollIFK1-313

❑ 92SpoIIIFK1-697
❑ 92SpoIIIFK1-784
❑ 93Bow-646
❑ 93ClaGam-74
❑ 93ColAllG-24
❑ 93ColPosP-1
❑ 93ColPosP-2
❑ 93ColPosP-3
❑ 93ColPosP-4
❑ 93ColPosP-5
❑ 93ColPosP-6
❑ 93ColPosP-7
❑ 93ColPosP-8
❑ 93DiaMar-86
❑ 93DodMot-4
❑ 93DodPol-20
❑ 93DodStaC-6
❑ 93Don-209
❑ 93DonEliD-8
❑ 93Fin-199
❑ 93FinRef-199
❑ 93Fla-75
❑ 93FlaWavotF-12
❑ 93FleMajLP-A13
❑ 93FunPac-6
❑ 93JimDeaR-8
❑ 93Lea-35
❑ 93LeaGolR-U4
❑ 93LeaGolRJ-U4
❑ 93OPC-314
❑ 93OPCPre-26
❑ 93PacJugC-34
❑ 93PacSpa-502
❑ 93Pin-252
❑ 93PinHomRC-26
❑ 93PinRooTP-3
❑ 93Sco-286
❑ 93ScoBoyoS-5
❑ 93Sel-347
❑ 93SelRoo-ROY2
❑ 93SelRooAR-5
❑ 93SP-98
❑ 93SPPlaP-PP15
❑ 93StaClu-585
❑ 93StaCluFDI-585
❑ 93StaCluMO-18
❑ 93StaCluMO-19
❑ 93StaCluMOP-585
❑ 93Stu-201
❑ 93StuSil-9
❑ 93Top-701
❑ 93TopFulS-6
❑ 93TopGol-701
❑ 93TopInaM-701
❑ 93TopInaR-701
❑ 93TopMic-701
❑ 93TopTra-24T
❑ 93Toy-22
❑ 93TriPla-55
❑ 93Ult-60
❑ 93Ult-300
❑ 93UltAllR-7
❑ 93UppDec-2
❑ 93UppDecDG-34
❑ 93UppDecGold-2
❑ 94Bow-387
❑ 94Bow-510
❑ 94BowBes-R81
❑ 94BowBes-X104
❑ 94BowBesR-R81
❑ 94BowBesR-X104
❑ 94BowPre-2
❑ 94ChuHomS-14
❑ 94ChuHomSG-14
❑ 94ColC-310
❑ 94ColC-318
❑ 94ColC-336
❑ 94ColC-400
❑ 94ColC-637
❑ 94ColChoGS-310
❑ 94ColChoGS-318
❑ 94ColChoGS-336
❑ 94ColChoGS-400
❑ 94ColChoGS-637
❑ 94ColChoHRA-HA8
❑ 94ColChoSS-310
❑ 94ColChoSS-318
❑ 94ColChoSS-336
❑ 94ColChoSS-400
❑ 94ColChoSS-637
❑ 94ColChoT-11
❑ 94DenHol-18
❑ 94DodDaiN-14
❑ 94DodMot-2
❑ 94DodPol-21
❑ 94Don-2
❑ 94DonAwaWJ-3
❑ 94DonDiaK-DK15
❑ 94DonDiaKJ-DK15
❑ 94DonEli-46
❑ 94DonLonBL-7
❑ 94DonMVP-7
❑ 94DonPro-5
❑ 94DonSpeE-2
❑ 94DonSpiotG-4
❑ 94DonSpiotGJ-4
❑ 94Fin-1
❑ 94FinJum-1
❑ 94FinRef-1
❑ 94Fla-182
❑ 94FlaHotN-7
❑ 94FlaInfP-7
❑ 94Fle-520
❑ 94Fle-713
❑ 94FleAllS-47
❑ 94FleAwaW-6
❑ 94FleExtB-294
❑ 94FleExtBGB-22
❑ 94FleExtBSYS-16
❑ 94FlePro-8
❑ 94FleRooS-14
❑ 94FleSun-20
❑ 94FleTeaL-21
❑ 94FUnPac-31
❑ 94FUnPac-185
❑ 94FUnPac-203
❑ 94FUnPac-208
❑ 94FUnPac-220
❑ 94FUnPac-231
❑ 94FUnPac-238
❑ 94KinDis-19
❑ 94Kra-27
❑ 94Lea-436
❑ 94LeaGam-12
❑ 94LeaL-120
❑ 94LeaLimGA-16
❑ 94LeaMVPC-N11
❑ 94LeaMVPCG-N11
❑ 94LeaPowB-6
❑ 94LeaPro-6
❑ 94LeaSli-2
❑ 94LeaStaS-4
❑ 94MotPia-1
❑ 94MotPia-2
❑ 94MotPia-3
❑ 94MotPia-4
❑ 94MotPia-1
❑ 94MotPia-2
❑ 94MotPia-3
❑ 94MotPia-4
❑ 94MotPia-BLUE
❑ 94MotPia-RED
❑ 94O-PJumAF-9
❑ 94OPC-147
❑ 94OPCAllR-9
❑ 94OPCDiaD-1
❑ 94OPCJumA-9
❑ 94OscMayR-27
❑ 94Pac-318
❑ 94Pac-658
❑ 94PacGolP-16
❑ 94PacPro-P6
❑ 94PacSilP-29
❑ 94PacSilPC-29
❑ 94PanSti-203
❑ 94Pin-28
❑ 94PinArtP-28
❑ 94PinMusC-28
❑ 94PinNewG-NG2
❑ 94PinPowS-PS17
❑ 94PinRunC-RC28
❑ 94PinTeaP-5
❑ 94PinTheN-19
❑ 94PinTri-TR7
❑ 94Pos-1
❑ 94PosCan-14
❑ 94ProMag-70
❑ 94RedFolMI-20
❑ 94RemUltP-1
❑ 94RemUltP-2
❑ 94RemUltP-3
❑ 94RemUltP-4
❑ 94RemUltP-5
❑ 94RemUltP-6
❑ 94RemUltPP-1
❑ 94RemUltPP-2
❑ 94Sco-476
❑ 94Sco-636
❑ 94ScoBoyoS-6
❑ 94ScoGolR-476
❑ 94ScoGolR-636
❑ 94ScoGolS-13
❑ 94Sel-4
❑ 94SelCroC-CC9
❑ 94SP-80
❑ 94SPDieC-80
❑ 94SPHol-29
❑ 94SPHolDC-29
❑ 94Spo-67
❑ 94Spo-189
❑ 94SpoFanA-AS5
❑ 94SpoRooGGG-GG5
❑ 94SpoSha-SH11
❑ 94SPPre-WR4
❑ 94StaClu-140
❑ 94StaClu-266
❑ 94StaCluDD-DD1
❑ 94StaCluF-F8
❑ 94StaCluFDI-140
❑ 94StaCluFDI-266
❑ 94StaCluFJ-F8
❑ 94StaCluGR-140
❑ 94StaCluGR-266
❑ 94StaCluMO-28
❑ 94StaCluMOP-140
❑ 94StaCluMOP-266
❑ 94StaCluMOP-F8
❑ 94StaCluMOP-DD1
❑ 94StaCluMOP-ST7
❑ 94StaCluST-ST7
❑ 94Stu-72
❑ 94StuEdiC-8
❑ 94StuSerS-6
❑ 94StuSerSG-6
❑ 94SucSav-17
❑ 94TomPiz-15
❑ 94Top-1
❑ 94Top-391
❑ 94TopBlaG-41
❑ 94TopGol-1
❑ 94TopGol-391
❑ 94TopSpa-1
❑ 94TopSpa-391
❑ 94TopSupS-34
❑ 94TopTraFI-2
❑ 94TriPla-88
❑ 94TriPlaP-6
❑ 94Ult-218
❑ 94UltAllS-11
❑ 94UltAwaW-25
❑ 94UltHitM-9
❑ 94UltHomRK-12
❑ 94UltRBIK-10
❑ 94UltRisS-9
❑ 94UltSecYS-9
❑ 94UppDec-33
❑ 94UppDec-47
❑ 94UppDec-273
❑ 94UppDec-500
❑ 94UppDecAJ-31
❑ 94UppDecAJG-31
❑ 94UppDecDC-W9
❑ 94UppDecED-33
❑ 94UppDecED-47
❑ 94UppDecED-273
❑ 94UppDecED-500
❑ 94UppDecMLS-MM15
❑ 94UppDecMLSED-MM15
❑ 94UppDecNG-13
❑ 94UppDecNGED-13
❑ 94USDepoT-1
❑ 94USPlaCA-4C
❑ 94USPlaCA-4D
❑ 94USPlaCR-1C
❑ 94USPlaCR-13H
❑ 94USPlaCR-JK
❑ 95Baz-77
❑ 95BazRedH-RH15
❑ 95Bow-310
❑ 95BowBes-R36
❑ 95BowBesJR-6
❑ 95BowBesR-R36
❑ 95ClaFanFPCP-5
❑ 95ClaPhoC-33
❑ 95ColCho-80
❑ 95ColCho-87
❑ 95ColChoCtA-6
❑ 95ColChoCtAGR-6
❑ 95ColChoCtG-CG15
❑ 95ColChoCtG-CG15B
❑ 95ColChoCtG-CG15C
❑ 95ColChoCtGE-15
❑ 95ColChoCtGG-CG15
❑ 95ColChoCtGG-CG15B
❑ 95ColChoCtGG-CG15C
❑ 95ColChoCtGGE-15
❑ 95ColChoGS-80
❑ 95ColChoGS-87
❑ 95ColChoSE-90
❑ 95ColChoSE-253
❑ 95ColChoSEGS-90
❑ 95ColChoSEGS-253
❑ 95ColChoSESS-90
❑ 95ColChoSESS-253
❑ 95ColChoSS-80
❑ 95ColChoSS-87
❑ 95DenHol-20
❑ 95DodMot-2
❑ 95DodPol-21
❑ 95DodROY-13
❑ 95Don-5
❑ 95DonAll-NL2
❑ 95DonDom-2
❑ 95DonEli-52
❑ 95DonLonBL-5
❑ 95DonPreP-5
❑ 95DonTopotO-271
❑ 95Emo-145
❑ 95EmoN-8
❑ 95Fin-113
❑ 95FinPowK-PK6
❑ 95FinRef-113
❑ 95Fla-155
❑ 95FlaHotN-7
❑ 95FlaInfP-7
❑ 95FlaTodS-9
❑ 95Fle-547
❑ 95FleAllF-1
❑ 95FleAllS-1
❑ 95FleTeaL-21
❑ 95FleUpdH-15
❑ 95FleUpdSS-8
❑ 95KinDis-16
❑ 95Kra-26
❑ 95Lea-218
❑ 95Lea300C-3
❑ 95LeaGolS-11
❑ 95LeaLim-79
❑ 95LeaLimG-16
❑ 95LeaLimIBP-10
❑ 95LeaLimL-6
❑ 95LeaOpeD-5
❑ 95NatPac-5
❑ 95Pac-224
❑ 95PacGolCDC-13
❑ 95PacGolP-17
❑ 95PacPri-72
❑ 95PanSti-24
❑ 95Pin-237
❑ 95Pin-300
❑ 95Pin-448
❑ 95Pin-450
❑ 95PinArtP-237
❑ 95PinArtP-300
❑ 95PinArtP-448
❑ 95PinArtP-450
❑ 95PinFan-23
❑ 95PinGatA-GA5
❑ 95PinMusC-237
❑ 95PinMusC-300
❑ 95PinMusC-448
❑ 95PinMusC-450
❑ 95PinPer-PP9
❑ 95PinPin-3
❑ 95PinPinR-3
❑ 95PinRedH-RH5
❑ 95PinTeaP-TP2
❑ 95PinUps-US3
❑ 95PinWhiH-WH5
❑ 95Pos-12
❑ 95RedFol-22
❑ 95Sco-17
❑ 95Sco-558
❑ 95ScoDreT-DG5
❑ 95ScoGolR-17
❑ 95ScoGolR-558
❑ 95ScoHaloG-HG10
❑ 95ScoPlaTS-17
❑ 95ScoPlaTS-558
❑ 95ScoRul-SR3
❑ 95ScoRulJ-SR3
❑ 95Sel-17
❑ 95Sel-248
❑ 95Sel-250
❑ 95SelArtP-17
❑ 95SelArtP-248
❑ 95SelArtP-250
❑ 95SelBigS-BS4
❑ 95SelCer-39
❑ 95SelCer-80
❑ 95SelCerC-5
❑ 95SelCerGT-5
❑ 95SelCerMG-39
❑ 95SelCerMG-80
❑ 95SelCerS-39
❑ 95SP-70
❑ 95SPCha-57
❑ 95SPCha-60
❑ 95SPChaDC-57
❑ 95SPChaDC-60
❑ 95SPChaDFC-4
❑ 95SPChaFCDC-4
❑ 95Spo-83
❑ 95Spo-167
❑ 95SpoArtP-83
❑ 95SpoArtP-167
❑ 95SpoDet-DE5
❑ 95SpoDouT-7
❑ 95SpoHamT-HT4
❑ 95SpoPro-PM5
❑ 95SPPlaP-PP6
❑ 95SPSil-70
❑ 95SPSpeF-43
❑ 95StaClu-149
❑ 95StaClu-320
❑ 95StaClu-502
❑ 95StaCluCC-CC1
❑ 95StaCluFDI-149
❑ 95StaCluMO-38
❑ 95StaCluMOP-149
❑ 95StaCluMOP-320
❑ 95StaCluMOP-502
❑ 95StaCluMOP-CC1
❑ 95StaCluSTDW-D7T
❑ 95StaCluSTDW-D149
❑ 95StaCluSTWS-149
❑ 95StaCluSTWS-320
❑ 95StaCluSTWS-502
❑ 95StaCluVR-78
❑ 95StaCluVRMO-78
❑ 95Stu-4
❑ 95StuGolS-4
❑ 95StuPlaS-4
❑ 95Sum-88
❑ 95Sum-178
❑ 95Sum-198
❑ 95SumBigB-BB5
❑ 95SumNthD-88
❑ 95SumNthD-178
❑ 95SumNthD-198
❑ 95Top-391
❑ 95Top-466
❑ 95TopCyb-261
❑ 95TopD3-27
❑ 95TopEmb-110
❑ 95TopEmbGI-110
❑ 95TopLeaL-LL40
❑ 95TopPre-PP2
❑ 95TopPreS-PP2
❑ 95TopTra-6T
❑ 95TopTra-163T
❑ 95TopTraPB-6
❑ 95UC3-39
❑ 95UC3-126
❑ 95UC3ArtP-39
❑ 95UC3ArtP-126
❑ 95UC3CycS-CS6
❑ 95UC3InM-IM4
❑ 95Ult-399
❑ 95UltAllS-15
❑ 95UltAllSGM-15
❑ 95UltGolM-399
❑ 95UltHitM-9
❑ 95UltHitMGM-9
❑ 95UltRBIK-10
❑ 95UltRBIKGM-10
❑ 95UltRisS-8
❑ 95UltRisSGM-8
❑ 95UppDec-320
❑ 95UppDecED-320
❑ 95UppDecEDG-320
❑ 95UppDecPAW-H8
❑ 95UppDecPAWE-H8
❑ 95UppDecPLL-R18
❑ 95UppDecPLL-R37
❑ 95UppDecPLL-R60
❑ 95UppDecPLLE-R18
❑ 95UppDecPLLE-R37
❑ 95UppDecPLLE-R60
❑ 95UppDecSE-35
❑ 95UppDecSEG-35
❑ 95UppDecSoaD-SD1
❑ 95Zen-76
❑ 95ZenAllS-3
❑ 95ZenZ-5
❑ 96Baz-8
❑ 96Bow-27
❑ 96BowBes-26
❑ 96BowBesAR-26
❑ 96BowBesC-9
❑ 96BowBesCAR-9
❑ 96BowBesCR-9
❑ 96BowBesMI-8
❑ 96BowBesMIAR-8
❑ 96BowBesMIR-8
❑ 96BowBesP-BBP7
❑ 96BowBesPAR-BBP7
❑ 96BowBesPR-BBP7
❑ 96BowBesR-26
❑ 96BowFoi-27
❑ 96Cir-146
❑ 96CirAcc-21
❑ 96CirBos-39
❑ 96CirRav-146
❑ 96ColCho-185
❑ 96ColCho-272
❑ 96ColCho-406
❑ 96ColChoCtG-CG21
❑ 96ColChoCtG-CG21B
❑ 96ColChoCtG-CG21C
❑ 96ColChoCtGE-CR21
❑ 96ColChoCtGG-CG21
❑ 96ColChoCtGG-CG21B
❑ 96ColChoCtGG-CG21C
❑ 96ColChoCtGGE-CR21
❑ 96ColChoGS-185
❑ 96ColChoGS-272
❑ 96ColChoGS-406
❑ 96ColChoSS-185
❑ 96ColChoSS-272
❑ 96ColChoSS-406
❑ 96ColChoYMtP-31
❑ 96ColChoYMtP-31A
❑ 96ColChoYMtPGS-31
❑ 96ColChoYMtPGS-31A
❑ 96DenHolGS-3
❑ 96DenHolGSAP-3
❑ 96DodFle-16
❑ 96DodMot-2
❑ 96DodPol-27
❑ 96Don-424
❑ 96DonFreF-8
❑ 96DonHitL-4
❑ 96DonPreP-424
❑ 96DonPurP-5
❑ 96DonRouT-7
❑ 96DonSam-7
❑ 96DonSho-5
❑ 96EmoLegoB-6
❑ 96EmoXL-215
❑ 96Fin-B113
❑ 96Fin-B275
❑ 96Fin-S11
❑ 96FinRef-B113
❑ 96FinRef-B275
❑ 96FinRef-S11
❑ 96Fla-298
❑ 96FlaDiaC-8
❑ 96FlaHotG-7
❑ 96FlaPow-6
❑ 96Fle-445
❑ 96FleChe-5
❑ 96FleLumC-6
❑ 96FleRoaW-5
❑ 96FleTeaL-21
❑ 96FleTif-445
❑ 96FleUpd-U235
❑ 96FleUpdH-15
❑ 96FleUpdSS-7
❑ 96FleUpdTC-U235
❑ 96FleZon-9
❑ 96Kin-16
❑ 96Lea-200
❑ 96LeaAllGMC-2
❑ 96LeaAllGMCG-2
❑ 96LeaAllGMCG-2A
❑ 96LeaGolS-5
❑ 96LeaLim-13
❑ 96LeaLimG-13
❑ 96LeaLimL-8
❑ 96LeaLimL-P8
❑ 96LeaLimLB-8
❑ 96LeaPicP-10
❑ 96LeaPicP-P10
❑ 96LeaPre-25
❑ 96LeaPre-150
❑ 96LeaPreP-25
❑ 96LeaPreP-150
❑ 96LeaPrePB-200
❑ 96LeaPrePG-200
❑ 96LeaPrePS-200
❑ 96LeaPreSG-51
❑ 96LeaPreSP-5
❑ 96LeaPreSta-12
❑ 96LeaPreSte-51

❑ 96LeaSig-1
❑ 96LeaSigPPG-1
❑ 96LeaSigPPP-1
❑ 96MetUni-187
❑ 96MetUniHM-6
❑ 96MetUniP-187
❑ 96MetUniT-6
❑ 96Pac-103
❑ 96PacBaeS-2
❑ 96PacCraC-CC7
❑ 96PacGolCD-DC7
❑ 96PacHom-HP1
❑ 96PacOctM-OM17
❑ 96PacPri-P38
❑ 96PacPriFB-FB13
❑ 96PacPriG-P38
❑ 96PacPriRHS-RH4
❑ 96PanSti-95
❑ 96Pin-4
❑ 96Pin-132
❑ 96Pin-138
❑ 96Pin-198
❑ 96Pin-265
❑ 96Pin-322
❑ 96Pin-398
❑ 96Pin-399
❑ 96PinAfi-124
❑ 96PinAfi-198
❑ 96PinAfiAP-124
❑ 96PinAfiAP-198
❑ 96PinAfiR-13
❑ 96PinAfiR-15
❑ 96PinAfiR-16
❑ 96PinAfiR-17
❑ 96PinAfiR-19
❑ 96PinAfiR-21
❑ 96PinAfiSP-1
❑ 96PinArtP-4
❑ 96PinArtP-65
❑ 96PinArtP-165
❑ 96PinArtP-197
❑ 96PinEssotG-10
❑ 96PinFan-10
❑ 96PinFoil-265
❑ 96PinFoil-322
❑ 96PinFoil-398
❑ 96PinFoil-399
❑ 96PinPow-7
❑ 96PinSam-4
❑ 96PinSky-7
❑ 96PinSlu-7
❑ 96PinSta-4
❑ 96PinSta-65
❑ 96PinSta-165
❑ 96PinSta-197
❑ 96PinTeaP-8
❑ 96PinTeaS-4
❑ 96Pro-10
❑ 96ProMagA-16
❑ 96ProMagDM-16
❑ 96ProSta-41
❑ 96RedF-30
❑ 96RemUltPP-1
❑ 96RemUltPP-2
❑ 96RemUltPP-3
❑ 96RemUltPP-4
❑ 96RemUltPP-5
❑ 96RemUltPP-6
❑ 96RemUltPP-7
❑ 96RemUltPP-8
❑ 96RemUltPP-9
❑ 96Sco-270
❑ 96Sco-317
❑ 96ScoBigB-5
❑ 96ScoDiaA-10
❑ 96ScoDreT-5
❑ 96ScoDugC-B42
❑ 96ScoDugCAP-B42
❑ 96ScoGolS-5
❑ 96ScoNumG-4
❑ 96ScoPowP-7
❑ 96ScoRef-12
❑ 96ScoTitT-11
❑ 96Sel-22
❑ 96Sel-155
❑ 96Sel-199
❑ 96SelArtP-22
❑ 96SelArtP-155
❑ 96SelArtP-199
❑ 96SelCer-30
❑ 96SelCer-138
❑ 96SelCerAP-30
❑ 96SelCerAP-138
❑ 96SelCerCB-30
❑ 96SelCerCB-138
❑ 96SelCerCR-30
❑ 96SelCerCR-138
❑ 96SelCerIP-4
❑ 96SelCerMB-30
❑ 96SelCerMB-138
❑ 96SelCerMG-30
❑ 96SelCerMG-138
❑ 96SelCerMR-30
❑ 96SelCerMR-138
❑ 96SelCerSF-10
❑ 96SelClaTF-12
❑ 96SelEnF-11
❑ 96SelTeaN-11
❑ 96SP-105
❑ 96SPBasH-87
❑ 96SPMarM-MM6
❑ 96SPMarMDC-6
❑ 96Spo-10
❑ 96Spo-102
❑ 96SpoArtP-10
❑ 96SpoArtP-102
❑ 96SpoDouT-7
❑ 96SpoHitP-4
❑ 96SpoPowS-6
❑ 96SpoPro-5
❑ 96SPPreF-6
❑ 96SPSpeFX-3
❑ 96SPSpeFXDC-3
❑ 96SPx-33
❑ 96SPx-MP1
❑ 96SPx-MPAU
❑ 96SPxBoufG-10
❑ 96SPxGol-33
❑ 96StaClu-216
❑ 96StaClu-442
❑ 96StaCluEPB-442
❑ 96StaCluEPG-442
❑ 96StaCluEPS-442
❑ 96StaCluEWB-EW2
❑ 96StaCluEWG-EW2
❑ 96StaCluEWS-EW2
❑ 96StaCluMM-MM2
❑ 96StaCluMO-34
❑ 96StaCluMOP-216
❑ 96StaCluMOP-442
❑ 96StaCluMOP-MM2
❑ 96StaCluMOP-PC7
❑ 96StaCluMOP-PP4
❑ 96StaCluPC-PC7
❑ 96StaCluPP-PP4
❑ 96Stu-80
❑ 96StuHitP-6
❑ 96StuMas-2
❑ 96StuMas-P2
❑ 96StuPrePB-80
❑ 96StuPrePG-80
❑ 96StuPrePS-80
❑ 96StuStaGS-6
❑ 96Sum-1
❑ 96Sum-156
❑ 96SumAbo&B-1
❑ 96SumAbo&B-156
❑ 96SumArtP-1
❑ 96SumArtP-156
❑ 96SumBal-11
❑ 96SumBigB-8
❑ 96SumBigBM-8
❑ 96SumFoi-1
❑ 96SumFoi-156
❑ 96SumHitI-13
❑ 96SumPos-5
❑ 96TeaOut-64
❑ 96TeaOut-C98
❑ 96Top-2
❑ 96Top-246
❑ 96TopChr-2
❑ 96TopChr-93
❑ 96TopChrR-2
❑ 96TopChrR-93
❑ 96TopChrWC-WC12
❑ 96TopChrWCR-WC12
❑ 96TopClaC-CC10
❑ 96TopGal-166
❑ 96TopGalE-1
❑ 96TopGalPPI-166
❑ 96TopLas-89
❑ 96TopLasPC-4
❑ 96TopMysF-M12
❑ 96TopMysF-M24
❑ 96TopMysFR-M12
❑ 96TopMysFR-M24
❑ 96TopPowB-2
❑ 96TopPro-NL7
❑ 96TopRoaW-RW12
❑ 96TopWreC-WC12
❑ 96Ult-224
❑ 96Ult-587
❑ 96UltChe-A6
❑ 96UltCheGM-A6
❑ 96UltDiaP-7
❑ 96UltDiaPGM-7
❑ 96UltGolM-224
❑ 96UltGolM-587
❑ 96UltHitM-7
❑ 96UltHitMGM-7
❑ 96UltOn-L-7
❑ 96UltOn-LGM-7
❑ 96UltPowP-6
❑ 96UltPowPGM-6
❑ 96UltPriL-10
❑ 96UltPriLGM-10
❑ 96UltRaw-8
❑ 96UltRawGM-8
❑ 96UppDec-145
❑ 96UppDec-360
❑ 96UppDec-383
❑ 96UppDecA-14
❑ 96UppDecDD-DD23
❑ 96UppDecDDG-DD23
❑ 96UppDecDDS-DD23
❑ 96UppDecG-GF6
❑ 96UppDecHC-HC14
❑ 96UppDecPD-PD12
❑ 96UppDecPHE-H38
❑ 96UppDecPRE-R36
❑ 96UppDecPRE-R46
❑ 96UppDecPRE-R59
❑ 96UppDecPreH-H38
❑ 96UppDecPreR-R36
❑ 96UppDecPreR-R46
❑ 96UppDecPreR-R59
❑ 96UppDecRunP-RP14
❑ 96UppDecVJLS-VJ17
❑ 96Zen-12
❑ 96Zen-138
❑ 96ZenArtP-12
❑ 96ZenArtP-138
❑ 96ZenDiaC-4
❑ 96ZenDiaCP-4
❑ 96ZenMoz-13
❑ 96ZenZ-8
❑ 97Bow-266
❑ 97BowBes-5
❑ 97BowBesAR-5
❑ 97BowBesBC-BC8
❑ 97BowBesBCAR-BC8
❑ 97BowBesBCR-BC8
❑ 97BowBesJ-5
❑ 97BowBesJAR-5
❑ 97BowBesJR-5
❑ 97BowBesMI-MI4
❑ 97BowBesMIAR-MI4
❑ 97BowBesMIARI-MI4
❑ 97BowBesMII-MI4
❑ 97BowBesMIR-MI4
❑ 97BowBesMIRI-MI4
❑ 97BowBesR-5
❑ 97BowChr-85
❑ 97BowChrI-85
❑ 97BowChrIR-85
❑ 97BowChrR-85
❑ 97BowInt-266
❑ 97Cir-356
❑ 97Cir-399
❑ 97CirBos-13
❑ 97CirIco-8
❑ 97CirLimA-11
❑ 97CirRav-356
❑ 97CirRav-399
❑ 97CirRavR-9
❑ 97CirSupB-13
❑ 97ColCho-365
❑ 97ColChoAC-26
❑ 97ColChoBS-18
❑ 97ColChoBSGS-18
❑ 97ColChoCtG-20A
❑ 97ColChoCtG-20B
❑ 97ColChoCtG-20C
❑ 97ColChoCtGE-CG20
❑ 97ColChoCtGIW-CG20
❑ 97ColChoNF-NF10
❑ 97ColChoPP-PP19
❑ 97ColChoPPG-PP19
❑ 97ColChoPPJ-PP19
❑ 97ColChoS-13
❑ 97ColChoSR-20
❑ 97ColChoT-LA10
❑ 97ColChoTBS-28
❑ 97ColChoTBSWH-28
❑ 97ColChoTotT-T15
❑ 97CraJac-15
❑ 97DenHol-20
❑ 97DodDWPM-5
❑ 97DodMot-3
❑ 97DodPol-23
❑ 97DodSco-2
❑ 97DodScoPl-2
❑ 97DodScoPr-2
❑ 97Don-134
❑ 97Don-402
❑ 97DonDiaK-7
❑ 97DonDiaKC-7
❑ 97DonDom-13
❑ 97DonEli-7
❑ 97DonEli-11
❑ 97DonEliGS-7
❑ 97DonFraFea-9
❑ 97DonGolPP-134
❑ 97DonGolPP-402
❑ 97DonLim-9
❑ 97DonLim-26
❑ 97DonLim-82
❑ 97DonLimE-9
❑ 97DonLimE-26
❑ 97DonLimE-82
❑ 97DonLimFotG-11
❑ 97DonLonL-9
❑ 97DonPowA-5
❑ 97DonPowADC-5
❑ 97DonPre-107
❑ 97DonPre-171
❑ 97DonPreCttC-107
❑ 97DonPreCttC-171
❑ 97DonPrePM-20
❑ 97DonPreS-5
❑ 97DonPreSS-5
❑ 97DonPreTB-15
❑ 97DonPreTBG-15
❑ 97DonPreTF-15
❑ 97DonPreTP-15
❑ 97DonPreTPG-15
❑ 97DonPreXP-9A
❑ 97DonRocL-4
❑ 97DonSig-7
❑ 97DonSigPPP-7
❑ 97DonSilPP-134
❑ 97DonSilPP-402
❑ 97DonTea-111
❑ 97DonTeaSMVP-2
❑ 97DonTeaSPE-111
❑ 97DonVxP1-34
❑ 97DonVxP1CD-3
❑ 97E-X2-82
❑ 97E-X2Cred-82
❑ 97E-X2EssCre-82
❑ 97E-X2Hall-15
❑ 97Fin-50
❑ 97Fin-151
❑ 97Fin-292
❑ 97FinEmb-151
❑ 97FinEmb-292
❑ 97FinEmbR-151
❑ 97FinEmbR-292
❑ 97FinRef-50
❑ 97FinRef-151
❑ 97FinRef-292
❑ 97FlaShoDC-12
❑ 97FlaShoHG-11
❑ 97FlaShoLC-31
❑ 97FlaShoLeg0-31
❑ 97FlaShoLeg1-31
❑ 97FlaShoM-A31
❑ 97FlaShoM-B31
❑ 97FlaShoM-C31
❑ 97FlaShoR0-31
❑ 97FlaShoR1-31
❑ 97FlaShoR2-31
❑ 97Fle-371
❑ 97Fle-497
❑ 97Fle-712
❑ 97Fle-734
❑ 97FleBleB-6
❑ 97FleDiaT-9
❑ 97FleGolM-8
❑ 97FleGouG-10
❑ 97FleGouGF-10
❑ 97FleHea-15
❑ 97FleLumC-13
❑ 97FleMilDM-14
❑ 97FleMilDMR-14
❑ 97FleNig&D-6
❑ 97FleSoaS-10
❑ 97FleSoaSG-10
❑ 97FleTeaL-21
❑ 97FleTif-371
❑ 97FleTif-497
❑ 97FleTif-712
❑ 97FleTif-734
❑ 97FleZon-14
❑ 97HigMinM-90
❑ 97HigMinM-91
❑ 97HigMinM-92
❑ 97HigMinMCT-26
❑ 97HigMinMCT-27
❑ 97HigMinMCT-28
❑ 97HigMinMM-15
❑ 97HigMinMM-17
❑ 97KinB-10
❑ 97Lea-191
❑ 97Lea-203
❑ 97Lea-373
❑ 97LeaDrefS-8
❑ 97LeaFraM-191
❑ 97LeaFraM-203
❑ 97LeaFraM-373
❑ 97LeaFraMDC-191
❑ 97LeaFraMDC-203
❑ 97LeaFraMDC-373
❑ 97LeaGet-3
❑ 97LeaGolS-24
❑ 97LeaKnoG-5
❑ 97LeaLeaotN-5
❑ 97LeaStaS-8
❑ 97MetUni-105
❑ 97MetUniBF-9
❑ 97MetUniML-8
❑ 97MetUniT-7
❑ 97NewPin-45
❑ 97NewPin-191
❑ 97NewPinAP-45
❑ 97NewPinAP-191
❑ 97NewPinIE-5
❑ 97NewPinKtP-18
❑ 97NewPinMC-45
❑ 97NewPinMC-191
❑ 97NewPinPP-45
❑ 97NewPinPP-191
❑ 97NewPinPP-I5A
❑ 97NewPinPP-K18
❑ 97NewPinPP-MP1
❑ 97NewPinPP-MP2
❑ 97NewPinPP-MP3
❑ 97NewPinPP-MP4
❑ 97NewPinPP-MP5
❑ 97NewPinPP-MP6
❑ 97NewPinS-MP1
❑ 97NewPinS-MP2
❑ 97NewPinS-MP3
❑ 97NewPinS-MP4
❑ 97NewPinS-MP5
❑ 97NewPinS-MP6
❑ 97Pac-339
❑ 97PacCar-31
❑ 97PacCarM-31
❑ 97PacCerCGT-10
❑ 97PacCraC-9
❑ 97PacFirD-17
❑ 97PacGolCD-31
❑ 97PacLigB-339
❑ 97PacPri-115
❑ 97PacPriGA-GA26
❑ 97PacPriGotD-GD161
❑ 97PacPriLB-115
❑ 97PacPriP-115
❑ 97PacPriSH-SH11A
❑ 97PacPriSL-SL11A
❑ 97PacSil-339
❑ 97PacTriCD-18
❑ 97Pin-103
❑ 97PinAllFP-6
❑ 97PinArtP-PP103
❑ 97PinCar-1
❑ 97PinCer-26
❑ 97PinCerCMGT-10
❑ 97PinCerCT-10
❑ 97PinCerMBla-26
❑ 97PinCerMBlu-26
❑ 97PinCerMG-26
❑ 97PinCerMR-26
❑ 97PinCerR-26
❑ 97PinEpixGO-E19
❑ 97PinEpixPE-E19
❑ 97PinFan-FF16
❑ 97PinHom-5
❑ 97PinHom-6
❑ 97PinIns-27
❑ 97PinInsC-19
❑ 97PinInsCE-27
❑ 97PinInsDD-4
❑ 97PinInsDE-27
❑ 97PinMin-7
❑ 97PinMinB-7
❑ 97PinMinCB-7
❑ 97PinMinCG-7
❑ 97PinMinCGR-7
❑ 97PinMinCN-7
❑ 97PinMinCSS-7
❑ 97PinMinG-7
❑ 97PinMinS-7
❑ 97PinMusC-103
❑ 97PinPastM-5
❑ 97PinPrePla-103
❑ 97PinPrePla-S8
❑ 97PinSha-8
❑ 97PinTeaP-5
❑ 97PinTeaP-10
❑ 97PinTotCPB-26
❑ 97PinTotCPG-26
❑ 97PinTotCPR-26
❑ 97PinX-P-16
❑ 97PinX-P-146
❑ 97PinX-PF&A-7
❑ 97PinX-PMoS-16
❑ 97PinX-PMoS-146
❑ 97PinX-PMW-7
❑ 97PinX-PMWG-7
❑ 97PinX-PMWS-7
❑ 97PinX-PSfF-47
❑ 97PinX-PSfFU-47
❑ 97PreCon-20
❑ 97Sco-22
❑ 97Sco-501
❑ 97Sco-550
❑ 97ScoAllF-16
❑ 97ScoArtPWB-22
❑ 97ScoArtPWB-501
❑ 97ScoArtPWB-550
❑ 97ScoBla-9
❑ 97ScoFra-5
❑ 97ScoFraG-5
❑ 97ScoHeaotO-22
❑ 97ScoHigZ-5
❑ 97ScoPreS-22
❑ 97ScoResC-501
❑ 97ScoResC-550
❑ 97ScoShoS-22
❑ 97ScoShoS-501
❑ 97ScoShoS-550
❑ 97ScoShoSAP-22
❑ 97ScoShoSAP-501
❑ 97ScoShoSAP-550
❑ 97ScoStaaD-13
❑ 97ScoSteS-9
❑ 97ScoTitT-2
❑ 97Sel-32
❑ 97Sel-147
❑ 97SelArtP-32
❑ 97SelArtP-147
❑ 97SelCom-32
❑ 97SelCom-147
❑ 97SelRegG-32
❑ 97SelRegG-147
❑ 97SelToootT-4
❑ 97SelToootTMB-4
❑ 97SP-95
❑ 97SPGamF-GF5
❑ 97SPInsI-16
❑ 97SPMarM-MM5
❑ 97SpoIll-112
❑ 97SpoIll-174
❑ 97SpoIllEE-112
❑ 97SpoIllEE-174
❑ 97SpoIllGS-15
❑ 97SPSpeF-5
❑ 97SPSpxF-7
❑ 97SPSPxFA-7
❑ 97SPx-30
❑ 97SPxBoufG-12
❑ 97SPxBro-30
❑ 97SPxCorotG-7
❑ 97SPxGol-30
❑ 97SPxGraF-30
❑ 97SPxSil-30
❑ 97SPxSte-30
❑ 97StaClu-31
❑ 97StaClu-383
❑ 97StaCluFR-F10
❑ 97StaCluFW-F10
❑ 97StaCluMat-31
❑ 97StaCluMOP-31
❑ 97StaCluMOP-383
❑ 97StaCluMOP-FB10
❑ 97StaCluMOP-PG18
❑ 97StaCluPG-PG18
❑ 97StrAll-50
❑ 97Stu-21
❑ 97StuHarH-10
❑ 97StuMasS-14
❑ 97StuMasS8-14
❑ 97StuPor8-7
❑ 97StuPrePG-21

❑ 97StuPrePS-21
❑ 97Top-20
❑ 97Top-104
❑ 97TopChr-9
❑ 97TopChrDD-DD8
❑ 97TopChrDDR-DD8
❑ 97TopChrJ-9
❑ 97TopChrR-9
❑ 97TopDodRotY-3
❑ 97TopGal-133
❑ 97TopGalGoH-GH7
❑ 97TopGalP-PP3
❑ 97TopGalPG-PG11
❑ 97TopGalPMS-10
❑ 97TopGalPMSSS-10
❑ 97TopGalPPI-133
❑ 97TopHobM-HM12
❑ 97TopIntF-ILM2
❑ 97TopIntFR-ILM2
❑ 97TopMem05-38
❑ 97TopScrPS-3
❑ 97TopScrPST-3
❑ 97TopSta-7
❑ 97TopSta97AS-AS6
❑ 97TopStaAM-7
❑ 97TopStaASM-ASM3
❑ 97TopSweS-SS12
❑ 97TopTeaT-TT16
❑ 97UD3-18
❑ 97UD3Marq-MA7
❑ 97Ult-223
❑ 97UltBasR-8
❑ 97UltChe-A6
❑ 97UltChe-B6
❑ 97UltDiaP-8
❑ 97UltDouT-15
❑ 97UltFamGam-5
❑ 97UltGolME-223
❑ 97UltHitM-6
❑ 97UltHRK-8
❑ 97UltPlaME-223
❑ 97UltPowP-A7
❑ 97UltPowP-B5
❑ 97UltSeaC-8
❑ 97UltStaR-6
❑ 97UltThu-9
❑ 97UltTop3-6
❑ 97UltTop3GM-6
❑ 97UppDec-95
❑ 97UppDecAG-AG20
❑ 97UppDecHC-HC13
❑ 97UppDecLDC-LD16
❑ 97UppDecMM-A6
❑ 97UppDecP-18
❑ 97UppDecPE-18
❑ 97UppDecPP-PP15
❑ 97UppDecPPJ-PP15
❑ 97UppDecRP-RP15
❑ 97UppDecSA-15
❑ 97UppDecSAG-15
❑ 97Zen-6
❑ 97Zen Z-Z-5
❑ 97Zen8x10-5
❑ 97Zen8x1D-5
❑ 97ZentheBP-5
❑ 97ZenV-2-4
❑ 98Bow-18
❑ 98BowBes-21
❑ 98BowBesAR-21
❑ 98BowBesMIF-MI20
❑ 98BowBesMIFAR-MI20
❑ 98BowBesMIFR-MI20
❑ 98BowBesR-21
❑ 98BowChr-18
❑ 98BowChrGA-18
❑ 98BowChrGAR-18
❑ 98BowChrI-18
❑ 98BowChrIR-18
❑ 98BowChrR-18
❑ 98BowChrR-35
❑ 98BowChrRR-35
❑ 98BowGolA-18
❑ 98BowInt-18
❑ 98CirThu-200
❑ 98CirThuB-15
❑ 98CirThuLA-12
❑ 98CirThuQS-9
❑ 98CirThuRav-200
❑ 98CirThuRR-12
❑ 98CirThuSupRav-200
❑ 98CirThuTB-9
❑ 98ColCho-4
❑ 98ColCho-145
❑ 98ColCho-185
❑ 98ColCho-268
❑ 98ColCho-279
❑ 98ColChoCG-4
❑ 98ColChoCtG-CG25A
❑ 98ColChoCtG-CG25B
❑ 98ColChoCtG-CG25C
❑ 98ColChoCtGExch-CG25
❑ 98ColChoCtGIW-CG25
❑ 98ColChoER-ER14
❑ 98ColChoGJ5-279
❑ 98ColChoMBH-17
❑ 98ColChoRJ-4
❑ 98ColChoRJ-145
❑ 98ColChoS'-15
❑ 98ColChoSQ-SQ44
❑ 98ColChoSQ-SQ84
❑ 98ColChoSQDouble-20
❑ 98ColChoSQHR-20
❑ 98ColChoSQSingle-20
❑ 98ColChoSQTriple-20
❑ 98CroRoy-90
❑ 98CroRoyAS-17
❑ 98CroRoyDK-13
❑ 98CroRoyFoB-14
❑ 98CroRoyFoBA-14
❑ 98CroRoyPotG-15
❑ 98DodPol-22
❑ 98DodSco-2
❑ 98DodScoP-2
❑ 98Don-31
❑ 98Don-159
❑ 98Don-371
❑ 98Don-409
❑ 98DonCol-31
❑ 98DonCol-159
❑ 98DonColE-404
❑ 98DonColE-521
❑ 98DonColL-291
❑ 98DonColL-351
❑ 98DonColP-556
❑ 98DonColP-723
❑ 98DonColS-31
❑ 98DonColS-159
❑ 98DonCruG-79
❑ 98DonCruP-79
❑ 98DonCruR-79
❑ 98DonDiaK-17
❑ 98DonDiaKC-17
❑ 98DonDom-29
❑ 98DonEli-4
❑ 98DonEli-121
❑ 98DonEliA-4
❑ 98DonEliA-121
❑ 98DonEliC-6
❑ 98DonEliI-13
❑ 98DonEliMC-6
❑ 98DonEliPN-5A
❑ 98DonEliPN-5B
❑ 98DonEliPN-5C
❑ 98DonEliPNDC-5A
❑ 98DonEliPNDC-5B
❑ 98DonEliPNDC-5C
❑ 98DonEliPNS-5A
❑ 98DonEliPNS-5B
❑ 98DonEliPNS-5C
❑ 98DonEliS-4
❑ 98DonEliS-121
❑ 98DonFANT-11
❑ 98DonFANTDC-11
❑ 98DonGolPP-31
❑ 98DonGolPP-159
❑ 98DonGolPP-371
❑ 98DonGolPP-409
❑ 98DonLonL-7
❑ 98DonPre-6
❑ 98DonPre-173
❑ 98DonPreGB-6
❑ 98DonPreGES-15
❑ 98DonPreGoB-6
❑ 98DonPreGX-15
❑ 98DonPreGXDC-15
❑ 98DonPrePM-6
❑ 98DonPreSeat-6
❑ 98DonPreSeat-173
❑ 98DonPreTP-6
❑ 98DonPreTPD-3
❑ 98DonPreTPG-6
❑ 98DonPreTPS-6
❑ 98DonPreTW-28
❑ 98DonPriCD-31
❑ 98DonPriCD-159
❑ 98DonPriCE-404
❑ 98DonPriCE-521
❑ 98DonPriCL-291
❑ 98DonPriCL-351
❑ 98DonPriCP-556
❑ 98DonPriCP-723
❑ 98DonProLO-5
❑ 98DonProLPI-8
❑ 98DonProLS-6
❑ 98DonSig-31
❑ 98DonSigP-31
❑ 98DonSilPP-31
❑ 98DonSilPP-159
❑ 98DonSilPP-371
❑ 98DonSilPP-409
❑ 98E-X2-15
❑ 98E-X2Cheap-7
❑ 98E-X2DesCoop-10
❑ 98E-X2ECFut-15
❑ 98E-X2ECNow-15
❑ 98Fin-15
❑ 98FinCen-C14
❑ 98FinCenR-C14
❑ 98FinMysF1-M2
❑ 98FinMysF1-M5
❑ 98FinMysF1-M8
❑ 98FinMysF1-M9
❑ 98FinMysF2-M13
❑ 98FinMysF2-M14
❑ 98FinMysF2-M15
❑ 98FinMysF2R-M13
❑ 98FinMysF2R-M14
❑ 98FinMysF2R-M15
❑ 98FinMysFR-M2
❑ 98FinMysFR-M5
❑ 98FinMysFR-M8
❑ 98FinMysFR-M9
❑ 98FinNo--15
❑ 98FinNo-R-15
❑ 98FinOve-A4
❑ 98FinOveR-A4
❑ 98FinPowZ-P15
❑ 98FinRef-15
❑ 98FinStaS-SS11
❑ 98FinStaSJ-5
❑ 98FinTheM-TM8
❑ 98FinTheMR-TM8
❑ 98FlaShoLeg0-17
❑ 98FlaShoLeg1-17
❑ 98FlaShoLeg2-17
❑ 98FlaShoLeg3-17
❑ 98FlaShoLegM-17
❑ 98FlaShoP1-4
❑ 98FlaShoR0-17
❑ 98FlaShoR1-17
❑ 98FlaShoR2-17
❑ 98FlaShoR3-17
❑ 98Fle-200
❑ 98Fle-334
❑ 98Fle-347
❑ 98Fle-391
❑ 98Fle-503
❑ 98FleDiaS-16
❑ 98FleDiaSCS-NNO
❑ 98FleDiaT-DT7
❑ 98FleIn TC-IC13
❑ 98FleLumC-11
❑ 98FlePowG-16
❑ 98FleVin'-32
❑ 98FleVin'-97
❑ 98FleVin'C-32
❑ 98FleVin'C-97
❑ 98FleZon-12
❑ 98HamHel-7
❑ 98KinDis-10
❑ 98Lea-92
❑ 98Lea-152
❑ 98LeaCruG-79
❑ 98LeaCruP-79
❑ 98LeaCruR-79
❑ 98LeaFraDA-92
❑ 98LeaFraDA-152
❑ 98LeaFraF-92
❑ 98LeaFraF-152
❑ 98LeaFraM-92
❑ 98LeaFraM-152
❑ 98LeaFraM-92
❑ 98LeaFraM-152
❑ 98LeaFraMDC-92
❑ 98LeaFraMDC-152
❑ 98LeaFraMDC-92
❑ 98LeaFraMDC-152
❑ 98LeaFraMZ2-92
❑ 98LeaFraMZ2-152
❑ 98LeaHeaftH-16
❑ 98LeaHeaftHS-16
❑ 98LeaRCMLHDSamp-8
❑ 98LeaRS-30
❑ 98LeaRS-144
❑ 98LeaRS-164
❑ 98LeaRS-312
❑ 98LeaRSExtM-6
❑ 98LeaRSExtMDC-6
❑ 98LeaRSGAHSamp-6
❑ 98LeaRSGreAH-6
❑ 98LeaRSGreAH-6B
❑ 98LeaRSGreAH-6C
❑ 98LeaRSGreHit-6
❑ 98LeaRSHRDerby-17
❑ 98LeaRSLHolo-30
❑ 98LeaRSLHolo-144
❑ 98LeaRSLHolo-164
❑ 98LeaRSLHolo-312
❑ 98LeaRSLMVP-15
❑ 98LeaRSLMVPPE-15
❑ 98LeaRSLong-30
❑ 98LeaRSLong-144
❑ 98LeaRSLong-164
❑ 98LeaRSLong-312
❑ 98LeaRSMLHD-8
❑ 98LeaRSMLHD-8B
❑ 98LeaRSMLHD-8C
❑ 98LeaRTrue-30
❑ 98LeaRTrue-144
❑ 98LeaRTrue-164
❑ 98LeaRTrue-312
❑ 98LeaStaS-4
❑ 98LeaStaSDC-4
❑ 98MetUni-106
❑ 98MetUni-212
❑ 98MetUniAT-14
❑ 98MetUniPMG-106
❑ 98MetUniPMG-212
❑ 98MetUniPP-11
❑ 98MetUniT-14
❑ 98MetUniUL-14
❑ 98Pac-339
❑ 98PacAur-149
❑ 98PacAurCube-10
❑ 98PacAurHC-10
❑ 98PacAurKotML-6
❑ 98PacAurODLC-10
❑ 98PacAurPF-31
❑ 98PacAurPFC-31
❑ 98PacAurPFPB-31
❑ 98PacAurPFR-31
❑ 98PacAurPFS-31
❑ 98PacCraCh-6
❑ 98PacGolCDC-21
❑ 98PacHomRH-13
❑ 98PacInCage-10
❑ 98PacInv-112
❑ 98PacInvCCDB-6
❑ 98PacInvCCG-6
❑ 98PacInvCCG-6
❑ 98PacInvCCLB-6
❑ 98PacInvCCP-6
❑ 98PacInvCCR-6
❑ 98PacInvGems-172
❑ 98PacInvInt-13N
❑ 98PacInvMiT-10
❑ 98PacInvPBlue-112
❑ 98PacInvPhoto-6
❑ 98PacInvSilv-112
❑ 98PacInvTeam-14
❑ 98PacOme-100
❑ 98PacOmeEP-17
❑ 98PacOmeEP1o1-17
❑ 98PacOmeFTF-3
❑ 98PacOmeOnIns-32
❑ 98PacOmeP-18
❑ 98PacOmeR-100
❑ 98PacOnl-488A
❑ 98PacOnl-488B
❑ 98PacOnl-494
❑ 98PacOnlR-488A
❑ 98PacOnlR-488B
❑ 98PacOnlR-494
❑ 98PacOnlWC-488A
❑ 98PacOnlWC-488B
❑ 98PacOnlWC-494
❑ 98PacPar-181
❑ 98PacParC-181
❑ 98PacParCB-4
❑ 98PacParCBPP-4
❑ 98PacParFC-10
❑ 98PacParG-181
❑ 98PacParHS-181
❑ 98PacParI-33
❑ 98PacParPB-181
❑ 98PacParR-181
❑ 98PacParSD-11
❑ 98PacParTC-22
❑ 98PacPlaB-339
❑ 98PacRedT-339
❑ 98PacSil-339
❑ 98PacTeaC-21
❑ 98Pin-7
❑ 98PinArtP-PP7
❑ 98PinEpixGE-E19
❑ 98PinEpixGP-E19
❑ 98PinEpixME-E19
❑ 98PinEpixMO-E19
❑ 98PinEpixMP-E19
❑ 98PinEpixPO-E19
❑ 98PinEpixPP-E19
❑ 98PinHitIH-3
❑ 98PinHitIHS-3
❑ 98PinIns-28
❑ 98PinInsBtN-5
❑ 98PinInsC-15
❑ 98PinInsCE-28
❑ 98PinInsCG-15
❑ 98PinInsDE-28
❑ 98PinInsSG-1AB
❑ 98PinInsSG-1CD
❑ 98PinInsSG-7AB
❑ 98PinInsSG-7CD
❑ 98PinInsSG-17AB
❑ 98PinInsSG-17CD
❑ 98PinInsSGS-1AB
❑ 98PinInsSGS-1CD
❑ 98PinInsSGS-7AB
❑ 98PinInsSGS-7CD
❑ 98PinInsSGS-17AB
❑ 98PinInsSGS-17CD
❑ 98PinMinB-17
❑ 98PinMinCB-17
❑ 98PinMinCBAP-17
❑ 98PinMinCGP-17
❑ 98PinMinCGPAP-17
❑ 98PinMinCN-17
❑ 98PinMinCNAP-17
❑ 98PinMinCSGR-17
❑ 98PinMinDC-17
❑ 98PinMinG-17
❑ 98PinMinMCSS-17
❑ 98PinMinS-17
❑ 98PinMinS-17
❑ 98PinMusC-PP7
❑ 98PinPer-6
❑ 98PinPer-144
❑ 98PinPerBB-3
❑ 98PinPerBBSamp-3
❑ 98PinPerBBSO-3
❑ 98PinPerLP-20
❑ 98PinPerPP-6
❑ 98PinPerPP-144
❑ 98PinPerPT-6
❑ 98PinPerSftF-44
❑ 98PinPerSftFShop-8
❑ 98PinPlu-33
❑ 98PinPlu-190
❑ 98PinPlu-195
❑ 98PinPluAE-19
❑ 98PinPluAEE-19
❑ 98PinPluAEP-19
❑ 98PinPluAP-PP18
❑ 98PinPluGAP-PP18
❑ 98PinPluLM-16
❑ 98PinPluMAP-PP18
❑ 98PinPluPieGame-6
❑ 98PinPluSamp-33
❑ 98PinPluTP-1
❑ 98PinPluTPG-1
❑ 98PinPluTPM-1
❑ 98PinPluY-12
❑ 98PinPowPJ-17
❑ 98PinPowPJS-17
❑ 98PinPreP-7
❑ 98PinPreP-E19
❑ 98PinPreP-H3
❑ 98PinSna-LAD1
❑ 98PinSna-LAD17
❑ 98PinSnaS-5
❑ 98PreCon-8
❑ 98Revo-96
❑ 98RevoFP-18
❑ 98RevoMLI-8
❑ 98RevoPTP-18
❑ 98RevoShow-33
❑ 98RevoSS-96
❑ 98Sco-24
❑ 98Sco-259
❑ 98ScoAllST-1
❑ 98ScoComP-5A
❑ 98ScoComP-5B
❑ 98ScoComP-5C
❑ 98ScoComPG-5A
❑ 98ScoComPG-5B
❑ 98ScoComPG-5C
❑ 98ScoEpix-E19
❑ 98ScoFirP-8
❑ 98ScoLoaL-LL5
❑ 98ScoRT-32
❑ 98ScoRT-263
❑ 98ScoRTSS-PP32
❑ 98ScoRTSS-PP156
❑ 98ScoRTSSAP-PP32
❑ 98ScoRTSSAP-PP156
❑ 98ScoRTSSAP1-PP32
❑ 98ScoRTSSAP1-PP156
❑ 98ScoRTStarGaz-6
❑ 98ScoSam-24
❑ 98ScoSS-PP120
❑ 98ScoSSAP-PP120
❑ 98SkyDugA-22
❑ 98SkyDugA-125
❑ 98SkyDugADH-DH13
❑ 98SkyDugAG-G6
❑ 98SkyDugAIA-22
❑ 98SkyDugAIA-125
❑ 98SP Aut-95
❑ 98SP Aut-SD40
❑ 98SP AutSD-SD40
❑ 98SP AutSDT-SD40
❑ 98SpoIll-101
❑ 98SpoIll-145
❑ 98SpoIllC-C1
❑ 98SpoIllEE-101
❑ 98SpoIllEE-145
❑ 98SpoIllFE-101
❑ 98SpoIllFE-145
❑ 98SpoIllODMP-OD15
❑ 98SpoIllTaN-121
❑ 98SpoIllTaNAotG-AG3
❑ 98SpoIllTaNEE-121
❑ 98SpoIllTaNGS-11
❑ 98SpoIllTaNRtC-RC8
❑ 98SpoIllWSF-117
❑ 98SpoIllWSFEE-117
❑ 98SpoIllWSFFE-117
❑ 98SpoIllWSFRJP-6
❑ 98SPxFin-31
❑ 98SPxFin-90
❑ 98SPxFin-157
❑ 98SPxFin-175
❑ 98SPxFin-230
❑ 98SPxFin-275
❑ 98SPxFin-340
❑ 98SPxFin-356
❑ 98SPxFinR-31
❑ 98SPxFinR-90
❑ 98SPxFinR-157
❑ 98SPxFinR-175
❑ 98SPxFinR-230
❑ 98SPxFinR-275
❑ 98SPxFinR-340
❑ 98SPxFinR-356
❑ 98SPxFinS-31
❑ 98SPxFinS-90
❑ 98SPxFinS-157
❑ 98SPxFinS-175
❑ 98SPxFinS-230
❑ 98SPxFinS-275
❑ 98SPxFinS-340
❑ 98SPxFinS-356
❑ 98StaCluBP-BP6
❑ 98StaCluFDI-337
❑ 98StaCluI-337
❑ 98StaCluNC-NC6
❑ 98StaCluOneK-337
❑ 98StaCluPP-337
❑ 98StaCluPWP-P9
❑ 98StaCluRC-RC3
❑ 98StaCluTIII-T6A
❑ 98StaCluTIII-T10A
❑ 98StaCluTLme-T6A
❑ 98StaCluTLme-T10A
❑ 98StaCluTLmo-T6A
❑ 98StaCluTLmo-T10A
❑ 98Stu-62
❑ 98Stu-CL2
❑ 98StuFF-8
❑ 98StuFFDC-8
❑ 98StuGPP-62
❑ 98StuGPP-CL2
❑ 98StuHitPar-3
❑ 98StuMast-15
❑ 98StuPor8x10-9
❑ 98StuPor8x10GP-9
❑ 98StuSPP-62
❑ 98StuSPP-CL2
❑ 98Top-100
❑ 98Top-479
❑ 98TopChr-100
❑ 98TopChr-479
❑ 98TopChrC9-C2
❑ 98TopChrC9R-C2
❑ 98TopChrHB-HB13
❑ 98TopChrHBR-HB13

❑ 98TopChrR-100
❑ 98TopChrR-479
❑ 98TopClo9-C2
❑ 98TopDevR-100
❑ 98TopDevR-479
❑ 98TopDia-100
❑ 98TopDia-479
❑ 98TopEtc-ES6
❑ 98TopFocP-FP12
❑ 98TopFruR-5
❑ 98TopGal-79
❑ 98TopGalGoH-GH8
❑ 98TopGalGoHJ-GH8
❑ 98TopGalGP-79
❑ 98TopGalOPP-79
❑ 98TopGalPG-PG6
❑ 98TopGalPPI-79
❑ 98TopGalPPIA-79
❑ 98TopGolLabC1-60
❑ 98TopGolLabC1B-60
❑ 98TopGolLabC1One-60
❑ 98TopGolLabC1R-60
❑ 98TopGolLabC2-60
❑ 98TopGolLabC2B-60
❑ 98TopGolLabC2One-60
❑ 98TopGolLabC2R-60
❑ 98TopGolLabC3-60
❑ 98TopGolLabC3B-60
❑ 98TopGolLabC3One-60
❑ 98TopGolLabC3R-60
❑ 98TopGolLP-PP3
❑ 98TopHal-HB13
❑ 98TopMiniC-100
❑ 98TopMiniC-479
❑ 98TopMysF-ILM13
❑ 98TopMysFB-M15
❑ 98TopMysFB-M15
❑ 98TopMysFBR-M15
❑ 98TopMysFBR-M15
❑ 98TopMysFR-ILM13
❑ 98TopOpeD-49
❑ 98TopPre-PP6
❑ 98TopSta-50
❑ 98TopSta'S-32
❑ 98TopSta'SGH-32
❑ 98TopStaB-50
❑ 98TopStaG-50
❑ 98TopStaGR-50
❑ 98TopStaLB-L6
❑ 98TopStaLG-L6
❑ 98TopStaLGR-L6
❑ 98TopStaLS-L6
❑ 98TopStaPre-PP1
❑ 98TopStaS-50
❑ 98TopStaSteG-32
❑ 98TopSup-11
❑ 98TopSup-11
❑ 98TopTek-86
❑ 98TopTekD-86
❑ 98UD3-40
❑ 98UD3-130
❑ 98UD3-220
❑ 98UD3DieCut-40
❑ 98UD3DieCut-130
❑ 98UD3DieCut-220
❑ 98UD3PCBlowup-40
❑ 98Ult-53
❑ 98Ult-485
❑ 98Ult-501
❑ 98UltArtT-9
❑ 98UltBigS-14
❑ 98UltDiaI-5
❑ 98UltDiaP-9
❑ 98UltDouT-8
❑ 98UltFalC-9
❑ 98UltGolM-53
❑ 98UltGolM-485
❑ 98UltGolM-501
❑ 98UltMas-53
❑ 98UltMas-485
❑ 98UltMas-501
❑ 98UltMilM-11
❑ 98UltNot-14
❑ 98UltPlaM-53
❑ 98UltPlaM-485
❑ 98UltPlaM-501
❑ 98UltPowP-5
❑ 98UltPriL-9
❑ 98UltTicS-5
❑ 98UltTop3-14
❑ 98UltWinN-15
❑ 98UppDec-13
❑ 98UppDec-149
❑ 98UppDec-400
❑ 98UppDec-453
❑ 98UppDec-537
❑ 98UppDec-605
❑ 98UppDec-681
❑ 98UppDec-681A
❑ 98UppDec10AP-14
❑ 98UppDec1APR-14
❑ 98UppDec5x7-400
❑ 98UppDec5x7-605
❑ 98UppDecAC-AS20
❑ 98UppDecAG-AG13
❑ 98UppDecAGDC-AG13
❑ 98UppDecCD-CD28
❑ 98UppDecNP-NP35
❑ 98UppDecPN-PN8
❑ 98UppDecPN-PN9
❑ 98UppDecPN-PN10
❑ 98UppDecPN-PN11
❑ 98UppDecPN-PN12
❑ 98UppDecPN-PN13
❑ 98UppDecPN-PN14
❑ 98UppDecR-63
❑ 98UppDecR-28
❑ 98UppDecRBBop-BB28
❑ 98UppDecRGKoG-G22
❑ 98UppDecRQL-Q17
❑ 98UppDecRTC-TC44
❑ 98UppDecSF-6
❑ 98UppDecSFPD-PZ4
❑ 98UppDecSFPZOB-PZ3
❑ 98UppDecSFPZPD-PZ3
❑ 98UppDecSFPZSX-PZ4
❑ 98UppDecTMT-15
❑ 98UppDecTMTG-15
❑ 98UppDecU-10
❑ 98Zen-14
❑ 98Zen5 xx7-21
❑ 98Zen5x7GoldImp-21
❑ 98Zen5x7Imp-21
❑ 98ZenEpi-E19
❑ 98ZenRaitB-5
❑ 98ZenSampL-Z21
❑ 98ZenSamS-14
❑ 98ZenZ-G-14
❑ 98ZenZ-S-14
❑ 98ZenZ-T-3
❑ 98ZenZ-T5x7-3
❑ 98ZenZ-TG-3
❑ 99199Fin-95
❑ 99199Fin-114
❑ 99199Fin-257
❑ 99AllMysFR-M28
❑ 99AurComP-6A
❑ 99AurComP-6B
❑ 99AurKinotML-6
❑ 99AurOn DL-11
❑ 99AurPenF-11
❑ 99AurPenF-11
❑ 99AurPenFB-11
❑ 99AurPenFS-11
❑ 99AurSty-11
❑ 99Bow-250
❑ 99BowBes-31
❑ 99BowBes-100
❑ 99BowBesAR-31
❑ 99BowBesAR-100
❑ 99BowBesFBMI-FB7
❑ 99BowBesFBMII-FB7
❑ 99BowBesFBMIII-FB7
❑ 99BowBesR-31
❑ 99BowBesR-100
❑ 99BowChrDA-DA10
❑ 99BowChrDAR-DA10
❑ 99BowEarR-ER1
❑ 99BowGol-250
❑ 99BowInt-250
❑ 99BowLatB-LB1
❑ 99CroRoyB-93
❑ 99CroRoyC2-5
❑ 99CroRoyCCDB-5
❑ 99CroRoyCCG-5
❑ 99CroRoyCCG-5
❑ 99CroRoyCCLB-5
❑ 99CroRoyCCP-5
❑ 99CroRoyCCP-5
❑ 99CroRoyCCR-5
❑ 99CroRoyL-93
❑ 99CroRoyLL-6
❑ 99CroRoyMP-9
❑ 99CroRoyOD-93
❑ 99CroRoyPotG-13
❑ 99CroRoyPP-13
❑ 99CroRoyPPN-13
❑ 99DumSet-154
❑ 99DumSet-ER1
❑ 99E-X Cen-3
❑ 99E-X CenECFut-3
❑ 99E-X CenECNow-3
❑ 99E-XCenFoF'-17
❑ 99FinCom-C1
❑ 99FinComDualR-C1
❑ 99FinFraR-FR6
❑ 99FinFraRR-FR6
❑ 99FinGolRef-95
❑ 99FinGolRef-114
❑ 99FinGolRef-257
❑ 99FinMil-M20
❑ 99FinProF-PF4
❑ 99FinProF-PF22
❑ 99FinRef-95
❑ 99FinRef-114
❑ 99FinRef-257
❑ 99FinSplS-SS9
❑ 99FinSplSDR-SS9
❑ 99FinTeaFB-TF10
❑ 99FinTeaFBR-TF10
❑ 99FinTeaFG-TF10
❑ 99FinTeaFGR-TF10
❑ 99FinTeaFR-TF10
❑ 99FinTeaFRR-TF10
❑ 99FlaShoLeg1-13
❑ 99FlaShoLeg2-13
❑ 99FlaShoLeg3-13
❑ 99FlaShoLegM1-13
❑ 99FlaShoLegM2-13
❑ 99FlaShoLegM3-13
❑ 99FlaShoMoG-10
❑ 99FlaShoR1-13
❑ 99FlaShoR2-13
❑ 99FlaShoR3-13
❑ 99Fle-41
❑ 99FleBri-30
❑ 99FleBri2G-30
❑ 99FleBriBlu-30
❑ 99FleBriGol-30
❑ 99FleBriSS-7
❑ 99FleBriSSP-7
❑ 99FleDatWD-7
❑ 99FleGoiYar-11
❑ 99FleGolM-10
❑ 99FleMys-98
❑ 99FleMys-154
❑ 99FleMysE-6
❑ 99FleMysG-98
❑ 99FleMysM-98
❑ 99FleMysM-154
❑ 99FleSta9-41
❑ 99FleVin'-41
❑ 99FleWarT-41
❑ 99HomHer-3
❑ 99KinDis-29
❑ 99MetUni-195
❑ 99MetUni-280
❑ 99MetUniBWTW-9
❑ 99MetUniDS-11
❑ 99MetUniGM-195
❑ 99MetUniGM-280
❑ 99MetUniL-1
❑ 99MetUniPM-11
❑ 99MetUniPMG-195
❑ 99MetUniPMG-280
❑ 99MetUniSamp-NNOA
❑ 99MetUniSamp-NNO
❑ 99Pac-286
❑ 99Pac-286A
❑ 99PacAur-123
❑ 99PacAurOD-123
❑ 99PacCroC-184
❑ 99PacCroCITC-10
❑ 99PacCroCPB-184
❑ 99PacCroCTC-19
❑ 99PacCroCTM-12
❑ 99PacDynaD-16
❑ 99PacDynaDT-16
❑ 99PacGolCDC-31
❑ 99PacInv-97
❑ 99PacInvDM-5
❑ 99PacInvFP-10
❑ 99PacInvGotG-5
❑ 99PacInvOD-97
❑ 99PacInvPB-97
❑ 99PacInvSF-10
❑ 99PacInvSF-10B
❑ 99PacInvSH-10
❑ 99PacInvSH-10B
❑ 99PacInvTA-10
❑ 99PacOme-156
❑ 99PacOme5T-22
❑ 99PacOme5TT-22
❑ 99PacOmeC-156
❑ 99PacOmeDD-5
❑ 99PacOmeDM-20
❑ 99PacOmeEP-10
❑ 99PacOmeEP1o1-10
❑ 99PacOmeG-156
❑ 99PacOmeH'-12
❑ 99PacOmePB-156
❑ 99PacPar-155
❑ 99PacParC-155
❑ 99PacParCB-6
❑ 99PacParCBPP-6
❑ 99PacParFC-11
❑ 99PacParG-155
❑ 99PacParHoloGold-155
❑ 99PacParHS-155
❑ 99PacParOD-155
❑ 99PacParPB-21
❑ 99PacParPB-155
❑ 99PacParRed-155
❑ 99PacParTC-19
❑ 99PacPlaB-286
❑ 99PacPlaB-286A
❑ 99PacPri-96
❑ 99PacPriAotG-12
❑ 99PacPriDG-12
❑ 99PacPriHB-96
❑ 99PacPriHG-96
❑ 99PacPriHM-96
❑ 99PacPriHP-96
❑ 99PacPriRed-96
❑ 99PacPriS-13
❑ 99PacPriS206-13
❑ 99PacPriS206R-13
❑ 99PacPriSE-13
❑ 99PacPriSP-13
❑ 99PacPriSP-13
❑ 99PacPriSV-13
❑ 99PacRed-286
❑ 99PacRed-286A
❑ 99PacTeaC-25
❑ 99PacTim-18
❑ 99Pin-20
❑ 99Rev-91
❑ 99RevDiaL-20
❑ 99RevFouP-11
❑ 99RevMLBIcon-5
❑ 99RevPremDate-91
❑ 99RevRet-91
❑ 99RevShaSS-91
❑ 99RevThoitS-10
❑ 99RevTri-6
❑ 99RevTri-6
❑ 99SkyMolM-137
❑ 99SkyMolMF-37
❑ 99SkyMolMFS-37
❑ 99SkyMolMFT-37
❑ 99SkyMolMX-137
❑ 99SkyPre-114
❑ 99SkyPre-292
❑ 99SkyPreIN-5
❑ 99SkyPreLB-5
❑ 99SkyPreR-114
❑ 99SkyPreR-292
❑ 99SkyPreSB-11
❑ 99SkyPreSotG-13
❑ 99SkyThu-254
❑ 99SkyThuDial1-D6
❑ 99SkyThuHip-H9
❑ 99SkyThuInD-ID7
❑ 99SkyThuRant-254
❑ 99SkyThuRave-254
❑ 99SkyThuTur-TC6
❑ 99SP Aut-54
❑ 99SP Aut-134
❑ 99SP AutEF-E20
❑ 99SP AutHRC-HR29
❑ 99SP AutR-R20
❑ 99SP SigAuto-MP
❑ 99SP SigAutoG-MP
❑ 99SPAutHRCDC-HR29
❑ 99SpoIll-76
❑ 99SpoIllH-18
❑ 99SPSig-11
❑ 99SPx-54
❑ 99SPxDom-FB12
❑ 99SPxFinR-54
❑ 99SPxFinS-54
❑ 99SPxPowE-PE19
❑ 99SPxPreS-PS13
❑ 99SPxStaF-SF17
❑ 99StaClu-275
❑ 99StaCluC-SCC13
❑ 99StaCluCR-SCC13
❑ 99StaCluFDI-275
❑ 99StaCluNC-NC12
❑ 99StaCluOoaK-275
❑ 99StaCluPP-275
❑ 99ThuSkySupR-254
❑ 99Top-340
❑ 99Top-459
❑ 99TopAllMF-M28
❑ 99TopBlaLC1-1
❑ 99TopBlaLC2-1
❑ 99TopBlaLC3-1
❑ 99TopChr-340
❑ 99TopChr-459
❑ 99TopChrF1-FF10
❑ 99TopChrF1R-FF10
❑ 99TopChrLotD-LD14
❑ 99TopChrLotDR-LD14
❑ 99TopChrR-340
❑ 99TopChrR-459
❑ 99TopChrRN-RN2
❑ 99TopChrRNR-RN2
❑ 99TopGal-14
❑ 99TopGal-110
❑ 99TopGalE-E19
❑ 99TopGalGoH-GH4
❑ 99TopGalHer-TH17
❑ 99TopGalHerP-TH17
❑ 99TopGalPP-14
❑ 99TopGalPP-110
❑ 99TopGalPPI-14
❑ 99TopGalPPI-110
❑ 99TopGolL-1
❑ 99TopGolLC1-1
❑ 99TopGolLC2-1
❑ 99TopGolLOtO-1
❑ 99TopLorotD-LD14
❑ 99TopMVPP-340
❑ 99TopMVPP-459
❑ 99TopOpeD-139
❑ 99TopOver-B4
❑ 99TopPowB-PB10
❑ 99TopPowBR-PB10
❑ 99TopRecN-RN2
❑ 99TopRecNG-RN2
❑ 99TopRedLC1-1
❑ 99TopRedLC2-1
❑ 99TopRedLC3-1
❑ 99TopSta-3
❑ 99TopSta-175
❑ 99TopSta'S-40
❑ 99TopSta'SG-40
❑ 99TopSta'SGDH-40
❑ 99TopSta1Foil-3
❑ 99TopSta2Foil-3
❑ 99TopSta3Foil-3
❑ 99TopSta4Foil-3
❑ 99TopStaFoil-3
❑ 99TopStaFoil-175
❑ 99TopStaFS-3
❑ 99TopStaOS-3
❑ 99TopStaTS-3
❑ 99TopStaTS-3
❑ 99TopSupC-25
❑ 99TopSupCR-25
❑ 99TopTek-15A
❑ 99TopTek-15B
❑ 99TopTekG-15A
❑ 99TopTekG-15B
❑ 99UD Cho-111
❑ 99UD ChoMBH-B17
❑ 99UD ChoPCR-111
❑ 99UD ChoS-6
❑ 99UD ChoSD-6
❑ 99UD ChoSHR-6
❑ 99UD ChoST-6
❑ 99UD ChoYW-Y19
❑ 99UD Ion-39
❑ 99UD Ion-80
❑ 99UD IonC-C5
❑ 99UD IonH-HG5
❑ 99UD IonH-H5
❑ 99UD IonN-N5
❑ 99UD IonR-39
❑ 99UD IonR-80
❑ 99UD IonWZ-WZ5
❑ 99UDHolo-36
❑ 99UDHoloAUsome-36
❑ 99UDHoloLau-L7
❑ 99UDHoloLauG-L7
❑ 99UDHoloStar-S7
❑ 99UDHoloStarG-S7
❑ 99Ult-65
❑ 99Ult-222
❑ 99UltDamI-11
❑ 99UltDiaP-5
❑ 99UltGolM-65
❑ 99UltGolM-222
❑ 99UltMas-65
❑ 99UltMas-222
❑ 99UltPlaM-65
❑ 99UltPlaM-222
❑ 99UltRBIK-15
❑ 99UltTheBook-15
❑ 99UltThu-12
❑ 99UppDec-151
❑ 99UppDec-525
❑ 99UppDec10AT-X1
❑ 99UppDec10ATD-X1
❑ 99UppDec10ATHR-X1
❑ 99UppDec10ATT-X1
❑ 99UppDecBD-52
❑ 99UppDecBDD-52
❑ 99UppDecBDDom-D13
❑ 99UppDecBDDomE-D13
❑ 99UppDecBDMN-M9
❑ 99UppDecBDMNE-M9
❑ 99UppDecBDQ-52
❑ 99UppDecBDT-52
❑ 99UppDecCf7-7
❑ 99UppDecCf7-C7
❑ 99UppDecCf7Cf7P-C7
❑ 99UppDecCf7LL-L14
❑ 99UppDecCf7SftF-S14
❑ 99UppDecCL-59
❑ 99UppDecCLCC-59
❑ 99UppDecCLM-C58
❑ 99UppDecCo7CE-7
❑ 99UppDecE-56
❑ 99UppDecE-147
❑ 99UppDecE-168
❑ 99UppDecE2C-2K3
❑ 99UppDecEDF-D9
❑ 99UppDecEDFFXG-D9
❑ 99UppDecEFXG-56
❑ 99UppDecEFXG-147
❑ 99UppDecEFXG-168
❑ 99UppDecEL1-151
❑ 99UppDecEL1-525
❑ 99UppDecEL2-151
❑ 99UppDecEL2-525
❑ 99UppDecEPE-P17
❑ 99UppDecF-F16
❑ 99UppDecFD-F16
❑ 99UppDecFQ-F16
❑ 99UppDecFT-F16
❑ 99UppDecGJ-MP
❑ 99UppDecIP-I18
❑ 99UppDecIPD-I18
❑ 99UppDecIPHR-I18
❑ 99UppDecIPT-I18
❑ 99UppDecM-130
❑ 99UppDecM-P11
❑ 99UppDecMD-D4
❑ 99UppDecMGS-130
❑ 99UppDecMGUS-GUMP
❑ 99UppDecMHFS-130
❑ 99UppDecMP-130
❑ 99UppDecMSS-130
❑ 99UppDecMST-T7
❑ 99UppDecMST-S11
❑ 99UppDecO-41
❑ 99UppDecO-89
❑ 99UppDecOAPoH-MP
❑ 99UppDecOMP-S1
❑ 99UppDecOSO-41
❑ 99UppDecOSO-89
❑ 99UppDecOWP-R18
❑ 99UppDecR-52
❑ 99UppDecRDR-D9
❑ 99UppDecRDRL2-D9
❑ 99UppDecRG-52
❑ 99UppDecRL-5
❑ 99UppDecROSS-S11
❑ 99UppDecROSS-S11
❑ 99UppDecRP-52
❑ 99UppDecRTA-T8
❑ 99UppDecRTAL2-T8
❑ 99UppDecTE-T15
❑ 99UppDecTED-T15
❑ 99UppDecTEQ-T15
❑ 99UppDecTET-T15
❑ 99UppDecVtaT-V17
❑ 99UppDecVtaTD-V17
❑ 99UppDecVtaTQ-V17
❑ 99UppDecVtaTT-V17
❑ 99UppDecWY-W21
❑ 99UppDecWYD-W21
❑ 99UppDecWYHR-W21
❑ 99UppDecWYT-W21
❑ 99Vic-251
❑ 99Vic-252
❑ 99Vic-458

Picano, John
❑ 92WesPalBEC-29

Picciolo, Dustin
❑ 87SpoIndP-25

Picciolo, Rob
❑ 76TucTorCa-1
❑ 76TusTorCr-9

❑ 78Top-528
❑ 79Top-378
❑ 80Top-158
❑ 81A'sGraG-8
❑ 81Don-357A
❑ 81Don-357B
❑ 81Fle-582
❑ 81Top-604
❑ 82A'sGraG-14
❑ 82Don-465
❑ 82Fle-106
❑ 82Top-293
❑ 82TopTra-89T
❑ 83BrePol-8
❑ 83Don-456
❑ 83Top-476
❑ 84AngSmo-22
❑ 84Don-455
❑ 84Nes792-88
❑ 84Top-88
❑ 84TopTif-88
❑ 84TopTra-94T
❑ 84TopTraT-94T
❑ 85A'sMot-13
❑ 85Top-756
❑ 85TopTif-756
❑ 85TopTifT-90T
❑ 85TopTra-90T
❑ 86Don-497
❑ 86OPC-3
❑ 86SpoIndC-177
❑ 86Top-672
❑ 86TopTif-672
❑ 87LasVegSP-26
❑ 87SpoIndP-26
❑ 91PadSmo-26
❑ 92PadMot-27
❑ 92PadPolD-15
❑ 92PadPolD-28
❑ 92PadSmo-23
❑ 93PadMot-28
❑ 94BreMilB-164
❑ 94PadMot-28
❑ 95PadMot-28
❑ 96PadMot-28
❑ 98PadMot-28

Picciuto, Nick
❑ 77TCMTheWY-16

Pichardo, Francisco
❑ 90EliTwiS-18
❑ 90KenTwiB-12
❑ 90KenTwiP-2309
❑ 90KenTwiS-19

Pichardo, Gilberto
❑ 98ButCopKG-27

Pichardo, Hipolito
❑ 90BasCitRS-19
❑ 91Cla/Bes-296
❑ 91LinDriAA-413
❑ 91MemChiLD-413
❑ 91MemChiP-650
❑ 92DonRoo-95
❑ 92FleUpd-32
❑ 92ScoRoo-103T
❑ 92TopTra-89T
❑ 92TopTraG-89T
❑ 93Don-571
❑ 93Fle-246
❑ 93LimRocDWB-128
❑ 93OPC-390
❑ 93PacSpa-493
❑ 93PacSpaPl-18
❑ 93Pin-450
❑ 93RoyPol-24
❑ 93RoyStaC-8
❑ 93Sco-336
❑ 93Sel-312
❑ 93StaClu-211
❑ 93StaCluFDI-211
❑ 93StaCluMOP-211
❑ 93Top-349
❑ 93TopGol-349
❑ 93TopInaM-349
❑ 93TopInaR-349
❑ 93TopMic-349
❑ 93Toy-89
❑ 93Ult-567
❑ 93UppDec-72
❑ 93UppDecGold-72
❑ 94ColC-231
❑ 94ColChoGS-231
❑ 94ColChoSS-231
❑ 94Don-391
❑ 94Fin-194
❑ 94FinRef-194
❑ 94Fle-171
❑ 94Lea-327
❑ 94Pac-299
❑ 94Pin-275
❑ 94PinArtP-275
❑ 94PinMusC-275
❑ 94Sco-218
❑ 94ScoGolR-218
❑ 94StaClu-223
❑ 94StaCluFDI-223
❑ 94StaCluGR-223
❑ 94StaCluMOP-223
❑ 94Top-482
❑ 94TopGol-482
❑ 94TopSpa-482
❑ 94Ult-71
❑ 95Don-376
❑ 95DonPreP-376
❑ 95Fle-171
❑ 95Pac-211
❑ 95StaClu-55
❑ 95StaCluFDI-55
❑ 95StaCluMOP-55
❑ 95StaCluSTWS-55
❑ 95Top-172
❑ 96Don-46
❑ 96DonPreP-46
❑ 96LeaSigEA-160
❑ 96Pac-327
❑ 96RoyPol-22
❑ 97Pac-108
❑ 97PacLigB-108
❑ 97PacSil-108
❑ 97RoyPol-18
❑ 97Sco-399
❑ 97ScoArtPWB-399
❑ 97ScoResC-399
❑ 97ScoShoS-399
❑ 97ScoShoSAP-399
❑ 98Pac-111
❑ 98PacOnl-349
❑ 98PacOnlR-349
❑ 98PacOnlWC-349
❑ 98PacPlaB-111
❑ 98PacRedT-111
❑ 98PacSil-111
❑ 99UppDecM-96
❑ 99UppDecMGS-96
❑ 99UppDecMHFS-96
❑ 99UppDecMSS-96
❑ 99Vic-187

Pichardo, Nelson
❑ 77WesHavYT-18

Pichardo, Sandy
❑ 92GulCoaMF-3492
❑ 93KinMetC-18
❑ 93KinMetF-3804
❑ 94CapCitBC-18
❑ 94CapCitBF-1759
❑ 94SouAtlLAF-SAL37
❑ 95StLucMTI-27
❑ 96TamYanY-20

Piche, Ron
❑ 61Top-61
❑ 62Top-582
❑ 63Top-179
❑ 65Top-464
❑ 76ExpRed-25
❑ 76MonExpP-24

Picinich, Val J.
❑ 20NatCarE-79
❑ 21Exh-128
❑ 21Exh-129
❑ 22E120-116
❑ 22W573-99
❑ 25Exh-67
❑ 29ExhFou-7
❑ 33Gou-118
❑ 34GouCanV-3
❑ 90DodTar-623
❑ 92ConTSN-479
❑ 93ConTSN-875

Pick, Charles
❑ 17Zee-95
❑ 18Zee-90
❑ 21Zee-79
❑ 22Zee-68
❑ 23Zee-93
❑ 24Zee-67

Pickens, Kevin
❑ 87EugEmeP-2676
❑ 89BasCitRS-21

Pickens, Ritchie
❑ 86DavLipB-17

Pickering, Calvin
❑ 96BluOriB-26
❑ 97Bes-53
❑ 97BesAutSBPP-15
❑ 97Bow-184
❑ 97BowChr-174
❑ 97BowChrI-174
❑ 97BowChrIR-174
❑ 97BowChrR-174
❑ 97BowInt-184
❑ 97DelSho-24
❑ 98Bes-86
❑ 98Bow-208
❑ 98BowBayM-25
❑ 98BowBes-199
❑ 98BowBesAR-199
❑ 98BowBesR-199
❑ 98BowChr-208
❑ 98BowChrGA-208
❑ 98BowChrGAR-208
❑ 98BowChrI-208
❑ 98BowChrIR-208
❑ 98BowChrR-208
❑ 98BowGolA-208
❑ 98BowInt-208
❑ 98EasLeaTPM-21
❑ 98FleUpd-U65
❑ 98SP MinPE-27
❑ 98SPMin-27
❑ 99199Fin-141
❑ 99BasAmeTP-82
❑ 99BasAmeTPA-35
❑ 99BasAmeTPBP-1
❑ 99BasAmeTPG-82
❑ 99BasAmeTPLM-10
❑ 99Bow-183
❑ 99BowAut-BA7
❑ 99BowBes-113
❑ 99BowBesAR-113
❑ 99BowBesR-113
❑ 99BowChr-183
❑ 99BowChrG-183
❑ 99BowChrGR-183
❑ 99BowChrI-183
❑ 99BowChrIR-183
❑ 99BowChrR-183
❑ 99BowChrSC-SC13
❑ 99BowChrSCR-SC13
❑ 99BowGol-183
❑ 99BowInt-183
❑ 99BowScoC-SC13
❑ 99FinGolRef-141
❑ 99FinRef-141
❑ 99FlaShoLeg1-75
❑ 99FlaShoLeg2-75
❑ 99FlaShoLeg3-75
❑ 99FlaShoLegM1-75
❑ 99FlaShoLegM2-75
❑ 99FlaShoLegM3-75
❑ 99FlaShoR1-75
❑ 99FlaShoR2-75
❑ 99FlaShoR3-75
❑ 99Fle-262
❑ 99FleBri-134
❑ 99FleBri2G-134
❑ 99FleBriBlu-134
❑ 99FleBriGol-134
❑ 99FleSta9-262
❑ 99FleWarT-262
❑ 99Rev-22
❑ 99RevPremDate-22
❑ 99RevRet-22
❑ 99RevShaSS-22
❑ 99SkyThu-262
❑ 99SkyThuRant-262
❑ 99SkyThuRave-262
❑ 99SkyThuUnl-U13
❑ 99SP Aut-94
❑ 99SP AutC-CP
❑ 99SP AutCG-CP
❑ 99SP SigAuto-CP
❑ 99SP SigAutoG-CP
❑ 99SP TopP-104
❑ 99SP TopPPE-104
❑ 99SpoIll-59
❑ 99SPSig-86
❑ 99SPx-86
❑ 99SPxFinR-86
❑ 99SPxFinS-86
❑ 99StaClu-168
❑ 99StaCluC-SCC38
❑ 99StaCluCR-SCC38
❑ 99StaCluFDI-168
❑ 99StaCluOoaK-168
❑ 99StaCluPP-168
❑ 99TeaBesR-9
❑ 99TeaBesRA-20
❑ 99ThuSkySupR-262
❑ 99Top-382
❑ 99TopAll-AM16
❑ 99TopChr-382
❑ 99TopChrA-AE16
❑ 99TopChrAR-AE16
❑ 99TopChrR-382
❑ 99TopMVPP-382
❑ 99UD Cho-16
❑ 99UD ChoPCR-16
❑ 99UppDec-285
❑ 99UppDecE-128
❑ 99UppDecEFXG-128
❑ 99UppDecEL1-285
❑ 99UppDecEL2-285
❑ 99UppDecM-28
❑ 99UppDecMGS-28
❑ 99UppDecMHFS-28
❑ 99UppDecMP-CP
❑ 99UppDecMSS-28
❑ 99UppDecO-80
❑ 99UppDecOSO-80
❑ 99Vic-44

Pickering, Oliver
❑ 03BreE10-117
❑ 09ColChiE-232A
❑ 09ColChiE-232B
❑ 09ColChiE-232C
❑ 09T206-455
❑ 12ColRedB-232A
❑ 12ColRedB-232B
❑ 12ColRedB-232C
❑ 12ColTinT-232A
❑ 12ColTinT-232B
❑ 12ColTinT-232C

Pickering, Urbane
❑ 25Zee-35
❑ 79RedSoxEF-14

Pickett, Antoine
❑ 87EugEmeP-2649
❑ 88ModA'sTI-28

Pickett, Bob
❑ 92WinHavRSC-19

Pickett, Danny
❑ 90ChaRaiB-18
❑ 90ChaRaiP-2033

Pickett, Eric
❑ 94StaCluDP-47
❑ 94StaCluDPFDI-47
❑ 95DanBraTI-21
❑ 96EugEmeB-20

Pickett, John
❑ 87OldJudN-399

Pickett, Rich
❑ 83LynMetT-21
❑ 84TidTidT-12

Pickett, Ricky
❑ 92BilMusF-3353
❑ 92BilMusSP-7
❑ 94ChaWheC-20
❑ 94ChaWheF-2701
❑ 95ChaLooTI-17
❑ 96PhoFirB-23
❑ 97PhoFirTI-18
❑ 98FreGriG-23

Pickett, Tony
❑ 87AppFoxP-23

Picketts, William
❑ 90SouOreAB-7
❑ 90SouOreAP-3435
❑ 91MadMusC-26
❑ 91MadMusP-2141
❑ 92RenSilSCLC-51

Pickford, Kevin
❑ 94ClaGolF-76
❑ 94WelPirC-18
❑ 94WelPirF-3495
❑ 96LynHilB-18
❑ 97CarMudC-8
❑ 98CarMudM-7

Pickich, Jeff
❑ 93WelPirC-22
❑ 93WelPirF-3358
❑ 94AugGreC-18
❑ 94AugGreF-3007

Pickle, V.H.
❑ 94DavLipB-10
❑ 95DavLipB-19

Pickler, Jeff
❑ 98TenKry-16

Pico, Brandon
❑ 92ClaDraP-107
❑ 92FroRowDP-14
❑ 92FroRowDPG-14
❑ 92FroRowDPS-14
❑ 92HunCubC-1
❑ 92HunCubF-3164
❑ 94MidLeaAF-MDW50
❑ 94PeoChiC-21
❑ 94PeoChiF-2281
❑ 96DayCubB-19

Pico, Jeff
❑ 86WinSpiP-20
❑ 87PitCubP-19
❑ 88CubDavB-41
❑ 88FleUpd-80
❑ 88FleUpdG-80
❑ 88IowCubC-3
❑ 88IowCubP-546
❑ 88PeoChiTI-25
❑ 88ScoRoo-94T
❑ 88ScoRooG-94T
❑ 88TopTra-87T
❑ 88TopTraT-87T
❑ 89CubMar-41
❑ 89Don-513
❑ 89Fle-436
❑ 89FleGlo-436
❑ 89PanSti-50
❑ 89PeoChiTI-28
❑ 89Sco-13
❑ 89Top-262
❑ 89TopTif-262
❑ 89ToyRoo-22
❑ 89UppDec-491
❑ 90CMC-82
❑ 90CubMar-15
❑ 90Don-585
❑ 90Fle-39
❑ 90FleCan-39
❑ 90IowCubC-7
❑ 90OPC-613
❑ 90PubIntS-200
❑ 90Sco-428
❑ 90Top-613
❑ 90TopTif-613
❑ 90TopTVCu-14
❑ 91Fle-428
❑ 91LinDriAAA-537
❑ 91OPC-311
❑ 91Sco-326
❑ 91TacTigLD-537
❑ 91TacTigP-2303
❑ 91Top-311
❑ 91TopDesS-311
❑ 91TopMic-311
❑ 91TopTif-311

Picollo, John
❑ 94OneYanC-17
❑ 94OneYanF-3794

Picota, Leny (Len)
❑ 87SavCarP-23
❑ 88St.PetCS-22
❑ 89ArkTraGS-18
❑ 90ArkTraGS-24
❑ 91LinDriAAA-243
❑ 91LouRedLD-243
❑ 91LouRedP-2914
❑ 92HarSenF-461
❑ 92HarSenS-296
❑ 93LinVenB-208
❑ 93OttLynF-2433
❑ 94VenLinU-239

Piechota, Al
❑ 77TCMTheWY-42

Piechowski, Tim
❑ 88JamExpP-1902

Piedra, Jorge
❑ 98GreFalDG-24

Piela, D.
❑ 88PulBraP-1765

Pieratt, Dan
❑ 91QuaCitAC-25
❑ 92QuaCitRBC-30

Pierce, Ben
❑ 87EugEmeP-2658
❑ 89AppFoxP-874
❑ 90BasCitRS-20

Pierce, Billy
❑ 47Exh-178
❑ 47PM1StaP1-163
❑ 51Bow-196
❑ 51TopBluB-45
❑ 52Bow-54
❑ 52RedMan-AL16
❑ 52StaCalL-73B
❑ 52StaCalS-87C
❑ 52Top-98
❑ 52WhiSoxHDP-6
❑ 53BowC-73
❑ 53Dor-121
❑ 53RedMan-AL16
❑ 53Top-143
❑ 54Bow-102
❑ 54RedHeaF-24
❑ 54RedMan-AL10
❑ 55Bow-214
❑ 55RobGouS-27
❑ 55RobGouW-27
❑ 56Top-160
❑ 57SwiFra-4
❑ 57Top-160
❑ 58JayPubA-15
❑ 58Top-50A
❑ 58Top-50B
❑ 58Top-334
❑ 58WhiSoxJP-8
❑ 59Baz-18
❑ 59Top-156
❑ 59Top-410
❑ 59Top-466
❑ 59Top-572
❑ 59TopVen-156
❑ 59WilSpoG-5
❑ 60Top-150
❑ 60Top-571
❑ 60TopTat-44
❑ 60TopTat-95
❑ 60TopVen-150
❑ 60WhiSoxTS-15
❑ 61Pos-21A
❑ 61Pos-21B
❑ 61Top-205
❑ 61TopStaI-126
❑ 61WhiSoxTS-12
❑ 62GiaJayP-12
❑ 62Jel-54
❑ 62Pos-54
❑ 62PosCan-54
❑ 62SalPlaC-2
❑ 62ShiPlaC-2
❑ 62Top-260
❑ 63GiaJayP-11
❑ 63Top-50
❑ 63Top-147
❑ 63Top-331
❑ 64Top-222
❑ 64TopVen-222
❑ 76ChiGre-16
❑ 76WhiSoxTAG-8
❑ 77GalGloG-30
❑ 79TCM50-16
❑ 80MarExh-22
❑ 80WhiSoxGT-5
❑ 81Gia196T-32
❑ 81WhiSox1T-29
❑ 83TopRep5-98
❑ 83YanYealT-2
❑ 85WhiSoxC-46
❑ 88WhiSoxC-22
❑ 89PacLegI-134
❑ 89SweBasG-57
❑ 90PacLeg-82
❑ 91TopArc1-143
❑ 92ActPacA-38
❑ 92BazQua5A-16
❑ 94UppDecAH-133
❑ 94UppDecAH1-133

Pierce, Brett
❑ 97EugEmeB-23

Pierce, Chris
❑ 86PriWilPP-19

Pierce, Dominic
❑ 88ButCopKSP-16
❑ 89GasRanP-1001
❑ 89GasRanS-18
❑ 89Sta-38

Pierce, Don Diego
❑ 82WauTimF-24

Pierce, Ed (Eddie)
❑ 89EugEmeB-9
❑ 91LinDriAA-414
❑ 91MemChiLD-414
❑ 91MemChiP-651
❑ 92MemChiF-2418
❑ 92MemChiS-442
❑ 92SkyAA F-187
❑ 93Don-147
❑ 93Fle-623
❑ 93MemChiF-375
❑ 93Top-803
❑ 93TopGol-803
❑ 93TopInaM-803
❑ 93TopInaR-803
❑ 93TopMic-803
❑ 94MemChiF-358

Pierce, George
❑ 15SpoNewM-138

Pierce, Jeff
❑ 91UtiBluSC-13

❑ 91UtiBluSP-3255
❑ 92MidLeaATI-32
❑ 92SouBenWSC-5
❑ 92SouBenWSF-175
❑ 93BirBarF-1192
❑ 93LinVenB-224
❑ 94ExcFS7-39
❑ 94NewBriRSF-647
Pierce, Jim
❑ 85CloHSS-34
Pierce, Kirk
❑ 95BatCliTI-26
❑ 96PieBolWB-20
❑ 97ClePhi-15
❑ 98ReaPhiM-4
❑ 98ReaPhiUM-17
Pierce, L. Jack
❑ 75DetTigP-25
❑ 76OPC-162
❑ 76SSP-368
❑ 76Top-162
❑ 78SanJosMMC-23
❑ 79SpoIndT-7
Pierce, Marvin
❑ 94BurIndF-3793
Pierce, Rob
❑ 92MadMusC-22
❑ 92MadMusF-1232
❑ 92RenSilSCLC-52
❑ 94HunStaF-1329
❑ 95HunStaTI-20
Pierce, Tony
❑ 67Top-542
❑ 68OPC-38
❑ 68Top-38
❑ 68TopVen-38
❑ 81TCM60I-401
Pierce, Walter
❑ 83ArkTraT-5
❑ 84ArkTraT-24
Piercey, William
❑ 15Zee-134
❑ 25Zee-99
Piercy, Bill
❑ 19Zee-60
❑ 21Exh-130
❑ 21Exh-131
❑ 21KoBreWSI-45
Piercy, Brad
❑ 98VerExpO-20
❑ 99TeaBesR-67
❑ 99TeaBesRG-67
❑ 99TeaBesRS-67
Pieretti, Chick (Marino)
❑ 47SenGunBP-8
❑ 49Bow-217
❑ 50Bow-181
❑ 50IndNumN-18
❑ 50IndTeal-20
❑ 52MotCoo-12
❑ 53MotCoo-35
Pierorazio, Wes
❑ 83WatIndF-23
❑ 85VisOakT-19
❑ 86VisOakP-15
❑ 87OrlTwiP-22
Pierre, Juan
❑ 98PorRocG-27
Pierre, Shape (Rogers)
❑ 93NegLeaRL2-29
Pierre-Louis, Danton
❑ 93MarPhiC-22
❑ 93MarPhiF-3484
❑ 94MarPhiC-17
❑ 94MarPhiF-3303
Piersall, Jim
❑ 47Exh-179
❑ 47PM1StaP1-164
❑ 51Bow-306
❑ 52Bow-189
❑ 53BowBW-36
❑ 53RedSoxTI-24
❑ 54Bow-66B
❑ 54Bow-210
❑ 54ColMeaPP-1
❑ 54ColMeaPP-2
❑ 54RedMan-AL11
❑ 55Bow-16
❑ 55RedMan-AL21
❑ 56Top-143
❑ 57Top-75
❑ 58RedSoxJP-7
❑ 58Top-280
❑ 59Ind-16
❑ 59RedSoxJP-7
❑ 59Top-355
❑ 60IndJayP-8
❑ 60Top-159
❑ 60TopVen-159
❑ 61Top-345
❑ 61TopStal-139
❑ 61WilSpoGH828-3
❑ 61WilSpoGH828-1-5
❑ 62Baz-36
❑ 62SalPlaC-88A
❑ 62SalPlaC-88B
❑ 62SenNewLP-1
❑ 62ShiPlaC-88
❑ 62Top-51
❑ 62Top-90
❑ 62TopBuc-68
❑ 62TopStal-100
❑ 62TopVen-51
❑ 62TopVen-90
❑ 63BasMagM-66
❑ 63ExhStaB-53
❑ 63Fle-29
❑ 63Top-443
❑ 64Top-586
❑ 65OPC-172
❑ 65Top-172
❑ 66AngDexP-11
❑ 66Top-565
❑ 67Top-584
❑ 77Spo-10224
❑ 79TCM50-188
❑ 80MarExh-23
❑ 81RedSoxBG2S-45
❑ 87CubCan-25
❑ 87SpoRea-14
❑ 89PacLegI-182
❑ 89SweBasG-83
❑ 90PacLeg-44
❑ 90SweBasG-92
❑ 91LinDri-20
❑ 91MetWIZ-316
❑ 91SweBasG-72
❑ 91TopArc1-286
❑ 92ActPacA-49
❑ 93RanKee-294
❑ 93TedWil-5
❑ 93UppDecAH-105
❑ 94UppDecAH-13
❑ 94UppDecAH-61
❑ 94UppDecAH1-13
❑ 94UppDecAH1-61
Pierson, Jason
❑ 92UtiBluSC-2
❑ 93MidLeaAGF-26
❑ 93SouBenWSC-17
❑ 93SouBenWSF-1429
❑ 94CarLeaAF-CAR11
❑ 94PriWilCC-19
❑ 94PriWilCF-1919
❑ 95PriWilCTI-21
❑ 96BinMetB-22
❑ 98PriWilCASM-15
Pierson, John
❑ 96RocCubTI-25
Pierson, Larry
❑ 88St.PetCS-23
❑ 89St.PetCS-22
❑ 90ArkTraGS-25
❑ 97LowSpiB-2
❑ 98MicBatCM-3
Pierzynski, A.J.
❑ 94SigRooDP-61
❑ 94SigRooDPS-61
❑ 95ForWayWTI-14
❑ 96BesAutS-72
❑ 96Bow-344
❑ 96BowFoi-344
❑ 96Exc-80
❑ 96ForWayWB-20
❑ 97ForMyeM-24
❑ 98Bow-319
❑ 98BowChr-319
❑ 98BowChrGA-319
❑ 98BowChrGAR-319
❑ 98BowChrI-319
❑ 98BowChrIR-319
❑ 98BowChrR-319
❑ 98BowGolA-319
❑ 98BowInt-319
❑ 98NewBriRCM-23
❑ 99Fle-487
❑ 99FleSta9-487
❑ 99FleWarT-487
❑ 99Pac-254
❑ 99PacPlaB-254
❑ 99PacRed-254
❑ 99SP Aut-108
❑ 99SP SigAuto-AJP
❑ 99SpoIll-69
❑ 99SPSig-94
❑ 99SPx-105
❑ 99SPxFinR-105
❑ 99SPxFinS-105
❑ 99UppDec-277
❑ 99UppDecE-120
❑ 99UppDecEFXG-120
❑ 99UppDecEL1-277
❑ 99UppDecEL2-277
❑ 99UppDecM-119
❑ 99UppDecMGS-119
❑ 99UppDecMHFS-119
❑ 99UppDecMSS-119
❑ 99Vic-223
Piet, Tony
❑ 33Gou-228
❑ 34BatR31-70
❑ 34BatR31-142
❑ 34DiaStaR-72
❑ 34ExhFou-4
❑ 34Gou-8
❑ 34GouCanV-63
❑ 35GouPuzR-1H
❑ 35GouPuzR-3F
❑ 35GouPuzR-14F
❑ 35GouPuzR-15F
❑ 36GouWidPPR-A84
❑ 36WorWidGV-95
❑ 72TCMthe3-87
❑ 83ConMar-28
❑ 88ConNatA-16
❑ 92ConTSN-524
Pietroburgo, Rob
❑ 79SpoIndT-18
❑ 80TacTigT-1
❑ 81ChaChaT-23
❑ 82ChaChaT-9
Pifer, Gary
❑ 87ChaWheP-10
❑ 88LakTigS-21
Pifferini, Raeann
❑ 91FreStaLBS-8
Pigg, Vic
❑ 23Zee-167
Piggot, Rusty
❑ 81QuaCitCT-4
Pignatano, Joe
❑ 58DodTeal-18
❑ 58Top-373
❑ 59DodMor-7
❑ 59DodTeal-20
❑ 59Top-16
❑ 59TopVen-16
❑ 60DodBelB-10
❑ 60Lea-126
❑ 60Top-292
❑ 60Top-442
❑ 61A'sTeal-15
❑ 61AthJayP-15
❑ 61Top-74
❑ 62Jel-97
❑ 62Pos-97
❑ 62PosCan-97
❑ 62SalPlaC-45
❑ 62ShiPlaC-45
❑ 62Top-247
❑ 73OPC-257
❑ 73Top-257A
❑ 73Top-257B
❑ 74OPC-179
❑ 74Top-179
❑ 79TCM50-204
❑ 81Gia196T-20
❑ 81TCM60I-407
❑ 82BraPol-52
❑ 83BraPol-52
❑ 84BraPol-52
❑ 84raPho-25
❑ 89MetRinP69-30
❑ 90DodTar-624
❑ 91MetWIZ-317
❑ 94Met69CCPP-5
❑ 94Met69CS-4
❑ 94Met69T-31
❑ 95ColSilB-24
❑ 96ColSilB-23
Pigott, Tony
❑ 97PriDevR-8
Pike, David
❑ 92IdaFalGF-3510
❑ 92IdaFalGSP-12
❑ 94ChaRanF-2495
Pike, Mark
❑ 87WatIndP-6
❑ 88WatIndP-683
❑ 89KinIndS-19
Pilarcik, Al
❑ 56BalOriP-45
❑ 57Top-311
❑ 58Hir-76
❑ 58HirTes-8
❑ 58OriJayP-9
❑ 58Top-259
❑ 59Top-7
❑ 59TopVen-7
❑ 60Top-498
❑ 61A'sTeal-16
❑ 61Top-62
❑ 79TCM50-212
❑ 91OriCro-362
Pilato, Chris
❑ 98BatMucTI-21
Pilkington, Eric
❑ 86CliGiaP-21
❑ 88SanJosGCLC-136
❑ 88SanJosGP-127
Pilkinton, Lem
❑ 86ElmPioRSP-15
❑ 87GreHorP-23
❑ 89PenPilS-19
❑ 89Sta-107
❑ 90CarLeaA-44
❑ 90PenPilS-15
❑ 91JacSunLD-350
❑ 91JacSunP-168
❑ 91LinDriAA-350
❑ 92BelMarF-1462
❑ 92SanBerC-29
Pill, Mike
❑ 78ChaPirT-18
Pilla, Tony
❑ 82OrlTwiT-11
❑ 83OrlTwiT-2
Pillette, Duane
❑ 51Bow-316
❑ 52Top-82
❑ 53BowBW-59
❑ 53Top-269
❑ 54Bow-133
❑ 54OriEss-30
❑ 54OriTeal-17
❑ 54Top-107
❑ 55Bow-244
❑ 55OriEss-22
❑ 55Top-168
❑ 57SeaPop-18
❑ 58SeaRalT-13
❑ 75OakOak2A-28
❑ 79DiaGre-199
❑ 79TCM50-191
❑ 83TopRep5-82
❑ 91OriCro-363
❑ 91TopArc1-269
❑ 94TopArc1-107
❑ 94TopArc1G-107
❑ 97BalOriP-41
Pillette, Herman
❑ 21Exh-132
❑ 21Nei-19
❑ 21Zee-59
❑ 22E120-57
❑ 22W572-76
❑ 22W573-100
❑ 26Zee-57
❑ 27Zee-35
❑ 28Zee-57
❑ 29Zee-55
❑ 30Zee-64
❑ 31Zee-38
❑ 32Zee-42
❑ 46SunBre-15
Pillette, Ted
❑ 24Zee-53
❑ 25Zee-50
❑ 30Zee-65
❑ 31Zee-39
❑ 33Zee-39A
❑ 33Zee-39B
Pilots, Seattle
❑ 69FleCloS-22
❑ 69FleCloS-38
❑ 69TopStaA-23
❑ 70Top-713
Pimentel, Ed
❑ 90Ft.LauYS-17
Pimentel, Jose
❑ 96SavSanB-24
❑ 97VerBeaD-20
❑ 98SanAntMG-23
Pimentel, Rafael D.
❑ 81ArkTraT-13
❑ 82ArkTraT-5
❑ 85DomLeaS-190
❑ 86MidAngP-19
Pimentel, Wander
❑ 90HamRedB-16
❑ 90HamRedS-19
❑ 91SavCarC-22
❑ 91SavCarP-1663
❑ 92SprCarC-8
❑ 92SprCarF-876
❑ 93ArkTraF-2820
❑ 94St.PetCC-22
❑ 94St.PetCF-2596
Pina, Horacio
❑ 71MLBOffS-548
❑ 71OPC-497
❑ 71SenTealW-19
❑ 71Top-497
❑ 72RanTeal-22
❑ 72Top-654
❑ 73OPC-138
❑ 73Top-138
❑ 74OPC-516
❑ 74Top-516
❑ 74TopTra-516T
❑ 75OPC-139
❑ 75Top-139
❑ 75TopMin-139
❑ 93RanKee-33
Pina, Mickey
❑ 87ElmPioRC-33
❑ 88ElmPio1C-3
❑ 88LynRedSS-17
❑ 89NewBriRSP-619
❑ 89NewBriRSS-14
❑ 89Sta-129
❑ 90Bow-270
❑ 90BowTif-270
❑ 90CMC-271
❑ 90PawRedSC-20
❑ 90PawRedSDD-19
❑ 90PawRedSP-473
❑ 90ProAAAF-445
❑ 90ScoRoo-104T
❑ 90TopTVRS-56
❑ 90TriAAAC-27
❑ 90UppDec-764
❑ 91LinDriAAA-364
❑ 91PawRedSDD-16
❑ 91PawRedSLD-364
❑ 91PawRedSP-50
Pina, Rafael
❑ 91EliTwiP-4298
❑ 92EliTwiC-12
❑ 92EliTwiF-3680
Pinales, Aquiles
❑ 96MacBraB-10
Pinango, Simon
❑ 93LinVenB-231
❑ 94VenLinU-143
❑ 96-97LinVen-78
Pincavitch, Kevin
❑ 92GreFalDSP-12
❑ 93YakBeaC-19
❑ 93YakBeaF-3883
❑ 94BakDodC-19
❑ 95AusFut-42
❑ 95VerBeaDTI-20
❑ 96Exc-181
❑ 96MauStiHWB-10
❑ 97SanBerS-13
Pinckes, Mike
❑ 90BurIndP-3016
❑ 91ColIndC-5
❑ 91ColIndP-1494
Pinder, Chris
❑ 88HagSunS-17
❑ 89HagSunB-27
❑ 89HagSunP-268
❑ 90KinIndTI-20
Pineda, Gabriel
❑ 90EugEmeGS-21
❑ 91AppFoxCB-9
❑ 91AppFoxP-1715
Pineda, Jose
❑ 91Ft.LauYC-17
❑ 91Ft.LauYP-2430
❑ 92ForLauYC-6
❑ 92ForLauYTI-23
❑ 92GreHorF-781
❑ 93AlbYanF-2166
Pineda, Lionel
❑ 95KanCouCTI-27
Pineda, Rafael
❑ 87QuaCitAP-15
❑ 87SalAngP-21
Pineiro, Joel
❑ 98WisTimRM-8
Pineiro, Michael
❑ 92BoiHawC-8
❑ 92BoiHawF-3632
❑ 93BenRocCB-22
❑ 93BenRocF-3272
❑ 94CenValRC-19
❑ 94CenValRF-3207
Pinelli, Babe (Ralph)
❑ 17Zee-54
❑ 18Zee-49
❑ 19Zee-61
❑ 20WalMaiW-41
❑ 21Nei-78
❑ 21Zee-35
❑ 22E120-177
❑ 22W572-77
❑ 22W573-101
❑ 26SpoComoA-31
❑ 28Zee-141
❑ 29Zee-139
❑ 30Zee-154
❑ 31Zee-111
❑ 32Zee-63
❑ 55Bow-307
❑ 87ConSer2-20
❑ 88ConSer4-22
❑ 92ConTSN-476
❑ 94ConTSN-1197
❑ 94ConTSNB-1197
Pinelli, Willie
❑ 87BakDodP-29
Pinero, Hugo
❑ 95LinVen-61
❑ 96-97LinVen-114
Pinhey, Lon
❑ 95TolMudHTI-4
❑ 97TolMudHB-32
❑ 98TolMudHQ-33
Piniella, Juan
❑ 98SavSanGM-21
Piniella, Lou
❑ 64Top-167
❑ 64TopVen-167
❑ 68OPC-16
❑ 68Top-16
❑ 68TopVen-16
❑ 69PilPos-25
❑ 69RoySol-13
❑ 69Top-394
❑ 70DayDaiNM-76
❑ 70MLBOffS-227
❑ 70OPC-321
❑ 70RoyTeal-27
❑ 70Top-321
❑ 70TopCanL-18
❑ 70TopScr-17
❑ 70TopSup-32
❑ 71MLBOffS-426
❑ 71OPC-35
❑ 71oySigST-21
❑ 71oySigST-22
❑ 71Top-35
❑ 71TopCoi-152
❑ 71TopGreM-38
❑ 71TopSup-62
❑ 71TopTat-77
❑ 72MilBra-275
❑ 72OPC-491
❑ 72oyTeal-19
❑ 72SevTraC-42
❑ 72Top-491
❑ 72Top-580
❑ 73Kel2D-24
❑ 73LinPor-135
❑ 73OPC-140
❑ 73SevTraC-59
❑ 73Top-140
❑ 73TopCanL-40
❑ 73TopCom-15
❑ 73TopPin-15
❑ 74OPC-390
❑ 74Top-390
❑ 74TopSta-188
❑ 74TopTra-390T
❑ 75Kel-34
❑ 75OPC-217
❑ 75Top-217
❑ 75TopMin-217
❑ 75YanSSP-11
❑ 76OPC-453
❑ 76SSP-445

❑ 76Top-453
❑ 77Kel-48
❑ 77PilPosR-25
❑ 77Top-96
❑ 77YanBurK-23
❑ 78OPC-82
❑ 78RCColC-90
❑ 78SSP270-3
❑ 78Top-159
❑ 78YanBurK-18
❑ 78YanPhoA-20
❑ 78YanSSPD-3
❑ 79BasPat-69
❑ 79Hos-69
❑ 79OPC-342
❑ 79Top-648
❑ 79YanBurK-18
❑ 79YanPicA-29
❑ 80OPC-120
❑ 80Top-225
❑ 80YanPhoA-19
❑ 81Don-109
❑ 81Fle-85
❑ 81FleStiC-45
❑ 81OPC-306
❑ 81Top-724
❑ 81YanPhoA-19
❑ 82Don-135
❑ 82Fle-48
❑ 82FleSta-114
❑ 82OPC-236
❑ 82Top-538
❑ 82YanPhoA-20
❑ 83Don-335
❑ 83Fle-392
❑ 83FleSta-151
❑ 83FleSti-45
❑ 83OPC-307
❑ 83Top-307
❑ 83YanPhoA-19
❑ 83YanRoyRD-8
❑ 84Don-274
❑ 84Fle-136
❑ 84Nes792-408
❑ 84OPC-351
❑ 84Top-408
❑ 84TopTif-408
❑ 85YanTCMP-5
❑ 86RoyGreT-5
❑ 86TopTra-86T
❑ 86TopTraT-86T
❑ 86YanTCM-38
❑ 87Top-168
❑ 87TopTif-168
❑ 88Top-44
❑ 88TopTif-44
❑ 90PacLeg-99
❑ 90RedKah-21
❑ 90TopTra-96T
❑ 90TopTraT-96T
❑ 91OPC-669
❑ 91OriCro-364
❑ 91RedKah-41
❑ 91RedPep-16
❑ 91Top-669
❑ 91TopDesS-669
❑ 91TopMic-669
❑ 91TopTif-669
❑ 92OPC-321
❑ 92RedFolS-123
❑ 92RedKah-41
❑ 92Top-321
❑ 92TopGol-321
❑ 92TopGolW-321
❑ 92TopMic-321
❑ 92YanWIZ7-128
❑ 92YanWIZ8-147
❑ 93MarMot-1
❑ 93Top-512
❑ 93TopGol-512
❑ 93TopInaM-512
❑ 93TopInaR-512
❑ 93TopMic-512
❑ 94MarMot-1
❑ 95MarMot-1
❑ 95MarPac-15
❑ 95MarPac-50
❑ 96MarMot-1
❑ 97UppDecMP-P20

Pinkerton, Wayne
❑ 76AshTouT-9
❑ 76AshTouT-11
❑ 76SanAntBTI-17
❑ 77TucTorC-6
❑ 78TucTorC-9
❑ 79TucTorT-12
❑ 80ChaChaT-3

Pinkham, Bill
❑ 72CedRapCT-1
❑ 83KnoBluJT-8

Pinkney, Alton
❑ 90KisDodD-22
❑ 91GreFalDSP-30
❑ 92VerBeaDC-4
❑ 92YakBeaC-3
❑ 92YakBeaF-3465
❑ 93VerBeaDF-2233

Pinkney, George
❑ 74BroClu-13
❑ 87OldJudN-400
❑ 90DodTar-625

Pinkston, Lal
❑ 52LavPro-62
❑ 55JetPos-12

Pinkus, Jeff
❑ 77SalPirT-19

Pinnell, Lance
❑ 89SanDieSAS-22

Pino, Rolando
❑ 83AppFoxFr-12
❑ 86BirBarTI-12
❑ 87BirBarB-19
❑ 89KenTwiP-1082
❑ 89KenTwiS-19
❑ 90GreBraB-20
❑ 92St.CatBJC-30
❑ 92St.CatBJF-3402
❑ 93St.CatBJC-26
❑ 93St.CatBJF-3990
❑ 94St.CatBJC-29
❑ 95DunBluJTI-18
❑ 96DunBluJB-29
❑ 96DunBluJTI-23

Pinol, Juan
❑ 87TamTarP-7

Pinoni, Scott
❑ 94EugEmeC-17
❑ 94EugEmeF-3722

Pinson, Chris
❑ 90ArkRaz-32

Pinson, Tom
❑ 92KinMetC-1
❑ 92KinMetF-1529

Pinson, Vada
❑ 47Exh-180
❑ 56RedBurB-17
❑ 58SeaRalT-14
❑ 58Top-420
❑ 59Kah-28
❑ 59RedBurBP-14
❑ 59RedBurBP-15
❑ 59RedBurBP-16
❑ 59RedShiBS-17
❑ 59Top-448
❑ 60ArmCoi-17
❑ 60Kah-33
❑ 60RedJayP-10
❑ 60Top-32
❑ 60Top-176
❑ 60TopVen-32
❑ 60TopVen-176
❑ 61Kah-33
❑ 61Pos-181A
❑ 61Pos-181B
❑ 61RedJayP-11
❑ 61Top-25
❑ 61Top-110
❑ 61TopStal-22
❑ 62Baz-3
❑ 62ExhStaB-30
❑ 62Jel-121
❑ 62Kah-31
❑ 62Pos-121
❑ 62PosCan-121
❑ 62RedEnq-26
❑ 62RedJayP-10
❑ 62SalPlaC-118
❑ 62ShiPlaC-118
❑ 62Top-52
❑ 62Top-80
❑ 62TopBuc-69
❑ 62TopStal-119
❑ 62TopVen-52
❑ 62TopVen-80
❑ 63BasMagM-67
❑ 63ExhStaB-54
❑ 63Fle-34
❑ 63Jel-130
❑ 63Kah-24
❑ 63Pos-130
❑ 63RedEnq-25
❑ 63RedFreBC-19
❑ 63RedJayP-10
❑ 63Top-265
❑ 64Kah-21
❑ 64RedJayP-9
❑ 64Top-80
❑ 64Top-162
❑ 64TopCoi-45
❑ 64TopCoi-152
❑ 64TopGia-56
❑ 64TopSta-2
❑ 64TopStaU-57
❑ 64TopVen-80
❑ 64TopVen-162
❑ 65Kah-35
❑ 65OldLonC-16
❑ 65RedEnq-23
❑ 65Top-355
❑ 65TopEmbl-42
❑ 65TopTral-24
❑ 66Kah-26
❑ 66OPC-180
❑ 66RedVolC-11
❑ 66Top-180
❑ 66TopVen-180
❑ 67CokCapA-29
❑ 67CokCapNLA-33
❑ 67CokCapR-11
❑ 67DexPre-169
❑ 67Kah-30
❑ 67Top-550
❑ 67TopVen-285
❑ 68AtlOilPBCC-35
❑ 68Baz-9
❑ 68Kah-A10
❑ 68Kah-B29
❑ 68OPC-90
❑ 68Top-90
❑ 68TopActS-10A
❑ 68TopVen-90
❑ 69MilBra-224
❑ 69OPC-160
❑ 69Top-160
❑ 69TopFou-4
❑ 69TopSta-119
❑ 69TopTeaP-18
❑ 70Ind-10
❑ 70MLBOffS-202
❑ 70OPC-445
❑ 70Top-445
❑ 70TopBoo-5
❑ 70TopSup-31
❑ 71Ind-10
❑ 71MLBOffS-382
❑ 71OPC-275
❑ 71Top-275
❑ 71TopCoi-18
❑ 71TopGreM-12
❑ 71TopTat-40
❑ 72MilBra-276
❑ 72OPC-135
❑ 72SevTraC-43
❑ 72Top-135
❑ 73OPC-75
❑ 73SevTraC-60
❑ 73Top-75
❑ 74OPC-490
❑ 74RoyPos-24
❑ 74Top-490
❑ 74TopSta-144
❑ 75OPC-295
❑ 75RoyPos-26
❑ 75SSP42-9
❑ 75Top-295
❑ 75TopMin-295
❑ 76OPC-415
❑ 76RedParC-22
❑ 76SSP-178
❑ 76Top-415
❑ 77MarPos-15
❑ 77Spo-2109
❑ 77Top-597
❑ 78TCM60I-146
❑ 80MarPos-18
❑ 80Red196T-3
❑ 82DiaCla-92
❑ 82Don-445
❑ 82MarPos-25
❑ 82OhiHaloF-52
❑ 86RedGreT-6
❑ 88TigPep-NNO
❑ 89TigMar-NNO
❑ 90TigCok-28
❑ 90TigTeal-19
❑ 91TigCok-NNO
❑ 93MarPub-28
❑ 94TedWil-23
❑ 94TedWil-140

Pinto, Gustavo
❑ 89NiaFalRP-19
❑ 93LinVenB-64
❑ 94VenLinU-69
❑ 95LinVen-245

Pinto, Mauro
❑ 80VenLeaS-171

Pinto, Rene
❑ 95LinVen-119
❑ 96-97LinVen-65
❑ 96GreBatB-19
❑ 97GreBatB-22
❑ 98GreBatM-14

Pioneer, Old
❑ 90ElmPioP-27

Pioneers, Elmira
❑ 88ElmPio1C-10
❑ 88ElmPio1C-11
❑ 88ElmPio1C-12
❑ 94ElmPioC-29B
❑ 94ElmPioC-30

Piotrowicz, Brian
❑ 90GreFalDSP-23
❑ 91BakDodCLC-8
❑ 92VerBeaDC-14
❑ 92VerBeaDF-2872
❑ 93SanAntMF-3003

Pipgras, Ed
❑ 90DodTar-626

Pipgras, Fred
❑ 29Zee-166
❑ 30Zee-184

Pipgras, George
❑ 28PorandAR-A29
❑ 28PorandAR-B29
❑ 28W56PlaC-S4A
❑ 32R33So2-404
❑ 33DouDisP-34
❑ 33Gou-12
❑ 33GouCanV-12
❑ 35DiaMatCS3T1-122
❑ 61Fle-134
❑ 75Yan192T-20
❑ 76GrePlaG-33
❑ 79DiaGre-6
❑ 79Yan192T-25
❑ 84Yan192G-27
❑ 91ConTSN-123

Piphus, Ben
❑ 83WatIndF-3

Pipik, Gary
❑ 89JamExpP-2138

Pipp, Wally
❑ 15SpoNewM-139
❑ 16BF2FP-36
❑ 16SpoNewM-138
❑ 17ColE13-134
❑ 19W514-84
❑ 20GasAmeMBD-14
❑ 20NatCarE-80
❑ 20WalMaiW-42
❑ 21E121So8-72
❑ 21Exh-133
❑ 21Nei-48
❑ 22AmeCarE122-54
❑ 22E120-70
❑ 22W572-78
❑ 22W573-102
❑ 22W575-99
❑ 22WilPatV-45
❑ 23W503-4
❑ 23W515-39
❑ 23W551-6
❑ 23WilChoV-124
❑ 25Exh-99
❑ 26Exh-29
❑ 26SpoComoA-32
❑ 27Exh-14
❑ 63GadFunC-62
❑ 74CapPub-54
❑ 91ConTSN-157

Pippen, Cotton (Henry)
❑ 39PlaBal-8
❑ 40PlaBal-136
❑ 46RemBre-24
❑ 47RemBre-13
❑ 47SigOil-51
❑ 47SmiClo-9

Pippin, Craig
❑ 83LynPirT-7
❑ 86IndTeal-34
❑ 86MaiGuiP-15
❑ 87OmaRoyP-15

Pippin, Harry
❑ 37Zee-59

Pirates, Pittsburgh
❑ 09SpoNewSM-18
❑ 10E-UOraBSC-1
❑ 13FatT20-15
❑ 36R31Pre-G26
❑ 38BasTabP-41
❑ 56Top-121
❑ 57Top-161
❑ 58PirTeal-14
❑ 58Top-341
❑ 59Top-528
❑ 60Top-484
❑ 60TopTat-61
❑ 61Top-554
❑ 61TopMagR-11
❑ 62GuyPotCP-16
❑ 62Top-409
❑ 63Top-151
❑ 64Top-373
❑ 64TopTatI-17
❑ 65OPC-209
❑ 65Top-209
❑ 66Top-404
❑ 66TopRubl-117
❑ 67Top-492
❑ 68LauWorS-24
❑ 68LauWorS-57
❑ 68Top-308
❑ 68TopVen-308
❑ 69FleCloS-19
❑ 69FleCloS-39
❑ 69TopStaA-19
❑ 70FleWorS-1
❑ 70FleWorS-24
❑ 70FleWorS-57
❑ 70Top-608
❑ 71FleWorS-7
❑ 71FleWorS-25
❑ 71FleWorS-58
❑ 71OPC-603
❑ 71Top-603
❑ 71TopTat-110
❑ 72OPC-1
❑ 72Top-1
❑ 73OPC-26
❑ 73OPCBTC-20
❑ 73Top-26
❑ 73TopBluTC-20
❑ 74OPC-626
❑ 74OPCTC-20
❑ 74Top-626
❑ 74TopStaA-20
❑ 74TopTeaC-20
❑ 78Top-606
❑ 83FleSta-244
❑ 83FleSti-NNO
❑ 83FleSti-NNO
❑ 87SpoTeaL-18
❑ 88PanSti-477
❑ 88RedFolSB-111
❑ 89FleWaxBC-C23
❑ 89TopTif-699
❑ 90KalTeaN-6
❑ 90PubIntS-630
❑ 90RedFolSB-116
❑ 92OPCBoxB-1
❑ 93TedWilPC-19
❑ 94ImpProP-25
❑ 94Sco-657
❑ 94ScoGolR-657
❑ 95PacPriTL-25
❑ 95PanSti-136
❑ 96PanSti-70
❑ 98CamPepP-88
❑ 99Vic-304

Pirkl, Greg
❑ 87BelMarL-7
❑ 89BelMarL-1
❑ 90Bes-233
❑ 90CMC-860
❑ 90SanBerSB-14
❑ 90SanBerSCLC-105
❑ 90SanBerSP-2637
❑ 91PenPilC-1
❑ 91SanBerSC-14
❑ 91SanBerSP-1990
❑ 92Bow-654
❑ 92CalCanF-3736
❑ 92ClaFS7-143
❑ 92DonRoo-96
❑ 92JacSunF-3710
❑ 92JacSunS-367
❑ 92SkyAA F-158
❑ 93Bow-571
❑ 93CalCanF-1173
❑ 93Don-589
❑ 94Fin-291
❑ 94FinRef-291
❑ 94MarMot-21
❑ 94ScoRoo-RT107
❑ 94ScoRooGR-RT107
❑ 94ScoRooSR-SU13
❑ 94Sel-414
❑ 94SpoRoo-98
❑ 94SpoRooAP-98
❑ 94StaClu-578
❑ 94StaCluFDI-578
❑ 94StaCluGR-578
❑ 94StaCluMOP-578
❑ 94Top-448
❑ 94TopGol-448
❑ 94TopSpa-448
❑ 95Bow-425
❑ 95ColCho-294
❑ 95ColChoGS-294
❑ 95ColChoSS-294
❑ 95Fle-274
❑ 95MarPac-39
❑ 95Sco-302
❑ 95ScoGolR-302
❑ 95ScoPlaTS-302
❑ 95Sel-48
❑ 95SelArtP-48
❑ 95Spo-156
❑ 95SpoArtP-156
❑ 95StaClu-396
❑ 95StaCluMOP-396
❑ 95StaCluSTWS-396
❑ 95TacRaiTI-16
❑ 95Ult-330
❑ 95UltGolM-330
❑ 96TacRaiB-21
❑ 98KinIndQ-18

Pirruccello, Mark
❑ 83ChaRoyT-1
❑ 84MemChiT-23

Pirtle, Jerry
❑ 79RocRedWT-12
❑ 79Top-720
❑ 89PacSenL-198

Pisacreta, Mike
❑ 89PulBraP-1890

Pisarkiewicz, Mike
❑ 77St.PetCT-19
❑ 78St.PetCT-20

Piscetta, Rob
❑ 89BakDodCLC-187

Pisciotta, Marc
❑ 91WelPirP-3570
❑ 92AugPirF-236
❑ 92ProFS7-314
❑ 93AugPirC-14
❑ 93AugPirF-1540
❑ 94CarLeaAF-CAR42
❑ 94SalBucC-15
❑ 94SalBucF-2321
❑ 94UppDecML-192
❑ 95CarMudF-153
❑ 97IowCub-22
❑ 98BesAutSS-42
❑ 98Don-281
❑ 98DonGolPP-281
❑ 98DonSilPP-281
❑ 98Fle-186
❑ 98LeaRS-296
❑ 98LeaRSLHolo-296
❑ 98LeaRSLong-296
❑ 98LeaRTrue-296
❑ 98PacOmeRS-30
❑ 98PacOmeRST5-30
❑ 98PacOnl-151
❑ 98PacOnlR-151
❑ 98PacOnlWC-151

Pisciotta, Scott
❑ 92JamExpC-9
❑ 92JamExpF-1500
❑ 92StaCluD-141
❑ 92UppDecML-149
❑ 93BurBeeC-19
❑ 93BurBeeF-156
❑ 94BurBeeC-22
❑ 94WesPalBEC-21
❑ 94WesPalBEF-36
❑ 96HarSenB-22

Pisel, Ron
❑ 78CedRapGT-22
❑ 83PhoGiaBHN-19

Pisker, Don
❑ 76DubPacT-26
❑ 78ChaChaT-12
❑ 79SyrChiT-8

❑ 79SyrChiTI-7
❑ 79Top-718
❑ 80SyrChiT-23
❑ 80SyrChiTI-17
❑ 81SalLakCGT-24
Piskol, Pete
❑ 84PriWilPT-8
Piskor, Kirk
❑ 90ArkRaz-21
Piskor, Steve
❑ 88LitFalMP-9
❑ 89PitMetS-19
Pisoni, Jim
❑ 57Top-402
❑ 59Top-259
❑ 92YanWIZ6-99
Pitcher, Scott
❑ 87BelMarL-19
❑ 89WauTimGS-8
❑ 90SanBerSB-17
❑ 90SanBerSCLC-95
❑ 90SanBerSP-2631
❑ 91SanBerSC-11
❑ 91SanBerSP-1987
❑ 92JacSunF-3706
❑ 92PenPilC-9
Pitler, Jake
❑ 48DodTeal-17
❑ 49EurSta-46
❑ 52Top-395
❑ 55DodGolS-28
❑ 56Dod-22
❑ 74dod195T-26
❑ 79TCM50-187
❑ 83TopRep5-395
❑ 95TopArcBD-32
Pitlock, Skip (Lee)
❑ 71OPC-19
❑ 71Top-19
❑ 75OPC-579
❑ 75Top-579
❑ 75TopMin-579
❑ 75TucTorC-19
❑ 76SalLakCGC-16
❑ 76TusTorCr-44
Pitt, Jye
❑ 97WilCubB-17
Pittaro, Chris
❑ 85FleUpd-87
❑ 85NasSouTI-18
❑ 85TopTifT-91T
❑ 85TopTra-91T
❑ 86Don-150
❑ 86Top-393
❑ 86TopTif-393
❑ 86TwiTeal-1
❑ 87PorBeaP-6
❑ 88PorBeaC-19
❑ 88PorBeaP-653
❑ 92SouOreAC-28
Pittenger, Clark A.
❑ 21Nei-42
❑ 22E120-10
❑ 22W573-103
❑ 29ExhFou-8
Pittinger, Charley
❑ 06FanCraNL-38
Pittman, Charles
❑ 92JohCitCC-14
❑ 92JohCitCF-3117
Pittman, Doug
❑ 87SalBucP-27
❑ 88KenTwiP-1388
Pittman, James
❑ 88OrlTwiB-8
Pittman, Joe
❑ 76DubPacT-27
❑ 77OrlTwiT-16
❑ 80TucTorT-3
❑ 81AstPos-14
❑ 81TucTorT-3
❑ 82Don-218
❑ 82Fle-222
❑ 82Top-119
❑ 82TopTra-90T
❑ 83Don-247
❑ 83Don-422
❑ 83Fle-369
❑ 83LasVegSBHN-17
❑ 83Top-346
❑ 85NasSouTI-19
❑ 87AstShoSPT-11
❑ 89PacSenL-38
❑ 89TopSenL-19
❑ 90EliSenL-101
❑ 91PacSenL-151
❑ 96QuaCitRB-2
Pittman, Mike
❑ 82SprCarF-5
❑ 83SprCarF-20
Pittman, Park
❑ 87VisOakP-11
❑ 89OrlTwiB-20
❑ 89OrlTwiP-1334
❑ 90Bow-408
❑ 90BowTif-408
❑ 90CMC-561
❑ 90FleUpd-109
❑ 90PorBeaC-9
❑ 90PorBeaP-177
❑ 90ProAAAF-247
Pittman, Thomas
❑ 98VerExpO-27
Pitts, Gaylen
❑ 75TucTorC-4
❑ 75TucTorTI-16
❑ 76TucTorCa-14
❑ 76TusTorCr-42
❑ 81ArkTraT-21
❑ 82ArkTraT-22
❑ 82LouRedE-23
❑ 83LouRedR-2
❑ 84LouRedR-2
❑ 87SprCarB-1
❑ 89ArkTraGS-1
❑ 89TexLeaAGS-19
❑ 90CMC-678
❑ 90LouRedBC-27
❑ 90LouRedBLBC-3
❑ 90LouRedBP-419
❑ 90ProAAAF-533
❑ 90SprCarDGB-27
❑ 90TopTVCa-61
❑ 97LouRedB-2
❑ 98MemRedG-16
Pitts, Jon
❑ 91HigSchPLS-28
❑ 92GulCoaRSP-3
❑ 93ButCopKSP-21
❑ 94ChaRanF-2501
Pitts, Kevin
❑ 93YakBeaC-20
❑ 93YakBeaF-3900
❑ 94VerBeaDC-14
❑ 94VerBeaDF-88
Pitts, Rick
❑ 96SpoIndB-21
❑ 98LanLugQ-23
Pittsley, Jim
❑ 92ClaDraP-80
❑ 92ClaFS7-405
❑ 92UppDecML-93
❑ 93ClaGolF-202
❑ 93RocRoyC-23
❑ 93RocRoyF-715
❑ 94BowBes-B48
❑ 94BowBesR-B48
❑ 94CarLeaAF-CAR21
❑ 94Cla-23
❑ 94ExcFS7-70
❑ 94StaClu-712
❑ 94StaCluFDI-712
❑ 94StaCluGR-712
❑ 94StaCluMOP-712
❑ 94WilBluRC-20
❑ 94WilBluRF-299
❑ 95Bow-100
❑ 95ColCho-31
❑ 95ColChoGS-31
❑ 95ColChoSS-31
❑ 95Exc-61
❑ 95ExcLeaL-12
❑ 95SelCer-95
❑ 95SelCerMG-95
❑ 95SigRooOJ-27
❑ 95SigRooOJP-27
❑ 95SigRooOJPS-27
❑ 95SigRooOJS-27
❑ 95SP-17
❑ 95SPSil-17
❑ 95Sum21C-TC4
❑ 95UppDecML-23
❑ 95UppDecMLFS-23
❑ 96ColCho-570
❑ 96ColChoGS-570
❑ 96ColChoSS-570
❑ 96Pin-183
❑ 96PinAfi-169
❑ 96PinAfiAP-169
❑ 96Sco-261
❑ 96Sel-184
❑ 96SelArtP-184
❑ 96SelCer-124
❑ 96SelCerAP-124
❑ 96SelCerCB-124
❑ 96SelCerCR-124
❑ 96SelCerMB-124
❑ 96SelCerMG-124
❑ 96SelCerMR-124
❑ 96Spo-125
❑ 96SpoArtP-125
❑ 96Sum-190
❑ 96SumAbo&B-190
❑ 96SumArtP-190
❑ 96SumFoi-190
❑ 97Bow-413
❑ 97BowChr-274
❑ 97BowChrI-274
❑ 97BowChrIR-274
❑ 97BowChrR-274
❑ 97BowInt-413
❑ 98PacOnl-350
❑ 98PacOnlR-350
❑ 98PacOnlWC-350
❑ 98StaCluFDI-136
❑ 98StaCluI-136
❑ 98StaCluOneK-136
❑ 98StaCluPP-136
Pitula, Stan
❑ 57IndTeal-18
Pitz, Michael
❑ 87BakDodP-28
❑ 88SanAntMB-3
❑ 89SanAntMB-23
❑ 90SanAntMGS-20
❑ 91JacSunLD-342
❑ 91JacSunP-149
❑ 91LinDriAA-342
Pivaral, Hugo
❑ 94FloStaLAF-FSL50
❑ 94VerBeaDF-68
❑ 95Bow-16
❑ 95SanBerSTI-15
❑ 95UppDecML-73
❑ 95UppDecMLFS-73
❑ 96BesAutSA-55
❑ 96SigRooOJ-27
❑ 96SigRooOJS-27
❑ 97BesAutAS-41
Pivnick, Phil
❑ 85AlbYanT-31
Pizarro, Germain
❑ 52LavPro-78
Pizarro, Juan
❑ 57Top-383
❑ 59Top-188
❑ 59TopVen-188
❑ 60BraLaktL-19
❑ 60BraSpiaS-17
❑ 60Lea-51
❑ 60Top-59
❑ 60TopVen-59
❑ 61Pos-112
❑ 61Top-227
❑ 61WhiSoxROLC-9
❑ 61WhiSoxTS-13
❑ 62Top-59
❑ 62Top-255
❑ 62TopBuc-70
❑ 62TopStal-28
❑ 62TopVen-59
❑ 62WhiSoxJP-9
❑ 62WhiSoxTS-16
❑ 63Jel-44
❑ 63Pos-44
❑ 63Top-10
❑ 63Top-160
❑ 63WhiSoxJP-11
❑ 63WhiSoxTS-21
❑ 64Top-2
❑ 64Top-430
❑ 64TopCoi-14
❑ 64TopGia-53
❑ 64TopSta-31
❑ 64TopStaU-58
❑ 64TopVen-2
❑ 64WheSta-36
❑ 64WhiSoxTS-19
❑ 65OPC-9
❑ 65OPC-125
❑ 65Top-9
❑ 65Top-125
❑ 65TopTral-25
❑ 65WhiSoxJP-7
❑ 66Top-335
❑ 66TopVen-335
❑ 67PirTeal-17
❑ 67Top-602
❑ 67TopPirS-5
❑ 67TopVen-272
❑ 68OPC-19
❑ 68PirKDK-29
❑ 68PirTeal-16
❑ 68Top-19
❑ 68TopVen-19
❑ 69Top-498
❑ 71MLBOffS-41
❑ 71OPC-647
❑ 71Top-647
❑ 72OPC-18
❑ 72Top-18A
❑ 72Top-18B
❑ 78TCM60I-79
❑ 80Bra195T-18
❑ 81RedSoxBG2S-103
❑ 84OCoandSI-197
❑ 89BlaYNPRWL-165
❑ 97RocCub-2
Pizarro, Melvin
❑ 95MarPhiTI-20
❑ 98BatMucTI-22
Pizarro, Miguel
❑ 78AshTouT-23
Pizzitola, Vince
❑ 52LavPro-112
Place, Eric
❑ 98St.CatSM-18
Place, Michael
❑ 90PulBraP-3106
❑ 91IdaFalBSP-2
❑ 92MacBraC-21
❑ 93MacBraC-19
Place, Mike
❑ 90PulBraB-8
❑ 92MacBraF-264
❑ 93MacBraF-1397
❑ 96PriWilCB-20
Placeres, Benigno
❑ 88St.CatBJP-2009
Pladson, Gordy
❑ 75DubPacT-23
❑ 76DubPacT-28
❑ 77CocAstT-17
❑ 79ChaChaT-13
❑ 80TucTorT-18
❑ 81Top-491
❑ 81TucTorT-18
❑ 82TucTorT-21
❑ 83TucTorT-7
Plainte, Brandon
❑ 80ElmPioRST-15
Plank, Ed
❑ 76PheGiaCr-28
❑ 76PhoGiaCa-18
❑ 76PhoGiaCC-18
❑ 76PhoGiaVNB-19
❑ 77GalGloG-156
❑ 77PhoGiaCC-19
❑ 77PhoGiaCP-19
❑ 77PhoGiaVNB-19
❑ 78PhoGiaC-21
❑ 79PhoGiaVNB-8
❑ 80PhoGiaVNB-6
Plank, Edward A.
❑ 03BreE10-118
❑ 04FanCraAL-41
❑ 08AmeCarE91-20
❑ 08AmeCarE91-58
❑ 08RosComP-64
❑ 09AmeCarE90-1-89
❑ 09PhiCarE-20
❑ 09RamT20-95
❑ 09SpoNewSM-39
❑ 09T206-293
❑ 10E-UOraBSC-19
❑ 10E12AmeCDCE125-31
❑ 10LuxCigPP-19
❑ 10NadE1-49
❑ 10PeoT21-45
❑ 10SepAnoP-21
❑ 10StaCarE-25
❑ 10W555-56
❑ 11A'sFirT20-16
❑ 11D35RocB-16
❑ 11DiaGumP-24
❑ 11PinT-5-503
❑ 11SpoLifCW-292
❑ 11SpoLifM-103
❑ 14CraJacE-6
❑ 14PolGroW-22
❑ 14TexTomE-38
❑ 15AmeCarE106-33
❑ 15CraJacE-6
❑ 39PC7AlbHoF-46
❑ 48ExhHoF-24
❑ 50CalHOFW-60
❑ 53ArtHaloFP-68
❑ 60Fle-46
❑ 61Fle-135
❑ 63BazA-9
❑ 68SCFOldT-26
❑ 72FleFamF-26
❑ 74A'sTCM1P-10
❑ 76ShaPiz-46
❑ 77BobParHoF-38
❑ 80Lau300-22
❑ 80MarExh-24
❑ 80PerHaloFP-46
❑ 80SSPHOF-46
❑ 81ConTSN-82
❑ 84GalHaloFRL-44
❑ 84OCoandSI-173
❑ 87ConSer2-49
❑ 88ConSer3-22
❑ 88FriBasCM-5
❑ 89HOFStiB-78
❑ 92ConTSN-463
❑ 93CraJac-19
❑ 94ConTSN-1002
❑ 94ConTSNB-1002
❑ 96PitPosH-10
Plante, Bill
❑ 85ElmPioT-16
❑ 86GreHorP-16
Plantenberg, Erik
❑ 89SanDieSAS-23
❑ 90ElmPioP-19
❑ 90SanDieSA3-8
❑ 91CarLeaAP-CAR26
❑ 91LynRedSC-6
❑ 91LynRedSP-1195
❑ 92LynRedSC-13
❑ 92LynRedSF-2904
❑ 93JacSunF-2711
❑ 94Don-647
❑ 94Fle-297
❑ 94JacSunF-1410
❑ 94StaClu-518
❑ 94StaCluFDI-518
❑ 94StaCluGR-518
❑ 94StaCluMOP-518
❑ 94Top-774
❑ 94TopGol-774
❑ 94TopSpa-773
❑ 96CanIndB-20
❑ 97PhiTeal-41
❑ 98FreGriG-24
Plantier, Phil
❑ 87ElmPioRC-34
❑ 88WinHavRSS-20
❑ 89LynRedSS-18
❑ 89Sta-170
❑ 90CMC-272
❑ 90PawRedSC-21
❑ 90PawRedSDD-20
❑ 90PawRedSP-474
❑ 90ProAAAF-446
❑ 90TopMag-67
❑ 90TopTVRS-57
❑ 91Bow-117
❑ 91Cla1-T22
❑ 91Cla2-T66
❑ 91ClaGam-128
❑ 91Don-41
❑ 91Fle-107
❑ 91LinDriAAA-365
❑ 91OPC-474
❑ 91PawRedSDD-17
❑ 91PawRedSLD-365
❑ 91PawRedSP-51
❑ 91RedSoxP-15
❑ 91Sco-348
❑ 91StaClu-459
❑ 91Stu-18
❑ 91Top-474
❑ 91TopDeb90-125
❑ 91TopDesS-474
❑ 91TopMic-474
❑ 91TopTif-474
❑ 91TriA AAGP-AAA31
❑ 91Ult-38
❑ 91UppDec-2
❑ 92Bow-459
❑ 92Cla1-T71
❑ 92ClaGam-111
❑ 92Don-488
❑ 92DonCraJ2-28
❑ 92Fle-44
❑ 92FleRooS-19
❑ 92Hig5-8
❑ 92Lea-50
❑ 92LeaBlaG-50
❑ 92LeaGolP-14
❑ 92LeaPre-14
❑ 92MVPPin-6
❑ 92OPC-782
❑ 92OPCPre-74
❑ 92Pin-51
❑ 92PinTea2-2
❑ 92ProFS7-14
❑ 92RedSoxDD-22
❑ 92Sco-406
❑ 92Sco100RS-86
❑ 92ScoImpP-20
❑ 92ScoProP-15
❑ 92StaClu-760
❑ 92StaCluNC-760
❑ 92StaPla-1
❑ 92StaPla-2
❑ 92StaPla-3
❑ 92StaPla-4
❑ 92StaPla-5
❑ 92StaPla-6
❑ 92StaPla-7
❑ 92StaPla-8
❑ 92StaPla-9
❑ 92StaPla-10
❑ 92StaPla-11
❑ 92Stu-136
❑ 92Top-782
❑ 92TopGol-782
❑ 92TopGolW-782
❑ 92TopMic-782
❑ 92TriPla-120
❑ 92Ult-318
❑ 92UppDec-425
❑ 92UppDecF-7
❑ 92UppDecFG-7
❑ 92UppDecWB-T18
❑ 93Bow-278
❑ 93Don-3
❑ 93Fla-136
❑ 93Fle-564
❑ 93FleFinE-144
❑ 93FunPac-140
❑ 93Lea-275
❑ 93OPC-332
❑ 93OPCPre-10
❑ 93PacSpa-599
❑ 93PadMot-8
❑ 93PanSti-99
❑ 93Pin-539
❑ 93RedFolS-74
❑ 93Sco-176
❑ 93Sel-242
❑ 93SelRoo-128T
❑ 93SP-171
❑ 93StaClu-282
❑ 93StaClu-614
❑ 93StaCluFDI-282
❑ 93StaCluFDI-614
❑ 93StaCluMOP-282
❑ 93StaCluMOP-614
❑ 93Top-592
❑ 93TopGol-592
❑ 93TopInaM-592
❑ 93TopInaR-592
❑ 93TopMic-592
❑ 93TopTra-42T
❑ 93Ult-475
❑ 93UppDec-274
❑ 93UppDec-474
❑ 93UppDec-774
❑ 93UppDecGold-274
❑ 93UppDecGold-474
❑ 93UppDecGold-774
❑ 94Bow-616
❑ 94ChuHomS-22
❑ 94ChuHomSG-22
❑ 94ColC-232
❑ 94ColChoGS-232
❑ 94ColChoSS-232
❑ 94Don-566
❑ 94Fin-84
❑ 94FinPre-84P
❑ 94FinRef-84
❑ 94Fla-235
❑ 94Fle-672
❑ 94FleExtB-376
❑ 94FUnPac-62
❑ 94Lea-59
❑ 94LeaL-153
❑ 94OPC-65
❑ 94Pac-532
❑ 94PacGolP-18
❑ 94PadMot-11

❑ 94PanSti-258
❑ 94Pin-80
❑ 94PinArtP-80
❑ 94PinMusC-80
❑ 94PinPowS-PS21
❑ 94ProMag-118
❑ 94Sco-404
❑ 94ScoGolR-404
❑ 94Sel-120
❑ 94SP-132
❑ 94SPDieC-132
❑ 94Spo-64
❑ 94StaClu-115
❑ 94StaCluFDI-115
❑ 94StaCluGR-115
❑ 94StaCluMOP-115
❑ 94Stu-135
❑ 94Top-13
❑ 94TopGol-13
❑ 94TopSpa-13
❑ 94TriPla-170
❑ 94Ult-583
❑ 94UppDec-145
❑ 94UppDecAJ-17
❑ 94UppDecAJG-17
❑ 94UppDecED-145
❑ 94USPlaCA-2C
❑ 95AstMot-15
❑ 95ColCho-120
❑ 95ColChoGS-120
❑ 95ColChoSE-164
❑ 95ColChoSEGS-164
❑ 95ColChoSESS-164
❑ 95ColChoSS-120
❑ 95Don-135
❑ 95DonPreP-135
❑ 95Emo-140
❑ 95Fin-275
❑ 95FinRef-275
❑ 95Fla-363
❑ 95Fle-566
❑ 95FleUpd-143
❑ 95Lea-308
❑ 95LeaLim-155
❑ 95Pac-368
❑ 95Pin-214
❑ 95PinArtP-214
❑ 95PinMusC-214
❑ 95Sco-430
❑ 95ScoGolR-430
❑ 95ScoPlaTS-430
❑ 95Sel-223
❑ 95SelArtP-223
❑ 95Spo-124
❑ 95SpoArtP-124
❑ 95StaClu-412
❑ 95StaClu-608
❑ 95StaCluMOP-412
❑ 95StaCluMOP-608
❑ 95StaCluSTWS-412
❑ 95StaCluSTWS-608
❑ 95StaCluVR-211
❑ 95StaCluVRMO-211
❑ 95Stu-108
❑ 95Top-176
❑ 95TopCyb-102
❑ 95TopTra-149T
❑ 95Ult-390
❑ 95UltGolM-390
❑ 95UppDec-273
❑ 95UppDec-474
❑ 95UppDecED-273
❑ 95UppDecEDG-273
❑ 95UppDecSE-177
❑ 95UppDecSEG-177
❑ 96A'sMot-15
❑ 96ColCho-358
❑ 96ColChoGS-358
❑ 96ColChoSS-358
❑ 96Don-528
❑ 96DonPreP-528
❑ 96Fle-119
❑ 96FleTif-119
❑ 96FleUpd-U75
❑ 96FleUpdTC-U75
❑ 96LeaSigA-182
❑ 96LeaSigAG-182
❑ 96LeaSigAS-182
❑ 96PacPri-P63
❑ 96PacPriG-P63
❑ 96Pin-29
❑ 96Sco-454
❑ 96Ult-287
❑ 96Ult-403
❑ 96UltGolM-287
❑ 96UltGolM-403
❑ 96UppDec-333
❑ 97LasVegS1A-25

Plants, Dan
❑ 84ElPasDT-17

Plaskett, Elmo
❑ 63Top-549

Plaster, Allen
❑ 91BluOriC-19
❑ 91BluOriP-4127
❑ 92FreKeyC-12
❑ 92FreKeyF-1803
❑ 93ModA'sC-16
❑ 93ModA'sF-797
❑ 94ModA'sC-19
❑ 94ModA'sF-3063
❑ 95HunStaTI-21

Platei, Mark
❑ 79AppFoxT-22
❑ 80GleFalWSBT-5
❑ 80GleFalWSCT-9
❑ 81AppFoxT-9

Platt, Mizell
❑ 49Bow-89
❑ 49Lea-159

Platts, Jim
❑ 87SpaPhiP-1
❑ 88SpaPhiP-1048

Plautz, Rick
❑ 82ForMyeRT-9

Plaza, Ron
❑ 62KahAtl-16
❑ 69PilPos-33
❑ 77PilPosR-33
❑ 80RedEnq-11
❑ 83Pil69G-23
❑ 86A'sMot-27

Pleasac, Joe
❑ 86ChaRaiP-21

Pledger, Kinnis
❑ 88SouBenWSGS-9
❑ 89SouBenWSGS-19
❑ 90SarWhiSS-20
❑ 91BirBarLD-70
❑ 91BirBarP-1467
❑ 91LinDriAA-70
❑ 92BirBarS-91
❑ 92SarWhiSF-221
❑ 92SkyAA F-44
❑ 93BirBarF-1205
❑ 96NorNavB-18
❑ 97WicWra-23
❑ 98BriBluM-23

Pleicones, Johnnie
❑ 86Ft.LauYP-18

Plein, Ronald
❑ 93CedRapKC-30
❑ 97CedRapK-21
❑ 98CedRapKTI-23

Pleis, Scott
❑ 83EriCarT-14

Pleis, William
❑ 62Top-124
❑ 62TopVen-124
❑ 63Top-293
❑ 63TwiVol-16
❑ 64Top-484
❑ 65OPC-122
❑ 65Top-122
❑ 78TCM60I-135
❑ 78TwiFri-41

Plemel, Lee
❑ 88HamRedP-1726
❑ 89SprCarB-11
❑ 90St.PetCS-18
❑ 91ArkTraLD-42
❑ 91ArkTraP-1285
❑ 91LinDriAA-42
❑ 92ArkTraF-1128
❑ 92ArkTraS-41

Plemmons, Ron
❑ 89UtiBluSP-18
❑ 90Bes-36
❑ 90SouBenWSB-7
❑ 90SouBenWSGS-13
❑ 91SarWhiSC-24
❑ 91SarWhiSP-1125
❑ 92SarWhiSF-222

Plemmons, Scott
❑ 90Bes-299
❑ 90ChaWheP-2238
❑ 92CedRapRC-22
❑ 92CedRapRF-1072

Plesac, Dan
❑ 86BrePol-37
❑ 86DonRoo-14
❑ 86FleUpd-90
❑ 86SpoRoo-10
❑ 86TopTra-87T
❑ 86TopTraT-87T
❑ 87BrePol-37
❑ 87BreTeal-10
❑ 87Don-214
❑ 87Fle-354
❑ 87FleGlo-354
❑ 87SpoTeaP-19
❑ 87Top-279
❑ 87TopSti-201
❑ 87TopTif-279
❑ 87ToyRoo-22
❑ 88BrePol-37
❑ 88BreTeal-29
❑ 88Don-109
❑ 88DonAll-18
❑ 88DonBasB-221
❑ 88Fle-171
❑ 88Fle-625
❑ 88FleGlo-171
❑ 88FleGlo-625
❑ 88FleMin-32
❑ 88FleStiC-39
❑ 88OPC-317
❑ 88PanSti-118
❑ 88RedFolSB-70
❑ 88Sco-77
❑ 88ScoGlo-77
❑ 88ScoYouS2-32
❑ 88Spo-191
❑ 88StaLinBre-13
❑ 88Top-670
❑ 88TopMinL-20
❑ 88TopSti-203
❑ 88TopStiB-65
❑ 88TopTif-670
❑ 89Bow-133
❑ 89BowTif-133
❑ 89BreGar-8
❑ 89BrePol-37
❑ 89BreYea-37
❑ 89CadEllD-40
❑ 89Don-382
❑ 89DonAll-22
❑ 89DonBasB-165
❑ 89Fle-195
❑ 89FleGlo-195
❑ 89FleLeaL-29
❑ 89FleSup-32
❑ 89OPC-167
❑ 89PanSti-367
❑ 89Sco-320
❑ 89ScoHot1S-32
❑ 89Spo-128
❑ 89Top-740
❑ 89TopBasT-131
❑ 89TopSti-197
❑ 89TopTif-740
❑ 89UppDec-630
❑ 90Bow-386
❑ 90BowTif-386
❑ 90BreMilB-19
❑ 90BrePol-37
❑ 90Don-175
❑ 90DonBesA-36
❑ 90El PasDAGTI-5
❑ 90Fle-334
❑ 90FleBasA-28
❑ 90FleBasAC-28
❑ 90FleCan-334
❑ 90FleLeaL-29
❑ 90FleLeaLC-29
❑ 90K-M-30
❑ 90Lea-216
❑ 90MLBBasB-85
❑ 90OPC-490
❑ 90PanSti-95
❑ 90PubIntS-503
❑ 90RedFolSB-74
❑ 90Sco-86
❑ 90Sco100S-86
❑ 90Spo-102
❑ 90Top-490
❑ 90TopBig-33
❑ 90TopMinL-21
❑ 90TopSti-200
❑ 90TopTif-490
❑ 90TopTVA-31
❑ 90UppDec-477
❑ 91Bow-34
❑ 91BreMilB-20
❑ 91BrePol-18
❑ 91ClaGam-33
❑ 91Don-104
❑ 91Fle-594
❑ 91Lea-287
❑ 91OPC-146
❑ 91PanFreS-212
❑ 91PanSti-163
❑ 91RedFolS-72
❑ 91Sco-275
❑ 91StaClu-7
❑ 91Top-146
❑ 91TopDesS-146
❑ 91TopMic-146
❑ 91TopTif-146
❑ 91Ult-179
❑ 91UppDec-322
❑ 92BrePol-19
❑ 92Don-682
❑ 92Fle-185
❑ 92OPC-303
❑ 92Pin-162
❑ 92Sco-567
❑ 92StaClu-532
❑ 92Top-303
❑ 92TopGol-303
❑ 92TopGolW-303
❑ 92TopMic-303
❑ 92Ult-388
❑ 92UppDec-550
❑ 93CubMar-20
❑ 93CubStaC-6
❑ 93Don-677
❑ 93Fle-633
❑ 93Lea-388
❑ 93OPC-297
❑ 93PacSpa-381
❑ 93Pin-433
❑ 93Sco-456
❑ 93StaClu-24
❑ 93StaCluFDI-24
❑ 93StaCluMOP-24
❑ 93Top-16
❑ 93TopGol-16
❑ 93TopInaM-16
❑ 93TopInaR-16
❑ 93TopMic-16
❑ 93TriPla-142
❑ 93Ult-318
❑ 93UppDec-804
❑ 93UppDecGold-804
❑ 94BreMilB-165
❑ 94Don-641
❑ 94Fle-393
❑ 94StaClu-256
❑ 94StaCluFDI-256
❑ 94StaCluGR-256
❑ 94StaCluMOP-256
❑ 94StaCluT-355
❑ 94StaCluTFDI-355
❑ 94Top-215
❑ 94TopGol-215
❑ 94TopSpa-215
❑ 95DonTopotO-324
❑ 95Fle-421
❑ 95FleUpd-151
❑ 95PirFil-26
❑ 96Fle-532
❑ 96FleTif-532
❑ 96Ult-537
❑ 96UltGolM-537
❑ 97BluJayOH-24
❑ 97BluJayS-9
❑ 98PacOnl-771
❑ 98PacOnlR-771
❑ 98PacOnlWC-771
❑ 99Fle-523
❑ 99FleSta9-523
❑ 99FleWarT-523

Pless, Rance
❑ 56A'sPos-34
❑ 56Top-339
❑ 79TCM50-176

Pletsch, John
❑ 93SanJosGC-29

Plews, Herb
❑ 57Top-169
❑ 58SeaTeal-22
❑ 58SenJayP-9
❑ 58Top-109
❑ 59Top-373
❑ 60MapLeaSF-16
❑ 61MapLeaBH-16

Plinski, Paul
❑ 79CedRapGT-17

Plitt, Norman
❑ 28Zee-38
❑ 29Zee-27
❑ 90DodTar-1051

Ploeger, Tim
❑ 91SpoIndC-13
❑ 91SpoIndP-3948
❑ 92SpoIndC-22
❑ 92SpoIndF-1292
❑ 93PocPosF-4208
❑ 93PocPosSP-17
❑ 94HigDesMC-20
❑ 94HigDesMF-2787

Plonk, Chad
❑ 92GulCoaYF-3791

Plonk, Chris
❑ 92HunCubC-23
❑ 92HunCubF-3156

Plooy, Eric
❑ 96BoiHawB-23

Ploucher, George
❑ 77CocAstT-18

Plumb, Dave
❑ 87SumBraP-13
❑ 88CarLeaAS-34
❑ 88DurBulS-17
❑ 89GreBraB-25
❑ 89GreBraP-1164
❑ 89GreBraS-17
❑ 89RicBraBC-20
❑ 90GreBraB-2
❑ 90GreBraP-1133
❑ 90GreBraS-15

Plumlee, Chris
❑ 93WatIndC-22
❑ 93WatIndF-3560
❑ 94ButCopKSP-18

Plummer, Bill Francis
❑ 70RelPam-9
❑ 73OPC-177
❑ 73Top-177
❑ 74OPC-524
❑ 74Top-524
❑ 75OPC-656
❑ 75Top-656
❑ 75TopMin-656
❑ 76OPC-627
❑ 76SSP-32
❑ 76Top-627
❑ 77Top-239
❑ 78SanJosMMC-19
❑ 78Top-106
❑ 79OPC-208
❑ 79SpoIndT-10
❑ 79Top-396
❑ 80SanJosMJitB-1
❑ 81WauTimT-29
❑ 82MarPos-26
❑ 84ChaLooT-8
❑ 86CalCanP-21
❑ 87CalCanP-2312
❑ 88CalCanC-24
❑ 88CalCanP-800
❑ 88TriAAAP-49
❑ 89MarMot-27
❑ 90MarMot-27
❑ 92MarMot-1
❑ 92OPC-171
❑ 92Top-171
❑ 92TopGol-171
❑ 92TopGolW-171
❑ 92TopMic-171
❑ 94RocPol-27
❑ 95JacSunTI-23
❑ 96JacSunB-2

Plummer, Dale
❑ 88LitFalMP-20
❑ 89JacMetGS-28
❑ 89St.LucMS-19
❑ 89Sta-23
❑ 90CMC-360
❑ 90ProAAAF-273
❑ 90TidTidC-9
❑ 90TidTidP-542
❑ 90TopTVM-53
❑ 91LinDriAAA-566
❑ 91TidTidLD-566
❑ 91TidTidP-2507
❑ 92TidTidF-894
❑ 92TidTidS-568
❑ 93NorTidF-2568
❑ 95PawRedSDD-21
❑ 95PawRedTI-19

Plummer, Raymond
❑ 97VerExpB-22
❑ 98CapFeaCM-16

Plummer, William
❑ 23Zee-168
❑ 25Zee-143
❑ 26Zee-170

Plunk, Eric
❑ 85HunStaJ-33
❑ 86DonRoo-40
❑ 86Fle-649
❑ 86TacTigP-16
❑ 87Don-178
❑ 87Fle-403
❑ 87FleGlo-403
❑ 87Top-587
❑ 87TopTif-587
❑ 88A'sMot-20
❑ 88Don-503
❑ 88DonBasB-267
❑ 88DonTeaBA-503
❑ 88Fle-291
❑ 88FleGlo-291
❑ 88Sco-614
❑ 88ScoGlo-614
❑ 88Top-173
❑ 88TopClo-88
❑ 88TopTif-173
❑ 89A'sMot-16
❑ 89Bow-191
❑ 89BowTif-191
❑ 89Don-125
❑ 89DonBasB-49
❑ 89Fle-20
❑ 89FleGlo-20
❑ 89OPC-141
❑ 89Sco-392
❑ 89Top-448
❑ 89TopTif-448
❑ 89UppDec-353
❑ 90Don-196
❑ 90Fle-452
❑ 90FleCan-452
❑ 90Lea-504
❑ 90OPC-9
❑ 90PubIntS-313
❑ 90Top-9
❑ 90TopTif-9
❑ 90TopTVY-17
❑ 90UppDec-630
❑ 90YanScoNW-20
❑ 91Don-593
❑ 91Fle-676
❑ 91OPC-786
❑ 91Sco-428
❑ 91StaClu-529
❑ 91Top-786
❑ 91TopDesS-786
❑ 91TopMic-786
❑ 91TopTif-786
❑ 91Ult-241
❑ 91UppDec-695
❑ 92Don-554
❑ 92Fle-241
❑ 92OPC-672
❑ 92Sco-379
❑ 92Top-672
❑ 92TopGol-672
❑ 92TopGolW-672
❑ 92TopMic-672
❑ 92UppDec-608
❑ 92YanWIZ8-148
❑ 93Fla-198
❑ 93Fle-599
❑ 93IndWUA-25
❑ 93PacSpa-417
❑ 93Sco-594
❑ 93StaClu-486
❑ 93StaCluFDI-486
❑ 93StaCluMOP-486
❑ 93UppDec-713
❑ 93UppDecGold-713
❑ 94Don-267
❑ 94Fla-288
❑ 94Fle-118
❑ 94Pac-182
❑ 94Pin-366
❑ 94PinArtP-366
❑ 94PinMusC-366
❑ 94Sco-131
❑ 94ScoGolR-131
❑ 94Top-577
❑ 94TopGol-577
❑ 94TopSpa-577
❑ 94Ult-47
❑ 95Don-396
❑ 95DonPreP-396
❑ 95DonTopotO-65
❑ 95Fle-144
❑ 95Sco-542
❑ 95ScoGolR-542
❑ 95ScoPlaTS-542
❑ 95Top-256
❑ 95Ult-40

❑ 95UltGolM-40
❑ 96Don-479
❑ 96DonPreP-479
❑ 96Fle-97
❑ 96FleTif-97
❑ 96IndFle-13
❑ 96LeaSigEA-161
❑ 97Fle-86
❑ 97FleTif-86
❑ 97IndScoU-14
❑ 97IndScoUTC-14
❑ 98PacInvGems-40
❑ 98PacOnl-228
❑ 98PacOnlR-228
❑ 98PacOnlWC-228
❑ 98UppDec-673

Plunkett, Wilson
❑ 75ForLauYS-23

Plympton, Jeff
❑ 88LynRedSS-18
❑ 89NewBriRSP-622
❑ 89NewBriRSS-16
❑ 90Bes-242
❑ 90EasLeaAP-EL33
❑ 90NewBriRSB-20
❑ 90NewBriRSP-1319
❑ 90NewBriRSS-15
❑ 90ProAaA-8
❑ 91LinDriAAA-366
❑ 91PawRedSDD-18
❑ 91PawRedSLD-366
❑ 91PawRedSP-38
❑ 92PawRedSF-920
❑ 92PawRedSS-362
❑ 92ProFS7-19
❑ 92Sco-823
❑ 92Sco100RS-13
❑ 92SkyAAAF-164
❑ 92StaClu-481
❑ 92TopDeb91-140
❑ 92UppDec-71
❑ 93PawRedSDD-21
❑ 93RedSoxWHP-21
❑ 97DunDonPPS-18

Poat, Ray
❑ 48Bow-42
❑ 48GiaTeal-21
❑ 49GiaTeal-22

Pocekay, Walter
❑ 53MotCoo-10

Poche, Gerry
❑ 76BatRouCT-18

Pocoroba, Biff
❑ 75AtlBraP-29
❑ 76AtlBraP-25
❑ 76OPC-103
❑ 76SSP-15
❑ 76Top-103
❑ 77Top-594
❑ 78BraCok-13
❑ 78Hos-99
❑ 78Top-296
❑ 79BasPat-70
❑ 79OPC-285
❑ 79Top-555
❑ 80OPC-73
❑ 80Top-132
❑ 81BraPol-4
❑ 81Fle-257
❑ 81Top-326
❑ 82BraBurKL-20
❑ 82BraPol-4
❑ 82Fle-446
❑ 82Top-88
❑ 83BraPol-4
❑ 83Don-436
❑ 83Fle-145
❑ 83OPC-367
❑ 83Top-676
❑ 84Don-77
❑ 84Fle-189
❑ 84Nes792-438
❑ 84Top-438
❑ 84TopTif-438

Podbielan, Bud (Clarence)
❑ 50WorWidGV-12
❑ 52Top-188
❑ 53BowBW-21
❑ 53Top-237
❑ 54Top-69
❑ 55Top-153
❑ 56SeaPop-14
❑ 56Top-224
❑ 57SeaPop-19
❑ 74dod195T-30
❑ 83TopRep5-188
❑ 90DodTar-627
❑ 91DodRinP2-7
❑ 91TopArc1-237
❑ 94TopArc1-69
❑ 94TopArc1G-69
❑ 95TopArcBD-10

Podesednik, Scott
❑ 96BreCouMB-25

Podgajny, Johnny
❑ 93ConTSN-948

Podjan, Jim
❑ 96OgdRapTI-45

Podres, Johnny
❑ 47PM1StaP1-165
❑ 47StaPinP2-32
❑ 52Par-76
❑ 53Top-263
❑ 54Top-166
❑ 55Bow-97
❑ 55DodGolS-4
❑ 55Top-25
❑ 55TopDouH-111
❑ 56Dod-23
❑ 56Top-173
❑ 57SwiFra-1
❑ 57Top-277
❑ 58DodBelB-7
❑ 58DodJayP-10
❑ 58DodTeal-19
❑ 58DodVol-10
❑ 58Hir-42
❑ 58Top-120
❑ 59ArmCoi-13
❑ 59DodMor-9
❑ 59DodPos-3
❑ 59DodTeal-21
❑ 59DodVol-11
❑ 59Top-262
❑ 59Top-495
❑ 60DodBelB-19
❑ 60DodJayP-11
❑ 60DodMor-9
❑ 60DodPos-9
❑ 60DodTeal-14
❑ 60DodUniO-14
❑ 60NuHi-2
❑ 60Top-425
❑ 61DodBelB-22
❑ 61DodJayP-8
❑ 61DodUniO-16
❑ 61NuSco-474
❑ 61Pos-169
❑ 61Top-109
❑ 61Top-207
❑ 61TopStal-31
❑ 62DodBelB-22
❑ 62DodJayP-8
❑ 62DodVol-21
❑ 62Jel-108
❑ 62Pos-108
❑ 62PosCan-108
❑ 62SalPlaC-172
❑ 62ShiPlaC-172
❑ 62Top-280
❑ 62TopBuc-71
❑ 62TopStal-138
❑ 63DodJayP-9
❑ 63SalMetC-9
❑ 63Top-150
❑ 63Top-412
❑ 64ChatheY-42
❑ 64Top-580
❑ 65ChaTheY-43
❑ 65DodTeal-16
❑ 65Top-387
❑ 66Top-468
❑ 67CokCapTi-15
❑ 67DexPre-170
❑ 67TigDexP-7
❑ 67Top-284
❑ 68LauWorS-52
❑ 69PadVol-6
❑ 69Top-659
❑ 70FleWorS-52
❑ 73OPC-12
❑ 73PadDea-21
❑ 73Top-12A
❑ 73Top-12B
❑ 78TCM60I-156
❑ 79TCM50-239
❑ 79TCM50-267
❑ 81TwiPos-21
❑ 82Don-566
❑ 82TwiPos-23
❑ 83TwiTeal-30
❑ 83TwiTeal-34
❑ 84MinTwiP-23
❑ 84TwiTeal-31
❑ 85TwiPos-20
❑ 85TwiTeal-18
❑ 85TwiTeal-33
❑ 87DodSmoA-26
❑ 88DodRinP1-6A
❑ 88PacLegI-105
❑ 89DodSmoG-63
❑ 90DodTar-628
❑ 90PacLeg-45
❑ 90SweBasG-104
❑ 91PhiMed-32
❑ 91SweBasG-73
❑ 91TopArc1-263
❑ 92DodStaTA-1
❑ 92PhiMed-24
❑ 93PhiMed-26
❑ 93TedWilM-8
❑ 93UppDecAH-106
❑ 94PhiMed-25
❑ 94TopArc1-166
❑ 94TopArc1G-166
❑ 94UppDecAH-63
❑ 94UppDecAH1-63
❑ 95Phi-23
❑ 95TopArcBD-56
❑ 95TopArcBD-77
❑ 95TopArcBD-93
❑ 95TopArcBD-120
❑ 95TopArcBD-127
❑ 95TopArcBD-153
❑ 96PhiTeal-26
❑ 99SpollIGotG-15
❑ 99SpollIGotGA-58
❑ 99SpollIGotGC-1

Podsednik, Scott
❑ 95HudValRTI-2
❑ 98Cha-20

Poe, Bill
❑ 72CedRapCT-28

Poe, Charles
❑ 90HigSchPLS-6
❑ 91SouBenWSC-10
❑ 91SouBenWSP-2870
❑ 92ClaFS7-261
❑ 92SouBenWSF-191
❑ 93SarWhiSC-21
❑ 93SarWhiSF-1384
❑ 94PriWilCC-20
❑ 94PriWilCF-1935
❑ 95SPML-34
❑ 96BesAutS-73
❑ 96BirBarB-25
❑ 96Exc-35
❑ 96HunStaTI-20
❑ 97MobBayBB-24
❑ 98Las-19

Poe, Rick
❑ 82JacMetT-13

Poe, Ryan
❑ 98HelBreM-28

Poehl, Michael
❑ 86WatIndP-21
❑ 87KinIndP-9
❑ 88EasLeaAP-42
❑ 88WilBilP-1325
❑ 91LinDriAA-415
❑ 91MemChiLD-415
❑ 91MemChiP-652

Poepping, Mike
❑ 75TacTwiK-21

Poff, John William
❑ 81EdmTraRR-2
❑ 94BreMilB-166

Poffenberger, Boots
❑ 79DiaGre-389
❑ 90DodTar-629

Pohl, Jeff
❑ 96BelGiaTI-21
❑ 97SalVolG-29

Pohle, Rich
❑ 88IdaFalBP-1861

Pohle, Walt
❑ 85BelBreT-2
❑ 86StoPorP-21
❑ 87ElPasDP-19

Poholsky, Tom
❑ 52Top-242
❑ 54CarHunW-15
❑ 54Top-142
❑ 55Bow-76
❑ 55CarHunW-16
❑ 56Top-196
❑ 57Top-235
❑ 83TopRep5-242
❑ 94TopArc1-142
❑ 94TopArc1G-142

Poindexter, Mike
❑ 81BatTroT-5
❑ 83WatIndF-24

Pointer, Aaron
❑ 67CokCapAs-11
❑ 67Top-564

Pointer, Corey
❑ 94SigRooDP-41
❑ 94SigRooDPS-41
❑ 94StaCluDP-89
❑ 94StaCluDPFDI-89
❑ 94TopTra-98T
❑ 95DanBraTI-22
❑ 96EugEmeB-1
❑ 97AugGre-30
❑ 97SouAtlTPB-4
❑ 98CarLeaAC-15
❑ 98CarLeaAC-25
❑ 98LynHilQ-22

Pointer-Jones, Carl
❑ 88BurBraP-2

Poissant, Rod
❑ 86LakTigP-17
❑ 87GleFalTP-16
❑ 89SanBerSCLC-75
❑ 90PenPilS-16
❑ 90StaFS7-78

Polak, Rich
❑ 90PriWilCTI-19
❑ 91Ft.LauYC-11
❑ 91Ft.LauYP-2424
❑ 92PriWilCC-17
❑ 92PriWilCF-144
❑ 93AlbYanF-2161
❑ 93LinVenB-267

Polakowski, Ted
❑ 84IdaFalATI-21

Polanco, Carlos
❑ 91BoiHawC-21
❑ 91BoiHawP-3888
❑ 91QuaCitAC-21
❑ 91QuaCitAP-2640

Polanco, Elvis
❑ 97RocCub-24
❑ 97WilCubB-18

Polanco, Enohel
❑ 97St.LucM-22
❑ 98BinMetQ-23

Polanco, Felipe
❑ 94AugGreC-19
❑ 94AugGreF-3018
❑ 94WelPirC-19
❑ 94WelPirF-3503

Polanco, Giovanni
❑ 91BelMarCB-26
❑ 91BelMarP-3660
❑ 92LetMouSP-3

Polanco, Juan
❑ 96SouOreTI-6

Polanco, Nicholas
❑ 89KinMetS-19
❑ 90KinMetB-12
❑ 90KinMetS-19

Polanco, Placido
❑ 95PeoChiTI-10
❑ 96StPetCB-24
❑ 97ArkTraB-17
❑ 97TexAllM-48
❑ 98Bes-87
❑ 98FleUpd-U77
❑ 98LeaRS-335
❑ 98LeaRSLHolo-335
❑ 98LeaRSLong-335
❑ 98LeaRTrue-335
❑ 98MemRedG-17
❑ 99Fle-566
❑ 99FleSta9-566
❑ 99FleWarT-566
❑ 99Pac-361
❑ 99PacCroC-235
❑ 99PacCroCPB-235
❑ 99PacPlaB-361
❑ 99PacRed-361
❑ 99Spolll-48

Polanco, Radhames
❑ 87LitFalMP-2402
❑ 88LitFalMP-10
❑ 89ColMetB-21
❑ 89ColMetGS-21

Polanco, Roger
❑ 75DubPacT-12
❑ 76VenLeaS-56

Poland, Philip
❑ 09T206-456

Poland, Trey
❑ 98Cha-4

Polasek, John
❑ 89AncGlaP-19
❑ 90JamExpP-24
❑ 91WesPalBEC-9
❑ 91WesPalBEP-1225
❑ 92FreKeyC-14
❑ 92FreKeyF-1804
❑ 92HagSunF-2553
❑ 93FreKeyC-21
❑ 93FreKeyF-1026

Polcovich, Kevin
❑ 92WelPirF-1332
❑ 93AugPirC-15
❑ 93AugPirF-1553
❑ 94CarMudF-1587
❑ 95CarMudF-168
❑ 97CalCanB-20
❑ 97CarMudC-18
❑ 97PirPos-28
❑ 97Sel-161
❑ 97SelCom-161
❑ 98ColCho-209
❑ 98ColChoSQ-SQ9
❑ 98Fle-228
❑ 98MetUni-78
❑ 98MetUniPMG-78
❑ 98Pac-400
❑ 98PacOnl-591
❑ 98PacOnlR-591
❑ 98PacOnlWC-591
❑ 98PacPlaB-400
❑ 98PacRedT-400
❑ 98PacSil-400
❑ 98Spolll-171
❑ 98SpollIEE-171
❑ 98SpollIFE-171
❑ 98StaCluFDI-341
❑ 98StaClul-341
❑ 98StaCluOneK-341
❑ 98StaCluPP-341
❑ 98Top-79
❑ 98TopChr-79
❑ 98TopChrR-79
❑ 98TopDevR-79
❑ 98TopDia-79
❑ 98TopMiniC-79
❑ 98Ult-115
❑ 98UltGolM-115
❑ 98UltMas-115
❑ 98UltPlaM-115
❑ 98UppDec-191
❑ 98UppDecSF-103
❑ 99StaClu-6
❑ 99StaCluFDI-6
❑ 99StaCluOoaK-6
❑ 99StaCluPP-6

Poldberg, Brian
❑ 81NasSouTI-13
❑ 82NasSouTI-18
❑ 83OmaRoyT-11
❑ 84OmaRoyT-23
❑ 85OmaRoyT-31
❑ 87AppFoxP-17
❑ 88AppFoxP-162
❑ 89AppFoxP-872
❑ 90BasCitRS-28
❑ 91LinDriAAA-350
❑ 91OmaRoyLD-350
❑ 91OmaRoyP-1051
❑ 92MemChiF-2435
❑ 92MemChiS-449
❑ 94EugEmeC-28
❑ 95SprSulTI-20
❑ 96LanLugB-1

Pole, Dick
❑ 74OPC-596
❑ 74Top-596
❑ 75OPC-513
❑ 75Top-513
❑ 75TopMin-513
❑ 76OPC-326
❑ 76Top-326
❑ 77MarPos-16
❑ 77Top-187
❑ 78Top-233
❑ 80PorBeaT-11
❑ 81BirBarT-19
❑ 83QuaCitCT-3
❑ 86PitCubP-19
❑ 87IowCubTI-21
❑ 88CubDavB-NNO
❑ 89CubMar-NNO
❑ 90CubMar-28
❑ 90TopTVCu-5
❑ 91CubVinL-21
❑ 92PawRedSF-941
❑ 92PawRedSS-375
❑ 93GiaMot-28
❑ 93GiaPos-27
❑ 94GiaMot-28
❑ 95GiaMot-28
❑ 96GiaMot-28
❑ 97DunDonPPS-19

Polemil, Miguel
❑ 85DomLeaS-102

Poles, Spot
❑ 74LauOldTBS-21

Polese, Joe
❑ 77NewCoPT-26

Polewski, Steve
❑ 90WelPirP-7
❑ 91AugPirC-17
❑ 91AugPirP-813

Polhemus, Mark
❑ 87BucN28-45

Polidor, Gus
❑ 80VenLeaS-185
❑ 81HolMilT-21
❑ 82HolMilT-18
❑ 83NasAngT-14
❑ 85EdmTraC-12
❑ 86EdmTraP-22
❑ 86Fle-650
❑ 87AngSmo-18
❑ 87CalAngPPS-30
❑ 87Don-579
❑ 88AngSmo-6
❑ 88Don-356
❑ 88Fle-501
❑ 88FleGlo-501
❑ 88Sco-341
❑ 88ScoGlo-341
❑ 88Top-708
❑ 88TopClo-89
❑ 88TopTif-708
❑ 89BrePol-14
❑ 90BrePol-14
❑ 90Don-412
❑ 90OPC-313
❑ 90Top-313
❑ 90TopTif-313
❑ 90UppDec-480
❑ 92TacTigF-2511
❑ 92TacTigS-544
❑ 93EdmTraF-1145
❑ 93LinVenB-225
❑ 94BreMilB-167
❑ 94VenLinU-64
❑ 95LinVen-241
❑ 95LinVen-330

Polidor, Wil
❑ 93HicCraC-19
❑ 93HicCraF-1287
❑ 93LinVenB-158
❑ 93SouBenWSC-18
❑ 94SouBenSHC-17
❑ 94SouBenSHF-602
❑ 94VenLinU-136
❑ 95LinVen-147
❑ 95PriWilCTI-10
❑ 96-97LinVen-231
❑ 97BirBarB-20

Poling, Mark
❑ 88CliGiaP-699

Polinski, Bob
❑ 76VenLeaS-65
❑ 78TacYanC-43
❑ 79ColCliT-15

Polis, Pete
❑ 92MedHatBJF-3211
❑ 92MedHatBJSP-16
❑ 93MedHatBJF-3741

Politte, Cliff
❑ 96MidLeaAB-21
❑ 96PeoChiB-24
❑ 97Bes-89
❑ 97BesGun-10
❑ 97Bow-419
❑ 97BowChr-279
❑ 97BowChrI-279
❑ 97BowChrIR-279
❑ 97BowChrR-279
❑ 97BowInt-419
❑ 97CalLeaATI-41
❑ 97CarLeaTP-12
❑ 97PriWilC-27
❑ 98ArkTraH-10
❑ 98Bow-330
❑ 98BowBes-168

❑ 98BowBesAR-168
❑ 98BowBesR-168
❑ 98BowCerBlueAU-60
❑ 98BowCerGA-60
❑ 98BowCerSA-60
❑ 98BowChr-330
❑ 98BowChrGA-330
❑ 98BowChrGAR-330
❑ 98BowChrI-330
❑ 98BowChrIR-330
❑ 98BowChrR-330
❑ 98BowGolA-330
❑ 98BowInt-330
❑ 98Don-293
❑ 98DonGolPP-293
❑ 98DonSilPP-293
❑ 98Fle-541
❑ 98LeaRS-289
❑ 98LeaRSLHolo-289
❑ 98LeaRSLong-289
❑ 98LeaRTrue-289
❑ 98MemRedG-18
❑ 98PacOmeRS-19
❑ 98PacOmeRST1-19
❑ 98PriWilCASM-6
❑ 98SkyDugA-95
❑ 98SkyDugAIA-95
❑ 98SP MinPE-104
❑ 98SPMin-104
❑ 98SPxFin-194
❑ 98SPxFinR-194
❑ 98SPxFinS-194
❑ 98Top-485
❑ 98TopChr-485
❑ 98TopChrR-485
❑ 98TopDevR-485
❑ 98TopDia-485
❑ 98TopMiniC-485
❑ 98UppDec-568
❑ 99MetUni-270
❑ 99MetUniGM-270
❑ 99MetUniPMG-270
❑ 99UppDecBD-114
❑ 99UppDecBDD-114
❑ 99UppDecBDQ-114
❑ 99UppDecBDT-114
Polk, Chad
❑ 98St.CatSM-24
Polk, Riley
❑ 87WatIndP-24
Polk, Ron
❑ 88MisStaB-25
❑ 89MisStaB-29
❑ 90MisStaB-30
❑ 91MisStaB-38
❑ 91TopTra-93T
❑ 91TopTraT-93T
❑ 92MisStaB-33
❑ 93MisStaB-36
Polk, Steve
❑ 88MisStaB-26
❑ 89MisStaB-30
❑ 90MisStaB-31
Polka, Fritz
❑ 86LitFalMP-23
❑ 87ColMetP-21
❑ 88FloStaLAS-17
❑ 88St.LucMS-19
Pollack, Chris
❑ 87JamExpP-2679
❑ 88RocExpLC-30
❑ 90WesPalBES-18
❑ 91HarSenLD-267
❑ 91HarSenP-624
❑ 91LinDriAA-267
❑ 92HarSenF-462
❑ 92HarSenS-297
Pollack, Rick
❑ 88BirBarB-15
Pollard, Damon
❑ 90EugEmeGS-23
❑ 91AppFoxCB-10
❑ 91AppFoxP-1716
❑ 92BasCitRC-6
❑ 92BasCitRF-3845
❑ 95HarSenTI-2
Pollard, Jim
❑ 52Whe-24A
❑ 52Whe-24B
Pollard, Nathaniel
❑ 93NegLeaRL2-30
Pollet, Howie (Howard)
❑ 39ExhSal-52A
❑ 39ExhSal-52B
❑ 46SeaSLP-48
❑ 46SpoExcW-8-2
❑ 49Bow-95
❑ 49EurSta-193
❑ 50Bow-72
❑ 51Bow-263
❑ 51R42SmaS-83
❑ 51TopRedB-7
❑ 52Bow-83
❑ 52Top-63
❑ 53NorBreL-21
❑ 53Top-83
❑ 54Top-89
❑ 55Top-76
❑ 55TopDouH-31
❑ 56Top-262
❑ 60Top-468
❑ 67AstTeal2-20
❑ 74CapPub-53
❑ 76TayBow4-37
❑ 77TCMTheWY-41
❑ 83Car194T-45
❑ 83TopRep5-63
❑ 85TCMPpl1-3
❑ 87AstSer1-30
❑ 91TopArc1-83
❑ 92BazQua5A-4
❑ 92CarMcD-49
❑ 94TopArc1-89
❑ 94TopArc1G-89
Polley, Dale
❑ 89GreBraB-15
❑ 89GreBraP-1160
❑ 89GreBraS-18
❑ 90CMC-279
❑ 90ProAAAF-403
❑ 90RicBraBC-14
❑ 90RicBraC-3
❑ 90RicBraP-258
❑ 90RicBraTI-26
❑ 90TriAllGP-AAA4
❑ 91LinDriAAA-437
❑ 91RicBraBC-13
❑ 91RicBraLD-437
❑ 91RicBraP-2565
❑ 91RicBraTI-23
❑ 92RicBraBB-17
❑ 92RicBraF-374
❑ 92RicBraRC-14
❑ 92RicBraS-436
❑ 93GreBraF-344
❑ 95RicBraTI-16
❑ 96ColCliB-25
❑ 97ColCliB-21
❑ 97ColCliD-18
❑ 97RicBraBC-17
Polley, Dave
❑ 88GreBraB-12
❑ 95RicBraRC-19
Polli, Crip (Lou)
❑ 36GouWidPPR-D27
❑ 36WorWidGV-84
Pollock, Elton
❑ 96AugGreB-23
Pollock, Jason
❑ 93PocPosF-4220
❑ 93PocPosSP-13
❑ 94OgdRapF-3749
❑ 94OgdRapSP-18
❑ 96NewJerCB-21
Pollock, Syd
❑ 76LauIndC-6
❑ 76LauIndC-23
Pollock, Wayne
❑ 91MelBusF-17
Pollreisz, Terry
❑ 98EveAquG-20
Polly, Nick
❑ 90DodTar-630
Poloni, John
❑ 76SanAntBTI-18
❑ 77TucTorC-35
❑ 80KnoBluJT-3
❑ 83WauTimF-2
❑ 87MyrBeaBJP-1451
❑ 88KnoBluJB-23
❑ 89KnoBluJB-29
❑ 89KnoBluJP-1147
❑ 89KnoBluJS-25
❑ 90KnoBluJB-19
❑ 90KnoBluJP-1261
❑ 90KnoBluJS-26
❑ 91LinDriAAA-522
❑ 91SyrChiLD-522
❑ 91SyrChiMB-19
❑ 91SyrChiP-2497
❑ 92SyrChiF-1987
❑ 92SyrChiMB-16
❑ 92SyrChiS-525
❑ 93RanKee-295
❑ 93SyrChiF-1014
❑ 94SyrChiF-987
❑ 94SyrChiTI-22
❑ 95DunBluJTI-19
Polonia, Israel
❑ 98KanCouC-23
❑ 98KanCouCCP-23
Polonia, Luis
❑ 84MadMusP-7
❑ 85DomLeaS-56
❑ 85HunStaJ-11
❑ 86TacTigP-17
❑ 87DonRoo-25
❑ 87FleUpd-99
❑ 87FleUpdG-99
❑ 87SpoRooI-18
❑ 87TopTra-96T
❑ 87TopTraT-96T
❑ 88Don-425
❑ 88DonTeaBA-425
❑ 88Fle-292
❑ 88FleGlo-292
❑ 88Lea-256
❑ 88OPC-238
❑ 88PanSti-177
❑ 88RedFolSB-71
❑ 88Sco-64
❑ 88ScoGlo-64
❑ 88ScoYouSI-22
❑ 88Spo-71
❑ 88StaLinAs-14
❑ 88TacTigC-16
❑ 88TacTigP-638
❑ 88Top-238
❑ 88TopBig-65
❑ 88TopRoo-14
❑ 88TopSti-172
❑ 88TopTif-238
❑ 88ToyRoo-24
❑ 89A'sMot-17
❑ 89Don-386
❑ 89Fle-21
❑ 89FleGlo-21
❑ 89OPC-386
❑ 89PanSti-425
❑ 89Sco-380
❑ 89ScoRoo-38T
❑ 89Spo-133
❑ 89Top-424
❑ 89TopTif-424
❑ 89UppDec-162
❑ 89YanScoNW-4
❑ 90Don-547
❑ 90DonBesA-116
❑ 90FleUpd-80
❑ 90Lea-295
❑ 90OPC-634
❑ 90PubIntS-314
❑ 90Sco-442
❑ 90ScoRoo-46T
❑ 90Top-634
❑ 90TopTif-634
❑ 90TopTra-97T
❑ 90TopTraT-97T
❑ 90TopTVY-32
❑ 90UppDec-316
❑ 91AngSmo-1
❑ 91Bow-209
❑ 91Don-93
❑ 91DonGraS-10
❑ 91Fle-322
❑ 91FouBal-16
❑ 91KinDis-10
❑ 91Lea-81
❑ 91OPC-107
❑ 91Sco-587
❑ 91StaClu-144
❑ 91Top-107
❑ 91TopDesS-107
❑ 91TopMic-107
❑ 91TopTif-107
❑ 91UltUpd-11
❑ 91UppDec-187
❑ 92AngPol-15
❑ 92Bow-582
❑ 92DenHol-12
❑ 92Don-252
❑ 92Fle-67
❑ 92Lea-45
❑ 92LeaBlaG-45
❑ 92OPC-37
❑ 92PanSti-10
❑ 92Pin-166
❑ 92RedFolS-75
❑ 92Sco-68
❑ 92StaClu-528
❑ 92Top-37
❑ 92TopGol-37
❑ 92TopGolW-37
❑ 92TopMic-37
❑ 92TriPla-99
❑ 92Ult-29
❑ 92UppDec-147
❑ 92UppDecTMH-40
❑ 92YanWIZ8-149
❑ 93AngMot-15
❑ 93AngPol-15
❑ 93AngStaCl-19
❑ 93Bow-413
❑ 93Don-461
❑ 93DonDiaK-DK26
❑ 93DonMVP-1
❑ 93DonSpiotG-SG7
❑ 93Fla-176
❑ 93Fle-196
❑ 93FunPac-41
❑ 93KinDis-7
❑ 93Lea-399
❑ 93LimRocDWB-111
❑ 93LinVenB-308
❑ 93LinVenB-320
❑ 93OPC-266
❑ 93PacBeiA-2
❑ 93PacSpa-50
❑ 93PacSpaPI-19
❑ 93PanSti-8
❑ 93Pin-31
❑ 93RedFolS-75
❑ 93Sco-39
❑ 93Sel-74
❑ 93SP-24
❑ 93StaClu-100
❑ 93StaCluFDI-100
❑ 93StaCluMOP-100
❑ 93Stu-170
❑ 93Top-760
❑ 93TopGol-760
❑ 93TopInaM-760
❑ 93TopInaR-760
❑ 93TopMic-760
❑ 93TriPla-12
❑ 93TriPla-190
❑ 93Ult-168
❑ 93UppDec-178
❑ 93UppDecGold-178
❑ 93USPlaCA-10H
❑ 94Bow-409
❑ 94ColC-504
❑ 94ColChoGS-504
❑ 94ColChoSS-504
❑ 94Don-255
❑ 94Fin-365
❑ 94FinRef-365
❑ 94Fla-323
❑ 94Fle-68
❑ 94FleExtB-138
❑ 94FleUpd-70
❑ 94Lea-390
❑ 94OPC-128
❑ 94Pac-87
❑ 94PanSti-41
❑ 94Pin-512
❑ 94PinArtP-512
❑ 94PinMusC-512
❑ 94ProMag-89
❑ 94Sco-45
❑ 94ScoGolR-45
❑ 94ScoRoo-RT9
❑ 94ScoRooGR-RT9
❑ 94Sel-251
❑ 94SpoRoo-10
❑ 94SpoRooAP-10
❑ 94StaClu-11
❑ 94StaClu-639
❑ 94StaCluFDI-11
❑ 94StaCluFDI-639
❑ 94StaCluGR-11
❑ 94StaCluGR-639
❑ 94StaCluMO-39
❑ 94StaCluMOP-11
❑ 94StaCluMOP-639
❑ 94StaCluT-208
❑ 94StaCluTFDI-208
❑ 94Top-566
❑ 94TopGol-566
❑ 94TopSpa-566
❑ 94TopTra-20T
❑ 94Ult-403
❑ 94UppDec-496
❑ 94UppDecED-496
❑ 94USPlaCA-11H
❑ 95ColCho-516
❑ 95ColChoGS-516
❑ 95ColChoSS-516
❑ 95Don-514
❑ 95DonPreP-514
❑ 95DonTopotO-124
❑ 95Fle-80
❑ 95Lea-162
❑ 95Pac-302
❑ 95PacPri-99
❑ 95Pin-445
❑ 95PinArtP-445
❑ 95PinMusC-445
❑ 95Sco-462
❑ 95ScoGolR-462
❑ 95ScoPlaTS-462
❑ 95StaClu-171
❑ 95StaCluFDI-171
❑ 95StaCluMOP-171
❑ 95StaCluSTWS-171
❑ 95StaCluVR-89
❑ 95StaCluVRMO-89
❑ 95Top-323
❑ 95TopCyb-176
❑ 95Ult-85
❑ 95UltGolM-85
❑ 96BalOriP-28
❑ 96ColCho-390T
❑ 96Fle-306
❑ 96FleTif-306
❑ 96Sco-489
Polson, Harold
❑ 20Zee-52
❑ 21Zee-60
Polverini, Steve
❑ 87AubAstP-9
Polvogt, Fred
❑ 29Zee-140
Pomeranz, Mike
❑ 89KenTwiP-1081
❑ 89KenTwiS-20
❑ 90CarLeaA-20
❑ 90SalBucS-16
Pomierski, Joe
❑ 93ClaGolF-145
❑ 94BelMarC-21
❑ 94BelMarF-3245
❑ 95EveAqaTI-15
❑ 96HudValRB-1
❑ 97St.PetDR-24
❑ 97St.PetDRUB-25
❑ 98St.PetDRM-26
Pomorski, John
❑ 36WorWidGV-92
Ponce, Carlos
❑ 81BurBeeT-22
❑ 83ElPasDT-19
❑ 84VanCanC-34
❑ 85VanCanC-224
❑ 86Don-595
❑ 87JapPlaB-5
❑ 90El PasDAGTI-10
❑ 91SumFlyC-28
❑ 91SumFlyP-2353
❑ 93HigDesMC-28
❑ 93HigDesMF-59
❑ 94BreCouMC-26
❑ 94BreMilB-259
Pond, Simon
❑ 96VerExpB-22
❑ 98JupHamQ-21
Ponder, Charles Elmer
❑ 20WalMaiW-43
❑ 22Zee-14
❑ 23WilChoV-125
❑ 23Zee-18
❑ 25Zee-100
❑ 27Zee-77
❑ 28Zee-97
Ponder, Kevin
❑ 88ColMetGS-10
❑ 89MiaMirIS-16
❑ 89MiaMirIS-16
❑ 90MiaMirIS-21
Ponder, Marcus
❑ 92LetMouSP-13
Pone, Vince
❑ 78NewWayCT-34
❑ 79BurBeeT-22
❑ 80BurBeeT-11
❑ 81BurBeeT-2
Ponio, Mike
❑ 89OklSoo-22
Ponson, Sidney
❑ 97Bes-27
❑ 97BesLimA-34
❑ 97Bow-74
❑ 97BowBay-25
❑ 97BowBes-130
❑ 97BowBesAR-130
❑ 97BowBesR-130
❑ 97BowCerBlaIA-CA63
❑ 97BowCerBluIA-CA63
❑ 97BowCerGolIA-CA63
❑ 97BowChr-102
❑ 97BowChrI-102
❑ 97BowChrIR-102
❑ 97BowChrR-102
❑ 97BowInt-74
❑ 97EasLeaTPB-8
❑ 98BesAutPOY-15
❑ 98BesFulCA-17
❑ 98BesPreA-38
❑ 98Bow-432
❑ 98BowChr-432
❑ 98BowChrGA-432
❑ 98BowChrGAR-432
❑ 98BowChrI-432
❑ 98BowChrIR-432
❑ 98BowChrR-432
❑ 98BowGolA-432
❑ 98BowInt-432
❑ 98FleUpd-U97
❑ 98LeaRS-250
❑ 98LeaRSLHolo-250
❑ 98LeaRSLong-250
❑ 98LeaRTrue-250
❑ 98PacOmeRS-1
❑ 98PacOmeRST3-1
❑ 98PacOnl-98
❑ 98PacOnlR-98
❑ 98PacOnlWC-98
❑ 98SP MinDTSPE-DS11
❑ 98SP MinPE-26
❑ 98SP MinSTHPE-H21
❑ 98SPMin-26
❑ 98SPMinDTS-DS11
❑ 98SPMinSTH-H21
❑ 98UppDec-594
❑ 99Fle-525
❑ 99FleSta9-525
❑ 99FleWarT-525
❑ 99MetUni-106
❑ 99MetUniGM-106
❑ 99MetUniPMG-106
❑ 99Pac-58
❑ 99PacCroC-40
❑ 99PacCroCPB-40
❑ 99PacPlaB-58
❑ 99PacRed-58
❑ 99SkyPre-2
❑ 99SkyPreR-2
❑ 99SP SigAuto-SP
❑ 99SPSig-96
❑ 99UppDec-321
❑ 99UppDecEL1-321
❑ 99UppDecEL2-321
Pont, Jon
❑ 94BelBreC-29
❑ 94BelBreFI-120
❑ 95BelBreTI-28
❑ 96El PasDB-3
❑ 97El PasDB-25
❑ 98El PasDG-25
Pontbriant, Matt
❑ 93AugPirC-16
❑ 93AugPirF-1541
❑ 94AugGreC-20
❑ 94AugGreF-3008
❑ 94SouAtlLAF-SAL35
❑ 95LynHilTI-22
❑ 96CarMudB-8
Ponte, Edward
❑ 90OscAstS-22
❑ 91OscAstC-9
❑ 91OscAstP-681
❑ 92JacGenS-344
❑ 92ProFS7-229
❑ 93QuaCitRBC-15
❑ 93QuaCitRBF-98
Pontes, Blossom
❑ 91HawWomS-11
Pontes, Dan
❑ 93GleFalRC-23
❑ 93GleFalRF-4002
❑ 95PeoChiTI-27
❑ 96StPetCB-25
❑ 98BinMetQ-24
Pontiff, Wally
❑ 74GasRanT-16

Pool, Bruce
❑ 92OneYanC-23
❑ 93GreHorC-18
❑ 93GreHorF-884
Pool, Harlin
❑ 31Zee-49
❑ 32Zee-64
❑ 33Zee-70
❑ 36GouWidPPR-D28
Pool, Matt
❑ 94BenRocC-19
❑ 94BenRocF-3591
❑ 95SalAvaTI-23
❑ 96SalAvaB-22
❑ 97NewHavRB-21
Poole, Ed
❑ 03BreE10-119
❑ 03BreE10-120
❑ 11SpoLifCW-293
Poole, Jim PCL
❑ 23Zee-74
❑ 24Zee-54
❑ 98GiaMot-22
Poole, Jimmy (James)
❑ 87PanAmTUBI-23
❑ 87PanAmTURB-13
❑ 88TopTra-88T
❑ 88TopTraT-88T
❑ 89TopBig-263
❑ 89VerBeaDS-22
❑ 90SanAntMGS-21
❑ 91BalOriP-24
❑ 91Cla1-T54
❑ 91Don-655
❑ 91Fle-217
❑ 91LinDriAAA-319
❑ 91OklCit8LD-319
❑ 91OklCit8P-176
❑ 91Sco-357
❑ 91TopDeb90-126
❑ 92BalOriP-29
❑ 92Don-600
❑ 92Fle-23
❑ 92OPC-683
❑ 92ProFS7-150
❑ 92Sco-693
❑ 92StaClu-412
❑ 92Top-683
❑ 92TopGol-683
❑ 92TopGolW-683
❑ 92TopMic-683
❑ 93BalOriP-27
❑ 93Don-295
❑ 93FleFinE-164
❑ 93PacSpa-348
❑ 93RanKee-296
❑ 93Top-793
❑ 93TopGol-793
❑ 93TopInaM-793
❑ 93TopInaR-793
❑ 93TopMic-793
❑ 94BalOriP-26
❑ 94Don-427
❑ 94Fla-7
❑ 94Fle-16
❑ 94OriPro-81
❑ 94OriUSPC-4S
❑ 94OriUSPC-9D
❑ 94Pac-42
❑ 94Sco-112
❑ 94ScoGolR-112
❑ 94StaCluT-293
❑ 94StaCluTFDI-293
❑ 94Top-449
❑ 94TopGol-449
❑ 94TopSpa-449
❑ 94Ult-8
❑ 95Pac-29
❑ 95Top-107
❑ 96Fle-98
❑ 96FleTif-98
❑ 96IndFle-14
❑ 96LeaSigEA-162
❑ 97PacPriGotD-GD219
❑ 98PacOnl-669
❑ 98PacOnlR-669
❑ 98PacOnlWC-669
Poole, Mark
❑ 83KinBluJTI-15
❑ 85SyrChiT-17
❑ 86SyrChiP-21
❑ 86TulDriTI-1
Poole, Ray
❑ 21Zee-61
❑ 22Zee-50
❑ 47A'sTeal-23
Poole, Stine
❑ 81BirBarT-20
❑ 82EvaTriT-13
❑ 83TolMudHT-12
Poor, Jeff
❑ 95BurBeeTI-15
❑ 95MidLeaA-40
❑ 96BurBeeTI-12
❑ 97SanJosG-17
Poorman, Thomas
❑ 87OldJudN-401
❑ 90KalBatN-45
Pope, Ashley
❑ 12Zee-45
❑ 13Zee-46
Pope, Dave
❑ 55Bow-198
❑ 55IndGolS-24
❑ 56BalOriP-11
❑ 56Top-154
❑ 57Top-249
❑ 61MapLeaBH-17
❑ 75TCM195CI-28
❑ 75TCM195CI-37
❑ 91OriCro-365
❑ 97BalOriP-42
Pope, Greg
❑ 81WatIndT-13
Pope, Matt
❑ 85CloHSS-35
Pope, Mike
❑ 78St.PetCT-21
Pope, Willie
❑ 95NegLeaL2-13
Popham, Art
❑ 80TacTigT-22
❑ 81TacTigT-3
❑ 82TacTigT-21
❑ 83TacTigT-23
Poplawski, Misty
❑ 91FreStaLBS-9
Popoff, Jim
❑ 92PitMetF-3292
❑ 93ExcFS7-78
❑ 93ExcLeaLF-10
Popov, Andrey
❑ 89EasLeaDDP-DD21
Popovich, Nick
❑ 77SpaPhiT-10
Popovich, Paul
❑ 67Top-536
❑ 68Top-266
❑ 68TopVen-266
❑ 69CubJewT-12
❑ 69OPC-47
❑ 69Top-47A
❑ 69Top-47B
❑ 69TopSta-48
❑ 69TopTeaP-22
❑ 70OPC-258
❑ 70Top-258
❑ 71MLBOffS-42
❑ 71OPC-726
❑ 71Top-726
❑ 72OPC-512
❑ 72Top-512
❑ 73OPC-309
❑ 73Top-309
❑ 74OPC-14
❑ 74Top-14
❑ 75OPC-359
❑ 75PitPirP-20
❑ 75Top-359
❑ 75TopMin-359
❑ 79CliDodT-8
❑ 90DodTar-631
Popowski, Eddie
❑ 73OPC-131
❑ 73Top-131A
❑ 73Top-131B
❑ 74OPC-403
❑ 74Top-403
❑ 87ElmPioBC-32
Popplewell, Tom
❑ 87OneYanP-9
❑ 88PriWilYS-19
❑ 89Ft.LauYS-19
❑ 90FloStaLAS-40
❑ 90Ft.LauYS-18
❑ 91AlbYanLD-13
❑ 91AlbYanP-1006
❑ 91LinDriAA-13
❑ 92AlbYanF-2227
❑ 92AlbYanSk-16
❑ 93AlbYanF-2162
❑ 94ElPasDF-3144
Popup, Mascot
❑ 98Cha-30
Poquette, Tom
❑ 75OPC-622
❑ 75Top-622
❑ 75TopMin-622
❑ 76KanCitRP-25
❑ 76RoyAaP-12
❑ 77BurCheD-66
❑ 77Kel-24
❑ 77OPC-66
❑ 77Top-93
❑ 78OPC-197
❑ 78Roy-19
❑ 78SSP270-239
❑ 78Top-357
❑ 79Top-476
❑ 80Top-597
❑ 81Top-153
❑ 82Roy-15
❑ 82Top-657
❑ 86RoyGreT-7
❑ 88OmaRoyP-1495
❑ 89OmaRoyC-25
❑ 89OmaRoyP-1741
❑ 90CMC-198
❑ 90OmaRoyC-23
❑ 90OmaRoyP-81
❑ 90ProAAAF-616
❑ 92AppFoxCB-27
❑ 92AppFoxFI-1001
❑ 93MemChiF-391
❑ 93RanKee-297
❑ 94OmaRoyF-1240
❑ 95OmaRoyTI-25
Porcelli, Joe
❑ 90GenCubP-3038
❑ 90GenCubS-20
❑ 91WinSpiC-10
❑ 91WinSpiP-2828
Port, Mike
❑ 87CalAngPPS-31
Portales, Nelson
❑ 94VenLinU-240
❑ 95LinVen-130
Porte, Carlos
❑ 80CedRapRT-6
❑ 83WatRedT-12
❑ 85CedRapRT-18
Porte, Nelson
❑ 96-97LinVen-94
Porter, Aaron
❑ 97ButCopKB-20
❑ 97ButCopKK-20
Porter, Andy
❑ 86NegLeaF-15
❑ 92NegLeaK-14
❑ 92NegLeaRLI-49
❑ 93UppDecS-17
❑ 95NegLeaL2-28
Porter, Bo
❑ 96DayCubB-20
❑ 96RocCubTI-26
❑ 98WesTenDJM-22
❑ 99SkyPre-247
❑ 99SkyPre-247
❑ 99SkyPreR-247
❑ 99SkyPreR-247
Porter, Bob
❑ 78GreBraT-19
❑ 79SavBraT-22
❑ 81RicBraT-7
❑ 82RicBraT-21
❑ 83RicBraT-20
❑ 85DurBulT-16
Porter, Brad
❑ 84EveGiaC-22A
Porter, Brian
❑ 89AubAstP-2169
❑ 90AubAstB-21
Porter, Carlos
❑ 80VenLeaS-17
Porter, Chuck
❑ 76QuaCitAT-27
❑ 78SalLakCGC-17
❑ 79SalLakCGT-19A
❑ 81VanCanT-2
❑ 82Top-333
❑ 82VanCanT-21
❑ 84BrePol-43
❑ 84Don-333
❑ 84Fle-211
❑ 84Nes792-452
❑ 84Top-452
❑ 84TopTif-452
❑ 85BreGar-16
❑ 85Don-115
❑ 85Fle-591
❑ 85Top-32
❑ 85TopTif-32
❑ 86Top-292
❑ 86TopTif-292
❑ 86VanCanP-22
❑ 94BreMilB-260
Porter, Colin
❑ 98AubDouTI-22
Porter, Darrell
❑ 72OPC-162
❑ 72Top-162
❑ 73OPC-582
❑ 73Top-582
❑ 74OPC-194
❑ 74Top-194
❑ 74TopSta-198
❑ 75Hos-62
❑ 75OPC-52
❑ 75Top-52
❑ 75TopMin-52
❑ 76BreA&P-10
❑ 76Hos-117
❑ 76OPC-645
❑ 76SSP-232
❑ 76Top-645
❑ 77OPC-116
❑ 77Top-214
❑ 78Hos-130
❑ 78OPC-66
❑ 78Roy-20
❑ 78SSP270-221
❑ 78Top-19
❑ 79BasPat-71
❑ 79Hos-4
❑ 79Kel-25
❑ 79OPC-295
❑ 79Top-571
❑ 80Kel-12
❑ 80OPC-188
❑ 80Top-360
❑ 80TopSup-39
❑ 81AllGamPI-133
❑ 81Car5x7-21
❑ 81CokTeaS-127
❑ 81Don-505
❑ 81Fle-36
❑ 81Top-610
❑ 81TopSti-224
❑ 81TopTra-814
❑ 82Don-498
❑ 82Fle-124
❑ 82FleSta-29
❑ 82OPC-98
❑ 82OPC-348
❑ 82Top-447
❑ 82Top-448
❑ 82TopSti-93
❑ 82TopStiV-93
❑ 83AllGamPI-134
❑ 83Car-21
❑ 83CarColBP-1
❑ 83Don-278
❑ 83Fle-18
❑ 83FleSta-152
❑ 83FleSti-3
❑ 83OPC-103
❑ 83PerCreC-12
❑ 83PerCreCG-12
❑ 83Top-103
❑ 83TopSti-148
❑ 83TopSti-149
❑ 83TopSti-182
❑ 83TopSti-183
❑ 84AllGamPI-44
❑ 84Car-22
❑ 84Car5x7-21
❑ 84Don-303
❑ 84Fle-331
❑ 84MilBra-19
❑ 84Nes792-285
❑ 84OPC-285
❑ 84Top-285
❑ 84TopRubD-31
❑ 84TopSti-143
❑ 84TopTif-285
❑ 85AllGamPI-133
❑ 85CarTeal-27
❑ 85Don-353
❑ 85Fle-237
❑ 85Lea-258
❑ 85OPC-246
❑ 85Top-525
❑ 85TopRubD-29
❑ 85TopSti-140
❑ 85TopTif-525
❑ 86BasStaB-84
❑ 86BreGreT-8
❑ 86CarKASD-16
❑ 86CarTeal-36
❑ 86Don-290
❑ 86Fle-45
❑ 86FleUpd-91
❑ 86OPC-84
❑ 86RanLit-5
❑ 86RanPer-17
❑ 86Spo-148
❑ 86Top-757
❑ 86TopTif-757
❑ 86TopTra-88T
❑ 86TopTraT-88T
❑ 87Don-593
❑ 87Fle-136
❑ 87FleGlo-136
❑ 87OPC-213
❑ 87RanMot-10
❑ 87RanSmo-10
❑ 87RedFolSB-52
❑ 87Top-689
❑ 87TopTif-689
❑ 88Sco-537
❑ 88ScoGlo-537
❑ 93RanKee-298
❑ 93RoySta2-10
❑ 94BreMilB-261
Porter, Dick
❑ 32OrbPinNP-36
❑ 32OrbPinUP-49
❑ 33TatOrb-49
❑ 34Gou-43
❑ 34GouCanV-88
❑ 93ConTSN-778
Porter, Eric
❑ 82WisRapTF-20
❑ 92Min-16
Porter, Griggy
❑ 73WicAerJPKB-12
❑ 74WicAerODF-118
Porter, Henry
❑ 87BucN28-17
❑ 87OldJudN-402
❑ 88GandBCGCE-32
❑ 88SpoTimM-20
Porter, J.W.
❑ 53Top-211
❑ 55Top-49
❑ 55TopDouH-9
❑ 58IndTeal-19
❑ 58Top-32A
❑ 58Top-32B
❑ 59SenTealW-13
❑ 59Top-246
❑ 91TopArc1-211
Porter, Jeff
❑ 83MemChiT-22
❑ 84IndIndTI-31
Porter, Merle
❑ 93NegLeaRL2-31
Porter, Mike
❑ 92BluOriC-5
❑ 92BluOriF-2359
❑ 93BluOriC-20
❑ 93BluOriF-4123
Porter, Mike 70s
❑ 79SpoIndT-3
Porter, Walter
❑ 30Zee-92
Porterfield, Bob (Erwin)
❑ 47Exh-181
❑ 49Bow-3
❑ 49YanTeal-16
❑ 50Bow-216
❑ 50YanTeal-16
❑ 51R42SmaS-81
❑ 52Bow-194
❑ 52RedMan-AL17
❑ 52TipTop-29
❑ 52Top-301
❑ 53BowC-22
❑ 53Bri-15
❑ 53RedMan-AL19
❑ 53Top-108
❑ 54Bow-24
❑ 54RedMan-AL18
❑ 55Bow-104
❑ 55DonWin-4
❑ 55RedMan-AL10
❑ 55RobGouS-7
❑ 55RobGouW-7
❑ 56Top-248
❑ 56YelBasP-25
❑ 57Top-118
❑ 58Top-344
❑ 59Top-181
❑ 59TopVen-181
❑ 79TCM50-284
❑ 81RedSoxBG2S-46
❑ 83TopRep5-301
❑ 91TopArc1-108
Porterfield, Ron
❑ 88AubAstP-1954
❑ 90ColMudS-26
❑ 95TucTotTI-20
❑ 96TusTorB-29
Portillo, Alex
❑ 95LinVen-142
❑ 96-97LinVen-222
❑ 96PriWilCB-21
Portillo, Luis
❑ 93LinVenB-105
❑ 94VenLinU-230
Portillo, Ramon
❑ 96MarPhiB-19
Portocarrero, Arnie (Arnold)
❑ 54A'STEAI-18
❑ 54Top-214
❑ 55A'sRodM-25
❑ 55A'sRodM-26
❑ 55A'sTeal-16
❑ 55Top-77
❑ 55TopDouH-11
❑ 56BalOriP-46
❑ 56Top-53
❑ 58Top-465
❑ 59Top-98
❑ 59TopVen-98
❑ 60Top-254
❑ 76A'sRodMC-17
❑ 79TCM50-196
❑ 91OriCro-366
❑ 94TopArc1-214
❑ 94TopArc1G-214
Portugal, Mark
❑ 82WisRapTF-14
❑ 83VisOakF-24
❑ 85TolMudHT-10
❑ 86DonRoo-44
❑ 87Don-566
❑ 87Fle-548
❑ 87FleGlo-548
❑ 87Top-419
❑ 87TopTif-419
❑ 87TwiPos-19
❑ 88PorBeaC-5
❑ 88PorBeaP-658
❑ 89Bow-318
❑ 89BowTif-318
❑ 89Fle-123
❑ 89FleGlo-123
❑ 89Sco-482
❑ 89Top-46
❑ 89TopTif-46
❑ 89TucTorJP-19
❑ 89UppDec-358
❑ 90AstLenH-17
❑ 90AstMot-10
❑ 90Bow-63
❑ 90BowTif-63
❑ 90ClaBlu-121
❑ 90Don-542
❑ 90Lea-399
❑ 90OPC-253
❑ 90Sco-552
❑ 90Top-253
❑ 90TopTif-253
❑ 90UppDec-502
❑ 91AstMot-10
❑ 91Bow-552
❑ 91Don-268
❑ 91Fle-512
❑ 91Lea-63
❑ 91OPC-647
❑ 91Sco-319
❑ 91StaClu-320
❑ 91Top-647
❑ 91TopDesS-647
❑ 91TopMic-647
❑ 91TopTif-647
❑ 91Ult-138
❑ 91UppDec-250
❑ 92AstMot-10
❑ 92Bow-656
❑ 92Don-188
❑ 92Fle-443
❑ 92OPC-114

❑ 92Pin-189
❑ 92RedFolS-76
❑ 92Sco-243
❑ 92StaClu-126
❑ 92Top-114
❑ 92TopGol-114
❑ 92TopGolW-114
❑ 92TopMic-114
❑ 92Ult-494
❑ 92UppDec-448
❑ 93AstMot-11
❑ 93AstStaC-30
❑ 93Don-612
❑ 93Fle-441
❑ 93Lea-467
❑ 93OPC-318
❑ 93PacSpa-126
❑ 93Pin-366
❑ 93StaClu-426
❑ 93StaCluFDI-426
❑ 93StaCluMOP-426
❑ 93Top-335
❑ 93TopGol-335
❑ 93TopInaM-335
❑ 93TopInaR-335
❑ 93TopMic-335
❑ 93Ult-394
❑ 93UppDec-99
❑ 93UppDecGold-99
❑ 94Bow-303
❑ 94ColC-568
❑ 94ColChoGS-568
❑ 94ColChoSS-568
❑ 94Don-199
❑ 94Fin-413
❑ 94FinRef-413
❑ 94Fla-246
❑ 94Fle-498
❑ 94FleExtB-391
❑ 94FleUpd-195
❑ 94GiaAMC-17
❑ 94GiaMot-10
❑ 94GiaTarBC-20
❑ 94Lea-429
❑ 94OPC-42
❑ 94Pac-273
❑ 94Pin-506
❑ 94PinArtP-506
❑ 94PinMusC-506
❑ 94Sco-193
❑ 94ScoGolR-193
❑ 94ScoRoo-RT64
❑ 94ScoRooGR-RT64
❑ 94Sel-316
❑ 94SpoRoo-62
❑ 94SpoRooAP-62
❑ 94StaClu-644
❑ 94StaCluFDI-644
❑ 94StaCluGR-644
❑ 94StaCluMOP-644
❑ 94StaCluT-20
❑ 94StaCluTFDI-20
❑ 94Top-734
❑ 94TopGol-734
❑ 94TopSpa-734
❑ 94TopTra-22T
❑ 94Ult-591
❑ 94UppDec-386
❑ 94UppDecED-386
❑ 94USPlaCA-11S
❑ 95ColCho-258
❑ 95ColChoGS-258
❑ 95ColChoSE-107
❑ 95ColChoSEGS-107
❑ 95ColChoSESS-107
❑ 95ColChoSS-258
❑ 95Don-268
❑ 95DonPreP-268
❑ 95DonTopotO-217
❑ 95Emo-196
❑ 95Fin-322
❑ 95FinRef-322
❑ 95Fla-210
❑ 95Fle-587
❑ 95GiaMot-8
❑ 95Lea-153
❑ 95Pac-383
❑ 95Pin-87
❑ 95PinArtP-87
❑ 95PinMusC-87
❑ 95Sco-446
❑ 95ScoGolR-446
❑ 95ScoPlaTS-446
❑ 95SP-117
❑ 95SPSil-117
❑ 95StaClu-378
❑ 95StaCluMOP-378
❑ 95StaCluSTWS-378
❑ 95Top-155
❑ 95Ult-243
❑ 95UltGolM-243
❑ 95UppDec-336
❑ 95UppDecED-336
❑ 95UppDecEDG-336
❑ 95UppDecSE-69
❑ 95UppDecSEG-69
❑ 96ColCho-99
❑ 96ColChoGS-99
❑ 96ColChoSS-99
❑ 96Don-540
❑ 96DonPreP-540
❑ 96EmoXL-167
❑ 96Fla-236
❑ 96Fle-349
❑ 96FleTif-349
❑ 96Pac-47
❑ 96Sco-458
❑ 96StaClu-417
❑ 96StaCluEPB-417
❑ 96StaCluEPG-417
❑ 96StaCluEPS-417
❑ 96StaCluMOP-417
❑ 96Top-328
❑ 96Ult-181
❑ 96UltGolM-181
❑ 96UppDec-309
❑ 97ColCho-421
❑ 97Fle-301
❑ 97Fle-684
❑ 97FleTif-301
❑ 97FleTif-684
❑ 97MetUni-49
❑ 97PacPriGotD-GD128
❑ 97PhiCopQ-22
❑ 97PhiTeal-21
❑ 97Top-33
❑ 97Ult-179
❑ 97Ult-466
❑ 97UltGolME-179
❑ 97UltGolME-466
❑ 97UltPlaME-179
❑ 97UltPlaME-466
❑ 98PhiTeal-27
❑ 99Pac-330
❑ 99PacPlaB-330
❑ 99PacRed-330
❑ 99UppDec-324
❑ 99UppDecEL1-324
❑ 99UppDecEL2-324
❑ 99UppDecM-36
❑ 99UppDecMGS-36
❑ 99UppDecMHFS-36
❑ 99UppDecMSS-36
Portwood, Craig
❑ 94DavLipB-21
Porzio, Mike
❑ 95OdgRapTI-23
❑ 98DanQ-C-22
Posada, Jorge
❑ 91OneYanP-4156
❑ 92GreHorC-7
❑ 92GreHorF-782
❑ 93CarLeaAGF-23
❑ 93PriWilCC-20
❑ 93PriWilCF-660
❑ 94Bow-38
❑ 94BowBes-B29
❑ 94BowBes-X106
❑ 94BowBesR-B29
❑ 94BowBesR-X106
❑ 94ColCliF-2955
❑ 94ColCliP-22
❑ 94ExcFS7-112
❑ 95Bow-56
❑ 95ColCliMCTI-2
❑ 95ColCliP-24
❑ 95ColCliTI-24
❑ 96ColCho-636
❑ 96ColChoGS-636
❑ 96ColChoSS-636
❑ 96ColCliB-26
❑ 96UppDec-159
❑ 97FlaShoLC-117
❑ 97FlaShoLeg0-117
❑ 97FlaShoLeg1-117
❑ 97FlaShoM-A117
❑ 97FlaShoM-B117
❑ 97FlaShoM-C117
❑ 97FlaShoR0-117
❑ 97FlaShoR1-117
❑ 97FlaShoR2-117
❑ 97FlaShoWotF-16
❑ 97Fle-522
❑ 97FleTif-522
❑ 97PinCer-125
❑ 97PinCerMBla-125
❑ 97PinCerMBlu-125
❑ 97PinCerMG-125
❑ 97PinCerMR-125
❑ 97PinCerR-125
❑ 97PinTotCPB-125
❑ 97PinTotCPG-125
❑ 97PinTotCPR-125
❑ 97Sco-481
❑ 97ScoArtPWB-481
❑ 97ScoResC-481
❑ 97ScoShoS-481
❑ 97ScoShoSAP-481
❑ 97Ult-536
❑ 97UltGolME-536
❑ 97UltPlaME-536
❑ 98Fin-217
❑ 98FinNo--217
❑ 98FinNo-R-217
❑ 98FinRef-217
❑ 98Fle-455
❑ 98Pac-156
❑ 98PacOnl-513
❑ 98PacOnlR-513
❑ 98PacOnlWC-513
❑ 98PacPlaB-156
❑ 98PacRedT-156
❑ 98PacSil-156
❑ 98PriWilCASM-24
❑ 98Sco-232
❑ 98TopGal-71
❑ 98TopGalGP-71
❑ 98TopGalOPP-71
❑ 98TopGalPPI-71
❑ 98TopGalPPIA-71
❑ 98YanSco-15
❑ 98YanScoP-15
❑ 99199Fin-26
❑ 99Bow-48
❑ 99BowChr-48
❑ 99BowChrG-48
❑ 99BowChrGR-48
❑ 99BowChrI-48
❑ 99BowChrIR-48
❑ 99BowChrR-48
❑ 99BowGol-48
❑ 99BowInt-48
❑ 99FinGolRef-26
❑ 99FinRef-26
❑ 99Fle-514
❑ 99FleBri-88
❑ 99FleBri2G-88
❑ 99FleBriBlu-88
❑ 99FleBriGol-88
❑ 99FleSta9-514
❑ 99FleWarT-514
❑ 99Pac-301
❑ 99PacAur-131
❑ 99PacAurOD-131
❑ 99PacCroC-195
❑ 99PacCroCPB-195
❑ 99PacPlaB-301
❑ 99PacRed-301
❑ 99SkyThu-142
❑ 99SkyThuRant-142
❑ 99SkyThuRave-142
❑ 99StaClu-58
❑ 99StaCluFDI-58
❑ 99StaCluOoaK-58
❑ 99StaCluPP-58
❑ 99ThuSkySupR-142
❑ 99Top-43
❑ 99TopChr-43
❑ 99TopChrR-43
❑ 99TopMVPP-43
❑ 99TopOpeD-25
❑ 99TopSta-91
❑ 99TopSta1Foil-91
❑ 99TopStaFoil-91
❑ 99TopStaOS-91
❑ 99UppDec-161
❑ 99UppDecEL1-161
❑ 99UppDecEL2-161
❑ 99Vic-276
❑ 99YanFle-24
Posada, Leo
❑ 61A'sTeal-17
❑ 61AthJayP-16
❑ 61Top-39
❑ 62Jel-96
❑ 62Pos-96
❑ 62PosCan-96
❑ 62SalPlaC-62
❑ 62ShiPlaC-62
❑ 62Top-168
❑ 62TopStal-55
❑ 62TopVen-168
❑ 73CedRapAT-25
❑ 74CedRapAT-25
❑ 75ForLauYS-25
❑ 76VenLeaS-38
❑ 78DayBeaAT-21
❑ 80VenLeaS-49
Pose, Scott
❑ 89BilMusP-2063
❑ 90Bes-91
❑ 90ChaWheB-24
❑ 90ChaWheP-2255
❑ 90CMC-696
❑ 90ProAaA-103
❑ 90SouAtlLAS-19
❑ 91ChaLooLD-164
❑ 91ChaLooP-1972
❑ 91LinDriAA-164
❑ 92ChaLooF-3831
❑ 92ChaLooS-192
❑ 92ClaFS7-442
❑ 92SkyAA F-85
❑ 92UppDecML-97
❑ 93Bow-318
❑ 93ClaGolF-54
❑ 93ExcFS7-27
❑ 93ExcLeaLF-13
❑ 93FleFinE-68
❑ 93Lea-272
❑ 93MarlStaClu-21
❑ 93MarUppD-762
❑ 93MarUSPC-5D
❑ 93PacSpa-469
❑ 93Pin-576
❑ 93PinExpOD-8
❑ 93StaClu-584
❑ 93StaCluFDI-584
❑ 93StaCluMOP-584
❑ 93TopTra-113T
❑ 93Ult-384
❑ 93UppDec-762
❑ 93UppDecGold-762
❑ 94NewOrlZF-1481
❑ 96SyrChiTI-23
❑ 97ColCliB-22
❑ 97ColCliD-19
❑ 98ColCliD-19
❑ 98ColCliM-23
❑ 98PacInvGems-78
Posedel, Bill
❑ 30Zee-111
❑ 31Zee-72
❑ 39PlaBal-121
❑ 40PlaBal-58
❑ 41Gou-19
❑ 47CenFlo-20
❑ 49EurSta-169
❑ 52Top-361
❑ 54CarHunW-16
❑ 55CarHunW-17
❑ 60Top-469
❑ 74PadDea-21
❑ 79DiaGre-221
❑ 83TopRep5-361
❑ 90DodTar-632
❑ 95ConTSN-1343
Posey, Bob
❑ 85DurBulT-29
❑ 86DurBulP-21
Posey, Cum
❑ 88NegLeaD-3
Posey, Gary
❑ 90ButCopKSP-6
Posey, John
❑ 87HagSunP-13
❑ 88ChaKniTI-11
❑ 89HagSunB-26
❑ 89HagSunS-14
❑ 89RocRedWC-12
❑ 90ChaKniTI-8
Posey, Marty
❑ 91GasRanC-26
❑ 91GasRanP-2703
❑ 91SouAtlLAGP-SAL24
Poss, David
❑ 87SalLakTTT-27
Post, David
❑ 92ClaDraP-103
❑ 92FroRowDP-70
❑ 92FroRowDPG-70
❑ 92FroRowDPS-70
❑ 92HigSchPLS-16
❑ 93YakBeaC-21
❑ 93YakBeaF-3890
❑ 94YakBeaC-12
❑ 94YakBeaF-3858
❑ 95VerBeaDTI-21
❑ 96WesPalBEB-27
❑ 97HarSen-22
❑ 98arSenW1-17
❑ 98HarSenM-17
Post, Jeff
❑ 92SouOreAC-16
❑ 92SouOreAF-3416
❑ 93PocPosF-4209
❑ 93PocPosSP-21
Post, John
❑ 88ElmPioC-28
Post, Sam
❑ 22KolMotBPP-23
Post, Wally
❑ 52Top-151
❑ 55Bow-32
❑ 55Kah-5
❑ 56Kah-13
❑ 56RedBurB-18
❑ 56Top-158
❑ 57Kah-24
❑ 57RedSoh-16
❑ 57Top-157
❑ 58Hir-14
❑ 58Kah-22
❑ 58PhiTeal-14
❑ 58Top-387
❑ 59HomRunD-15
❑ 59Top-398
❑ 60PhiJayP-10
❑ 60Top-13
❑ 60TopVen-13
❑ 61Kah-34
❑ 61Top-378
❑ 61TopStal-23
❑ 62Jel-128
❑ 62Kah-32
❑ 62Pos-128
❑ 62PosCan-128
❑ 62RedEnq-27
❑ 62RedJayP-11
❑ 62Top-148
❑ 62TopVen-148
❑ 63RedEnq-26
❑ 63Top-462
❑ 64Top-253
❑ 64TopVen-253
❑ 77RedCarP-8
❑ 79DiaGre-273
❑ 80Red196T-2
❑ 82OhiHaloF-53
❑ 83TopRep5-151
❑ 91TopArc1-294
Postema, Andy
❑ 90EriSaiS-18
❑ 91RenSilSCLC-9
Postier, Paul
❑ 87GasRanP-16
❑ 88TulDriTI-24
❑ 89TulDriGS-21
❑ 89TulDriTI-19
❑ 90TulDriP-1164
❑ 90TulDriTI-20
❑ 91LinDriAAA-320
❑ 91OklCit8LD-320
❑ 91OklCit8P-188
❑ 92OklCit8S-319
Postiff, J.P.
❑ 90FreStaS-11
❑ 90HunCubP-3292
❑ 91WinSpiP-2838
❑ 92PeoChiC-20
❑ 92PeoChiTI-20
❑ 93PocPosF-4217
❑ 93PocPosSP-7
Poston, Mark
❑ 85BeaGolGT-16
❑ 86BeaGolGP-20
❑ 87LasVegSP-10
Pote, Lou
❑ 92ShrCapF-3867
❑ 92ShrCapS-589
❑ 93ShrCapF-2757
❑ 94Bow-547
❑ 94ShrCapF-1603
❑ 95UppDecML-177
❑ 95UppDecMLFS-177
❑ 96HarSenB-23
❑ 98MidAngG-24
❑ 98MidAngO-26
Potenziano, Benjamin
❑ 95BelGiaTI-NNO
❑ 96SanJosGB-30
❑ 97ShrCap-5
❑ 97ShrCapB-5
❑ 98ShrCapM-6
❑ 98ShrCapWS-6
Potestio, Doug
❑ 86lowCubP-22
❑ 86StaoftFT-6
❑ 87lowCubTI-6
Potestio, Frank
❑ 87DayBeaAP-17
❑ 88SprCarB-10
❑ 89ArkTraGS-19
❑ 89LouRedBTI-31
Pott, Larry
❑ 85TulDriTI-17
Potter, Lonnie
❑ 90BenBucL-9
Potter, Mike
❑ 76TulOilGP-15
❑ 78SprRedWK-3
Potter, Nelson
❑ 41DouPlaR-129
❑ 46SeaSLP-49
❑ 47TipTop-70
❑ 49EurSta-16
❑ 79DiaGre-193
❑ 85TCMPpl1-12
❑ 93ConTSN-717
❑ 96Bro194F-7
Potter, Scott
❑ 89EasLeaDDP-DD48
Potthoff, Michael
❑ 89GreFalDSP-4
❑ 90BakDodCLC-240
Pottinger, Mark
❑ 86ClePhiP-20
❑ 87LakTigP-20
Potts, Dave
❑ 86AubAstP-19
❑ 87OscAstP-16
❑ 88OscAstS-21
❑ 89OscAstS-18
Potts, Mike
❑ 92DurBulC-21
❑ 92DurBulF-1096
❑ 92DurBulTI-5
❑ 93GreBraF-345
❑ 94BraUSPC-4S
❑ 94RicBraF-2845
❑ 95RicBraRC-20
❑ 95RicBraTI-17
❑ 96BrePol-21
❑ 96LeaSigA-183
❑ 96LeaSigAG-183
❑ 96LeaSigAS-183
Pough, Pork Chop (Clyde)
❑ 89BurlndS-21
❑ 90RenSilSCLC-264
❑ 90WatIndS-16
❑ 91KinIndC-18
❑ 91KinIndP-330
❑ 92KinIndC-20
❑ 92KinIndF-2487
❑ 92UppDecML-199
❑ 93KinIndC-22
❑ 93KinIndF-2256
❑ 93KinIndTI-22
❑ 94CanIndF-3126
❑ 95Bes-5
❑ 95TreThuTI-22
❑ 96Exc-17
❑ 96PawRedSDD-23
❑ 97OmaRoyB-19
Poulin, Jim
❑ 88BelBreGS-3
❑ 89StoPorB-25
❑ 89StoPorCLC-178
❑ 89StoPorP-387
❑ 89StoPorS-27
Poulis, George
❑ 90WatDiaB-21
❑ 91WatDiaC-27
❑ 96MemChiB-3
❑ 97MobBayBB-8
Poulsen, Chris
❑ 98DanBraQ-20
Poulsen, Ken
❑ 77FriOneYW-23
Pound, John
❑ 78QuaCitAT-18
Pounders, Brad
❑ 87TexLeaAF-5
❑ 87WicPilRD-8
❑ 88LasVegSC-15

❑ 88LasVegSP-247
❑ 89Fle-642
❑ 89FleGlo-642
Poupart, Melvin
❑ 96PitMetB-19
❑ 97PitMet-23
Pourron, Joe
❑ 98YakBeaG-26
Poveda, Crispin
❑ 90IBAWorA-14
Powalski, Richard
❑ 98WilCubM-21
Powell, Alonzo
❑ 83CliGiaF-14
❑ 86SouLeaAJ-15
❑ 86WesPalBEP-24
❑ 87DonOpeD-93
❑ 87ExpPos-20
❑ 87IndIndTI-33
❑ 87SpoRooP-8
❑ 87SpoTeaP-20
❑ 88IndIndC-15
❑ 88IndIndP-520
❑ 88StaLinE-12
❑ 89IndIndP-1210
❑ 89WesPalBES-18
❑ 90PorBeaP-193
❑ 90ProAAAF-263
❑ 91CalCanLD-69
❑ 91CalCanP-529
❑ 91FleUpd-55
❑ 91Lea-521
❑ 91LinDriAAA-69
❑ 92CalCanS-66
❑ 92Don-213
❑ 92Fle-290
❑ 92OPC-295
❑ 92Sco-413
❑ 92StaClu-547
❑ 92Top-295
❑ 92TopGol-295
❑ 92TopGolW-295
❑ 92TopMic-295
Powell, Bill (William Burris)
❑ 11PinT-5-852
❑ 11PinT-5-854
❑ 72ClaCar-113
Powell, Boog (John)
❑ 47Exh-182
❑ 62BalOriP-20
❑ 62Top-99
❑ 62TopVen-99
❑ 63BalOriP-26
❑ 63Jel-62
❑ 63Pos-62
❑ 63Top-398
❑ 64BalOriP-28
❑ 64OriJayP-9
❑ 64Top-89
❑ 64TopCoi-104
❑ 64TopSta-36
❑ 64TopStaU-59
❑ 64TopTatI-64
❑ 64TopVen-89
❑ 65BalOriP-27
❑ 65Baz-11
❑ 65OldLonC-33
❑ 65OPC-3
❑ 65Top-3
❑ 65Top-560
❑ 65TopEmbI-29
❑ 65TopTraI-63
❑ 66BalOriP-27
❑ 66OPC-167
❑ 66Top-167
❑ 66TopVen-167
❑ 67BalOriP-81
❑ 67BalOriP-82
❑ 67BalOriP-83
❑ 67CokCapO-11
❑ 67DexPre-171
❑ 67OPCPapI-1
❑ 67Top-230
❑ 67Top-241
❑ 67Top-243
❑ 67Top-521
❑ 67TopPos-1
❑ 67TopTesF-18
❑ 67TopVen-199
❑ 68AtlOilPBCC-36
❑ 68BalOriDPCP-10
❑ 68CokCapO-11
❑ 68DexPre-64
❑ 68Top-381
❑ 68Top3-D-8
❑ 69MilBra-225
❑ 69MLBOffS-7
❑ 69MLBPin-22
❑ 69OPC-15
❑ 69OPCDec-17
❑ 69Top-15
❑ 69TopDec-2
❑ 69TopSta-128
❑ 69TopTeaP-5
❑ 70BalOriP-24
❑ 70DayDaiNM-34
❑ 70Kel-19
❑ 70MilBra-22
❑ 70MLBOffS-153
❑ 70OPC-64
❑ 70OPC-200
❑ 70OPC-201
❑ 70OPC-410
❑ 70OPC-451
❑ 70Ori-10
❑ 70Top-64
❑ 70Top-200
❑ 70Top-201
❑ 70Top-410
❑ 70Top-451
❑ 70TopScr-18
❑ 70TopSup-38
❑ 70TraSta-11C
❑ 71AllBasA-18
❑ 71BalOriP-21
❑ 71Kel-20
❑ 71MilDud-25
❑ 71MLBOffS-307
❑ 71MLBOffS-570
❑ 71OPC-63
❑ 71OPC-195
❑ 71OPC-327
❑ 71OPC-700
❑ 71Top-63
❑ 71Top-195
❑ 71Top-327
❑ 71Top-700
❑ 71TopCoi-74
❑ 71TopSup-5
❑ 71TopTat-56
❑ 71TopTat-57
❑ 72MilBra-277
❑ 72OPC-250
❑ 72OriDMV-7
❑ 72OriPos-24
❑ 72OriPos-25
❑ 72ProStaP-34
❑ 72Top-250
❑ 73BalOriP-34
❑ 73OPC-325
❑ 73OriJohP-26
❑ 73OriTeal-24
❑ 73Top-325
❑ 74OPC-460
❑ 74Top-460
❑ 75CleIndP-22
❑ 75IndJB R-6
❑ 75OPC-208
❑ 75OPC-625
❑ 75Top-208
❑ 75Top-625
❑ 75TopMin-208
❑ 75TopMin-625
❑ 76Hos-75
❑ 76IndTeal-7
❑ 76Kel-50
❑ 76OPC-45
❑ 76SSP-524
❑ 76Top-45
❑ 77Top-206
❑ 78TCM60I-80
❑ 81Ori6F-26
❑ 82K-M-17
❑ 82TCMGreS-42
❑ 83FraBroR-22
❑ 83FraBroR-23
❑ 83FraBroR-26
❑ 83YanYeaIT-16
❑ 86OriGreT-11
❑ 90BasWit-9
❑ 90DodTar-633
❑ 90PacLeg-46
❑ 90SweBasG-16
❑ 91Kel3D-13
❑ 91MDAA-12
❑ 91OriCro-367
❑ 91SweBasG-74
❑ 91UppDecS-3
❑ 91UppDecS-5
❑ 92ActPacA-80
❑ 92MDAMVP-7
❑ 92MVP2H-18
❑ 93MetIma-16
❑ 93OriCroASU-11
❑ 93TedWil-84
❑ 93TedWil-143
❑ 94BalOriP-27
❑ 94UppDecAH-195
❑ 94UppDecAH1-195
❑ 95BalOriP-41
❑ 95MrTurBG-4
❑ 99SpoIllGotG-26
❑ 99SpoIllGotG-59
Powell, Brian
❑ 96LakTigB-19
❑ 96Top-244
❑ 97LakTigB-27
❑ 98JacSunM-19
❑ 98UppDec-581
Powell, Charlie
❑ 78ChaPirT-19
Powell, Colin
❑ 91Bow-533
Powell, Corey
❑ 91MidLeaAP-MWL48
❑ 91RocExpC-10
❑ 91RocExpP-2045
❑ 92WesPalBEC-17
❑ 92WesPalBEF-2088
❑ 93BurBeeC-20
❑ 93BurBeeF-172
❑ 94OscAstC-19
❑ 94OscAstF-1146
Powell, Dante
❑ 93BazTeaU-2
❑ 93TopTra-45T
❑ 94ClaUpdCotC-CC19
❑ 94EveGiaF-3669
❑ 94SigRooDP-22
❑ 94SigRooDPS-22
❑ 95Exc-292
❑ 95ExcFirYP-9
❑ 95SPML-148
❑ 95UppDecML-100
❑ 95UppDecMLFS-100
❑ 95UppDecMLOP-OP25
❑ 96BesAutS-74
❑ 96BesAutSA-56
❑ 96Bow-201
❑ 96BowFoi-201
❑ 96DouAllB-54
❑ 96Exc-246
❑ 96TexLeaAB-13
❑ 97Bow-166
❑ 97BowBes-148
❑ 97BowBesAR-148
❑ 97BowBesR-148
❑ 97BowChr-162
❑ 97BowChrI-162
❑ 97BowChrIR-162
❑ 97BowChrR-162
❑ 97BowInt-166
❑ 97ColChoU-U26
❑ 97FlaShoLC-79
❑ 97FlaShoLeg0-79
❑ 97FlaShoLeg1-79
❑ 97FlaShoM-A79
❑ 97FlaShoM-B79
❑ 97FlaShoM-C79
❑ 97FlaShoR0-79
❑ 97FlaShoR1-79
❑ 97FlaShoR2-79
❑ 97Fle-644
❑ 97FleTif-644
❑ 97PhoFirTI-19
❑ 97SpoIll-19
❑ 97SpoIllEE-19
❑ 97Top-206
❑ 97Ult-467
❑ 97UltGolME-467
❑ 97UltPlaME-467
❑ 97UppDec-544
❑ 98Bow-214
❑ 98BowChr-214
❑ 98BowChrGA-214
❑ 98BowChrGAR-214
❑ 98BowChrI-214
❑ 98BowChrIR-214
❑ 98BowChrR-214
❑ 98BowGolA-214
❑ 98BowInt-214
❑ 98ColCho-233
❑ 98ColChoSQ-SQ16
❑ 98Don-267
❑ 98DonGolPP-267
❑ 98DonSigA-71
❑ 98DonSigAM-93
❑ 98DonSilPP-267
❑ 98Fle-226
❑ 98FreGriG-25
❑ 98PacInvGems-219
❑ 98SPxFin-28
❑ 98SPxFinR-28
❑ 98SPxFinS-28
❑ 98StaCluFDI-126
❑ 98StaCluI-126
❑ 98StaCluOneK-126
❑ 98StaCluPP-126
❑ 98Ult-341
❑ 98UltGolM-341
❑ 98UltMas-341
❑ 98UltPlaM-341
❑ 98UppDec-219
❑ 98UppDecSF-121
❑ 99Fle-313
❑ 99FleSta9-313
❑ 99FleWarT-313
❑ 99PacInv-9
❑ 99PacInvOD-9
❑ 99PacInvPB-9
Powell, Dennis
❑ 85AlbDukCr-154
❑ 86DodCokP-24
❑ 86DodPol-48
❑ 86Don-250
❑ 87CalCanP-2314
❑ 87Don-499
❑ 87Fle-450
❑ 87FleGlo-450
❑ 87Top-47
❑ 87TopTif-47
❑ 88CalCanC-4
❑ 88CalCanP-796
❑ 88Top-453
❑ 88TopTif-453
❑ 89FleUpd-61
❑ 89TopTra-97T
❑ 89TopTraT-97T
❑ 90BreMilB-20
❑ 90CMC-47
❑ 90DenZepC-22
❑ 90DenZepP-624
❑ 90DodTar-634
❑ 90Fle-521
❑ 90FleCan-521
❑ 90ProAAAF-649
❑ 90Sco-308
❑ 90UppDec-229
❑ 91CalCanLD-68
❑ 91CalCanP-514
❑ 91LinDriAAA-68
❑ 92Bow-426
❑ 92MarMot-12
❑ 93CalCanF-1165
❑ 93Fle-312
❑ 93MarMot-23
❑ 93StaClu-108
❑ 93StaCluFDI-108
❑ 93StaCluMOP-108
❑ 94BreMilB-345
❑ 94NasSouF-1250
Powell, Gordon
❑ 90HelBreSP-12
❑ 91BelBreCB-15
❑ 91BelBreP-2111
❑ 92BelBreCB-22
❑ 92BelBreFI-414
Powell, Grover
❑ 64Top-113
❑ 64TopVen-113
❑ 76Met63 S-11
❑ 91MetWIZ-318
Powell, Hosken
❑ 77TacTwiDQ-6
❑ 78TwiFriP-14
❑ 79OPC-346
❑ 79Top-656
❑ 79TwiFriP-21
❑ 80Top-471
❑ 80TwiPos-23
❑ 81Don-567
❑ 81Fle-559
❑ 81Top-137
❑ 81TwiPos-22
❑ 82Don-228
❑ 82Fle-558
❑ 82Top-584
❑ 82TopSti-206
❑ 82TopStiV-206
❑ 82TopTra-91T
❑ 83Don-644
❑ 83Fle-440
❑ 83FleSta-153
❑ 83FleSti-106
❑ 83OPC-77
❑ 83Top-77
❑ 84VanCanC-38
Powell, Jake (Alvin Jacob)
❑ 38OurNatGPP-23
❑ 39PlaBal-1
❑ 40PlaBal-11
❑ 75YanDyn1T-36
❑ 75YanDyn1T-51
❑ 91ConTSN-83
Powell, James E.
❑ 87OldJudN-403
Powell, Jay
❑ 91MisStaB-39
❑ 92MisStaB-34
❑ 93AusFut-66
❑ 93MisStaB-31
❑ 94Bow-655
❑ 94Cla-179
❑ 94ClaGolF-8
❑ 94ClaGolN1PLF-LP11
❑ 94ClaGolREF-RE11
❑ 94ClaTriF-T4
❑ 94ExcFS7-14
❑ 94FreKeyC-19
❑ 94FreKeyF-2612
❑ 94OriPro-82
❑ 94Pin-435
❑ 94PinArtP-435
❑ 94PinMusC-435
❑ 94Sco-575
❑ 94ScoGolR-575
❑ 94SigRoo-36
❑ 94SigRooS-36
❑ 94Top-745
❑ 94TopGol-745
❑ 94TopSpa-745
❑ 95PorSeaDTI-21
❑ 96Bow-170
❑ 96BowBes-103
❑ 96BowBesAR-103
❑ 96BowBesR-103
❑ 96BowFoi-170
❑ 96ColCho-559
❑ 96ColChoGS-559
❑ 96ColChoSS-559
❑ 96Pin-381
❑ 96PinAfi-167
❑ 96PinAfiAP-167
❑ 96PinFoil-381
❑ 96Sel-186
❑ 96SelArtP-186
❑ 96SelCer-128
❑ 96SelCerAP-128
❑ 96SelCerCB-128
❑ 96SelCerCR-128
❑ 96SelCerMB-128
❑ 96SelCerMG-128
❑ 96SelCerMR-128
❑ 97MarPac-18
❑ 97StaClu-366
❑ 97StaCluMOP-366
❑ 97Top-339
❑ 98ColCho-376
❑ 98PacInvGems-156
❑ 98PacOnl-303
❑ 98PacOnlR-303
❑ 98PacOnlWC-303
❑ 98PorSeaD5AQ-23
❑ 98Ult-371
❑ 98UltGolM-371
❑ 98UltMas-371
❑ 98UltPlaM-371
❑ 98UppDec-379
❑ 99Fle-467
❑ 99FleSta9-467
❑ 99FleWarT-467
❑ 99Ult-55
❑ 99UltGolM-55
❑ 99UltMas-55
❑ 99UltPlaM-55
Powell, Jeremy
❑ 94SigRooDPBSDP-9
❑ 95SigRooMOP-P4
❑ 95SigRooMOPS-P4
❑ 96DelShoB-25
❑ 98AriFalLTP-25
❑ 98arSenW1-18
❑ 98EasLeaTPM-22
❑ 98FleUpd-U21
❑ 98HarSenM-18
❑ 99Fle-491
❑ 99FleSta9-491
❑ 99FleWarT-491
Powell, John
❑ 93BazTeaU-16
❑ 93TopTra-131T
❑ 94TopTra-59T
❑ 95TulDriTI-20
❑ 96TulDriTI-21
❑ 97TexAllM-24
❑ 97TulDriTI-21
❑ 98TulDriTI-20
Powell, John GA
❑ 89GeoColC-24
Powell, John J.
❑ 03BreE10-121
❑ 03BreE10-122
❑ 08RosComP-71
❑ 09RamT20-96
❑ 09T206-294
❑ 10DarChoE-25
❑ 11HelSta-64
❑ 11PinT-5-1002
❑ 11SpoLifCW-294
❑ 11SpoLifM-115
❑ 72ClaCar-8
❑ 98CamPepP-62
Powell, Kelly
❑ 89SanDieSAS-24
Powell, Kenny
❑ 90Bes-275
❑ 90GasRanB-5
❑ 90GasRanP-2534
❑ 90GasRanS-18
❑ 91ChaRanC-24
❑ 91ChaRanP-1328
❑ 92ClaFS7-112
❑ 92GasRanF-2266
❑ 93ChaRanF-1953
❑ 93ClaFS7-111
Powell, Lawrence
❑ 37Zee-84
Powell, Paul Ray
❑ 74AlbDukCa-75
❑ 74AlbDukTI-13
❑ 76SSP-82
❑ 90DodTar-635
Powell, Ray
❑ 21Exh-134
❑ 21Exh-135
❑ 21Nei-95
❑ 22E120-133
❑ 22W572-79
❑ 23WilChoV-126
Powell, Red (John)
❑ 14Zee-144
❑ 14Zee-144
Powell, Robert LeRoy
❑ 56Top-144
Powell, Ross
❑ 89CedRapRAB-31
❑ 89CedRapRS-30
❑ 90CedRapRDGB-31
❑ 90ChaLooGS-24
❑ 91LinDriAAA-270
❑ 91NasSouLD-270
❑ 91NasSouP-2155
❑ 93IndIndF-1486
❑ 94IndIndF-1808
❑ 94Pin-401
❑ 94PinArtP-401
❑ 94PinMusC-401
❑ 94Sco-589
❑ 94ScoBoyoS-56
❑ 94ScoGolR-589
❑ 94TopTra-84T
❑ 94TucTorF-761
❑ 96IndIndB-20
Powell, Watt
❑ 11Zee-98
❑ 12HomRunKE-72
❑ 12Zee-126
Powell, William
❑ 93NegLeaRL2-32
Power, John
❑ 86WatIndP-22
Power, Ted
❑ 80AlbDukTc-22
❑ 80VenLeaS-28
❑ 81AlbDukTc-5
❑ 82Fle-17
❑ 84Don-447
❑ 84Fle-478
❑ 84Nes792-554
❑ 84RedEnq-22
❑ 84Top-554
❑ 84TopTif-554
❑ 85Don-286
❑ 85Fle-547

❑ 85RedYea-12
❑ 85Top-342
❑ 85TopSti-50
❑ 85TopTif-342
❑ 86Don-408
❑ 86Fle-187
❑ 86OPC-108
❑ 86RedTexG-48
❑ 86SevCoi-S12
❑ 86Spo-166
❑ 86Top-108
❑ 86TopSti-140
❑ 86TopTif-108
❑ 87Don-536
❑ 87Fle-210
❑ 87FleGlo-210
❑ 87RedKah-48
❑ 87Top-437
❑ 87TopTif-437
❑ 88Don-142
❑ 88Fle-245
❑ 88FleGlo-245
❑ 88FleUpd-33
❑ 88FleUpdG-33
❑ 88OPC-236
❑ 88PanSti-272
❑ 88RoySmo-14
❑ 88RoyTeal-24
❑ 88Sco-242
❑ 88ScoGlo-242
❑ 88StaLinRe-16
❑ 88Top-236
❑ 88TopTif-236
❑ 88TopTra-89T
❑ 88TopTraT-89T
❑ 89CarTeal-24
❑ 89Don-153
❑ 89Fle-142
❑ 89FleGlo-142
❑ 89LouRedBC-10
❑ 89LouRedBP-1249
❑ 89LouRedBTI-32
❑ 89OPC-331
❑ 89Sco-348
❑ 89Top-777
❑ 89TopTif-777
❑ 90DodTar-636
❑ 90Don-653
❑ 90Fle-258
❑ 90FleCan-258
❑ 90FleUpd-50
❑ 90Lea-473
❑ 90OPC-59
❑ 90PirHomC-23
❑ 90Top-59
❑ 90TopTif-59
❑ 90UppDec-340
❑ 91Bow-688
❑ 91Don-608
❑ 91Fle-46
❑ 91FleUpd-85
❑ 91OPC-621
❑ 91RedKah-48
❑ 91Sco-255
❑ 91SimandSMLBL-34
❑ 91Top-621
❑ 91TopDesS-621
❑ 91TopMic-621
❑ 91TopTif-621
❑ 91UppDec-450
❑ 92Don-586
❑ 92Fle-416
❑ 92IndFanC-24
❑ 92Sco-113
❑ 92StaClu-812
❑ 92UppDec-680
❑ 93Don-766
❑ 93Fle-600
❑ 93IndWUA-26
❑ 93Lea-61
❑ 93PacSpa-418
❑ 93StaClu-82
❑ 93StaCluFDI-82
❑ 93StaCluMOP-82
❑ 94StaClu-163
❑ 94StaCluFDI-163
❑ 94StaCluGR-163
❑ 94StaCluMOP-163
❑ 94Top-319
❑ 94TopGol-319
❑ 94TopSpa-319
❑ 94Ult-123

Power, Vic
❑ 54A'STEAI-19
❑ 54Top-52
❑ 55A'sRodM-27
❑ 55A'sRodM-28
❑ 55A'sTeal-17
❑ 55Top-30
❑ 55TopDouH-29
❑ 56A'sPos-35
❑ 56A'sRodM-7
❑ 56Top-67
❑ 56TopPin-14
❑ 57Top-167
❑ 58A'sJayP-7
❑ 58IndTeal-30
❑ 58Top-406
❑ 59Ind-17
❑ 59Kah-29
❑ 59Top-229
❑ 60Baz-16
❑ 60IndJayP-9
❑ 60Kah-34
❑ 60Lea-65
❑ 60Top-75
❑ 60TopVen-75
❑ 61Kah-35
❑ 61Pos-63A
❑ 61Pos-63B
❑ 61Top-255
❑ 61TwiCloD-21
❑ 62Jel-37
❑ 62Kah-33A
❑ 62Kah-33B
❑ 62Pos-37
❑ 62PosCan-37
❑ 62SalPlaC-44
❑ 62ShiPlaC-44
❑ 62Top-445
❑ 62TopBuc-72
❑ 62TopStal-39
❑ 63Fle-23
❑ 63Jel-1
❑ 63Pos-1
❑ 63Top-40
❑ 63TwiJayP-9
❑ 63TwiVol-17
❑ 64PhiPhiB-18
❑ 64Top-355
❑ 64TopVen-355
❑ 65Top-442
❑ 66OPC-192
❑ 66Top-192
❑ 66TopVen-192
❑ 76A'sRodMC-18
❑ 78TCM60I-196
❑ 79TCM50-147
❑ 81SanDieSC-5
❑ 84OCoandSI-114
❑ 90HOFStiB-56
❑ 94TopArc1-52
❑ 94TopArc1G-52

Powers, Ellis
❑ 31Zee-50

Powers, Jack
❑ 89AncBucTI-28

Powers, Jeff
❑ 98WatIndTI-25

Powers, John
❑ 57JetPos-17
❑ 58Kah-23
❑ 58Top-432
❑ 59RedEnq-21
❑ 59Top-489
❑ 60Top-422
❑ 91OriCro-368
❑ 97RanCucQG-22
❑ 98MobBayBTI-21
❑ 99SP TopP-105
❑ 99SP TopPPE-105

Powers, Larry
❑ 79LodDodT-11

Powers, Les
❑ 33Zee-138

Powers, Michael Riley
❑ 03BreE10-123

Powers, Mike
❑ 09T206-295
❑ 82OhiHaloF-9

Powers, Randy
❑ 90BoiHawP-3305
❑ 90ProAaA-159
❑ 91PalSprAP-2012
❑ 92SalSpuC-5

Powers, Robert
❑ 92HelBreF-1722
❑ 92HelBreSP-11
❑ 93HelBreF-4105
❑ 93HelBreSP-1

Powers, Scott
❑ 87ElmPioBC-12
❑ 87ElmPioRC-12
❑ 88LynRedSS-19
❑ 89LynRedSS-19
❑ 90LynRedSTI-7
❑ 91LinDriAA-468
❑ 91NewBriRSLD-468
❑ 91NewBriRSP-359

Powers, Steve
❑ 75QuaCitAT-20
❑ 77SalPirT-20A
❑ 77SalPirT-20B
❑ 90AshTouC-8
❑ 90AubAstB-11
❑ 90AubAstP-3407
❑ 91AshTouP-566
❑ 92BurAstC-13
❑ 92BurAstF-542
❑ 93OscAstC-18
❑ 93OscAstF-626

Powers, Tad
❑ 89PenPilS-20
❑ 90RenSilSCLC-285
❑ 91SalLakTP-3209
❑ 91SalLakTSP-3
❑ 91SydWavF-12

Powers, Terry
❑ 91WinHavRSC-7
❑ 91WinHavRSP-487
❑ 92ClaFS7-192
❑ 92WinHavRSC-10
❑ 92WinHavRSF-1775
❑ 93WesPalBEC-19
❑ 93WesPalBEF-1338
❑ 94WesPalBEC-22
❑ 94WesPalBEF-37

Powers, Thomas
❑ 87OldJudN-404
❑ 88SFHesCreN32-25A
❑ 88SFHesCreN32-25B

Powis, Carl
❑ 91OriCro-369

Powles, George
❑ 30Zee-155

Pozo, Arquimedez
❑ 92SanBerSF-967
❑ 93RivPilCLC-14
❑ 94Bow-9
❑ 94BowBes-B78
❑ 94BowBes-X103
❑ 94BowBesR-B78
❑ 94BowBesR-X103
❑ 94Cla-198
❑ 94JacSunF-1419
❑ 94UppDec-535
❑ 94UppDecED-535
❑ 94UppDecML-131
❑ 95ActPacF-41
❑ 95Exc-120
❑ 95MarPac-40
❑ 95TacRaiTI-17
❑ 95Top-540
❑ 95UppDecML-74
❑ 95UppDecMLFS-74
❑ 95UppDecMLOP-OP26
❑ 96ColCho-729
❑ 96ColChoGS-23
❑ 96ColChoGS-729
❑ 96ColChoSS-23
❑ 96ColChoSS-729
❑ 96TacRaiB-22
❑ 96UppDec-224
❑ 96UppDecFSP-FS17
❑ 96UppDecPHE-H26
❑ 96UppDecPreH-H26
❑ 97PawRedS-21
❑ 97RedSoxS-13
❑ 97RedSoxSPl-13
❑ 97RedSoxSPr-13
❑ 97Sco-312
❑ 97ScoArtPWB-312
❑ 97ScoPreS-312
❑ 97ScoShoS-312
❑ 97ScoShoSAP-312
❑ 98PawRedSQ-24
❑ 99BasAmeTP-83
❑ 99BasAmeTPG-83

Pozo, Joel
❑ 94VenLinU-249

Pozo, Melanio
❑ 85DomLeaS-193

Pozo, Yohel
❑ 94BenRocF-3598
❑ 95AshTouTI-33

Prada, Nelson
❑ 97ForWayW-26
❑ 98ForMyeMTI-25

Prado, Jose
❑ 91MiaHurBB-10
❑ 94BakDodC-20
❑ 95SanAntMTI-55
❑ 97St.PauS-22
❑ 98St.PauSTI-19

Prager, Howard
❑ 88CapCodPPaLP-175
❑ 89AubAstP-2175
❑ 90OscAstS-23
❑ 91OscAstP-694
❑ 92JacGenF-4009
❑ 92JacGenS-345
❑ 92SkyAA F-144
❑ 93ArkTraF-2825
❑ 94LouRedF-2989
❑ 95LouRedF-284

Prall, Wilford
❑ 74WicAerODF-111

Pramesa, John
❑ 47PM1StaP1-166
❑ 51Bow-324
❑ 52Bow-247
❑ 52Top-105
❑ 55DesMoiHB-16
❑ 79DiaGre-270
❑ 83TopRep5-105

Pransky, Jim
❑ 98SouOreTG-27

Prappas, Jim
❑ 52LavPro-99

Prater, Andy
❑ 93ElmPioC-15
❑ 93ElmPioF-3826
❑ 94KanCouCC-19
❑ 94KanCouCF-165
❑ 94KanCouCTI-23
❑ 95BreCouMF-249
❑ 97AugGre-15
❑ 97EriSeaWB-27
❑ 97Top-482
❑ 98EriSeaWM-20

Prater, Pete
❑ 94EveGiaC-23
❑ 94EveGiaF-3652
❑ 95BurBeeTI-16

Prather, Mark
❑ 93Tex-5

Prats, Jean
❑ 52LavPro-27

Prats, Mario
❑ 91AshTouP-567

Pratt, Cressy (Crestwell)
❑ 82WatRedT-22
❑ 83TamTarT-20

Pratt, Del (Derrill)
❑ 14B18B-33A
❑ 14B18B-33B
❑ 14CraJacE-93
❑ 15CraJacE-93
❑ 15SpoNewM-140
❑ 16SpoNewM-139
❑ 17ColE13-135
❑ 17HolBreD-80
❑ 20NatCarE-81
❑ 21E121So1-76
❑ 21Exh-136
❑ 21Exh-137
❑ 21OxfConE-13
❑ 22E120-11
❑ 22W573-104
❑ 23W501-11
❑ 23WilChoV-127
❑ 91ConTSN-162

Pratt, Evan
❑ 93SouAtlLAPI-32

Pratt, Louis A.
❑ 79SavBraT-21
❑ 81ArkTraT-20

Pratt, Rich
❑ 94HicCraF-2175
❑ 95Exc-30
❑ 95PriWilCTI-22
❑ 96BirBarB-18

Pratt, Scott
❑ 99JustheS-39
❑ 99JustheSJB-39
❑ 99TeaBesR-68
❑ 99TeaBesRG-68
❑ 99TeaBesRS-68

Pratt, Steve
❑ 89CliGiaP-908

Pratt, Todd
❑ 85ElmPioT-17
❑ 86GreHorP-17
❑ 87WinHavRSP-29
❑ 88EasLeaAP-22
❑ 88NewBriRSP-906
❑ 89NewBriRSP-624
❑ 89NewBriRSS-15
❑ 90NewBriRSP-1321
❑ 90NewBriRSS-16
❑ 91LinDriAAA-367
❑ 91PawRedSDD-19
❑ 91PawRedSLD-367
❑ 91PawRedSP-41
❑ 92ReaPhiS-540
❑ 92ScrRedBF-2450
❑ 92SkyAA F-235
❑ 93Don-620
❑ 93Fle-497
❑ 93LinVenB-9
❑ 93LinVenB-288
❑ 93PhiMed-27
❑ 93Pin-598
❑ 93Sco-276
❑ 93Top-479
❑ 93TopGol-479
❑ 93TopInaM-479
❑ 93TopInaR-479
❑ 93TopMic-479
❑ 93Ult-444
❑ 94Don-188
❑ 94Fle-598
❑ 94Pac-484
❑ 94PhiMed-26
❑ 94PhiMel-18
❑ 94PhiUSPC-3S
❑ 94PhiUSPC-9D
❑ 94StaClu-84
❑ 94StaCluFDI-84
❑ 94StaCluGR-84
❑ 94StaCluMOP-84
❑ 94StaCluT-227
❑ 94StaCluTFDI-227
❑ 94Top-597
❑ 94TopGol-597
❑ 94TopSpa-597
❑ 94VenLinU-135
❑ 95Pac-336
❑ 97NorTid-26
❑ 97NorTidB-26
❑ 98NorTidP-21
❑ 98NorTidQ-20
❑ 98PacOnl-489
❑ 98PacOnlR-489
❑ 98PacOnlWC-489
❑ 98PinSna-NYM12
❑ 98Ult-311
❑ 98UltGolM-311
❑ 98UltMas-311
❑ 98UltPlaM-311

Pratt, Wes
❑ 94AubAstC-11
❑ 94AubAstF-3771
❑ 95AubAstTI-10
❑ 95QuaCitRBTI-18
❑ 96AubDouB-3
❑ 97QuaCitRBB-21

Pratte, Evan
❑ 91NiaFalRC-12
❑ 91NiaFalRP-3643
❑ 92FayGenC-22
❑ 92FayGenF-2178
❑ 93LonTigF-2317

Pratts, Tato (Alberto)
❑ 88ElmPioC-2
❑ 89WinHavRSS-17
❑ 90LynRedSTI-20
❑ 90NewBriRSB-22
❑ 91ElmPioC-26
❑ 91ElmPioP-3271

Preikszas, Dave
❑ 91HelBreSP-14

Premack, Clayton
❑ 94LetMouF-3879
❑ 94LetMouSP-17

Prempas, Lyle
❑ 96HelBreTI-20

Prendergast, Jim
❑ 50WorWidGV-39

Prensi, Dagoberto
❑ 94MedHatBJF-3694
❑ 94MedHatBJSP-7
❑ 95HagSunF-81

Prentice, Elton
❑ 18Zee-50

Preqenger, John
❑ 77FriOneYW-92

Prescott, George
❑ 60TacBan-15
❑ 61UniOil-H3

Preseren, Ken
❑ 76BatTroTI-16

Presko, Joe
❑ 52Bow-62
❑ 52Top-220
❑ 53CarHunW-17
❑ 54Bow-190
❑ 54CarHunW-17
❑ 54Top-135
❑ 79TCM50-178
❑ 83TopRep5-220
❑ 94TopArc1-135
❑ 94TopArc1G-135

Presley, Billy
❑ 80ChaO'sP-15
❑ 80ChaO'sW-16

Presley, Jim
❑ 80WauTimT-13
❑ 81MarPos-25
❑ 81WauTimT-20
❑ 82LynSaiT-13
❑ 84SalLakCGC-184
❑ 85DomLeaS-150
❑ 85Don-240
❑ 85Fle-500
❑ 85MarMot-20
❑ 85TopTifT-92T
❑ 85TopTra-92T
❑ 86Don-313
❑ 86Fle-473
❑ 86FleMin-98
❑ 86FleStiC-89
❑ 86KayB-24
❑ 86Lea-183
❑ 86MarMot-7
❑ 86OPC-228
❑ 86SevCoi-W14
❑ 86Spo-40
❑ 86Top-598
❑ 86TopSti-219
❑ 86TopTat-12
❑ 86TopTif-598
❑ 87ClaGam-48
❑ 87Don-23
❑ 87Don-120
❑ 87DonAll-29
❑ 87DonOpeD-123
❑ 87DonSupD-23
❑ 87Fle-594
❑ 87FleGlo-594
❑ 87FleLimE-33
❑ 87FleMin-82
❑ 87FleStiC-91
❑ 87Lea-23
❑ 87Lea-154
❑ 87MarMot-4
❑ 87OPC-45
❑ 87RedFolSB-19
❑ 87Spo-179
❑ 87SpoTeaP-25
❑ 87Top-45
❑ 87TopSti-214
❑ 87TopTif-45
❑ 88Don-366
❑ 88DonBasB-219
❑ 88Fle-385
❑ 88FleGlo-385
❑ 88MarMot-4
❑ 88OPC-285
❑ 88PanSti-189
❑ 88Sco-46
❑ 88ScoGlo-46
❑ 88Spo-54
❑ 88StaLinMa-14
❑ 88Top-285
❑ 88TopBig-90
❑ 88TopSti-217
❑ 88TopTif-285
❑ 89Bow-214
❑ 89BowTif-214
❑ 89ChaLooLITI-24
❑ 89Don-379
❑ 89DonBasB-331
❑ 89Fle-555
❑ 89FleGlo-555
❑ 89MarMot-4
❑ 89OPC-112
❑ 89PanSti-437
❑ 89Sco-73
❑ 89Spo-7
❑ 89Top-112
❑ 89TopBig-75
❑ 89TopSti-223
❑ 89TopTif-112
❑ 89UppDec-642

❑ 90Bow-18
❑ 90BowTif-18
❑ 90BraDubP-23
❑ 90BraDubS-26
❑ 90ClaYel-T21
❑ 90Don-497
❑ 90DonBesN-37
❑ 90Fle-522
❑ 90FleCan-522
❑ 90FleUpd-6
❑ 90Lea-277
❑ 90OPC-346
❑ 90PubIntS-439
❑ 90Sco-34
❑ 90ScoRoo-36T
❑ 90Top-346
❑ 90TopBig-304
❑ 90TopSti-224
❑ 90TopTif-346
❑ 90TopTra-98T
❑ 90TopTraT-98T
❑ 90UppDec-315
❑ 90UppDec-760
❑ 91Bow-646
❑ 91Don-173
❑ 91Fle-700
❑ 91OPC-643
❑ 91PadMag-23A
❑ 91PanFreS-21
❑ 91PanSti-24
❑ 91RedFolS-73
❑ 91Sco-771
❑ 91Top-643
❑ 91TopDesS-643
❑ 91TopMic-643
❑ 91TopTif-643
❑ 91UppDec-282
❑ 91UppDec-791
❑ 92OklCit8F-1924
❑ 92OklCit8S-320
❑ 96AriBlaDB-3
❑ 97SouBenSH-8

Presley, Kirk
❑ 94ActPac-8
❑ 94Bow-324
❑ 94BowBes-B26
❑ 94BowBesR-B26
❑ 94Cla-50
❑ 94ClaBonB-BB2
❑ 94ClaCreotC-C2
❑ 94ColC-26
❑ 94ColChoGS-26
❑ 94ColChoSS-26
❑ 94Pin-436
❑ 94PinArtP-436
❑ 94PinMusC-436
❑ 94PitMetC-17
❑ 94PitMetF-3521
❑ 94Sco-518
❑ 94ScoGolR-518
❑ 94SigRoo-45
❑ 94SigRooS-45
❑ 94SP-14
❑ 94SPDieC-14
❑ 94Top-740
❑ 94TopGol-740
❑ 94TopSpa-740
❑ 94UppDecAHNIL-11
❑ 94UppDecML-TC2
❑ 95Bow-164
❑ 95Exc-236
❑ 95UppDecML-30
❑ 95UppDecMLFS-30
❑ 96PitMetB-20

Press, Greg
❑ 94ElmPioC-16
❑ 94ElmPioF-3472
❑ 95KanCouCTI-26
❑ 95MidLeaA-41
❑ 96BreCouMB-26
❑ 97PorSeaD-24

Pressley, Kasey
❑ 97WilCubB-19

Pressnell, Tot (Forest)
❑ 39PlaBal-134
❑ 40DodTeal-19
❑ 40PlaBal-146
❑ 41CubTeal-20
❑ 42CubTeal-19
❑ 74TCMNic-25
❑ 90DodTar-637

Presto, Nick
❑ 96BilMusTI-26
❑ 98ChaLooG-21

Preston, Dayton
❑ 88ColAstB-24

Preston, Doyle
❑ 94PriRedF-3271
❑ 95BilMusTI-22

Preston, George
❑ 94BelBreC-19
❑ 94BelBreFl-97
❑ 94HelBreSP-8

Preston, Steve
❑ 88EugEmeB-20
❑ 89AppFoxP-861

Preumer, Dave
❑ 97ForMyeM-4

Prevost, Eric
❑ 78WisRapTT-15

Prewitt, Larry
❑ 80PhoGiaVNB-5

Price, Al
❑ 81ElPasDT-24
❑ 82ElPasDT-24
❑ 83ElPasDT-18
❑ 85VanCanC-225
❑ 87DenZepP-3
❑ 98RocRedWQ-5

Price, Bill
❑ 81WisRapTT-18

Price, Bryan
❑ 85MidAngT-2
❑ 86PalSprAP-27
❑ 86PalSprAS-15
❑ 88VerMarP-940
❑ 89CalCanC-9
❑ 89CalCanP-540
❑ 89WilBilS-16
❑ 91PenPilP-396
❑ 92BelMarF-1463
❑ 93RivPilCLC-29
❑ 94BelMarF-3233
❑ 95EveAqaTI-16
❑ 96PorCitRB-3

Price, Chris
❑ 95SprSulTI-21
❑ 97PorRocG-20
❑ 98AshTouM-17

Price, Corey
❑ 96BilMusTI-27
❑ 98BurBeeM-16

Price, Duane
❑ 98BilMusTI-27

Price, Harris
❑ 75AppFoxT-23
❑ 76AppFoxT-19

Price, Harry
❑ 12HomRunKE-53
❑ 12Zee-91
❑ 15Zee-49

Price, Jamey
❑ 96WesMicWB-21
❑ 97HunStaTI-22
❑ 97SouLeaTP-14
❑ 99WesMicWAM-20

Price, Jimmie
❑ 67OPC-123
❑ 67Top-123
❑ 68TigDetFPB-18
❑ 68Top-226
❑ 68TopVen-226
❑ 69TigTealC-14
❑ 69Top-472
❑ 70OPC-129
❑ 70Top-129
❑ 71MLBOffS-403
❑ 71OPC-444
❑ 71Top-444
❑ 72MilBra-278
❑ 88TigDom-20

Price, Joe
❑ 79NaSouTI-19
❑ 80IndIndTI-5
❑ 81Fle-210
❑ 81Top-258
❑ 82Don-481
❑ 82Fle-81
❑ 82RedCok-18
❑ 82Top-492
❑ 83Don-481
❑ 83Fle-600
❑ 83RedYea-49
❑ 83Top-191
❑ 84Don-506
❑ 84Fle-479
❑ 84Nes792-686
❑ 84OPC-159
❑ 84RedEnq-17
❑ 84Top-686
❑ 84TopSti-58
❑ 84TopTif-686
❑ 85Don-627
❑ 85Fle-548
❑ 85OPC-82
❑ 85RedYea-13
❑ 85Top-82
❑ 85TopMin-82
❑ 85TopSti-56
❑ 85TopTif-82
❑ 86Don-506
❑ 86Fle-188
❑ 86RedTexG-49
❑ 86Top-523
❑ 86TopTif-523
❑ 87Fle-211
❑ 87FleGlo-211
❑ 87PhoFirP-17
❑ 87Top-332
❑ 87TopTif-332
❑ 88Don-655
❑ 88GiaMot-26
❑ 88GiaPos-25
❑ 88Top-786
❑ 88TopTif-786
❑ 89Don-376
❑ 89Fle-339
❑ 89FleGlo-339
❑ 89GiaMot-26
❑ 89Sco-444
❑ 89Top-217
❑ 89TopTif-217
❑ 89UppDec-505
❑ 90BalOriP-22
❑ 90Bow-245
❑ 90BowTif-245
❑ 90Fle-282
❑ 90FleCan-282
❑ 90OPC-473
❑ 90Top-473
❑ 90TopTif-473
❑ 91Fle-488
❑ 91LinDriAAA-464
❑ 91OPC-127
❑ 91OriCro-370
❑ 91RocRedWLD-464
❑ 91Top-127
❑ 91TopDesS-127
❑ 91TopMic-127
❑ 91TopTif-127

Price, John Thomas
❑ 46RemBre-16

Price, Kevin
❑ 82DanSunF-9
❑ 83RedPioT-21
❑ 86JacExpT-14
❑ 86SouLeaAJ-25
❑ 87JacExpP-448
❑ 87SouLeaAJ-17
❑ 88ChaKniTI-4

Price, Nathan
❑ 97SalVolG-30

Price, Phil
❑ 87SpaPhiP-25
❑ 88VirGenS-18

Price, Ray
❑ 77ColCliT-19

Price, Ryan
❑ 98AshTouM-18
❑ 98SouAtlLPM-16

Price, Tom
❑ 94GreFalDSP-25
❑ 95SanBerSTI-16
❑ 97NewHavRB-25
❑ 98NewHavRM-23
❑ 98NewHavRMA-23

Prichard, Brian
❑ 91BriTigC-8
❑ 91BriTigP-3608

Pricher, John
❑ 92BoiHawC-18
❑ 92BoiHawF-3623
❑ 93ClaFS7-238
❑ 93ExcFS7-147
❑ 93PalSprAC-17
❑ 93PalSprAF-67
❑ 94ClaGolF-139
❑ 94ExcFS7-30
❑ 94MidAngF-2437
❑ 94MidAngOHP-21

Priddy, Jerry (Gerald)
❑ 41DouPlaR-109
❑ 49Bow-4A
❑ 49Bow-4B
❑ 49Lea-111
❑ 50Bow-212
❑ 51Bow-71
❑ 51R42SmaS-79
❑ 51TopBluB-46
❑ 52Bow-139
❑ 52NatTeaL-21
❑ 52Top-28
❑ 53DixLid-15
❑ 53DixPre-15
❑ 53NorBreL-22
❑ 53TigGle-25
❑ 53Top-113
❑ 54SeaPop-21
❑ 67OPC-26
❑ 77TCMTheWY-33
❑ 79TCM50-213
❑ 83TopRep5-28
❑ 91TopArc1-113

Priddy, Robert
❑ 64Top-74
❑ 64TopVen-74
❑ 65Top-482
❑ 66Top-572
❑ 67SenPos-20
❑ 67Top-26A
❑ 67Top-26B
❑ 68Top-391
❑ 69Top-248
❑ 70Top-687
❑ 71MLBOffS-20
❑ 71OPC-147
❑ 71Top-147

Pride, Charley
❑ 73A'sPos-31
❑ 73A'sPos-32

Pride, Curtis
❑ 89PitMetS-20
❑ 91FloStaLAP-FSL33
❑ 91St.LucMC-2
❑ 91St.LucMP-725
❑ 92BinMetF-530
❑ 92BinMetS-65
❑ 92ClaFS7-159
❑ 92SkyAA F-30
❑ 93HarSenF-280
❑ 94ActPac-33
❑ 94AriFalLS-15
❑ 94Cla-197
❑ 94ColC-233
❑ 94ColChoGS-233
❑ 94ColChoSS-233
❑ 94Don-646
❑ 94FleMajLP-29
❑ 94Pac-387
❑ 94Pin-230
❑ 94PinArtP-230
❑ 94PinMusC-230
❑ 94Spo-167
❑ 94Top-237
❑ 94TopGol-237
❑ 94TopSpa-237
❑ 94UppDec-250
❑ 94UppDecED-250
❑ 95ActPacF-45
❑ 96Fle-464
❑ 96FleTif-464
❑ 96LeaSig-137
❑ 96LeaSigA-184
❑ 96LeaSigAG-184
❑ 96LeaSigAS-184
❑ 96LeaSigPPG-137
❑ 96LeaSigPPP-137
❑ 96TigHebN-18
❑ 96TolMudHB-23
❑ 97Cir-331
❑ 97CirRav-331
❑ 97ColCho-107
❑ 97Don-192
❑ 97DonEli-145
❑ 97DonEliGS-145
❑ 97DonGolPP-192
❑ 97DonSilPP-192
❑ 97Fle-104
❑ 97FleTif-104
❑ 97Lea-143
❑ 97LeaFraM-143
❑ 97LeaFraMDC-143
❑ 97Pac-94
❑ 97PacLigB-94
❑ 97PacSil-94
❑ 97PinIns-123
❑ 97PinInsCE-123
❑ 97PinInsDE-123
❑ 97Sco-217
❑ 97ScoArtPWB-217
❑ 97ScoPreS-217
❑ 97ScoShoS-217
❑ 97ScoShoSAP-217
❑ 97Top-376
❑ 97Ult-62
❑ 97UltGolME-62
❑ 97UltPlaME-62
❑ 98PacOnl-72
❑ 98PacOnlR-72
❑ 98PacOnlWC-72

Pridy, Todd
❑ 92EriSaiC-20
❑ 92EriSaiF-1633
❑ 93ClaFS7-112
❑ 93ExcFS7-39
❑ 93KanCouCC-16
❑ 93KanCouCF-924
❑ 93KanCouCTI-17
❑ 93Top-441
❑ 93TopGol-441
❑ 93TopInaM-441
❑ 93TopInaR-441
❑ 93TopMic-441
❑ 94BreCouMC-13
❑ 94BreCouMF-20
❑ 95SigRoo-42
❑ 95SigRooSig-42

Priebe, Kevin
❑ 97HelBreB-27
❑ 98BelSnaM-21

Pries, Jeff
❑ 86AlbYanT-15
❑ 86ColCliP-17
❑ 86ColCliP-19
❑ 87AlbYanP-18

Priess, Matt
❑ 97SalVolG-31

Priessman, Kraig
❑ 83SanJosBC-17

Priest, Adam
❑ 95TenVolW-10

Priest, Chris
❑ 94LetMouF-3892
❑ 94LetMouSP-4

Priest, Eddie
❑ 94BilMusF-3667
❑ 94BilMusSP-19
❑ 94StaCluDP-45
❑ 94StaCluDPFDI-45
❑ 95Exc-180
❑ 95Top-316
❑ 97SouAtlTPB-11
❑ 98ChaLooG-22
❑ 98IndIndQ-15
❑ 99SpoIll-64

Prieto, Alejandro
❑ 94VenLinU-72
❑ 95SprSulTI-22
❑ 96-97LinVen-241
❑ 96WilBluRB-22
❑ 97CarLeaTP-16
❑ 97WilBluR-9
❑ 98WicWraM-12

Prieto, Ariel
❑ 95A'sCHP-8
❑ 95AthMot-29
❑ 95LeaLim-121
❑ 95SPCha-10
❑ 95SPChaDC-10
❑ 95UppDec-453
❑ 96Bow-56
❑ 96BowFoi-56
❑ 96ColCho-14
❑ 96ColChoGS-14
❑ 96ColChoSS-14
❑ 96Don-231
❑ 96DonPreP-231
❑ 96EmoXL-106
❑ 96Fla-152
❑ 96Fle-216
❑ 96FleTif-216
❑ 96Lea-84
❑ 96LeaPrePB-84
❑ 96LeaPrePG-84
❑ 96LeaPrePS-84
❑ 96LeaSigA-185
❑ 96LeaSigAG-185
❑ 96LeaSigAS-185
❑ 96Pac-392
❑ 96Pin-316
❑ 96PinFoil-316
❑ 96Sco-127
❑ 96ScoDugC-A79
❑ 96ScoDugCAP-A79
❑ 96SP-138
❑ 96TopGal-137
❑ 96TopGalPPI-137
❑ 96Ult-116
❑ 96UltGolM-116
❑ 96UppDec-164
❑ 97A'sMot-14
❑ 97Cir-153
❑ 97CirRav-153
❑ 97ColCho-186
❑ 97Fle-659
❑ 97FleTif-659
❑ 97Pac-174
❑ 97PacLigB-174
❑ 97PacSil-174
❑ 97Sco-351
❑ 97ScoArtPWB-351
❑ 97ScoResC-351
❑ 97ScoShoS-351
❑ 97ScoShoSAP-351
❑ 97Top-279
❑ 97Ult-368
❑ 97UltGolME-368
❑ 97UltPlaME-368
❑ 97UppDec-446
❑ 98ColCho-199
❑ 98Pac-171
❑ 98PacOnl-542
❑ 98PacOnlR-542
❑ 98PacOnlWC-542
❑ 98PacPlaB-171
❑ 98PacRedT-171
❑ 98PacSil-171
❑ 98StaCluFDI-235
❑ 98StaCluI-235
❑ 98StaCluOneK-235
❑ 98StaCluPP-235
❑ 98UppDec-182
❑ 98UppDecSF-98

Prieto, Arnie
❑ 88MiaMarS-19
❑ 89MiaMirIS-23

Prieto, Chris
❑ 93SpoIndC-16
❑ 93SpoIndF-3604
❑ 94RanCucQC-22
❑ 94RanCucQF-1650
❑ 95RanCucQT-1
❑ 96RanCucQB-22
❑ 97MobBayBB-11
❑ 97RanCucQUG-7
❑ 98Las-20

Prieto, Omar
❑ 80VenLeaS-241

Prieto, Pete (Pedro)
❑ 76DubPacT-29
❑ 77CocAstT-19

Prieto, Rick
❑ 93WatIndC-23
❑ 93WatIndF-3572
❑ 94ColRedC-16
❑ 94ColRedF-457
❑ 95BakBlaTI-7
❑ 95KinIndTI-22
❑ 97RanCucQG-23
❑ 98Las-21
❑ 98MobBayBTI-22

Prihoda, Steve
❑ 95SpoIndTI-19
❑ 96CarLeaA1B-5
❑ 96CarLeaA2B-5
❑ 96WilBluRB-5
❑ 97WicWra-8
❑ 98WicWraM-6

Prim, Ray
❑ 43CubTeal-20
❑ 47SigOil-34

Primmante, Val
❑ 80ColAstT-2

Prince, Bob
❑ 95PirCocP-22

Prince, Don
❑ 77FriOneYW-55

Prince, Doug
❑ 75TopPho-119

Prince, Ray
❑ 77DayBealT-16

Prince, Tom
❑ 86PriWilPP-20
❑ 87HarSenP-3
❑ 88BufBisC-19
❑ 88BufBisP-1488
❑ 88Don-538
❑ 88TriAAAP-5
❑ 89Don-527
❑ 89Fle-217
❑ 89FleGlo-217
❑ 89Sco-626
❑ 89ScoHot1R-45
❑ 89Top-453
❑ 89TopTif-453
❑ 89UppDec-311

❑ 90Bow-176
❑ 90BowTif-176
❑ 90BufBisC-14
❑ 90BufBisP-376
❑ 90BufBisTI-19
❑ 90CMC-14
❑ 90ProAAAF-491
❑ 90PubIntS-161
❑ 92BufBisBS-15
❑ 92Sco-618
❑ 92StaClu-332
❑ 92Ult-559
❑ 93PacSpa-591
❑ 93PirHil-11
❑ 93PirNatl-25
❑ 94DodPol-22
❑ 94Fle-618
❑ 94Pac-505
❑ 97DodMot-20
❑ 97DodPol-24
❑ 97PacPriGotD-GD162
❑ 98DodMot-20
❑ 98DodPol-23
❑ 98PacInvGems-173
❑ 98PacOnl-383
❑ 98PacOnlR-383
❑ 98PacOnlWC-383
Princi, Peter
❑ 98PitMetM-23
Prinz, Paul
❑ 87BriYouC-21
Prioleau, Laney
❑ 86LakTigP-18
Prior, Dan
❑ 80CarMudF-20
❑ 81ReaPhiT-5
❑ 82ReaPhiT-6
Pritchard, Buddy (Harold)
❑ 58Top-151
Pritchard, Michael
❑ 94HelBreF-3622
❑ 94HelBreSP-2
Pritchett, Anthony
❑ 91BenBucCB-18
❑ 91BenBucP-3707
Pritchett, Chris
❑ 91BoiHawC-2
❑ 91BoiHawP-3889
❑ 91Cla/Bes-445
❑ 91FroRowDP-54
❑ 91FroRowDPG-54
❑ 91FroRowDPS-54
❑ 92MidLeaATI-33
❑ 92QuaCitRBC-26
❑ 92QuaCitRBF-820
❑ 92StaCluD-142
❑ 92UppDecML-152
❑ 93Bow-665
❑ 93ExcFS7-148
❑ 93MidAngF-330
❑ 94ExcFS7-31
❑ 94MidAngF-2446
❑ 94MidAngOHP-22
❑ 96Top-103
❑ 96VanCanB-23
❑ 97MidAngOHP-23
❑ 97VanCanB-23
❑ 98VanCanG-21
❑ 99DumSet-125
❑ 99FleMys-125
❑ 99FleMysM-125
❑ 99PacOme-7
❑ 99PacOmeC-7
❑ 99PacOmeG-7
❑ 99PacOmePB-7
Pritikin, James
❑ 86BelMarCr-113
❑ 88WauTimGS-12
❑ 89SanBerSB-14
❑ 89SanBerSCLC-86
Probst, Alan
❑ 92AubAstC-16
❑ 92AubAstF-1356
❑ 93AshTouC-16
❑ 93AshTouF-2279
❑ 94MidLeaAF-MDW53
❑ 94QuaCitRBC-16
❑ 94QuaCitRBF-538
❑ 95QuaCitRBTI-19
❑ 96JacGenB-23
❑ 97JacGen-22
❑ 97JacGenS-20
❑ 98KnoSG-18
Probst, Thomas
❑ 92BenRocCB-27
Procopio, Jim
❑ 87IdaFalBP-16
❑ 88IdaFalBP-1853
❑ 92LetMouSP-26
Procter, Craig
❑ 88SpoIndP-1944
Proctor, Bill
❑ 94SouBenSHC-18
❑ 94SouBenSHF-592
Proctor, Dave
❑ 88LitFalMP-21
❑ 89Bow-378
❑ 89BowTif-378
❑ 89St.LucMS-20
❑ 90JacMetGS-14
❑ 91Cla/Bes-257
❑ 91St.LucMP-707
❑ 92St.LucMF-1745
Proctor, Jim
❑ 60Top-141
❑ 60TopVen-141
Proctor, Murph
❑ 89AncGlaP-20
❑ 91YakBeaC-5
❑ 91YakBeaP-4254
❑ 92BakDodCLC-20
❑ 92CalLeaACL-30
❑ 92ProFS7-248
❑ 93SanAntMF-3014
❑ 94CanIndF-3127
❑ 97SanBerS-24
Proctor, Scott
❑ 98YakBeaG-27
Proctor, Steve
❑ 93SavCarC-28
❑ 94MadHatC-29
Prodanov, Peter
❑ 92OklStaC-23
❑ 97MicBatC-22
❑ 98FarRedHM-23
Proffitt, Mike
❑ 72CedRapCT-19
Proffitt, Steve
❑ 89HigSchPLS-9
Prohaska, Tim
❑ 89NiaFalRP-28
Prokop, Mike
❑ 98PitMetM-24
Prokopec, Luke
❑ 95GreFalDTI-16
❑ 96SavSanB-7
❑ 98SanBerS-25
❑ 98SanBerSTIS-22
❑ 99Bow-391
❑ 99BowGol-391
❑ 99BowInt-391
Proly, Michael
❑ 75TulOil7-14
❑ 76St.LouCP-25
❑ 76TulOilGP-16
❑ 77TacTwiDQ-17
❑ 79Top-514
❑ 80Top-399
❑ 81Don-596
❑ 81Fle-358
❑ 81Top-83
❑ 81TopTra-815
❑ 82CubRedL-36
❑ 82Don-345
❑ 82Fle-254
❑ 82IowCubT-22
❑ 82Top-183
❑ 82TopTra-92T
❑ 83CubThoAV-36
❑ 83Don-225
❑ 83Fle-505
❑ 83Top-597
❑ 84Don-320
❑ 84Fle-501
❑ 84Nes792-437
❑ 84SyrChiT-16
❑ 84Top-437
❑ 84TopTif-437
Prospero, Teo
❑ 95BelGiaTI-2
❑ 96BelGiaTI-8
Prothro, Doc
❑ 26Zee-100
❑ 27Zee-78
❑ 40PhiTeal-19
❑ 41PhiTeal-21
❑ 93ConTSN-964
Prough, Bill
❑ 22Zee-69
❑ 24Zee-68
Prough, Herschel
❑ 14Zee-46
❑ 15Zee-50
❑ 16Zee-43
❑ 17Zee-38
❑ 18Zee-33
❑ 19Zee-62
❑ 20Zee-73
❑ 21Zee-80
Provence, Todd
❑ 86VenGulP-21
❑ 87KnoBluJP-1504
❑ 88MyrBeaBJP-1192
❑ 89MyrBeaBJP-1455
❑ 90MyrBeaBJP-2790
Prts, Mario
❑ 90AshTouC-9
Prud'homme, Johnny
❑ 28LaPre-8
Pruemer, Dave
❑ 98NewBriRCM-4
Pruett, Hub (Hubert)
❑ 23W503-45
❑ 25Zee-36
❑ 26Zee-85
❑ 73FleWilD-34
❑ 87ConSer2-50
❑ 88ConSer5-24
❑ 92MegRut-100
❑ 93ConTSN-904
Pruett, Jim
❑ 45A'sTeal-26
Pruett, Matt
❑ 97PriDevR-27
Pruiett, Charles
❑ 14Zee-47
❑ 15Zee-51
❑ 16Zee-44
❑ 17Zee-39
Pruiett, Tex
❑ 08RosComP-5
Pruitt, Charles
❑ 13Zee-47
Pruitt, Darrell Ray
❑ 86PenWhiSP-21
❑ 87BirBarB-21
❑ 88ChaLooB-11
❑ 88SouLeaAJ-6
❑ 89GreBraB-3
❑ 89GreBraP-1171
❑ 89GreBraS-19
Pruitt, Donald
❑ 90HelBreSP-20
❑ 91BelBreCB-6
❑ 91BelBreP-2101
❑ 91MidLeaAP-MWL34
❑ 92BelBreCB-9
❑ 92BelBreFI-403
❑ 93StoPorC-19
❑ 93StoPorF-744
Pruitt, Ed
❑ 86JacMetT-8
❑ 87JacMetF-14
Pruitt, Jason
❑ 91ClaDraP-26
❑ 91FroRowDP-26
❑ 91FroRowDPG-26
❑ 91FroRowDPS-26
❑ 91HigSchPLS-31
❑ 92AppFoxCB-26
❑ 92AppFoxFI-983
❑ 92ClaFS7-358
❑ 92EugEmeC-21
❑ 92EugEmeF-3028
❑ 92OPC-246
❑ 92StaCluD-143
❑ 92Top-246
❑ 92TopGol-246
❑ 92TopGolW-246
❑ 92TopMic-246
Pruitt, Ron
❑ 75SpoIndC-11
❑ 76IndTeal-8
❑ 77IndTeal-21
❑ 77Top-654
❑ 78IndTeal-25
❑ 78Top-198
❑ 79Top-226
❑ 80IndTeal-24
❑ 80Top-13
❑ 81Top-442
❑ 82PhoGiaVNB-13
❑ 83PorBeaT-21
❑ 89PacSenL-103
❑ 89TopSenL-74
❑ 93RanKee-299
Pruitt, Russell
❑ 79ElmPioRST-12
Prusia, Greg
❑ 89AppFoxP-858
Prybylinski, Bruce
❑ 88OneYanP-2061
❑ 89PriWilCS-17
❑ 90PriWilCTI-20
❑ 91Ft.LauYC-12
❑ 91Ft.LauYP-2425
❑ 92PriWilCC-1
❑ 92PriWilCF-145
❑ 92ProFS7-117
Prybylinski, Don
❑ 91ArkTraLD-43
❑ 91ArkTraP-1289
❑ 91LinDriAA-43
❑ 92ArkTraF-1133
❑ 92ArkTraS-42
❑ 92ClaFS7-333
❑ 92SkyAA F-18
❑ 92StaClu-748
Pryce, Ken
❑ 81QuaCitCT-22
❑ 83MidCubT-11
❑ 84IowCubT-1
❑ 85IowCubT-20
❑ 86IowCubP-23
Pryer-Fuller, Pamela
❑ 97NegLeaPC-12H
Pryor, Buddy
❑ 83CedRapRF-2
❑ 83CedRapRT-14
❑ 86VerRedP-15
❑ 87NasSouTI-17
❑ 89TacTigC-15
❑ 89TacTigP-1558
Pryor, Greg
❑ 76SacSolC-10
❑ 78SSP270-145
❑ 79Top-559
❑ 80OPC-91
❑ 80Top-164
❑ 81Don-278
❑ 81Fle-359
❑ 81Top-608
❑ 82Don-521
❑ 82Fle-356
❑ 82Roy-16
❑ 82Top-76
❑ 82TopTra-93T
❑ 83Don-264
❑ 83Fle-121
❑ 83RoyPos-22
❑ 83Top-418
❑ 84Don-374
❑ 84Fle-353
❑ 84Nes792-317
❑ 84RoyPos-25
❑ 84Top-317
❑ 84TopTif-317
❑ 85Don-277
❑ 85Fle-210
❑ 85RoyTeal-25
❑ 85Top-188
❑ 85TopTif-188
❑ 86Don-344
❑ 86RoyNatP-4
❑ 86RoyTeal-19
❑ 86Top-773
❑ 86TopTif-773
❑ 87Don-378
❑ 87OPC-268
❑ 87Top-761
❑ 87TopTif-761
❑ 93RanKee-300
Pryor, Jim
❑ 76CedRapGT-22
❑ 77CedRapGT-13
Pryor, Pete
❑ 96HicCraB-15
Pryor, Randy
❑ 88CapCodPPaLP-107
Przybycien, Tony
❑ 66TolMudHTI-20
Przybylinski, Rodney
❑ 89TenTecGE-21
Psaltis, Spiro
❑ 82ChaRoyT-19
❑ 85MidAngT-16
Puccinelli, George
❑ 28LaPre-24
❑ 36ExhFou-14
❑ 36WorWidGV-127
❑ 38ExhFou-1
Puchales, Javier
❑ 90KisDodD-23
❑ 91GreFalDSP-29
❑ 93VerBeaDC-20
❑ 93VerBeaDF-2234
❑ 94SanAntMF-2484
❑ 95SanAntMTI-33
Puchkov, Evgeny
❑ 89EasLeaDDP-DD6
❑ 93Top-633
❑ 93TopGol-633
❑ 93TopInaM-633
❑ 93TopInaR-633
❑ 93TopMic-633
Puckett, Kirby
❑ 83VisOakF-6
❑ 84FleUpd-93
❑ 84OCoandSI-243
❑ 85AllGamPI-68
❑ 85Don-438
❑ 85Fle-286
❑ 85FleStaS-122
❑ 85Lea-107
❑ 85OPC-10
❑ 85Top-536
❑ 85TopSti-307
❑ 85TopSti-376
❑ 85TopTif-536
❑ 85Twi7-1
❑ 85TwiPos-21
❑ 85TwiTeal-24
❑ 86Don-72
❑ 86DonHig-7
❑ 86Fle-401
❑ 86FleLeaL-32
❑ 86FleMin-85
❑ 86FleSluBC-M5
❑ 86FleStiC-90
❑ 86KayB-25
❑ 86Lea-69
❑ 86OPC-329
❑ 86Spo-93
❑ 86Top-329
❑ 86TopSti-285
❑ 86TopTat-13
❑ 86TopTat-22
❑ 86TopTif-329
❑ 86TwiTeal-24
❑ 86WilGloT-2
❑ 87ClaGam-55
❑ 87ClaUpdY-112
❑ 87Don-19
❑ 87Don-149
❑ 87DonAll-4
❑ 87DonHig-30
❑ 87DonOpeD-221
❑ 87DonP-4
❑ 87DonSupD-19
❑ 87Dra-19
❑ 87Fle-549
❑ 87Fle-633
❑ 87FleAll-5
❑ 87FleAwaW-30
❑ 87FleBasA-32
❑ 87FleGlo-549
❑ 87FleGlo-633
❑ 87FleLeaL-36
❑ 87FleMin-83
❑ 87FleSlu-31
❑ 87FleStiC-92
❑ 87FleWaxBC-C11
❑ 87GenMilB-3I
❑ 87HosSti-26
❑ 87KayB-24
❑ 87KraFoo-27
❑ 87Lea-19
❑ 87Lea-56
❑ 87MandMSL-15
❑ 87OPC-82
❑ 87RedFolSB-23
❑ 87SmoAmeL-8
❑ 87Spo-7
❑ 87Spo-198
❑ 87SpoIllS-10
❑ 87SpoSupD-11
❑ 87SpoTeaP-17
❑ 87StuPan-22
❑ 87Top-450
❑ 87Top-611
❑ 87TopCoi-20
❑ 87TopGloA-19
❑ 87TopGloS-57
❑ 87TopMinL-63
❑ 87TopSti-146
❑ 87TopSti-274
❑ 87TopTif-450
❑ 87TopTif-611
❑ 87TwiPos-20
❑ 87TwiTeal-23
❑ 88Baz-14
❑ 88CheBoy-13
❑ 88ClaRed-164
❑ 88Don-368
❑ 88DonAll-15
❑ 88DonBasB-186
❑ 88DonBonM-BC15
❑ 88Dra-19
❑ 88Fle-19
❑ 88Fle-638
❑ 88FleAwaW-29
❑ 88FleBasA-30
❑ 88FleBasM-26
❑ 88FleExcS-30
❑ 88FleGlo-19
❑ 88FleGlo-638
❑ 88FleGlo-WS8
❑ 88FleHotS-30
❑ 88FleLeaL-30
❑ 88FleMin-36
❑ 88FleRecS-29
❑ 88FleSlu-30
❑ 88FleStiC-45
❑ 88FleSup-28
❑ 88FleTeaL-26
❑ 88FleWaxBC-C7
❑ 88FleWorS-8
❑ 88GreBasS-43
❑ 88KayB-23
❑ 88KeyFooD-6
❑ 88KinDis-3
❑ 88Lea-144
❑ 88MSAFanSD-1
❑ 88MSAIceTD-6
❑ 88Nes-39
❑ 88OPC-120
❑ 88OurOwnTD-6
❑ 88PanSti-144
❑ 88PanSti-444
❑ 88RedFolSB-72
❑ 88Sco-24
❑ 88Sco-653
❑ 88ScoGlo-24
❑ 88ScoGlo-653
❑ 88Spo-8
❑ 88Spo-180
❑ 88StaLinAl-21
❑ 88StaLinTw-15
❑ 88StaPuc-1
❑ 88StaPuc-2
❑ 88StaPuc-3
❑ 88StaPuc-4
❑ 88StaPuc-5
❑ 88StaPuc-6
❑ 88StaPuc-7
❑ 88StaPuc-8
❑ 88StaPuc-9
❑ 88StaPuc-10
❑ 88StaPuc-11
❑ 88TarPla-31
❑ 88TetTeaD-6
❑ 88Top-120
❑ 88Top-391
❑ 88TopBig-36
❑ 88TopCoi-23
❑ 88TopGloS-27
❑ 88TopMinL-23
❑ 88TopRevLL-21
❑ 88TopRitTM-21
❑ 88TopSti-283
❑ 88TopStiB-52
❑ 88TopTif-120
❑ 88TopTif-391
❑ 88TopUKM-57
❑ 88TopUKMT-57
❑ 88TwiMasBD-8
❑ 88TwiSmoC-12
❑ 88WeiMarD-6
❑ 88Woo-31
❑ 89Bow-162
❑ 89BowTif-162
❑ 89CadEllD-41
❑ 89CerSup-8
❑ 89ClaLigB-15
❑ 89ClaTraP-176
❑ 89Don-182
❑ 89DonAll-23
❑ 89DonBasB-130
❑ 89DonBonM-BC1
❑ 89Fle-124
❑ 89Fle-639
❑ 89FleBasA-32
❑ 89FleBasM-32
❑ 89FleExcS-34
❑ 89FleGlo-124

❑ 89FleGlo-639
❑ 89FleHeroB-31
❑ 89FleLeaL-30
❑ 89FleSup-33
❑ 89FleWaxBC-C20
❑ 89K-M-16
❑ 89KayB-24
❑ 89KeyFooD-12
❑ 89MasBreD-2
❑ 89MSAHolD-8
❑ 89MSAIceTD-12
❑ 89Nis-8
❑ 89OPC-132
❑ 89OurOwnTD-12
❑ 89PanSti-247
❑ 89PanSti-393
❑ 89Sco-20
❑ 89ScoHot1S-11
❑ 89Scomast-19
❑ 89Spo-156
❑ 89SpollIFKI-167
❑ 89TetTeaD-12
❑ 89Top-403
❑ 89Top-650
❑ 89TopAme2C-24
❑ 89TopBasT-46
❑ 89TopBatL-4
❑ 89TopBig-167
❑ 89TopCapC-20
❑ 89TopCoi-48
❑ 89TopDouA-7
❑ 89TopGloS-1
❑ 89TopHeaUT-20
❑ 89TopHilTM-23
❑ 89TopMinL-62
❑ 89TopSti-293
❑ 89TopStiB-19
❑ 89TopTif-403
❑ 89TopTif-650
❑ 89TopUKM-60
❑ 89TVSpoM-102
❑ 89UppDec-376
❑ 89WeiMarD-12
❑ 90AllBasT-12
❑ 90Baz-7
❑ 90Bow-424
❑ 90BowTif-424
❑ 90ClaBlu-28
❑ 90Col-33
❑ 90Don-269
❑ 90Don-683A
❑ 90Don-683B
❑ 90DonBesA-23
❑ 90DOnBonM-BC8
❑ 90DonLeaS-46
❑ 90DonPre-12
❑ 90Fle-383
❑ 90Fle-635
❑ 90FleAll-7
❑ 90FleAwaW-26
❑ 90FleBasA-29
❑ 90FleBasAC-29
❑ 90FleBasM-29
❑ 90FleBasMC-29
❑ 90FleCan-383
❑ 90FleCan-635
❑ 90FleLeaL-30
❑ 90FleLeaLC-30
❑ 90FleWaxBC-C22
❑ 90GooHumICBLS-15
❑ 90Hot50PS-31
❑ 90K-M-22
❑ 90KayB-23
❑ 90KinDis-21
❑ 90Lea-123
❑ 90M.Vpin-58
❑ 90MLBBasB-98
❑ 90MSAHolD-17
❑ 90MSAIceTD-13
❑ 90NikMin-2
❑ 90OPC-391
❑ 90OPC-700
❑ 90PanSti-105
❑ 90PanSti-183
❑ 90PanSti-199
❑ 90Pos-3
❑ 90PubIntS-292
❑ 90PubIntS-335
❑ 90RedFolSB-75
❑ 90Sco-400
❑ 90Sco-690
❑ 90Sco100S-1
❑ 90Spo-11
❑ 90SunSee-5
❑ 90SupActM-4
❑ 90Top-391
❑ 90Top-700
❑ 90TopAmeA-24
❑ 90TopBatL-3
❑ 90TopBig-2
❑ 90TopCoi-4
❑ 90TopDou-49
❑ 90TopGaloC-7
❑ 90TopGloA-18
❑ 90TopGloS-48
❑ 90TopHeaU-20
❑ 90TopHilHM-27
❑ 90TopMag-24
❑ 90TopMinL-23
❑ 90TopSti-157
❑ 90TopSti-286
❑ 90TopStiB-52
❑ 90TopTif-391
❑ 90TopTif-700
❑ 90TopTVA-6
❑ 90UppDec-48
❑ 90UppDec-236
❑ 90USPlaCA-8S
❑ 90WinDis-2
❑ 90WonBreS-9
❑ 91BasBesHM-15
❑ 91Bow-320
❑ 91CadEllD-42
❑ 91Cla1-T57
❑ 91Cla3-T74
❑ 91ClaGam-111
❑ 91Col-7
❑ 91DodPho-27
❑ 91Don-490
❑ 91Fle-623
❑ 91FlePro-1
❑ 91JimDea-11
❑ 91KinDis-23
❑ 91Lea-208
❑ 91LeaPre-21
❑ 91MajLeaCP-12
❑ 91MooSna-2
❑ 91OPC-300
❑ 91OPCPre-96
❑ 91PanFreS-305
❑ 91PanSti-248
❑ 91PepSup-13
❑ 91PetSta-17
❑ 91Pos-28
❑ 91PosCan-30
❑ 91RedFolS-74
❑ 91Sco-200
❑ 91Sco-855
❑ 91Sco-891
❑ 91Sco100S-7
❑ 91SevCoi-A11
❑ 91SevCoi-F13
❑ 91SimandSMLBL-35
❑ 91StaClu-110
❑ 91StaPinB-36
❑ 91Stu-90
❑ 91Top-300
❑ 91TopCraJI-34
❑ 91TopDesS-300
❑ 91TopMic-300
❑ 91TopTif-300
❑ 91TopTriH-A9
❑ 91Ult-195
❑ 91UltGol-8
❑ 91UppDec-544
❑ 91USPlaCA-4D
❑ 92Bow-80
❑ 92Cla1-T72
❑ 92Cla2-T90
❑ 92ClaGam-101
❑ 92ColAllG-9
❑ 92ColAllP-9
❑ 92Don-617
❑ 92DonCraJ2-32
❑ 92DonEli-17
❑ 92DonMcD-21
❑ 92Fle-217
❑ 92Fle-704
❑ 92FleAll-22
❑ 92FleCitTP-11
❑ 92FleTeaL-5
❑ 92Fre-7
❑ 92Hig5-84
❑ 92HitTheBB-26
❑ 92KinDis-20
❑ 92Lea-98
❑ 92LeaBlaG-98
❑ 92MooSna-6
❑ 92Mr.TurS-18
❑ 92MSABenSHD-7
❑ 92MVPPin-7
❑ 92OPC-575
❑ 92OPCBoxB-4
❑ 92OPCPre-102
❑ 92PanSti-120
❑ 92PepDieM-27
❑ 92Pin-20
❑ 92Pin-289
❑ 92PinSlu-13
❑ 92Pos-7
❑ 92PosCan-17
❑ 92RedFolS-77
❑ 92RevSup1-10
❑ 92RevSup1-11
❑ 92RevSup1-12
❑ 92Sco-600
❑ 92Sco-796
❑ 92Sco-886
❑ 92Sco100S-7
❑ 92ScoFacI-B6
❑ 92ScoProaG-6
❑ 92ScoProP-4
❑ 92SevCoi-18
❑ 92SpollIFK1-29
❑ 92SpoStaCC-36
❑ 92StaClu-500
❑ 92StaCluD-144
❑ 92StaCluD-145
❑ 92StaPuc-1
❑ 92StaPuc-2
❑ 92StaPuc-3
❑ 92StaPuc-4
❑ 92StaPuc-5
❑ 92StaPuc-6
❑ 92StaPuc-7
❑ 92StaPuc-8
❑ 92StaPuc-9
❑ 92StaPuc-10
❑ 92StaPuc-11
❑ 92Stu-209
❑ 92StuHer-BC14
❑ 92StuPre-2
❑ 92SunSee-5
❑ 92Top-575
❑ 92TopGol-575
❑ 92TopGolW-575
❑ 92TopKid-109
❑ 92TopMcD-19
❑ 92TopMic-575
❑ 92TriPla-202
❑ 92TriPlaP-7
❑ 92Ult-97
❑ 92UltAllS-8
❑ 92UltAwaW-23
❑ 92UppDec-254
❑ 92UppDecF-35
❑ 92UppDecFG-35
❑ 92UppDecTMH-41
❑ 92UppDecWB-T9
❑ 93Bow-325
❑ 93CadDis-45
❑ 93ClaGam-75
❑ 93ColAllG-5
❑ 93CosBroPP-1
❑ 93DenHol-26
❑ 93DiaMar-87
❑ 93DiaMarP-6
❑ 93Don-607
❑ 93DonDiaK-DK4
❑ 93DonMasotG-13
❑ 93DonMVP-18
❑ 93DurPowP1-5
❑ 93Fin-112
❑ 93FinJum-112
❑ 93FinRef-112
❑ 93Fla-242
❑ 93Fle-273
❑ 93Fle-355
❑ 93FleAll-AL9
❑ 93FleAtl-18
❑ 93FleFruotL-52
❑ 93FleTeaL-AL1
❑ 93FunPac-191
❑ 93FunPac-195
❑ 93FunPacA-AS9
❑ 93Hos-29
❑ 93HumDumC-11
❑ 93JimDea-13
❑ 93Kra-11
❑ 93Lea-378
❑ 93LeaGolA-R17
❑ 93LeaGolA-U7
❑ 93LeaHeaftH-9
❑ 93MetBak-16
❑ 93OPC-306
❑ 93OPCPreSP-11
❑ 93OPCPreSPF-11
❑ 93PacSpa-177
❑ 93PanSti-130
❑ 93Pin-426
❑ 93PinCoo-12
❑ 93PinCooD-12
❑ 93PinSlu-16
❑ 93PinTeaP-9
❑ 93Pos-3
❑ 93PosCan-8
❑ 93RedFolS-76
❑ 93RedFolS-121
❑ 93Sco-505
❑ 93Sco-533
❑ 93Sco-550
❑ 93Sco-606
❑ 93ScoFra-9
❑ 93ScoGolDT-2
❑ 93Sel-4
❑ 93SelChaS-18
❑ 93SelStaL-2
❑ 93SelStaL-7
❑ 93SP-7
❑ 93StaClu-283
❑ 93StaClu-597
❑ 93StaCluFDI-283
❑ 93StaCluFDI-597
❑ 93StaCluM-28
❑ 93StaCluMMP-7
❑ 93StaCluMO-20
❑ 93StaCluMOP-283
❑ 93StaCluMOP-597
❑ 93StaCluMP-6
❑ 93Stu-214
❑ 93Top-200
❑ 93Top-406
❑ 93TOPBLAG-40
❑ 93TopGol-200
❑ 93TopGol-406
❑ 93TopInaM-200
❑ 93TopInaM-406
❑ 93TopInaR-200
❑ 93TopInaR-406
❑ 93TopMic-200
❑ 93TopMic-406
❑ 93TopMic-P200
❑ 93TriPla-260
❑ 93TriPlaA-20
❑ 93Ult-236
❑ 93UltAllS-18
❑ 93UltAwaW-17
❑ 93UppDec-34
❑ 93UppDec-50
❑ 93UppDec-565
❑ 93UppDecCP-R17
❑ 93UppDecDG-26
❑ 93UppDecFH-61
❑ 93UppDecGold-34
❑ 93UppDecGold-50
❑ 93UppDecGold-565
❑ 93UppDecHRH-HR24
❑ 93UppDecIC-WI24
❑ 93UppDecICJ-WI24
❑ 93UppDecOD-D19
❑ 93UppDecTriCro-TC6
❑ 93USPlaCA-12D
❑ 94Bow-460
❑ 94BowBes-R75
❑ 94BowBesR-R75
❑ 94ChuHomS-5
❑ 94ChuHomSG-5
❑ 94ColC-319
❑ 94ColC-353
❑ 94ColC-425
❑ 94ColC-638
❑ 94ColChoGS-319
❑ 94ColChoGS-353
❑ 94ColChoGS-425
❑ 94ColChoGS-638
❑ 94ColChoSS-319
❑ 94ColChoSS-353
❑ 94ColChoSS-425
❑ 94ColChoSS-638
❑ 94ColChoT-12
❑ 94Don-343
❑ 94DonAwaWJ-5
❑ 94DonDom-B5
❑ 94DonDomJ-B5
❑ 94DonMVP-23
❑ 94DonSpeE-343
❑ 94Fin-204
❑ 94FinJum-204
❑ 94FinRef-204
❑ 94Fla-77
❑ 94FlaHotG-7
❑ 94FlaOutP-8
❑ 94Fle-217
❑ 94Fle-712
❑ 94FleAllS-20
❑ 94FleExtB-123
❑ 94FleExtBGB-23
❑ 94FleSun-21
❑ 94FleTeaL-9
❑ 94FleUpdDT-9
❑ 94FUnPac-34
❑ 94FUnPac-206
❑ 94FUnPac-232
❑ 94KinDis-12
❑ 94Kra-9
❑ 94Lea-294
❑ 94LeaGam-9
❑ 94LeaL-51
❑ 94LeaLimGA-9
❑ 94LeaMVPC-A11
❑ 94LeaMVPCG-A11
❑ 94O-PJumAF-17
❑ 94OPC-93
❑ 94OPCAllR-17
❑ 94OPCJumA-17
❑ 94OscMayR-10
❑ 94Pac-365
❑ 94PacSilP-11
❑ 94PacSilPC-11
❑ 94PanSti-96
❑ 94Pin-21
❑ 94PinArtP-21
❑ 94PinMusC-21
❑ 94PinRunC-RC20
❑ 94PinTheN-11
❑ 94Pos-4
❑ 94PosCan-18
❑ 94ProMag-77
❑ 94RedFolMI-21
❑ 94Sco-21
❑ 94ScoGolR-21
❑ 94ScoGolS-52
❑ 94Sel-17
❑ 94SelSam-17
❑ 94SP-186
❑ 94SPDieC-186
❑ 94SPHol-30
❑ 94SPHolDC-30
❑ 94Spo-42
❑ 94SpoFanA-AS8
❑ 94SpoMov-MM4
❑ 94SPPre-CR3
❑ 94StaClu-359
❑ 94StaCluFDI-359
❑ 94StaCluGR-359
❑ 94StaCluMOP-359
❑ 94StaCluMOP-DD5
❑ 94StaCluMOP-ST23
❑ 94StaCluST-ST23
❑ 94Stu-200
❑ 94TomPiz-25
❑ 94Top-100
❑ 94Top-607
❑ 94TopBlaG-17
❑ 94TopGol-100
❑ 94TopGol-607
❑ 94TopSpa-100
❑ 94TopSpa-607
❑ 94TopSupS-35
❑ 94TriPla-258
❑ 94TriPlaM-11
❑ 94Ult-394
❑ 94UppDec-289
❑ 94UppDec-325
❑ 94UppDecAJ-14
❑ 94UppDecAJG-14
❑ 94UppDecDC-C4
❑ 94UppDecED-289
❑ 94UppDecED-325
❑ 94UppDecNG-14
❑ 94UppDecNGED-14
❑ 95Baz-113
❑ 95Bow-280
❑ 95BowBes-R27
❑ 95BowBesR-R27
❑ 95ClaPhoC-35
❑ 95ColCho-77
❑ 95ColChoGS-77
❑ 95ColChoSE-230
❑ 95ColChoSEGS-230
❑ 95ColChoSESS-230
❑ 95ColChoSS-77
❑ 95DenHol-21
❑ 95Don-330
❑ 95Don-380
❑ 95DonAll-AL9
❑ 95DonDiaK-DK19
❑ 95DonDom-9
❑ 95DonEli-57
❑ 95DonPreP-330
❑ 95DonPreP-380
❑ 95DonTopotO-113
❑ 95Emo-58
❑ 95Fin-167
❑ 95FinRef-167
❑ 95Fla-62
❑ 95FlaOutP-8
❑ 95Fle-212
❑ 95FleAllS-8
❑ 95FleLeaL-3
❑ 95FleTeaL-9
❑ 95FleUpdH-16
❑ 95KinDis-17
❑ 95Kra-11
❑ 95Lea-183
❑ 95Lea300C-17
❑ 95LeaGolS-13
❑ 95LeaGreG-12
❑ 95LeaHeaftH-5
❑ 95LeaLim-122
❑ 95LeaLimG-11
❑ 95LeaLimIBP-16
❑ 95LeaLimL-7
❑ 95LeaStaS-6
❑ 95Pac-255
❑ 95PacGolCDC-14
❑ 95PacGolP-26
❑ 95PacPri-82
❑ 95PanSti-82
❑ 95PanSti-124
❑ 95Pin-296
❑ 95Pin-340
❑ 95PinArtP-296
❑ 95PinArtP-340
❑ 95PinFan-5
❑ 95PinGatA-GA7
❑ 95PinMusC-296
❑ 95PinMusC-340
❑ 95PinPer-PP14
❑ 95PinPin-18
❑ 95PinPinR-18
❑ 95PinRedH-RH9
❑ 95PinTeaP-TP9
❑ 95PinWhiH-WH9
❑ 95Pos-6
❑ 95PosCan-9
❑ 95RedFol-24
❑ 95Sco-237
❑ 95Sco-559
❑ 95ScoDouGC-GC11
❑ 95ScoGolR-237
❑ 95ScoGolR-559
❑ 95ScoHaloG-HG11
❑ 95ScoPlaTS-237
❑ 95ScoPlaTS-559
❑ 95ScoRul-SR12
❑ 95ScoRulJ-SR12
❑ 95Sel-79
❑ 95SelArtP-79
❑ 95SelCer-33
❑ 95SelCerGT-11
❑ 95SelCerMG-33
❑ 95SP-170
❑ 95SPCha-111
❑ 95SPCha-167
❑ 95SPCha-170
❑ 95SPChaCP-CP8
❑ 95SPChaCPDC-CP8
❑ 95SPChaDC-111
❑ 95SPChaDC-167
❑ 95SPChaDC-170
❑ 95Spo-25
❑ 95SpoArtP-25
❑ 95SpoDouT-11
❑ 95SpoHamT-HT12
❑ 95SpoPro-PM12
❑ 95SPSil-170
❑ 95SPSpeF-13
❑ 95StaClu-319
❑ 95StaClu-450
❑ 95StaClu-518
❑ 95StaCluCC-CC12
❑ 95StaCluCT-2
❑ 95StaCluMO-39
❑ 95StaCluMOP-319
❑ 95StaCluMOP-450
❑ 95StaCluMOP-518
❑ 95StaCluMOP-CC12
❑ 95StaCluMOP-RL24
❑ 95StaCluRL-RL24
❑ 95StaCluSTWS-319
❑ 95StaCluSTWS-450
❑ 95StaCluSTWS-518
❑ 95StaCluVR-241
❑ 95StaCluVRMO-241
❑ 95Stu-22

❑ 95StuGolS-22
❑ 95StuPlaS-22
❑ 95Sum-32
❑ 95Sum-184
❑ 95SumBigB-BB11
❑ 95SumNthD-32
❑ 95SumNthD-184
❑ 95TomPiz-13
❑ 95Top-390
❑ 95Top-534
❑ 95TopCyb-319
❑ 95TopD3Z-2
❑ 95TopEmb-71
❑ 95TopEmbGI-71
❑ 95TopFinIns-13
❑ 95TopLeaL-LL12
❑ 95TopTra-162T
❑ 95UC3-33
❑ 95UC3-138
❑ 95UC3ArtP-33
❑ 95UC3ArtP-138
❑ 95UC3CycS-CS8
❑ 95UC3InM-IM7
❑ 95Ult-76
❑ 95UltAllS-16
❑ 95UltAllSGM-16
❑ 95UltGolM-76
❑ 95UltRBIK-1
❑ 95UltRBIKGM-1
❑ 95UppDec-430
❑ 95UppDecED-430
❑ 95UppDecEDG-430
❑ 95UppDecPAW-H4
❑ 95UppDecPAWE-H4
❑ 95UppDecPC-MLB12
❑ 95UppDecPLL-R14
❑ 95UppDecPLL-R55
❑ 95UppDecPLLE-R14
❑ 95UppDecPLLE-R55
❑ 95UppDecSE-85
❑ 95UppDecSEG-85
❑ 95Zen-65
❑ 95ZenAllS-4
❑ 96Baz-24
❑ 96Bow-98
❑ 96BowBes-78
❑ 96BowBesAR-78
❑ 96BowBesR-78
❑ 96BowFoi-98
❑ 96Cir-59
❑ 96CirAcc-9
❑ 96CirBos-14
❑ 96CirRav-59
❑ 96ColCho-200
❑ 96ColChoGS-200
❑ 96ColChoSS-200
❑ 96ColChoYMtP-32
❑ 96ColChoYMtP-32A
❑ 96ColChoYMtPGS-32
❑ 96ColChoYMtPGS-32A
❑ 96DenHol-11
❑ 96DenHolGS-10
❑ 96DenHolGSAP-10
❑ 96Don-50
❑ 96Don-330
❑ 96DonDiaK-22
❑ 96DonHitL-8
❑ 96DonPreP-50
❑ 96DonPreP-330
❑ 96EmoXL-85
❑ 96Fin-B271
❑ 96Fin-G18
❑ 96Fin-S79
❑ 96FinRef-B271
❑ 96FinRef-G18
❑ 96FinRef-S79
❑ 96Fla-120
❑ 96Fle-172
❑ 96FleTeaL-9
❑ 96FleTif-172
❑ 96Kin-7
❑ 96Lea-77
❑ 96LeaAllGMC-16
❑ 96LeaAllGMCG-16
❑ 96LeaLim-70
❑ 96LeaLimG-70
❑ 96LeaPre-63
❑ 96LeaPreP-63
❑ 96LeaPrePB-77
❑ 96LeaPrePG-77
❑ 96LeaPrePS-77
❑ 96LeaPreSG-41
❑ 96LeaPreSte-41
❑ 96LeaSig-99
❑ 96LeaSigEA-163
❑ 96LeaSigEACM-24
❑ 96LeaSigPPG-99
❑ 96LeaSigPPP-99
❑ 96LeaTotB-5
❑ 96MetUni-80
❑ 96MetUniP-80
❑ 96Pac-365
❑ 96PacGolCD-DC25
❑ 96PacHom-HP17
❑ 96PacPri-P117
❑ 96PacPriFB-FB14
❑ 96PacPriG-P117
❑ 96PacPriRHS-RH9
❑ 96PanSti-200
❑ 96Pin-155
❑ 96Pin-203
❑ 96Pin-268
❑ 96Pin-318
❑ 96PinAfi-24
❑ 96PinAfiAP-24
❑ 96PinAfiFPP-24
❑ 96PinAfiSP-28
❑ 96PinArtP-82
❑ 96PinArtP-103
❑ 96PinArtP-168
❑ 96PinArtP-196
❑ 96PinEssotG-8
❑ 96PinFan-14
❑ 96PinFirR-6
❑ 96PinFoil-203
❑ 96PinFoil-268
❑ 96PinFoil-318
❑ 96PinSky-14
❑ 96PinSta-82
❑ 96PinSta-103
❑ 96PinSta-168
❑ 96PinSta-196
❑ 96Pro-11
❑ 96ProMagDM-17
❑ 96ProSta-127
❑ 96RedF-32
❑ 96Sco-52
❑ 96Sco-358
❑ 96ScoDugC-A45
❑ 96ScoDugC-B83
❑ 96ScoDugCAP-A45
❑ 96ScoDugCAP-B83
❑ 96Sel-64
❑ 96SelArtP-64
❑ 96SelCer-62
❑ 96SelCerAP-62
❑ 96SelCerCB-62
❑ 96SelCerCR-62
❑ 96SelCerIP-15
❑ 96SelCerMB-62
❑ 96SelCerMG-62
❑ 96SelCerMR-62
❑ 96SelClaTF-17
❑ 96SelEnF-14
❑ 96SelTeaN-19
❑ 96SP-115
❑ 96Spo-6
❑ 96SpoArtP-6
❑ 96SpoDouT-10
❑ 96SpoHitP-10
❑ 96SPSpeFX-16
❑ 96SPSpeFXDC-16
❑ 96SPx-36
❑ 96SPxGol-36
❑ 96StaClu-23
❑ 96StaCluEPB-23
❑ 96StaCluEPG-23
❑ 96StaCluEPS-23
❑ 96StaCluMM-MM9
❑ 96StaCluMO-35
❑ 96StaCluMOP-23
❑ 96StaCluMOP-MM9
❑ 96Stu-74
❑ 96StuHitP-5
❑ 96StuPrePB-74
❑ 96StuPrePG-74
❑ 96StuPrePS-74
❑ 96Sum-77
❑ 96SumAbo&B-77
❑ 96SumArtP-77
❑ 96SumBal-17
❑ 96SumFoi-77
❑ 96Top-50
❑ 96Top-221
❑ 96TopChr-19
❑ 96TopChr-81
❑ 96TopChrMotG-15
❑ 96TopChrMotGR-15
❑ 96TopChrR-19
❑ 96TopChrR-81
❑ 96TopClaC-CC4
❑ 96TopGal-152
❑ 96TopGalE-4
❑ 96TopGalPG-PG11
❑ 96TopGalPPI-152
❑ 96TopLas-109
❑ 96TopLasSS-7
❑ 96TopMasotG-15
❑ 96TopMysF-M8
❑ 96TopMysFR-M8
❑ 96Ult-92
❑ 96UltDiaP-8
❑ 96UltDiaPGM-8
❑ 96UltGolM-92
❑ 96UltPriL-8
❑ 96UltPriLGM-8
❑ 96UltRes-6
❑ 96UltResGM-6
❑ 96UltThu-16
❑ 96UltThuGM-16
❑ 96UppDec-130
❑ 96UppDec-384
❑ 96UppDecDD-DD24
❑ 96UppDecDDG-DD24
❑ 96UppDecDDS-DD24
❑ 96UppDecHC-HC7
❑ 96Zen-90
❑ 96Zen-149
❑ 96ZenArtP-90
❑ 96ZenArtP-149
❑ 96ZenMoz-19
❑ 96ZenZ-17
❑ 97ColCho-151
❑ 97ColChoS-26
❑ 97ColChoTBS-30
❑ 97ColChoTBSWH-30
❑ 97DonEli-95
❑ 97DonEliGS-95
❑ 97DonEliPtT-4
❑ 97DonEliPtT-6
❑ 97DonEliPtTA-4
❑ 97DonEliPtTA-6
❑ 97Fle-154
❑ 97FleTif-154
❑ 97HigMinM-95
❑ 97HigMinM-96
❑ 97HigMinMCT-29
❑ 97HigMinMCT-30
❑ 97PacPriGotD-GD64
❑ 97PucSigN-1
❑ 97SpollIAM-3
❑ 97SpollICC-10
❑ 97UD3-40
❑ 97Ult-93
❑ 97UltGolME-93
❑ 97UltPlaME-93
❑ 97UppDec-105
❑ 97UppDec-214
❑ 97UppDec-414
❑ 97UppDecAG-AG13
❑ 97UppDecHC-HC20
❑ 98ScoAllST-11
❑ 98SpollITaN-24
❑ 98SpollITaNC-C2
❑ 98SpollITaNEE-24
❑ 98SpollITaNGS-25
❑ 98SpollIWSFAE-2
❑ 98SpollIWSFAEG-2
❑ 98UppDecR-55
❑ 98UppDecRSotT-KP

Pudlo, Scott
❑ 91EriSaiC-22
❑ 91EriSaiP-4068

Pueschner, Craig
❑ 90ChaRaiB-19
❑ 90ChaRaiP-2052
❑ 90SouAtlLAS-40
❑ 91Cla/Bes-366
❑ 91WatDiaC-22
❑ 91WatDiaP-1269
❑ 92CedRapRC-21
❑ 92CedRapRF-1086
❑ 93WinSpiC-19
❑ 93WinSpiF-1582

Puetz, Matt
❑ 86AncGlaPTI-30

Puffer, Aaron
❑ 93BoiHawC-22
❑ 93BoiHawF-3915

Puffer, Brandon
❑ 98ChaAllCM-9

Puffinbarger, Rusty
❑ 98WatIndTI-26

Pugh, Josh
❑ 97EugEmeB-20

Pugh, Scott
❑ 91SpoIndC-5
❑ 91SpoIndP-3958
❑ 92WatDiaC-4
❑ 92WatDiaF-2151
❑ 93RanCucQC-24
❑ 93RanCucQF-841
❑ 94WicWraF-200

Pugh, Tim
❑ 89BilMusP-2064
❑ 90Bes-186
❑ 90ChaWheB-7
❑ 90ChaWheP-2239
❑ 90CMC-694
❑ 90ProAaA-92
❑ 91ChaLooLD-165
❑ 91ChaLooP-1958
❑ 91Cla/Bes-299
❑ 91LinDriAA-165
❑ 92MarPhiC-17
❑ 92MarPhiF-3056
❑ 92NasSouF-1832
❑ 92NasSouS-289
❑ 92SkyAAAF-135
❑ 93BatCliCB-24
❑ 93BatCliF-3144
❑ 93Bow-442
❑ 93Don-162
❑ 93Fle-40
❑ 93Lea-331
❑ 93OPCPre-75
❑ 93Pin-270
❑ 93RedKah-18
❑ 93Sco-247
❑ 93StaClu-265
❑ 93StaCluFDI-265
❑ 93StaCluMOP-265
❑ 93Top-702
❑ 93TopGol-702
❑ 93TopInaM-702
❑ 93TopInaR-702
❑ 93TopMic-702
❑ 93Ult-332
❑ 93UppDec-26
❑ 93UppDecGold-26
❑ 94ColC-234
❑ 94ColChoGS-234
❑ 94ColChoSS-234
❑ 94Don-277
❑ 94Fin-67
❑ 94FinRef-67
❑ 94Fle-419
❑ 94Lea-91
❑ 94Pac-154
❑ 94Pin-481
❑ 94PinArtP-481
❑ 94PinMusC-481
❑ 94RedKah-22
❑ 94StaClu-243
❑ 94StaCluFDI-243
❑ 94StaCluGR-243
❑ 94StaCluMOP-243
❑ 94Top-95
❑ 94TopGol-95
❑ 94TopSpa-95
❑ 94UppDec-481
❑ 94UppDecED-481
❑ 94USPlaCR-5S
❑ 95RedKah-22
❑ 95TopTra-120T
❑ 95UppDec-403
❑ 95UppDecED-403
❑ 95UppDecEDG-403
❑ 97TolMudHB-28
❑ 98St.PauSTI-20

Pugmire, Rob
❑ 97AppLeaTPB-5
❑ 97BurIndG-21

Puhl, Terry
❑ 75DubPacT-2
❑ 78AstBurK-19
❑ 78AstPos-18
❑ 78Top-553
❑ 79AstPos-17
❑ 79AstTeal-10
❑ 79Kel-33
❑ 79Top-617
❑ 80OPC-82
❑ 80Top-147
❑ 81AllGamPI-159
❑ 81AstPos-15
❑ 81CokTeaS-67
❑ 81Don-24
❑ 81Fle-62
❑ 81Kel-42
❑ 81OPC-64
❑ 81Top-411
❑ 81TopScr-88
❑ 81TopSti-171
❑ 81TopSupHT-100
❑ 82AstAstI-5
❑ 82AstPos-17
❑ 82Don-370
❑ 82Fle-223
❑ 82FleSta-44
❑ 82OPC-277
❑ 82Top-277
❑ 82TopSti-42
❑ 83AllGamPI-157
❑ 83AstPos-21
❑ 83Don-167
❑ 83Fle-458
❑ 83FleSti-209
❑ 83OPC-39
❑ 83Top-39
❑ 83TopSti-239
❑ 84AllGamPI-65
❑ 84AstMot-10
❑ 84AstPos-21
❑ 84Don-476
❑ 84Fle-235
❑ 84Nes792-383
❑ 84OPC-383
❑ 84Top-383
❑ 84TopSti-67
❑ 84TopTif-383
❑ 85AllGamPI-156
❑ 85AstHouP-7
❑ 85AstMot-7
❑ 85Don-426
❑ 85Fle-356
❑ 85GenMilS-6
❑ 85Lea-80
❑ 85OPC-283
❑ 85SevCoi-C14
❑ 85SubDis-39
❑ 85ThoMcAD-39
❑ 85Top-613
❑ 85TopMin-613
❑ 85TopSti-67
❑ 85TopTif-613
❑ 86AstMilL-16
❑ 86AstMot-16
❑ 86AstPol-21
❑ 86AstTeal-11
❑ 86BasStaB-85
❑ 86Don-206
❑ 86Fle-308
❑ 86Lea-138
❑ 86OPC-161
❑ 86Top-763
❑ 86TopTif-763
❑ 87AstMot-7
❑ 87AstPol-15
❑ 87AstShoSPT-12
❑ 87Don-431
❑ 87Fle-65
❑ 87FleGlo-65
❑ 87OPC-227
❑ 87Top-693
❑ 87TopTif-693
❑ 88AstMot-7
❑ 88AstPol-17
❑ 88Don-533
❑ 88FleUpd-90
❑ 88FleUpdG-90
❑ 88Sco-282
❑ 88ScoGlo-282
❑ 88StaLinAst-12
❑ 88Top-587
❑ 88TopClo-91
❑ 88TopTif-587
❑ 89AstLenH-22
❑ 89AstMot-6
❑ 89AstSmo-31
❑ 89Don-472
❑ 89DonBasB-294
❑ 89Fle-364
❑ 89FleGlo-364
❑ 89Sco-567
❑ 89Top-119
❑ 89TopTif-119
❑ 90AstLenH-18
❑ 90AstMot-9
❑ 90Don-354
❑ 90Fle-233
❑ 90FleCan-233
❑ 90MLBBasB-60
❑ 90OPC-494
❑ 90PanSti-256
❑ 90PubIntS-98
❑ 90Sco-473
❑ 90Top-494
❑ 90TopTif-494
❑ 90UppDec-201
❑ 91MetColP-44
❑ 91SimandSMLBL-36

Puig, Benny
❑ 89BlaYNPRWL-183
❑ 94OttLynF-2899

Puig, Ed
❑ 87StoPorP-27
❑ 88BlaYNPRWL-12
❑ 88ElPasDB-22
❑ 88TexLeaAGS-31
❑ 89ElPasDGS-14
❑ 90CMC-27
❑ 90DenZepC-2
❑ 90DenZepP-625
❑ 90ElPasDGS-24
❑ 90ProAAAF-650
❑ 91DenZepLD-148
❑ 91DenZepP-123
❑ 91LinDriAAA-148
❑ 92MemChiF-2419
❑ 92MemChiS-443

Puig, Rich
❑ 91MetWIZ-319

Puikunas, Ed
❑ 85FreGiaSB-15
❑ 86ShrCapP-21
❑ 87ShrCapP-15
❑ 88PhoFirC-11
❑ 88PhoFirP-74
❑ 88ShrCapP-1301
❑ 89PhoFirC-2
❑ 89PhoFirP-1492

Pujals, Denis
❑ 96ButCopKB-25
❑ 97FloStaLTPB-20
❑ 97St.PetDR-25
❑ 97St.PetDRUB-26
❑ 98St.PetDRM-14

Pujols, Luis
❑ 73CedRapAT-11
❑ 74CedRapAT-11
❑ 75DubPacT-21
❑ 78AstPos-19
❑ 78ChaChaT-13
❑ 79ChaChaT-14
❑ 79Top-139
❑ 81AstPos-16
❑ 81Don-379A
❑ 81Don-379B
❑ 81Fle-68
❑ 81Top-313
❑ 82AstAstI-8
❑ 82AstPos-18
❑ 82Don-576
❑ 82Fle-224
❑ 82Top-582
❑ 83AstPos-22
❑ 83Don-642
❑ 83Fle-459
❑ 83OPC-112
❑ 83Top-752
❑ 83TucTorT-13
❑ 84Fle-236
❑ 84Nes792-446
❑ 84Top-446
❑ 84TopTif-446
❑ 84TucTorC-71
❑ 85DomLeaS-22
❑ 85RanPer-8
❑ 86OklCit8P-18
❑ 87AstShoSPO-24
❑ 87IndIndTI-6
❑ 89PacSenL-167
❑ 89TopSenL-130
❑ 89WesPalBES-26
❑ 93ExpPosN-18
❑ 93RanKee-301

Pujols, Rafael
❑ 98SouOreTG-28

Pujols, Ruben
❑ 88VirGenS-19
❑ 89BasCitRS-22

Pulchinski, Thomas
❑ 77WatIndT-16
❑ 78WatIndT-16

Puleo, Charles
❑ 80KnoBluJT-21
❑ 81TidTidT-13
❑ 82MetPhoA-17
❑ 82TopTra-94T
❑ 83Don-128
❑ 83Fle-552
❑ 83OPC-358
❑ 83RedYea-25
❑ 83Top-549
❑ 83TopTra-88T

❑ 84Don-530
❑ 84Fle-480
❑ 84Nes792-273
❑ 84Top-273
❑ 84TopTif-273
❑ 84WicAerRD-1
❑ 86RicBraP-17
❑ 87BraSmo-2
❑ 88Don-537
❑ 88Fle-548
❑ 88FleGlo-548
❑ 88Sco-454
❑ 88ScoGlo-454
❑ 88Top-179
❑ 88TopClo-92
❑ 88TopTif-179
❑ 89Bow-263
❑ 89BowTif-263
❑ 89Don-286
❑ 89Fle-598
❑ 89FleGlo-598
❑ 89RicBraBC-21
❑ 89Sco-448
❑ 89Top-728
❑ 89TopTif-728
❑ 89UppDec-589
❑ 90PubIntS-119
❑ 91MetWIZ-320
❑ 92BluOriF-2376
❑ 93AlbPolCB-24
❑ 93AlbPolF-2043
❑ 94BluOriC-24
❑ 94BluOriF-3580
❑ 96BluOriB-3
❑ 98BluOriQ-3

Pulford, Don
❑ 47CenFlo-21

Pulido, Alfonso
❑ 84HawIslC-121
❑ 85ColCliP-18
❑ 85ColCliT-8
❑ 85YanTCMP-16
❑ 86ColCliP-18
❑ 86ColCliP-20
❑ 86StaoftFT-3
❑ 87ColCliP-20
❑ 87ColCliP-20
❑ 87ColCliT-7
❑ 87TopTif-642
❑ 92YanWIZ8-150

Pulido, Carlos
❑ 85Don-34
❑ 87Top-642
❑ 90KenTwiB-24
❑ 90KenTwiP-2293
❑ 90KenTwiS-20
❑ 91VisOakC-9
❑ 92OrlSunRF-2848
❑ 92OrlSunRS-517
❑ 92SkyAA F-224
❑ 93PorBeaF-2383
❑ 94Bow-328
❑ 94ColC-611
❑ 94ColChoGS-611
❑ 94ColChoSS-611
❑ 94FleUpd-64
❑ 94Sel-410
❑ 94SpoRoo-126
❑ 94SpoRooAP-126
❑ 95Don-353
❑ 95DonPreP-353
❑ 95LinVen-305
❑ 95Pac-256
❑ 96IowCubB-21

Pulido, Juan Carlos
❑ 93LinVenB-85
❑ 94VenLinU-22
❑ 95LinVen-93
❑ 96-97LinVen-22

Pulido, Phil
❑ 77DayBealT-17

Pull, Elizabeth
❑ 08AllLadBC-5

Pullen, Shane
❑ 94MarPhiC-18
❑ 94MarPhiF-3309
❑ 95Exc-245
❑ 95PiePhiF-195
❑ 95Top-237
❑ 96PieBolWB-21

Pulli, Frank
❑ 88T/MUmp-14
❑ 89T/MUmp-12
❑ 89T/MUmp-60
❑ 90T/MUmp-12

Pulliam, Harry C.
❑ 06FanCraNL-39

Pulliam, Harvey
❑ 88BasCitRS-19
❑ 89MemChiB-15
❑ 89MemChiP-1204
❑ 89MemChiS-19
❑ 89SouLeaAJ-1
❑ 90CMC-192
❑ 90OmaRoyC-17
❑ 90OmaRoyP-78
❑ 90ProAAAF-613
❑ 91Bow-303
❑ 91LinDriAAA-344
❑ 91OmaRoyLD-344
❑ 91OmaRoyP-1048
❑ 92DonRoo-97
❑ 92Fle-166
❑ 92OmaRoyS-342
❑ 92OPC-687
❑ 92Pin-279
❑ 92Sco-761
❑ 92ScoRoo-22
❑ 92SkyAAAF-156
❑ 92StaClu-428
❑ 92Top-687
❑ 92TopDeb91-141
❑ 92TopGol-687
❑ 92TopGolW-687
❑ 92TopMic-687
❑ 92UppDec-457
❑ 93PacSpa-494
❑ 93RoyStaC-28
❑ 94LasVegSF-882
❑ 96ColSprSSTI-26
❑ 97ColSprSATTI-4
❑ 97ColSprSTI-19

Pullins, Jimmie
❑ 89IdaFalBP-2011
❑ 90PulBraB-23
❑ 90PulBraP-3110

Pulsipher, Bill
❑ 92PitMetC-1
❑ 92PitMetF-3293
❑ 92StaClu-676
❑ 92StaCluECN-676
❑ 94ActPac-36
❑ 94BinMetF-703
❑ 94Bow-212
❑ 94Bow-361
❑ 94BowBes-B3
❑ 94BowBes-X109
❑ 94BowBesR-B3
❑ 94BowBesR-X109
❑ 94Cla-110
❑ 94ClaCreotC-C19
❑ 94ClaTriF-T52
❑ 94ExcFS7-237
❑ 94FleExtB-322
❑ 94FleExtBMLH-7
❑ 94MetShuST-1
❑ 94Top-785
❑ 94TopGol-785
❑ 94TopSpa-785
❑ 94Ult-532
❑ 94UppDecML-205
❑ 94UppDecMLPotYF-PY15
❑ 95Bow-270
❑ 95BowBes-B61
❑ 95BowBesR-B61
❑ 95BowGolF-270
❑ 95ColCho-35
❑ 95ColChoGS-35
❑ 95ColChoSE-4
❑ 95ColChoSEGS-4
❑ 95ColChoSESS-4
❑ 95ColChoSS-35
❑ 95Emo-161
❑ 95Exc-237
❑ 95ExcLeaL-13
❑ 95Fin-294
❑ 95FinRef-294
❑ 95Fle-379
❑ 95NorTidTI-23
❑ 95Sel-212
❑ 95SelArtP-212
❑ 95SelCer-125
❑ 95SelCerMG-125
❑ 95SP-84
❑ 95SPCha-5
❑ 95SPChaDC-5
❑ 95SPSil-84
❑ 95StaCluCB-CB13
❑ 95StaCluMOP-CB13
❑ 95Top-156
❑ 95UppDec-2
❑ 95UppDecED-2
❑ 95UppDecEDG-2
❑ 95UppDecML-4
❑ 95UppDecML-106
❑ 95UppDecMLFS-4
❑ 95UppDecMLFS-106
❑ 95UppDecMLOP-OP18
❑ 95UppDecMLT1PF-5
❑ 95UppDecSE-59
❑ 95UppDecSEG-59
❑ 95Zen-130
❑ 95ZenRooRC-6
❑ 96Baz-127
❑ 96ColCho-223
❑ 96ColChoGS-223
❑ 96ColChoSS-223
❑ 96Don-100
❑ 96DonPreP-100
❑ 96EmoXL-238
❑ 96Fin-S38
❑ 96FinRef-S38
❑ 96Fla-326
❑ 96Fle-487
❑ 96FleTif-487
❑ 96Lea-173
❑ 96LeaPrePB-173
❑ 96LeaPrePG-173
❑ 96LeaPrePS-173
❑ 96LeaSig-129
❑ 96LeaSigA-186
❑ 96LeaSigAG-186
❑ 96LeaSigAS-186
❑ 96LeaSigPPG-129
❑ 96LeaSigPPP-129
❑ 96MetKah-27
❑ 96MetKah-28
❑ 96MetUni-205
❑ 96MetUniP-205
❑ 96Pac-137
❑ 96PanSti-30
❑ 96Pin-2
❑ 96PinArtP-2
❑ 96PinSam-2
❑ 96PinSta-2
❑ 96RedF-2
❑ 96Sco-43
❑ 96ScoDiaA-12
❑ 96ScoDugC-A38
❑ 96ScoDugCAP-A38
❑ 96ScoFutF-12
❑ 96Sel-4
❑ 96SelArtP-4
❑ 96SelTeaN-21
❑ 96SigRooOJMR-M5
❑ 96Spo-52
❑ 96SpoArtP-52
❑ 96StaClu-18
❑ 96StaCluEPB-18
❑ 96StaCluEPG-18
❑ 96StaCluEPS-18
❑ 96StaCluMOP-18
❑ 96Top-144
❑ 96TopGal-94
❑ 96TopGalPPI-94
❑ 96Ult-247
❑ 96UltGolM-247
❑ 96UppDec-139
❑ 96UppDecBCP-BC4
❑ 97Cir-116
❑ 97CirRav-116
❑ 97Don-131
❑ 97DonEli-80
❑ 97DonEliGS-80
❑ 97DonGolPP-131
❑ 97DonPre-18
❑ 97DonPreCttC-18
❑ 97DonSilPP-131
❑ 97Lea-230
❑ 97LeaFraM-230
❑ 97LeaFraMDC-230
❑ 97LeaGet-15
❑ 97NewPin-131
❑ 97NewPinAP-131
❑ 97NewPinMC-131
❑ 97NewPinPP-131
❑ 97NorTid-27
❑ 97NorTidB-27
❑ 97PinIns-73
❑ 97PinInsCE-73
❑ 97PinInsDE-73
❑ 97Sco-130
❑ 97ScoArtPWB-130
❑ 97ScoPreS-130
❑ 97ScoShoS-130
❑ 97ScoShoSAP-130
❑ 97Sel-43
❑ 97SelArtP-43
❑ 97SelCom-43
❑ 97SelRegG-43
❑ 97Stu-40
❑ 97StuPrePG-40
❑ 97StuPrePS-40
❑ 97Top-408
❑ 98FleUpd-U62
❑ 98NorTidP-22
❑ 98NorTidQ-21
❑ 98PinSna-NYM10
❑ 99Fle-548
❑ 99FleSta9-548
❑ 99FleWarT-548

Pumphrey, Kenny
❑ 96BesAutS-75
❑ 96PitMetB-21
❑ 97CapCitB-8
❑ 98St.LucMM-8

Punto, Nick
❑ 98BatMucTI-23

Puorto, Jamie
❑ 97LetBlaDB-27
❑ 98SouBenSHM-21

Purcell, Gary
❑ 77BriRedST-15

Purcell, William
❑ 87BucN28-4
❑ 87OldJudN-405
❑ 94OriofB-32

Purcey, Walter
❑ 36GouWidPPR-D29

Purdin, John
❑ 65DodTeal-17
❑ 65Top-331
❑ 68Top-336
❑ 68TopVen-336
❑ 69OPC-161
❑ 69Top-161
❑ 69TopFou-9
❑ 71OPC-748
❑ 71Top-748
❑ 85SpoIndGC-16
❑ 90DodTar-638

Purdy, Alan
❑ 93WelPirC-23
❑ 94SalBucC-16
❑ 94SalBucF-2330

Purdy, Pid (Everett V.)
❑ 28StaPlaCE-51
❑ 29ExhFou-8
❑ 92ConTSN-406

Purdy, Shawn
❑ 91BoiHawC-12
❑ 91BoiHawP-3876
❑ 91Cla/Bes-447
❑ 91MiaHurBB-11
❑ 92ClaFS7-212
❑ 92PalSprAC-16
❑ 92PalSprAF-836
❑ 94LakElsSC-13
❑ 94LakElsSF-1660
❑ 94MidAngF-2438
❑ 97MidAngOHP-24
❑ 97PhoFirTI-20
❑ 98RicBraQ-12

Purkey, Bob
❑ 54Top-202
❑ 55Top-118
❑ 55TopDouH-113
❑ 56RedBurB-19
❑ 57Top-368
❑ 58Kah-24
❑ 58RedEnq-30
❑ 58RedJayP-10
❑ 58Top-311
❑ 59Kah-30
❑ 59RedBurBP-17
❑ 59RedBurBP-18
❑ 59RedShiBS-18
❑ 59Top-506
❑ 60Kah-35
❑ 60Lea-67
❑ 60RedJayP-11
❑ 60Top-4
❑ 60TopVen-4
❑ 61Kah-36
❑ 61Pos-184A
❑ 61Pos-184B
❑ 61SevElev-4
❑ 61Top-9
❑ 62Jel-123
❑ 62Kah-34A
❑ 62Kah-34B
❑ 62Pos-123
❑ 62PosCan-123
❑ 62RedEnq-28
❑ 62SalPlaC-153
❑ 62ShiPlaC-153
❑ 62Top-120
❑ 62Top-263
❑ 62TopBuc-73
❑ 62TopStal-120
❑ 62TopVen-120
❑ 63Baz-26
❑ 63Fle-35
❑ 63Jel-134
❑ 63Kah-25
❑ 63Pos-134
❑ 63RedEnq-27
❑ 63RedFreBC-20
❑ 63RedJayP-11
❑ 63SalMetC-6
❑ 63Top-5
❑ 63Top-7
❑ 63Top-350
❑ 63TopStil-32
❑ 64Kah-22
❑ 64RedJayP-10
❑ 64Top-480
❑ 65CarJayP-7
❑ 65CarTeal-18
❑ 65OPC-214
❑ 65Top-214
❑ 66Top-551
❑ 79TCM50-260
❑ 80Red196T-29
❑ 88PacLegl-77
❑ 94TopArc1-202
❑ 94TopArc1G-202

Purkiss, Matt
❑ 98GreBatM-15

Purnell, Byron
❑ 76LauindC-18

Purpura, Dan
❑ 82AmaGolST-8
❑ 83BeaGolGT-10

Purpura, Joe
❑ 78CliDodT-26

Pursell, Joe
❑ 83KinBluJTI-16

Purtell, William
❑ 09ColChiE-233A
❑ 09ColChiE-233B
❑ 09ColChiE-233C
❑ 09T206-296
❑ 10ChiE-17
❑ 10CouT21-208
❑ 10RedCroT-149
❑ 10RedCroT-236
❑ 11PinT-5-654
❑ 11SpoLifCW-295
❑ 11SpoLifM-28
❑ 12ColRedB-233A
❑ 12ColRedB-233B
❑ 12ColRedB-233C
❑ 12ColTinT-233A
❑ 12ColTinT-233B
❑ 12ColTinT-233C
❑ 12ImpTobC-30
❑ 15Zee-135
❑ 72ClaCar-86
❑ 72ClaCar-120

Purvis, Glenn
❑ 75AndRanT-10
❑ 76AshTouT-21
❑ 77VisOakT-10

Puryear, Nate
❑ 76BatTroTI-17
❑ 77WatIndT-17
❑ 79TacTugT-17
❑ 81ChaChaT-22
❑ 82ChaLooT-1

Pust, John
❑ 87VisOakP-21

Putman, Ed
❑ 80EvaTriT-7
❑ 80Top-59
❑ 81RocRedWT-13
❑ 81RocRedWW-13

Putnam, Pat
❑ 75LynRanT-21
❑ 76AshTouT-15
❑ 77TucTorC-51
❑ 78Top-706
❑ 78TucTorC-32
❑ 79Top-713
❑ 80OPC-8
❑ 80Top-22
❑ 81Don-265
❑ 81Fle-630
❑ 81OPC-302
❑ 81Top-498
❑ 82Don-520
❑ 82Fle-327
❑ 82FleSta-180
❑ 82OPC-149
❑ 82Top-149
❑ 82TopSti-241
❑ 82TopStiV-241
❑ 83TopTra-89T
❑ 84Don-145
❑ 84Fle-617
❑ 84MarMot-16
❑ 84Nes792-336
❑ 84Nes792-636
❑ 84OPC-226
❑ 84Top-336
❑ 84Top-636
❑ 84TopRubD-23
❑ 84TopSti-339
❑ 84TopTif-336
❑ 84TopTif-636
❑ 85Fle-287
❑ 85OmaRoyT-9
❑ 85Top-535
❑ 85TopTif-535
❑ 86MarGreT-1
❑ 87JapPlaB-31
❑ 89PacSenL-85
❑ 89T/MSenL-87
❑ 90EliSenL-75
❑ 93RanKee-302

Putnicki, Billy
❑ 98KanCouC-24
❑ 98KanCouCCP-24

Putrich, Josh
❑ 94HunCubC-23
❑ 94HunCubF-3552

Puttman, Ambrose
❑ 05RotCP-1
❑ 09T206-457
❑ 11SpoLifCW-296

Puttman, Shannon
❑ 94WelPirC-20
❑ 94WelPirF-3496

Puzey, James W.
❑ 86St.PetCP-25
❑ 87SprCarB-5
❑ 88ArkTraGS-22
❑ 88LouRedBTI-40
❑ 89LouRedBC-12
❑ 89LouRedBP-1243
❑ 89LouRedBTI-33

Pyburn, James
❑ 56BalOriP-4
❑ 57Top-276
❑ 91OriCro-371

Pyburn, Jeff
❑ 82HawIslT-12

Pyc, David
❑ 92GreFalDSP-9
❑ 94SanAntMF-2467
❑ 95SanAntMTI-57
❑ 96SanAntMB-17
❑ 97AlbDukGS-26

Pye, Eddie
❑ 88GreFalDTI-9
❑ 89BakDodCLC-198
❑ 89CalLeaA-19
❑ 90SanAntMGS-22
❑ 90TexLeaAGS-2
❑ 91AlbDukLD-18
❑ 91AlbDukP-1150
❑ 91LinDriAAA-18
❑ 92AlbDukF-729
❑ 92AlbDukS-9
❑ 93AlbDukF-1471
❑ 94AlbDukF-852
❑ 95DodPol-22

Pyfrom, Joel
❑ 82MiaMarT-6

Pyle, John
❑ 94HudValRC-19
❑ 94HudValRF-3389

Pyle, Scott
❑ 81WesHavAT-23
❑ 82WesHavAT-28
❑ 83TacTigT-26

Pyrtle, Joe
❑ 95PitMetTI-25
❑ 97PitMet-24

Pytlak, Frank A.
❑ 33TatOrbSDR-180
❑ 34DiaMatCSB-149
❑ 34ExhFou-11
❑ 35DiaMatCS3T1-123
❑ 36GouWidPPR-A85

- ❑ 36GouWidPPR-A119
- ❑ 36OveCanR-36
- ❑ 37ExhFou-11
- ❑ 38GouHeaU-245
- ❑ 38GouHeaU-269
- ❑ 39GouPreR303A-37
- ❑ 39WorWidGTP-37
- ❑ 39WorWidGV-20
- ❑ 41DouPlaR-107
- ❑ 75RedSox1T-31
- ❑ 91ConTSN-280

Pyznarski, Tim
- ❑ 82WesHavAT-17
- ❑ 83AlbA'sT-13
- ❑ 84TacTigC-87
- ❑ 85LasVegSC-122
- ❑ 86LasVegSP-13
- ❑ 87DenZepP-2
- ❑ 87Don-654
- ❑ 87Spo-158
- ❑ 87SpoTeaP-19
- ❑ 87Top-429
- ❑ 87TopTif-429
- ❑ 88DenZepC-11
- ❑ 88DenZepP-1273
- ❑ 88RocRedWGCP-21
- ❑ 88TriAAAP-13
- ❑ 89OmaRoyP-1726

Quaccia, Luke
- ❑ 97NewJerCB-22
- ❑ 98PeoChiM-19

Quade, Mike
- ❑ 82AleDukT-10
- ❑ 83AleDukT-28
- ❑ 86MacPirP-20
- ❑ 87JacExpP-455
- ❑ 89RocExpLC-23
- ❑ 90RocExpLC-19
- ❑ 90RocExpP-2710
- ❑ 91HarSenLD-274
- ❑ 91HarSenP-642
- ❑ 91LinDriAA-274
- ❑ 92HarSenF-475
- ❑ 92HarSenS-299
- ❑ 93OttLynF-2449
- ❑ 94ScrRedBF-935
- ❑ 95ScrRedBTI-22
- ❑ 96WesMicWB-1
- ❑ 97HunStaTI-23

Quade, Scott
- ❑ 93JamExpC-17
- ❑ 93JamExpF-3335

Quakes, Rancho Cucamanga
- ❑ 96RanCucQB-30

Qualls, Jim
- ❑ 69CubJewT-13
- ❑ 69Top-602
- ❑ 70OPC-192
- ❑ 70Top-192
- ❑ 71OPC-731
- ❑ 71Top-731
- ❑ 88BoiHawP-1610

Qualls, Kent
- ❑ 95PawRedSDD-22
- ❑ 95PawRedTI-NNO

Qualters, Tom
- ❑ 54Top-174
- ❑ 55Top-33
- ❑ 55TopDouH-107
- ❑ 58Top-453
- ❑ 59Top-341
- ❑ 94TopArc1-174
- ❑ 94TopArc1G-174

Quantrill, Paul
- ❑ 89ElmPioP-31
- ❑ 90WinHavRSS-21
- ❑ 91LinDriAA-469
- ❑ 91NewBriRSLD-469
- ❑ 91NewBriRSP-351
- ❑ 91PawRedSDD-20
- ❑ 92Bow-23
- ❑ 92PawRedSF-921
- ❑ 92PawRedSS-363
- ❑ 92SkyAAAF-165
- ❑ 93Don-327
- ❑ 93Fle-181
- ❑ 93Lea-544
- ❑ 93PacSpa-362
- ❑ 93Pin-175
- ❑ 93RedSoxP-25
- ❑ 93RedSoxWHP-11
- ❑ 93Sco-221
- ❑ 93SelRoo-46T
- ❑ 93Top-528
- ❑ 93TopGol-528
- ❑ 93TopInaM-528
- ❑ 93TopInaR-528
- ❑ 93TopMic-528
- ❑ 93Ult-155
- ❑ 94Don-644
- ❑ 94Fle-38
- ❑ 94FleUpd-169
- ❑ 94Pac-62
- ❑ 94PhiMel-19
- ❑ 94Sco-583
- ❑ 94ScoGolR-583
- ❑ 94Top-417
- ❑ 94TopGol-417
- ❑ 94TopSpa-417
- ❑ 94Ult-317
- ❑ 94USPlaCR-2S
- ❑ 95FleUpd-124
- ❑ 95Phi-24
- ❑ 95PhiMel-18
- ❑ 95StaClu-577
- ❑ 95StaCluMOP-577
- ❑ 95StaCluSTWS-577
- ❑ 95TopTra-127T
- ❑ 96BluJayOH-26
- ❑ 96ColCho-248
- ❑ 96ColChoGS-248
- ❑ 96ColChoSS-248
- ❑ 96Don-348
- ❑ 96DonPreP-348
- ❑ 96Fla-191
- ❑ 96Fle-281
- ❑ 96FleTif-281
- ❑ 96FleUpd-U101
- ❑ 96FleUpdTC-U101
- ❑ 96LeaSigEA-164
- ❑ 96Pac-158
- ❑ 96ProSta-89
- ❑ 96Ult-258
- ❑ 96Ult-435
- ❑ 96UltGolM-258
- ❑ 96UltGolM-435
- ❑ 97BluJayOH-25
- ❑ 97BluJayS-21
- ❑ 97DunDonPPS-20
- ❑ 98Pac-226
- ❑ 98PacOnl-772
- ❑ 98PacOnlR-772
- ❑ 98PacOnlWC-772
- ❑ 98PacPlaB-226
- ❑ 98PacRedT-226
- ❑ 98PacSil-226
- ❑ 99Fle-545
- ❑ 99FleSta9-545
- ❑ 99FleWarT-545

Quarles, Melvin
- ❑ 78QuaCitAT-19

Quatraro, Matt
- ❑ 96ButCopKB-26
- ❑ 97ChaRivDG-22
- ❑ 97SouAtlTPB-9
- ❑ 97Top-252
- ❑ 98St.PetDRM-16

Quatrine, Mike
- ❑ 90ElmPioP-26

Quealey, Steve
- ❑ 82BirBarT-20

Queen, Mel D.
- ❑ 64Top-33
- ❑ 64TopVen-33
- ❑ 66Top-556
- ❑ 67Top-374A
- ❑ 67Top-374B
- ❑ 67TopVen-296
- ❑ 68Top-283
- ❑ 68TopVen-283
- ❑ 69OPC-81
- ❑ 69Top-81
- ❑ 71MLBOffS-354
- ❑ 71OPC-736
- ❑ 71Top-736
- ❑ 72OPC-196
- ❑ 72Top-196
- ❑ 79WatIndT-23
- ❑ 80TacTigT-7
- ❑ 81ChaChaT-21
- ❑ 82Ind-29
- ❑ 82IndBurK-8
- ❑ 82IndBurK-9
- ❑ 82IndWhe-17
- ❑ 87SyrChiT-28
- ❑ 96BluJayOH-25
- ❑ 97BluJayOH-26
- ❑ 97BluJayS-27

Queen, Mel J.
- ❑ 47TipTop-55
- ❑ 50PirTeal-18
- ❑ 51Bow-309
- ❑ 52Bow-171

Queen, Mike
- ❑ 97PitMet-25
- ❑ 98CapCitBF5-13
- ❑ 98CapCitBM-13

Quellich, George
- ❑ 32Zee-13
- ❑ 33Zee-71

Querecuto, Juan
- ❑ 90St.CatBJP-3453
- ❑ 92St.CatBJC-4
- ❑ 92St.CatBJF-3390
- ❑ 93LinVenB-180
- ❑ 93St.CatBJC-20
- ❑ 93St.CatBJF-3978
- ❑ 94DunBluJC-22
- ❑ 94DunBluJF-2566
- ❑ 94VenLinU-113
- ❑ 95DunBluJTI-20
- ❑ 95LinVen-173
- ❑ 96-97LinVen-41

Quero, Juan
- ❑ 91ChaRanC-8
- ❑ 91ChaRanP-1312
- ❑ 94VenLinU-66

Quero, Pedro
- ❑ 98VerExpO-30

Querry, Wray
- ❑ 24Zee-55

Quesada, Ed
- ❑ 89EveGiaS-24

Quevedo, Ruben
- ❑ 97DanBraB-23
- ❑ 98MacBraM-14
- ❑ 99Bow-402
- ❑ 99BowGol-402
- ❑ 99BowInt-402

Quezada, Edward
- ❑ 96VerExpB-23
- ❑ 98CapFeaCM-17

Quezada, Rafael
- ❑ 80AndBraT-29

Quezada, Silvano
- ❑ 75LafDriT-21
- ❑ 76PheGiaCr-32
- ❑ 76PhoGiaCa-4
- ❑ 76PhoGiaCC-19
- ❑ 76PhoGiaVNB-20
- ❑ 85DomLeaS-41

Quick, Gene
- ❑ 76CliPilT-27

Quick, Jim
- ❑ 88T/MUmp-26
- ❑ 89T/MUmp-24
- ❑ 90T/MUmp-23

Quick, Ron
- ❑ 81ShrCapT-17

Quigley, Donald
- ❑ 96SpoIndB-22
- ❑ 97SpoIndG-24

Quigley, Ernest
- ❑ 34DiaMatCSB-150
- ❑ 94ConTSN-1206
- ❑ 94ConTSNB-1206

Quigley, Jerry
- ❑ 76QuaCitAT-28

Quijada, Ed
- ❑ 90AshTouP-2758
- ❑ 90CMC-662
- ❑ 92BurAstC-14
- ❑ 92BurAstF-543

Quiles, Henry
- ❑ 91BriTigP-3602

Quiles, Victor
- ❑ 87WytCubP-8

Quilici, Frank
- ❑ 66Top-207
- ❑ 66TopVen-207
- ❑ 66TwiFaiG-13
- ❑ 67TwiTeal-16
- ❑ 68Top-557
- ❑ 69MilBra-226
- ❑ 69Top-356
- ❑ 70Top-572
- ❑ 71MLBOffS-471
- ❑ 71OPC-141
- ❑ 71Top-141
- ❑ 72MilBra-279
- ❑ 72TwiPos-17
- ❑ 72TwiTeal-11
- ❑ 73OPC-49
- ❑ 73Top-49A
- ❑ 73Top-49B
- ❑ 74OPC-447
- ❑ 74Top-447
- ❑ 75OPC-443
- ❑ 75Top-443
- ❑ 75TopMin-443
- ❑ 75TwiPos-19
- ❑ 75TwiTeal-22
- ❑ 78TwiFri-18

Quillin, Lee
- ❑ 09T206-458

Quillin, Ty
- ❑ 91KinMetC-7
- ❑ 91KinMetP-3827
- ❑ 92PitMetC-4
- ❑ 92PitMetF-3307
- ❑ 94PitMetC-18
- ❑ 94PitMetF-3522

Quinlan, Craig
- ❑ 91St.CatBJC-10
- ❑ 91St.CatBJP-3399

Quinlan, Thomas PCL
- ❑ 14Zee-48A
- ❑ 14Zee-48B
- ❑ 16Zee-88
- ❑ 17Zee-73
- ❑ 18Zee-69

Quinlan, Tom
- ❑ 87MyrBeaBJP-1445
- ❑ 88KnoBluJB-25
- ❑ 89KnoBluJB-20
- ❑ 89KnoBluJP-1123
- ❑ 89KnoBluJS-16
- ❑ 90Bes-247
- ❑ 90CMC-773
- ❑ 90KnoBluJB-22
- ❑ 90KnoBluJP-1252
- ❑ 90KnoBluJS-14
- ❑ 90ProAaA-62
- ❑ 91LinDriAAA-514
- ❑ 91SyrChiLD-514
- ❑ 91SyrChiMB-20
- ❑ 91SyrChiP-2487
- ❑ 91TopDeb90-127
- ❑ 92SkyAAAF-230
- ❑ 92SyrChiF-1977
- ❑ 92SyrChiMB-17
- ❑ 92SyrChiS-514
- ❑ 93BluJayD4-27
- ❑ 93BluJayFS-23
- ❑ 93Don-161
- ❑ 93Sco-309
- ❑ 93SyrChiF-1006
- ❑ 94ScrRedBF-928
- ❑ 94SpoRoo-67
- ❑ 94SpoRooAP-67
- ❑ 95Pac-337
- ❑ 96LeaSigEA-165
- ❑ 97ColSprSTI-20
- ❑ 97PacPriGotD-GD65
- ❑ 98OklRedM-12

Quinn, Bob
- ❑ 79RedSoxEF-22
- ❑ 94ConTSN-1111
- ❑ 94ConTSNB-1111

Quinn, Frank W.
- ❑ 49RedSoxTI-19
- ❑ 51Bow-276

Quinn, Jack (John Picus)
- ❑ 09T206-297
- ❑ 10CouT21-209
- ❑ 10CouT21-210
- ❑ 10CouT21-311
- ❑ 10DomDisP-100
- ❑ 10RedCroT-63
- ❑ 10RedCroT-237
- ❑ 10SweCapPP-37
- ❑ 11HelSta-45
- ❑ 11PinT-5-809
- ❑ 11S74Sil-24
- ❑ 11T205-141
- ❑ 12HasTriFT-4
- ❑ 12T207-152
- ❑ 14PieStaT-87
- ❑ 15VicT21-24
- ❑ 16Zee-140
- ❑ 17Zee-115
- ❑ 20GasAmeMBD-15
- ❑ 21E121So8-73
- ❑ 21KoBreWSI-46
- ❑ 22E120-12
- ❑ 22W572-80
- ❑ 22W575-100
- ❑ 25Exh-68
- ❑ 26Exh-68
- ❑ 27AmeCarE126-14
- ❑ 31Exh-4
- ❑ 31W517-17
- ❑ 33Gou-78
- ❑ 33GouCanV-53
- ❑ 74A's192T-21
- ❑ 81ConTSN-93
- ❑ 87ConSer2-51
- ❑ 88ConSer3-23
- ❑ 90DodTar-639
- ❑ 91ConTSN-287
- ❑ 93ConTSN-709
- ❑ 94ConTSN-1148
- ❑ 94ConTSNB-1148

Quinn, James
- ❑ 77NewCoPT-27

Quinn, Joseph J.
- ❑ 87OldJudN-407
- ❑ 89N526N7C-11
- ❑ 93AusFut-119

Quinn, Mark
- ❑ 95SpoIndTI-20
- ❑ 96LanLugB-19
- ❑ 96MidLeaAB-39
- ❑ 97CalLeaATI-42
- ❑ 97WilBluR-13
- ❑ 98TexLeaTPG-29
- ❑ 98WicWraM-26
- ❑ 99Bow-79
- ❑ 99BowChr-79
- ❑ 99BowChrG-79
- ❑ 99BowChrGR-79
- ❑ 99BowChrI-79
- ❑ 99BowChrIR-79
- ❑ 99BowChrR-79
- ❑ 99BowGol-79
- ❑ 99BowInt-79

Quinn, Mike
- ❑ 92BriTigC-29
- ❑ 97TulDriTI-22
- ❑ 98TexLeaC-17
- ❑ 98TulDriTI-25

Quinn, Owen
- ❑ 16Zee-62

Quinn, Pat
- ❑ 80PhiBul-21

Quinn, Thomas G.
- ❑ 87OldJudN-406

Quinn, Tom
- ❑ 90MisStaB-32
- ❑ 91MisStaB-40
- ❑ 92MisStaB-35

Quinones, Elliot
- ❑ 90BilMusP-3234
- ❑ 90ProAaA-197
- ❑ 91ChaWheC-25
- ❑ 91ChaWheP-2900
- ❑ 92ChaWheF-22
- ❑ 92ChaWVWC-11
- ❑ 93ClaGolF-188
- ❑ 93SouAtlLAPI-33

Quinones, Hector
- ❑ 83BelBreFr-26
- ❑ 86FreGiaSB-18

Quinones, Luis
- ❑ 83AlbA'sT-14
- ❑ 84MaiGuiT-20
- ❑ 85MaiGuiT-21
- ❑ 86FleUpd-92
- ❑ 86PhoFirP-21
- ❑ 87IowCubTI-20
- ❑ 87Top-362
- ❑ 87TopTif-362
- ❑ 88BlaYNPRWL-76
- ❑ 88Don-365
- ❑ 88NasSouC-14
- ❑ 88NasSouP-490
- ❑ 88NasSouTI-19
- ❑ 88Top-667
- ❑ 88TopTif-667
- ❑ 89BlaYNPRWL-84
- ❑ 89NasSouC-17
- ❑ 89NasSouP-1272
- ❑ 90ClaBlu-132
- ❑ 90Don-595
- ❑ 90Fle-428
- ❑ 90FleCan-428
- ❑ 90OPC-176
- ❑ 90RedKah-22
- ❑ 90Sco-499
- ❑ 90Top-176
- ❑ 90TopTif-176
- ❑ 90UppDec-593
- ❑ 91Don-459
- ❑ 91Fle-77
- ❑ 91Lea-233
- ❑ 91OPC-581
- ❑ 91RedKah-10
- ❑ 91Sco-822
- ❑ 91Top-581
- ❑ 91TopDesS-581
- ❑ 91TopMic-581
- ❑ 91TopTif-581
- ❑ 91UltUpd-77
- ❑ 92Fle-417
- ❑ 92OPC-356
- ❑ 92PorBeaF-2676
- ❑ 92PorBeaS-405
- ❑ 92Sco-638
- ❑ 92StaClu-151
- ❑ 92Top-356
- ❑ 92TopGol-356
- ❑ 92TopGolW-356
- ❑ 92TopMic-356
- ❑ 93TucTorF-3070
- ❑ 94CalCanF-798

Quinones, Rene
- ❑ 77BurBeeT-23
- ❑ 79HolMilT-1
- ❑ 80VanCanT-16
- ❑ 81VanCanT-18
- ❑ 83BufBisT-18
- ❑ 83ElPasDT-8
- ❑ 84BufBisT-5
- ❑ 93WinSpiC-20
- ❑ 93WinSpiF-1569
- ❑ 94WinSpiC-19
- ❑ 94WinSpiF-269

Quinones, Rey F.
- ❑ 86DonRoo-48
- ❑ 86FleUpd-93
- ❑ 86PawRedSP-17
- ❑ 86TopTra-89T
- ❑ 86TopTraT-89T
- ❑ 87Don-638
- ❑ 87DonOpeD-121
- ❑ 87Fle-595
- ❑ 87FleGlo-595
- ❑ 87MarMot-20
- ❑ 87Top-561
- ❑ 87TopTif-561
- ❑ 88Don-198
- ❑ 88DonBasB-275
- ❑ 88Fle-386
- ❑ 88FleGlo-386
- ❑ 88MarMot-20
- ❑ 88OPC-358
- ❑ 88PanSti-186
- ❑ 88PanSti-190
- ❑ 88Sco-192
- ❑ 88ScoGlo-192
- ❑ 88StaLinMa-15
- ❑ 88Top-358
- ❑ 88TopSti-215
- ❑ 88TopTif-358
- ❑ 89BimBreD-4
- ❑ 89BlaYNPRWL-150
- ❑ 89Bow-213
- ❑ 89BowTif-213
- ❑ 89Don-330
- ❑ 89DonBasB-185
- ❑ 89Fle-556
- ❑ 89FleGlo-556
- ❑ 89OPC-246
- ❑ 89PanSti-438
- ❑ 89Sco-361
- ❑ 89Top-246
- ❑ 89TopSti-224
- ❑ 89TopTif-246
- ❑ 89TopTra-98T
- ❑ 89TopTraT-98T
- ❑ 89UppDec-508
- ❑ 89UppDec-750

Quintal, Craig
- ❑ 97WesMicW-19
- ❑ 98LakTigM-9

Quintana, Al
- ❑ 86WatPirP-17

Quintana, Carlos
- ❑ 85ElmPioT-18
- ❑ 86GreHorP-18
- ❑ 87NewBriRSP-12
- ❑ 88PawRedSC-20
- ❑ 88PawRedSP-453
- ❑ 88TriAAC-22
- ❑ 89ClaTraO-133
- ❑ 89Don-37
- ❑ 89Fle-95
- ❑ 89FleGlo-95
- ❑ 89PawRedSC-13
- ❑ 89PawRedSP-688
- ❑ 89PawRedSTI-19
- ❑ 89Sco-623
- ❑ 89ScoHot1R-13
- ❑ 89Top-704

❑ 89TopBig-142
❑ 89TopTif-704
❑ 89UppDec-26
❑ 90ClaYel-T44
❑ 90Don-517
❑ 90DonBesA-140
❑ 90Fle-283
❑ 90FleCan-283
❑ 90Hot50RS-36
❑ 90Lea-394
❑ 90OPC-18
❑ 90RedSoxP-15
❑ 90Sco-658
❑ 90Sco100RS-49
❑ 90ScoYouS2-42
❑ 90Top-18
❑ 90TopBig-273
❑ 90TopTif-18
❑ 90TopTVRS-32
❑ 90UppDec-465
❑ 91Bow-126
❑ 91Cla3-T75
❑ 91Don-568
❑ 91Fle-108
❑ 91Lea-473
❑ 91OPC-206
❑ 91PanFreS-264
❑ 91PanSti-221
❑ 91RedSoxP-16
❑ 91RedSoxP-22
❑ 91Sco-149
❑ 91StaClu-12
❑ 91Top-206
❑ 91TopDesS-206
❑ 91TopMic-206
❑ 91TopTif-206
❑ 91Ult-39
❑ 91UppDec-232
❑ 92Cla1-T73
❑ 92Don-609
❑ 92Fle-45
❑ 92OPC-127
❑ 92PanSti-85
❑ 92Pin-358
❑ 92RedSoxDD-23
❑ 92Sco-189
❑ 92StaClu-25
❑ 92Top-127
❑ 92TopGol-127
❑ 92TopGolW-127
❑ 92TopMic-127
❑ 92Ult-19
❑ 92UppDec-421
❑ 93Bow-227
❑ 93FleFinE-176
❑ 93Lea-437
❑ 93LinVenB-269
❑ 93PacJugC-13
❑ 93PacSpa-35
❑ 93Pin-564
❑ 93RedSoxP-26
❑ 93SP-203
❑ 93StaClu-605
❑ 93StaCluFDI-605
❑ 93StaCluMOP-605
❑ 93Ult-514
❑ 93UppDec-747
❑ 93UppDecGold-747
❑ 94Don-219
❑ 94Fle-39
❑ 94Pac-63
❑ 94Pin-175
❑ 94PinArtP-175
❑ 94PinMusC-175
❑ 94Sco-499
❑ 94ScoGolR-499
❑ 94StaClu-290
❑ 94StaCluFDI-290
❑ 94StaCluGR-290
❑ 94StaCluMOP-290
❑ 94Top-349
❑ 94TopGol-349
❑ 94TopPre-294
❑ 94TopSpa-349
❑ 94VenLinU-233
❑ 95LinVen-42
❑ 96-97LinVen-104
❑ 96-97LinVen-282

Quintana, Luis
❑ 75SalLakCC-16
❑ 76AtlBraP-26
❑ 76SalLakCGC-17
❑ 77SalLakCGC-16
❑ 80ChaO'sP-16
❑ 80ChaO'sW-17
❑ 82WicAerTI-13
❑ 83WicAerDS-15

Quintana, Urbano
❑ 96MarPhiB-20
❑ 97BatCliTI-31

Quintana, Willibaldo
❑ 76VenLeaS-94
❑ 80VenLeaS-96

Quintell, John
❑ 91OneYanP-4157
❑ 92AlbYanSk-17
❑ 92Ft.LauYF-2615

Quintero, Frank
❑ 77VisOakT-11
❑ 78OrlTwiT-16

Quinzer, Paul
❑ 86SpoIndC-165
❑ 88WicPilRD-23
❑ 89WicUpdR-16
❑ 89WicWraR-27
❑ 90LasVegSP-121
❑ 90ProAAAF-9

Quire, Jeremy
❑ 97LetBlaDB-10
❑ 98SouBenSHM-3

Quirico, Rafael
❑ 90Bes-147
❑ 90GreHorB-10
❑ 90GreHorP-2662
❑ 90GreHorS-16
❑ 90OneYanP-3371
❑ 91GreHorP-3057
❑ 91SouAtlLAGP-SAL29
❑ 92PriWilCF-146
❑ 92ProFS7-126
❑ 92UppDecML-229
❑ 93AlbYanF-2163
❑ 93LimRocDWB-13
❑ 94ColCliF-2953
❑ 94ColCliP-23
❑ 95ColCliMCTI-3
❑ 95ColCliP-25
❑ 95ColCliTI-25
❑ 96ReaPhiB-11
❑ 97MidAng-22

Quirk, Art
❑ 62BalOriP-21
❑ 62Top-591
❑ 63Top-522
❑ 91OriCro-372

Quirk, Jamie
❑ 75OmaRoyTI-14
❑ 76KanCitRP-26
❑ 76OPC-598
❑ 76Top-598
❑ 77Top-463
❑ 78SpoIndC-5
❑ 78Top-95
❑ 79Top-26
❑ 80Top-248
❑ 81Don-341
❑ 81Fle-50
❑ 81Top-507
❑ 82Don-212
❑ 82Fle-421
❑ 82Roy-17
❑ 82Top-173
❑ 83Car-22
❑ 83Top-264
❑ 83TopTra-90T
❑ 84Fle-332
❑ 84Nes792-671
❑ 84Top-671
❑ 84TopTif-671
❑ 85OmaRoyT-16
❑ 86RoyTeal-20
❑ 87Fle-377
❑ 87FleGlo-377
❑ 87Top-354
❑ 87TopTif-354
❑ 88Don-404
❑ 88Fle-266
❑ 88FleGlo-266
❑ 88PanSti-103
❑ 88RoySmo-19
❑ 88RoyTeal-25
❑ 88Sco-577
❑ 88ScoGlo-577
❑ 88StaLinRo-12
❑ 88Top-477
❑ 88TopTif-477
❑ 89Bow-173
❑ 89BowTif-173
❑ 89Fle-290
❑ 89FleGlo-290
❑ 89Sco-461
❑ 89Top-702
❑ 89TopTif-702
❑ 89UppDec-620
❑ 90A'sMot-15
❑ 91A'sMot-15
❑ 91Don-588
❑ 91Fle-21
❑ 91Lea-431
❑ 91OPC-132
❑ 91OriCro-373
❑ 91StaClu-573
❑ 91Top-132
❑ 91TopDesS-132
❑ 91TopMic-132
❑ 91TopTif-132
❑ 92AthMot-15
❑ 92Don-472
❑ 92Fle-265
❑ 92OPC-19
❑ 92Sco-526
❑ 92StaClu-83
❑ 92Top-19
❑ 92TopGol-19
❑ 92TopGolW-19
❑ 92TopMic-19
❑ 92YanWIZ8-151
❑ 93Fle-667
❑ 94BreMilB-68

Quirk, John
❑ 94HicCraC-18
❑ 94HicCraF-2176
❑ 96PriWilCB-22

Quiros, Gus
❑ 79VanCanT-11
❑ 80VanCanT-4
❑ 80VenLeaS-252
❑ 81VanCanT-11

Quiroz, Juan
❑ 76VenLeaS-24

Quisenberry, Dan
❑ 75WatRoyT-24
❑ 76WatRoyT-24
❑ 77JacSunT-20
❑ 79RoyTeal-8
❑ 80Top-667
❑ 81CokTeaS-79
❑ 81Don-222
❑ 81Fle-31
❑ 81FleStiC-24
❑ 81OPC-206
❑ 81RoyProPS-2
❑ 81Top-8
❑ 81Top-493
❑ 81TopSti-7
❑ 82Don-112
❑ 82Fle-422
❑ 82FleSta-204
❑ 82Roy-18
❑ 82Top-264
❑ 83AllGamPI-84
❑ 83Don-70
❑ 83Fle-122
❑ 83FleSta-154
❑ 83FleSti-100
❑ 83Kel-32
❑ 83OPC-155
❑ 83OPC-396
❑ 83RoyPol-6
❑ 83RoyPos-23
❑ 83Top-155
❑ 83Top-396
❑ 83Top-708
❑ 83TopFol-4
❑ 83TopSti-22
❑ 83TopSti-74
❑ 83TopSti-165
❑ 84AllGamPI-186
❑ 84Don-583
❑ 84DonActAS-56
❑ 84Fle-354
❑ 84Fle-635
❑ 84FleSti-73
❑ 84FunFooP-25
❑ 84Nes792-3
❑ 84Nes792-138
❑ 84Nes792-407
❑ 84Nes792-570
❑ 84Nes792-718
❑ 84NesDreT-11
❑ 84OPC-69
❑ 84OPC-273
❑ 84RalPur-25
❑ 84RoyPos-26
❑ 84SevCoi-C24
❑ 84Top-3
❑ 84Top-138
❑ 84Top-407
❑ 84Top-570
❑ 84Top-718
❑ 84TopCer-25
❑ 84TopGloS-38
❑ 84TopRubD-10
❑ 84TopSti-9
❑ 84TopSti-10
❑ 84TopSti-279
❑ 84TopSti-290
❑ 84TopSup-9
❑ 84TopTif-3
❑ 84TopTif-138
❑ 84TopTif-407
❑ 84TopTif-570
❑ 84TopTif-718
❑ 85AllGamPI-84
❑ 85Don-6
❑ 85Don-95
❑ 85DonActA-8
❑ 85DonSupD-6
❑ 85Dra-39
❑ 85Fle-211
❑ 85FleLimE-25
❑ 85FleStaS-99
❑ 85KASDis-9
❑ 85KitCloD-9
❑ 85Lea-6
❑ 85OPC-270
❑ 85RoyTeal-24
❑ 85SevCoi-C15
❑ 85SubDis-16
❑ 85ThoMcAD-16
❑ 85Top-270
❑ 85Top-711
❑ 85Top3-D-24
❑ 85TopGaloC-8
❑ 85TopGloS-35
❑ 85TopRubD-10
❑ 85TopSti-173
❑ 85TopSti-269
❑ 85TopSup-8
❑ 85TopTif-270
❑ 85TopTif-711
❑ 85Woo-28
❑ 86BasStaB-86
❑ 86Don-541
❑ 86Fle-18
❑ 86FleAll-9
❑ 86FleMin-2
❑ 86FleStiC-91
❑ 86GenMilB-2H
❑ 86Lea-208
❑ 86OPC-50
❑ 86QuaGra-29
❑ 86RoyKitCD-8
❑ 86RoyNatP-29
❑ 86RoyTeal-21
❑ 86SevCoi-C7
❑ 86SevCoi-E7
❑ 86SevCoi-S7
❑ 86SevCoi-W7
❑ 86Spo-55
❑ 86Spo-180
❑ 86Spo-186
❑ 86Top-50
❑ 86Top-722
❑ 86Top3-D-21
❑ 86TopGaloC-9
❑ 86TopGloS-35
❑ 86TopSti-257
❑ 86TopSup-5
❑ 86TopTat-3
❑ 86TopTif-50
❑ 86TopTif-722
❑ 87Don-177
❑ 87Fle-378
❑ 87FleBasA-33
❑ 87FleGlo-378
❑ 87FleMin-84
❑ 87FleStiC-93
❑ 87GenMilB-3J
❑ 87OPC-15
❑ 87RedFolSB-7
❑ 87Spo-167
❑ 87SpoTeaP-13
❑ 87Top-714
❑ 87TopSti-257
❑ 87TopTif-714
❑ 88Don-471
❑ 88Fle-267
❑ 88FleGlo-267
❑ 88GreBasS-80
❑ 88OPC-195
❑ 88PanSti-101
❑ 88RoySmo-15
❑ 88RoyTeal-26
❑ 88Sco-290
❑ 88ScoGlo-290
❑ 88ScoRoo-18T
❑ 88ScoRooG-18T
❑ 88Spo-76
❑ 88StaLinAl-22
❑ 88StaLinRo-13
❑ 88Top-195
❑ 88TopSti-256
❑ 88TopTif-195
❑ 89CarSmo-19
❑ 89CarTeal-25
❑ 89FleUpd-120
❑ 89OPC-13
❑ 89Sco-520
❑ 89Top-612
❑ 89TopTif-612
❑ 89UppDec-533
❑ 90Don-437
❑ 90Fle-259
❑ 90FleCan-259
❑ 90OPC-312
❑ 90PubIntS-227
❑ 90Sco-475
❑ 90Top-312
❑ 90TopTif-312
❑ 90UppDec-659
❑ 92KelAll-9
❑ 93RoySta2-11

Quittner, Peter
❑ 97ButCopKB-21
❑ 97ButCopKK-21

Ra, Michael
❑ 93AubAstC-30
❑ 94AubAstC-26
❑ 97JacGen-4
❑ 97JacGenS-21
❑ 98JacGenM-27

Raabe, Brian
❑ 91CalLeLA-8
❑ 91VisOakC-19
❑ 91VisOakP-1751
❑ 92Ft.MyeMCB-8
❑ 92Ft.MyeMF-2755
❑ 93ClaGolF-165
❑ 93NasXprF-410
❑ 94SalLakBF-824
❑ 94TriAAF-AAA17
❑ 97Sco-326
❑ 97ScoArtPWB-326
❑ 97ScoShoS-326
❑ 97ScoShoSAP-326
❑ 97TacRai-22

Raasch, Glen
❑ 91PenPilP-382
❑ 93PeoChiTI-21

Rabb, John
❑ 79CedRapGT-5
❑ 81ShrCapT-2
❑ 82PhoGiaVNB-5
❑ 83PhoGiaBHN-1
❑ 84Don-143
❑ 84GiaPos-22
❑ 84Nes792-228
❑ 84Top-228
❑ 84TopTif-228
❑ 85DomLeaS-97
❑ 85Don-236
❑ 85IntLeaAT-12
❑ 85PhoGiaC-183
❑ 85RicBraT-22
❑ 85Top-696
❑ 85TopTif-696
❑ 86RicBraP-18
❑ 87RicBraBC-17
❑ 87RicBraC-20
❑ 87RicBraT-20
❑ 91RenSilSCLC-1

Rabbit, Dodger
❑ 95GreFalDTI-38

Rabe, Charles
❑ 57SeaPop-20
❑ 58Kah-25
❑ 58RedEnq-31
❑ 58Top-376
❑ 59RedEnq-22
❑ 59SeaPop-9

Rabouin, Andre
❑ 88AppFoxP-159
❑ 89AppFoxP-871
❑ 90AppFoxBS-20
❑ 90AppFoxP-2113
❑ 98ChaAllCM-27

Raccoon, Rocky
❑ 95ChaLooTI-30

Rachac, Max
❑ 26Zee-101
❑ 27Zee-100
❑ 28Zee-117
❑ 29Zee-119

Rachels, Wes
❑ 98BatMucTI-24

Rackley, Keifer
❑ 93BelMarCB-22
❑ 93BelMarF-3223
❑ 94RivPilCLC-13
❑ 95PorCitRTI-18
❑ 96WilBluRB-21

Rackley, Marv
❑ 43ParSpo-81
❑ 47TipTop-103
❑ 90DodTar-640

Racobaldo, Mike
❑ 90KisDodD-24

Raczka, Mike
❑ 86ChaOriW-22
❑ 87ChaO'sW-10
❑ 88RocRedWGCP-22
❑ 89RocRedWC-5
❑ 89RocRedWP-1648
❑ 92ModA'sC-18
❑ 92TacTigF-2500
❑ 93Don-183
❑ 93Pin-277
❑ 93TacTigF-3030
❑ 94NewBriRSF-648
❑ 95LouRedF-276

Radachowsky, Gregg
❑ 90NiaFalRP-13
❑ 91NiaFalRP-3637

Radar, Keith
❑ 91SalLakTSP-1

Radatz, Dick
❑ 47PM1StaP1-167
❑ 61SeaPop-18
❑ 62Top-591
❑ 63Top-363
❑ 64ChatheY-43
❑ 64RedSoxTI-6
❑ 64Top-170
❑ 64TopCoi-30
❑ 64TopGia-40
❑ 64TopSta-41
❑ 64TopVen-170
❑ 64WheSta-37
❑ 65Baz-10
❑ 65ChaTheY-44
❑ 65OldLonC-34
❑ 65RedSoxTI-11
❑ 65Top-295
❑ 65TopEmbl-48
❑ 65TopTral-64
❑ 66RedSoxTI-10
❑ 66Top-475
❑ 66TopRubl-76
❑ 67CokCapl-16
❑ 67OPC-174
❑ 67Top-174
❑ 69Top-663
❑ 74LauAllG-63
❑ 78TCM60I-76
❑ 81RedSoxBG2S-104
❑ 86RedSoxGT-11
❑ 89PacLegI-122
❑ 89SweBasG-46

Radbourn, Hoss (Charles)
❑ 36Halof FP-20
❑ 39PC7AlbHoF-24
❑ 50CalHOFW-61
❑ 63GadFunC-8
❑ 75FlePio-5
❑ 75TCMAllG-26
❑ 76ShaPiz-25
❑ 80PerHaloFP-24
❑ 80SSPHOF-24
❑ 84GalHaloFRL-25
❑ 87BucN28-11A
❑ 87BucN28-11B
❑ 87OldJudN-408A
❑ 87OldJudN-408B
❑ 89N526N7C-12
❑ 90BasWit-92
❑ 90HOFStiB-2
❑ 94OriofB-42

Radcliff, Rip (Ray)
❑ 33WorCig(-70
❑ 36GouWidPPR-A86
❑ 36NatChiFPR-102
❑ 36OveCanR-37
❑ 36SandSW-45
❑ 37OPCBatUV-125

❑ 37WheBB14-13
❑ 37WheBB7-29H
❑ 38BasTabP-24
❑ 38GouHeaU-261
❑ 38GouHeaU-285
❑ 91ConTSN-98
Radcliff, Vic
❑ 97LanLugTS-21
❑ 98LanLugQ-24
Radcliffe, Alex
❑ 91PomBlaBPB-5
❑ 97NegLeaPC-5C
Radcliffe, Double-Duty (Ted)
❑ 78LauLonABS-36
❑ 86NegLeaF-64
❑ 91NegLeaRL-25
❑ 92NegLeaK-7
❑ 92NegLeaRLI-50
❑ 93UppDecS-17
❑ 94TedWil-110
❑ 95NegLeaL2-6
❑ 95NegLeaLI-25
❑ 97NegLeaPC-JKO
Radcliffe, Ernest
❑ 87EriCarP-9
❑ 88VirGenS-20
Rader, Dave
❑ 72OPC-232
❑ 72Top-232
❑ 73OPC-121
❑ 73Top-121
❑ 74OPC-213
❑ 74Top-213
❑ 74TopSta-108
❑ 75Gia-8
❑ 75GiaTeal-14
❑ 75OPC-31
❑ 75Top-31
❑ 75TopMin-31
❑ 76Hos-21
❑ 76HosTwi-21
❑ 76OPC-54
❑ 76SanFraGP-17
❑ 76SSP-101
❑ 76Top-54
❑ 77Car5-19
❑ 77CarTeal-18
❑ 77Top-427
❑ 78SSP270-246
❑ 78Top-563
❑ 79OPC-369
❑ 79Top-489
❑ 79Top-693
❑ 80Top-296
❑ 81Don-512
❑ 81OPC-359
❑ 81Top-378
Rader, Donald
❑ 16Zee-123
❑ 16Zee-141
❑ 19Zee-43
Rader, Doug
❑ 67Ast-24
❑ 67Top-412
❑ 68CokCapA-11
❑ 68Top-332
❑ 68TopVen-332
❑ 69MilBra-227
❑ 69MLBOffS-142
❑ 69OPC-119
❑ 69Top-119
❑ 69TopFou-15
❑ 69TopSta-37
❑ 69TopTeaP-6
❑ 70AstPho-21
❑ 70AstTeal-10
❑ 70MLBOffS-46
❑ 70OPC-355
❑ 70Top-355
❑ 71AstCok-9
❑ 71AstTeal-19
❑ 71MLBOffS-90
❑ 71OPC-425
❑ 71Top-425
❑ 71TopCoi-17
❑ 72AstTeal-20
❑ 72Kel-14
❑ 72MilBra-280
❑ 72Top-536
❑ 73OPC-76
❑ 73Top-76
❑ 74AstFouTIP-2
❑ 74OPC-395
❑ 74Top-395
❑ 74TopDecE-14
❑ 74TopSta-35
❑ 75AstPos-24
❑ 75Hos-89A
❑ 75Hos-89B
❑ 75OPC-165
❑ 75Top-165
❑ 75TopMin-165
❑ 76OPC-44
❑ 76SSP-59
❑ 76Top-44
❑ 76TopTra-44T
❑ 77BurCheD-128
❑ 77PadSchC-44
❑ 77Top-9
❑ 78OPC-166
❑ 78Top-651
❑ 79PadFamF-32
❑ 80HawIsIT-2
❑ 81HawIsIT-21
❑ 82AstAstI-2
❑ 82HawIsIT-23
❑ 83RanAffF-11
❑ 83TopTra-91T
❑ 84Nes792-412
❑ 84RanJarP-11
❑ 84Top-412
❑ 84TopTif-412
❑ 85Top-519
❑ 85TopTif-519
❑ 86AstGreT-4
❑ 87AstSer1-26
❑ 87AstShoSO-19
❑ 87AstShoSPO-25
❑ 87AstShoSTw-24
❑ 87AstShoSTw-27
❑ 87AstShowSTh-25
❑ 89TopTra-99T
❑ 89TopTraT-99T
❑ 90OPC-51
❑ 90Top-51
❑ 90TopTif-51
❑ 91OPC-231
❑ 91Top-231
❑ 91TopDesS-231
❑ 91TopMic-231
❑ 91TopTif-231
❑ 92AthMot-28
❑ 93MarPub-28
❑ 93RanKee-303
Rader, Keith
❑ 91SalLakTP-3220
Radford, Paul
❑ 87OldJudN-409
Radinsky, Scott
❑ 87PenWhiSP-12
❑ 89SouBenWSGS-7
❑ 90Bow-308
❑ 90BowTif-308
❑ 90ClaYel-T5
❑ 90DonRoo-40
❑ 90FleUpd-86
❑ 90Lea-484
❑ 90ScoRoo-90T
❑ 90TopTra-99T
❑ 90TopTraT-99T
❑ 90UppDec-725
❑ 90WhiSoxC-22
❑ 90WhiSoxC-28
❑ 91Baz-22
❑ 91Bow-365
❑ 91Don-332
❑ 91Fle-135
❑ 91Lea-463
❑ 91OPC-299
❑ 91Sco-62
❑ 91Sco100RS-83
❑ 91StaClu-311
❑ 91Top-299
❑ 91TopDeb90-128
❑ 91TopDesS-299
❑ 91TopMic-299
❑ 91TopRoo-25
❑ 91TopTif-299
❑ 91ToyRoo-25
❑ 91UltUpd-18
❑ 91UppDec-621
❑ 91WhiSoxK-31
❑ 92Don-299
❑ 92Fle-96
❑ 92Lea-281
❑ 92LeaBlaG-281
❑ 92OPC-701
❑ 92Pin-389
❑ 92PinTea2-46
❑ 92PinTeaP-12
❑ 92Sco-444
❑ 92Top-701
❑ 92TopGol-701
❑ 92TopGolW-701
❑ 92TopMic-701
❑ 92Ult-340
❑ 92UppDec-594
❑ 92WhiSoxK-31
❑ 93Don-169
❑ 93Fle-208
❑ 93PacSpa-74
❑ 93Pin-451
❑ 93Sco-182
❑ 93StaClu-275
❑ 93StaCluFDI-275
❑ 93StaCluMOP-275
❑ 93Top-550
❑ 93TopGol-550
❑ 93TopInaM-550
❑ 93TopInaR-550
❑ 93TopMic-550
❑ 93Ult-177
❑ 93UppDec-298
❑ 93UppDecGold-298
❑ 93WhiSoxK-23
❑ 93WhiSoxSC-19
❑ 94ColC-235
❑ 94ColChoGS-235
❑ 94ColChoSS-235
❑ 94Don-230
❑ 94Fle-92
❑ 94Pac-135
❑ 94Pin-135
❑ 94PinArtP-135
❑ 94PinMusC-135
❑ 94Sco-276
❑ 94ScoGolR-276
❑ 94StaClu-434
❑ 94StaCluFDI-434
❑ 94StaCluGR-434
❑ 94StaCluMOP-434
❑ 94StaCluT-125
❑ 94StaCluTFDI-125
❑ 94Top-421
❑ 94TopGol-421
❑ 94TopSpa-421
❑ 95TopTra-71T
❑ 95WhiSoxK-25
❑ 96DodMot-22
❑ 97DodMot-21
❑ 97DodPol-25
❑ 98DodMot-9
❑ 98DodPol-24
❑ 98PacOnl-384
❑ 98PacOnlR-384
❑ 98PacOnlWC-384
❑ 99Fle-559
❑ 99FleSta9-559
❑ 99FleWarT-559
Radison, Dan
❑ 88HamRedP-1732
❑ 89BlaYNPRWL-97
❑ 89SprCarB-29
❑ 91AlbYanLD-24
❑ 91AlbYanP-1023
❑ 91LinDriAA-24
❑ 92AlbYanF-2348
❑ 92AlbYanSk-24
❑ 93PadMot-28
❑ 94PadMot-28
Radke, Brad
❑ 92KenTwiC-22
❑ 92KenTwiF-601
❑ 93ForMyeMC-20
❑ 93ForMyeMF-2652
❑ 94Cla-88
❑ 94NasXprF-384
❑ 95Exc-88
❑ 95Fla-281
❑ 95FleUpd-62
❑ 95StaClu-560
❑ 95StaCluMOP-560
❑ 95StaCluSTWS-560
❑ 95TopTra-79T
❑ 95UppDec-257
❑ 95UppDecED-257
❑ 95UppDecEDG-257
❑ 96ColCho-201
❑ 96ColChoGS-201
❑ 96ColChoSS-201
❑ 96Don-10
❑ 96DonPreP-10
❑ 96EmoXL-86
❑ 96Fla-121
❑ 96Fle-173
❑ 96FleTif-173
❑ 96Lea-131
❑ 96LeaPrePB-131
❑ 96LeaPrePG-131
❑ 96LeaPrePS-131
❑ 96LeaSigA-187
❑ 96LeaSigAG-187
❑ 96LeaSigAS-187
❑ 96MetUni-81
❑ 96MetUniP-81
❑ 96MetUniProS-81
❑ 96MetUniProS-XX
❑ 96Pac-356
❑ 96Pin-37
❑ 96Sco-77
❑ 96ScoDugC-A63
❑ 96ScoDugCAP-A63
❑ 96SP-114
❑ 96StaClu-163
❑ 96StaCluMOP-163
❑ 96Sum-6
❑ 96SumAbo&B-6
❑ 96SumArtP-6
❑ 96SumFoi-6
❑ 96Top-163
❑ 96Ult-93
❑ 96UltGolM-93
❑ 96UppDec-126
❑ 97Cir-389
❑ 97CirRav-389
❑ 97ColCho-380
❑ 97Fle-155
❑ 97FleTif-155
❑ 97Sel-188
❑ 97SelCom-188
❑ 97StaClu-265
❑ 97StaCluMOP-265
❑ 97Top-257
❑ 97Ult-345
❑ 97UltGolME-345
❑ 97UltPlaME-345
❑ 97UppDec-413
❑ 98Bow-13
❑ 98BowChr-13
❑ 98BowChrGA-13
❑ 98BowChrGAR-13
❑ 98BowChrI-13
❑ 98BowChrIR-13
❑ 98BowChrR-13
❑ 98BowGolA-13
❑ 98BowInt-13
❑ 98CirThu-246
❑ 98CirThuRav-246
❑ 98CirThuSupRav-246
❑ 98ColCho-157
❑ 98ColChoSQ-SQ31
❑ 98Don-48
❑ 98DonCol-48
❑ 98DonColL-245
❑ 98DonColP-644
❑ 98DonColS-48
❑ 98DonGolPP-48
❑ 98DonPre-94
❑ 98DonPreSeat-94
❑ 98DonPriCD-48
❑ 98DonPriCL-245
❑ 98DonPriCP-644
❑ 98DonSilPP-48
❑ 98Fin-21
❑ 98FinNo--21
❑ 98FinNo-R-21
❑ 98FinRef-21
❑ 98FlaShoLeg0-98
❑ 98FlaShoLeg1-98
❑ 98FlaShoLeg2-98
❑ 98FlaShoLeg3-98
❑ 98FlaShoLegM-98
❑ 98FlaShoR0-98
❑ 98FlaShoR1-98
❑ 98FlaShoR2-98
❑ 98FlaShoR3-98
❑ 98Fle-85
❑ 98Lea-46
❑ 98LeaFraDA-46
❑ 98LeaFraF-46
❑ 98LeaFraM-46
❑ 98LeaFraM-46
❑ 98LeaFraMDC-46
❑ 98LeaFraMDC-46
❑ 98LeaFraMZ2-46
❑ 98LeaRS-90
❑ 98LeaRSLHolo-90
❑ 98LeaRSLong-90
❑ 98LeaRTrue-90
❑ 98MetUni-49
❑ 98MetUniPMG-49
❑ 98Pac-140
❑ 98PacAur-54
❑ 98PacInv-48
❑ 98PacInvPBlue-48
❑ 98PacInvSilv-48
❑ 98PacInvTeam-16
❑ 98PacOme-144
❑ 98PacOmeR-144
❑ 98PacOnl-433
❑ 98PacOnlR-433
❑ 98PacOnlWC-433
❑ 98PacPar-65
❑ 98PacParC-65
❑ 98PacParG-65
❑ 98PacParHS-65
❑ 98PacParPB-65
❑ 98PacParR-65
❑ 98PacPlaB-140
❑ 98PacRedT-140
❑ 98PacSil-140
❑ 98Pin-35
❑ 98PinArtP-PP34
❑ 98PinMusC-PP34
❑ 98PinPreP-35
❑ 98Revo-85
❑ 98RevoSS-85
❑ 98Sco-168
❑ 98ScoRT-110
❑ 98ScoSS-PP72
❑ 98ScoSSAP-PP72
❑ 98SkyDugA-72
❑ 98SkyDugAIA-72
❑ 98SP Aut-122
❑ 98SpoIll-102
❑ 98SpoIllEE-102
❑ 98SpoIllFE-102
❑ 98SpoIllWSF-120
❑ 98SpoIllWSFEE-120
❑ 98SpoIllWSFFE-120
❑ 98SPxFin-97
❑ 98SPxFinR-97
❑ 98SPxFinS-97
❑ 98StaCluFDI-277
❑ 98StaCluI-277
❑ 98StaCluOneK-277
❑ 98StaCluPP-277
❑ 98Stu-131
❑ 98StuGPP-131
❑ 98StuSPP-131
❑ 98Top-113
❑ 98Top-474
❑ 98TopChr-113
❑ 98TopChr-474
❑ 98TopChrR-113
❑ 98TopChrR-474
❑ 98TopDevR-113
❑ 98TopDevR-474
❑ 98TopDia-113
❑ 98TopDia-474
❑ 98TopGal-102
❑ 98TopGalGP-102
❑ 98TopGalOPP-102
❑ 98TopGalPPI-102
❑ 98TopGalPPIA-102
❑ 98TopMiniC-113
❑ 98TopMiniC-474
❑ 98TopOpeD-59
❑ 98TopSta-83
❑ 98TopStaB-83
❑ 98TopStaG-83
❑ 98TopStaGR-83
❑ 98TopStaS-83
❑ 98Ult-8
❑ 98UltGolM-8
❑ 98UltMas-8
❑ 98UltPlaM-8
❑ 98UppDec-133
❑ 98UppDecR-56
❑ 98UppDecSF-81
❑ 99199Fin-37
❑ 99CroRoyB-83
❑ 99CroRoyL-83
❑ 99CroRoyOD-83
❑ 99FinGolRef-37
❑ 99FinRef-37
❑ 99Fle-265
❑ 99FleSta9-265
❑ 99FleWarT-265
❑ 99KinDis-23
❑ 99MetUni-201
❑ 99MetUniGM-201
❑ 99MetUniPMG-201
❑ 99Pac-255
❑ 99PacAur-107
❑ 99PacAurOD-107
❑ 99PacOme-139
❑ 99PacOmeC-139
❑ 99PacOmeG-139
❑ 99PacOmePB-139
❑ 99PacPar-136
❑ 99PacParC-136
❑ 99PacParG-136
❑ 99PacParHoloGold-136
❑ 99PacParHS-136
❑ 99PacParOD-136
❑ 99PacParPB-136
❑ 99PacParRed-136
❑ 99PacParTC-17
❑ 99PacPlaB-255
❑ 99PacRed-255
❑ 99Rev-81
❑ 99RevPremDate-81
❑ 99RevRet-81
❑ 99RevShaSS-81
❑ 99SkyPre-100
❑ 99SkyPreR-100
❑ 99SkyThu-227
❑ 99SkyThuRant-227
❑ 99SkyThuRave-227
❑ 99SP Aut-50
❑ 99SP SigAuto-BR
❑ 99SPSig-123
❑ 99StaClu-224
❑ 99StaCluFDI-224
❑ 99StaCluOoaK-224
❑ 99StaCluPP-224
❑ 99ThuSkySupR-227
❑ 99Top-19
❑ 99TopChr-19
❑ 99TopChrR-19
❑ 99TopMVPP-19
❑ 99TopOpeD-14
❑ 99UD Cho-107
❑ 99UD ChoPCR-107
❑ 99Ult-149
❑ 99UltGolM-149
❑ 99UltMas-149
❑ 99UltPlaM-149
❑ 99UppDecCLM-C53
❑ 99UppDecM-117
❑ 99UppDecMGS-117
❑ 99UppDecMHFS-117
❑ 99UppDecMP-117
❑ 99UppDecMSS-117
❑ 99Vic-225
Radloff, Scott
❑ 83CedRapRF-21
❑ 83CedRapRT-15
Radlosky, Rob
❑ 95ForWayWTI-12
❑ 96FtMyeMB-7
❑ 98NewBriRCM-24
Radmanovich, Ryan
❑ 94ForWayWC-19
❑ 94ForWayWF-2016
❑ 94MidLeaAF-MDW14
❑ 95ForMyeMTI-22
❑ 96DouAllB-21
❑ 96HarCitRCB-24
❑ 97SalLakB-21
❑ 98Bow-104
❑ 98BowChr-104
❑ 98BowChrGA-104
❑ 98BowChrGAR-104
❑ 98BowChrI-104
❑ 98BowChrIR-104
❑ 98BowChrR-104
❑ 98BowGolA-104
❑ 98BowInt-104
❑ 98TacRaiQ-24
Radonitz, William
❑ 33Zee-161
❑ 37Zee-48
Radovich, Robert
❑ 65SeaPop-14
❑ 65SeaPop-15
Radtke, Jack
❑ 90DodTar-641
Radziewicz, Doug
❑ 91JohCitCC-8
❑ 91JohCitCP-3986
❑ 92SprCarC-5
❑ 92SprCarF-877
❑ 93St.PetCC-20
❑ 93St.PetCF-2636
❑ 94ArkTraF-3103
❑ 94ExcFS7-273
Raelhn, Gary
❑ 93HolLeg-13
Raeside, John
❑ 82LynMetT-23
Raether, Peter
❑ 90ArkRaz-22
Raether, Richard

❑ 85MiaHur-12
❑ 86TulDriTI-22
❑ 87PorChaRP-9
❑ 88BlaYNPRWL-28
❑ 88TulDriTI-26
❑ 90TulDriDGB-10

Raffensberger, Ken
❑ 49Bow-176
❑ 49EurSta-93
❑ 51Bow-48
❑ 52Bow-55
❑ 52TipTop-30
❑ 52Top-118
❑ 53BowC-106
❑ 53Top-276
❑ 54Bow-92
❑ 54Top-46
❑ 83TopRep5-118
❑ 91TopArc1-276
❑ 94TopArc1-46
❑ 94TopArc1G-46
❑ 95ConTSN-1414

Raffo, Greg
❑ 91BriTigC-16
❑ 91BriTigP-3603
❑ 92NiaFalRC-26
❑ 92NiaFalRF-3322
❑ 93LakTigF-1308

Raffo, Thomas
❑ 88CapCodPB-9
❑ 88CapCodPPaLP-79
❑ 88MisStaB-27
❑ 89MisStaB-31
❑ 90MiaMirIS-20
❑ 90MisStaB-33
❑ 91ChaWheC-19
❑ 91ChaWheP-2896
❑ 91Cla/Bes-261
❑ 91SouAtlLAGP-SAL10
❑ 92CedRapRC-5
❑ 92CedRapRF-1080

Raftery, Thomas
❑ 12HomRunKE-73
❑ 12Zee-127

Ragan, Pat (Don C.P.)
❑ 09ObaT21-20
❑ 12T207-153
❑ 16FleBreD-74
❑ 16SpoNewM-140
❑ 75WhiSox1T-19
❑ 90DodTar-642

Raggio, Brady
❑ 94NewJerCF-3418
❑ 95MidLeaA-42
❑ 95PeoChiTI-37
❑ 96ArkTraB-23
❑ 96DouAllB-56
❑ 96TexLeaAB-14
❑ 97Bow-306
❑ 97BowInt-306
❑ 97Fle-584
❑ 97FleTif-584
❑ 97LouRedB-26
❑ 97NewJerCB-2
❑ 97Ult-519
❑ 97UltGolME-519
❑ 97UltPlaME-519
❑ 98Fle-242

Ragland, Tom
❑ 72OPC-334
❑ 72Top-334
❑ 73IndTeal-22
❑ 74OPC-441
❑ 74Top-441
❑ 93RanKee-34

Ragland, Trace
❑ 91WelPirC-14
❑ 91WelPirP-3589
❑ 93SalBucC-19
❑ 93SalBucF-447

Ragni, John
❑ 52MotCoo-34

Ragsdale, Jerry
❑ 83AndBraT-27

Rahan, Johnny
❑ 52LavPro-67

Raich, Eric
❑ 76OPC-484
❑ 76Top-484
❑ 77Top-62

Raifstanger, John
❑ 94UtiBluSC-23
❑ 96MicBatCB-21
❑ 97SarRedS-20

Raimondi, Albert
❑ 33Zee-72
❑ 37Zee-24
❑ 37Zee-38

Raimondi, Bill
❑ 37Zee-40
❑ 46RemBre-25
❑ 47RemBre-1
❑ 47SigOil-52
❑ 47SmiClo-2
❑ 48SigOil-19
❑ 48SmiClo-1
❑ 49BowPCL-18
❑ 49RemBre-22
❑ 53MotCoo-36

Raimondi, Ernest
❑ 37Zee-85

Raimondo, Pasquale
❑ 81VerBeaDT-15

Rain, Steve
❑ 94HunCubC-24
❑ 94HunCubF-3553
❑ 95MidLeaA-43
❑ 95RocCubTI-28
❑ 96OrlCubB-22
❑ 97Bow-189
❑ 97BowChr-177
❑ 97BowChrI-177
❑ 97BowChrIR-177
❑ 97BowChrR-177
❑ 97BowInt-189
❑ 97IowCub-23
❑ 98IowCubQ-20

Rainbolt, Ray
❑ 74GasRanT-17
❑ 75LynRanT-22
❑ 76SanAntBTI-19
❑ 79TulDriT-8

Rainbows, Charlestown
❑ 89ChaRaiP-970

Rainer, Rick
❑ 84JacMetT-11
❑ 85TidTidT-28
❑ 86TidTidP-25
❑ 87TidTidP-30
❑ 87TidTidT-25

Raineri, Joe
❑ 92OklStaC-24

Raines, Kenneth
❑ 94IdaFalBF-3583
❑ 94IdaFalBSP-21
❑ 95DanBraTI-23
❑ 95DurBulTI-26
❑ 96HudValRB-9

Raines, Larry
❑ 57IndTeal-19
❑ 58Top-243

Raines, Mike
❑ 81CedRapRT-5

Raines, Ned
❑ 79CedRapGT-21

Raines, Rock (Tim)
❑ 79MemChiT-20
❑ 81Don-538
❑ 81ExpPos-9
❑ 81OPC-136
❑ 81Top-479
❑ 81TopTra-816
❑ 82Don-214
❑ 82ExpHygM-16
❑ 82ExpPos-31
❑ 82ExpZel-3
❑ 82FBIDis-17
❑ 82Fle-202
❑ 82Fle-207
❑ 82FleSta-31
❑ 82Kel-53
❑ 82OPC-70
❑ 82OPCPos-17
❑ 82PerAll-13
❑ 82PerAllG-13
❑ 82PerCreC-6
❑ 82PerCreCG-6
❑ 82Top-3
❑ 82Top-70
❑ 82Top-164
❑ 82TopSti-7
❑ 82TopSti-62
❑ 82TopSti-116
❑ 83AllGamPI-158
❑ 83Don-540
❑ 83ExpPos-23
❑ 83ExpStu-9
❑ 83Fle-292
❑ 83FleSta-155
❑ 83FleSti-265
❑ 83OPC-227
❑ 83OPC-352
❑ 83PerAll-14
❑ 83PerAllG-14
❑ 83Top-403
❑ 83Top-595
❑ 83Top-704
❑ 83TopSti-210
❑ 83TopSti-253
❑ 84AllGamPI-66
❑ 84Don-299
❑ 84ExpPos-22
❑ 84ExpStu-20
❑ 84ExpStu-36
❑ 84ExpStu-37
❑ 84Fle-281
❑ 84Fle-631
❑ 84FleSti-51
❑ 84FleSti-88
❑ 84FunFooP-41
❑ 84Nes792-134
❑ 84Nes792-370
❑ 84Nes792-390
❑ 84NesDreT-17
❑ 84OPC-370
❑ 84OPC-390
❑ 84SevCoi-E20
❑ 84Top-134
❑ 84Top-370
❑ 84Top-390
❑ 84TopGloA-17
❑ 84TopGloS-37
❑ 84TopRubD-23
❑ 84TopSti-91
❑ 84TopSti-179
❑ 84TopSti-201
❑ 84TopStiB-4
❑ 84TopTif-134
❑ 84TopTif-370
❑ 84TopTif-390
❑ 85AllGamPI-157
❑ 85Don-299
❑ 85DonActA-1
❑ 85Dra-24
❑ 85ExpCup-1
❑ 85ExpPos-17
❑ 85Fle-405
❑ 85FleLimE-26
❑ 85FleStaS-42
❑ 85FleStaS-58
❑ 85Lea-218
❑ 85Lea-252
❑ 85OPC-277
❑ 85OPCPos-7
❑ 85SevCoi-S12
❑ 85Top-630
❑ 85Top3-D-17
❑ 85TopMin-630
❑ 85TopRubD-9
❑ 85TopSti-82
❑ 85TopSti-282
❑ 85TopSup-15
❑ 85TopTif-630
❑ 86Don-177
❑ 86DonAll-20
❑ 86Dra-15
❑ 86ExpProPa-7
❑ 86ExpProPo-1
❑ 86Fle-256
❑ 86Fle-632
❑ 86FleLeaL-33
❑ 86FleMin-54
❑ 86FleStiC-92
❑ 86GenMilB-6E
❑ 86Lea-108
❑ 86OPC-280
❑ 86QuaGra-10
❑ 86SevCoi-E12
❑ 86Spo-11
❑ 86Spo-127
❑ 86Spo-144
❑ 86SpoDecG-74
❑ 86Top-280
❑ 86TopGloS-15
❑ 86TopMinL-49
❑ 86TopSti-75
❑ 86TopSup-42
❑ 86TopTat-17
❑ 86TopTif-280
❑ 87BoaandB-24
❑ 87ClaGam-29
❑ 87Don-56
❑ 87DonAll-36
❑ 87DonHig-7
❑ 87DonHig-16
❑ 87ExpPos-21
❑ 87Fle-328
❑ 87Fle-642
❑ 87FleAll-12
❑ 87FleBasA-34
❑ 87FleExcS-34
❑ 87FleGlo-328
❑ 87FleGlo-642
❑ 87FleMin-85
❑ 87FleRecS-30
❑ 87FleSlu-32
❑ 87FleStiC-94
❑ 87GenMilB-5E
❑ 87KayB-25
❑ 87Lea-149
❑ 87OPC-30
❑ 87RedFolSB-39
❑ 87Spo-34
❑ 87Spo-152
❑ 87Spo-197
❑ 87Spo-199
❑ 87SpoDeaP-1
❑ 87SpoSupD-15
❑ 87StaRai-1
❑ 87StaRai-2
❑ 87StaRai-3
❑ 87StaRai-4
❑ 87StaRai-5
❑ 87StaRai-6
❑ 87StaRai-7
❑ 87StaRai-8
❑ 87StaRai-9
❑ 87StaRai-10
❑ 87StaRai-11
❑ 87StaRai-12
❑ 87StuPan-7
❑ 87Top-30
❑ 87TopGaloC-8
❑ 87TopGloS-48
❑ 87TopMinL-17
❑ 87TopSti-85
❑ 87TopTif-30
❑ 87Woo-11
❑ 88Baz-15
❑ 88ClaRed-168
❑ 88Don-2
❑ 88Don-345
❑ 88DonAll-57
❑ 88DonAll-62
❑ 88DonBasB-180
❑ 88DonBonM-BC18
❑ 88DonSupD-2
❑ 88Dra-2
❑ 88ExpPos-27
❑ 88Fle-193
❑ 88Fle-631
❑ 88FleAwaW-30
❑ 88FleBasA-31
❑ 88FleBasM-27
❑ 88FleExcS-31
❑ 88FleGlo-193
❑ 88FleGlo-631
❑ 88FleHea-6
❑ 88FleHotS-31
❑ 88FleLeaL-31
❑ 88FleMin-90
❑ 88FleRecS-30
❑ 88FleStiC-97
❑ 88FleSup-29
❑ 88FleTeaL-27
❑ 88GreBasS-51
❑ 88K-M-19
❑ 88KayB-24
❑ 88Lea-2
❑ 88Lea-114
❑ 88Lea-211
❑ 88MSAFanSD-16
❑ 88MSAHosD-11
❑ 88MSAJifPD-14
❑ 88Nes-31
❑ 88OPC-243
❑ 88PanSti-325
❑ 88PanSti-330
❑ 88Sco-3
❑ 88Sco-649
❑ 88ScoGlo-3
❑ 88ScoGlo-649
❑ 88Spo-2
❑ 88StaLinAl-23
❑ 88StaLinE-13
❑ 88TarPla-32
❑ 88Top-403
❑ 88Top-720
❑ 88TopBig-116
❑ 88TopCoi-49
❑ 88TopGloS-12
❑ 88TopMinL-57
❑ 88TopRevLL-5
❑ 88TopRitTM-6
❑ 88TopSti-76
❑ 88TopStiB-20
❑ 88TopTif-403
❑ 88TopTif-720
❑ 88TopUKM-58
❑ 88TopUKMT-58
❑ 89Bow-369
❑ 89BowTif-369
❑ 89CerSup-6
❑ 89ClaLigB-42
❑ 89Don-97
❑ 89DonBasB-258
❑ 89ExpPos-24
❑ 89Fle-391
❑ 89FleGlo-391
❑ 89K-M-27
❑ 89KayB-25
❑ 89OPC-87
❑ 89PanSti-125
❑ 89RedFolSB-91
❑ 89Sco-40
❑ 89ScoHot1S-95
❑ 89Spo-150
❑ 89SpoIllFKI-178
❑ 89Top-81
❑ 89Top-560
❑ 89TopBasT-80
❑ 89TopBatL-7
❑ 89TopBig-73
❑ 89TopCoi-22
❑ 89TopGloS-53
❑ 89TopSti-77
❑ 89TopTif-81
❑ 89TopTif-560
❑ 89TopUKM-61
❑ 89TVSpoM-13
❑ 89UppDec-402
❑ 89UppDecS-2
❑ 90Bow-118
❑ 90BowTif-118
❑ 90ClaBlu-118
❑ 90Don-216
❑ 90DonBesN-104
❑ 90DOnBonM-BC7
❑ 90ExpPos-28
❑ 90Fle-359
❑ 90FleBasM-30
❑ 90FleBasMC-30
❑ 90FleCan-359
❑ 90GooHumICBLS-16
❑ 90Hot50PS-32
❑ 90KayB-24
❑ 90KinDis-6
❑ 90Lea-212
❑ 90M.Vpin-61
❑ 90MSAHolD-2
❑ 90OPC-180
❑ 90PanSti-283
❑ 90PubIntS-186
❑ 90Sco-409
❑ 90Sco100S-75
❑ 90Spo-69
❑ 90StaLonJS-23
❑ 90StaLonJS-39
❑ 90SunSee-14
❑ 90SupActM-16
❑ 90Top-180
❑ 90TopAmeA-17
❑ 90TopBatL-7
❑ 90TopBig-154
❑ 90TopCoi-54
❑ 90TopDou-50
❑ 90TopGloS-38
❑ 90TopMinL-63
❑ 90TopSti-69
❑ 90TopStiB-18
❑ 90TopTif-180
❑ 90TopTVA-55
❑ 90UppDec-29
❑ 90UppDec-177
❑ 91BasBesHM-16
❑ 91Bow-362
❑ 91Cla2-T9
❑ 91ClaGam-174
❑ 91DenHol-26
❑ 91Don-457
❑ 91Fle-244
❑ 91FleUpd-15
❑ 91Lea-413
❑ 91OPC-360
❑ 91OPCPre-97
❑ 91PanFreS-143
❑ 91PanSti-63
❑ 91RedFolS-75
❑ 91Sco-35
❑ 91Sco100S-89
❑ 91ScoRoo-10T
❑ 91StaClu-523
❑ 91StaPro-4
❑ 91Stu-37
❑ 91StuPre-4
❑ 91Top-360
❑ 91TopCraJI-3
❑ 91TopDesS-360
❑ 91TopMic-360
❑ 91TopTif-360
❑ 91TopTra-94T
❑ 91TopTraT-94T
❑ 91Ult-81
❑ 91UppDec-143
❑ 91UppDec-773
❑ 91WhiSoxK-30
❑ 92Bow-204
❑ 92ClaGam-99
❑ 92Don-312
❑ 92Fle-97
❑ 92Lea-37
❑ 92LeaBlaG-37
❑ 92OPC-426
❑ 92PanSti-131
❑ 92Pin-178
❑ 92Pin-605
❑ 92RedFolS-78
❑ 92Sco-635
❑ 92StaClu-426
❑ 92Stu-156
❑ 92Top-426
❑ 92TopGol-426
❑ 92TopGolW-426
❑ 92TopKid-104
❑ 92TopMic-426
❑ 92TriPla-107
❑ 92Ult-43
❑ 92UppDec-575
❑ 92WhiSoxK-30
❑ 93Bow-499
❑ 93Don-565
❑ 93ExpDonM-6
❑ 93Fin-183
❑ 93FinRef-183
❑ 93Fle-209
❑ 93FunPac-201
❑ 93Lea-420
❑ 93OPC-290
❑ 93PacSpa-75
❑ 93PanSti-140
❑ 93Pin-53
❑ 93RedFolS-77
❑ 93Sco-658
❑ 93Sel-236
❑ 93SP-259
❑ 93StaClu-43
❑ 93StaCluFDI-43
❑ 93StaCluMOP-43
❑ 93Stu-215
❑ 93Top-675
❑ 93TopGol-675
❑ 93TopInaM-675
❑ 93TopInaR-675
❑ 93TopMic-675
❑ 93TriPla-108
❑ 93Ult-178
❑ 93UppDec-597
❑ 93UppDecGold-597
❑ 93USPlaCA-6H
❑ 93WhiSoxK-24
❑ 93WhiSoxSC-5
❑ 94Bow-127
❑ 94ColC-385
❑ 94ColChoGS-385
❑ 94ColChoSS-385
❑ 94Don-220
❑ 94Don-258
❑ 94Fin-192
❑ 94FinRef-192
❑ 94Fla-35
❑ 94Fle-93
❑ 94FleExtB-52
❑ 94Lea-116
❑ 94LeaL-23
❑ 94OPC-228
❑ 94Pac-136
❑ 94Pin-462
❑ 94PinArtP-462
❑ 94PinMusC-462
❑ 94ProMag-27
❑ 94Sco-379
❑ 94ScoGolR-379
❑ 94Sel-92
❑ 94StaClu-350
❑ 94StaClu-525

❑ 94StaCluFDI-350
❑ 94StaCluFDI-525
❑ 94StaCluGR-350
❑ 94StaCluGR-525
❑ 94StaCluMOP-350
❑ 94StaCluMOP-525
❑ 94StaCluT-136
❑ 94StaCluTFDI-136
❑ 94Stu-208
❑ 94SucSav-4
❑ 94Top-243
❑ 94TopGol-243
❑ 94TopSpa-243
❑ 94TriPla-268
❑ 94Ult-341
❑ 94UppDec-254
❑ 94UppDecAJ-42
❑ 94UppDecAJG-42
❑ 94UppDecED-254
❑ 94WhiSoxK-25
❑ 95Bow-291
❑ 95ColCho-495
❑ 95ColChoGS-495
❑ 95ColChoSS-495
❑ 95Don-75
❑ 95DonPreP-75
❑ 95DonTopotO-53
❑ 95Emo-28
❑ 95Fin-187
❑ 95FinRef-187
❑ 95Fla-248
❑ 95Fle-127
❑ 95Lea-208
❑ 95LeaLim-94
❑ 95Pac-95
❑ 95Sco-112
❑ 95ScoGolR-112
❑ 95ScoPlaTS-112
❑ 95SP-139
❑ 95SPCha-139
❑ 95SPChaDC-139
❑ 95SPSil-139
❑ 95StaClu-302
❑ 95StaClu-410
❑ 95StaCluMOP-302
❑ 95StaCluMOP-410
❑ 95StaCluMOP-RL12
❑ 95StaCluRL-RL12
❑ 95StaCluSTWS-302
❑ 95StaCluSTWS-410
❑ 95StaCluVR-158
❑ 95StaCluVRMO-158
❑ 95Stu-148
❑ 95Top-77
❑ 95TopCyb-54
❑ 95TopEmb-130
❑ 95TopEmbGI-130
❑ 95Ult-33
❑ 95UltGolM-33
❑ 95UppDec-198
❑ 95UppDecED-198
❑ 95UppDecEDG-198
❑ 95UppDecSE-157
❑ 95UppDecSEG-157
❑ 95WhiSoxK-26
❑ 96ColCho-95
❑ 96ColCho-779
❑ 96ColChoGS-95
❑ 96ColChoSS-95
❑ 96Don-384
❑ 96DonPreP-384
❑ 96EmoXL-94
❑ 96Fin-B224
❑ 96FinRef-B224
❑ 96Fla-135
❑ 96Fle-75
❑ 96FleTif-75
❑ 96FleUpd-U66
❑ 96FleUpdTC-U66
❑ 96LeaSig-136
❑ 96LeaSigPPG-136
❑ 96LeaSigPPP-136
❑ 96MetUni-93
❑ 96MetUniP-93
❑ 96MLBPin-28
❑ 96Pac-284
❑ 96PanSti-174
❑ 96Pin-364
❑ 96PinFoil-364
❑ 96Sco-449
❑ 96StaClu-418
❑ 96StaCluEPB-418
❑ 96StaCluEPG-418
❑ 96StaCluEPS-418
❑ 96StaCluMOP-418
❑ 96Stu-59
❑ 96StuPrePB-59
❑ 96StuPrePG-59
❑ 96StuPrePS-59
❑ 96Top-272
❑ 96TopChrMotG-7
❑ 96TopChrMotGR-7
❑ 96TopMasotG-7
❑ 96Ult-43
❑ 96Ult-393
❑ 96UltGolM-43
❑ 96UltGolM-393
❑ 96UppDec-111
❑ 96UppDec-409
❑ 97Cir-292
❑ 97CirRav-292
❑ 97ColCho-182
❑ 97ColChoT-NY7
❑ 97Fle-503
❑ 97FleTif-503
❑ 97Lea-274
❑ 97LeaFraM-274
❑ 97LeaFraMDC-274
❑ 97Pac-157
❑ 97PacLigB-157
❑ 97PacSil-157
❑ 97Sco-391
❑ 97ScoArtPWB-391
❑ 97ScoResC-391
❑ 97ScoShoS-391
❑ 97ScoShoSAP-391
❑ 97Top-334
❑ 97Ult-461
❑ 97UltGolME-461
❑ 97UltPlaME-461
❑ 97UppDec-443
❑ 98ColCho-192
❑ 98DonColL-300
❑ 98DonPriCL-300
❑ 98Fle-437
❑ 98Lea-101
❑ 98LeaFraDA-101
❑ 98LeaFraF-101
❑ 98LeaFraM-101
❑ 98LeaFraM-101
❑ 98LeaFraMDC-101
❑ 98LeaFraMDC-101
❑ 98LeaFraMZ2-101
❑ 98PacOnl-514
❑ 98PacOnlR-514
❑ 98PacOnlWC-514
❑ 98PinSna-NYY6
❑ 98UppDec-449
❑ 98YanUppD-449
❑ 99BowGol-363
❑ 99BowInt-363
❑ 99CroRoyB-104
❑ 99CroRoyL-104
❑ 99CroRoyOD-104
❑ 99Fle-535
❑ 99FleSta9-535
❑ 99FleWarT-535
❑ 99Pac-302
❑ 99PacPar-173
❑ 99PacParC-173
❑ 99PacParG-173
❑ 99PacParHoloGold-173
❑ 99PacParHS-173
❑ 99PacParOD-173
❑ 99PacParPB-173
❑ 99PacParRed-173
❑ 99PacPlaB-302
❑ 99PacRed-302
❑ 99YanFle-9
Raines, Tim Jr.
❑ 99Bow-363
Rainey, Chuck
❑ 80Top-662
❑ 81Top-199
❑ 82Fle-303
❑ 82RedSoxC-15
❑ 82Top-522
❑ 83CubThoAV-30
❑ 83Don-334
❑ 83Fle-192
❑ 83Top-56
❑ 83TopTra-92T
❑ 84Don-76
❑ 84Fle-502
❑ 84Nes792-334
❑ 84OPC-334
❑ 84Top-334
❑ 84TopSti-47
❑ 84TopTif-334
❑ 85Don-618
Rainey, Scott
❑ 83CliGiaF-9
❑ 87WicPilRD-16
Rainout, Chief
❑ 87PeoChiPW-6
Raisanen, Keith
❑ 87WatPirP-8
❑ 88SalBucS-16
❑ 89AugPirP-506
❑ 89SouAtlLAGS-9
❑ 90SalBucS-17
Rajotte, Jason
❑ 95WesMicWTI-20
❑ 96ModA'sB-10
❑ 97HunStaTI-24
Rajsich, Dave
❑ 75ForLauYS-7
❑ 78TacYanC-28
❑ 79Top-710
❑ 80Top-548
❑ 81Don-267
❑ 83OklCit8T-15
❑ 85RocRedWT-21
❑ 86LouRedTI-25
❑ 88LouRedBC-9
❑ 88LouRedBP-443
❑ 88LouRedBTI-41
❑ 89PacSenL-3
❑ 91BelBreCB-26
❑ 91BelBreP-2120
❑ 91PacSenL-154
❑ 91PacSenL-160
❑ 92AugPirF-256
❑ 92YanWIZ7-129
❑ 93RanKee-304
❑ 93SalBucC-27
❑ 93SalBucF-449
❑ 94SalBucC-27
❑ 94SalBucF-2341
❑ 95CarMudF-174
❑ 97CalCanB-3
❑ 98CarMudM-25
Rajsich, Gary
❑ 77CocAstT-20
❑ 80TucTorT-16
❑ 81TidTidT-9
❑ 82MetPhoA-18
❑ 83Don-599
❑ 83Fle-553
❑ 83TidTidT-8
❑ 83Top-317
❑ 84LouRedR-6
❑ 85GiaMot-24
❑ 85GiaPos-25
❑ 87JapPlaB-14
❑ 89PacSenL-7
❑ 89TopSenL-124
❑ 90EliSenL-12
❑ 91MetWIZ-321
❑ 91PacSenL-156
❑ 91PacSenL-160
Rakers, Jason
❑ 95WatIndTI-24
❑ 97IdaFalBTI-14
❑ 97KinIndB-20
❑ 98AkrAerM-14
❑ 98Bow-389
❑ 98BowChr-389
❑ 98BowChrGA-389
❑ 98BowChrGAR-389
❑ 98BowChrI-389
❑ 98BowChrIR-389
❑ 98BowChrR-389
❑ 98BowGolA-389
❑ 98BowInt-389
❑ 98BufBisG-24
❑ 98EasLeaTPM-23
❑ 99Bow-80
❑ 99BowAut-BA16
❑ 99BowChr-80
❑ 99BowChrG-80
❑ 99BowChrGR-80
❑ 99BowChrI-80
❑ 99BowChrIR-80
❑ 99BowChrR-80
❑ 99BowGol-80
❑ 99BowInt-80
❑ 99SpoIll-55
❑ 99Top-429
❑ 99TopChr-429
❑ 99TopChrR-429
❑ 99TopMVPP-429
❑ 99UppDecMP-JRA
Rakow, Ed
❑ 58MonRoyF-18
❑ 59O'KAleMR-16
❑ 60Top-551
❑ 61AthJayP-17
❑ 61Top-147
❑ 62Top-342
❑ 63Jel-90
❑ 63Pos-90
❑ 63Top-82
❑ 64TigJayP-9
❑ 64TigLid-12
❑ 64Top-491
❑ 65Top-454
❑ 90DodTar-643
Raleigh, John
❑ 09ObaT21-353
❑ 11PacCoaBD-52
❑ 11Zee-120
❑ 12HomRunKE-90
❑ 12ObaPreT-102
❑ 12Zee-153
❑ 13Zee-147
Raleigh, Matt (Matthew)
❑ 92JamExpC-23
❑ 92JamExpF-1508
❑ 93JamExpC-18
❑ 94BurBeeC-1
❑ 94BurBeeF-1092
❑ 95Bow-135
❑ 95Exc-225
❑ 95UppDecML-210
❑ 95UppDecMLFS-210
❑ 96FreKeyB-19
❑ 97BinMetB-23
Raley, Dan
❑ 89LakTigS-17
❑ 90LakTigS-20
❑ 91LinDriAA-400
❑ 91LonTigLD-400
❑ 91LonTigP-1894
❑ 92LakTigC-29
❑ 92LakTigF-2295
❑ 93LonTigF-2324
❑ 94LakTigC-29
❑ 94LakTigF-3053
Raley, Tim
❑ 88BelBreGS-5
❑ 89StoPorB-20
❑ 89StoPorCLC-169
❑ 89StoPorP-401
❑ 89StoPorS-9
❑ 90StoPorB-13
❑ 90StoPorCLC-198
❑ 90StoPorP-2198
❑ 91HagSunLD-243
❑ 91HagSunP-2469
❑ 91LinDriAA-243
Rally, Mascot
❑ 90BraDubS-27
❑ 92BraLykS-28
❑ 93BraLykS-30
❑ 94MasMan-13
❑ 95NewHavRTI-NNO
Ralph, Curtis
❑ 90PriWilCTI-21
❑ 91PriWilCC-10
❑ 91PriWilCP-1426
❑ 92ForLauYC-12
❑ 92ForLauYTI-24
❑ 92PriWilCC-25
❑ 92PriWilCF-147
❑ 93PriWilCC-21
❑ 93PriWilCF-654
❑ 94AlbYanF-1439
Ralston, Bill
❑ 74TacTwiC-19
❑ 75TacTwiK-5
Ralston, Bobby (Robert)
❑ 84AriWilP-16
❑ 85OrlTwiT-10
❑ 86TolMudHP-18
❑ 87OrlTwiP-6
❑ 88PorBeaC-21
❑ 88PorBeaP-657
❑ 89PorBeaC-15
❑ 89PorBeaP-232
❑ 90HunStaB-18
❑ 97WilCubB-28
❑ 98WilCubM-28
Ralston, Doc
❑ 11PinT-5-557
Ralston, Kris
❑ 93EugEmeC-21
❑ 93EugEmeF-3854
❑ 94CarLeaAF-CAR22
❑ 94ExcFS7-71
❑ 94WilBluRC-21
❑ 94WilBluRF-300
❑ 95WicWraTI-35
❑ 96OmaRoyB-23
❑ 96SigRooOJTP-T9
Rama, Shelby
❑ 94SpaPhiF-1721
❑ 94SparPhiC-17
❑ 97St.PetDR-26
Ramage, W. C.
❑ 23Zee-169
Ramanouchi, Kenichi
❑ 91SalSpuC-7
❑ 91SalSpuP-2254
Ramazzotti, Bob
❑ 49EurSta-67
❑ 51Bow-247
❑ 52Top-184
❑ 53BowBW-41
❑ 83TopRep5-184
❑ 90DodTar-644
Rambadt, Charles
❑ 90HelBreSP-22
Rambis, Randy
❑ 79WatIndT-17
Rambo, Dan
❑ 90Bes-123
❑ 90CalLeaACLC-53
❑ 90CMC-717
❑ 90ProAaA-145
❑ 90SanJosGB-23
❑ 90SanJosGCLC-44
❑ 90SanJosGP-2006
❑ 90SanJosGS-18
❑ 91LinDriAA-318
❑ 91ShrCapLD-318
❑ 91ShrCapP-1821
❑ 92PhoFirF-2820
❑ 92ShrCapF-3868
❑ 92ShrCapS-590
❑ 92SkyAA F-260
❑ 93LinVenB-86
❑ 93PhoFirF-1515
Rambo, Matt
❑ 87UtiBluSP-26
❑ 88SpaPhiP-1025
❑ 88SpaPhiS-16
❑ 89ClePhiS-17
❑ 91Cla/Bes-53
❑ 91OscAstC-10
❑ 91OscAstP-682
❑ 92JacGenS-346
❑ 92SkyAA F-145
Rametta, Steve
❑ 75SanAntBT-16
Ramey, Jeff
❑ 92BilMusF-3358
❑ 92BilMusSP-17
❑ 93PriRedC-24
❑ 93PriRedF-4189
Ramharter, Steve
❑ 89AncGlaP-21
❑ 90ButCopKSP-17
Ramie, Vern
❑ 82KnoBluJT-17
❑ 83SyrChiT-23
Ramirez, Alex
❑ 76VenLeaS-165
❑ 80OrlTwiT-18
❑ 80VenLeaS-142
Ramirez, Alex (Alexander)
❑ 93BurIndC-21
❑ 93BurIndF-3313
❑ 94Bow-335
❑ 94ColRedC-17
❑ 94ColRedF-458
❑ 94VenLinU-104
❑ 95BakBlaTI-3
❑ 95LinVen-156
❑ 96-97LinVen-204
❑ 96CanIndB-21
❑ 97BufBis-23
❑ 98Bow-326
❑ 98BowChr-326
❑ 98BowChrGA-326
❑ 98BowChrGAR-326
❑ 98BowChrI-326
❑ 98BowChrIR-326
❑ 98BowChrR-326
❑ 98BowGolA-326
❑ 98BowInt-326
❑ 98BufBisG-25
❑ 99Bow-169
❑ 99BowAut-BA15
❑ 99BowChr-169
❑ 99BowChrG-169
❑ 99BowChrGR-169
❑ 99BowChrI-169
❑ 99BowChrIR-169
❑ 99BowChrR-169
❑ 99BowGol-169
❑ 99BowInt-169
Ramirez, Allan (D. Allan)
❑ 80ChaO'sP-17
❑ 80ChaO'sW-18
❑ 82RocRedWT-5
❑ 83OriPos-22
❑ 83RocRedWT-7
❑ 84Don-332
❑ 84Nes792-347
❑ 84RocRedWT-16
❑ 84Top-347
❑ 84TopTif-347
❑ 85ChaO'sT-25
❑ 91OriCro-374
Ramirez, Angel
❑ 93MedHatBJF-3750
❑ 93MedHatBJSP-3
❑ 94HagSunC-19
❑ 94HagSunF-2744
❑ 95DunBluJTI-21
❑ 96BesAutS-76
❑ 96BesAutSA-57
❑ 97BesAutAS-42
❑ 97KnoSmo-19
❑ 98ColCliD-20
❑ 98ColCliM-24
❑ 98NorNavQ-19
Ramirez, Aramis
❑ 96EriSeaB-20
❑ 97Bes-18
❑ 97Bes-91
❑ 97BesAutSBPP-34
❑ 97BesDiaB-12
❑ 97BesLimA-35
❑ 97Bow-310
❑ 97BowChr-214
❑ 97BowChrI-214
❑ 97BowChrIR-214
❑ 97BowChrR-214
❑ 97BowInt-310
❑ 97CarLeaTP-2
❑ 97LynHil-17
❑ 98Bes-40
❑ 98Bes-88
❑ 98BesFulCA-18
❑ 98BesPreA-39
❑ 98Bow-215
❑ 98BowBes-109
❑ 98BowBesAR-109
❑ 98BowBesP-BP9
❑ 98BowBesPAR-BP9
❑ 98BowBesPR-BP9
❑ 98BowBesR-109
❑ 98BowCerBlueAU-59
❑ 98BowCerGA-59
❑ 98BowCerSA-59
❑ 98BowChr-215
❑ 98BowChrGA-215
❑ 98BowChrGAR-215
❑ 98BowChrI-215
❑ 98BowChrIR-215
❑ 98BowChrR-215
❑ 98BowGolA-215
❑ 98BowInt-215
❑ 98BowScoC-SC17
❑ 98DonSig-94
❑ 98DonSigA-72
❑ 98DonSigAC-92
❑ 98DonSigAM-94
❑ 98DonSigP-94
❑ 98FleUpd-U15
❑ 98LeaRS-318
❑ 98LeaRSLHolo-318
❑ 98LeaRSLong-318
❑ 98LeaRTrue-318
❑ 98NasSouTI-26
❑ 98NasSouTISS-24
❑ 98SP MinDTSPE-DS21
❑ 98SP MinPE-9
❑ 98SP MinPE-101
❑ 98SPMin-9
❑ 98SPMin-101
❑ 98SPMinDTS-DS21
❑ 98SpoIllWSF-128
❑ 98SpoIllWSFEE-128
❑ 98SpoIllWSFFE-128
❑ 98Top-488
❑ 98TopChr-488
❑ 98TopChrR-488
❑ 98TopDevR-488
❑ 98TopDia-488

❑ 98TopMiniC-488
❑ 98TopTek-31
❑ 98TopTekD-31
❑ 98UppDecR-129
❑ 98UppDecRNF-NF29
❑ 99199Fin-128
❑ 99199Fin-196
❑ 99Bow-142
❑ 99BowChr-142
❑ 99BowChrG-142
❑ 99BowChrGR-142
❑ 99BowChrI-142
❑ 99BowChrIR-142
❑ 99BowChrR-142
❑ 99BowGol-142
❑ 99BowInt-142
❑ 99FinGolRef-128
❑ 99FinGolRef-196
❑ 99FinRef-128
❑ 99FinRef-196
❑ 99Fle-228
❑ 99FleSta9-228
❑ 99FleWarT-228
❑ 99MetUni-272
❑ 99MetUniGM-272
❑ 99MetUniPMG-272
❑ 99Pac-344
❑ 99PacAur-149
❑ 99PacAurOD-149
❑ 99PacCroC-224
❑ 99PacCroCPB-224
❑ 99PacPlaB-344
❑ 99PacPri-115
❑ 99PacPriHB-115
❑ 99PacPriHG-115
❑ 99PacPriHM-115
❑ 99PacPriHP-115
❑ 99PacPriRed-115
❑ 99PacPriS-130
❑ 99PacPriS206-130
❑ 99PacPriS206R-130
❑ 99PacRed-344
❑ 99SkyThu-146
❑ 99SkyThuRant-146
❑ 99SkyThuRave-146
❑ 99SP Aut-67
❑ 99SP SigAuto-ARA
❑ 99SP SigAutoG-ARA
❑ 99SpoIll-62
❑ 99SPSig-76
❑ 99SPx-62
❑ 99SPxFinR-62
❑ 99SPxFinS-62
❑ 99StaClu-223
❑ 99StaCluFDI-223
❑ 99StaCluOoaK-223
❑ 99StaCluPP-223
❑ 99ThuSkySupR-146
❑ 99Top-113
❑ 99TopChr-113
❑ 99TopChrNB-NB14
❑ 99TopChrNBR-NB14
❑ 99TopChrR-113
❑ 99TopMVPP-113
❑ 99TopNewB-NB14
❑ 99TopSta-95
❑ 99TopSta1Foil-95
❑ 99TopStaFoil-95
❑ 99TopStaOS-95
❑ 99UD Cho-129
❑ 99UD ChoMBH-B22
❑ 99UD ChoPCR-129
❑ 99UD Ion-48
❑ 99UD IonR-48
❑ 99Ult-231
❑ 99UltGolM-231
❑ 99UltMas-231
❑ 99UltPlaM-231
❑ 99UppDec-11
❑ 99UppDecBD-113
❑ 99UppDecBDD-113
❑ 99UppDecBDQ-113
❑ 99UppDecBDT-113
❑ 99UppDecCLM-C75
❑ 99UppDecEL1-11
❑ 99UppDecEL2-11
❑ 99UppDecM-163
❑ 99UppDecMGS-163
❑ 99UppDecMHFS-163
❑ 99UppDecMSC-SC6
❑ 99UppDecMSS-163
❑ 99Vic-314

Ramirez, Daniel
❑ 91KanCouCC-19
❑ 91KanCouCP-2666
❑ 91KanCouCTI-16
❑ 92FreKeyC-27
❑ 92FreKeyF-1814
❑ 93FreKeyC-22
❑ 93FreKeyF-1036
❑ 96PitMetB-22

Ramirez, Daniel E.
❑ 97CapCitB-29
❑ 98St.LucMM-11

Ramirez, Fausto
❑ 86BelMarCr-125
❑ 87BelMarTI-27
❑ 88WauTimGS-3

Ramirez, Felix
❑ 97SarRedS-21

Ramirez, Francisco
❑ 91EliTwiP-4304

Ramirez, Frank
❑ 87IdaFalBP-23

Ramirez, Hector
❑ 91KinMetC-19
❑ 91KinMetP-3811
❑ 92ColMetC-2
❑ 92ColMetF-293
❑ 92ColMetPI-27
❑ 94St.LucMC-19
❑ 94St.LucMF-1194
❑ 95BinMetTI-31
❑ 96BinMetB-23
❑ 97RocRedW-20
❑ 98ChaKniQ-24

Ramirez, Horacio
❑ 98EugEme-21
❑ 98MacBraM-16

Ramirez, J.D.
❑ 89SalLakTTI-11
❑ 90RocExpLC-20
❑ 90RocExpP-2703
❑ 91WesPalBEC-23
❑ 91WesPalBEP-1238
❑ 94MidAngF-2447
❑ 94MidAngOHP-23
❑ 95MidAngOHP-26
❑ 95MidAngTI-23

Ramirez, Jack
❑ 79TulDriT-12

Ramirez, Joel
❑ 94BelMarC-22
❑ 94BelMarF-3246
❑ 95EveAqaTI-17
❑ 96MidLeaAB-5
❑ 96WisTimRB-17
❑ 97LanJet-20
❑ 98LanJetG-18

Ramirez, Jose
❑ 96FayGenB-25
❑ 98WesMicWM-17

Ramirez, Juan
❑ 94KinMetC-16
❑ 94KinMetF-3837

Ramirez, Julio
❑ 96BesAutS-77
❑ 97MidLeaTP-12
❑ 98Bes-89
❑ 98Bow-379
❑ 98BowBes-157
❑ 98BowBesAR-157
❑ 98BowBesR-157
❑ 98BowChr-379
❑ 98BowChrGA-379
❑ 98BowChrGAR-379
❑ 98BowChrI-379
❑ 98BowChrIR-379
❑ 98BowChrR-379
❑ 98BowGolA-379
❑ 98BowInt-379
❑ 98Don-340
❑ 98DonGolPP-340
❑ 98DonSig-121
❑ 98DonSigP-121
❑ 98DonSilPP-340
❑ 98LeaRS-218
❑ 98LeaRSLHolo-218
❑ 98LeaRSLong-218
❑ 98LeaRTrue-218
❑ 98UppDec-573
❑ 99Bow-111
❑ 99BowChr-111
❑ 99BowChrG-111
❑ 99BowChrGR-111
❑ 99BowChrI-111
❑ 99BowChrIR-111
❑ 99BowChrR-111
❑ 99BowGol-111
❑ 99BowInt-111

Ramirez, Leo
❑ 93MacBraC-20
❑ 93MacBraF-1398
❑ 93SouAtlLAGF-42
❑ 94ClaGolF-116

Ramirez, Luis
❑ 78NewWayCT-35
❑ 92GulCoaYF-3792

Ramirez, Luis I.
❑ 98BluOriQ-32

Ramirez, Manny
❑ 91BurIndP-3316
❑ 91ClaDraP-10
❑ 91FroRowDP-47
❑ 91FroRowDPG-47
❑ 91FroRowDPS-47
❑ 91HigSchPLS-7
❑ 92Bow-532
❑ 92Bow-676
❑ 92ClaFS7-155
❑ 92DonRoo-98
❑ 92KinIndF-2488
❑ 92OPC-156
❑ 92Pin-295
❑ 92ProFS7-62
❑ 92Sco-800
❑ 92StaCluD-146
❑ 92Top-156
❑ 92TopGol-156
❑ 92TopGolW-156
❑ 92TopMic-156
❑ 92UppDec-63
❑ 92UppDecML-35
❑ 92UppDecML-55
❑ 92UppDecML-146
❑ 93Bow-365
❑ 93Bow-669
❑ 93CanIndF-2849
❑ 93ClaGolF-124
❑ 93ClaYouG-YG18
❑ 93ExcFS7-164
❑ 93FlaWavotF-13
❑ 93FleFinE-204
❑ 93SP-285
❑ 93Ult-545
❑ 93UppDec-433
❑ 93UppDecGold-433
❑ 94Bow-55
❑ 94Bow-371
❑ 94BowBes-R88
❑ 94BowBes-X107
❑ 94BowBesR-R88
❑ 94BowBesR-X107
❑ 94ColC-16
❑ 94ColChoGS-16
❑ 94ColChoSS-16
❑ 94Don-322
❑ 94Fin-430
❑ 94FinJum-430
❑ 94FinRef-430
❑ 94Fla-43
❑ 94Fle-119
❑ 94FleExtB-66
❑ 94FleExtBRS-16
❑ 94FUnPac-1
❑ 94LeaGolR-6
❑ 94LeaL-30
❑ 94LeaLimRP-9
❑ 94OPC-121
❑ 94OPCHotP-6
❑ 94Pac-183
❑ 94Pin-244
❑ 94PinArtP-244
❑ 94PinMusC-244
❑ 94PinNewG-NG17
❑ 94PinPowS-PS13
❑ 94PinRooTP-6
❑ 94ProMag-39
❑ 94Sco-645
❑ 94ScoBoyoS-38
❑ 94ScoGolR-645
❑ 94ScoRoo-RT72
❑ 94ScoRooGR-RT72
❑ 94ScoRooS-SU2
❑ 94ScoRooSR-SU2
❑ 94Sel-181
❑ 94SelRooS-RS10
❑ 94SP-101
❑ 94SPDieC-101
❑ 94SPHol-31
❑ 94SPHolDC-31
❑ 94Spo-151
❑ 94SpoRoo-R01
❑ 94SpoRooRS-TR2
❑ 94SpoSha-SH12
❑ 94SPPre-CR4
❑ 94StaClu-320
❑ 94StaClu-627
❑ 94StaCluFDI-320
❑ 94StaCluFDI-627
❑ 94StaCluGR-320
❑ 94StaCluGR-627
❑ 94StaCluMOP-320
❑ 94StaCluMOP-627
❑ 94Stu-95
❑ 94Top-216
❑ 94TopGol-216
❑ 94TopSpa-216
❑ 94TopSupS-36
❑ 94TopTraFI-8
❑ 94TriPla-286
❑ 94Ult-351
❑ 94UppDec-23
❑ 94UppDecDC-C5
❑ 94UppDecED-23
❑ 94UppDecMLS-MM16
❑ 94UppDecMLSED-MM16
❑ 94UppDecNG-15
❑ 94UppDecNGED-15
❑ 95Baz-109
❑ 95Bow-352
❑ 95BowBes-R12
❑ 95BowBes-X2
❑ 95BowBesR-R12
❑ 95BowBesR-X2
❑ 95ClaPhoC-18
❑ 95ColCho-275
❑ 95ColChoCtA-7
❑ 95ColChoCtAGR-7
❑ 95ColChoCtG-CG16
❑ 95ColChoCtG-CG16B
❑ 95ColChoCtG-CG16C
❑ 95ColChoCtGE-16
❑ 95ColChoCtGG-CG16
❑ 95ColChoCtGG-CG16B
❑ 95ColChoCtGG-CG16C
❑ 95ColChoCtGGE-16
❑ 95ColChoGS-275
❑ 95ColChoSE-117
❑ 95ColChoSEGS-117
❑ 95ColChoSESS-117
❑ 95ColChoSS-275
❑ 95Don-370
❑ 95DonPreP-370
❑ 95DonTopotO-66
❑ 95Emo-37
❑ 95EmoN-9
❑ 95Fin-4
❑ 95FinPowK-PK5
❑ 95FinRef-4
❑ 95Fla-35
❑ 95FlaTodS-10
❑ 95Fle-145
❑ 95FlePro-6
❑ 95FleRooS-14
❑ 95Lea-280
❑ 95LeaLim-66
❑ 95LeaLimG-23
❑ 95LeaLimIBP-7
❑ 95LeaLimL-14
❑ 95Pac-128
❑ 95PacGolCDC-8
❑ 95PacGolP-32
❑ 95PacLatD-28
❑ 95PacPri-41
❑ 95PanSti-105
❑ 95Pin-287
❑ 95Pin-350
❑ 95PinArtP-287
❑ 95PinArtP-350
❑ 95PinMusC-287
❑ 95PinMusC-350
❑ 95PinPer-PP13
❑ 95PinRedH-RH15
❑ 95PinUps-US11
❑ 95PinWhiH-WH15
❑ 95Sco-445
❑ 95Sco-568
❑ 95ScoAi-AM15
❑ 95ScoGolR-445
❑ 95ScoGolR-568
❑ 95ScoHaloG-HG38
❑ 95ScoPlaTS-445
❑ 95ScoPlaTS-568
❑ 95ScoRul-SR24
❑ 95ScoRulJ-SR24
❑ 95Sel-81
❑ 95SelArtP-81
❑ 95SelCanM-CM5
❑ 95SelCer-48
❑ 95SelCerC-7
❑ 95SelCerMG-48
❑ 95SelCerPU-2
❑ 95SelCerPU9-2
❑ 95SigRooMR-MR4
❑ 95SigRooMRS-MR4
❑ 95SigRooOJSS-10
❑ 95SigRooOJSSS-10
❑ 95SP-151
❑ 95SPCha-150
❑ 95SPChaDC-150
❑ 95Spo-105
❑ 95SpoArtP-105
❑ 95SpoHamT-HT13
❑ 95SpoSam-105
❑ 95SPPlaP-PP15
❑ 95SPSil-151
❑ 95SPSpeF-11
❑ 95StaClu-264
❑ 95StaCluFDI-264
❑ 95StaCluMO-46
❑ 95StaCluMOP-264
❑ 95StaCluSTDW-I264
❑ 95StaCluSTMP-18
❑ 95StaCluSTWS-264
❑ 95StaCluVR-132
❑ 95StaCluVRMO-132
❑ 95Stu-32
❑ 95StuGolS-32
❑ 95Sum-18
❑ 95SumNewA-NA2
❑ 95SumNthD-18
❑ 95Top-577
❑ 95TopCyb-351
❑ 95TopEmb-136
❑ 95TopEmbGI-136
❑ 95UC3-48
❑ 95UC3-134
❑ 95UC3ArtP-48
❑ 95UC3ArtP-134
❑ 95Ult-41
❑ 95UltAllR-9
❑ 95UltAllRGM-9
❑ 95UltGolM-41
❑ 95UltSecYS-11
❑ 95UltSecYSGM-11
❑ 95UppDec-97
❑ 95UppDecED-97
❑ 95UppDecEDG-97
❑ 95UppDecPLL-R35
❑ 95UppDecPLLE-R35
❑ 95UppDecSE-161
❑ 95UppDecSEG-161
❑ 95Zen-69
❑ 95ZenAllS-5
❑ 95ZenZ-10
❑ 96Baz-106
❑ 96Bow-85
❑ 96BowBes-52
❑ 96BowBesAR-52
❑ 96BowBesC-10
❑ 96BowBesCAR-10
❑ 96BowBesCR-10
❑ 96BowBesR-52
❑ 96BowFoi-85
❑ 96Cir-37
❑ 96CirAcc-7
❑ 96CirBos-10
❑ 96CirRav-37
❑ 96ColCho-125
❑ 96ColCho-329
❑ 96ColCho-382T
❑ 96ColChoCtG-CG12
❑ 96ColChoCtG-CG12B
❑ 96ColChoCtG-CG12C
❑ 96ColChoCtGE-CR12
❑ 96ColChoCtGG-CG12
❑ 96ColChoCtGG-CG12B
❑ 96ColChoCtGG-CG12C
❑ 96ColChoCtGGE-CR12
❑ 96ColChoGS-125
❑ 96ColChoGS-329
❑ 96ColChoSS-125
❑ 96ColChoSS-329
❑ 96Don-40
❑ 96DonDiaK-3
❑ 96DonEli-67
❑ 96DonPowA-9
❑ 96DonPowADC-9
❑ 96DonPreP-40
❑ 96DonPurP-7
❑ 96DonSam-6
❑ 96DonSho-8
❑ 96EmoLegoB-7
❑ 96EmoRarB-9
❑ 96EmoXL-55
❑ 96EmoXL-P55
❑ 96Fin-B298
❑ 96Fin-S95
❑ 96FinRef-B298
❑ 96FinRef-S95
❑ 96Fla-74
❑ 96FlaPow-7
❑ 96Fle-99
❑ 96FleChe-6
❑ 96FleLumC-7
❑ 96FleRoaW-6
❑ 96FleTif-99
❑ 96FleTomL-9
❑ 96FleUpd-U236
❑ 96FleUpdH-16
❑ 96FleUpdSS-8
❑ 96FleUpdTC-U236
❑ 96IndFle-15
❑ 96Lea-38
❑ 96LeaAllGMC-13
❑ 96LeaAllGMCG-13
❑ 96LeaGolS-14
❑ 96LeaLim-8
❑ 96LeaLimG-8
❑ 96LeaPicP-4
❑ 96LeaPre-5
❑ 96LeaPreP-5
❑ 96LeaPrePB-38
❑ 96LeaPrePG-38
❑ 96LeaPrePS-38
❑ 96LeaPreSG-77
❑ 96LeaPreSte-77
❑ 96LeaSig-11
❑ 96LeaSigA-188
❑ 96LeaSigAG-188
❑ 96LeaSigAS-188
❑ 96LeaSigPPG-11
❑ 96LeaSigPPP-11
❑ 96MetUni-52
❑ 96MetUniML-7
❑ 96MetUniP-52
❑ 96MetUniPP-9
❑ 96Pac-301
❑ 96PacCraC-CC9
❑ 96PacEstL-EL25
❑ 96PacGolCD-DC6
❑ 96PacHom-HP9
❑ 96PacOctM-OM18
❑ 96PacPri-P98
❑ 96PacPriG-P98
❑ 96PacPriRHS-RH14
❑ 96PanSti-176
❑ 96Pin-46
❑ 96Pin-149
❑ 96Pin-278
❑ 96PinAfi-109
❑ 96PinAfiAP-109
❑ 96PinAfiSP-13
❑ 96PinArtP-18
❑ 96PinArtP-76
❑ 96PinArtP-178
❑ 96PinChrBC-11
❑ 96PinFan-24
❑ 96PinFirR-14
❑ 96PinFoil-278
❑ 96PinPow-16
❑ 96PinProS-14
❑ 96PinSky-17
❑ 96PinSlu-13
❑ 96PinSta-18
❑ 96PinSta-76
❑ 96PinSta-178
❑ 96PinTeaT-4
❑ 96ProSta-59
❑ 96SchDis-6
❑ 96Sco-305
❑ 96ScoAll-19
❑ 96ScoBigB-11
❑ 96ScoDiaA-16
❑ 96ScoDreT-8
❑ 96ScoDugC-B30
❑ 96ScoDugCAP-B30
❑ 96ScoFutF-6
❑ 96ScoGolS-30
❑ 96ScoNumG-12
❑ 96ScoPowP-14
❑ 96ScoRef-6
❑ 96ScoTitT-15
❑ 96Sel-8
❑ 96SelArtP-8
❑ 96SelCer-51
❑ 96SelCerAP-51
❑ 96SelCerCB-51
❑ 96SelCerCR-51
❑ 96SelCerIP-8
❑ 96SelCerMB-51
❑ 96SelCerMG-51
❑ 96SelCerMR-51
❑ 96SelCerSF-14

❑ 96SelEnF-24
❑ 96SelTeaN-1
❑ 96SP-74
❑ 96SPBasH-88
❑ 96Spo-30
❑ 96Spo-113
❑ 96SpoArtP-30
❑ 96SpoArtP-113
❑ 96SpoDouT-11
❑ 96SpoPowS-17
❑ 96SpoPro-15
❑ 96SPSpeFX-43
❑ 96SPSpeFXDC-43
❑ 96SPx-21
❑ 96SPxBoufG-8
❑ 96SPxGol-21
❑ 96StaClu-215
❑ 96StaClu-368
❑ 96StaCluEPB-368
❑ 96StaCluEPG-368
❑ 96StaCluEPS-368
❑ 96StaCluMO-36
❑ 96StaCluMOP-215
❑ 96StaCluMOP-368
❑ 96Stu-114
❑ 96StuMas-4
❑ 96StuPrePB-114
❑ 96StuPrePG-114
❑ 96StuPrePS-114
❑ 96StuStaGS-11
❑ 96Sum-85
❑ 96SumAbo&B-85
❑ 96SumArtP-85
❑ 96SumBigB-10
❑ 96SumBigBM-10
❑ 96SumFoi-85
❑ 96SumHitI-10
❑ 96SumPos-9
❑ 96TeaOut-65
❑ 96Top-400
❑ 96TopChr-161
❑ 96TopChrR-161
❑ 96TopGal-126
❑ 96TopGalPPI-126
❑ 96TopLas-13
❑ 96TopMysF-M10
❑ 96TopMysFR-M10
❑ 96TopRoaW-RW13
❑ 96Ult-53
❑ 96Ult-599
❑ 96UltChe-A7
❑ 96UltCheGM-A7
❑ 96UltFreF-9
❑ 96UltFreFGM-9
❑ 96UltGolM-53
❑ 96UltGolM-599
❑ 96UltHomRK-8
❑ 96UltHomRKGM-8
❑ 96UltHomRKR-8
❑ 96UltHomRKRGM-8
❑ 96UltPowP-7
❑ 96UltPowPGM-7
❑ 96UltRBIK-6
❑ 96UltRBIKGM-6
❑ 96UltRisS-9
❑ 96UltRisSGM-9
❑ 96UppDec-55
❑ 96UppDecBCP-BC20
❑ 96UppDecDD-DD17
❑ 96UppDecDDG-DD17
❑ 96UppDecDDS-DD17
❑ 96UppDecHC-HC6
❑ 96UppDecPD-PD13
❑ 96UppDecPRE-R17
❑ 96UppDecPreR-R17
❑ 96UppDecRunP-RP15
❑ 96Zen-34
❑ 96Zen-142
❑ 96ZenArtP-34
❑ 96ZenArtP-142
❑ 96ZenMoz-18
❑ 96ZenZ-12
❑ 97Bow-34
❑ 97BowBes-62
❑ 97BowBesAR-62
❑ 97BowBesR-62
❑ 97BowChr-29
❑ 97BowChrI-29
❑ 97BowChrIR-29
❑ 97BowChrR-29
❑ 97BowInt-34
❑ 97Cir-280
❑ 97CirBos-14
❑ 97CirRav-280
❑ 97CirSupB-14
❑ 97ColCho-310
❑ 97ColChoAC-15
❑ 97ColChoCtG-11A
❑ 97ColChoCtG-11B
❑ 97ColChoCtG-11C
❑ 97ColChoCtGE-CG11
❑ 97ColChoCtGIW-CG11
❑ 97ColChoNF-NF27
❑ 97ColChoS-6
❑ 97ColChoSR-21
❑ 97ColChoT-CI13
❑ 97ColChoTBS-19
❑ 97ColChoTBSWH-19
❑ 97ColChoTotT-T13
❑ 97Don-11
❑ 97Don-412
❑ 97DonEli-18
❑ 97DonEliGS-18
❑ 97DonEliLaL-9
❑ 97DonGolPP-11
❑ 97DonGolPP-412
❑ 97DonLim-8
❑ 97DonLim-117
❑ 97DonLim-142
❑ 97DonLimE-8
❑ 97DonLimE-117
❑ 97DonLimE-142
❑ 97DonLimENG-142
❑ 97DonLimFotG-9
❑ 97DonPowA-13
❑ 97DonPowADC-13
❑ 97DonPre-38
❑ 97DonPre-180
❑ 97DonPreCttC-38
❑ 97DonPreCttC-180
❑ 97DonPreTB-16
❑ 97DonPreTBG-16
❑ 97DonPreTF-16
❑ 97DonPreTP-16
❑ 97DonPreTPG-16
❑ 97DonPreXP-1A
❑ 97DonRocL-12
❑ 97DonSig-20
❑ 97DonSigA-80
❑ 97DonSigAC-99
❑ 97DonSigAM-99
❑ 97DonSigPPP-20
❑ 97DonSilPP-11
❑ 97DonSilPP-412
❑ 97DonTea-76
❑ 97DonTeaSPE-76
❑ 97DonVxP1-46
❑ 97E-X2-17
❑ 97E-X2ACA-8
❑ 97E-X2Cred-17
❑ 97E-X2EssCre-17
❑ 97Fin-138
❑ 97Fin-265
❑ 97Fin-349
❑ 97FinEmb-138
❑ 97FinEmb-349
❑ 97FinEmbR-138
❑ 97FinEmbR-349
❑ 97FinRef-138
❑ 97FinRef-265
❑ 97FinRef-349
❑ 97FlaShoDC-14
❑ 97FlaShoLC-33
❑ 97FlaShoLeg0-33
❑ 97FlaShoLeg1-33
❑ 97FlaShoM-A33
❑ 97FlaShoM-B33
❑ 97FlaShoM-C33
❑ 97FlaShoR0-33
❑ 97FlaShoR1-33
❑ 97FlaShoR2-33
❑ 97Fle-87
❑ 97Fle-713
❑ 97Fle-728
❑ 97FleNig&D-7
❑ 97FleTif-87
❑ 97FleTif-713
❑ 97FleTif-728
❑ 97IndSco-8
❑ 97IndScoPI-8
❑ 97IndScoPr-8
❑ 97IndScoU-8
❑ 97IndScoUTC-8
❑ 97Lea-105
❑ 97Lea-359
❑ 97LeaFraM-105
❑ 97LeaFraM-359
❑ 97LeaFraMDC-105
❑ 97LeaFraMDC-359
❑ 97LeaWarT-7
❑ 97MetUni-86
❑ 97NewPin-42
❑ 97NewPinAP-42
❑ 97NewPinMC-42
❑ 97NewPinPP-42
❑ 97Pac-78
❑ 97PacLatotML-9
❑ 97PacLigB-78
❑ 97PacPriSL-SL3B
❑ 97PacSil-78
❑ 97Pin-196
❑ 97PinArtP-PP196
❑ 97PinCar-9
❑ 97PinCer-68
❑ 97PinCerLI-19
❑ 97PinCerMBla-68
❑ 97PinCerMBlu-68
❑ 97PinCerMG-68
❑ 97PinCerMR-68
❑ 97PinCerR-68
❑ 97PinFan-FF13
❑ 97PinIns-67
❑ 97PinInsC-4
❑ 97PinInsCE-67
❑ 97PinInsDD-13
❑ 97PinInsDE-67
❑ 97PinMin-14
❑ 97PinMinB-14
❑ 97PinMinCB-14A
❑ 97PinMinCB-14B
❑ 97PinMinCG-14
❑ 97PinMinCGR-14
❑ 97PinMinCN-14
❑ 97PinMinCSS-14
❑ 97PinMinG-14
❑ 97PinMinS-14
❑ 97PinMusC-196
❑ 97PinPastM-16
❑ 97PinPrePla-196
❑ 97PinTotCPB-68
❑ 97PinTotCPG-68
❑ 97PinTotCPR-68
❑ 97PinX-P-61
❑ 97PinX-PF&A-17
❑ 97PinX-PMoS-61
❑ 97PinX-PMP-5
❑ 97PinX-PMW-18
❑ 97PinX-PMWG-18
❑ 97PinX-PMWS-18
❑ 97PinX-PreMPS-5
❑ 97PreCon-11
❑ 97Sco-162
❑ 97Sco-496
❑ 97ScoArtPWB-162
❑ 97ScoArtPWB-496
❑ 97ScoHeatO-13
❑ 97ScoPreS-162
❑ 97ScoResC-496
❑ 97ScoShoS-162
❑ 97ScoShoS-496
❑ 97ScoShoSAP-162
❑ 97ScoShoSAP-496
❑ 97ScoStaaD-17
❑ 97Sel-4
❑ 97SelArtP-4
❑ 97SelCom-4
❑ 97SelRegG-4
❑ 97SelToootT-12
❑ 97SelToootTMB-12
❑ 97SP-60
❑ 97SPInsI-12
❑ 97SPMarM-MM11
❑ 97SpoIII-67
❑ 97SpoIIIEE-67
❑ 97SPSpeF-30
❑ 97SPSpxF-8
❑ 97SPSPxFA-8
❑ 97SPx-21
❑ 97SPxBoufG-9
❑ 97SPxBro-21
❑ 97SPxGol-21
❑ 97SPxGraF-21
❑ 97SPxSil-21
❑ 97SPxSte-21
❑ 97StaClu-244
❑ 97StaCluMat-244
❑ 97StaCluMOP-244
❑ 97Stu-32
❑ 97StuMasS-13
❑ 97StuMasS8-13
❑ 97StuPor8-16
❑ 97StuPrePG-32
❑ 97StuPrePS-32
❑ 97Top-318
❑ 97TopChr-106
❑ 97TopChrDD-DD4
❑ 97TopChrDDR-DD4
❑ 97TopChrR-106
❑ 97TopGal-116
❑ 97TopGalPPI-116
❑ 97TopMem05-39
❑ 97TopSta-35
❑ 97TopStaAM-35
❑ 97UD3-51
❑ 97UD3GenNex-GN20
❑ 97Ult-54
❑ 97UltGolME-54
❑ 97UltHitM-13
❑ 97UltPlaME-54
❑ 97UltTop3-18
❑ 97UltTop3GM-18
❑ 97UppDec-188
❑ 97UppDec-345
❑ 97UppDecAG-AG16
❑ 97UppDecBCP-BC4
❑ 97UppDecHC-HC14
❑ 97UppDecLDC-LD19
❑ 97UppDecMM-A5
❑ 97UppDecPP-PP14
❑ 97UppDecPPJ-PP14
❑ 97UppDecRP-RP16
❑ 97UppDecRSF-RS10
❑ 97UppDecTTS-TS20
❑ 98Bow-284
❑ 98BowBes-14
❑ 98BowBesAR-14
❑ 98BowBesR-14
❑ 98BowChr-284
❑ 98BowChrGA-284
❑ 98BowChrGAR-284
❑ 98BowChrI-284
❑ 98BowChrIR-284
❑ 98BowChrR-284
❑ 98BowChrR-36
❑ 98BowChrRR-36
❑ 98BowGolA-284
❑ 98BowInt-284
❑ 98BowMinLM-MVP9
❑ 98CirThu-24
❑ 98CirThuRav-24
❑ 98CirThuSupRav-24
❑ 98ColCho-75
❑ 98ColChoCtG-CG21A
❑ 98ColChoCtG-CG21B
❑ 98ColChoCtG-CG21C
❑ 98ColChoCtGExch-CG21
❑ 98ColChoCtGIW-CG21
❑ 98ColChoRJ-SQ69
❑ 98ColChoS'-11
❑ 98ColChoSQ-SQ69
❑ 98CroRoy-45
❑ 98CroRoyFoB-9
❑ 98CroRoyFoBA-9
❑ 98Don-131
❑ 98Don-355
❑ 98DonCol-131
❑ 98DonColE-419
❑ 98DonColE-536
❑ 98DonColL-232
❑ 98DonColP-581
❑ 98DonColS-131
❑ 98DonCruG-18
❑ 98DonCruP-18
❑ 98DonCruR-18
❑ 98DonDom-23
❑ 98DonEli-19
❑ 98DonEli-136
❑ 98DonEliA-19
❑ 98DonEliA-136
❑ 98DonEliS-19
❑ 98DonEliS-136
❑ 98DonGolPP-131
❑ 98DonGolPP-355
❑ 98DonLonL-16
❑ 98DonPre-31
❑ 98DonPreGES-11
❑ 98DonPreGX-11
❑ 98DonPreGXDC-11
❑ 98DonPreSeat-31
❑ 98DonPreTW-24
❑ 98DonPriCD-131
❑ 98DonPriCE-419
❑ 98DonPriCE-536
❑ 98DonPriCL-232
❑ 98DonPriCP-581
❑ 98DonProLPI-11
❑ 98DonProLS-8
❑ 98DonSig-55
❑ 98DonSigP-55
❑ 98DonSilPP-131
❑ 98DonSilPP-355
❑ 98E-X2-75
❑ 98E-X2ECFut-75
❑ 98E-X2ECNow-75
❑ 98Fin-244
❑ 98FinNo--244
❑ 98FinNo-R-244
❑ 98FinOve-B5
❑ 98FinOveR-B5
❑ 98FinRef-244
❑ 98FinStaS-SS22
❑ 98FlaShoLeg0-49
❑ 98FlaShoLeg1-49
❑ 98FlaShoLeg2-49
❑ 98FlaShoLeg3-49
❑ 98FlaShoLegM-49
❑ 98FlaShoR0-49
❑ 98FlaShoR1-49
❑ 98FlaShoR2-49
❑ 98FlaShoR3-49
❑ 98Fle-335
❑ 98Fle-388
❑ 98Lea-32
❑ 98LeaCruG-18
❑ 98LeaCruP-18
❑ 98LeaCruR-18
❑ 98LeaFraDA-32
❑ 98LeaFraF-32
❑ 98LeaFraM-32
❑ 98LeaFraM-32
❑ 98LeaFraMDC-32
❑ 98LeaFraMDC-32
❑ 98LeaFraMZ2-32
❑ 98LeaRCMLHDSamp-14
❑ 98LeaRS-4
❑ 98LeaRS-133
❑ 98LeaRSLHolo-4
❑ 98LeaRSLHolo-133
❑ 98LeaRSLong-4
❑ 98LeaRSLong-133
❑ 98LeaRSMLHD-14
❑ 98LeaRSTicMas-16
❑ 98LeaRSTicMasDC-16
❑ 98LeaRTrue-4
❑ 98LeaRTrue-133
❑ 98LeaStaRep-10
❑ 98MetUni-36
❑ 98MetUniPMG-36
❑ 98Pac-78
❑ 98PacAur-32
❑ 98PacAurCube-7
❑ 98PacAurODLC-7
❑ 98PacAurPF-38
❑ 98PacAurPFC-38
❑ 98PacAurPFPB-38
❑ 98PacAurPFR-38
❑ 98PacAurPFS-38
❑ 98PacGolCDC-12
❑ 98PacInv-25
❑ 98PacInvGems-41
❑ 98PacInvPBlue-25
❑ 98PacInvSilv-25
❑ 98PacInvTeam-8
❑ 98PacLatotML-10
❑ 98PacNes-6
❑ 98PacOme-74
❑ 98PacOmeEP-5
❑ 98PacOmeEP1o1-5
❑ 98PacOmeFTF-10
❑ 98PacOmeOnIns-7
❑ 98PacOmeP-5
❑ 98PacOmeR-74
❑ 98PacOnl-229
❑ 98PacOnl-236
❑ 98PacOnlR-229
❑ 98PacOnlR-236
❑ 98PacOnlWC-229
❑ 98PacOnlWC-236
❑ 98PacPar-40
❑ 98PacParC-40
❑ 98PacParG-40
❑ 98PacParHS-40
❑ 98PacParl-30
❑ 98PacParPB-40
❑ 98PacParR-40
❑ 98PacParTC-5
❑ 98PacPlaB-78
❑ 98PacRedT-78
❑ 98PacSil-78
❑ 98PacTeaC-5
❑ 98Pin-45
❑ 98PinArtP-PP42
❑ 98PinIns-108
❑ 98PinInsCE-108
❑ 98PinInsDE-108
❑ 98PinInsSG-11AB
❑ 98PinInsSG-11CD
❑ 98PinInsSG-23AB
❑ 98PinInsSG-23CD
❑ 98PinInsSGS-11AB
❑ 98PinInsSGS-11CD
❑ 98PinInsSGS-23AB
❑ 98PinInsSGS-23CD
❑ 98PinMusC-PP42
❑ 98PinPer-32
❑ 98PinPerBB-15
❑ 98PinPerBBSamp-15
❑ 98PinPerBBSO-15
❑ 98PinPerPP-32
❑ 98PinPerSftF-18
❑ 98PinPlu-119
❑ 98PinPluAP-PP38
❑ 98PinPluGAP-PP38
❑ 98PinPluMAP-PP38
❑ 98PinPreP-45
❑ 98PinSna-CI1
❑ 98Revo-46
❑ 98RevoFP-5
❑ 98RevoShow-6
❑ 98RevoSS-46
❑ 98ScoComP-10A
❑ 98ScoComP-10B
❑ 98ScoComP-10C
❑ 98ScoComPG-10A
❑ 98ScoComPG-10B
❑ 98ScoComPG-10C
❑ 98ScoRT-40
❑ 98ScoRTSS-PP40
❑ 98ScoRTSSAP-PP40
❑ 98ScoRTSSAP1-PP40
❑ 98SP Aut-79
❑ 98SP Aut-SD18
❑ 98SP AutSD-SD18
❑ 98SP AutSDT-SD18
❑ 98SpoIll-103
❑ 98SpoIllC-C5
❑ 98SpoIllEE-103
❑ 98SpoIllFE-103
❑ 98SpoIllTaN-122
❑ 98SpoIllTaNEE-122
❑ 98SpoIllWSF-118
❑ 98SpoIllWSFEE-118
❑ 98SpoIllWSFFE-118
❑ 98SPxFin-43
❑ 98SPxFin-77
❑ 98SPxFin-153
❑ 98SPxFin-224
❑ 98SPxFinR-43
❑ 98SPxFinR-77
❑ 98SPxFinR-153
❑ 98SPxFinR-224
❑ 98SPxFinS-43
❑ 98SPxFinS-77
❑ 98SPxFinS-153
❑ 98SPxFinS-224
❑ 98StaCluFDI-91
❑ 98StaCluI-91
❑ 98StaCluNC-NC18
❑ 98StaCluOneK-91
❑ 98StaCluPP-91
❑ 98StaCluTIII-T8B
❑ 98StaCluTLme-T8B
❑ 98StaCluTLmo-T8B
❑ 98Stu-164
❑ 98StuGPP-164
❑ 98StuHitPar-5
❑ 98StuSPP-164
❑ 98Top-125
❑ 98TopChr-125
❑ 98TopChrR-125
❑ 98TopDevR-125
❑ 98TopDia-125
❑ 98TopGal-132
❑ 98TopGalGP-132
❑ 98TopGalOPP-132
❑ 98TopGalPPI-132
❑ 98TopGalPPIA-132
❑ 98TopGolLabC1-94
❑ 98TopGolLabC1B-94
❑ 98TopGolLabC1One-94
❑ 98TopGolLabC1R-94
❑ 98TopGolLabC2-94
❑ 98TopGolLabC2B-94
❑ 98TopGolLabC2One-94
❑ 98TopGolLabC2R-94
❑ 98TopGolLabC3-94
❑ 98TopGolLabC3B-94
❑ 98TopGolLabC3One-94
❑ 98TopGolLabC3R-94
❑ 98TopMiniC-125
❑ 98TopOpeD-61
❑ 98TopSta-109
❑ 98TopSta'S-33
❑ 98TopSta'SGH-33
❑ 98TopStaB-109
❑ 98TopStaG-109

❑ 98TopStaGR-109
❑ 98TopStaS-109
❑ 98TopStaSteG-33
❑ 98TopTek-66
❑ 98TopTekD-66
❑ 98UD3-41
❑ 98UD3-131
❑ 98UD3-221
❑ 98UD3DieCut-41
❑ 98UD3DieCut-131
❑ 98UD3DieCut-221
❑ 98Ult-205
❑ 98UltBigS-9
❑ 98UltDouT-20
❑ 98UltGolM-205
❑ 98UltMas-205
❑ 98UltPlaM-205
❑ 98UppDec-350
❑ 98UppDec10AP-46
❑ 98UppDec1APR-46
❑ 98UppDecAC-AS14
❑ 98UppDecAG-AG24
❑ 98UppDecAGDC-AG24
❑ 98UppDecNP-NP9
❑ 98UppDecR-30
❑ 98UppDecRBBop-BB9
❑ 98UppDecRTC-TC11
❑ 98UppDecTMT-11
❑ 98UppDecTMTG-11
❑ 98Zen-47
❑ 98Zen5 xx7-56
❑ 98Zen5x7GoldImp-56
❑ 98Zen5x7Imp-56
❑ 98ZenZ-G-47
❑ 98ZenZ-S-47
❑ 99199Fin-15
❑ 99AllMysFR-M17
❑ 99AurOn DL-6
❑ 99AurPenF-8
❑ 99AurPenF-8
❑ 99AurPenFB-8
❑ 99AurPenFS-8
❑ 99AurSty-8
❑ 99Bow-35
❑ 99BowBes-27
❑ 99BowBesAR-27
❑ 99BowBesR-27
❑ 99BowChr-35
❑ 99BowChrG-35
❑ 99BowChrGR-35
❑ 99BowChrI-35
❑ 99BowChrIR-35
❑ 99BowChrR-35
❑ 99BowGol-35
❑ 99BowInt-35
❑ 99CroRoyB-45
❑ 99CroRoyL-45
❑ 99CroRoyOD-45
❑ 99CroRoyPotG-9
❑ 99CroRoyPP-9
❑ 99CroRoyPPN-9
❑ 99E-X Cen-90
❑ 99E-X CenECFut-90
❑ 99E-X CenECNow-90
❑ 99FinGolRef-15
❑ 99FinProF-PF8
❑ 99FinRef-15
❑ 99FinSplS-SS6
❑ 99FinSplSDR-SS6
❑ 99FlaShoLeg1-40
❑ 99FlaShoLeg2-40
❑ 99FlaShoLeg3-40
❑ 99FlaShoLegM1-40
❑ 99FlaShoLegM2-40
❑ 99FlaShoLegM3-40
❑ 99FlaShoMoG-11
❑ 99FlaShoR1-40
❑ 99FlaShoR2-40
❑ 99FlaShoR3-40
❑ 99Fle-35
❑ 99FleBri-28
❑ 99FleBri2G-28
❑ 99FleBriBlu-28
❑ 99FleBriGol-28
❑ 99FleBriSS-15
❑ 99FleBriSSP-15
❑ 99FleMys-53
❑ 99FleMysD-9
❑ 99FleMysG-53
❑ 99FleMysM-53
❑ 99FleSta9-35
❑ 99FleVin'-35
❑ 99FleWarT-35
❑ 99HomHer-16
❑ 99MetUni-211
❑ 99MetUniGM-211
❑ 99MetUniPMG-211
❑ 99Pac-134
❑ 99Pac-134A
❑ 99PacAur-54
❑ 99PacAurOD-54
❑ 99PacCroC-88
❑ 99PacCroC-8
❑ 99PacCroCITC-6
❑ 99PacCroCPB-88
❑ 99PacCroCTC-9
❑ 99PacCroCTM-6
❑ 99PacGolCDC-8
❑ 99PacInv-46
❑ 99PacInvFP-8
❑ 99PacInvOD-46
❑ 99PacInvPB-46
❑ 99PacInvSF-8
❑ 99PacInvSF-8B
❑ 99PacInvSH-8
❑ 99PacInvSH-8B
❑ 99PacInvTA-7
❑ 99PacOme-75
❑ 99PacOme5T-13
❑ 99PacOme5TT-13
❑ 99PacOmeC-75
❑ 99PacOmeDM-13
❑ 99PacOmeEP-8
❑ 99PacOmeEP1o1-8
❑ 99PacOmeG-75
❑ 99PacOmeH'-8
❑ 99PacOmePB-75
❑ 99PacPar-75
❑ 99PacParC-75
❑ 99PacParFC-8
❑ 99PacParG-75
❑ 99PacParHoloGold-75
❑ 99PacParHS-75
❑ 99PacParOD-75
❑ 99PacParPB-13
❑ 99PacParPB-75
❑ 99PacParRed-75
❑ 99PacParTC-9
❑ 99PacPlaB-134
❑ 99PacPlaB-134A
❑ 99PacPri-45
❑ 99PacPriAotG-9
❑ 99PacPriHB-45
❑ 99PacPriHG-45
❑ 99PacPriHM-45
❑ 99PacPriHP-45
❑ 99PacPriRed-45
❑ 99PacPriS-14
❑ 99PacPriS206-14
❑ 99PacPriS206R-14
❑ 99PacPriSE-14
❑ 99PacPriSP-14
❑ 99PacPriSP-14
❑ 99PacPriSV-14
❑ 99PacRed-134
❑ 99PacRed-134A
❑ 99PacTeaC-5
❑ 99Rev-45
❑ 99RevDiaL-12
❑ 99RevFouP-7
❑ 99RevPremDate-45
❑ 99RevRet-45
❑ 99RevShaSS-45
❑ 99RevThoitS-8
❑ 99RevTri-13
❑ 99RevTri-13
❑ 99SkyMolM-121
❑ 99SkyMolMF-21
❑ 99SkyMolMFS-21
❑ 99SkyMolMFT-21
❑ 99SkyMolMX-121
❑ 99SkyPre-18
❑ 99SkyPreR-18
❑ 99SkyThu-246
❑ 99SkyThuDial1-D7
❑ 99SkyThuRant-246
❑ 99SkyThuRave-246
❑ 99SkyThuTur-TC7
❑ 99SP Aut-27
❑ 99SP AutEF-E13
❑ 99SP AutHRC-HR9
❑ 99SP AutR-R13
❑ 99SP SigAuto-MR
❑ 99SP SigAutoG-MR
❑ 99SPAutHRCDC-HR9
❑ 99SpoIll-166
❑ 99SpoIllF4-9
❑ 99SpoIllF4E-9
❑ 99SpoIllH-10
❑ 99SPSig-25
❑ 99SPx-35
❑ 99SPxFinR-35
❑ 99SPxFinS-35
❑ 99SPxPowE-PE12
❑ 99SPxStaF-SF11
❑ 99StaClu-205
❑ 99StaCluC-SCC11
❑ 99StaCluCR-SCC11
❑ 99StaCluFDI-205
❑ 99StaCluOoaK-205
❑ 99StaCluPP-205
❑ 99ThuSkySupR-246
❑ 99Top-15
❑ 99Top-455
❑ 99TopAll-AM9
❑ 99TopAllMF-M17
❑ 99TopBlaLC1-82
❑ 99TopBlaLC2-82
❑ 99TopBlaLC3-82
❑ 99TopChr-15
❑ 99TopChr-455
❑ 99TopChrA-AE9
❑ 99TopChrAR-AE9
❑ 99TopChrF1-FF15
❑ 99TopChrF1R-FF15
❑ 99TopChrR-15
❑ 99TopChrR-455
❑ 99TopGal-46
❑ 99TopGalE-E15
❑ 99TopGalPP-46
❑ 99TopGalPPI-46
❑ 99TopGolL-82
❑ 99TopGolLC1-82
❑ 99TopGolLC2-82
❑ 99TopGolLOtO-82
❑ 99TopMVPP-15
❑ 99TopMVPP-455
❑ 99TopOpeD-10
❑ 99TopPowB-PB18
❑ 99TopPowBR-PB18
❑ 99TopRedLC1-82
❑ 99TopRedLC2-82
❑ 99TopRedLC3-82
❑ 99TopSta-26
❑ 99TopSta-159
❑ 99TopSta'S-10
❑ 99TopSta'SG-10
❑ 99TopSta'SGDH-10
❑ 99TopSta1Foil-26
❑ 99TopSta2Foil-26
❑ 99TopStaFoil-26
❑ 99TopStaFoil-159
❑ 99TopStaOS-26
❑ 99TopStaTS-26
❑ 99TopSupC-3
❑ 99TopSupCR-3
❑ 99TopTek-32A
❑ 99TopTek-32B
❑ 99TopTekG-32A
❑ 99TopTekG-32B
❑ 99UD Cho-76
❑ 99UD ChoP-76
❑ 99UD ChoPCR-76
❑ 99UD ChoYW-Y10
❑ 99UD Ion-21
❑ 99UD Ion-73
❑ 99UD IonR-21
❑ 99UD IonR-73
❑ 99UDHolo-19
❑ 99UDHoloAUsome-19
❑ 99Ult-103
❑ 99UltGolM-103
❑ 99UltMas-103
❑ 99UltPlaM-103
❑ 99UltRBIK-9
❑ 99UppDec-351
❑ 99UppDecCf7-28
❑ 99UppDecCf7-77
❑ 99UppDecCf7-C22
❑ 99UppDecCf7Cf7P-C22
❑ 99UppDecCf7LL-L29
❑ 99UppDecCL-89
❑ 99UppDecCLCC-89
❑ 99UppDecCLM-C28
❑ 99UppDecCo7CE-28
❑ 99UppDecCo7CE-77
❑ 99UppDecE-28
❑ 99UppDecE-142
❑ 99UppDecEFXG-28
❑ 99UppDecEFXG-142
❑ 99UppDecEL1-351
❑ 99UppDecEL2-351
❑ 99UppDecEPE-P11
❑ 99UppDecGJ-MR
❑ 99UppDecIP-I19
❑ 99UppDecIPD-I19
❑ 99UppDecIPHR-I19
❑ 99UppDecIPT-I19
❑ 99UppDecM-66
❑ 99UppDecM-P13
❑ 99UppDecMGS-66
❑ 99UppDecMHFS-66
❑ 99UppDecMP-66
❑ 99UppDecMSS-66
❑ 99UppDecR-24
❑ 99UppDecRG-24
❑ 99UppDecRI-MR
❑ 99UppDecRIL2-MR
❑ 99UppDecRP-24
❑ 99UppDecVtaT-V11
❑ 99UppDecVtaTD-V11
❑ 99UppDecVtaTQ-V11
❑ 99UppDecVtaTT-V11
❑ 99UppDecWY-W22
❑ 99UppDecWYD-W22
❑ 99UppDecWYHR-W22
❑ 99UppDecWYT-W22
❑ 99Vic-116
❑ 99Vic-117

Ramirez, Mario
❑ 76WauMetT-22
❑ 77LynMetT-23
❑ 78TidTidT-20
❑ 79TidTidT-12
❑ 81HawIslT-23
❑ 83PadTeal-20
❑ 84Fle-309
❑ 84Nes792-94
❑ 84PadMot-23
❑ 84Top-94
❑ 84TopTif-94
❑ 85PadMot-16
❑ 85Top-427
❑ 85TopTif-427
❑ 86Don-568
❑ 86TolMudHP-19
❑ 86Top-262
❑ 86TopTif-262
❑ 91MetWIZ-322

Ramirez, Milt
❑ 70CarTeal-21
❑ 71MLBOffS-281
❑ 71OPC-702
❑ 71Top-702
❑ 76VenLeaS-120
❑ 77SanJosMC-5
❑ 80OgdA'sT-14

Ramirez, Nelson
❑ 90HunCubP-3280

Ramirez, Nick
❑ 88ChaWheB-26
❑ 88GenCubP-1634

Ramirez, Omar
❑ 91WatIndC-27
❑ 91WatIndP-3382
❑ 92KinIndC-4
❑ 93CanIndF-2850
❑ 93ExcFS7-165
❑ 93LimRocDP-P3
❑ 93LimRocDWB-113
❑ 93LimRocDWB-149
❑ 94ChaKniF-908
❑ 94Cla-59
❑ 94ExcFS7-49
❑ 94UppDecML-172
❑ 94UppDecMLPotYF-PY12

Ramirez, Orlando
❑ 75CalAngP-30
❑ 76SSP-197
❑ 77Top-131

Ramirez, Pete
❑ 96BurBeeTI-13
❑ 97SanJosG-16

Ramirez, Rafael
❑ 78GreBraT-20
❑ 79SavBraT-23
❑ 80RicBraT-2
❑ 81BraPol-16
❑ 81Fle-266
❑ 81Top-192
❑ 82BraBurKL-21
❑ 82BraPol-16
❑ 82Don-546
❑ 82Fle-447
❑ 82Top-536
❑ 83AllGamPI-112
❑ 83BraPol-16
❑ 83Don-310
❑ 83Fle-146
❑ 83FleSta-156
❑ 83FleSti-85
❑ 83Top-439
❑ 84AllGamPI-23
❑ 84BraPol-16
❑ 84Don-589
❑ 84Fle-190
❑ 84FleSti-26
❑ 84Nes792-234
❑ 84OPC-234
❑ 84raPho-26
❑ 84Top-234
❑ 84TopSti-33
❑ 84TopTif-234
❑ 85AllGamPI-113
❑ 85BraHos-20
❑ 85BraPol-16
❑ 85Don-141
❑ 85Fle-339
❑ 85Lea-86
❑ 85OPC-232
❑ 85Top-647
❑ 85TopSti-27
❑ 85TopTif-647
❑ 86BraPol-16
❑ 86Don-263
❑ 86Fle-526
❑ 86OPC-107
❑ 86Top-107
❑ 86TopSti-42
❑ 86TopTat-11
❑ 86TopTif-107
❑ 87BraSmo-18
❑ 87Don-202
❑ 87Fle-526
❑ 87FleGlo-526
❑ 87Top-31
❑ 87Top-76
❑ 87TopSti-42
❑ 87TopTif-31
❑ 87TopTif-76
❑ 88AstMot-17
❑ 88AstPol-18
❑ 88Don-448
❑ 88FleUpd-91
❑ 88FleUpdG-91
❑ 88OPC-379
❑ 88PanSti-247
❑ 88Sco-426
❑ 88ScoGlo-426
❑ 88ScoRoo-12T
❑ 88ScoRooG-12T
❑ 88StaLinAst-13
❑ 88Top-379
❑ 88TopTif-379
❑ 88TopTra-90T
❑ 88TopTraT-90T
❑ 89AstLenH-16
❑ 89AstMot-16
❑ 89AstSmo-32
❑ 89Bow-330
❑ 89BowTif-330
❑ 89Don-509
❑ 89DonBasB-64
❑ 89Fle-365
❑ 89FleGlo-365
❑ 89OPC-261
❑ 89PanSti-90
❑ 89Sco-113
❑ 89Top-749
❑ 89TopBig-268
❑ 89TopSti-17
❑ 89TopTif-749
❑ 89UppDec-341
❑ 90AstLenH-19
❑ 90AstMot-19
❑ 90Don-241
❑ 90DonBesN-77
❑ 90Fle-234
❑ 90FleCan-234
❑ 90Lea-135
❑ 90OPC-558
❑ 90PanSti-266
❑ 90PubIntS-99
❑ 90Sco-42
❑ 90Top-558
❑ 90TopBig-183
❑ 90TopSti-18
❑ 90TopTif-558
❑ 90UppDec-144
❑ 91AstMot-19
❑ 91Bow-564
❑ 91Don-586
❑ 91Fle-513
❑ 91OPC-423
❑ 91PanFreS-10
❑ 91Sco-305
❑ 91StaClu-107
❑ 91StaCluP-33
❑ 91Top-423
❑ 91TopDesS-423
❑ 91TopMic-423
❑ 91TopTif-423
❑ 91Ult-139
❑ 91UppDec-210
❑ 92AstMot-19
❑ 92Sco-388
❑ 92StaClu-451
❑ 92Ult-495
❑ 92UppDec-582
❑ 93PacSpa-127

Ramirez, Randy
❑ 84ChaLooT-21

Ramirez, Ray
❑ 86OrlTwiP-16
❑ 87OklCit8P-24
❑ 88OklCit8P-51
❑ 89OklCit8P-1533
❑ 90CMC-174
❑ 90OklCit8C-24

Ramirez, Rich
❑ 95ModA'sTI-22
❑ 96ModA'sB-29

Ramirez, Richard
❑ 87GasRanP-23
❑ 93BurIndC-22
❑ 93BurIndF-3307

Ramirez, Roberto
❑ 91CliGiaP-848
❑ 91EveGiaC-27
❑ 91EveGiaP-3922
❑ 92SouOreAF-3422
❑ 94RivPilCLC-20
❑ 95PorCitRTI-19
❑ 96PorCitRB-23
❑ 97VisOakG-24

Ramirez, Roberto Pitcher
❑ 91WelPirC-24
❑ 91WelPirP-3571
❑ 94CarMudF-1578
❑ 99DumSet-102
❑ 99FleMys-102
❑ 99FleMysM-102

Ramirez, Russell
❑ 78NewWayCT-36
❑ 79BurBeeT-2

Ramirez, Victor
❑ 85DomLeaS-75
❑ 92ButCopKSP-30
❑ 92KinIndF-2489

Ramon, Julio
❑ 87OneYanP-16

Ramon, Ray
❑ 86ReaPhiP-22

Ramos, Bobby (Roberto)
❑ 75WesPalBES-7
❑ 79SalLakCGT-21B
❑ 80ExpPos-23
❑ 81ExpPos-10
❑ 81Fle-162
❑ 81OPC-136
❑ 81Top-479
❑ 82ColCliP-31
❑ 82ColCliT-18
❑ 82Fle-203
❑ 82OPC-354
❑ 82Top-354
❑ 83ExpPos-24
❑ 83ExpStu-20
❑ 83TopTra-93T
❑ 84Don-209
❑ 84ExpPos-23
❑ 84ExpStu-9
❑ 84Fle-282
❑ 84Nes792-32
❑ 84OPC-32
❑ 84Top-32
❑ 84TopTif-32
❑ 85EdmTraC-15
❑ 85OPC-269
❑ 85Top-407
❑ 85TopTif-407
❑ 86IowCubP-24
❑ 87OmaRoyP-21
❑ 88PhoFirC-13
❑ 88PhoFirP-69
❑ 89ColMudB-20
❑ 89ColMudP-121
❑ 89ColMudS-24
❑ 89PacSenL-65
❑ 89TopSenL-18
❑ 90OscAstS-29
❑ 91OscAstC-20
❑ 92YanWIZ8-152

❑ 93AshTouC-25
❑ 93AshTouF-2293
Ramos, Cesar
❑ 93BurIndC-23
❑ 93BurIndF-3297
❑ 94ColRedC-18
❑ 94ColRedF-441
Ramos, Domingo
❑ 76ForLauYS-9
❑ 77WesHavYT-19
❑ 78TacYanC-17
❑ 79SyrChiT-6
❑ 79SyrChiTI-1
❑ 80SyrChiT-22
❑ 81SyrChiTI-17
❑ 82SalLakCGT-16
❑ 84Don-440
❑ 84MarMot-18
❑ 84Nes792-194
❑ 84Top-194
❑ 84TopTif-194
❑ 85DomLeaS-146
❑ 85MarMot-12
❑ 85Top-349
❑ 85TopTif-349
❑ 86MarMot-12
❑ 86Top-462
❑ 86TopTif-462
❑ 87MarMot-21
❑ 87Top-641
❑ 87TopTif-641
❑ 88ColSprSSC-16
❑ 88ColSprSSP-1534
❑ 88Don-622
❑ 88FleUpd-23
❑ 88FleUpdG-23
❑ 88IndTeal-28
❑ 88Sco-362
❑ 88ScoGlo-362
❑ 88Top-206
❑ 88TopTif-206
❑ 89CubMar-15
❑ 90CubMar-16
❑ 90Don-491
❑ 90Lea-440
❑ 90OPC-37
❑ 90Sco-489
❑ 90Top-37
❑ 90TopTif-37
❑ 90TopTVCu-24
❑ 90UppDec-150
❑ 91Fle-429
❑ 91OPC-541
❑ 91Top-541
❑ 91TopDesS-541
❑ 91TopMic-541
❑ 91TopTif-541
❑ 91UppDec-85
❑ 92YanWIZ7-130
Ramos, Eddie
❑ 91Cla/Bes-440
❑ 91ClaDraP-45
❑ 91FroRowDP-33
❑ 91FroRowDPG-33
❑ 91FroRowDPS-33
❑ 92AshTouC-15
❑ 92ClaFS7-382
❑ 92StaCluD-147
❑ 93QuaCitRBC-16
❑ 93QuaCitRBF-109
❑ 94QuaCitRBC-17
❑ 94QuaCitRBF-544
Ramos, Edgar
❑ 94QuaCitRBC-18
❑ 94QuaCitRBF-531
❑ 95QuaCitRBTI-20
❑ 96KisCobB-21
❑ 97Fle-649
❑ 97FleTif-649
❑ 98JacGenM-18
Ramos, George
❑ 78GreBraT-21
Ramos, Jairo
❑ 91MedHatBJP-4116
❑ 91MedHatBJSP-8
❑ 93LinVenB-27
❑ 94VenLinU-89
❑ 95LinVen-223
❑ 96-97LinVen-229
Ramos, John
❑ 87PriWilYP-28
❑ 88CarLeaAS-15
❑ 88PriWilYS-20
❑ 89AlbYanB-13
❑ 89AlbYanP-336
❑ 89AlbYanSt-15
❑ 89EasLeaAP-22
❑ 89Sta-100
❑ 90AlbYanB-12
❑ 90AlbYanP-1177
❑ 90AlbYanSt-13
❑ 90Bes-152
❑ 90EasLeaAP-EL42
❑ 91AlbYanCB-4
❑ 91ColCliLD-115
❑ 91ColCliP-15
❑ 91ColCliP-599
❑ 91LinDriAAA-115
❑ 91Ult-385
❑ 92ColCliF-356
❑ 92ColCliP-14
❑ 92ColCliS-113
❑ 92Don-15
❑ 92Fle-242
❑ 92ProFS7-105
❑ 92Sco-818
❑ 92ScoRoo-8
❑ 92SkyAAAF-53
❑ 92TopDeb91-142
❑ 92TopGol-658
❑ 92TopGolW-658
❑ 94LasVegSF-875
❑ 95SyrChiTI-20
❑ 96SyrChiTI-24
Ramos, Jorge
❑ 90SouBenWSB-8
❑ 90SouBenWSGS-14
❑ 91SouBenWSC-4
❑ 91SouBenWSP-2864
Ramos, Jose
❑ 87FayGenP-2
❑ 88FayGenP-1086
❑ 89LonTigP-1387
❑ 90CMC-384
❑ 90ProAAAF-376
❑ 90TolMudHC-7
❑ 90TolMudHP-146
❑ 90WicStaSGD-30
❑ 91LinDriAA-394
❑ 91LonTigLD-394
❑ 91LonTigP-1877
❑ 92LonTigS-414
❑ 93LinVenB-73
❑ 95LinVen-243
❑ 96-97LinVen-214
Ramos, Kelly
❑ 98PitMetM-25
Ramos, Ken
❑ 88NebCor-14
❑ 90CarLeaA-43
❑ 90KinIndTI-9
❑ 91CanIndLD-97
❑ 91CanIndP-991
❑ 91LinDriAA-97
❑ 92CanIndF-702
❑ 92CanIndS-115
❑ 93Bow-473
❑ 93ChaKniF-558
❑ 93ClaFS7-239
❑ 93ClaGolF-7
❑ 93ExcFS7-166
❑ 93ExcLeaLF-20
❑ 94TucTorF-776
❑ 94VenLinU-224
❑ 95TucTotTI-21
❑ 96TusTorB-21
❑ 98NewOrlZM-18
Ramos, Luis
❑ 90IBAWorA-19
Ramos, Papo
❑ 92EveGiaC-17
❑ 92EveGiaF-1704
❑ 93CliGiaC-18
Ramos, Pedro
❑ 56Top-49
❑ 57Top-326
❑ 58SeaTeal-23
❑ 58SenJayP-10
❑ 58Top-331
❑ 59SenTealW-14
❑ 59Top-78
❑ 59Top-291
❑ 59TopVen-78
❑ 60Lea-21
❑ 60SenJayP-12
❑ 60Top-175
❑ 60TopVen-175
❑ 61Pos-98A
❑ 61Pos-98B
❑ 61Top-50
❑ 61Top-528
❑ 61TopStal-184
❑ 61TwiCloD-22
❑ 61TwiPetM-3
❑ 61TwiUniMC-12
❑ 62IndJayP-11
❑ 62Top-485
❑ 62TopBuc-74
❑ 62TopStal-79
❑ 63ReqKP-13
❑ 63Top-14
❑ 64IndJayP-9
❑ 64Kah-23
❑ 64Top-562
❑ 65ChaTheY-18
❑ 65OPC-13
❑ 65Top-13
❑ 66Top-439
❑ 67OPC-187
❑ 67Top-187
❑ 78TCM60I-38
❑ 89PacSenL-68
❑ 89PacSenL-217
❑ 92YanWIZ6-100
Ramos, Richard
❑ 82WicAerTI-14
❑ 83WicAerDS-16
Ramos, Wolf
❑ 80ElmPioRST-24
❑ 80VenLeaS-12
Ramppen, Frank
❑ 83VisOakF-7
Ramsay, Robert
❑ 97SarRedS-22
❑ 98TreThuM-18
Ramsberger, Thomas
❑ 98OrlRayM-26
Ramsdell, Willie (J. Willard)
❑ 49W72HolS-17
❑ 51Bow-251
❑ 52Bow-22
❑ 52Top-114
❑ 53MotCoo-3
❑ 79TCM50-279
❑ 83TopRep5-114
❑ 90DodTar-645
Ramsey, Bill
❑ 47SigOil-66
❑ 47SigOil-84
❑ 47SunBre-18
Ramsey, C. A.
❑ 26Zee-171
❑ 27Zee-143
Ramsey, Fernando
❑ 87GenCubP-10
❑ 88ChaWheB-22
❑ 89PeoChiTI-21
❑ 89PeoChiTI-25
❑ 90WinSpiTI-11
❑ 91ChaKniLD-139
❑ 91ChaKniP-1701
❑ 91LinDriAA-139
❑ 92IowCubF-4061
❑ 92IowCubS-216
❑ 92ProFS7-203
❑ 92SkyAAAF-104
❑ 93CubStaC-29
❑ 93Don-539
❑ 93IowCubF-2145
❑ 93LinVenB-174
❑ 93Pin-273
❑ 93UppDec-382
❑ 93UppDecGold-382
❑ 95NasSouTI-17
❑ 96NasSouB-17
Ramsey, Jeff
❑ 90RocExpLC-21
❑ 90RocExpP-2707
Ramsey, Matthew
❑ 89MisStaB-32
❑ 90MisStaB-34
Ramsey, Mike (Michael James)
❑ 87AlbDukD-30
❑ 88AlbDukCm-14
❑ 88AlbDukP-267
❑ 88BlaYNPRWLU-43
❑ 88Sco-267
❑ 88ScoGlo-267
❑ 89EdmTraC-16
❑ 89EdmTraP-561
❑ 90DodTar-646
❑ 91SprCarP-759
Ramsey, Mike (Michael Jeffery)
❑ 76ArkTraT-8
❑ 77ArkTraT-7A
❑ 77ArkTraT-7B
❑ 78SprRedWK-5
❑ 81Fle-549
❑ 81Top-366
❑ 82Don-316
❑ 82Fle-125
❑ 82Top-574
❑ 83Car-23
❑ 83Don-568
❑ 83Fle-19
❑ 83Top-128
❑ 84Don-382
❑ 84Fle-333
❑ 84Nes792-467
❑ 84Top-467
❑ 84TopTif-467
❑ 85Fle-406
❑ 85OPC-62
❑ 85Top-62
❑ 85TopTif-62
❑ 86TamTarP-15
❑ 87DodMot-11
❑ 87DonOpeD-80
❑ 87EdmTraP-2066
❑ 90DodTar-647
❑ 91PacSenL-18
❑ 91SprCarC-11
❑ 92SavCarC-23
❑ 92SavCarF-679
❑ 93SprCarC-28
❑ 93SprCarF-1868
❑ 94St.PetCC-28
❑ 94St.PetCF-2602
❑ 95ArkTraTI-23
❑ 96CliLumKTI-21
❑ 97MobBayBB-5
❑ 98MobBayBTI-23
Ramsey, Rob
❑ 98BesAutSS-43
❑ 99SP TopP-107
❑ 99SP TopPPE-107
Ramsey, Thomas
❑ 87OldJudN-410
❑ 88SpoTimM-21
❑ 89EdgR.WG-18
Ramstack, Curt
❑ 76AppFoxT-20
Rand, Dick
❑ 54CarHunW-19
❑ 58JetPos-15
❑ 58Top-218
Rand, Ian
❑ 95BelGiaTI-24
❑ 96BelGiaTI-7
❑ 97BakBlaB-8
❑ 97BakBlaTI-8
Rand, Kevin
❑ 85AlbYanT-27
❑ 87ColCliP-2
❑ 89EasLeaDDP-DD49
Randa, Joe
❑ 91EugEmeC-14
❑ 91EugEmeP-3736
❑ 92AppFoxCB-1
❑ 92AppFoxFI-995
❑ 92BasCitRF-3852
❑ 92Bow-560
❑ 92ClaFS7-11
❑ 92MidLeaATI-34
❑ 92ProFS7-78
❑ 92UppDecML-325
❑ 93Bow-237
❑ 93ClaFS7-240
❑ 93ClaGolF-5
❑ 93ExcFS7-177
❑ 93MemChiF-383
❑ 93RoyStaC-20
❑ 94AriFalLS-16
❑ 94Bow-199
❑ 94Cla-89
❑ 94ExcFS7-72
❑ 94OmaRoyF-1231
❑ 94UppDecML-75
❑ 94UppDecML-96
❑ 95ColCho-14
❑ 95ColChoGS-14
❑ 95ColChoSS-14
❑ 95Exc-62
❑ 95FleUpd-48
❑ 95Sel-180
❑ 95SelArtP-180
❑ 95SelCer-121
❑ 95SelCerMG-121
❑ 95SigRoo-43
❑ 95SigRooSig-43
❑ 95StaClu-532
❑ 95StaCluMOP-532
❑ 95StaCluSTWS-532
❑ 95Sum-139
❑ 95SumNthD-139
❑ 95Top-637
❑ 95UC3-107
❑ 95UC3ArtP-107
❑ 95UppDec-243
❑ 95UppDecED-243
❑ 95UppDecEDG-243
❑ 95UppDecML-31
❑ 95UppDecMLFS-31
❑ 96Cir-47
❑ 96CirRav-47
❑ 96ColCho-577
❑ 96ColCho-652
❑ 96ColChoGS-577
❑ 96ColChoGS-652
❑ 96ColChoSS-577
❑ 96ColChoSS-652
❑ 96FleUpd-U43
❑ 96FleUpdTC-U43
❑ 96LeaSigA-189
❑ 96LeaSigAG-189
❑ 96LeaSigAS-189
❑ 96RoyPol-23
❑ 96Sco-268
❑ 96StaClu-450
❑ 96StaCluMOP-450
❑ 96UppDec-353
❑ 97Cir-61
❑ 97CirRav-61
❑ 97ColCho-133
❑ 97ColCho-429
❑ 97Don-349
❑ 97DonGolPP-349
❑ 97DonLim-50
❑ 97DonLimE-50
❑ 97DonLimENG-50
❑ 97DonSigA-81
❑ 97DonSigAC-100
❑ 97DonSigAM-100
❑ 97DonSilPP-349
❑ 97Fle-120
❑ 97Fle-680
❑ 97FleTif-120
❑ 97FleTif-680
❑ 97Lea-15
❑ 97LeaFraM-15
❑ 97LeaFraMDC-15
❑ 97NewPin-90
❑ 97NewPinAP-90
❑ 97NewPinMC-90
❑ 97NewPinPP-90
❑ 97Pac-109
❑ 97PacLigB-109
❑ 97PacSil-109
❑ 97PirPos-29
❑ 97SP-143
❑ 97StaClu-271
❑ 97StaCluMOP-271
❑ 97Top-216
❑ 97Ult-399
❑ 97UltGolME-399
❑ 97UltPlaME-399
❑ 97UppDec-89
❑ 98CirThu-84
❑ 98CirThuRav-84
❑ 98CirThuSupRav-84
❑ 98ColCho-367
❑ 98Don-227
❑ 98DonColL-243
❑ 98DonColP-635
❑ 98DonGolPP-227
❑ 98DonPre-85
❑ 98DonPreSeat-85
❑ 98DonPriCL-243
❑ 98DonPriCP-635
❑ 98DonSilPP-227
❑ 98Fle-407
❑ 98Lea-44
❑ 98LeaFraDA-44
❑ 98LeaFraF-44
❑ 98LeaFraM-44
❑ 98LeaFraM-44
❑ 98LeaFraMDC-44
❑ 98LeaFraMDC-44
❑ 98LeaFraMZ2-44
❑ 98Pac-401
❑ 98PacOnl-281
❑ 98PacOnlR-281
❑ 98PacOnlWC-281
❑ 98PacPlaB-401
❑ 98PacRedT-401
❑ 98PacSil-401
❑ 98PinIns-100
❑ 98PinInsCE-100
❑ 98PinInsDE-100
❑ 98SPxFin-273
❑ 98SPxFinR-273
❑ 98SPxFinS-273
❑ 98Stu-33
❑ 98StuGPP-33
❑ 98StuSPP-33
❑ 98Top-441
❑ 98TopChr-441
❑ 98TopChrR-441
❑ 98TopDevR-441
❑ 98TopDia-441
❑ 98TopMiniC-441
❑ 98Ult-432
❑ 98UltGolM-432
❑ 98UltMas-432
❑ 98UltPlaM-432
❑ 98UppDec-678
❑ 99Fle-554
❑ 99FleSta9-554
❑ 99FleWarT-554
❑ 99PacOme-116
❑ 99PacOmeC-116
❑ 99PacOmeG-116
❑ 99PacOmePB-116
❑ 99PacPar-114
❑ 99PacParC-114
❑ 99PacParG-114
❑ 99PacParHoloGold-114
❑ 99PacParHS-114
❑ 99PacParOD-114
❑ 99PacParPB-114
❑ 99PacParRed-114
❑ 99StaClu-86
❑ 99StaCluFDI-86
❑ 99StaCluOoaK-86
❑ 99StaCluPP-86
❑ 99UppDec-391
❑ 99UppDecEL1-391
❑ 99UppDecEL2-391
❑ 99Vic-185
Randahl, Rick
❑ 81TacTigT-2
Randall, Bob
❑ 70RelPam-10
❑ 74AlbDukCa-78
❑ 74AlbDukTI-14
❑ 75AlbDukCa-6
❑ 75IntLeaASB-24
❑ 75PacCoaLAB-24
❑ 76MinTwiP-12
❑ 77BurCheD-52
❑ 77Top-578
❑ 78Top-363
❑ 78TwiFriP-15
❑ 79Top-58
❑ 79TwiFriP-22
❑ 80OPC-90
❑ 80TolMudHT-2
❑ 80Top-162
❑ 80TwiPos-24
Randall, Mark
❑ 89MarPhiS-26
❑ 90ClePhiS-18
❑ 91SpaPhiC-12
❑ 91SpaPhiP-897
❑ 92ClePhiF-2057
❑ 92SpaPhiC-14
❑ 93ClePhiC-18
❑ 93ClePhiF-2682
Randall, Newton
❑ 09T206-459
❑ 16Zee-45
Randall, Sap (James)
❑ 82RedPioT-8
❑ 83NasAngT-18
❑ 84EdmTraC-101
❑ 85EdmTraC-10
❑ 86MidAngP-20
❑ 87EdmTraP-2076
❑ 88BlaYNPRWL-29
❑ 88TriAAAP-46
❑ 88VanCanC-20
❑ 88VanCanP-765
Randall, Scott
❑ 96AshTouB-29
❑ 97Bow-379
❑ 97BowInt-379
❑ 97CarLeaTP-29
❑ 97SalAva-26
❑ 98Bow-320
❑ 98BowChr-320
❑ 98BowChrGA-320
❑ 98BowChrGAR-320
❑ 98BowChrI-320

❑ 98BowChrIR-320
❑ 98BowChrR-320
❑ 98BowGolA-320
❑ 98BowInt-320
❑ 98EasLeaTPM-24
❑ 98NewHavRM-25
❑ 98NewHavRMA-25
❑ 99Bow-88
❑ 99BowAut-BA49
❑ 99BowChr-88
❑ 99BowChrG-88
❑ 99BowChrGR-88
❑ 99BowChrI-88
❑ 99BowChrIR-88
❑ 99BowChrR-88
❑ 99BowGol-88
❑ 99BowInt-88

Randle, Carl
❑ 88ButCopKSP-7
❑ 89GasRanP-1005
❑ 89GasRanS-19
❑ 90GasRanB-3
❑ 90GasRanP-2519
❑ 90GasRanS-19
❑ 91ChaRanC-9
❑ 91ChaRanP-1313

Randle, Len
❑ 71SenTealW-20
❑ 72RanTeal-23
❑ 72Top-737
❑ 73OPC-378
❑ 73Top-378
❑ 74OPC-446
❑ 74Top-446
❑ 75OPC-259
❑ 75RanPos-27
❑ 75RanPos-28
❑ 75Top-259
❑ 75TopMin-259
❑ 76OPC-31
❑ 76SSP-266
❑ 76Top-31
❑ 76VenLeaS-90
❑ 77BurCheD-21
❑ 77Top-196
❑ 78Hos-102
❑ 78Kel-22
❑ 78MetDaiPA-20
❑ 78OPC-132
❑ 78Top-544
❑ 79OPC-236
❑ 79Top-454
❑ 81Don-485
❑ 81Fle-301
❑ 81MarPol-9
❑ 81MarPos-26
❑ 81Top-692
❑ 81TopTra-817
❑ 82Don-307
❑ 82Fle-516
❑ 82MarPos-27
❑ 82OPC-312
❑ 82Top-312
❑ 82TopSti-230
❑ 86RanGreT-8
❑ 87WatIndP-27
❑ 89PacSenL-11
❑ 89T/MSenL-88
❑ 89TopSenL-38
❑ 90EliSenL-13
❑ 90OrlSunRB-11
❑ 90SweBasG-53
❑ 91FouBal-13
❑ 91MetWIZ-323
❑ 91PacSenL-116
❑ 92YanWIZ7-131
❑ 93RanKee-35

Randle, Michael
❑ 87KenTwiP-3
❑ 88CalLeaACLC-37
❑ 88VisOakCLC-147
❑ 88VisOakP-85
❑ 89OrlTwiB-21
❑ 89OrlTwiP-1339
❑ 90OrlSunRP-1097
❑ 90OrlSunRS-15

Randle, Randy
❑ 86OscAstP-20
❑ 87OscAstP-5
❑ 88ModA'sCLC-77
❑ 89NewBriRSP-618
❑ 89NewBriRSS-17
❑ 90NewBriRSB-19
❑ 90NewBriRSP-1328
❑ 90NewBriRSS-17
❑ 91LinDriAA-470
❑ 91NewBriRSLD-470
❑ 91NewBriRSP-360

Randolph, Bob
❑ 81LynSaiT-26
❑ 83ChaLooT-13

Randolph, Carl
❑ 94OneYanC-30
❑ 98NorNavQ-30

Randolph, Ed
❑ 96WisTimRB-18

Randolph, Jaisen
❑ 98MidLeaPM-22
❑ 98RocCubM-24
❑ 98RocCubTI-25

Randolph, Scott
❑ 87SalAngP-29

Randolph, Steve
❑ 96GreBatB-20
❑ 97TamYan-22
❑ 98HigDesMG-21

Randolph, Tommy
❑ 86DavLipB-18

Randolph, Willie
❑ 76OPC-592
❑ 76SSP-584
❑ 76Top-592
❑ 76TopTra-592T
❑ 77BurCheD-175
❑ 77OPC-110
❑ 77Top-359
❑ 77YanBurK-13
❑ 77YanNedC-4
❑ 78Hos-89
❑ 78OPC-228
❑ 78SSP270-27
❑ 78Top-411
❑ 78Top-620
❑ 78YanBurK-13
❑ 78YanPhoA-21
❑ 78YanSSPD-27
❑ 79OPC-125
❑ 79RawActT-1
❑ 79Top-250
❑ 79YanBurK-13
❑ 79YanPicA-30
❑ 80OPC-239
❑ 80Top-460
❑ 80YanPhoA-20
❑ 81AllGamPI-15
❑ 81Don-345
❑ 81Fle-109
❑ 81FleStiC-107
❑ 81OPC-60
❑ 81PerAll-16
❑ 81Top-60
❑ 81TopScr-36
❑ 81TopSti-108
❑ 81TopSti-242
❑ 81TopSupHT-70
❑ 81YanPhoA-20
❑ 82Don-461
❑ 82Fle-49
❑ 82FleSta-121
❑ 82OPC-37
❑ 82OPC-159
❑ 82OPC-213
❑ 82Top-548
❑ 82Top-569
❑ 82Top-570
❑ 82TopSti-219
❑ 82YanPhoA-21
❑ 83AllGamPI-14
❑ 83Don-283
❑ 83Fle-393
❑ 83FleSta-157
❑ 83FleSti-44
❑ 83OPC-140
❑ 83Top-140
❑ 83TopSti-95
❑ 83YanPhoA-20
❑ 83YanRoyRD-9
❑ 84AllGamPI-105
❑ 84Don-417
❑ 84Fle-137
❑ 84FunFooP-20
❑ 84Nes792-360
❑ 84OPC-360
❑ 84Top-360
❑ 84TopSti-324
❑ 84TopTif-360
❑ 85AllGamPI-15
❑ 85Don-92
❑ 85Fle-140
❑ 85Lea-83
❑ 85OPC-8
❑ 85PolMet-Y1
❑ 85Top-765
❑ 85TopSti-312
❑ 85TopTif-765
❑ 85YanTCMP-30
❑ 86BasStaB-87
❑ 86Don-16
❑ 86Don-92
❑ 86DonSupD-16
❑ 86Fle-115
❑ 86Lea-16
❑ 86OPC-332
❑ 86Top-276
❑ 86Top-455
❑ 86TopSti-305
❑ 86TopTat-15
❑ 86TopTif-276
❑ 86TopTif-455
❑ 86YanTCM-27
❑ 87Don-154
❑ 87DonOpeD-246
❑ 87Fle-109
❑ 87FleBasA-35
❑ 87FleGlo-109
❑ 87Lea-58
❑ 87OPC-377
❑ 87RedFolSB-2
❑ 87SpoTeaP-7
❑ 87Top-701
❑ 87TopSti-302
❑ 87TopTif-701
❑ 88Don-228
❑ 88DonAll-3
❑ 88DonBasB-108
❑ 88DonPop-3
❑ 88DonReaBY-228
❑ 88Dra-18
❑ 88Fle-218
❑ 88FleBasA-32
❑ 88FleBasM-28
❑ 88FleGlo-218
❑ 88FleMin-42
❑ 88FleStiC-50
❑ 88Lea-162
❑ 88Nes-22
❑ 88OPC-210
❑ 88PanSti-153
❑ 88PanSti-228
❑ 88Sco-266
❑ 88ScoBoxC-3
❑ 88ScoGlo-266
❑ 88Spo-47
❑ 88SpoGam-6
❑ 88StaLinAl-24
❑ 88StaLinY-11
❑ 88Top-210
❑ 88Top-387
❑ 88Top-459
❑ 88TopBig-76
❑ 88TopGloA-3
❑ 88TopGloS-42
❑ 88TopMinL-28
❑ 88TopSti-162
❑ 88TopSti-294
❑ 88TopStiB-37
❑ 88TopTif-210
❑ 88TopTif-387
❑ 88TopTif-459
❑ 88TopUKM-59
❑ 88TopUKMT-59
❑ 89Bow-344
❑ 89BowTif-344
❑ 89DodMot-10
❑ 89DodPol-8
❑ 89DodSmoG-57
❑ 89DodStaSV-11
❑ 89Don-395
❑ 89DonBasB-148
❑ 89DonTra-8
❑ 89Fle-265
❑ 89FleGlo-265
❑ 89FleUpd-93
❑ 89OPC-244
❑ 89PanSti-405
❑ 89RedFolSB-92
❑ 89Sco-45
❑ 89ScoRoo-41T
❑ 89Top-519
❑ 89Top-635
❑ 89TopBig-244
❑ 89TopSti-309
❑ 89TopTif-519
❑ 89TopTif-635
❑ 89TopTra-100T
❑ 89TopTraT-100T
❑ 89UppDec-237
❑ 89UppDec-777
❑ 90Bow-90
❑ 90BowTif-90
❑ 90ClaBlu-122
❑ 90ClaYel-T71
❑ 90DodPol-12
❑ 90DodTar-648
❑ 90Don-19
❑ 90Don-250
❑ 90DonBesA-110
❑ 90DonSupD-19
❑ 90Fle-406
❑ 90FleCan-406
❑ 90Lea-345
❑ 90OPC-25
❑ 90PanSti-279
❑ 90PubIntS-16
❑ 90Sco-395
❑ 90Sco100S-4
❑ 90ScoRoo-51T
❑ 90Spo-175
❑ 90Top-25
❑ 90TopBig-43
❑ 90TopCoi-55
❑ 90TopSti-66
❑ 90TopTif-25
❑ 90TopTra-100T
❑ 90TopTraT-100T
❑ 90UppDec-183
❑ 90UppDec-704
❑ 91Bow-46
❑ 91BreMilB-21
❑ 91BrePol-19
❑ 91Don-217
❑ 91Don-766
❑ 91Fle-22
❑ 91FleUpd-33
❑ 91Lea-419
❑ 91OPC-525
❑ 91PanFreS-193
❑ 91Sco-194
❑ 91ScoRoo-35T
❑ 91StaClu-545
❑ 91Stu-74
❑ 91Top-525
❑ 91TopDesS-525
❑ 91TopMic-525
❑ 91TopTif-525
❑ 91TopTra-95T
❑ 91TopTraT-95T
❑ 91TopTriH-A10
❑ 91UltUpd-32
❑ 91UppDec-421
❑ 91UppDec-720
❑ 92Bow-681
❑ 92Cla1-T74
❑ 92ClaGam-169
❑ 92DodStaTA-28
❑ 92Don-625
❑ 92Fle-186
❑ 92Lea-240
❑ 92LeaBlaG-240
❑ 92MetColP-9
❑ 92MetKah-12
❑ 92OPC-116
❑ 92OPCPre-67
❑ 92PanSti-36
❑ 92Pin-382
❑ 92Sco-30
❑ 92ScoRoo-35T
❑ 92StaClu-890
❑ 92Top-116
❑ 92TopGol-116
❑ 92TopGolW-116
❑ 92TopMic-116
❑ 92TopTra-90T
❑ 92TopTraG-90T
❑ 92Ult-536
❑ 92UppDec-211
❑ 92UppDec-795
❑ 92YanWIZ7-132
❑ 92YanWIZ8-153
❑ 92YanWIZA-60
❑ 93Don-644
❑ 93Fle-479
❑ 93PacSpa-200
❑ 93Sco-613
❑ 93Sel-195
❑ 93Top-324
❑ 93TopGol-324
❑ 93TopInaM-324
❑ 93TopInaR-324
❑ 93TopMic-324
❑ 93UppDec-419
❑ 93UppDecGold-419
❑ 94BreMilB-69
❑ 96MetMod-8

Ranew, Merritt
❑ 62Top-156
❑ 62TopVen-156
❑ 63Col45'JP-8
❑ 64Top-78
❑ 64TopVen-78
❑ 65SeaPop-16
❑ 66OPC-62
❑ 66SeaPop-18
❑ 66Top-62A
❑ 66Top-62B
❑ 66TopVen-62
❑ 67SeaPop-14
❑ 83Pil69G-31
❑ 89AstCol4S-11

Rangel, Julio
❑ 97GreBatB-23
❑ 98TamYanM-24

Ranger, Rowdy
❑ 91GasRanC-30

Rangers, Texas
❑ 69FleCloS-23
❑ 69FleCloS-40
❑ 72Top-668
❑ 73OPC-7
❑ 73OPCBTC-24
❑ 73Top-7
❑ 73TopBluTC-24
❑ 74OPC-184
❑ 74OPCTC-24
❑ 74Top-184
❑ 74TopStaA-24
❑ 74TopTeaC-24
❑ 78Top-659
❑ 83FleSta-249
❑ 83FleSti-NNO
❑ 87SpoTeaL-1
❑ 88PanSti-467
❑ 88RedFolSB-123
❑ 90PubIntS-640
❑ 90RedFolSB-106
❑ 93RanKee-SP1
❑ 94HudValRC-29
❑ 94ImpProP-13
❑ 94Sco-329
❑ 94ScoGolR-329
❑ 95PacPriTL-13
❑ 95PanSti-153
❑ 96PanSti-235
❑ 96RanFle-19
❑ 97ColChoT-TR
❑ 99Vic-393

Rannow, John
❑ 86EveGiaC-19
❑ 86EveGiaPC-22
❑ 87CliGiaP-10

Ransom, Cody
❑ 98SalVol-29

Ransom, Gene
❑ 82MadMusF-9
❑ 83MadMusF-18

Ransom, Jeff
❑ 81PhoGiaVNB-22
❑ 83PhoGiaBHN-5
❑ 87TolMudHP-24
❑ 87TolMudHT-11

Rantz, Mike
❑ 83IdaFalAT-24

Raper, Ron
❑ 88CapCodPPaLP-37

Rapp, Craig
❑ 91IdaFalBP-4327
❑ 91IdaFalBSP-20

Rapp, Earl
❑ 49RemBre-23
❑ 50RemBre-21
❑ 53MotCoo-30
❑ 75Gia195T-23

Rapp, Goldie (Joe)
❑ 12PCLPin-19
❑ 20NatCarE-82
❑ 20W52-15
❑ 21Exh-138
❑ 21Nei-104
❑ 22E120-205
❑ 22W572-81
❑ 22W573-105
❑ 23WilChoV-128

Rapp, Pat (Patrick)
❑ 90CliGiaB-23
❑ 90CliGiaP-2547
❑ 90ProAaA-117
❑ 91CalLeLA-39
❑ 91Cla/Bes-275
❑ 91SanJosGC-20
❑ 91SanJosGP-9
❑ 92DonRoo-99
❑ 92PhoFirF-2821
❑ 92PhoFirS-394
❑ 92SkyAAAF-180
❑ 93ClaFS7-247
❑ 93EdmTraF-1134
❑ 93Fle-429
❑ 93MarPub-19
❑ 93Top-791
❑ 93TopGol-791
❑ 93TopInaM-791
❑ 93TopInaR-791
❑ 93TopMic-791
❑ 94ColC-236
❑ 94ColChoGS-236
❑ 94ColChoSS-236
❑ 94Fle-473
❑ 94MarTeal-13
❑ 94Pin-189
❑ 94PinArtP-189
❑ 94PinMusC-189
❑ 94Sco-310
❑ 94ScoGolR-310
❑ 94StaClu-606
❑ 94StaCluFDI-606
❑ 94StaCluGR-606
❑ 94StaCluMOP-606
❑ 94StaCluT-65
❑ 94StaCluTFDI-65
❑ 94Top-227
❑ 94TopGol-227
❑ 94TopSpa-227
❑ 94Ult-496
❑ 95ColCho-304
❑ 95ColChoGS-304
❑ 95ColChoSE-131
❑ 95ColChoSEGS-131
❑ 95ColChoSESS-131
❑ 95ColChoSS-304
❑ 95Don-121
❑ 95DonPreP-121
❑ 95Fle-340
❑ 95Lea-142
❑ 95Pac-176
❑ 95Pin-198
❑ 95PinArtP-198
❑ 95PinMusC-198
❑ 95Sco-492
❑ 95ScoGolR-492
❑ 95ScoPlaTS-492
❑ 95StaClu-364
❑ 95StaCluMOP-364
❑ 95StaCluSTWS-364
❑ 95StaCluVR-191
❑ 95StaCluVRMO-191
❑ 95Top-497
❑ 95TopCyb-287
❑ 95Ult-166
❑ 95UltGolM-166
❑ 95UppDec-356
❑ 95UppDecED-356
❑ 95UppDecEDG-356
❑ 96ColCho-558
❑ 96ColChoGS-558
❑ 96ColChoSS-558
❑ 96Don-392
❑ 96DonPreP-392
❑ 96EmoXL-189
❑ 96Fla-267
❑ 96Fle-393
❑ 96FleTif-393
❑ 96LeaSigA-190
❑ 96LeaSigAG-190
❑ 96LeaSigAS-190
❑ 96MetUni-168
❑ 96MetUniP-168
❑ 96Pac-72
❑ 96Sco-481
❑ 96StaClu-41
❑ 96StaClu-248
❑ 96StaCluMOP-41
❑ 96StaCluMOP-248
❑ 96Top-54
❑ 96Ult-480
❑ 96UltGolM-480
❑ 96UppDec-338
❑ 97ColCho-346
❑ 97ColChoT-FM11
❑ 97Fle-334
❑ 97FleTif-334
❑ 97MarPac-19
❑ 97Sco-441
❑ 97ScoArtPWB-441
❑ 97ScoResC-441
❑ 97ScoShoS-441
❑ 97ScoShoSAP-441

❑ 98PacOnl-351
❑ 98PacOnlR-351
❑ 98PacOnlWC-351
Rapp, Travis
❑ 97BriWhiSB-12
Rapp, Vern
❑ 77Car5-20
❑ 77CarTeal-19
❑ 77Top-183
❑ 78Top-324
❑ 79ExpPos-20
❑ 80ExpPos-24
❑ 82ExpPos-32
❑ 83ExpPos-25
❑ 83ExpStu-3
❑ 84RedEnq-32
❑ 84TopTra-95T
❑ 84TopTraT-95T
Rappoli, Paul
❑ 91ElmPioC-12
❑ 91ElmPioP-3285
❑ 92LynRedSC-10
❑ 92LynRedSF-2922
❑ 93NewBriRSF-1235
❑ 94SarRedSC-23
❑ 94SarRedSF-1967
❑ 96TreThuB-25
Rapps, William
❑ 09ObaT21-126
❑ 09ObaT21-298
❑ 11PacCoaBD-53
❑ 11Zee-56
❑ 12ObaPreT-47
❑ 12Zee-71
❑ 12Zee-72
Rariden, Bill (William A.)
❑ 09ColChiE-234
❑ 11PinT-5-711
❑ 12ColRedB-234
❑ 12ColTinT-234
❑ 14CraJacE-137
❑ 15CraJacE-137
❑ 15SpoNewM-141
❑ 16FleBreD-75
❑ 16SpoNewM-141
❑ 17ColE13-136
❑ 17HolBreD-81
❑ 20RedWorCP-15
❑ 88PacEigMO-86
❑ 94ConTSN-1024
❑ 94ConTSNB-1024
Raschi, Vic (Victor)
❑ 47Exh-183
❑ 47PM1StaP1-168
❑ 48BluTin-32
❑ 48YanTeal-22
❑ 49Bow-35
❑ 49YanTeal-17
❑ 50Bow-100
❑ 50YanTeal-17
❑ 51BerRos-C4
❑ 51Bow-25
❑ 52BerRos-50
❑ 52Bow-37
❑ 52StaCalL-70D
❑ 52StaCalS-84A
❑ 53BowC-27
❑ 53ExhCan-5
❑ 54Bow-33A
❑ 54Bow-33B
❑ 54CarHunW-18
❑ 55A'sRodM-29
❑ 55A'sTeal-18
❑ 55Bow-185
❑ 55CarHunW-18
❑ 74LauAllG-48
❑ 75JohMiz-20
❑ 76A'sRodMC-19
❑ 79TCM50-186
❑ 83YanASFY-34
❑ 85TCMPpl1-31
❑ 88PacLegI-70
❑ 90BasWit-53
❑ 92YanWIZA-61
Rascon, Rene
❑ 95ElmPioTI-22
❑ 95ElmPioUTI-22
❑ 96KanCouCTI-22
Rash, Joshua
❑ 93GreFalDSP-7
❑ 94YakBeaC-13
❑ 94YakBeaF-3864
Rashid, Ralph
❑ 93PeoChiC-27
Rasmus, Tony
❑ 86TriTriC-191
❑ 87SalAngP-14
Rasmussen, Dennis
❑ 81HolMilT-25
❑ 83ColCliT-8
❑ 84ColCliP-19
❑ 84ColCliT-25
❑ 84Don-446
❑ 85Don-518
❑ 85Fle-141
❑ 85Lea-48
❑ 85Top-691
❑ 85TopTif-691
❑ 85YanTCMP-17
❑ 86Don-336
❑ 86Top-301
❑ 86TopTif-301
❑ 86YanTCM-12
❑ 87ClaGam-87
❑ 87Don-175
❑ 87DonOpeD-247
❑ 87Fle-110
❑ 87FleExcS-35
❑ 87FleGamW-35
❑ 87FleGlo-110
❑ 87FleMin-86
❑ 87FleStiC-95
❑ 87Lea-260
❑ 87OPC-364
❑ 87Spo-71A
❑ 87Spo-71B
❑ 87SpoTeaP-7
❑ 87Top-555
❑ 87TopMinL-66
❑ 87TopSti-303
❑ 87TopTif-555
❑ 88Don-575
❑ 88Fle-246
❑ 88FleGlo-246
❑ 88FleUpd-126
❑ 88FleUpdG-126
❑ 88Sco-560
❑ 88ScoGlo-560
❑ 88StaLinRe-17
❑ 88Top-135
❑ 88TopSti-145
❑ 88TopTif-135
❑ 88TopTra-91T
❑ 88TopTraT-91T
❑ 89Bow-450
❑ 89BowTif-450
❑ 89ClaLigB-86
❑ 89Don-559
❑ 89Fle-314
❑ 89FleGlo-314
❑ 89OPC-32
❑ 89PadCok-12
❑ 89PadMag-17
❑ 89PadPos-24
❑ 89PanSti-195
❑ 89Sco-562
❑ 89Spo-212
❑ 89Top-32
❑ 89TopTif-32
❑ 89UppDec-645
❑ 90Bow-205
❑ 90BowTif-205
❑ 90Don-420
❑ 90Fle-165
❑ 90FleCan-165
❑ 90Lea-471
❑ 90M.Vpin-87
❑ 90OPC-449
❑ 90PadCok-14
❑ 90PadMag-4
❑ 90PubIntS-56
❑ 90Sco-129
❑ 90Top-449
❑ 90TopTif-449
❑ 90UppDec-594
❑ 91Don-458
❑ 91Fle-539
❑ 91OPC-774
❑ 91PadMag-2
❑ 91PadSmo-27
❑ 91Sco-457
❑ 91StaClu-169
❑ 91StaCluP-34
❑ 91Top-774
❑ 91TopDesS-774
❑ 91TopMic-774
❑ 91TopTif-774
❑ 91Ult-309
❑ 91UppDec-230
❑ 92Don-245
❑ 92Fle-617
❑ 92OPC-252
❑ 92RocRedWS-463
❑ 92Sco-536
❑ 92StaClu-749
❑ 92StaCluECN-749
❑ 92Top-252
❑ 92TopGol-252
❑ 92TopGolW-252
❑ 92TopMic-252
❑ 92UppDec-439
❑ 92YanWIZ8-154
❑ 93Don-778
❑ 93RoyStaC-12
❑ 93Sco-392
❑ 94PhoFirF-1518
❑ 96ButCopKB-5
❑ 97ChaRivDG-23
❑ 98LowSpiM-2
Rasmussen, Eric (Harold)
❑ 75TulOil7-11
❑ 76OPC-182
❑ 76SSP-296
❑ 76St.LouCP-26
❑ 76Top-182
❑ 77Car5-21
❑ 77CarTeal-20
❑ 77Top-404
❑ 78CarTeal-24
❑ 78PadFamF-23
❑ 78Top-281
❑ 79Top-57
❑ 80Top-301
❑ 81Don-123
❑ 81Fle-497
❑ 81Top-342
❑ 83Car-24
❑ 83Top-594
❑ 84Nes792-724
❑ 84OPC-377
❑ 84Top-724
❑ 84TopTif-724
❑ 84TucTorC-49
❑ 86MiaMarP-21
❑ 86RocRedWP-17
❑ 87RocRedWP-8
❑ 87RocRedWT-8
❑ 88WatIndP-686
❑ 89CanIndB-11
❑ 89CanIndP-1308
❑ 89CanIndS-2
❑ 89PacSenL-107
❑ 90EliSenL-76
❑ 96FtMyeMB-3
❑ 97ForMyeM-2
❑ 98NewBriRCM-2
Rasmussen, Jim
❑ 81OklCit8T-25
❑ 82OklCit8T-16
❑ 82OklCit8T-18
❑ 82ReaPhiT-7
❑ 84NasSouTI-18
❑ 87HawIslP-11
Rasmussen, Mark
❑ 87HawRai-3
Rasmussen, Nate
❑ 94GreFalDSP-18
❑ 95YakBeaTI-26
Rasmussen, Neil
❑ 73CedRapAT-10
❑ 75BurBeeT-20
❑ 77HolMilT-20
❑ 78HolMilT-18
Rasp, Ronnie
❑ 88WytCubP-2001
❑ 89ChaWheB-17
❑ 89ChaWheP-1764
❑ 90PeoChiTI-27
❑ 90WinSpiTI-13
Ratekin, Mark
❑ 91BoiHawC-28
❑ 91BoiHawP-3877
❑ 92QuaCitRBC-4
❑ 92QuaCitRBF-808
❑ 92StaCluD-148
❑ 93PalSprAC-18
❑ 93PalSprAF-68
❑ 94Bow-647
❑ 94MidAngOHP-24
❑ 95MidAngOHP-27
❑ 97MidAngOHP-25
Rath, Fred
❑ 96ForWayWB-21
❑ 96MidLeaAB-31
❑ 97ForMyeM-25
❑ 98SalLakBO-22
Rath, Fred Helsher
❑ 77FriOneYW-35
Rath, Gary
❑ 92MisStaB-36
❑ 93MisStaB-37
❑ 94StaCluDP-20
❑ 94StaCluDPFDI-20
❑ 95BowBes-B58
❑ 95BowBesR-B58
❑ 95SanAntMTI-19
❑ 95SPML-78
❑ 95TopTra-88T
❑ 96BesAutS-78
❑ 96BesAutSA-58
❑ 96Bow-290
❑ 96BowFoi-290
❑ 96Top-429
❑ 97AlbDukGS-27
❑ 97BesAutAS-43
❑ 98AlbDukG-20
Rath, Maurice
❑ 09ColChiE-235
❑ 12ColRedB-235
❑ 12ColTinT-235
❑ 12T207-155
❑ 16Zee-89
❑ 17Zee-74
❑ 19W514-57
❑ 20RedWorCP-16
❑ 21Zee-130
❑ 88PacEigMO-85
Rathbun, Jason
❑ 94GreBatF-471
❑ 95TamYanYI-21
❑ 97GreBatC-16
Rather, Dody
❑ 86FloStaLAP-39
❑ 86OscAstP-21
❑ 87ColAstP-17
Rathjen, Dennis
❑ 80CliGiaT-2
Rathjen, Edwin
❑ 26Zee-149
Ratliff, Chris
❑ 95BurBeeTI-18
Ratliff, Danny
❑ 86StoPorP-22
Ratliff, Daryl
❑ 89PriPirS-15
❑ 90AugPirP-2478
❑ 90CMC-724
❑ 91CarLeaAP-CAR36
❑ 91SalBucC-12
❑ 91SalBucP-966
❑ 92Bow-71
❑ 92CarMudF-1194
❑ 92CarMudS-139
❑ 92SkyAA F-65
❑ 93CarMudF-2069
❑ 93CarMudTI-16
❑ 93ClaFS7-289
❑ 94SalBucC-17
Ratliff, Jon
❑ 93GenCubC-1
❑ 93GenCubF-3172
❑ 94Bow-334
❑ 94Cla-65
❑ 94ClaGolF-52
❑ 94ClaGolN1PLF-LP12
❑ 94ClaGolREF-RE12
❑ 94ClaTriF-T13
❑ 94DayCubC-20
❑ 94DayCubF-2350
❑ 94ExcFS7-166
❑ 94Pin-437
❑ 94PinArtP-437
❑ 94PinMusC-437
❑ 94Sco-454
❑ 94ScoGolR-454
❑ 94Top-739
❑ 94TopGol-739
❑ 94TopSpa-739
❑ 94UppDecML-231
❑ 95OrlCubF-8
❑ 95SPML-31
❑ 96BesAutS-79
❑ 96IowCubB-30
❑ 97IowCub-24
❑ 98RicBraQ-13
Ratliff, Kelly Eugene
❑ 65Top-553
❑ 67AstTeal2-21
Ratliff, Paul
❑ 63Top-549
❑ 70OPC-267
❑ 70Top-267
❑ 70TwiTeal-6
❑ 71OPC-607
❑ 71Top-607
❑ 94BreMilB-70
Ratto, Len
❑ 49SolSunP-9
Ratzer, Steve
❑ 81ExpPos-11
❑ 82TidTidT-21
Rau, Doug
❑ 73OPC-602
❑ 73Top-602
❑ 74OPC-64
❑ 74Top-64
❑ 75OPC-269
❑ 75Top-269
❑ 75TopMin-269
❑ 76LinSup-119
❑ 76OPC-124
❑ 76SSP-71
❑ 76Top-124
❑ 77BurCheD-149
❑ 77DodPho-11
❑ 77Kel-11
❑ 77OPC-128
❑ 77Top-421
❑ 78OPC-24
❑ 78SSP270-78
❑ 78Top-641
❑ 79DodBlu-10
❑ 79Kel-56
❑ 79OPC-178
❑ 79Top-347
❑ 80DodPol-31
❑ 80Top-527
❑ 81Fle-133
❑ 81RedPioT-9
❑ 81Top-174
❑ 81TopTra-818
❑ 90DodTar-649
Raub, Tommy
❑ 11SpoLifCW-297
Raubolt, Art
❑ 86LakTigP-19
Rauch, Bob
❑ 91MetWIZ-324
Rauch, Rocky (Al)
❑ 78WatIndT-17
Rauer, Troy
❑ 96SouOreTI-4
❑ 96WesMicWB-22
❑ 97VisOakG-25
Rauls, Ian
❑ 98BatMucTI-25
Rauth, Chris
❑ 85LitFalMT-8
❑ 86ColMetP-20
❑ 87LynMetP-15
❑ 89JacMetGS-24
❑ 90KnoBluJB-16
❑ 92TidTidF-895
❑ 92TidTidS-569
Rautzhan, Lance (Clarence G.)
❑ 75WatDodT-17
❑ 78Top-709
❑ 79HolMilT-25
❑ 79OPC-193
❑ 79Top-373
❑ 80VanCanT-9
❑ 90DodTar-650
❑ 94BreMilB-71
Ravelo, Graciano
❑ 76VenLeaS-110
❑ 80VenLeaS-183
❑ 93LinVenB-72
Raven, Luis
❑ 91BoiHawC-3
❑ 91BoiHawP-3897
❑ 92PalSprAC-15
❑ 92PalSprAF-850
❑ 93MidAngF-334·
❑ 94MidAngF-2448
❑ 94MidAngOHP-25
❑ 94VenLinU-9
❑ 95Exc-24
❑ 95LinVen-82
❑ 95MidAngOHP-28
❑ 95UppDecML-76
❑ 95UppDecMLFS-76
❑ 96-97LinVen-6
❑ 96SigRooOJTP-T4
❑ 97BirBarB-12
❑ 97MidAngOHP-26
Raven, Rally
❑ 97NewHavRB-1
❑ 98NewHavRM-24
❑ 98NewHavRMA-24
Ravens, New Haven
❑ 98NewHavRM-31
❑ 98NewHavRMA-31
Ravitz, David
❑ 93YakBeaC-22
❑ 93YakBeaF-3891
Rawdon, Chris
❑ 86ElmPioRSP-16
Rawitzer, Kevin
❑ 93EugEmeF-3855
❑ 94ExcFS7-73
❑ 94MidLeaAF-MDW24
❑ 94RocRoyC-18
❑ 94RocRoyF-562
❑ 95WilBluRTI-36
❑ 96WicWraB-10
❑ 97WicWra-11
❑ 98WicWraM-7
Rawley, Billy
❑ 83CedRapRT-6
Rawley, Shane
❑ 75WesPalBES-21
❑ 77MarPos-17
❑ 79OPC-30
❑ 79Top-74
❑ 80MarPos-19
❑ 80OPC-368
❑ 80Top-723
❑ 81Don-167
❑ 81MarPol-16
❑ 81MarPos-27
❑ 81OPC-51
❑ 81Top-423
❑ 81TopSti-129
❑ 82Don-352A
❑ 82Don-352B
❑ 82Fle-517
❑ 82Top-197
❑ 82TopTra-95T
❑ 82YanPhoA-22
❑ 83AllGamPI-85
❑ 83Don-513
❑ 83Fle-394
❑ 83Top-592
❑ 83YanPhoA-21
❑ 84Don-295
❑ 84Fle-138
❑ 84FleUpd-94
❑ 84Nes792-254
❑ 84OPC-254
❑ 84Top-254
❑ 84TopTif-254
❑ 85AllGamPI-174
❑ 85Don-599
❑ 85DonHig-39
❑ 85Fle-263
❑ 85Lea-31
❑ 85OPC-169
❑ 85PhiCIG-15
❑ 85PhiTas-9
❑ 85PhiTas-22
❑ 85Top-636
❑ 85TopTif-636
❑ 86BasStaB-88
❑ 86Don-233
❑ 86Fle-446
❑ 86Lea-109
❑ 86OPC-361
❑ 86PhiCIG-6
❑ 86PhiTas-28
❑ 86Top-361
❑ 86TopSti-123
❑ 86TopTif-361
❑ 87Don-83
❑ 87DonAll-56
❑ 87DonOpeD-159
❑ 87Fle-180
❑ 87FleGlo-180
❑ 87FleRecS-31
❑ 87FleStiC-96
❑ 87Lea-139
❑ 87OPC-239
❑ 87PhiTas-28
❑ 87RedFolSB-124
❑ 87Spo-181
❑ 87SpoTeaP-6
❑ 87StuPan-9
❑ 87Top-771
❑ 87TopSti-120
❑ 87TopTif-771
❑ 88Don-13
❑ 88Don-83
❑ 88DonBasB-240
❑ 88DonSupD-13

88Fle-311
88FleGlo-311
88FleHotS-32
88FleMin-100
88FleStiC-109
88FleSupBC-C4
88FleWaxBC-C8
88Lea-13
88Lea-92
88OPC-66
88PanSti-352
88PhiTas-19
88Sco-375
88ScoGlo-375
88Spo-51
88StaLinPh-13
88Top-66
88Top-406
88TopClo-93
88TopGloS-45
88TopMinL-65
88TopSti-121
88TopTif-66
88TopTif-406
89Bow-151
89BowTif-151
89Don-251
89Fle-579
89FleGlo-579
89FleUpd-44
89OPC-24
89Sco-170
89Top-494
89TopSti-118
89TopTif-494
89TopTra-101T
89TopTraT-101T
89UppDec-427
89UppDec-786
90Don-537
90Fle-384
90FleCan-384
90OPC-101
90PubIntS-336
90Sco-71
90Top-101
90TopTif-101
90UppDec-438
92YanWIZ8-155

Rawlings, John
20GasAmeMBD-31
21E121So1-77
21E121So8-74
21KoBreWSI-18
22E120-190
22W573-106
22W575-101
23W501-61
23W503-26
23WilChoV-129
93ConTSN-699

Rawlings, Reggie
25Zee-51

Rawls, Mike
97YakBeaG-27

Ray, Art
83AleDukT-9

Ray, Bregg
84ButCopKT-21

Ray, Glenn
81ChaRoyT-7

Ray, Jay
86BakDodP-23
88VerBeaDS-21

Ray, Jim F.
67Ast-25
68DexPre-37
68Top-539
69Top-257
70AstPho-22
70MLBOffS-124
70OPC-113
70Top-113
71AstTeal-20
71MLBOffS-91
71MLBOffS-249
71OPC-242
71Top-242
72AstTeal-21
72MilBra-135
72Top-603
73OPC-313
73Top-313
74OPC-458
74Tig-10
74Top-458
74TopTra-458T
75CedRapGT-16
75OPC-89
75Top-89
75TopMin-89
82AstAstI-2
87AstShowSTh-19

Ray, Johnny
80ColAstT-7
81TucTorT-10
82Don-528
82Fle-492
82Top-291
82TopTra-96T
83AllGamPI-106
83Don-437
83Fle-317
83FleSta-158
83FleSti-76
83Kel-24
83OPC-149
83Top-149
83TopSti-327
84AllGamPI-14
84Don-308
84Fle-260
84FunFooP-69
84Nes792-387
84Nes792-537
84NesDreT-13
84OPC-323
84OPC-387
84Pir-16
84Top-387
84Top-537
84TopGloS-5
84TopRubD-9
84TopSti-183
84TopSti-186
84TopStiB-7
84TopTif-387
84TopTif-537
85AllGamPI-103
85Don-186
85DonActA-50
85Fle-473
85FleStaS-43
85GenMilS-7
85Lea-212
85OPC-96
85Pir-16
85SubDis-40
85ThoMcAD-40
85Top-96
85TopMin-96
85TopRubD-5
85TopSti-130
85TopTif-96
86Don-19
86Don-186
86DonHig-9
86DonSupD-19
86Fle-617
86FleStiC-93
86Lea-19
86OPC-37
86Top-615
86TopSti-124
86TopTat-4
86TopTif-615
87AstShoSPT-22
87Don-144
87DonOpeD-162
87DonOpeD-163A
87Fle-618
87FleAwaW-31
87FleExcS-36
87FleGlo-618
87FleMin-87
87FleStiC-97
87KraFoo-14
87Lea-147
87OPC-291
87RedFolSB-51
87SmoNatL-8
87Spo-116
87Spo-121
87SpoTeaP-18
87StuPan-10
87Top-747
87TopGloS-55
87TopSti-135
87TopTif-747
88AngSmo-2
88Don-428
88DonBasB-171
88Fle-502
88FleGlo-502
88FleSlu-31
88Lea-260
88OPC-115
88Sco-254
88ScoGlo-254
88Spo-186
88StaLinAn-17
88Top-115
88TopBig-97
88TopTif-115
89AngSmo-20
89Bow-49
89BowTif-49
89CadEllD-42
89Don-12
89Don-331
89DonAll-25
89DonBasB-195
89DonSupD-12
89Fle-487
89FleBasA-33
89FleGlo-487
89FleHeroB-32
89OPC-109
89PanSti-292
89RedFolSB-93
89Sco-14
89ScoHot1S-99
89Spo-195
89Top-455
89TopBatL-18
89TopBig-7
89TopCoi-49
89TopHilTM-24
89TopMinL-50
89TopSti-182
89TopTif-455
89TopUKM-62
89TVSpoM-111
89UppDec-481
90AngSmo-14
90Bow-302
90BowTif-302
90ChaWheB-8
90ChaWheP-2240
90Don-234
90DonBesA-73
90Fle-143
90FleCan-143
90Lea-208
90OPC-334
90PanSti-33
90PubIntS-378
90Sco-293
90Spo-82
90Top-334
90TopBatL-18
90TopBig-95
90TopSti-174
90TopTif-334
90UppDec-509
91ChaWheC-8
91ChaWheP-2885
91Don-622
91Fle-323
91OPC-273
91PanFreS-181
91PanSti-138
91Sco-31
91Top-273
91TopDesS-273
91TopMic-273
91TopTif-273
91UppDec-678
92CedRapRC-4
92ChaLooF-3817
92ChaLooS-193
92SkyAA F-86
93ChaLooF-2361

Ray, Ken
94RocRoyC-19
94RocRoyF-563
95Bow-38
95Exc-63
95WilBluRTI-24
96WicWraB-11
97OmaRoyB-13

Ray, Larry
82TucTorT-10
83TucTorT-20
84TucTorC-70
86ColAstP-22
86SouLeaAJ-11
87VanCanP-1617

Ray, Rick
89UtiBluSP-31
91UtiBluSC-25

Ray, Steve
83GreHorT-11

Raybon, Shannon
86VisOakP-16
87VisOakP-27
88OrlTwiB-25

Rayborn, Kenny
97LowSpiB-23
98MicBatCM-26

Rayborn, Kris
98JohCCTI-27
99TeaBesR-69
99TeaBesRG-69
99TeaBesRS-69

Raydon, Curt
59Top-305
60Top-49
60TopVen-49

Rayford, Floyd
78AngFamF-29
78SSP270-200
79SalLakCGT-20B
80RocRedWT-18
81RocRedWT-14
81RocRedWW-14
81Top-399
83RocRedWT-13
83Top-192
84BalOriP-26
84Fle-334
84FleUpd-95
84Nes792-514
84Top-514
84TopTif-514
84TopTra-96T
84TopTraT-96T
85BalOriP-22
85BalOriP-23
85Don-576
85Fle-186
85OriHea-14
85Top-341
85TopTif-341
86BalOriHMP-14
86BalOriP-14
86Don-332
86Fle-283
86Lea-197
86Top-623
86TopTif-623
87BalOriP-27
87OriFreB-6
87Top-426
87TopTif-426
88Sco-359
88ScoGlo-359
88Top-296
88TopTif-296
89ScrRedBC-22
89ScrRedBP-727
90CMC-248
90El PasDAGTI-39
90ScrRedBC-22
91LinDriAAA-500
91OriCro-375
91ScrRedBLD-500
91ScrRedBP-2556
92BatCliCB-29
92BatCliF-3284
94BatCliC-28
94BatCliF-3464
97PieBolWB-2
98BelSnaM-26

Raymer, Fred
09ObaT21-44
09ObaT21-148
09ObaT21-420
10BisCoaLE99-25
11SpoLifCW-298
12ObaPreT-169

Raymer, Greg
83MiaMarT-9
86JacExpT-12

Raymond, Bugs (Arthur)
09ColChiE-236
09RamT20-97
09SpoNewSM-35
09T206-298
11PinT-5-261
11S74Sil-93
11SpoLifM-216
11T205-142
11TurRedT-113
12ColRedB-236
12ColTinT-236
12HasTriFT-69

Raymond, Claude
63Top-519
64Top-504
65OPC-48
65Top-48
66Top-586
67AstTeal2-22
67CokCapAs-4
67Top-364
68BraPos-26
68OPC-166
68Top-166
68TopVen-166
69Top-446
70DayDaiNM-132
70ExpPin-12
70MLBOffS-68
70OPC-268
70Top-268
71ExpPS-20
71MLBOffS-138
71OPC-202
71OPC-536
71Top-536
78TCM60I-46
81WhiSox1T-39
86AstMot-4
87AstSer1-19
87AstShoSTw-13
92Nab-23
92UppDecS-21
93ExpDonM-26

Raymondi, Michael
96HudValRB-21

Raynor, Mark
95BatCliTI-27
96PieBolWB-22
97ClePhi-16
98ReaPhiUM-18

Raynor, Tom
92ForLauYTI-25
93PriWilCC-30

Raziano, Barry
75IntLeaASB-25
75PacCoaLAB-25
75SalLakCC-15

Raziano, Michael S.
88SprCarB-16

Razjigaev, Rudy
93BoiHawC-23
93BoiHawF-3916
93Top-633
93TopGol-633
93TopInaM-633
93TopInaR-633
93TopMic-633

Razook, Mark
87AncGlaP-24
89WauTimGS-12
89WilBilS-17
90CMC-756
90WilBilB-19
90WilBilP-1066
90WilBilS-20

Razorback, The
90ArkRaz-11

Razorbacks, Arkansas
90ArkRaz-31

Rea, Clarke
91NiaFalRC-8
91NiaFalRP-3638
92LetMouSP-10
93FayGenC-20
93FayGenF-133

Rea, Shayne
90EugEmeGS-24
91AppFoxCB-11
91AppFoxP-1717
91Cla/Bes-250
92AppFoxCB-17
92AppFoxFI-984

Read, Addison
21Zee-36
22Zee-37
23Zee-54
23Zee-55
24Zee-36
25Zee-37
26Zee-86
27Zee-60
28Zee-86
29Zee-80
30Zee-93
31Zee-51
32Zee-65

Read, James
88PacEigMO-11

Reade, Bill
80UtiBluJT-30

Reade, Curtis
81VerBeaDT-16

Ready, Jerry
78TucTorC-48

Ready, Randy
81BurBeeT-17
82ElPasDT-7
84BrePol-2
84TopTra-97T
84TopTraT-97T
85BrePol-2
85Fle-592
86BrePol-2
86Don-481
86Fle-498
86Top-209
86TopTif-209
87FleUpd-100
87FleUpdG-100
87PadBohHB-5
87TopTra-97T
87TopTraT-97T
88Don-264
88Fle-594
88FleGlo-594
88OPC-151
88PadCok-5
88PadSmo-23
88PanSti-407
88Sco-512
88ScoGlo-512
88StaLinPa-10
88Top-426
88TopBig-102
88TopTif-426
89Don-365
89DonBasB-215
89Fle-315
89FleGlo-315
89OPC-82
89PadCok-13
89PanSti-201
89PhiTas-45
89Sco-426
89ScoRoo-60T
89Top-551
89TopSti-106
89TopTif-551
89TopTra-102T
89TopTraT-102T
89UppDec-474
90Don-396
90El PasDAGTI-13
90Fle-571
90FleCan-571
90Lea-500
90OPC-356
90PanSti-311
90PhiTas-26
90PubIntS-57
90Sco-376
90Top-356
90TopBig-150
90TopSti-120
90TopTif-356
90UppDec-404
91Bow-495
91Don-148
91Fle-410A
91Fle-410B
91Lea-82
91OPC-137
91PanFreS-104
91PhiMed-33
91Sco-615
91StaClu-265
91Top-137
91TopDesS-137
91TopMic-137
91TopTif-137
91Ult-271
91UppDec-540
92AthMot-25
92Don-179
92Fle-542
92Lea-246
92LeaBlaG-246
92OPC-63
92Sco-59

❑ 92ScoProP-13
❑ 92Stu-228
❑ 92Top-63
❑ 92TopGol-63
❑ 92TopGolW-63
❑ 92TopMic-63
❑ 92Ult-427
❑ 92UppDec-408
❑ 94BreMilB-72
❑ 94Fle-547
❑ 95Phi-25
❑ 95PhiMel-19
Reagan, Don
❑ 20Zee-34
Reagan, Edward
❑ 09T206-510
❑ 10CouT21-55
Reagan, Kyle
❑ 89BilMusP-2047
Reagan, Ronald
❑ 84WilMay-39
❑ 86TopRos-88
Reagans, Javan
❑ 88JamExpP-1917
Reames, Britt
❑ 95NewJerCTI-23
❑ 96MidLeaAB-22
❑ 96PeoChiB-25
❑ 97Bes-43
❑ 97BesLimA-36
❑ 98BesCasT-8
❑ 98BesFulCA-19
❑ 98BesPreA-40
Reames, Jay
❑ 96NewJerCB-22
❑ 97PeoChi-21
Reams, Ronald
❑ 90MedHatBJB-22
❑ 91MyrBeaHC-25
❑ 91MyrBeaHP-2959
❑ 92MyrBeaHC-9
❑ 92MyrBeaHF-2212
❑ 93KnoSmoF-1264
Reardon, Beans
❑ 94ConTSN-1188
❑ 94ConTSNB-1188
Reardon, Jeff
❑ 77LynMetT-24
❑ 79TidTidT-5
❑ 81Don-156
❑ 81ExpPos-12
❑ 81Fle-335
❑ 81OPC-79
❑ 81Top-456
❑ 81TopTra-819
❑ 82Don-547
❑ 82ExpHygM-17
❑ 82ExpPos-33
❑ 82Fle-204
❑ 82FleSta-37
❑ 82OPC-123
❑ 82OPCPos-23
❑ 82Top-667
❑ 83Don-194
❑ 83ExpPos-26
❑ 83ExpStu-5
❑ 83Fle-293
❑ 83FleSta-159
❑ 83FleSti-267
❑ 83OPC-290
❑ 83Top-290
❑ 83TopSti-254
❑ 84Don-279
❑ 84ExpPos-24
❑ 84ExpStu-13
❑ 84Fle-283
❑ 84FleSti-71
❑ 84JacMetF-10
❑ 84Nes792-595
❑ 84OPC-116
❑ 84Top-595
❑ 84TopSti-89
❑ 84TopTif-595
❑ 85Don-331
❑ 85Fle-407
❑ 85Lea-126
❑ 85OPC-375
❑ 85OPCPos-12
❑ 85Top-375
❑ 85TopMin-375
❑ 85TopSti-85
❑ 85TopTif-375
❑ 86Don-209
❑ 86DonAll-33
❑ 86DonHig-14
❑ 86ExpProPa-13
❑ 86ExpProPo-11
❑ 86Fle-257
❑ 86FleLimE-35
❑ 86FleSlu-26
❑ 86FleStiC-94
❑ 86GenMilB-6F
❑ 86Lea-214
❑ 86OPC-35
❑ 86SevCoi-E10
❑ 86Spo-119
❑ 86Top-35
❑ 86Top-711
❑ 86Top3-D-20
❑ 86TopGaloC-10
❑ 86TopGloS-55
❑ 86TopSti-76
❑ 86TopSup-6
❑ 86TopTat-22
❑ 86TopTif-35
❑ 86TopTif-711
❑ 87ClaGam-94
❑ 87Don-98
❑ 87DonAll-52
❑ 87DonWaxBC-PC11
❑ 87Fle-329
❑ 87FleGlo-329
❑ 87FleLimE-34
❑ 87FleMin-88
❑ 87FleSlu-33
❑ 87FleStiC-98
❑ 87FleUpd-101
❑ 87FleUpdG-101
❑ 87KraFoo-40
❑ 87Lea-143
❑ 87OPC-165
❑ 87RedFolSB-65
❑ 87Spo-77
❑ 87SpoTeaP-17
❑ 87Top-165
❑ 87TopGloS-15
❑ 87TopMinL-18
❑ 87TopSti-81
❑ 87TopTif-165
❑ 87TopTra-98T
❑ 87TopTraT-98T
❑ 87TwiPos-21
❑ 87TwiTeal-26
❑ 88Don-122
❑ 88DonBasB-242
❑ 88Fle-20
❑ 88FleAwaW-31
❑ 88FleBasA-33
❑ 88FleGlo-20
❑ 88FleMin-37
❑ 88FleSlu-32
❑ 88FleStiC-46
❑ 88FleTeaL-28
❑ 88Nes-27
❑ 88OPC-99
❑ 88PanSti-133
❑ 88RedFolSB-73
❑ 88Sco-91
❑ 88ScoGlo-91
❑ 88Spo-53
❑ 88StaLinTw-16
❑ 88Top-425
❑ 88TopBig-10
❑ 88TopMinL-24
❑ 88TopRitTM-28
❑ 88TopSti-14
❑ 88TopSti-280
❑ 88TopTif-425
❑ 88TwiMasBD-4
❑ 88TwiSmoC-4
❑ 89Bow-148
❑ 89BowTif-148
❑ 89CadEllD-43
❑ 89Don-155
❑ 89DonAll-24
❑ 89DonBasB-242
❑ 89Fle-125
❑ 89FleGlo-125
❑ 89FleSup-34
❑ 89OPC-86
❑ 89PanSti-382
❑ 89RedFolSB-94
❑ 89Sco-305
❑ 89ScoHot1S-24
❑ 89Spo-168
❑ 89Top-775
❑ 89TopBasT-136
❑ 89TopGloS-54
❑ 89TopMinL-63
❑ 89TopSti-8
❑ 89TopSti-284
❑ 89TopStiB-33
❑ 89TopTif-775
❑ 89UppDec-596
❑ 89Woo-17
❑ 90Bow-265
❑ 90BowTif-265
❑ 90ClaBlu-101
❑ 90ClaYel-T55
❑ 90Don-119
❑ 90DonBesA-72
❑ 90Fle-385
❑ 90FleCan-385
❑ 90FleUpd-75
❑ 90Lea-276
❑ 90OPC-235
❑ 90OPCBoxB-K
❑ 90PanSti-108
❑ 90PubIntS-293
❑ 90PubIntS-337
❑ 90RedFolSB-76
❑ 90RedSoxP-16
❑ 90Sco-522
❑ 90ScoRoo-17T
❑ 90Spo-37
❑ 90Top-235
❑ 90TopBig-285
❑ 90TopMag-93
❑ 90TopSti-6
❑ 90TopSti-289
❑ 90TopTif-235
❑ 90TopTra-101T
❑ 90TopTraT-101T
❑ 90TopTVRS-15
❑ 90TopWaxBC-K
❑ 90UppDec-417
❑ 90UppDec-729
❑ 90Woo-17
❑ 91Bow-107
❑ 91Don-369
❑ 91Fle-109
❑ 91Lea-252
❑ 91MetWIZ-325
❑ 91OPC-605
❑ 91OPCBoxB-M
❑ 91OPCPre-98
❑ 91PanFreS-272
❑ 91PanSti-218
❑ 91RedFolS-76
❑ 91RedSoxP-17
❑ 91RedSoxP-24
❑ 91Sco-164
❑ 91StaClu-354
❑ 91StaCluMO-25
❑ 91Stu-19
❑ 91Top-605
❑ 91TopDesS-605
❑ 91TopMic-605
❑ 91TopTif-605
❑ 91TopWaxBC-M
❑ 91Ult-40
❑ 91UppDec-418
❑ 91USPlaCA-5D
❑ 91Woo-17
❑ 92Bow-475
❑ 92Don-89
❑ 92DonUpd-U9
❑ 92Fle-46
❑ 92FleUpd-71
❑ 92FleUpdH-3
❑ 92Hig5-9
❑ 92Lea-151
❑ 92LeaBlaG-151
❑ 92OPC-3
❑ 92OPC-182
❑ 92PepDieM-8
❑ 92Pin-158
❑ 92RedSoxDD-24
❑ 92Sco-58
❑ 92Sco100S-5
❑ 92ScoRoo-46T
❑ 92StaClu-657
❑ 92StaCluD-149
❑ 92StaCluNC-657
❑ 92Stu-137
❑ 92SunSee-1
❑ 92Top-3
❑ 92Top-182
❑ 92TopGol-3
❑ 92TopGol-182
❑ 92TopGolW-3
❑ 92TopGolW-182
❑ 92TopMic-3
❑ 92TopMic-182
❑ 92Ult-20
❑ 92UppDec-501
❑ 93Don-739
❑ 93ExpDonM-11
❑ 93Fle-370
❑ 93FleFinE-18
❑ 93Lea-389
❑ 93OPC-342
❑ 93Pin-535
❑ 93RedKah-19
❑ 93Sco-514
❑ 93Sco-564
❑ 93Sel-362
❑ 93SelRoo-135T
❑ 93StaClu-161
❑ 93StaClu-602
❑ 93StaCluFDI-161
❑ 93StaCluFDI-602
❑ 93StaCluMO-21
❑ 93StaCluMOP-161
❑ 93StaCluMOP-602
❑ 93Top-475
❑ 93TopGol-475
❑ 93TopInaM-475
❑ 93TopInaR-475
❑ 93TopMic-475
❑ 93Ult-333
❑ 93UppDec-541
❑ 93UppDecGold-541
❑ 93UppDecSH-HI15
❑ 94ColC-592
❑ 94ColChoGS-592
❑ 94ColChoSS-592
❑ 94Fle-420
❑ 94Pac-155
❑ 94Pin-521
❑ 94PinArtP-521
❑ 94PinMusC-521
❑ 94Sco-251
❑ 94ScoGolR-251
Reaves, Scott
❑ 87UtiBluSP-20
❑ 88ClePhiS-20
❑ 88SpaPhiS-1
❑ 89ClePhiS-18
Reavis, Kelly
❑ 91OklStaC-19
Reberger, Frank
❑ 69Top-637
❑ 70Gia-12
❑ 70MLBOffS-117
❑ 70OPC-103
❑ 70Top-103
❑ 71MLBOffS-262
❑ 71OPC-251
❑ 71Top-251
❑ 72Top-548
❑ 83NasAngT-21
❑ 84EdmTraC-242
❑ 85EdmTraC-23
❑ 86EdmTraP-23
❑ 87EdmTraP-2077
❑ 92SanJosGC-28
❑ 93MarPub-28
❑ 96VanCanB-2
❑ 97ShrCap-4
❑ 97ShrCapB-4
Reboulet, James
❑ 83EriCarT-4
❑ 84SavCarT-10
❑ 86FloStaLAP-40
❑ 86St.PetCP-26
❑ 87ArkTraP-23
❑ 88BufBisC-17
❑ 88BufBisP-1470
❑ 88BufBisTI-7
Reboulet, Jeff
❑ 87OrlTwiP-15
❑ 88OrlTwiB-19
❑ 89OrlTwiP-1345
❑ 90LSUTigGM-4
❑ 90OrlSunRB-27
❑ 90OrlSunRP-1093
❑ 90OrlSunRS-16
❑ 91LinDriAAA-415
❑ 91PorBeaLD-415
❑ 91PorBeaP-1572
❑ 92DonRoo-100
❑ 92PorBeaS-417
❑ 93Don-179
❑ 93Fle-642
❑ 93PacSpa-525
❑ 93Sco-233
❑ 93StaClu-146
❑ 93StaCluFDI-146
❑ 93StaCluMOP-146
❑ 93Top-172
❑ 93TopGol-172
❑ 93TopInaM-172
❑ 93TopInaR-172
❑ 93TopMic-172
❑ 93UppDec-733
❑ 93UppDecGold-733
❑ 94Don-85
❑ 94Fle-218
❑ 94Pac-366
❑ 94StaClu-183
❑ 94StaCluFDI-183
❑ 94StaCluGR-183
❑ 94StaCluMOP-183
❑ 94TopTra-123T
❑ 95ColCho-488
❑ 95ColChoGS-488
❑ 95ColChoSS-488
❑ 95Don-432
❑ 95DonPreP-432
❑ 95Fle-213
❑ 95Sco-545
❑ 95ScoGolR-545
❑ 95ScoPlaTS-545
❑ 95StaClu-137
❑ 95StaCluFDI-137
❑ 95StaCluMOP-137
❑ 95StaCluSTWS-137
❑ 95Top-359
❑ 96ColCho-607
❑ 96ColChoGS-607
❑ 96ColChoSS-607
❑ 96Don-512
❑ 96DonPreP-512
❑ 96Fle-174
❑ 96FleTif-174
❑ 96LeaSigEA-166
❑ 96Sco-440
❑ 97BalOriP-27
❑ 97Pac-144
❑ 97PacLigB-144
❑ 97PacSil-144
❑ 98Pac-32
❑ 98PacOnl-99
❑ 98PacOnlR-99
❑ 98PacOnlWC-99
❑ 98PacPlaB-32
❑ 98PacRedT-32
❑ 98PacSil-32
Rech, Ed
❑ 82LynMetT-8
Rector, Bobby
❑ 95BurBeeTI-17
❑ 96SanJosGB-25
❑ 97BakBlaB-25
❑ 97BakBlaTI-25
❑ 98PorSeaDQ-9
Red Birds, Columbus
❑ 36R31Pre-G22
❑ 38BasTabP-42
Red Sox, Boston
❑ 09MaxPubP-22
❑ 09SpoNewSM-82
❑ 13FatT20-1
❑ 35GouPreR-1
❑ 36R31Pre-G19A
❑ 36R31Pre-G19B
❑ 38BasTabP-43
❑ 46SpoExcW-10-3
❑ 51TopTea-1
❑ 56Top-111
❑ 57Top-171
❑ 58Top-312
❑ 59Top-248
❑ 60Top-537
❑ 60TopTat-65
❑ 61Top-373
❑ 61TopMagR-5
❑ 62GuyPotCP-2
❑ 62Top-334
❑ 63GadFunC-14
❑ 63Top-202
❑ 64Top-579
❑ 64TopTatI-2
❑ 65Top-403
❑ 66Top-259
❑ 66TopRubI-102
❑ 66TopVen-259
❑ 67Top-604
❑ 68LauWorS-9
❑ 68LauWorS-15
❑ 69FleCloS-3
❑ 69FleCloS-42
❑ 69TopStaA-3
❑ 70FleWorS-1
❑ 70FleWorS-9
❑ 70FleWorS-15
❑ 70FleWorS-64
❑ 70Top-563
❑ 71FleWorS-10
❑ 71FleWorS-14
❑ 71FleWorS-65
❑ 71OPC-386
❑ 71Top-386
❑ 71TopTat-15
❑ 72OPC-328
❑ 72Top-328
❑ 72TopCloT-26
❑ 73OPC-596
❑ 73OPCBTC-3
❑ 73Top-596
❑ 73TopBluTC-3
❑ 74OPC-567
❑ 74OPCTC-3
❑ 74Top-567
❑ 74TopStaA-3
❑ 74TopTeaC-3
❑ 78Top-424
❑ 83FleSta-227
❑ 83FleSti-NNO
❑ 83FleSti-NNO
❑ 87FleWaxBC-C5
❑ 87SpoTeaL-9
❑ 88PanSti-456
❑ 88RedFolSB-119
❑ 89FleWaxBC-C17
❑ 90PubIntS-642
❑ 90RedFolSB-109
❑ 91PanCanT1-122
❑ 91PanCanT1-125
❑ 94ImpProP-2
❑ 94Sco-318
❑ 94ScoGolR-318
❑ 95PacPriTL-2
❑ 95PanSti-149
❑ 96FleRedS-19
❑ 96PanSti-139
❑ 99Vic-56
Red Sox, Memphis
❑ 92NegLeaRLI-89
❑ 92NegLeaRLI-90
❑ 93NegLeaRL2-54
❑ 93NegLeaRL2-74
Red Sox, Pawtucket
❑ 87IntLeaAT-41
❑ 89PawRedSTI-30
❑ 90PawRedSDD-31
❑ 91PawRedSDD-31
❑ 93PawRedSDD-31
❑ 94PawRedSDD-31
❑ 95PawRedSDD-31
❑ 96PawRedSDD-30
❑ 97DunDonPPS-31
Red Stockings, Cincinnati
❑ 63GadFunC-16
❑ 69RedStoPaS-1
❑ 90BasWit-90
❑ 94OriofB-19
❑ 94UppDecAH-101
❑ 94UppDecAH1-101
❑ 94UppDecAJ-43
❑ 94UppDecAJG-43
❑ 94UppDecMPC-NNO
Red Wings, Rochester
❑ 81RocRedWW-20
❑ 87IntLeaAT-44
❑ 88RocRedWGCP-1
❑ 88RocRedWGCP-33
❑ 88RocRedWGCP-34
❑ 88RocRedWGCP-35
❑ 88RocRedWGCP-36
Redd, Rick R.
❑ 88HarSenP-840
Redd, Ricky Joe
❑ 91MisStaB-41
❑ 92MisStaB-37
❑ 93MisStaB-38
Redd, Ulysses A.
❑ 93NegLeaRL2-33
Redding, Cannonball (Dick)
❑ 74LauOldTBS-25
❑ 86NegLeaF-112
❑ 90NegLeaS-3
Redding, Corey
❑ 95DavLipB-20
Redding, Mike
❑ 86KenTwiP-21
❑ 87VisOakP-16
❑ 88VisOakCLC-160
❑ 88VisOakP-93
❑ 89OrlTwiB-22
❑ 89OrlTwiP-1333
❑ 90OrlSunRB-19
❑ 90OrlSunRP-1081

❑ 90OrlSunRS-17
❑ 90StaFS7-47
Redding, Tim
❑ 98AubDouTI-23
Reddish, Mike
❑ 83NasSouTI-17
❑ 85ChaO'sT-10
❑ 86RocRedWP-18
Redfern, Pete
❑ 76MinTwiP-13
❑ 77Top-249
❑ 78Top-81
❑ 78TwiFriP-16
❑ 79Top-113
❑ 79TwiFriP-23
❑ 80Top-403
❑ 80TwiPos-25
❑ 81Don-548
❑ 81Fle-560
❑ 81Top-714
❑ 81TwiPos-23
❑ 82Don-51
❑ 82Fle-559
❑ 82Top-309
❑ 82TwiPos-24
❑ 83Don-256
❑ 83Fle-623
❑ 83Top-559
❑ 88AlaGolAA70TI-14
Redfield, Joe
❑ 86ChaOriW-23
❑ 87MidAngP-13
❑ 87TexLeaAF-12
❑ 88EdmTraC-20
❑ 88EdmTraP-555
❑ 89ScrRedBC-20
❑ 89ScrRedBP-731
❑ 90CMC-34
❑ 90DenZepC-9
❑ 90DenZepP-634
❑ 90ProAAAF-659
❑ 90TriAllGP-AAA25
❑ 91BufBisLD-41
❑ 91BufBisP-549
❑ 91LinDriAAA-41
❑ 92Bow-438
❑ 92BufBisBS-16
❑ 92BufBisF-335
❑ 92BufBisS-39
❑ 92Fle-563
❑ 92Sco-412
❑ 93HolLeg-16
Redick, Kevin
❑ 86EveGiaC-6
❑ 86EveGiaPC-23
❑ 87CliGiaP-13
Reding, Josh
❑ 98CapFeaCM-18
❑ 98SouAtlLPM-17
Redington, Thomas
❑ 88SumBraP-412
❑ 89BurBraP-1610
❑ 89BurBraS-17
❑ 90Bes-75
❑ 90GreBraB-5
❑ 90GreBraP-1137
❑ 90GreBraS-16
❑ 90StaFS7-95
❑ 91Cla/Bes-327
❑ 91LinDriAA-615
❑ 91WicWraLD-615
❑ 91WicWraP-2605
❑ 91WicWraRD-15
❑ 92BirBarF-2593
❑ 92BirBarS-87
❑ 92ClaFS7-32
❑ 92OPC-473
❑ 92Top-473
❑ 92TopGol-473
❑ 92TopGolW-473
❑ 92TopMic-473
❑ 94LakElsSC-14
❑ 94LakElsSF-1673
❑ 95AusFut-80
❑ 95LakElsSTI-19
Redman, Augustus
❑ 26Zee-16
Redman, Mark
❑ 95Bes-132
❑ 95BowBes-X2
❑ 95BowBesR-X2
❑ 95ForMyeMTI-9
❑ 95SPML-109
❑ 96BesAutSA-59
❑ 96Bow-382
❑ 96BowFoi-382
❑ 96Exc-81
❑ 96FtMyeMB-8
❑ 96HarCitRCB-25
❑ 96Top-14
❑ 96TopPowB-14
❑ 97BesAutAS-44
❑ 97BesAutP-R10
❑ 97Bow-126
❑ 97BowBes-161
❑ 97BowBesAR-161
❑ 97BowBesR-161
❑ 97BowInt-126
❑ 97SalLakB-22
❑ 97Top-494
❑ 98Bow-210
❑ 98BowChr-210
❑ 98BowChrGA-210
❑ 98BowChrGAR-210
❑ 98BowChrI-210
❑ 98BowChrIR-210
❑ 98BowChrR-210
❑ 98BowGolA-210
❑ 98BowInt-210
❑ 98NewBriRCM-25
Redman, Tike
❑ 97LynHil-18
❑ 98CarLeaTPQ-23
❑ 98LynHilQ-23
Redman, Tim
❑ 87EriCarP-29
❑ 88HamRedP-1729
❑ 89HamRedS-22
❑ 90St.PetCS-19
❑ 91ArkTraP-1290
❑ 92LouRedF-1890
❑ 95NewJerCTI-24
Redmon, Glenn
❑ 74PhoGiaC-83
❑ 75PhoGiaC-8
❑ 75PhoGiaCK-13
❑ 76WilTomT-19
Redmond, Andre
❑ 89PriPirS-16
❑ 90WelPirP-25
❑ 91AugPirP-805
Redmond, Dan
❑ 87WatIndP-28
❑ 89CanIndB-9
Redmond, H. Wayne
❑ 71OPC-728
❑ 71Top-728
Redmond, Mike
❑ 93KanCouCC-17
❑ 93KanCouCF-919
❑ 93KanCouCTI-18
❑ 94KanCouCC-20
❑ 94KanCouCF-166
❑ 94KanCouCTI-24
❑ 95PorSeaDTI-22
❑ 96PorSeaDB-22
❑ 97ChaKni-25
❑ 98PorSeaD5AQ-6
❑ 98PorSeaDQ-14
❑ 99Fle-556
❑ 99FleSta9-556
❑ 99FleWarT-556
Reds, Cincinnati
❑ 09MaxPubP-24
❑ 13FatT20-12
❑ 20RedWorCP-25
❑ 38BasTabP-44
❑ 41HarHarW-30
❑ 41HarHarW-31
❑ 51TopTea-4
❑ 56Top-90A
❑ 56Top-90B
❑ 56Top-90C
❑ 57Top-322
❑ 58Top-428A
❑ 58Top-428B
❑ 59Top-111
❑ 59TopVen-111
❑ 60Top-164
❑ 60TopTat-57
❑ 60TopVen-164
❑ 61Top-249
❑ 61TopMagR-15
❑ 62GuyPotCP-5
❑ 62Top-465
❑ 63Top-63
❑ 64Top-403
❑ 64TopTatI-6
❑ 65Top-316
❑ 66OPC-59
❑ 66Top-59
❑ 66TopRubI-106
❑ 66TopVen-59
❑ 67Top-407
❑ 68LauWorS-16
❑ 68LauWorS-37
❑ 68Top-574
❑ 69FleCloS-7
❑ 69FleCloS-41
❑ 69TopStaA-7
❑ 70FleWorS-16
❑ 70FleWorS-36
❑ 70FleWorS-37
❑ 70OPC-544
❑ 70Top-544
❑ 71FleWorS-17
❑ 71FleWorS-37
❑ 71FleWorS-38
❑ 71FleWorS-68
❑ 71OPC-357
❑ 71Top-357
❑ 71TopTat-52
❑ 72Top-651
❑ 73OPC-641
❑ 73OPCBTC-7
❑ 73Top-641
❑ 73TopBluTC-7
❑ 74OPC-459
❑ 74OPCTC-7
❑ 74Top-459
❑ 74TopStaA-7
❑ 74TopTeaC-7
❑ 78Top-526
❑ 83FleSta-231
❑ 83FleSti-NNO
❑ 83FleSti-NNO
❑ 86JosHalC-5
❑ 87SpoTeaL-4
❑ 88PanSti-269
❑ 88PanSti-471
❑ 88RedFolSB-130
❑ 90PubIntS-624
❑ 90RedFolSB-107
❑ 90TopMag-37
❑ 91FleWorS-8
❑ 91PanCanT1-117
❑ 91PanCanT1-128
❑ 91PanCanT1-131
❑ 91Woo-32
❑ 93TedWilPC-6
❑ 94ImpProP-17
❑ 94Sco-649
❑ 94ScoGolR-649
❑ 95PacPriTL-17
❑ 95PanSti-131
❑ 96PanSti-53
❑ 99Vic-102
Redus, Gary
❑ 81WatRedT-15
❑ 82IndIndTI-17
❑ 83RedYea-2
❑ 83TopTra-94T
❑ 84AllGamPI-67
❑ 84Don-184
❑ 84DonActAS-16
❑ 84Fle-481
❑ 84Nes792-475
❑ 84OPC-231
❑ 84RedBor-2
❑ 84RedEnq-9
❑ 84Top-475
❑ 84TopRubD-20
❑ 84TopSti-52
❑ 84TopTif-475
❑ 85Don-306
❑ 85Fle-549
❑ 85IndIndTI-34
❑ 85Lea-47
❑ 85OPC-146
❑ 85Top-146
❑ 85TopRubD-20
❑ 85TopSti-49
❑ 85TopTif-146
❑ 86Don-306
❑ 86Fle-189
❑ 86FleUpd-94
❑ 86OPC-342
❑ 86PhiCIG-12
❑ 86PhiKel-3
❑ 86PhiTas-22
❑ 86Top-342
❑ 86TopTif-342
❑ 86TopTra-90T
❑ 86TopTraT-90T
❑ 87Don-288
❑ 87DonOpeD-229
❑ 87Fle-181
❑ 87FleGlo-181
❑ 87FleUpd-102
❑ 87FleUpdG-102
❑ 87OPC-42
❑ 87Top-42
❑ 87TopSti-119
❑ 87TopTif-42
❑ 87TopTra-99T
❑ 87TopTraT-99T
❑ 87WhiSoxC-24
❑ 88Don-370
❑ 88Fle-408
❑ 88FleGlo-408
❑ 88OPC-332
❑ 88PanSti-64
❑ 88Sco-443
❑ 88ScoGlo-443
❑ 88StaLinWS-15
❑ 88Top-657
❑ 88TopMinL-9
❑ 88TopTif-657
❑ 88WhiSoxC-24
❑ 89Bow-425
❑ 89BowTif-425
❑ 89Don-605
❑ 89Fle-218
❑ 89FleGlo-218
❑ 89OPC-281
❑ 89PirVerFJ-2
❑ 89Sco-177
❑ 89Top-281
❑ 89TopBig-131
❑ 89TopTif-281
❑ 89UppDec-419
❑ 90Bow-180
❑ 90BowTif-180
❑ 90Don-597
❑ 90Fle-476
❑ 90FleCan-476
❑ 90Lea-209
❑ 90OPC-507
❑ 90PanSti-331
❑ 90PirHomC-24
❑ 90PubIntS-162
❑ 90Sco-14
❑ 90Top-507
❑ 90TopBig-52
❑ 90TopSti-127
❑ 90TopTif-507
❑ 90UppDec-248
❑ 91Bow-516
❑ 91Don-587
❑ 91Fle-47
❑ 91Lea-254
❑ 91OPC-771
❑ 91Sco-226
❑ 91StaClu-486
❑ 91Top-771
❑ 91TopDesS-771
❑ 91TopMic-771
❑ 91TopTif-771
❑ 91Ult-285
❑ 91UppDec-38
❑ 92Don-67
❑ 92Fle-564
❑ 92Lea-223
❑ 92LeaBlaG-223
❑ 92OPC-453
❑ 92PirNatI-19
❑ 92Sco-303
❑ 92StaClu-524
❑ 92Top-453
❑ 92TopGol-453
❑ 92TopGolW-453
❑ 92TopMic-453
❑ 92Ult-560
❑ 92UppDec-519
❑ 93Don-516
❑ 93Fle-504
❑ 93Lea-426
❑ 93PacSpa-250
❑ 93RanKee-425
❑ 93RanStaC-14
❑ 93Ult-634
❑ 94Don-275
❑ 94Fle-318
❑ 94Lea-387
❑ 94Pac-626
❑ 94RanMagM-32
❑ 94Sco-191
❑ 94ScoGolR-191
❑ 94StaClu-514
❑ 94StaCluFDI-514
❑ 94StaCluGR-514
❑ 94StaCluMOP-514
❑ 94StaCluT-264
❑ 94StaCluTFDI-264
❑ 94Top-108
❑ 94TopGol-108
❑ 94TopSpa-108
❑ 95Sco-103
❑ 95ScoGolR-103
❑ 95ScoPlaTS-103
Reece, Bob
❑ 78ExpPos-11
❑ 83WicAerDS-17
Reece, Jeff
❑ 86StoPorP-23
❑ 87WicPilRD-14
Reece, John
❑ 93DanBraC-19
❑ 93DanBraF-3633
Reece, Thad
❑ 83MadMusF-9
❑ 84AlbA'sT-5
❑ 85TacTigC-135
❑ 86TacTigP-18
❑ 87TacTigP-10
❑ 88MemChiB-24
❑ 90AlbDecGB-35
❑ 90CMC-195
❑ 90OmaRoyC-20
❑ 90OmaRoyP-74
❑ 90ProAAAF-609
Reed, Billy
❑ 89HigSchPLS-23
❑ 89WatDiaP-1788
❑ 89WatDiaS-23
❑ 90Bes-314
❑ 90WatDiaB-14
❑ 90WatDiaP-2379
❑ 91HigDesMC-9
❑ 91HigDesMP-2392
❑ 95HudValRTI-5
Reed, Bob E.
❑ 29Zee-141
❑ 30Zee-156
❑ 70OPC-207
❑ 70Top-207
❑ 71MLBOffS-404
❑ 71OPC-732
❑ 71Top-732
Reed, Bobby
❑ 88MisStaB-28
❑ 89MisStaB-33
❑ 90MisStaB-35
❑ 91LinDriAA-591
❑ 91TulDriLD-591
❑ 91TulDriP-2771
❑ 91TulDriTI-22
❑ 92Bow-522
❑ 92UppDecML-232
Reed, Brandon
❑ 94BriTigC-20
❑ 94BriTigF-3500
❑ 95Bes-19
❑ 95Bes-110
❑ 95FayGenTI-20
❑ 96Exc-52
❑ 96ExcSeaC-7
❑ 96JacSunB-24
❑ 96Top-431
❑ 97Bow-325
❑ 97BowInt-325
❑ 97JacSun-19
❑ 97TexAllM-25
❑ 98TolMudHQ-25
❑ 99Bow-303
❑ 99BowGol-303
❑ 99BowInt-303
Reed, Brian
❑ 94ButCopKSP-8
❑ 95PeoChiTI-21
❑ 96StPetCB-26
Reed, Chris
❑ 91PriRedC-6
❑ 91PriRedP-3512
❑ 92BilMusF-3354
❑ 92BilMusSP-15
❑ 94ChaWheC-21
❑ 94ChaWheF-2702
❑ 96ChaLooB-23
❑ 97ChaLoo-21
Reed, Curt
❑ 82AppFoxFr-12
❑ 83GleFalWST-9
Reed, Curtis
❑ 81HawIslT-10
Reed, Dan
❑ 97CalLeaATI-43
❑ 97FreKey-21
Reed, Darren
❑ 86AlbYanT-23
❑ 87AlbYanP-16
❑ 88MetColP-44
❑ 88TidTidCa-17
❑ 88TidTidCM-16
❑ 88TidTidP-1603
❑ 89MetColP-49
❑ 89TidTidC-17
❑ 89TidTidP-1957
❑ 90AlbDecGB-20
❑ 90CMC-376
❑ 90FleUpd-39
❑ 90MetColP-45
❑ 90ProAAAF-288
❑ 90TidTidC-25
❑ 90TidTidP-557
❑ 90TopTVM-54
❑ 91Fle-159
❑ 91MetColP-20
❑ 91MetWIZ-326
❑ 91Sco-368
❑ 91TopDeb90-129
❑ 92Bow-537
❑ 92DonRoo-101
❑ 92StaClu-824
❑ 92TopTra-91T
❑ 92TopTraG-91T
❑ 93Don-105
❑ 93MetColP-44
❑ 93MetKah-21
❑ 93Top-482
❑ 93TopGol-482
❑ 93TopInaM-482
❑ 93TopInaR-482
❑ 93TopMic-482
❑ 94BufBisF-1850
❑ 95RicBraTI-18
Reed, Dennis
❑ 87AncGlaP-25
❑ 90AshTouC-10
❑ 91AshTouP-568
❑ 92BurAstC-11
❑ 92BurAstF-544
Reed, Howard
❑ 60Lea-84
❑ 61UniOil-SP9
❑ 65DodTeal-18
❑ 65Top-544
❑ 66Top-387
❑ 70Top-548
❑ 71ExpLaPR-10
❑ 71ExpPS-21
❑ 71OPC-398
❑ 71Top-398
❑ 90DodTar-651
Reed, Jack
❑ 61Yan61RL-36
❑ 91YanRinP12-10
❑ 92YanWIZ6-101
Reed, Jamie
❑ 84ChaO'sT-14
❑ 85RocRedWT-28
❑ 87RocRedWP-22
❑ 88RocRedWGCP-31
❑ 88RocRedWP-214
Reed, Jason
❑ 94YakBeaC-14
❑ 94YakBeaF-3844
❑ 95GreFalDTI-19
❑ 95VerBeaDTI-22
Reed, Jeff
❑ 81WisRapTT-14
❑ 83OrlTwiT-5
❑ 84MinTwiP-24
❑ 84TolMudHT-2
❑ 84TwiTeal-7
❑ 85Don-30
❑ 85IntLeaAT-38
❑ 85TolMudHT-14
❑ 85TwiTeal-7
❑ 86FleUpd-95
❑ 86TwiTeal-7
❑ 87DonOpeD-92
❑ 87ExpPos-22
❑ 87Fle-550
❑ 87FleGlo-550
❑ 87Top-247
❑ 87TopTif-247
❑ 87TopTra-100T
❑ 87TopTraT-100T
❑ 88Don-88
❑ 88ExpPos-28
❑ 88Fle-194
❑ 88FleGlo-194
❑ 88OPC-176
❑ 88Sco-408
❑ 88ScoGlo-408

- 88StaLinE-14
- 88Top-176
- 88TopTif-176
- 89Don-469
- 89Fle-167
- 89FleGlo-167
- 89RedKah-34
- 89Sco-99
- 89Top-626
- 89TopBig-158
- 89TopTif-626
- 89UppDec-276
- 90Don-351
- 90Fle-429
- 90FleCan-429
- 90Lea-505
- 90OPC-772
- 90PublntS-37
- 90RedKah-23
- 90Sco-147
- 90Top-772
- 90TopTif-772
- 90UppDec-165
- 91Don-741
- 91Fle-78
- 91Lea-102
- 91OPC-419
- 91RedKah-34
- 91RedPep-17
- 91StaClu-534
- 91Top-419
- 91TopDesS-419
- 91TopMic-419
- 91TopTif-419
- 91Ult-101
- 92Don-451
- 92Fle-418
- 92OPC-91
- 92RedKah-34
- 92Sco-311
- 92StaClu-487
- 92Top-91
- 92TopGol-91
- 92TopGolW-91
- 92TopMic-91
- 92Ult-195
- 92UppDec-299
- 93Fle-397
- 93FleFinE-154
- 93GiaMot-25
- 93GiaPos-28
- 93GiaStaC-13
- 93PacSpa-87
- 93Ult-488
- 94Fle-698
- 94GiaAMC-18
- 94GiaMot-21
- 94GiaTarBC-21
- 94GiaUSPC-4C
- 94GiaUSPC-10H
- 94Pac-552
- 94StaClu-504
- 94StaCluFDI-504
- 94StaCluGR-504
- 94StaCluMOP-504
- 94StaCluT-17
- 94StaCluTFDI-17
- 94Top-291
- 94TopGol-291
- 94TopSpa-291
- 95GiaMot-21
- 95Top-181
- 96FleUpd-U130
- 96FleUpdTC-U130
- 96LeaSigEA-167
- 97DonTea-103
- 97DonTeaSPE-103
- 97Fle-314
- 97FleTif-314
- 97Pac-285
- 97PacLigB-285
- 97PacPriGotD-GD137
- 97PacSil-285
- 97Top-486
- 97Ult-188
- 97UltGolME-188
- 97UltPlaME-188
- 98Fin-193
- 98FinNo--193
- 98FinNo-R-193
- 98FinRef-193
- 98PacOnl-256
- 98PacOnlR-256
- 98PacOnlWC-256
- 98PacPar-156
- 98PacParC-156
- 98PacParG-156
- 98PacParHS-156
- 98PacParPB-156
- 98PacParR-156
- 98Top-199
- 98TopChr-199
- 98TopChrR-199
- 98TopDevR-199
- 98TopDia-199
- 98TopMiniC-199
- 99Fle-552
- 99FleSta9-552
- 99FleWarT-552
- 99Pac-152
- 99PacCroC-100
- 99PacCroCPB-100
- 99PacPlaB-152
- 99PacRed-152
- 99Top-144
- 99TopChr-144
- 99TopChrR-144
- 99TopMVPP-144
- 99UppDec-366
- 99UppDecEL1-366
- 99UppDecEL2-366

Reed, Jerry M.

- 80VenLeaS-247
- 81ReaPhiT-1
- 82OklCit8T-9
- 83ChaChaT-4
- 83IndPos-28
- 84MaiGuiT-2
- 85IndPol-35
- 85MaiGuiT-8
- 86CalCanP-22
- 86Fle-592
- 86Top-172
- 86TopTif-172
- 87MarMot-22
- 87Top-619
- 87TopTif-619
- 88Don-517
- 88Fle-387
- 88FleGlo-387
- 88MarMot-22
- 88Sco-488
- 88ScoGlo-488
- 88StaLinMa-16
- 88Top-332
- 88TopTif-332
- 89Don-657
- 89Fle-557
- 89FleGlo-557
- 89MarMot-22
- 89Sco-427
- 89Top-441
- 89TopTif-441
- 89UppDec-529
- 90Don-614
- 90Fle-523
- 90FleCan-523
- 90FleUpd-76
- 90Lea-368
- 90OPC-247
- 90PublntS-440
- 90Sco-492
- 90Top-247
- 90TopTif-247
- 90TopTVRS-58
- 90UppDec-210
- 91Fle-110
- 91PacSenL-141

Reed, Jody

- 86NewBriRSP-21
- 87IntLeaAT-21
- 87PawRedSP-56
- 87PawRedST-17
- 88Don-41
- 88DonBasB-196
- 88DonRoo-44
- 88DonTeaBRS-41
- 88Fle-360
- 88FleGlo-360
- 88Lea-41
- 88Sco-625
- 88ScoGlo-625
- 88Spo-225
- 88StaLinRS-15
- 88Top-152
- 88TopBig-202
- 88TopTif-152
- 89Bow-30
- 89BowTif-30
- 89Don-305
- 89DonBasB-289
- 89Fle-96
- 89FleGlo-96
- 89OPC-232
- 89PanSti-268
- 89RedFolSB-95
- 89Sco-486
- 89ScoHot1R-85
- 89ScoYouSI-2
- 89Spo-210
- 89Top-321
- 89Top-734
- 89TopBig-97
- 89TopGloS-60
- 89TopTif-321
- 89TopTif-734
- 89ToyRoo-23
- 89UppDec-370
- 90Bow-272
- 90BowTif-272
- 90ClaYel-T54
- 90Don-398
- 90DonBesA-16
- 90Fle-284
- 90FleCan-284
- 90Lea-150
- 90OPC-96
- 90PanSti-25
- 90PublntS-462
- 90RedSoxP-17
- 90Sco-11
- 90Top-96
- 90TopBig-167
- 90TopMinL-6
- 90TopTif-96
- 90TopTVRS-25
- 90UppDec-321
- 91Bow-120
- 91Don-123
- 91Fle-111
- 91Lea-69
- 91OPC-247
- 91PanFreS-265
- 91PanSti-220
- 91RedSoxP-18
- 91RedSoxP-25
- 91Sco-173
- 91StaClu-33
- 91Top-247
- 91TopDesS-247
- 91TopMic-247
- 91TopTif-247
- 91Ult-41
- 91UppDec-184
- 92Bow-642
- 92Don-47
- 92Fle-47
- 92Lea-413
- 92LeaBlaG-413
- 92OPC-598
- 92PanSti-86
- 92Pin-222
- 92RedSoxDD-25
- 92Sco-85
- 92ScoProP-24
- 92StaClu-816
- 92StaCluNC-816
- 92Stu-138
- 92Top-598
- 92TopGol-598
- 92TopGolW-598
- 92TopMic-598
- 92TriPla-25
- 92Ult-21
- 92UppDec-404
- 93Bow-506
- 93DodMot-9
- 93DodPol-21
- 93DodStaC-3
- 93Don-165
- 93Fla-76
- 93FlaPro-6
- 93Fle-182
- 93FleFinE-83
- 93Lea-299
- 93OPC-357
- 93OPCPre-115
- 93PacSpa-503
- 93Pin-519
- 93Sco-414
- 93Sel-120
- 93SelRoo-93T
- 93StaClu-612
- 93StaCluFDI-612
- 93StaCluMOP-612
- 93Stu-177
- 93Top-103
- 93TopGol-103
- 93TopInaM-103
- 93TopInaR-103
- 93TopMic-103
- 93TriPla-253
- 93Ult-403
- 93UppDec-96
- 93UppDec-568
- 93UppDecGold-96
- 93UppDecGold-568
- 94BreMilB-346
- 94BrePol-22
- 94BreTeal-21
- 94ColC-564
- 94ColChoGS-564
- 94ColChoSS-564
- 94Don-236
- 94Fin-346
- 94FinRef-346
- 94Fla-308
- 94Fle-521
- 94FleExtB-107
- 94FleUpd-56
- 94Lea-376
- 94Pac-319
- 94Pin-519
- 94PinArtP-519
- 94PinMusC-519
- 94Sco-368
- 94ScoGolR-368
- 94ScoRoo-RT49
- 94ScoRooGR-RT49
- 94Sel-336
- 94StaClu-13
- 94StaClu-642
- 94StaCluFDI-13
- 94StaCluFDI-642
- 94StaCluGR-13
- 94StaCluGR-642
- 94StaCluMOP-13
- 94StaCluMOP-642
- 94Top-325
- 94TopGol-325
- 94TopSpa-325
- 94TopTra-57T
- 94Ult-377
- 94UppDec-473
- 94UppDecED-473
- 95ColCho-171
- 95ColCho-565T
- 95ColChoGS-171
- 95ColChoSS-171
- 95Don-414
- 95DonPreP-414
- 95DonTopotO-344
- 95Fin-50
- 95FinRef-50
- 95Fle-187
- 95FleUpd-189
- 95Pac-240
- 95PadCHP-13
- 95PadMot-13
- 95Sco-176
- 95ScoGolR-176
- 95ScoPlaTS-176
- 95StaClu-38
- 95StaCluFDI-38
- 95StaCluMOP-38
- 95StaCluSTWS-38
- 95StaCluVR-27
- 95StaCluVRMO-27
- 95Top-418
- 95TopCyb-218
- 96ColCho-298
- 96ColChoGS-298
- 96ColChoSS-298
- 96Don-336
- 96DonPreP-336
- 96EmoXL-282
- 96Fla-380
- 96Fle-576
- 96FleTif-576
- 96Pac-195
- 96PadMot-10
- 96ProSta-85
- 96StaClu-352
- 96StaCluMOP-352
- 96Ult-288
- 96UltGolM-288
- 96UppDec-446
- 97Fle-468
- 97FleTif-468
- 97Pac-431
- 97PacLigB-431
- 97PacSil-431
- 97StaClu-285
- 97StaCluMOP-285
- 97Top-109
- 98Pac-95
- 98PacPlaB-95
- 98PacRedT-95
- 98PacSil-95

Reed, Ken

- 86BirBarTI-3
- 87DayBeaAP-7

Reed, Kenny

- 93BluOriC-21
- 93BluOriF-4129
- 94AlbPolC-20
- 94AlbPolF-2245
- 94MarPhiC-19
- 94MarPhiF-3291
- 95MarPhiTI-21

Reed, Marty

- 86KinEagP-18
- 87MidAngP-27
- 87TexLeaAF-15
- 88EdmTraC-9
- 88EdmTraP-562

Reed, Milton

- 15Zee-70

Reed, Patrick

- 91GreFalDSP-27
- 92YakBeaC-7
- 92YakBeaF-3466
- 93WelPirC-24
- 93WelPirF-3375

Reed, Rick (Richard Allen)

- 87MacPirP-10
- 88SalBucS-17
- 89BlaYNPRWL-160
- 89BlaYNPRWLU-66
- 89BlaYNPRWLU-67
- 89BlaYNPRWLU-68
- 89BlaYNPRWLU-70
- 89BlaYNPRWLU-71
- 89BufBisC-9
- 89BufBisP-1675
- 90BufBisC-8
- 90BufBisP-371
- 90CMC-8
- 90Don-527
- 90Fle-477
- 90FleCan-477
- 90Lea-427
- 90ProAAAF-486
- 90Sco-544
- 90Sco100RS-8
- 90UppDec-89A
- 91BufBisLD-42
- 91BufBisP-540
- 91LinDriAAA-42
- 91Sco-584
- 91TriA AAGP-AAA4
- 92OmaRoyS-1
- 92OmaRoyS-343
- 92Sco100RS-73
- 92SkyAAAF-295
- 92StaClu-434
- 93OmaRoyF-1678
- 93RanKee-426
- 93Top-212
- 93TopGol-212
- 93TopInaM-212
- 93TopInaR-212
- 93TopMic-212
- 93TriAAAGF-42
- 94RanMagM-13
- 94RanMagM-33
- 96NorTidB-25
- 98Fin-67
- 98FinNo--67
- 98FinNo-R-67
- 98FinRef-67
- 98Top-132
- 98TopChr-132
- 98TopChrR-132
- 98TopDevR-132
- 98TopDia-132
- 98TopMiniC-132
- 99199Fin-28
- 99FinGolRef-28
- 99FinRef-28
- 99StaClu-31
- 99StaCluFDI-31
- 99StaCluOoaK-31
- 99StaCluPP-31
- 99Top-53
- 99TopChr-53
- 99TopChrR-53
- 99TopMVPP-53

Reed, Rick (Umpire)

- 88T/MUmp-48
- 89T/MUmp-46
- 90T/MUmp-44

Reed, Robert

- 28Zee-142

Reed, Ron

- 68BraPos-27
- 68OPC-76
- 68Top-76
- 68TopVen-76
- 69AtlBraBPPS-20
- 69OPC-177
- 69Top-177
- 69TopFou-8
- 69TopSta-9
- 70MLBOffS-12
- 70OPC-546
- 70Top-546
- 71MLBOffS-21
- 71OPC-359
- 71Top-359
- 72MilBra-281
- 72Top-787
- 73OPC-72
- 73Top-72
- 74OPC-346
- 74Top-346
- 75AtlBraP-30
- 75OPC-81
- 75St.LouCP-21
- 75Top-81
- 75TopMin-81
- 76OPC-58
- 76PhiPhiP-23
- 76Top-58
- 76TopTra-58T
- 77Top-243
- 78SSP270-30
- 78Top-472
- 79OPC-84
- 79PhiBurK-7
- 79Top-177
- 80OPC-318
- 80PhiBurK-21
- 80Top-609
- 81Don-44
- 81Fle-11
- 81Top-376
- 82Don-399
- 82Fle-255
- 82Top-581
- 83Don-567
- 83Fle-169
- 83FleSta-160
- 83FleSti-172
- 83PhiPosGPaM-13
- 83PhiTas-23
- 83Top-728
- 83TopFol-4
- 84Don-529
- 84Fle-45
- 84FleUpd-96
- 84Nes792-43
- 84Top-43
- 84TopTif-43
- 84TopTra-98T
- 84TopTraT-98T
- 84WhiSoxTV-26
- 85Don-282
- 85Fle-524
- 85Top-221
- 85TopTif-221
- 90RicBra2ATI-20

Reed, Sean

- 88WytCubP-1981
- 89ChaWheB-16
- 89ChaWheP-1762

Reed, Steve Vincent

- 88PocGiaP-2082
- 89CliGiaP-906
- 90ShrCapP-1443
- 90ShrCapS-20
- 91LinDriAA-319
- 91ShrCapLD-319
- 91ShrCapP-1822
- 92PhoFirF-2822
- 92ShrCapF-3869
- 92ShrCapS-591
- 92SkyAA F-261
- 93Don-375
- 93Fle-414
- 93FleFinE-40
- 93PacSpa-435
- 93Pin-584
- 93RocStaC-26
- 93RocUSPC-5H

❑ 93RocUSPC-11D
❑ 93Sco-573
❑ 93Sel-351
❑ 93StaClu-674
❑ 93StaCluFDI-674
❑ 93StaCluMOP-674
❑ 93Top-461
❑ 93TopGol-461
❑ 93TopInaM-461
❑ 93TopInaR-461
❑ 93TopMic-461
❑ 93Ult-356
❑ 93UppDec-752
❑ 93UppDecGold-752
❑ 94Don-438
❑ 94Fle-450
❑ 94Pac-204
❑ 94RocPol-20
❑ 94Sco-170
❑ 94ScoGolR-170
❑ 94StaClu-475
❑ 94StaCluFDI-475
❑ 94StaCluGR-475
❑ 94StaCluMOP-475
❑ 94StaCluT-112
❑ 94StaCluTFDI-112
❑ 94Top-627
❑ 94TopGol-627
❑ 94TopSpa-627
❑ 94Ult-187
❑ 94USPlaCR-3S
❑ 95Don-123
❑ 95DonPreP-123
❑ 95DonTopotO-230
❑ 95Fle-526
❑ 95Pac-143
❑ 95StaClu-64
❑ 95StaCluFDI-64
❑ 95StaCluMOP-64
❑ 95StaCluSTWS-64
❑ 95Top-321
❑ 95Ult-156
❑ 95UltGolM-156
❑ 96ColCho-539
❑ 96ColChoGS-539
❑ 96ColChoSS-539
❑ 96Don-146
❑ 96DonPreP-146
❑ 96Fla-249
❑ 96Fle-370
❑ 96FleTif-370
❑ 96LeaSigEA-168
❑ 96Pac-51
❑ 96RocFle-11
❑ 96RocPol-16
❑ 96Ult-472
❑ 96UltGolM-472
❑ 96UppDec-66
❑ 97Cir-360
❑ 97CirRav-360
❑ 97Fle-315
❑ 97FleTif-315
❑ 98GiaMot-24
❑ 98Pac-288
❑ 98PacOnl-670
❑ 98PacOnlR-670
❑ 98PacOnlWC-670
❑ 98PacPlaB-288
❑ 98PacRedT-288
❑ 98PacSil-288

Reed, Steve Xavier
❑ 96JohCitCTI-26
❑ 97PeoChi-22
❑ 98ArkTraM-22

Reed, Steven
❑ 78BurBeeT-22
❑ 79HolMilT-21
❑ 80HolMilT-18

Reed, Tom
❑ 84VisOakT-13

Reed, Toncie
❑ 89AubAstP-2167
❑ 90OscAstS-24

Reeder, Bill E.
❑ 49EurSta-194
❑ 52MotCoo-48

Reeder, Cory
❑ 98StoPorUG-4

Reeder, Jim
❑ 96AubDouB-16
❑ 97QuaCitRBB-22
❑ 98KisCobQ-22

Reeder, Mike
❑ 87GenCubP-14
❑ 88ChaWheB-5

Reelhorn, John
❑ 81OklCit8T-15
❑ 82OklCit8T-19

Rees, Robert
❑ 90KinMetB-14
❑ 90KinMetS-20
❑ 91ColMetPI-8
❑ 91ColMetPPI-4
❑ 92ColMetF-294
❑ 93QuaCitRBC-17
❑ 93QuaCitRBF-99

Rees, Sean
❑ 89AlaGol-11
❑ 89AriStaB-22
❑ 92PenPilC-7
❑ 92PenPilF-2930
❑ 92StaCluD-150
❑ 93RivPilCLC-15

Reese, Andrew
❑ 28PorandAR-A30
❑ 28PorandAR-B30
❑ 29ExhFou-9
❑ 31Zee-52

Reese, Chip
❑ 83AndBraT-10
❑ 89BoiHawP-1979

Reese, Jason
❑ 90MedHatBJB-2
❑ 91PocPioP-3780
❑ 91PocPioSP-11

Reese, Jimmie
❑ 25Zee-38
❑ 26Zee-87
❑ 27Zee-61
❑ 28ExhPCL-21
❑ 29Zee-81
❑ 31Exh-26
❑ 33Zee-10
❑ 65SeaPop-17
❑ 73OPC-421
❑ 73Top-421A
❑ 73Top-421B
❑ 74OPC-276
❑ 74Top-276
❑ 75CalAngP-31
❑ 76SSP-630
❑ 78AngFamF-30
❑ 87CalAngPPS-32
❑ 91Bow-186
❑ 91Stu-21
❑ 92UppDecS-13
❑ 93AngMot-28
❑ 93AngPol-12
❑ 93ConTSN-690
❑ 93PacRya2S-245
❑ 94UppDecAH-199
❑ 94UppDecAH1-199

Reese, Kyle
❑ 28Zee-87
❑ 86EriCarP-24
❑ 87Ft.MyeRP-27
❑ 88VirGenS-21
❑ 89MemChiB-16
❑ 89MemChiP-1206
❑ 89MemChiS-20
❑ 90MemChiB-12
❑ 90MemChiP-1011
❑ 90MemChiS-23

Reese, Matt
❑ 93SouOreAC-21
❑ 93SouOreAF-4079
❑ 94WesMicWC-20
❑ 94WesMicWF-2311
❑ 95ModA'sTI-23

Reese, Pee Wee (Harold H.)
❑ 40DodTeal-20
❑ 41DouPlaR-23
❑ 41PlaBal-54
❑ 41WheM5-18
❑ 42DodTeal-16
❑ 43MPR302-1-20
❑ 46DodTeal-17
❑ 46SpoExcW-4-6
❑ 47DodTeal-17
❑ 47Exh-184A
❑ 47Exh-184B
❑ 47HomBon-38
❑ 47PM1StaP1-169
❑ 47PM1StaP1-170
❑ 47PM1StaP1-171
❑ 47PM1StaP1-172
❑ 48DodTeal-18
❑ 48SweSpoT-18
❑ 49Bow-36
❑ 49EurSta-47
❑ 49MPR302-2-106
❑ 50AmeNut&CCP-14
❑ 50Bow-21
❑ 50Dra-19
❑ 50RoyDes-2
❑ 51Bow-80
❑ 51R42SmaS-86
❑ 52BerRos-51
❑ 52Bow-8
❑ 52CokTip-7
❑ 52RedMan-NL17
❑ 52RoyPre-9
❑ 52StaCalL-79B
❑ 52StaCalS-91A
❑ 52Top-333
❑ 53BowC-33
❑ 53Dor-127
❑ 53ExhCan-21
❑ 53RedMan-NL10
❑ 53Top-76
❑ 54Bow-58
❑ 54NewYorJA-14
❑ 54RedMan-NL15
❑ 55ArmCoi-15
❑ 55BigLeaIS-15
❑ 55Bow-37
❑ 55DaiQueS-15
❑ 55DodGolS-16
❑ 55RedMan-NL17
❑ 56Dod-24
❑ 56Top-260
❑ 56YelBasP-26
❑ 57Top-30
❑ 58DodBelB-8
❑ 58DodJayP-11
❑ 58DodTeal-20
❑ 58DodVol-11
❑ 58Hir-23
❑ 58Top-375
❑ 59DodTeal-22
❑ 59DodVol-12
❑ 60NuHi-37
❑ 61NuSco-437
❑ 69EquSpoHoF-BB15
❑ 73Dod194T-23
❑ 74dod195T-33
❑ 75DodTCMA-8
❑ 75TCMGua-9
❑ 76SSP-594
❑ 76SSPYanOD-8
❑ 76TayBow4-16
❑ 77GalGloG-31
❑ 78DodTCM4-2
❑ 78DodTCM4-38
❑ 79DiaGre-90
❑ 79TCM50-84
❑ 80DodGreT-3
❑ 80PacLeg-52
❑ 80PerHaloFP-189
❑ 80PerHaloFPS-54
❑ 80SSPHOF-188
❑ 82DiaCla-16
❑ 82GSGalAG-11
❑ 83TCMPla1942-28
❑ 83TopRep5-333
❑ 84FifNatCT-13
❑ 84OCoandSI-48
❑ 84SpoDesPW-34
❑ 85TCMPhoC-18
❑ 86SpoDecG-21
❑ 86TCMSupS-16
❑ 87Dod195T-6
❑ 87LeaSpeO*-H8
❑ 88DodRinP1-5A
❑ 88PacLegI-21
❑ 89DodSmoG-23
❑ 89PerCelP-34
❑ 90DodTar-652
❑ 90PerGreM-26
❑ 90PerGreM-91
❑ 91TopArc1-76
❑ 92BazQua5A-15
❑ 92Zip-6
❑ 95TopArcBD-24
❑ 95TopArcBD-43
❑ 95TopArcBD-89
❑ 95TopArcBD-123
❑ 95TopArcBD-159
❑ 98SpollITaN-25
❑ 98SpollITaNEE-25

Reese, Pokey (Calvin)
❑ 91Cla/Bes-412
❑ 91ClaDraP-16
❑ 91FroRowDP-23
❑ 91FroRowDPG-23
❑ 91FroRowDPS-23
❑ 91PriRedC-15
❑ 91PriRedP-3523
❑ 92Bow-86
❑ 92ChaWheF-17
❑ 92ChaWVWC-1
❑ 92ClaFS7-59
❑ 92OPC-714
❑ 92ProFS7-220
❑ 92StaCluD-151
❑ 92Top-714
❑ 92TopGol-714
❑ 92TopGolW-714
❑ 92TopMic-714
❑ 92UppDecML-70
❑ 92UppDecML-226
❑ 93Bow-146
❑ 93ChaLooF-2369
❑ 93ClaFS7-248
❑ 93ClaGolF-189
❑ 93ExcFS7-28
❑ 93SouAtlLAIPI-10
❑ 93SouAtlLAPI-34
❑ 94ActPac-49
❑ 94Bow-270
❑ 94Bow-355
❑ 94BowBes-B9
❑ 94BowBesR-B9
❑ 94ChaLooF-1367
❑ 94Cla-108
❑ 94ColC-666
❑ 94ColChoGS-666
❑ 94ColChoSS-666
❑ 94SigRoo-44
❑ 94SigRooS-44
❑ 94Top-278
❑ 94TopGol-278
❑ 94TopSpa-278
❑ 94UppDec-544
❑ 94UppDecED-544
❑ 94UppDecML-117
❑ 95ActPacF-47
❑ 95ARuFalLS-16
❑ 95Bes-63
❑ 95Bow-264
❑ 95BowBes-B24
❑ 95BowBesR-B24
❑ 95BowGolF-264
❑ 95Exc-181
❑ 95IndIndF-103
❑ 95SPML-38
❑ 95Sum21C-TC2
❑ 95Top-171
❑ 95UppDecML-28
❑ 95UppDecMLFS-28
❑ 96Bow-200
❑ 96BowBes-98
❑ 96BowBesAR-98
❑ 96BowBesP-BBP12
❑ 96BowBesPAR-BBP12
❑ 96BowBesPR-BBP12
❑ 96BowBesR-98
❑ 96BowFoi-200
❑ 96IndIndB-21
❑ 97Bow-155
❑ 97BowBes-119
❑ 97BowBesAR-119
❑ 97BowBesR-119
❑ 97BowCerBlaIA-CA64
❑ 97BowCerBluIA-CA64
❑ 97BowCerGolIA-CA64
❑ 97BowChr-155
❑ 97BowChrI-155
❑ 97BowChrIR-155
❑ 97BowChrR-155
❑ 97BowInt-155
❑ 97ColCho-308
❑ 97Don-369
❑ 97DonFraFea-14
❑ 97DonGolPP-369
❑ 97DonLim-49
❑ 97DonLim-116
❑ 97DonLimE-49
❑ 97DonLimE-116
❑ 97DonLimFotG-39
❑ 97DonPre-157
❑ 97DonPreCttC-157
❑ 97DonSig-68
❑ 97DonSigA-82
❑ 97DonSigAC-101
❑ 97DonSigAM-101
❑ 97DonSigPPP-68
❑ 97DonSilPP-369
❑ 97Fle-686
❑ 97FleTif-686
❑ 97IndInd-18
❑ 97Lea-323
❑ 97LeaFraM-323
❑ 97LeaFraMDC-323
❑ 97PinCer-119
❑ 97PinCerMBla-119
❑ 97PinCerMBlu-119
❑ 97PinCerMG-119
❑ 97PinCerMR-119
❑ 97PinCerR-119
❑ 97PinTotCPB-119
❑ 97PinTotCPG-119
❑ 97PinTotCPR-119
❑ 97Sel-198
❑ 97SelCom-198
❑ 97SpoIll-20
❑ 97SpoIllEE-20
❑ 97TopStaFAS-FAS11
❑ 97Ult-460
❑ 97UltGolME-460
❑ 97UltPlaME-460
❑ 98ColCho-69
❑ 98Don-112
❑ 98DonCol-112
❑ 98DonCol-184
❑ 98DonColE-510
❑ 98DonColL-301
❑ 98DonColP-664
❑ 98DonColS-112
❑ 98DonColS-179
❑ 98DonCruG-64
❑ 98DonCruP-64
❑ 98DonCruR-64
❑ 98DonEli-110
❑ 98DonEliA-110
❑ 98DonEliS-110
❑ 98DonGolPP-112
❑ 98DonPre-114
❑ 98DonPreSeat-114
❑ 98DonPriCD-112
❑ 98DonPriCD-184
❑ 98DonPriCE-510
❑ 98DonPriCL-301
❑ 98DonPriCP-664
❑ 98DonRatR-9
❑ 98DonRatRM-9
❑ 98DonSilPP-112
❑ 98Fin-268
❑ 98FinNo--268
❑ 98FinNo-R-268
❑ 98FinRef-268
❑ 98Fle-154
❑ 98Lea-102
❑ 98LeaCruG-64
❑ 98LeaCruP-64
❑ 98LeaCruR-64
❑ 98LeaFraDA-102
❑ 98LeaFraF-102
❑ 98LeaFraM-102
❑ 98LeaFraM-102
❑ 98LeaFraMDC-102
❑ 98LeaFraMDC-102
❑ 98LeaFraMZ2-102
❑ 98MetUni-154
❑ 98MetUniPMG-154
❑ 98Pac-270
❑ 98PacOnl-197
❑ 98PacOnlR-197
❑ 98PacOnlWC-197
❑ 98PacPlaB-270
❑ 98PacRedT-270
❑ 98PacSil-270
❑ 98Pin-175
❑ 98PinArtP-PP78
❑ 98PinIns-18
❑ 98PinInsCE-18
❑ 98PinInsDE-18
❑ 98PinMusC-PP78
❑ 98PinPreP-175
❑ 98Sco-240
❑ 98ScoRT-196
❑ 98ScoRTSS-PP109
❑ 98ScoRTSSAP-PP109
❑ 98ScoRTSSAP1-PP109
❑ 98StaCluFDI-64
❑ 98StaCluI-64
❑ 98StaCluOneK-64
❑ 98StaCluPP-64
❑ 98Stu-107
❑ 98StuGPP-107
❑ 98StuSPP-107
❑ 98Top-159
❑ 98TopChr-159
❑ 98TopChrR-159
❑ 98TopDevR-159
❑ 98TopDia-159
❑ 98TopMiniC-159
❑ 98Ult-168
❑ 98UltGolM-168
❑ 98UltMas-168
❑ 98UltPlaM-168
❑ 98UppDec-68
❑ 99PacOme-66
❑ 99PacOmeC-66
❑ 99PacOmeG-66
❑ 99PacOmePB-66
❑ 99PacPar-65
❑ 99PacParC-65
❑ 99PacParG-65
❑ 99PacParHoloGold-65
❑ 99PacParHS-65
❑ 99PacParOD-65
❑ 99PacParPB-65
❑ 99PacParRed-65
❑ 99Top-424
❑ 99TopChr-424
❑ 99TopChrR-424
❑ 99TopMVPP-424
❑ 99UppDecM-58
❑ 99UppDecMGS-58
❑ 99UppDecMHFS-58
❑ 99UppDecMP-58
❑ 99UppDecMSS-58

Reese, Rich
❑ 65Top-597
❑ 67Top-486
❑ 67TwiTeal-17
❑ 68OPC-111
❑ 68Top-111
❑ 68TopVen-111
❑ 69MilBra-228
❑ 69OPC-56
❑ 69Top-56
❑ 70DayDaiNM-120
❑ 70MLBOffS-238
❑ 70OPC-404
❑ 70Top-404
❑ 70TwiSupV-10
❑ 70TwiTeal-7
❑ 71MLBOffS-472
❑ 71OPC-349
❑ 71Top-349
❑ 71TopCoi-72
❑ 72MilBra-282
❑ 72Top-611
❑ 72TwiPos-18
❑ 72TwiTeal-12
❑ 78TwiFri-19
❑ 89PacLegI-112

Reese, Stan
❑ 79AshTouT-27

Reeser, Jeffery
❑ 89PeoChiTI-34

Reeve, Bob
❑ 85AncGlaPTI-41

Reeves, Dave
❑ 91BilMusP-3751
❑ 91BilMusSP-22

Reeves, Glenn
❑ 94KanCouCC-21
❑ 94KanCouCF-177
❑ 94KanCouCTI-25
❑ 95BreCouMF-259
❑ 96BreCouMB-27
❑ 97PorSeaD-25
❑ 98PorSeaDQ-25

Reeves, Jim
❑ 78St.PetCT-22

Reeves, Matt
❑ 79CliDodT-5
❑ 82VerBeaDT-10

Reeves, Mel
❑ 47SmiClo-24

Reeves, Mickey
❑ 91HunCubC-18
❑ 91HunCubP-3348
❑ 92HunCubC-12
❑ 92HunCubF-3165

Reeves, Robert E.
❑ 29ExhFou-17
❑ 31Exh-17
❑ 33Zee-27

Regalado, Maximo
❑ 97GreFalDTI-19

Regalado, Rudy
❑ 55Bow-142
❑ 59SeaPop-31
❑ 60HenHouW-14
❑ 75TCM195Cl-29

Regalado, Uvaldo
❑ 82DayBeaAT-6
❑ 83DayBeaAT-9
❑ 85DomLeaS-103

Regan, Frank
❑ 79WatIndT-7

❑ 80WatIndT-24
Regan, Jason
❑ 97WisTimR-21
❑ 98LanJetG-19
Regan, Michael J.
❑ 09ColChiE-237
❑ 12ColRedB-237
❑ 12ColTinT-237
Regan, Phil
❑ 61Top-439
❑ 62Jel-24
❑ 62Pos-24
❑ 62PosCan-24
❑ 62TigPosCF-16
❑ 62Top-366
❑ 63Top-494
❑ 64TigJayP-10
❑ 64TigLid-13
❑ 64Top-535
❑ 65OPC-191
❑ 65Top-191
❑ 66Top-347
❑ 66TopVen-347
❑ 67Baz-29
❑ 67CokCapD-1
❑ 67CokCapDA-1
❑ 67DexPre-172
❑ 67OPC-130
❑ 67Top-130
❑ 68OPC-88
❑ 68Top-88
❑ 68TopVen-88
❑ 69CubJewT-14
❑ 69CubPho-9
❑ 69CubTeaIC-7
❑ 69MilBra-229
❑ 69MLBOffS-124
❑ 69Top-535
❑ 69TopSta-18
❑ 70DayDaiNM-129
❑ 70MLBOffS-21
❑ 70OPC-334
❑ 70Top-334
❑ 71MLBOffS-43
❑ 71OPC-634
❑ 71Top-634
❑ 72MilBra-283
❑ 72OPC-485
❑ 72Top-485
❑ 84CubUno-9
❑ 85DomLeaS-177
❑ 85MarMot-27
❑ 86MarMot-28
❑ 87DodSmoA-27
❑ 88DodSmo-9
❑ 89DodSmoG-72
❑ 90DodTar-653
❑ 92DodStaTA-5
❑ 93LinVenB-205
❑ 94VenLinU-58
❑ 95BalOriP-42
❑ 95LinVen-37
❑ 96-97LinVen-165
Regan, William W.
❑ 28StaPlaCE-52
❑ 29ExhFou-18
❑ 29PorandAR-69
❑ 93ConTSN-813
Reger, Roy
❑ 85CloHSS-36
Reggins, Mark
❑ 92LouRedS-275
Regira, Gary
❑ 89JamExpP-2154
❑ 90RocExpLC-22
❑ 90RocExpP-2688
❑ 91WesPalBEC-10
❑ 91WesPalBEP-1226
Rego, Jimmy
❑ 33Zee-73
Rego, Tony
❑ 28Zee-98
❑ 29Zee-96
Rehbaum, Chris
❑ 80BatTroT-27
❑ 80WatIndT-16
❑ 81BatTroT-23
❑ 82WatIndF-17
❑ 82WatIndT-22
Rehg, Walter
❑ 30Zee-14
Rehkopf, Rob
❑ 94WilCubC-19
❑ 94WilCubF-3763
Rehm, Vic
❑ 60Lea-61
Rehwinkel, Pat
❑ 89HelBreSP-4
Reiber, Frank
❑ 36WorWidGV-111
❑ 39WorWidGV-21
❑ 74TigTCM1AC-24
Reiber, Lee
❑ 93LetMouF-4153
❑ 93LetMouSP-21
Reich, Andy
❑ 89ColMetB-19
❑ 89ColMetGS-22
❑ 89SouAtlLAGS-16
❑ 90St.LucMS-21
❑ 91St.LucMC-18
❑ 91St.LucMP-708
❑ 92BinMetF-513
❑ 93BinMetF-2331
Reich, Herman
❑ 49EurSta-68
Reich, Steve
❑ 93BazTeaU-4
❑ 93TopTra-85T
Reichard, Bud (Clyde)
❑ 78WisRapTT-16
❑ 85TulDriTI-37
❑ 89PenPilS-21
❑ 89PenPilS-26
Reichardt, Kevin
❑ 87BelMarTI-5
Reichardt, Rick
❑ 65AngMatSA-4
❑ 65OPC-194
❑ 65SeaPop-18
❑ 65SeaPop-19
❑ 65Top-194
❑ 66AngDexP-12
❑ 66Top-321
❑ 66TopVen-321
❑ 67Baz-1
❑ 67OPC-40
❑ 67Top-40
❑ 67TopVen-202
❑ 68Top-570
❑ 68TopActS-3C
❑ 68TopActS-14C
❑ 69AngJacitB-10
❑ 69MilBra-230
❑ 69MLBOffS-25
❑ 69MLBPin-23
❑ 69OPC-205
❑ 69Top-205
❑ 69TopDecI-34
❑ 69TopFou-7
❑ 69TopSta-147
❑ 69TopSup-8
❑ 69TopTeaP-17
❑ 69TraSta-18
❑ 70Kel-18
❑ 70MLBOffS-177
❑ 70Top-720
❑ 70TraSta-12C
❑ 71OPC-643
❑ 71Top-643
❑ 71TopCoi-102
❑ 72MilBra-284
❑ 72WhiSoxTI1-10
❑ 73LinPor-52
❑ 81TCM60I-337
❑ 86AngGreT-7
Reichel, Tom
❑ 87PenWhiSP-19
Reichenbach, Eric
❑ 91PitMetC-24
❑ 91PitMetP-3420
❑ 92ClaFS7-81
❑ 92ColMetC-23
❑ 92ColMetF-295
❑ 92ColMetPI-17
❑ 93CapCitBC-18
❑ 93CapCitBF-459
Reichert, Dan
❑ 97SpoIndG-25
❑ 98BesNumOP-37
❑ 98Bow-427
❑ 98BowBes-188
❑ 98BowBesAR-188
❑ 98BowBesR-188
❑ 98BowChr-427
❑ 98BowChrGA-427
❑ 98BowChrGAR-427
❑ 98BowChrI-427
❑ 98BowChrIR-427
❑ 98BowChrR-427
❑ 98BowGolA-427
❑ 98BowInt-427
❑ 98Top-493
❑ 98TopChr-493
❑ 98TopChrR-493
❑ 98TopDevR-493
❑ 98TopDia-493
❑ 98TopMiniC-493
❑ 98WicWraM-28
❑ 99Bow-147
❑ 99Bow-377
❑ 99BowChr-147
❑ 99BowChrG-147
❑ 99BowChrGR-147
❑ 99BowChrI-147
❑ 99BowChrIR-147
❑ 99BowChrR-147
❑ 99BowGol-147
❑ 99BowGol-377
❑ 99BowInt-147
❑ 99BowInt-377
Reichle, Darrin
❑ 87SpoIndP-2
❑ 88ChaRaiP-1208
❑ 88SouAtlLAGS-11
❑ 89RivRedWB-14
❑ 89RivRedWCLC-15
❑ 89RivRedWP-1393
❑ 90Bes-151
❑ 90CMC-853
❑ 90RivRedWB-24
❑ 90RivRedWCLC-23
❑ 90RivRedWP-2607
❑ 91LinDriAA-616
❑ 91WicWraLD-616
❑ 91WicWraP-2596
❑ 91WicWraRD-7
Reichler, Joe
❑ 90LitSunW-7
Reichow, Robert
❑ 96BurIndB-14
Reichstein, Derek
❑ 95ElmPioTI-23
❑ 95ElmPioUTI-23
Reid, Derek
❑ 90EveGiaB-26
❑ 90EveGiaP-3142
❑ 90ProAaA-172
❑ 91Cla/Bes-273
❑ 91SanJosGC-28
❑ 91SanJosGP-25
❑ 92ShrCapF-3884
❑ 92UppDecML-87
❑ 94SanBerSC-19
❑ 94SanBerSF-2772
❑ 95BurBeeTI-19
❑ 96SanJosGB-9
Reid, Gregory
❑ 91MadMusC-19
❑ 91MadMusP-2143
❑ 92MadMusC-5
❑ 92MadMusF-1250
Reid, Jessie
❑ 84ShrCapFB-16
❑ 85FreGiaSB-18
❑ 86PhoFirP-22
❑ 86StaoftFT-36
❑ 87PhoFirP-16
❑ 88Fle-643
❑ 88FleGlo-643
❑ 89TacTigC-17
❑ 89TacTigP-1549
Reid, John
❑ 91NiaFalRC-20
❑ 92FayGenC-4
❑ 92FayGenF-2166
❑ 92LakTigF-2277
Reid, Rayon
❑ 96AugGreB-24
Reid, Scott D.
❑ 70OPC-56
❑ 70Top-56
❑ 71OPC-439
❑ 71Top-439
Reid, Terry
❑ 91MelBusF-15
Reidy, Bill
❑ 09ObaT21-21
❑ 11SpoLifCW-299
❑ 12Zee-128
❑ 90DodTar-654
Reightley, Ryan
❑ 97UCLBruTI-18
Reilley, John
❑ 88SumBraP-394
❑ 89WauTimGS-5
❑ 90SalSpuCLC-129
❑ 90SalSpuP-2720
Reilly, Alex
❑ 11PinT-5-1054
❑ 20Zee-93
Reilly, Charles T.
❑ 87OldJudN-413
Reilly, Ed
❑ 83DayBeaAT-10
Reilly, John
❑ 94St.CatBJC-17
❑ 94St.CatBJF-3647
❑ 95StCatSTI-15
Reilly, John G.
❑ 87OldJudN-412
❑ 88SpoTimM-22
❑ 89EdgR.WG-13
Reilly, Mike
❑ 88T/MUmp-33
❑ 89T/MUmp-31
❑ 90T/MUmp-30
Reilly, Neil
❑ 85BurRanT-6
Reilly, Thomas H.
❑ 09ColChiE-238
❑ 09ColChiE-239
❑ 09RamT20-98
❑ 12ColRedB-238
❑ 12ColRedB-239
❑ 12ColTinT-238
❑ 12ColTinT-239
Reimer, Gerry
❑ 67VanMouSO-18
Reimer, Kevin
❑ 86SalRedBP-23
❑ 87PorChaRP-26
❑ 88TulDriTI-25
❑ 89Fle-641
❑ 89FleGlo-641
❑ 89OklCit8C-19
❑ 89OklCit8P-1527
❑ 89ScoHot1R-59
❑ 90CMC-169
❑ 90Fle-310
❑ 90FleCan-310
❑ 90OklCit8C-19
❑ 90OklCit8P-446
❑ 90ProAAAF-692
❑ 90TulDriDGB-30
❑ 91Don-80
❑ 91Fle-298
❑ 91OPC-304
❑ 91RanMot-15
❑ 91Sco-836
❑ 91Top-304
❑ 91TopDesS-304
❑ 91TopMic-304
❑ 91TopTif-304
❑ 91UltUpd-57
❑ 91UppDec-494
❑ 92Bow-115
❑ 92Don-251
❑ 92Fle-315
❑ 92Lea-93
❑ 92LeaBlaG-93
❑ 92OPC-737
❑ 92Pin-340
❑ 92RanMot-15
❑ 92RanTeal-18
❑ 92Sco-152
❑ 92StaClu-57
❑ 92Top-737
❑ 92TopGol-737
❑ 92TopGolW-737
❑ 92TopMic-737
❑ 92Ult-444
❑ 92UppDec-201
❑ 93Bow-479
❑ 93BrePol-21
❑ 93BreSen5-4
❑ 93Don-55
❑ 93Fla-228
❑ 93Fle-326
❑ 93FleFinE-232
❑ 93Lea-377
❑ 93OPC-284
❑ 93OPCPre-131
❑ 93PacSpa-515
❑ 93PanSti-43
❑ 93Pin-531
❑ 93RanKee-305
❑ 93Sco-628
❑ 93Sel-268
❑ 93SelRoo-101T
❑ 93SP-69
❑ 93StaClu-699
❑ 93StaCluFDI-699
❑ 93StaCluMOP-699
❑ 93Top-87
❑ 93TopGol-87
❑ 93TopInaM-87
❑ 93TopInaR-87
❑ 93TopMic-87
❑ 93Ult-576
❑ 93UppDec-578
❑ 93UppDecGold-578
❑ 94BreMilB-168
❑ 94ColC-237
❑ 94ColChoGS-237
❑ 94ColChoSS-237
❑ 94Don-233
❑ 94Fle-189
❑ 94PanSti-85
❑ 94Sco-477
❑ 94ScoGolR-477
❑ 94Top-585
❑ 94TopGol-585
❑ 94TopSpa-585
❑ 94Ult-82
❑ 97TacRai-23
Reimer, Matt
❑ 93AlbPolCB-18
Reimer, Robin
❑ 86EveGiaPC-25
Reimers, Tom
❑ 96HicCraB-16
❑ 97BriWhiSB-9
Reimink, Robert
❑ 89NiaFalRP-20
❑ 90LakTigS-21
❑ 91LinDriAA-395
❑ 91LonTigLD-395
❑ 91LonTigP-1887
❑ 92LonTigF-641
❑ 92LonTigS-415
❑ 93TolMudHF-1661
Reimsnyder, Brian
❑ 90EriSaiS-19
Rein, Fred
❑ 77ChaPatT-14
❑ 77SalPirT-21
Reinbach, Mike
❑ 75IntLeaAT-5
❑ 79TCMJapPB-81
❑ 91OriCro-376
Reincke, Corey
❑ 91FayGenC-7
❑ 91FayGenP-1167
❑ 91NiaFalRC-28
❑ 91NiaFalRP-3631
❑ 93NiaFalRF-3385
Reindeer, Rhubard the
❑ 98TacRaiQ-30
Reinebold, Jim
❑ 88SouBenWSGS-16
❑ 89SouBenWSGS-3
❑ 90SouBenWSB-29
❑ 90SouBenWSGS-29
❑ 91SouBenWSP-2876
❑ 92SouBenWSF-196
❑ 93SouBenWSC-27
❑ 93SouBenWSF-1449
❑ 94SouBenSHC-27
❑ 94SouBenSHF-612
❑ 97SouBenSH-29
❑ 98SouBenSHM-27
Reinert, Greg
❑ 91IdaFalBSP-9
Reinhart, Art
❑ 20Zee-130
❑ 21Zee-17
❑ 27MidBre-13
❑ 91ConTSN-242
Reinheimer, Christian
❑ 94JohCitCC-24
❑ 94JohCitCF-3701
Reinholtz, Eric
❑ 87SalAngP-10
Reinike, Chris
❑ 98WatIndTI-27
❑ 99JustheS-40
❑ 99JustheSJB-40
❑ 99TeaBesR-70
❑ 99TeaBesRG-70
❑ 99TeaBesRS-70
Reinisch, Paul
❑ 90BriTigP-3170
❑ 90BriTigS-19
Reinke, Jeff
❑ 75CliPilT-30
Reis, Bobby (Robert)
❑ 36GouWidPPR-A87
❑ 90DodTar-655
Reis, Dave
❑ 88PulBraP-1757
❑ 89BurBraP-1619
❑ 89BurBraS-18
❑ 90Bes-195
❑ 90BurBraB-7
❑ 90BurBraP-2347
❑ 90BurBraS-20
❑ 90MidLeaASGS-47
Reis, Paul
❑ 88PulBraP-1759
❑ 89SumBraP-1090
❑ 90BurBraB-17
❑ 90BurBraP-2359
❑ 90BurBraS-21
Reis, Tom
❑ 47CenFlo-22
Reiser, James
❑ 86MedA'sC-52
❑ 87MadMusP-15
❑ 87MadMusP-10
❑ 88MadMusP-18
Reiser, Pete
❑ 36OveCanR-38
❑ 39ExhSal-53A
❑ 39ExhSal-53B
❑ 41DouPlaR-17
❑ 42DodTeal-17
❑ 43MPR302-1-21
❑ 46DodTeal-18
❑ 46SpoExcW-8-3
❑ 47DodTeal-18
❑ 47PM1StaP1-173
❑ 48Bow-7
❑ 48DodTeal-19
❑ 48SweSpoT-2
❑ 49Bow-185
❑ 49EurSta-17
❑ 49Lea-146
❑ 50Bow-193
❑ 51Bow-238
❑ 52Top-189
❑ 60DodTeal-15
❑ 60DodUniO-23
❑ 60Top-463
❑ 73Dod194T-24
❑ 73OPC-81
❑ 73Top-81A
❑ 73Top-81B
❑ 78DodTCM4-36
❑ 80MarExh-25
❑ 80PacLeg-88
❑ 83TopRep5-189
❑ 86TCMSupS-44
❑ 87SpoRea-34
❑ 88WilMulP-7
❑ 89DodSmoG-47
❑ 90DodTar-656
❑ 91DodRinP3-8
Reish, Steve
❑ 83KinBluJTI-17
❑ 84MemChiT-17
Reisigl, Jacob
❑ 15Zee-114
❑ 16Zee-90
Reisinger, Eric
❑ 97SalVolG-32
Reisling, Doc (Frank)
❑ 11PinT-5-559
❑ 11SpoLifM-131
❑ 90DodTar-1052
Reiter, Gary
❑ 81DurBulT-24
❑ 82DurBulT-20
❑ 83RicBraT-8
❑ 84RicBraT-15
❑ 85RicBraT-7
Reith, Brian
❑ 98GreBatM-16
Reitmeister, Ben
❑ 87HawRai-27
Reitmyer, Paul
❑ 13Zee-87
Reitsma, Chris
❑ 97Bes-31
❑ 97Bow-219
❑ 97BowChr-196
❑ 97BowChrI-196
❑ 97BowChrIR-196
❑ 97BowChrR-196
❑ 97BowInt-219
❑ 97MicBatC-23
❑ 97MidLeaTP-16
❑ 97Top-273
❑ 98Bow-313
❑ 98BowChr-313

❑ 98BowChrGA-313
❑ 98BowChrGAR-313
❑ 98BowChrI-313
❑ 98BowChrIR-313
❑ 98BowChrR-313
❑ 98BowGolA-313
❑ 98BowInt-313
Reitz, Heinie (Henry)
❑ 94OriTeal-13
Reitz, Ken
❑ 73OPC-603
❑ 73Top-603
❑ 74OPC-372
❑ 74Top-372
❑ 75OPC-27
❑ 75St.LouCP-22
❑ 75Top-27
❑ 75TopMin-27
❑ 76OPC-158
❑ 76SanFraGP-18
❑ 76SSP-280
❑ 76Top-158
❑ 76TopTra-158T
❑ 77BurCheD-13
❑ 77Car5-22
❑ 77CarTeal-21
❑ 77Kel-38A
❑ 77Kel-38B
❑ 77Top-297
❑ 78CarTeal-25
❑ 78Hos-106
❑ 78Top-692
❑ 79Hos-23
❑ 79OPC-307
❑ 79Top-587
❑ 80OPC-103
❑ 80Top-182
❑ 81AllGamPI-125
❑ 81CokTeaS-19
❑ 81Don-307
❑ 81Fle-530
❑ 81OPC-316
❑ 81Top-441
❑ 81TopScr-101
❑ 81TopSti-158
❑ 81TopSupHT-28
❑ 81TopTra-820
❑ 82Don-277
❑ 82Fle-602
❑ 82FleSta-91
❑ 82OPC-245
❑ 82Top-245
❑ 82TopSti-26
❑ 85TulDriTI-1
❑ 86SanJosBP-17
❑ 87SanJosBP-3
❑ 89PacSenL-213
❑ 89T/MSenL-89
❑ 89TopSenL-35
❑ 90EliSenL-61
❑ 91PacSenL-33
❑ 91SweBasG-119
❑ 92CarMcD-41
Reitzel, Mark
❑ 87HawRai-18
Reitzel, Mike
❑ 90MiaMirIS-22
Rekar, Bryan
❑ 93BenRocCB-1
❑ 93BenRocF-3267
❑ 94Bow-554
❑ 94CenValRC-20
❑ 94CenValRF-3202
❑ 94ExcFS7-187
❑ 95Bow-160
❑ 95BowBes-B76
❑ 95BowBesR-B76
❑ 95NewHavRTI-35
❑ 96ColCho-542
❑ 96ColChoGS-542
❑ 96ColChoSS-542
❑ 96ColSprSSTI-27
❑ 96Don-444
❑ 96DonPreP-444
❑ 96Fin-B119
❑ 96FinRef-B119
❑ 96Fle-371
❑ 96FleTif-371
❑ 96LeaSigA-191
❑ 96LeaSigAG-191
❑ 96LeaSigAS-191
❑ 96Pac-61
❑ 96PacPri-P22
❑ 96PacPriG-P22
❑ 96Pin-48
❑ 96RocPol-17
❑ 96Sco-463
❑ 96StaClu-107
❑ 96StaCluMOP-107
❑ 96Top-416
❑ 96Ult-473
❑ 96UltGolM-473
❑ 96UppDec-64
❑ 97ColSprSTI-21
❑ 97Pac-286
❑ 97PacLigB-286
❑ 97PacSil-286
❑ 98UppDec-732
❑ 99Pac-417
❑ 99PacPlaB-417
❑ 99PacRed-417
Relaford, Desi
❑ 92ClaFS7-387
❑ 92PenPilC-8
❑ 92PenPilF-2941
❑ 92StaCluD-152
❑ 93Bow-163
❑ 93ClaFS7-249
❑ 93ExcFS7-230
❑ 93JacSunF-2718
❑ 93MariStaClu-2
❑ 94AriFalLS-17
❑ 94Bow-529
❑ 94JacSunF-1420
❑ 94RivPilCLC-3
❑ 94UppDecML-186
❑ 95Bes-40
❑ 95Bow-153
❑ 95BowBes-B89
❑ 95BowBesR-B89
❑ 95PorCitRTI-20
❑ 95SPML-152
❑ 95Top-642
❑ 95UppDecML-77
❑ 95UppDecMLFS-77
❑ 96Bow-186
❑ 96BowBes-166
❑ 96BowBesAR-166
❑ 96BowBesMI-2
❑ 96BowBesMIAR-2
❑ 96BowBesMIR-2
❑ 96BowBesR-166
❑ 96BowFoi-186
❑ 96Exc-106
❑ 96SigRooOJTP-T5
❑ 96TacRaiB-23
❑ 96Top-426
❑ 97Don-397
❑ 97DonGolPP-397
❑ 97DonSilPP-397
❑ 97Lea-171
❑ 97LeaFraM-171
❑ 97LeaFraMDC-171
❑ 97Sco-298
❑ 97ScoArtPWB-298
❑ 97ScoPreS-298
❑ 97ScoShoS-298
❑ 97ScoShoSAP-298
❑ 97ScrRedB-7
❑ 98Bow-334
❑ 98BowChr-334
❑ 98BowChrGA-334
❑ 98BowChrGAR-334
❑ 98BowChrI-334
❑ 98BowChrIR-334
❑ 98BowChrR-334
❑ 98BowGolA-334
❑ 98BowInt-334
❑ 98ColCho-459
❑ 98Don-312
❑ 98DonGolPP-312
❑ 98DonSilPP-312
❑ 98Fle-547
❑ 98LeaRS-284
❑ 98LeaRSLHolo-284
❑ 98LeaRSLong-284
❑ 98LeaRTrue-284
❑ 98PacAur-172
❑ 98PacInvGems-188
❑ 98PacOmeRS-20
❑ 98PacOmeRST1-20
❑ 98PacOnl-570
❑ 98PacOnlR-570
❑ 98PacOnlWC-570
❑ 98PacPar-215
❑ 98PacParC-215
❑ 98PacParG-215
❑ 98PacParHS-215
❑ 98PacParPB-215
❑ 98PacParR-215
❑ 98PhiTeal-28
❑ 98PinIns-106
❑ 98PinInsCE-106
❑ 98PinInsDE-106
❑ 98Revo-110
❑ 98RevoRooHH-17
❑ 98RevoRooHHG-17
❑ 98RevoSS-110
❑ 98ScrRedB1ATI-14
❑ 98SkyDugA-107
❑ 98SkyDugAIA-107
❑ 98Ult-340
❑ 98UltGolM-340
❑ 98UltMas-340
❑ 98UltPlaM-340
❑ 98UppDec-714
❑ 99Fle-306
❑ 99FleSta9-306
❑ 99FleWarT-306
❑ 99MetUni-168
❑ 99MetUniGM-168
❑ 99MetUniPMG-168
❑ 99Pac-331
❑ 99PacAur-142
❑ 99PacAurOD-142
❑ 99PacOme-181
❑ 99PacOmeC-181
❑ 99PacOmeG-181
❑ 99PacOmePB-181
❑ 99PacPar-180
❑ 99PacParC-180
❑ 99PacParG-180
❑ 99PacParHoloGold-180
❑ 99PacParHS-180
❑ 99PacParOD-180
❑ 99PacParPB-180
❑ 99PacParRed-180
❑ 99PacPlaB-331
❑ 99PacRed-331
❑ 99Rev-107
❑ 99RevPremDate-107
❑ 99RevRet-107
❑ 99RevShaSS-107
❑ 99SkyPre-74
❑ 99SkyPreR-74
❑ 99Top-336
❑ 99TopChr-336
❑ 99TopChrR-336
❑ 99TopMVPP-336
❑ 99UD Cho-125
❑ 99UD ChoPCR-125
❑ 99UppDec-174
❑ 99UppDecBD-65
❑ 99UppDecBDD-65
❑ 99UppDecBDQ-65
❑ 99UppDecBDT-65
❑ 99UppDecEL1-174
❑ 99UppDecEL2-174
❑ 99Vic-299
Relaford, Winnie
❑ 88SumBraP-400
❑ 89SumBraP-1103
Relaigh, Matt
❑ 93JamExpF-3336
Rembielak, Rick
❑ 82MiaMarT-16
Remington, Jake
❑ 95IdaFalBTI-21
❑ 96CliLumKTI-22
Remlinger, Mike
❑ 87EveGiaC-31
❑ 88ShrCapP-1296
❑ 89ShrCapP-1832
❑ 90Bow-227
❑ 90BowTif-227
❑ 90ShrCapP-1444
❑ 90ShrCapS-21
❑ 91DonRoo-37
❑ 91GiaPacGaE-27
❑ 91LinDriAAA-390
❑ 91PhoFirLD-390
❑ 91PhoFirP-64
❑ 91UppDecFE-36F
❑ 92CalCanF-3729
❑ 92CalCanS-68
❑ 92Don-336
❑ 92Fle-646
❑ 92Sco-410
❑ 92Sco100RS-49
❑ 92SkyAAAF-31
❑ 92TopDeb91-143
❑ 92UppDec-585
❑ 93CalCanF-1166
❑ 94FleUpd-159
❑ 94NorTidF-2919
❑ 95MetColP-26
❑ 96IndIndB-22
❑ 98PacOnl-198
❑ 98PacOnlR-198
❑ 98PacOnlWC-198
❑ 98UppDec-341
❑ 99Fle-410
❑ 99FleSta9-410
❑ 99FleWarT-410
❑ 99Pac-116
❑ 99PacPlaB-116
❑ 99PacRed-116
Remmerswaal, Win
❑ 77BriRedST-16
❑ 81Don-98
❑ 81PawRedST-7
❑ 81Top-38
Remneas, Alexander
❑ 15Zee-52
Remo, Bryon
❑ 91OklStaC-20
Remo, Jeff
❑ 82QuaCitCT-16
Remy, Jerry
❑ 75CalAngP-32
❑ 76OPC-229
❑ 76SSP-198
❑ 76Top-229
❑ 77BurCheD-121
❑ 77Kel-44
❑ 77Top-342
❑ 78Hos-66
❑ 78PapGinD-2
❑ 78SSP270-186
❑ 78Top-478
❑ 79OPC-325
❑ 79Top-618
❑ 80OPC-85
❑ 80Top-155
❑ 81Don-215
❑ 81Fle-238
❑ 81OPC-131
❑ 81Top-549
❑ 82Don-156
❑ 82Fle-304
❑ 82FleSta-171
❑ 82OPC-25
❑ 82RedSoxC-16
❑ 82Squ-2
❑ 82Top-25
❑ 82TopSti-132
❑ 82TopSti-149
❑ 83AllGamPI-15
❑ 83Don-74
❑ 83Fle-193
❑ 83FleSti-68
❑ 83OPC-295
❑ 83Top-295
❑ 83TopSti-33
❑ 84AllGamPI-106
❑ 84AllGamPI-187
❑ 84Don-172
❑ 84Fle-407
❑ 84Nes792-445
❑ 84OPC-58
❑ 84Top-445
❑ 84TopRubD-21
❑ 84TopSti-215
❑ 84TopTif-445
❑ 85Fle-167
❑ 85OPC-173
❑ 85Top-761
❑ 85TopRubD-21
❑ 85TopSti-218
❑ 85TopTif-761
Rende, Sal
❑ 79TacTugT-11
❑ 80TacTigT-14
❑ 81ChaLooT-17
❑ 82ChaLooT-11
❑ 83BufBisT-13
❑ 87ChaLooB-1
❑ 88ChaLooLTI-25
❑ 88MemChiB-26
❑ 89OmaRoyC-23
❑ 89OmaRoyP-1740
❑ 89TriAAAP-AAA37
❑ 90CMC-200
❑ 90OmaRoyC-25
❑ 90OmaRoyP-80
❑ 90ProAAAF-615
❑ 91LinDriAAA-349
❑ 91OmaRoyLD-349
❑ 91OmaRoyP-1049
❑ 91TriA AAGP-AAA27
❑ 93EdmTraF-1152
❑ 94EdmTraF-2890
❑ 95ChaKniTI-1
❑ 96ChaKniB-1
❑ 97PorSeaD-3
❑ 98PorSeaDQ-27
Rendell, Ed
❑ 96PinFan-ER1
Rendina, Mike
❑ 88BriTigP-1877
❑ 89BriTigS-21
❑ 89FayGenP-1584
❑ 90FayGenP-2416
❑ 90SouAtlLAS-20
❑ 91LakTigC-22
❑ 91LakTigP-275
❑ 92LakTigC-2
❑ 92LakTigF-2288
❑ 93LonTigF-2318
❑ 94TreThuF-2129
Rendon, Miguel
❑ 96-97LinVen-230
Renegade, Rookie the
❑ 96HudValRB-29
Renegades, Hudson Valley
❑ 98HudValR-30
Renfroe, Chad
❑ 93UtiBluSC-21
❑ 93UtiBluSF-3533
❑ 94LynRedSC-21
❑ 94LynRedSF-1891
❑ 95MicBatCTI-22
❑ 96SigRooOJ-28
❑ 96SigRooOJS-28
Renfroe, Chico
❑ 92NegLeaRLI-51
Renfroe, Laddie (Cohen)
❑ 86WinSpiP-21
❑ 87PitCubP-8
❑ 88IowCubC-4
❑ 88IowCubP-551
❑ 89ChaKniTI-1
❑ 90CMC-83
❑ 90IowCubC-8
❑ 90IowCubP-318
❑ 90ProAAAF-625
❑ 90TopTVCu-58
❑ 91IowCubLD-214
❑ 91IowCubP-1059
❑ 91LinDriAAA-214
❑ 91TriA AAGP-AAA19
❑ 92IowCubF-4050
❑ 92IowCubS-217
❑ 92Sco-875
❑ 92SkyAAAF-105
❑ 92TopDeb91-144
❑ 97NegLeaPC-4S
Renfroe, Marshall
❑ 60Lea-99
❑ 60TacBan-16
Renick, Rick
❑ 68Top-301
❑ 68TopVen-301
❑ 69MilBra-231
❑ 70OPC-93
❑ 70Top-93
❑ 71MLBOffS-473
❑ 71OPC-694
❑ 71Top-694
❑ 72MilBra-285
❑ 72OPC-459
❑ 72Top-459
❑ 73TacTwiC-18
❑ 74TacTwiC-20
❑ 75TacTwiK-8
❑ 76TacTwiDQ-17
❑ 78TwiFri-42
❑ 83MemChiT-23
❑ 85ExpPos-18
❑ 86ExpProPa-28
❑ 87TwiPos-22
❑ 87TwiTeal-29
❑ 92VanCanF-2734
❑ 92VanCanS-649
❑ 93NasSouF-583
❑ 94NasSouF-1265
❑ 95NasSouTI-18
❑ 96NasSouB-1
❑ 97PirPos-30
Reniff, Hal
❑ 61Yan61RL-25
❑ 62Top-139B
❑ 62Top-139C
❑ 62Top-159
❑ 62TopVen-159
❑ 63Top-546
❑ 64ChatheY-20
❑ 64Top-36
❑ 64TopVen-36
❑ 65ChaTheY-19
❑ 65Top-413
❑ 66OPC-68
❑ 66Top-68
❑ 66TopVen-68
❑ 67CokCapYM-V10
❑ 67Top-201
❑ 67YanPhoS-93
❑ 78TCM60I-106
❑ 83Yan196-25
❑ 91MetWIZ-327
❑ 91YanRinP12-7
❑ 92YanWIZ6-102
Renko, Steve
❑ 69ExpPin-6
❑ 70OPC-87
❑ 70Top-87
❑ 71ExpPS-22
❑ 71MLBOffS-139
❑ 71OPC-209
❑ 71Top-209
❑ 72Dia-38
❑ 72OPC-307
❑ 72OPC-308
❑ 72ProStaP-10
❑ 72Top-307
❑ 72Top-308
❑ 73OPC-623
❑ 73Top-623
❑ 74ExpWes-8
❑ 74OPC-49
❑ 74Top-49
❑ 74TopSta-58
❑ 75ExpPos-28
❑ 75Hos-69
❑ 75OPC-34
❑ 75Top-34
❑ 75TopMin-34
❑ 76CubTri-19
❑ 76OPC-264
❑ 76Top-264
❑ 77Top-586
❑ 78Top-493
❑ 79Top-352
❑ 80Top-184
❑ 81Don-337
❑ 81Fle-231
❑ 81LonBeaPT-24
❑ 81Top-63
❑ 81TopTra-821
❑ 82Don-38
❑ 82Fle-472
❑ 82Top-702
❑ 83Don-393
❑ 83Fle-99
❑ 83FleSti-24
❑ 83OPC-236
❑ 83RoyPos-24
❑ 83Top-236
❑ 83TopTra-95T
❑ 84Fle-355
❑ 84Nes792-444
❑ 84Top-444
❑ 84TopTif-444
❑ 91WesPalBEC-11
❑ 91WesPalBEP-1227
❑ 92WinHavRSF-1776
❑ 93ExpDonM-27
❑ 93HagSunC-21
❑ 93HagSunF-1878
❑ 94WicWraF-188
❑ 96CedRapKTI-28
❑ 97BirBarB-29
❑ 98BirBarG-22
❑ 98BriBluM-24
Renna, Bill
❑ 54A'STEAI-20
❑ 54Top-112
❑ 55A'sRodM-30
❑ 55A'sRodM-31
❑ 55A'sTeal-19
❑ 55Top-121
❑ 55TopDouH-99
❑ 56Top-82
❑ 58Top-473
❑ 59Top-72
❑ 59TopVen-72
❑ 76A'sRodMC-20
❑ 94TopArc1-112
❑ 94TopArc1G-112
Renneau, Charlie
❑ 77VisOakT-12
Rennert, Dutch
❑ 88T/MUmp-18
❑ 89T/MUmp-18

❑ 90T/MUmp-16
Rennhack, Mike
❑ 92HigSchPLS-4
❑ 93AshTouC-17
❑ 93AshTouF-2291
❑ 94QuaCitRBC-19
❑ 94QuaCitRBF-548
❑ 95QuaCitRBTI-21
❑ 96StoPorB-15
❑ 97El PasDB-11
❑ 98El PasDG-26
Rennicke, Dean
❑ 83AlbDukTc-5
❑ 84AlbDukCr-160
❑ 85AlbDukCr-151
Renninger, Bob
❑ 74CedRapAT-1
Rennspies, Dustin
❑ 92GreFalDSP-21
Rensa, Tony
❑ 34DiaMatCSB-151
❑ 93ConTSN-950
Renteria, David
❑ 92GulCoaYF-3799
❑ 93OneYanC-17
❑ 93OneYanF-3513
❑ 94GreBatF-485
❑ 95NorNagUTI-2
❑ 97GreBatC-17
Renteria, Ed (Edison)
❑ 87AubAstP-23
❑ 88AshTouP-1058
❑ 89OscAstS-19
❑ 90ColMudB-23
❑ 90ColMudP-1355
❑ 90ColMudS-20
❑ 91OscAstC-21
❑ 91OscAstP-695
Renteria, Edgar
❑ 93ClaYouG-YG19
❑ 93KanCouCC-18
❑ 93KanCouCF-925
❑ 93KanCouCTI-19
❑ 94Bow-94
❑ 94BowBes-B63
❑ 94BowBesR-B63
❑ 94BreCouMC-1
❑ 94BreCouMF-21
❑ 94Cla-111
❑ 94ClaTriF-T31
❑ 94FloStaLAF-FSL30
❑ 94PorSeaDF-688
❑ 95Bes-70
❑ 95Bes-104
❑ 95BesFra-F7
❑ 95Bow-120
❑ 95KanCouCLTI-12
❑ 95PorSeaDTI-23
❑ 95SPML-62
❑ 95UppDecML-186
❑ 95UppDecMLFS-186
❑ 96Bow-377
❑ 96BowBes-130
❑ 96BowBesAR-130
❑ 96BowBesR-130
❑ 96BowFoi-377
❑ 96ChaKniB-23
❑ 96ColCho-446
❑ 96ColChoGS-446
❑ 96ColChoSS-446
❑ 96Exc-166
❑ 96Fin-B332
❑ 96FinRef-B332
❑ 96LeaPre-142
❑ 96LeaPreP-142
❑ 96LeaSig-96
❑ 96LeaSigPPG-96
❑ 96LeaSigPPP-96
❑ 96SP-9
❑ 96UppDec-256
❑ 96Zen-115
❑ 96ZenArtP-115
❑ 97Bow-2
❑ 97BowBes-65
❑ 97BowBesAR-65
❑ 97BowBesR-65
❑ 97BowInt-2
❑ 97Cir-10
❑ 97CirRav-10
❑ 97ColCho-116
❑ 97ColChoT-FM6
❑ 97Don-326
❑ 97DonGolPP-326
❑ 97DonLim-13
❑ 97DonLimE-13
❑ 97DonLimENG-13
❑ 97DonPre-134
❑ 97DonPreCttC-134
❑ 97DonRatR-19
❑ 97DonSigA-83
❑ 97DonSigAC-102
❑ 97DonSigAM-102
❑ 97DonSilPP-326
❑ 97E-X2-73
❑ 97E-X2Cred-73
❑ 97E-X2EssCre-73
❑ 97Fin-17
❑ 97FinRef-17
❑ 97FlaShoLC-60
❑ 97FlaShoLeg0-60
❑ 97FlaShoLeg1-60
❑ 97FlaShoM-A60
❑ 97FlaShoM-B60
❑ 97FlaShoM-C60
❑ 97FlaShoR0-60
❑ 97FlaShoR1-60
❑ 97FlaShoR2-60
❑ 97Fle-335
❑ 97FleRooS-11
❑ 97FleTif-335
❑ 97Lea-8
❑ 97LeaFraM-8
❑ 97LeaFraMDC-8
❑ 97MarPac-20
❑ 97MetUni-178
❑ 97MetUniMF-7
❑ 97MetUniPP-9
❑ 97NewPin-111
❑ 97NewPinAP-111
❑ 97NewPinMC-111
❑ 97NewPinPP-111
❑ 97Pac-306
❑ 97PacGolCD-27
❑ 97PacLigB-306
❑ 97PacPri-103
❑ 97PacPriLB-103
❑ 97PacPriP-103
❑ 97PacSil-306
❑ 97Pin-182
❑ 97PinArtP-PP182
❑ 97PinCer-103
❑ 97PinCerMBla-103
❑ 97PinCerMBlu-103
❑ 97PinCerMG-103
❑ 97PinCerMR-103
❑ 97PinCerR-103
❑ 97PinIns-140
❑ 97PinInsCE-140
❑ 97PinInsDE-140
❑ 97PinMusC-182
❑ 97PinPrePla-182
❑ 97PinTotCPB-103
❑ 97PinTotCPG-103
❑ 97PinTotCPR-103
❑ 97PinX-P-90
❑ 97PinX-PMoS-90
❑ 97PinX-PMP-17
❑ 97PinX-PreMPS-17
❑ 97Sco-50
❑ 97ScoArtPWB-50
❑ 97ScoPreS-50
❑ 97ScoShoS-50
❑ 97ScoShoSAP-50
❑ 97SelRooR-4
❑ 97SP-77
❑ 97SpoIll-68
❑ 97SpoIllEE-68
❑ 97StaClu-154
❑ 97StaCluM-M17
❑ 97StaCluMOP-154
❑ 97StaCluMOP-M17
❑ 97Stu-138
❑ 97StuPrePG-138
❑ 97StuPrePS-138
❑ 97Top-211
❑ 97TopAwel-AI15
❑ 97TopChr-79
❑ 97TopChrR-79
❑ 97TopGal-142
❑ 97TopGalPPI-142
❑ 97UD3-43
❑ 97UD3GenNex-GN7
❑ 97Ult-201
❑ 97UltGolME-201
❑ 97UltPlaME-201
❑ 97UltRooR-9
❑ 97UppDec-77
❑ 97UppDec-183
❑ 97UppDecBCP-BC11
❑ 98Bow-25
❑ 98BowChr-25
❑ 98BowChrGA-25
❑ 98BowChrGAR-25
❑ 98BowChrI-25
❑ 98BowChrIR-25
❑ 98BowChrR-25
❑ 98BowGolA-25
❑ 98BowInt-25
❑ 98CirThu-127
❑ 98CirThuRav-127
❑ 98CirThuSupRav-127
❑ 98ColCho-127
❑ 98ColChoMBH-15
❑ 98CroRoy-60
❑ 98Don-126
❑ 98DonCol-126
❑ 98DonColP-668
❑ 98DonColS-126
❑ 98DonGolPP-126
❑ 98DonPre-118
❑ 98DonPreSeat-118
❑ 98DonPriCD-126
❑ 98DonPriCP-668
❑ 98DonSilPP-126
❑ 98E-X2-53
❑ 98E-X2ECFut-53
❑ 98E-X2ECNow-53
❑ 98Fin-147
❑ 98FinNo--147
❑ 98FinNo-R-147
❑ 98FinRef-147
❑ 98FlaShoLeg0-48
❑ 98FlaShoLeg1-48
❑ 98FlaShoLeg2-48
❑ 98FlaShoLeg3-48
❑ 98FlaShoLegM-48
❑ 98FlaShoR0-48
❑ 98FlaShoR1-48
❑ 98FlaShoR2-48
❑ 98FlaShoR3-48
❑ 98Fle-67
❑ 98FleVin'-27
❑ 98FleVin'C-27
❑ 98LeaRS-107
❑ 98LeaRSLHolo-107
❑ 98LeaRSLong-107
❑ 98LeaRTrue-107
❑ 98MetUni-155
❑ 98MetUniPMG-155
❑ 98Pac-307
❑ 98PacAur-133
❑ 98PacInv-100
❑ 98PacInvGems-157
❑ 98PacInvInt-10N
❑ 98PacInvPBlue-100
❑ 98PacInvSilv-100
❑ 98PacInvTeam-11
❑ 98PacLatotML-17
❑ 98PacOme-101
❑ 98PacOmeR-101
❑ 98PacOnl-304
❑ 98PacOnlR-304
❑ 98PacOnlWC-304
❑ 98PacPar-164
❑ 98PacParC-164
❑ 98PacParG-164
❑ 98PacParHS-164
❑ 98PacParI-14
❑ 98PacParPB-164
❑ 98PacParR-164
❑ 98PacPlaB-307
❑ 98PacRedT-307
❑ 98PacSil-307
❑ 98Pin-95
❑ 98PinPer-90
❑ 98PinPerPP-90
❑ 98PinPreP-95
❑ 98PorSeaD5AQ-2
❑ 98Revo-63
❑ 98RevoSS-63
❑ 98ScoRT-131
❑ 98ScoRTSS-PP80
❑ 98ScoRTSSAP-PP80
❑ 98ScoRTSSAP1-PP80
❑ 98SkyDugA-17
❑ 98SkyDugAIA-17
❑ 98SP Aut-93
❑ 98SpoIll-104
❑ 98SpoIll-129
❑ 98SpoIllEE-104
❑ 98SpoIllEE-129
❑ 98SpoIllFE-104
❑ 98SpoIllFE-129
❑ 98SpoIllTaN-123
❑ 98SpoIllTaNEE-123
❑ 98SpoIllWSF-20
❑ 98SpoIllWSF-30
❑ 98SpoIllWSFEE-20
❑ 98SpoIllWSFEE-30
❑ 98SpoIllWSFFE-20
❑ 98SpoIllWSFFE-30
❑ 98SPxFin-277
❑ 98SPxFinR-277
❑ 98SPxFinS-277
❑ 98StaCluFDI-55
❑ 98StaCluI-55
❑ 98StaCluOneK-55
❑ 98StaCluPP-55
❑ 98Stu-213
❑ 98StuGPP-213
❑ 98StuSPP-213
❑ 98Top-93
❑ 98TopChr-93
❑ 98TopChrR-93
❑ 98TopDevR-93
❑ 98TopDia-93
❑ 98TopGal-117
❑ 98TopGalGP-117
❑ 98TopGalOPP-117
❑ 98TopGalPPI-117
❑ 98TopGalPPIA-117
❑ 98TopMiniC-93
❑ 98TopOpeD-46
❑ 98TopSta-19
❑ 98TopStaB-19
❑ 98TopStaG-19
❑ 98TopStaGR-19
❑ 98TopStaS-19
❑ 98TopTek-46
❑ 98TopTekD-46
❑ 98Ult-128
❑ 98UltGolM-128
❑ 98UltMas-128
❑ 98UltNot-3
❑ 98UltPlaM-128
❑ 98UppDec-93
❑ 98UppDec-432
❑ 98UppDecNP-NP3
❑ 98UppDecSF-57
❑ 99199Fin-218
❑ 99Bow-254
❑ 99BowGol-254
❑ 99BowInt-254
❑ 99E-X Cen-40
❑ 99E-X CenECFut-40
❑ 99E-X CenECNow-40
❑ 99FinGolRef-218
❑ 99FinRef-218
❑ 99FlaShoLeg1-91
❑ 99FlaShoLeg2-91
❑ 99FlaShoLeg3-91
❑ 99FlaShoLegM1-91
❑ 99FlaShoLegM2-91
❑ 99FlaShoLegM3-91
❑ 99FlaShoR1-91
❑ 99FlaShoR2-91
❑ 99FlaShoR3-91
❑ 99Fle-242
❑ 99FleBri-105
❑ 99FleBri2G-105
❑ 99FleBriBlu-105
❑ 99FleBriGol-105
❑ 99FleSta9-242
❑ 99FleWarT-242
❑ 99MetUni-32
❑ 99MetUniGM-32
❑ 99MetUniPMG-32
❑ 99Pac-183
❑ 99PacAur-158
❑ 99PacAurOD-158
❑ 99PacCroC-118
❑ 99PacCroCPB-118
❑ 99PacOme-198
❑ 99PacOmeC-198
❑ 99PacOmeG-198
❑ 99PacOmePB-198
❑ 99PacPar-195
❑ 99PacParC-195
❑ 99PacParG-195
❑ 99PacParHoloGold-195
❑ 99PacParHS-195
❑ 99PacParOD-195
❑ 99PacParPB-195
❑ 99PacParRed-195
❑ 99PacPlaB-183
❑ 99PacPri-64
❑ 99PacPriHB-64
❑ 99PacPriHG-64
❑ 99PacPriHM-64
❑ 99PacPriHP-64
❑ 99PacPriRed-64
❑ 99PacPriS-131
❑ 99PacPriS206-131
❑ 99PacPriS206R-131
❑ 99PacRed-183
❑ 99SkyMolM-5
❑ 99SkyMolMX-5
❑ 99SkyPre-10
❑ 99SkyPreR-10
❑ 99SkyThu-41
❑ 99SkyThuRant-41
❑ 99SkyThuRave-41
❑ 99SpoIll-116
❑ 99ThuSkySupR-41
❑ 99Top-379
❑ 99TopChr-379
❑ 99TopChrR-379
❑ 99TopMVPP-379
❑ 99UD Ion-28
❑ 99UD IonR-28
❑ 99Ult-43
❑ 99UltGolM-43
❑ 99UltMas-43
❑ 99UltPlaM-43
❑ 99UppDec-464
❑ 99UppDecCLM-C78
❑ 99UppDecEL1-464
❑ 99UppDecEL2-464
❑ 99UppDecM-171
❑ 99UppDecMGS-171
❑ 99UppDecMHFS-171
❑ 99UppDecMSS-171
❑ 99Vic-325
Renteria, Rich
❑ 82AleDukT-27
❑ 83LynPirT-17
❑ 85MexCitTT-22
❑ 86HawIslP-20
❑ 87MarMot-23
❑ 88MarMot-23
❑ 89Bow-212
❑ 89BowTif-212
❑ 89MarMot-20
❑ 89Sco-142
❑ 89TopBig-109
❑ 89UppDec-547
❑ 93Bow-10
❑ 93FleFinE-69
❑ 93MarFloA-7
❑ 93MarPub-20
❑ 93MarUSPC-6D
❑ 93MarUSPC-13H
❑ 93PacSpa-470
❑ 93TopTra-2T
❑ 93Ult-385
❑ 94Don-499
❑ 94Fle-474
❑ 94MarTeal-14
❑ 94PanSti-184
❑ 94StaClu-87
❑ 94StaCluFDI-87
❑ 94StaCluGR-87
❑ 94StaCluMOP-87
❑ 94StaCluT-63
❑ 94StaCluTFDI-63
❑ 94Top-681
❑ 94TopGol-681
❑ 94TopSpa-681
❑ 95Top-340
Rentschuler, Tom
❑ 83PeoSunF-16
❑ 83RedPioT-22
Renwick, Richard
❑ 80QuaCitCT-9
Renz, Kevin
❑ 86PenWhiSP-22
❑ 87PenWhiSP-2
❑ 88BirBarB-28
Replogle, Andy
❑ 77ArkTraT-8A
❑ 77ArkTraT-8B
❑ 79Top-427
❑ 79VanCanT-8
❑ 81VanCanT-16
❑ 94BreMilB-169
Repoz, Craig
❑ 85LitFalMT-21
❑ 86ColMetP-21
❑ 87LynMetP-1
❑ 88St.LucMS-20
❑ 89JacMetGS-4
❑ 90WicWraRD-17
Repoz, Jeff
❑ 90PriPatD-16
Repoz, Roger
❑ 66OPC-138
❑ 66Top-138
❑ 66TopVen-138
❑ 67CokCapAt-13
❑ 67DexPre-173
❑ 67Top-416
❑ 68Top-587
❑ 69MilBra-232
❑ 69MLBOffS-26
❑ 69OPC-103
❑ 69Top-103
❑ 69TopSta-148
❑ 69TopTeaP-17
❑ 70MLBOffS-178
❑ 70OPC-397
❑ 70Top-397
❑ 71MLBOffS-355
❑ 71OPC-508
❑ 71Top-508
❑ 72MilBra-286
❑ 72Top-541
❑ 81TCM60I-458
❑ 92YanWIZ6-103
Repulski, Rip
❑ 53Top-172
❑ 54Bow-46
❑ 54CarHunW-20
❑ 54RedMan-NL17
❑ 54Top-115
❑ 55Bow-205
❑ 55CarHunW-19
❑ 55Top-55
❑ 55TopDouH-125
❑ 56Top-201
❑ 57Top-245
❑ 58Hir-15
❑ 58PhiJayP-8
❑ 58Top-14
❑ 59DodTeal-23
❑ 59DodVol-13
❑ 59Top-195
❑ 59TopVen-195
❑ 60DodBelB-5
❑ 60Lea-86
❑ 60Top-265
❑ 61Top-128
❑ 90DodTar-657
❑ 91TopArc1-172
❑ 94TopArc1-115
❑ 94TopArc1G-115
Rescigno, Xavier
❑ 47SigOil-13
❑ 49BowPCL-5
Resendez, Oscar
❑ 91BurIndP-3302
❑ 92ColRedF-2389
❑ 92ProFS7-61
❑ 92WatIndC-7
❑ 92WatIndF-3232
❑ 93ColRedC-19
❑ 93ColRedF-594
❑ 94HigDesMC-21
❑ 94HigDesMF-2788
Resetar, Gary
❑ 89KenTwiP-1075
❑ 89KenTwiS-21
❑ 90Bes-174
❑ 90OrlSunRB-12
❑ 90OrlSunRP-1087
❑ 90OrlSunRS-18
❑ 91CanIndLD-92
❑ 91CanIndP-982
❑ 91LinDriAA-92
Resinger, Grover
❑ 66BraPos-21
❑ 75CalAngP-33
Resnikoff, Bob
❑ 88SouBenWSGS-24
❑ 89SarWhiSS-19
❑ 90SarWhiSS-21
❑ 90StaFS7-60
❑ 91OscAstP-683
Respondek, Mark
❑ 91WavRedF-11
❑ 92AlbPolCB-12
❑ 92AlbPolF-2304
❑ 93AusFut-85
❑ 93JamExpC-19
❑ 93JamExpF-3325
❑ 95AusFut-77
❑ 95AusFut-91
Restilli, Dino
❑ 48SomandK-12
❑ 49SomandK-17
❑ 50Bow-123
❑ 85TCMPpl1-20
Restin, Eric
❑ 76BurBeeT-27
❑ 77BurBeeT-24
Restovich, Michael
❑ 99Bow-358

❑ 99BowGol-358
❑ 99BowInt-358
Resz, Greg
❑ 93OneYanC-18
❑ 93OneYanF-3501
❑ 94GreBatF-472
❑ 96TamYanY-21
❑ 97NorNav-28
❑ 97NorNavTI-25
❑ 98ColCliD-21
❑ 98ColCliM-25
❑ 98NorNavQ-20
Retes, Lorenzo
❑ 85MexCitTT-10
Rettenmund, Merv
❑ 67BalOriP-84
❑ 67BalOriP-85
❑ 67BalOriP-86
❑ 69OPC-66
❑ 69Top-66
❑ 70BalOriP-25
❑ 70DayDaiNM-143
❑ 70Ori-11
❑ 70Top-629
❑ 71BalOriP-22
❑ 71MLBOffS-308
❑ 71OPC-393
❑ 71Top-393
❑ 72Kel-11
❑ 72MilBra-287
❑ 72OPC-86
❑ 72OPC-235
❑ 72OriDMV-9
❑ 72OriPos-26
❑ 72ProStaP-35
❑ 72Top-86
❑ 72Top-235
❑ 73BalOriP-35
❑ 73OPC-56
❑ 73OriJohP-14
❑ 73OriTeal-25
❑ 73Top-56
❑ 74OPC-585
❑ 74Top-585
❑ 74TopTra-585T
❑ 75OPC-369
❑ 75Top-369
❑ 75TopMin-369
❑ 76OPC-283
❑ 76SSP-46
❑ 76Top-283
❑ 77PadSchC-45
❑ 77Top-659
❑ 78AngFamF-31
❑ 78Top-566
❑ 79Top-48
❑ 80Top-402
❑ 83RanAffF-NNO
❑ 84RanJarP-NNO
❑ 89A'sMot-27
❑ 90A'sMot-27
❑ 91OriCro-377
❑ 91PadSmo-28
❑ 92PadMot-27
❑ 92PadPolD-16
❑ 92PadPolD-28
❑ 92PadSmo-24
❑ 93PadMot-28
❑ 93RanKee-306
❑ 94PadMot-28
❑ 95PadMot-28
❑ 96PadMot-28
❑ 98PadMot-28
Retzer, Ed
❑ 83MadMusF-10
❑ 83TacTigT-31
Retzer, Ken
❑ 55DonWin-36
❑ 61SenJayP-8
❑ 62Top-594
❑ 63Jel-94
❑ 63Pos-94
❑ 63Top-471
❑ 64Top-277
❑ 64TopVen-277
❑ 65OPC-278
❑ 65Top-278
Reucor, Randy
❑ 72CedRapCT-16
Reulbach, Ed
❑ 06FanCraNL-40
❑ 07CubA.CDPP-10
❑ 07CubGFGCP-10
❑ 08AmeCarE91-21
❑ 08AmeCarE91-59
❑ 08RosComP-107
❑ 09ColChiE-240
❑ 09PhiCarE-21
❑ 09RamT20-101
❑ 09T206-299
❑ 09T206-300
❑ 10CouT21-211
❑ 10CouT21-212
❑ 10CouT21-213
❑ 10CouT21-312
❑ 10DomDisP-101
❑ 10JuJuDE-34
❑ 10RedCroT-64
❑ 10RedCroT-150
❑ 10RedCroT-238
❑ 10SweCapPP-88
❑ 11HelSta-100
❑ 11JonKeyaAC-317
❑ 11PinT-5-215
❑ 11S74Sil-67
❑ 11SpoLifCW-300
❑ 11SpoLifM-179
❑ 11T205-143
❑ 12ColRedB-240
❑ 12ColTinT-240
❑ 12HasTriFT-36D
❑ 12T207-156
❑ 14CraJacE-80
❑ 14FatPlaT-41
❑ 14PieStaT-88
❑ 15CraJacE-80
❑ 50CubGreB-14
❑ 69Baz-12
❑ 72FleFamF-29
❑ 84CubBriPC-5H
❑ 87Cub190T-3
❑ 90DodTar-658
❑ 90HOFStiB-12
❑ 92ConTSN-549
Reuschel, Paul
❑ 73WicAerJPKB-13
❑ 74WicAerODF-112
❑ 76VenLeaS-170
❑ 77CubJewT-13
❑ 77Top-333
❑ 77Top-634
❑ 78SSP270-247
❑ 78Top-663
❑ 79Top-511
Reuschel, Rick
❑ 73OPC-482
❑ 73Top-482
❑ 74OPC-136
❑ 74Top-136
❑ 74TopSta-18
❑ 75Hos-51
❑ 75OPC-153
❑ 75Top-153
❑ 75TopMin-153
❑ 76CubTri-20
❑ 76Hos-17
❑ 76HosTwi-17
❑ 76OPC-359
❑ 76SSP-301
❑ 76Top-359
❑ 77BurCheD-193
❑ 77Hos-103
❑ 77OPC-214
❑ 77Spo-4307
❑ 77Top-530
❑ 77Top-634
❑ 78Hos-131
❑ 78Kel-45
❑ 78OPC-56
❑ 78RCColC-91
❑ 78SSP270-245
❑ 78Top-50
❑ 79BasPat-75
❑ 79Hos-67
❑ 79Kel-47
❑ 79OPC-123
❑ 79Top-240
❑ 80OPC-99
❑ 80Top-175
❑ 81CokTeaS-20
❑ 81Don-561
❑ 81Fle-293
❑ 81FleStiC-93
❑ 81OPC-205
❑ 81Top-645
❑ 81TopSti-157
❑ 81TopSupHT-29
❑ 81TopTra-822
❑ 81YanPhoA-21
❑ 82Don-157
❑ 82Fle-50
❑ 82OPC-204
❑ 82Top-405
❑ 84CubBriPC-12S
❑ 84CubChiT-22
❑ 84CubSev-47
❑ 85Fle-63
❑ 85FleUpd-88
❑ 85HawIslC-230
❑ 85OPC-306
❑ 85Top-306
❑ 85TopMin-306
❑ 85TopTif-306
❑ 85TopTifT-93T
❑ 85TopTra-93T
❑ 86Don-532
❑ 86Fle-618
❑ 86FleSlu-27
❑ 86FleStiC-95
❑ 86Lea-207
❑ 86Top-779
❑ 86TopMinL-57
❑ 86TopSti-126
❑ 86TopTat-7
❑ 86TopTif-779
❑ 87Don-188
❑ 87Fle-619
❑ 87FleGlo-619
❑ 87OPC-154
❑ 87RedFolSB-129
❑ 87Top-521
❑ 87TopSti-128
❑ 87TopTif-521
❑ 88Don-613
❑ 88DonAll-52
❑ 88DonBasB-218
❑ 88Fle-94
❑ 88FleGlo-94
❑ 88FleLeaL-32
❑ 88FleStiC-130
❑ 88GiaMot-15
❑ 88GiaPos-26
❑ 88Lea-219
❑ 88OPC-278
❑ 88Sco-519
❑ 88ScoGlo-519
❑ 88Spo-136
❑ 88StaLinG-14
❑ 88Top-660
❑ 88TopBig-188
❑ 88TopMinL-76
❑ 88TopRevLL-13
❑ 88TopRitTM-30
❑ 88TopTif-660
❑ 89Bow-466
❑ 89BowTif-466
❑ 89Don-11
❑ 89Don-335
❑ 89DonBasB-162
❑ 89DonSupD-11
❑ 89Fle-340
❑ 89FleGlo-340
❑ 89GiaMot-15
❑ 89OPC-65
❑ 89PanSti-210
❑ 89Sco-5
❑ 89ScoHot1S-22
❑ 89Spo-72
❑ 89Top-65
❑ 89TopBasT-83
❑ 89TopMinL-42
❑ 89TopSti-79
❑ 89TopTif-65
❑ 89TopUKM-63
❑ 89TVSpoM-50
❑ 89UppDec-194
❑ 90Bow-223
❑ 90BowTif-223
❑ 90Don-112
❑ 90Don-663A
❑ 90Don-663B
❑ 90Fle-68
❑ 90FleCan-68
❑ 90GiaMot-8
❑ 90KayB-25
❑ 90MLBBasB-23
❑ 90OPC-190
❑ 90OPCBoxB-L
❑ 90PanSti-206
❑ 90PanSti-370
❑ 90PubIntS-79
❑ 90RedFolSB-77
❑ 90Sco-465
❑ 90Sco100S-7
❑ 90Spo-161
❑ 90Top-190
❑ 90TopBig-328
❑ 90TopGloA-10
❑ 90TopGloS-18
❑ 90TopMinL-87
❑ 90TopSti-89
❑ 90TopSti-154
❑ 90TopStiB-26
❑ 90TopTif-190
❑ 90TopWaxBC-L
❑ 90UppDec-696
❑ 90Woo-18
❑ 91Don-518
❑ 91Fle-270
❑ 91GiaMot-14
❑ 91OPC-422
❑ 91Sco-544
❑ 91Top-422
❑ 91TopDesS-422
❑ 91TopMic-422
❑ 91TopTif-422
❑ 91UppDec-249
❑ 92CubOldS-19
❑ 92YanWIZ8-156
Reuss, Jerry
❑ 70CarTeal-22
❑ 70OPC-96
❑ 70Top-96
❑ 71CarTeal-19
❑ 71CarTeal-30
❑ 71OPC-158
❑ 71Top-158
❑ 72AstTeal-22
❑ 72Top-775
❑ 73LinPor-83
❑ 73OPC-446
❑ 73Top-446
❑ 74OPC-116
❑ 74Top-116
❑ 74TopSta-38
❑ 75OPC-124
❑ 75PitPirP-21
❑ 75Top-124
❑ 75TopMin-124
❑ 76BlaDis-47
❑ 76BucDis-47
❑ 76CarDis-47
❑ 76CraDis-47
❑ 76DailsID-47
❑ 76Hos-29
❑ 76HosTwi-29
❑ 76IsaDis-47
❑ 76Kel-43
❑ 76OPC-60
❑ 76OrbDis-47
❑ 76PirPos-17
❑ 76RedBarD-47
❑ 76SafDis-47
❑ 76SSP-562
❑ 76Top-60
❑ 76TowCluD-47
❑ 77BurCheD-181
❑ 77ChiWilD-54
❑ 77DailsID-54
❑ 77DetCaeD-54
❑ 77HolInnD-54
❑ 77Hos-119
❑ 77MSADis-54
❑ 77OPC-97
❑ 77PepGloD-65
❑ 77PirPosP-21
❑ 77SagDis-54
❑ 77sDis-54
❑ 77Top-645
❑ 77WenDis-54
❑ 77ZipDis-54
❑ 78Top-255
❑ 79Top-536
❑ 80DodPol-41
❑ 80Top-318
❑ 81Dod-9
❑ 81Dod-24
❑ 81DodPol-41
❑ 81DodPos-7
❑ 81Don-417
❑ 81Fle-118
❑ 81LonBeaPT-9
❑ 81OPC-153
❑ 81Top-440
❑ 81TopScr-103
❑ 81TopSti-181
❑ 81TopSupHT-50
❑ 82DodPol-41
❑ 82DodUniOV-16
❑ 82DogBuiE-6
❑ 82Don-284
❑ 82Fle-18
❑ 82FleSta-7
❑ 82OPC-278
❑ 82SevSluC-21
❑ 82Top-710
❑ 82TopSti-56
❑ 82TopSti-259
❑ 83AllGamPI-173
❑ 83DodPol-41
❑ 83DodPos-12
❑ 83Don-158
❑ 83Fle-216
❑ 83FleSta-161
❑ 83FleSti-123
❑ 83OPC-90
❑ 83Top-90
❑ 83TopFol-1
❑ 83TopSti-247
❑ 84DodPol-41
❑ 84DodUniO-6
❑ 84Don-418
❑ 84Fle-110
❑ 84Nes792-170
❑ 84OPC-170
❑ 84Top-170
❑ 84TopSti-81
❑ 84TopTif-170
❑ 85DodCokP-26
❑ 85Don-226
❑ 85Fle-380
❑ 85OPC-66
❑ 85ReuCysF-1
❑ 85Top-680
❑ 85TopTif-680
❑ 86BasStaB-89
❑ 86DodCokP-25
❑ 86DodPol-41
❑ 86DodUniOP-15
❑ 86Don-104
❑ 86Fle-141
❑ 86OPC-236
❑ 86Spo-53
❑ 86Top-577
❑ 86TopSti-66
❑ 86TopTif-577
❑ 87AstShowSTh-20
❑ 87AstShowSTh-26
❑ 87DodPol-21
❑ 87DodSmoA-28
❑ 87Fle-451
❑ 87FleGlo-451
❑ 87OPC-373
❑ 87Top-682
❑ 87TopTif-682
❑ 88DodSmo-6
❑ 88Sco-270
❑ 88ScoGlo-270
❑ 88ScoRoo-61T
❑ 88ScoRooG-61T
❑ 88Top-216
❑ 88TopTif-216
❑ 88WhiSoxC-23
❑ 89Bow-57
❑ 89BowTif-57
❑ 89Don-413
❑ 89DonBasB-305
❑ 89Fle-510
❑ 89FleGlo-510
❑ 89Sco-489
❑ 89Top-357
❑ 89TopTif-357
❑ 89UppDec-151
❑ 89WhiSoxC-22
❑ 90DodTar-659
❑ 90Don-528
❑ 90Fle-335
❑ 90FleCan-335
❑ 90KayB-26
❑ 90OPC-424
❑ 90PubIntS-400
❑ 90Top-424
❑ 90TopTif-424
❑ 90UppDec-96
❑ 91DodUno7P-4
❑ 92DodStaTA-19
❑ 94BreMilB-170
Reuteman, AGM (R.C.)
❑ 88TidTidCa-26
Reutter, Derrick
❑ 83KinBluJTI-18
Revak, Ray
❑ 86GreHorP-19
Reveira, Frank
❑ 60TacBan-17
❑ 61TacBan-18
Revelle, Dutch (R.H.)
❑ 09T206-511
Revenig, Todd
❑ 90SouOreAB-8
❑ 90SouOreAP-3445
❑ 91MadMusP-2130
❑ 92Bow-198
❑ 92HunStaF-3950
❑ 92HunStaS-319
❑ 92SkyAA F-136
❑ 93AthStaC-26
❑ 93Top-766
❑ 93TopGol-766
❑ 93TopInaM-766
❑ 93TopInaR-766
❑ 93TopMic-766
❑ 95EdmTraTI-19
Revering, Dave
❑ 76IndIndTI-7
❑ 77IndIndTI-4
❑ 78Top-706
❑ 79Hos-139
❑ 79OPC-113
❑ 79Top-224
❑ 80OPC-227
❑ 80Top-438
❑ 80TopSup-58
❑ 81A'sGraG-13
❑ 81Don-117
❑ 81Fle-576
❑ 81FleStiC-4
❑ 81OPC-57
❑ 81Top-568
❑ 81TopScr-22
❑ 81TopSti-117
❑ 81TopTra-823
❑ 81YanPhoA-22
❑ 82Don-234
❑ 82Fle-51
❑ 82OPC-109
❑ 82Top-109
❑ 82TopTra-97T
❑ 83Fle-484
❑ 83OPC-291
❑ 83Top-677
❑ 85IndIndTI-29
❑ 92YanWIZ8-157
Revson, Peter
❑ 74NewYorNTDiS-16
Rex, Mike
❑ 76CedRapGT-23
❑ 79PhoGiaVNB-23
❑ 80PhoGiaVNB-18
❑ 81PhoGiaVNB-11
❑ 82PhoGiaVNB-26
Rexrode, Jackie
❑ 97SouBenSH-25
❑ 97Top-469
❑ 98HigDesMG-22
❑ 98SouBenSHM-6
❑ 99Bow-327
❑ 99BowAut-BA54
❑ 99BowGol-327
❑ 99BowInt-327
❑ 99Top-433
❑ 99TopChr-433
❑ 99TopChrR-433
❑ 99TopMVPP-433
Rey, Everett
❑ 80WatIndT-25
❑ 81ChaLooT-9
❑ 82ChaLooT-3
❑ 83BufBisT-12
Reyan, Julio
❑ 87BelMarL-8
❑ 89BelMarL-2
❑ 91BelMarP-3661
Reyes, Alberto
❑ 92AlbPolCB-19
❑ 92AlbPolF-2305
❑ 93BurBeeC-21
❑ 93BurBeeF-157
❑ 93LimRocDWB-2
❑ 93MidLeaAGF-33
❑ 94HarSenF-2089
❑ 95Exc-226
❑ 95Fin-308
❑ 95Fla-275
❑ 95FleUpd-56
❑ 96ColCho-196
❑ 96ColChoGS-196
❑ 96ColChoSS-196
❑ 96Fle-156
❑ 96FleTif-156
❑ 97PacPriGotD-GD57
❑ 98PacOnl-410
❑ 98PacOnlR-410
❑ 98PacOnlWC-410
❑ 99PacCroC-153

❑ 99PacCroCPB-153
Reyes, Ambiorix
❑ 98MarPhiG-24
Reyes, Amner
❑ 90BenBucL-24
Reyes, Basilo
❑ 84IdaFalATI-22
Reyes, Cananea
❑ 81MarPos-28
Reyes, Carlos
❑ 86AshTouP-22
Reyes, Carlos Alberto
❑ 92MacBraC-20
❑ 92MacBraF-265
❑ 93AusFut-98
❑ 93AusFut-108
❑ 93AusFut-118
❑ 93AusFut-128
❑ 93GreBraF-346
❑ 94A'sMot-20
❑ 94Bow-492
❑ 94Fin-302
❑ 94FinRef-302
❑ 94Fla-332
❑ 94FleUpd-77
❑ 94Lea-296
❑ 94ScoRoo-RT117
❑ 94ScoRooGR-RT117
❑ 94SpoRoo-97
❑ 94SpoRooAP-97
❑ 94TopTra-128T
❑ 94Ult-410
❑ 95AthMot-20
❑ 95FinRef-308
❑ 95Fle-252
❑ 95Pac-319
❑ 95Sco-489
❑ 95ScoGolR-489
❑ 95ScoPlaTS-489
❑ 95Top-72
❑ 96A'sMot-21
❑ 96Fle-217
❑ 96FleTif-217
❑ 96LeaSigEA-169
❑ 96Pac-394
❑ 97Pac-175
❑ 97PacLigB-175
❑ 97PacSil-175
❑ 98Pac-172
❑ 98PacOnl-646
❑ 98PacOnlR-646
❑ 98PacOnlWC-646
❑ 98PacPlaB-172
❑ 98PacRedT-172
❑ 98PacSil-172
❑ 98PadMot-26
Reyes, Dennis
❑ 94GreFalDSP-26
❑ 94VerBeaDC-15
❑ 94VerBeaDF-69
❑ 96SanBerSB-21
❑ 97AlbDukUG-4
❑ 97Bow-391
❑ 97BowChr-258
❑ 97BowChrI-258
❑ 97BowChrIR-258
❑ 97BowChrR-258
❑ 97BowInt-391
❑ 97DonLim-60
❑ 97DonLimE-60
❑ 97DonLimENG-60
❑ 97DonSigA-84
❑ 97DonSigAC-103
❑ 97DonSigAM-103
❑ 97SanAntMB-8
❑ 97TexLeaTP-17
❑ 98AlbDukG-21
❑ 98Bow-108
❑ 98BowChr-108
❑ 98BowChrGA-108
❑ 98BowChrGAR-108
❑ 98BowChrI-108
❑ 98BowChrIR-108
❑ 98BowChrR-108
❑ 98BowGolA-108
❑ 98BowInt-108
❑ 98CirThu-159
❑ 98CirThuRav-159
❑ 98CirThuSupRav-159
❑ 98ColCho-107
❑ 98Don-141
❑ 98DonCol-141
❑ 98DonCol-199
❑ 98DonColL-270
❑ 98DonColP-703
❑ 98DonColS-141
❑ 98DonColS-194
❑ 98DonGolPP-141
❑ 98DonPre-153
❑ 98DonPreSeat-153
❑ 98DonPriCD-141
❑ 98DonPriCD-199
❑ 98DonPriCL-270
❑ 98DonPriCP-703
❑ 98DonRatR-24
❑ 98DonRatRM-24
❑ 98DonSilPP-141
❑ 98Fle-97
❑ 98Lea-71
❑ 98LeaFraDA-71
❑ 98LeaFraF-71
❑ 98LeaFraM-71
❑ 98LeaFraM-71
❑ 98LeaFraMDC-71
❑ 98LeaFraMDC-71
❑ 98LeaFraMS-71
❑ 98LeaFraMZ2-71
❑ 98LeaRS-308
❑ 98LeaRSLHolo-308
❑ 98LeaRSLong-308
❑ 98LeaRTrue-308
❑ 98Pac-340
❑ 98PacPlaB-340
❑ 98PacRedT-340
❑ 98PacSil-340
❑ 98PinSna-LAD15
❑ 98SanAntMM-8
❑ 98SpoIll-170
❑ 98SpoIllEE-170
❑ 98SpoIllFE-170
❑ 98Stu-144
❑ 98StuGPP-144
❑ 98StuSPP-144
❑ 98Top-443
❑ 98TopChr-443
❑ 98TopChrR-443
❑ 98TopDevR-443
❑ 98TopDia-443
❑ 98TopMiniC-443
❑ 98Ult-266
❑ 98UltGolM-266
❑ 98UltMas-266
❑ 98UltPlaM-266
❑ 98UppDec-257
❑ 98UppDecSF-139
❑ 99MetUni-121
❑ 99MetUniGM-121
❑ 99MetUniPMG-121
❑ 99StaClu-246
❑ 99StaCluFDI-246
❑ 99StaCluOoaK-246
❑ 99StaCluPP-246
❑ 99Top-311
❑ 99TopChr-311
❑ 99TopChrR-311
❑ 99TopMVPP-311
Reyes, Eddy
❑ 97HudValRB-6
❑ 98ChaRivDG-22
Reyes, Freddy
❑ 96AppLeaAB-18
❑ 97ForWayW-27
Reyes, Gilberto
❑ 85AlbDukCr-170
❑ 86AlbDukP-20
❑ 86Don-581
❑ 87AlbDukD-17
❑ 87DodPol-7
❑ 88AlbDukCm-21
❑ 88AlbDukP-257
❑ 89IndIndC-11
❑ 89IndIndP-1240
❑ 90DodTar-1053
❑ 91Bow-447
❑ 91ExpPos-17
❑ 91FleUpd-99
❑ 91Lea-451
❑ 91UltUpd-92
❑ 92Don-381
❑ 92Fle-489
❑ 92OPC-286
❑ 92PanSti-201
❑ 92Pin-428
❑ 92Sco-229
❑ 92StaClu-173
❑ 92Top-286
❑ 92TopGol-286
❑ 92TopGolW-286
❑ 92TopMic-286
❑ 92Ult-225
❑ 92UppDec-230
❑ 93ColSprSSF-3089
❑ 93LimRocDWB-71
❑ 98MadBlaW-13
Reyes, Giovanny
❑ 86QuaCitAP-26
❑ 86SalAngC-77
❑ 87QuaCitAP-5
❑ 88PalSprACLC-109
Reyes, Jesus
❑ 73CedRapAT-8
❑ 74CedRapAT-3
❑ 76VenLeaS-187
Reyes, Jimmy
❑ 93HicCraC-20
❑ 93HicCraF-1288
❑ 94SouBenSHC-19
❑ 94SouBenSHF-603
Reyes, Jose
❑ 77CliDodT-20
❑ 80OrlTwiT-7
❑ 82OrlTwi8SCT-22
❑ 84MemChiT-21
❑ 85DomLeaS-189
❑ 86OmaRoyP-18
❑ 90BenBucL-13
❑ 91CliGiaC-9
❑ 91CliGiaP-833
❑ 96AugGreB-25
❑ 97EriSeaWB-28
Reyes, Joselito
❑ 85KinBluJT-18
Reyes, Juan
❑ 86BelBreP-19
❑ 89BenBucL-6
❑ 89BriTigS-22
Reyes, Michael
❑ 94ElmPioC-17
❑ 94ElmPioF-3488
❑ 95KanCouCTI-13
Reyes, Nap
❑ 83TCMPla1945-35
Reyes, Nate
❑ 97GreFalDTI-20
Reyes, Orlando
❑ 76VenLeaS-191
Reyes, Pablo
❑ 85KinBluJT-9
❑ 86VenGulP-22
Reyes, Rafael
❑ 91RocExpC-11
❑ 91RocExpP-2046
Reyes, Sergio
❑ 91HunCubC-19
❑ 91HunCubP-3349
Reyes, Steve
❑ 88BilMusP-1810
Reyes, Victor
❑ 90ButCopKSP-20
Reyes, Wascar
❑ 78ChaPirT-20
Reyes, Winston
❑ 94MarPhiC-20
❑ 94MarPhiF-3304
Reyna, Dion
❑ 88MadMusP-19
Reyna, Luis
❑ 86VenGulP-23
❑ 87KnoBluJP-1502
❑ 88SyrChiC-12
❑ 88SyrChiP-810
Reynolds, Allie
❑ 47StaPinP2-33
❑ 47TipTop-56
❑ 47YanTeaT-20
❑ 48BluTin-21
❑ 48Bow-14
❑ 48YanTeal-23
❑ 49Bow-114
❑ 49YanTeal-18
❑ 50Bow-138
❑ 50Dra-28
❑ 50YanTeal-18
❑ 51BerRos-C3
❑ 51Bow-109
❑ 51R42SmaS-89
❑ 51TopRedB-6
❑ 52BasPho-4
❑ 52BerRos-52
❑ 52DixLid-15
❑ 52DixPre-15
❑ 52H-OInsOR-3
❑ 52StaCalL-70A
❑ 52StaCalS-84A
❑ 52TipTop-31
❑ 52Top-67
❑ 53BowC-68
❑ 53DixLid-16
❑ 53DixPre-16
❑ 53Dor-109
❑ 53NorBreL-23
❑ 53SpoMagP-8
❑ 53Top-141
❑ 54Bow-113
❑ 54NewYorJA-56
❑ 55ArmCoi-16
❑ 55Bow-201
❑ 59OklTodML-6
❑ 61Fle-69
❑ 68LauWorS-46
❑ 69EquSpoHoF-BB16
❑ 70FleWorS-46
❑ 71FleWorS-48
❑ 75JohMiz-13
❑ 76GrePlaG-5
❑ 77GalGloG-33
❑ 79TCM50-185
❑ 82TCMGreP-13
❑ 83TopRep5-67
❑ 83YanASFY-35
❑ 83YanYealT-12
❑ 84FifNatCT-14
❑ 85TCMPla1-8
❑ 88PacLegI-41
❑ 89SweBasG-101
❑ 91TopArc1-141
❑ 92BazQua5A-5
❑ 92UppDecS-16
❑ 92YanWIZA-62
❑ 93ActPacA-135
Reynolds, Archie
❑ 71MLBOffS-356
❑ 71OPC-664
❑ 71Top-664
❑ 72Top-672
❑ 94BreMilB-171
Reynolds, Bob
❑ 82IowCubT-28
Reynolds, Carl
❑ 28PorandAR-C4
❑ 29ExhFou-20
❑ 30ChiEveAP-19
❑ 30WhiSoxTI-21
❑ 31Exh-20
❑ 32OrbPinNP-2
❑ 32OrbPinUP-50
❑ 33ButCanV-39
❑ 33CraJacP-18
❑ 33GeoCMil-25
❑ 33Gou-120
❑ 33TatOrb-50
❑ 34BabRutG-52
❑ 34BatR31-49
❑ 34BatR31-95
❑ 34ButPreR-51
❑ 34GouCanV-12
❑ 35AlDemDCR3-74
❑ 35GouPuzR-6E
❑ 35GouPuzR-11G
❑ 35GouPuzR-13E
❑ 35GouPuzR-15E
❑ 39CubTeal-20
❑ 85BigLeaC3-79
❑ 91ConTSN-80
Reynolds, Chance
❑ 93EveGiaC-21
❑ 93EveGiaF-3772
❑ 96CarMudB-15
Reynolds, Charles
❑ 87OldJudN-414
Reynolds, Chris
❑ 97PriDevR-28
Reynolds, Craig
❑ 70RelPam-11
❑ 76OPC-596
❑ 76SSP-582
❑ 76Top-596
❑ 76VenLeaS-158
❑ 77MarPos-18
❑ 77Top-474
❑ 78Top-199
❑ 79AstPos-18
❑ 79AstTeal-11
❑ 79Kel-51
❑ 79OPC-251
❑ 79Top-482
❑ 80OPC-71
❑ 80Top-129
❑ 81AstPos-17
❑ 81Don-378
❑ 81Fle-74
❑ 81OPC-12
❑ 81Top-617
❑ 82AstAstI-4
❑ 82AstPos-19
❑ 82Don-344
❑ 82Fle-225
❑ 82OPC-57
❑ 82Top-57
❑ 82TopSti-46
❑ 83AstPos-23
❑ 83Don-317
❑ 83Fle-460
❑ 83Top-328
❑ 84AstMot-26
❑ 84AstPos-22
❑ 84Don-405
❑ 84Fle-237
❑ 84Nes792-776
❑ 84Top-776
❑ 84TopTif-776
❑ 85AllGamPI-114
❑ 85AstHouP-8
❑ 85AstMot-14
❑ 85Don-328
❑ 85Fle-357
❑ 85OPC-156
❑ 85Top-156
❑ 85TopMin-156
❑ 85TopSti-65
❑ 85TopTif-156
❑ 86AstMilL-17
❑ 86AstMot-18
❑ 86AstPol-13
❑ 86AstTeal-12
❑ 86Don-232
❑ 86Fle-309
❑ 86Lea-107
❑ 86OPC-298
❑ 86Top-298
❑ 86TopTif-298
❑ 87AstMot-19
❑ 87AstPol-10
❑ 87AstShoSPT-13
❑ 87Don-384
❑ 87DonOpeD-19
❑ 87Fle-66
❑ 87FleGlo-66
❑ 87OPC-298
❑ 87Top-779
❑ 87TopTif-779
❑ 88AstMot-19
❑ 88AstPol-19
❑ 88Don-209
❑ 88Fle-454
❑ 88FleGlo-454
❑ 88Lea-205
❑ 88OPC-18
❑ 88PanSti-297
❑ 88Sco-207
❑ 88ScoGlo-207
❑ 88StaLinAst-14
❑ 88Top-557
❑ 88TopBig-219
❑ 88TopTif-557
❑ 89AstLenH-15
❑ 89AstMot-18
❑ 89AstSmo-33
❑ 89Bow-328
❑ 89BowTif-328
❑ 89Don-477
❑ 89Fle-366
❑ 89FleGlo-366
❑ 89PAORelT-5
❑ 89Sco-468
❑ 89Top-428
❑ 89TopBig-312
❑ 89TopTif-428
❑ 89UppDec-284
❑ 90OPC-637
❑ 90PubIntS-100
❑ 90Top-637
❑ 90TopTif-637
Reynolds, Dave
❑ 86AppFoxP-19
❑ 87PenWhiSP-11
❑ 88TamTarS-21
❑ 89SarWhiSS-20
❑ 90BirBarB-21
❑ 90BirBarP-1109
Reynolds, Don
❑ 70RelPam-12
❑ 78PadFamF-24
❑ 79HawIslT-13
❑ 79Top-292
❑ 80HawIslT-23
❑ 87BelMarL-29
❑ 88SanBerSB-2
❑ 88SanBerSCLC-55
❑ 91JacGenLD-575
❑ 91JacGenP-941
❑ 91LinDriAA-575
❑ 92JacGenF-4016
❑ 94JacGenF-232
❑ 95TucTotTI-22
❑ 96TusTorB-27
Reynolds, Doug
❑ 89EriOriS-18
❑ 90FreKeyTI-9
❑ 91FreKeyC-14
❑ 91FreKeyP-2368
❑ 91KanCouCTI-17
Reynolds, Harold
❑ 81WauTimT-18
❑ 82LynSaiT-17
❑ 83SalLakCGT-22
❑ 84SalLakCGC-185
❑ 85MarMot-23
❑ 86CalCanP-23
❑ 86Don-484
❑ 86MarPacNB-11
❑ 86Top-769
❑ 86TopTif-769
❑ 87Don-489
❑ 87DonOpeD-117
❑ 87Fle-596
❑ 87FleGlo-596
❑ 87MarMot-10
❑ 87Top-91
❑ 87TopSti-216
❑ 87TopTif-91
❑ 88Don-563
❑ 88DonAll-13
❑ 88DonBasB-304
❑ 88Fle-388
❑ 88FleAwaW-32
❑ 88FleGlo-388
❑ 88FleMin-53
❑ 88FleRecS-31
❑ 88FleStiC-62
❑ 88Lea-227
❑ 88MarMot-10
❑ 88OPC-7
❑ 88PanSti-188
❑ 88PanSti-219
❑ 88Sco-277
❑ 88ScoGlo-277
❑ 88Spo-127
❑ 88StaLinMa-17
❑ 88Top-485
❑ 88Top-519
❑ 88TopBig-142
❑ 88TopMinL-35
❑ 88TopRevLL-19
❑ 88TopSti-221
❑ 88TopTif-485
❑ 88TopTif-519
❑ 88TopUKM-60
❑ 88TopUKMT-60
❑ 89Bow-210
❑ 89BowTif-210
❑ 89ClaTraO-147
❑ 89Don-21
❑ 89Don-93
❑ 89DonAll-27
❑ 89DonBasB-51
❑ 89DonSupD-21
❑ 89Fle-558
❑ 89FleBasA-34
❑ 89FleGlo-558
❑ 89FleHeroB-33
❑ 89FleLeaL-31
❑ 89K-M-13
❑ 89MarMot-10
❑ 89OPC-208
❑ 89PanSti-436
❑ 89RedFolSB-96
❑ 89Sco-310
❑ 89ScoHot1S-82
❑ 89Spo-165
❑ 89Top-580
❑ 89TopBasT-143
❑ 89TopBig-2
❑ 89TopMinL-74
❑ 89TopSti-226
❑ 89TopStiB-5
❑ 89TopTif-580
❑ 89TVSpoM-123
❑ 89UppDec-249
❑ 90Bow-478
❑ 90BowTif-478
❑ 90ClaBlu-128
❑ 90Don-227
❑ 90DonBesA-138
❑ 90Fle-524
❑ 90FleAwaW-27

❑ 90FleCan-524
❑ 90Hot50PS-33
❑ 90Lea-140
❑ 90M.Vpin-96
❑ 90MarMot-6
❑ 90MLBBasB-118
❑ 90OPC-161
❑ 90PanSti-144
❑ 90PubIntS-294
❑ 90PubIntS-441
❑ 90Sco-167
❑ 90Sco100S-43
❑ 90Spo-119
❑ 90Top-161
❑ 90TopBig-321
❑ 90TopDou-51
❑ 90TopHeaU-17
❑ 90TopMinL-34
❑ 90TopSti-221
❑ 90TopTif-161
❑ 90UppDec-179
❑ 91Bow-252
❑ 91ClaGam-47
❑ 91Don-175
❑ 91Fle-460
❑ 91Lea-297
❑ 91MarCouH-3
❑ 91OPC-260
❑ 91PanCanT1-55
❑ 91PanCanT1-111
❑ 91PanFreS-229
❑ 91PanSti-191
❑ 91Sco-48
❑ 91SevCoi-NW13
❑ 91StaClu-217
❑ 91Stu-119
❑ 91Top-260
❑ 91TopDesS-260
❑ 91TopMic-260
❑ 91TopTif-260
❑ 91TopTriH-A12
❑ 91Ult-343
❑ 91UppDec-32
❑ 91UppDec-148
❑ 92Bow-503
❑ 92Don-239
❑ 92Fle-291
❑ 92Hig5-110
❑ 92HitTheBB-27
❑ 92Lea-38
❑ 92LeaBlaG-38
❑ 92MarMot-3
❑ 92OPC-670
❑ 92PanSti-56
❑ 92Pin-59
❑ 92RedFolS-79
❑ 92Sco-250
❑ 92StaClu-181
❑ 92Stu-239
❑ 92Top-670
❑ 92TopGol-670
❑ 92TopGolW-670
❑ 92TopKid-123
❑ 92TopMic-670
❑ 92TriPla-203
❑ 92Ult-129
❑ 92UppDec-314
❑ 93BalOriP-28
❑ 93BalOriP-29
❑ 93Bow-57
❑ 93Don-639
❑ 93Fin-50
❑ 93FinRef-50
❑ 93Fla-156
❑ 93Fle-680
❑ 93FleFinE-165
❑ 93Lea-370
❑ 93OPC-279
❑ 93OPCPre-89
❑ 93PacSpa-349
❑ 93Pin-530
❑ 93Sco-559
❑ 93Sel-134
❑ 93SelRoo-14T
❑ 93StaClu-23
❑ 93StaClu-668
❑ 93StaCluFDI-23
❑ 93StaCluFDI-668
❑ 93StaCluMOP-23
❑ 93StaCluMOP-668
❑ 93Stu-129
❑ 93Top-757
❑ 93TopGol-757
❑ 93TopInaM-757
❑ 93TopInaR-757
❑ 93TopMic-757
❑ 93Ult-499
❑ 93UppDec-35
❑ 93UppDec-803
❑ 93UppDecGold-35
❑ 93UppDecGold-803
❑ 94AngLAT-22
❑ 94AngMot-12
❑ 94ColC-384
❑ 94ColChoGS-384
❑ 94ColChoSS-384
❑ 94Don-271
❑ 94Fla-273
❑ 94Fle-17
❑ 94FleExtB-38
❑ 94FleUpd-21
❑ 94Lea-428
❑ 94Pac-43
❑ 94PanSti-22
❑ 94Pin-475
❑ 94PinArtP-475
❑ 94PinMusC-475
❑ 94Sco-441
❑ 94ScoGolR-441
❑ 94ScoRoo-RT20
❑ 94ScoRooGR-RT20
❑ 94Sel-313
❑ 94StaClu-625
❑ 94StaCluFDI-625
❑ 94StaCluGR-625
❑ 94StaCluMOP-625
❑ 94Top-355
❑ 94TopGol-355
❑ 94TopSpa-355
❑ 94Ult-332
❑ 94UppDec-423
❑ 94UppDecED-423
❑ 95ColCho-93
❑ 95Top-69

Reynolds, Jeff
❑ 83SyrChiT-19
❑ 86JacExpT-21
❑ 87IndIndTI-16
❑ 88TolMudHC-15
❑ 88TolMudHP-585
❑ 89NasSouTI-19

Reynolds, Ken
❑ 71OPC-664
❑ 71Top-664
❑ 72OPC-252
❑ 72Top-252
❑ 73OPC-638
❑ 73Top-638
❑ 75TulOil7-4
❑ 76HawIsIC-14
❑ 76SSP-292
❑ 78SyrChiT-16
❑ 79SyrChiT-19
❑ 79SyrChiTI-15
❑ 87GenCubP-6
❑ 89GenCubP-1885
❑ 94BreMilB-173

Reynolds, Larry
❑ 80TulDriT-9
❑ 81TulDriT-7
❑ 82ArkTraT-21
❑ 83ArkTraT-22
❑ 84ArkTraT-9

Reynolds, Mark
❑ 85OscAstTI-14

Reynolds, Mike
❑ 79RicBraT-2
❑ 82RicBraT-18
❑ 84RicBraT-1
❑ 85DurBulT-30
❑ 86DurBulP-22

Reynolds, Neil
❑ 87SalLakTTT-5

Reynolds, R.J. (Robert J.)
❑ 81VerBeaDT-17
❑ 84AlbDukCr-148
❑ 84FleUpd-97
❑ 85DodCokP-27
❑ 85DomLeaS-24
❑ 85Don-128
❑ 85Fle-381
❑ 85Top-369
❑ 85TopTif-369
❑ 86Don-552
❑ 86Fle-619
❑ 86FleMin-120
❑ 86Lea-212
❑ 86OPC-306
❑ 86Top-417
❑ 86TopTif-417
❑ 87Don-65
❑ 87Fle-620
❑ 87FleGlo-620
❑ 87GenMilB-5F
❑ 87OPC-109
❑ 87RedFolSB-77
❑ 87SpoTeaP-18
❑ 87StuPan-10
❑ 87Top-109
❑ 87TopSti-134
❑ 87TopTif-109
❑ 88Don-65
❑ 88DonBasB-201
❑ 88Fle-339
❑ 88FleGlo-339
❑ 88OPC-27
❑ 88PanSti-379
❑ 88PirTeal-27
❑ 88Sco-34
❑ 88ScoGlo-34
❑ 88StaLinPi-17
❑ 88Top-27
❑ 88TopTif-27
❑ 89Don-134
❑ 89DonBasB-257
❑ 89Fle-219
❑ 89FleGlo-219
❑ 89PirVerFJ-23
❑ 89Sco-91
❑ 89Top-658
❑ 89TopTif-658
❑ 89UppDec-315
❑ 90DodTar-660
❑ 90Don-447
❑ 90Fle-478
❑ 90FleCan-478
❑ 90Lea-381
❑ 90OPC-592
❑ 90PirHomC-25
❑ 90PubIntS-163
❑ 90Sco-469
❑ 90Top-592
❑ 90TopSti-126
❑ 90TopTif-592
❑ 90UppDec-540
❑ 91Don-101
❑ 91Fle-48
❑ 91OPC-198
❑ 91Sco-273
❑ 91Top-198
❑ 91TopDesS-198
❑ 91TopMic-198
❑ 91TopTif-198
❑ 91UppDec-150

Reynolds, Randy
❑ 76AshTouT-2

Reynolds, Robert Allen
❑ 71OPC-664
❑ 71Top-664
❑ 72OPC-162
❑ 72Top-162
❑ 73BalOriP-36
❑ 73OPC-612
❑ 73OriJohP-34
❑ 73OriTeal-26
❑ 73Top-612
❑ 74OPC-259
❑ 74Top-259
❑ 75BalOriP-24
❑ 75DetTigP-26
❑ 75OPC-142
❑ 75Top-142
❑ 75TopMin-142
❑ 91OriCro-378
❑ 94BreMilB-172

Reynolds, Ronn
❑ 82JacMetT-11
❑ 84TidTidT-25
❑ 85MetColP-30
❑ 85MetTCM-20
❑ 86Fle-92
❑ 86PhiTas-29
❑ 86PorBeaP-19
❑ 86Top-649
❑ 86TopTif-649
❑ 87PhiTas-29
❑ 87Top-471
❑ 87TopTif-471
❑ 87TucTorP-20
❑ 88DenZepC-16
❑ 88DenZepP-1262
❑ 89UppDec-627A
❑ 90CMC-515
❑ 90LasVegSC-12
❑ 90LasVegSP-127
❑ 90ProAAAF-15
❑ 91MetWIZ-328
❑ 91PacSenL-109

Reynolds, Shane
❑ 89AubAstP-2161
❑ 90ColMudB-12
❑ 90ColMudP-1345
❑ 91Cla/Bes-67
❑ 91JacGenLD-572
❑ 91JacGenP-926
❑ 91LinDriAA-572
❑ 92Bow-327
❑ 92DonRoo-102
❑ 92SkyAAAF-275
❑ 92TucTorF-485
❑ 92TucTorS-617
❑ 93Don-164
❑ 93Pin-254
❑ 93Sco-282
❑ 93Top-522
❑ 93TopGol-522
❑ 93TopInaM-522
❑ 93TopInaR-522
❑ 93TopMic-522
❑ 93TucTorF-3058
❑ 94AstMot-22
❑ 94Fla-392
❑ 94FleExtB-280
❑ 94FleUpd-147
❑ 94LeaLimR-41
❑ 94Sco-586
❑ 94ScoGolR-586
❑ 94ScoRoo-RT86
❑ 94ScoRooGR-RT86
❑ 94Sel-196
❑ 94SpoRoo-123
❑ 94SpoRooAP-123
❑ 94StaClu-558
❑ 94StaCluFDI-558
❑ 94StaCluGR-558
❑ 94StaCluMOP-558
❑ 94Ult-511
❑ 95AstMot-21
❑ 95ColCho-117
❑ 95ColChoGS-117
❑ 95ColChoSS-117
❑ 95Don-307
❑ 95DonPreP-307
❑ 95DonTopotO-260
❑ 95Fla-364
❑ 95Fle-467
❑ 95FleRooS-15
❑ 95Lea-245
❑ 95Pac-193
❑ 95Sco-538
❑ 95ScoGolR-538
❑ 95ScoPlaTS-538
❑ 95StaClu-270
❑ 95StaCluFDI-270
❑ 95StaCluMOP-270
❑ 95StaCluSTWS-270
❑ 95StaCluVR-135
❑ 95StaCluVRMO-135
❑ 95Top-257
❑ 95Ult-176
❑ 95UltGolM-176
❑ 95UppDec-23
❑ 95UppDecED-23
❑ 95UppDecEDG-23
❑ 95USPlaCMLA-7S
❑ 96AstMot-13
❑ 96Cir-139
❑ 96CirRav-139
❑ 96ColCho-164
❑ 96ColChoGS-164
❑ 96ColChoSS-164
❑ 96Don-411
❑ 96DonPreP-411
❑ 96EmoXL-203
❑ 96Fin-B31
❑ 96FinRef-B31
❑ 96Fla-284
❑ 96Fle-418
❑ 96FleTif-418
❑ 96LeaSigA-192
❑ 96LeaSigAG-192
❑ 96LeaSigAS-192
❑ 96MetUni-180
❑ 96MetUniP-180
❑ 96Pac-95
❑ 96PanSti-60
❑ 96ProSta-15
❑ 96Sco-212
❑ 96StaClu-110
❑ 96StaCluEPB-110
❑ 96StaCluEPG-110
❑ 96StaCluEPS-110
❑ 96StaCluMOP-110
❑ 96Top-169
❑ 96TopChr-49
❑ 96TopChrR-49
❑ 96TopGal-66
❑ 96TopGalPPI-66
❑ 96TopLas-61
❑ 96Ult-214
❑ 96UltGolM-214
❑ 96UppDec-79
❑ 97AstMot-6
❑ 97Cir-44
❑ 97CirRav-44
❑ 97ColCho-124
❑ 97Don-59
❑ 97DonEli-132
❑ 97DonEliGS-132
❑ 97DonGolPP-59
❑ 97DonLim-109
❑ 97DonLimE-109
❑ 97DonLimENG-109
❑ 97DonSilPP-59
❑ 97Fin-258
❑ 97FinRef-258
❑ 97Fle-353
❑ 97FleTif-353
❑ 97Lea-70
❑ 97LeaFraM-70
❑ 97LeaFraMDC-70
❑ 97MetUni-140
❑ 97PacPri-109
❑ 97PacPriLB-109
❑ 97PacPriP-109
❑ 97PacPriSH-SH10B
❑ 97Pin-130
❑ 97PinArtP-PP130
❑ 97PinIns-103
❑ 97PinInsCE-103
❑ 97PinInsDE-103
❑ 97PinMusC-130
❑ 97PinPrePla-130
❑ 97Sco-284
❑ 97ScoArtPWB-284
❑ 97ScoPreS-284
❑ 97ScoShoS-284
❑ 97ScoShoSAP-284
❑ 97SP-83
❑ 97SpoIll-69
❑ 97SpoIllEE-69
❑ 97StaClu-45
❑ 97StaCluMat-45
❑ 97StaCluMOP-45
❑ 97Stu-58
❑ 97StuPrePG-58
❑ 97StuPrePS-58
❑ 97Top-430
❑ 97Ult-211
❑ 97UltGolME-211
❑ 97UltPlaME-211
❑ 97UppDec-369
❑ 98CirThu-96
❑ 98CirThuRav-96
❑ 98CirThuSupRav-96
❑ 98ColCho-132
❑ 98Fin-79
❑ 98FinNo--79
❑ 98FinNo-R-79
❑ 98FinRef-79
❑ 98Fle-569
❑ 98FleVin'-96
❑ 98FleVin'C-96
❑ 98Pac-324
❑ 98PacOme-110
❑ 98PacOmeR-110
❑ 98PacOnl-331
❑ 98PacOnlR-331
❑ 98PacOnlWC-331
❑ 98PacPar-173
❑ 98PacParC-173
❑ 98PacParG-173
❑ 98PacParHS-173
❑ 98PacParPB-173
❑ 98PacParR-173
❑ 98PacPlaB-324
❑ 98PacRedT-324
❑ 98PacSil-324
❑ 98PinPlu-113
❑ 98Sco-190
❑ 98ScoSS-PP88
❑ 98ScoSSAP-PP88
❑ 98SpoIllWSF-150
❑ 98SpoIllWSFEE-150
❑ 98SpoIllWSFFE-150
❑ 98StaCluFDI-313
❑ 98StaCluI-313
❑ 98StaCluOneK-313
❑ 98StaCluPP-313
❑ 98Top-380
❑ 98TopChr-380
❑ 98TopChrR-380
❑ 98TopDevR-380
❑ 98TopDia-380
❑ 98TopMiniC-380
❑ 98Ult-304
❑ 98UltGolM-304
❑ 98UltMas-304
❑ 98UltPlaM-304
❑ 98UppDec-384
❑ 99199Fin-57
❑ 99Bow-70
❑ 99BowChr-70
❑ 99BowChrG-70
❑ 99BowChrGR-70
❑ 99BowChrI-70
❑ 99BowChrIR-70
❑ 99BowChrR-70
❑ 99BowGol-70
❑ 99BowInt-70
❑ 99FinGolRef-57
❑ 99FinRef-57
❑ 99Fle-193
❑ 99FleBri-69
❑ 99FleBri2G-69
❑ 99FleBriBlu-69
❑ 99FleBriGol-69
❑ 99FleSta9-193
❑ 99FleWarT-193
❑ 99MetUni-133
❑ 99MetUniGM-133
❑ 99MetUniPMG-133
❑ 99Pac-197
❑ 99PacAur-84
❑ 99PacAurOD-84
❑ 99PacCroC-129
❑ 99PacCroCPB-129
❑ 99PacPlaB-197
❑ 99PacRed-197
❑ 99SkyPre-126
❑ 99SkyPreR-126
❑ 99SkyThu-42
❑ 99SkyThuRant-42
❑ 99SkyThuRave-42
❑ 99StaClu-53
❑ 99StaCluFDI-53
❑ 99StaCluOoaK-53
❑ 99StaCluPP-53
❑ 99ThuSkySupR-42
❑ 99Top-260
❑ 99TopChr-260
❑ 99TopChrR-260
❑ 99TopMVPP-260
❑ 99TopOpeD-111
❑ 99Ult-18
❑ 99UltGolM-18
❑ 99UltMas-18
❑ 99UltPlaM-18
❑ 99UppDec-387
❑ 99UppDecEL1-387
❑ 99UppDecEL2-387
❑ 99UppDecR-36
❑ 99UppDecRG-36
❑ 99UppDecRP-36
❑ 99Vic-176

Reynolds, Tim
❑ 83CedRapRF-1
❑ 83CedRapRT-9

Reynolds, Tommie (Thomas D.)
❑ 64Top-528
❑ 65Top-333
❑ 67Top-487
❑ 69A'sJacitB-12
❑ 69Top-467
❑ 70OPC-259
❑ 70Top-259
❑ 71OPC-676
❑ 71Top-676
❑ 74SacSolC-46
❑ 75IntLeaASB-26
❑ 75PacCoaLAB-26
❑ 75SacSolC-3
❑ 76SpoIndC-16
❑ 77SpoIndC-15
❑ 78SpoIndC-15
❑ 86ModA'sC-25
❑ 86ModA'sP-21
❑ 87ModA'sC-23
❑ 87ModA'sP-23
❑ 88HunStaTI-15
❑ 89A'sMot-27
❑ 90A'sMot-27
❑ 91A'sMot-28

❑ 91MetWIZ-329
❑ 92AthMot-28
❑ 93AthMot-27
❑ 94A'sMot-28
❑ 94BreMilB-174
❑ 95AthMot-28
Reynolds, Walker
❑ 95DanBraTI-24
Reynolds, William
❑ 86MedA'sC-56
Reynoso, Armando
❑ 91BraSubS-31
❑ 91LinDriAAA-438
❑ 91RicBraBC-14
❑ 91RicBraLD-438
❑ 91RicBraP-2566
❑ 91RicBraTI-1
❑ 91TriA AAGP-AAA38
❑ 92Fle-367
❑ 92OPC-631
❑ 92RicBraBB-7
❑ 92RicBraF-375
❑ 92RicBraRC-15
❑ 92RicBraS-437
❑ 92Sco-877
❑ 92SkyAAAF-201
❑ 92SkyAAAF-296
❑ 92StaClu-763
❑ 92StaCluECN-763
❑ 92Top-631
❑ 92TopDeb91-145
❑ 92TopGol-631
❑ 92TopGolW-631
❑ 92TopMic-631
❑ 92UppDec-674
❑ 93Don-752
❑ 93FleFinE-41
❑ 93Lea-454
❑ 93PacJugC-35
❑ 93PacSpa-436
❑ 93SelRoo-38T
❑ 93SP-224
❑ 93StaClu-652
❑ 93StaCluFDI-652
❑ 93StaCluMOP-652
❑ 93TopTra-116T
❑ 93UppDec-793
❑ 93UppDecGold-793
❑ 94Bow-198
❑ 94ColC-238
❑ 94ColChoGS-238
❑ 94ColChoSS-238
❑ 94Don-497
❑ 94Fin-14
❑ 94FinJum-14
❑ 94FinRef-14
❑ 94Fla-157
❑ 94Fle-451
❑ 94FleExtB-252
❑ 94FleRooS-15
❑ 94Lea-148
❑ 94OPC-114
❑ 94Pac-205
❑ 94Pin-220
❑ 94PinArtP-220
❑ 94PinMusC-220
❑ 94RocPol-21
❑ 94Sco-227
❑ 94ScoGolR-227
❑ 94Sel-344
❑ 94StaClu-332
❑ 94StaCluFDI-332
❑ 94StaCluGR-332
❑ 94StaCluMOP-332
❑ 94StaCluT-103
❑ 94StaCluTFDI-103
❑ 94Top-49
❑ 94TopGol-49
❑ 94TopSpa-49
❑ 94TriPla-230
❑ 94Ult-188
❑ 94UppDec-348
❑ 94UppDecED-348
❑ 94USPlaCR-12S
❑ 95Pac-144
❑ 95Sco-497
❑ 95ScoGolR-497
❑ 95ScoPlaTS-497
❑ 95Top-349
❑ 96ColCho-536
❑ 96ColChoGS-536
❑ 96ColChoSS-536
❑ 96Pac-57
❑ 96RocPol-18
❑ 96Ult-191
❑ 96UltGolM-191
❑ 96UppDec-321
❑ 97Cir-237
❑ 97CirRav-237
❑ 97ColCho-96
❑ 97Fle-316
❑ 97Fle-673
❑ 97FleTif-316
❑ 97FleTif-673
❑ 97Pac-287
❑ 97PacLigB-287
❑ 97PacSil-287
❑ 97RicBraBC-2
❑ 97RocSco-11
❑ 97RocScoPl-11
❑ 97RocScoPr-11
❑ 97Sco-204
❑ 97ScoArtPWB-204
❑ 97ScoPreS-204
❑ 97ScoShoS-204
❑ 97ScoShoSAP-204
❑ 97Top-217
❑ 97Ult-506
❑ 97UltGolME-506
❑ 97UltPlaME-506
❑ 98PacInvGems-185
❑ 98UppDec-167
❑ 98UppDecNP-NP23
❑ 99PacCroC-185
❑ 99PacCroCPB-185
Reynoso, Ben
❑ 96IdaFalB-20
❑ 97RanCucQG-24
❑ 98RanCucQG-24
❑ 98RanCucQG-24
Reynoso, Gabriel
❑ 92MedHatBJF-3209
❑ 92MedHatBJSP-21
Reynoso, Henry
❑ 90BelBreB-19
❑ 90BelBreS-17
Reynoso, Ismael
❑ 98KanCouC-25
❑ 98KanCouCCP-25
Reynoso, Querbin
❑ 92GulCoaRSP-23
❑ 93ChaRaiC-16
❑ 93ChaRaiF-1909
❑ 94ChaRivC-16
❑ 94ChaRivF-2670
Reznik, Brad
❑ 89BirBarB-30
Rezotko, Joe
❑ 33WorCig(-71
Rhawn, Bobby
❑ 48GiaTeal-22
❑ 49AngTeal-30
❑ 49GiaTeal-23
❑ 52Par-2
Rhea, Allen
❑ 90St.CatBJP-3469
Rhea, Chip
❑ 96AriBlaDB-26
Rhea, Thad
❑ 98EriSeaWM-21
Rhein, Jeff
❑ 92AubAstC-7
❑ 92AubAstF-1367
❑ 93QuaCitRBC-18
❑ 93QuaCitRBF-113
Rhem, Flint (Charles)
❑ 28W56PlaC-S3A
❑ 31CarMet-23
❑ 33DouDisP-35
❑ 33Gou-136
❑ 34GouCanV-5
❑ 35GouPuzR-8L
❑ 35GouPuzR-9L
❑ 74Car193T-21
❑ 85BigLeaC3-40
❑ 87ConSer2-52
❑ 88ConSer4-23
❑ 91ConTSN-325
Rhiel, William
❑ 31Zee-73
❑ 36GouWidPPR-D30
❑ 36WorWidGV-81
❑ 90DodTar-661
Rhine, Kendall
❑ 93AubAstC-19
❑ 93AubAstF-3441
❑ 94AubAstC-12
❑ 94AubAstF-3756
❑ 94ClaGolF-17
❑ 95HagSunF-68
❑ 96DunBluJB-20
❑ 96DunBluJTI-24
❑ 97KnoSmo-20
Rhinehart, Dallas
❑ 92BoiHawF-3624
Rhines, Billy
❑ 98CamPepP-63
Rhoades, James
❑ 88AugPirP-387
Rhoads, Robert
❑ 05IndSouPSoCP-15
❑ 08RosComP-29
❑ 09T206-301
❑ 09T206-302
❑ 10CouT21-56
❑ 11SpoLifCW-301
❑ 11TurRedT-114
Rhoda, Gary
❑ 93HelBreF-4091
❑ 93HelBreSP-22
Rhodas, Kevin
❑ 83MiaMarT-10
Rhoden, Rick
❑ 74AlbDukTI-15
❑ 75OPC-618
❑ 75Top-618
❑ 75TopMin-618
❑ 76LinSup-124
❑ 76OPC-439
❑ 76SSP-72
❑ 76Top-439
❑ 77BurCheD-148
❑ 77DodPho-12
❑ 77OPC-57
❑ 77Top-245
❑ 78OPC-159
❑ 78SSP270-59
❑ 78Top-605
❑ 79OPC-66
❑ 79Top-145
❑ 80PorBeaT-27
❑ 80Top-92
❑ 81AllGamPI-172
❑ 81Fle-377
❑ 81OPC-312
❑ 81Top-312
❑ 82Don-423
❑ 82Fle-493
❑ 82Top-513
❑ 82TopSti-82
❑ 83Don-250
❑ 83Fle-318
❑ 83FleSta-162
❑ 83OPC-181
❑ 83Top-781
❑ 84Don-552
❑ 84Fle-261
❑ 84Nes792-485
❑ 84Nes792-696
❑ 84OPC-46
❑ 84Pir-17
❑ 84Top-485
❑ 84Top-696
❑ 84TopTif-485
❑ 84TopTif-696
❑ 85Don-552
❑ 85Fle-474
❑ 85FleStaS-97
❑ 85Lea-63
❑ 85OPC-53
❑ 85Pir-17
❑ 85Top-695
❑ 85TopSti-127
❑ 85TopTif-695
❑ 86Don-166
❑ 86DonHig-20
❑ 86Fle-620
❑ 86OPC-232
❑ 86Top-232
❑ 86Top-756
❑ 86TopSti-130
❑ 86TopTat-9
❑ 86TopTif-232
❑ 86TopTif-756
❑ 87DodSmoA-29
❑ 87Don-10
❑ 87Don-435
❑ 87DonAll-24
❑ 87DonSupD-10
❑ 87Fle-621
❑ 87FleGlo-621
❑ 87FleUpd-103
❑ 87FleUpdG-103
❑ 87Lea-10
❑ 87OPC-365
❑ 87RedFolSB-103
❑ 87Spo-129
❑ 87SpoTeaP-7
❑ 87Top-365
❑ 87TopMinL-31
❑ 87TopSti-130
❑ 87TopTif-365
❑ 87TopTra-101T
❑ 87TopTraT-101T
❑ 88Don-128
❑ 88DonBasB-161
❑ 88DonReaBY-128
❑ 88Fle-219
❑ 88FleGlo-219
❑ 88FleStiC-51
❑ 88FleSup-30
❑ 88Lea-98
❑ 88OPC-185
❑ 88PanSti-149
❑ 88RedFolSB-74
❑ 88Sco-74
❑ 88ScoGlo-74
❑ 88Spo-104
❑ 88SpoGam-16
❑ 88StaLinY-12
❑ 88Top-185
❑ 88TopBig-108
❑ 88TopSti-298
❑ 88TopTif-185
❑ 89AstLenH-3
❑ 89AstMot-24
❑ 89AstSmo-34
❑ 89Bow-323
❑ 89BowTif-323
❑ 89DodSmoG-87
❑ 89Don-429
❑ 89DonTra-40
❑ 89Fle-266
❑ 89FleGlo-266
❑ 89FleUpd-89
❑ 89OPC-18
❑ 89PanSti-399
❑ 89Sco-317
❑ 89Top-18
❑ 89TopBig-237
❑ 89TopDouM-23
❑ 89TopTif-18
❑ 89UppDec-56
❑ 90DodTar-662
❑ 90Fle-235
❑ 90FleCan-235
❑ 90OPC-588
❑ 90PubIntS-101
❑ 90Top-588
❑ 90TopTif-588
❑ 90UppDec-504
❑ 92DonStaTA-15
❑ 92YanWIZ8-158
Rhodes, Art (Arthur Lee)
❑ 89EriOriS-19
❑ 90FreKeyTI-29
❑ 91Bow-95
❑ 91Cla/Bes-335
❑ 91ClaGolB-BC14
❑ 91HagSunLD-244
❑ 91HagSunP-2457
❑ 91LeaGolR-BC6
❑ 91LeaGolRNV-270
❑ 91LinDriAA-244
❑ 91UppDecFE-13F
❑ 92BalOriP-30
❑ 92Bow-631
❑ 92Cla1-T75
❑ 92ClaGam-146
❑ 92Don-727
❑ 92Fle-24
❑ 92Lea-394
❑ 92LeaBlaG-394
❑ 92OPC-771
❑ 92Pin-251
❑ 92ProFS7-6
❑ 92RocRedWF-1939
❑ 92RocRedWS-464
❑ 92Sco-736
❑ 92ScoImpP-35
❑ 92ScoRoo-7
❑ 92SkyAAAF-211
❑ 92StaClu-641
❑ 92StaCluECN-641
❑ 92Top-771
❑ 92TopDeb91-146
❑ 92TopGol-771
❑ 92TopGolW-771
❑ 92TopMic-771
❑ 92UppDec-17
❑ 93BalOriP-30
❑ 93Bow-169
❑ 93Don-133
❑ 93Fle-174
❑ 93FleRooS-RSB8
❑ 93Lea-397
❑ 93OPC-329
❑ 93PacSpa-350
❑ 93Pin-326
❑ 93Sco-360
❑ 93Sel-300
❑ 93SelChaR-14
❑ 93StaClu-560
❑ 93StaCluFDI-560
❑ 93StaCluMOP-560
❑ 93Top-554
❑ 93TopGol-554
❑ 93TopInaM-554
❑ 93TopInaR-554
❑ 93TopMic-554
❑ 93Toy-28
❑ 93Ult-500
❑ 93UppDec-384
❑ 93UppDecGold-384
❑ 93USPlaCR-6C
❑ 94BalOriP-28
❑ 94ColC-373
❑ 94ColChoGS-373
❑ 94ColChoSS-373
❑ 94Don-299
❑ 94Fin-335
❑ 94FinRef-335
❑ 94Fle-18
❑ 94OPC-17
❑ 94OriPro-83
❑ 94OriUSPC-5C
❑ 94OriUSPC-10H
❑ 94RocRedWTI-19
❑ 94StaClu-129
❑ 94StaCluFDI-129
❑ 94StaCluGR-129
❑ 94StaCluMOP-129
❑ 94StaCluT-280
❑ 94StaCluTFDI-280
❑ 94Top-477
❑ 94TopGol-477
❑ 94TopSpa-477
❑ 94Ult-309
❑ 95BalOriP-43
❑ 95Fla-8
❑ 95Fle-18
❑ 95StaClu-453
❑ 95StaCluMOP-453
❑ 95StaCluSTWS-453
❑ 95Top-289
❑ 95TopCyb-156
❑ 95Ult-257
❑ 95UltGolM-257
❑ 95UppDec-369
❑ 95UppDecED-369
❑ 95UppDecEDG-369
❑ 96BalOriP-29
❑ 96LeaSigA-193
❑ 96LeaSigAG-193
❑ 96LeaSigAS-193
❑ 97BalOriP-28
❑ 97PacPriGotD-GD14
❑ 97Top-53
❑ 97Ult-10
❑ 97UltGolME-10
❑ 97UltPlaME-10
❑ 98OriSco-15
❑ 98OriScoP-15
❑ 98PacInvGems-14
❑ 98PacOnl-100
❑ 98PacOnlR-100
❑ 98PacOnlWC-100
❑ 98Sco-228
❑ 98StaCluFDI-214
❑ 98StaCluI-214
❑ 98StaCluOneK-214
❑ 98StaCluPP-214
❑ 99Pac-59
❑ 99PacPlaB-59
❑ 99PacRed-59
Rhodes, Charles
❑ 09PC7HHB-37
❑ 09T206-303
Rhodes, Dusty
❑ 89HelBreSP-27
❑ 91HelBreSP-29
Rhodes, Dusty (James L.)
❑ 54NewYorJA-34
❑ 54Top-170
❑ 55GiaGolS-23
❑ 55RedMan-NL22
❑ 55StaMey-10
❑ 55Top-1
❑ 55TopDouH-27
❑ 56Top-50
❑ 56TopHocF-A4
❑ 56TopHocF-B6
❑ 57Top-61
❑ 60TacBan-18
❑ 61TacBan-19
❑ 61UniOil-T26
❑ 68LauWorS-51
❑ 79TCM50-190
❑ 84FifNatCT-15
❑ 91TopArc1-299
❑ 94TedWilM-M23
❑ 94TopArc1-170
❑ 94TopArc1G-170
Rhodes, Dusty A.
❑ 98OneYanG-22
Rhodes, Dusty PCL
❑ 28ExhPCL-22
Rhodes, Gordon
❑ 28Zee-17
❑ 35DiaMatCS3T1-124
❑ 93ConTSN-983
Rhodes, Harry(Lefty)
❑ 93NegLeaRL2-34
Rhodes, Jeff
❑ 83CedRapRF-15
❑ 83CedRapRT-24
Rhodes, Joey
❑ 96HigDesMB-23
❑ 97FreKey-22
Rhodes, Mike
❑ 83ArkTraT-1
❑ 86ArkTraP-17
❑ 89Ft.LauYS-20
❑ 89Sta-79
❑ 90GreHorB-24
❑ 90GreHorP-2676
❑ 90GreHorS-17
Rhodes, Ricky
❑ 89OneYanP-2123
❑ 90Bes-249
❑ 90CMC-823
❑ 90GreHorB-11
❑ 90GreHorP-2663
❑ 90GreHorS-18
❑ 90ProAaA-86
❑ 91Cla/Bes-235
❑ 91PriWilCC-11
❑ 91PriWilCP-1427
❑ 92ForLauYC-22
❑ 92ForLauYTI-26
❑ 92Ft.LauYF-2610
Rhodes, Tuffy (Karl)
❑ 87AshTouP-1
❑ 88FloStaLAS-18
❑ 88OscAstS-22
❑ 89ColMudB-22
❑ 89ColMudP-142
❑ 89ColMudS-19
❑ 90Bow-79
❑ 90BowTif-79
❑ 90CMC-620
❑ 90ProAAAF-208
❑ 90TucTorC-18
❑ 90TucTorP-218
❑ 91AstMot-14
❑ 91Bow-544
❑ 91ClaGam-72
❑ 91Don-698
❑ 91Fle-514
❑ 91Lea-195
❑ 91OPC-516
❑ 91Sco-365
❑ 91ScoRoo-32
❑ 91StaClu-52
❑ 91Top-516
❑ 91TopDeb90-130
❑ 91TopDesS-516
❑ 91TopMic-516
❑ 91TopTif-516
❑ 91UppDec-466
❑ 91UppDec-702
❑ 92StaClu-241
❑ 92TucTorS-618
❑ 93LinVenB-229
❑ 93OmaRoyF-1694
❑ 93TriAAAGF-43
❑ 93Ult-395
❑ 94Bow-222
❑ 94ColC-489
❑ 94ColChoGS-489
❑ 94ColChoSS-489
❑ 94Fin-330
❑ 94FinRef-330
❑ 94Fla-140

❑ 94FleExtB-222
❑ 94FleUpd-110
❑ 94Lea-356
❑ 94Pac-106
❑ 94Pin-497
❑ 94PinArtP-497
❑ 94PinMusC-497
❑ 94Sco-447
❑ 94ScoGolR-447
❑ 94Sel-141
❑ 94StaClu-608
❑ 94StaCluFDI-608
❑ 94StaCluGR-608
❑ 94StaCluMOP-608
❑ 94StaCluT-344
❑ 94StaCluTFDI-344
❑ 94Stu-62
❑ 94Top-657
❑ 94TopGol-657
❑ 94TopSpa-657
❑ 94Ult-463
❑ 94UppDec-492
❑ 94UppDecED-492
❑ 94VenLinU-87
❑ 95Don-334
❑ 95DonPreP-334
❑ 95Fla-115
❑ 95Fle-422
❑ 95Pac-76
❑ 95Pin-213
❑ 95PinArtP-213
❑ 95PinMusC-213
❑ 95Sco-121
❑ 95ScoGolR-121
❑ 95ScoPlaTS-121
❑ 95StaClu-369
❑ 95StaCluMOP-369
❑ 95StaCluSTWS-369
❑ 95Top-178
❑ 95Ult-362
❑ 95UltGolM-362

Rhodriguez, Rory
❑ 91PriRedC-22
❑ 91PriRedP-3513
❑ 96WesPalBEB-13

Rhomberg, Kevin
❑ 78WatIndT-18
❑ 80TacTigT-20
❑ 80VenLeaS-255
❑ 81ChaLooT-23
❑ 82ChaChaT-17
❑ 83ChaChaT-17
❑ 83IndPos-29
❑ 84Ind-25
❑ 85PhoGiaC-193
❑ 88ChaLooLTI-26

Rhone, O.J.
❑ 93EugEmeC-22
❑ 93EugEmeF-3871
❑ 94RocRoyC-20
❑ 94RocRoyF-578

Rhubarb, Mascot
❑ 95TacRaiTI-30
❑ 96TacRaiB-30
❑ 97TacRai-30

Rhyne, Hal
❑ 23Zee-143
❑ 24Zee-99
❑ 25Zee-119
❑ 28ExhPCL-23
❑ 28Zee-143
❑ 29ExhFou-18
❑ 31Exh-18
❑ 33ExhFou-9
❑ 33Zee-139A
❑ 33Zee-139B
❑ 33Zee-140
❑ 37Zee-86
❑ 91ConTSN-195

Rial, Cliff
❑ 89MisStaB-45

Ribant, Dennis
❑ 65OPC-73
❑ 65Top-73
❑ 66Top-241
❑ 66TopVen-241
❑ 67Kah-31
❑ 67PirTeal-18
❑ 67Top-527
❑ 67TopPirS-3
❑ 68CokCapT-13
❑ 68Top-326
❑ 68TopVen-326
❑ 69Top-463
❑ 81TCM60I-443
❑ 91MetWIZ-330

Ribaudo, Mike
❑ 97WilCubB-20
❑ 98PitMetM-26

Ribbie, Mascot
❑ 85WhiSoxC-NNO
❑ 86WhiSoxC-NNO
❑ 87WhiSoxC-25
❑ 88WhiSoxC-25

Ricabal, Dan
❑ 94YakBeaC-15
❑ 94YakBeaF-3845
❑ 95Exc-217
❑ 95SanBerSTI-17
❑ 96HilStaHWB-NNO
❑ 96SavSanB-13
❑ 97VerBeaD-21
❑ 98SanAntMG-24

Ricanelli, John
❑ 76QuaCitAT-29
❑ 78SalLakCGC-11

Riccelli, Frank
❑ 74OPC-599
❑ 74Top-599A
❑ 74Top-599B
❑ 74Top-599C
❑ 75LafDriT-15
❑ 76PheGiaCr-30
❑ 76PhoGiaCa-7
❑ 76PhoGiaCC-20
❑ 76PhoGiaVNB-21
❑ 77Gia-19
❑ 77PhoGiaCC-20
❑ 77PhoGiaCP-20
❑ 77PhoGiaVNB-20
❑ 78SprRedWK-17
❑ 79AstPos-19
❑ 80Top-247
❑ 81BufBisT-24
❑ 82SyrChiT-6
❑ 89PacSenL-59
❑ 91PacSenL-67

Ricci, Chuck
❑ 89WatDiaP-1783
❑ 89WatDiaS-24
❑ 91FreKeyC-7
❑ 91FreKeyP-2362
❑ 92HagSunF-2554
❑ 93BowBayF-2186
❑ 94ReaPhiF-2061
❑ 95ScrRedBTI-23
❑ 96PawRedSDD-24

Ricci, Frank
❑ 81NasSouTI-15
❑ 82NasSouTI-19
❑ 83BeaGolGT-23

Ricci, Peter
❑ 30Zee-94
❑ 31Zee-53
❑ 32Zee-43

Ricciardi, J.P.
❑ 88SouOreAP-1714

Riccitant, Chuck
❑ 90FreKeyTI-26

Rice, Andy
❑ 94Top-208
❑ 94TopGol-208
❑ 94TopSpa-208

Rice, Charles
❑ 94ClaGolF-77
❑ 96AugGreB-26
❑ 96EriSeaB-21
❑ 96Exc-223
❑ 97LynHil-19

Rice, David
❑ 89BenBucL-9

Rice, Del
❑ 46SeaSLP-50
❑ 47Exh-185
❑ 47TipTop-161
❑ 49EurSta-195
❑ 49MPR302-2-112
❑ 50Bow-125
❑ 51Bow-156
❑ 51R42SmaS-87
❑ 52Bow-107
❑ 52Top-100
❑ 53BowC-53
❑ 53CarHunW-18
❑ 53Top-68
❑ 54Bow-30
❑ 54CarHunW-21
❑ 54RedMan-NL9
❑ 55Bow-106
❑ 55CarHunW-20
❑ 57Top-193
❑ 58Top-51
❑ 59Top-104
❑ 59TopVen-104
❑ 60Top-248
❑ 61Top-448
❑ 72Top-718
❑ 80Bra195T-22
❑ 83Car194T-32
❑ 83TopRep5-100
❑ 91OriCro-379
❑ 91TopArc1-68

Rice, Gary
❑ 91AdeGiaF-2

Rice, Grantland
❑ 90LitSunW-5
❑ 92MegRut-163
❑ 92MegRutP-138

Rice, Hal
❑ 51Bow-300
❑ 52Top-398
❑ 53CarHunW-19
❑ 53Top-93
❑ 54Bow-219
❑ 54Top-95
❑ 55Bow-52
❑ 83TopRep5-398
❑ 91TopArc1-93
❑ 94TopArc1-95
❑ 94TopArc1G-95

Rice, Harry F.
❑ 27MidBre-38
❑ 29ExhFou-23
❑ 29PorandAR-70
❑ 31SenTeaPW-26
❑ 34DiaMatCSB-152
❑ 91ConTSN-216

Rice, Jim
❑ 57JetPos-18

Rice, Jim Ed
❑ 75OPC-616
❑ 75SSPPuzB-21
❑ 75Top-616
❑ 75TopMin-616
❑ 76Hos-127
❑ 76Kel-10
❑ 76LinSup-113
❑ 76OPC-340
❑ 76RedSox-7
❑ 76RedSoxSM-13
❑ 76SSP-405
❑ 76Top-340
❑ 77BurCheD-29
❑ 77Hos-23
❑ 77OPC-62
❑ 77Spo-3810
❑ 77Top-60
❑ 78Hos-45
❑ 78Kel-49
❑ 78OPC-2
❑ 78OPC-163
❑ 78PapGinD-14
❑ 78RCColC-77
❑ 78SSP270-189
❑ 78Top-202
❑ 78Top-670
❑ 78WifBalD-61
❑ 79BasPat-72
❑ 79Hos-2
❑ 79Kel-15
❑ 79OPC-210
❑ 79PapGloT-1
❑ 79Top-2
❑ 79Top-3
❑ 79Top-400
❑ 79TopCom-2
❑ 80BurKinPHR-20
❑ 80Kel-44
❑ 80OPC-112
❑ 80Top-200
❑ 80TopSup-5
❑ 80WilGloT-5
❑ 80WilGloT-6
❑ 81AllGamPI-66
❑ 81CokTeaS-9
❑ 81Don-338
❑ 81Dra-8
❑ 81Fle-222
❑ 81FleStiC-53
❑ 81Kel-9
❑ 81OPC-68
❑ 81PerCreC-23
❑ 81Squ-7
❑ 81Top-500
❑ 81TopScr-13
❑ 81TopSti-41
❑ 81TopSupHT-8
❑ 81TopSupN-11
❑ 82Don-200
❑ 82Dra-27
❑ 82FBIDis-18
❑ 82Fle-305
❑ 82FleSta-163
❑ 82K-M-33
❑ 82OPC-366
❑ 82RedSoxC-17
❑ 82Top-750
❑ 82TopSti-150
❑ 82WilSpoG-6
❑ 83AllGamPI-67
❑ 83Don-208
❑ 83Dra-22
❑ 83Fle-194
❑ 83FleSta-163
❑ 83FleSti-66
❑ 83Kel-13
❑ 83Oco& SSBG-13
❑ 83OPC-30
❑ 83PerAll-4
❑ 83PerAllG-4
❑ 83PerCreC-31
❑ 83PerCreCG-31
❑ 83Top-30
❑ 83Top-381
❑ 83TopFol-2
❑ 83TopFol-3
❑ 83TopSti-37
❑ 84AllGamPI-157
❑ 84Don-50
❑ 84DonActAS-52
❑ 84DonCha-4
❑ 84Dra-25
❑ 84Fle-408
❑ 84FleSti-20
❑ 84FleSti-37
❑ 84FunFooP-5
❑ 84Nes792-132
❑ 84Nes792-133
❑ 84Nes792-401
❑ 84Nes792-550
❑ 84NesDreT-5
❑ 84OCoandSI-31
❑ 84OPC-184
❑ 84OPC-364
❑ 84RalPur-9
❑ 84SevCoi-E15
❑ 84Top-132
❑ 84Top-133
❑ 84Top-401
❑ 84Top-550
❑ 84TopCer-9
❑ 84TopGloA-6
❑ 84TopGloS-22
❑ 84TopRubD-16
❑ 84TopSti-102A
❑ 84TopSti-189
❑ 84TopSti-200B
❑ 84TopSti-217
❑ 84TopSup-5
❑ 84TopTif-132
❑ 84TopTif-133
❑ 84TopTif-401
❑ 84TopTif-550
❑ 85AllGamPI-69
❑ 85Don-15
❑ 85Don-50
❑ 85DonActA-27
❑ 85DonSupD-15
❑ 85Dra-25
❑ 85Fle-168
❑ 85FleLimE-27
❑ 85FleStaS-13
❑ 85FleStaS-23
❑ 85GenMilS-22
❑ 85Lea-15
❑ 85OPC-150
❑ 85SevCoi-E4
❑ 85SevCoi-W2
❑ 85SpoSam-1
❑ 85Top-150
❑ 85Top3-D-6
❑ 85TopGloS-6
❑ 85TopMin-150
❑ 85TopRubD-14
❑ 85TopSti-208
❑ 85TopSup-50
❑ 85TopTif-150
❑ 86BasStaB-90
❑ 86BurKinA-8
❑ 86Don-213
❑ 86DonAll-16
❑ 86DonPop-16
❑ 86DorChe-20
❑ 86Dra-13
❑ 86Fle-358
❑ 86FleMin-76
❑ 86FleStiC-96
❑ 86GenMilB-1G
❑ 86Lea-146
❑ 86MeaGolSB-14
❑ 86MSAJifPD-1
❑ 86OPC-320
❑ 86QuaGra-30
❑ 86SevCoi-C5
❑ 86SevCoi-E5
❑ 86SevCoi-S5
❑ 86SevCoi-W5
❑ 86Spo-17
❑ 86Spo-52
❑ 86Spo-61
❑ 86Spo-139
❑ 86Spo-146
❑ 86SpoDecG-57
❑ 86StaRic-1
❑ 86StaRic-2
❑ 86StaRic-3
❑ 86StaRic-4
❑ 86StaRic-5
❑ 86StaRic-6
❑ 86StaRic-7
❑ 86StaRic-8
❑ 86StaRic-9
❑ 86StaRic-10
❑ 86StaRic-11
❑ 86StaRic-12
❑ 86Top-320
❑ 86Top3-D-23
❑ 86TopGloA-6
❑ 86TopGloS-36
❑ 86TopSti-161
❑ 86TopSti-246
❑ 86TopSup-43
❑ 86TopTat-20
❑ 86TopTif-320
❑ 86TruVal-7
❑ 86WilGloT-2
❑ 86Woo-28
❑ 87BoaandB-5
❑ 87BurKinA-16
❑ 87ClaGam-59
❑ 87Don-92
❑ 87DonAll-45
❑ 87DonOpeD-182
❑ 87Dra-15
❑ 87Fle-41
❑ 87Fle-633
❑ 87FleExcS-37
❑ 87FleGlo-41
❑ 87FleGlo-633
❑ 87FleHea-6
❑ 87FleLimE-35
❑ 87FleMin-89
❑ 87FleStiC-99
❑ 87K-M-18
❑ 87KayB-26
❑ 87KraFoo-5
❑ 87Lea-247
❑ 87MSAJifPD-19
❑ 87OPC-146
❑ 87OPCBoxB-F
❑ 87RedFolSB-44
❑ 87RedSoxP-16
❑ 87RedSoxSAP-10
❑ 87SevCoi-E14
❑ 87SevCoi-M14
❑ 87Spo-80
❑ 87Spo-97
❑ 87SpoDeaP-3
❑ 87SpoTeaP-9
❑ 87Top-480
❑ 87Top-610
❑ 87TopCoi-21
❑ 87TopGloS-42
❑ 87TopMinL-44
❑ 87TopSti-17
❑ 87TopSti-248
❑ 87TopTif-480
❑ 87TopTif-610
❑ 87TopWaxBC-F
❑ 87Woo-5
❑ 87Woo-27
❑ 88CheBoy-21
❑ 88Don-399
❑ 88DonBasB-28
❑ 88DonTeaBRS-399
❑ 88Fle-361
❑ 88FleGlo-361
❑ 88Lea-215
❑ 88OPC-61
❑ 88PanSti-33
❑ 88Sco-14
❑ 88ScoGlo-14
❑ 88Spo-158
❑ 88StaLinRS-16
❑ 88Top-662
❑ 88Top-675
❑ 88TopBig-181
❑ 88TopSti-247
❑ 88TopTif-662
❑ 88TopTif-675
❑ 89Bow-33
❑ 89BowTif-33
❑ 89Don-122
❑ 89Fle-97
❑ 89FleGlo-97
❑ 89OPC-245
❑ 89OPCBoxB-I
❑ 89PanSti-281
❑ 89Sco-85
❑ 89Spo-173
❑ 89Top-245
❑ 89TopBasT-112
❑ 89TopBatL-9
❑ 89TopBig-18
❑ 89TopSti-256
❑ 89TopTif-245
❑ 89TopWaxBC-I
❑ 89UppDec-413
❑ 90KayB-27
❑ 90MLBBasB-70
❑ 90OPC-785
❑ 90OPCBoxB-M
❑ 90PubIntS-463
❑ 90Top-785
❑ 90TopAmeA-3
❑ 90TopBatL-9
❑ 90TopHilHM-8
❑ 90TopTif-785
❑ 90TopWaxBC-M
❑ 90UppDec-373
❑ 91PacSenL-148
❑ 92KelAll-8
❑ 92MDAMVP-12
❑ 93ActPacA-166
❑ 93Yoo-14

Rice, Lance
❑ 88GreFalDTI-7
❑ 89BakDodCLC-192
❑ 89CalLeaA-5
❑ 90SanAntMGS-23
❑ 91LinDriAA-539
❑ 91SanAntMLD-539
❑ 91SanAntMP-2979
❑ 92SanAntMF-3978
❑ 94HarSenF-2108
❑ 96BowBayB-24

Rice, Len
❑ 47PadTeal-16

Rice, Pat
❑ 87WauTimP-24
❑ 88SanBerSB-6
❑ 88SanBerSCLC-43
❑ 89WilBilP-646
❑ 89WilBilS-18
❑ 90CalCanC-4
❑ 90CalCanP-650
❑ 90CMC-431
❑ 90ProAAAF-115
❑ 91CalCanLD-70
❑ 91CalCanP-515
❑ 91Cla3-T76
❑ 91LinDriAAA-70
❑ 92CalCanF-3730
❑ 92CalCanS-69
❑ 92Fle-658
❑ 92Sco-423
❑ 92SkyAAAF-32
❑ 92TopDeb91-147
❑ 96WisTimRB-2
❑ 97WisTimR-2
❑ 98OrlRayM-25

Rice, Pete
❑ 83AleDukT-8
❑ 85NasPirT-19
❑ 86NasPirP-22
❑ 87SalBucP-7
❑ 88TolMudHC-23
❑ 88TolMudHP-598

Rice, Rich
❑ 86ChaOriW-24

Rice, Sam (Edgar)
❑ 17ColE13-137
❑ 17HolBreD-82
❑ 19W514-79
❑ 20NatCarE-83
❑ 20WalMaiW-44

❑ 21E121So1-78
❑ 21E121So8-75
❑ 21Exh-140
❑ 22AmeCarE122-55
❑ 22E120-117
❑ 22W572-83
❑ 22W575-102
❑ 23W501-14
❑ 23WilChoV-130
❑ 26SpoComoA-34
❑ 26SpoNewSM-7
❑ 27AmeCarE126-29
❑ 27YorCarE-36
❑ 28W502-36
❑ 28Yue-36
❑ 29ExhFou-32
❑ 29PorandAR-71
❑ 31Exh-32
❑ 31SenTeaIPW-27
❑ 33DouDisP-36
❑ 33Gou-134
❑ 34DiaStaR-32
❑ 34GouCanV-18
❑ 53ArtHaloFP-69
❑ 60Fle-34
❑ 60SenUniMC-16
❑ 61Fle-70
❑ 73TCMAllG-16
❑ 75SenTCM1-26
❑ 75TCMAllG-27
❑ 76RowExh-10
❑ 76ShaPiz-93
❑ 77GalGloG-108
❑ 80PerHaloFP-93
❑ 80SSPHOF-93
❑ 81SpoHaloF-19
❑ 82DiaCla-11
❑ 82TCMGreH-33
❑ 91ConTSN-54
❑ 92ConTSN-436
❑ 93ConTSN-887
❑ 94ConTSN-1256
❑ 94ConTSNB-1256
Rice, Tim
❑ 86WinSpiP-22
❑ 87PitCubP-24
❑ 88BasCitRS-20
Rice, Woolsey
❑ 83BelBreFr-2
Rich, Bart
❑ 94KanCouCC-22
Rich, Billy
❑ 99TeaBesR-71
❑ 99TeaBesRG-71
❑ 99TeaBesRS-71
Rich, Ted
❑ 92UtiBluSC-10
❑ 93SouBenWSC-19
Rich, Woody
❑ 39GouPreR303A-38
❑ 39WorWidGTP-38
Richard, Bee Bee (Lee)
❑ 72OPC-476
❑ 72Top-476
❑ 75OPC-653
❑ 75Top-653
❑ 75TopMin-653
❑ 76OPC-533
❑ 76SSP-145
❑ 76St.LouCP-27
❑ 76Top-533
Richard, Chris
❑ 95NewJerCTI-25
❑ 96StPetCB-27
❑ 97ArkTraB-18
❑ 97NewJerCB-3
Richard, J.R.
❑ 72OPC-101
❑ 72Top-101
❑ 74OPC-522
❑ 74Top-522
❑ 74TopSta-36
❑ 75AstPos-25
❑ 75OPC-73
❑ 75Top-73
❑ 75TopMin-73
❑ 76Hos-110
❑ 76HouAstP-26
❑ 76OPC-625
❑ 76Top-625
❑ 77AstPho-11
❑ 77BurCheD-1
❑ 77Hos-112
❑ 77OPC-227
❑ 77RCColC-55
❑ 77Spo-7103
❑ 77Top-260
❑ 78AstBurK-4
❑ 78AstPos-21
❑ 78Hos-92
❑ 78OPC-149
❑ 78RCColC-49
❑ 78Top-470
❑ 79AstPos-20
❑ 79AstTeaI-12
❑ 79Hos-29
❑ 79Kel-19
❑ 79OPC-310
❑ 79Top-6
❑ 79Top-203
❑ 79Top-590
❑ 79TopCom-23
❑ 80BurKinPHR-8
❑ 80Kel-58
❑ 80OPC-28
❑ 80Top-50
❑ 80Top-206
❑ 80Top-207
❑ 80TopSup-25
❑ 81AstPos-18
❑ 81CokTeaS-68
❑ 81Don-140
❑ 81Fle-56
❑ 81FleStiC-44
❑ 81Kel-16
❑ 81MSAMinD-26
❑ 81OPC-350
❑ 81Top-350
❑ 82AstPos-20
❑ 82Fle-226
❑ 82OnDecD-26
❑ 82OPC-190
❑ 82Top-190
❑ 86AstGreT-9
❑ 86AstMot-21
❑ 87AstShoSO-20
❑ 87AstShoSPO-26
❑ 87AstShoSPT-14
❑ 87AstShowSTh-26
❑ 88HouSho-18
❑ 92UppDecS-26
❑ 93UppDecS-11
Richard, Ray
❑ 79WatIndT-32
Richard, Ron
❑ 91YakBeaC-4
❑ 91YakBeaP-4255
Richardi, Rick
❑ 85MiaHur-13
❑ 87MiaMarP-8
❑ 88MiaMarS-20
Richards, Bob
❑ 68AtlOil-9
Richards, Dave
❑ 78LodDodT-13
❑ 81AlbDukTc-8
❑ 82HawIslT-2
Richards, Dave T.
❑ 88FayGenP-1095
❑ 89LakTigS-18
❑ 90LonTigP-1267
❑ 91JacSunLD-343
❑ 91JacSunP-150
❑ 91LinDriAA-343
❑ 92ArkTraF-1129
❑ 92ElPasDF-3919
❑ 93El PasDF-2949
Richards, Fuzzy (Fred)
❑ 53MotCoo-50
Richards, Gene (Eugene)
❑ 76HawIslC-13
❑ 77PadSchC-46A
❑ 77PadSchC-46B
❑ 77Top-473
❑ 78PadFamF-25
❑ 78Top-292
❑ 79PadFamF-5
❑ 79Top-364
❑ 80OPC-323
❑ 80Top-616
❑ 81AllGamPI-160
❑ 81Don-4
❑ 81Fle-486
❑ 81FleStiC-17
❑ 81OPC-171
❑ 81PadFamF-15
❑ 81Top-171
❑ 81TopScr-86
❑ 81TopSti-225
❑ 82Don-499
❑ 82Fle-580
❑ 82FleSta-104
❑ 82OPC-253
❑ 82Top-708
❑ 82TopSti-103
❑ 83AllGamPI-159
❑ 83Don-271
❑ 83Fle-370
❑ 83OPC-7
❑ 83PadTeaI-21
❑ 83Top-7
❑ 83TopSti-294
❑ 84Don-429
❑ 84Fle-310
❑ 84FleUpd-98
❑ 84GiaPos-23
❑ 84Nes792-594
❑ 84Top-594
❑ 84TopTif-594
❑ 84TopTra-99T
❑ 84TopTraT-99T
❑ 85Fle-619
❑ 85Top-434
❑ 85TopTif-434
❑ 86PadGreT-5
❑ 89PacSenL-48
❑ 89T/MSenL-90
❑ 89TopSenL-63
❑ 90EliSenL-102
❑ 91LinDriAA-450
❑ 91MidAngOHP-21
❑ 91MidAngP-450
❑ 92CalLeaACL-52
❑ 92PalSprAC-29
❑ 92PalSprAF-857
❑ 93PalSprAC-27
❑ 93PalSprAF-88
Richards, Kevin
❑ 81TulDriT-22
❑ 82TulDriT-8
Richards, Mark
❑ 98PorSeaDQ-10
Richards, Nicky
❑ 83ChaRoyT-2
Richards, Paul
❑ 33Gou-142
❑ 33WorCig(-72
❑ 51Bow-195
❑ 52Bow-93
❑ 52Top-305
❑ 53BowC-39
❑ 54Wil-14
❑ 55Bow-225
❑ 56BalOriP-24
❑ 56BalOriP-47
❑ 58BalOriP-13
❑ 58OriJayP-10
❑ 60Lea-112
❑ 60OriJayP-6
❑ 60Top-224
❑ 61Top-131
❑ 61Top-566
❑ 62Col.45B-16
❑ 62Col45'JP-10
❑ 63BasMagM-68
❑ 70SpoCarfCOP-18
❑ 72TCMthe3-58
❑ 79DiaGre-383
❑ 81TigDetN-40
❑ 83TCMPla1944-5
❑ 83TopRep5-305
❑ 88ConSer5-25
❑ 90DodTar-663
❑ 91TopArc1-322
❑ 93ConTSN-765
❑ 97BalOriP-43
Richards, Rowan
❑ 96HudValRB-3
❑ 97TulDriTI-23
❑ 98Cha-23
❑ 98TexLeaC-18
Richards, Rusty
❑ 87SumBraP-8
❑ 89RicBraBC-22
❑ 89RicBraC-7
❑ 89RicBraP-829
❑ 89RicBraTI-18
❑ 90CMC-280
❑ 90ProAAAF-404
❑ 90RicBraBC-17
❑ 90RicBraC-4
❑ 90RicBraP-259
❑ 90RicBraTI-27
❑ 90TopDeb89-99
❑ 91LinDriAAA-439
❑ 91RicBraBC-4
❑ 91RicBraLD-439
❑ 91RicBraTI-9
❑ 92OrlSunRS-518
❑ 92SkyAA F-225
❑ 92TexLon-33
Richards, Ryan
❑ 91OklStaC-21
Richards, Todd
❑ 80BatTroT-4
❑ 81BatTroT-6
Richardson, A.J.
❑ 88VisOakCLC-157
❑ 88VisOakP-87
❑ 89OrlTwiB-23
❑ 89OrlTwiP-1346
Richardson, Bobby
❑ 47Exh-186
❑ 57Top-286
❑ 58Top-101A
❑ 58Top-101B
❑ 59Top-76
❑ 59Top-237
❑ 59TopVen-76
❑ 60Top-405
❑ 61NuSco-415
❑ 61Pos-8A
❑ 61Pos-8B
❑ 61Top-180
❑ 61Top-308
❑ 61TopDicG-13
❑ 61Yan61RL-2
❑ 61YanJayP-10
❑ 62AmeTraS-43A
❑ 62AmeTraS-43B
❑ 62AmeTraS-43C
❑ 62AmeTraS-43D
❑ 62Jel-2
❑ 62Pos-2
❑ 62PosCan-2
❑ 62SalPlaC-64
❑ 62ShiPlaC-64
❑ 62Top-65
❑ 62TopStaI-90
❑ 62TopVen-65
❑ 62YanJayP-11
❑ 63Fle-25
❑ 63Jel-13
❑ 63Kah-26
❑ 63Pos-13
❑ 63ReqKP-14
❑ 63SalMetC-52
❑ 63Top-173
❑ 63Top-420
❑ 63TopStiI-33
❑ 63YanJayP-10
❑ 64ChatheY-21
❑ 64Top-190
❑ 64TopCoi-72
❑ 64TopCoi-123
❑ 64TopSta-12
❑ 64TopStaU-60
❑ 64TopVen-190
❑ 64WheSta-38
❑ 64YanJayP-10
❑ 65ChaTheY-20
❑ 65MacSta-9
❑ 65OPC-115
❑ 65Top-115
❑ 65TopEmbI-65
❑ 65TopTraI-26
❑ 66Top-490
❑ 66TopRubI-77
❑ 66YanTeaI-10
❑ 70FleWorS-61
❑ 77GalGloG-247
❑ 78TCM60I-112
❑ 81TCM60I-477
❑ 83FraBroR-16
❑ 83Yan196-2
❑ 83YanASFY-36
❑ 84OCoandSI-210
❑ 87Yan196T-3
❑ 88PacLegI-74
❑ 89SweBasG-49
❑ 90HOFStiB-61
❑ 90PacLeg-100
❑ 91LinDri-4
❑ 91SweBasG-75
❑ 91UppDecS-16
❑ 91YanRinP11-11
❑ 92ActPacA-31
❑ 92YanWIZ6-104
❑ 92YanWIZA-63
❑ 93UppDecAH-107
❑ 94TedWil-63
❑ 94TedWilM-M28
❑ 94UppDecAH-131
❑ 94UppDecAH1-131
❑ 94UppDecS-2
❑ 97BobRic-1
❑ 97FleMilDM-27
❑ 97FleMilDMR-27
❑ 98SpoIllWSF-28
❑ 98SpoIllWSFEE-28
❑ 98SpoIllWSFFE-28
Richardson, Brad
❑ 96OgdRapTI-28
Richardson, Brian
❑ 92GulCoaDF-3575
❑ 93GreFalDSP-28
❑ 94VerBeaDC-16
❑ 94VerBeaDF-82
❑ 94YakBeaC-16
❑ 94YakBeaF-3859
❑ 95SanBerSTI-18
❑ 97SanAntMB-20
❑ 97TexLeaTP-18
❑ 98AlbDukG-22
❑ 98SanAntMM-20
Richardson, C.N.
❑ 29ExhFou-24
Richardson, Danny (Daniel)
❑ 86OldJudN-12
❑ 87BucN28-72A
❑ 87BucN28-72B
❑ 87OldJudN-416
❑ 88AugBecN-27
❑ 88GandBCGCE-33
❑ 88WG1CarG-43
❑ 89SFHaCN-15
❑ 90DodTar-664
❑ 90KalBatN-46
Richardson, David
❑ 89SprCarB-16
❑ 90LouRedBLBC-35
❑ 90St.PetCS-20
❑ 91LinDriAAA-244
❑ 91LouRedLD-244
❑ 91LouRedP-2915
Richardson, Don
❑ 86WinSpiP-23
Richardson, Eric
❑ 92StaCluD-153
❑ 93HicCraC-21
❑ 93HicCraF-1294
❑ 94HicCraC-19
❑ 94HicCraF-2190
Richardson, Gordon
❑ 66OPC-51
❑ 66Top-51
❑ 66TopVen-51
❑ 81TCM60I-460
❑ 91MetWIZ-331
Richardson, Hardy (A.H.)
❑ 76SSP188WS-17
❑ 87BucN28-33A
❑ 87BucN28-33B
❑ 87OldJudN-415
❑ 87ScrDC-15
❑ 88WG1CarG-23
❑ 89N526N7C-14
Richardson, James
❑ 22Zee-136
❑ 88KinIndS-19
Richardson, Jeff
❑ 85LitFalMT-9
❑ 86LynMetP-18
❑ 87LynMetP-24
❑ 87TamTarP-12
❑ 88ChaLooB-22
❑ 88PalSprACLC-92
❑ 88PalSprAP-1463
❑ 89NasSouC-18
❑ 89NasSouP-1291
❑ 89NasSouTI-20
❑ 89PalSprAP-469
❑ 90BufBisC-12
❑ 90BufBisP-382
❑ 90BufBisTI-20
❑ 90CMC-12
❑ 90ProAAAF-497
❑ 91BufBisLD-43
❑ 91BufBisP-550
❑ 91LinDriAAA-43
❑ 92BufBisBS-17
❑ 92BufBisF-328
❑ 92BufBisS-40
❑ 92SkyAAAF-18
❑ 93PawRedSF-2417
❑ 93SouOreAF-4080
❑ 94LouRedF-2990
❑ 94SouOreAC-22
❑ 94SouOreAF-3639
❑ 95LynHilTI-23
❑ 96EriSeaB-1
❑ 97AugGre-2
❑ 98LynHilQ-24
Richardson, Jeffrey Scott
❑ 89PalSprACLC-51
❑ 90TopDeb89-100
❑ 91Bow-198
❑ 91TopDeb90-131
❑ 93SouOreAC-22
❑ 93TopTra-81T
Richardson, Jesse
❑ 95HelBreTI-28
Richardson, Jim
❑ 87WatIndP-3
❑ 88AlaGolTI-14
❑ 89KinIndS-20
Richardson, Jon
❑ 78RicBraT-12
❑ 79RicBraT-7
Richardson, Kasey
❑ 96ForWayWB-22
❑ 97ForWayW-28
❑ 98FreKeyM-15
Richardson, Keith
❑ 88WatPirP-1
❑ 89SalBucS-17
❑ 89Sta-95
❑ 90HarSenP-1191
❑ 90HarSenS-16
Richardson, Kenny
❑ 78NewWayCT-37
Richardson, Kerry
❑ 87KinIndP-23
❑ 88WilBilP-1328
Richardson, Lenny
❑ 88CapCodPPaLP-5
Richardson, Mike
❑ 89EriOriS-20
❑ 90FreKeyTI-6
❑ 93NiaFalRF-3386
Richardson, Milt
❑ 88EugEmeB-27
❑ 89EugEmeB-18
Richardson, Nolan
❑ 77CinRedT-3
Richardson, Ron
❑ 83MidCubT-18
Richardson, Ronnie
❑ 87ElmPioBC-27
❑ 87ElmPioRC-27
❑ 88ElmPio1C-4
❑ 88LynRedSS-20
❑ 89LynRedSS-28
Richardson, Scott
❑ 92HelBreF-1723
❑ 92HelBreSP-21
❑ 93BelBreCB-18
❑ 93BelBreFI-1720
❑ 94StoPorC-20
❑ 94StoPorF-1706
❑ 95ElPasDTI-20
❑ 96SanBerSB-22
❑ 97SanAntMB-25
❑ 98AlbDukG-23
❑ 98SanAntMM-25
Richardson, Tim
❑ 86HagSunP-15
❑ 87HagSunP-19
❑ 90HagSunDGB-21
Richardson, Tracey
❑ 90WatIndS-28
Richardt, Mike
❑ 79AshTouT-26
❑ 80ChaChaT-8
❑ 83Don-368
❑ 83Fle-575
❑ 83FleSta-164
❑ 83RanAffF-2
❑ 83Top-371
❑ 84Nes792-641
❑ 84Top-641
❑ 84TopTif-641
❑ 93RanKee-307
Richartz, Scott
❑ 75AppFoxT-24
❑ 76AppFoxT-21
Richbourg, Lance
❑ 29ExhFou-2
❑ 29PorandAR-72
❑ 31Exh-2
❑ 33ExhFou-1

❑ 93ConTSN-701
Richeal, Ryan
❑ 94BurBeeC-29
❑ 95BurBeeTI-22
Richer, Troy
❑ 92CalLeaACL-35
Richert, Pete
❑ 62Top-131
❑ 62TopVen-131
❑ 63Top-383
❑ 64Top-51
❑ 64TopVen-51
❑ 65OPC-252
❑ 65Top-252
❑ 66Baz-43
❑ 66OPC-95
❑ 66SenTeal-11
❑ 66Top-95
❑ 66TopRubI-78
❑ 66TopVen-95
❑ 67BalOriP-87
❑ 67BalOriP-88
❑ 67Baz-43
❑ 67CokCapS-4
❑ 67DexPre-174
❑ 67SenTeal-11
❑ 67Top-590
❑ 68CokCapO-12
❑ 68Top-354
❑ 68TopVen-354
❑ 69MLBPin-24
❑ 69OPC-86
❑ 69Top-86
❑ 70BalOriP-26
❑ 70Top-601
❑ 71BalOriP-23
❑ 71MLBOffS-311
❑ 71OPC-273
❑ 71OriCha-12
❑ 71Top-273
❑ 72Top-649
❑ 73OPC-239
❑ 73Top-239
❑ 74OPC-348
❑ 74Top-348
❑ 74TopTra-348T
❑ 88ModA'sCLC-82
❑ 88ModA'sTI-2
❑ 89ModA'sC-2
❑ 89ModA'sCLC-287
❑ 90DodTar-665
❑ 90ModA'sC-34
❑ 90ModA'sCLC-172
❑ 90ModA'sP-2230
❑ 91ModA'sC-18
❑ 91ModA'sP-3107
❑ 91OriCro-380
❑ 92CalLeaACL-22
❑ 92ModA'sC-26
❑ 92ModA'sF-3911
❑ 93ModA'sC-27
❑ 93ModA'sF-816
❑ 94ModA'sC-27
❑ 94ModA'sF-3079
❑ 95EdmTraTI-20
Richey, Jeff
❑ 92EveGiaC-20
❑ 92EveGiaF-1687
❑ 93CliGiaC-19
❑ 93CliGiaF-2488
❑ 94ExcFS7-294
❑ 94SanJosGC-20
❑ 94SanJosGF-2815
❑ 95Exc-293
Richey, Mikal
❑ 96GreFalDB-22
❑ 96GreFalDTI-30
❑ 97GreFalDTI-21
Richey, Rodney
❑ 88IdaFalBP-1838
❑ 89SumBraP-1104
❑ 90DurBulTI-24
Richie, Bennie
❑ 83VisOakF-19
❑ 84VisOakT-1
Richie, Lewis
❑ 09AmeCarE90-1-90
❑ 10DomDisP-102
❑ 10SweCapPP-89
❑ 11HelSta-101
❑ 11PinT-5-214
❑ 11SpoLifM-180
❑ 11T205-144
❑ 12HasTriFT-53
Richie, Rob
❑ 88BasAmeAAB-3
❑ 88EasLeaAP-11
❑ 88GleFalTP-925
❑ 89TolMudHP-765
❑ 90OPC-146
❑ 90Top-146
❑ 90TopDeb89-101
❑ 90TopTif-146
❑ 90TriAAAC-29
❑ 90UppDec-76
Richman, Arthur
❑ 88MetColP-54
Richmond, Bob
❑ 87CliGiaP-25
Richmond, Bob Seattle
❑ 69PilPos-24
❑ 77PilPosR-24
Richmond, Clarence
❑ 91KisDodP-4203
❑ 92GulCoaDF-3582
Richmond, Don
❑ 47A'sTeal-24
❑ 50WorWidGV-43
❑ 51Bow-264
Richmond, Ryan
❑ 89PitMetS-21
❑ 89Sta-161
❑ 90ColMetGS-18
❑ 90ColMetPPI-3
Richter, Francis C.
❑ 90LitSunW-4
Richter, Reggie
❑ 11HelSta-102
Rick, Dean
❑ 78SalPirT-13
Ricken, Ray
❑ 94OneYanC-18
❑ 94OneYanF-3790
❑ 94StaCluDP-60
❑ 94StaCluDPFDI-60
❑ 95Bes-36
❑ 95GreBatTI-20
❑ 95TamYanYI-22
❑ 96Bow-327
❑ 96BowFoi-327
❑ 96Exc-92
❑ 96ExcCli-8
❑ 96NorNavB-19
❑ 96Top-428
❑ 97Bow-209
❑ 97BowCerBlaIA-CA65
❑ 97BowCerBluIA-CA65
❑ 97BowCerGolIA-CA65
❑ 97BowInt-209
❑ 97ColCliB-23
❑ 97ColCliD-20
❑ 97NorNav-29
Ricker, Drew
❑ 86EveGiaC-9
❑ 86EveGiaPC-24
❑ 87CliGiaP-22
Ricker, Troy
❑ 85UtiBluST-22
❑ 86JamExpP-19
❑ 87JamExpP-2550
❑ 88RocExpLC-31
❑ 89WesPalBES-19
❑ 90JamExpP-25
❑ 90RocExpLC-22
❑ 90RocExpP-2708
❑ 91WesPalBEC-28
❑ 91WesPalBEP-1242
❑ 92ClaFS7-297
❑ 92VisOakC-22
❑ 92VisOakF-1027
❑ 93ClaFS7-250
❑ 93ExcFS7-35
Rickert, Marv
❑ 47TipTop-115
❑ 52Top-50
❑ 83TopRep5-50
❑ 84TCMPla1-31
Rickert, Rick
❑ 49EurSta-18
Ricketts, Chad
❑ 96RocCubTI-27
❑ 97RocCub-25
Ricketts, Dave
❑ 65Top-581
❑ 67Top-589
❑ 68OPC-46
❑ 68Top-46
❑ 68TopVen-46
❑ 69MilBra-233
❑ 69Top-232
❑ 70Top-626
❑ 72MilBra-288
❑ 73OPC-517
❑ 73Top-517A
❑ 73Top-517B
❑ 78CarTeal-26
❑ 79Car5-22
❑ 81Car5x7-22
❑ 83Car-25
❑ 84Car-23
❑ 84Car5x7-22
❑ 85CarTeal-28
❑ 86CarTeal-37
❑ 87CarTeal-27
❑ 88CarTeal-29
❑ 89CarTeal-26
❑ 90TopTVCa-4
Ricketts, Dick
❑ 59Top-137
❑ 59TopVen-137
❑ 60Top-236
Rickey, Ralph
❑ 73WicAerJPKB-14
Rickey, W. Branch
❑ 14CraJacE-133
❑ 15CraJacE-133
❑ 23WilChoV-131
❑ 31CarMet-24
❑ 41CarW75-22
❑ 60Fle-55
❑ 76ShaPiz-106
❑ 77GalGloG-124
❑ 80PerHaloFP-105
❑ 80SSPHOF-105
❑ 82OhiHaloF-29
❑ 88DodRinP1-6B
❑ 88WilMulP-9
❑ 89HOFStiB-91
❑ 90BasWit-101
❑ 90PerGreM-84
❑ 92YanWIZH-27
❑ 93CraJac-12
❑ 94UppDecTAE-55
❑ 95ConTSN-1399
Rickman, Andy
❑ 88GreHorP-1568
❑ 89CedRapRB-13
❑ 89CedRapRP-932
❑ 89CedRapRS-15
Ricks, Ed
❑ 89MadMusS-19
Ricks, Ron
❑ 97ButCopKB-22
❑ 97ButCopKK-22
❑ 98CedRapKTI-24
Rico, Alfredo
❑ 70Top-552
Rico, Carlos
❑ 92AriWilP-14
Rico, Ron
❑ 92HelBreF-1714
❑ 92HelBreSP-19
Riconda, Harry
❑ 25Zee-52
❑ 90DodTar-666
Riddle, David
❑ 89EriOriS-21
❑ 89SanDieSAS-25
❑ 90Bes-317
❑ 90CMC-693
❑ 90WauTimB-12
❑ 90WauTimP-2125
❑ 90WauTimS-19
❑ 91FreKeyC-8
❑ 91FreKeyP-2363
Riddle, Elmer
❑ 41HarHarW-19
❑ 49EurSta-170
❑ 79DiaGre-261
❑ 83TCMPla1943-28
❑ 84OCoandSI-166
Riddle, Johnny (John L.)
❑ 53Top-274
❑ 54CarHunW-22
❑ 54Top-147
❑ 55CarHunW-21
❑ 55Top-98
❑ 58RedEnq-32
❑ 75CedRapGT-6
❑ 80Bra195T-34
❑ 83TCMPla1945-42
❑ 91TopArc1-274
❑ 94TopArc1-147
❑ 94TopArc1G-147
Riddleberger, Dennis
❑ 71OPC-93
❑ 71SenTealW-21
❑ 71Top-93
❑ 72Top-642
❑ 73OPC-157
❑ 73Top-157
Riddoch, Greg
❑ 88PadSmo-24
❑ 89PadPos-25
❑ 90PadMag-22
❑ 90TopTra-102T
❑ 90TopTraT-102T
❑ 91OPC-109
❑ 91PadCok-7
❑ 91PadMag-1
❑ 91PadSmo-29
❑ 91Top-109
❑ 91TopDesS-109
❑ 91TopMic-109
❑ 91TopTif-109
❑ 92OPC-351
❑ 92PadCarJ-16
❑ 92PadMot-1
❑ 92PadPolD-17
❑ 92PadSmo-25
❑ 92Top-351
❑ 92TopGol-351
❑ 92TopGolW-351
❑ 92TopMic-351
Riddoch, Rory
❑ 92SanBerC-30
Rideau, Greg
❑ 92BurIndC-14
❑ 92BurIndF-1654
Ridenour, Dana
❑ 87Ft.LauYP-9
❑ 88AlbYanP-1342
❑ 88EasLeaAP-4
❑ 89WilBilP-647
❑ 90Bes-55
❑ 90EasLeaAP-EL18
❑ 90WilBilB-20
❑ 90WilBilP-1057
❑ 90WilBilS-21
❑ 91IndIndLD-192
❑ 91IndIndP-460
❑ 91LinDriAAA-192
❑ 91TriA AAGP-AAA16
❑ 92IndIndF-1856
❑ 92IndIndS-190
❑ 93ColSprSSF-3085
❑ 94EdmTraF-2875
Ridenour, Ryan
❑ 90BatCliP-3069
❑ 98OneYanG-23
❑ 99TeaBesR-72
❑ 99TeaBesRG-72
❑ 99TeaBesRS-72
Ridley, Brian
❑ 98AubDouTI-24
Ridzik, Steve
❑ 53BowBW-48
❑ 54Bow-223
❑ 55Bow-111
❑ 57Top-123
❑ 60MapLeaSF-17
❑ 60Top-489
❑ 61MapLeaBH-18
❑ 64Top-92
❑ 64TopVen-92
❑ 65OPC-211
❑ 65Top-211
❑ 66Top-294
❑ 66TopVen-294
Riebe, Harvey
❑ 95PacHarR-1
Riedling, John
❑ 94BilMusF-3668
❑ 95BilMusTI-15
❑ 97BurBeeB-18
❑ 98ChaLooG-23
Rieger, Elmer
❑ 09PC7HHB-36
❑ 14Zee-72
❑ 19Zee-144
❑ 20Zee-92
❑ 21Zee-106
❑ 22Zee-86
Riegert, Tim
❑ 96JohCitCTI-27
❑ 97PeoChi-23
❑ 98PeoChiM-20
Riel, Franich
❑ 40SolHug-16
Riemer, Matt
❑ 92BluOriC-17
❑ 92BluOriF-2368
❑ 93BluOriC-1
❑ 93BluOriF-4134
❑ 94AlbPolC-21
❑ 94AlbPolF-2246
❑ 94OriPro-84
Riemer, Robin
❑ 86EveGiaC-183
Riemer, Tim
❑ 89WatIndS-19
Riesgo, Nikco
❑ 88SpoIndP-1936
❑ 89ChaRaiP-995
❑ 90FloStaLAS-16
❑ 90St.LucMS-22
❑ 90StaFS7-10
❑ 91Bow-536
❑ 91ReaPhiP-1375
❑ 92ProFS7-298
❑ 92TopDeb91-148
Riewerts, Tom
❑ 82AubAstT-15
Rife, Jackie
❑ 93MarPhiC-23
❑ 93MarPhiF-3473
❑ 94MarPhiC-21
❑ 94MarPhiF-3292
Riffle, Brian
❑ 78QuaCitAT-20
Rigby, Bob
❑ 82MonNew-12
Rigby, Brad
❑ 94SigRooDP-34
❑ 94SigRooDPS-34
❑ 94StaCluDP-28
❑ 94StaCluDPFDI-28
❑ 95ModA'sTI-24
❑ 95SPML-124
❑ 96BesAutS-80
❑ 96Bow-321
❑ 96BowFoi-321
❑ 96Exc-100
❑ 96HunStaTI-21
❑ 97Bow-354
❑ 97BowCerBlaIA-CA66
❑ 97BowCerBluIA-CA66
❑ 97BowCerGolIA-CA66
❑ 97BowChr-239
❑ 97BowChrI-239
❑ 97BowChrIR-239
❑ 97BowChrR-239
❑ 97BowInt-354
❑ 98CirThu-230
❑ 98CirThuRav-230
❑ 98CirThuSupRav-230
❑ 98ColCho-126
❑ 98Fle-277
❑ 98StaCluFDI-152
❑ 98StaCluI-152
❑ 98StaCluOneK-152
❑ 98StaCluPP-152
❑ 98Top-415
❑ 98TopChr-415
❑ 98TopChrR-415
❑ 98TopDevR-415
❑ 98TopDia-415
❑ 98TopMiniC-415
❑ 98UppDec-272
Rigby, Kevin
❑ 81DurBulT-3
Rigdon, Paul
❑ 96WatIndTI-25
❑ 98KinIndQ-19
❑ 99BasAmeTP-84
❑ 99BasAmeTPG-84
Riggan, Jerrod
❑ 96BoiHawB-24
❑ 96HilStaHWB-24
Riggar, Butch
❑ 77ForLauYS-28
❑ 79HolMilT-18
Riggert, Joe
❑ 90DodTar-667
Riggins, Mark A.
❑ 81ArkTraT-14
❑ 82ArkTraT-7
❑ 83St.PetCT-11
❑ 86ArkTraP-18
❑ 87SprCarB-2
❑ 89BlaYNPRWL-98
❑ 89LouRedBC-24
❑ 89LouRedBP-1254
❑ 90CMC-679
❑ 90LouRedBC-28
❑ 90LouRedBLBC-4
❑ 90LouRedBP-420
❑ 90ProAAAF-534
❑ 90TopTVCa-62
❑ 91LinDriAAA-250
❑ 91LouRedLD-250
❑ 91LouRedP-2933
❑ 91LouRedTI-31
❑ 92LouRedF-1903
❑ 94LouRedF-2997
Riggleman, James D.
❑ 75WatDodT-18
❑ 77ArkTraT-9A
❑ 77ArkTraT-9B
❑ 79ArkTraT-5
❑ 80ArkTraT-4
❑ 81ArkTraT-19
❑ 83St.PetCT-29
❑ 86ArkTraP-19
❑ 87ArkTraP-7
❑ 88ArkTraGS-4
❑ 89BlaYNPRWL-69
❑ 89CarTeal-27
❑ 90TopTVCa-5
❑ 91LasVegSLD-299
❑ 91LasVegSP-253
❑ 91LinDriAAA-299
❑ 92LasVegSF-2809
❑ 92LasVegSS-249
❑ 93PadMot-1
❑ 93Top-513
❑ 93TopGol-513
❑ 93TopInaM-513
❑ 93TopInaR-513
❑ 93TopMic-513
❑ 94PadMot-1
Riggs, Adam
❑ 94GreFalDSP-19
❑ 95Bes-78
❑ 95SanBerSTI-19
❑ 95SPML-4
❑ 95SPML-75
❑ 95SPMLA-21
❑ 95SPMLDtS-DS6
❑ 96BesAutSA-60
❑ 96Bow-319
❑ 96BowFoi-319
❑ 96Exc-182
❑ 96ExcAll-3
❑ 96ExcTL-8
❑ 96SanAntMB-18
❑ 96Top-426
❑ 97AlbDukGS-28
❑ 97BesAutAS-45
❑ 97BesAutP-R11
❑ 97Bow-85
❑ 97BowCerBlaIA-CA67
❑ 97BowCerBluIA-CA67
❑ 97BowCerGolIA-CA67
❑ 97BowInt-85
❑ 97ColCho-474
❑ 98AlbDukG-24
❑ 98ColCho-19
❑ 98ColCho-148
❑ 98Fle-182
❑ 98PacInvGems-174
❑ 98UppDec-279
❑ 99DodPol-22
❑ 99Vic-195
Riggs, Eric
❑ 98VerBeaDM-21
Riggs, Jim
❑ 82OneYanT-2
❑ 83GreHorT-22
❑ 85AlbYanT-18
❑ 86AlbYanT-1
Riggs, Kevin
❑ 90BilMusP-3231
❑ 91CedRapRC-19
❑ 91CedRapRP-2728
❑ 92CedRapRC-18
❑ 92CedRapRF-1081
❑ 92MidLeaATI-35
❑ 93StoPorC-20
❑ 93StoPorF-753
❑ 94ClaGolF-176
❑ 94ElPasDF-3154
❑ 94ExcFS7-84
❑ 94UppDecML-234
❑ 95NorNavTI-41
❑ 96DouAllB-22
❑ 96NorNavB-20
❑ 97AkrAer-22
Riggs, Lew
❑ 34DiaStaR-96
❑ 36GouWidPPR-A88
❑ 37ExhFou-4
❑ 38ExhFou-4
❑ 38RedOraW-22

❑ 39OrcPhoAP-19
❑ 39PlaBal-77
❑ 39RedTeal-18
❑ 40PlaBal-78
❑ 41DodTeal-6
❑ 41DouPlaR-141
❑ 41HarHarW-20
❑ 42DodTeal-18
❑ 73Dod194T-25
❑ 77CinRedT-35
❑ 77TCMTheWY-78
❑ 78DodTCM4-22
❑ 90DodTar-668
❑ 92ConTSN-567
Riggs, Tony
❑ 92GulCoaRSP-26
❑ 93NewOrlZF-983
Righetti, Dave
❑ 79WesHavYT-21
❑ 80ColCliP-24
❑ 80ColCliT-17
❑ 81ColCliP-24
❑ 81ColCliT-9
❑ 81YanPhoA-23
❑ 82Don-73
❑ 82Fle-52
❑ 82Top-439
❑ 82YanPhoA-23
❑ 83Don-199
❑ 83Fle-395
❑ 83OPC-176
❑ 83Top-81
❑ 83Top-176
❑ 83YanPhoA-22
❑ 84Don-10
❑ 84Don-10A
❑ 84Don-103
❑ 84DonActAS-59
❑ 84Fle-139
❑ 84Fle-639
❑ 84FleSti-86
❑ 84FunFooP-116
❑ 84Nes792-5
❑ 84Nes792-635
❑ 84OPC-277
❑ 84Top-5
❑ 84Top-635
❑ 84TopGloS-28
❑ 84TopRubD-24
❑ 84TopSti-287B
❑ 84TopSti-315
❑ 84TopTif-5
❑ 84TopTif-635
❑ 85AllGamPI-85
❑ 85Don-336
❑ 85DonHig-37
❑ 85Dra-40
❑ 85Fle-142
❑ 85FleStaS-102
❑ 85Lea-219
❑ 85OPC-260
❑ 85PolMet-Y5
❑ 85SevCoi-E13
❑ 85Top-260
❑ 85TopRubD-24
❑ 85TopSti-314
❑ 85TopSup-58
❑ 85TopTif-260
❑ 85YanTCMP-18
❑ 86BasStaB-91
❑ 86Don-214
❑ 86DonHig-52
❑ 86Fle-116
❑ 86FleMin-25
❑ 86FleStiC-97
❑ 86GenMilB-1H
❑ 86Lea-89
❑ 86OPC-34
❑ 86SevCoi-E10
❑ 86Spo-41
❑ 86Spo-72
❑ 86Spo-141
❑ 86SpoRoo-48
❑ 86Top-560
❑ 86TopSti-303
❑ 86TopSup-44
❑ 86TopTat-11
❑ 86TopTif-560
❑ 86YanTCM-13
❑ 87ClaGam-86
❑ 87Don-128
❑ 87DonAll-55
❑ 87Fle-111
❑ 87Fle-627
❑ 87FleAwaW-32
❑ 87FleGlo-111
❑ 87FleGlo-627
❑ 87FleHotS-31
❑ 87FleMin-90
❑ 87FleRecS-32
❑ 87FleSlu-34
❑ 87FleStiC-100
❑ 87FleWaxBC-C12
❑ 87KayB-27
❑ 87KeyFooD-20
❑ 87Lea-53
❑ 87MSAIceTD-20
❑ 87OPC-40
❑ 87OurOwnTD-20
❑ 87SevCoi-E9
❑ 87Spo-57
❑ 87Spo-119
❑ 87Spo-194
❑ 87SpoTeaP-7
❑ 87Top-5
❑ 87Top-40
❑ 87Top-616
❑ 87TopCoi-22
❑ 87TopGaloC-9
❑ 87TopGloS-24
❑ 87TopMinL-67
❑ 87TopSti-8
❑ 87TopSti-9
❑ 87TopSti-299
❑ 87TopTif-5
❑ 87TopTif-40
❑ 87TopTif-616
❑ 87WeiMarD-20
❑ 87Woo-14
❑ 88Baz-16
❑ 88Don-93
❑ 88DonAll-29
❑ 88DonBasB-164
❑ 88DonReaBY-93
❑ 88Fle-220
❑ 88Fle-625
❑ 88FleAwaW-33
❑ 88FleGlo-220
❑ 88FleGlo-625
❑ 88FleMin-43
❑ 88FleRecS-32
❑ 88FleSlu-33
❑ 88FleStiC-52
❑ 88FleTeaL-29
❑ 88K-M-20
❑ 88Lea-57
❑ 88Nes-28
❑ 88OPC-155
❑ 88PanSti-150
❑ 88RedFolSB-75
❑ 88Sco-351
❑ 88ScoGlo-351
❑ 88Spo-135
❑ 88SpoGam-19
❑ 88StaLinAl-25
❑ 88StaLinY-13
❑ 88Top-790
❑ 88TopGaloC-10
❑ 88TopMinL-29
❑ 88TopSti-300
❑ 88TopStiB-66
❑ 88TopTif-790
❑ 88Woo-16
❑ 89Bow-167
❑ 89BowTif-167
❑ 89Don-78
❑ 89DonBasB-76
❑ 89Fle-267
❑ 89FleGlo-267
❑ 89OPC-335
❑ 89PanSti-400
❑ 89RedFolSB-97
❑ 89Sco-225
❑ 89ScoHot1S-37
❑ 89Spo-158
❑ 89Top-335
❑ 89TopBasT-73
❑ 89TopDouM-18
❑ 89TopSti-307
❑ 89TopTif-335
❑ 89TVSpoM-84
❑ 89UppDec-59
❑ 89YanScoNW-6
❑ 90Bow-426
❑ 90BowTif-426
❑ 90ClaBlu-41
❑ 90Don-311
❑ 90DonBesA-136
❑ 90DonLeaS-14
❑ 90Fle-453
❑ 90FleCan-453
❑ 90M.Vpin-69
❑ 90OPC-160
❑ 90PanSti-124
❑ 90PublntS-545
❑ 90RedFolSB-79
❑ 90Sco-194
❑ 90Sco100S-39
❑ 90Spo-88
❑ 90Top-160
❑ 90TopBig-102
❑ 90TopTif-160
❑ 90TopTVY-18
❑ 90UppDec-479
❑ 90YanScoNW-16
❑ 91BasBesRB-12
❑ 91Bow-632
❑ 91ClaGam-87
❑ 91Don-21
❑ 91Don-275
❑ 91DonSupD-21
❑ 91Fle-677
❑ 91FleUpd-131
❑ 91GiaMot-8
❑ 91GiaPacGaE-15
❑ 91GiaSFE-12
❑ 91Lea-301
❑ 91OPC-410
❑ 91OPCPre-99
❑ 91PanFreS-332
❑ 91PanSti-266
❑ 91RedFolS-77
❑ 91Sco-24
❑ 91Sco100S-68
❑ 91ScoRoo-53T
❑ 91StaClu-356
❑ 91Stu-258
❑ 91Top-410
❑ 91TopDesS-410
❑ 91TopMic-410
❑ 91TopTif-410
❑ 91TopTra-96T
❑ 91TopTraT-96T
❑ 91UppDec-448
❑ 91UppDec-778
❑ 92Bow-324
❑ 92ClaGam-43
❑ 92Don-174
❑ 92Fle-647
❑ 92GiaMot-8
❑ 92GiaPacGaE-30
❑ 92Lea-135
❑ 92LeaBlaG-135
❑ 92OPC-35
❑ 92PanSti-219
❑ 92Pin-82
❑ 92Sco-260
❑ 92StaClu-107
❑ 92Top-35
❑ 92TopGol-35
❑ 92TopGolW-35
❑ 92TopKid-62
❑ 92TopMic-35
❑ 92TriPla-23
❑ 92Ult-594
❑ 92UppDec-171
❑ 92UppDecTMH-42
❑ 92YanWIZ7-133
❑ 92YanWIZ8-159
❑ 92YanWIZA-64
❑ 93Don-552
❑ 93Fle-537
❑ 93GiaMot-10
❑ 93GiaPos-29
❑ 93GiaStaC-2
❑ 93PacSpa-614
❑ 93StaClu-431
❑ 93StaCluFDI-431
❑ 93StaCluMOP-431
❑ 93Top-310
❑ 93TopGol-310
❑ 93TopInaM-310
❑ 93TopInaR-310
❑ 93TopMic-310
❑ 93UppDec-579
❑ 93UppDecGold-579
❑ 94Pac-553
❑ 95NasSouTI-19
Righetti, Leo
❑ 53SanFraSTI-16
❑ 56SeaPop-15
❑ 57SeaPop-21
Righetti, Steve
❑ 78AshTouT-24
❑ 79AshTouT-15
Rightnowar, Ron
❑ 87FayGenP-24
❑ 88LakTigS-22
❑ 89LonTigP-1369
❑ 90LonTigP-1268
❑ 91TolMudHP-1931
❑ 92TolMudHF-1043
❑ 93TolMudHF-1654
❑ 94NewOrlZF-1466
❑ 94TriAAF-AAA8
Riginos, Tom
❑ 88CapCodPPaLP-58
Rigler, Cy
❑ 21Exh-141
❑ 94ConTSN-1202
❑ 94ConTSNB-1202
Rigney, Bill (William J.)
❑ 47PM1StaP1-174
❑ 48Bow-32
❑ 48GiaTeal-23
❑ 49Bow-170
❑ 49EurSta-123
❑ 49GiaTeal-24
❑ 50Bow-117
❑ 50JJKCopP-13
❑ 51Bow-125
❑ 52BerRos-53
❑ 52NatTeaL-22
❑ 52Top-125
❑ 53BowBW-3
❑ 56GiaJayP-9
❑ 57GiaJayP-7
❑ 58GiaSFCB-19
❑ 58PacBel-6
❑ 60MacSta-18
❑ 60Top-7
❑ 60Top-225
❑ 60TopVen-7
❑ 61AngJayP-10
❑ 61Top-225
❑ 62AngJayP-9
❑ 62Top-549
❑ 63AngJayP-14
❑ 63Top-294
❑ 64Top-383
❑ 65OPC-66
❑ 65Top-66
❑ 66Top-249
❑ 66TopVen-249
❑ 67Top-494
❑ 68Top-416
❑ 69OPC-182
❑ 69Top-182
❑ 70OPC-426
❑ 70Top-426
❑ 70TwiTeal-8
❑ 71OPC-532
❑ 71Top-532
❑ 72GiaTeal-16
❑ 72OPC-389
❑ 72Top-389
❑ 72TwiTeal-13
❑ 75Gia195T-24
❑ 76SanFraGP-19
❑ 78TwiFri-20
❑ 79DiaGre-41
❑ 81TCM60I-457
❑ 83TopRep5-125
❑ 84TCMPla1-43
❑ 86AngGreT-12
❑ 89AngSmo-1
❑ 91TopArc1-328
❑ 92BazQua5A-19
Rigney, John D.
❑ 33WorCig(-73
❑ 39WhiSoxTI-14
❑ 41DouPlaR-71
❑ 47TipTop-26
❑ 79DiaGre-133
❑ 94ConTSN-1225
❑ 94ConTSNB-1225
Rigney, Topper (Emory E.)
❑ 21Exh-142
❑ 21Nei-17
❑ 22E120-58
❑ 22W572-84
❑ 22W573-107
❑ 25Exh-94
❑ 26Exh-69
❑ 26SpoComoA-35
❑ 27YorCarE-38
❑ 93ConTSN-728
Rigoli, Joe
❑ 79NewCoPT-3
❑ 83EriCarT-2
❑ 85LouRedR-2
❑ 86EriCarP-25
❑ 87EriCarP-3
❑ 96PhiTeal-27
❑ 97PhiTeal-59
Rigos, John
❑ 83EriCarT-3
❑ 85SprCarT-1
❑ 86St.PetCP-27
❑ 87SalBucP-14
❑ 88HarSenP-834
Rigsby, Rickey
❑ 88PulBraP-1761
❑ 89IdaFalBP-2013
Rigsby, Tim
❑ 90MiaMirIS-21
❑ 90MiaMirIS-26
❑ 91KinIndC-19
❑ 91KinIndP-331
❑ 92SalLakTSP-6
Rijo, Fernando
❑ 98GreFalDG-25
Rijo, Jose
❑ 84FleUpd-99
❑ 84TopTra-100T
❑ 84TopTraT-100T
❑ 85DomLeaS-35
❑ 85Don-492
❑ 85Fle-143
❑ 85TacTigC-133
❑ 85Top-238
❑ 85TopTif-238
❑ 86A'sMot-13
❑ 86Don-522
❑ 86DonHig-2
❑ 86Fle-431
❑ 86Top-536
❑ 86TopTif-536
❑ 87Don-55
❑ 87Fle-404
❑ 87FleGlo-404
❑ 87Lea-119
❑ 87SpoTeaP-23
❑ 87Top-34
❑ 87TopTif-34
❑ 88Don-548
❑ 88FleUpd-86
❑ 88FleUpdG-86
❑ 88RedKah-27
❑ 88Sco-392
❑ 88ScoGlo-392
❑ 88ScoRoo-27T
❑ 88ScoRooG-27T
❑ 88Top-316
❑ 88TopTif-316
❑ 88TopTra-92T
❑ 88TopTraT-92T
❑ 89Bow-300
❑ 89BowTif-300
❑ 89ClaTraO-141
❑ 89Don-375
❑ 89DonBasB-278
❑ 89Fle-168
❑ 89FleGlo-168
❑ 89OPC-135
❑ 89PanSti-68
❑ 89RedKah-27
❑ 89Sco-552A
❑ 89Sco-552B
❑ 89ScoYouSI-31
❑ 89SpoIllFKI-240
❑ 89Top-135
❑ 89TopMinL-12
❑ 89TopSti-140
❑ 89TopTif-135
❑ 89UppDec-619
❑ 90Bow-45
❑ 90BowTif-45
❑ 90Don-115
❑ 90Fle-430
❑ 90FleCan-430
❑ 90Lea-282
❑ 90OPC-627
❑ 90PanSti-243
❑ 90PublntS-38
❑ 90RedKah-24
❑ 90Sco-511
❑ 90Top-627
❑ 90TopBig-257
❑ 90TopSti-137
❑ 90TopTif-627
❑ 90UppDec-216
❑ 91Bow-681
❑ 91Cla1-T97
❑ 91Cla2-T31
❑ 91ClaGam-109
❑ 91Col-27
❑ 91Don-722
❑ 91Don-742
❑ 91Fle-79
❑ 91FleWorS-7
❑ 91KinDis-24
❑ 91Lea-326
❑ 91OPC-493
❑ 91PanFreS-134
❑ 91PepSup-5
❑ 91RedKah-27
❑ 91RedPep-18
❑ 91Sco-658
❑ 91StaClu-11
❑ 91Top-493
❑ 91TopCraJI-9
❑ 91TopDesS-493
❑ 91TopMic-493
❑ 91TopTif-493
❑ 91Ult-102
❑ 91UppDec-298
❑ 91Woo-31
❑ 91Woo-33
❑ 92Bow-680
❑ 92ClaGam-77
❑ 92Don-223
❑ 92Fle-419
❑ 92Hig5-34
❑ 92Lea-139
❑ 92LeaBlaG-139
❑ 92MooSna-3
❑ 92OPC-220
❑ 92PanSti-269
❑ 92Pin-508
❑ 92RedKah-27
❑ 92Sco-232
❑ 92Sco100S-43
❑ 92ScoImpP-83
❑ 92StaClu-800
❑ 92Stu-26
❑ 92Top-220
❑ 92TopGol-220
❑ 92TopGolW-220
❑ 92TopKid-42
❑ 92TopMic-220
❑ 92Ult-196
❑ 92UppDec-258
❑ 92UppDec-712
❑ 92UppDecTMH-43
❑ 92YanWIZ8-160
❑ 93Bow-62
❑ 93DiaMar-88
❑ 93Don-454
❑ 93Fin-24
❑ 93FinRef-24
❑ 93Fla-31
❑ 93Fle-41
❑ 93FleFruotL-53
❑ 93HumDumC-29
❑ 93KinDis-8
❑ 93Lea-411
❑ 93MSABenSPD-15
❑ 93OPC-286
❑ 93PacBeiA-21
❑ 93PacSpa-88
❑ 93PacSpaGE-9
❑ 93PacSpaPI-5
❑ 93PanSti-289
❑ 93Pin-77
❑ 93RedKah-20
❑ 93Sco-105
❑ 93Sel-163
❑ 93SP-213
❑ 93StaClu-233
❑ 93StaCluFDI-233
❑ 93StaCluMOP-233
❑ 93Stu-211
❑ 93Top-165
❑ 93TopComotH-20
❑ 93TopGol-165
❑ 93TopInaM-165
❑ 93TopInaR-165
❑ 93TopMic-165
❑ 93Ult-33
❑ 93UppDec-226
❑ 93UppDec-473
❑ 93UppDecGold-226
❑ 93UppDecGold-473
❑ 93USPlaCA-6S
❑ 94Bow-402
❑ 94BowBes-R56
❑ 94BowBesR-R56
❑ 94ColC-239
❑ 94ColChoGS-239
❑ 94ColChoSS-239
❑ 94DenHol-19
❑ 94Don-361
❑ 94DonMVP-3

- 94DonSpeE-361
- 94Fin-308
- 94FinRef-308
- 94Fla-148
- 94Fle-421
- 94FleExtB-237
- 94FleExtBPD-7
- 94FleSmo'nH-9
- 94FUnPac-84
- 94Lea-340
- 94OPC-50
- 94OscMayR-28
- 94Pac-156
- 94PacAll-10
- 94PanSti-15
- 94PanSti-167
- 94Pin-322
- 94PinArtP-322
- 94PinMusC-322
- 94ProMag-33
- 94RedFolMI-35
- 94RedKah-23
- 94Sco-52
- 94ScoGolR-52
- 94Sel-40
- 94SP-161
- 94SPDieC-161
- 94Spo-112
- 94StaClu-596
- 94StaClu-715
- 94StaCluFDI-596
- 94StaCluFDI-715
- 94StaCluGR-596
- 94StaCluGR-715
- 94StaCluMO-40
- 94StaCluMOP-596
- 94StaCluMOP-715
- 94Stu-171
- 94Top-705
- 94TopGol-705
- 94TopSpa-705
- 94TriPla-218
- 94TriPlaM-14
- 94Ult-476
- 94UltLeaL-10
- 94UltStrK-4
- 94UppDec-143
- 94UppDecAJ-26
- 94UppDecAJG-26
- 94UppDecED-143
- 94USPlaCA-13S
- 95Baz-88
- 95Bow-374
- 95ColCho-434
- 95ColChoGS-434
- 95ColChoSE-197
- 95ColChoSEGS-197
- 95ColChoSESS-197
- 95ColChoSS-434
- 95Don-292
- 95DonPreP-292
- 95DonTopotO-218
- 95Fin-35
- 95FinFlaT-FT7
- 95FinRef-35
- 95Fla-122
- 95Fle-443
- 95FleTeaL-17
- 95Lea-102
- 95LeaLim-130
- 95LinVen-308
- 95LinVen-318
- 95LinVen-319
- 95Pac-111
- 95PacLatD-29
- 95PacPri-35
- 95Pin-223
- 95PinArtP-223
- 95PinMusC-223
- 95PinSam-223
- 95RedFol-15
- 95RedKah-23
- 95Sco-270
- 95ScoGolR-270
- 95ScoHaloG-HG30
- 95ScoPlaTS-270
- 95Sel-138
- 95SelArtP-138
- 95SP-46
- 95Spo-40
- 95SpoArtP-40
- 95SPSil-46
- 95StaClu-300
- 95StaCluMOP-300
- 95StaCluSTDW-RE300
- 95StaCluSTWS-300
- 95StaCluVR-157
- 95StaCluVRMO-157
- 95Stu-85
- 95Top-529
- 95TopCyb-314
- 95TopD3-38
- 95TopEmb-26
- 95TopEmbGI-26
- 95TopLeaL-LL47
- 95Ult-147
- 95UltGolM-147
- 95UltStrK-6
- 95UltStrKGM-6
- 95UppDec-407
- 95UppDecED-407
- 95UppDecEDG-407
- 95UppDecSE-28
- 95UppDecSEG-28
- 95USPlaCMLA-5S
- 95Zen-57
- 96AubDouB-10
- 96ColCho-113
- 96ColChoGS-113
- 96ColChoSS-113
- 96Don-500
- 96DonPreP-500
- 96Fin-B150
- 96FinRef-B150
- 96Fla-237
- 96Fle-350
- 96FleTif-350
- 96PacPriFT-FT6
- 96Pin-44
- 96ProSta-104
- 96Sco-208
- 96Sel-43
- 96SelArtP-43
- 96StaClu-428
- 96StaCluEPB-428
- 96StaCluEPG-428
- 96StaCluEPS-428
- 96StaCluMOP-428
- 96Top-120
- 96Ult-465
- 96UltGolM-465
- 96UppDec-307
- 97Pac-275
- 97PacLigB-275
- 97PacSil-275
- 97QuaCitRBB-23
- 97Top-373
- 98KisCobQ-23

Rijo, Rafael
- 89SalDodTI-26
- 90YakBeaTI-13
- 91VerBeaDC-25
- 91VerBeaDP-790
- 92RocExpC-27
- 92RocExpF-2128

Rijo-Berger, Jose
- 97PitMet-26

Riker, Robert
- 90BriTigP-3161
- 90BriTigS-20

Riles, Earnest
- 83ElPasDT-21
- 84VanCanC-35
- 85FleUpd-89
- 85VanCanC-207
- 86BrePol-1
- 86Don-359
- 86Fle-499
- 86FleLeaL-34
- 86FleMin-102
- 86FleStiC-98
- 86KayB-26
- 86Lea-161
- 86MSAJayPCD-14
- 86SevCoi-C13
- 86Spo-16
- 86Top-398
- 86TopGloS-40
- 86TopSti-310
- 86TopTif-398
- 87BrePol-1
- 87Don-151
- 87Fle-355
- 87FleGamW-36
- 87FleGlo-355
- 87FleMin-91
- 87Lea-66
- 87OPC-318
- 87SpoTeaP-19
- 87Top-523
- 87TopSti-203
- 87TopTif-523
- 88BlaYNPRWL-124
- 88BrePol-1
- 88Don-478
- 88Fle-172
- 88FleGlo-172
- 88FleUpd-130
- 88FleUpdG-130
- 88Sco-349
- 88ScoGlo-349
- 88ScoRoo-57T
- 88ScoRooG-57T
- 88StaLinBre-14
- 88Top-88
- 88TopTif-88
- 88TopTra-93T
- 88TopTraT-93T
- 89Bow-475
- 89BowTif-475
- 89BreGar-14
- 89ClaLigB-87
- 89Don-625
- 89DonBasB-50
- 89Fle-341
- 89FleGlo-341
- 89GiaMot-16
- 89Sco-458
- 89Top-676
- 89TopTif-676
- 89UppDec-497
- 90Bow-239
- 90BowTif-239
- 90Don-131
- 90El PasDAGTI-9
- 90Fle-69
- 90FleCan-69
- 90GiaMot-15
- 90GiaSmo-16
- 90OPC-732
- 90PubIntS-80
- 90Sco-447
- 90Top-732
- 90TopSti-81
- 90TopTif-732
- 90UppDec-378
- 91A'sMot-16
- 91Bow-217
- 91Don-461
- 91Fle-271
- 91FleUpd-51
- 91Lea-358
- 91OPC-408
- 91Sco-626
- 91ScoRoo-55T
- 91StaClu-432
- 91Top-408
- 91TopDesS-408
- 91TopMic-408
- 91TopTif-408
- 91TopTra-97T
- 91TopTraT-97T
- 91UltUpd-47
- 91UppDec-780
- 92OPC-187
- 92Sco-222
- 92Top-187
- 92TopGol-187
- 92TopGolW-187
- 92TopMic-187
- 92TucTorF-498
- 92UppDec-494
- 93RedSoxP-27
- 94BreMilB-175
- 94Fle-40
- 94VanCanF-1871

Riley, Cash
- 96GreFalDB-23
- 96GreFalDTI-31
- 97YakBeaG-28
- 98VerBeaDM-30

Riley, Darren
- 85CedRapRT-24
- 86FloStaLAP-41
- 86TamTarP-16
- 87VerRedP-25
- 88ChaLooB-24
- 91ParPatF-5
- 94ButCopKSP-22

Riley, Ed
- 89ElmPioP-14
- 90WinHavRSS-22
- 91LynRedSC-7
- 91LynRedSP-1196
- 92NewBriRSF-431
- 92NewBriRSS-493
- 92SkyAA F-212
- 93ClaGolF-29
- 93ExcFS7-136
- 93NewBriRSF-1217
- 94NewBriRSF-649

Riley, George
- 80WicAerT-20
- 81Don-588
- 81Top-514
- 83ReaPhiT-8
- 84PorBeaC-206
- 86ExpPos-12

Riley, Jim
- 92EveGiaC-16
- 92EveGiaF-1688

Riley, Marquis
- 92BoiHawC-1
- 92BoiHawF-3644
- 92ClaDraP-48
- 92FroRowDP-26
- 92FroRowDPG-26
- 92FroRowDPS-26
- 93ClaFS7-113
- 93PalSprAC-1
- 93PalSprAF-83
- 93StaCluM-199
- 94Bow-263
- 94ExcFS7-32
- 94MidAngF-2451
- 94MidAngOHP-26
- 94UppDecML-33
- 94UppDecMLPotYF-PY1
- 95Bow-188
- 97VanCanB-24

Riley, Matt
- 99BasAmeTPA-36
- 99TeaBesRA-21
- 99TeaBesRBG-8

Riley, Mike
- 79WisRapTT-3
- 82CedRapRT-6

Riley, Mike Eugene
- 96BelGiaTI-18
- 97SalVolG-33

Riley, P.J.
- 89AubAstP-2180

Riley, Randy
- 84NewOriT-1

Riley, Tim
- 77DayBeaIT-18

Riley, Tom
- 83CedRapRF-5
- 83CedRapRT-16
- 84CedRapRT-15
- 85CedRapRT-31

Rima, Tom
- 74CedRapAT-5
- 75DubPacT-4

Rincon, Andy (Andrew)
- 80ArkTraT-9
- 81Top-244
- 82LouRedE-24
- 82Top-135
- 83LouRedR-17
- 89ArkTraGS-20

Rincon, Juan
- 98ForWayW!-23

Rincon, Ricardo
- 97Fle-519
- 97FleTif-519
- 97PirPos-31
- 97SpoIll-51
- 97SpoIllEE-51
- 98Fle-192
- 98Pac-402
- 98PacOnl-592
- 98PacOnlR-592
- 98PacOnlWC-592
- 98PacPlaB-402
- 98PacRedT-402
- 98PacSil-402
- 98SpoIll-186
- 98SpoIllEE-186
- 98SpoIllFE-186
- 98Top-267
- 98TopChr-267
- 98TopChrR-267
- 98TopDevR-267
- 98TopDia-267
- 98TopMiniC-267
- 98Ult-195
- 98UltGolM-195
- 98UltMas-195
- 98UltPlaM-195
- 98UppDec-532
- 99Fle-538
- 99FleSta9-538
- 99FleWarT-538
- 99Pac-345
- 99PacCroC-225
- 99PacCroCPB-225
- 99PacPlaB-345
- 99PacRed-345
- 99StaCluC-CS23
- 99StaCluC-CS28
- 99StaCluC-CS35
- 99StaCluC-CS40
- 99Top-76
- 99TopChr-76
- 99TopChrR-76
- 99TopMVPP-76

Rincones, Hector
- 80VenLeaS-6
- 81WatRedT-16
- 83WatRedT-13
- 84WicAerRD-3
- 85AlbDukCr-157
- 86MemChiSTOS-22
- 86MemChiTOS-22
- 93LinVenB-189
- 95LinVen-100
- 96-97LinVen-29

Rincones, Wuarrner
- 96-97LinVen-206

Rinderknecht, Bob
- 93BluOriF-4124

Rineer, Jeff
- 78RocRedWT-14
- 79RocRedWT-16
- 80RocRedWT-8
- 91OriCro-381

Rinehart, Dallas
- 92BoiHawC-21
- 93CedRapKC-14
- 93PalSprAC-19
- 93PalSprAF-69

Rinehart, Robert
- 86ColMetP-22

Riner, Willard
- 89GeoColC-25
- 90GeoColC-25

Rines, Doug
- 89TenTecGE-22

Ring, Dave
- 90ElmPioP-20

Ring, James J.
- 19W514-98
- 20NatCarE-84
- 20RedWorCP-17
- 20W516-11
- 21Exh-143
- 21Nei-120
- 22E120-206
- 22W575-103
- 23W503-47
- 23WilChoV-132
- 26Exh-39
- 27AmeCarE126-24
- 27MidBre-14
- 28Exh-22
- 88PacEigMO-87
- 92ConTSN-614

Ringgold, Keith
- 90EveGiaB-27
- 90EveGiaP-3143
- 91BenBucCB-19
- 91BenBucP-3708

Ringkamp, Mark
- 92Ft.MyeMCB-9
- 92Ft.MyeMF-2745

Ringler, Tim
- 88KnoBluJB-22
- 89KnoBluJB-30
- 89KnoBluJP-1122

Riordan, James
- 13Zee-70

Rios, Armando
- 92LSUTigM-9
- 93LSUTigM-4
- 94CliLumC-19
- 94CliLumF-1995
- 94LSUTigMP-12
- 97ShrCap-21
- 97ShrCapB-21
- 98FleUpd-U31
- 98FreGriG-26
- 98LeaRS-336
- 98LeaRSLHolo-336
- 98LeaRSLong-336
- 98LeaRTrue-336
- 99Bow-160
- 99BowChr-160
- 99BowChrG-160
- 99BowChrGR-160
- 99BowChrI-160
- 99BowChrIR-160
- 99BowChrR-160
- 99BowGol-160
- 99BowInt-160
- 99DumSet-127
- 99E-X Cen-102
- 99E-X CenECFut-102
- 99E-X CenECNow-102
- 99Fle-274
- 99FleBri-166
- 99FleBri2G-166
- 99FleBriBlu-166
- 99FleBriGol-166
- 99FleMys-127
- 99FleMysM-127
- 99FleSta9-274
- 99FleWarT-274
- 99Pac-387
- 99Pac-387A
- 99PacCroC-255
- 99PacCroCPB-255
- 99PacPlaB-387
- 99PacPlaB-387A
- 99PacPriS-132
- 99PacPriS206-132
- 99PacPriS206R-132
- 99PacRed-387
- 99PacRed-387A
- 99SkyThu-237
- 99SkyThuRant-237
- 99SkyThuRave-237
- 99SpoIll-54
- 99ThuSkySupR-237
- 99Top-432
- 99TopChr-432
- 99TopChrR-432
- 99UppDecE-105
- 99UppDecEFXG-105
- 99Vic-350

Rios, Brian
- 98WesMicWM-18

Rios, Carlos Rafael
- 77AppFoxT-20
- 78ChaPirT-21
- 81BufBisT-19
- 82KnoBluJT-15
- 85IntLeaAT-5
- 85RicBraT-15
- 86GreBraTI-15
- 88BlaYNPRWL-139
- 88BobCamRB-3
- 88RicBraC-18
- 88RicBraP-8
- 89BlaYNPRWL-12
- 89RicBraBC-23
- 89RicBraC-13
- 89RicBraP-842
- 89RicBraTI-19

Rios, Coronel (Carlos)
- 87GreBraB-5

Rios, Danny
- 95TamYanYI-23
- 96NorNavB-21
- 97ColCliB-24
- 97ColCliD-21
- 97GreBatC-18

Rios, Eddie
- 95Bow-49
- 95SanAntMTI-21

Rios, Eduardo
- 93GreFalDSP-10
- 94VenLinU-44
- 94VerBeaDC-17
- 94VerBeaDF-83
- 95LinVen-20
- 96-97LinVen-135
- 96SanAntMB-19

Rios, Enrique
- 87KenTwiP-29
- 88CarLeaAS-16
- 88LynRedSS-21

Rios, Fernando
- 98BurBeeM-17

Rios, Jesus
- 85MexCitTT-1

Rios, Juan
- 69RoyTeal-11
- 69Top-619
- 70OPC-89
- 70Top-89
- 72MilBra-289

Ripken, Bill
- 86ChaOriW-25
- 86SouLeaAJ-1

❑ 87BalOriP-28
❑ 87DonRoo-16
❑ 87IntLeaAT-27
❑ 87OriFreB-3
❑ 87RocRedWP-12
❑ 87RocRedWT-13
❑ 87SpoRoo2-28
❑ 88ClaRed-163
❑ 88Don-336
❑ 88Don-625
❑ 88DonBasB-254
❑ 88Fle-569
❑ 88Fle-640
❑ 88FleGlo-569
❑ 88FleGlo-640
❑ 88KeyFooD-7
❑ 88Lea-134
❑ 88MSAIceTD-7
❑ 88OPC-352
❑ 88OriFreB-7
❑ 88OriPos-26
❑ 88OurOwnTD-7
❑ 88PanSti-9
❑ 88Sco-200
❑ 88ScoGlo-200
❑ 88ScoYouSI-20
❑ 88Spo-216
❑ 88StaLinO-12
❑ 88TetTeaD-7
❑ 88Top-352
❑ 88TopRoo-1
❑ 88TopSti-227
❑ 88TopTif-352
❑ 88ToyRoo-25
❑ 88WeiMarD-7
❑ 89BalOriP-25
❑ 89Bow-12
❑ 89BowTif-12
❑ 89Don-259
❑ 89DonBasB-318
❑ 89Fle-616A
❑ 89Fle-616B
❑ 89Fle-616C
❑ 89Fle-616D
❑ 89FleGlo-616
❑ 89OPC-22
❑ 89OriFreB-3
❑ 89PanSti-261
❑ 89RedFolSB-98
❑ 89Sco-18
❑ 89Top-571
❑ 89TopBig-27
❑ 89TopTif-571
❑ 89TVSpoM-92
❑ 89UppDec-283
❑ 90BalOriP-23
❑ 90Bow-256
❑ 90BowTif-256
❑ 90Don-164
❑ 90Fle-186
❑ 90FleCan-186
❑ 90HagSunDGB-22
❑ 90Lea-271
❑ 90M.Vpin-6
❑ 90MLBBasB-113
❑ 90OPC-468
❑ 90PanSti-3
❑ 90PubIntS-583
❑ 90Sco-174
❑ 90Top-468
❑ 90TopBig-244
❑ 90TopSti-235
❑ 90TopTif-468
❑ 90UppDec-184
❑ 91BalOriP-25
❑ 91Bow-87
❑ 91Don-167
❑ 91Fle-489
❑ 91Lea-7
❑ 91OPC-677
❑ 91OriCro-382
❑ 91PanFreS-241
❑ 91Sco-487
❑ 91SevCoi-A12
❑ 91StaClu-222
❑ 91StaCluP-35
❑ 91StaPinB-37
❑ 91Top-677
❑ 91TopDesS-677
❑ 91TopMic-677
❑ 91TopTif-677
❑ 91Ult-23
❑ 91UppDec-550
❑ 92BalOriP-31
❑ 92Bow-373
❑ 92Don-734
❑ 92Fle-25
❑ 92Lea-184
❑ 92LeaBlaG-184
❑ 92OPC-752
❑ 92PanSti-66
❑ 92Pin-336
❑ 92RedFolS-80
❑ 92Sco-97
❑ 92StaClu-533
❑ 92Top-752
❑ 92TopGol-752
❑ 92TopGolW-752
❑ 92TopMic-752
❑ 92Ult-10
❑ 92UppDec-82
❑ 92UppDec-250
❑ 93Bow-517
❑ 93Don-59
❑ 93Fle-550
❑ 93FleFinE-282
❑ 93Lea-435
❑ 93OPCPre-59
❑ 93PacSpa-645
❑ 93PanSti-72
❑ 93Pin-153
❑ 93RanKee-427
❑ 93RanStaC-29
❑ 93StaClu-603
❑ 93StaCluFDI-603
❑ 93StaCluMOP-603
❑ 93Ult-635
❑ 93UppDec-181
❑ 93UppDec-511
❑ 93UppDecGold-181
❑ 93UppDecGold-511
❑ 94Fin-339
❑ 94FinRef-339
❑ 94FleUpd-95
❑ 94RanMagM-34
❑ 94StaClu-369
❑ 94StaCluFDI-369
❑ 94StaCluGR-369
❑ 94StaCluMOP-369
❑ 94StaCluT-268
❑ 94StaCluTFDI-268
❑ 95Fle-294
❑ 95Sco-499
❑ 95ScoGolR-499
❑ 95ScoPlaTS-499
❑ 96BalOriP-30
❑ 97PacPriGotD-GD15
❑ 97RanDr P-26
❑ 97RanMot-20
❑ 98Pac-207
❑ 98PacOnl-282
❑ 98PacOnlR-282
❑ 98PacOnlWC-282
❑ 98PacPlaB-207
❑ 98PacRedT-207
❑ 98PacSil-207
❑ 98Ult-318
❑ 98UltGolM-318
❑ 98UltMas-318
❑ 98UltPlaM-318

Ripken, Cal Jr.

❑ 80ChaO'sP-18
❑ 80ChaO'sW-19
❑ 81BalOriP-15
❑ 81RocRedWT-15
❑ 81RocRedWW-1
❑ 82BalOriP-4
❑ 82Don-405
❑ 82Fle-176
❑ 82Top-21
❑ 82TopTra-98T
❑ 83AllGamPI-23
❑ 83Don-279
❑ 83DonActA-52
❑ 83Dra-23
❑ 83Fle-70
❑ 83FleSta-165
❑ 83FleSti-198
❑ 83OPC-163
❑ 83OriPos-23
❑ 83Top-163
❑ 83TopSti-26
❑ 83TopSti-315
❑ 84AllGamPI-113
❑ 84BalOriP-27
❑ 84Don-106
❑ 84DonActAS-20
❑ 84DonCha-48
❑ 84Dra-26
❑ 84Fle-17
❑ 84FleSti-15
❑ 84FleSti-29
❑ 84FunFooP-118
❑ 84MilBra-20
❑ 84MLBPen-1
❑ 84Nes792-400
❑ 84Nes792-426
❑ 84Nes792-490
❑ 84NesDreT-4
❑ 84OCoandSI-9
❑ 84OCoandSI-82
❑ 84OCoandSI-222
❑ 84OPC-2
❑ 84OPC-363
❑ 84OriEng-11
❑ 84RawGloT-2
❑ 84SevCoi-E14
❑ 84Top-400
❑ 84Top-426
❑ 84Top-490
❑ 84TopRubD-30
❑ 84TopSti-24
❑ 84TopSti-197
❑ 84TopSti-204
❑ 84TopStiB-13
❑ 84TopSup-1
❑ 84TopTif-400
❑ 84TopTif-426
❑ 84TopTif-490
❑ 85AllGamPI-25
❑ 85BalOriP-24
❑ 85Don-14
❑ 85Don-169
❑ 85DonActA-7
❑ 85DonSupD-14
❑ 85Dra-26
❑ 85Fle-187
❑ 85Fle-626
❑ 85Fle-641
❑ 85FleLimE-28
❑ 85FleStaS-41
❑ 85KASDis-10
❑ 85KitCloD-10
❑ 85Lea-14
❑ 85OPC-30
❑ 85OriHea-15
❑ 85SevCoi-E14
❑ 85SubDis-17
❑ 85ThoMcAD-17
❑ 85Top-30
❑ 85Top-704
❑ 85Top3-D-16
❑ 85TopGloA-16
❑ 85TopGloS-24
❑ 85TopRubD-31
❑ 85TopSti-185
❑ 85TopSti-197
❑ 85TopSup-48
❑ 85TopTif-30
❑ 85TopTif-704
❑ 86BalOriHMP-15
❑ 86BalOriP-15
❑ 86BasStaB-92
❑ 86BurKinA-15
❑ 86Don-210
❑ 86DonAll-14
❑ 86DonPop-14
❑ 86DorChe-4
❑ 86Dra-11
❑ 86Fle-284
❑ 86Fle-633
❑ 86FleAll-5
❑ 86FleLeaL-35
❑ 86FleLimE-36
❑ 86FleMin-59
❑ 86FleSlu-28
❑ 86FleStiC-99
❑ 86GenMilB-1I
❑ 86Lea-142
❑ 86MeaGolBB-11
❑ 86MeaGolM-8
❑ 86MeaGolSB-11
❑ 86MSAJifPD-9
❑ 86OPC-340
❑ 86QuaGra-31
❑ 86SevCoi-C3
❑ 86SevCoi-E3
❑ 86SevCoi-S3
❑ 86SevCoi-W3
❑ 86Spo-8
❑ 86Spo-54
❑ 86Spo-57
❑ 86Spo-69
❑ 86Spo-73
❑ 86Spo-128
❑ 86SpoDecG-73
❑ 86SpoRoo-48
❑ 86Top-340
❑ 86Top-715
❑ 86TopGloA-5
❑ 86TopGloS-14
❑ 86TopMinL-2
❑ 86TopSti-159
❑ 86TopSti-226
❑ 86TopSup-45
❑ 86TopTat-4
❑ 86TopTif-340
❑ 86TopTif-715
❑ 86TruVal-22
❑ 87BalOriP-29
❑ 87BoaandB-22
❑ 87ClaGam-52
❑ 87Don-89
❑ 87DonAll-5
❑ 87DonHig-38
❑ 87DonOpeD-133
❑ 87DonP-5
❑ 87Dra-6
❑ 87Fle-478
❑ 87FleAwaW-33
❑ 87FleBasA-36
❑ 87FleGamW-37
❑ 87FleGlo-478
❑ 87FleMin-92
❑ 87FleSlu-35
❑ 87FleStiC-101
❑ 87KeyFooD-14
❑ 87KraFoo-3
❑ 87Lea-98
❑ 87MandMSL-13
❑ 87MSAIceTD-14
❑ 87MSAJifPD-8
❑ 87OPC-312
❑ 87OriFreB-8
❑ 87OurOwnTD-14
❑ 87RalPur-12
❑ 87RedFolSB-118
❑ 87SevCoi-M16
❑ 87Spo-9
❑ 87Spo-113
❑ 87SpoDeaP-4
❑ 87SpoSupD-8
❑ 87SpoTeaP-21
❑ 87StuPan-14
❑ 87Top-609
❑ 87Top-784
❑ 87TopCoi-23
❑ 87TopGloA-16
❑ 87TopGloS-37
❑ 87TopMinL-40
❑ 87TopSti-151
❑ 87TopSti-233
❑ 87TopTif-609
❑ 87TopTif-784
❑ 87WeiMarD-14
❑ 88Baz-17
❑ 88CheBoy-7
❑ 88ClaRed-176
❑ 88Don-26
❑ 88Don-171
❑ 88Don-625
❑ 88DonAll-5
❑ 88DonBasB-198
❑ 88DonBonM-BC1
❑ 88DonPop-5
❑ 88DonSupD-26
❑ 88Dra-25
❑ 88Fle-570
❑ 88Fle-635
❑ 88Fle-640
❑ 88FleGlo-570
❑ 88FleGlo-635
❑ 88FleGlo-640
❑ 88FleRecS-33
❑ 88FleSlu-34
❑ 88FleStiC-3
❑ 88FleSup-31
❑ 88FleTeaL-30
❑ 88GreBasS-74
❑ 88K-M-21
❑ 88KayB-25
❑ 88KinDis-24
❑ 88Lea-26
❑ 88Lea-100
❑ 88OPC-74
❑ 88OriFreB-8
❑ 88OriPos-27
❑ 88PanSti-11
❑ 88PanSti-13
❑ 88PanSti-230
❑ 88RedFolSB-76
❑ 88Sco-550
❑ 88Sco-651
❑ 88ScoBoxC-5
❑ 88ScoGlo-550
❑ 88ScoGlo-651
❑ 88Spo-152
❑ 88StaLinAl-26
❑ 88StaLinO-13
❑ 88TarPla-33
❑ 88Top-51
❑ 88Top-650
❑ 88TopBig-62
❑ 88TopCoi-24
❑ 88TopGloA-5
❑ 88TopGloS-6
❑ 88TopRitTM-13
❑ 88TopSti-160
❑ 88TopSti-228
❑ 88TopStiB-44
❑ 88TopTif-51
❑ 88TopTif-650
❑ 88TopUKM-61
❑ 88TopUKMT-61
❑ 89BalOriP-26
❑ 89Bow-9
❑ 89Bow-260
❑ 89BowTif-9
❑ 89BowTif-260
❑ 89CadEIID-44
❑ 89ClaLigB-56
❑ 89Don-51
❑ 89DonAll-5
❑ 89DonAll-32
❑ 89DonBasB-142
❑ 89DonBonM-BC15
❑ 89DonPop-5
❑ 89Fle-617
❑ 89FleBasA-35
❑ 89FleGlo-617
❑ 89FleHeroB-34
❑ 89FleLeaL-32
❑ 89K-M-15
❑ 89KeyFooD-16
❑ 89MasBreD-12
❑ 89MSAIceTD-16
❑ 89OPC-250
❑ 89OPCBoxB-J
❑ 89OriFreB-8
❑ 89OurOwnTD-16
❑ 89PanSti-241
❑ 89PanSti-262
❑ 89RedFolSB-99
❑ 89Sco-15
❑ 89ScoHot1S-77
❑ 89Scomast-3
❑ 89Spo-66
❑ 89SpoIllFKI-69
❑ 89TetTeaD-16
❑ 89Top-250
❑ 89TopBasT-77
❑ 89TopBig-286
❑ 89TopCapC-6
❑ 89TopCoi-50
❑ 89TopGloA-5
❑ 89TopGloS-47
❑ 89TopSti-150
❑ 89TopSti-237
❑ 89TopStiB-11
❑ 89TopTif-250
❑ 89TopUKM-64
❑ 89TopWaxBC-J
❑ 89TVSpoM-89
❑ 89UppDec-467
❑ 89UppDec-682
❑ 89UppDecS-2
❑ 89WeiMarD-16
❑ 90AllBasT-4
❑ 90Bow-255
❑ 90BowTif-255
❑ 90ClaBlu-24
❑ 90Don-96
❑ 90Don-676A
❑ 90Don-676B
❑ 90DonBesA-57
❑ 90DOnBonM-BC18
❑ 90DonLeaS-19
❑ 90Fle-187
❑ 90Fle-624A
❑ 90Fle-624B
❑ 90Fle-634
❑ 90FleAll-8
❑ 90FleBasA-30
❑ 90FleBasAC-30
❑ 90FleBasM-31
❑ 90FleBasMC-31
❑ 90FleCan-187
❑ 90FleCan-624
❑ 90FleCan-624
❑ 90FleCan-634
❑ 90Hot50PS-34
❑ 90K-M-16
❑ 90K-M-20
❑ 90Lea-197
❑ 90M.Vpin-7
❑ 90MLBBasB-112
❑ 90OPC-8
❑ 90OPC-388
❑ 90OPC-570
❑ 90OPCBoxB-N
❑ 90PanSti-7
❑ 90PanSti-202
❑ 90PanSti-388
❑ 90Pos-21
❑ 90PubIntS-584
❑ 90RedFolSB-78
❑ 90Sco-2
❑ 90Sco100S-66
❑ 90Spo-100
❑ 90StaRip-1
❑ 90StaRip-2
❑ 90StaRip-3
❑ 90StaRip-4
❑ 90StaRip-5
❑ 90StaRip-6
❑ 90StaRip-7
❑ 90StaRip-8
❑ 90StaRip-9
❑ 90StaRip-10
❑ 90StaRip-11
❑ 90SunSee-23
❑ 90SupActM-10
❑ 90Top-8
❑ 90Top-388
❑ 90Top-570
❑ 90TopAmeA-15
❑ 90TopBig-327
❑ 90TopCoi-24
❑ 90TopDou-52
❑ 90TopGloA-16
❑ 90TopGloS-51
❑ 90TopHilHM-32
❑ 90TopMag-49
❑ 90TopSti-5
❑ 90TopSti-160
❑ 90TopSti-231
❑ 90TopStiB-44
❑ 90TopTif-8
❑ 90TopTif-388
❑ 90TopTif-570
❑ 90TopTVA-19
❑ 90TopWaxBC-N
❑ 90UppDec-266
❑ 90USPlaCA-6S
❑ 90WinDis-9
❑ 90Woo-19
❑ 91BalOriP-26
❑ 91BasBesRB-13
❑ 91Bow-104
❑ 91CadEIID-43
❑ 91Cla2-T3
❑ 91Cla3-T77
❑ 91Cla3-NNO
❑ 91ClaGam-110
❑ 91Col-2
❑ 91DenHol-20
❑ 91Don-52
❑ 91Don-223
❑ 91DonBonC-BC17
❑ 91Fle-490
❑ 91JimDea-15
❑ 91Lea-430
❑ 91MajLeaCP-29
❑ 91MooSna-14
❑ 91MSAHolD-20
❑ 91OPC-5
❑ 91OPC-150
❑ 91OPCPre-100
❑ 91OriCro-383
❑ 91PanFreS-170
❑ 91PanFreS-243
❑ 91PanSti-192
❑ 91PepSup-8
❑ 91PetSta-1
❑ 91Pos-19
❑ 91PosCan-22
❑ 91RedFolS-78
❑ 91RedFolS-124
❑ 91Sco-95
❑ 91Sco-849
❑ 91Sco100S-21
❑ 91SevCoi-A13
❑ 91SilHol-4
❑ 91StaClu-430
❑ 91StaCluMO-26
❑ 91StaPinB-38

❑ 91Stu-9
❑ 91Top-5
❑ 91Top-150
❑ 91TopCraJI-13
❑ 91TopDesS-5
❑ 91TopDesS-150
❑ 91TopGloA-5
❑ 91TopMic-5
❑ 91TopMic-150
❑ 91TopSta-28
❑ 91TopTif-5
❑ 91TopTif-150
❑ 91TopTriH-A1
❑ 91Ult-24
❑ 91UppDec-347
❑ 91UppDecFE-85F
❑ 91USPlaCA-13D
❑ 91Woo-18
❑ 92BalOriP-32
❑ 92Bow-400
❑ 92Cla1-T76
❑ 92Cla2-T56
❑ 92ClaGam-190
❑ 92ColAllG-5
❑ 92ColAllP-5
❑ 92DenHol-9
❑ 92Don-22
❑ 92Don-35
❑ 92DonBonC-BC1
❑ 92DonCraJ1-13
❑ 92DonDiaK-DK5
❑ 92DonEli-S2
❑ 92DonMcD-1
❑ 92DonPre-10
❑ 92DonSupD-DK5
❑ 92Fle-26
❑ 92Fle-703
❑ 92Fle-711
❑ 92FleAll-20
❑ 92FleCitTP-5
❑ 92FleLumC-L7
❑ 92FleTeaL-17
❑ 92Fre-13
❑ 92Hig5-5
❑ 92Hig5S-24
❑ 92HitTheBB-28
❑ 92JimDeaLL-5
❑ 92KinDis-12
❑ 92LaKdec-23
❑ 92Lea-52
❑ 92Lea-199
❑ 92LeaBlaG-52
❑ 92LeaBlaG-199
❑ 92LeaGolP-13
❑ 92LeaPre-13
❑ 92MooSna-23
❑ 92Mr.TurS-19
❑ 92MSABenSHD-6
❑ 92MVPPin-18
❑ 92New-21
❑ 92OPC-40
❑ 92OPCPre-137
❑ 92PanSti-68
❑ 92PanSti-275
❑ 92PepDieM-17
❑ 92Pin-200
❑ 92PinRool-11
❑ 92PinSlu-14
❑ 92PinTeaP-7
❑ 92Pos-9
❑ 92PosCan-15
❑ 92RedFolS-81
❑ 92RedFolS-124
❑ 92Sco-433
❑ 92Sco-540
❑ 92Sco-788
❑ 92Sco-794
❑ 92Sco-884
❑ 92Sco100S-89
❑ 92ScoProaG-5
❑ 92SevCoi-9
❑ 92SpoIllFK1-132
❑ 92SpoIllFK1-455
❑ 92SpoIllFK1-627
❑ 92SpoStaCC-37
❑ 92StaClu-1
❑ 92StaClu-595
❑ 92StaCluD-154
❑ 92StaCluMP-10
❑ 92Stu-129
❑ 92StuHer-BC7
❑ 92StuPre-5
❑ 92SunSee-9
❑ 92Top-40
❑ 92Top-400
❑ 92TopGol-40
❑ 92TopGol-400
❑ 92TopGolPS-40
❑ 92TopGolW-40
❑ 92TopGolW-400
❑ 92TopKid-63
❑ 92TopMcD-13
❑ 92TopMic-40
❑ 92TopMic-400
❑ 92TriPla-199
❑ 92TriPla-253
❑ 92TriPlaG-GS11
❑ 92Ult-11
❑ 92UltAllS-3
❑ 92UltAwaW-5
❑ 92UltAwaW-21A
❑ 92UltAwaW-21B
❑ 92UppDec-82
❑ 92UppDec-165
❑ 92UppDec-645
❑ 92UppDecF-36
❑ 92UppDecFG-36
❑ 92UppDecHRH-HR4
❑ 92UppDecTMH-1
❑ 92UppDecTMH-44
❑ 93BalOriP-31
❑ 93Ble-28
❑ 93Ble-29
❑ 93Ble-30
❑ 93Ble-31
❑ 93Ble-32
❑ 93Ble-33
❑ 93Bow-225
❑ 93CadDis-46
❑ 93ClaGam-76
❑ 93ColAllG-9
❑ 93ColPosRJ-1
❑ 93ColPosRJ-2
❑ 93ColPosRJ-3
❑ 93ColPosRJ-4
❑ 93ColPosRJ-5
❑ 93ColPosRJ-6
❑ 93ColPosRJ-7
❑ 93DenHol-16
❑ 93DiaMar-89
❑ 93Don-559
❑ 93DonEliD-19
❑ 93DonMasotG-6
❑ 93DonMVP-14
❑ 93DonPre-12
❑ 93DurPowP2-1
❑ 93Fin-96
❑ 93FinJum-96
❑ 93FinRef-96
❑ 93Fla-157
❑ 93Fle-551
❑ 93FleAtl-19
❑ 93FleFruotL-54
❑ 93FunPac-32
❑ 93FunPac-130
❑ 93FunPac-135
❑ 93FunPac-218
❑ 93FunPacA-AS6
❑ 93Hos-26
❑ 93HumDumC-1
❑ 93JimDea-3
❑ 93KinDis-3
❑ 93Kra-12
❑ 93Lea-431
❑ 93LeaGolA-R14
❑ 93LeaGolA-U6
❑ 93LeaHeaftH-5
❑ 93MetBak-17
❑ 93MilBonSS-12
❑ 93OPC-352
❑ 93OPCPre-125
❑ 93OriCroASU-7
❑ 93PacSpa-24
❑ 93PanSti-73
❑ 93Pin-20
❑ 93Pin-305
❑ 93Pin-471
❑ 93PinCoo-17
❑ 93PinCooD-17
❑ 93PinHomRC-47
❑ 93Pos-9
❑ 93PosCan-7
❑ 93RedFolS-78
❑ 93RedFolS-122
❑ 93Sco-6
❑ 93ScoFra-1
❑ 93Sel-18
❑ 93SelChaS-15
❑ 93SelDufIP-10
❑ 93SP-8
❑ 93StaClu-40
❑ 93StaCluFDI-40
❑ 93StaCluM-141
❑ 93StaCluMOP-40
❑ 93StaCluMP-7
❑ 93Stu-80
❑ 93Top-300
❑ 93TopFulS-11
❑ 93TopGol-300
❑ 93TopInaM-300
❑ 93TopInaR-300
❑ 93TopMic-300
❑ 93TriPla-3
❑ 93TriPlaA-17
❑ 93TriPlaP-3
❑ 93Ult-501
❑ 93UltAllS-14
❑ 93UltAwaW-15
❑ 93UppDec-36
❑ 93UppDec-44
❑ 93UppDec-585
❑ 93UppDecDG-16
❑ 93UppDecGold-36
❑ 93UppDecGold-44
❑ 93UppDecGold-585
❑ 93UppDecIC-WI15
❑ 93UppDecICJ-WI15
❑ 93UppDecTAN-TN4
❑ 93UppDecTriCro-TC7
❑ 93USPlaCA-WCO
❑ 94BalOriP-29
❑ 94Bow-75
❑ 94BowBes-R71
❑ 94BowBes-X94
❑ 94BowBesR-R71
❑ 94BowBesR-X94
❑ 94BurKinR-1
❑ 94BurKinR-2
❑ 94BurKinR-3
❑ 94BurKinR-4
❑ 94BurKinR-5
❑ 94BurKinR-6
❑ 94BurKinR-7
❑ 94BurKinR-8
❑ 94BurKinR-9
❑ 94BurKinRG-1
❑ 94BurKinRG-2
❑ 94BurKinRG-3
❑ 94BurKinRG-4
❑ 94BurKinRG-5
❑ 94BurKinRG-6
❑ 94BurKinRG-7
❑ 94BurKinRG-8
❑ 94BurKinRG-9
❑ 94ChuHomS-7
❑ 94ChuHomSG-7
❑ 94ClaUpdCotC-CR1
❑ 94ClaUpdCotC-AU1
❑ 94ColC-240
❑ 94ColC-343
❑ 94ColChoGS-240
❑ 94ColChoGS-343
❑ 94ColChoSS-240
❑ 94ColChoSS-343
❑ 94ColChoT-13
❑ 94DenHol-20
❑ 94Don-40
❑ 94Don-140
❑ 94DonAnn8-6
❑ 94DonMVP-15
❑ 94DonSpeE-40
❑ 94Fin-235
❑ 94FinJum-235
❑ 94FinRef-235
❑ 94Fla-8
❑ 94FlaHotG-8
❑ 94FlaHotN-8
❑ 94FlaInfP-8
❑ 94Fle-19
❑ 94FleAllS-21
❑ 94FleExtB-12
❑ 94FleExtBGB-24
❑ 94FleTeaL-1
❑ 94FleUpdDT-10
❑ 94FUnPac-108
❑ 94FUnPac-180
❑ 94FUnPac-219
❑ 94Kra-10
❑ 94Lea-1
❑ 94LeaL-5
❑ 94LeaLimGA-7
❑ 94LeaMVPC-A12
❑ 94LeaMVPCG-A12
❑ 94LeaPro-7
❑ 94LeaStaS-10
❑ 94O-PJumAF-15
❑ 94OPC-185
❑ 94OPCAllR-15
❑ 94OPCJumA-15
❑ 94OriPro-85
❑ 94OriUSPC-1H
❑ 94OriUSPC-9C
❑ 94OscMayR-11
❑ 94Pac-44
❑ 94PacSilP-15
❑ 94PacSilPC-15
❑ 94PanSti-23
❑ 94Pin-50
❑ 94PinArtP-50
❑ 94PinMusC-50
❑ 94PinTeaP-4
❑ 94PinTheN-23
❑ 94PinTri-TR13
❑ 94Pos-25
❑ 94PosCan-13
❑ 94ProMag-8
❑ 94RedFolMI-22
❑ 94Sco-85
❑ 94ScoGolR-85
❑ 94ScoGolS-36
❑ 94Sel-249
❑ 94Sel-SS1
❑ 94SP-126
❑ 94SPDieC-126
❑ 94SPHol-32
❑ 94SPHolDC-32
❑ 94Spo-69
❑ 94Spo-179
❑ 94SpoFanA-AS4
❑ 94SPPre-ER5
❑ 94StaClu-373
❑ 94StaCluDD-DD4
❑ 94StaCluFDI-373
❑ 94StaCluGR-373
❑ 94StaCluMOP-373
❑ 94StaCluMOP-DD4
❑ 94StaCluMOP-ST15
❑ 94StaCluST-ST15
❑ 94StaCluT-271
❑ 94StaCluTF-8
❑ 94StaCluTFDI-271
❑ 94Stu-127
❑ 94StuSerS-7
❑ 94StuSerSG-7
❑ 94SucSav-15
❑ 94TomPiz-26
❑ 94Top-200
❑ 94Top-387
❑ 94Top-604
❑ 94TopBlaG-18
❑ 94TopGol-200
❑ 94TopGol-387
❑ 94TopGol-604
❑ 94TopSpa-200
❑ 94TopSpa-387
❑ 94TopSpa-604
❑ 94TopSupS-37
❑ 94TriPla-159
❑ 94TriPlaM-7
❑ 94TriPlaN-6
❑ 94Ult-9
❑ 94UltAllS-4
❑ 94UltCarA-3
❑ 94UppDec-281
❑ 94UppDec-425
❑ 94UppDecAJ-15
❑ 94UppDecAJG-15
❑ 94UppDecDC-E9
❑ 94UppDecED-281
❑ 94UppDecED-425
❑ 94USDepoT-2
❑ 95BalOriP-44
❑ 95BalSunRVC-1
❑ 95Baz-2
❑ 95BazRedH-RH2
❑ 95Bow-413
❑ 95BowBes-R10
❑ 95BowBesJR-7
❑ 95BowBesR-R10
❑ 95ClaFanFPCP-6
❑ 95ClaPhoC-5
❑ 95ColCho-85
❑ 95ColChoGS-85
❑ 95ColChoSE-155
❑ 95ColChoSE-263
❑ 95ColChoSEGS-155
❑ 95ColChoSEGS-263
❑ 95ColChoSESS-155
❑ 95ColChoSESS-263
❑ 95ColChoSS-85
❑ 95Don-83
❑ 95DonAll-AL6
❑ 95DonDom-6
❑ 95DonPreP-83
❑ 95DonTopotO-15
❑ 95Emo-8
❑ 95Emo-P8
❑ 95EmoMas-8
❑ 95EmoR-1
❑ 95EmoR-2
❑ 95EmoR-3
❑ 95EmoR-4
❑ 95EmoR-5
❑ 95EmoR-6
❑ 95EmoR-7
❑ 95EmoR-8
❑ 95EmoR-9
❑ 95EmoR-10
❑ 95EmoR-11
❑ 95EmoR-12
❑ 95EmoR-13
❑ 95EmoR-14
❑ 95EmoR-15
❑ 95Fin-120
❑ 95FinRef-120
❑ 95Fla-9
❑ 95FlaHotG-9
❑ 95FlaHotN-8
❑ 95FlaRip-1
❑ 95FlaRip-2
❑ 95FlaRip-3
❑ 95FlaRip-4
❑ 95FlaRip-5
❑ 95FlaRip-6
❑ 95FlaRip-7
❑ 95FlaRip-8
❑ 95FlaRip-9
❑ 95FlaRip-10
❑ 95FlaRip-11
❑ 95FlaRip-12
❑ 95FlaRip-13
❑ 95FlaRip-14
❑ 95FlaRip-15
❑ 95Fle-19
❑ 95FleAllF-4
❑ 95FleAllS-5
❑ 95FleTeaL-1
❑ 95FleUpdSL-8
❑ 95KinDis-18
❑ 95Kra-12
❑ 95Lea-134
❑ 95LeaGreG-14
❑ 95LeaHeaftH-6
❑ 95LeaLim-97
❑ 95LeaLimG-7
❑ 95LeaLimL-16
❑ 95LeaOpeD-6
❑ 95LeaSli-4A
❑ 95LeaSli-4B
❑ 95LeaStaS-7
❑ 95MetImpRi-1
❑ 95MetImpRi-2
❑ 95MetImpRi-3
❑ 95MetImpRi-4
❑ 95MetImpRi-5
❑ 95MetImpRi-6
❑ 95MetImpRi-7
❑ 95MetImpRi-8
❑ 95MetImpRi-9
❑ 95MetImpRi-10
❑ 95NatPac-10
❑ 95Pac-30
❑ 95PacGolCDC-4
❑ 95PacGolP-9
❑ 95PacPri-10
❑ 95PanSti-68
❑ 95Pin-204
❑ 95Pin-305
❑ 95PinArtP-204
❑ 95PinArtP-305
❑ 95PinFan-1
❑ 95PinGatA-GA3
❑ 95PinMusC-204
❑ 95PinMusC-305
❑ 95PinPin-10
❑ 95PinPinR-10
❑ 95PinRedH-RH1
❑ 95PinTeaP-TP5
❑ 95PinWhiH-WH1
❑ 95Pos-8
❑ 95PosCan-18
❑ 95RedFol-7
❑ 95Sco-3
❑ 95Sco-556
❑ 95ScoDouGC-GC12
❑ 95ScoDreT-DG3
❑ 95ScoGolR-3
❑ 95ScoGolR-556
❑ 95ScoHaloG-HG6
❑ 95ScoPlaTS-3
❑ 95ScoPlaTS-556
❑ 95ScoRul-SR18
❑ 95ScoRulJ-SR18
❑ 95ScoSam-HG5
❑ 95Sel-1
❑ 95Sel-245
❑ 95SelArtP-1
❑ 95SelArtP-245
❑ 95SelBigS-BS3
❑ 95SelCer-72
❑ 95SelCer-2131
❑ 95SelCerC-3
❑ 95SelCerGT-3
❑ 95SelCerMG-72
❑ 95SelCerMG-2131
❑ 95SelCerS-3
❑ 95SP-1
❑ 95SPCha-99
❑ 95SPCha-115
❑ 95SPCha-120
❑ 95SPCha-CR1
❑ 95SPCha-CR1
❑ 95SPChaDC-99
❑ 95SPChaDC-115
❑ 95SPChaDC-120
❑ 95Spo-122
❑ 95Spo-170
❑ 95SpoArtP-122
❑ 95SpoArtP-170
❑ 95SpoDouT-5
❑ 95SpoHamT-HT5
❑ 95SpoPro-PM3
❑ 95SpoSam-122
❑ 95SPPlaP-PP16
❑ 95SPSil-1
❑ 95SPSpeF-16
❑ 95StaClu-1
❑ 95StaClu-239
❑ 95StaClu-314
❑ 95StaClu-510
❑ 95StaCluCT-20
❑ 95StaCluFDI-1
❑ 95StaCluFDI-239
❑ 95StaCluMO-40
❑ 95StaCluMOP-1
❑ 95StaCluMOP-239
❑ 95StaCluMOP-314
❑ 95StaCluMOP-510
❑ 95StaCluMOP-RL27
❑ 95StaCluRL-RL27
❑ 95StaCluSTWS-1
❑ 95StaCluSTWS-239
❑ 95StaCluSTWS-314
❑ 95StaCluSTWS-510
❑ 95StaCluVR-1
❑ 95StaCluVRMO-1
❑ 95StaRip-1
❑ 95StaRip-2
❑ 95StaRip-3
❑ 95StaRip-4
❑ 95StaRip-5
❑ 95StaRip-6
❑ 95StaRip-7
❑ 95StaRip-8
❑ 95StaRip-9
❑ 95StaRip-10
❑ 95StaRip-11
❑ 95StaRip-12
❑ 95StaRip-13
❑ 95StaRip-14
❑ 95StaRip-15
❑ 95StaRip-16
❑ 95StaRip-17
❑ 95StaRip-18
❑ 95StaRip-19
❑ 95StaRip-20
❑ 95StaRip-21
❑ 95StaRip-22
❑ 95StaRip-23
❑ 95StaRip-24
❑ 95StaRip-25
❑ 95StaRip-26
❑ 95StaRip-27
❑ 95StaRip-28
❑ 95StaRip-29
❑ 95StaRip-30
❑ 95StaRip-31
❑ 95StaRip-32
❑ 95StaRip-33
❑ 95StaRip-34
❑ 95StaRip-35
❑ 95StaRip-36
❑ 95StaRip-37
❑ 95StaRip-38
❑ 95StaRip-39
❑ 95StaRip-40

❑ 95StaRip-41
❑ 95StaRip-42
❑ 95StaRip-43
❑ 95StaRip-44
❑ 95StaRip-45
❑ 95StaRip-46
❑ 95StaRip-47
❑ 95StaRip-48
❑ 95StaRip-49
❑ 95StaRip-50
❑ 95StaRip-51
❑ 95StaRip-52
❑ 95StaRip-53
❑ 95StaRip-54
❑ 95StaRip-55
❑ 95StaRip-56
❑ 95StaRip-57
❑ 95StaRip-58
❑ 95StaRip-59
❑ 95StaRip-60
❑ 95StaRip-61
❑ 95StaRip-62
❑ 95StaRip-63
❑ 95StaRip-64
❑ 95StaRip-65
❑ 95StaRip-66
❑ 95StaRip-67
❑ 95StaRip-68
❑ 95StaRip-69
❑ 95StaRip-70
❑ 95StaRip-71
❑ 95StaRip-72
❑ 95StaRip-73
❑ 95StaRip-74
❑ 95StaRip-75
❑ 95StaRip-76
❑ 95StaRip-77
❑ 95StaRip-78
❑ 95StaRip-79
❑ 95StaRip-80
❑ 95Stu-8
❑ 95StuGolS-8
❑ 95StuPlaS-8
❑ 95Sum-79
❑ 95Sum-176
❑ 95Sum-196
❑ 95SumBigB-BB3
❑ 95SumNthD-79
❑ 95SumNthD-176
❑ 95SumNthD-196
❑ 95SumSam-79
❑ 95TomPiz-14
❑ 95Top-387
❑ 95Top-588
❑ 95TopCyb-360
❑ 95TopD3-2
❑ 95TopEmb-113
❑ 95TopEmbGI-113
❑ 95TopTra-5T
❑ 95TopTra-159T
❑ 95TopTraPB-5
❑ 95UC3-75
❑ 95UC3-123
❑ 95UC3ArtP-75
❑ 95UC3ArtP-123
❑ 95UC3CycS-CS4
❑ 95UC3InM-IM1
❑ 95UDAUnsBC-CR1
❑ 95UDAUnsBC-NH2
❑ 95Ult-258
❑ 95UltAllS-17
❑ 95UltAllSGM-17
❑ 95UltGolM-258
❑ 95UppDec-365
❑ 95UppDecED-365
❑ 95UppDecEDG-365
❑ 95UppDecPAW-H21
❑ 95UppDecPAWE-H21
❑ 95UppDecPC-MLB13
❑ 95UppDecSE-46
❑ 95UppDecSEG-46
❑ 95Zen-12
❑ 95ZenAllS-1
❑ 95ZenAllS-18
❑ 95ZenSam-12
❑ 95ZenZ-1
❑ 96BalOriP-31
❑ 96Baz-15
❑ 96Bow-1
❑ 96BowBes-3
❑ 96BowBesAR-3
❑ 96BowBesC-11
❑ 96BowBesCAR-11
❑ 96BowBesCR-11
❑ 96BowBesMI-4
❑ 96BowBesMIAR-4
❑ 96BowBesMIR-4
❑ 96BowBesP-BBP28
❑ 96BowBesPAR-BBP28
❑ 96BowBesPR-BBP28
❑ 96BowBesR-3
❑ 96BowFoi-1
❑ 96Cir-8
❑ 96Cir-199
❑ 96CirAcc-1
❑ 96CirBos-2
❑ 96CirBos-P2
❑ 96CirRav-8
❑ 96CirRav-199
❑ 96Cla7/1PC-1
❑ 96ColCho-1
❑ 96ColCho-362
❑ 96ColCho-421
❑ 96ColChoCtG-CG4
❑ 96ColChoCtG-CG4B
❑ 96ColChoCtG-CG4C
❑ 96ColChoCtGE-CR4
❑ 96ColChoCtGG-CG4
❑ 96ColChoCtGG-CG4B
❑ 96ColChoCtGG-CG4C
❑ 96ColChoCtGGE-CR4
❑ 96ColChoGS-1
❑ 96ColChoGS-362
❑ 96ColChoGS-421
❑ 96ColChoSS-1
❑ 96ColChoSS-362
❑ 96ColChoSS-421
❑ 96ColChoYMtP-33
❑ 96ColChoYMtP-33A
❑ 96ColChoYMtPGS-33
❑ 96ColChoYMtPGS-33A
❑ 96CUIMCR-1
❑ 96CUIMCR-2
❑ 96CUIMCR-3
❑ 96CUIMCR-4
❑ 96CUIMCR-NNO
❑ 96DenHol-2
❑ 96DenHolGS-1
❑ 96DenHolGSAP-1
❑ 96Don-110
❑ 96Don-145
❑ 96DonDiaK-30
❑ 96DonEli-61
❑ 96DonFreF-3
❑ 96DonPreP-110
❑ 96DonPreP-145
❑ 96DonRouT-8
❑ 96DonSam-5
❑ 96DonSho-6
❑ 96EmoN-8
❑ 96EmoXL-9
❑ 96EmoXLD-8
❑ 96Fin-B281
❑ 96Fin-G25
❑ 96Fin-S165
❑ 96FinLan-3
❑ 96FinRef-B281
❑ 96FinRef-G25
❑ 96FinRef-S165
❑ 96Fla-12
❑ 96FlaDiaC-9
❑ 96FlaHotG-8
❑ 96Fle-20
❑ 96Fle-P20
❑ 96FleChe-7
❑ 96FleGolM-8
❑ 96FleTeaL-1
❑ 96FleTif-20
❑ 96FleUpd-U237
❑ 96FleUpd-8
❑ 96FleUpdH-17
❑ 96FleUpdSL-9
❑ 96FleUpdTC-U237
❑ 96Kin-22
❑ 96Lea-21
❑ 96LeaAllGMC-4
❑ 96LeaAllGMCG-4
❑ 96LeaGolS-8
❑ 96LeaHatO-1
❑ 96LeaLim-15
❑ 96LeaLimG-15
❑ 96LeaLimL-3
❑ 96LeaLimLB-3
❑ 96LeaLimPC-2
❑ 96LeaPicP-2
❑ 96LeaPre-22
❑ 96LeaPreP-22
❑ 96LeaPrePB-21
❑ 96LeaPrePG-21
❑ 96LeaPrePS-21
❑ 96LeaPreSG-17
❑ 96LeaPreSP-4
❑ 96LeaPreSta-7
❑ 96LeaPreSte-17
❑ 96LeaSig-15
❑ 96LeaSigPPG-15
❑ 96LeaSigPPP-15
❑ 96LeaStaS-1
❑ 96LibSpo-1
❑ 96MetUni-9
❑ 96MetUniML-8
❑ 96MetUniP-9
❑ 96MetUniT-7
❑ 96MLBPin-29
❑ 96OriFle-15
❑ 96Pac-230
❑ 96PacCraC-CC3
❑ 96PacGolCD-DC15
❑ 96PacHom-HP6
❑ 96PacMil-M10
❑ 96PacPri-P77
❑ 96PacPriFB-FB15
❑ 96PacPriG-P77
❑ 96PacPriRHS-RH19
❑ 96PanSti-128
❑ 96Pin-136
❑ 96Pin-196
❑ 96Pin-214
❑ 96Pin-258
❑ 96Pin-393
❑ 96Pin-399
❑ 96Pin-CR1
❑ 96PinAfi-18
❑ 96PinAfiAP-18
❑ 96PinAfiFPP-18
❑ 96PinAfiMN-8
❑ 96PinAfiR-2
❑ 96PinAfiR-3
❑ 96PinAfiR-5
❑ 96PinAfiR-7
❑ 96PinAfiR-10
❑ 96PinAfiR-12
❑ 96PinAfiSP-2
❑ 96PinArtP-63
❑ 96PinArtP-114
❑ 96PinArtP-158
❑ 96PinEssotG-1
❑ 96PinFan-1
❑ 96PinFoil-214
❑ 96PinFoil-258
❑ 96PinFoil-393
❑ 96PinFoil-399
❑ 96PinSky-4
❑ 96PinSta-63
❑ 96PinSta-114
❑ 96PinSta-158
❑ 96PinTeaP-4
❑ 96PinTeaS-5
❑ 96Pro-12
❑ 96ProMagA-5
❑ 96ProMagDM-4
❑ 96ProSta-76
❑ 96RedF-15
❑ 96SchDis-13
❑ 96Sco-60
❑ 96Sco-274
❑ 96Sco-356
❑ 96Sco-NNO
❑ 96ScoAll-4
❑ 96ScoBigB-1
❑ 96ScoDiaA-5
❑ 96ScoDreT-1
❑ 96ScoDugC-A52
❑ 96ScoDugC-B81
❑ 96ScoDugCAP-A52
❑ 96ScoDugCAP-B81
❑ 96ScoGolS-25
❑ 96ScoNumG-1
❑ 96ScoRef-1
❑ 96Sel-19
❑ 96Sel-153
❑ 96Sel-200
❑ 96SelArtP-19
❑ 96SelArtP-153
❑ 96SelArtP-200
❑ 96SelCer-53
❑ 96SelCer-139
❑ 96SelCerAP-53
❑ 96SelCerAP-139
❑ 96SelCerCB-53
❑ 96SelCerCB-139
❑ 96SelCerCR-53
❑ 96SelCerCR-139
❑ 96SelCerIP-14
❑ 96SelCerMB-53
❑ 96SelCerMB-139
❑ 96SelCerMG-53
❑ 96SelCerMG-139
❑ 96SelCerMR-53
❑ 96SelCerMR-139
❑ 96SelCerSF-5
❑ 96SelClaTF-1
❑ 96SelEnF-3
❑ 96SelTeaN-20
❑ 96SP-30
❑ 96SP-187
❑ 96SPMarM-MM9
❑ 96SPMarMDC-9
❑ 96Spo-54
❑ 96Spo-100
❑ 96Spo-144
❑ 96SpoArtP-54
❑ 96SpoArtP-100
❑ 96SpoArtP-144
❑ 96SpoDouT-1
❑ 96SpoHitP-2
❑ 96SpoPowS-4
❑ 96SpoPro-1
❑ 96SPSpeFX-20
❑ 96SPSpeFXDC-20
❑ 96SPx-5
❑ 96SPxBoufG-4
❑ 96SPxGol-5
❑ 96StaClu-198
❑ 96StaClu-424
❑ 96StaCluEPB-424
❑ 96StaCluEPG-424
❑ 96StaCluEPS-424
❑ 96StaCluMet-M7
❑ 96StaCluMM-MM6
❑ 96StaCluMOP-198
❑ 96StaCluMOP-424
❑ 96StaCluMOP-M7
❑ 96StaCluMOP-MM6
❑ 96StaCluMOP-TSCA1
❑ 96StaCluTA-1
❑ 96Stu-1
❑ 96StuMas-5
❑ 96StuPrePB-1
❑ 96StuPrePG-1
❑ 96StuPrePS-1
❑ 96StuStaGS-1
❑ 96Sum-19
❑ 96Sum-154
❑ 96Sum-200
❑ 96SumAbo&B-19
❑ 96SumAbo&B-154
❑ 96SumAbo&B-200
❑ 96SumArtP-19
❑ 96SumArtP-154
❑ 96SumArtP-200
❑ 96SumBal-1
❑ 96SumBigB-6
❑ 96SumBigBM-6
❑ 96SumFoi-19
❑ 96SumFoi-200
❑ 96SumHitI-9
❑ 96SumPos-4
❑ 96TeaOut-66
❑ 96TeaOut-C99
❑ 96Top-96
❑ 96Top-200
❑ 96Top-222
❑ 96TopBigC-7
❑ 96TopChr-28
❑ 96TopChr-67
❑ 96TopChr-82
❑ 96TopChrMotG-9
❑ 96TopChrMotGR-9
❑ 96TopChrR-28
❑ 96TopChrR-67
❑ 96TopChrR-82
❑ 96TopClaC-CC2
❑ 96TopGal-168
❑ 96TopGalPG-PG3
❑ 96TopGalPPI-168
❑ 96TopLas-90
❑ 96TopLasSS-8
❑ 96TopMasotG-9
❑ 96TopMysF-M7
❑ 96TopMysF-M23
❑ 96TopMysFR-M7
❑ 96TopMysFR-M23
❑ 96TopPro-AL8
❑ 96Ult-11
❑ 96Ult-588
❑ 96Ult-DD1
❑ 96Ult-DD2
❑ 96UltCaltH-7
❑ 96UltCaltHGM-7
❑ 96UltChe-A8
❑ 96UltChe-B9
❑ 96UltCheGM-A8
❑ 96UltCheGM-B9
❑ 96UltDiaP-9
❑ 96UltDiaPGM-9
❑ 96UltGolM-11
❑ 96UltGolM-588
❑ 96UltPriL-4
❑ 96UltPriLGM-4
❑ 96UltPro-NNO
❑ 96UltRaw-9
❑ 96UltRawGM-9
❑ 96UltRes-7
❑ 96UltResGM-7
❑ 96UltSeaC-8
❑ 96UltSeaCGM-8
❑ 96UltThu-17
❑ 96UltThuGM-17
❑ 96UppDec-1
❑ 96UppDec-115
❑ 96UppDec-280
❑ 96UppDec-385
❑ 96UppDecA-15
❑ 96UppDecDD-DD6
❑ 96UppDecDDG-DD6
❑ 96UppDecDDS-DD6
❑ 96UppDecG-GF5
❑ 96UppDecHC-HC15
❑ 96UppDecPHE-H6
❑ 96UppDecPreH-H6
❑ 96UppDecRCJ-1
❑ 96UppDecRCJ-2
❑ 96UppDecRCJ-3
❑ 96UppDecRCJ-4
❑ 96UppDecRCJ-5
❑ 96UppDecRCJ-6
❑ 96UppDecRCJ-7
❑ 96UppDecRCJ-8
❑ 96UppDecRCJ-9
❑ 96UppDecRCJ-10
❑ 96UppDecRCJ-11
❑ 96UppDecRCJ-12
❑ 96UppDecRCJ-13
❑ 96UppDecRCJ-14
❑ 96UppDecRCJ-15
❑ 96UppDecRCJ-16
❑ 96UppDecRCJ-17
❑ 96UppDecRCJ-18
❑ 96UppDecRCJ-19
❑ 96UppDecRCJ-20
❑ 96UppDecRCJ-21
❑ 96UppDecRCJ-22
❑ 96UppDecRipC-1
❑ 96UppDecRipC-2
❑ 96UppDecRipC-3
❑ 96UppDecRipC-4
❑ 96UppDecRipC-5
❑ 96UppDecRipC-6
❑ 96UppDecRipC-7
❑ 96UppDecRipC-8
❑ 96UppDecRipC-9
❑ 96UppDecRipC-10
❑ 96UppDecRipC-11
❑ 96UppDecRipC-12
❑ 96UppDecRipC-13
❑ 96UppDecRipC-14
❑ 96UppDecRipC-15
❑ 96UppDecRipC-16
❑ 96UppDecRipC-17
❑ 96UppDecRipC-18
❑ 96UppDecRipC-19
❑ 96UppDecRipC-20
❑ 96UppDecRipC-21
❑ 96UppDecRipC-22
❑ 96UppDecRipC-NNO
❑ 96Zen-76
❑ 96Zen-132
❑ 96ZenArtP-76
❑ 96ZenArtP-132
❑ 96ZenDiaC-5
❑ 96ZenDiaCP-5
❑ 96ZenMoz-8
❑ 96ZenZ-3
❑ 97BalOriP-29
❑ 97Bow-18
❑ 97BowBes-64
❑ 97BowBesAR-64
❑ 97BowBesBC-BC4
❑ 97BowBesBCAR-BC4
❑ 97BowBesBCR-BC4
❑ 97BowBesJ-64
❑ 97BowBesJAR-64
❑ 97BowBesJR-64
❑ 97BowBesP-7
❑ 97BowBesPAR-7
❑ 97BowBesPR-7
❑ 97BowBesR-64
❑ 97BowChr-14
❑ 97BowChrI-14
❑ 97BowChrIR-14
❑ 97BowChrR-14
❑ 97BowInt-18
❑ 97BurKinR-1
❑ 97BurKinR-2
❑ 97BurKinR-3
❑ 97BurKinR-4
❑ 97BurKinR-5
❑ 97BurKinR-6
❑ 97BurKinR-7
❑ 97BurKinR-8
❑ 97BurKinR-AU
❑ 97BurKinRG-1
❑ 97BurKinRG-2
❑ 97BurKinRG-3
❑ 97BurKinRG-4
❑ 97BurKinRG-5
❑ 97BurKinRG-6
❑ 97BurKinRG-7
❑ 97BurKinRG-8
❑ 97Cir-8
❑ 97Cir-398
❑ 97CirBos-15
❑ 97CirIco-9
❑ 97CirLimA-12
❑ 97CirRav-8
❑ 97CirRav-398
❑ 97CirRavR-10
❑ 97CirSupB-15
❑ 97ColCho-41
❑ 97ColChoAC-13
❑ 97ColChoBS-8
❑ 97ColChoBSGS-8
❑ 97ColChoCtG-6A
❑ 97ColChoCtG-6B
❑ 97ColChoCtG-6C
❑ 97ColChoCtGE-CG6
❑ 97ColChoCtGIW-CG6
❑ 97ColChoNF-NF35
❑ 97ColChoS-20
❑ 97ColChoSR-22
❑ 97ColChoT-BO5
❑ 97ColChoTBS-5
❑ 97ColChoTBSWH-5
❑ 97ColChoTotT-T7
❑ 97CraJac-3
❑ 97Don-121
❑ 97Don-400
❑ 97Don-448
❑ 97DonArmaD-8
❑ 97DonDiaK-2
❑ 97DonDiaKC-2
❑ 97DonDom-4
❑ 97DonEli-6
❑ 97DonEli-9
❑ 97DonEliGS-6
❑ 97DonEliLaL-6
❑ 97DonEliPtT-1
❑ 97DonEliPtT-3
❑ 97DonEliPtTA-1
❑ 97DonEliPtTA-3
❑ 97DonFraFea-13
❑ 97DonGolPP-121
❑ 97DonGolPP-400
❑ 97DonGolPP-448
❑ 97DonLim-5
❑ 97DonLim-36
❑ 97DonLim-37
❑ 97DonLimE-5
❑ 97DonLimE-36
❑ 97DonLimE-37
❑ 97DonLimENG-5
❑ 97DonLimFotG-1
❑ 97DonLimFotG-43
❑ 97DonPowA-3
❑ 97DonPowADC-3
❑ 97DonPre-98
❑ 97DonPre-169
❑ 97DonPreCttC-98
❑ 97DonPreCttC-169
❑ 97DonPrePM-18
❑ 97DonPreS-4
❑ 97DonPreSS-4
❑ 97DonPreTB-17
❑ 97DonPreTBG-17
❑ 97DonPreTF-17
❑ 97DonPreTP-17
❑ 97DonPreTPG-17
❑ 97DonPreXP-5B
❑ 97DonRipOWIK-1
❑ 97DonRipOWIK-2
❑ 97DonRipOWIK-3
❑ 97DonRipOWIK-4
❑ 97DonRipOWIK-5
❑ 97DonRipOWIK-6
❑ 97DonRipOWIK-7

❑ 97DonRipOWIK-8
❑ 97DonRipOWIK-9
❑ 97DonRipOWIK-10
❑ 97DonRipOWIK-10A
❑ 97DonRocL-15
❑ 97DonSig-58
❑ 97DonSigAC-104
❑ 97DonSigAM-104
❑ 97DonSigPPP-58
❑ 97DonSilPP-121
❑ 97DonSilPP-400
❑ 97DonSilPP-448
❑ 97DonTea-35
❑ 97DonTeaSMVP-9
❑ 97DonTeaSPE-35
❑ 97DonUpdRIC-1
❑ 97DonVxP1-11
❑ 97DonVxP1CD-4
❑ 97E-X2-8
❑ 97E-X2Cred-8
❑ 97E-X2EssCre-8
❑ 97E-X2Hall-4
❑ 97Fin-135
❑ 97Fin-252
❑ 97Fin-334
❑ 97FinEmb-135
❑ 97FinEmb-334
❑ 97FinEmbR-135
❑ 97FinEmbR-334
❑ 97FinRef-135
❑ 97FinRef-252
❑ 97FinRef-334
❑ 97FlaShoDC-15
❑ 97FlaShoHG-12
❑ 97FlaShoLC-8
❑ 97FlaShoLeg0-8
❑ 97FlaShoLeg1-8
❑ 97FlaShoM-A8
❑ 97FlaShoM-B8
❑ 97FlaShoM-C8
❑ 97FlaShoR0-8
❑ 97FlaShoR1-8
❑ 97FlaShoR2-8
❑ 97Fle-13
❑ 97Fle-498
❑ 97Fle-714
❑ 97Fle-723
❑ 97FleDecoE-10
❑ 97FleDecoERT-10
❑ 97FleDiaT-10
❑ 97FleGolM-9
❑ 97FleGouG-11
❑ 97FleGouGF-11
❑ 97FleHea-16
❑ 97FleMilDM-8
❑ 97FleMilDMR-8
❑ 97FleTeaL-1
❑ 97FleTif-13
❑ 97FleTif-498
❑ 97FleTif-714
❑ 97FleTif-723
❑ 97HigMinESC-30
❑ 97HigMinESC-31
❑ 97HigMinESC-32
❑ 97HigMinM-100
❑ 97HigMinM-101
❑ 97HigMinM-102
❑ 97HigMinM-103
❑ 97HigMinMCT-31
❑ 97HigMinMCT-32
❑ 97HigMinMM-19
❑ 97HigMinMM-21
❑ 97HigMinMM-23
❑ 97HigMinMSM-10
❑ 97HigMinMSM-11
❑ 97HigMinMSM-12
❑ 97Lea-188
❑ 97Lea-218
❑ 97Lea-370
❑ 97LeaDrefS-2
❑ 97LeaFraM-188
❑ 97LeaFraM-218
❑ 97LeaFraM-370
❑ 97LeaFraMDC-188
❑ 97LeaFraMDC-218
❑ 97LeaFraMDC-370
❑ 97LeaGet-15
❑ 97LeaGolS-21
❑ 97LeaKnoG-8
❑ 97LeaLeaotN-2
❑ 97LeaStaS-9
❑ 97MetUni-8
❑ 97MetUniMF-8
❑ 97MetUniML-9
❑ 97MetUniT-8
❑ 97NewPin-91
❑ 97NewPin-178
❑ 97NewPinAP-91
❑ 97NewPinAP-178
❑ 97NewPinIE-4
❑ 97NewPinKtP-14
❑ 97NewPinMC-91
❑ 97NewPinMC-178
❑ 97NewPinPP-91
❑ 97NewPinPP-178
❑ 97NewPinPP-I4A
❑ 97NewPinPP-K14
❑ 97NewPinPP-CR1
❑ 97NewPinPP-CR2
❑ 97NewPinPP-CR3
❑ 97NewPinPP-CR4
❑ 97NewPinPP-CR5
❑ 97NewPinPP-CR6
❑ 97NewPinS-CR1
❑ 97NewPinS-CR2
❑ 97NewPinS-CR3
❑ 97NewPinS-CR4
❑ 97NewPinS-CR5
❑ 97NewPinS-CR6
❑ 97OriSco-7
❑ 97OriScoPl-7
❑ 97OriScoPr-7
❑ 97OriSun-7
❑ 97Pac-29
❑ 97PacCar-4
❑ 97PacCarM-4
❑ 97PacCerCGT-7
❑ 97PacFirD-4
❑ 97PacGolCD-5
❑ 97PacLigB-29
❑ 97PacPri-12
❑ 97PacPriGA-GA3
❑ 97PacPriGotD-GD16
❑ 97PacPriLB-12
❑ 97PacPriP-12
❑ 97PacPriSH-SH1A
❑ 97PacPriSL-SL1A
❑ 97PacSil-29
❑ 97Pin-191
❑ 97PinArtP-PP191
❑ 97PinCar-3
❑ 97PinCer-28
❑ 97PinCer-146
❑ 97PinCerCMGT-7
❑ 97PinCerCT-7
❑ 97PinCerLI-1
❑ 97PinCerMBla-28
❑ 97PinCerMBla-146
❑ 97PinCerMBlu-28
❑ 97PinCerMBlu-146
❑ 97PinCerMG-28
❑ 97PinCerMG-146
❑ 97PinCerMR-28
❑ 97PinCerMR-146
❑ 97PinCerR-28
❑ 97PinCerR-146
❑ 97PinEpixPE-E14
❑ 97PinFan-FF7
❑ 97PinHom-21
❑ 97PinHom-22
❑ 97PinIns-23
❑ 97PinInsC-22
❑ 97PinInsCE-23
❑ 97PinInsDD-1
❑ 97PinInsDE-23
❑ 97PinMin-4
❑ 97PinMinB-4
❑ 97PinMinCB-4
❑ 97PinMinCG-4
❑ 97PinMinCGR-4
❑ 97PinMinCN-4
❑ 97PinMinCSS-4
❑ 97PinMinG-4
❑ 97PinMinS-4
❑ 97PinMusC-191
❑ 97PinPasttM-4
❑ 97PinPrePla-191
❑ 97PinPrePla-S5
❑ 97PinSha-5
❑ 97PinTotCPB-28
❑ 97PinTotCPB-146
❑ 97PinTotCPG-28
❑ 97PinTotCPG-146
❑ 97PinTotCPR-28
❑ 97PinTotCPR-146
❑ 97PinX-P-57
❑ 97PinX-PMoS-57
❑ 97PinX-PMP-18
❑ 97PinX-PMW-6
❑ 97PinX-PMWG-6
❑ 97PinX-PMWS-6
❑ 97PinX-PreMPS-18
❑ 97PinX-PSfF-48
❑ 97PinX-PSfFU-48
❑ 97PreCon-5
❑ 97Sco-151
❑ 97Sco-546
❑ 97ScoArtPWB-151
❑ 97ScoArtPWB-546
❑ 97ScoFra-3
❑ 97ScoFraG-3
❑ 97ScoHeaotO-12
❑ 97ScoHigZ-15
❑ 97ScoPitP-1
❑ 97ScoPitP-3
❑ 97ScoPreS-151
❑ 97ScoResC-546
❑ 97ScoShoS-151
❑ 97ScoShoS-546
❑ 97ScoShoSAP-151
❑ 97ScoShoSAP-546
❑ 97ScoStaaD-23
❑ 97Sel-71
❑ 97SelArtP-71
❑ 97SelCom-71
❑ 97SelRegG-71
❑ 97SelToootT-3
❑ 97SelToootTMB-3
❑ 97SP-34
❑ 97SPGamF-GF4
❑ 97SPInsI-8
❑ 97SPMarM-MM14
❑ 97SpoIll-33
❑ 97SpoIll-124
❑ 97SpoIll-177
❑ 97SpoIllAM-2
❑ 97SpoIllEE-33
❑ 97SpoIllEE-124
❑ 97SpoIllEE-177
❑ 97SpoIllGS-7
❑ 97SPSpeF-8
❑ 97SPx-12
❑ 97SPxBoufG-5
❑ 97SPxBro-12
❑ 97SPxCorotG-8
❑ 97SPxGol-12
❑ 97SPxGraF-12
❑ 97SPxSil-12
❑ 97SPxSte-12
❑ 97StaClu-8
❑ 97StaCluMat-8
❑ 97StaCluMOP-8
❑ 97StaCluMOP-PG16
❑ 97StaCluPG-PG16
❑ 97StrAll-51
❑ 97Stu-51
❑ 97StuHarH-6
❑ 97StuMasS-11
❑ 97StuMasS8-11
❑ 97StuPor8-5
❑ 97StuPrePG-51
❑ 97StuPrePS-51
❑ 97Top-400
❑ 97TopAll-AS9
❑ 97TopChr-140
❑ 97TopChrAS-AS9
❑ 97TopChrDD-DD7
❑ 97TopChrDDR-DD7
❑ 97TopChrJ-140
❑ 97TopChrR-140
❑ 97TopChrSAR-AS9
❑ 97TopGal-4
❑ 97TopGalGoH-GH5
❑ 97TopGalPMS-7
❑ 97TopGalPMSSS-7
❑ 97TopGalPPI-4
❑ 97TopHobM-HM2
❑ 97TopIntF-ILM12
❑ 97TopIntFR-ILM12
❑ 97TopMem05-40
❑ 97TopScr-17
❑ 97TopScrPS-4
❑ 97TopScrPST-4
❑ 97TopScrT-17
❑ 97TopSta-3
❑ 97TopSta97AS-AS7
❑ 97TopStaAM-3
❑ 97TopStaASM-ASM1
❑ 97UD3-25
❑ 97UD3Marq-MA8
❑ 97Ult-11
❑ 97Ult-P11
❑ 97UltBasR-9
❑ 97UltChe-A7
❑ 97UltChe-B5
❑ 97UltDiaP-9
❑ 97UltDouT-1
❑ 97UltFamGam-4
❑ 97UltFieC-15
❑ 97UltGolME-11
❑ 97UltGolME-NNO
❑ 97UltHitM-5
❑ 97UltLeaS-3
❑ 97UltPlaME-11
❑ 97UltPowP-A8
❑ 97UltPowP-B4
❑ 97UltStaR-5
❑ 97UltTop3-5
❑ 97UltTop3GM-5
❑ 97UppDec-20
❑ 97UppDec-147
❑ 97UppDecAG-AG15
❑ 97UppDecHC-HC8
❑ 97UppDecMM-A3
❑ 97UppDecP-7
❑ 97UppDecPE-7
❑ 97UppDecSA-13
❑ 97UppDecSAG-13
❑ 97Zen-35
❑ 97Zen Z-Z-6
❑ 97Zen8x10-19
❑ 97Zen8x1D-19
❑ 97ZentheBP-19
❑ 97ZenV-2-6
❑ 98Bow-222
❑ 98BowBes-11
❑ 98BowBesAR-11
❑ 98BowBesMIF-MI5
❑ 98BowBesMIFAR-MI5
❑ 98BowBesMIFR-MI5
❑ 98BowBesR-11
❑ 98BowChr-222
❑ 98BowChrGA-222
❑ 98BowChrGAR-222
❑ 98BowChrI-222
❑ 98BowChrIR-222
❑ 98BowChrR-222
❑ 98BowGolA-222
❑ 98BowInt-222
❑ 98CirThu-8
❑ 98CirThu-P8
❑ 98CirThuB-16
❑ 98CirThuRav-8
❑ 98CirThuSupRav-8
❑ 98ColCho-22
❑ 98ColCho-40
❑ 98ColCho-267
❑ 98ColChoCtG-CG5A
❑ 98ColChoCtG-CG5B
❑ 98ColChoCtG-CG5C
❑ 98ColChoCtGExch-CG5
❑ 98ColChoCtGIW-CG5
❑ 98ColChoER-ER3
❑ 98ColChoMBH-6
❑ 98ColChoRJ-40
❑ 98ColChoS'-3
❑ 98ColChoSQ-SQ27
❑ 98ColChoSQ-SQ50
❑ 98ColChoSQDouble-3
❑ 98ColChoSQHR-3
❑ 98ColChoSQSingle-3
❑ 98ColChoSQTriple-3
❑ 98CroRoy-23
❑ 98CroRoyAS-2
❑ 98CroRoyCCPA-1
❑ 98CroRoyCCPrem-1
❑ 98CroRoyDK-4
❑ 98CroRoyFoB-4
❑ 98CroRoyFoBA-4
❑ 98CroRoyPotG-5
❑ 98Don-61
❑ 98Don-160
❑ 98Don-389
❑ 98DonCol-61
❑ 98DonCol-160
❑ 98DonColE-406
❑ 98DonColE-523
❑ 98DonColL-332
❑ 98DonColL-376
❑ 98DonColP-553
❑ 98DonColP-720
❑ 98DonColS-61
❑ 98DonColS-160
❑ 98DonCruG-8
❑ 98DonCruP-8
❑ 98DonCruR-8
❑ 98DonDay-8
❑ 98DonDiaK-1
❑ 98DonDiaKC-1
❑ 98DonDom-21
❑ 98DonEli-6
❑ 98DonEli-123
❑ 98DonEliA-6
❑ 98DonEliA-123
❑ 98DonEliBttF-1
❑ 98DonEliBttFA-1B
❑ 98DonEliBttFA-NNO
❑ 98DonEliC-4
❑ 98DonEliI-16
❑ 98DonEliMC-4
❑ 98DonEliPN-4A
❑ 98DonEliPN-4B
❑ 98DonEliPN-4C
❑ 98DonEliPNDC-4A
❑ 98DonEliPNDC-4B
❑ 98DonEliPNDC-4C
❑ 98DonEliPNS-4A
❑ 98DonEliPNS-4B
❑ 98DonEliPNS-4C
❑ 98DonEliS-6
❑ 98DonEliS-123
❑ 98DonFANT-3
❑ 98DonFANTDC-3
❑ 98DonGolPP-61
❑ 98DonGolPP-160
❑ 98DonGolPP-389
❑ 98DonPre-3
❑ 98DonPre-170
❑ 98DonPreGB-3
❑ 98DonPreGES-13
❑ 98DonPreGoB-3
❑ 98DonPreGX-13
❑ 98DonPreGXDC-13
❑ 98DonPrePM-3
❑ 98DonPreSeat-3
❑ 98DonPreSeat-170
❑ 98DonPreTP-3
❑ 98DonPreTPD-2
❑ 98DonPreTPG-3
❑ 98DonPreTPS-3
❑ 98DonPreTW-6
❑ 98DonPriCD-61
❑ 98DonPriCD-160
❑ 98DonPriCE-406
❑ 98DonPriCE-523
❑ 98DonPriCL-332
❑ 98DonPriCL-376
❑ 98DonPriCP-553
❑ 98DonPriCP-720
❑ 98DonProLS-20
❑ 98DonSig-9
❑ 98DonSig-109
❑ 98DonSigAC-93
❑ 98DonSigAM-95
❑ 98DonSigP-9
❑ 98DonSigP-109
❑ 98DonSigSP-22
❑ 98DonSilPP-61
❑ 98DonSilPP-160
❑ 98DonSilPP-389
❑ 98DonSonM9-1
❑ 98E-X2-9
❑ 98E-X2DesCoop-3
❑ 98E-X2ECFut-9
❑ 98E-X2ECNow-9
❑ 98Fin-135
❑ 98FinMysF1-M21
❑ 98FinMysF1-M22
❑ 98FinMysF1-M23
❑ 98FinMysF1-M24
❑ 98FinMysFR-M21
❑ 98FinMysFR-M22
❑ 98FinMysFR-M23
❑ 98FinMysFR-M24
❑ 98FinNo--135
❑ 98FinNo-R-135
❑ 98FinOve-A2
❑ 98FinOveR-A2
❑ 98FinRef-135
❑ 98FinStaS-SS9
❑ 98FinTheM-TM5
❑ 98FinTheMR-TM5
❑ 98FlaShoLeg0-8
❑ 98FlaShoLeg1-8
❑ 98FlaShoLeg2-8
❑ 98FlaShoLeg3-8
❑ 98FlaShoLegM-8
❑ 98FlaShoP1-2
❑ 98FlaShoR0-8
❑ 98FlaShoR1-8
❑ 98FlaShoR2-8
❑ 98FlaShoR3-8
❑ 98FlaShoRSS-NNO
❑ 98Fle-8
❑ 98Fle-348
❑ 98Fle-574
❑ 98Fle-593
❑ 98FleDecERT-12
❑ 98FleDecoE-12
❑ 98FleDiaSCS-NNO
❑ 98FleDiaT-DT8
❑ 98FleLumC-12
❑ 98FleUpd-U8
❑ 98FleVin'-8
❑ 98FleVin'C-8
❑ 98Lea-133
❑ 98Lea-177
❑ 98LeaFraDA-133
❑ 98LeaFraDA-177
❑ 98LeaFraF-133
❑ 98LeaFraF-177
❑ 98LeaFraM-133
❑ 98LeaFraM-177
❑ 98LeaFraM-133
❑ 98LeaFraM-177
❑ 98LeaFraMDC-133
❑ 98LeaFraMDC-177
❑ 98LeaFraMDC-133
❑ 98LeaFraMDC-177
❑ 98LeaFraMZ2-133
❑ 98LeaFraMZ2-177
❑ 98LeaHeaftH-17
❑ 98LeaHeaftHS-17
❑ 98LeaRCMLHDSamp-6
❑ 98LeaRS-28
❑ 98LeaRS-188
❑ 98LeaRSGAHSamp-2
❑ 98LeaRSGreAH-2
❑ 98LeaRSGreHit-3
❑ 98LeaRSLHolo-28
❑ 98LeaRSLHolo-188
❑ 98LeaRSLMVP-3
❑ 98LeaRSLMVPPE-3
❑ 98LeaRSLong-28
❑ 98LeaRSLong-188
❑ 98LeaRSMLHD-6
❑ 98LeaRSSOSamp-6
❑ 98LeaRSStaOva-6
❑ 98LeaRSTicMas-3
❑ 98LeaRSTicMasDC-3
❑ 98LeaRTrue-28
❑ 98LeaRTrue-188
❑ 98LeaStaRep-4
❑ 98LeaStaS-6
❑ 98LeaStaSDC-6
❑ 98MetUni-200
❑ 98MetUni-213
❑ 98MetUniAT-8
❑ 98MetUniDH-6
❑ 98MetUniPMG-200
❑ 98MetUniPMG-213
❑ 98MetUniPP-6
❑ 98MetUniT-8
❑ 98MetUniUL-8
❑ 98OriSco-3
❑ 98OriScoP-3
❑ 98Pac-33
❑ 98PacAur-14
❑ 98PacAurCube-4
❑ 98PacAurHC-4
❑ 98PacAurKotML-3
❑ 98PacAurODLC-4
❑ 98PacAurPF-8
❑ 98PacAurPFC-8
❑ 98PacAurPFPB-8
❑ 98PacAurPFR-8
❑ 98PacAurPFS-8
❑ 98PacCraCh-3
❑ 98PacGolCDC-6
❑ 98PacHomRH-HRC2
❑ 98PacInCage-3
❑ 98PacInv-12
❑ 98PacInvCCDB-3
❑ 98PacInvCCG-3
❑ 98PacInvCCG-3
❑ 98PacInvCCLB-3
❑ 98PacInvCCP-3
❑ 98PacInvCCR-3
❑ 98PacInvGems-15
❑ 98PacInvInt-2A
❑ 98PacInvMiT-2
❑ 98PacInvPBlue-12
❑ 98PacInvPhoto-2
❑ 98PacInvSilv-12
❑ 98PacInvTeam-3
❑ 98PacOme-34
❑ 98PacOmeEP-1
❑ 98PacOmeEP1o1-1
❑ 98PacOmeFTF-5
❑ 98PacOmeOnIns-1
❑ 98PacOmeP-1
❑ 98PacOmeR-34
❑ 98PacOnl-101A
❑ 98PacOnl-101B
❑ 98PacOnl-105
❑ 98PacOnlR-101A

❑ 98PacOnlR-101B
❑ 98PacOnlR-105
❑ 98PacOnlWC-101A
❑ 98PacOnlWC-101B
❑ 98PacOnlWC-105
❑ 98PacPar-17
❑ 98PacParC-17
❑ 98PacParCB-2
❑ 98PacParCBPP-2
❑ 98PacParFC-3
❑ 98PacParG-17
❑ 98PacParHS-17
❑ 98PacParPB-17
❑ 98PacParR-17
❑ 98PacParSD-3
❑ 98PacParTC-2
❑ 98PacPlaB-33
❑ 98PacRedT-33
❑ 98PacSil-33
❑ 98PacTeaC-2
❑ 98Pin-183
❑ 98PinArtP-PP86
❑ 98PinEpixME-E14
❑ 98PinEpixMO-E14
❑ 98PinEpixMP-E14
❑ 98PinEpixPO-E14
❑ 98PinEpixPP-E14
❑ 98PinEpixSE-E14
❑ 98PinEpixSO-E14
❑ 98PinEpixSP-E14
❑ 98PinIns-8
❑ 98PinIns-144
❑ 98PinInsBtN-2
❑ 98PinInsC-16
❑ 98PinInsCE-8
❑ 98PinInsCE-144
❑ 98PinInsCG-16
❑ 98PinInsDE-8
❑ 98PinInsDE-144
❑ 98PinInsSG-1AB
❑ 98PinInsSG-1CD
❑ 98PinInsSG-8AB
❑ 98PinInsSG-8CD
❑ 98PinInsSG-15AB
❑ 98PinInsSG-15CD
❑ 98PinInsSGS-1AB
❑ 98PinInsSGS-1CD
❑ 98PinInsSGS-8AB
❑ 98PinInsSGS-8CD
❑ 98PinInsSGS-15AB
❑ 98PinInsSGS-15CD
❑ 98PinMinB-18
❑ 98PinMinCB-18
❑ 98PinMinCBAP-18
❑ 98PinMinCGP-18
❑ 98PinMinCGPAP-18
❑ 98PinMinCN-18
❑ 98PinMinCNAP-18
❑ 98PinMinCSGR-18
❑ 98PinMinDC-18
❑ 98PinMinG-18
❑ 98PinMinMCSS-18
❑ 98PinMinS-18
❑ 98PinMinS-18
❑ 98PinMusC-PP86
❑ 98PinPer-3
❑ 98PinPer-140
❑ 98PinPerBB-8
❑ 98PinPerBBSamp-8
❑ 98PinPerBBSO-8
❑ 98PinPerLP-9
❑ 98PinPerPP-3
❑ 98PinPerPP-140
❑ 98PinPerPT-5
❑ 98PinPerSftF-19
❑ 98PinPerSftFShop-9
❑ 98PinPlu-21
❑ 98PinPlu-185
❑ 98PinPluAE-14
❑ 98PinPluAEE-14
❑ 98PinPluAEP-14
❑ 98PinPluAP-PP11
❑ 98PinPluGAP-PP11
❑ 98PinPluLM-8
❑ 98PinPluMAP-PP11
❑ 98PinPluPieGame-5
❑ 98PinPluTP-5
❑ 98PinPluTPG-5
❑ 98PinPluTPM-5
❑ 98PinPowPJ-2
❑ 98PinPowPJS-2
❑ 98PinPreP-183
❑ 98PinPreP-E14
❑ 98PinPreP-S44
❑ 98PinPreP-S45
❑ 98PinPreP-S46

❑ 98PinSna-BO1
❑ 98PinSna-BO13
❑ 98PinSnaS-2
❑ 98PinSpe-44
❑ 98PinSpe-45
❑ 98PinSpe-46
❑ 98PinUnc-183
❑ 98PreCon-9
❑ 98Revo-22
❑ 98RevoFP-1
❑ 98RevoMLI-1
❑ 98RevoPTP-1
❑ 98RevoRooHH-23
❑ 98RevoShow-1
❑ 98RevoSS-22
❑ 98Sco-43
❑ 98Sco-257
❑ 98Sco-268
❑ 98ScoAllST-7
❑ 98ScoComP-4A
❑ 98ScoComP-4B
❑ 98ScoComP-4C
❑ 98ScoComPG-4A
❑ 98ScoComPG-4B
❑ 98ScoComPG-4C
❑ 98ScoEpix-E14
❑ 98ScoFirP-4
❑ 98ScoLoaL-LL7
❑ 98ScoNewS-NS15
❑ 98ScoRT-28
❑ 98ScoRT-267
❑ 98ScoRTSS-PP28
❑ 98ScoRTSS-PP160
❑ 98ScoRTSSAP-PP28
❑ 98ScoRTSSAP-PP160
❑ 98ScoRTSSAP1-PP28
❑ 98ScoRTSSAP1-PP160
❑ 98ScoRTStarGaz-5
❑ 98ScoSam-43
❑ 98ScoSS-PP128
❑ 98ScoSSAP-PP128
❑ 98SkyDugA-52
❑ 98SkyDugA-123
❑ 98SkyDugADH-DH14
❑ 98SkyDugAIA-52
❑ 98SkyDugAIA-123
❑ 98SkyDugAS-SH7
❑ 98SP Aut-55
❑ 98SP Aut-SD8
❑ 98SP AutSD-SD8
❑ 98SP AutSDT-SD8
❑ 98SpolII-105
❑ 98SpolIIC-C4
❑ 98SpolIIEC-EC7
❑ 98SpolIIEE-105
❑ 98SpolIIFE-105
❑ 98SpolIIODMP-OD4
❑ 98SpolIITaN-40
❑ 98SpolIITaN-124
❑ 98SpolIITaNAotG-AG6
❑ 98SpolIITaNC-C7
❑ 98SpolIITaNEE-40
❑ 98SpolIITaNEE-124
❑ 98SpolIITaNGS-6
❑ 98SpolIITaNRtC-RC9
❑ 98SpolIIWSF-119
❑ 98SpolIIWSF-P8
❑ 98SpolIIWSFEE-119
❑ 98SpolIIWSFFE-119
❑ 98SPxFin-64
❑ 98SPxFin-145
❑ 98SPxFin-172
❑ 98SPxFin-354
❑ 98SPxFinR-64
❑ 98SPxFinR-145
❑ 98SPxFinR-172
❑ 98SPxFinR-354
❑ 98SPxFinS-64
❑ 98SPxFinS-145
❑ 98SPxFinS-172
❑ 98SPxFinS-354
❑ 98StaCluFDI-83
❑ 98StaClul-83
❑ 98StaClul-NNO
❑ 98StaClul-NNO
❑ 98StaCluNC-NC1
❑ 98StaCluOneK-83
❑ 98StaCluPP-83
❑ 98StaCluPWP-P4
❑ 98StaCluRC-RC6
❑ 98StaCluTIII-T5B
❑ 98StaCluTIII-T13A
❑ 98StaCluTLme-T5B
❑ 98StaCluTLme-T13A
❑ 98StaCluTLmo-T5B
❑ 98StaCluTLmo-T13A

❑ 98Stu-113
❑ 98Stu-CL4
❑ 98StuFF-4
❑ 98StuFFDC-4
❑ 98StuGPP-113
❑ 98StuGPP-CL4
❑ 98StuMast-18
❑ 98StuPor8x10-8
❑ 98StuPor8x10GP-8
❑ 98StuSony99-1
❑ 98StuSPP-113
❑ 98StuSPP-CL4
❑ 98Top-320
❑ 98TopChr-320
❑ 98TopChrF-FB5
❑ 98TopChrFR-FB5
❑ 98TopChrHB-HB6
❑ 98TopChrHBR-HB6
❑ 98TopChrM-MS9
❑ 98TopChrMR-MS9
❑ 98TopChrR-320
❑ 98TopDevR-320
❑ 98TopDia-320
❑ 98TopEtc-ES7
❑ 98TopFla-FB5
❑ 98TopFocP-FP4
❑ 98TopFruR-6
❑ 98TopGal-77
❑ 98TopGalGoH-GH9
❑ 98TopGalGoHJ-GH9
❑ 98TopGalGP-77
❑ 98TopGalOPP-77
❑ 98TopGalPG-PG4
❑ 98TopGalPPI-77
❑ 98TopGalPPIA-77
❑ 98TopGolLabC1-29
❑ 98TopGolLabC1B-29
❑ 98TopGolLabC1One-29
❑ 98TopGolLabC1R-29
❑ 98TopGolLabC2-29
❑ 98TopGolLabC2B-29
❑ 98TopGolLabC2One-29
❑ 98TopGolLabC2R-29
❑ 98TopGolLabC3-29
❑ 98TopGolLabC3B-29
❑ 98TopGolLabC3One-29
❑ 98TopGolLabC3R-29
❑ 98TopHal-HB6
❑ 98TopMil-MS9
❑ 98TopMiniC-320
❑ 98TopMysF-ILM2
❑ 98TopMysFB-M16
❑ 98TopMysFB-M16
❑ 98TopMysFBR-M16
❑ 98TopMysFBR-M16
❑ 98TopMysFR-ILM2
❑ 98TopOpeD-146
❑ 98TopSta-51
❑ 98TopSta'S-34
❑ 98TopSta'SGH-34
❑ 98TopStaB-51
❑ 98TopStaG-51
❑ 98TopStaGR-51
❑ 98TopStaS-51
❑ 98TopStaSteG-34
❑ 98TopSup-27
❑ 98TopSup-27
❑ 98TopTek-51
❑ 98TopTekD-51
❑ 98UD3-65
❑ 98UD3-155
❑ 98UD3-245
❑ 98UD3DieCut-65
❑ 98UD3DieCut-155
❑ 98UD3DieCut-245
❑ 98Ult-143
❑ 98Ult-250
❑ 98Ult-474
❑ 98Ult-477
❑ 98UltArtT-5
❑ 98UltDial-4
❑ 98UltDiaP-5
❑ 98UltDouT-7
❑ 98UltFalC-5
❑ 98UltGolM-143
❑ 98UltGolM-250
❑ 98UltGolM-474
❑ 98UltGolM-477
❑ 98UltMas-143
❑ 98UltMas-250
❑ 98UltMas-474
❑ 98UltMas-477
❑ 98UltMilM-3
❑ 98UltNot-18
❑ 98UltPlaM-143
❑ 98UltPlaM-250

❑ 98UltPlaM-474
❑ 98UltPlaM-477
❑ 98UltPriL-5
❑ 98UltTicS-13
❑ 98UltTop3-22
❑ 98UltWinN-3
❑ 98UppDec-145
❑ 98UppDec-310
❑ 98UppDec-614
❑ 98UppDec10AP-40
❑ 98UppDec1APR-40
❑ 98UppDec5x7-310
❑ 98UppDec5x7-614
❑ 98UppDecAC-AS8
❑ 98UppDecAG-AG8
❑ 98UppDecAGDC-AG8
❑ 98UppDecCD-CD8
❑ 98UppDecNP-NP37
❑ 98UppDecPN-PN29
❑ 98UppDecPN-PN30
❑ 98UppDecPN-PN31
❑ 98UppDecPN-PN32
❑ 98UppDecPN-PN33
❑ 98UppDecPN-PN34
❑ 98UppDecPN-PN35
❑ 98UppDecR-11
❑ 98UppDecR-4
❑ 98UppDecRBBop-BB3
❑ 98UppDecRGKoG-G2
❑ 98UppDecRL-6
❑ 98UppDecRQL-Q2
❑ 98UppDecRTC-TC3
❑ 98UppDecU-8
❑ 98Zen-3
❑ 98Zen5 xx7-50
❑ 98Zen5x7GoldImp-50
❑ 98Zen5x7Imp-50
❑ 98ZenEpi-E14
❑ 98ZenRaitB-7
❑ 98ZenZ-G-3
❑ 98ZenZ-S-3
❑ 98ZenZ-T-4
❑ 98ZenZ-T5x7-4
❑ 98ZenZ-TG-4
❑ 99199Fin-82
❑ 99199Fin-119
❑ 99199Fin-272
❑ 99AurComP-1A
❑ 99AurComP-1B
❑ 99AurKinotML-1
❑ 99AurOn DL-2
❑ 99AurPenF-3
❑ 99AurPenF-3
❑ 99AurPenFB-3
❑ 99AurPenFS-3
❑ 99AurSty-3
❑ 99Bow-5
❑ 99BowBes-75
❑ 99BowBesAR-75
❑ 99BowBesR-75
❑ 99BowChr-5
❑ 99BowChrG-5
❑ 99BowChrGR-5
❑ 99BowChrI-5
❑ 99BowChrIR-5
❑ 99BowChrR-5
❑ 99BowEarR-ER2
❑ 99BowGol-5
❑ 99BowInt-5
❑ 99CroRoyB-22
❑ 99CroRoyC2-1
❑ 99CroRoyCCDB-1
❑ 99CroRoyCCG-1
❑ 99CroRoyCCG-1
❑ 99CroRoyCCLB-1
❑ 99CroRoyCCP-1
❑ 99CroRoyCCP-1
❑ 99CroRoyCCR-1
❑ 99CroRoyL-22
❑ 99CroRoyLL-2
❑ 99CroRoyMP-3
❑ 99CroRoyOD-22
❑ 99CroRoyPotG-5
❑ 99CroRoyPP-5
❑ 99CroRoyPPN-5
❑ 99DumSet-157
❑ 99DumSet-ER2
❑ 99E-X Cen-19
❑ 99E-X CenECFut-19
❑ 99E-X CenECNow-19
❑ 99E-XCenFoF'-9
❑ 99E-XCenMotC-6
❑ 99FinDouF-DF6
❑ 99FinDouFDualR-DF6
❑ 99FinFraR-FR7
❑ 99FinFraRR-FR7

❑ 99FinGolRef-82
❑ 99FinGolRef-119
❑ 99FinGolRef-272
❑ 99FinMil-M2
❑ 99FinRef-82
❑ 99FinRef-119
❑ 99FinRef-272
❑ 99FinSplS-SS5
❑ 99FinSplSDR-SS5
❑ 99FlaShoLeg1-8
❑ 99FlaShoLeg2-8
❑ 99FlaShoLeg3-8
❑ 99FlaShoLegM1-8
❑ 99FlaShoLegM2-8
❑ 99FlaShoLegM3-8
❑ 99FlaShoMoG-12
❑ 99FlaShoR1-8
❑ 99FlaShoR2-8
❑ 99FlaShoR3-8
❑ 99Fle-8
❑ 99Fle-596
❑ 99FleBri-8
❑ 99FleBri2G-8
❑ 99FleBriBlu-8
❑ 99FleBriGol-8
❑ 99FleBriSS-10
❑ 99FleBriSSP-10
❑ 99FleDatWD-8
❑ 99FleGolM-11
❑ 99FleMys-18
❑ 99FleMys-157
❑ 99FleMysE-7
❑ 99FleMysG-18
❑ 99FleMysM-18
❑ 99FleMysM-157
❑ 99FleSta9-8
❑ 99FleSta9-596
❑ 99FleVin'-8
❑ 99FleWarT-8
❑ 99FleWarT-596
❑ 99MetUni-49
❑ 99MetUni-241
❑ 99MetUni-290
❑ 99MetUniBWTW-13
❑ 99MetUniDS-1
❑ 99MetUniGM-49
❑ 99MetUniGM-241
❑ 99MetUniGM-290
❑ 99MetUniL-9
❑ 99MetUniPM-3
❑ 99MetUniPMG-49
❑ 99MetUniPMG-241
❑ 99MetUniPMG-290
❑ 99Pac-60
❑ 99Pac-60A
❑ 99PacAur-25
❑ 99PacAurOD-25
❑ 99PacCraCho-1
❑ 99PacCroC-41
❑ 99PacCroCITC-2
❑ 99PacCroCPB-41
❑ 99PacCroCPC-1
❑ 99PacCroCTC-4
❑ 99PacDynaD-1
❑ 99PacDynaDT-1
❑ 99PacGolCDC-2
❑ 99PacInv-22
❑ 99PacInvDM-1
❑ 99PacInvFP-4
❑ 99PacInvGotG-1
❑ 99PacInvOD-22
❑ 99PacInvPB-22
❑ 99PacInvSF-4
❑ 99PacInvSF-4B
❑ 99PacInvSH-4
❑ 99PacInvSH-4B
❑ 99PacInvTA-3
❑ 99PacOme-37
❑ 99PacOme5T-25
❑ 99PacOme5TT-25
❑ 99PacOmeC-37
❑ 99PacOmeDM-7
❑ 99PacOmeEP-4
❑ 99PacOmeEP1o1-4
❑ 99PacOmeG-37
❑ 99PacOmePB-37
❑ 99PacPar-36
❑ 99PacParC-36
❑ 99PacParCB-2
❑ 99PacParCBPP-2
❑ 99PacParFC-3
❑ 99PacParG-36
❑ 99PacParHoloGold-36
❑ 99PacParHS-36
❑ 99PacParOD-36
❑ 99PacParPB-7

❑ 99PacParPB-36
❑ 99PacParRed-36
❑ 99PacParTC-4
❑ 99PacPlaB-60
❑ 99PacPlaB-60A
❑ 99PacPri-21
❑ 99PacPriAotG-4
❑ 99PacPriBL-1
❑ 99PacPriDG-5
❑ 99PacPriEP-1
❑ 99PacPriHB-21
❑ 99PacPriHG-21
❑ 99PacPriHM-21
❑ 99PacPriHP-21
❑ 99PacPriRed-21
❑ 99PacPriS-15
❑ 99PacPriS206-15
❑ 99PacPriS206R-15
❑ 99PacPriSE-15
❑ 99PacPriSHRH-22
❑ 99PacPriSP-15
❑ 99PacPriSP-15
❑ 99PacPriSV-15
❑ 99PacRed-60
❑ 99PacRed-60A
❑ 99PacTeaC-2
❑ 99PacTim-1
❑ 99Pin-21
❑ 99Rev-23
❑ 99RevDiaL-8
❑ 99RevFouP-3
❑ 99RevMLBIcon-1
❑ 99RevPremDate-23
❑ 99RevRet-23
❑ 99RevShaSS-23
❑ 99RevThoitS-4
❑ 99RevTri-2
❑ 99RevTri-2
❑ 99SkyMolM-132
❑ 99SkyMolMF-32
❑ 99SkyMolMFS-32
❑ 99SkyMolMFT-32
❑ 99SkyMolMX-132
❑ 99SkyPre-208
❑ 99SkyPre-281
❑ 99SkyPreIN-1
❑ 99SkyPreLB-15
❑ 99SkyPreR-208
❑ 99SkyPreR-281
❑ 99SkyPreSB-7
❑ 99SkyPreSotG-11
❑ 99SkyThu-285
❑ 99SkyThuHip-H10
❑ 99SkyThuRant-285
❑ 99SkyThuRave-285
❑ 99SP Aut-12
❑ 99SP Aut-125
❑ 99SP AutC-CR
❑ 99SP AutCG-CR
❑ 99SP AutEF-E7
❑ 99SP AutR-R7
❑ 99SpolII-34
❑ 99SpolII-85
❑ 99SpolIIH-8
❑ 99SPx-20
❑ 99SPxDom-FB3
❑ 99SPxFinR-20
❑ 99SPxFinS-20
❑ 99SPxPreS-PS11
❑ 99SPxStaF-SF3
❑ 99StaClu-175
❑ 99StaCluC-SCC14
❑ 99StaCluCR-SCC14
❑ 99StaCluFDI-175
❑ 99StaCluNC-NC11
❑ 99StaCluOoaK-175
❑ 99StaCluPP-175
❑ 99ThuSkySupR-285
❑ 99Top-270
❑ 99TopActF-9
❑ 99TopActFAU-9
❑ 99TopActFCU-9
❑ 99TopBlaLC1-67
❑ 99TopBlaLC2-67
❑ 99TopBlaLC3-67
❑ 99TopChr-270
❑ 99TopChrR-270
❑ 99TopChrRN-RN9
❑ 99TopChrRNR-RN9
❑ 99TopGal-19
❑ 99TopGal-113
❑ 99TopGalE-E9
❑ 99TopGalHer-TH13
❑ 99TopGalHerP-TH13
❑ 99TopGalPP-19
❑ 99TopGalPP-113

❑ 99TopGalPPI-19
❑ 99TopGalPPI-113
❑ 99TopGolL-67
❑ 99TopGolLC1-67
❑ 99TopGolLC2-67
❑ 99TopGolLOtO-67
❑ 99TopMVPP-270
❑ 99TopOpeD-144
❑ 99TopOver-B2
❑ 99TopRecN-RN9
❑ 99TopRecNG-RN9
❑ 99TopRedLC1-67
❑ 99TopRedLC2-67
❑ 99TopRedLC3-67
❑ 99TopSta-20
❑ 99TopSta-157
❑ 99TopSta'S-15
❑ 99TopSta'SG-15
❑ 99TopSta'SGDH-15
❑ 99TopSta1Foil-20
❑ 99TopSta2Foil-20
❑ 99TopSta3Foil-20
❑ 99TopStaFoil-20
❑ 99TopStaFoil-157
❑ 99TopStaOS-20
❑ 99TopStaTS-20
❑ 99TopStaTS-20
❑ 99TopTek-25A
❑ 99TopTek-25B
❑ 99TopTekG-25A
❑ 99TopTekG-25B
❑ 99UD Cho-36
❑ 99UD Cho-58
❑ 99UD ChoBU-4
❑ 99UD ChoBUCG-6
❑ 99UD ChoMBH-B4
❑ 99UD ChoP-58
❑ 99UD ChoPCR-36
❑ 99UD ChoPCR-58
❑ 99UD ChoS-21
❑ 99UD ChoSD-21
❑ 99UD ChoSHR-21
❑ 99UD ChoST-21
❑ 99UD Ion-10
❑ 99UD Ion-66
❑ 99UD IonC-C2
❑ 99UD IonH-HG2
❑ 99UD IonH-H2
❑ 99UD IonN-N2
❑ 99UD IonR-10
❑ 99UD IonR-66
❑ 99UD IonWZ-WZ2
❑ 99UDHolo-10
❑ 99UDHoloAUsome-10
❑ 99UDHoloFF-F2
❑ 99UDHoloFFG-F2
❑ 99Ult-83
❑ 99Ult-213
❑ 99UltDamI-3
❑ 99UltDiaP-4
❑ 99UltGolM-83
❑ 99UltGolM-213
❑ 99UltMas-83
❑ 99UltMas-213
❑ 99UltPlaM-83
❑ 99UltPlaM-213
❑ 99UltRBIK-22
❑ 99UltTheBook-18
❑ 99UltThu-3
❑ 99UppDec-49
❑ 99UppDec-530
❑ 99UppDec10AT-X5
❑ 99UppDec10ATD-X5
❑ 99UppDec10ATHR-X5
❑ 99UppDec10ATT-X5
❑ 99UppDecBD-11
❑ 99UppDecBDD-11
❑ 99UppDecBDDom-D8
❑ 99UppDecBDDomE-D8
❑ 99UppDecBDMN-M13
❑ 99UppDecBDMNE-M13
❑ 99UppDecBDQ-11
❑ 99UppDecBDT-11
❑ 99UppDecCf7-27
❑ 99UppDecCf7-81
❑ 99UppDecCf7LL-L4
❑ 99UppDecCL-55
❑ 99UppDecCLCC-55
❑ 99UppDecCLEM-EM7
❑ 99UppDecCLM-C10
❑ 99UppDecCo7CE-27
❑ 99UppDecCo7CE-81
❑ 99UppDecE-11
❑ 99UppDecEFXG-11
❑ 99UppDecEL1-49
❑ 99UppDecEL1-530
❑ 99UppDecEL2-49
❑ 99UppDecEL2-530
❑ 99UppDecEPE-P7
❑ 99UppDecEUR-U14
❑ 99UppDecF-F7
❑ 99UppDecFD-F7
❑ 99UppDecFQ-F7
❑ 99UppDecFT-F7
❑ 99UppDecIP-I20
❑ 99UppDecIPD-I20
❑ 99UppDecIPHR-I20
❑ 99UppDecIPT-I20
❑ 99UppDecM-23
❑ 99UppDecMD-D13
❑ 99UppDecMGS-23
❑ 99UppDecMGUS-GUCR
❑ 99UppDecMHFS-23
❑ 99UppDecMP-23
❑ 99UppDecMSS-23
❑ 99UppDecMST-T12
❑ 99UppDecO-18
❑ 99UppDecO-83
❑ 99UppDecOAPoH-CR
❑ 99UppDecOMP-S4
❑ 99UppDecOSO-18
❑ 99UppDecOSO-83
❑ 99UppDecOWP-R6
❑ 99UppDecR-13
❑ 99UppDecRDR-D3
❑ 99UppDecRDRL2-D3
❑ 99UppDecRG-13
❑ 99UppDecROSS-S4
❑ 99UppDecROSS-S4
❑ 99UppDecRP-13
❑ 99UppDecRTA-T11
❑ 99UppDecRTAL2-T11
❑ 99UppDecTE-T5
❑ 99UppDecTED-T5
❑ 99UppDecTEQ-T5
❑ 99UppDecTET-T5
❑ 99UppDecVtaT-V7
❑ 99UppDecVtaTD-V7
❑ 99UppDecVtaTQ-V7
❑ 99UppDecVtaTT-V7
❑ 99UppDecWY-W23
❑ 99UppDecWYD-W23
❑ 99UppDecWYHR-W23
❑ 99UppDecWYT-W23
❑ 99Vic-45
❑ 99Vic-46
❑ 99Vic-452

Ripken, Cal Sr.
❑ 76BalOriP-32
❑ 78BalOriP-25
❑ 82Don-579
❑ 83OriPos-24
❑ 84BalOriP-28
❑ 85BalOriP-25
❑ 85Fle-641
❑ 86BalOriP-16
❑ 87BalOriP-30
❑ 87OriFreB-7
❑ 87TopTra-102T
❑ 87TopTraT-102T
❑ 88Don-625
❑ 88OriPos-28
❑ 88Top-444
❑ 88TopTif-444
❑ 89BalOriP-27
❑ 89Bow-260
❑ 89BowTif-260
❑ 89OriFreB-7

Ripley, Allen
❑ 78PapGinD-1
❑ 78SSP270-188
❑ 79Top-702
❑ 80GiaTeal-24
❑ 80Top-413
❑ 81Fle-454
❑ 81GiaTeal-15
❑ 81Top-144
❑ 82CubRedL-33
❑ 82Don-125
❑ 82Fle-299
❑ 82Top-529
❑ 82TopTra-99T
❑ 83Don-57
❑ 83Fle-506
❑ 83Top-73

Ripley, Walter
❑ 79RedSoxEF-6

Rippelmeyer, Brad
❑ 91IdaFalBP-4333
❑ 91IdaFalBSP-3
❑ 92DurBulC-13
❑ 92DurBulF-1105
❑ 92DurBulTI-15
❑ 93GreBraF-354
❑ 94DurBulC-15
❑ 94DurBulF-331
❑ 94DurBulTI-16
❑ 95BreBtaTI-9
❑ 97ChaRivDG-24
❑ 98HudValR-20

Rippelmeyer, Ray
❑ 60HenHouW-28
❑ 60SeaPop-11
❑ 60UniOil-10
❑ 61Top-276
❑ 62Top-271
❑ 73OPC-486
❑ 73PhiTeal-26
❑ 73Top-486A
❑ 73Top-486B
❑ 74OPC-119
❑ 74Top-119
❑ 75PhiPhiP-25
❑ 76PhiPhiP-36
❑ 78SSP270-35
❑ 89NasSouC-24
❑ 89NasSouP-1280
❑ 89NasSouTI-29
❑ 90CMC-150
❑ 90NasSouC-25
❑ 90NasSouP-250
❑ 90ProAAAF-562
❑ 97NorTid-3
❑ 97NorTidB-3
❑ 98NorTidP-23
❑ 98NorTidQ-34

Ripple, Charles
❑ 47CenFlo-23
❑ 47SigOil-67

Ripple, Jimmy
❑ 28LaPre-17
❑ 36WorWidGV-28
❑ 38ExhFou-5
❑ 38OurNatGPP-24
❑ 39PlaBal-66
❑ 41DouPlaR-11
❑ 41DouPlaR-95
❑ 41HarHarW-21
❑ 44CenFlo-18
❑ 77CinRedT-8
❑ 90DodTar-669
❑ 91ConTSN-86

Rippley, Steve
❑ 88T/MUmp-49
❑ 89T/MUmp-47
❑ 90T/MUmp-45

Ripslager, Charles
❑ 87OldJudN-417

Ris, Greg
❑ 78QuaCitAT-21

Risberg, Swede (Charles)
❑ 15Zee-136
❑ 16Zee-142
❑ 18WhiSoxTI-18
❑ 19W514-105
❑ 75WhiSox1T-20
❑ 88LitSunBS-6
❑ 88PacEigMO-16
❑ 88PacEigMO-26
❑ 88PacEigMO-70
❑ 88PacEigMO-103
❑ 92Man191BSR-19
❑ 94ConTSN-1032
❑ 94ConTSNB-1032

Riscen, Fred
❑ 88SalLakCTTI-21

Riske, David
❑ 97KinIndB-21
❑ 98CarLeaAC-23
❑ 98KinIndQ-20
❑ 99Bow-120
❑ 99BowChr-120
❑ 99BowChrG-120
❑ 99BowChrGR-120
❑ 99BowChrI-120
❑ 99BowChrIR-120
❑ 99BowChrR-120
❑ 99BowGol-120
❑ 99BowInt-120

Risley, Bill (William)
❑ 88GreHorP-1551
❑ 89CedRapRB-6
❑ 89CedRapRP-912
❑ 89CedRapRS-16
❑ 90CedRapRB-14
❑ 90CedRapRP-2313
❑ 90ProAaA-121
❑ 91ChaLooLD-166
❑ 91ChaLooP-1959
❑ 91LinDriAA-166
❑ 92DonRoo-103
❑ 92IndIndF-1857
❑ 93Bow-44
❑ 93FleFinE-96
❑ 93OttLynF-2434
❑ 94CalCanF-787
❑ 94Fla-339
❑ 94FleExtB-171
❑ 94FleUpd-85
❑ 95Don-205
❑ 95DonPreP-205
❑ 95DonTopotO-154
❑ 95Fla-302
❑ 95Fle-275
❑ 95FleRooS-16
❑ 95MarMot-27
❑ 95MarPac-41
❑ 95Top-448
❑ 95TopCyb-244
❑ 95Ult-105
❑ 95UltGolM-105
❑ 95UltSecYS-12
❑ 95UltSecYSGM-12
❑ 96BluJayOH-27
❑ 96Don-438
❑ 96DonPreP-438
❑ 96Fla-192
❑ 96Fle-242
❑ 96FleTif-242
❑ 96FleUpd-U102
❑ 96FleUpdTC-U102
❑ 96LeaSigEA-170
❑ 96Ult-436
❑ 96UltGolM-436
❑ 97BluJayOH-27
❑ 98PacOnl-773
❑ 98PacOnlR-773
❑ 98PacOnlWC-773

Ritch, Harry
❑ 85VerBeaDT-13

Ritchey, Claude
❑ 03BreE10-124
❑ 06FanCraNL-41
❑ 08RosComP-93
❑ 09ColChiE-241
❑ 09RamT20-99
❑ 09T206-304
❑ 11SpoLifCW-303
❑ 12ColRedB-241
❑ 12ColTinT-241
❑ 98CamPepP-64

Ritchey, Larry
❑ 86MedA'sC-60

Ritchie, Dave
❑ 89EugEmeB-11

Ritchie, Gregg
❑ 86EveGiaC-5
❑ 86EveGiaPC-26
❑ 87CliGiaP-4
❑ 88SanJosGCLC-127
❑ 88SanJosGP-131
❑ 89ShrCapP-1841
❑ 90CMC-541
❑ 90PhoFirC-14
❑ 90PhoFirP-25
❑ 90ProAAAF-51
❑ 91LinDriAAA-391
❑ 91PhoFirLD-391
❑ 91PhoFirP-81
❑ 92PhoFirF-2835
❑ 92PhoFirS-395
❑ 96BriWhiSB-2
❑ 97BriWhiSB-26
❑ 98HicCraM-3
❑ 98HicCraUO-3

Ritchie, Jay
❑ 64SeaPop-14
❑ 65Top-494
❑ 67BraPho-25

Ritchie, Lewis
❑ 09SpoNewSM-87
❑ 14PieStaT-89

Ritchie, Peter
❑ 18Zee-91
❑ 19Zee-119
❑ 22Zee-137
❑ 23Zee-170
❑ 24Zee-100
❑ 25Zee-120

Ritchie, Todd
❑ 90CIaDraP-12
❑ 90EliTwiS-19
❑ 91Bow-332
❑ 91Cla/Bes-319
❑ 91Cla1-T58
❑ 91KenTwiC-22
❑ 91KenTwiP-2072
❑ 91MidLeaAP-MWL39
❑ 91Sco-678
❑ 92Bow-524
❑ 92ClaFS7-298
❑ 92ProFS7-99
❑ 92UppDecML-106
❑ 92VisOakC-23
❑ 92VisOakF-1014
❑ 93ClaFS7-251
❑ 93ClaGolF-44
❑ 93NasXprF-403
❑ 94Bow-272
❑ 94NasXprF-385
❑ 94SigRoo-17
❑ 94SigRooS-17
❑ 94UppDecML-167
❑ 95HarCitRCTI-20
❑ 96HarCitRCB-26
❑ 98PacInvGems-66
❑ 98PacOnl-434
❑ 98PacOnlR-434
❑ 98PacOnlWC-434
❑ 98SalLakBO-23

Ritchie, Wally
❑ 86ClePhiP-21
❑ 87FleUpd-104
❑ 87FleUpdG-104
❑ 87MaiGuiP-17
❑ 87TopTra-103T
❑ 87TopTraT-103T
❑ 88BlaYNPRWLU-9
❑ 88Don-555
❑ 88Fle-312
❑ 88FleGlo-312
❑ 88OPC-322
❑ 88PhiTas-20
❑ 88Sco-526
❑ 88ScoGlo-526
❑ 88Top-494
❑ 88TopTif-494
❑ 89ScrRedBC-9
❑ 89ScrRedBP-715
❑ 90CMC-232
❑ 90ProAAAF-300
❑ 90ScrRedBC-6
❑ 90ScrRedBP-598
❑ 91LinDriAAA-493
❑ 91ScrRedBLD-493
❑ 91ScrRedBP-2536
❑ 92Don-631
❑ 92Fle-543
❑ 92Lea-443
❑ 92LeaBlaG-443
❑ 92PhiMed-25
❑ 92Sco-619
❑ 92StaClu-324
❑ 93TolMudHF-1655
❑ 93TriAAAGF-39
❑ 94ClaGolF-179
❑ 98ScrRedB1ATI-15

Ritter, Chris
❑ 86PriWilPP-21
❑ 87HarSenP-25
❑ 88HarSenP-845

Ritter, Darren
❑ 89PulBraP-1905
❑ 90Bes-47
❑ 90BurBraB-25
❑ 90BurBraP-2348
❑ 90BurBraS-22
❑ 91DurBulUP-6
❑ 91MacBraC-7
❑ 91MacBraP-861
❑ 92DurBulC-9
❑ 92DurBulF-1097
❑ 92DurBulTI-31

Ritter, Jason
❑ 94EugEmeC-18
❑ 94EugEmeF-3710
❑ 95SpoIndTI-21
❑ 96LanLugB-20

Ritter, Ken
❑ 89MedAthB-15

Ritter, Lawrence
❑ 90LitSunW-12

Ritter, Lou (Louis)
❑ 09ColChiE-242
❑ 09T206-460
❑ 11SpoLifCW-304
❑ 12ColRedB-242
❑ 12ColTinT-242
❑ 90DodTar-670

Ritter, Reggie
❑ 83WatIndF-15
❑ 85WatIndT-11
❑ 86IndOhH-53
❑ 86IndTeal-35
❑ 86MaiGuiP-16
❑ 87BufBisP-19
❑ 88ColSprSSC-7
❑ 88ColSprSSP-1540
❑ 89BlaYNPRWLU-4

Ritter, Ryan
❑ 95HelBreTI-15
❑ 96BelSnaTI-32

Ritter, Wallace
❑ 29Zee-10

Ritter, William
❑ 17ColE13-138

Rittman, Alvin
❑ 89BelMarL-24
❑ 90SprCarB-2

Rittwage, James
❑ 65Top-501
❑ 70WicAerM-13

Rittweger, Bill
❑ 82JacMetT-18

Ritz, Kevin
❑ 87GleFalTP-6
❑ 88GleFalTP-926
❑ 89TolMudHC-7
❑ 89TolMudHP-786
❑ 90Bow-350
❑ 90BowTif-350
❑ 90ClaBlu-131
❑ 90CMC-385
❑ 90Don-415
❑ 90Fle-613
❑ 90FleCan-613
❑ 90Hot50RS-37
❑ 90OPC-237
❑ 90ProAAAF-377
❑ 90Sco-572
❑ 90Sco100RS-11
❑ 90Spo-29
❑ 90TigCok-18
❑ 90TolMudHC-8
❑ 90TolMudHP-147
❑ 90Top-237
❑ 90TopDeb89-102
❑ 90TopTif-237
❑ 90UppDec-98
❑ 91LinDriAAA-596
❑ 91TigCok-31
❑ 91TolMudHLD-596
❑ 91TolMudHP-1932
❑ 92Bow-419
❑ 92Lea-386
❑ 92LeaBlaG-386
❑ 92StaClu-337
❑ 92TigKro-22
❑ 92Ult-368
❑ 93Don-99
❑ 93Fle-415
❑ 93Top-771
❑ 93TopGol-771
❑ 93TopInaM-771
❑ 93TopInaR-771
❑ 93TopMic-771
❑ 94ColSprSSF-732
❑ 94FleUpd-130
❑ 95Fle-527
❑ 95StaClu-576
❑ 95StaCluMOP-576
❑ 95StaCluSTWS-576
❑ 95TopTra-115T
❑ 95Ult-157
❑ 95UltGolM-157
❑ 96ColCho-137
❑ 96ColChoGS-137
❑ 96ColChoSS-137
❑ 96Don-383
❑ 96DonPreP-383
❑ 96EmoXL-176
❑ 96Fla-250
❑ 96Fle-372
❑ 96FleTif-372
❑ 96LeaSigEA-171
❑ 96Pac-52
❑ 96RocFle-12
❑ 96RocPol-19
❑ 96Sco-45
❑ 96StaClu-377
❑ 96StaCluMOP-377
❑ 96Ult-192
❑ 96UltGolM-192
❑ 96UppDec-324
❑ 97Cir-220

❑ 97CirRav-220
❑ 97ColCho-97
❑ 97ColChoT-CR3
❑ 97Fle-317
❑ 97FleTif-317
❑ 97Lea-96
❑ 97LeaFraM-96
❑ 97LeaFraMDC-96
❑ 97MetUni-75
❑ 97Pac-288
❑ 97PacLigB-288
❑ 97PacSil-288
❑ 97RocSco-2
❑ 97RocScoPl-2
❑ 97RocScoPr-2
❑ 97Sco-29
❑ 97ScoArtPWB-29
❑ 97ScoPreS-29
❑ 97ScoShoS-29
❑ 97ScoShoSAP-29
❑ 97StaClu-158
❑ 97StaCluMOP-158
❑ 97Top-233
❑ 97Ult-189
❑ 97UltGolME-189
❑ 97UltPlaME-189
❑ 97UppDec-58
❑ 98UppDec-356

Ritz, Trey
❑ 92HamRedC-17
❑ 92HamRedF-1603
❑ 93GleFalRC-24
❑ 93GleFalRF-4014

Ritzi, Mike
❑ 97BurBeeB-29

Rivard, John
❑ 89MiaMirlS-17

Rivas, Hector
❑ 80VenLeaS-213

Rivas, Javier
❑ 91PulBraC-15
❑ 91PulBraP-4019

Rivas, Limbert
❑ 90AshTouP-2746

Rivas, Luis
❑ 97Bes-76
❑ 97ForWayW-1
❑ 97MidLeaTP-10
❑ 98Bes-90
❑ 98Bow-400
❑ 98BowBes-141
❑ 98BowBesAR-141
❑ 98BowBesR-141
❑ 98BowChr-400
❑ 98BowChrGA-400
❑ 98BowChrGAR-400
❑ 98BowChrl-400
❑ 98BowChrlR-400
❑ 98BowChrR-400
❑ 98BowGolA-400
❑ 98BowInt-400
❑ 98ForMyeMTI-26
❑ 98SP MinPE-77
❑ 98SPMin-77

Rivas, Martin
❑ 77ChaPatT-15
❑ 85DomLeaS-160

Rivas, Oscar
❑ 89AriStaB-23
❑ 89BelMarL-12
❑ 90PenPilS-17
❑ 91SanBerSP-1988

Rivas, Rafael
❑ 80UtiBluJT-31

Rivas, Ralph
❑ 83KinBluJTI-19

Rivas, Rene
❑ 85DomLeaS-159

Rivas, Tony
❑ 75OakOak2A-29

Rivell, Robert
❑ 88CapCodPPaLP-72
❑ 91WatDiaC-19
❑ 91WatDiaP-1266

River Rascal, Crash the
❑ 94WesMicWC-28
❑ 95WesMicWTI-99
❑ 96WesMicWB-4
❑ 97WesMicW-4
❑ 98WesMicWM-1

Rivera, Alvin
❑ 97AshTou-21
❑ 97PorRocG-21

Rivera, Angel
❑ 88JamExpP-1900

Rivera, Ben
❑ 88SumBraP-410
❑ 89DurBullS-18
❑ 89DurBullS-18
❑ 89DurBulTI-18
❑ 90DurBulUTI-4
❑ 90GreBraB-6
❑ 90GreBraP-1126
❑ 90GreBraS-17
❑ 91Bow-579
❑ 91GreBraC-3
❑ 91GreBraLD-214
❑ 91GreBraP-2997
❑ 91LinDriAA-214
❑ 92DonRoo-104
❑ 92FleUpd-111
❑ 92PhiMed-45
❑ 92Pin-554
❑ 92Ult-463
❑ 93Don-412
❑ 93Fle-107
❑ 93Lea-393
❑ 93LimRocDWB-44
❑ 93OPC-330
❑ 93PacSpa-580
❑ 93PhiMed-28
❑ 93PhiStaC-20
❑ 93Pin-437
❑ 93Sco-242
❑ 93Sel-329
❑ 93StaClu-654
❑ 93StaCluFDI-654
❑ 93StaCluMOP-654
❑ 93Top-622
❑ 93TopGol-622
❑ 93TopInaM-622
❑ 93TopInaR-622
❑ 93TopMic-622
❑ 93Ult-93
❑ 93UppDec-389
❑ 93UppDecGold-389
❑ 94ColC-626
❑ 94ColChoGS-626
❑ 94ColChoSS-626
❑ 94Don-216
❑ 94Fla-211
❑ 94Fle-599
❑ 94Lea-213
❑ 94Pac-485
❑ 94PhiMed-27
❑ 94PhiUSPC-5H
❑ 94PhiUSPC-12C
❑ 94Pin-178
❑ 94PinArtP-178
❑ 94PinMusC-178
❑ 94Sco-293
❑ 94ScoGolR-293
❑ 94StaClu-252
❑ 94StaCluFDI-252
❑ 94StaCluGR-252
❑ 94StaCluMOP-252
❑ 94StaCluT-232
❑ 94StaCluTFDI-232
❑ 94Top-352
❑ 94TopGol-352
❑ 94TopSpa-352
❑ 94Ult-252
❑ 95Top-239

Rivera, Bombo (Jesus)
❑ 75ExpPos-29
❑ 76ExpRed-26
❑ 76MonExpP-25
❑ 77OPC-54
❑ 77Top-178
❑ 78Top-657
❑ 78TwiFriP-17
❑ 79Top-449
❑ 79TwiFriP-24
❑ 80OPC-22
❑ 80Top-43
❑ 80TwiPos-26
❑ 81Don-593
❑ 81Fle-556
❑ 81OmaRoyT-23
❑ 81Top-256
❑ 82OmaRoyT-20
❑ 83OmaRoyT-19
❑ 88BlaYNPRWL-14

Rivera, Carlos
❑ 87FayGenP-14
❑ 88ElmPioC-11
❑ 88WinHavRSS-21
❑ 89BlaYNPRWLU-17
❑ 89ElmPioP-15
❑ 97AugGre-22
❑ 98AugGreM-6

Rivera, Charlie
❑ 95NegLeaL2-21

Rivera, Dave
❑ 76AshTouT-4
❑ 77AshTouT-18
❑ 82ChaChaT-22

Rivera, David
❑ 88BlaYNPRWL-113
❑ 89BlaYNPRWL-184
❑ 91KenTwiC-6
❑ 91KenTwiP-2084
❑ 92VisOakC-18
❑ 92VisOakF-1023
❑ 93NasXprF-411

Rivera, Elvin
❑ 86QuaCitAP-27
❑ 87QuaCitAP-16
❑ 88RenSilSCLC-269

Rivera, Ernesto
❑ 92OklStaC-25

Rivera, German
❑ 78CliDodT-27
❑ 83AlbDukTc-17
❑ 84DodPol-25
❑ 85AlbDukCr-162
❑ 85Don-638
❑ 85Fle-382
❑ 85Top-626
❑ 85TopTif-626
❑ 86NasSouTI-20
❑ 87TolMudHP-4
❑ 87TolMudHT-3
❑ 88BlaYNPRWL-13
❑ 88DenZepC-12
❑ 88DenZepP-1253
❑ 88TriAAAP-14
❑ 88TriAAC-9
❑ 90DodTar-671
❑ 90IndIndP-305
❑ 90ProAAAF-588
❑ 90TriAllGP-AAA9

Rivera, Hector
❑ 89WesPalBES-20
❑ 90CMC-670
❑ 90GatCitPP-3349
❑ 90GatCitPSP-20
❑ 90JacExpB-23
❑ 90JacExpP-1374
❑ 91Bow-444
❑ 91HarSenLD-261
❑ 91HarSenP-625
❑ 91LinDriAA-261

Rivera, Jim (Manuel J.)
❑ 53Top-156
❑ 54Top-34
❑ 55Top-58
❑ 55TopDouH-89
❑ 56Top-70
❑ 56TopHocF-A11
❑ 56TopHocF-B13
❑ 56TopPin-35
❑ 57Top-107
❑ 58Top-11A
❑ 58Top-11B
❑ 58WhiSoxJP-9
❑ 59Top-213
❑ 60Lea-55
❑ 60Top-116
❑ 60TopVen-116
❑ 60WhiSoxTS-16
❑ 61Pos-33A
❑ 61Pos-33B
❑ 61Top-367
❑ 81WhiSox1T-10
❑ 83AndBraT-14
❑ 84DurBulT-26
❑ 91TopArc1-156
❑ 94TopArc1-34
❑ 94TopArc1G-34

Rivera, Jose
❑ 83GreHorT-23
❑ 83QuaCitCT-23
❑ 87MemChiB-4
❑ 87MemChiP-23
❑ 88BlaYNPRWL-15
❑ 88MemChiB-25
❑ 89BlaYNPRWL-151

Rivera, Juan
❑ 98SpoIndG-27
❑ 99Bow-386
❑ 99BowGol-386
❑ 99BowInt-386

Rivera, Lino
❑ 88BlaYNPRWL-74
❑ 88ChaRanS-20
❑ 89BlaYNPRWL-85
❑ 89FayGenP-1573
❑ 89SouAtlLAGS-21
❑ 90LakTigS-22
❑ 90StaFS7-37
❑ 91LakTigC-11
❑ 91LakTigP-266
❑ 92ArkTraS-43

Rivera, Luis A.
❑ 97VerExpB-23
❑ 98JupHamQ-28

Rivera, Luis Antonio
❑ 83VerBeaDT-13
❑ 86IndIndTI-28
❑ 87ExpPos-23
❑ 87Fle-330
❑ 87FleGlo-330
❑ 87IndIndTI-27
❑ 88BlaYNPRWL-77
❑ 88ExpPos-29
❑ 88StaLinE-15
❑ 88TopBig-223
❑ 88TopTra-94T
❑ 88TopTraT-94T
❑ 89BlaYNPRWL-86
❑ 89Bow-29
❑ 89BowTif-29
❑ 89Don-578
❑ 89Fle-392
❑ 89FleGlo-392
❑ 89OPC-257
❑ 89PawRedSC-20
❑ 89PawRedSP-697
❑ 89PawRedSTI-20
❑ 89Sco-169
❑ 89Top-431
❑ 89TopSti-68
❑ 89TopTif-431
❑ 89UppDec-423
❑ 90Don-421
❑ 90Fle-285
❑ 90FleCan-285
❑ 90Lea-283
❑ 90OPC-601
❑ 90RedSoxP-18
❑ 90Top-601
❑ 90TopTif-601
❑ 90TopTVRS-26
❑ 90UppDec-482
❑ 91Don-234
❑ 91Fle-112
❑ 91Lea-408
❑ 91OPC-338
❑ 91PanFreS-267
❑ 91RedSoxP-19
❑ 91RedSoxP-26
❑ 91Sco-271
❑ 91StaClu-55
❑ 91Top-338
❑ 91TopDesS-338
❑ 91TopMic-338
❑ 91TopTif-338
❑ 91Ult-42
❑ 91UppDec-182
❑ 92Bow-355
❑ 92Don-332
❑ 92Fle-48
❑ 92Lea-355
❑ 92LeaBlaG-355
❑ 92OPC-97
❑ 92PanSti-88
❑ 92Pin-346
❑ 92RedSoxDD-26
❑ 92Sco-159
❑ 92StaClu-255
❑ 92Top-97
❑ 92TopGol-97
❑ 92TopGolW-97
❑ 92TopMic-97
❑ 92Ult-22
❑ 92UppDec-308
❑ 93Don-591
❑ 93Fle-565
❑ 93PacSpa-36
❑ 93PanSti-94
❑ 93Pin-159
❑ 93RedSoxP-28
❑ 93RedSoxWHP-24
❑ 93StaClu-533
❑ 93StaCluFDI-533
❑ 93StaCluMOP-533
❑ 93Top-296
❑ 93TopGol-296
❑ 93TopInaM-296
❑ 93TopInaR-296
❑ 93TopMic-296
❑ 93TriPla-246
❑ 93Ult-515
❑ 93UppDec-602
❑ 93UppDecGold-602
❑ 94MetColP-21
❑ 94Pac-64
❑ 94StaCluMOP-ST16
❑ 94StaCluST-ST16
❑ 95Pac-286
❑ 95StaCluSTDW-RS1T
❑ 96NorTidB-26
❑ 98NewOrlZM-19
❑ 98PacInvGems-165

Rivera, Luis Gutierrez
❑ 97AppLeaTPB-3
❑ 97DanBraB-24
❑ 98Bes-91
❑ 98Bow-317
❑ 98BowChr-317
❑ 98BowChrGA-317
❑ 98BowChrGAR-317
❑ 98BowChrl-317
❑ 98BowChrlR-317
❑ 98BowChrR-317
❑ 98BowGolA-317
❑ 98BowInt-317
❑ 98MacBraM-18
❑ 99Bow-212
❑ 99BowChr-212
❑ 99BowChrG-212
❑ 99BowChrGR-212
❑ 99BowChrl-212
❑ 99BowChrlR-212
❑ 99BowChrR-212
❑ 99BowGol-212
❑ 99BowInt-212
❑ 99TeaBesRFS-2

Rivera, Luis J.
❑ 98CapFeaCM-19
❑ 98VerExpO-21

Rivera, Mariano
❑ 90TamYanD-17
❑ 91GreHorP-3058
❑ 92Bow-302
❑ 92Ft.LauYF-2611
❑ 93Bow-327
❑ 94TamYanC-20
❑ 94TamYanF-2382
❑ 95Bow-165
❑ 95Exc-102
❑ 95StaClu-592
❑ 95StaCluMOP-592
❑ 95StaCluSTWS-592
❑ 95TopTra-130T
❑ 96ColCho-19
❑ 96ColChoGS-19
❑ 96ColChoSS-19
❑ 96Don-67
❑ 96DonPreP-67
❑ 96Fle-195
❑ 96FleTif-195
❑ 96LeaSig-107
❑ 96LeaSigA-194
❑ 96LeaSigAG-194
❑ 96LeaSigAS-194
❑ 96LeaSigPPG-107
❑ 96LeaSigPPP-107
❑ 96Pac-382
❑ 96Pin-189
❑ 96Sco-225
❑ 96StaClu-411
❑ 96StaCluMOP-411
❑ 96Ult-105
❑ 96UltGolM-105
❑ 97Bow-27
❑ 97BowBes-32
❑ 97BowBesAR-32
❑ 97BowBesR-32
❑ 97BowChr-23
❑ 97BowChrl-23
❑ 97BowChrlR-23
❑ 97BowChrR-23
❑ 97BowInt-27
❑ 97BowIntB-BBI9
❑ 97BowIntBAR-BBI9
❑ 97BowIntBR-BBI9
❑ 97Cir-3
❑ 97CirFasT-7
❑ 97CirRav-3
❑ 97ColCho-405
❑ 97ColChoBS-7
❑ 97ColChoBSGS-7
❑ 97Don-133
❑ 97DonEli-118
❑ 97DonEliGS-118
❑ 97DonGolPP-133
❑ 97DonLim-134
❑ 97DonLimE-134
❑ 97DonLimENG-134
❑ 97DonPre-123
❑ 97DonPreCttC-123
❑ 97DonSilPP-133
❑ 97DonTea-128
❑ 97DonTeaSPE-128
❑ 97Fin-117
❑ 97FinEmb-117
❑ 97FinEmbR-117
❑ 97FinRef-117
❑ 97FlaShoLC-142
❑ 97FlaShoLeg0-142
❑ 97FlaShoLeg1-142
❑ 97FlaShoM-A142
❑ 97FlaShoM-B142
❑ 97FlaShoM-C142
❑ 97FlaShoR0-142
❑ 97FlaShoR1-142
❑ 97FlaShoR2-142
❑ 97Fle-176
❑ 97FleTif-176
❑ 97Lea-147
❑ 97LeaFraM-147
❑ 97LeaFraMDC-147
❑ 97LeaGet-16
❑ 97MetUni-122
❑ 97NewPin-87
❑ 97NewPinAP-87
❑ 97NewPinMC-87
❑ 97NewPinPP-87
❑ 97Pac-158
❑ 97PacGolCD-13
❑ 97PacLatotML-14
❑ 97PacLigB-158
❑ 97PacPri-54
❑ 97PacPriLB-54
❑ 97PacPriP-54
❑ 97PacSil-158
❑ 97Pin-128
❑ 97PinArtP-PP128
❑ 97PinCar-14
❑ 97PinCer-62
❑ 97PinCerMBla-62
❑ 97PinCerMBlu-62
❑ 97PinCerMG-62
❑ 97PinCerMR-62
❑ 97PinCerR-62
❑ 97PinIns-113
❑ 97PinInsCE-113
❑ 97PinInsDD-17
❑ 97PinInsDE-113
❑ 97PinMusC-128
❑ 97PinPrePla-128
❑ 97PinTotCPB-62
❑ 97PinTotCPG-62
❑ 97PinTotCPR-62
❑ 97PinX-P-25
❑ 97PinX-PMoS-25
❑ 97Sco-116
❑ 97Sco-527
❑ 97ScoArtPWB-116
❑ 97ScoArtPWB-527
❑ 97ScoPreS-116
❑ 97ScoResC-527
❑ 97ScoShoS-116
❑ 97ScoShoS-527
❑ 97ScoShoSAP-116
❑ 97ScoShoSAP-527
❑ 97ScoStaaD-12
❑ 97Sel-87
❑ 97SelArtP-87
❑ 97SelCom-87
❑ 97SelRegG-87
❑ 97SelRooR-18
❑ 97SP-127
❑ 97Spolll-132
❑ 97SpollIEE-132
❑ 97StaClu-11
❑ 97StaCluMat-11
❑ 97StaCluMOP-11
❑ 97StrAll-52
❑ 97Stu-104
❑ 97StuPrePG-104
❑ 97StuPrePS-104
❑ 97Top-256
❑ 97TopAwel-AI16
❑ 97TopChr-89
❑ 97TopChrR-89
❑ 97TopGal-158
❑ 97TopGalPPI-158
❑ 97TopSta-94
❑ 97TopStaAM-94
❑ 97Ult-103

❑ 97UltGolME-103
❑ 97UltPlaME-103
❑ 97UppDec-69
❑ 97UppDec-439
❑ 97YanSco-7
❑ 97YanScoPl-7
❑ 97YanScoPr-7
❑ 98Bow-269
❑ 98BowChr-269
❑ 98BowChrGA-269
❑ 98BowChrGAR-269
❑ 98BowChrI-269
❑ 98BowChrIR-269
❑ 98BowChrR-269
❑ 98BowGolA-269
❑ 98BowInt-269
❑ 98CirThu-89
❑ 98CirThuRav-89
❑ 98CirThuSupRav-89
❑ 98ColCho-451
❑ 98Don-209
❑ 98DonGolPP-209
❑ 98DonSigA-73
❑ 98DonSigAC-94
❑ 98DonSigAM-96
❑ 98DonSilPP-209
❑ 98Fin-29
❑ 98FinNo--29
❑ 98FinNo-R-29
❑ 98FinRef-29
❑ 98Fle-205
❑ 98FleVin'-42
❑ 98FleVin'C-42
❑ 98MetUni-53
❑ 98MetUniPMG-53
❑ 98Pac-157
❑ 98PacAur-63
❑ 98PacInv-55
❑ 98PacInvPBlue-55
❑ 98PacInvSilv-55
❑ 98PacInvTeam-19
❑ 98PacLatotML-27
❑ 98PacOme-170
❑ 98PacOmeR-170
❑ 98PacOnl-515
❑ 98PacOnlR-515
❑ 98PacOnlWC-515
❑ 98PacPar-74
❑ 98PacParC-74
❑ 98PacParG-74
❑ 98PacParHS-74
❑ 98PacParPB-74
❑ 98PacParR-74
❑ 98PacPlaB-157
❑ 98PacRedT-157
❑ 98PacSil-157
❑ 98PinIns-99
❑ 98PinInsCE-99
❑ 98PinInsDE-99
❑ 98PinPlu-22
❑ 98PinSna-NYY7
❑ 98Sco-113
❑ 98ScoRT-64
❑ 98ScoSS-PP147
❑ 98ScoSSAP-PP147
❑ 98SPxFin-303
❑ 98SPxFinR-303
❑ 98SPxFinS-303
❑ 98StaCluFDI-38
❑ 98StaCluI-38
❑ 98StaCluOneK-38
❑ 98StaCluPP-38
❑ 98Stu-69
❑ 98StuGPP-69
❑ 98StuSPP-69
❑ 98Top-8
❑ 98TopChr-8
❑ 98TopChrR-8
❑ 98TopDevR-8
❑ 98TopDia-8
❑ 98TopGal-76
❑ 98TopGalGP-76
❑ 98TopGalOPP-76
❑ 98TopGalPPI-76
❑ 98TopGalPPIA-76
❑ 98TopGolLabC1-41
❑ 98TopGolLabC1B-41
❑ 98TopGolLabC1One-41
❑ 98TopGolLabC1R-41
❑ 98TopGolLabC2-41
❑ 98TopGolLabC2B-41
❑ 98TopGolLabC2One-41
❑ 98TopGolLabC2R-41
❑ 98TopGolLabC3-41
❑ 98TopGolLabC3B-41
❑ 98TopGolLabC3One-41
❑ 98TopGolLabC3R-41
❑ 98TopMiniC-8
❑ 98TopOpeD-7
❑ 98TopSta-52
❑ 98TopStaB-52
❑ 98TopStaG-52
❑ 98TopStaGR-52
❑ 98TopStaS-52
❑ 98Ult-147
❑ 98UltDouT-18
❑ 98UltGolM-147
❑ 98UltMas-147
❑ 98UltPlaM-147
❑ 98UppDec-465
❑ 98UppDecNP-NP26
❑ 98YanSco-9
❑ 98YanScoP-9
❑ 98YanUppD-465
❑ 98Zen-65
❑ 98ZenZ-G-65
❑ 98ZenZ-S-65
❑ 99199Fin-239
❑ 99Bow-58
❑ 99BowChr-58
❑ 99BowChrG-58
❑ 99BowChrGR-58
❑ 99BowChrI-58
❑ 99BowChrIR-58
❑ 99BowChrR-58
❑ 99BowGol-58
❑ 99BowInt-58
❑ 99FinGolRef-239
❑ 99FinRef-239
❑ 99Fle-234
❑ 99FleSta9-234
❑ 99FleWarT-234
❑ 99MetUni-22
❑ 99MetUniGM-22
❑ 99MetUniPMG-22
❑ 99Pac-303
❑ 99PacCroC-196
❑ 99PacCroC-14
❑ 99PacCroCPB-196
❑ 99PacPlaB-303
❑ 99PacRed-303
❑ 99SkyMolM-77
❑ 99SkyMolMX-77
❑ 99SkyPre-136
❑ 99SkyPreR-136
❑ 99SkyThu-111
❑ 99SkyThuRant-111
❑ 99SkyThuRave-111
❑ 99SP SigAuto-MRI
❑ 99SPSig-139
❑ 99StaClu-75
❑ 99StaCluFDI-75
❑ 99StaCluOoaK-75
❑ 99StaCluPP-75
❑ 99ThuSkySupR-111
❑ 99Top-172
❑ 99Top-240
❑ 99TopChr-172
❑ 99TopChr-240
❑ 99TopChrR-172
❑ 99TopChrR-240
❑ 99TopMVPP-172
❑ 99TopOpeD-95
❑ 99TopSta-126
❑ 99TopStaFoil-126
❑ 99Ult-136
❑ 99UltGolM-136
❑ 99UltMas-136
❑ 99UltPlaM-136
❑ 99UppDec-158
❑ 99UppDec-240
❑ 99UppDecEL1-158
❑ 99UppDecEL1-240
❑ 99UppDecEL2-158
❑ 99UppDecEL2-240
❑ 99UppDecM-146
❑ 99UppDecMGS-146
❑ 99UppDecMHFS-146
❑ 99UppDecMSS-146
❑ 99Vic-275
❑ 99YanFle-4

Rivera, Maximo
❑ 93WelPirC-25
❑ 93WelPirF-3369

Rivera, Michael
❑ 98WesMicWM-19

Rivera, Miguel
❑ 94JohCitCC-25
❑ 94JohCitCF-3712
❑ 96PeoChiB-26
❑ 97PeoChi-24
❑ 98ArkTraM-23

Rivera, Oscar
❑ 92BelMarCB-15
❑ 92BelMarF-1442
❑ 94AppFoxC-16
❑ 94AppFoxFl-1053
❑ 95GreFalDTI-5

Rivera, Pablo
❑ 89BlaYNPRWL-13
❑ 89ChaKniTI-25

Rivera, Rafael
❑ 91SalSpuC-2
❑ 91SalSpuP-2247
❑ 92SalSpuC-9
❑ 92SalSpuF-3759
❑ 96EveAquB-18
❑ 97LanJet-21

Rivera, Ricardo
❑ 82AubAstT-17
❑ 83DayBeaAT-22

Rivera, Roberto
❑ 89BurIndS-22
❑ 90WatIndS-17
❑ 91ColIndC-15
❑ 91ColIndP-1482
❑ 92KinIndC-15
❑ 92KinIndF-2474
❑ 93CanIndF-2837
❑ 94PeoChiC-22
❑ 94PeoChiF-2266
❑ 95OrlCubF-9
❑ 96IowCubB-22
❑ 96Pac-32
❑ 97DelSho-21
❑ 98NewOrlZM-20

Rivera, Ruben
❑ 92GulCoaYF-3705
❑ 93OneYanC-1
❑ 93OneYanF-3518
❑ 94AriFalLS-18
❑ 94Bow-348
❑ 94BowBes-X99
❑ 94BowBesR-X99
❑ 94Cla-73
❑ 94ExcFS7-113
❑ 94GreBatF-489
❑ 94SouAtlLAF-SAL16
❑ 95ActPac2G-10G
❑ 95ActPacF-31
❑ 95ActPacF-71
❑ 95Bow-231
❑ 95BowBes-B42
❑ 95BowBes-X9
❑ 95BowBesR-B42
❑ 95BowBesR-X9
❑ 95BowGolF-231
❑ 95ColCho-28
❑ 95ColChoGS-28
❑ 95ColChoSS-28
❑ 95ColCliP-26
❑ 95ColCliTI-26
❑ 95Emo-66
❑ 95Exc-103
❑ 95ExcAll-8
❑ 95NorNagUTI-24
❑ 95NorNavTI-24
❑ 95SigRooFD-FD4
❑ 95SigRooFDS-FD4
❑ 95SigRooOJ-36
❑ 95SigRooOJHP-HP4
❑ 95SigRooOJHPS-HP4
❑ 95SigRooOJSS-1
❑ 95SigRooOJSSS-1
❑ 95SigRooP'P-P2
❑ 95SP-10
❑ 95SPCha-9
❑ 95SPChaDC-9
❑ 95SPSil-10
❑ 95StaCluCB-CB12
❑ 95StaCluMOP-CB12
❑ 95Sum21C-TC5
❑ 95Top-640
❑ 95UppDec-1
❑ 95UppDecED-1
❑ 95UppDecEDG-1
❑ 95UppDecML-8
❑ 95UppDecML-112
❑ 95UppDecMLFS-8
❑ 95UppDecMLFS-112
❑ 95UppDecMLOP-OP19
❑ 95UppDecMLT1PF-4
❑ 95UppDecSE-144
❑ 95UppDecSEG-144
❑ 96Bow-168
❑ 96BowBes-96
❑ 96BowBesAR-96
❑ 96BowBesC-12
❑ 96BowBesCAR-12
❑ 96BowBesCR-12
❑ 96BowBesMI-5
❑ 96BowBesMIAR-5
❑ 96BowBesMIR-5
❑ 96BowBesP-BBP19
❑ 96BowBesPAR-BBP19
❑ 96BowBesPR-BBP19
❑ 96BowBesR-96
❑ 96BowFoi-168
❑ 96BowMinLP-11
❑ 96Cir-69
❑ 96CirRav-69
❑ 96ColCho-20
❑ 96ColChoGS-20
❑ 96ColChoSS-20
❑ 96ColCliB-27
❑ 96Don-397
❑ 96DonPreP-397
❑ 96EmoXL-95
❑ 96Fin-B340
❑ 96FinRef-B340
❑ 96Fla-136
❑ 96FlaWavotF-19
❑ 96FlePro-8
❑ 96FleUpd-U67
❑ 96FleUpdTC-U67
❑ 96Lea-215
❑ 96LeaLimR-3
❑ 96LeaLimRG-3
❑ 96LeaPre-137
❑ 96LeaPreP-137
❑ 96LeaPrePB-215
❑ 96LeaPrePG-215
❑ 96LeaPrePS-215
❑ 96LeaSig-92
❑ 96LeaSigPPG-92
❑ 96LeaSigPPP-92
❑ 96MLBPin-30
❑ 96PacPri-P122
❑ 96PacPriG-P122
❑ 96Pin-165
❑ 96PinArtP-92
❑ 96PinSam-165
❑ 96PinSta-92
❑ 96PinTeaT-1
❑ 96Sco-263
❑ 96Sco-381
❑ 96ScoDugC-A109
❑ 96ScoDugC-B106
❑ 96ScoDugCAP-A109
❑ 96ScoDugCAP-B106
❑ 96ScoFutF-8
❑ 96SelCer-134
❑ 96SelCerAP-134
❑ 96SelCerCB-134
❑ 96SelCerCR-134
❑ 96SelCerMB-134
❑ 96SelCerMG-134
❑ 96SelCerMR-134
❑ 96Spo-109
❑ 96Spo-126
❑ 96SpoArtP-109
❑ 96SpoArtP-126
❑ 96SpoDouT-4
❑ 96SpoPowS-13
❑ 96SpoPro-19
❑ 96StaClu-258
❑ 96StaCluMOP-258
❑ 96Top-430
❑ 96TopChr-138
❑ 96TopChrR-138
❑ 96Ult-394
❑ 96Ult-600
❑ 96UltGolM-394
❑ 96UltGolM-600
❑ 96UltGolP-10
❑ 96UltGolPGM-10
❑ 96UppDec-230
❑ 96UppDecBCP-BC9
❑ 96Zen-111
❑ 96ZenArtP-111
❑ 96ZenDiaC-15
❑ 96ZenDiaCP-15
❑ 97Bow-118
❑ 97BowBes-142
❑ 97BowBesAR-142
❑ 97BowBesP-14
❑ 97BowBesPAR-14
❑ 97BowBesPR-14
❑ 97BowBesR-142
❑ 97BowCerBlaIA-CA68
❑ 97BowCerBluIA-CA68
❑ 97BowCerGolIA-CA68
❑ 97BowInt-118
❑ 97BowIntB-BBI15
❑ 97BowIntBAR-BBI15
❑ 97BowIntBR-BBI15
❑ 97Cir-312
❑ 97CirRav-312
❑ 97ColCho-178
❑ 97ColChoT-NY4
❑ 97Don-106
❑ 97DonEli-27
❑ 97DonEliGS-27
❑ 97DonEliTotC-18
❑ 97DonEliTotCDC-18
❑ 97DonGolPP-106
❑ 97DonSilPP-106
❑ 97E-X2-35
❑ 97E-X2Cred-35
❑ 97E-X2EssCre-35
❑ 97Fin-280
❑ 97FinEmb-280
❑ 97FinEmbR-280
❑ 97FinRef-280
❑ 97FlaShoWotF-17
❑ 97Fle-177
❑ 97FleTif-177
❑ 97GreBatC-1
❑ 97Lea-30
❑ 97LeaFraM-30
❑ 97LeaFraMDC-30
❑ 97Pac-159
❑ 97PacLatotML-15
❑ 97PacLigB-159
❑ 97PacSil-159
❑ 97PinIns-130
❑ 97PinInsCE-130
❑ 97PinInsDE-130
❑ 97PinPasttM-25
❑ 97Sco-114
❑ 97ScoArtPWB-114
❑ 97ScoPreS-114
❑ 97ScoShoS-114
❑ 97ScoShoSAP-114
❑ 97Sel-110
❑ 97SelArtP-110
❑ 97SelCom-110
❑ 97SelRegG-110
❑ 97SelRooR-15
❑ 97SelToootT-14
❑ 97SelToootTMB-14
❑ 97StaClu-90
❑ 97StaCluMOP-90
❑ 97Stu-158
❑ 97StuPrePG-158
❑ 97StuPrePS-158
❑ 97Top-403
❑ 97TopAwel-AI17
❑ 97TopChr-141
❑ 97TopChrR-141
❑ 97TopGal-159
❑ 97TopGalPPI-159
❑ 97UD3-53
❑ 97UD3GenNex-GN16
❑ 97Ult-104
❑ 97UltGolME-104
❑ 97UltGolP-9
❑ 97UltPlaME-104
❑ 97UppDec-121
❑ 97UppDec-199
❑ 97UppDec-381
❑ 97UppDecBCP-BC18
❑ 97UppDecTTS-TS6
❑ 97YanSco-6
❑ 97YanScoPl-6
❑ 97YanScoPr-6
❑ 98Bes-92
❑ 98Bow-425
❑ 98BowBes-138
❑ 98BowBesAR-138
❑ 98BowBesR-138
❑ 98BowChr-425
❑ 98BowChrGA-425
❑ 98BowChrGAR-425
❑ 98BowChrI-425
❑ 98BowChrIR-425
❑ 98BowChrR-425
❑ 98BowGolA-425
❑ 98BowInt-425
❑ 98CroRoy-118
❑ 98Don-143
❑ 98DonCol-143
❑ 98DonColE-515
❑ 98DonColL-209
❑ 98DonColP-701
❑ 98DonColS-143
❑ 98DonEli-115
❑ 98DonEliA-115
❑ 98DonEliS-115
❑ 98DonGolPP-143
❑ 98DonPre-151
❑ 98DonPreSeat-151
❑ 98DonPriCD-143
❑ 98DonPriCE-515
❑ 98DonPriCL-209
❑ 98DonPriCP-701
❑ 98DonSilPP-143
❑ 98FlaShoWotF-6
❑ 98Las-22
❑ 98Lea-9
❑ 98LeaFraDA-9
❑ 98LeaFraF-9
❑ 98LeaFraM-9
❑ 98LeaFraM-9
❑ 98LeaFraMDC-9
❑ 98LeaFraMDC-9
❑ 98LeaFraMS-9
❑ 98LeaFraMZ2-9
❑ 98MetUni-98
❑ 98MetUniPMG-98
❑ 98PacAur-193
❑ 98PacPar-239
❑ 98PacParC-239
❑ 98PacParG-239
❑ 98PacParHS-239
❑ 98PacParPB-239
❑ 98PacParR-239
❑ 98PinIns-74
❑ 98PinInsCE-74
❑ 98PinInsDE-74
❑ 98PinPlu-47
❑ 98RevoRooHH-18
❑ 98RevoRooHHG-18
❑ 98StaCluFDI-348
❑ 98StaCluI-348
❑ 98StaCluOneK-348
❑ 98StaCluPP-348
❑ 98Stu-149
❑ 98StuGPP-149
❑ 98StuSPP-149
❑ 98Ult-242
❑ 98UltGolM-242
❑ 98UltMas-242
❑ 98UltPlaM-242
❑ 99Bow-3
❑ 99BowChr-3
❑ 99BowChrG-3
❑ 99BowChrGR-3
❑ 99BowChrI-3
❑ 99BowChrIR-3
❑ 99BowChrR-3
❑ 99BowGol-3
❑ 99BowInt-3
❑ 99FlaShoLeg1-90
❑ 99FlaShoLeg2-90
❑ 99FlaShoLeg3-90
❑ 99FlaShoLegM1-90
❑ 99FlaShoLegM2-90
❑ 99FlaShoLegM3-90
❑ 99FlaShoR1-90
❑ 99FlaShoR2-90
❑ 99FlaShoR3-90
❑ 99Fle-462
❑ 99FleSta9-462
❑ 99FleWarT-462
❑ 99Pac-374
❑ 99PacAur-164
❑ 99PacAurOD-164
❑ 99PacCroC-246
❑ 99PacCroCPB-246
❑ 99PacOme-206
❑ 99PacOmeC-206
❑ 99PacOmeG-206
❑ 99PacOmePB-206
❑ 99PacPar-203
❑ 99PacParC-203
❑ 99PacParG-203
❑ 99PacParHoloGold-203
❑ 99PacParHS-203
❑ 99PacParOD-203
❑ 99PacParPB-203
❑ 99PacParRed-203
❑ 99PacPlaB-374
❑ 99PacRed-374
❑ 99SkyMolM-15
❑ 99SkyMolMX-15
❑ 99SP AutC-RR
❑ 99SP AutCG-RR
❑ 99SPx-66
❑ 99SPxFinR-66
❑ 99SPxFinS-66
❑ 99Top-249
❑ 99TopChr-249
❑ 99TopChrR-249
❑ 99TopMVPP-249
❑ 99UppDec-473

❑ 99UppDecCLM-C81
❑ 99UppDecEL1-473
❑ 99UppDecEL2-473
❑ 99UppDecM-178
❑ 99UppDecMGS-178
❑ 99UppDecMHFS-178
❑ 99UppDecMP-RR
❑ 99UppDecMSS-178
❑ 99Vic-341
Rivera, Santiago
❑ 93SpolndC-17
❑ 94SprSulC-19
❑ 94SprSulF-2046
❑ 95RanCucQT-26
Rivera, Willie
❑ 94UtiBluSC-24
❑ 94UtiBluSF-3834
❑ 96MicBatCB-22
RiverDog, Charlie the
❑ 94ChaRivC-30
❑ 95ChaRivTI-30
❑ 96ChaRivTI-9605
❑ 98ChaRivDG-9
RiverDog, Shamrock the
❑ 96ChaRivTI-9604
Riverdogs, Charleston
❑ 95ChaRivUTIS-39
❑ 96ChaRivTI-9631
Rivero, Eddie
❑ 97ClePhi-17
❑ 98ReaPhiM-16
❑ 98ReaPhiUM-19
Rivero, Marty
❑ 87GenCubP-13
❑ 88PeoChiTI-26
❑ 89WinSpiS-14
Rivers, Jonathan
❑ 94MedHatBJF-3695
❑ 94MedHatBJSP-8
❑ 95HagSunF-82
❑ 96DunBluJB-21
❑ 96DunBluJTI-25
❑ 97DunBluJTI-24
❑ 98KnoSG-19
Rivers, Ken
❑ 87DunBluJP-949
❑ 88KnoBluJB-14
❑ 89KnoBluJB-21
❑ 89KnoBluJP-1132
❑ 89KnoBluJS-17
❑ 90MyrBeaBJP-2779
❑ 91LinDriAA-441
❑ 91MidAngLD-441
❑ 91MidAngOHP-22
❑ 91MidAngP-437
Rivers, Mickey
❑ 88ElmPioC-23
❑ 89WinHavRSS-18
❑ 90LynRedSTI-4
❑ 91Cla/Bes-90
❑ 91WinHavRSC-24
❑ 91WinHavRSP-503
Rivers, Mickey Sr.
❑ 72OPC-272
❑ 72Top-272
❑ 73OPC-597
❑ 73Top-597
❑ 74OPC-76
❑ 74Top-76
❑ 75CalAngP-34
❑ 75GreHeroBP-1
❑ 75Hos-22
❑ 75HosTwi-22
❑ 75OPC-164
❑ 75Top-164
❑ 75TopMin-164
❑ 76Hos-102
❑ 76Kel-41A
❑ 76Kel-41B
❑ 76OPC-85
❑ 76OPC-198
❑ 76SSP-203
❑ 76Top-85
❑ 76Top-198
❑ 76TopTra-85T
❑ 77BurCheD-180
❑ 77Kel-55
❑ 77OPC-69
❑ 77Top-305
❑ 77YanBurK-18
❑ 78Hos-110
❑ 78Kel-17
❑ 78OPC-182
❑ 78SSP270-13
❑ 78Top-690
❑ 78YanBurK-20
❑ 78YanPhoA-22
❑ 78YanSSPD-13
❑ 79OPC-24
❑ 79Top-60
❑ 79YanBurK-20
❑ 80OPC-251
❑ 80Top-485
❑ 81AllGamPI-67
❑ 81Don-496
❑ 81Fle-617
❑ 81FleStiC-32
❑ 81OPC-145
❑ 81Top-145
❑ 81TopScr-31
❑ 81TopSti-132
❑ 81TopSupHT-94
❑ 82Don-242
❑ 82Fle-328
❑ 82FleSta-174
❑ 82OPC-51
❑ 82OPC-356
❑ 82Top-704
❑ 82Top-705
❑ 82TopSti-243
❑ 83Don-394
❑ 83Fle-576
❑ 83OPC-224
❑ 83RanAffF-17
❑ 83Top-224
❑ 83TopFol-5
❑ 84Don-465
❑ 84Fle-425
❑ 84Nes792-504
❑ 84OPC-269
❑ 84RanJarP-17
❑ 84Top-504
❑ 84TopSti-361
❑ 84TopTif-504
❑ 85Don-465
❑ 85Fle-565
❑ 85Lea-35
❑ 85OPC-371
❑ 85Top-371
❑ 85TopSti-355
❑ 85TopTif-371
❑ 86RanGreT-10
❑ 89PacSenL-163
❑ 89T/MSenL-91
❑ 89TopSenL-115
❑ 90EliSenL-28
❑ 92YanWIZ7-134
❑ 92YanWIZA-65
❑ 93RanKee-308
❑ 99SpollIGotG-72
❑ 99SpollIGotGA-60
Rives, Sherron
❑ 95FayGenTI-21
Rivette, Scott
❑ 96WesMicWB-23
❑ 97ModA'sG-25
❑ 98HunStaTI-3
Rixey, Eppa
❑ 15SpoNewM-142
❑ 16SpoNewM-142
❑ 17ColE13-139
❑ 17HolBreD-83
❑ 21E121So1-79A
❑ 21E121So1-79B
❑ 21E121So8-76
❑ 21Exh-144
❑ 22AmeCarE122-56
❑ 22E120-178
❑ 22W572-85
❑ 22W575-104
❑ 23W501-54
❑ 23WilChoV-133
❑ 25Exh-30
❑ 26Exh-30
❑ 27Exh-15
❑ 27YorCarE-16
❑ 28StaPlaCE-53
❑ 28W502-16
❑ 28Yue-16
❑ 33Gou-74
❑ 34GouCanV-32
❑ 53ArtHaloFP-70
❑ 61Fle-71
❑ 76RowExh-6
❑ 76ShaPiz-94
❑ 77BobParHoF-39
❑ 77GalGloG-99
❑ 77RedCarP-14
❑ 80PerHaloFP-94
❑ 80SSPHOF-94
❑ 82OhiHaloF-41
❑ 82TCMGreP-35
❑ 86RedGreT-4
❑ 89HOFStiB-69
❑ 91ConTSN-39
❑ 93ConTSN-906
❑ 95ConTSN-1327
Rizo, Miguel
❑ 98JohCCTI-28
Rizza, Jerry
❑ 88SouOreAP-1715
❑ 90EriSaiS-20
Rizzo, Johnny
❑ 39ExhSal-54
❑ 39PlaBal-11
❑ 40PlaBal-108
❑ 41DouPlaR-123
❑ 42DodTeal-19
❑ 47SigOil-68
❑ 47SunBre-19
❑ 77CinRedT-37
❑ 90DodTar-672
❑ 93ConTSN-944
Rizzo, Mike
❑ 83PeoSunF-14
Rizzo, Nick
❑ 98KanCouC-26
❑ 98KanCouCCP-26
Rizzo, Rick
❑ 81ChaRoyT-23
❑ 82ForMyeRT-1
❑ 84MemChiT-3
Rizzo, Todd
❑ 92YakBeaC-16
❑ 92YakBeaF-3447
❑ 95PriWilCTI-23
❑ 97BirBarB-14
Rizzo, Tom
❑ 88PulBraP-1754
❑ 89SumBraP-1087
❑ 90IdaFalBP-3246
Rizzuto, Phil
❑ 41DouPlaR-61
❑ 41DouPlaR-63
❑ 46SpoExcW-5-6
❑ 47Exh-187A
❑ 47Exh-187B
❑ 47HomBon-39
❑ 47PM1StaP1-175
❑ 47StaPinP2-34
❑ 47TipTop-57
❑ 47YanTeaT-21
❑ 48Bow-8
❑ 48YanTeal-24
❑ 49Bow-98A
❑ 49Bow-98B
❑ 49Lea-11
❑ 49YanTeal-19
❑ 50AmeNut&CCP-15
❑ 50Bow-11
❑ 50Dra-25
❑ 50RoyDes-11
❑ 50YanTeal-19
❑ 51BerRos-A3
❑ 51Bow-26
❑ 51R42SmaS-90
❑ 51TopCurA-9
❑ 51TopRedB-5
❑ 52BerRos-54A
❑ 52BerRos-54B
❑ 52Bow-52
❑ 52RoyPre-10
❑ 52StaCalL-70F
❑ 52StaCalS-84C
❑ 52TipTop-32
❑ 52TipTop-33
❑ 52Top-11
❑ 52Whe-25A
❑ 52Whe-25B
❑ 53BowC-9
❑ 53BowC-93
❑ 53Bri-39
❑ 53Dor-101
❑ 53Dor-101A
❑ 53ExhCan-25
❑ 53RedMan-AL10
❑ 53StaMey-7
❑ 53Top-114
❑ 54Bow-1
❑ 54DanDee-19
❑ 54NewYorJA-57
❑ 54RedMan-AL17
❑ 54StaMey-11
❑ 54Top-17
❑ 55Bow-10
❑ 55StaMey-11
❑ 55Top-189
❑ 56Top-113
❑ 56TopPin-29
❑ 56YanTeal-20
❑ 60NuHi-45
❑ 61NuSco-445
❑ 61Top-471
❑ 67TopVen-186
❑ 75TCMGua-1
❑ 75YanAllTT-8
❑ 77GalGloG-37
❑ 79TCM50-144
❑ 80PacLeg-82
❑ 80PerHaloFP-219
❑ 80PerHaloFPS-78
❑ 80YanGreT-4
❑ 82DiaCla-45
❑ 82GSGalAG-10
❑ 82TCMStaot5-3
❑ 83MLBPin-15
❑ 83TopRep5-11
❑ 83YanASFY-37
❑ 83YanYealT-3
❑ 84OCoandSI-54
❑ 84TCMPla1-7
❑ 86SpoDecG-22
❑ 86TCMSupS-9
❑ 86TCMSupS-19
❑ 88PacLegI-10
❑ 89SweBasG-111
❑ 89YanCitAG-4
❑ 90PacLeg-101
❑ 90PerGreM-105
❑ 90YanMomPRP-5
❑ 91TopArc1-114
❑ 92BazQua5A-2
❑ 92UppDecS-16
❑ 92YanWIZA-66
❑ 93Yoo-15
❑ 94TopArc1-17
❑ 94TopArc1G-17
❑ 94Yoo-12
❑ 95ComIma-6
❑ 95ComImaP-1
❑ 98DonSigSS-13
❑ 98SpollITaN-26
❑ 98SpollITaNEE-26
Roa, Hector
❑ 90PulBraB-17
❑ 90PulBraP-3097
❑ 91MiaMirC-23
❑ 91MiaMirP-417
❑ 92DurBulC-5
❑ 92DurBulF-1110
❑ 92DurBulTI-2
❑ 93Bow-2
❑ 93GreBraF-359
❑ 93LimRocDWB-50
❑ 94GreBraF-422
❑ 94GreBraTI-18
❑ 95RicBraRC-21
❑ 95RicBraTI-19
Roa, Joe
❑ 90PulBraB-9
❑ 90PulBraP-3107
❑ 91MacBraC-8
❑ 91MacBraP-862
❑ 92St.LucMCB-10
❑ 92St.LucMF-1746
❑ 93BinMetF-2332
❑ 96BufBisB-17
❑ 97Fle-583
❑ 97FleTif-583
❑ 97PacPriGotD-GD39
❑ 97SpollI-21
❑ 97SpollIEE-21
❑ 98FreGriG-27
Roa, Pedro
❑ 89BelMarL-19
❑ 90BenBucL-27
Roach, Brett
❑ 88BriTigP-1884
❑ 89FayGenP-1589
Roach, Jason
❑ 97PitMet-27
❑ 98CapCitBF5-25
❑ 98CapCitBM-25
Roach, John
❑ 19Zee-27
❑ 87OldJudN-418
Roach, Kevin
❑ 89CarNewE-4
Roach, Mel
❑ 54Top-181
❑ 55BraGolS-28
❑ 55Top-117
❑ 59Top-54
❑ 59TopVen-54
❑ 60BraLaktL-20
❑ 60BraSpiaS-18
❑ 60Top-491
❑ 61Pos-163
❑ 61Top-217
❑ 62Top-581
❑ 80Bra195T-20
❑ 94TopArc1-181
❑ 94TopArc1G-181
Roach, Petie
❑ 92EveGiaC-2
❑ 92EveGiaF-1699
❑ 93CliGiaC-20
❑ 93CliGiaF-2501
❑ 93EveGiaC-22
❑ 93EveGiaF-3778
❑ 94YakBeaF-3846
❑ 95SanBerSTI-20
❑ 96SanAntMB-20
❑ 96VerBeaDB-24
❑ 97AlbDukUG-5
❑ 97SanAntMB-9
❑ 98AlbDukG-25
❑ 98SanAntMM-9
Roadcap, Steve
❑ 83QuaCitCT-16
❑ 86PitCubP-20
❑ 88WytCubP-1991
❑ 89WytCubS-29
❑ 90HunCubP-3303
❑ 91HunCubC-30
❑ 91HunCubP-3353
❑ 92PeoChiC-28
❑ 92PeoChiTI-21
❑ 93PeoChiF-1100
❑ 93PeoChiTI-22
❑ 94PeoChiC-26
❑ 94PeoChiF-2283
❑ 95RocCubTI-NNO
❑ 96RocCubTI-28
Roarke, Mike
❑ 61Top-376
❑ 62TigPosCF-17
❑ 62Top-87
❑ 62TopVen-87
❑ 63Top-224
❑ 64TigJayP-11
❑ 64Top-292
❑ 64TopVen-292
❑ 74WicAerODF-109
❑ 83PawRedST-26
❑ 84Car-24
❑ 84Car5x7-23
❑ 85CarTeal-29
❑ 86CarTeal-38
❑ 87CarTeal-28
❑ 88CarTeal-30
❑ 89CarTeal-28
❑ 90TopTVCa-6
❑ 91PadSmo-30
❑ 92PadMot-27
❑ 92PadPolD-28
❑ 92PadSmo-26
❑ 93PadMot-28
Roarke, Tom
❑ 82AubAstT-1
Robarge, Dennis
❑ 88ElmPioC-29
❑ 89ElmPioP-26
❑ 94SalBucC-29
Robb, David
❑ 98VisOakG-25
Robbe, Fletcher
❑ 53MotCoo-5
Robbins, Bruce
❑ 80EvaTriT-18
❑ 80Top-666
❑ 80VenLeaS-104
❑ 81BirBarT-6
❑ 81Don-129
❑ 81Fle-477
❑ 81Top-79
❑ 82EvaTriT-6
❑ 83BirBarT-10
Robbins, Doug
❑ 88TopTra-95T
❑ 88TopTraT-95T
❑ 89TopBig-49
❑ 90Bes-53
❑ 90HagSunB-3
❑ 90HagSunP-1416
❑ 90HagSunS-21
❑ 91HagSunLD-245
❑ 91HagSunP-2460
❑ 91LinDriAA-245
❑ 92OPC-58
❑ 92RocRedWF-1943
❑ 92RocRedWS-465
❑ 92Top-58
❑ 92TopGol-58
❑ 92TopGolW-58
❑ 92TopMic-58
❑ 93TacTigF-3036
Robbins, Jake
❑ 96GreBatB-21
❑ 97GreBatB-24
❑ 98TamYanM-25
Robbins, Jason
❑ 93PriRedC-25
❑ 93PriRedF-4178
❑ 94BilMusF-3669
❑ 94BilMusSP-20
❑ 95Exc-182
❑ 95SPML-42
❑ 95UppDecML-104
❑ 95UppDecMLFS-104
❑ 96ChaLooB-24
❑ 97HigDesMG-21
Robbins, Johnny Lee
❑ 79CliDodT-3
Robbins, Lance
❑ 95CedRapKTI-15
❑ 97St.PauS-23
Robbins, Leroy
❑ 79WatA'sT-7
❑ 80WesHavWCT-3
Robbins, Mike
❑ 96LanLugB-21
❑ 97WilBluR-23
Robbins, Ted
❑ 98QuaCitRBG-22
Robbins, Tim
❑ 88BulDurM-2
Robbins, Wes
❑ 81NasSouTI-16
Robbs, Bill
❑ 92SpolndC-5
❑ 92SpolndF-1308
❑ 93RanCucQC-25
❑ 93RanCucQF-845
Robbs, Don
❑ 87HawRai-30
Roberge, Al
❑ 50WorWidGV-46
❑ 95ConTSN-1341
Roberge, Bert
❑ 77CocAstT-21
❑ 79AstPos-21
❑ 80Top-329
❑ 80TucTorT-23
❑ 81TucTorT-21
❑ 82AstAstI-3
❑ 82AstAstI-10
❑ 82TucTorT-15
❑ 83Don-496
❑ 83Fle-461
❑ 83Top-611
❑ 83TucTorT-8
❑ 85ExpPos-19
❑ 85Fle-525
❑ 85Top-388
❑ 85TopTif-388
❑ 85TopTifT-94T
❑ 85TopTra-94T
❑ 86Don-575
❑ 86ExpProPa-16
❑ 86Fle-258
❑ 86OPC-154
❑ 86Top-154
❑ 86TopTif-154
Roberge, J.P.
❑ 94GreFalDSP-20
❑ 95SanBerSTI-21
❑ 96SanAntMB-21
❑ 97SanAntMB-21
❑ 98AlbDukG-26
❑ 98SanAntMM-21
Roberson, Charles
❑ 97WatIndTI-23
Roberson, Gerald
❑ 94IdaFalBF-3593
❑ 94IdaFalBSP-18
Roberson, Kevin
❑ 88WytCubP-1978
❑ 89ChaWheB-7
❑ 89ChaWheP-1747
❑ 90WinSpiTI-10
❑ 91ChaKniLD-140
❑ 91ChaKniP-1702
❑ 91Cla/Bes-2
❑ 91LinDriAA-140

❑ 92IowCubF-4062
❑ 92IowCubS-218
❑ 92SkyAAAF-106
❑ 92UppDecML-124
❑ 93Bow-60
❑ 93ClaFS7-14
❑ 93ExcFS7-12
❑ 93Lea-458
❑ 93SelRoo-89T
❑ 93SP-88
❑ 93TriAAAGF-5
❑ 94ColC-241
❑ 94ColChoGS-241
❑ 94ColChoSS-241
❑ 94Don-235
❑ 94Fin-77
❑ 94FinRef-77
❑ 94Fle-394
❑ 94IowCubF-1287
❑ 94Pac-107
❑ 94Sco-604
❑ 94ScoBoyoS-9
❑ 94ScoGolR-604
❑ 94StaClu-383
❑ 94StaCluFDI-383
❑ 94StaCluGR-383
❑ 94StaCluMOP-383
❑ 94StaCluT-348
❑ 94StaCluTFDI-348
❑ 94Top-119
❑ 94TopGol-119
❑ 94TopSpa-119
❑ 94Ult-165
❑ 94UppDec-199
❑ 94UppDecED-199
❑ 95ColCho-211
❑ 95ColChoGS-211
❑ 95ColChoSS-211
❑ 95Pac-77
❑ 95UppDec-311
❑ 95UppDecED-311
❑ 95UppDecEDG-311
❑ 95UppDecSE-122
❑ 95UppDecSEG-122
❑ 96FleUpd-U161
❑ 96FleUpdTC-U161
❑ 96LeaSigEA-172
❑ 97PhoFirTI-21

Roberson, Sid
❑ 93StoPorC-21
❑ 93StoPorF-745
❑ 94ElPasDF-3145
❑ 94ExcFS7-85
❑ 95Bow-109
❑ 95BowBes-B40
❑ 95BowBesR-B40
❑ 95Exc-74
❑ 95TopTra-97T
❑ 96ColCho-189
❑ 96ColChoGS-189
❑ 96ColChoSS-189
❑ 96Don-26
❑ 96DonPreP-26
❑ 96Pac-351
❑ 96Top-47

Roberts, Bill
❑ 76DubPacT-30

Roberts, Bip (Leon)
❑ 86DonRoo-33
❑ 86FleUpd-96
❑ 86TopTra-91T
❑ 86TopTraT-91T
❑ 87Don-114
❑ 87Fle-427
❑ 87FleGlo-427
❑ 87LasVegSP-23
❑ 87Top-637
❑ 87TopTif-637
❑ 88LasVegSC-14
❑ 88LasVegSP-245
❑ 89FleUpd-126
❑ 89PadCok-14
❑ 89PadPos-26
❑ 89TopTra-103T
❑ 89TopTraT-103T
❑ 90Bow-222
❑ 90BowTif-222
❑ 90Don-347
❑ 90DonBesN-60
❑ 90Fle-166
❑ 90FleCan-166
❑ 90Lea-233
❑ 90OPC-307
❑ 90PadCok-15
❑ 90PadMag-26
❑ 90PanSti-359
❑ 90Sco-51
❑ 90ScoYouSI-23
❑ 90Spo-116
❑ 90Top-307
❑ 90TopBig-149
❑ 90TopSti-103
❑ 90TopTif-307
❑ 90UppDec-303
❑ 91Bow-654
❑ 91Don-195
❑ 91Fle-540
❑ 91Lea-478
❑ 91OPC-538
❑ 91PadCok-8
❑ 91PadMag-9
❑ 91PadMag-23B
❑ 91PadSmo-31
❑ 91PanFreS-96
❑ 91PanSti-97
❑ 91Sco-28
❑ 91StaClu-18
❑ 91Stu-248
❑ 91Top-538
❑ 91TopCraJ2-31
❑ 91TopDesS-538
❑ 91TopMic-538
❑ 91TopTif-538
❑ 91Ult-310
❑ 91UppDec-271
❑ 92Bow-525
❑ 92ClaGam-192
❑ 92Don-371
❑ 92Fle-618
❑ 92FleUpd-82
❑ 92Lea-252
❑ 92LeaBlaG-252
❑ 92OPC-20
❑ 92OPCPre-69
❑ 92PanSti-233
❑ 92Pin-404
❑ 92RedKah-10
❑ 92Sco-123
❑ 92ScoRoo-79T
❑ 92StaClu-48
❑ 92StaClu-645
❑ 92StaCluNC-645
❑ 92Stu-27
❑ 92Top-20
❑ 92TopGol-20
❑ 92TopGolPS-20
❑ 92TopGolW-20
❑ 92TopKid-56
❑ 92TopMic-20
❑ 92TopPreS-20
❑ 92TopTra-92T
❑ 92TopTraG-92T
❑ 92Ult-485
❑ 92UppDec-141
❑ 92UppDec-763
❑ 93Bow-582
❑ 93ClaGam-77
❑ 93Don-106
❑ 93DonDiaK-DK11
❑ 93DonMVP-23
❑ 93DonSpiotG-SG9
❑ 93DurPowP1-18
❑ 93Fin-15
❑ 93FinRef-15
❑ 93Fla-32
❑ 93Fle-42
❑ 93FleGolM-B2
❑ 93FunPac-172
❑ 93Lea-414
❑ 93OPC-305
❑ 93PacSpa-89
❑ 93PanSti-292
❑ 93Pin-358
❑ 93RedFolS-79
❑ 93RedFolS-123
❑ 93RedKah-21
❑ 93Sco-85
❑ 93Sco-516
❑ 93Sel-111
❑ 93SelStaL-60
❑ 93SP-214
❑ 93StaClu-30
❑ 93StaCluFDI-30
❑ 93StaCluM-30
❑ 93StaCluMOP-30
❑ 93StaCluMP-8
❑ 93Stu-135
❑ 93Top-219
❑ 93TOPBLAG-16
❑ 93TopGol-219
❑ 93TopInaM-219
❑ 93TopInaR-219
❑ 93TopMic-219
❑ 93TriPla-88
❑ 93Ult-34
❑ 93UppDec-112
❑ 93UppDecGold-112
❑ 93UppDecSH-HI16
❑ 93USPlaCA-4H
❑ 93USPlaCA-9D
❑ 94Bow-64
❑ 94ColC-476
❑ 94ColC-479
❑ 94ColChoGS-476
❑ 94ColChoGS-479
❑ 94ColChoSS-479
❑ 94Don-304
❑ 94Fin-363
❑ 94FinRef-363
❑ 94Fla-440
❑ 94Fle-422
❑ 94FleExtB-377
❑ 94FleUpd-189
❑ 94FUnPac-110
❑ 94Lea-299
❑ 94LeaL-154
❑ 94OPC-111
❑ 94Pac-157
❑ 94PadMot-4
❑ 94Pin-500
❑ 94PinArtP-500
❑ 94PinMusC-500
❑ 94ProMag-120
❑ 94Sco-108
❑ 94ScoGolR-108
❑ 94ScoRoo-RT46
❑ 94ScoRooGR-RT46
❑ 94Sel-218
❑ 94SP-133
❑ 94SPDieC-133
❑ 94StaClu-186
❑ 94StaClu-698
❑ 94StaCluFDI-186
❑ 94StaCluFDI-698
❑ 94StaCluGR-186
❑ 94StaCluGR-698
❑ 94StaCluMOP-186
❑ 94StaCluMOP-698
❑ 94Top-733
❑ 94TopGol-733
❑ 94TopSpa-733
❑ 94TopTra-81T
❑ 94Ult-584
❑ 94UppDec-382
❑ 94UppDecED-382
❑ 95Baz-56
❑ 95Bow-343
❑ 95ColCho-352
❑ 95ColChoGS-352
❑ 95ColChoSE-166
❑ 95ColChoSEGS-166
❑ 95ColChoSESS-166
❑ 95ColChoSS-352
❑ 95Don-450
❑ 95DonPreP-450
❑ 95DonTopotO-345
❑ 95Fin-85
❑ 95FinRef-85
❑ 95Fla-205
❑ 95Fle-567
❑ 95Lea-92
❑ 95LeaLim-113
❑ 95Pac-369
❑ 95PacPri-118
❑ 95PadCHP-7
❑ 95PadMot-4
❑ 95Pin-388
❑ 95PinArtP-388
❑ 95PinMusC-388
❑ 95Sco-40
❑ 95ScoGolR-40
❑ 95ScoPlaTS-40
❑ 95SP-110
❑ 95SPCha-92
❑ 95SPChaDC-92
❑ 95SPSil-110
❑ 95StaClu-344
❑ 95StaCluMOP-344
❑ 95StaCluSTWS-344
❑ 95StaCluVR-182
❑ 95StaCluVRMO-182
❑ 95Stu-118
❑ 95Top-265
❑ 95TopCyb-144
❑ 95TopD3-47
❑ 95TopEmb-57
❑ 95TopEmbGI-57
❑ 95Ult-441
❑ 95UltGolM-441
❑ 95UppDec-136
❑ 95UppDecED-136
❑ 95UppDecEDG-136
❑ 96Cir-48
❑ 96CirRav-48
❑ 96ColCho-295
❑ 96ColCho-774
❑ 96ColChoGS-295
❑ 96ColChoSS-295
❑ 96Don-120
❑ 96DonPreP-120
❑ 96EmoXL-70
❑ 96Fin-B259
❑ 96FinRef-B259
❑ 96Fla-94
❑ 96Fle-577
❑ 96FleTif-577
❑ 96FleUpd-U44
❑ 96FleUpdTC-U44
❑ 96Pac-189
❑ 96Pin-325
❑ 96PinFoil-325
❑ 96RoyPol-24
❑ 96Sco-38
❑ 96ScoDugC-A36
❑ 96ScoDugCAP-A36
❑ 96SP-99
❑ 96StaClu-90
❑ 96StaCluEPB-90
❑ 96StaCluEPG-90
❑ 96StaCluEPS-90
❑ 96StaCluMOP-90
❑ 96Stu-10
❑ 96StuPrePB-10
❑ 96StuPrePG-10
❑ 96StuPrePS-10
❑ 96Top-288
❑ 96Ult-360
❑ 96UltGolM-360
❑ 96UppDec-188
❑ 96UppDec-350
❑ 96UppDec-417
❑ 97Cir-315
❑ 97CirRav-315
❑ 97ColCho-361
❑ 97Don-311
❑ 97DonGolPP-311
❑ 97DonLim-79
❑ 97DonLimE-79
❑ 97DonLimENG-79
❑ 97DonSilPP-311
❑ 97Fin-92
❑ 97FinRef-92
❑ 97Fle-121
❑ 97FleTif-121
❑ 97Lea-285
❑ 97LeaFraM-285
❑ 97LeaFraMDC-285
❑ 97Pac-110
❑ 97PacLigB-110
❑ 97PacSil-110
❑ 97RoyPol-19
❑ 97Sco-396
❑ 97ScoArtPWB-396
❑ 97ScoResC-396
❑ 97ScoShoS-396
❑ 97ScoShoSAP-396
❑ 97StaClu-339
❑ 97StaCluMOP-339
❑ 97Top-55
❑ 97TopGal-24
❑ 97TopGalPPI-24
❑ 97Ult-70
❑ 97UltGolME-70
❑ 97UltPlaME-70
❑ 97UppDec-394
❑ 98DonColL-318
❑ 98DonPriCL-318
❑ 98Fle-422
❑ 98Lea-119
❑ 98LeaFraDA-119
❑ 98LeaFraF-119
❑ 98LeaFraM-119
❑ 98LeaFraM-119
❑ 98LeaFraMDC-119
❑ 98LeaFraMDC-119
❑ 98LeaFraMZ2-119
❑ 98PacAur-40
❑ 98PacOme-92
❑ 98PacOmeR-92
❑ 98PacOnl-283
❑ 98PacOnlR-283
❑ 98PacOnlWC-283
❑ 98PacPar-50
❑ 98PacParC-50
❑ 98PacParG-50
❑ 98PacParHS-50
❑ 98PacParPB-50
❑ 98PacParR-50
❑ 98Sco-132
❑ 98ScoSS-PP55
❑ 98ScoSSAP-PP55
❑ 98TolMudHQ-26
❑ 98Top-345
❑ 98TopChr-345
❑ 98TopChrR-345
❑ 98TopDevR-345
❑ 98TopDia-345
❑ 98TopMiniC-345
❑ 98Ult-452
❑ 98UltGolM-452
❑ 98UltMas-452
❑ 98UltPlaM-452
❑ 98UppDec-679
❑ 99Pac-315
❑ 99PacPlaB-315
❑ 99PacRed-315

Roberts, Bobby
❑ 89TenTecGE-23

Roberts, Brent
❑ 88BurIndP-1772

Roberts, Brett
❑ 93ForMyeMC-21
❑ 93ForMyeMF-2653
❑ 94ForMyeMC-20
❑ 94ForMyeMF-1168
❑ 95HarCitRCTI-21
❑ 97SalLakB-23

Roberts, Brian
❑ 91ButCopKSP-25
❑ 92Ft.MyeMCB-4
❑ 92Ft.MyeMF-2750

Roberts, Chris
❑ 91TopTra-98T
❑ 91TopTraT-98T
❑ 92Bow-569
❑ 92ClaDraP-13
❑ 92ClaDraPFB-BC12
❑ 92FroRowDP-50
❑ 92FroRowDPG-50
❑ 92FroRowDPS-50
❑ 92StaCluD-155
❑ 92TopDaiQTU-25
❑ 92TopTra-93T
❑ 92TopTraG-93T
❑ 93ClaFS7-252
❑ 93FloStaLAF-41
❑ 93Pin-467
❑ 93Sco-499
❑ 93Sel-297
❑ 93St.LucMC-20
❑ 93St.LuMF-2920
❑ 93StaCluM-4
❑ 93StaCluM-170
❑ 93StaCluMMP-8
❑ 94BinMetF-704
❑ 94Bow-596
❑ 94Cla-156
❑ 94ClaGolF-124
❑ 94ExcFS7-238
❑ 94MetShuST-4
❑ 94UppDecML-80
❑ 95Bow-28
❑ 95Exc-238
❑ 95NorTidTI-24
❑ 95Top-653
❑ 95UppDecML-80
❑ 95UppDecMLFS-80
❑ 97BinMetB-24

Roberts, Cliff
❑ 77DayBealT-19

Roberts, Curt
❑ 54DanDee-20
❑ 54Top-242
❑ 55Top-107
❑ 55TopDouH-11
❑ 56PirTeal-19
❑ 56Top-306
❑ 58MonRoyF-19
❑ 59O'KAleMR-17
❑ 60DarFar-6
❑ 61UniOil-SP10
❑ 94TopArc1-242
❑ 94TopArc1G-242

Roberts, Dale
❑ 92YanWIZ6-105

Roberts, Dave A.
❑ 69Top-536
❑ 70OPC-151
❑ 70RelPam-13
❑ 70Top-151
❑ 71MLBOffS-235
❑ 71OPC-448
❑ 71Top-448
❑ 72AstTeal-23
❑ 72Kel-15A
❑ 72Kel-15B
❑ 72OPC-91
❑ 72OPC-360
❑ 72SevTraC-44
❑ 72Top-91
❑ 72Top-360
❑ 73LinPor-84
❑ 73OPC-39
❑ 73Top-39
❑ 74AstFouTIP-1
❑ 74OPC-177
❑ 74Top-177
❑ 74TopSta-37
❑ 75AstPos-26
❑ 75OPC-301
❑ 75Top-301
❑ 75TopMin-301
❑ 76DetTigP-23
❑ 76OPC-649
❑ 76Top-649
❑ 76TopTra-649T
❑ 77Hos-101
❑ 77OPC-38
❑ 77Top-363
❑ 79GiaPol-25
❑ 79Top-473
❑ 80MarPos-20
❑ 80Top-212
❑ 81Don-501
❑ 81Fle-636
❑ 81Top-431
❑ 86AstGreT-10
❑ 87AstShoSPT-25
❑ 87AstShoSTw-14
❑ 87AstShowSTh-26
❑ 91MetWIZ-332

Roberts, Dave L.
❑ 63Top-158
❑ 66Top-571

Roberts, Dave R.
❑ 94JamJamC-20
❑ 94JamJamF-3981
❑ 95Bes-17
❑ 97JacSun-20
❑ 98JacSunM-20
❑ 99Bow-392
❑ 99BowGol-392
❑ 99BowInt-392

Roberts, Dave W.
❑ 73LinPor-156
❑ 73OPC-133
❑ 73PadDea-22
❑ 73Top-133
❑ 74OPC-309
❑ 74PadDea-22
❑ 74PadMcDD-11
❑ 74PadTeal-10
❑ 74PadTeal-11
❑ 74Top-309A
❑ 74Top-309B
❑ 74TopSta-99
❑ 75HawIsIC-5
❑ 75IntLeaASB-27
❑ 75OPC-558
❑ 75PacCoaLAB-27
❑ 75Top-558
❑ 75TopMin-558
❑ 76HawIsIC-5
❑ 76OPC-107
❑ 76Top-107
❑ 77OPC-193
❑ 77PadFamF-5
❑ 77PadSchC-47
❑ 77Top-537
❑ 78PadFamF-26
❑ 78SSP270-266
❑ 78Top-501
❑ 79Top-342
❑ 80Top-93
❑ 81AstPos-19
❑ 81Don-490A
❑ 81Don-490B
❑ 81Fle-607
❑ 81Top-57
❑ 81TopTra-824
❑ 82Don-625
❑ 82Fle-227
❑ 82PhoGiaVNB-8
❑ 82Top-218
❑ 83Don-273
❑ 83Top-148

❑ 86PadGreT-4
❑ 87AstShoSPT-24
❑ 93RanKee-309
Roberts, Drex
❑ 85KinBluJT-20
Roberts, Grant
❑ 97BesAutSBPP-42
❑ 97BesGun-4
❑ 97Bow-299
❑ 97BowChr-207
❑ 97BowChrI-207
❑ 97BowChrIR-207
❑ 97BowChrR-207
❑ 97BowInt-299
❑ 97CapCitB-9
❑ 97SouAtlTPB-8
❑ 98Bes-41
❑ 98Bes-93
❑ 98BesAutSS-44
❑ 98Bow-171
❑ 98BowCerBlueAU-30
❑ 98BowCerGA-30
❑ 98BowCerSA-30
❑ 98BowChr-171
❑ 98BowChrGA-171
❑ 98BowChrGAR-171
❑ 98BowChrI-171
❑ 98BowChrIR-171
❑ 98BowChrR-171
❑ 98BowGolA-171
❑ 98BowInt-171
❑ 98SP MinPE-84
❑ 98SP SPTSC-GR
❑ 98SPMin-84
❑ 98St.LucMM-2
❑ 99BasAmeTP-85
❑ 99BasAmeTPG-85
❑ 99Bow-141
❑ 99BowAut-BA10
❑ 99BowChr-141
❑ 99BowChrG-141
❑ 99BowChrGR-141
❑ 99BowChrI-141
❑ 99BowChrIR-141
❑ 99BowChrR-141
❑ 99BowGol-141
❑ 99BowInt-141
❑ 99SP TopP-109
❑ 99SP TopPPE-109
Roberts, James Newsom
❑ 90DodTar-673
Roberts, Jay
❑ 83AndBraT-31
Roberts, Jeff
❑ 86WauTimP-19
Roberts, John
❑ 86GreHorP-20
❑ 87GreHorP-8
❑ 88EasLeaAP-23
❑ 88NewBriRSP-894
❑ 89PawRedSC-21
❑ 89PawRedSP-693
❑ 89PawRedSTI-21
❑ 92ChaRaiC-7
❑ 92ChaRaiF-134
❑ 93WatDiaC-24
❑ 93WatDiaF-1782
❑ 94SprSulC-20
❑ 94SprSulF-2051
❑ 95RanCucQT-23
❑ 96RanCucQB-23
Roberts, Keith
❑ 90BriTigP-3150
❑ 90BriTigS-21
Roberts, Leon (Leon K.)
❑ 75DetTigP-27
❑ 75OPC-620
❑ 75Top-620
❑ 75TopMin-620
❑ 76HouAstP-27
❑ 76OPC-292
❑ 76SSP-362
❑ 76Top-292
❑ 76TopTra-292T
❑ 77BurCheD-3
❑ 77Top-456
❑ 79Hos-37
❑ 79OPC-81
❑ 79Top-166
❑ 79TopCom-15
❑ 80MarPos-21
❑ 80OPC-266
❑ 80Top-507
❑ 81Don-48
❑ 81Fle-608
❑ 81Top-368
❑ 81TopTra-825
❑ 82Don-415
❑ 82Fle-329
❑ 82OPC-186
❑ 82Top-688
❑ 83OPC-89
❑ 83RoyPos-25
❑ 83Top-89
❑ 83TopTra-96T
❑ 84Don-399
❑ 84Fle-356
❑ 84Nes792-784
❑ 84PriWilPT-1
❑ 84RoyPos-27
❑ 84Top-784
❑ 84TopTif-784
❑ 85NasPirT-20
❑ 85NasSouTI-20
❑ 85Top-217
❑ 85TopTif-217
❑ 86MarGreT-5
❑ 86NasSouTI-21
❑ 87TolMudHP-20
❑ 87TolMudHT-21
❑ 88FayGenP-1104
❑ 89PacSenL-30
❑ 89T/MSenL-92
❑ 89TopSenL-113
❑ 90EliSenL-103
❑ 91PacSenL-97
❑ 92DurBulC-25
❑ 92DurBulF-1115
❑ 92DurBulTI-7
❑ 93DurBulC-26
❑ 93DurBulF-503
❑ 93DurBulTI-1
❑ 93RanKee-310
❑ 94MacBraC-27
❑ 94MacBraF-2222
Roberts, Lonell
❑ 90MedHatBJB-9
❑ 91Cla/Bes-99
❑ 91MyrBeaHC-26
❑ 91MyrBeaHP-2960
❑ 92St.CatBJC-17
❑ 92St.CatBJF-3399
❑ 93HagSunC-22
❑ 93HagSunF-1894
❑ 94DunBluJC-23
❑ 94DunBluJF-2571
❑ 95AusFut-70
❑ 95Bow-182
❑ 95KnoSmoF-52
❑ 96BesAutSA-61
❑ 96KnoSmoB-21
❑ 97BesAutAS-46
❑ 97BesAutP-R12
❑ 97SyrSkyCB-19
❑ 98GreBraG-19
Roberts, Mark
❑ 96HicCraB-17
❑ 98WinWar-23
Roberts, Mel
❑ 77ReaPhiT-19
❑ 88SouAtlLAGS-2
❑ 88SpaPhiP-1033
❑ 88SpaPhiS-6
❑ 89SpaPhiP-1050
❑ 89SpaPhiS-26
❑ 90SpaPhiB-25
❑ 90SpaPhiP-2508
❑ 90SpaPhiS-27
❑ 91SpaPhiC-28
❑ 91SpaPhiP-913
❑ 92PhiMed-26
❑ 93PhiMed-29
❑ 94PhiMed-28
❑ 95Phi-26
❑ 96GreBraB-3
❑ 96GreBraTI-30
❑ 97GreBraG-24
❑ 98GreBraG-20
Roberts, Mike
❑ 80TulDriT-5
❑ 81TulDriT-17
❑ 97EugEmeB-11
Roberts, Norman
❑ 86HagSunP-16
Roberts, Pete
❑ 88LasVegSC-5
❑ 88LasVegSP-228
❑ 89LasVegSC-9
❑ 89LasVegSP-13
❑ 90CMC-510
❑ 90LasVegSC-7
❑ 90LasVegSP-122
❑ 90ProAAAF-10
Roberts, Ray
❑ 94EugEmeC-19
❑ 94EugEmeF-3711
❑ 95SprSulTI-23
Roberts, Robin
❑ 47Exh-188A
❑ 47Exh-188B
❑ 47PM1StaP1-176
❑ 47PM1StaP1-177
❑ 49Bow-46
❑ 49EurSta-143
❑ 49OlmStu-6
❑ 49PhiBul-43
❑ 49PhiLumPB-8
❑ 50Bow-32
❑ 50JJKCopP-14
❑ 50PhiPhil-18
❑ 51BerRos-D8
❑ 51Bow-3
❑ 51TopCurA-10
❑ 52BerRos-55
❑ 52Bow-4
❑ 52NatTeaL-23
❑ 52RedMan-NL18
❑ 52TipTop-34
❑ 52Top-59
❑ 53BowC-65
❑ 53MacSta-3
❑ 53RedMan-NL11
❑ 53SpoMagP-9
❑ 54Bow-95
❑ 54RedMan-NL18
❑ 55Bow-171
❑ 56PhiPos-5
❑ 56Top-180
❑ 56YelBasP-27
❑ 57Top-15
❑ 58JayPubA-16
❑ 58PhiJayP-9
❑ 58PhiTeal-15
❑ 58Top-90
❑ 59Top-156
❑ 59Top-352
❑ 59TopVen-156
❑ 60Baz-26
❑ 60KeyChal-39
❑ 60MacSta-19
❑ 60NuHi-44
❑ 60PhiJayP-11
❑ 60Top-264
❑ 60TopTat-45
❑ 61NuSco-444
❑ 61Pos-117A
❑ 61Pos-117B
❑ 61Top-20
❑ 61TopStal-58
❑ 62BalOriP-22
❑ 62Jel-198
❑ 62Pos-198
❑ 62PosCan-198
❑ 62Top-243
❑ 63BalOriP-27
❑ 63Jel-66
❑ 63Pos-66
❑ 63Top-6
❑ 63Top-125
❑ 64BalOriP-29
❑ 64OriJayP-10
❑ 64Top-285
❑ 64TopVen-285
❑ 65BalOriP-28
❑ 65OPC-15
❑ 65Top-15
❑ 66Top-530
❑ 69EquSpoHoF-BB17
❑ 74NewYorNTDiS-19
❑ 75Phi195T-23
❑ 76GalBasGHoF-23
❑ 76JerJonPC-8
❑ 76RowExh-6
❑ 76ShaPiz-157
❑ 76ShaPiz-158
❑ 77BobParHoF-72
❑ 77GalGloG-4
❑ 77PhiFav-14
❑ 78ReaRem-16
❑ 79BasGre-67
❑ 79DiaGre-317
❑ 79PhiTeal-7
❑ 79TCM50-4
❑ 80PacLeg-56
❑ 80PerHaloFP-157
❑ 80PerHaloFPS-32
❑ 80Phi195T-23
❑ 80SSPHOF-157
❑ 81TCM60I-459
❑ 82CraJac-14
❑ 82DiaCla-108
❑ 82TCMGreP-6
❑ 82TCMStaot5-10
❑ 83DonHOFH-41
❑ 83MLBPin-30
❑ 83PhiPosGM-8
❑ 83PhiPosGPaM-2
❑ 83TopRep5-59
❑ 84OCoandSI-64
❑ 85TCMPpl1-15
❑ 86PhiTas-36
❑ 86SpoDecG-39
❑ 86SpoDesJM-21
❑ 86TCMSupS-26
❑ 87AstShowSTh-24
❑ 87Phi195T-9
❑ 88PacLegl-15
❑ 89TopBasT-40
❑ 90PacLeg-47
❑ 90PerGreM-17
❑ 90PhiTas-31
❑ 90SweBasG-11
❑ 91LinDri-33
❑ 91OriCro-384
❑ 91SweBasG-77
❑ 91TopArc1-288
❑ 91UppDecS-3
❑ 92ActPacA-12
❑ 92ActPacA2-12G
❑ 92BazQua5A-21
❑ 92UppDecF-54
❑ 92UppDecFG-54
❑ 92UppDecHH-HI7
❑ 92UppDecS-35
❑ 93ActPacAC-12
❑ 93TedWil-73
❑ 93UppDecAH-108
❑ 94UppDecAH-36
❑ 94UppDecAH-223
❑ 94UppDecAH1-36
❑ 94UppDecAH1-223
❑ 97TopStaHRR-12
❑ 97TopStaRRAU-12
❑ 98SpollITaN-27
❑ 98SpollITaNEE-27
❑ 99SpollIGotG-36
❑ 99SpollIGotGA-61
Roberts, Scott
❑ 84VanCanC-42
❑ 85VanCanC-218
❑ 86IndTeal-36
❑ 86MaiGuiP-17
❑ 87BufBisP-20
Roberts, Tim
❑ 91EriSaiC-23
❑ 91EriSaiP-4069
Roberts, Vaughn
❑ 29Zee-28
❑ 30Zee-38
Roberts, Willis
❑ 93BriTigC-17
❑ 94BriTigC-21
❑ 94BriTigF-3501
❑ 95FayGenTI-22
❑ 96LakTigB-20
❑ 97JacSun-21
❑ 98JacSunM-21
Robertson, Andre
❑ 81ColCliP-2
❑ 81ColCliT-3
❑ 82ColCliP-2
❑ 82ColCliT-17
❑ 82Top-83
❑ 82YanPhoA-24
❑ 83Don-387
❑ 83Fle-396
❑ 83Top-281
❑ 83TopSti-316
❑ 83YanPhoA-23
❑ 83YanRoyRD-10
❑ 84ColCliP-20
❑ 84ColCliT-9
❑ 84Don-347
❑ 84Fle-140
❑ 84Nes792-592
❑ 84OPC-282
❑ 84Top-592
❑ 84TopSti-323
❑ 84TopTif-592
❑ 85Fle-144
❑ 85Top-354
❑ 85TopTif-354
❑ 85YanTCMP-31
❑ 86ColCliP-19
❑ 86ColCliP-21
❑ 86Don-469
❑ 86Fle-117
❑ 86StaoftFT-5
❑ 86Top-738
❑ 86TopTif-738
❑ 86YanTCM-28
❑ 87ChaLooB-25
❑ 88HunStaTI-16
❑ 88TacTigC-19
❑ 88TacTigP-634
❑ 89OklCit8C-14
❑ 89OklCit8P-1514
❑ 92TexLon-34
❑ 92YanWIZ8-161
Robertson, Bill
❑ 90BelBreB-2
❑ 90BelBreS-18
Robertson, Bob E.
❑ 68OPC-36
❑ 68Top-36
❑ 68TopVen-36
❑ 69PirJacitB-10
❑ 69Top-468A
❑ 69Top-468B
❑ 69TopTeaP-16
❑ 70Top-664
❑ 71Kel-4
❑ 71MLBOffS-212
❑ 71OPC-255
❑ 71Pir-5
❑ 71PirActP-22
❑ 71PirArc-9
❑ 71Top-255
❑ 72Kel-45
❑ 72OPC-429
❑ 72OPC-430
❑ 72PirTeal-6
❑ 72Top-429
❑ 72Top-430
❑ 73OPC-422
❑ 73Top-422
❑ 74OPC-540
❑ 74Top-540
❑ 75OPC-409
❑ 75PitPirP-23
❑ 75Top-409
❑ 75TopMin-409
❑ 76OPC-449
❑ 76PirPos-18
❑ 76SSP-578
❑ 76Top-449
❑ 77Top-176
❑ 79OPC-158
❑ 79Top-312
❑ 89SweBasG-107
❑ 90AshTouC-28
❑ 91AshTouP-586
❑ 92AshTouC-27
❑ 93OscAstC-27
❑ 93OscAstF-645
Robertson, Bryant
❑ 85LitFalMT-27
Robertson, Charles
❑ 21Exh-145
❑ 21Nei-10
❑ 22E120-26
❑ 22W573-108
❑ 22W575-105
❑ 23W503-54
❑ 75WhiSox1T-21
❑ 92ConTSN-354
❑ 93ConTSN-815
Robertson, Dale
❑ 81PawRedST-13
❑ 84PawRedST-4
Robertson, Daryl
❑ 77FriOneYW-19
Robertson, David A.
❑ 15SpoNewM-143
❑ 16FleBreD-76
❑ 16SpoNewM-143
❑ 17ColE13-140
❑ 17HolBreD-84
❑ 23W503-3
❑ 23WilChoV-134
Robertson, Doug
❑ 85EveGialC-14
❑ 86CliGiaP-22
❑ 87CliGiaP-1
❑ 88CalLeaACLC-6
❑ 88SanJosGCLC-137
❑ 88SanJosGP-115
❑ 89ShrCapP-1851
❑ 90CMC-457
❑ 90ColSprSSC-5
❑ 90ColSprSSP-32
❑ 90IndTeal-33
❑ 90ProAAAF-213
❑ 91LinDriAA-442
❑ 91MidAngLD-442
❑ 91MidAngOHP-23
❑ 91MidAngP-433
❑ 96SouOreTI-9
Robertson, Gene (Eugene E.)
❑ 92ConTSN-386
Robertson, Jason
❑ 89HigSchPLS-14
❑ 90Bes-288
❑ 90GreHorB-25
❑ 90GreHorP-2677
❑ 90GreHorS-19
❑ 91PriWilCC-22
❑ 91PriWilCP-1440
❑ 92ClaFS7-225
❑ 92PriWilCC-24
❑ 92PriWilCF-163
❑ 92ProFS7-123
❑ 93AlbYanF-2176
❑ 94AlbYanF-1456
❑ 95NorNagUTI-22
❑ 95NorNavTI-22
❑ 96ChaKniB-24
Robertson, Jay
❑ 78DunBluJT-18
❑ 80SyrChiT-6
❑ 80SyrChiTI-18
Robertson, Jenny
❑ 88BulDurM-3
Robertson, Jeriome
❑ 97QuaCitRBB-24
❑ 98KisCobQ-24
Robertson, Jerry L.
❑ 66St.PetCTI-12
❑ 69Top-284
❑ 70Top-661
❑ 71OPC-651
❑ 71Top-651
Robertson, Jim (Alfred J.)
❑ 54A'STEAI-21
❑ 54Bow-211
❑ 54Top-149
❑ 55A'sRodM-32
❑ 55Bow-5
❑ 55Top-177
❑ 56SeaPop-16
❑ 94TopArc1-149
❑ 94TopArc1G-149
Robertson, Lawrence
❑ 23Zee-19
Robertson, Michael
❑ 86JamExpP-20
Robertson, Mike
❑ 87St.PetCP-5
❑ 88ArkTraGS-20
❑ 89ArkTraGS-21
❑ 92Bow-687
❑ 92ClaFS7-375
❑ 92SarWhiSCB-20
❑ 92SarWhiSF-215
❑ 92StaCluD-156
❑ 92UppDecML-48
❑ 92UppDecML-156
❑ 93BirBarF-1200
❑ 93Bow-315
❑ 93ClaFS7-87
❑ 93ClaGolF-78
❑ 93UppDec-448
❑ 93UppDecGold-448
❑ 94BirBarC-19
❑ 94BirBarF-634
❑ 94Bow-43
❑ 94UppDecML-40
❑ 94VenLinU-147
❑ 95LinVen-150
❑ 95NasSouTI-20
❑ 96NasSouB-18
❑ 97ScrRedB-18
❑ 98TusSidM-24
Robertson, Rich Wayne
❑ 90WelPirP-26
❑ 91SalBucC-18
❑ 91SalBucP-948
❑ 92CarMudF-1178
❑ 93Bow-123
❑ 93BufBisF-515
❑ 93FleFinE-117

❑ 94BufBisF-1834
❑ 94TriAAF-AAA27
❑ 96Fle-175
❑ 96FleTif-175
❑ 96LeaSigEA-173
❑ 96Ult-379
❑ 96UltGolM-379
❑ 97PacPriGotD-GD66
❑ 97PhoFirDTTI-23
❑ 98ColCho-162
❑ 98PacOnl-21
❑ 98PacOnlR-21
❑ 98PacOnlWC-21
❑ 98UppDec-434
❑ 98VanCanG-22
Robertson, Richard P.
❑ 69OPC-16
❑ 69Top-16
❑ 70OPC-229
❑ 70Top-229
❑ 71MLBOffS-263
❑ 71OPC-443
❑ 71Top-443
❑ 72Top-618
Robertson, Robby
❑ 93AppFoxCB-20
❑ 93AppFoxFI-2475
Robertson, Rod (Roderick)
❑ 86BenPhiC-130
❑ 88SpaPhiP-1034
❑ 88SpaPhiS-2
❑ 89ClePhiS-19
❑ 90ReaPhiB-18
❑ 90ReaPhiP-1228
❑ 90ReaPhiS-21
❑ 91LinDriAA-515
❑ 91ReaPhiLD-515
❑ 91ReaPhiP-1376
❑ 92LonTigF-642
❑ 92LonTigS-416
❑ 93TolMudHF-1662
❑ 94OrlCubF-1393
❑ 95RocRedWTI-30
Robertson, Ryan
❑ 96KanCouCTI-23
❑ 98PorSeaDQ-15
Robertson, Shawn
❑ 91SpoIndC-10
❑ 91SpoIndP-3961
❑ 92WatDiaC-18
❑ 92WatDiaF-2154
Robertson, Sherry
❑ 47SenGunBP-9
❑ 50Bow-161
❑ 51Bow-95
❑ 52A'sTeal-23
❑ 52Top-245
❑ 83TopRep5-245
Robertson, Stan
❑ 92AlbPolCB-23
❑ 92AlbPolF-2320
❑ 92JamExpF-1515
Robertson, Tommy
❑ 92SanBerC-10
❑ 92SanBerSF-972
❑ 93RivPilCLC-16
❑ 95LynHilTI-24
Robicheaux, Randy
❑ 86WatPirP-18
Robidoux, Billy Jo
❑ 83BelBreFr-21
❑ 86BrePol-13
❑ 86Don-515
❑ 86Fle-652
❑ 86FleUpd-97
❑ 86Spo-178
❑ 86SpoRoo-28
❑ 86TopTra-92T
❑ 86TopTraT-92T
❑ 87BrePol-13
❑ 87BreTeal-11
❑ 87Don-240
❑ 87DonOpeD-51
❑ 87Fle-356
❑ 87FleGlo-356
❑ 87SpoTeaP-19
❑ 87Top-401
❑ 87TopRoo-13
❑ 87TopSti-202
❑ 87TopTif-401
❑ 88BreTeal-30
❑ 88DenZepC-13
❑ 88DenZepP-1267
❑ 88Sco-334
❑ 88ScoGlo-334
❑ 88StaLinBre-15
❑ 89WhiSoxC-23
❑ 90TopTVRS-27
❑ 90UppDec-782
❑ 94BreMilB-262
Robinette, Gary
❑ 81AppFoxT-22
Robinson, Aaron
❑ 46SpoExcW-9-3
❑ 47HomBon-40
❑ 47TipTop-58
❑ 47YanTeaT-22
❑ 48WhiSoxTI-24
❑ 49Bow-133
❑ 50Bow-95
❑ 51Bow-142
❑ 53MotCoo-6
❑ 92YanWIZA-67
Robinson, Adam
❑ 97SouOreTB-8
❑ 98VisOakG-26
Robinson, Alan
❑ 92HamRedC-21
❑ 92HamRedF-1608
Robinson, Bill
❑ 87SalAngP-8
❑ 88QuaCitAGS-8
Robinson, Bill H.
❑ 67Top-442
❑ 68Top-337
❑ 68Top3-D-9
❑ 68TopVen-337
❑ 68YanPhoS-76
❑ 69MilBra-234
❑ 69MLBOffS-78
❑ 69Top-313
❑ 69TopSta-207
❑ 69TopTeaP-19
❑ 69YanMal-7
❑ 69YanPhoS-48
❑ 70MLBOffS-249
❑ 70OPC-23
❑ 70Top-23
❑ 72MilBra-290
❑ 73OPC-37
❑ 73PhiTeal-15
❑ 73Top-37
❑ 74OPC-174
❑ 74PhiJohP-24
❑ 74Top-174
❑ 74TopSta-78
❑ 75OPC-501
❑ 75PitPirP-22
❑ 75Top-501
❑ 75TopMin-501
❑ 76OPC-137
❑ 76PirPos-19
❑ 76SSP-577
❑ 76Top-137
❑ 77BurCheD-183
❑ 77PirPos-22
❑ 77Top-335
❑ 78OPC-128
❑ 78Top-455
❑ 79OPC-336
❑ 79Top-637
❑ 80OPC-138
❑ 80Top-264
❑ 81Don-137
❑ 81Fle-373
❑ 81Top-51
❑ 82Don-402
❑ 82Fle-494
❑ 82Top-543
❑ 82TopTra-100T
❑ 83Fle-170
❑ 83PhiTas-24
❑ 83Top-754
❑ 85MetTCM-3
❑ 85PolMet-M1
❑ 86MetTCM-34
❑ 87MetColP-45
❑ 88MetColP-45
❑ 88MetKah-28
❑ 89MetColP-50
❑ 89MetKah-23
❑ 90SweBasG-114
❑ 92ShrCapF-3887
❑ 92ShrCapS-599
❑ 92YanWIZ6-106
❑ 94ReaPhiF-2080
❑ 95ReaPhiELC-30
❑ 96ReaPhiB-26
❑ 97ScrRedB-26
❑ 98ScrRedBQ-23
Robinson, Bo
❑ 98EveAquG-21
Robinson, Bob
❑ 92VisOakC-10
❑ 92VisOakF-1015
❑ 93ForMyeMC-22
Robinson, Bobby
❑ 86NegLeaF-65
❑ 91NegLeaRL-12
❑ 92NegLeaRLI-52
❑ 95NegLeaL2-7
❑ 95NegLeaLI-12
Robinson, Brad
❑ 88GreHorP-1557
Robinson, Brett
❑ 87GenCubP-2
❑ 88PeoChiTI-27
❑ 89PeoChiTI-7
❑ 90ChaKniTI-17
Robinson, Brian
❑ 85CedRapRT-19
❑ 86VerRedP-16
❑ 87CedRapRP-17
Robinson, Brooks
❑ 47Exh-189
❑ 47PM1StaP1-178
❑ 55DonWin-37
❑ 56BalOriP-48
❑ 57Top-328
❑ 58BalOriP-14
❑ 58Top-307
❑ 59OriJayP-7
❑ 59Top-439
❑ 60Lea-27
❑ 60OriJayP-7
❑ 60Top-28
❑ 60TopVen-28
❑ 61BalOriP-16
❑ 61Pos-75A
❑ 61Pos-75B
❑ 61Raw-9
❑ 61Top-10
❑ 61Top-572
❑ 61TopDicG-14
❑ 61TopStal-104
❑ 62BalOriP-23
❑ 62Pos-29
❑ 62PosCan-29
❑ 62SalPlaC-40
❑ 62ShiPlaC-40
❑ 62Top-45
❑ 62Top-468
❑ 62TopBuc-75
❑ 62TopStal-8
❑ 62TopVen-45
❑ 63BalOriP-28
❑ 63BasMagM-69
❑ 63Baz-30
❑ 63ExhStaB-55
❑ 63Fle-4
❑ 63Jel-59
❑ 63Pos-59
❑ 63SalMetC-53
❑ 63Top-345
❑ 63TopStil-34
❑ 64BalOriP-30
❑ 64Baz-30
❑ 64OriJayP-11
❑ 64Raw-7
❑ 64Top-230
❑ 64TopCoi-18
❑ 64TopCoi-125
❑ 64TopGia-50
❑ 64TopSta-21
❑ 64TopStaU-61
❑ 64TopVen-230
❑ 64WheSta-39
❑ 65BalOriP-29
❑ 65Baz-30
❑ 65OldLonC-35
❑ 65OPC-1
❑ 65OPC-5
❑ 65OPC-150
❑ 65Top-1
❑ 65Top-5
❑ 65Top-150
❑ 65TopEmbl-16
❑ 65TopTral-65
❑ 66BalOriP-28
❑ 66Baz-34
❑ 66Top-390
❑ 66TopRubl-79
❑ 67BalOriP-89
❑ 67BalOriP-90
❑ 67BalOriP-91
❑ 67BalOriP-92
❑ 67BalOriP-93
❑ 67Baz-34
❑ 67CokCapA-3
❑ 67CokCapAAm-21
❑ 67CokCapO-10
❑ 67DexPre-175
❑ 67DexPre-176
❑ 67OPC-1
❑ 67OPC-154
❑ 67OPCPapl-3
❑ 67Top-1
❑ 67Top-154
❑ 67Top-531
❑ 67Top-600
❑ 67TopPos-3
❑ 67TopTesF-19
❑ 67TopVen-211
❑ 68AtlOilPBCC-37
❑ 68BalOriDPCP-11
❑ 68Baz-8
❑ 68CokCapO-10
❑ 68DexPre-65
❑ 68OPC-20
❑ 68Top-20
❑ 68Top-365
❑ 68Top-530
❑ 68TopActS-12C
❑ 68TopGamI-9
❑ 68TopVen-20
❑ 68TopVen-365
❑ 69BalOriPC-3
❑ 69EquSpoHoF-BB18
❑ 69MilBra-235
❑ 69MLBOffS-8
❑ 69MLBPin-25
❑ 69NabTeaF-18
❑ 69OPCDec-18
❑ 69Top-421
❑ 69Top-504
❑ 69Top-550
❑ 69TopDec-1
❑ 69TopSta-129
❑ 69TopSup-3
❑ 69TopTeaP-5
❑ 69TraSta-13
❑ 70BalOriP-27
❑ 70DayDaiNM-154
❑ 70Kel-21
❑ 70MLBOffS-154
❑ 70OPC-230
❑ 70OPC-455
❑ 70Top-230
❑ 70Top-455
❑ 71AllBasA-19
❑ 71BalOriP-24
❑ 71BazNumT-22
❑ 71BazUnn-31
❑ 71MilDud-26
❑ 71MLBOffS-309
❑ 71MLBOffS-571
❑ 71OPC-300
❑ 71OPC-331
❑ 71OriCha-13
❑ 71Top-300
❑ 71Top-331
❑ 71TopCoi-114
❑ 71TopGreM-9
❑ 71TopSup-59
❑ 71TopTat-6
❑ 71TopTat-7
❑ 72MilBra-291
❑ 72OPC-222
❑ 72OPC-498
❑ 72OriDMV-8
❑ 72OriPos-27
❑ 72ProStaP-36
❑ 72SevTraC-45
❑ 72Top-222
❑ 72Top-498
❑ 72Top-550
❑ 73BalOriP-37
❑ 73LinPor-13
❑ 73OPC-90
❑ 73OriJohP-5A
❑ 73OriJohP-5B
❑ 73OriTeal-27
❑ 73SevTraC-61
❑ 73Top-90
❑ 73TopCanL-41
❑ 73TopCom-16
❑ 73TopPin-16
❑ 74LauAllG-66
❑ 74OPC-160
❑ 74OPC-334
❑ 74Top-160
❑ 74Top-334
❑ 74TopDecE-25
❑ 74TopSta-129
❑ 75BalOriP-25
❑ 75Hos-144
❑ 75Kel-18
❑ 75OPC-50
❑ 75OPC-202
❑ 75SSP42-6
❑ 75Top-50
❑ 75Top-202
❑ 75TopMin-50
❑ 75TopMin-202
❑ 76BalOriP-33
❑ 76BalOriP-34
❑ 76BlaDis-48
❑ 76BucDis-48
❑ 76CarDis-48
❑ 76CraDis-48
❑ 76DailsID-48
❑ 76Hos-36
❑ 76HosTwi-36
❑ 76IsaDis-48
❑ 76LauDiaJ-11
❑ 76OPC-95
❑ 76OrbDis-48
❑ 76RedBarD-48
❑ 76SafDis-48
❑ 76SSP-392
❑ 76Top-95
❑ 76TowCluD-48
❑ 77BalOriP-16
❑ 77BalOriP-17
❑ 77BurCheD-43
❑ 77ChiWilD-55
❑ 77DailsID-55
❑ 77DetCaeD-55
❑ 77HolInnD-55
❑ 77MSADis-55
❑ 77SagDis-55
❑ 77sDis-55
❑ 77Spo-1607
❑ 77Top-285
❑ 77WenDis-55
❑ 77ZipDis-55
❑ 78OPC-239
❑ 78TCM60I-190
❑ 78Top-4
❑ 80MarExh-26
❑ 80PacLeg-54
❑ 80PerHaloFP-184
❑ 80PerHaloFPS-49
❑ 80SSPHOF-181
❑ 81Ori6F-27
❑ 82CraJac-8
❑ 82DiaCla-67
❑ 82K-M-5
❑ 83ASABroR-1
❑ 83ASABroR-2
❑ 83ASABroR-3
❑ 83ASABroR-4
❑ 83ASABroR-5
❑ 83ASABroR-6
❑ 83ASABroR-7
❑ 83ASABroR-8
❑ 83ASABroR-9
❑ 83ASABroR-10
❑ 83ASABroR-11
❑ 83ASABroR-12
❑ 83FraBroR-1
❑ 83FraBroR-2
❑ 83FraBroR-3
❑ 83FraBroR-4
❑ 83FraBroR-5
❑ 83FraBroR-6
❑ 83FraBroR-7
❑ 83FraBroR-8
❑ 83FraBroR-9
❑ 83FraBroR-10
❑ 83FraBroR-11
❑ 83FraBroR-12
❑ 83FraBroR-13
❑ 83FraBroR-14
❑ 83FraBroR-15
❑ 83FraBroR-16
❑ 83FraBroR-17
❑ 83FraBroR-18
❑ 83FraBroR-19
❑ 83FraBroR-20
❑ 83FraBroR-21
❑ 83FraBroR-22
❑ 83FraBroR-23
❑ 83FraBroR-24
❑ 83FraBroR-25
❑ 83FraBroR-26
❑ 83FraBroR-27
❑ 83FraBroR-28
❑ 83FraBroR-29
❑ 83FraBroR-30
❑ 83FraBroR-31
❑ 83FraBroR-32
❑ 83FraBroR-33
❑ 83FraBroR-34
❑ 83FraBroR-35
❑ 83FraBroR-36
❑ 83FraBroR-37
❑ 83FraBroR-38
❑ 83FraBroR-39
❑ 83FraBroR-40
❑ 83MLBPin-16
❑ 83TigAlKS-69
❑ 83TopTraBP-9
❑ 84OCoandSI-33
❑ 84OCoandSI-76
❑ 84SpoDesPW-7
❑ 85DalNatCC-4
❑ 86OriGreT-10
❑ 86SpoDecG-45
❑ 86SpoDesJM-10
❑ 86TCM-13
❑ 86TCMSupS-30
❑ 87BalOriP-31
❑ 87HygAllG-36
❑ 87K-M-9
❑ 87LeaSpeO*-H9
❑ 87NesDreT-14
❑ 88GreBasS-21
❑ 88HouSho-1
❑ 88PacLegI-3
❑ 89KahCoo-9
❑ 89PacLegI-129
❑ 89PerCelP-35
❑ 89SweBasG-134
❑ 89TopBasT-10
❑ 90AGFA-13
❑ 90BasWit-17
❑ 90PacLeg-102
❑ 90PerGreM-39
❑ 91BalOriP-27
❑ 91MDAA-14
❑ 91MDAA-NNO
❑ 91OriCro-385
❑ 91SweBasG-146
❑ 91UppDecS-3
❑ 91UppDecS-11
❑ 92FroRowBR-1
❑ 92FroRowBR-1AU
❑ 92FroRowBR-2
❑ 92FroRowBR-3
❑ 92FroRowBR-4
❑ 92FroRowBR-5
❑ 92KodCelD-4
❑ 92MDAMVP-4
❑ 92PMGol-1
❑ 92PMGol-2
❑ 92UppDecF-51
❑ 92UppDecFG-51
❑ 92UppDecHH-HI8
❑ 92UppDecS-17
❑ 92UppDecS-26
❑ 92UppDecS-34
❑ 92Zip-5
❑ 93ActPacA-120
❑ 93ActPacA2-54G
❑ 93CouTimLBR-1
❑ 93CouTimLBR-2
❑ 93CouTimLBR-3
❑ 93CouTimLBR-4
❑ 93CouTimLBR-5
❑ 93CouTimLBR-6
❑ 93CouTimLBR-7
❑ 93NabAllA-5
❑ 93OriCroASU-3
❑ 93TedWilBR-1
❑ 93TedWilBR-2
❑ 93TedWilBR-3
❑ 93TedWilBR-4
❑ 93TedWilBR-5
❑ 93TedWilBR-6
❑ 93TedWilBR-7
❑ 93TedWilBR-8
❑ 93TedWilBR-9
❑ 93TedWilBR-AU
❑ 93UppDecS-18
❑ 93Yoo-16
❑ 94TedWil-10
❑ 94Yoo-13
❑ 95BalOriP-45
❑ 95MCIAmb-15
❑ 95TopLegot6M-10
❑ 96AriLot-3
❑ 97ClaBroR-1
❑ 97DonSigSS-17
❑ 97FleMilDM-5

❑ 97FleMilDMR-5
❑ 97HigMinMCT-33
❑ 97HigMinMCT-34
❑ 97JimDea-2
❑ 97SpollICC-8
❑ 97TopStaHRR-13
❑ 97TopStaRRAU-13
❑ 98SpollIAuto-6
❑ 98SpollITaN-28
❑ 98SpollITaNAotG-AG4
❑ 98SpollITaNEE-28
❑ 98SpollITaNGS-21
❑ 98SpollIWSF-7
❑ 98SpollIWSFEE-7
❑ 98SpollIWSFFE-7
❑ 98SpollIWSFMC-2
❑ 98UppDecR-12
❑ 98UppDecRSotT-BR
❑ 99TopHaloFC-HOF2

Robinson, Bruce
❑ 79ColCliT-16
❑ 79Top-711
❑ 80ColCliP-26
❑ 80ColCliT-15
❑ 81Top-424
❑ 84TacTigC-73
❑ 92YanWIZ7-135
❑ 92YanWIZ8-162

Robinson, Carl
❑ 11PinT-5-1107

Robinson, Chris
❑ 91BoiHawC-27
❑ 91BoiHawP-3878
❑ 92PalSprAC-4
❑ 92PalSprAF-837

Robinson, Clyde
❑ 09ColChiE-243
❑ 11SpoLifCW-305
❑ 12ColRedB-243

Robinson, Connie
❑ 83FraBroR-10

Robinson, Craig
❑ 74OPC-23
❑ 74Top-23
❑ 74TopTra-23T
❑ 75AtlBraP-31
❑ 75OPC-367
❑ 75Top-367
❑ 75TopMin-367
❑ 76AtlBraP-27
❑ 76SSP-12
❑ 76VenLeaS-51
❑ 81RicBraT-23
❑ 82RicBraT-29
❑ 83RicBraT-24

Robinson, Daniel
❑ 93KanCouCC-19
❑ 93KanCouCF-928
❑ 93KanCouCTI-20
❑ 93Top-599
❑ 93TopGol-599
❑ 93TopInaM-599
❑ 93TopInaR-599
❑ 93TopMic-599
❑ 94BreCouMC-14
❑ 94BreCouMF-24
❑ 95BreCouMF-260

Robinson, Darek
❑ 93JohCitCC-16
❑ 93JohCitCF-3689
❑ 94NewJerCC-20
❑ 94NewJerCF-3425
❑ 95PeoChiTI-3

Robinson, Darryl
❑ 87EugEmeP-2648
❑ 88AppFoxP-144
❑ 88MidLeaAGS-38
❑ 89AppFoxP-860
❑ 90BasCitRS-21
❑ 91LinDriAA-416
❑ 91MemChiLD-416
❑ 91MemChiP-663
❑ 92MemChiF-2428
❑ 92MemChiS-444

Robinson, David
❑ 88SanDieS-17
❑ 88SanDieSAAG-17
❑ 89SanDieSAG-16
❑ 95BatCliTI-28
❑ 96PieBolWB-23

Robinson, David T.
❑ 71OPC-262
❑ 71Top-262

Robinson, Dewey
❑ 78AppFoxT-15
❑ 79IowOakP-13
❑ 80IowOakP-10
❑ 80Top-664
❑ 81Top-487
❑ 82Top-176
❑ 87PenWhiSP-7
❑ 93WhiSoxK-30

Robinson, Don
❑ 77ShrCapT-18
❑ 79Top-264
❑ 80Top-719
❑ 81Don-375
❑ 81Fle-366
❑ 81OPC-168
❑ 81Top-168
❑ 82Fle-495
❑ 82OPC-332
❑ 82Top-332
❑ 83Don-171
❑ 83Fle-319
❑ 83OPC-44
❑ 83Top-44
❑ 83TopSti-277
❑ 84Don-532
❑ 84Fle-262
❑ 84Nes792-616
❑ 84OPC-22
❑ 84Pir-18
❑ 84Top-616
❑ 84TopTif-616
❑ 85Don-264
❑ 85Fle-475
❑ 85OPC-129
❑ 85Pir-18
❑ 85Top-537
❑ 85TopTif-537
❑ 86Don-357
❑ 86Fle-621
❑ 86Lea-159
❑ 86Top-731
❑ 86TopTif-731
❑ 87Don-608
❑ 87Fle-622
❑ 87FleGlo-622
❑ 87OPC-387
❑ 87Top-712
❑ 87TopTif-712
❑ 88Don-573
❑ 88Fle-95
❑ 88FleGlo-95
❑ 88FleMin-120
❑ 88FleStiC-131
❑ 88FleTeaL-31
❑ 88GiaMot-22
❑ 88GiaPos-27
❑ 88Sco-619
❑ 88ScoGlo-619
❑ 88Spo-90
❑ 88StaLinG-15
❑ 88Top-52
❑ 88TopSti-94
❑ 88TopTif-52
❑ 89Bow-463
❑ 89BowTif-463
❑ 89Don-571
❑ 89DonBasB-191
❑ 89Fle-342
❑ 89FleBasA-36
❑ 89FleGlo-342
❑ 89GiaMot-22
❑ 89PanSti-211
❑ 89Sco-440
❑ 89Top-473
❑ 89TopSti-86
❑ 89TopTif-473
❑ 89UppDec-523
❑ 90Don-258
❑ 90Fle-70
❑ 90FleCan-70
❑ 90GiaMot-20
❑ 90GiaSmo-17
❑ 90Lea-267
❑ 90OPC-217
❑ 90PubIntS-81
❑ 90Sco-112
❑ 90Top-217
❑ 90TopBig-193
❑ 90TopSti-84
❑ 90TopTif-217
❑ 90UppDec-616
❑ 91Bow-384
❑ 91Bow-619
❑ 91Don-581
❑ 91Fle-272
❑ 91GiaMot-20
❑ 91GiaPacGaE-21
❑ 91GiaSFE-13
❑ 91Lea-188
❑ 91OPC-104
❑ 91PanFreS-73
❑ 91PanSti-74
❑ 91PulBraC-13
❑ 91PulBraP-4020
❑ 91Sco-639
❑ 91StaClu-167
❑ 91Top-104
❑ 91TopDesS-104
❑ 91TopMic-104
❑ 91TopTif-104
❑ 91Ult-327
❑ 91UppDec-402
❑ 91UppDecSS-SS16
❑ 92MacBraC-24
❑ 92MacBraF-282
❑ 92OPC-373
❑ 92PhiMed-46
❑ 92Pin-463
❑ 92ProFS7-192
❑ 92StaClu-729
❑ 92StaCluNC-729
❑ 92Top-373
❑ 92TopGol-373
❑ 92TopGolW-373
❑ 92TopMic-373
❑ 92Ult-329
❑ 93DurBulC-14
❑ 93DurBulF-498
❑ 93DurBulTI-32
❑ 94GreBraF-426
❑ 94GreBraTI-19

Robinson, Dustin
❑ 98ChaAllCM-10

Robinson, Dwight
❑ 91PitMetC-3
❑ 91PitMetP-3432
❑ 92ColMetC-20
❑ 92ColMetF-305
❑ 92ColMetPI-22
❑ 93CapCitBC-19
❑ 93CapCitBF-470
❑ 94ClaGolF-24
❑ 94St.LucMC-20
❑ 94St.LucMF-1205

Robinson, Earl
❑ 60DarFar-20
❑ 61Top-343
❑ 62BalOriP-24
❑ 62Top-272
❑ 64BalOriP-31
❑ 78TCM60I-81
❑ 90DodTar-674
❑ 91OriCro-386

Robinson, Eddie (William E.)
❑ 47Exh-190
❑ 47IndTeal-22
❑ 47IndVanPP-21
❑ 48IndTeal-26
❑ 50Bow-18
❑ 50RoyDes-22
❑ 51Bow-88
❑ 51TopRedB-51
❑ 52BerRos-56
❑ 52Bow-77
❑ 52NatTeaL-24
❑ 52RedMan-AL18
❑ 52RoyPre-11
❑ 52StaCalL-73C
❑ 52StaCalS-87A
❑ 52Top-32
❑ 52WhiSoxHDP-7
❑ 53A'sTeal-26
❑ 53BowBW-20
❑ 53Dor-135
❑ 53MotCoo-59
❑ 53RedMan-AL11
❑ 53Top-73
❑ 54Bow-193
❑ 54NewYorJA-58
❑ 54Top-62
❑ 55Bow-153
❑ 56BalOriP-52
❑ 56Top-302
❑ 56YanTeal-21
❑ 57Top-238
❑ 60Top-455
❑ 76WhiSoxTAG-9
❑ 79DiaGre-298
❑ 79TCM50-283
❑ 80WhiSoxGT-12
❑ 83FraBroR-11
❑ 83TopRep5-32
❑ 85TCMPpl1-34
❑ 91OriCro-387
❑ 91TopArc1-73
❑ 94TopArc1-62
❑ 94TopArc1G-62

Robinson, Eli
❑ 91PriRedC-17
❑ 91PriRedP-3524
❑ 92PriRedC-2
❑ 92PriRedF-3096
❑ 93BilMusF-3955
❑ 93BilMusSP-11

Robinson, Emmett
❑ 86KinEagP-19

Robinson, Floyd
❑ 47Exh-191
❑ 62SalPlaC-214
❑ 62ShiPlaC-214
❑ 62Top-454
❑ 62TopBuc-76
❑ 62TopStal-29
❑ 62WhiSoxJP-10
❑ 62WhiSoxTS-17
❑ 63Baz-24
❑ 63Jel-39
❑ 63Pos-39
❑ 63Top-2
❑ 63Top-405
❑ 63TopStil-35
❑ 63WhiSoxTS-22
❑ 64Baz-24
❑ 64Top-195
❑ 64TopCoi-39
❑ 64TopSta-18
❑ 64TopStaU-62
❑ 64TopVen-195
❑ 64WhiSoxl-22
❑ 64WhiSoxTS-20
❑ 65Top-345
❑ 65WhiSoxJP-8
❑ 66OPC-8
❑ 66Top-8
❑ 66Top-199
❑ 66TopRubl-80
❑ 66TopVen-8
❑ 66TopVen-199
❑ 67CokCapR-16
❑ 67OPC-120
❑ 67Top-120
❑ 68Top-404

Robinson, Frank
❑ 47Exh-192
❑ 56Kah-14
❑ 56RedBurB-20
❑ 57Kah-25
❑ 57RedSoh-17
❑ 57SwiFra-16
❑ 57Top-35
❑ 58Kah-26
❑ 58RedEnq-33
❑ 58RedJayP-11
❑ 58Top-285
❑ 58Top-386
❑ 58Top-484
❑ 59ArmCoi-14
❑ 59HomRunD-16
❑ 59Kah-31
❑ 59RedBurBP-19
❑ 59RedBurBP-20
❑ 59RedShiBS-19
❑ 59Top-435
❑ 60Baz-29
❑ 60Kah-36
❑ 60MacSta-20
❑ 60RedJayP-12
❑ 60Top-352
❑ 60Top-490
❑ 60TopTat-46
❑ 61Baz-31
❑ 61Kah-37
❑ 61Pos-182A
❑ 61Pos-182B
❑ 61RedJayP-12
❑ 61Top-25
❑ 61Top-360
❑ 61Top-581
❑ 61TopDicG-15
❑ 61TopStal-24
❑ 62AurRec-14
❑ 62Baz-26
❑ 62Jel-122
❑ 62Kah-35
❑ 62Pos-122
❑ 62PosCan-122
❑ 62RedEnq-29
❑ 62RedJayP-12
❑ 62SalPlaC-165
❑ 62ShiPlaC-165
❑ 62Top-54
❑ 62Top-350
❑ 62Top-396
❑ 62TopBuc-77
❑ 62TopStal-121
❑ 62TopVen-54
❑ 63BasMagM-70
❑ 63Baz-31
❑ 63ExhStaB-56
❑ 63Jel-131
❑ 63Kah-27
❑ 63Pos-131A
❑ 63Pos-131B
❑ 63RedEnq-28
❑ 63RedFreBC-22
❑ 63RedJayP-12
❑ 63SalMetC-29
❑ 63Top-1
❑ 63Top-3
❑ 63Top-400
❑ 63TopStil-36
❑ 64Baz-31
❑ 64Kah-24
❑ 64RedJayP-11
❑ 64Top-260
❑ 64TopCoi-37
❑ 64TopCoi-154
❑ 64TopGia-29
❑ 64TopSta-15
❑ 64TopStaU-63
❑ 64TopTatl-65
❑ 64TopVen-260
❑ 65Baz-31
❑ 65Kah-36
❑ 65OldLonC-17
❑ 65OPC-120
❑ 65RedEnq-24
❑ 65Top-120
❑ 65TopEmbl-22
❑ 65TopTral-66
❑ 66BalOriP-29
❑ 66Baz-32
❑ 66Top-219
❑ 66Top-310
❑ 66TopRubl-81
❑ 66TopVen-219
❑ 66TopVen-310
❑ 67AshOil-8
❑ 67BalOriP-94
❑ 67Baz-32
❑ 67CokCapA-23
❑ 67CokCapAAm-32
❑ 67CokCapO-4
❑ 67DexPre-177
❑ 67DexPre-178
❑ 67OPC-1
❑ 67OPC-62
❑ 67OPC-100
❑ 67OPCPapl-19
❑ 67Top-1
❑ 67Top-62
❑ 67Top-100
❑ 67Top-239
❑ 67Top-241
❑ 67Top-243
❑ 67TopGiaSU-3
❑ 67TopPos-19
❑ 67TopTesF-20
❑ 67TopVen-194
❑ 68AtlOilPBCC-38
❑ 68BalOriDPCP-12
❑ 68Baz-3
❑ 68CokCapO-4
❑ 68DexPre-66
❑ 68OPC-2
❑ 68OPC-4
❑ 68Top-2
❑ 68Top-4
❑ 68Top-373
❑ 68Top-454A
❑ 68Top-454B
❑ 68Top-500
❑ 68Top-530
❑ 68TopActS-3B
❑ 68TopActS-4A
❑ 68TopActS-13A
❑ 68TopActS-15B
❑ 68TopGaml-7
❑ 68TopPla-11
❑ 68TopPos-24
❑ 68TopVen-2
❑ 68TopVen-4
❑ 68TopVen-6
❑ 69MilBra-236
❑ 69MLBOffS-9
❑ 69MLBPin-26
❑ 69NabTeaF-19
❑ 69Top-250
❑ 69TopDecl-35
❑ 69TopSta-130
❑ 69TopSup-2
❑ 69TopTeaP-5
❑ 69TraSta-16
❑ 70BalOriP-28
❑ 70DayDaiNM-5
❑ 70Kel-15
❑ 70MilBra-23
❑ 70MLBOffS-155
❑ 70OPC-463
❑ 70Ori-12
❑ 70Top-463
❑ 70Top-700
❑ 70TopCanL-19
❑ 70TopPos-12
❑ 70TopSup-37
❑ 70TraSta-12A
❑ 71AllBasA-20
❑ 71BalOriP-25
❑ 71BazNumT-2
❑ 71Kel-15
❑ 71MatMin-13
❑ 71MatMin-14
❑ 71MilDud-27
❑ 71MLBOffS-310
❑ 71MLBOffS-572
❑ 71OPC-63
❑ 71OPC-329
❑ 71OPC-640
❑ 71OriCha-14
❑ 71Top-329
❑ 71Top-640
❑ 71TopCoi-50
❑ 71TopTat-93
❑ 72MilBra-292
❑ 72OPC-88
❑ 72OPC-100
❑ 72OPC-228
❑ 72ProStaP-20
❑ 72SevTraC-46
❑ 72Top-88
❑ 72Top-100
❑ 72Top-228
❑ 72Top-754
❑ 73LinPor-34
❑ 73OPC-175
❑ 73Top-175
❑ 73TopCanL-42
❑ 74LauAllG-59
❑ 74OPC-55
❑ 74Top-55
❑ 74TopDecE-66
❑ 74TopSta-145
❑ 75CleIndP-23
❑ 75IndJB R-7
❑ 75OPC-199
❑ 75OPC-204
❑ 75OPC-331
❑ 75OPC-580
❑ 75SSP42-8
❑ 75Top-199
❑ 75Top-204
❑ 75Top-331
❑ 75Top-580
❑ 75TopMin-199
❑ 75TopMin-204
❑ 75TopMin-331
❑ 75TopMin-580
❑ 76BlaDis-49
❑ 76BucDis-49
❑ 76CarDis-49
❑ 76CraDis-49
❑ 76DailsID-49
❑ 76IsaDis-49
❑ 76LauDiaJ-5
❑ 76OPC-477
❑ 76OrbDis-49
❑ 76RedBarD-49
❑ 76SafDis-49
❑ 76SSP-525
❑ 76Top-477
❑ 76TowCluD-49
❑ 76UPIS-11
❑ 77IndTeal-22
❑ 77RedCarP-16
❑ 77Spo-5920
❑ 77Top-18
❑ 78BalOriP-26
❑ 78RocRedWT-15
❑ 78TCM60I-140
❑ 80Lau300-23
❑ 80PacLeg-123

❑ 80PerHaloFP-180
❑ 80PerHaloFPS-45
❑ 80Red196T-4
❑ 80SSPHOF-178
❑ 81GiaTeal-16
❑ 81Ori6F-28
❑ 82Don-424
❑ 82Gia25tATI-26
❑ 82K-M-9
❑ 82OhiHaloF-30
❑ 82TCMGreS-12
❑ 82TCMStaot5-17
❑ 83ASAFraR-1
❑ 83ASAFraR-2
❑ 83ASAFraR-3
❑ 83ASAFraR-4
❑ 83ASAFraR-5
❑ 83ASAFraR-6
❑ 83ASAFraR-7
❑ 83ASAFraR-8
❑ 83ASAFraR-9
❑ 83ASAFraR-10
❑ 83ASAFraR-11
❑ 83ASAFraR-12
❑ 83Don-564
❑ 83Don-648
❑ 83DonHOFH-19
❑ 83FraBroR-23
❑ 83FraBroR-24
❑ 83FraBroR-25
❑ 83GiaMot-1
❑ 83GiaPos-24
❑ 83Oco& SSBG-14
❑ 83Top-576
❑ 83TopSti-4
❑ 84DonCha-43
❑ 84GiaPos-24
❑ 84Nes792-171
❑ 84OCoandSI-70
❑ 84Top-171
❑ 84TopTif-171
❑ 85BalOriP-26
❑ 85CirK-4
❑ 85DonHOFS-8
❑ 85Woo-29
❑ 86BalOriP-17
❑ 86BigLeaC-4
❑ 86OriGreT-7
❑ 86RedGreT-5
❑ 86SpoDecG-41
❑ 86Top-404
❑ 86TopTif-404
❑ 87BalOriP-32
❑ 87K-M-10
❑ 87NesDreT-16
❑ 87OriFreB-20
❑ 88GreBasS-57
❑ 88OriFreB-20
❑ 88OriPos-29
❑ 88TopTra-96T
❑ 88TopTraT-96T
❑ 89AngSmo-8
❑ 89BalOriP-28
❑ 89DodSmoG-24
❑ 89OriFreB-20
❑ 89Top-774
❑ 89TopTif-774
❑ 90BalOriP-24
❑ 90BasWit-48
❑ 90DodTar-675
❑ 90OPC-381
❑ 90PerGreM-94
❑ 90Top-381
❑ 90TopTif-381
❑ 91BalOriP-28
❑ 91OPC-639
❑ 91OriCro-388
❑ 91Top-639
❑ 91TopDesS-639
❑ 91TopEasCN-4
❑ 91TopMic-639
❑ 91TopTif-639
❑ 91UppDecS-3
❑ 92TVSpoMF5HRC-11
❑ 93OriCroASU-4
❑ 93SelTriC-3
❑ 93UppDecS-18
❑ 94NabAllA-3
❑ 94UppDecS-10
❑ 94UppDecTAE-68
❑ 95BalParF-2
❑ 95TopLegot6M-5
❑ 95UppDecA-5
❑ 97DonSigSS-18
❑ 97FleMilDM-11
❑ 97FleMilDMR-11
❑ 97SpollIAM-5
❑ 97SpollICC-12
❑ 97St.VinHHS-14
❑ 98SpollITaN-29
❑ 98SpollITaNC-C6
❑ 98SpollITaNEE-29
❑ 98SpollIWSF-8
❑ 98SpollIWSFEE-8
❑ 98SpollIWSFFE-8
❑ 98SpollIWSFMC-1
❑ 99SP SigAuto-FR
❑ 99SpollIGotG-20
❑ 99SpollIGotGA-62
❑ 99SpollIGotGC-19
❑ 99SPSig-178
❑ 99TopStaRR-1
❑ 99TopStaRRA-1
❑ 99UppDecAP-FR
❑ 99UppDecAPH5AU-FRAU
❑ 99UppDecCL-22
❑ 99UppDecCL-135
❑ 99UppDecCLCC-22
❑ 99UppDecCLCC-135
❑ 99UppDecCLES-FR
❑ 99UppDecCLESC-FR
❑ 99UppDecR-107
❑ 99UppDecRG-107
❑ 99UppDecRP-107

Robinson, Hank
❑ 14B18B-87A
❑ 14B18B-87B

Robinson, Hassan
❑ 94AubAstC-13
❑ 94AubAstF-3772
❑ 95AubAstTI-27
❑ 96QuaCitRB-22
❑ 97KisCob-19

Robinson, Henry
❑ 86Ft.MyeRP-22

Robinson, Humberto
❑ 52LavPro-91
❑ 55Top-182
❑ 59Top-366
❑ 60Lea-70
❑ 60Top-416

Robinson, Jackie R.
❑ 47BonBreR-1
❑ 47BonBreR-2
❑ 47BonBreR-3
❑ 47BonBreR-4
❑ 47BonBreR-5
❑ 47BonBreR-6
❑ 47BonBreR-7
❑ 47BonBreR-8
❑ 47BonBreR-9
❑ 47BonBreR-10
❑ 47BonBreR-11
❑ 47BonBreR-12
❑ 47BonBreR-13
❑ 47DodTeal-19
❑ 47Exh-193
❑ 47HomBon-41
❑ 47PM1StaP1-179
❑ 47PM1StaP1-180
❑ 47PM1StaP1-181
❑ 47PM1StaP1-182
❑ 47PM1StaP1-183
❑ 47PM1StaP1-184
❑ 47PM1StaP1-185
❑ 47PM1StaP1-186
❑ 47StaPinP2-33A
❑ 48BluTin-36
❑ 48DodTeal-20
❑ 48SweSpoT-3
❑ 49Bow-50
❑ 49EurSta-48
❑ 49Lea-79
❑ 50Bow-22
❑ 50JJKCopP-15
❑ 51R42SmaS-91
❑ 52BerRos-57
❑ 52StaCalL-79G
❑ 52StaCalS-91B
❑ 52Top-312
❑ 53ArtHaloFP-71
❑ 53ExhCan-19
❑ 53Top-1
❑ 54NewYorJA-15
❑ 54Top-10
❑ 55DodGolS-15
❑ 55Top-50
❑ 55TopDouH-25
❑ 56Dod-25
❑ 56Top-30
❑ 56TopHocF-A14
❑ 56TopPin-51
❑ 60NuHi-53
❑ 60RawGloT-27
❑ 61NuSco-428
❑ 63BasMagM-71
❑ 63HalofFB-15
❑ 64TopRooAB-5
❑ 67TopVen-184
❑ 70Houof J-24
❑ 72TopTes5-2
❑ 73HalofFPP-14
❑ 74CapPub-4
❑ 74dod195T-34
❑ 74LauAllG-49
❑ 75DodTCMA-9
❑ 75TCMAllG-28
❑ 75TCMHouoJ-26
❑ 76GalBasGHoF-24
❑ 76LauDiaJ-26
❑ 76ShaPiz-88
❑ 76TayBow4-17
❑ 77BobParHoF-40
❑ 77GalGloG-20
❑ 77GalGloG-228
❑ 77Spo-923
❑ 79BasGre-77
❑ 79TCM50-291
❑ 80DodGreT-4
❑ 80LauFamF-18
❑ 80PacLeg-15
❑ 80PerHaloFP-89
❑ 80SSPHOF-89
❑ 81SanDieSC-6
❑ 81SpoHaloF-18
❑ 82BasCarN-13
❑ 82BHCRSpoL-7
❑ 82DavHaloFB-19
❑ 82DiaCla-48
❑ 82GSGalAG-24
❑ 82TCMGreH-5
❑ 82TCMStaot5-15
❑ 83DonHOFH-6
❑ 83MLBPin-31
❑ 83TopRep5-312
❑ 83TopTraBP-8
❑ 84FifNatCT-16
❑ 84OCoandSI-97
❑ 84OCoandSI-135
❑ 84SpoDesPW-1
❑ 85TCMPhoC-2
❑ 85TCMPhoC-18
❑ 85TCMPla1-27
❑ 86NegLeaF-11
❑ 86NegLeaF-25
❑ 86SpoDecG-28
❑ 86TCM-7
❑ 86TCMSupS-21
❑ 86TCMSupS-48
❑ 87Dod195T-3
❑ 87HygAllG-37
❑ 87NegLeaPD-33
❑ 87NesDreT-24
❑ 87SpoRea-35
❑ 88DodRinP1-3C
❑ 88DodRinP1-6B
❑ 88GreBasS-19
❑ 88PacLegl-40
❑ 88WilMulP-10
❑ 89BowInsT-9
❑ 89BowRepl-9
❑ 89BowTif-R9
❑ 89DodSmoG-25
❑ 89HOFStiB-12
❑ 89SpollIFKI-212
❑ 89USPLegSC-3
❑ 90BasWit-52
❑ 90DodTar-676
❑ 90PerGreM-3
❑ 90PerGreM-91
❑ 91PomBlaBPB-2
❑ 91TopArc1-1
❑ 92BazQua5A-14
❑ 93Ble-34
❑ 94TopArc1-10
❑ 94TopArc1G-10
❑ 94UppDecTAE-50
❑ 94UppDecTAEGM-7
❑ 94UppDecTAELD-LD9
❑ 95DodROY-1
❑ 95TopArcBD-18
❑ 95TopArcBD-37
❑ 95TopArcBD-66
❑ 95TopArcBD-95
❑ 95TopArcBD-117
❑ 95TopArcBD-142
❑ 95UDAUnsBC-NNO
❑ 97BluJayJR-1
❑ 97BrePol-23
❑ 97ColCho-55
❑ 97DenHol-29
❑ 97FanJacR-1
❑ 97FanJacR-2
❑ 97FanJacR-3
❑ 97FanJacR-4
❑ 97FanJacR-5
❑ 97FleMilDM-17
❑ 97FleMilDMR-17
❑ 97HowUniR-1
❑ 97Lea-NNO
❑ 97LeaJacRSNWG-1
❑ 97NegLeaPC-1D
❑ 97PhiCopQ-23
❑ 97St.VinHHS-17
❑ 97Top-42
❑ 97TopChr-42
❑ 97TopChrR-42
❑ 97TopDodRotY-1
❑ 97UppDec-1
❑ 97UppDec-2
❑ 97UppDec-3
❑ 97UppDec-4
❑ 97UppDec-5
❑ 97UppDec-6
❑ 97UppDec-7
❑ 97UppDec-8
❑ 97UppDec-9
❑ 98BowChrR-2
❑ 98BowChrRR-2
❑ 99SpollIGotG-42
❑ 99SpollIGotGRB-7
❑ 99SpollIGotGRBG-7
❑ 99UppDecCL-44
❑ 99UppDecCL-132
❑ 99UppDecCLCC-44
❑ 99UppDecCLCC-132
❑ 99UppDecCLEM-EM2
❑ 99UppDecCLJotC-AC5

Robinson, Jeff (Jeffrey D.)
❑ 84FleUpd-100
❑ 84GiaPos-25
❑ 84TopTra-101T
❑ 84TopTraT-101T
❑ 85Don-201
❑ 85Fle-620
❑ 85OPC-5
❑ 85Top-592
❑ 85TopMin-592
❑ 85TopTif-592
❑ 86GiaMot-15
❑ 86GiaPos-26
❑ 86TopTra-93T
❑ 86TopTraT-93T
❑ 87Don-559
❑ 87Fle-283
❑ 87FleGlo-283
❑ 87GiaMot-25
❑ 87GiaPos-27
❑ 87Top-389
❑ 87TopTif-389
❑ 88Don-558
❑ 88DonBasB-241
❑ 88OPC-244
❑ 88PirTeal-28
❑ 88Sco-439
❑ 88ScoGlo-439
❑ 88StaLinPi-18
❑ 88Top-244
❑ 88TopBig-123
❑ 88TopSti-133
❑ 88TopTif-244
❑ 89Bow-410
❑ 89BowTif-410
❑ 89Don-370
❑ 89DonBasB-129
❑ 89Fle-220
❑ 89FleGlo-220
❑ 89OPC-351
❑ 89PanSti-164
❑ 89PirVerFJ-49
❑ 89Sco-309
❑ 89Top-681
❑ 89TopBig-45
❑ 89TopSti-129
❑ 89TopTif-681
❑ 89TVSpoM-72
❑ 89UppDec-332
❑ 90Bow-427
❑ 90BowTif-427
❑ 90Don-134
❑ 90Fle-479
❑ 90FleCan-479
❑ 90Lea-412
❑ 90OPC-23
❑ 90PubIntS-164
❑ 90Sco-333
❑ 90Top-723
❑ 90TopTif-723
❑ 90TopTraT-103T
❑ 90TopTVY-19
❑ 90UppDec-403
❑ 90YanScoNW-23
❑ 91AngSmo-18
❑ 91Bow-193
❑ 91Don-291
❑ 91Fle-678
❑ 91Lea-307
❑ 91OPC-19
❑ 91Sco-192
❑ 91StaClu-542
❑ 91Top-19
❑ 91TopDesS-19
❑ 91TopMic-19
❑ 91TopTif-19
❑ 91TopTra-99T
❑ 91TopTraT-99T
❑ 92CubMar-38
❑ 92Don-59
❑ 92IowCubS-219
❑ 92OPC-137
❑ 92Sco-186
❑ 92StaClu-756
❑ 92Top-137
❑ 92TopGol-137
❑ 92TopGolW-137
❑ 92TopMic-137
❑ 93Fle-382

Robinson, Jeff (Jeffrey M.)
❑ 85PhoGiaC-184
❑ 86NasSouTI-22
❑ 87DonRoo-13
❑ 87FleUpd-105
❑ 87FleUpdG-105
❑ 87SpoRoo2-46
❑ 87TopTra-104T
❑ 87TopTraT-104T
❑ 88Don-296
❑ 88Fle-68A
❑ 88Fle-68B
❑ 88FleGlo-68
❑ 88Sco-549
❑ 88ScoGlo-549
❑ 88TigPep-44
❑ 88TigPol-10
❑ 88Top-449
❑ 88TopTif-449
❑ 89Bow-97
❑ 89BowTif-97
❑ 89ClaLigB-93
❑ 89Don-18
❑ 89Don-470
❑ 89DonSupD-18
❑ 89Fle-143
❑ 89FleGlo-143
❑ 89FleLeaL-33
❑ 89OPC-267
❑ 89PanSti-335
❑ 89Sco-284
❑ 89ScoHot1S-34
❑ 89ScoYouS2-8
❑ 89Spo-193
❑ 89TigMar-44
❑ 89TigPol-44
❑ 89Top-267
❑ 89TopBig-274
❑ 89TopTif-267
❑ 89UppDec-472
❑ 90Don-417
❑ 90Fle-614
❑ 90FleCan-614
❑ 90Lea-429
❑ 90OPC-42
❑ 90PubIntS-481
❑ 90PubIntS-603
❑ 90TigCok-19
❑ 90Top-42
❑ 90TopSti-284
❑ 90TopTif-42
❑ 90TopTra-103T
❑ 90UppDec-552
❑ 91BalOriP-29
❑ 91Bow-90
❑ 91Don-245
❑ 91Fle-349
❑ 91Lea-464
❑ 91OPC-766
❑ 91OriCro-500
❑ 91Sco-129
❑ 91StaClu-441
❑ 91Top-766
❑ 91TopDesS-766
❑ 91TopMic-766
❑ 91TopTif-766
❑ 91TopTra-100T
❑ 91TopTraT-100T
❑ 91UppDec-676
❑ 91UppDec-796
❑ 92Don-77
❑ 92Pin-516
❑ 92RanMot-16
❑ 92Sco-274
❑ 92StaClu-715
❑ 92UppDec-320
❑ 93RanKee-311

Robinson, Jerry
❑ 63Top-466

Robinson, Jim
❑ 78NewWayCT-38
❑ 79BurBeeT-4
❑ 88MisStaB-29
❑ 89MisStaB-34
❑ 90MisStaB-36
❑ 90PeoChiUTI-U2
❑ 91GenCubC-16
❑ 91GenCubP-4222
❑ 92ChaKniF-2774
❑ 92ChaKniS-164
❑ 92ProFS7-211
❑ 93OriCubF-2789

Robinson, Joseph Jr
❑ 97AubDouTI-27

Robinson, Ken
❑ 91MedHatBJP-4099
❑ 92MyrBeaHF-2196
❑ 93HagSunC-23
❑ 93HagSunF-1879
❑ 94HagSunC-20
❑ 94HagSunF-2728
❑ 95SyrChiTI-21
❑ 96Fle-282
❑ 96FleTif-282
❑ 96SyrChiTI-25
❑ 97SyrSkyCB-20

Robinson, Kerry
❑ 96MidLeaAB-23
❑ 96PeoChiB-27
❑ 97ArkTraB-24
❑ 97Bes-88
❑ 97BesLimA-37
❑ 97Bow-382
❑ 97BowChr-252
❑ 97BowChrI-252
❑ 97BowChrIR-252
❑ 97BowChrR-252
❑ 97BowInt-382
❑ 97TexAllM-50
❑ 97TexLeaTP-2
❑ 98BesFulCA-20
❑ 98BesPreA-41
❑ 98Bow-342
❑ 98BowChr-342
❑ 98BowChrGA-342
❑ 98BowChrGAR-342
❑ 98BowChrI-342
❑ 98BowChrIR-342
❑ 98BowChrR-342
❑ 98BowGolA-342
❑ 98BowInt-342
❑ 98OrlRayM-15
❑ 98SouLeaTPG-30
❑ 99SpollI-50

Robinson, Kevin
❑ 87EriCarP-20
❑ 88HamRedP-1730

Robinson, Lee
❑ 74AlbDukCa-74
❑ 74AlbDukTI-16
❑ 75AlbDukCa-4

Robinson, Lynn
❑ 88BurBraP-1

Robinson, M.C.
❑ 87OldJudN-420

Robinson, Marteese
❑ 88MadMusP-20
❑ 89MadMusS-27
❑ 89ModA'sCLC-285
❑ 90Bes-280

Robinson, Marty
❑ 96GreBatB-22

Robinson, Mike
❑ 83EriCarT-24
❑ 85SprCarT-25
❑ 86ArkTraP-20

❑ 87ArkTraP-2
❑ 88ArkTraGS-19
❑ 88LouRedBTI-42
Robinson, Napoleon
❑ 89SalDodTI-27
❑ 90BakDodCLC-233
❑ 91GreBraC-4
❑ 91GreBraLD-215
❑ 91GreBraP-2998
❑ 91LinDriAA-215
❑ 92Bow-34
❑ 92ProFS7-184
❑ 92RicBraBB-20
❑ 92RicBraF-376
❑ 92RicBraRC-16
❑ 92RicBraS-438
❑ 92SkyAAAF-202
❑ 93ExcFS7-5
❑ 93RicBraBB-4
❑ 93RicBraF-183
❑ 93RicBraP-15
❑ 93RicBraRC-3
❑ 93RicBraRC-24
❑ 97RicBraBC-18
Robinson, Randall
❑ 87ChaWheP-27
Robinson, Randy
❑ 83ButCopKT-9
❑ 88SouBenWSGS-25
Robinson, Raul
❑ 91MacBraC-26
❑ 91MacBraP-879
Robinson, Rhett
❑ 89GeoColC-26
❑ 89GeoColC-28
Robinson, Rogers
❑ 64TulOil-6
Robinson, Ron
❑ 81CedRapRT-6
❑ 82WatRedT-9
❑ 84WicAerRD-8
❑ 85Don-649
❑ 85Fle-650
❑ 86Don-121
❑ 86Fle-190
❑ 86RedTexG-33
❑ 86Top-442
❑ 86TopTif-442
❑ 87Don-310
❑ 87Fle-212
❑ 87FleGamW-38
❑ 87FleGlo-212
❑ 87FleMin-93
❑ 87RedKah-33
❑ 87Top-119
❑ 87TopTif-119
❑ 88Don-166
❑ 88DonBasB-308
❑ 88Fle-247
❑ 88FleGlo-247
❑ 88FleMin-75
❑ 88OPC-342
❑ 88RedKah-33
❑ 88Sco-476
❑ 88ScoGlo-476
❑ 88Top-81
❑ 88Top-517
❑ 88TopTif-81
❑ 88TopTif-517
❑ 89Bow-303
❑ 89BowTif-303
❑ 89CedRapRAB-14
❑ 89Don-308
❑ 89Fle-169
❑ 89FleGlo-169
❑ 89OPC-16
❑ 89RedKah-33
❑ 89Sco-559
❑ 89Top-16
❑ 89TopBig-132
❑ 89TopTif-16
❑ 89UppDec-187
❑ 90BreMilB-21
❑ 90CedRapRDGB-14
❑ 90Don-553
❑ 90Fle-431
❑ 90FleCan-431
❑ 90Lea-467
❑ 90OPC-604
❑ 90Sco-495
❑ 90Top-604
❑ 90TopTif-604
❑ 90TopTra-104T
❑ 90TopTraT-104T
❑ 91Bow-39
❑ 91BreMilB-22
❑ 91BrePol-20
❑ 91Don-254
❑ 91Fle-595
❑ 91Lea-14
❑ 91OPC-313
❑ 91Sco-517
❑ 91StaClu-296
❑ 91Stu-75
❑ 91Top-313
❑ 91TopDesS-313
❑ 91TopMic-313
❑ 91TopTif-313
❑ 91UppDec-620
❑ 92BrePol-20
❑ 92Fle-187
❑ 92OPC-395
❑ 92StaClu-739
❑ 92StaCluECN-739
❑ 92UppDec-198
❑ 93Fle-634
❑ 94BreMilB-263
Robinson, Scott
❑ 90BilMusP-3220
❑ 91CedRapRC-11
❑ 91CedRapRP-2718
❑ 92ChaLooF-3818
❑ 92ChaWVWC-18
❑ 93ChaLooF-2362
❑ 93SouAtlLAIPI-7
❑ 93SouAtlLAPI-35
❑ 94PhoFirF-1519
❑ 95AusFut-66
❑ 95PhoFirTI-14
Robinson, Ted
❑ 98GiaMot-27
Robinson, Terry
❑ 91PocPioP-3799
❑ 91PocPioSP-5
Robinson, Tony
❑ 96LynHilB-19
❑ 97AugGre-23
Robinson, Wilbert
❑ 15SpoNewM-144
❑ 16SpoNewM-144
❑ 21E121So1-80
❑ 21E121So8-77
❑ 22W575-106
❑ 23W501-97
❑ 23W515-53
❑ 27YorCarE-43
❑ 39PC7AlbHoF-38
❑ 50CalHOFW-62
❑ 53ArtHaloFP-72
❑ 60Fle-33
❑ 63BazA-27
❑ 70SpoCarfCOP-17
❑ 72FleFamF-10
❑ 72LauGreF-30
❑ 75TCMAllG-29
❑ 76ShaPiz-38
❑ 77BobParHoF-98
❑ 77GalGloG-162
❑ 77Ind192T-22
❑ 80PerHaloFP-38
❑ 80SSPHOF-38
❑ 84GalHaloFRL-38
❑ 87OldJudN-419
❑ 89DodSmoG-104
❑ 89HOFStiB-86
❑ 90DodTar-677A
❑ 90KalBatN-47
❑ 90KalBatN-48
❑ 93ConMasC-8
❑ 93ConTSN-846
❑ 94DukCabN-4
❑ 94OriTeal-14
❑ 95May-36
Robinson, Yank (William H.)
❑ 76SSP188WS-15
❑ 87BucN28-103
❑ 87LonJacN-11
❑ 87OldJudN-421A
❑ 87OldJudN-421B
❑ 87ScrDC-8
Robitaille, Martin
❑ 88JamExpP-1921
❑ 92JamExpC-28
❑ 92JamExpF-1518
Robledo, Nilson
❑ 91SouBenWSC-24
❑ 91SouBenWSP-2860
❑ 92SarWhiSF-209
❑ 93FloStaLAF-24
❑ 93SarWhiSC-22
❑ 93SarWhiSF-1371
❑ 94SouBenSHC-20
❑ 94SouBenSHF-597
❑ 95MidLeaA-44
❑ 96Exc-36
❑ 96PriWilCB-23
Robles, Gabby (Gabriel)
❑ 86KinEagP-20
❑ 87WinSpiP-18
Robles, Greg
❑ 82IdaFalAT-21
❑ 83MadMusF-22
❑ 84AlbA'sT-25
Robles, Javier
❑ 91BurIndP-3309
Robles, Jorge
❑ 89BlaYNPRWL-50
❑ 89WauTimGS-19
❑ 90PenPilS-18
Robles, Josman
❑ 90DurBulTI-18
Robles, Juan
❑ 96LanLugB-22
❑ 96SpoIndB-23
❑ 97LanLugTS-22
Robles, Oscar
❑ 94SigRooDP-66
❑ 94SigRooDPS-66
❑ 94StaCluDP-38
❑ 94StaCluDPFDI-38
❑ 95AubAstTI-12
❑ 96KisCobB-22
❑ 98KisCobQ-25
Robles, Rafael
❑ 69Top-592
❑ 70Top-573
❑ 71OPC-408
❑ 71Top-408
❑ 72PadPos-21
❑ 94NewJerCC-21
❑ 94NewJerCF-3426
Robles, Ruben
❑ 83TucTorT-26
❑ 84TucTorC-66
❑ 85DomLeaS-82
Robles, Scott
❑ 90KenTwiB-25
❑ 90KenTwiP-2294
❑ 90KenTwiS-21
Robles, Sergio
❑ 73OPC-601
❑ 73Top-601
❑ 74OPC-603
❑ 74Top-603
❑ 75TulOil7-21
❑ 90DodTar-678B
❑ 91OriCro-389
Robles, Silvano
❑ 75AppFoxT-25
❑ 76AppFoxT-22
❑ 76CliPilT-28
Robson, David
❑ 89AriStaB-24
❑ 92NiaFalRC-2
❑ 92NiaFalRF-3327
Robson, Gary
❑ 88BelBreGS-2
Robson, Tom
❑ 74SpoIndC-38
❑ 75IntLeaASB-28
❑ 75PacCoaLAB-28
❑ 75SpoIndC-1
❑ 79WauTimT-16
❑ 80AshTouT-2
❑ 86RanPer-NNO
❑ 87RanMot-28
❑ 87RanSmo-21
❑ 88RanMot-27
❑ 89RanMot-27
❑ 89RanSmo-26
❑ 90RanMot-27
❑ 91RanMot-28
❑ 92RanMot-28
❑ 93RanKee-312
Roby, Ellis
❑ 86SumBraP-22
❑ 87DurBulP-10
❑ 88DurBulS-18
❑ 89GreBraB-9
❑ 89GreBraP-1159
❑ 89GreBraS-20
Roca, Gilbert
❑ 86MacPirP-21
❑ 87SalBucP-16
❑ 88HarSenP-851
❑ 89JacMetGS-17
❑ 90TopTVM-55
❑ 94VenLinU-144
Rocco, Mickey (Michael)
❑ 47CenFlo-24
❑ 47SigOil-85
❑ 48SomandK-26
❑ 49SomandK-14
Rocha, Juan
❑ 95SprSulTI-24
❑ 96LanLugB-23
❑ 96MidLeaAB-40
❑ 97WilBluR-14
Roche, Jack
❑ 09ObaT21-422
❑ 12ObaPreT-171
❑ 16Zee-63
❑ 17Zee-40
Roche, Marlon
❑ 96QuaCitRB-23
❑ 97QuaCitRBB-25
Roche, Rod
❑ 86VerBeaDP-20
❑ 87BakDodP-17
Roche, Steve
❑ 80WauTimT-7
❑ 81ChaLooT-8
❑ 82ChaLooT-15
❑ 82WatIndF-10
Roche, Tim
❑ 77CliDodT-21
❑ 78LodDodT-14
Roche, Titi
❑ 87LitFalMP-2406
❑ 88LitFalMP-11
❑ 89St.LucMS-21
❑ 89Sta-24
Rochelli, Lou
❑ 90DodTar-1055
Rochford, Mike
❑ 84PawRedST-21
❑ 86PawRedSP-18
❑ 87PawRedSP-59
❑ 87PawRedST-9
❑ 88PawRedSC-2
❑ 88PawRedSP-447
❑ 89Fle-650
❑ 89FleGlo-650
❑ 89PawRedSC-6
❑ 89PawRedSP-700
❑ 89PawRedSTI-22
❑ 90Bow-264
❑ 90BowTif-264
❑ 90CMC-254
❑ 90PawRedSC-3
❑ 90PawRedSDD-21
❑ 90PawRedSP-460
❑ 90ProAAAF-432
❑ 90TopTVRS-16
❑ 90UppDec-694
❑ 91Sco-739
Rock Cats, Hardware City
❑ 96HarCitRCB-1
Rock, Bob
❑ 77ChaPatT-16
❑ 78SalPirT-14
❑ 80BufBisT-12
❑ 81BufBisT-10
Rock, Royal
❑ 09ColChiE-244
❑ 12ColRedB-244
❑ 12ColTinT-244
❑ 12ImpTobC-10
Rockenfeld, Isaac B.
❑ 09T206-512
❑ 10CouT21-57
Rockenfield, Isaac
❑ 09ObaT21-231
❑ 09ObaT21-401
❑ 12ObaPreT-150
Rocker, John
❑ 94DanBraC-22
❑ 94DanBraF-3530
❑ 95EugEmeTI-17
❑ 95MacBraTI-24
❑ 96MacBraB-11
❑ 97DurBulTI-15
❑ 98FleUpd-U64
❑ 98LeaRS-302
❑ 98LeaRSLHolo-302
❑ 98LeaRSLong-302
❑ 98LeaRTrue-302
❑ 99Fle-280
❑ 99FleSta9-280
❑ 99FleWarT-280
❑ 99SkyMolMOA-25
❑ 99SkyThu-131
❑ 99SkyThuRant-131
❑ 99SkyThuRave-131
❑ 99ThuSkySupR-131
❑ 99Top-429
❑ 99TopChr-429
❑ 99TopChrR-429
❑ 99TopMVPP-429
❑ 99UppDec-312
❑ 99UppDecEL1-312
❑ 99UppDecEL2-312
Rockett, Pat
❑ 78Top-502
❑ 79RicBraT-20
❑ 80SyrChiT-5
❑ 80SyrChiTI-19
Rockey, Jim
❑ 86DurBulP-23
Rockey, Mascot
❑ 98MemRedG-19
Rockhill, Ron
❑ 75LynRanT-23
Rockies, Colorado
❑ 83KelCerB-3
❑ 92DonBonC-BC7
❑ 92HitTheBB-11
❑ 94ImpProP-18
❑ 94Sco-650
❑ 94ScoGolR-650
❑ 95PacPriTL-18
❑ 95PanSti-135
❑ 96PanSti-85
❑ 96RocFle-19
❑ 97ColChoT-CR
❑ 99Vic-127
Rockman, Marv
❑ 88GasRanP-995
❑ 89TulDriGS-22
❑ 89TulDriTI-20
❑ 90TulDriP-1152
❑ 90TulDriTI-21
Rockmore, Thurston
❑ 94LetMouF-3893
❑ 94LetMouSP-5
Rockne, Knute
❑ 87SpoCubG-1
Rockweiler, Dean
❑ 86JamExpP-21
Rodarte, Raul
❑ 92PenPilC-10
❑ 92PenPilF-2942
❑ 93RivPilCLC-17
❑ 94JacSunF-1421
❑ 95LynHilTI-25
❑ 96GreBraB-23
❑ 96GreBraTI-9
❑ 96RicBraRC-20
❑ 96RicBraUB-23
Rodas, Rick (Richard)
❑ 82AlbDukTc-9
❑ 83AlbDukTc-6
❑ 84AlbDukCr-147
❑ 84DodPol-56
❑ 85AlbDukCr-174
❑ 90DodTar-678
Rodda, William
❑ 26Zee-58
❑ 27Zee-36
❑ 28Zee-58
❑ 29Zee-56
❑ 30Zee-66
❑ 33WorCig(-74
Roddy, Phil
❑ 77AshTouT-19
Rode, Don
❑ 48SomandK-30
Rodeheaver, Roger
❑ 98BatMucTI-26
Rodgers, Andre
❑ 57Top-377
❑ 59Top-216
❑ 60Lea-42
❑ 60Top-431
❑ 61Pos-153A
❑ 61Pos-153B
❑ 61Top-183
❑ 62Jel-185
❑ 62Pos-185
❑ 62PosCan-185
❑ 62SalPlaC-155A
❑ 62SalPlaC-155B
❑ 62ShiPlaC-155
❑ 62Top-477
❑ 63CubJayP-10
❑ 63Jel-173
❑ 63Pos-173
❑ 63Top-193
❑ 64CubJayP-10
❑ 64Top-336
❑ 64TopVen-336
❑ 65Top-536
❑ 66PirEasH-16
❑ 66Top-592
❑ 67PirTeal-19
❑ 67Top-554
❑ 78TCM60I-52
Rodgers, Bobby
❑ 72TwiTeal-14
❑ 97Top-200
Rodgers, Bobby Jonathan
❑ 96LowSpiB-22
Rodgers, Buck (Robert L.)
❑ 47Exh-195
❑ 62Top-431
❑ 62TopStal-68
❑ 63AngJayP-15
❑ 63Baz-2
❑ 63Fle-20
❑ 63Jel-31
❑ 63Pos-31
❑ 63Top-280
❑ 63TopStil-37
❑ 64Top-61
❑ 64Top-426
❑ 64TopVen-61
❑ 65Top-342
❑ 65TopTral-27
❑ 66AngDexP-13
❑ 66Top-462
❑ 67CokCapDA-26
❑ 67Top-281
❑ 68Top-433
❑ 69MilBra-237
❑ 69MLBOffS-27
❑ 69OPC-157
❑ 69Top-157
❑ 69TopFou-16
❑ 69TopSta-149
❑ 69TopTeaP-17
❑ 70TwiTeal-9
❑ 73OPC-49
❑ 73Top-49A
❑ 73Top-49B
❑ 74OPC-447
❑ 74Top-447
❑ 78TCM60I-63
❑ 80BreTeal-20
❑ 81Don-327
❑ 81Top-668
❑ 82BrePol-NNO
❑ 82BrePol-NNO
❑ 82Don-232
❑ 84IndIndTI-2
❑ 85ExpPos-20
❑ 85IndIndTI-36
❑ 85TopTifT-95T
❑ 85TopTra-95T
❑ 86AngGreT-8
❑ 86ExpProPa-3
❑ 86ExpProPo-4
❑ 86OPC-141
❑ 86Top-171
❑ 86TopTif-171
❑ 87ExpPos-24
❑ 87OPC-293
❑ 87Top-293
❑ 87TopTif-293
❑ 88ExpPos-30
❑ 88OPC-134
❑ 88Top-504
❑ 88TopTif-504
❑ 89ExpPos-25
❑ 89OPC-193
❑ 89Top-474
❑ 89TopTif-474
❑ 90El PasDAGTI-19
❑ 90ExpPos-29
❑ 90OPC-81
❑ 90Top-81
❑ 90TopTif-81
❑ 91OPC-321
❑ 91Top-321
❑ 91TopDesS-321
❑ 91TopMic-321
❑ 91TopTif-321
❑ 92OPC-21
❑ 92Top-21
❑ 92TopGol-21
❑ 92TopGolW-21

❑ 92TopMic-21
❑ 93AngMot-1
❑ 93AngPol-3
❑ 93ExpDonM-32
❑ 93Top-503
❑ 93TopGol-503
❑ 93TopInaM-503
❑ 93TopInaR-503
❑ 93TopMic-503
Rodgers, Charlie
❑ 91MiaMirC-11
Rodgers, Darrell
❑ 85EveGiaIC-15
❑ 86FreGiaSB-15
❑ 88MidLeaAGS-13
❑ 89ChaLooB-15
❑ 89ChaLooGS-21
❑ 92PriRedC-28
Rodgers, Doc
❑ 91PriRedP-3532
❑ 92PriRedF-3103
Rodgers, John
❑ 93PeoChiTI-23
Rodgers, Marcus
❑ 97BriWhiSB-10
Rodgers, Paul
❑ 87MyrBeaBJP-1464
❑ 88DunBluJS-14
❑ 89DunBluJS-13
❑ 90KnoBluJB-12
❑ 90KnoBluJP-1255
❑ 90KnoBluJS-15
❑ 91Cla/Bes-3
❑ 91KnoBluJLD-364
❑ 91KnoBluJP-1782
❑ 91LinDriAA-364
Rodgers, Tim
❑ 83KinBluJTI-20
❑ 84SyrChiT-17
❑ 86TulDriTI-7
❑ 87OklCit8P-17
Rodgers, Wilbur
❑ 09ObaT21-299
❑ 11Zee-57
❑ 12HomRunKE-44
❑ 12ObaPreT-48
❑ 12Zee-73
❑ 13Zee-71
❑ 14Zee-73A
❑ 14Zee-73B
❑ 18Zee-51
❑ 19Zee-63
❑ 21Zee-81
❑ 29Zee-97
Rodgers, William
❑ 16FleBreD-77
❑ 20Zee-74
Rodiles, Jose
❑ 85Ft.MyeRT-30
❑ 86MemChiSTOS-23
❑ 86MemChiTOS-23
❑ 87ColAstP-18
Rodiles, Steve
❑ 85IowCubT-36
Rodin, Eric
❑ 59SeaPop-32
Rodrigues, Rynee
❑ 91HawWomS-12
Rodriguez, A.
❑ 86AshTouP-23
Rodriguez, Abimael
❑ 90JamExpP-4
❑ 91SumFlyC-19
❑ 91SumFlyP-2344
Rodriguez, Adam
❑ 93BriTigF-3648
❑ 94FayGenC-20
❑ 94FayGenF-2150
❑ 96LakTigB-21
❑ 97TolMudHB-29
Rodriguez, Adriano
❑ 85DomLeaS-181
Rodriguez, Ahmed
❑ 89JohCitCS-18
❑ 89SavCarP-353
❑ 90HamRedB-17
❑ 90HamRedS-20
❑ 91SprCarC-22
❑ 91SprCarP-750
❑ 92SprCarF-878
Rodriguez, Al
❑ 91EveGiaC-3
❑ 91EveGiaP-3923
❑ 92CliGiaC-18
❑ 93LinVenB-223
Rodriguez, Alex
(Alexander E.)
❑ 92SpollFK1-543
❑ 93Ble-35
❑ 93Ble-36
❑ 93ClaCP-1
❑ 94ActPac-1
❑ 94ActPac-55
❑ 94ActPac2G-1G
❑ 94ActPac2GD-1G
❑ 94AppFoxC-1
❑ 94AppFoxFl-1063
❑ 94Cla-51
❑ 94Cla-100
❑ 94Cla-151
❑ 94ClaBonB-BB3
❑ 94ClaCreotC-C11
❑ 94ClaTriF-T73
❑ 94ColC-647
❑ 94ColChoGS-647
❑ 94ColChoSS-647
❑ 94Fla-340
❑ 94FlaWavotF-B8
❑ 94FleUpd-86
❑ 94LeaLimRP-10
❑ 94MidLeaAF-MDW5
❑ 94ScoRoo-HC1
❑ 94SP-15
❑ 94SPDieC-15
❑ 94SPHol-33
❑ 94SPHolDC-33
❑ 94SpoRoo-148
❑ 94SpoRooAP-148
❑ 94SpoRooRS-TR11
❑ 94UppDec-24
❑ 94UppDec-298
❑ 94UppDec-A298
❑ 94UppDecED-24
❑ 94UppDecED-298
❑ 94UppDecML-TC1
❑ 94UppDecMLT1PMF-8
❑ 94UppDecNG-16
❑ 94UppDecNGED-16
❑ 95ColCho-5
❑ 95ColCho-527
❑ 95ColChoCtG-CG17
❑ 95ColChoCtG-CG17B
❑ 95ColChoCtG-CG17C
❑ 95ColChoCtGE-17
❑ 95ColChoCtGG-CG17
❑ 95ColChoCtGG-CG17B
❑ 95ColChoCtGG-CG17C
❑ 95ColChoCtGGE-17
❑ 95ColChoGS-5
❑ 95ColChoGS-527
❑ 95ColChoSE-1
❑ 95ColChoSEGS-1
❑ 95ColChoSESS-1
❑ 95ColChoSS-5
❑ 95ColChoSS-527
❑ 95Don-114
❑ 95DonPreP-114
❑ 95DonTopotO-155
❑ 95Emo-82
❑ 95EmoRoo-10
❑ 95Fla-85
❑ 95FleMajLP-10
❑ 95FleUpd-77
❑ 95FleUpdRU-9
❑ 95Lea-313
❑ 95LeaGolR-1
❑ 95LeaLim-14
❑ 95LeaLimG-19
❑ 95MarMot-7
❑ 95MarPac-42
❑ 95NatPac-12
❑ 95Pac-402
❑ 95PacGolCDC-17
❑ 95PacLatD-30
❑ 95PacPri-129
❑ 95Pin-132
❑ 95Pin-283
❑ 95PinArtP-132
❑ 95PinArtP-283
❑ 95PinMusC-132
❑ 95PinMusC-283
❑ 95PinNewB-NB1
❑ 95PinSam-132
❑ 95Sco-312
❑ 95Sco-569
❑ 95ScoAi-AM17
❑ 95ScoConR-AD1
❑ 95ScoGolR-312
❑ 95ScoGolR-569
❑ 95ScoHaloG-HG41
❑ 95ScoPlaTS-312
❑ 95ScoPlaTS-569
❑ 95ScoRooDT-RDT3
❑ 95ScoRul-SR5
❑ 95ScoRulJ-SR5
❑ 95Sel-203
❑ 95Sel-241
❑ 95SelArtP-203
❑ 95SelArtP-241
❑ 95SelCanM-CM10
❑ 95SelCer-118
❑ 95SelCerF-10
❑ 95SelCerMG-118
❑ 95SelCerPU-20
❑ 95SelCerPU9-20
❑ 95SelSam-241
❑ 95SigRooMR-MR5
❑ 95SigRooMRS-MR5
❑ 95SP-188
❑ 95SPCha-184
❑ 95SPChaDC-184
❑ 95Spo-141
❑ 95SpoArtP-141
❑ 95SpoDouT-6
❑ 95SPSil-188
❑ 95SPSpeF-20
❑ 95Stu-18
❑ 95StuGolS-18
❑ 95StuPlaS-18
❑ 95Sum-133
❑ 95SumNewA-NA4
❑ 95SumNthD-133
❑ 95TacRaiTI-18
❑ 95UC3-115
❑ 95UC3ArtP-115
❑ 95UC3CleS-CS1
❑ 95Ult-331
❑ 95UltGolM-331
❑ 95UltGolP-9
❑ 95UltGolPGM-9
❑ 95UppDec-215
❑ 95UppDec-J215
❑ 95UppDecED-215
❑ 95UppDecEDG-215
❑ 95UppDecPAW-H15
❑ 95UppDecPAWE-H15
❑ 95UppDecSE-120
❑ 95UppDecSEG-120
❑ 95Zen-146
❑ 95ZenRooRC-1
❑ 96Cir-81
❑ 96CirRav-81
❑ 96ColCho-316
❑ 96ColChoGS-316
❑ 96ColChoSS-316
❑ 96ColChoYMtP-34
❑ 96ColChoYMtP-34A
❑ 96ColChoYMtPGS-34
❑ 96ColChoYMtPGS-34A
❑ 96Don-8
❑ 96DonPreP-8
❑ 96EmoXL-117
❑ 96Fla-164
❑ 96Fle-243
❑ 96FleTif-243
❑ 96Lea-24
❑ 96LeaLim-31
❑ 96LeaLimG-31
❑ 96LeaLimL-5
❑ 96LeaLimLB-5
❑ 96LeaLimPC-8
❑ 96LeaPre-35
❑ 96LeaPreP-35
❑ 96LeaPrePB-24
❑ 96LeaPrePG-24
❑ 96LeaPrePS-24
❑ 96LeaPreSG-8
❑ 96LeaPreSta-2
❑ 96LeaPreSte-8
❑ 96LeaSig-16
❑ 96LeaSigA-195
❑ 96LeaSigAG-195
❑ 96LeaSigAS-195
❑ 96LeaSigEA-174
❑ 96LeaSigEACM-25
❑ 96LeaSigPPG-16
❑ 96LeaSigPPP-16
❑ 96MarMot-9
❑ 96MetUni-110
❑ 96MetUniP-110
❑ 96MetUniProS-110
❑ 96Pac-416
❑ 96PacEstL-EL26
❑ 96PanSti-224
❑ 96Pin-275
❑ 96PinAfi-136
❑ 96PinAfiAP-136
❑ 96PinAfiSP-20
❑ 96PinArtP-175
❑ 96PinFirR-5
❑ 96PinFoil-275
❑ 96PinProS-5
❑ 96PinSta-175
❑ 96PinTeaT-8
❑ 96ProMagA-10
❑ 96ProSta-65
❑ 96Sco-20
❑ 96Sco-361
❑ 96ScoDiaA-15
❑ 96ScoDugC-A19
❑ 96ScoDugC-B86
❑ 96ScoDugCAP-A19
❑ 96ScoDugCAP-B86
❑ 96ScoFutF-4
❑ 96ScoNumG-30
❑ 96ScoRef-2
❑ 96Sel-45
❑ 96SelArtP-45
❑ 96SelCer-6
❑ 96SelCerAP-6
❑ 96SelCerCB-6
❑ 96SelCerCR-6
❑ 96SelCerMB-6
❑ 96SelCerMG-6
❑ 96SelCerMR-6
❑ 96SelEnF-21
❑ 96SigRooOJMR-M1
❑ 96SP-171
❑ 96Spo-20
❑ 96SpoArtP-20
❑ 96SpoDouT-9
❑ 96SPx-57
❑ 96SPxGol-57
❑ 96Stu-65
❑ 96StuPrePB-65
❑ 96StuPrePG-65
❑ 96StuPrePS-65
❑ 96Sum-84
❑ 96SumAbo&B-84
❑ 96SumArtP-84
❑ 96SumFoi-84
❑ 96SumPos-4
❑ 96TeaOut-67
❑ 96TeaOut-C99
❑ 96Ult-130
❑ 96UltGolM-130
❑ 96UppDec-202
❑ 96UppDecBCP-BC15
❑ 96UppDecDD-DD38
❑ 96UppDecDDG-DD38
❑ 96UppDecDDS-DD38
❑ 96Zen-99
❑ 96ZenArtP-99
❑ 96ZenDiaC-9
❑ 96ZenDiaCP-9
❑ 96ZenMoz-5
❑ 97Cir-100
❑ 97Cir-397
❑ 97Cir-P100
❑ 97CirBos-16
❑ 97CirEmeA-100
❑ 97CirEmeAR-AU4
❑ 97CirFasT-8
❑ 97CirIco-10
❑ 97CirLimA-13
❑ 97CirRav-100
❑ 97CirRav-397
❑ 97CirRavR-11
❑ 97CirSupB-16
❑ 97ColCho-56
❑ 97ColCho-235
❑ 97ColCho-332
❑ 97ColChoAC-4
❑ 97ColChoBS-5
❑ 97ColChoBSGS-5
❑ 97ColChoCtG-29A
❑ 97ColChoCtG-29B
❑ 97ColChoCtG-29C
❑ 97ColChoCtGE-CG29
❑ 97ColChoCtGIW-CG29
❑ 97ColChoNF-NF1
❑ 97ColChoPP-PP18
❑ 97ColChoPPG-PP18
❑ 97ColChoPPJ-PP18
❑ 97ColChoS-3
❑ 97ColChoSR-23
❑ 97ColChoT-SM6
❑ 97ColChoTBS-41
❑ 97ColChoTBSWH-41
❑ 97ColChoTotT-T28
❑ 97DenHol-11
❑ 97Don-44
❑ 97Don-404
❑ 97DonArmaD-6
❑ 97DonDom-5
❑ 97DonEli-2
❑ 97DonEli-6
❑ 97DonEliGS-2
❑ 97DonEliLaL-2
❑ 97DonEliPtT-2
❑ 97DonEliPtT-3
❑ 97DonEliPtTA-2
❑ 97DonEliPtTA-3
❑ 97DonEliTotC-1
❑ 97DonEliTotCDC-1
❑ 97DonFraFea-3
❑ 97DonGolPP-44
❑ 97DonGolPP-404
❑ 97DonLim-13
❑ 97DonLim-69
❑ 97DonLim-122
❑ 97DonLimE-13
❑ 97DonLimE-69
❑ 97DonLimE-122
❑ 97DonLimENG-13
❑ 97DonPowA-7
❑ 97DonPowADC-7
❑ 97DonPre-92
❑ 97DonPre-167
❑ 97DonPreCttC-92
❑ 97DonPreCttC-167
❑ 97DonPrePM-15
❑ 97DonPreS-1
❑ 97DonPreSS-1
❑ 97DonPreTB-18
❑ 97DonPreTBG-18
❑ 97DonPreTF-18
❑ 97DonPreTP-18
❑ 97DonPreTPG-18
❑ 97DonPreXP-7B
❑ 97DonSig-61
❑ 97DonSigAC-105
❑ 97DonSigAM-105
❑ 97DonSigPPP-61
❑ 97DonSilPP-44
❑ 97DonSilPP-404
❑ 97DonTea-137
❑ 97DonTeaSMVP-7
❑ 97DonTeaSPE-137
❑ 97DonVxP1-3
❑ 97DonVxP1CD-5
❑ 97E-X2-43
❑ 97E-X2-P43
❑ 97E-X2-S43
❑ 97E-X2-NNO
❑ 97E-X2ACA-3
❑ 97E-X2Cred-43
❑ 97E-X2EmeAuto-43
❑ 97E-X2EmeAutoR-AU4
❑ 97E-X2EssCre-43
❑ 97E-X2Hall-9
❑ 97E-X2SD2000-1
❑ 97FlaShoDC-16
❑ 97FlaShoHG-13
❑ 97FlaShoLC-3
❑ 97FlaShoLeg0-3
❑ 97FlaShoLeg1-3
❑ 97FlaShoM-A3
❑ 97FlaShoM-B3
❑ 97FlaShoM-C3
❑ 97FlaShoR0-3
❑ 97FlaShoR1-3
❑ 97FlaShoR2-3
❑ 97FlaShoR2-NNO
❑ 97Fle-213
❑ 97Fle-499
❑ 97Fle-715
❑ 97FleBleB-7
❑ 97FleDiaT-11
❑ 97FleGouG-12
❑ 97FleGouGF-12
❑ 97FleHea-17
❑ 97FleLumC-14
❑ 97FleMilDM-28
❑ 97FleMilDMR-28
❑ 97FleNig&D-8
❑ 97FleSoaS-11
❑ 97FleSoaSG-11
❑ 97FleTif-213
❑ 97FleTif-499
❑ 97FleTif-715
❑ 97FleZon-15
❑ 97HigMinESC-40
❑ 97HigMinESC-41
❑ 97HigMinESC-42
❑ 97HigMinM-105
❑ 97HigMinM-106
❑ 97HigMinM-107
❑ 97HigMinMSM-15
❑ 97HigMinMSM-16
❑ 97Lea-16
❑ 97Lea-350
❑ 97Lea-368
❑ 97LeaBanS-5
❑ 97LeaDrefS-11
❑ 97LeaFraM-16
❑ 97LeaFraM-350
❑ 97LeaFraM-368
❑ 97LeaFraMDC-16
❑ 97LeaFraMDC-350
❑ 97LeaFraMDC-368
❑ 97LeaGet-5
❑ 97LeaGolS-2
❑ 97LeaLeaotN-12
❑ 97LeaStaS-4
❑ 97MarSco-3
❑ 97MarScoPl-3
❑ 97MarScoPr-3
❑ 97MetUni-149
❑ 97MetUni-P149
❑ 97MetUniBF-10
❑ 97MetUniEA-AU4
❑ 97MetUniEAR-AU4
❑ 97MetUniMF-9
❑ 97MetUniML-10
❑ 97MetUniPP-10
❑ 97MetUniT-9
❑ 97NewPin-81
❑ 97NewPin-180
❑ 97NewPin-190
❑ 97NewPinAP-81
❑ 97NewPinAP-180
❑ 97NewPinAP-190
❑ 97NewPinIE-8
❑ 97NewPinKtP-5
❑ 97NewPinMC-81
❑ 97NewPinMC-180
❑ 97NewPinMC-190
❑ 97NewPinPP-81
❑ 97NewPinPP-180
❑ 97NewPinPP-190
❑ 97NewPinPP-I8A
❑ 97NewPinPP-K5
❑ 97NewPinPP-AR1
❑ 97NewPinPP-AR2
❑ 97NewPinPP-AR3
❑ 97NewPinPP-AR4
❑ 97NewPinS-AR1
❑ 97NewPinS-AR2
❑ 97NewPinS-AR3
❑ 97NewPinS-AR4
❑ 97Pac-192
❑ 97PacCar-18
❑ 97PacCarM-18
❑ 97PacCerCGT-5
❑ 97PacCraC-6
❑ 97PacFirD-12
❑ 97PacGolCD-18
❑ 97PacLatotML-20
❑ 97PacLigB-192
❑ 97PacPri-65
❑ 97PacPriGA-GA15
❑ 97PacPriGotD-GD91
❑ 97PacPriLB-65
❑ 97PacPriP-65
❑ 97PacPriSH-SH7A
❑ 97PacPriSL-SL6B
❑ 97PacSil-192
❑ 97PacTriCD-10
❑ 97Pin-92
❑ 97PinArtP-PP92
❑ 97PinCar-19
❑ 97PinCer-22
❑ 97PinCer-144
❑ 97PinCerCMGT-5
❑ 97PinCerCT-5
❑ 97PinCerLI-12
❑ 97PinCerMBla-22
❑ 97PinCerMBla-144
❑ 97PinCerMBlu-22
❑ 97PinCerMBlu-144
❑ 97PinCerMG-22
❑ 97PinCerMG-144
❑ 97PinCerMR-22
❑ 97PinCerMR-144
❑ 97PinCerR-22
❑ 97PinCerR-144
❑ 97PinEpixPE-E13
❑ 97PinFan-FF5
❑ 97PinHom-11
❑ 97PinHom-12
❑ 97PinIns-8
❑ 97PinInsC-5
❑ 97PinInsCE-8
❑ 97PinInsDD-1
❑ 97PinInsDE-8

❑ 97PinMin-3
❑ 97PinMinB-3
❑ 97PinMinCB-3
❑ 97PinMinCG-3
❑ 97PinMinCGR-3
❑ 97PinMinCN-3
❑ 97PinMinCSS-3
❑ 97PinMinG-3
❑ 97PinMinS-3
❑ 97PinMusC-92
❑ 97PinPasttM-6
❑ 97PinPrePla-92
❑ 97PinPrePla-S10
❑ 97PinSha-10
❑ 97PinTeaP-4
❑ 97PinTeaP-10
❑ 97PinTotCPB-22
❑ 97PinTotCPB-144
❑ 97PinTotCPG-22
❑ 97PinTotCPG-144
❑ 97PinTotCPR-22
❑ 97PinTotCPR-144
❑ 97PinX-P-15
❑ 97PinX-P-147
❑ 97PinX-PF&A-18
❑ 97PinX-PMoS-15
❑ 97PinX-PMoS-147
❑ 97PinX-PMP-7
❑ 97PinX-PMP-P7
❑ 97PinX-PMW-4
❑ 97PinX-PMWG-4
❑ 97PinX-PMWS-4
❑ 97PinX-PreMPS-7
❑ 97PreCon-21
❑ 97Sco-95
❑ 97Sco-507
❑ 97ScoAllF-5
❑ 97ScoArtPWB-95
❑ 97ScoArtPWB-507
❑ 97ScoBla-12
❑ 97ScoHeaotO-7
❑ 97ScoHigZ-10
❑ 97ScoPitP-2
❑ 97ScoPitP-3
❑ 97ScoPreS-95
❑ 97ScoResC-507
❑ 97ScoShoS-95
❑ 97ScoShoS-507
❑ 97ScoShoSAP-95
❑ 97ScoShoSAP-507
❑ 97ScoStaaD-6
❑ 97ScoSteS-8
❑ 97ScoTitT-17
❑ 97Sel-53
❑ 97Sel-141
❑ 97SelArtP-53
❑ 97SelArtP-141
❑ 97SelCom-53
❑ 97SelCom-141
❑ 97SelRegG-53
❑ 97SelRegG-141
❑ 97SelToootT-24
❑ 97SelToootTMB-24
❑ 97SP-166
❑ 97SPGamF-GF1
❑ 97SPInsI-10
❑ 97SPMarM-MM8
❑ 97SpollI-70
❑ 97SpollI-158
❑ 97SpollI-170
❑ 97SpollI-179
❑ 97SpollI-P158
❑ 97SpollIAM-1
❑ 97SpollIEE-70
❑ 97SpollIEE-158
❑ 97SpollIEE-170
❑ 97SpollIEE-179
❑ 97SpollIGS-23
❑ 97SPSpeF-10
❑ 97SPSpeF-49
❑ 97SPSpxF-6
❑ 97SPSPxFA-6
❑ 97SPVinAu-24
❑ 97SPVinAu-25
❑ 97SPVinAu-26
❑ 97SPx-46
❑ 97SPxBoufG-18
❑ 97SPxBoufGSS-4
❑ 97SPxBro-46
❑ 97SPxCorotG-10
❑ 97SPxGol-46
❑ 97SPxGraF-46
❑ 97SPxSil-46
❑ 97SPxSte-46
❑ 97StrAll-53
❑ 97Stu-43
❑ 97Stu-165
❑ 97StuHarH-8
❑ 97StuMasS-8
❑ 97StuMasS8-8
❑ 97StuPor8-3
❑ 97StuPrePG-43
❑ 97StuPrePG-165
❑ 97StuPrePS-43
❑ 97StuPrePS-165
❑ 97UD3-50
❑ 97UD3GenNex-GN1
❑ 97UD3Marq-MA10
❑ 97Ult-126
❑ 97UltAutE-5
❑ 97UltChe-B4
❑ 97UltDiaP-10
❑ 97UltDouT-9
❑ 97UltFamGam-3
❑ 97UltFieC-16
❑ 97UltGolME-126
❑ 97UltHitM-4
❑ 97UltLeaS-2
❑ 97UltPlaME-126
❑ 97UltPowP-A9
❑ 97UltPowP-B3
❑ 97UltSeaC-9
❑ 97UltStaR-4
❑ 97UltThu-6
❑ 97UltTop3-4
❑ 97UltTop3GM-4
❑ 97UppDec-319
❑ 97UppDec-422
❑ 97UppDec-500
❑ 97UppDecAG-AG3
❑ 97UppDecAWJ-1
❑ 97UppDecBCP-BC20
❑ 97UppDecHC-HC1
❑ 97UppDecHTH-HT1
❑ 97UppDecLDC-LD15
❑ 97UppDecMM-A10
❑ 97UppDecMP-P4
❑ 97UppDecP-27
❑ 97UppDecPE-27
❑ 97UppDecRP-RP10
❑ 97UppDecRSF-RS1
❑ 97UppDecSA-11
❑ 97UppDecSAG-11
❑ 97UppDecTTS-TS10
❑ 97Zen-22
❑ 97Zen Z-Z-4
❑ 97Zen8x10-13
❑ 97Zen8x1D-13
❑ 97ZentheBP-13
❑ 97ZenV-2-5
❑ 98Bow-232
❑ 98BowBes-45
❑ 98BowBesAR-45
❑ 98BowBesMIF-MI4
❑ 98BowBesMIFAR-MI4
❑ 98BowBesMIFR-MI4
❑ 98BowBesR-45
❑ 98BowChr-232
❑ 98BowChrGA-232
❑ 98BowChrGAR-232
❑ 98BowChrI-232
❑ 98BowChrIR-232
❑ 98BowChrR-232
❑ 98BowGolA-232
❑ 98BowInt-232
❑ 98CirThu-3
❑ 98CirThu-298
❑ 98CirThuB-17
❑ 98CirThuLA-13
❑ 98CirThuQS-10
❑ 98CirThuRav-3
❑ 98CirThuRR-13
❑ 98CirThuSupRav-3
❑ 98ColCho-272
❑ 98ColCho-495
❑ 98ColChoB5-495
❑ 98ColChoCtG-CG24A
❑ 98ColChoCtG-CG24B
❑ 98ColChoCtG-CG24C
❑ 98ColChoCtGExch-CG24
❑ 98ColChoCtGIW-CG24
❑ 98ColChoGJ5-272
❑ 98ColChoMBH-26
❑ 98ColChoS'-26
❑ 98ColChoSQ-SQ35
❑ 98ColChoSQ-SQ85
❑ 98ColChoSQDouble-7
❑ 98ColChoSQHR-7
❑ 98ColChoSQSingle-7
❑ 98ColChoSQTriple-7
❑ 98CroRoy-128
❑ 98CroRoyAS-8
❑ 98CroRoyCCPA-3
❑ 98CroRoyCCPrem-3
❑ 98CroRoyDK-21
❑ 98CroRoyFoB-21
❑ 98CroRoyFoBA-21
❑ 98CroRoyHRF-8
❑ 98CroRoyPotG-23
❑ 98Don-34
❑ 98Don-163
❑ 98Don-370
❑ 98Don-408
❑ 98DonCol-34
❑ 98DonCol-163
❑ 98DonColE-403
❑ 98DonColE-520
❑ 98DonColL-364
❑ 98DonColP-554
❑ 98DonColP-721
❑ 98DonColS-34
❑ 98DonColS-163
❑ 98DonCruG-40
❑ 98DonCruP-40
❑ 98DonCruR-40
❑ 98DonDiaK-19
❑ 98DonDiaKC-19
❑ 98DonDom-14
❑ 98DonEli-3
❑ 98DonEli-120
❑ 98DonEliA-3
❑ 98DonEliA-120
❑ 98DonEliBttF-8
❑ 98DonEliBttFA-8
❑ 98DonEliC-3
❑ 98DonElil-17
❑ 98DonEliMC-3
❑ 98DonEliPN-11A
❑ 98DonEliPN-11B
❑ 98DonEliPN-11C
❑ 98DonEliPNDC-11A
❑ 98DonEliPNDC-11B
❑ 98DonEliPNDC-11C
❑ 98DonEliPNS-11A
❑ 98DonEliPNS-11B
❑ 98DonEliPNS-11C
❑ 98DonEliS-3
❑ 98DonEliS-120
❑ 98DonFANT-7
❑ 98DonFANTDC-7
❑ 98DonGolPP-34
❑ 98DonGolPP-163
❑ 98DonGolPP-370
❑ 98DonGolPP-408
❑ 98DonPre-4
❑ 98DonPre-171
❑ 98DonPreGB-4
❑ 98DonPreGES-6
❑ 98DonPreGoB-4
❑ 98DonPreGX-6
❑ 98DonPreGXDC-6
❑ 98DonPrePM-4
❑ 98DonPreSeat-4
❑ 98DonPreSeat-171
❑ 98DonPreTP-4
❑ 98DonPreTPD-2
❑ 98DonPreTPG-4
❑ 98DonPreTPS-4
❑ 98DonPreTW-16
❑ 98DonPriCD-34
❑ 98DonPriCD-163
❑ 98DonPriCE-403
❑ 98DonPriCE-520
❑ 98DonPriCL-364
❑ 98DonPriCP-554
❑ 98DonPriCP-721
❑ 98DonProLPI-6
❑ 98DonProLS-16
❑ 98DonSig-37
❑ 98DonSigAC-95
❑ 98DonSigAM-97
❑ 98DonSigP-37
❑ 98DonSigSP-23
❑ 98DonSilPP-34
❑ 98DonSilPP-163
❑ 98DonSilPP-370
❑ 98DonSilPP-408
❑ 98E-X2-1
❑ 98E-X2-NNO
❑ 98E-X2ARodHawaii-NNO
❑ 98E-X2DesCoop-1
❑ 98E-X2ECFut-1
❑ 98E-X2ECNow-1
❑ 98E-X2Sig2001-16
❑ 98Fin-157
❑ 98FinCen-C13
❑ 98FinCenR-C13
❑ 98FinMysF2-M8
❑ 98FinMysF2-M10
❑ 98FinMysF2-M12
❑ 98FinMysF2-M33
❑ 98FinMysF2R-M8
❑ 98FinMysF2R-M10
❑ 98FinMysF2R-M12
❑ 98FinMysF2R-M33
❑ 98FinMysFO-1
❑ 98FinMysFOR-1
❑ 98FinNo--157
❑ 98FinNo-R-157
❑ 98FinRef-157
❑ 98FinStaS-SS2
❑ 98FinStaSJ-2
❑ 98FinTheM-TM10
❑ 98FinTheMR-TM10
❑ 98FlaShoLeg0-7
❑ 98FlaShoLeg1-7
❑ 98FlaShoLeg2-7
❑ 98FlaShoLeg3-7
❑ 98FlaShoLegM-7
❑ 98FlaShoP1-9
❑ 98FlaShoR0-7
❑ 98FlaShoR1-7
❑ 98FlaShoR2-7
❑ 98FlaShoR3-7
❑ 98Fle-100
❑ 98Fle-336
❑ 98Fle-349
❑ 98Fle-594
❑ 98Fle-P100
❑ 98FleDiamInk-8
❑ 98FleDiaS-17
❑ 98FleDiaT-DT9
❑ 98FleLumC-13
❑ 98FleUpd-U10
❑ 98FleVin'-58
❑ 98FleVin'C-58
❑ 98FleZon-13
❑ 98Lea-165
❑ 98LeaCruG-40
❑ 98LeaCruP-40
❑ 98LeaCruR-40
❑ 98LeaFraDA-165
❑ 98LeaFraF-165
❑ 98LeaFraM-165
❑ 98LeaFraM-165
❑ 98LeaFraMDC-165
❑ 98LeaFraMDC-165
❑ 98LeaFraMZ2-165
❑ 98LeaRCMLHDSamp-7
❑ 98LeaRS-29
❑ 98LeaRS-143
❑ 98LeaRSCross-3
❑ 98LeaRSGAHSamp-4
❑ 98LeaRSGreAH-4
❑ 98LeaRSGreHit-4
❑ 98LeaRSLHolo-29
❑ 98LeaRSLHolo-143
❑ 98LeaRSLMVP-4
❑ 98LeaRSLMVPPE-4
❑ 98LeaRSLong-29
❑ 98LeaRSLong-143
❑ 98LeaRSMLHD-7
❑ 98LeaRSTicMas-1
❑ 98LeaRSTicMasDC-1
❑ 98LeaRTrue-29
❑ 98LeaRTrue-143
❑ 98LeaStaRep-3
❑ 98LeaStaS-3
❑ 98LeaStaSDC-3
❑ 98MarSco-2
❑ 98MarScoP-2
❑ 98MetUni-100
❑ 98MetUni-214
❑ 98MetUni-219
❑ 98MetUni-NNO
❑ 98MetUniAT-13
❑ 98MetUniDH-4
❑ 98MetUniPMG-100
❑ 98MetUniPMG-214
❑ 98MetUniPP-10
❑ 98MetUniT-13
❑ 98MetUniUL-13
❑ 98Pac-193
❑ 98PacAur-76
❑ 98PacAurCube-17
❑ 98PacAurHC-17
❑ 98PacAurKotML-10
❑ 98PacAurODLC-17
❑ 98PacAurPF-3
❑ 98PacAurPFC-3
❑ 98PacAurPFPB-3
❑ 98PacAurPFR-3
❑ 98PacAurPFS-3
❑ 98PacGolCDC-32
❑ 98PacHomRH-19
❑ 98PacInCage-18
❑ 98PacInv-67
❑ 98PacInvGems-96
❑ 98PacInvInt-10A
❑ 98PacInvMiT-18
❑ 98PacInvPBlue-67
❑ 98PacInvPhoto-15
❑ 98PacInvSilv-67
❑ 98PacInvTeam-26
❑ 98PacLatotML-33
❑ 98PacNes-3A
❑ 98PacOme-225
❑ 98PacOmeEP-8
❑ 98PacOmeEP1o1-8
❑ 98PacOmeFTF-1
❑ 98PacOmeOnIns-15
❑ 98PacOmeP-10
❑ 98PacOmeR-225
❑ 98PacOnl-693A
❑ 98PacOnl-693B
❑ 98PacOnlR-693A
❑ 98PacOnlR-693B
❑ 98PacOnlWC-693A
❑ 98PacOnlWC-693B
❑ 98PacPar-90
❑ 98PacParC-90
❑ 98PacParFC-17
❑ 98PacParG-90
❑ 98PacParHS-90
❑ 98PacParPB-90
❑ 98PacParR-90
❑ 98PacParSD-19
❑ 98PacPlaB-193
❑ 98PacRedT-193
❑ 98PacSil-193
❑ 98PacTeaC-12
❑ 98Pin-182
❑ 98PinArtP-PP85
❑ 98PinEpixME-E13
❑ 98PinEpixMO-E13
❑ 98PinEpixMP-E13
❑ 98PinEpixPO-E13
❑ 98PinEpixPP-E13
❑ 98PinEpixSE-E13
❑ 98PinEpixSO-E13
❑ 98PinEpixSP-E13
❑ 98PinIns-3
❑ 98PinIns-139
❑ 98PinInsBtN-3
❑ 98PinInsC-17
❑ 98PinInsCE-3
❑ 98PinInsCE-139
❑ 98PinInsCG-17
❑ 98PinInsDE-3
❑ 98PinInsDE-139
❑ 98PinInsSG-2AB
❑ 98PinInsSG-2CD
❑ 98PinInsSG-4AB
❑ 98PinInsSG-4CD
❑ 98PinInsSG-6AB
❑ 98PinInsSG-6CD
❑ 98PinInsSG-25AB
❑ 98PinInsSG-25CD
❑ 98PinInsSGS-2AB
❑ 98PinInsSGS-2CD
❑ 98PinInsSGS-4AB
❑ 98PinInsSGS-4CD
❑ 98PinInsSGS-6AB
❑ 98PinInsSGS-6CD
❑ 98PinInsSGS-25AB
❑ 98PinInsSGS-25CD
❑ 98PinMinB-19
❑ 98PinMinCB-19
❑ 98PinMinCBAP-19
❑ 98PinMinCGP-19
❑ 98PinMinCGPAP-19
❑ 98PinMinCN-19
❑ 98PinMinCNAP-19
❑ 98PinMinCSGR-19
❑ 98PinMinDC-19
❑ 98PinMinG-19
❑ 98PinMinMCSS-19
❑ 98PinMinS-19
❑ 98PinMusC-PP85
❑ 98PinPer-4
❑ 98PinPer-141
❑ 98PinPerBB-5
❑ 98PinPerBBSamp-5
❑ 98PinPerBBSO-5
❑ 98PinPerLP-19
❑ 98PinPerPP-4
❑ 98PinPerPP-141
❑ 98PinPerPT-2
❑ 98PinPerSftF-20
❑ 98PinPerSftFShop-10
❑ 98PinPlu-25
❑ 98PinPlu-184
❑ 98PinPluAE-13
❑ 98PinPluAEE-13
❑ 98PinPluAEP-13
❑ 98PinPluAP-PP13
❑ 98PinPluGAP-PP13
❑ 98PinPluLM-23
❑ 98PinPluMAP-PP13
❑ 98PinPluPieGame-3
❑ 98PinPluTP-4
❑ 98PinPluTPG-4
❑ 98PinPluTPM-4
❑ 98PinPowPJ-1
❑ 98PinPowPJS-1
❑ 98PinPreP-182
❑ 98PinPreP-E13
❑ 98PinSna-SM1
❑ 98PinSna-SM11
❑ 98PinSnaS-6
❑ 98PinUnc-182
❑ 98PreCon-10
❑ 98Revo-135
❑ 98RevoFP-9
❑ 98RevoMLI-5
❑ 98RevoPTP-9
❑ 98RevoRooHH-29
❑ 98RevoShow-15
❑ 98RevoSS-135
❑ 98Sco-10
❑ 98ScoEpix-E13
❑ 98ScoFirP-3
❑ 98ScoNewS-NS6
❑ 98ScoRT-30
❑ 98ScoRT-255
❑ 98ScoRTComPla-3A
❑ 98ScoRTComPla-3B
❑ 98ScoRTComPla-3C
❑ 98ScoRTCPSamp-3A
❑ 98ScoRTCPSamp-3B
❑ 98ScoRTCPSamp-3C
❑ 98ScoRTSS-PP30
❑ 98ScoRTSS-PP148
❑ 98ScoRTSSAP-PP30
❑ 98ScoRTSSAP-PP148
❑ 98ScoRTSSAP1-PP30
❑ 98ScoRTSSAP1-PP148
❑ 98ScoRTStarGaz-11
❑ 98ScoSam-10
❑ 98ScoSS-PP116
❑ 98ScoSSAP-PP116
❑ 98SelSelSamp-6
❑ 98SkyDugA-81
❑ 98SkyDugA-132
❑ 98SkyDugA-NNO
❑ 98SkyDugAAR-11
❑ 98SkyDugAIA-81
❑ 98SkyDugAIA-132
❑ 98SkyDugAS-SH8
❑ 98SP Aut-179
❑ 98SP Aut-SD11
❑ 98SP AutC-AR
❑ 98SP AutSD-SD11
❑ 98SP AutSDT-SD11
❑ 98SP AutTrade-13
❑ 98SPAutGJ5x7-4
❑ 98SpollI-106
❑ 98SpollI-P106
❑ 98SpollI-NNO
❑ 98SpollIEC-EC2
❑ 98SpollIEE-106
❑ 98SpollIFE-106
❑ 98SpollITaN-125
❑ 98SpollITaN-P125
❑ 98SpollITaN-NNO
❑ 98SpollITaNAotG-AG2
❑ 98SpollITaNEE-125
❑ 98SpollITaNGS-3
❑ 98SpollIWSF-108
❑ 98SpollIWSFEE-108
❑ 98SpollIWSFFE-108
❑ 98SpollIWSFRJP-11
❑ 98SPxFin-47
❑ 98SPxFin-133
❑ 98SPxFin-167
❑ 98SPxFin-179
❑ 98SPxFin-219
❑ 98SPxFin-357
❑ 98SPxFinHRH-HR5
❑ 98SPxFinR-47
❑ 98SPxFinR-133
❑ 98SPxFinR-167
❑ 98SPxFinR-179
❑ 98SPxFinR-219
❑ 98SPxFinR-357
❑ 98SPxFinS-47

❑ 98SPxFinS-133
❑ 98SPxFinS-167
❑ 98SPxFinS-179
❑ 98SPxFinS-219
❑ 98SPxFinS-357
❑ 98StaCluFDI-288
❑ 98StaCluI-288
❑ 98StaCluOneK-288
❑ 98StaCluPP-288
❑ 98StaCluPWP-P7
❑ 98StaCluRC-RC10
❑ 98StaCluTIII-T14C
❑ 98StaCluTLme-T14C
❑ 98StaCluTLmo-T14C
❑ 98Stu-42
❑ 98StuFF-5
❑ 98StuFFDC-5
❑ 98StuGPP-42
❑ 98StuMast-17
❑ 98StuPor8x10-20
❑ 98StuPor8x10GP-20
❑ 98StuSPP-42
❑ 98Top-504
❑ 98TopChr-504
❑ 98TopChrR-504
❑ 98TopDevR-504
❑ 98TopDia-504
❑ 98TopGal-125
❑ 98TopGalGoH-GH4
❑ 98TopGalGoHJ-GH4
❑ 98TopGalGP-125
❑ 98TopGalOPP-125
❑ 98TopGalPG-PG1
❑ 98TopGalPPI-125
❑ 98TopGalPPIA-125
❑ 98TopGolLabC1-25
❑ 98TopGolLabC1B-25
❑ 98TopGolLabC1One-25
❑ 98TopGolLabC1R-25
❑ 98TopGolLabC2-25
❑ 98TopGolLabC2B-25
❑ 98TopGolLabC2One-25
❑ 98TopGolLabC2R-25
❑ 98TopGolLabC3-25
❑ 98TopGolLabC3B-25
❑ 98TopGolLabC3One-25
❑ 98TopGolLabC3R-25
❑ 98TopMiniC-504
❑ 98TopSta-139
❑ 98TopStaB-139
❑ 98TopStaG-G8
❑ 98TopStaG-139
❑ 98TopStaGG-G8
❑ 98TopStaGGR-G8
❑ 98TopStaGR-139
❑ 98TopStaGS-G8
❑ 98TopStaLB-L13
❑ 98TopStaLG-L13
❑ 98TopStaLGR-L13
❑ 98TopStaLS-L13
❑ 98TopStaS-139
❑ 98TopSup-36
❑ 98TopSup-36
❑ 98TopTek-9
❑ 98TopTekD-9
❑ 98UD3-48
❑ 98UD3-138
❑ 98UD3-228
❑ 98UD3DieCut-48
❑ 98UD3DieCut-138
❑ 98UD3DieCut-228
❑ 98UD3PCBlowup-48
❑ 98Ult-83
❑ 98Ult-247
❑ 98Ult-479
❑ 98Ult-S100
❑ 98UltArtT-3
❑ 98UltBacttF-2
❑ 98UltDial-3
❑ 98UltDiaP-3
❑ 98UltDouT-1
❑ 98UltFalC-3
❑ 98UltGolM-83
❑ 98UltGolM-247
❑ 98UltGolM-479
❑ 98UltKidG-2
❑ 98UltMas-83
❑ 98UltMas-247
❑ 98UltMas-479
❑ 98UltMilM-6
❑ 98UltNot-19
❑ 98UltPlaM-83
❑ 98UltPlaM-247
❑ 98UltPlaM-479
❑ 98UltPowP-3
❑ 98UltPriL-3
❑ 98UltTicS-15
❑ 98UltTop3-20
❑ 98UltWinN-1
❑ 98UppDec-18
❑ 98UppDec-146
❑ 98UppDec-457
❑ 98UppDec-510
❑ 98UppDec-617
❑ 98UppDec10AP-42
❑ 98UppDec1APR-42
❑ 98UppDec5x7-510
❑ 98UppDec5x7-617
❑ 98UppDecAC-AS15
❑ 98UppDecAG-AG3
❑ 98UppDecAGDC-AG3
❑ 98UppDecAPA1-7
❑ 98UppDecAPA1-8
❑ 98UppDecBCP-BC10
❑ 98UppDecCD-CD3
❑ 98UppDecDS-DS43
❑ 98UppDecNP-NP38
❑ 98UppDecR-92
❑ 98UppDecR-29
❑ 98UppDecRBBop-BB14
❑ 98UppDecRGKoG-G9
❑ 98UppDecRQL-Q8
❑ 98UppDecRTC-TC19
❑ 98UppDecSF-3
❑ 98UppDecSFPD-PZ8
❑ 98UppDecSFPZSX-PZ8
❑ 98UppDecTMT-18
❑ 98UppDecTMTG-18
❑ 98UppDecU-15
❑ 98Zen-16
❑ 98Zen5 xx7-14
❑ 98Zen5x7GoldImp-14
❑ 98Zen5x7Imp-14
❑ 98ZenEpi-E13
❑ 98ZenRaitB-3
❑ 98ZenZ-G-16
❑ 98ZenZ-S-16
❑ 98ZenZ-T-5
❑ 98ZenZ-T5x7-5
❑ 98ZenZ-TG-5
❑ 99199Fin-85
❑ 99199Fin-105
❑ 99199Fin-253
❑ 99AllMysFR-M7
❑ 99AurComP-10A
❑ 99AurComP-10B
❑ 99AurKinotML-10
❑ 99AurOn DL-18
❑ 99AurPenF-18
❑ 99AurPenF-18
❑ 99AurPenFB-18
❑ 99AurPenFS-18
❑ 99AurSty-18
❑ 99Bow-265
❑ 99BowBes-50
❑ 99BowBes-92
❑ 99BowBesAR-50
❑ 99BowBesAR-92
❑ 99BowBesFBMI-FB5
❑ 99BowBesFBMII-FB5
❑ 99BowBesFBMIII-FB5
❑ 99BowBesMI-M1
❑ 99BowBesMIAR-M1
❑ 99BowBesMIR-M1
❑ 99BowBesR-50
❑ 99BowBesR-92
❑ 99BowChrDA-DA18
❑ 99BowChrDAR-DA18
❑ 99BowGol-265
❑ 99BowInt-265
❑ 99CroRoyB-130
❑ 99CroRoyC2-10
❑ 99CroRoyL-130
❑ 99CroRoyLL-10
❑ 99CroRoyMP-18
❑ 99CroRoyOD-130
❑ 99CroRoyPotG-23
❑ 99CroRoyPP-23
❑ 99CroRoyPPN-23
❑ 99DumSet-155
❑ 99E-X Cen-6
❑ 99E-X CenECFut-6
❑ 99E-X CenECNow-6
❑ 99E-XCenFoF'-6
❑ 99E-XCenMotC-7
❑ 99FinAarAwC-HA7
❑ 99FinAarAwCR-HA7
❑ 99FinDouF-DF1
❑ 99FinDouFDualR-DF1
❑ 99FinGolRef-85
❑ 99FinGolRef-105
❑ 99FinGolRef-253
❑ 99FinLeal-L8
❑ 99FinMil-M8
❑ 99FinMil-M14
❑ 99FinMil-M28
❑ 99FinMil-M37
❑ 99FinPeelHyp-9
❑ 99FinPeelSpark-9
❑ 99FinPeeSS-9
❑ 99FinProF-PF7
❑ 99FinProF-PF24
❑ 99FinProF-PF39
❑ 99FinProF-PF50
❑ 99FinRef-85
❑ 99FinRef-105
❑ 99FinRef-253
❑ 99FinSplS-SS2
❑ 99FinSplSDR-SS2
❑ 99FinTeaFB-TF5
❑ 99FinTeaFBR-TF5
❑ 99FinTeaFG-TF5
❑ 99FinTeaFGR-TF5
❑ 99FinTeaFR-TF5
❑ 99FinTeaFRR-TF5
❑ 99FlaShoLeg1-14
❑ 99FlaShoLeg2-14
❑ 99FlaShoLeg3-14
❑ 99FlaShoLegM1-14
❑ 99FlaShoLegM2-14
❑ 99FlaShoLegM3-14
❑ 99FlaShoMoG-13
❑ 99FlaShoR1-14
❑ 99FlaShoR2-14
❑ 99FlaShoR3-14
❑ 99Fle-9
❑ 99Fle-587
❑ 99Fle-593
❑ 99FleBri-39
❑ 99FleBri2G-39
❑ 99FleBriBlu-39
❑ 99FleBriGol-39
❑ 99FleBriSS-6
❑ 99FleBriSSP-6
❑ 99FleDatWD-9
❑ 99FleDiaM-12
❑ 99FleDiaSkiSheet-NNO
❑ 99FleGoiYar-12
❑ 99FleGolM-12
❑ 99FleMys-74
❑ 99FleMys-155
❑ 99FleMysE-8
❑ 99FleMysFI-22
❑ 99FleMysFtG-6
❑ 99FleMysG-74
❑ 99FleMysM-74
❑ 99FleMysM-155
❑ 99FleSta9-9
❑ 99FleSta9-587
❑ 99FleSta9-593
❑ 99FleVin'-9
❑ 99FleWarT-9
❑ 99FleWarT-587
❑ 99FleWarT-593
❑ 99HomHer-11
❑ 99MetUni-50
❑ 99MetUni-235
❑ 99MetUni-275
❑ 99MetUni-300
❑ 99MetUniBWTW-15
❑ 99MetUniDS-2
❑ 99MetUniGM-50
❑ 99MetUniGM-235
❑ 99MetUniGM-275
❑ 99MetUniGM-300
❑ 99MetUniL-10
❑ 99MetUniPM-1
❑ 99MetUniPMG-50
❑ 99MetUniPMG-235
❑ 99MetUniPMG-275
❑ 99MetUniPMG-300
❑ 99MetUniSamp-NNOA
❑ 99MetUniSamp-NNO
❑ 99Pac-40
❑ 99Pac-40A
❑ 99PacAur-179
❑ 99PacAurOD-179
❑ 99PacCraCho-5
❑ 99PacCroC-267
❑ 99PacCroC-17
❑ 99PacCroCITC-18
❑ 99PacCroCPB-267
❑ 99PacCroCPC-5
❑ 99PacCroCTM-17
❑ 99PacDynaD-7
❑ 99PacDynaDT-7
❑ 99PacGolCDC-14
❑ 99PacInv-136
❑ 99PacInvDM-10
❑ 99PacInvFP-19
❑ 99PacInvGotG-10
❑ 99PacInvOD-136
❑ 99PacInvPB-136
❑ 99PacInvSF-18
❑ 99PacInvSF-18B
❑ 99PacInvSH-19
❑ 99PacInvSH-19B
❑ 99PacInvTA-18
❑ 99PacOme-224
❑ 99PacOme5T-29
❑ 99PacOme5TT-29
❑ 99PacOmeC-224
❑ 99PacOmeDD-3
❑ 99PacOmeDM-31
❑ 99PacOmeEP-18
❑ 99PacOmeEP1o1-18
❑ 99PacOmeG-224
❑ 99PacOmeH'-18
❑ 99PacOmePB-224
❑ 99PacPar-220
❑ 99PacParC-220
❑ 99PacParCB-10
❑ 99PacParCBPP-10
❑ 99PacParFC-18
❑ 99PacParG-220
❑ 99PacParHoloGold-220
❑ 99PacParHS-220
❑ 99PacParOD-220
❑ 99PacParPB-33
❑ 99PacParPB-220
❑ 99PacParRed-220
❑ 99PacPlaB-40
❑ 99PacPlaB-40A
❑ 99PacPri-135
❑ 99PacPriAotG-19
❑ 99PacPriBL-5
❑ 99PacPriDG-19
❑ 99PacPriEP-6
❑ 99PacPriHB-135
❑ 99PacPriHG-135
❑ 99PacPriHM-135
❑ 99PacPriHP-135
❑ 99PacPriRed-135
❑ 99PacPriS-16
❑ 99PacPriS206-16
❑ 99PacPriS206R-16
❑ 99PacPriSE-16
❑ 99PacPriSP-16
❑ 99PacPriSP-16
❑ 99PacPriSV-16
❑ 99PacRed-40
❑ 99PacRed-40A
❑ 99PacTim-8
❑ 99Pin-22
❑ 99Rev-133
❑ 99RevDiaL-32
❑ 99RevFouP-19
❑ 99RevMLBIcon-10
❑ 99RevPremDate-133
❑ 99RevRet-133
❑ 99RevShaSS-133
❑ 99RevThoitS-18
❑ 99RevTri-10
❑ 99RevTri-10
❑ 99SkyMolM-138
❑ 99SkyMolMF-38
❑ 99SkyMolMFS-38
❑ 99SkyMolMFT-38
❑ 99SkyMolMX-138
❑ 99SkyPre-1
❑ 99SkyPre-288
❑ 99SkyPreA-45
❑ 99SkyPreABlue-45
❑ 99SkyPreIN-15
❑ 99SkyPreLB-7
❑ 99SkyPreR-1
❑ 99SkyPreR-288
❑ 99SkyPreSB-8
❑ 99SkyPreSotG-1
❑ 99SkyThu-276
❑ 99SkyThuDial1-D8
❑ 99SkyThuHip-H11
❑ 99SkyThuRant-276
❑ 99SkyThuRave-276
❑ 99SkyThuTur-TC8
❑ 99SkyThuwww-WB7
❑ 99SP Aut-77
❑ 99SP Aut-130
❑ 99SP AutEF-E27
❑ 99SP AutHRC-HR15
❑ 99SP AutHRC-HR40
❑ 99SP AutR-R27
❑ 99SP SigAuto-AR
❑ 99SP SigAutoG-AR
❑ 99SPAutHRCDC-HR15
❑ 99SPAutHRCDC-HR40
❑ 99SpoIII-36
❑ 99SpoIII-149
❑ 99SpoIIIDD-10
❑ 99SpoIIIF4-12
❑ 99SpoIIIF4E-12
❑ 99SpoIIIH-13
❑ 99SPSig-4
❑ 99SPx-69
❑ 99SPxDom-FB17
❑ 99SPxFinR-69
❑ 99SPxFinS-69
❑ 99SPxPowE-PE26
❑ 99SPxPreS-PS22
❑ 99SPxStaF-SF25
❑ 99StaClu-1
❑ 99StaCluA-SCA1
❑ 99StaCluC-SCC21
❑ 99StaCluC-CS3
❑ 99StaCluC-CS9
❑ 99StaCluC-CS15
❑ 99StaCluC-CS20
❑ 99StaCluCR-SCC21
❑ 99StaCluFDI-1
❑ 99StaCluNC-NC6
❑ 99StaCluOoaK-1
❑ 99StaCluPP-1
❑ 99StaCluTI-T3C
❑ 99StaCluTI-T9A
❑ 99StaCluTL-T3C
❑ 99StaCluTL-T9A
❑ 99StaCluTL-T3C
❑ 99StaCluTL-T9A
❑ 99StaCluVR-VR5
❑ 99ThuSkySupR-276
❑ 99Top-228
❑ 99Top-300
❑ 99Top-452
❑ 99TopActF-10
❑ 99TopActFAU-10
❑ 99TopActFCU-10
❑ 99TopAll-AM12
❑ 99TopAllMF-M7
❑ 99TopAut-A4
❑ 99TopBlaLC1-25
❑ 99TopBlaLC2-25
❑ 99TopBlaLC3-25
❑ 99TopChr-228
❑ 99TopChr-300
❑ 99TopChr-452
❑ 99TopChrA-AE12
❑ 99TopChrAR-AE12
❑ 99TopChrERttH-ER3
❑ 99TopChrERttH-ER3
❑ 99TopChrF1-FF1
❑ 99TopChrF1R-FF1
❑ 99TopChrLotD-LD7
❑ 99TopChrLotDR-LD7
❑ 99TopChrNB-NB10
❑ 99TopChrNBR-NB10
❑ 99TopChrR-228
❑ 99TopChrR-300
❑ 99TopChrR-452
❑ 99TopGal-57
❑ 99TopGal-106
❑ 99TopGalE-E13
❑ 99TopGalGoH-GH10
❑ 99TopGalHer-TH7
❑ 99TopGalHerP-TH7
❑ 99TopGalPP-57
❑ 99TopGalPP-106
❑ 99TopGalPPI-57
❑ 99TopGalPPI-106
❑ 99TopGolL-25
❑ 99TopGolLC1-25
❑ 99TopGolLC2-25
❑ 99TopGolLOtO-25
❑ 99TopGolLRtA-RA3
❑ 99TopGolLRtA-RA8
❑ 99TopGolLRtAB-RA3
❑ 99TopGolLRtAB-RA8
❑ 99TopGolLRtAOtO-RA3
❑ 99TopGolLRtAOtO-RA8
❑ 99TopGolLRtAR-RA3
❑ 99TopGolLRtAR-RA8
❑ 99TopLorotD-LD7
❑ 99TopMVPP-300
❑ 99TopMVPP-452
❑ 99TopNewB-NB10
❑ 99TopOpeD-135
❑ 99TopOver-B3
❑ 99TopPowB-PB6
❑ 99TopPowBR-PB6
❑ 99TopRedLC1-25
❑ 99TopRedLC2-25
❑ 99TopRedLC3-25
❑ 99TopSta-10
❑ 99TopSta-173
❑ 99TopSta'S-4
❑ 99TopSta'SG-4
❑ 99TopSta'SGDH-4
❑ 99TopSta1Foil-10
❑ 99TopSta2Foil-10
❑ 99TopSta3Foil-10
❑ 99TopSta4Foil-10
❑ 99TopStaFoil-10
❑ 99TopStaFoil-173
❑ 99TopStaFS-10
❑ 99TopStaG-G4
❑ 99TopStaGFoil-G4
❑ 99TopStaOS-10
❑ 99TopStaTS-10
❑ 99TopStaTS-10
❑ 99TopSupC-26
❑ 99TopSupCR-26
❑ 99TopTek-42A
❑ 99TopTek-42B
❑ 99TopTekG-42A
❑ 99TopTekG-42B
❑ 99TopTekT-T7
❑ 99UD Cho-143
❑ 99UD ChoBU-8
❑ 99UD ChoMBH-B26
❑ 99UD ChoP-143
❑ 99UD ChoPCR-143
❑ 99UD ChoS-3
❑ 99UD ChoSD-3
❑ 99UD ChoSHR-3
❑ 99UD ChoST-3
❑ 99UD ChoYW-Y26
❑ 99UD Ion-53
❑ 99UD Ion-87
❑ 99UD IonC-C6
❑ 99UD IonH-HG6
❑ 99UD IonH-H6
❑ 99UD IonN-N6
❑ 99UD IonR-53
❑ 99UD IonR-87
❑ 99UD IonWZ-WZ6
❑ 99UDHolo-54
❑ 99UDHoloAUsome-54
❑ 99UDHoloLau-L8
❑ 99UDHoloLauG-L8
❑ 99UDHoloStar-S8
❑ 99UDHoloStarG-S8
❑ 99Ult-173
❑ 99Ult-212
❑ 99Ult-216
❑ 99UltDamI-1
❑ 99UltDiaP-3
❑ 99UltGolM-173
❑ 99UltGolM-212
❑ 99UltGolM-216
❑ 99UltMas-173
❑ 99UltMas-212
❑ 99UltMas-216
❑ 99UltPlaM-173
❑ 99UltPlaM-212
❑ 99UltPlaM-216
❑ 99UltPromo-NNO
❑ 99UltRBIK-20
❑ 99UltTheBook-20
❑ 99UltThu-1
❑ 99UppDec-487
❑ 99UppDec-524
❑ 99UppDec-534
❑ 99UppDec10AT-X16
❑ 99UppDec10ATD-X16
❑ 99UppDec10ATHR-X16
❑ 99UppDec10ATT-X16
❑ 99UppDecBD-77
❑ 99UppDecBDD-77
❑ 99UppDecBDDom-D3
❑ 99UppDecBDDomE-D3
❑ 99UppDecBDMN-M5
❑ 99UppDecBDMNE-M5
❑ 99UppDecBDQ-77
❑ 99UppDecBDT-77
❑ 99UppDecCf7-4
❑ 99UppDecCf7-82
❑ 99UppDecCf7-C4
❑ 99UppDecCf7Cf7P-C4
❑ 99UppDecCf7LL-L8
❑ 99UppDecCf7SftF-S4
❑ 99UppDecCL-61
❑ 99UppDecCL-109
❑ 99UppDecCLCC-61
❑ 99UppDecCLCC-109
❑ 99UppDecCLES-AR
❑ 99UppDecCLESC-AR
❑ 99UppDecCLM-C87

❑ 99UppDecCo7CE-4
❑ 99UppDecCo7CE-82
❑ 99UppDecCo7SftFA-AR
❑ 99UppDecE-82
❑ 99UppDecE-141
❑ 99UppDecE-180
❑ 99UppDecE2C-2K7
❑ 99UppDecEDF-D5
❑ 99UppDecEDFFXG-D5
❑ 99UppDecEFXG-82
❑ 99UppDecEFXG-141
❑ 99UppDecEFXG-180
❑ 99UppDecEL1-487
❑ 99UppDecEL1-524
❑ 99UppDecEL1-534
❑ 99UppDecEL2-487
❑ 99UppDecEL2-524
❑ 99UppDecEL2-534
❑ 99UppDecEPE-P27
❑ 99UppDecEUR-U5
❑ 99UppDecF-F25
❑ 99UppDecFD-F25
❑ 99UppDecFQ-F25
❑ 99UppDecFT-F25
❑ 99UppDecGJ-AR
❑ 99UppDecIP-I21
❑ 99UppDecIPD-I21
❑ 99UppDecIPHR-I21
❑ 99UppDecIPT-I21
❑ 99UppDecM-191
❑ 99UppDecM-P4
❑ 99UppDecMD-D2
❑ 99UppDecMGS-191
❑ 99UppDecMHFS-191
❑ 99UppDecMP-191
❑ 99UppDecMSS-191
❑ 99UppDecMST-T2
❑ 99UppDecMST-S5
❑ 99UppDecO-28
❑ 99UppDecO-90
❑ 99UppDecOAPoH-AR
❑ 99UppDecOMP-S11
❑ 99UppDecOSO-28
❑ 99UppDecOSO-90
❑ 99UppDecOWP-R4
❑ 99UppDecR-77
❑ 99UppDecRDR-D7
❑ 99UppDecRDRL2-D7
❑ 99UppDecRG-77
❑ 99UppDecRL-6
❑ 99UppDecROSS-S2
❑ 99UppDecROSS-S2
❑ 99UppDecRP-77
❑ 99UppDecRTA-T6
❑ 99UppDecRTAL2-T6
❑ 99UppDecTE-T26
❑ 99UppDecTED-T26
❑ 99UppDecTEQ-T26
❑ 99UppDecTET-T26
❑ 99UppDecVtaT-V27
❑ 99UppDecVtaTD-V27
❑ 99UppDecVtaTQ-V27
❑ 99UppDecVtaTT-V27
❑ 99UppDecWY-W24
❑ 99UppDecWYD-W24
❑ 99UppDecWYHR-W24
❑ 99UppDecWYT-W24
❑ 99Vic-367
❑ 99Vic-369
❑ 99Vic-371
❑ 99Vic-373
❑ 99Vic-466

Rodriguez, Alexander
❑ 75BurBeeT-21

Rodriguez, Amando
❑ 91IdaFalBSP-4

Rodriguez, Andres
❑ 90PriWilCTI-22
❑ 91Ft.LauYC-23
❑ 91Ft.LauYP-2436
❑ 92ForLauYC-5
❑ 92ForLauYTI-27
❑ 92Ft.LauYF-2621

Rodriguez, Andy
❑ 75SanAntBT-17
❑ 78QuaCitAT-22

Rodriguez, Angel
❑ 85BelBreT-10
❑ 87StoPorP-10
❑ 88BlaYNPRWL-16
❑ 88ElPasDB-23
❑ 88StoPorCLC-198
❑ 88StoPorP-742

Rodriguez, Anthony
❑ 91KisDodP-4189
❑ 92GulCoaDF-3569

Rodriguez, Armando
❑ 90PulBraB-24
❑ 90PulBraP-3109
❑ 91IdaFalBP-4340

Rodriguez, Aurelio
❑ 69AngJacitB-11
❑ 69SenTeal-13
❑ 69Top-653
❑ 70MLBOffS-179
❑ 70OPC-228
❑ 70SenPolY-8
❑ 70Top-228
❑ 71MLBOffS-405
❑ 71OPC-464
❑ 71Top-464
❑ 72MilBra-293
❑ 72OPC-319
❑ 72Top-319
❑ 72TopCloT-27
❑ 73LinPor-77
❑ 73OPC-218
❑ 73TigJew-16
❑ 73Top-218
❑ 74OPC-72
❑ 74Top-72
❑ 74TopSta-179
❑ 75DetTigP-28
❑ 75OPC-221
❑ 75Top-221
❑ 75TopMin-221
❑ 76DetTigP-24
❑ 76OPC-267
❑ 76SSP-366
❑ 76Top-267
❑ 77BurCheD-93
❑ 77Hos-120
❑ 77OPC-136
❑ 77Top-574
❑ 78OPC-64
❑ 78TigBurK-14
❑ 78TigTeal-22
❑ 78Top-342
❑ 79OPC-83
❑ 79Top-176
❑ 80OPC-245
❑ 80Top-468
❑ 81Fle-105
❑ 81TigDetN-47
❑ 81Top-34
❑ 81YanPhoA-24
❑ 82Fle-53
❑ 82OPCPos-10
❑ 82Top-334
❑ 82TopTra-101T
❑ 83Don-369
❑ 83Fle-249
❑ 83Top-758
❑ 83TopTra-97T
❑ 84Nes792-269
❑ 84Top-269
❑ 84TopTif-269
❑ 88ColSprSSC-25
❑ 88ColSprSSP-1536
❑ 90CMC-402
❑ 90ProAAAF-396
❑ 90TolMudHC-25
❑ 90TolMudHP-166
❑ 91OriCro-390
❑ 92UppDecS-30
❑ 92YanWIZ8-163
❑ 96BurlndB-23
❑ 97WatIndTI-24

Rodriguez, Beto
❑ 90JohCitCS-21
❑ 91SprCarC-23
❑ 91SprCarP-751

Rodriguez, Bobby
❑ 97DelSho-17
❑ 98DelShoM-4

Rodriguez, Buena
❑ 89JamExpP-2131
❑ 90RocExpLC-24
❑ 90RocExpP-2705

Rodriguez, Carlos Marquez
❑ 76VenLeaS-50
❑ 88Ft.LauYS-18
❑ 89Ft.LauYS-21
❑ 90AlbYanP-1178
❑ 90AlbYanSt-14
❑ 90ColCliP-683
❑ 90ProAAAF-333
❑ 90TopTVY-58
❑ 91ColCliLD-116
❑ 91ColCliP-16
❑ 91ColCliP-604
❑ 91DonRoo-41
❑ 91LinDriAAA-116
❑ 92AlbYanF-2233
❑ 92AlbYanSk-18
❑ 92Sco-411
❑ 92TopDeb91-149
❑ 92UppDec-77
❑ 93ColCliF-1117
❑ 93ColCliP-15
❑ 94PawRedSDD-18
❑ 94PawRedSF-953
❑ 94SpoRoo-61
❑ 94SpoRooAP-61
❑ 95ColCho-407
❑ 95ColChoGS-407
❑ 95ColChoSS-407
❑ 95Don-144
❑ 95DonPreP-144
❑ 95Fle-37
❑ 95Pac-44
❑ 95PacLatD-32
❑ 95PacPri-15
❑ 95Sco-453
❑ 95ScoGolR-453
❑ 95ScoPlaTS-453
❑ 95Top-562
❑ 95TopCyb-338

Rodriguez, Cecil
❑ 93ExcFS7-194

Rodriguez, Chad
❑ 97LanLugTS-23

Rodriguez, Chris
❑ 91HunCubC-20
❑ 91HunCubP-3333
❑ 92GenCubC-8
❑ 92GenCubF-1559
❑ 93PeoChiC-17
❑ 93PeoChiF-1083
❑ 94DayCubC-21
❑ 94DayCubF-2351
❑ 96WatIndTI-26
❑ 97AshTou-22
❑ 97PorRocG-22

Rodriguez, Dave
❑ 83TacTigT-30B
❑ 92BriTigC-14
❑ 92BriTigF-1409
❑ 93NiaFalRF-3387

Rodriguez, Eddie
❑ 83PeoSunF-28
❑ 86QuaCitAP-28
❑ 87QuaCitAP-18
❑ 87SalAngP-1
❑ 88QuaCitAGS-1
❑ 89QuaCitAB-2
❑ 89QuaCitAGS-1
❑ 90MidAngGS-1
❑ 92GreFalDSP-15

Rodriguez, Eddy Alberto
❑ 89BriTigS-23
❑ 90NiaFalRP-23
❑ 91FayGenC-8
❑ 91FayGenP-1168
❑ 92LakTigC-25
❑ 92LakTigF-2278

Rodriguez, Edgal Antonio
❑ 87QuaCitAP-3
❑ 88BlaYNPRWL-17
❑ 88QuaCitAGS-7
❑ 89PalSprACLC-41
❑ 89PalSprAP-465
❑ 90QuaCitAGS-28
❑ 91PalSprAP-2032

Rodriguez, Eduardo
❑ 71MLBOffS-449
❑ 74OPC-171
❑ 74Top-171
❑ 75OPC-582
❑ 75Top-582
❑ 75TopMin-582
❑ 76OPC-92
❑ 76SSP-228
❑ 76Top-92
❑ 77BurCheD-86
❑ 77Top-361
❑ 78Top-623
❑ 79Top-108
❑ 80Top-273
❑ 81HolMilT-1
❑ 94BreMilB-264

Rodriguez, Edwin
❑ 83ColCliT-18
❑ 84LasVegSC-240
❑ 85LasVegSC-108
❑ 86LasVegSP-14
❑ 87LasVegSP-19
❑ 92YanWIZ8-164

Rodriguez, Eligio
❑ 88GenCubP-1646

Rodriguez, Ellie (Eliseo)
❑ 69OPC-49
❑ 69RoySol-14
❑ 69Top-49A
❑ 69Top-49B
❑ 69TopTeaP-7
❑ 70OPC-402
❑ 70RoyTeal-28
❑ 70Top-402
❑ 71BreTeal-13
❑ 71OPC-344
❑ 71Top-344
❑ 71TopCoi-124
❑ 72MilBra-294
❑ 72OPC-421
❑ 72Top-421
❑ 73Kel2D-2
❑ 73OPC-45
❑ 73SevTraC-62
❑ 73Top-45
❑ 73TopCanL-43
❑ 74OPC-405
❑ 74Top-405
❑ 74TopSta-146
❑ 75CalAngP-35
❑ 75Hos-34
❑ 75HosTwi-34
❑ 75OPC-285
❑ 75Top-285
❑ 75TopMin-285
❑ 76OPC-512
❑ 76SSP-193
❑ 76Top-512
❑ 77Top-148
❑ 81TCM60I-421
❑ 89BlaYNPRWL-166
❑ 90DodTar-679
❑ 92YanWIZ6-107
❑ 93UppDecS-4
❑ 94BreMilB-265

Rodriguez, Ernesto
❑ 91Cla/Bes-40
❑ 91MyrBeaHC-22
❑ 91MyrBeaHP-2956
❑ 91SouAtlLAGP-SAL39
❑ 92DunBluJC-19
❑ 92DunBluJF-2008

Rodriguez, Ernie
❑ 85BenPhiC-20
❑ 88ButCopKSP-28
❑ 89ButCopKSP-28
❑ 93PocPosF-4222
❑ 93PocPosSP-24

Rodriguez, F. Boi
❑ 87JamExpP-2544
❑ 88WesPalBES-22
❑ 89JacExpB-16
❑ 89JacExpP-177
❑ 90JacExpB-24
❑ 91GreBraC-24
❑ 91GreBraLD-216
❑ 91LinDriAA-216
❑ 91RicBraBC-35
❑ 92RicBraBB-25
❑ 92RicBraF-385
❑ 92RicBraRC-17
❑ 92RicBraS-439
❑ 92SkyAAAF-203
❑ 93RicBraBB-24
❑ 93RicBraF-194
❑ 93RicBraP-20
❑ 93RicBraRC-4
❑ 93RicBraRC-25
❑ 97RicBraBC-11

Rodriguez, Felix Antonio
❑ 76VenLeaS-178
❑ 77ShrCapT-19
❑ 80VenLeaS-144
❑ 91KisDodP-4190
❑ 92GreFalDSP-6
❑ 93VerBeaDC-21
❑ 93VerBeaDF-2217
❑ 94SanAntMF-2468
❑ 95Bow-81
❑ 95BowBes-B27
❑ 95BowBesR-B27
❑ 95TopTra-63T
❑ 96Bow-286
❑ 96BowFoi-286
❑ 96ColCho-587
❑ 96ColChoGS-587
❑ 96ColChoSS-587
❑ 96Fle-446
❑ 96FleTif-446
❑ 97Indlnd-19
❑ 98Bow-416
❑ 98BowChr-416
❑ 98BowChrGA-416
❑ 98BowChrGAR-416
❑ 98BowChrI-416
❑ 98BowChrIR-416
❑ 98BowChrR-416
❑ 98BowGolA-416
❑ 98BowInt-416
❑ 98ColCho-296
❑ 98DiaBacP-9
❑ 98DiaMcD-17
❑ 98DonSigA-74
❑ 98DonSigAC-96
❑ 98DonSigAM-98
❑ 98Fle-421
❑ 98LeaRS-300
❑ 98LeaRSLHolo-300
❑ 98LeaRSLong-300
❑ 98LeaRTrue-300
❑ 98Pac-271
❑ 98PacOnl-44
❑ 98PacOnlR-44
❑ 98PacOnlWC-44
❑ 98PacPlaB-271
❑ 98PacRedT-271
❑ 98PacSil-271
❑ 98Ult-454
❑ 98UltGolM-454
❑ 98UltMas-454
❑ 98UltPlaM-454
❑ 98UppDec-644
❑ 99PacCroC-18
❑ 99PacCroCPB-18

Rodriguez, Fernando
❑ 88BlaYNPRWL-18
❑ 89BlaYNPRWLU-37

Rodriguez, Frank (Francisco)
❑ 66St.PetCTI-13
❑ 91Cla/Bes-397
❑ 91ClaDraP-NNO
❑ 91ClaGolB-BC17
❑ 91ElmPioC-14
❑ 91ElmPioP-3279
❑ 91FroRowDP-1
❑ 91FroRowDPG-1
❑ 91FroRowDPS-1
❑ 91FroRowFR-1
❑ 91FroRowFR-2
❑ 91FroRowFR-3
❑ 91FroRowFR-4
❑ 91UppDecFE-21F
❑ 92Bow-45
❑ 92ClaBluBF-BC20
❑ 92ClaFS7-391
❑ 92ClaPro-8
❑ 92ClaRedB-BC20
❑ 92LynRedSC-1
❑ 92LynRedSF-2905
❑ 92ProFS7-23
❑ 92UppDecML-43
❑ 92UppDecML-54
❑ 92UppDecML-266
❑ 92UppDecMLTPHF-TP6
❑ 93Bow-143
❑ 93Bow-362
❑ 93ClaGolF-22
❑ 93ClaYouG-YG20
❑ 93ExcFS7-137
❑ 93HelBreSP-2
❑ 93NewBriRSF-1218
❑ 93UppDec-442
❑ 93UppDecGold-442
❑ 94ActPac-22
❑ 94ActPac-AU1
❑ 94Bow-368
❑ 94Bow-615
❑ 94BowBes-B30
❑ 94BowBesR-B30
❑ 94Cla-94
❑ 94ClaCreotC-C23
❑ 94ClaGolA-SH5
❑ 94ClaGolF-112
❑ 94PawRedSDD-19
❑ 94PawRedSF-947
❑ 94StoPorC-21
❑ 94StoPorF-1693
❑ 94Top-112
❑ 94TopGol-112
❑ 94TopSpa-112
❑ 94UppDecML-115
❑ 94UppDecML-262
❑ 94UppDecMLPotYF-PY21
❑ 95ActPac2G-16G
❑ 95ActPacF-26
❑ 95ActPacF-77
❑ 95Bow-126
❑ 95ElPasDTI-21
❑ 95Exc-14
❑ 95Fla-230
❑ 95FleAllR-M9
❑ 95PawRedSDD-23
❑ 95PawRedTI-30
❑ 95Sel-166
❑ 95SelArtP-166
❑ 95SelCer-123
❑ 95SelCerMG-123
❑ 95SelCerPU-13
❑ 95SelCerPU9-13
❑ 95StaClu-580
❑ 95StaCluMOP-580
❑ 95StaCluSTWS-580
❑ 95Sum-131
❑ 95SumNewA-NA13
❑ 95SumNthD-131
❑ 95Top-244
❑ 95UC3-109
❑ 95UC3ArtP-109
❑ 95UppDec-236
❑ 95UppDec-492
❑ 95UppDecED-236
❑ 95UppDecEDG-236
❑ 95UppDecML-24
❑ 95UppDecMLFS-24
❑ 96ColCho-25
❑ 96ColChoGS-25
❑ 96ColChoSS-25
❑ 96Don-23
❑ 96DonPreP-23
❑ 96Fin-S153
❑ 96FinRef-S153
❑ 96Fla-122
❑ 96Fle-176
❑ 96FleTif-176
❑ 96LeaSigA-196
❑ 96LeaSigAG-196
❑ 96LeaSigAS-196
❑ 96PinAfi-138
❑ 96PinAfiAP-138
❑ 96Sco-155
❑ 96ScoDugC-A90
❑ 96ScoDugCAP-A90
❑ 96Sel-130
❑ 96SelArtP-130
❑ 96StaClu-379
❑ 96StaCluMOP-379
❑ 96Sum-117
❑ 96SumAbo&B-117
❑ 96SumArtP-117
❑ 96SumFoi-117
❑ 96Top-254
❑ 96Ult-380
❑ 96UltGolM-380
❑ 96UppDec-368
❑ 97Cir-122
❑ 97CirRav-122
❑ 97ColCho-158
❑ 97Don-247
❑ 97DonGolPP-247
❑ 97DonSilPP-247
❑ 97El PasDB-19
❑ 97Fin-33
❑ 97FinRef-33
❑ 97Fle-156
❑ 97FleTif-156
❑ 97Lea-61
❑ 97LeaFraM-61
❑ 97LeaFraMDC-61
❑ 97MetUni-213
❑ 97Pin-89
❑ 97PinArtP-PP89
❑ 97PinMusC-89
❑ 97PinPrePla-89
❑ 97Sco-108
❑ 97ScoArtPWB-108
❑ 97ScoPreS-108
❑ 97ScoShoS-108
❑ 97ScoShoSAP-108
❑ 97SP-107
❑ 97StaClu-179
❑ 97StaCluMOP-179
❑ 97Top-77
❑ 97Ult-94
❑ 97UltGolME-94

❑ 97UltPlaME-94
❑ 97UppDec-107
❑ 98PacOnl-435
❑ 98PacOnlR-435
❑ 98PacOnlWC-435
❑ 98SalLakBO-24
❑ 98StaCluFDI-220
❑ 98StaClul-220
❑ 98StaCluOneK-220
❑ 98StaCluPP-220
❑ 99PacCroC-165
❑ 99PacCroCPB-165
Rodriguez, Frankie
❑ 93HelBreF-4092
❑ 94ExcFS7-21
❑ 98LouRedQ-26
❑ 98PacInvGems-67
Rodriguez, Fred
❑ 590'KAleMR-18
Rodriguez, Gabriel
❑ 87GenCubP-15
❑ 88BlaYNPRWL-114
❑ 88Ft.LauYS-19
❑ 88PeoChiTI-28
❑ 89BlaYNPRWL-123
❑ 89Ft.LauYS-22
❑ 89Sta-80
❑ 89WinSpiS-NNO
❑ 90GenCubS-21
❑ 90OscAstS-25
Rodriguez, Gary
❑ 96WatIndTI-27
❑ 98KinIndQ-21
Rodriguez, Guillermo
❑ 96BelGiaTI-2
❑ 97SalVolG-34
Rodriguez, Hector
❑ 91AugPirC-18
❑ 91AugPirP-814
❑ 94NewJerCC-22
❑ 94NewJerCF-3427
❑ 96BoiHawB-25
❑ 97BoiHawG-23
❑ 98CedRapKTI-25
Rodriguez, Hector (Antonio H.)
❑ 52WhiSoxHDP-8
❑ 53BowC-98
Rodriguez, Henry
❑ 89VerBeaDS-23
❑ 90SanAntMGS-24
❑ 90TexLeaAGS-8
❑ 91AlbDukLD-19
❑ 91AlbDukP-1156
❑ 91Bow-185
❑ 91Cla2-T51
❑ 91DodPho-24
❑ 91LeaGolR-BC8
❑ 91LeaGolRNV-272
❑ 91LinDriAAA-19
❑ 91Ult-386
❑ 91UppDec-21
❑ 92AlbDukF-735
❑ 92AlbDukS-19
❑ 92Bow-108
❑ 92DonRoo-105
❑ 92Fle-661
❑ 92OPC-656
❑ 92ProFS7-241
❑ 92SkyAAAF-10
❑ 92SpollIFK1-505
❑ 92StaClu-268
❑ 92Top-656
❑ 92TopGol-656
❑ 92TopGolW-656
❑ 92TopMic-656
❑ 92TriA AAS-19
❑ 93AlbDukF-1477
❑ 93DodPol-22
❑ 93Don-218
❑ 93Fle-453
❑ 93LimRocDWB-84
❑ 93Pin-182
❑ 93Sco-244
❑ 93Sel-404
❑ 93StaClu-226
❑ 93StaCluFDI-226
❑ 93StaCluMOP-226
❑ 93Top-284
❑ 93TopGol-284
❑ 93TopInaM-284
❑ 93TopInaR-284
❑ 93TopMic-284
❑ 93Toy-38
❑ 93UppDec-391
❑ 93UppDecGold-391
❑ 94ColC-596
❑ 94ColChoGS-596
❑ 94ColChoSS-596
❑ 94DodDaiN-3
❑ 94DodMot-8
❑ 94DodPol-23
❑ 94Don-264
❑ 94Fla-399
❑ 94Fle-522
❑ 94FleExtB-295
❑ 94Lea-385
❑ 94LeaL-121
❑ 94Pac-320
❑ 94Sel-320
❑ 94StaClu-176
❑ 94StaCluFDI-176
❑ 94StaCluGR-176
❑ 94StaCluMOP-176
❑ 94Top-727
❑ 94TopGol-727
❑ 94TopSpa-727
❑ 94Ult-521
❑ 94UppDec-436
❑ 94UppDecED-436
❑ 95ColCho-224
❑ 95ColCho-551T
❑ 95ColChoGS-224
❑ 95ColChoSS-224
❑ 95DodPol-23
❑ 95Don-280
❑ 95DonPreP-280
❑ 95Fle-548
❑ 95Lea-36
❑ 95LinVen-314
❑ 95Pac-225
❑ 95PacPri-73
❑ 95Sco-52
❑ 95ScoGolR-52
❑ 95ScoPlaTS-52
❑ 95StaClu-491
❑ 95StaCluMOP-491
❑ 95StaCluSTWS-491
❑ 95StaCluVR-270
❑ 95StaCluVRMO-270
❑ 95Top-400
❑ 95TopCyb-201
❑ 95Ult-184
❑ 95UltGolM-184
❑ 96Bow-82
❑ 96BowBes-18
❑ 96BowBesAR-18
❑ 96BowBesR-18
❑ 96BowFoi-82
❑ 96Cir-151
❑ 96CirAcc-23
❑ 96CirBos-41
❑ 96CirRav-151
❑ 96ColCho-616
❑ 96ColChoGS-616
❑ 96ColChoSS-616
❑ 96ExpDis-15
❑ 96Fin-B325
❑ 96FinRef-B325
❑ 96FleUpd-U151
❑ 96FleUpdTC-U151
❑ 96LeaLim-85
❑ 96LeaLimG-85
❑ 96LeaPre-97
❑ 96LeaPreP-97
❑ 96LeaSig-35
❑ 96LeaSigPPG-35
❑ 96LeaSigPPP-35
❑ 96Pac-127
❑ 96Ult-508
❑ 96UltGolM-508
❑ 96Zen-50
❑ 96ZenArtP-50
❑ 96ZenMoz-17
❑ 97Bow-47
❑ 97BowInt-47
❑ 97Cir-293
❑ 97CirRav-293
❑ 97ColCho-160
❑ 97Don-10
❑ 97DonDiaK-6
❑ 97DonDiaKC-6
❑ 97DonEli-100
❑ 97DonEliGS-100
❑ 97DonGolPP-10
❑ 97DonLim-150
❑ 97DonLim-164
❑ 97DonLimE-150
❑ 97DonLimE-164
❑ 97DonLimENG-150
❑ 97DonPre-40
❑ 97DonPreCttC-40
❑ 97DonRocL-13
❑ 97DonSigA-85
❑ 97DonSigAC-106
❑ 97DonSigAM-106
❑ 97DonSilPP-10
❑ 97E-X2-84
❑ 97E-X2Cred-84
❑ 97E-X2EssCre-84
❑ 97Fin-232
❑ 97FinRef-232
❑ 97FlaShoLC-101
❑ 97FlaShoLeg0-101
❑ 97FlaShoLeg1-101
❑ 97FlaShoM-A101
❑ 97FlaShoM-B101
❑ 97FlaShoM-C101
❑ 97FlaShoR0-101
❑ 97FlaShoR1-101
❑ 97FlaShoR2-101
❑ 97Fle-384
❑ 97Fle-737
❑ 97FleTeaL-22
❑ 97FleTif-384
❑ 97FleTif-737
❑ 97Lea-71
❑ 97LeaFraM-71
❑ 97LeaFraMDC-71
❑ 97MetUni-159
❑ 97NewPin-110
❑ 97NewPinAP-110
❑ 97NewPinMC-110
❑ 97NewPinPP-110
❑ 97Pac-350
❑ 97PacFirD-18
❑ 97PacLatotML-32
❑ 97PacLigB-350
❑ 97PacPri-120
❑ 97PacPriGotD-GD170
❑ 97PacPriLB-120
❑ 97PacPriP-120
❑ 97PacSil-350
❑ 97PinCer-91
❑ 97PinCerMBla-91
❑ 97PinCerMBlu-91
❑ 97PinCerMG-91
❑ 97PinCerMR-91
❑ 97PinCerR-91
❑ 97PinIns-38
❑ 97PinInsCE-38
❑ 97PinInsDE-38
❑ 97PinMin-26
❑ 97PinMinB-26
❑ 97PinMinCB-26
❑ 97PinMinCG-26
❑ 97PinMinCGR-26
❑ 97PinMinCN-26
❑ 97PinMinCSS-26
❑ 97PinMinG-26
❑ 97PinMinS-26
❑ 97PinPasttM-18
❑ 97PinTotCPB-91
❑ 97PinTotCPG-91
❑ 97PinTotCPR-91
❑ 97PinX-P-76
❑ 97PinX-PMoS-76
❑ 97PinX-PSfF-49
❑ 97PinX-PSfFU-49
❑ 97Sco-228
❑ 97Sco-517
❑ 97ScoArtPWB-228
❑ 97ScoArtPWB-517
❑ 97ScoPreS-228
❑ 97ScoResC-517
❑ 97ScoShoS-228
❑ 97ScoShoS-517
❑ 97ScoShoSAP-228
❑ 97ScoShoSAP-517
❑ 97ScoSteS-15
❑ 97Sel-40
❑ 97SelArtP-40
❑ 97SelCom-40
❑ 97SelRegG-40
❑ 97SP-114
❑ 97Spolll-85
❑ 97SpolllEE-85
❑ 97StaClu-28
❑ 97StaCluMat-28
❑ 97StaCluMOP-28
❑ 97Stu-27
❑ 97StuPrePG-27
❑ 97StuPrePS-27
❑ 97Top-210
❑ 97TopChr-78
❑ 97TopChrR-78
❑ 97TopGal-131
❑ 97TopGalPPI-131
❑ 97TopIntF-ILM11
❑ 97Ult-233
❑ 97UltDouT-16
❑ 97UltGolME-233
❑ 97UltPlaME-233
❑ 97UppDec-109
❑ 98Bow-275
❑ 98BowChr-275
❑ 98BowChrGA-275
❑ 98BowChrGAR-275
❑ 98BowChrl-275
❑ 98BowChrlR-275
❑ 98BowChrR-275
❑ 98BowGolA-275
❑ 98BowInt-275
❑ 98CirThu-34
❑ 98CirThuRav-34
❑ 98CirThuSupRav-34
❑ 98ColCho-335
❑ 98Don-228
❑ 98DonColP-629
❑ 98DonGolPP-228
❑ 98DonPre-79
❑ 98DonPreSeat-79
❑ 98DonPriCP-629
❑ 98DonSigA-75
❑ 98DonSigAC-97
❑ 98DonSigAM-99
❑ 98DonSilPP-228
❑ 98E-X2-52
❑ 98E-X2ECFut-52
❑ 98E-X2ECNow-52
❑ 98FlaShoLeg0-117
❑ 98FlaShoLeg1-117
❑ 98FlaShoLeg2-117
❑ 98FlaShoLeg3-117
❑ 98FlaShoLegM-117
❑ 98FlaShoR0-117
❑ 98FlaShoR1-117
❑ 98FlaShoR2-117
❑ 98FlaShoR3-117
❑ 98Fle-377
❑ 98FleVin'-83
❑ 98FleVin'C-83
❑ 98LeaRS-81
❑ 98LeaRSLHolo-81
❑ 98LeaRSLong-81
❑ 98LeaRTrue-81
❑ 98MetUni-172
❑ 98MetUniPMG-172
❑ 98Pac-353
❑ 98PacAur-115
❑ 98PacInv-116
❑ 98PacInvPBlue-116
❑ 98PacInvSilv-116
❑ 98PacInvTeam-17
❑ 98PacOme-50
❑ 98PacOmeR-50
❑ 98PacOnl-152
❑ 98PacOnlR-152
❑ 98PacOnlWC-152
❑ 98PacPlaB-353
❑ 98PacRedT-353
❑ 98PacSil-353
❑ 98PacTeaC-22
❑ 98Pin-73
❑ 98PinPer-105
❑ 98PinPerPP-105
❑ 98PinPlu-111
❑ 98PinPreP-73
❑ 98Revo-31
❑ 98RevoSS-31
❑ 98ScoRT-170
❑ 98SkyDugA-8
❑ 98SkyDugAIA-8
❑ 98SP Aut-64
❑ 98Spolll-107
❑ 98SpolllEE-107
❑ 98SpolllFE-107
❑ 98SpolllTaN-126
❑ 98SpolllTaNEE-126
❑ 98SpolllWSF-111
❑ 98SpolllWSFEE-111
❑ 98SpolllWSFFE-111
❑ 98SPxFin-257
❑ 98SPxFin-336
❑ 98SPxFinR-257
❑ 98SPxFinR-336
❑ 98SPxFinS-257
❑ 98SPxFinS-336
❑ 98StaCluFDI-366
❑ 98StaClul-366
❑ 98StaCluOneK-366
❑ 98StaCluPP-366
❑ 98Stu-167
❑ 98StuGPP-167
❑ 98StuSPP-167
❑ 98Top-99
❑ 98TopChr-99
❑ 98TopChrR-99
❑ 98TopDevR-99
❑ 98TopDia-99
❑ 98TopGal-7
❑ 98TopGalGP-7
❑ 98TopGalOPP-7
❑ 98TopGalPPI-7
❑ 98TopGalPPIA-7
❑ 98TopGolLabC1-35
❑ 98TopGolLabC1B-35
❑ 98TopGolLabC1One-35
❑ 98TopGolLabC1R-35
❑ 98TopGolLabC2-35
❑ 98TopGolLabC2B-35
❑ 98TopGolLabC2One-35
❑ 98TopGolLabC2R-35
❑ 98TopGolLabC3-35
❑ 98TopGolLabC3B-35
❑ 98TopGolLabC3One-35
❑ 98TopGolLabC3R-35
❑ 98TopMiniC-99
❑ 98TopOpeD-48
❑ 98TopSta-34
❑ 98TopStaB-34
❑ 98TopStaG-34
❑ 98TopStaGR-34
❑ 98TopStaS-34
❑ 98Ult-185
❑ 98Ult-369
❑ 98UltGolM-185
❑ 98UltGolM-369
❑ 98UltMas-185
❑ 98UltMas-369
❑ 98UltPlaM-185
❑ 98UltPlaM-369
❑ 98UppDec-657
❑ 99199Fin-212
❑ 99CroRoyB-29
❑ 99CroRoyL-29
❑ 99CroRoyOD-29
❑ 99FinGolRef-212
❑ 99FinRef-212
❑ 99FlaShoLeg1-77
❑ 99FlaShoLeg2-77
❑ 99FlaShoLeg3-77
❑ 99FlaShoLegM1-77
❑ 99FlaShoLegM2-77
❑ 99FlaShoLegM3-77
❑ 99FlaShoR1-77
❑ 99FlaShoR2-77
❑ 99FlaShoR3-77
❑ 99Fle-209
❑ 99FleBri-94
❑ 99FleBri2G-94
❑ 99FleBriBlu-94
❑ 99FleBriGol-94
❑ 99FleMys-32
❑ 99FleMysG-32
❑ 99FleMysM-32
❑ 99FleSta9-209
❑ 99FleWarT-209
❑ 99MetUni-112
❑ 99MetUniGM-112
❑ 99MetUniPMG-112
❑ 99Pac-90
❑ 99PacCroC-59
❑ 99PacCroCPB-59
❑ 99PacInv-31
❑ 99PacInvOD-31
❑ 99PacInvPB-31
❑ 99PacOme-51
❑ 99PacOmeC-51
❑ 99PacOmeG-51
❑ 99PacOmePB-51
❑ 99PacPar-51
❑ 99PacParC-51
❑ 99PacParG-51
❑ 99PacParHoloGold-51
❑ 99PacParHS-51
❑ 99PacParOD-51
❑ 99PacParPB-51
❑ 99PacParRed-51
❑ 99PacPlaB-90
❑ 99PacPriS-133
❑ 99PacPriS206-133
❑ 99PacPriS206R-133
❑ 99PacRed-90
❑ 99Rev-30
❑ 99RevPremDate-30
❑ 99RevRet-30
❑ 99RevShaSS-30
❑ 99SkyPre-158
❑ 99SkyPreR-158
❑ 99SkyThu-99
❑ 99SkyThuRant-99
❑ 99SkyThuRave-99
❑ 99SP AutHRC-HR31
❑ 99SPAutHRCDC-HR31
❑ 99StaClu-261
❑ 99StaCluFDI-261
❑ 99StaCluOoaK-261
❑ 99StaCluPP-261
❑ 99ThuSkySupR-99
❑ 99Top-357
❑ 99TopChr-357
❑ 99TopChrR-357
❑ 99TopMVPP-357
❑ 99TopOpeD-122
❑ 99Ult-148
❑ 99UltGolM-148
❑ 99UltMas-148
❑ 99UltPlaM-148
❑ 99UppDec-63
❑ 99UppDecBD-19
❑ 99UppDecBDD-19
❑ 99UppDecBDQ-19
❑ 99UppDecBDT-19
❑ 99UppDecEL1-63
❑ 99UppDecEL2-63
❑ 99UppDecM-41
❑ 99UppDecMGS-41
❑ 99UppDecMHFS-41
❑ 99UppDecMP-41
❑ 99UppDecMSS-41
❑ 99Vic-86
Rodriguez, Iggy
❑ 86WesPalBEP-25
Rodriguez, Inocencio
❑ 90IBAWorA-12
Rodriguez, Ismael
❑ 93LinVenB-7
Rodriguez, Ivan Minors
❑ 78BurBeeT-23
❑ 80HolMilT-6
❑ 81VanCanT-8
Rodriguez, Ivan Torres
❑ 89BlaYNPRWL-51
❑ 89GasRanP-1006
❑ 89GasRanS-20
❑ 89SouAtlLAGS-26
❑ 90ChaRanS-22
❑ 90FloStaLAS-41
❑ 90StaFS7-26
❑ 91Bow-272
❑ 91Cla/Bes-136
❑ 91Cla2-T82
❑ 91Cla3-T78
❑ 91ClaGolB-BC7
❑ 91DonRoo-33
❑ 91FleUpd-62
❑ 91LinDriAA-592
❑ 91ScoRoo-82T
❑ 91TopTra-101T
❑ 91TopTraT-101T
❑ 91TulDriLD-592
❑ 91TulDriP-2776
❑ 91TulDriTI-23
❑ 91UltUpd-58
❑ 91UppDecFE-55F
❑ 92Bow-1
❑ 92Cla1-T77
❑ 92Cla2-T69
❑ 92ClaGam-159
❑ 92ColAllG-23
❑ 92ColAllP-23
❑ 92Don-289
❑ 92DonCraJ1-27
❑ 92Fle-316
❑ 92FleRooS-12
❑ 92Lea-194
❑ 92LeaBlaG-194
❑ 92OPC-78
❑ 92OPCPre-55
❑ 92PanSti-74
❑ 92Pin-156
❑ 92PinTea2-8
❑ 92PinTeaP-3
❑ 92ProFS7-153
❑ 92RanMot-5
❑ 92RanTeal-19
❑ 92Sco-700
❑ 92Sco100RS-77
❑ 92ScoImpP-5
❑ 92SpollIFK1-518
❑ 92StaClu-415
❑ 92Stu-246
❑ 92Top-78

❑ 92TopDeb91-150
❑ 92TopGol-78
❑ 92TopGolW-78
❑ 92TopMcD-41
❑ 92TopMic-78
❑ 92TriPla-51
❑ 92Ult-139
❑ 92UppDec-245
❑ 92UppDecF-2
❑ 92UppDecFG-2
❑ 93Bow-489
❑ 93ClaGam-78
❑ 93ColAllG-11
❑ 93DiaMar-90
❑ 93Don-187
❑ 93Fin-47
❑ 93FinRef-47
❑ 93Fla-285
❑ 93Fle-327
❑ 93Fle-355
❑ 93FunPac-159
❑ 93FunPacA-AS2
❑ 93HumDumC-17
❑ 93Lea-5
❑ 93LeaFas-15
❑ 93LeaGolA-R1
❑ 93LeaGolA-U2
❑ 93OPC-331
❑ 93PacBeiA-4
❑ 93PacBeiA-16
❑ 93PacJugC-14
❑ 93PacSpa-316
❑ 93PacSpaPl-20
❑ 93PanSti-80
❑ 93Pin-21
❑ 93Pin-301
❑ 93PinTea2-29
❑ 93PinTeaP-3
❑ 93RanKee-428
❑ 93RanStaC-10
❑ 93RedFolS-80
❑ 93RedFolS-124
❑ 93Sco-25
❑ 93Sco-507
❑ 93Sco-537
❑ 93ScoGolDT-6
❑ 93Sel-136
❑ 93SelChaS-17
❑ 93SP-9
❑ 93StaClu-524
❑ 93StaClu-592
❑ 93StaCluFDI-524
❑ 93StaCluFDI-592
❑ 93StaCluM-175
❑ 93StaCluMOP-524
❑ 93StaCluMOP-592
❑ 93Stu-133
❑ 93Top-360
❑ 93TopGol-360
❑ 93TopInaM-360
❑ 93TopInaR-360
❑ 93TopMic-360
❑ 93Toy-33
❑ 93ToyMasP-10
❑ 93TriPla-16
❑ 93Ult-284
❑ 93UltAllS-11
❑ 93UltAwaW-11
❑ 93UppDec-52
❑ 93UppDec-123
❑ 93UppDec-450
❑ 93UppDec-468
❑ 93UppDecFA-A12
❑ 93UppDecFAJ-A12
❑ 93UppDecGold-52
❑ 93UppDecGold-123
❑ 93UppDecGold-450
❑ 93UppDecGold-468
❑ 93UppDecS-19
❑ 94Bow-101
❑ 94ChuHomS-27
❑ 94ChuHomSG-27
❑ 94ColC-625
❑ 94ColChoGS-625
❑ 94ColChoSS-625
❑ 94Don-376
❑ 94DonDiaK-DK10
❑ 94DonDiaKJ-DK10
❑ 94DonSpeE-376
❑ 94Fin-126
❑ 94FinPre-126P
❑ 94FinRef-126
❑ 94Fla-346
❑ 94Fle-319
❑ 94FleAllS-22
❑ 94FleExtB-184
❑ 94FUnPac-70
❑ 94FUnPac-176
❑ 94Lea-338
❑ 94LeaL-74
❑ 94LeaLimGA-15
❑ 94OPC-87
❑ 94Pac-627
❑ 94PacAll-13
❑ 94PanSti-132
❑ 94Pin-349
❑ 94PinArtP-349
❑ 94PinMusC-349
❑ 94PinTeaP-5
❑ 94ProMag-135
❑ 94RanAllP-20
❑ 94RanAllP-21
❑ 94RanAllP-22
❑ 94RanMagM-35
❑ 94Sco-31
❑ 94ScoGolR-31
❑ 94ScoGolS-58
❑ 94Sel-214
❑ 94SelSki-SK8
❑ 94SP-151
❑ 94SPDieC-151
❑ 94Spo-88
❑ 94SpoFanA-AS5
❑ 94StaClu-116
❑ 94StaCluFDI-116
❑ 94StaCluGR-116
❑ 94StaCluMOP-116
❑ 94StaCluMOP-ST27
❑ 94StaCluST-ST27
❑ 94StaCluT-265
❑ 94StaCluTFDI-265
❑ 94Stu-157
❑ 94Top-165
❑ 94TopGol-165
❑ 94TopSpa-165
❑ 94TriPla-199
❑ 94Ult-132
❑ 94UltAwaW-1
❑ 94UppDec-245
❑ 94UppDecAJ-34
❑ 94UppDecAJG-34
❑ 94UppDecED-245
❑ 95Baz-16
❑ 95Bow-344
❑ 95BowBes-X1
❑ 95BowBesR-X1
❑ 95ClaPhoC-55
❑ 95ColCho-391
❑ 95ColChoGS-391
❑ 95ColChoSE-188
❑ 95ColChoSEGS-188
❑ 95ColChoSESS-188
❑ 95ColChoSS-391
❑ 95Don-423
❑ 95DonAll-AL2
❑ 95DonDom-2
❑ 95DonPreP-423
❑ 95DonTopotO-165
❑ 95Emo-88
❑ 95Fin-109
❑ 95FinRef-109
❑ 95Fla-92
❑ 95FlaHotG-10
❑ 95Fle-295
❑ 95FleAllS-1
❑ 95FleUpdSL-9
❑ 95KinDis-19
❑ 95Kra-13
❑ 95Lea-107
❑ 95LeaGreG-16
❑ 95LeaLim-131
❑ 95Pac-433
❑ 95PacLatD-31
❑ 95PacPri-137
❑ 95PanSti-28
❑ 95Pin-122
❑ 95PinArtP-122
❑ 95PinFan-10
❑ 95PinMusC-122
❑ 95PinSam-122
❑ 95RanCra-28
❑ 95Sco-367
❑ 95ScoConR-AD2
❑ 95ScoGolR-367
❑ 95ScoHaloG-HG74
❑ 95ScoPlaTS-367
❑ 95Sel-63
❑ 95SelArtP-63
❑ 95SelCer-77
❑ 95SelCerMG-77
❑ 95SP-198
❑ 95SPCha-192
❑ 95SPChaDC-192
❑ 95Spo-33
❑ 95SpoArtP-33
❑ 95SPSil-198
❑ 95StaClu-197
❑ 95StaCluFDI-197
❑ 95StaCluMOP-197
❑ 95StaCluSTWS-197
❑ 95StaCluVR-103
❑ 95StaCluVRMO-103
❑ 95Stu-117
❑ 95Sum-82
❑ 95SumNthD-82
❑ 95TomPiz-15
❑ 95Top-543
❑ 95TopCyb-324
❑ 95TopD3-32
❑ 95TopEmb-54
❑ 95TopEmbGI-54
❑ 95TopTra-163T
❑ 95UC3-82
❑ 95UC3ArtP-82
❑ 95Ult-113
❑ 95UltAllS-18
❑ 95UltAllSGM-18
❑ 95UltAwaW-1
❑ 95UltAwaWGM-1
❑ 95UltGolM-113
❑ 95UppDec-391
❑ 95UppDecED-391
❑ 95UppDecEDG-391
❑ 95UppDecSE-41
❑ 95UppDecSEG-41
❑ 95Zen-39
❑ 95ZenAllS-12
❑ 96Baz-104
❑ 96Bow-3
❑ 96BowBes-30
❑ 96BowBesAR-30
❑ 96BowBesMI-8
❑ 96BowBesMIAR-8
❑ 96BowBesMIR-8
❑ 96BowBesR-30
❑ 96BowFoi-3
❑ 96Cir-92
❑ 96CirRav-92
❑ 96Cla7/1PC-8
❑ 96ColCho-345
❑ 96ColChoGS-345
❑ 96ColChoSS-345
❑ 96DenHol-21
❑ 96Don-350
❑ 96DonPreP-350
❑ 96EmoXL-127
❑ 96EmoXLD-9
❑ 96Fin-B258
❑ 96Fin-S3
❑ 96FinRef-B258
❑ 96FinRef-S3
❑ 96Fla-178
❑ 96FlaHotG-9
❑ 96Fle-260
❑ 96FleTif-260
❑ 96Kin-21
❑ 96Lea-151
❑ 96LeaLim-1
❑ 96LeaLimG-1
❑ 96LeaPre-21
❑ 96LeaPreP-21
❑ 96LeaPrePB-151
❑ 96LeaPrePG-151
❑ 96LeaPrePS-151
❑ 96LeaSig-40
❑ 96LeaSigEA-175
❑ 96LeaSigEACM-26
❑ 96LeaSigPPG-40
❑ 96LeaSigPPP-40
❑ 96MetUni-116
❑ 96MetUniP-116
❑ 96MetUniProS-116
❑ 96Pac-420
❑ 96PacEstL-EL27
❑ 96PacGolCD-DC24
❑ 96PacPri-P138
❑ 96PacPriG-P138
❑ 96PanSti-234
❑ 96Pin-59
❑ 96PinAfi-69
❑ 96PinAfiAP-69
❑ 96PinAfiFPP-69
❑ 96PinArtP-23
❑ 96PinFan-22
❑ 96PinSta-23
❑ 96PinTeaP-8
❑ 96ProMagA-7
❑ 96ProSta-99
❑ 96RanDr P-27
❑ 96RanFle-14
❑ 96RanMot-4
❑ 96RedF-11
❑ 96Sco-302
❑ 96ScoDugC-B27
❑ 96ScoDugCAP-B27
❑ 96ScoGolS-22
❑ 96ScoNumG-24
❑ 96Sel-9
❑ 96SelArtP-9
❑ 96SelCer-35
❑ 96SelCerAP-35
❑ 96SelCerCB-35
❑ 96SelCerCR-35
❑ 96SelCerMB-35
❑ 96SelCerMG-35
❑ 96SelCerMR-35
❑ 96SelTeaN-14
❑ 96SP-180
❑ 96Spo-11
❑ 96SpoArtP-11
❑ 96SpoDouT-7
❑ 96StaClu-380
❑ 96StaCluEPB-380
❑ 96StaCluEPG-380
❑ 96StaCluEPS-380
❑ 96StaCluMM-MM2
❑ 96StaCluMOP-380
❑ 96StaCluMOP-MM2
❑ 96Stu-139
❑ 96StuPrePB-139
❑ 96StuPrePG-139
❑ 96StuPrePS-139
❑ 96Sum-12
❑ 96SumAbo&B-12
❑ 96SumArtP-12
❑ 96SumFoi-12
❑ 96SumPos-5
❑ 96TeaOut-68
❑ 96Top-140
❑ 96Top-227
❑ 96TopChr-39
❑ 96TopChr-87
❑ 96TopChrR-39
❑ 96TopChrR-87
❑ 96TopGal-52
❑ 96TopGalPPI-52
❑ 96TopLas-91
❑ 96Ult-139
❑ 96UltGolM-139
❑ 96UltPriL-1
❑ 96UltPriLGM-1
❑ 96UppDec-210
❑ 96Zen-7
❑ 96ZenArtP-7
❑ 96ZenMoz-2
❑ 97Bow-261
❑ 97BowBes-84
❑ 97BowBesAR-84
❑ 97BowBesMI-MI4
❑ 97BowBesMIAR-MI4
❑ 97BowBesMIARI-MI4
❑ 97BowBesMII-MI4
❑ 97BowBesMIR-MI4
❑ 97BowBesMIRI-MI4
❑ 97BowBesR-84
❑ 97BowChr-83
❑ 97BowChrI-83
❑ 97BowChrIR-83
❑ 97BowChrR-83
❑ 97BowInt-261
❑ 97Cir-259
❑ 97CirRav-259
❑ 97ColCho-243
❑ 97ColChoAC-8
❑ 97ColChoT-TR7
❑ 97CraJac-14
❑ 97Don-31
❑ 97Don-438
❑ 97DonArmaD-4
❑ 97DonDiaK-8
❑ 97DonDiaKC-8
❑ 97DonEli-13
❑ 97DonEliGS-13
❑ 97DonEliLaL-5
❑ 97DonGolPP-31
❑ 97DonGolPP-438
❑ 97DonLim-28
❑ 97DonLim-44
❑ 97DonLim-171
❑ 97DonLimE-28
❑ 97DonLimE-44
❑ 97DonLimE-171
❑ 97DonLimENG-171
❑ 97DonLimFotG-3
❑ 97DonPowA-20
❑ 97DonPowADC-20
❑ 97DonPre-49
❑ 97DonPre-186
❑ 97DonPreCttC-49
❑ 97DonPreCttC-186
❑ 97DonPrePM-8
❑ 97DonPreS-20
❑ 97DonPreSS-20
❑ 97DonPreTB-19
❑ 97DonPreTBG-19
❑ 97DonPreTF-19
❑ 97DonPreTP-19
❑ 97DonPreTPG-19
❑ 97DonPreXP-3A
❑ 97DonSig-71
❑ 97DonSigAC-107
❑ 97DonSigAM-107
❑ 97DonSigNN-7
❑ 97DonSigPPP-71
❑ 97DonSilPP-31
❑ 97DonSilPP-438
❑ 97DonTeaSMVP-1
❑ 97DonVxP1-28
❑ 97E-X2-47
❑ 97E-X2Cred-47
❑ 97E-X2EssCre-47
❑ 97Fin-90
❑ 97Fin-152
❑ 97Fin-289
❑ 97FinEmb-152
❑ 97FinEmb-289
❑ 97FinEmbR-152
❑ 97FinEmbR-289
❑ 97FinRef-90
❑ 97FinRef-152
❑ 97FinRef-289
❑ 97FlaShoHG-14
❑ 97FlaShoLC-57
❑ 97FlaShoLeg0-57
❑ 97FlaShoLeg1-57
❑ 97FlaShoM-A57
❑ 97FlaShoM-B57
❑ 97FlaShoM-C57
❑ 97FlaShoR0-57
❑ 97FlaShoR1-57
❑ 97FlaShoR2-57
❑ 97Fle-231
❑ 97FleTif-231
❑ 97Lea-194
❑ 97Lea-221
❑ 97Lea-384
❑ 97LeaDrefS-16
❑ 97LeaFraM-194
❑ 97LeaFraM-221
❑ 97LeaFraM-384
❑ 97LeaFraMDC-194
❑ 97LeaFraMDC-221
❑ 97LeaFraMDC-384
❑ 97LeaGet-12
❑ 97LeaGolS-9
❑ 97LeaLeaotN-5
❑ 97MetUni-168
❑ 97NewPin-61
❑ 97NewPin-185
❑ 97NewPinAP-61
❑ 97NewPinAP-185
❑ 97NewPinIE-5
❑ 97NewPinKtP-3
❑ 97NewPinMC-61
❑ 97NewPinMC-185
❑ 97NewPinPP-61
❑ 97NewPinPP-185
❑ 97NewPinPP-I5B
❑ 97NewPinPP-K3
❑ 97NewPinPP-IR1
❑ 97NewPinPP-IR2
❑ 97NewPinPP-IR3
❑ 97NewPinPP-IR4
❑ 97NewPinPP-IR5
❑ 97NewPinS-IR1
❑ 97NewPinS-IR2
❑ 97NewPinS-IR3
❑ 97NewPinS-IR4
❑ 97NewPinS-IR5
❑ 97Pac-209
❑ 97PacBaeS-3
❑ 97PacCar-20
❑ 97PacCarM-20
❑ 97PacCerCGT-9
❑ 97PacGolCD-20
❑ 97PacLatotML-22
❑ 97PacLigB-209
❑ 97PacPri-71
❑ 97PacPriLB-71
❑ 97PacPriP-71
❑ 97PacPriSL-SL7C
❑ 97PacSil-209
❑ 97Pin-47
❑ 97PinAllFP-7
❑ 97PinArtP-PP47
❑ 97PinCar-13
❑ 97PinCer-79
❑ 97PinCerCMGT-9
❑ 97PinCerCT-9
❑ 97PinCerMBla-79
❑ 97PinCerMBlu-79
❑ 97PinCerMG-79
❑ 97PinCerMR-79
❑ 97PinCerR-79
❑ 97PinEpixGO-E4
❑ 97PinEpixPE-E4
❑ 97PinFan-FF15
❑ 97PinIns-48
❑ 97PinInsC-17
❑ 97PinInsCE-48
❑ 97PinInsDD-4
❑ 97PinInsDE-48
❑ 97PinMin-25
❑ 97PinMinB-25
❑ 97PinMinCB-25
❑ 97PinMinCG-25
❑ 97PinMinCGR-25
❑ 97PinMinCN-25
❑ 97PinMinCSS-25
❑ 97PinMinG-25
❑ 97PinMinS-25
❑ 97PinMusC-47
❑ 97PinPasttM-12
❑ 97PinPrePla-47
❑ 97PinTeaP-5
❑ 97PinTeaP-10
❑ 97PinTotCPB-79
❑ 97PinTotCPG-79
❑ 97PinTotCPR-79
❑ 97PinX-P-35
❑ 97PinX-P-141
❑ 97PinX-PMoS-35
❑ 97PinX-PMoS-141
❑ 97PinX-PMP-10
❑ 97PinX-PreMPS-10
❑ 97RanCup-4
❑ 97RanDr P-27
❑ 97RanMot-4
❑ 97RanSco-12
❑ 97RanScoPl-12
❑ 97RanScoPr-12
❑ 97Sco-203
❑ 97Sco-547
❑ 97ScoAllF-15
❑ 97ScoArtPWB-203
❑ 97ScoArtPWB-547
❑ 97ScoHeaotO-2
❑ 97ScoPitP-5
❑ 97ScoPreS-203
❑ 97ScoResC-547
❑ 97ScoShoS-203
❑ 97ScoShoS-547
❑ 97ScoShoSAP-203
❑ 97ScoShoSAP-547
❑ 97Sel-25
❑ 97SelArtP-25
❑ 97SelCom-25
❑ 97SelRegG-25
❑ 97SelToootT-20
❑ 97SelToootTMB-20
❑ 97SP-170
❑ 97SpoIll-71
❑ 97SpoIllEE-71
❑ 97SPSpeF-18
❑ 97SPSpxF-8
❑ 97SPSPxFA-8
❑ 97SPx-49
❑ 97SPxBro-49
❑ 97SPxCorotG-7
❑ 97SPxGol-49
❑ 97SPxGraF-49
❑ 97SPxSil-49
❑ 97SPxSte-49
❑ 97StaClu-200
❑ 97StaCluMat-200
❑ 97StaCluMOP-200
❑ 97StaCluMOP-PL1
❑ 97StaCluPL-PL1
❑ 97StrAll-54
❑ 97Stu-108
❑ 97StuHarH-1
❑ 97StuPrePG-108
❑ 97StuPrePS-108
❑ 97Top-340
❑ 97TopAll-AS1
❑ 97TopChr-114

❑ 97TopChrAS-AS1
❑ 97TopChrDD-DD6
❑ 97TopChrDDR-DD6
❑ 97TopChrR-114
❑ 97TopChrSAR-AS1
❑ 97TopGal-111
❑ 97TopGalPPI-111
❑ 97TopMemO5-41
❑ 97TopSta-16
❑ 97TopSta97AS-AS5
❑ 97TopStaAM-16
❑ 97UD3-28
❑ 97Ult-140
❑ 97UltFieC-17
❑ 97UltGolME-140
❑ 97UltPlaME-140
❑ 97UppDec-138
❑ 97UppDec-203
❑ 97UppDec-211
❑ 97UppDecHTH-HT9
❑ 97UppDecRSF-RS11
❑ 97Zen-15
❑ 97Zen8x10-9
❑ 97Zen8x1D-9
❑ 98Bow-4
❑ 98BowBes-82
❑ 98BowBesAR-82
❑ 98BowBesMIF-MI10
❑ 98BowBesMIFAR-MI10
❑ 98BowBesMIFR-MI10
❑ 98BowBesR-82
❑ 98BowChr-4
❑ 98BowChrGA-4
❑ 98BowChrGAR-4
❑ 98BowChrI-4
❑ 98BowChrIR-4
❑ 98BowChrR-4
❑ 98BowChrR-27
❑ 98BowChrRR-27
❑ 98BowGolA-4
❑ 98BowInt-4
❑ 98Cha-29
❑ 98CirThu-63
❑ 98CirThuRav-63
❑ 98CirThuSupRav-63
❑ 98ColCho-186
❑ 98ColCho-249
❑ 98ColChoRJ-249
❑ 98ColChoS'-28
❑ 98ColChoSQ-SQ64
❑ 98CroRoy-138
❑ 98CroRoyAS-10
❑ 98CroRoyDK-24
❑ 98CroRoyFoB-24
❑ 98CroRoyFoBA-24
❑ 98Don-17
❑ 98Don-398
❑ 98DonCol-17
❑ 98DonColE-418
❑ 98DonColE-535
❑ 98DonColL-251
❑ 98DonColP-575
❑ 98DonColP-738
❑ 98DonColS-17
❑ 98DonCruG-46
❑ 98DonCruP-46
❑ 98DonCruR-46
❑ 98DonDay-3
❑ 98DonDiaK-3
❑ 98DonDiaKC-3
❑ 98DonDom-8
❑ 98DonEli-18
❑ 98DonEli-135
❑ 98DonEliA-18
❑ 98DonEliA-135
❑ 98DonEliC-25
❑ 98DonEliI-7
❑ 98DonEliMC-25
❑ 98DonEliS-18
❑ 98DonEliS-135
❑ 98DonGolPP-17
❑ 98DonGolPP-398
❑ 98DonPre-25
❑ 98DonPre-188
❑ 98DonPreGES-18
❑ 98DonPreGX-18
❑ 98DonPreGXDC-18
❑ 98DonPrePM-22
❑ 98DonPreSeat-25
❑ 98DonPreSeat-188
❑ 98DonPreTW-15
❑ 98DonPriCD-17
❑ 98DonPriCE-418
❑ 98DonPriCE-535
❑ 98DonPriCL-251
❑ 98DonPriCP-575
❑ 98DonPriCP-738
❑ 98DonSig-7
❑ 98DonSigP-7
❑ 98DonSilPP-17
❑ 98DonSilPP-398
❑ 98E-X2-14
❑ 98E-X2DesCoop-15
❑ 98E-X2ECFut-14
❑ 98E-X2ECNow-14
❑ 98Fin-125
❑ 98FinNo--125
❑ 98FinNo-R-125
❑ 98FinRef-125
❑ 98FlaShoLeg0-28
❑ 98FlaShoLeg1-28
❑ 98FlaShoLeg2-28
❑ 98FlaShoLeg3-28
❑ 98FlaShoLegM-28
❑ 98FlaShoR0-28
❑ 98FlaShoR1-28
❑ 98FlaShoR2-28
❑ 98FlaShoR3-28
❑ 98Fle-170
❑ 98FleVin'-61
❑ 98FleVin'C-61
❑ 98Lea-52
❑ 98LeaCruG-46
❑ 98LeaCruP-46
❑ 98LeaCruR-46
❑ 98LeaFraDA-52
❑ 98LeaFraF-52
❑ 98LeaFraM-52
❑ 98LeaFraM-52
❑ 98LeaFraMDC-52
❑ 98LeaFraMDC-52
❑ 98LeaFraMZ2-52
❑ 98LeaHeaftH-18
❑ 98LeaHeaftHS-18
❑ 98LeaRS-49
❑ 98LeaRS-140
❑ 98LeaRSCross-6
❑ 98LeaRSGreHit-19
❑ 98LeaRSLHolo-49
❑ 98LeaRSLHolo-140
❑ 98LeaRSLMVP-5
❑ 98LeaRSLMVPPE-5
❑ 98LeaRSLong-49
❑ 98LeaRSLong-140
❑ 98LeaRSSOSamp-10
❑ 98LeaRSStaOva-10
❑ 98LeaRSTicMas-8
❑ 98LeaRSTicMasDC-8
❑ 98LeaRTrue-49
❑ 98LeaRTrue-140
❑ 98LeaStaRep-21
❑ 98MetUni-4
❑ 98MetUniPMG-4
❑ 98Pac-208
❑ 98PacAur-89
❑ 98PacAurHC-18
❑ 98PacAurPF-7
❑ 98PacAurPFC-7
❑ 98PacAurPFPB-7
❑ 98PacAurPFR-7
❑ 98PacAurPFS-7
❑ 98PacGolCDC-34
❑ 98PacInCage-20
❑ 98PacInv-71
❑ 98PacInvGems-106
❑ 98PacInvInt-13A
❑ 98PacInvPBlue-71
❑ 98PacInvPhoto-16
❑ 98PacInvSilv-71
❑ 98PacInvTeam-27
❑ 98PacLatotML-35
❑ 98PacNes-3B
❑ 98PacOme-241
❑ 98PacOmeEP-10
❑ 98PacOmeEP1o1-10
❑ 98PacOmeOnIns-18
❑ 98PacOmeR-241
❑ 98PacOnl-743A
❑ 98PacOnl-743B
❑ 98PacOnlR-743A
❑ 98PacOnlR-743B
❑ 98PacOnlWC-743A
❑ 98PacOnlWC-743B
❑ 98PacPar-107
❑ 98PacParC-107
❑ 98PacParFC-19
❑ 98PacParG-107
❑ 98PacParHS-107
❑ 98PacParI-19
❑ 98PacParPB-107
❑ 98PacParR-107
❑ 98PacParTC-13
❑ 98PacPlaB-208
❑ 98PacRedT-208
❑ 98PacSil-208
❑ 98PacTeaC-13
❑ 98PinEpixGE-E4
❑ 98PinEpixGP-E4
❑ 98PinEpixPO-E4
❑ 98PinEpixPP-E4
❑ 98PinEpixSE-E4
❑ 98PinEpixSO-E4
❑ 98PinEpixSP-E4
❑ 98PinIns-7
❑ 98PinInsBtN-11
❑ 98PinInsCE-7
❑ 98PinInsDE-7
❑ 98PinInsSG-7AB
❑ 98PinInsSG-7CD
❑ 98PinInsSG-18AB
❑ 98PinInsSG-18CD
❑ 98PinInsSGS-7AB
❑ 98PinInsSGS-7CD
❑ 98PinInsSGS-18AB
❑ 98PinInsSGS-18CD
❑ 98PinMinB-20
❑ 98PinMinCB-20
❑ 98PinMinCBAP-20
❑ 98PinMinCGP-20
❑ 98PinMinCGPAP-20
❑ 98PinMinCN-20
❑ 98PinMinCNAP-20
❑ 98PinMinCSGR-20
❑ 98PinMinDC-20
❑ 98PinMinG-20
❑ 98PinMinMCSS-20
❑ 98PinMinS-20
❑ 98PinPer-25
❑ 98PinPerLP-13
❑ 98PinPerPP-25
❑ 98PinPlu-27
❑ 98PinPluAE-4
❑ 98PinPluAEE-4
❑ 98PinPluAEP-4
❑ 98PinPluAP-PP14
❑ 98PinPluGAP-PP14
❑ 98PinPluLM-22
❑ 98PinPluMAP-PP14
❑ 98PinPluTP-1
❑ 98PinPluTPG-1
❑ 98PinPluTPM-1
❑ 98PinPreP-E4
❑ 98PinSna-TR1
❑ 98PreCon-15
❑ 98RanPinM-4
❑ 98Revo-144
❑ 98RevoFP-11
❑ 98RevoPTP-11
❑ 98RevoShow-18
❑ 98RevoSS-144
❑ 98Sco-88
❑ 98ScoAllST-2
❑ 98ScoEpix-E4
❑ 98ScoFirP-19
❑ 98ScoRT-33
❑ 98ScoRTASEpix-4
❑ 98ScoRTComPla-7A
❑ 98ScoRTComPla-7B
❑ 98ScoRTComPla-7C
❑ 98ScoRTCPSamp-7A
❑ 98ScoRTCPSamp-7B
❑ 98ScoRTCPSamp-7C
❑ 98ScoRTSS-PP33
❑ 98ScoRTSSAP-PP33
❑ 98ScoRTSSAP1-PP33
❑ 98ScoSS-PP138
❑ 98ScoSSAP-PP138
❑ 98SkyDugA-86
❑ 98SkyDugA-140
❑ 98SkyDugADH-DH15
❑ 98SkyDugAIA-86
❑ 98SkyDugAIA-140
❑ 98SP Aut-192
❑ 98SP Aut-SD22
❑ 98SP AutC-IR
❑ 98SP AutSD-SD22
❑ 98SP AutSDT-SD22
❑ 98SpollI-108
❑ 98SpollIEE-108
❑ 98SpollIFE-108
❑ 98SpollIODMP-OD29
❑ 98SpollITaN-127
❑ 98SpollITaNC-C12
❑ 98SpollITaNEE-127
❑ 98SpollIWSF-141
❑ 98SpollIWSFEE-141
❑ 98SpollIWSFFE-141
❑ 98SPxFin-137
❑ 98SPxFin-169
❑ 98SPxFinR-137
❑ 98SPxFinR-169
❑ 98SPxFinS-137
❑ 98SPxFinS-169
❑ 98StaCluFDI-223
❑ 98StaCluI-223
❑ 98StaCluNC-NC2
❑ 98StaCluOneK-223
❑ 98StaCluPP-223
❑ 98StaCluTIII-T10C
❑ 98StaCluTLme-T10C
❑ 98StaCluTLmo-T10C
❑ 98Stu-3
❑ 98StuFF-18
❑ 98StuFFDC-18
❑ 98StuGPP-3
❑ 98StuMast-4
❑ 98StuPor8x10-7
❑ 98StuPor8x10GP-7
❑ 98StuSPP-3
❑ 98Top-292
❑ 98TopChr-292
❑ 98TopChrR-292
❑ 98TopDevR-292
❑ 98TopDia-292
❑ 98TopFocP-FP6
❑ 98TopFruR-7
❑ 98TopGal-69
❑ 98TopGalGP-69
❑ 98TopGalOPP-69
❑ 98TopGalPPI-69
❑ 98TopGalPPIA-69
❑ 98TopGolLabC1-80
❑ 98TopGolLabC1B-80
❑ 98TopGolLabC1One-80
❑ 98TopGolLabC1R-80
❑ 98TopGolLabC2-80
❑ 98TopGolLabC2B-80
❑ 98TopGolLabC2One-80
❑ 98TopGolLabC2R-80
❑ 98TopGolLabC3-80
❑ 98TopGolLabC3B-80
❑ 98TopGolLabC3One-80
❑ 98TopGolLabC3R-80
❑ 98TopMiniC-292
❑ 98TopOpeD-119
❑ 98TopSta-130
❑ 98TopSta'S-35
❑ 98TopSta'SGH-35
❑ 98TopStaB-130
❑ 98TopStaG-130
❑ 98TopStaGR-130
❑ 98TopStaLB-L12
❑ 98TopStaLG-L12
❑ 98TopStaLGR-L12
❑ 98TopStaLS-L12
❑ 98TopStaPre-PP5
❑ 98TopStaS-130
❑ 98TopStaSteG-35
❑ 98TopSup-17
❑ 98TopSup-17
❑ 98TopTek-5
❑ 98TopTekD-5
❑ 98UD3-74
❑ 98UD3-164
❑ 98UD3-254
❑ 98UD3DieCut-74
❑ 98UD3DieCut-164
❑ 98UD3DieCut-254
❑ 98Ult-210
❑ 98UltDouT-10
❑ 98UltGolM-210
❑ 98UltMas-210
❑ 98UltPlaM-210
❑ 98UltTop3-2
❑ 98UppDec-230
❑ 98UppDec10AP-15
❑ 98UppDec1APR-15
❑ 98UppDec5x7-230
❑ 98UppDecCD-CD6
❑ 98UppDecNP-NP29
❑ 98UppDecR-96
❑ 98UppDecRGKoG-G11
❑ 98UppDecRQL-Q28
❑ 98UppDecRTC-TC23
❑ 98UppDecSF-130
❑ 98Zen-19
❑ 98Zen5 xx7-35
❑ 98Zen5x7GoldImp-35
❑ 98Zen5x7Imp-35
❑ 98ZenEpi-E4
❑ 98ZenRaitB-6
❑ 98ZenSampL-Z35
❑ 98ZenSamS-19
❑ 98ZenZ-G-19
❑ 98ZenZ-S-19
❑ 99199Fin-195
❑ 99199Fin-265
❑ 99AllMysFR-M29
❑ 99AurOn DL-20
❑ 99AurPenF-20
❑ 99AurPenF-20
❑ 99AurPenFB-20
❑ 99AurPenFS-20
❑ 99AurSty-20
❑ 99Bow-37
❑ 99BowBes-22
❑ 99BowBesAR-22
❑ 99BowBesR-22
❑ 99BowChr-37
❑ 99BowChrG-37
❑ 99BowChrGR-37
❑ 99BowChrI-37
❑ 99BowChrIR-37
❑ 99BowChrR-37
❑ 99BowGol-37
❑ 99BowInt-37
❑ 99CroRoyB-140
❑ 99CroRoyL-140
❑ 99CroRoyMP-20
❑ 99CroRoyOD-140
❑ 99CroRoyPotG-25
❑ 99CroRoyPP-25
❑ 99CroRoyPPN-25
❑ 99E-X Cen-28
❑ 99E-X CenECFut-28
❑ 99E-X CenECNow-28
❑ 99E-XCenFoF'-10
❑ 99FinCom-C1
❑ 99FinComDualR-C1
❑ 99FinGolRef-195
❑ 99FinGolRef-265
❑ 99FinRef-195
❑ 99FinRef-265
❑ 99FinSplS-SS9
❑ 99FinSplSDR-SS9
❑ 99FlaShoLeg1-62
❑ 99FlaShoLeg2-62
❑ 99FlaShoLeg3-62
❑ 99FlaShoLegM1-62
❑ 99FlaShoLegM2-62
❑ 99FlaShoLegM3-62
❑ 99FlaShoR1-62
❑ 99FlaShoR2-62
❑ 99FlaShoR3-62
❑ 99Fle-202
❑ 99FleBri-97
❑ 99FleBri2G-97
❑ 99FleBriBlu-97
❑ 99FleBriGol-97
❑ 99FleMys-79
❑ 99FleMysG-79
❑ 99FleMysM-79
❑ 99FleSta9-202
❑ 99FleWarT-202
❑ 99MetUni-23
❑ 99MetUniGM-23
❑ 99MetUniPMG-23
❑ 99Pac-429
❑ 99Pac-429A
❑ 99PacAur-194
❑ 99PacAurOD-194
❑ 99PacCroC-288
❑ 99PacCroC-21
❑ 99PacCroCITC-20
❑ 99PacCroCPB-288
❑ 99PacCroCTM-19
❑ 99PacGolCDC-17
❑ 99PacInv-146
❑ 99PacInvOD-146
❑ 99PacInvPB-146
❑ 99PacInvSF-20
❑ 99PacInvSF-20B
❑ 99PacInvTA-20
❑ 99PacOme-239
❑ 99PacOme5T-30
❑ 99PacOme5TT-30
❑ 99PacOmeC-239
❑ 99PacOmeDM-35
❑ 99PacOmeG-239
❑ 99PacOmePB-239
❑ 99PacPar-238
❑ 99PacParC-238
❑ 99PacParFC-20
❑ 99PacParG-238
❑ 99PacParHoloGold-238
❑ 99PacParHS-238
❑ 99PacParOD-238
❑ 99PacParPB-36
❑ 99PacParPB-238
❑ 99PacParRed-238
❑ 99PacPlaB-429
❑ 99PacPlaB-429A
❑ 99PacPri-144
❑ 99PacPriAotG-20
❑ 99PacPriHB-144
❑ 99PacPriHG-144
❑ 99PacPriHM-144
❑ 99PacPriHP-144
❑ 99PacPriRed-144
❑ 99PacPriS-17
❑ 99PacPriS206-17
❑ 99PacPriS206R-17
❑ 99PacPriSE-17
❑ 99PacPriSP-17
❑ 99PacPriSP-17
❑ 99PacPriSV-17
❑ 99PacRed-429
❑ 99PacRed-429A
❑ 99Pin-23
❑ 99Rev-143
❑ 99RevDiaL-35
❑ 99RevPremDate-143
❑ 99RevRet-143
❑ 99RevShaSS-143
❑ 99RevThoitS-20
❑ 99RevTri-30
❑ 99RevTri-30
❑ 99SkyMolM-112
❑ 99SkyMolMF-12
❑ 99SkyMolMFS-12
❑ 99SkyMolMFT-12
❑ 99SkyMolMX-112
❑ 99SkyPre-75
❑ 99SkyPreR-75
❑ 99SkyThu-209
❑ 99SkyThuRant-209
❑ 99SkyThuRave-209
❑ 99SP Aut-85
❑ 99SP AutC-IR
❑ 99SP AutCG-IR
❑ 99SP SigAuto-PG
❑ 99SP SigAutoG-PG
❑ 99SpollI-100
❑ 99SpollIH-20
❑ 99SPSig-39
❑ 99SPx-76
❑ 99SPxFinR-76
❑ 99SPxFinS-76
❑ 99SPxPowE-PE30
❑ 99SPxStaF-SF29
❑ 99SPxWinM-IR
❑ 99StaClu-270
❑ 99StaCluC-SCC4
❑ 99StaCluCR-SCC4
❑ 99StaCluFDI-270
❑ 99StaCluOoaK-270
❑ 99StaCluPP-270
❑ 99ThuSkySupR-209
❑ 99Top-399
❑ 99Top-459
❑ 99TopAllMF-M29
❑ 99TopBlaLC1-39
❑ 99TopBlaLC2-39
❑ 99TopBlaLC3-39
❑ 99TopChr-399
❑ 99TopChr-459
❑ 99TopChrERttH-ER9
❑ 99TopChrERttH-ER9
❑ 99TopChrR-399
❑ 99TopChrR-459
❑ 99TopGal-40
❑ 99TopGalPP-40
❑ 99TopGalPPI-40
❑ 99TopGolL-39
❑ 99TopGolLC1-39
❑ 99TopGolLC2-39
❑ 99TopGolLOtO-39
❑ 99TopMVPP-399
❑ 99TopMVPP-459
❑ 99TopOpeD-147
❑ 99TopRedLC1-39
❑ 99TopRedLC2-39
❑ 99TopRedLC3-39
❑ 99TopSta-75
❑ 99TopSta'S-33
❑ 99TopSta'SG-33
❑ 99TopSta'SGDH-33
❑ 99TopSta1Foil-75
❑ 99TopStaFoil-75
❑ 99TopStaOS-75
❑ 99TopSupC-27
❑ 99TopSupCR-27
❑ 99TopTek-23A
❑ 99TopTek-23B
❑ 99TopTekG-23A
❑ 99TopTekG-23B

❑ 99UD Cho-149
❑ 99UD ChoPCR-149
❑ 99UD ChoS-20
❑ 99UD ChoSD-20
❑ 99UD ChoSHR-20
❑ 99UD ChoST-20
❑ 99UD Ion-57
❑ 99UD IonC-C20
❑ 99UD IonR-57
❑ 99UDHolo-57
❑ 99UDHoloAUsome-57
❑ 99Ult-37
❑ 99UltGolM-37
❑ 99UltMas-37
❑ 99UltPlaM-37
❑ 99UltRBIK-3
❑ 99UppDec-220
❑ 99UppDec-243
❑ 99UppDec10AT-X12
❑ 99UppDec10ATD-X12
❑ 99UppDec10ATHR-X12
❑ 99UppDec10ATT-X12
❑ 99UppDecBD-86
❑ 99UppDecBDD-86
❑ 99UppDecBDDom-D7
❑ 99UppDecBDDomE-D7
❑ 99UppDecBDQ-86
❑ 99UppDecBDT-86
❑ 99UppDecCf7-32
❑ 99UppDecCf7-C25
❑ 99UppDecCf7Cf7P-C25
❑ 99UppDecCf7LL-L22
❑ 99UppDecCL-80
❑ 99UppDecCLCC-80
❑ 99UppDecCLM-C95
❑ 99UppDecCo7CE-32
❑ 99UppDecE-86
❑ 99UppDecE-149
❑ 99UppDecE-175
❑ 99UppDecEFXG-86
❑ 99UppDecEFXG-149
❑ 99UppDecEFXG-175
❑ 99UppDecEL1-220
❑ 99UppDecEL1-243
❑ 99UppDecEL2-220
❑ 99UppDecEL2-243
❑ 99UppDecF-F27
❑ 99UppDecFD-F27
❑ 99UppDecFQ-F27
❑ 99UppDecFT-F27
❑ 99UppDecGJ-IR
❑ 99UppDecM-205
❑ 99UppDecMGS-205
❑ 99UppDecMHFS-205
❑ 99UppDecMP-IR
❑ 99UppDecMSS-205
❑ 99UppDecMST-S10
❑ 99UppDecO-58
❑ 99UppDecOMP-S9
❑ 99UppDecOSO-58
❑ 99UppDecOWP-R19
❑ 99UppDecR-83
❑ 99UppDecRDR-D14
❑ 99UppDecRDRL2-D14
❑ 99UppDecRG-83
❑ 99UppDecRI-IR
❑ 99UppDecRIL2-IR
❑ 99UppDecRP-83
❑ 99UppDecTE-T29
❑ 99UppDecTED-T29
❑ 99UppDecTEQ-T29
❑ 99UppDecTET-T29
❑ 99Vic-398
Rodriguez, Javier
❑ 95EveAqaTI-18
Rodriguez, John
❑ 97IdaFalBTI-15
❑ 98GreBatM-17
Rodriguez, Jonis
❑ 84GreHorT-20
Rodriguez, Jorge
❑ 98OneYanG-24
Rodriguez, Jose
❑ 79WisRapTT-21
❑ 81BufBisT-13
❑ 82JacMetT-8
❑ 82PorBeaT-21
❑ 83LynPirT-22
❑ 83St.PetCT-23
❑ 86ArkTraP-21
❑ 86BurExpP-18
❑ 87AppFoxP-20
❑ 89BriTigS-24
❑ 89PriPirS-17
❑ 93IdaFalBSP-17
❑ 94IdaFalBF-3589
❑ 94IdaFalBSP-25
Rodriguez, Joshua
❑ 90MidAngGS-NNO
Rodriguez, Juan
❑ 77DayBeaIT-20
❑ 96BoiHawB-26
❑ 97CedRapK-22
❑ 98LakElsSG-23
Rodriguez, Julian
❑ 76BatTroTI-18
Rodriguez, Larry
❑ 96AriBlaDB-27
❑ 97Bow-137
❑ 97BowInt-137
❑ 97Top-250
❑ 98Bow-190
❑ 98BowChr-190
❑ 98BowChrGA-190
❑ 98BowChrGAR-190
❑ 98BowChrI-190
❑ 98BowChrIR-190
❑ 98BowChrR-190
❑ 98BowGolA-190
❑ 98BowInt-190
❑ 98Top-253
❑ 98TopChr-253
❑ 98TopChrR-253
❑ 98TopDevR-253
❑ 98TopDia-253
❑ 98TopMiniC-253
Rodriguez, Leo
❑ 58JetPos-16
Rodriguez, Liu
❑ 96HicCraB-18
❑ 97HicCraB-24
❑ 97HicCraRB-29
❑ 98WinWar-24
Rodriguez, Luis
❑ 95BelGiaTI-15
❑ 95StCatSTI-14
❑ 96-97LinVen-141
❑ 96HagSunB-18
❑ 97HagSunB-18
❑ 98DunBluJSB-2
❑ 98DunBluJTI-26
Rodriguez, Luis E.
❑ 81OklCit8T-16
Rodriguez, Manuel
❑ 90JohCitCS-22
❑ 91JohCitCC-24
❑ 91JohCitCP-3976
Rodriguez, Marcos
❑ 79CliDodT-15
Rodriguez, Maximo
❑ 95KanCouCTI-11
❑ 96BreCouMB-28
❑ 97BreCouMB-26
Rodriguez, Miguel
❑ 80UtiBluJT-32
❑ 96OgdRapTI-25
❑ 97JohCitCTI-28
❑ 97StoPor-21
❑ 98LetBlaDG-24
❑ 98StoPorG-28
Rodriguez, Mike
❑ 77ModA'sC-7
❑ 79OgdA'sT-4
❑ 96StCatSB-23
❑ 97HagSunB-19
❑ 98HagSunM-22
Rodriguez, Nate
❑ 93MarPhiC-24
❑ 93MarPhiF-3485
Rodriguez, Nelson
❑ 80AppFoxT-12
Rodriguez, Nerio
❑ 93HicCraC-22
❑ 93HicCraF-1281
❑ 96FreKeyB-17
❑ 97BalOriP-30
❑ 97Bow-190
❑ 97BowChr-178
❑ 97BowChrI-178
❑ 97BowChrIR-178
❑ 97BowChrR-178
❑ 97BowInt-190
❑ 97DonRatR-6
❑ 97OriSco-9
❑ 97OriScoPl-9
❑ 97OriScoPr-9
❑ 97RocRedW-21
❑ 97Sco-308
❑ 97ScoArtPWB-308
❑ 97ScoPreS-308
❑ 97ScoShoS-308
❑ 97ScoShoSAP-308
❑ 97StaClu-267
❑ 97StaCluMOP-267
❑ 97UppDec-273
❑ 98Bow-333
❑ 98BowChr-333
❑ 98BowChrGA-333
❑ 98BowChrGAR-333
❑ 98BowChrI-333
❑ 98BowChrIR-333
❑ 98BowChrR-333
❑ 98BowGolA-333
❑ 98BowInt-333
❑ 98PacInvGems-16
❑ 98PacOmeRS-1
❑ 98PacOmeRST3-1
❑ 98PacOnl-102
❑ 98PacOnlR-102
❑ 98PacOnlWC-102
❑ 98Ult-256
❑ 98UltGolM-256
❑ 98UltMas-256
❑ 98UltPlaM-256
Rodriguez, Noel
❑ 93AshTouC-18
❑ 93AshTouF-2292
❑ 93AubAstC-20
❑ 93AubAstF-3456
❑ 94QuaCitRBC-20
❑ 94QuaCitRBF-549
❑ 95QuaCitRBTI-22
❑ 96KisCobB-23
❑ 97JacGen-23
❑ 97JacGenS-22
❑ 98KisCobQ-26
Rodriguez, Peter
❑ 98PitMetM-27
Rodriguez, Ramon
❑ 85SpoIndC-20
❑ 86ChaRaiP-22
Rodriguez, Rich (Richard A.)
❑ 84LitFalMT-25
❑ 86LynMetP-19
❑ 87LynMetP-19
❑ 88Fle-293
❑ 88FleGlo-293
❑ 88FleUpd-24
❑ 88FleUpdG-24
❑ 88JacMetGS-13
❑ 88MetColP-46
❑ 88Top-166
❑ 88TopTif-166
❑ 89WicStaR-19
❑ 89WicWraR-29
❑ 90CMC-512
❑ 90LasVegSC-9
❑ 90LasVegSP-123
❑ 90ProAAAF-11
❑ 91Don-769
❑ 91Fle-541
❑ 91Lea-448
❑ 91OPC-573
❑ 91PadMag-16
❑ 91Sco-593
❑ 91StaClu-565
❑ 91Top-573
❑ 91TopDeb90-132
❑ 91TopDesS-573
❑ 91TopMic-573
❑ 91TopTif-573
❑ 91UppDec-640
❑ 92Don-388
❑ 92Fle-619
❑ 92Lea-319
❑ 92LeaBlaG-319
❑ 92OPC-462
❑ 92PadCarJ-17
❑ 92PadMot-22
❑ 92PadPolD-29
❑ 92PadSmo-27
❑ 92Sco-149
❑ 92StaClu-712
❑ 92StaCluNC-712
❑ 92Top-462
❑ 92TopGol-462
❑ 92TopGolW-462
❑ 92TopMic-462
❑ 92Ult-581
❑ 92UppDec-568
❑ 93Don-338
❑ 93Fle-145
❑ 93Lea-368
❑ 93MarPub-21
❑ 93PacSpa-262
❑ 93PadMot-11
❑ 93Sco-466
❑ 93StaClu-137
❑ 93StaCluFDI-137
❑ 93StaCluMOP-137
❑ 93Top-693
❑ 93TopGol-693
❑ 93TopInaM-693
❑ 93TopInaR-693
❑ 93TopMic-693
❑ 93TopTra-71T
❑ 93Ult-120
❑ 93UppDec-330
❑ 93UppDecGold-330
❑ 94Don-635
❑ 94Fle-475
❑ 94FleUpd-182
❑ 94Sco-295
❑ 94ScoGolR-295
❑ 94StaCluT-76
❑ 94StaCluTFDI-76
❑ 94Top-312
❑ 94TopGol-312
❑ 94TopSpa-312
❑ 95Fle-508
❑ 95Top-601
❑ 95TopCyb-372
❑ 96OmaRoyB-24
❑ 98GiaMot-15
❑ 98PacInvGems-220
❑ 98PacOnl-671
❑ 98PacOnlR-671
❑ 98PacOnlWC-671
❑ 99PacCroC-256
❑ 99PacCroCPB-256
Rodriguez, Richard
❑ 77ChaPatT-17
❑ 89WicChaR-4
Rodriguez, Rick
❑ 85ModA'sC-18
❑ 86TacTigP-19
❑ 88ColSprSSC-8
❑ 88ColSprSSP-1549
❑ 88IndTeal-29
❑ 89VanCanC-8
❑ 89VanCanP-580
❑ 91LinDriAAA-392
❑ 91PhoFirLD-392
❑ 91PhoFirP-65
❑ 91PocPioP-3801
❑ 91PocPioSP-29
❑ 93SouOreAC-29
❑ 95ModA'sTI-25
❑ 96ModA'sB-25
❑ 97ModA'sG-26
❑ 98ModA'sG-26
Rodriguez, Rigo
❑ 85BeaGolGT-10
Rodriguez, Roberto
❑ 67VanMouSO-19
❑ 68Top-199
❑ 68TopVen-199
❑ 69Top-358
❑ 71MLBOffS-44
❑ 71OPC-424
❑ 71Top-424
❑ 74WicAerODF-104
Rodriguez, Roman
❑ 89PriPirS-18
❑ 90AugPirP-2474
❑ 91SalBucC-7
❑ 91SalBucP-961
❑ 92CarMudS-140
❑ 94StoPorC-22
❑ 94StoPorF-1703
❑ 95LynHilTI-26
Rodriguez, Rosario
❑ 88GreHorP-1567
❑ 89CedRapRAB-24
❑ 90CedRapRDGB-24
❑ 90ChaLooGS-25
❑ 90NasSouP-231
❑ 90ProAAAF-543
❑ 90TopDeb89-103
❑ 91BufBisLD-44
❑ 91BufBisP-541
❑ 91LinDriAAA-44
❑ 91OPC-688
❑ 91Sco-373
❑ 91Top-688
❑ 91TopDesS-688
❑ 91TopMic-688
❑ 91TopTif-688
❑ 92Bow-498
❑ 92BufBisBS-18
❑ 92BufBisS-34
❑ 92Don-748
❑ 92Fle-565
❑ 92SkyAAAF-19
❑ 92StaClu-697
❑ 92StaCluNC-697
Rodriguez, Ruben
❑ 83AleDukT-26
❑ 85DomLeaS-57
❑ 85NasPirT-21
❑ 86NasPirP-23
❑ 87SalLakTTT-7
❑ 87VanCanP-1620
❑ 88SalLakCTTI-3
❑ 89BoiHawP-1992
❑ 89DenZepC-18
❑ 89DenZepP-34
❑ 89SalLakTTI-3
❑ 90EriSaiS-21
❑ 91LinDriAA-396
❑ 91LonTigLD-396
❑ 91LonTigP-1881
❑ 92PawRedSF-926
❑ 92PawRedSS-364
❑ 93LimRocDWB-47
❑ 93PawRedSDD-22
❑ 93PawRedSF-2411
❑ 93PawRedSTI-19
❑ 94PawRedSDD-20
❑ 94PawRedSF-949
Rodriguez, Ryan
❑ 98St.PauSTI-21
Rodriguez, Sammy
❑ 96PitMetB-23
❑ 97PitMet-28
❑ 98St.LucMM-5
Rodriguez, Serafin
❑ 98ChaAllCM-25
❑ 98SouAtlLPM-18
Rodriguez, Steve
❑ 91TopTra-102T
❑ 91TopTraT-102T
❑ 92ClaDraP-112
❑ 92FroRowDP-84
❑ 92FroRowDPG-84
❑ 92FroRowDPS-84
❑ 92StaCluD-157
❑ 92TopDaiQTU-26
❑ 92TopTra-94T
❑ 92TopTraG-94T
❑ 93ClaFS7-114
❑ 93LynRedSC-22
❑ 93LynRedSF-2525
❑ 93StaCluM-10
❑ 93StaCluM-50
❑ 94NewBriRSF-660
❑ 94PawRedSDD-21
❑ 94UppDecML-66
❑ 95Bow-59
❑ 95FleUpd-13
❑ 95PawRedSDD-24
❑ 95PawRedTI-7
❑ 95Sum-152
❑ 95SumNthD-152
❑ 95UppDec-246
❑ 95UppDecED-246
❑ 95UppDecEDG-246
❑ 96ColCho-544
❑ 96ColChoGS-544
❑ 96ColChoSS-544
❑ 96Pac-320
❑ 96Sco-254
❑ 96StaClu-445
❑ 96StaCluMOP-445
❑ 96TolMudHB-24
❑ 97TolMudHB-30
Rodriguez, Tomas
❑ 88BilMusP-1816
❑ 89BilMusP-2044
❑ 89BlaYNPRWL-152
Rodriguez, Tony
❑ 91ElmPioC-13
❑ 91ElmPioP-3280
❑ 92LynRedSC-7
❑ 92LynRedSF-2917
❑ 93NewBriRSF-1230
❑ 94PawRedSDD-22
❑ 94SarRedSC-24
❑ 94SarRedSF-1961
❑ 95PawRedSDD-25
❑ 95PawRedTI-2
❑ 96PawRedSDD-25
❑ 96SarRedSB-27
❑ 97PawRedS-22
Rodriguez, Victor
❑ 82RocRedWT-16
❑ 84BalOriP-29
❑ 85Don-535
❑ 85LasVegSC-101
❑ 87LouRedTI-26
❑ 88BlaYNPRWL-115
❑ 88PorBeaC-20
❑ 88PorBeaP-649
❑ 89BlaYNPRWL-52
❑ 89PorBeaC-17
❑ 89PorBeaP-210
❑ 89TriAAAP-AAA40
❑ 90CMC-564
❑ 90PorBeaC-12
❑ 90PorBeaP-188
❑ 90ProAAAF-258
❑ 91LinDriAAA-416
❑ 91OriCro-391
❑ 91PorBeaLD-416
❑ 91PorBeaP-1573
❑ 92ScrRedBF-2454
❑ 93ScrRedBF-2550
❑ 93ScrRedBTI-22
❑ 94EdmTraF-2882
❑ 95KanCouCLTI-13
❑ 95KanCouCTI-24
❑ 95MidLeaA-45
❑ 95UppDecML-214
❑ 95UppDecMLFS-214
❑ 96BreCouMB-29
❑ 96SarRedSB-3
❑ 96SigRooOJ-29
❑ 96StCatSB-24
❑ 97PorSeaD-26
❑ 97SarRedS-29
❑ 98PorSeaDQ-20
Rodriguez, Wilfredo
❑ 98MidLeaPM-20
❑ 98QuaCitRBG-23
Rodriques, Cecil
❑ 92HelBreF-1730
❑ 92HelBreSP-20
❑ 93BelBreCB-19
❑ 93BelBreFI-1724
❑ 94BelBreC-20
❑ 94BelBreFI-117
❑ 96El PasDB-24
Roe, Chan
❑ 98DunBluJTI-27
Roe, Preacher
❑ 47Exh-194
❑ 47PM1StaP1-187
❑ 47TipTop-145
❑ 48DodTeal-21
❑ 49Bow-162
❑ 50Bow-167
❑ 50Dra-1
❑ 51Bow-118
❑ 51TopRedB-16
❑ 52BerRos-58
❑ 52Bow-168
❑ 52DixLid-16
❑ 52DixPre-16
❑ 52NatTeaL-25
❑ 52StaCalL-79F
❑ 52StaCalS-91C
❑ 52Top-66
❑ 52Whe-26A
❑ 52Whe-26B
❑ 53BowBW-26
❑ 53DixLid-17
❑ 53DixPre-17
❑ 53ExhCan-1
❑ 53NorBreL-24
❑ 53Top-254
❑ 54Bow-218
❑ 54DixLid-13
❑ 54NewYorJA-16
❑ 54Top-14
❑ 55Bow-216
❑ 68LauWorS-46
❑ 70FleWorS-46
❑ 71FleWorS-47
❑ 74dod195T-31
❑ 74TCMNic-21
❑ 79DiaGre-87
❑ 79TCM50-145
❑ 79TCM50-239
❑ 83TCMPla1945-32
❑ 83TopRep5-66
❑ 88DodRinP1-9C
❑ 89DodSmoG-56
❑ 90DodTar-680
❑ 91TopArc1-254
❑ 92BazQua5A-9
❑ 94TopArc1-14
❑ 94TopArc1G-14
❑ 95TopArcBD-8
❑ 95TopArcBD-53
❑ 95TopArcBD-67

Roe, Rocky
❑ 88T/MUmp-42
❑ 89T/MUmp-40
❑ 90T/MUmp-38
Roebig, Stuart
❑ 91BriBanF-9
Roebuck, Ed
❑ 52LaPat-14
❑ 52Par-75
❑ 53ExhCan-41
❑ 55DodGolS-24
❑ 55Top-195
❑ 56Dod-26
❑ 56Top-58
❑ 58DodTeal-21
❑ 58Top-435
❑ 60DodBelB-13
❑ 60DodUniO-15
❑ 60Top-519
❑ 61DodBelB-37
❑ 61Pos-170
❑ 61Top-6
❑ 61TopStaI-32
❑ 62DodBelB-37
❑ 62DodVol-19
❑ 62Top-535
❑ 63Top-295
❑ 64PhiPhiB-19
❑ 64Top-187
❑ 64TopCoi-20
❑ 64TopSta-35
❑ 64TopStaU-64
❑ 64TopVen-187
❑ 65OPC-52
❑ 65Top-52
❑ 78TCM60I-165A
❑ 87Dod195T-8
❑ 90DodTar-681
❑ 91DodRinP3-12
❑ 95TopArcBD-106
❑ 95TopArcBD-144
Roebuck, Joe
❑ 89HelBreSP-13
❑ 90EriSaiS-22
❑ 91RenSilSCLC-13
❑ 92ChaRanC-8
❑ 92ChaRanF-2239
Roebuck, Ron
❑ 86AshTouP-24
❑ 86AubAstP-20
Roebuck, Scott
❑ 83WauTimF-20
Roeder, Jack
❑ 82WauTimF-3
Roeder, Jason
❑ 97SpoIndG-26
Roeder, Steve
❑ 90WelPirP-27
❑ 91WelPirC-19
❑ 92PulBraC-23
❑ 92PulBraF-3175
Roenicke, Gary
❑ 76SSP-338
❑ 78BalOriP-27
❑ 80BalOriP-16
❑ 80Top-568
❑ 81Don-116
❑ 81Fle-187
❑ 81OPC-37
❑ 81Top-37
❑ 82Don-509
❑ 82Fle-177
❑ 82Top-204
❑ 83Don-27
❑ 83Fle-71
❑ 83OPC-382
❑ 83OriPos-25
❑ 83Top-605
❑ 84BalOriP-30
❑ 84Don-392
❑ 84Fle-18
❑ 84Nes792-372
❑ 84OPC-372
❑ 84OriEng-12
❑ 84Top-372
❑ 84TopSti-205
❑ 84TopTif-372
❑ 85BalOriP-27
❑ 85Don-123
❑ 85Fle-188
❑ 85OPC-109
❑ 85Top-109
❑ 85TopMin-109
❑ 85TopTif-109
❑ 86Don-472
❑ 86Fle-285
❑ 86FleUpd-98
❑ 86OPC-183
❑ 86Top-494
❑ 86TopTif-494
❑ 86TopTra-94T
❑ 86TopTraT-94T
❑ 86YanTCM-37
❑ 87BraSmo-23
❑ 87DonOpeD-47
❑ 87Fle-112
❑ 87FleGlo-112
❑ 87OPC-283
❑ 87Top-683
❑ 87TopTif-683
❑ 87TopTra-105T
❑ 87TopTraT-105T
❑ 88PanSti-252
❑ 88Sco-482
❑ 88ScoGlo-482
❑ 88StaLinBra-15
❑ 88Top-523
❑ 88TopClo-95
❑ 88TopTif-523
❑ 91OriCro-392
❑ 91PacSenL-85
❑ 91PacSenL-104
❑ 92YanWIZ8-165
❑ 95IdaFalBTI-19
Roenicke, Ron
❑ 78LodDodT-15
❑ 80AlbDukTc-6
❑ 81AlbDukTc-9
❑ 82DodPol-40
❑ 82DodUniOV-17
❑ 82Fle-19
❑ 82Top-681
❑ 83DodPol-40
❑ 83Don-327
❑ 83Fle-217
❑ 83FleSta-166
❑ 83Top-113
❑ 84Don-484
❑ 84Fle-618
❑ 84LasVegSC-237
❑ 84Nes792-647
❑ 84Top-647
❑ 84TopTif-647
❑ 86FleUpd-99
❑ 86Top-63
❑ 86TopTif-63
❑ 87Don-412
❑ 87Fle-182
❑ 87FleGlo-182
❑ 87PhiTas-17
❑ 87Top-329
❑ 87TopTif-329
❑ 88NasSouC-21
❑ 88NasSouP-475
❑ 88NasSouTI-20
❑ 88Sco-566
❑ 88ScoGlo-566
❑ 88Top-783
❑ 88TopTif-783
❑ 89OklCit8C-16
❑ 89OklCit8P-1519
❑ 90DodTar-682
❑ 91PacSenL-85
❑ 91PacSenL-106
❑ 91SanAntMP-2993
❑ 92DodMot-28
❑ 92DodPol-NNO
❑ 93DodMot-28
❑ 93DodPol-30
❑ 94GreFalDSP-30
❑ 95SanBerSTI-31
❑ 97SanAntMB-27
❑ 97TexAllM-31
❑ 98SanAntMG-25
❑ 98SanAntMM-27
Roesch, John
❑ 77NewCoPT-28
❑ 78NewWayCT-39
Roesler, Mike
❑ 86CedRapRT-8
❑ 87TamTarP-5
❑ 88NasSouC-11
❑ 88NasSouP-492
❑ 89BlaYNPRWL-161
❑ 89NasSouC-7
❑ 89NasSouP-1282
❑ 89NasSouTI-21
❑ 90BufBisTI-21
❑ 90Fle-645
❑ 90FleCan-645
❑ 90OPC-203
❑ 90Sco-648
❑ 90Top-203
❑ 90TopDeb89-104
❑ 90TopTif-203
❑ 91CarMudLD-115
❑ 91CarMudP-1085
❑ 91LinDriAA-115
❑ 92BufBisBS-19
❑ 92BufBisF-322
❑ 92BufBisS-41
Roessler, Pat
❑ 90BirBarB-29
❑ 90BirBarP-1399
❑ 91BirBarP-1472
❑ 91LinDriAA-75
❑ 92BirBarF-2599
❑ 93SarWhiSF-1388
Roetter, Randy
❑ 82QuaCitCT-28
❑ 88WauTimGS-28
❑ 89WilBilP-634
❑ 90CalCanC-25
❑ 90CMC-452
❑ 96TacRaiB-4
❑ 97TacRai-4
❑ 98TacRaiQ-4
Roettgen, Mark
❑ 96PeoChiB-28
Roettger, Oscar F.L.
❑ 78HalHalR-14
❑ 81ConTSN-94
❑ 90DodTar-683
Roettger, Wally (Walter H.)
❑ 27MidBre-15
❑ 31CarMet-25
❑ 31Exh-8
❑ 33ButCanV-40
❑ 34DiaMatCSB-153
❑ 81ConTSN-95
❑ 92ConTSN-653
Rogaliner, Chris
❑ 90NiaFalRP-30
Rogalski, Wayne
❑ 86AshTouP-25
Rogan, Bullet (Wilbur)
❑ 74LauOldTBS-19
❑ 86NegLeaF-32
❑ 87NegLeaPD-34
❑ 90NegLeaS-29
❑ 94TedWil-111
Rogan, Pat
❑ 65Top-486
Rogascozv, Boris
❑ 89EasLeaDDP-DD12
Rogell, William
❑ 33Gou-11
❑ 33GouCanV-11
❑ 34BatR31-177
❑ 34DiaMatCSB-154
❑ 34DiaStaR-76
❑ 34TigTeal-15
❑ 35GolMedFR-11
❑ 35GouPuzR-1D
❑ 35GouPuzR-2D
❑ 35GouPuzR-16D
❑ 35GouPuzR-17D
❑ 36GouWidPPR-A89
❑ 36NatChiFPR-65
❑ 36WorWidGV-52
❑ 38CloFotW-72
❑ 74TigTCM1AC-25
❑ 76TigOldTS-18
❑ 80TigGreT-2
❑ 81TigDetN-16
❑ 81TigSecNP-29
❑ 83TigAlKS-39
❑ 86TigSpoD-7
❑ 94ConTSN-1236
❑ 94ConTSNB-1236
Rogers, Brad
❑ 88BatCliP-1691
Rogers, Brian C.
❑ 98OneYanG-25
❑ 99TeaBesR-73
❑ 99TeaBesRG-73
❑ 99TeaBesRS-73
Rogers, Brown
❑ 13Zee-19
❑ 14Zee-22
Rogers, Bryan
❑ 90St.LucMS-23
❑ 91LinDriAA-641
❑ 91WilBilLD-641
❑ 91WilBilP-290
❑ 92BinMetF-514
❑ 92BinMetS-66
❑ 93BinMetF-2333
❑ 94NorTidF-2920
❑ 95NorTidTI-25
❑ 97RicBra-20
Rogers, Charlie
❑ 90MiaMirIS-22
❑ 90MiaMirIS-27
❑ 91Cla/Bes-375
❑ 91MiaMirP-407
❑ 92StoPorC-11
❑ 92StoPorF-35
❑ 93El PasDF-2950
❑ 94ExcFS7-86
❑ 94NewOrlZF-1467
Rogers, Danny
❑ 87SumBraP-22
❑ 88CedRapRP-1162
❑ 90NiaFalRP-1
❑ 91Cla/Bes-379
❑ 91FayGenC-22
❑ 91FayGenP-1181
Rogers, Dave
❑ 77SalPirT-22
Rogers, Dennis
❑ 86NasPirP-24
❑ 87MacPirP-24
❑ 91SouOreAAP-SOA28
Rogers, Doug
❑ 89IdaFalBP-2027
Rogers, Dusty
❑ 86TamTarP-17
❑ 87CedRapRP-11
Rogers, Jason
❑ 94BluOriC-18
❑ 94BluOriF-3562
❑ 96FreKeyB-18
❑ 97FreKey-23
❑ 98BowBayM-26
❑ 98FreKeyM-16
Rogers, Jesse
❑ 96NegLeaBMKC-8
Rogers, Jimmy
❑ 88MyrBeaBJP-1190
❑ 88SouAtlLAGS-22
❑ 89KnoBluJB-22
❑ 89KnoBluJP-1133
❑ 89KnoBluJS-18
❑ 90Bes-176
❑ 90CMC-855
❑ 90KnoBluJB-2
❑ 90KnoBluJP-1241
❑ 90KnoBluJS-16
❑ 91KnoBluJLD-365
❑ 91KnoBluJP-1764
❑ 91LinDriAA-365
❑ 94SyrChiF-970
❑ 94SyrChiTI-23
❑ 95SyrChiTI-22
❑ 96SyrChiTI-26
Rogers, Kenny
❑ 88TulDriTI-28
❑ 89DonBasB-315
❑ 89DonRoo-13
❑ 89RanMot-21
❑ 89RanSmo-27
❑ 89ScoRoo-107T
❑ 89TopTra-104T
❑ 89TopTraT-104T
❑ 90Don-283
❑ 90Fle-311
❑ 90FleCan-311
❑ 90Lea-311
❑ 90OPC-683
❑ 90RanMot-22
❑ 90Sco-301
❑ 90Sco100RS-46
❑ 90ScoYouSI-21
❑ 90Spo-216
❑ 90Top-683
❑ 90TopDeb89-105
❑ 90TopRoo-24
❑ 90TopTif-683
❑ 90ToyRoo-22
❑ 90UppDec-606
❑ 91Bow-290
❑ 91Don-258
❑ 91Fle-299
❑ 91Lea-105
❑ 91OPC-332
❑ 91RanMot-22
❑ 91Sco-155
❑ 91StaClu-258
❑ 91Top-332
❑ 91TopDesS-332
❑ 91TopMic-332
❑ 91TopTif-332
❑ 91Ult-353
❑ 91UppDec-606
❑ 92Don-368
❑ 92Fle-317
❑ 92Lea-173
❑ 92LeaBlaG-173
❑ 92OPC-511
❑ 92Pin-482
❑ 92RanMot-22
❑ 92RanTeal-20
❑ 92Sco-101
❑ 92StaClu-311
❑ 92Top-511
❑ 92TopGol-511
❑ 92TopGolW-511
❑ 92TopMic-511
❑ 92Ult-445
❑ 92UppDec-651
❑ 93Don-509
❑ 93Fle-328
❑ 93Lea-92
❑ 93OPC-356
❑ 93PacSpa-646
❑ 93Pin-381
❑ 93RanKee-429
❑ 93RanStaC-19
❑ 93Sco-204
❑ 93StaClu-55
❑ 93StaCluFDI-55
❑ 93StaCluMOP-55
❑ 93Top-169
❑ 93TopGol-169
❑ 93TopInaM-169
❑ 93TopInaR-169
❑ 93TopMic-169
❑ 93Ult-285
❑ 93UppDec-92
❑ 93UppDecGold-92
❑ 94Bow-429
❑ 94ColC-242
❑ 94ColChoGS-242
❑ 94ColChoSS-242
❑ 94Don-410
❑ 94Fin-94
❑ 94FinRef-94
❑ 94Fla-347
❑ 94Fle-320
❑ 94FleExtB-185
❑ 94Lea-293
❑ 94Pac-628
❑ 94Pin-221
❑ 94PinArtP-221
❑ 94PinMusC-221
❑ 94RanMagM-36
❑ 94Sco-212
❑ 94ScoGolR-212
❑ 94Sel-297
❑ 94StaClu-467
❑ 94StaCluFDI-467
❑ 94StaCluGR-467
❑ 94StaCluMOP-467
❑ 94StaCluT-252
❑ 94StaCluTFDI-252
❑ 94Stu-158
❑ 94Top-413
❑ 94TopGol-413
❑ 94TopSpa-413
❑ 94TriPla-200
❑ 94Ult-133
❑ 94UppDec-457
❑ 94UppDecED-457
❑ 95Bow-289
❑ 95BowBes-R61
❑ 95BowBesR-R61
❑ 95ColCho-65
❑ 95ColCho-398
❑ 95ColChoGS-65
❑ 95ColChoGS-398
❑ 95ColChoSE-183
❑ 95ColChoSE-264
❑ 95ColChoSEGS-183
❑ 95ColChoSEGS-264
❑ 95ColChoSESS-183
❑ 95ColChoSESS-264
❑ 95ColChoSS-65
❑ 95ColChoSS-398
❑ 95Don-531
❑ 95DonPreP-531
❑ 95DonTopotO-166
❑ 95Emo-89
❑ 95Fin-178
❑ 95FinRef-178
❑ 95Fla-309
❑ 95Fle-296
❑ 95FleTeaL-13
❑ 95Lea-222
❑ 95LeaLim-136
❑ 95Pin-327
❑ 95PinArtP-327
❑ 95PinMusC-327
❑ 95RanCra-29
❑ 95Sco-315
❑ 95Sco-425
❑ 95ScoGolR-315
❑ 95ScoGolR-425
❑ 95ScoPlaTS-315
❑ 95ScoPlaTS-425
❑ 95SP-199
❑ 95SPCha-193
❑ 95SPChaDC-193
❑ 95SPSil-199
❑ 95StaClu-67
❑ 95StaCluFDI-67
❑ 95StaCluMOP-67
❑ 95StaCluSTWS-67
❑ 95StaCluVR-41
❑ 95StaCluVRMO-41
❑ 95Top-13
❑ 95TopCyb-11
❑ 95UppDec-394
❑ 95UppDecC-4A
❑ 95UppDecED-394
❑ 95UppDecEDG-394
❑ 95UppDecSE-38
❑ 95UppDecSEG-38
❑ 95Zen-40
❑ 96Baz-22
❑ 96ColCho-781
❑ 96Don-163
❑ 96DonPreP-163
❑ 96EmoXL-96
❑ 96Fin-B195
❑ 96FinRef-B195
❑ 96Fla-137
❑ 96Fle-261
❑ 96FleTif-261
❑ 96FleUpd-U68
❑ 96FleUpdTC-U68
❑ 96MetUni-94
❑ 96MetUniP-94
❑ 96Pac-427
❑ 96PanSti-233
❑ 96Pin-31
❑ 96Pin-341
❑ 96PinAfi-47
❑ 96PinAfiAP-47
❑ 96PinAfiFPP-47
❑ 96PinFoil-341
❑ 96RanCup-3
❑ 96RedF-13
❑ 96Sco-319
❑ 96ScoDugC-B44
❑ 96ScoDugCAP-B44
❑ 96Spo-80
❑ 96SpoArtP-80
❑ 96StaClu-143
❑ 96StaClu-238
❑ 96StaCluEPB-143
❑ 96StaCluEPG-143
❑ 96StaCluEPS-143
❑ 96StaCluMOP-143
❑ 96StaCluMOP-238
❑ 96Sum-54
❑ 96SumAbo&B-54
❑ 96SumArtP-54
❑ 96SumFoi-54
❑ 96Top-130
❑ 96TopGal-72
❑ 96TopGalPPI-72
❑ 96TopLas-127
❑ 96Ult-140
❑ 96Ult-395
❑ 96UltGolM-140
❑ 96UltGolM-395
❑ 96UppDec-504U
❑ 96UppDecPHE-H18
❑ 96UppDecPreH-H18
❑ 97ColCho-407
❑ 97Fle-178
❑ 97FleTif-178
❑ 97Pac-160
❑ 97PacLigB-160
❑ 97PacSil-160
❑ 97Sco-225
❑ 97ScoArtPWB-225
❑ 97ScoPreS-225
❑ 97ScoShoS-225
❑ 97ScoShoSAP-225
❑ 97StaClu-98
❑ 97StaCluMOP-98
❑ 97Top-372
❑ 97Ult-105

❑ 97UltGolME-105
❑ 97UltPlaME-105
❑ 97YanSco-14
❑ 97YanScoPl-14
❑ 97YanScoPr-14
❑ 98A'sMot-6
❑ 98Bow-263
❑ 98BowChr-263
❑ 98BowChrGA-263
❑ 98BowChrGAR-263
❑ 98BowChrI-263
❑ 98BowChrIR-263
❑ 98BowChrR-263
❑ 98BowGolA-263
❑ 98BowInt-263
❑ 98CirThu-44
❑ 98CirThuRav-44
❑ 98CirThuSupRav-44
❑ 98ColCho-453
❑ 98Fle-370
❑ 98PacAur-69
❑ 98PacOme-179
❑ 98PacOmeR-179
❑ 98PacOnl-543
❑ 98PacOnlR-543
❑ 98PacOnlWC-543
❑ 98Pin-139
❑ 98PinPlu-143
❑ 98PinPreP-139
❑ 98SP Aut-149
❑ 98Ult-448
❑ 98UltGolM-448
❑ 98UltMas-448
❑ 98UltPlaM-448
❑ 98UppDec-706
❑ 99199Fin-31
❑ 99FinGolRef-31
❑ 99FinRef-31
❑ 99Fle-197
❑ 99FleBri-77
❑ 99FleBri2G-77
❑ 99FleBriBlu-77
❑ 99FleBriGol-77
❑ 99FleSta9-197
❑ 99FleWarT-197
❑ 99MetUni-81
❑ 99MetUniGM-81
❑ 99MetUniPMG-81
❑ 99Pac-316
❑ 99PacCroC-206
❑ 99PacCroCPB-206
❑ 99PacOme-173
❑ 99PacOmeC-173
❑ 99PacOmeG-173
❑ 99PacOmePB-173
❑ 99PacPlaB-316
❑ 99PacRed-316
❑ 99SkyPre-34
❑ 99SkyPreR-34
❑ 99SkyThu-201
❑ 99SkyThuRant-201
❑ 99SkyThuRave-201
❑ 99SpoIll-102
❑ 99StaClu-67
❑ 99StaCluFDI-67
❑ 99StaCluOoaK-67
❑ 99StaCluPP-67
❑ 99ThuSkySupR-201
❑ 99Top-27
❑ 99TopChr-27
❑ 99TopChrR-27
❑ 99TopMVPP-27
❑ 99TopOpeD-18
❑ 99Ult-210
❑ 99UltGolM-210
❑ 99UltMas-210
❑ 99UltPlaM-210
❑ 99UppDec-168
❑ 99UppDecEL1-168
❑ 99UppDecEL2-168
❑ 99Vic-287

Rogers, Kevin
❑ 88PocGiaP-2091
❑ 89CliGiaP-891
❑ 90Bes-76
❑ 90CalLeaACLC-50
❑ 90CMC-716
❑ 90SanJosGB-24
❑ 90SanJosGCLC-51
❑ 90SanJosGP-2003
❑ 90SanJosGS-19
❑ 91Bow-638
❑ 91Cla/Bes-221
❑ 91LinDriAA-320
❑ 91ShrCapLD-320
❑ 91ShrCapP-1823
❑ 92Bow-415
❑ 92ShrCapF-3870
❑ 92ShrCapS-593
❑ 92SkyAA F-262
❑ 93Bow-576
❑ 93FleFinE-155
❑ 93FleMajLP-A10
❑ 93GiaMot-24
❑ 93GiaPos-30
❑ 93GiaStaC-8
❑ 93LeaGolR-R11
❑ 93LeaGolRJ-R11
❑ 93PacSpa-615
❑ 93Pin-613
❑ 93PinRooTP-2
❑ 93Sco-319
❑ 93SelRoo-64T
❑ 93Top-822
❑ 93TopGol-822
❑ 93TopInaM-822
❑ 93TopInaR-822
❑ 93TopMic-822
❑ 93Ult-489
❑ 93UppDec-8
❑ 93UppDecGold-8
❑ 94ColC-243
❑ 94ColChoGS-243
❑ 94ColChoSS-243
❑ 94Don-508
❑ 94Fle-699
❑ 94GiaAMC-19
❑ 94GiaTarBC-22
❑ 94GiaUSPC-3S
❑ 94GiaUSPC-9D
❑ 94Pac-554
❑ 94Pin-365
❑ 94PinArtP-365
❑ 94PinMusC-365
❑ 94Sco-581
❑ 94ScoGolR-581
❑ 94StaClu-459
❑ 94StaCluFDI-459
❑ 94StaCluGR-459
❑ 94StaCluMOP-459
❑ 94StaCluT-23
❑ 94StaCluTFDI-23
❑ 94Top-3
❑ 94TopGol-3
❑ 94TopSpa-3
❑ 94Ult-592
❑ 95Fla-211
❑ 95Top-219
❑ 97RicBra-21

Rogers, Lamarr
❑ 93CenValRF-2901
❑ 93Top-746
❑ 93TopGol-746
❑ 93TopInaM-746
❑ 93TopInaR-746
❑ 93TopMic-746
❑ 94NewHavRF-1558
❑ 95NewHavRTI-5
❑ 97St.PauS-24
❑ 98St.PauSTI-22

Rogers, Lee
❑ 39WorWidGV-22
❑ 79RedSoxEF-6
❑ 90DodTar-684

Rogers, Mac
❑ 85DurBulT-9
❑ 86DurBulP-24

Rogers, Marte
❑ 85ElmPioT-19

Rogers, Packy
❑ 88ElmPio1C-5
❑ 90DodTar-685

Rogers, Randy
❑ 78TidTidT-21
❑ 83AndBraT-15

Rogers, Robbie
❑ 88RenSilSCLC-283

Rogers, Roy
❑ 75JohMiz-14

Rogers, Steve
❑ 72Dia-39
❑ 73ExpPos-6
❑ 74OPC-169
❑ 74Top-169
❑ 74TopDecE-65
❑ 74TopSta-59
❑ 75ExpPos-30
❑ 75OPC-173
❑ 75Top-173
❑ 75TopMin-173
❑ 76BlaDis-50
❑ 76BucDis-50
❑ 76CarDis-50
❑ 76CraDis-50
❑ 76DailsID-50
❑ 76ExpRed-27
❑ 76IsaDis-50
❑ 76MonExpP-26
❑ 76OPC-71
❑ 76OrbDis-50
❑ 76RedBarD-50
❑ 76SafDis-50
❑ 76SSP-349
❑ 76Top-71
❑ 76TowCluD-50
❑ 77BurCheD-159
❑ 77ExpPos-26
❑ 77Hos-22
❑ 77OPC-153
❑ 77Top-316
❑ 78OPC-9
❑ 78Top-425
❑ 78WifBalD-62
❑ 79ExpPos-21
❑ 79OPC-120
❑ 79Top-235
❑ 80ExpPos-25
❑ 80Kel-8
❑ 80OPC-271
❑ 80Top-520
❑ 81Don-330A
❑ 81Don-330B
❑ 81ExpPos-13
❑ 81Fle-143
❑ 81FleStiC-57
❑ 81OPC-344
❑ 81OPCPos-9
❑ 81Top-725
❑ 81TopScr-106
❑ 81TopSti-190
❑ 82Don-36
❑ 82ExpHygM-18
❑ 82ExpPos-34
❑ 82ExpZel-2
❑ 82FBIDis-19
❑ 82Fle-205
❑ 82FleSta-36
❑ 82OPC-52
❑ 82OPCPos-20
❑ 82PerAll-15
❑ 82PerAllG-15
❑ 82Top-605
❑ 82TopSti-59
❑ 83AllGamPI-174
❑ 83Don-18
❑ 83Don-320
❑ 83ExpPos-27
❑ 83ExpStu-10
❑ 83Fle-294
❑ 83FleSta-167
❑ 83FleSti-260
❑ 83OPC-106
❑ 83OPC-111
❑ 83OPC-320
❑ 83Top-111
❑ 83Top-320
❑ 83Top-405
❑ 83Top-707
❑ 83TopSti-208
❑ 83TopSti-256
❑ 84Don-219
❑ 84DonActAS-48
❑ 84ExpPos-25
❑ 84ExpStu-19
❑ 84ExpStu-36
❑ 84Fle-284
❑ 84Nes792-80
❑ 84Nes792-394
❑ 84Nes792-708
❑ 84OPC-80
❑ 84OPC-394
❑ 84SevCoi-W20
❑ 84Top-80
❑ 84Top-394
❑ 84Top-708
❑ 84TopGloS-3
❑ 84TopRubD-30
❑ 84TopSti-88
❑ 84TopSti-182
❑ 84TopTif-80
❑ 84TopTif-394
❑ 84TopTif-708
❑ 85Don-219
❑ 85Fle-408
❑ 85Lea-192
❑ 85OPC-205
❑ 85OPCPos-11
❑ 85Top-205
❑ 85TopMin-205
❑ 85TopRubD-31
❑ 85TopSti-89
❑ 85TopTif-205
❑ 86ExpGreT-9
❑ 88GreBasS-34
❑ 91UppDecS-23
❑ 92Nab-33
❑ 92UppDecS-21
❑ 93ExpDonM-28
❑ 93UppDecS-27
❑ 94TedWil-51

Rogers, Stu
❑ 85BurRanT-23

Rogers, Thomas
❑ 21E121So1-81
❑ 21E121So8-78
❑ 21KoBreWSI-47
❑ 22W575-107
❑ 23W501-28

Roggenburk, Garry
❑ 63Top-386
❑ 63TwiVol-18
❑ 64Top-258
❑ 64TopVen-258
❑ 66Top-582
❑ 67Top-429
❑ 68Top-581
❑ 81TCM60I-336
❑ 91ElmPioC-28
❑ 91ElmPioP-3288
❑ 92ElmPioC-25
❑ 92ElmPioF-1397
❑ 93UtiBluSC-26
❑ 93UtiBluSF-3549
❑ 94UtiBluSC-29
❑ 94UtiBluSF-3837

Roggendorf, Kip
❑ 93St.CatBJC-21
❑ 93St.CatBJF-3983
❑ 94St.CatBJC-28
❑ 94St.CatBJF-3653

Rogodzinski, Mike
❑ 73PhiTeal-21
❑ 74OPC-492
❑ 74Top-492
❑ 76SSP-607

Rogovin, Saul
❑ 47PM1StaP1-188
❑ 52Bow-165
❑ 52RedMan-AL19
❑ 52TipTop-35
❑ 52Top-159
❑ 53BowC-75
❑ 54Bow-140
❑ 57Top-129
❑ 91OriCro-393
❑ 97BalOriP-44

Rogow, Mark
❑ 96CarMudB-28
❑ 96HonShaHWB-NNO

Rogozenski, Karl
❑ 83St.PetCT-28

Rohan, Tony
❑ 85NewOriT-7
❑ 87MiaMarP-9
❑ 88MiaMarS-22

Rohde, Brad
❑ 86BelMarCr-112
❑ 86WauTimP-20

Rohde, Dave
❑ 86AriWilP-12
❑ 86AubAstP-21
❑ 87OscAstP-29
❑ 88ColAstB-11
❑ 89ColMudB-21
❑ 89ColMudP-123
❑ 89ColMudS-20
❑ 89Sta-2
❑ 89TucTorJP-20
❑ 90AstLenH-20
❑ 90Bow-75
❑ 90BowTif-75
❑ 90CMC-621
❑ 90FleUpd-17
❑ 90TucTorC-19
❑ 91AstMot-18
❑ 91Bow-558
❑ 91Don-743
❑ 91Lea-424
❑ 91OPC-531
❑ 91Sco100RS-69
❑ 91StaClu-137
❑ 91Top-531
❑ 91TopDeb90-133
❑ 91TopDesS-531
❑ 91TopMic-531
❑ 91TopTif-531
❑ 91UppDec-662
❑ 92ColSprSSF-760
❑ 92StaClu-753
❑ 92StaCluECN-753
❑ 93BufBisF-526
❑ 93PacSpa-100
❑ 94BufBisF-1844
❑ 95TucTotTI-23

Rohde, Dr. Richard
❑ 63RedFreBC-21

Rohe, George
❑ 11SpoLifCW-306

Rohlfing, Wayne
❑ 79QuaCitCT-6
❑ 80QuaCitCT-24

Rohlof, Scott
❑ 86VisOakP-17

Rohm, Dave
❑ 78DunBluJT-19

Rohn, Andy
❑ 87EveGiaC-7

Rohn, Dan
❑ 80VenLeaS-115
❑ 80WicAerT-6
❑ 82IowCubT-8
❑ 83IowCubT-19
❑ 84CubChiT-23
❑ 84IowCubT-8
❑ 85IntLeaAT-36
❑ 85MaiGuiT-22
❑ 86IndOhH-15
❑ 86IndTeal-37
❑ 87TacTigP-16
❑ 88OklCit8C-20
❑ 88OklCit8P-31
❑ 89OklCit8C-15
❑ 89OklCit8P-1530
❑ 91PacSenL-21
❑ 92Ft.MyeMCB-26
❑ 92Ft.MyeMF-2760
❑ 94SalLakBF-833
❑ 95ForWayWTI-26
❑ 96ForWayWB-27
❑ 98OrlRayM-23

Rohr, Les
❑ 68Top-569
❑ 91MetWIZ-333

Rohr, William
❑ 67Top-547
❑ 68Top-314
❑ 68TopVen-314
❑ 70WicAerM-14

Rohrer, William
❑ 12Zee-46
❑ 13Zee-48
❑ 14Zee-91
❑ 15Zee-87

Rohrmeier, Dan
❑ 88FloStaLAS-48
❑ 88TamTarS-22
❑ 89SarWhiSS-21
❑ 90ProAaA-70
❑ 90TexLeaAGS-29
❑ 90TulDriP-1169
❑ 90TulDriTI-22
❑ 91LinDriAA-593
❑ 91TulDriLD-593
❑ 91TulDriP-2787
❑ 91TulDriTI-24
❑ 92MemChiF-2433
❑ 92MemChiS-445
❑ 93ClaGolF-26
❑ 93ExcFS7-178
❑ 93OmaRoyF-1695
❑ 94MemChiF-371
❑ 95ChaLooTI-18
❑ 96MemChiB-26
❑ 97TacRai-24
❑ 98TacRaiQ-25

Rohrwild, Shawn
❑ 90IdaFalBP-3266
❑ 91MacBraC-9
❑ 91MacBraP-863

Rohwer, Ray
❑ 23Zee-171
❑ 25Zee-53
❑ 26Zee-102
❑ 27Zee-101
❑ 28Zee-118
❑ 29Zee-120
❑ 30Zee-129
❑ 31Zee-92

Roig, Tony
❑ 59DarFar-19
❑ 60DarFar-16
❑ 61UniOil-SD8
❑ 77FriOneYW-12

Rois, Luis
❑ 80GleFalWSBT-6
❑ 80GleFalWSCT-17
❑ 81GleFalWST-20

Rojano, Rafael
❑ 95GreBatTI-32

Rojas, Alejandro
❑ 98MarPhiG-25

Rojas, Arquimedes
❑ 95LinVen-162

Rojas, Christian
❑ 94PriRedC-20
❑ 94PriRedF-3272
❑ 95BilMusTI-6
❑ 96Exc-149
❑ 97BurBeeB-19
❑ 98BurBeeM-18
❑ 98WatIndTI-28

Rojas, Cookie
❑ 62RedEnq-30
❑ 63Top-221
❑ 64PhiPhiB-20
❑ 64PhiTeaS-5
❑ 64Top-448
❑ 65Top-474
❑ 66OPC-170
❑ 66PhiTeal-10
❑ 66Top-170
❑ 66TopRubI-82
❑ 66TopVen-170
❑ 67CokCapPh-11
❑ 67DexPre-179
❑ 67PhiPol-11
❑ 67Top-595
❑ 68OPC-39
❑ 68Top-39
❑ 68TopVen-39
❑ 69MilBra-238
❑ 69MLBOffS-176
❑ 69PhiTeal-7
❑ 69Top-507
❑ 69TopSta-77
❑ 69TopSup-55
❑ 69TopTeaP-8
❑ 69TraSta-55
❑ 70CarTeal-23
❑ 70DayDaiNM-131
❑ 70MLBOffS-142
❑ 70RoyTeal-29
❑ 70Top-569
❑ 71MLBOffS-427
❑ 71OPC-118
❑ 71oySigST-23
❑ 71Top-118
❑ 72Kel-39A
❑ 72Kel-39B
❑ 72MilBra-295
❑ 72OPC-415
❑ 72oyTeal-20
❑ 72Top-415
❑ 73LinPor-90
❑ 73OPC-188
❑ 73Top-188
❑ 74Kel-42
❑ 74OPC-278
❑ 74RoyPos-25
❑ 74Top-278
❑ 74TopSta-189
❑ 75Hos-2
❑ 75HosTwi-2
❑ 75OPC-169
❑ 75RoyPos-27
❑ 75Top-169
❑ 75TopMin-169
❑ 76KanCitRP-27
❑ 76OPC-311
❑ 76RoyAaP-13
❑ 76SSP-171
❑ 76Top-311
❑ 77Top-509
❑ 83PhiPosGPaM-8
❑ 85DomLeaS-179
❑ 86RoyGreT-2
❑ 88AngSmo-1
❑ 88TopTra-97T
❑ 88TopTraT-97T
❑ 93MarPub-28
❑ 93UppDecS-28
❑ 94TopSpa-L9

Rojas, Eliser
❑ 97HelBreB-28
❑ 98HelBreM-29

Rojas, Francisco

❑ 78CedRapGT-23
Rojas, Freddy
❑ 93KinMetC-19
❑ 93KinMetF-3805
Rojas, Homar
❑ 85MexCitTT-17
❑ 87SanAntDTI-21
❑ 88FloStaLAS-19
❑ 88VerBeaDS-22
❑ 89SanAntMB-21
❑ 90SanAntMGS-25
Rojas, Jeff
❑ 85VisOakT-18
Rojas, Luis
❑ 82WesHavAT-24
Rojas, Mel (Melquiades)
❑ 87BurExpP-1093
❑ 89JacExpB-28
❑ 89JacExpP-156
❑ 89SouLeaAJ-20
❑ 90Bow-108
❑ 90BowTif-108
❑ 90IndIndP-302
❑ 90ProAAAF-585
❑ 90UppDec-772
❑ 91Don-681
❑ 91ExpPos-18
❑ 91Fle-245
❑ 91OPC-252
❑ 91OPCPre-101
❑ 91Sco-729
❑ 91ScoRoo-1
❑ 91Top-252
❑ 91TopDeb90-134
❑ 91TopDesS-252
❑ 91TopMic-252
❑ 91TopTif-252
❑ 91UppDec-357
❑ 92Don-435
❑ 92ExpPos-25
❑ 92Fle-490
❑ 92IndIndS-191
❑ 92OPC-583
❑ 92OPCPre-124
❑ 92Sco-725
❑ 92StaClu-489
❑ 92Top-583
❑ 92TopGol-583
❑ 92TopGolW-583
❑ 92TopMic-583
❑ 92UppDec-683
❑ 93Don-408
❑ 93ExpColP7-6
❑ 93ExpPosN-19
❑ 93Fle-79
❑ 93Lea-364
❑ 93LimRocDWB-14
❑ 93OPC-347
❑ 93PacSpa-537
❑ 93Pin-419
❑ 93Sco-363
❑ 93StaClu-553
❑ 93StaCluFDI-553
❑ 93StaCluMOP-553
❑ 93Top-341
❑ 93TopGol-341
❑ 93TopInaM-341
❑ 93TopInaR-341
❑ 93TopMic-341
❑ 93Ult-70
❑ 93UppDec-190
❑ 93UppDecGold-190
❑ 94ColC-244
❑ 94ColChoGS-244
❑ 94ColChoSS-244
❑ 94Don-491
❑ 94Fla-403
❑ 94Fle-548
❑ 94FleExtB-310
❑ 94Lea-47
❑ 94Pac-388
❑ 94Pin-176
❑ 94PinArtP-176
❑ 94PinMusC-176
❑ 94Sco-162
❑ 94ScoGolR-162
❑ 94StaClu-14
❑ 94StaCluFDI-14
❑ 94StaCluGR-14
❑ 94StaCluMOP-14
❑ 94Top-78
❑ 94TopGol-78
❑ 94TopSpa-78
❑ 94Ult-525
❑ 94UppDec-366
❑ 94UppDecED-366
❑ 95Baz-67
❑ 95ColCho-248
❑ 95ColChoGS-248
❑ 95ColChoSS-248
❑ 95Don-322
❑ 95DonPreP-322
❑ 95DonTopotO-284
❑ 95Fla-378
❑ 95Fle-357
❑ 95Lea-237
❑ 95Pac-272
❑ 95Pin-59
❑ 95PinArtP-59
❑ 95PinMusC-59
❑ 95Sco-488
❑ 95ScoGolR-488
❑ 95ScoPlaTS-488
❑ 95StaClu-266
❑ 95StaCluFDI-266
❑ 95StaCluMOP-266
❑ 95StaCluSTWS-266
❑ 95Top-74
❑ 95TopCyb-51
❑ 95Ult-193
❑ 95UltGolM-193
❑ 96ColCho-216
❑ 96ColChoGS-216
❑ 96ColChoSS-216
❑ 96Don-156
❑ 96DonPreP-156
❑ 96EmoXL-225
❑ 96ExpDis-16
❑ 96Fin-B132
❑ 96FinRef-B132
❑ 96Fla-312
❑ 96Fle-465
❑ 96FleTif-465
❑ 96LeaSigA-197
❑ 96LeaSigAG-197
❑ 96LeaSigAS-197
❑ 96Pac-119
❑ 96PacPri-P43
❑ 96PacPriG-P43
❑ 96Sco-431
❑ 96StaClu-167
❑ 96StaCluEPB-167
❑ 96StaCluEPG-167
❑ 96StaCluEPS-167
❑ 96StaCluMOP-167
❑ 96Top-186
❑ 96TopGal-47
❑ 96TopGalPPI-47
❑ 96Ult-235
❑ 96UltGolM-235
❑ 96UppDec-393
❑ 97Bow-61
❑ 97BowInt-61
❑ 97Cir-306
❑ 97CirRav-306
❑ 97ColCho-289
❑ 97Fin-274
❑ 97FinRef-274
❑ 97FlaShoLC-84
❑ 97FlaShoLeg0-84
❑ 97FlaShoLeg1-84
❑ 97FlaShoM-A84
❑ 97FlaShoM-B84
❑ 97FlaShoM-C84
❑ 97FlaShoR0-84
❑ 97FlaShoR1-84
❑ 97FlaShoR2-84
❑ 97Fle-385
❑ 97Fle-665
❑ 97FleTif-385
❑ 97FleTif-665
❑ 97Lea-82
❑ 97LeaFraM-82
❑ 97LeaFraMDC-82
❑ 97Pac-351
❑ 97PacLigB-351
❑ 97PacSil-351
❑ 97Sco-460
❑ 97ScoArtPWB-460
❑ 97ScoResC-460
❑ 97ScoShoS-460
❑ 97ScoShoSAP-460
❑ 97SP-42
❑ 97StaClu-148
❑ 97StaCluMOP-148
❑ 97Top-26
❑ 97Ult-312
❑ 97UltGolME-312
❑ 97UltPlaME-312
❑ 97UppDec-527
❑ 98Fle-447
❑ 98PacOnl-490
❑ 98PacOnlR-490
❑ 98PacOnlWC-490
❑ 98Top-361
❑ 98TopChr-361
❑ 98TopChrR-361
❑ 98TopDevR-361
❑ 98TopDia-361
❑ 98TopMiniC-361
❑ 98UppDec-448
Rojas, Mike
❑ 83IdaFalAT-17
❑ 93BirBarF-1210
❑ 97AubDouTI-14
❑ 98QuaCitRBG-24
Rojas, Minnie
❑ 66SeaPop-19
❑ 66SeaPop-20
❑ 67CokCapDA-33
❑ 67OPC-104
❑ 67Top-104
❑ 68Top-305
❑ 68TopVen-305
❑ 69Top-502
Rojas, Moises
❑ 98LowSpiM-15
Rojas, Olinto
❑ 76VenLeaS-172
❑ 80VenLeaS-139
Rojas, Renny
❑ 97ButCopKB-23
❑ 97ButCopKK-23
Rojas, Ricky
❑ 86Ft.MyeRP-23
❑ 87Ft.MyeRP-20
❑ 88EasLeaAP-36
❑ 88VerMarP-959
❑ 89WilBilS-19
❑ 90Bes-73
❑ 90WilBilB-21
❑ 90WilBilP-1058
❑ 90WilBilS-22
❑ 91CalCanLD-71
❑ 91CalCanP-516
❑ 91LinDriAAA-71
❑ 92LonTigF-631
❑ 92LonTigS-417
❑ 93LinVenB-81
Rojas, Roberto
❑ 92BriTigF-1428
❑ 93FayGenC-21
❑ 93FayGenF-143
❑ 93LimRocDWB-38
❑ 93SouAtlLAGF-17
❑ 94LakTigC-18
❑ 94LakTigF-3050
Rojas, Wilberto
❑ 90St.CatBJP-3478
Rojek, Stan
❑ 46DodTeal-19
❑ 47DodTeal-20
❑ 47PM1StaP1-189
❑ 49Bow-135
❑ 49EurSta-171
❑ 50Bow-86
❑ 50PirTeal-19
❑ 50RoyDes-15A
❑ 50RoyDes-15B
❑ 51Bow-166
❑ 52Bow-137
❑ 52NatTeaL-26
❑ 52Top-163
❑ 83TopRep5-163
❑ 90DodTar-686
Rokosz, Keith
❑ 77AppFoxT-21
Roland, James
❑ 63Top-522
❑ 63TwiVol-19
❑ 64Top-341
❑ 64TopVen-341
❑ 65OPC-171
❑ 65Top-171
❑ 67TwiTeal-18
❑ 68Top-276
❑ 68TopVen-276
❑ 69Top-336
❑ 70Top-719
❑ 71MLBOffS-524
❑ 71OPC-642
❑ 71Top-642
❑ 72OPC-464
❑ 72Top-464
❑ 78TwiFri-43
❑ 92YanWIZ7-136
❑ 93RanKee-36
Roland, William
❑ 95SpoIndTI-22
Roldan, Sal
❑ 88MiaMarS-21
❑ 88SalLakCTTI-27
Rolen, Scott
❑ 94ClaGolF-120
❑ 94SpaPhiF-1731
❑ 94SparPhiC-1
❑ 95Bes-89
❑ 95Bes-105
❑ 95Bow-271
❑ 95BowBes-B87
❑ 95BowBesR-B87
❑ 95BowGolF-271
❑ 95Exc-246
❑ 95ReaPhiELC-31
❑ 95SPML-130
❑ 95SPMLA-22
❑ 95SPMLDtS-DS13
❑ 95UppDecML-78
❑ 95UppDecMLFS-78
❑ 95UppDecMLOP-OP21
❑ 96BesAutSA-62
❑ 96Bow-114
❑ 96BowBes-145
❑ 96BowBesAR-145
❑ 96BowBesMI-3
❑ 96BowBesMIAR-3
❑ 96BowBesMIR-3
❑ 96BowBesR-145
❑ 96BowFoi-114
❑ 96Exc-212
❑ 96ExcCli-9
❑ 96LeaSig-122
❑ 96LeaSigPPG-122
❑ 96LeaSigPPP-122
❑ 96ReaPhiB-21
❑ 96Top-434
❑ 97Bow-294
❑ 97BowBes-194
❑ 97BowBesA-194
❑ 97BowBesAAR-194
❑ 97BowBesAR-194
❑ 97BowBesAR-194
❑ 97BowBesBC-BC15
❑ 97BowBesBCAR-BC15
❑ 97BowBesBCR-BC15
❑ 97BowBesP-12
❑ 97BowBesPAR-12
❑ 97BowBesPR-12
❑ 97BowBesR-194
❑ 97BowCerBlaIA-CA70
❑ 97BowCerBluIA-CA70
❑ 97BowCerGolIA-CA70
❑ 97BowChr-202
❑ 97BowChrI-202
❑ 97BowChrIR-202
❑ 97BowChrR-202
❑ 97BowChrSHR-SHR11
❑ 97BowChrSHRR-SHR11
❑ 97BowInt-294
❑ 97BowScoHR-11
❑ 97Cir-283
❑ 97CirEmeA-283
❑ 97CirEmeAR-AU5
❑ 97CirFasT-9
❑ 97CirRav-283
❑ 97ColCho-15
❑ 97ColChoBS-4
❑ 97ColChoBSGS-4
❑ 97ColChoNF-NF40
❑ 97ColChoTotT-T23
❑ 97DenHol-28
❑ 97Don-357
❑ 97DonEli-57
❑ 97DonEliGS-57
❑ 97DonEliTotC-5
❑ 97DonEliTotC-P5
❑ 97DonEliTotCDC-5
❑ 97DonFraFea-13
❑ 97DonGolPP-357
❑ 97DonLim-36
❑ 97DonLim-72
❑ 97DonLimE-36
❑ 97DonLimE-72
❑ 97DonLimENG-72
❑ 97DonLimFotG-63
❑ 97DonPre-160
❑ 97DonPre-198
❑ 97DonPreCttC-160
❑ 97DonPreCttC-198
❑ 97DonRatR-3
❑ 97DonRooDK-3
❑ 97DonRooDKC-3
❑ 97DonSig-50
❑ 97DonSigA-86
❑ 97DonSigAC-108
❑ 97DonSigAM-108
❑ 97DonSigPPP-50
❑ 97DonSilPP-357
❑ 97DonVxP1-5
❑ 97E-X2-89
❑ 97E-X2Cred-89
❑ 97E-X2EmeAuto-89
❑ 97E-X2EmeAutoR-AU5
❑ 97E-X2EssCre-89
❑ 97E-X2SD2000-11
❑ 97Fin-133
❑ 97FinEmb-133
❑ 97FinEmbR-133
❑ 97FinRef-133
❑ 97FlaShoLC-6
❑ 97FlaShoLeg0-6
❑ 97FlaShoLeg1-6
❑ 97FlaShoM-A6
❑ 97FlaShoM-B6
❑ 97FlaShoM-C6
❑ 97FlaShoR0-6
❑ 97FlaShoR1-6
❑ 97FlaShoR2-6
❑ 97FlaShoWotF-19
❑ 97Fle-418
❑ 97FleNewH-11
❑ 97FleRooS-18
❑ 97FleTif-418
❑ 97Lea-174
❑ 97LeaFraM-174
❑ 97LeaFraMDC-174
❑ 97LeaGolS-29
❑ 97LeaLeaotN-13
❑ 97MetUni-205
❑ 97MetUniEA-AU5
❑ 97MetUniEAR-AU5
❑ 97MetUniMfG-9
❑ 97NewPin-172
❑ 97NewPin-200
❑ 97NewPinAP-172
❑ 97NewPinAP-200
❑ 97NewPinMC-172
❑ 97NewPinMC-200
❑ 97NewPinPP-172
❑ 97NewPinPP-200
❑ 97PacPriGotD-GD186
❑ 97PhiCopQ-24
❑ 97PhiTeal-17
❑ 97PinCer-112
❑ 97PinCerMBla-112
❑ 97PinCerMBlu-112
❑ 97PinCerMG-112
❑ 97PinCerMR-112
❑ 97PinCerR-112
❑ 97PinEpixGO-E11
❑ 97PinIns-132
❑ 97PinInsCE-132
❑ 97PinInsDE-132
❑ 97PinTotCPB-112
❑ 97PinTotCPG-112
❑ 97PinTotCPR-112
❑ 97PinX-P-134
❑ 97PinX-PMoS-134
❑ 97PreCon-29
❑ 97Sco-474
❑ 97ScoArtPWB-316
❑ 97ScoArtPWB-474
❑ 97ScoResC-474
❑ 97ScoShoS-474
❑ 97ScoShoSAP-316
❑ 97ScoShoSAP-474
❑ 97Sel-102
❑ 97SelArtP-102
❑ 97SelCom-102
❑ 97SelRegG-102
❑ 97SelRooR-13
❑ 97SelToootT-17
❑ 97SelToootTMB-17
❑ 97SP-135
❑ 97SPInsI-18
❑ 97SpoIll-22
❑ 97SpoIllEE-22
❑ 97SPSpeF-46
❑ 97SPSpxF-10
❑ 97SPSPxFA-10
❑ 97SPx-39
❑ 97SPxBro-39
❑ 97SPxGol-39
❑ 97SPxGraF-39
❑ 97SPxSil-39
❑ 97SPxSte-39
❑ 97StaClu-172
❑ 97StaClu-193
❑ 97StaCluC-CO4
❑ 97StaCluM-M38
❑ 97StaCluMOP-172
❑ 97StaCluMOP-193
❑ 97StaCluMOP-M38
❑ 97Stu-155
❑ 97StuAut-24
❑ 97StuHarH-22
❑ 97StuPor8-24
❑ 97StuPrePG-155
❑ 97StuPrePS-155
❑ 97Top-268
❑ 97TopAwel-AI18
❑ 97TopChr-96
❑ 97TopChrR-96
❑ 97TopGal-154
❑ 97TopGalPPI-154
❑ 97TopMem05-54
❑ 97TopStaFAS-FAS4
❑ 97UD3-58
❑ 97UD3GenNex-GN19
❑ 97Ult-255
❑ 97UltAutE-3
❑ 97UltGolME-255
❑ 97UltPlaME-255
❑ 97UltRooR-10
❑ 97UppDec-229
❑ 97UppDecBCP-BC3
❑ 97Zen-49
❑ 97Zen8x10-24
❑ 97Zen8x1D-24
❑ 98Bow-2
❑ 98BowBes-18
❑ 98BowBesAR-18
❑ 98BowBesR-18
❑ 98BowCerBlueAU-17
❑ 98BowCerGA-17
❑ 98BowCerSA-17
❑ 98BowChr-2
❑ 98BowChrGA-2
❑ 98BowChrGAR-2
❑ 98BowChrI-2
❑ 98BowChrIR-2
❑ 98BowChrR-2
❑ 98BowChrR-48
❑ 98BowChrRR-48
❑ 98BowGolA-2
❑ 98BowInt-2
❑ 98CirThu-144
❑ 98CirThuB-18
❑ 98CirThuFT-9
❑ 98CirThuRav-144
❑ 98CirThuRS-1
❑ 98CirThuSupRav-144
❑ 98ColCho-12
❑ 98ColCho-261
❑ 98ColCho-463
❑ 98ColChoB5-463
❑ 98ColChoER-ER21
❑ 98ColChoMBH-21
❑ 98ColChoSQ-SQ2
❑ 98ColChoSQ-SQ52
❑ 98ColChoSQDouble-24
❑ 98ColChoSQHR-24
❑ 98ColChoSQSingle-24
❑ 98ColChoSQTriple-24
❑ 98CroRoy-106
❑ 98CroRoyPotG-19
❑ 98Don-85
❑ 98Don-169
❑ 98Don-400
❑ 98DonCol-85
❑ 98DonCol-169
❑ 98DonColE-481
❑ 98DonColE-546
❑ 98DonColL-333
❑ 98DonColL-398
❑ 98DonColP-567
❑ 98DonColP-734
❑ 98DonColS-85
❑ 98DonColS-169
❑ 98DonCruG-88
❑ 98DonCruP-88
❑ 98DonCruR-88
❑ 98DonEli-81
❑ 98DonEli-146
❑ 98DonEliA-81
❑ 98DonEliA-146
❑ 98DonEliC-11
❑ 98DonEliMC-11
❑ 98DonEliS-81
❑ 98DonEliS-146
❑ 98DonFANT-19
❑ 98DonFANTDC-19
❑ 98DonGolPP-85
❑ 98DonGolPP-169
❑ 98DonGolPP-400

❑ 98DonLonL-22
❑ 98DonPre-17
❑ 98DonPre-184
❑ 98DonPreGB-20
❑ 98DonPreGES-22
❑ 98DonPreGoB-20
❑ 98DonPreGX-22
❑ 98DonPreGXDC-22
❑ 98DonPrePM-17
❑ 98DonPreSeat-17
❑ 98DonPreSeat-184
❑ 98DonPreTP-20
❑ 98DonPreTPD-10
❑ 98DonPreTPG-20
❑ 98DonPreTPS-20
❑ 98DonPreTW-2
❑ 98DonPriCD-85
❑ 98DonPriCD-169
❑ 98DonPriCE-481
❑ 98DonPriCE-546
❑ 98DonPriCL-333
❑ 98DonPriCL-398
❑ 98DonPriCP-567
❑ 98DonPriCP-734
❑ 98DonProLPI-15
❑ 98DonSig-17
❑ 98DonSigA-76
❑ 98DonSigAC-98
❑ 98DonSigAM-100
❑ 98DonSigP-17
❑ 98DonSigSB-26
❑ 98DonSilPP-85
❑ 98DonSilPP-169
❑ 98DonSilPP-400
❑ 98E-X2-97
❑ 98E-X2Cheap-16
❑ 98E-X2ECFut-97
❑ 98E-X2ECNow-97
❑ 98Fin-142
❑ 98FinCen-C4
❑ 98FinCenR-C4
❑ 98FinMysF2-M3
❑ 98FinMysF2-M5
❑ 98FinMysF2-M6
❑ 98FinMysF2-M32
❑ 98FinMysF2R-M3
❑ 98FinMysF2R-M5
❑ 98FinMysF2R-M6
❑ 98FinMysF2R-M32
❑ 98FinNo--142
❑ 98FinNo-R-142
❑ 98FinRef-142
❑ 98FinTheM-TM17
❑ 98FinTheMR-TM17
❑ 98FlaShoLeg0-20
❑ 98FlaShoLeg1-20
❑ 98FlaShoLeg2-20
❑ 98FlaShoLeg3-20
❑ 98FlaShoLegM-20
❑ 98FlaShoP1-8
❑ 98FlaShoR0-20
❑ 98FlaShoR1-20
❑ 98FlaShoR2-20
❑ 98FlaShoR3-20
❑ 98Fle-150
❑ 98Fle-595
❑ 98FleDiamInk-9
❑ 98FleDiaSCS-NNO
❑ 98FleRooS-17
❑ 98FleVin'-45
❑ 98FleVin'C-45
❑ 98Lea-134
❑ 98Lea-199
❑ 98LeaFraDA-134
❑ 98LeaFraDA-199
❑ 98LeaFraF-134
❑ 98LeaFraF-199
❑ 98LeaFraM-134
❑ 98LeaFraM-199
❑ 98LeaFraM-134
❑ 98LeaFraM-199
❑ 98LeaFraMDC-134
❑ 98LeaFraMDC-199
❑ 98LeaFraMDC-134
❑ 98LeaFraMDC-199
❑ 98LeaFraMZ2-134
❑ 98LeaFraMZ2-199
❑ 98LeaRCMLHDSamp-16
❑ 98LeaRS-42
❑ 98LeaRS-160
❑ 98LeaRS-184
❑ 98LeaRSGreHit-15
❑ 98LeaRSHRDerby-7
❑ 98LeaRSLHolo-42
❑ 98LeaRSLHolo-160
❑ 98LeaRSLHolo-184
❑ 98LeaRSLong-42
❑ 98LeaRSLong-160
❑ 98LeaRSLong-184
❑ 98LeaRSMLHD-16
❑ 98LeaRTrue-42
❑ 98LeaRTrue-160
❑ 98LeaRTrue-184
❑ 98LeaStaRep-7
❑ 98LeaStaS-16
❑ 98LeaStaSDC-16
❑ 98MetUni-67
❑ 98MetUniAT-18
❑ 98MetUniPMG-67
❑ 98MetUniT-6
❑ 98MetUniUL-20
❑ 98Pac-386
❑ 98PacAur-173
❑ 98PacAurHC-13
❑ 98PacAurPF-17
❑ 98PacAurPFC-17
❑ 98PacAurPFPB-17
❑ 98PacAurPFR-17
❑ 98PacAurPFS-17
❑ 98PacInv-126
❑ 98PacInv-148
❑ 98PacInvGems-189
❑ 98PacInvInt-3N
❑ 98PacInvMiT-14
❑ 98PacInvPBlue-126
❑ 98PacInvPBlue-148
❑ 98PacInvSilv-126
❑ 98PacInvSilv-148
❑ 98PacInvTeam-21
❑ 98PacOme-185
❑ 98PacOmeOnIns-33
❑ 98PacOmeR-185
❑ 98PacOnl-571
❑ 98PacOnl-577
❑ 98PacOnlR-571
❑ 98PacOnlR-577
❑ 98PacOnlWC-571
❑ 98PacOnlWC-577
❑ 98PacPar-216
❑ 98PacParC-216
❑ 98PacParG-216
❑ 98PacParHS-216
❑ 98PacParI-45
❑ 98PacParPB-216
❑ 98PacParR-216
❑ 98PacParTC-26
❑ 98PacPlaB-386
❑ 98PacRedT-386
❑ 98PacSil-386
❑ 98PacTeaC-24
❑ 98PhiTeal-29
❑ 98Pin-39
❑ 98PinArtP-PP37
❑ 98PinEpixGE-E11
❑ 98PinEpixGP-E11
❑ 98PinEpixME-E11
❑ 98PinEpixMO-E11
❑ 98PinEpixMP-E11
❑ 98PinEpixSE-E11
❑ 98PinEpixSO-E11
❑ 98PinEpixSP-E11
❑ 98PinIns-17
❑ 98PinInsBtN-7
❑ 98PinInsC-18
❑ 98PinInsCE-17
❑ 98PinInsCG-18
❑ 98PinInsDE-17
❑ 98PinInsSG-2AB
❑ 98PinInsSG-2CD
❑ 98PinInsSG-8AB
❑ 98PinInsSG-8CD
❑ 98PinInsSGS-2AB
❑ 98PinInsSGS-2CD
❑ 98PinInsSGS-8AB
❑ 98PinInsSGS-8CD
❑ 98PinMinB-30
❑ 98PinMinCB-30
❑ 98PinMinCBAP-30
❑ 98PinMinCGP-30
❑ 98PinMinCGPAP-30
❑ 98PinMinCN-30
❑ 98PinMinCNAP-30
❑ 98PinMinCSGR-30
❑ 98PinMinDC-30
❑ 98PinMinG-30
❑ 98PinMinMCSS-30
❑ 98PinMinMG-6
❑ 98PinMinMGC-6
❑ 98PinMinS-30
❑ 98PinMusC-PP37
❑ 98PinPer-17
❑ 98PinPerLP-11
❑ 98PinPerPP-17
❑ 98PinPerSftF-45
❑ 98PinPerSftFShop-11
❑ 98PinPlu-178
❑ 98PinPluAE-11
❑ 98PinPluAEE-11
❑ 98PinPluAEP-11
❑ 98PinPluAP-PP59
❑ 98PinPluGAP-PP59
❑ 98PinPluLM-6
❑ 98PinPluMAP-PP59
❑ 98PinPluTP-14
❑ 98PinPluTPG-14
❑ 98PinPluTPM-14
❑ 98PinPowPJ-24
❑ 98PinPowPJS-24
❑ 98PinPreP-39
❑ 98PinPreP-E11
❑ 98PinPreP-S21
❑ 98PinPreP-S22
❑ 98PinPreP-S23
❑ 98PinPreP-S24
❑ 98PinPreP-S25
❑ 98PinSpe-21
❑ 98PinSpe-22
❑ 98PinSpe-23
❑ 98PinSpe-24
❑ 98PinSpe-25
❑ 98Revo-111
❑ 98RevoSS-111
❑ 98Sco-68
❑ 98ScoEpix-E11
❑ 98ScoFirP-13
❑ 98ScoRT-21
❑ 98ScoRT-265
❑ 98ScoRTASEpix-11
❑ 98ScoRTSS-PP21
❑ 98ScoRTSS-PP158
❑ 98ScoRTSSAP-PP21
❑ 98ScoRTSSAP-PP158
❑ 98ScoRTSSAP1-PP21
❑ 98ScoRTSSAP1-PP158
❑ 98ScoRTStarGaz-14
❑ 98ScoSS-PP29
❑ 98ScoSSAP-PP29
❑ 98SelSelSamp-9
❑ 98SkyDugA-34
❑ 98SkyDugA-122
❑ 98SkyDugAAR-12
❑ 98SkyDugAAR-13
❑ 98SkyDugADH-DH16
❑ 98SkyDugAIA-34
❑ 98SkyDugAIA-122
❑ 98SP Aut-150
❑ 98SP Aut-SD13
❑ 98SP AutC-SR
❑ 98SP AutSD-SD13
❑ 98SP AutSDT-SD13
❑ 98SpoIll-109
❑ 98SpoIll-196
❑ 98SpoIllEE-109
❑ 98SpoIllEE-196
❑ 98SpoIllFE-109
❑ 98SpoIllFE-196
❑ 98SpoIllTaN-128
❑ 98SpoIllTaNA-6
❑ 98SpoIllTaNAR-6
❑ 98SpoIllTaNEE-128
❑ 98SpoIllTaNGS-12
❑ 98SpoIllWSF-116
❑ 98SpoIllWSFEE-116
❑ 98SpoIllWSFFE-116
❑ 98SPxFin-15
❑ 98SPxFin-228
❑ 98SPxFin-308
❑ 98SPxFinR-15
❑ 98SPxFinR-228
❑ 98SPxFinR-308
❑ 98SPxFinS-15
❑ 98SPxFinS-228
❑ 98SPxFinS-308
❑ 98StaCluBP-BP2
❑ 98StaCluC-CS1
❑ 98StaCluC-CS4
❑ 98StaCluC-CS5
❑ 98StaCluFDI-315
❑ 98StaCluI-315
❑ 98StaCluOneK-315
❑ 98StaCluPP-315
❑ 98Stu-15
❑ 98StuFF-15
❑ 98StuFFDC-15
❑ 98StuGPP-15
❑ 98StuHitPar-13
❑ 98StuPor8x10-17
❑ 98StuPor8x10GP-17
❑ 98StuSPP-15
❑ 98Top-25
❑ 98TopBabB-BB2
❑ 98TopChr-25
❑ 98TopChrBB-BB2
❑ 98TopChrBBR-BB2
❑ 98TopChrR-25
❑ 98TopDevR-25
❑ 98TopDia-25
❑ 98TopGal-74
❑ 98TopGalAG-AG6
❑ 98TopGalGP-74
❑ 98TopGalOPP-74
❑ 98TopGalPPI-74
❑ 98TopGalPPIA-74
❑ 98TopGolLabC1-53
❑ 98TopGolLabC1B-53
❑ 98TopGolLabC1One-53
❑ 98TopGolLabC1R-53
❑ 98TopGolLabC2-53
❑ 98TopGolLabC2B-53
❑ 98TopGolLabC2One-53
❑ 98TopGolLabC2R-53
❑ 98TopGolLabC3-53
❑ 98TopGolLabC3B-53
❑ 98TopGolLabC3One-53
❑ 98TopGolLabC3R-53
❑ 98TopMiniC-25
❑ 98TopMysFB-M3
❑ 98TopMysFB-M3
❑ 98TopMysFBR-M3
❑ 98TopMysFBR-M3
❑ 98TopOpeD-18
❑ 98TopSta-46
❑ 98TopSta'S-36
❑ 98TopSta'SGH-36
❑ 98TopStaB-46
❑ 98TopStaG-46
❑ 98TopStaGR-46
❑ 98TopStaS-46
❑ 98TopStaSteG-36
❑ 98TopSup-7
❑ 98TopSup-7
❑ 98TopTek-88
❑ 98TopTekD-88
❑ 98UD3-15
❑ 98UD3-105
❑ 98UD3-195
❑ 98UD3DieCut-15
❑ 98UD3DieCut-105
❑ 98UD3DieCut-195
❑ 98Ult-70
❑ 98Ult-219
❑ 98Ult-490
❑ 98UltArtT-16
❑ 98UltBacttF-6
❑ 98UltGolM-70
❑ 98UltGolM-219
❑ 98UltGolM-490
❑ 98UltKidG-7
❑ 98UltMas-70
❑ 98UltMas-219
❑ 98UltMas-490
❑ 98UltMilM-8
❑ 98UltNot-9
❑ 98UltPlaM-70
❑ 98UltPlaM-219
❑ 98UltPlaM-490
❑ 98UltTicS-3
❑ 98UltTop3-11
❑ 98UltWinN-19
❑ 98UppDec-479
❑ 98UppDec-613
❑ 98UppDecAC-AS12
❑ 98UppDecBCP-BC2
❑ 98UppDecDS-DS12
❑ 98UppDecR-74
❑ 98UppDecREP-2
❑ 98UppDecRGKoG-G25
❑ 98UppDecRQL-Q18
❑ 98UppDecRSotT-SR
❑ 98UppDecRTC-TC45
❑ 98Zen-24
❑ 98Zen5 xx7-16
❑ 98Zen5x7GoldImp-16
❑ 98Zen5x7Imp-16
❑ 98ZenEpi-E11
❑ 98ZenZ-G-24
❑ 98ZenZ-S-24
❑ 98ZenZ-T-18
❑ 98ZenZ-TG-18
❑ 99199Fin-35
❑ 99199Fin-118
❑ 99199Fin-273
❑ 99AllMysFR-M12
❑ 99Bow-260
❑ 99BowBes-55
❑ 99BowBesAR-55
❑ 99BowBesFF-FR2A
❑ 99BowBesFF-FR2C
❑ 99BowBesFFA-FR2A
❑ 99BowBesFFA-FR2C
❑ 99BowBesR-55
❑ 99BowEarR-ER9
❑ 99BowGol-260
❑ 99BowInt-260
❑ 99CroRoyB-107
❑ 99CroRoyL-107
❑ 99CroRoyMP-12
❑ 99CroRoyOD-107
❑ 99CroRoyPP-18
❑ 99CroRoyPPN-18
❑ 99DumSet-ER9
❑ 99E-X Cen-1
❑ 99E-X CenECFut-1
❑ 99E-X CenECNow-1
❑ 99E-XCenA-8
❑ 99E-XCenFoF'-19
❑ 99FinDouF-DF7
❑ 99FinDouFDualR-DF7
❑ 99FinGolRef-35
❑ 99FinGolRef-118
❑ 99FinGolRef-273
❑ 99FinRef-35
❑ 99FinRef-118
❑ 99FinRef-273
❑ 99FinSplS-SS8
❑ 99FinSplSDR-SS8
❑ 99FlaShoLeg1-17
❑ 99FlaShoLeg2-17
❑ 99FlaShoLeg3-17
❑ 99FlaShoLegM1-17
❑ 99FlaShoLegM2-17
❑ 99FlaShoLegM3-17
❑ 99FlaShoR1-17
❑ 99FlaShoR2-17
❑ 99FlaShoR3-17
❑ 99FlaShoSamp-17
❑ 99FlaShoSamp-17
❑ 99FlaShoSamp-17
❑ 99Fle-24
❑ 99Fle-588
❑ 99FleBri-33
❑ 99FleBri2G-33
❑ 99FleBriBlu-33
❑ 99FleBriGol-33
❑ 99FleMys-35
❑ 99FleMysD-3
❑ 99FleMysFI-23
❑ 99FleMysG-35
❑ 99FleMysM-35
❑ 99FleSta9-24
❑ 99FleSta9-588
❑ 99FleVin'-24
❑ 99FleWarT-24
❑ 99FleWarT-588
❑ 99KinDis-3
❑ 99MetUni-188
❑ 99MetUni-277
❑ 99MetUniBWTW-6
❑ 99MetUniDS-13
❑ 99MetUniGM-188
❑ 99MetUniGM-277
❑ 99MetUniPM-9
❑ 99MetUniPMG-188
❑ 99MetUniPMG-277
❑ 99Pac-332
❑ 99PacAur-143
❑ 99PacAurOD-143
❑ 99PacCroC-214
❑ 99PacCroCPB-214
❑ 99PacCroCTC-22
❑ 99PacGolCDC-32
❑ 99PacInv-112
❑ 99PacInvFP-14
❑ 99PacInvOD-112
❑ 99PacInvPB-112
❑ 99PacInvTA-13
❑ 99PacOme-182
❑ 99PacOme5T-27
❑ 99PacOme5TT-27
❑ 99PacOmeC-182
❑ 99PacOmeDM-24
❑ 99PacOmeEP-13
❑ 99PacOmeEP1o1-13
❑ 99PacOmeG-182
❑ 99PacOmePB-182
❑ 99PacPar-181
❑ 99PacParC-181
❑ 99PacParG-181
❑ 99PacParHoloGold-181
❑ 99PacParHS-181
❑ 99PacParOD-181
❑ 99PacParPB-27
❑ 99PacParPB-181
❑ 99PacParRed-181
❑ 99PacParTC-22
❑ 99PacPlaB-332
❑ 99PacPri-109
❑ 99PacPriHB-109
❑ 99PacPriHG-109
❑ 99PacPriHM-109
❑ 99PacPriHP-109
❑ 99PacPriRed-109
❑ 99PacPriS-134
❑ 99PacPriS206-134
❑ 99PacPriS206R-134
❑ 99PacRed-332
❑ 99PacTeaC-26
❑ 99Rev-108
❑ 99RevDiaL-25
❑ 99RevFouP-14
❑ 99RevPremDate-108
❑ 99RevRet-108
❑ 99RevShaSS-108
❑ 99RevTri-28
❑ 99RevTri-28
❑ 99SkyMolM-144
❑ 99SkyMolMF-44
❑ 99SkyMolMFS-44
❑ 99SkyMolMFT-44
❑ 99SkyMolMX-144
❑ 99SkyPre-19
❑ 99SkyPre-274
❑ 99SkyPreA-46
❑ 99SkyPreABlue-46
❑ 99SkyPreIN-7
❑ 99SkyPreLB-8
❑ 99SkyPreR-19
❑ 99SkyPreR-274
❑ 99SkyPreSB-14
❑ 99SkyPreSotG-6
❑ 99SkyThu-279
❑ 99SkyThuRant-279
❑ 99SkyThuRave-279
❑ 99SkyThuwww-WB8
❑ 99SP Aut-64
❑ 99SP AutC-SR
❑ 99SP AutCG-SR
❑ 99SP AutEF-E22
❑ 99SP AutHRC-HR34
❑ 99SP AutR-R22
❑ 99SP SigAuto-SR
❑ 99SP SigAutoG-SR
❑ 99SPAutHRCDC-HR34
❑ 99SpoIll-80
❑ 99SpoIllH-12
❑ 99SPSig-35
❑ 99SPx-60
❑ 99SPxFinR-60
❑ 99SPxFinS-60
❑ 99SPxPowE-PE22
❑ 99SPxPreS-PS18
❑ 99StaClu-220
❑ 99StaCluC-CS3
❑ 99StaCluC-CS10
❑ 99StaCluC-CS16
❑ 99StaCluC-CS20
❑ 99StaCluFDI-220
❑ 99StaCluOoaK-220
❑ 99StaCluPP-220
❑ 99StaCluTI-T12C
❑ 99StaCluTL-T12C
❑ 99StaCluTL-T12C
❑ 99ThuSkySupR-279
❑ 99Top-125
❑ 99Top-453
❑ 99TopAllMF-M12
❑ 99TopAut-A3
❑ 99TopBlaLC1-74
❑ 99TopBlaLC2-74
❑ 99TopBlaLC3-74
❑ 99TopChr-125
❑ 99TopChr-453
❑ 99TopChrNB-NB6
❑ 99TopChrNBR-NB6
❑ 99TopChrR-125
❑ 99TopChrR-453
❑ 99TopGal-12
❑ 99TopGal-127
❑ 99TopGalE-E18
❑ 99TopGalHer-TH11
❑ 99TopGalHerP-TH11
❑ 99TopGalP-PP1
❑ 99TopGalPP-12
❑ 99TopGalPP-127
❑ 99TopGalPPI-12
❑ 99TopGalPPI-127

❑ 99TopGolL-74
❑ 99TopGolLC1-74
❑ 99TopGolLC2-74
❑ 99TopGolLOtO-74
❑ 99TopMVPP-125
❑ 99TopMVPP-453
❑ 99TopNewB-NB6
❑ 99TopOpeD-73
❑ 99TopRedLC1-74
❑ 99TopRedLC2-74
❑ 99TopRedLC3-74
❑ 99TopSta-44
❑ 99TopSta-152
❑ 99TopSta'S-17
❑ 99TopSta'SG-17
❑ 99TopSta'SGDH-17
❑ 99TopSta1Foil-44
❑ 99TopSta2Foil-44
❑ 99TopStaFoil-44
❑ 99TopStaFoil-152
❑ 99TopStaOS-44
❑ 99TopStaTS-44
❑ 99TopTek-22A
❑ 99TopTek-22B
❑ 99TopTekG-22A
❑ 99TopTekG-22B
❑ 99UD Cho-43
❑ 99UD Cho-124
❑ 99UD ChoMBH-B21
❑ 99UD ChoP-124
❑ 99UD ChoPCR-43
❑ 99UD ChoPCR-124
❑ 99UD ChoS-19
❑ 99UD ChoSD-19
❑ 99UD ChoSHR-19
❑ 99UD ChoST-19
❑ 99UD Ion-46
❑ 99UD Ion-82
❑ 99UD IonC-C13
❑ 99UD IonH-H13
❑ 99UD IonR-46
❑ 99UD IonR-82
❑ 99UD IonWZ-WZ13
❑ 99UDHolo-44
❑ 99UDHoloAUsome-44
❑ 99Ult-200
❑ 99UltDamI-13
❑ 99UltGolM-200
❑ 99UltMas-200
❑ 99UltPlaM-200
❑ 99UltRBIK-12
❑ 99UltTheBook-11
❑ 99UltThu-15
❑ 99UppDec-175
❑ 99UppDecBD-63
❑ 99UppDecBDD-63
❑ 99UppDecBDDom-D17
❑ 99UppDecBDDomE-D17
❑ 99UppDecBDMN-M12
❑ 99UppDecBDMNE-M12
❑ 99UppDecBDQ-63
❑ 99UppDecBDT-63
❑ 99UppDecCf7-39
❑ 99UppDecCf7-C28
❑ 99UppDecCf7Cf7P-C28
❑ 99UppDecCf7LL-L24
❑ 99UppDecCL-104
❑ 99UppDecCLCC-104
❑ 99UppDecCLM-C72
❑ 99UppDecCo7CE-39
❑ 99UppDecE-67
❑ 99UppDecE-155
❑ 99UppDecE-177
❑ 99UppDecEFXG-67
❑ 99UppDecEFXG-155
❑ 99UppDecEFXG-177
❑ 99UppDecEL1-175
❑ 99UppDecEL2-175
❑ 99UppDecEPE-P22
❑ 99UppDecF-F20
❑ 99UppDecFD-F20
❑ 99UppDecFQ-F20
❑ 99UppDecFT-F20
❑ 99UppDecIP-I22
❑ 99UppDecIPD-I22
❑ 99UppDecIPHR-I22
❑ 99UppDecIPT-I22
❑ 99UppDecM-156
❑ 99UppDecMGS-156
❑ 99UppDecMGUS-GUSR
❑ 99UppDecMHFS-156
❑ 99UppDecMP-156
❑ 99UppDecMSS-156
❑ 99UppDecO-24
❑ 99UppDecOSO-24
❑ 99UppDecR-64
❑ 99UppDecRG-64
❑ 99UppDecROSS-S25
❑ 99UppDecROSS-S25
❑ 99UppDecRP-64
❑ 99UppDecTE-T20
❑ 99UppDecTED-T20
❑ 99UppDecTEQ-T20
❑ 99UppDecTET-T20
❑ 99UppDecVtaT-V22
❑ 99UppDecVtaTD-V22
❑ 99UppDecVtaTQ-V22
❑ 99UppDecVtaTT-V22
❑ 99UppDecWY-W29
❑ 99UppDecWYD-W29
❑ 99UppDecWYHR-W29
❑ 99UppDecWYT-W29
❑ 99Vic-293
❑ 99Vic-294

Rolen, Steve
❑ 90CliGiaB-25
❑ 90CliGiaP-2559
❑ 91Cla/Bes-112
❑ 91SanJosGC-11
❑ 91SanJosGP-20
❑ 92SanJosGC-3

Rolfe, Red (Robert)
❑ 34BatR31-22
❑ 34BatR31-181
❑ 34DiaStaR-29
❑ 34DiaStaR-104
❑ 34Gou-94
❑ 35GouPuzR-8E
❑ 35GouPuzR-9E
❑ 36GouWidPPR-A90
❑ 36OveCanR-39
❑ 36WorWidGV-38
❑ 41DouPlaR-65
❑ 42GilRazL-1
❑ 46SpoExcW-8-12
❑ 51Bow-319
❑ 52Top-296
❑ 71FleWorS-34
❑ 72FleFamF-22
❑ 72TCMthe3-84
❑ 74CapPub-52
❑ 75YanAllTT-9
❑ 75YanDyn1T-37
❑ 75YanDyn1T-52
❑ 80YanGreT-3
❑ 83TopRep5-296
❑ 87SpoCubG-2
❑ 92ConTSN-576
❑ 92YanWIZA-68

Rolish, Chad
❑ 94SouOreAC-23
❑ 94SouOreAF-3621

Rolison, Nate
❑ 96KanCouCTI-24
❑ 96KanCouCUTI-11
❑ 96MauStiHWB-29
❑ 97Bow-197
❑ 97BowChr-184
❑ 97BowChrI-184
❑ 97BowChrIR-184
❑ 97BowChrR-184
❑ 97BowInt-197
❑ 97BreCouMB-27
❑ 97FloStaLTPB-2
❑ 98PorSeaDQ-21
❑ 98SP MinPE-57
❑ 98SPMin-57
❑ 99BasAmeTP-86
❑ 99BasAmeTPG-86

Rolland, Dave
❑ 82BirBarT-13
❑ 86DayBealP-23
❑ 87SanJosBP-15

Rollin, Rondal
❑ 84EvaTriT-3
❑ 86BirBarTI-28
❑ 87BirBarB-7
❑ 87SouLeaAJ-2
❑ 89BirBarADB-29
❑ 90BirBarADB-29

Rollings, Bill
❑ 79TulDriT-23

Rollings, Red (William R.)
❑ 29Zee-11
❑ 33Gou-88
❑ 34GouCanV-40

Rollins, Jimmy
❑ 96AppLeaAB-25
❑ 96MarPhiB-21
❑ 97PieBolWB-24
❑ 98Bes-94
❑ 98Bow-181
❑ 98BowChr-181
❑ 98BowChrGA-181
❑ 98BowChrGAR-181
❑ 98BowChrI-181
❑ 98BowChrIR-181
❑ 98BowChrR-181
❑ 98BowGolA-181
❑ 98BowInt-181
❑ 98ClePhiM-19
❑ 98ClePhiUM-19

Rollins, Michael
❑ 92DavLipB-21
❑ 93DavLipB-18

Rollins, Pep (Patrick)
❑ 91UtiBluSC-28
❑ 91UtiBluSP-3250

Rollins, Rich
❑ 47Exh-196
❑ 61TwiCloD-23
❑ 62Top-596
❑ 63Fle-24
❑ 63Jel-4
❑ 63Pos-4
❑ 63SalMetC-49
❑ 63Top-110
❑ 63TwiJayP-10
❑ 63TwiVol-20
❑ 64Baz-10
❑ 64ChatheY-44
❑ 64Top-8
❑ 64Top-270
❑ 64TopCoi-51
❑ 64TopSta-52
❑ 64TopStaU-65
❑ 64TopVen-8
❑ 64TopVen-270
❑ 64TwiJayP-10
❑ 65ChaTheY-45
❑ 65OPC-90
❑ 65Top-90
❑ 65TwiPos-9
❑ 66Top-473
❑ 66TwiFaiG-14
❑ 67CokCapTw-8
❑ 67DexPre-180
❑ 67OPC-98
❑ 67Top-98
❑ 67TwiTeal-19
❑ 68DexPre-67
❑ 68Top-243
❑ 68TopVen-243
❑ 69MilBra-239
❑ 69MLBOffS-98
❑ 69PilPos-10
❑ 69Top-451A
❑ 69Top-451B
❑ 69TopSta-229
❑ 69TopTeaP-9
❑ 70BreMcD-25
❑ 70BreMil-20
❑ 70MLBOffS-276
❑ 70Top-652
❑ 72MilBra-296
❑ 77PilPosR-10
❑ 78TCM60I-119
❑ 83Pil69G-16
❑ 89PacLegI-169
❑ 94BreMilB-266

Rolls, Damian
❑ 96BesAutS1RP-FR10
❑ 96YakBeaTI-29
❑ 97SouAtlTPB-30
❑ 98VerBeaDM-31
❑ 99BasAmeTP-87
❑ 99BasAmeTPG-87

Rolls, David
❑ 88EugEmeB-12
❑ 90EugEmeGS-25
❑ 91SalLakTP-3213
❑ 91SalLakTSP-9
❑ 92ChaRanC-13
❑ 92ChaRanF-2228
❑ 93TulDriF-2736
❑ 93TulDriTI-24
❑ 94TulDriF-247
❑ 94TulDriTI-19

Rolocut, Brian
❑ 93GreFalDSP-12
❑ 94YakBeaC-17
❑ 94YakBeaF-3847
❑ 95SanBerSTI-22
❑ 96VerBeaDB-25
❑ 97RocCub-26

Romagna, Randy
❑ 83KinBluJTI-21
❑ 85KinBluJT-14
❑ 86KinEagP-21

Roman, Bob
❑ 77SpaPhiT-20

Roman, Dan
❑ 87OneYanP-7
❑ 88Ft.LauYS-20
❑ 89Ft.LauYS-23
❑ 92EriSaiC-11
❑ 92EriSaiF-1622
❑ 93LetMouF-4149
❑ 93LetMouSP-16
❑ 93Top-782
❑ 93TopGol-782
❑ 93TopInaM-782
❑ 93TopInaR-782
❑ 93TopMic-782

Roman, Jose
❑ 81BatTroT-3
❑ 82WatIndF-24
❑ 83WatIndF-12
❑ 84BufBisT-8
❑ 85Fle-646
❑ 85MaiGuiT-13
❑ 86IndTeal-38
❑ 86MaiGuiP-18
❑ 87BufBisP-21
❑ 87TidTidP-23
❑ 87TidTidT-29
❑ 88MetColP-47
❑ 88TidTidCa-25
❑ 88TidTidCM-9
❑ 88TidTidP-1601

Roman, Junior
❑ 77WatIndT-18
❑ 78WauMetT-23
❑ 92GulCoaMF-3497

Roman, Luis
❑ 85DomLeaS-107

Roman, Melvin
❑ 94EveGiaC-24
❑ 94EveGiaF-3661

Roman, Miguel
❑ 81BatTroT-26
❑ 83WatIndF-13
❑ 86IndTeal-39
❑ 86WatIndP-20
❑ 87WilBilP-13
❑ 88JacMetGS-17

Roman, Ray
❑ 87ReaPhiP-11
❑ 88ReaPhiP-885

Roman, Vince
❑ 90AshTouC-22
❑ 90AubAstB-10
❑ 90AubAstP-3405
❑ 91AshTouP-580
❑ 92OscAstC-24
❑ 92OscAstF-2544
❑ 93QuaCitRBC-19
❑ 93QuaCitRBF-114

Roman, William A.
❑ 65Top-493

Romanick, Ron
❑ 81RedPioT-5
❑ 82HolMilT-8
❑ 83NasAngT-6
❑ 84AngSmo-23
❑ 84FleUpd-101
❑ 84TopTra-102T
❑ 84TopTraT-102T
❑ 85AngSmo-11
❑ 85Don-451
❑ 85Fle-309
❑ 85OPC-280
❑ 85Top-579
❑ 85TopSti-231
❑ 85TopTif-579
❑ 86AngSmo-11
❑ 86Don-85
❑ 86Fle-166
❑ 86FleMin-34
❑ 86FleStiC-100
❑ 86Lea-81
❑ 86OPC-76
❑ 86Top-733
❑ 86TopSti-180
❑ 86TopTif-733
❑ 87ColCliP-21
❑ 87ColCliP-23
❑ 87ColCliT-8
❑ 87OPC-136
❑ 87Top-136
❑ 87TopTif-136
❑ 88StoPorCLC-176
❑ 88StoPorP-731
❑ 94RivPilCLC-30
❑ 95PorCitRTI-22
❑ 98TacRaiQ-3

Romano, Andy
❑ 89MajLeaM-5
❑ 89MajLeaM-11

Romano, James
❑ 52Par-73
❑ 90DodTar-1056

Romano, Jason
❑ 97TopSta-111
❑ 97TopStaAM-111
❑ 98BesNumOP-38
❑ 98Bow-149
❑ 98BowChr-149
❑ 98BowChrGA-149
❑ 98BowChrGAR-149
❑ 98BowChrI-149
❑ 98BowChrIR-149
❑ 98BowChrR-149
❑ 98BowGolA-149
❑ 98BowInt-149
❑ 98SavSanGM-22
❑ 98SouAtlLPM-19
❑ 98Top-248
❑ 98TopChr-248
❑ 98TopChrR-248
❑ 98TopDevR-248
❑ 98TopDia-248
❑ 98TopMiniC-248
❑ 99BasAmeTPA-37
❑ 99Bow-376
❑ 99BowGol-376
❑ 99BowInt-376
❑ 99TeaBesRA-22

Romano, John
❑ 59Top-138
❑ 59TopVen-138
❑ 60IndJayP-10
❑ 60Top-323
❑ 61Kah-38
❑ 61Pos-67A
❑ 61Pos-67B
❑ 61SevElev-6
❑ 61Top-5
❑ 61TopMagR-19
❑ 61TopStaI-142
❑ 62Baz-31
❑ 62IndJayP-12
❑ 62Jel-42
❑ 62Kah-36
❑ 62Pos-42
❑ 62PosCan-42
❑ 62SalPlaC-94
❑ 62ShiPlaC-94
❑ 62Top-330
❑ 62TopBuc-78
❑ 62TopStaI-40
❑ 63Baz-18
❑ 63IndJayP-11
❑ 63Jel-76
❑ 63Pos-76
❑ 63SalMetC-46
❑ 63Top-72
❑ 63Top-392
❑ 63TopStiI-38
❑ 64Baz-18
❑ 64IndJayP-10
❑ 64Kah-25
❑ 64Top-515
❑ 64TopCoi-9
❑ 64TopGia-59
❑ 64TopSta-48
❑ 64TopStaU-66
❑ 64TopTatI-66
❑ 65OPC-17
❑ 65Top-17
❑ 65TopEmbI-10
❑ 65WhiSoxJP-9
❑ 66Top-199
❑ 66Top-413
❑ 66TopVen-199
❑ 67OPC-196
❑ 67Top-196
❑ 81WhiSox1T-13

Romano, Mike
❑ 94HagSunC-21
❑ 94HagSunF-2729
❑ 94SouAtlLAF-SAL18
❑ 95DunBluJTI-22
❑ 96KnoSmoB-22
❑ 97SyrSkyCB-21
❑ 98SyrSkyG-24

Romano, Scott
❑ 90Bes-270
❑ 90GreHorB-18
❑ 90GreHorP-2670
❑ 90GreHorS-20
❑ 90OneYanP-3373
❑ 91GreHorP-3067
❑ 92ForLauYC-15
❑ 92ForLauYTI-28
❑ 92Ft.LauYF-2622
❑ 93GreHorC-19
❑ 93GreHorF-896
❑ 94FloStaLAF-FSL25
❑ 94TamYanC-21
❑ 94TamYanF-2395
❑ 95AusFut-12
❑ 95NorNavTI-34
❑ 95SPML-116
❑ 95UppDecML-94
❑ 95UppDecMLFS-94
❑ 97St.PetDR-27
❑ 97St.PetDRUB-27

Romano, Thomas
❑ 82MadMusF-28
❑ 83AlbA'sT-19
❑ 84TacTigC-77
❑ 85TacTigC-131
❑ 86IndIndTI-7
❑ 87IndIndTI-14
❑ 88BlaYNPRWLU-10
❑ 88BufBisC-13
❑ 88BufBisP-1485
❑ 88BufBisTI-4
❑ 89BufBisC-21
❑ 89BufBisP-1670

Romanoli, Paul
❑ 92SprCarC-7
❑ 92SprCarF-864
❑ 93St.PetCC-21
❑ 93St.PetCF-2626

Romanov, Vitalyi
❑ 89EasLeaDDP-DD2

Romanovsky, Mike
❑ 86PalSprAP-28
❑ 86PalSprAS-10
❑ 87MidAngP-22

Romay, Willie
❑ 89BelMarL-28
❑ 91PenPilC-17
❑ 91PenPilP-391
❑ 94BreCouMF-25

Rombard, Rich
❑ 91FayGenP-1187

Romberger, Al
❑ 55JetPos-13

Romboli, Curt
❑ 96MicBatCB-23
❑ 96MidLeaAB-47
❑ 97MicBatC-24

Romero, Al
❑ 83NasAngT-19
❑ 85EdmTraC-25
❑ 86EdmTraP-24

Romero, Alejandro
❑ 97GreFalDTI-22

Romero, Brian
❑ 89ButCopKSP-6
❑ 90Bes-301
❑ 90GasRanB-7
❑ 90GasRanP-2520
❑ 90GasRanS-20
❑ 90ProAaA-79
❑ 90SouAtlLAS-21
❑ 90StaFS7-97
❑ 91LinDriAA-594
❑ 91TulDriLD-594
❑ 91TulDriP-2772
❑ 91TulDriTI-25
❑ 92SkyAA F-265
❑ 92TulDriF-2693
❑ 92TulDriS-601
❑ 93TulDriF-2734
❑ 93TulDriTI-25

Romero, Charlie
❑ 88QuaCitAGS-24
❑ 89PalSprACLC-36
❑ 89PalSprAP-470
❑ 94CedRapKC-25
❑ 94CedRapKF-1126
❑ 96CedRapKTI-29

Romero, Ed Ralph
❑ 76BurBeeT-28
❑ 77HolMilT-21
❑ 78SpoIndC-10
❑ 79Top-708
❑ 79VanCanT-17
❑ 80VanCanT-13
❑ 81Top-659
❑ 82BrePol-11

❑ 82Don-536
❑ 82Top-408
❑ 83BreGar-15
❑ 83BrePol-11
❑ 83Don-584
❑ 83Fle-44
❑ 83Top-271
❑ 84BreGar-16
❑ 84BrePol-11
❑ 84Don-89
❑ 84Fle-212
❑ 84Nes792-146
❑ 84Top-146
❑ 84TopTif-146
❑ 85BreGar-17
❑ 85BrePol-11
❑ 85Don-515
❑ 85Fle-593
❑ 85SubDis-18
❑ 85ThoMcAD-18
❑ 85Top-498
❑ 85TopTif-498
❑ 86Don-455
❑ 86Fle-500
❑ 86OPC-317
❑ 86Top-317
❑ 86TopTif-317
❑ 86TopTra-95T
❑ 86TopTraT-95T
❑ 87Don-606
❑ 87Fle-42
❑ 87FleGlo-42
❑ 87OPC-158
❑ 87RedSoxP-17
❑ 87Top-675
❑ 87TopTif-675
❑ 88BlaYNPRWL-174
❑ 88Don-623
❑ 88DonTeaBRS-623
❑ 88Fle-362
❑ 88FleGlo-362
❑ 88Sco-259
❑ 88ScoGlo-259
❑ 88StaLinRS-17
❑ 88Top-37
❑ 88TopTif-37
❑ 89TopTra-105T
❑ 89TopTraT-105T
❑ 89UppDec-40
❑ 90Bow-361
❑ 90BowTif-361
❑ 90TigCok-20
❑ 91LasVegSLD-291
❑ 91LasVegSP-244
❑ 91LinDriAAA-291
❑ 92BreCarT-19
❑ 92SpoIndC-27
❑ 92SpoIndF-1310
❑ 93WatDiaC-28
❑ 93WatDiaF-1784
❑ 94BreMilB-267
❑ 94SprSulC-28
❑ 94SprSulF-2052
❑ 96DouAllB-25
❑ 96MemChiB-1
❑ 98El PasDG-27

Romero, Eddie
❑ 92SpoIndC-30

Romero, Elbi
❑ 87SpaPhiP-19

Romero, Elvis
❑ 86BenPhiC-140
❑ 87KenTwiP-23

Romero, Esmyel
❑ 82RedPioT-9

Romero, J.C.
❑ 98NewBriRCM-26

Romero, John
❑ 97ButCopKB-24
❑ 97ButCopKK-24

Romero, Jonathan
❑ 92MidAngF-4034
❑ 92PalSprAC-6

Romero, Jordan
❑ 98DelShoM-26

Romero, Mandy
❑ 89AugPirP-498
❑ 89SouAtlLAGS-10
❑ 90CarLeaA-21
❑ 90SalBucS-18
❑ 91CarMudLD-103
❑ 91CarMudP-1090
❑ 91LinDriAA-103
❑ 92CarMudF-1185
❑ 92CarMudS-141
❑ 92ClaFS7-326
❑ 92SkyAA F-66
❑ 93BufBisF-521
❑ 94BufBisF-1841
❑ 95WicWraTI-29
❑ 96Exc-66
❑ 96MemChiB-27
❑ 97MobBayBB-26
❑ 98Las-23

Romero, Philip
❑ 91FreStaBS-10
❑ 92MarPhiC-9
❑ 92MarPhiF-3066
❑ 93SpaPhiC-22
❑ 93SpaPhiF-1063

Romero, Ramon
❑ 78WatIndT-19
❑ 79WauTimT-14
❑ 80WatIndT-6
❑ 81AppFoxT-23
❑ 81WatIndT-14
❑ 82AppFoxFr-6
❑ 82WatIndT-9
❑ 83BufBisT-9
❑ 83GleFalWST-10
❑ 83IndPos-30
❑ 84BufBisT-16
❑ 84MaiGuiT-1
❑ 85BufBisT-11
❑ 85Ind-25
❑ 85IndPol-50
❑ 86Don-495
❑ 86TolMudHP-20
❑ 86Top-208
❑ 86TopTif-208
❑ 90HagSunDGB-23

Romero, Richard
❑ 93LinVenB-244
❑ 95LinVen-178
❑ 96-97LinVen-174

Romero, Robinson
❑ 96BriWhiSB-27
❑ 97BriWhiSB-13
❑ 98BriWhiSQ-22

Romero, Ronaldo
❑ 89GasRanP-1016
❑ 89GasRanS-21
❑ 90GasRanB-2
❑ 90GasRanP-2521
❑ 90GasRanS-21

Romero, Tony
❑ 87ElmPioBC-21
❑ 87ElmPioRC-21
❑ 88ElmPio1C-6

Romero, Willie
❑ 93GreFalDSP-20
❑ 93LinVenB-243
❑ 94BakDodC-21
❑ 94VerBeaDC-18
❑ 94VerBeaDF-89
❑ 95LinVen-15
❑ 95SanAntMTI-35
❑ 96-97LinVen-137
❑ 96SanAntMB-22
❑ 97SanAntMB-26
❑ 98AlbDukG-27
❑ 98SanAntMM-26

Romine, Jason
❑ 96PorRocB-25
❑ 97AshTou-23

Romine, Kevin
❑ 84PawRedST-13
❑ 85PawRedST-11
❑ 86PawRedSP-19
❑ 87PawRedSP-54
❑ 87PawRedST-18
❑ 87Top-121
❑ 87TopTif-121
❑ 88DonTeaBRS-NEW
❑ 88Fle-363
❑ 88FleGlo-363
❑ 88Sco-644
❑ 88ScoGlo-644
❑ 88StaLinRS-18
❑ 89Fle-98A
❑ 89Fle-98B
❑ 89FleGlo-98
❑ 89PawRedSC-18
❑ 89PawRedSP-682
❑ 89PawRedSTI-23
❑ 89Sco-541
❑ 89UppDec-524
❑ 90Bow-273
❑ 90BowTif-273
❑ 90Don-476
❑ 90Fle-286
❑ 90FleCan-286
❑ 90Lea-414
❑ 90RedSoxP-19
❑ 90Sco-458
❑ 90TopTra-105T
❑ 90TopTraT-105T
❑ 90TopTVRS-33
❑ 90UppDec-441
❑ 91Don-290
❑ 91Fle-113
❑ 91OPC-652
❑ 91RedSoxP-27
❑ 91Sco-116
❑ 91ScoPro-116
❑ 91Top-652
❑ 91TopDesS-652
❑ 91TopMic-652
❑ 91TopTif-652

Rommel, Ed
❑ 20WalMaiW-45
❑ 21E121So1-82A
❑ 21E121So1-82B
❑ 21Exh-146
❑ 21Nei-9
❑ 22E120-88
❑ 22W572-86
❑ 22W573-109
❑ 22W575-108
❑ 23W501-1
❑ 23W515-5
❑ 23WilChoV-135
❑ 25Exh-111
❑ 26Exh-111
❑ 27YorCarE-55
❑ 28W502-55
❑ 28Yue-55
❑ 29PorandAR-73
❑ 30W554-14
❑ 33ButCre-20
❑ 34DiaMatCSB-155
❑ 55Bow-239
❑ 74A's192T-22
❑ 77GalGloG-196
❑ 87ConSer2-19
❑ 94ConTSN-1156
❑ 94ConTSNB-1156

Rommell, Rick
❑ 23W501-103
❑ 80ElPasDT-6
❑ 81HolMilT-26

Romo, Enrique
❑ 77MarPos-19
❑ 78OPC-186
❑ 78Top-278
❑ 79OPC-281
❑ 79Top-548
❑ 80Top-332
❑ 81Don-255
❑ 81Fle-385
❑ 81OPC-28
❑ 81Top-28
❑ 82Don-59
❑ 82Fle-496
❑ 82Top-106
❑ 83Fle-320
❑ 83Top-226

Romo, Greg
❑ 97WesMicW-20
❑ 98LakTigM-10
❑ 98WesMicWM-20

Romo, Robert
❑ 87AubAstP-16

Romo, Vicente
❑ 69Top-267
❑ 70MLBOffS-163
❑ 70OPC-191
❑ 70Top-191
❑ 71MLBOffS-329
❑ 71OPC-723
❑ 71Top-723
❑ 72MilBra-297
❑ 72OPC-499
❑ 72Top-499
❑ 73OPC-381
❑ 73PadDea-23
❑ 73Top-381
❑ 74OPC-197
❑ 74PadDea-23
❑ 74PadTeal-12
❑ 74Top-197A
❑ 74Top-197B
❑ 75OPC-274
❑ 75Top-274
❑ 75TopMin-274
❑ 81RedSoxBG2S-105
❑ 83Fle-218
❑ 83Top-633
❑ 90DodTar-687

Romonosky, John
❑ 59SenTealW-15
❑ 59Top-267
❑ 60Top-87
❑ 60TopVen-87

Ronan, Kernan
❑ 82CliGiaF-16
❑ 83PhoGiaBHN-10
❑ 84ShrCapFB-17
❑ 89PalSprACLC-62
❑ 89PalSprAP-481
❑ 90PalSprACLC-229
❑ 90PalSprAP-2595
❑ 91LinDriAA-450
❑ 91MidAngLD-450
❑ 91MidAngOHP-24
❑ 91MidAngP-451
❑ 92MidAngF-4042
❑ 93MidAngF-339
❑ 94MidAngF-2455
❑ 94MidAngOHP-27
❑ 95MidAngOHP-29
❑ 95MidAngTI-24
❑ 96MidAngB-2
❑ 96MidAngOHP-22
❑ 98LakElsSG-24

Ronan, Marc
❑ 88AlaGolTI-15
❑ 89AlaGol-15
❑ 90HamRedB-14
❑ 91Cla/Bes-5
❑ 91SavCarC-14
❑ 91SavCarP-1654
❑ 92ClaFS7-270
❑ 92SprCarC-2
❑ 92SprCarF-872
❑ 93St.PetCC-22
❑ 93St.PetCF-2630
❑ 94LouRedF-2984
❑ 95LouRedF-278
❑ 96ChaKniB-25
❑ 97ColCliB-25
❑ 97ColCliD-22
❑ 98NewOrlZM-21

Ronca, Joe
❑ 90WelPirP-14
❑ 91AugPirC-22
❑ 91AugPirP-821
❑ 92SalBucF-77

Rondon, Alberto
❑ 76DubPacT-31

Rondon, Alex
❑ 95WesMicWTI-28
❑ 96SouOreTI-17
❑ 96WesMicWB-24

Rondon, Alfie
❑ 89PacSenL-173
❑ 91PacSenL-68
❑ 91PacSenL-78

Rondon, Gil (Gilbert)
❑ 76HouAstP-28
❑ 89PacSenL-196
❑ 90KinMetB-26
❑ 90KinMetS-27
❑ 91MedHatBJP-4118
❑ 91MedHatBJSP-24
❑ 91PacSenL-11
❑ 92MedHatBJSP-28

Rondon, Isidro
❑ 86TamTarP-18

Roneberg, Brett
❑ 98KanCouC-27
❑ 98KanCouCCP-27

Roney, Chad
❑ 97VerBeaD-22

Roney, Matt
❑ 99BowBes-180
❑ 99BowBesAR-180
❑ 99BowBesR-180
❑ 99StaClu-343
❑ 99StaCluFDI-343
❑ 99StaCluOoaK-343
❑ 99StaCluPP-343
❑ 99Top-438
❑ 99TopChr-438
❑ 99TopChrR-438
❑ 99TopMVPP-438

Ronk, Jeff
❑ 82AmaGolST-7
❑ 83BeaGolGT-14
❑ 84BeaGolGT-25

Ronning, Al
❑ 52Par-49
❑ 53ExhCan-56

Ronson, Tod
❑ 86EveGiaC-21
❑ 86EveGiaPC-27
❑ 87CliGiaP-8
❑ 88SanJosGCLC-128
❑ 88SanJosGP-126
❑ 89SalSpuCLC-143
❑ 89SalSpuP-1821

Roobarb, Mascot
❑ 85WhiSoxC-NNO
❑ 86WhiSoxC-NNO
❑ 87WhiSoxC-25
❑ 88WhiSoxC-25

Rood, Nelson
❑ 86TucTorP-19
❑ 87TucTorP-15
❑ 88TucTorC-13
❑ 88TucTorJP-19
❑ 88TucTorP-191
❑ 90CMC-491
❑ 90EdmTraC-14
❑ 90EdmTraP-525
❑ 90ProAAAF-101
❑ 92CliGiaC-27
❑ 92CliGiaF-3613

Roof, Gene (Eugene L.)
❑ 78St.PetCT-23
❑ 79ArkTraT-22
❑ 80VenLeaS-118
❑ 82Don-615
❑ 82LouRedE-25
❑ 82Top-561
❑ 83Fle-20
❑ 83LouRedR-5
❑ 84LouRedR-5
❑ 85RicBraT-20
❑ 86NasSouTI-23
❑ 87TolMudHP-22
❑ 87TolMudHT-22
❑ 88TolMudHP-599
❑ 89FayGenP-1577
❑ 90FayGenP-2423
❑ 90SouAtlLAS-23
❑ 91LinDriAA-399
❑ 91LonTigLD-399
❑ 91LonTigP-1892
❑ 92TigTeal-28
❑ 93TigGat-28
❑ 98TolMudHQ-2

Roof, Phil
❑ 63Top-324
❑ 64Top-541
❑ 65Top-537
❑ 66Top-382
❑ 67CokCapAt-9
❑ 67DexPre-181
❑ 67OPC-129
❑ 67Top-129
❑ 68Top-484
❑ 69MilBra-240
❑ 69Top-334
❑ 70BreMcD-26
❑ 70BreMil-21
❑ 70BreTeal-10
❑ 70OPC-359
❑ 70SunPin-15
❑ 70Top-359
❑ 71BreTeal-14
❑ 71MLBOffS-450
❑ 71OPC-22
❑ 71Top-22
❑ 72MilBra-298
❑ 72OPC-201
❑ 72Top-201
❑ 72TwiPos-19
❑ 73OPC-598
❑ 73Top-598
❑ 74OPC-388
❑ 74Top-388
❑ 75OPC-576
❑ 75Top-576
❑ 75TopMin-576
❑ 75TwiPos-20
❑ 75TwiTeal-23
❑ 76MinTwiP-14
❑ 76OPC-424
❑ 76SSP-224
❑ 76Top-424
❑ 77OPC-121
❑ 77Top-392
❑ 78PadFamF-27
❑ 83OrlTwiT-1
❑ 84MarMot-27
❑ 85MarMot-27
❑ 86MarMot-28
❑ 87MarMot-28
❑ 90CubMar-28
❑ 90TopTVCu-6
❑ 91CubMar-NNO
❑ 91CubVinL-22
❑ 92OrlSunRF-2862
❑ 92OrlSunRS-524
❑ 93NasXprF-417
❑ 94BreMilB-347
❑ 94NasXprF-401
❑ 97SalLakB-3
❑ 98SalLakBO-1

Rooker, Dave
❑ 83ButCopKT-26
❑ 86PriWilPP-22
❑ 87HarSenP-4

Rooker, Jim
❑ 69Top-376
❑ 70OPC-222
❑ 70RoyTeal-30
❑ 70Top-222
❑ 71MLBOffS-428
❑ 71OPC-730
❑ 71Top-730
❑ 71TopCoi-32
❑ 72oyTeal-21
❑ 72Top-742
❑ 74OPC-402
❑ 74Top-402
❑ 75OPC-148
❑ 75PitPirP-24
❑ 75Top-148
❑ 75TopMin-148
❑ 76OPC-243
❑ 76PirPos-20
❑ 76SSP-566
❑ 76Top-243
❑ 77OPC-161
❑ 77PirPosP-23
❑ 77Top-82
❑ 78Top-308
❑ 79Top-584
❑ 80Top-694
❑ 81Fle-368
❑ 88PirTeal-29
❑ 93PirNatl-26

Rooker, Michael
❑ 88PacEigMO-9

Rookie, Ray the
❑ 96MauStiHWB-NNO

Rooks, George
❑ 87BucN28-51
❑ 87OldJudN-422

Roomes, Rolando
❑ 82QuaCitCT-24
❑ 83QuaCitCT-27
❑ 86WinSpiP-24
❑ 87PitCubP-25
❑ 88BlaYNPRWLU-36
❑ 88TriAAC-7
❑ 89Don-577
❑ 89Fle-644
❑ 89FleGlo-644
❑ 89FleUpd-86
❑ 89NasSouC-22
❑ 89NasSouP-1286
❑ 89RedKah-36
❑ 89ScoHot1R-37
❑ 89ScoRoo-109T
❑ 89UppDec-6
❑ 90Bow-56
❑ 90BowTif-56
❑ 90ClaBlu-38
❑ 90Don-360
❑ 90Fle-432
❑ 90FleCan-432
❑ 90OPC-364
❑ 90PanSti-254
❑ 90Sco-417
❑ 90Sco100RS-92
❑ 90ScoYouSI-22
❑ 90Top-364
❑ 90TopBig-87
❑ 90TopSti-143
❑ 90TopTif-364
❑ 90UppDec-170
❑ 91DenZepP-136

Rooney, Jim
❑ 84NewOriT-16

Rooney, Mike
❑ 97LetBlaDB-28
❑ 98SouBenSHM-22

Rooney, Pat
❑ 79MemChiT-22
❑ 80MemChiT-17
❑ 82WicAerTI-15
❑ 83WicAerDS-18

❑ 84ColCliP-21
❑ 84ColCliT-3
❑ 85SyrChiT-16
Roosevelt, Franklin Delano
❑ 94UppDecTAE-47
Rooster, Rowdy the
❑ 95PorCitRTI-21
❑ 96PorCitRB-29
Root, Charley H.
❑ 24Zee-15
❑ 28Exh-11
❑ 28StaPlaCE-54
❑ 29ExhFou-6
❑ 29PorandAR-74
❑ 30ChiEveAP-8
❑ 30CubTeal-15
❑ 30SchR33-44
❑ 31CubTeal-18
❑ 31Exh-6
❑ 32CubTeal-20
❑ 32OrbPinUP-51
❑ 33ButCre-21
❑ 33ExhFou-3
❑ 33Gou-226
❑ 33TatOrb-51
❑ 33TatOrbSDR-190
❑ 34DiaMatCSB-156
❑ 35DiaMatCS3T1-125
❑ 36CubTeal-25
❑ 36DiaMatCS3T2-20
❑ 39CubTeal-21
❑ 39GouPreR303A-39
❑ 39WorWidGTP-39
❑ 41CubTeal-21
❑ 60Top-457
❑ 75TCMLarFP-3
❑ 77CubAllT-10
❑ 77GalGloG-59
❑ 80Bra195T-17
❑ 80CubGreT-2
❑ 84CubBriPC-7C
❑ 85BigLeaC3-20
❑ 88ConSer3-24
❑ 91ConTSN-93
❑ 92CubOldS-20
Root, Derek
❑ 95AubAstTI-3
❑ 96QuaCitRB-24
❑ 97KisCob-20
❑ 98KisCobQ-27
Root, Mitch
❑ 91HunCubC-21
❑ 91HunCubP-3343
❑ 92HunCubC-19
❑ 92HunCubF-3157
❑ 94JamJamC-21
❑ 94JamJamF-3975
❑ 95MidLeaA-46
Roper, Brian
❑ 89ButCopKSP-3
Roper, Chad
❑ 92ClaDraP-46
❑ 92FroRowDP-60
❑ 92FroRowDPG-60
❑ 92FroRowDPS-60
❑ 92HigSchPLS-22
❑ 92HigSchPLS-NNO
❑ 93ClaFS7-15
❑ 93ForMyeMC-1
❑ 93ForMyeMF-2665
❑ 93StaCluM-177
❑ 94Bow-572
❑ 94BowBes-B53
❑ 94BowBesR-B53
❑ 94FloStaLAF-FSL12
❑ 94ForMyeMC-21
❑ 94ForMyeMF-1175
❑ 94UppDecML-243
❑ 95HarCitRCTI-22
❑ 96HarCitRCB-27
❑ 97ForMyeM-26
❑ 98ForMyeMTI-27
❑ 98MadBlaW-14
Roper, John
❑ 91ChaWheC-9
❑ 91ChaWheP-2886
❑ 91Cla/Bes-276
❑ 91SouAtlLAGP-SAL11
❑ 92Bow-528
❑ 92ChaLooF-3819
❑ 92ChaLooS-194
❑ 92ClaFS7-72
❑ 92ProFS7-218
❑ 92SkyAA F-87
❑ 92UppDecML-44
❑ 92UppDecML-233
❑ 93Bow-34
❑ 93ClaFS7-16
❑ 93ClaGolF-55
❑ 93ExcFS7-29
❑ 93FlaWavotF-14
❑ 93FleFinE-19
❑ 93IndIndF-1487
❑ 93SelRoo-34T
❑ 93Ult-334
❑ 94BowBes-B34
❑ 94BowBesR-B34
❑ 94Cla-114
❑ 94ColC-245
❑ 94ColChoGS-245
❑ 94ColChoSS-245
❑ 94Don-551
❑ 94Fla-369
❑ 94Fle-423
❑ 94IndIndF-1809
❑ 94Pin-137
❑ 94PinArtP-137
❑ 94PinMusC-137
❑ 94RedKah-24
❑ 94Sco-623
❑ 94ScoGolR-623
❑ 94StaClu-476
❑ 94StaCluFDI-476
❑ 94StaCluGR-476
❑ 94StaCluMOP-476
❑ 94Top-581
❑ 94TopGol-581
❑ 94TopSpa-581
❑ 94Ult-175
❑ 94UppDec-68
❑ 94UppDecED-68
❑ 95ColCho-437
❑ 95ColChoGS-437
❑ 95ColChoSS-437
❑ 95Don-442
❑ 95DonPreP-442
❑ 95Fin-141
❑ 95FinRef-141
❑ 95Fla-123
❑ 95Fle-444
❑ 95Lea-286
❑ 95RedKah-24
❑ 95Sco-356
❑ 95ScoGolR-356
❑ 95ScoPlaTS-356
❑ 95StaClu-269
❑ 95StaCluFDI-269
❑ 95StaCluMOP-269
❑ 95StaCluSTWS-269
❑ 95Top-604
❑ 95TopCyb-375
❑ 95Ult-369
❑ 95UltGolM-369
❑ 95UppDec-171
❑ 95UppDecED-171
❑ 95UppDecEDG-171
❑ 96ChaLooB-25
Roque, Francisco
❑ 96HelBreTI-21
❑ 98BelSnaM-22
Roque, Jorge
❑ 96NewJerCB-23
Roque, Jorge Vargas
❑ 72OPC-316
❑ 72Top-316
❑ 73OPC-606
❑ 73Top-606
Roque, Rafael
❑ 92GulCoaMF-3479
❑ 93KinMetC-20
❑ 93KinMetF-3794
❑ 95StLucMTI-28
❑ 96BinMetB-24
❑ 97BinMetB-25
❑ 98El PasDG-28
❑ 99Bow-349
❑ 99BowGol-349
❑ 99BowInt-349
❑ 99DumSet-138
❑ 99Fle-121
❑ 99FleMys-138
❑ 99FleMysM-138
❑ 99FleSta9-121
❑ 99FleWarT-121
❑ 99PacCroC-154
❑ 99PacCroCPB-154
❑ 99SkyThu-80
❑ 99SkyThuRant-80
❑ 99SkyThuRave-80
❑ 99SP SigAuto-RR
❑ 99SP SigAutoG-RR
❑ 99SpoIll-47
❑ 99SPSig-29
❑ 99ThuSkySupR-80
❑ 99UppDec-404
❑ 99UppDecEL1-404
❑ 99UppDecEL2-404
❑ 99UppDecEM-MC9
❑ 99UppDecEMFXG-MC9
❑ 99Vic-209
Roques, Ryan
❑ 97UCLBruTI-19
Rorex, Troy
❑ 92DavLipB-22
❑ 93DavLipB-19
Rosa, Cristy
❑ 97PorRocG-23
❑ 98AshTouM-19
Rosa, Erick
❑ 97WatIndTI-25
Rosa, Julio
❑ 88BriTigP-1869
❑ 89FayGenP-1587
Rosado, Ed (Edwin)
❑ 88MarPhiS-28
❑ 89BatCliP-1944
❑ 89BlaYNPRWL-124
❑ 89SpaPhiP-1029
❑ 89SpaPhiS-20
❑ 90ClePhiS-19
❑ 91LinDriAA-516
❑ 91ReaPhiLD-516
❑ 91ReaPhiP-1373
❑ 92ReaPhiF-579
❑ 92ReaPhiS-541
❑ 93ReaPhiF-298
Rosado, Jose
❑ 95WilBluRTI-26
❑ 96Bow-229
❑ 96BowFoi-229
❑ 96OmaRoyB-25
❑ 96WicWraB-12
❑ 97BowBes-106
❑ 97BowBesAR-106
❑ 97BowBesR-106
❑ 97Cir-11
❑ 97CirRav-11
❑ 97ColCho-354
❑ 97Don-366
❑ 97DonGolPP-366
❑ 97DonLim-172
❑ 97DonLimE-172
❑ 97DonPre-89
❑ 97DonPreCttC-89
❑ 97DonSilPP-366
❑ 97Fin-268
❑ 97FinRef-268
❑ 97Fle-122
❑ 97FleTif-122
❑ 97MetUni-97
❑ 97RoyPol-20
❑ 97Sco-286
❑ 97ScoArtPWB-286
❑ 97ScoPreS-286
❑ 97ScoShoS-286
❑ 97ScoShoSAP-286
❑ 97Sel-162
❑ 97SelCom-162
❑ 97SpoIll-72
❑ 97SpoIllEE-72
❑ 97StaClu-83
❑ 97StaCluM-M26
❑ 97StaCluMOP-83
❑ 97StaCluMOP-M26
❑ 97StrAll-55
❑ 97Top-409
❑ 97TopChr-144
❑ 97TopChrR-144
❑ 97TopGal-174
❑ 97TopGalPPI-174
❑ 97TopSta-97
❑ 97TopStaAM-97
❑ 97Ult-71
❑ 97UltGolME-71
❑ 97UltPlaME-71
❑ 97UppDec-388
❑ 98ColCho-136
❑ 98Fin-103
❑ 98FinNo--103
❑ 98FinNo-R-103
❑ 98FinRef-103
❑ 98Fle-206
❑ 98Pac-112
❑ 98PacInvTeam-13
❑ 98PacOnl-352
❑ 98PacOnlR-352
❑ 98PacOnlWC-352
❑ 98PacPar-58
❑ 98PacParC-58
❑ 98PacParG-58
❑ 98PacParHS-58
❑ 98PacParPB-58
❑ 98PacParR-58
❑ 98PacPlaB-112
❑ 98PacRedT-112
❑ 98PacSil-112
❑ 98PinPlu-23
❑ 98Sco-114
❑ 98ScoSS-PP148
❑ 98ScoSSAP-PP148
❑ 98StaCluFDI-100
❑ 98StaCluI-100
❑ 98StaCluOneK-100
❑ 98StaCluPP-100
❑ 98Top-174
❑ 98TopChr-174
❑ 98TopChrR-174
❑ 98TopDevR-174
❑ 98TopDia-174
❑ 98TopGal-131
❑ 98TopGalGP-131
❑ 98TopGalOPP-131
❑ 98TopGalPPI-131
❑ 98TopGalPPIA-131
❑ 98TopMiniC-174
❑ 98TopOpeD-93
❑ 98UppDec-110
❑ 98UppDecSF-68
❑ 99Fle-432
❑ 99FleSta9-432
❑ 99FleWarT-432
❑ 99Pac-211
❑ 99PacCroC-136
❑ 99PacCroCPB-136
❑ 99PacPlaB-211
❑ 99PacRed-211
❑ 99SkyPre-214
❑ 99SkyPreR-214
Rosado, Juan
❑ 96VerExpB-24
❑ 98StoPorUG-5
Rosado, Papo (Luis)
❑ 78TidTidT-22
❑ 79SyrChiT-18
❑ 79SyrChiTI-2
❑ 80TidTidT-22
❑ 84RocRedWT-12
❑ 85RocRedWT-3
❑ 91MetWIZ-334
Rosar, Buddy (Warren)
❑ 41Gou-4
❑ 46SpoExcW-6-6
❑ 47A'sTeal-25
❑ 48A'sTeal-19
❑ 48BluTin-19
❑ 48Bow-10
❑ 49A'sTeal-27
❑ 49Bow-138
❑ 49Lea-128
❑ 49PhiBul-44
❑ 50Bow-136
❑ 50RedSoxTI-20
❑ 51Bow-236
❑ 63GadFunC-29
❑ 75YanDyn1T-38
❑ 76TayBow4-83
❑ 79DiaGre-15
❑ 84TCMPla1-23
❑ 92YanWIZA-69
Rosar, Greg
❑ 94ButCopKSP-9
Rosario, Alfonso
❑ 78CedRapGT-24
❑ 85DomLeaS-207
Rosario, David
❑ 87PeoChiP-16
❑ 88BlaYNPRWL-140
❑ 88WinSpiS-15
❑ 89BlaYNPRWL-14
❑ 89BlaYNPRWLU-55
❑ 89ChaKniTI-13
❑ 91IowCubLD-215
❑ 91IowCubP-1060
❑ 91LinDriAA-215
❑ 92ColCliF-349
❑ 92ColCliP-8
❑ 92ColCliS-114
❑ 92SkyAAAF-54
Rosario, Eliezel
❑ 90AshTouP-2747
❑ 95IdaFalBTI-2
Rosario, Felix
❑ 94MedHatBJF-3696
❑ 94MedHatBJSP-9
❑ 95StCatSTI-23
Rosario, Francisco
❑ 88SavCarP-358
❑ 90MarPhiP-3194
Rosario, Gabriel
❑ 91MedHatBJP-4108
❑ 91MedHatBJSP-15
❑ 92MyrBeaHC-22
❑ 92MyrBeaHF-2205
❑ 93DunBluJC-18
❑ 93DunBluJFFN-20
Rosario, Jimmy (Angel)
❑ 72OPC-366
❑ 72Top-366
❑ 74PhoGiaC-87
❑ 75SacSolC-12
❑ 76SpoIndC-2
❑ 94BreMilB-348
Rosario, Jose
❑ 78DunBluJT-20
Rosario, Jossy
❑ 87WytCubP-7
❑ 89ChaWheB-8
❑ 89ChaWheP-1750
Rosario, Juan
❑ 98HudValR-21
Rosario, Julio
❑ 86ElmPioRSP-17
❑ 87ElmPioBC-8
❑ 87ElmPioRC-8
❑ 88ElmPio1C-7
❑ 88ElmPioC-18
❑ 88WinHavRSS-22
❑ 89ElmPioP-16
❑ 93GreFalDSP-8
Rosario, Liriano
❑ 94KnoSmoF-1311
Rosario, Maximo
❑ 83AndBraT-16
Rosario, Mel
❑ 92SpoIndC-14
❑ 92SpoIndF-1297
❑ 93SpoIndC-18
❑ 93SpoIndF-3596
❑ 96HigDesMB-24
❑ 97Bow-420
❑ 97BowChr-280
❑ 97BowChrI-280
❑ 97BowChrIR-280
❑ 97BowChrR-280
❑ 97BowInt-420
❑ 98Bow-121
❑ 98BowCerBlueAU-7
❑ 98BowCerGA-7
❑ 98BowCerSA-7
❑ 98BowChr-121
❑ 98BowChrGA-121
❑ 98BowChrGAR-121
❑ 98BowChrI-121
❑ 98BowChrIR-121
❑ 98BowChrR-121
❑ 98BowGolA-121
❑ 98BowInt-121
❑ 98RocRedWQ-25
Rosario, Melvin
❑ 86KinEagP-22
❑ 87Ft.LauYP-26
❑ 88AlbYanP-1343
❑ 88BlaYNPRWL-49
❑ 89BlaYNPRWL-53
❑ 89Ft.LauYS-24
❑ 90ChaLooGS-26
❑ 93WatDiaC-25
❑ 93WatDiaF-1778
❑ 97BowBay-26
❑ 97EasLeaTPB-9
❑ 97TexAllM-26
❑ 98PorRocG-28
❑ 98SpoIll-160
❑ 98SpoIllEE-160
❑ 98SpoIllFE-160
Rosario, Ruben
❑ 96JohCitCTI-28
❑ 97NewJerCB-23
❑ 98NewJerCM-25
❑ 98PeoChiM-21
Rosario, Sal
❑ 75BurBeeT-22
Rosario, Santiago
❑ 77FriOneYW-108
Rosario, Simon
❑ 76DubPacT-32
❑ 77CocAstT-22
❑ 78DayBeaAT-22
❑ 80ColAstT-14
❑ 81TucTorT-8
❑ 84DurBulT-1
❑ 85DomLeaS-201
❑ 85GreBraTI-14
Rosario, Victor
❑ 85ElmPioT-20
❑ 86GreHorP-21
❑ 87GreHorP-19
❑ 88MarPhiS-29
❑ 89ReaPhiS-20
❑ 89ScrRedBC-23
❑ 89ScrRedBP-710
❑ 90CMC-241
❑ 90ProAAAF-309
❑ 90ScrRedBC-15
❑ 90ScrRedBP-607
❑ 91Fle-701
❑ 91LinDriAAA-440
❑ 91RicBraBC-21
❑ 91RicBraLD-440
❑ 91RicBraP-2577
❑ 91RicBraTI-11
❑ 91TopDeb90-135
❑ 92SkyAAAF-267
❑ 92TolMudHF-1051
❑ 92TolMudHS-595
❑ 93LimRocDWB-135
Roscoe, Greg
❑ 88WatIndP-691
❑ 89KinIndS-21
❑ 89WatIndS-20
❑ 90CanIndB-23
❑ 90CanIndP-1308
❑ 90CanIndS-15
❑ 91CanIndLD-93
❑ 91CanIndP-980
❑ 91LinDriAA-93
❑ 92ColSprSSF-750
❑ 92ColSprSSS-94
Rose, Bobby (Robert)
❑ 86QuaCitAP-29
❑ 88MidLeaAGS-23
❑ 88QuaCitAGS-14
❑ 89MidAngGS-27
❑ 89TexLeaAGS-3
❑ 90Bow-293
❑ 90BowTif-293
❑ 90ClaUpd-T41
❑ 90CMC-492
❑ 90EdmTraC-15
❑ 90EdmTraP-526
❑ 90Fle-651
❑ 90FleCan-651
❑ 90ProAAAF-102
❑ 90Sco-604
❑ 90TopDeb89-106
❑ 90UppDec-77
❑ 91Bow-206
❑ 91EdmTraLD-169
❑ 91EdmTraP-1524
❑ 91Fle-324
❑ 91LinDriAAA-169
❑ 92AngPol-16
❑ 92Don-90
❑ 92Fle-68
❑ 92Lea-250
❑ 92LeaBlaG-250
❑ 92OPC-652
❑ 92OPCPre-169
❑ 92Sco-558
❑ 92StaClu-79
❑ 92Top-652
❑ 92TopGol-652
❑ 92TopGolW-652
❑ 92TopMic-652
❑ 92Ult-330
❑ 92UppDec-611
Rose, Brian
❑ 94BenRocC-20
❑ 94BenRocF-3592
❑ 94StaCluDP-35
❑ 94StaCluDPFDI-35
❑ 95AshTouUTI-8
❑ 95MicBatCTI-23
❑ 96Bow-357
❑ 96BowFoi-357
❑ 96TreThuB-13
❑ 97Bes-29
❑ 97BesAutSBPP-37
❑ 97BesGun-5
❑ 97Bow-105
❑ 97Bow98ROY-ROY14
❑ 97BowBes-144
❑ 97BowBesAR-144

❑ 97BowBesR-144
❑ 97BowChr-125
❑ 97BowChr1RFR-ROY14
❑ 97BowChr98RF-ROY14
❑ 97BowChrI-125
❑ 97BowChrIR-125
❑ 97BowChrR-125
❑ 97BowInt-105
❑ 97PawRedS-1
❑ 98BesAutPOY-16
❑ 98BesCon-9
❑ 98BesCon-10
❑ 98BesDiaB-7
❑ 98BesPos-3
❑ 98BesYouG-9
❑ 98BesYouG-10
❑ 98Bow-103
❑ 98BowBes-135
❑ 98BowBesAR-135
❑ 98BowBesR-135
❑ 98BowCerBlueAU-32
❑ 98BowCerGA-32
❑ 98BowCerSA-32
❑ 98BowChr-103
❑ 98BowChrGA-103
❑ 98BowChrGAR-103
❑ 98BowChrI-103
❑ 98BowChrIR-103
❑ 98BowChrR-103
❑ 98BowGolA-103
❑ 98BowInt-103
❑ 98BowScoC-SC14
❑ 98CirThu-180
❑ 98CirThuRav-180
❑ 98CirThuSupRav-180
❑ 98ColCho-111
❑ 98Don-309
❑ 98DonColL-208
❑ 98DonColP-716
❑ 98DonGolPP-309
❑ 98DonPre-166
❑ 98DonPreSeat-166
❑ 98DonPriCL-208
❑ 98DonPriCP-716
❑ 98DonSigA-77
❑ 98DonSigAC-99
❑ 98DonSigAM-101
❑ 98DonSilPP-309
❑ 98FlaShoLeg0-31
❑ 98FlaShoLeg1-31
❑ 98FlaShoLeg2-31
❑ 98FlaShoLeg3-31
❑ 98FlaShoLegM-31
❑ 98FlaShoR0-31
❑ 98FlaShoR1-31
❑ 98FlaShoR2-31
❑ 98FlaShoR3-31
❑ 98Fle-259
❑ 98FleProF-PF16
❑ 98Lea-8
❑ 98LeaFraDA-8
❑ 98LeaFraF-8
❑ 98LeaFraM-8
❑ 98LeaFraM-8
❑ 98LeaFraMDC-8
❑ 98LeaFraMDC-8
❑ 98LeaFraMZ2-8
❑ 98LeaRCrusUP-124
❑ 98LeaRS-272
❑ 98LeaRSCrusUG-124
❑ 98LeaRSCrusUR-124
❑ 98LeaRSLHolo-272
❑ 98LeaRSLong-272
❑ 98LeaRTrue-272
❑ 98PacOme-41
❑ 98PacOmeR-41
❑ 98PacOmeRS-13
❑ 98PacOmeRST5-13
❑ 98PacOnl-124
❑ 98PacOnlR-124
❑ 98PacOnlWC-124
❑ 98PinPer-137
❑ 98PinPerPP-137
❑ 98PinPlu-175
❑ 98PinSna-BRS2
❑ 98ScoRT-102
❑ 98ScoRTSS-PP69
❑ 98ScoRTSSAP-PP69
❑ 98ScoRTSSAP1-PP69
❑ 98SkyDugA-104
❑ 98SkyDugAIA-104
❑ 98SpoIll-153
❑ 98SpoIllEE-153
❑ 98SpoIllFE-153
❑ 98SpoIllWSF-33
❑ 98SpoIllWSFEE-33
❑ 98SpoIllWSFFE-33
❑ 98Stu-90
❑ 98StuGPP-90
❑ 98StuSPP-90
❑ 98Top-485
❑ 98TopChr-485
❑ 98TopChrR-485
❑ 98TopDevR-485
❑ 98TopDia-485
❑ 98TopMiniC-485
❑ 98TreThuM-19
❑ 98Ult-225
❑ 98UltGolM-225
❑ 98UltMas-225
❑ 98UltPlaM-225
❑ 98UltRoctS-5
❑ 98UppDec-274
❑ 98UppDecBCP-BC23
❑ 99PacOme-46
❑ 99PacOmeC-46
❑ 99PacOmeG-46
❑ 99PacOmePB-46

Rose, Carl
❑ 86WatPirP-19

Rose, Don
❑ 73OPC-178
❑ 73Top-178
❑ 75PhoGiaC-21
❑ 75PhoGiaCK-7
❑ 91MetWIZ-335

Rose, Edward
❑ 27Zee-37
❑ 28Zee-59

Rose, Guy
❑ 71RicBraTI-16

Rose, Harry
❑ 33WorCig(-75

Rose, Heath
❑ 92BurAstF-545
❑ 93QuaCitRBC-20

Rose, Johnathan
❑ 98MarPhiG-26

Rose, Kevin
❑ 79NewCoPT-20

Rose, Mark
❑ 91OneYanP-4169
❑ 92GreHorC-27
❑ 92GreHorF-798
❑ 93GreHorF-905
❑ 94OneYanC-27

Rose, Mike
❑ 96AubDouB-23
❑ 97QuaCitRBB-26
❑ 98QuaCitRBG-25

Rose, Pete Edward
❑ 56RedBurB-21
❑ 63RedEnq-32
❑ 63RedFreBC-23
❑ 63Top-537
❑ 64Kah-26
❑ 64RedJayP-12
❑ 64Top-125
❑ 64TopCoi-82
❑ 64TopVen-125
❑ 65Kah-37
❑ 65OPC-207
❑ 65RedEnq-25
❑ 65Top-207
❑ 66Baz-38
❑ 66Kah-27
❑ 66OPC-30
❑ 66RedVolC-12
❑ 66Top-30
❑ 66TopRubI-83
❑ 66TopVen-30
❑ 67Baz-38
❑ 67CokCapA-2
❑ 67CokCapNLA-30
❑ 67CokCapR-13
❑ 67DexPre-182
❑ 67Kah-32
❑ 67Top-430
❑ 67TopGiaSU-1
❑ 67TopVen-270
❑ 68AtlOilPBCC-39
❑ 68Baz-6
❑ 68Baz-15
❑ 68Top-230
❑ 68TopActS-5C
❑ 68TopGamI-30
❑ 68TopPla-21
❑ 68TopPos-23
❑ 68TopVen-230
❑ 69CitMetC-14
❑ 69KelPin-15
❑ 69MilBra-241
❑ 69MLBOffS-135
❑ 69MLBPin-55
❑ 69NabTeaF-20
❑ 69OPC-2
❑ 69OPC-120
❑ 69Top-2
❑ 69Top-120
❑ 69Top-424
❑ 69TopDec-21
❑ 69TopDecI-36
❑ 69TopFou-19
❑ 69TopSta-29
❑ 69TopSup-41
❑ 69TopTeaP-20
❑ 69TraSta-54
❑ 70DayDaiNM-1
❑ 70Kel-2
❑ 70MilBra-24
❑ 70MLBOffS-35
❑ 70OPC-61
❑ 70OPC-458
❑ 70Top-61
❑ 70Top-458
❑ 70Top-580
❑ 70TopBoo-15
❑ 70TopSup-34
❑ 70TraSta-1A
❑ 71AllBasA-21
❑ 71BazNumT-32
❑ 71BazUnn-5
❑ 71Kel-65
❑ 71MilDud-60
❑ 71MLBOffS-68
❑ 71MLBOffS-573
❑ 71OPC-100
❑ 71Top-100
❑ 71Top-511
❑ 71TopCoi-101
❑ 71TopGreM-15
❑ 71TopSup-20
❑ 71TopTat-113
❑ 72Dia-63
❑ 72Kel-6
❑ 72MilBra-299
❑ 72ProStaP-21
❑ 72SevTraC-47
❑ 72Top-559
❑ 72Top-560
❑ 72TopPos-11
❑ 73Kel2D-6
❑ 73LinPor-59
❑ 73OPC-130
❑ 73Top-130
❑ 73TopCanL-44
❑ 74Kel-38
❑ 74NewYorNTDiS-22
❑ 74OPC-201
❑ 74OPC-300
❑ 74OPC-336
❑ 74Top-201
❑ 74Top-300
❑ 74Top-336
❑ 74TopDecE-16
❑ 74TopSta-30
❑ 75BlaBacD-5
❑ 75Hos-29
❑ 75HosTwi-29
❑ 75Kel-11
❑ 75OPC-211
❑ 75OPC-320
❑ 75SSPPuzB-22
❑ 75Top-211
❑ 75Top-320
❑ 75TopMin-211
❑ 75TopMin-320
❑ 76BlaDis-51
❑ 76BucDis-51
❑ 76CarDis-51
❑ 76CraDis-51
❑ 76DailsID-51
❑ 76Hos-66
❑ 76IsaDis-51
❑ 76Kel-55
❑ 76LinSup-97
❑ 76OPC-240
❑ 76OrbDis-51
❑ 76RedBarD-51
❑ 76RedIceL-12
❑ 76RedKro-16
❑ 76SafDis-51
❑ 76SafSupLB-4
❑ 76SafSupLB-6
❑ 76SafSupLB-10
❑ 76SafSupLB-13
❑ 76SafSupLB-15
❑ 76SSP-41
❑ 76Top-240
❑ 76TowCluD-51
❑ 77BurCheD-204
❑ 77ChiWilD-56
❑ 77DailsID-56
❑ 77DetCaeD-56
❑ 77HolInnD-56
❑ 77Hos-8
❑ 77Kel-20
❑ 77MSADis-56
❑ 77OPC-240
❑ 77PepGloD-43
❑ 77RCColC-56
❑ 77RedCarP-11
❑ 77SagDis-56
❑ 77sDis-56
❑ 77Spo-804
❑ 77Top-277
❑ 77Top-450
❑ 77TopCloS-38
❑ 77WenDis-56
❑ 77ZipDis-56
❑ 78Hos-128
❑ 78OPC-100
❑ 78OPC-240
❑ 78Pep-21
❑ 78RCColC-3
❑ 78SSP270-132
❑ 78Top-5
❑ 78Top-20
❑ 78WifBalD-63
❑ 79BasPat-73
❑ 79Hos-144
❑ 79Kel-22
❑ 79OPC-343
❑ 79PhiBurK-13
❑ 79PhiTeal-8
❑ 79Top-204
❑ 79Top-650
❑ 79TopCom-28
❑ 80BurKinPHR-21
❑ 80Kel-35
❑ 80OPC-282
❑ 80PhiBul-28
❑ 80PhiBurK-4
❑ 80Top-4
❑ 80Top-540
❑ 80TopSup-19
❑ 81AllGamPI-98
❑ 81CokTeaS-104
❑ 81Don-131
❑ 81Don-131B
❑ 81Don-251
❑ 81Don-371
❑ 81Dra-3
❑ 81Fle-1
❑ 81Fle-645
❑ 81Fle-645B
❑ 81FleStiC-43
❑ 81FleStiC-74
❑ 81Kel-63
❑ 81MSAMinD-27
❑ 81OPC-180
❑ 81PerAll-7
❑ 81PerCreC-5
❑ 81Squ-11
❑ 81Top-180
❑ 81Top-205
❑ 81TopScr-62
❑ 81TopSti-200
❑ 81TopSupHT-86
❑ 81TopSupN-12
❑ 82Don-1
❑ 82Don-168
❑ 82Don-585
❑ 82Dra-28
❑ 82FBIDis-20
❑ 82Fle-256
❑ 82Fle-640
❑ 82FleSta-51
❑ 82FleSta-107
❑ 82FleSta-109
❑ 82K-M-24
❑ 82K-M-44
❑ 82Kel-18
❑ 82MonNew-13
❑ 82OnDecD-27
❑ 82OPC-24
❑ 82OPC-337
❑ 82OPC-361
❑ 82PerAll-16
❑ 82PerAllG-16
❑ 82PerCreC-9
❑ 82PerCreCG-9
❑ 82SevSluC-22
❑ 82Squ-12
❑ 82Top-4
❑ 82Top-337
❑ 82Top-636
❑ 82Top-780
❑ 82Top-781
❑ 82TopSti-78
❑ 82TopSti-117
❑ 82TopSti-121
❑ 83AllGamPI-98
❑ 83Don-42
❑ 83DonActA-31
❑ 83Dra-24
❑ 83Fle-171
❑ 83Fle-634
❑ 83FleSta-168
❑ 83FleSti-143
❑ 83FleSti-145
❑ 83FleSti-174
❑ 83Kel-6
❑ 83Oco& SSBG-15
❑ 83OPC-100
❑ 83OPC-101
❑ 83OPC-373
❑ 83PerCreC-13
❑ 83PerCreCG-13
❑ 83PhiPosGM-13
❑ 83PhiPosGPaM-7
❑ 83PhiTas-25
❑ 83Top-100
❑ 83Top-101
❑ 83Top-397
❑ 83TopFol-3
❑ 83TopGloS-14
❑ 83TopSti-272
❑ 83TopStiB-7
❑ 83TopTraBP-3
❑ 84AllGamPI-68
❑ 84Don-61
❑ 84DonActAS-54
❑ 84DonCha-27
❑ 84Dra-27
❑ 84ExpGla-2
❑ 84ExpPos-26
❑ 84ExpStu-17
❑ 84Fle-46
❑ 84Fle-636
❑ 84FleSti-99
❑ 84FleSti-119
❑ 84FleUpd-102
❑ 84FunFooP-4
❑ 84MilBra-21
❑ 84Nes792-300
❑ 84Nes792-701
❑ 84Nes792-702
❑ 84OCoandSI-30
❑ 84OCoandSI-108
❑ 84OCoandSI-125
❑ 84OCoandSI-134
❑ 84OCoandSI-184
❑ 84OPC-300
❑ 84RalPur-4
❑ 84SevCoi-C22
❑ 84Top-300
❑ 84Top-701
❑ 84Top-702
❑ 84TopCer-4
❑ 84TopGaloC-9
❑ 84TopGloS-1
❑ 84TopRubD-24
❑ 84TopSti-115
❑ 84TopTif-300
❑ 84TopTif-701
❑ 84TopTif-702
❑ 84TopTra-103T
❑ 84TopTraT-103T
❑ 85AllGamPI-98
❑ 85Don-254
❑ 85Don-641
❑ 85DonHig-10
❑ 85DonHig-40
❑ 85Fle-550
❑ 85Fle-640
❑ 85FleLimE-29
❑ 85FleStaS-1
❑ 85FleStaS-2
❑ 85FleStaS-3
❑ 85Lea-144
❑ 85OPC-116
❑ 85RedYea-14
❑ 85SevCoi-G10
❑ 85SpoSam-43
❑ 85Top-6
❑ 85Top-547
❑ 85Top-600
❑ 85Top3-D-5
❑ 85TopGloS-10
❑ 85TopRubD-24
❑ 85TopSti-57
❑ 85TopSup-32
❑ 85TopTif-6
❑ 85TopTif-547
❑ 85TopTif-600
❑ 85Woo-30
❑ 86BasStaB-93
❑ 86BurKinA-4
❑ 86Don-62
❑ 86Don-644
❑ 86Don-653
❑ 86DonAll-34
❑ 86DonSupD-27
❑ 86Dra-22
❑ 86Fle-191
❑ 86Fle-628
❑ 86Fle-638
❑ 86FleFutHoF-1
❑ 86FleLeaL-36
❑ 86FleLimE-37
❑ 86FleMin-40
❑ 86FleSlu-29
❑ 86FleStiC-101
❑ 86Lea-53
❑ 86Lea-209
❑ 86Lea-260
❑ 86MeaGolBB-12
❑ 86MeaGolM-9
❑ 86MeaGolSB-8
❑ 86MSAJifPD-11
❑ 86OPC-1
❑ 86OPCBoxB-N
❑ 86QuaGra-11
❑ 86RedTexG-14A
❑ 86RedTexG-14B
❑ 86RedTexG-14C
❑ 86SevCoi-C2
❑ 86SevCoi-E2
❑ 86SevCoi-S2
❑ 86SevCoi-S16
❑ 86SevCoi-W2
❑ 86Spo-50
❑ 86Spo-51
❑ 86Spo-56
❑ 86Spo-58
❑ 86Spo-69
❑ 86Spo-130
❑ 86Spo-138
❑ 86Spo-181
❑ 86Spo-182
❑ 86SpoDecG-60
❑ 86SpoRoo-46
❑ 86Top-1
❑ 86Top-2
❑ 86Top-3
❑ 86Top-4
❑ 86Top-5
❑ 86Top-6
❑ 86Top-7
❑ 86Top-206
❑ 86Top-741
❑ 86Top3-D-22
❑ 86TopGaloC-11
❑ 86TopGloS-51
❑ 86TopRos-1
❑ 86TopRos-2
❑ 86TopRos-3
❑ 86TopRos-4
❑ 86TopRos-5
❑ 86TopRos-6
❑ 86TopRos-7
❑ 86TopRos-8
❑ 86TopRos-9
❑ 86TopRos-10
❑ 86TopRos-11
❑ 86TopRos-12
❑ 86TopRos-13
❑ 86TopRos-14
❑ 86TopRos-15
❑ 86TopRos-16
❑ 86TopRos-17
❑ 86TopRos-18
❑ 86TopRos-19
❑ 86TopRos-20
❑ 86TopRos-21
❑ 86TopRos-22
❑ 86TopRos-23
❑ 86TopRos-24
❑ 86TopRos-25
❑ 86TopRos-26
❑ 86TopRos-27
❑ 86TopRos-28
❑ 86TopRos-29
❑ 86TopRos-30
❑ 86TopRos-31

❑ 86TopRos-32
❑ 86TopRos-33
❑ 86TopRos-34
❑ 86TopRos-35
❑ 86TopRos-36
❑ 86TopRos-37
❑ 86TopRos-38
❑ 86TopRos-39
❑ 86TopRos-40
❑ 86TopRos-41
❑ 86TopRos-42
❑ 86TopRos-43
❑ 86TopRos-44
❑ 86TopRos-45
❑ 86TopRos-46
❑ 86TopRos-47
❑ 86TopRos-48
❑ 86TopRos-49
❑ 86TopRos-50
❑ 86TopRos-51
❑ 86TopRos-52
❑ 86TopRos-53
❑ 86TopRos-54
❑ 86TopRos-55
❑ 86TopRos-56
❑ 86TopRos-57
❑ 86TopRos-58
❑ 86TopRos-59
❑ 86TopRos-60
❑ 86TopRos-61
❑ 86TopRos-62
❑ 86TopRos-63
❑ 86TopRos-64
❑ 86TopRos-65
❑ 86TopRos-66
❑ 86TopRos-67
❑ 86TopRos-68
❑ 86TopRos-69
❑ 86TopRos-70
❑ 86TopRos-71
❑ 86TopRos-72
❑ 86TopRos-73
❑ 86TopRos-74
❑ 86TopRos-75
❑ 86TopRos-76
❑ 86TopRos-77
❑ 86TopRos-78
❑ 86TopRos-79
❑ 86TopRos-80
❑ 86TopRos-81
❑ 86TopRos-82
❑ 86TopRos-83
❑ 86TopRos-84
❑ 86TopRos-85
❑ 86TopRos-86
❑ 86TopRos-87
❑ 86TopRos-88
❑ 86TopRos-89
❑ 86TopRos-90
❑ 86TopRos-91
❑ 86TopRos-92
❑ 86TopRos-93
❑ 86TopRos-94
❑ 86TopRos-95
❑ 86TopRos-96
❑ 86TopRos-97
❑ 86TopRos-98
❑ 86TopRos-99
❑ 86TopRos-100
❑ 86TopRos-101
❑ 86TopRos-102
❑ 86TopRos-103
❑ 86TopRos-104
❑ 86TopRos-105
❑ 86TopRos-106
❑ 86TopRos-107
❑ 86TopRos-108
❑ 86TopRos-109
❑ 86TopRos-110
❑ 86TopRos-111
❑ 86TopRos-112
❑ 86TopRos-113
❑ 86TopRos-114
❑ 86TopRos-115
❑ 86TopRos-116
❑ 86TopRos-117
❑ 86TopRos-118
❑ 86TopRos-119
❑ 86TopRos-120
❑ 86TopSti-1
❑ 86TopSti-2
❑ 86TopSti-134
❑ 86TopSup-46
❑ 86TopTat-6
❑ 86TopTif-1
❑ 86TopTif-2
❑ 86TopTif-3
❑ 86TopTif-4
❑ 86TopTif-5
❑ 86TopTif-6
❑ 86TopTif-7
❑ 86TopTif-206
❑ 86TopTif-741
❑ 86TopWaxBC-N
❑ 86TruVal-4
❑ 86Woo-29
❑ 87ClaGam-1
❑ 87ClaUpdY-103
❑ 87Don-186
❑ 87Fle-213
❑ 87FleBasA-37
❑ 87FleExcS-38
❑ 87FleGlo-213
❑ 87FleHotS-32
❑ 87FleLeaL-37
❑ 87FleLimE-36
❑ 87FleRecS-33
❑ 87FleStiC-102
❑ 87K-M-19
❑ 87KraFoo-34
❑ 87Lea-129
❑ 87OPC-200
❑ 87RedFolSB-64
❑ 87RedKah-NNO
❑ 87Spo-25
❑ 87SpoRea-19
❑ 87SpoRea-22
❑ 87SpoSupD-17
❑ 87SpoTeaP-4
❑ 87Top-200
❑ 87Top-281
❑ 87Top-393
❑ 87TopGloS-41
❑ 87TopSti-139
❑ 87TopTif-200
❑ 87TopTif-281
❑ 87TopTif-393
❑ 88ClaBlu-226
❑ 88GreBasS-79
❑ 88K-M-22
❑ 88RedKah-14
❑ 88Top-475
❑ 88TopClo-96
❑ 88TopTif-475
❑ 89ClaLigB-71
❑ 89RedKah-14
❑ 89Top-505
❑ 89TopTif-505
❑ 90HOFStiB-84
❑ 91FouBal-5
❑ 91TopRut-7
❑ 92DynRos-1
❑ 92DynRos-2
❑ 92DynRos-3
❑ 92DynRos-4
❑ 92DynRos-5
❑ 92DynRos-6
❑ 92DynRos-7
❑ 92DynRos-8
❑ 92DynRos-9
❑ 92DynRos-10
❑ 92DynRos-11
❑ 92DynRos-12
❑ 92DynRos-13
❑ 92DynRos-14
❑ 93Yoo-17
❑ 94UppDecTAE-77
❑ 96Red76K-3

Rose, Pete Jr.
❑ 82Fle-640
❑ 86TopRos-5
❑ 86TopRos-83
❑ 89EriOriS-22
❑ 89FreKeyS-27
❑ 89KahComC-2
❑ 89Sta-175
❑ 89StaFutS-5
❑ 89StaFutS-6
❑ 89TopBasT-34
❑ 90ClaBlu-75
❑ 90FreKeyTI-20
❑ 91SarWhiSC-18
❑ 91SarWhiSP-1120
❑ 92ColRedC-1
❑ 92ColRedF-2420
❑ 93ClaFS7-17
❑ 93KinIndC-1
❑ 93KinIndF-2257
❑ 93KinIndTI-23
❑ 94HicCraC-20
❑ 94HicCraF-2185
❑ 95MidLeaA-47
❑ 96BirBarB-12
❑ 97ChaLoo-22
❑ 98IndIndQ-27
❑ 98PriWilCASM-20
❑ 98Top-240
❑ 98TopChr-240
❑ 98TopChrR-240
❑ 98TopDevR-240
❑ 98TopDia-240
❑ 98TopMiniC-240
❑ 98TopOpeD-109

Rose, Pete PCL
❑ 21Zee-82
❑ 21Zee-107

Rose, Russ
❑ 75OakOak2A-30

Rose, Scott
❑ 91ModA'sC-13
❑ 91ModA'sP-3087
❑ 92MadMusC-23
❑ 92MadMusF-1233
❑ 93SanBerSF-768
❑ 94HunStaF-1330
❑ 95HunStaTI-22
❑ 98ColCliM-26

Rose, Ted
❑ 98ChaLooG-24

Rose, Tyler
❑ 86TopRos-56

Roseboro, Jaime
❑ 86LitFalMP-24
❑ 87ColMetP-6
❑ 88ColMetGS-24
❑ 89St.LucMS-22
❑ 89Sta-117
❑ 90Bow-134
❑ 90BowTif-134
❑ 90JacMetGS-10
❑ 90TopTVM-56
❑ 91TidTidP-2525
❑ 92HarSenF-474

Roseboro, Johnny
❑ 58Top-42
❑ 59DodMor-10
❑ 59DodPos-12
❑ 59DodTeal-24
❑ 59Top-441
❑ 60DodBelB-7
❑ 60DodJayP-12
❑ 60DodMor-10
❑ 60DodPos-10
❑ 60DodTeal-16
❑ 60DodUniO-16
❑ 60MacSta-21
❑ 60Top-88
❑ 60Top-292
❑ 60TopVen-88
❑ 61DodBelB-8
❑ 61DodJayP-9
❑ 61DodUniO-17
❑ 61Pos-166A
❑ 61Pos-166B
❑ 61Top-363
❑ 61TopStal-33
❑ 62DodBelB-8
❑ 62DodJayP-9
❑ 62DodVol-6
❑ 62Jel-107
❑ 62Pos-107
❑ 62PosCan-107
❑ 62SalPlaC-133
❑ 62ShiPlaC-133
❑ 62Top-32
❑ 62Top-397
❑ 62TopStal-139
❑ 62TopVen-32
❑ 63Jel-120
❑ 63Pos-120
❑ 63SalMetC-12
❑ 63Top-487
❑ 64DodHea-9
❑ 64Top-88
❑ 64TopVen-88
❑ 65DodJayP-11
❑ 65DodTeal-19
❑ 65Top-405
❑ 65TopTral-28
❑ 66OPC-189
❑ 66Top-189
❑ 66TopRubl-84
❑ 66TopVen-189
❑ 67CokCapD-9
❑ 67CokCapDA-9
❑ 67Top-365
❑ 67TopVen-268
❑ 68Baz-7
❑ 68DexPre-68
❑ 68OPC-65
❑ 68Top-65
❑ 68TopVen-65
❑ 69MilBra-242
❑ 69MLBOffS-70
❑ 69OPC-218
❑ 69Top-218
❑ 69TopFou-9
❑ 69TopSta-198
❑ 69TopTeaP-15
❑ 70MLBOffS-285
❑ 70SenPolY-9
❑ 70Top-655
❑ 72MilBra-300
❑ 73OPC-421
❑ 73Top-421A
❑ 73Top-421B
❑ 74OPC-276
❑ 74Top-276
❑ 78TCM60I-185
❑ 87DodSmoA-30
❑ 88DodSmo-2
❑ 89DodSmoG-64
❑ 90DodTar-688
❑ 90MetColP-46
❑ 91DodRinP2-2
❑ 92DodStaTA-1

Roselli, Bob
❑ 56Top-131
❑ 61Top-529
❑ 61WhiSoxTS-14
❑ 62Top-363
❑ 62WhiSoxTS-18

Rosello, Dave
❑ 73WicAerJPKB-15
❑ 74OPC-607
❑ 74Top-607
❑ 76CubTri-21
❑ 76OPC-546
❑ 76Top-546
❑ 77Top-92
❑ 78Top-423
❑ 80IndTeal-25
❑ 80Top-122
❑ 81Don-79
❑ 82ChaChaT-18
❑ 82Don-617
❑ 82Fle-377
❑ 82Top-724

Roseman, James
❑ 87BucN28-63
❑ 87FouBasHN-9
❑ 87OldJudN-423
❑ 88AugBecN-28
❑ 88GandBCGCE-34
❑ 90KalBatN-49

Rosen, Al
❑ 47PM1StaP1-190
❑ 49IndTeal-22
❑ 50Bow-232
❑ 50IndNumN-19
❑ 50IndTeal-21
❑ 51BerRos-A1
❑ 51Bow-187
❑ 51IndHag-6
❑ 51R42SmaS-85
❑ 51TopRedB-35
❑ 52Bow-151
❑ 52IndNumN-10
❑ 52NatTeaL-27
❑ 52StaCalL-74B
❑ 52StaCalS-88C
❑ 52Top-10
❑ 53BowC-8
❑ 53IndPenCBP-23
❑ 53NorBreL-25
❑ 53RedMan-AL24
❑ 53Top-135
❑ 54DanDee-21
❑ 54DixLid-14
❑ 54RedHeaF-25
❑ 54RedMan-AL12
❑ 54Top-15
❑ 55ArmCoi-17
❑ 55BigLeaIS-16
❑ 55DaiQueS-16
❑ 55Ind-7
❑ 55IndCarBL-7
❑ 55IndGolS-14
❑ 55RedMan-AL11
❑ 55Top-70
❑ 55TopDouH-1
❑ 56Top-35
❑ 56TopHocF-A8
❑ 56TopPin-10
❑ 61Top-474
❑ 72TopTes5-4
❑ 74LauAllG-54
❑ 75OPC-191
❑ 75TCM195Cl-30
❑ 75Top-191
❑ 75TopMin-191
❑ 77GalGloG-35
❑ 79TCM50-175
❑ 82DiaCla-73
❑ 82OhiHaloF-60
❑ 83TopRep5-10
❑ 85TCMHomRC-8
❑ 86IndGreT-4
❑ 90PacLeg-78
❑ 90SweBasG-39
❑ 91SweBasG-78
❑ 91TopArc1-135
❑ 92ActPacA-70
❑ 92BazQua5A-20
❑ 93UppDecAH-109
❑ 94TedWil-28
❑ 94TopArc1-15
❑ 94TopArc1G-15
❑ 94UppDecAH-67
❑ 94UppDecAH1-67

Rosen, David
❑ 85OscAstTI-30

Rosen, Goody (Goodwin)
❑ 39PlaBal-76
❑ 83TCMPla1945-31
❑ 90DodTar-689
❑ 91DodRinP2-4

Rosenbalm, Marc
❑ 92SanBerC-9

Rosenberg, Harry
❑ 30Zee-67
❑ 33Zee-40
❑ 37Zee-25
❑ 37Zee-49

Rosenberg, Steve
❑ 87AlbYanP-1
❑ 88BlaYNPRWL-30
❑ 88VanCanC-3
❑ 88VanCanP-754
❑ 89Don-219
❑ 89FleUpd-22
❑ 89Top-616
❑ 89TopTif-616
❑ 89UppDec-715
❑ 89WhiSoxC-24
❑ 90AlbDecGB-30
❑ 90CMC-638
❑ 90Don-253
❑ 90Fle-547
❑ 90FleCan-547
❑ 90OPC-379
❑ 90ProAAAF-167
❑ 90Sco-523
❑ 90Top-379
❑ 90TopTif-379
❑ 90UppDec-522
❑ 90VanCanC-11
❑ 90VanCanP-489
❑ 91LasVegSLD-292
❑ 91LasVegSP-234
❑ 91LinDriAAA-292
❑ 91PadSmo-32

Rosenbohm, Jim
❑ 92ClaDraP-30
❑ 92FroRowDP-92
❑ 92FroRowDPG-92
❑ 92FroRowDPS-92
❑ 93CliGiaC-1
❑ 93CliGiaF-2489
❑ 93MidLeaAGF-41
❑ 93Top-667
❑ 93TopGol-667
❑ 93TopInaM-667
❑ 93TopInaR-667
❑ 93TopMic-667
❑ 94CliLumC-20
❑ 94CliLumF-1979
❑ 95AubAstTI-16
❑ 96PitMetB-24

Rosenfeld, Max
❑ 72TCMthe3-59
❑ 90DodTar-1057

Rosenfield, Dave
❑ 88TidTidCa-5

Rosengren, John
❑ 92BriTigC-9
❑ 93NiaFalRF-3388
❑ 94ExcFS7-60
❑ 94FloStaLAF-FSL14
❑ 94LakTigC-19
❑ 94LakTigF-3035
❑ 95JacSunTI-24
❑ 96JacSunB-25
❑ 97TolMudHB-31

Rosengren, Rosey (John)
❑ 92BriTigF-1410
❑ 95Exc-52

Rosenkranz, Terry
❑ 92ButCopKSP-12
❑ 98BriBluM-25

Rosenthal, Larry
❑ 33WorCig(-76
❑ 39WhiSoxTI-15
❑ 40WhiSoxL-15
❑ 79DiaGre-130
❑ 94ConTSN-1309
❑ 94ConTSNB-1309

Rosenthal, Todd
❑ 92SalLakTSP-11

Rosenthal, Wayne
❑ 87GasRanP-18
❑ 88ChaRanS-21
❑ 89ChaRanS-20
❑ 89TulDriTI-21
❑ 90TulDriP-1153
❑ 91LinDriAAA-321
❑ 91OklCit8LD-321
❑ 91OklCit8P-178
❑ 92Fle-318
❑ 92OklCit8F-1915
❑ 92OklCit8S-304
❑ 92OPC-584
❑ 92OPCPre-30
❑ 92Sco-749
❑ 92SkyAAAF-147
❑ 92StaClu-658
❑ 92Top-584
❑ 92TopDeb91-151
❑ 92TopGol-584
❑ 92TopGolW-584
❑ 92TopMic-584
❑ 92Ult-446
❑ 93RanKee-313
❑ 98JupHamQ-2

Rosfelder, Chris
❑ 89ElmPioP-17

Rosinski, Brian
❑ 80WicAerT-17

Roskom, Bryan
❑ 89KenTwiP-1069
❑ 89KenTwiS-22
❑ 90KenTwiB-15
❑ 90KenTwiS-29

Roskos, John
❑ 94ClaGolF-74
❑ 94ElmPioC-18
❑ 94ElmPioF-3479
❑ 95KanCouCTI-22
❑ 95MidLeaA-48
❑ 96PorSeaDB-23
❑ 97Bes-69
❑ 97BesAutSBPP-33
❑ 97PorSeaD-27
❑ 98BesAutSS-45
❑ 98Bow-170
❑ 98BowChr-170
❑ 98BowChrGA-170
❑ 98BowChrGAR-170
❑ 98BowChrI-170
❑ 98BowChrIR-170
❑ 98BowChrR-170
❑ 98BowGolA-170
❑ 98BowInt-170
❑ 98ChaKniQ-25
❑ 98LeaRS-125
❑ 98LeaRSLHolo-125
❑ 98LeaRSLong-125
❑ 98LeaRTrue-125
❑ 98PacOmeRS-27
❑ 98PacOmeRST2-27
❑ 98PorSeaD5AQ-14

Roslund, John
❑ 75QuaCitAT-21

Roso, Jimmy (James)
❑ 89BluOriS-17
❑ 89Sta-115
❑ 90CMC-870
❑ 90WauTimB-16
❑ 90WauTimP-2129
❑ 90WauTimS-20
❑ 91KanCouCC-13
❑ 91KanCouCP-2660
❑ 91KanCouCTI-18
❑ 92FreKeyC-24

❑ 92FreKeyF-1808
❑ 93BowBayF-2191
Ross, Arthur
❑ 09ObaT21-354
❑ 11PacCoaBD-54
❑ 12ObaPreT-103
Ross, Bob (Floyd Robert)
❑ 52Top-298
❑ 54Top-189
❑ 83TopRep5-298
❑ 94TopArc1-189
❑ 94TopArc1G-189
Ross, Brandi
❑ 91HawWomS-13
Ross, Chelcie
❑ 89MajLeaM-6
Ross, Chester
❑ 41Gou-31
Ross, Chuck
❑ 76BurBeeT-29
❑ 77BurBeeT-25
❑ 78HolMilT-19
Ross, Dan
❑ 89LonTigP-1361
Ross, David
❑ 89MarPhiS-27
❑ 90BatCliP-3066
❑ 91PeoChiC-1
❑ 91PeoChiP-1341
❑ 91PeoChiTI-12
❑ 98YakBeaG-28
Ross, Don
❑ 47RoyMon-3
❑ 49BowPCL-20
❑ 83TCMPla1945-13
❑ 90DodTar-690
Ross, Duncan C.
❑ 88KimN18-37
Ross, Gary Douglas
❑ 69Top-404
❑ 70Top-694
❑ 71MLBOffS-236
❑ 71OPC-153
❑ 71Top-153
❑ 72PadPos-22
❑ 73OPC-112
❑ 73PadDea-24
❑ 73Top-112
❑ 75HawIslC-16
❑ 75IntLeaASB-29
❑ 75PacCoaLAB-29
❑ 77Top-544
❑ 78Top-291
❑ 90BenBucL-26
❑ 91MadMusP-2131
Ross, Jackie
❑ 92HelBreF-1731
❑ 92HelBreSP-13
❑ 93BelBreCB-20
❑ 93BelBreFI-1725
Ross, Jason
❑ 96DanBraB-18
❑ 97MacBra-25
❑ 98DanQ-C-15
Ross, Jeremy
❑ 95ElmPioTI-24
❑ 95ElmPioUTI-24
Ross, Joe
❑ 89OneYanP-2125
Ross, Justin
❑ 98ButCopKG-28
❑ 98TenKry-17
Ross, Mark
❑ 82TucTorT-3
❑ 84TucTorC-68
❑ 85TucTorC-54
❑ 86TucTorP-20
❑ 87VanCanP-1602
❑ 88SyrChiC-5
❑ 88SyrChiP-824
❑ 89SyrChiC-4
❑ 89SyrChiMB-19
❑ 89SyrChiP-814
❑ 90BufBisC-9
❑ 90BufBisP-372
❑ 90BufBisTI-22
❑ 90CMC-9
❑ 90ProAAAF-487
❑ 91LinDriAAA-441
❑ 91RicBraBC-15
❑ 91RicBraLD-441
❑ 91RicBraP-2567
❑ 91RicBraTI-28
❑ 92GreBraF-1169
❑ 93IdaFalBF-4052
❑ 94IdaFalBSP-29
❑ 96MacBraB-28
❑ 97MacBra-28
❑ 98MacBraM-28
Ross, Michael
❑ 88HamRedP-1727
❑ 89SprCarB-10
❑ 90ArkTraGS-26
❑ 90IBAWorA-37
❑ 91LinDriAAA-245
❑ 91LouRedLD-245
❑ 91LouRedP-2931
❑ 92ArkTraF-1139
❑ 92ArkTraS-44
Ross, Ron
❑ 89NiaFalRP-27
Ross, Samuel
❑ 20Zee-53
❑ 21Zee-62
❑ 22Zee-51
Ross, Sean
❑ 87SumBraP-27
❑ 88BurBraP-20
❑ 89DurBullS-19
❑ 89DurBullS-19
❑ 89DurBulTI-19
❑ 91Cla/Bes-156
❑ 91GreBraC-22
❑ 91GreBraLD-217
❑ 91GreBraP-3017
❑ 91LinDriAA-217
❑ 92RicBraBB-19
❑ 92RicBraF-389
❑ 92RicBraRC-18
❑ 92RicBraS-440
❑ 93ColSprSSF-3100
❑ 93PawRedSF-2422
❑ 93PawRedSTI-20
❑ 97RicBraBC-5
Ross, Sid
❑ 21Zee-83
Ross, Tony
❑ 94AubAstC-14
❑ 94AubAstF-3773
❑ 95MidLeaA-49
❑ 95QuaCitRBTI-23
❑ 96KisCobB-24
❑ 97KisCob-21
Rosselli, Joe
❑ 90EveGiaB-11
❑ 90EveGiaP-3127
❑ 90ProAaA-165
❑ 91CliGiaC-6
❑ 92CalLeaACL-17
❑ 92ClaFS7-250
❑ 92SanJosGC-2
❑ 92UppDecML-295
❑ 92UppDecMLPotY-PY11
❑ 93Bow-632
❑ 93ClaFS7-58
❑ 93ClaGolF-68
❑ 94Bow-575
❑ 94ShrCapF-1604
❑ 94Ult-593
❑ 95Bow-107
❑ 95Exc-294
❑ 95Fla-428
❑ 95Fle-588
❑ 95GiaMot-17
❑ 95StaClu-570
❑ 95StaCluMOP-570
❑ 95StaCluSTWS-570
❑ 95Sum-157
❑ 95SumNthD-157
❑ 95Top-248
❑ 95UppDec-231
❑ 95UppDecED-231
❑ 95UppDecEDG-231
❑ 95UppDecML-79
❑ 95UppDecMLFS-79
❑ 96ColCho-307
❑ 96ColChoGS-307
❑ 96ColChoSS-307
❑ 96Sco-239
❑ 96VanCanB-24
Rossen, Bob
❑ 77LynMetT-25
Rosser, Rex
❑ 75OklCit8TI-24
Rossi, Joe
❑ 52Top-379
❑ 53Top-74
❑ 83TopRep5-379
❑ 91TopArc1-74
Rossi, Tom
❑ 83EriCarT-21
Rossiter, Mike
❑ 91ClaDraP-34
❑ 91FroRowDP-14
❑ 91FroRowDPG-14
❑ 91FroRowDPS-14
❑ 91HigSchPLS-21
❑ 92ClaFS7-374
❑ 92MadMusC-20
❑ 92MadMusF-1234
❑ 92MidLeaATI-36
❑ 92OPC-474
❑ 92StaCluD-158
❑ 92Top-474
❑ 92TopGol-474
❑ 92TopGolW-474
❑ 92TopMic-474
❑ 92UppDecML-214
❑ 93ModA'sC-17
❑ 93ModA'sF-798
❑ 95ModA'sTI-26
❑ 96HunStaTI-22
❑ 97StoPor-9
❑ 98MobBayBTI-24
Rossler, Ross (Brett)
❑ 91KinMetC-12
❑ 91KinMetP-3817
❑ 92PitMetC-9
❑ 92PitMetF-3300
Rossman, Claude
❑ 07TigACDPP-12
❑ 08RosComP-39
❑ 09BriE97-26
❑ 09T206-305
❑ 09TigMorBBBP-13
❑ 09TigMorPWBPP-10
❑ 09WolNewDTPP-14
❑ 10CouT21-58
❑ 11PinT-5-953
❑ 11SpoLifCW-307
❑ 12PhiCarE-26
❑ 72ClaCar-35
Rossum, Floyd
❑ 85BenPhiC-21
Rossy, Elem
❑ 86MiaMarP-22
❑ 88BlaYNPRWL-141
❑ 89BlaYNPRWL-15
Rossy, Rico
❑ 85NewOriT-14
❑ 86ChaOriW-26
❑ 87ChaO'sW-5
❑ 88BufBisC-18
❑ 88BufBisP-1471
❑ 89HarSenP-289
❑ 89HarSenS-15
❑ 90GreBraP-1138
❑ 90RicBraBC-19
❑ 91LinDriAAA-442
❑ 91RicBraBC-22
❑ 91RicBraLD-442
❑ 91RicBraP-2578
❑ 91RicBraTI-3
❑ 92Bow-390
❑ 92DonRoo-106
❑ 92Fle-676
❑ 92OmaRoyS-2
❑ 92OmaRoyS-344
❑ 92Sco-817
❑ 92StaClu-629
❑ 92StaCluECN-629
❑ 92TopDeb91-152
❑ 92Ult-376
❑ 93OmaRoyF-1687
❑ 93OPCPre-123
❑ 93PacSpa-495
❑ 93StaClu-106
❑ 93StaCluFDI-106
❑ 93StaCluMOP-106
❑ 94Fle-172
❑ 94Pac-300
❑ 94TriAAF-AAA11
❑ 96LasVegSB-20
❑ 98TacRaiQ-26
Rostel, Bud
❑ 86AncGlaPTI-31
❑ 87AncGlaP-26
Rotblatt, Marv
❑ 51Bow-303
Roth, Bob F.
❑ 15SpoNewM-145
❑ 16SpoNewM-145
❑ 17ColE13-141
❑ 17HolBreD-85
❑ 19W514-47
❑ 20GasAmeMBD-16
❑ 21E121So8-79
❑ 21KoBreWSI-48
❑ 22W575-109
❑ 28Zee-18
Roth, Frank
❑ 11SpoLifCW-308
Roth, Greg
❑ 89SouBenWSGS-26
❑ 90BirBarB-8
❑ 90BirBarP-1115
❑ 91BirBarLD-71
❑ 91BirBarP-1464
❑ 91LinDriAA-71
❑ 92BirBarS-92
❑ 92HagSunF-2564
❑ 92RocRedWS-466
Roth, Kris
❑ 86PeoChiP-20
❑ 87WinSpiP-22
❑ 88PitCubP-1376
Rothan, Bill
❑ 76TulOilGP-17
❑ 78SprRedWK-19
Rothermal, Russ
❑ 75IowOakT-15
❑ 79ChaChaT-3
Rothey, Mark
❑ 81CedRapRT-7
❑ 82CedRapRT-1
❑ 83WatRedT-7
Rothford, Jim
❑ 81ShrCapT-19
Rothrock, Brian
❑ 77OrlTwiT-17
Rothrock, John
❑ 28StaPlaCE-55
❑ 29ExhFou-17
❑ 31Exh-17
❑ 34DiaMatCSB-157
❑ 34ExhFou-8
❑ 35DiaMatCS3T1-126
❑ 74Car193T-22
❑ 79DiaGre-153
❑ 79RedSoxEF-3
❑ 79RedSoxEF-14
❑ 93ConTSN-851
Rothschild, Larry
❑ 77IndIndTI-17
❑ 79IndIndTI-9
❑ 80IndIndTI-14
❑ 81EvaTriT-6
❑ 82EvaTriT-7
❑ 83LasVegSBHN-18
❑ 85IowCubT-21
❑ 89CedRapRB-26
❑ 89CedRapRP-933
❑ 90RedKah-27
❑ 91RedKah-NNO
❑ 92RedKah-NNO
❑ 97MarPac-30
Rothstein, Arnold
❑ 88LitSunBS-14
❑ 88PacEigMO-28
Roundtree, Brian
❑ 92MisStaB-38
Rounsifer, Aaron
❑ 92ClaDraP-99
Rountree, Brian
❑ 89BriTigS-25
❑ 90FayGenP-2405
Rountree, Jerrold
❑ 91SpoIndC-11
❑ 91SpoIndP-3962
Rountree, Mike
❑ 86WatIndP-23
❑ 88RenSilSCLC-284
Rouse, Chuck
❑ 77ChaPatT-18
Rouse, Randy
❑ 76DubPacT-33
❑ 77CocAstT-23
❑ 78DayBeaAT-23
Rousey, Steve
❑ 87WesPalBEP-676
Roush, Edd
❑ 15CraJacE-161
❑ 15SpoNewM-146
❑ 16FleBreD-78
❑ 16SpoNewM-146
❑ 17ColE13-142
❑ 17HolBreD-86
❑ 19W514-85
❑ 20NatCarE-85
❑ 20RedWorCP-18
❑ 20W516-29
❑ 21E121So1-83
❑ 21E121So8-81
❑ 21Nei-79
❑ 21OxfConE-14
❑ 22E120-179
❑ 22W572-87
❑ 22W575-110
❑ 22WilPatV-1
❑ 23MapCriV-28
❑ 23W501-53
❑ 23W515-57
❑ 23WilChoV-136
❑ 25Exh-31
❑ 26Exh-31
❑ 27YorCarE-53
❑ 28Exh-20
❑ 28W502-53
❑ 28W513-61
❑ 28Yue-53
❑ 29PorandAR-75
❑ 31W517-3
❑ 38RedOraW-23
❑ 39RedTeal-19
❑ 53ArtHaloFP-73
❑ 61Fle-72
❑ 73TCMAllG-17
❑ 76ISCHooHA-1
❑ 76RowExh-8
❑ 76ShaPiz-90
❑ 77BobParHoF-41
❑ 77GalGloG-93
❑ 77RedCarP-7
❑ 77SerSta-19
❑ 78DexHaloFP-41
❑ 79DiaGre-251
❑ 80PacLeg-70
❑ 80PerHaloFP-90
❑ 80PerHaloFPS-9
❑ 80SSPHOF-90
❑ 82DiaCla-44
❑ 82OhiHaloF-10
❑ 84OCoandSI-155
❑ 86RedGreT-11
❑ 87ConSer2-54
❑ 88PacEigMO-84
❑ 89PacLegI-216
❑ 89SweBasG-35
❑ 90SweBasG-35
❑ 91ConTSN-55
❑ 91SweBasG-134
❑ 93ActPacA-93
❑ 93ActPacA2-27G
❑ 94ConTSN-993
❑ 94ConTSN-1023
❑ 94ConTSNB-993
❑ 94ConTSNB-1023
Roush, Ryan
❑ 98LowSpiM-16
Rovasio, Dom
❑ 89KenTwiP-1066
Rover, Vince
❑ 83CedRapRF-19
❑ 83CedRapRT-21
Rowan, John Albert
❑ 09ColChiE-245A
❑ 09ColChiE-245B
❑ 10DomDisP-103
❑ 10JuJuDE-35
❑ 10SweCapPP-131
❑ 11HelSta-103
❑ 11PinT-5-407
❑ 11S74Sil-104
❑ 11SpoLifCW-309
❑ 11SpoLifM-201
❑ 11T205-145
❑ 12ColRedB-245A
❑ 12ColRedB-245B
❑ 12ColTinT-245A
❑ 12ColTinT-245B
❑ 12HasTriFT-13D
❑ 14PieStaT-90
Rowand, Aaron
❑ 98HicCraUO-24
❑ 99TeaBesR-74
❑ 99TeaBesRFS-6
❑ 99TeaBesRG-74
❑ 99TeaBesRS-74
Rowdie, Mascot
❑ 96IndIndB-29
❑ 97IndInd-30
❑ 98IndIndQ-35
Rowdon, Wade
❑ 82AppFoxFr-5
❑ 83WatRedT-14
❑ 84WicAerRD-21
❑ 85Don-642
❑ 87IowCubTI-19
❑ 87Top-569
❑ 87TopTif-569
❑ 88Fle-430
❑ 88FleGlo-430
❑ 88OriPos-30
❑ 88RocRedWGCP-23
❑ 91OriCro-394
Rowe, Butch (Harold)
❑ 78WisRapTT-17
Rowe, Davis E.
❑ 87OldJudN-424
Rowe, Don
❑ 58JetPos-17
❑ 61ColJet-2
❑ 63Top-562
❑ 83RedPioT-28
❑ 84VanCanC-243
❑ 87HawIsIP-10
❑ 91DenZepP-139
❑ 91LinDriAAA-150
❑ 91MetWIZ-336
❑ 92BrePol-30
Rowe, Jim
❑ 85BelBreT-4
❑ 86BelBreP-20
❑ 87BelBreP-11
❑ 88ElPasDB-11
❑ 94PawRedSDD-23
Rowe, John Charles
❑ 76SSP188WS-5
❑ 87OldJudN-425
❑ 87ScrDC-16
❑ 88WG1CarG-24
Rowe, Ken
❑ 63Top-562
❑ 65Top-518
❑ 82RocRedWT-22
❑ 85BalOriP-28
❑ 86BalOriP-18
❑ 87ColCliP-25
❑ 87ColCliP-2
❑ 87ColCliT-24
❑ 89ColCliC-24
❑ 89ColCliP-24
❑ 89ColCliP-755
❑ 90CMC-224
❑ 90ColCliC-24
❑ 90ColCliP-1
❑ 90ColCliP-693
❑ 90DodTar-691
❑ 90ProAAAF-343
❑ 91OriCro-395
❑ 92CanIndF-708
❑ 92CanIndS-125
❑ 93CanIndF-2854
❑ 94CanIndF-3135
❑ 95WatIndTI-25
❑ 96KenIndB-29
❑ 97KinIndB-27
❑ 98ColRedSM-28
Rowe, Matt
❑ 86SumBraP-23
Rowe, Mike
❑ 76BatTroTI-19
Rowe, Pete
❑ 78DunBluJT-21
❑ 80KnoBluJT-4
❑ 82AleDukT-14
❑ 83LynPirT-13
❑ 90SalSpuCLC-146
❑ 90SalSpuP-2737
❑ 91DunBluJC-27
Rowe, Ralph
❑ 72TwiPos-20
❑ 72TwiTeal-15
❑ 73OPC-49
❑ 73Top-49A
❑ 73Top-49B
❑ 74OPC-447
❑ 74Top-447
❑ 75TwiPos-21
❑ 76SSP-603
❑ 81BalOriP-16
❑ 83OriPos-26
❑ 84BalOriP-31
❑ 89SumBraP-1091
❑ 90SumBraP-2453
Rowe, Schoolboy (Lynwood)
❑ 34BatR31-184
❑ 34DiaStaR-33
❑ 34DiaStaR-98
❑ 34TigTeal-16
❑ 34WarBakSP-7
❑ 35ExhFou-12
❑ 35GouPreR-15
❑ 35GouPuzR-8F

❑ 35GouPuzR-9F
❑ 36ExhFou-12
❑ 36GouWidPPR-A91
❑ 36GouWidPPR-C21
❑ 36NatChiFPR-66
❑ 36OveCanR-40
❑ 36R31PasP-49
❑ 36R31Pre-G13
❑ 36WheBB4-9
❑ 36WorWidGV-44
❑ 37ExhFou-12
❑ 37OPCBatUV-134
❑ 38BasTabP-25
❑ 39PlaBal-60
❑ 42DodTeal-20
❑ 43PhiTeal-20
❑ 49Bow-216
❑ 49EurSta-144
❑ 49PhiBul-45
❑ 49PhiLumPB-9
❑ 54Top-197
❑ 61Fle-73
❑ 74TigTCM1AC-26
❑ 74TigTCM1AC-35
❑ 76TayBow4-50
❑ 76TigOldTS-19
❑ 77GalGloG-83
❑ 78TigDeaCS-3
❑ 80LauFamF-17
❑ 81TigDetN-93
❑ 81TigSecNP-21
❑ 83TCMPla1942-15
❑ 86TigSpoD-8
❑ 90DodTar-692
❑ 91ConTSN-256
❑ 93ConTSN-718
❑ 94TopArc1-197
❑ 94TopArc1G-197
❑ 95MegRut-24

Rowe, Tom A.
❑ 80RocRedWT-9
❑ 81RocRedWT-16
❑ 81RocRedWW-6
❑ 84ChaLooT-19
❑ 85IntLeaAT-42
❑ 85MaiGuiT-9
❑ 86MaiGuiP-19

Rowe, William A.
❑ 88KimN18-38

Rowell, Carvel
❑ 41DouPlaR-43
❑ 47TipTop-83

Rowen, Rob
❑ 87SanAntDTI-6
❑ 88FreSunCLC-19
❑ 88FreSunP-1244

Rowher, Claude
❑ 23Zee-94
❑ 24Zee-69

Rowland, Donnie
❑ 85MiaHur-14
❑ 86FloStaLAP-42
❑ 86LakTigP-20
❑ 87LakTigP-6
❑ 88TolMudHC-22
❑ 88TolMudHP-589
❑ 89LonTigP-1363

Rowland, Mike
❑ 78PhoGiaC-22
❑ 79PhoGiaVNB-3
❑ 80PhoGiaVNB-4
❑ 81PhoGiaVNB-10
❑ 81Top-502
❑ 82PhoGiaVNB-4
❑ 97PhoFirDTTI-22

Rowland, Pants (Clarence)
❑ 15SpoNewM-147
❑ 16BF2FP-16
❑ 16SpoNewM-147
❑ 17ColE13-143
❑ 18WhiSoxTI-19
❑ 25Zee-54
❑ 92ConTSN-485
❑ 92Man191BSR-20

Rowland, Rich
❑ 88BriTigP-1872
❑ 89FayGenP-1578
❑ 90LonTigP-1271
❑ 91Cla2-T95
❑ 91LinDriAAA-597
❑ 91TolMudHLD-597
❑ 91TolMudHP-1936
❑ 91TopDeb90-136
❑ 92OPC-472
❑ 92SkyAAAF-268
❑ 92StaClu-508
❑ 92TolMudHF-1047
❑ 92TolMudHS-596
❑ 92Top-472
❑ 92TopGol-472
❑ 92TopGolW-472
❑ 92TopMic-472
❑ 93Don-77
❑ 93Fle-610
❑ 93Pin-264
❑ 93Sco-283
❑ 93ScoBoyoS-30
❑ 93StaClu-519
❑ 93StaCluFDI-519
❑ 93StaCluMOP-519
❑ 93TolMudHF-1656
❑ 93TriAAAGF-40
❑ 94Don-645
❑ 94Pac-228
❑ 94Sco-228
❑ 94ScoGolR-228
❑ 94ScoRoo-RT98
❑ 94ScoRooGR-RT98
❑ 94Sel-392
❑ 94SpoRoo-105
❑ 94SpoRooAP-105
❑ 94Top-588
❑ 94TopGol-588
❑ 94TopSpa-588
❑ 94TopTra-122T
❑ 95Don-505
❑ 95DonPreP-505
❑ 95Fle-38
❑ 95Lea-57
❑ 95Sco-62
❑ 95ScoGolR-62
❑ 95ScoPlaTS-62
❑ 95StaClu-483
❑ 95StaCluMOP-483
❑ 95StaCluSTWS-483
❑ 95Top-272
❑ 95Ult-14
❑ 95UltGolM-14
❑ 96SyrChiTI-27
❑ 97PhoFirTI-22

Rowley, Bill
❑ 87IndIndTI-36

Rowley, Steve
❑ 89ButCopKSP-10
❑ 90ChaRanS-24
❑ 91ChaRanC-10
❑ 91ChaRanP-1314
❑ 91TulDriTI-26
❑ 92SkyAA F-273
❑ 92TulDriS-617
❑ 94TulDriF-243
❑ 94TulDriTI-20

Rowson, James
❑ 96EveAquB-19

Roy, Jean-Pierre
❑ 43ParSpo-82
❑ 50W720HolS-24
❑ 52Par-90

Roy, Kevin
❑ 83WauTimF-13

Roy, Luther
❑ 90DodTar-693

Roy, Norman
❑ 51Bow-278

Roy, Pat
❑ 76CedRapGT-24
❑ 95FRIAAG-168

Roy, Walt
❑ 90BurBraB-14
❑ 90BurBraP-2349
❑ 90BurBraS-23
❑ 91DurBulP-1542

Royals, Kansas City
❑ 69FleCloS-11
❑ 69FleCloS-43
❑ 69TopStaA-11
❑ 70OPC-422
❑ 70Top-422
❑ 71OPC-742
❑ 71Top-742
❑ 71TopTat-33
❑ 72Top-617
❑ 73OPC-347
❑ 73OPCBTC-11
❑ 73Top-347
❑ 73TopBluTC-11
❑ 74OPC-343
❑ 74OPCTC-11
❑ 74Top-343
❑ 74TopStaA-11
❑ 74TopTeaC-11
❑ 78Top-724
❑ 83FleSta-236
❑ 83FleSti-NNO
❑ 83FleSti-NNO
❑ 86FleWaxBC-C1
❑ 87SpoTeaL-13
❑ 88PanSti-461
❑ 88RedFolSB-112
❑ 90FleWaxBC-C23
❑ 90PubIntS-637
❑ 90RedFolSB-126
❑ 94ImpProP-7
❑ 94Sco-323
❑ 94ScoGolR-323
❑ 95PacPriTL-7
❑ 95PanSti-145
❑ 96PanSti-187
❑ 99Vic-180

Royals, Montreal
❑ 43ParSpo-83

Royalty, Doug
❑ 87AubAstP-26
❑ 88AshTouP-1065

Royer, Stan
❑ 88SouOreAP-1701
❑ 89Bow-195
❑ 89BowTif-195
❑ 89CalLeaA-31
❑ 89ModA'sC-25
❑ 89ModA'sCLC-276
❑ 90Bes-240
❑ 90HunStaB-19
❑ 90LouRedBLBC-36
❑ 91LinDriAAA-246
❑ 91LouRedLD-246
❑ 91LouRedP-2924
❑ 91LouRedTI-22
❑ 91SouOreAAP-SOA7
❑ 92Don-602
❑ 92LouRedF-1894
❑ 92LouRedS-268
❑ 92Pin-263
❑ 92Sco-822
❑ 92SkyAAAF-129
❑ 92StaClu-286
❑ 92TopDeb91-153
❑ 93CarPol-18
❑ 93Don-680
❑ 93FleFinE-130
❑ 93LouRedF-224
❑ 93PacSpa-636
❑ 93Top-820
❑ 93TopGol-820
❑ 93TopInaM-820
❑ 93TopInaR-820
❑ 93TopMic-820
❑ 94CarPol-18
❑ 94Pac-603
❑ 94ScoRoo-RT140
❑ 94ScoRooGR-RT140
❑ 94SpoRoo-119
❑ 94SpoRooAP-119
❑ 94StaCluT-311
❑ 94StaCluTFDI-311

Royster, Aaron
❑ 94MarPhiC-22
❑ 94MarPhiF-3310
❑ 95PiePhiF-198
❑ 97ReaPhi-24
❑ 97TexAllM-51
❑ 98ReaPhiM-1
❑ 98ReaPhiUM-20

Royster, Jerry
❑ 74AlbDukCa-76
❑ 74AlbDukTI-17
❑ 75AlbDukCa-3
❑ 75IntLeaASB-30
❑ 75PacCoaLAB-30
❑ 76AtlBraP-28
❑ 76OPC-592
❑ 76Top-592
❑ 77BurCheD-212
❑ 77Hos-38
❑ 77OPC-251
❑ 77Top-549
❑ 78BraCok-14
❑ 78Top-187
❑ 79Top-344
❑ 80OPC-241
❑ 80Top-463
❑ 81BraPol-1
❑ 81Don-339
❑ 81Fle-250
❑ 81Top-268
❑ 82BraBurKL-22
❑ 82BraPol-1
❑ 82Don-555
❑ 82Fle-448
❑ 82Top-608
❑ 83BraPol-1
❑ 83Don-425
❑ 83Fle-147
❑ 83FleSta-169
❑ 83FleSti-92
❑ 83Top-26
❑ 84BraPol-1
❑ 84Don-531
❑ 84Fle-191
❑ 84Nes792-572
❑ 84raPho-27
❑ 84Top-572
❑ 84TopSti-37
❑ 84TopTif-572
❑ 85Fle-340
❑ 85FleUpd-90
❑ 85PadMot-18
❑ 85Top-776
❑ 85TopTif-776
❑ 85TopTifT-96T
❑ 85TopTra-96T
❑ 86Don-446
❑ 86Fle-333
❑ 86OPC-118
❑ 86Top-118
❑ 86TopTif-118
❑ 87Don-534
❑ 87Fle-428
❑ 87FleGlo-428
❑ 87OPC-324
❑ 87Top-403
❑ 87TopTif-403
❑ 87TopTra-106T
❑ 87TopTraT-106T
❑ 87WhiSoxC-26
❑ 88Don-660
❑ 88Fle-221
❑ 88FleGlo-221
❑ 88StaLinY-14
❑ 88Top-257
❑ 88TopTif-257
❑ 89UppDec-433
❑ 90DodTar-694
❑ 90EliSenL-47
❑ 90YakBeaTI-23
❑ 91VerBeaDC-30
❑ 91VerBeaDP-791
❑ 92SanAntMF-3988
❑ 92SanAntMS-574
❑ 92YanWIZ8-166
❑ 94JacSunF-1428
❑ 95MemChiTI-1
❑ 96LasVegSB-2
❑ 97LasVegS1A-2
❑ 98Las-2
❑ 99SpoIllGotG-86
❑ 99SpoIllGotGA-63

Royster, Willie
❑ 79RocRedWT-5
❑ 80ChaO'sP-19
❑ 80ChaO'sW-20
❑ 82RocRedWT-11
❑ 83EvaTriT-12
❑ 91OriCro-396

Rozek, Richard
❑ 50IndTeal-22
❑ 52IndNumN-11
❑ 52Top-363
❑ 83TopRep5-363

Rozema, Dave
❑ 75CliPilT-2
❑ 77TigBurK-3
❑ 78Hos-36
❑ 78Kel-21
❑ 78OPC-38
❑ 78TigBurK-5
❑ 78TigTeal-23
❑ 78Top-124
❑ 79OPC-12
❑ 79TigFreP-5
❑ 79Top-33
❑ 80OPC-151
❑ 80Top-288
❑ 81Don-9
❑ 81Fle-464
❑ 81Top-614
❑ 82Don-259
❑ 82Fle-279
❑ 82FleSta-153
❑ 82Top-319
❑ 83Don-133
❑ 83Fle-340
❑ 83TigPos-25
❑ 83Top-562
❑ 84Don-272
❑ 84Fle-90
❑ 84Nes792-457
❑ 84OPC-133
❑ 84TigFarJ-13
❑ 84TigTeal-28
❑ 84TigWavP-30
❑ 84Top-457
❑ 84TopTif-457
❑ 85Don-125
❑ 85Fle-21
❑ 85FleUpd-91
❑ 85RanPer-30
❑ 85SevCoi-D5
❑ 85Top-47
❑ 85TopTif-47
❑ 85TopTifT-97T
❑ 85TopTra-97T
❑ 86Don-343
❑ 86Fle-570
❑ 86Lea-154
❑ 86OPC-208
❑ 86Top-739
❑ 86TopTif-739
❑ 91PacSenL-135
❑ 93RanKee-314

Rozman, Richard
❑ 88SouOreAP-1694

Roznovsky, Ron
❑ 75IowOakT-16

Roznovsky, Vic
❑ 65Top-334
❑ 66BalOriP-30
❑ 66Top-467
❑ 67BalOriP-95
❑ 67OPC-163
❑ 67Top-163
❑ 68Top-428
❑ 69Top-368
❑ 81Ori6F-29
❑ 91OriCro-397

Rub, Jerry
❑ 88PriWilYS-21
❑ 89AlbYanB-12
❑ 89AlbYanP-328
❑ 89AlbYanSt-16
❑ 90AlbYanP-1035
❑ 90AlbYanSt-15
❑ 90CMC-781
❑ 91AlbYanLD-14
❑ 91AlbYanP-1007
❑ 91LinDriAA-14

Rub, Ron
❑ 87Ft.LauYP-15

Rubel, John
❑ 83ButCopKT-27

Rubel, Mike
❑ 82TulDriT-28
❑ 83TulDriT-15
❑ 84OklCit8T-14
❑ 85OklCit8T-22
❑ 87PhoFirP-27
❑ 90TulDriDGB-12

Rubeling, Albert
❑ 52Par-82
❑ 79DiaGre-336

Ruberto, Sonny (John E.)
❑ 66St.PetCTI-14
❑ 76IndIndTI-11
❑ 77Car5-23
❑ 77CarTeal-22
❑ 78CarTeal-27
❑ 80ArkTraT-5

Rubio, Jorge
❑ 66SeaPop-21
❑ 77FriOneYW-34

Ruble, Art
❑ 33WorCig(-77
❑ 33WorCig(-78
❑ 33WorCig(-79

Ruble, William
❑ 28Zee-163

Ruby, J. Gary
❑ 87QuaCitAP-20
❑ 88CalLeaACLC-36
❑ 88PalSprACLC-114
❑ 88PalSprAP-1435
❑ 89MidAngGS-3
❑ 90MidAngGS-2
❑ 91EdmTraP-1532
❑ 91LinDriAAA-175
❑ 92EdmTraF-3554
❑ 93VanCanF-2614
❑ 94VanCanF-1879
❑ 97BufBis-2
❑ 98ScrRedBQ-24

Ruch, Rob
❑ 94EliTwiC-21
❑ 94EliTwiF-3731

Rucker, Dave
❑ 80EvaTriT-9
❑ 80VenLeaS-122
❑ 82EvaTriT-8
❑ 82Top-261
❑ 83Don-641
❑ 83EvaTriT-9
❑ 83Fle-341
❑ 83TigPos-26
❑ 83Top-304
❑ 84Car-25
❑ 84Car5x7-24
❑ 84Don-260
❑ 84Nes792-699
❑ 84Top-699
❑ 84TopTif-699
❑ 85Don-260
❑ 85Fle-238
❑ 85FleUpd-92
❑ 85PorBeaC-26
❑ 85Top-421
❑ 85TopTif-421
❑ 85TopTifT-98T
❑ 85TopTra-98T
❑ 86Don-448
❑ 86Fle-447
❑ 86PhiTas-39
❑ 86Top-39
❑ 86TopTif-39
❑ 87OklCit8P-27
❑ 88BufBisC-8
❑ 88BufBisP-1472
❑ 89BufBisC-5
❑ 89BufBisP-1662
❑ 89UppDec-436

Rucker, Johnny
❑ 40PlaBal-213
❑ 41DouPlaR-137
❑ 47CenFlo-25
❑ 49BowPCL-7

Rucker, Nap (George)
❑ 03WilCarE-26
❑ 08RosComP-99
❑ 09ColChiE-246
❑ 09RamT20-100
❑ 09SpoNewSM-10
❑ 09T206-306
❑ 09T206-307
❑ 10CouT21-214
❑ 10CouT21-215
❑ 10CouT21-313
❑ 10DomDisP-104
❑ 10RedCroT-65
❑ 10RedCroT-151
❑ 10RedCroT-239
❑ 10SweCapPP-75A
❑ 10SweCapPP-75B
❑ 11HelSta-88
❑ 11L1L-117
❑ 11MecDFT-14
❑ 11PinT-5-462
❑ 11PloCanE-54
❑ 11S74Sil-54
❑ 11S81LarS-92
❑ 11SpoLifM-162
❑ 11T205-146
❑ 11TurRedT-34
❑ 12ColRedB-246
❑ 12ColTinT-246
❑ 12HasTriFT-3B
❑ 12PhiCarE-27
❑ 12T207-157
❑ 13NatGamW-34
❑ 13TomBarW-32
❑ 14B18B-60
❑ 14CraJacE-51
❑ 14PieStaT-91
❑ 14PolGroW-23
❑ 15CraJacE-51
❑ 15SpoNewM-148
❑ 16BF2FP-64
❑ 16FleBreD-79
❑ 16SpoNewM-148
❑ 82DiaCla-104
❑ 90DodTar-695
❑ 92ConTSN-333
❑ 94ConTSN-1263
❑ 94ConTSNB-1263

Ruckman, Scott
❑ 86BenPhiC-133
❑ 87UtiBluSP-5

❑ 88SpaPhiP-1037
❑ 88SpaPhiS-3
Rudi, Joe
❑ 69Top-587
❑ 70OPC-102
❑ 70Top-102
❑ 71MLBOffS-525
❑ 71OPC-407
❑ 71Top-407
❑ 72OPC-209
❑ 72Top-209
❑ 73A'sPos-41
❑ 73Kel2D-36
❑ 73OPC-360
❑ 73SevTraC-63
❑ 73Top-360
❑ 74A'sPos-50
❑ 74OPC-264
❑ 74Top-264
❑ 74TopSta-229
❑ 75Hos-40
❑ 75HosTwi-40
❑ 75Kel-28
❑ 75OPC-45
❑ 75OPC-465
❑ 75Top-45
❑ 75Top-465
❑ 75TopMin-45
❑ 75TopMin-465
❑ 76Kel-7
❑ 76OPC-475
❑ 76SSP-490
❑ 76Top-475
❑ 77BurCheD-125
❑ 77ChiWilD-57
❑ 77DailsID-57
❑ 77DetCaeD-57
❑ 77HollnnD-57
❑ 77Hos-146
❑ 77MSADis-57
❑ 77OPC-206
❑ 77RCColC-57
❑ 77SagDis-57
❑ 77sDis-57
❑ 77Spo-2105
❑ 77Top-155
❑ 77TopCloS-39
❑ 77WenDis-57
❑ 77ZipDis-57
❑ 78AngFamF-32
❑ 78Hos-114
❑ 78OPC-28
❑ 78RCColC-40
❑ 78SSP270-214
❑ 78Top-635
❑ 78WifBalD-64
❑ 79BasPat-74
❑ 79Hos-84
❑ 79OPC-134
❑ 79Top-267
❑ 80OPC-289
❑ 80Top-556
❑ 81Don-174
❑ 81Fle-272
❑ 81FleStiC-113
❑ 81OPC-362
❑ 81Top-701
❑ 81TopTra-826
❑ 82Don-586
❑ 82Fle-306
❑ 82OPC-388
❑ 82Top-388
❑ 82TopTra-102T
❑ 83Don-287
❑ 83Fle-532
❑ 83Top-87
❑ 84OCoandSI-190
❑ 86A'sGreT-5
❑ 87A'sMot-9
❑ 87ModA'sC-A2
❑ 91UppDecS-19
❑ 93MCIAmb-7
❑ 99SpollIGotG-52
❑ 99SpollIGotGA-64
❑ 99SpollIGotGC-32
Rudison, Karl
❑ 90PulBraB-18
❑ 90PulBraP-3094
Rudolph, Blaine
❑ 88BriTigP-1879
❑ 89FayGenP-1579
❑ 90DunBluJS-15
Rudolph, F. Don
❑ 58Top-347
❑ 59SeaPop-33
❑ 59Top-179
❑ 59TopVen-179
❑ 60HenHouW-33
❑ 60SeaPop-12
❑ 60UniOil-17
❑ 62Top-224
❑ 63Top-291
❑ 64Top-427
❑ 81WhiSox1T-38
Rudolph, Greg
❑ 92St.PetCC-25
❑ 92St.PetCF-2037
❑ 93SprCarC-21
❑ 93SprCarF-1864
Rudolph, Jeremi
❑ 96MedHatBJTI-24
Rudolph, Ken
❑ 70OPC-46
❑ 70Top-46
❑ 71MLBOffS-45
❑ 71OPC-472
❑ 71Top-472
❑ 72OPC-271
❑ 72Top-271
❑ 73OPC-414
❑ 73Top-414
❑ 74OPC-584
❑ 74Top-584
❑ 75OPC-289
❑ 75St.LouCP-23
❑ 75Top-289
❑ 75TopMin-289
❑ 76OPC-601
❑ 76SSP-287
❑ 76St.LouCP-28
❑ 76Top-601
❑ 78SprRedWK-24
❑ 91OriCro-398
Rudolph, Mason
❑ 90KinMetB-6
❑ 90KinMetS-21
❑ 91ColMetPI-25
❑ 91ColMetPPI-2
❑ 92St.LucMCB-16
❑ 92St.LucMF-1749
❑ 93St.LucMC-21
❑ 93St.LuMF-2925
❑ 95PorSeaDTI-24
Rudolph, Richard
❑ 09ColChiE-247A
❑ 09ColChiE-247B
❑ 09T206-461
❑ 10CouT21-216
❑ 10CouT21-314
❑ 12ColRedB-247A
❑ 12ColRedB-247B
❑ 12ColTinT-247A
❑ 12ColTinT-247B
❑ 12ImpTobC-22
❑ 15CraJacE-154
❑ 15SpoNewM-149
❑ 16BF2FP-57
❑ 16FleBreD-80
❑ 16SpoNewM-149
❑ 17ColE13-144
❑ 19W514-13
❑ 20W516-15
❑ 55DonWin-38
❑ 80BraTCM1-19
❑ 93ConTSN-704
Rudstrom, Tom
❑ 89BenBucL-15
Ruebel, Matt
❑ 90OklSoo-18
❑ 91WelPirC-20
❑ 91WelPirP-3572
❑ 92AugPirC-12
❑ 92AugPirF-237
❑ 92ClaFS7-19
❑ 93SalBucC-20
❑ 93SalBucF-430
❑ 93SouAtlLAPI-36
❑ 94CarMudF-1579
❑ 95Bes-94
❑ 95CarMudF-154
❑ 96BowBes-122
❑ 96BowBesAR-122
❑ 96BowBesR-122
❑ 96Top-430
❑ 97Fle-435
❑ 97FleTif-435
❑ 97PirPos-32
❑ 97StaClu-340
❑ 97StaCluMOP-340
❑ 97Ult-266
❑ 97UltGolME-266
❑ 97UltPlaME-266
❑ 98DurBulTI-25
Ruecker, Dion
❑ 97LowSpiB-16
Ruel, Muddy (Harold)
❑ 21E121So1-84
❑ 21Exh-147
❑ 22E120-13
❑ 22W573-110
❑ 22W575-111
❑ 23MapCriV-24
❑ 23W501-10
❑ 23WilChoV-137
❑ 25Exh-128
❑ 26Exh-128
❑ 27AmeCarE126-25
❑ 27Exh-63
❑ 28Exh-64
❑ 28StaPlaCE-56
❑ 29ExhFou-31
❑ 29PorandAR-76
❑ 33ButCre-22
❑ 33DouDisP-37
❑ 33ExhFou-12
❑ 33Gou-18
❑ 33GouCanV-18
❑ 35DiaMatCS3T1-127
❑ 35GouPuzR-5A
❑ 35GouPuzR-6A
❑ 35GouPuzR-11J
❑ 35GouPuzR-13A
❑ 40PlaBal-127
❑ 48IndTeal-27
❑ 49IndTeal-29
❑ 67SpoHobFC-20
❑ 75SenTCM1-27
❑ 79RedSoxEF-21
❑ 91ConTSN-284
❑ 93ConTSN-865
Ruess, Matt
❑ 94JamJamC-22
❑ 94JamJamF-3963
Rueter, Kirk
❑ 92RocExpC-13
❑ 92RocExpF-2114
❑ 93HarSenF-269
❑ 93SelRoo-88T
❑ 94Bow-60
❑ 94ColC-246
❑ 94ColChoGS-246
❑ 94ColChoSS-246
❑ 94Don-237
❑ 94Fin-9
❑ 94FinJum-9
❑ 94FinRef-9
❑ 94Fla-194
❑ 94Fle-549
❑ 94FleExtB-311
❑ 94FleExtBSYS-17
❑ 94FleRooS-16
❑ 94FUnPac-142
❑ 94Lea-8
❑ 94OPC-255
❑ 94OPCDiaD-8
❑ 94Pac-389
❑ 94Pin-382
❑ 94PinArtP-382
❑ 94PinMusC-382
❑ 94Sco-312
❑ 94ScoBoyoS-11
❑ 94ScoGolR-312
❑ 94Sel-172
❑ 94StaClu-302
❑ 94StaCluFDI-302
❑ 94StaCluGR-302
❑ 94StaCluMOP-302
❑ 94Top-628
❑ 94TopGol-628
❑ 94TopSpa-628
❑ 94TriPla-98
❑ 94Ult-231
❑ 94UltRisS-10
❑ 94UppDec-171
❑ 94UppDecED-171
❑ 94USPlaCR-9S
❑ 95ColCho-249
❑ 95ColChoGS-249
❑ 95ColChoSS-249
❑ 95Don-486
❑ 95DonPreP-486
❑ 95Fla-165
❑ 95Fle-358
❑ 95Lea-241
❑ 95Sco-171
❑ 95ScoGolR-171
❑ 95ScoPlaTS-171
❑ 95StaClu-139
❑ 95StaCluFDI-139
❑ 95StaCluMOP-139
❑ 95StaCluSTWS-139
❑ 95Top-344
❑ 95TopCyb-186
❑ 95Ult-406
❑ 95UltGolM-406
❑ 95UppDec-330
❑ 95UppDecED-330
❑ 95UppDecEDG-330
❑ 96ColCho-611
❑ 96ColChoGS-611
❑ 96ColChoSS-611
❑ 96Fle-466
❑ 96FleTif-466
❑ 96Ult-509
❑ 96UltGolM-509
❑ 97DonSigA-87
❑ 97DonSigAC-109
❑ 97DonSigAM-109
❑ 97Ult-478
❑ 97UltGolME-478
❑ 97UltPlaME-478
❑ 98CirThu-57
❑ 98CirThuRav-57
❑ 98CirThuSupRav-57
❑ 98ColCho-231
❑ 98ColCho-492
❑ 98Fin-19
❑ 98FinNo--19
❑ 98FinNo-R-19
❑ 98FinRef-19
❑ 98Fle-28
❑ 98GiaMot-9
❑ 98Pac-447
❑ 98PacOnl-672
❑ 98PacOnlR-672
❑ 98PacOnlWC-672
❑ 98PacPlaB-447
❑ 98PacRedT-447
❑ 98PacSil-447
❑ 98StaCluFDI-213
❑ 98StaClul-213
❑ 98StaCluOneK-213
❑ 98StaCluPP-213
❑ 98Top-359
❑ 98TopChr-359
❑ 98TopChrR-359
❑ 98TopDevR-359
❑ 98TopDia-359
❑ 98TopMiniC-359
❑ 98UppDec-504
❑ 99Fle-290
❑ 99FleSta9-290
❑ 99FleWarT-290
❑ 99Pac-388
❑ 99PacPlaB-388
❑ 99PacRed-388
❑ 99SkyThu-121
❑ 99SkyThuRant-121
❑ 99SkyThuRave-121
❑ 99ThuSkySupR-121
❑ 99Top-256
❑ 99TopChr-256
❑ 99TopChrR-256
❑ 99TopMVPP-256
❑ 99UppDec-483
❑ 99UppDecEL1-483
❑ 99UppDecEL2-483
Ruether, Dutch (Walter)
❑ 16Zee-91
❑ 19W514-108
❑ 20RedWorCP-19
❑ 21E121So1-85
❑ 21Exh-139
❑ 21Nei-64
❑ 22E120-147
❑ 22W572-82
❑ 22W573-111
❑ 23W501-99
❑ 23W503-56
❑ 23W515-40
❑ 26SpoComoA-33
❑ 27YorCarE-2
❑ 28W502-2
❑ 28Yue-2
❑ 75SenTCM1-28
❑ 75Yan192T-21
❑ 79Yan192T-26
❑ 84Yan192G-26
❑ 88PacEigMO-83
❑ 90DodTar-696
❑ 91ConTSN-104
Ruff, Anthony
❑ 93IdaFalBSP-8
❑ 94DanBraC-23
Ruff, Dan
❑ 91BriTigC-24
❑ 91BriTigP-3616
❑ 92LakTigC-4
❑ 92LakTigF-2289
❑ 93LakTigC-22
❑ 93LakTigF-1325
Ruffcorn, Scott
❑ 91Cla/Bes-409
❑ 91ClaDraP-21
❑ 91FroRowDP-4
❑ 91FroRowDPG-4
❑ 91FroRowDPP-3
❑ 91FroRowDPS-4
❑ 92Bow-88
❑ 92ClaBluBF-BC18
❑ 92ClaFS7-373
❑ 92ClaRedB-BC18
❑ 92OPC-36
❑ 92Pin-300
❑ 92SarWhiSCB-1
❑ 92SarWhiSF-205
❑ 92Sco-806
❑ 92StaCluD-159
❑ 92Top-36
❑ 92TopGol-36
❑ 92TopGolW-36
❑ 92TopMic-36
❑ 92UppDecML-246
❑ 93BirBarF-1193
❑ 93Bow-443
❑ 93ClaFisN-16
❑ 93ClaGolF-79
❑ 93ClaYouG-YG21
❑ 93ExcFS7-154
❑ 93FleFinE-197
❑ 94ActPac-20
❑ 94Bow-595
❑ 94BowBes-B36
❑ 94BowBes-X100
❑ 94BowBesR-B36
❑ 94BowBesR-X100
❑ 94Cla-102
❑ 94ClaCreotC-C21
❑ 94ClaGolREF-RE2
❑ 94ColC-247
❑ 94ColChoGS-247
❑ 94ColChoSS-247
❑ 94Don-619
❑ 94Fin-440
❑ 94FinJum-440
❑ 94FinRef-440
❑ 94LeaGolR-5
❑ 94LeaLimR-10
❑ 94NasSouF-1251
❑ 94Pin-255
❑ 94PinArtP-255
❑ 94PinMusC-255
❑ 94PinNewG-NG16
❑ 94Sco-611
❑ 94ScoGolR-611
❑ 94SigRooTPD-T1
❑ 94SigRooTPS-T1
❑ 94Spo-169
❑ 94StaCluT-127
❑ 94StaCluTFDI-127
❑ 94Top-356
❑ 94TopGol-356
❑ 94TopSpa-356
❑ 94TriAAF-AAA7
❑ 94UppDec-25
❑ 94UppDecED-25
❑ 95ActPac2G-17G
❑ 95ActPacF-12
❑ 95ActPacF-78
❑ 95Bow-423
❑ 95ColCho-2
❑ 95ColChoGS-2
❑ 95ColChoSS-2
❑ 95Don-504
❑ 95DonPreP-504
❑ 95FleUpd-37
❑ 95Lea-273
❑ 95Pin-256
❑ 95PinArtP-256
❑ 95PinMusC-256
❑ 95Sel-178
❑ 95Sel-232
❑ 95SelArtP-178
❑ 95SelArtP-232
❑ 95SelCer-94
❑ 95SelCerMG-94
❑ 95SelCerPU-4
❑ 95SelCerPU9-4
❑ 95Spo-157
❑ 95SpoArtP-157
❑ 95StaClu-480
❑ 95StaCluMOP-480
❑ 95StaCluSTWS-480
❑ 95Sum-118
❑ 95SumNthD-118
❑ 95Top-488
❑ 95UC3-96
❑ 95UC3ArtP-96
❑ 95Ult-276
❑ 95UltGolM-276
❑ 95UppDec-199
❑ 95UppDecED-199
❑ 95UppDecEDG-199
❑ 95UppDecPAW-H33
❑ 95UppDecPAWE-H33
❑ 95Zen-121
❑ 96NasSouB-19
❑ 96Sco-163
❑ 97Fle-530
❑ 97FleTif-530
❑ 97PhiTeal-33
❑ 97Ult-483
❑ 97UltGolME-483
❑ 97UltPlaME-483
❑ 98IndIndQ-16
Ruffin, Bruce
❑ 86ReaPhiP-23
❑ 86SpoRoo-29
❑ 87Don-555
❑ 87Fle-183
❑ 87FleGlo-183
❑ 87FleHotS-33
❑ 87Lea-168
❑ 87PhiTas-47
❑ 87SpoTeaP-6
❑ 87Top-499
❑ 87TopRoo-14
❑ 87TopSti-123
❑ 87TopSti-312
❑ 87TopTif-499
❑ 87ToyRoo-23
❑ 88Don-165
❑ 88Fle-313
❑ 88FleGlo-313
❑ 88OPC-268
❑ 88PanSti-353
❑ 88PhiTas-21
❑ 88Sco-492
❑ 88ScoGlo-492
❑ 88StaLinPh-14
❑ 88Top-268
❑ 88TopSti-119
❑ 88TopTif-268
❑ 89Bow-393
❑ 89BowTif-393
❑ 89Don-515
❑ 89Fle-580
❑ 89FleGlo-580
❑ 89OPC-222
❑ 89PanSti-148
❑ 89PhiTas-28
❑ 89Sco-328
❑ 89ScrRedBP-728
❑ 89Top-518
❑ 89TopSti-122
❑ 89TopTif-518
❑ 89UppDec-319
❑ 90Fle-572
❑ 90FleCan-572
❑ 90Lea-151
❑ 90OPC-22
❑ 90PhiTas-27
❑ 90Top-22
❑ 90TopTif-22
❑ 90UppDec-580
❑ 91Fle-411
❑ 91LinDriAAA-494
❑ 91OPC-637
❑ 91Sco-524
❑ 91ScrRedBLD-494
❑ 91ScrRedBP-2537
❑ 91StaClu-89
❑ 91Top-637
❑ 91TopDesS-637
❑ 91TopMic-637
❑ 91TopTif-637
❑ 91UppDec-410
❑ 92Bow-354
❑ 92BrePol-21
❑ 92Don-680
❑ 92Fle-544
❑ 92Lea-414
❑ 92LeaBlaG-414
❑ 92OPC-307
❑ 92Sco-161

❑ 92ScoRoo-71T
❑ 92StaClu-867
❑ 92TexLon-35
❑ 92Top-307
❑ 92TopGol-307
❑ 92TopGolW-307
❑ 92TopMic-307
❑ 92TopTra-95T
❑ 92TopTraG-95T
❑ 92UppDec-309
❑ 93FleFinE-42
❑ 93PacSpa-437
❑ 93RocStaC-15
❑ 93RocUSPC-7D
❑ 93RocUSPC-12S
❑ 93StaClu-270
❑ 93StaCluFDI-270
❑ 93StaCluMOP-270
❑ 93Ult-357
❑ 93UppDec-670
❑ 93UppDecGold-670
❑ 94BreMilB-349
❑ 94ColC-407
❑ 94ColChoGS-407
❑ 94ColChoSS-407
❑ 94Don-305
❑ 94Fin-199
❑ 94FinRef-199
❑ 94Fla-158
❑ 94Fle-452
❑ 94FleExtB-253
❑ 94Pac-206
❑ 94RocPol-22
❑ 94StaCluT-101
❑ 94StaCluTFDI-101
❑ 94Top-407
❑ 94TopGol-407
❑ 94TopSpa-407
❑ 94Ult-189
❑ 95ColCho-451
❑ 95ColChoGS-451
❑ 95ColChoSS-451
❑ 95Don-476
❑ 95DonPreP-476
❑ 95DonTopotO-231
❑ 95Fla-133
❑ 95Fle-528
❑ 95FleTeaL-18
❑ 95Lea-296
❑ 95Pac-145
❑ 95Sco-189
❑ 95ScoGolR-189
❑ 95ScoPlaTS-189
❑ 95StaClu-5
❑ 95StaCluFDI-5
❑ 95StaCluMOP-5
❑ 95StaCluSTWS-5
❑ 95Top-625
❑ 95TopCyb-392
❑ 95Ult-158
❑ 95UltGolM-158
❑ 96Don-367
❑ 96DonPreP-367
❑ 96Fle-373
❑ 96FleTif-373
❑ 96LeaSigEA-176
❑ 96RocPol-20
❑ 96Ult-474
❑ 96UltGolM-474
❑ 97Cir-65
❑ 97CirRav-65
❑ 97ColCho-321
❑ 97DonTea-100
❑ 97DonTeaSPE-100
❑ 97Fle-318
❑ 97FleTif-318
❑ 97Pac-289
❑ 97PacLigB-289
❑ 97PacSil-289
❑ 97RocSco-14
❑ 97RocScoPl-14
❑ 97RocScoPr-14
❑ 97Sco-332
❑ 97ScoArtPWB-332
❑ 97ScoResC-332
❑ 97ScoShoS-332
❑ 97ScoShoSAP-332
❑ 97Top-136
❑ 97Ult-340
❑ 97UltGolME-340
❑ 97UltPlaME-340

Ruffin, Johnny
❑ 89UtiBluSP-19
❑ 90SouBenWSGS-15
❑ 91Bow-347
❑ 91Cla/Bes-95
❑ 91SarWhiSC-9
❑ 91SarWhiSP-1112
❑ 92BirBarS-93
❑ 92Bow-451
❑ 92ClaFS7-33
❑ 92DonRoo-107
❑ 92LeaGolR-BC13
❑ 92ProFS7-43
❑ 92SarWhiSF-206
❑ 92SkyAA F-45
❑ 92UppDecML-224
❑ 93BirBarF-1194
❑ 93Bow-147
❑ 93ClaFS7-88
❑ 93WhiSoxSC-26
❑ 94Bow-102
❑ 94ColC-17
❑ 94ColChoGS-17
❑ 94ColChoSS-17
❑ 94Don-135
❑ 94Fin-283
❑ 94FinRef-283
❑ 94Fla-370
❑ 94Fle-424
❑ 94FleExtB-238
❑ 94Lea-305
❑ 94LeaLimR-18
❑ 94Pin-410
❑ 94PinArtP-410
❑ 94PinMusC-410
❑ 94RedKah-25
❑ 94ScoRoo-RT144
❑ 94ScoRooGR-RT144
❑ 94Sel-394
❑ 94SpoRoo-96
❑ 94SpoRooAP-96
❑ 94Top-779
❑ 94TopGol-779
❑ 94TopSpa-779
❑ 94Ult-176
❑ 94UppDec-170
❑ 94UppDecED-170
❑ 95ColChoGS-435
❑ 95ColChoSS-435
❑ 95Don-287
❑ 95DonPreP-287
❑ 95Fle-445
❑ 95FleRooS-17
❑ 95IndIndF-93
❑ 95Lea-109
❑ 95Pac-112
❑ 95RedKah-25
❑ 95Sco-67
❑ 95ScoGolR-67
❑ 95ScoPlaTS-67
❑ 95StaClu-276
❑ 95StaCluMOP-276
❑ 95StaCluSTWS-276
❑ 95Top-270
❑ 95TopCyb-146
❑ 95Ult-148
❑ 95UltGolM-148
❑ 97PawRedS-23
❑ 98LouRedQ-25
❑ 98NorTidQ-22

Ruffing, Red (Charles H.)
❑ 25Exh-69
❑ 26Exh-70
❑ 29ExhFou-17
❑ 29PorandAR-77
❑ 32USCar*-20
❑ 33CraJacP-19
❑ 33GeoCMil-26
❑ 33Gou-56
❑ 33WorCig-79
❑ 34BabRutG-53
❑ 34ButPreR-52
❑ 34DiaStaR-60
❑ 34GouCanV-48
❑ 35GouPuzR-4D
❑ 35GouPuzR-7D
❑ 35GouPuzR-12D
❑ 36ExhFou-13
❑ 36NatChiFPR-92
❑ 36R31PasP-20
❑ 36R31Pre-L11
❑ 36WorWidGV-102
❑ 37OPCBatUV-136
❑ 37WheBB6-2
❑ 38OurNatGPP-25
❑ 39PlaBal-3
❑ 40PlaBal-10
❑ 40WheM4-1A
❑ 40WheM4-1B
❑ 41DouPlaR-67
❑ 41DouPlaR-85
❑ 41PlaBal-20
❑ 43MPR302-1-22
❑ 47PM1StaP1-191
❑ 60Fle-63
❑ 61Fle-74
❑ 69EquSpoHoF-BB19
❑ 72TCMthe3-60
❑ 72TCMthe3-61
❑ 73SevTraC-64
❑ 73TCMAllG-18
❑ 75YanAllTT-10
❑ 75YanDyn1T-39
❑ 76GrePlaG-35
❑ 76RowExh-1
❑ 76ShaPiz-105
❑ 77GalGloG-54
❑ 80PacLeg-109
❑ 80PerHaloFP-106
❑ 80SSPHOF-106
❑ 80YanGreT-9
❑ 82DiaCla-107
❑ 82MetGal62-31
❑ 82OhiHaloF-11
❑ 82TCMGreP-28
❑ 83Car194T-64
❑ 83DonHOFH-31
❑ 86SpoDecG-14
❑ 89HOFStiB-83
❑ 91ConTSN-13
❑ 91ConTSN-227
❑ 92YanWIZA-70
❑ 92YanWIZH-28
❑ 93ConTSN-882
❑ 94ConTSN-1078
❑ 94ConTSNB-1078

Ruffner, Mark
❑ 89ReaPhiB-24

Rugg, Rusty
❑ 89HelBreSP-6
❑ 91HelBreSP-19

Ruhl, Dan
❑ 92LetMouSP-4

Ruhle, Vern
❑ 75DetTigP-29
❑ 75OPC-614
❑ 75Top-614
❑ 75TopMin-614
❑ 76DetTigP-25
❑ 76Hos-46
❑ 76HosTwi-46
❑ 76OPC-89
❑ 76Top-89
❑ 77OPC-212
❑ 77Top-311
❑ 78ChaChaT-14
❑ 78Top-456
❑ 79AstPos-22
❑ 79Top-49
❑ 80Top-234
❑ 81AstPos-20
❑ 81Don-261A
❑ 81Don-261B
❑ 81Fle-53
❑ 81Top-642
❑ 82AstAstI-7
❑ 82AstPos-21
❑ 82Don-293
❑ 82Fle-228
❑ 82Top-539
❑ 83AstPos-24
❑ 83Don-627
❑ 83Fle-462
❑ 83Top-172
❑ 84AstMot-23
❑ 84AstPos-23
❑ 84Don-564
❑ 84Fle-238
❑ 84Nes792-328
❑ 84Top-328
❑ 84TopTif-328
❑ 85Don-380
❑ 85Fle-358
❑ 85FleUpd-93
❑ 85Ind-26
❑ 85IndPol-48
❑ 85Top-426
❑ 85TopTif-426
❑ 85TopTifT-99T
❑ 85TopTra-99T
❑ 86Fle-593
❑ 86Top-768
❑ 86TopTif-768
❑ 87AstShoSPO-27
❑ 87CalAngPPS-33
❑ 87Fle-91
❑ 87FleGlo-91
❑ 87Top-221
❑ 87TopTif-221
❑ 90SweBasG-128
❑ 91SweBasG-76

Ruiz, Augie
❑ 79LodDodT-2
❑ 81BirBarT-23
❑ 82EvaTriT-9
❑ 83RicBraT-9

Ruiz, Benny
❑ 86GleFalTP-19
❑ 87GleFalTP-14
❑ 88TolMudHC-16
❑ 88TolMudHP-602

Ruiz, Cecilio
❑ 83LasVegSBHN-19

Ruiz, Cesar
❑ 94BriTigC-22
❑ 94BriTigF-3512
❑ 96FayGenB-26

Ruiz, Chico (Hiraldo S.)
❑ 62RedEnq-31
❑ 63Top-407
❑ 64Top-356
❑ 64TopVen-356
❑ 65RedEnq-26
❑ 65Top-554
❑ 66OPC-159
❑ 66Top-159
❑ 66TopVen-159
❑ 67CokCapR-12
❑ 67Top-339
❑ 67TopVen-305
❑ 68Kah-B30
❑ 68Top-213
❑ 68TopVen-213
❑ 69MilBra-243
❑ 69Top-469
❑ 70Top-606
❑ 71MLBOffS-357
❑ 71OPC-686
❑ 71Top-686
❑ 72MilBra-301
❑ 77SerSta-20
❑ 78TCM60I-35

Ruiz, Chico (Manuel)
❑ 78RicBraT-13
❑ 79RicBraT-13
❑ 81RicBraT-9
❑ 82RicBraT-15
❑ 83RicBraT-15
❑ 90RicBra2ATI-21

Ruiz, Estuar
❑ 92KanCouCTI-26

Ruiz, Mauricio
❑ 93LinVenB-240
❑ 95LinVen-141
❑ 96-97LinVen-220

Ruiz, Nelson
❑ 80BatTroT-29

Ruiz, Rafael
❑ 96HicCraB-19

Ruiz, Stewart
❑ 91BluOriC-3
❑ 91BluOriP-4136
❑ 92KanCouCF-102
❑ 94VenLinU-161

Ruiz, Willy
❑ 98SpoIndG-28

Rujff, Anthony
❑ 93IdaFalBF-4048

Ruling, Stephen
❑ 77SpoIndC-8
❑ 78SpoIndC-11

Rumer, Tim
❑ 90TamYanD-18
❑ 91Ft.LauYC-13
❑ 91Ft.LauYP-2426
❑ 92ClaFS7-224
❑ 92PriWilCC-13
❑ 92PriWilCF-148
❑ 94AlbYanF-1440
❑ 95ColCliMCTI-4
❑ 95ColCliP-27
❑ 95ColCliTI-27
❑ 96NorNavB-22
❑ 97ColCliB-26
❑ 97ColCliD-23

Rumfield, Toby
❑ 91Cla/Bes-413
❑ 91FroRowDP-35
❑ 91FroRowDPG-35
❑ 91FroRowDPS-35
❑ 91PriRedC-13
❑ 91PriRedP-3518
❑ 92BilMusF-3359
❑ 92BilMusSP-6
❑ 93WesVirWF-2869
❑ 94CarLeaAF-CAR50
❑ 94WinSpiC-20
❑ 94WinSpiF-282
❑ 95ChaLooTI-19
❑ 96ChaLooB-26
❑ 97ChaLoo-23
❑ 98GreBraG-21

Rumler, William G.
❑ 17ColE13-145
❑ 19Zee-74
❑ 20Zee-94
❑ 29Zee-12
❑ 30Zee-15

Rumsey, Dan
❑ 89AriStaB-25
❑ 91CliGiaP-849
❑ 92MidAngF-4039
❑ 92PalSprAC-26
❑ 93MidAngF-335
❑ 97MidAngOHP-27

Rumsey, Derrell
❑ 91VisOakC-23
❑ 91VisOakP-1755
❑ 92ClaFS7-371
❑ 92Ft.MyeMCB-12
❑ 92Ft.MyeMF-2757

Rundels, Matt
❑ 92JamExpC-6
❑ 92JamExpF-1509
❑ 93BurBeeC-22
❑ 93BurBeeF-167
❑ 94HarSenF-2100
❑ 95HarSenTI-4
❑ 96SigRooOJ-30
❑ 96SigRooOJS-30

Rundles, Gary
❑ 89CarNewE-21

Runge, Ed
❑ 55Bow-277
❑ 90T/MUmp-64

Runge, Paul E.
❑ 88T/MUmp-17
❑ 89T/MUmp-17
❑ 90T/MUmp-17
❑ 90T/MUmp-64

Runge, Paul W.
❑ 81RicBraT-10
❑ 82RicBraT-16
❑ 83RicBraT-16
❑ 84raPho-28
❑ 84RicBraT-24
❑ 85BraPol-12
❑ 85TopTifT-100T
❑ 85TopTra-100T
❑ 86RicBraP-19
❑ 86Top-409
❑ 86TopTif-409
❑ 87RicBraBC-18
❑ 87RicBraC-12
❑ 87RicBraT-14
❑ 88FleUpd-71
❑ 88FleUpdG-71
❑ 88StaLinBra-16
❑ 89LasVegSC-21
❑ 89Top-38
❑ 89TopBig-23
❑ 89TopTif-38
❑ 89UppDec-55
❑ 90CMC-343
❑ 90ProAAAF-359
❑ 90SyrChiC-17
❑ 90SyrChiMB-19
❑ 90SyrChiP-579
❑ 93IdaFalBF-4050
❑ 93IdaFalBSP-30
❑ 94DanBraC-30
❑ 94DanBraF-3548
❑ 95EugEmeTI-29
❑ 96MacBraB-26
❑ 97DurBulTI-2
❑ 98DanQ-C-28

Runge, Scott
❑ 86WatPirP-20
❑ 87WatPirP-5
❑ 88AugPirP-376
❑ 89SanBerSB-19
❑ 89WilBilP-638

Runion, Jeff
❑ 92GulCoaRSP-24
❑ 93ChaRaiC-17
❑ 93ChaRaiF-1910
❑ 93ClaGolF-108
❑ 94ChaRivC-17
❑ 94ChaRivF-2671
❑ 95ChaRivTI-17

Runion, Tony
❑ 94ColRedC-19
❑ 95KinIndTI-23
❑ 96KenIndB-22
❑ 98LynHilQ-12

Runk, David
❑ 98BilMusTI-28

Runnells, Tom
❑ 81PhoGiaVNB-23
❑ 82PhoGiaVNB-21
❑ 83PhoGiaBHN-9
❑ 84WicAerRD-11
❑ 86Don-569
❑ 87VerRedP-16
❑ 88ChaLooB-14
❑ 89ChaLooLITI-25
❑ 89IndIndC-25
❑ 89IndIndP-1220
❑ 90ExpPos-30
❑ 91ExpPos-19
❑ 91TopTra-103T
❑ 91TopTraT-103T
❑ 92ExpDonD-15A
❑ 92ExpPos-26
❑ 92OPC-51
❑ 92Top-51
❑ 92TopGol-51
❑ 92TopGolW-51
❑ 92TopMic-51
❑ 93LonTigF-2322
❑ 94TreThuF-2134
❑ 95TolMudHTI-1
❑ 96TolMudHB-2

Runnels, Pete (James E.)
❑ 47Exh-197
❑ 52Top-2
❑ 53BowC-139
❑ 53Bri-16
❑ 53Top-219
❑ 54Top-6
❑ 55Bow-255
❑ 55RedMan-AL20
❑ 56Top-234
❑ 57Top-64
❑ 58Hir-38
❑ 58RedSoxJP-8
❑ 58Top-265
❑ 59Top-370
❑ 59Top-519
❑ 59WilSpoG-6
❑ 60KeyChal-40
❑ 60RedSoxJP-8
❑ 60Top-15
❑ 60TopTat-47
❑ 60TopVen-15
❑ 61Baz-32
❑ 61NuSco-407
❑ 61Pos-47A
❑ 61Pos-47B
❑ 61SevElev-11
❑ 61Top-42
❑ 61Top-210
❑ 61TopMagR-29
❑ 61TopStal-116
❑ 62Jel-57
❑ 62Pos-57
❑ 62PosCan-57
❑ 62RedSoxJP-8
❑ 62SalPlaC-47A
❑ 62SalPlaC-47B
❑ 62ShiPlaC-47
❑ 62Top-3
❑ 62TopBuc-79
❑ 62TopStal-17
❑ 62TopVen-3
❑ 63BasMagM-72
❑ 63Col45"P-12
❑ 63Col45"P-18
❑ 63Col45'JP-9
❑ 63ExhStaB-57
❑ 63Jel-77
❑ 63Pos-77
❑ 63SalMetC-61
❑ 63Top-2
❑ 63Top-230
❑ 64Col.45JP-6
❑ 64Top-121
❑ 64TopVen-121
❑ 80MarExh-27
❑ 81RedSoxBG2S-47
❑ 83TopRep5-2
❑ 85TCMPhoC-38

❑ 90PacLeg-103
❑ 91TopArc1-219
❑ 94TopArc1-6
❑ 94TopArc1G-6
Runyan, Paul
❑ 94PriRedC-21
❑ 94PriRedF-3261
Runyan, Sean
❑ 92FroRowDP-41
❑ 92FroRowDPG-41
❑ 92FroRowDPS-41
❑ 92HigSchPLS-14
❑ 93Bow-616
❑ 93ClaGolF-161
❑ 93StaCluM-89
❑ 94AubAstC-15
❑ 94AubAstF-3757
❑ 96QuaCitRB-25
❑ 97MobBayBB-27
❑ 98Fle-550
❑ 98PacOmeRS-2
❑ 98PacOmeRST1-2
❑ 98PacOnl-284
❑ 98PacOnlR-284
❑ 98PacOnlWC-284
❑ 99Fle-557
❑ 99FleSta9-557
❑ 99FleWarT-557
Runyon, Curt
❑ 75AndRanT-16
Runzi, Andy
❑ 93BoiHawF-3917
Ruocchio, James
❑ 91BoiHawC-6
❑ 91BoiHawP-3890
Ruotsinoja, Jacob
❑ 97CliLumG-22
❑ 98CliLumG-20
Rupcich, Mike
❑ 89FreStaBS-17
❑ 90FreStaS-12
❑ 91FreStaBS-16
Rupe, Brian
❑ 83VisOakF-25
Rupe, Ryan
❑ 99BasAmeTP-88
❑ 99BasAmeTPA-38
❑ 99BasAmeTPG-88
❑ 99Bow-347
❑ 99BowGol-347
❑ 99BowInt-347
❑ 99DumSet-117
❑ 99FleMys-117
❑ 99FleMysM-117
❑ 99SkyPre-261
❑ 99SkyPre-261
❑ 99SkyPreDD-3
❑ 99SkyPreR-261
❑ 99SkyPreR-261
❑ 99TeaBesR-75
❑ 99TeaBesRG-75
❑ 99TeaBesRS-75
Rupert, Bryan
❑ 98PeoChiM-22
Rupkey, Rich
❑ 90HamRedB-12
❑ 90HamRedS-21
Rupp, Brian
❑ 93Bow-700
❑ 93ClaFS7-115
❑ 93SavCarC-21
❑ 93SavCarF-694
❑ 93SouAtlLAGF-51
❑ 94ClaGolF-160
❑ 94ExcFS7-274
❑ 94St.PetCC-23
❑ 94St.PetCF-2598
❑ 94UppDecML-184
❑ 96ArkTraB-24
❑ 97ArkTraB-19
❑ 97LouRedB-27
❑ 98MemRedG-20
Rupp, Chad
❑ 93EliTwiC-19
❑ 93EliTwiF-3422
❑ 94ForWayWC-20
❑ 94ForWayWF-2017
❑ 95ForMyeMTI-23
❑ 96HarCitRCB-28
❑ 97SalLakB-24
❑ 98SalLakBO-25
Rupp, Mark
❑ 89EriOriS-23
❑ 90HelBreSP-21
Rupp, Terry
❑ 89SpoIndSP-9
❑ 90WatDiaB-15
❑ 90WatDiaP-2386
Ruppert, Colonel (Jacob)
❑ 75Yan192T-22
❑ 75YanDyn1T-33
❑ 79Yan192T-27
❑ 84Yan192G-10
❑ 89CMCRut-15
❑ 90YanMomPRP-10
❑ 95ConTSN-1398
Rusch, Glendon
❑ 94RocRoyC-21
❑ 94RocRoyF-564
❑ 95Bes-23
❑ 95Exc-64
❑ 95SPML-70
❑ 95WilBluRTI-18
❑ 96BesAutSA-63
❑ 96Bow-289
❑ 96BowBes-105
❑ 96BowBesAR-105
❑ 96BowBesR-105
❑ 96BowFoi-289
❑ 96Exc-67
❑ 96ExcSeaC-8
❑ 96OmaRoyB-26
❑ 97BesAutAS-47
❑ 97BesAutP-R13
❑ 97Bow-415
❑ 97BowBes-126
❑ 97BowBesAR-126
❑ 97BowBesR-126
❑ 97BowInt-415
❑ 97ColCho-461
❑ 97Don-370
❑ 97DonGolPP-370
❑ 97DonPre-148
❑ 97DonPreCttC-148
❑ 97DonSilPP-370
❑ 97Fle-567
❑ 97FleTif-567
❑ 97PinCer-123
❑ 97PinCerMBla-123
❑ 97PinCerMBlu-123
❑ 97PinCerMG-123
❑ 97PinCerMR-123
❑ 97PinCerR-123
❑ 97PinTotCPB-123
❑ 97PinTotCPG-123
❑ 97PinTotCPR-123
❑ 97Sco-476
❑ 97ScoArtPWB-476
❑ 97ScoResC-476
❑ 97ScoShoS-476
❑ 97ScoShoSAP-476
❑ 97Sel-154
❑ 97SelCom-154
❑ 97SpoIll-23
❑ 97SpoIllEE-23
❑ 97StaClu-191
❑ 97StaCluMOP-191
❑ 97Top-207
❑ 97Ult-475
❑ 97UltGolME-475
❑ 97UltPlaME-475
❑ 98ColCho-388
❑ 98Fle-103
❑ 98PacInvGems-55
❑ 98PacOnl-353
❑ 98PacOnlR-353
❑ 98PacOnlWC-353
❑ 98PinIns-112
❑ 98PinInsCE-112
❑ 98PinInsDE-112
❑ 98ScoRT-88
❑ 98Top-231
❑ 98TopChr-231
❑ 98TopChrR-231
❑ 98TopDevR-231
❑ 98TopDia-231
❑ 98TopMiniC-231
❑ 98Ult-81
❑ 98UltGolM-81
❑ 98UltMas-81
❑ 98UltPlaM-81
❑ 98UppDec-393
❑ 99Pac-212
❑ 99PacPlaB-212
❑ 99PacRed-212
❑ 99UppDec-117
❑ 99UppDecEL1-117
❑ 99UppDecEL2-117
Rusciano, Chris
❑ 92IdaFalGF-3511
❑ 92IdaFalGSP-4
❑ 93IdaFalBF-4028
❑ 93IdaFalBSP-15
❑ 94IdaFalBF-3584
❑ 94IdaFalBSP-22
❑ 94MacBraC-17
❑ 94MacBraF-2202
Rush, Andy
❑ 89ElmPioP-18
❑ 90DodTar-1058
❑ 90WinHavRSS-23
❑ 91LynRedSC-28
❑ 91LynRedSP-1197
❑ 92LynRedSC-14
❑ 92LynRedSF-2906
❑ 93RanCucQF-833
Rush, Bob
❑ 49EurSta-69
❑ 50Bow-61
❑ 51Bow-212
❑ 52NatTeaL-28
❑ 52StaCalL-80D
❑ 52StaCalS-92C
❑ 52Top-153
❑ 53BowC-110
❑ 54Bow-77
❑ 55Bow-182
❑ 55RobGouS-13
❑ 55RobGouW-13
❑ 56Top-214
❑ 57Top-137
❑ 58Top-313
❑ 59Top-396
❑ 60BraJayP-9
❑ 60BraLaktL-21
❑ 60BraSpiaS-19
❑ 60Top-404
❑ 79DiaGre-115
❑ 79TCM50-164
❑ 83TopRep5-153
Rush, Eddie (Edward)
❑ 88CedRapRP-1155
❑ 89GreHorP-418
❑ 90CedRapRB-6
❑ 90CedRapRP-2329
❑ 91CedRapRP-2729
❑ 91MidLeaAP-MWL23
Rush, Larry
❑ 79HolMilT-20
❑ 80VanCanT-1
❑ 81VanCanT-12
❑ 82VanCanT-7
Rush, Miles
❑ 98NasSouTI-27
❑ 98NasSouTISS-25
Rush, Rod
❑ 84EveGiaC-13B
Rush, Tony
❑ 94OneYanF-3791
Rushing, Will
❑ 96FtMyeMB-9
❑ 97ForMyeM-27
❑ 98FarRedHM-29
Rushworth, Jim
❑ 92JamExpC-22
❑ 92JamExpF-1501
❑ 93BurBeeC-23
❑ 93BurBeeF-158
❑ 94WesPalBEC-23
❑ 94WesPalBEF-38
Rusie, Amos
❑ 75FlePio-12
❑ 76ISCHooHA-5
❑ 78DexHaloFP-42
❑ 80PerHaloFP-162
❑ 80SSPHOF-162
❑ 81ConTSN-72
❑ 86IndIndTI-8
❑ 87ConSer2-53
❑ 87OldJudN-426A
❑ 87OldJudN-426B
❑ 92ConTSN-535
❑ 94OriofB-68
❑ 95May-26A
❑ 95May-26B
❑ 95NewN566-175
Rusin, Dave
❑ 91PerHeaF-4
Rusk, Mike
❑ 75ForLauYS-28
Rusk, Troy
❑ 90PriPatD-17
❑ 91SpaPhiC-15
❑ 91SpaPhiP-902
❑ 92ClePhiF-2065
❑ 92SpaPhiC-4
❑ 92SpaPhiF-1272
❑ 93ClePhiC-19
❑ 93ClePhiF-2687
❑ 94ReaPhiF-2066
Ruskey, Jason
❑ 94BelMarC-23
❑ 94BelMarF-3231
Ruskin, Scott
❑ 87MacPirP-22
❑ 88SalBucS-18
❑ 89BlaYNPRWLU-31
❑ 89SalBucS-18
❑ 90Bow-167
❑ 90BowTif-167
❑ 90DonRoo-27
❑ 90Lea-512
❑ 90TopTra-106T
❑ 90TopTraT-106T
❑ 90UppDec-713
❑ 91Don-612
❑ 91ExpPos-20
❑ 91Fle-246
❑ 91OPC-589
❑ 91Sco-799
❑ 91Top-589
❑ 91TopDeb90-137
❑ 91TopDesS-589
❑ 91TopMic-589
❑ 91TopRoo-26
❑ 91TopTif-589
❑ 91Ult-209
❑ 91UppDec-383
❑ 92Don-394
❑ 92Fle-491
❑ 92FleUpd-83
❑ 92Lea-521
❑ 92LeaBlaG-521
❑ 92OPC-692
❑ 92RedKah-28
❑ 92Sco-121
❑ 92ScoRoo-57T
❑ 92StaClu-777
❑ 92StaCluNC-777
❑ 92Top-692
❑ 92TopGol-692
❑ 92TopGolW-692
❑ 92TopMic-692
❑ 92TopTra-96T
❑ 92TopTraG-96T
❑ 92UppDec-384
❑ 93Fle-398
❑ 93IndIndF-1488
❑ 93StaClu-199
❑ 93StaCluFDI-199
❑ 93StaCluMOP-199
❑ 93Top-328
❑ 93TopGol-328
❑ 93TopInaM-328
❑ 93TopInaR-328
❑ 93TopMic-328
❑ 93TriAAAGF-9
Russ, Kevin
❑ 84IdaFalATI-23
❑ 86MadMusP-18
Russell, Alan
❑ 91BoiHawC-30
❑ 93BoiHawC-30
Russell, Allen
❑ 23WilChoV-138
❑ 75SenTCM1-29
Russell, Bill E.
❑ 70MLBOffS-56
❑ 70OPC-304
❑ 70Top-304
❑ 71Dod-12
❑ 71DodTic-14
❑ 71MLBOffS-113
❑ 71OPC-226
❑ 71Top-226
❑ 72Top-736
❑ 73LinPor-96
❑ 73OPC-108
❑ 73Top-108
❑ 74OPC-239
❑ 74Top-239
❑ 74TopDecE-40
❑ 74TopSta-49
❑ 75Hos-91
❑ 75OPC-23
❑ 75Top-23
❑ 75TopMin-23
❑ 76LinSup-116
❑ 76OPC-22
❑ 76Top-22
❑ 77DodPho-13
❑ 77Top-322
❑ 78SSP270-56
❑ 78Top-128
❑ 79DodBlu-11
❑ 79Top-546
❑ 80DodPol-18
❑ 80OPC-40
❑ 80Top-75
❑ 81AllGamPI-113
❑ 81Dod-25
❑ 81DodPol-18
❑ 81Don-57
❑ 81Fle-117
❑ 81FleStiC-68
❑ 81LonBeaPT-3A
❑ 81LonBeaPT-3B
❑ 81OPC-20
❑ 81Top-465
❑ 81TopSti-179
❑ 81TopSupHT-51
❑ 82DodPol-18
❑ 82DodUniOV-18
❑ 82Don-453
❑ 82Fle-20
❑ 82FleSta-8
❑ 82Top-279
❑ 83AllGamPI-113
❑ 83DodPol-18
❑ 83DodPos-13
❑ 83Don-210
❑ 83Fle-219
❑ 83FleSti-116
❑ 83OPC-123
❑ 83Top-661
❑ 83TopSti-249
❑ 84AllGamPI-24
❑ 84DodPol-18
❑ 84Don-587
❑ 84Fle-111
❑ 84Nes792-792
❑ 84OPC-14
❑ 84Top-792
❑ 84TopRubD-21
❑ 84TopSti-77
❑ 84TopTif-792
❑ 85AllGamPI-115
❑ 85DodCokP-28
❑ 85Don-93
❑ 85Fle-383
❑ 85Lea-232
❑ 85OPC-343
❑ 85SpoIndGC-17
❑ 85Top-343
❑ 85TopMin-343
❑ 85TopRubD-21
❑ 85TopSti-76
❑ 85TopTif-343
❑ 86DodCokP-26
❑ 86DodPol-18
❑ 86DodUniOP-16
❑ 86Don-153
❑ 86Fle-142
❑ 86Top-506
❑ 86Top-696
❑ 86TopTif-506
❑ 86TopTif-696
❑ 87DodMot-27
❑ 87DodPol-29
❑ 87DodSmoA-31
❑ 87Fle-452
❑ 87FleGlo-452
❑ 87Top-116
❑ 87TopTif-116
❑ 88DodMot-28
❑ 88DodSmo-13
❑ 88DodSmo-15
❑ 89DodMot-27
❑ 89DodPol-1
❑ 89DodSmoG-81
❑ 90DodMot-28
❑ 90DodPol-NNO
❑ 90DodTar-697
❑ 91DodMot-28
❑ 91DodPho-6
❑ 91DodPol-NNO
❑ 91DodUno7P-1
❑ 92AlbDukF-737
❑ 92AlbDukS-24
❑ 92DodStaTA-15
❑ 92UppDecS-15
❑ 93AlbDukF-1478
❑ 93TriAAAGF-15
❑ 94DodMot-28
❑ 94DodPol-30
❑ 95DodMot-28
❑ 95DodPol-30
❑ 96DodMot-28
❑ 96DodPol-8
❑ 97DodMot-1
❑ 97DodPol-26
❑ 98DodPol-25
Russell, Dan
❑ 88ModA'sTI-25
Russell, Fred
❑ 88EugEmeB-15
❑ 89EugEmeB-19
❑ 90AppFoxBS-21
❑ 90AppFoxP-2103
❑ 90CMC-698
❑ 91BasCitRC-20
❑ 91BasCitRP-1406
❑ 91Cla/Bes-122
Russell, Jack Erwin
❑ 29PorandAR-78
❑ 33Gou-123
❑ 33Gou-167
❑ 33WorCig-80
❑ 34DiaMatCSB-158
❑ 39CubTeal-23
❑ 79DiaGre-67
❑ 85BigLeaC3-85
❑ 94ConTSN-1048
❑ 94ConTSNB-1048
Russell, Jake
❑ 94MarPhiC-23
❑ 94MarPhiF-3305
❑ 95BatCliTI-29
❑ 97BurIndG-22
❑ 98KinIndQ-22
Russell, Jeff
❑ 82WatRedT-8
❑ 83IndIndTI-14
❑ 84Don-569
❑ 84Nes792-270
❑ 84RedBor-46
❑ 84RedEnq-16
❑ 84Top-270
❑ 84TopTif-270
❑ 85Don-487
❑ 85Fle-551
❑ 85RedYea-15
❑ 85Top-651
❑ 85TopTif-651
❑ 86Don-586
❑ 86OklCit8P-19
❑ 86RanPer-40
❑ 87Don-550
❑ 87Fle-137
❑ 87FleGlo-137
❑ 87RanMot-26
❑ 87RanSmo-32
❑ 87Top-444
❑ 87TopTif-444
❑ 88Don-531
❑ 88Fle-478
❑ 88FleGlo-478
❑ 88RanMot-26
❑ 88RanSmo-17
❑ 88Sco-514
❑ 88ScoGlo-514
❑ 88StaLinRa-14
❑ 88Top-114
❑ 88TopTif-114
❑ 89Bow-226
❑ 89BowTif-226
❑ 89Don-403
❑ 89DonAll-26
❑ 89DonBasB-200
❑ 89Fle-531
❑ 89FleGlo-531
❑ 89OPC-166
❑ 89PanSti-447
❑ 89RanMot-6
❑ 89RanSmo-28
❑ 89Sco-438
❑ 89Top-565
❑ 89TopBig-309
❑ 89TopSti-243
❑ 89TopTif-565
❑ 89UppDec-461
❑ 90Bow-485
❑ 90BowTif-485
❑ 90Don-284
❑ 90DonBesA-99
❑ 90Fle-312
❑ 90Fle-633
❑ 90FleAwaW-28
❑ 90FleCan-312
❑ 90FleCan-633
❑ 90Lea-152
❑ 90Lea-442
❑ 90OPC-80
❑ 90OPC-395
❑ 90PanSti-159

❑ 90PubIntS-420
❑ 90RanMot-8
❑ 90RedFolSB-80
❑ 90Sco-263
❑ 90Sco100S-23
❑ 90Spo-192
❑ 90Top-80
❑ 90Top-395
❑ 90TopBig-15
❑ 90TopGaloC-8
❑ 90TopMinL-38
❑ 90TopSti-252
❑ 90TopStiB-66
❑ 90TopTif-80
❑ 90TopTif-395
❑ 90UppDec-638
❑ 91Bow-267
❑ 91Don-202
❑ 91Fle-300
❑ 91Lea-291
❑ 91OPC-344
❑ 91RanMot-8
❑ 91Sco-277
❑ 91StaClu-421
❑ 91Top-344
❑ 91TopDesS-344
❑ 91TopMic-344
❑ 91TopTif-344
❑ 91Ult-354
❑ 91UppDec-648
❑ 92Bow-218
❑ 92Don-129
❑ 92Fle-319
❑ 92Lea-90
❑ 92LeaBlaG-90
❑ 92OPC-257
❑ 92Pin-209
❑ 92RanMot-8
❑ 92RanTeal-21
❑ 92Sco-124
❑ 92StaClu-28
❑ 92Stu-247
❑ 92Top-257
❑ 92TopGol-257
❑ 92TopGolW-257
❑ 92TopMic-257
❑ 92Ult-140
❑ 92UppDec-695
❑ 93Bow-115
❑ 93Don-711
❑ 93Fla-167
❑ 93Fle-668
❑ 93FleFinE-177
❑ 93Lea-494
❑ 93OPCPre-9
❑ 93Pin-444
❑ 93RanKee-315
❑ 93RedSoxP-29
❑ 93Sco-413
❑ 93Sel-365
❑ 93SelRoo-7T
❑ 93SP-204
❑ 93StaClu-635
❑ 93StaCluFDI-635
❑ 93StaCluMOP-635
❑ 93Top-736
❑ 93TopGol-736
❑ 93TopInaM-736
❑ 93TopInaR-736
❑ 93TopMic-736
❑ 93TopTra-25T
❑ 93Ult-516
❑ 93UppDec-702
❑ 93UppDecGold-702
❑ 94ColC-583
❑ 94ColChoGS-583
❑ 94ColChoSS-583
❑ 94Don-248
❑ 94Fin-90
❑ 94FinPre-90P
❑ 94FinRef-90
❑ 94Fle-41
❑ 94FleExtB-23
❑ 94Lea-336
❑ 94OPC-113
❑ 94Pac-65
❑ 94Pin-46
❑ 94PinArtP-46
❑ 94PinMusC-46
❑ 94RanAllP-16
❑ 94RanAllP-17
❑ 94Sco-529
❑ 94ScoGolR-529
❑ 94Sel-272
❑ 94StaClu-710
❑ 94StaCluFDI-710
❑ 94StaCluGR-710
❑ 94StaCluMOP-710
❑ 94Top-55
❑ 94TopGol-55
❑ 94TopSpa-55
❑ 94TriPla-206
❑ 94Ult-17
❑ 94UppDec-213
❑ 94UppDecED-213
❑ 95ColCho-271
❑ 95ColChoGS-271
❑ 95ColChoSS-271
❑ 95DonTopotO-167
❑ 95Fla-310
❑ 95Fle-146
❑ 95FleUpd-86
❑ 95RanCra-30
❑ 95TopTra-89T
❑ 96ColCho-344
❑ 96ColChoGS-344
❑ 96ColChoSS-344
❑ 96Don-201
❑ 96DonPreP-201
❑ 96Fle-262
❑ 96FleTif-262
❑ 96Pac-430
❑ 96RanDr P-28
❑ 97PacPriGotD-GD99

Russell, Jim
❑ 47TipTop-146
❑ 49Bow-235
❑ 49EurSta-20
❑ 50Bow-223
❑ 52MotCoo-52
❑ 52Top-51
❑ 83TCMPla1944-27
❑ 83TopRep5-51
❑ 90DodTar-698
❑ 95TopArcBD-6

Russell, Joe
❑ 75AndRanT-46
❑ 76AshTouT-1
❑ 79TulDriT-2
❑ 81TulDriT-27

Russell, John
❑ 15Zee-53
❑ 20Zee-35
❑ 83PorBeaT-17
❑ 84PhiTas-42
❑ 84PorBeaC-208
❑ 85Don-648
❑ 85Fle-653
❑ 85PhiTas-11
❑ 85PhiTas-31
❑ 86Don-82
❑ 86Fle-448
❑ 86PhiCIG-14
❑ 86PhiTas-6
❑ 86Top-392
❑ 86TopTif-392
❑ 87Don-207
❑ 87Fle-184
❑ 87FleGlo-184
❑ 87PhiTas-6
❑ 87Top-379
❑ 87TopTif-379
❑ 88MaiPhiC-12
❑ 88MaiPhiP-285
❑ 88PhiTas-37
❑ 88Top-188
❑ 88TopTif-188
❑ 89BraDub-21
❑ 89UppDec-532
❑ 90CMC-161
❑ 90DodTar-699
❑ 90Don-458
❑ 90OklCit8C-11
❑ 90OklCit8P-436
❑ 90ProAAAF-682
❑ 90PubIntS-120
❑ 90RanMot-26
❑ 90TopTra-107T
❑ 90TopTraT-107T
❑ 91Fle-301
❑ 91OPC-734
❑ 91RanMot-26
❑ 91Sco-802
❑ 91StaClu-474
❑ 91Top-734
❑ 91TopDesS-734
❑ 91TopMic-734
❑ 91TopTif-734
❑ 91UppDec-191
❑ 92Sco-339
❑ 92StaClu-846
❑ 92StaCluECN-846
❑ 92TulDriF-2699
❑ 92TulDriS-618
❑ 93PacSpa-647
❑ 93RanKee-430
❑ 93RanStaC-23
❑ 96FtMyeMB-1
❑ 97ForMyeM-1
❑ 98NewBriRCM-1

Russell, LaGrande
❑ 91BelMarCB-28
❑ 92PenPilC-12
❑ 92PenPilF-2931
❑ 93Bow-403
❑ 93JacSunF-2712
❑ 95PorCitRTI-23
❑ 96PorCitRB-24
❑ 97OrlRayB-21

Russell, Larry
❑ 88CapCodPPaLP-28

Russell, Matt
❑ 89BenBucL-25
❑ 90BenBucL-31

Russell, Mike
❑ 94StaCluDP-7
❑ 94StaCluDPFDI-7

Russell, Reb (Ewell A.)
❑ 14CraJacE-15
❑ 14PolGroW-24
❑ 15CraJacE-15
❑ 15SpoNewM-150
❑ 16BF2FP-17
❑ 16SpoNewM-150
❑ 17ColE13-146A
❑ 17ColE13-146B
❑ 18WhiSoxTI-20
❑ 75WhiSox1T-22
❑ 92ConTSN-482
❑ 92Man191BSR-21

Russell, Richard
❑ 91BelMarP-3662

Russell, Rip (Glen David)
❑ 39CubTeal-22
❑ 39ExhSal-55
❑ 42CubTeal-20
❑ 46RedSoxTI-20
❑ 47RedSoxTI-21
❑ 47TipTop-12
❑ 75RedSox1T-32
❑ 93ConTSN-727

Russell, Rob
❑ 85PriWilPT-7
❑ 86PriWilPP-23
❑ 87HarSenP-12
❑ 88HarSenP-858
❑ 89HarSenP-303
❑ 89HarSenS-16

Russell, Ron
❑ 86DayBealP-24

Russell, Todd
❑ 90BenBucL-14
❑ 91MadMusC-1

Russell, Tony
❑ 83GreHorT-26
❑ 85AlbYanT-21
❑ 86AlbYanT-10
❑ 87AlbYanP-2

Russin, Tom
❑ 98VisOakG-27

Russo, Dennis
❑ 98BilMusTI-29

Russo, Marius
❑ 41DouPlaR-111
❑ 43YanSta-22
❑ 75YanDyn1T-40
❑ 79DiaGre-14
❑ 83YanASFY-38
❑ 89SweBasG-101
❑ 92YanWIZA-71

Russo, Pat
❑ 91KenTwiC-15
❑ 91KenTwiP-2073

Russo, Paul
❑ 90EliTwiS-20
❑ 91Bow-695
❑ 91Cla/Bes-344
❑ 91KenTwiP-2085
❑ 92ClaFS7-203
❑ 92OPC-473
❑ 92OrlSunRF-2856
❑ 92OrlSunRS-519
❑ 92SkyAA F-226
❑ 92Top-473
❑ 92TopGol-473
❑ 92TopGolW-473
❑ 92TopMic-473
❑ 93ClaFS7-18
❑ 93ClaGolF-94
❑ 93PorBeaF-2390
❑ 94SalLakBF-825
❑ 95MemChiTI-27
❑ 96LasVegSB-21
❑ 97ColCliB-27
❑ 97ColCliD-24
❑ 98NewOrlZM-22

Russo, Tony
❑ 87EriCarP-16
❑ 88SavCarP-333
❑ 89St.PetCS-23

Russoniello, Michael
❑ 97BoiHawG-24

Rust, Brian
❑ 95EugEmeTI-8
❑ 96EugEmeB-22
❑ 97DurBulTI-24
❑ 98GreBraG-22

Rusteck, Dick
❑ 77FriOneYW-43
❑ 81TCM60I-420
❑ 91MetWIZ-337

Ruszkowski, Hank
❑ 47IndTeal-23
❑ 47IndVanPP-22

Ruth, Babe (George Herman)
❑ 14BalIntR-1
❑ 15SpoNewM-151
❑ 16SpoNewM-151
❑ 17ColE13-147
❑ 17HolBreD-87
❑ 19W514-2
❑ 20NatCarE-86
❑ 20W516-1
❑ 20W52-13
❑ 21E121So1-86A
❑ 21E121So1-86B
❑ 21E121So1-86C
❑ 21E121So1-86D
❑ 21E121So1-86E
❑ 21E121So8-82A
❑ 21E121So8-82B
❑ 21E121So8-82C
❑ 21Exh-148
❑ 21Exh-149
❑ 21KoBreWSI-49
❑ 21Nei-37
❑ 21OxfConE-15
❑ 21PatRut-1
❑ 22AmeCarE122-57
❑ 22E120-71
❑ 22W572-88
❑ 22W573-112
❑ 22W575-112
❑ 22WilPatV-25
❑ 23Lec-7
❑ 23MapCriV-8
❑ 23W501-49
❑ 23W503-32
❑ 23W515-3
❑ 23W515-47
❑ 23W551-7
❑ 23WilChoV-139
❑ 24MrsShePP-7
❑ 25Exh-100
❑ 26Exh-102
❑ 26SpoComoA-36
❑ 26SpoNewSM-2
❑ 27AmeCarE126-38
❑ 27Exh-52
❑ 27YorCarE-6
❑ 28BabRCCE-1
❑ 28BabRCCE-2
❑ 28BabRCCE-3
❑ 28BabRCCE-4
❑ 28BabRCCE-5
❑ 28BabRCCE-6
❑ 28Exh-51
❑ 28FroJoy-1
❑ 28FroJoy-2
❑ 28FroJoy-3
❑ 28FroJoy-4
❑ 28FroJoy-5
❑ 28FroJoy-6
❑ 28PorandAR-A31
❑ 28PorandAR-B31
❑ 28StaPlaCE-57
❑ 28W502-6
❑ 28W512-6
❑ 28W56PlaC-JOK
❑ 28Yue-6
❑ 29ExhFou-26
❑ 29PorandAR-79
❑ 30SchR33-26
❑ 30SchR33-42
❑ 30UncJac-24
❑ 30W554-15
❑ 31Exh-26
❑ 31W517-4
❑ 31W517-20
❑ 32R33So2-402
❑ 32USCar*-32
❑ 33ButCanV-41
❑ 33ButCre-23
❑ 33ExhFou-13
❑ 33Gou-53
❑ 33Gou-144
❑ 33Gou-149
❑ 33Gou-181
❑ 33GouCanV-80
❑ 33GouCanV-93
❑ 33RitCE-1S
❑ 33RitCE-13C
❑ 33SpoKin-2
❑ 33WorCig-81
❑ 34BabRutG-54
❑ 34ButPreR-53
❑ 34ExhFou-13
❑ 34GouCanV-28
❑ 34GouPreR-4
❑ 35AlDemDCR3-4
❑ 35ClaBreD3-4
❑ 35ExhFou-1
❑ 35GouPuzR-1J
❑ 35GouPuzR-3A
❑ 35GouPuzR-14A
❑ 35GouPuzR-15A
❑ 35QuaBabRP-1
❑ 36Halof FP-21
❑ 36NatChiFPR-84
❑ 38QuaOatR-1
❑ 39PC7AlbHoF-4
❑ 46SpoExcW-8-4
❑ 47PM1StaP1-192
❑ 48BabRutS-1
❑ 48BabRutS-25
❑ 48BabRutS-26
❑ 48BabRutS-27
❑ 48BabRutS-28
❑ 48BaeRutSP-1
❑ 48ExhHoF-25A
❑ 48ExhHoF-25B
❑ 48SweSpoT-12
❑ 49Lea-3
❑ 49LeaPre-7
❑ 50CalHOFW-63
❑ 50H80FouMH-3
❑ 51R42SmaS-92
❑ 51TopConMA-9
❑ 53ArtHaloFP-74
❑ 56TopHocF-B1
❑ 58HarSta-2
❑ 58JayPubAG-9
❑ 59FleWil-2
❑ 59FleWil-75
❑ 60ExhWriH-20
❑ 60Fle-3
❑ 60KeyChal-41
❑ 60NuHi-1
❑ 60NuHi-16
❑ 60NuHi-47
❑ 60RawGloT-28
❑ 61Fle-75
❑ 61GolPre-3
❑ 61NuSco-447
❑ 61NuSco-455
❑ 61Top-401
❑ 62Top-135
❑ 62Top-136
❑ 62Top-137
❑ 62Top-138
❑ 62Top-139A
❑ 62Top-140
❑ 62Top-141
❑ 62Top-142
❑ 62Top-143
❑ 62Top-144
❑ 62TopVen-135
❑ 62TopVen-136
❑ 62TopVen-137
❑ 62TopVen-138
❑ 62TopVen-139
❑ 62TopVen-140
❑ 62TopVen-141
❑ 62TopVen-142
❑ 62TopVen-143
❑ 62TopVen-144
❑ 63BasMagM-73
❑ 63BazA-17
❑ 63GadFunC-1
❑ 63GadFunC-34
❑ 63HalofFB-16
❑ 66AurSpoMK-4
❑ 67TopVen-147
❑ 68AtlOil-10
❑ 68LauWorS-12
❑ 68LauWorS-13
❑ 68LauWorS-20
❑ 68LauWorS-25
❑ 68LauWorS-29
❑ 68SCFOldT-1
❑ 68SpoMemAG-11
❑ 69Baz-5
❑ 69Baz-9
❑ 69Baz-10
❑ 69Baz-11
❑ 69EquSpoHoF-BB20
❑ 70FleWorS-12
❑ 70FleWorS-13
❑ 70FleWorS-20
❑ 70FleWorS-25
❑ 70FleWorS-29
❑ 70Houof J-25
❑ 70MetMusoAB-6
❑ 70SpoCarfCOP-1
❑ 70SpoCarfCOP-8
❑ 70SpoCarfCOP-31
❑ 70SpoCarfCOP-32
❑ 71FleWorS-16
❑ 71FleWorS-30
❑ 72FleFamF-20
❑ 72KelATG-6
❑ 72KelATG-14
❑ 72LauGreF-32
❑ 73BooProC-11
❑ 73BooProC-17
❑ 73HalofFPP-15
❑ 73OPC-1
❑ 73OPC-474
❑ 73SevTraC-65
❑ 73SyrChiTI-24
❑ 73Top-1
❑ 73Top-474
❑ 74CapPub-1
❑ 74LauAllG-33
❑ 74SyrChiTI-23
❑ 74TCMNic-2
❑ 75SyrChiTI-17
❑ 75TCMAllG-30
❑ 75TCMAllG-31
❑ 75TCMHouoJ-27
❑ 75Yan192T-23
❑ 75YanAllTT-11
❑ 76ChePri-3
❑ 76GalBasGHoF-25
❑ 76LauDiaJ-32
❑ 76MotOldT-9
❑ 76OPC-345
❑ 76RowExh-16
❑ 76ShaPiz-2
❑ 76TayBow4-3
❑ 76TayBow4-49
❑ 76TayBow4-113
❑ 76Top-345
❑ 77BobParHoF-42
❑ 77BobParMBC-1
❑ 77BobParMBC-17
❑ 77GalGloG-69
❑ 77GalGloG-91
❑ 77GalGloG-165
❑ 77GalGloG-193
❑ 77GalGloG-227
❑ 77SerSta-21
❑ 77ShaPiz-20
❑ 77Spo-511
❑ 77Spo-6818
❑ 78DexHaloFP-43
❑ 79Pew-14
❑ 79Yan192T-28
❑ 80FraBabR-1
❑ 80FraBabR-2
❑ 80FraBabR-3
❑ 80FraBabR-4
❑ 80FraBabR-5
❑ 80FraBabR-6
❑ 80FraBabR-7
❑ 80FraBabR-8
❑ 80FraBabR-9
❑ 80FraBabR-10
❑ 80FraBabR-11
❑ 80FraBabR-12
❑ 80FraBabR-13
❑ 80FraBabR-14
❑ 80FraBabR-15

❑ 80FraBabR-16
❑ 80FraBabR-17
❑ 80FraBabR-18
❑ 80FraBabR-19
❑ 80FraBabR-20
❑ 80FraBabR-21
❑ 80FraBabR-22
❑ 80FraBabR-23
❑ 80FraBabR-24
❑ 80FraBabR-25
❑ 80FraBabR-26
❑ 80FraBabR-27
❑ 80FraBabR-28
❑ 80FraBabR-29
❑ 80FraBabR-30
❑ 80FraBabR-31
❑ 80FraBabR-32
❑ 80FraBabR-33
❑ 80FraBabR-34
❑ 80FraBabR-35
❑ 80FraBabR-36
❑ 80FraBabR-37
❑ 80FraBabR-38
❑ 80FraBabR-39
❑ 80FraBabR-40
❑ 80FraBabR-41
❑ 80FraBabR-42
❑ 80FraBabR-43
❑ 80FraBabR-44
❑ 80FraBabR-45
❑ 80FraBabR-46
❑ 80FraBabR-47
❑ 80FraBabR-48
❑ 80FraBabR-49
❑ 80FraBabR-50
❑ 80FraBabR-51
❑ 80FraBabR-52
❑ 80FraBabR-53
❑ 80FraBabR-54
❑ 80FraBabR-55
❑ 80FraBabR-56
❑ 80FraBabR-57
❑ 80FraBabR-58
❑ 80FraBabR-59
❑ 80FraBabR-60
❑ 80FraBabR-61
❑ 80FraBabR-62
❑ 80FraBabR-63
❑ 80FraBabR-64
❑ 80FraBabR-65
❑ 80FraBabR-66
❑ 80FraBabR-67
❑ 80FraBabR-68
❑ 80FraBabR-69
❑ 80FraBabR-70
❑ 80FraBabR-71
❑ 80FraBabR-72
❑ 80FraBabR-73
❑ 80FraBabR-74
❑ 80FraBabR-75
❑ 80FraBabR-76
❑ 80FraBabR-77
❑ 80FraBabR-78
❑ 80FraBabR-79
❑ 80FraBabR-80
❑ 80Lau300-2
❑ 80LauFamF-16
❑ 80PacLeg-1
❑ 80PerHaloFP-4
❑ 80SSPHOF-1
❑ 80YanGreT-5
❑ 81ConTSN-4
❑ 81SpoHaloF-3
❑ 82BasCarN-20
❑ 82BHCRSpoL-2
❑ 82DavHaloFB-20
❑ 82DiaCla-13
❑ 82TCMGreH-19
❑ 82TCMGreS-18
❑ 83BigLeaCOA-20
❑ 83ConMar-17
❑ 83TCMRut-1
❑ 83TCMRut-5
❑ 83TCMRut-6
❑ 83TopSti-2
❑ 84CubBriPC-13H
❑ 84DonCha-1
❑ 84GalHaloFRL-2
❑ 84OCoandSI-90
❑ 84SpoDesPW-47
❑ 84Yan192G-2
❑ 85BigLeaC3-54
❑ 85CirK-2
❑ 85DonHOFS-1
❑ 85FegMurCG-15
❑ 85FegMurCG-16
❑ 85GeoSteM-8
❑ 85TCMPhoC-4
❑ 85TCMPhoC-8
❑ 85TCMPhoC-9
❑ 85UltBasC-3
❑ 85Woo-31
❑ 86BigLeaC-2
❑ 86ConSer1-13
❑ 86ConSer1-20
❑ 86ConSer1-48
❑ 86ConSer1-50
❑ 86ConSer1-54
❑ 86SpoDecG-1
❑ 86TCM-12
❑ 86TCMSupS-2
❑ 86TCMSupS-9
❑ 86TCMSupS-14
❑ 86TCMSupS-42
❑ 86TCMSupS-43
❑ 86TopRos-87
❑ 87HygAllG-38
❑ 87NesDreT-5
❑ 87SpoCubG-1
❑ 87SpoRea-2
❑ 87Yan192T-9
❑ 88ConAmeA-21
❑ 88ConSer3-25
❑ 88GreBasS-81
❑ 88WilMulP-5
❑ 89CadEllD-45
❑ 89CMCBasG-4
❑ 89CMCRut-1
❑ 89CMCRut-2
❑ 89CMCRut-3
❑ 89CMCRut-4
❑ 89CMCRut-5
❑ 89CMCRut-6
❑ 89CMCRut-7
❑ 89CMCRut-8
❑ 89CMCRut-9
❑ 89CMCRut-10
❑ 89CMCRut-11
❑ 89CMCRut-12
❑ 89CMCRut-13
❑ 89CMCRut-14
❑ 89CMCRut-15
❑ 89CMCRut-16
❑ 89CMCRut-17
❑ 89CMCRut-18
❑ 89CMCRut-19
❑ 89CMCRut-20
❑ 89CMCRut-P1
❑ 89DodSmoG-26
❑ 89HOFStiB-47
❑ 89PacLegI-176
❑ 89SpoIllFKI-216
❑ 89SweBasG-1
❑ 89TopBasT-20
❑ 89USPLegSC-4
❑ 89YanCitAG-5
❑ 90BasWit-86
❑ 90Col-10
❑ 90HOFStiB-25
❑ 90PerGreM-1
❑ 90SweBasG-10
❑ 90YanMomPRP-2
❑ 91CadEllD-44
❑ 91ConTSN-110
❑ 91ConTSN-145
❑ 91ConTSNP-145
❑ 91DenBal-3
❑ 91HomCooC-1
❑ 91SweBasG-124
❑ 91USGamSBL-2C
❑ 91USGamSBL-2D
❑ 91USGamSBL-2H
❑ 91USGamSBL-2S
❑ 92ConTSN-426
❑ 92ConTSN1N-663
❑ 92ConTSNAP-663G
❑ 92ConTSNCI-4
❑ 92DelRut-1
❑ 92GolEntR-1
❑ 92GolEntR-2
❑ 92GolEntR-3
❑ 92GolEntR-4
❑ 92GolEntR-5
❑ 92MegRut-1
❑ 92MegRut-2
❑ 92MegRut-3
❑ 92MegRut-4
❑ 92MegRut-5
❑ 92MegRut-6
❑ 92MegRut-7
❑ 92MegRut-8
❑ 92MegRut-9
❑ 92MegRut-10
❑ 92MegRut-11
❑ 92MegRut-12
❑ 92MegRut-13
❑ 92MegRut-14
❑ 92MegRut-15
❑ 92MegRut-16
❑ 92MegRut-17
❑ 92MegRut-18
❑ 92MegRut-19
❑ 92MegRut-20
❑ 92MegRut-21
❑ 92MegRut-22
❑ 92MegRut-23
❑ 92MegRut-24
❑ 92MegRut-25
❑ 92MegRut-26
❑ 92MegRut-27
❑ 92MegRut-28
❑ 92MegRut-29
❑ 92MegRut-30
❑ 92MegRut-31
❑ 92MegRut-32
❑ 92MegRut-33
❑ 92MegRut-34
❑ 92MegRut-35
❑ 92MegRut-36
❑ 92MegRut-37
❑ 92MegRut-38
❑ 92MegRut-39
❑ 92MegRut-40
❑ 92MegRut-41
❑ 92MegRut-42
❑ 92MegRut-43
❑ 92MegRut-44
❑ 92MegRut-45
❑ 92MegRut-46
❑ 92MegRut-47
❑ 92MegRut-48
❑ 92MegRut-49
❑ 92MegRut-50
❑ 92MegRut-51
❑ 92MegRut-52
❑ 92MegRut-53
❑ 92MegRut-54
❑ 92MegRut-55
❑ 92MegRut-56
❑ 92MegRut-57
❑ 92MegRut-58
❑ 92MegRut-59
❑ 92MegRut-60
❑ 92MegRut-61
❑ 92MegRut-62
❑ 92MegRut-63
❑ 92MegRut-64
❑ 92MegRut-65
❑ 92MegRut-66
❑ 92MegRut-67
❑ 92MegRut-68
❑ 92MegRut-69
❑ 92MegRut-70
❑ 92MegRut-71
❑ 92MegRut-72
❑ 92MegRut-73
❑ 92MegRut-74
❑ 92MegRut-75
❑ 92MegRut-76
❑ 92MegRut-77
❑ 92MegRut-78
❑ 92MegRut-79
❑ 92MegRut-80
❑ 92MegRut-81
❑ 92MegRut-82
❑ 92MegRut-83
❑ 92MegRut-84
❑ 92MegRut-85
❑ 92MegRut-86
❑ 92MegRut-87
❑ 92MegRut-88
❑ 92MegRut-89
❑ 92MegRut-90
❑ 92MegRut-91
❑ 92MegRut-92
❑ 92MegRut-93
❑ 92MegRut-94
❑ 92MegRut-95
❑ 92MegRut-96
❑ 92MegRut-97
❑ 92MegRut-98
❑ 92MegRut-99
❑ 92MegRut-100
❑ 92MegRut-101
❑ 92MegRut-102
❑ 92MegRut-103
❑ 92MegRut-104
❑ 92MegRut-105
❑ 92MegRut-106
❑ 92MegRut-107
❑ 92MegRut-108
❑ 92MegRut-109
❑ 92MegRut-110
❑ 92MegRut-111
❑ 92MegRut-112
❑ 92MegRut-113
❑ 92MegRut-114
❑ 92MegRut-115
❑ 92MegRut-116
❑ 92MegRut-117
❑ 92MegRut-118
❑ 92MegRut-119
❑ 92MegRut-120
❑ 92MegRut-121
❑ 92MegRut-122
❑ 92MegRut-123
❑ 92MegRut-124
❑ 92MegRut-125
❑ 92MegRut-126
❑ 92MegRut-127
❑ 92MegRut-128
❑ 92MegRut-129
❑ 92MegRut-130
❑ 92MegRut-131
❑ 92MegRut-132
❑ 92MegRut-133
❑ 92MegRut-134
❑ 92MegRut-135
❑ 92MegRut-136
❑ 92MegRut-137
❑ 92MegRut-138
❑ 92MegRut-139
❑ 92MegRut-140
❑ 92MegRut-141
❑ 92MegRut-142
❑ 92MegRut-143
❑ 92MegRut-144
❑ 92MegRut-145
❑ 92MegRut-146
❑ 92MegRut-147
❑ 92MegRut-148
❑ 92MegRut-149
❑ 92MegRut-150
❑ 92MegRut-151
❑ 92MegRut-152
❑ 92MegRut-153
❑ 92MegRut-154
❑ 92MegRut-155
❑ 92MegRut-156
❑ 92MegRut-157
❑ 92MegRut-158
❑ 92MegRut-159
❑ 92MegRut-160
❑ 92MegRut-161
❑ 92MegRut-162
❑ 92MegRut-163
❑ 92MegRutP-14
❑ 92MegRutP-31
❑ 92MegRutP-75
❑ 92MegRutP-106
❑ 92MegRutP-124
❑ 92MegRutP-129
❑ 92MegRutP-134
❑ 92MegRutP-138
❑ 92MegRutP-154
❑ 92PMGolRP-1
❑ 92Sco-879
❑ 92St.VinHHS-9
❑ 92TVSpoMF5HRC-12
❑ 92WhiLegtL-3
❑ 92WhiPro-3
❑ 92YanWIZA-72
❑ 92YanWIZH-29
❑ 93ActPacA-94
❑ 93ActPacA2-28G
❑ 93Ble-37
❑ 93CadDis-47
❑ 93ConMasB-2
❑ 93ConMasC-5
❑ 93ConTSN-663
❑ 93ConTSN-888
❑ 93ConTSNP-888
❑ 93Hoy-6
❑ 93LegFoi-9
❑ 93LegFoiHI-1
❑ 93SpeHOFI-1
❑ 93TedWil-121
❑ 93TedWilLC-6
❑ 93UppDecAH-110
❑ 93UppDecAH-131
❑ 93UppDecAH-133
❑ 93UppDecAH-134
❑ 93UppDecAH-146
❑ 93UppDecAH-149
❑ 93UppDecAH-151
❑ 93UppDecAH-152
❑ 94ConTSN-1080
❑ 94ConTSNB-1080
❑ 94ConTSNCI-33
❑ 94ConTSNCI-35
❑ 94MegRutS-1
❑ 94MegRutS-2
❑ 94MegRutS-3
❑ 94MegRutS-4
❑ 94MegRutS-5
❑ 94TedWil5C-6
❑ 94TedWilTfB-T1
❑ 94TedWilTfB-T2
❑ 94TedWilTfB-T3
❑ 94TedWilTfB-T4
❑ 94TedWilTfB-T5
❑ 94TedWilTfB-T6
❑ 94TedWilTfB-T7
❑ 94TedWilTfB-T8
❑ 94TedWilTfB-T9
❑ 94UppDecAH-60
❑ 94UppDecAH-110
❑ 94UppDecAH-165
❑ 94UppDecAH1-60
❑ 94UppDecAH1-110
❑ 94UppDecAH1-165
❑ 94UppDecAJ-45
❑ 94UppDecAJG-45
❑ 94UppDecTAE-30
❑ 94UppDecTAE-BC3
❑ 94UppDecTAEGM-8
❑ 95ConTSN-1405
❑ 95ConTSN-NNO
❑ 95ConTSNGJ-1
❑ 95ConTSNP-3C
❑ 95ConTSNP-1535
❑ 95MegRut-1
❑ 95MegRut-2
❑ 95MegRut-3
❑ 95MegRut-4
❑ 95MegRut-5
❑ 95MegRut-6
❑ 95MegRut-7
❑ 95MegRut-8
❑ 95MegRut-9
❑ 95MegRut-10
❑ 95MegRut-11
❑ 95MegRut-12
❑ 95MegRut-13
❑ 95MegRut-14
❑ 95MegRut-15
❑ 95MegRut-16
❑ 95MegRut-17
❑ 95MegRut-18
❑ 95MegRut-19
❑ 95MegRut-20
❑ 95MegRut-21
❑ 95MegRut-22
❑ 95MegRut-23
❑ 95MegRut-24
❑ 95MegRut-25
❑ 95Top-3
❑ 95UppDecRH-73
❑ 95UppDecRH-74
❑ 95UppDecRH-75
❑ 95UppDecRH-76
❑ 95UppDecRH-77
❑ 95UppDecRH-78
❑ 95UppDecRH-79
❑ 95UppDecRH-80
❑ 95UppDecRH-81
❑ 95UppDecRH-NNO
❑ 95UppDecSHoB-3
❑ 96BalHOF1C-4
❑ 96ColCho-500
❑ 96ColChoGS-500
❑ 96ColChoSS-500
❑ 96MetImpR-1
❑ 96MetImpR-2
❑ 96MetImpR-3
❑ 96MetImpR-4
❑ 96MetImpR-5
❑ 97FleMilDM-3
❑ 97FleMilDMR-3
❑ 97HigMinMSM-19
❑ 97HigMinMSM-20
❑ 97HigMinMSM-21
❑ 98SpoIllWSFAE-3
❑ 98SpoIllWSFAEG-3
❑ 98UppDecRLC-#LC
❑ 99SP SigLC-BR
❑ 99SpoIllGotG-3
❑ 99SpoIllGotGRB-3
❑ 99SpoIllGotGRBG-3
❑ 99UppDecAP-BR
❑ 99UppDecAPoH-PH
❑ 99UppDecAPoH-LCPH
❑ 99UppDecBD-90
❑ 99UppDecBDD-90
❑ 99UppDecBDDom-D30
❑ 99UppDecBDDomE-D30
❑ 99UppDecBDMN-M1
❑ 99UppDecBDMNE-M1
❑ 99UppDecBDQ-90
❑ 99UppDecBDT-90
❑ 99UppDecCL-1
❑ 99UppDecCL-S1
❑ 99UppDecCLA-1910
❑ 99UppDecCLCC-1
❑ 99UppDecCLJotC-AC1
❑ 99UppDecCLLC-BR
❑ 99UppDecCLMS-HR1
❑ 99UppDecR-104
❑ 99UppDecRG-104
❑ 99UppDecRL-7
❑ 99UppDecRL-12
❑ 99UppDecRL-14
❑ 99UppDecRL-16
❑ 99UppDecRP-104

Ruth, Claire
❑ 92MegRut-121

Ruth, Dorothy
❑ 92MegRut-151

Ruth, Helen
❑ 92MegRut-120

Ruth, Julia
❑ 92MegRut-152
❑ 92MegRut-153

Ruth, Pat
❑ 85CloHSS-37
❑ 89FreStaBS-18
❑ 91BatCliCB-4
❑ 91BatCliP-3486
❑ 92ClaFS7-265
❑ 92SpaPhiF-1277
❑ 93SpaPhiC-23

Rutherford, Daryl
❑ 96IdaFalB-21
❑ 97IdaFalBTI-16

Rutherford, John
❑ 52Top-320
❑ 53Top-137
❑ 74dod195T-32
❑ 83TopRep5-320
❑ 90DodTar-700
❑ 91TopArc1-137
❑ 95TopArcBD-21
❑ 95TopArcBD-48

Rutherford, Mark
❑ 98ClePhiM-20
❑ 98ClePhiUM-20

Ruthven, Dick
❑ 73PhiTeal-16
❑ 74OPC-47
❑ 74Top-47
❑ 75OPC-267
❑ 75PhiProPS-13
❑ 75Top-267
❑ 75TopMin-267
❑ 76AtlBraP-29
❑ 76OPC-431
❑ 76SSP-477
❑ 76Top-431
❑ 77BurCheD-208
❑ 77Hos-74
❑ 77Top-575
❑ 78Top-75
❑ 79PhiBurK-6
❑ 79Top-419
❑ 80PhiBurK-19
❑ 80Top-136
❑ 81AllGamPI-173
❑ 81Don-153
❑ 81Fle-16
❑ 81OPC-285
❑ 81Top-691
❑ 81TopSupHT-87
❑ 82Don-525
❑ 82Fle-257
❑ 82FleSta-52
❑ 82OPC-317
❑ 82Top-317
❑ 83CubThoAV-44
❑ 83Don-497
❑ 83Fle-172
❑ 83OPC-313
❑ 83PhiTas-26
❑ 83Top-484
❑ 83TopTra-98T
❑ 84CubChiT-24
❑ 84CubSev-44

❑ 84Don-510
❑ 84Fle-503
❑ 84Nes792-736
❑ 84OPC-156
❑ 84Top-736
❑ 84TopSti-49
❑ 84TopTif-736
❑ 85CubLioP-18
❑ 85CubSev-44
❑ 85Fle-64
❑ 85OPC-268
❑ 85Top-563
❑ 85TopMin-563
❑ 85TopTif-563
❑ 86Don-564
❑ 86Fle-377
❑ 86Top-98
❑ 86TopTif-98
Rutkay, Gary
❑ 52LavPro-38
Rutledge, Jeff
❑ 82QuaCitCT-19
❑ 86PitCubP-21
Rutledge, Trey
❑ 93PriRedC-26
❑ 93PriRedF-4179
❑ 94ChaWheC-22
❑ 94ChaWheF-2703
❑ 94LSUTigMP-13
Rutter, Sam
❑ 92BelBreCB-5
❑ 92BelBreFl-404
Rutz, Ryan
❑ 94HudValRC-20
❑ 94HudValRF-3393
❑ 95ChaRivTI-13
❑ 95ChaRivUTIS-36
Ruyak, Craig
❑ 90JohCitCS-23
Ruyak, Todd
❑ 92PriRedC-12
❑ 92PriRedF-3088
❑ 93WesVirWC-22
❑ 93WesVirWF-2866
❑ 94KinIndC-16
❑ 94KinIndF-2640
Ruzek, Don
❑ 77LodDodT-15
❑ 78LodDodT-16
❑ 83AppFoxFr-27
Ryal, Mark
❑ 82OmaRoyT-21
❑ 83OmaRoyT-20
❑ 84OmaRoyT-24
❑ 85BufBisT-15
❑ 86EdmTraP-25
❑ 87AngSmo-14
❑ 87CalAngPPS-34
❑ 87Don-583
❑ 88Fle-503
❑ 88FleGlo-503
❑ 88LouRedBTI-43
❑ 88Top-243
❑ 88TopTif-243
❑ 89BlaYNPRWL-162
❑ 89PhiTas-29
❑ 90BufBisC-20
❑ 90BufBisP-383
❑ 90BufBisTI-23
❑ 90CMC-20
❑ 90ProAAAF-498
❑ 93EdmTraF-1149
Ryan, Bill
❑ 09ObaT21-332
❑ 11Zee-99
❑ 12ObaPreT-81
❑ 20GasAmeMBD-32
❑ 21E121So1-87
❑ 21E121So8-80
❑ 23W503-5
Ryan, Blondy (John C.)
❑ 30WhiSoxTI-22
❑ 33ButCanV-42
❑ 33WorCig-82
❑ 34BabRutG-55
❑ 34DiaMatCSB-159
❑ 34DiaStaR-40
❑ 34ExhFou-5
❑ 34Gou-32
❑ 34GouCanV-73
❑ 35AlDemDCR3-84
❑ 35ExhFou-6
❑ 81ConTSN-25
❑ 93ConTSN-694
Ryan, Bobby
❑ 90WatIndS-18
❑ 91RocExpC-12
❑ 91RocExpP-2047
❑ 92SalLakTSP-22
Ryan, Colin
❑ 88CapCodPPaLP-71
❑ 89EugEmeB-13
❑ 90AppFoxBS-22
❑ 90AppFoxP-2098
❑ 91BasCitRC-15
❑ 91BasCitRP-1401
❑ 91Cla/Bes-130
Ryan, Connie
❑ 47TipTop-84
❑ 49EurSta-19
❑ 51Bow-216
❑ 52Bow-164
❑ 52DixLid-17
❑ 52DixPre-17
❑ 52Top-107
❑ 53BowC-131
❑ 53NorBreL-26
❑ 53Top-102
❑ 54Top-136
❑ 58SeaRalT-15
❑ 74OPC-634
❑ 74Top-634
❑ 75TCMGua-14
❑ 79DiaGre-222
❑ 80Bra195T-35
❑ 83TCMPla1944-40
❑ 83TopRep5-107
❑ 91JesHSA-3
❑ 91TopArc1-102
❑ 93RanKee-316
❑ 94TopArc1-136
❑ 94TopArc1G-136
Ryan, Craig
❑ 79VanCanT-5
❑ 80VanCanT-15
❑ 80VenLeaS-124
Ryan, Dan
❑ 09ObaT21-127
❑ 89SalLakTTI-8
Ryan, Duffy
❑ 81RedPioT-11
Ryan, Ellis
❑ 50IndTeal-23
Ryan, Jack
❑ 13Zee-20
❑ 14TexTomE-39
❑ 14Zee-23
❑ 15Zee-18
❑ 16Zee-15
❑ 17Zee-14
❑ 88SFHesCreN32-26
❑ 90DodTar-701
❑ 90DodTar-1059
❑ 98CamPepP-65
Ryan, James E.
❑ 03BreE10-125
❑ 87BucN28-23
❑ 87OldJudN-427
❑ 88AllandGN-6
❑ 88AllandGN-6
❑ 88AugBecN-29
❑ 88GandBCGCE-35
❑ 88WG1CarG-15
❑ 95May-37
Ryan, Jason
❑ 95Bow-12
❑ 95Exc-169
❑ 96Bow-256
❑ 96BowFoi-256
❑ 96OrlCubB-23
❑ 98SouLeaTPG-20
❑ 98WesTenDJM-23
Ryan, Jody
❑ 86BelMarCr-117
❑ 87WauTimP-3
❑ 88SanBerSB-7
❑ 88SanBerSCLC-42
❑ 89SanBerSB-21
❑ 89SanBerSCLC-67
Ryan, John Budd
❑ 08BufBisFJO-14
❑ 09ColChiE-248
❑ 09ColChiE-249
❑ 09ObaT21-32
❑ 09ObaT21-128
❑ 09ObaT21-300
❑ 11PacCoaBD-55
❑ 11Zee-58
❑ 12ColRedB-248
❑ 12ColRedB-249
❑ 12ColTinT-248
❑ 12ColTinT-249
❑ 12ObaPreT-49
❑ 12T207-158
❑ 14Zee-74
❑ 15Zee-88
❑ 16Zee-92
❑ 17Zee-75
❑ 18Zee-70
❑ 21Zee-84
❑ 22Zee-70
❑ 23Zee-95
❑ 25Zee-75
❑ 26Zee-125
❑ 27Zee-102
❑ 28Zee-119
❑ 29Zee-121
❑ 30Zee-130
❑ 31Zee-93
❑ 34ButPreR-54
Ryan, Ken (Kenneth Frederick)
❑ 86ElmPioRSP-18
❑ 87GreHorP-6
❑ 88LynRedSS-22
❑ 89WinHavRSS-19
❑ 90LynRedSTI-21
❑ 91WinHavRSC-8
❑ 91WinHavRSP-488
❑ 92NewBriRSF-432
❑ 92NewBriRSS-494
❑ 92SkyAA F-213
❑ 93Bow-3
❑ 93Don-383
❑ 93FleMajLP-B18
❑ 93LeaGolR-R13
❑ 93LeaGolRJ-R13
❑ 93OPCPre-41
❑ 93PawRedSDD-23
❑ 93Pin-278
❑ 93Sco-329
❑ 93SelRoo-65T
❑ 93Top-786
❑ 93TopGol-786
❑ 93TopInaM-786
❑ 93TopInaR-786
❑ 93TopMic-786
❑ 93TopTra-103T
❑ 93Ult-517
❑ 93UppDec-772
❑ 93UppDecGold-772
❑ 94ColC-248
❑ 94ColChoGS-248
❑ 94ColChoSS-248
❑ 94Don-276
❑ 94Fla-266
❑ 94Fle-42
❑ 94FleExtB-24
❑ 94SarRedSC-25
❑ 94Sco-592
❑ 94ScoGolR-592
❑ 94StaClu-404
❑ 94StaCluFDI-404
❑ 94StaCluGR-404
❑ 94StaCluMOP-404
❑ 94Top-264
❑ 94TopGol-264
❑ 94TopSpa-264
❑ 95ColCho-417
❑ 95ColChoGS-417
❑ 95ColChoSS-417
❑ 95Don-44
❑ 95DonPreP-44
❑ 95DonTopotO-25
❑ 95Fle-39
❑ 95Lea-217
❑ 95Pin-353
❑ 95PinArtP-353
❑ 95PinMusC-353
❑ 95Sco-498
❑ 95ScoGolR-498
❑ 95ScoPlaTS-498
❑ 95StaClu-81
❑ 95StaCluFDI-81
❑ 95StaCluMOP-81
❑ 95StaCluSTWS-81
❑ 95Top-63
❑ 95TopCyb-45
❑ 95TopEmb-60
❑ 95TopEmbGI-60
❑ 95Ult-15
❑ 95UltGolM-15
❑ 95UppDec-401
❑ 95UppDecED-401
❑ 95UppDecEDG-401
❑ 95UppDecSE-79
❑ 95UppDecSEG-79
❑ 96FleUpd-U169
❑ 96FleUpdTC-U169
❑ 96LeaSigA-198
❑ 96LeaSigAG-198
❑ 96LeaSigAS-198
❑ 96PhiTeal-28
❑ 97Fle-419
❑ 97FleTif-419
❑ 97PhiTeal-51
❑ 97Top-144
❑ 98PacInvGems-190
Ryan, Kevin
❑ 85AncGlaPTI-26
❑ 91BluOriC-17
❑ 91BluOriP-4128
❑ 92FreKeyC-26
❑ 92FreKeyF-1805
❑ 93BowBayF-2187
❑ 94BowBayF-2413
❑ 94OriPro-86
❑ 95BowBayTI-40
❑ 95RocRedWTI-31
Ryan, Matt
❑ 94AugGreC-21
❑ 94AugGreF-3009
❑ 95CarMudF-155
❑ 97BesAutAS-48
❑ 98NasSouTI-28
❑ 98NasSouTISS-26
Ryan, Mike
❑ 65Top-573
❑ 66RedSoxTI-11
❑ 66Top-419
❑ 67CokCapRS-9
❑ 67Top-223
❑ 67TopRedSS-14
❑ 68Top-306
❑ 68TopVen-306
❑ 69MLBOffS-177
❑ 69OPC-28
❑ 69PhiTeal-8
❑ 69Top-28
❑ 69TopTeaP-8
❑ 70MLBOffS-93
❑ 70Top-591
❑ 71MLBOffS-186
❑ 71OPC-533
❑ 71Top-533
❑ 72MilBra-302
❑ 72OPC-324
❑ 72Top-324
❑ 73OPC-467
❑ 73PhiTeal-17
❑ 73Top-467
❑ 74OPC-564
❑ 74Top-564
❑ 81RedSoxBG2S-106
❑ 84PhiTas-13
❑ 85PhiTas-6
❑ 85PhiTas-8
❑ 86PhiTas-5
❑ 87PhiTas-xx0
❑ 88PhiTas-29
❑ 88Top-669
❑ 88TopTif-669
❑ 89PhiTas-30
❑ 90PhiTas-34
❑ 92PhiMed-27
❑ 93PhiMed-30
❑ 94PhiMed-29
❑ 95Phi-27
Ryan, Mike S.
❑ 98ForWayW!-10
Ryan, Nolan
❑ 68OPC-177
❑ 68Top-177
❑ 68TopVen-177
❑ 69MetNewYDN-15
❑ 69MetTeal-12
❑ 69Top-533
❑ 70MetTra-24A
❑ 70MLBOffS-81
❑ 70OPC-197
❑ 70OPC-198
❑ 70Top-197
❑ 70Top-198
❑ 70Top-712
❑ 71MetTeal-16
❑ 71MLBOffS-162
❑ 71OPC-513
❑ 71Top-355
❑ 71Top-513
❑ 72Top-595
❑ 73BooProC-18
❑ 73Kel2D-16
❑ 73LinPor-35
❑ 73MetAllEB-9
❑ 73OPC-67
❑ 73OPC-220
❑ 73SevTraC-66
❑ 73Top-67
❑ 73Top-220
❑ 73TopCanL-45
❑ 73TopCom-17
❑ 73TopPin-17
❑ 74Kel-8
❑ 74NewYorNTDiS-15
❑ 74OPC-20
❑ 74OPC-207
❑ 74Top-20
❑ 74Top-207
❑ 74TopDecE-41
❑ 74TopPuz-9
❑ 74TopSta-147
❑ 75CalAngP-36
❑ 75Hos-58
❑ 75HosTwi-58
❑ 75Kel-26
❑ 75OPC-5
❑ 75OPC-7
❑ 75OPC-312
❑ 75OPC-500
❑ 75SSP42-10
❑ 75Top-5
❑ 75Top-7
❑ 75Top-312
❑ 75Top-500
❑ 75TopMin-5
❑ 75TopMin-7
❑ 75TopMin-312
❑ 75TopMin-500
❑ 76BlaDis-52
❑ 76BucDis-52
❑ 76CarDis-52
❑ 76CraDis-52
❑ 76DailsID-52
❑ 76Hos-79
❑ 76IsaDis-52
❑ 76LauDiaJ-1
❑ 76OPC-330
❑ 76OrbDis-52
❑ 76RedBarD-52
❑ 76SafDis-52
❑ 76SSP-187
❑ 76SSP-593A
❑ 76SSP-593B
❑ 76Top-330
❑ 76TowCluD-52
❑ 77BurCheD-123
❑ 77ChiWilD-58
❑ 77DailsID-58
❑ 77DetCaeD-58
❑ 77HollnnD-58
❑ 77Hos-81
❑ 77MSADis-58
❑ 77OPC-6
❑ 77OPC-65
❑ 77OPC-264
❑ 77PepGloD-24
❑ 77SagDis-58
❑ 77sDis-58
❑ 77Spo-216
❑ 77Spo-2304
❑ 77Top-6
❑ 77Top-234
❑ 77Top-650
❑ 77TopCloS-40
❑ 77WenDis-58
❑ 77ZipDis-58
❑ 78AngFamF-33
❑ 78Hos-83
❑ 78Kel-51
❑ 78OPC-6
❑ 78OPC-105
❑ 78OPC-241
❑ 78Pep-37
❑ 78RCColC-93
❑ 78SSP270-203
❑ 78Top-6
❑ 78Top-206
❑ 78Top-400
❑ 78WifBalD-65
❑ 79BasPat-76
❑ 79Hos-101
❑ 79OPC-51
❑ 79Top-6
❑ 79Top-115
❑ 79Top-417
❑ 79TopCom-4
❑ 80BurKinPHR-9
❑ 80Kel-20
❑ 80OPC-303
❑ 80Top-206
❑ 80Top-580
❑ 80TopSup-20
❑ 81AllGamPI-174
❑ 81AstPos-21
❑ 81CokTeaS-69
❑ 81Don-260
❑ 81Fle-57
❑ 81FleStiC-108
❑ 81Kel-6
❑ 81OPC-240
❑ 81PerCreC-26
❑ 81Top-240
❑ 81TopSti-30
❑ 81TopSti-173
❑ 81TopSupHT-101
❑ 82AstAstI-7
❑ 82AstPos-22
❑ 82Don-13
❑ 82Don-419
❑ 82FBIDis-21
❑ 82Fle-229
❑ 82FleSta-42
❑ 82FleSta-242
❑ 82Kel-11
❑ 82OPC-90
❑ 82SevSluC-23
❑ 82Top-5
❑ 82Top-66
❑ 82Top-90
❑ 82Top-167
❑ 82TopSti-13
❑ 82TopSti-41
❑ 82TopStiV-41
❑ 83AllGamPI-175
❑ 83AstPos-25
❑ 83Don-118
❑ 83DonActA-23
❑ 83Fle-463
❑ 83FleSta-170
❑ 83FleSti-141
❑ 83FleSti-207
❑ 83Kel-31
❑ 83KelCerB-2
❑ 83OPC-360
❑ 83OPC-361
❑ 83Top-360
❑ 83Top-361
❑ 83TopFol-1
❑ 83TopGloS-28
❑ 83TopSti-235
❑ 84AllGamPI-86
❑ 84AstMot-1
❑ 84AstPos-24
❑ 84Don-60
❑ 84DonActAS-14
❑ 84DonCha-39
❑ 84Fle-239
❑ 84FleSti-82
❑ 84FunFooP-109
❑ 84Nes792-4
❑ 84Nes792-66
❑ 84Nes792-470
❑ 84Nes792-707
❑ 84OCoandSI-7
❑ 84OCoandSI-211
❑ 84OCoandSI-244
❑ 84OPC-66
❑ 84RalPur-14
❑ 84RawGloT-3
❑ 84SevCoi-W13
❑ 84Top-4
❑ 84Top-66
❑ 84Top-470
❑ 84Top-707
❑ 84TopCer-14
❑ 84TopGaloC-10
❑ 84TopGloS-15
❑ 84TopPewB-7
❑ 84TopRubD-26
❑ 84TopSti-66
❑ 84TopSup-28
❑ 84TopTif-4
❑ 84TopTif-66
❑ 84TopTif-470
❑ 84TopTif-707
❑ 85AllGamPI-175
❑ 85AngStrH-11
❑ 85AstHouP-3
❑ 85AstMot-2
❑ 85Don-60
❑ 85DonActA-20
❑ 85DonHig-22
❑ 85Fle-359
❑ 85FleLimE-30
❑ 85FleStaS-115

❑ 85Lea-216
❑ 85OPC-63
❑ 85SevCoi-C1
❑ 85SevCoi-S3
❑ 85StaRya-1
❑ 85StaRya-2
❑ 85StaRya-3
❑ 85StaRya-4
❑ 85StaRya-5
❑ 85StaRya-6
❑ 85StaRya-7
❑ 85StaRya-8
❑ 85StaRya-9
❑ 85StaRya-10
❑ 85StaRya-11
❑ 85StaRya-12
❑ 85Top-7
❑ 85Top-760
❑ 85TopMin-760
❑ 85TopRubD-26
❑ 85TopSti-58
❑ 85TopSup-23
❑ 85TopTif-7
❑ 85TopTif-760
❑ 85Woo-32
❑ 86AstMilL-18
❑ 86AstMot-23
❑ 86AstPol-2
❑ 86AstTeal-13
❑ 86BasStaB-94
❑ 86Don-258
❑ 86DonAll-21
❑ 86Dra-33
❑ 86Fle-310
❑ 86FleFutHoF-5
❑ 86FleMin-65
❑ 86FleSlu-30
❑ 86FleStiC-102
❑ 86Lea-132
❑ 86MSAJifPD-13
❑ 86OPC-100
❑ 86QuaGra-12
❑ 86SevCoi-C8
❑ 86SevCoi-E8
❑ 86SevCoi-S8
❑ 86SevCoi-W8
❑ 86Spo-43
❑ 86Spo-141
❑ 86Spo-143
❑ 86Spo-182
❑ 86SpoDecG-63
❑ 86Top-100
❑ 86TopGloS-45
❑ 86TopMinL-43
❑ 86TopSti-9
❑ 86TopSti-24
❑ 86TopSup-47
❑ 86TopTat-24
❑ 86TopTif-100
❑ 86TruVal-26
❑ 87AstMot-8
❑ 87AstPol-16
❑ 87AstShoSPT-15
❑ 87AstShoSPT-16
❑ 87AstShoSPT-23
❑ 87ClaGam-82
❑ 87Don-138
❑ 87DonHig-53
❑ 87Dra-32.
❑ 87Fle-67
❑ 87FleBasA-38
❑ 87FleGlo-67
❑ 87FleStiC-103
❑ 87K-M-20
❑ 87KraFoo-48
❑ 87Lea-257
❑ 87MandMSL-22
❑ 87OPC-155
❑ 87RalPur-1
❑ 87RedFolSB-121
❑ 87Spo-125
❑ 87SpoRea-22
❑ 87SpoTeaP-8
❑ 87StuPan-5
❑ 87Top-757
❑ 87TopCoi-40
❑ 87TopSti-27
❑ 87TopTif-757
❑ 88AstMot-8
❑ 88AstPol-20
❑ 88ClaRed-179
❑ 88Don-61
❑ 88DonBasB-232
❑ 88Fle-455
❑ 88FleBasA-34
❑ 88FleGlo-455
❑ 88FleMin-79
❑ 88FleStiC-88
❑ 88GreBasS-22
❑ 88HouSho-12
❑ 88K-M-23
❑ 88Lea-77
❑ 88Nes-43
❑ 88OPC-250
❑ 88OPCBoxB-N
❑ 88PanSti-288
❑ 88PanSti-435
❑ 88Sco-575
❑ 88ScoGlo-575
❑ 88Spo-39
❑ 88StaLinAl-27
❑ 88StaLinAst-15
❑ 88TarPla-34
❑ 88Top-6
❑ 88Top-250
❑ 88Top-661
❑ 88TopBig-29
❑ 88TopCoi-50
❑ 88TopGaloC-11
❑ 88TopMinL-50
❑ 88TopRevLL-8
❑ 88TopSti-7
❑ 88TopTif-6
❑ 88TopTif-250
❑ 88TopTif-661
❑ 88TopUKM-62
❑ 88TopUKMT-62
❑ 88TopWaxBC-N
❑ 88Woo-6
❑ 89AngSmo-7
❑ 89BesWesR-NNO
❑ 89Bow-225
❑ 89BowTif-225
❑ 89CadEllD-46
❑ 89ClaTraP-164
❑ 89Don-154
❑ 89DonBasB-55
❑ 89DonTra-19
❑ 89Fle-368
❑ 89FleGlo-368
❑ 89FleUpd-67
❑ 89KinDis-10
❑ 89MetRinP69-24
❑ 89OPC-366
❑ 89OPCBoxB-K
❑ 89PanSti-83
❑ 89PanSti-226
❑ 89RanMot-2
❑ 89RanSmo-29
❑ 89RedFolSB-100
❑ 89Sco-300
❑ 89ScoHot1S-64
❑ 89Scomast-5
❑ 89ScoRoo-2T
❑ 89Spo-115
❑ 89SpollIFKI-81
❑ 89Top-530
❑ 89TopBasT-70
❑ 89TopMinL-14
❑ 89TopSti-20
❑ 89TopTif-530
❑ 89TopTra-106T
❑ 89TopTraT-106T
❑ 89TopWaxBC-K
❑ 89UppDec-145
❑ 89UppDec-669
❑ 89UppDec-774
❑ 90AllBasT-16
❑ 90BasWit-55
❑ 90Bow-486
❑ 90BowIns-8
❑ 90BowInsL-8
❑ 90BowInsT-8
❑ 90BowTif-486
❑ 90BowTif-A8
❑ 90ClaBlu-1
❑ 90ClaUpd-T26
❑ 90ClaYel-T84
❑ 90ClaYel-T91
❑ 90ClaYel-NNO0
❑ 90Col-14
❑ 90Don-166
❑ 90Don-659
❑ 90Don-659A
❑ 90Don-665
❑ 90Don-665A
❑ 90Don-665C
❑ 90DonBesA-49
❑ 90DonLeaS-24
❑ 90DonPre-7
❑ 90DonSupD-NNO
❑ 90Fle-313
❑ 90Fle-636
❑ 90FleAwaW-29
❑ 90FleCan-313
❑ 90FleCan-636
❑ 90FleLeaL-31
❑ 90FleLeaLC-31
❑ 90FleUpd-131
❑ 90GooHumICBLS-17
❑ 90HOFStiB-77
❑ 90Hot50PS-35
❑ 90K-M-25
❑ 90KayB-28
❑ 90KinDis-22
❑ 90Lea-21
❑ 90Lea-264
❑ 90Lea-265
❑ 90M.Vpin-103
❑ 90MotRya-1
❑ 90MotRya-2
❑ 90MotRya-3
❑ 90MotRya-4
❑ 90MSAIceTD-20
❑ 90OPC-1
❑ 90OPC-2
❑ 90OPC-3
❑ 90OPC-4
❑ 90OPC-5
❑ 90OPCBoxB-O
❑ 90PanSti-160
❑ 90PanSti-185
❑ 90PanSti-387
❑ 90Pos-11
❑ 90PubIntS-421
❑ 90RanMot-2
❑ 90RedFolSB-81
❑ 90RinPosR1-1
❑ 90RinPosR1-2
❑ 90RinPosR1-3
❑ 90RinPosR1-4
❑ 90RinPosR1-5
❑ 90RinPosR1-6
❑ 90RinPosR1-7
❑ 90RinPosR1-8
❑ 90RinPosR1-9
❑ 90RinPosR1-10
❑ 90RinPosR1-11
❑ 90RinPosR1-12
❑ 90RinPosR2-1
❑ 90RinPosR2-2
❑ 90RinPosR2-3
❑ 90RinPosR2-4
❑ 90RinPosR2-5
❑ 90RinPosR2-6
❑ 90RinPosR2-7
❑ 90RinPosR2-8
❑ 90RinPosR2-9
❑ 90RinPosR2-10
❑ 90RinPosR2-11
❑ 90RinPosR2-12
❑ 90RyaArlYP-1
❑ 90Sco-250
❑ 90Sco-696
❑ 90Sco100S-44
❑ 90ScoSpoR-NNO
❑ 90Spo-8
❑ 90StaLonJS-13
❑ 90StaLonJS-26
❑ 90StaRya-1
❑ 90StaRya-2
❑ 90StaRya-3
❑ 90StaRya-4
❑ 90StaRya-5
❑ 90StaRya-6
❑ 90StaRya-7
❑ 90StaRya-8
❑ 90StaRya-9
❑ 90StaRya-10
❑ 90StaRya-11
❑ 90SupActM-5
❑ 90Top-1
❑ 90Top-2
❑ 90Top-3
❑ 90Top-4
❑ 90Top-5
❑ 90TopBig-171
❑ 90TopCoi-25
❑ 90TopDou-53
❑ 90TopGaloC-9
❑ 90TopGloS-2
❑ 90TopMag-10
❑ 90TopMag-109
❑ 90TopMag-110
❑ 90TopMag-111
❑ 90TopMag-112
❑ 90TopMinL-39
❑ 90TopSti-3
❑ 90TopSti-242
❑ 90TopStiB-58
❑ 90TopTif-1
❑ 90TopTif-2
❑ 90TopTif-3
❑ 90TopTif-4
❑ 90TopTif-5
❑ 90TopTVA-9
❑ 90TopWaxBC-O
❑ 90UppDec-34
❑ 90UppDec-544
❑ 90UppDec-734A
❑ 90UppDec-734B
❑ 90UppDecS-1
❑ 90UppDecS-2
❑ 90WonBreS-16
❑ 90Woo-20
❑ 91BasBesRB-14
❑ 91BlePro-3
❑ 91BlePro-4
❑ 91BlePro-5
❑ 91BlePro-6
❑ 91BlePro-7
❑ 91Bow-280
❑ 91CadEllD-45
❑ 91Cla1-T86
❑ 91Cla2-T80
❑ 91Cla2-T97
❑ 91Cla3-T79
❑ 91Cla3-T98
❑ 91ClaGam-196
❑ 91ClaNolR1-1
❑ 91ClaNolR1-2
❑ 91ClaNolR1-3
❑ 91ClaNolR1-4
❑ 91ClaNolR1-5
❑ 91ClaNolR1-6
❑ 91ClaNolR1-7
❑ 91ClaNolR1-8
❑ 91ClaNolR1-9
❑ 91ClaNolR1-10
❑ 91Col-3
❑ 91Don-89
❑ 91DonBonC-BC3
❑ 91DonBonC-BC15
❑ 91DonEli-L1
❑ 91DonPre-7
❑ 91Fle-302
❑ 91FleWaxBC-3
❑ 91JimDea-24
❑ 91Lea-423
❑ 91LeaGolR-BC25
❑ 91LeaPre-25
❑ 91MajLeaCP-35
❑ 91MetWIZ-338
❑ 91MotRya-1
❑ 91MotRya-2
❑ 91MotRya-3
❑ 91MotRya-4
❑ 91MSAHolD-19
❑ 91OPC-1
❑ 91OPC-6
❑ 91OPCBoxB-N
❑ 91OPCPre-102
❑ 91PacRya7N-1
❑ 91PacRya7N-2
❑ 91PacRya7N-3
❑ 91PacRya7N-4
❑ 91PacRya7N-5
❑ 91PacRya7N-6
❑ 91PacRya7N-7
❑ 91PacRyaI8-1
❑ 91PacRyaI8-2
❑ 91PacRyaI8-3
❑ 91PacRyaI8-4
❑ 91PacRyaI8-5
❑ 91PacRyaI8-6
❑ 91PacRyaI8-7
❑ 91PacRyaI8-8
❑ 91PacRyaTEI-1
❑ 91PacRyaTEI-2
❑ 91PacRyaTEI-3
❑ 91PacRyaTEI-4
❑ 91PacRyaTEI-5
❑ 91PacRyaTEI-6
❑ 91PacRyaTEI-7
❑ 91PacRyaTEI-8
❑ 91PacRyaTEI-9
❑ 91PacRyaTEI-10
❑ 91PacRyaTEI-11
❑ 91PacRyaTEI-12
❑ 91PacRyaTEI-13
❑ 91PacRyaTEI-14
❑ 91PacRyaTEI-15
❑ 91PacRyaTEI-16
❑ 91PacRyaTEI-17
❑ 91PacRyaTEI-18
❑ 91PacRyaTEI-19
❑ 91PacRyaTEI-20
❑ 91PacRyaTEI-21
❑ 91PacRyaTEI-22
❑ 91PacRyaTEI-23
❑ 91PacRyaTEI-24
❑ 91PacRyaTEI-25
❑ 91PacRyaTEI-26
❑ 91PacRyaTEI-27
❑ 91PacRyaTEI-28
❑ 91PacRyaTEI-29
❑ 91PacRyaTEI-30
❑ 91PacRyaTEI-31
❑ 91PacRyaTEI-32
❑ 91PacRyaTEI-33
❑ 91PacRyaTEI-34
❑ 91PacRyaTEI-35
❑ 91PacRyaTEI-36
❑ 91PacRyaTEI-37
❑ 91PacRyaTEI-38
❑ 91PacRyaTEI-39
❑ 91PacRyaTEI-40
❑ 91PacRyaTEI-41
❑ 91PacRyaTEI-42
❑ 91PacRyaTEI-43
❑ 91PacRyaTEI-44
❑ 91PacRyaTEI-45
❑ 91PacRyaTEI-46
❑ 91PacRyaTEI-47
❑ 91PacRyaTEI-48
❑ 91PacRyaTEI-49
❑ 91PacRyaTEI-50
❑ 91PacRyaTEI-51
❑ 91PacRyaTEI-52
❑ 91PacRyaTEI-53
❑ 91PacRyaTEI-54
❑ 91PacRyaTEI-55
❑ 91PacRyaTEI-56
❑ 91PacRyaTEI-57
❑ 91PacRyaTEI-58
❑ 91PacRyaTEI-59
❑ 91PacRyaTEI-60
❑ 91PacRyaTEI-61
❑ 91PacRyaTEI-62
❑ 91PacRyaTEI-63
❑ 91PacRyaTEI-64
❑ 91PacRyaTEI-65
❑ 91PacRyaTEI-66
❑ 91PacRyaTEI-67
❑ 91PacRyaTEI-68
❑ 91PacRyaTEI-69
❑ 91PacRyaTEI-70
❑ 91PacRyaTEI-71
❑ 91PacRyaTEI-72
❑ 91PacRyaTEI-73
❑ 91PacRyaTEI-74
❑ 91PacRyaTEI-75
❑ 91PacRyaTEI-76
❑ 91PacRyaTEI-77
❑ 91PacRyaTEI-78
❑ 91PacRyaTEI-79
❑ 91PacRyaTEI-80
❑ 91PacRyaTEI-81
❑ 91PacRyaTEI-82
❑ 91PacRyaTEI-83
❑ 91PacRyaTEI-84
❑ 91PacRyaTEI-85
❑ 91PacRyaTEI-86
❑ 91PacRyaTEI-87
❑ 91PacRyaTEI-88
❑ 91PacRyaTEI-89
❑ 91PacRyaTEI-90
❑ 91PacRyaTEI-91
❑ 91PacRyaTEI-92
❑ 91PacRyaTEI-93
❑ 91PacRyaTEI-94
❑ 91PacRyaTEI-95
❑ 91PacRyaTEI-96
❑ 91PacRyaTEI-97
❑ 91PacRyaTEI-98
❑ 91PacRyaTEI-99
❑ 91PacRyaTEI-100
❑ 91PacRyaTEI-101
❑ 91PacRyaTEI-102
❑ 91PacRyaTEI-103
❑ 91PacRyaTEI-104
❑ 91PacRyaTEI-105
❑ 91PacRyaTEI-106
❑ 91PacRyaTEI-107
❑ 91PacRyaTEI-108
❑ 91PacRyaTEI-109
❑ 91PacRyaTEI-110
❑ 91PanCanT1-77
❑ 91PanFreS-259
❑ 91PanFreS-354
❑ 91PanSti-3
❑ 91PanSti-205
❑ 91PetSta-25
❑ 91Pos-17
❑ 91PosCan-27
❑ 91RanMot-2
❑ 91RedFolS-79
❑ 91Sco-4
❑ 91Sco-417
❑ 91Sco-686
❑ 91Sco-701
❑ 91Sco100S-25
❑ 91ScoCoo-B7
❑ 91ScoRyaLaT-1
❑ 91ScoRyaLaT-2
❑ 91ScoRyaLaT-3
❑ 91ScoRyaLaT-4
❑ 91SevCoi-A14
❑ 91SevCoi-F14
❑ 91SevCoi-T11
❑ 91SevCoi-NC8
❑ 91SevCoi-NW14
❑ 91SevCoi-SC12
❑ 91SilHol-2
❑ 91StaClu-200
❑ 91StaCluCM-24
❑ 91StaCluCM-25
❑ 91StaCluCM-NNO
❑ 91StaCluMO-7
❑ 91StaCluMO-27
❑ 91StaCluP-36
❑ 91StaPinB-39
❑ 91StaRya-1
❑ 91StaRya-2
❑ 91StaRya-3
❑ 91StaRya-4
❑ 91StaRya-5
❑ 91StaRya-6
❑ 91StaRya-7
❑ 91StaRya-8
❑ 91StaRya-9
❑ 91StaRya-10
❑ 91StaRya-11
❑ 91Stu-128
❑ 91SunSee-20
❑ 91Top-1
❑ 91Top-6
❑ 91TopCraJI-1
❑ 91TopDesS-1
❑ 91TopDesS-6
❑ 91TopMic-1
❑ 91TopMic-6
❑ 91TopSta-29
❑ 91TopTif-1
❑ 91TopTif-6
❑ 91TopTriH-A13
❑ 91TopWaxBC-N
❑ 91Ult-355
❑ 91Ult-395
❑ 91Ult-400
❑ 91UppDec-345
❑ 91UppDec-SP2
❑ 91UppDecCBP-1
❑ 91UppDecCBP-3
❑ 91UppDecRH-10
❑ 91UppDecRH-11
❑ 91UppDecRH-12
❑ 91UppDecRH-13
❑ 91UppDecRH-14
❑ 91UppDecRH-15
❑ 91UppDecRH-16
❑ 91UppDecRH-17
❑ 91UppDecRH-18
❑ 91UppDecRH-AU2
❑ 91Woo-19
❑ 92Ble23KR-1
❑ 92Ble23KR-2
❑ 92Ble23KR-3
❑ 92Bow-222
❑ 92Cla1-T78
❑ 92Cla1-NNO
❑ 92Cla2-T67
❑ 92ClaBluBF-BC1
❑ 92ClaFS7-1
❑ 92ClaGam-183
❑ 92ClaPro-1
❑ 92ClaRedB-BC1
❑ 92ColPro-12
❑ 92ColRya-1
❑ 92ColRya-2
❑ 92ColRya-3
❑ 92ColRya-4
❑ 92ColRya-5
❑ 92ColRya-6
❑ 92ColRya-7
❑ 92ColRya-8

❑ 92ColRya-9
❑ 92ColRya-10
❑ 92ColRya-11
❑ 92ColRya-12
❑ 92ColRya-AU
❑ 92ConTSNGI-934G
❑ 92DEL-AU3
❑ 92Don-154
❑ 92Don-555
❑ 92Don-707
❑ 92DonCokR-1
❑ 92DonCokR-2
❑ 92DonCokR-3
❑ 92DonCokR-4
❑ 92DonCokR-5
❑ 92DonCokR-6
❑ 92DonCokR-7
❑ 92DonCokR-8
❑ 92DonCokR-9
❑ 92DonCokR-10
❑ 92DonCokR-11
❑ 92DonCokR-12
❑ 92DonCokR-13
❑ 92DonCokR-14
❑ 92DonCokR-15
❑ 92DonCokR-16
❑ 92DonCokR-17
❑ 92DonCokR-18
❑ 92DonCokR-19
❑ 92DonCokR-20
❑ 92DonCokR-21
❑ 92DonCokR-22
❑ 92DonCokR-23
❑ 92DonCokR-24
❑ 92DonCokR-25
❑ 92DonCokR-26
❑ 92DonCraJ1-15
❑ 92DonMcD-5
❑ 92DonPre-11
❑ 92Fle-320
❑ 92Fle-682
❑ 92Fle-710
❑ 92FleCitTP-1
❑ 92FleSmo'nH-S5
❑ 92Hig5-114
❑ 92Hig5S-25
❑ 92Hig5S-34
❑ 92JimDeaLL-6
❑ 92KinDis-7
❑ 92LaKdec-24
❑ 92Lea-41
❑ 92Lea-133
❑ 92LeaBlaG-41
❑ 92LeaBlaG-133
❑ 92LeaGolP-25
❑ 92LeaPre-25
❑ 92MooSna-20
❑ 92MotRya7N-1
❑ 92MotRya7N-2
❑ 92MotRya7N-3
❑ 92MotRya7N-4
❑ 92MotRya7N-5
❑ 92MotRya7N-6
❑ 92MotRya7N-7
❑ 92MotRya7N-8
❑ 92MotRyaA-1
❑ 92MotRyaA-2
❑ 92MotRyaA-3
❑ 92MotRyaA-4
❑ 92MotRyaA-5
❑ 92MotRyaA-6
❑ 92Mr.TurS-20
❑ 92MVPPin-22
❑ 92New-22
❑ 92OPC-1
❑ 92OPC-4
❑ 92OPCPre-81
❑ 92PacRyaG-1
❑ 92PacRyaG-2
❑ 92PacRyaG-3
❑ 92PacRyaG-4
❑ 92PacRyaG-5
❑ 92PacRyaG-6
❑ 92PacRyaG-7
❑ 92PacRyaG-8
❑ 92PacRyaL-1
❑ 92PacRyaL-2
❑ 92PacRyaL-3
❑ 92PacRyaL-4
❑ 92PacRyaL-5
❑ 92PacRyaL-6
❑ 92PacRyaL-AU
❑ 92PacRyaM6-1
❑ 92PacRyaM6-2
❑ 92PacRyaM6-3
❑ 92PacRyaM6-4
❑ 92PacRyaM6-5
❑ 92PacRyaM6-6
❑ 92PacRyaTEI-111
❑ 92PacRyaTEI-112
❑ 92PacRyaTEI-113
❑ 92PacRyaTEI-114
❑ 92PacRyaTEI-115
❑ 92PacRyaTEI-116
❑ 92PacRyaTEI-117
❑ 92PacRyaTEI-118
❑ 92PacRyaTEI-119
❑ 92PacRyaTEI-120
❑ 92PacRyaTEI-121
❑ 92PacRyaTEI-122
❑ 92PacRyaTEI-123
❑ 92PacRyaTEI-124
❑ 92PacRyaTEI-125
❑ 92PacRyaTEI-126
❑ 92PacRyaTEI-127
❑ 92PacRyaTEI-128
❑ 92PacRyaTEI-129
❑ 92PacRyaTEI-130
❑ 92PacRyaTEI-131
❑ 92PacRyaTEI-132
❑ 92PacRyaTEI-133
❑ 92PacRyaTEI-134
❑ 92PacRyaTEI-135
❑ 92PacRyaTEI-136
❑ 92PacRyaTEI-137
❑ 92PacRyaTEI-138
❑ 92PacRyaTEI-139
❑ 92PacRyaTEI-140
❑ 92PacRyaTEI-141
❑ 92PacRyaTEI-142
❑ 92PacRyaTEI-143
❑ 92PacRyaTEI-144
❑ 92PacRyaTEI-145
❑ 92PacRyaTEI-146
❑ 92PacRyaTEI-147
❑ 92PacRyaTEI-148
❑ 92PacRyaTEI-149
❑ 92PacRyaTEI-150
❑ 92PacRyaTEI-151
❑ 92PacRyaTEI-152
❑ 92PacRyaTEI-153
❑ 92PacRyaTEI-154
❑ 92PacRyaTEI-155
❑ 92PacRyaTEI-156
❑ 92PacRyaTEI-157
❑ 92PacRyaTEI-158
❑ 92PacRyaTEI-159
❑ 92PacRyaTEI-160
❑ 92PacRyaTEI-161
❑ 92PacRyaTEI-162
❑ 92PacRyaTEI-163
❑ 92PacRyaTEI-164
❑ 92PacRyaTEI-165
❑ 92PacRyaTEI-166
❑ 92PacRyaTEI-167
❑ 92PacRyaTEI-168
❑ 92PacRyaTEI-169
❑ 92PacRyaTEI-170
❑ 92PacRyaTEI-171
❑ 92PacRyaTEI-172
❑ 92PacRyaTEI-173
❑ 92PacRyaTEI-174
❑ 92PacRyaTEI-175
❑ 92PacRyaTEI-176
❑ 92PacRyaTEI-177
❑ 92PacRyaTEI-178
❑ 92PacRyaTEI-179
❑ 92PacRyaTEI-180
❑ 92PacRyaTEI-181
❑ 92PacRyaTEI-182
❑ 92PacRyaTEI-183
❑ 92PacRyaTEI-184
❑ 92PacRyaTEI-185
❑ 92PacRyaTEI-186
❑ 92PacRyaTEI-187
❑ 92PacRyaTEI-188
❑ 92PacRyaTEI-189
❑ 92PacRyaTEI-190
❑ 92PacRyaTEI-191
❑ 92PacRyaTEI-192
❑ 92PacRyaTEI-193
❑ 92PacRyaTEI-194
❑ 92PacRyaTEI-195
❑ 92PacRyaTEI-196
❑ 92PacRyaTEI-197
❑ 92PacRyaTEI-198
❑ 92PacRyaTEI-199
❑ 92PacRyaTEI-200
❑ 92PacRyaTEI-201
❑ 92PacRyaTEI-202
❑ 92PacRyaTEI-203
❑ 92PacRyaTEI-204
❑ 92PacRyaTEI-205
❑ 92PacRyaTEI-206
❑ 92PacRyaTEI-207
❑ 92PacRyaTEI-208
❑ 92PacRyaTEI-209
❑ 92PacRyaTEI-210
❑ 92PacRyaTEI-211
❑ 92PacRyaTEI-212
❑ 92PacRyaTEI-213
❑ 92PacRyaTEI-214
❑ 92PacRyaTEI-215
❑ 92PacRyaTEI-216
❑ 92PacRyaTEI-217
❑ 92PacRyaTEI-218
❑ 92PacRyaTEI-219
❑ 92PacRyaTEI-220
❑ 92PacSea-82
❑ 92PacSea-85
❑ 92PanSti-82
❑ 92Pin-50
❑ 92Pin-281
❑ 92Pin-294
❑ 92Pin-618
❑ 92PinRool-12
❑ 92Pos-27
❑ 92RanMot-2
❑ 92RanTeal-22
❑ 92RedFolS-82
❑ 92Sco-2
❑ 92Sco-425
❑ 92Sco100S-50
❑ 92ScoProP-1
❑ 92ScoProP-14
❑ 92SevCoi-11
❑ 92SpoIllFK1-168
❑ 92SpoStaCC-38
❑ 92StaClu-605
❑ 92StaClu-770
❑ 92StaCluECN-605
❑ 92StaCluMP-11
❑ 92Stu-248
❑ 92Top-1
❑ 92Top-4
❑ 92TopGol-1
❑ 92TopGol-4
❑ 92TopGolPS-1
❑ 92TopGolW-1
❑ 92TopGolW-4
❑ 92TopKid-127
❑ 92TopMcD-24
❑ 92TopMic-1
❑ 92TopMic-4
❑ 92TopMic-G1
❑ 92TriPla-22
❑ 92Ult-141
❑ 92UppDec-92
❑ 92UppDec-655
❑ 92UppDecF-37
❑ 92UppDecFG-37
❑ 92UppDecS-13
❑ 92UppDecTMH-45
❑ 93Ble-38
❑ 93Ble-39
❑ 93Ble-40
❑ 93Ble-41
❑ 93Ble-42
❑ 93Ble-43
❑ 93Ble-44
❑ 93Ble-45
❑ 93Ble-46
❑ 93Ble-47
❑ 93BlePro-4
❑ 93BlePro-5
❑ 93BlePro-6
❑ 93BlePro-7
❑ 93BlePro-8
❑ 93BlePro-9
❑ 93BleRya6-1
❑ 93BleRya6-2
❑ 93BleRya6-3
❑ 93BleRya6-4
❑ 93BleRya6-5
❑ 93BleRya6-6
❑ 93Bow-405
❑ 93CadDis-48
❑ 93ClaGam-79
❑ 93ConMasC-3
❑ 93ConTSN-928
❑ 93ConTSN-929
❑ 93ConTSN-930
❑ 93ConTSN-931
❑ 93ConTSN-932
❑ 93ConTSN-933
❑ 93ConTSN-934
❑ 93ConTSN-935
❑ 93ConTSNP-934
❑ 93DiaMar-91
❑ 93DiaMarA-6
❑ 93Don-423
❑ 93DonEliD-10
❑ 93DonEliD-AU10
❑ 93DonEliS-20
❑ 93DonMasotG-2
❑ 93DurPowP1-20
❑ 93Fin-107
❑ 93FinJum-107
❑ 93FinPro-107
❑ 93FinProR-107
❑ 93FinRef-107
❑ 93Fla-286
❑ 93FlaPro-7
❑ 93Fle-690
❑ 93FleAtl-20
❑ 93FleFinEDT-6
❑ 93FleFruotL-55
❑ 93FunPac-18
❑ 93FunPac-26
❑ 93FunPac-33
❑ 93FunPac-160
❑ 93FunPac-214
❑ 93HumDumC-16
❑ 93JimDea-16
❑ 93KinDis-17
❑ 93Kra-13
❑ 93Lea-115
❑ 93LeaGolA-R19
❑ 93LeaHeaftH-1
❑ 93MetBak-35
❑ 93MotRyaF-1
❑ 93MotRyaF-2
❑ 93MotRyaF-3
❑ 93MotRyaF-4
❑ 93MotRyaF-5
❑ 93MotRyaF-6
❑ 93MotRyaF-7
❑ 93MotRyaF-8
❑ 93MotRyaF-9
❑ 93MotRyaF-10
❑ 93OPC-229
❑ 93OPCPreSP-20
❑ 93OPCPreSPF-20
❑ 93PacJugC-15
❑ 93PacRya2S-221
❑ 93PacRya2S-222
❑ 93PacRya2S-223
❑ 93PacRya2S-224
❑ 93PacRya2S-225
❑ 93PacRya2S-226
❑ 93PacRya2S-227
❑ 93PacRya2S-228
❑ 93PacRya2S-229
❑ 93PacRya2S-230
❑ 93PacRya2S-231
❑ 93PacRya2S-232
❑ 93PacRya2S-233
❑ 93PacRya2S-234
❑ 93PacRya2S-235
❑ 93PacRya2S-236
❑ 93PacRya2S-237
❑ 93PacRya2S-238
❑ 93PacRya2S-239
❑ 93PacRya2S-240
❑ 93PacRya2S-241
❑ 93PacRya2S-242
❑ 93PacRya2S-243
❑ 93PacRya2S-244
❑ 93PacRya2S-245
❑ 93PacRya2S-246
❑ 93PacRya2S-247
❑ 93PacRya2S-248
❑ 93PacRya2S-249
❑ 93PacRya2S-250
❑ 93PacRyaFM-1
❑ 93PacRyaFM-2
❑ 93PacRyaFM-3
❑ 93PacRyaFM-4
❑ 93PacRyaFM-5
❑ 93PacRyaFM-6
❑ 93PacRyaFM-7
❑ 93PacRyaFM-8
❑ 93PacRyaFM-9
❑ 93PacRyaFM-10
❑ 93PacRyaFM-11
❑ 93PacRyaFM-12
❑ 93PacRyaFM-13
❑ 93PacRyaFM-14
❑ 93PacRyaFM-15
❑ 93PacRyaFM-16
❑ 93PacRyaFM-17
❑ 93PacRyaFM-18
❑ 93PacRyaFM-19
❑ 93PacRyaFM-20
❑ 93PacRyaL-7
❑ 93PacRyaL-8
❑ 93PacRyaL-9
❑ 93PacRyaL-10
❑ 93PacRyaL-11
❑ 93PacRyaL-12
❑ 93PacRyaPI-1
❑ 93PacRyaPI-2
❑ 93PacRyaPI-3
❑ 93PacRyaPI-4
❑ 93PacRyaPI-5
❑ 93PacRyaPI-6
❑ 93PacRyaPI-7
❑ 93PacRyaPI-8
❑ 93PacRyaPI-9
❑ 93PacRyaPI-10
❑ 93PacRyaPI-11
❑ 93PacRyaPI-12
❑ 93PacRyaPI-13
❑ 93PacRyaPI-14
❑ 93PacRyaPI-15
❑ 93PacRyaPI-16
❑ 93PacRyaPI-17
❑ 93PacRyaPI-18
❑ 93PacRyaPI-19
❑ 93PacRyaPI-20
❑ 93PacSpa-317
❑ 93PanSti-87
❑ 93PhoFilR-1
❑ 93PhoFilR-2
❑ 93PhoFilR-3
❑ 93PhoFilR-4
❑ 93PhoFilR-5
❑ 93PhoFilR-6
❑ 93PhoFilR-7
❑ 93Pin-75
❑ 93Pin-290
❑ 93PinCoo-1
❑ 93PinCooD-1
❑ 93PinTri-6
❑ 93PinTri-7
❑ 93PinTri-8
❑ 93PinTri-9
❑ 93PinTri-10
❑ 93Pos-20
❑ 93RanDrP-3
❑ 93RanKee-431
❑ 93RanStaC-1
❑ 93RedFolS-81
❑ 93Sco-59
❑ 93Sel-90
❑ 93SelRoo-NR1
❑ 93SP-198
❑ 93SpeRya1-1
❑ 93SpeRya1-2
❑ 93SpeRya1-3
❑ 93SpeRya1-4
❑ 93SpeRya1-5
❑ 93SpeRya1-6
❑ 93SpeRya1-7
❑ 93SpeRya1-8
❑ 93SpeRya1-9
❑ 93SpeRya1-10
❑ 93SpeRya2-1
❑ 93SpeRya2-2
❑ 93SpeRya2-3
❑ 93SpeRya5-1
❑ 93SpeRya5-2
❑ 93SpeRya5-3
❑ 93SpeRya5-4
❑ 93SpeRya5-5
❑ 93SpeRyaTS-1
❑ 93StaClu-353
❑ 93StaCluFDI-353
❑ 93StaCluMOP-353
❑ 93StaCluMP-21
❑ 93Stu-71
❑ 93StuSil-10
❑ 93TexSupRS-1
❑ 93TexSupRS-2
❑ 93TexSupRS-3
❑ 93TexSupRS-4
❑ 93TexSupRS-5
❑ 93TexSupRS-6
❑ 93TexSupRS-7
❑ 93TexSupRS-8
❑ 93TexSupRS-9
❑ 93TexSupRS-10
❑ 93TexSupRS-11
❑ 93TexSupRS-12
❑ 93TexSupRS-13
❑ 93TexSupRS-14
❑ 93TexSupRS-15
❑ 93TexSupRS-16
❑ 93TexSupRS-17
❑ 93TexSupRS-18
❑ 93TexSupRS-19
❑ 93TexSupRS-20
❑ 93TexSupRS-21
❑ 93TexSupRS-22
❑ 93TexSupRS-23
❑ 93TexSupRS-24
❑ 93TexSupRS-25
❑ 93TexSupRS-26
❑ 93TexSupRS-27
❑ 93TexSupRS-28
❑ 93TexSupRS-29
❑ 93TexSupRS-30
❑ 93Top-700
❑ 93TopGol-700
❑ 93TopInaM-700
❑ 93TopInaR-700
❑ 93TopMagJRC-4
❑ 93TopMic-700
❑ 93TopMic-P700
❑ 93TriPla-96
❑ 93TriPlaN-7
❑ 93Ult-636
❑ 93UltStrK-4
❑ 93UppDec-37
❑ 93UppDec-155
❑ 93UppDec-SP6
❑ 93UppDecDG-30
❑ 93UppDecFA-A5
❑ 93UppDecFAJ-A5
❑ 93UppDecGold-37
❑ 93UppDecGold-155
❑ 93UppDecIC-WI19
❑ 93UppDecICJ-WI19
❑ 93UppDecOD-D20
❑ 93UppDecS-19
❑ 93UppDecSH-HI17
❑ 93UppDecTAN-TN5
❑ 93WhaRya-1
❑ 93WhaRya-2
❑ 93WhaRya-3
❑ 93WhaRya-4
❑ 93WhaRya-5
❑ 93WhaRya-6
❑ 93WhaRya-7
❑ 93WhaRya-8
❑ 93WhaRya-9
❑ 93WhaRya-10
❑ 94ColC-249
❑ 94ColC-320
❑ 94ColChoGS-249
❑ 94ColChoGS-320
❑ 94ColChoSS-249
❑ 94ColChoSS-320
❑ 94ConTSNCI-30
❑ 94Don-1
❑ 94DonAnn8-5
❑ 94DonSpeE-1
❑ 94Fle-321
❑ 94FleGolM-7
❑ 94FleGolMJ-7
❑ 94FleSmo'nH-10
❑ 94HarStaR-1
❑ 94LegPosR-1
❑ 94Met69CCPP-27
❑ 94Met69CS-26
❑ 94Met69T-7
❑ 94RanAllP-17
❑ 94RyaSSC-1
❑ 94RyaSSC-2
❑ 94RyaSSC-3
❑ 94RyaSSC-4
❑ 94RyaSSC-5
❑ 94RyaSSC-6
❑ 94RyaSSC-7
❑ 94RyaSSC-8
❑ 94RyaSSC-9
❑ 94RyaSSC-10
❑ 94RyaSSC-11
❑ 94RyaSSC-12
❑ 94SigRooFCS-AU7
❑ 94SigRooFCS-AU8
❑ 94SigRooG-2
❑ 94StaClu-34
❑ 94StaCluFDI-34
❑ 94StaCluGR-34
❑ 94StaCluMOP-34
❑ 94Top-34
❑ 94TopGol-34
❑ 94TopPorP-700
❑ 94TopPre-700
❑ 94TopSpa-34
❑ 94UppDecAH-15
❑ 94UppDecAH-34
❑ 94UppDecAH-120
❑ 94UppDecAH-125
❑ 94UppDecAH1-15

❑ 94UppDecAH1-34
❑ 94UppDecAH1-120
❑ 94UppDecAH1-125
❑ 94UppDecTAE-79
❑ 95ColCho-46
❑ 95ColCho-52
❑ 95ColChoGS-46
❑ 95ColChoGS-52
❑ 95ColChoSS-46
❑ 95ColChoSS-52
❑ 95EagBalL-1
❑ 95FanRya-1
❑ 95FanRya-2
❑ 95FanRya-3
❑ 95FanRya-4
❑ 95FanRya-5
❑ 95SP-2
❑ 95SPChaCP-CP2
❑ 95SPChaCPDC-CP2
❑ 95SPSil-2
❑ 95UppDec-448
❑ 95UppDecED-448
❑ 95UppDecEDG-448
❑ 95UppDecSE-175
❑ 95UppDecSEG-175
❑ 95UppDecSHoB-6
❑ 96MetImpRy-1
❑ 96MetImpRy-2
❑ 96MetImpRy-3
❑ 96MetImpRy-4
❑ 96MetImpRy-5
❑ 96MetImpRy-6
❑ 96MetImpRy-7
❑ 96MetImpRy-8
❑ 96MetImpRy-9
❑ 96MetImpRy-10
❑ 96PacNolR-1
❑ 96PacNolR-2
❑ 96PacNolR-3
❑ 96PacNolR-4
❑ 96PacNolR-5
❑ 96PacNolR-6
❑ 96PacNolR-7
❑ 96PacNolR-8
❑ 96PacNolR-9
❑ 96PacNolR-10
❑ 96PacNolR-11
❑ 96PacNolR-12
❑ 96PacNolR-13
❑ 96PacNolR-14
❑ 96PacNolR-15
❑ 96PacNolR-16
❑ 96PacNolR-17
❑ 96PacNolR-18
❑ 96PacNolR-19
❑ 96PacNolR-20
❑ 96PacNolR-21
❑ 96PacNolR-22
❑ 96PacNolR-23
❑ 96PacNolR-24
❑ 96PacNolR-25
❑ 96PacNolR-26
❑ 96PacNolR-27
❑ 96PacNolR-A
❑ 96PacNolR-B
❑ 96Pro-13
❑ 96RanCup-4
❑ 97HigMinMCP-11
❑ 97HigMinMCP-12
❑ 97HigMinMCP-13
❑ 97HigMinMCT-35
❑ 97HigMinMCT-36
❑ 97HigMinMM-4
❑ 97HigMinMM-5
❑ 97HigMinMM-7
❑ 97HigMinMSM-25
❑ 97HigMinMSM-26
❑ 98DonEliBttF-7
❑ 98DonEliBttFA-7
❑ 98DonSigSS-14
❑ 98DonSigSS-R1
❑ 98PinPlu-NNO
❑ 98UppDecR-97
❑ 98UppDecRSotT-NR
❑ 98UppDecRTC-TC24
❑ 99SP SigAuto-NR
❑ 99SpollIGotG-34
❑ 99SpollIGotGA-65
❑ 99SpollIGotGC-29
❑ 99SpollIGotGC-37
❑ 99SpollIGotGC-48
❑ 99SpollIGotGC-49
❑ 99SpollIGotGRB-6
❑ 99SpollIGotGRBG-6
❑ 99SPSig-167
❑ 99Top-34
❑ 99TopChr-34
❑ 99TopChrR-34
❑ 99TopMVPP-34
❑ 99TopOpeD-21
❑ 99TopRyaAut-1
❑ 99TopRyaAut-2
❑ 99TopRyaAut-3
❑ 99TopRyaAut-4
❑ 99TopRyaAut-5
❑ 99TopRyaAut-6
❑ 99TopRyaAut-7
❑ 99TopRyaAut-8
❑ 99TopRyaAut-9
❑ 99TopRyaAut-10
❑ 99TopRyaAut-11
❑ 99TopRyaAut-12
❑ 99TopRyaAut-13
❑ 99TopRyaAut-14
❑ 99TopRyaAut-15
❑ 99TopRyaAut-16
❑ 99TopRyaAut-17
❑ 99TopRyaAut-18
❑ 99TopRyaAut-19
❑ 99TopRyaAut-20
❑ 99TopRyaAut-21
❑ 99TopRyaAut-22
❑ 99TopRyaAut-23
❑ 99TopRyaAut-24
❑ 99TopRyaAut-25
❑ 99TopRyaAut-26
❑ 99TopRyaAut-27
❑ 99TopRyan-1
❑ 99TopRyan-2
❑ 99TopRyan-3
❑ 99TopRyan-4
❑ 99TopRyan-5
❑ 99TopRyan-6
❑ 99TopRyan-7
❑ 99TopRyan-8
❑ 99TopRyan-9
❑ 99TopRyan-10
❑ 99TopRyan-11
❑ 99TopRyan-12
❑ 99TopRyan-13
❑ 99TopRyan-14
❑ 99TopRyan-15
❑ 99TopRyan-16
❑ 99TopRyan-17
❑ 99TopRyan-18
❑ 99TopRyan-19
❑ 99TopRyan-20
❑ 99TopRyan-21
❑ 99TopRyan-22
❑ 99TopRyan-23
❑ 99TopRyan-24
❑ 99TopRyan-25
❑ 99TopRyan-26
❑ 99TopRyan-27
❑ 99TopRyanF-1
❑ 99TopRyanF-2
❑ 99TopRyanF-3
❑ 99TopRyanF-4
❑ 99TopRyanF-5
❑ 99TopRyanF-6
❑ 99TopRyanF-7
❑ 99TopRyanF-8
❑ 99TopRyanF-9
❑ 99TopRyanF-10
❑ 99TopRyanF-11
❑ 99TopRyanF-12
❑ 99TopRyanF-13
❑ 99TopRyanF-14
❑ 99TopRyanF-15
❑ 99TopRyanF-16
❑ 99TopRyanF-17
❑ 99TopRyanF-18
❑ 99TopRyanF-19
❑ 99TopRyanF-20
❑ 99TopRyanF-21
❑ 99TopRyanF-22
❑ 99TopRyanF-23
❑ 99TopRyanF-24
❑ 99TopRyanF-25
❑ 99TopRyanF-26
❑ 99TopRyanF-27
❑ 99TopRyanFR-1
❑ 99TopRyanFR-2
❑ 99TopRyanFR-3
❑ 99TopRyanFR-4
❑ 99TopRyanFR-5
❑ 99TopRyanFR-6
❑ 99TopRyanFR-7
❑ 99TopRyanFR-8
❑ 99TopRyanFR-9
❑ 99TopRyanFR-10
❑ 99TopRyanFR-11
❑ 99TopRyanFR-12
❑ 99TopRyanFR-13
❑ 99TopRyanFR-14
❑ 99TopRyanFR-15
❑ 99TopRyanFR-16
❑ 99TopRyanFR-17
❑ 99TopRyanFR-18
❑ 99TopRyanFR-19
❑ 99TopRyanFR-20
❑ 99TopRyanFR-21
❑ 99TopRyanFR-22
❑ 99TopRyanFR-23
❑ 99TopRyanFR-24
❑ 99TopRyanFR-25
❑ 99TopRyanFR-26
❑ 99TopRyanFR-27
❑ 99TopSupC-7
❑ 99TopSupCR-7
❑ 99UppDec10AT-X9
❑ 99UppDec10ATD-X9
❑ 99UppDec10ATHR-X9
❑ 99UppDec10ATT-X9
❑ 99UppDecCL-41
❑ 99UppDecCLA-1980
❑ 99UppDecCLCC-41
❑ 99UppDecCLEM-EM3
❑ 99UppDecCLES-NR
❑ 99UppDecCLESC-NR
❑ 99UppDecCLJotC-NR
❑ 99UppDecGJ-NRA
❑ 99UppDecGJ-NRB
❑ 99UppDecGJ-NRAS
❑ 99UppDecR-89
❑ 99UppDecRG-89
❑ 99UppDecRI-NR
❑ 99UppDecRIL2-NR
❑ 99UppDecRP-89

Ryan, Pat
❑ 97IdaFalBTI-17
❑ 98CliLumG-21

Ryan, Ray
❑ 09T206-513

Ryan, Reese
❑ 92PacRyaTEI-149

Ryan, Reid
❑ 90ClaYel-T91
❑ 94HudValRC-21
❑ 94HudValRF-3385
❑ 94SigRooFCD-4
❑ 94SigRooFCS-AU7
❑ 94SigRooFCS-AU8
❑ 94TopTra-101T
❑ 95ChaRivTI-1
❑ 95ColCho-45
❑ 95ColChoGS-45
❑ 95ColChoSS-45
❑ 95Exc-131
❑ 95UppDec-15
❑ 95UppDecED-15
❑ 95UppDecEDG-15

Ryan, Rob
❑ 94LetMouF-3887
❑ 94LetMouSP-14
❑ 96AriBlaDB-28
❑ 97SouBenSH-26
❑ 98BilMusTI-30
❑ 98TusSidM-28
❑ 99Bow-403
❑ 99BowGol-403
❑ 99BowInt-403

Ryan, Rosy (Wilfred)
❑ 21KoBreWSI-19
❑ 22W575-113
❑ 23W501-75
❑ 23WilChoV-140
❑ 33WorCig-83
❑ 33WorCig(-80
❑ 90DodTar-702
❑ 93ConTSN-746

Ryan, Sean
❑ 90BatCliP-3076
❑ 91Cla/Bes-117
❑ 91LinDriAA-517
❑ 91ReaPhiLD-517
❑ 91ReaPhiP-1377
❑ 92ClaFS7-234
❑ 92ReaPhiF-583
❑ 92ReaPhiS-542
❑ 92SkyAA F-236
❑ 92UppDecML-120
❑ 93ScrRedBF-2551
❑ 93ScrRedBTI-23

Ryba, Jason
❑ 98BluOriQ-31

Ryba, Mike (Dominic)
❑ 42RedSoxTI-21
❑ 43RedSoxTI-21
❑ 46RedSoxTI-21
❑ 54CarHunW-23
❑ 54Top-237
❑ 75RedSox1T-33
❑ 83TCMPla1944-11
❑ 94TopArc1-237
❑ 94TopArc1G-237
❑ 95ConTSN-1401

Rychel, Kevin
❑ 90AugPirP-2461
❑ 91SalBucC-19
❑ 91SalBucP-949
❑ 92AugPirC-9
❑ 92SalBucF-63
❑ 93SalBucC-21
❑ 93SalBucF-431
❑ 94CarMudF-1580
❑ 95CarMudF-156
❑ 96CarMudB-9

Ryden, Karl
❑ 97IdaFalBTI-18

Ryder, Brian
❑ 80NasSouTI-17
❑ 81ColCliP-35
❑ 81ColCliT-14
❑ 82IndIndTI-11
❑ 83IndIndTI-11

Ryder, Derek
❑ 95CedRapKTI-20
❑ 96CedRapKTI-20
❑ 97LakElsSG-24

Ryder, Scott
❑ 90IdaFalBP-3245
❑ 91PulBraC-26
❑ 91PulBraP-4003
❑ 92DurBulC-4
❑ 92DurBulF-1098
❑ 92DurBulTI-26
❑ 93DurBulC-15
❑ 93DurBulF-484

Ryder, Steve
❑ 94HunCubC-25
❑ 94HunCubF-3563

Ryerson, Gary
❑ 75SalLakCC-14
❑ 94BreMilB-350

Rymer, Carlos
❑ 80AndBraT-16

Ryun, Jim
❑ 74NewYorNTDiS-8

Saa, Humberto
❑ 90HunCubP-3293
❑ 91GenCubC-17
❑ 91GenCubP-4227

Saatzer, Michael
❑ 82RedPioT-10
❑ 83NasAngT-7
❑ 86QuaCitAP-30

Saavedra, Ed
❑ 78WatIndT-20
❑ 79WatIndT-21
❑ 81WatIndT-27
❑ 82ChaLooT-4
❑ 83BufBisT-20
❑ 84BufBisT-22

Saavedra, Justo
❑ 80BatTroT-23

Sabathia, C.C.
❑ 99199Fin-294
❑ 99Bow-344
❑ 99BowBes-171
❑ 99BowBesAR-171
❑ 99BowBesR-171
❑ 99BowGol-344
❑ 99BowInt-344
❑ 99FinGolRef-294
❑ 99FinRef-294
❑ 99TeaBesR-76
❑ 99TeaBesRFS-8
❑ 99TeaBesRG-76
❑ 99TeaBesRS-76

Sabel, Erik
❑ 96AriBlaDB-29
❑ 97HigDesMG-22
❑ 98TexLeaC-19
❑ 98TulDriTI-16

Saberhagen, Bret
❑ 84FleUpd-103
❑ 84RoyPos-28
❑ 84TopTra-104T
❑ 84TopTraT-104T
❑ 85Don-222
❑ 85DonHig-26
❑ 85Fle-212
❑ 85FleStaS-124
❑ 85OPC-23
❑ 85RoyTeal-26
❑ 85Top-23
❑ 85TopTif-23
❑ 86BasStaB-95
❑ 86Don-11
❑ 86Don-100
❑ 86DonSupD-11
❑ 86Dra-29
❑ 86Fle-19
❑ 86FleLeaL-37
❑ 86FleLimE-38
❑ 86FleMin-3
❑ 86FleSlu-31
❑ 86FleStiC-103
❑ 86GenMilB-2I
❑ 86KayB-27
❑ 86Lea-11
❑ 86OPC-249
❑ 86OPCBoxB-O
❑ 86QuaGra-19
❑ 86RoyKitCD-3
❑ 86RoyNatP-31
❑ 86RoyTeal-22
❑ 86SevCoi-C6
❑ 86SevCoi-E6
❑ 86SevCoi-S6
❑ 86SevCoi-W6
❑ 86Spo-10
❑ 86Spo-176
❑ 86Spo-185
❑ 86Spo-186
❑ 86Top-487
❑ 86Top-720
❑ 86Top3-D-25
❑ 86TopGaloC-12
❑ 86TopGloS-27
❑ 86TopMinL-20
❑ 86TopSti-17
❑ 86TopSti-260
❑ 86TopSup-3
❑ 86TopTat-2
❑ 86TopTif-487
❑ 86TopTif-720
❑ 86TopWaxBC-O
❑ 87ClaGam-88
❑ 87ClaUpdY-116
❑ 87Don-132
❑ 87DonHig-6
❑ 87Fle-379
❑ 87FleAwaW-34
❑ 87FleGlo-379
❑ 87FleLimBC-C5
❑ 87FleSlu-36
❑ 87Lea-261
❑ 87OPC-140
❑ 87Spo-145
❑ 87SpoTeaP-13
❑ 87StuPan-20
❑ 87Top-140
❑ 87TopTif-140
❑ 88ClaRed-172
❑ 88Don-96
❑ 88DonAll-8
❑ 88DonBasB-231
❑ 88DonPop-8
❑ 88Fle-268
❑ 88Fle-626
❑ 88FleGlo-268
❑ 88FleGlo-626
❑ 88FleLeaL-33
❑ 88FleMin-26
❑ 88FleStiC-32
❑ 88FleTeaL-32
❑ 88GreBasS-53
❑ 88Lea-68
❑ 88MSAJifPD-15
❑ 88Nes-11
❑ 88OPC-5
❑ 88PanSti-102
❑ 88PanSti-106
❑ 88PanSti-107
❑ 88PanSti-229
❑ 88RedFolSB-77
❑ 88RoySmo-16
❑ 88RoyTeal-27
❑ 88Sco-89
❑ 88ScoBoxC-9
❑ 88ScoGlo-89
❑ 88ScoYouS2-17
❑ 88Spo-15
❑ 88StaLinRo-14
❑ 88Top-141
❑ 88Top-540
❑ 88TopBig-94
❑ 88TopCoi-25
❑ 88TopGloA-10
❑ 88TopMinL-14
❑ 88TopSti-163
❑ 88TopSti-254
❑ 88TopStiB-60
❑ 88TopTif-141
❑ 88TopTif-540
❑ 88TopUKM-63
❑ 88TopUKMT-63
❑ 89Bow-111
❑ 89BowTif-111
❑ 89ClaLigB-62
❑ 89Don-144
❑ 89DonBasB-95
❑ 89Fle-291
❑ 89FleGlo-291
❑ 89OPC-157
❑ 89PanSti-352
❑ 89RoyTasD-11
❑ 89Sco-251
❑ 89Spo-109
❑ 89Top-750
❑ 89TopAwaW-4
❑ 89TopBasT-92
❑ 89TopBig-6
❑ 89TopSti-263
❑ 89TopTif-750
❑ 89UppDec-37
❑ 90BasWit-21
❑ 90Baz-4
❑ 90Bow-364
❑ 90BowIns-9
❑ 90BowInsL-9
❑ 90BowInsT-9
❑ 90BowTif-364
❑ 90BowTif-A9
❑ 90ClaBlu-139
❑ 90ClaUpd-NNO
❑ 90Col-30
❑ 90Don-89
❑ 90DonBesA-21
❑ 90Fle-116
❑ 90FleAwaW-30
❑ 90FleBasA-31
❑ 90FleBasAC-31
❑ 90FleBasM-32
❑ 90FleBasMC-32
❑ 90FleCan-116
❑ 90FleLeaL-32
❑ 90FleLeaLC-32
❑ 90GooHumICBLS-18
❑ 90Hot50PS-36
❑ 90K-M-26
❑ 90Lea-72
❑ 90M.Vpin-46
❑ 90MSAHolD-5
❑ 90MSAIceTD-17
❑ 90OPC-350
❑ 90OPC-393
❑ 90PanSti-81
❑ 90PubIntS-354
❑ 90RoyPos-21
❑ 90Sco-195A
❑ 90Sco-195B
❑ 90Spo-94
❑ 90StaLonJS-19
❑ 90StaLonJS-36
❑ 90StaSab-1
❑ 90StaSab-2
❑ 90StaSab-4
❑ 90StaSab-6
❑ 90StaSab-8
❑ 90StaSab-10
❑ 90Top-350
❑ 90Top-393
❑ 90TopBig-21
❑ 90TopCoi-2
❑ 90TopDou-54
❑ 90TopGaloC-10
❑ 90TopGloS-13
❑ 90TopHeaU-7
❑ 90TopMag-5
❑ 90TopMinL-17
❑ 90TopSti-266
❑ 90TopStiB-59
❑ 90TopTif-350
❑ 90TopTif-393
❑ 90TopTVA-15
❑ 90UppDec-326
❑ 90USPlaCA-3C
❑ 90WinDis-4
❑ 90Woo-3
❑ 91BasBesAotM-14
❑ 91Bow-291
❑ 91CadEllD-46
❑ 91Cla3-T80

- 91ClaGam-36
- 91Don-88
- 91Fle-567
- 91Lea-118
- 91OPC-280
- 91PanFreS-283
- 91PanSti-225
- 91RedFolS-80
- 91RoyPol-18
- 91Sco-6
- 91Sco100S-59
- 91SimandSMLBL-37
- 91StaClu-38
- 91StaCluMO-28
- 91StaPinB-40
- 91Stu-69
- 91Top-280
- 91TopCraJ2-14
- 91TopDesS-280
- 91TopMic-280
- 91TopTif-280
- 91TopTriH-A7
- 91Ult-154
- 91UppDec-33
- 91UppDec-435
- 92Bow-586
- 92ClaGam-175
- 92Don-128
- 92Don-434
- 92Fle-167
- 92Hig5-65
- 92Lea-376
- 92LeaBlaG-376
- 92MetColP-5
- 92MetKah-18
- 92New-23
- 92OPC-75
- 92OPCPre-82
- 92PanSti-101
- 92Pin-442
- 92Sco-6
- 92Sco-786
- 92Sco100S-11
- 92ScoRoo-20T
- 92SpoStaCC-39
- 92StaClu-755
- 92Stu-69
- 92Top-75
- 92TopGol-75
- 92TopGolW-75
- 92TopKid-107
- 92TopMic-75
- 92TopTra-97T
- 92TopTraG-97T
- 92Ult-537
- 92UppDec-233
- 92UppDec-751
- 93Bow-510
- 93CadDis-49
- 93Don-222
- 93Fin-53
- 93FinRef-53
- 93Fla-96
- 93Fle-93
- 93FunPac-129
- 93Lea-93
- 93MetColP-25
- 93MetKah-18
- 93OPC-302
- 93PacSpa-201
- 93Pin-185
- 93RedFolS-82
- 93RoySta2-12
- 93Sco-115
- 93Sel-123
- 93SP-153
- 93StaClu-335
- 93StaCluFDI-335
- 93StaCluMOP-335
- 93Stu-112
- 93Top-600
- 93TopGol-600
- 93TopInaM-600
- 93TopInaR-600
- 93TopMic-600
- 93TriPla-124
- 93Ult-79
- 93UppDec-282
- 93UppDecGold-282
- 94Bow-16
- 94ColC-250
- 94ColChoGS-250
- 94ColChoSS-250
- 94Don-298
- 94Fin-419
- 94FinRef-419
- 94Fla-409
- 94Fle-576
- 94FleExtB-323
- 94FleExtBPD-8
- 94Lea-437
- 94LeaL-132
- 94MetColP-22
- 94MetShuST-3
- 94OPC-46
- 94Pac-416
- 94PanSti-222
- 94Pin-203
- 94PinArtP-203
- 94PinMusC-203
- 94ProMag-95
- 94Sco-92
- 94ScoGolR-92
- 94Sel-101
- 94SP-120
- 94SPDieC-120
- 94StaClu-368
- 94StaCluFDI-368
- 94StaCluGR-368
- 94StaCluMOP-368
- 94Stu-119
- 94Top-245
- 94TopGol-245
- 94TopSpa-245
- 94TriPla-148
- 94Ult-533
- 94UppDec-428
- 94UppDecED-428
- 95Baz-86
- 95Bow-322
- 95BowBes-R40
- 95BowBesR-R40
- 95ColCho-325
- 95ColChoGS-325
- 95ColChoSE-150
- 95ColChoSE-251
- 95ColChoSEGS-150
- 95ColChoSEGS-251
- 95ColChoSESS-150
- 95ColChoSESS-251
- 95ColChoSS-325
- 95DenHol-22
- 95Don-431
- 95DonMouM-4
- 95DonPreP-431
- 95DonTopotO-232
- 95Emo-162
- 95Fin-166
- 95FinFlaT-FT8
- 95FinRef-166
- 95Fla-175
- 95Fle-380
- 95FleTeaL-23
- 95Kra-27
- 95Lea-74
- 95LeaLim-173
- 95MetColP-5
- 95Pac-287
- 95PanSti-7
- 95Pin-355
- 95PinArtP-355
- 95PinMusC-355
- 95RedFol-26
- 95Sco-21
- 95ScoGolR-21
- 95ScoHaloG-HG43
- 95ScoPlaTS-21
- 95Sel-128
- 95SelArtP-128
- 95SelCer-46
- 95SelCerMG-46
- 95SP-85
- 95SPCha-72
- 95SPChaCP-CP9
- 95SPChaCPDC-CP9
- 95SPChaDC-72
- 95Spo-38
- 95SpoArtP-38
- 95SPSil-85
- 95SPSpeF-45
- 95StaClu-45
- 95StaClu-138
- 95StaCluFDI-45
- 95StaCluFDI-138
- 95StaCluMOP-45
- 95StaCluMOP-138
- 95StaCluSTWS-45
- 95StaCluSTWS-138
- 95StaCluVR-71
- 95StaCluVRMO-71
- 95Stu-99
- 95Sum-106
- 95SumNthD-106
- 95TomPiz-28
- 95Top-459
- 95TopCyb-254
- 95TopEmb-124
- 95TopEmbGI-124
- 95TopLeaL-LL49
- 95UC3-46
- 95UC3ArtP-46
- 95Ult-415
- 95UltGolM-415
- 95UppDec-120
- 95UppDec-490
- 95UppDecED-120
- 95UppDecEDG-120
- 95UppDecSE-195
- 95UppDecSEG-195
- 95USPlaCMLA-12S
- 95Zen-10
- 96Baz-114
- 96ColCho-130
- 96ColChoGS-130
- 96ColChoSS-130
- 96Don-53
- 96DonPreP-53
- 96Fla-251
- 96Fle-374
- 96FleTif-374
- 96Lea-29
- 96LeaPrePB-29
- 96LeaPrePG-29
- 96LeaPrePS-29
- 96LeaSigA-199
- 96LeaSigAG-199
- 96LeaSigAS-199
- 96MetKah-28
- 96MetMod-9
- 96MetUni-157
- 96MetUniP-157
- 96Pac-63
- 96PanSti-82
- 96Pin-251
- 96PinArtP-151
- 96PinFoil-251
- 96PinSta-151
- 96RocFle-13
- 96RocPol-21
- 96Sco-292
- 96ScoDugC-B17
- 96ScoDugCAP-B17
- 96StaClu-55
- 96StaCluMOP-55
- 96Top-292
- 96TopChrMotG-14
- 96TopChrMotGR-14
- 96TopMasotG-14
- 96Ult-475
- 96UltGolM-475
- 96UppDec-61
- 98Bow-279
- 98BowChr-279
- 98BowChrGA-279
- 98BowChrGAR-279
- 98BowChrI-279
- 98BowChrIR-279
- 98BowChrR-279
- 98BowGolA-279
- 98BowInt-279
- 98ColCho-46
- 98PacOnl-125
- 98PacOnlR-125
- 98PacOnlWC-125
- 98PinSna-BRS18
- 98SpoIllWSFMC-4
- 99FlaShoLeg1-127
- 99FlaShoLeg2-127
- 99FlaShoLeg3-127
- 99FlaShoLegM1-127
- 99FlaShoLegM2-127
- 99FlaShoLegM3-127
- 99FlaShoR1-127
- 99FlaShoR2-127
- 99FlaShoR3-127
- 99Fle-452
- 99FleSta9-452
- 99FleWarT-452
- 99MetUni-169
- 99MetUniGM-169
- 99MetUniPMG-169
- 99Pac-73
- 99PacCroC-49
- 99PacCroCPB-49
- 99PacPlaB-73
- 99PacRed-73
- 99SkyPre-134
- 99SkyPreR-134
- 99SkyThu-185
- 99SkyThuRant-185
- 99SkyThuRave-185
- 99SpoIll-89
- 99StaClu-239
- 99StaCluFDI-239
- 99StaCluOoaK-239
- 99StaCluPP-239
- 99ThuSkySupR-185
- 99Top-122
- 99TopChr-122
- 99TopChrR-122
- 99TopMVPP-122
- 99TopOpeD-71
- 99Ult-135
- 99UltGolM-135
- 99UltMas-135
- 99UltPlaM-135
- 99UppDec-55
- 99UppDecEL1-55
- 99UppDecEL2-55
- 99Vic-71

Sabino, Miguel

- 87SumBraP-3
- 88GreBraB-7
- 89GreBraB-27
- 89GreBraP-1170
- 89GreBraS-21
- 90CanIndB-15
- 90CanIndP-1305
- 90CanIndS-16
- 90CMC-721
- 91CanIndLD-94
- 91CanIndP-992
- 91LinDriAA-94
- 93LimRocDWB-36

Sable, Luke

- 88GasRanP-1002
- 89ChaRanS-21
- 90ChaRanS-25
- 91LinDriAA-595
- 91TulDriLD-595
- 91TulDriP-2782
- 91TulDriTI-27
- 92TulDriF-2704
- 92TulDriS-619
- 93OklCit8F-1634

Sabo, Chris

- 87NasSouTI-18
- 88DonBasB-278
- 88DonRoo-30
- 88FleSlu-35
- 88FleUpd-87
- 88FleUpdG-87
- 88RedKah-17
- 88ScoRoo-100T
- 88ScoRooG-100T
- 88TarPla-35
- 88Top-288
- 88TopTra-98T
- 88TopTraT-98T
- 89Baz-18
- 89Bow-309
- 89BowTif-309
- 89CedRapRAB-4
- 89ClaLigB-53
- 89Don-4
- 89Don-317
- 89DonAll-59
- 89DonBasB-222
- 89DonSupD-4
- 89Fle-170
- 89Fle-637
- 89FleBasM-33
- 89FleExcS-35
- 89FleGlo-170
- 89FleGlo-637
- 89FleSup-35
- 89FleWaxBC-C21
- 89K-M-3
- 89KinDis-7
- 89OPC-156
- 89PanSti-64
- 89PanSti-476
- 89RedKah-17
- 89Sco-104
- 89ScoHot1R-76
- 89ScoYouSI-10
- 89Spo-13
- 89SpoIllFKI-48
- 89Top-490
- 89TopBasT-140
- 89TopBig-251
- 89TopCoi-3
- 89TopGaloC-9
- 89TopGloS-40
- 89TopMinL-13
- 89TopRoo-17
- 89TopSti-142
- 89TopSti-325
- 89TopTif-490
- 89TopUKM-65
- 89ToyRoo-24
- 89TVSpoM-38
- 89TVSpoM-139
- 89UppDec-180
- 89UppDec-663
- 89Woo-6
- 90Bow-53
- 90BowTif-53
- 90CedRapRDGB-4
- 90ClaUpd-T43
- 90Don-242
- 90DonBesN-64
- 90Fle-433
- 90FleCan-433
- 90KinDis-10
- 90Lea-146
- 90M.Vpin-30
- 90MLBBasB-19
- 90MSAIceTD-3
- 90OPC-737
- 90PanSti-248
- 90PubIntS-39
- 90RedKah-25
- 90Sco-70
- 90StaLonJS-20
- 90StaLonJS-25
- 90SupActM-12
- 90Top-737
- 90TopBig-121
- 90TopMag-18
- 90TopSti-140
- 90TopTif-737
- 90UppDec-181
- 90USPlaCA-5H
- 91Bow-674
- 91CadEIID-47
- 91Cla1-T26
- 91ClaGam-108
- 91Don-153
- 91Don-412
- 91Don-440
- 91Fle-80
- 91FleWorS-5
- 91Lea-65
- 91MooSna-21
- 91OPC-45
- 91PanFreS-129
- 91PanFreS-160
- 91PanSti-127
- 91Pos-13
- 91PosCan-10
- 91RedFolS-81
- 91RedFolS-125
- 91RedKah-17
- 91RedPep-19
- 91Sco-462
- 91Sco-795
- 91Sco100S-28
- 91SimandSMLBL-38
- 91StaClu-165
- 91StaPinB-41
- 91Stu-170
- 91Top-45
- 91TopCraJ2-29
- 91TopDesS-45
- 91TopGloA-15
- 91TopMic-45
- 91TopTif-45
- 91TopTriH-N3
- 91Ult-103
- 91UltGol-9
- 91UppDec-77
- 91UppDec-135
- 91UppDecFE-94F
- 91USPlaCA-12C
- 91Woo-29
- 92Bow-595
- 92ClaGam-79
- 92Don-50
- 92Don-424
- 92DonCraJ2-16
- 92Fle-420
- 92FleTeaL-3
- 92Fre-14
- 92Hig5-35
- 92HitTheBB-29
- 92JimDea-6
- 92KinDis-2
- 92Lea-271
- 92LeaBlaG-271
- 92LeaGolP-3
- 92LeaPre-3
- 92Mr.TurS-21
- 92MVPPin-44
- 92OPC-485
- 92OPCPre-23
- 92PanSti-264
- 92PanSti-283
- 92Pin-135
- 92RedFolS-83
- 92RedFolS-125
- 92RedKah-17
- 92Sco-70
- 92StaClu-273
- 92StaCluD-160
- 92Stu-28
- 92SunSee-10
- 92Top-485
- 92TopGol-485
- 92TopGolW-485
- 92TopKid-39
- 92TopMic-485
- 92TriPla-90
- 92Ult-197
- 92UppDec-123
- 92UppDecF-38
- 92UppDecFG-38
- 93Bow-286
- 93CadDis-50
- 93Don-58
- 93Fin-39
- 93FinRef-39
- 93Fla-33
- 93Fle-43
- 93Lea-418
- 93OPC-333
- 93PacSpa-90
- 93PanSti-294
- 93Pin-47
- 93RedKah-22
- 93Sco-149
- 93Sel-135
- 93SP-215
- 93StaClu-286
- 93StaCluFDI-286
- 93StaCluMOP-286
- 93Stu-73
- 93Top-245
- 93TopGol-245
- 93TopInaM-245
- 93TopInaR-245
- 93TopMic-245
- 93TriPla-184
- 93Ult-35
- 93UppDec-147
- 93UppDecGold-147
- 94BalOriP-30
- 94Bow-187
- 94ColC-485
- 94ColChoGS-485
- 94ColChoSS-485
- 94Don-330
- 94Fin-418
- 94FinRef-418
- 94Fla-9
- 94Fle-425
- 94FleExtB-13
- 94FleUpd-6
- 94Lea-324
- 94OPC-136
- 94OriPro-87
- 94OriUSPC-6D
- 94Pac-158
- 94PanSti-168
- 94Pin-490
- 94PinArtP-490
- 94PinMusC-490
- 94Sco-360
- 94ScoGolR-360
- 94ScoRoo-RT17
- 94ScoRooGR-RT17
- 94Sel-314
- 94SpoRoo-51
- 94SpoRooAP-51
- 94StaClu-676
- 94StaCluFDI-676
- 94StaCluGR-676
- 94StaCluMOP-676
- 94StaCluT-291
- 94StaCluTFDI-291
- 94Top-542
- 94TopGol-542
- 94TopSpa-542
- 94TopTra-125T
- 94TriPla-160
- 94Ult-310

❑ 94UppDec-347
❑ 94UppDecED-347
❑ 95ColCho-333
❑ 95ColChoGS-333
❑ 95ColChoSS-333
❑ 95Fle-20
❑ 95FleUpd-38
❑ 95Lea-314
❑ 95Pin-405
❑ 95PinArtP-405
❑ 95PinMusC-405
❑ 95Sco-385
❑ 95ScoGolR-385
❑ 95ScoPlaTS-385
❑ 95Top-137
❑ 95TopCyb-84
❑ 95UppDec-433
❑ 95UppDecED-433
❑ 95UppDecEDG-433
❑ 95UppDecSE-152
❑ 95UppDecSEG-152
❑ 96FleUpd-U125
❑ 96FleUpdTC-U125
❑ 96Ult-466
❑ 96UltGolM-466
Sabo, Scott
❑ 84IdaFalATI-24
❑ 85MadMusP-21
❑ 85MadMusT-1
❑ 86MadMusP-17
❑ 86MadMusP-19
❑ 87WilBilP-20
Sabol, Tony
❑ 46RemBre-13
❑ 47RemBre-15
❑ 47SigOil-53
❑ 47SmiClo-13
Saccavino, Craig
❑ 92EliTwiC-3
❑ 92EliTwiF-3681
❑ 93ForMyeMC-23
❑ 93ForMyeMF-2654
❑ 94ForMyeMC-22
❑ 94ForMyeMF-1169
Saccomanno, Joseph
❑ 89BurBraP-1600
❑ 89BurBraS-19
Sachen, Bob
❑ 85RedWinA-8
❑ 86RedWinA-7
Sachs, Brent
❑ 98MadBlaW-15
Sachse, Matt
❑ 95Bow-96
❑ 95EveAqaTI-19
❑ 96BesAutSA-64
❑ 96EveAquB-20
❑ 97WisTimR-22
❑ 98LanJetG-20
Sacka, Frank
❑ 89ChaLooLITI-26
Sackinsky, Brian
❑ 92ClaDraP-28
❑ 92ClaFS7-420
❑ 93AlbPolF-2025
❑ 93ClaFS7-59
❑ 93StaCluM-160
❑ 93Top-647
❑ 93TopGol-647
❑ 93TopInaM-647
❑ 93TopInaR-647
❑ 93TopMic-647
❑ 94BowBayF-2414
❑ 94ExcFS7-15
❑ 94OriPro-88
❑ 94UppDecML-191
❑ 95Bow-8
❑ 95RocRedWTI-32
❑ 95Top-429
❑ 95UppDecML-134
❑ 95UppDecMLFS-134
❑ 96RocRedWB-23
Sadecki, Ray
❑ 60Top-327
❑ 61Top-32
❑ 62Top-383
❑ 62TopStal-190
❑ 63CarJayP-16
❑ 63CarJayP-17
❑ 63Top-486
❑ 64CarTeal-7
❑ 64Top-147
❑ 64TopVen-147
❑ 65CarTeal-19
❑ 65OPC-10
❑ 65OPC-230
❑ 65Top-10
❑ 65Top-230
❑ 66OPC-26
❑ 66Top-26
❑ 66TopVen-26
❑ 67CokCapG-14
❑ 67Top-409
❑ 67TopVen-323
❑ 68DexPre-69
❑ 68Top-494
❑ 69MilBra-244
❑ 69OPC-125
❑ 69Top-125
❑ 69TopFou-17
❑ 70Top-679
❑ 71MLBOffS-163
❑ 71OPC-406
❑ 71Top-406
❑ 72MilBra-303
❑ 72Top-563
❑ 72Top-564
❑ 73OPC-283
❑ 73Top-283
❑ 74MetDaiPA-12
❑ 74OPC-216
❑ 74Top-216
❑ 75AtlBraP-32
❑ 75OPC-349
❑ 75SSP18-14
❑ 75St.LouCP-24
❑ 75Top-349
❑ 75TopMin-349
❑ 77MetDaiPA-20
❑ 77Top-26
❑ 91MetWIZ-339
❑ 92PeoChiTI-22
❑ 94BreMilB-73
Sadecki, Steve
❑ 92ChaRanF-2225
❑ 92ClaFS7-113
❑ 92GasRanC-2
❑ 93ChaRanC-19
❑ 93ChaRanF-1940
❑ 94TulDriF-244
❑ 94TulDriTI-21
Sadek, Mike
❑ 74OPC-577
❑ 74PhoGiaC-81
❑ 74Top-577
❑ 75PhoGiaCK-3
❑ 76OPC-234
❑ 76SanFraGP-20
❑ 76Top-234
❑ 77Gia-20
❑ 77GiaTeal-21
❑ 77Top-129
❑ 78GiaTeal-23
❑ 78Top-8
❑ 79GiaPol-3
❑ 79Top-256
❑ 80GiaPol-3
❑ 80GiaTeal-25
❑ 80OPC-240
❑ 80Top-462
❑ 81Don-498
❑ 81GiaTeal-17
❑ 81Top-384
❑ 96GiaMot-28
Sadler, Al
❑ 97El PasDB-20
❑ 98El PasDG-29
Sadler, Alan
❑ 85BelBreT-21
❑ 86StoPorP-24
❑ 87ElPasDP-24
❑ 88StoPorCLC-181
❑ 88StoPorP-726
❑ 89BlaYNPRWLU-22
❑ 89DenZepC-9
❑ 89DenZepP-44
❑ 90CMC-44
❑ 90DenZepC-19
❑ 90DenZepP-626
❑ 90ProAAAF-651
❑ 93BelBreCB-21
❑ 93BelBreFI-1708
Sadler, Donnie
❑ 95Bes-7
❑ 95Bow-191
❑ 95MicBatCTI-24
❑ 95MidLeaA-50
❑ 96BesAutSA-65
❑ 96Bow-376
❑ 96BowBes-165
❑ 96BowBesAR-165
❑ 96BowBesMI-6
❑ 96BowBesMIAR-6
❑ 96BowBesMIR-6
❑ 96BowBesR-165
❑ 96BowFoi-376
❑ 96Exc-18
❑ 96TreThuB-29
❑ 97Bes-35
❑ 97BesAutAS-49
❑ 97BesAutP-H8
❑ 97BesAutSBPP-11
❑ 97BesWhe-1
❑ 97Bow-140
❑ 97BowBes-193
❑ 97BowBesAR-193
❑ 97BowBesMI-MI8
❑ 97BowBesMIAR-MI8
❑ 97BowBesMIARI-MI8
❑ 97BowBesMII-MI8
❑ 97BowBesMIR-MI8
❑ 97BowBesMIRI-MI8
❑ 97BowBesR-193
❑ 97BowCerBlaIA-CA72
❑ 97BowCerBluIA-CA72
❑ 97BowCerGolIA-CA72
❑ 97BowChr-148
❑ 97BowChrI-148
❑ 97BowChrIR-148
❑ 97BowChrR-148
❑ 97BowInt-140
❑ 97PawRedS-24
❑ 98Bow-201
❑ 98BowBes-117
❑ 98BowBesAR-117
❑ 98BowBesR-117
❑ 98BowChr-201
❑ 98BowChrGA-201
❑ 98BowChrGAR-201
❑ 98BowChrI-201
❑ 98BowChrIR-201
❑ 98BowChrR-201
❑ 98BowGolA-201
❑ 98BowInt-201
❑ 98Don-337
❑ 98DonGolPP-337
❑ 98DonSilPP-337
❑ 98Fle-440
❑ 98LeaRS-279
❑ 98LeaRSLHolo-279
❑ 98LeaRSLong-279
❑ 98LeaRTrue-279
❑ 98PacOnl-126
❑ 98PacOnlR-126
❑ 98PacOnlWC-126
❑ 98PawRedSQ-25
❑ 98SP MinPE-28
❑ 98SPMin-28
❑ 98Ult-280
❑ 98UltGolM-280
❑ 98UltMas-280
❑ 98UltPlaM-280
❑ 99Fle-549
❑ 99FleSta9-549
❑ 99FleWarT-549
❑ 99PacInv-27
❑ 99PacInvOD-27
❑ 99PacInvPB-27
❑ 99PacPar-44
❑ 99PacParC-44
❑ 99PacParG-44
❑ 99PacParHoloGold-44
❑ 99PacParHS-44
❑ 99PacParOD-44
❑ 99PacParPB-44
❑ 99PacParRed-44
❑ 99SP Aut-16
❑ 99SP SigAuto-DS
❑ 99SpoIll-65
❑ 99SPSig-136
❑ 99UppDecM-35
❑ 99UppDecMGS-35
❑ 99UppDecMHFS-35
❑ 99UppDecMSS-35
❑ 99Vic-68
Sadler, Sean
❑ 90NiaFalRP-14
❑ 91FayGenC-15
❑ 91FayGenP-1173
Sadowski, Ed
❑ 59Top-139
❑ 59TopVen-139
❑ 60Lea-113
❑ 60Top-403
❑ 61Top-163
❑ 62AngJayP-10
❑ 62Top-569
❑ 63AngJayP-16
❑ 63Top-527
❑ 64Top-61
❑ 64TopVen-61
Sadowski, Jim
❑ 76VenLeaS-92
Sadowski, Robert F.
❑ 61TopStal-174
❑ 62KahAtl-17
❑ 62Top-595
❑ 63Top-568
❑ 64BraJayP-10
❑ 64Top-271
❑ 64TopVen-271
❑ 65BraTeal-11
❑ 65OPC-156
❑ 65Top-156
❑ 66RedSoxTI-12
❑ 66Top-523
❑ 67SeaPop-15
❑ 78TCM60I-167
Sadowski, Ted
❑ 61SyrChi-2
❑ 61Top-254
❑ 61TwiCloD-24
Sadowsky, Clinton
❑ 91BriTigC-17
❑ 91BriTigP-3604
Saeki, Kazushi
❑ 79TCMJapPB-36
Saenz, Jason
❑ 99TeaBesR-77
❑ 99TeaBesRFS-14
❑ 99TeaBesRG-77
❑ 99TeaBesRS-77
Saenz, Olmedo
❑ 92SouBenWSC-13
❑ 92SouBenWSF-187
❑ 93SarWhiSC-23
❑ 93SarWhiSF-1379
❑ 94BowBes-B84
❑ 94BowBesR-B84
❑ 94ExcFS7-40
❑ 94NasSouF-1259
❑ 95ColCho-497
❑ 95ColChoGS-497
❑ 95ColChoSS-497
❑ 95LinVen-152
❑ 95NasSouTI-21
❑ 95Pac-96
❑ 95Top-634
❑ 96Bow-313
❑ 96BowFoi-313
❑ 96NasSouB-20
❑ 98PitMetM-28
❑ 99PacOme-176
❑ 99PacOmeC-176
❑ 99PacOmeG-176
❑ 99PacOmePB-176
❑ 99Rev-104
❑ 99RevPremDate-104
❑ 99RevRet-104
❑ 99RevShaSS-104
Saetre, Damon
❑ 90PenPilS-19
❑ 91PenPilC-16
❑ 91PenPilP-392
Saferight, Harry
❑ 75ShrCapT-18
❑ 76ShrCapT-18
❑ 77ShrCapT-20
❑ 78ColCliT-21
❑ 79PorBeaT-21
❑ 80RicBraT-16
❑ 80Top-683
❑ 81RicBraT-24
❑ 82TolMudHT-10
Saffell, Tom
❑ 49PorBeaP-3
❑ 51Bow-130
❑ 52MotCoo-36
❑ 59DarFar-20
Saffer, Jeffrey
❑ 96GreBatB-23
❑ 97GreBatB-25
Saffer, Jon
❑ 93ClaGolF-140
❑ 93JamExpC-20
❑ 93JamExpF-3339
❑ 93StaCluM-166
❑ 94VerExpC-19
❑ 94VerExpF-3922
❑ 96HarSenB-24
Safly, Joel
❑ 90VisOakCLC-82
❑ 92VisOakC-26
❑ 93ForMyeMC-28
Sagawa, Kiyoshi
❑ 89VisOakCLC-103
❑ 89VisOakP-1434
Sage, Henry
❑ 87OldJudN-428
❑ 87OldJudN-429
Sagedal, Brent
❑ 95HudValRTI-25
Sager, A.J.
❑ 88SpoIndP-1933
❑ 89ChaRaiP-971
❑ 90WicWraRD-18
❑ 91LinDriAA-617
❑ 91WicWraLD-617
❑ 91WicWraP-2597
❑ 91WicWraRD-8
❑ 92LasVegSF-2795
❑ 92LasVegSS-238
❑ 94Bow-474
❑ 94PadMot-18
❑ 95Pac-370
❑ 96TolMudHB-25
❑ 97ColSprSATTI-6
❑ 97Fle-105
❑ 97FleTif-105
❑ 97PacPriGotD-GD44
❑ 98PacInvGems-50
❑ 98PacOnl-285
❑ 98PacOnlR-285
❑ 98PacOnlWC-285
Sagmoen, Marc
❑ 93EriSaiC-20
❑ 93EriSaiF-3130
❑ 94ChaRanF-2509
❑ 96TulDriTI-22
❑ 97Fle-586
❑ 97FleTif-586
❑ 97Ult-537
❑ 97UltGolME-537
❑ 97UltPlaME-537
❑ 98OklRedM-13
Saier, Matt
❑ 95SpoIndTI-23
❑ 96WilBluRB-26
❑ 97WilBluR-24
❑ 98OmaRoyM-19
Saier, Vic
❑ 12T207-159
❑ 14CraJacE-104
❑ 14FatPlaT-42
❑ 15CraJacE-104
❑ 15SpoNewM-152
❑ 16BF2FP-69
❑ 16SpoNewM-152
❑ 17ColE13-148
Sailors, Jamie
❑ 93JohCitCC-17
❑ 93JohCitCF-3674
❑ 94MadHatC-20
❑ 94MadHatF-130
Sain, Joe
❑ 83WisRapTF-5
Sain, Johnny
❑ 46SpoExcW-7-6
❑ 47Exh-198
❑ 47HomBon-42
❑ 47TipTop-85
❑ 48Bow-12
❑ 49Bow-47
❑ 49EurSta-21
❑ 49MPR302-2-122
❑ 50AmeNut&CCP-16
❑ 51Bow-314
❑ 51FisBakL-24
❑ 51TopBluB-9
❑ 52BerRos-59
❑ 52Top-49A
❑ 52Top-49B
❑ 53BowBW-25
❑ 53Dor-116
❑ 53Dor-116A
❑ 53Top-119
❑ 54Top-205
❑ 55A'sRodM-33
❑ 55A'sTeal-20
❑ 55Top-193
❑ 61Yan61RL-39
❑ 62SaiSpiP-1
❑ 68TigDetFPB-20
❑ 73BooProC-12
❑ 73OPC-356
❑ 73Top-356
❑ 74OPC-221
❑ 74Top-221
❑ 75SSP42-2
❑ 76A'sRodMC-21
❑ 76TayBow4-40
❑ 78AtlCon-21
❑ 78RicBraT-14
❑ 79RicBraT-3
❑ 80RicBraT-9
❑ 81RicBraT-1
❑ 81TCM60I-481
❑ 82RicBraT-28
❑ 83ASAWS-4
❑ 83RicBraT-25
❑ 83TopRep5-49
❑ 83Yan196-NNO
❑ 83YanASFY-40
❑ 84RicBraT-26
❑ 84TCMPla1-35
❑ 85BraPol-33
❑ 86BraPol-33
❑ 89SweBasG-121
❑ 91TopArc1-119
❑ 92BazQua5A-15
❑ 92YanWIZA-73
❑ 93ActPacA-136
❑ 94TopArc1-205
❑ 94TopArc1G-205
Sain, Tom
❑ 76TacTwiDQ-18
❑ 77TacTwiDQ-7
❑ 78OrlTwiT-17
❑ 79TolMudHT-15
Saints, St Paul
❑ 38BasTabP-45
Saipe, Mike
❑ 94BenRocC-21
❑ 94BenRocF-3593
❑ 95SalAvaTI-19
❑ 96NewHavRB-21
❑ 97NewHavRB-23
❑ 97TexAllM-52
❑ 98Bow-352
❑ 98BowChr-352
❑ 98BowChrGA-352
❑ 98BowChrGAR-352
❑ 98BowChrI-352
❑ 98BowChrIR-352
❑ 98BowChrR-352
❑ 98BowGolA-352
❑ 98BowInt-352
❑ 98ColSprSS-28
Saitoh, Takayuki
❑ 96HonShaHWB-4
Saitta, Pat
❑ 87DunBluJP-951
Saitta, Rich
❑ 96YakBeaTI-4
❑ 97YakBeaG-29
❑ 98SanBerS-26
❑ 98SanBerSTIS-23
Saitz, Robbie
❑ 91FreStaBS-11
❑ 92ClaFS7-361
❑ 92PalSprAC-2
❑ 92PalSprAF-838
Sajonia, Brian
❑ 88JamExpP-1907
Sak, James
❑ 96CliLumKTI-23
❑ 96RanCucQB-24
❑ 97RanCucQG-25
❑ 98MobBayBTI-25
Sakamoto, Toshizo
❑ 79TCMJapPB-3
Sakata, Lenn
❑ 76SpoIndC-19
❑ 77SpoIndC-11
❑ 79VanCanT-22B
❑ 80BalOriP-17
❑ 80Top-668
❑ 81BalOriP-17
❑ 81Don-499
❑ 81Fle-194
❑ 81Top-287
❑ 82Don-644
❑ 82Fle-178
❑ 82Top-136
❑ 83Don-205
❑ 83Fle-72
❑ 83OriPos-27
❑ 83Top-319
❑ 84BalOriP-32
❑ 84Don-620
❑ 84Fle-19
❑ 84Nes792-578
❑ 84Top-578
❑ 84TopTif-578
❑ 85BalOriP-29
❑ 85Fle-189

❑ 85Top-81
❑ 85TopTif-81
❑ 86TacTigP-20
❑ 86Top-446
❑ 86TopTif-446
❑ 88SouOreAP-1717
❑ 88Top-716
❑ 88TopClo-97
❑ 88TopTif-716
❑ 89ModA'sCLC-288
❑ 91EdmTraLD-175
❑ 91EdmTraP-1533
❑ 91LinDriAAA-175
❑ 91OriCro-399
❑ 91PacSenL-91
❑ 92EdmTraF-3555
❑ 92EdmTraS-175
❑ 92YanWIZ8-167
❑ 93VanCanF-2615
❑ 94BreMilB-74
❑ 94VanCanF-1880

Sakowski, Vince
❑ 83TriTriT-19

Sakumoto, Masahiro
❑ 96MauStiHWB-16

Sakurai, Teruhide
❑ 79TCMJapPB-65

Sala, David J.
❑ 87SprCarB-16
❑ 89SavCarP-367

Salado, Jose
❑ 74SacSolC-56

Salado, Tim
❑ 94OgdRapF-3737
❑ 94OgdRapSP-21

Salaiz, David
❑ 89ColMudB-5
❑ 89ColMudP-138

Salamon, John
❑ 91MarPhiC-18
❑ 91MarPhiP-3453
❑ 93AugPirC-17
❑ 93AugPirF-1542
❑ 94BelBreC-21
❑ 94BelBreFl-98
❑ 94MidLeaAF-MDW10
❑ 95AusFut-46
❑ 98NewHavRM-26
❑ 98NewHavRMA-26

Salas, Jose
❑ 76VenLeaS-127

Salas, Mark
❑ 82ArkTraT-11
❑ 82NasSouTl-20
❑ 83ArkTraT-12
❑ 84Car-26
❑ 84LouRedR-27
❑ 85Don-547
❑ 85FleUpd-94
❑ 85TopTifT-101T
❑ 85TopTra-101T
❑ 85TwiPos-22
❑ 85TwiTeal-9
❑ 85TwiTeal-19
❑ 86Don-316
❑ 86Fle-402
❑ 86FleStiC-104
❑ 86KayB-28
❑ 86Lea-185
❑ 86OPC-43
❑ 86Spo-177
❑ 86Spo-178
❑ 86Top-537
❑ 86TopSti-278
❑ 86TopSti-315
❑ 86TopTat-17
❑ 86TopTif-537
❑ 86TwiTeal-8
❑ 87Fle-551
❑ 87FleGlo-551
❑ 87FleUpd-106
❑ 87FleUpdG-106
❑ 87OPC-87
❑ 87SpoTeaP-17
❑ 87Top-87
❑ 87TopTif-87
❑ 87TopTra-107T
❑ 87TopTraT-107T
❑ 87TwiPos-23
❑ 88Sco-232
❑ 88ScoGlo-232
❑ 88ScoRoo-52T
❑ 88ScoRooG-52T
❑ 88StaLinWS-16
❑ 88TopTra-99T
❑ 88TopTraT-99T
❑ 88WhiSoxC-26
❑ 89ColSprSSC-20
❑ 89ColSprSSP-240
❑ 89Fle-511
❑ 89FleGlo-511
❑ 89Sco-542
❑ 89Top-384
❑ 89TopTif-384
❑ 89UppDec-460
❑ 90TigCok-21
❑ 91Don-65
❑ 91Fle-350
❑ 91OPC-498
❑ 91StaClu-456
❑ 91TigCok-27
❑ 91TigPol-10
❑ 91Top-498
❑ 91TopDesS-498
❑ 91TopMic-498
❑ 91TopTif-498
❑ 91Ult-127
❑ 91UppDec-205
❑ 92Don-512
❑ 92Fle-144
❑ 92Sco-394
❑ 92YanWIZ8-168
❑ 93HicCraC-29
❑ 93HicCraF-1297
❑ 95WhiSoxK-31

Salava, Randy
❑ 82ReaPhiT-18
❑ 83ReaPhiT-19
❑ 84PorBeaC-203
❑ 85PhiTas-45
❑ 85PorBeaC-37

Salazar, Angel (Argenis)
❑ 80VenLeaS-209
❑ 83WicAerDS-19
❑ 84Don-33
❑ 84ExpPos-27
❑ 84ExpStu-31
❑ 85Don-523
❑ 85OPC-154
❑ 85Top-154
❑ 85TopMin-154
❑ 85TopTif-154
❑ 86FleUpd-100
❑ 86RoyTeal-23
❑ 86TopTra-96T
❑ 86TopTraT-96T
❑ 87Don-624
❑ 87Fle-380
❑ 87FleGlo-380
❑ 87Top-533
❑ 87TopSti-259
❑ 87TopTif-533
❑ 88CubDavB-18
❑ 88Don-502
❑ 88DonTeaBC-NEW
❑ 88Fle-269
❑ 88FleGlo-269
❑ 88OPC-29
❑ 88PanSti-109
❑ 88Sco-330
❑ 88ScoGlo-330
❑ 88Top-29
❑ 88TopTif-29
❑ 89Sco-527
❑ 89Top-642
❑ 89TopTif-642
❑ 89UppDec-222

Salazar, Carlos
❑ 90SouOreAB-19
❑ 90SouOreAP-3436
❑ 91ModA'sP-3099
❑ 92ModA'sC-19
❑ 92ModA'sF-3907

Salazar, Jeff
❑ 83PeoSunF-17

Salazar, Jeremy
❑ 98BatMucTl-27

Salazar, Juan
❑ 97RocCub-27
❑ 98RocCubM-25
❑ 98RocCubTl-26

Salazar, Julian
❑ 91BelBreCB-16
❑ 91BelBreP-2112
❑ 92StoPorF-42
❑ 93PocPosF-4218
❑ 93PocPosSP-22

Salazar, Lazerio
❑ 86NegLeaF-93

Salazar, Luis Ernesto
❑ 76VenLeaS-134
❑ 77SalPirT-23
❑ 78SalPirT-15
❑ 79BufBisT-16
❑ 80PorBeaT-9
❑ 80VenLeaS-200
❑ 81Fle-501
❑ 81PadFamF-16
❑ 81Top-309
❑ 81TopSti-228
❑ 82Don-472
❑ 82Fle-581
❑ 82OPC-133
❑ 82Top-366
❑ 82Top-662
❑ 82TopSti-101
❑ 82TopStiV-101
❑ 83Don-548
❑ 83Fle-371
❑ 83OPC-156
❑ 83PadTeal-22
❑ 83Top-533
❑ 84Don-356
❑ 84Fle-311
❑ 84Nes792-68
❑ 84OPC-68
❑ 84PadMot-24
❑ 84PadSmo-20
❑ 84Top-68
❑ 84TopSti-159
❑ 84TopTif-68
❑ 85Don-568
❑ 85Fle-43
❑ 85FleUpd-95
❑ 85Top-789
❑ 85TopTif-789
❑ 85TopTifT-102T
❑ 85TopTra-102T
❑ 85WhiSoxC-5
❑ 86Don-302
❑ 86Fle-215
❑ 86Top-103
❑ 86TopTif-103
❑ 87Top-454
❑ 87TopTif-454
❑ 87TopTra-108T
❑ 87TopTraT-108T
❑ 88Fle-595
❑ 88FleGlo-595
❑ 88FleUpd-30
❑ 88FleUpdG-30
❑ 88OPC-276
❑ 88Sco-284
❑ 88ScoGlo-284
❑ 88ScoRoo-13T
❑ 88ScoRooG-13T
❑ 88TigPep-12
❑ 88Top-276
❑ 88TopTif-276
❑ 88TopTra-100T
❑ 88TopTraT-100T
❑ 89ClaLigB-72
❑ 89Don-352
❑ 89Fle-144
❑ 89FleGlo-144
❑ 89OPC-122
❑ 89PadCok-15
❑ 89PadPos-27
❑ 89PanSti-342
❑ 89Sco-316
❑ 89Top-553
❑ 89TopSti-276
❑ 89TopTif-553
❑ 89TopTra-107T
❑ 89TopTraT-107T
❑ 89UppDec-136
❑ 90Bow-40
❑ 90BowTif-40
❑ 90BriTigP-3164
❑ 90BriTigS-22
❑ 90CubMar-17
❑ 90Don-513
❑ 90FleUpd-9
❑ 90Lea-388
❑ 90OPC-378
❑ 90Sco-92
❑ 90Top-378
❑ 90TopBig-182
❑ 90TopTif-378
❑ 90TopTVCu-25
❑ 90UppDec-6
❑ 91Bow-428
❑ 91CubMar-10
❑ 91CubVinL-24
❑ 91Don-372
❑ 91Fle-430
❑ 91Lea-185
❑ 91OPC-614
❑ 91PanFreS-45
❑ 91Sco-207
❑ 91StaClu-94
❑ 91Top-614
❑ 91TopDesS-614
❑ 91TopMic-614
❑ 91TopTif-614
❑ 91Ult-67
❑ 91UppDec-311
❑ 92CubMar-10
❑ 92Don-152
❑ 92OPC-67
❑ 92PanSti-184
❑ 92Pin-372
❑ 92Sco-508
❑ 92StaClu-21
❑ 92Top-67
❑ 92TopGol-67
❑ 92TopGolW-67
❑ 92TopMic-67
❑ 92Ult-179
❑ 92UppDec-638
❑ 93Fle-383
❑ 93PacSpa-60
❑ 93StaClu-549
❑ 93StaCluFDI-549
❑ 93StaCluMOP-549
❑ 93Top-21
❑ 93TopGol-21
❑ 93TopInaM-21
❑ 93TopInaR-21
❑ 93TopMic-21
❑ 95LinVen-257
❑ 96BelSnaTl-33
❑ 97BelSnaB-2
❑ 98LouRedQ-33

Salazar, Luis R.
❑ 88St.CatBJP-2006
❑ 93LinVenB-1
❑ 93LinVenB-207
❑ 93LinVenB-343
❑ 94VenLinU-60
❑ 94VenLinU-255
❑ 95LinVen-210
❑ 95LinVen-252
❑ 96-97LinVen-188
❑ 96StoPorB-10

Salazar, Mike
❑ 93NiaFalRF-3389
❑ 94FayGenC-21
❑ 94FayGenF-2144
❑ 96LakTigB-22

Salazar, Terry
❑ 81BufBisT-21

Salazar, Tomas
❑ 96-97LinVen-223

Salcedo, Edwin
❑ 90TamYanD-19
❑ 92PriWilCC-14
❑ 92PriWilCF-153
❑ 94TamYanF-2387

Salcedo, Jose
❑ 91KisDodP-4182
❑ 94StoPorC-23
❑ 94StoPorF-1694

Salcedo, Luis
❑ 87MadMusP-16
❑ 87MadMusP-24

Salcedo, Ron
❑ 84ChaO'sT-4
❑ 85ChaO'sT-11
❑ 86ChaOriW-27
❑ 87RocRedWP-4
❑ 87RocRedWT-19
❑ 88RocRedWC-16
❑ 88RocRedWGCP-24
❑ 88RocRedWP-200
❑ 88RocRedWTI-19
❑ 89ScrRedBC-16
❑ 89ScrRedBP-707
❑ 90HagSunDGB-24

Salcedo, Yamil
❑ 94TamYanC-22
❑ 95NorNavTl-45

Salery, Johnny
❑ 82WisRapTF-9
❑ 83WisRapTF-13

Saleski, Stan
❑ 77ForLauYS-24

Salfran, Francisco
❑ 52LavPro-110

Salinas, Manual V.
❑ 86BirBarTl-2
❑ 87BirBarB-23
❑ 88JacMetGS-18
❑ 88TexLeaAGS-14
❑ 89JacMetGS-13
❑ 89TidTidP-1951

Salinas, Trey
❑ 96ButCopKB-27

Salinsen, Michael
❑ 33Zee-74

Salisbury, Jim
❑ 86SumBraP-24
❑ 87DurBulP-24

Salkeld, Bill
❑ 33Zee-141
❑ 49Bow-88A
❑ 49Bow-88B
❑ 49EurSta-22
❑ 50Bow-237

Salkeld, Roger
❑ 89BelMarL-13
❑ 90Bes-14
❑ 90Bow-465
❑ 90BowTif-465
❑ 90CalLeaACLC-21
❑ 90CMC-858
❑ 90OPC-44
❑ 90ProAaA-135
❑ 90SanBerSB-1
❑ 90SanBerSCLC-87
❑ 90SanBerSP-2632
❑ 90Sco-674
❑ 90Top-44
❑ 90TopMag-75
❑ 90TopTif-44
❑ 91Bow-262
❑ 91Cla/Bes-106
❑ 91Cla2-T59
❑ 91JacSunLD-344
❑ 91JacSunP-151
❑ 91LeaGolR-BC19
❑ 91LinDriAA-344
❑ 91UppDec-63
❑ 92Bow-369
❑ 92CalCanS-51
❑ 92Don-7
❑ 92OPC-676
❑ 92ProFS7-140
❑ 92SkyAAAF-33
❑ 92Top-676
❑ 92TopGol-676
❑ 92TopGolW-676
❑ 92TopMic-676
❑ 92UppDec-15
❑ 92UppDecML-257
❑ 94Bow-145
❑ 94CalCanF-788
❑ 94ColC-589
❑ 94ColChoGS-589
❑ 94ColChoSS-589
❑ 94Fin-318
❑ 94FinRef-318
❑ 94Fla-341
❑ 94FleExtB-172
❑ 94FleMajLP-30
❑ 94FleUpd-87
❑ 94LeaLimR-79
❑ 94Pac-580
❑ 94Pin-393
❑ 94PinArtP-393
❑ 94PinMusC-393
❑ 94Sco-644
❑ 94ScoGolR-644
❑ 94ScoRoo-RT79
❑ 94ScoRooGR-RT79
❑ 94Sel-388
❑ 94SpoRoo-131
❑ 94SpoRooAP-131
❑ 94StaClu-495
❑ 94StaCluFDI-495
❑ 94StaCluGR-495
❑ 94StaCluMOP-495
❑ 94Top-376
❑ 94TopGol-376
❑ 94TopSpa-376
❑ 94Ult-424
❑ 94UppDec-164
❑ 94UppDecED-164
❑ 95Don-107
❑ 95DonPreP-107
❑ 95Fle-276
❑ 95Lea-189
❑ 95Pin-345
❑ 95PinArtP-345
❑ 95PinMusC-345
❑ 95Sco-458
❑ 95ScoGolR-458
❑ 95ScoPlaTS-458
❑ 96Fin-B331
❑ 96FinRef-B331
❑ 96FleUpd-U126
❑ 96FleUpdTC-U126
❑ 97Fle-302
❑ 97FleTif-302
❑ 97IndInd-20
❑ 97PacPriGotD-GD129
❑ 97Top-178
❑ 98NewOrlZM-23

Sallee, Andy
❑ 91MarPhiC-7
❑ 91MarPhiP-3464
❑ 92BatCliCB-28
❑ 92BatCliF-3274
❑ 93SpaPhiC-24
❑ 93SpaPhiF-1064

Sallee, H. Slim
❑ 09ColChiE-250
❑ 09PC7HHB-38
❑ 09RamT20-102
❑ 10DarChoE-26
❑ 11HelSta-177
❑ 11PinT-5-358
❑ 11PloCanE-55
❑ 11SpoLifCW-310
❑ 11SpoLifM-278
❑ 11TurRedT-37
❑ 12ColRedB-250
❑ 12ColTinT-250
❑ 14B18B-88A
❑ 14B18B-88B
❑ 14CraJacE-123
❑ 14FatPlaT-43
❑ 15CraJacE-123
❑ 15SpoNewM-153
❑ 16BF2FP-97
❑ 16SpoNewM-153
❑ 17ColE13-149
❑ 17HolBreD-88
❑ 17HolBreD-89
❑ 19W514-86
❑ 20RedWorCP-20
❑ 21E121So8-83A
❑ 21E121So8-83B
❑ 21KoBreWSI-20
❑ 22AmeCarE122-58
❑ 22MrsShePP-16
❑ 22W575-114
❑ 23WilChoV-141
❑ 88ConSer4-24
❑ 88PacEigMO-82
❑ 93ConTSN-780
❑ 94ConTSN-1020
❑ 94ConTSNB-1020

Salles, John
❑ 89PeoChiTl-8
❑ 90CarLeaA-47
❑ 90WinSpiTl-3
❑ 91ChaKniLD-141
❑ 91ChaKniP-1687
❑ 91LinDriAA-141
❑ 92IowCubS-220
❑ 92SkyAAAF-107
❑ 93ClaFS7-19
❑ 93OrlCubF-2782

Salley, Anthony
❑ 98HagSunM-23

Salmon, Chico
❑ 64Top-499
❑ 65OPC-105
❑ 65Top-105
❑ 66Top-594
❑ 67BalOriP-96
❑ 67CokCapl-11
❑ 67OPC-43
❑ 67Top-43
❑ 68Top-318
❑ 68TopVen-318
❑ 69MilBra-245
❑ 69MLBOffS-99
❑ 69OPC-62
❑ 69PilPos-8
❑ 69Top-62
❑ 69TopSta-230
❑ 69TopTeaP-9
❑ 70BalOriP-29
❑ 70MLBOffS-156
❑ 70OPC-301
❑ 70Ori-13
❑ 70Top-301
❑ 71BalOriP-26
❑ 71MLBOffS-312
❑ 71OPC-249
❑ 71Top-249
❑ 72MilBra-304
❑ 72OriPos-28

❑ 72Top-646
❑ 77PilPosR-8
❑ 91OriCro-400

Salmon, Fabian

❑ 93HelBreF-4093
❑ 93HelBreSP-13
❑ 94BelBreC-22
❑ 94BelBreFl-99

Salmon, Tim

❑ 88CapCodPPaLP-176
❑ 89BenBucL-23
❑ 90CMC-854
❑ 90PalSprACLC-215
❑ 90PalSprAP-2593
❑ 90TopMag-104
❑ 91Bow-203
❑ 91Cla/Bes-329
❑ 91Cla3-T81
❑ 91LinDriAA-443
❑ 91MidAngLD-443
❑ 91MidAngOHP-25
❑ 91MidAngP-447
❑ 92Bow-259
❑ 92DonRooP-BC10
❑ 92EdmTraF-3551
❑ 92EdmTraS-165
❑ 92FleUpd-10
❑ 92ProFS7-32
❑ 92ScoRoo-93T
❑ 92SkyAAAF-81
❑ 92TriA AAS-165
❑ 93AngAdoF-3
❑ 93AngMot-7
❑ 93AngPol-20
❑ 93AngStaCl-13
❑ 93Bow-229
❑ 93Bow-341
❑ 93DiaMar-92
❑ 93Don-176
❑ 93DonEliD-7
❑ 93Fin-163
❑ 93FinRef-163
❑ 93Fla-177
❑ 93FlaWavotF-15
❑ 93Fle-197
❑ 93FunPac-7
❑ 93FunPac-37
❑ 93JimDeaR-9
❑ 93Lea-445
❑ 93LeaGolR-R10
❑ 93LeaGolRJ-R10
❑ 93OPC-292
❑ 93OPCPre-37
❑ 93PacSpa-51
❑ 93Pin-276
❑ 93Pin-303
❑ 93PinHomRC-42
❑ 93PinRooTP-8
❑ 93PinTea2-20
❑ 93Sco-346
❑ 93ScoBoyoS-2
❑ 93Sel-339
❑ 93SelChaR-11
❑ 93SelRoo-ROY1
❑ 93SelRooAR-8
❑ 93SP-25
❑ 93SPPlaP-PP16
❑ 93StaClu-249
❑ 93StaCluFDI-249
❑ 93StaCluMO-22
❑ 93StaCluMOP-249
❑ 93Stu-114
❑ 93Top-20
❑ 93TopFulS-9
❑ 93TopGol-20
❑ 93TopInaM-20
❑ 93TopInaR-20
❑ 93TopMic-20
❑ 93TopMic-P20
❑ 93Toy-67
❑ 93TriPla-37
❑ 93Ult-523
❑ 93UltAllR-8
❑ 93UppDec-1
❑ 93UppDec-25
❑ 93UppDec-812
❑ 93UppDecDG-1
❑ 93UppDecFA-A15
❑ 93UppDecFAJ-A15
❑ 93UppDecGold-1
❑ 93UppDecGold-25
❑ 93UppDecGold-812
❑ 93UppDecIC-WI1
❑ 93UppDecICJ-WI1
❑ 93UppDecOD-D21
❑ 93UppDecS-19
❑ 94AngLAT-21
❑ 94AngMot-5
❑ 94Bow-395
❑ 94BowBes-R25
❑ 94BowBes-X102
❑ 94BowBesR-R25
❑ 94BowBesR-X102
❑ 94ChuHomS-9
❑ 94ChuHomSG-9
❑ 94ColC-251
❑ 94ColC-328
❑ 94ColC-639
❑ 94ColChoGS-251
❑ 94ColChoGS-328
❑ 94ColChoGS-639
❑ 94ColChoSS-251
❑ 94ColChoSS-328
❑ 94ColChoSS-639
❑ 94ColChoT-10
❑ 94DenHol-21
❑ 94Don-353
❑ 94DonAwaWJ-8
❑ 94DonDiaK-DK4
❑ 94DonDiaKJ-DK4
❑ 94DonEli-39
❑ 94DonMVP-17
❑ 94DonPro-6
❑ 94DonSpeE-353
❑ 94DonSpiotG-7
❑ 94DonSpiotGJ-7
❑ 94Fin-18
❑ 94FinJum-18
❑ 94FinRef-18
❑ 94Fla-27
❑ 94FlaHotG-9
❑ 94FlaOutP-9
❑ 94Fle-69
❑ 94Fle-P69
❑ 94FleAwaW-5
❑ 94FleExtB-39
❑ 94FleExtBGB-25
❑ 94FleExtBSYS-18
❑ 94FleRooS-17
❑ 94FleSal-1
❑ 94FleSal-2
❑ 94FleSal-3
❑ 94FleSal-4
❑ 94FleSal-5
❑ 94FleSal-6
❑ 94FleSal-7
❑ 94FleSal-8
❑ 94FleSal-9
❑ 94FleSal-10
❑ 94FleSal-11
❑ 94FleSal-12
❑ 94FleSal-13
❑ 94FleSal-14
❑ 94FleSal-15
❑ 94FleSal-AU0
❑ 94FleSun-22
❑ 94FleTeaL-3
❑ 94FUnPac-15
❑ 94FUnPac-203
❑ 94FUnPac-239
❑ 94KinDis-7
❑ 94Lea-109
❑ 94LeaL-18
❑ 94LeaSli-8
❑ 94MotPia-1
❑ 94MotPia-2
❑ 94MotPia-3
❑ 94MotPia-4
❑ 94MotPia-BLUE
❑ 94MotPia-RED
❑ 94MotSal-1
❑ 94MotSal-2
❑ 94MotSal-3
❑ 94MotSal-4
❑ 94O-PJumAF-10
❑ 94OPC-194
❑ 94OPCAllR-10
❑ 94OPCDiaD-11
❑ 94OPCJumA-10
❑ 94OscMayR-12
❑ 94Pac-88
❑ 94Pac-659
❑ 94PacGolP-9
❑ 94PacPro-P7
❑ 94PacSilP-12
❑ 94PacSilPC-12
❑ 94PanSti-42
❑ 94Pin-9
❑ 94PinArtP-9
❑ 94PinMusC-9
❑ 94PinNewG-NG1
❑ 94PinPowS-PS4
❑ 94PinRunC-RC13
❑ 94PinTeaP-8
❑ 94PinTheN-9
❑ 94Pos-26
❑ 94ProMag-18
❑ 94RedFolMI-23
❑ 94Sco-539
❑ 94Sco-635
❑ 94ScoBoyoS-24
❑ 94ScoGolR-539
❑ 94ScoGolR-635
❑ 94ScoGolS-44
❑ 94Sel-309
❑ 94SP-26
❑ 94SPDieC-26
❑ 94SPHol-34
❑ 94SPHolDC-34
❑ 94Spo-89
❑ 94SpoRooGGG-GG7
❑ 94SpoSha-SH2
❑ 94SPPre-WR5
❑ 94StaClu-36
❑ 94StaClu-181
❑ 94StaCluDD-DD8
❑ 94StaCluF-F9
❑ 94StaCluFDI-36
❑ 94StaCluFDI-181
❑ 94StaCluFJ-F9
❑ 94StaCluGR-36
❑ 94StaCluGR-181
❑ 94StaCluMO-47
❑ 94StaCluMOP-36
❑ 94StaCluMOP-181
❑ 94StaCluMOP-F9
❑ 94StaCluMOP-DD8
❑ 94StaCluMOP-ST17
❑ 94StaCluP-36
❑ 94StaCluST-ST17
❑ 94Stu-15
❑ 94StuEdiC-6
❑ 94TedWil-158
❑ 94TedWil-159
❑ 94TedWil-160
❑ 94TedWil-161
❑ 94TomPiz-27
❑ 94Top-397
❑ 94TopBlaG-19
❑ 94TopGol-397
❑ 94TopSpa-397
❑ 94TopSupS-38
❑ 94TriPla-19
❑ 94TriPlaP-7
❑ 94Ult-27
❑ 94UltAwaW-24
❑ 94UltRisS-11
❑ 94UltSecYS-4
❑ 94UppDec-54
❑ 94UppDec-111
❑ 94UppDec-283
❑ 94UppDecAJ-10
❑ 94UppDecAJG-10
❑ 94UppDecDC-W10
❑ 94UppDecED-54
❑ 94UppDecED-111
❑ 94UppDecED-283
❑ 94UppDecMLS-MM17
❑ 94UppDecMLSED-MM17
❑ 94UppDecNG-17
❑ 94UppDecNGED-17
❑ 94USPlaCR-6H
❑ 94USPlaCR-13C
❑ 94USPlaCR-JK
❑ 95AngCHP-1
❑ 95AngMot-4
❑ 95Baz-119
❑ 95Bow-353
❑ 95BowBes-R33
❑ 95BowBesR-R33
❑ 95ClaPhoC-10
❑ 95ColCho-100
❑ 95ColChoGS-100
❑ 95ColChoSE-35
❑ 95ColChoSEGS-35
❑ 95ColChoSESS-35
❑ 95ColChoSS-100
❑ 95DenHol-23
❑ 95Don-403
❑ 95DonPreP-403
❑ 95DonTopotO-42
❑ 95Emo-21
❑ 95Fin-79
❑ 95FinRef-79
❑ 95Fla-21
❑ 95FlaTodS-11
❑ 95Fle-235
❑ 95FlePro-5
❑ 95FleTeaL-3
❑ 95FleUpdH-17
❑ 95FleUpdSS-9
❑ 95Lea-264
❑ 95LeaLim-30
❑ 95LeaLimG-13
❑ 95LeaLimIBP-20
❑ 95NatPac-8
❑ 95Pac-64
❑ 95PacGolP-5
❑ 95PacPri-21
❑ 95PanSti-88
❑ 95Pin-286
❑ 95Pin-391
❑ 95PinArtP-286
❑ 95PinArtP-391
❑ 95PinFan-12
❑ 95PinMusC-286
❑ 95PinMusC-391
❑ 95PinPer-PP8
❑ 95PinRedH-RH19
❑ 95PinUps-US8
❑ 95PinWhiH-WH19
❑ 95RedFol-12
❑ 95Sco-420
❑ 95ScoGolR-420
❑ 95ScoHaloG-HG78
❑ 95ScoPlaTS-420
❑ 95ScoRul-SR20
❑ 95ScoRulJ-SR20
❑ 95Sel-59
❑ 95SelArtP-59
❑ 95SelCer-17
❑ 95SelCerMG-17
❑ 95SP-135
❑ 95SPCha-135
❑ 95SPChaDC-135
❑ 95Spo-68
❑ 95SpoArtP-68
❑ 95SpoHamT-HT18
❑ 95SPPlaP-PP17
❑ 95SPSil-135
❑ 95SPSpeF-4
❑ 95StaClu-473
❑ 95StaClu-512
❑ 95StaCluMOP-473
❑ 95StaCluMOP-512
❑ 95StaCluMOP-SS7
❑ 95StaCluSS-SS7
❑ 95StaCluSTWS-473
❑ 95StaCluSTWS-512
❑ 95StaCluVR-259
❑ 95StaCluVRMO-259
❑ 95Stu-13
❑ 95StuGolS-13
❑ 95StuPlaS-13
❑ 95Sum-35
❑ 95SumBigB-BB19
❑ 95SumNthD-35
❑ 95Top-200
❑ 95TopCyb-114
❑ 95TopD3-16
❑ 95TopEmb-108
❑ 95TopEmbGI-108
❑ 95UC3-14
❑ 95UC3ArtP-14
❑ 95UC3CycS-CS18
❑ 95Ult-23
❑ 95UltGolM-23
❑ 95UppDec-270
❑ 95UppDecED-270
❑ 95UppDecEDG-270
❑ 95UppDecPLL-R36
❑ 95UppDecPLLE-R36
❑ 95UppDecSE-126
❑ 95UppDecSEG-126
❑ 95Zen-102
❑ 96AngMot-4
❑ 96Baz-111
❑ 96Bow-43
❑ 96BowBes-9
❑ 96BowBesAR-9
❑ 96BowBesC-13
❑ 96BowBesCAR-13
❑ 96BowBesCR-13
❑ 96BowBesP-BBP6
❑ 96BowBesPAR-BBP6
❑ 96BowBesPR-BBP6
❑ 96BowBesR-9
❑ 96BowFoi-43
❑ 96Cir-22
❑ 96CirAcc-3
❑ 96CirBos-5
❑ 96CirRav-22
❑ 96ColCho-75
❑ 96ColCho-416
❑ 96ColChoCtG-CG8
❑ 96ColChoCtG-CG8B
❑ 96ColChoCtG-CG8C
❑ 96ColChoCtGG-CG8
❑ 96ColChoCtGG-CG8B
❑ 96ColChoCtGG-CG8C
❑ 96ColChoGS-75
❑ 96ColChoGS-416
❑ 96ColChoSS-75
❑ 96ColChoSS-416
❑ 96ColChoYMtP-35
❑ 96ColChoYMtP-35A
❑ 96ColChoYMtPGS-35
❑ 96ColChoYMtPGS-35A
❑ 96DenHol-16
❑ 96Don-477
❑ 96DonDiaK-7
❑ 96DonEli-65
❑ 96DonHitL-13
❑ 96DonPowA-5
❑ 96DonPowADC-5
❑ 96DonPreP-477
❑ 96DonRouT-4
❑ 96EmoLegoB-8
❑ 96EmoXL-30
❑ 96Fin-B97
❑ 96Fin-G249
❑ 96Fin-S22
❑ 96FinRef-B97
❑ 96FinRef-G249
❑ 96FinRef-S22
❑ 96Fla-41
❑ 96Fle-57
❑ 96FleLumC-8
❑ 96FleRoaW-7
❑ 96FleTif-57
❑ 96FleUpd-U238
❑ 96FleUpdH-18
❑ 96FleUpdTC-U238
❑ 96Lea-45
❑ 96LeaAllGMC-10
❑ 96LeaAllGMCG-10
❑ 96LeaGolS-6
❑ 96LeaLim-17
❑ 96LeaLimG-17
❑ 96LeaPre-28
❑ 96LeaPreP-28
❑ 96LeaPrePB-45
❑ 96LeaPrePG-45
❑ 96LeaPrePS-45
❑ 96LeaPreSG-25
❑ 96LeaPreSte-25
❑ 96LeaSig-9
❑ 96LeaSigA-200
❑ 96LeaSigAG-200
❑ 96LeaSigAS-200
❑ 96LeaSigPPG-9
❑ 96LeaSigPPP-9
❑ 96LibSpo-NNO
❑ 96MetUni-32
❑ 96MetUniML-9
❑ 96MetUniP-32
❑ 96Pac-264
❑ 96PacGolCD-DC12
❑ 96PacPri-P86
❑ 96PacPriFB-FB16
❑ 96PacPriG-P86
❑ 96PacPriRHS-RH5
❑ 96PanSti-209
❑ 96Pin-26
❑ 96Pin-142
❑ 96Pin-276
❑ 96PinAfi-122
❑ 96PinAfiAP-122
❑ 96PinAfiSP-29
❑ 96PinArtP-12
❑ 96PinArtP-69
❑ 96PinArtP-176
❑ 96PinEssotG-14
❑ 96PinFoil-276
❑ 96PinPow-14
❑ 96PinSta-12
❑ 96PinSta-69
❑ 96PinSta-176
❑ 96PinTeaP-5
❑ 96ProMagDM-7
❑ 96ProSta-2
❑ 96RedF-20
❑ 96Sco-328
❑ 96ScoAll-13
❑ 96ScoDiaA-30
❑ 96ScoDugC-B53
❑ 96ScoDugCAP-B53
❑ 96ScoGolS-4
❑ 96ScoPowP-16
❑ 96ScoTitT-8
❑ 96Sel-10
❑ 96SelArtP-10
❑ 96SelCer-37
❑ 96SelCerAP-37
❑ 96SelCerCB-37
❑ 96SelCerCR-37
❑ 96SelCerIP-17
❑ 96SelCerMB-37
❑ 96SelCerMG-37
❑ 96SelCerMR-37
❑ 96SelEnF-22
❑ 96SelTeaN-23
❑ 96SP-45
❑ 96SPMarM-MM5
❑ 96SPMarMDC-5
❑ 96Spo-2
❑ 96Spo-106
❑ 96SpoArtP-2
❑ 96SpoArtP-106
❑ 96SpoPowS-10
❑ 96SpoPro-18
❑ 96SPSpeFX-42
❑ 96SPSpeFXDC-42
❑ 96SPx-12
❑ 96SPxGol-12
❑ 96StaClu-213
❑ 96StaClu-405
❑ 96StaCluEPB-405
❑ 96StaCluEPG-405
❑ 96StaCluEPS-405
❑ 96StaCluMO-37
❑ 96StaCluMOP-213
❑ 96StaCluMOP-405
❑ 96StaCluMOP-PP9
❑ 96StaCluMOP-PS13
❑ 96StaCluPP-PP9
❑ 96StaCluPS-PS13
❑ 96Stu-56
❑ 96StuHitP-9
❑ 96StuPrePB-56
❑ 96StuPrePG-56
❑ 96StuPrePS-56
❑ 96Sum-81
❑ 96Sum-160
❑ 96SumAbo&B-81
❑ 96SumAbo&B-160
❑ 96SumArtP-81
❑ 96SumArtP-160
❑ 96SumBal-16
❑ 96SumBigB-11
❑ 96SumBigBM-11
❑ 96SumFoi-81
❑ 96SumFoi-160
❑ 96SumHitI-3
❑ 96TeaOut-69
❑ 96Top-319
❑ 96TopChr-126
❑ 96TopChrR-126
❑ 96TopGal-154
❑ 96TopGalPPI-154
❑ 96TopLas-110
❑ 96TopLasPC-5
❑ 96TopPro-AL20
❑ 96TopRoaW-RW14
❑ 96Ult-33
❑ 96Ult-589
❑ 96UltGolM-33
❑ 96UltGolM-589
❑ 96UltHitM-8
❑ 96UltHitMGM-8
❑ 96UltHomRK-9
❑ 96UltHomRKGM-9
❑ 96UltHomRKR-9
❑ 96UltHomRKRGM-9
❑ 96UltOn-L-8
❑ 96UltOn-LGM-8
❑ 96UltPowP-8
❑ 96UltPowPGM-8
❑ 96UltPriL-9
❑ 96UltPriLGM-9
❑ 96UppDec-290
❑ 96UppDecHC-HC16
❑ 96UppDecPD-PD14
❑ 96UppDecPHE-H5
❑ 96UppDecPRE-R7
❑ 96UppDecPRE-R28
❑ 96UppDecPreH-H5
❑ 96UppDecPreR-R7
❑ 96UppDecPreR-R28
❑ 96UppDecRunP-RP16
❑ 96UppDecVJLS-VJ16
❑ 96Zen-39
❑ 96ZenArtP-39
❑ 96ZenMoz-7
❑ 97AngMot-2

❑ 97Bow-5
❑ 97BowBes-98
❑ 97BowBesA-98
❑ 97BowBesAAR-98
❑ 97BowBesAR-98
❑ 97BowBesAR-98
❑ 97BowBesR-98
❑ 97BowChr-4
❑ 97BowChrl-4
❑ 97BowChrlR-4
❑ 97BowChrR-4
❑ 97BowInt-5
❑ 97Cir-5
❑ 97CirRav-5
❑ 97ColCho-260
❑ 97ColChoNF-NF9
❑ 97ColChoTBS-13
❑ 97ColChoTBSWH-13
❑ 97DenHol-1
❑ 97Don-76
❑ 97Don-447
❑ 97DonEli-23
❑ 97DonEliGS-23
❑ 97DonGolPP-76
❑ 97DonGolPP-447
❑ 97DonLim-75
❑ 97DonLim-142
❑ 97DonLimE-75
❑ 97DonLimE-142
❑ 97DonLimENG-142
❑ 97DonLimFotG-46
❑ 97DonPre-51
❑ 97DonPreCttC-51
❑ 97DonPreXP-6A
❑ 97DonSig-5
❑ 97DonSigPPP-5
❑ 97DonSilPP-76
❑ 97DonSilPP-447
❑ 97DonTea-2
❑ 97DonTeaSPE-2
❑ 97DonVxP1-30
❑ 97Fin-144
❑ 97Fin-246
❑ 97FinEmb-144
❑ 97FinEmbR-144
❑ 97FinRef-144
❑ 97FinRef-246
❑ 97FlaShoLC-30
❑ 97FlaShoLeg0-30
❑ 97FlaShoLeg1-30
❑ 97FlaShoM-A30
❑ 97FlaShoM-B30
❑ 97FlaShoM-C30
❑ 97FlaShoR0-30
❑ 97FlaShoR1-30
❑ 97FlaShoR2-30
❑ 97Fle-50
❑ 97Fle-721
❑ 97FleTif-50
❑ 97FleTif-721
❑ 97HigMinMCT-37
❑ 97HigMinMCT-38
❑ 97KinB-11
❑ 97Lea-129
❑ 97LeaFraM-129
❑ 97LeaFraMDC-129
❑ 97MetUni-43
❑ 97NewPin-20
❑ 97NewPinAP-20
❑ 97NewPinMC-20
❑ 97NewPinPP-20
❑ 97Pac-13
❑ 97PacLigB-13
❑ 97PacPri-5
❑ 97PacPriLB-5
❑ 97PacPriP-5
❑ 97PacSil-13
❑ 97Pin-53
❑ 97PinArtP-PP53
❑ 97PinCer-23
❑ 97PinCerMBla-23
❑ 97PinCerMBlu-23
❑ 97PinCerMG-23
❑ 97PinCerMR-23
❑ 97PinCerR-23
❑ 97PinIns-85
❑ 97PinInsCE-85
❑ 97PinInsDE-85
❑ 97PinMin-24
❑ 97PinMinB-24
❑ 97PinMinCB-24
❑ 97PinMinCG-24
❑ 97PinMinCGR-24
❑ 97PinMinCN-24
❑ 97PinMinCSS-24
❑ 97PinMinG-24
❑ 97PinMinS-24
❑ 97PinMusC-53
❑ 97PinPrePla-53
❑ 97PinTotCPB-23
❑ 97PinTotCPG-23
❑ 97PinTotCPR-23
❑ 97PinX-P-49
❑ 97PinX-PMoS-49
❑ 97PinX-PSfF-50
❑ 97PinX-PSfFU-50
❑ 97Sco-149
❑ 97Sco-494
❑ 97ScoArtPWB-149
❑ 97ScoArtPWB-494
❑ 97ScoBla-18
❑ 97ScoHeaotO-32
❑ 97ScoPitP-7
❑ 97ScoPreS-149
❑ 97ScoResC-494
❑ 97ScoShoS-149
❑ 97ScoShoS-494
❑ 97ScoShoSAP-149
❑ 97ScoShoSAP-494
❑ 97Sel-44
❑ 97SelArtP-44
❑ 97SelCom-44
❑ 97SelRegG-44
❑ 97SelToootT-13
❑ 97SelToootTMB-13
❑ 97SP-20
❑ 97SPMarM-MM6
❑ 97SpoIll-163
❑ 97SpoIllEE-163
❑ 97SPSpeF-32
❑ 97SPx-3
❑ 97SPxBro-3
❑ 97SPxGol-3
❑ 97SPxGraF-3
❑ 97SPxSil-3
❑ 97SPxSte-3
❑ 97StaClu-7
❑ 97StaCluMat-7
❑ 97StaCluMOP-7
❑ 97Stu-67
❑ 97StuHarH-16
❑ 97StuPrePG-67
❑ 97StuPrePS-67
❑ 97Top-320
❑ 97TopChr-107
❑ 97TopChrR-107
❑ 97TopGal-102
❑ 97TopGalPPI-102
❑ 97TopIntF-ILM2
❑ 97TopIntFR-ILM2
❑ 97TopMem05-42
❑ 97UD3-22
❑ 97Ult-30
❑ 97UltDouT-3
❑ 97UltGolME-30
❑ 97UltPlaME-30
❑ 97UppDec-290
❑ 97UppDecPP-PP12
❑ 97UppDecPPJ-PP12
❑ 97UppDecRP-RP19
❑ 98AngSco-6
❑ 98AngScoP-6
❑ 98Bow-27
❑ 98BowBes-85
❑ 98BowBesAR-85
❑ 98BowBesR-85
❑ 98BowChr-27
❑ 98BowChrGA-27
❑ 98BowChrGAR-27
❑ 98BowChrl-27
❑ 98BowChrlR-27
❑ 98BowChrR-27
❑ 98BowChrR-26
❑ 98BowChrRR-26
❑ 98BowGolA-27
❑ 98BowInt-27
❑ 98CirThu-15
❑ 98CirThuRav-15
❑ 98CirThuSupRav-15
❑ 98ColCho-280
❑ 98ColChoCtG-CG6A
❑ 98ColChoCtG-CG6B
❑ 98ColChoCtG-CG6C
❑ 98ColChoCtGExch-CG6
❑ 98ColChoCtGIW-CG6
❑ 98ColChoER-ER1
❑ 98ColChoMBH-1
❑ 98ColChoSQ-SQ28
❑ 98CroRoy-4
❑ 98Don-77
❑ 98Don-359
❑ 98DonCol-77
❑ 98DonColE-437
❑ 98DonColL-216
❑ 98DonColP-589
❑ 98DonColS-77
❑ 98DonCruG-1
❑ 98DonCruP-1
❑ 98DonCruR-1
❑ 98DonEli-37
❑ 98DonEliA-37
❑ 98DonEliS-37
❑ 98DonGolPP-77
❑ 98DonGolPP-359
❑ 98DonLonL-12
❑ 98DonPre-39
❑ 98DonPreGES-12
❑ 98DonPreGX-12
❑ 98DonPreGXDC-12
❑ 98DonPreSeat-39
❑ 98DonPriCD-77
❑ 98DonPriCE-437
❑ 98DonPriCL-216
❑ 98DonPriCP-589
❑ 98DonProLS-14
❑ 98DonSig-57
❑ 98DonSigP-57
❑ 98DonSilPP-77
❑ 98DonSilPP-359
❑ 98DonSonM9-12
❑ 98E-X2-43
❑ 98E-X2ECFut-43
❑ 98E-X2ECNow-43
❑ 98Fin-97
❑ 98FinNo--97
❑ 98FinNo-R-97
❑ 98FinRef-97
❑ 98FlaShoLeg0-45
❑ 98FlaShoLeg1-45
❑ 98FlaShoLeg2-45
❑ 98FlaShoLeg3-45
❑ 98FlaShoLegM-45
❑ 98FlaShoR0-45
❑ 98FlaShoR1-45
❑ 98FlaShoR2-45
❑ 98FlaShoR3-45
❑ 98Fle-15
❑ 98FleVin'-2
❑ 98FleVin'C-2
❑ 98KinDis-11
❑ 98Lea-16
❑ 98LeaFraDA-16
❑ 98LeaFraF-16
❑ 98LeaFraM-16
❑ 98LeaFraM-16
❑ 98LeaFraMDC-16
❑ 98LeaFraMDC-16
❑ 98LeaFraMZ2-16
❑ 98LeaRS-12
❑ 98LeaRS-132
❑ 98LeaRSLHolo-12
❑ 98LeaRSLHolo-132
❑ 98LeaRSLong-12
❑ 98LeaRSLong-132
❑ 98LeaRSTicMas-18
❑ 98LeaRSTicMasDC-18
❑ 98LeaRTrue-12
❑ 98LeaRTrue-132
❑ 98LeaStaRep-9
❑ 98MetUni-94
❑ 98MetUniPMG-94
❑ 98Pac-15
❑ 98PacAur-8
❑ 98PacAurPF-34
❑ 98PacAurPFC-34
❑ 98PacAurPFPB-34
❑ 98PacAurPFR-34
❑ 98PacAurPFS-34
❑ 98PacInv-5
❑ 98PacInvGems-7
❑ 98PacInvPBlue-5
❑ 98PacInvSilv-5
❑ 98PacInvTeam-1
❑ 98PacOme-8
❑ 98PacOmeR-8
❑ 98PacOnl-22
❑ 98PacOnlR-22
❑ 98PacOnlWC-22
❑ 98PacPar-9
❑ 98PacParC-9
❑ 98PacParG-9
❑ 98PacParHS-9
❑ 98PacParl-46
❑ 98PacParPB-9
❑ 98PacParR-9
❑ 98PacParTC-1
❑ 98PacPlaB-15
❑ 98PacRedT-15
❑ 98PacSil-15
❑ 98PacTeaC-1
❑ 98Pin-51
❑ 98PinArtP-PP46
❑ 98PinIns-42
❑ 98PinInsCE-42
❑ 98PinInsDE-42
❑ 98PinInsSG-16AB
❑ 98PinInsSG-16CD
❑ 98PinInsSGS-16AB
❑ 98PinInsSGS-16CD
❑ 98PinMusC-PP46
❑ 98PinPer-40
❑ 98PinPerPP-40
❑ 98PinPerSftF-21
❑ 98PinPlu-141
❑ 98PinPluAP-PP47
❑ 98PinPluGAP-PP47
❑ 98PinPluMAP-PP47
❑ 98PinPreP-51
❑ 98PinSna-AA7
❑ 98Revo-5
❑ 98RevoSS-5
❑ 98Sco-117
❑ 98ScoRT-14
❑ 98ScoRTSS-PP14
❑ 98ScoRTSSAP-PP14
❑ 98ScoRTSSAP1-PP14
❑ 98ScoSS-PP48
❑ 98ScoSSAP-PP48
❑ 98SkyDugA-50
❑ 98SkyDugAIA-50
❑ 98SP Aut-35
❑ 98SpoIll-110
❑ 98SpoIllEE-110
❑ 98SpoIllFE-110
❑ 98SpoIllODMP-OD1
❑ 98SpoIllTaN-129
❑ 98SpoIllTaNEE-129
❑ 98SpoIllWSF-121
❑ 98SpoIllWSFEE-121
❑ 98SpoIllWSFFE-121
❑ 98SPxFin-38
❑ 98SPxFin-54
❑ 98SPxFin-221
❑ 98SPxFinR-38
❑ 98SPxFinR-54
❑ 98SPxFinR-221
❑ 98SPxFinS-38
❑ 98SPxFinS-54
❑ 98SPxFinS-221
❑ 98StaCluC-CS26
❑ 98StaCluC-CS28
❑ 98StaCluC-CS30
❑ 98StaCluFDI-265
❑ 98StaClul-265
❑ 98StaCluNC-NC19
❑ 98StaCluOneK-265
❑ 98StaCluPP-265
❑ 98StaCluTIll-T17A
❑ 98StaCluTLme-T17A
❑ 98StaCluTLmo-T17A
❑ 98Stu-203
❑ 98StuFF-28
❑ 98StuFFDC-28
❑ 98StuGPP-203
❑ 98StuSony99-12
❑ 98StuSPP-203
❑ 98Top-312
❑ 98TopChr-312
❑ 98TopChrR-312
❑ 98TopDevR-312
❑ 98TopDia-312
❑ 98TopGal-126
❑ 98TopGalGP-126
❑ 98TopGalOPP-126
❑ 98TopGalPG-PG8
❑ 98TopGalPPI-126
❑ 98TopGalPPIA-126
❑ 98TopGolLabC1-71
❑ 98TopGolLabC1B-71
❑ 98TopGolLabC1One-71
❑ 98TopGolLabC1R-71
❑ 98TopGolLabC2-71
❑ 98TopGolLabC2B-71
❑ 98TopGolLabC2One-71
❑ 98TopGolLabC2R-71
❑ 98TopGolLabC3-71
❑ 98TopGolLabC3B-71
❑ 98TopGolLabC3One-71
❑ 98TopGolLabC3R-71
❑ 98TopMiniC-312
❑ 98TopMysF-ILM16
❑ 98TopMysFR-ILM16
❑ 98TopOpeD-138
❑ 98TopSta-102
❑ 98TopSta'S-37
❑ 98TopSta'SGH-37
❑ 98TopStaB-102
❑ 98TopStaG-102
❑ 98TopStaGR-102
❑ 98TopStaS-102
❑ 98TopStaSteG-37
❑ 98TopTek-72
❑ 98TopTekD-72
❑ 98UD3-51
❑ 98UD3-141
❑ 98UD3-231
❑ 98UD3DieCut-51
❑ 98UD3DieCut-141
❑ 98UD3DieCut-231
❑ 98Ult-7
❑ 98UltGolM-7
❑ 98UltMas-7
❑ 98UltPlaM-7
❑ 98UppDec-290
❑ 98UppDecR-3
❑ 98UppDecTMT-28
❑ 98UppDecTMTG-28
❑ 98Zen-9
❑ 98Zen5 xx7-25
❑ 98Zen5x7GoldImp-25
❑ 98Zen5x7Imp-25
❑ 98ZenZ-G-9
❑ 98ZenZ-S-9
❑ 99199Fin-69
❑ 99AllMysFR-M20
❑ 99Bow-273
❑ 99BowBes-30
❑ 99BowBesAR-30
❑ 99BowBesR-30
❑ 99BowGol-273
❑ 99BowInt-273
❑ 99CroRoyB-4
❑ 99CroRoyL-4
❑ 99CroRoyOD-4
❑ 99E-X Cen-61
❑ 99E-X CenECFut-61
❑ 99E-X CenECNow-61
❑ 99FinGolRef-69
❑ 99FinRef-69
❑ 99FlaShoLeg1-24
❑ 99FlaShoLeg2-24
❑ 99FlaShoLeg3-24
❑ 99FlaShoLegM1-24
❑ 99FlaShoLegM2-24
❑ 99FlaShoLegM3-24
❑ 99FlaShoR1-24
❑ 99FlaShoR2-24
❑ 99FlaShoR3-24
❑ 99Fle-235
❑ 99FleBri-90
❑ 99FleBri2G-90
❑ 99FleBriBlu-90
❑ 99FleBriGol-90
❑ 99FleMys-42
❑ 99FleMysG-42
❑ 99FleMysM-42
❑ 99FleSta9-235
❑ 99FleWarT-235
❑ 99KinDis-9
❑ 99MetUni-82
❑ 99MetUniGM-82
❑ 99MetUniPMG-82
❑ 99Pac-12
❑ 99Pac-12A
❑ 99PacAur-5
❑ 99PacAurOD-5
❑ 99PacCroC-9
❑ 99PacCroCPB-9
❑ 99PacInv-4
❑ 99PacInvOD-4
❑ 99PacInvPB-4
❑ 99PacOme-8
❑ 99PacOmeC-8
❑ 99PacOmeG-8
❑ 99PacOmePB-8
❑ 99PacPar-8
❑ 99PacParC-8
❑ 99PacParG-8
❑ 99PacParHoloGold-8
❑ 99PacParHS-8
❑ 99PacParOD-8
❑ 99PacParPB-8
❑ 99PacParRed-8
❑ 99PacPlaB-12
❑ 99PacPlaB-12A
❑ 99PacPri-5
❑ 99PacPriHB-5
❑ 99PacPriHG-5
❑ 99PacPriHM-5
❑ 99PacPriHP-5
❑ 99PacPriRed-5
❑ 99PacPriS-44
❑ 99PacPriS206-44
❑ 99PacPriS206R-44
❑ 99PacPriSP-44
❑ 99PacPriSV-44
❑ 99PacRed-12
❑ 99PacRed-12A
❑ 99Rev-4
❑ 99RevPremDate-4
❑ 99RevRet-4
❑ 99RevShaSS-4
❑ 99SkyMolM-106
❑ 99SkyMolMF-6
❑ 99SkyMolMFS-6
❑ 99SkyMolMFT-6
❑ 99SkyMolMX-106
❑ 99SkyPre-135
❑ 99SkyPreR-135
❑ 99SkyThu-211
❑ 99SkyThuRant-211
❑ 99SkyThuRave-211
❑ 99SpoIll-94
❑ 99StaClu-241
❑ 99StaCluFDI-241
❑ 99StaCluOoaK-241
❑ 99StaCluPP-241
❑ 99ThuSkySupR-211
❑ 99Top-360
❑ 99Top-456
❑ 99TopAllMF-M20
❑ 99TopBlaLC1-29
❑ 99TopBlaLC2-29
❑ 99TopBlaLC3-29
❑ 99TopChr-360
❑ 99TopChr-456
❑ 99TopChrR-360
❑ 99TopChrR-456
❑ 99TopGal-54
❑ 99TopGalPP-54
❑ 99TopGalPPI-54
❑ 99TopGolL-29
❑ 99TopGolLC1-29
❑ 99TopGolLC2-29
❑ 99TopGolLOtO-29
❑ 99TopMVPP-360
❑ 99TopMVPP-456
❑ 99TopOpeD-115
❑ 99TopRedLC1-29
❑ 99TopRedLC2-29
❑ 99TopRedLC3-29
❑ 99TopSta-101
❑ 99TopSta'S-28
❑ 99TopSta'SG-28
❑ 99TopSta'SGDH-28
❑ 99TopStaFoil-101
❑ 99UD Cho-46
❑ 99UD ChoP-46
❑ 99UD ChoPCR-46
❑ 99UDHolo-3
❑ 99UDHoloAUsome-3
❑ 99Ult-168
❑ 99UltGolM-168
❑ 99UltMas-168
❑ 99UltPlaM-168
❑ 99UppDec-25
❑ 99UppDecBD-2
❑ 99UppDecBDD-2
❑ 99UppDecBDQ-2
❑ 99UppDecBDT-2
❑ 99UppDecEL1-25
❑ 99UppDecEL2-25
❑ 99UppDecM-6
❑ 99UppDecMGS-6
❑ 99UppDecMHFS-6
❑ 99UppDecMP-6
❑ 99UppDecMSS-6
❑ 99UppDecR-3
❑ 99UppDecRG-3
❑ 99UppDecRP-3
❑ 99Vic-6

Saltzgaber, Brian

❑ 90NiaFalRP-9
❑ 91FayGenC-16
❑ 91FayGenP-1174
❑ 91SouAtlLAGP-SAL21
❑ 92LakTigC-10
❑ 92LakTigF-2283
❑ 93LonTigF-2311
❑ 94TreThuF-2133

Saltzgaver, Jack

❑ 35DiaMatCS3T1-128
❑ 72TCMthe3-76
❑ 75YanDyn1T-41
❑ 93ConTSN-972

Salva, Elias

❑ 80WauTimT-8
Salveson, John
❑ 33ButCanV-43
❑ 49W72HolS-18
❑ 50W720HolS-25
Salvior, Troy
❑ 90HamRedB-10
❑ 90HamRedS-22
❑ 91Cla/Bes-310
❑ 91St.PetCC-10
❑ 91St.PetCP-2274
❑ 92St.PetCF-2027
Salvo, Manny
❑ 32Zee-88
❑ 33Zee-94
❑ 47PadTeal-17
❑ 94ConTSN-1294
❑ 94ConTSNB-1294
Salyer, Ron
❑ 75SanAntBT-18
Salyers, Jeremy
❑ 97VerExpB-24
❑ 98CapFeaCM-20
Salzano, Jerry
❑ 93HelBreF-4106
❑ 93HelBreSP-10
❑ 94BelBreC-23
❑ 94BelBreFI-112
❑ 94WilCubC-20
❑ 94WilCubF-3773
❑ 96LakTigB-23
❑ 98GreBraG-23
Samaniego, Art
❑ 79ElmPioRST-5
Sambel, Arnie
❑ 90EugEmeGS-26
Sambito, Joe
❑ 74CedRapAT-6
❑ 77AstPho-12
❑ 77Top-227
❑ 78AstBurK-10
❑ 78AstPos-22
❑ 78Top-498
❑ 79AstPos-23
❑ 79AstTeal-13
❑ 79Top-158
❑ 80Top-571
❑ 81AstPos-22
❑ 81CokTeaS-70
❑ 81Don-21
❑ 81Fle-65
❑ 81OPC-334
❑ 81Top-385
❑ 81TopSti-172
❑ 82AstAstI-4
❑ 82AstPos-23
❑ 82Don-65
❑ 82Fle-230
❑ 82FleSta-47
❑ 82Top-34
❑ 83AstPos-26
❑ 83Don-244
❑ 83Fle-464
❑ 83OPC-296
❑ 83Top-662
❑ 84AstPos-25
❑ 85Don-572
❑ 85Fle-360
❑ 85FleUpd-96
❑ 85Top-264
❑ 85TopTif-264
❑ 85TopTifT-103T
❑ 85TopTra-103T
❑ 86AstMot-19
❑ 86FleUpd-101
❑ 86TopTra-97T
❑ 86TopTraT-97T
❑ 87AstShoSPO-28
❑ 87Don-421
❑ 87Fle-43
❑ 87FleGlo-43
❑ 87OPC-262
❑ 87RedSoxP-18
❑ 87Top-451
❑ 87TopTif-451
❑ 88Fle-364
❑ 88FleGlo-364
❑ 88Sco-314
❑ 88ScoGlo-314
❑ 88Top-784
❑ 88TopClo-98
❑ 88TopTif-784
❑ 88TucTorJP-20
❑ 89PacSenL-18
❑ 89T/MSenL-93
❑ 89TopSenL-95
❑ 91MetWIZ-340
❑ 91PacSenL-157
❑ 93UppDecAH-111
Sambo, Ramon
❑ 87VerRedP-7
❑ 88CedRapRP-1149
❑ 89ElPasDGS-28
❑ 89TexLeaAGS-15
❑ 90CMC-642
❑ 90ProAAAF-181
❑ 90VanCanC-15
❑ 90VanCanP-503
❑ 91LinDriAA-444
❑ 91MidAngLD-444
❑ 91MidAngOHP-26
❑ 91MidAngP-448
❑ 93LimRocDWB-122
Samboy, Alvaro
❑ 91SpoIndC-25
❑ 91SpoIndP-3949
Samboy, Javier
❑ 96AriBlaDB-30
Samboy, Nelson
❑ 96KisCobB-25
❑ 97KisCob-22
❑ 98KisCobQ-28
Samcoff, Ed
❑ 48SmiClo-19
❑ 49RemBre-24
Samford, Ron
❑ 59SenTealW-16
❑ 59Top-242
❑ 60Top-409
❑ 76DalCon-9
❑ 79TCM50-102
Sammons, Lee
❑ 90BenBucL-22
❑ 91MadMusC-28
❑ 91TacTigP-2319
❑ 92JacGenF-4013
❑ 92JacGenS-347
❑ 92SkyAA F-146
Samonds, Shereen
❑ 89OrlTwiB-28
❑ 94ColSilBC-7
❑ 95ColSilB9-2
Sampen, Bill
❑ 86WatPirP-21
❑ 87SalBucP-21
❑ 89HarSenP-290
❑ 89HarSenS-17
❑ 90Bow-104
❑ 90BowTif-104
❑ 90DonRoo-12
❑ 90ExpPos-31
❑ 90FleUpd-31
❑ 90ScoRoo-79T
❑ 90TopTra-108T
❑ 90TopTraT-108T
❑ 90UppDec-724
❑ 91Don-351
❑ 91Fle-247
❑ 91Lea-318
❑ 91OPC-649
❑ 91PanFreS-149
❑ 91Sco-68
❑ 91Sco100RS-64
❑ 91StaClu-249
❑ 91StaCluP-37
❑ 91Stu-199
❑ 91Top-649
❑ 91TopDeb90-138
❑ 91TopDesS-649
❑ 91TopMic-649
❑ 91TopTif-649
❑ 91ToyRoo-26
❑ 91UppDec-661
❑ 92Bow-348
❑ 92Don-571
❑ 92ExpDonD-3A
❑ 92ExpPos-27
❑ 92Fle-492
❑ 92OPC-566
❑ 92Sco-166
❑ 92StaClu-277
❑ 92Top-566
❑ 92TopGol-566
❑ 92TopGolW-566
❑ 92TopMic-566
❑ 92TriPla-221
❑ 92Ult-522
❑ 93Don-337
❑ 93Fle-624
❑ 93OmaRoyF-1679
❑ 93PacSpa-188
❑ 93RoyStaC-22
❑ 94AngLAT-10
Sample, Billy
❑ 78TucTorC-19
❑ 79Top-713
❑ 80Top-458
❑ 81Don-268
❑ 81Fle-637
❑ 81OPC-283
❑ 81Top-283
❑ 82Don-69
❑ 82Fle-330
❑ 82OPC-112
❑ 82Top-112
❑ 83Don-242
❑ 83Fle-577
❑ 83FleSti-166
❑ 83RanAffF-5
❑ 83Top-641
❑ 84Don-403
❑ 84Fle-426
❑ 84Nes792-12
❑ 84OPC-12
❑ 84RanJarP-5
❑ 84Top-12
❑ 84TopSti-352
❑ 84TopTif-12
❑ 85Don-464
❑ 85Fle-566
❑ 85FleUpd-97
❑ 85Top-337
❑ 85TopSti-351
❑ 85TopTif-337
❑ 85YanTCMP-25
❑ 86BraPol-5
❑ 86Don-539
❑ 86Fle-118
❑ 86FleUpd-102
❑ 86Top-533
❑ 86TopTif-533
❑ 86TopTra-98T
❑ 86TopTraT-98T
❑ 87Don-143
❑ 87Fle-527
❑ 87FleGlo-527
❑ 87Top-104
❑ 87TopTif-104
❑ 90SweBasG-118
❑ 91SweBasG-79
❑ 92YanWIZ8-169
❑ 93RanKee-317
Sample, Deron
❑ 89KinMetS-20
❑ 90ColMetGS-10
❑ 90ColMetPPI-1
❑ 90SouAtlLAS-41
❑ 91St.LucMC-17
❑ 91St.LucMP-709
❑ 92EriSaiC-7
❑ 92EriSaiF-1623
Sample, Frank
❑ 91HunCubC-22
❑ 91HunCubP-3334
Samples, Todd
❑ 90JamExpP-11
❑ 91SouAtlLAGP-SAL47
❑ 91SumFlyC-24
❑ 91SumFlyP-2349
❑ 92RocExpC-25
❑ 92RocExpF-2129
❑ 93StoPorC-22
❑ 93StoPorF-758
❑ 94ElPasDF-3160
❑ 94StoPorC-24
❑ 94StoPorF-1707
Samplinski, Rich
❑ 88CapCodPPaLP-104
❑ 89OklSoo-23
❑ 90OklSoo-7
Sampson, Benj
❑ 94ForWayWC-1
❑ 94ForWayWF-2010
❑ 95ForMyeMTI-24
❑ 96BesAutS-81
❑ 97NewBriRC-25
❑ 98FleUpd-U83
❑ 98SalLakBO-26
❑ 99Fle-511
❑ 99FleSta9-511
❑ 99FleWarT-511
❑ 99SkyPreA-47
❑ 99SkyPreABlue-47
❑ 99SkyThu-170
❑ 99SkyThuRant-170
❑ 99SkyThuRave-170
❑ 99SpoIll-69
❑ 99ThuSkySupR-170
Sampson, Jacob
❑ 98YakBeaG-29
Sampson, Mark
❑ 86SpoIndC-166
Sampson, Michael
❑ 89VerBeaDS-24
❑ 90YakBeaTI-3
❑ 91VerBeaDC-11
❑ 91VerBeaDP-772
Sampson, Tommy
❑ 92NegLeaK-15
❑ 92NegLeaRLI-53
❑ 95NegLeaL2-20
Sams, Aaron
❑ 98WilCubM-22
❑ 99TeaBesR-78
❑ 99TeaBesRFS-7
❑ 99TeaBesRG-78
❑ 99TeaBesRS-78
Sams, Andre
❑ 78GreBraT-22
Samson, Fred (Frederic)
❑ 87PorChaRP-14
❑ 89TulDriGS-23
❑ 89TulDriTI-22
❑ 90ChaRanS-26
❑ 90FloStaLAS-42
❑ 90StaFS7-27
❑ 91LinDriAA-596
❑ 91TulDriLD-596
❑ 91TulDriP-2783
❑ 91TulDriTI-28
Samson, William
❑ 52Par-51
❑ 53ExhCan-54
Samuel, Amado
❑ 62Top-597
❑ 64Top-129
❑ 64TopVen-129
❑ 91MetWIZ-341
Samuel, Cody
❑ 94OneYanC-19
❑ 94OneYanF-3803
❑ 96GreBatB-24
❑ 97TamYan-24
Samuel, Juan
❑ 83PorBeaT-2
❑ 83ReaPhiT-17
❑ 84Fle-47
❑ 84FunFooP-68
❑ 84PhiTas-32
❑ 84TopTra-105T
❑ 84TopTraT-105T
❑ 85AllGamPI-104
❑ 85Don-23
❑ 85Don-183
❑ 85DonActA-56
❑ 85DonSupD-23
❑ 85Dra-27
❑ 85Fle-264
❑ 85Fle-634
❑ 85FleStaS-44
❑ 85FleStaS-59
❑ 85Lea-23
❑ 85OPC-265
❑ 85PhiCIG-1
❑ 85PhiTas-11
❑ 85PhiTas-32
❑ 85SevCoi-E15
❑ 85Top-8
❑ 85Top-265
❑ 85TopGloS-31
❑ 85TopRubD-16
❑ 85TopSti-114
❑ 85TopSti-369
❑ 85TopSup-28
❑ 85TopTif-8
❑ 85TopTif-265
❑ 86BurKinA-10
❑ 86Don-326
❑ 86DonHig-37
❑ 86Fle-449
❑ 86FleLeaL-38
❑ 86FleLimE-39
❑ 86FleMin-93
❑ 86FleStiC-105
❑ 86KayB-29
❑ 86Lea-196
❑ 86OPC-237
❑ 86PhiCIG-1
❑ 86PhiKel-4
❑ 86PhiTas-8
❑ 86SevCoi-E12
❑ 86Spo-94
❑ 86Top-475
❑ 86TopMinL-54
❑ 86TopSti-121
❑ 86TopTat-15
❑ 86TopTif-475
❑ 87Don-165
❑ 87DonOpeD-156
❑ 87Fle-185
❑ 87Fle-642
❑ 87FleBasA-39
❑ 87FleGlo-185
❑ 87FleGlo-642
❑ 87FleLeaL-38
❑ 87FleMin-94
❑ 87FleStiC-104
❑ 87Lea-132
❑ 87OPC-255
❑ 87PhiCha-3
❑ 87PhiTas-8
❑ 87Spo-123
❑ 87SpoTeaP-6
❑ 87StuPan-9
❑ 87Top-255
❑ 87Top-481
❑ 87TopMinL-29
❑ 87TopSti-125
❑ 87TopTif-255
❑ 87TopTif-481
❑ 88Baz-18
❑ 88Don-288
❑ 88Don-576
❑ 88DonAll-55
❑ 88DonBasB-215
❑ 88Dra-20
❑ 88Fle-314
❑ 88FleAll-10
❑ 88FleBasA-35
❑ 88FleGlo-314
❑ 88FleMin-101
❑ 88FleStiC-110
❑ 88FleTeaL-33
❑ 88KayB-26
❑ 88Lea-146
❑ 88Nes-16
❑ 88OPC-19
❑ 88PanSti-359
❑ 88PhiTas-22
❑ 88Sco-32
❑ 88ScoGlo-32
❑ 88Spo-96
❑ 88SpoGam-12
❑ 88StaLinPh-15
❑ 88Top-398
❑ 88Top-705
❑ 88TopBig-67
❑ 88TopClo-99
❑ 88TopCoi-51
❑ 88TopGloS-43
❑ 88TopMinL-66
❑ 88TopRevLL-7
❑ 88TopSti-120
❑ 88TopStiB-5
❑ 88TopTif-398
❑ 88TopTif-705
❑ 88TopUKM-64
❑ 88TopUKMT-64
❑ 89Bow-405
❑ 89BowTif-405
❑ 89CadEllD-47
❑ 89ClaTraO-146
❑ 89Don-76
❑ 89DonBasB-238
❑ 89Fle-581
❑ 89FleGlo-581
❑ 89FleUpd-102
❑ 89MetKah-24
❑ 89OPC-372
❑ 89PanSti-152
❑ 89PhiTas-31
❑ 89RedFolSB-101
❑ 89Sco-255
❑ 89ScoHot1S-26
❑ 89ScoRoo-21T
❑ 89Spo-17
❑ 89Top-575
❑ 89TopAme2C-25
❑ 89TopBasT-95
❑ 89TopBig-321
❑ 89TopCoi-23
❑ 89TopGloS-13
❑ 89TopHilTM-25
❑ 89TopMinL-29
❑ 89TopSti-117
❑ 89TopStiB-37
❑ 89TopTif-575
❑ 89TopTra-108T
❑ 89TopTraT-108T
❑ 89TopUKM-66
❑ 89TVSpoM-29
❑ 89UppDec-336
❑ 90Bow-91
❑ 90BowTif-91
❑ 90ClaYel-T45
❑ 90DodMot-7
❑ 90DodPol-10
❑ 90Don-53
❑ 90DonBesN-29
❑ 90Fle-215
❑ 90FleCan-215
❑ 90FleUpd-25
❑ 90Lea-226
❑ 90OPC-85
❑ 90PubIntS-249
❑ 90Sco-198
❑ 90ScoRoo-33T
❑ 90Top-85
❑ 90TopAmeA-25
❑ 90TopBig-283
❑ 90TopMinL-68
❑ 90TopTif-85
❑ 90TopTra-109T
❑ 90TopTraT-109T
❑ 90UppDec-583
❑ 90UppDec-795
❑ 91Bow-596
❑ 91Cla3-T82
❑ 91DodMot-7
❑ 91DodPho-23
❑ 91DodPol-10
❑ 91Don-62
❑ 91Fle-218
❑ 91Lea-10
❑ 91MetWIZ-342
❑ 91OPC-645
❑ 91OPCBoxB-O
❑ 91PanFreS-56
❑ 91Sco-446
❑ 91StaClu-495
❑ 91Stu-188
❑ 91Top-645
❑ 91TopDesS-645
❑ 91TopMic-645
❑ 91TopTif-645
❑ 91TopWaxBC-O
❑ 91Ult-168
❑ 91UppDec-117
❑ 91USPlaCA-8C
❑ 92Bow-253
❑ 92ClaGam-37
❑ 92DodMot-24
❑ 92DodPol-10
❑ 92DodSmo-10492
❑ 92DodStaTA-30
❑ 92Don-105
❑ 92Fle-469
❑ 92Lea-125
❑ 92LeaBlaG-125
❑ 92OPC-315
❑ 92PanSti-193
❑ 92Pin-99
❑ 92RedFolS-126
❑ 92Sco-73
❑ 92ScoProP-16
❑ 92StaClu-11
❑ 92StaCluD-161
❑ 92Top-315
❑ 92TopGol-315
❑ 92TopGolW-315
❑ 92TopMic-315
❑ 92TriPla-73
❑ 92TriPla-125
❑ 92Ult-216
❑ 92UppDec-195
❑ 93PacBeiA-21
❑ 93PacSpa-404
❑ 93RedKah-23
❑ 93Sco-611
❑ 93Sel-237
❑ 93SelRoo-129T
❑ 93Ult-335
❑ 93UppDec-527
❑ 93UppDecGold-527
❑ 94Fle-426
❑ 94FleUpd-46
❑ 94Pac-159
❑ 94StaClu-679
❑ 94StaCluFDI-679
❑ 94StaCluGR-679
❑ 94StaCluMOP-679
❑ 95Don-506
❑ 95DonPreP-506
❑ 95Fle-60
❑ 95Pac-159

❑ 95Sco-527
❑ 95ScoGolR-527
❑ 95ScoPlaTS-527
❑ 96BluJayOH-28
❑ 96Fle-137
❑ 96FleTif-137
❑ 96FleUpd-U103
❑ 96FleUpdTC-U103
❑ 96LeaSigEA-177
❑ 96Pac-323
❑ 97BluJayOH-28
❑ 97Pac-227
❑ 97PacLigB-227
❑ 97PacSil-227
❑ 98PacInvGems-114
❑ 98PacOnl-774
❑ 98PacOnlR-774
❑ 98PacOnlWC-774
❑ 99Pac-447
❑ 99PacCroC-300
❑ 99PacCroCPB-300
❑ 99PacPlaB-447
❑ 99PacRed-447

Samuel, Mike
❑ 81BurBeeT-19
❑ 82BelBreFr-19
❑ 84ElPasDT-9
❑ 85BelBreT-1

Samuels, Geoff
❑ 91BenBucCB-10
❑ 91BenBucP-3695
❑ 92SalSpuC-3
❑ 92SalSpuF-3752

Samuels, Roger
❑ 86ColAstP-23
❑ 88BlaYNPRWL-125
❑ 88FleUpd-131
❑ 88FleUpdG-131
❑ 88PhoFirC-8
❑ 88PhoFirP-70
❑ 90CMC-370
❑ 90ProAAAF-274
❑ 90TidTidC-19
❑ 90TidTidP-543
❑ 90TopTVM-57

Samuels, Scott
❑ 92ClaFS7-443
❑ 92EriSaiC-13
❑ 92EriSaiF-1639
❑ 94BreCouMC-15
❑ 94BreCouMF-26
❑ 95Bes-59
❑ 96OrlCubB-24
❑ 97OrlRayB-22
❑ 98arSenW1-19
❑ 98HarSenM-19

Sanborn, Kyle
❑ 88CapCodPPaLP-112

Sanchez, Adam
❑ 92PeoChiTI-31
❑ 93PocPosSP-25

Sanchez, Adrian
❑ 90HunCubP-3281
❑ 91HunCubC-23
❑ 91HunCubP-3335
❑ 92MidLeaATI-37
❑ 92PeoChiC-18
❑ 92PeoChiTI-23
❑ 93PeoChiTI-24

Sanchez, Alejandro
❑ 81ReaPhiT-22
❑ 82OklCit8T-7
❑ 83PorBeaT-22
❑ 84PhoGiaC-8
❑ 85Don-43
❑ 85Fle-648
❑ 85FleUpd-98
❑ 86Don-415
❑ 86Fle-236
❑ 86Top-563
❑ 86TopTif-563
❑ 86TwiTeal-13
❑ 87TacTigP-20

Sanchez, Alex
❑ 97Bow-333
❑ 97BowBes-200
❑ 97BowBesAR-200
❑ 97BowBesR-200
❑ 97BowChr-229
❑ 97BowChrI-229
❑ 97BowChrIR-229
❑ 97BowChrR-229
❑ 97BowInt-333
❑ 97ChaRivDG-25
❑ 97Top-252
❑ 98Bes-42
❑ 98Bow-152
❑ 98BowBes-147
❑ 98BowBesAR-147
❑ 98BowBesR-147
❑ 98BowCerBlueAU-64
❑ 98BowCerGA-64
❑ 98BowCerSA-64
❑ 98BowChr-152
❑ 98BowChrGA-152
❑ 98BowChrGAR-152
❑ 98BowChrI-152
❑ 98BowChrIR-152
❑ 98BowChrR-152
❑ 98BowGolA-152
❑ 98BowInt-152
❑ 98SP MinPE-120
❑ 98SPMin-120
❑ 98St.PetDRM-27
❑ 98Top-250
❑ 98TopChr-250
❑ 98TopChrR-250
❑ 98TopDevR-250
❑ 98TopDia-250
❑ 98TopMiniC-250

Sanchez, Alex Anthony
❑ 88BasAmeAAB-13
❑ 88KnoBluJB-1
❑ 88OPC-194
❑ 88SouLeaAJ-26
❑ 88TacTigC-17
❑ 88TacTigP-637
❑ 89Bow-245
❑ 89BowTif-245
❑ 89Don-47
❑ 89FleUpd-71
❑ 89SyrChiC-10
❑ 89SyrChiMB-20
❑ 89SyrChiP-813
❑ 89TopTra-109T
❑ 89TopTraT-109T
❑ 90BluJayFS-24
❑ 90CMC-327
❑ 90Don-45
❑ 90Fle-92
❑ 90FleCan-92
❑ 90OPC-563
❑ 90ProAAAF-350
❑ 90SyrChiC-1
❑ 90SyrChiMB-20
❑ 90SyrChiP-570
❑ 90Top-563
❑ 90TopDeb89-107
❑ 90TopTif-563
❑ 90ToyRoo-23
❑ 90TriAAAC-25
❑ 90UppDec-757
❑ 91LinDriAAA-515
❑ 91SyrChiK-3
❑ 91SyrChiLD-515
❑ 91SyrChiMB-21
❑ 91SyrChiP-2479
❑ 92BasCitRF-3846
❑ 93MemChiF-376
❑ 94CalCanF-789

Sanchez, Arturo
❑ 80VenLeaS-53

Sanchez, Carlos
❑ 88PocGiaP-2077

Sanchez, Celerino
❑ 73OPC-103
❑ 73SyrChiTI-25
❑ 73Top-103
❑ 74OPC-623
❑ 74SyrChiTI-24
❑ 74Top-623
❑ 92YanWIZ7-137

Sanchez, Daniel
❑ 90GreHorB-19
❑ 90GreHorP-2671
❑ 90GreHorS-21
❑ 91PriWilCC-19
❑ 91PriWilCP-1436

Sanchez, Francisco
❑ 87GasRanP-28

Sanchez, Frank
❑ 78WauMetT-24

Sanchez, Geraldo
❑ 86HagSunP-17
❑ 87HagSunP-28
❑ 88BlaYNPRWL-175
❑ 89BlaYNPRWL-54

Sanchez, Gordon
❑ 92FroRowDP-38
❑ 92FroRowDPG-38
❑ 92FroRowDPS-38
❑ 92OneYanC-6
❑ 93ColCliF-1114
❑ 93ColCliP-12
❑ 94TamYanC-23
❑ 94TamYanF-2388
❑ 95NorNavTI-48

Sanchez, Israel
❑ 83ChaRoyT-22
❑ 85Ft.MyeRT-15
❑ 86MemChiSTOS-24
❑ 86MemChiTOS-24
❑ 87OmaRoyP-18
❑ 88FleUpd-34
❑ 88FleUpdG-34
❑ 88OmaRoyC-11
❑ 88OmaRoyP-1496
❑ 89Don-474
❑ 89Top-452
❑ 89TopTif-452
❑ 89UppDec-326
❑ 90UppDec-384
❑ 91LinDriAAA-465
❑ 91RocRedWLD-465
❑ 91RocRedWP-1901
❑ 92RocRedWS-467

Sanchez, Jesus
❑ 94KinMetC-17
❑ 94KinMetF-3821
❑ 96StLucMTI-26
❑ 97Bes-79
❑ 97BinMetB-26
❑ 97EasLeaTPB-6
❑ 97TexAllM-53
❑ 98Bow-314
❑ 98BowChr-314
❑ 98BowChrGA-314
❑ 98BowChrGAR-314
❑ 98BowChrI-314
❑ 98BowChrIR-314
❑ 98BowChrR-314
❑ 98BowGolA-314
❑ 98BowInt-314
❑ 98Fle-506
❑ 98LeaRS-304
❑ 98LeaRSLHolo-304
❑ 98LeaRSLong-304
❑ 98LeaRTrue-304
❑ 98PacOmeRS-16
❑ 98PacOmeRST1-16
❑ 98PacOnl-305
❑ 98PacOnlR-305
❑ 98PacOnlWC-305
❑ 98UppDec-552
❑ 99Fle-459
❑ 99FleSta9-459
❑ 99FleWarT-459
❑ 99PacCroC-119
❑ 99PacCroCPB-119
❑ 99SP SigAuto-JS
❑ 99SPSig-166
❑ 99Top-419
❑ 99TopChr-419
❑ 99TopChrR-419
❑ 99TopMVPP-419

Sanchez, Jose
❑ 93AppFoxCB-21
❑ 93AppFoxFI-2459

Sanchez, Juan
❑ 87ClePhiP-22

Sanchez, Leo
❑ 84PriWilPT-28
❑ 85DomLeaS-51
❑ 85NasPirT-22

Sanchez, Luis
❑ 73CedRapAT-15
❑ 74CedRapAT-13

Sanchez, Luis M.
❑ 76VenLeaS-139
❑ 80VenLeaS-196
❑ 81LonBeaPT-16
❑ 82Top-653
❑ 83Don-519
❑ 83Fle-100
❑ 83Top-623
❑ 84AllGamPI-188
❑ 84AngSmo-24
❑ 84Don-597
❑ 84Fle-527
❑ 84Nes792-258
❑ 84OPC-258
❑ 84Top-258
❑ 84TopSti-233
❑ 84TopTif-258
❑ 85AngSmo-16
❑ 85Don-352
❑ 85Fle-310
❑ 85OPC-42
❑ 85Top-42
❑ 85TopTif-42
❑ 86Top-124
❑ 86TopTif-124
❑ 87JapPlaB-11
❑ 93LinVenB-98
❑ 94VenLinU-138
❑ 95LinVen-132

Sanchez, Manuel
❑ 97EugEmeB-24
❑ 98EugEme-22

Sanchez, Marcos
❑ 80VenLeaS-227
❑ 95IdaFalBTI-34
❑ 96CliLumKTI-24
❑ 97CliLumG-23
❑ 98RanCucQG-25
❑ 98RanCucQG-25

Sanchez, Martin
❑ 96MacBraB-12
❑ 98HigDesMG-23

Sanchez, Mike
❑ 95YakBeaTI-27
❑ 96GreFalDB-24
❑ 96GreFalDTI-12
❑ 96SanBerSB-23

Sanchez, Omar
❑ 94St.CatBJC-18
❑ 94St.CatBJF-3657
❑ 94VenLinU-118
❑ 95DunBluJTI-23
❑ 95LinVen-174
❑ 95StCatSTI-25
❑ 96-97LinVen-45
❑ 96DunBluJUTI-11
❑ 96HagSunB-19

Sanchez, Orlando
❑ 81Car5x7-23
❑ 82Don-636
❑ 82Fle-126
❑ 82LouRedE-26
❑ 82Top-604
❑ 83LouRedR-24
❑ 85MaiGuiT-23
❑ 88BlaYNPRWL-176
❑ 91OriCro-401
❑ 97SarRedS-23

Sanchez, Ozzir (Osvaldo)
❑ 87SpoIndP-1
❑ 88ChaRaiP-1200
❑ 89BlaYNPRWL-153
❑ 89WatDiaP-1786
❑ 89WatDiaS-25
❑ 90Bes-281
❑ 90CMC-701
❑ 90WatDiaB-16
❑ 90WatDiaP-2391
❑ 91HigDesMC-28
❑ 91HigDesMP-2411
❑ 92DurBulC-6
❑ 92DurBulF-1111
❑ 92DurBulTI-17
❑ 93ClaFS7-290
❑ 93DurBulC-16
❑ 93DurBulF-499

Sanchez, Pedro
❑ 75BurBeeT-23
❑ 85DomLeaS-104
❑ 86AubAstP-22
❑ 87AshTouP-27
❑ 88OscAstS-23
❑ 89ColMudB-6
❑ 89ColMudP-127
❑ 89ColMudS-21
❑ 90CMC-624
❑ 90ProAAAF-197
❑ 90TucTorC-22
❑ 90TucTorP-207

Sanchez, Perry
❑ 90GatCitPP-3360
❑ 90GatCitPSP-21
❑ 91WesPalBEC-17
❑ 91WesPalBEP-1233

Sanchez, Raul
❑ 57Top-393
❑ 60Top-311
❑ 61MapLeaBH-19

Sanchez, Rey
❑ 88BlaYNPRWLU-21
❑ 88ChaRanS-NNO
❑ 89BlaYNPRWL-16
❑ 89OklCit8C-18
❑ 89OklCit8P-1511
❑ 91IowCubLD-216
❑ 91IowCubP-1067
❑ 91LinDriAAA-216
❑ 91TriA AAGP-AAA20
❑ 92CubMar-6
❑ 92Don-412
❑ 92FleUpd-75
❑ 92IowCubS-221
❑ 92Pin-550
❑ 92ProFS7-200
❑ 92StaClu-308
❑ 92TopDeb91-154
❑ 92TopTra-98T
❑ 92TopTraG-98T
❑ 92Ult-180
❑ 92UppDec-562
❑ 93Bow-496
❑ 93CubMar-22
❑ 93CubStaC-24
❑ 93Don-424
❑ 93Fle-24
❑ 93Lea-88
❑ 93PacBeiA-18
❑ 93PacSpa-61
❑ 93Pin-317
❑ 93Sco-324
❑ 93StaClu-36
❑ 93StaCluFDI-36
❑ 93StaCluMOP-36
❑ 93Top-292
❑ 93TopGol-292
❑ 93TopInaM-292
❑ 93TopInaR-292
❑ 93TopMic-292
❑ 93Toy-60
❑ 93Ult-319
❑ 93Ult-648
❑ 93UppDec-612
❑ 93UppDecGold-612
❑ 93USPlaCR-8H
❑ 94ColC-558
❑ 94ColChoGS-558
❑ 94ColChoSS-558
❑ 94Don-383
❑ 94Fin-249
❑ 94FinRef-249
❑ 94Fla-362
❑ 94Fle-395
❑ 94FleExtB-223
❑ 94Pac-108
❑ 94Sco-482
❑ 94ScoGolR-482
❑ 94StaClu-104
❑ 94StaCluFDI-104
❑ 94StaCluGR-104
❑ 94StaCluMOP-104
❑ 94StaCluT-338
❑ 94StaCluTFDI-338
❑ 94Top-422
❑ 94TopGol-422
❑ 94TopSpa-422
❑ 95ColCho-202
❑ 95ColChoGS-202
❑ 95ColChoSS-202
❑ 95Don-173
❑ 95DonPreP-173
❑ 95DonTopotO-203
❑ 95Fin-66
❑ 95FinRef-66
❑ 95Fla-116
❑ 95Fle-423
❑ 95Lea-160
❑ 95Pac-78
❑ 95PacPri-25
❑ 95Pin-315
❑ 95PinArtP-315
❑ 95PinMusC-315
❑ 95Sco-63
❑ 95ScoGolR-63
❑ 95ScoPlaTS-63
❑ 95StaClu-21
❑ 95StaCluFDI-21
❑ 95StaCluMOP-21
❑ 95StaCluSTWS-21
❑ 95StaCluVR-15
❑ 95StaCluVRMO-15
❑ 95Top-57
❑ 95TopD3-53
❑ 95TopEmb-59
❑ 95TopEmbGI-59
❑ 95Ult-138
❑ 95UltGolM-138
❑ 95UppDec-63
❑ 95UppDecED-63
❑ 95UppDecEDG-63
❑ 96ColCho-496
❑ 96ColChoGS-496
❑ 96ColChoSS-496
❑ 96CubFle-14
❑ 96Don-111
❑ 96DonPreP-111
❑ 96EmoXL-158
❑ 96Fla-222
❑ 96Fle-327
❑ 96FleTif-327
❑ 96LeaSigA-201
❑ 96LeaSigAG-201
❑ 96LeaSigAS-201
❑ 96MetUni-144
❑ 96MetUniP-144
❑ 96Pac-27
❑ 96Sco-395
❑ 96StaClu-389
❑ 96StaCluMOP-389
❑ 96Top-287
❑ 96Ult-169
❑ 96UltGolM-169
❑ 96UppDec-296
❑ 97ColCho-68
❑ 97Pac-256
❑ 97PacLigB-256
❑ 97PacSil-256
❑ 97Sco-429
❑ 97ScoArtPWB-429
❑ 97ScoResC-429
❑ 97ScoShoS-429
❑ 97ScoShoSAP-429
❑ 97StaClu-349
❑ 97StaCluMOP-349
❑ 97Top-179
❑ 97UppDec-32
❑ 98GiaMot-18
❑ 98Pac-158
❑ 98PacOnl-673
❑ 98PacOnlR-673
❑ 98PacOnlWC-673
❑ 98PacPlaB-158
❑ 98PacRedT-158
❑ 98PacSil-158
❑ 99Pac-389
❑ 99PacCroC-257
❑ 99PacCroCPB-257
❑ 99PacPlaB-389
❑ 99PacRed-389
❑ 99Top-57
❑ 99TopChr-57
❑ 99TopChrR-57
❑ 99TopMVPP-57
❑ 99Vic-190

Sanchez, Sammye
❑ 88LitFalMP-12

Sanchez, Sergio
❑ 93ElmPioC-16
❑ 93ElmPioF-3831

Sanchez, Simon
❑ 98LetBlaDG-25

Sanchez, Stan
❑ 87SanBerSP-6
❑ 89SanBerSB-26
❑ 89SanBerSCLC-91

Sanchez, Toby
❑ 98ChaAllCM-21

Sanchez, Victor
❑ 94AubAstC-16
❑ 94AubAstF-3763
❑ 95QuaCitRBTI-24
❑ 96JacGenB-24
❑ 97JacGen-24
❑ 97JacGenS-23
❑ 98JacGenM-19

Sanchez, Wellington
❑ 97HelBreB-29
❑ 98BelSnaM-23

Sanchez, Yuri
❑ 92BriTigC-20
❑ 92BriTigF-1421
❑ 92ClaDraP-39
❑ 92ClaFS7-427
❑ 93ClaFS7-116
❑ 93FayGenC-1
❑ 93FayGenF-138
❑ 94Cla-4
❑ 94LakTigC-20
❑ 94LakTigF-3045
❑ 94UppDecML-129
❑ 95JacSunTI-25
❑ 95UppDecML-206
❑ 95UppDecMLFS-206
❑ 97BurBeeB-20
❑ 98BinMetQ-25

Sanchez, Zoilo
❑ 86LynMetP-20
❑ 87JacMetF-6

- ❑ 87MetColP-46
- ❑ 88JacMetGS-2
- ❑ 89JacMetGS-15
- ❑ 90CMC-377
- ❑ 90ProAAAF-289
- ❑ 90TidTidC-26
- ❑ 90TidTidP-558
- ❑ 90TopTVM-58

Sand, Heinie (John Henry)

- ❑ 18Zee-71
- ❑ 21Exh-150
- ❑ 21Zee-108
- ❑ 22Zee-87
- ❑ 25Exh-47
- ❑ 26Exh-47
- ❑ 28Exh-23
- ❑ 33Gou-85
- ❑ 34GouCanV-27
- ❑ 92ConTSN-615

Sandberg, Chuck

- ❑ 81BriRedST-11

Sandberg, Gus

- ❑ 25Zee-11
- ❑ 26Zee-32
- ❑ 27Zee-17
- ❑ 28Zee-39
- ❑ 29Zee-29

Sandberg, Jared

- ❑ 97AppLeaTPB-10
- ❑ 97PriDevR-17
- ❑ 97Top-470
- ❑ 98Bes-43
- ❑ 98BesDiaB-8
- ❑ 98Bow-78
- ❑ 98BowCerBlueAU-29
- ❑ 98BowCerGA-29
- ❑ 98BowCerSA-29
- ❑ 98BowChr-78
- ❑ 98BowChrGA-78
- ❑ 98BowChrGAR-78
- ❑ 98BowChrI-78
- ❑ 98BowChrIR-78
- ❑ 98BowChrR-78
- ❑ 98BowGolA-78
- ❑ 98BowInt-78
- ❑ 98ChaRivDG-23
- ❑ 98HudValR-22
- ❑ 98Top-250
- ❑ 98TopChr-250
- ❑ 98TopChrR-250
- ❑ 98TopDevR-250
- ❑ 98TopDia-250
- ❑ 98TopMiniC-250
- ❑ 99Bow-118
- ❑ 99BowAut-BA57
- ❑ 99BowChr-118
- ❑ 99BowChrG-118
- ❑ 99BowChrGR-118
- ❑ 99BowChrI-118
- ❑ 99BowChrIR-118
- ❑ 99BowChrR-118
- ❑ 99BowGol-118
- ❑ 99BowInt-118

Sandberg, Ryne

- ❑ 80CarMudF-22
- ❑ 81OklCit8T-17
- ❑ 82CubRedL-23
- ❑ 83AllGamPI-107
- ❑ 83CubThoAV-23
- ❑ 83Don-277
- ❑ 83Fle-507
- ❑ 83OPC-83
- ❑ 83Top-83
- ❑ 83Top-282
- ❑ 83TopSti-328
- ❑ 84AllGamPI-15
- ❑ 84CubBriPC-6S
- ❑ 84CubChiT-25
- ❑ 84CubSev-23
- ❑ 84CubUno-2
- ❑ 84CubUno-3
- ❑ 84CubUno-7
- ❑ 84CubUno-12
- ❑ 84CubUno-15
- ❑ 84Don-311
- ❑ 84DonActAS-43
- ❑ 84Fle-504
- ❑ 84FunFooP-13
- ❑ 84Nes792-596
- ❑ 84OCoandSI-102
- ❑ 84OCoandSI-202
- ❑ 84OPC-64
- ❑ 84Top-596
- ❑ 84TopSti-45
- ❑ 84TopTif-596
- ❑ 85AllGamPI-105
- ❑ 85CubLioP-19
- ❑ 85CubSev-23
- ❑ 85Don-1
- ❑ 85Don-67
- ❑ 85DonActA-24
- ❑ 85DonSupD-1
- ❑ 85DonWaxBC-PC2
- ❑ 85Dra-28
- ❑ 85Fle-65
- ❑ 85Fle-630
- ❑ 85FleLimE-31
- ❑ 85FleStaS-11
- ❑ 85FleStaS-45
- ❑ 85GenMilS-8
- ❑ 85KASDis-11
- ❑ 85KitCloD-11
- ❑ 85Lea-1
- ❑ 85OPC-296
- ❑ 85SevCoi-G11
- ❑ 85SubDis-41
- ❑ 85ThoMcAD-41
- ❑ 85Top-460
- ❑ 85Top-713
- ❑ 85Top3-D-7
- ❑ 85TopGaloC-9
- ❑ 85TopGloA-3
- ❑ 85TopGloS-21
- ❑ 85TopRubD-9
- ❑ 85TopSti-34
- ❑ 85TopSti-175
- ❑ 85TopSup-1
- ❑ 85TopTif-460
- ❑ 85TopTif-713
- ❑ 86BasStaB-96
- ❑ 86CubGat-23
- ❑ 86CubUno-15
- ❑ 86Don-67
- ❑ 86DonAll-32
- ❑ 86DorChe-14
- ❑ 86Dra-19
- ❑ 86Fle-378
- ❑ 86FleLeaL-39
- ❑ 86FleLimE-40
- ❑ 86FleMin-80
- ❑ 86FleSlu-32
- ❑ 86FleStiC-106
- ❑ 86GenMilB-4G
- ❑ 86Lea-62
- ❑ 86MeaGolBB-13
- ❑ 86MeaGolM-10
- ❑ 86MeaGolSB-12
- ❑ 86MSAJayPCD-15
- ❑ 86MSAJifPD-12
- ❑ 86OPC-19
- ❑ 86QuaGra-13
- ❑ 86SevCoi-C9
- ❑ 86Spo-20
- ❑ 86Spo-51
- ❑ 86Spo-127
- ❑ 86Top-690
- ❑ 86TopGloS-34
- ❑ 86TopMinL-39
- ❑ 86TopSti-55
- ❑ 86TopSup-48
- ❑ 86TopTat-8
- ❑ 86TopTif-690
- ❑ 86TruVal-14
- ❑ 87BoaandB-30
- ❑ 87BurKinA-18
- ❑ 87ClaGam-35
- ❑ 87CubCan-26
- ❑ 87CubDavB-23
- ❑ 87Don-77
- ❑ 87DonAll-13
- ❑ 87DonOpeD-75
- ❑ 87DonP-13
- ❑ 87Dra-21
- ❑ 87Fle-572
- ❑ 87Fle-639
- ❑ 87FleAwaW-35
- ❑ 87FleGlo-572
- ❑ 87FleGlo-639
- ❑ 87FleLeaL-39
- ❑ 87FleMin-95
- ❑ 87FleStiC-105
- ❑ 87FleWaxBC-C14
- ❑ 87GenMilB-5G
- ❑ 87HosSti-8
- ❑ 87KayB-28
- ❑ 87KraFoo-8
- ❑ 87Lea-234
- ❑ 87MandMSL-4
- ❑ 87MSAJifPD-1
- ❑ 87OPC-143
- ❑ 87RalPur-15
- ❑ 87RedFolSB-16
- ❑ 87SevCoi-C14
- ❑ 87SevCoi-M11
- ❑ 87Spo-8
- ❑ 87Spo-116
- ❑ 87Spo-197
- ❑ 87SpoIIS-11
- ❑ 87SpoSupD-3
- ❑ 87SpoTeaP-22
- ❑ 87Top-680
- ❑ 87TopCoi-41
- ❑ 87TopGloA-3
- ❑ 87TopSti-61
- ❑ 87TopSti-156
- ❑ 87TopTif-680
- ❑ 88Baz-19
- ❑ 88CarSmo-16
- ❑ 88CheBoy-11
- ❑ 88ClaRed-169
- ❑ 88CubDavB-23
- ❑ 88Don-242
- ❑ 88DonAll-35
- ❑ 88DonBasB-116
- ❑ 88DonPop-13
- ❑ 88DonTeaBC-242
- ❑ 88Fle-431
- ❑ 88Fle-628
- ❑ 88FleBasM-29
- ❑ 88FleExcS-32
- ❑ 88FleGlo-431
- ❑ 88FleGlo-628
- ❑ 88FleMin-70
- ❑ 88FleStiC-80
- ❑ 88FleSupBC-C5
- ❑ 88FleWaxBC-C10
- ❑ 88GreBasS-49
- ❑ 88Lea-207
- ❑ 88OPC-10
- ❑ 88PanSti-234
- ❑ 88PanSti-260
- ❑ 88Sco-26
- ❑ 88ScoBoxC-12
- ❑ 88ScoGlo-26
- ❑ 88Spo-12
- ❑ 88StaLinAl-28
- ❑ 88StaLinCu-10
- ❑ 88TarPla-36
- ❑ 88Top-10
- ❑ 88TopBig-16
- ❑ 88TopCoi-52
- ❑ 88TopGloA-14
- ❑ 88TopGloS-14
- ❑ 88TopSti-57
- ❑ 88TopSti-147
- ❑ 88TopStiB-6
- ❑ 88TopTif-10
- ❑ 88TopUKM-65
- ❑ 88TopUKMT-65
- ❑ 89Bow-290
- ❑ 89BowTif-290
- ❑ 89CadEllD-48
- ❑ 89ClaLigB-99
- ❑ 89CubMar-23
- ❑ 89Don-105
- ❑ 89DonAll-35
- ❑ 89DonBasB-26
- ❑ 89DonPop-35
- ❑ 89Fle-437
- ❑ 89FleGlo-437
- ❑ 89FleHeroB-35
- ❑ 89K-M-24
- ❑ 89KayB-26
- ❑ 89KinDis-5
- ❑ 89OPC-360
- ❑ 89PanSti-56
- ❑ 89PanSti-233
- ❑ 89Sco-35
- ❑ 89ScoHot1S-54
- ❑ 89Scomast-23
- ❑ 89Spo-201
- ❑ 89SpoIllFKI-121
- ❑ 89Top-360
- ❑ 89Top-387
- ❑ 89TopAme2C-26
- ❑ 89TopBasT-69
- ❑ 89TopBig-212
- ❑ 89TopDouA-14
- ❑ 89TopGloA-14
- ❑ 89TopGloS-34
- ❑ 89TopHeaUT-9
- ❑ 89TopSti-55
- ❑ 89TopSti-155
- ❑ 89TopStiB-38
- ❑ 89TopTif-360
- ❑ 89TopTif-387
- ❑ 89TopUKM-67
- ❑ 89TVSpoM-18
- ❑ 89UppDec-120
- ❑ 89UppDec-675
- ❑ 90AllBasT-19
- ❑ 90Bow-30
- ❑ 90BowTif-30
- ❑ 90ClaBlu-27
- ❑ 90ClaYel-T86
- ❑ 90Col-29
- ❑ 90CubMar-18
- ❑ 90Don-105
- ❑ 90Don-692A
- ❑ 90Don-692B
- ❑ 90DonBesN-26
- ❑ 90DOnBonM-BC10
- ❑ 90DonLeaS-11
- ❑ 90Fle-40
- ❑ 90Fle-625
- ❑ 90Fle-639
- ❑ 90FleAll-9
- ❑ 90FleAwaW-31
- ❑ 90FleBasA-32
- ❑ 90FleBasAC-32
- ❑ 90FleBasM-33
- ❑ 90FleBasMC-33
- ❑ 90FleCan-40
- ❑ 90FleCan-625
- ❑ 90FleCan-639
- ❑ 90FleLeaL-33
- ❑ 90FleLeaLC-33
- ❑ 90GooHumICBLS-19
- ❑ 90Hot50PS-37
- ❑ 90K-M-2
- ❑ 90Lea-98
- ❑ 90Lea-528
- ❑ 90M.Vpin-20
- ❑ 90MLBBasB-47
- ❑ 90MSAIceTD-12
- ❑ 90OPC-210
- ❑ 90OPC-398
- ❑ 90OPCBoxB-P
- ❑ 90PanSti-212
- ❑ 90PanSti-231
- ❑ 90Pos-9
- ❑ 90PubIntS-201
- ❑ 90PubIntS-270
- ❑ 90Sco-90
- ❑ 90Sco-561A
- ❑ 90Sco-561B
- ❑ 90Sco-691
- ❑ 90Sco100S-32
- ❑ 90ScoMcD-8
- ❑ 90Spo-54
- ❑ 90StaSan-1
- ❑ 90StaSan-2
- ❑ 90StaSan-3
- ❑ 90StaSan-4
- ❑ 90StaSan-5
- ❑ 90StaSan-6
- ❑ 90StaSan-7
- ❑ 90StaSan-8
- ❑ 90StaSan-9
- ❑ 90StaSan-10
- ❑ 90StaSan-11
- ❑ 90SunSee-20
- ❑ 90SupActM-20
- ❑ 90Top-210
- ❑ 90Top-398
- ❑ 90TopBig-75
- ❑ 90TopCoi-56
- ❑ 90TopDou-55
- ❑ 90TopGloA-3
- ❑ 90TopGloS-1
- ❑ 90TopHeaU-9
- ❑ 90TopMag-25
- ❑ 90TopMinL-51
- ❑ 90TopSti-12
- ❑ 90TopSti-46
- ❑ 90TopSti-152
- ❑ 90TopStiB-6
- ❑ 90TopTif-210
- ❑ 90TopTif-398
- ❑ 90TopTVA-51
- ❑ 90TopTVCu-26
- ❑ 90TopWaxBO-P
- ❑ 90UppDec-324
- ❑ 90UppDecS-5
- ❑ 90USPlaCA-4H
- ❑ 90WonBreS-20
- ❑ 90Woo-21
- ❑ 91BasBesHM-17
- ❑ 91BasBesRB-15
- ❑ 91Baz-9
- ❑ 91Bow-377
- ❑ 91Bow-416
- ❑ 91CadEllD-48
- ❑ 91Cla1-T29
- ❑ 91Cla1-NNO
- ❑ 91Cla2-T67
- ❑ 91ClaGam-107
- ❑ 91Col-15
- ❑ 91ColPosS-1
- ❑ 91ColPosS-2
- ❑ 91ColPosS-3
- ❑ 91ColPosS-4
- ❑ 91ColPosS-5
- ❑ 91ColPosS-6
- ❑ 91ColPosS-7
- ❑ 91ColPosS-8
- ❑ 91ColSan-1
- ❑ 91ColSan-2
- ❑ 91ColSan-3
- ❑ 91ColSan-4
- ❑ 91ColSan-5
- ❑ 91ColSan-6
- ❑ 91ColSan-7
- ❑ 91ColSan-8
- ❑ 91ColSan-9
- ❑ 91ColSan-10
- ❑ 91ColSan-11
- ❑ 91ColSan-12
- ❑ 91ColSan-xx
- ❑ 91CubMar-23
- ❑ 91CubVinL-23
- ❑ 91CubVinL-36
- ❑ 91Don-14
- ❑ 91Don-404
- ❑ 91Don-433
- ❑ 91Don-504
- ❑ 91DonBonC-BC7
- ❑ 91DonEli-S1
- ❑ 91DonPre-9
- ❑ 91DonSupD-14
- ❑ 91Fle-431
- ❑ 91Fle-709
- ❑ 91Fle-713
- ❑ 91FleAll-1
- ❑ 91FlePro-F3
- ❑ 91JimDea-6
- ❑ 91KinDis-19
- ❑ 91Lea-207
- ❑ 91LeaPre-2
- ❑ 91LinDriS-1
- ❑ 91LinDriS-2
- ❑ 91LinDriS-3
- ❑ 91LinDriS-4
- ❑ 91LinDriS-5
- ❑ 91LinDriS-6
- ❑ 91LinDriS-7
- ❑ 91LinDriS-8
- ❑ 91LinDriS-9
- ❑ 91LinDriS-10
- ❑ 91LinDriS-11
- ❑ 91LinDriS-12
- ❑ 91LinDriS-13
- ❑ 91LinDriS-14
- ❑ 91LinDriS-15
- ❑ 91LinDriS-16
- ❑ 91LinDriS-17
- ❑ 91LinDriS-18
- ❑ 91LinDriS-19
- ❑ 91LinDriS-20
- ❑ 91MajLeaCP-68
- ❑ 91MooSna-5
- ❑ 91MSAHolD-6
- ❑ 91OPC-7
- ❑ 91OPC-398
- ❑ 91OPC-740
- ❑ 91OPCPre-103
- ❑ 91PacPro-1
- ❑ 91PanCanT1-9
- ❑ 91PanCanT1-27
- ❑ 91PanCanT1-34
- ❑ 91PanCanT1-49
- ❑ 91PanCanT1-101
- ❑ 91PanFreS-44
- ❑ 91PanFreS-159
- ❑ 91PanSti-40
- ❑ 91PepSup-3
- ❑ 91PetSta-4
- ❑ 91Pos-16
- ❑ 91RedFolS-82
- ❑ 91RedFolS-126
- ❑ 91Sco-3
- ❑ 91Sco-665
- ❑ 91Sco-815
- ❑ 91Sco-862
- ❑ 91Sco100S-60
- ❑ 91SevCoi-M11
- ❑ 91SevCoi-T12
- ❑ 91SevCoi-NW8
- ❑ 91StaClu-230
- ❑ 91StaCluCM-26
- ❑ 91StaPinB-42
- ❑ 91Stu-158
- ❑ 91Top-7
- ❑ 91Top-398
- ❑ 91Top-740
- ❑ 91TopCraJI-6
- ❑ 91TopDesS-7
- ❑ 91TopDesS-398
- ❑ 91TopDesS-740
- ❑ 91TopGaloC-10
- ❑ 91TopGloA-14
- ❑ 91TopMic-7
- ❑ 91TopMic-398
- ❑ 91TopMic-740
- ❑ 91TopSta-30
- ❑ 91TopTif-7
- ❑ 91TopTif-398
- ❑ 91TopTif-740
- ❑ 91TopTriH-N2
- ❑ 91Ult-66
- ❑ 91UltGol-10
- ❑ 91UppDec-132
- ❑ 91UppDec-725
- ❑ 91UppDecFE-79F
- ❑ 91UppDecFE-93F
- ❑ 91UppDecSS-SS8
- ❑ 91USPlaCA-12S
- ❑ 91Woo-20
- ❑ 92Bow-300
- ❑ 92Cla1-T79
- ❑ 92Cla2-T29
- ❑ 92Cla2-NNO
- ❑ 92ClaGam-131
- ❑ 92ColAllG-4
- ❑ 92ColAllP-4
- ❑ 92ColPro-13
- ❑ 92CubMar-23
- ❑ 92DenHol-10
- ❑ 92Don-429
- ❑ 92Don-576
- ❑ 92DonCraJ1-28
- ❑ 92DonMcD-6
- ❑ 92Fle-389
- ❑ 92FleAll-14
- ❑ 92FleCitTP-3
- ❑ 92FleLumC-L4
- ❑ 92Fre-12
- ❑ 92Hig5-30
- ❑ 92Hig5S-26
- ❑ 92HitTheBB-30
- ❑ 92JimDea-18
- ❑ 92KinDis-19
- ❑ 92LaKdec-25
- ❑ 92Lea-317
- ❑ 92Lea-331
- ❑ 92LeaBlaG-317
- ❑ 92LeaBlaG-331
- ❑ 92LeaGolP-2
- ❑ 92LeaPre-2
- ❑ 92Mr.TurS-22
- ❑ 92MSABenSHD-19
- ❑ 92MVPPin-42
- ❑ 92New-24
- ❑ 92OPC-110
- ❑ 92OPCPre-34
- ❑ 92PanSti-183
- ❑ 92PanSti-282
- ❑ 92PepDieM-16
- ❑ 92Pin-10
- ❑ 92Pin-617
- ❑ 92PinRool-13
- ❑ 92PinSlu-9
- ❑ 92PinTeaP-5
- ❑ 92Pos-2
- ❑ 92PosCan-4
- ❑ 92RedFolS-84
- ❑ 92RedFolS-127
- ❑ 92RevSup1-7
- ❑ 92RevSup1-8
- ❑ 92RevSup1-9
- ❑ 92Sco-200
- ❑ 92Sco-442
- ❑ 92Sco-774
- ❑ 92Sco100S-85
- ❑ 92ScoProaG-12
- ❑ 92ScoProP-4
- ❑ 92ScoSam-5
- ❑ 92SevCoi-15
- ❑ 92StaClu-50
- ❑ 92StaClu-600
- ❑ 92StaCluD-162
- ❑ 92StaSan-1
- ❑ 92StaSan-2
- ❑ 92StaSan-3
- ❑ 92StaSan-4

❑ 92StaSan-5
❑ 92StaSan-6
❑ 92StaSan-7
❑ 92StaSan-8
❑ 92StaSan-9
❑ 92StaSan-10
❑ 92StaSan-11
❑ 92Stu-18
❑ 92StuHer-BC1
❑ 92StuPre-3
❑ 92Top-110
❑ 92Top-387
❑ 92TopGol-110
❑ 92TopGol-387
❑ 92TopGolW-110
❑ 92TopGolW-387
❑ 92TopKid-1
❑ 92TopMcD-5
❑ 92TopMic-110
❑ 92TopMic-387
❑ 92TriPla-229
❑ 92Ult-181
❑ 92UltAllS-12
❑ 92UltAwaW-25
❑ 92UppDec-145
❑ 92UppDecF-39
❑ 92UppDecFG-39
❑ 92UppDecTMH-46
❑ 93Ble-48
❑ 93Ble-49
❑ 93Ble-50
❑ 93BlePro-10
❑ 93BlePro-11
❑ 93BlePro-12
❑ 93BlePro-13
❑ 93Bow-200
❑ 93CadDis-51
❑ 93ClaGam-80
❑ 93ColAllG-10
❑ 93CubMar-21
❑ 93CubStaC-1
❑ 93DenHol-8
❑ 93DiaMar-93
❑ 93DiaMarP-7
❑ 93Don-344
❑ 93DonDiaK-DK2
❑ 93DonEli-20
❑ 93DonEliD-1
❑ 93DonEliS-2
❑ 93DonLonBL-LL15
❑ 93DonMasotG-5
❑ 93DonMVP-22
❑ 93DonPre-2
❑ 93DonSpiotG-SG14
❑ 93DurPowP2-13
❑ 93Fin-105
❑ 93FinJum-105
❑ 93FinRef-105
❑ 93Fla-20
❑ 93Fle-25
❑ 93Fle-356
❑ 93FleAtl-21
❑ 93FleFruotL-56
❑ 93FleTeaL-NL6
❑ 93FunPac-19
❑ 93FunPac-80
❑ 93FunPac-84
❑ 93FunPacA-AS4
❑ 93Hos-2
❑ 93JimDea-25
❑ 93KinDis-22
❑ 93Kra-27
❑ 93Lea-224
❑ 93LeaGolA-R4
❑ 93LeaGolA-U4
❑ 93LeaHeaftH-8
❑ 93MetBak-18
❑ 93OPC-274
❑ 93OPCPreSP-4
❑ 93OPCPreSPF-4
❑ 93PacSpa-62
❑ 93PanSti-204
❑ 93Pin-15
❑ 93PinCoo-8
❑ 93PinCooD-8
❑ 93PinHomRC-12
❑ 93PinSlu-27
❑ 93Pos-13
❑ 93PosCan-14
❑ 93RedFolS-83
❑ 93Sco-4
❑ 93Sco-530
❑ 93ScoFra-16
❑ 93Sel-97
❑ 93SelChaS-2
❑ 93SelDufIP-11
❑ 93SelStaL-11
❑ 93SP-17
❑ 93SPPlaP-PP17
❑ 93StaClu-366
❑ 93StaClu-600
❑ 93StaCluFDI-366
❑ 93StaCluFDI-600
❑ 93StaClul-B3
❑ 93StaCluM-44
❑ 93StaCluMMP-9
❑ 93StaCluMOP-366
❑ 93StaCluMOP-600
❑ 93StaCluMOP-MB3
❑ 93Stu-176
❑ 93Top-3
❑ 93Top-402
❑ 93TOPBLAG-17
❑ 93TopGol-3
❑ 93TopGol-402
❑ 93TopInaM-3
❑ 93TopInaM-402
❑ 93TopInaR-3
❑ 93TopInaR-402
❑ 93TopMic-3
❑ 93TopMic-402
❑ 93TopPos-1
❑ 93TriPla-10
❑ 93TriPlaA-4
❑ 93TriPlaN-3
❑ 93TriPlaP-10
❑ 93Ult-320
❑ 93UltAllS-3
❑ 93UppDec-38
❑ 93UppDec-175
❑ 93UppDec-483
❑ 93UppDec-735
❑ 93UppDecCP-R18
❑ 93UppDecDG-8
❑ 93UppDecGold-38
❑ 93UppDecGold-175
❑ 93UppDecGold-483
❑ 93UppDecGold-735
❑ 93UppDecHRH-HR11
❑ 93UppDecOD-D22
❑ 93UppDecTAN-TN6
❑ 94Bow-250
❑ 94Bow-388
❑ 94ChuHomS-16
❑ 94ChuHomSG-16
❑ 94ColC-335
❑ 94ColC-555
❑ 94ColChoGS-335
❑ 94ColChoGS-555
❑ 94ColChoSS-335
❑ 94ColChoSS-555
❑ 94ColChoT-14
❑ 94DenHol-22
❑ 94Don-18
❑ 94Don-110
❑ 94DonAnn8-9
❑ 94DonSpeE-18
❑ 94Fin-210
❑ 94FinJum-210
❑ 94FinRef-210
❑ 94Fla-141
❑ 94FlaHotN-9
❑ 94Fle-396
❑ 94FleAllS-48
❑ 94FleTeaL-16
❑ 94FUnPac-60
❑ 94KinDis-22
❑ 94Lea-425
❑ 94LeaPro-8
❑ 94LeaSli-4
❑ 94O-PJumAF-7
❑ 94OPC-16
❑ 94OPCAllR-7
❑ 94OPCJumA-7
❑ 94OscMayR-29
❑ 94Pac-109
❑ 94PacSilP-26
❑ 94PacSilPC-26
❑ 94PanSti-156
❑ 94Pin-6
❑ 94PinArtP-6
❑ 94PinMusC-6
❑ 94PinTheN-14
❑ 94RedFolMI-36
❑ 94Sco-20
❑ 94ScoGolR-20
❑ 94Sel-32
❑ 94SP-71
❑ 94SPDieC-71
❑ 94Spo-45
❑ 94SpoFanA-AS2
❑ 94SpoMov-MM2
❑ 94StaClu-397
❑ 94StaClu-719
❑ 94StaCluFDI-397
❑ 94StaCluFDI-719
❑ 94StaCluGR-397
❑ 94StaCluGR-719
❑ 94StaCluMOP-397
❑ 94StaCluMOP-719
❑ 94StaCluT-331
❑ 94StaCluTF-9
❑ 94StaCluTFDI-331
❑ 94Stu-63
❑ 94StuHer-5
❑ 94Top-300
❑ 94Top-602
❑ 94TopGol-300
❑ 94TopGol-602
❑ 94TopSpa-300
❑ 94TopSpa-602
❑ 94TopSupS-39
❑ 94TopTra-130T
❑ 94TopTra-131T
❑ 94TriPla-77
❑ 94TriPlaM-6
❑ 94TriPlaN-2
❑ 94Ult-166
❑ 94UltAllS-13
❑ 94UltCarA-4
❑ 94UppDec-92
❑ 94UppDecAJ-5
❑ 94UppDecAJG-5
❑ 94UppDecDC-C6
❑ 94UppDecED-92
❑ 94Yoo-14
❑ 95ColCho-48
❑ 95ColChoGS-48
❑ 95ColChoSS-48
❑ 95UppDec-447
❑ 95UppDecED-447
❑ 95UppDecEDG-447
❑ 95UppDecSE-258
❑ 95UppDecSEG-258
❑ 96Bow-51
❑ 96BowBes-8
❑ 96BowBesAR-8
❑ 96BowBesR-8
❑ 96BowFoi-51
❑ 96Cir-111
❑ 96CirBos-29
❑ 96CirRav-111
❑ 96ColCho-495
❑ 96ColChoGS-495
❑ 96ColChoSS-495
❑ 96CubFle-15
❑ 96DenHol-9
❑ 96EmoXL-159
❑ 96Fin-G39
❑ 96Fin-S234
❑ 96FinRef-G39
❑ 96FinRef-S234
❑ 96Fla-223
❑ 96Fle-328
❑ 96FleTif-328
❑ 96FleUpd-U239
❑ 96FleUpd-U249
❑ 96FleUpdTC-U239
❑ 96FleUpdTC-U249
❑ 96LeaLim-77
❑ 96LeaLimG-77
❑ 96LeaPre-91
❑ 96LeaPreP-91
❑ 96LeaPreSG-66
❑ 96LeaPreSte-66
❑ 96LeaSig-84
❑ 96LeaSigPPG-84
❑ 96LeaSigPPP-84
❑ 96MetUni-145
❑ 96MetUniML-10
❑ 96MetUniP-145
❑ 96Pin-342
❑ 96PinAfi-16
❑ 96PinAfiAP-16
❑ 96PinAfiFPP-16
❑ 96PinAfiSP-16
❑ 96PinFan-12
❑ 96PinFoil-342
❑ 96Sel-140
❑ 96SelArtP-140
❑ 96SelCer-28
❑ 96SelCerAP-28
❑ 96SelCerCB-28
❑ 96SelCerCR-28
❑ 96SelCerIP-19
❑ 96SelCerMB-28
❑ 96SelCerMG-28
❑ 96SelCerMR-28
❑ 96SelTeaN-15
❑ 96SP-53
❑ 96SPx-14
❑ 96SPxGol-14
❑ 96Stu-6
❑ 96StuPrePB-6
❑ 96StuPrePG-6
❑ 96StuPrePS-6
❑ 96Sum-70
❑ 96SumAbo&B-70
❑ 96SumArtP-70
❑ 96SumBal-10
❑ 96SumFoi-70
❑ 96SumHitI-15
❑ 96TeaOut-70
❑ 96Top-356
❑ 96TopBigC-8
❑ 96TopChr-144
❑ 96TopChrR-144
❑ 96TopGal-38
❑ 96TopGalPPI-38
❑ 96TopLas-48
❑ 96TopLasSS-15
❑ 96Ult-457
❑ 96UltCaltt H-8
❑ 96UltCalttHGM-8
❑ 96UltGolM-457
❑ 96UltRes-8
❑ 96UltResGM-8
❑ 96UltThu-18
❑ 96UltThuGM-18
❑ 96UppDec-486U
❑ 96Zen-16
❑ 96ZenArtP-16
❑ 96ZenMoz-6
❑ 97Bow-22
❑ 97BowBes-8
❑ 97BowBesAR-8
❑ 97BowBesR-8
❑ 97BowChr-18
❑ 97BowChrI-18
❑ 97BowChrIR-18
❑ 97BowChrR-18
❑ 97BowInt-22
❑ 97Cir-23
❑ 97CirRav-23
❑ 97ColCho-66
❑ 97ColChoAC-29
❑ 97ColChoNF-NF16
❑ 97Don-72
❑ 97DonEli-70
❑ 97DonEliGS-70
❑ 97DonGolPP-72
❑ 97DonLim-30
❑ 97DonLim-68
❑ 97DonLimE-30
❑ 97DonLimE-68
❑ 97DonLimENG-30
❑ 97DonLimFotG-47
❑ 97DonPre-96
❑ 97DonPreCttC-96
❑ 97DonPreTB-20
❑ 97DonPreTBG-20
❑ 97DonPreTF-20
❑ 97DonPreTP-20
❑ 97DonPreTPG-20
❑ 97DonSig-21
❑ 97DonSigA-88
❑ 97DonSigAC-110
❑ 97DonSigAM-110
❑ 97DonSigPPP-21
❑ 97DonSilPP-72
❑ 97DonVxP1-50
❑ 97E-X2-62
❑ 97E-X2Cred-62
❑ 97E-X2EssCre-62
❑ 97E-X2Hall-5
❑ 97Fin-2
❑ 97Fin-303
❑ 97FinEmb-303
❑ 97FinEmbR-303
❑ 97FinRef-2
❑ 97FinRef-303
❑ 97FlaShoLC-23
❑ 97FlaShoLeg0-23
❑ 97FlaShoLeg1-23
❑ 97FlaShoM-A23
❑ 97FlaShoM-B23
❑ 97FlaShoM-C23
❑ 97FlaShoR0-23
❑ 97FlaShoR1-23
❑ 97FlaShoR2-23
❑ 97Fle-282
❑ 97Fle-716
❑ 97Fle-725
❑ 97FleDecoE-11
❑ 97FleDecoERT-11
❑ 97FleGouG-13
❑ 97FleGouGF-13
❑ 97FleHea-18
❑ 97FleTif-282
❑ 97FleTif-716
❑ 97FleTif-725
❑ 97HigMinM-109
❑ 97HigMinMCT-39
❑ 97HigMinMCT-40
❑ 97KinB-26
❑ 97Lea-196
❑ 97Lea-205
❑ 97LeaFraM-196
❑ 97LeaFraM-205
❑ 97LeaFraMDC-196
❑ 97LeaFraMDC-205
❑ 97LeaGolS-32
❑ 97MetUni-14
❑ 97NewPin-140
❑ 97NewPinAP-140
❑ 97NewPinMC-140
❑ 97NewPinPP-140
❑ 97Pac-257
❑ 97PacCar-25
❑ 97PacCarM-25
❑ 97PacGolCD-25
❑ 97PacLigB-257
❑ 97PacPri-88
❑ 97PacPriGA-GA20
❑ 97PacPriGotD-GD121
❑ 97PacPriLB-88
❑ 97PacPriP-88
❑ 97PacSil-257
❑ 97Pin-99
❑ 97PinArtP-PP99
❑ 97PinCer-4
❑ 97PinCerLI-18
❑ 97PinCerMBla-4
❑ 97PinCerMBlu-4
❑ 97PinCerMG-4
❑ 97PinCerMR-4
❑ 97PinCerR-4
❑ 97PinEpixGO-E6
❑ 97PinEpixPE-E6
❑ 97PinIns-37
❑ 97PinInsCE-37
❑ 97PinInsDE-37
❑ 97PinMusC-99
❑ 97PinPrePla-99
❑ 97PinTotCPB-4
❑ 97PinTotCPG-4
❑ 97PinTotCPR-4
❑ 97PinX-P-45
❑ 97PinX-PMoS-45
❑ 97PreCon-12
❑ 97SanCom-1
❑ 97Sco-94
❑ 97Sco-537
❑ 97ScoAllF-4
❑ 97ScoArtPWB-94
❑ 97ScoArtPWB-537
❑ 97ScoPreS-94
❑ 97ScoResC-537
❑ 97ScoShoS-94
❑ 97ScoShoS-537
❑ 97ScoShoSAP-94
❑ 97ScoShoSAP-537
❑ 97Sel-33
❑ 97SelArtP-33
❑ 97SelCom-33
❑ 97SelRegG-33
❑ 97SelToootT-18
❑ 97SelToootTMB-18
❑ 97SP-43
❑ 97SpoIll-95
❑ 97SpoIllEE-95
❑ 97SpoIllGS-11
❑ 97SPSpeF-36
❑ 97SPx-15
❑ 97SPxBro-15
❑ 97SPxCorotG-6
❑ 97SPxGol-15
❑ 97SPxGraF-15
❑ 97SPxSil-15
❑ 97SPxSte-15
❑ 97StaClu-229
❑ 97StaCluMat-229
❑ 97StaCluMOP-229
❑ 97Stu-41
❑ 97StuPor8-23
❑ 97StuPrePG-41
❑ 97StuPrePS-41
❑ 97Top-167
❑ 97TopChr-67
❑ 97TopChrR-67
❑ 97TopGal-29
❑ 97TopGalPPI-29
❑ 97TopSta-59
❑ 97TopStaAM-59
❑ 97Ult-168
❑ 97UltFamGam-16
❑ 97UltGolME-168
❑ 97UltHitM-15
❑ 97UltLeaS-9
❑ 97UltPlaME-168
❑ 97UltTop3-20
❑ 97UltTop3GM-20
❑ 97UppDec-325
❑ 97UppDecMM-B6
❑ 97Zen-42
❑ 98ColCho-14
❑ 98ColCho-55
❑ 98ColChoRJ-55
❑ 98ColChoS'-6
❑ 98ColChoSQ-SQ59
❑ 98LeaHeaftH-19
❑ 98LeaHeaftHS-19
❑ 98MetUni-84
❑ 98MetUniPMG-84
❑ 98Pac-256
❑ 98PacInvGems-134
❑ 98PacInvTeam-5
❑ 98PacPlaB-256
❑ 98PacRedT-256
❑ 98PacSil-256
❑ 98PinEpixGE-E6
❑ 98PinEpixGP-E6
❑ 98PinEpixPO-E6
❑ 98PinEpixPP-E6
❑ 98PinEpixSE-E6
❑ 98PinEpixSO-E6
❑ 98PinEpixSP-E6
❑ 98PinInsSG-14AB
❑ 98PinInsSG-14CD
❑ 98PinInsSG-21AB
❑ 98PinInsSG-21CD
❑ 98PinInsSGS-14AB
❑ 98PinInsSGS-14CD
❑ 98PinInsSGS-21AB
❑ 98PinInsSGS-21CD
❑ 98PinPluAE-6
❑ 98PinPluAEE-6
❑ 98PinPluAEP-6
❑ 98PinPreP-E6
❑ 98ScoAllST-5
❑ 98ScoEpix-E6
❑ 98ScoRTASEpix-6
❑ 98Ult-160
❑ 98UltGolM-160
❑ 98UltMas-160
❑ 98UltPlaM-160
❑ 98UppDec-50
❑ 98UppDec-247
❑ 98UppDec10AP-28
❑ 98UppDec1APR-28
❑ 98UppDec5x7-50
❑ 98ZenEpi-E6

Sander, Mike
❑ 87NewOriP-12
❑ 88HagSunS-18
❑ 89EasLeaDDP-DD40
❑ 89HagSunB-25
❑ 89HagSunP-275
❑ 89HagSunS-15
❑ 90HagSunB-21
❑ 90HagSunDGB-25
❑ 90HagSunP-1413
❑ 90HagSunS-22

Sander, Rick
❑ 77LodDodT-16

Sanderlin, Rick
❑ 77PhoGiaCC-21
❑ 77PhoGiaCP-21
❑ 77PhoGiaVNB-21
❑ 78PhoGiaC-23
❑ 79PhoGiaVNB-21

Sanders, Adam
❑ 90UtiBluSP-6

Sanders, Al
❑ 88ElmPioC-10
❑ 89ElmPioP-19
❑ 89WinHavRSS-20
❑ 90StaFS7-5
❑ 90WinHavRSS-24
❑ 91LinDriAA-471
❑ 91NewBriRSLD-471
❑ 91NewBriRSP-352
❑ 92NewBriRSF-433
❑ 92NewBriRSS-495

Sanders, Alexander
❑ 87OldJudN-431

Sanders, Allen
❑ 95SpoIndTI-24
❑ 96SpoIndB-24
❑ 97LanLugTS-24
Sanders, Anthony
❑ 93MedHatBJF-3751
❑ 93MedHatBJSP-16
❑ 94St.CatBJC-19
❑ 94St.CatBJF-3658
❑ 95HagSunF-83
❑ 96DunBluJB-22
❑ 96DunBluJTI-26
❑ 96DunBluJUTI-12
❑ 96MauStiHWB-18
❑ 97Bow-127
❑ 97BowChr-139
❑ 97BowChrI-139
❑ 97BowChrIR-139
❑ 97BowChrR-139
❑ 97BowInt-127
❑ 97TexAllM-27
❑ 98Bow-95
❑ 98BowCerBlueAU-35
❑ 98BowCerGA-35
❑ 98BowCerSA-35
❑ 98BowChr-95
❑ 98BowChrGA-95
❑ 98BowChrGAR-95
❑ 98BowChrI-95
❑ 98BowChrIR-95
❑ 98BowChrR-95
❑ 98BowGolA-95
❑ 98BowInt-95
❑ 98SyrSkyG-25
❑ 98UppDec-553
Sanders, Craig
❑ 95SpoIndTI-25
❑ 96LanLugB-24
Sanders, Deion
❑ 89AlbYanB-1
❑ 89AlbYanP-338
❑ 89AlbYanSt-23
❑ 89ClaTraP-200
❑ 89DonRoo-6
❑ 89FleUpd-53
❑ 89Sta-150
❑ 89StaFutS-13
❑ 89StaFutS-14
❑ 89TopTra-110T
❑ 89TopTraT-110T
❑ 89YanScoNW-22
❑ 90AlbDecGB-1
❑ 90ClaBlu-21A
❑ 90ClaBlu-21B
❑ 90Don-427
❑ 90Fle-454
❑ 90FleCan-454
❑ 90Hot50RS-38
❑ 90Lea-359
❑ 90OPC-61
❑ 90Sco-586
❑ 90Sco100RS-40
❑ 90ScoYouS2-27
❑ 90Spo-221
❑ 90Top-61
❑ 90TopDeb89-108
❑ 90TopMag-82
❑ 90TopTif-61
❑ 90TopTVY-33
❑ 90UppDec-13
❑ 90YanScoNW-22
❑ 91Bow-588
❑ 91BraDubP-24
❑ 91BraSubS-32
❑ 91Lea-436
❑ 91RicBraBC-37
❑ 91Sco100RS-6
❑ 91ScoRoo-34T
❑ 91StaClu-442
❑ 91UppDec-352
❑ 91UppDec-743
❑ 92Bow-160
❑ 92BraKryPS-1
❑ 92BraLykP-24
❑ 92BraLykS-29
❑ 92Cla1-T80
❑ 92Cla2-T13
❑ 92ClaGam-127
❑ 92Don-564
❑ 92Fle-368
❑ 92Lea-448
❑ 92LeaBlaG-448
❑ 92LeaGolP-27
❑ 92OPC-645
❑ 92OPCPre-91
❑ 92Pin-170
❑ 92PinTea2-31
❑ 92Sco-571
❑ 92SpoIllFK1-617
❑ 92StaClu-15
❑ 92StaCluMP-12
❑ 92Stu-9
❑ 92Top-645
❑ 92TopGol-645
❑ 92TopGolW-645
❑ 92TopMic-645
❑ 92TriPla-186
❑ 92Ult-464
❑ 92UltAllS-17
❑ 92UppDec-247
❑ 92UppDec-SP3
❑ 92YanWIZ8-170
❑ 93BluJayDM-17
❑ 93Bow-438
❑ 93BraLykP-25
❑ 93BraLykS-31
❑ 93BraStaC-22
❑ 93ClaGam-81
❑ 93DiaMar-94
❑ 93Don-158
❑ 93DonMasotG-16
❑ 93DurPowP2-7
❑ 93Fin-141
❑ 93FinRef-141
❑ 93Fla-10
❑ 93Fle-13
❑ 93FunPac-34
❑ 93FunPac-67
❑ 93FunPac-219
❑ 93Lea-222
❑ 93OPC-372
❑ 93OPCPreSP-10
❑ 93OPCPreSPF-10
❑ 93PacSpa-11
❑ 93PanSti-188
❑ 93Pin-4
❑ 93RedFolS-84
❑ 93Sco-123
❑ 93Sel-84
❑ 93SelStaL-22
❑ 93SP-62
❑ 93StaClu-408
❑ 93StaCluFDI-408
❑ 93StaCluMOP-408
❑ 93Top-795
❑ 93TopGol-795
❑ 93TopInaM-795
❑ 93TopInaR-795
❑ 93TopMic-795
❑ 93Toy-82
❑ 93TriPla-162
❑ 93TriPlaA-9
❑ 93TriPlaN-8
❑ 93Ult-12
❑ 93UppDec-166
❑ 93UppDecGold-166
❑ 94Bow-301
❑ 94BowBes-R38
❑ 94BowBesR-R38
❑ 94BraLykS-28
❑ 94BraUSPC-7C
❑ 94BraUSPC-9S
❑ 94BraUSPC-13H
❑ 94ColC-575
❑ 94ColChoGS-575
❑ 94ColChoSS-575
❑ 94Don-430
❑ 94Fin-22
❑ 94FinPre-22P
❑ 94FinRef-22
❑ 94Fla-371
❑ 94Fle-373
❑ 94FleExtB-239
❑ 94FleUpd-121
❑ 94FUnPac-164
❑ 94Lea-101
❑ 94LeaL-98
❑ 94LeaMVPC-N12
❑ 94LeaMVPCG-N12
❑ 94OPC-118
❑ 94Pac-21
❑ 94PanSti-150
❑ 94Pin-174
❑ 94PinArtP-174
❑ 94PinMusC-174
❑ 94RedKah-26
❑ 94Sco-496
❑ 94ScoGolR-496
❑ 94ScoGolS-6
❑ 94ScoRoo-RT57
❑ 94ScoRooCP-CP10
❑ 94ScoRooGR-RT57
❑ 94Sel-305
❑ 94SP-162
❑ 94SPDieC-162
❑ 94Spo-108
❑ 94SpoRoo-25
❑ 94SpoRooAP-25
❑ 94SpoRooS-25
❑ 94StaClu-472
❑ 94StaCluFDI-472
❑ 94StaCluGR-472
❑ 94StaCluMOP-472
❑ 94StaCluT-54
❑ 94StaCluTFDI-54
❑ 94Stu-172
❑ 94Top-375
❑ 94TopGol-375
❑ 94TopSpa-375
❑ 94TopTra-103T
❑ 94TriPla-49
❑ 94Ult-156
❑ 94UppDec-85
❑ 94UppDecED-85
❑ 95Baz-115
❑ 95Bow-277
❑ 95BowBes-X3
❑ 95BowBesR-X3
❑ 95ClaPhoC-49
❑ 95ColCho-425
❑ 95ColChoGS-425
❑ 95ColChoSE-199
❑ 95ColChoSEGS-199
❑ 95ColChoSESS-199
❑ 95ColChoSS-425
❑ 95Don-415
❑ 95DonPreP-415
❑ 95DonTopotO-356
❑ 95Emo-118
❑ 95Fin-205
❑ 95FinRef-205
❑ 95Fla-340
❑ 95Fle-446
❑ 95Lea-94
❑ 95LeaLim-90
❑ 95LeaLim-98
❑ 95LeaLimG-24
❑ 95NatPac-17
❑ 95Pac-113
❑ 95PacPri-36
❑ 95PanSti-80
❑ 95Pin-341
❑ 95PinArtP-341
❑ 95PinFan-19
❑ 95PinMusC-341
❑ 95PinRedH-RH22
❑ 95PinUps-US25
❑ 95PinWhiH-WH22
❑ 95RedKah-26
❑ 95Sco-266
❑ 95ScoGolR-266
❑ 95ScoHaloG-HG27
❑ 95ScoPlaTS-266
❑ 95Sel-116
❑ 95SelArtP-116
❑ 95SelCer-8
❑ 95SelCerMG-8
❑ 95SP-43
❑ 95SPCha-93
❑ 95SPChaDC-93
❑ 95Spo-77
❑ 95SpoArtP-77
❑ 95SPSil-43
❑ 95StaClu-122
❑ 95StaCluFDI-122
❑ 95StaCluMO-41
❑ 95StaCluMOP-122
❑ 95StaCluMOP-SS8
❑ 95StaCluMOP-VRE8
❑ 95StaCluSS-SS8
❑ 95StaCluSTWS-122
❑ 95StaCluVE-VRE8
❑ 95StaCluVR-61
❑ 95StaCluVRMO-61
❑ 95Stu-20
❑ 95StuGolS-20
❑ 95StuPlaS-20
❑ 95Sum-36
❑ 95SumNthD-36
❑ 95Top-508
❑ 95TopCyb-297
❑ 95TopEmb-12
❑ 95TopEmbGI-12
❑ 95TopLeaL-LL19
❑ 95UC3-4
❑ 95UC3ArtP-4
❑ 95Ult-149
❑ 95UltGolM-149
❑ 95UppDec-170
❑ 95UppDec-465
❑ 95UppDecED-170
❑ 95UppDecEDG-170
❑ 95UppDecSE-165
❑ 95UppDecSEG-165
❑ 95USPlaCMLA-10H
❑ 95Zen-26
❑ 96Baz-130
❑ 96ColCho-306
❑ 96ColChoGS-306
❑ 96ColChoSS-306
❑ 96Don-405
❑ 96DonPreP-405
❑ 96Fle-595
❑ 96FleTif-595
❑ 96Lea-34
❑ 96LeaPrePB-34
❑ 96LeaPrePG-34
❑ 96LeaPrePS-34
❑ 96MetUni-245
❑ 96MetUniP-245
❑ 96Pac-200
❑ 96PacGolCD-DC30
❑ 96PacPri-P67
❑ 96PacPriG-P67
❑ 96PanSti-110
❑ 96Pin-25
❑ 96PinArtP-11
❑ 96PinSta-11
❑ 96ProSta-53
❑ 96Sco-18
❑ 96ScoDugC-A17
❑ 96ScoDugCAP-A17
❑ 96Spo-83
❑ 96SpoArtP-83
❑ 96StaClu-11
❑ 96StaCluEPB-11
❑ 96StaCluEPG-11
❑ 96StaCluEPS-11
❑ 96StaCluMeg-MH9
❑ 96StaCluMOP-11
❑ 96StaCluMOP-MH9
❑ 96Top-315
❑ 96Ult-298
❑ 96UltGolM-298
❑ 96UppDec-192
❑ 97Bow-70
❑ 97BowBes-44
❑ 97BowBesAR-44
❑ 97BowBesR-44
❑ 97BowChr-51
❑ 97BowChrI-51
❑ 97BowChrIR-51
❑ 97BowChrR-51
❑ 97BowInt-70
❑ 97Cir-81
❑ 97CirRav-81
❑ 97ColCho-305
❑ 97ColChoBS-9
❑ 97ColChoBSGS-9
❑ 97ColChoNF-NF22
❑ 97Don-304
❑ 97DonGolPP-304
❑ 97DonLim-42
❑ 97DonLim-61
❑ 97DonLim-181
❑ 97DonLimE-42
❑ 97DonLimE-61
❑ 97DonLimE-181
❑ 97DonLimENG-42
❑ 97DonLimFotG-16
❑ 97DonSig-86
❑ 97DonSigPPP-86
❑ 97DonSilPP-304
❑ 97E-X2-65
❑ 97E-X2Cred-65
❑ 97E-X2EssCre-65
❑ 97Fin-299
❑ 97FinEmb-299
❑ 97FinEmbR-299
❑ 97FinRef-299
❑ 97FlaShoLC-47
❑ 97FlaShoLeg0-47
❑ 97FlaShoLeg1-47
❑ 97FlaShoM-A47
❑ 97FlaShoM-B47
❑ 97FlaShoM-C47
❑ 97FlaShoR0-47
❑ 97FlaShoR1-47
❑ 97FlaShoR2-47
❑ 97Fle-650
❑ 97FleTif-650
❑ 97HigMinMCT-41
❑ 97HigMinMCT-42
❑ 97Lea-209
❑ 97Lea-397
❑ 97LeaFraM-209
❑ 97LeaFraM-397
❑ 97LeaFraMDC-209
❑ 97LeaFraMDC-397
❑ 97LeaGolS-8
❑ 97LeaLeaotN-9
❑ 97LeaWarT-16
❑ 97NewPin-125
❑ 97NewPinAP-125
❑ 97NewPinMC-125
❑ 97NewPinPP-125
❑ 97Sco-431
❑ 97ScoArtPWB-431
❑ 97ScoResC-431
❑ 97ScoShoS-431
❑ 97ScoShoSAP-431
❑ 97Sel-183
❑ 97SelCom-183
❑ 97SP-53
❑ 97SpoIll-97
❑ 97SpoIllEE-97
❑ 97SpoIllGS-12
❑ 97SPx-20
❑ 97SPxBro-20
❑ 97SPxGol-20
❑ 97SPxGraF-20
❑ 97SPxSil-20
❑ 97SPxSte-20
❑ 97Stu-134
❑ 97StuPrePG-134
❑ 97StuPrePS-134
❑ 97Ult-346
❑ 97UltGolME-346
❑ 97UltPlaME-346
❑ 97UppDec-528
❑ 97Zen-34
❑ 98ColCho-70
❑ 98Don-89
❑ 98DonCol-89
❑ 98DonColE-470
❑ 98DonColL-290
❑ 98DonColP-614
❑ 98DonColS-89
❑ 98DonCruG-65
❑ 98DonCruP-65
❑ 98DonCruR-65
❑ 98DonEli-70
❑ 98DonEliA-70
❑ 98DonEliS-70
❑ 98DonGolPP-89
❑ 98DonPre-64
❑ 98DonPreSeat-64
❑ 98DonPriCD-89
❑ 98DonPriCE-470
❑ 98DonPriCL-290
❑ 98DonPriCP-614
❑ 98DonSilPP-89
❑ 98Fle-229
❑ 98FleVin'-13
❑ 98FleVin'C-13
❑ 98Lea-91
❑ 98LeaFraDA-91
❑ 98LeaFraF-91
❑ 98LeaFraM-91
❑ 98LeaFraM-91
❑ 98LeaFraMDC-91
❑ 98LeaFraMDC-91
❑ 98LeaFraMZ2-91
❑ 98MetUni-99
❑ 98MetUni-207
❑ 98MetUniPMG-99
❑ 98MetUniPMG-207
❑ 98Pac-272
❑ 98PacInv-87
❑ 98PacInvGems-139
❑ 98PacInvPBlue-87
❑ 98PacInvSilv-87
❑ 98PacInvTeam-7
❑ 98PacPlaB-272
❑ 98PacRedT-272
❑ 98PacSil-272
❑ 98PacTeaC-17
❑ 98Pin-58
❑ 98PinArtP-PP51
❑ 98PinMusC-PP51
❑ 98PinPreP-58
❑ 98Sco-59
❑ 98ScoSS-PP22
❑ 98ScoSSAP-PP22
❑ 98SpoIllC-C9
❑ 98StaCluFDI-225
❑ 98StaCluI-225
❑ 98StaCluOneK-225
❑ 98StaCluPP-225
❑ 98Top-10
❑ 98TopChr-10
❑ 98TopChrF-FB9
❑ 98TopChrFR-FB9
❑ 98TopChrR-10
❑ 98TopDevR-10
❑ 98TopDia-10
❑ 98TopFla-FB9
❑ 98TopMiniC-10
❑ 98TopOpeD-9
❑ 98Ult-42
❑ 98UltGolM-42
❑ 98UltMas-42
❑ 98UltPlaM-42
❑ 98UppDec-67
❑ 98UppDec5x7-68
Sanders, Doug
❑ 95TacRaiTI-19
Sanders, Earl
❑ 87DunBluJP-946
❑ 88DunBluJS-15
❑ 89DunBluJS-14
❑ 90KnoBluJB-23
❑ 90KnoBluJP-1245
❑ 90KnoBluJS-17
❑ 91GreBraC-5
❑ 91GreBraLD-218
❑ 91GreBraP-2999
❑ 91LinDriAA-218
Sanders, Frankie
❑ 97KinIndB-22
❑ 98AkrAerM-15
Sanders, Herbert
❑ 26Zee-33
❑ 27Zee-18
Sanders, John
❑ 97PinFan-PC7
Sanders, Ken
❑ 66Top-356
❑ 66TopVen-356
❑ 67VanMouSO-20
❑ 70SunPin-16
❑ 71BreTeal-15
❑ 71MLBOffS-451
❑ 71OPC-116
❑ 71Top-116
❑ 72OPC-391
❑ 72Top-391
❑ 73OPC-246
❑ 73Top-246
❑ 74MetTeal-18
❑ 74OPC-638
❑ 74Top-638
❑ 75OPC-366
❑ 75Top-366
❑ 75TopMin-366
❑ 76OPC-291
❑ 76SSP-550
❑ 76Top-291
❑ 77SpoIndC-20
❑ 77Top-171
❑ 91MetWIZ-343
❑ 94BreMilB-75
Sanders, Lance
❑ 89UtiBluSP-20
❑ 93MarPhiC-25
❑ 93MarPhiF-3474
❑ 94SpaPhiF-1722
❑ 94SparPhiC-18
Sanders, Matt
❑ 91BluOriC-16
❑ 91BluOriP-4129
❑ 92KanCouCC-7
❑ 92KanCouCF-92
❑ 92KanCouCTI-27
Sanders, Pat
❑ 93SouOreAC-23
❑ 93SouOreAF-4073
❑ 94SouOreAC-24
❑ 94SouOreAF-3633
❑ 95WesMicWTI-26
Sanders, Paul
❑ 91EugEmeC-8
❑ 91EugEmeP-3729
Sanders, Ray
❑ 47TipTop-86
❑ 79DiaGre-167
❑ 83Car194T-11
❑ 83TCMPla1944-23
Sanders, Reggie (Reginald Jerome)
❑ 74OPC-600
❑ 74Top-600
❑ 75OPC-617
❑ 75Top-617
❑ 75TopMin-617
❑ 78SSP270-149

❑ 99FleMys-92
❑ 99FleMysG-92
❑ 99FleMysM-92

Sanders, Reggie (Reginald Laverne)

❑ 88BilMusP-1822
❑ 89GreHorP-415
❑ 89SouAtlLAGS-23
❑ 90CedRapRB-11
❑ 90CedRapRP-2334
❑ 90CMC-655
❑ 90MidLeaASGS-48
❑ 90ProAaA-128
❑ 90TopMag-66
❑ 91Bow-537
❑ 91ChaLooLD-167
❑ 91ChaLooP-1973
❑ 91Cla/Bes-41
❑ 91ClaGam-70
❑ 91ClaGolB-BC4
❑ 91LeaGolR-BC10
❑ 91LeaGolRNV-274
❑ 91LinDriAA-167
❑ 91LinDriP-167
❑ 91UppDec-71
❑ 91UppDecFE-1F
❑ 91UppDecFE-11F
❑ 92Bow-118
❑ 92Cla1-T81
❑ 92Cla2-T72
❑ 92Cla2-NNO
❑ 92ClaGam-141
❑ 92Don-415
❑ 92DonCraJ2-15
❑ 92Fle-421
❑ 92JimDeaRS-5
❑ 92Lea-360
❑ 92LeaBlaG-360
❑ 92LeaGolP-33
❑ 92OPC-283
❑ 92OPCPre-25
❑ 92Pin-440
❑ 92PinRoo-22
❑ 92PinRool-1
❑ 92PinTea2-70
❑ 92ProFS7-214
❑ 92RedKah-16
❑ 92Sco-829
❑ 92ScoImpP-76
❑ 92ScoRoo-35
❑ 92StaClu-865
❑ 92StaCluNC-865
❑ 92Stu-29
❑ 92Top-283
❑ 92TopDeb91-155
❑ 92TopGol-283
❑ 92TopGolW-283
❑ 92TopMic-283
❑ 92TriPla-109
❑ 92Ult-486
❑ 92UltAllR-8
❑ 92UppDec-27
❑ 92UppDecSR-SR20
❑ 93Bow-666
❑ 93ClaGam-82
❑ 93DiaMar-95
❑ 93Don-402
❑ 93Fin-20
❑ 93FinRef-20
❑ 93Fla-34
❑ 93Fle-44
❑ 93FleRooS-RSA7
❑ 93Lea-428
❑ 93OPC-358
❑ 93PacSpa-405
❑ 93PanSti-298
❑ 93Pin-158
❑ 93PinTea2-24
❑ 93RedFolS-85
❑ 93RedKah-24
❑ 93Sco-171
❑ 93Sel-274
❑ 93SelChaR-3
❑ 93SP-216
❑ 93StaClu-471
❑ 93StaCluFDI-471
❑ 93StaCluMOP-471
❑ 93Top-83
❑ 93TopGol-83
❑ 93TopInaM-83
❑ 93TopInaR-83
❑ 93TopMic-83
❑ 93Toy-27
❑ 93Ult-36
❑ 93UppDec-354
❑ 93UppDec-469
❑ 93UppDecGold-354
❑ 93UppDecGold-469
❑ 93USPlaCR-10C
❑ 94Bow-242
❑ 94ColC-252
❑ 94ColChoGS-252
❑ 94ColChoSS-252
❑ 94Don-436
❑ 94Fin-43
❑ 94FinPre-43P
❑ 94FinRef-43
❑ 94Fla-149
❑ 94Fle-427
❑ 94FleExtB-240
❑ 94FUnPac-116
❑ 94Lea-106
❑ 94LeaL-99
❑ 94OPC-207
❑ 94Pac-160
❑ 94PanSti-169
❑ 94Pin-360
❑ 94PinArtP-360
❑ 94PinMusC-360
❑ 94PinPowS-PS10
❑ 94ProMag-34
❑ 94RedFolMI-15
❑ 94RedKah-27
❑ 94Sco-394
❑ 94ScoGolR-394
❑ 94Sel-71
❑ 94SP-163
❑ 94SPDieC-163
❑ 94StaClu-136
❑ 94StaCluFDI-136
❑ 94StaCluGR-136
❑ 94StaCluMOP-136
❑ 94StaCluMOP-ST3
❑ 94StaCluST-ST3
❑ 94Stu-173
❑ 94Top-647
❑ 94TopGol-647
❑ 94TopSpa-647
❑ 94TriPla-219
❑ 94Ult-177
❑ 94UppDec-222
❑ 94UppDecED-222
❑ 95Bow-312
❑ 95ClaPhoC-16
❑ 95ColCho-431
❑ 95ColChoGS-431
❑ 95ColChoSE-202
❑ 95ColChoSEGS-202
❑ 95ColChoSESS-202
❑ 95ColChoSS-431
❑ 95Don-204
❑ 95DonPreP-204
❑ 95DonTopotO-219
❑ 95Emo-119
❑ 95Fin-127
❑ 95FinRef-127
❑ 95Fla-124
❑ 95Fle-447
❑ 95Lea-47
❑ 95LeaLim-160
❑ 95Pac-114
❑ 95Pin-76
❑ 95PinArtP-76
❑ 95PinMusC-76
❑ 95RedKah-27
❑ 95Sco-366
❑ 95ScoGolR-366
❑ 95ScoHaloG-HG69
❑ 95ScoPlaTS-366
❑ 95Sel-104
❑ 95SelArtP-104
❑ 95SelCer-2
❑ 95SelCerMG-2
❑ 95SelCerS-2
❑ 95SP-41
❑ 95SPCha-34
❑ 95SPChaDC-34
❑ 95Spo-112
❑ 95SpoArtP-112
❑ 95SPSil-41
❑ 95SPSpeF-35
❑ 95StaClu-333
❑ 95StaCluMOP-333
❑ 95StaCluSTDW-RE3T
❑ 95StaCluSTDW-RE333
❑ 95StaCluSTWS-333
❑ 95StaCluVR-173
❑ 95StaCluVRMO-173
❑ 95Stu-88
❑ 95Sum-110
❑ 95Top-411
❑ 95TopCyb-211
❑ 95Ult-370
❑ 95UltGolM-370
❑ 95UppDec-404
❑ 95UppDecED-404
❑ 95UppDecEDG-404
❑ 95UppDecSE-30
❑ 95UppDecSEG-30
❑ 95Zen-86
❑ 96Baz-4
❑ 96Bow-58
❑ 96BowBes-35
❑ 96BowBesAR-35
❑ 96BowBesR-35
❑ 96BowFoi-58
❑ 96Cir-118
❑ 96CirBos-32
❑ 96CirRav-118
❑ 96ColCho-115
❑ 96ColChoGS-115
❑ 96ColChoSS-115
❑ 96Don-219
❑ 96DonDiaK-10
❑ 96DonEli-63
❑ 96DonPowA-3
❑ 96DonPowADC-3
❑ 96DonPreP-219
❑ 96EmoXL-168
❑ 96Fin-B196
❑ 96Fin-S86
❑ 96FinRef-B196
❑ 96FinRef-S86
❑ 96Fla-238
❑ 96Fle-351
❑ 96FleTif-351
❑ 96FleUpd-U240
❑ 96FleUpdTC-U240
❑ 96Lea-146
❑ 96LeaAllGMC-6
❑ 96LeaAllGMCG-6
❑ 96LeaLim-6
❑ 96LeaLimG-6
❑ 96LeaPre-4
❑ 96LeaPreP-4
❑ 96LeaPrePB-146
❑ 96LeaPrePG-146
❑ 96LeaPrePS-146
❑ 96LeaPreSG-73
❑ 96LeaPreSte-73
❑ 96LeaSig-25
❑ 96LeaSigPPG-25
❑ 96LeaSigPPP-25
❑ 96MetUni-151
❑ 96MetUniP-151
❑ 96Pac-44
❑ 96PacGolCD-DC21
❑ 96PacOctM-OM19
❑ 96PacPri-P17
❑ 96PacPriG-P17
❑ 96PanSti-52
❑ 96Pin-20
❑ 96Pin-143
❑ 96Pin-264
❑ 96PinAfi-96
❑ 96PinAfiAP-96
❑ 96PinAfiFPP-96
❑ 96PinAfiSP-17
❑ 96PinArtP-10
❑ 96PinArtP-70
❑ 96PinArtP-164
❑ 96PinEssotG-6
❑ 96PinFoil-264
❑ 96PinPow-6
❑ 96PinSlu-12
❑ 96PinSta-10
❑ 96PinSta-70
❑ 96PinSta-164
❑ 96PinTeaP-6
❑ 96ProSta-102
❑ 96Sco-311
❑ 96ScoAll-16
❑ 96ScoBigB-18
❑ 96ScoDiaA-18
❑ 96ScoDugC-B36
❑ 96ScoDugCAP-B36
❑ 96ScoGolS-3
❑ 96ScoNumG-18
❑ 96ScoRef-11
❑ 96Sel-24
❑ 96SelArtP-24
❑ 96SelCer-24
❑ 96SelCerAP-24
❑ 96SelCerCB-24
❑ 96SelCerCR-24
❑ 96SelCerIP-8
❑ 96SelCerMB-24
❑ 96SelCerMG-24
❑ 96SelCerMR-24
❑ 96SelClaTF-9
❑ 96SelEnF-10
❑ 96SelTeaN-25
❑ 96SP-65
❑ 96Spo-35
❑ 96Spo-107
❑ 96SpoArtP-35
❑ 96SpoArtP-107
❑ 96SpoPowS-11
❑ 96SpoPro-17
❑ 96StaClu-214
❑ 96StaClu-435
❑ 96StaCluB&B-BB3
❑ 96StaCluEPB-435
❑ 96StaCluEPG-435
❑ 96StaCluEPS-435
❑ 96StaCluMO-38
❑ 96StaCluMOP-214
❑ 96StaCluMOP-435
❑ 96StaCluMOP-BB3
❑ 96Stu-48
❑ 96StuPrePB-48
❑ 96StuPrePG-48
❑ 96StuPrePS-48
❑ 96Sum-4
❑ 96SumAbo&B-4
❑ 96SumArtP-4
❑ 96SumFoi-4
❑ 96Top-330
❑ 96TopChr-132
❑ 96TopChrR-132
❑ 96TopClaC-CC7
❑ 96TopGal-151
❑ 96TopGalE-17
❑ 96TopGalPPI-151
❑ 96TopLas-77
❑ 96TopPro-NL8
❑ 96TopRoaW-RW15
❑ 96Ult-182
❑ 96UltGolM-182
❑ 96UltPowP-9
❑ 96UltPowPGM-9
❑ 96UltRBIK-7
❑ 96UltRBIKGM-7
❑ 96UppDec-45
❑ 96UppDecPD-PD15
❑ 96UppDecPRE-R47
❑ 96UppDecPreR-R47
❑ 96Zen-63
❑ 96ZenArtP-63
❑ 96ZenMoz-10
❑ 97Bow-233
❑ 97BowBes-76
❑ 97BowBesAR-76
❑ 97BowBesR-76
❑ 97BowChr-60
❑ 97BowChrI-60
❑ 97BowChrIR-60
❑ 97BowChrR-60
❑ 97BowInt-233
❑ 97Cir-284
❑ 97CirRav-284
❑ 97ColCho-78
❑ 97ColCho-306
❑ 97Don-100
❑ 97DonGolPP-100
❑ 97DonLim-154
❑ 97DonLimE-154
❑ 97DonLimENG-154
❑ 97DonPre-23
❑ 97DonPreCttC-23
❑ 97DonSilPP-100
❑ 97E-X2-66
❑ 97E-X2Cred-66
❑ 97E-X2EssCre-66
❑ 97Fin-14
❑ 97FinRef-14
❑ 97FlaShoLC-55
❑ 97FlaShoLeg0-55
❑ 97FlaShoLeg1-55
❑ 97FlaShoM-A55
❑ 97FlaShoM-B55
❑ 97FlaShoM-C55
❑ 97FlaShoR0-55
❑ 97FlaShoR1-55
❑ 97FlaShoR2-55
❑ 97Fle-303
❑ 97FleTif-303
❑ 97Lea-228
❑ 97LeaFraM-228
❑ 97LeaFraMDC-228
❑ 97MetUni-50
❑ 97NewPin-22
❑ 97NewPinAP-22
❑ 97NewPinMC-22
❑ 97NewPinPP-22
❑ 97Pac-276
❑ 97PacLigB-276
❑ 97PacPri-94
❑ 97PacPriLB-94
❑ 97PacPriP-94
❑ 97PacSil-276
❑ 97Sco-19
❑ 97ScoArtPWB-19
❑ 97ScoPreS-19
❑ 97ScoShoS-19
❑ 97ScoShoSAP-19
❑ 97SP-52
❑ 97SpoIll-98
❑ 97SpoIllEE-98
❑ 97StaClu-34
❑ 97StaCluMat-34
❑ 97StaCluMOP-34
❑ 97Stu-103
❑ 97StuPrePG-103
❑ 97StuPrePS-103
❑ 97Top-80
❑ 97TopChr-30
❑ 97TopChrR-30
❑ 97TopGal-108
❑ 97TopGalPPI-108
❑ 97Ult-180
❑ 97UltGolME-180
❑ 97UltPlaME-180
❑ 97UppDec-46
❑ 98CirThu-72
❑ 98CirThuRav-72
❑ 98CirThuSupRav-72
❑ 98CroRoy-41
❑ 98Don-75
❑ 98DonCol-75
❑ 98DonColS-75
❑ 98DonGolPP-75
❑ 98DonPriCD-75
❑ 98DonSilPP-75
❑ 98Fin-30
❑ 98FinNo--30
❑ 98FinNo-R-30
❑ 98FinRef-30
❑ 98FlaShoLeg0-114
❑ 98FlaShoLeg1-114
❑ 98FlaShoLeg2-114
❑ 98FlaShoLeg3-114
❑ 98FlaShoLegM-114
❑ 98FlaShoR0-114
❑ 98FlaShoR1-114
❑ 98FlaShoR2-114
❑ 98FlaShoR3-114
❑ 98Fle-16
❑ 98MetUni-54
❑ 98MetUniPMG-54
❑ 98Pac-273
❑ 98PacAur-121
❑ 98PacInv-88
❑ 98PacInvPBlue-88
❑ 98PacInvSilv-88
❑ 98PacInvTeam-7
❑ 98PacOme-67
❑ 98PacOmeR-67
❑ 98PacOnl-199
❑ 98PacOnlR-199
❑ 98PacOnlWC-199
❑ 98PacPar-148
❑ 98PacParC-148
❑ 98PacParG-148
❑ 98PacParHS-148
❑ 98PacParI-40
❑ 98PacParPB-148
❑ 98PacParR-148
❑ 98PacPlaB-273
❑ 98PacRedT-273
❑ 98PacSil-273
❑ 98Pin-97
❑ 98PinIns-94
❑ 98PinInsCE-94
❑ 98PinInsDE-94
❑ 98PinPlu-70
❑ 98PinPreP-97
❑ 98Revo-41
❑ 98RevoSS-41
❑ 98Sco-124
❑ 98ScoRT-93
❑ 98ScoSS-PP52
❑ 98ScoSSAP-PP52
❑ 98SkyDugA-12
❑ 98SkyDugAIA-12
❑ 98SP Aut-73
❑ 98SpoIllWSF-115
❑ 98SpoIllWSFEE-115
❑ 98SpoIllWSFFE-115
❑ 98SPxFin-263
❑ 98SPxFinR-263
❑ 98SPxFinS-263
❑ 98StaCluFDI-71
❑ 98StaCluI-71
❑ 98StaCluOneK-71
❑ 98StaCluPP-71
❑ 98Top-364
❑ 98TopChr-364
❑ 98TopChrR-364
❑ 98TopDevR-364
❑ 98TopDia-364
❑ 98TopGal-73
❑ 98TopGalGP-73
❑ 98TopGalOPP-73
❑ 98TopGalPPI-73
❑ 98TopGalPPIA-73
❑ 98TopGolLabC1-13
❑ 98TopGolLabC1B-13
❑ 98TopGolLabC1One-13
❑ 98TopGolLabC1R-13
❑ 98TopGolLabC2-13
❑ 98TopGolLabC2B-13
❑ 98TopGolLabC2One-13
❑ 98TopGolLabC2R-13
❑ 98TopGolLabC3-13
❑ 98TopGolLabC3B-13
❑ 98TopGolLabC3One-13
❑ 98TopGolLabC3R-13
❑ 98TopMiniC-364
❑ 98TopSta-149
❑ 98TopStaB-149
❑ 98TopStaG-149
❑ 98TopStaGR-149
❑ 98TopStaS-149
❑ 98Ult-149
❑ 98UltGolM-149
❑ 98UltMas-149
❑ 98UltPlaM-149
❑ 98UppDec-340
❑ 99CroRoyB-122
❑ 99CroRoyL-122
❑ 99CroRoyOD-122
❑ 99FlaShoLeg1-134
❑ 99FlaShoLeg2-134
❑ 99FlaShoLeg3-134
❑ 99FlaShoLegM1-134
❑ 99FlaShoLegM2-134
❑ 99FlaShoLegM3-134
❑ 99FlaShoR1-134
❑ 99FlaShoR2-134
❑ 99FlaShoR3-134
❑ 99Fle-212
❑ 99FleSta9-212
❑ 99FleWarT-212
❑ 99MetUni-83
❑ 99MetUniGM-83
❑ 99MetUniPMG-83
❑ 99Pac-117
❑ 99PacAur-165
❑ 99PacAurOD-165
❑ 99PacCroC-79
❑ 99PacCroCPB-79
❑ 99PacInv-125
❑ 99PacInvOD-125
❑ 99PacInvPB-125
❑ 99PacOme-207
❑ 99PacOmeC-207
❑ 99PacOmeG-207
❑ 99PacOmePB-207
❑ 99PacPlaB-117
❑ 99PacPri-39
❑ 99PacPriHB-39
❑ 99PacPriHG-39
❑ 99PacPriHM-39
❑ 99PacPriHP-39
❑ 99PacPriRed-39
❑ 99PacRed-117
❑ 99Rev-123
❑ 99RevPremDate-123
❑ 99RevRet-123
❑ 99RevShaSS-123
❑ 99SkyPre-159
❑ 99SkyPreR-159
❑ 99SkyThu-97
❑ 99SkyThuRant-97
❑ 99SkyThuRave-97
❑ 99ThuSkySupR-97
❑ 99Ult-201
❑ 99UltGolM-201
❑ 99UltMac-201
❑ 99UltPlaM-201
❑ 99UppDec-472
❑ 99UppDecEL1-472
❑ 99UppDecEL2-472
❑ 99Vic-340

Sanders, Rod

❑ 92PriRedC-21
❑ 92PriRedF-3097
❑ 93PriRedC-27
❑ 93PriRedF-4197
❑ 94PriRedC-22
❑ 94PriRedF-3273
Sanders, Satch
❑ 81MiaOriT-9
Sanders, Scott
❑ 90SpoIndSP-14
❑ 91Cla/Bes-338
❑ 91WatDiaC-8
❑ 91WatDiaP-1255
❑ 92SkyAA F-286
❑ 92WicWraS-644
❑ 93Bow-110
❑ 93ClaFS7-253
❑ 93LasVegSF-943
❑ 93Ult-476
❑ 94ColC-528
❑ 94ColChoGS-528
❑ 94ColChoSS-528
❑ 94Don-489
❑ 94Fla-441
❑ 94FleExtB-378
❑ 94FleMajLP-31
❑ 94FleUpd-190
❑ 94Lea-37
❑ 94PadMot-17
❑ 94Pin-381
❑ 94PinArtP-381
❑ 94PinMusC-381
❑ 94ScoRoo-RT122
❑ 94ScoRooGR-RT122
❑ 94Top-789
❑ 94TopGol-789
❑ 94TopSpa-789
❑ 94Ult-282
❑ 94UppDec-362
❑ 94UppDecED-362
❑ 95ColCho-359
❑ 95ColChoGS-359
❑ 95ColChoSS-359
❑ 95Don-528
❑ 95DonPreP-528
❑ 95Emo-190
❑ 95Fle-568
❑ 95Lea-203
❑ 95PadCHP-6
❑ 95PadMot-22
❑ 95Sco-508
❑ 95ScoGolR-508
❑ 95ScoPlaTS-508
❑ 95StaClu-260
❑ 95StaCluFDI-260
❑ 95StaCluMOP-260
❑ 95StaCluSTWS-260
❑ 95StaCluVR-128
❑ 95StaCluVRMO-128
❑ 95Top-33
❑ 95TopCyb-25
❑ 95Ult-237
❑ 95UltGolM-237
❑ 96ColCho-703
❑ 96ColChoGS-703
❑ 96ColChoSS-703
❑ 96Don-6
❑ 96DonPreP-6
❑ 96Fle-578
❑ 96FleTif-578
❑ 96LeaSigA-202
❑ 96LeaSigAG-202
❑ 96LeaSigAS-202
❑ 96PadMot-6
❑ 96Top-58
❑ 97Cir-47
❑ 97CirRav-47
❑ 97ColCho-459
❑ 97DonTea-149
❑ 97DonTeaSPE-149
❑ 97Fle-469
❑ 97Fle-595
❑ 97FleTif-469
❑ 97FleTif-595
❑ 97MetUni-224
❑ 97NewPin-48
❑ 97NewPinAP-48
❑ 97NewPinMC-48
❑ 97NewPinPP-48
❑ 97PacPriGotD-GD209
❑ 97Top-362
❑ 97Ult-400
❑ 97UltGolME-400
❑ 97UltPlaME-400
❑ 97UppDecMP-P14
❑ 98ColCho-373
❑ 98UppDec-358
Sanders, Stan
❑ 82OneYanT-7
Sanders, Tracy
❑ 90BurIndP-3023
❑ 90ProAaA-188
❑ 91CarLeaAP-CAR19
❑ 91Cla/Bes-202
❑ 91KinIndC-27
❑ 91KinIndP-339
❑ 92Bow-42
❑ 92CanIndF-703
❑ 92CanIndS-116
❑ 92ClaFS7-40
❑ 92ProFS7-53
❑ 92SkyAA F-54
❑ 92UppDecML-127
❑ 93Bow-9
❑ 93CanIndF-2851
❑ 93ClaFS7-20
❑ 93ExcFS7-167
❑ 93Top-616
❑ 93TopGol-616
❑ 93TopInaM-616
❑ 93TopInaR-616
❑ 93TopMic-616
❑ 93WicWraF-2992
❑ 94BinMetF-719
❑ 95NorTidTI-26
❑ 96MidAngB-26
❑ 96TulDriTI-23
❑ 97CarMudC-24
❑ 97TexAllM-54
❑ 98CarMudM-16
Sanderski, John
❑ 86WinHavRSP-20
❑ 87GreHorP-24
Sanderson, David
❑ 94KinMetC-18
❑ 94KinMetF-3838
❑ 97St.LucM-23
Sanderson, Scott
❑ 79ExpPos-22
❑ 79Top-720
❑ 80ExpPos-26
❑ 80OPC-301
❑ 80Top-578
❑ 81AllGamPI-175
❑ 81Don-450
❑ 81ExpPos-14
❑ 81Fle-166
❑ 81OPC-235
❑ 81OPCPos-12
❑ 81Top-235
❑ 82Don-288
❑ 82ExpHygM-19
❑ 82ExpPos-35
❑ 82ExpZel-17
❑ 82Fle-206
❑ 82FleSta-40
❑ 82OPC-7
❑ 82OPCPos-22
❑ 82Top-7
❑ 82TopSti-63
❑ 83Don-446
❑ 83ExpPos-28
❑ 83ExpStu-17
❑ 83Fle-295
❑ 83FleSti-259
❑ 83OPC-54
❑ 83Top-717
❑ 84CubChiT-26
❑ 84CubSev-24
❑ 84Don-341
❑ 84Fle-285
❑ 84FleUpd-104
❑ 84Nes792-164
❑ 84OPC-164
❑ 84Top-164
❑ 84TopTif-164
❑ 84TopTra-106T
❑ 84TopTraT-106T
❑ 85CubLioP-20
❑ 85CubSev-21
❑ 85Don-266
❑ 85Fle-66
❑ 85Lea-194
❑ 85OPC-373
❑ 85Top-616
❑ 85TopSti-40
❑ 85TopTif-616
❑ 86BasStaB-97
❑ 86CubGat-21
❑ 86CubUno-16
❑ 86Don-442
❑ 86Fle-379
❑ 86Top-406
❑ 86TopTif-406
❑ 87CubCan-27
❑ 87CubDavB-21
❑ 87Don-447
❑ 87Fle-573
❑ 87FleGlo-573
❑ 87SpoTeaP-22
❑ 87Top-534
❑ 87TopSti-60
❑ 87TopTif-534
❑ 88AlaGolAA70TI-21
❑ 88CubDavB-21
❑ 88Don-646
❑ 88DonTeaBC-646
❑ 88Fle-432
❑ 88FleGlo-432
❑ 88Sco-544
❑ 88ScoGlo-544
❑ 88StaLinCu-11
❑ 88Top-311
❑ 88TopTif-311
❑ 89CubMar-21
❑ 89Don-629
❑ 89FleUpd-78
❑ 89Top-212
❑ 89TopTif-212
❑ 89UppDec-342
❑ 90A'sMot-11
❑ 90Bow-447
❑ 90BowTif-447
❑ 90Don-647
❑ 90Fle-41
❑ 90FleCan-41
❑ 90FleUpd-118
❑ 90Lea-194
❑ 90OPC-67
❑ 90PubIntS-202
❑ 90Sco-488
❑ 90ScoRoo-61T
❑ 90Top-67
❑ 90TopTif-67
❑ 90TopTra-110T
❑ 90TopTraT-110T
❑ 90UppDec-39
❑ 90UppDec-739
❑ 91Bow-177
❑ 91Don-533
❑ 91Fle-23
❑ 91Lea-169
❑ 91OPC-728
❑ 91OPCPre-104
❑ 91Sco-118
❑ 91ScoPro-118
❑ 91ScoRoo-78T
❑ 91Stu-99
❑ 91Top-728
❑ 91TopDesS-728
❑ 91TopMic-728
❑ 91TopTif-728
❑ 91TopTra-104T
❑ 91TopTraT-104T
❑ 91UltUpd-43
❑ 91UppDec-582
❑ 91UppDec-750
❑ 91USPlaCA-3D
❑ 92Don-227
❑ 92DonDiaK-DK10
❑ 92DonSupD-DK10
❑ 92Fle-243
❑ 92Lea-152
❑ 92LeaBlaG-152
❑ 92OPC-480
❑ 92PanSti-142
❑ 92Pin-337
❑ 92Pin-587
❑ 92Sco-211
❑ 92Sco100S-59
❑ 92StaClu-496
❑ 92StaCluD-163
❑ 92Stu-219
❑ 92Top-480
❑ 92TopGol-480
❑ 92TopGolW-480
❑ 92TopMic-480
❑ 92TriPla-39
❑ 92TriPla-77
❑ 92Ult-414
❑ 92UppDec-415
❑ 92UppDecTMH-47
❑ 92YanWIZA-74
❑ 93AngMot-9
❑ 93AngPol-9
❑ 93AngStaCl-7
❑ 93Don-726
❑ 93Fla-178
❑ 93Fle-655
❑ 93FleFinE-188
❑ 93Lea-419
❑ 93OPCPre-100
❑ 93PacSpa-211
❑ 93PanSti-145
❑ 93Pin-574
❑ 93Sco-618
❑ 93Sel-261
❑ 93StaClu-679
❑ 93StaCluFDI-679
❑ 93StaCluMOP-679
❑ 93Stu-15
❑ 93Top-525
❑ 93TopGol-525
❑ 93TopInaM-525
❑ 93TopInaR-525
❑ 93TopMic-525
❑ 93Ult-524
❑ 93UppDec-734
❑ 93UppDecGold-734
❑ 94Don-266
❑ 94Fle-700
❑ 94FleUpd-30
❑ 94Lea-406
❑ 94Sco-401
❑ 94ScoGolR-401
❑ 94ScoRoo-RT54
❑ 94ScoRooGR-RT54
❑ 94StaClu-551
❑ 94StaCluFDI-551
❑ 94StaCluGR-551
❑ 94StaCluMOP-551
❑ 94WhiSoxK-26
❑ 95AngMot-24
❑ 95ColCho-498
❑ 95ColChoGS-498
❑ 95ColChoSS-498
❑ 95Don-521
❑ 95DonPreP-521
❑ 95Sco-53
❑ 95ScoGolR-53
❑ 95ScoPlaTS-53
❑ 96AngMot-24
❑ 96ColCho-488
❑ 96ColChoGS-488
❑ 96ColChoSS-488
Sanderson, Shaun
❑ 89SalLakTTI-17
❑ 90EriSaiS-23
Sandillo, Bill
❑ 96HarCitRCB-5
Sandling, Bob
❑ 80ElmPioRST-14
Sandlock, Mike
❑ 46DodTeal-20
❑ 49W72HolS-19
❑ 50W720HolS-26
❑ 53Top-247
❑ 54Top-104
❑ 79DiaGre-217
❑ 90DodTar-703
❑ 91TopArc1-247
❑ 94TopArc1-104
❑ 94TopArc1G-104
Sandoval, Danny
❑ 98HicCraM-25
❑ 98HicCraUO-25
❑ 98SouAtlLPM-20
Sandoval, Dennis
❑ 77WauMetT-16
Sandoval, Guillermo
❑ 89BelBre2S-24
❑ 90StoPorB-22
❑ 90StoPorCLC-183
❑ 90StoPorP-2183
❑ 91StoPorC-10
Sandoval, Jesus
❑ 86AppFoxP-20
Sandoval, Jhensy
❑ 97LetBlaDB-16
❑ 97Top-468
❑ 98Bow-197
❑ 98BowCerBlueAU-10
❑ 98BowCerGA-10
❑ 98BowCerSA-10
❑ 98BowChr-197
❑ 98BowChrGA-197
❑ 98BowChrGAR-197
❑ 98BowChrI-197
❑ 98BowChrIR-197
❑ 98BowChrR-197
❑ 98BowGolA-197
❑ 98BowInt-197
❑ 98HigDesMG-24
❑ 98Top-498
❑ 98TopChr-498
❑ 98TopChrR-498
❑ 98TopDevR-498
❑ 98TopDia-498
❑ 98TopMiniC-498
Sandoval, Jose
❑ 76VenLeaS-42
Sandoval, Jose 90s
❑ 93Bow-78
❑ 93BufBisF-527
Sandoval, Marcos
❑ 98St.CatSM-19
Sandoval, Mike
❑ 87WatPirP-31
❑ 90HarSenS-25
❑ 92BufBisBS-20
❑ 96AugGreB-3
❑ 97CarMudC-28
❑ 98CarMudM-28
Sandry, Bill
❑ 83AppFoxFr-28
Sands, Charlie
❑ 71PirActP-23
❑ 72Top-538
❑ 74OPC-381
❑ 74Top-381
❑ 75OPC-548
❑ 75Top-548
❑ 75TopMin-548
❑ 75TucTorTI-17
❑ 76TucTorCa-20
❑ 76TusTorCr-39
❑ 92YanWIZ6-108
Sands, John
❑ 19Zee-75
❑ 20Zee-95
Sandt, Tommy
❑ 75TucTorC-2
❑ 75TucTorTI-18
❑ 76VenLeaS-21
❑ 77Top-616
❑ 78SyrChiT-17
❑ 79PorBeaT-6
❑ 80PorBeaT-8
❑ 81PorBeaT-21
❑ 82BufBisT-18
❑ 83LynPirT-23
❑ 84HawIslC-137
❑ 85HawIslC-233
❑ 86HawIslP-6
❑ 88PirTeal-30
❑ 89PirVerFJ-31
❑ 90PirHomC-26
❑ 93PirNatl-27
❑ 94PirQui-21
❑ 97MarPac-31
Sandy, Tim
❑ 90KinMetB-17
❑ 90KinMetS-22
❑ 91PitMetC-8
❑ 91PitMetP-3436
❑ 92St.LucMCB-3
❑ 92St.LucMF-1762
❑ 93BinMetF-2348
❑ 93St.LuMF-2935
Saneaux, Francisco
❑ 92BluOriC-7
❑ 92BluOriF-2360
❑ 94AlbPolC-22
❑ 94AlbPolF-2236
❑ 94OriPro-89
❑ 97FreKey-24
Sanford, Chance
❑ 92WelPirC-20
❑ 92WelPirF-1333
❑ 93SalBucC-22
❑ 93SalBucF-442
❑ 94CarLeaAF-CAR43
❑ 94SalBucC-18
❑ 94SalBucF-2331
❑ 96CarMudB-21
❑ 97CalCanB-21
❑ 97CarMudC-19
❑ 98NasSouTI-29
❑ 98NasSouTISS-27
Sanford, Ed
❑ 82ArkTraT-8
Sanford, Jack (John S.)
❑ 47PM1StaP1-193
❑ 57Top-387
❑ 58Hir-39
❑ 58PhiJayP-10
❑ 58Top-264
❑ 59Top-275
❑ 60GiaJayP-11
❑ 60Lea-54
❑ 60Top-165
❑ 60TopVen-165
❑ 61Pos-154
❑ 61Top-258
❑ 61Top-383
❑ 61TopStal-84
❑ 62Jel-141
❑ 62Pos-141
❑ 62PosCan-141
❑ 62Top-538
❑ 63GiaJayP-12
❑ 63Jel-110
❑ 63Pos-110
❑ 63Top-7
❑ 63Top-143
❑ 63Top-325
❑ 63TopStil-39
❑ 64GiaJayP-11
❑ 64Top-414
❑ 65OPC-228
❑ 65Top-228
❑ 66OPC-23
❑ 66Top-23
❑ 66TopVen-23
❑ 67CokCapDA-27
❑ 67Top-549
❑ 79TCM50-125
❑ 81Gia196T-29
Sanford, John F.
❑ 47TipTop-71
❑ 48AngTeal-23
❑ 49Bow-236
❑ 49YanTeal-20
❑ 50Bow-156
❑ 50YanTeal-20
❑ 51BerRos-D3
❑ 51Bow-145
❑ 52MotCoo-53
❑ 85TCMPla1-41
Sanford, Mo (Meredith)
❑ 89GreHorP-423
❑ 89SouAtlLAGS-31
❑ 90CedRapRB-23
❑ 90CedRapRP-2321
❑ 90MidLeaASGS-49
❑ 90ProAaA-120
❑ 91ChaLooLD-168
❑ 91ChaLooP-1960
❑ 91Cla/Bes-47
❑ 91FleUpd-86
❑ 91LinDriAA-168
❑ 92Bow-281
❑ 92Cla1-T82
❑ 92ClaGam-197
❑ 92Don-417
❑ 92NasSouS-290
❑ 92OPC-674
❑ 92OPCPre-17
❑ 92Pin-254
❑ 92PinTea2-77
❑ 92ProFS7-215
❑ 92Sco-769
❑ 92ScoRoo-40
❑ 92SkyAAAF-136
❑ 92StaClu-336
❑ 92Top-674
❑ 92TopDeb91-156
❑ 92TopGol-674
❑ 92TopGolW-674
❑ 92TopMic-674
❑ 92UppDec-45
❑ 92UppDecML-253
❑ 93ColSprSSF-3086
❑ 93Don-760
❑ 93Pin-230
❑ 93SelRoo-33T
❑ 93Top-634
❑ 93TopGol-634
❑ 93TopInaM-634
❑ 93TopInaR-634
❑ 93TopMic-634
❑ 94Fle-453
❑ 94SalLakBF-815
❑ 94Sco-253
❑ 94ScoGolR-253
❑ 94Top-343
❑ 94TopGol-343
❑ 94TopSpa-343
❑ 96OklCit8B-17
Sangeado, Juan
❑ 95GreFalDTI-8
Sanguillen, Manny
❑ 68PirKDK-35
❑ 68PirTeal-17

- 68Top-251
- 68TopVen-251
- 69PirJacitB-11
- 69PirTeal-20
- 69Top-509
- 70DayDaiNM-148
- 70MLBOffS-106
- 70OPC-188
- 70PirTeal-16
- 70Top-188
- 71Kel-13
- 71MilDud-61
- 71MLBOffS-213
- 71OPC-62
- 71OPC-480
- 71PirActP-10
- 71PirArc-10
- 71Top-62
- 71Top-480
- 71TopTat-41
- 72EssCoi-12
- 72Kel-19
- 72MilBra-305
- 72OPC-60
- 72OPC-225
- 72OPC-228
- 72PirTeal-7
- 72Top-60
- 72Top-225
- 72Top-228
- 73Kel2D-42
- 73LinPor-152
- 73OPC-250
- 73SevTraC-67
- 73Top-250
- 73TopCanL-46
- 74Kel-15
- 74OPC-28
- 74Top-28
- 74TopDecE-22
- 74TopSta-87
- 75Hos-21
- 75HosTwi-21
- 75OPC-515
- 75PitPirP-25
- 75Top-515
- 75TopMin-515
- 76BlaDis-53
- 76BucDis-53
- 76CarDis-53
- 76CraDis-53
- 76DailsID-53
- 76Hos-72
- 76IsaDis-53
- 76Kel-42
- 76OPC-191
- 76OPC-220
- 76OrbDis-53
- 76PirPos-21
- 76RedBarD-53
- 76SafDis-53
- 76SSP-571
- 76Top-191
- 76Top-220
- 76TowCluD-53
- 77BurCheD-111
- 77ChiWilD-59
- 77DailsID-59
- 77DetCaeD-59
- 77HolInnD-59
- 77MSADis-59
- 77OPC-231
- 77PepGloD-4
- 77SagDis-59
- 77sDis-59
- 77Top-61
- 77WenDis-59
- 77ZipDis-59
- 78Hos-58
- 78Top-658
- 78WifBalD-66
- 79BasPat-77
- 79Top-447
- 80PirGreT-8
- 80Top-148
- 81Don-14
- 81Fle-376
- 81Top-226
- 86PirGreT-8
- 89SweBasG-29
- 90PacLeg-75
- 90SweBasG-126
- 91KelLey-10
- 91SweBasG-80
- 93MCIAmb-9
- 93TedWil-80
- 93TedWilM-13
- 93UppDecAH-112
- 94MCIAmb-9
- 94MCIAmb-S4
- 94UppDecAH-29
- 94UppDecAH-224
- 94UppDecAH1-29
- 94UppDecAH1-224

Sanjurjo, Jose
- 91BriTigC-11
- 91BriTigP-3620
- 93BriTigC-18
- 93BriTigF-3665

Sankey, Ben
- 32Zee-44
- 36GouWidPPR-D31
- 36WorWidGV-83

Sankey, Brian
- 96YakBeaTI-17
- 97SanBerS-25
- 98VerBeaDM-23

Sanner, Dale
- 75TucTorC-7
- 75TucTorTI-19
- 76TusTorCr-14

Sano, Motokuni
- 88MiaMarS-23

Santa, Jeff
- 97LetBlaDB-29

Santa, Roberto
- 94HudValRC-22
- 94HudValRF-3394
- 95ChaRivTI-22

SantaCruz, Nick
- 88BatCliP-1678
- 89SpaPhiP-1043
- 89SpaPhiS-21
- 90SpaPhiB-18
- 90SpaPhiP-2501
- 90SpaPhiS-18

Santaella, Alexis
- 90TamYanD-20
- 94GreBatF-473
- 94VenLinU-195
- 95LinVen-127
- 96-97LinVen-83
- 97GreBatC-19

SantaMaria, Silverio
- 90ElmPioP-21
- 91WinHavRSC-9
- 91WinHavRSP-489
- 92WinHavRSC-13
- 93ForLauRSC-23
- 93ForLauRSFP-1598
- 94SarRedSF-1949

Santamaria, William
- 96BesAutSA-66
- 97BesAutAS-50
- 97CapCitB-10

Santana, Andres
- 87PocGiaTB-23
- 88CliGiaP-705
- 88MidLeaAGS-2
- 89SanJosGB-1
- 89SanJosGCLC-226
- 89SanJosGP-450
- 89SanJosGS-23
- 89Sta-87
- 90Bow-230
- 90BowTif-230
- 90ShrCapP-1449
- 90ShrCapS-22
- 90TexLeaAGS-23
- 91LinDriAAA-393
- 91PhoFirLD-393
- 91PhoFirP-76
- 91Sco-762
- 91TopDeb90-139
- 91TriA AAGP-AAA34
- 91Ult-328
- 91UppDec-87
- 92PhoFirF-2831
- 92Sco100RS-32
- 92StaClu-491

Santana, Ernesto
- 87MacPirP-1
- 88WatPirP-10
- 89St.CatBJP-2087
- 90UtiBluSP-22

Santana, Humberto
- 98CapCitBF5-14
- 98CapCitBM-14
- 98PitMetM-29

Santana, Johan
- 98AubDouTI-25

Santana, Jose
- 89AubAstP-2165
- 90AshTouP-2763
- 90BoiHawP-3318
- 92AubAstC-11
- 92AubAstF-1363
- 93AshTouC-19
- 93AshTouF-2285
- 94OscAstC-20
- 94OscAstF-1147
- 95QuaCitRBTI-25

Santana, Julio
- 94ChaRivC-18
- 94ChaRivF-2672
- 94Cla-6
- 94SouAtlLAF-SAL5
- 95Bes-45
- 95BowBes-B26
- 95BowBesR-B26
- 95Exc-132
- 95SPML-160
- 95TulDriTI-2
- 95UppDecML-211
- 95UppDecMLFS-211
- 95UppDecMLOP-OP27
- 96Bow-130
- 96BowBes-144
- 96BowBesAR-144
- 96BowBesR-144
- 96BowFoi-130
- 96OklCit8B-18
- 97ColCho-488
- 97Fle-691
- 97FleTif-691
- 97RanDr P-28
- 97RanMot-24
- 97Sco-490
- 97ScoArtPWB-490
- 97ScoResC-490
- 97ScoShoS-490
- 97ScoShoSAP-490
- 98UppDec-234

Santana, Manuel
- 93AugPirC-18
- 93AugPirF-1543
- 94SalBucC-19
- 94SalBucF-2322

Santana, Marino
- 93BelMarCB-23
- 93BelMarF-3206
- 94BelMarC-24
- 94BelMarF-3232
- 95Bes-44
- 95Exc-121
- 95MidLeaA-51
- 96Bow-198
- 96BowFoi-198
- 96Exc-107
- 96LanJetB-23
- 97JacSun-22
- 98TolMudHQ-27
- 99FleSta9-405
- 99FleWarT-405
- 99PacCroC-109
- 99PacCroCPB-109
- 99SpollI-68

Santana, Miguel
- 88FloStaLAS-20
- 88VerBeaDS-23
- 90JacExpB-12
- 90JacExpP-1387
- 93LimRocDWB-59

Santana, Osmany
- 98WatIndTI-29

Santana, Pedro
- 97LowSpiB-24
- 97WesMicW-21
- 98MicBatCM-27
- 98MidLeaPM-26
- 98WesMicWM-21

Santana, Rafael
- 80NasSouTI-18
- 82LouRedE-27
- 83Car-26
- 84TidTidT-16
- 85DomLeaS-148
- 85Don-610
- 85Fle-90
- 85MetTCM-29
- 85Top-67
- 85TopTif-67
- 86Don-319
- 86Fle-93
- 86MetTCM-22
- 86MetWorSC-7
- 86OPC-102
- 86Top-587
- 86TopSti-102
- 86TopTif-587
- 87Don-569
- 87DonOpeD-126
- 87Fle-21
- 87FleGlo-21
- 87Lea-167
- 87Top-378
- 87TopTif-378
- 88Don-633
- 88DonBasB-273
- 88DonReaBY-NEW
- 88Fle-149
- 88FleGlo-149
- 88FleUpd-50
- 88FleUpdG-50
- 88PanSti-344
- 88Sco-316
- 88ScoGlo-316
- 88ScoRoo-54T
- 88ScoRooG-54T
- 88StaLinMe-17
- 88Top-233
- 88TopBig-246
- 88TopClo-100
- 88TopTif-233
- 88TopTra-101T
- 88TopTraT-101T
- 89Bow-174
- 89BowTif-174
- 89Don-309
- 89Fle-268
- 89FleGlo-268
- 89PanSti-407
- 89Sco-296
- 89Top-792
- 89TopBig-192
- 89TopDouM-21
- 89TopSti-313
- 89TopTif-792
- 89UppDec-216
- 89YanScoNW-11
- 90OPC-651
- 90PubIntS-546
- 90Top-651
- 90TopTif-651
- 91MetWIZ-344
- 92BasCitRC-25
- 92BasCitRF-3861
- 92YanWIZ8-171
- 93WilBluRC-29
- 93WilBluRF-2015
- 94EugEmeC-30
- 95SprSulTI-25
- 97LowSpiB-3

Santana, Ralph
- 80KnoBluJT-11

Santana, Raul
- 91SumFlyC-15
- 91SumFlyP-2338
- 92RocExpC-3
- 92RocExpF-2120
- 93WesPalBEC-20
- 93WesPalBEF-1345
- 94HigDesMC-22
- 94HigDesMF-2793

Santana, Rodolfo
- 80ElmPioRST-43

Santana, Ruben
- 85MetColP-2
- 87MetColP-20
- 90PenPilS-20
- 91SanBerSC-20
- 91SanBerSP-1997
- 92ClaFS7-215
- 92PenPilC-14
- 92PenPilF-2943
- 93ClaFS7-254
- 93ExcFS7-231
- 93JacSunF-2719
- 93LimRocDWB-23
- 93LimRocDWB-148
- 94ClaGolF-102
- 94ColC-667
- 94ColChoGS-667
- 94ColChoSS-667
- 94ExcFS7-127
- 94JacSunF-1422
- 94Top-527
- 94TopGol-527
- 94TopSpa-527
- 94UppDec-88
- 94UppDecED-88
- 94UppDecML-95
- 94UppDecML-173
- 94UppDecMLPotYF-PY13
- 95ChaLooTI-20
- 96ChaLooB-27

Santana, Simon
- 77ChaPatT-19

Santangelo, F.P.
- 88CapCodPPaLP-156
- 89JamExpP-2132
- 90WesPalBES-19
- 91HarSenLD-268
- 91HarSenP-636
- 91LinDriAA-268
- 92IndIndF-1869
- 92IndIndS-192
- 93OttLynF-2447
- 94OttLynF-2906
- 96Fle-467
- 96FleTif-467
- 96Pac-124
- 96Pin-388
- 96PinFoil-388
- 96Sco-256
- 97Cir-31
- 97CirRav-31
- 97ColCho-389
- 97Don-225
- 97DonGolPP-225
- 97DonLim-97
- 97DonLimE-97
- 97DonLimENG-97
- 97DonSilPP-225
- 97Fle-386
- 97FleTif-386
- 97Lea-317
- 97LeaFraM-317
- 97LeaFraMDC-317
- 97Pac-352
- 97PacLigB-352
- 97PacPri-121
- 97PacPriLB-121
- 97PacPriP-121
- 97PacSil-352
- 97Pin-157
- 97PinArtP-PP157
- 97PinCer-70
- 97PinCerMBla-70
- 97PinCerMBlu-70
- 97PinCerMG-70
- 97PinCerMR-70
- 97PinCerR-70
- 97PinMusC-157
- 97PinPrePla-157
- 97PinTotCPB-70
- 97PinTotCPG-70
- 97PinTotCPR-70
- 97Sco-276
- 97ScoArtPWB-276
- 97ScoPreS-276
- 97ScoShoS-276
- 97ScoShoSAP-276
- 97SelRooR-7
- 97StaClu-290
- 97StaCluMOP-290
- 97Top-17
- 97UppDec-429
- 98ColCho-169
- 98Fin-112
- 98FinNo--112
- 98FinNo-R-112
- 98FinRef-112
- 98Fle-448
- 98Pac-354
- 98PacAur-158
- 98PacOme-151
- 98PacOmeR-151
- 98PacOnl-460
- 98PacOnlR-460
- 98PacOnlWC-460
- 98PacPar-197
- 98PacParC-197
- 98PacParG-197
- 98PacParHS-197
- 98PacParPB-197
- 98PacParR-197
- 98PacPlaB-354
- 98PacRedT-354
- 98PacSil-354
- 98StaCluFDI-53
- 98StaClul-53
- 98StaCluOneK-53
- 98StaCluPP-53
- 98Top-42
- 98TopChr-42
- 98TopChrR-42
- 98TopDevR-42
- 98TopDia-42
- 98TopMiniC-42
- 98Ult-267
- 98UltGolM-267
- 98UltMas-267
- 98UltPlaM-267
- 98UppDec-153
- 98UppDec-159
- 98UppDecSF-84
- 99Pac-269
- 99PacCroC-173
- 99PacCroCPB-173
- 99PacPlaB-269
- 99PacRed-269
- 99SPSig-126
- 99StaClu-51
- 99StaCluFDI-51
- 99StaCluOoaK-51
- 99StaCluPP-51
- 99Top-77
- 99TopChr-77
- 99TopChrR-77
- 99TopMVPP-77
- 99UppDec-484
- 99UppDecEL1-484
- 99UppDecEL2-484
- 99UppDecM-185
- 99UppDecMGS-185
- 99UppDecMHFS-185
- 99UppDecMSS-185
- 99Vic-360

Santarelli, Cal
- 85WatIndT-9
- 86WatIndP-21

Santiago, Angelo
- 90GatCitPP-3354
- 90GatCitPSP-16

Santiago, Antonio
- 97WilCubB-21

Santiago, Arnold
- 94BurIndC-22
- 94BurIndF-3805

Santiago, Benny (Benito)
- 83MiaMarT-20
- 84OCoandSI-238
- 85BeaGolGT-21
- 86Fle-644
- 86LasVegSP-15
- 86PadFirPTB-5
- 87ClaUpdY-132
- 87Don-31
- 87DonHig-45
- 87DonHig-55
- 87DonOpeD-148
- 87DonRoo-44
- 87Fle-429
- 87FleGlo-429
- 87Lea-31
- 87PadBohHB-9
- 87Spo-118
- 87SpoRool-19
- 87SpoRooP-9
- 87SpoTeaP-16
- 87TopTra-109T
- 87TopTraT-109T
- 88Baz-20
- 88ClaBlu-219
- 88ClaRed-160
- 88Don-3
- 88Don-114
- 88DonBasB-301
- 88DonSupD-3
- 88Fle-596
- 88FleAwaW-34
- 88FleBasM-30
- 88FleExcS-33
- 88FleGlo-596
- 88FleHotS-33
- 88FleLeaL-34
- 88FleMin-115
- 88FleRecS-34
- 88FleStiC-125
- 88FleSup-32
- 88GreBasS-59
- 88K-M-24
- 88KeyFooD-15
- 88Lea-3
- 88Lea-58
- 88MSAIceTD-15
- 88Nes-12
- 88OPC-86
- 88OurOwnTD-15
- 88PadCok-9
- 88PadSmo-25
- 88PanSti-402
- 88PanSti-405

❑ 88PanSti-433
❑ 88RedFolSB-78
❑ 88Sco-25
❑ 88Sco-654
❑ 88ScoGlo-25
❑ 88ScoGlo-654
❑ 88ScoYouSI-2
❑ 88Spo-22
❑ 88Spo-222
❑ 88SpoGam-10
❑ 88StaLinPa-11
❑ 88TarPla-37
❑ 88TetTeaD-15
❑ 88Top-7
❑ 88Top-404
❑ 88Top-693
❑ 88Top-699
❑ 88TopBig-12
❑ 88TopCoi-35
❑ 88TopGaloC-12
❑ 88TopGloS-30
❑ 88TopRoo-18
❑ 88TopSti-2
❑ 88TopSti-112
❑ 88TopTif-7
❑ 88TopTif-404
❑ 88TopTif-693
❑ 88TopTif-699
❑ 88TopUKM-66
❑ 88TopUKMT-66
❑ 88ToyRoo-26
❑ 88WeiMarD-15
❑ 88Woo-14
❑ 89BimBreD-3
❑ 89Bow-453
❑ 89BowTif-453
❑ 89CadEllD-49
❑ 89ClaLigB-73
❑ 89Don-205
❑ 89Fle-316
❑ 89FleGlo-316
❑ 89KeyFooD-9
❑ 89MSAIceTD-9
❑ 89OPC-256
❑ 89OurOwnTD-9
❑ 89PadCok-16
❑ 89PadMag-11
❑ 89PadPos-28
❑ 89PanSti-199
❑ 89RedFolSB-102
❑ 89Sco-4
❑ 89ScoHot1S-47
❑ 89Spo-22
❑ 89StaSan-1
❑ 89StaSan-2
❑ 89StaSan-3
❑ 89StaSan-4
❑ 89StaSan-5
❑ 89StaSan-6
❑ 89StaSan-7
❑ 89StaSan-8
❑ 89StaSan-9
❑ 89StaSan-10
❑ 89StaSan-11
❑ 89TetTeaD-9
❑ 89Top-256
❑ 89TopBasT-148
❑ 89TopBig-134
❑ 89TopCoi-24
❑ 89TopGloS-15
❑ 89TopSti-101
❑ 89TopStiB-57
❑ 89TopTif-256
❑ 89TopUKM-68
❑ 89TVSpoM-46
❑ 89TVSpoM-138
❑ 89UppDec-165
❑ 89WeiMarD-9
❑ 90Bow-218
❑ 90BowTif-218
❑ 90ClaUpd-T44
❑ 90Don-465
❑ 90Don-708A
❑ 90Don-708B
❑ 90DonBesN-121
❑ 90DonLeaS-4
❑ 90Fle-167
❑ 90FleAwaW-32
❑ 90FleCan-167
❑ 90GooHumICBLS-20
❑ 90HOFStiB-92
❑ 90Lea-207
❑ 90M.Vpin-88
❑ 90MLBBasB-58
❑ 90OPC-35
❑ 90PadCok-16
❑ 90PadMag-2
❑ 90PadMag-21
❑ 90PanSti-213
❑ 90PanSti-358
❑ 90PubIntS-58
❑ 90PubIntS-271
❑ 90RedFolSB-82
❑ 90Sco-454
❑ 90Sco100S-63
❑ 90ScoMcD-15
❑ 90Spo-115
❑ 90SupActM-15
❑ 90Top-35
❑ 90TopBig-125
❑ 90TopDou-56
❑ 90TopGloA-9
❑ 90TopSti-110
❑ 90TopSti-153
❑ 90TopStiB-23
❑ 90TopTif-35
❑ 90UppDec-12
❑ 90UppDec-325
❑ 90USPlaCA-10H
❑ 91Bow-383
❑ 91Bow-656
❑ 91CadEllD-49
❑ 91Cla2-T43
❑ 91ClaGam-175
❑ 91DenHol-18
❑ 91Don-449
❑ 91Fle-542
❑ 91FleAll-9
❑ 91KinDis-20
❑ 91Lea-432
❑ 91OPC-760
❑ 91OPCPre-105
❑ 91PadMag-26
❑ 91PadSmo-33
❑ 91PanCanT1-99
❑ 91PanFreS-90
❑ 91PanFreS-157
❑ 91PanSti-93
❑ 91PosCan-13
❑ 91RedFolS-83
❑ 91Sco-416
❑ 91Sco-663
❑ 91Sco-810
❑ 91Sco-870
❑ 91Sco-893
❑ 91Sco100S-61
❑ 91SevCoi-SC13
❑ 91StaClu-105
❑ 91StaPinB-43
❑ 91Stu-249
❑ 91Top-760
❑ 91TopCraJI-33
❑ 91TopDesS-760
❑ 91TopMic-760
❑ 91TopTif-760
❑ 91TopTriH-N10
❑ 91Ult-311
❑ 91UppDec-467
❑ 91UppDecFE-91F
❑ 91UppDecSS-SS17
❑ 91USPlaCA-11S
❑ 92Bow-395
❑ 92ClaGam-62
❑ 92ColAllG-14
❑ 92ColAllP-14
❑ 92Don-40
❑ 92Don-430
❑ 92Fle-620
❑ 92Fre-10
❑ 92Hig5-125
❑ 92Lea-321
❑ 92LeaBlaG-321
❑ 92New-25
❑ 92OPC-185
❑ 92OPCPre-154
❑ 92PadCarJ-18
❑ 92PadMot-6
❑ 92PadPolD-18
❑ 92PadSmo-28
❑ 92PanSti-231
❑ 92PanSti-280
❑ 92Pin-2
❑ 92Pin-601
❑ 92Pin-615
❑ 92PinTeaP-3
❑ 92PosCan-2
❑ 92RedFolS-85
❑ 92RedFolS-128
❑ 92Sco-245
❑ 92Sco100S-36
❑ 92ScoCokD-19
❑ 92ScoImpP-58
❑ 92ScoProaG-10
❑ 92StaClu-130
❑ 92StaCluD-164
❑ 92StaPro-8
❑ 92Stu-107
❑ 92Top-185
❑ 92TopGol-185
❑ 92TopGolW-185
❑ 92TopKid-54
❑ 92TopMcD-2
❑ 92TopMic-185
❑ 92TriPla-70
❑ 92Ult-283
❑ 92UppDec-253
❑ 92UppDecF-40
❑ 92UppDecFG-40
❑ 93Bow-178
❑ 93CadDis-52
❑ 93DenHol-14
❑ 93DiaMar-96
❑ 93Don-522
❑ 93DurPowP2-10
❑ 93Fin-138
❑ 93FinRef-138
❑ 93Fla-53
❑ 93Fle-523
❑ 93FleFinE-70
❑ 93FunPac-117
❑ 93FunPac-121
❑ 93Hos-21
❑ 93HumDumC-31
❑ 93JimDea-21
❑ 93KinDis-6
❑ 93Lea-410
❑ 93MarFloA-4
❑ 93MarlStaClu-12
❑ 93MarPub-22
❑ 93MarUppD-776
❑ 93MarUSPC-1H
❑ 93MarUSPC-2S
❑ 93OPC-353
❑ 93OPCPre-43
❑ 93PacBeiA-23
❑ 93PacSpa-263
❑ 93PacSpa-471
❑ 93PacSpaGE-10
❑ 93PacSpaPI-6
❑ 93Pin-502
❑ 93PinExpOD-2
❑ 93RedFolS-86
❑ 93Sco-591
❑ 93Sel-269
❑ 93SelRoo-26T
❑ 93SP-142
❑ 93StaClu-274
❑ 93StaClu-319
❑ 93StaCluFDI-274
❑ 93StaCluFDI-319
❑ 93StaCluM-5
❑ 93StaCluMOP-274
❑ 93StaCluMOP-319
❑ 93Stu-127
❑ 93Top-220
❑ 93TopGol-220
❑ 93TopInaM-220
❑ 93TopInaR-220
❑ 93TopMic-220
❑ 93TopPos-2
❑ 93TopPos-3
❑ 93TopTra-44T
❑ 93TriPla-210
❑ 93TriPlaG-GS9
❑ 93Ult-386
❑ 93UppDec-776
❑ 93UppDecDG-14
❑ 93UppDecGold-776
❑ 94Bow-122
❑ 94ColC-374
❑ 94ColChoGS-374
❑ 94ColChoSS-374
❑ 94Don-348
❑ 94DonSpeE-348
❑ 94Fin-366
❑ 94FinRef-366
❑ 94Fla-384
❑ 94Fle-476
❑ 94FleExtB-265
❑ 94Lea-96
❑ 94LeaL-108
❑ 94MarTeal-15
❑ 94OPC-150
❑ 94Pac-249
❑ 94PacAll-1
❑ 94PanSti-185
❑ 94Pin-305
❑ 94PinArtP-305
❑ 94PinMusC-305
❑ 94ProMag-53
❑ 94Sco-40
❑ 94ScoGolR-40
❑ 94Sel-354
❑ 94Spo-13
❑ 94StaClu-143
❑ 94StaCluFDI-143
❑ 94StaCluGR-143
❑ 94StaCluMOP-143
❑ 94StaCluT-79
❑ 94StaCluTFDI-79
❑ 94Stu-111
❑ 94SucSav-6
❑ 94Top-370
❑ 94TopGol-370
❑ 94TopSpa-370
❑ 94TriPla-139
❑ 94Ult-497
❑ 94UppDec-397
❑ 94UppDecED-397
❑ 95ColCho-306
❑ 95ColCho-577T
❑ 95ColChoGS-306
❑ 95ColChoSE-136
❑ 95ColChoSEGS-136
❑ 95ColChoSESS-136
❑ 95ColChoSS-306
❑ 95Don-484
❑ 95DonPreP-484
❑ 95Fla-341
❑ 95Fle-341
❑ 95FleUpd-135
❑ 95Lea-257
❑ 95Pac-177
❑ 95PanSti-25
❑ 95Pin-400
❑ 95PinArtP-400
❑ 95PinMusC-400
❑ 95RedFol-19
❑ 95RedKah-28
❑ 95Sco-158
❑ 95ScoGolR-158
❑ 95ScoPlaTS-158
❑ 95StaClu-23
❑ 95StaClu-566
❑ 95StaCluFDI-23
❑ 95StaCluMOP-23
❑ 95StaCluMOP-566
❑ 95StaCluSTDW-RE566
❑ 95StaCluSTWS-23
❑ 95StaCluSTWS-566
❑ 95Top-160
❑ 95TopCyb-95
❑ 95TopTra-34T
❑ 95Ult-383
❑ 95UltGolM-383
❑ 95UppDec-486
❑ 95UppDec-TC3
❑ 95UppDecSE-167
❑ 95UppDecSEG-167
❑ 95UppDecT-TC3
❑ 96ColCho-116
❑ 96ColCho-669
❑ 96ColChoGS-116
❑ 96ColChoGS-669
❑ 96ColChoSS-116
❑ 96ColChoSS-669
❑ 96Don-493
❑ 96DonPreP-493
❑ 96EmoXL-248
❑ 96Fin-S277
❑ 96FinRef-S277
❑ 96Fla-337
❑ 96Fle-352
❑ 96FleTif-352
❑ 96FleUpd-U170
❑ 96FleUpdTC-U170
❑ 96Pac-49
❑ 96PacPri-P18
❑ 96PacPriG-P18
❑ 96PhiTeal-29
❑ 96Pin-327
❑ 96PinFoil-327
❑ 96ProSta-103
❑ 96Sco-126
❑ 96SP-143
❑ 96StaClu-56
❑ 96StaCluEPB-56
❑ 96StaCluEPG-56
❑ 96StaCluEPS-56
❑ 96StaCluMOP-56
❑ 96TeaOut-71
❑ 96Top-394
❑ 96Ult-523
❑ 96UltGolM-523
❑ 96UppDec-432
❑ 97BluJayB-11
❑ 97BluJayOH-29
❑ 97BluJayS-5
❑ 97Cir-235
❑ 97CirRav-235
❑ 97ColChoU-U30
❑ 97Don-71
❑ 97Don-280
❑ 97DonGolPP-71
❑ 97DonGolPP-280
❑ 97DonSilPP-71
❑ 97DonSilPP-280
❑ 97Fin-247
❑ 97FinRef-247
❑ 97FlaShoLC-62
❑ 97FlaShoLeg0-62
❑ 97FlaShoLeg1-62
❑ 97FlaShoM-A62
❑ 97FlaShoM-B62
❑ 97FlaShoM-C62
❑ 97FlaShoR0-62
❑ 97FlaShoR1-62
❑ 97FlaShoR2-62
❑ 97Fle-420
❑ 97Fle-687
❑ 97FleTif-420
❑ 97FleTif-687
❑ 97Lea-296
❑ 97LeaFraM-296
❑ 97LeaFraMDC-296
❑ 97MetUni-206
❑ 97Pac-384
❑ 97PacLigB-384
❑ 97PacPri-131
❑ 97PacPriLB-131
❑ 97PacPriP-131
❑ 97PacSil-384
❑ 97Sco-455
❑ 97ScoArtPWB-455
❑ 97ScoResC-455
❑ 97ScoShoS-455
❑ 97ScoShoSAP-455
❑ 97StaClu-178
❑ 97StaCluMOP-178
❑ 97Top-82
❑ 97TopSta-88
❑ 97TopStaAM-88
❑ 97Ult-306
❑ 97UltGolME-306
❑ 97UltPlaME-306
❑ 98Pac-227
❑ 98PacPlaB-227
❑ 98PacRedT-227
❑ 98PacSil-227
❑ 98ScoRT-139
❑ 98StaCluFDI-50
❑ 98StaCluI-50
❑ 98StaCluOneK-50
❑ 98StaCluPP-50
❑ 98Ult-349
❑ 98UltGolM-349
❑ 98UltMas-349
❑ 98UltPlaM-349
❑ 98UppDec-243
❑ 99Pac-448
❑ 99PacPlaB-448
❑ 99PacRed-448
❑ 99SkyPre-11
❑ 99SkyPreR-11
❑ 99UppDec-335
❑ 99UppDecEL1-335
❑ 99UppDecEL2-335
❑ 99UppDecM-43
❑ 99UppDecMGS-43
❑ 99UppDecMHFS-43
❑ 99UppDecMSS-43
❑ 99Vic-82

Santiago, Cedric
❑ 90ElmPioP-22

Santiago, Delvy
❑ 89BlaYNPRWLU-32
❑ 89PriPirS-19
❑ 90AugPirP-2462
❑ 91CollndC-16
❑ 91CollndP-1483

Santiago, Derek
❑ 98KanCouC-28
❑ 98KanCouCCP-28

Santiago, Gus
❑ 91SumFlyC-20
❑ 91SumFlyP-2345

Santiago, Jorge
❑ 91BurIndP-3310
❑ 97PitMet-29

Santiago, Jose
❑ 95SpoIndTI-26
❑ 96LanLugB-25
❑ 98WicWraM-8
❑ 99PacCroC-137
❑ 99PacCroCPB-137
❑ 99PacOme-118
❑ 99PacOmeC-118
❑ 99PacOmeG-118
❑ 99PacOmePB-118

Santiago, Jose G.
❑ 56A'sPos-36
❑ 56Top-59
❑ 75TCM195Cl-31
❑ 75TCM195Cl-39

Santiago, Jose R.
❑ 65Top-557
❑ 66Top-203
❑ 66TopVen-203
❑ 67CokCapRS-4
❑ 67DexPre-183
❑ 67Top-473
❑ 67TopRedSS-15
❑ 67TopVen-240
❑ 68AtlOilPBCC-40
❑ 68CokCapRS-10
❑ 68OPC-123
❑ 68Top-123
❑ 68TopVen-123
❑ 69MilBra-246
❑ 69MLBOffS-16
❑ 69OPC-21
❑ 69Top-21
❑ 69TopSta-137
❑ 69TopTeaP-3
❑ 70Top-708
❑ 81RedSoxBG2S-107

Santiago, Mike
❑ 85DurBulT-11
❑ 86JacMetT-9
❑ 87JacMetF-25
❑ 88JacMetGS-9

Santiago, Norm
❑ 86Ft.LauYP-19
❑ 87JacExpP-431
❑ 88WesPalBES-23

Santiago, Rafael
❑ 90ChaRaiB-20
❑ 90ChaRaiP-2031

Santiago, Sandi
❑ 90TamYanD-21
❑ 91OneYanP-4153
❑ 92OneYanC-13
❑ 93GreHorC-20
❑ 93GreHorF-885
❑ 94SanBerSC-20
❑ 94SanBerSF-2758
❑ 95TamYanYI-24

Santini, Aaron
❑ 94ForWayWC-21
❑ 94ForWayWF-2018

Santo, Jose
❑ 96ChaRivTI-9627

Santo, Ron
❑ 47Exh-199
❑ 61Baz-3
❑ 61CubJayP-10
❑ 61Pos-196A
❑ 61Pos-196B
❑ 61Top-35
❑ 61WilSpoGH828-1-6
❑ 62Baz-34
❑ 62CubJayP-9
❑ 62Jel-184
❑ 62Pos-184
❑ 62PosCan-184
❑ 62SalPlaC-136
❑ 62ShiPlaC-136
❑ 62Top-170
❑ 62TopStal-109
❑ 62TopVen-170
❑ 63BasMagM-74
❑ 63CubJayP-11
❑ 63ExhStaB-58
❑ 63Fle-32
❑ 63Jel-170
❑ 63Pos-170
❑ 63Top-113
❑ 63Top-252
❑ 64ChatheY-45
❑ 64CubJayP-11
❑ 64Top-375
❑ 64TopCoi-68
❑ 64TopCoi-146
❑ 64TopGia-58
❑ 64TopRooAB-2
❑ 64TopSta-33

- ❑ 64TopStaU-67
- ❑ 64WheSta-40
- ❑ 65Baz-28
- ❑ 65ChaTheY-46
- ❑ 65CubJayP-10
- ❑ 65OPC-6
- ❑ 65OPC-110
- ❑ 65Top-6
- ❑ 65Top-110
- ❑ 65TopEmbl-28
- ❑ 65TopTral-67
- ❑ 66Baz-39
- ❑ 66CubTeal-11
- ❑ 66Top-290
- ❑ 66TopRubl-85
- ❑ 66TopVen-290
- ❑ 67AshOil-9
- ❑ 67Baz-39
- ❑ 67CokCapA-6
- ❑ 67CokCapC-11
- ❑ 67CokCapNLA-23
- ❑ 67CubProPS-11
- ❑ 67DexPre-184
- ❑ 67DexPre-185
- ❑ 67OPC-70
- ❑ 67OPCPapl-26
- ❑ 67ProPizC-13
- ❑ 67Top-70
- ❑ 67TopGiaSU-22
- ❑ 67TopPos-26
- ❑ 67TopTesF-21
- ❑ 67TopVen-309
- ❑ 68AtlOilPBCC-41
- ❑ 68Baz-6
- ❑ 68Baz-15
- ❑ 68Kah-B31
- ❑ 68OPC-5
- ❑ 68Top-5
- ❑ 68Top-235
- ❑ 68Top-366
- ❑ 68TopActS-4B
- ❑ 68TopActS-5A
- ❑ 68TopActS-16B
- ❑ 68TopGaml-19
- ❑ 68TopPla-22
- ❑ 68TopPos-21
- ❑ 68TopVen-5
- ❑ 68TopVen-235
- ❑ 68TopVen-366
- ❑ 69CitMetC-13
- ❑ 69CubBumS-5
- ❑ 69CubJewT-15
- ❑ 69CubPho-10
- ❑ 69CubTealC-8
- ❑ 69Kah-B18
- ❑ 69KelPin-16
- ❑ 69MilBra-247
- ❑ 69MLBOffS-125
- ❑ 69MLBPin-56
- ❑ 69NabTeaF-21
- ❑ 69OPC-4
- ❑ 69OPCDec-19
- ❑ 69Top-4
- ❑ 69Top-420
- ❑ 69Top-570
- ❑ 69TopDec-19
- ❑ 69TopDecl-37
- ❑ 69TopSta-19
- ❑ 69TopSup-38
- ❑ 69TopTeaP-4
- ❑ 69TraSta-42
- ❑ 70CubDunD-5
- ❑ 70DayDaiNM-121
- ❑ 70Kel-42
- ❑ 70MilBra-25
- ❑ 70MLBOffS-22
- ❑ 70OPC-63
- ❑ 70OPC-454
- ❑ 70SunPin-8
- ❑ 70Top-63
- ❑ 70Top-454
- ❑ 70Top-670
- ❑ 70TopPos-5
- ❑ 70TopSup-21
- ❑ 70TraSta-2A
- ❑ 71MilDud-62
- ❑ 71MLBOffS-46
- ❑ 71OPC-220
- ❑ 71Top-220
- ❑ 71TopCoi-95
- ❑ 71TopSup-35
- ❑ 71TopTat-108
- ❑ 72CubChi-7
- ❑ 72CubTeal-11
- ❑ 72MilBra-306
- ❑ 72Top-555
- ❑ 72Top-556
- ❑ 73Kel2D-54
- ❑ 73LinPor-44
- ❑ 73OPC-115
- ❑ 73SevTraC-68
- ❑ 73Top-115
- ❑ 74Kel-7A
- ❑ 74Kel-7B
- ❑ 74OPC-270
- ❑ 74OPC-334
- ❑ 74Top-270
- ❑ 74Top-334
- ❑ 74TopSta-19
- ❑ 74TopTra-270T
- ❑ 75OPC-35
- ❑ 75Top-35
- ❑ 75TopMin-35
- ❑ 77CubAllT-11
- ❑ 78TCM60I-22
- ❑ 80CubGreT-3
- ❑ 83MLBPin-32
- ❑ 84CubBriPC-3D
- ❑ 84CubUno-2
- ❑ 84CubUno-7
- ❑ 84OCoandSI-232
- ❑ 88PacLegI-97
- ❑ 89SweBasG-36
- ❑ 90BasWit-14
- ❑ 90PacLeg-48
- ❑ 90SweBasG-64
- ❑ 91LinDri-5
- ❑ 91MDAA-5
- ❑ 91SweBasG-81
- ❑ 91UppDecS-21
- ❑ 92ActPacA-39
- ❑ 92CubOldS-21
- ❑ 92UppDecS-28
- ❑ 93TedWil-23
- ❑ 93UppDecAH-113
- ❑ 94UppDecAH-201
- ❑ 94UppDecAH1-201
- ❑ 99SpollIGotG-65
- ❑ 99SpollIGotGA-66
- ❑ 99SpollIGotGC-17

SantoDomingo, Rafael
- ❑ 78IndIndTI-17
- ❑ 79NaSouTI-20
- ❑ 80IndIndTI-22

Santop, Louis
- ❑ 74LauOldTBS-16
- ❑ 90NegLeaS-33

Santora, Jack
- ❑ 97UCLBruTI-21

Santora, Steve
- ❑ 85EveGiaC-15
- ❑ 85EveGialC-16

Santorini, Al
- ❑ 69PadVol-7
- ❑ 69Top-592
- ❑ 70OPC-212
- ❑ 70Top-212
- ❑ 71CarTeal-20
- ❑ 71CarTeal-31
- ❑ 71MLBOffS-237
- ❑ 71OPC-467
- ❑ 71Top-467
- ❑ 72Top-723
- ❑ 73OPC-24
- ❑ 73Top-24

Santoro, Gary
- ❑ 95ElmPioTI-25
- ❑ 95ElmPioUTI-25
- ❑ 96KanCouCTI-25
- ❑ 97BreCouMB-18

Santoro, Pat
- ❑ 98LowSpiM-17

Santos, Don
- ❑ 86WatIndP-24
- ❑ 87WatIndP-20

Santos, Ed
- ❑ 77LodDodT-17

Santos, Eddie
- ❑ 83KinBluJTI-22

Santos, Faustoe
- ❑ 85MadMusP-22
- ❑ 85MadMusT-2

Santos, Henry
- ❑ 92BriTigC-10
- ❑ 92BriTigF-1411
- ❑ 93NiaFalRF-3390
- ❑ 94FayGenC-22
- ❑ 94FayGenF-2145
- ❑ 96El PasDB-25

Santos, Jerry (Gerald)
- ❑ 91JohCitCC-21
- ❑ 91JohCitCP-3977
- ❑ 92MidLeaATI-38
- ❑ 92ProFS7-329
- ❑ 92SprCarC-24
- ❑ 92SprCarF-865
- ❑ 93ArkTraF-2812
- ❑ 93ExcFS7-105
- ❑ 94ArkTraF-3089
- ❑ 94Bow-452

Santos, Jose
- ❑ 97ButCopKB-25
- ❑ 97ButCopKK-25
- ❑ 98ButCopKG-29
- ❑ 98SavSanGM-23
- ❑ 98SouAtlLPM-21
- ❑ 99BasAmeTP-89
- ❑ 99BasAmeTPG-89

Santos, Josh
- ❑ 98SalVol-30

Santos, Juan
- ❑ 93EugEmeC-23
- ❑ 93EugEmeF-3856

Santos, Leigh
- ❑ 94ButCopKSP-10

Santos, Luis
- ❑ 80WisRapTT-2

Santos, Matthew
- ❑ 95ModA'sTI-27

Santos, Ray
- ❑ 97St.PauS-25

Santos, Victor
- ❑ 97LakTigB-28

Santovenia, Nelson
- ❑ 83MemChiT-8
- ❑ 86JacExpT-8
- ❑ 87JacExpP-433
- ❑ 87SouLeaAJ-5
- ❑ 88ExpPos-31
- ❑ 88FleUpd-103
- ❑ 88FleUpdG-103
- ❑ 88IndIndC-18
- ❑ 88IndIndP-500
- ❑ 88ScoRoo-96T
- ❑ 88ScoRooG-96T
- ❑ 88TopTra-102T
- ❑ 88TopTraT-102T
- ❑ 89Bow-361
- ❑ 89BowTif-361
- ❑ 89Don-366
- ❑ 89DonBasB-146
- ❑ 89ExpPos-26
- ❑ 89Fle-393
- ❑ 89FleGlo-393
- ❑ 89OPC-228
- ❑ 89PanSti-112
- ❑ 89Sco-346
- ❑ 89ScoHot1R-71
- ❑ 89Top-228
- ❑ 89TopBig-98
- ❑ 89TopRoo-18
- ❑ 89TopSti-78
- ❑ 89TopTif-228
- ❑ 89ToyRoo-25
- ❑ 89UppDec-380
- ❑ 90Don-224
- ❑ 90ExpPos-32
- ❑ 90Fle-360
- ❑ 90FleCan-360
- ❑ 90Lea-502
- ❑ 90OPC-614
- ❑ 90PanSti-289
- ❑ 90PubIntS-187
- ❑ 90Sco-451
- ❑ 90Spo-162
- ❑ 90Top-614
- ❑ 90TopTif-614
- ❑ 90UppDec-432
- ❑ 91ExpPos-21
- ❑ 91Fle-248
- ❑ 91OPC-744
- ❑ 91Sco-777
- ❑ 91StaClu-416
- ❑ 91Top-744
- ❑ 91TopDesS-744
- ❑ 91TopMic-744
- ❑ 91TopTif-744
- ❑ 92OPC-732
- ❑ 92Top-732
- ❑ 92TopGol-732
- ❑ 92TopGolW-732
- ❑ 92TopMic-732
- ❑ 92VanCanF-2726
- ❑ 92VanCanS-646
- ❑ 93OmaRoyF-1682
- ❑ 94OmaRoyF-1227

Santoya, Cristobal
- ❑ 91IdaFalBSP-18

Santucci, Steve
- ❑ 93GleFalRC-25
- ❑ 93GleFalRF-4020
- ❑ 94MadHatC-21
- ❑ 94MadHatF-148
- ❑ 94NewJerCC-23
- ❑ 94NewJerCF-3432
- ❑ 96StPetCB-28

Sapienza, Rich
- ❑ 87TamTarP-29
- ❑ 88CedRapRP-1148

Sapp, Damian
- ❑ 96MicBatCB-24
- ❑ 97Bow-195
- ❑ 97BowInt-195
- ❑ 98Bow-321
- ❑ 98BowChr-321
- ❑ 98BowChrGA-321
- ❑ 98BowChrGAR-321
- ❑ 98BowChrI-321
- ❑ 98BowChrIR-321
- ❑ 98BowChrR-321
- ❑ 98BowGolA-321
- ❑ 98BowInt-321

Sarandon, Susan
- ❑ 88BulDurM-4

Sarazen, Gene
- ❑ 32USCar*-9
- ❑ 41WheM5-19

Sarbaugh, Mike
- ❑ 90CalLeaACLC-46
- ❑ 91KinIndC-20
- ❑ 91KinIndP-332
- ❑ 92CanIndF-699
- ❑ 92CanIndS-117
- ❑ 94CanIndF-3128
- ❑ 95KinIndTI-24
- ❑ 98KinIndQ-28

Sarcia, Joe
- ❑ 91GenCubC-18
- ❑ 91GenCubP-4228

Sardinha, Ed
- ❑ 86ElmPioRSP-19
- ❑ 96DelShoB-3

Sargent, J. A.
- ❑ 22Zee-52

Sarmiento, Danny
- ❑ 92GulCoaDF-3565
- ❑ 93GreFalDSP-17
- ❑ 98ColRedSM-9

Sarmiento, Manny
- ❑ 76IndIndTI-16
- ❑ 76VenLeaS-174
- ❑ 77IndIndTI-25
- ❑ 77Top-475
- ❑ 78Pep-22
- ❑ 78SSP270-122
- ❑ 78Top-377
- ❑ 79IndIndTI-21
- ❑ 79OPC-69
- ❑ 79Top-149
- ❑ 80SpoIndT-12
- ❑ 80Top-21
- ❑ 80VenLeaS-151
- ❑ 81PawRedST-10
- ❑ 81Top-649
- ❑ 82PorBeaT-8
- ❑ 83Don-502
- ❑ 83Fle-321
- ❑ 83FleSta-171
- ❑ 83FleSti-75
- ❑ 83Top-566
- ❑ 84Don-200
- ❑ 84Fle-263
- ❑ 84Nes792-209
- ❑ 84Pir-19
- ❑ 84Top-209
- ❑ 84TopTif-209
- ❑ 85HawIslC-248

Sarmiento, Oscar
- ❑ 93LinVenB-75
- ❑ 94VenLinU-133

Sarmiento, Wally
- ❑ 80TolMudHT-12
- ❑ 81TolMudHT-8

Sarmiento, Wilfredo
- ❑ 80VenLeaS-7

Sarni, Bill
- ❑ 54Top-194
- ❑ 55Bow-30
- ❑ 55CarHunW-22
- ❑ 55RedMan-NL9
- ❑ 56Top-247
- ❑ 57GiaJayP-8
- ❑ 57Top-86
- ❑ 79TCM50-106
- ❑ 94TopArc1-194
- ❑ 94TopArc1G-194

Sarrett, Daniel
- ❑ 80WatRedT-17

Sartain, Dave
- ❑ 91EliTwiP-4299
- ❑ 92ClaFS7-152
- ❑ 92KenTwiC-4
- ❑ 92KenTwiF-602
- ❑ 92ProFS7-100
- ❑ 94HigDesMC-23
- ❑ 94HigDesMF-2789

Sasaki, Kenichi
- ❑ 94CenValRC-21
- ❑ 94CenValRF-3203

Sasaki, Kyosuke
- ❑ 79TCMJapPB-48

Sasaki, Shigehi
- ❑ 90SalSpuCLC-118
- ❑ 90SalSpuP-2719

Sass, James
- ❑ 90StoPorB-10
- ❑ 90StoPorCLC-195
- ❑ 90StoPorP-2195
- ❑ 91BelBreCB-9
- ❑ 91BelBreP-2118

Sasser, Don
- ❑ 75CedRapGT-12
- ❑ 76CedRapGT-26

Sasser, Mackey
- ❑ 85FreGiaSB-8
- ❑ 86ShrCapP-22
- ❑ 87PhoFirP-20
- ❑ 88Don-28
- ❑ 88DonRoo-51
- ❑ 88DonTeaBM-NEW
- ❑ 88FleUpd-106
- ❑ 88FleUpdG-106
- ❑ 88Lea-28
- ❑ 88MetKah-2
- ❑ 88Sco-642
- ❑ 88ScoGlo-642
- ❑ 88ScoRoo-30T
- ❑ 88ScoRooG-30T
- ❑ 88TopTra-103T
- ❑ 88TopTraT-103T
- ❑ 89ClaLigB-26
- ❑ 89Don-454
- ❑ 89Fle-48
- ❑ 89FleGlo-48
- ❑ 89MetColP-17
- ❑ 89MetKah-25
- ❑ 89Sco-303
- ❑ 89ScoHot1R-82
- ❑ 89ScoYouSI-38
- ❑ 89Top-457
- ❑ 89TopRoo-19
- ❑ 89TopTif-457
- ❑ 89ToyRoo-26
- ❑ 89UppDec-561
- ❑ 90ClaBlu-78
- ❑ 90Don-471
- ❑ 90Fle-216
- ❑ 90FleCan-216
- ❑ 90Lea-435
- ❑ 90MetColP-24
- ❑ 90MetKah-2
- ❑ 90OPC-656
- ❑ 90PubIntS-144
- ❑ 90Sco-510
- ❑ 90Top-656
- ❑ 90TopTif-656
- ❑ 90TopTVM-22
- ❑ 90UppDec-185
- ❑ 91ClaGam-37
- ❑ 91Don-136
- ❑ 91Fle-160
- ❑ 91Lea-361
- ❑ 91MetColP-21
- ❑ 91MetKah-2
- ❑ 91MetPerPA-25
- ❑ 91MetTro-8
- ❑ 91MetWIZ-345
- ❑ 91OPC-382
- ❑ 91PanFreS-78
- ❑ 91Sco-307
- ❑ 91Sco100S-75
- ❑ 91StaClu-172
- ❑ 91Top-382
- ❑ 91TopDesS-382
- ❑ 91TopMic-382
- ❑ 91TopTif-382
- ❑ 91Ult-226
- ❑ 91UppDec-103
- ❑ 92Don-256
- ❑ 92Fle-515
- ❑ 92Lea-108
- ❑ 92LeaBlaG-108
- ❑ 92MetColP-18
- ❑ 92MetKah-2
- ❑ 92OPC-533
- ❑ 92Pin-447
- ❑ 92Sco-472
- ❑ 92StaClu-249
- ❑ 92Top-533
- ❑ 92TopGol-533
- ❑ 92TopGolW-533
- ❑ 92TopMic-533
- ❑ 92Ult-237
- ❑ 93Don-512
- ❑ 93Fle-480
- ❑ 93FleFinE-274
- ❑ 93MariStaClu-11
- ❑ 93MarMot-22
- ❑ 93OPC-328
- ❑ 93Top-788
- ❑ 93TopGol-788
- ❑ 93TopInaM-788
- ❑ 93TopInaR-788
- ❑ 93TopMic-788
- ❑ 94Fle-298
- ❑ 94MarMot-22
- ❑ 94Pac-581
- ❑ 94Sco-439
- ❑ 94ScoGolR-439
- ❑ 94StaClu-510
- ❑ 94StaCluFDI-510
- ❑ 94StaCluGR-510
- ❑ 94StaCluMOP-510
- ❑ 94Ult-124
- ❑ 94VenLinU-120

Sasser, Robert
- ❑ 94IdaFalBF-3594
- ❑ 94IdaFalBSP-24
- ❑ 95DanBraTI-25
- ❑ 95EugEmeTI-26
- ❑ 96MacBraB-19
- ❑ 97CedRapK-23
- ❑ 98TulDriTI-18
- ❑ 99SpolII-63

Sassone, Mike
- ❑ 87St.PetCP-4
- ❑ 88ArkTraGS-18

Satnat, Dave
- ❑ 86SalRedBP-24

Sato, Shin-Ichi
- ❑ 90IBAWorA-23
- ❑ 90IBAWorA-45
- ❑ 90IBAWorA-52

Satoh, Hideki
- ❑ 96HonShaHWB-16

Satoh, Hiroyuki
- ❑ 90GatCitPP-3340
- ❑ 90GatCitPSP-19

Satre, Jason
- ❑ 89GreHorP-414
- ❑ 90Bes-42
- ❑ 90ChaWheB-9
- ❑ 90ChaWheP-2241
- ❑ 90CMC-707
- ❑ 91CedRapRC-12
- ❑ 91CedRapRP-2719
- ❑ 92ChaLooF-3820
- ❑ 93BowBayF-2188
- ❑ 94OriPro-90
- ❑ 94RocRedWF-998
- ❑ 94RocRedWTI-20
- ❑ 94VenLinU-234

Satriano, Gina
- ❑ 94ColSilBC-8
- ❑ 95ColSilB-25
- ❑ 95ColSilB9-4

Satriano, Tom
- ❑ 63Top-548
- ❑ 64Top-521
- ❑ 65OPC-124
- ❑ 65SeaPop-20
- ❑ 65Top-124
- ❑ 66Top-361
- ❑ 66TopVen-361
- ❑ 67Top-343
- ❑ 68Top-238
- ❑ 68TopVen-238
- ❑ 69MilBra-248
- ❑ 69OPC-78
- ❑ 69Top-78
- ❑ 69TopSta-150
- ❑ 70MLBOffS-164
- ❑ 70Top-581
- ❑ 71MLBOffS-330
- ❑ 71OPC-557
- ❑ 71Top-557

❑ 72MilBra-307
Satterfield, Cory
❑ 88HamRedP-1731
❑ 89SprCarB-18
❑ 90St.PetCS-21
Satterfield, Jeremy
❑ 96MedHatBJTI-25
Sattler, Bill
❑ 82WicAerTI-16
❑ 83WicAerDS-20
❑ 84IndIndTI-19
❑ 84IndIndTI-21
Saturnino, Sherton
❑ 92IdaFalGF-3528
❑ 92IdaFalGSP-11
❑ 93DanBraC-20
❑ 93DanBraF-3634
❑ 94MacBraC-18
❑ 94MacBraF-2220
Saturria, Luis
❑ 96AppLeaAB-21
❑ 96JohCitCTI-29
❑ 97PeoChi-25
❑ 98PriWilCQ-26
❑ 99FleBri-172
❑ 99FleBri2G-172
❑ 99FleBriBlu-172
❑ 99FleBriGol-172
❑ 99SkyPreA-48
❑ 99SkyPreABlue-48
Satzinger, Jeff
❑ 86MacPirP-22
❑ 87KenTwiP-17
❑ 88OrlTwiB-13
❑ 89OrlTwiB-24
❑ 89OrlTwiP-1330
❑ 90CMC-158
❑ 90OklCit8C-8
❑ 90OklCit8P-433
❑ 90ProAAAF-679
Saucier, Kevin
❑ 77ReaPhiT-20
❑ 80PhiBurK-22
❑ 80Top-682
❑ 81Fle-24A
❑ 81Fle-24B
❑ 81Fle-24C
❑ 81Top-53
❑ 81TopTra-827
❑ 82Don-485
❑ 82Fle-275
❑ 82FleSta-158
❑ 82OPC-238
❑ 82Top-238
❑ 83Top-373
Sauer, Ed
❑ 44CubTeal-20
❑ 47SigOil-35
❑ 48AngTeal-24
❑ 49EurSta-196
Sauer, Hank (Henry)
❑ 47Exh-200
❑ 47PM1StaP1-194
❑ 48Bow-45
❑ 49Bow-5
❑ 49Lea-20
❑ 49MPR302-2-113
❑ 50Bow-25
❑ 50JJKCopP-16
❑ 51Bow-22
❑ 51TopBluB-49
❑ 52DixLid-18
❑ 52DixPre-18
❑ 52NatTeaL-29
❑ 52StaCalL-80E
❑ 52StaCalS-92C
❑ 52Top-35
❑ 53BowC-48
❑ 53DixLid-18
❑ 53DixPre-18
❑ 53ExhCan-7
❑ 53NorBreL-27
❑ 53RedMan-NL16
❑ 53Top-111
❑ 54RedHeaF-26
❑ 54Top-4
❑ 54Wil-15
❑ 55Top-45
❑ 55TopDouH-103
❑ 56Top-41
❑ 56TopHocF-A3
❑ 56TopPin-6
❑ 57Top-197
❑ 58GiaArmT-8
❑ 58GiaJayP-9
❑ 58GiaSFCB-20
❑ 58Hir-49
❑ 58PacBel-7
❑ 58Top-378
❑ 59Top-404
❑ 61Top-481
❑ 74LauAllG-52
❑ 75OPC-190
❑ 75Top-190
❑ 75TopMin-190
❑ 76ChiGre-17
❑ 77GalGloG-27
❑ 77Gia-21
❑ 79DiaGre-125
❑ 79TCM50-70
❑ 82GSGalAG-19
❑ 83TopRep5-35
❑ 84CubBriPC-13D
❑ 84CubUno-3
❑ 85TCMPhoC-32
❑ 88PacLegI-23
❑ 91TopArc1-111
❑ 92BazQua5A-2
❑ 92CubOldS-22
❑ 94TopArc1-4
❑ 94TopArc1G-4
Sauerbeck, Scott
❑ 94PitMetC-19
❑ 94PitMetF-3523
❑ 95StLucMTI-29
❑ 96StLucMTI-32
❑ 97BinMetB-27
❑ 98NorTidP-24
❑ 98NorTidQ-23
❑ 99SkyPre-223
❑ 99SkyPre-223
❑ 99SkyPreR-223
❑ 99SkyPreR-223
Sauget, Rich
❑ 96HicCraB-20
Saugstad, Mark
❑ 92EveGiaC-1
❑ 92EveGiaF-1700
❑ 93CliGiaC-21
❑ 93EveGiaC-23
❑ 93EveGiaF-3767
❑ 94HigDesMC-24
❑ 94HigDesMF-2790
Saul, Jim
❑ 62KahAtl-18
❑ 80ElPasDT-7
❑ 81HolMilT-2
❑ 82PorBeaT-23
❑ 83NasSouTI-18
❑ 84NasSouTI-19
❑ 85AlbYanT-25
❑ 86AlbYanT-16
❑ 89BurBraP-1615
❑ 89BurBraS-27
❑ 90BurBraB-28
❑ 90BurBraP-2365
❑ 90BurBraS-27
❑ 96EugEmeB-25
❑ 97EugEmeB-1
❑ 98EugEme-23
Saulter, Kevin
❑ 91PulBraC-29
❑ 91PulBraP-4004
❑ 92MacBraC-14
❑ 92MacBraF-266
Saunders, Chris
❑ 92PitMetF-3305
❑ 93ClaFS7-21
❑ 93ClaGolF-168
❑ 93St.LucMC-22
❑ 93St.LuMF-2930
❑ 94BinMetF-712
❑ 95BinMetTI-35
❑ 96BinMetB-25
❑ 96DouAllB-14
❑ 97NorTid-28
❑ 97NorTidB-28
Saunders, Dennis
❑ 71OPC-423
❑ 71Top-423
Saunders, Doug
❑ 89ColMetB-20
❑ 89ColMetGS-23
❑ 90St.LucMS-24
❑ 91St.LucMC-5
❑ 91St.LucMP-721
❑ 92BinMetF-525
❑ 92BinMetS-67
❑ 93FleFinE-105
❑ 93NorTidF-2577
❑ 93TopTra-43T
❑ 94BinMetF-713
❑ 98LanJetG-21
Saunders, Henri
❑ 90LSUTigA-16
Saunders, Mark
❑ 79ElmPioRST-28
Saunders, Tony
❑ 94BreCouMC-16
❑ 94BreCouMF-10
❑ 96PorSeaDB-24
❑ 97Bow-123
❑ 97BowCerBlaIA-CA71
❑ 97BowCerBluIA-CA71
❑ 97BowCerGolIA-CA71
❑ 97BowChr-137
❑ 97BowChrI-137
❑ 97BowChrIR-137
❑ 97BowChrR-137
❑ 97BowInt-123
❑ 97ColChoU-U14
❑ 97Fle-581
❑ 97FleTif-581
❑ 97MarPac-21
❑ 98CirThu-241
❑ 98CirThuRav-241
❑ 98CirThuSupRav-241
❑ 98ColCho-508
❑ 98DevRayP-8
❑ 98Don-322
❑ 98DonGolPP-322
❑ 98DonSilPP-322
❑ 98Fin-239
❑ 98FinNo--239
❑ 98FinNo-R-239
❑ 98FinRef-239
❑ 98Fle-221
❑ 98Fle-404
❑ 98LeaRS-252
❑ 98LeaRSLHolo-252
❑ 98LeaRSLong-252
❑ 98LeaRTrue-252
❑ 98MetUni-107
❑ 98MetUniPMG-107
❑ 98PacInvGems-158
❑ 98PacOnl-717
❑ 98PacOnlR-717
❑ 98PacOnlWC-717
❑ 98Pin-176
❑ 98PinArtP-PP79
❑ 98PinMusC-PP79
❑ 98PinPlu-67
❑ 98PinPreP-176
❑ 98PinSna-TBDR10
❑ 98PorSeaD5AQ-27
❑ 98ScoRT-180
❑ 98SP Aut-183
❑ 98SpoIll-198
❑ 98SpoIllEE-198
❑ 98SpoIllFE-198
❑ 98SPxFin-322
❑ 98SPxFinR-322
❑ 98SPxFinS-322
❑ 98StaCluFDI-322
❑ 98StaCluI-322
❑ 98StaCluOneK-322
❑ 98StaCluPP-322
❑ 98Stu-209
❑ 98StuGPP-209
❑ 98StuSPP-209
❑ 98Top-497
❑ 98TopChr-497
❑ 98TopChrR-497
❑ 98TopDevR-497
❑ 98TopDia-497
❑ 98TopGal-18
❑ 98TopGalGP-18
❑ 98TopGalOPP-18
❑ 98TopGalPPI-18
❑ 98TopGalPPIA-18
❑ 98TopMiniC-497
❑ 98Ult-179
❑ 98Ult-465
❑ 98UltGolM-179
❑ 98UltGolM-465
❑ 98UltMas-179
❑ 98UltMas-465
❑ 98UltPlaM-179
❑ 98UltPlaM-465
❑ 98UppDec-97
❑ 98UppDec-517
❑ 98UppDec-724
❑ 99Fle-444
❑ 99FleSta9-444
❑ 99FleWarT-444
❑ 99StaClu-214
❑ 99StaCluFDI-214
❑ 99StaCluOoaK-214
❑ 99StaCluPP-214
❑ 99Top-373
❑ 99TopChr-373
❑ 99TopChrR-373
❑ 99TopMVPP-373
❑ 99UppDec-496
❑ 99UppDecEL1-496
❑ 99UppDecEL2-496
Saunier, Randy
❑ 82CliGiaF-12
Sauritch, Chris
❑ 94BluOriF-3571
❑ 96HigDesMB-25
Sauve, Erik
❑ 94HudValRC-23
❑ 94HudValRF-3395
Sauve, Jeff
❑ 96MicBatCB-25
Sauveur, Rich
❑ 84PriWilPT-23
❑ 85NasPirT-23
❑ 86NasPirP-25
❑ 87HarSenP-24
❑ 88JacExpB-3
❑ 88JacExpP-986
❑ 89IndIndP-1228
❑ 90MiaMirIS-23
❑ 91LinDriAAA-567
❑ 91TidTidLD-567
❑ 91TidTidP-2508
❑ 92OmaRoyF-2962
❑ 92OmaRoyS-345
❑ 93TopGol-396
❑ 94IndIndF-1810
❑ 95IndIndF-94
❑ 96NasSouB-21
❑ 97PacSil-62
Savage, Ashleigh
❑ 89AncGlaP-22
Savage, Jack
❑ 86BakDodP-24
❑ 87SanAntDTI-22
❑ 87TexLeaAF-34
❑ 88Fle-650
❑ 88FleGlo-650
❑ 88MetColP-48
❑ 88TidTidCa-27
❑ 88TidTidCM-1
❑ 88TidTidP-1583
❑ 89Don-618
❑ 89MetColP-51
❑ 89TidTidC-5
❑ 89TidTidP-1971
❑ 90DodTar-1060
❑ 90TopTra-111T
❑ 90TopTraT-111T
❑ 91LinDriAAA-417
❑ 91OPC-357
❑ 91PorBeaLD-417
❑ 91PorBeaP-1564
❑ 91Top-357
❑ 91TopDesS-357
❑ 91TopMic-357
❑ 91TopTif-357
Savage, Jim
❑ 90BatCliP-3077
❑ 91BenBucCB-13
❑ 91BenBucP-3703
❑ 91SpaPhiC-18
❑ 91SpaPhiP-903
Savage, John
❑ 88RenSilSCLC-275
Savage, John Robert
❑ 47A'sTeal-26
❑ 48A'sTeal-20
❑ 49Bow-204
Savage, Ted
❑ 62Top-104
❑ 62TopVen-104
❑ 63PirIDL-20
❑ 63Top-508
❑ 64Top-62
❑ 64TopVen-62
❑ 67Top-552
❑ 68OPC-119
❑ 68Top-119
❑ 68TopVen-119
❑ 69Top-471A
❑ 69Top-471B
❑ 70BreMcD-27
❑ 70BreMil-22
❑ 70BreTeal-11
❑ 70SunPin-17
❑ 70Top-602
❑ 71BreTeal-16
❑ 71MLBOffS-434
❑ 71OPC-76
❑ 71oySigST-24
❑ 71Top-76
❑ 71TopCoi-44
❑ 71TopSup-3
❑ 71TopTat-58
❑ 72MilBra-308
❑ 81TCM60I-343
❑ 90DodTar-704
❑ 94BreMilB-76
Savarino, Bill (William)
❑ 86MedA'sC-51
❑ 87ModA'sC-14
❑ 87ModA'sP-2
❑ 88ModA'sCLC-75
❑ 89CalLeaA-44
❑ 89HunStaB-4
❑ 89ModA'sC-21
Savary, Scott
❑ 94BilMusF-3683
❑ 94BilMusSP-12
Saverine, Bob
❑ 63BalOriP-29
❑ 63Top-158
❑ 64BalOriP-32
❑ 64Top-221
❑ 64TopVen-221
❑ 65Top-427
❑ 66Top-312
❑ 66TopVen-312
❑ 67CokCapS-13
❑ 67DexPre-186
❑ 67OPC-27
❑ 67SenPos-21
❑ 67Top-27
❑ 68OPC-149
❑ 68Top-149
❑ 68TopVen-149
❑ 78TCM60I-14
❑ 91OriCro-402
Saverino, Mike
❑ 82DanSunF-23
❑ 83PeoSunF-27
Savinon, Odalis
❑ 89JohCitCS-19
❑ 91SprCarC-24
❑ 91SprCarP-757
❑ 92St.PetCC-21
❑ 93ArkTraF-2826
Savoy, Annie
❑ 89BulDurOS-5
Sawatski, Carl
❑ 47Exh-201A
❑ 47Exh-201B
❑ 47Exh-201C
❑ 53Top-202
❑ 54Top-198
❑ 55Top-122
❑ 55TopDouH-93
❑ 58Top-234
❑ 59Top-56
❑ 59TopVen-56
❑ 60Lea-120
❑ 60Top-545
❑ 61Top-198
❑ 62Jel-162
❑ 62Pos-162
❑ 62PosCan-162
❑ 62SalPlaC-119
❑ 62ShiPlaC-119
❑ 62Top-106
❑ 62TopVen-106
❑ 63Top-267
❑ 64Top-24
❑ 64TopVen-24
❑ 80Bra195T-30
❑ 89TexLeaAGS-40
❑ 91TopArc1-202
❑ 94TopArc1-198
❑ 94TopArc1G-198
Sawatski, John
❑ 72CedRapCT-6
Sawkiw, Warren
❑ 88CapCodPPaLP-3
❑ 90NiaFalRP-10
❑ 91LakTigC-27
❑ 91LakTigP-276
❑ 92LakTigC-24
❑ 95KnoSmoF-53
❑ 97BirBarB-18
Sawyer, Carl
❑ 14Zee-24
❑ 22Zee-159
❑ 23Zee-195
Sawyer, Eddie
❑ 49EurSta-145
❑ 49PhiBul-46
❑ 50Bow-225
❑ 51Bow-184
❑ 58PhiTeal-16
❑ 60PhiJayP-12
❑ 60Top-226
❑ 75Phi195T-24
❑ 77PhiFav-22
❑ 79DiaGre-325
❑ 80Phi195T-24
❑ 83PhiPosGPaM-11
❑ 87Phi195T-1
Sawyer, Rick
❑ 75SyrChiTI-18
❑ 76SSP-426
❑ 77PadFamF-6
❑ 77PadSchC-48
❑ 77Top-268
❑ 92YanWIZ7-138
Sawyer, Zach
❑ 93MadMusC-22
❑ 93MadMusF-1821
❑ 94WesMicWC-21
❑ 94WesMicWF-2294
❑ 95ModA'sTI-28
Sax, Dave
❑ 79CliDodT-18
❑ 82AlbDukTc-13
❑ 83DodPol-23
❑ 84AlbDukCr-152
❑ 84Don-519
❑ 85PawRedST-15
❑ 86Top-307
❑ 86TopTif-307
❑ 87Don-647
❑ 87PawRedST-25
❑ 88BufBisC-22
❑ 88BufBisP-1483
❑ 89ColCliC-26
❑ 89ColCliP-756
❑ 90CMC-219
❑ 90ColCliC-19
❑ 90ColCliP-7
❑ 90ColCliP-680
❑ 90DodTar-705
❑ 90ProAAAF-330
❑ 90TopTVY-59
❑ 91ColCliLD-117
❑ 91ColCliP-17
❑ 91ColCliP-600
❑ 91LinDriAAA-117
❑ 91PacSenL-34
❑ 92ColCliF-357
❑ 92ColCliP-15
❑ 92ColCliS-115
Sax, Steve
❑ 79CliDodT-10
❑ 82DodPol-52
❑ 82DodPos-7
❑ 82DodUniOV-19
❑ 82DogBuiE-7
❑ 82Don-624
❑ 82Fle-21
❑ 82Top-681
❑ 82TopTra-103T
❑ 83AllGamPI-108
❑ 83DodPol-3
❑ 83DodPos-14
❑ 83Don-336
❑ 83Fle-220
❑ 83FleSta-172
❑ 83FleSti-118
❑ 83OPC-245
❑ 83PerAll-15
❑ 83PerAllG-15
❑ 83SevCoi-2
❑ 83Top-245
❑ 83TopSti-329
❑ 84AllGamPI-16
❑ 84DodPol-3
❑ 84DodSmo-3
❑ 84Don-104
❑ 84Fle-112
❑ 84Fle-633
❑ 84FleSti-90
❑ 84FunFooP-45
❑ 84MilBra-22
❑ 84Nes792-610
❑ 84OPC-144
❑ 84SevCoi-W22
❑ 84Top-610
❑ 84TopGloA-14
❑ 84TopRubD-19
❑ 84TopSti-78
❑ 84TopTif-610

❑ 85AllGamPI-106
❑ 85DodCokP-29
❑ 85Don-418
❑ 85Fle-384
❑ 85FleLimE-32
❑ 85Lea-90
❑ 85OPC-369
❑ 85Top-470
❑ 85TopMin-470
❑ 85TopRubD-18
❑ 85TopSti-77
❑ 85TopTif-470
❑ 86BasStaB-98
❑ 86DodCokP-27
❑ 86DodPol-3
❑ 86DodUniOP-17
❑ 86Don-540
❑ 86DonHig-50
❑ 86Fle-143
❑ 86GenMilB-5H
❑ 86OPC-175
❑ 86Spo-56
❑ 86Spo-95
❑ 86SpoRoo-48
❑ 86Top-175
❑ 86TopSti-72
❑ 86TopTat-21
❑ 86TopTif-175
❑ 87ClaGam-20
❑ 87DodMot-3
❑ 87DodPho-12
❑ 87DodPol-2
❑ 87DodSmoA-32
❑ 87Don-26
❑ 87Don-278
❑ 87DonAll-28
❑ 87DonOpeD-85
❑ 87DonSupD-26
❑ 87Dra-25
❑ 87Fle-453
❑ 87FleAll-4
❑ 87FleGamW-39
❑ 87FleGlo-453
❑ 87FleHotS-34
❑ 87FleMin-96
❑ 87FleRecS-34
❑ 87FleStiC-106
❑ 87GenMilB-6H
❑ 87KraFoo-38
❑ 87Lea-26
❑ 87Lea-203
❑ 87MandMSL-21
❑ 87OPC-254
❑ 87SevCoi-W10
❑ 87SmoNatL-1
❑ 87Spo-12
❑ 87SpoTeaP-14
❑ 87Top-596
❑ 87Top-769
❑ 87TopCoi-42
❑ 87TopMinL-15
❑ 87TopSti-70
❑ 87TopTif-596
❑ 87TopTif-769
❑ 88DodMot-3
❑ 88DodPol-3
❑ 88DodSmo-25
❑ 88Don-176
❑ 88DonBasB-204
❑ 88Fle-523
❑ 88FleGlo-523
❑ 88FleMin-85
❑ 88FleStiC-93
❑ 88Lea-185
❑ 88OPC-305
❑ 88PanSti-311
❑ 88Sco-35
❑ 88ScoGlo-35
❑ 88StaLinAl-29
❑ 88StaLinD-14
❑ 88Top-305
❑ 88TopBig-46
❑ 88TopSti-74
❑ 88TopTif-305
❑ 89Bow-178
❑ 89BowTif-178
❑ 89CadEllD-50
❑ 89ClaTraP-179
❑ 89DodSmoG-99
❑ 89Don-84
❑ 89DonBasB-20
❑ 89DonTra-23
❑ 89Fle-70
❑ 89FleGlo-70
❑ 89FleGlo-WS9
❑ 89FleUpd-52
❑ 89FleWorS-9
❑ 89OPC-40
❑ 89PanSti-106
❑ 89RedFolSB-103
❑ 89Sco-69
❑ 89ScoHot1S-33
❑ 89ScoRoo-20T
❑ 89Spo-58
❑ 89Top-40
❑ 89TopBasT-100
❑ 89TopBig-111
❑ 89TopDouM-19
❑ 89TopMinL-19
❑ 89TopSti-57
❑ 89TopStiB-39
❑ 89TopTif-40
❑ 89TopTra-111T
❑ 89TopTraT-111T
❑ 89TopUKM-69
❑ 89UppDec-53
❑ 89UppDec-748
❑ 89YanScoNW-2
❑ 90Bow-442
❑ 90BowTif-442
❑ 90ClaBlu-149
❑ 90DodTar-706
❑ 90Don-2
❑ 90Don-78
❑ 90DonBesA-24
❑ 90DOnBonM-BC22
❑ 90DonSupD-2
❑ 90Fle-455
❑ 90FleBasA-33
❑ 90FleBasAC-33
❑ 90FleCan-455
❑ 90FleLeaL-34
❑ 90FleLeaLC-34
❑ 90Hot50PS-38
❑ 90Lea-96
❑ 90LeaPre-1
❑ 90M.Vpin-70
❑ 90MLBBasB-62
❑ 90MSAHolD-16
❑ 90MSAIceTD-19
❑ 90OPC-560
❑ 90PanSti-129
❑ 90PubIntS-547
❑ 90RedFolSB-83
❑ 90Sco-125
❑ 90Sco100S-2
❑ 90ScoMcD-22
❑ 90Spo-12
❑ 90Top-560
❑ 90TopBig-141
❑ 90TopCoi-26
❑ 90TopDou-57
❑ 90TopGloS-8
❑ 90TopMinL-25
❑ 90TopSti-310
❑ 90TopStiB-38
❑ 90TopTif-560
❑ 90TopTVA-18
❑ 90TopTVY-26
❑ 90UppDec-18
❑ 90UppDec-172
❑ 90USPlaCA-4S
❑ 90WinDis-7
❑ 90YanScoNW-3
❑ 91Bow-170
❑ 91CadEllD-50
❑ 91Cla2-T17
❑ 91ClaGam-106
❑ 91Don-48
❑ 91Don-163
❑ 91Fle-679
❑ 91Lea-220
❑ 91OPC-290
❑ 91PanCanT1-46
❑ 91PanFreS-168
❑ 91PanFreS-325
❑ 91PanSti-271
❑ 91RedFolS-84
❑ 91RedFolS-127
❑ 91Sco-32
❑ 91Sco100S-72
❑ 91StaClu-204
❑ 91StaCluP-38
❑ 91StaPinB-44
❑ 91Stu-100
❑ 91Top-290
❑ 91TopCraJ2-30
❑ 91TopDesS-290
❑ 91TopGloA-3
❑ 91TopMic-290
❑ 91TopTif-290
❑ 91TopTriH-A10
❑ 91Ult-242
❑ 91UppDec-462
❑ 92Bow-469
❑ 92ClaGam-195
❑ 92DodStaTA-25
❑ 92Don-729
❑ 92Fle-244
❑ 92Hig5-90
❑ 92LaKdec-26
❑ 92Lea-217
❑ 92LeaBlaG-217
❑ 92OPC-430
❑ 92OPCPre-43
❑ 92PanSti-136
❑ 92Pin-328
❑ 92Sco-475
❑ 92ScoRoo-4T
❑ 92SpoStaCC-40
❑ 92StaClu-635
❑ 92StaCluNC-635
❑ 92Stu-157
❑ 92Top-430
❑ 92TopGol-430
❑ 92TopGolW-430
❑ 92TopKid-85
❑ 92TopMic-430
❑ 92TopTra-99T
❑ 92TopTraG-99T
❑ 92TriPlaG-GS4
❑ 92Ult-108
❑ 92Ult-341
❑ 92UppDec-358
❑ 92UppDec-743
❑ 92WhiSoxK-7
❑ 92YanWIZ8-172
❑ 92YanWIZA-75
❑ 93CadDis-53
❑ 93Don-123
❑ 93Fle-588
❑ 93Lea-107
❑ 93OPC-307
❑ 93PacSpa-395
❑ 93PanSti-137
❑ 93Pin-335
❑ 93Sco-418
❑ 93Sel-102
❑ 93StaClu-482
❑ 93StaCluFDI-482
❑ 93StaCluMOP-482
❑ 93Top-367
❑ 93TopGol-367
❑ 93TopInaM-367
❑ 93TopInaR-367
❑ 93TopMic-367
❑ 93TriPla-47
❑ 93Ult-179
❑ 93UppDec-369
❑ 93UppDecGold-369
❑ 93WhiSoxK-25
❑ 94Don-286
❑ 94Fle-94
❑ 94Lea-210
❑ 94Pac-137
❑ 94Sco-254
❑ 94ScoGolR-254
❑ 94StaCluT-128
❑ 94StaCluTFDI-128
❑ 94Top-662
❑ 94TopGol-662
❑ 94TopSpa-662
❑ 95DodROY-11

Sayers, Gale
❑ 68AtlOil-11

Sayers, Keith
❑ 95OdgRapTI-24
❑ 96OgdRapTI-NNO
❑ 98BelSnaM-28

Sayler, Barry
❑ 83St.PetCT-24

Sayles, Bill
❑ 90DodTar-707

Sayles, Steve
❑ 83MiaMarT-24

Saylor, Jamie
❑ 98JacGenM-20

Saylor, Ryan
❑ 97VerExpB-25
❑ 98CapFeaCM-21

Sbrocco, Jon
❑ 94CliLumC-21
❑ 94CliLumF-1989
❑ 96SanJosGB-3
❑ 97ShrCap-22
❑ 97ShrCapB-22

Scafa, Bob
❑ 93BazTeaU-17
❑ 93TopTra-120T
❑ 94YakBeaC-18
❑ 95BakBlaTI-19

Scaglione, Tony
❑ 88WatIndP-690
❑ 89KinIndS-22

Scala, Dominic
❑ 77ModA'sC-4

Scala, Jerry
❑ 50WorWidGV-28

Scales, George
❑ 78LauLonABS-26

Scales, Matthew
❑ 92LetMouSP-19

Scalzitti, Will
❑ 92BenRocCB-20
❑ 92BenRocF-1476
❑ 93CenValRC-21
❑ 93CenValRF-2895
❑ 93Top-476
❑ 93TopGol-476
❑ 93TopInaM-476
❑ 93TopInaR-476
❑ 93TopMic-476
❑ 94CenValRC-22
❑ 94CenValRF-3208
❑ 95NewHavRTI-15

Scanlan, Bob
❑ 86ClePhiP-22
❑ 87PhiTas-39B
❑ 87ReaPhiP-20
❑ 88MaiPhiC-9
❑ 88MaiPhiP-294
❑ 89ReaPhiB-8
❑ 89ReaPhiP-652
❑ 89ReaPhiS-21
❑ 90CMC-233
❑ 90ProAAAF-301
❑ 90ScrRedBC-7
❑ 90ScrRedBP-599
❑ 91CubMar-30
❑ 91IowCubLD-223
❑ 91IowCubP-1061
❑ 91Lea-520
❑ 91LinDriAAA-223
❑ 91ScoRoo-102T
❑ 91TopTra-105T
❑ 91TopTraT-105T
❑ 91UppDecFE-48F
❑ 92CubMar-30
❑ 92Don-474
❑ 92FleUpd-76
❑ 92Lea-437
❑ 92LeaBlaG-437
❑ 92OPC-274
❑ 92OPCPre-14
❑ 92Sco-285
❑ 92Sco100RS-59
❑ 92StaClu-112
❑ 92Top-274
❑ 92TopDeb91-157
❑ 92TopGol-274
❑ 92TopGolW-274
❑ 92TopMic-274
❑ 92Ult-473
❑ 93CubMar-23
❑ 93CubStaC-22
❑ 93Don-292
❑ 93Fle-26
❑ 93Lea-13
❑ 93OPC-325
❑ 93Pin-417
❑ 93Sco-361
❑ 93StaClu-444
❑ 93StaCluFDI-444
❑ 93StaCluMOP-444
❑ 93Top-47
❑ 93TopGol-47
❑ 93TopInaM-47
❑ 93TopInaR-47
❑ 93TopMic-47
❑ 93Ult-22
❑ 93UppDec-617
❑ 93UppDecGold-617
❑ 94BreMilB-351
❑ 94BrePol-23
❑ 94BreTeal-22
❑ 94Don-263
❑ 94Fin-310
❑ 94FinRef-310
❑ 94Fle-397
❑ 94FleUpd-57
❑ 94Top-451
❑ 94TopGol-451
❑ 94TopSpa-451
❑ 95Don-56
❑ 95DonPreP-56
❑ 95Fle-188

Scanlan, Doc (William)
❑ 10DomDisP-105A
❑ 10DomDisP-105B
❑ 10SweCapPP-76
❑ 11HelSta-151
❑ 11PinT-5-461
❑ 11S74Sil-55
❑ 11SpoLifM-163
❑ 11T205-147
❑ 12HasTriFT-43
❑ 12T207-160

Scanlin, Michael
❑ 87GasRanP-19
❑ 88TulDriTI-1

Scanlon, Ken
❑ 80AndBraT-23
❑ 81DurBulT-4
❑ 82DurBulT-7
❑ 83DurBulT-12

Scanlon, Pat (James P.)
❑ 75ExpPos-31
❑ 76SSP-332
❑ 77PadFamF-7
❑ 78Top-611

Scanlon, Steve
❑ 88VisOakCLC-161
❑ 88VisOakP-94

Scannell, Larry
❑ 87ElmPioBC-5
❑ 87ElmPioRC-5
❑ 88ElmPioC-24
❑ 89WinHavRSS-21

Scantlebury, Pat
❑ 60MapLeaSF-18
❑ 61MapLeaBH-20
❑ 86NegLeaF-35

Scarbery, Randy
❑ 77SanJosMC-18
❑ 80Top-291

Scarborough, Carey
❑ 75BurBeeT-24

Scarborough, Ray
❑ 47SenGunBP-10
❑ 49Bow-140
❑ 50Bow-108
❑ 50Dra-29
❑ 50RoyDes-14A
❑ 50RoyDes-14B
❑ 50RoyDes-14C
❑ 51Bow-39
❑ 51TopRedB-42
❑ 52Bow-140
❑ 52RoyPre-12
❑ 52TipTop-36
❑ 52Top-43
❑ 53Dor-108
❑ 53Top-213
❑ 67BalOriP-97
❑ 79DiaGre-72
❑ 79TCM50-208
❑ 83TopRep5-43
❑ 91TopArc1-213

Scarce, Bubba
❑ 98DanBraQ-2

Scarce, Mac
❑ 73OPC-6
❑ 73PhiTeal-18
❑ 73Top-6
❑ 74OPC-149
❑ 74Top-149
❑ 75OPC-527
❑ 75Top-527
❑ 75TopMin-527
❑ 76IndIndTI-22
❑ 77IndIndTI-15
❑ 91MetWIZ-346

Scarpace, Ken
❑ 81CedRapRT-17
❑ 82WatRedT-19

Scarpetta, Dan
❑ 83BelBreFr-25
❑ 87DenZepP-15
❑ 88ElPasDB-3
❑ 88TexLeaAGS-6
❑ 89SanAntMB-18

Scarpitti, Jeff
❑ 94EugEmeC-20
❑ 94EugEmeF-3712

Scarsella, Les
❑ 36GouWidPPR-D32
❑ 38RedOraW-24
❑ 39OrcPhoAP-20
❑ 39RedTeal-20
❑ 46RemBre-26
❑ 47RemBre-2
❑ 47SigOil-54
❑ 47SmiClo-3
❑ 48SigOil-20
❑ 48SmiClo-6
❑ 49BowPCL-25
❑ 49RemBre-25
❑ 77CinRedT-31

Scarsone, Steve (Stephen)
❑ 86BenPhiC-135
❑ 87ChaWheP-5
❑ 88ClePhiS-22
❑ 89EasLeaDDP-DD25
❑ 89ReaPhiB-4
❑ 89ReaPhiP-665
❑ 89ReaPhiS-22
❑ 89ReaPhiS-27
❑ 90ClePhiS-20
❑ 91LinDriAA-518
❑ 91ReaPhiLD-518
❑ 91ScrRedBP-2548
❑ 91TriA AAGP-AAA41
❑ 92DonRoo-108
❑ 92ScrRedBF-2455
❑ 92ScrRedBS-492
❑ 92SkyAAAF-222
❑ 92TriA AAS-492
❑ 93Don-381
❑ 93GiaStaC-21
❑ 94Fle-701
❑ 94GiaAMC-20
❑ 94GiaMot-9
❑ 94GiaTarBC-23
❑ 94GiaUSPC-4H
❑ 94GiaUSPC-11S
❑ 94Pac-555
❑ 94Sco-596
❑ 94ScoGolR-596
❑ 94StaClu-3
❑ 94StaCluFDI-3
❑ 94StaCluGR-3
❑ 94StaCluMOP-3
❑ 94StaCluT-9
❑ 94StaCluTFDI-9
❑ 94Top-729
❑ 94TopGol-729
❑ 94TopSpa-729
❑ 95Don-462
❑ 95DonPreP-462
❑ 95DonTopotO-357
❑ 95FleUpd-196
❑ 95GiaMot-13
❑ 95StaClu-603
❑ 95StaCluMOP-603
❑ 95StaCluSTWS-603
❑ 96ColCho-718
❑ 96ColChoGS-718
❑ 96ColChoSS-718
❑ 96Don-387
❑ 96DonPreP-387
❑ 96Fle-596
❑ 96FleTif-596
❑ 96GiaMot-18
❑ 96LeaSigA-203
❑ 96LeaSigAG-203
❑ 96LeaSigAS-203
❑ 96Ult-570
❑ 96UltGolM-570
❑ 97CarPol-23
❑ 97Pac-447
❑ 97PacLigB-447
❑ 97PacSil-447
❑ 98VanCanG-23

Scavo, Vinny
❑ 87PanAmTUBI-NNO
❑ 94BreCouMC-27
❑ 95BreCouMF-264

Schaaf, Bob
❑ 94YakBeaC-19
❑ 94YakBeaF-3860
❑ 95SanBerSTI-23
❑ 96VerBeaDB-26

Schaaf, Jim
❑ 64TopRooAB-20

Schaal, Paul
❑ 65Top-517
❑ 66AngDexP-14
❑ 66Top-376
❑ 67CokCapDA-21
❑ 67OPC-58
❑ 67Top-58A
❑ 67Top-58B
❑ 68Top-474

❑ 69MilBra-249
❑ 69MLBOffS-62
❑ 69Top-352
❑ 69TopSta-188
❑ 70MLBOffS-228
❑ 70OPC-338
❑ 70RoyTeal-31
❑ 70Top-338
❑ 71MLBOffS-429
❑ 71OPC-487
❑ 71Top-487
❑ 72MilBra-309
❑ 72OPC-177
❑ 72OPC-178
❑ 72oyTeal-22
❑ 72Top-177
❑ 72Top-178
❑ 73OPC-416
❑ 73Top-416
❑ 74OPC-514
❑ 74Top-514
❑ 86RoyGreT-4
Schacht, Al
❑ 22KolMotBPP-24
❑ 31SenTealPW-28
❑ 34DiaMatCSB-160
❑ 36GouWidPPR-A92
❑ 36NatChiFPR-98
❑ 36R31PasP-40
❑ 36WorWidGV-29
❑ 39PlaBal-113
❑ 40PlaBal-116
❑ 79RedSoxEF-15
❑ 87ConSer2-9
❑ 92ConTSN-559
❑ 93ConTSN-920
Schaefer, Bob
❑ 82TidTidT-22
❑ 84TidTidT-10
❑ 85IntLeaAT-1
❑ 85TidTidT-27
❑ 86GleFalTP-20
❑ 87MemChiB-1
❑ 87MemChiP-10
❑ 88RoySmo-2
❑ 88RoyTeal-28
❑ 91RoyPol-26
Schaefer, Chris
❑ 88CapCodPPaLP-31
❑ 89EugEmeB-1
❑ 90AppFoxBS-23
❑ 90AppFoxP-2093
Schaefer, Doug
❑ 79PhoGiaVNB-1
❑ 80PhoGiaVNB-3
❑ 81PhoGiaVNB-7
Schaefer, Germany (Herman)
❑ 07TigACDPP-13
❑ 08RosComP-40
❑ 09AmeCarE90-1-91
❑ 09RamT20-103
❑ 09T206-308
❑ 09T206-309
❑ 09TigMorBBBP-14
❑ 09TigMorPWBPP-11
❑ 09WolNewDTPP-15
❑ 09WolNewDTPP-16
❑ 10CouT21-217
❑ 10CouT21-218
❑ 10CouT21-219
❑ 10CouT21-315
❑ 10DomDisP-106
❑ 10E101-37
❑ 10E102-20
❑ 10MelMinE-37
❑ 10NadCarE-44
❑ 10PeoT21-46A
❑ 10PeoT21-46B
❑ 10RedCroT-66
❑ 10RedCroT-152
❑ 10RedCroT-153
❑ 10RedCroT-240
❑ 10SepAnoP-10
❑ 10SweCapPP-63
❑ 11HelSta-76
❑ 11PinT-5-560
❑ 11S74Sil-40
❑ 11SpoLifCW-311
❑ 11SpoLifM-132
❑ 11T205-148
❑ 12HasTriFT-58
❑ 12HasTriFT-59
❑ 12T207-161
❑ 14PieStaT-92
❑ 15AmeCarE106-34
❑ 15SpoNewM-154
❑ 16TanBraE-16
❑ 77GalGloG-167
❑ 81TigDetN-102
❑ 95ConTSN-1372
Schaefer, Jacob
❑ 88KimN18-39
Schaefer, Jeff
❑ 84RocRedWT-10
❑ 85ChaO'sT-12
❑ 85UtiBluST-14
❑ 86MidAngP-21
❑ 87SanAntDTI-1
❑ 88VanCanC-21
❑ 88VanCanP-753
❑ 89VanCanC-24
❑ 89WhiSoxC-25
❑ 90CalCanP-660
❑ 90FleUpd-120
❑ 90ProAAAF-125
❑ 90TopDeb89-109
❑ 91FleUpd-56
❑ 91MarCouH-2
❑ 91OPC-681
❑ 91Top-681
❑ 91TopDesS-681
❑ 91TopMic-681
❑ 91TopTif-681
❑ 92Don-525
❑ 92Lea-513
❑ 92LeaBlaG-513
❑ 92MarMot-24
❑ 92OPC-391
❑ 92Sco-629
❑ 92StaClu-108
❑ 93ChaKniF-552
Schaefer, Jim
❑ 80AshTouT-6
❑ 88RoySmo-2
Schaefer, Steve
❑ 79ElmPioRST-15
Schaeffer, Harry
❑ 78ReaRem-17
Schaeffer, Jon
❑ 98ForWayW!-11
Schaeffer, Mark
❑ 72PadPos-23
Schaeffer, Trevor
❑ 98DunBluJSB-20
Schafer, Bill
❑ 90SumBraB-18
❑ 90SumBraP-2430
Schafer, Brett
❑ 95SpoIndTI-27
❑ 96LanLugB-26
❑ 97LanLugTS-25
Schafer, Dennis
❑ 81CliGiaT-13
Schafer, George
❑ 09ObaT21-186
Schafer, Randy
❑ 79MemChiT-11
Schaffer, Jake
❑ 98LakTigM-18
Schaffer, Jim
❑ 61UniOil-P11
❑ 62Top-579
❑ 63Top-81
❑ 64Top-359
❑ 64TopVen-359
❑ 65Top-313
❑ 68Top-463
❑ 78TCM60I-152
❑ 78TCM60I-169
❑ 78TCM60I-184
❑ 79TulDriT-13
❑ 83RoyPos-26
❑ 84RoyPos-29
❑ 85RoyTeal-27
❑ 88RoyTeal-29
❑ 89HagSunB-10
❑ 89HagSunP-282
❑ 89HagSunS-22
❑ 91MetWIZ-347
❑ 93RanKee-318
Schaffer, John
❑ 86RedWinA-9
Schaffer, Trevor
❑ 97RocCub-28
❑ 98DunBluJTI-28
Schaffernoth, Joe
❑ 61Top-58
❑ 63Top-463
Schaffner, Eric
❑ 96GreBatB-25
❑ 97GreBatB-26
Schaffrath, Pam
❑ 95ColSilB-26
❑ 96ColSilB-24
Schaive, John
❑ 82BufBisT-6
❑ 83LynPirT-18
Schaive, John Sr.
❑ 61Top-259
❑ 62Top-529
❑ 63Top-356
Schalk, Ray
❑ 09ColChiE-251
❑ 09SpoNewSM-96
❑ 12ColRedB-251
❑ 12ColTinT-251
❑ 14CraJacE-61
❑ 15CraJacE-61
❑ 15SpoNewM-155
❑ 16BF2FP-18
❑ 16SpoNewM-154
❑ 17ColE13-150
❑ 17HolBreD-90
❑ 18WhiSoxTI-21
❑ 19W514-60
❑ 20W516-4
❑ 21E121So1-88A
❑ 21E121So1-88B
❑ 21E121So8-84
❑ 21Exh-151
❑ 21OxfConE-16
❑ 22AmeCarE122-59
❑ 22E120-27
❑ 22W572-89
❑ 22W573-113
❑ 22W575-115
❑ 22WilPatV-16
❑ 23MapCriV-3
❑ 23W501-43
❑ 23W515-51
❑ 25Exh-78
❑ 26Exh-78
❑ 26SpoComoA-37
❑ 27AmeCarE126-8
❑ 27Exh-40
❑ 27YorCarE-23
❑ 28W502-23
❑ 28Yue-23
❑ 30CubTeal-16
❑ 31CubTeal-20
❑ 36WorWidGV-124
❑ 50CalHOFW-64
❑ 53ArtHaloFP-75
❑ 60Fle-56
❑ 61Fle-136
❑ 74CapPub-47
❑ 75WhiSox1T-23
❑ 75WhiSox1T-24
❑ 76GrePlaG-24
❑ 76MotOldT-6
❑ 76ShaPiz-79
❑ 76WhiSoxTAG-10
❑ 77GalGloG-177
❑ 78DexHaloFP-44
❑ 80PacLeg-85
❑ 80PerHaloFP-78
❑ 80SSPHOF-78
❑ 80WhiSoxGT-9
❑ 85WhiSoxC-72
❑ 87ConSer2-55
❑ 88PacEigMO-43
❑ 88PacEigMO-45
❑ 88PacEigMO-50
❑ 88PacEigMO-51
❑ 88PacEigMO-52
❑ 88PacEigMO-100
❑ 89WhiSoxK-3
❑ 91ConTSN-48
❑ 92Man191BSR-22
❑ 93ConTSN-879
❑ 94ConTSN-1033
❑ 94ConTSNB-1033
❑ 94ConTSNCI-38
❑ 95ConTSN-1384
Schall, Gene
❑ 91BatCliCB-2
❑ 91BatCliP-3493
❑ 91FroRowDP-6
❑ 91FroRowDPG-6
❑ 91FroRowDPS-6
❑ 92ClaFS7-266
❑ 92SpaPhiF-1278
❑ 92StaCluD-165
❑ 93Bow-512
❑ 93PhiStaC-18
❑ 93ReaPhiF-304
❑ 94Bow-280
❑ 94Cla-113
❑ 94ExcFS7-248
❑ 94ScrRedBF-929
❑ 94Top-786
❑ 94TopGol-786
❑ 94TopSpa-786
❑ 94TriAAF-AAA44
❑ 94UppDecML-193
❑ 95Exc-247
❑ 95ScrRedBTI-24
❑ 95Top-79
❑ 95UppDecML-82
❑ 95UppDecMLFS-82
❑ 96ColCho-32
❑ 96ColChoGS-32
❑ 96ColChoSS-32
❑ 96Don-453
❑ 96DonPreP-453
❑ 96Fle-506
❑ 96FleTif-506
❑ 96ScrRedBB-23
❑ 96Ult-524
❑ 96UltGolM-524
❑ 97Pac-385
❑ 97PacLigB-385
❑ 97PacSil-385
❑ 97Pin-54
❑ 97PinArtP-PP54
❑ 97PinMusC-54
❑ 97PinPrePla-54
❑ 98RicBraQ-23
❑ 98ScrRedB1ATI-16
Schaller, Walter
❑ 13Zee-120
❑ 14Zee-119
❑ 15Zee-115
❑ 16Zee-117
❑ 17Zee-96
❑ 20Zee-54
Schallock, Art
❑ 49W72HolS-20
❑ 50W720HolS-28
❑ 56SeaPop-17
❑ 91OriCro-403
❑ 97BalOriP-45
Schammel, Bill
❑ 83MidCubT-1
Schang, Bobby
❑ 20Zee-75
❑ 21Zee-85
❑ 22Zee-71
❑ 23Zee-96
❑ 24Zee-70
❑ 25Zee-76
❑ 27MidBre-16
Schang, Wally (Walter H.)
❑ 14CraJacE-58
❑ 14FatPlaT-44
❑ 15CraJacE-58
❑ 15SpoNewM-156
❑ 16BF2FP-41
❑ 16FleBreD-81
❑ 16SpoNewM-155
❑ 17ColE13-151
❑ 17HolBreD-91
❑ 19W514-99
❑ 20GasAmeMBD-17
❑ 20NatCarE-87
❑ 21E121So1-89
❑ 21E121So8-85
❑ 21Exh-152
❑ 21Exh-157
❑ 21KoBreWSI-50
❑ 21Nei-20
❑ 22AmeCarE122-60
❑ 22E120-72
❑ 22W572-90
❑ 22W573-114
❑ 22W575-116
❑ 22WilPatV-11
❑ 23W501-27
❑ 23W503-2
❑ 23W515-17
❑ 23WilChoV-142
❑ 25Exh-101
❑ 28Exh-59
❑ 28StaPlaCE-58
❑ 29ExhFou-29
❑ 31Exh-24
❑ 67SpoHobFC-18
❑ 68SCFOldT-25
❑ 74A'sl92T-23
❑ 80BraTCM1-30
❑ 91ConTSN-249
❑ 92ConTSN-448
❑ 93ConTSN-872
❑ 94ConTSN-1231
❑ 94ConTSNB-1231
Schanz, Charley
❑ 50RedSoxTI-21
❑ 52MotCoo-41
❑ 53MotCoo-40
❑ 79DiaGre-311
❑ 83TCMPla1944-44
Schanz, Scott
❑ 91PenPilC-10
❑ 91PenPilP-376
❑ 92SanBerC-12
❑ 92SanBerSF-953
❑ 93JacSunF-2713
❑ 94JacSunF-1411
Schar, Art
❑ 35AlDemDCR3-48
Schardt, Bill (Wilbur)
❑ 09ColChiE-252A
❑ 09ColChiE-252B
❑ 12ColRedB-252A
❑ 12ColRedB-252B
❑ 12ColTinT-252A
❑ 12ColTinT-252B
❑ 12T207-162
❑ 90DodTar-708
Scharein, George
❑ 41PhiTeal-22
❑ 47SigOil-86
Scharff, Tony
❑ 91SouOreAC-19
❑ 91SouOreAP-3842
❑ 92MadMusC-24
Scharrer, Jim
❑ 95TopTra-126T
❑ 96AppLeaAB-14
❑ 96DanBraB-19
❑ 96Top-21
❑ 96TopPowB-21
❑ 97MacBra-12
❑ 98DanQ-C-16
Schattinger, Jeff
❑ 80OmaRoyP-22
❑ 81OmaRoyT-12
❑ 82EdmTraT-25
Schatz, Dan
❑ 87VisOakP-25
Schatzeder, Dan
❑ 77ExpPos-27
❑ 78ExpPos-13
❑ 78Top-709
❑ 79OPC-56
❑ 79Top-124
❑ 80OPC-140
❑ 80Top-267
❑ 81Don-248
❑ 81Fle-482
❑ 81OPC-112
❑ 81Top-417
❑ 82Don-385
❑ 82ExpPos-36
❑ 82Fle-281
❑ 82OPC-106
❑ 82Top-691
❑ 82TopTra-104T
❑ 83ExpPos-29
❑ 83ExpStu-22
❑ 83Fle-296
❑ 83OPC-189
❑ 83Top-189
❑ 84Don-132
❑ 84ExpPos-28
❑ 84ExpStu-7
❑ 84Fle-286
❑ 84Nes792-57
❑ 84OPC-57
❑ 84Top-57
❑ 84TopTif-57
❑ 85Don-543
❑ 85Fle-409
❑ 85Lea-59
❑ 85OPC-293
❑ 85Top-501
❑ 85TopMin-501
❑ 85TopTif-501
❑ 86ExpPos-13
❑ 86ExpProPa-12
❑ 86Fle-259
❑ 86OPC-324
❑ 86Top-324
❑ 86TopTif-324
❑ 87Don-482
❑ 87ExpPos-25
❑ 87Fle-186
❑ 87FleGlo-186
❑ 87OPC-168
❑ 87PhiTas-35
❑ 87Top-789
❑ 87TopTif-789
❑ 87TwiTeal-20
❑ 88Fle-21A
❑ 88Fle-21B
❑ 88FleGlo-21
❑ 88IndGat-31
❑ 88IndTeal-30
❑ 88StaLinTw-17
❑ 88Top-218
❑ 88TopClo-101
❑ 88TopTif-218
❑ 89AstLenH-9
❑ 89AstSmo-35
❑ 89FleUpd-90
❑ 89TucTorC-10
❑ 89TucTorJP-21
❑ 89TucTorP-198
❑ 90AstLenH-21
❑ 90AstMot-18
❑ 90Bow-69
❑ 90BowTif-69
❑ 90Don-594
❑ 90Fle-236
❑ 90FleCan-236
❑ 90Sco-418
❑ 91Don-497
❑ 91MetWIZ-348
Schaub, Greg
❑ 96HelBreTI-22
❑ 97BelSnaB-25
❑ 98StoPorG-26
Schauer, Rube (A.J.)
❑ 16FleBreD-82
Scheckla, Roddy
❑ 88AubAstP-1960
❑ 89AshTouP-946
Scheer, Greg
❑ 95EveAqaTI-20
❑ 96WisTimRB-19
Scheer, Ron
❑ 83WisRapTF-2
❑ 84VisOakT-21
❑ 86PenWhiSP-23
❑ 87PenWhiSP-17
Scheetz, Brian
❑ 90ButCopKSP-19
Scheetz, Rick
❑ 82WisRapTF-11
Scheffer, Aaron
❑ 95EveAqaTI-21
❑ 96WisTimRB-20
❑ 97LanJet-22
❑ 98LanJetG-22
Scheffer, Lawrence
❑ 95OdgRapTI-25
Scheffing, Bob
❑ 41CubTeal-22
❑ 42CubTeal-21
❑ 49Bow-83A
❑ 49Bow-83B
❑ 49EurSta-71
❑ 49Lea-160
❑ 50Bow-168
❑ 54Top-76
❑ 60BraLaktL-22
❑ 60BraSpiaS-20
❑ 60Top-464
❑ 61TigJayP-12
❑ 61Top-223
❑ 62TigJayP-11
❑ 62Top-72
❑ 62Top-416
❑ 62TopVen-72
❑ 63TigJayP-10
❑ 63Top-134
❑ 79DiaGre-114
❑ 85TCMPla1-29
❑ 94TopArc1-76
❑ 94TopArc1G-76
Scheffler, Craig
❑ 93GreFalDSP-9
❑ 94VerBeaDC-19
❑ 94VerBeaDF-70
❑ 94YakBeaC-20
❑ 94YakBeaF-3848
❑ 95BakBlaTI-20
❑ 96VerBeaDB-27
Scheffler, Jim
❑ 90PitMetP-21
❑ 91PitMetC-17
❑ 91PitMetP-3421
Schefsky, Steve
❑ 84BeaGolGT-13

❑ 85BeaGolGT-11
Scheib, Carl
❑ 47A'sTeal-27
❑ 48A'sTeal-21
❑ 49A'sTeal-28
❑ 49Bow-25
❑ 49OlmStu-7
❑ 49PhiBul-47
❑ 50A'sTeal-22
❑ 50Bow-213
❑ 51A'sTeal-28
❑ 51Bow-83
❑ 52A'sTeal-24
❑ 52Bow-46
❑ 52Top-116
❑ 53A'sTeal-27
❑ 53BowC-150
❑ 53Top-57
❑ 54A'STEAl-22
❑ 54Bow-67
❑ 54Top-118
❑ 60RawGloT-29
❑ 70Houof J-26
❑ 75TCMHouoJ-28
❑ 76TayBow4-109
❑ 79DiaGre-338
❑ 83TopRep5-116
❑ 85TCMPla1-44
❑ 91TopArc1-57
❑ 94TopArc1-118
❑ 94TopArc1G-118
Scheibe, Britton
❑ 92SpoIndC-3
❑ 92SpoIndF-1309
❑ 93SpoIndC-19
❑ 93SpoIndF-3605
Scheibeck, Frank
❑ 87OldJudN-432
Scheid, Rich
❑ 87Ft.LauYP-18
❑ 88PitCubP-1372
❑ 89IowCubC-9
❑ 89IowCubP-1713
❑ 90Bes-175
❑ 90BirBarB-22
❑ 90BirBarP-1110
❑ 91LinDriAAA-645
❑ 91VanCanLD-645
❑ 91VanCanP-1594
❑ 92VanCanF-2721
❑ 92VanCanS-647
❑ 93EdmTraF-1135
❑ 93Top-646
❑ 93TopGol-646
❑ 93TopInaM-646
❑ 93TopInaR-646
❑ 93TopMic-646
❑ 94EdmTraF-2876
❑ 94TriAAF-AAA30
❑ 95ChaKniTI-22
❑ 95FleUpd-99
Scheinblum, Richie
❑ 65Top-577
❑ 68OPC-16
❑ 68Top-16
❑ 68TopVen-16
❑ 69Top-479
❑ 70OPC-161
❑ 70Top-161
❑ 70WicAerM-15
❑ 71OPC-326
❑ 71Top-326
❑ 72OPC-468
❑ 72oyTeal-23
❑ 72Top-468
❑ 73OPC-78
❑ 73SevTraC-69
❑ 73Top-78
❑ 74OPC-323
❑ 74Top-323
❑ 74TopSta-148
Schell, Danny (Clyde)
❑ 55Top-79
❑ 55TopDouH-81
Scheller, Rod
❑ 77LodDodT-18
❑ 78LodDodT-17A
❑ 78LodDodT-17B
Schellhasse, Albert
❑ 87OldJudN-433
Schelzo, Phil
❑ 96VerExpB-6
❑ 97VerExpB-6
❑ 98VerExpO-5
Schemer, Mike
❑ 47SunBre-20
Schenbeck, Tom
❑ 92HelBreF-1715
❑ 92HelBreSP-22
❑ 93BelBreCB-22
❑ 93BelBreFl-1709
❑ 94StoPorC-25
❑ 94StoPorF-1695
Schenck, Bruce
❑ 91PocPioP-3781
❑ 91PocPioSP-6
Schenck, Larry
❑ 89GeoColC-27
❑ 90GeoColC-26
❑ 90GeoColC-33
Schenkle, William
❑ 87OldJudN-434
Schenz, Henry
❑ 50PirTeal-20
❑ 52MotCoo-30
Scherer, Doug
❑ 84ModA'sC-20
❑ 85ModA'sC-23
❑ 85TacTigC-141
❑ 86HunStaDJ-40
❑ 87HunStaTI-20
❑ 88KnoBluJB-11
Scherger, George
❑ 73OPC-296
❑ 73Top-296
❑ 74OPC-326
❑ 74Top-326
❑ 79NaSouTI-21
❑ 81WatRedT-22
❑ 82IndIndTI-2
❑ 84RedEnq-29
❑ 86RedTexG-NNO
Scherger, Joe
❑ 82AmaGolST-4
Scherman, Fred
❑ 71MLBOffS-406
❑ 71OPC-316
❑ 71Top-316
❑ 72OPC-6
❑ 72Top-6
❑ 73LinPor-78
❑ 73OPC-660
❑ 73TigJew-17
❑ 73Top-660
❑ 74OPC-186
❑ 74Top-186
❑ 74TopTra-186T
❑ 75AstPos-27
❑ 75ExpPos-32
❑ 75OPC-252
❑ 75SSP18-10
❑ 75Top-252
❑ 75TopMin-252
❑ 76ExpRed-28
❑ 76MonExpP-27
❑ 76OPC-188
❑ 76SSP-343
❑ 76Top-188
❑ 77ColCliT-20
❑ 87AstShoSTw-15
Scherrer, Bill
❑ 80WatRedT-7
❑ 81WatRedT-7
❑ 84Don-203
❑ 84Fle-482
❑ 84Nes792-373
❑ 84RedEnq-18
❑ 84Top-373
❑ 84TopSti-62
❑ 84TopTif-373
❑ 85Fle-22
❑ 85TigCaiD-17
❑ 85TigWen-19
❑ 85Top-586
❑ 85TopTif-586
❑ 86Don-516
❑ 86Fle-237
❑ 86Top-217
❑ 86TopTif-217
❑ 87Top-98
❑ 87TopTif-98
❑ 88RocRedWC-9
❑ 88RocRedWP-209
❑ 88RocRedWTI-20
❑ 89OklCit8C-3
❑ 89TidTidP-1955
❑ 91OriCro-404
Schesser, Heath
❑ 98WesMicWM-22
Schettler, Louis
❑ 11PinT-5-313
❑ 11SpoLifM-239
Scheuer, Chris
❑ 89AugPirP-520
Scheznayder, Wade
❑ 78QuaCitAT-23
❑ 81RedPioT-12
Schick, Maurice
❑ 19Zee-100
❑ 20Zee-114
❑ 21Zee-131
❑ 22Zee-88
Schiefelbein, Mike
❑ 92AriWilP-15
❑ 94EveGiaC-25
❑ 94EveGiaF-3653
❑ 95BelGiaTI-30
Schiel, Rob
❑ 90KenTwiB-13
❑ 90KenTwiP-2304
❑ 90KenTwiS-22
Schildknecht, Bill
❑ 87OldJudN-435
Schiller, Jon
❑ 89EveGiaS-25
Schilling, Chuck
❑ 47PM1StaP1-195
❑ 47PM1StaP1-196
❑ 61Top-499
❑ 62Baz-21
❑ 62Jel-56
❑ 62Pos-56
❑ 62PosCan-56
❑ 62RedSoxJP-9
❑ 62Top-345
❑ 62Top-467
❑ 62TopStal-18
❑ 63Top-52
❑ 64Top-182
❑ 64Top-481
❑ 64TopCoi-103
❑ 64TopVen-182
❑ 65OPC-272
❑ 65Top-272
❑ 66OPC-6
❑ 66Top-6
❑ 66TopVen-6
❑ 78TCM60I-183
❑ 81RedSoxBG2S-108
❑ 85TCMPhoC-21
Schilling, Curt
❑ 86ElmPioRSP-20
❑ 87GreHorP-2
❑ 88NewBriRSP-908
❑ 89BalOriP-29
❑ 89Don-635
❑ 89RocRedWC-7
❑ 89RocRedWP-1655
❑ 90Bow-246
❑ 90BowTif-246
❑ 90CMC-306
❑ 90Don-667
❑ 90FleUpd-68
❑ 90OPC-97
❑ 90ProAAAF-458
❑ 90RocRedWC-5
❑ 90RocRedWGC-14
❑ 90RocRedWP-701
❑ 90Sco-581
❑ 90Sco100RS-94
❑ 90Spo-133
❑ 90Top-97
❑ 90TopTif-97
❑ 91AstMot-15
❑ 91Bow-560
❑ 91Don-556
❑ 91Fle-491
❑ 91Lea-292
❑ 91OPC-569
❑ 91OriCro-405
❑ 91Sco-788
❑ 91ScoRoo-80T
❑ 91Stu-179
❑ 91Top-569
❑ 91TopDesS-569
❑ 91TopMic-569
❑ 91TopTif-569
❑ 91UppDec-528
❑ 92Don-757
❑ 92FleUpd-112
❑ 92Lea-516
❑ 92LeaBlaG-516
❑ 92OPC-316
❑ 92PhiMed-28
❑ 92Sco-671
❑ 92ScoRoo-25T
❑ 92SpollIFK1-721
❑ 92StaClu-279
❑ 92Top-316
❑ 92TopGol-316
❑ 92TopGolW-316
❑ 92TopMic-316
❑ 92TopTra-100T
❑ 92TopTraG-100T
❑ 92Ult-208
❑ 92Ult-548
❑ 93Bow-680
❑ 93Don-118
❑ 93Fin-10
❑ 93FinRef-10
❑ 93Fla-107
❑ 93Fle-108
❑ 93Lea-4
❑ 93OPC-354
❑ 93PacSpa-581
❑ 93PanSti-268
❑ 93PhiMed-31
❑ 93PhiStaC-14
❑ 93Pin-402
❑ 93Sco-52
❑ 93Sel-229
❑ 93SelStaL-65
❑ 93SP-178
❑ 93StaClu-422
❑ 93StaCluFDI-422
❑ 93StaCluMO-23
❑ 93StaCluMOP-422
❑ 93Stu-131
❑ 93Top-421
❑ 93TopComotH-25
❑ 93TopGol-421
❑ 93TopInaM-421
❑ 93TopInaR-421
❑ 93TopMic-421
❑ 93TriPla-129
❑ 93TriPla-230
❑ 93Ult-445
❑ 93UppDec-267
❑ 93UppDecGold-67
❑ 93USPlaCA-12S
❑ 94Bow-308
❑ 94ColC-253
❑ 94ColChoGS-253
❑ 94ColChoSS-253
❑ 94Don-577
❑ 94Fin-150
❑ 94FinRef-150
❑ 94Fla-417
❑ 94Fle-600
❑ 94FleExtB-341
❑ 94FleExtBPD-6
❑ 94FleSmo'nH-11
❑ 94FUnPac-38
❑ 94Lea-320
❑ 94OPC-66
❑ 94Pac-486
❑ 94PanSti-230
❑ 94PhiMed-30
❑ 94PhiMel-20
❑ 94PhiUSPC-7C
❑ 94PhiUSPC-12H
❑ 94Pin-105
❑ 94PinArtP-105
❑ 94PinMusC-105
❑ 94ProMag-105
❑ 94Sco-88
❑ 94ScoGolR-88
❑ 94Sel-161
❑ 94Spo-51
❑ 94StaClu-289
❑ 94StaCluFDI-289
❑ 94StaCluGR-289
❑ 94StaCluMOP-289
❑ 94StaCluT-229
❑ 94StaCluTFDI-229
❑ 94Top-142
❑ 94TopGol-142
❑ 94TopSpa-142
❑ 94TriPla-179
❑ 94Ult-554
❑ 94UppDec-460
❑ 94UppDecED-460
❑ 95ColCho-374
❑ 95ColChoGS-374
❑ 95ColChoSS-374
❑ 95Don-21
❑ 95DonPreP-21
❑ 95DonTopotO-309
❑ 95Emo-170
❑ 95Fla-395
❑ 95Fle-403
❑ 95Lea-205
❑ 95Phi-28
❑ 95PhiMel-20
❑ 95Pin-100
❑ 95PinArtP-100
❑ 95PinMusC-100
❑ 95Sco-163
❑ 95ScoGolR-163
❑ 95ScoPlaTS-163
❑ 95SP-91
❑ 95SPSil-91
❑ 95StaClu-4
❑ 95StaCluFDI-4
❑ 95StaCluMOP-4
❑ 95StaCluSTWS-4
❑ 95Top-297
❑ 95TopCyb-160
❑ 95Ult-209
❑ 95UltGolM-209
❑ 95UppDec-381
❑ 95UppDecED-381
❑ 95UppDecEDG-381
❑ 96Cir-169
❑ 96CirRav-169
❑ 96ColCho-672
❑ 96ColChoGS-672
❑ 96ColChoSS-672
❑ 96Don-309
❑ 96DonPreP-309
❑ 96EmoXL-249
❑ 96Fla-338
❑ 96Fle-507
❑ 96FleTif-507
❑ 96LeaSigA-204
❑ 96LeaSigAG-204
❑ 96LeaSigAS-204
❑ 96Sco-153
❑ 96StaClu-292
❑ 96StaCluMOP-292
❑ 96Top-128
❑ 96Ult-525
❑ 96UltGolM-525
❑ 97Bow-272
❑ 97BowChr-59
❑ 97BowChrI-59
❑ 97BowChrIR-59
❑ 97BowChrR-59
❑ 97BowInt-232
❑ 97Cir-338
❑ 97CirRav-338
❑ 97ColCho-197
❑ 97Don-306
❑ 97DonGolPP-306
❑ 97DonLim-114
❑ 97DonLimE-114
❑ 97DonLimENG-114
❑ 97DonSilPP-306
❑ 97Fin-104
❑ 97FinEmb-104
❑ 97FinEmbR-104
❑ 97FinRef-104
❑ 97FlaShoLC-138
❑ 97FlaShoLeg0-138
❑ 97FlaShoLeg1-138
❑ 97FlaShoM-A138
❑ 97FlaShoM-B138
❑ 97FlaShoM-C138
❑ 97FlaShoR0-138
❑ 97FlaShoR1-138
❑ 97FlaShoR2-138
❑ 97Fle-421
❑ 97Fle-741
❑ 97FleTeaL-24
❑ 97FleTif-421
❑ 97FleTif-741
❑ 97Lea-252
❑ 97LeaFraM-252
❑ 97LeaFraMDC-252
❑ 97MetUni-207
❑ 97Pac-386
❑ 97PacLigB-386
❑ 97PacSil-386
❑ 97PhiCopQ-25
❑ 97PhiCopQ-26
❑ 97PhiTeal-38
❑ 97Pin-9
❑ 97PinArtP-PP9
❑ 97PinMusC-9
❑ 97PinPrePla-9
❑ 97Sco-416
❑ 97ScoArtPWB-416
❑ 97ScoResC-416
❑ 97ScoShoS-416
❑ 97ScoShoSAP-416
❑ 97SP-137
❑ 97SpolII-91
❑ 97SpolIIEE-91
❑ 97StaClu-152
❑ 97StaCluMOP-152
❑ 97StrAll-56
❑ 97Top-368
❑ 97TopGal-54
❑ 97TopGalPPI-54
❑ 97TopSta-84
❑ 97TopStaAM-84
❑ 97Ult-256
❑ 97UltGolME-256
❑ 97UltPlaME-256
❑ 97UppDec-156
❑ 98Bow-51
❑ 98BowBes-94
❑ 98BowBesAR-94
❑ 98BowBesR-94
❑ 98BowChr-51
❑ 98BowChrGA-51
❑ 98BowChrGAR-51
❑ 98BowChrI-51
❑ 98BowChrIR-51
❑ 98BowChrR-51
❑ 98BowGolA-51
❑ 98BowInt-51
❑ 98CirThu-38
❑ 98CirThuRav-38
❑ 98CirThuSupRav-38
❑ 98ColCho-258
❑ 98ColCho-460
❑ 98ColChoS'-21
❑ 98ColChoSQ-SQ33
❑ 98CroRoy-107
❑ 98Don-123
❑ 98DonCol-123
❑ 98DonColL-284
❑ 98DonColP-638
❑ 98DonColS-123
❑ 98DonGolPP-123
❑ 98DonPre-88
❑ 98DonPreSeat-88
❑ 98DonPriCD-123
❑ 98DonPriCL-284
❑ 98DonPriCP-638
❑ 98DonSig-74
❑ 98DonSigA-78
❑ 98DonSigAC-100
❑ 98DonSigAM-102
❑ 98DonSigP-74
❑ 98DonSigSP-24
❑ 98DonSilPP-123
❑ 98E-X2-37
❑ 98E-X2ECFut-37
❑ 98E-X2ECNow-37
❑ 98Fin-99
❑ 98FinNo--99
❑ 98FinNo-R-99
❑ 98FinRef-99
❑ 98FlaShoLeg0-100
❑ 98FlaShoLeg1-100
❑ 98FlaShoLeg2-100
❑ 98FlaShoLeg3-100
❑ 98FlaShoLegM-100
❑ 98FlaShoR0-100
❑ 98FlaShoR1-100
❑ 98FlaShoR2-100
❑ 98FlaShoR3-100
❑ 98Fle-38
❑ 98Fle-309
❑ 98Fle-319
❑ 98Fle-596
❑ 98FleDiaS-18
❑ 98FlePowG-17
❑ 98FleVin'-46
❑ 98FleVin'C-46
❑ 98Lea-85
❑ 98LeaFraDA-85
❑ 98LeaFraF-85
❑ 98LeaFraM-85
❑ 98LeaFraM-85
❑ 98LeaFraMDC-85
❑ 98LeaFraMDC-85
❑ 98LeaFraMZ2-85
❑ 98LeaRS-88
❑ 98LeaRSLHolo-88
❑ 98LeaRSLong-88
❑ 98LeaRTrue-88
❑ 98MetUni-108
❑ 98MetUniPMG-108
❑ 98Pac-387
❑ 98PacAur-174
❑ 98PacInv-127
❑ 98PacInvPBlue-127
❑ 98PacInvSilv-127
❑ 98PacInvTeam-21
❑ 98PacOme-186
❑ 98PacOmeR-186
❑ 98PacOnl-572
❑ 98PacOnlR-572

❑ 98PacOnlWC-572
❑ 98PacPar-217
❑ 98PacParC-217
❑ 98PacParG-217
❑ 98PacParHS-217
❑ 98PacParI-10
❑ 98PacParPB-217
❑ 98PacParR-217
❑ 98PacPlaB-387
❑ 98PacRedT-387
❑ 98PacSil-387
❑ 98PacTeaC-24
❑ 98PhiTeal-31
❑ 98Pin-4
❑ 98PinArtP-PP4
❑ 98PinMusC-PP4
❑ 98PinPlu-81
❑ 98PinPreP-4
❑ 98Revo-112
❑ 98RevoSS-112
❑ 98ScoRT-85
❑ 98SkyDugA-35
❑ 98SkyDugAD-D5
❑ 98SkyDugAIA-35
❑ 98SP Aut-151
❑ 98SpoIII-111
❑ 98SpoIII-182
❑ 98SpoIIIEE-111
❑ 98SpoIIIEE-182
❑ 98SpoIIIFE-111
❑ 98SpoIIIFE-182
❑ 98SpoIIIODMP-OD22
❑ 98SpoIIITaN-130
❑ 98SpoIIITaNEE-130
❑ 98SpoIIIWSF-113
❑ 98SpoIIIWSFEE-113
❑ 98SpoIIIWSFFE-113
❑ 98SPxFin-115
❑ 98SPxFin-161
❑ 98SPxFin-214
❑ 98SPxFinR-115
❑ 98SPxFinR-161
❑ 98SPxFinR-214
❑ 98SPxFinS-115
❑ 98SPxFinS-161
❑ 98SPxFinS-214
❑ 98StaCluFDI-59
❑ 98StaCluI-59
❑ 98StaCluOneK-59
❑ 98StaCluPP-59
❑ 98Stu-152
❑ 98StuGPP-152
❑ 98StuSPP-152
❑ 98Top-332
❑ 98Top-476
❑ 98TopChr-332
❑ 98TopChr-476
❑ 98TopChrR-332
❑ 98TopChrR-476
❑ 98TopDevR-332
❑ 98TopDevR-476
❑ 98TopDia-332
❑ 98TopDia-476
❑ 98TopGal-127
❑ 98TopGalGP-127
❑ 98TopGalOPP-127
❑ 98TopGalPPI-127
❑ 98TopGalPPIA-127
❑ 98TopGolLabC1-62
❑ 98TopGolLabC1B-62
❑ 98TopGolLabC1One-62
❑ 98TopGolLabC1R-62
❑ 98TopGolLabC2-62
❑ 98TopGolLabC2B-62
❑ 98TopGolLabC2One-62
❑ 98TopGolLabC2R-62
❑ 98TopGolLabC3-62
❑ 98TopGolLabC3B-62
❑ 98TopGolLabC3One-62
❑ 98TopGolLabC3R-62
❑ 98TopMiniC-332
❑ 98TopMiniC-476
❑ 98TopOpeD-159
❑ 98TopSta-126
❑ 98TopStaB-126
❑ 98TopStaG-126
❑ 98TopStaGR-126
❑ 98TopStaS-126
❑ 98TopTek-32
❑ 98TopTekD-32
❑ 98UD3-88
❑ 98UD3-178
❑ 98UD3-268
❑ 98UD3DieCut-88
❑ 98UD3DieCut-178
❑ 98UD3DieCut-268
❑ 98Ult-82
❑ 98UltGolM-82
❑ 98UltMas-82
❑ 98UltPlaM-82
❑ 98UppDec-475
❑ 98UppDec-538
❑ 98UppDecR-75
❑ 98UppDecRTC-TC46
❑ 99199Fin-175
❑ 99Bow-24
❑ 99BowBes-28
❑ 99BowBesAR-28
❑ 99BowBesR-28
❑ 99BowChr-24
❑ 99BowChrG-24
❑ 99BowChrGR-24
❑ 99BowChrI-24
❑ 99BowChrIR-24
❑ 99BowChrR-24
❑ 99BowGol-24
❑ 99BowInt-24
❑ 99CroRoyB-108
❑ 99CroRoyL-108
❑ 99CroRoyOD-108
❑ 99E-X Cen-69
❑ 99E-X CenECFut-69
❑ 99E-X CenECNow-69
❑ 99FinGolRef-175
❑ 99FinRef-175
❑ 99FlaShoLeg1-100
❑ 99FlaShoLeg2-100
❑ 99FlaShoLeg3-100
❑ 99FlaShoLegM1-100
❑ 99FlaShoLegM2-100
❑ 99FlaShoLegM3-100
❑ 99FlaShoR1-100
❑ 99FlaShoR2-100
❑ 99FlaShoR3-100
❑ 99Fle-270
❑ 99FleBri-98
❑ 99FleBri2G-98
❑ 99FleBriBlu-98
❑ 99FleBriGol-98
❑ 99FleMys-44
❑ 99FleMysG-44
❑ 99FleMysM-44
❑ 99FleSta9-270
❑ 99FleWarT-270
❑ 99MetUni-223
❑ 99MetUniGM-223
❑ 99MetUniPMG-223
❑ 99Pac-333
❑ 99PacAur-144
❑ 99PacAurOD-144
❑ 99PacCroC-215
❑ 99PacCroCPB-215
❑ 99PacInv-113
❑ 99PacInvOD-113
❑ 99PacInvPB-113
❑ 99PacOme-183
❑ 99PacOmeC-183
❑ 99PacOmeG-183
❑ 99PacOmePB-183
❑ 99PacPar-182
❑ 99PacParC-182
❑ 99PacParG-182
❑ 99PacParHoloGold-182
❑ 99PacParHS-182
❑ 99PacParOD-182
❑ 99PacParPB-182
❑ 99PacParRed-182
❑ 99PacPlaB-333
❑ 99PacPri-110
❑ 99PacPriHB-110
❑ 99PacPriHG-110
❑ 99PacPriHM-110
❑ 99PacPriHP-110
❑ 99PacPriRed-110
❑ 99PacPriS-135
❑ 99PacPriS206-135
❑ 99PacPriS206R-135
❑ 99PacRed-333
❑ 99Pin-24
❑ 99Rev-109
❑ 99RevPremDate-109
❑ 99RevRet-109
❑ 99RevShaSS-109
❑ 99SkyMolM-27
❑ 99SkyMolMX-27
❑ 99SkyPre-20
❑ 99SkyPreA-49
❑ 99SkyPreABlue-49
❑ 99SkyPreR-20
❑ 99SkyThu-287
❑ 99SkyThuRant-287
❑ 99SkyThuRave-287
❑ 99SP Aut-65
❑ 99SpoIII-15
❑ 99SpoIII-40
❑ 99SpoIII-155
❑ 99SPxStaF-SF21
❑ 99StaClu-180
❑ 99StaCluFDI-180
❑ 99StaCluOoaK-180
❑ 99StaCluPP-180
❑ 99ThuSkySupR-287
❑ 99Top-385
❑ 99Top-447
❑ 99TopAll-AM26
❑ 99TopBlaLC1-51
❑ 99TopBlaLC2-51
❑ 99TopBlaLC3-51
❑ 99TopChr-385
❑ 99TopChr-447
❑ 99TopChrA-AE26
❑ 99TopChrAR-AE26
❑ 99TopChrR-385
❑ 99TopChrR-447
❑ 99TopGal-70
❑ 99TopGalPP-70
❑ 99TopGalPPI-70
❑ 99TopGolL-51
❑ 99TopGolLC1-51
❑ 99TopGolLC2-51
❑ 99TopGolLOtO-51
❑ 99TopMVPP-385
❑ 99TopMVPP-447
❑ 99TopOpeD-134
❑ 99TopRecN-RN3
❑ 99TopRecNG-RN3
❑ 99TopRedLC1-51
❑ 99TopRedLC2-51
❑ 99TopRedLC3-51
❑ 99TopSta-104
❑ 99TopStaFoil-104
❑ 99UD ChoS-29
❑ 99UD ChoSD-29
❑ 99UD ChoSHR-29
❑ 99UD ChoST-29
❑ 99UD Ion-47
❑ 99UD IonR-47
❑ 99Ult-172
❑ 99UltGolM-172
❑ 99UltMas-172
❑ 99UltPlaM-172
❑ 99UppDec-451
❑ 99UppDec-535
❑ 99UppDecCL-73
❑ 99UppDecCLCC-73
❑ 99UppDecCLM-C71
❑ 99UppDecE-68
❑ 99UppDecEFXG-68
❑ 99UppDecEL1-535
❑ 99UppDecEL2-451
❑ 99UppDecEL2-535
❑ 99UppDecM-155
❑ 99UppDecMGS-155
❑ 99UppDecMHFS-155
❑ 99UppDecMP-155
❑ 99UppDecMSS-155
❑ 99UppDecO-26
❑ 99UppDecOSO-26
❑ 99UppDecR-65
❑ 99UppDecRG-65
❑ 99UppDecRP-65
❑ 99Vic-300
Schilling, Jarrett
❑ 85CloHSS-38
Schimdt, Eric
❑ 77CliDodT-22
❑ 88ColCliC-8
Schimming, Mark
❑ 84IowCubT-13
Schimpf, Rex
❑ 82DayBeaAT-7
❑ 83DayBeaAT-11
Schinkle, Adolph
❑ 17Zee-76
Schino, Stanley
❑ 29Zee-142
❑ 30Zee-95
❑ 31Zee-54
Schiraldi, Calvin
❑ 84JacMetT-4
❑ 85Don-38
❑ 85FleUpd-99
❑ 85MetTCM-16
❑ 85TidTidT-5
❑ 86Don-652
❑ 86PawRedSP-20
❑ 86SpoRoo-44
❑ 86Top-210
❑ 86TopTif-210
❑ 87Don-641
❑ 87Fle-44
❑ 87FleGlo-44
❑ 87Lea-137
❑ 87RedSoxP-19
❑ 87SpoTeaP-9
❑ 87Top-94
❑ 87TopTif-94
❑ 87Woo-20
❑ 88CubDavB-32
❑ 88Don-375
❑ 88DonBasB-194
❑ 88DonTeaBC-NEW
❑ 88Fle-365
❑ 88FleGlo-365
❑ 88OPC-62
❑ 88Sco-218
❑ 88ScoGlo-218
❑ 88ScoRoo-39T
❑ 88ScoRooG-39T
❑ 88StaLinCu-12
❑ 88Top-599
❑ 88TopTif-599
❑ 88TopTra-104T
❑ 88TopTraT-104T
❑ 89CubMar-32
❑ 89Don-285
❑ 89DonBasB-82
❑ 89Fle-438
❑ 89FleGlo-438
❑ 89OPC-337
❑ 89Sco-321
❑ 89Top-337
❑ 89TopSti-56
❑ 89TopTif-337
❑ 89UppDec-82
❑ 90Don-672
❑ 90Fle-168
❑ 90FleCan-168
❑ 90OPC-693
❑ 90PadCok-17
❑ 90PadMag-13
❑ 90PublntS-203
❑ 90Top-693
❑ 90TopTif-693
❑ 90UppDec-643
❑ 91Don-308
❑ 91Fle-543
❑ 91LinDriAAA-610
❑ 91MetWIZ-349
❑ 91OPC-424
❑ 91PadMag-15A
❑ 91Sco-611
❑ 91Top-424
❑ 91TopDesS-424
❑ 91TopMic-424
❑ 91TopTif-424
❑ 91TucTorLD-610
❑ 91TucTorP-2212
❑ 92TexLon-36
❑ 93RanKee-319
Schirm, George
❑ 08BufBisFJO-15
❑ 09ColChiE-254A
❑ 09ColChiE-254B
❑ 09T206-462
❑ 12ColRedB-254A
❑ 12ColRedB-254B
❑ 12ColTinT-254A
❑ 12ColTinT-254B
❑ 12ImpTobC-29
❑ 13Zee-49
Schlafly, Harry
❑ 09ColChiE-255
❑ 09T206-463
❑ 12ColRedB-255
❑ 12ColTinT-255
Schlei, Admiral (George)
❑ 08RosComP-181
❑ 09BriE97-27
❑ 09RamT20-105
❑ 09T206-310
❑ 09T206-311
❑ 09T206-312
❑ 10CouT21-220
❑ 10CouT21-221
❑ 10E101-38
❑ 10MelMinE-38
❑ 10NadCarE-45
❑ 10NadE1-50
❑ 10PeoT21-47
❑ 11PinT-5-263
❑ 11S74Sil-94
❑ 11SpoLifCW-312
❑ 11SpoLifM-217
❑ 11T205-149
❑ 11TurRedT-115
Schleighoffer, Mike
❑ 86AlbDukP-21
Schlesinger, Bill
❑ 65Top-573
❑ 68Top-258
❑ 68TopVen-258
Schley, Van
❑ 88SalLakCTTI-16
❑ 89SalLakTTI-18
Schlicher, B.J.
❑ 96AppLeaAB-26
❑ 96MarPhiB-22
Schlichting, John
❑ 85VerBeaDT-3
❑ 86VerBeaDP-21
Schlitzer, Victor
❑ 09AmeCarE90-1-92
Schlomann, Brett
❑ 95GreBatTI-21
❑ 96TamYanY-22
❑ 97TamYan-25
❑ 98NorNavQ-21
Schlopy, Butch
❑ 86WatPirP-22
❑ 88AugPirP-374
❑ 89SalBucS-19
❑ 90SalBucS-19
Schloss, M.
❑ 88KimN18-40
Schlutt, Jason
❑ 93SpoIndC-20
❑ 93SpoIndF-3591
❑ 94SprSulC-21
❑ 94SprSulF-2035
❑ 95RanCucQT-27
❑ 97St.PauS-26
Schlyder, Brett
❑ 95AusFut-54
Schmack, Brian
❑ 96HicCraB-21
❑ 98WinWar-25
Schmakel, Jim
❑ 84TigWavP-31
Schmaltz, Darin
❑ 97YakBeaG-31
Schmandt, Ray
❑ 20NatCarE-88
❑ 22E120-148
❑ 22W573-115
❑ 23WilChoV-143
❑ 90DodTar-1062
Schmees, George
❑ 50W720HolS-29
❑ 50WorWidGV-20
❑ 52Bow-245
❑ 53MotCoo-13
❑ 54SeaPop-22
❑ 55SeaPop-17
Schmelz, Al
❑ 91MetWIZ-350
Schmelz, Heinrich
❑ 87OldJudN-436
Schmid, Michael
❑ 82BurRanF-18
❑ 82BurRanT-8
Schmidt, Augie
❑ 83KnoBluJT-12
❑ 84SyrChiT-8
❑ 85PhoGiaC-194
Schmidt, Bill
❑ 40SolHug-17
❑ 91OneYanP-4170
❑ 92OneYanC-28
❑ 93OneYanC-28
❑ 93OneYanF-3523
Schmidt, Bob (Robert B.)
❑ 58GiaJayP-10
❑ 58GiaSFCB-21
❑ 58Top-468
❑ 59Top-109
❑ 59TopVen-109
❑ 60GiaJayP-12
❑ 60Top-501
❑ 61GiaJayP-12
❑ 61Pos-151
❑ 61Top-31
❑ 62SalPlaC-179
❑ 62ShiPlaC-179
❑ 62Top-262
❑ 63Top-94
❑ 65Top-582
❑ 66TolMudHTI-21
❑ 79TCM50-246
❑ 80Red196T-24
❑ 84GiaMot-14
❑ 92YanWIZ6-109
Schmidt, Boss (Charles)
❑ 07TigACDPP-14
❑ 08RosComP-41
❑ 09T206-313
❑ 09T206-314
❑ 09TigMorPWBPP-12
❑ 09TigTaCP-15
❑ 09WolNewDTPP-17
❑ 10CouT21-59
❑ 10CouT21-222
❑ 10DomDisP-107
❑ 10E101-39
❑ 10E102-21
❑ 10MelMinE-39
❑ 10NadCarE-46
❑ 10PeoT21-48
❑ 10SweCapPP-30A
❑ 10SweCapPP-30B
❑ 11HelSta-36
❑ 11PinT-5-157
❑ 11PinT-5-175
❑ 11PloCanE-56
❑ 11SpoLifCW-313
❑ 11SpoLifM-68
❑ 11T205-150
❑ 11TurRedT-116
❑ 15SpoNewM-157
❑ 23Lec-8
❑ 72ClaCar-59
Schmidt, Butcher (Charles John)
❑ 12ImpTobC-12
❑ 14CraJacE-127
❑ 15CraJacE-127
❑ 80BraTCM1-20
Schmidt, Curtis
❑ 92JamExpC-18
❑ 92JamExpF-1502
❑ 93WesPalBEC-21
❑ 93WesPalBEF-1339
❑ 94HarSenF-2090
Schmidt, Dave
❑ 96NewJerCB-24
Schmidt, Dave (David F.)
❑ 80TulDriT-22
❑ 82Top-418
❑ 87FleUpdG-107
❑ 91OPC-136
❑ 98DelShoM-3
Schmidt, Dave (David J.)
❑ 80AshTouT-25
❑ 83Don-321
❑ 83Fle-578
❑ 83RanAffF-24
❑ 83Top-116
❑ 84Don-586
❑ 84Fle-427
❑ 84Nes792-584
❑ 84RanJarP-24
❑ 84Top-584
❑ 84TopTif-584
❑ 85Don-586
❑ 85Fle-567
❑ 85OPC-313
❑ 85RanPer-24
❑ 85Top-313
❑ 85TopMin-313
❑ 85TopTif-313
❑ 86Don-378
❑ 86Fle-571
❑ 86FleUpd-103
❑ 86OPC-79
❑ 86Top-79
❑ 86TopTif-79
❑ 86TopTra-99T
❑ 86TopTraT-99T
❑ 86WhiSoxC-24
❑ 87BalOriP-33
❑ 87Don-182
❑ 87Fle-505
❑ 87FleGlo-505
❑ 87FleUpd-107
❑ 87OPC-372
❑ 87OriFreB-24
❑ 87Top-703
❑ 87TopTif-703
❑ 87TopTra-110T
❑ 87TopTraT-110T

❑ 88Don-371
❑ 88DonBasB-333
❑ 88Fle-571
❑ 88FleGlo-571
❑ 88FleMin-2
❑ 88OPC-214
❑ 88OriFreB-24
❑ 88OriPos-31
❑ 88PanSti-6
❑ 88Sco-103
❑ 88ScoGlo-103
❑ 88StaLinO-14
❑ 88Top-214
❑ 88TopSti-226
❑ 88TopTif-214
❑ 89BalOriP-30
❑ 89Bow-5
❑ 89BowTif-5
❑ 89Don-13
❑ 89Don-215
❑ 89DonSupD-13
❑ 89Fle-618
❑ 89FleGlo-618
❑ 89OPC-231
❑ 89OriFreB-24
❑ 89PanSti-255
❑ 89Sco-292
❑ 89Top-677
❑ 89TopBig-130
❑ 89TopTif-677
❑ 89UppDec-447
❑ 90Bow-110
❑ 90BowTif-110
❑ 90Don-524
❑ 90ExpPos-33
❑ 90Fle-188
❑ 90FleCan-188
❑ 90FleUpd-32
❑ 90Lea-457
❑ 90OPC-497
❑ 90PublntS-585
❑ 90Sco-30
❑ 90Top-497
❑ 90TopTif-497
❑ 90TopTra-112T
❑ 90TopTraT-112T
❑ 90UppDec-641
❑ 91Fle-249
❑ 91OriCro-406
❑ 91Sco-156
❑ 91Top-136
❑ 91TopDesS-136
❑ 91TopMic-136
❑ 91TopTif-136
❑ 91UppDec-684
❑ 92CalCanS-70
❑ 93LynRedSF-2526
❑ 93RanKee-320

Schmidt, Dave B.
❑ 98ArkTraM-24

Schmidt, David M.
❑ 92WinHavRSC-4
❑ 92WinHavRSF-1787

Schmidt, Donnie
❑ 96PorRocB-26
❑ 97PorRocG-24
❑ 98WisTimRM-9

Schmidt, Eric
❑ 78LodDodT-18
❑ 79CliDodT-12
❑ 86AlbYanT-21
❑ 87AlbYanP-4
❑ 88ColCliP-9
❑ 88ColCliP-313

Schmidt, Fred
❑ 83Car194T-56

Schmidt, George
❑ 98FarRedHM-28

Schmidt, Gregg
❑ 86Ft.MyeRP-24

Schmidt, Haven
❑ 58RedEnq-34

Schmidt, Henry M.
❑ 90DodTar-1063

Schmidt, J.D.
❑ 89BoiHawP-1978

Schmidt, Jason
❑ 92ClaFS7-260
❑ 92MacBraC-25
❑ 92MacBraF-267
❑ 93ClaFS7-22
❑ 93DurBulC-17
❑ 93DurBulF-485
❑ 93DurBulTI-29
❑ 94GreBraF-411
❑ 94GreBraTI-20
❑ 94TopTra-56T
❑ 94UppDecML-67
❑ 95Bow-194
❑ 95BowBes-B31
❑ 95BowBesR-B31
❑ 95Fla-329
❑ 95FleUpd-93
❑ 95RicBraRC-22
❑ 95RicBraTI-20
❑ 95SigRoo-44
❑ 95SigRooSig-44
❑ 96Bow-53
❑ 96BowFoi-53
❑ 96BraFle-15
❑ 96ColCho-48
❑ 96ColChoGS-48
❑ 96ColChoSS-48
❑ 96EmoXL-148
❑ 96Fin-B268
❑ 96FinRef-B268
❑ 96Fla-209
❑ 96Fle-307
❑ 96FleTif-307
❑ 96Lea-213
❑ 96LeaPre-126
❑ 96LeaPreP-126
❑ 96LeaPrePB-213
❑ 96LeaPrePG-213
❑ 96LeaPrePS-213
❑ 96LeaSigA-205
❑ 96LeaSigAG-205
❑ 96LeaSigAS-205
❑ 96Pin-371
❑ 96PinAfi-162
❑ 96PinAfiAP-162
❑ 96PinChrBC-9
❑ 96PinFoil-371
❑ 96RicBraB-24
❑ 96RicBraUB-24
❑ 96Sco-228
❑ 96Sel-164
❑ 96SelArtP-164
❑ 96SelCer-110
❑ 96SelCerAP-110
❑ 96SelCerCB-110
❑ 96SelCerCR-110
❑ 96SelCerMB-110
❑ 96SelCerMG-110
❑ 96SelCerMR-110
❑ 96SP-20
❑ 96Spo-138
❑ 96SpoArtP-138
❑ 96SpoRooJ-1
❑ 96StaClu-112
❑ 96StaCluMOP-112
❑ 96Stu-127
❑ 96StuPrePB-127
❑ 96StuPrePG-127
❑ 96StuPrePS-127
❑ 96Sum-184
❑ 96SumAbo&B-184
❑ 96SumArtP-184
❑ 96SumFoi-184
❑ 96TopLasBS-6
❑ 96Ult-445
❑ 96UltGolM-445
❑ 96UppDec-250
❑ 96UppDecBCP-BC16
❑ 96Zen-116
❑ 96ZenArtP-116
❑ 97Cir-203
❑ 97CirRav-203
❑ 97ColCho-463
❑ 97Fle-436
❑ 97FleTif-436
❑ 97PirPos-33
❑ 97Sco-446
❑ 97ScoArtPWB-446
❑ 97ScoResC-446
❑ 97ScoShoS-446
❑ 97ScoShoSAP-446
❑ 97SP-144
❑ 97Top-383
❑ 97Ult-414
❑ 97UltGolME-414
❑ 97UltPlaME-414
❑ 97UppDec-463
❑ 98CirThu-104
❑ 98CirThuRav-104
❑ 98CirThuSupRav-104
❑ 98ColCho-214
❑ 98CroRoy-110
❑ 98Fle-91
❑ 98PacOnl-593
❑ 98PacOnlR-593
❑ 98PacOnlWC-593
❑ 98Revo-115
❑ 98RevoSS-115
❑ 98SP Aut-156
❑ 98SPxFin-116
❑ 98SPxFinR-116
❑ 98SPxFinS-116
❑ 98StaCluFDI-96
❑ 98StaCluFDI-309
❑ 98StaCluI-96
❑ 98StaCluI-309
❑ 98StaCluOneK-96
❑ 98StaCluOneK-309
❑ 98StaCluPP-96
❑ 98StaCluPP-309
❑ 98Top-445
❑ 98TopChr-445
❑ 98TopChrR-445
❑ 98TopDevR-445
❑ 98TopDia-445
❑ 98TopMiniC-445
❑ 98UppDec-484
❑ 99199Fin-164
❑ 99FinGolRef-164
❑ 99FinRef-164
❑ 99Fle-256
❑ 99FleSta9-256
❑ 99FleWarT-256
❑ 99MetUni-124
❑ 99MetUniGM-124
❑ 99MetUniPMG-124
❑ 99Pac-346
❑ 99PacPlaB-346
❑ 99PacRed-346
❑ 99SkyMolMOA-17
❑ 99SkyPre-218
❑ 99SkyPreR-218
❑ 99SkyThu-175
❑ 99SkyThuRant-175
❑ 99SkyThuRave-175
❑ 99StaClu-99
❑ 99StaCluFDI-99
❑ 99StaCluOoaK-99
❑ 99StaCluPP-99
❑ 99ThuSkySupR-175
❑ 99Top-168
❑ 99TopChr-168
❑ 99TopChrR-168
❑ 99TopMVPP-168
❑ 99Ult-120
❑ 99UltGolM-120
❑ 99UltMas-120
❑ 99UltPlaM-120
❑ 99UppDec-179
❑ 99UppDecEL1-179
❑ 99UppDecEL2-179

Schmidt, Jeff
❑ 92BoiHawC-27
❑ 92BoiHawF-3625
❑ 92ClaDraP-21
❑ 92ClaFS7-413
❑ 92FroRowDP-57
❑ 92FroRowDPG-57
❑ 92FroRowDPS-57
❑ 93CedRapKC-15
❑ 93CedRapKF-1734
❑ 93Pin-469
❑ 93Sco-501
❑ 93StaCluM-113
❑ 94ClaGolF-99
❑ 94LakElsSC-15
❑ 94LakElsSF-1661
❑ 95MidAngOHP-30
❑ 95MidAngTI-25
❑ 96VanCanB-25
❑ 97Fle-51
❑ 97FleTif-51
❑ 97PacPriGotD-GD7
❑ 97Ult-31
❑ 97UltGolME-31
❑ 97UltPlaME-31
❑ 97VanCanB-25
❑ 98VanCanG-24

Schmidt, Keith
❑ 89BluOriS-20
❑ 90WauTimB-27
❑ 90WauTimP-2141
❑ 90WauTimS-21
❑ 91Cla/Bes-59
❑ 91KanCouCC-25
❑ 91KanCouCP-2673
❑ 92KanCouCC-15
❑ 92KanCouCF-107
❑ 92KanCouCTI-28
❑ 93AlbPolF-2039
❑ 94DurBulC-16
❑ 94DurBulF-341
❑ 94DurBulTI-17

Schmidt, Mike
❑ 73OPC-615
❑ 73PhiTeal-19
❑ 73Top-615
❑ 74OPC-283
❑ 74PhiJohP-20
❑ 74Top-283
❑ 75Hos-133
❑ 75Kel-56
❑ 75OPC-70
❑ 75OPC-307
❑ 75PhiPhiP-26
❑ 75PhiProPS-14
❑ 75Top-70
❑ 75Top-307
❑ 75TopMin-70
❑ 75TopMin-307
❑ 76BlaDis-54
❑ 76BucDis-54
❑ 76CarDis-54
❑ 76CraDis-54
❑ 76DailsID-54
❑ 76Hos-84
❑ 76IsaDis-54
❑ 76OPC-193
❑ 76OPC-480
❑ 76OrbDis-54
❑ 76PhiPhiP-25
❑ 76RedBarD-54
❑ 76SafDis-54
❑ 76SSP-470
❑ 76Top-193
❑ 76Top-480
❑ 76TowCluD-54
❑ 77BurCheD-168
❑ 77ChiWilD-60
❑ 77DailsID-60
❑ 77DetCaeD-60
❑ 77HolInnD-60
❑ 77Hos-43
❑ 77MSADis-60
❑ 77OPC-2
❑ 77OPC-245
❑ 77PepGloD-70
❑ 77RCColC-58
❑ 77SagDis-60
❑ 77sDis-60
❑ 77Spo-3402
❑ 77Spo-8124
❑ 77Top-2
❑ 77Top-140
❑ 77TopCloS-41
❑ 77WenDis-60
❑ 77ZipDis-60
❑ 78Hos-113
❑ 78Kel-3
❑ 78OPC-225
❑ 78RCColC-18
❑ 78SSP270-46
❑ 78Top-360
❑ 78WifBalD-67
❑ 79BasPat-78
❑ 79Hos-9
❑ 79OPC-323
❑ 79PhiBurK-16
❑ 79PhiTeal-9
❑ 79Top-610
❑ 80Kel-2
❑ 80OPC-141
❑ 80PerHaloFP-223
❑ 80PerHaloFPS-80
❑ 80PhiBurK-6
❑ 80Top-270
❑ 80TopSup-2
❑ 81AllGamPI-126
❑ 81CokTeaS-105
❑ 81Don-11
❑ 81Don-590
❑ 81Dra-7
❑ 81Fle-5
❑ 81Fle-640
❑ 81Fle-640B
❑ 81Fle-645
❑ 81Fle-645B
❑ 81FleStiC-9
❑ 81FleStiC-43
❑ 81FleStiC-128
❑ 81Kel-5
❑ 81MSAMinD-28
❑ 81OPC-207
❑ 81PerAll-8
❑ 81PerCreC-2
❑ 81Squ-8
❑ 81Top-2
❑ 81Top-3
❑ 81Top-206
❑ 81Top-540
❑ 81TopScr-60
❑ 81TopSti-19
❑ 81TopSti-21
❑ 81TopSti-199
❑ 81TopSti-254
❑ 81TopSupHT-88
❑ 81TopSupN-13
❑ 82Don-294
❑ 82Don-585
❑ 82Dra-29
❑ 82FBIDis-22
❑ 82Fle-258
❑ 82Fle-637
❑ 82Fle-641
❑ 82FleSta-53
❑ 82K-M-39
❑ 82K-M-41
❑ 82Kel-16
❑ 82MonNew-14
❑ 82OnDecD-28
❑ 82OPC-100
❑ 82OPC-101
❑ 82OPC-339
❑ 82PerAll-17
❑ 82PerAllG-17
❑ 82PerCreC-3
❑ 82PerCreCG-3
❑ 82SevSluC-24
❑ 82Squ-14
❑ 82Top-100
❑ 82Top-101
❑ 82Top-162
❑ 82Top-163
❑ 82Top-339
❑ 82TopSti-3
❑ 82TopSti-5
❑ 82TopSti-74
❑ 82TopSti-123
❑ 83AllGamPI-125
❑ 83Don-168
❑ 83DonActA-57
❑ 83Dra-25
❑ 83Fle-173
❑ 83FleSta-173
❑ 83FleSti-145
❑ 83FleSti-170
❑ 83Kel-58
❑ 83OPC-300
❑ 83OPC-301
❑ 83OPC-342
❑ 83PerAll-16
❑ 83PerAllG-16
❑ 83PerCreC-14
❑ 83PerCreCG-14
❑ 83PhiPosGM-5
❑ 83PhiPosGPaM-10
❑ 83PhiTas-27
❑ 83StaSch-1
❑ 83StaSch-2
❑ 83StaSch-3
❑ 83StaSch-4
❑ 83StaSch-5
❑ 83StaSch-6
❑ 83StaSch-7
❑ 83StaSch-8
❑ 83StaSch-9
❑ 83StaSch-10
❑ 83StaSch-11
❑ 83StaSch-12
❑ 83StaSch-13
❑ 83StaSch-14
❑ 83StaSch-15
❑ 83Top-300
❑ 83Top-301
❑ 83Top-399
❑ 83TopFol-2
❑ 83TopGloS-8
❑ 83TopSti-10
❑ 83TopSti-172
❑ 83TopSti-270
❑ 83TopStiB-3
❑ 84AllGamPI-35
❑ 84Don-23
❑ 84Don-23A
❑ 84Don-183
❑ 84DonActAS-57
❑ 84DonCha-11
❑ 84Dra-28
❑ 84Fle-48
❑ 84FleSti-16
❑ 84FleSti-35
❑ 84FleSti-48
❑ 84FraGloT-1
❑ 84FunFooP-11
❑ 84MilBra-23
❑ 84MLBPen-16
❑ 84Nes792-132
❑ 84Nes792-388
❑ 84Nes792-700
❑ 84Nes792-703
❑ 84NesDreT-14
❑ 84OCoandSI-69
❑ 84OCoandSI-87
❑ 84OPC-361
❑ 84OPC-388
❑ 84PhiTas-6
❑ 84PhiTas-33
❑ 84RalPur-22
❑ 84SevCoi-C4
❑ 84SevCoi-E4
❑ 84SevCoi-W4
❑ 84Top-132
❑ 84Top-388
❑ 84Top-700
❑ 84Top-703
❑ 84TopCer-22
❑ 84TopGaloC-11
❑ 84TopGloA-15
❑ 84TopGloS-39
❑ 84TopRubD-23
❑ 84TopSti-101
❑ 84TopSti-117
❑ 84TopSti-188
❑ 84TopSup-6
❑ 84TopTif-132
❑ 84TopTif-388
❑ 84TopTif-700
❑ 84TopTif-703
❑ 85AllGamPI-125
❑ 85CirK-19
❑ 85Don-61
❑ 85DonActA-17
❑ 85Dra-29
❑ 85Fle-265
❑ 85Fle-627
❑ 85Fle-630
❑ 85FleLimE-33
❑ 85FleStaS-17
❑ 85FleStaS-34
❑ 85FleStaS-74
❑ 85FleStaS-75
❑ 85FleStaS-76
❑ 85FleStaS-77
❑ 85FleStaS-78
❑ 85FleStaS-79
❑ 85GenMilS-9
❑ 85KASDis-12
❑ 85KitCloD-12
❑ 85Lea-205
❑ 85OPC-67
❑ 85PhiCIG-4
❑ 85PhiTas-11
❑ 85PhiTas-33
❑ 85SevCoi-C4
❑ 85SevCoi-E16
❑ 85SevCoi-W1
❑ 85SpoPro-2
❑ 85SpoSam-1
❑ 85SubDis-42
❑ 85ThoMcAD-42
❑ 85Top-500
❑ 85Top-714
❑ 85Top3-D-1
❑ 85TopGaloC-10
❑ 85TopGloA-4
❑ 85TopGloS-23
❑ 85TopMin-500
❑ 85TopRubD-9
❑ 85TopSti-94
❑ 85TopSti-111
❑ 85TopSti-193
❑ 85TopSup-12
❑ 85TopTif-500
❑ 85TopTif-714
❑ 86BasStaB-99
❑ 86BurKinA-5
❑ 86Don-61
❑ 86DonHig-4
❑ 86DonHig-36
❑ 86DorChe-8
❑ 86Dra-26
❑ 86Fle-450
❑ 86FleLimE-41
❑ 86FleMin-94
❑ 86FleSlu-33
❑ 86FleStiC-107
❑ 86FraGloT-4
❑ 86FraGloT-5
❑ 86GenMilB-4H
❑ 86Lea-51

❑ 86MeaGolBB-14
❑ 86MeaGolM-11
❑ 86MeaGolSB-16
❑ 86MSAJifPD-17
❑ 86OPC-200
❑ 86PhiCIG-10
❑ 86PhiKel-5
❑ 86PhiTas-20
❑ 86QuaGra-14
❑ 86SevCoi-C5
❑ 86SevCoi-E5
❑ 86SevCoi-S5
❑ 86SevCoi-W5
❑ 86Spo-44
❑ 86Spo-62
❑ 86Spo-68
❑ 86Spo-139
❑ 86Spo-148
❑ 86SpoDecG-55
❑ 86Top-200
❑ 86Top3-D-24
❑ 86TopGloS-17
❑ 86TopMinL-55
❑ 86TopSti-114
❑ 86TopSup-49
❑ 86TopTat-7
❑ 86TopTif-200
❑ 86TruVal-28
❑ 86Woo-30
❑ 87BoaandB-1
❑ 87BurKinA-17
❑ 87ClaGam-62
❑ 87ClaUpdY-101
❑ 87Don-139
❑ 87DonAll-17
❑ 87DonHig-2
❑ 87DonOpeD-160
❑ 87DonP-17
❑ 87Dra-23
❑ 87Fle-187
❑ 87FleAll-6
❑ 87FleAwaW-36
❑ 87FleBasA-40
❑ 87FleGamW-40
❑ 87FleGlo-187
❑ 87FleHotS-35
❑ 87FleLeaL-40
❑ 87FleLimE-37
❑ 87FleMin-97
❑ 87FleRecS-35
❑ 87FleSlu-37
❑ 87FleStiC-107
❑ 87FleWaxBC-C15
❑ 87GenMilB-5H
❑ 87HosSti-13
❑ 87K-M-31
❑ 87KayB-29
❑ 87KeyFooD-11
❑ 87KraFoo-30
❑ 87Lea-122
❑ 87MandMSL-3
❑ 87MSAIceTD-11
❑ 87MSAJifPD-16
❑ 87OPC-396
❑ 87OurOwnTD-11
❑ 87PhiCha-4
❑ 87PhiTas-20
❑ 87RalPur-14
❑ 87RedFolSB-46
❑ 87Spo-30
❑ 87Spo-115
❑ 87Spo-156
❑ 87SpoDeaP-1
❑ 87SpoSupD-4
❑ 87SpoTeaP-6
❑ 87StuPan-9
❑ 87Top-430
❑ 87Top-597
❑ 87TopCoi-43
❑ 87TopGaloC-10
❑ 87TopGloA-4
❑ 87TopGloS-28
❑ 87TopMinL-30
❑ 87TopSti-116
❑ 87TopSti-160
❑ 87TopTif-430
❑ 87TopTif-597
❑ 87WeiMarD-11
❑ 87Woo-8
❑ 88CheBoy-14
❑ 88ClaRed-167
❑ 88Don-330
❑ 88DonAll-39
❑ 88DonBasB-271
❑ 88DonBonM-BC4
❑ 88DonPop-17
❑ 88Dra-8
❑ 88Fle-315
❑ 88Fle-636
❑ 88FleAwaW-35
❑ 88FleBasA-36
❑ 88FleBasM-31
❑ 88FleExcS-34
❑ 88FleGlo-315
❑ 88FleGlo-636
❑ 88FleHotS-34
❑ 88FleLeaL-35
❑ 88FleMin-102
❑ 88FleRecS-35
❑ 88FleSlu-36
❑ 88FleStiC-111
❑ 88FleSup-33
❑ 88FleTeaL-34
❑ 88FleWaxBC-C11
❑ 88GreBasS-23
❑ 88K-M-25
❑ 88KayB-27
❑ 88KeyFooD-16
❑ 88KinDis-1
❑ 88Lea-124
❑ 88MSAFanSD-19
❑ 88MSAIceTD-16
❑ 88Nes-6
❑ 88OPC-321
❑ 88OPCBoxB-O
❑ 88OurOwnTD-16
❑ 88PanSti-234
❑ 88PanSti-360
❑ 88PanSti-429
❑ 88PhiTas-23
❑ 88RedFolSB-79
❑ 88Sco-16
❑ 88Sco-657
❑ 88ScoBoxC-13
❑ 88ScoGlo-16
❑ 88ScoGlo-657
❑ 88Spo-35
❑ 88Spo-180
❑ 88SpoGam-21
❑ 88StaLinAl-30
❑ 88StaLinPh-16
❑ 88StaMat/S-1
❑ 88StaMat/S-2
❑ 88StaMat/S-4
❑ 88StaMat/S-6
❑ 88StaMat/S-8
❑ 88StaMat/S-10
❑ 88TarPla-38
❑ 88TetTeaD-16
❑ 88Top-600
❑ 88TopBig-88
❑ 88TopCoi-53
❑ 88TopGloA-15
❑ 88TopGloS-3
❑ 88TopMinL-67
❑ 88TopRitTM-8
❑ 88TopSti-9
❑ 88TopSti-125
❑ 88TopSti-149
❑ 88TopStiB-8
❑ 88TopTif-600
❑ 88TopUKM-67
❑ 88TopUKMT-67
❑ 88TopWaxBC-O
❑ 88WeiMarD-16
❑ 88Woo-7
❑ 89Bow-402
❑ 89BowTif-402
❑ 89CadEllD-51
❑ 89CerSup-4
❑ 89ClaLigB-48
❑ 89ClaTraP-153
❑ 89Don-193
❑ 89Fle-582
❑ 89FleGlo-582
❑ 89FleSup-36
❑ 89FleUpd-131
❑ 89KayB-27
❑ 89OPC-100
❑ 89OPCBoxB-L
❑ 89PanSti-3
❑ 89PanSti-153
❑ 89PhiTas-32
❑ 89RedFolSB-104
❑ 89Sco-149
❑ 89ScoHot1S-76
❑ 89Spo-21
❑ 89SpollIFKI-90
❑ 89Top-100
❑ 89Top-489
❑ 89TopAme2C-27
❑ 89TopBasT-72
❑ 89TopBig-220
❑ 89TopCapC-16
❑ 89TopHeaUT-24
❑ 89TopSti-120
❑ 89TopTif-100
❑ 89TopTif-489
❑ 89TopUKM-70
❑ 89TopWaxBC-L
❑ 89TVSpoM-32
❑ 89UppDec-406
❑ 89UppDec-684
❑ 90AGFA-21
❑ 90BasWit-39
❑ 90Don-643
❑ 90HOFStiB-94
❑ 90OPC-662
❑ 90PerGreM-100
❑ 90PhiTas-32
❑ 90PhiTas-36
❑ 90PubIntS-250
❑ 90Top-662
❑ 90TopTif-662
❑ 90UppDec-20
❑ 91BasBesRB-16
❑ 91Cla/Bes-1
❑ 91Cla/Bes-AU1
❑ 91ClaGolB-BC1
❑ 91UppDecS-2
❑ 92ClaFS7-100
❑ 92DEL-AU4
❑ 92KelAll-10
❑ 92PhiDaiN-7
❑ 92TVSpoMF5HRC-13
❑ 93UppDecS-12
❑ 94TedWil-75
❑ 94TedWil-141
❑ 94TedWil-151
❑ 94TedWil5C-7
❑ 94TedWilMS-MS1
❑ 94TedWilMS-MS2
❑ 94TedWilMS-MS3
❑ 94TedWilMS-MS4
❑ 94TedWilMS-MS5
❑ 94TedWilMS-MS6
❑ 94TedWilMS-MS7
❑ 94TedWilMS-MS8
❑ 94Yoo-15
❑ 95ColCho-50
❑ 95ColChoGS-50
❑ 95ColChoSS-50
❑ 95JimDeaAG-4
❑ 95Phi-29
❑ 95PirCocP-7
❑ 95SP-4
❑ 95SPCha-112
❑ 95SPChaDC-112
❑ 95SPSil-4
❑ 95UppDec-450
❑ 95UppDecC-5B
❑ 95UppDecED-450
❑ 95UppDecEDG-450
❑ 95UppDecSE-208
❑ 95UppDecSEG-208
❑ 95UppDecSHoB-5
❑ 97DonSigSS-19
❑ 97HigMinMCT-43
❑ 97HigMinMCT-44
❑ 98TopStaRR-4
❑ 98TopStaRRA-4
❑ 99BowBesFF-FR2B
❑ 99BowBesFF-FR2C
❑ 99BowBesFFA-FR2B
❑ 99BowBesFFA-FR2C
❑ 99SP SigAuto-MS
❑ 99SPSig-171
❑ 99TopHaloFC-HOF1
❑ 99UppDecAP-MS
❑ 99UppDecAPH5AU-MSAU
❑ 99UppDecCL-28
❑ 99UppDecCLA-1970
❑ 99UppDecCLCC-28
❑ 99UppDecCLES-MS
❑ 99UppDecCLESC-MS
❑ 99UppDecCLJotC-AC6
❑ 99UppDecCLJotC-MS
❑ 99UppDecR-110
❑ 99UppDecRG-110
❑ 99UppDecRP-110

Schmidt, Pete
❑ 87BelMarL-10

Schmidt, Todd
❑ 96BesAutSA-67
❑ 97NewJerCB-24
❑ 98NewJerCM-26

Schmidt, Tom
❑ 92BenRocCB-21
❑ 92BenRocF-1482
❑ 93CenValRC-22
❑ 93CenValRF-2902
❑ 93Top-433
❑ 93TopGol-433
❑ 93TopInaM-433
❑ 93TopInaR-433
❑ 93TopMic-433
❑ 94Bow-114
❑ 94CenValRC-23
❑ 94CenValRF-3213
❑ 95NewHavRTI-34
❑ 96JacSunB-26
❑ 97JacSun-23

Schmidt, Walter
❑ 09ObaT21-333
❑ 12HomRunKE-74
❑ 12ObaPreT-82
❑ 12Zee-129
❑ 13Zee-121
❑ 14Zee-120
❑ 15Zee-116
❑ 20WalMaiW-46
❑ 21Nei-113
❑ 22E120-223
❑ 22W572-91
❑ 22W573-116
❑ 92ConTSN-571

Schmidt, Walton
❑ 29Zee-143

Schmidt, Willard
❑ 53CarHunW-20
❑ 53Top-168
❑ 56Top-323
❑ 57Top-206
❑ 58RedEnq-35
❑ 58Top-214
❑ 59RedEnq-23
❑ 59Top-171
❑ 59TopVen-171
❑ 60SeaPop-13
❑ 62KahAtl-19
❑ 79TCM50-153
❑ 91TopArc1-168

Schmitt, Chris
❑ 93HelBreF-4094
❑ 93HelBreSP-23
❑ 94BelBreC-24
❑ 94BelBreFl-100
❑ 96DurBulBlB-19
❑ 96DurBulBrB-20

Schmitt, Todd
❑ 92SpoIndC-7
❑ 92SpoIndF-1293
❑ 93WatDiaC-26
❑ 93WatDiaF-1768
❑ 94RanCucQC-23
❑ 94RanCucQF-1639
❑ 95Exc-287
❑ 95MemChiTI-20
❑ 97BesAutAS-51
❑ 97LasVegS1A-26

Schmittou, Larry
❑ 79NaSouTI-22
❑ 89NasSouTI-28
❑ 95NasSouTI-22

Schmittou, Mike
❑ 89TenTecGE-24

Schmitz, Dan
❑ 79WesHavYT-5
❑ 80NasSouTI-19
❑ 81ColCliP-6
❑ 82ColCliP-6
❑ 82ColCliT-16
❑ 82NasSouTI-21
❑ 83TidTidT-17
❑ 84TolMudHT-7
❑ 85VisOakT-25
❑ 86VisOakP-18

Schmitz, John
❑ 42CubTeaI-22
❑ 47Exh-202
❑ 47TipTop-116
❑ 49Bow-52
❑ 49EurSta-70
❑ 49Lea-48
❑ 50Bow-24
❑ 51Bow-69
❑ 51TopBluB-41
❑ 52Bow-224
❑ 52NatTeaL-30
❑ 52Top-136
❑ 53Bri-17
❑ 54Top-33
❑ 55Bow-105
❑ 55Top-159
❑ 56BalOriP-34
❑ 56Top-298
❑ 56TopHocF-A16
❑ 56TopHocF-B18
❑ 74dod195T-36
❑ 79DiaGre-113
❑ 83TopRep5-136
❑ 85TCMPla1-30
❑ 90DodTar-709
❑ 91OriCro-407
❑ 94TopArc1-33
❑ 94TopArc1G-33
❑ 95TopArcBD-9

Schmitz, Mike
❑ 93OneYanC-19
❑ 93OneYanF-3514
❑ 94GreBatF-486
❑ 97GreBatC-20

Schmutz, Charlie
❑ 09ObaT21-402
❑ 12ObaPreT-151
❑ 90DodTar-1064

Schnabel, Matt
❑ 98KanCouC-29
❑ 98KanCouCCP-29

Schnacke, Ken
❑ 92ColCliP-1
❑ 93ColCliP-25
❑ 97ColCliD-25

Schneck, Dave
❑ 76IndIndTI-15
❑ 91MetWIZ-351

Schneider, Brian
❑ 95TopTra-122T
❑ 98CapFeaCM-22

Schneider, Dan
❑ 94EveGiaC-26
❑ 94EveGiaF-3654
❑ 95BurBeeTI-20

Schneider, Dan Louis
❑ 63Top-299
❑ 64Top-351
❑ 64TopVen-351
❑ 65Top-366
❑ 66BraPos-22
❑ 67Top-543
❑ 68OPC-57
❑ 68Top-57
❑ 68TopVen-57
❑ 69Top-656
❑ 87AstShoSTw-29

Schneider, Herm
❑ 95WhiSoxK-27

Schneider, Jeff
❑ 80RocRedWT-10
❑ 81BalOriP-18
❑ 81RocRedWW-7
❑ 82SpoIndT-7
❑ 82Top-21
❑ 83SyrChiT-11
❑ 91OriCro-408
❑ 94St.CatBJC-20
❑ 94St.CatBJF-3642

Schneider, Paul
❑ 83WauTimF-19
❑ 86ChaLooP-22
❑ 86SouLeaAJ-20
❑ 87CalCanP-2316
❑ 88CalCanC-2
❑ 88CalCanP-793

Schneider, Pete
❑ 16FleBreD-83
❑ 21Zee-167
❑ 22Zee-160
❑ 23Zee-196
❑ 24Zee-138

Schneider, Phil
❑ 93BenRocCB-23
❑ 93BenRocF-3268
❑ 94NewHavRF-1548
❑ 95NewHavRTI-18
❑ 95Top-648

Schneider, Tom
❑ 93JamExpC-21
❑ 93JamExpF-3326
❑ 94BurBeeC-23
❑ 94BurBeeF-1081

Schnoor, Chuck
❑ 82LynMetT-14

Schnur, Curt
❑ 95DanBraTI-26

Schnurbusch, Chris
❑ 88FayGenP-1097
❑ 89CedRapRB-16
❑ 89CedRapRP-934
❑ 89CedRapRS-17

Schober, Dave
❑ 84MadMusP-3
❑ 85MadMusP-23
❑ 85MadMusT-25
❑ 86MadMusP-25
❑ 86MadMusP-20
❑ 87MadMusP-23
❑ 87MadMusP-2
❑ 89HunStaB-19

Schock, Will (William)
❑ 88HunStaTI-17
❑ 88MadMusP-21
❑ 88MidLeaAGS-54
❑ 89HunStaB-2
❑ 90Bes-197
❑ 90HunStaB-9
❑ 91LinDriAAA-544
❑ 91TacTigLD-544
❑ 91TacTigP-2304

Schockman, Mark
❑ 85NewOriT-16

Schoen, Jerry
❑ 91BenBucCB-14
❑ 91BenBucP-3704

Schoen, Jerry Thomas
❑ 69PilPos-19
❑ 77PilPosR-19

Schoen, Mark
❑ 98LynHilQ-27

Schoendienst, Kevin
❑ 81QuaCitCT-10

Schoendienst, Red (Albert)
❑ 46SeaSLP-51
❑ 47Exh-203A
❑ 47Exh-203B
❑ 47Exh-203C
❑ 48Bow-38
❑ 49Bow-111
❑ 49EurSta-197
❑ 50Bow-71
❑ 50JJKCopP-17
❑ 51Bow-10
❑ 51FisBakL-25
❑ 51R42SmaS-97
❑ 51TopBluB-6
❑ 52BasPho-5
❑ 52BerRos-60
❑ 52Bow-30
❑ 52DixLid-19
❑ 52DixPre-19
❑ 52RedMan-NL19
❑ 52StaCalL-81A
❑ 52StaCalS-93B
❑ 52TipTop-37
❑ 52Top-91
❑ 53BowC-101
❑ 53CarHunW-21
❑ 53DixLid-19
❑ 53DixPre-19
❑ 53MacSta-4
❑ 53NorBreL-28
❑ 53RedMan-NL12
❑ 53Top-78
❑ 54Bow-110
❑ 54CarHunW-24
❑ 54DanDee-22
❑ 54DixLid-15
❑ 54RedHeaF-27
❑ 54RedMan-NL10
❑ 54Wil-16
❑ 55Bow-29
❑ 55CarHunW-23
❑ 55RedMan-NL18
❑ 55RobGouS-3
❑ 55RobGouW-3
❑ 56Top-165
❑ 56YelBasP-28
❑ 57BraSpiaS4-17
❑ 57GiaJayP-9
❑ 57Top-154
❑ 58BraJayP-11
❑ 58Top-190
❑ 59Top-480
❑ 60BraJayP-10
❑ 60BraLaktL-23
❑ 60BraSpiaS-21
❑ 60MacSta-22
❑ 60NuHi-25
❑ 60Top-335
❑ 61NuSco-425
❑ 61Pos-111
❑ 61Top-505
❑ 62SalPlaC-151

❑ 62ShiPlaC-151
❑ 62Top-575
❑ 65CarJayP-8
❑ 65CarTeal-20
❑ 65Top-556
❑ 66CarCoi-12
❑ 66CarTeal-9
❑ 66OPC-76
❑ 66Top-76
❑ 66TopVen-76
❑ 67Top-512
❑ 67TopVen-297
❑ 68Top-294
❑ 68TopVen-294
❑ 69Top-462
❑ 70CarTeal-24
❑ 70OPC-346
❑ 70Top-346
❑ 71CarTeal-21
❑ 71CarTeal-32
❑ 71OPC-239
❑ 71Top-239
❑ 72OPC-67
❑ 72Top-67
❑ 73OPC-497
❑ 73Top-497A
❑ 73Top-497B
❑ 74LauAllG-50
❑ 74OPC-236
❑ 74OPC-236
❑ 74Top-236
❑ 75OPC-246
❑ 75Top-246
❑ 75TopMin-246
❑ 76GrePlaG-32
❑ 76OPC-581
❑ 76SSP-300
❑ 76St.LouCP-29
❑ 76Top-581
❑ 78BraTCC-11
❑ 78CarTeal-28
❑ 79Car5-24
❑ 79TCM50-94
❑ 80Bra195T-40
❑ 80PerHaloFP-203
❑ 80PerHaloFPS-66
❑ 81Car5x7-24
❑ 81Don-431
❑ 81TCM60I-395
❑ 83Car-27
❑ 83Car194T-31
❑ 83CarGreT-12
❑ 83TopRep5-91
❑ 84Car-27
❑ 84Car5x7-25
❑ 84TCMPla1-24
❑ 85CarTeal-30
❑ 85TCMPhoC-28
❑ 86CarTeal-39
❑ 87Bra195T-5
❑ 87CarTeal-29
❑ 88CarTeal-31
❑ 88PacLegI-2
❑ 88ScoBoxC-T5
❑ 88Top-351
❑ 88TopTif-351
❑ 89CarTeal-29
❑ 90PerGreM-55
❑ 90TopTra-113T
❑ 90TopTraT-113T
❑ 91TopArc1-78
❑ 91UppDecS-14
❑ 92BazQua5A-11
❑ 92CarMcD-21
❑ 92UppDecS-11
❑ 93ActPacA-114
❑ 93ActPacA2-48G
❑ 93ActPacAC-4
❑ 94TedWil-83
❑ 96IllLot-4
❑ 98SpoIllTaN-30
❑ 98SpoIllTaNEE-30
❑ 99SpoIllGotG-2
❑ 99SpoIllGotGA-67
❑ 99SpoIllGotGC-7

Schoeneck, Jumbo (Louis N.)
❑ 87OldJudN-437

Schoeneweis, Scott
❑ 96LakElsSB-11
❑ 97Bow-370
❑ 97BowInt-370
❑ 97MidAng-23
❑ 97TexLeaTP-14
❑ 98Bes-44
❑ 98Bow-126
❑ 98BowChr-126
❑ 98BowChrGA-126
❑ 98BowChrGAR-126
❑ 98BowChrI-126
❑ 98BowChrIR-126
❑ 98BowChrR-126
❑ 98BowGolA-126
❑ 98BowInt-126
❑ 98SP MinPE-14
❑ 98SPMin-14
❑ 98VanCanG-25
❑ 99Bow-150
❑ 99BowChr-150
❑ 99BowChrG-150
❑ 99BowChrGR-150
❑ 99BowChrI-150
❑ 99BowChrIR-150
❑ 99BowChrR-150
❑ 99BowGol-150
❑ 99BowInt-150
❑ 99DumSet-106
❑ 99FleMys-106
❑ 99FleMysM-106

Schoenhaus, Ted
❑ 76CedRapGT-27

Schoenvogel, Chad
❑ 91FroRowDP-3
❑ 91FroRowDPG-3
❑ 91FroRowDPP-4
❑ 91FroRowDPS-3
❑ 92ClaFS7-325
❑ 92StaCluD-166
❑ 92WinHavRSC-16
❑ 92WinHavRSF-1777

Schofield, Andy
❑ 96NewJerCB-25

Schofield, Dick (Richard C.)
❑ 59TopVen-68
❑ 82DanSunF-27
❑ 84AllGamPI-114
❑ 84AngSmo-25
❑ 84Don-35
❑ 84FleUpd-105
❑ 84TopTra-107T
❑ 84TopTraT-107T
❑ 85AngSmo-13
❑ 85Don-329
❑ 85Fle-311
❑ 85Top-138
❑ 85Top-629
❑ 85TopTif-138
❑ 85TopTif-629
❑ 86AngSmo-13
❑ 86Don-133
❑ 86Fle-167
❑ 86OPC-311
❑ 86Top-311
❑ 86TopTif-311
❑ 87AngSmo-15
❑ 87CalAngPPS-35
❑ 87Don-283
❑ 87DonOpeD-4
❑ 87Fle-92
❑ 87FleGlo-92
❑ 87OPC-54
❑ 87SevCoi-W9
❑ 87Top-502
❑ 87TopSti-176
❑ 87TopTif-502
❑ 88AngSmo-16
❑ 88Don-233
❑ 88DonBasB-195
❑ 88Fle-504
❑ 88FleGlo-504
❑ 88Lea-178
❑ 88OPC-43
❑ 88PanSti-45
❑ 88RedFolSB-80
❑ 88Sco-274
❑ 88ScoGlo-274
❑ 88StaLinAn-18
❑ 88Top-43
❑ 88TopBig-204
❑ 88TopSti-177
❑ 88TopTif-43
❑ 89Bow-46
❑ 89BowTif-46
❑ 89Don-108
❑ 89DonBasB-251
❑ 89Fle-488
❑ 89FleGlo-488
❑ 89OPC-286
❑ 89PanSti-294
❑ 89Sco-16
❑ 89Top-477
❑ 89TopBig-53
❑ 89TopSti-174
❑ 89TopTif-477
❑ 89UppDec-201
❑ 90AngSmo-15
❑ 90Bow-291
❑ 90BowTif-291
❑ 90DodTar-710
❑ 90Don-288
❑ 90DonBesA-131
❑ 90Fle-144
❑ 90FleCan-144
❑ 90Lea-419
❑ 90OPC-189
❑ 90PubIntS-379
❑ 90Sco-44
❑ 90Top-189
❑ 90TopBig-211
❑ 90TopTif-189
❑ 90UppDec-669
❑ 91AngSmo-14
❑ 91Bow-191
❑ 91Don-262
❑ 91Fle-325
❑ 91Lea-59
❑ 91OPC-736
❑ 91PanFreS-183
❑ 91Sco-776
❑ 91StaClu-59
❑ 91Top-736
❑ 91TopDesS-736
❑ 91TopMic-736
❑ 91TopTif-736
❑ 91Ult-52
❑ 91UppDec-169
❑ 92Don-44
❑ 92Fle-69
❑ 92FleUpd-105
❑ 92Lea-419
❑ 92LeaBlaG-419
❑ 92MetKah-11
❑ 92OPC-230
❑ 92PanSti-8
❑ 92Pin-338
❑ 92Sco-552
❑ 92ScoRoo-26T
❑ 92StaClu-16
❑ 92StaClu-738
❑ 92Top-230
❑ 92TopGol-230
❑ 92TopGolW-230
❑ 92TopMic-230
❑ 92TopTra-101T
❑ 92TopTraG-101T
❑ 92Ult-30
❑ 92Ult-538
❑ 92UppDec-269
❑ 92UppDec-791
❑ 93BluJayD-23
❑ 93BluJayDM-30
❑ 93BluJayFS-24
❑ 93Fle-94
❑ 93Lea-382
❑ 93OPCPre-129
❑ 93PacSpa-202
❑ 93Top-79
❑ 93TopGol-79
❑ 93TopInaM-79
❑ 93TopInaR-79
❑ 93TopMic-79
❑ 93Ult-646
❑ 93UppDec-768
❑ 93UppDecGold-768
❑ 94BluJayUSPC-10S
❑ 94ColC-569
❑ 94ColChoGS-569
❑ 94ColChoSS-569
❑ 94Fle-341
❑ 94Lea-211
❑ 94StaClu-234
❑ 94StaCluFDI-234
❑ 94StaCluGR-234
❑ 94StaCluMOP-234
❑ 94StaCluT-160
❑ 94StaCluTFDI-160
❑ 95ColCho-153
❑ 95ColChoGS-153
❑ 95ColChoSS-153
❑ 95Fle-103
❑ 96AngMot-27

Schofield, Ducky (John R.)
❑ 54CarHunW-25
❑ 54Top-191
❑ 55CarHunW-24
❑ 55Top-143
❑ 58Top-106
❑ 59Top-68
❑ 60KeyChal-42
❑ 60Top-104
❑ 60TopVen-104
❑ 61Kah-39
❑ 61Top-453
❑ 62Top-484
❑ 63PirIDL-21
❑ 63Top-34
❑ 64PirKDK-23
❑ 64Top-284
❑ 64TopVen-284
❑ 65OPC-218
❑ 65Top-218
❑ 66OPC-156
❑ 66Top-156
❑ 66Top-474
❑ 66TopVen-156
❑ 67Top-381
❑ 68Top-588
❑ 69OPC-18
❑ 69Top-18
❑ 70OPC-251
❑ 70Top-251
❑ 71MLBOffS-282
❑ 71OPC-396
❑ 71Top-396
❑ 72MilBra-310
❑ 77PirTCM1WC-13
❑ 78TCM60I-199
❑ 81RedSoxBG2S-109
❑ 85Top-138
❑ 85TopTif-138
❑ 92YanWIZ6-110
❑ 94BreMilB-77
❑ 94TopArc1-191
❑ 94TopArc1G-191

Schofield, John
❑ 86KinEagP-23
❑ 87PorChaRP-2

Scholan, Jarrod
❑ 96DayCubB-30

Scholzen, Jeffrey
❑ 91PocPioP-3791
❑ 91PocPioSP-22

Schooler, Aaron
❑ 94EliTwiC-22
❑ 94EliTwiF-3732

Schooler, Mike (Michael)
❑ 86WauTimP-21
❑ 87ChaLooB-8
❑ 88CalCanC-9
❑ 88CalCanP-795
❑ 88ScoRoo-91T
❑ 88ScoRooG-91T
❑ 88TopTra-105T
❑ 88TopTraT-105T
❑ 89ChaLooLITI-27
❑ 89Don-637
❑ 89Fle-559
❑ 89FleGlo-559
❑ 89MarMot-25
❑ 89Sco-528
❑ 89ScoHot1R-73
❑ 89ScoYouS2-34
❑ 89Top-199
❑ 89TopTif-199
❑ 89ToyRoo-27
❑ 89UppDec-28
❑ 90Bow-470
❑ 90BowTif-470
❑ 90ClaBlu-79
❑ 90Don-330
❑ 90DonBesA-82
❑ 90Fle-525
❑ 90FleCan-525
❑ 90Lea-258
❑ 90MarMot-21
❑ 90OPC-681
❑ 90PanSti-151
❑ 90RedFolSB-84
❑ 90Sco-149
❑ 90Spo-187
❑ 90Top-681
❑ 90TopBig-235
❑ 90TopMinL-35
❑ 90TopSti-228
❑ 90TopTif-681
❑ 90UppDec-214
❑ 91Bow-241
❑ 91Don-302
❑ 91Fle-461
❑ 91Lea-230
❑ 91MarCouH-25
❑ 91OPC-365
❑ 91PanFreS-236
❑ 91PanSti-184
❑ 91RedFolS-85
❑ 91Sco-489
❑ 91SevCoi-NW15
❑ 91StaClu-508
❑ 91Top-365
❑ 91TopDesS-365
❑ 91TopMic-365
❑ 91TopTif-365
❑ 91UppDec-638
❑ 92Bow-336
❑ 92Don-444
❑ 92Fle-292
❑ 92MarMot-10
❑ 92OPC-28
❑ 92Pin-171
❑ 92Sco-654
❑ 92StaClu-313
❑ 92Top-28
❑ 92TopGol-28
❑ 92TopGolW-28
❑ 92TopMic-28
❑ 92UppDec-405
❑ 93Don-449
❑ 93Fle-313
❑ 93OklCit8F-1626
❑ 93OPC-350
❑ 93RanKee-432
❑ 93Sco-544
❑ 93Sel-392
❑ 93StaClu-198
❑ 93StaCluFDI-198
❑ 93StaCluMOP-198
❑ 93Top-258
❑ 93TopGol-258
❑ 93TopInaM-258
❑ 93TopInaR-258
❑ 93TopMic-258
❑ 93Ult-271
❑ 94WicWraF-189
❑ 95MidAngOHP-31
❑ 95MidAngTI-26

Schoon, Peter
❑ 90IBAWorA-7

Schoonmaker, Jerry
❑ 56Top-216
❑ 57Top-334

Schoonover, Gary
❑ 87BriYouC-19
❑ 88IdaFalBP-1836
❑ 89BurBraP-1602
❑ 89BurBraS-20

Schoppee, Dave
❑ 81BriRedST-9
❑ 83PawRedST-10

Schorr, Bill
❑ 88ButCopKSP-8

Schorr, Bradley
❑ 91KinMetC-22
❑ 91KinMetP-3812
❑ 92ColMetC-5
❑ 92ColMetF-296
❑ 92ColMetPI-20
❑ 93St.LucMC-23
❑ 93St.LuMF-2921
❑ 94St.LucMC-21
❑ 94St.LucMF-1195

Schorr, Charles
❑ 20Zee-131
❑ 24Zee-101

Schorzman, Steve
❑ 96BriWhiSB-28
❑ 98HicCraUO-26

Schott, Arthur Eugene
❑ 36R31PasP-21
❑ 38RedOraW-25

Schott, Marge
❑ 93RedKah-25

Schottzie, Schottzie
❑ 91RedKah-0
❑ 92RedKah-2
❑ 94RedKah-28
❑ 95RedKah-29

Schourek, Pete
❑ 88LitFalMP-22
❑ 89ColMetB-14
❑ 89ColMetGS-24
❑ 90MetColP-47
❑ 90St.LucMS-25
❑ 90TexLeaAGS-33
❑ 90TopTVM-59
❑ 91Bow-482
❑ 91FleUpd-104
❑ 91LeaGolR-BC15
❑ 91MetColP-45
❑ 91MetKah-48
❑ 91MetPerPA-26
❑ 91OPCPre-106
❑ 91ScoRoo-87T
❑ 91TopTra-106T
❑ 91TopTraT-106T
❑ 91UppDec-766
❑ 92Don-535
❑ 92Fle-516
❑ 92Lea-176
❑ 92LeaBlaG-176
❑ 92MetColP-27
❑ 92OPC-287
❑ 92OPCPre-58
❑ 92Pin-141
❑ 92Sco-332
❑ 92Sco100RS-20
❑ 92SkyAAAF-255
❑ 92StaClu-521
❑ 92TidTidS-570
❑ 92Top-287
❑ 92TopDeb91-158
❑ 92TopGol-287
❑ 92TopGolW-287
❑ 92TopMic-287
❑ 92Ult-539
❑ 92UppDec-673
❑ 93Don-198
❑ 93Fle-95
❑ 93MetColP-45
❑ 93MetKah-48
❑ 93PacSpa-203
❑ 93Pin-324
❑ 93StaClu-238
❑ 93StaCluFDI-238
❑ 93StaCluMOP-238
❑ 93Top-352
❑ 93TopGol-352
❑ 93TopInaM-352
❑ 93TopInaR-352
❑ 93TopMic-352
❑ 93Ult-433
❑ 93UppDec-658
❑ 93UppDecGold-658
❑ 94Don-652
❑ 94Fle-577
❑ 94MetShuST-6
❑ 94RedKah-29
❑ 94StaClu-439
❑ 94StaCluFDI-439
❑ 94StaCluGR-439
❑ 94StaCluMOP-439
❑ 94Top-699
❑ 94TopGol-699
❑ 94TopSpa-699
❑ 94TriPla-149
❑ 95ColCho-423
❑ 95ColChoGS-423
❑ 95ColChoSS-423
❑ 95DonTopotO-220
❑ 95Emo-120
❑ 95Fla-125
❑ 95Fle-448
❑ 95Pin-430
❑ 95PinArtP-430
❑ 95PinMusC-430
❑ 95RedKah-30
❑ 95Top-484
❑ 95TopCyb-276
❑ 95Ult-371
❑ 95UltGolM-371
❑ 95UppDec-167
❑ 95UppDecED-167
❑ 95UppDecEDG-167
❑ 96ColCho-114
❑ 96ColCho-372T
❑ 96ColChoGS-114
❑ 96ColChoSS-114
❑ 96Don-85
❑ 96DonPreP-85
❑ 96EmoXL-169
❑ 96Fin-B137
❑ 96FinRef-B137
❑ 96Fla-239
❑ 96Fle-353
❑ 96FleTif-353
❑ 96Lea-86
❑ 96LeaPrePB-86
❑ 96LeaPrePG-86
❑ 96LeaPrePS-86
❑ 96MetUni-152
❑ 96MetUniP-152
❑ 96Pac-43
❑ 96PanSti-50
❑ 96Pin-70

❑ 96Pin-216
❑ 96PinAfi-74
❑ 96PinAfiAP-74
❑ 96PinAfiFPP-74
❑ 96PinArtP-94
❑ 96PinArtP-116
❑ 96PinFoil-216
❑ 96PinSta-94
❑ 96PinSta-116
❑ 96Sco-190
❑ 96Sel-84
❑ 96SelArtP-84
❑ 96SP-64
❑ 96Spo-86
❑ 96SpoArtP-86
❑ 96StaClu-396
❑ 96StaCluEPB-396
❑ 96StaCluEPG-396
❑ 96StaCluEPS-396
❑ 96StaCluMOP-396
❑ 96Sum-42
❑ 96SumAbo&B-42
❑ 96SumArtP-42
❑ 96SumFoi-42
❑ 96Top-112
❑ 96TopGal-49
❑ 96TopGalPPI-49
❑ 96Ult-183
❑ 96UltGolM-183
❑ 96UppDec-46
❑ 96UppDecPHE-H47
❑ 96UppDecPreH-H47
❑ 97Cir-161
❑ 97CirRav-161
❑ 97ColCho-83
❑ 97Fin-49
❑ 97FinRef-49
❑ 97Fle-304
❑ 97FleTif-304
❑ 97Sco-458
❑ 97ScoArtPWB-458
❑ 97ScoResC-458
❑ 97ScoShoS-458
❑ 97ScoShoSAP-458
❑ 97StaClu-323
❑ 97StaCluMOP-323
❑ 97Top-349
❑ 97UppDec-47
❑ 98Pin-145
❑ 98PinPreP-145
❑ 98Top-426
❑ 98TopChr-426
❑ 98TopChrR-426
❑ 98TopDevR-426
❑ 98TopDia-426
❑ 98TopMiniC-426

Schrager, Tony
❑ 98WilCubM-23

Schramka, Paul
❑ 77FriOneYW-14

Schramm, Carl
❑ 91GenCubC-27
❑ 91GenCubP-4213
❑ 92PeoChiC-8
❑ 92PeoChiTI-24
❑ 93DayCubC-16
❑ 93DayCubF-856
❑ 96SanJosGB-23
❑ 97SanJosG-15

Schreckengost, Ossie
❑ 03BreE10-126
❑ 04FanCraAL-42
❑ 08AmeCarE91-23
❑ 08RosComP-65
❑ 09T206-464
❑ 72ClaCar-109

Schreiber, Bruce
❑ 89PriPirS-20
❑ 89Sta-174
❑ 90CarLeaA-23
❑ 90SalBucS-20
❑ 90StaFS7-1
❑ 91CarMudLD-116
❑ 91CarMudP-1094
❑ 91Cla/Bes-225
❑ 91LinDriAA-116
❑ 92CarMudF-1189
❑ 92SalBucC-5
❑ 93CarMudF-2064
❑ 93CarMudTI-5
❑ 94CarMudF-1588

Schreiber, Hank
❑ 20RedWorCP-21

Schreiber, Marty
❑ 84DurBulT-27
❑ 85DurBulT-12
❑ 86OscAstP-22

Schreiber, Paul
❑ 92CalLeaACL-24

Schreiber, Paul Frederick
❑ 54Top-217
❑ 75YanDyn1T-42
❑ 94TopArc1-217
❑ 94TopArc1G-217

Schreiber, Stan
❑ 96AugGreB-27
❑ 97AugGre-24

Schreiber, Ted
❑ 61SeaPop-19
❑ 61SeaPop-20
❑ 62SeaPop-10
❑ 62SeaPop-11
❑ 76Met63 S-12
❑ 77FriOneYW-103
❑ 91MetWIZ-352

Schreimann, Eric
❑ 94MarPhiF-3298
❑ 95MarPhiTI-22
❑ 96PieBolWB-24

Schreiner, John
❑ 91BasCitRC-21
❑ 91BasCitRP-1407

Schreiser, Andre
❑ 52LavPro-82

Schrenk, Steve
❑ 88SouBenWSGS-26
❑ 89SouBenWSGS-15
❑ 90Bes-104
❑ 90SouBenWSB-16
❑ 90SouBenWSGS-16
❑ 92SarWhiSCB-15
❑ 92SarWhiSF-207
❑ 93ExcFS7-155
❑ 94NasSouF-1252
❑ 95Bow-47
❑ 96NasSouB-22
❑ 97RocRedW-22

Schriver, Pop (William)
❑ 63GadFunC-13
❑ 87OldJudN-438
❑ 98CamPepP-66

Schroder, Bob
❑ 65Top-589

Schroeck, Bob
❑ 82ElPasDT-16
❑ 83ElPasDT-24
❑ 84ElPasDT-3

Schroeder, Bill (Alfred W.)
❑ 81ElPasDT-13
❑ 82VanCanT-3
❑ 84BrePol-21
❑ 84Don-515
❑ 84Nes792-738
❑ 84Top-738
❑ 84TopTif-738
❑ 85BreGar-18
❑ 85BrePol-21
❑ 85Don-124
❑ 85Fle-594
❑ 85Top-176
❑ 85TopTif-176
❑ 86BrePol-21
❑ 86Don-211
❑ 86Fle-501
❑ 86Top-662
❑ 86TopTif-662
❑ 87BrePol-21
❑ 87BreTeal-12
❑ 87Don-486
❑ 87DonOpeD-49
❑ 87Fle-357
❑ 87FleGlo-357
❑ 87Top-302
❑ 87TopTif-302
❑ 88BrePol-21
❑ 88BreTeal-31
❑ 88Don-419
❑ 88Fle-173
❑ 88FleGlo-173
❑ 88Sco-311
❑ 88ScoGlo-311
❑ 88StaLinBre-16
❑ 88Top-12
❑ 88TopTif-12
❑ 89Bow-44
❑ 89BowTif-44
❑ 89Don-644
❑ 89Top-563
❑ 89TopTif-563
❑ 89UppDec-627A
❑ 89UppDec-627B
❑ 90Don-567
❑ 90El PasDAGTI-18
❑ 90OPC-244
❑ 90Sco-362
❑ 90Top-244
❑ 90TopTif-244
❑ 90UppDec-149
❑ 91OPC-452
❑ 91Top-452
❑ 91TopDesS-452
❑ 91TopMic-452
❑ 91TopTif-452
❑ 94BreMilB-176

Schroeder, Chad
❑ 97WesMicW-22
❑ 98WesMicWM-23

Schroeder, Clyde
❑ 20Zee-55
❑ 23Zee-75
❑ 24Zee-56

Schroeder, Jay
❑ 83KinBluJTI-23

Schroeder, John
❑ 94SigRooDP-85
❑ 94SigRooDPS-85
❑ 96ForWayWB-23
❑ 98ForMyeMTI-28

Schroeder, Scott A.
❑ 96IdaFalB-22

Schroeder, Todd
❑ 91WelPirC-3
❑ 91WelPirP-3582
❑ 92AugPirC-6
❑ 92SalBucC-20
❑ 92SalBucF-72

Schroeffel, Scott
❑ 96PorRocB-27
❑ 97SalAva-27
❑ 98SalAvaC-23

Schroll, Al
❑ 55Bow-319
❑ 59Top-546
❑ 60Lea-95
❑ 60Top-357
❑ 62Top-102
❑ 62TopVen-102

Schrom, Dave
❑ 80VenLeaS-78

Schrom, Ken
❑ 77QuaCitAT-24
❑ 80SalLakCGT-7
❑ 81Fle-425
❑ 81OPC-238
❑ 81SyrChiT-21
❑ 81SyrChiTI-18
❑ 81Top-577
❑ 82SyrChiT-7
❑ 82SyrChiTI-19
❑ 83TolMudHT-9
❑ 84Don-72
❑ 84Fle-572
❑ 84MinTwiP-25
❑ 84Nes792-11
❑ 84Nes792-322
❑ 84OPC-322
❑ 84Top-11
❑ 84Top-322
❑ 84TopSti-308
❑ 84TopTif-11
❑ 84TopTif-322
❑ 84TwiTeal-13
❑ 85Don-486
❑ 85Fle-288
❑ 85OPC-161
❑ 85Top-161
❑ 85TopTif-161
❑ 85TwiPos-23
❑ 85TwiTeal-13
❑ 85TwiTeal-20
❑ 86Don-635
❑ 86Fle-403
❑ 86FleUpd-104
❑ 86IndOhH-18
❑ 86IndTeal-40
❑ 86OPC-71
❑ 86Top-71
❑ 86TopTif-71
❑ 86TopTra-100T
❑ 86TopTraT-100T
❑ 87Don-403
❑ 87DonAll-53
❑ 87Fle-258
❑ 87FleGlo-258
❑ 87FleMin-98
❑ 87IndGat-18
❑ 87OPC-171
❑ 87Spo-107
❑ 87SpoTeaP-3
❑ 87Top-635
❑ 87TopSti-204
❑ 87TopTif-635
❑ 88Don-501
❑ 88Fle-614
❑ 88FleGlo-614
❑ 88OPC-256
❑ 88Sco-574
❑ 88ScoGlo-574
❑ 88StaLinl-17
❑ 88Top-256
❑ 88TopTif-256
❑ 90El PasDAGTI-36

Schu, Rick
❑ 84PorBeaC-209
❑ 85Don-448
❑ 85FleUpd-100
❑ 85PhiTas-43
❑ 85PorBeaC-34
❑ 85TopTifT-104T
❑ 85TopTra-104T
❑ 86Don-570
❑ 86Fle-451
❑ 86OPC-16
❑ 86PhiTas-15
❑ 86SevCoi-E9
❑ 86Top-16
❑ 86TopSti-122
❑ 86TopTif-16
❑ 87Don-509
❑ 87Fle-188
❑ 87FleGlo-188
❑ 87PhiTas-15
❑ 87Top-209
❑ 87TopTif-209
❑ 88Don-432
❑ 88Fle-316
❑ 88FleGlo-316
❑ 88OriFreB-25
❑ 88OriPos-32
❑ 88Sco-448
❑ 88ScoGlo-448
❑ 88StaLinPh-17
❑ 88Top-731
❑ 88TopBig-122
❑ 88TopTif-731
❑ 89BalOriP-31
❑ 89Don-406
❑ 89Fle-619
❑ 89FleGlo-619
❑ 89OPC-352
❑ 89RedFolSB-105
❑ 89RocRedWC-23
❑ 89RocRedWP-1642
❑ 89Sco-452
❑ 89TigMar-35
❑ 89Top-352
❑ 89TopBig-164
❑ 89TopTif-352
❑ 89TopTra-112T
❑ 89TopTraT-112T
❑ 89UppDec-490
❑ 90Don-599
❑ 90OPC-498
❑ 90Top-498
❑ 90TopTif-498
❑ 91Fle-326
❑ 91LinDriAAA-495
❑ 91OriCro-409
❑ 91ScrRedBLD-495
❑ 91ScrRedBP-2547
❑ 92ScrRedBF-2456
❑ 92ScrRedBS-493
❑ 92SkyAAAF-223
❑ 92TriA AAS-493
❑ 98ScrRedB1ATI-17
❑ 98SouBenSHM-26

Schubert, Brian
❑ 90NiaFalRP-24

Schuble, Henry
❑ 32R33So2-411
❑ 33Gou-4
❑ 33GouCanV-4
❑ 34TigTeal-17
❑ 35GouPuzR-5F
❑ 35GouPuzR-6F
❑ 35GouPuzR-11H
❑ 35GouPuzR-13F
❑ 74TigTCM1AC-27
❑ 76TigOldTS-20

Schubmehl, Brian
❑ 98BelSnaM-24

Schuckert, Wayne
❑ 81AppFoxT-12
❑ 82AppFoxFr-18
❑ 83GleFalWST-19

Schueler, Ron
❑ 73OPC-169
❑ 73Top-169
❑ 74OPC-544
❑ 74PhiJohP-37
❑ 74Top-544
❑ 74TopTra-544T
❑ 75OPC-292
❑ 75PhiPhiP-27
❑ 75Top-292
❑ 75TopMin-292
❑ 76OPC-586
❑ 76PhiPhiP-26
❑ 76Top-586
❑ 77Top-337
❑ 78SSP270-138
❑ 78Top-409
❑ 79Top-686
❑ 84A'sMot-27

Schueler, Russ
❑ 87BurExpP-1080

Schuerholz, John
❑ 82Roy-19
❑ 83RoyPos-27
❑ 84RoyPos-30
❑ 85RoyTeal-28

Schuermann, Lance
❑ 91ButCopKSP-16
❑ 92Ft.MyeMCB-24
❑ 92Ft.MyeMF-2746
❑ 93ChaRanC-20
❑ 93ChaRanF-1941
❑ 94TulDriF-245
❑ 94TulDriTI-22
❑ 96BowBayB-25

Schugel, Jeff
❑ 84VisOakT-14
❑ 85VisOakT-6

Schula, Kevin
❑ 92IdaFalGF-3516

Schuldt, Matt
❑ 98HudValR-24

Schuler, Dave
❑ 77WatIndT-19
❑ 78SalLakCGC-20
❑ 79SalLakCGT-17A
❑ 80SalLakCGT-6
❑ 81SalLakCGT-11
❑ 82OmaRoyT-8
❑ 83OmaRoyT-9
❑ 85RicBraT-8
❑ 86OmaRoyP-19
❑ 86OmaRoyT-19
❑ 87DenZepP-11
❑ 88VerMarP-941
❑ 90Ft.LauYS-24
❑ 91PriWilCC-25
❑ 91PriWilCP-1443
❑ 92PriWilCF-166
❑ 93AlbYanF-2179
❑ 94AlbYanF-1459
❑ 96SanJosGB-29

Schulhofer, Adam
❑ 92GenCubC-7
❑ 92GenCubF-1560
❑ 93PeoChiC-18
❑ 93PeoChiF-1084

Schullstrom, Erik
❑ 88AlaGolTI-16
❑ 89FreStaBS-19
❑ 90FreStaS-13
❑ 92ClaFS7-121
❑ 92HagSunF-2555
❑ 92HagSunS-268
❑ 92SkyAA F-112
❑ 93BowBayF-2189
❑ 94NasXprF-386
❑ 95Ult-306
❑ 95UltGolM-306
❑ 96Pac-359
❑ 96PawRedSDD-26
❑ 96TreThuB-15

Schulmerich, Wes
❑ 28Zee-40
❑ 29Zee-30
❑ 34DiaMatCSB-161
❑ 34ExhFou-6
❑ 34Gou-54
❑ 83ConMar-30
❑ 88ConNatA-17

Schult, Art
❑ 53Top-167
❑ 56SeaPop-18
❑ 58Top-58A
❑ 58Top-58B
❑ 60Lea-123
❑ 60Top-93
❑ 60TopVen-93
❑ 79TCM50-253
❑ 91TopArc1-167

Schult, Rob
❑ 97UCLBruTI-22

Schulte, Fred
❑ 14PieStaT-93
❑ 28Exh-60
❑ 29ExhFou-30
❑ 29PorandAR-80
❑ 30CubTeal-17
❑ 31Exh-29
❑ 33Gou-112
❑ 33Gou-190
❑ 34BatR31-50
❑ 35DiaMatCS3T1-129
❑ 35ExhFou-16
❑ 79DiaGre-52
❑ 91ConTSN-286
❑ 91ConTSN-304

Schulte, Joe
❑ 86AshTouP-26
❑ 87OscAstP-14

Schulte, John
❑ 90HigSchPLS-12
❑ 90WelPirP-9
❑ 92AugPirC-15
❑ 92AugPirF-254

Schulte, John C.
❑ 31Zee-23
❑ 33Gou-186
❑ 40PlaBal-12
❑ 43YanSta-23
❑ 75YanDyn1T-43
❑ 94ConTSN-1046
❑ 94ConTSNB-1046

Schulte, Len
❑ 46SeaSLP-51
❑ 96Bro194F-8

Schulte, Mark
❑ 84ArkTraT-13
❑ 86ArkTraP-22
❑ 87Ft.MyeRP-12

Schulte, Rich
❑ 91AubAstC-10
❑ 91AubAstP-4287
❑ 92BurAstC-24
❑ 92BurAstF-559
❑ 93OscAstC-19
❑ 93OscAstF-640

Schulte, Todd
❑ 83BurRanF-2
❑ 83BurRanT-10

Schulte, Troy
❑ 93AubAstC-21
❑ 93AubAstF-3442
❑ 94AubAstC-17
❑ 94AubAstF-3758
❑ 95AubAstTI-17

Schulte, Wildfire (Frank)
❑ 07CubA.CDPP-11
❑ 07CubGFGCP-11
❑ 08AmeCarE91-24
❑ 08AmeCarE91-61
❑ 08RosComP-108
❑ 09ColChiE-256
❑ 09MaxPubP-10
❑ 09MaxPubP-21
❑ 09RamT20-106
❑ 09SpoNewSM-66
❑ 09T206-315
❑ 09T206-316
❑ 10ChiE-8
❑ 10CouT21-223
❑ 10CouT21-316
❑ 10DomDisP-108
❑ 10RedCroT-67
❑ 10RedCroT-154
❑ 10RedCroT-241
❑ 10SweCapPP-90
❑ 11BasBatEU-32
❑ 11HelSta-104
❑ 11PinT-5-206
❑ 11S74Sil-68
❑ 11SpoLifCW-314
❑ 11SpoLifM-181
❑ 11T205-151
❑ 11TurRedT-117
❑ 12ColRedB-256
❑ 12ColTinT-256

❑ 12HasTriFT-66
❑ 12T207-163
❑ 14CraJacE-101
❑ 14E&SP-5
❑ 14FatPlaT-45
❑ 14PolGroW-25
❑ 15CraJacE-101
❑ 15SpoNewM-158
❑ 15VicT21-25
❑ 16BF2FP-70
❑ 16SpoNewM-156
❑ 17ColE13-152
❑ 19W514-10
❑ 22Zee-38
❑ 22Zee-139
❑ 72ClaCar-70
❑ 87Cub190T-7

Schultea, Chris
❑ 92SalLakTSP-12

Schultea, Matt
❑ 95OdgRapTI-26

Schultz, Barney (George)
❑ 62CubJayP-10
❑ 62Top-89
❑ 62TopStal-110
❑ 62TopVen-89
❑ 63Top-452
❑ 65OPC-28
❑ 65Top-28
❑ 71CarTeal-22
❑ 71CarTeal-33
❑ 73OPC-497
❑ 73Top-497A
❑ 73Top-497B
❑ 74OPC-236
❑ 74OPC-236
❑ 74Top-236
❑ 78TCM60I-15

Schultz, Bob D.
❑ 52Top-401
❑ 53Top-144
❑ 54Bow-59
❑ 83TopRep5-401
❑ 91TopArc1-144

Schultz, Bobby
❑ 77Car5-24
❑ 91BurIndP-3317

Schultz, Buddy (Charles)
❑ 77CarTeal-23
❑ 78CarTeal-29
❑ 78Top-301
❑ 79Car5-25
❑ 79Top-532
❑ 80Top-601
❑ 82ArkTraT-9

Schultz, Carl
❑ 93DanBraF-3617
❑ 94CarLeaAF-CAR30

Schultz, Eric
❑ 98FarRedHM-27

Schultz, Greg
❑ 83AlbDukTc-18
❑ 84AlbDukCr-157
❑ 85PhoGiaC-196

Schultz, Howie
❑ 90DodTar-711

Schultz, Jeffrey
❑ 98SouOreTG-29

Schultz, Joseph C. Jr.
❑ 46SeaSLP-56
❑ 47TipTop-72
❑ 62KahAtl-20
❑ 65CarTeal-21
❑ 69PilPos-5
❑ 69Top-254
❑ 70RoyTeal-32
❑ 75DetTigP-30
❑ 76DetTigP-26
❑ 83Pil69G-2
❑ 89PacLegI-162
❑ 93ConTSN-790
❑ 96Bro194F-18

Schultz, Joseph C. Sr.
❑ 13Zee-88
❑ 17Zee-15
❑ 21Nei-114
❑ 22E120-236
❑ 22W572-92
❑ 22W573-117
❑ 90DodTar-1065

Schultz, Scott
❑ 87LakTigP-5
❑ 92LSUTigM-6
❑ 93LSUTigM-16
❑ 94LSUTig-9
❑ 94LSUTigMP-15
❑ 95WatIndTI-26

Schultz, Ted
❑ 76AppFoxT-23

Schultz, Wallace
❑ 19Zee-120

Schulz, Harry
❑ 75CliPilT-25

Schulz, Jeff
❑ 83ButCopKT-28
❑ 86OmaRoyP-20
❑ 86OmaRoyT-6
❑ 87OmaRoyP-23
❑ 88OmaRoyC-15
❑ 88OmaRoyP-1508
❑ 89OmaRoyC-22
❑ 89OmaRoyP-1736
❑ 90CMC-193
❑ 90OmaRoyC-18
❑ 90OmaRoyP-79
❑ 90ProAAAF-614
❑ 90TopDeb89-110
❑ 91BufBisLD-45
❑ 91BufBisP-554
❑ 91Don-687
❑ 91Fle-568
❑ 91LinDriAAA-45
❑ 91Sco-336
❑ 91Sco100RS-25
❑ 91UppDec-607
❑ 92IowCubF-4063
❑ 92NasSouS-291

Schulz, Pat
❑ 93WatIndC-23
❑ 93WatIndF-3578

Schulze, Don
❑ 81QuaCitCT-29
❑ 83IowCubT-9
❑ 84IndWhe-37
❑ 84IowCubT-22
❑ 85AllGamPI-86
❑ 85Don-639
❑ 85Fle-454
❑ 85Ind-27
❑ 85Top-93
❑ 85TopTif-93
❑ 86IndOhH-37
❑ 86IndTeal-41
❑ 86Top-542
❑ 86TopTif-542
❑ 87BufBisP-22
❑ 87Fle-259
❑ 87FleGlo-259
❑ 87TidTidP-25
❑ 87TidTidT-26
❑ 87Top-297
❑ 87TopTif-297
❑ 88TolMudHC-3
❑ 88TolMudHP-604
❑ 88Top-131
❑ 88TopTif-131
❑ 89ColCliC-6
❑ 89ColCliP-11
❑ 89ColCliP-753
❑ 89PadPos-30
❑ 89TidTidC-11
❑ 91MetWIZ-353
❑ 92YanWIZ8-173
❑ 93RocRedWF-238

Schumacher, Garry
❑ 64TopRooAB-16

Schumacher, Hal
❑ 33Gou-129
❑ 33Gou-240
❑ 33NatLeaAC-14
❑ 33WorCig-84
❑ 34BatR31-52
❑ 34BatR31-110
❑ 35GouPuzR-1K
❑ 35GouPuzR-3B
❑ 35GouPuzR-14B
❑ 35GouPuzR-15B
❑ 35WheBB1-23
❑ 36WorWidGV-23
❑ 38OurNatGPP-26
❑ 39PlaBal-73
❑ 40PlaBal-85
❑ 48SweSpoT-7
❑ 61Fle-137
❑ 72TCMthe3-62
❑ 74Bra193NLA-14
❑ 77GalGloG-221
❑ 83BigLeaCOA-35
❑ 83ConMar-46
❑ 88ConNatA-18
❑ 94ConTSN-1127
❑ 94ConTSNB-1127

Schumacher, Roy
❑ 81AppFoxT-11

Schumaker, Mark
❑ 94FreKeyC-29

Schuman, Rich
❑ 87AriWilP-11

Schumate, Jack
❑ 79WisRapTT-22

Schunk, Jerry
❑ 87DunBluJP-947
❑ 88DunBluJS-16
❑ 89KnoBluJB-23
❑ 89KnoBluJP-1142
❑ 89KnoBluJS-19
❑ 90KnoBluJB-25
❑ 90KnoBluJP-1250
❑ 90KnoBluJS-18
❑ 90StaFS7-89
❑ 91BluJayS-34
❑ 91Bow-20
❑ 91LinDriAAA-516
❑ 91SyrChiLD-516
❑ 91SyrChiMB-22
❑ 91SyrChiP-2488
❑ 92SkyAAAF-231
❑ 92SyrChiF-1978
❑ 92SyrChiMB-18
❑ 92SyrChiS-515
❑ 93PorBeaF-2391
❑ 94PorSeaDTI-27
❑ 95ChaKniTI-23

Schupp, Ferdie
❑ 16FleBreD-84
❑ 17ColE13-153
❑ 21E121So1-90
❑ 21E121So8-86A
❑ 21E121So8-86B
❑ 22AmeCarE122-61
❑ 22AmeCarE122-62
❑ 22W575-117
❑ 90DodTar-712

Schurman, Ryan
❑ 96DanBraB-20
❑ 97EugEmeB-12
❑ 98MacBraM-20

Schurr, Wayne
❑ 64Top-548
❑ 65OPC-149
❑ 65Top-149

Schuster, Bill
❑ 44CubTeal-21
❑ 47SigOil-36
❑ 48AngTeal-25
❑ 49AngTeal-31
❑ 49W725AngTI-25
❑ 54SeaPop-23

Schuster, Frank
❑ 74TacTwiC-9

Schuster, Mark
❑ 79HolMilT-7
❑ 80HolMilT-3
❑ 81VanCanT-5
❑ 82ElPasDT-8
❑ 84PhoGiaC-7
❑ 85PhoGiaC-185

Schutz, Carl
❑ 93DanBraC-21
❑ 94DurBulC-17
❑ 94DurBulF-326
❑ 94DurBulTI-18
❑ 95BreBtaTI-49
❑ 95Exc-156
❑ 96RicBraB-25
❑ 96RicBraRC-6
❑ 96RicBraUB-25
❑ 97RicBra-22
❑ 98GreBraG-24

Schwab, Chris
❑ 94Bow-556
❑ 94BurBeeC-24
❑ 94BurBeeF-1096
❑ 94ClaGolF-73
❑ 94ClaGolN1PLF-LP13
❑ 94ClaGolREF-RE13
❑ 94UppDecML-178
❑ 96DelShoB-26
❑ 98JupHamQ-24

Schwab, Ken
❑ 80CliGiaT-8

Schwabe, Mike
❑ 88GleFalTP-927
❑ 89BlaYNPRWL-27
❑ 89FleUpd-32
❑ 89LonTigP-1375
❑ 90CMC-386
❑ 90ProAAAF-378
❑ 90TolMudHC-9
❑ 90TolMudHP-148
❑ 90TopDeb89-111
❑ 91Fle-351
❑ 92PorBeaF-2665
❑ 92PorBeaS-418

Schwall, Don
❑ 62Baz-37
❑ 62Jel-64
❑ 62Pos-64
❑ 62PosCan-64
❑ 62RedSoxJP-10
❑ 62SalPlaC-210
❑ 62ShiPlaC-210
❑ 62Top-35
❑ 62TopBuc-80
❑ 62TopStal-19
❑ 62TopVen-35
❑ 63Top-344
❑ 64PirKDK-24
❑ 64Top-558
❑ 65Top-362
❑ 66OPC-144
❑ 66Top-144
❑ 66TopVen-144
❑ 67CokCapB-15
❑ 67Top-267
❑ 78TCM60I-118
❑ 81RedSoxBG2S-110

Schwanke, Jim
❑ 91OklStaC-22
❑ 92OklStaC-5

Schwankl, Darren
❑ 92Min-17

Schwarber, Mike
❑ '80BatTroT-10
❑ 81WatIndT-15
❑ 82ChaLooT-10

Schwarber, Tom
❑ 91BriTigC-23
❑ 91BriTigP-3605
❑ 92FayGenC-19
❑ 92FayGenF-2167
❑ 93LakTigF-1309
❑ 93LonTigF-2306

Schwartz, Dave
❑ 91EliTwiP-4300

Schwartz, Randy
❑ 67OPC-33
❑ 67Top-33
❑ 67VanMouSO-21

Schwartzbauer, Whitey
❑ 97PorRocG-25
❑ 98AshTouM-20

Schwarz, Jeff
❑ 88WinSpiS-19
❑ 89HagSunB-24
❑ 89HagSunP-263
❑ 89HagSunS-16
❑ 91ElPasDLD-195
❑ 91ElPasDP-2748
❑ 91LinDriAA-195
❑ 92BirBarF-2581
❑ 92BirBarS-94
❑ 92VanCanF-2722
❑ 93FleFinE-198
❑ 93WhiSoxK-26
❑ 94Fle-95
❑ 94Sco-588
❑ 94ScoGolR-588
❑ 94StaClu-482
❑ 94StaCluFDI-482
❑ 94StaCluGR-482
❑ 94StaCluMOP-482
❑ 94StaCluT-137
❑ 94StaCluTFDI-137
❑ 94Top-33
❑ 94TopGol-33
❑ 94TopSpa-33
❑ 94Ult-38

Schwarz, Tom
❑ 86VisOakP-19
❑ 87OrlTwiP-18
❑ 88ReaPhiP-863

Schwegman, Harry
❑ 59O'KAleMR-19

Schweighoffer, Mike
❑ 85VerBeaDT-18
❑ 87SanAntDTI-13
❑ 88SanAntMB-10

Schweitzer, Al
❑ 09PC7HHB-39
❑ 10JHDABE-15
❑ 11PinT-5-111
❑ 11SpoLifCW-315
❑ 11SpoLifM-116

Schweitzer, Rick
❑ 97MobBayBB-30

Schweitzer, Tim
❑ 92AriWilP-16

Schwenck, Rudolph
❑ 12HomRunKE-54
❑ 12Zee-92

Schwenke, Matt
❑ 94BakDodC-22
❑ 96LasVegSB-22
❑ 96RanCucQB-25
❑ 97RanCucQG-26

Schwerman, Brian
❑ 77ChaPatT-20
❑ 78ChaPirT-22

Scioneaux, Damian
❑ 97HudValRB-5
❑ 98ChaRivDG-25

Sciortino, Michael
❑ 90PitMetP-15
❑ 91PitMetC-9
❑ 91PitMetP-3433

Scioscia, Mike
❑ 77CliDodT-23
❑ 79AlbDukTc-10
❑ 80AlbDukTc-26
❑ 81Dod-26
❑ 81DodPol-14
❑ 81DodPos-8
❑ 81Fle-131
❑ 81LonBeaPT-8
❑ 81Top-302
❑ 82DodPol-14
❑ 82DodPos-8
❑ 82DodUniOV-20
❑ 82Don-598
❑ 82Fle-22
❑ 82OPC-173
❑ 82Top-642
❑ 83DodPol-14
❑ 83DodPos-15
❑ 83Don-75
❑ 83Fle-221
❑ 83Top-352
❑ 84DodPol-14
❑ 84Fle-113
❑ 84Nes792-64
❑ 84Top-64
❑ 84TopTif-64
❑ 85AllGamPI-134
❑ 85DodCokP-30
❑ 85Don-459
❑ 85Fle-385
❑ 85Lea-118
❑ 85Top-549
❑ 85TopSti-79
❑ 85TopTif-549
❑ 86DodCokP-28
❑ 86DodPol-14
❑ 86DodUniOP-18
❑ 86Don-93
❑ 86Fle-144
❑ 86Lea-87
❑ 86OPC-111
❑ 86Spo-167
❑ 86Top-468
❑ 86TopMinL-46
❑ 86TopSti-68
❑ 86TopTat-19
❑ 86TopTif-468
❑ 87DodMot-10
❑ 87DodPho-13
❑ 87DodPol-6
❑ 87Don-130
❑ 87DonOpeD-82
❑ 87Fle-454
❑ 87FleGlo-454
❑ 87Lea-123
❑ 87OPC-144
❑ 87SevCoi-W12
❑ 87Spo-67
❑ 87Spo-151
❑ 87SpoTeaP-14
❑ 87Top-144
❑ 87TopSti-73
❑ 87TopTif-144
❑ 88DodMot-10
❑ 88DodPol-14
❑ 88Don-106
❑ 88DonBasB-260
❑ 88Fle-524
❑ 88FleGlo-524
❑ 88Lea-97
❑ 88OPC-225
❑ 88PanSti-307
❑ 88Sco-53
❑ 88ScoGlo-53
❑ 88Spo-110
❑ 88StaLinD-15
❑ 88Top-225
❑ 88TopBig-72
❑ 88TopSti-67
❑ 88TopTif-225
❑ 89Bow-342
❑ 89BowTif-342
❑ 89DodMot-3
❑ 89DodPol-9
❑ 89DodSmoG-31
❑ 89DodStaSV-12
❑ 89Don-77
❑ 89DonBasB-66
❑ 89Fle-71
❑ 89FleAll-9
❑ 89FleGlo-71
❑ 89FleGlo-WS4
❑ 89FleWorS-4
❑ 89OPC-7
❑ 89PanSti-104
❑ 89Sco-121
❑ 89Spo-138
❑ 89Top-755
❑ 89TopBig-281
❑ 89TopSti-58
❑ 89TopTif-755
❑ 89TVSpoM-36
❑ 89UppDec-116
❑ 90Bow-89
❑ 90BowTif-89
❑ 90DodMot-4
❑ 90DodPol-14
❑ 90DodTar-713
❑ 90Don-316
❑ 90DonBesN-5
❑ 90DonGraS-7
❑ 90Fle-407
❑ 90FleCan-407
❑ 90Lea-49
❑ 90M.Vpin-49
❑ 90OPC-605
❑ 90PanSti-276
❑ 90PubIntS-17
❑ 90Sco-398
❑ 90Sco100S-48
❑ 90Spo-163
❑ 90Top-605
❑ 90TopBig-67
❑ 90TopDou-58
❑ 90TopGloS-34
❑ 90TopSti-64
❑ 90TopStiB-24
❑ 90TopTif-605
❑ 90UppDec-298
❑ 90USPlaCA-2H
❑ 91Bow-613
❑ 91DodMot-4
❑ 91DodPho-25
❑ 91DodPol-14
❑ 91DodSt.V-3
❑ 91Don-112
❑ 91Don-436A
❑ 91Don-436B
❑ 91Fle-219
❑ 91Lea-24
❑ 91OPC-305
❑ 91OPC-404
❑ 91PanFreS-54
❑ 91PanSti-57
❑ 91RedFolS-128
❑ 91Sco-520
❑ 91StaClu-19
❑ 91StaCluP-39
❑ 91StaPinB-45
❑ 91Stu-189
❑ 91Top-305
❑ 91Top-404
❑ 91TopDesS-305
❑ 91TopDesS-404
❑ 91TopGloA-20
❑ 91TopMic-305
❑ 91TopMic-404
❑ 91TopTif-305
❑ 91TopTif-404
❑ 91Ult-169
❑ 91UppDec-139
❑ 92Bow-368
❑ 92DodMot-9
❑ 92DodPol-14
❑ 92DodSmo-5192
❑ 92DodStaTA-29

❑ 92Don-480
❑ 92Fle-470
❑ 92HitTheBB-31
❑ 92Lea-165
❑ 92LeaBlaG-165
❑ 92New-26
❑ 92OPC-13
❑ 92PanSti-191
❑ 92Pin-210
❑ 92Sco-226
❑ 92Sco-782
❑ 92SpoStaCC-41
❑ 92StaClu-140
❑ 92Stu-48
❑ 92Top-13
❑ 92TopGol-13
❑ 92TopGolW-13
❑ 92TopMic-13
❑ 92TriPla-191
❑ 92Ult-217
❑ 92UppDec-152
❑ 93Don-508
❑ 93Fle-67
❑ 93OPC-326
❑ 93PadMot-23
❑ 93PanSti-213
❑ 93Pin-498
❑ 93RedFolS-87
❑ 93Sco-623
❑ 93Sel-69
❑ 93StaClu-46
❑ 93StaCluFDI-46
❑ 93StaCluMOP-46
❑ 93StaCluMP-9
❑ 93Top-202
❑ 93TopGol-202
❑ 93TopInaM-202
❑ 93TopInaR-202
❑ 93TopMic-202
❑ 93TriPla-196
❑ 93UppDec-688
❑ 93UppDecGold-688
❑ 94StaCluT-255
❑ 94StaCluTFDI-255
❑ 98DodMot-28
❑ 98DodPol-30

Scoble, Troy
❑ 91AdeGiaF-15
❑ 93AusFut-10
❑ 95AusFutSFP-SFFP1

Scoggins, Lynn
❑ 15Zee-19
❑ 16Zee-16

Scolaro, Don
❑ 94AubAstC-18
❑ 94AubAstF-3767
❑ 95AubAstTI-6

Sconiers, Daryl
❑ 78QuaCitAT-24
❑ 80ElPasDT-14
❑ 81SalLakCGT-20
❑ 82Top-653
❑ 83Don-141
❑ 83TopTra-99T
❑ 84AngSmo-26
❑ 84Don-451
❑ 84Fle-528
❑ 84FleSti-112
❑ 84Nes792-27
❑ 84Top-27
❑ 84TopTif-27
❑ 85Don-620
❑ 85Fle-312
❑ 85OPC-256
❑ 85Top-604
❑ 85TopTif-604
❑ 86Fle-168
❑ 86SanJosBP-18
❑ 86Top-193
❑ 86TopTif-193
❑ 87SanJosBP-28
❑ 88VanCanC-22
❑ 88VanCanP-766
❑ 91LinDriAA-445
❑ 91MidAngLD-445
❑ 91MidAngP-443

Scooch, Mascot
❑ 92SyrChiMB-19

Scopio, Joe
❑ 94WilCubC-21
❑ 94WilCubF-3780

Scoras, John
❑ 78MemChiBC-9
❑ 79MemChiT-17

Score, Herb
❑ 47Exh-204A
❑ 47Exh-204B
❑ 55IndCarBL-8
❑ 55IndGolS-7
❑ 56Top-140
❑ 57IndSoh-12
❑ 57IndTeal-20
❑ 57Top-50
❑ 58IndTeal-20
❑ 58Top-352
❑ 58Top-495
❑ 59Ind-18
❑ 59Kah-32
❑ 59Top-88
❑ 59TopVen-88
❑ 60Kah-37
❑ 60Top-360
❑ 60TopTat-48
❑ 61Top-185
❑ 61Top-337
❑ 61UniOil-SD9
❑ 61WhiSoxTS-15
❑ 62Top-116
❑ 62TopVen-116
❑ 62WhiSoxTS-19
❑ 76SSP-595
❑ 77SerSta-22
❑ 78ReaRem-18
❑ 79DiaGre-300
❑ 79TCM50-134
❑ 80MarExh-28
❑ 86IndIndTI-24
❑ 87SpoRea-16
❑ 89PacLegI-126
❑ 89SweBasG-114
❑ 90PacLeg-49
❑ 90SweBasG-32
❑ 91SweBasG-82
❑ 92ActPacA-79
❑ 94TopArc1-256
❑ 94TopArc1G-256
❑ 94UppDecAH-56
❑ 94UppDecAH1-56

Scott, Andrew
❑ 91AdeGiaF-16
❑ 93AusFut-4

Scott, Brian
❑ 97HicCraB-25
❑ 98HicCraUO-27
❑ 98WinWar-26

Scott, Charles
❑ 86WatIndP-25
❑ 88ColSprSSC-9
❑ 88ColSprSSP-1529
❑ 88IndTeal-31
❑ 89ColSprSSP-8
❑ 90CMC-559
❑ 90PorBeaC-7
❑ 90PorBeaP-178
❑ 90ProAAAF-248
❑ 91LinDriAAA-419
❑ 91PorBeaLD-419
❑ 91PorBeaP-1565

Scott, Craig
❑ 89KinMetS-21

Scott, Dale
❑ 88T/MUmp-58
❑ 89T/MUmp-56
❑ 90T/MUmp-54

Scott, Darryl
❑ 88CapCodPPaLP-34
❑ 90BoiHawP-3313
❑ 91QuaCitAC-10
❑ 91QuaCitAP-2627
❑ 92MidAngF-4027
❑ 92MidAngOHP-22
❑ 92MidAngS-469
❑ 92ProFS7-35
❑ 92SkyAA F-200
❑ 93AngStaCl-26
❑ 93FleFinE-189
❑ 93TriAAAGF-33
❑ 93VanCanF-2596
❑ 94Pin-225
❑ 94PinArtP-225
❑ 94PinMusC-225
❑ 96BufBisB-18
❑ 97BufBis-24

Scott, Death Valley (James)
❑ 11SpoLifM-29
❑ 11T205-152
❑ 14CraJacE-26
❑ 15CraJacE-26
❑ 18WhiSoxTI-22
❑ 19Zee-101
❑ 20Zee-115
❑ 92Man191BSR-23

Scott, Dick
❑ 92MadMusF-1252

Scott, Dick (Richard E.)
❑ 82ColCliT-15
❑ 85AlbYanT-19
❑ 87ColCliP-13
❑ 88AlbYanP-1350
❑ 89TacTigC-20
❑ 89TacTigP-1554
❑ 90CMC-601
❑ 90ProAAAF-150
❑ 90TacTigC-24
❑ 90TacTigP-103
❑ 90TopDeb89-112
❑ 92MadMusC-26
❑ 93SouOreAC-28
❑ 93SouOreAF-4081
❑ 94ModA'sC-26
❑ 94ModA'sF-3078
❑ 95HunStaTI-23
❑ 96HunStaTI-23
❑ 97SouBenSH-3

Scott, Dick (Richard L.)
❑ 77FriOneYW-38
❑ 90DodTar-714

Scott, Donnie
❑ 84OklCit8T-19
❑ 95BilMusTI-27

Scott, Donnie (Donald M.)
❑ 80AshTouT-21
❑ 81TulDriT-13
❑ 82TulDriT-11
❑ 83OklCit8T-23
❑ 84RanJarP-43
❑ 85CalCanC-81
❑ 85Don-544
❑ 85Fle-568
❑ 85Top-496
❑ 85TopTif-496
❑ 85TopTifT-105T
❑ 85TopTra-105T
❑ 86Fle-474
❑ 86RocRedWP-19
❑ 86Top-568
❑ 86TopTif-568
❑ 87ElPasDP-3
❑ 88ElPasDB-2
❑ 89DenZepC-6
❑ 89DenZepP-52
❑ 90CMC-137
❑ 90NasSouC-12
❑ 90NasSouP-237
❑ 90ProAAAF-549
❑ 91LinDriAAA-271
❑ 91NasSouLD-271
❑ 91NasSouP-2160
❑ 92BilMusF-3373
❑ 92BilMusSP-30
❑ 93BilMusF-3962
❑ 93BilMusSP-27
❑ 93RanKee-321
❑ 94BilMusF-3685
❑ 94BilMusSP-23

Scott, Gary
❑ 88CapCodPPaLP-88
❑ 89GenCubP-1877
❑ 90CarLeaA-49
❑ 90TopMag-54
❑ 90WinSpiTI-1
❑ 91Bow-535
❑ 91Cla2-T88
❑ 91CubVinL-25
❑ 91FleUpd-80
❑ 91IowCubP-1068
❑ 91LeaGolR-BC4
❑ 91LeaGolRNV-268
❑ 91OPCPre-107
❑ 91ScoAllF-3
❑ 91ScoRoo-90T
❑ 91StaClu-596
❑ 91Stu-159
❑ 91TopTra-107T
❑ 91TopTraT-107T
❑ 91UltUpd-72
❑ 91UppDec-58
❑ 92Bow-128
❑ 92Lea-6
❑ 92LeaBlaG-6
❑ 92Pin-269
❑ 92PinRoo-15
❑ 92PinTea2-73
❑ 92Sco100RS-81
❑ 92StaClu-708
❑ 92Stu-19
❑ 92TopDeb91-159
❑ 92TopTra-102T
❑ 92TopTraG-102T
❑ 92Ult-474
❑ 93Don-750
❑ 93IndIndF-1498
❑ 93Sco-547
❑ 93Top-656
❑ 93TopGol-656
❑ 93TopInaM-656
❑ 93TopInaR-656
❑ 93TopMic-656
❑ 93TriPla-84
❑ 94PhoFirF-1529
❑ 95PhoFirTI-21

Scott, George C.
❑ 92ElmPioC-1
❑ 92ElmPioF-1392
❑ 93LynRedSC-23
❑ 93LynRedSF-2532

Scott, George Charles
❑ 47PM1StaP1-197
❑ 66Top-558
❑ 67CokCapA-34
❑ 67CokCapAAm-22
❑ 67CokCapRS-12
❑ 67DexPre-187
❑ 67OPC-75
❑ 67Top-75
❑ 67TopRedSS-16
❑ 67TopVen-200
❑ 68AtlOilPBCC-42
❑ 68Baz-7
❑ 68CokCapRS-12
❑ 68DexPre-70
❑ 68Top-233
❑ 68TopActS-2C
❑ 68TopActS-13C
❑ 68TopGamI-22
❑ 68TopVen-233
❑ 69MLBOffS-17
❑ 69RedSoxAO-10
❑ 69RedSoxTI-9
❑ 69RedSoxTI-7
❑ 69Top-574
❑ 69TopSta-138
❑ 69TopTeaP-3
❑ 70MLBOffS-165
❑ 70OPC-385
❑ 70RedSoxCPPC-12
❑ 70Top-385
❑ 71MilDud-28
❑ 71MLBOffS-331
❑ 71OPC-9
❑ 71RedSoxA-8
❑ 71RedSoxTI-9
❑ 71Top-9
❑ 71TopCoi-98
❑ 72MilBra-311
❑ 72SevTraC-48
❑ 72Top-585
❑ 73LinPor-103
❑ 73OPC-263
❑ 73Top-263
❑ 73TopCanL-47
❑ 73TopCom-18
❑ 73TopPin-18
❑ 74OPC-27
❑ 74Top-27
❑ 74TopDecE-30
❑ 74TopSta-199
❑ 75Hos-26
❑ 75HosTwi-26
❑ 75OPC-360
❑ 75Top-360
❑ 75TopMin-360
❑ 76BreA&P-11
❑ 76Hos-54
❑ 76HosTwi-54
❑ 76Kel-21
❑ 76OPC-15
❑ 76OPC-194
❑ 76OPC-196
❑ 76RedSox-8
❑ 76SSP-237
❑ 76Top-15
❑ 76Top-194
❑ 76Top-196
❑ 77Hos-148
❑ 77OPC-210
❑ 77Top-255
❑ 78Hos-24
❑ 78OPC-12
❑ 78PapGinD-15
❑ 78SSP270-183
❑ 78Top-125
❑ 79BasPat-79
❑ 79OPC-340
❑ 79Top-645
❑ 80Top-414
❑ 80VenLeaS-77
❑ 81RedSoxBG2S-66
❑ 81RedSoxBG2S-111
❑ 86BreGreT-1
❑ 92UppDecS-6
❑ 92YanWIZ7-139
❑ 94BreMilB-177

Scott, Jeff
❑ 75LynRanT-24
❑ 77AshTouT-20
❑ 79AshTouT-22
❑ 87UtiBluSP-11

Scott, Jim
❑ 09T206-317
❑ 11HelSta-15
❑ 11PinT-5-759
❑ 12T207-164
❑ 14PieStaT-94
❑ 14PolGroW-26
❑ 15SpoNewM-159
❑ 16BF2FP-19
❑ 16SpoNewM-158
❑ 21Zee-132
❑ 22Zee-107
❑ 23Zee-144
❑ 24Zee-102
❑ 63GadFunC-51
❑ 86VerRedP-17
❑ 92ConTSN-341

Scott, Joe
❑ 86NegLeaF-58
❑ 92NegLeaRLI-54

Scott, Joe Burt
❑ 92NegLeaRLI-55

Scott, John H.
❑ 75OPC-616
❑ 75Top-616
❑ 75TopMin-616
❑ 76HawIsIC-7
❑ 76SSP-131
❑ 77OPC-94
❑ 77Top-473
❑ 78SprRedWK-4
❑ 78Top-547
❑ 79TCMJapPB-21

Scott, John William
❑ 23W503-63
❑ 23W515-25
❑ 91ConTSN-97

Scott, Kelly
❑ 83NasSouTI-19
❑ 84ColCliP-22
❑ 84ColCliT-19
❑ 85ColCliP-19
❑ 85ColCliT-9

Scott, Kevin
❑ 89AubAstP-2183
❑ 90AshTouP-2752
❑ 91Cla/Bes-37
❑ 91OscAstC-28
❑ 91OscAstP-689
❑ 92OscAstC-14
❑ 92OscAstF-2534
❑ 93AusFut-120
❑ 93OscAstC-20
❑ 93OscAstF-632

Scott, L. Everett
❑ 15SpoNewM-160
❑ 16SpoNewM-157
❑ 17ColE13-154
❑ 17HolBreD-92
❑ 19W514-90
❑ 20NatCarE-89
❑ 21E121So1-91
❑ 21E121So8-87
❑ 21Exh-153
❑ 21Exh-154
❑ 22AmeCarE122-63
❑ 22E120-73
❑ 22W575-118
❑ 22W575-119
❑ 22WilPatV-27
❑ 23W501-30
❑ 23W515-46
❑ 23WilChoV-144
❑ 28W512-7
❑ 75SenTCM1-31
❑ 77BobParMBC-18
❑ 91ConTSN-149

Scott, Mark
❑ 80ChaChaT-2

Scott, Mark ANN
❑ 59HomRunD-17

Scott, Marty (Martin)
❑ 79TucTorT-10
❑ 80VenLeaS-27
❑ 81TulDriT-4
❑ 82BurRanF-28
❑ 82BurRanT-25
❑ 83TulDriT-25
❑ 90TulDriDGB-34
❑ 97St.PauS-27
❑ 98St.PauSTI-23

Scott, Michael Wm.
❑ 87GreBraB-28
❑ 87SprCarB-19

Scott, Mickey (Ralph)
❑ 70Top-669
❑ 72OriPos-29
❑ 72Top-724
❑ 73BalOriP-38
❑ 73OPC-553
❑ 73Top-553
❑ 75CalAngP-37
❑ 76OPC-276
❑ 76Top-276
❑ 77Top-401
❑ 78ColCliT-22
❑ 91OriCro-410

Scott, Mike (Michael Warren)
❑ 76VenLeaS-188
❑ 78TidTidT-23
❑ 79TidTidT-15
❑ 80TidTidT-23
❑ 80Top-681
❑ 81Don-37
❑ 81Top-109
❑ 82Don-128
❑ 82Fle-535
❑ 82MetPhoA-19
❑ 82Top-246
❑ 82Top-432
❑ 83AstPos-27
❑ 83Fle-554
❑ 83Top-679
❑ 83TopTra-100T
❑ 84AstMot-14
❑ 84AstPos-26
❑ 84Don-136
❑ 84Fle-240
❑ 84Nes792-559
❑ 84Top-559
❑ 84TopTif-559
❑ 85AstHouP-16
❑ 85AstMot-18
❑ 85Don-258
❑ 85Fle-361
❑ 85OPC-17
❑ 85Top-17
❑ 85TopMin-17
❑ 85TopTif-17
❑ 86AstMilL-19
❑ 86AstPol-3
❑ 86AstTeal-14
❑ 86Don-476
❑ 86DonHig-46
❑ 86Fle-311
❑ 86FleMin-66
❑ 86FleStiC-108
❑ 86GreBraTI-16
❑ 86Lea-235
❑ 86SevCoi-S11
❑ 86Spo-195
❑ 86Top-268
❑ 86TopSti-27
❑ 86TopTat-23
❑ 86TopTif-268
❑ 87AstMot-2
❑ 87AstPol-11
❑ 87ClaGam-81
❑ 87ClaUpdY-123
❑ 87Don-18
❑ 87Don-163
❑ 87DonAll-32
❑ 87DonAllB-PC13
❑ 87DonOpeD-15
❑ 87DonSupD-18
❑ 87Dra-33
❑ 87Fle-68
❑ 87Fle-630
❑ 87FleAwaW-37
❑ 87FleGlo-68
❑ 87FleGlo-630
❑ 87FleLimE-38
❑ 87FleMin-99

❑ 87FleRecS-36
❑ 87FleSlu-38
❑ 87FleStiC-108
❑ 87GenMilB-6I
❑ 87HosSti-10
❑ 87KayB-30
❑ 87KraFoo-4
❑ 87Lea-18
❑ 87Lea-258
❑ 87MandMSL-18
❑ 87MSAJifPD-18
❑ 87OPC-330
❑ 87SmoNatL-5
❑ 87Spo-19
❑ 87Spo-119
❑ 87Spo-120
❑ 87SpoSupD-2
❑ 87SpoTeaP-8
❑ 87StuPan-5
❑ 87Top-330
❑ 87TopCoi-44
❑ 87TopGaloC-11
❑ 87TopMinL-11
❑ 87TopSti-15
❑ 87TopSti-35
❑ 87TopTif-330
❑ 87Woo-18
❑ 88AstMot-2
❑ 88AstPol-21
❑ 88CheBoy-19
❑ 88ClaBlu-221
❑ 88Don-112
❑ 88DonAll-40
❑ 88DonBasB-206
❑ 88DonBonM-BC12
❑ 88DonPop-18
❑ 88Fle-456
❑ 88Fle-632
❑ 88FleAwaW-36
❑ 88FleBasA-37
❑ 88FleBasM-32
❑ 88FleExcS-35
❑ 88FleGlo-456
❑ 88FleGlo-632
❑ 88FleHotS-35
❑ 88FleLeaL-36
❑ 88FleMin-80
❑ 88FleRecS-36
❑ 88FleSlu-37
❑ 88FleStiC-89
❑ 88FleSup-34
❑ 88FleTeaL-35
❑ 88GreBasS-50
❑ 88K-M-26
❑ 88KinDis-13
❑ 88Lea-54
❑ 88OPC-227
❑ 88PanSti-233
❑ 88PanSti-289
❑ 88RedFolSB-81
❑ 88Sco-335
❑ 88ScoBoxC-18
❑ 88ScoGlo-335
❑ 88Spo-66
❑ 88StaLinAl-31
❑ 88StaLinAst-16
❑ 88StaSco-1
❑ 88StaSco-2
❑ 88StaSco-3
❑ 88StaSco-4
❑ 88StaSco-5
❑ 88StaSco-6
❑ 88StaSco-7
❑ 88StaSco-8
❑ 88StaSco-9
❑ 88StaSco-10
❑ 88StaSco-11
❑ 88TarPla-39
❑ 88Top-760
❑ 88TopBig-140
❑ 88TopCoi-54
❑ 88TopGloA-21
❑ 88TopGloS-5
❑ 88TopMinL-51
❑ 88TopRitTM-4
❑ 88TopSti-30
❑ 88TopSti-154
❑ 88TopStiB-26
❑ 88TopTif-760
❑ 88TopUKM-68
❑ 88TopUKMT-68
❑ 89AstLenH-4
❑ 89AstMot-2
❑ 89AstSmo-36
❑ 89Bow-322
❑ 89BowTif-322
❑ 89ClaLigB-23
❑ 89Don-69
❑ 89DonBasB-94
❑ 89DonBonM-BC2
❑ 89Fle-367
❑ 89FleBasM-34
❑ 89FleGlo-367
❑ 89FleLeaL-34
❑ 89FleSup-37
❑ 89OPC-180
❑ 89PanSti-84
❑ 89RedFolSB-106
❑ 89Sco-550
❑ 89ScoHot1S-60
❑ 89Scomast-4
❑ 89Spo-120
❑ 89SpoIllFKI-144
❑ 89Top-180
❑ 89TopBasT-50
❑ 89TopBig-51
❑ 89TopMinL-15
❑ 89TopSti-15
❑ 89TopTif-180
❑ 89TVSpoM-53
❑ 89UppDec-295
❑ 90AstLenH-22
❑ 90AstMot-4
❑ 90BasWit-12
❑ 90Bow-71
❑ 90BowTif-71
❑ 90ClaBlu-29
❑ 90Don-207
❑ 90DonBesN-16
❑ 90DonLeaS-50
❑ 90Fle-237
❑ 90Fle-636
❑ 90FleAll-10
❑ 90FleAwaW-33
❑ 90FleCan-237
❑ 90FleCan-636
❑ 90FleLeaL-35
❑ 90FleLeaLC-35
❑ 90GooHumICBLS-21
❑ 90Hot50PS-39
❑ 90K-M-9
❑ 90KinDis-1
❑ 90Lea-4
❑ 90M.Vpin-42
❑ 90MLBBasB-43
❑ 90OPC-405
❑ 90OPC-460
❑ 90PanSti-262
❑ 90Pos-20
❑ 90PubIntS-102
❑ 90RedFolSB-85
❑ 90Sco-40
❑ 90Sco-692
❑ 90Sco100S-97
❑ 90Spo-55
❑ 90SunSee-22
❑ 90Top-405
❑ 90Top-460
❑ 90TopBig-249
❑ 90TopDou-59
❑ 90TopGloS-14
❑ 90TopMag-8
❑ 90TopMinL-56
❑ 90TopSti-19
❑ 90TopStiB-27
❑ 90TopTif-405
❑ 90TopTif-460
❑ 90TopTVA-42
❑ 90UppDec-88
❑ 90UppDec-125
❑ 91AstMot-4
❑ 91BasBesAotM-15
❑ 91Bow-546
❑ 91ClaGam-38
❑ 91Don-483
❑ 91Fle-515
❑ 91MetWIZ-354
❑ 91OPC-240
❑ 91PanFreS-14
❑ 91PanSti-16
❑ 91PetSta-8
❑ 91RedFolS-86
❑ 91Sco-46
❑ 91SevCoi-T9
❑ 91StaClu-209
❑ 91Stu-180
❑ 91Top-240
❑ 91TopDesS-240
❑ 91TopMic-240
❑ 91TopTif-240
❑ 91Ult-140
❑ 91UppDec-531
❑ 94TedWil-36

Scott, Pete (Floyd John)
❑ 29Zee-57
❑ 33Gou-70
❑ 33Zee-23
❑ 34GouCanV-33
❑ 92ConTSN-578

Scott, Philip
❑ 90PitMetP-1
❑ 91GreHorP-3068

Scott, Rennie
❑ 90LynRedSTI-22
❑ 91LynRedSC-8
❑ 91LynRedSP-1198

Scott, Rodney
❑ 72Dia-40
❑ 76SSP-172
❑ 78Top-191
❑ 79ExpPos-23
❑ 79ExpPos-24
❑ 79Top-86
❑ 80ExpPos-27
❑ 80OPC-360
❑ 80Top-712
❑ 81AllGamPI-106
❑ 81Don-209
❑ 81Fle-155
❑ 81OPC-227
❑ 81OPCPos-2
❑ 81Top-204
❑ 81Top-539
❑ 81TopSti-185
❑ 82Don-240
❑ 82ExpPos-37
❑ 82Fle-207
❑ 82FleSta-38
❑ 82OPC-259
❑ 82OPCPos-14
❑ 82Top-259
❑ 89PacSenL-177
❑ 89T/MSenL-94
❑ 89TopSenL-29
❑ 90EliSenL-29
❑ 91PacSenL-69
❑ 92Nab-13
❑ 92YanWIZ8-174
❑ 93ExpDonM-18

Scott, Ron
❑ 93JohCitCC-18
❑ 93JohCitCF-3675
❑ 94SavCarC-24
❑ 94SavCarF-505
❑ 95PeoChiTI-19

Scott, Sean
❑ 92SouOreAC-26
❑ 92SouOreAF-3435

Scott, Shawn
❑ 90St.CatBJP-3480
❑ 91DunBluJC-23
❑ 91DunBluJP-221
❑ 92KnoBluJF-3004
❑ 92KnoBluJS-392
❑ 93SyrChiF-1012

Scott, Steve
❑ 87SalLakTTT-26

Scott, Tary
❑ 85GreHorT-3
❑ 86FloStaLAP-43
❑ 86WinHavRSP-21
❑ 87NewBriRSP-22

Scott, Tim
❑ 83CedRapRF-3
❑ 83CedRapRT-8
❑ 87HawIsIP-14
❑ 87SanAntDTI-4
❑ 88BakDodCLC-258
❑ 89SanAntMB-24
❑ 90AlbDukCm-9
❑ 90AlbDukP-344
❑ 90AlbDukTr-26
❑ 90CMC-411
❑ 90ProAAAF-65
❑ 91LasVegSLD-293
❑ 91LasVegSP-235
❑ 91LinDriAAA-293
❑ 92BenRocCB-22
❑ 92BenRocF-1483
❑ 92Bow-454
❑ 92DonRoo-109
❑ 92LasVegSF-2796
❑ 92LasVegSS-239
❑ 92PadPolD-29
❑ 92StaClu-881
❑ 92StaCluECN-881
❑ 92TopDeb91-160
❑ 93Don-362
❑ 93Fle-524
❑ 93Lea-174
❑ 93PacSpa-600
❑ 93PadMot-27
❑ 93SanBerSC-14
❑ 93SanBerSF-779
❑ 93Sco-251
❑ 93StaClu-76
❑ 93StaCluFDI-76
❑ 93StaCluMOP-76
❑ 93Top-166
❑ 93TopGol-166
❑ 93TopInaM-166
❑ 93TopInaR-166
❑ 93TopMic-166
❑ 93Ult-477
❑ 93UppDec-662
❑ 93UppDecGold-662
❑ 94Don-265
❑ 94Fle-550
❑ 94Lea-219
❑ 94Top-373
❑ 94TopGol-373
❑ 94TopSpa-373
❑ 95Don-208
❑ 95DonPreP-208
❑ 95DonTopotO-285
❑ 95Fla-166
❑ 95Fle-359
❑ 95TopTra-62T
❑ 95Ult-407
❑ 95UltGolM-407
❑ 96ColCho-609
❑ 96ColChoGS-609
❑ 96ColChoSS-609
❑ 96Don-162
❑ 96DonPreP-162
❑ 96ExpBoo-4
❑ 96ExpDis-17
❑ 96Fle-468
❑ 96FleTif-468
❑ 96LeaSigEA-178
❑ 97PadMot-26

Scott, Tom
❑ 95BilMusTI-18

Scott, Tony
❑ 75ExpPos-33
❑ 76SSP-339
❑ 77Car5-25
❑ 77CarTeal-24
❑ 78CarTeal-30
❑ 78Top-352
❑ 79Car5-23
❑ 79Top-143
❑ 80OPC-17
❑ 80Top-33
❑ 81CokTeaS-128
❑ 81Don-191
❑ 81Fle-531
❑ 81Top-165
❑ 81TopSti-223
❑ 81TopTra-828
❑ 82AstAstI-9
❑ 82AstPos-24
❑ 82Don-522
❑ 82Fle-231
❑ 82FleSta-46
❑ 82Top-698
❑ 83AstPos-28
❑ 83Don-293
❑ 83Fle-465
❑ 83Top-507
❑ 84AstMot-20
❑ 84Don-527
❑ 84Fle-241
❑ 84Nes792-292
❑ 84Top-292
❑ 84TopTif-292
❑ 85OPC-367
❑ 85Top-733
❑ 85TopTif-733
❑ 87AstShoSPT-26
❑ 89TopSenL-91
❑ 90EliSenL-104
❑ 91BatCliP-3502
❑ 91PacSenL-121
❑ 92SpaPhiC-23
❑ 92SpaPhiF-1282
❑ 93SpaPhiC-26
❑ 93SpaPhiF-1073
❑ 94SpaPhiF-1740
❑ 94SparPhiC-27

Scott, Tyrone
❑ 90AubAstB-19
❑ 90AubAstP-3402
❑ 91BurAstC-8
❑ 91BurAstP-2799
❑ 92BurAstC-9
❑ 92BurAstF-546

Scranton, Jim
❑ 84OmaRoyT-27
❑ 85OmaRoyT-17
❑ 86OmaRoyP-21
❑ 86OmaRoyT-7

Scripture, Billy
❑ 78ChaPirT-23

Scrivener, Chuck (Churck)
❑ 76DetTigP-27
❑ 77Top-173
❑ 78Top-94
❑ 79SyrChiTI-3

Scruggs, John
❑ 70WicAerM-16

Scruggs, Ron
❑ 86AppFoxP-21
❑ 87PenWhiSP-25

Scruggs, Tony
❑ 88ChaRanS-22
❑ 89TulDriGS-24
❑ 89TulDriTI-23
❑ 90Bes-19
❑ 90CMC-654
❑ 90GasRanB-1
❑ 90GasRanP-2535
❑ 90GasRanS-22
❑ 90ProAaA-98
❑ 90SouAtlLAS-22
❑ 90StaFS7-98
❑ 91Bow-289
❑ 91LinDriAAA-304
❑ 91OklCit8LD-304
❑ 92OklCit8F-1928
❑ 92OklCit8S-321
❑ 92TopDeb91-161
❑ 93JacSunF-2723
❑ 93RanKee-322

Scudder, Bill
❑ 83VerBeaDT-10
❑ 85AlbDukCr-166

Scudder, Scott
❑ 87CedRapRP-7
❑ 88CedRapRP-1157
❑ 88MidLeaAGS-14
❑ 89CedRapRAB-15
❑ 89FleUpd-87
❑ 89NasSouC-8
❑ 89NasSouP-1293
❑ 89NasSouTI-22
❑ 89ScoRoo-99T
❑ 90Bow-46
❑ 90BowTif-46
❑ 90CedRapRDGB-15
❑ 90CMC-135
❑ 90Don-435
❑ 90Fle-434
❑ 90FleCan-434
❑ 90Hot50RS-39
❑ 90Lea-413
❑ 90NasSouC-10
❑ 90NasSouP-232
❑ 90OPC-553
❑ 90ProAAAF-544
❑ 90Sco-518
❑ 90Sco100RS-65
❑ 90Top-553
❑ 90TopDeb89-113
❑ 90TopTif-553
❑ 90UppDec-164
❑ 91Don-265
❑ 91Fle-81
❑ 91Lea-183
❑ 91OPC-713
❑ 91RedKah-47
❑ 91Sco-642
❑ 91Top-713
❑ 91TopDesS-713
❑ 91TopMic-713
❑ 91TopTif-713
❑ 91UppDec-615
❑ 92Bow-571
❑ 92ClaGam-180
❑ 92Don-306
❑ 92Fle-422
❑ 92IndFanC-25
❑ 92Lea-429
❑ 92LeaBlaG-429
❑ 92OPC-48
❑ 92OPCPre-181
❑ 92Pin-480
❑ 92Sco-209
❑ 92ScoRoo-67T
❑ 92StaClu-644
❑ 92StaCluNC-644
❑ 92Top-48
❑ 92TopGol-48
❑ 92TopGolW-48
❑ 92TopMic-48
❑ 92Ult-356
❑ 92UppDec-485
❑ 92UppDec-787
❑ 93Don-653
❑ 93Fle-601
❑ 93IndWUA-27
❑ 93PacSpa-101
❑ 93StaClu-243
❑ 93StaCluFDI-243
❑ 93StaCluMOP-243
❑ 93Top-248
❑ 93TopGol-248
❑ 93TopInaM-248
❑ 93TopInaR-248
❑ 93TopMic-248
❑ 93Ult-190
❑ 93UppDec-208
❑ 93UppDecGold-208
❑ 94BufBisF-1835

Scull, Angel
❑ 53Bri-18
❑ 54Top-204
❑ 59O'KAleMR-20
❑ 94TopArc1-204
❑ 94TopArc1G-204

Scully, Vin
❑ 59DodVol-14
❑ 60DodUniO-22
❑ 61DodUniO-24
❑ 71DodTic-20
❑ 82DodUniOV-21

Scurry, Rod
❑ 76ShrCapT-7
❑ 77ShrCapT-21
❑ 78ColCliT-23
❑ 79PorBeaT-22
❑ 81Fle-380
❑ 81Top-194
❑ 82Don-185
❑ 82Fle-497
❑ 82Top-207
❑ 83AllGamPI-177
❑ 83Don-376
❑ 83Fle-322
❑ 83Top-537
❑ 84Don-235
❑ 84Fle-264
❑ 84Nes792-69
❑ 84Pir-20
❑ 84Top-69
❑ 84TopTif-69
❑ 85Don-142
❑ 85Fle-476
❑ 85Pir-19
❑ 85Top-641
❑ 85TopTif-641
❑ 86Top-449
❑ 86TopTif-449
❑ 86YanTCM-14
❑ 87Don-374
❑ 87Fle-113
❑ 87FleGlo-113
❑ 87OPC-393
❑ 87Top-665
❑ 87TopTif-665
❑ 88CalCanC-10
❑ 88CalCanP-779
❑ 89Sco-516
❑ 89UppDec-208
❑ 92YanWIZ8-175

Scutaro, Marco
❑ 96-97LinVen-208
❑ 97KinIndB-23
❑ 98AkrAerM-24

Scutero, Brian
❑ 95BoiHawTI-26
❑ 96CedRapKTI-21
❑ 97CedRapK-24
❑ 97LakElsSG-25

Sea Dog, Slugger the
❑ 98PorSeaD5AQ-36
❑ 98PorSeaDQ-30

Sea Dogs, Portland
❑ 94PorSeaDTI-2
❑ 95PorSeaDTI-30

Seabol, Scott
❑ 98GreBatM-18

Seabury, Jaron
❑ 96MedHatBJTI-26

❑ 97St.CatSB-25
❑ 98HagSunM-24
Seal, Mike
❑ 88OklSoo-23
❑ 89MyrBeaBJP-1462
Seal, Scott
❑ 97IdaFalBTI-19
❑ 98RanCucQG-26
❑ 98RanCucQG-26
Seale, Jay
❑ 98St.CatSM-20
Seale, Johnnie
❑ 77FriOneYW-87
Sealer, Joel
❑ 88NebCor-15
Seals, Joey
❑ 89GreFalDSP-15
❑ 91GreFalDSP-10
Sealy, Randy
❑ 75ShrCapT-19
❑ 76ShrCapT-12
❑ 80WesHavWCT-23B
Sealy, Scot
❑ 92GasRanF-2256
❑ 93ChaRaiC-18
❑ 93ChaRaiF-1914
❑ 93ClaGolF-206
❑ 96LanJetB-24
❑ 98TacRaiQ-27
Seaman, Kim
❑ 77WauMetT-17
❑ 81HawIslT-16
❑ 82HawIslT-22
❑ 82WicAerTI-17
Seamon, Jonathan
❑ 86DavLipB-19
Seanez, Rudy
❑ 87WatIndP-18
❑ 88WatIndP-692
❑ 89KinIndS-23
❑ 90Bes-164
❑ 90CanIndB-24
❑ 90CanIndP-1293
❑ 90CMC-832
❑ 90Fle-640
❑ 90FleCan-640
❑ 90IndTeal-34
❑ 90Lea-417
❑ 90ProAaA-10
❑ 90TopDeb89-114
❑ 91ColSprSSLD-89
❑ 91ColSprSSP-2181
❑ 91Don-218
❑ 91Fle-376
❑ 91LinDriAAA-89
❑ 91UppDec-358
❑ 92Don-552
❑ 92Fle-122
❑ 92SanAntMS-575
❑ 92Sco-696
❑ 92StaClu-713
❑ 92StaCluECN-713
❑ 93Don-758
❑ 93OPC-391
❑ 93RocStaC-16
❑ 93Top-676
❑ 93TopGol-676
❑ 93TopInaM-676
❑ 93TopInaR-676
❑ 93TopMic-676
❑ 94AlbDukF-842
❑ 95DodMot-24
❑ 95DodPol-24
❑ 95Fla-156
❑ 95Fle-549
❑ 95TopTra-143T
❑ 97NorTid-29
❑ 97NorTidB-34
❑ 98RicBraQ-14
❑ 99Fle-399
❑ 99FleSta9-399
❑ 99FleWarT-399
❑ 99PacCroC-31
❑ 99PacCroCPB-31
Searage, Ray
❑ 77St.PetCT-7
❑ 79ArkTraT-20
❑ 81TidTidT-24
❑ 82ChaChaT-10
❑ 82Top-478
❑ 84VanCanC-30
❑ 85BrePol-41
❑ 85Fle-595
❑ 86Don-536
❑ 86Fle-502
❑ 86Top-642
❑ 86TopTif-642
❑ 86VanCanP-23
❑ 87Fle-506
❑ 87FleGlo-506
❑ 87Top-149
❑ 87TopTif-149
❑ 87WhiSoxC-27
❑ 88AlbDukCm-4
❑ 88AlbDukP-262
❑ 88Don-429
❑ 88Fle-409
❑ 88FleGlo-409
❑ 88StaLinWS-17
❑ 88Top-788
❑ 88TopTif-788
❑ 89DodMot-22
❑ 89DodPol-30
❑ 89DodStaSV-13
❑ 89FleUpd-94
❑ 90DodMot-22
❑ 90DodPol-59
❑ 90DodTar-1066
❑ 90Don-649
❑ 90Fle-408
❑ 90FleCan-408
❑ 90OPC-84
❑ 90Top-84
❑ 90TopTif-84
❑ 91Fle-220
❑ 91LinDriAAA-496
❑ 91MetWIZ-355
❑ 91ScrRedBLD-496
❑ 91ScrRedBP-2538
❑ 92EdmTraF-3539
❑ 94BreMilB-178
❑ 94MadHatC-28
❑ 94MadHatF-150
❑ 95PeoChiTI-39
❑ 96PeoChiB-2
❑ 97PriWilC-3
❑ 98HudValR-23
Search, Michael
❑ 90BoiHawP-3316
❑ 90PalSprACLC-223
❑ 90PalSprAP-2576
Searcy, Steve
❑ 86GleFalTP-21
❑ 87TolMudHP-2
❑ 87TolMudHT-16
❑ 88TolMudHC-4
❑ 88TolMudHP-609
❑ 88TriAAC-25
❑ 89Bow-95
❑ 89BowTif-95
❑ 89ClaLigB-78
❑ 89Don-29
❑ 89Fle-145
❑ 89FleGlo-145
❑ 89Sco-627
❑ 89ScoHot1R-47
❑ 89ScoYouS2-27
❑ 89Top-167
❑ 89TopTif-167
❑ 89UppDec-764
❑ 90CMC-387
❑ 90Fle-615
❑ 90FleCan-615
❑ 90Hot50RS-40
❑ 90OPC-487
❑ 90ProAAAF-379
❑ 90Sco100RS-97
❑ 90TolMudHC-10
❑ 90TolMudHP-149
❑ 90Top-487
❑ 90TopTif-487
❑ 90TriAllGP-AAA20
❑ 90UppDec-575
❑ 91Don-549
❑ 91Lea-187
❑ 91OPC-369
❑ 91Sco-649
❑ 91Sco100RS-76
❑ 91StaClu-352
❑ 91TigCok-49
❑ 91Top-369
❑ 91TopDesS-369
❑ 91TopMic-369
❑ 91TopTif-369
❑ 91UppDec-338
❑ 92Fle-545
❑ 92OPC-599
❑ 92PhiMed-29
❑ 92Sco-698
❑ 92ScrRedBF-2445
❑ 92StaClu-648
❑ 92Top-599
❑ 92TopGol-599
❑ 92TopGolW-599
❑ 92TopMic-599
❑ 93RocRedWF-239
Searles, Bob
❑ 87CubCan-28
Sears, Allen
❑ 83DurBulT-23
❑ 91BoiHawC-20
Sears, Jimmy
❑ 91BoiHawP-3891
Sears, Ken
❑ 43YanSta-24
❑ 46SeaSLP-53
Sears, Mike
❑ 86FloStaLAP-44
❑ 86WinHavRSP-22
❑ 87WinHavRSP-19
Sears, Todd
❑ 98AshTouM-21
❑ 98SouAtlLPM-22
❑ 99BasAmeTP-90
❑ 99BasAmeTPG-90
❑ 99Bow-207
❑ 99BowChr-207
❑ 99BowChrG-207
❑ 99BowChrGR-207
❑ 99BowChrI-207
❑ 99BowChrIR-207
❑ 99BowChrR-207
❑ 99BowGol-207
❑ 99BowInt-207
Seaton, Billy
❑ 91GulCoaRSP-13
❑ 92GulCoaRSP-13
Seaton, Tom
❑ 09ObaT21-129
❑ 09ObaT21-201
❑ 09ObaT21-301
❑ 09ObaT21-375
❑ 11PacCoaBD-56
❑ 11Zee-59
❑ 12ObaPreT-50
❑ 12ObaPreT-124
❑ 12PCLPin-20
❑ 14CraJacE-100
❑ 15CraJacE-100
❑ 15SpoNewM-161
❑ 16SpoNewM-159
❑ 19Zee-102
❑ 20Zee-116
Seats, Dean
❑ 81CedRapRT-13
Seats, Tom
❑ 37Zee-60
❑ 47PadTeal-18
❑ 49BowPCL-35
❑ 90DodTar-715
Seaver, Anne
❑ 92PacSea-63
Seaver, Mark
❑ 96MauStiHWB-36
❑ 97CalLeaATI-44
❑ 97CarLeaTP-17
❑ 97FreKey-25
Seaver, Nancy
❑ 92PacSea-63
Seaver, Sarah
❑ 92PacSea-63
Seaver, Tom
❑ 67MetPos-3
❑ 67MetPos-5
❑ 67Top-581
❑ 68Baz-1
❑ 68OPC-45
❑ 68Top-45
❑ 68TopActS-3C
❑ 68TopActS-14C
❑ 68TopVen-45
❑ 69MetBoyS-1
❑ 69MetCit-8
❑ 69MetNewYDN-16
❑ 69MetTeal-13
❑ 69MetTealC-4
❑ 69MilBra-250
❑ 69MLBOffS-170
❑ 69NabTeaF-22
❑ 69Top-480
❑ 69TopDecl-38
❑ 69TopSta-68
❑ 69TopSup-52
❑ 69TopTeaP-24
❑ 69TraSta-48
❑ 70DayDaiNM-8
❑ 70Kel-7
❑ 70MetTeal-10
❑ 70MetTealC-4
❑ 70MetTra-21C
❑ 70MilBra-26
❑ 70MLBOffS-82
❑ 70OPC-69
❑ 70OPC-195
❑ 70OPC-300
❑ 70Top-69
❑ 70Top-195
❑ 70Top-300
❑ 70TopCanL-21
❑ 70TopScr-19
❑ 70TopSup-5
❑ 70TraSta-4C
❑ 71AllBasA-22
❑ 71BazNumT-35
❑ 71Kel-2
❑ 71MatMin-15
❑ 71MatMin-16
❑ 71MetTeal-17
❑ 71MilDud-63
❑ 71MLBOffS-164
❑ 71MLBOffS-574
❑ 71OPC-68
❑ 71OPC-72
❑ 71OPC-160
❑ 71Top-68
❑ 71Top-72
❑ 71Top-160
❑ 71TopCoi-127
❑ 71TopSup-53
❑ 71TopTat-114
❑ 71TopTat-115
❑ 72Kel-1A
❑ 72Kel-1B
❑ 72MetTeal-5
❑ 72MilBra-312
❑ 72OPC-91
❑ 72OPC-93
❑ 72OPC-95
❑ 72OPC-347
❑ 72OPC-445
❑ 72OPC-446
❑ 72ProStaP-22
❑ 72SevTraC-49
❑ 72Top-91
❑ 72Top-93
❑ 72Top-95
❑ 72Top-347
❑ 72Top-445
❑ 72Top-446
❑ 72TopPos-13
❑ 73Kel2D-46
❑ 73LinPor-122
❑ 73MetAllEB-10
❑ 73MetTeal-11
❑ 73NewYorSNM-3
❑ 73OPC-350
❑ 73SevTraC-70
❑ 73Top-350
❑ 73TopCanL-48
❑ 73TopCom-19
❑ 73TopPin-19
❑ 74Kel-52
❑ 74LauAllG-68
❑ 74MetDaiPA-8
❑ 74MetJapEB-9
❑ 74MetTeal-19
❑ 74NewYorNTDiS-13
❑ 74OPC-80
❑ 74OPC-206
❑ 74OPC-207
❑ 74Top-80
❑ 74Top-206
❑ 74Top-207
❑ 74TopDecE-9
❑ 74TopPuz-10
❑ 74TopSta-70
❑ 75BlaBacD-6
❑ 75Hos-75
❑ 75MetSSP-12
❑ 75OPC-370
❑ 75SSP42-15
❑ 75SSPPuzB-23
❑ 75SSPSam-6
❑ 75Top-370
❑ 75TopMin-370
❑ 76BlaDis-55
❑ 76BucDis-55
❑ 76CarDis-55
❑ 76CraDis-55
❑ 76DailsID-55
❑ 76Hos-35
❑ 76HosTwi-35
❑ 76IsaDis-55
❑ 76Kel-32A
❑ 76Kel-32B
❑ 76MetMSAP-1
❑ 76OPC-5
❑ 76OPC-199
❑ 76OPC-201
❑ 76OPC-203
❑ 76OPC-600
❑ 76OrbDis-55
❑ 76RedBarD-55
❑ 76SafDis-55
❑ 76SafSupLB-5
❑ 76SafSupLB-9
❑ 76SafSupLB-12
❑ 76SafSupLB-14A
❑ 76SafSupLB-15
❑ 76SSP-551
❑ 76Top-5
❑ 76Top-199
❑ 76Top-201
❑ 76Top-203
❑ 76Top-600
❑ 76TowCluD-55
❑ 77BurCheD-142
❑ 77ChiWilD-61
❑ 77DailsID-61
❑ 77DetCaeD-61
❑ 77HolInnD-61
❑ 77Hos-7
❑ 77MetDaiPA-21
❑ 77MSADis-61
❑ 77OPC-6
❑ 77OPC-205
❑ 77PepGloD-67
❑ 77RCColC-59
❑ 77SagDis-61
❑ 77sDis-61
❑ 77Spo-121
❑ 77Spo-2922
❑ 77Top-6
❑ 77Top-150
❑ 77TopCloS-42
❑ 77WenDis-61
❑ 77ZipDis-61
❑ 78Hos-149
❑ 78Kel-27
❑ 78OPC-120
❑ 78Pep-23
❑ 78RCColC-36
❑ 78SagDis-10
❑ 78SSP270-116
❑ 78TasDis-10
❑ 78Top-450
❑ 78WifBalD-68
❑ 79BasPat-80
❑ 79Hos-65
❑ 79Kel-29
❑ 79OPC-44
❑ 79SpaGloT-2
❑ 79Top-100
❑ 79TopCom-22
❑ 80BurKinPHR-10
❑ 80Kel-49
❑ 80OPC-260
❑ 80PerHaloFP-215
❑ 80PerHaloFPS-75
❑ 80RawActTS-1
❑ 80RedEnq-41
❑ 80Top-500
❑ 80TopSup-15
❑ 81AllGamPI-176
❑ 81CokTeaS-46
❑ 81Don-422
❑ 81Don-425
❑ 81Fle-200
❑ 81FleStiC-49
❑ 81Kel-38
❑ 81MSAMinD-29
❑ 81OPC-220
❑ 81PerCreC-11
❑ 81Top-220
❑ 81TopScr-107
❑ 81TopSti-165
❑ 81TopSupHT-41
❑ 81TopSupN-14
❑ 82Don-16
❑ 82Don-148
❑ 82Don-628
❑ 82FBIDis-23
❑ 82Fle-82
❑ 82Fle-634
❑ 82Fle-645
❑ 82FleSta-11
❑ 82Kel-8
❑ 82OnDecD-29
❑ 82OPC-30
❑ 82OPC-31
❑ 82OPC-346
❑ 82PerCreC-2
❑ 82PerCreCG-2
❑ 82RedCok-19
❑ 82Squ-21
❑ 82Top-30
❑ 82Top-31
❑ 82Top-165
❑ 82Top-346
❑ 82Top-346B
❑ 82Top-756
❑ 82TopSti-9
❑ 82TopSti-36
❑ 83AllGamPI-176
❑ 83Don-122
❑ 83Fle-601
❑ 83FleSta-174
❑ 83FleSti-218
❑ 83Oco& SSBG-16
❑ 83OPC-52
❑ 83OPC-354
❑ 83Top-580
❑ 83Top-581
❑ 83TopFol-1
❑ 83TopSti-233
❑ 83TopTra-101T
❑ 84Don-116
❑ 84DonActAS-53
❑ 84DonCha-40
❑ 84Fle-595
❑ 84FleUpd-106
❑ 84FunFooP-15
❑ 84MLBPen-8
❑ 84Nes792-246
❑ 84Nes792-706
❑ 84Nes792-707
❑ 84Nes792-708
❑ 84Nes792-740
❑ 84OCoandSI-105
❑ 84OCoandSI-164
❑ 84OPC-261
❑ 84RalPur-8
❑ 84SevCoi-E8
❑ 84Top-246
❑ 84Top-706
❑ 84Top-707
❑ 84Top-708
❑ 84Top-740
❑ 84TopCer-8
❑ 84TopGaloC-12
❑ 84TopPewB-1
❑ 84TopRubD-17
❑ 84TopSti-106
❑ 84TopTif-246
❑ 84TopTif-706
❑ 84TopTif-707
❑ 84TopTif-708
❑ 84TopTif-740
❑ 84TopTra-108T
❑ 84TopTraT-108T
❑ 84WhiSoxTV-27
❑ 85AllGamPI-87
❑ 85Don-424A
❑ 85Don-424B
❑ 85DonHig-1
❑ 85DonHig-30
❑ 85Dra-41
❑ 85Fle-526
❑ 85FleLimE-34
❑ 85FleStaS-68
❑ 85FleStaS-69
❑ 85FleStaS-70
❑ 85FleStaS-71
❑ 85FleStaS-72
❑ 85FleStaS-73
❑ 85KASDis-13
❑ 85KitCloD-13
❑ 85Lea-101
❑ 85OPC-1
❑ 85SevCoi-G12
❑ 85SpoSam-45
❑ 85SubDis-19
❑ 85ThoMcAD-19
❑ 85Top-670
❑ 85Top3-D-30
❑ 85TopMin-670
❑ 85TopSti-235
❑ 85TopSup-31
❑ 85TopTif-670
❑ 85WhiSoxC-41
❑ 86Don-609
❑ 86Don-609B
❑ 86Fle-216
❑ 86Fle-630
❑ 86FleFutHoF-3
❑ 86FleLeaL-40

❑ 86FleMin-46
❑ 86FleSlu-34
❑ 86FleStiC-109
❑ 86Lea-234
❑ 86MSAJayPCD-16
❑ 86OPC-390
❑ 86QuaGra-32
❑ 86SevCoi-C8
❑ 86SevCoi-E8
❑ 86SevCoi-S8
❑ 86SevCoi-W8
❑ 86Spo-25
❑ 86Spo-60
❑ 86Spo-67
❑ 86Spo-70
❑ 86Spo-134
❑ 86Spo-135
❑ 86Spo-142
❑ 86Spo-182
❑ 86SpoDecG-52
❑ 86SpoRoo-47
❑ 86StaSea-1
❑ 86StaSea-2
❑ 86StaSea-3
❑ 86StaSea-4
❑ 86StaSea-5
❑ 86StaSea-6
❑ 86StaSea-7
❑ 86StaSea-8
❑ 86StaSea-9
❑ 86StaSea-10
❑ 86StaSea-11
❑ 86StaSea-12
❑ 86Top-390
❑ 86Top-402
❑ 86TopGloS-22
❑ 86TopSti-10
❑ 86TopSti-287
❑ 86TopSup-50
❑ 86TopTat-10
❑ 86TopTif-390
❑ 86TopTif-402
❑ 86TopTra-101T
❑ 86TopTraT-101T
❑ 86TruVal-12
❑ 86WhiSoxC-41
❑ 87Don-375
❑ 87Fle-45
❑ 87FleGlo-45
❑ 87K-M-21
❑ 87Lea-263
❑ 87OPC-49
❑ 87Spo-28
❑ 87SpoRea-22
❑ 87Top-306
❑ 87Top-425
❑ 87TopSti-246
❑ 87TopTif-306
❑ 87TopTif-425
❑ 88AlaGolAA60TI-3
❑ 89Met196C-11
❑ 89MetRinP69-26
❑ 89TopBasT-15
❑ 90AGFA-14
❑ 90BasWit-46
❑ 90HOFStiB-76
❑ 90MetHaloF-4
❑ 90PacLeg-60
❑ 90PerGreM-73
❑ 90SouCalS-11
❑ 90SweBasG-1
❑ 91MetWIZ-356
❑ 91SweBasG-107
❑ 91UppDecRH-10
❑ 92FroRowAH-3
❑ 92FroRowSe-1
❑ 92FroRowSe-1AU
❑ 92FroRowSe-2
❑ 92FroRowSe-3
❑ 92FroRowSe-4
❑ 92FroRowSe-5
❑ 92KelAll-5
❑ 92PacSea-1
❑ 92PacSea-2
❑ 92PacSea-3
❑ 92PacSea-4
❑ 92PacSea-5
❑ 92PacSea-6
❑ 92PacSea-7
❑ 92PacSea-8
❑ 92PacSea-9
❑ 92PacSea-10
❑ 92PacSea-11
❑ 92PacSea-12
❑ 92PacSea-13
❑ 92PacSea-14
❑ 92PacSea-15
❑ 92PacSea-16
❑ 92PacSea-17
❑ 92PacSea-18
❑ 92PacSea-19
❑ 92PacSea-20
❑ 92PacSea-21
❑ 92PacSea-22
❑ 92PacSea-23
❑ 92PacSea-24
❑ 92PacSea-25
❑ 92PacSea-26
❑ 92PacSea-27
❑ 92PacSea-28
❑ 92PacSea-29
❑ 92PacSea-30
❑ 92PacSea-31
❑ 92PacSea-32
❑ 92PacSea-33
❑ 92PacSea-34
❑ 92PacSea-35
❑ 92PacSea-36
❑ 92PacSea-37
❑ 92PacSea-38
❑ 92PacSea-39
❑ 92PacSea-40
❑ 92PacSea-41
❑ 92PacSea-42
❑ 92PacSea-43
❑ 92PacSea-44
❑ 92PacSea-45
❑ 92PacSea-46
❑ 92PacSea-47
❑ 92PacSea-48
❑ 92PacSea-49
❑ 92PacSea-50
❑ 92PacSea-51
❑ 92PacSea-52
❑ 92PacSea-53
❑ 92PacSea-54
❑ 92PacSea-55
❑ 92PacSea-56
❑ 92PacSea-57
❑ 92PacSea-58
❑ 92PacSea-59
❑ 92PacSea-60
❑ 92PacSea-61
❑ 92PacSea-62
❑ 92PacSea-63
❑ 92PacSea-64
❑ 92PacSea-65
❑ 92PacSea-66
❑ 92PacSea-67
❑ 92PacSea-68
❑ 92PacSea-69
❑ 92PacSea-70
❑ 92PacSea-71
❑ 92PacSea-72
❑ 92PacSea-73
❑ 92PacSea-74
❑ 92PacSea-75
❑ 92PacSea-76
❑ 92PacSea-77
❑ 92PacSea-78
❑ 92PacSea-79
❑ 92PacSea-80
❑ 92PacSea-81
❑ 92PacSea-82
❑ 92PacSea-83
❑ 92PacSea-84
❑ 92PacSea-85
❑ 92PacSea-86
❑ 92PacSea-87
❑ 92PacSea-88
❑ 92PacSea-89
❑ 92PacSea-90
❑ 92PacSea-91
❑ 92PacSea-92
❑ 92PacSea-93
❑ 92PacSea-94
❑ 92PacSea-95
❑ 92PacSea-96
❑ 92PacSea-97
❑ 92PacSea-98
❑ 92PacSea-99
❑ 92PacSea-100
❑ 92PacSea-101
❑ 92PacSea-102
❑ 92PacSea-103
❑ 92PacSea-104
❑ 92PacSea-105
❑ 92PacSea-106
❑ 92PacSea-107
❑ 92PacSea-108
❑ 92PacSea-109
❑ 92PacSea-110
❑ 92PacSeaI6-1
❑ 92PacSeaI6-2
❑ 92PacSeaI6-3
❑ 92PacSeaI6-4
❑ 92PacSeaI6-5
❑ 92PacSeaI6-6
❑ 92PacSeaI6-AU1
❑ 92PhoFilHoF-3
❑ 92PhoFilHoF-4
❑ 93ActPacA-129
❑ 93ActPacA2-63G
❑ 93ActPacSP-TS1
❑ 93ActPacSP-TS2
❑ 93ActPacSP-TS3
❑ 93ActPacSP-TS4
❑ 93ActPacSP-TS5
❑ 93PacRya2S-241
❑ 93PacRya2S-250
❑ 93SpeGolSS-1
❑ 93Yoo-18
❑ 94Met69CCPP-28
❑ 94Met69CS-27
❑ 94Met69SP-P1
❑ 94Met69SP-P3
❑ 94Met69T-3
❑ 94Met69T-42
❑ 94Met69T-52
❑ 94UppDecAH-120
❑ 94UppDecAH-177
❑ 94UppDecAH-180
❑ 94UppDecAH1-120
❑ 94UppDecAH1-177
❑ 94UppDecAH1-180
❑ 94UppDecAHA-4
❑ 94UppDecTAE-70
❑ 95EagBalL-3
❑ 95UppDecSHoB-9
❑ 97DonSigSS-20
❑ 98UppDecR-64
❑ 98UppDecRSotT-TS
❑ 99SP SigAuto-TSE
❑ 99SPSig-170
❑ 99TopStaRR-5
❑ 99TopStaRRA-5
❑ 99UppDecCL-32
❑ 99UppDecCL-133
❑ 99UppDecCLA-1970
❑ 99UppDecCLCC-32
❑ 99UppDecCLCC-133
❑ 99UppDecCLES-TS
❑ 99UppDecCLESC-TS

Seay, Bobby
❑ 97ChaRivDG-26
❑ 97SouAtlTPB-10
❑ 98Bes-95
❑ 98ChaRivDG-26
❑ 99199Fin-292
❑ 99Bow-425
❑ 99BowBes-166
❑ 99BowBesAR-166
❑ 99BowBesR-166
❑ 99BowGol-425
❑ 99BowInt-425
❑ 99FinGolRef-292
❑ 99FinRef-292
❑ 99TopBlaLC1-54
❑ 99TopBlaLC2-54
❑ 99TopBlaLC3-54
❑ 99TopGolL-54
❑ 99TopGolLC1-54
❑ 99TopGolLC2-54
❑ 99TopGolLOtO-54
❑ 99TopRedLC1-54
❑ 99TopRedLC2-54
❑ 99TopRedLC3-54
❑ 99TopSta-107
❑ 99TopStaFoil-107

Seay, Dick
❑ 78LauLonABS-14

Seay, Mark
❑ 87SanJosBP-16

Sebach, Kyle
❑ 92BoiHawF-3626
❑ 92QuaCitRBC-20
❑ 92QuaCitRBF-809
❑ 93CedRapKC-16
❑ 93CedRapKF-1735
❑ 94LakElsSC-16
❑ 94LakElsSF-1662
❑ 94MidAngOHP-28
❑ 96LakElsSB-10
❑ 96MidAngB-27

Seberino, Ronnie
❑ 97PriDevR-29
❑ 97Top-253
❑ 98HudValR-25

Sebra, Bob
❑ 83TriTriT-1
❑ 85OklCit8T-19
❑ 86IndIndTI-23
❑ 87Don-468
❑ 87ExpPos-26
❑ 87Fle-331
❑ 87FleGlo-331
❑ 87Lea-213
❑ 87OPC-314
❑ 87Top-479
❑ 87TopTif-479
❑ 88Don-458
❑ 88Fle-195
❑ 88FleGlo-195
❑ 88IndIndC-3
❑ 88IndIndP-511
❑ 88OPC-93
❑ 88Sco-337
❑ 88ScoGlo-337
❑ 88Top-93
❑ 88TopTif-93
❑ 88TriAAAP-17
❑ 89BlaYNPRWL-163
❑ 89ScrRedBC-4
❑ 89ScrRedBP-718
❑ 90BreMilB-22
❑ 90CMC-136
❑ 90NasSouC-11
❑ 90NasSouP-233
❑ 90ProAAAF-545
❑ 90TulDriDGB-8
❑ 92IowCubF-4051
❑ 92OklCit8S-322
❑ 92SkyAAAF-148
❑ 93LouRedF-213
❑ 93RanKee-323
❑ 94BreMilB-179

Sebring, James
❑ 09RamT20-107
❑ 72ClaCar-82
❑ 90DodTar-716

Sebring, Jeff
❑ 96PorRocB-28
❑ 97PorRocG-26

Secoda, Jason
❑ 96SouBenSHS-22

Secoda, Joseph
❑ 97JohCitCTI-30
❑ 98NewJerCM-27

Secory, Frank
❑ 55Bow-286

Secrest, Charlie
❑ 59Top-140
❑ 59TopVen-140

Secrist, Don
❑ 69Top-654

Secrist, Reed
❑ 93AugPirC-19
❑ 93AugPirF-1554
❑ 94SalBucC-20
❑ 94SalBucF-2332
❑ 95LynHilTI-27
❑ 96Exc-224
❑ 97CalCanB-22
❑ 98MemRedG-21

Seda, Israel
❑ 91PenPilC-22
❑ 91PenPilP-387

Sedar, Ed
❑ 83AppFoxFr-18
❑ 86PenWhiSP-24
❑ 87DayBeaAP-19
❑ 88SouBenWSGS-17
❑ 91PocPioP-3802
❑ 91PocPioSP-28

Sedlacek, Shawn
❑ 98SpoIndG-29

See, Charles
❑ 20RedWorCP-22
❑ 22Zee-108
❑ 23Zee-145

See, Larry
❑ 82VerBeaDT-20
❑ 84AlbDukCr-162
❑ 86AlbDukP-22
❑ 87AlbDukD-21
❑ 89TolMudHC-14
❑ 89TolMudHP-784
❑ 90DodTar-717
❑ 93RanKee-324

Seeburger, John
❑ 88OneYanP-2050
❑ 89Ft.LauYS-25

Seeds, Robert Ira
❑ 32OrbPinUP-52
❑ 33ExhFou-10
❑ 33TatOrb-52
❑ 36GouWidPPR-D33
❑ 36WorWidGV-27
❑ 39PlaBal-32
❑ 40PlaBal-91
❑ 72TCMthe3-75
❑ 75YanDyn1T-44

Seefried, Tate
❑ 90TamYanD-22
❑ 91OneYanP-4163
❑ 92ClaFS7-307
❑ 92GreHorC-25
❑ 92GreHorF-789
❑ 93CarLeaAGF-24
❑ 93PriWilCC-1
❑ 93PriWilCF-666
❑ 94AlbYanF-1451
❑ 94AlbYanTI-3
❑ 94Bow-661
❑ 94BowBes-B20
❑ 94BowBesR-B20
❑ 94Cla-174
❑ 94ExcFS7-114
❑ 94UppDecML-87
❑ 95Bow-139
❑ 95Exc-104
❑ 95NorNagUTI-31
❑ 95SigRooOJ-29
❑ 95SigRooOJP-29
❑ 95SigRooOJPS-29
❑ 95SigRooOJS-29
❑ 95UppDecML-96
❑ 95UppDecMLFS-96
❑ 96Bow-141
❑ 96BowFoi-141
❑ 96NorNavB-23
❑ 97BinMetB-28
❑ 98PriWilCASM-25

Seeger, Mark
❑ 81AppFoxT-24

Seegers, Pat
❑ 78NewWayCT-40
❑ 79BurBeeT-3

Seelbach, Christopher
❑ 92ClaFS7-252
❑ 92MacBraC-22
❑ 92MacBraF-268
❑ 92StaCluD-167
❑ 92UppDecML-94
❑ 93ClaFS7-255
❑ 93DurBulC-18
❑ 93DurBulF-486
❑ 93DurBulTI-31
❑ 94GreBraF-412
❑ 94GreBraTI-21
❑ 94UppDecML-78
❑ 95Exc-157
❑ 95RicBraRC-23
❑ 95RicBraTI-21
❑ 96ChaKniB-26
❑ 97ChaKni-26
❑ 98OrlRayM-16

Seelbach, Chuck
❑ 73OPC-51
❑ 73Top-51
❑ 74OPC-292
❑ 74Tig-11
❑ 74Top-292

Seerey, James Pat
❑ 47IndTeal-24
❑ 47IndVanPP-23
❑ 49AngTeal-32
❑ 49Lea-73
❑ 77TCMTheWY-13
❑ 85TCMPla1-35
❑ 94TedWil-152

Seery, John Emmett
❑ 87BucN28-46A
❑ 87BucN28-46B
❑ 87OldJudN-439
❑ 88WG1CarG-35

Sees, Eric
❑ 96SpoIndB-25

Seesz, Brian
❑ 92GulCoaRSP-21
❑ 93ChaRaiC-19
❑ 93ChaRaiF-1915

Sefcik, Kevin
❑ 93BatCliCB-25
❑ 93BatCliF-3155
❑ 94ClePhiC-22
❑ 94ClePhiF-2537
❑ 95ReaPhiELC-32
❑ 95ReaPhiTI-9
❑ 96Bow-262
❑ 96BowFoi-262
❑ 96FleUpd-U171
❑ 96FleUpdTC-U171
❑ 96LeaSigEA-179
❑ 96ScrRedBB-24
❑ 96Ult-526
❑ 96UltGolM-526
❑ 97Fle-422
❑ 97FleTif-422
❑ 97Pac-387
❑ 97PacLigB-387
❑ 97PacSil-387
❑ 97PhiTeal-31A
❑ 98PacInvGems-191
❑ 98PacOnl-573
❑ 98PacOnlR-573
❑ 98PacOnlWC-573
❑ 98PhiTeal-30
❑ 99Fle-489
❑ 99FleSta9-489
❑ 99FleWarT-489
❑ 99Pac-334
❑ 99PacAur-145
❑ 99PacAurOD-145
❑ 99PacCroC-216
❑ 99PacCroCPB-216
❑ 99PacPlaB-334
❑ 99PacRed-334

Sefly, Joel
❑ 91VisOakC-27

Segelke, Herman
❑ 82IowCubT-23
❑ 83PhoGiaBHN-13
❑ 84PhoGiaC-10

Segrist, Kal
❑ 58UniOil-7
❑ 91OriCro-411

Segui, Daniel
❑ 89PitMetS-25
❑ 89Sta-166
❑ 90VisOakCLC-77
❑ 90VisOakP-2164

Segui, David
❑ 88HagSunS-19
❑ 89FreKeyS-21
❑ 90BalOriP-25
❑ 90Bow-251
❑ 90Bow-251B
❑ 90BowTif-251A
❑ 90BowTif-251B
❑ 90FleUpd-69
❑ 90HagSunDGB-26
❑ 90RocRedWGC-2
❑ 90ScoRoo-95T
❑ 90TriAllGP-AAA54
❑ 90UppDec-773
❑ 91BalOriP-30
❑ 91Bow-102
❑ 91Cla1-T15
❑ 91Don-730
❑ 91Fle-492
❑ 91LinDriAAA-466
❑ 91MajLeaCP-30
❑ 91OPC-724
❑ 91OriCro-412
❑ 91RocRedWLD-466
❑ 91RocRedWP-1910
❑ 91Sco-362
❑ 91Sco100RS-61
❑ 91ScoRoo-31
❑ 91SevCoi-A15
❑ 91StaClu-50
❑ 91StaCluP-40
❑ 91Stu-10
❑ 91Top-724
❑ 91TopDeb90-140
❑ 91TopDesS-724
❑ 91TopMic-724
❑ 91TopTif-724
❑ 91Ult-25
❑ 91UppDec-342
❑ 92BalOriP-33
❑ 92Don-321
❑ 92Fle-27
❑ 92OPC-447
❑ 92OPCPre-153
❑ 92Pin-185
❑ 92ProFS7-5
❑ 92Sco-554
❑ 92Sco100RS-33
❑ 92StaClu-783
❑ 92StaCluNC-783
❑ 92Top-447
❑ 92TopGol-447
❑ 92TopGolW-447
❑ 92TopMic-447

❑ 92Ult-308
❑ 92UppDec-316
❑ 93BalOriP-32
❑ 93Don-397
❑ 93Fle-175
❑ 93Lea-306
❑ 93PacSpa-25
❑ 93Pin-325
❑ 93Sco-610
❑ 93SP-162
❑ 93StaClu-479
❑ 93StaCluFDI-479
❑ 93StaCluMOP-479
❑ 93Top-82
❑ 93TopGol-82
❑ 93TopInaM-82
❑ 93TopInaR-82
❑ 93TopMic-82
❑ 93Toy-45
❑ 93TriPla-12
❑ 93TriPlaP-12
❑ 93Ult-146
❑ 93UppDec-792
❑ 93UppDecGold-792
❑ 94ColC-254
❑ 94ColC-529
❑ 94ColChoGS-254
❑ 94ColChoGS-529
❑ 94ColChoSS-254
❑ 94ColChoSS-529
❑ 94Don-624
❑ 94Fin-103
❑ 94FinRef-103
❑ 94Fla-410
❑ 94Fle-20
❑ 94FleExtB-324
❑ 94FleUpd-160
❑ 94Lea-352
❑ 94MetColP-23
❑ 94OriPro-91
❑ 94OriUSPC-7C
❑ 94OriUSPC-12H
❑ 94Pac-45
❑ 94PanSti-24
❑ 94Pin-131
❑ 94PinArtP-131
❑ 94PinMusC-131
❑ 94Sco-361
❑ 94ScoGolR-361
❑ 94ScoRoo-RT35
❑ 94ScoRooGR-RT35
❑ 94Sel-322
❑ 94StaClu-95
❑ 94StaClu-696
❑ 94StaCluFDI-95
❑ 94StaCluFDI-696
❑ 94StaCluGR-95
❑ 94StaCluGR-696
❑ 94StaCluMOP-95
❑ 94StaCluMOP-696
❑ 94StaCluT-285
❑ 94StaCluTFDI-285
❑ 94Top-571
❑ 94TopGol-571
❑ 94TopSpa-571
❑ 94TopTra-94T
❑ 94Ult-534
❑ 94UppDec-421
❑ 94UppDecED-421
❑ 95ColCho-313
❑ 95ColChoGS-313
❑ 95ColChoSS-313
❑ 95Don-242
❑ 95DonPreP-242
❑ 95DonTopotO-286
❑ 95Fle-381
❑ 95Lea-262
❑ 95MetColP-27
❑ 95Pac-288
❑ 95Pin-313
❑ 95PinArtP-313
❑ 95PinMusC-313
❑ 95Sco-388
❑ 95ScoGolR-388
❑ 95ScoPlaTS-388
❑ 95StaClu-83
❑ 95StaCluFDI-83
❑ 95StaCluMOP-83
❑ 95StaCluSTWS-83
❑ 95Top-101
❑ 95TopCyb-65
❑ 95Ult-416
❑ 95UltGolM-416
❑ 95UppDec-358
❑ 95UppDec-464
❑ 95UppDecED-358
❑ 95UppDecEDG-358
❑ 95UppDecSE-57
❑ 95UppDecSEG-57
❑ 96Baz-110
❑ 96Cir-152
❑ 96CirRav-152
❑ 96ColCho-210
❑ 96ColChoGS-210
❑ 96ColChoSS-210
❑ 96Don-78
❑ 96DonPreP-78
❑ 96EmoXL-226
❑ 96ExpBoo-5
❑ 96ExpDis-18
❑ 96ExpDis-19
❑ 96Fin-B36
❑ 96FinRef-B36
❑ 96Fla-313
❑ 96Fle-469
❑ 96FleTif-469
❑ 96Lea-162
❑ 96LeaPrePB-162
❑ 96LeaPrePG-162
❑ 96LeaPrePS-162
❑ 96LeaSigA-206
❑ 96LeaSigAG-206
❑ 96LeaSigAS-206
❑ 96MetUni-194
❑ 96MetUniP-194
❑ 96Pac-121
❑ 96PacEstL-EL28
❑ 96PacPri-P44
❑ 96PacPriG-P44
❑ 96PanSti-23
❑ 96Pin-39
❑ 96ProSta-48
❑ 96Sco-133
❑ 96ScoDugC-A84
❑ 96ScoDugCAP-A84
❑ 96StaClu-28
❑ 96StaCluMOP-28
❑ 96Stu-77
❑ 96StuPrePB-77
❑ 96StuPrePG-77
❑ 96StuPrePS-77
❑ 96Top-151
❑ 96TopChr-44
❑ 96TopChrR-44
❑ 96TopGal-45
❑ 96TopGalPPI-45
❑ 96Ult-236
❑ 96UltGolM-236
❑ 96UppDec-131
❑ 97Cir-181
❑ 97CirRav-181
❑ 97ColCho-159
❑ 97Don-187
❑ 97DonGolPP-187
❑ 97DonSilPP-187
❑ 97Fin-131
❑ 97FinEmb-131
❑ 97FinEmbR-131
❑ 97FinRef-131
❑ 97Fle-387
❑ 97FleTif-387
❑ 97Lea-315
❑ 97LeaFraM-315
❑ 97LeaFraMDC-315
❑ 97Pac-353
❑ 97PacLigB-353
❑ 97PacSil-353
❑ 97Pin-59
❑ 97PinArtP-PP59
❑ 97PinMusC-59
❑ 97PinPrePla-59
❑ 97Sco-420
❑ 97ScoArtPWB-420
❑ 97ScoResC-420
❑ 97ScoShoS-420
❑ 97ScoShoSAP-420
❑ 97StaClu-64
❑ 97StaCluMOP-64
❑ 97Top-36
❑ 97Ult-421
❑ 97UltGolME-421
❑ 97UltPlaME-421
❑ 97UppDec-113
❑ 98Bow-278
❑ 98BowChr-278
❑ 98BowChrGA-278
❑ 98BowChrGAR-278
❑ 98BowChrI-278
❑ 98BowChrIR-278
❑ 98BowChrR-278
❑ 98BowGolA-278
❑ 98BowInt-278
❑ 98CirThu-285
❑ 98CirThuRav-285
❑ 98CirThuSupRav-285
❑ 98ColCho-496
❑ 98CroRoy-129
❑ 98Don-260
❑ 98DonGolPP-260
❑ 98DonSig-119
❑ 98DonSigP-119
❑ 98DonSilPP-260
❑ 98Fle-86
❑ 98Fle-403
❑ 98LeaRS-120
❑ 98LeaRSLHolo-120
❑ 98LeaRSLong-120
❑ 98LeaRTrue-120
❑ 98Pac-355
❑ 98PacAur-77
❑ 98PacInv-117
❑ 98PacInvPBlue-117
❑ 98PacInvSilv-117
❑ 98PacInvTeam-17
❑ 98PacOme-226
❑ 98PacOmeR-226
❑ 98PacOnl-694
❑ 98PacOnlWC-694
❑ 98PacPar-91
❑ 98PacParC-91
❑ 98PacParG-91
❑ 98PacParHS-91
❑ 98PacParPB-91
❑ 98PacParR-91
❑ 98PacPlaB-355
❑ 98PacRedT-355
❑ 98PacSil-355
❑ 98Pin-113
❑ 98PinPreP-113
❑ 98Revo-136
❑ 98RevoSS-136
❑ 98Sco-176
❑ 98ScoSS-PP78
❑ 98ScoSSAP-PP78
❑ 98StaCluFDI-263
❑ 98StaCluI-263
❑ 98StaCluOneK-263
❑ 98StaCluPP-263
❑ 98Stu-93
❑ 98StuGPP-93
❑ 98StuSPP-93
❑ 98Top-154
❑ 98TopChr-154
❑ 98TopChrR-154
❑ 98TopDevR-154
❑ 98TopDia-154
❑ 98TopMiniC-154
❑ 98TopOpeD-81
❑ 98TopSta-29
❑ 98TopStaB-29
❑ 98TopStaG-29
❑ 98TopStaGR-29
❑ 98TopStaS-29
❑ 98Ult-287
❑ 98UltGolM-287
❑ 98UltMas-287
❑ 98UltPlaM-287
❑ 98UppDec-511
❑ 99199Fin-48
❑ 99CroRoyB-131
❑ 99CroRoyL-131
❑ 99CroRoyOD-131
❑ 99FinGolRef-48
❑ 99FinRef-48
❑ 99Fle-257
❑ 99FleSta9-257
❑ 99FleWarT-257
❑ 99MetUni-33
❑ 99MetUniGM-33
❑ 99MetUniPMG-33
❑ 99Pac-402
❑ 99PacAur-180
❑ 99PacAurOD-180
❑ 99PacCroC-268
❑ 99PacCroC-18
❑ 99PacCroCPB-268
❑ 99PacInv-137
❑ 99PacInvOD-137
❑ 99PacInvPB-137
❑ 99PacPar-221
❑ 99PacParC-221
❑ 99PacParG-221
❑ 99PacParHoloGold-221
❑ 99PacParHS-221
❑ 99PacParOD-221
❑ 99PacParPB-221
❑ 99PacParRed-221
❑ 99PacPlaB-402
❑ 99PacPri-136
❑ 99PacPriHB-136
❑ 99PacPriHG-136
❑ 99PacPriHM-136
❑ 99PacPriHP-136
❑ 99PacPriRed-136
❑ 99PacPriS-136
❑ 99PacPriS206-136
❑ 99PacPriS206R-136
❑ 99PacRed-402
❑ 99Rev-134
❑ 99RevPremDate-134
❑ 99RevRet-134
❑ 99RevShaSS-134
❑ 99SkyPre-8
❑ 99SkyPreA-50
❑ 99SkyPreABlue-50
❑ 99SkyPreR-8
❑ 99SkyThu-26
❑ 99SkyThuRant-26
❑ 99SkyThuRave-26
❑ 99SP SigAuto-DSE
❑ 99SPSig-157
❑ 99StaClu-61
❑ 99StaCluFDI-61
❑ 99StaCluOoaK-61
❑ 99StaCluPP-61
❑ 99ThuSkySupR-26
❑ 99Top-17
❑ 99TopChr-17
❑ 99TopChrR-17
❑ 99TopMVPP-17
❑ 99TopOpeD-12
❑ 99Ult-19
❑ 99UltGolM-19
❑ 99UltMas-19
❑ 99UltPlaM-19
❑ 99UppDec-207
❑ 99UppDecEL1-207
❑ 99UppDecEL2-207
❑ 99UppDecM-195
❑ 99UppDecMGS-195
❑ 99UppDecMHFS-195
❑ 99UppDecMSS-195
❑ 99Vic-378

Segui, Diego
❑ 61UniOil-H4
❑ 63Top-157
❑ 64A's-14
❑ 64AthJayP-11
❑ 64Top-508
❑ 64TopCoi-24
❑ 65OPC-197
❑ 65Top-197
❑ 65TopEmbl-24
❑ 65TopTral-68
❑ 66Top-309
❑ 66TopVen-309
❑ 67VanMouSO-22
❑ 68Top-517
❑ 69PilPos-11
❑ 69PilWhe-8
❑ 69Top-511A
❑ 69Top-511B
❑ 70OPC-2
❑ 70Top-2
❑ 71MLBOffS-526
❑ 71OPC-67
❑ 71OPC-215
❑ 71Top-67
❑ 71Top-215
❑ 72Top-735
❑ 73OPC-383
❑ 73Top-383
❑ 74OPC-151
❑ 74Top-151
❑ 74TopTra-151T
❑ 75OPC-232
❑ 75Top-232
❑ 75TopMin-232
❑ 76SSP-423
❑ 76VenLeaS-83
❑ 77PilPosR-11
❑ 77Top-653
❑ 80VenLeaS-16
❑ 83Pil69G-25
❑ 87PocGiaTB-30
❑ 88PocGiaP-2100
❑ 89EveGiaS-31
❑ 90EveGiaP-3146
❑ 90PacLeg-104

Seguignol, Fernando
❑ 94OneYanC-20
❑ 94OneYanF-3805
❑ 96DelShoB-27
❑ 98arSenW1-20
❑ 98Bow-394
❑ 98BowChr-394
❑ 98BowChrGA-394
❑ 98BowChrGAR-394
❑ 98BowChrI-394
❑ 98BowChrIR-394
❑ 98BowChrR-394
❑ 98BowGolA-394
❑ 98BowInt-394
❑ 98DonSig-138
❑ 98DonSigP-138
❑ 98FleUpd-U30
❑ 98HarSenM-20
❑ 98LeaRS-331
❑ 98LeaRSLHolo-331
❑ 98LeaRSLong-331
❑ 98LeaRTrue-331
❑ 99199Fin-282
❑ 99BasAmeTP-91
❑ 99BasAmeTPG-91
❑ 99Bow-205
❑ 99BowAut-BA25
❑ 99BowBes-144
❑ 99BowBesAR-144
❑ 99BowBesR-144
❑ 99BowChr-205
❑ 99BowChrDA-DA3
❑ 99BowChrDAR-DA3
❑ 99BowChrG-205
❑ 99BowChrGR-205
❑ 99BowChrI-205
❑ 99BowChrIR-205
❑ 99BowChrR-205
❑ 99BowGol-205
❑ 99BowInt-205
❑ 99DumSet-BF5
❑ 99DumSet-BF5
❑ 99FinFutF-FF10
❑ 99FinGolRef-282
❑ 99FinRef-282
❑ 99FlaShoLeg1-30
❑ 99FlaShoLeg2-30
❑ 99FlaShoLeg3-30
❑ 99FlaShoLegM1-30
❑ 99FlaShoLegM2-30
❑ 99FlaShoLegM3-30
❑ 99FlaShoR1-30
❑ 99FlaShoR2-30
❑ 99FlaShoR3-30
❑ 99Fle-99
❑ 99FleBri-145
❑ 99FleBri2G-145
❑ 99FleBriBlu-145
❑ 99FleBriGol-145
❑ 99FleSta9-99
❑ 99FleWarT-99
❑ 99Pac-270
❑ 99Pac-270A
❑ 99PacAur-115
❑ 99PacAurOD-115
❑ 99PacCroC-174
❑ 99PacCroCPB-174
❑ 99PacInv-92
❑ 99PacInvOD-92
❑ 99PacInvPB-92
❑ 99PacPlaB-270
❑ 99PacPlaB-270A
❑ 99PacPri-89
❑ 99PacPriHB-89
❑ 99PacPriHG-89
❑ 99PacPriHM-89
❑ 99PacPriHP-89
❑ 99PacPriRed-89
❑ 99PacRed-270
❑ 99PacRed-270A
❑ 99SkyThu-82
❑ 99SkyThuRant-82
❑ 99SkyThuRave-82
❑ 99SP Aut-110
❑ 99SP SigAuto-FS
❑ 99SP SigAutoG-FS
❑ 99SP TopP-110
❑ 99SP TopPPE-110
❑ 99SpoIll-53
❑ 99SpoIllOTW-11
❑ 99SPSig-83
❑ 99SPx-107
❑ 99SPxFinR-107
❑ 99SPxFinS-107
❑ 99StaClu-348
❑ 99StaCluFDI-348
❑ 99StaCluOoaK-348
❑ 99StaCluPP-348
❑ 99ThuSkySupR-82
❑ 99Top-432
❑ 99TopChr-432
❑ 99TopChrR-432
❑ 99TopMVPP-432
❑ 99TopSta-27
❑ 99TopSta1Foil-27
❑ 99TopSta2Foil-27
❑ 99TopStaFoil-27
❑ 99TopStaOS-27
❑ 99TopStaTS-27
❑ 99UD Cho-18
❑ 99UD ChoPCR-18
❑ 99UppDec-290
❑ 99UppDecE-133
❑ 99UppDecEFXG-133
❑ 99UppDecEL1-290
❑ 99UppDecEL2-290
❑ 99UppDecM-129
❑ 99UppDecMGS-129
❑ 99UppDecMHFS-129
❑ 99UppDecMSS-129
❑ 99Vic-235

Segura, Angel
❑ 89CarNewE-19

Segura, Jose
❑ 85DomLeaS-135
❑ 85KinBluJT-10
❑ 86KnoBluJP-19
❑ 87SyrChiP-1936
❑ 87SyrChiT-7
❑ 88FleUpd-20
❑ 88FleUpdG-20
❑ 88WhiSoxC-27
❑ 89VanCanC-6
❑ 89VanCanP-591
❑ 90CMC-639
❑ 90ProAAAF-168
❑ 90VanCanC-12
❑ 90VanCanP-490
❑ 91LinDriAAA-394
❑ 91PhoFirLD-394
❑ 91PhoFirP-66
❑ 92NasSouS-292
❑ 92Sco-278
❑ 93LimRocDWB-69

Segura, Juan
❑ 93LetMouF-4157
❑ 93LetMouSP-20
❑ 94AugGreC-22
❑ 94SalBucC-21
❑ 94SalBucF-2333

Sehorn, Jason
❑ 90HunCubP-3302

Seibert, Gib
❑ 85PorBeaC-27
❑ 87MaiGuiP-15
❑ 87MaiGuiT-16

Seibert, Kurt
❑ 80TolMudHT-20
❑ 81TolMudHT-14

Seibert, Mal
❑ 90FayGenP-2406

Seibert, Rick
❑ 89PenPilS-22

Seibold, Socks (Harry)
❑ 20Zee-132
❑ 21Zee-38
❑ 24Zee-37
❑ 29PorandAR-84
❑ 33DouDisP-38
❑ 93ConTSN-975

Seidel, Dick
❑ 83GreHorT-12

Seidel, Ryan
❑ 96RocCubTI-29

Seidensticker, Andy
❑ 88VisOakCLC-172
❑ 88VisOakP-106

Seidholz, Don
❑ 78KnoKnoST-18
❑ 79KnoKnoST-9

Seifert, Keith
❑ 87WatIndP-21
❑ 88WatIndP-678

Seifert, Ryan
❑ 97PorRocG-27
❑ 98AshTouM-22

Seiler, Keith
❑ 90TamYanD-23
❑ 91GreHorP-3059
❑ 92PriWilCC-20
❑ 92PriWilCF-149
❑ 93PriWilCC-22
❑ 93PriWilCF-655
❑ 94AlbYanF-1441
❑ 95NorNavTI-20

Seilheimer, Rick

❑ 80GleFalWSBT-7
❑ 80GleFalWSCT-8
❑ 81GleFalWST-9
❑ 82EdmTraT-21
❑ 86BirBarTI-14

Seip, Rod
❑ 92GulCoaRSP-1
❑ 93EriSaiC-21
❑ 93EriSaiF-3115
❑ 94ChaRivC-19
❑ 94ChaRivF-2673

Seitz, Charles
❑ 09T206-514

Seitz, David
❑ 86SumBraP-25

Seitz, Paul
❑ 67VanMouSO-23

Seitzer, Brad
❑ 91BluOriC-8
❑ 91BluOriP-4137
❑ 91KanCouCTI-19
❑ 92ClaFS7-146
❑ 92FreKeyC-11
❑ 92FreKeyF-1815
❑ 93FreKeyC-23
❑ 93FreKeyF-1037
❑ 96El PasDB-26
❑ 97Top-490
❑ 97TucTorB-26
❑ 98TacRaiQ-28

Seitzer, Kevin
❑ 83ButCopKT-20
❑ 85Ft.MyeRT-9
❑ 86OmaRoyP-22
❑ 86OmaRoyT-3
❑ 87ClaUpdY-139
❑ 87DonHig-26
❑ 87DonHig-47
❑ 87DonOpeD-207
❑ 87DonRoo-15
❑ 87Fle-652
❑ 87FleGlo-652
❑ 87FleSlu-39
❑ 87FleUpd-108
❑ 87FleUpdG-108
❑ 87Spo-158
❑ 87SpoRooI-20
❑ 87SpoTeaP-13
❑ 87TopTra-111T
❑ 87TopTraT-111T
❑ 88ClaBlu-218
❑ 88ClaRed-159
❑ 88Don-280
❑ 88DonAll-27
❑ 88DonBasB-175
❑ 88DonBonM-BC17
❑ 88Fle-270
❑ 88FleAwaW-37
❑ 88FleBasA-38
❑ 88FleBasM-33
❑ 88FleExcS-36
❑ 88FleGlo-270
❑ 88FleHotS-36
❑ 88FleLeaL-37
❑ 88FleMin-27
❑ 88FleRecS-37
❑ 88FleSlu-38
❑ 88FleStiC-33
❑ 88FleSup-35
❑ 88FleTeaL-36
❑ 88FleWaxBC-C12
❑ 88K-M-27
❑ 88KeyFooD-8
❑ 88Lea-105
❑ 88MSAIceTD-8
❑ 88OPC-275
❑ 88OurOwnTD-8
❑ 88PanSti-108
❑ 88PanSti-436
❑ 88RoySmo-21
❑ 88RoyTeal-30
❑ 88Sco-6
❑ 88ScoGlo-6
❑ 88ScoYouSI-10
❑ 88Spo-17
❑ 88SpoGam-13
❑ 88StaLinRo-15
❑ 88StaSei-1
❑ 88StaSei-2
❑ 88StaSei-3
❑ 88StaSei-4
❑ 88StaSei-5
❑ 88StaSei-6
❑ 88StaSei-7
❑ 88StaSei-8
❑ 88StaSei-9
❑ 88StaSei-10
❑ 88StaSei-11
❑ 88TarPla-40
❑ 88TetTeaD-8
❑ 88Top-275
❑ 88TopBig-115
❑ 88TopGloS-9
❑ 88TopMinL-15
❑ 88TopRevLL-22
❑ 88TopRitTM-19
❑ 88TopRoo-9
❑ 88TopSti-261
❑ 88TopSti-306
❑ 88TopTif-275
❑ 88TopUKM-69
❑ 88TopUKMT-69
❑ 88ToyRoo-27
❑ 88WeiMarD-8
❑ 89Bow-123
❑ 89BowTif-123
❑ 89CadEllD-52
❑ 89ClaLigB-65
❑ 89Don-10
❑ 89Don-238
❑ 89DonBasB-207
❑ 89DonSupD-10
❑ 89Fle-292
❑ 89FleExcS-36
❑ 89FleGlo-292
❑ 89FleHeroB-36
❑ 89FleWaxBC-C22
❑ 89MSAHolD-9
❑ 89Nis-9
❑ 89OPC-58
❑ 89PanSti-357
❑ 89RedFolSB-107
❑ 89RoyTasD-2
❑ 89Sco-55
❑ 89ScoHot1S-17
❑ 89Spo-55
❑ 89Top-670
❑ 89TopBasT-120
❑ 89TopBig-313
❑ 89TopSti-264
❑ 89TopTif-670
❑ 89TVSpoM-106
❑ 89UppDec-510
❑ 89UppDecS-3
❑ 90Bow-380
❑ 90BowTif-380
❑ 90Don-85
❑ 90DonBesA-91
❑ 90Fle-117
❑ 90FleCan-117
❑ 90Lea-230
❑ 90MLBBasB-102
❑ 90OPC-435
❑ 90PanSti-86
❑ 90PubIntS-355
❑ 90RedFolSB-86
❑ 90RoyPos-22
❑ 90Sco-199
❑ 90Sco100S-88
❑ 90Spo-46
❑ 90Top-435
❑ 90TopBig-76
❑ 90TopMinL-18
❑ 90TopSti-267
❑ 90TopTif-435
❑ 90UppDec-363
❑ 91Bow-305
❑ 91ClaGam-40
❑ 91Don-73
❑ 91Fle-569
❑ 91KinDis-2
❑ 91Lea-133
❑ 91OPC-695
❑ 91PanFreS-278
❑ 91PanSti-227
❑ 91RoyPol-19
❑ 91Sco-279
❑ 91Sco100S-97
❑ 91SimandSMLBL-39
❑ 91StaClu-88
❑ 91StuPre-5
❑ 91Top-695
❑ 91TopDesS-695
❑ 91TopMic-695
❑ 91TopTif-695
❑ 91Ult-155
❑ 91UppDec-433
❑ 92Bow-126
❑ 92BrePol-22
❑ 92Don-577
❑ 92DonUpd-U15
❑ 92Fle-168
❑ 92FleUpd-38
❑ 92Lea-399
❑ 92LeaBlaG-399
❑ 92OPC-577
❑ 92OPCPre-27
❑ 92Pin-11
❑ 92RedFolS-86
❑ 92RoyPol-24
❑ 92Sco-310
❑ 92ScoProP-5
❑ 92ScoRoo-2T
❑ 92StaClu-285
❑ 92StaClu-820
❑ 92Top-577
❑ 92TopGol-577
❑ 92TopGolW-577
❑ 92TopMic-577
❑ 92TopTra-103T
❑ 92TopTraG-103T
❑ 92Ult-389
❑ 92UppDec-327
❑ 92UppDec-783
❑ 93AthMot-21
❑ 93AthStaC-5
❑ 93Bow-597
❑ 93Don-603
❑ 93Fle-256
❑ 93FleFinE-262
❑ 93Lea-353
❑ 93OPC-312
❑ 93OPCPre-121
❑ 93PacSpa-164
❑ 93PanSti-40
❑ 93Pin-117
❑ 93Sco-571
❑ 93Sel-87
❑ 93StaClu-57
❑ 93StaClu-657
❑ 93StaCluFDI-57
❑ 93StaCluFDI-657
❑ 93StaCluMOP-57
❑ 93StaCluMOP-657
❑ 93Stu-169
❑ 93Top-44
❑ 93TopGol-44
❑ 93TopInaM-44
❑ 93TopInaR-44
❑ 93TopMic-44
❑ 93Ult-612
❑ 93UppDec-295
❑ 93UppDec-616
❑ 93UppDecGold-295
❑ 93UppDecGold-616
❑ 94BreMilB-180
❑ 94BrePol-24
❑ 94BreTeal-23
❑ 94ColC-379
❑ 94ColChoGS-379
❑ 94ColChoSS-379
❑ 94Don-261
❑ 94Fin-314
❑ 94FinRef-314
❑ 94Fla-70
❑ 94Fle-190
❑ 94FleExtB-108
❑ 94Lea-339
❑ 94Pac-341
❑ 94PanSti-86
❑ 94ProMag-72
❑ 94Sco-519
❑ 94ScoGolR-519
❑ 94Sel-355
❑ 94StaClu-90
❑ 94StaCluFDI-90
❑ 94StaCluGR-90
❑ 94StaCluMOP-90
❑ 94Stu-47
❑ 94Top-411
❑ 94TopGol-411
❑ 94TopSpa-411
❑ 94Ult-378
❑ 94UppDec-378
❑ 94UppDecED-378
❑ 95BowBes-R67
❑ 95BowBesR-R67
❑ 95ColCho-172
❑ 95ColChoGS-172
❑ 95ColChoSS-172
❑ 95Don-10
❑ 95DonDiaK-DK13
❑ 95DonPreP-10
❑ 95DonTopotO-102
❑ 95Emo-55
❑ 95Fin-210
❑ 95FinRef-210
❑ 95Fla-276
❑ 95Fle-189
❑ 95Lea-86
❑ 95LeaLim-61
❑ 95Pin-46
❑ 95PinArtP-46
❑ 95PinMusC-46
❑ 95Sco-45
❑ 95ScoGolR-45
❑ 95ScoPlaTS-45
❑ 95SP-166
❑ 95SPCha-165
❑ 95SPChaDC-165
❑ 95SPSil-166
❑ 95StaClu-435
❑ 95StaCluMOP-435
❑ 95StaCluSTWS-435
❑ 95StaCluVR-230
❑ 95StaCluVRMO-230
❑ 95Stu-145
❑ 95TomPiz-16
❑ 95Top-309
❑ 95TopCyb-166
❑ 95Ult-68
❑ 95UltGolM-68
❑ 95UppDec-302
❑ 95UppDecED-302
❑ 95UppDecEDG-302
❑ 95Zen-64
❑ 96Baz-46
❑ 96BrePol-22
❑ 96Cir-53
❑ 96CirRav-53
❑ 96ColCho-190
❑ 96ColChoGS-190
❑ 96ColChoSS-190
❑ 96DenHol-26
❑ 96Don-503
❑ 96DonPreP-503
❑ 96EmoXL-77
❑ 96Fin-B70
❑ 96FinRef-B70
❑ 96Fla-106
❑ 96Fle-157
❑ 96FleTif-157
❑ 96Lea-74
❑ 96LeaPre-89
❑ 96LeaPreP-89
❑ 96LeaPrePB-74
❑ 96LeaPrePG-74
❑ 96LeaPrePS-74
❑ 96LeaSigA-207
❑ 96LeaSigAG-207
❑ 96LeaSigAS-207
❑ 96MetUni-73
❑ 96MetUniP-73
❑ 96PanSti-197
❑ 96Pin-231
❑ 96PinAfi-7
❑ 96PinAfiAP-7
❑ 96PinAfiFPP-7
❑ 96PinArtP-131
❑ 96PinFan-19
❑ 96PinFoil-231
❑ 96PinSta-131
❑ 96ProSta-26
❑ 96RedF-31
❑ 96Sco-59
❑ 96Sel-28
❑ 96SelArtP-28
❑ 96SelTeaN-28
❑ 96SP-109
❑ 96Spo-93
❑ 96SpoArtP-93
❑ 96StaClu-33
❑ 96StaCluMOP-33
❑ 96Stu-84
❑ 96StuPrePB-84
❑ 96StuPrePG-84
❑ 96StuPrePS-84
❑ 96Sum-10
❑ 96SumAbo&B-10
❑ 96SumArtP-10
❑ 96SumFoi-10
❑ 96TeaOut-72
❑ 96Top-111
❑ 96TopChr-30
❑ 96TopChrR-30
❑ 96Ult-83
❑ 96UltGolM-83
❑ 96UppDec-365
❑ 96ZenMoz-14
❑ 97Cir-152
❑ 97CirRav-152
❑ 97ColCho-316
❑ 97Don-324
❑ 97DonEli-139
❑ 97DonEliGS-139
❑ 97DonGolPP-324
❑ 97DonSilPP-324
❑ 97DonTea-88
❑ 97DonTeaSPE-88
❑ 97Fin-231
❑ 97FinRef-231
❑ 97Fle-88
❑ 97FleTif-88
❑ 97IndSco-11
❑ 97IndScoPl-11
❑ 97IndScoPr-11
❑ 97IndScoU-11
❑ 97IndScoUTC-11
❑ 97Lea-286
❑ 97LeaFraM-286
❑ 97LeaFraMDC-286
❑ 97Pin-79
❑ 97PinArtP-PP79
❑ 97PinMusC-79
❑ 97PinPrePla-79
❑ 97Sco-207
❑ 97ScoArtPWB-207
❑ 97ScoPreS-207
❑ 97ScoShoS-207
❑ 97ScoShoSAP-207
❑ 97StaClu-305
❑ 97StaCluMOP-305
❑ 97Stu-72
❑ 97StuPrePG-72
❑ 97StuPrePS-72
❑ 97Top-421
❑ 97UppDec-341
❑ 98PacInvGems-42

Seja, Aaron
❑ 91FayGenP-1184
❑ 91NiaFalRC-7
❑ 91NiaFalRP-3648

Sekany, Jason
❑ 97MicBatC-25
❑ 98TreThuM-20

Selak, Ron**
❑ 76VenLeaS-59
❑ 78SprRedWK-21

Selbach, Kip (Albert)
❑ 03BreE10-127
❑ 11SpoLifCW-317

Selby, Bill
❑ 92ElmPioC-19
❑ 92ElmPioF-1393
❑ 92FroRowDP-49
❑ 92FroRowDPG-49
❑ 92FroRowDPS-49
❑ 93LynRedSC-24
❑ 93LynRedSF-2527
❑ 94CarLeaAF-CAR5
❑ 94LynRedSC-22
❑ 94LynRedSF-1902
❑ 95Bow-63
❑ 95Exc-15
❑ 95TreThuTI-23
❑ 95UppDecML-187
❑ 95UppDecMLFS-187
❑ 96BowBes-173
❑ 96BowBesAR-173
❑ 96BowBesR-173
❑ 96Exc-19
❑ 96PawRedSDD-27
❑ 97Ult-18
❑ 97UltGolME-18
❑ 97UltPlaME-18
❑ 98BufBisG-26

Sele, Aaron
❑ 91Cla/Bes-437
❑ 91ClaDraP-19
❑ 91FroRowDP-2
❑ 91FroRowDPG-2
❑ 91FroRowDPS-2
❑ 92Bow-311
❑ 92ClaBluBF-BC11
❑ 92ClaFS7-175
❑ 92ClaRedB-BC11
❑ 92LynRedSC-16
❑ 92LynRedSF-2907
❑ 92OPC-504
❑ 92Sco-809
❑ 92StaCluD-168
❑ 92Top-504
❑ 92TopGol-504
❑ 92TopGolW-504
❑ 92TopMic-504
❑ 92UppDecML-291
❑ 92UppDecMLPotY-PY20
❑ 93Bow-255
❑ 93ClaFisN-8
❑ 93ClaFS7-23
❑ 93ClaGolF-23
❑ 93ExcAllF-7
❑ 93ExcFS7-138
❑ 93FlaWavotF-16
❑ 93FleFinE-178
❑ 93Lea-518
❑ 93PawRedSDD-24
❑ 93PawRedSF-2408
❑ 93PawRedSTI-21
❑ 93SelRoo-86T
❑ 93SP-205
❑ 93TopTra-3T
❑ 94Bow-643
❑ 94BowBes-R44
❑ 94BowBesR-R44
❑ 94ColC-255
❑ 94ColChoGS-255
❑ 94ColChoSS-255
❑ 94Don-303
❑ 94Fin-6
❑ 94FinJum-6
❑ 94FinRef-6
❑ 94Fla-15
❑ 94Fla-P15
❑ 94Fle-43
❑ 94FleExtB-25
❑ 94FleExtBPD-4
❑ 94FleExtBSYS-19
❑ 94FleRooS-18
❑ 94FUnPac-36
❑ 94Lea-199
❑ 94LeaL-11
❑ 94OPC-89
❑ 94OPCDiaD-17
❑ 94Pac-66
❑ 94Pin-95
❑ 94PinArtP-95
❑ 94PinMusC-95
❑ 94PinNewG-NG5
❑ 94Sco-561
❑ 94ScoBoyoS-2
❑ 94ScoGolR-561
❑ 94Sel-337
❑ 94SP-156
❑ 94SPDieC-156
❑ 94Spo-37
❑ 94StaClu-179
❑ 94StaClu-678
❑ 94StaCluFDI-179
❑ 94StaCluFDI-678
❑ 94StaCluGR-179
❑ 94StaCluGR-678
❑ 94StaCluMOP-179
❑ 94StaCluMOP-678
❑ 94Stu-164
❑ 94Top-445
❑ 94TopGol-445
❑ 94TopSpa-445
❑ 94TriPla-207
❑ 94Ult-18
❑ 94UltRisS-12
❑ 94UltSecYS-5
❑ 94UppDec-45
❑ 94UppDec-80
❑ 94UppDecAJ-21
❑ 94UppDecAJG-21
❑ 94UppDecED-45
❑ 94UppDecED-80
❑ 94USPlaCR-8S
❑ 95Bow-314
❑ 95ColCho-406
❑ 95ColChoGS-406
❑ 95ColChoSE-191
❑ 95ColChoSEGS-191
❑ 95ColChoSESS-191
❑ 95ColChoSS-406
❑ 95Don-17
❑ 95DonPreP-17
❑ 95DonTopotO-26
❑ 95Emo-15
❑ 95Fin-201
❑ 95FinRef-201
❑ 95Fla-13
❑ 95Fle-40
❑ 95Lea-7
❑ 95LeaLim-137
❑ 95Pac-45
❑ 95Pin-259
❑ 95PinArtP-259
❑ 95PinMusC-259
❑ 95PinUps-US18
❑ 95RedFol-11
❑ 95Sco-335
❑ 95ScoGolR-335
❑ 95ScoPlaTS-335
❑ 95Sel-29

❑ 95SelArtP-29
❑ 95SP-129
❑ 95Spo-57
❑ 95SpoArtP-57
❑ 95SPSil-129
❑ 95StaClu-464
❑ 95StaCluMOP-464
❑ 95StaCluSTDW-RS464
❑ 95StaCluSTWS-464
❑ 95StaCluVR-253
❑ 95StaCluVRMO-253
❑ 95Stu-150
❑ 95Top-301
❑ 95TopCyb-162
❑ 95UC3-16
❑ 95UC3ArtP-16
❑ 95Ult-264
❑ 95UltGolM-264
❑ 95UppDec-162
❑ 95UppDecED-162
❑ 95UppDecEDG-162
❑ 96ColCho-476
❑ 96ColChoGS-476
❑ 96ColChoSS-476
❑ 96Don-157
❑ 96DonPreP-157
❑ 96Fla-24
❑ 96Fle-33
❑ 96FleRedS-12
❑ 96FleTif-33
❑ 96Lea-202
❑ 96LeaPrePB-202
❑ 96LeaPrePG-202
❑ 96LeaPrePS-202
❑ 96Sco-416
❑ 96Top-332
❑ 96Ult-319
❑ 96UltGolM-319
❑ 96UppDec-284
❑ 97Cir-19
❑ 97CirRav-19
❑ 97ColCho-49
❑ 97Don-319
❑ 97DonGolPP-319
❑ 97DonSilPP-319
❑ 97DonTea-57
❑ 97DonTeaSPE-57
❑ 97Fle-662
❑ 97FleTif-662
❑ 97Lea-302
❑ 97LeaFraM-302
❑ 97LeaFraMDC-302
❑ 97PacPriGotD-GD25
❑ 97Sco-395
❑ 97ScoArtPWB-395
❑ 97ScoResC-395
❑ 97ScoShoS-395
❑ 97ScoShoSAP-395
❑ 97StaClu-177
❑ 97StaCluMOP-177
❑ 97Top-243
❑ 97Ult-539
❑ 97UltGolME-539
❑ 97UltPlaME-539
❑ 98CirThu-240
❑ 98CirThuRav-240
❑ 98CirThuSupRav-240
❑ 98ColCho-50
❑ 98ColCho-518
❑ 98CroRoy-139
❑ 98Fle-78
❑ 98Fle-486
❑ 98PacOme-242
❑ 98PacOmeR-242
❑ 98PacOnl-744
❑ 98PacOnlR-744
❑ 98PacOnlWC-744
❑ 98PinSna-TR11
❑ 98RedSoxS-2
❑ 98RedSoxSP-2
❑ 98Revo-145
❑ 98RevoSS-145
❑ 98Sco-29
❑ 98ScoRT-211
❑ 98Top-169
❑ 98TopChr-169
❑ 98TopChrR-169
❑ 98TopDevR-169
❑ 98TopDia-169
❑ 98TopMiniC-169
❑ 98Ult-301
❑ 98UltGolM-301
❑ 98UltMas-301
❑ 98UltPlaM-301
❑ 98UppDec-46
❑ 98UppDec-742
❑ 99199Fin-89
❑ 99FinGolRef-89
❑ 99FinRef-89
❑ 99Fle-232
❑ 99FleSta9-232
❑ 99FleWarT-232
❑ 99Pac-430
❑ 99PacCroC-289
❑ 99PacCroCPB-289
❑ 99PacPar-239
❑ 99PacParC-239
❑ 99PacParG-239
❑ 99PacParHoloGold-239
❑ 99PacParHS-239
❑ 99PacParOD-239
❑ 99PacParPB-239
❑ 99PacParRed-239
❑ 99PacPlaB-430
❑ 99PacPri-145
❑ 99PacPriHB-145
❑ 99PacPriHG-145
❑ 99PacPriHM-145
❑ 99PacPriHP-145
❑ 99PacPriRed-145
❑ 99PacRed-430
❑ 99SkyThu-240
❑ 99SkyThuRant-240
❑ 99SkyThuRave-240
❑ 99StaClu-137
❑ 99StaCluFDI-137
❑ 99StaCluOoaK-137
❑ 99StaCluPP-137
❑ 99ThuSkySupR-240
❑ 99Top-86
❑ 99TopChr-86
❑ 99TopChrR-86
❑ 99TopMVPP-86
❑ 99TopOpeD-49
❑ 99Ult-134
❑ 99UltGolM-134
❑ 99UltMas-134
❑ 99UltPlaM-134
❑ 99UppDec-504
❑ 99UppDecEL1-504
❑ 99UppDecEL2-504
❑ 99Vic-402

Selig, Bud
❑ 96PinFan-BS1

Selkirk, George
❑ 34DiaStaR-88
❑ 35DiaMatCS3T1-130
❑ 36WorWidGV-11
❑ 37KelPepS-BB12
❑ 37OPCBatUV-108
❑ 38CloFotW-73
❑ 38OurNatGPP-27
❑ 39PlaBal-25
❑ 40PlaBal-8
❑ 72TCMthe3-63
❑ 75YanDyn1T-45
❑ 75YanDyn1T-51
❑ 79DiaGre-7
❑ 83YanASFY-41
❑ 85BigLeaC3-65
❑ 92ConTSN-388
❑ 92YanWIZA-76

Sell, Chip
❑ 94YakBeaC-21
❑ 94YakBeaF-3865
❑ 95VerBeaDTI-23
❑ 96SanBerSB-24
❑ 97VerBeaD-23
❑ 98SanAntMG-26

Sellas, Marcelino
❑ 88CapCodPPaLP-91

Selleck, Tom
❑ 92UppDec-SP4

Sellers, Alvy
❑ 24Zee-139

Sellers, Jeff
❑ 86DonRoo-29
❑ 86PawRedSP-21
❑ 87Don-544
❑ 87Fle-46
❑ 87FleGlo-46
❑ 87Lea-158
❑ 87RedSoxP-20
❑ 87Top-12
❑ 87TopTif-12
❑ 88Don-585
❑ 88DonTeaBRS-585
❑ 88Fle-366
❑ 88FleGlo-366
❑ 88Sco-541
❑ 88ScoGlo-541
❑ 88Top-653
❑ 88TopTif-653
❑ 89Bow-299
❑ 89BowTif-299
❑ 89Don-517
❑ 89NasSouP-1270
❑ 89Sco-491
❑ 89Top-544
❑ 89TopTif-544
❑ 92TulDriF-2694

Sellers, Justin
❑ 97IdaFalBTI-20

Sellers, Rick
❑ 89NiaFalRP-21
❑ 90FayGenP-2412
❑ 91LakTigC-16
❑ 92LonTigF-637
❑ 92LonTigS-418
❑ 93LonTigF-2312
❑ 95ChaLooTI-21

Sellheimer, Rick
❑ 85BufBisT-5

Sellick, John
❑ 88SavCarP-347
❑ 88SouAtlLAGS-25
❑ 89SprCarB-14
❑ 90St.PetCS-22
❑ 91ArkTraLD-44
❑ 91ArkTraP-1296
❑ 91LinDriAA-44
❑ 92ArkTraF-1140
❑ 92ArkTraS-45
❑ 92SkyAA F-19

Sellner, Scott
❑ 88BilMusP-1807
❑ 89CedRapRB-17
❑ 89CedRapRP-925
❑ 89CedRapRS-18
❑ 90ChaLooGS-27
❑ 91ChaLooLD-169
❑ 91ChaLooP-1968
❑ 91LinDriAA-169

Sells, Dave
❑ 74OPC-37
❑ 74Top-37
❑ 75CalAngP-38
❑ 90DodTar-718

Sells, George
❑ 88CapCodPPaLP-117
❑ 90HamRedB-9
❑ 90HamRedS-23
❑ 91St.PetCP-2275

Selma, Dick
❑ 66OPC-67
❑ 66Top-67
❑ 66TopVen-67
❑ 67Top-386
❑ 68Top-556
❑ 69CubJewT-16
❑ 69MLBOffS-195
❑ 69OPC-197
❑ 69Top-197
❑ 69TopDecl-39
❑ 69TopFou-6
❑ 69TopSta-98
❑ 69TopSup-62
❑ 69TopTeaP-12
❑ 70MLBOffS-23
❑ 70OPC-24
❑ 70Top-24
❑ 71Kel-21
❑ 71MLBOffS-187
❑ 71OPC-705
❑ 71PhiArcO-10
❑ 71Top-705
❑ 72Top-726
❑ 73OPC-632
❑ 73Top-632
❑ 75AlbDukCa-11
❑ 91MetWIZ-357
❑ 94BreMilB-181

Selmo, Feliberto
❑ 93DanBraC-15
❑ 93DanBraF-3625

Selna, Charles
❑ 88SFHesCreN32-27

Seltzer, Randy
❑ 76AppFoxT-24
❑ 77AppFoxT-22

Semall, Paul
❑ 79ColCliT-3
❑ 80WicAerT-15
❑ 83OklCit8T-16
❑ 84HawIslC-125
❑ 85HawIslC-232

Sember, Mike
❑ 79SyrChiT-10
❑ 79SyrChiTI-10

Sembera, Carroll
❑ 66Top-539
❑ 67OPC-136
❑ 67Top-136
❑ 68Top-207
❑ 68TopVen-207
❑ 69Top-351

Sementelli, Chris
❑ 89SpaPhiP-1049

Semerano, Bob
❑ 77ChaPatT-21

Seminara, Frank
❑ 88OneYanP-2071
❑ 89OneYanP-2121
❑ 89PriWilCS-18
❑ 90CarLeaA-14
❑ 90PriWilCTI-23
❑ 91Cla/Bes-382
❑ 91LinDriAA-618
❑ 91WicWraLD-618
❑ 91WicWraP-2598
❑ 91WicWraRD-9
❑ 92Bow-561
❑ 92Don-10
❑ 92DonRooP-BC17
❑ 92FleUpd-124
❑ 92LasVegSS-240
❑ 92PadPolD-19
❑ 92PadSmo-29
❑ 92PinRoo-25
❑ 92ProFS7-334
❑ 92ScoRoo-97T
❑ 92SkyAAAF-116
❑ 92TopTra-104T
❑ 92TopTraG-104T
❑ 93Bow-222
❑ 93ClaGam-83
❑ 93Don-550
❑ 93Fle-146
❑ 93Lea-64
❑ 93OPC-282
❑ 93PacSpa-601
❑ 93PadMot-16
❑ 93Pin-561
❑ 93Sco-342
❑ 93Sel-305
❑ 93StaClu-438
❑ 93StaCluFDI-438
❑ 93StaCluMOP-438
❑ 93Top-247
❑ 93TopGol-247
❑ 93TopInaM-247
❑ 93TopInaR-247
❑ 93TopMic-247
❑ 93Toy-57
❑ 93Ult-121
❑ 93UppDec-307
❑ 93UppDecGold-307
❑ 93USPlaCR-10D
❑ 94Fle-673
❑ 94MetShuST-8
❑ 94NorTidF-2921
❑ 94Pac-533
❑ 94Ult-283
❑ 95RocRedWTI-33

Seminick, Andy
❑ 47Exh-205
❑ 47PM1StaP1-198
❑ 49Bow-30
❑ 49EurSta-146
❑ 49PhiBul-48
❑ 49PhiLumPB-10
❑ 50Bow-121
❑ 50PhiPhil-19
❑ 50RoyDes-7A
❑ 50RoyDes-7B
❑ 51BerRos-C7
❑ 51Bow-51
❑ 51TopRedB-45
❑ 52DixLid-20
❑ 52DixPre-20
❑ 52RoyPre-13
❑ 52Top-297
❑ 53BowBW-7
❑ 53Top-153
❑ 54Bow-172
❑ 55Bow-93
❑ 56Top-296
❑ 75Phi195T-25
❑ 76TayBow4-51
❑ 77PhiFav-13
❑ 79DiaGre-315
❑ 80Phi195T-25
❑ 83PhiPosGPaM-3
❑ 83TCMPla1945-43
❑ 83TopRep5-297
❑ 91TopArc1-153

Seminoff, Rich
❑ 93ElmPioC-17
❑ 93ElmPioF-3832
❑ 94ElmPioF-3484

Semore, Enos
❑ 88OklSoo-6
❑ 89OklSoo-1

Semprini, John
❑ 82JacMetT-9
❑ 84ChaLooT-11

Semproch, Roman
❑ 58PhiTeal-17
❑ 58Top-474
❑ 59Top-197
❑ 60Top-286
❑ 61Top-174
❑ 61TopStal-206

Sempsprott, Ed
❑ 75WatRoyT-25

Sempsrott, Ed
❑ 76WatRoyT-25
❑ 77DayBealT-21

Sena, Sean
❑ 90YakBeaTI-22

Senators, Mascot
❑ 98arSenW1-28
❑ 98HarSenM-28

Senators, Washington
❑ 13FatT20-8
❑ 24SenWri&D-1
❑ 35GouPreR-3
❑ 38BasTabP-39
❑ 51TopTea-9
❑ 56Top-146
❑ 57Top-270
❑ 58SeaTeal-29
❑ 58Top-44
❑ 59Top-397
❑ 60Top-43
❑ 60TopTat-71
❑ 60TopVen-43
❑ 61TopMagR-4
❑ 62GuyPotCP-19
❑ 62Top-206
❑ 63Top-131
❑ 64Top-343
❑ 64TopTatl-20
❑ 64TopVen-343
❑ 65OPC-267
❑ 65Top-267
❑ 66OPC-194
❑ 66Top-194
❑ 66TopRubl-120
❑ 66TopVen-194
❑ 67Top-437
❑ 68LauWorS-21
❑ 69FleCloS-24
❑ 69FleCloS-44
❑ 69TopStaA-24
❑ 70Top-676
❑ 71OPC-462
❑ 71Top-462
❑ 71TopTat-94

Sencion, Pablo
❑ 96MedHatBJTI-27
❑ 97St.CatSB-26

Sendoh, Mikio
❑ 79TCMJapPB-42

Senegal, Terence
❑ 98BilMusTI-31

Senften, Dave
❑ 98AugGreM-29

Senger, Charles
❑ 66TolMudHTI-22

Seninger, Glenn
❑ 88SalLakCTTI-4

Senior, Shawn
❑ 94LynRedSC-23
❑ 94LynRedSF-1892
❑ 95Bow-169
❑ 95SigRooOJ-30
❑ 95SigRooOJP-30
❑ 95SigRooOJPS-30
❑ 95SigRooOJS-30
❑ 95TreThuTI-14
❑ 96Bow-118
❑ 96BowFoi-118
❑ 96TreThuB-14

Senjem, Guye
❑ 98St.PauSTI-24

Senkowitz, Mark
❑ 92ElmPioC-17
❑ 92ElmPioF-1385
❑ 93UtiBluSC-22
❑ 93UtiBluSF-3536

Senn, Terry
❑ 75TidTidTI-18

Senne, Michael
❑ 86AriWilP-13
❑ 87St.PetCP-9
❑ 88ArkTraGS-25
❑ 89ShrCapP-1840

Senne, Tim
❑ 86VisOakP-20
❑ 87VisOakP-14

Senteney, Steve
❑ 82SyrChiT-8
❑ 82SyrChiTI-20
❑ 83Don-52
❑ 83TidTidT-10

Sentlinger, Rick
❑ 77QuaCitAT-25

Seo, Jae Weong
❑ 98Bow-438
❑ 98BowBes-106
❑ 98BowBesAR-106
❑ 98BowBesR-106
❑ 98BowChr-438
❑ 98BowChrGA-438
❑ 98BowChrGAR-438
❑ 98BowChrl-438
❑ 98BowChrIR-438
❑ 98BowChrR-438
❑ 98BowGolA-438
❑ 98BowInt-438
❑ 98St.LucMM-16

Seo, Yoshihiro
❑ 96HonShaHWB-27

Seoane, Manny (Manuel)
❑ 76OklCit8TI-26
❑ 76VenLeaS-215
❑ 80WicAerT-21
❑ 81BirBarT-4
❑ 81EvaTriT-7

Seoane, Mitch
❑ 84GreHorT-25
❑ 86PalSprAS-24
❑ 87MidAngP-20
❑ 89QuaCitAB-25
❑ 89QuaCitAGS-2
❑ 90QuaCitAGS-3
❑ 91QuaCitAC-27
❑ 91QuaCitAP-2645
❑ 92QuaCitRBC-27
❑ 92QuaCitRBF-826
❑ 93CedRapKC-26
❑ 93CedRapKF-1754
❑ 94LakElsSC-26
❑ 94LakElsSF-1680
❑ 95LakElsSTI-20
❑ 96LakElsSB-26
❑ 97MidAng-1
❑ 98VanCanG-26

Seok, Tae
❑ 96HilStaHWB-29

Sepanek, Rob
❑ 86Ft.LauYP-20
❑ 87PriWilYP-10
❑ 88AlbYanP-1332
❑ 89AlbYanB-9
❑ 89AlbYanP-330
❑ 89AlbYanSt-17
❑ 89EasLeaAP-8
❑ 90AlbDecGB-29
❑ 90CMC-221
❑ 90ColCliC-21
❑ 90ColCliP-22
❑ 90ColCliP-684
❑ 90ProAAAF-334

Sepeda, Jamie
❑ 92BatCliCB-1
❑ 92BatCliF-3264
❑ 93ClaGolF-152
❑ 93ClePhiC-20
❑ 93ClePhiF-2683
❑ 94ClePhiC-23
❑ 94ClePhiF-2526

Sepela, Thom
❑ 86ElmPioRSP-21
❑ 87ElmPioBC-20
❑ 87ElmPioRC-20

Septimo, Felix
❑ 90MedHatBJB-11
❑ 91St.CatBJP-3409

Sepulveda, Jorge
❑ 86VerBeaDP-22

Sepulveda, Louis
❑ 13Zee-122
❑ 14Zee-121

❑ 15Zee-117
❑ 16Zee-118
Sequea, Jacobo
❑ 98ChaAllCM-30
Serad, William
❑ 87OldJudN-440
Serafin, Ricardo
❑ 95MarPhiTI-23
❑ 96MarPhiB-23
Serafini, Dan
❑ 92ClaBluBF-BC28
❑ 92ClaDraP-20
❑ 92ClaFS7-411
❑ 92UppDecML-104
❑ 93Bow-397
❑ 93ClaFS7-256
❑ 93ClaGolF-114
❑ 93ForWayWC-1
❑ 93ForWayWF-1968
❑ 93Pin-465
❑ 93Sco-497
❑ 93Sel-352
❑ 93StaCluM-43
❑ 93Top-307
❑ 93TopGol-307
❑ 93TopInaM-307
❑ 93TopInaR-307
❑ 93TopMic-307
❑ 94Cla-132
❑ 94ClaGolF-67
❑ 94ExcFS7-98
❑ 94ForMyeMC-23
❑ 94UppDecML-108
❑ 95Bes-29
❑ 95HarCitRCTI-23
❑ 95SPML-89
❑ 96Bow-139
❑ 96BowFoi-139
❑ 96ColCho-777
❑ 96Exc-82
❑ 96UppDec-264
❑ 97SalLakB-25
❑ 98Bow-163
❑ 98BowChr-163
❑ 98BowChrGA-163
❑ 98BowChrGAR-163
❑ 98BowChrI-163
❑ 98BowChrIR-163
❑ 98BowChrR-163
❑ 98BowGolA-163
❑ 98BowInt-163
❑ 98Fle-261
❑ 98SalLakBO-27
Serafini, Rudy
❑ 83QuaCitCT-14
Serbalik, Mike
❑ 92YakBeaF-3460
Serbin, Scott
❑ 90SarWhiSS-30
Serena, Bill
❑ 50Bow-230
❑ 51Bow-246
❑ 52Top-325
❑ 53BowC-122
❑ 54Bow-93
❑ 55Bow-233
❑ 75OakOak2A-31
❑ 83TopRep5-325
Serena, Danny
❑ 93AusFut-38
Sergio, Thomas
❑ 98Cha-16
❑ 98TulDriTI-12
Serna, Joe
❑ 93WelPirC-26
Serna, Paul
❑ 81LynSaiT-18
❑ 82Don-567
❑ 82MarPos-28
❑ 83ChaLooT-2
❑ 83Top-492
❑ 84ChaLooT-12
❑ 85CalCanC-79
❑ 86WauTimP-23
Serna, Ramon
❑ 87ElPasDP-25
❑ 88ElPasDB-7
Serra, Armando
❑ 88St.CatBJP-2037
Serra, Jose
❑ 92BluOriC-8
❑ 92BluOriF-2369
❑ 93AlbPolCB-19
❑ 93AlbPolF-2035
❑ 94AlbPolC-23
❑ 94AlbPolF-2247
❑ 94OriPro-92
Serrano, Andy
❑ 79ElmPioRST-17
Serrano, Danny
❑ 98CedRapKTI-26
Serrano, Elio
❑ 98BatMucTI-28
Serrano, Jim
❑ 98VerExpO-35
Serrano, Marty
❑ 77DayBealT-22
Serrano, Nestor
❑ 93BelMarCB-24
❑ 93BelMarF-3224
❑ 94BelMarC-25
❑ 94BelMarF-3247
❑ 96-97LinVen-143
Serrano, Sammy
❑ 98SalVol-31
❑ 99TeaBesR-79
❑ 99TeaBesRG-79
❑ 99TeaBesRS-79
Serrano, Wascar
❑ 97IdaFalBTI-21
❑ 98CliLumG-22
Serrato, Jacob
❑ 93HunCubC-23
❑ 93HunCubF-3239
Serrell, Barney
❑ 95NegLeaL2-11
❑ 97NegLeaPC-4D
Serritella, John
❑ 83ButCopKT-10
❑ 83ChaRoyT-23
Serum, Gary
❑ 77OrlTwiT-18
❑ 77TacTwiDQ-16A
❑ 78TwiFriP-18
❑ 79Top-627
❑ 79TwiFriP-25
❑ 80TolMudHT-5
❑ 80Top-61
❑ 82OrlTwi8SCT-23
Servais, Scott
❑ 87PanAmTUBI-28
❑ 87PanAmTURB-3
❑ 88TopTra-106T
❑ 88TopTraT-106T
❑ 89OscAstS-20
❑ 89Sta-17
❑ 89TopBig-291
❑ 90CMC-623
❑ 90ProAAAF-196
❑ 90TucTorC-21
❑ 90TucTorP-206
❑ 91LinDriAAA-618
❑ 91TucTorLD-618
❑ 91TucTorP-2216
❑ 91UppDecFE-68F
❑ 92AstMot-17
❑ 92Bow-463
❑ 92Don-763
❑ 92Fle-444
❑ 92Lea-121
❑ 92LeaBlaG-121
❑ 92OPC-437
❑ 92Pin-255
❑ 92Sco-816
❑ 92ScoRoo-36
❑ 92StaClu-509
❑ 92Top-437
❑ 92TopDeb91-162
❑ 92TopGol-437
❑ 92TopGolW-437
❑ 92TopMic-437
❑ 92Ult-496
❑ 92UppDec-561
❑ 93AstMot-6
❑ 93AstStaC-13
❑ 93Don-108
❑ 93Fle-442
❑ 93Lea-33
❑ 93OPC-339
❑ 93PacSpa-480
❑ 93StaClu-363
❑ 93StaCluFDI-363
❑ 93StaCluMOP-363
❑ 93Top-36
❑ 93TopGol-36
❑ 93TopInaM-36
❑ 93TopInaR-36
❑ 93TopMic-36
❑ 93Ult-396
❑ 93UppDec-613
❑ 93UppDecGold-613
❑ 93USPlaCR-8C
❑ 94AstMot-19
❑ 94ColC-256
❑ 94ColChoGS-256
❑ 94ColChoSS-256
❑ 94Don-381
❑ 94Fin-135
❑ 94FinRef-135
❑ 94Fla-175
❑ 94Fle-499
❑ 94FleExtB-281
❑ 94Lea-332
❑ 94Pac-274
❑ 94Pin-134
❑ 94PinArtP-134
❑ 94PinMusC-134
❑ 94Sco-257
❑ 94ScoGolR-257
❑ 94StaClu-150
❑ 94StaCluFDI-150
❑ 94StaCluGR-150
❑ 94StaCluMOP-150
❑ 94Top-674
❑ 94TopGol-674
❑ 94TopSpa-674
❑ 94Ult-209
❑ 94UppDec-404
❑ 94UppDecED-404
❑ 95AstMot-6
❑ 95ColCho-113
❑ 95ColChoGS-113
❑ 95ColChoSS-113
❑ 95Don-313
❑ 95DonPreP-313
❑ 95DonTopotO-204
❑ 95Fle-468
❑ 95Lea-39
❑ 95Sco-486
❑ 95ScoGolR-486
❑ 95ScoPlaTS-486
❑ 95StaClu-163
❑ 95StaCluFDI-163
❑ 95StaCluMOP-163
❑ 95StaCluSTWS-163
❑ 95Top-342
❑ 95TopCyb-185
❑ 95Ult-177
❑ 95UltGolM-177
❑ 96ColCho-493
❑ 96ColChoGS-493
❑ 96ColChoSS-493
❑ 96CubFle-16
❑ 96Don-4
❑ 96DonPreP-4
❑ 96Fla-224
❑ 96Fle-329
❑ 96FleTif-329
❑ 96LeaSigA-208
❑ 96LeaSigAG-208
❑ 96LeaSigAS-208
❑ 96Pac-20
❑ 96StaClu-309
❑ 96StaCluMOP-309
❑ 96TeaOut-73
❑ 96Ult-170
❑ 96UltGolM-170
❑ 96UppDec-297
❑ 97ColCho-64
❑ 97Don-186
❑ 97DonGolPP-186
❑ 97DonSilPP-186
❑ 97Fle-283
❑ 97FleTif-283
❑ 97Lea-66
❑ 97LeaFraM-66
❑ 97LeaFraMDC-66
❑ 97Pac-258
❑ 97PacLigB-258
❑ 97PacSil-258
❑ 97Pin-126
❑ 97PinArtP-PP126
❑ 97PinMusC-126
❑ 97PinPrePla-126
❑ 97Sco-290
❑ 97ScoArtPWB-290
❑ 97ScoPreS-290
❑ 97ScoShoS-290
❑ 97ScoShoSAP-290
❑ 97StaClu-279
❑ 97StaCluMOP-279
❑ 97Top-284
❑ 97UppDec-33
❑ 98ColCho-333
❑ 98Fin-133
❑ 98FinNo--133
❑ 98FinNo-R-133
❑ 98FinRef-133
❑ 98Fle-396
❑ 98Pac-257
❑ 98PacOnl-153
❑ 98PacOnlR-153
❑ 98PacOnlWC-153
❑ 98PacPlaB-257
❑ 98PacRedT-257
❑ 98PacSil-257
❑ 98StaCluFDI-65
❑ 98StaCluI-65
❑ 98StaCluOneK-65
❑ 98StaCluPP-65
❑ 98Top-92
❑ 98TopChr-92
❑ 98TopChrR-92
❑ 98TopDevR-92
❑ 98TopDia-92
❑ 98TopMiniC-92
❑ 98UppDec-326
❑ 99Fle-492
❑ 99FleSta9-492
❑ 99FleWarT-492
❑ 99Pac-91
❑ 99PacPlaB-91
❑ 99PacRed-91
❑ 99Top-79
❑ 99TopChr-79
❑ 99TopChrR-79
❑ 99TopMVPP-79
Servello, Dan
❑ 91EugEmeC-12
❑ 91EugEmeP-3740
❑ 92AppFoxCB-20
❑ 92AppFoxFI-1000
Service, Scott
❑ 88ReaPhiP-868
❑ 89Fle-653
❑ 89FleGlo-653
❑ 89ReaPhiB-6
❑ 89ReaPhiP-657
❑ 89ReaPhiS-23
❑ 90Bow-143
❑ 90BowTif-143
❑ 90CMC-234
❑ 90ProAAAF-302
❑ 90ScrRedBC-8
❑ 90ScrRedBP-600
❑ 90UppDec-35
❑ 91IndIndLD-193
❑ 91IndIndP-461
❑ 91LinDriAAA-193
❑ 92IndIndS-193
❑ 93IndIndF-1489
❑ 94Fle-428
❑ 94IndIndF-1811
❑ 94Top-306
❑ 94TopGol-306
❑ 94TopSpa-306
❑ 95IndIndF-95
❑ 96IndIndB-23
❑ 97IndInd-21
❑ 98PacOnl-354
❑ 98PacOnlR-354
❑ 98PacOnlWC-354
❑ 99UppDec-389
❑ 99UppDecEL1-389
❑ 99UppDecEL2-389
Servoss, Bob
❑ 76WilTomT-18
Sessi, Walter
❑ 46SeaSLP-54
❑ 83Car194T-38
Sessions, Doug
❑ 98AubDouTI-26
Sevcik, John
❑ 65Top-597
Sever, Carl
❑ 33Zee-142
Severeid, Henry
❑ 12T207-165
❑ 17ColE13-155
❑ 17HolBreD-93
❑ 21E121So8-88
❑ 21Exh-155
❑ 21Nei-25
❑ 22AmeCarE122-64
❑ 22E120-99
❑ 22W572-93
❑ 22W573-118
❑ 22W575-120
❑ 23WilChoV-145
❑ 25Exh-116
❑ 27Zee-103
❑ 28ExhPCL-24
❑ 28Zee-120
❑ 29Zee-122
❑ 30Zee-16
❑ 31Zee-6
❑ 75SenTCM1-30
❑ 93ConTSN-855
Severino, Eddy
❑ 96MedHatBJTI-28
Severino, Jose
❑ 93BriTigC-19
❑ 95NewJerCTI-26
Severinsen, Al
❑ 67BalOriP-98
❑ 70OPC-477
❑ 70Top-477
❑ 71MLBOffS-238
❑ 71OPC-747
❑ 71Top-747
❑ 72OPC-274
❑ 72Top-274
❑ 72TopCloT-28
❑ 91OriCro-413
Severns, Bill
❑ 77HolMilT-22
❑ 78SpoIndC-7
❑ 79VanCanT-21
❑ 80VanCanT-8
Severson, Rich
❑ 71MLBOffS-430
❑ 71OPC-103
❑ 71Top-103
Seward, Ed
❑ 87OldJudN-441
Sewell, Joe
❑ 91AubAstC-9
❑ 91AubAstP-4273
❑ 92BurAstC-7
❑ 92BurAstF-547
❑ 93OscAstC-21
❑ 93OscAstF-627
Sewell, Joe (Joseph W.)
❑ 20NatCarE-90
❑ 20WalMaiW-47
❑ 21E121So1-92
❑ 21Exh-156
❑ 21Nei-12
❑ 22E120-40
❑ 22W572-94
❑ 22W573-119
❑ 22W575-121
❑ 23MapCriV-12
❑ 23W501-16
❑ 23WilChoV-146
❑ 25Exh-85
❑ 26Exh-84
❑ 26SpoComoA-38
❑ 27YorCarE-10
❑ 28Exh-43
❑ 28StaPlaCE-59
❑ 28W502-10
❑ 28Yue-10
❑ 29ExhFou-21
❑ 29PorandAR-81
❑ 31W517-46
❑ 32OrbPinNP-116
❑ 33Gou-165
❑ 33GouCanV-89
❑ 61Fle-76
❑ 72LauGreF-40
❑ 77GalGloG-107
❑ 77Ind192T-16
❑ 79DiaGre-5
❑ 80PerHaloFP-163
❑ 80PerHaloFPS-35
❑ 80SSPHOF-163
❑ 81ConTSN-53
❑ 82DiaCla-97
❑ 82OhiHaloF-42
❑ 83YanYealT-13
❑ 89HOFStiB-22
❑ 89PacLegI-125
❑ 89PerCelP-36
❑ 90HOFStiB-33
❑ 90PacLeg-67
❑ 90PerGreM-68
❑ 91ConTSN-40
❑ 91ConTSN-275
❑ 92YanWIZH-30
❑ 93ConTSN-786
❑ 94ConTSN-992
❑ 94ConTSN-1175
❑ 94ConTSNB-992
❑ 94ConTSNB-1175
❑ 95ConTSN-1363
Sewell, Luke
❑ 23W503-61
❑ 28StaPlaCE-60
❑ 28W56PlaC-H5
❑ 29ExhFou-22
❑ 29PorandAR-82
❑ 31Exh-22
❑ 33ExhFou-11
❑ 33Gou-114
❑ 33Gou-163
❑ 33GouCanV-91
❑ 33WorCig-85
❑ 34BatR31-155
❑ 35GouPuzR-1I
❑ 35GouPuzR-2F
❑ 35GouPuzR-16F
❑ 35GouPuzR-17F
❑ 36GouWidPPR-A93
❑ 36NatChiFPR-103
❑ 36NatChiFPR-115
❑ 36R31PasP-43
❑ 36WorWidGV-62
❑ 38ExhFou-10
❑ 39PlaBal-5
❑ 40PlaBal-48
❑ 41BroW75-25
❑ 46SeaSLP-55
❑ 46SpoExcW-8-5
❑ 49EurSta-94
❑ 51Bow-322
❑ 52Bow-94
❑ 56SeaPop-19
❑ 61Fle-138
❑ 79DiaGre-65
❑ 81ConTSN-54
❑ 82DiaCla-99
❑ 82OhiHaloF-12
❑ 91ConTSN-193
❑ 94ConTSN-996
❑ 94ConTSN-1175
❑ 94ConTSNB-996
❑ 94ConTSNB-1175
❑ 96Bro194F-17
Sewell, T. Rip
❑ 34DiaMatCSB-162
❑ 46SpoExcW-6-1A
❑ 47Exh-206
❑ 47TipTop-147
❑ 49Bow-234
❑ 49EurSta-172
❑ 77TCMTheWY-20
❑ 79DiaGre-363
❑ 83TCMPla1943-34
❑ 85BigLeaC3-26
❑ 89PacLegI-202
Sexauer, Elmer
❑ 90DodTar-1067
Sexson, Richie
❑ 93BurIndC-24
❑ 93BurIndF-3308
❑ 94ColRedC-20
❑ 94ColRedF-451
❑ 94SouAtlLAF-SAL10
❑ 95Bes-15
❑ 95BowBes-B10
❑ 95BowBesR-B10
❑ 95KinIndTI-25
❑ 95SPML-46
❑ 95TopTra-122T
❑ 96BesAutSA-68
❑ 96Bow-335
❑ 96BowBes-138
❑ 96BowBesAR-138
❑ 96BowBesMI-1
❑ 96BowBesMIAR-1
❑ 96BowBesMIR-1
❑ 96BowBesP-BBP24
❑ 96BowBesPAR-BBP24
❑ 96BowBesPR-BBP24
❑ 96BowBesR-138
❑ 96BowFoi-335
❑ 96CanIndB-22
❑ 96Exc-46
❑ 96ExcSeaC-9
❑ 96Top-425
❑ 97BesAutAS-52
❑ 97BesAutP-R14
❑ 97BesAutSBPP-49
❑ 97Bow-160
❑ 97BowCerBlaIA-CA73
❑ 97BowCerBluIA-CA73
❑ 97BowCerGolIA-CA73
❑ 97BowChr-158
❑ 97BowChrI-158
❑ 97BowChrIR-158
❑ 97BowChrR-158
❑ 97BowInt-160
❑ 97BufBis-25
❑ 97ColCho-463

❑ 97FlaShoWotF-8
❑ 97Fle-529
❑ 97FleTif-529
❑ 97Sel-136
❑ 97SelArtP-136
❑ 97SelCom-136
❑ 97SelRegG-136
❑ 97Ult-485
❑ 97UltGolME-485
❑ 97UltPlaME-485
❑ 98Bow-92
❑ 98Bow99ROYF-ROY7
❑ 98BowBes-107
❑ 98BowBesAR-107
❑ 98BowBesP-BP8
❑ 98BowBesPAR-BP8
❑ 98BowBesPR-BP8
❑ 98BowBesR-107
❑ 98BowCerBlueAU-15
❑ 98BowCerGA-15
❑ 98BowCerSA-15
❑ 98BowChr-92
❑ 98BowChrGA-92
❑ 98BowChrGAR-92
❑ 98BowChrI-92
❑ 98BowChrIR-92
❑ 98BowChrR-92
❑ 98BowGolA-92
❑ 98BowInt-92
❑ 98BufBisG-27
❑ 98ColCho-78
❑ 98Don-325
❑ 98DonColL-391
❑ 98DonGolPP-325
❑ 98DonPriCL-391
❑ 98DonSig-125
❑ 98DonSigA-79
❑ 98DonSigAC-101
❑ 98DonSigAM-103
❑ 98DonSigP-125
❑ 98DonSilPP-325
❑ 98Fle-265
❑ 98Lea-192
❑ 98LeaFraDA-192
❑ 98LeaFraF-192
❑ 98LeaFraM-192
❑ 98LeaFraM-192
❑ 98LeaFraMDC-192
❑ 98LeaFraMDC-192
❑ 98LeaFraMZ2-192
❑ 98LeaRS-249
❑ 98LeaRSLHolo-249
❑ 98LeaRSLong-249
❑ 98LeaRTrue-249
❑ 98PinIns-125
❑ 98PinInsCE-125
❑ 98PinInsDE-125
❑ 98PinPer-128
❑ 98PinPerPP-128
❑ 98ScoRT-233
❑ 98ScoRTSS-PP126
❑ 98ScoRTSSAP-PP126
❑ 98ScoRTSSAP1-PP126
❑ 98SP MinPE-43
❑ 98SPMin-43
❑ 98SPxFin-23
❑ 98SPxFinR-23
❑ 98SPxFinS-23
❑ 98Stu-195
❑ 98StuGPP-195
❑ 98StuSPP-195
❑ 98Top-257
❑ 98TopChr-257
❑ 98TopChrR-257
❑ 98TopDevR-257
❑ 98TopDia-257
❑ 98TopMiniC-257
❑ 98UppDec-258
❑ 98UppDecSF-141
❑ 99199Fin-233
❑ 99Bow-333
❑ 99BowAut-BA34
❑ 99BowBesRLRGUB-RB6
❑ 99BowBesRLRGWJ-RJ1
❑ 99BowGol-333
❑ 99BowInt-333
❑ 99FinGolRef-233
❑ 99FinRef-233
❑ 99FlaShoLeg1-80
❑ 99FlaShoLeg2-80
❑ 99FlaShoLeg3-80
❑ 99FlaShoLegM1-80
❑ 99FlaShoLegM2-80
❑ 99FlaShoLegM3-80
❑ 99FlaShoR1-80
❑ 99FlaShoR2-80
❑ 99FlaShoR3-80
❑ 99Fle-42
❑ 99Fle-589
❑ 99FleBri-23
❑ 99FleBri2G-23
❑ 99FleBriBlu-23
❑ 99FleBriGol-23
❑ 99FleBriI-13
❑ 99FleRooFla-14
❑ 99FleSta9-42
❑ 99FleSta9-589
❑ 99FleVin'-42
❑ 99FleWarT-42
❑ 99FleWarT-589
❑ 99MetUni-19
❑ 99MetUniGM-19
❑ 99MetUniPMG-19
❑ 99Pac-135
❑ 99PacAur-55
❑ 99PacAurOD-55
❑ 99PacOme-76
❑ 99PacOmeC-76
❑ 99PacOmeG-76
❑ 99PacOmePB-76
❑ 99PacPar-76
❑ 99PacParC-76
❑ 99PacParG-76
❑ 99PacParHoloGold-76
❑ 99PacParHS-76
❑ 99PacParOD-76
❑ 99PacParPB-76
❑ 99PacParRed-76
❑ 99PacPlaB-135
❑ 99PacPri-46
❑ 99PacPriHB-46
❑ 99PacPriHG-46
❑ 99PacPriHM-46
❑ 99PacPriHP-46
❑ 99PacPriRed-46
❑ 99PacPriS-137
❑ 99PacPriS206-137
❑ 99PacPriS206R-137
❑ 99PacRed-135
❑ 99Rev-46
❑ 99RevPremDate-46
❑ 99RevRet-46
❑ 99RevShaSS-46
❑ 99SkyMolM-34
❑ 99SkyMolMX-34
❑ 99SkyPre-219
❑ 99SkyPreR-219
❑ 99SkyThu-248
❑ 99SkyThuRant-248
❑ 99SkyThuRave-248
❑ 99SkyThuUnl-U14
❑ 99SpoIllOTW-10
❑ 99StaClu-288
❑ 99StaCluC-CS1
❑ 99StaCluC-CS8
❑ 99StaCluC-CS14
❑ 99StaCluC-CS19
❑ 99StaCluFDI-288
❑ 99StaCluOoaK-288
❑ 99StaCluPP-288
❑ 99ThuSkySupR-248
❑ 99Top-252
❑ 99TopChr-252
❑ 99TopChrR-252
❑ 99TopMVPP-252
❑ 99UppDec-359
❑ 99UppDecEL1-359
❑ 99UppDecEL2-359
Sexton, Chris
❑ 93BilMusF-3956
❑ 93BilMusSP-2
❑ 94ChaWheC-2
❑ 94ChaWheF-2714
❑ 94Top-527
❑ 94TopGol-527
❑ 94TopSpa-527
❑ 94UppDecML-213
❑ 95SalAvaTI-9
❑ 96NewHavRB-22
❑ 96NewHavRUSTI-16
❑ 97NewHavRB-13
❑ 97TexAllM-55
❑ 98ColSprSS-4
Sexton, Jeff
❑ 94WatIndC-24
❑ 94WatIndF-3936
❑ 96CanIndB-23
❑ 97AkrAer-23
❑ 98AkrAerM-16
❑ 98BesPreA-42
Sexton, Jimmy
❑ 75ShrCapT-20
❑ 76ShrCapT-8
❑ 77SanJosMC-22
❑ 78AstPos-23
❑ 79AstPos-24
❑ 79Top-232
❑ 80Top-11
❑ 80TucTorT-2
❑ 81TacTigT-15
❑ 82TacTigT-38
❑ 83Don-449
❑ 83Fle-533
❑ 83Top-709
❑ 87AstShoSPT-17
Sexton, Twink (Wayne)
❑ 79JacMetT-4
Seybold, Socks (Ralph)
❑ 03BreE10-128
❑ 08AmeCarE91-25
❑ 08RosComP-66
Seyfried, Gordon
❑ 64Top-499
Seymour, Bob
❑ 82VerBeaDT-25
Seymour, Cy (James B.)
❑ 06FanCraNL-42
❑ 08AmeCarE91-26
❑ 08AmeCarE91-62
❑ 08RosComP-131
❑ 09ColChiE-259A
❑ 09ColChiE-259B
❑ 09T206-318
❑ 09T206-319
❑ 09T206-320
❑ 10E12AmeCDCE125-32
❑ 10NadE1-51
❑ 11BasBatEU-33
❑ 11MecDFT-18
❑ 11PinT-5-258
❑ 11SpoLifCW-318
❑ 11SpoLifM-218
❑ 11SpoLifM-289
❑ 12ColRedB-259A
❑ 12ColRedB-259B
❑ 12ColTinT-259A
❑ 12ColTinT-259B
❑ 12ImpTobC-38
Seymour, Harold
❑ 90LitSunW-16
Seymour, Paul
❑ 81BatTroT-29
Seymour, Steve
❑ 91KinMetC-20
❑ 91KinMetP-3813
❑ 92PitMetC-7
❑ 92PitMetF-3294
Seymour, Winston
❑ 89SalBucS-20
❑ 89WelPirP-21
❑ 90AugPirP-2475
Seys, John
❑ 31CubTeal-21
❑ 36CubTeal-26
Sferrazza, Matt
❑ 86JacExpT-13
❑ 87GleFalTP-13
Sferrazza, Vince
❑ 86FreGiaSB-3
❑ 87ShrCapP-23
❑ 88ShrCapP-1284
❑ 89SprCarB-26
Shaab, Doug
❑ 85OscAstTI-12
Shabazz, Basil
❑ 91JohCitCC-15
❑ 91JohCitCP-3990
❑ 92JohCitCC-1
❑ 92JohCitCF-3131
❑ 92StaCluD-169
❑ 93Bow-108
❑ 93CarStaC-23
❑ 93ExcFS7-106
❑ 93MidLeaAGF-53
❑ 93SprCarC-22
❑ 93SprCarF-1865
❑ 94Bow-292
❑ 94Cla-26
❑ 94ClaTriF-T76
❑ 94FloStaLAF-FSL44
❑ 94St.PetCC-24
❑ 94St.PetCF-2599
❑ 94UppDecML-244
❑ 95SigRoo-45
Shabosky, Brian
❑ 88CapCodPB-7
❑ 88CapCodPPaLP-186
Shackelford, Brett
❑ 93DavLipB-25
Shackelford, Brian
❑ 98SpoIndG-30
Shackle, Richard
❑ 89JohCitCS-20
❑ 89Sta-167
❑ 90SavCarP-2068
❑ 90SouAtlLAS-42
❑ 91FloStaLAP-FSL35
❑ 91St.PetCC-12
❑ 91St.PetCP-2276
❑ 92ArkTraF-1130
❑ 92ArkTraS-46
❑ 93ArkTraF-2813
Shadburne, Adam
❑ 96BatCliTI-12
Shaddix, Jeffrey
❑ 98OneYanG-26
Shaddy, Chris
❑ 83KnoBluJT-14
❑ 86KnoBluJP-20
❑ 87KnoBluJP-1495
❑ 88SyrChiC-22
❑ 88SyrChiP-833
❑ 89RicBraBC-24
❑ 89RicBraC-22
❑ 89RicBraP-824
❑ 89RicBraTI-20
Shade, Mick (Mike)
❑ 83SprCarF-11
❑ 85LouRedR-24
❑ 87JacExpP-442
❑ 88JacExpB-2
❑ 88JacExpP-985
Shade, Steve
❑ 86EriCarP-26
Shader, George
❑ 18Zee-34
Shafer, Bill
❑ 92PulBraC-24
❑ 92PulBraF-3176
❑ 93DanBraC-22
❑ 93DanBraF-3618
❑ 94MacBraC-19
❑ 94MacBraF-2203
❑ 95BreBtaTI-28
Shafer, Frank T.
❑ 87OldJudN-443
Shafer, George
❑ 87OldJudN-442
Shafer, Tillie (Arthur Joseph)
❑ 11HelSta-136
❑ 11SpoLifM-219
Shaff, Chris
❑ 97DanBraB-7
❑ 98DanBraQ-30
Shaffer, Duane
❑ 78KnoKnoST-19
❑ 79AppFoxT-21
❑ 80GleFalWSBT-25
❑ 80GleFalWSCT-24
Shaffer, Travis
❑ 92KinMetC-4
❑ 92KinMetF-1530
❑ 93PitMetC-17
❑ 93PitMetF-3708
❑ 94St.LucMC-22
❑ 94St.LucMF-1196
Shagena, Randy
❑ 94ElmPioC-19
❑ 94ElmPioF-3473
Shambaugh, Mike
❑ 86AncGlaPTI-32
❑ 88BoiHawP-1611
Shamblin, Bill
❑ 87KinIndP-1
❑ 88RenSilSCLC-272
Shamburg, Ken
❑ 90FreKeyTI-17
❑ 90RocRedWGC-31
❑ 91HagSunLD-246
❑ 91HagSunP-2465
❑ 91LinDriAA-246
❑ 92RocRedWF-1947
❑ 92RocRedWS-468
❑ 92SkyAAAF-212
Shamsky, Art
❑ 65RedEnq-27
❑ 65Top-398
❑ 66OPC-119
❑ 66Top-119
❑ 66TopVen-119
❑ 67CokCapR-17
❑ 67DexPre-188
❑ 67Kah-33
❑ 67OPC-96
❑ 67Top-96
❑ 68Kah-B32
❑ 68Top-292
❑ 68TopVen-292
❑ 69MetBoyS-4
❑ 69MetNewYDN-17
❑ 69MetTeal-14
❑ 69MilBra-251
❑ 69Top-221
❑ 69TopSta-69
❑ 70DayDaiNM-69
❑ 70MetTeal-11
❑ 70MetTra-23A
❑ 70OPC-137
❑ 70Top-137
❑ 71MetTeal-18
❑ 71MetTealA-5
❑ 71MLBOffS-165
❑ 71OPC-445
❑ 71Top-445
❑ 71TopCoi-43
❑ 72MilBra-313
❑ 72OPC-353
❑ 72Top-353
❑ 72TopCloT-29
❑ 78TCM60I-278
❑ 89MetRinP69-27
❑ 91MetWIZ-358
❑ 93UppDecS-3
❑ 94Met69CCPP-29
❑ 94Met69CS-28
❑ 94Met69T-11
❑ 96Met69Y-7
Shanahan, Bill
❑ 92ColMetPI-35
Shanahan, Chris
❑ 91PitMetC-16
❑ 91PitMetP-3422
❑ 92St.LucMCB-4
❑ 92St.LucMF-1747
❑ 93CapCitBC-20
❑ 93CapCitBF-460
Shanahan, Damien
❑ 95AusFut-76
Shanahan, Greg (Paul)
❑ 74AlbDukCa-73
❑ 74AlbDukTI-18
❑ 74OPC-599
❑ 74Top-599A
❑ 74Top-599B
❑ 74Top-599C
❑ 75AlbDukCa-12
❑ 76VenLeaS-196
❑ 90DodTar-719
Shanahan, Jason
❑ 95ElmPioTI-26
❑ 95ElmPioUTI-26
❑ 96BreCouMB-30
Shandor, Ted
❑ 53SanFraSTI-17
Shaner, Wally
❑ 94ConTSN-1292
❑ 94ConTSNB-1292
Shankle, Ron
❑ 93BluOriC-22
❑ 93BluOriF-4135
❑ 94LetMouF-3888
❑ 94LetMouSP-21
Shanklin, Paul
❑ 97DanBraB-25
Shanklin, Robert
❑ 29Zee-98
❑ 30Zee-68
Shankman, Herbert
❑ 52LavPro-9
Shanks, Cliff
❑ 95ButCopKtI-18
Shanks, Hank (Howard S.)
❑ 14B18B-46
❑ 15SpoNewM-162
❑ 16SpoNewM-160
❑ 17ColE13-156
❑ 21Exh-157
❑ 22E120-118
❑ 23WilChoV-147
❑ 93ConTSN-729
Shanks, Willie
❑ 85KinBluJT-11
❑ 86VenGulP-24
Shannon, Dan
❑ 89HamRedS-23
❑ 90SpaPhiB-21
❑ 90SpaPhiP-2504
❑ 90SpaPhiS-19
Shannon, Daniel
❑ 87OldJudN-444
Shannon, Maurice J.
❑ 20NatCarE-91
Shannon, Mike
❑ 90LitSunW-24
Shannon, Mike (Thomas Michael)
❑ 61UniOil-P12
❑ 62KahAtl-21
❑ 64Top-262
❑ 64TopVen-262
❑ 65CarJayP-9
❑ 65CarTeal-22
❑ 65OPC-43
❑ 65OPC-132
❑ 65Top-43
❑ 65Top-132
❑ 66Top-293
❑ 66TopVen-293
❑ 67Top-605
❑ 67TopVen-266
❑ 68Top-445
❑ 69MilBra-252
❑ 69MLBOffS-215
❑ 69OPC-110
❑ 69Top-110
❑ 69TopFou-18
❑ 69TopSta-120
❑ 69TopTeaP-18
❑ 70CarTeal-25
❑ 70MLBOffS-143
❑ 70Top-614
❑ 71MLBOffS-283
❑ 71OPC-735
❑ 71Top-735
❑ 72MilBra-314
❑ 78TCM60I-275
❑ 91UppDecS-14
❑ 92CarMcD-31
Shannon, Robert
❑ 86JamExpP-22
Shannon, Scott
❑ 91St.CatBJC-24
❑ 92St.CatBJC-29
❑ 93St.CatBJC-29
❑ 96KnoSmoB-3
❑ 97KnoSmo-4
Shannon, Spike (William P.)
❑ 08RosComP-132
❑ 09T206-465
❑ 11SpoLifCW-319
Shannon, Thomas L.
❑ 87NewOriP-26
❑ 88RocExpLC-32
Shannon, Wally
❑ 60Lea-93
Shannon, William
❑ 52LavPro-63
Shantz, Bobby
❑ 47PM1StaP1-199
❑ 47PM1StaP1-200
❑ 49A'sTeal-29
❑ 49PhiBul-49
❑ 50A'sTeal-23
❑ 50Bow-234
❑ 51A'sTeal-29
❑ 51Bow-227
❑ 52A'sTeal-25
❑ 52DixLid-21
❑ 52DixPre-21
❑ 52RedMan-AL20
❑ 52StaCalL-76C
❑ 52Top-219
❑ 53A'sTeal-28
❑ 53BowC-11
❑ 53DixLid-20
❑ 53DixPre-20
❑ 53Dor-114
❑ 53NorBreL-29
❑ 53RedMan-AL20
❑ 53SpoMagP-10
❑ 53Top-225
❑ 54A'STEAI-24
❑ 54Bow-19
❑ 54Top-21
❑ 55A'sRodM-34
❑ 55A'sRodM-35
❑ 55A'sTeal-22
❑ 55Bow-139
❑ 55Bow-140

❑ 56A'sPos-37
❑ 56A'sRodM-8
❑ 56Top-261
❑ 57Top-272
❑ 58Top-289
❑ 58Top-419
❑ 58YanJayP-11
❑ 59Top-222
❑ 60RawGloT-30
❑ 60Top-315
❑ 61Pos-15
❑ 61Top-379
❑ 61Top-473
❑ 61TopStal-198
❑ 62Col.45B-17
❑ 62Col45'HC-14
❑ 62SalPlaC-188
❑ 62ShiPlaC-188
❑ 62Top-177
❑ 62TopBuc-81
❑ 62TopStal-128
❑ 62TopVen-177
❑ 63Top-533
❑ 64PhiPhiB-21
❑ 64Top-278
❑ 64TopVen-278
❑ 70Houof J-27
❑ 75OPC-190
❑ 75TCMHouoJ-29
❑ 75Top-190
❑ 75TopMin-190
❑ 76A'sRodMC-22
❑ 77PhiFav-20
❑ 79DiaGre-349
❑ 79TCM50-171
❑ 81TCM60I-456
❑ 83TopRep5-219
❑ 83YanASFY-42
❑ 84OCoandSI-49
❑ 84OCoandSI-218
❑ 88PacLegI-61
❑ 89AstCol4S-7
❑ 89SweBasG-131
❑ 90PacLeg-105
❑ 91SweBasG-83
❑ 91TopArc1-225
❑ 92ActPacA-78
❑ 92BazQua5A-3
❑ 92YanWIZ6-112
❑ 92YanWIZA-77
❑ 93TedWil-69
❑ 94TopArc1-21
❑ 94TopArc1G-21

Shantz, Wilmer
❑ 54A'STEAI-23
❑ 55A'sRodM-36
❑ 55A'sRodM-37
❑ 55A'sTeal-21
❑ 55Bow-139
❑ 55Bow-175
❑ 66TolMudHTI-22
❑ 66TolMudHTI-23
❑ 76A'sRodMC-23
❑ 92YanWIZ6-111

Shapiro, Tony
❑ 95ButCopKtl-19

Shapley, Joe
❑ 90NebCor-21

Sharitt, Kelly
❑ 89OneYanP-2108
❑ 90GreHorS-26
❑ 90SouAtlLAS-25

Sharkey, Jack
❑ 32USCar*-25

Sharkey, Tom
❑ 98CamPepP-67

Sharko, Gary
❑ 89CliGiaP-887
❑ 90SanJosGB-19
❑ 90SanJosGCLC-46
❑ 90SanJosGP-2005
❑ 90SanJosGS-20
❑ 91CalLeLA-35
❑ 91SanJosGC-21
❑ 91SanJosGP-10
❑ 92ProFS7-352

Sharon, Dick
❑ 74OPC-48
❑ 74Tig-12
❑ 74Top-48
❑ 75OPC-293
❑ 75PadDea-22
❑ 75Top-293
❑ 75TopMin-293

Sharp, Bill
❑ 74OPC-519
❑ 74Top-519
❑ 75OPC-373
❑ 75Top-373
❑ 75TopMin-373
❑ 76BreA&P-12
❑ 76OPC-244
❑ 76SSP-246
❑ 76Top-244
❑ 77SpoIndC-6
❑ 94BreMilB-182

Sharp, Gary
❑ 82BurRanF-19
❑ 82BurRanT-9

Sharp, Mike
❑ 91YakBeaC-26
❑ 91YakBeaP-4247
❑ 92BakDodCLC-21
❑ 92CalLeaACL-34
❑ 92ProFS7-251

Sharp, Scott
❑ 94PriRedC-23
❑ 94PriRedF-3265
❑ 97BurBeeB-21

Sharpe, Bayard
❑ 07NewEveWS-12
❑ 09T206-466
❑ 11PinT-5-707
❑ 11SpoLifM-143
❑ 11T205-153
❑ 12ImpTobC-31
❑ 12PCLPin-21
❑ 12Zee-47

Sharpe, Grant
❑ 96AppLeaAB-10
❑ 96BurIndB-24
❑ 97BurIndG-23

Sharpe, Justin
❑ 98EugEme-24

Sharpe, Ken
❑ 91ParPatF-1

Sharpe, William
❑ 31Zee-40

Sharperson, Mike
❑ 83KinBluJTI-24
❑ 85SyrChiT-19
❑ 86SyrChiP-22
❑ 87BluJayFS-27
❑ 87Don-565
❑ 87DonOpeD-31
❑ 88AlbDukCm-16
❑ 88AlbDukP-253
❑ 88DodPol-27
❑ 88Fle-525
❑ 88FleGlo-525
❑ 89AlbDukCm-14
❑ 89AlbDukP-59
❑ 89Bow-348
❑ 89BowTif-348
❑ 89DodPol-17
❑ 89DodStaSV-14
❑ 89Fle-72
❑ 89FleGlo-72
❑ 89Sco-602
❑ 90DodMot-20
❑ 90DodPol-27
❑ 90DodTar-720
❑ 90Don-603
❑ 90Lea-490
❑ 90OPC-117
❑ 90Top-117
❑ 90TopTif-117
❑ 91Bow-602
❑ 91DodMot-20
❑ 91DodPol-27
❑ 91Don-168
❑ 91Fle-221
❑ 91OPC-53
❑ 91Sco-546
❑ 91StaClu-541
❑ 91Top-53
❑ 91TopDesS-53
❑ 91TopMic-53
❑ 91TopTif-53
❑ 91Ult-170
❑ 91UppDec-598
❑ 92DodMot-25
❑ 92DodPol-27
❑ 92DodSmo-10592
❑ 92DodStaTA-31
❑ 92Don-526
❑ 92FleUpd-93
❑ 92Lea-318
❑ 92LeaBlaG-318
❑ 92OPC-627
❑ 92Pin-167
❑ 92Sco-592
❑ 92StaClu-93
❑ 92Stu-49
❑ 92Top-627
❑ 92TopGol-627
❑ 92TopGolW-627
❑ 92TopMic-627
❑ 92Ult-218
❑ 93DodMot-14
❑ 93DodPol-23
❑ 93DodStaC-9
❑ 93Don-166
❑ 93Fle-68
❑ 93OPC-346
❑ 93PacSpa-154
❑ 93PanSti-217
❑ 93Pin-37
❑ 93Sco-429
❑ 93Sel-157
❑ 93StaClu-307
❑ 93StaCluFDI-307
❑ 93StaCluM-164
❑ 93StaCluMOP-307
❑ 93Top-526
❑ 93TopGol-526
❑ 93TopInaM-526
❑ 93TopInaR-526
❑ 93TopMic-526
❑ 93Ult-404
❑ 93UppDec-316
❑ 93UppDecGold-316
❑ 94Fle-523
❑ 94Sco-287
❑ 94ScoGolR-287
❑ 95RicBraRC-24
❑ 95RicBraTI-22
❑ 96LasVegSB-1

Sharpnack, Bob
❑ 86ModA'sC-18
❑ 86ModA'sP-22
❑ 87MadMusP-17
❑ 87MadMusP-25
❑ 88HunStaTI-18
❑ 89HunStaB-11

Sharrott, George
❑ 90DodTar-1068

Sharsig, William J.
❑ 87OldJudN-445

Sharts, Scott
❑ 91WatIndC-22
❑ 91WatIndP-3377
❑ 92WatIndC-4
❑ 92WatIndF-3233
❑ 93ColRedC-20
❑ 93ColRedF-595

Sharts, Stephen
❑ 85BenPhiC-22
❑ 87ClePhiP-16
❑ 88ReaPhiP-865
❑ 89ReaPhiB-5
❑ 89ReaPhiP-651
❑ 90CMC-235
❑ 90ProAAAF-303
❑ 90ScrRedBC-9
❑ 90ScrRedBP-601

Shartzer, Phil
❑ 58SeaRalT-16

Shatley, Andy
❑ 96StCatSB-25
❑ 97HagSunB-20

Shaughnessy, Shag (Francis)
❑ 09T206-515
❑ 36GouWidPPR-D34
❑ 36WorWidGV-78

Shaute, Joe
❑ 28StaPlaCE-61
❑ 72TCMthe3-64
❑ 90DodTar-721
❑ 93ConTSN-857

Shave, Jon
❑ 88MisStaB-30
❑ 89MisStaB-35
❑ 90ButCopKSP-26
❑ 90MisStaB-38
❑ 91Cla/Bes-380
❑ 91GasRanC-22
❑ 91GasRanP-2699
❑ 92ClaFS7-445
❑ 92SkyAA F-274
❑ 92TulDriF-2705
❑ 92TulDriS-620
❑ 92UppDecML-312
❑ 93Bow-59
❑ 93ClaGolF-9
❑ 93ExcFS7-236
❑ 93FleFinE-283
❑ 93OklCit8F-1635
❑ 93RanKee-433
❑ 93StaClu-725
❑ 93StaCluFDI-725
❑ 93StaCluMOP-725
❑ 93Top-451
❑ 93TopGol-451
❑ 93TopInaM-451
❑ 93TopInaR-451
❑ 93TopMic-451
❑ 93TopTra-78T
❑ 94OklCit8F-1501
❑ 94Pac-629
❑ 94Pin-422
❑ 94PinArtP-422
❑ 94PinMusC-422
❑ 94PinRooTP-3
❑ 94StaClu-199
❑ 94StaCluFDI-199
❑ 94StaCluGR-199
❑ 94StaCluMOP-199
❑ 94StaCluT-247
❑ 94StaCluTFDI-247
❑ 94Top-775
❑ 94TopGol-775
❑ 94TopSpa-775
❑ 95Top-643
❑ 96OklCit8B-19
❑ 97SalLakB-26
❑ 98SalLakBO-28

Shaver, Jeff
❑ 86MadMusP-18
❑ 86MadMusP-21
❑ 87HunStaTI-21
❑ 88TacTigC-8
❑ 88TacTigP-619
❑ 89TacTigC-11
❑ 89TacTigP-1559
❑ 91SouOreAAP-SOA9

Shaver, Tony
❑ 95QuaCitRBTI-26
❑ 96KisCobB-26

Shaw, Al
❑ 09T206-321

Shaw, Bob
❑ 58Top-206
❑ 59TigGraASP-14
❑ 59Top-159
❑ 59TopVen-159
❑ 60Lea-83
❑ 60Top-380
❑ 60WhiSoxJP-9
❑ 60WhiSoxTS-17
❑ 61Pos-23
❑ 61Top-352
❑ 61TopStal-127
❑ 61WhiSoxTS-16
❑ 62Top-109
❑ 62TopStal-56
❑ 62TopVen-109
❑ 63BraJayP-9
❑ 63Jel-154
❑ 63Pos-154A
❑ 63Pos-154B
❑ 63SalMetC-7
❑ 63Top-5
❑ 63Top-255
❑ 64GiaJayP-12
❑ 64Top-328
❑ 64TopVen-328
❑ 65Top-428
❑ 65TopEmbl-57
❑ 66Top-260
❑ 66TopVen-260
❑ 67CokCapYM-V25
❑ 67DexPre-189
❑ 67Kah-34
❑ 67MetTeal-10
❑ 67Top-470
❑ 73OPC-646
❑ 73Top-646
❑ 79DiaGre-149
❑ 81WhiSox1T-28
❑ 91MetWIZ-359

Shaw, Cedric
❑ 88ButCopKSP-9
❑ 89ChaRanS-22
❑ 90TulDriP-1154
❑ 90TulDriTI-23
❑ 91LinDriAA-597
❑ 91TulDriLD-597
❑ 91TulDriP-2773
❑ 91TulDriTI-29
❑ 92SkyAA F-275
❑ 92TulDriF-2695
❑ 92TulDriS-621
❑ 93OklCit8F-1627

Shaw, Curtis (Malcolm)
❑ 90ProAaA-164
❑ 90SouOreAB-17
❑ 90SouOreAP-3427
❑ 91MadMusC-14
❑ 92Bow-174
❑ 92CalLeaACL-19
❑ 92ClaFS7-190
❑ 92ModA'sC-2
❑ 92ModA'sF-3898
❑ 93Bow-513
❑ 93ClaFS7-257
❑ 93ClaGolF-75
❑ 93ExcFS7-218
❑ 93HunStaF-2082
❑ 94Bow-52
❑ 94Cla-119
❑ 94ClaTriF-T58
❑ 94HunStaF-1331
❑ 94TacTigF-3173
❑ 94UppDecML-26
❑ 95EdmTraTI-21
❑ 96ModA'sB-14
❑ 97CalCanB-23
❑ 97CarMudC-9

Shaw, Don
❑ 66MetTeal-10
❑ 67Top-587
❑ 68Top-521
❑ 69OPC-183
❑ 69Top-183
❑ 70ExpPos-2
❑ 70OPC-476
❑ 70Top-476
❑ 71CarTeal-23
❑ 71CarTeal-34
❑ 71OPC-654
❑ 71Top-654
❑ 72OPC-479
❑ 72Top-479
❑ 81TCM60I-449
❑ 88SanDieS-18
❑ 88SanDieSAAG-18
❑ 89SanDieSAG-17
❑ 91MetWIZ-360

Shaw, Jeff
❑ 87WatIndP-16
❑ 88WilBilP-1309
❑ 89CanIndB-3
❑ 89CanIndP-1298
❑ 89CanIndS-19
❑ 90Bow-329
❑ 90BowTif-329
❑ 90ColSprSSP-33
❑ 90DonRoo-53
❑ 90IndTeal-35
❑ 90ProAAAF-214
❑ 91ColSprSSLD-95
❑ 91ColSprSSP-2182
❑ 91LinDriAAA-95
❑ 91Sco-746
❑ 91TopDeb90-141
❑ 92Bow-410
❑ 92ColSprSSF-751
❑ 92ColSprSSS-95
❑ 92Don-595
❑ 92Sco-624
❑ 92SkyAAAF-41
❑ 92StaClu-843
❑ 92StaCluNC-843
❑ 92UppDec-660
❑ 93ExpPosN-20
❑ 93FleFinE-97
❑ 94Fle-551
❑ 94Top-469
❑ 94TopGol-469
❑ 94TopSpa-469
❑ 94VenLinU-38
❑ 95Fla-167
❑ 95Fle-360
❑ 95StaClu-478
❑ 95StaCluMOP-478
❑ 95StaCluSTWS-478
❑ 95Ult-408
❑ 95UltGolM-408
❑ 96LeaSigEA-180
❑ 97ColSprSATTI-7
❑ 98CirThu-146
❑ 98CirThuRav-146
❑ 98CirThuSupRav-146
❑ 98ColCho-71
❑ 98ColCho-260
❑ 98DodMot-21
❑ 98Fin-128
❑ 98FinNo--128
❑ 98FinNo-R-128
❑ 98FinRef-128
❑ 98Fle-293
❑ 98FleUpd-U86
❑ 98MetUni-72
❑ 98MetUniPMG-72
❑ 98Pac-274
❑ 98PacOnl-200
❑ 98PacOnlR-200
❑ 98PacOnlWC-200
❑ 98PacPlaB-274
❑ 98PacRedT-274
❑ 98PacSil-274
❑ 98StaCluFDI-260
❑ 98StaCluI-260
❑ 98StaCluOneK-260
❑ 98StaCluPP-260
❑ 98Top-81
❑ 98TopChr-81
❑ 98TopChrR-81
❑ 98TopDevR-81
❑ 98TopDia-81
❑ 98TopMiniC-81
❑ 98TopSta-61
❑ 98TopStaB-61
❑ 98TopStaG-61
❑ 98TopStaGR-61
❑ 98TopStaS-61
❑ 98Ult-140
❑ 98UltGolM-140
❑ 98UltMas-140
❑ 98UltPlaM-140
❑ 98UppDec-69
❑ 98UppDecSF-42
❑ 99199Fin-178
❑ 99Bow-28
❑ 99BowChr-28
❑ 99BowChrG-28
❑ 99BowChrGR-28
❑ 99BowChrI-28
❑ 99BowChrIR-28
❑ 99BowChrR-28
❑ 99BowGol-28
❑ 99BowInt-28
❑ 99DodPol-23
❑ 99FinGolRef-178
❑ 99FinRef-178
❑ 99Fle-553
❑ 99FleSta9-553
❑ 99FleWarT-553
❑ 99MetUni-89
❑ 99MetUniGM-89
❑ 99MetUniPMG-89
❑ 99Pac-227
❑ 99PacPlaB-227
❑ 99PacRed-227
❑ 99SkyPre-99
❑ 99SkyPreR-99
❑ 99StaClu-36
❑ 99StaCluFDI-36
❑ 99StaCluOoaK-36
❑ 99StaCluPP-36
❑ 99Top-410
❑ 99TopChr-410
❑ 99TopChrR-410
❑ 99TopMVPP-410
❑ 99Ult-188
❑ 99UltGolM-188
❑ 99UltMas-188
❑ 99UltPlaM-188

Shaw, John W.
❑ 87OldJudN-447

Shaw, Kerry
❑ 88SalLakCTTI-17
❑ 89SalSpuCLC-144
❑ 89SalSpuP-1803
❑ 90SanJosGB-2
❑ 90SanJosGCLC-29
❑ 90SanJosGP-2020
❑ 90SanJosGS-21

Shaw, Kevin
❑ 88AppFoxP-140
❑ 89BasCitRS-8
❑ 89Sta-63
❑ 90BasCitRS-22
❑ 91BasCitRC-11
❑ 91BasCitRP-1398
❑ 91FloStaLAP-FSL3
❑ 92BasCitRC-2
❑ 92BasCitRF-3847
❑ 93WinSpiC-21
❑ 93WinSpiF-1570

Shaw, Rick
❑ 82AmaGolST-22

Shaw, Robert

❑ 12ImpTobC-83
Shaw, Royal N.
❑ 09ObaT21-166
❑ 09ObaT21-334
❑ 09T206-467
❑ 11Zee-100
❑ 12ObaPreT-83
Shaw, Samuel E.
❑ 87OldJudN-446
Shaw, Scott
❑ 86Ft.LauYP-21
❑ 87Ft.LauYP-7
❑ 88AlbYanP-1345
❑ 89AlbYanB-4
❑ 89AlbYanP-317
❑ 89AlbYanSt-18
Shaw, Shelby
❑ 92ChaRanC-22
❑ 92ChaRanF-2226
Shaw, Theo
❑ 81ChaRoyT-8
❑ 84OmaRoyT-17
❑ 85Ft.MyeRT-20
❑ 86OmaRoyP-23
❑ 86OmaRoyT-20
❑ 87MemChiB-12
❑ 87MemChiP-15
❑ 88WilBilP-1318
❑ 89ColSprSSP-259
❑ 90CalCanC-20
❑ 90CMC-447
❑ 94EugEmeC-29
Shawkey, J. Bob
❑ 09ColChiE-260
❑ 12ColRedB-260
❑ 12ColTinT-260
❑ 15CraJacE-164
❑ 15SpoNewM-163
❑ 16SpoNewM-161
❑ 17ColE13-157
❑ 17HolBreD-94
❑ 19W514-29
❑ 20NatCarE-92
❑ 21E121So1-93
❑ 21E121So8-89
❑ 21KoBreWSI-51
❑ 21Nei-39
❑ 22E120-74
❑ 22W572-95
❑ 22W573-120
❑ 22W575-122
❑ 22WilPatV-12
❑ 23Lec-9
❑ 23W501-31
❑ 23W515-9
❑ 25Exh-102
❑ 26Exh-103
❑ 27AmeCarE126-37
❑ 27YorCarE-59
❑ 28LaPre-1
❑ 28PorandAR-A32
❑ 28PorandAR-B32
❑ 61Fle-139
❑ 75Yan192T-24
❑ 79DiaGre-4
❑ 79Yan192T-29
❑ 84Yan192G-5
❑ 88ConSer5-26
❑ 91ConTSN-156
❑ 95ConTSN-1328
Shay, Dan
❑ 08AmeCarE91-27
❑ 11SpoLifCW-320
Shay, Speck
❑ 24Zee-71
Shea, Bill
❑ 90BasWit-27
Shea, Ed
❑ 87WatPirP-4
Shea, Elmer
❑ 22Zee-72
❑ 23Zee-98
❑ 25Zee-77
❑ 26Zee-126
❑ 27Zee-104
❑ 28Zee-121
Shea, John
❑ 87MyrBeaBJP-1452
❑ 88KnoBluJB-3
❑ 89KnoBluJB-24
❑ 89KnoBluJP-1140
❑ 89KnoBluJS-20
❑ 90CMC-334
❑ 90ProAAAF-351
❑ 90SyrChiC-8
❑ 90SyrChiMB-21
❑ 90SyrChiP-571
❑ 91LinDriAAA-517
❑ 91SyrChiLD-517
❑ 91SyrChiMB-23
❑ 91SyrChiP-2480
❑ 92SyrChiF-1965
❑ 92SyrChiMB-20
❑ 92SyrChiS-516
❑ 93NewBriRSF-1219
❑ 94ElPasDF-3146
❑ 95RocRedWTI-34
Shea, John E.
❑ 07NewEveWS-13
Shea, Joseph
❑ 88SFHesCreN32-28
Shea, Kevin
❑ 87VerBeaDP-29
Shea, Kurt
❑ 88BriTigP-1887
❑ 89FayGenP-1582
Shea, Mervyn D.J.
❑ 23Zee-97
❑ 24Zee-72
❑ 25Zee-78
❑ 26Zee-127
❑ 29ExhFou-24
❑ 35AlDemDCR3-13
❑ 35DiaMatCS3T1-131
❑ 72TCMthe1-175
❑ 90DodTar-722
❑ 92ConTSN-412
Shea, Red (Patrick)
❑ 20GasAmeMBD-33
❑ 20WalMaiW-48
❑ 21E121So1-94
❑ 21E121So8-90A
❑ 21E121So8-90B
❑ 21KoBreWSI-21
❑ 22W575-123
❑ 23W501-63
❑ 23Zee-146
❑ 24Zee-103
Shea, Spec (Frank)
❑ 47PM1StaP1-201
❑ 47YanTeaT-23
❑ 48BluTin-13
❑ 48Bow-26
❑ 48YanTeal-25
❑ 49Bow-49
❑ 49YanTeal-21
❑ 50Bow-155
❑ 52Bow-230
❑ 52Top-248
❑ 53BowC-141
❑ 53Bri-19
❑ 53Top-164
❑ 54Bow-104
❑ 55Bow-207
❑ 83TopRep5-248
❑ 83YanASFY-43
❑ 91TopArc1-164
❑ 92YanWIZA-78
Shea, Steven F.
❑ 69Top-499
Sheaffer, Danny
❑ 85PawRedST-12
❑ 86PawRedSP-22
❑ 87PawRedST-8
❑ 89ColSprSSC-21
❑ 89ColSprSSP-241
❑ 90BufBisC-15
❑ 90BufBisP-377
❑ 90BufBisTI-24
❑ 90CMC-15
❑ 90ProAAAF-492
❑ 91LinDriAAA-418
❑ 91PorBeaLD-418
❑ 91PorBeaP-1568
❑ 92PorBeaF-2671
❑ 92PorBeaS-419
❑ 92SkyAAAF-191
❑ 93FleFinE-43
❑ 93RocStaC-28
❑ 93RocUSPC-6C
❑ 93RocUSPC-9H
❑ 93TopTra-39T
❑ 93Ult-358
❑ 94Don-610
❑ 94Fle-454
❑ 94RocPol-23
❑ 94Sco-197
❑ 94ScoGolR-197
❑ 94StaClu-185
❑ 94StaCluFDI-185
❑ 94StaCluGR-185
❑ 94StaCluMOP-185
❑ 94StaCluT-96
❑ 94StaCluTFDI-96
❑ 94Top-314
❑ 94TopGol-314
❑ 94TopSpa-314
❑ 96Fle-555
❑ 96FleTif-555
❑ 96LeaSigEA-181
❑ 97CarPol-24
❑ 98MemRedG-22
Shealy, Al
❑ 30CubTeal-18
Shean, David
❑ 09AmeCarE90-1-94
❑ 10E101-41
❑ 10E102-22
❑ 10JuJuDE-36
❑ 10MelMinE-41
❑ 10NadCarE-48
❑ 10PeoT21-49
❑ 11HelSta-105
❑ 11PinT-5-701
❑ 11S74Sil-46
❑ 11SpoLifCW-321
❑ 11SpoLifM-144
❑ 11T205-154A
❑ 11T205-154B
❑ 12HasTriFT-13E
Shean, Larry
❑ 19W514-116
Shearer, Ray
❑ 58Top-283
Shearn, Thomas
❑ 97AubDouTI-7
❑ 98QuaCitRBG-26
Sheary, Kevin
❑ 85MiaHur-15
❑ 88RocExpLC-33
Sheckard, James
❑ 03BreE10-129
❑ 06FanCraNL-43
❑ 07CubA.CDPP-12
❑ 07CubGFGCP-12
❑ 08AmeCarE91-22
❑ 08AmeCarE91-60
❑ 08RosComP-109
❑ 09AmeCarE90-1-95
❑ 09ColChiE-253
❑ 09RamT20-104
❑ 09T206-322
❑ 09T206-323
❑ 10ChiE-9
❑ 10DarChoE-27
❑ 10DomDisP-109
❑ 10JHDABE-14
❑ 10RedCroT-68
❑ 10RedCroT-242
❑ 10SweCapPP-91
❑ 11BasBatEU-34
❑ 11HelSta-106
❑ 11PinT-5-212
❑ 11PloCanE-57
❑ 11S74Sil-69
❑ 11SpoLifCW-322
❑ 11SpoLifM-182
❑ 11T205-155
❑ 12ColRedB-253
❑ 12ColTinT-253
❑ 12HasTriFT-66
❑ 17ColE13-158
❑ 90DodTar-723
❑ 93ConTSN-900
Sheehan, Al
❑ 33WorCig(-81
Sheehan, Chris
❑ 92EugEmeC-22
❑ 92EugEmeF-3029
❑ 93RocRoyC-24
❑ 93RocRoyF-716
❑ 94ExcFS7-74
❑ 95WicWraTI-36
❑ 95WilBluRTI-38
Sheehan, Jack
❑ 90DodTar-724
Sheehan, John
❑ 17Zee-41
❑ 27Zee-122
❑ 87AshTouP-28
❑ 88OscAstS-24
❑ 89OscAstS-21
❑ 90ColMudB-18
❑ 90ColMudP-1346
❑ 90ColMudS-21
Sheehan, Ken
❑ 33Zee-143
❑ 33Zee-144
❑ 37Zee-41
❑ 37Zee-87
Sheehan, Leslie
❑ 12PCLPin-22
❑ 16Zee-119
❑ 21Zee-86
❑ 22Zee-73
❑ 23Zee-115
❑ 26Zee-17
❑ 27Zee-7
Sheehan, Terry
❑ 76SeaRaiC-15
❑ 78OrlTwiT-18
❑ 79TolMudHT-10
❑ 80OrlTwiT-16
Sheehan, Tommy
❑ 08RosComP-100
❑ 09ObaT21-302
❑ 11PacCoaBD-57
❑ 11Zee-60
❑ 12HomRunKE-55
❑ 12ObaPreT-51
❑ 12Zee-93
❑ 32Zee-14
❑ 78HalHalR-8
❑ 90DodTar-1069
Sheehy, Mark
❑ 84AlbDukCr-246
❑ 87BakDodP-16
❑ 88SanAntMB-25
Sheely, Earl Homer
❑ 17Zee-77
❑ 18Zee-72
❑ 19Zee-76
❑ 20Zee-96
❑ 21E121So1-95
❑ 21Exh-158
❑ 21Nei-34
❑ 22E120-28
❑ 22W572-96
❑ 22W573-121
❑ 22W575-124
❑ 23W501-46
❑ 23WilChoV-148
❑ 25Exh-79
❑ 26Exh-79
❑ 27YorCarE-37
❑ 28ExhPCL-25
❑ 28W502-37
❑ 28Yue-37
❑ 28Zee-122
❑ 29ExhFou-13
❑ 30Zee-157
❑ 31Exh-2
❑ 33ExhFou-1
❑ 33Zee-83
❑ 46SunBre-16
❑ 47CenFlo-26
❑ 92ConTSN-515
Sheen, Charlie
❑ 88PacEigMO-10
❑ 89MajLeaM-7
❑ 89MajLeaM-10
Sheets, Andy
❑ 92LSUTigM-10
❑ 93RivPilCLC-18
❑ 94RivPilCLC-16
❑ 95TacRaiTI-20
❑ 96TacRaiB-24
❑ 97PacPriGotD-GD92
❑ 97TacRai-25
❑ 98PacInvGems-97
❑ 98PacOnl-647
❑ 98PacOnlR-647
❑ 98PacOnlWC-647
❑ 98PadMot-17
Sheets, Larry
❑ 84BalOriP-33
❑ 84RocRedWT-1
❑ 85BalOriP-30
❑ 85Don-36
❑ 85FleUpd-101
❑ 85OriHea-16
❑ 85TopTifT-106T
❑ 85TopTra-106T
❑ 86BalOriHMP-16
❑ 86BalOriP-19
❑ 86Don-350
❑ 86Fle-286
❑ 86SevCoi-E9
❑ 86Spo-177
❑ 86Top-147
❑ 86TopGloS-50
❑ 86TopSti-308
❑ 86TopTat-7
❑ 86TopTif-147
❑ 87BalOriP-34
❑ 87Don-248
❑ 87Fle-479
❑ 87FleGlo-479
❑ 87FleHotS-36
❑ 87OriFreB-18
❑ 87SmoAmeL-10
❑ 87SpoTeaP-21
❑ 87Top-552
❑ 87TopSti-229
❑ 87TopTif-552
❑ 88ClaRed-188
❑ 88Don-273
❑ 88DonBasB-286
❑ 88Dra-23
❑ 88Fle-572
❑ 88FleAwaW-38
❑ 88FleBasM-34
❑ 88FleExcS-37
❑ 88FleGlo-572
❑ 88FleHotS-37
❑ 88FleLeaL-38
❑ 88FleMin-3
❑ 88FleStiC-4
❑ 88OPC-327
❑ 88OriFreB-18
❑ 88OriPos-33
❑ 88PanSti-16
❑ 88Sco-219
❑ 88ScoGlo-219
❑ 88Spo-161
❑ 88StaLinO-15
❑ 88Top-327
❑ 88TopBig-26
❑ 88TopSti-230
❑ 88TopTif-327
❑ 88TopUKM-70
❑ 88TopUKMT-70
❑ 89BalOriP-32
❑ 89Bow-16
❑ 89BowTif-16
❑ 89Don-333
❑ 89Fle-620
❑ 89FleGlo-620
❑ 89OPC-98
❑ 89OriFreB-19
❑ 89PanSti-264
❑ 89Sco-81
❑ 89Top-98
❑ 89Top-381
❑ 89TopBig-113
❑ 89TopSti-239
❑ 89TopTif-98
❑ 89TopTif-381
❑ 89TVSpoM-91
❑ 89UppDec-254
❑ 90Don-495
❑ 90Fle-189
❑ 90FleCan-189
❑ 90FleUpd-100
❑ 90HagSunDGB-27
❑ 90Lea-350
❑ 90OPC-708
❑ 90PubIntS-586
❑ 90Sco-111
❑ 90ScoRoo-65T
❑ 90TigCok-22
❑ 90Top-708
❑ 90TopTif-708
❑ 90UppDec-287
❑ 91Fle-352
❑ 91OPC-281
❑ 91OriCro-414
❑ 91Sco-176
❑ 91Top-281
❑ 91TopDesS-281
❑ 91TopMic-281
❑ 91TopTif-281
❑ 91UppDec-340
❑ 93NewOrlZF-980
❑ 95BalOriP-46
Sheff, Chris
❑ 92ClaDraP-101
❑ 92FroRowDP-59
❑ 92FroRowDPG-59
❑ 92FroRowDPS-59
❑ 93Bow-642
❑ 93KanCouCC-20
❑ 93KanCouCF-929
❑ 93KanCouCTI-21
❑ 93MidLeaAGF-10
❑ 94BreCouMF-27
❑ 95PorSeaDTI-25
❑ 95SigRooOJ-28
❑ 95SigRooOJP-28
❑ 95SigRooOJPS-28
❑ 95SigRooOJS-28
❑ 96Bow-284
❑ 96BowFoi-284
❑ 96Exc-167
❑ 96PorSeaDB-25
❑ 97ChaKni-27
❑ 98PorSeaD5AQ-13
Sheffer, Chad
❑ 95EveAqaTI-22
❑ 96WisTimRB-21
Sheffield, Gary
❑ 87StoPorP-1
❑ 88BasAmeAAB-22
❑ 88ElPasDB-1
❑ 88TexLeaAGS-26
❑ 88TriAAC-14
❑ 89Baz-19
❑ 89Bow-142
❑ 89BowTif-142
❑ 89BrePol-1
❑ 89BreYea-1
❑ 89ClaTraO-101
❑ 89Don-31
❑ 89DonBasB-113
❑ 89DonRoo-1
❑ 89Fle-196
❑ 89FleGlo-196
❑ 89PanSti-364
❑ 89Sco-625
❑ 89ScoHot1R-10
❑ 89ScoYouSI-25
❑ 89Spo-41
❑ 89Spo-223
❑ 89Top-343
❑ 89TopBig-55
❑ 89TopHeaUT-13
❑ 89TopRoo-20
❑ 89TopTif-343
❑ 89ToyRoo-28
❑ 89UppDec-13
❑ 89UppDec-13A
❑ 90Baz-16
❑ 90Bow-391
❑ 90BowTif-391
❑ 90BreMilB-23
❑ 90BrePol-11
❑ 90ClaBlu-14
❑ 90Don-501
❑ 90DonBesA-121
❑ 90El PasDAGTI-27
❑ 90Fle-336
❑ 90FleCan-336
❑ 90Hot50RS-41
❑ 90Lea-157
❑ 90OPC-718
❑ 90PubIntS-504
❑ 90PubIntS-604
❑ 90Sco-97
❑ 90Sco100RS-20
❑ 90ScoMcD-12
❑ 90Spo-52
❑ 90Top-718
❑ 90TopBig-163
❑ 90TopCoi-27
❑ 90TopGloS-10
❑ 90TopHeaU-13
❑ 90TopMag-91
❑ 90TopRoo-25
❑ 90TopSti-202
❑ 90TopSti-326
❑ 90TopTif-718
❑ 90ToyRoo-24
❑ 90UppDec-157
❑ 91Bow-52
❑ 91BreMilB-23
❑ 91BrePol-20
❑ 91CadEllD-51
❑ 91Cla2-T13
❑ 91ClaGam-103
❑ 91Don-751
❑ 91Fle-596
❑ 91JimDea-7
❑ 91Lea-173
❑ 91OPC-68
❑ 91PanFreS-206
❑ 91PanSti-170
❑ 91Pos-15
❑ 91Sco-473
❑ 91Sco100S-30
❑ 91StaClu-95
❑ 91Stu-76
❑ 91Top-68
❑ 91TopDesS-68
❑ 91TopMic-68
❑ 91TopTif-68
❑ 91Ult-180

❑ 91UppDec-266
❑ 92Bow-214
❑ 92Cla2-T59
❑ 92ColAllG-20
❑ 92ColAllP-20
❑ 92Don-192
❑ 92DonUpd-U11
❑ 92Fle-188
❑ 92FleUpd-125
❑ 92Lea-446
❑ 92LeaBlaG-446
❑ 92OPC-695
❑ 92PadCarJ-19
❑ 92PadMot-3
❑ 92PadPolD-20
❑ 92PadPolD-30
❑ 92PadSmo-30
❑ 92Pin-235
❑ 92PinTea2-59
❑ 92RedFolS-87
❑ 92Sco-589
❑ 92ScoRoo-1T
❑ 92StaClu-309
❑ 92StaClu-766
❑ 92StaCluECN-766
❑ 92StaCluMO-12
❑ 92Stu-108
❑ 92Top-695
❑ 92TopGol-695
❑ 92TopGolW-695
❑ 92TopMic-695
❑ 92TopTra-105T
❑ 92TopTraG-105T
❑ 92TriPla-53
❑ 92Ult-83
❑ 92Ult-582
❑ 92UltAllS-14
❑ 92UppDec-84
❑ 92UppDec-234
❑ 92UppDec-745
❑ 93Bow-490
❑ 93CadDis-54
❑ 93ClaGam-84
❑ 93ClaGolF-216
❑ 93ClaGolF-AU2
❑ 93DenHol-17
❑ 93DiaMar-97
❑ 93Don-444
❑ 93DonDiaK-DK21
❑ 93DonEli-28
❑ 93DonEliS-10
❑ 93DonLonBL-LL16
❑ 93DonMasotG-3
❑ 93DonMVP-26
❑ 93DonPre-10
❑ 93DonSpiotG-SG12
❑ 93DurPowP2-18
❑ 93Fin-31
❑ 93FinRef-31
❑ 93Fla-54
❑ 93Fle-147
❑ 93Fle-351
❑ 93Fle-356
❑ 93Fle-704
❑ 93FleAll-NL3
❑ 93FleAtl-22
❑ 93FleFinE-71
❑ 93FleFruotL-57
❑ 93FlePro-A3
❑ 93FleTeaL-NL5
❑ 93FunPac-20
❑ 93FunPac-25
❑ 93FunPac-141
❑ 93Hos-6
❑ 93JimDea-18
❑ 93Kra-28
❑ 93Lea-307
❑ 93LeaGolA-R15
❑ 93LeaGolA-U5
❑ 93MarPub-23
❑ 93OPC-317
❑ 93OPCPreSP-6
❑ 93OPCPreSPF-6
❑ 93PacSpa-264
❑ 93PadMot-2
❑ 93PanSti-158
❑ 93PanSti-261
❑ 93Pin-1
❑ 93Pin-300
❑ 93PinHomRC-6
❑ 93PinSlu-7
❑ 93PinTeaP-6
❑ 93Pos-11
❑ 93PosCan-16
❑ 93RedFolS-125
❑ 93Sco-2
❑ 93Sco-531
❑ 93Sco-534
❑ 93ScoFra-25
❑ 93ScoGolDT-3
❑ 93Sel-41
❑ 93SelChaS-4
❑ 93SelRoo-4T
❑ 93SelSam-41
❑ 93SelStaL-4
❑ 93SelStaL-30
❑ 93SelStaL-47
❑ 93SP-18
❑ 93SPPlaP-PP18
❑ 93StaClu-300
❑ 93StaClu-618
❑ 93StaCluFDI-300
❑ 93StaCluFDI-618
❑ 93StaCluM-17
❑ 93StaCluMMP-10
❑ 93StaCluMOP-300
❑ 93StaCluMOP-618
❑ 93Stu-207
❑ 93Top-140
❑ 93Top-403
❑ 93TOPBLAG-18
❑ 93TopFulS-18
❑ 93TopGol-140
❑ 93TopGol-403
❑ 93TopInaM-140
❑ 93TopInaM-403
❑ 93TopInaR-140
❑ 93TopInaR-403
❑ 93TopMic-140
❑ 93TopMic-403
❑ 93TopTra-51T
❑ 93Toy-64
❑ 93ToyMasP-11
❑ 93TriPla-6
❑ 93TriPlaA-10
❑ 93TriPlaLL-L6
❑ 93TriPlaP-6
❑ 93Ult-122
❑ 93UltAllS-5
❑ 93UltAwaW-25
❑ 93UltHomRK-8
❑ 93UltPer-8
❑ 93UppDec-222
❑ 93UppDec-474
❑ 93UppDec-492
❑ 93UppDec-494
❑ 93UppDec-828
❑ 93UppDecFA-A2
❑ 93UppDecFAJ-A2
❑ 93UppDecGold-222
❑ 93UppDecGold-474
❑ 93UppDecGold-492
❑ 93UppDecGold-494
❑ 93UppDecGold-828
❑ 93UppDecS-19
❑ 93UppDecTriCro-TC8
❑ 93USPlaCA-7C
❑ 93USPlaCA-13D
❑ 94Bow-290
❑ 94BowBes-R13
❑ 94BowBesR-R13
❑ 94BreMilB-268
❑ 94ChuHomS-18
❑ 94ChuHomSG-18
❑ 94ColC-257
❑ 94ColC-341
❑ 94ColChoGS-257
❑ 94ColChoGS-341
❑ 94ColChoSS-257
❑ 94ColChoSS-341
❑ 94ColChoT-6
❑ 94DenHol-23
❑ 94Don-5
❑ 94DonDiaK-DK25
❑ 94DonDiaKJ-DK25
❑ 94DonPro-10
❑ 94DonSpeE-5
❑ 94Fin-225
❑ 94FinJum-225
❑ 94FinRef-225
❑ 94Fla-166
❑ 94Fle-477
❑ 94FleAllS-49
❑ 94FleExtB-266
❑ 94FleExtBGB-26
❑ 94FleTeaL-19
❑ 94FUnPac-10
❑ 94Kra-28
❑ 94Lea-319
❑ 94LeaL-109
❑ 94LeaMVPC-N13
❑ 94LeaMVPCG-N13
❑ 94MarTeal-16
❑ 94OPC-45
❑ 94Pac-250
❑ 94PanSti-186
❑ 94Pin-88
❑ 94PinArtP-88
❑ 94PinMusC-88
❑ 94PinPowS-PS15
❑ 94PinTheN-18
❑ 94PinTheN-P18
❑ 94Pos-5
❑ 94ProMag-54
❑ 94RedFolMI-24
❑ 94Sco-100
❑ 94ScoGolR-100
❑ 94ScoGolS-20
❑ 94Sel-256
❑ 94SP-114
❑ 94SPDieC-114
❑ 94SPHol-35
❑ 94SPHolDC-35
❑ 94Spo-28
❑ 94SpoFanA-AS8
❑ 94SpoRooGGG-GG1
❑ 94SpoRooS-GG1
❑ 94StaClu-4
❑ 94StaClu-180
❑ 94StaCluFDI-4
❑ 94StaCluFDI-180
❑ 94StaCluGR-4
❑ 94StaCluGR-180
❑ 94StaCluMOP-4
❑ 94StaCluMOP-180
❑ 94StaCluT-67
❑ 94StaCluTF-10
❑ 94StaCluTFDI-67
❑ 94Stu-112
❑ 94Top-560
❑ 94TopGol-560
❑ 94TopSpa-560
❑ 94TopSupS-40
❑ 94TriPla-140
❑ 94TriPlaM-10
❑ 94TriPlaN-3
❑ 94Ult-199
❑ 94UppDec-50
❑ 94UppDec-271
❑ 94UppDec-475
❑ 94UppDecAJ-3
❑ 94UppDecAJG-3
❑ 94UppDecDC-E10
❑ 94UppDecED-50
❑ 94UppDecED-271
❑ 94UppDecED-475
❑ 94UppDecNG-18
❑ 94UppDecNGED-18
❑ 95Baz-44
❑ 95Bow-325
❑ 95BowBes-R5
❑ 95BowBesR-R5
❑ 95ColCho-300
❑ 95ColChoCtG-CG18
❑ 95ColChoCtG-CG18B
❑ 95ColChoCtG-CG18C
❑ 95ColChoCtGE-18
❑ 95ColChoCtGG-CG18
❑ 95ColChoCtGG-CG18B
❑ 95ColChoCtGG-CG18C
❑ 95ColChoCtGGE-18
❑ 95ColChoGS-300
❑ 95ColChoSE-130
❑ 95ColChoSEGS-130
❑ 95ColChoSESS-130
❑ 95ColChoSS-300
❑ 95DenHol-24
❑ 95Don-168
❑ 95DonPreP-168
❑ 95DonTopotO-247
❑ 95Emo-132
❑ 95Fin-119
❑ 95FinPowK-PK14
❑ 95FinRef-119
❑ 95Fla-141
❑ 95FlaOutP-9
❑ 95Fle-342
❑ 95KinDis-21
❑ 95Lea-182
❑ 95LeaLim-126
❑ 95Pac-178
❑ 95PacPri-57
❑ 95PanSti-74
❑ 95Pin-119
❑ 95PinArtP-119
❑ 95PinFan-29
❑ 95PinMusC-119
❑ 95PinSam-119
❑ 95RedFol-19
❑ 95Sco-340
❑ 95ScoGolR-340
❑ 95ScoHaloG-HG61
❑ 95ScoPlaTS-340
❑ 95Sel-62
❑ 95SelArtP-62
❑ 95SelCer-28
❑ 95SelCerMG-28
❑ 95SP-55
❑ 95SPCha-47
❑ 95SPChaDC-47
❑ 95Spo-46
❑ 95SpoArtP-46
❑ 95SPSil-55
❑ 95SPSpeF-37
❑ 95StaClu-90
❑ 95StaClu-500
❑ 95StaCluCC-CC13
❑ 95StaCluFDI-90
❑ 95StaCluMOP-90
❑ 95StaCluMOP-500
❑ 95StaCluMOP-CC13
❑ 95StaCluMOP-RL15
❑ 95StaCluRL-RL15
❑ 95StaCluSTWS-90
❑ 95StaCluSTWS-500
❑ 95StaCluVR-56
❑ 95StaCluVRMO-56
❑ 95Stu-181
❑ 95Sum-43
❑ 95SumNthD-43
❑ 95Top-440
❑ 95TopCyb-236
❑ 95TopEmb-2
❑ 95TopEmbGI-2
❑ 95UC3-28
❑ 95UC3ArtP-28
❑ 95Ult-167
❑ 95UltGolM-167
❑ 95UppDec-355
❑ 95UppDecED-355
❑ 95UppDecEDG-355
❑ 95UppDecPC-MLB14
❑ 95UppDecPLL-R40
❑ 95UppDecPLLE-R40
❑ 95UppDecSE-115
❑ 95UppDecSEG-115
❑ 95Zen-35
❑ 96Baz-132
❑ 96BowBes-53
❑ 96BowBesAR-53
❑ 96BowBesR-53
❑ 96BowFoi-42
❑ 96Cir-131
❑ 96CirAcc-18
❑ 96CirBos-36
❑ 96CirRav-131
❑ 96ColCho-399
❑ 96ColCho-560
❑ 96ColChoCtG-CG18
❑ 96ColChoCtG-CG18B
❑ 96ColChoCtG-CG18C
❑ 96ColChoCtGE-CR18
❑ 96ColChoCtGG-CG18
❑ 96ColChoCtGG-CG18B
❑ 96ColChoCtGG-CG18C
❑ 96ColChoCtGGE-CR18
❑ 96ColChoGS-399
❑ 96ColChoGS-560
❑ 96ColChoSS-399
❑ 96ColChoSS-560
❑ 96ColChoYMtP-36
❑ 96ColChoYMtP-36A
❑ 96ColChoYMtPGS-36
❑ 96ColChoYMtPGS-36A
❑ 96DenHol-12
❑ 96Don-36
❑ 96DonPreP-36
❑ 96EmoXL-190
❑ 96Fin-B309
❑ 96Fin-S60
❑ 96Fin-S337
❑ 96FinRef-B309
❑ 96FinRef-S60
❑ 96FinRef-S337
❑ 96Fla-268
❑ 96Fle-394
❑ 96FleTif-394
❑ 96FleUpd-U241
❑ 96FleUpdTC-U241
❑ 96Lea-14
❑ 96LeaLim-3
❑ 96LeaLimG-3
❑ 96LeaPre-27
❑ 96LeaPreP-27
❑ 96LeaPrePB-14
❑ 96LeaPrePG-14
❑ 96LeaPrePS-14
❑ 96LeaPreSG-19
❑ 96LeaPreSte-19
❑ 96LeaSig-30
❑ 96LeaSigPPG-30
❑ 96LeaSigPPP-30
❑ 96LibSpo-10
❑ 96MetUni-169
❑ 96MetUniP-169
❑ 96Pac-83
❑ 96PacPri-P27
❑ 96PacPriG-P27
❑ 96PanSti-15
❑ 96Pin-123
❑ 96Pin-271
❑ 96PinAfi-94
❑ 96PinAfiAP-94
❑ 96PinAfiFPP-94
❑ 96PinArtP-32
❑ 96PinArtP-171
❑ 96PinFan-17
❑ 96PinFirR-7
❑ 96PinFoil-271
❑ 96PinSky-11
❑ 96PinSlu-11
❑ 96PinSta-32
❑ 96PinSta-171
❑ 96ProSta-66
❑ 96Sco-281
❑ 96ScoDugC-B6
❑ 96ScoDugCAP-B6
❑ 96ScoGolS-7
❑ 96ScoPowP-6
❑ 96ScoTitT-16
❑ 96Sel-29
❑ 96SelArtP-29
❑ 96SelCer-3
❑ 96SelCerAP-3
❑ 96SelCerCB-3
❑ 96SelCerCR-3
❑ 96SelCerIP-16
❑ 96SelCerMB-3
❑ 96SelCerMG-3
❑ 96SelCerMR-3
❑ 96SelCerSF-15
❑ 96SelEnF-17
❑ 96SelTeaN-16
❑ 96SP-86
❑ 96Spo-45
❑ 96Spo-108
❑ 96SpoArtP-45
❑ 96SpoArtP-108
❑ 96SpoHitP-12
❑ 96SpoPowS-12
❑ 96SPSpeFX-11
❑ 96SPSpeFXDC-11
❑ 96SPx-27
❑ 96SPxGol-27
❑ 96StaClu-400
❑ 96StaCluEPB-400
❑ 96StaCluEPG-400
❑ 96StaCluEPS-400
❑ 96StaCluEWB-EW9
❑ 96StaCluEWG-EW9
❑ 96StaCluEWS-EW9
❑ 96StaCluMOP-400
❑ 96Stu-64
❑ 96StuPrePB-64
❑ 96StuPrePG-64
❑ 96StuPrePS-64
❑ 96Sum-100
❑ 96SumAbo&B-100
❑ 96SumArtP-100
❑ 96SumFoi-100
❑ 96SumPos-9
❑ 96TeaOut-74
❑ 96Top-80
❑ 96TopChr-27
❑ 96TopChrR-27
❑ 96TopGal-177
❑ 96TopGalE-9
❑ 96TopGalPPI-177
❑ 96TopLas-78
❑ 96TopPro-NL19
❑ 96Ult-481
❑ 96UltGolM-481
❑ 96UppDec-340
❑ 96UppDecDD-DD20
❑ 96UppDecDDG-DD20
❑ 96UppDecDDS-DD20
❑ 96Zen-21
❑ 96Zen-143
❑ 96ZenArtP-21
❑ 96ZenArtP-143
❑ 96ZenDiaC-14
❑ 96ZenDiaCP-14
❑ 96ZenMoz-16
❑ 96ZenZ-13
❑ 97Bow-231
❑ 97BowBes-35
❑ 97BowBesAR-35
❑ 97BowBesMI-MI6
❑ 97BowBesMIAR-MI6
❑ 97BowBesMIARI-MI6
❑ 97BowBesMII-MI6
❑ 97BowBesMIR-MI6
❑ 97BowBesMIRI-MI6
❑ 97BowBesP-9
❑ 97BowBesPAR-9
❑ 97BowBesPR-9
❑ 97BowBesR-35
❑ 97BowChr-58
❑ 97BowChrI-58
❑ 97BowChrIR-58
❑ 97BowChrR-58
❑ 97BowInt-231
❑ 97Cir-299
❑ 97CirRav-299
❑ 97ColCho-345
❑ 97ColChoAC-34
❑ 97ColChoCtG-17A
❑ 97ColChoCtG-17B
❑ 97ColChoCtG-17C
❑ 97ColChoCtGE-CG17
❑ 97ColChoCtGIW-CG17
❑ 97ColChoNF-NF32
❑ 97ColChoPP-PP10
❑ 97ColChoPPG-PP10
❑ 97ColChoPPJ-PP10
❑ 97ColChoS-17
❑ 97ColChoSR-24
❑ 97ColChoT-FM9
❑ 97ColChoTBS-22
❑ 97ColChoTBSWH-22
❑ 97CraJac-10
❑ 97DenHol-21
❑ 97Don-159
❑ 97Don-403
❑ 97DonDom-20
❑ 97DonEli-43
❑ 97DonEliGS-43
❑ 97DonFraFea-11
❑ 97DonGolPP-159
❑ 97DonGolPP-403
❑ 97DonLim-3
❑ 97DonLim-24
❑ 97DonLim-127
❑ 97DonLimE-3
❑ 97DonLimE-24
❑ 97DonLimE-127
❑ 97DonLimENG-24
❑ 97DonLimFotG-29
❑ 97DonLimFotG-67
❑ 97DonPowA-17
❑ 97DonPowADC-17
❑ 97DonPre-101
❑ 97DonPre-191
❑ 97DonPreCttC-101
❑ 97DonPreCttC-191
❑ 97DonPreS-17
❑ 97DonPreSS-17
❑ 97DonPreTB-21
❑ 97DonPreTBG-21
❑ 97DonPreTF-21
❑ 97DonPreTP-21
❑ 97DonPreTPG-21
❑ 97DonRocL-10
❑ 97DonSig-23
❑ 97DonSigAC-111
❑ 97DonSigAM-111
❑ 97DonSigPPP-23
❑ 97DonSilPP-159
❑ 97DonSilPP-403
❑ 97DonVxP1-24
❑ 97E-X2-74
❑ 97E-X2Cred-74
❑ 97E-X2EssCre-74
❑ 97Fin-109
❑ 97Fin-176
❑ 97Fin-326
❑ 97FinEmb-109
❑ 97FinEmb-326
❑ 97FinEmbR-109
❑ 97FinEmbR-326
❑ 97FinRef-109
❑ 97FinRef-176
❑ 97FinRef-326
❑ 97FlaShoLC-38
❑ 97FlaShoLeg0-38
❑ 97FlaShoLeg1-38

- ❑ 97FlaShoM-A38
- ❑ 97FlaShoM-B38
- ❑ 97FlaShoM-C38
- ❑ 97FlaShoR0-38
- ❑ 97FlaShoR1-38
- ❑ 97FlaShoR2-38
- ❑ 97Fle-336
- ❑ 97Fle-731
- ❑ 97FleLumC-15
- ❑ 97FleTeaL-19
- ❑ 97FleTif-336
- ❑ 97FleTif-731
- ❑ 97FleZon-16
- ❑ 97KinB-22
- ❑ 97Lea-49
- ❑ 97Lea-357
- ❑ 97LeaDrefS-6
- ❑ 97LeaFraM-49
- ❑ 97LeaFraM-357
- ❑ 97LeaFraMDC-49
- ❑ 97LeaFraMDC-357
- ❑ 97LeaLeaotN-11
- ❑ 97LeaWarT-10
- ❑ 97MarPac-22
- ❑ 97MetUni-179
- ❑ 97NewPin-94
- ❑ 97NewPin-186
- ❑ 97NewPinAP-94
- ❑ 97NewPinAP-186
- ❑ 97NewPinMC-94
- ❑ 97NewPinMC-186
- ❑ 97NewPinPP-94
- ❑ 97NewPinPP-186
- ❑ 97Pac-307
- ❑ 97PacCar-27
- ❑ 97PacCarM-27
- ❑ 97PacCerCGT-16
- ❑ 97PacLigB-307
- ❑ 97PacPri-104
- ❑ 97PacPriLB-104
- ❑ 97PacPriP-104
- ❑ 97PacSil-307
- ❑ 97PinCar-11
- ❑ 97PinCer-44
- ❑ 97PinCerCMGT-16
- ❑ 97PinCerCT-16
- ❑ 97PinCerMBla-44
- ❑ 97PinCerMBlu-44
- ❑ 97PinCerMG-44
- ❑ 97PinCerMR-44
- ❑ 97PinCerR-44
- ❑ 97PinIns-45
- ❑ 97PinInsCE-45
- ❑ 97PinInsDE-45
- ❑ 97PinInsFS-15
- ❑ 97PinMin-23
- ❑ 97PinMinB-23
- ❑ 97PinMinCB-23
- ❑ 97PinMinCG-23
- ❑ 97PinMinCGR-23
- ❑ 97PinMinCN-23
- ❑ 97PinMinCSS-23
- ❑ 97PinMinG-23
- ❑ 97PinMinS-23
- ❑ 97PinPrePla-S4
- ❑ 97PinSha-4
- ❑ 97PinTeaP-8
- ❑ 97PinTeaP-10
- ❑ 97PinTotCPB-44
- ❑ 97PinTotCPG-44
- ❑ 97PinTotCPR-44
- ❑ 97PinX-P-80
- ❑ 97PinX-PF&A-10
- ❑ 97PinX-PMoS-80
- ❑ 97PinX-PSfF-51
- ❑ 97PinX-PSfFU-51
- ❑ 97PreCon-6
- ❑ 97Sco-184
- ❑ 97Sco-514
- ❑ 97ScoArtPWB-184
- ❑ 97ScoArtPWB-515
- ❑ 97ScoBla-13
- ❑ 97ScoPreS-184
- ❑ 97ScoResC-515
- ❑ 97ScoShoS-184
- ❑ 97ScoShoS-515
- ❑ 97ScoShoSAP-184
- ❑ 97ScoShoSAP-515
- ❑ 97ScoSteS-17
- ❑ 97ScoTitT-16
- ❑ 97Sel-11
- ❑ 97SelArtP-11
- ❑ 97SelCom-11
- ❑ 97SelRegG-11
- ❑ 97SelToootT-12
- ❑ 97SelToootTMB-12
- ❑ 97SP-75
- ❑ 97SPMarM-MM16
- ❑ 97SpoIll-83
- ❑ 97SpoIllEE-83
- ❑ 97SPSpeF-22
- ❑ 97SPSpxF-4
- ❑ 97SPSPxFA-4
- ❑ 97SPVinAu-27
- ❑ 97SPVinAu-28
- ❑ 97SPVinAu-29
- ❑ 97SPVinAu-30
- ❑ 97SPx-26
- ❑ 97SPxBoufG-10
- ❑ 97SPxBoufGSS-5
- ❑ 97SPxBro-26
- ❑ 97SPxGol-26
- ❑ 97SPxGraF-26
- ❑ 97SPxSil-26
- ❑ 97SPxSte-26
- ❑ 97StaClu-2
- ❑ 97StaClu-381
- ❑ 97StaCluMat-2
- ❑ 97StaCluMOP-2
- ❑ 97StaCluMOP-381
- ❑ 97StaCluMOP-PG9
- ❑ 97StaCluPG-PG9
- ❑ 97StaCluPP-PP3
- ❑ 97Stu-2
- ❑ 97StuMasS-21
- ❑ 97StuMasS8-21
- ❑ 97StuPor8-22
- ❑ 97StuPrePG-2
- ❑ 97StuPrePS-2
- ❑ 97Top-264
- ❑ 97TopAll-AS16
- ❑ 97TopChr-94
- ❑ 97TopChrAS-AS16
- ❑ 97TopChrJ-94
- ❑ 97TopChrR-94
- ❑ 97TopChrSAR-AS16
- ❑ 97TopGal-55
- ❑ 97TopGalPG-PG10
- ❑ 97TopGalPPI-55
- ❑ 97TopIntF-ILM14
- ❑ 97TopIntFR-ILM14
- ❑ 97TopMem05-43
- ❑ 97TopSta-53
- ❑ 97TopStaAM-53
- ❑ 97TopSweS-SS13
- ❑ 97TopTeaT-TT13
- ❑ 97UD3-10
- ❑ 97Ult-202
- ❑ 97UltGolME-202
- ❑ 97UltPlaME-202
- ❑ 97UppDec-215
- ❑ 97UppDec-360
- ❑ 97UppDecLDC-LD10
- ❑ 97UppDecP-16
- ❑ 97UppDecPE-16
- ❑ 97UppDecPP-PP11
- ❑ 97UppDecPPJ-PP11
- ❑ 97UppDecRP-RP12
- ❑ 97Zen-29
- ❑ 98Bow-68
- ❑ 98BowBes-19
- ❑ 98BowBesAR-19
- ❑ 98BowBesR-19
- ❑ 98BowChr-68
- ❑ 98BowChrGA-68
- ❑ 98BowChrGAR-68
- ❑ 98BowChrI-68
- ❑ 98BowChrIR-68
- ❑ 98BowChrR-68
- ❑ 98BowChrR-11
- ❑ 98BowChrRR-11
- ❑ 98BowGolA-68
- ❑ 98BowInt-68
- ❑ 98BowMinLM-MVP10
- ❑ 98CirThu-26
- ❑ 98CirThuRav-26
- ❑ 98CirThuSupRav-26
- ❑ 98ColCho-95
- ❑ 98ColChoER-ER11
- ❑ 98ColChoRJ-95
- ❑ 98ColChoS'-13
- ❑ 98ColChoSQDouble-28
- ❑ 98ColChoSQHR-28
- ❑ 98ColChoSQSingle-28
- ❑ 98ColChoSQTriple-28
- ❑ 98CroRoy-72
- ❑ 98CroRoyAS-11
- ❑ 98CroRoyFoB-11
- ❑ 98CroRoyFoBA-11
- ❑ 98DodFanA-4
- ❑ 98DodMot-5
- ❑ 98Don-138
- ❑ 98DonCol-138
- ❑ 98DonColE-439
- ❑ 98DonColL-221
- ❑ 98DonColP-586
- ❑ 98DonColP-745
- ❑ 98DonColS-138
- ❑ 98DonCruG-72
- ❑ 98DonCruP-72
- ❑ 98DonCruR-72
- ❑ 98DonEli-39
- ❑ 98DonEliA-39
- ❑ 98DonEliS-39
- ❑ 98DonGolPP-138
- ❑ 98DonPre-36
- ❑ 98DonPre-195
- ❑ 98DonPreGES-16
- ❑ 98DonPreGX-16
- ❑ 98DonPreGXDC-16
- ❑ 98DonPreSeat-36
- ❑ 98DonPreSeat-195
- ❑ 98DonPreTW-4
- ❑ 98DonPriCD-138
- ❑ 98DonPriCE-439
- ❑ 98DonPriCL-221
- ❑ 98DonPriCP-586
- ❑ 98DonPriCP-745
- ❑ 98DonProLO-11
- ❑ 98DonSig-36
- ❑ 98DonSigP-36
- ❑ 98DonSilPP-138
- ❑ 98DonSonM9-9
- ❑ 98E-X2-22
- ❑ 98E-X2ECFut-22
- ❑ 98E-X2ECNow-22
- ❑ 98Fin-25
- ❑ 98FinMysF1-M41
- ❑ 98FinMysF1-M42
- ❑ 98FinMysF1-M43
- ❑ 98FinMysF1-M44
- ❑ 98FinMysFR-M41
- ❑ 98FinMysFR-M42
- ❑ 98FinMysFR-M43
- ❑ 98FinMysFR-M44
- ❑ 98FinNo--25
- ❑ 98FinNo-R-25
- ❑ 98FinPowZ-P8
- ❑ 98FinRef-25
- ❑ 98FinStaS-SS16
- ❑ 98FlaShoLeg0-68
- ❑ 98FlaShoLeg1-68
- ❑ 98FlaShoLeg2-68
- ❑ 98FlaShoLeg3-68
- ❑ 98FlaShoLegM-68
- ❑ 98FlaShoR0-68
- ❑ 98FlaShoR1-68
- ❑ 98FlaShoR2-68
- ❑ 98FlaShoR3-68
- ❑ 98Fle-6
- ❑ 98Fle-521
- ❑ 98FleVin'-28
- ❑ 98FleVin'-104
- ❑ 98FleVin'C-28
- ❑ 98FleVin'C-104
- ❑ 98KinDis-16
- ❑ 98Lea-21
- ❑ 98LeaFraDA-21
- ❑ 98LeaFraF-21
- ❑ 98LeaFraM-21
- ❑ 98LeaFraM-21
- ❑ 98LeaFraMDC-21
- ❑ 98LeaFraMDC-21
- ❑ 98LeaFraMZ2-21
- ❑ 98LeaRS-9
- ❑ 98LeaRS-187
- ❑ 98LeaRSLHolo-9
- ❑ 98LeaRSLHolo-187
- ❑ 98LeaRSLong-9
- ❑ 98LeaRSLong-187
- ❑ 98LeaRTrue-9
- ❑ 98LeaRTrue-187
- ❑ 98MetUni-193
- ❑ 98MetUniPMG-193
- ❑ 98Pac-308
- ❑ 98PacAur-134
- ❑ 98PacGolCDC-17
- ❑ 98PacInv-101
- ❑ 98PacInvGems-159
- ❑ 98PacInvPBlue-101
- ❑ 98PacInvSilv-101
- ❑ 98PacInvTeam-11
- ❑ 98PacOme-128
- ❑ 98PacOmeR-128
- ❑ 98PacOnl-385
- ❑ 98PacOnl-389
- ❑ 98PacOnlR-385
- ❑ 98PacOnlR-389
- ❑ 98PacOnlWC-385
- ❑ 98PacOnlWC-389
- ❑ 98PacPar-165
- ❑ 98PacParC-165
- ❑ 98PacParG-165
- ❑ 98PacParHS-165
- ❑ 98PacParI-16
- ❑ 98PacParPB-165
- ❑ 98PacParR-165
- ❑ 98PacPlaB-308
- ❑ 98PacRedT-308
- ❑ 98PacSil-308
- ❑ 98Pin-40
- ❑ 98PinArtP-PP38
- ❑ 98PinIns-22
- ❑ 98PinInsCE-22
- ❑ 98PinInsDE-22
- ❑ 98PinMusC-PP38
- ❑ 98PinPer-37
- ❑ 98PinPerLP-17
- ❑ 98PinPerPP-37
- ❑ 98PinPerSftF-46
- ❑ 98PinPlu-140
- ❑ 98PinPluAP-PP46
- ❑ 98PinPluGAP-PP46
- ❑ 98PinPluMAP-PP46
- ❑ 98PinPreP-40
- ❑ 98Revo-77
- ❑ 98RevoFP-17
- ❑ 98RevoShow-31
- ❑ 98RevoSS-77
- ❑ 98ScoRT-47
- ❑ 98ScoRTSS-PP47
- ❑ 98ScoRTSSAP-PP47
- ❑ 98ScoRTSSAP1-PP47
- ❑ 98SkyDugA-18
- ❑ 98SkyDugAIA-18
- ❑ 98SP Aut-110
- ❑ 98SP AutC-GS
- ❑ 98SP AutTrade-14
- ❑ 98SPAutGJ5x7-2
- ❑ 98SpoIll-112
- ❑ 98SpoIllEE-112
- ❑ 98SpoIllFE-112
- ❑ 98SpoIllTaN-131
- ❑ 98SpoIllTaNEE-131
- ❑ 98SpoIllWSF-112
- ❑ 98SpoIllWSFEE-112
- ❑ 98SpoIllWSFFE-112
- ❑ 98SPxFin-289
- ❑ 98SPxFin-350
- ❑ 98SPxFinR-289
- ❑ 98SPxFinR-350
- ❑ 98SPxFinS-289
- ❑ 98SPxFinS-350
- ❑ 98StaCluFDI-262
- ❑ 98StaCluI-262
- ❑ 98StaCluOneK-262
- ❑ 98StaCluPP-262
- ❑ 98Stu-97
- ❑ 98StuFF-24
- ❑ 98StuFFDC-24
- ❑ 98StuGPP-97
- ❑ 98StuSony99-9
- ❑ 98StuSPP-97
- ❑ 98Top-166
- ❑ 98Top-279
- ❑ 98Top-483
- ❑ 98TopChr-166
- ❑ 98TopChr-279
- ❑ 98TopChr-483
- ❑ 98TopChrF-FB8
- ❑ 98TopChrFR-FB8
- ❑ 98TopChrR-166
- ❑ 98TopChrR-279
- ❑ 98TopChrR-483
- ❑ 98TopDevR-166
- ❑ 98TopDevR-279
- ❑ 98TopDevR-483
- ❑ 98TopDia-166
- ❑ 98TopDia-279
- ❑ 98TopDia-483
- ❑ 98TopFla-FB8
- ❑ 98TopGal-130
- ❑ 98TopGalGP-130
- ❑ 98TopGalOPP-130
- ❑ 98TopGalPPI-130
- ❑ 98TopGalPPIA-130
- ❑ 98TopGolLabC1-90
- ❑ 98TopGolLabC1B-90
- ❑ 98TopGolLabC1One-90
- ❑ 98TopGolLabC1R-90
- ❑ 98TopGolLabC2-90
- ❑ 98TopGolLabC2B-90
- ❑ 98TopGolLabC2One-90
- ❑ 98TopGolLabC2R-90
- ❑ 98TopGolLabC3-90
- ❑ 98TopGolLabC3B-90
- ❑ 98TopGolLabC3One-90
- ❑ 98TopGolLabC3R-90
- ❑ 98TopMiniC-166
- ❑ 98TopMiniC-279
- ❑ 98TopMiniC-483
- ❑ 98TopOpeD-87
- ❑ 98TopSta-5
- ❑ 98TopSta'S-38
- ❑ 98TopSta'SGH-38
- ❑ 98TopStaB-5
- ❑ 98TopStaG-5
- ❑ 98TopStaGR-5
- ❑ 98TopStaS-5
- ❑ 98TopStaSteG-38
- ❑ 98TopSup-14
- ❑ 98TopSup-14
- ❑ 98TopTek-29
- ❑ 98TopTekD-29
- ❑ 98UD3-32
- ❑ 98UD3-122
- ❑ 98UD3-212
- ❑ 98UD3DieCut-32
- ❑ 98UD3DieCut-122
- ❑ 98UD3DieCut-212
- ❑ 98Ult-43
- ❑ 98Ult-253
- ❑ 98UltGolM-43
- ❑ 98UltGolM-253
- ❑ 98UltMas-43
- ❑ 98UltMas-253
- ❑ 98UltPlaM-43
- ❑ 98UltPlaM-253
- ❑ 98UppDec-95
- ❑ 98UppDec-369
- ❑ 98UppDec-428
- ❑ 98UppDec-688
- ❑ 98UppDec10AP-53
- ❑ 98UppDec1APR-53
- ❑ 98UppDec5x7-95
- ❑ 98UppDecAG-AG28
- ❑ 98UppDecAGDC-AG28
- ❑ 98UppDecAPA1-9
- ❑ 98UppDecAPA1-10
- ❑ 98UppDecAPA2-GS
- ❑ 98UppDecCD-CD11
- ❑ 98UppDecR-48
- ❑ 98UppDecR-18
- ❑ 98UppDecRBBop-BB27
- ❑ 98UppDecRTC-TC42
- ❑ 98UppDecSF-59
- ❑ 98Zen-58
- ❑ 98Zen5 xx7-38
- ❑ 98Zen5x7GoldImp-38
- ❑ 98Zen5x7Imp-38
- ❑ 98ZenZ-G-58
- ❑ 98ZenZ-S-58
- ❑ 99199Fin-99
- ❑ 99Bow-11
- ❑ 99BowBes-19
- ❑ 99BowBesAR-19
- ❑ 99BowBesR-19
- ❑ 99BowChr-11
- ❑ 99BowChrG-11
- ❑ 99BowChrGR-11
- ❑ 99BowChrI-11
- ❑ 99BowChrIR-11
- ❑ 99BowChrR-11
- ❑ 99BowGol-11
- ❑ 99BowInt-11
- ❑ 99CroRoyB-75
- ❑ 99CroRoyL-75
- ❑ 99CroRoyOD-75
- ❑ 99DodPol-24
- ❑ 99E-X Cen-36
- ❑ 99E-X CenECFut-36
- ❑ 99E-X CenECNow-36
- ❑ 99FinGolRef-99
- ❑ 99FinRef-99
- ❑ 99FlaShoLeg1-69
- ❑ 99FlaShoLeg2-69
- ❑ 99FlaShoLeg3-69
- ❑ 99FlaShoLegM1-69
- ❑ 99FlaShoLegM2-69
- ❑ 99FlaShoLegM3-69
- ❑ 99FlaShoR1-69
- ❑ 99FlaShoR2-69
- ❑ 99FlaShoR3-69
- ❑ 99Fle-40
- ❑ 99FleBri-73
- ❑ 99FleBri2G-73
- ❑ 99FleBriBlu-73
- ❑ 99FleBriGol-73
- ❑ 99FleSta9-40
- ❑ 99FleVin'-40
- ❑ 99FleWarT-40
- ❑ 99MetUni-147
- ❑ 99MetUniGM-147
- ❑ 99MetUniPMG-147
- ❑ 99Pac-228
- ❑ 99PacAur-96
- ❑ 99PacAurOD-96
- ❑ 99PacCroC-145
- ❑ 99PacCroCPB-145
- ❑ 99PacInv-78
- ❑ 99PacInvOD-78
- ❑ 99PacInvPB-78
- ❑ 99PacOme-125
- ❑ 99PacOmeC-125
- ❑ 99PacOmeG-125
- ❑ 99PacOmePB-125
- ❑ 99PacPar-121
- ❑ 99PacParC-121
- ❑ 99PacParG-121
- ❑ 99PacParHoloGold-121
- ❑ 99PacParHS-121
- ❑ 99PacParOD-121
- ❑ 99PacParPB-121
- ❑ 99PacParRed-121
- ❑ 99PacPlaB-228
- ❑ 99PacPri-77
- ❑ 99PacPriHB-77
- ❑ 99PacPriHG-77
- ❑ 99PacPriHM-77
- ❑ 99PacPriHP-77
- ❑ 99PacPriRed-77
- ❑ 99PacPriS-138
- ❑ 99PacPriS206-138
- ❑ 99PacPriS206R-138
- ❑ 99PacRed-228
- ❑ 99Rev-73
- ❑ 99RevPremDate-73
- ❑ 99RevRet-73
- ❑ 99RevShaSS-73
- ❑ 99SkyMolM-92
- ❑ 99SkyMolMX-92
- ❑ 99SkyPre-220
- ❑ 99SkyPreR-220
- ❑ 99SkyThu-251
- ❑ 99SkyThuRant-251
- ❑ 99SkyThuRave-251
- ❑ 99SP Aut-44
- ❑ 99SpoIll-134
- ❑ 99SPx-47
- ❑ 99SPxFinR-47
- ❑ 99SPxFinS-47
- ❑ 99StaClu-215
- ❑ 99StaCluC-SCC6
- ❑ 99StaCluCR-SCC6
- ❑ 99StaCluFDI-215
- ❑ 99StaCluOoaK-215
- ❑ 99StaCluPP-215
- ❑ 99ThuSkySupR-251
- ❑ 99Top-55
- ❑ 99TopBlaLC1-20
- ❑ 99TopBlaLC2-20
- ❑ 99TopBlaLC3-20
- ❑ 99TopChr-55
- ❑ 99TopChrR-55
- ❑ 99TopGal-63
- ❑ 99TopGalPP-63
- ❑ 99TopGalPPI-63
- ❑ 99TopGolL-20
- ❑ 99TopGolLC1-20
- ❑ 99TopGolLC2-20
- ❑ 99TopGolLOtO-20
- ❑ 99TopMVPP-55
- ❑ 99TopOpeD-30
- ❑ 99TopRedLC1-20
- ❑ 99TopRedLC2-20
- ❑ 99TopRedLC3-20
- ❑ 99TopSta-62
- ❑ 99TopSta'S-36
- ❑ 99TopSta'SG-36
- ❑ 99TopSta'SGDH-36
- ❑ 99TopSta1Foil-62
- ❑ 99TopStaFoil-62
- ❑ 99TopStaOS-62
- ❑ 99UD Cho-98
- ❑ 99UD ChoP-98
- ❑ 99UD ChoPCR-98
- ❑ 99UD ChoYW-Y17
- ❑ 99Ult-142
- ❑ 99UltGolM-142
- ❑ 99UltMas-142
- ❑ 99UltPlaM-142
- ❑ 99UppDec-124
- ❑ 99UppDecBD-44
- ❑ 99UppDecBDD-44
- ❑ 99UppDecBDQ-44
- ❑ 99UppDecBDT-44

❑ 99UppDecCL-98
❑ 99UppDecCLCC-98
❑ 99UppDecCLM-C50
❑ 99UppDecE-47
❑ 99UppDecEFXG-47
❑ 99UppDecEL1-124
❑ 99UppDecEL2-124
❑ 99UppDecM-109
❑ 99UppDecMGS-109
❑ 99UppDecMHFS-109
❑ 99UppDecMP-109
❑ 99UppDecMSS-109
❑ 99UppDecO-57
❑ 99UppDecOSO-57
❑ 99Vic-204

Sheffield, Tony
❑ 92ClaDraP-40
❑ 92ClaFS7-428
❑ 92FroRowDP-17
❑ 92FroRowDPG-17
❑ 92FroRowDPS-17
❑ 92HigSchPLS-5
❑ 93StaCluM-85
❑ 93Top-687
❑ 93TopGol-687
❑ 93TopInaM-687
❑ 93TopInaR-687
❑ 93TopMic-687
❑ 94UtiBluSC-25
❑ 94UtiBluSF-3835

Sheffield, Travis
❑ 86DayBealP-25

Sheffler, Jim
❑ 89KinMetS-22

Shehan, Brian
❑ 88CapCodPPaLP-38

Shelby, Anthony
❑ 95GreBatTI-22
❑ 96GreBatB-26
❑ 97TamYan-26
❑ 98ColCliD-22
❑ 98ColCliM-27

Shelby, John
❑ 80ChaO'sP-20
❑ 80ChaO'sW-21
❑ 81BalOriP-19
❑ 82RocRedWT-17
❑ 83TopTra-102T
❑ 84Don-291
❑ 84Fle-20
❑ 84FleSti-114
❑ 84Nes792-86
❑ 84Top-86
❑ 84TopTif-86
❑ 85BalOriP-31
❑ 85Don-472
❑ 85Fle-190
❑ 85OPC-264
❑ 85OriHea-17
❑ 85RocRedWT-13
❑ 85Top-508
❑ 85TopSti-204
❑ 85TopTif-508
❑ 86BalOriHMP-17
❑ 86BalOriP-20
❑ 86Don-643
❑ 86Fle-287
❑ 86FleMin-60
❑ 86Top-309
❑ 86TopTif-309
❑ 87BalOriP-35
❑ 87Don-354
❑ 87DonOpeD-139
❑ 87Fle-480
❑ 87FleGlo-480
❑ 87FleUpd-109
❑ 87FleUpdG-109
❑ 87Top-208
❑ 87TopTif-208
❑ 87TopTra-112T
❑ 87TopTraT-112T
❑ 88DodMot-14
❑ 88DodPol-31
❑ 88Don-352
❑ 88DonBasB-290
❑ 88Fle-526
❑ 88FleGlo-526
❑ 88OPC-307
❑ 88PanSti-316
❑ 88Sco-286
❑ 88ScoGlo-286
❑ 88StaLinD-16
❑ 88Top-428
❑ 88TopBig-218
❑ 88TopTif-428
❑ 89Bow-349
❑ 89BowTif-349
❑ 89DodMot-14
❑ 89DodPol-20
❑ 89DodStaSV-15
❑ 89Don-314
❑ 89Fle-73
❑ 89FleGlo-73
❑ 89OPC-175
❑ 89PanSti-109
❑ 89Sco-103
❑ 89Top-175
❑ 89TopSti-63
❑ 89TopTif-175
❑ 89UppDec-75
❑ 90DodMot-25
❑ 90DodPol-31
❑ 90DodTar-725
❑ 90PubIntS-18
❑ 91Don-563
❑ 91Fle-353
❑ 91OPC-746
❑ 91OriCro-415
❑ 91Sco-609
❑ 91TigCok-25
❑ 91TigPol-11
❑ 91Top-746
❑ 91TopDesS-746
❑ 91TopMic-746
❑ 91TopTif-746
❑ 91UppDec-201
❑ 92PawRedSF-937
❑ 92PawRedSS-365
❑ 93ButCopKSP-22
❑ 94BakDodC-27
❑ 95SanAntMTI-31
❑ 96SanAntMB-30
❑ 97DunDonPPS-21
❑ 98DodMot-28

Sheldon, Bob
❑ 74SacSolC-63
❑ 75OPC-623
❑ 75SacSolC-8
❑ 75Top-623
❑ 75TopMin-623
❑ 76OPC-626
❑ 76SpoIndC-1
❑ 76SSP-256
❑ 76Top-626
❑ 77SpoIndC-12
❑ 94BreMilB-269

Sheldon, Dave
❑ 86AppFoxP-22

Sheldon, Kyle
❑ 98VerExpO-16

Sheldon, Roland
❑ 61Top-541
❑ 61Yan61RL-23
❑ 62Top-185
❑ 62TopVen-185
❑ 63Top-507
❑ 65OPC-254
❑ 65Top-254
❑ 66OPC-18
❑ 66Top-18
❑ 66TopVen-18
❑ 69Top-413
❑ 83Yan196-23
❑ 91YanRinP13-7
❑ 92YanWIZ6-113

Sheldon, Scott
❑ 91SouOreAC-13
❑ 91SouOreAP-3857
❑ 92ClaFS7-179
❑ 92MadMusC-15
❑ 92MadMusF-1246
❑ 92MidLeaATI-39
❑ 93MadMusC-23
❑ 93MadMusF-1831
❑ 93MidLeaAGF-15
❑ 94HunStaF-1337
❑ 95EdmTraTI-22
❑ 98OklRedM-14
❑ 99SpoIll-63

Sheldon, Shane
❑ 95HelBreTI-24

Sheldon-Collins, Mathew
❑ 91WavRedF-9
❑ 93AusFut-91

Sheldon-Collins, Simon
❑ 93AusFut-90
❑ 93AusFut-107
❑ 95AusFut-75

Shell, Scott
❑ 91EliTwiP-4308

Shellenback, Frank
❑ 20Zee-149
❑ 23Zee-197
❑ 24Zee-140
❑ 25Zee-79
❑ 26Zee-18
❑ 28ExhPCL-26
❑ 28Zee-19
❑ 31Zee-7
❑ 32Zee-15
❑ 33Zee-3
❑ 75Gia195T-33
❑ 75WhiSox1T-24

Shellenback, Jim
❑ 67Top-592
❑ 68PirTeal-18
❑ 69Top-567
❑ 70OPC-389
❑ 70Top-389
❑ 71MLBOffS-549
❑ 71OPC-351
❑ 71SenTealW-22
❑ 71Top-351
❑ 74OPC-657
❑ 74SpoIndC-31
❑ 74Top-657
❑ 75HawIslC-14
❑ 76HawIslC-2
❑ 84TolMudHT-21
❑ 85TolMudHT-27
❑ 87OrlTwiP-7
❑ 88PorBeaC-25
❑ 88PorBeaP-644
❑ 89PorBeaC-25
❑ 89PorBeaP-226
❑ 90CMC-573
❑ 90PorBeaC-21
❑ 90PorBeaP-194
❑ 90ProAAAF-264
❑ 91LinDriAA-496
❑ 91OrlSunRLD-496
❑ 91OrlSunRP-1867
❑ 92OrlSunRF-2864
❑ 93ForMyeMC-27
❑ 93ForMyeMF-2673
❑ 93RanKee-37

Shelley, Hugh
❑ 74TigTCM1AC-28

Shelley, Jason
❑ 93DanBraC-23
❑ 93DanBraF-3635

Shelly, Mascot
❑ 98ArkTraM-30

Shelton, Andrew
❑ 12ColRedB-261
❑ 12ColTinT-261

Shelton, Barry
❑ 96HicCraB-22

Shelton, Ben
❑ 88AugPirP-370
❑ 89AugPirP-511
❑ 90SalBucS-21
❑ 91ParPatF-3
❑ 91SalBucC-8
❑ 91SalBucP-962
❑ 92Bow-568
❑ 92CarMudF-1190
❑ 92CarMudS-142
❑ 92ClaFS7-45
❑ 92SkyAA F-67
❑ 92UppDecML-282
❑ 93BufBisF-528
❑ 93FleFinE-118

Shelton, Derek
❑ 92OneYanC-10
❑ 98GreBatM-28

Shelton, Harry
❑ 86GenCubP-24
❑ 87PeoChiP-19
❑ 88ChaWheB-21
❑ 89PeoChiTI-26
❑ 90MiaMirIS-24
❑ 90MiaMirIS-23

Shelton, Mike
❑ 86ReaPhiP-24
❑ 87ReaPhiP-9
❑ 88MaiPhiC-7
❑ 88MaiPhiP-282
❑ 88TriAAAP-25

Shelton, Ron
❑ 90LitSunW-17

Shenk, Larry
❑ 64TopRooAB-18
❑ 93AlbPolCB-26
❑ 93AlbPolF-2026
❑ 94FreKeyC-20
❑ 94FreKeyF-2613
❑ 94OriPro-93

Shepard, Bert Robert
❑ 77TCMTheWY-43

Shepard, David
❑ 96BilMusTI-28
❑ 98ChaAllCM-11

Shepard, Greg
❑ 96SouBenSHS-23
❑ 97HicCraB-26
❑ 97HicCraRB-30
❑ 98WinWar-27

Shepard, Jack
❑ 55Top-73
❑ 55TopDouH-23
❑ 56PirTeal-20
❑ 79TCM50-112

Shepard, Kelvin
❑ 87JamExpP-2549
❑ 89RocExpLC-24

Shepard, Ken
❑ 88GenCubP-1656

Shepard, Larry
❑ 68PirKDK-7
❑ 68PirTeal-19
❑ 68Top-584
❑ 69PirGre-7
❑ 69PirTeal-21
❑ 69Top-384
❑ 73OPC-296
❑ 73Top-296
❑ 74OPC-326
❑ 74Top-326
❑ 79GiaPol-8

Shepard, Laurie
❑ 96ColSilB-25

Sheperd, Alvie
❑ 97BesAutAS-53

Shepherd, Alvie
❑ 96BesAutSA-69
❑ 96Bow-325
❑ 96BowFoi-325
❑ 96FreKeyB-1
❑ 96Top-234
❑ 97BesAutP-R15
❑ 97BesAutSBPP-17
❑ 97BowBay-27
❑ 98BowBayM-27

Shepherd, Brian
❑ 94EveGiaF-3655

Shepherd, Keith
❑ 87WatPirP-15
❑ 88AugPirP-375
❑ 89BasCitRS-23
❑ 90RenSilSCLC-276
❑ 90WatIndS-19
❑ 91SouBenWSC-20
❑ 91SouBenWSP-2856
❑ 92BirBarF-2582
❑ 92BirBarS-95
❑ 93Don-332
❑ 93Fle-109
❑ 93FleFinE-44
❑ 93Top-447
❑ 93TopGol-447
❑ 93TopInaM-447
❑ 93TopInaR-447
❑ 93TopMic-447
❑ 94ColSprSSF-733
❑ 94Pac-207
❑ 96RocRedWB-24
❑ 97NorTid-30
❑ 97NorTidB-29

Shepherd, Mike
❑ 90PulBraB-10
❑ 90PulBraP-3105

Shepherd, Ron
❑ 82KnoBluJT-20
❑ 83SyrChiT-24
❑ 84SyrChiT-5
❑ 85FleUpd-102
❑ 86SyrChiP-23
❑ 87IndIndTI-12
❑ 87OPC-117
❑ 87Top-643
❑ 87TopTif-643
❑ 88IndIndC-16
❑ 88IndIndP-524
❑ 89LouRedBC-22
❑ 89LouRedBP-1261
❑ 89LouRedBTI-34

Sheppard, Brandon
❑ 97St.LucM-24

Sheppard, Don
❑ 89HigSchPLS-22
❑ 91SouBenWSC-11
❑ 91SouBenWSP-2871
❑ 92SalSpuC-13
❑ 92SalSpuF-3772
❑ 93DunBluJC-19
❑ 93DunBluJFFN-21
❑ 94KnoSmoF-1317

Sheppard, Phillip
❑ 84VisOakT-8

Shepperd, Richard
❑ 90BoiHawP-3329
❑ 91SalSpuC-13
❑ 91SalSpuP-2259

Shepston, Mike
❑ 79QuaCitCT-24

Sherdel, Bill
❑ 21Nei-100
❑ 22E120-237
❑ 22W572-97
❑ 25Exh-63
❑ 26Exh-63
❑ 27AmeCarE126-12
❑ 27MidBre-17
❑ 28W56PlaC-C8A
❑ 31W517-6
❑ 91ConTSN-194
❑ 92ConTSN-619

Sheridan, Bobby
❑ 87SpoIndP-13
❑ 89RivRedWCLC-19
❑ 89RivRedWP-1418
❑ 89SpoIndSP-22

Sheridan, Jack
❑ 88SFHesCreN32-29

Sheridan, John
❑ 94ConTSN-1198
❑ 94ConTSNB-1198

Sheridan, Neil
❑ 52Par-16

Sheridan, Pat
❑ 81OmaRoyT-24
❑ 82OmaRoyT-22
❑ 83OmaRoyT-21
❑ 84Don-588
❑ 84Fle-357
❑ 84Nes792-121
❑ 84RoyPos-31
❑ 84Top-121
❑ 84TopSti-286
❑ 84TopTif-121
❑ 85Don-339
❑ 85Fle-213
❑ 85RoyTeal-29
❑ 85Top-359
❑ 85TopSti-272
❑ 85TopTif-359
❑ 86Don-155
❑ 86Fle-20
❑ 86OPC-240
❑ 86RoyKitCD-11
❑ 86Top-743
❑ 86TopTif-743
❑ 87Fle-162
❑ 87FleGlo-162
❑ 87TigCaiD-18
❑ 87TigCok-6
❑ 87Top-234
❑ 87TopTif-234
❑ 88Don-522
❑ 88Fle-69
❑ 88FleGlo-69
❑ 88PanSti-97
❑ 88Sco-171
❑ 88ScoGlo-171
❑ 88StaLinTi-17
❑ 88TigPep-15
❑ 88Top-514
❑ 88TopClo-102
❑ 88TopTif-514
❑ 89Bow-107
❑ 89BowTif-107
❑ 89Don-417
❑ 89Fle-146
❑ 89FleGlo-146
❑ 89Sco-204
❑ 89ScoRoo-71T
❑ 89TigMar-15
❑ 89TigPol-15
❑ 89Top-288
❑ 89TopBig-150
❑ 89TopTif-288
❑ 89UppDec-652A
❑ 89UppDec-652B
❑ 90Don-367
❑ 90Fle-71
❑ 90FleCan-71
❑ 90OPC-422
❑ 90PubIntS-482
❑ 90Sco-509
❑ 90Top-422
❑ 90TopTif-422
❑ 90UppDec-460
❑ 91ColCliP-610

Sheridan, Shane
❑ 89AncGlaP-23

Sheriff, Dave
❑ 81LynSaiT-9
❑ 82IdaFalAT-33
❑ 83IdaFalAT-34
❑ 84IdaFalATI-25

Sherling, Ed
❑ 25Zee-55

Sherlock, Glenn
❑ 85OscAstTI-15
❑ 86OscAstP-23
❑ 87ColCliP-22
❑ 87ColCliP-3
❑ 87ColCliT-25
❑ 88ColCliP-304
❑ 89AlbYanB-7
❑ 89AlbYanP-339
❑ 90AlbYanP-1183
❑ 90AlbYanSt-26
❑ 90TamYanD-28
❑ 91Ft.LauYC-3
❑ 91Ft.LauYP-2443

Sherlock, Jack
❑ 26Zee-172
❑ 27Zee-144
❑ 28Zee-164
❑ 29Zee-58
❑ 32Zee-16
❑ 33Zee-4

Sherlock, Vince
❑ 32Zee-45
❑ 33Zee-18
❑ 90DodTar-726

Sherman, Darrell
❑ 89SpoIndSP-26
❑ 90Bes-286
❑ 90CalLeaACLC-10
❑ 90CMC-719
❑ 90ProAaA-147
❑ 90RivRedWB-17
❑ 90RivRedWCLC-3
❑ 90RivRedWP-2620
❑ 91Cla/Bes-153
❑ 91LinDriAA-619
❑ 91WicWraLD-619
❑ 91WicWraP-2613
❑ 91WicWraRD-23
❑ 92ClaFS7-347
❑ 92SkyAA F-287
❑ 92UppDecML-61
❑ 92UppDecML-249
❑ 92WicWraS-645
❑ 93Bow-602
❑ 93LeaGolR-R20
❑ 93LeaGolRJ-R20
❑ 93OPCPre-118
❑ 93PacSpa-602
❑ 93PadMot-15
❑ 93Pin-619
❑ 93StaClu-739
❑ 93StaCluFDI-739
❑ 93StaCluMOP-739
❑ 93Top-576
❑ 93TopGol-576
❑ 93TopInaM-576
❑ 93TopInaR-576
❑ 93TopMic-576
❑ 93Ult-478
❑ 93UppDec-784
❑ 93UppDecGold-784
❑ 94ColSprSSF-746
❑ 94RocPol-24
❑ 94Sco-595
❑ 94ScoBoyoS-54
❑ 94ScoGolR-595
❑ 94StaCluT-94
❑ 94StaCluTFDI-94
❑ 95TacRaiTI-21

Sherman, Jack
❑ 47SigOil-14

Sherman, Jim
❑ 83ColAstT-5
❑ 86TucTorP-21

Sherman, Steve
❑ 76CedRapGT-28
❑ 77CedRapGT-17

Sherman, Tyril
❑ 92GulCoaMF-3480

Shermet, Dave

❑ 86AriWilP-14
❑ 87AriWilP-12
❑ 88AriWilP-11
❑ 88AubAstP-1958
❑ 89AshTouP-948
Shermeyer, Keith
❑ 77WauMetT-18
❑ 78WauMetT-25
Sherow, Dennis
❑ 79MemChiT-19
❑ 80MemChiT-18
❑ 81WesHavAT-19
❑ 82TacTigT-18
❑ 82WesHavAT-25
❑ 83TacTigT-27
Sherrill, Dennis
❑ 79ColCliT-19
❑ 80ColCliP-12
❑ 80ColCliT-23
❑ 92YanWIZ8-176
Sherrill, Tim
❑ 88SavCarP-334
❑ 89St.PetCS-24
❑ 90CMC-122
❑ 90LouRedBC-22
❑ 90LouRedBLBC-37
❑ 90LouRedBP-403
❑ 90ProAAAF-517
❑ 90TopTVCa-63
❑ 91LinDriAAA-247
❑ 91LouRedLD-247
❑ 91LouRedTI-6
❑ 91OPC-769
❑ 91Top-769
❑ 91TopDeb90-142
❑ 91TopDesS-769
❑ 91TopMic-769
❑ 91TopTif-769
❑ 92LouRedF-1887
❑ 92LouRedS-269
❑ 92Sco-404
❑ 92Sco100RS-90
❑ 92StaClu-822
❑ 92StaCluECN-822
Sherry, Larry
❑ 59WilSpoG-7
❑ 60Baz-17
❑ 60DodJayP-13
❑ 60DodMor-11
❑ 60DodPos-11
❑ 60DodTeal-17
❑ 60DodUniO-17
❑ 60Top-105
❑ 60TopVen-105
❑ 61DodBelB-51
❑ 61DodJayP-10
❑ 61DodUniO-18
❑ 61NuSco-431
❑ 61Pos-161A
❑ 61Pos-161B
❑ 61Top-412
❑ 61Top-521
❑ 61TopStal-34
❑ 62DodBelB-51
❑ 62DodVol-5
❑ 62Jel-111
❑ 62Pos-111
❑ 62PosCan-111
❑ 62Top-435
❑ 63Top-565
❑ 64Top-474
❑ 65Top-408
❑ 66Top-289
❑ 66TopVen-289
❑ 67CokCapTi-1
❑ 67Top-571
❑ 68LauWorS-56
❑ 68SeaPop-13
❑ 68Top-468
❑ 77PirPosP-24
❑ 87AstShowSTh-21
❑ 90DodTar-727
❑ 90HOFStiB-59
Sherry, Norm
❑ 59DarFar-21
❑ 60DodUniO-18
❑ 60Top-529
❑ 61DodBelB-34
❑ 61DodUniO-19
❑ 61Top-521
❑ 62DodBelB-34
❑ 62DodVol-8
❑ 62Top-238
❑ 63Top-316
❑ 74SalLakCAC-97
❑ 75IntLeaASB-31
❑ 75PacCoaLAB-31
❑ 75SalLakCC-20
❑ 76Met63 S-13
❑ 77Top-34
❑ 78ExpPos-12
❑ 79ExpPos-25
❑ 80ExpPos-28
❑ 83PadTeal-23
❑ 84PadMot-27
❑ 84PadSmo-21
❑ 85SpoIndC-21
❑ 86GiaMot-28
❑ 86GiaPos-27
❑ 87GiaMot-27
❑ 87GiaPos-28
❑ 88GiaMot-27
❑ 88GiaPos-28
❑ 89GiaMot-28
❑ 90DodTar-728
❑ 90GiaMot-21
❑ 90GiaSmo-18
❑ 91GiaMot-27
❑ 91MetWIZ-361
❑ 92EveGiaC-30
❑ 92EveGiaF-1706
Shetrone, Barry
❑ 60Top-348
❑ 63Top-276
❑ 64SeaPop-15
❑ 91OriCro-416
Shevlin, Jim
❑ 90SalSpuCLC-138
❑ 90SalSpuP-2727
Shibata, Kazuya
❑ 96HonShaHWB-25
Shibata, Keith
❑ 87EugEmeP-2659
❑ 88AppFoxP-153
❑ 88EugEmeB-29
Shibata, Osao
❑ 79TCMJapPB-60
Shibilo, Andy
❑ 98NewJerCM-28
Shidawara, Cliff
❑ 86PhoFirP-23
❑ 87PhoFirP-19
❑ 88PhoFirP-66
Shields, Doug
❑ 88CapCodPPaLP-40
❑ 90EugEmeGS-27
❑ 91BasCitRC-27
❑ 91BasCitRP-1413
❑ 92MemChiF-2434
Shields, Mike
❑ 79SavBraT-9
Shields, Scot
❑ 97BoiHawG-25
❑ 98CedRapKTI-27
Shields, Steve
❑ 81BriRedST-17
❑ 83PawRedST-11
❑ 84RicBraT-17
❑ 85RicBraT-9
❑ 86Fle-527
❑ 86RicBraP-20
❑ 87TopTra-113T
❑ 87TopTraT-113T
❑ 88ColCliC-6
❑ 88ColCliP-10
❑ 88ColCliP-314
❑ 88DonReaBY-NEW
❑ 88Sco-396
❑ 88ScoGlo-396
❑ 88ScoRoo-47T
❑ 88ScoRooG-47T
❑ 88Top-632
❑ 88TopTif-632
❑ 89Fle-269
❑ 89FleGlo-269
❑ 89PorBeaC-4
❑ 89PorBeaP-218
❑ 89Sco-578
❑ 89Top-484
❑ 89TopTif-484
❑ 90PubIntS-338
❑ 92YanWIZ8-177
Shields, Tom
❑ 86WatPirP-23
❑ 88HarSenP-836
❑ 88TopClo-103
❑ 89EasLeaDDP-DD26
❑ 89HarSenP-298
❑ 89HarSenS-18
❑ 89Sta-20
❑ 90BufBisC-21
❑ 90BufBisP-384
❑ 90BufBisTI-25
❑ 90CMC-21
❑ 90ProAAAF-499
❑ 91LinDriAAA-467
❑ 91RocRedWLD-467
❑ 91RocRedWP-1911
❑ 92RocRedWF-1948
❑ 92RocRedWS-469
❑ 93Bow-228
❑ 93PacSpa-382
❑ 93Ult-321
❑ 94IowCubF-1283
❑ 94Pac-110
❑ 94StaCluT-336
❑ 94StaCluTFDI-336
❑ 97DelSho-5
❑ 98FreKeyM-3
Shiell, Jason
❑ 96DanBraB-21
❑ 97MacBra-15
❑ 98DanQ-C-21
Shiera, Norman
❑ 76VenLeaS-190
❑ 76VenLeaS-210
❑ 80VenLeaS-223
Shifflett, Steve
❑ 90AppFoxBS-24
❑ 90AppFoxP-2094
❑ 91LinDriAA-417
❑ 91MemChiLD-417
❑ 91MemChiP-653
❑ 92DonRoo-110
❑ 92OmaRoyF-2961
❑ 92OmaRoyS-346
❑ 92SkyAAAF-158
❑ 93Don-73
❑ 93Fle-625
❑ 93OmaRoyF-1680
❑ 93Sco-266
❑ 93StaClu-84
❑ 93StaCluFDI-84
❑ 93StaCluMOP-84
❑ 93Top-735
❑ 93TopGol-735
❑ 93TopInaM-735
❑ 93TopInaR-735
❑ 93TopMic-735
❑ 93Ult-216
❑ 94OmaRoyF-1223
Shifflett, Chris
❑ 88GasRanP-1001
❑ 89ButCopKSP-14
❑ 90TulDriP-1155
❑ 91LinDriAA-598
❑ 91TulDriLD-598
❑ 91TulDriP-2774
Shifflett, Mark
❑ 83NasSouTI-20
❑ 84NasSouTI-20
❑ 87MemChiB-13
❑ 87MemChiP-6
❑ 90AlbYanSt-27
❑ 90OneYanP-3391
❑ 91GreHorP-3077
❑ 91SouAtlLAGP-SAL30
❑ 92ForLauYC-24
❑ 92ForLauYTI-29
❑ 92Ft.LauYF-3010
❑ 93PriWilCC-29
❑ 93PriWilCF-675
❑ 97TamYan-3
❑ 98TamYanM-2
Shifflett, Matt
❑ 87JamExpP-2562
❑ 89RocExpLC-25
❑ 91DurBulC-1
❑ 91DurBulP-1543
Shikles, Larry
❑ 86GreHorP-22
❑ 87WinHavRSP-4
❑ 88NewBriRSP-899
❑ 89NewBriRSP-613
❑ 89NewBriRSS-18
❑ 90CMC-255
❑ 90PawRedSC-4
❑ 90PawRedSDD-22
❑ 90PawRedSP-461
❑ 90ProAAAF-433
❑ 90TopTVRS-59
❑ 91LinDriAAA-368
❑ 91PawRedSDD-21
❑ 91PawRedSLD-368
❑ 91PawRedSP-39
❑ 92PawRedSF-922
❑ 92PawRedSS-366
❑ 92SkyAAAF-166
❑ 93TacTigF-3031
❑ 97DunDonPPS-22
Shillinglaw, Dave
❑ 86MadMusP-26
❑ 86MadMusP-22
Shimp, Tommy Joe
❑ 80MemChiT-19
❑ 83MemChiT-10
❑ 84TulDriTI-37
❑ 85OklCit8T-13
❑ 86OklCit8P-20
Shinall, Zakary
❑ 88BakDodCLC-259
❑ 89VerBeaDS-25
❑ 90SanAntMGS-26
❑ 91Bow-612
❑ 91Cla/Bes-384
❑ 91DodPho-26
❑ 91DodSt.V-18
❑ 91LinDriAA-540
❑ 91SanAntMLD-540
❑ 91SanAntMP-2972
❑ 92AlbDukF-721
❑ 92AlbDukS-20
❑ 93ChaKniF-541
Shindle, William
❑ 87OldJudN-448
❑ 90DodTar-729
❑ 95May-38
❑ 98CamPepP-68
Shines, Razor
❑ 83MemChiT-21
❑ 84IndIndTI-17
❑ 84IndIndTI-26
❑ 85Don-401
❑ 85ExpPos-21
❑ 85Lea-164
❑ 86OPC-132
❑ 86Top-132
❑ 86TopTif-132
❑ 87IndIndTI-8
❑ 88IndIndC-12
❑ 88IndIndP-514
❑ 89IndIndC-12
❑ 89IndIndP-1219
❑ 91IndIndLD-194
❑ 91IndIndP-471
❑ 91LinDriAAA-194
❑ 91PacSenL-128
❑ 92IndIndF-1870
❑ 92IndIndS-194
❑ 93IndIndF-1505
Shingledecker, Gary
❑ 89EriOriS-24
❑ 90WauTimB-19
❑ 90WauTimP-2132
Shinholster, Vince
❑ 87SanBerSP-12
Shinjyo, Tsuyoshi
❑ 96HilStaHWB-1
Shinn, James
❑ 09ObaT21-45
❑ 09ObaT21-149
❑ 09ObaT21-316
❑ 11BigEatEU-16
❑ 11Zee-77
❑ 12HomRunKE-56
❑ 12ObaPreT-65
❑ 12Zee-94
❑ 13Zee-89
❑ 14Zee-92
❑ 15Zee-89
❑ 16Zee-93
❑ 17Zee-78
Shinners, Ralph
❑ 22E120-191
❑ 22W573-122
❑ 23WilChoV-149
❑ 27Zee-62A
❑ 27Zee-62B
Shiotani, Kazu
❑ 94BriTigC-23
Shiozaki, Kenny
❑ 88ButCopKSP-11
Shipanoff, Dave
❑ 83KnoBluJT-7
❑ 84SyrChiT-25
❑ 85PorBeaC-28
❑ 86Don-34
❑ 86Fle-452
❑ 86Lea-29
❑ 86PhiTas-33
❑ 86PorBeaP-20
❑ 87EdmTraP-2065
Shipke, William
❑ 08RosComP-85
❑ 09RamT20-108
❑ 09T206-324
Shipley, Craig
❑ 85AlbDukCr-155
❑ 86AlbDukP-23
❑ 87AlbDukD-22
❑ 88JacMetGS-12
❑ 89MetColP-52
❑ 89TidTidC-22
❑ 89TidTidP-1961
❑ 90DodTar-730
❑ 90TopTVM-60
❑ 91LasVegSP-245
❑ 91MetWIZ-362
❑ 92Don-667
❑ 92Fle-621
❑ 92OPC-308
❑ 92OPCPre-33
❑ 92PadCarJ-20
❑ 92PadMot-25
❑ 92PadPolD-21
❑ 92PadSmo-31
❑ 92Sco-856
❑ 92StaClu-374
❑ 92Top-308
❑ 92TopGol-308
❑ 92TopGolW-308
❑ 92TopMic-308
❑ 92Ult-583
❑ 93Don-206
❑ 93Lea-395
❑ 93PacSpa-603
❑ 93PadMot-20
❑ 93PanSti-260
❑ 93StaClu-258
❑ 93StaCluFDI-258
❑ 93StaCluMOP-258
❑ 93Stu-130
❑ 93Top-601
❑ 93TopGol-601
❑ 93TopInaM-601
❑ 93TopInaR-601
❑ 93TopMic-601
❑ 93Ult-123
❑ 93UppDec-788
❑ 93UppDecGold-788
❑ 94Don-516
❑ 94Fle-674
❑ 94Pac-534
❑ 94PadMot-14
❑ 94PanSti-259
❑ 94StaClu-460
❑ 94StaCluFDI-460
❑ 94StaCluGR-460
❑ 94StaCluMOP-460
❑ 94Top-184
❑ 94TopGol-184
❑ 94TopSpa-184
❑ 95AstMot-20
❑ 95Don-534
❑ 95DonPreP-534
❑ 95Fle-569
❑ 95FleUpd-144
❑ 95Pin-187
❑ 95PinArtP-187
❑ 95PinMusC-187
❑ 95Top-328
❑ 96ColCho-358
❑ 96ColChoGS-358
❑ 96ColChoSS-358
❑ 96FleUpd-U199
❑ 96FleUpdTC-U199
❑ 96LeaSigEA-182
❑ 96PadMot-15
❑ 96Sco-211
❑ 97Pac-432
❑ 97PacLigB-432
❑ 97PacSil-432
❑ 97PadMot-15
❑ 98PacInvGems-211
❑ 98PacOnl-23
❑ 98PacOnlR-23
❑ 98PacOnlWC-23
Shipley, Joe
❑ 59Top-141
❑ 59TopVen-141
❑ 60Top-239
Shipley, Mark
❑ 91SydWavF-1
❑ 93AusFut-80
❑ 93AusFut-100
❑ 93AusFut-107
❑ 95AusFut-79
Shipman, Mike
❑ 92MarPhiC-19
❑ 92MarPhiF-3061
❑ 93MarPhiC-26
❑ 93MarPhiF-3479
❑ 94BatCliC-21
❑ 94BatCliF-3451
Shipp, Kevin
❑ 97BatCliTI-5
❑ 98PieBolWM-24
Shipp, Skip
❑ 96EriSeaB-22
❑ 97AugGre-19
Shippy, Greg
❑ 75CliPilT-20
Shirahata, Hiro
❑ 83SanJosBC-10
Shireman, Jeff
❑ 89SprCarB-12
❑ 90St.PetCS-23
❑ 91ArkTraLD-45
❑ 91ArkTraP-1297
❑ 91LinDriAA-45
❑ 92LouRedF-1895
❑ 92LouRedS-270
❑ 93ArkTraF-2821
❑ 93LouRedF-225
❑ 94ArkTraF-3097
❑ 94ClaGolF-14
❑ 95ArkTraTI-24
❑ 96ArkTraB-2
❑ 97NewJerCB-1
❑ 98PeoChiM-27
Shires, Art (Charles A.)
❑ 28PorandAR-C5
❑ 29PorandAR-83
❑ 30ChiEveAP-20
❑ 31W517-43
❑ 92ConTSN-608
Shirley, Al
❑ 91ClaDraP-14
❑ 91FroRowDP-43
❑ 91FroRowDPG-43
❑ 91FroRowDPS-43
❑ 91HigSchPLS-2
❑ 92KinMetC-9
❑ 92KinMetF-1544
❑ 92OPC-306
❑ 92Pin-297
❑ 92Sco-802
❑ 92StaCluD-170
❑ 92Top-306
❑ 92TopGol-306
❑ 92TopGolW-306
❑ 92TopMic-306
❑ 93Bow-566
❑ 93CapCitBC-1
❑ 93CapCitBF-472
❑ 93ClaFS7-117
❑ 93ExcFS7-79
❑ 94CapCitBC-19
❑ 94CapCitBF-1764
❑ 94MetShuST-7
❑ 95AusFut-14
❑ 95StLucMTI-30
❑ 96WilBluRB-17
❑ 98WicWraM-15
Shirley, Bart
❑ 66Top-591
❑ 67Top-287
❑ 69Top-289
❑ 90DodTar-731
❑ 91MetWIZ-363
❑ 92TexLon-37
Shirley, Bob
❑ 77PadSchC-49
❑ 78PadFamF-28
❑ 78Top-266
❑ 79PadFamF-36
❑ 79Top-594
❑ 80OPC-248
❑ 80Top-476
❑ 81Car5x7-25
❑ 81Don-242
❑ 81Fle-495
❑ 81OPC-49
❑ 81Top-49
❑ 81TopTra-829
❑ 82Don-120
❑ 82Fle-127
❑ 82OPC-33
❑ 82Top-749
❑ 82TopTra-105T
❑ 83Fle-602
❑ 83Top-112
❑ 83TopTra-103T
❑ 83YanPhoA-24
❑ 84Don-214

❑ 84Fle-141
❑ 84Nes792-684
❑ 84Top-684
❑ 84TopTif-684
❑ 85Don-370
❑ 85Fle-145
❑ 85Top-328
❑ 85TopTif-328
❑ 85YanTCMP-19
❑ 86Don-458
❑ 86Fle-119
❑ 86Top-213
❑ 86TopTif-213
❑ 86YanTCM-15
❑ 87Don-463
❑ 87Fle-114
❑ 87FleGlo-114
❑ 87Top-524
❑ 87TopTif-524
❑ 88SyrChiC-7
❑ 88SyrChiP-827
❑ 89PacSenL-207
❑ 89St.CatBJP-2095
❑ 89T/MSenL-95
❑ 89TopSenL-6
❑ 90CMC-333
❑ 90ProAAAF-369
❑ 90SyrChiC-7
❑ 90SyrChiMB-22
❑ 90SyrChiP-589
❑ 92YanWIZ8-179

Shirley, Mike
❑ 91BurIndP-3318
❑ 92Ft.MyeMCB-7
❑ 92Ft.MyeMF-2758

Shirley, Mule (Ernest)
❑ 75SenTCM1-32

Shirley, Steve
❑ 77LodDodT-19
❑ 78LodDodT-19
❑ 81AlbDukTc-3
❑ 85HawIslC-235
❑ 85NasSouTI-21
❑ 86AlbDukP-24
❑ 87OmaRoyP-14
❑ 88IndIndC-4
❑ 88IndIndP-505
❑ 90DodTar-732

Shirley, Tex (Alvis)
❑ 42A'sTeal-27
❑ 46SeaSLP-57
❑ 96Bro194F-24

Shirley, Tom
❑ 82AlbDukTc-8

Shive, Chuck
❑ 89MarPhiS-28

Shivers, Ivy
❑ 33WorCig(-82

Shoals, Leo
❑ 94CarLeaA-DJ18

Shoch, George
❑ 87OldJudN-449
❑ 88WG1CarG-70
❑ 90DodTar-1071

Shocker, Urban
❑ 20NatCarE-93
❑ 21E121So1-96
❑ 21Exh-159
❑ 21Nei-40
❑ 22E120-100
❑ 22W572-98
❑ 22W573-123
❑ 22W575-125
❑ 23W501-2
❑ 23W503-55
❑ 23W515-48
❑ 23WilChoV-150
❑ 25Exh-103
❑ 26Exh-104
❑ 26SpoComoA-39
❑ 27AmeCarE126-36
❑ 28Exh-52
❑ 75Yan192T-25
❑ 79Yan192T-30
❑ 84Yan192G-7
❑ 91ConTSN-114
❑ 93ConTSN-711

Shockey, Greg
❑ 92BelMarCB-2
❑ 92BelMarF-1459
❑ 93ClaGolF-192
❑ 93RivPilCLC-19
❑ 95LakElsSTI-21
❑ 95SPML-29
❑ 96BesAutS-82
❑ 96MidAngB-28
❑ 96MidAngOHP-23
❑ 96TexLeaAB-35
❑ 97RanCucQG-27

Shockey, Richard
❑ 90ModA'sC-27

Shockey, Scott
❑ 88CapCodPPaLP-63
❑ 89MedAthB-2
❑ 90CMC-659
❑ 90MadMusP-2278
❑ 91Cla/Bes-237
❑ 91HunStaC-21
❑ 91HunStaLD-293
❑ 91HunStaP-1805
❑ 91HunStaTI-19
❑ 91LinDriAA-293
❑ 93ModA'sC-18
❑ 93ModA'sF-809
❑ 94ClaGolF-127
❑ 94HunStaF-1338

Shockley, Costen (John Costen)
❑ 65OPC-107
❑ 65Top-107
❑ 88ChaLooLTI-27

Shockley, Keith
❑ 96MarPhiB-24
❑ 97BatCliTI-10

Shoebridge, Terry
❑ 77BurBeeT-26
❑ 78BurBeeT-24
❑ 80HolMilT-9
❑ 81ElPasDT-5

Shoemaker, Charlie
❑ 77FriOneYW-89

Shoemaker, John
❑ 78LodDodT-20
❑ 81VerBeaDT-26
❑ 82VerBeaDT-29
❑ 83VerBeaDT-26
❑ 85VerBeaDT-27
❑ 86VerBeaDP-23
❑ 87VerBeaDP-30
❑ 88FloStaLAS-1
❑ 88VerBeaDS-18B
❑ 89SanAntMB-25
❑ 90SanAntMGS-1
❑ 91LinDriAA-549
❑ 91SanAntMLD-549
❑ 91SanAntMP-2991
❑ 92GulCoaDF-3583
❑ 93YakBeaC-28
❑ 93YakBeaF-3901
❑ 94VerBeaDC-29
❑ 95GreFalDTI-31
❑ 96SavSanB-1
❑ 97VerBeaD-1
❑ 98VerBeaDM-1

Shoemaker, Steve
❑ 92MadMusC-12
❑ 92MadMusF-1235
❑ 93SanBerSC-15
❑ 93SanBerSF-769
❑ 94HunStaF-1332
❑ 94OneYanC-21
❑ 94OneYanF-3792
❑ 94SigRooDPBSDP-10
❑ 94SigRooDP-79
❑ 94SigRooDPS-79
❑ 94StaCluDP-52
❑ 94StaCluDPFDI-52
❑ 95GreBatTI-23
❑ 95HunStaTI-24
❑ 96BesAutS-83
❑ 96BesAutSA-70
❑ 96SalAvaB-24
❑ 97BesAutAS-54
❑ 97SalAva-28
❑ 98Bes-45
❑ 98Bow-426
❑ 98BowChr-426
❑ 98BowChrGA-426
❑ 98BowChrGAR-426
❑ 98BowChrI-426
❑ 98BowChrIR-426
❑ 98BowChrR-426
❑ 98BowGolA-426
❑ 98BowInt-426
❑ 98ColSprSS-15

Shoen, Gerry
❑ 77FriOneYW-20

Shoeneck, Lewis
❑ 88WG1CarG-36

Shoffner, Milburn
❑ 38CloFotW-74
❑ 39OrcPhoAP-21
❑ 39PlaBal-87
❑ 40PlaBal-149
❑ 41HarHarW-22
❑ 77CinRedT-25
❑ 93ConTSN-925

Shofner, Frank S.
❑ 48SomandK-9
❑ 49SomandK-15

Sholl, Derek
❑ 87EugEmeP-2663
❑ 88EugEmeB-25

Sholton, Craig
❑ 91WelPirC-15

Shombert, Otto
❑ 87BucN28-47
❑ 87OldJudN-450

Shook, Wes
❑ 92ButCopKSP-9
❑ 93EriSaiC-1
❑ 93EriSaiF-3121
❑ 94ExcFS7-137

Shoop, Brian
❑ 88MisStaB-31
❑ 89MisStaB-42

Shopay, Tom
❑ 67YanPhoS-94
❑ 70OPC-363
❑ 70Top-363
❑ 71BalOriP-27
❑ 72OPC-418
❑ 72OriPos-30
❑ 72Top-418
❑ 75BalOriP-26
❑ 76BalOriP-35
❑ 76SSP-401
❑ 77BalOriP-18
❑ 78ColCliT-24
❑ 89PacSenL-71
❑ 91OriCro-417
❑ 92YanWIZ6-114

Shore, Ernie (Ernest)
❑ 15SpoNewM-164
❑ 16FleBreD-85
❑ 16SpoNewM-162
❑ 17ColE13-159
❑ 21Zee-149
❑ 22Zee-138
❑ 73FleWilD-31
❑ 86WinSpiP-5
❑ 86WinSpiP-6
❑ 87ConSer2-56
❑ 90HOFStiB-15
❑ 91ConTSN-141
❑ 92ConTSN-351

Shore, Jeff
❑ 89ChaRanS-23

Shore, Ray
❑ 52Par-18
❑ 63RedFreBC-24

Shores, Brad
❑ 86BurExpP-19
❑ 89AppFoxP-869
❑ 91AppFoxCB-21

Shores, Scott
❑ 94BatCliC-22
❑ 94BatCliF-3460
❑ 94SigRooDPBSDP-10
❑ 94StaCluDP-61
❑ 94StaCluDPFDI-61
❑ 95ClePhiF-230
❑ 95SigRooMOP-P9
❑ 95SigRooMOPS-P9
❑ 96ReaPhiB-25

Shores, Walter
❑ 32Zee-75

Shores, William
❑ 31W517-7
❑ 37Zee-88
❑ 94ConTSN-1145
❑ 94ConTSNB-1145

Short, Barry
❑ 96StLucMTI-5

Short, Ben
❑ 91OneYanP-4154
❑ 92GreHorC-9
❑ 92GreHorF-778

Short, Bill
❑ 60Top-142
❑ 60TopVen-142
❑ 61Top-252
❑ 62BalOriP-25
❑ 62Top-221
❑ 66BalOriP-31
❑ 67Top-577
❑ 68Top-536
❑ 69Top-259
❑ 91MetWIZ-364
❑ 91OriCro-418
❑ 92YanWIZ6-115

Short, Chris
❑ 47StaPinP2-35
❑ 58PhiTeal-18
❑ 64PhiJayP-9
❑ 64PhiPhiB-22
❑ 64PhiTeaS-6
❑ 65PhiJayP-9
❑ 66PhiTeal-11
❑ 67CokCapPh-15
❑ 67DexPre-190
❑ 67PhiPol-12
❑ 67Top-395
❑ 67TopVen-329
❑ 68OPC-7
❑ 68OPC-139
❑ 68Top-7
❑ 68Top-139
❑ 68TopActS-9C
❑ 68TopVen-7
❑ 68TopVen-9
❑ 68TopVen-139
❑ 69MilBra-253
❑ 69MLBOffS-178
❑ 69PhiTeal-9
❑ 69Top-395
❑ 69TopDecl-40
❑ 69TopSta-78
❑ 69TopSup-54
❑ 69TopTeaP-8
❑ 70Kel-41
❑ 70MLBOffS-94
❑ 70OPC-270
❑ 70PhiTeal-10
❑ 70Top-270
❑ 71Kel-75
❑ 71MLBOffS-188
❑ 71OPC-511
❑ 71PhiArcO-11
❑ 71Top-511
❑ 72MilBra-315
❑ 72Top-665
❑ 83PhiPosGPaM-9
❑ 84OCoandSI-229
❑ 86PhiGreT-6
❑ 94BreMilB-270
❑ 94CarLeaA-DJ15

Short, Rick
❑ 94BluOriC-19
❑ 94BluOriF-3572
❑ 96FreKeyB-21
❑ 97FreKey-26

Shorten, Chick (Charles)
❑ 17ColE13-160
❑ 22E120-101
❑ 23W503-41
❑ 91ConTSN-136

Shotkoski, David
❑ 88HunStaTI-19
❑ 88ModA'sCLC-57
❑ 88ModA'sTI-31
❑ 89HunStaB-15
❑ 91LinDriAA-446
❑ 91MidAngLD-446
❑ 91MidAngOHP-27
❑ 91MidAngP-434

Shotton, Burt
❑ 14B18B-34A
❑ 14B18B-34B
❑ 14CraJacE-86
❑ 15CraJacE-86
❑ 15SpoNewM-165
❑ 16SpoNewM-163
❑ 17ColE13-161
❑ 17HolBreD-96
❑ 19W514-78
❑ 47DodTeal-21
❑ 48DodTeal-22
❑ 49EurSta-49
❑ 60RawGloT-31
❑ 70Houof J-28
❑ 75TCMHouoJ-30
❑ 85BigLeaC3-66
❑ 90DodTar-733
❑ 91ConTSN-152

Shotton, Craig
❑ 91WelPirP-3590
❑ 92WelPirC-21

Shoulders, Bob
❑ 87NewOriP-13

Shoun, Clyde
❑ 36CubTeal-27
❑ 36DiaMatCS3T2-21
❑ 38CloFotW-75
❑ 41CarW75-23
❑ 50RemBre-22
❑ 51R42SmaS-99
❑ 83Car194T-50
❑ 92ConTSN-379

Shoup, Eric
❑ 88BriTigP-1876

Shouppe, Jamey
❑ 83DayBeaAT-12

Shourds, Anthony
❑ 98SavSanGM-24

Shourds, Jeff
❑ 77CedRapGT-23

Shouse, Brian
❑ 90WelPirP-28
❑ 91AugPirC-11
❑ 92CarMudF-1179
❑ 92CarMudS-143
❑ 93BufBisF-516
❑ 94BufBisF-1836
❑ 95CarMudF-157
❑ 97RocRedW-23
❑ 98PacOmeRS-13
❑ 98PacOmeRST5-13
❑ 98PacOnl-127
❑ 98PacOnlR-127
❑ 98PacOnlWC-127
❑ 98PawRedSQ-26

Show, Eric
❑ 81HawIslT-19
❑ 82TopTra-106T
❑ 83AllGamPI-178
❑ 83Don-439
❑ 83Fle-372
❑ 83FleSta-175
❑ 83FleSti-225
❑ 83OPC-68
❑ 83PadTeal-24
❑ 83Top-68
❑ 83TopSti-330
❑ 84AllGamPI-87
❑ 84Don-406
❑ 84Fle-312
❑ 84Nes792-532
❑ 84OPC-238
❑ 84PadMot-4
❑ 84PadSmo-22
❑ 84Top-532
❑ 84TopRubD-27
❑ 84TopSti-162
❑ 84TopTif-532
❑ 85Don-202
❑ 85DonActA-59
❑ 85Fle-44
❑ 85Lea-137
❑ 85OPC-118
❑ 85PadMot-9
❑ 85Top-118
❑ 85TopRubD-27
❑ 85TopSti-156
❑ 85TopTif-118
❑ 86Don-234
❑ 86Fle-334
❑ 86Lea-111
❑ 86OPC-209
❑ 86Top-762
❑ 86TopTif-762
❑ 87Don-164
❑ 87DonOpeD-149
❑ 87Fle-430
❑ 87FleGlo-430
❑ 87FleHotS-37
❑ 87OPC-354
❑ 87PadBohHB-30
❑ 87Top-730
❑ 87TopSti-112
❑ 87TopTif-730
❑ 88Don-387
❑ 88Fle-597
❑ 88FleGlo-597
❑ 88PadCok-30
❑ 88PadSmo-26
❑ 88PanSti-400
❑ 88Sco-338
❑ 88ScoGlo-338
❑ 88StaLinPa-12
❑ 88Top-303
❑ 88TopTif-303
❑ 89Bow-446
❑ 89BowTif-446
❑ 89Don-482
❑ 89Fle-317
❑ 89FleGlo-317
❑ 89OPC-147
❑ 89PadCok-17
❑ 89PadMag-7
❑ 89PadPos-29
❑ 89PadShoK-1
❑ 89PanSti-196
❑ 89Sco-254
❑ 89Top-427
❑ 89TopBig-35
❑ 89TopTif-427
❑ 89UppDec-171
❑ 90Bow-209
❑ 90BowTif-209
❑ 90Don-559
❑ 90Fle-169
❑ 90FleCan-169
❑ 90Lea-115
❑ 90OPC-239
❑ 90PadCok-18
❑ 90PadMag-5
❑ 90PubIntS-59
❑ 90Sco-493
❑ 90Top-239
❑ 90TopBig-71
❑ 90TopSti-111
❑ 90TopTif-239
❑ 90UppDec-587
❑ 91A'sMot-23
❑ 91A'sSFE-11
❑ 91Bow-223
❑ 91Fle-544
❑ 91Lea-354
❑ 91OPC-613
❑ 91Sco-563
❑ 91ScoRoo-64T
❑ 91StaClu-138
❑ 91Stu-108
❑ 91Top-613
❑ 91TopDesS-613
❑ 91TopMic-613
❑ 91TopTif-613
❑ 91UppDec-293
❑ 91UppDec-798
❑ 92OPC-132
❑ 92Sco-662
❑ 92Top-132
❑ 92TopGol-132
❑ 92TopGolW-132
❑ 92TopMic-132

Showalter, Buck (William N.)
❑ 77ForLauYS-10
❑ 79WesHavYT-7
❑ 80NasSouTI-20
❑ 81ColCliP-11
❑ 81ColCliT-20
❑ 81NasSouTI-17
❑ 82NasSouTI-22
❑ 83NasSouTI-21
❑ 88FloStaLAS-27
❑ 89AlbYanB-8
❑ 89AlbYanP-326
❑ 89AlbYanSt-22
❑ 89EasLeaAP-26
❑ 92OPC-201
❑ 92Top-201
❑ 92TopGol-201
❑ 92TopGolW-201
❑ 92TopMic-201
❑ 93Top-510
❑ 93TopGol-510
❑ 93TopInaM-510
❑ 93TopInaR-510
❑ 93TopMic-510
❑ 96StaClu-356
❑ 96StaCluMOP-356
❑ 96UppDec-476
❑ 98DiaMcD-18

Showalter, J.R.
❑ 90BoiHawP-3326
❑ 91PalSprAP-2026

Shreimann, Eric
❑ 94MarPhiC-24

Shrev, Ben
❑ 88WytCubP-1992

Shreve, Leven
❑ 87OldJudN-451
❑ 88GenCubP-1652

Shrum, Dennis
❑ 94AubAstC-19
❑ 94AubAstF-3759

Shuba, George
❑ 52Top-326
❑ 53BowC-145
❑ 53Top-34
❑ 54Bow-202
❑ 54NewYorJA-17
❑ 55Bow-66
❑ 55DodGolS-26

❑ 74dod195T-35
❑ 79TCM50-277
❑ 82Bow195E-267
❑ 83TopRep5-326
❑ 88DodRinP1-5B
❑ 90DodTar-734
❑ 91TopArc1-34
❑ 95TopArcBD-23
❑ 95TopArcBD-41
❑ 95TopArcBD-90
❑ 95TopArcBD-126
Shubert, Rich
❑ 74GasRanT-18
❑ 76SanAntBTI-20
❑ 77HolMilT-23
Shucks, Mr.
❑ 95CedRapKTI-NNO
Shuey, Paul
❑ 91TopTra-108T
❑ 91TopTraT-108T
❑ 92ClaBluBF-BC21
❑ 92ClaDraP-2
❑ 92ClaDraPFB-BC2
❑ 92ClaDraPP-BB2
❑ 92ClaFS7-401
❑ 92ColRedF-2390
❑ 92StaCluD-171
❑ 92TopDaiQTU-32
❑ 92UppDecML-142
❑ 93CanIndF-2838
❑ 93ClaFisN-19
❑ 93ClaFS7-1
❑ 93ClaGolF-14
❑ 93ClaInsC-7
❑ 93ExcFS7-168
❑ 94Cla-160
❑ 94ClaGolF-107
❑ 94Fla-289
❑ 94FleExtB-67
❑ 94FleUpd-37
❑ 94KinIndF-2641
❑ 94LeaLimR-7
❑ 94ScoRoo-RT109
❑ 94ScoRooGR-RT109
❑ 94Sel-411
❑ 94SigRoo-42
❑ 94SigRooS-42
❑ 94SpoRoo-46
❑ 94SpoRooAP-46
❑ 94TopTra-78T
❑ 94UppDec-522
❑ 94UppDecED-522
❑ 94UppDecML-47
❑ 95Bow-252
❑ 95BowBes-B86
❑ 95BowBesR-B86
❑ 95BowGolF-252
❑ 95ColCho-26
❑ 95ColChoGS-26
❑ 95ColChoSE-22
❑ 95ColChoSEGS-22
❑ 95ColChoSESS-22
❑ 95ColChoSS-26
❑ 95Don-479
❑ 95DonPreP-479
❑ 95Fle-147
❑ 95Lea-91
❑ 95Pin-155
❑ 95PinArtP-155
❑ 95PinMusC-155
❑ 95Sco-138
❑ 95ScoGolR-138
❑ 95ScoPlaTS-138
❑ 95StaClu-288
❑ 95StaCluMOP-288
❑ 95StaCluSTWS-288
❑ 95TopTra-112T
❑ 96BufBisB-19
❑ 97Fle-607
❑ 97FleTif-607
❑ 97StaClu-302
❑ 97StaCluMOP-302
❑ 97Top-16
❑ 98PacInvGems-43
❑ 98PacOnl-230
❑ 98PacOnlR-230
❑ 98PacOnlWC-230
❑ 99Fle-555
❑ 99FleSta9-555
❑ 99FleWarT-555
Shuffield, Jack
❑ 83ChaRoyT-12
Shugars, Shawn
❑ 94HudValRC-24
❑ 94HudValRF-3401
❑ 95ChaRivTI-27
Shuler, Dave
❑ 92PriWilCC-27
Shull, Mike
❑ 87PalSprP-10
❑ 90PalSprACLC-222
Shulleeta, Mike
❑ 82QuaCitCT-11
Shulock, John
❑ 88T/MUmp-39
❑ 89T/MUmp-37
❑ 90T/MUmp-35
Shultea, Chris
❑ 91SalLakTSP-19
Shultis, Chris
❑ 86EveGiaC-22
❑ 86EveGiaPC-28
❑ 88BoiHawP-1613
Shultis, Lane
❑ 21Zee-37
Shumake, Brooks
❑ 86VerRedP-18
Shumaker, Anthony
❑ 95BatCliTI-30
❑ 95MarPhiTI-24
❑ 96PieBolWB-25
❑ 97ClePhi-18
❑ 98ReaPhiM-25
❑ 98ReaPhiUM-21
❑ 99Bow-417
❑ 99BowGol-417
❑ 99BowInt-417
Shumate, Jacob
❑ 94DanBraC-1
❑ 94SigRooDP-26
❑ 94SigRooDPS-26
❑ 94StaCluDP-1
❑ 94StaCluDPFDI-1
❑ 94TopTra-13T
❑ 95Exc-158
❑ 95MacBraTI-27
❑ 95Pin-172
❑ 95PinArtP-172
❑ 95PinMusC-172
❑ 95ScoDraP-DP9
❑ 95StaClu-99
❑ 95StaCluFDI-99
❑ 95StaCluMOP-99
❑ 95StaCluSTWS-99
❑ 95Top-6
❑ 95UppDecML-191
❑ 95UppDecMLFS-191
❑ 97EugEmeB-13
❑ 98MacBraM-22
Shumpert, Derek
❑ 94OneYanC-22
❑ 94OneYanF-3806
❑ 96GreBatB-27
❑ 97GreBatB-27
Shumpert, Terry
❑ 87EugEmeP-2674
❑ 88AppFoxP-142
❑ 89BlaYNPRWLU-9
❑ 89OmaRoyC-18
❑ 89OmaRoyP-1721
❑ 90ClaYel-T65
❑ 90DonBesA-134
❑ 90DonRoo-55
❑ 90FleUpd-104
❑ 90Lea-409
❑ 90RoyPos-23
❑ 90ScoRoo-110T
❑ 90TopTra-114T
❑ 90TopTraT-114T
❑ 90UppDec-733
❑ 91Bow-314
❑ 91Don-297
❑ 91Fle-570
❑ 91Lea-104
❑ 91MajLeaCP-22
❑ 91OPC-322
❑ 91OPCPre-108
❑ 91RoyPol-20
❑ 91Sco-349
❑ 91Sco100RS-3
❑ 91ScoAllF-9
❑ 91ScoRoo-27
❑ 91SevCoi-F15
❑ 91StaClu-111
❑ 91Top-322
❑ 91TopDeb90-143
❑ 91TopDesS-322
❑ 91TopMic-322
❑ 91TopTif-322
❑ 91Ult-156
❑ 91UppDec-521
❑ 92Bow-157
❑ 92Cla1-T83
❑ 92Don-562
❑ 92Fle-169
❑ 92Lea-347
❑ 92LeaBlaG-347
❑ 92OmaRoyF-2972
❑ 92OPC-483
❑ 92PanSti-95
❑ 92Pin-203
❑ 92RoyPol-25
❑ 92Sco-248
❑ 92Sco100RS-44
❑ 92StaClu-165
❑ 92Top-483
❑ 92TopGol-483
❑ 92TopGolW-483
❑ 92TopMic-483
❑ 92UppDec-348
❑ 93Don-601
❑ 93OmaRoyF-1688
❑ 93PacSpa-141
❑ 93TriAAAGF-44
❑ 94FleUpd-51
❑ 94VenLinU-88
❑ 95Don-176
❑ 95DonPreP-176
❑ 95Fle-172
❑ 95Sco-523
❑ 95ScoGolR-523
❑ 95ScoPlaTS-523
❑ 95Top-87
❑ 95Ult-61
❑ 95UltGolM-61
❑ 96IowCubB-23
❑ 97LasVegS1A-27
❑ 97PacPriGotD-GD122
❑ 98ColSprSS-6
Shupe, Vince
❑ 47PadTeal-19
Shupe, Wilford
❑ 20WalMaiW-49
Shwan, Dan
❑ 88SalLakCTTI-3
❑ 89SalLakTTI-3
❑ 91SalLakTP-3229
❑ 91SalLakTSP-27
Shy, Jason
❑ 95EugEmeTI-15
❑ 96DanBraB-22
Siberz, Bo
❑ 90OneYanP-3381
❑ 91GreHorP-3060
Siblerud, Daniel
❑ 86ColMetP-23
Siciliano, Jess
❑ 96EriSeaB-23
❑ 97EriSeaWB-29
Sick, David
❑ 94BoiHawC-22
❑ 94BoiHawF-3354
❑ 95CedRapKTI-28
❑ 96CedRapKTI-22
Sicking, Eddie
❑ 33WorCig(-83
Siddall, Joe
❑ 88JamExpP-1908
❑ 89RocExpLC-26
❑ 90WesPalBES-20
❑ 91HarSenLD-269
❑ 91HarSenP-631
❑ 91LinDriAA-269
❑ 92HarSenF-464
❑ 92HarSenS-298
❑ 93OttLynF-2439
❑ 94OttLynF-2901
❑ 94Pac-390
❑ 97PacPriGotD-GD147
❑ 98TolMudHQ-28
Sides, Craig
❑ 92BurIndC-5
❑ 92BurIndF-1655
Siebern, Norm
❑ 47Exh-207
❑ 58Top-54
❑ 59Top-308
❑ 60A's-9
❑ 60A'sJayP-8
❑ 60A'sTeal-14
❑ 60Top-11
❑ 60TopVen-11
❑ 61A'sTeal-18
❑ 61AthJayP-18
❑ 61AthJayP-19
❑ 61Pos-82A
❑ 61Pos-82B
❑ 61Top-119
❑ 61Top-267
❑ 61TopDicG-16
❑ 61TopStal-165
❑ 62Baz-33
❑ 62ExhStaB-31
❑ 62Jel-92
❑ 62Pos-92
❑ 62PosCan-92
❑ 62SalPlaC-85
❑ 62ShiPlaC-85
❑ 62Top-127
❑ 62Top-275
❑ 62TopBuc-82
❑ 62TopStal-57
❑ 62TopVen-127
❑ 63AthJayP-9
❑ 63BasMagM-75
❑ 63Baz-4
❑ 63ExhStaB-59
❑ 63Fle-17
❑ 63Jel-85
❑ 63Pos-85
❑ 63SalMetC-51
❑ 63Top-2
❑ 63Top-430
❑ 63TopStil-40
❑ 64BalOriP-33
❑ 64OriJayP-12
❑ 64Top-145
❑ 64TopCoi-49
❑ 64TopSta-14
❑ 64TopStaU-68
❑ 64TopTatI-67
❑ 64TopVen-145
❑ 64WheSta-41
❑ 65BalOriP-30
❑ 65Top-455
❑ 66AngDexP-15
❑ 66OPC-14
❑ 66Top-14
❑ 66TopVen-14
❑ 67CokCapG-5
❑ 67DexPre-191
❑ 67Top-299
❑ 68CokCapRS-15
❑ 68Top-537
❑ 78TCM60I-178
❑ 79TCM50-223
❑ 81RedSoxBG2S-112
❑ 83FraBroR-18
❑ 91OriCro-419
Siebert, Dick
❑ 40PlaBal-192
❑ 41DouPlaR-127
❑ 42A'sTeal-29
❑ 43A'STEAI-19
❑ 45A'sTeal-28
❑ 77TCMTheWY-22
❑ 83TCMPla1943-23
❑ 90DodTar-735
❑ 93ConTSN-926
Siebert, Mac
❑ 89BriTigS-26
Siebert, Paul
❑ 75IowOakT-17
❑ 75OPC-614
❑ 75Top-614
❑ 75TopMin-614
❑ 76VenLeaS-138
❑ 78MetDaiPA-21
❑ 87AstShoSPT-18
❑ 89PacSenL-212
❑ 91MetWIZ-365
Siebert, Rick
❑ 86DurBulP-25
❑ 87DurBulP-18
❑ 88SumBraP-402
Siebert, Sonny
❑ 64Top-552
❑ 65OPC-96
❑ 65Top-96
❑ 66IndVolC-10
❑ 66Kah-28
❑ 66Top-197
❑ 66Top-222
❑ 66Top-226
❑ 66TopVen-197
❑ 66TopVen-222
❑ 66TopVen-226
❑ 67CokCapI-8
❑ 67Kah-35
❑ 67OPC-95
❑ 67Top-95
❑ 67Top-463
❑ 67TopVen-246
❑ 68OPC-8
❑ 68Top-8
❑ 68Top-295
❑ 68TopVen-8
❑ 68TopVen-295
❑ 69MLBOffS-43
❑ 69Top-455
❑ 69TopSta-167
❑ 69TopTeaP-13
❑ 70MLBOffS-166
❑ 70RedSoxCPPC-13
❑ 70Top-597
❑ 71Kel-24
❑ 71MLBOffS-332
❑ 71OPC-710
❑ 71RedSoxA-9
❑ 71RedSoxTI-10
❑ 71Top-710
❑ 71TopCoi-122
❑ 72Kel-36
❑ 72OPC-290
❑ 72SevTraC-50
❑ 72Top-290
❑ 73OPC-14
❑ 73RanTeal-20
❑ 73Top-14
❑ 74OPC-548
❑ 74Top-548
❑ 75OPC-328
❑ 75Top-328
❑ 75TopMin-328
❑ 76SSP-484
❑ 81RedSoxBG2S-113
❑ 85LasVegSC-121
❑ 87LasVegSP-6
❑ 88LasVegSC-25
❑ 88LasVegSP-248
❑ 91WatDiaC-26
❑ 91WatDiaP-1274
❑ 92WicWraS-650
❑ 93RanKee-325
❑ 93WicWraF-2994
❑ 94PadMot-28
❑ 95PadMot-28
❑ 96ColSprSSTI-28
❑ 97ColSprSTI-22
❑ 98ColSprSS-42
Siebert, Steve
❑ 90SpoIndSP-13
❑ 91UtiBluSC-15
❑ 91UtiBluSP-3251
Siebler, Dwight
❑ 64Top-516
❑ 65Top-326
❑ 66Top-546
❑ 67OPC-164
❑ 67Top-164
❑ 78TCM60I-126
Siegel, Bob
❑ 86WauTimP-24
Siegel, Dan
❑ 94PriRedC-29
❑ 98ChaAllCM-29
Siegel, Justin
❑ 96HudValRB-16
❑ 98SavSanGM-25
Siegel, Lanny
❑ 89AncBucTI-26
Siegle, John H.
❑ 09AmeCarE90-1-93
❑ 10E101-40
❑ 10MelMinE-40
❑ 10NadCarE-47
❑ 10PeoT21-50
Siegle, Tony
❑ 89PadPos-31
Sieradzki, Al
❑ 89BluOriS-21
Sierra, Candy (Ulises)
❑ 85BeaGolGT-9
❑ 86BeaGolGP-21
❑ 87WicPilRD-20
❑ 88NasSouTI-21
❑ 89BlaYNPRWL-154
❑ 89Fle-171
❑ 89FleGlo-171
❑ 89Top-711
❑ 89TopTif-711
❑ 90RivRedWB-23
❑ 90RivRedWP-2609
Sierra, Ernie
❑ 89SanJosGB-30
Sierra, Ruben
❑ 85TulDriTI-12
❑ 86DonRoo-52
❑ 86FleUpd-105
❑ 86OklCit8P-21
❑ 86RanPer-3
❑ 86SpoRoo-16
❑ 87ClaUpdY-149
❑ 87Don-346
❑ 87DonOpeD-172
❑ 87Fle-138
❑ 87FleGlo-138
❑ 87FleMin-100
❑ 87Lea-225
❑ 87RanMot-13
❑ 87RanSmo-17
❑ 87SpoTeaP-1
❑ 87Top-6
❑ 87Top-261
❑ 87TopRoo-15
❑ 87TopSti-10
❑ 87TopTif-6
❑ 87TopTif-261
❑ 87ToyRoo-24
❑ 88BlaYNPRWLU-52
❑ 88ClaRed-180
❑ 88Don-223
❑ 88DonBasB-200
❑ 88DonBonM-BC26
❑ 88Fle-479
❑ 88FleExcS-38
❑ 88FleGlo-479
❑ 88FleHotS-38
❑ 88FleLeaL-39
❑ 88FleMin-58
❑ 88FleStiC-69
❑ 88FleSup-36
❑ 88KayB-28
❑ 88Lea-206
❑ 88OPC-319
❑ 88PanSti-209
❑ 88RanMot-10
❑ 88RanSmo-9
❑ 88Sco-113
❑ 88ScoGlo-113
❑ 88ScoYouSI-36
❑ 88Spo-113
❑ 88StaLinRa-15
❑ 88Top-771
❑ 88TopCoi-26
❑ 88TopGloS-4
❑ 88TopRitTM-25
❑ 88TopSti-234
❑ 88TopTif-771
❑ 88TopUKM-71
❑ 88TopUKMT-71
❑ 89BimBreD-6
❑ 89Bow-235
❑ 89BowTif-235
❑ 89ClaTraP-162
❑ 89Don-48
❑ 89DonBasB-111
❑ 89DonBonM-BC26
❑ 89Fle-532
❑ 89FleBasA-37
❑ 89FleBasM-35
❑ 89FleExcS-37
❑ 89FleGlo-532
❑ 89FleHeroB-37
❑ 89OPC-53
❑ 89PanSti-457
❑ 89RanMot-7
❑ 89RanSmo-30
❑ 89RedFolSB-108
❑ 89Sco-43
❑ 89Scomast-31
❑ 89Spo-189
❑ 89SpoIllFKI-165
❑ 89Top-53
❑ 89TopBig-82
❑ 89TopCoi-51
❑ 89TopHilTM-26
❑ 89TopSti-242
❑ 89TopTif-53
❑ 89TopUKM-71
❑ 89TulDriTI-27
❑ 89TVSpoM-117
❑ 89UppDec-416
❑ 89UppDec-686
❑ 90Bow-490
❑ 90BowTif-490
❑ 90ClaBlu-7
❑ 90ClaBlu-59A
❑ 90ClaBlu-59B
❑ 90ClaYel-T77
❑ 90Col-7
❑ 90Don-3A
❑ 90Don-3B
❑ 90Don-174
❑ 90Don-673A
❑ 90Don-673B

- 90DonBesA-143
- 90DonSupD-3
- 90Fle-314
- 90FleAll-11
- 90FleAwaW-34
- 90FleBasA-34
- 90FleBasAC-34
- 90FleBasM-34
- 90FleBasMC-34
- 90FleCan-314
- 90FleLeaL-36
- 90FleLeaLC-36
- 90FleWaxBC-C25
- 90Hot50PS-40
- 90Lea-257
- 90M.Vpin-104
- 90OPC-185
- 90OPC-390
- 90PanSti-162
- 90PanSti-203
- 90PubIntS-422
- 90PubIntS-605
- 90RanMot-3
- 90Sco-420
- 90Sco100S-85
- 90Spo-188
- 90StaLonJS-8
- 90StaLonJS-33
- 90Top-185
- 90Top-390
- 90TopAmeA-32
- 90TopBig-175
- 90TopCoi-28
- 90TopDou-60
- 90TopGloA-19
- 90TopGloS-26
- 90TopHilHM-20
- 90TopMag-4
- 90TopMinL-40
- 90TopSti-161
- 90TopSti-244
- 90TopStiB-53
- 90TopTif-185
- 90TopTif-390
- 90TopTVA-7
- 90TulDriDGB-35
- 90UppDec-355
- 90UppDecS-1
- 91BasBesHRK-16
- 91Bow-283
- 91CadElID-52
- 91Cla3-T83
- 91ClaGam-41
- 91DenHol-21
- 91Don-567
- 91Fle-303
- 91FlePro-3
- 91KinDis-9
- 91Lea-97
- 91MooSna-16
- 91OPC-535
- 91OPCPre-109
- 91PanFreS-257
- 91PanSti-202
- 91RanMot-3
- 91RedFolS-87
- 91Sco-495
- 91Sco-859
- 91Sco100S-12
- 91SevCoi-T13
- 91StaClu-123
- 91StaPinB-46
- 91Stu-129
- 91Top-535
- 91TopCraJ2-18
- 91TopDesS-535
- 91TopMic-535
- 91TopTif-535
- 91Ult-356
- 91UniWayS-1
- 91UppDec-455
- 91USPlaCA-9H
- 92Bow-225
- 92Cla2-T65
- 92ClaGam-151
- 92DenHol-25
- 92Don-298
- 92DonCraJ2-26
- 92Fle-321
- 92FleCitTP-18
- 92FleUpd-51
- 92Hig5-115
- 92HitTheBB-32
- 92Lea-383
- 92LeaBlaG-383
- 92OPC-700
- 92OPCPre-66
- 92PanSti-79
- 92Pin-14
- 92Pin-616
- 92PinSlu-10
- 92PinTeaP-10
- 92RanMot-3
- 92RanTeal-23
- 92RedFolS-88
- 92Sco-437
- 92Sco-490
- 92Sco100S-87
- 92ScoImpP-46
- 92ScoRoo-63T
- 92StaClu-387
- 92StaCluD-172
- 92Stu-249
- 92StuPre-1
- 92Top-403
- 92Top-700
- 92TopGol-403
- 92TopGol-700
- 92TopGolW-403
- 92TopGolW-700
- 92TopKid-128
- 92TopMic-403
- 92TopMic-700
- 92TopMic-G403
- 92TriPla-238
- 92Ult-142
- 92UppDec-176
- 92UppDecF-41
- 92UppDecFG-41
- 92UppDecTMH-48
- 92UppDecWB-T10
- 93AthMot-5
- 93AthStaC-10
- 93Bow-245
- 93ClaGam-85
- 93DiaMar-98
- 93Don-637
- 93DurPowP2-6
- 93Fin-158
- 93FinRef-158
- 93Fla-262
- 93Fle-298
- 93FunPac-52
- 93Lea-29
- 93OPC-243
- 93PacSpa-225
- 93PacSpaGE-18
- 93PanSti-21
- 93Pin-200
- 93PinHomRC-46
- 93PinSlu-12
- 93RanKee-326
- 93RedFolS-126
- 93Sco-608
- 93Sel-366
- 93SP-43
- 93StaClu-580
- 93StaCluFDI-580
- 93StaCluM-47
- 93StaCluMOP-580
- 93StaCluMP-22
- 93Stu-113
- 93Top-440
- 93TopGol-440
- 93TopInaM-440
- 93TopInaR-440
- 93TopMic-440
- 93TriPla-60
- 93Ult-613
- 93UppDec-49
- 93UppDec-145
- 93UppDecGold-49
- 93UppDecGold-145
- 94A'sMot-7
- 94Bow-24
- 94BowBes-R57
- 94BowBesR-R57
- 94ChuHomS-3
- 94ChuHomSG-3
- 94ColC-258
- 94ColChoGS-258
- 94ColChoSS-258
- 94Don-33
- 94DonDiaK-DK18
- 94DonDiaKJ-DK18
- 94DonMVP-25
- 94DonSpeE-33
- 94Fin-371
- 94FinRef-371
- 94Fla-333
- 94Fle-273
- 94FleExtB-155
- 94FUnPac-141
- 94Lea-67
- 94LeaL-63
- 94OPC-195
- 94OscMayR-13
- 94Pac-462
- 94PacAll-12
- 94PanSti-112
- 94Pin-61
- 94PinArtP-61
- 94PinMusC-61
- 94ProMag-98
- 94RanAllP-17
- 94RanAllP-19
- 94RanAllP-20
- 94Sco-409
- 94ScoGolR-409
- 94Sel-45
- 94SP-37
- 94SPDieC-37
- 94Spo-73
- 94StaClu-307
- 94StaClu-536
- 94StaCluFDI-307
- 94StaCluFDI-536
- 94StaCluGR-307
- 94StaCluGR-536
- 94StaCluMOP-307
- 94StaCluMOP-536
- 94Stu-6
- 94TomPiz-28
- 94Top-680
- 94TopGol-680
- 94TopSpa-680
- 94TriPla-8
- 94Ult-411
- 94UppDec-380
- 94UppDecAJ-2
- 94UppDecAJG-2
- 94UppDecED-380
- 95AthMot-7
- 95Baz-100
- 95Bow-360
- 95BowBes-R8
- 95BowBesR-R8
- 95ColCho-135
- 95ColChoGS-135
- 95ColChoSE-50
- 95ColChoSEGS-50
- 95ColChoSESS-50
- 95ColChoSS-135
- 95Don-406
- 95DonDiaK-DK5
- 95DonPreP-406
- 95DonTopotO-125
- 95Emo-74
- 95Fin-208
- 95FinRef-208
- 95Fla-295
- 95FlaOutP-10
- 95Fle-253
- 95FleTeaL-11
- 95Lea-243
- 95LeaLim-56
- 95LinVen-313
- 95LinVen-321
- 95Pac-320
- 95PacPri-103
- 95PanSti-87
- 95Pin-45
- 95PinArtP-45
- 95PinMusC-45
- 95Sco-351
- 95ScoGolR-351
- 95ScoHaloG-HG84
- 95ScoPlaTS-351
- 95Sel-15
- 95SelArtP-15
- 95SP-184
- 95SPCha-180
- 95SPChaDC-180
- 95Spo-86
- 95SpoArtP-86
- 95SPSil-184
- 95SPSpeF-17
- 95StaClu-96
- 95StaClu-520
- 95StaCluCC-CC2
- 95StaCluCT-14
- 95StaCluFDI-96
- 95StaCluMOP-96
- 95StaCluMOP-520
- 95StaCluMOP-CC2
- 95StaCluMOP-RL29
- 95StaCluRL-RL29
- 95StaCluSTWS-96
- 95StaCluSTWS-520
- 95StaCluVR-59
- 95StaCluVRMO-59
- 95Stu-111
- 95Sum-108
- 95SumNthD-108
- 95TomPiz-17
- 95Top-310
- 95TopCyb-167
- 95TopD3-3
- 95TopEmb-14
- 95TopEmbGI-14
- 95UC3-86
- 95UC3ArtP-86
- 95Ult-96
- 95UltGolM-96
- 95UppDec-280
- 95UppDec-494
- 95UppDecED-280
- 95UppDecEDG-280
- 95UppDecPLL-R46
- 95UppDecPLLE-R46
- 95UppDecSE-110
- 95UppDecSEG-110
- 95Zen-95
- 96ColCho-630
- 96ColChoGS-630
- 96ColChoSS-630
- 96Don-171
- 96DonPreP-171
- 96EmoXL-97
- 96Fin-B169
- 96FinRef-B169
- 96Fla-138
- 96Fle-196
- 96FleTif-196
- 96Lea-168
- 96LeaPrePB-168
- 96LeaPrePG-168
- 96LeaPrePS-168
- 96MetUni-95
- 96MetUniP-95
- 96Pac-379
- 96PacEstL-EL29
- 96Pin-116
- 96PinAfi-40
- 96PinAfiAP-40
- 96PinAfiFPP-40
- 96Sco-342
- 96ScoDugC-B67
- 96ScoDugCAP-B67
- 96Sel-118
- 96SelArtP-118
- 96SP-133
- 96StaClu-354
- 96StaCluEPB-354
- 96StaCluEPG-354
- 96StaCluEPS-354
- 96StaCluMOP-354
- 96Stu-69
- 96StuPrePB-69
- 96StuPrePG-69
- 96StuPrePS-69
- 96Sum-58
- 96SumAbo&B-58
- 96SumArtP-58
- 96SumFoi-58
- 96Top-290
- 96TopGal-14
- 96TopGalPPI-14
- 96Ult-106
- 96UltGolM-106
- 96UppDec-158
- 97Cir-247
- 97CirRav-247
- 97Don-259
- 97DonEli-66
- 97DonEliGS-66
- 97DonGolPP-259
- 97DonPre-44
- 97DonPreCttC-44
- 97DonSilPP-259
- 97Fle-106
- 97FleTif-106
- 97NewPin-145
- 97NewPinAP-145
- 97NewPinMC-145
- 97NewPinPP-145
- 97Pac-95
- 97PacLigB-95
- 97PacSil-95
- 97Pin-39
- 97PinArtP-PP39
- 97PinIns-21
- 97PinInsCE-21
- 97PinInsDE-21
- 97PinMusC-39
- 97PinPrePla-39
- 97PinPrePla-123
- 97Sco-143
- 97Sco-342
- 97ScoArtPWB-143
- 97ScoArtPWB-342
- 97ScoPreS-143
- 97ScoResC-342
- 97ScoShoS-143
- 97ScoShoS-342
- 97ScoShoSAP-143
- 97ScoShoSAP-342
- 97StaClu-277
- 97StaCluMOP-277
- 97Stu-26
- 97StuPrePG-26
- 97StuPrePS-26
- 97SyrSkyCB-22
- 97Top-452
- 97Ult-422
- 97UltGolME-422
- 97UltPlaME-422
- 98NorTidQ-24
- 98PacOnl-178
- 98PacOnlR-178
- 98PacOnlWC-178
- 98Ult-418
- 98UltGolM-418
- 98UltMas-418
- 98UltPlaM-418
- 98UppDec-661

Siever, Edward
- 03BreE10-130
- 07TigACDPP-15
- 08IndPos-17
- 09WolNewDTPP-18
- 11SpoLifCW-323

Sievers, Jason
- 90EveGiaB-15
- 90EveGiaP-3131
- 92EveGiaF-1694
- 93ButCopKSP-2
- 94CliLumC-22
- 94CliLumF-1984

Sievers, Roy
- 47Exh-208A
- 47Exh-208B
- 47Exh-208C
- 47Exh-208D
- 47StaPinP2-36
- 50Bow-16
- 51Bow-67
- 51FisBakL-26
- 51TopRedB-9
- 52Top-64
- 53Top-67
- 54Top-245
- 55DonWin-5
- 55Top-16
- 55TopDouH-79
- 56Top-75
- 56TopPin-59
- 57Top-89
- 58SeaTeal-24
- 58SenJayP-11
- 58Top-250
- 59ArmCoi-15
- 59Baz-19
- 59Top-74
- 59Top-340
- 59Top-465
- 59Top-566
- 59TopVen-74
- 60NuHi-23
- 60SenUniMC-17
- 60Top-25
- 60TopVen-25
- 60WhiSoxJP-10
- 60WhiSoxTS-18
- 61NuSco-423
- 61Pos-26A
- 61Pos-26B
- 61SevElev-9
- 61Top-470
- 61TopStal-128
- 61WhiSoxTS-17
- 62Jel-46
- 62Pos-46
- 62PosCan-46
- 62SalPlaC-66
- 62ShiPlaC-66
- 62Top-220
- 62TopBuc-83
- 62TopStal-58
- 62TopStal-169
- 63BasMagM-76
- 63Jel-177
- 63Pos-177
- 63Top-283
- 64PhiTeaS-7
- 64Top-43
- 64TopVen-43
- 65Top-574
- 76GrePlaG-36
- 77GalGloG-43
- 78TCM60I-242
- 79DiaGre-75
- 79TCM50-206
- 82TCMGreS-41
- 83TopRep5-64
- 83YanYealT-9
- 88PacLegI-26
- 89SweBasG-47
- 91TopArc1-67
- 94TopArc1-245
- 94TopArc1G-245

Sievert, Mark
- 93MedHatBJF-3735
- 93MedHatBJSP-15
- 94St.CatBJC-21
- 94St.CatBJF-3643
- 95HagSunF-69
- 95SPML-164
- 96BowBes-123
- 96BowBesAR-123
- 96BowBesR-123
- 96DouAllB-26
- 96Exc-119
- 96KnoSmoB-23
- 97SyrSkyCB-23
- 98SyrSkyG-26

Sigafoos, Francis
- 28Zee-99
- 30Zee-39

Sigler, Allen
- 85CedRapRT-25
- 86CedRapRT-22

Sigler, Brad
- 93HunCubC-24
- 93HunCubF-3246

Siglin, Paddy (W.)
- 17Zee-56
- 18Zee-73
- 19Zee-44
- 20WalMaiW-50
- 20Zee-56
- 21Zee-109
- 22Zee-89
- 23Zee-99
- 24Zee-73
- 25Zee-80
- 26Zee-59

Sigman, Lee
- 78BurBeeT-25
- 80HolMilT-25
- 83ElPasDT-25

Sigmund, John
- 63GadFunC-68

Signore, Tom
- 97VerExpB-3

Sigwart, Clete
- 93SpaPhiC-28
- 94ClePhiC-30
- 95ClePhiF-234
- 97ClePhi-29
- 98ClePhiM-30
- 98ClePhiUM-30

Sikes, Jason
- 94MarPhiC-25
- 94MarPhiF-3293
- 94SigRooDP-78
- 94SigRooDPS-78
- 94StaCluDP-53
- 94StaCluDPFDI-53
- 95MarPhiTI-25
- 96PieBolWB-26
- 97PieBolWB-25

Sikes, Ken
- 93GreFalDSP-14
- 94YakBeaC-22
- 94YakBeaF-3849
- 95Exc-218
- 95VerBeaDTI-26
- 96SanBerSB-25

Sikorski, Brian
- 95AubAstTI-14
- 96BesAutSA-71
- 96MidLeaAB-28
- 96QuaCitRB-26
- 97BesAutAS-55
- 97KisCob-23

❑ 98Bow-136
❑ 98BowChr-136
❑ 98BowChrGA-136
❑ 98BowChrGAR-136
❑ 98BowChrI-136
❑ 98BowChrIR-136
❑ 98BowChrR-136
❑ 98BowGolA-136
❑ 98BowInt-136
❑ 98JacGenM-21
Silch, Edward
❑ 87OldJudN-452
Silcox, Rusty
❑ 90SpoIndSP-3
❑ 91HigDesMC-10
❑ 91HigDesMP-2393
❑ 92HigDesMC-1
❑ 93BinMetF-2334
Siler, Jeff
❑ 96LakTigB-24
Siler, Mike
❑ 87BakDodP-26
Silicato, Tom
❑ 77ReaPhiT-21
Silkwood, Joe
❑ 83SprCarF-12
❑ 84ArkTraT-20
Silva, Carlos
❑ 96MarPhiB-25
❑ 97AppLeaTPB-14
❑ 98MarPhiG-27
Silva, Douglas
❑ 98SavSanGM-26
Silva, Freddie
❑ 82SprCarF-6
❑ 83St.PetCT-12
Silva, Herman
❑ 76VenLeaS-52
Silva, Ildemero
❑ 80VenLeaS-60
Silva, Jose
❑ 93HagSunC-24
❑ 93HagSunF-1880
❑ 94ActPac-47
❑ 94ActPac-62
❑ 94ActPac2G-8G
❑ 94ActPac2GD-8G
❑ 94BowBes-B86
❑ 94BowBesR-B86
❑ 94Cla-3
❑ 94ClaTriF-T82
❑ 94ColC-648
❑ 94ColChoGS-648
❑ 94ColChoSS-648
❑ 94DunBluJC-24
❑ 94DunBluJF-2556
❑ 94ExcFS7-148
❑ 94ExcLeaLF-16
❑ 94SP-16
❑ 94SPDieC-16
❑ 94TedWil-130
❑ 94UppDec-526
❑ 94UppDecAHNIL-12
❑ 94UppDecED-526
❑ 94UppDecML-50
❑ 94UppDecML-254
❑ 94UppDecMLT1PJF-TP9
❑ 94UppDecMLT1PMF-9
❑ 95ActPacF-16
❑ 95ColChoSE-16
❑ 95ColChoSEGS-16
❑ 95ColChoSESS-16
❑ 95Exc-141
❑ 95UppDecML-29
❑ 95UppDecML-113
❑ 95UppDecMLFS-29
❑ 95UppDecMLFS-113
❑ 95UppDecMLOP-OP28
❑ 95UppDecMLT1PF-6
❑ 97CalCanB-24
❑ 97PirPos-34
❑ 98Don-248
❑ 98DonGolPP-248
❑ 98DonSilPP-248
❑ 98Fle-457
❑ 98PacOmeRS-11
❑ 98PacOmeRST4-11
❑ 98PacOnl-594
❑ 98PacOnlR-594
❑ 98PacOnlWC-594
❑ 98PinPlu-115
❑ 99Fle-517
❑ 99FleSta9-517
❑ 99FleWarT-517
Silva, Luis
❑ 95LinVen-68
❑ 95WesMicWTI-24
Silva, Mark
❑ 83NasSouTI-22
❑ 85ColCliP-20
❑ 85ColCliT-24
❑ 85DomLeaS-200
❑ 86ColCliP-20
❑ 86ColCliP-22
Silva, Natalio
❑ 80VenLeaS-100
Silva, Ryan
❑ 86BenPhiC-149
Silva, Ted
❑ 95ChaRivUTIS-32
❑ 97TulDriTI-24
Silva, Troy
❑ 97BurIndG-24
Silvas, Brian
❑ 81BatTroT-7
Silver, Chad
❑ 89CarNewE-12
❑ 90PriPatD-18
Silver, Keith
❑ 84EveGiaC-10A
❑ 86ShrCapP-23
Silver, Larry
❑ 78St.PetCT-24
Silver, Long Ball
❑ 94SalBucC-30
Silver, Roy
❑ 86St.PetCP-28
❑ 87ArkTraP-12
❑ 87TexLeaAF-2
❑ 88LouRedBC-22
❑ 88LouRedBP-431
❑ 88LouRedBTI-44
❑ 89ArkTraGS-22
❑ 89BlaYNPRWL-87
❑ 89BlaYNPRWLU-53
❑ 89TexLeaAGS-38
❑ 90CMC-116
❑ 90LouRedBC-16
❑ 90LouRedBLBC-38
❑ 90LouRedBP-418
❑ 90ProAAAF-532
❑ 90TopTVCa-64
❑ 91SavCarC-2
❑ 91SavCarP-1669
❑ 92SprCarC-28
❑ 92SprCarF-886
❑ 94NewJerCC-29
❑ 95PeoChiTI-38
❑ 96PeoChiB-1
❑ 97PriWilC-2
❑ 98St.PetDRM-28
Silvera, Al
❑ 56Top-137
Silvera, Charlie
❑ 50YanTeal-21
❑ 52Bow-197
❑ 52Top-168
❑ 53Dor-119
❑ 53Top-242
❑ 54Top-96
❑ 55Top-188
❑ 56YanTeal-22
❑ 57Top-255
❑ 73OPC-323
❑ 73Top-323
❑ 74OPC-379
❑ 74Top-379
❑ 75RanPos-29
❑ 79TCM50-266
❑ 83TopRep5-168
❑ 91TopArc1-242
❑ 93RanKee-327
❑ 94TopArc1-96
❑ 94TopArc1G-96
Silverio, Francisco
❑ 86TamTarP-19
❑ 87CedRapRP-23
Silverio, Luis
❑ 75WatRoyT-26
❑ 76WatRoyT-26
❑ 77JacSunT-21
❑ 82OmaRoyT-23
❑ 85DomLeaS-53
❑ 88FloStaLAS-30
❑ 89BasCitRS-27
Silverio, Nelson
❑ 86MadMusP-19
❑ 86MadMusP-23
❑ 88ChaRaiP-1220
Silverio, Tom
❑ 72OPC-213
❑ 72Top-213
Silverio, Victor
❑ 91QuaCitAC-11
❑ 91QuaCitAP-2628
❑ 92PalSprAC-5
❑ 92PalSprAF-839
❑ 93LimRocDWB-3
Silverman, Aaron
❑ 52Par-3
Silverman, Bob
❑ 80KnoBluJT-9
Silverman, Don
❑ 85IowCubT-27
Silverman, Eric
❑ 50WorWidGV-19
Silverstein, Allan
❑ 88MyrBeaBJP-1187
❑ 89DunBluJS-15
❑ 90DunBluJS-16
Silvestre, Juan
❑ 98WisTimRM-24
Silvestri, David
❑ 87PanAmTUBI-5
❑ 87PanAmTURB-24
❑ 88TopTra-107T
❑ 88TopTraT-107T
❑ 89OscAstS-22
❑ 89Sta-18
❑ 89TopBig-141
❑ 90PriWilCTI-24
❑ 91AlbYanLD-15
❑ 91AlbYanP-1016
❑ 91LinDriAA-15
❑ 92Bow-87
❑ 92Cla2-T95
❑ 92ColCliF-361
❑ 92ColCliP-19
❑ 92ColCliS-116
❑ 92DonRoo-111
❑ 92LeaGolR-BC20
❑ 92Pin-531
❑ 92ProFS7-111
❑ 92SkyAAAF-55
❑ 93ClaFS7-291
❑ 93ColCliF-1118
❑ 93ColCliP-16
❑ 93FleFinE-252
❑ 93FleMajLP-B5
❑ 93Pin-180
❑ 93Sco-252
❑ 93Top-529
❑ 93TopGol-529
❑ 93TopInaM-529
❑ 93TopInaR-529
❑ 93TopMic-529
❑ 94ColCliF-2960
❑ 94ColCliP-24
❑ 94StaCluT-191
❑ 94StaCluTFDI-191
❑ 95Sco-298
❑ 95ScoGolR-298
❑ 95ScoPlaTS-298
❑ 96LeaSigEA-183
❑ 97Pac-354
❑ 97PacLigB-354
❑ 97PacSil-354
❑ 98DurBulTI-26
Silvestri, Ken
❑ 39WhiSoxTI-16
❑ 40WhiSoxL-16
❑ 47YanTeaT-24
❑ 49EurSta-147
❑ 49PhiBul-50
❑ 50PhiPhil-20
❑ 51Bow-256
❑ 52Bow-200
❑ 60Top-466
❑ 66BraPos-23
❑ 67BraPho-27
❑ 68BraPos-28
❑ 73OPC-237
❑ 73Top-237A
❑ 73Top-237B
❑ 74OPC-634
❑ 74Top-634
❑ 75AtlBraP-33
❑ 75Phi195T-26
❑ 78KnoKnoST-20
❑ 80Phi195T-26
❑ 87PorBeaP-23
❑ 89WatIndS-26
❑ 90WatIndS-25
Silvey, Jeff
❑ 90GeoColC-27
Silvey, Jim
❑ 72CedRapCT-21
Silvia, Brian
❑ 92PriRedC-18
❑ 92PriRedF-3090
❑ 93PriRedC-28
❑ 93PriRedF-4183
❑ 94NewJerCC-24
❑ 94NewJerCF-3420
Sima, Al
❑ 52Top-93
❑ 53Bri-20
❑ 53Top-241
❑ 54Top-216
❑ 83TopRep5-93
❑ 88ChaLooLTI-28
❑ 91TopArc1-241
❑ 94TopArc1-216
❑ 94TopArc1G-216
Simas, Bill Anthony
❑ 92BoiHawC-29
❑ 92BoiHawF-3627
❑ 93CedRapKC-17
❑ 93CedRapKF-1736
❑ 94LakElsSC-17
❑ 94LakElsSF-1663
❑ 95Bow-197
❑ 95NasSouTI-23
❑ 96Bow-175
❑ 96BowFoi-175
❑ 96FleUpd-U27
❑ 96FleUpdTC-U27
❑ 96Ult-335
❑ 96UltGolM-335
❑ 97WhiSoxTI-41
❑ 98PacOnl-179
❑ 98PacOnlR-179
❑ 98PacOnlWC-179
❑ 99Fle-551
❑ 99FleSta9-551
❑ 99FleWarT-551
❑ 99Top-273
❑ 99TopChr-273
❑ 99TopChrR-273
❑ 99TopMVPP-273
Simas, William
❑ 31Zee-94
❑ 32Zee-89
Simcox, Larry
❑ 82DayBeaAT-23
❑ 83ColAstT-7
❑ 98TenKry-4
Simmermacher, Bret
❑ 86BelMarCr-114
Simmons, Al (Aloysius)
❑ 21Exh-160
❑ 26SpoComoA-40
❑ 26SpoNewSM-8
❑ 28Exh-56
❑ 28PorandAR-A33
❑ 28PorandAR-B33
❑ 28W56PlaC-C11
❑ 29PorandAR-85
❑ 30SchR33-1
❑ 30UncJac-25
❑ 30W554-16
❑ 31Exh-27
❑ 31W517-40
❑ 32OrbPinNP-39
❑ 32OrbPinUP-53
❑ 32R33So2-415
❑ 32USCar*-17
❑ 33ButCanV-44
❑ 33ButCre-24
❑ 33CraJacP-20
❑ 33DelR33-2
❑ 33DouDisP-39
❑ 33ExhFou-14
❑ 33GeoCMil-27
❑ 33Gou-35
❑ 33GouCanV-35
❑ 33RitCE-9D
❑ 33TatOrb-53
❑ 33TatOrbSDR-154
❑ 33WorCig-86
❑ 33WorCig-87
❑ 34BabRutG-56
❑ 34BatR31-34
❑ 34ButPreR-55
❑ 34DiaStaR-2A
❑ 34DiaStaR-2B
❑ 34ExhFou-10
❑ 34ExhFou-14
❑ 35AlDemDCR3-14
❑ 35AlDemDCR3-16
❑ 35ExhFou-10
❑ 35GouPuzR-5A
❑ 35GouPuzR-6A
❑ 35GouPuzR-11J
❑ 35GouPuzR-13A
❑ 35WheBB1-24
❑ 36GouWidPPR-A94
❑ 36GouWidPPR-B19
❑ 36NatChiFPR-67
❑ 36NatChiFPR-90
❑ 36OveCanR-41
❑ 36WorWidGV-77
❑ 38BasTabP-26
❑ 38CloFotW-76
❑ 38OurNatGPP-28
❑ 39GouPreR303A-40
❑ 39GouPreR303B-21
❑ 39WorWidGTP-40
❑ 42A'sTeal-30
❑ 43RedSoxTI-22
❑ 45A'sTeal-29
❑ 46A'sTeal-12
❑ 47A'sTeal-28
❑ 48A'sTeal-22
❑ 49PhiBul-51
❑ 50CalHOFW-65
❑ 51R42SmaS-102
❑ 53ArtHaloFP-76
❑ 60ExhWriH-21
❑ 60Fle-32
❑ 61Fle-77
❑ 61GolPre-20
❑ 63BazA-21
❑ 67TopVen-170
❑ 69Baz-2
❑ 69Baz-9
❑ 74A's192T-24
❑ 74CapPub-58
❑ 76GrePlaG-8
❑ 76RowExh-13
❑ 76ShaPiz-64
❑ 76WhiSoxTAG-11
❑ 77BobParHoF-43
❑ 77CinRedT-11
❑ 77GalGloG-58
❑ 77GalGloG-190
❑ 77PhiFav-5
❑ 78DexHaloFP-45
❑ 80LauFamF-3
❑ 80PacLeg-119
❑ 80PerHaloFP-68
❑ 80SSPHOF-68
❑ 80WhiSoxGT-8
❑ 81ConTSN-81
❑ 82DiaCla-9
❑ 82TCMGreH-26
❑ 82TCMGreS-24
❑ 83A'sGreT-5
❑ 83BigLeaCOA-10
❑ 83ConMar-4
❑ 83MiaMarT-16
❑ 85FegMurCG-17
❑ 86SpoDecG-5
❑ 87HygAllG-39
❑ 88ConAmeA-22
❑ 88ConSer4-25
❑ 91ConTSN-49
❑ 91ConTSN-311
❑ 91TopArc1-326
❑ 92ConTSN-423
❑ 92ConTSN-554
❑ 92ConTSNCI-13
❑ 93ConTSN-666
❑ 94ConTSN-1084
❑ 94ConTSN-1136
❑ 94ConTSNB-1084
❑ 94ConTSNB-1136
❑ 94TedWil-70
❑ 95ConTSN-1375
❑ 95MegRut-3
❑ 99UppDecCL-43
❑ 99UppDecCLCC-43
Simmons, Brad
❑ 77DayBeaIT-23
Simmons, Brian
❑ 96MidLeaAB-55
❑ 96SouBenSHS-24
❑ 97BirBarB-9
❑ 97SouLeaTP-1
❑ 98BesAutSS-47
❑ 98FleUpd-U50
❑ 98SP MinPE-37
❑ 98SPMin-37
❑ 99Bow-146
❑ 99BowChr-146
❑ 99BowChrG-146
❑ 99BowChrGR-146
❑ 99BowChrI-146
❑ 99BowChrIR-146
❑ 99BowChrR-146
❑ 99BowGol-146
❑ 99BowInt-146
❑ 99CroRoyB-35
❑ 99CroRoyL-35
❑ 99CroRoyOD-35
❑ 99Fle-229
❑ 99FleBri-142
❑ 99FleBri2G-142
❑ 99FleBriBlu-142
❑ 99FleBriGol-142
❑ 99FleSta9-229
❑ 99FleWarT-229
❑ 99SkyThu-187
❑ 99SkyThuRant-187
❑ 99SkyThuRave-187
❑ 99SpoIll-70
❑ 99ThuSkySupR-187
❑ 99UppDec-341
❑ 99UppDecEL1-341
❑ 99UppDecEL2-341
❑ 99Vic-100
Simmons, Carlos
❑ 96ChaRivTI-9628
Simmons, Chris
❑ 94OgdRapF-3750
❑ 94OgdRapSP-19
Simmons, Curt
❑ 47Exh-209
❑ 47PM1StaP1-202
❑ 49Bow-14
❑ 49EurSta-148
❑ 49PhiBul-52
❑ 49PhiLumPB-11
❑ 50Bow-68
❑ 50JJKCopP-18
❑ 50PhiPhil-21
❑ 51BerRos-D9
❑ 51Bow-111
❑ 52Bow-184
❑ 52StaCalL-77C
❑ 52Top-203
❑ 53BowC-64
❑ 54Bow-79
❑ 54RedMan-NL12
❑ 55ArmCoi-18
❑ 55Bow-64
❑ 55RedMan-NL24
❑ 55RobGouS-6
❑ 55RobGouW-6
❑ 56PhiPos-6
❑ 56Top-290
❑ 57Top-158
❑ 58Hir-28
❑ 58PhiJayP-11
❑ 58PhiTeal-19
❑ 58Top-404
❑ 59Top-382
❑ 60Top-451
❑ 61Top-11
❑ 61TopStal-93
❑ 62CarJayP-11
❑ 62Jel-167
❑ 62Pos-167
❑ 62PosCan-167
❑ 62Top-56
❑ 62Top-285
❑ 62TopVen-56
❑ 63CarJayP-18
❑ 63CarJayP-19
❑ 63Top-22
❑ 64Top-385
❑ 65CarTeal-23
❑ 65Top-373
❑ 66CarTeal-10
❑ 66Top-489
❑ 67CokCapC-16
❑ 67OPC-39
❑ 67Top-39
❑ 75Phi195T-27
❑ 79DiaGre-319
❑ 79TCM50-54
❑ 80Phi195T-27
❑ 83PhiPosGPaM-9
❑ 83TopRep5-203
❑ 87Phi195T-2
❑ 91TopArc1-318
❑ 99SpoIllGotG-18
❑ 99SpoIllGotGA-68
Simmons, Deon
❑ 86AncGlaPTI-41
Simmons, Enoch
❑ 89MedAthB-26
❑ 90MadMusB-10
❑ 90MadMusP-2281
❑ 91Cla/Bes-256

❑ 91ModA'sC-23
❑ 91ModA'sP-3105
❑ 92CalLeaACL-11
❑ 92RenSilSCLC-53
❑ 93HunStaF-2096
❑ 94TacTigF-3189

Simmons, George
❑ 11T205-156
❑ 12ImpTobC-75
❑ 67SpoHobFC-3

Simmons, Greg
❑ 85BelBreT-17
❑ 86BelBreP-21

Simmons, Gus
❑ 63GadFunC-77

Simmons, Hack
❑ 11DiaGumP-25

Simmons, Jason
❑ 93IdaFalBF-4029
❑ 93IdaFalBSP-10

Simmons, Jerry
❑ 98EugEme-25

Simmons, John
❑ 92IdaFalGF-3512
❑ 92IdaFalGSP-1
❑ 93MacBraC-21
❑ 93MacBraF-1399
❑ 94DurBulC-18
❑ 94DurBulF-327
❑ 94DurBulTI-19
❑ 95BreBtaTI-50

Simmons, John Earl
❑ 50WorWidGV-5
❑ 52Par-62
❑ 53ExhCan-35

Simmons, Josh
❑ 92HunCubC-10
❑ 92HunCubF-3158
❑ 93PeoChiTI-25

Simmons, Mark
❑ 92BoiHawC-7
❑ 92BoiHawF-3639
❑ 93BoiHawF-3931
❑ 93CedRapKC-18
❑ 93CedRapKF-1748
❑ 94CedRapKC-20
❑ 94CedRapKF-1118
❑ 95LakElsSTI-22

Simmons, Mitch
❑ 92AlbPolF-2315

Simmons, Nelson
❑ 83BirBarT-16
❑ 84EvaTriT-9
❑ 85DomLeaS-138
❑ 85FleUpd-103
❑ 85NasSouTI-22
❑ 86Don-272
❑ 86Fle-238
❑ 86RocRedWP-21
❑ 86TigCaiD-16
❑ 86Top-121
❑ 86TopTif-121
❑ 87RocRedWP-18
❑ 88CalCanC-19
❑ 88CalCanP-802
❑ 88TopClo-104
❑ 89BlaYNPRWLU-10
❑ 89Don-212
❑ 90HunStaB-22
❑ 91LinDriAAA-545
❑ 91OriCro-420
❑ 91TacTigLD-545
❑ 91TacTigP-2320
❑ 93LinVenB-315

Simmons, Randy
❑ 88PulBraP-1768
❑ 89SouAtlLAGS-44
❑ 89SumBraP-1110
❑ 90Bes-81
❑ 90BurBraB-24
❑ 90BurBraP-2364
❑ 90BurBraS-24
❑ 91DurBulP-1561

Simmons, Scott
❑ 91HamRedP-4038
❑ 92ClaFS7-271
❑ 92MidLeaATI-40
❑ 92SprCarC-22
❑ 92SprCarF-866
❑ 93St.PetCC-23
❑ 93St.PetCF-2627
❑ 94ArkTraF-3090
❑ 95ArkTraTI-25
❑ 95Exc-274
❑ 96LouRedB-25

Simmons, Ted
❑ 70CarTeal-26
❑ 71CarTeal-24
❑ 71CarTeal-35
❑ 71CarTeal-36
❑ 71OPC-117
❑ 71Top-117
❑ 72CarTeal-14
❑ 72OPC-154
❑ 72Top-154
❑ 73LinPor-169
❑ 73OPC-85
❑ 73SevTraC-71
❑ 73Top-85
❑ 74Kel-21
❑ 74OPC-260
❑ 74Top-260
❑ 74TopDecE-10
❑ 74TopSta-116
❑ 75Hos-95
❑ 75OPC-75
❑ 75St.LouCP-25
❑ 75Top-75
❑ 75TopMin-75
❑ 76BlaDis-56
❑ 76BucDis-56
❑ 76CarDis-56
❑ 76CraDis-56
❑ 76DailsID-56
❑ 76Hos-113
❑ 76IsaDis-56
❑ 76Kel-57
❑ 76OPC-191
❑ 76OPC-290
❑ 76OrbDis-56
❑ 76RedBarD-56
❑ 76SafDis-56
❑ 76Spo-5
❑ 76SSP-274
❑ 76St.LouCP-30
❑ 76Top-191
❑ 76Top-290
❑ 76TowCluD-56
❑ 77BurCheD-16
❑ 77Car5-26
❑ 77CarTeal-25
❑ 77Hos-61
❑ 77OPC-196
❑ 77Top-470
❑ 77TopCloS-43
❑ 78CarTeal-31
❑ 78Hos-65
❑ 78OPC-150
❑ 78Pep-38
❑ 78Top-380
❑ 78WifBalD-69
❑ 79BasPat-81
❑ 79Car5-26
❑ 79Hos-44
❑ 79Kel-2
❑ 79OPC-267
❑ 79Top-510
❑ 79TopCom-30
❑ 80Kel-45
❑ 80OPC-47
❑ 80Top-85
❑ 80TopSup-36
❑ 81AllGamPI-43
❑ 81Don-308
❑ 81Fle-528
❑ 81FleStiC-120
❑ 81OPC-352
❑ 81PerCreC-17
❑ 81Top-705
❑ 81TopScr-63
❑ 81TopSti-94
❑ 81TopSupN-15
❑ 81TopTra-830
❑ 82BrePol-23
❑ 82Don-106
❑ 82Fle-152
❑ 82FleSta-137
❑ 82OPC-150
❑ 82Top-150
❑ 82TopSti-201
❑ 82TopStiV-201
❑ 83AllGamPI-43
❑ 83BreGar-16
❑ 83BrePol-23
❑ 83Don-332
❑ 83Fle-45
❑ 83FleSta-176
❑ 83FleSti-22
❑ 83OPC-33
❑ 83OPC-284
❑ 83PerAll-5
❑ 83PerAllG-5
❑ 83Top-450
❑ 83Top-451
❑ 83TopSti-85
❑ 84AllGamPI-133
❑ 84BreGar-17
❑ 84BrePol-23
❑ 84Don-473
❑ 84DonActAS-58
❑ 84Fle-213
❑ 84FunFooP-124
❑ 84MilBra-24
❑ 84Nes792-404
❑ 84Nes792-630
❑ 84Nes792-713
❑ 84Nes792-726
❑ 84OPC-94
❑ 84OPC-122
❑ 84RalPur-3
❑ 84SevCoi-C21
❑ 84Top-404
❑ 84Top-630
❑ 84Top-713
❑ 84Top-726
❑ 84TopCer-3
❑ 84TopGloA-9
❑ 84TopGloS-18
❑ 84TopSti-193
❑ 84TopSti-293
❑ 84TopStiB-2
❑ 84TopTif-404
❑ 84TopTif-630
❑ 84TopTif-713
❑ 84TopTif-726
❑ 85BreGar-19
❑ 85BrePol-23
❑ 85Don-414
❑ 85Fle-596
❑ 85Lea-104
❑ 85OPC-318
❑ 85Top-318
❑ 85TopSti-294
❑ 85TopTif-318
❑ 86BasStaB-100
❑ 86BraPol-23
❑ 86Don-292
❑ 86Fle-503
❑ 86FleUpd-106
❑ 86Lea-167
❑ 86Spo-196
❑ 86SpoDecG-62
❑ 86Top-237
❑ 86TopSti-199
❑ 86TopTat-4
❑ 86TopTif-237
❑ 86TopTra-102T
❑ 86TopTraT-102T
❑ 87BraSmo-13
❑ 87Don-537
❑ 87Fle-528
❑ 87FleGlo-528
❑ 87Top-516
❑ 87TopTif-516
❑ 88Don-560
❑ 88Fle-549
❑ 88FleGlo-549
❑ 88Lea-222
❑ 88Sco-285
❑ 88ScoGlo-285
❑ 88StaLinBra-17
❑ 88Top-791
❑ 88TopTif-791
❑ 89Fle-599
❑ 89FleGlo-599
❑ 89Sco-611
❑ 89UppDec-570
❑ 91MDAA-2
❑ 92BreCarT-20
❑ 92CarMcD-35
❑ 93PirNatI-28
❑ 94BreMilB-352
❑ 94BreMilB-353

Simmons, Todd
❑ 86BeaGolGP-22
❑ 87LasVegSP-11
❑ 88Fle-650
❑ 88FleGlo-650
❑ 88LasVegSC-6
❑ 88LasVegSP-240
❑ 89DenZepC-10
❑ 89DenZepP-30
❑ 89Fle-318
❑ 89FleGlo-318

Simmons, Wendell
❑ 98YakBeaG-30

Simms, Mike (Michael)
❑ 87AshTouP-17
❑ 88FloStaLAS-21
❑ 88OscAstS-25
❑ 89ColMudB-7
❑ 89ColMudP-141
❑ 89ColMudS-22
❑ 89Sta-3
❑ 90CMC-622
❑ 90ProAAAF-198
❑ 90TucTorC-20
❑ 90TucTorP-208
❑ 91Bow-551
❑ 91Cla2-T90
❑ 91Fle-516
❑ 91LinDriAAA-619
❑ 91OPC-32
❑ 91Sco-766
❑ 91StaClu-281
❑ 91Top-32
❑ 91TopDeb90-144
❑ 91TopDesS-32
❑ 91TopMic-32
❑ 91TopTif-32
❑ 91TucTorLD-619
❑ 91TucTorP-2221
❑ 91UppDec-664
❑ 92Don-747
❑ 92Fle-445
❑ 92OPC-463
❑ 92PanSti-156
❑ 92Sco-632
❑ 92SkyAAAF-276
❑ 92StaClu-262
❑ 92Top-463
❑ 92TopGol-463
❑ 92TopGolW-463
❑ 92TopMic-463
❑ 92TucTorF-501
❑ 92TucTorS-619
❑ 92UppDec-584
❑ 93Don-32
❑ 93LasVegSF-953
❑ 93PacSpa-128
❑ 94BufBisF-1845
❑ 95TucTotTI-24
❑ 96AstMot-24
❑ 96ColCho-566
❑ 96ColChoGS-566
❑ 96ColChoSS-566
❑ 96Don-499
❑ 96DonPreP-499
❑ 97RanMot-23
❑ 98PacInvGems-107
❑ 98PacOnl-745
❑ 98PacOnlR-745
❑ 98PacOnlWC-745
❑ 99Fle-544
❑ 99FleSta9-544
❑ 99FleWarT-544

Simon, Ben
❑ 96YakBeaTI-41
❑ 98VerBeaDM-16

Simon, Michael
❑ 75TopPho-30

Simon, Michael Edward
❑ 10PirHerICP-10
❑ 10PirTipTD-19
❑ 11HelSta-165
❑ 11MecDFT-40
❑ 11PinT-5-858
❑ 11SpoLifM-259
❑ 12T207-166
❑ 14CraJacE-25
❑ 15CraJacE-25
❑ 17Zee-116

Simon, Randall
❑ 93DanBraC-24
❑ 93DanBraF-3626
❑ 94MacBraC-20
❑ 94MacBraF-2216
❑ 95DurBulTI-27
❑ 96BesAutSA-72
❑ 96GreBraB-24
❑ 96GreBraTI-18
❑ 97BesAutAS-56
❑ 97BesAutP-H9
❑ 97BesAutSBPP-35
❑ 97Bow-131
❑ 97BowChr-143
❑ 97BowChrI-143
❑ 97BowChrIR-143
❑ 97BowChrR-143
❑ 97BowInt-131
❑ 97FlaShoWotF-3
❑ 97Fle-653
❑ 97FleTif-653
❑ 97RicBra-23
❑ 97Ult-508
❑ 97UltGolME-508
❑ 97UltPlaME-508
❑ 98BowBes-169
❑ 98BowBesAR-169
❑ 98BowBesR-169
❑ 98CirThu-88
❑ 98CirThuRav-88
❑ 98CirThuSupRav-88
❑ 98ColCho-37
❑ 98Don-323
❑ 98DonGolPP-323
❑ 98DonSigA-80
❑ 98DonSigAC-102
❑ 98DonSigAM-104
❑ 98DonSigSP-25
❑ 98DonSilPP-323
❑ 98E-X2Sig2001-10
❑ 98Fle-62
❑ 98LeaRS-251
❑ 98LeaRSLHolo-251
❑ 98LeaRSLong-251
❑ 98LeaRTrue-251
❑ 98PacInvGems-126
❑ 98PinSna-AB4
❑ 98RicBraQ-24
❑ 98SpoIll-151
❑ 98SpoIllEE-151
❑ 98SpoIllFE-151
❑ 98StaCluFDI-189
❑ 98StaCluI-189
❑ 98StaCluITW-W13
❑ 98StaCluOneK-189
❑ 98StaCluPP-189
❑ 98Stu-143
❑ 98StuGPP-143
❑ 98StuSPP-143
❑ 98UppDec-301
❑ 99BasAmeTPA-39
❑ 99CroRoyB-17
❑ 99CroRoyL-17
❑ 99CroRoyOD-17
❑ 99UltWorP-6

Simon, Richie (Richard)
❑ 86AubAstP-23
❑ 87AubAstP-25
❑ 88AshTouP-1069
❑ 89OscAstS-23
❑ 90ColMudB-13
❑ 90ColMudP-1347
❑ 90ColMudS-22
❑ 91JacGenLD-573
❑ 91JacGenP-927
❑ 91LinDriAA-564
❑ 91LinDriAA-573
❑ 92JacGenF-4000
❑ 92JacGenS-343
❑ 92SkyAA F-147
❑ 92TucTorF-486
❑ 93ShrCapF-2758
❑ 94ShrCapF-1605

Simon, Rick
❑ 74GasRanT-19

Simon, Willie
❑ 76WauMetT-23

Simond, Rob
❑ 80LynSaiT-6
❑ 81LynSaiT-10

Simonds, Dan
❑ 88FreSunCLC-6
❑ 88FreSunP-1230
❑ 89EasLeaDDP-DD29
❑ 89FreKeyS-22
❑ 89HagSunB-23
❑ 90HagSunB-2
❑ 90HagSunP-1417
❑ 91IowCubLD-217
❑ 91IowCubP-1064
❑ 91LinDriAAA-217
❑ 93CubMar-24
❑ 96BluOriB-2
❑ 96BowBayB-3
❑ 97CliLumG-24
❑ 98CliLumG-27

Simoneaux, Wayne
❑ 91IdaFalBSP-19

Simons, Doug
❑ 89CalLeaA-17
❑ 89VisOakCLC-95
❑ 89VisOakP-1435
❑ 90CMC-749
❑ 90OrlSunRB-21
❑ 90OrlSunRP-1082
❑ 90OrlSunRS-19
❑ 91Bow-463
❑ 91Cla2-T86
❑ 91DonRoo-26
❑ 91MetColP-46
❑ 91MetKah-43
❑ 91MetPerPA-27
❑ 91OPCPre-110
❑ 91ScoRoo-91T
❑ 91TopTra-109T
❑ 91TopTraT-109T
❑ 91UppDecFE-63F
❑ 92Don-688
❑ 92IndIndF-1858
❑ 92MetColP-28
❑ 92OPC-82
❑ 92Sco-479
❑ 92Sco100RS-91
❑ 92Top-82
❑ 92TopDeb91-163
❑ 92TopGol-82
❑ 92TopGolW-82
❑ 92TopMic-82
❑ 93Don-276
❑ 93OttLynF-2435
❑ 94OmaRoyF-1224
❑ 96JacGenB-25
❑ 96TexLeaAB-15
❑ 98PitMetM-2

Simons, Mitchel
❑ 91JamExpC-12
❑ 91JamExpP-3555
❑ 91OklStaC-23
❑ 92AlbPolCB-25
❑ 93WesPalBEC-22
❑ 93WesPalBEF-1350
❑ 97SalLakB-27
❑ 98RocRedWQ-26

Simons, Neil
❑ 82DayBeaAT-15

Simonson, Bob
❑ 85BelBreT-6
❑ 86BelBreP-22
❑ 88BelBreGS-9
❑ 93ChaRaiC-20
❑ 93ChaRaiF-1925

Simontacchi, Jason
❑ 96SpoIndB-26
❑ 97LanLugTS-26

Simonton, Benji
❑ 92ClaDraP-55
❑ 92EveGiaC-9
❑ 92EveGiaF-1705
❑ 93Bow-112
❑ 93CliGiaF-2502
❑ 93StaCluM-60
❑ 94CliLumC-1
❑ 94CliLumF-1996
❑ 94MidLeaAF-MDW41
❑ 95Exc-295
❑ 95ExcLeaL-14
❑ 95UppDecML-55
❑ 95UppDecMLFS-55
❑ 97ShrCap-23
❑ 97ShrCapB-23
❑ 98SanJosGQ-11

Simonton, Cy
❑ 95EveAqaTI-23
❑ 96EveAquB-21

Simpson, Allan
❑ 97EveAquG-23
❑ 98WisTimRM-10

Simpson, Cory
❑ 98DanBraQ-16

Simpson, Danny
❑ 83TriTriT-22

Simpson, Dick
❑ 63Top-407
❑ 64Top-127
❑ 64TopVen-127
❑ 65SeaPop-21
❑ 65Top-374
❑ 66Top-311
❑ 66TopVen-311
❑ 67CokCapR-18
❑ 67OPC-6
❑ 67Top-6
❑ 68Top-459
❑ 69MilBra-254
❑ 69Top-608
❑ 69YanPhoS-49
❑ 87AstShowSTh-22
❑ 92YanWIZ6-116

Simpson, Greg
❑ 86CedRapRT-9
❑ 87VerRedP-6

❑ 88CedRapRP-1137
Simpson, Herb
❑ 92NegLeaRLI-56
Simpson, Jay
❑ 92BoiHawC-10
❑ 93PalSprAC-20
❑ 93PalSprAF-84
❑ 94LakElsSC-18
❑ 94LakElsSF-1677
Simpson, Jeramie
❑ 96StLucMTI-10
Simpson, Joe
❑ 75AlbDukCa-2
❑ 75IntLeaASB-32
❑ 75PacCoaLAB-32
❑ 79Top-719
❑ 80Top-637
❑ 81Don-168
❑ 81Fle-616
❑ 81MarPol-15
❑ 81MarPos-29
❑ 81Top-116
❑ 82Don-55
❑ 82Fle-518
❑ 82MarPos-29
❑ 82Top-382
❑ 83Fle-485
❑ 83RoyPos-28
❑ 83Top-567
❑ 83TopTra-104T
❑ 84Don-496
❑ 84EdmTraC-115
❑ 84Fle-358
❑ 84Nes792-219
❑ 84Top-219
❑ 84TopTif-219
❑ 89CarNewE-9
❑ 90DodTar-736
Simpson, O.J.
❑ 74NewYorNTDiS-32
Simpson, Shelton
❑ 90WelPirP-29
Simpson, Suitcase (Harry)
❑ 52Bow-223
❑ 52IndNumN-17
❑ 52Top-193
❑ 53BowC-86
❑ 53Top-150
❑ 55A'sRodM-38
❑ 55A'sTeal-23
❑ 56A'sPos-38
❑ 56A'sRodM-9
❑ 56Top-239
❑ 57Top-225
❑ 58Top-299
❑ 59Top-333
❑ 60Lea-81
❑ 60Top-180
❑ 60TopVen-180
❑ 61UniOil-SD10
❑ 76A'sRodMC-24
❑ 79TCM50-79
❑ 81WhiSox1T-15
❑ 83TopRep5-193
❑ 84OCoandSI-123
❑ 86NegLeaF-92
❑ 91TopArc1-150
Simpson, Wayne
❑ 70DayDaiNM-68
❑ 70Top-683
❑ 71Kel-1
❑ 71MilDud-64
❑ 71MLBOffS-69
❑ 71OPC-68
❑ 71OPC-339
❑ 71Top-68
❑ 71Top-339
❑ 71TopCoi-53
❑ 72Top-762
❑ 73OPC-428
❑ 73Top-428
❑ 76SalLakCGC-14
❑ 76SSP-599
Simpson, William
❑ 77AshTouT-21
❑ 78AshTouT-25
Sims, Daniel
❑ 89IdaFalBP-2018
❑ 90SumBraB-20
❑ 90SumBraP-2448
Sims, Duke (Duane)
❑ 66OPC-169
❑ 66Top-169
❑ 66TopVen-169
❑ 67OPC-3
❑ 67Top-3
❑ 68Top-508
❑ 69MilBra-255
❑ 69Top-414
❑ 69TopSta-168
❑ 69TopTeaP-13
❑ 70MLBOffS-203
❑ 70OPC-275
❑ 70Top-275
❑ 71Dod-13
❑ 71DodTic-15
❑ 71MLBOffS-114
❑ 71OPC-172
❑ 71Top-172
❑ 71TopCoi-66
❑ 72MilBra-316
❑ 72OPC-63
❑ 72Top-63
❑ 73OPC-304
❑ 73Top-304
❑ 74OPC-398
❑ 74Top-398
❑ 86AppFoxP-23
❑ 89SweBasG-128
❑ 90DodTar-737
❑ 92YanWIZ7-140
❑ 93RanKee-328
Sims, Greg
❑ 89AugPirP-517
❑ 89SouAtlLAGS-5
❑ 90SalBucS-22
❑ 91VisOakP-1756
Sims, Gregory E.
❑ 66Top-596
Sims, Harry
❑ 52LavPro-33
Sims, Joe Beely
❑ 86JamExpP-23
❑ 87JamExpP-2545
Sims, Kenny
❑ 98BluOriQ-9
Sims, Kinney
❑ 88RenSilSCLC-278
Sims, Mark
❑ 87SpaPhiP-6
❑ 88ClePhiS-21
❑ 89ClePhiS-20
❑ 90Bes-182
❑ 90EasLeaAP-EL22
❑ 90ReaPhiB-10
❑ 90ReaPhiP-1220
❑ 90ReaPhiS-22
❑ 91LinDriAA-519
❑ 91ReaPhiLD-519
❑ 91ReaPhiP-1370
❑ 92ScrRedBF-2446
❑ 92ScrRedBS-494
❑ 93PorBeaF-2384
❑ 94ButCopKSP-28
Sims, Mike
❑ 83TamTarT-29
❑ 86VerRedP-19
❑ 93ElmPioC-18
❑ 93ElmPioF-3827
❑ 94BreCouMC-17
❑ 94BreCouMF-15
❑ 95BreCouMF-250
Sims, Wesley
❑ 93EriSaiC-22
❑ 93EriSaiF-3125
❑ 94ChaRanF-2506
Simunic, Doug
❑ 79MemChiT-7
❑ 80MemChiT-22
❑ 83ChaChaT-7
❑ 84BufBisT-6
❑ 84MaiGuiT-5
❑ 89AubAstP-2184
❑ 89PacSenL-35
❑ 89TopSenL-84
❑ 90EliSenL-105
❑ 91KisDodP-4205
❑ 91PacSenL-55
❑ 92GulCoaDF-3586
❑ 98FarRedHM-26
Sinacori, Chris
❑ 91GreFalDSP-21
❑ 92VerBeaDC-16
❑ 92VerBeaDF-2873
❑ 93VerBeaDC-22
❑ 93VerBeaDF-2218
❑ 94VerBeaDC-20
❑ 94VerBeaDF-71
❑ 95DunBluJTI-24
Sinatro, Greg
❑ 77SanJosMC-8
Sinatro, Matt
❑ 81RicBraT-20
❑ 82Don-149
❑ 82RicBraT-12
❑ 83Don-622
❑ 83RicBraT-11
❑ 85GreBraTI-15
❑ 87TacTigP-9
❑ 88TacTigC-18
❑ 88TacTigP-616
❑ 89BlaYNPRWLU-38
❑ 89TucTorC-11
❑ 89TucTorP-201
❑ 90CalCanC-13
❑ 90CalCanP-654
❑ 90CMC-440
❑ 90ProAAAF-119
❑ 90TopTra-115T
❑ 90TopTraT-115T
❑ 91OPC-709
❑ 91Top-709
❑ 91TopDesS-709
❑ 91TopMic-709
❑ 91TopTif-709
❑ 92Bow-462
❑ 92MarMot-18
❑ 92StaClu-872
❑ 95MarMot-28
❑ 96MarMot-28
Sinclair, John
❑ 87BriYouC-12
Sinclair, Ken
❑ 84SavCarT-25
Sinclair, Steve
❑ 91MedHatBJP-4100
❑ 91MedHatBJSP-12
❑ 93MedHatBJF-3736
❑ 93MedHatBJSP-2
❑ 94HagSunC-22
❑ 94HagSunF-2730
❑ 95DunBluJTI-25
❑ 96DunBluJB-23
❑ 96DunBluJTI-27
❑ 97DunBluJTI-25
❑ 98PacOmeRS-12
❑ 98PacOmeRST2-12
❑ 98PacOnl-775
❑ 98PacOnlR-775
❑ 98PacOnlWC-775
❑ 98SyrSkyG-27
❑ 99Fle-570
❑ 99FleSta9-570
❑ 99FleWarT-570
Siner, Hosea John
❑ 09ColChiE-262
❑ 12ColRedB-262
❑ 12ColTinT-262
Singer, Bill
❑ 66Top-288
❑ 66TopVen-288
❑ 67OPC-12
❑ 67Top-12
❑ 68Top-249
❑ 68TopVen-249
❑ 69MLBOffS-152
❑ 69OPC-12
❑ 69Top-12
❑ 69Top-575
❑ 69TopSta-49
❑ 69TopTeaP-22
❑ 70Kel-17
❑ 70MLBOffS-57
❑ 70OPC-71
❑ 70OPC-490
❑ 70Top-71
❑ 70Top-490
❑ 70TopBoo-17
❑ 71Dod-14
❑ 71DodTic-16
❑ 71MLBOffS-115
❑ 71OPC-145
❑ 71Top-145
❑ 72MilBra-317
❑ 72OPC-25
❑ 72Top-25
❑ 73LinPor-36
❑ 73OPC-570
❑ 73Top-570
❑ 74Kel-12
❑ 74OPC-210
❑ 74Top-210
❑ 74TopSta-149
❑ 75CalAngP-39
❑ 75Hos-82
❑ 75HosTwi-82
❑ 75OPC-40
❑ 75Top-40
❑ 75TopMin-40
❑ 76MinTwiP-15
❑ 76OPC-411
❑ 76SSP-188
❑ 76Top-411
❑ 76TopTra-411T
❑ 77ChiWilD-62
❑ 77DailsID-62
❑ 77DetCaeD-62
❑ 77HolInnD-62
❑ 77Hos-139
❑ 77MSADis-62
❑ 77OPC-85
❑ 77RCColC-60
❑ 77SagDis-62
❑ 77sDis-62
❑ 77Top-346
❑ 77TopCloS-44
❑ 77WenDis-62
❑ 77ZipDis-62
❑ 78RCColC-2
❑ 84DodUniO-6
❑ 87DodSmoA-33
❑ 88DodSmo-6
❑ 89DodSmoG-75
❑ 90DodTar-738
❑ 91DodUno7P-4
❑ 92DodStaTA-8
❑ 92Nab-18
❑ 93RanKee-329
Singer, Tom
❑ 90St.CatBJP-3457
❑ 91MyrBeaHC-10
❑ 91MyrBeaHP-2944
❑ 92DunBluJC-16
❑ 92DunBluJF-1999
❑ 93DunBluJC-20
❑ 93DunBluJF-1795
❑ 93DunBluJFFN-22
❑ 94DunBluJC-25
❑ 94DunBluJF-2557
Singletary, Chico
❑ 87SavCarP-15
Singletary, Daniel
❑ 98LetBlaDG-26
Singleton, Bert Elmer
❑ 49Bow-147
❑ 49SomandK-25
❑ 52MotCoo-17
❑ 53SanFraSTI-18
❑ 55SeaPop-18
❑ 56SeaPop-20
❑ 57Top-378
❑ 59Top-548
❑ 62SeaPop-12
❑ 63MilSau-6
❑ 63SeaPop-9
Singleton, Chris
❑ 94Cla-176
❑ 94ClaGolF-63
❑ 94ClaTriF-T70
❑ 94SanJosGC-21
❑ 94SanJosGF-2829
❑ 96Cir-194
❑ 96CirRav-194
❑ 96FleUpd-U209
❑ 96FleUpdTC-U209
❑ 96TexLeaAB-16
❑ 96UltGolP-15
❑ 96UltGolPHGM-15
❑ 97ShrCap-24
❑ 97ShrCapB-24
❑ 97Ult-298
❑ 97UltGolME-298
❑ 97UltPlaME-298
❑ 98ColCliD-23
❑ 98ColCliM-28
❑ 99Bow-407
❑ 99BowGol-407
❑ 99BowInt-407
❑ 99PacOme-61
❑ 99PacOmeC-61
❑ 99PacOmeG-61
❑ 99PacOmePB-61
❑ 99SkyPre-239
❑ 99SkyPre-239
❑ 99SkyPreR-239
❑ 99SkyPreR-239
Singleton, Duane
❑ 92Bow-679
❑ 92ClaFS7-285
❑ 92StoPorC-7
❑ 92UppDecML-196
❑ 93AusFut-127
❑ 93Bow-43
❑ 93ClaGolF-100
❑ 93El PasDF-2965
❑ 94Bow-533
❑ 94BreMilB-354
❑ 95Bow-255
❑ 95BowGolF-255
❑ 95ColChoSE-21
❑ 95ColChoSEGS-21
❑ 95ColChoSESS-21
❑ 95Pin-150
❑ 95PinArtP-150
❑ 95PinMusC-150
❑ 95Sco-581
❑ 95ScoGolR-581
❑ 95ScoPlaTS-581
❑ 95Sel-218
❑ 95SelArtP-218
❑ 95Spo-159
❑ 95SpoArtP-159
❑ 95Top-638
❑ 95Ult-299
❑ 95UltGolM-299
❑ 96Don-549
❑ 96DonPreP-549
❑ 96TolMudHB-26
❑ 97PacPriGotD-GD45
❑ 97VanCanB-26
❑ 98BriBluM-26
Singleton, John
❑ 23Zee-116
❑ 27Zee-105
❑ 28Zee-123
Singleton, Ken
❑ 71MetTeal-19
❑ 71MetTealA-6
❑ 71OPC-16
❑ 71Top-16
❑ 72OPC-425
❑ 72OPC-426
❑ 72ProStaP-11
❑ 72Top-425
❑ 72Top-426
❑ 73OPC-232
❑ 73Top-232
❑ 74ExpWes-9
❑ 74Kel-48
❑ 74OPC-25
❑ 74Top-25
❑ 74TopSta-60
❑ 75BalOriP-27
❑ 75Kel-40
❑ 75OPC-125
❑ 75Top-125
❑ 75TopMin-125
❑ 76BalOriP-36
❑ 76Hos-76
❑ 76Kel-12
❑ 76OPC-175
❑ 76SSP-400
❑ 76Top-175
❑ 77BalOriP-19
❑ 77BurCheD-41
❑ 77Hos-107
❑ 77OPC-19
❑ 77Top-445
❑ 78BalOriP-28
❑ 78Hos-75
❑ 78Kel-55
❑ 78OPC-80
❑ 78Top-65
❑ 79Hos-135
❑ 79OPC-324
❑ 79Top-615
❑ 80BalOriP-18
❑ 80Kel-30
❑ 80OPC-178
❑ 80Top-340
❑ 80TopSup-11
❑ 81AllGamPI-68
❑ 81BalOriP-20
❑ 81Don-115
❑ 81Dra-12
❑ 81Fle-188
❑ 81FleStiC-103
❑ 81Kel-39
❑ 81OPC-281
❑ 81PerAll-17
❑ 81Top-570
❑ 81TopScr-17
❑ 81TopSti-33
❑ 82BalOriP-5
❑ 82Don-24
❑ 82Don-105
❑ 82Dra-30
❑ 82FBIDis-24
❑ 82Fle-179
❑ 82FleSta-150
❑ 82Kel-58
❑ 82OPC-2
❑ 82OPC-290
❑ 82Top-290
❑ 82Top-552
❑ 82TopSti-136
❑ 82TopSti-144
❑ 83AllGamPI-68
❑ 83Don-257
❑ 83Dra-26
❑ 83Fle-73
❑ 83FleSta-177
❑ 83FleSti-195
❑ 83OPC-85
❑ 83OriPos-28
❑ 83Top-85
❑ 83TopSti-28
❑ 84AllGamPI-159
❑ 84BalOriP-34
❑ 84Don-610
❑ 84Fle-21
❑ 84FleSti-46
❑ 84FleSti-55
❑ 84Nes792-165
❑ 84OPC-165
❑ 84OriEng-13
❑ 84Top-165
❑ 84TopRubD-29
❑ 84TopSti-206
❑ 84TopStiB-8
❑ 84TopTif-165
❑ 85Fle-191
❑ 85OPC-326
❑ 85Top-755
❑ 85TopMin-755
❑ 85TopSti-201
❑ 85TopTif-755
❑ 86ExpGreT-5
❑ 86OriGreT-8
❑ 89SweBasG-26
❑ 91MetWIZ-366
❑ 91OriCro-421
❑ 92Nab-3
❑ 93ExpDonM-19
❑ 93OriCroASU-12
Singleton, Scott
❑ 94SpoIndC-22
❑ 94SpoIndF-3324
Singley, Joe
❑ 87PenWhiSP-6
❑ 89UtiBluSP-21
❑ 90SouBenWSB-9
❑ 90SouBenWSGS-25
Sington, Fred
❑ 39PlaBal-68
❑ 90DodTar-739
Sinibaldi, Caesar
❑ 33Zee-145
Sinner, Greg
❑ 92BurIndC-13
❑ 92BurIndF-1656
❑ 93WatIndC-25
❑ 93WatIndF-3561
Sinnes, David
❑ 94HagSunC-23
❑ 94HagSunF-2731
❑ 94SouAtlLAF-SAL19
❑ 95Exc-142
❑ 95WilBluRTI-23
Sinnett, Lou
❑ 85AncGlaPTI-40
Sipe, Pat
❑ 87WesPalBEP-659
❑ 88JacExpB-20
❑ 88JacExpP-981
❑ 89JacExpB-8
❑ 89JacExpP-165
Sipin, John
❑ 79TCMJapPB-59
Sipple, John
❑ 89ChaRanS-24
Siracusa, John
❑ 75OklCit8TI-11
Sirak, Kenny
❑ 88NebCor-26
❑ 91SpaPhiC-19
❑ 91SpaPhiP-904
❑ 92ClePhiC-10
❑ 92ClePhiF-2066
❑ 93ClePhiC-21
❑ 93ClePhiF-2692
Siriano, Rick
❑ 82DurBulT-8
❑ 83DurBulT-13
Sirotka, Mike

- ❑ 92LSUTigM-11
- ❑ 93LSUTigM-5
- ❑ 94LSUTigMP-14
- ❑ 94MidLeaAF-MDW28
- ❑ 94SouBenSHC-21
- ❑ 94SouBenSHF-593
- ❑ 95Exc-31
- ❑ 95NasSouTI-24
- ❑ 96BirBarB-26
- ❑ 96Fle-76
- ❑ 96FleTif-76
- ❑ 96NasSouB-23
- ❑ 98PacInvGems-34
- ❑ 98PacOnl-180
- ❑ 98PacOnlR-180
- ❑ 98PacOnlWC-180
- ❑ 98UppDec-662
- ❑ 99Fle-573
- ❑ 99FleSta9-573
- ❑ 99FleWarT-573
- ❑ 99MetUni-24
- ❑ 99MetUniGM-24
- ❑ 99MetUniPMG-24
- ❑ 99Pac-105
- ❑ 99PacOme-59
- ❑ 99PacOmeC-59
- ❑ 99PacOmeG-59
- ❑ 99PacOmePB-59
- ❑ 99PacPlaB-105
- ❑ 99PacRed-105
- ❑ 99SkyPre-103
- ❑ 99SkyPreR-103
- ❑ 99UppDec-69
- ❑ 99UppDecEL1-69
- ❑ 99UppDecEL2-69
- ❑ 99Vic-94

Sisco, Mike
- ❑ 87BelMarTI-21

Sisco, Steve
- ❑ 92EugEmeC-23
- ❑ 92EugEmeF-3039
- ❑ 93MidLeaAGF-18
- ❑ 93RocRoyC-25
- ❑ 93RocRoyF-725
- ❑ 95WicWraTI-26
- ❑ 96WicWraB-22
- ❑ 97WicWra-18
- ❑ 98OmaRoyM-20

Sisemore, Jerry
- ❑ 80PhiBul-9

Sisk, Doug
- ❑ 82JacMetT-10
- ❑ 83TopTra-105T
- ❑ 84Don-615
- ❑ 84Fle-596
- ❑ 84JacMetF-11
- ❑ 84Nes792-599
- ❑ 84OPC-21
- ❑ 84Top-599
- ❑ 84TopTif-599
- ❑ 85Don-441
- ❑ 85Fle-91
- ❑ 85Lea-187
- ❑ 85MetColP-5
- ❑ 85MetFanC-7
- ❑ 85MetTCM-17
- ❑ 85OPC-315
- ❑ 85Top-315
- ❑ 85TopSti-103
- ❑ 85TopTif-315
- ❑ 86Fle-94
- ❑ 86MetTCM-12
- ❑ 86MetWorSC-9
- ❑ 86TidTidP-26
- ❑ 86Top-144
- ❑ 86TopTif-144
- ❑ 87Fle-22
- ❑ 87FleGlo-22
- ❑ 87MetColP-47
- ❑ 87Top-404
- ❑ 87TopTif-404
- ❑ 88Don-642
- ❑ 88Fle-150
- ❑ 88FleGlo-150
- ❑ 88FleUpd-3
- ❑ 88FleUpdG-3
- ❑ 88OriPos-34
- ❑ 88Sco-227
- ❑ 88ScoGlo-227
- ❑ 88Top-763
- ❑ 88TopClo-105
- ❑ 88TopTif-763
- ❑ 89Fle-621
- ❑ 89FleGlo-621
- ❑ 89Sco-264
- ❑ 89Top-13
- ❑ 89TopTif-13
- ❑ 89UppDec-261
- ❑ 90IndTeal-36
- ❑ 91BraDubP-25
- ❑ 91MetWIZ-367
- ❑ 91OriCro-422

Sisk, Kevin
- ❑ 91ButCopKSP-21

Sisk, Tommie
- ❑ 63Top-169
- ❑ 64PirKDK-25
- ❑ 64Top-224
- ❑ 64TopVen-224
- ❑ 65Top-558
- ❑ 66PirEasH-25
- ❑ 66Top-441
- ❑ 67OPC-84
- ❑ 67PirTeal-20
- ❑ 67Top-84
- ❑ 67TopPirS-21
- ❑ 68PirKDK-25
- ❑ 68PirTeal-20
- ❑ 68Top-429
- ❑ 69MLBOffS-196
- ❑ 69OPC-152
- ❑ 69Top-152
- ❑ 69TopFou-11
- ❑ 70MLBOffS-118
- ❑ 70OPC-374
- ❑ 70Top-374

Sisler, Dave
- ❑ 57Top-56
- ❑ 58Hir-40
- ❑ 58Top-59
- ❑ 59RedSoxJP-8
- ❑ 59Top-346
- ❑ 59Top-384
- ❑ 60Lea-64
- ❑ 60Top-186
- ❑ 60TopVen-186
- ❑ 61Pos-44
- ❑ 61SevElev-1
- ❑ 61Top-239
- ❑ 61TopStal-155
- ❑ 62RedEnq-32
- ❑ 62Top-171
- ❑ 62TopVen-171
- ❑ 63RedEnq-29
- ❑ 63Top-284
- ❑ 81RedSoxBG2S-48

Sisler, Dick
- ❑ 46SeaSLP-58
- ❑ 47Exh-210
- ❑ 47TipTop-162
- ❑ 49Bow-205
- ❑ 49EurSta-149
- ❑ 49Lea-143
- ❑ 49PhiBul-53
- ❑ 50Bow-119
- ❑ 50Dra-10
- ❑ 50PhiPhil-22
- ❑ 50RoyDes-19A
- ❑ 50RoyDes-19B
- ❑ 51BerRos-C8
- ❑ 51Bow-52
- ❑ 51TopBluB-8
- ❑ 52Bow-127
- ❑ 52RoyPre-14
- ❑ 52TipTop-38
- ❑ 52Top-113
- ❑ 53BowBW-10
- ❑ 53CarHunW-22
- ❑ 53ExhCan-62
- ❑ 60HenHouW-8
- ❑ 60SeaPop-14
- ❑ 63RedFreBC-25
- ❑ 64Top-162
- ❑ 64TopVen-162
- ❑ 65OPC-158
- ❑ 65RedEnq-28
- ❑ 65Top-158
- ❑ 66CarCoi-4
- ❑ 70CarTeal-27
- ❑ 74NewYorNTDiS-26
- ❑ 75PadDea-4
- ❑ 75PadDea-23
- ❑ 75Phi195T-28
- ❑ 76SSP-622
- ❑ 79DiaGre-170
- ❑ 79TCM50-152
- ❑ 80Phi195T-28
- ❑ 80Red196T-7
- ❑ 83Car194T-34
- ❑ 83PhiPosGM-2
- ❑ 83TopRep5-113
- ❑ 84TCMPla1-25
- ❑ 87Phi195T-8
- ❑ 89JohCitCS-24

Sisler, George
- ❑ 80ColCliP-NNO
- ❑ 80ColCliT-27
- ❑ 81ColCliP-NNO
- ❑ 81ColCliT-27
- ❑ 82ColCliP-NNO
- ❑ 82ColCliT-26
- ❑ 84ColCliP-23
- ❑ 84ColCliT-24
- ❑ 85ColCliP-21
- ❑ 85ColCliT-29
- ❑ 86ColCliP-21
- ❑ 87ColCliP-23
- ❑ 89ColCliP-25

Sisler, George Sr.
- ❑ 15SpoNewM-166
- ❑ 16BF2FP-45
- ❑ 16SpoNewM-164
- ❑ 17ColE13-162
- ❑ 17HolBreD-97
- ❑ 19W514-101
- ❑ 20NatCarE-94
- ❑ 20WalMaiW-51
- ❑ 21E121So1-97A
- ❑ 21E121So1-97B
- ❑ 21E121So8-91A
- ❑ 21E121So8-91B
- ❑ 21Exh-161
- ❑ 21Nei-32
- ❑ 21OxfConE-17
- ❑ 22AmeCarE122-65
- ❑ 22AmeCarE122-66
- ❑ 22E120-102
- ❑ 22W572-99
- ❑ 22W573-124
- ❑ 22W575-126
- ❑ 22WilPatV-4
- ❑ 23W501-4
- ❑ 23W503-13
- ❑ 23W515-11
- ❑ 23W551-8
- ❑ 23WilChoV-151
- ❑ 24MrsShePP-8
- ❑ 25Exh-117
- ❑ 26Exh-118
- ❑ 26SpoComoA-41
- ❑ 27AmeCarE126-49
- ❑ 27Exh-59
- ❑ 27MidBre-39
- ❑ 27YorCarE-54
- ❑ 28StaPlaCE-62
- ❑ 28W502-54
- ❑ 28Yue-54
- ❑ 29ExhFou-1
- ❑ 39PC7AlbHoF-25
- ❑ 40PlaBal-179
- ❑ 48ExhHoF-26
- ❑ 50CalHOFW-66
- ❑ 51R42SmaS-103
- ❑ 53ArtHaloFP-77
- ❑ 60Fle-13
- ❑ 61Fle-78
- ❑ 61Fle-89
- ❑ 61GolPre-13
- ❑ 63HalofFB-17
- ❑ 67SpoHobFC-13
- ❑ 67TopVen-154
- ❑ 72KelATG-5
- ❑ 72LauGreF-5
- ❑ 73FleWilD-12
- ❑ 74CapPub-64
- ❑ 74NewYorNTDiS-22
- ❑ 75TCMAllG-32
- ❑ 76RowExh-2
- ❑ 76ShaPiz-20
- ❑ 77BobParHoF-73
- ❑ 77GalGloG-94
- ❑ 77SerSta-23
- ❑ 77ShaPiz-11
- ❑ 79Top-411
- ❑ 80Lau300-24
- ❑ 80LauFamF-9
- ❑ 80PacLeg-108
- ❑ 80PerHaloFP-25
- ❑ 80SSPHOF-25
- ❑ 81ConTSN-83
- ❑ 81SpoHaloF-21
- ❑ 82OhiHaloF-31
- ❑ 82TCMGreH-22
- ❑ 84GalHaloFRL-20
- ❑ 85Woo-33
- ❑ 87ConSer2-58
- ❑ 87HygAllG-40
- ❑ 88ConSer4-26
- ❑ 90HOFStiB-23
- ❑ 91ConTSN-66
- ❑ 92ConTSN-595
- ❑ 93ConTSN-798
- ❑ 93ConTSN-836
- ❑ 99UppDecCL-33
- ❑ 99UppDecCLCC-33

Sismondo, Ron
- ❑ 83WauTimF-24

Sisney, Lorenzo
- ❑ 88WauTimGS-5

Sisson, Doug
- ❑ 91ButCopKSP-27
- ❑ 92ChaRanC-28
- ❑ 92ChaRanF-2241
- ❑ 93EriSaiC-27
- ❑ 93EriSaiF-3131
- ❑ 94HudValRC-26
- ❑ 94HudValRF-3402
- ❑ 96DelShoB-1
- ❑ 96DelShoUB-1
- ❑ 98JupHamQ-1

Sisti, Sibby
- ❑ 41DouPlaR-41
- ❑ 46SpoExcW-9-12
- ❑ 47TipTop-87
- ❑ 49Bow-201
- ❑ 49EurSta-23
- ❑ 50Bow-164
- ❑ 50JJKCopP-19
- ❑ 51Bow-170
- ❑ 52Bow-100
- ❑ 52Top-293
- ❑ 53BraJohC-13
- ❑ 53Top-124
- ❑ 54BraJohC-13
- ❑ 58UniOil-8
- ❑ 79DiaGre-219
- ❑ 83Bra53F-13
- ❑ 83Pil69G-22
- ❑ 83TopRep5-293
- ❑ 91TopArc1-124

Sitton, Red
- ❑ 11PinT-5-1066

Siuda, Matt
- ❑ 85AncGlaPTI-33
- ❑ 88MadMusP-22

Sivik, Mike
- ❑ 77AppFoxT-23
- ❑ 78AppFoxT-16
- ❑ 79AppFoxT-13

Siwa, Joe
- ❑ 90KenTwiB-14
- ❑ 90KenTwiP-2298
- ❑ 90KenTwiS-23
- ❑ 91LinDriAA-493
- ❑ 91OrlSunRLD-493
- ❑ 91OrlSunRP-1853
- ❑ 92OrlSunRF-2850
- ❑ 92OrlSunRS-520

Siwy, Jim
- ❑ 81AppFoxT-10
- ❑ 82EdmTraT-3
- ❑ 85Ind-28
- ❑ 85MaiGuiT-12
- ❑ 86LasVegSP-16
- ❑ 87LasVegSP-25

Sizemore, Bill
- ❑ 93LetMouF-4166
- ❑ 93LetMouSP-26
- ❑ 94LetMouF-3896
- ❑ 94LetMouSP-28
- ❑ 95ElmPioTI-27
- ❑ 95ElmPioUTI-27

Sizemore, Ted
- ❑ 69Top-552
- ❑ 70MLBOffS-58
- ❑ 70OPC-174
- ❑ 70Top-174
- ❑ 71CarTeal-25
- ❑ 71CarTeal-37
- ❑ 71MLBOffS-284
- ❑ 71OPC-571
- ❑ 71Top-571
- ❑ 71TopCoi-65
- ❑ 72CarTeal-15
- ❑ 72OPC-514
- ❑ 72Top-514
- ❑ 73OPC-128
- ❑ 73Top-128
- ❑ 74OPC-209
- ❑ 74Top-209
- ❑ 74TopSta-117
- ❑ 75Hos-71
- ❑ 75OPC-404
- ❑ 75St.LouCP-26
- ❑ 75Top-404
- ❑ 75TopMin-404
- ❑ 76Hos-70
- ❑ 76LinSup-125
- ❑ 76OPC-522
- ❑ 76SSP-284
- ❑ 76Top-522
- ❑ 77Top-366
- ❑ 78OPC-118
- ❑ 78SSP270-39
- ❑ 78Top-136
- ❑ 79OPC-148
- ❑ 79Top-297
- ❑ 80OPC-46
- ❑ 80Top-81
- ❑ 85SpoIndGC-18
- ❑ 90DodTar-740
- ❑ 95DodROY-7

Skaalen, Jim
- ❑ 87PorChaRP-24
- ❑ 88TulDriTI-10
- ❑ 89OklCit8C-23
- ❑ 89OklCit8P-1508
- ❑ 90TulDriDGB-29
- ❑ 93AppFoxCB-29

Skadan, Scott
- ❑ 93AlbPolCB-27
- ❑ 94AlbPolC-30

Skaff, Frank (Francis)
- ❑ 43A'STEAI-20
- ❑ 52Par-91
- ❑ 54OriEss-31
- ❑ 90DodTar-741
- ❑ 97BalOriP-46

Skaggs, David
- ❑ 77BalOriP-20
- ❑ 78BalOriP-29
- ❑ 78Top-593
- ❑ 79Top-367
- ❑ 80Top-211
- ❑ 81Top-48
- ❑ 91OriCro-423
- ❑ 91PacSenL-100

Skaggs, Steve
- ❑ 80CedRapRT-14

Skalisky, Rocky
- ❑ 77ReaPhiT-22

Skalski, Joe
- ❑ 87WilBilP-27
- ❑ 88ColSprSSC-10
- ❑ 88ColSprSSP-1533
- ❑ 89ColSprSSC-9
- ❑ 89IndTeal-23
- ❑ 89UppDec-716
- ❑ 90Bow-323
- ❑ 90BowTif-323
- ❑ 90CMC-455
- ❑ 90ColSprSSC-3
- ❑ 90ColSprSSP-34
- ❑ 90IndTeal-37
- ❑ 90ProAAAF-215
- ❑ 90Sco-618A
- ❑ 90Sco-618B
- ❑ 90TopDeb89-115

Skaugstad, Dave
- ❑ 58RedEnq-36

Skeels, Andy
- ❑ 87SpoIndP-7
- ❑ 88RivRedWCLC-226
- ❑ 88RivRedWP-1425
- ❑ 89CalLeaA-20
- ❑ 89RivRedWB-15
- ❑ 89RivRedWCLC-12
- ❑ 89RivRedWP-1414
- ❑ 90AlbYanB-13
- ❑ 90AlbYanP-1038
- ❑ 90AlbYanSt-16
- ❑ 91AlbYanP-1012
- ❑ 92SalSpuF-3760

Skeels, David
- ❑ 09ObaT21-377
- ❑ 12ObaPreT-126
- ❑ 96EveAquB-22
- ❑ 97LanJet-23
- ❑ 98VisOakG-28

Skeels, Mark
- ❑ 92EriSaiC-8
- ❑ 92EriSaiF-1627
- ❑ 93HigDesMC-18
- ❑ 93HigDesMF-45
- ❑ 93Top-558
- ❑ 93TopGol-558
- ❑ 93TopInaM-558
- ❑ 93TopInaR-558
- ❑ 93TopMic-558
- ❑ 94BreCouMF-16

Skeen, Archie
- ❑ 62SeaPop-13
- ❑ 63MilSau-7
- ❑ 63SeaPop-10
- ❑ 64Top-428

Skeete, Rafael
- ❑ 87HagSunP-22
- ❑ 88ChaKniTI-15
- ❑ 89HagSunB-22
- ❑ 89HagSunP-278
- ❑ 89HagSunS-17
- ❑ 90ElPasDGS-25

Skelton, Bryan
- ❑ 93DavLipB-20
- ❑ 94DavLipB-22
- ❑ 95DavLipB-21

Skelton, John
- ❑ 87KenTwiP-28
- ❑ 88KenTwiP-1400

Skett, Will
- ❑ 96StCatSB-26
- ❑ 97DunBluJTI-26
- ❑ 98KnoSG-20

Skiba, Daniel
- ❑ 77WatIndT-20

Skidmore, Roe (Robert)
- ❑ 71OPC-121
- ❑ 71Top-121

Skiff, Bill (William)
- ❑ 20WalMaiW-52
- ❑ 43CenFlo-21
- ❑ 44CenFlo-20
- ❑ 45CenFlo-22

Skillicorn, Dirk
- ❑ 90NebCor-22

Skinner, Bob
- ❑ 47Exh-221A
- ❑ 55Top-88
- ❑ 55TopDouH-55
- ❑ 56PirTeal-21
- ❑ 56Top-297
- ❑ 57PirTeal-8
- ❑ 57Top-209
- ❑ 58Hir-30
- ❑ 58JayPubA-17
- ❑ 58Kah-27
- ❑ 58PirTeal-9
- ❑ 58Top-94
- ❑ 59ArmCoi-16
- ❑ 59Kah-33
- ❑ 59Top-320
- ❑ 59Top-543
- ❑ 60Kah-38
- ❑ 60KeyChal-43
- ❑ 60PirJayP-11
- ❑ 60PirTag-4
- ❑ 60Top-113
- ❑ 60TopVen-113
- ❑ 61Kah-40
- ❑ 61PirJayP-10
- ❑ 61Pos-131A
- ❑ 61Pos-131B
- ❑ 61Top-204
- ❑ 61TopStal-69
- ❑ 62Jel-174
- ❑ 62Pos-174
- ❑ 62PosCan-174
- ❑ 62SalPlaC-143
- ❑ 62ShiPlaC-143
- ❑ 62Top-115
- ❑ 62TopVen-115
- ❑ 63Jel-141
- ❑ 63PirJayP-11
- ❑ 63Pos-141
- ❑ 63RedFreBC-26
- ❑ 63Top-18
- ❑ 63Top-215
- ❑ 64Top-377
- ❑ 65CarTeal-24
- ❑ 65Top-591
- ❑ 66Top-471
- ❑ 69PhiTeal-10
- ❑ 69Top-369
- ❑ 73OPC-12
- ❑ 73PadDea-25
- ❑ 73Top-12A
- ❑ 73Top-12B
- ❑ 74OPC-489
- ❑ 74Top-489
- ❑ 76PirPos-22
- ❑ 77PadSchC-50
- ❑ 77PirTCM1WC-8
- ❑ 78AngFamF-34
- ❑ 79DiaGre-373
- ❑ 79TCM50-248

❑ 85Top-139
❑ 85TopTif-139
❑ 86BraPol-4
❑ 87Pir196T-5
❑ 89TucTorC-25
❑ 89TucTorP-203
❑ 90CMC-627
❑ 90ProAAAF-209
❑ 90SweBasG-129
❑ 90TucTorC-25
❑ 90TucTorP-219
❑ 91LinDriAAA-624
❑ 91TriA AAGP-AAA53
❑ 91TucTorLD-624
❑ 91TucTorP-2228
❑ 92TucTorF-503
❑ 92TucTorS-624
Skinner, Joel
❑ 82GleFalWST-10
❑ 84Don-27
❑ 85BufBisT-6
❑ 85Don-574
❑ 85Fle-646
❑ 85Top-139
❑ 85Top-488
❑ 85TopTif-139
❑ 85TopTif-488
❑ 85WhiSoxC-22
❑ 86Don-330
❑ 86Top-239
❑ 86TopTif-239
❑ 86WhiSoxC-22
❑ 87Don-545
❑ 87DonOpeD-240
❑ 87Fle-115
❑ 87FleGlo-115
❑ 87SpoTeaP-7
❑ 87Top-626
❑ 87TopTif-626
❑ 88Don-474
❑ 88DonBasB-300
❑ 88DonReaBY-474
❑ 88Sco-532
❑ 88ScoGlo-532
❑ 88Top-109
❑ 88TopClo-106
❑ 88TopTif-109
❑ 89Don-427
❑ 89DonBasB-224
❑ 89DonTra-22
❑ 89Fle-270
❑ 89FleGlo-270
❑ 89IndTeal-24
❑ 89OPC-127
❑ 89Sco-447
❑ 89ScoRoo-76T
❑ 89Top-536
❑ 89TopTif-536
❑ 89UppDec-328
❑ 90Don-73
❑ 90Fle-501
❑ 90FleCan-501
❑ 90IndTeal-38
❑ 90Lea-286
❑ 90OPC-54
❑ 90PubIntS-567
❑ 90Top-54
❑ 90TopTif-54
❑ 90UppDec-369
❑ 91Don-120
❑ 91Fle-377
❑ 91IndFanC-25
❑ 91Lea-211
❑ 91OPC-783
❑ 91Sco-809
❑ 91StaClu-561
❑ 91Top-783
❑ 91TopDesS-783
❑ 91TopMic-783
❑ 91TopTif-783
❑ 91UppDec-121
❑ 92Don-99
❑ 92Fle-123
❑ 92IndFanC-26
❑ 92Lea-181
❑ 92LeaBlaG-181
❑ 92OPC-378
❑ 92Sco-227
❑ 92StaClu-278
❑ 92Top-378
❑ 92TopGol-378
❑ 92TopGolW-378
❑ 92TopMic-378
❑ 92UppDec-199
❑ 92YanWIZ8-180
❑ 93IndWUA-28
❑ 95WatIndTI-27
❑ 97KinIndB-26
❑ 98AkrAerM-1
Skinner, John
❑ 82AppFoxFr-14
Skinner, Matt
❑ 85NewOriT-23
Skinner, Mike
❑ 86RocRedWP-22
❑ 87RocRedWP-5
❑ 87RocRedWT-9
Skizas, Lou
❑ 56A'sPos-39
❑ 57Top-83
❑ 58Top-319
❑ 59SeaPop-34
❑ 59Top-328
❑ 60SeaPop-15
❑ 60UniOil-15
❑ 81WhiSox1T-22
Skjerpen, Trevor
❑ 94WelPirC-22
❑ 94WelPirF-3497
Sklar, Joel
❑ 86LitFalMP-25
Skodny, Joe
❑ 86EugEmeC-48
❑ 87AppFoxP-11
❑ 88BasCitRS-21
Skoglund, Brad
❑ 83WisRapTF-23
Skok, Craig
❑ 76SacSolC-4
❑ 79Top-363
❑ 80RicBraT-20
❑ 80VenLeaS-20
❑ 93RanKee-330
Skolfield, Stan
❑ 97LowSpiB-30
Skoog, Jack
❑ 89SanDieSAS-26
Skorochocki, John
❑ 77NewCoPT-29
❑ 78BurBeeT-26
❑ 80HolMilT-2
❑ 81ElPasDT-4
❑ 82VanCanT-6
Skowron, Bill
❑ 47Exh-211A
❑ 47Exh-211B
❑ 47StaPinP2-37
❑ 53Dor-140
❑ 54Top-239
❑ 55Bow-160
❑ 55Top-22
❑ 55TopDouH-21
❑ 56Top-61
❑ 56TopPin-30
❑ 56YanTeal-23
❑ 57Top-135
❑ 57YanJayP-13
❑ 58JayPubA-18
❑ 58Top-240
❑ 58Top-477
❑ 58YanJayP-12
❑ 59Top-90
❑ 59Top-554
❑ 59TopVen-90
❑ 59Yoo-6
❑ 60MacSta-23
❑ 60Top-370
❑ 60Top-553
❑ 60YanJayP-10
❑ 61Pos-3A
❑ 61Pos-3B
❑ 61Top-42
❑ 61Top-371
❑ 61Top-568
❑ 61Yan61RL-5
❑ 61YanJayP-11
❑ 62Jel-1
❑ 62Pos-1
❑ 62PosCan-1
❑ 62SalPlaC-59
❑ 62ShiPlaC-59
❑ 62Top-110
❑ 62TopStal-91
❑ 62TopVen-110
❑ 62YanJayP-12
❑ 63DodJayP-11
❑ 63Jel-12
❑ 63Pos-12
❑ 63Top-180
❑ 64ChatheY-46
❑ 64Top-445
❑ 64TopGia-60
❑ 65OPC-70
❑ 65Top-70
❑ 65TopEmbl-5
❑ 65TopTral-69
❑ 65WhiSoxJP-10
❑ 66Baz-33
❑ 66Top-199
❑ 66Top-590
❑ 66TopRubl-86
❑ 66TopVen-199
❑ 67CokCapWS-13
❑ 67DexPre-192
❑ 67Top-357
❑ 70FleWorS-60
❑ 78TCM60I-230
❑ 79TCM50-210
❑ 81TCM60I-474
❑ 82ASAMicM-42
❑ 83MLBPin-17
❑ 83TigAIKS-18
❑ 83Yan196-5
❑ 83YanASFY-44
❑ 85WhiSoxC-23
❑ 87Yan196T-1
❑ 88PacLegI-82
❑ 90DodTar-742
❑ 91YanRinP11-3
❑ 92ActPacA-35
❑ 92YanWIZ6-117
❑ 92YanWIZA-79
❑ 93MetIma-17
❑ 93UppDecAH-114
❑ 94TedWil-64
❑ 94TopArc1-239
❑ 94TopArc1G-239
❑ 94UppDecAH-66
❑ 94UppDecAH1-66
❑ 99SpollIGotG-53
❑ 99SpollIGotGA-69
Skrehot, Shaun
❑ 98EriSeaWM-22
Skripko, Joseph
❑ 85GreHorT-8
Skripko, Scott
❑ 86WinHavRSP-23
❑ 87NewBriRSP-10
❑ 89LynRedSS-25
Skrmetta, Matt
❑ 93BriTigC-20
❑ 94JamJamC-23
❑ 94JamJamF-3964
❑ 95FayGenTI-23
❑ 96LakTigB-25
❑ 96WesOahCHWB-23
❑ 97MobBayBB-28
❑ 98MobBayBTI-26
Skryd, Chris
❑ 89SalLakTTI-19
Skube, Bob
❑ 81ElPasDT-15
❑ 82VanCanT-1
❑ 83BrePol-26
❑ 85VanCanC-214
❑ 94BreMilB-271
Skurla, John
❑ 86FreGiaSB-23
❑ 88ShrCapP-1297
❑ 88TexLeaAGS-15
❑ 89PhoFirC-23
❑ 89PhoFirP-1496
❑ 90CMC-489
❑ 90EdmTraC-12
❑ 90EdmTraP-530
❑ 90ProAAAF-106
Skurski, Andy
❑ 47SigOil-15
❑ 49W72HolS-21
Skuse, Nick
❑ 94BoiHawC-23
❑ 94BoiHawF-3355
❑ 95CedRapKTI-38
❑ 96CedRapKTI-23
❑ 97LakElsSG-26
❑ 98JacSunM-22
Skyta, Damon
❑ 86EveGiaPC-29
Slack, Bill
❑ 85GreBraTI-16
❑ 86GreBraTI-17
❑ 87DurBulP-15
❑ 89GreBraB-18
❑ 89GreBraP-1168
❑ 89GreBraS-25
❑ 90GreBraP-1144
❑ 91GreBraC-26
❑ 91GreBraP-3020
❑ 91LinDriAA-225
❑ 92GreBraF-1170
❑ 93GreBraF-366
❑ 94CarLeaA-DJ37
❑ 94DurBulC-28
❑ 94DurBulF-347
❑ 94DurBulTI-20
❑ 95DurBulTI-28
❑ 96GreBraB-2
❑ 96GreBraTI-27
❑ 97DurBulTI-4
❑ 98DanBraQ-28
Slade, Gordon
❑ 25Zee-160
❑ 26Zee-60
❑ 27Zee-38
❑ 28ExhPCL-27
❑ 28Zee-60
❑ 29Zee-59
❑ 34DiaMatCSB-163
❑ 35DiaMatCS2-18
❑ 37Zee-5
❑ 37Zee-26
❑ 72TCMthe3-65
❑ 90DodTar-743
Slade, Oski
❑ 24Zee-141
Slade, Shawn
❑ 93BoiHawC-24
❑ 93BoiHawF-3918
❑ 94CedRapKC-21
❑ 94CedRapKF-1108
❑ 95CedRapKTI-9
Slage, Walter
❑ 12HomRunKE-15
Slagle, Eric
❑ 92Min-18
Slagle, James J.
❑ 07CubA.CDPP-14
❑ 07CubGFGCP-13
❑ 08AmeCarE91-28
❑ 08RosComP-110
❑ 09T206-468
❑ 11SpoLifCW-324
Slagle, Lee
❑ 92JamExpC-29
❑ 93WesPalBEC-28
❑ 94VerExpC-23
Slagle, Roger
❑ 76ForLauYS-22
❑ 77WesHavYT-20
❑ 78TacYanC-10
❑ 80ColCliP-18
❑ 80ColCliT-2
❑ 80NasSouTI-21
❑ 81NasSouTI-18
❑ 82NasSouTI-23
❑ 91PacSenL-17
❑ 92YanWIZ7-141
Slagle, Walter
❑ 08IndPos-18
❑ 12Zee-19
❑ 14Zee-93
Slamka, John
❑ 94SigRooDP-84
❑ 94SigRooDPS-84
❑ 95AshTouUTI-28
❑ 97AshTou-24
Slater, Bob
❑ 76QuaCitAT-30
❑ 79SalLakCGT-21A
❑ 79Top-703
Slater, Vernon
❑ 90EugEmeGS-28
❑ 91AppFoxCB-7
❑ 91EugEmeC-10
❑ 91EugEmeP-3741
Slater, Wayne
❑ 97YakBeaG-30
Slaton, Jim
❑ 72Top-744
❑ 73OPC-628
❑ 73Top-628
❑ 74OPC-371
❑ 74Top-371
❑ 74TopSta-200
❑ 75OPC-281
❑ 75Top-281
❑ 75TopMin-281
❑ 76BreA&P-13
❑ 76OPC-163
❑ 76SSP-229
❑ 76Top-163
❑ 77BurCheD-83
❑ 77Hos-105
❑ 77OPC-29
❑ 77Top-604
❑ 78Hos-14
❑ 78OPC-146
❑ 78TigBurK-7
❑ 78TigTeal-24
❑ 78Top-474
❑ 79TigFreP-9
❑ 79Top-541
❑ 80OPC-10
❑ 80Top-24
❑ 81Don-447
❑ 81Fle-518
❑ 81Top-357
❑ 82BrePol-41
❑ 82Don-80
❑ 82Fle-153
❑ 82Top-221
❑ 83AllGamPI-86
❑ 83BreGar-17
❑ 83BrePol-41
❑ 83Don-330A
❑ 83Don-330B
❑ 83Fle-46
❑ 83OPC-114
❑ 83Top-114
❑ 84AngSmo-27
❑ 84Don-481
❑ 84Fle-214
❑ 84FleUpd-107
❑ 84Nes792-772
❑ 84OPC-104
❑ 84Top-772
❑ 84TopSti-302
❑ 84TopTif-772
❑ 84TopTra-109T
❑ 84TopTraT-109T
❑ 85AllGamPI-88
❑ 85AngSmo-17
❑ 85Don-545
❑ 85Fle-313
❑ 85Top-657
❑ 85TopTif-657
❑ 86AngSmo-17
❑ 86Don-402
❑ 86Fle-169
❑ 86Top-579
❑ 86TopTif-579
❑ 87Fle-163
❑ 87FleGlo-163
❑ 87Top-432
❑ 87TopTif-432
❑ 89PacSenL-110
❑ 89T/MSenL-96
❑ 91SouOreAP-3867
❑ 92BreCarT-21
❑ 92RenSilSCLC-61
❑ 92SouOreAC-29
❑ 94BreMilB-272
❑ 96DayCubB-27
❑ 97LanJet-2
❑ 98LanJetG-23
Slattery, Chris
❑ 88CapCodPPaLP-161
Slattery, Don
❑ 92JohCitCC-17
❑ 92JohCitCF-3125
Slattery, Jack
❑ 11SpoLifCW-325
Slattery, Kevin
❑ 75CliPilT-17
Slattery, Mike
❑ 87OldJudN-453
❑ 89SFHaCN-16
Slaught, Don
❑ 82OmaRoyT-12
❑ 83Don-196
❑ 83Fle-123
❑ 83RoyPos-29
❑ 84Don-419
❑ 84Fle-359
❑ 84Nes792-196
❑ 84RoyPos-32
❑ 84Top-196
❑ 84TopTif-196
❑ 85Don-496
❑ 85Fle-214
❑ 85FleUpd-104
❑ 85OPC-159
❑ 85RanPer-4
❑ 85Top-542
❑ 85TopSti-279
❑ 85TopTif-542
❑ 85TopTifT-107T
❑ 85TopTra-107T
❑ 86BasStaB-101
❑ 86Don-281
❑ 86Fle-572
❑ 86Lea-155
❑ 86OPC-24
❑ 86RanLit-6
❑ 86RanPer-4
❑ 86Top-761
❑ 86TopSti-243
❑ 86TopTif-761
❑ 87Don-136
❑ 87DonOpeD-176
❑ 87Fle-139
❑ 87FleGlo-139
❑ 87OPC-308
❑ 87RanMot-12
❑ 87RanSmo-9
❑ 87Spo-32
❑ 87Spo-154
❑ 87SpoTeaP-1
❑ 87Top-308
❑ 87TopSti-241
❑ 87TopTif-308
❑ 88AlaGolAA70TI-13
❑ 88DonBasB-188
❑ 88DonReaBY-NEW
❑ 88FleUpd-51
❑ 88FleUpdG-51
❑ 88Sco-268
❑ 88ScoGlo-268
❑ 88ScoRoo-19T
❑ 88ScoRooG-19T
❑ 88StaLinRa-16
❑ 88StaLinY-15
❑ 88Top-462
❑ 88TopTif-462
❑ 88TopTra-108T
❑ 88TopTraT-108T
❑ 89Bow-172
❑ 89BowTif-172
❑ 89Don-190
❑ 89DonBasB-105
❑ 89Fle-271
❑ 89FleGlo-271
❑ 89OPC-238
❑ 89PanSti-403
❑ 89Sco-561
❑ 89Spo-218
❑ 89Top-611
❑ 89TopBig-138
❑ 89TopTif-611
❑ 89UppDec-178
❑ 89YanScoNW-12
❑ 90Bow-182
❑ 90BowTif-182
❑ 90Don-277
❑ 90Fle-456
❑ 90FleCan-456
❑ 90FleUpd-51
❑ 90Lea-354
❑ 90MLBBasB-65
❑ 90OPC-26
❑ 90PirHomC-27
❑ 90PubIntS-548
❑ 90Sco-79
❑ 90ScoRoo-13T
❑ 90Top-26
❑ 90TopSti-318
❑ 90TopTif-26
❑ 90TopTra-116T
❑ 90TopTraT-116T
❑ 90UppDec-152
❑ 91Bow-532
❑ 91Don-213
❑ 91Fle-49
❑ 91Lea-29
❑ 91OPC-221
❑ 91Sco-610
❑ 91SimandSMLBL-40
❑ 91StaClu-358
❑ 91Stu-228
❑ 91Top-221
❑ 91TopDesS-221
❑ 91TopMic-221
❑ 91TopTif-221
❑ 91Ult-286
❑ 91UppDec-181
❑ 92Don-653
❑ 92Fle-566
❑ 92Lea-124
❑ 92LeaBlaG-124
❑ 92OPC-524
❑ 92Pin-416
❑ 92PirNatl-20
❑ 92Sco-280
❑ 92StaClu-545
❑ 92Top-524
❑ 92TopGol-524

❑ 92TopGolW-524
❑ 92TopMic-524
❑ 92Ult-258
❑ 92UppDec-540
❑ 92YanWIZ8-181
❑ 93Bow-430
❑ 93Don-438
❑ 93Fla-116
❑ 93Fle-119
❑ 93Lea-6
❑ 93PacSpa-251
❑ 93Pin-188
❑ 93PirNatl-29
❑ 93RanKee-331
❑ 93Sco-181
❑ 93Sel-171
❑ 93SP-187
❑ 93StaClu-127
❑ 93StaCluFDI-127
❑ 93StaCluMOP-127
❑ 93Stu-209
❑ 93Top-778
❑ 93TopGol-778
❑ 93TopInaM-778
❑ 93TopInaR-778
❑ 93TopMic-778
❑ 93Ult-455
❑ 93UppDec-743
❑ 93UppDecGold-743
❑ 94Bow-602
❑ 94ColC-259
❑ 94ColChoGS-259
❑ 94ColChoSS-259
❑ 94Don-217
❑ 94Fin-127
❑ 94FinRef-127
❑ 94Fla-219
❑ 94Fle-619
❑ 94FleExtB-351
❑ 94Lea-135
❑ 94Pac-506
❑ 94PanSti-238
❑ 94Pin-217
❑ 94PinArtP-217
❑ 94PinMusC-217
❑ 94PirQui-22
❑ 94ProMag-108
❑ 94Sco-86
❑ 94ScoGolR-86
❑ 94Sel-65
❑ 94StaClu-137
❑ 94StaCluFDI-137
❑ 94StaCluGR-137
❑ 94StaCluMOP-137
❑ 94Stu-149
❑ 94SucSav-9
❑ 94Top-405
❑ 94TopGol-405
❑ 94TopSpa-405
❑ 94TriPla-188
❑ 94Ult-260
❑ 94UppDec-479
❑ 94UppDecED-479
❑ 95ColCho-387
❑ 95ColChoGS-387
❑ 95ColChoSS-387
❑ 95Don-498
❑ 95DonPreP-498
❑ 95Fin-43
❑ 95FinRef-43
❑ 95Fla-189
❑ 95Fle-488
❑ 95Lea-136
❑ 95Pac-351
❑ 95Pin-322
❑ 95PinArtP-322
❑ 95PinMusC-322
❑ 95PirFil-27
❑ 95Sco-73
❑ 95ScoGolR-73
❑ 95ScoPlaTS-73
❑ 95StaClu-299
❑ 95StaCluMOP-299
❑ 95StaCluSTWS-299
❑ 95StaCluVR-156
❑ 95StaCluVRMO-156
❑ 95Top-345
❑ 95TopCyb-187
❑ 95Ult-219
❑ 95UltGolM-219
❑ 95UppDec-387
❑ 95UppDecED-387
❑ 95UppDecEDG-387
❑ 96AngMot-25
❑ 96Don-335
❑ 96DonPreP-335
❑ 96Fle-533
❑ 96FleTif-533
❑ 96FleUpd-U21
❑ 96FleUpdTC-U21
❑ 96LeaSigA-209
❑ 96LeaSigAG-209
❑ 96LeaSigAS-209
❑ 97PadMot-12
❑ 97Ult-515
❑ 97UltGolME-515
❑ 97UltPlaME-515

Slaughter, Enos
❑ 41CarW75-24
❑ 41DouPlaR-39
❑ 46SeaSLP-59
❑ 46SpoExcW-9-2
❑ 47Exh-212
❑ 47HomBon-43
❑ 47PM1StaP1-203
❑ 47StaPinP2-38
❑ 47TipTop-163
❑ 48BluTin-34
❑ 48Bow-17
❑ 49Bow-65
❑ 49EurSta-198
❑ 49Lea-127
❑ 50AmeNut&CCP-17
❑ 50Bow-35
❑ 50Dra-36
❑ 51Bow-58
❑ 51R42SmaS-96
❑ 51TopBluB-30
❑ 52Bow-232
❑ 52DixLid-22
❑ 52DixPre-22
❑ 52NatTeaL-31
❑ 52RedMan-NL20
❑ 52StaCalL-81D
❑ 52StaCalS-93B
❑ 52TipTop-39
❑ 52Top-65
❑ 53BowC-81
❑ 53CarHunW-23
❑ 53DixLid-21
❑ 53DixPre-21
❑ 53Dor-133
❑ 53NorBreL-30
❑ 53RedMan-NL13
❑ 53Top-41
❑ 54Bow-62
❑ 54CarHunW-26
❑ 54DixLid-22
❑ 54RedHeaF-28
❑ 54RedMan-NL19A
❑ 54Wil-17
❑ 55A'sRodM-39
❑ 55A'sTeal-24
❑ 55Bow-60
❑ 56A'sPos-40
❑ 56A'sRodM-10
❑ 56Top-109
❑ 57Top-215
❑ 57YanJayP-14
❑ 58Top-142
❑ 59Top-155
❑ 59TopVen-155
❑ 66CarCoi-11
❑ 68LauWorS-43
❑ 70FleWorS-43
❑ 71FleWorS-44
❑ 74LauAllG-53
❑ 75JohMiz-16
❑ 76A'sRodMC-25
❑ 76TayBow4-18
❑ 77GalGloG-40
❑ 79DiaGre-166
❑ 79TCM50-240
❑ 80PacLeg-32
❑ 80PerHaloFP-191
❑ 80PerHaloFPS-56
❑ 80SSPHOF-194
❑ 82DiaCla-2
❑ 83Car194T-17
❑ 83TopRep5-65
❑ 84OCoandSI-51
❑ 84SpoDesPW-27
❑ 85DalNatCC-6
❑ 85TCMPhoC-33
❑ 85TCMPla1-2
❑ 85UltBasC-15
❑ 86SpoDecG-18
❑ 88HouSho-16
❑ 88PacLegI-84
❑ 89PacLegI-137
❑ 89PerCelP-37
❑ 89SweBasG-65
❑ 90PacLeg-50
❑ 90PerGreM-29
❑ 90SweBasG-54
❑ 91ConTSN-56
❑ 91SweBasG-84
❑ 91TopArc1-41
❑ 92ActPacA-15
❑ 92ActPacA2-15G
❑ 92BazQua5A-13
❑ 92CarMcD-23
❑ 92ConTSN-642
❑ 92UppDecS-11
❑ 92YanWIZH-31
❑ 93ActPacAC-15
❑ 93TedWil-92
❑ 93TedWilLC-7
❑ 93UppDecAH-115
❑ 94ConTSNCI-27
❑ 94UppDecAH-14
❑ 94UppDecAH-134
❑ 94UppDecAH1-14
❑ 94UppDecAH1-134
❑ 97TopStaHRR-14
❑ 97TopStaRRAU-14
❑ 98SpollITaN-31
❑ 98SpollITaNEE-31
❑ 98SpollIWSF-26
❑ 98SpollIWSFEE-26
❑ 98SpollIWSFFE-26
❑ 99SpollIGotG-9
❑ 99SpollIGotGA-70

Slaughter, Garland
❑ 89WelPirP-22

Slaughter, Sterling
❑ 64Top-469
❑ 65Top-314
❑ 97AriStaBG-19

Slavic, Joseph
❑ 86LakTigP-21
❑ 88LakTigS-23

Slavin, Dave
❑ 88PocGiaP-2094
❑ 89CliGiaP-909

Slavin, Tim
❑ 83WauTimF-8

Slayback, Bill
❑ 73OPC-537
❑ 73Top-537

Slaymaker, Joe
❑ 75BurBeeT-25

Sleater, Lou
❑ 52Top-306
❑ 53Top-224
❑ 55A'sRodM-40
❑ 55A'sTeal-25
❑ 56BalOriP-49
❑ 58Top-46A
❑ 58Top-46B
❑ 59TigGraASP-15
❑ 76A'sRodMC-26
❑ 83TopRep5-306
❑ 91OriCro-424
❑ 91TopArc1-224

Slemmer, Ben
❑ 98SpoIndG-31

Slemmer, Dave
❑ 97VisOakG-26
❑ 98HunStaTI-20A
❑ 98VisOakG-29

Slettvet, Doug
❑ 75QuaCitAT-22
❑ 76QuaCitAT-31
❑ 77QuaCitAT-26

Slezak, Robert
❑ 82VerBeaDT-11
❑ 83VerBeaDT-12

Slider, Mascot
❑ 93IndWUA-34
❑ 94MasMan-14
❑ 95StLucMTI-36
❑ 96StLucMTI-29
❑ 97PinFan-PC12

Slider, Rac (Rachel)
❑ 61UniOil-H5
❑ 63SeaPop-11
❑ 85IntLeaAT-45
❑ 85PawRedST-14
❑ 90TopTVRS-6

Slifko, Paul
❑ 86NewBriRSP-22
❑ 87WinHavRSP-20

Sline, Fred
❑ 12ImpTobC-9

Slininger, Dennis
❑ 91JohCitCC-20
❑ 91JohCitCP-3978
❑ 92SprCarC-15
❑ 92SprCarF-867
❑ 93MidLeaAGF-54
❑ 93SprCarC-23
❑ 93SprCarF-1850
❑ 94ClaGolF-26

Sliwinski, Kevin
❑ 86KnoBluJP-21
❑ 87KnoBluJP-1503
❑ 88HunStaTI-20
❑ 88TacTigC-20
❑ 88TacTigP-626

Sloan, Dave
❑ 76SeaRaiC-16

Sloan, Shae
❑ 95ColSilB-27
❑ 96ColSilB-26

Sloat, Lefty (Dwain)
❑ 90DodTar-744

Slocum, Ron
❑ 70Top-573
❑ 71MLBOffS-239
❑ 71OPC-274
❑ 71Top-274

Slocumb, Heathcliff
❑ 86LitFalMP-26
❑ 87WinSpiP-7
❑ 88WinSpiS-16
❑ 89PeoChiTI-9
❑ 90ChaKniTI-6
❑ 91Bow-421
❑ 91Cla3-T84
❑ 91CubMar-51
❑ 91CubVinL-26
❑ 91DonRoo-25
❑ 91FleUpd-81
❑ 91Lea-370
❑ 91ScoRoo-84T
❑ 91UltUpd-73
❑ 91UppDec-767
❑ 92Don-334
❑ 92Fle-390
❑ 92OPC-576
❑ 92Sco-213
❑ 92Sco100RS-28
❑ 92StaClu-382
❑ 92Top-576
❑ 92TopDeb91-164
❑ 92TopGol-576
❑ 92TopGolW-576
❑ 92TopMic-576
❑ 92UppDec-569
❑ 93Don-664
❑ 93IowCubF-2132
❑ 93Top-783
❑ 93TopGol-783
❑ 93TopInaM-783
❑ 93TopInaR-783
❑ 93TopMic-783
❑ 94FleUpd-170
❑ 94PhiMed-31
❑ 94PhiMel-21
❑ 94StaClu-681
❑ 94StaCluFDI-681
❑ 94StaCluGR-681
❑ 94StaCluMOP-681
❑ 94StaCluT-231
❑ 94StaCluTFDI-231
❑ 94TopTra-43T
❑ 95Don-263
❑ 95DonPreP-263
❑ 95DonTopotO-310
❑ 95Emo-171
❑ 95Fin-264
❑ 95FinRef-264
❑ 95Fla-396
❑ 95Fle-404
❑ 95Lea-132
❑ 95Phi-30
❑ 95PhiMel-21
❑ 95SP-92
❑ 95SPCha-77
❑ 95SPChaDC-77
❑ 95SPSil-92
❑ 95StaClu-610
❑ 95StaCluMOP-610
❑ 95StaCluSTWS-610
❑ 95Top-98
❑ 95Ult-210
❑ 95UltGolM-210
❑ 95UppDec-477
❑ 96Baz-16
❑ 96ColCho-257
❑ 96ColChoGS-257
❑ 96ColChoSS-257
❑ 96Don-65
❑ 96DonPreP-65
❑ 96Fin-B125
❑ 96Fin-B318
❑ 96FinRef-B125
❑ 96FinRef-B318
❑ 96Fla-25
❑ 96Fle-508
❑ 96FleRedS-13
❑ 96FleTif-508
❑ 96FleUpd-U17
❑ 96FleUpdTC-U17
❑ 96MetUni-213
❑ 96MetUniP-213
❑ 96Pac-165
❑ 96PanSti-35
❑ 96StaClu-82
❑ 96StaCluEPB-82
❑ 96StaCluEPG-82
❑ 96StaCluEPS-82
❑ 96StaCluMOP-82
❑ 96Top-11
❑ 96Top-385
❑ 96TopChr-11
❑ 96TopChrR-11
❑ 96TopGal-13
❑ 96TopGalPPI-13
❑ 96TopPowB-11
❑ 96Ult-259
❑ 96Ult-320
❑ 96UltGolM-259
❑ 96UltGolM-320
❑ 96UppDec-172
❑ 96UppDec-287
❑ 97Cir-171
❑ 97CirRav-171
❑ 97ColCho-46
❑ 97Fin-228
❑ 97FinRef-228
❑ 97Fle-29
❑ 97FleTif-29
❑ 97Pac-45
❑ 97PacLigB-45
❑ 97PacSil-45
❑ 97StaClu-354
❑ 97StaCluMOP-354
❑ 97Top-379
❑ 97Ult-19
❑ 97UltGolME-19
❑ 97UltPlaME-19
❑ 97UppDec-310
❑ 98Fle-469
❑ 98MarSco-11
❑ 98MarScoP-11
❑ 98Pac-194
❑ 98PacOnl-695
❑ 98PacOnlR-695
❑ 98PacOnlWC-695
❑ 98PacPlaB-194
❑ 98PacRedT-194
❑ 98PacSil-194
❑ 98Pin-149
❑ 98PinPreP-149
❑ 98Sco-157
❑ 98StaCluFDI-41
❑ 98StaClul-41
❑ 98StaCluOneK-41
❑ 98StaCluPP-41
❑ 98Top-388
❑ 98TopChr-388
❑ 98TopChrR-388
❑ 98TopDevR-388
❑ 98TopDia-388
❑ 98TopMiniC-388
❑ 98Ult-346
❑ 98UltGolM-346
❑ 98UltMas-346
❑ 98UltPlaM-346
❑ 98UppDec-516
❑ 99UppDec-320
❑ 99UppDecEL1-320
❑ 99UppDecEL2-320

Slominski, Rich
❑ 86WauTimP-22

Slomkowski, Bob
❑ 98LowSpiM-30

Slomkowski, Rich
❑ 89WatDiaP-1798
❑ 89WatDiaS-19
❑ 90FreKeyTI-8

Sloniger, Chris
❑ 88SalLakCTTI-5
❑ 89MiaMirIS-17

Slosson, Bill
❑ 91SumFlyC-29
❑ 94BenRocC-30
❑ 95AshTouTI-NNO
❑ 96AshTouB-5
❑ 97AshTou-30

Slotnick, Joe
❑ 86BurExpP-20

Slowik, Tad
❑ 86PeoChiP-21
❑ 87WinSpiP-11
❑ 93AubAstC-29
❑ 93AubAstF-3461

Sluggerr, Mascot
❑ 94PorSeaDTI-21
❑ 96PorSeaDB-5
❑ 97RoyPol-23

Slusarski, Joe
❑ 87PanAmTUBI-24
❑ 87PanAmTURB-20
❑ 88TopTra-109T
❑ 88TopTraT-109T
❑ 89ModA'sC-15
❑ 89ModA'sCLC-266
❑ 89TopBig-213
❑ 90Bes-203
❑ 90HunStaB-10
❑ 91Bow-233
❑ 91Cla3-T85
❑ 91ScoRoo-105T
❑ 91TacTigP-2305
❑ 91UppDec-777
❑ 92AthMot-19
❑ 92Bow-58
❑ 92Don-626
❑ 92Fle-266
❑ 92Lea-431
❑ 92LeaBlaG-431
❑ 92OPC-651
❑ 92Pin-187
❑ 92Sco-309
❑ 92Sco100RS-18
❑ 92StaClu-782
❑ 92StaCluECN-782
❑ 92Top-651
❑ 92TopDaiQTU-14
❑ 92TopDeb91-165
❑ 92TopGol-651
❑ 92TopGolW-651
❑ 92TopMic-651
❑ 92UppDec-663
❑ 93StaClu-376
❑ 93StaCluFDI-376
❑ 93StaCluMOP-376
❑ 93TacTigF-3032

Sly, Kian
❑ 92PulBraC-4
❑ 92PulBraF-3193
❑ 93MacBraC-22
❑ 93MacBraF-1415

Smajstra, Craig
❑ 83AppFoxFr-10
❑ 86WatIndP-22
❑ 87BufBisP-10
❑ 88TucTorC-23
❑ 88TucTorJP-21
❑ 88TucTorP-168
❑ 89TucTorC-12
❑ 89TucTorJP-22
❑ 89TucTorP-200
❑ 90CMC-611
❑ 90ProAAAF-199
❑ 90TriAllGP-AAA40
❑ 90TucTorC-9
❑ 90TucTorP-209
❑ 91IowCubLD-205
❑ 91IowCubP-1069
❑ 91LinDriAAA-205

Smaldone, Ed
❑ 89GenCubP-1859
❑ 89GenCubP-1861

Smale, Robert
❑ 18Zee-35

Small, Aaron
❑ 90MyrBeaBJP-2777
❑ 91Cla/Bes-361
❑ 91DunBluJC-10
❑ 91DunBluJP-206
❑ 92ClaFS7-162
❑ 92KnoBluJF-2991
❑ 92KnoBluJS-393
❑ 92SkyAA F-167
❑ 93Bow-631
❑ 93KnoSmoF-1251
❑ 94BowBes-B83
❑ 94BowBesR-B83
❑ 94KnoSmoF-1304
❑ 94SpoRoo-88
❑ 94SpoRooAP-88
❑ 95BluJayOH-29

❑ 95Pin-141
❑ 95PinArtP-141
❑ 95PinMusC-141
❑ 95Sco-592
❑ 95ScoGolR-592
❑ 95ScoPlaTS-592
❑ 96LeaSigEA-184
❑ 97A'sMot-27
❑ 98A'sMot-27
❑ 98PacInv-60
❑ 98PacInvPBlue-60
❑ 98PacInvSilv-60
❑ 98PacOnl-544
❑ 98PacOnlR-544
❑ 98PacOnlWC-544
❑ 98PacPar-82
❑ 98PacParC-82
❑ 98PacParG-82
❑ 98PacParHS-82
❑ 98PacParPB-82
❑ 98PacParR-82
❑ 99Pac-23
❑ 99PacPlaB-23
❑ 99PacRed-23

Small, Andru
❑ 93ElmPioC-19
❑ 93ElmPioF-3833

Small, Chris
❑ 88AubAstP-1949

Small, Hank
❑ 78RicBraT-15

Small, Jeff
❑ 86PeoChiP-22
❑ 87WinSpiP-24
❑ 90CMC-95
❑ 90IowCubC-20
❑ 90IowCubP-325
❑ 90ProAAAF-632
❑ 90TopTVCu-59
❑ 90TriAllGP-AAA35
❑ 91IowCubLD-218
❑ 91IowCubP-1070
❑ 91LinDriAAA-218
❑ 92NasSouF-1841
❑ 92NasSouS-293
❑ 93EdmTraF-1146

Small, Jim
❑ 56Top-207
❑ 57Top-33
❑ 61UniOil-H6

Small, Lefty (Nataniel)
❑ 76LauIndC-7

Small, Mark
❑ 89AubAstP-2188
❑ 90AshTouP-2748
❑ 91OscAstC-11
❑ 91OscAstP-684
❑ 92OscAstC-12
❑ 92OscAstF-2530
❑ 93JacGenF-2109
❑ 94JacGenF-217
❑ 95TucTotTI-25
❑ 96AstMot-27
❑ 96TusTorB-22
❑ 98OklRedM-15

Small, Robert
❑ 89JamExpP-2133

Smalley, Dave
❑ 84GreHorT-13

Smalley, Roy
❑ 75RanPos-30
❑ 75SpoIndC-6
❑ 76MinTwiP-16
❑ 76OPC-70
❑ 76OPC-657
❑ 76SSP-267
❑ 76Top-70
❑ 76Top-657
❑ 77Hos-66
❑ 77Spo-8504
❑ 77Top-66
❑ 78Hos-118
❑ 78Top-471
❑ 78TwiFriP-19
❑ 79Hos-60
❑ 79OPC-110
❑ 79Top-219
❑ 79TwiFriP-26
❑ 80Kel-13
❑ 80OPC-296
❑ 80Top-570
❑ 80TopSup-40
❑ 80TwiPos-27
❑ 81AllGamPI-23
❑ 81Don-487
❑ 81Fle-551
❑ 81FleStiC-55
❑ 81MSAMinD-30
❑ 81OPC-115
❑ 81Top-115
❑ 81TopScr-43
❑ 81TopSti-100
❑ 81TwiPos-24
❑ 82Don-22
❑ 82Don-573
❑ 82Fle-560
❑ 82FleSta-228
❑ 82OnDecD-30
❑ 82OPC-197
❑ 82Top-767
❑ 82TopSti-207
❑ 82TopTra-107T
❑ 82YanPhoA-25
❑ 83AllGamPI-24
❑ 83Don-209
❑ 83Fle-397
❑ 83FleSta-178
❑ 83FleSti-37
❑ 83OPC-38
❑ 83Top-460
❑ 83TopSti-96
❑ 83YanPhoA-25
❑ 83YanRoyRD-11
❑ 84Don-225
❑ 84Fle-142
❑ 84Nes792-305
❑ 84OPC-305
❑ 84Top-305
❑ 84TopTif-305
❑ 85Don-622
❑ 85Fle-527
❑ 85FleUpd-105
❑ 85OPC-26
❑ 85Top-26
❑ 85Top-140
❑ 85TopSti-237
❑ 85TopTif-26
❑ 85TopTif-140
❑ 85TopTifT-108T
❑ 85TopTra-108T
❑ 85Twi7-6
❑ 85TwiPos-24
❑ 85TwiTeal-2
❑ 86Don-486
❑ 86Fle-404
❑ 86Lea-237
❑ 86OPC-156
❑ 86Top-613
❑ 86TopTif-613
❑ 86TwiTeal-3
❑ 87Don-443
❑ 87Fle-552
❑ 87FleGlo-552
❑ 87OPC-47
❑ 87SpoTeaP-17
❑ 87Top-744
❑ 87TopSti-282
❑ 87TopTif-744
❑ 87TwiPos-24
❑ 87TwiTeal-2
❑ 88Don-566
❑ 88Fle-22
❑ 88FleGlo-22
❑ 88Lea-233
❑ 88Sco-606
❑ 88ScoGlo-606
❑ 88StaLinTw-18
❑ 88Top-239
❑ 88TopTif-239
❑ 90SouCalS-12
❑ 92YanWIZ8-182
❑ 93RanKee-332

Smalley, Roy Sr.
❑ 47PM1StaP1-204
❑ 49EurSta-72
❑ 49Lea-77
❑ 50Bow-115
❑ 51Bow-44
❑ 51FisBakL-27
❑ 51TopBluB-17
❑ 52Bow-64
❑ 52Top-173
❑ 53BowBW-56
❑ 54Bow-109
❑ 54Top-231
❑ 55Bow-252
❑ 55BraJohC-30
❑ 57Top-397
❑ 60DarFar-3
❑ 76OPC-70
❑ 76Top-70
❑ 79DiaGre-116
❑ 83TopRep5-173
❑ 85Top-140
❑ 85TopTif-140
❑ 91TopArc1-297
❑ 94TopArc1-231
❑ 94TopArc1G-231

Smalls, Roberto
❑ 88WytCubP-1986
❑ 89ChaWheB-15
❑ 89ChaWheP-1761
❑ 90GenCubP-3052
❑ 90GenCubS-22

Smallwood, Kevin
❑ 90ArkRaz-29

Smallwood, Walter
❑ 21Zee-168

Smallwood, Woody (DeWitt)
❑ 93NegLeaRL2-35

Smart, J.D.
❑ 95TopTra-49T
❑ 96DelShoB-28
❑ 98arSenW1-21
❑ 98Bow-324
❑ 98BowChr-324
❑ 98BowChrGA-324
❑ 98BowChrGAR-324
❑ 98BowChrI-324
❑ 98BowChrIR-324
❑ 98BowChrR-324
❑ 98BowGolA-324
❑ 98BowInt-324
❑ 98HarSenM-21
❑ 99Bow-337
❑ 99BowAut-BA27
❑ 99BowGol-337
❑ 99BowInt-337

Smedes, Mike
❑ 89AncGlaP-24

Smelko, Mark
❑ 82RedPioT-11
❑ 83RedPioT-23

Smelser, Don
❑ 80ElPasDT-15

Smetana, Steve
❑ 96LowSpiB-23
❑ 97MicBatC-26
❑ 98TreThuM-21

Smetek, Peter
❑ 98HudValR-26

Smiley, John
❑ 85PriWilPT-22
❑ 86PriWilPP-24
❑ 87DonRoo-39
❑ 87FleUpd-110
❑ 87FleUpdG-110
❑ 87SpoRooI-21
❑ 87SpoRooP-7
❑ 87SpoTeaP-18
❑ 87TopTra-114T
❑ 87TopTraT-114T
❑ 88Don-449
❑ 88DonBasB-257
❑ 88Fle-340
❑ 88FleGlo-340
❑ 88PirTeal-31
❑ 88RedFolSB-82
❑ 88Sco-287
❑ 88ScoGlo-287
❑ 88StaLinPi-19
❑ 88Top-423
❑ 88TopTif-423
❑ 88ToyRoo-28
❑ 89Bow-413
❑ 89BowTif-413
❑ 89ClaTraP-191
❑ 89Don-329
❑ 89DonBasB-157
❑ 89Fle-221
❑ 89FleGlo-221
❑ 89OPC-322
❑ 89PanSti-167
❑ 89PirVerFJ-57
❑ 89Sco-409
❑ 89ScoYouSI-37
❑ 89Top-322
❑ 89TopBig-85
❑ 89TopSti-124
❑ 89TopTif-322
❑ 89UppDec-516
❑ 90ClaBlu-126
❑ 90Don-17
❑ 90Don-54
❑ 90DonBesN-21
❑ 90DonSupD-17
❑ 90Fle-480
❑ 90FleCan-480
❑ 90Lea-328
❑ 90OPC-568
❑ 90PanSti-323
❑ 90PirHomC-30
❑ 90PubIntS-165
❑ 90Sco-334
❑ 90Sco100S-65
❑ 90Spo-191
❑ 90Top-568
❑ 90TopBig-79
❑ 90TopSti-132
❑ 90TopTif-568
❑ 90UppDec-387
❑ 91Bow-509
❑ 91Cla3-T86
❑ 91Don-664
❑ 91Fle-50
❑ 91Lea-123
❑ 91OPC-143
❑ 91Sco-465
❑ 91StaClu-471
❑ 91Stu-229
❑ 91Top-143
❑ 91TopDesS-143
❑ 91TopMic-143
❑ 91TopTif-143
❑ 91UltUpd-102
❑ 91UppDec-669
❑ 91USPlaCA-3C
❑ 92Bow-257
❑ 92Cla2-T88
❑ 92ClaGam-156
❑ 92Don-331
❑ 92Fle-567
❑ 92FleUpd-41
❑ 92Fre-5
❑ 92Hig5-93
❑ 92Hig5S-27
❑ 92Lea-526
❑ 92LeaBlaG-526
❑ 92MooSna-12
❑ 92OPC-232
❑ 92OPCPre-2
❑ 92Pin-184
❑ 92RedFolS-89
❑ 92Sco-659
❑ 92Sco100S-3
❑ 92ScoImpP-79
❑ 92ScoRoo-22T
❑ 92StaClu-380
❑ 92StaClu-625
❑ 92StaCluD-173
❑ 92StaCluNC-625
❑ 92Stu-210
❑ 92SunSee-17
❑ 92Top-232
❑ 92TopGol-232
❑ 92TopGolW-232
❑ 92TopMic-232
❑ 92TopTra-106T
❑ 92TopTraG-106T
❑ 92TriPla-52
❑ 92Ult-259
❑ 92Ult-400
❑ 92UppDec-467
❑ 92UppDec-785
❑ 93Bow-230
❑ 93ClaGam-86
❑ 93Don-475
❑ 93Fin-14
❑ 93FinRef-14
❑ 93Fle-643
❑ 93FleFinE-20
❑ 93Lea-433
❑ 93OPC-335
❑ 93OPCPre-56
❑ 93PacSpa-406
❑ 93Pin-543
❑ 93PinTeaP-2
❑ 93RedKah-26
❑ 93Sco-624
❑ 93Sel-75
❑ 93SelAce-13
❑ 93SelRoo-100T
❑ 93SelSam-75
❑ 93StaClu-190
❑ 93StaCluFDI-190
❑ 93StaCluMOP-190
❑ 93Top-363
❑ 93TopComotH-10
❑ 93TopGol-363
❑ 93TopInaM-363
❑ 93TopInaR-363
❑ 93TopMic-363
❑ 93Ult-336
❑ 93UppDec-268
❑ 93UppDec-694
❑ 93UppDecGold-268
❑ 93UppDecGold-694
❑ 94ColChoSS-473
❑ 94Don-105
❑ 94Fin-179
❑ 94FinRef-179
❑ 94Fla-150
❑ 94Fle-429
❑ 94FleExtB-241
❑ 94Lea-24
❑ 94Pac-161
❑ 94Pin-99
❑ 94PinArtP-99
❑ 94PinMusC-99
❑ 94ProMag-31
❑ 94RedKah-30
❑ 94Sco-424
❑ 94ScoGolR-424
❑ 94Sel-169
❑ 94StaClu-487
❑ 94StaCluFDI-487
❑ 94StaCluGR-487
❑ 94StaCluMOP-487
❑ 94Stu-174
❑ 94Top-12
❑ 94TopGol-12
❑ 94TopSpa-12
❑ 94TriPla-220
❑ 94Ult-178
❑ 94UppDec-327
❑ 94UppDecED-327
❑ 95ColCho-436
❑ 95ColChoGS-436
❑ 95ColChoSS-436
❑ 95Don-11
❑ 95DonPreP-11
❑ 95DonTopotO-221
❑ 95Emo-121
❑ 95Fla-126
❑ 95Fle-449
❑ 95Lea-343
❑ 95Pin-51
❑ 95PinArtP-51
❑ 95PinMusC-51
❑ 95RedKah-31
❑ 95Sco-471
❑ 95ScoGolR-471
❑ 95ScoPlaTS-471
❑ 95SPCha-38
❑ 95SPChaDC-38
❑ 95StaClu-416
❑ 95StaCluMOP-416
❑ 95StaCluSTDW-RE416
❑ 95StaCluSTWS-416
❑ 95StaCluVR-214
❑ 95StaCluVRMO-214
❑ 95Top-56
❑ 95TopCyb-41
❑ 95Ult-372
❑ 95UltGolM-372
❑ 95UppDec-402
❑ 95UppDecED-402
❑ 95UppDecEDG-402
❑ 96Cir-119
❑ 96CirRav-119
❑ 96ColCho-522
❑ 96ColChoGS-522
❑ 96ColChoSS-522
❑ 96Don-139
❑ 96DonPreP-139
❑ 96EmoXL-170
❑ 96Fla-240
❑ 96Fle-354
❑ 96FleTif-354
❑ 96MetUni-153
❑ 96MetUniP-153
❑ 96Pac-38
❑ 96PanSti-51
❑ 96Sco-94
❑ 96SP-66
❑ 96StaClu-124
❑ 96StaClu-244
❑ 96StaCluEPB-124
❑ 96StaCluEPG-124
❑ 96StaCluEPS-124
❑ 96StaCluMOP-124
❑ 96StaCluMOP-244
❑ 96Top-257
❑ 96Ult-184
❑ 96UltGolM-184
❑ 96UppDec-47
❑ 97Cir-351
❑ 97CirRav-351
❑ 97ColCho-82
❑ 97Fin-89
❑ 97FinRef-89
❑ 97Fle-305
❑ 97FleTif-305
❑ 97MetUni-51
❑ 97PacPriGotD-GD130
❑ 97Sco-388
❑ 97ScoArtPWB-388
❑ 97ScoResC-388
❑ 97ScoShoS-388
❑ 97ScoShoSAP-388
❑ 97StaClu-150
❑ 97StaCluMOP-150
❑ 97Top-119
❑ 97Ult-181
❑ 97UltGolME-181
❑ 97UltPlaME-181
❑ 97UppDec-338
❑ 98Fin-274
❑ 98FinNo--274
❑ 98FinNo-R-274
❑ 98FinRef-274
❑ 98PinSna-CI15
❑ 98StaCluFDI-264
❑ 98StaCluI-264
❑ 98StaCluOneK-264
❑ 98StaCluPP-264
❑ 98Top-419
❑ 98TopChr-419
❑ 98TopChrR-419
❑ 98TopDevR-419
❑ 98TopDia-419
❑ 98TopMiniC-419
❑ 98Ult-99
❑ 98UltGolM-99
❑ 98UltMas-99
❑ 98UltPlaM-99
❑ 98UppDec-344

Smiley, Reuben
❑ 88PocGiaP-2087
❑ 89CliGiaP-894
❑ 90Bes-310
❑ 90CalLeaACLC-45
❑ 90SanJosGB-3
❑ 90SanJosGCLC-30
❑ 90SanJosGP-2024
❑ 90SanJosGS-22
❑ 90SanJosGS-26
❑ 91LinDriAA-321
❑ 91ShrCapLD-321
❑ 91ShrCapP-1836
❑ 92ShrCapF-3885
❑ 92ShrCapS-594
❑ 93PhoFirF-1531
❑ 94PhoFirF-1534

Smith, Ackroyd
❑ 52LavPro-77

Smith, Adam
❑ 88PocGiaP-2092

Smith, Al (Alfred J.)
❑ 28Zee-41
❑ 33ButCanV-45
❑ 46SunBre-17
❑ 47SigOil-69
❑ 47SunBre-21
❑ 54Top-248
❑ 55Bow-20
❑ 55IndCarBL-9
❑ 55IndGolS-17
❑ 55Top-197
❑ 56Top-105
❑ 56TopPin-11
❑ 57IndSoh-13
❑ 57IndTeal-21
❑ 57Top-145
❑ 58Top-177
❑ 58WhiSoxJP-10
❑ 59Top-22
❑ 59TopVen-22
❑ 60Top-428
❑ 60WhiSoxJP-11
❑ 60WhiSoxTS-19
❑ 61Pos-24A
❑ 61Pos-24B
❑ 61Top-42
❑ 61Top-170
❑ 61TopStal-129
❑ 61WhiSoxTS-18
❑ 62Jel-48
❑ 62Pos-48
❑ 62PosCan-48
❑ 62SalPlaC-29
❑ 62ShiPlaC-29
❑ 62Top-410
❑ 62WhiSoxJP-11

❑ 62WhiSoxTS-20
❑ 63BalOriP-30
❑ 63Jel-38
❑ 63Pos-38
❑ 63Top-16
❑ 64IndJayP-11
❑ 64Top-317
❑ 64TopVen-317
❑ 75TCM195Cl-32
❑ 76GrePlaG-38
❑ 81WhiSox1T-7
❑ 83TCMPla1943-8
❑ 84OCoandSI-206
❑ 91OriCro-425
❑ 92ConTSN-580
❑ 93DiaStaES-149
❑ 94TopArc1-248
❑ 94TopArc1G-248
Smith, Alex
❑ 87DurBulP-14
❑ 88BobCamRB-16
❑ 88RicBraC-13
❑ 88RicBraP-25
❑ 89RicBraBC-25
❑ 89RicBraP-841
❑ 89RicBraTI-21
❑ 96OklCit8B-20
Smith, Andy
❑ 94SouOreAC-25
❑ 94SouOreAF-3622
❑ 95WesMicWTI-31
❑ 96WesMicWB-25
❑ 97VisOakG-27
Smith, Anthony
❑ 09RamT20-109
Smith, Archie
❑ 87EugEmeP-2655
Smith, Arthur
❑ 11PacCoaBD-58
❑ 11Zee-101
❑ 24Zee-74
Smith, Ballard
❑ 77PadSchC-51
Smith, Ben
❑ 89KinMetS-29
❑ 90KinMetS-30
Smith, Bernie
❑ 71OPC-204
❑ 71Top-204
❑ 83RedPioT-29
❑ 94BreMilB-273
Smith, Big
❑ 88SFHesCreN32-30
Smith, Bill
❑ 83AppFoxFr-1
Smith, Bill (William Garland)
❑ 60MapLeaSF-19
❑ 61MapLeaBH-21
Smith, Bill PCL
❑ 19Zee-103
Smith, Billy
❑ 85EveGialC-17
Smith, Billy Edward
❑ 75CalAngP-40
❑ 76SalLakCGC-9
❑ 76SSP-199
❑ 77BalOriP-21
❑ 78BalOriP-30
❑ 78Top-666
❑ 79Top-237
❑ 80Top-367
❑ 81GiaTeal-18
❑ 82Fle-400
❑ 82Top-593
❑ 91OriCro-426
Smith, Billy Franklin
❑ 84BluJayFS-27
❑ 85BluJayFS-26
❑ 86BluJayFS-28
❑ 87BluJayFS-28
❑ 88BluJayFS-26
Smith, Billy Lavern
❑ 78DayBeaAT-24
❑ 80TucTorT-11
❑ 81TucTorT-24
❑ 82Top-441
❑ 82TucTorT-18
Smith, Bob
❑ 52LavPro-13
❑ 60MapLeaSF-20
❑ 61MapLeaBH-22
❑ 63Top-241
Smith, Bob (Robert Eldridge)
❑ 21Exh-166
❑ 28Exh-3
❑ 29ExhFou-2
❑ 29PorandAR-86
❑ 31CubTeal-19
❑ 32CubTeal-21
❑ 33Gou-185
❑ 34BatR31-47
❑ 34DiaMatCSB-164
❑ 91ConTSN-217
Smith, Bob Gilchrist
❑ 58Top-226
❑ 59Top-83
❑ 59TopVen-83
❑ 91MetWIZ-368
Smith, Bob W.
❑ 58Top-445
Smith, Bobby (Robert Eugene)
❑ 94CarLeaAF-CAR31
❑ 94DurBulC-19
❑ 94DurBulTI-21
❑ 95BreBtaTI-2
❑ 96BesAutS-85
❑ 96Bow-296
❑ 96BowFoi-296
❑ 96ColCho-441
❑ 96ColChoGS-441
❑ 96ColChoSS-441
❑ 96Exc-133
❑ 96RicBraB-26
❑ 96RicBraRC-8
❑ 96RicBraUB-26
❑ 96UppDec-259
❑ 97BesAutAS-57
❑ 97Bow-86
❑ 97BowInt-86
❑ 97RicBra-24
❑ 97Sel-123
❑ 97SelArtP-123
❑ 97SelCom-123
❑ 97SelRegG-123
❑ 98Bow-301
❑ 98BowChr-301
❑ 98BowChrGA-301
❑ 98BowChrGAR-301
❑ 98BowChrI-301
❑ 98BowChrIR-301
❑ 98BowChrR-301
❑ 98BowGolA-301
❑ 98BowInt-301
❑ 98CirThu-203
❑ 98CirThuRav-203
❑ 98CirThuSupRav-203
❑ 98CroRoy-134
❑ 98DevRayP-18
❑ 98Don-288
❑ 98DonGolPP-288
❑ 98DonSilPP-288
❑ 98Fle-474
❑ 98LeaRS-285
❑ 98LeaRSLHolo-285
❑ 98LeaRSLong-285
❑ 98LeaRTrue-285
❑ 98PacOmeRS-15
❑ 98PacOmeRST3-15
❑ 98PacOnl-718
❑ 98PacOnlR-718
❑ 98PacOnlWC-718
❑ 98SPxFin-202
❑ 98SPxFinR-202
❑ 98SPxFinS-202
❑ 98Top-466
❑ 98TopChr-466
❑ 98TopChrR-466
❑ 98TopDevR-466
❑ 98TopDia-466
❑ 98TopMiniC-466
❑ 99Fle-231
❑ 99FleSta9-231
❑ 99FleWarT-231
❑ 99MetUni-64
❑ 99MetUniGM-64
❑ 99MetUniPMG-64
❑ 99SkyPre-168
❑ 99SkyPreR-168
❑ 99SkyThu-119
❑ 99SkyThuRant-119
❑ 99SkyThuRave-119
❑ 99SP SigAuto-BS
❑ 99SpoIllOTW-13
❑ 99SPSig-133
❑ 99ThuSkySupR-119
❑ 99Top-391
❑ 99TopChr-391
❑ 99TopChrR-391
❑ 99TopMVPP-391
❑ 99UD Cho-147
❑ 99UD ChoPCR-147
❑ 99UppDec-6
❑ 99UppDecEL1-6
❑ 99UppDecEL2-6
❑ 99UppDecM-202
❑ 99UppDecMGS-202
❑ 99UppDecMHFS-202
❑ 99UppDecMSS-202
❑ 99UppDecR-81
❑ 99UppDecRG-81
❑ 99UppDecRP-81
❑ 99Vic-384
Smith, Bobby Gene
❑ 57Top-384
❑ 58Top-402
❑ 59Top-162
❑ 59TopVen-162
❑ 60Top-194
❑ 60TopVen-194
❑ 61Top-316
❑ 62Jel-196
❑ 62Pos-196
❑ 62PosCan-196
❑ 62SalPlaC-176A
❑ 62SalPlaC-176B
❑ 62ShiPlaC-176
❑ 62Top-531
Smith, Bobby Glen
❑ 78BurBeeT-27
❑ 79HolMilT-6
❑ 80VanCanT-5
❑ 81VanCanT-19
Smith, Brad
❑ 88ClePhiS-23
Smith, Brandon
❑ 94PitMetC-20
❑ 98AubDouTI-27
Smith, Brent
❑ 93EveGiaC-24
❑ 93EveGiaF-3768
Smith, Brett
❑ 94OgdRapF-3738
❑ 94OgdRapSP-11
Smith, Brian
❑ 94MedHatBJF-3679
❑ 94MedHatBJSP-19
❑ 95HagSunF-70
❑ 96KnoSmoB-24
❑ 97EveAquG-24
❑ 97SyrSkyCB-24
Smith, Brick
❑ 84ChaLooT-4
❑ 86ChaLooP-23
❑ 86SouLeaAJ-17
❑ 87CalCanP-2320
❑ 87SpoRooP-5
❑ 88CalCanP-803
❑ 89ChaLooLITI-28
❑ 89TucTorC-17
❑ 89TucTorJP-23
❑ 89TucTorP-193
Smith, Broadway (Alexander B.)
❑ 90DodTar-1072
❑ 98CamPepP-69
Smith, Brook
❑ 93EveGiaC-25
❑ 93EveGiaF-3769
❑ 95BurBeeTI-28
Smith, Bryan
❑ 80VenLeaS-250
❑ 86BakDodP-25
❑ 87VerBeaDP-24
❑ 90AubAstB-12
❑ 90AubAstP-3406
❑ 91BurAstC-22
❑ 91BurAstP-2816
❑ 91Cla/Bes-313
Smith, Bryn
❑ 79MemChiT-5
❑ 80MemChiT-20
❑ 82ExpHygM-20
❑ 82ExpPos-38
❑ 82OPC-118
❑ 82Top-118
❑ 83Don-88A
❑ 83Don-88B
❑ 83ExpPos-30
❑ 83ExpStu-29
❑ 83Fle-297
❑ 83OPC-234
❑ 83Top-447
❑ 84AllGamPI-88
❑ 84Don-453
❑ 84ExpPos-29
❑ 84ExpStu-21
❑ 84Fle-287
❑ 84Nes792-656
❑ 84OPC-77
❑ 84Top-656
❑ 84TopTif-656
❑ 85AllGamPI-176
❑ 85Don-209
❑ 85ExpPos-22
❑ 85Fle-410
❑ 85Lea-171
❑ 85OPC-88
❑ 85Top-88
❑ 85TopMin-88
❑ 85TopSti-90
❑ 85TopTif-88
❑ 86Don-299
❑ 86ExpPos-14
❑ 86ExpProPa-19
❑ 86ExpProPo-2
❑ 86Fle-260
❑ 86FleMin-55
❑ 86FleSlu-35
❑ 86FleStiC-110
❑ 86GenMilB-6G
❑ 86Lea-174
❑ 86OPC-299
❑ 86Spo-120
❑ 86Top-299
❑ 86TopSti-79
❑ 86TopSup-51
❑ 86TopTat-22
❑ 86TopTif-299
❑ 87Don-159
❑ 87ExpPos-27
❑ 87Fle-332
❑ 87FleGlo-332
❑ 87GenMilB-4F
❑ 87Lea-60
❑ 87OPC-281
❑ 87StuPan-8
❑ 87Top-505
❑ 87TopSti-83
❑ 87TopTif-505
❑ 88Don-335
❑ 88DonBasB-202
❑ 88ExpPos-32
❑ 88Fle-196
❑ 88FleGlo-196
❑ 88Lea-129
❑ 88OPC-161
❑ 88PanSti-320
❑ 88Sco-356
❑ 88ScoGlo-356
❑ 88StaLinE-16
❑ 88Top-161
❑ 88TopBig-250
❑ 88TopTif-161
❑ 89Bow-353
❑ 89BowTif-353
❑ 89Don-216
❑ 89DonBasB-124
❑ 89ExpPos-27
❑ 89Fle-394
❑ 89FleGlo-394
❑ 89OPC-131
❑ 89PanSti-116
❑ 89Sco-428
❑ 89Top-464
❑ 89TopBig-47
❑ 89TopTif-464
❑ 89UppDec-78
❑ 90Bow-184
❑ 90BowTif-184
❑ 90CarSmo-20
❑ 90Don-25
❑ 90Don-106
❑ 90DonBesN-10
❑ 90DonSupD-25
❑ 90Fle-361
❑ 90FleCan-361
❑ 90Lea-393
❑ 90OPC-352
❑ 90PubIntS-188
❑ 90Sco-419
❑ 90ScoRoo-55T
❑ 90Top-352
❑ 90TopSti-78
❑ 90TopTif-352
❑ 90TopTra-117T
❑ 90TopTraT-117T
❑ 90TopTVCa-18
❑ 90UppDec-579
❑ 90UppDec-794
❑ 91Bow-407
❑ 91CarPol-36
❑ 91Don-113
❑ 91Fle-644
❑ 91Lea-226
❑ 91OPC-743
❑ 91Sco-444
❑ 91StaClu-17
❑ 91Top-743
❑ 91TopDesS-743
❑ 91TopMic-743
❑ 91TopTif-743
❑ 91Ult-294
❑ 91UppDec-307
❑ 92CarPol-17
❑ 92Don-323
❑ 92Fle-590
❑ 92Lea-157
❑ 92LeaBlaG-157
❑ 92OPC-31
❑ 92Pin-474
❑ 92Sco-529
❑ 92StaClu-368
❑ 92Top-31
❑ 92TopGol-31
❑ 92TopGolW-31
❑ 92TopMic-31
❑ 92Ult-269
❑ 92UppDec-591
❑ 93Fle-515
❑ 93Lea-409
❑ 93PacSpa-438
❑ 93RocStaC-4
❑ 93RocUSPC-5D
❑ 93RocUSPC-8H
❑ 93Ult-359
❑ 93UppDec-723
❑ 93UppDecGold-723
❑ 97SalAva-3
Smith, Bubba (Charles)
❑ 91BelMarCB-12
❑ 91BelMarP-3675
❑ 91Cla/Bes-446
❑ 92ClaFS7-216
❑ 92PenPilC-1
❑ 92PenPilF-2944
❑ 92UppDecML-170
❑ 93Bow-346
❑ 93ClaGolF-34
❑ 93ClaMVPF-1
❑ 93ExcFS7-232
❑ 93ExcLeaLF-2
❑ 93JacSunF-2720
❑ 93Top-423
❑ 93TopGol-423
❑ 93TopInaM-423
❑ 93TopInaR-423
❑ 93TopMic-423
❑ 94Bow-344
❑ 94ChaLooF-1368
❑ 95ForMyeMTI-25
❑ 95HarCitRCTI-24
❑ 96DouAllB-53
❑ 96TexLeaAB-17
❑ 96TulDriTI-24
❑ 97OklCit8-21
Smith, Bud (Robert)
❑ 98JohCCTI-29
Smith, C.L.
❑ 90RocExpLC-25
Smith, Calvin
❑ 91HunCubC-24
❑ 91HunCubP-3344
Smith, Cameron
❑ 93BriTigC-1
❑ 94FayGenC-23
❑ 94FayGenF-2146
❑ 95FayGenTI-24
❑ 96Bow-182
❑ 96BowFoi-182
❑ 96LakTigB-26
❑ 96WesOahCHWB-16
❑ 97MobBayBB-25
Smith, Carlisle
❑ 23Zee-198
Smith, Carlos
❑ 09T206-516
Smith, Casey
❑ 97BurIndG-25
❑ 98WatIndTI-30
Smith, Chad
❑ 88BurBraP-4
❑ 89SumBraP-1108
❑ 90DurBulTI-23
❑ 90MiaMirIS-25
❑ 92HamRedC-3
❑ 92HamRedF-1591
❑ 93SprCarC-24
❑ 93SprCarF-1851
Smith, Charles Edwin
❑ 09SenBarP-8
❑ 11SpoLifCW-326
Smith, Charles M.
❑ 08RosComP-86
❑ 11PinT-5-663
❑ 11TurRedT-118
❑ 72ClaCar-88
Smith, Charles W.
❑ 11SpoLifM-145
❑ 60DarFar-12
❑ 61SevElev-26
❑ 62SalPlaC-135A
❑ 62SalPlaC-135B
❑ 62ShiPlaC-135
❑ 62Top-283
❑ 62WhiSoxTS-21
❑ 63Top-424
❑ 63WhiSoxTS-23
❑ 64Top-519
❑ 65OPC-22
❑ 65Top-22
❑ 66CarTeal-11
❑ 66Top-358
❑ 66TopVen-358
❑ 67CokCapYM-V11
❑ 67DexPre-193
❑ 67Top-257
❑ 67YanPhoS-95
❑ 68Top-596
❑ 68YanPhoS-77
❑ 69Top-538
❑ 78TCM60I-289
❑ 90DodTar-745
❑ 91MetWIZ-369
❑ 92YanWIZ6-118
❑ 94CarLeaA-DJ14
Smith, Chris
❑ 92BoiHawC-26
❑ 92BoiHawF-3640
❑ 92ClaDraP-33
❑ 92ClaFS7-423
❑ 93CedRapKC-19
❑ 93CedRapKF-1749
❑ 93MidLeaAGF-36
❑ 93StaCluM-132
❑ 94Bow-154
❑ 94Cla-41
❑ 94MidAngF-2449
❑ 94MidAngOHP-29
❑ 96LakElsSB-21
Smith, Chris W.
❑ 80MemChiT-21
❑ 82WicAerTI-18
❑ 83PhoGiaBHN-22
❑ 84Don-46
❑ 87SalAngP-33
Smith, Chuck
❑ 92AshTouC-23
❑ 93QuaCitRBC-21
❑ 93QuaCitRBF-100
❑ 94OscAstC-21
❑ 94OscAstF-1138
❑ 96PriWilCB-24
❑ 97BirBarB-8
Smith, Clarence
❑ 16Zee-64
Smith, Clay
❑ 79CliDodT-2
Smith, Cleo
❑ 75AlbDukCa-9
Smith, Clint
❑ 99TeaBesR-80
❑ 99TeaBesRG-80
❑ 99TeaBesRS-80
Smith, Coleman
❑ 92HunCubC-17
❑ 92HunCubF-3166
❑ 94PeoChiC-23
❑ 94PeoChiF-2282
Smith, Coley
❑ 74TacTwiC-10
❑ 75TacTwiK-17
Smith, Corey
❑ 87UtiBluSP-30
Smith, Craig
❑ 93HelBreSP-5
❑ 94StoPorC-26
❑ 94StoPorF-1704
Smith, D.L. (David Lee)
❑ 86ChaOriW-28
❑ 87RocRedWP-14
❑ 88RocRedWP-195

❑ 88RocRedWTI-21
❑ 89BelMarL-29
❑ 89ElPasDGS-24
❑ 89TexLeaAGS-16
❑ 90CMC-35
❑ 90DenZepC-10
❑ 90DenZepP-635
❑ 90ProAAAF-660
❑ 90SanBerSCLC-99
❑ 90SanBerSP-2647
❑ 91DenZepLD-126
❑ 91DenZepP-132
❑ 91LinDriAAA-126
❑ 92ColSprSSS-96
Smith, D.W. (David Wayne)
❑ 82HolMilT-10
❑ 83NasAngT-8
❑ 84EdmTraC-103
❑ 84NewOriT-11
❑ 85EdmTraC-16
❑ 86EdmTraP-26
Smith, Dan
❑ 75CedRapGT-17
❑ 78TidTidT-24
❑ 79JacMetT-17
❑ 86BakDodP-26
❑ 87OrlTwiP-3
❑ 91RocExpC-21
Smith, Dan (Daniel Scott)
❑ 90ButCopKSP-7
❑ 90ClaDraP-16
❑ 91Bow-275
❑ 91LinDriAAA-322
❑ 91OklCit8LD-322
❑ 91OklCit8P-179
❑ 91PacRyaTEI-61
❑ 91Sco-384
❑ 92Bow-391
❑ 92ClaFS7-291
❑ 92SkyAA F-276
❑ 92TulDriF-2696
❑ 92TulDriS-622
❑ 93Bow-109
❑ 93ClaGolF-10
❑ 93DayCubC-17
❑ 93DayCubF-866
❑ 93Don-374
❑ 93Fle-329
❑ 93PacSpa-648
❑ 93Pin-603
❑ 93RanKee-333
❑ 93RanStaC-6
❑ 93Top-607
❑ 93TopGol-607
❑ 93TopInaM-607
❑ 93TopInaR-607
❑ 93TopMic-607
❑ 93Toy-68
❑ 93Ult-637
❑ 93UppDec-7
❑ 93UppDecGold-7
❑ 94ChaRivC-20
❑ 94ChaRivF-2674
❑ 94DayCubC-22
❑ 94DayCubF-2363
❑ 94SigRoo-43
❑ 94SigRooS-43
❑ 94SpoRoo-33
❑ 94SpoRooAP-33
❑ 94UppDecML-174
❑ 95Pac-434
❑ 95Top-127
❑ 98TulDriTI-11
Smith, Dan Independent League
❑ 98St.PauSTI-25
Smith, Dana
❑ 86HagSunP-18
❑ 88ChaKniTI-21
❑ 89HagSunB-21
❑ 89HagSunP-286
❑ 89HagSunS-18
Smith, Danny
❑ 85CedRapRT-12
❑ 86VerRedP-20
❑ 97TulDriTI-25
Smith, Daryl
❑ 80AshTouT-19
❑ 83TulDriT-7
❑ 86WatIndP-23
❑ 87WilBilP-12
❑ 88BirBarB-19
❑ 90MemChiS-24
❑ 91LinDriAAA-345
❑ 91OmaRoyLD-345
❑ 91OmaRoyP-1035
❑ 91TopDeb90-145
Smith, Dave
❑ 76BurBeeT-30
❑ 77HolMilT-24
❑ 78HolMilT-20
❑ 79ChaChaT-11A
❑ 79ChaChaT-11B
❑ 80SpoIndT-2
❑ 81LynSaiT-11
❑ 83WauTimF-27
❑ 94SarRedSC-26
❑ 94SarRedSF-1962
❑ 97RanCucQG-28
Smith, Dave (David S.)
❑ 77CocAstT-24
❑ 81AstPos-23
❑ 81Don-23A
❑ 81Don-23B
❑ 81Fle-71
❑ 81OPC-287
❑ 81Top-534
❑ 82AstAstI-5
❑ 82AstPos-26
❑ 82Don-191
❑ 82Fle-232
❑ 82OPC-297
❑ 82Top-761
❑ 83AstPos-29
❑ 83Don-370
❑ 83Fle-466
❑ 83OPC-247
❑ 83Top-247
❑ 84AstMot-13
❑ 84AstPos-27
❑ 84Don-548
❑ 84Fle-242
❑ 84Nes792-361
❑ 84Top-361
❑ 84TopTif-361
❑ 85AstHouP-13
❑ 85AstMot-21
❑ 85Don-548
❑ 85Fle-362
❑ 85Top-123
❑ 85TopTif-123
❑ 86AstMilL-20
❑ 86AstPol-11
❑ 86Don-328
❑ 86Fle-312
❑ 86FleStiC-111
❑ 86OPC-222
❑ 86SevCoi-S12
❑ 86Top-408
❑ 86TopSti-31
❑ 86TopTif-408
❑ 87AstMot-20
❑ 87AstPol-17
❑ 87AstShoSPT-19
❑ 87ClaGam-66
❑ 87Don-308
❑ 87DonAll-30
❑ 87Fle-69
❑ 87FleGlo-69
❑ 87FleHotS-38
❑ 87FleStiC-109
❑ 87Lea-224
❑ 87OPC-50
❑ 87Spo-77
❑ 87Spo-94
❑ 87SpoTeaP-8
❑ 87Top-50
❑ 87TopMinL-12
❑ 87TopTif-50
❑ 88AlaGolAA70TI-24
❑ 88AstMot-20
❑ 88AstPol-22
❑ 88Don-410
❑ 88DonBasB-262
❑ 88Fle-457
❑ 88FleGlo-457
❑ 88FleHotS-39
❑ 88FleMin-81
❑ 88FleStiC-90
❑ 88FleTeaL-37
❑ 88OPC-73
❑ 88PanSti-290
❑ 88SanDieSAAG-19
❑ 88Sco-365
❑ 88ScoGlo-365
❑ 88Spo-208
❑ 88StaLinAst-17
❑ 88Top-520
❑ 88TopSti-26
❑ 88TopTif-520
❑ 89AstLenH-19
❑ 89AstMot-19
❑ 89AstSmo-37
❑ 89Bow-317
❑ 89BowTif-317
❑ 89ClaLigB-22
❑ 89Don-272
❑ 89DonBasB-232
❑ 89Fle-369
❑ 89FleBasA-38
❑ 89FleGlo-369
❑ 89OPC-305
❑ 89PanSti-87
❑ 89SanDieSAG-18
❑ 89Sco-245
❑ 89Top-305
❑ 89TopSti-13
❑ 89TopTif-305
❑ 89UppDec-302
❑ 90AstLenH-23
❑ 90AstMot-17
❑ 90Bow-62
❑ 90BowTif-62
❑ 90ClaBlu-94
❑ 90Don-88
❑ 90DonBesN-40
❑ 90Fle-238
❑ 90FleCan-238
❑ 90Lea-122
❑ 90OPC-746
❑ 90PanSti-257
❑ 90PubIntS-103
❑ 90RedFolSB-87
❑ 90Sco-45
❑ 90Sco100S-19
❑ 90Spo-140
❑ 90Top-746
❑ 90TopBig-145
❑ 90TopSti-16
❑ 90TopSti-190
❑ 90TopTif-746
❑ 90TopTVA-49
❑ 90UppDec-448
❑ 90USPlaCA-8D
❑ 91Bow-425
❑ 91Cla3-T87
❑ 91CubMar-42
❑ 91CubVinL-27
❑ 91Don-212
❑ 91Fle-517
❑ 91FleUpd-82
❑ 91Lea-456
❑ 91OPC-215
❑ 91OPCPre-111
❑ 91PanSti-12
❑ 91Sco-314
❑ 91ScoRoo-9T
❑ 91StaClu-345
❑ 91Stu-160
❑ 91Top-215
❑ 91TopDesS-215
❑ 91TopMic-215
❑ 91TopTif-215
❑ 91TopTra-110T
❑ 91TopTraT-110T
❑ 91UppDec-513
❑ 91UppDec-704
❑ 92Bow-333
❑ 92ClaGam-31
❑ 92CubMar-42
❑ 92Don-53
❑ 92Fle-391
❑ 92Lea-30
❑ 92LeaBlaG-30
❑ 92OPC-601
❑ 92Pin-94
❑ 92Sco-98
❑ 92StaClu-219
❑ 92Top-601
❑ 92TopGol-601
❑ 92TopGolW-601
❑ 92TopMic-601
❑ 92Ult-475
❑ 92UppDec-549
❑ 94SpoIndF-3341
❑ 95RanCucQT-37
❑ 98Las-3
Smith, David
❑ 95MicBatCTI-25
Smith, David (Marvin David)
❑ 23Zee-56
❑ 26Zee-104
❑ 88KenTwiP-1391
❑ 89VisOakCLC-117
❑ 89VisOakP-1448
❑ 90SanBerSB-20
Smith, David A.
❑ 82HolMilT-9
Smith, Del Roy
❑ 85IowCubT-35
Smith, Demond
❑ 91KinMetC-2
❑ 91KinMetP-3828
❑ 92PitMetC-2
❑ 92PitMetF-3308
❑ 93CapCitBF-473
❑ 94BoiHawC-24
❑ 94BoiHawF-3369
❑ 94LakElsSC-19
❑ 94LakElsSF-1678
❑ 95CedRapKTI-24
❑ 95MidLeaA-52
❑ 96BesAutS-84
❑ 96Exc-101
❑ 96HunStaTI-24
❑ 96Top-437
❑ 99WesMicWAM-21
Smith, Dick (Richard Arthur)
❑ 53MotCoo-39
❑ 55Bow-288
❑ 64Top-398
❑ 65Top-579
❑ 76Met63 S-14
❑ 90DodTar-746
❑ 91MetWIZ-370
Smith, Don
❑ 84AlbDukCr-155
❑ 85AlbDukCr-171
Smith, Duke (John)
❑ 82MadMusF-5
Smith, Dwight
❑ 86PeoChiP-23
❑ 87PitCubP-26
❑ 88BlaYNPRWL-188
❑ 88IowCubC-21
❑ 88IowCubP-530
❑ 88TriAAAP-19
❑ 89Bow-297
❑ 89BowTif-297
❑ 89CubMar-18
❑ 89DonBasB-205
❑ 89DonRoo-32
❑ 89FleUpd-79
❑ 89IowCubC-22
❑ 89IowCubP-1708
❑ 89Sco-642
❑ 89ScoHot1R-64
❑ 89TopTra-113T
❑ 89TopTraT-113T
❑ 89UppDec-780
❑ 90Bow-32
❑ 90BowTif-32
❑ 90ClaBlu-30
❑ 90CubMar-19
❑ 90Don-393
❑ 90DonBesN-63
❑ 90Fle-42
❑ 90FleBasM-35
❑ 90FleBasMC-35
❑ 90FleCan-42
❑ 90FleSoaS-12
❑ 90Hot50RS-42
❑ 90Lea-255
❑ 90OPC-311
❑ 90PanSti-235
❑ 90PubIntS-204
❑ 90Sco-240
❑ 90Sco100RS-4
❑ 90ScoYouSI-2
❑ 90Spo-152
❑ 90Top-311
❑ 90TopBig-151
❑ 90TopCoi-57
❑ 90TopDeb89-116
❑ 90TopHeaU-23
❑ 90TopRoo-26
❑ 90TopSti-52
❑ 90TopTif-311
❑ 90TopTVCu-33
❑ 90ToyRoo-25
❑ 90UppDec-376
❑ 91CubMar-18
❑ 91CubVinL-28
❑ 91Don-559
❑ 91Fle-432
❑ 91OPC-463
❑ 91PanFreS-47
❑ 91Sco-301
❑ 91StaClu-181
❑ 91Top-463
❑ 91TopDesS-463
❑ 91TopMic-463
❑ 91TopTif-463
❑ 91Ult-68
❑ 91UppDec-452
❑ 92CubMar-18
❑ 92Don-561
❑ 92Fle-392
❑ 92OPC-168
❑ 92Pin-293
❑ 92Sco-612
❑ 92StaClu-196
❑ 92Top-168
❑ 92TopGol-168
❑ 92TopGolW-168
❑ 92TopMic-168
❑ 93CubMar-25
❑ 93CubStaC-11
❑ 93Don-476
❑ 93Fla-21
❑ 93Fle-384
❑ 93Lea-547
❑ 93PacSpa-63
❑ 93Sco-637
❑ 93StaClu-278
❑ 93StaCluFDI-278
❑ 93StaCluMOP-278
❑ 93Top-688
❑ 93TopGol-688
❑ 93TopInaM-688
❑ 93TopInaR-688
❑ 93TopMic-688
❑ 93TriPla-172
❑ 93Ult-23
❑ 94AngLAT-12
❑ 94AngMot-8
❑ 94ColC-582
❑ 94ColChoGS-582
❑ 94ColChoSS-582
❑ 94Don-570
❑ 94Fle-398
❑ 94FleUpd-7
❑ 94Pac-111
❑ 94PanSti-157
❑ 94Pin-66
❑ 94PinArtP-66
❑ 94PinMusC-66
❑ 94Sco-408
❑ 94ScoGolR-408
❑ 94Top-536
❑ 94TopGol-536
❑ 94TopSpa-536
❑ 94TopTra-52T
❑ 95ColCho-336
❑ 95ColChoGS-336
❑ 95ColChoSS-336
❑ 95Top-261
❑ 96ColCho-451
❑ 96ColChoGS-451
❑ 96ColChoSS-451
❑ 96FleUpd-U106
❑ 96FleUpdTC-U106
❑ 96MLBPin-31
❑ 97DonSigA-89
❑ 97DonSigAC-112
❑ 97DonSigAM-112
❑ 97St.PauS-28
❑ 98RocRedWQ-27
Smith, Earl L.
❑ 22W573-125
❑ 23WilChoV-152
❑ 28Exh-26
❑ 28W502-48
❑ 28Yue-48
Smith, Earl S.
❑ 20GasAmeMBD-34
❑ 20NatCarE-95
❑ 21E121So1-98
❑ 21E121So8-92
❑ 21Exh-162
❑ 21Exh-163
❑ 21KoBreWSI-22
❑ 22E120-119
❑ 22E120-192
❑ 22W572-100
❑ 22W573-126
❑ 22W575-128
❑ 23W501-71
❑ 23W503-28
❑ 23WilChoV-153
❑ 25Exh-54
❑ 26Exh-54
❑ 27Exh-27
❑ 91ConTSN-74
Smith, Ed
❑ 88SouBenWSGS-5
❑ 89SouBenWSGS-28
❑ 90SarWhiSS-22
❑ 91SarWhiSC-19
❑ 91SarWhiSP-1121
❑ 92ElPasDF-3932
❑ 92StoPorC-4
❑ 92StoPorF-43
❑ 93El PasDF-2959
❑ 94OrlCubF-1394
Smith, Eddie (Edgar)
❑ 39WhiSoxTI-17
❑ 40WhiSoxL-17
❑ 79DiaGre-129
❑ 84TCMPla1-13
Smith, Elmer E.
❑ 87OldJudN-456
❑ 88SpoTimM-23
❑ 98CamPepP-70
Smith, Elmer John
❑ 17ColE13-163
❑ 21E121So1-99
❑ 21Exh-164
❑ 22E120-14
❑ 22W572-101
❑ 22W575-127
❑ 23W501-110
❑ 26Zee-103
❑ 27Zee-79
❑ 68SCFOldT-8
❑ 77Ind192T-17
❑ 95ConTSN-1367
Smith, Eric
❑ 92BatCliCB-12
❑ 92BatCliF-3265
❑ 94ClePhiC-24
❑ 94ClePhiF-2527
❑ 95AubAstTI-15
❑ 96QuaCitRB-27
❑ 97KisCob-24
Smith, Ernie
❑ 33WorCig(-84
❑ 33WorCig(-85
❑ 33WorCig(-86
Smith, Frank
❑ 90KisDodD-25
❑ 91GreFalDSP-1
❑ 92GreFalDSP-27
❑ 93BakDodCLC-22
❑ 94VerBeaDC-21
❑ 94VerBeaDF-84
❑ 95SanBerSTI-24
Smith, Frank T.
❑ 52Bow-186
❑ 52Top-179
❑ 53Top-116
❑ 54Bow-188
❑ 54Top-71
❑ 55CarHunW-25
❑ 55Top-204
❑ 83TopRep5-179
❑ 91TopArc1-116
❑ 94TopArc1-71
❑ 94TopArc1G-71
Smith, Fred
❑ 92WatIndC-13
❑ 92WatIndF-3234
❑ 93ColRedC-21
❑ 93ColRedF-596
Smith, Freddie
❑ 81MiaOriT-3
Smith, Garry J.
❑ 77WesHavYT-21
❑ 78TacYanC-39B
❑ 79ColCliT-5
❑ 80ColCliP-15
❑ 80ColCliT-5
❑ 81ColCliP-13
❑ 82ColCliP-13
❑ 82ColCliT-14
❑ 82NasSouTI-24
Smith, Gary
❑ 81ColCliT-21
Smith, Gene
❑ 81BurBeeT-5
Smith, George A.
❑ 23WilChoV-154
❑ 87OldJudN-458
❑ 90DodTar-747
Smith, George C.
❑ 65Top-483
❑ 66RedSoxTI-13
❑ 66Top-542
❑ 67CokCapRS-13
❑ 67DexPre-194
❑ 67Top-444

❑ 67TopRedSS-18
Smith, George H.
❑ 08BufBisFJO-16
❑ 09ColChiE-265
❑ 09T206-469
❑ 12ColRedB-265
❑ 12ColTinT-265
Smith, Germany (George J.)
❑ 74BroClu-14
❑ 90DodTar-748
❑ 95May-39
❑ 98CamPepP-71
Smith, Glenn
❑ 75LynRanT-25
Smith, Greg
❑ 81VerBeaDT-18
❑ 86EriCarP-27
❑ 87EriCarP-11
❑ 87OklCit8P-19
❑ 88SpoIndP-1932
❑ 91AlbDukLD-20
❑ 91AlbDukP-1151
Smith, Greg (Gregory A.)
❑ 85BeaGolGT-6
❑ 86LasVegSP-17
❑ 87PeoChiP-14
❑ 88CarLeaAS-35
❑ 88WinSpiS-17
❑ 89ChaKniTI-11
❑ 89ChaRaiP-979
❑ 89SouLeaAJ-11
❑ 90Bow-31
❑ 90BowTif-31
❑ 90CMC-88
❑ 90Fle-643
❑ 90FleCan-643
❑ 90IowCubC-13
❑ 90IowCubP-326
❑ 90ProAAAF-633
❑ 90RivRedWB-18
❑ 90RivRedWCLC-2
❑ 90RivRedWP-2621
❑ 90Sco-614
❑ 90TopDeb89-117
❑ 90TopTVCu-27
❑ 90UppDec-738
❑ 91Bow-594
❑ 91Don-574
❑ 91Fle-433
❑ 91LinDriAAA-20
❑ 91OPC-560
❑ 91StaClu-554
❑ 91Top-560
❑ 91TopDesS-560
❑ 91TopMic-560
❑ 91TopTif-560
❑ 92TolMudHF-1052
❑ 92TolMudHS-597
❑ 93IowCubF-2142
❑ 94NewOrlZF-1477
❑ 97SpoIndG-27
Smith, Hal R.
❑ 56Top-283
❑ 57Top-111
❑ 58CarJayP-14
❑ 58Top-273
❑ 59Top-497
❑ 60CarJayP-10
❑ 60KeyChal-44
❑ 60Lea-94
❑ 60Top-84
❑ 60TopVen-84
❑ 61CarJayP-11
❑ 61Pos-180A
❑ 61Pos-180B
❑ 61Top-549
❑ 61TopStal-70
❑ 61TopStal-94
❑ 62SalPlaC-190
❑ 62ShiPlaC-190
❑ 77PirTCM1WC-12
Smith, Hal W.
❑ 55OriEss-23
❑ 55Top-8
❑ 56A'sPos-41
❑ 56BalOriP-10
❑ 56Top-62
❑ 56TopHocF-A15
❑ 56TopPin-3
❑ 57Top-41
❑ 58A'sJayP-8
❑ 58Top-257
❑ 59Top-227
❑ 60Lea-58
❑ 60Lea-94
❑ 60Lea-119
❑ 60Top-48
❑ 60TopVen-48
❑ 61Kah-41
❑ 61Pos-139
❑ 61Top-242
❑ 62Col.45B-18
❑ 62Col45'HC-15
❑ 62Col45'JP-11
❑ 62Jel-181
❑ 62Pos-181
❑ 62PosCan-181
❑ 62Top-492
❑ 62TopBuc-84
❑ 62TopStal-129
❑ 63Col45'JP-10
❑ 63Top-153
❑ 64Top-233
❑ 64TopVen-233
❑ 79TCM50-127
❑ 89AstCol4S-12
❑ 91OriCro-427
❑ 97BalOriP-47
Smith, Hamlin
❑ 94LetMouSP-27
Smith, Hap (Henry J.)
❑ 09T206-328
❑ 10DomDisP-110
❑ 10SweCapPP-77
❑ 90DodTar-1073
Smith, Harold
❑ 33ButCanV-46
❑ 89TenTecGE-25
Smith, Harry Thomas
❑ 03BreE10-131
❑ 11SpoLifCW-329
❑ 11SpoLifM-146
Smith, Herb
❑ 91PomBlaBPB-23
Smith, Hilton
❑ 78LauLonABS-34
❑ 86NegLeaF-27
❑ 87NegLeaPD-27
❑ 97NegLeaPC-9H
Smith, Hugh
❑ 09ObaT21-92
❑ 09ObaT21-265
❑ 11PacCoaBD-59
❑ 11Zee-19A
❑ 11Zee-19B
❑ 12HomRunKE-16
❑ 12ObaPreT-14
❑ 12Zee-20
❑ 88SFHesCreN32-31
Smith, Hut
❑ 92ClaDraP-75
❑ 92HigSchPLS-18
❑ 93StaCluM-95
❑ 94AlbPolC-24
❑ 94AlbPolF-2237
❑ 97FreKey-27
❑ 98ReaPhiUM-22
Smith, Indiana (Mike)
❑ 92FroRowDP-78
❑ 92FroRowDPG-78
❑ 92FroRowDPS-78
❑ 92GasRanF-2262
❑ 93ChaRanC-21
❑ 93ChaRanF-1950
❑ 93StaCluM-101
Smith, Ira
❑ 90GreFalDSP-28
❑ 92BakDodCLC-22
❑ 93RanCucQC-26
❑ 93RanCucQF-846
❑ 94ClaGolF-143
❑ 94ExcFS7-286
❑ 94WicWraF-203
❑ 95Exc-288
❑ 95MemChiTI-9
❑ 96LasVegSB-23
❑ 97JacSun-24
❑ 98TolMudHQ-29
Smith, Jack
❑ 20WalMaiW-53
❑ 21Exh-165
❑ 21Nei-75
❑ 22E120-238
❑ 22W572-102
❑ 22W573-127
❑ 27AmeCarE126-51
❑ 81BirBarT-15
❑ 82WesHavAT-9
❑ 83ColAstT-20
❑ 92ConTSN-507
Smith, Jack (Jack Everett)
❑ 86TamTarP-20
❑ 87TamTarP-14
❑ 88GreHorP-1569
❑ 89EasLeaAP-20
❑ 89WilBilP-643
❑ 89WilBilS-20
❑ 91JacSunLD-345
❑ 91JacSunP-160
❑ 91LinDriAA-345
❑ 92OrlSunRS-521
❑ 92TacTigF-2512
❑ 93CalCanF-1174
Smith, Jack H.
❑ 63Top-496
❑ 90DodTar-749
Smith, Jackie
❑ 78AppFoxT-17
❑ 79KnoKnoST-17
Smith, James PCL
❑ 20Zee-150
❑ 21Zee-169
❑ 24Zee-104
❑ 98BriWhiSQ-23
Smith, Jason
❑ 92ElmPioC-6
❑ 92ElmPioF-1386
❑ 93BenRocCB-24
❑ 93BenRocF-3273
❑ 94AshTouC-19
❑ 94AshTouF-1786
❑ 94SouAtlLAF-SAL30
❑ 95AshTouTI-30
❑ 97WilCubB-22
❑ 98RocCubM-26
❑ 98RocCubTI-27
Smith, Jed
❑ 82LouRedE-28
❑ 83LouRedR-30
❑ 84LouRedR-10
❑ 85LouRedR-10
❑ 86LouRedTI-29
Smith, Jeff
❑ 75DubPacT-3
❑ 76DubPacT-34
❑ 81RedPioT-6
❑ 82RedPioT-12
❑ 86BelBreP-23
❑ 87LitFalMP-2391
❑ 91EugEmeC-20
❑ 91EugEmeP-3727
❑ 92AppFoxCB-21
❑ 92AppFoxFI-1091
❑ 93CarLeaAGF-16
❑ 93WilBluRC-20
❑ 93WilBluRF-1997
❑ 94WilBluRC-22
❑ 94WilBluRF-301
Smith, Jeff Harold
❑ 96ForWayWB-24
❑ 97ForMyeM-28
❑ 98ForMyeMTI-29
❑ 98SalLakBO-29
Smith, Jem
❑ 88KimN18-41
Smith, Jesse
❑ 98HelBreM-30
Smith, Jim
❑ 88EugEmeB-8
❑ 91LinDriAA-418
❑ 91MemChiLD-418
❑ 91MemChiP-654
Smith, Jimmy (James Lawrence)
❑ 14FatPlaT-46
❑ 20RedWorCP-23
Smith, Jimmy (James Lorne)
❑ 77ChaPatT-22
❑ 79BufBisT-17
❑ 79RocRedWT-13
❑ 80RocRedWT-17
❑ 80TidTidT-20
❑ 81PorBeaT-22
❑ 83Don-402
❑ 83Fle-323
❑ 83Top-122
Smith, Joe
❑ 92BakDodCLC-23
Smith, Joel
❑ 88SouOreAP-1697
❑ 89RocExpLC-27
❑ 90WesPalBES-22
❑ 92BoiHawC-4
❑ 92BoiHawF-3633
❑ 93PalSprAC-21
❑ 93PalSprAF-79
❑ 95LakElsSTI-23
Smith, John
❑ 58RedEnq-37
❑ 78CedRapGT-25
❑ 89UtiBluSP-22
❑ 90UtiBluSP-23
❑ 92PitMetF-3309
❑ 93St.LucMC-24
❑ 93St.LuMF-2936
❑ 94SouOreAC-26
❑ 94SouOreAF-3623
❑ 94St.LucMC-23
❑ 94St.LucMF-1208
❑ 95BelBreTI-3
Smith, John Francis
❑ 87OldJudN-455A
❑ 87OldJudN-455B
❑ 88SFHesCreN32-32
Smith, John W.
❑ 20NatCarE-96
❑ 23WilChoV-155
Smith, JoJo
❑ 91YakBeaC-27
❑ 91YakBeaP-4248
Smith, Joseph
❑ 09ObaT21-130
Smith, Josh
❑ 97IdaFalBTI-22
Smith, Jud
❑ 09ObaT21-7
❑ 09ObaT21-93
Smith, Julie
❑ 91FreStaLBS-10
Smith, Justin
❑ 94PriRedC-24
❑ 94PriRedF-3262
❑ 95BatCliTI-31
Smith, Keilan
❑ 94St.CatBJC-22
❑ 94St.CatBJF-3644
❑ 95DunBluJTI-26
❑ 96DunBluJUTI-13
❑ 97LakTigB-29
❑ 98JacSunM-23
Smith, Keith L.
❑ 74GasRanT-20
❑ 76SacSolC-2
❑ 77TucTorC-11
❑ 78Top-710
❑ 78TucTorC-15B
❑ 81Don-539
❑ 81Fle-534
❑ 83NasSouTI-23
❑ 84NasSouTI-21
❑ 85ColCliP-22
❑ 85ColCliT-19
❑ 86ColCliP-22
❑ 86ColCliP-23
❑ 87DenZepP-25
❑ 88BlaYNPRWLU-29
❑ 88DenZepC-14
❑ 88DenZepP-1261
❑ 89VanCanC-13
❑ 89VanCanP-578
❑ 90CMC-646
❑ 90ProAAAF-174
❑ 90VanCanC-19
❑ 90VanCanP-496
❑ 92RicBraBB-3
❑ 92RicBraF-386
❑ 92RicBraRC-20
❑ 92RicBraS-441
❑ 92YanWIZ8-183
❑ 93RanKee-334
❑ 94BriTigF-3513
❑ 95PeoChiTI-30
Smith, Kelly
❑ 82PhoGiaVNB-20
Smith, Kelvin
❑ 83CliGiaF-20
Smith, Ken
❑ 79SavBraT-24
❑ 80RicBraT-18
❑ 81RicBraT-4
❑ 82BraBurKL-23
❑ 82RicBraT-23
❑ 83BraPol-11
❑ 83Fle-148
❑ 84RicBraT-3
❑ 85RicBraT-16
❑ 86RocRedWP-23
❑ 88SavCarP-332
❑ 89St.PetCS-25
Smith, Kevin
❑ 91KisDodP-4183
❑ 92GulCoaDF-3566
❑ 93AubAstC-22
❑ 93AubAstF-3443
Smith, Kielan
❑ 93MedHatBJF-3737
Smith, Lance
❑ 90AshTouC-20
❑ 91AshTouP-572
❑ 92BurAstC-10
❑ 92BurAstF-551
Smith, Larry
❑ 83IdaFalAT-11
❑ 85HunStaJ-30
❑ 87SanBerSP-2
❑ 89WelPirP-31
❑ 93WelPirC-29
❑ 94WelPirC-30
❑ 94WelPirF-3512
❑ 96EriSeaB-2
Smith, Larry (Lawrence)
❑ 89MiaMirIS-18
Smith, Lee Arthur
❑ 80WicAerT-12
❑ 82CubRedL-46
❑ 82Don-252
❑ 82Fle-603
❑ 82Fle-603B
❑ 82Top-452
❑ 83CubThoAV-46
❑ 83Don-403
❑ 83Fle-508
❑ 83Top-699
❑ 84AllGamPI-89
❑ 84CubChiT-27
❑ 84CubSev-46
❑ 84CubUno-9
❑ 84Don-289
❑ 84Fle-505
❑ 84FleSti-67
❑ 84FunFooP-108
❑ 84Nes792-176
❑ 84OPC-176
❑ 84Top-176
❑ 84TopSti-44
❑ 84TopTif-176
❑ 85AllGamPI-177
❑ 85CubLioP-21
❑ 85CubSev-46
❑ 85Don-311
❑ 85Fle-67
❑ 85FleStaS-105
❑ 85Lea-128
❑ 85OPC-43
❑ 85Top-511
❑ 85TopMin-511
❑ 85TopSti-41
❑ 85TopTif-511
❑ 86BasStaB-102
❑ 86CubGat-46
❑ 86CubUno-17
❑ 86Don-144
❑ 86DonAllB-PC8
❑ 86Fle-380
❑ 86FleLeaL-41
❑ 86FleLimE-42
❑ 86FleStiC-112
❑ 86GenMilB-4I
❑ 86Lea-64
❑ 86MSAJayPCD-17
❑ 86OPC-355
❑ 86SevCoi-C11
❑ 86Spo-45
❑ 86Spo-55
❑ 86Top-355
❑ 86Top-636
❑ 86TopSti-56
❑ 86TopSup-52
❑ 86TopTat-1
❑ 86TopTif-355
❑ 86TopTif-636
❑ 87CubCan-29
❑ 87CubDavB-46
❑ 87Don-292
❑ 87Fle-574
❑ 87FleExcS-39
❑ 87FleGlo-574
❑ 87FleLimE-39
❑ 87FleMin-101
❑ 87FleStiC-110
❑ 87Lea-80
❑ 87OPC-23
❑ 87RedFolSB-42
❑ 87SevCoi-C16
❑ 87SevCoi-M15
❑ 87Spo-104
❑ 87SpoTeaP-22
❑ 87Top-23
❑ 87TopMinL-3
❑ 87TopSti-56
❑ 87TopTif-23
❑ 88Don-292
❑ 88DonAll-60
❑ 88DonBasB-252
❑ 88DonTeaBRS-NEW
❑ 88Fle-433
❑ 88FleGlo-433
❑ 88FleMin-9
❑ 88FleUpd-8
❑ 88FleUpdG-8
❑ 88OPC-240
❑ 88PanSti-256
❑ 88Sco-31
❑ 88ScoGlo-31
❑ 88ScoRoo-20T
❑ 88ScoRooG-20T
❑ 88Spo-179
❑ 88StaLinCu-13
❑ 88StaLinRS-19
❑ 88Top-240
❑ 88TopGloS-56
❑ 88TopMinL-44
❑ 88TopSti-64
❑ 88TopStiB-33
❑ 88TopTif-240
❑ 88TopTra-110T
❑ 88TopTraT-110T
❑ 89Bow-19
❑ 89BowTif-19
❑ 89Don-66
❑ 89DonBasB-84
❑ 89Fle-99
❑ 89FleGlo-99
❑ 89OPC-149
❑ 89PanSti-272
❑ 89RedFolSB-109
❑ 89Sco-150
❑ 89ScoHot1S-18
❑ 89Spo-148
❑ 89SpoIllFKI-294
❑ 89Top-760
❑ 89TopBasT-144
❑ 89TopSti-251
❑ 89TopTif-760
❑ 89TVSpoM-68
❑ 89UppDec-521
❑ 90Bow-263
❑ 90BowTif-263
❑ 90CarSmo-21
❑ 90ClaBlu-137
❑ 90Don-110
❑ 90DonBesN-120
❑ 90Fle-287
❑ 90FleCan-287
❑ 90FleUpd-53
❑ 90Lea-524
❑ 90M.Vpin-12
❑ 90OPC-495
❑ 90PanSti-14
❑ 90PubIntS-464
❑ 90Sco-37
❑ 90ScoRoo-48T
❑ 90Top-495
❑ 90TopMag-71
❑ 90TopSti-262
❑ 90TopTif-495
❑ 90TopTra-118T
❑ 90TopTraT-118T
❑ 90TopTVRS-17
❑ 90UppDec-393
❑ 91Bow-387
❑ 91CarPol-47
❑ 91Don-169
❑ 91Don-403
❑ 91Fle-645
❑ 91Lea-44
❑ 91OPC-660
❑ 91PanCanT1-83
❑ 91PanFreS-39
❑ 91PanSti-38
❑ 91Sco-81
❑ 91StaClu-42
❑ 91Stu-237
❑ 91Top-660
❑ 91TopDesS-660
❑ 91TopMic-660
❑ 91TopTif-660
❑ 91Ult-295
❑ 91UppDec-348
❑ 91USPlaCA-10C
❑ 92Bow-505

❑ 92CarMcD-53
❑ 92CarPol-18
❑ 92Cla2-T28
❑ 92ClaGam-23
❑ 92Don-112
❑ 92DonCraJ2-4
❑ 92Fle-591
❑ 92Fle-697
❑ 92FleAll-8
❑ 92FleSmo'nH-S1
❑ 92Fre-6
❑ 92Hig5-98
❑ 92Lea-254
❑ 92LeaBlaG-254
❑ 92OPC-565
❑ 92OPCPre-190
❑ 92PanSti-179
❑ 92Pin-195
❑ 92Sco-630
❑ 92Sco-781
❑ 92Sco100S-28
❑ 92StaClu-180
❑ 92StaCluD-174
❑ 92Stu-97
❑ 92Top-396
❑ 92Top-565
❑ 92TopGol-396
❑ 92TopGol-565
❑ 92TopGolW-396
❑ 92TopGolW-565
❑ 92TopKid-28
❑ 92TopMic-396
❑ 92TopMic-565
❑ 92TriPla-62
❑ 92Ult-270
❑ 92UppDec-376
❑ 92UppDecTMH-49
❑ 93Bow-600
❑ 93CarPol-19
❑ 93CarStaC-13
❑ 93ClaGam-87
❑ 93CubRol-2
❑ 93Don-548
❑ 93Fin-95
❑ 93FinJum-95
❑ 93FinRef-95
❑ 93Fla-127
❑ 93Fle-133
❑ 93FleAll-NL12
❑ 93FleFinEDT-7
❑ 93FunPac-77
❑ 93Kra-29
❑ 93Lea-154
❑ 93OPC-324
❑ 93PacSpa-303
❑ 93PanSti-160
❑ 93PanSti-192
❑ 93Pin-416
❑ 93RedFolS-88
❑ 93Sco-103
❑ 93Sco-529
❑ 93Sel-83
❑ 93SelChaS-12
❑ 93SelDufIP-12
❑ 93SelRoo-31T
❑ 93SelStaL-70
❑ 93SP-78
❑ 93StaClu-462
❑ 93StaCluFDI-462
❑ 93StaCluM-128
❑ 93StaCluMO-24
❑ 93StaCluMOP-462
❑ 93Stu-147
❑ 93Top-12
❑ 93Top-411
❑ 93TOPBLAG-19
❑ 93TopGol-12
❑ 93TopGol-411
❑ 93TopInaM-12
❑ 93TopInaM-411
❑ 93TopInaR-12
❑ 93TopInaR-411
❑ 93TopMic-12
❑ 93TopMic-411
❑ 93TriPla-83
❑ 93Ult-112
❑ 93UltAllS-10
❑ 93UppDec-82
❑ 93UppDecGold-82
❑ 94BalOriP-31
❑ 94Bow-299
❑ 94BowBes-R5
❑ 94BowBesR-R5
❑ 94ColC-260
❑ 94ColC-556
❑ 94ColChoGS-260
❑ 94ColChoGS-556
❑ 94ColChoSS-260
❑ 94ColChoSS-556
❑ 94Don-650
❑ 94Fin-351
❑ 94FinRef-351
❑ 94Fla-258
❑ 94Fle-246
❑ 94FleExtB-14
❑ 94FleUpd-8
❑ 94Lea-357
❑ 94LeaL-6
❑ 94OriPro-94
❑ 94Pac-436
❑ 94Pin-499
❑ 94PinArtP-499
❑ 94PinMusC-499
❑ 94PinTri-TR18
❑ 94Sco-245
❑ 94Sco-627
❑ 94ScoGolR-245
❑ 94ScoGolR-627
❑ 94ScoRoo-RT2
❑ 94ScoRooCP-CP8
❑ 94ScoRooGR-RT2
❑ 94ScoRooS-RT2
❑ 94Sel-217
❑ 94SP-127
❑ 94SPDieC-127
❑ 94SpoRoo-38
❑ 94SpoRooAP-38
❑ 94StaClu-543
❑ 94StaClu-605
❑ 94StaCluFDI-543
❑ 94StaCluFDI-605
❑ 94StaCluGR-543
❑ 94StaCluGR-605
❑ 94StaCluMOP-543
❑ 94StaCluMOP-605
❑ 94Stu-128
❑ 94Top-110
❑ 94TopGol-110
❑ 94TopSpa-110
❑ 94TopTra-100T
❑ 94Ult-311
❑ 94UppDec-505
❑ 94UppDecED-505
❑ 95AngCHP-15
❑ 95AngMot-13
❑ 95Baz-3
❑ 95Bow-330
❑ 95BowBes-R59
❑ 95BowBesR-R59
❑ 95ColCho-57
❑ 95ColCho-105
❑ 95ColChoGS-57
❑ 95ColChoGS-105
❑ 95ColChoSE-144
❑ 95ColChoSE-152
❑ 95ColChoSEGS-144
❑ 95ColChoSEGS-152
❑ 95ColChoSESS-144
❑ 95ColChoSESS-152
❑ 95ColChoSS-57
❑ 95ColChoSS-105
❑ 95Don-133
❑ 95DonPreP-133
❑ 95DonTopotO-43
❑ 95Emo-22
❑ 95Fin-172
❑ 95Fin-241
❑ 95FinRef-172
❑ 95FinRef-241
❑ 95Fla-239
❑ 95Fle-21
❑ 95FleAllS-24
❑ 95FleUpd-68
❑ 95Lea-346
❑ 95LeaLim-189
❑ 95Pac-31
❑ 95PacPri-11
❑ 95PanSti-17
❑ 95PanSti-128
❑ 95Pin-64
❑ 95PinArtP-64
❑ 95PinMusC-64
❑ 95Sco-91
❑ 95ScoDreT-DG12
❑ 95ScoGolR-91
❑ 95ScoHaloG-HG40
❑ 95ScoPlaTS-91
❑ 95SPCha-130
❑ 95SPChaDC-130
❑ 95StaClu-12
❑ 95StaClu-627
❑ 95StaCluFDI-12
❑ 95StaCluMO-42
❑ 95StaCluMOP-12
❑ 95StaCluMOP-627
❑ 95StaCluSTWS-12
❑ 95StaCluSTWS-627
❑ 95StaCluVR-7
❑ 95StaCluVRMO-7
❑ 95Stu-92
❑ 95Top-394
❑ 95Top-425
❑ 95Top-659
❑ 95Top-660
❑ 95TopCyb-223
❑ 95TopTra-66T
❑ 95Ult-272
❑ 95UltGolM-272
❑ 95UltLeaL-5
❑ 95UltLeaLGM-5
❑ 95UppDec-16
❑ 95UppDecED-16
❑ 95UppDecEDG-16
❑ 95UppDecSE-261
❑ 95UppDecSEG-261
❑ 96AngMot-11
❑ 96Baz-60
❑ 96ColCho-77
❑ 96ColChoGS-77
❑ 96ColChoSS-77
❑ 96ColChoYMtP-37
❑ 96ColChoYMtP-37A
❑ 96ColChoYMtPGS-37
❑ 96ColChoYMtPGS-37A
❑ 96Don-291
❑ 96DonPreP-291
❑ 96EmoXL-31
❑ 96Fin-S142
❑ 96FinRef-S142
❑ 96Fla-42
❑ 96Fle-58
❑ 96FleTif-58
❑ 96Lea-110
❑ 96LeaPrePB-110
❑ 96LeaPrePG-110
❑ 96LeaPrePS-110
❑ 96MetUni-33
❑ 96MetUniP-33
❑ 96Pac-270
❑ 96Pin-222
❑ 96PinAfi-43
❑ 96PinAfiAP-43
❑ 96PinAfiFPP-43
❑ 96PinArtP-122
❑ 96PinFoil-222
❑ 96PinSta-122
❑ 96Sco-150
❑ 96ScoDugC-A88
❑ 96ScoDugCAP-A88
❑ 96Sel-141
❑ 96SelArtP-141
❑ 96StaClu-66
❑ 96StaCluEPB-66
❑ 96StaCluEPG-66
❑ 96StaCluEPS-66
❑ 96StaCluMOP-66
❑ 96Stu-91
❑ 96StuPrePB-91
❑ 96StuPrePG-91
❑ 96StuPrePS-91
❑ 96Sum-89
❑ 96SumAbo&B-89
❑ 96SumArtP-89
❑ 96SumFoi-89
❑ 96Top-251
❑ 96TopChr-98
❑ 96TopChrMotG-8
❑ 96TopChrMotGR-8
❑ 96TopChrR-98
❑ 96TopGal-46
❑ 96TopGalPPI-46
❑ 96TopMasotG-8
❑ 96Ult-34
❑ 96UltGolM-34
❑ 96UppDec-113
❑ 96UppDec-288
❑ 96UppDecPHE-H19
❑ 96UppDecPreH-H19
❑ 97Cir-242
❑ 97CirRav-242
❑ 97ColCho-85
❑ 97ColCho-390
❑ 97Fle-685
❑ 97FleTif-685
❑ 97PacPriGotD-GD131
❑ 97Sco-379
❑ 97ScoArtPWB-379
❑ 97ScoResC-379
❑ 97ScoShoS-379
❑ 97ScoShoSAP-379
❑ 97Ult-446
❑ 97UltGolME-446
❑ 97UltPlaME-446
❑ 97UppDec-48
❑ 98ColCho-165
❑ 98UppDec-155
❑ 98UppDec10AP-11
❑ 98UppDec1APR-11

Smith, Lillian

❑ 88KimN18-42

Smith, Lonnie

❑ 76OklCit8TI-4
❑ 79Top-722
❑ 80PhiBul-41
❑ 80PhiBurK-14
❑ 81CokTeaS-106
❑ 81Don-295
❑ 81Fle-15
❑ 81OPC-317
❑ 81Top-317
❑ 82Don-606
❑ 82Fle-259
❑ 82Fle-641
❑ 82FleSta-60
❑ 82OPC-127
❑ 82Top-127
❑ 82TopTra-108T
❑ 83AllGamPI-160
❑ 83Car-28
❑ 83CarPanP-6
❑ 83Don-91
❑ 83DonActA-34
❑ 83Fle-21
❑ 83Fle-636
❑ 83FleSta-179
❑ 83FleSti-4
❑ 83Kel-30
❑ 83OPC-273
❑ 83PerCreC-15
❑ 83PerCreCG-15
❑ 83Top-465
❑ 83Top-561
❑ 83TopFol-3
❑ 83TopSti-283
❑ 84AllGamPI-70
❑ 84Car-28
❑ 84Car5x7-26
❑ 84Don-231
❑ 84Don-625
❑ 84DonCha-23
❑ 84Fle-335
❑ 84FleSti-7
❑ 84Nes792-186
❑ 84Nes792-580
❑ 84OPC-113
❑ 84SevCoi-C14
❑ 84Top-186
❑ 84Top-580
❑ 84TopRubD-1
❑ 84TopSti-140
❑ 84TopStiB-5
❑ 84TopTif-186
❑ 84TopTif-580
❑ 85AllGamPI-158
❑ 85Don-231
❑ 85Fle-239
❑ 85FleStaS-61
❑ 85FleUpd-106
❑ 85Lea-225
❑ 85OPC-255
❑ 85Top-255
❑ 85TopMin-255
❑ 85TopRubD-1
❑ 85TopSti-139
❑ 85TopTif-255
❑ 85TopTifT-109T
❑ 85TopTra-109T
❑ 86BasStaB-103
❑ 86Don-399
❑ 86Fle-21
❑ 86FleMin-4
❑ 86Lea-188
❑ 86OPC-7
❑ 86RoyKitCD-1
❑ 86RoyNatP-21
❑ 86RoyTeal-24
❑ 86Spo-186
❑ 86Top-617
❑ 86TopMinL-21
❑ 86TopSti-264
❑ 86TopTif-617
❑ 87Don-225
❑ 87Fle-381
❑ 87FleGlo-381
❑ 87FleLimE-40
❑ 87FleStiC-111
❑ 87SpoTeaP-13
❑ 87Top-69
❑ 87TopSti-262
❑ 87TopTif-69
❑ 88BlaYNPRWL-154
❑ 88BobCamRB-5
❑ 88Don-527
❑ 88PanSti-111
❑ 88RicBraC-14
❑ 88RicBraP-1
❑ 88Sco-263
❑ 88ScoGlo-263
❑ 88Top-777
❑ 88TopTif-777
❑ 88TriAAC-24
❑ 89Bow-278
❑ 89BowTif-278
❑ 89BraDub-22
❑ 89DonBasB-114
❑ 89FleUpd-74
❑ 89TopBig-242
❑ 89TopTra-114T
❑ 89TopTraT-114T
❑ 89UppDec-731
❑ 90Bow-12
❑ 90BowTif-12
❑ 90BraDubP-24
❑ 90BraDubS-28
❑ 90ClaBlu-52
❑ 90Don-222
❑ 90DonBesN-86
❑ 90Fle-593
❑ 90FleAwaW-35
❑ 90FleCan-593
❑ 90FleLeaL-37
❑ 90FleLeaLC-37
❑ 90GooHumICBLS-22
❑ 90Lea-217
❑ 90M.Vpin-3
❑ 90OPC-152
❑ 90PanSti-227
❑ 90PubIntS-121
❑ 90RedFolSB-88
❑ 90Sco-399
❑ 90Sco100S-82
❑ 90Spo-65
❑ 90Top-152
❑ 90TopBatL-19
❑ 90TopBig-7
❑ 90TopCoi-58
❑ 90TopDou-61
❑ 90TopMinL-46
❑ 90TopSti-24
❑ 90TopStiB-19
❑ 90TopTif-152
❑ 90UppDec-215
❑ 91Bow-567
❑ 91BraDubP-26
❑ 91BraSubS-33
❑ 91Don-364
❑ 91Fle-702
❑ 91Lea-13
❑ 91OPC-306
❑ 91PanFreS-24
❑ 91PanSti-22
❑ 91Sco-543
❑ 91SimandSMLBL-41
❑ 91StaClu-97
❑ 91Top-306A
❑ 91Top-306B
❑ 91TopDesS-306
❑ 91TopMic-306
❑ 91TopTif-306
❑ 91Ult-11
❑ 91UppDec-305
❑ 92BraLykP-25
❑ 92BraLykS-30
❑ 92Don-517
❑ 92Fle-369
❑ 92Lea-480
❑ 92LeaBlaG-480
❑ 92OPC-467
❑ 92PanSti-168
❑ 92Pin-465
❑ 92Sco-13
❑ 92ScoFacI-B4
❑ 92ScoProP-1
❑ 92StaClu-282
❑ 92Top-467
❑ 92TopGol-467
❑ 92TopGolW-467
❑ 92TopMic-467
❑ 92TriPla-40
❑ 92Ult-168
❑ 92UppDec-301
❑ 93Don-658
❑ 93Fle-371
❑ 93FleFinE-119
❑ 93Lea-394
❑ 93Pin-454
❑ 93PirNatI-30
❑ 93Sco-431
❑ 93StaClu-658
❑ 93StaCluFDI-658
❑ 93StaCluM-182
❑ 93StaCluMOP-658
❑ 93Ult-456
❑ 93UppDec-716
❑ 93UppDecGold-716
❑ 94BalOriP-32
❑ 94OriPro-95
❑ 94Sco-462
❑ 94ScoGolR-462
❑ 94StaClu-643
❑ 94StaCluFDI-643
❑ 94StaCluGR-643
❑ 94StaCluMOP-643
❑ 95Sco-75
❑ 95ScoGolR-75
❑ 95ScoPlaTS-75

Smith, Luther

❑ 15Zee-118
❑ 17Zee-97
❑ 18Zee-92
❑ 19Zee-104
❑ 20Zee-117

Smith, Mandy

❑ 81WisRapTT-19

Smith, Mark

❑ 83BirBarT-7
❑ 83RocRedWT-8

Smith, Mark Edward

❑ 88CapCodPPaLP-146
❑ 90HamRedB-7
❑ 90HamRedS-24
❑ 91ClaDraP-6
❑ 91St.PetCC-13
❑ 92Bow-556
❑ 92ClaDraP-91
❑ 92ClaFS7-122
❑ 92HagSunF-2569
❑ 92HagSunS-269
❑ 92SkyAA F-113
❑ 92SprCarC-14
❑ 92SprCarF-868
❑ 92UppDec-66
❑ 92UppDecML-38
❑ 92UppDecML-281
❑ 92UppDecMLPotY-PY15
❑ 93Bow-253
❑ 93ClaFS7-89
❑ 93ClaGolF-59
❑ 93ExcFS7-127
❑ 93FreKeyC-24
❑ 93FreKeyF-1027
❑ 93RocRedWF-254
❑ 93TriAAAGF-30
❑ 94Bow-47
❑ 94Cla-99
❑ 94ClaGolF-145
❑ 94LeaLimR-64
❑ 94OriPro-96
❑ 94RocRedWF-1011
❑ 94RocRedWTI-21
❑ 94ScoRoo-RT108
❑ 94ScoRooGR-RT108
❑ 94Sel-408
❑ 94TopTra-4T
❑ 94UppDecML-232
❑ 95BalOriP-47
❑ 95Don-372
❑ 95DonPreP-372
❑ 95Pac-32
❑ 95Pin-166
❑ 95PinArtP-166
❑ 95PinMusC-166
❑ 95RocRedWTI-35
❑ 95Sco-284
❑ 95ScoGolR-284
❑ 95ScoPlaTS-284
❑ 95Top-631
❑ 96BalOriP-32
❑ 96RocRedWB-25
❑ 96Sco-236
❑ 96ScoDugC-A105
❑ 96ScoDugCAP-A105
❑ 96StaClu-395
❑ 96StaCluMOP-395
❑ 97PacPriGotD-GD17
❑ 97PirPos-35

❑ 98PacInvGems-196
❑ 98PacOnl-595
❑ 98PacOnlR-595
❑ 98PacOnlWC-595
❑ 98UppDec-483
❑ 98UppDec-532

Smith, Mason

❑ 94MedHatBJF-3680
❑ 94MedHatBJSP-20

Smith, Matt

❑ 94ClaUpdCotC-CC14
❑ 94SigRooDP-16
❑ 94SigRooDPS-16
❑ 94StaCluDP-4
❑ 94StaCluDPFDI-4
❑ 94TopTra-116T
❑ 95Bow-210
❑ 95ScoDraP-DP16
❑ 95SPML-73
❑ 95SprSulTI-26
❑ 95StaClu-110
❑ 95StaCluFDI-110
❑ 95StaCluMOP-110
❑ 95StaCluSTWS-110
❑ 95Top-53
❑ 95UppDec-12
❑ 95UppDecED-12
❑ 95UppDecEDG-12
❑ 95UppDecML-180
❑ 95UppDecMLFS-180
❑ 95UppDecSE-56
❑ 95UppDecSEG-56
❑ 96BesAutSA-73
❑ 96HonShaHWB-23
❑ 96WilBluRB-1
❑ 97BesAutAS-58
❑ 97TexLeaTP-30
❑ 97WicWra-19

Smith, Mayo (Edward)

❑ 55Top-130
❑ 55TopDouH-69
❑ 56Top-60
❑ 56TopHocF-A9
❑ 56TopPin-21
❑ 58PhiJayP-12
❑ 59RedEnq-24
❑ 67Top-321
❑ 68TigDetFPB-21
❑ 68Top-544
❑ 69OPC-40
❑ 69TigTeal-10
❑ 69TigTealC-15
❑ 69Top-40
❑ 70OPC-313
❑ 70Top-313
❑ 78TigDeaCS-11
❑ 81TigDetN-35

Smith, Mike

❑ 76AppFoxT-25
❑ 82RicBraT-26
❑ 94HigDesMC-25
❑ 94HigDesMF-2797
❑ 95TulDriTI-21

Smith, Milt

❑ 56SeaPop-21
❑ 56SeaPop-22
❑ 61UniOil-H7

Smith, Mississippi (Michael A.)

❑ 87IndIndTI-23
❑ 88IndIndC-7
❑ 88IndIndP-509
❑ 89RocRedWC-8
❑ 89RocRedWP-1634
❑ 89RocRedWP-1637
❑ 90OPC-552
❑ 90TamYanD-24
❑ 90Top-552
❑ 90TopTif-552

Smith, Myrl

❑ 77RocRedWM-20
❑ 79TucTorT-2

Smith, Nate

❑ 91OriCro-429
❑ 98NewJerCM-29

Smith, Nestor

❑ 98ForWayW!-12

Smith, Nick

❑ 87OldJudN-460

Smith, Nig (Frank Elmer)

❑ 07WhiSoxGWH-10
❑ 08RosComP-17
❑ 09T206-325
❑ 09T206-326
❑ 09T206-327
❑ 10ChiE-18
❑ 10CouT21-224
❑ 10E101-42
❑ 10E102-23
❑ 10MelMinE-42
❑ 10NadCarE-49
❑ 10RedCroT-69
❑ 10RedCroT-155
❑ 10RedCroT-156
❑ 10RedCroT-243
❑ 11PinT-5-655
❑ 11SpoLifCW-328
❑ 11SpoLifM-30
❑ 12T207-168
❑ 14CraJacE-90
❑ 15CraJacE-90

Smith, Ottis

❑ 91PitMetC-15
❑ 91PitMetP-3423
❑ 92ColMetC-3
❑ 92ColMetPI-19
❑ 93St.LucMC-25
❑ 93St.LuMF-2922
❑ 94OrlCubF-1383
❑ 95OrlCubF-10

Smith, Ozzie

❑ 78PadFamF-29
❑ 79Hos-102
❑ 79OPC-52
❑ 79PadFamF-3
❑ 79Top-116
❑ 80OPC-205
❑ 80Top-393
❑ 81AllGamPI-114
❑ 81Don-1
❑ 81Fle-488
❑ 81OPC-254
❑ 81PadFamF-17
❑ 81Top-207
❑ 81Top-254
❑ 81TopScr-68
❑ 81TopSti-230
❑ 82Don-21
❑ 82Don-94
❑ 82Fle-582
❑ 82FleSta-101
❑ 82Kel-6
❑ 82OPC-95
❑ 82Top-95
❑ 82TopSti-104
❑ 82TopTra-109T
❑ 83AllGamPI-114
❑ 83Car-29
❑ 83Don-120
❑ 83Fle-22
❑ 83Fle-636
❑ 83FleSta-180
❑ 83FleSti-10
❑ 83Kel-21
❑ 83OPC-14
❑ 83PerAll-17
❑ 83PerAllG-17
❑ 83PerCreC-16
❑ 83PerCreCG-16
❑ 83Top-540
❑ 83TopSti-168
❑ 83TopSti-180
❑ 83TopSti-186
❑ 83TopSti-288
❑ 84AllGamPI-25
❑ 84Car-29
❑ 84Car5x7-27
❑ 84Don-59
❑ 84Don-625
❑ 84Fle-336
❑ 84FunFooP-71
❑ 84MilBra-25
❑ 84MLBPen-14
❑ 84Nes792-130
❑ 84Nes792-389
❑ 84NesDreT-15
❑ 84OPC-130
❑ 84OPC-389
❑ 84RalPur-2
❑ 84RawGloT-4
❑ 84SevCoi-C19
❑ 84Top-130
❑ 84Top-389
❑ 84TopCer-2
❑ 84TopGloA-16
❑ 84TopGloS-17
❑ 84TopRubD-28
❑ 84TopSti-144
❑ 84TopSti-187
❑ 84TopTif-130
❑ 84TopTif-389
❑ 85AllGamPI-116
❑ 85CarTeal-31
❑ 85Don-59
❑ 85DonActA-28
❑ 85Fle-240
❑ 85Fle-631
❑ 85FleLimE-35
❑ 85GenMilS-10
❑ 85KASDis-14
❑ 85KitCloD-14
❑ 85Lea-60
❑ 85OPC-191
❑ 85SevCoi-C16
❑ 85Top-605
❑ 85Top-715
❑ 85TopGloA-5
❑ 85TopRubD-28
❑ 85TopSti-137
❑ 85TopSti-181
❑ 85TopSup-47
❑ 85TopTif-605
❑ 85TopTif-715
❑ 86BasStaB-104
❑ 86CarIGAS-11
❑ 86CarKASD-7
❑ 86CarSchM-21
❑ 86CarTeal-40
❑ 86Don-59
❑ 86DonAll-8
❑ 86DonPop-8
❑ 86Fle-46
❑ 86FleLeaL-42
❑ 86FleMin-10
❑ 86FleStiC-113
❑ 86GenMilB-4J
❑ 86KonTraCOS-1
❑ 86KonTraCOS-2
❑ 86KonTraCOS-3
❑ 86KonTraCOS-4
❑ 86KonTraCOS-5
❑ 86KonTraCOS-6
❑ 86KonTraCOS-7
❑ 86KonTraCOS-8
❑ 86KonTraCOS-9
❑ 86KonTraCOS-10
❑ 86KonTraCOS-11
❑ 86KonTraCOS-12
❑ 86KonTraCOS-13
❑ 86KonTraCOS-14
❑ 86KonTraCOS-15
❑ 86KonTraCOS-16
❑ 86KonTraCOS-17
❑ 86KonTraCOS-18
❑ 86KonTraCOS-19
❑ 86KonTraCOS-20
❑ 86Lea-47
❑ 86OPC-297
❑ 86QuaGra-15
❑ 86SevCoi-S10
❑ 86Spo-121
❑ 86Top-704
❑ 86Top-730
❑ 86TopGloA-16
❑ 86TopGloS-46
❑ 86TopSti-11
❑ 86TopSti-46
❑ 86TopSti-153
❑ 86TopSup-53
❑ 86TopTat-16
❑ 86TopTif-704
❑ 86TopTif-730
❑ 86TruVal-9
❑ 87BurKinA-14
❑ 87CarSmo-17
❑ 87CarTeal-30
❑ 87ClaGam-32
❑ 87Don-5
❑ 87Don-60
❑ 87DonAll-15
❑ 87DonOpeD-65
❑ 87DonP-15
❑ 87DonSupD-5
❑ 87Fle-308
❑ 87FleAwaW-38
❑ 87FleBasA-41
❑ 87FleGlo-308
❑ 87FleMin-102
❑ 87FleStiC-112
❑ 87GenMilB-5I
❑ 87HosSti-15
❑ 87KraFoo-16
❑ 87Lea-5
❑ 87Lea-108
❑ 87MandMSL-24
❑ 87MSAJifPD-7
❑ 87OPC-107
❑ 87RalPur-13
❑ 87RedFolSB-112
❑ 87SmoNatL-9
❑ 87Spo-79
❑ 87Spo-142
❑ 87SpoIIS-12
❑ 87SpoTeaP-12
❑ 87StuPan-11
❑ 87Top-598
❑ 87Top-749
❑ 87TopCoi-45
❑ 87TopGloA-5
❑ 87TopGloS-23
❑ 87TopSti-46
❑ 87TopSti-162
❑ 87TopTif-598
❑ 87TopTif-749
❑ 88ActPacT-6
❑ 88CarSmo-18
❑ 88CarTeal-32
❑ 88CheBoy-5
❑ 88ClaBlu-210
❑ 88Don-263
❑ 88DonAll-37
❑ 88DonAll-63
❑ 88DonBasB-243
❑ 88DonBonM-BC22
❑ 88DonPop-15
❑ 88Fle-47
❑ 88Fle-628
❑ 88FleAwaW-39
❑ 88FleBasA-39
❑ 88FleBasM-35
❑ 88FleGlo-47
❑ 88FleGlo-628
❑ 88FleGlo-WS4
❑ 88FleHotS-40
❑ 88FleMin-109
❑ 88FleRecS-38
❑ 88FleStiC-120
❑ 88FleTeaL-38
❑ 88FleWorS-4
❑ 88GreBasS-35
❑ 88K-M-28
❑ 88KinDis-4
❑ 88Lea-115
❑ 88MSAFanSD-11
❑ 88Nes-5
❑ 88OPC-39
❑ 88PanSti-235
❑ 88PanSti-393
❑ 88Sco-12
❑ 88ScoBoxC-14
❑ 88ScoGlo-12
❑ 88Spo-68
❑ 88StaLinAl-32
❑ 88StaLinCa-18
❑ 88TarPla-41
❑ 88Top-400
❑ 88Top-460
❑ 88TopBig-228
❑ 88TopClo-107
❑ 88TopCoi-55
❑ 88TopGloA-16
❑ 88TopGloS-47
❑ 88TopMinL-72
❑ 88TopSti-53
❑ 88TopSti-153
❑ 88TopStiB-12
❑ 88TopTif-400
❑ 88TopTif-460
❑ 88TopUKM-72
❑ 88TopUKMT-72
❑ 89Bow-436
❑ 89BowTif-436
❑ 89CadEllD-53
❑ 89CarSmo-20
❑ 89CarTeal-30
❑ 89CerSup-1
❑ 89ClaLigB-58
❑ 89ColPosOS-1
❑ 89ColPosOS-2
❑ 89ColPosOS-3
❑ 89ColPosOS-4
❑ 89ColPosOS-5
❑ 89ColPosOS-6
❑ 89ColPosOS-7
❑ 89ColPosOS-8
❑ 89Don-63
❑ 89DonAll-37
❑ 89DonAll-62
❑ 89DonBasB-44
❑ 89DonBonM-BC14
❑ 89DonPop-37
❑ 89Fle-463
❑ 89FleExcS-38
❑ 89FleGlo-463
❑ 89FleLeaL-35
❑ 89KayB-28
❑ 89MSAHolD-3
❑ 89OPC-230
❑ 89PanSti-186
❑ 89PanSti-235
❑ 89RedFolSB-110
❑ 89Sco-80
❑ 89ScoHot1S-88
❑ 89Scomast-27
❑ 89Spo-105
❑ 89SpoIllFKI-43
❑ 89Top-230
❑ 89Top-389
❑ 89TopBasT-45
❑ 89TopBig-110
❑ 89TopCoi-25
❑ 89TopDouA-16
❑ 89TopGloA-16
❑ 89TopGloS-42
❑ 89TopHeaUT-17
❑ 89TopMinL-37
❑ 89TopSti-44
❑ 89TopSti-161
❑ 89TopStiB-45
❑ 89TopTif-230
❑ 89TopTif-389
❑ 89TopUKM-72
❑ 89TVSpoM-25
❑ 89UppDec-265
❑ 89UppDec-674
❑ 90AllBasT-10
❑ 90BasWit-41
❑ 90Bow-195
❑ 90BowTif-195
❑ 90CarSmo-22
❑ 90ClaBlu-18
❑ 90Col-5
❑ 90Don-201
❑ 90Don-710A
❑ 90Don-710B
❑ 90DonBesN-83
❑ 90DonLeaS-9
❑ 90Fle-260
❑ 90FleAwaW-36
❑ 90FleBasA-35
❑ 90FleBasAC-35
❑ 90FleBasM-36
❑ 90FleBasMC-36
❑ 90FleCan-260
❑ 90GooHumICBLS-23
❑ 90Hot50PS-41
❑ 90K-M-4
❑ 90KayB-29
❑ 90KinDis-4
❑ 90Lea-142
❑ 90Lea-364
❑ 90LeaPre-12
❑ 90M.Vpin-99
❑ 90MLBBasB-30
❑ 90OPC-400
❑ 90OPC-590
❑ 90PanSti-206
❑ 90PanSti-338
❑ 90Pos-6
❑ 90PubIntS-228
❑ 90PubIntS-272
❑ 90RedFolSB-89
❑ 90Sco-285
❑ 90Sco100S-6
❑ 90ScoMcD-24
❑ 90Spo-16
❑ 90Top-400
❑ 90Top-590
❑ 90TopBig-203
❑ 90TopDou-62
❑ 90TopGloA-5
❑ 90TopGloS-16
❑ 90TopMag-57
❑ 90TopSti-42
❑ 90TopSti-145
❑ 90TopStiB-12
❑ 90TopTif-400
❑ 90TopTif-590
❑ 90TopTVA-52
❑ 90TopTVCa-29
❑ 90UppDec-225
❑ 90USPlaCA-6H
❑ 90WonBreS-5
❑ 91BasBesRB-17
❑ 91Bow-398
❑ 91CadEllD-53
❑ 91CarPol-1
❑ 91ClaGam-39
❑ 91Don-240
❑ 91Don-437
❑ 91Fle-646
❑ 91JimDea-20
❑ 91Lea-80
❑ 91MajLeaCP-49
❑ 91MooSna-8
❑ 91OPC-130
❑ 91OPCPre-112
❑ 91PanCanT1-103
❑ 91PanFreS-34
❑ 91PanFreS-161
❑ 91PanSti-39
❑ 91PepSup-12
❑ 91PetSta-18
❑ 91PosCan-8
❑ 91RedFolS-129
❑ 91Sco-825
❑ 91Sco100S-18
❑ 91SevCoi-M12
❑ 91StaClu-154
❑ 91StaPinB-47
❑ 91Stu-238
❑ 91SunSee-1
❑ 91Top-130
❑ 91TopCraJ2-27
❑ 91TopDesS-130
❑ 91TopGloA-16
❑ 91TopMic-130
❑ 91TopSta-31
❑ 91TopTif-130
❑ 91TopTriH-N12
❑ 91Ult-296
❑ 91UppDec-162
❑ 91UppDecFE-95F
❑ 91USPlaCA-13S
❑ 92Bow-675
❑ 92CarMcD-38
❑ 92CarPol-19
❑ 92Cla1-T51
❑ 92Cla2-T26
❑ 92ClaGam-24
❑ 92ColAllG-6
❑ 92ColAllP-6
❑ 92Don-423
❑ 92Don-432
❑ 92DonCraJ1-6
❑ 92DonMcD-26
❑ 92Fle-592
❑ 92Fre-13
❑ 92Hig5-99
❑ 92HitTheBB-33
❑ 92JimDeaLL-3
❑ 92LaKdec-27
❑ 92Lea-400
❑ 92LeaBlaG-400
❑ 92Mr.TurS-23
❑ 92New-27
❑ 92OPC-760
❑ 92OPCPre-84
❑ 92PanSti-175
❑ 92PanSti-284
❑ 92PepDieM-19
❑ 92Pin-6
❑ 92Pin-285
❑ 92PinRool-15
❑ 92Pos-8
❑ 92PosCan-6
❑ 92RedFolS-90
❑ 92RedFolS-129
❑ 92Sco-590
❑ 92Sco100S-47
❑ 92ScoCokD-20
❑ 92ScoFacI-B9
❑ 92ScoProaG-14
❑ 92ScoProP-5
❑ 92SevCoi-14
❑ 92SpoStaCC-42
❑ 92StaClu-680
❑ 92StaCluD-175
❑ 92StaCluMO-9
❑ 92StaCluMO-10
❑ 92StaCluNC-680
❑ 92Stu-98
❑ 92StuPre-20
❑ 92Top-760
❑ 92TopGol-760
❑ 92TopGolW-760
❑ 92TopKid-25
❑ 92TopMcD-11
❑ 92TopMic-760
❑ 92TriPla-244
❑ 92Ult-271
❑ 92UltAwaW-9
❑ 92UppDec-177
❑ 92UppDec-716
❑ 92UppDecF-42

❑ 92UppDecFG-42
❑ 92UppDecTMH-50
❑ 93Bow-460
❑ 93CadDis-55
❑ 93CarPol-20
❑ 93CarStaC-1
❑ 93ClaGam-88
❑ 93ColAllG-22
❑ 93DiaMar-99
❑ 93Don-520
❑ 93DurPowP1-11
❑ 93Fin-28
❑ 93FinRef-28
❑ 93Fla-128
❑ 93FleFinE-131
❑ 93FleFinEDT-8
❑ 93FunPac-35
❑ 93FunPac-74
❑ 93FunPac-78
❑ 93FunPac-215
❑ 93FunPacA-AS6
❑ 93HumDumC-50
❑ 93KinDis-12
❑ 93Lea-328
❑ 93LeaHeaftH-10
❑ 93MetBak-36
❑ 93OPC-313
❑ 93PacSpa-302
❑ 93PanSti-194
❑ 93Pin-329
❑ 93PinCoo-9
❑ 93PinCooD-9
❑ 93PinTeaP-7
❑ 93Pos-26
❑ 93PosCan-17
❑ 93RedFolS-89
❑ 93RedFolS-127
❑ 93Sco-522
❑ 93Sco-532
❑ 93Sco-562
❑ 93ScoGolDT-1
❑ 93Sel-15
❑ 93SelChaS-3
❑ 93SP-79
❑ 93StaClu-548
❑ 93StaCluFDI-548
❑ 93StaCluM-147
❑ 93StaCluMOP-548
❑ 93Stu-217
❑ 93StuHer-6
❑ 93Top-40
❑ 93TOPBLAG-20
❑ 93TopGol-40
❑ 93TopInaM-40
❑ 93TopInaR-40
❑ 93TopMic-40
❑ 93TriPla-122
❑ 93TriPlaA-3
❑ 93TriPlaN-9
❑ 93Ult-113
❑ 93UltAwaW-6
❑ 93UppDec-146
❑ 93UppDec-482
❑ 93UppDecDG-31
❑ 93UppDecGold-146
❑ 93UppDecGold-482
❑ 93UppDecIC-WI7
❑ 93UppDecICJ-WI7
❑ 93UppDecTAN-TN7
❑ 93USPlaCA-3H
❑ 94Bow-424
❑ 94BowBes-R3
❑ 94BowBesR-R3
❑ 94CarMagG-1
❑ 94CarPol-19
❑ 94ChuHomS-26
❑ 94ChuHomSG-26
❑ 94ColC-334
❑ 94ColC-545
❑ 94ColChoGS-334
❑ 94ColChoGS-545
❑ 94ColChoSS-334
❑ 94ColChoSS-545
❑ 94ColChoT-14
❑ 94DenHol-24
❑ 94Don-35
❑ 94DonSpeE-35
❑ 94Fin-136
❑ 94FinPre-136P
❑ 94FinRef-136
❑ 94Fla-228
❑ 94Fle-646
❑ 94FleExtB-363
❑ 94FlePro-5
❑ 94FUnPac-101
❑ 94Kra-29
❑ 94Lea-409
❑ 94LeaL-147
❑ 94LeaLimGA-8
❑ 94OPC-181
❑ 94Pac-604
❑ 94PanSti-248
❑ 94Pin-389
❑ 94PinArtP-389
❑ 94PinMusC-389
❑ 94PinTri-TR10
❑ 94ProMag-114
❑ 94RedFolMI-14
❑ 94Sco-384
❑ 94ScoGolR-384
❑ 94Sel-30
❑ 94SP-65
❑ 94SPDieC-65
❑ 94SPHol-36
❑ 94SPHolDC-36
❑ 94Spo-41
❑ 94SpoFanA-AS4
❑ 94StaClu-417
❑ 94StaClu-541
❑ 94StaCluFDI-417
❑ 94StaCluFDI-541
❑ 94StaCluGR-417
❑ 94StaCluGR-541
❑ 94StaCluMOP-417
❑ 94StaCluMOP-541
❑ 94StaCluT-301
❑ 94StaCluTF-11
❑ 94StaCluTFDI-301
❑ 94Stu-54
❑ 94SucSav-8
❑ 94Top-320
❑ 94TopGol-320
❑ 94TopSpa-320
❑ 94TriPla-66
❑ 94Ult-568
❑ 94UppDec-278
❑ 94UppDec-360
❑ 94UppDecDC-C7
❑ 94UppDecED-278
❑ 94UppDecED-360
❑ 95Baz-28
❑ 95Bow-370
❑ 95ClaFanFPCP-7
❑ 95ClaPhoC-52
❑ 95ColCho-200
❑ 95ColChoGS-200
❑ 95ColChoSE-75
❑ 95ColChoSEGS-75
❑ 95ColChoSESS-75
❑ 95ColChoSS-200
❑ 95DenHol-25
❑ 95Don-50
❑ 95DonAll-NL6
❑ 95DonPreP-50
❑ 95DonTopotO-335
❑ 95Emo-183
❑ 95Fin-217
❑ 95FinRef-217
❑ 95Fla-195
❑ 95Fle-509
❑ 95FleAllS-5
❑ 95KinDis-20
❑ 95Kra-28
❑ 95Lea-212
❑ 95LeaGreG-13
❑ 95LeaLim-62
❑ 95Pac-416
❑ 95PacPri-133
❑ 95PanSti-63
❑ 95Pin-282
❑ 95Pin-333
❑ 95PinArtP-282
❑ 95PinArtP-333
❑ 95PinFan-18
❑ 95PinMusC-282
❑ 95PinMusC-333
❑ 95PinPin-9
❑ 95PinPinR-9
❑ 95PinTeaP-TP5
❑ 95RedFol-31
❑ 95Sco-26
❑ 95ScoGolR-26
❑ 95ScoHaloG-HG24
❑ 95ScoPlaTS-26
❑ 95Sel-123
❑ 95SelArtP-123
❑ 95SelCer-55
❑ 95SelCerMG-55
❑ 95SP-100
❑ 95SPCha-83
❑ 95SPCha-85
❑ 95SPChaCP-CP7
❑ 95SPChaCPDC-CP7
❑ 95SPChaDC-83
❑ 95SPChaDC-85
❑ 95Spo-108
❑ 95SpoArtP-108
❑ 95SpoDouT-5
❑ 95SPSil-100
❑ 95StaClu-65
❑ 95StaCluFDI-65
❑ 95StaCluMOP-65
❑ 95StaCluMOP-RL3
❑ 95StaCluRL-RL3
❑ 95StaCluSTWS-65
❑ 95StaCluVR-39
❑ 95StaCluVRMO-39
❑ 95Stu-41
❑ 95StuGolS-41
❑ 95Sum-40
❑ 95SumNthD-40
❑ 95TomPiz-29
❑ 95Top-347
❑ 95TopCyb-188
❑ 95TopD3-58
❑ 95TopEmb-75
❑ 95TopEmbGI-75
❑ 95TopTra-159T
❑ 95UC3-56
❑ 95UC3ArtP-56
❑ 95Ult-227
❑ 95UltGolM-227
❑ 95UppDec-60
❑ 95UppDecED-60
❑ 95UppDecEDG-60
❑ 95UppDecPC-MLB15
❑ 95UppDecSE-225
❑ 95UppDecSEG-225
❑ 95UppDecSoaD-SD8
❑ 95Zen-79
❑ 96CarPol-23
❑ 96Cir-181
❑ 96CirAcc-26
❑ 96CirBos-46
❑ 96CirRav-181
❑ 96ColCho-104
❑ 96ColCho-280
❑ 96ColCho-404
❑ 96ColCho-756
❑ 96ColChoGS-104
❑ 96ColChoGS-280
❑ 96ColChoGS-404
❑ 96ColChoGS-756
❑ 96ColChoSS-104
❑ 96ColChoSS-280
❑ 96ColChoSS-404
❑ 96ColChoSS-756
❑ 96ColChoYMtP-38
❑ 96ColChoYMtP-38A
❑ 96ColChoYMtPGS-38
❑ 96ColChoYMtPGS-38A
❑ 96DenHol-20
❑ 96Don-352
❑ 96DonPreP-352
❑ 96EmoXL-271
❑ 96Fla-367
❑ 96Fle-556
❑ 96FleTif-556
❑ 96FleUpd-9
❑ 96Lea-163
❑ 96LeaLim-66
❑ 96LeaLimG-66
❑ 96LeaPre-31
❑ 96LeaPreP-31
❑ 96LeaPrePB-163
❑ 96LeaPrePG-163
❑ 96LeaPrePS-163
❑ 96LeaSig-52
❑ 96LeaSigPPG-52
❑ 96LeaSigPPP-52
❑ 96MetUni-229
❑ 96MetUniP-229
❑ 96MLBPin-32
❑ 96Pac-226
❑ 96PacPri-P72
❑ 96PacPriG-P72
❑ 96PanSti-74
❑ 96Pin-104
❑ 96Pin-281
❑ 96PinAfi-5
❑ 96PinAfiAP-5
❑ 96PinAfiFPP-5
❑ 96PinArtP-39
❑ 96PinArtP-181
❑ 96PinFan-15
❑ 96PinFoil-281
❑ 96PinSta-39
❑ 96PinSta-181
❑ 96Pro-14
❑ 96ProSta-35
❑ 96RedF-7
❑ 96Sco-61
❑ 96ScoDugC-A53
❑ 96ScoDugCAP-A53
❑ 96Sel-67
❑ 96SelArtP-67
❑ 96SelCer-50
❑ 96SelCerAP-50
❑ 96SelCerCB-50
❑ 96SelCerCR-50
❑ 96SelCerMB-50
❑ 96SelCerMG-50
❑ 96SelCerMR-50
❑ 96SelTeaN-2
❑ 96SP-155
❑ 96Spo-53
❑ 96SpoArtP-53
❑ 96SPx-48
❑ 96SPxGol-48
❑ 96StaCluMeg-MH4
❑ 96StaCluMOP-MH4
❑ 96Stu-22
❑ 96StuPrePB-22
❑ 96StuPrePG-22
❑ 96StuPrePS-22
❑ 96Sum-102
❑ 96Sum-153
❑ 96SumAbo&B-102
❑ 96SumAbo&B-153
❑ 96SumArtP-102
❑ 96SumArtP-153
❑ 96SumFoi-102
❑ 96SumFoi-154
❑ 96TeaOut-75
❑ 96TeaOut-C97
❑ 96Top-301
❑ 96TopChr-120
❑ 96TopChrMotG-5
❑ 96TopChrMotGR-5
❑ 96TopChrR-120
❑ 96TopMasotG-5
❑ 96Ult-279
❑ 96UltCaltH-9
❑ 96UltCaltHGM-9
❑ 96UltGolM-279
❑ 96UppDec-108
❑ 96UppDec-386
❑ 96UppDec-440
❑ 96UppDecDD-DD31
❑ 96UppDecDDG-DD31
❑ 96UppDecDDS-DD31
❑ 96Zen-2
❑ 96ZenArtP-2
❑ 96ZenMoz-11
❑ 97ColCho-200
❑ 97ColChoS-1
❑ 97ColChoTBS-38
❑ 97ColChoTBSWH-38
❑ 97Don-231
❑ 97DonEli-125
❑ 97DonEliGS-125
❑ 97DonEliPtT-10
❑ 97DonEliPtT-12
❑ 97DonEliPtTA-10
❑ 97DonEliPtTA-12
❑ 97DonGolPP-231
❑ 97DonSilPP-231
❑ 97Fle-452
❑ 97FleGolM-10
❑ 97FleTif-452
❑ 97HigMinM-110
❑ 97HigMinMCT-45
❑ 97HigMinMCT-46
❑ 97Lea-152
❑ 97LeaFraM-152
❑ 97LeaFraMDC-152
❑ 97Pac-416
❑ 97PacLigB-416
❑ 97PacPri-141
❑ 97PacPriGA-GA29
❑ 97PacPriGotD-GD203
❑ 97PacPriLB-141
❑ 97PacPriP-141
❑ 97PacSil-416
❑ 97Pin-122
❑ 97PinArtP-PP122
❑ 97PinMusC-122
❑ 97PinPrePla-122
❑ 97ScoHigZ-13
❑ 97UD3-39
❑ 97Ult-276
❑ 97UltGolME-276
❑ 97UltPlaME-276
❑ 97UppDec-148
❑ 97UppDec-161
❑ 97UppDec-214
❑ 98DonSigSS-15
❑ 98DonSigSS-R2
❑ 99SkyOzzSC-NNO
❑ 99UppDecCLJotC-OZ
❑ 99UppDecR-95
❑ 99UppDecRG-95
❑ 99UppDecRI-OZ
❑ 99UppDecRIL2-OZ
❑ 99UppDecRP-95

Smith, Paul
❑ 54DanDee-23
❑ 54Top-11
❑ 57Top-345
❑ 58Top-269
❑ 61SeaPop-21
❑ 61SeaPop-22
❑ 63MilSau-8
❑ 94TopArc1-11
❑ 94TopArc1G-11

Smith, Pete J.
❑ 62SeaPop-14
❑ 63SeaPop-12
❑ 64SeaPop-16
❑ 86GreBraTI-18
❑ 87GreBraB-24
❑ 88Don-571
❑ 88DonBasB-197
❑ 88DonRoo-10
❑ 88Fle-647
❑ 88FleGlo-647
❑ 88FleUpd-73
❑ 88FleUpdG-73
❑ 88ScoRoo-84T
❑ 88ScoRooG-84T
❑ 88TopTra-111T
❑ 88TopTraT-111T
❑ 89Bow-269
❑ 89BowTif-269
❑ 89BraDub-23
❑ 89Don-263
❑ 89Fle-600
❑ 89FleGlo-600
❑ 89OPC-388
❑ 89PanSti-36
❑ 89Sco-207
❑ 89ScoHot1R-74
❑ 89ScoYouSI-19
❑ 89Top-537
❑ 89TopSti-31
❑ 89TopTif-537
❑ 89ToyRoo-29
❑ 89UppDec-412
❑ 90BraDubP-25
❑ 90BraDubS-29
❑ 90Don-499
❑ 90Fle-594
❑ 90FleCan-594
❑ 90Lea-144
❑ 90OPC-771
❑ 90PubIntS-122
❑ 90Sco-225
❑ 90Top-771
❑ 90TopBig-161
❑ 90TopTif-771
❑ 90UppDec-613
❑ 91BraDubP-27
❑ 91BraSubS-34
❑ 91Fle-703
❑ 91OPC-383
❑ 91Sco-205
❑ 91StaClu-519
❑ 91Top-383
❑ 91TopDesS-383
❑ 91TopMic-383
❑ 91TopTif-383
❑ 91UppDec-622
❑ 92Fle-370
❑ 92OPC-226
❑ 92RicBraBB-18
❑ 92RicBraF-3014
❑ 92RicBraRC-21
❑ 92RicBraS-442
❑ 92Sco-464
❑ 92StaClu-632
❑ 92Top-226
❑ 92TopGol-226
❑ 92TopGolW-226
❑ 92TopMic-226
❑ 92TriA AAS-442
❑ 93BraLykP-26
❑ 93BraLykS-32
❑ 93BraStaC-13
❑ 93Don-498
❑ 93Fle-372
❑ 93Lea-214
❑ 93OPC-222
❑ 93Pin-541
❑ 93Sco-408
❑ 93StaClu-237
❑ 93StaCluFDI-237
❑ 93StaCluMOP-237
❑ 93Top-413
❑ 93TopGol-413
❑ 93TopInaM-413
❑ 93TopInaR-413
❑ 93TopMic-413
❑ 93Ult-311
❑ 93UppDec-589
❑ 93UppDecGold-589
❑ 94Bow-624
❑ 94ColC-509
❑ 94ColChoGS-509
❑ 94ColChoSS-509
❑ 94Don-585
❑ 94Fin-350
❑ 94FinRef-350
❑ 94Fle-374
❑ 94FleExtB-325
❑ 94FleUpd-161
❑ 94Lea-419
❑ 94MetColP-24
❑ 94MetShuST-6
❑ 94ScoRoo-RT52
❑ 94ScoRooGR-RT52
❑ 94Sel-318
❑ 94SpoRoo-4
❑ 94SpoRooAP-4
❑ 94Top-658
❑ 94TopGol-658
❑ 94TopSpa-658
❑ 94Ult-535
❑ 94UppDec-419
❑ 94UppDecED-419
❑ 95Don-451
❑ 95DonPreP-451
❑ 95Fle-382
❑ 95FleUpd-136
❑ 95Top-43
❑ 96LasVegSB-24
❑ 97LasVegS1A-28
❑ 97RicBraBC-10
❑ 98PacInvGems-212
❑ 98PacOnl-648
❑ 98PacOnlR-648
❑ 98PacOnlWC-648
❑ 98PadMot-23
❑ 98UppDec-498

Smith, Peter L.
❑ 63MilSau-9
❑ 64Top-428

Smith, Phil
❑ 82DayBeaAT-24

Smith, Pop (Charles Marvin)
❑ 87BucN28-91
❑ 87OldJudN-459
❑ 88WG1CarG-62

Smith, Ramon
❑ 94MedHatBJF-3681
❑ 94MedHatBJSP-21

Smith, Randy
❑ 76QuaCitAT-32
❑ 89IdaFalBP-2008
❑ 90IdaFalBP-3263
❑ 91IdaFalBP-4346
❑ 91RocExpP-2056
❑ 94St.CatBJC-23
❑ 94St.CatBJF-3645
❑ 95StCatSTI-8

Smith, Ray
❑ 77VisOakT-13
❑ 78OrlTwiT-19
❑ 79TolMudHT-22
❑ 80TolMudHT-16
❑ 81TwiPos-25
❑ 82TolMudHT-11
❑ 83TwiTeal-3
❑ 83TwiTeal-32
❑ 84Fle-573
❑ 84Nes792-46
❑ 84TolMudHT-4
❑ 84Top-46
❑ 84TopTif-46
❑ 85LasVegSC-114
❑ 86TacTigP-21
❑ 89EliTwiS-29
❑ 90EliTwiS-24
❑ 91EliTwiP-4315
❑ 92EliTwiC-23
❑ 92EliTwiF-3697

❑ 93EliTwiF-3430
❑ 94EliTwiF-3746
Smith, Red
❑ 90LitSunW-8
Smith, Red (James C.)
❑ 11S74Sil-56
❑ 14B18B-61
❑ 15SpoNewM-167
❑ 16FleBreD-86
❑ 16SpoNewM-165
❑ 17ColE13-164
❑ 17HolBreD-98
❑ 22Zee-161
❑ 80BraTCM1-28
❑ 90DodTar-1074
Smith, Reggie (Carl R.)
❑ 67Top-314
❑ 67TopRedSS-12
❑ 68OPC-61
❑ 68RedSoxTI-7
❑ 68Top-61
❑ 68TopVen-61
❑ 69MilBra-256
❑ 69MLBOffS-18
❑ 69RedSoxAO-11
❑ 69RedSoxTI-10
❑ 69RedSoxTI-8
❑ 69Top-660
❑ 69TopSta-139
❑ 69TopTeaP-3
❑ 70Kel-46
❑ 70MLBOffS-167
❑ 70OPC-62
❑ 70OPC-215
❑ 70RedSoxCPPC-14
❑ 70Top-62
❑ 70Top-215
❑ 70TopPos-20
❑ 71Kel-52
❑ 71MilDud-29
❑ 71MLBOffS-333
❑ 71OPC-305
❑ 71RedSoxA-10
❑ 71RedSoxTI-11
❑ 71Top-305
❑ 71TopCoi-78
❑ 71TopSup-1
❑ 71TopTat-67
❑ 72Kel-35
❑ 72MilBra-318
❑ 72OPC-88
❑ 72SevTraC-51
❑ 72Top-88
❑ 72Top-565
❑ 72Top-566
❑ 73LinPor-170
❑ 73OPC-40
❑ 73SevTraC-72
❑ 73Top-40
❑ 74OPC-285
❑ 74Top-285
❑ 74TopSta-118
❑ 75Hos-59
❑ 75Kel-3
❑ 75OPC-490
❑ 75St.LouCP-27
❑ 75Top-490
❑ 75TopMin-490
❑ 76BatTroTI-20
❑ 76BlaDis-57
❑ 76BucDis-57
❑ 76CarDis-57
❑ 76CraDis-57
❑ 76DailsID-57
❑ 76Hos-30
❑ 76HosTwi-30
❑ 76IsaDis-57
❑ 76OPC-215
❑ 76OrbDis-57
❑ 76RedBarD-57
❑ 76SafDis-57
❑ 76SSP-278
❑ 76St.LouCP-31
❑ 76Top-215
❑ 76TowCluD-57
❑ 77BurCheD-152
❑ 77DodPho-14
❑ 77OPC-223
❑ 77Top-345
❑ 78Hos-30
❑ 78Kel-34
❑ 78OPC-57
❑ 78RCColC-95
❑ 78SSP270-58
❑ 78Top-168
❑ 78WifBalD-70
❑ 79BasPat-82
❑ 79Hos-72
❑ 79OPC-243
❑ 79Top-465
❑ 79TopCom-25
❑ 80DodPol-8
❑ 80OPC-350
❑ 80Top-695
❑ 81AllGamPI-161
❑ 81Dod-27
❑ 81DodPol-8
❑ 81Don-59
❑ 81Fle-111
❑ 81FleStiC-87
❑ 81Kel-36
❑ 81LonBeaPT-17
❑ 81OPC-75
❑ 81RedSoxBG2S-114
❑ 81Top-75
❑ 81TopScr-57
❑ 81TopSti-178
❑ 81TopSupHT-52
❑ 82Don-488
❑ 82Fle-23
❑ 82Gia25tATI-27
❑ 82OPC-5
❑ 82OPC-228
❑ 82Top-545
❑ 82Top-546
❑ 82TopTra-110T
❑ 83Don-611
❑ 83Fle-272
❑ 83FleSta-181
❑ 83FleSti-49
❑ 83OPC-282
❑ 83OPC-283
❑ 83Top-282
❑ 83Top-283
❑ 83TopSti-12
❑ 83TopSti-302
❑ 84DodUniO-8
❑ 87DodSmoA-34
❑ 88DodSmo-21
❑ 89DodSmoG-88
❑ 90DodTar-750
❑ 91DodUno7P-5
❑ 92CarMcD-34
❑ 92DodStaTA-16
❑ 93ActPacA-159
❑ 94DodMot-28
❑ 94DodPol-30
❑ 95DodMot-28
❑ 95DodPol-30
❑ 96DodMot-28
❑ 96DodPol-8
❑ 98DodPol-30
Smith, Rhett
❑ 89OklSoo-24
Smith, Richard
❑ 90WauTimB-7
❑ 90WauTimP-2120
❑ 90WauTimS-22
❑ 96BelSnaTI-34
Smith, Rick
❑ 88BakDodCLC-267
❑ 95HelBreTI-12
Smith, Riverboat (Robert Walkay)
❑ 81RedSoxBG2S-49
Smith, Rob (Robert D.)
❑ 88StoPorCLC-192
❑ 88StoPorP-741
❑ 89StoPorB-23
❑ 89StoPorCLC-168
❑ 89StoPorP-394
❑ 89StoPorS-18
❑ 90BelBreS-19
Smith, Robbie
❑ 86OrlTwiP-17
❑ 87OrlTwiP-2
Smith, Robbie (Robert A.)
❑ 91ColIndC-28
❑ 91ColIndP-1495
❑ 92ColRedC-23
❑ 92ColRedF-2401
Smith, Rod (Rodriguez John)
❑ 94SigRooDP-50
❑ 94SigRooDPS-50
❑ 95GreBatTI-25
❑ 96GreBatB-28
❑ 97GreBatB-28
❑ 98TamYanM-26
Smith, Rogers
❑ 89MisStaB-45
❑ 90MisStaB-44
❑ 91MisStaB-55
Smith, Ron
❑ 75BurBeeT-26
❑ 76BurBeeT-31
❑ 76WatRoyT-27
❑ 80PenPilBT-20
❑ 80PenPilCT-26
❑ 81ReaPhiT-15
Smith, Ronald
❑ 93HunCubC-25
❑ 93HunCubF-3247
Smith, Ronnie
❑ 47SigOil-70
Smith, Roosevelt
❑ 91EriSaiC-24
❑ 91EriSaiP-4070
Smith, Roy
❑ 80PenPilBT-12
❑ 80PenPilCT-4
❑ 81ReaPhiT-7
❑ 82ReaPhiT-8
❑ 83ChaChaT-5
❑ 84IndWhe-33
❑ 84MaiGuiT-3
❑ 85Don-611
❑ 85Fle-455
❑ 85Ind-29
❑ 85IndPol-33
❑ 85MaiGuiT-10
❑ 85Top-381
❑ 85TopTif-381
❑ 86Don-468
❑ 86Top-9
❑ 86TopTif-9
❑ 86TwiTeal-14
❑ 87PorBeaP-8
❑ 88PorBeaC-6
❑ 88PorBeaP-645
❑ 88TriAAAP-33
❑ 90Don-273
❑ 90Fle-386
❑ 90FleCan-386
❑ 90Lea-400
❑ 90OPC-672
❑ 90PanSti-107
❑ 90Sco-568
❑ 90Top-672
❑ 90TopTif-672
❑ 90UppDec-284
❑ 91BalOriP-31
❑ 91Don-470
❑ 91Fle-624
❑ 91OPC-503
❑ 91RocRedWP-1902
❑ 91Sco-151
❑ 91Top-503
❑ 91TopDesS-503
❑ 91TopMic-503
❑ 91TopTif-503
❑ 91UppDec-490
❑ 92Fle-28
❑ 92Sco-256
❑ 93BufBisF-517
❑ 93TriAAAGF-21
❑ 96WisTimRB-22
❑ 98St.PauSTI-26
Smith, Ryan
❑ 92BelMarCB-14
❑ 92BelMarF-1443
❑ 96PorCitRB-25
❑ 98SavSanGM-27
Smith, Samuel
❑ 87OldJudN-454
❑ 87OldJudN-457
Smith, Scott
❑ 93EriSaiC-23
❑ 93EriSaiF-3116
❑ 94ChaRanF-2496
❑ 95TulDriTI-22
❑ 96MidLeaAB-6
❑ 96WisTimRB-23
Smith, Sean
❑ 92GreHorC-8
❑ 92GreHorF-779
❑ 93ClaGolF-150
❑ 93DanBraC-25
❑ 93DanBraF-3622
❑ 93StaCluM-152
❑ 94MacBraC-21
❑ 94MacBraF-2210
❑ 95DurBulTI-29
❑ 96DurBulBlB-23
❑ 96DurBulBrB-24
Smith, Shad
❑ 91GreHorP-3061
❑ 92PriWilCC-18
❑ 92PriWilCF-150
❑ 93ShrCapF-2759
❑ 94ShrCapF-1606
Smith, Shawn
❑ 94AubAstC-27
❑ 95AubAstTI-1
❑ 96BatCliTI-27
Smith, Sherry (Sherrod)
❑ 20NatCarE-97
❑ 21Exh-167
❑ 21Exh-168
❑ 22E120-149
❑ 23W503-48
❑ 25Exh-86
❑ 26Exh-85
❑ 27AmeCarE126-22
❑ 27YorCarE-31
❑ 28W502-31
❑ 28Yue-31
❑ 90DodTar-751
❑ 92ConTSN-609
Smith, Sloan
❑ 94GreBatF-490
❑ 94OneYanC-23
❑ 94OneYanF-3807
❑ 94Top-748
❑ 94TopGol-748
❑ 94TopSpa-748
❑ 95TamYanYI-25
❑ 96NorNavB-24
❑ 97GreBatC-21
❑ 97TamYan-27
Smith, Snuffy (Donald)
❑ 47SmiClo-16
Smith, Stephen
❑ 96BilMusTI-29
Smith, Steve
❑ 84ShrCapFB-18
❑ 85FreGiaSB-23
❑ 86FreGiaSB-17
❑ 90MisStaB-41
❑ 90WicStaSGD-31
❑ 91MisStaB-42
❑ 92MisStaB-39
❑ 93MisStaB-39
Smith, Steve J.
❑ 79HawIslT-14
❑ 80HawIslT-18
❑ 81HawIslT-4
❑ 82HawIslT-3
❑ 86BeaGolGP-23
❑ 87TexLeaAF-13
❑ 87WicPilRD-9
❑ 88LasVegSC-24
❑ 88LasVegSP-244
❑ 89LasVegSC-24
❑ 89LasVegSP-25
❑ 89TriAAAP-AAA50
❑ 90CMC-171
❑ 90OklCit8C-21
❑ 90OklCit8P-448
❑ 91PenPilP-394
❑ 93AppFoxFI-2478
❑ 94CalCanF-804
❑ 95TacRaiTI-1
❑ 96MarMot-28
Smith, Syd
❑ 09T206-517
❑ 10CouT21-60
❑ 11PinT-5-624
Smith, Tad
❑ 93PitMetC-18
❑ 93PitMetF-3719
Smith, Taylor
❑ 98St.CatSM-21
Smith, Ted
❑ 77ModA'sC-1
Smith, Terry
❑ 86LakTigP-22
❑ 87LakTigP-11
❑ 90LakTigS-28
❑ 90PriPatD-19
❑ 96TreThuB-4
Smith, Texas (Michael A.)
❑ 86CedRapRT-10
❑ 87VerRedP-12
❑ 88ChaLooB-21
❑ 89RocRedWC-9
❑ 90CMC-309
❑ 90OPC-249
❑ 90ProAAAF-459
❑ 90RocRedWC-8
❑ 90RocRedWGC-23
❑ 90RocRedWP-702
❑ 90Sco-635
❑ 90Top-249
❑ 90TopDeb89-118
❑ 90TopTif-249
❑ 91OriCro-428
Smith, Tim
❑ 84NewOriT-14
❑ 90ElmPioP-23
❑ 91CarLeaAP-CAR27
❑ 91LynRedSC-9
❑ 91LynRedSP-1199
❑ 91SouOreAC-3
❑ 91SouOreAP-3843
❑ 92NewBriRSF-434
❑ 92NewBriRSS-496
❑ 92ProFS7-22
❑ 92RenSilSCLC-54
❑ 92SkyAA F-214
❑ 92StaCluD-176
❑ 93NewBriRSF-1220
❑ 93SanBerSC-16
❑ 93SanBerSF-770
❑ 94NewBriRSF-650
❑ 94TacTigF-3174
Smith, Tobe
❑ 87NegLeaPD-14
Smith, Toby
❑ 94RocRoyC-22
❑ 94RocRoyF-565
❑ 95WilBluRTI-34
❑ 96WicWraB-25
❑ 97OmaRoyB-14
Smith, Todd
❑ 86MiaMarP-23
❑ 87SalBucP-26
❑ 89MedAthB-30
❑ 90ModA'sC-28
❑ 90ModA'sCLC-151
❑ 90ModA'sP-2212
❑ 91ModA'sC-14
❑ 91ModA'sP-3088
❑ 91OklStaC-24
❑ 92HunStaS-320
❑ 92ProFS7-132
❑ 92SkyAA F-137
Smith, Tom
❑ 52LavPro-70
❑ 81QuaCitCT-18
❑ 83PeoSunF-10
❑ 91AppFoxCB-25
❑ 91AppFoxP-1730
❑ 92BasCitRC-7
❑ 92BasCitRF-3858
❑ 92Bow-383
❑ 92ClaFS7-145
❑ 93WilBluRC-21
❑ 93WilBluRF-2011
Smith, Tommy
❑ 75AndRanT-1
❑ 75LafDriT-5
❑ 80ChaO'sP-21
❑ 80ChaO'sW-22
❑ 80RocRedWT-19
Smith, Tommy A.
❑ 74OPC-606
❑ 74Top-606
❑ 75OklCit8TI-15
❑ 75OPC-619
❑ 75Top-619
❑ 75TopMin-619
❑ 76SSP-530
❑ 77OPC-92
❑ 77Top-14
❑ 78SalLakCGC-1
Smith, Tony
❑ 11PinT-5-452
❑ 11T205-157
❑ 12ImpTobC-32
❑ 90DodTar-1075
Smith, Tracy
❑ 88GenCubP-1647
❑ 89PeoChiTI-20
❑ 90WinSpiTI-21
Smith, Travis
❑ 95HelBreTI-11
❑ 96StoPorB-14
❑ 97El PasDB-21
❑ 97TexLeaTP-6
❑ 98LouRedQ-24
❑ 98Top-259
❑ 98TopChr-259
❑ 98TopChrR-259
❑ 98TopDevR-259
❑ 98TopDia-259
❑ 98TopMiniC-259
Smith, Vinnie
❑ 52MotCoo-59
Smith, Wallace H.
❑ 12T207-167
❑ 18Zee-74
Smith, Ward
❑ 75AndRanT-47
❑ 76AshTouT-8
Smith, Wib
❑ 09PC7HHB-40
Smith, Willie
❑ 65OPC-85
❑ 65Top-85
❑ 66AngDexP-16
❑ 66DexPre-2
❑ 66Top-438
❑ 67Top-397
❑ 68Top-568
❑ 69CubJewT-17
❑ 69CubTealC-9
❑ 69MilBra-257
❑ 69OPC-198
❑ 69Top-198
❑ 69TopFou-23
❑ 70OPC-318
❑ 70Top-318
❑ 71OPC-457
❑ 71Top-457
❑ 72MilBra-319
❑ 90BatCliP-3070
❑ 91SalLakTSP-15
❑ 92SalLakTSP-9
Smith, Willie Everett
❑ 88AugPirP-377
❑ 89SalBucS-21
❑ 90AlbYanB-7
❑ 90Bow-425
❑ 90BowTif-425
❑ 90CMC-207
❑ 90ColCliC-7
❑ 90ColCliP-14
❑ 90ColCliP-676
❑ 90ProAAAF-326
❑ 90TopTVY-60
❑ 91AlbYanCB-5
❑ 91AlbYanLD-17
❑ 91AlbYanP-1008
❑ 91Bow-160
❑ 91Cla/Bes-332
❑ 91LinDriAA-17
❑ 91SalLakTP-3214
❑ 92CanIndF-689
❑ 92CanIndS-120
❑ 92ColSprSSF-752
❑ 92ProFS7-113
❑ 94Bow-508
❑ 96SigRooOJ-31
❑ 96SigRooOJS-31
Smith, Wilma
❑ 97PinFan-PC9
Smith, Woody
❑ 88WytCubP-1990
❑ 89PeoChiTI-22
❑ 90PeoChiTI-13
Smith, Woody (Forest)
❑ 75SanAntBT-19
❑ 77WatIndT-21
❑ 78WatIndT-21
❑ 81ChaLooT-24
Smith, Zane
❑ 83DurBulT-24
❑ 85BraPol-34
❑ 85Fle-651
❑ 86BraPol-34
❑ 86Don-565
❑ 86Fle-528
❑ 86Lea-222
❑ 86OPC-167
❑ 86Top-167
❑ 86TopTif-167
❑ 87BraSmo-1
❑ 87Don-167
❑ 87Fle-529
❑ 87FleGlo-529
❑ 87OPC-226
❑ 87RedFolSB-73
❑ 87SpoTeaP-24
❑ 87Top-544
❑ 87TopTif-544
❑ 88Don-167
❑ 88DonBasB-170
❑ 88Fle-550

❑ 88FleGlo-550
❑ 88FleMin-66
❑ 88FleStiC-78
❑ 88FleTeaL-39
❑ 88OPC-297
❑ 88PanSti-240
❑ 88Sco-410
❑ 88ScoGlo-410
❑ 88Spo-134
❑ 88StaLinBra-18
❑ 88Top-297
❑ 88TopBig-193
❑ 88TopMinL-42
❑ 88TopSti-40
❑ 88TopTif-297
❑ 88TopUKM-73
❑ 88TopUKMT-73
❑ 89Bow-262
❑ 89BowTif-262
❑ 89Don-499
❑ 89Fle-601
❑ 89FleGlo-601
❑ 89FleUpd-99
❑ 89OPC-339
❑ 89RedFolSB-111
❑ 89Sco-492
❑ 89ScoRoo-56T
❑ 89Top-688
❑ 89TopSti-27
❑ 89TopTif-688
❑ 89UppDec-71
❑ 90Don-460
❑ 90ExpPos-34
❑ 90Fle-362
❑ 90FleCan-362
❑ 90Lea-238
❑ 90OPC-48
❑ 90PubIntS-123
❑ 90Sco-477A
❑ 90Sco-477B
❑ 90Top-48
❑ 90TopTif-48
❑ 90UppDec-607
❑ 91Bow-524
❑ 91ClaGam-82
❑ 91Don-532
❑ 91Fle-51
❑ 91Lea-495
❑ 91OPC-441
❑ 91PanCanT1-66
❑ 91Sco-845
❑ 91StaClu-260
❑ 91StaCluP-41
❑ 91Top-441
❑ 91TopDesS-441
❑ 91TopMic-441
❑ 91TopTif-441
❑ 91UppDec-759
❑ 92Bow-409
❑ 92Don-360
❑ 92Fle-568
❑ 92Hig5-94
❑ 92Lea-96
❑ 92LeaBlaG-96
❑ 92OPC-345
❑ 92Pin-237
❑ 92PirNatl-21
❑ 92Sco-493
❑ 92StaClu-807
❑ 92StaCluD-177
❑ 92StaCluECN-807
❑ 92Top-345
❑ 92TopGol-345
❑ 92TopGolW-345
❑ 92TopMic-345
❑ 92Ult-260
❑ 92UppDec-486
❑ 93Don-94
❑ 93Fle-120
❑ 93FunPac-150
❑ 93Lea-152
❑ 93OPC-170
❑ 93PacSpa-252
❑ 93PanSti-278
❑ 93Pin-403
❑ 93PirNatl-31
❑ 93Sco-121
❑ 93Sel-231
❑ 93StaClu-343
❑ 93StaCluFDI-343
❑ 93StaCluMOP-343
❑ 93Top-560
❑ 93TopGol-560
❑ 93TopInaM-560
❑ 93TopInaR-560
❑ 93TopMic-560
❑ 93Ult-101
❑ 93UppDec-349
❑ 93UppDecGold-349
❑ 94ColC-571
❑ 94ColChoGS-571
❑ 94ColChoSS-571
❑ 94Don-559
❑ 94Fin-381
❑ 94FinRef-381
❑ 94Fla-220
❑ 94Fle-620
❑ 94Lea-374
❑ 94Pac-507
❑ 94PanSti-239
❑ 94PirQui-23
❑ 94Sco-239
❑ 94ScoGolR-239
❑ 94StaClu-310
❑ 94StaCluFDI-310
❑ 94StaCluGR-310
❑ 94StaCluMOP-310
❑ 94Top-707
❑ 94TopGol-707
❑ 94TopSpa-707
❑ 94Ult-559
❑ 94UppDec-251
❑ 94UppDecED-251
❑ 95ColCho-389
❑ 95ColChoGS-389
❑ 95ColChoSE-176
❑ 95ColChoSEGS-176
❑ 95ColChoSESS-176
❑ 95ColChoSS-389
❑ 95Don-457
❑ 95DonPreP-457
❑ 95Fle-489
❑ 95FleTeaL-25
❑ 95Pac-352
❑ 95Sco-157
❑ 95ScoGolR-157
❑ 95ScoPlaTS-157
❑ 95StaClu-44
❑ 95StaCluFDI-44
❑ 95StaCluMOP-44
❑ 95StaCluSTWS-44
❑ 95TopTra-55T
❑ 95Ult-426
❑ 95UltGolM-426
❑ 95UppDec-147
❑ 95UppDecED-147
❑ 95UppDecEDG-147
❑ 96ColCho-63
❑ 96ColChoGS-63
❑ 96ColChoSS-63
❑ 96Fle-34
❑ 96FleTif-34
❑ 96FleUpd-U180
❑ 96FleUpdTC-U180
❑ 96LeaSigA-210
❑ 96LeaSigAG-210
❑ 96LeaSigAS-210

Smithberg, Roger
❑ 89BlaYNPRWLU-23
❑ 89LasVegSP-17
❑ 90Bow-203
❑ 90BowTif-203
❑ 90CMC-503
❑ 90LasVegSC-1
❑ 90LasVegSP-124
❑ 90ProAAAF-12
❑ 91HigDesMC-11
❑ 91HigDesMP-2394
❑ 91WicWraP-2599
❑ 93HunStaF-2083
❑ 94Don-421
❑ 94TacTigF-3175
❑ 94Top-652
❑ 94TopGol-652
❑ 94TopSpa-652

Smithson, Mike
❑ 80VenLeaS-165
❑ 81PawRedST-11
❑ 83RanAffF-48
❑ 83TopTra-106T
❑ 84AllGamPI-176
❑ 84Don-221
❑ 84Fle-428
❑ 84FleUpd-108
❑ 84MinTwiP-26
❑ 84Nes792-89
❑ 84Top-89
❑ 84TopTif-89
❑ 84TopTra-110T
❑ 84TopTraT-110T
❑ 84TwiTeal-32
❑ 85Don-316
❑ 85Fle-289
❑ 85OPC-359
❑ 85Top-483
❑ 85TopSti-301
❑ 85TopTif-483
❑ 85Twi7-11
❑ 85TwiPos-25
❑ 85TwiTeal-22
❑ 85TwiTeal-34
❑ 86Don-147
❑ 86Fle-405
❑ 86Lea-73
❑ 86OPC-101
❑ 86Top-695
❑ 86TopMinL-24
❑ 86TopSti-282
❑ 86TopTat-10
❑ 86TopTif-695
❑ 86TwiTeal-33
❑ 87Don-245
❑ 87Fle-553
❑ 87FleGlo-553
❑ 87OPC-225
❑ 87Top-225
❑ 87TopSti-275
❑ 87TopTif-225
❑ 87TwiPos-25
❑ 88DonTeaBRS-NEW
❑ 88Fle-23
❑ 88FleGlo-23
❑ 88FleUpd-9
❑ 88FleUpdG-9
❑ 88OPC-389
❑ 88ScoRoo-59T
❑ 88ScoRooG-59T
❑ 88Top-554
❑ 88TopTif-554
❑ 89Don-628
❑ 89Fle-100
❑ 89FleGlo-100
❑ 89Sco-403
❑ 89Top-377
❑ 89TopBig-222
❑ 89TopTif-377
❑ 89UppDec-38
❑ 90Don-464
❑ 90Fle-288
❑ 90FleCan-288
❑ 90OPC-188
❑ 90PubIntS-465
❑ 90Sco-512
❑ 90Top-188
❑ 90TopTif-188
❑ 90UppDec-610
❑ 93RanKee-335

Smock, Greg
❑ 92RenSilSCLC-58
❑ 93MadMusC-24
❑ 94ModA'sC-20

Smokey, Mascot
❑ 95TenVolW-13
❑ 98TenKry-6

Smolen, Bruce
❑ 91BatCliCB-11
❑ 91BatCliP-3494

Smoll, Clyde
❑ 40PhiTeal-20
❑ 41PhiTeal-23
❑ 87ElmPioBC-1
❑ 87ElmPioRC-1
❑ 88ElmPioC-30
❑ 89ElmPioP-25

Smoltz, John
❑ 86LakTigP-23
❑ 87GleFalTP-24
❑ 88BobCamRB-8
❑ 88FleUpd-74
❑ 88FleUpdG-74
❑ 88RicBraC-3
❑ 88RicBraP-23
❑ 88TriAAC-30
❑ 89Bow-266
❑ 89BowTif-266
❑ 89BraDub-24
❑ 89ClaTraP-174
❑ 89Don-642
❑ 89DonBasB-85
❑ 89Fle-602
❑ 89FleGlo-602
❑ 89Sco-616
❑ 89Top-382
❑ 89TopBig-260
❑ 89TopTif-382
❑ 89UppDec-17
❑ 90Bow-10
❑ 90BowTif-10
❑ 90BraDubP-26
❑ 90BraDubS-30
❑ 90ClaBlu-13
❑ 90Don-8
❑ 90Don-121
❑ 90DonBesN-50
❑ 90DOnBonM-BC12A
❑ 90DOnBonM-BC12B
❑ 90DonSupD-8
❑ 90Fle-595
❑ 90FleBasA-36
❑ 90FleBasAC-36
❑ 90FleCan-595
❑ 90Hot50PS-42
❑ 90Lea-59
❑ 90M.Vpin-4
❑ 90OPC-535
❑ 90PanSti-228
❑ 90PubIntS-124
❑ 90RedFolSB-90
❑ 90Sco-370
❑ 90Sco100S-35
❑ 90ScoYouSI-36
❑ 90Spo-61
❑ 90StaLonJS-14
❑ 90StaLonJS-34
❑ 90Top-535
❑ 90TopBig-306
❑ 90TopMinL-47
❑ 90TopSti-30
❑ 90TopTif-535
❑ 90UppDec-84
❑ 90UppDec-535
❑ 91Bow-580
❑ 91BraDubP-28
❑ 91BraSubS-35
❑ 91Cla2-T27
❑ 91ClaGam-180
❑ 91Don-75
❑ 91Fle-704
❑ 91Lea-27
❑ 91OPC-157
❑ 91PanFreS-26
❑ 91PanSti-26
❑ 91Sco-208
❑ 91StaClu-365
❑ 91Stu-149
❑ 91Top-157
❑ 91TopDesS-157
❑ 91TopMic-157
❑ 91TopTif-157
❑ 91Ult-12
❑ 91UppDec-264
❑ 92Bow-347
❑ 92BraLykP-26
❑ 92BraLykS-31
❑ 92ClaGam-18
❑ 92Don-442
❑ 92Fle-371
❑ 92Lea-191
❑ 92LeaBlaG-191
❑ 92OPC-245
❑ 92Pin-191
❑ 92PinTea2-30
❑ 92Sco-287
❑ 92ScoImpP-30
❑ 92SpoIllFK1-503
❑ 92StaClu-459
❑ 92StaCluD-178
❑ 92Stu-10
❑ 92Top-245
❑ 92TopGol-245
❑ 92TopGolW-245
❑ 92TopMic-245
❑ 92TriPla-172
❑ 92Ult-169
❑ 92UppDec-322
❑ 93Bow-494
❑ 93BraLykP-27
❑ 93BraLykS-33
❑ 93BraStaC-12
❑ 93ClaGam-89
❑ 93DiaMar-100
❑ 93Don-130
❑ 93Fin-166
❑ 93FinRef-166
❑ 93Fla-11
❑ 93Fle-14
❑ 93FunPac-68
❑ 93HumDumC-27
❑ 93Lea-104
❑ 93MSABenSPD-8
❑ 93OPC-364
❑ 93PacSpa-12
❑ 93Pin-143
❑ 93Pin-298
❑ 93Sco-61
❑ 93Sel-177
❑ 93SelAce-17
❑ 93SelStaL-66
❑ 93SelStaL-76
❑ 93SP-63
❑ 93StaClu-463
❑ 93StaClu-599
❑ 93StaCluFDI-463
❑ 93StaCluFDI-599
❑ 93StaCluM-86
❑ 93StaCluM-135
❑ 93StaCluMOP-463
❑ 93StaCluMOP-599
❑ 93Stu-61
❑ 93Top-35
❑ 93TopComotH-30
❑ 93TopGol-35
❑ 93TopInaM-35
❑ 93TopInaR-35
❑ 93TopMic-35
❑ 93TriPla-67
❑ 93Ult-312
❑ 93UltStrK-5
❑ 93UppDec-363
❑ 93UppDec-472
❑ 93UppDecCP-R19
❑ 93UppDecGold-363
❑ 93UppDecGold-472
❑ 94Bow-629
❑ 94BraLykP-30
❑ 94BraLykS-29
❑ 94BraUSPC-6D
❑ 94BraUSPC-12C
❑ 94ColC-420
❑ 94ColChoGS-420
❑ 94ColChoSS-420
❑ 94Don-260
❑ 94Fin-100
❑ 94FinPre-100P
❑ 94FinRef-100
❑ 94Fla-357
❑ 94Fle-375
❑ 94FleAllS-50
❑ 94FleExtB-213
❑ 94FleSmo'nH-12
❑ 94FUnPac-233
❑ 94Lea-309
❑ 94OPC-39
❑ 94Pac-22
❑ 94PanSti-151
❑ 94Pin-342
❑ 94PinArtP-342
❑ 94PinMusC-342
❑ 94Sco-366
❑ 94ScoGolR-366
❑ 94Sel-174
❑ 94Spo-136
❑ 94StaClu-405
❑ 94StaClu-714
❑ 94StaCluFDI-405
❑ 94StaCluFDI-714
❑ 94StaCluGR-405
❑ 94StaCluGR-714
❑ 94StaCluMO-7
❑ 94StaCluMOP-405
❑ 94StaCluMOP-714
❑ 94StaCluT-35
❑ 94StaCluTFDI-35
❑ 94Top-687
❑ 94TopGol-687
❑ 94TopSpa-687
❑ 94TriPla-50
❑ 94Ult-157
❑ 94UltStrK-5
❑ 94UppDec-87
❑ 94UppDecED-87
❑ 95BraAtlC-7
❑ 95ColCho-167
❑ 95ColChoGS-167
❑ 95ColChoSS-167
❑ 95Don-461
❑ 95DonPreP-461
❑ 95DonTopotO-193
❑ 95Emo-108
❑ 95Fin-313
❑ 95FinRef-313
❑ 95Fla-108
❑ 95Fle-318
❑ 95Lea-18
❑ 95Pac-15
❑ 95Pin-25
❑ 95PinArtP-25
❑ 95PinMusC-25
❑ 95Sco-468
❑ 95ScoGolR-468
❑ 95ScoHaloG-HG66
❑ 95ScoPlaTS-468
❑ 95Sel-189
❑ 95SelArtP-189
❑ 95StaClu-397
❑ 95StaCluMOP-397
❑ 95StaCluSTDW-B397
❑ 95StaCluSTMP-9
❑ 95StaCluSTWS-397
❑ 95Top-145
❑ 95Ult-133
❑ 95UltGolM-133
❑ 95UppDec-294
❑ 95UppDecED-294
❑ 95UppDecEDG-294
❑ 96BowBes-72
❑ 96BowBesAR-72
❑ 96BowBesR-72
❑ 96BraFle-16
❑ 96Cir-107
❑ 96CirAcc-15
❑ 96CirBos-28
❑ 96CirRav-107
❑ 96ColCho-49
❑ 96ColChoGS-49
❑ 96ColChoSS-49
❑ 96Don-363
❑ 96DonPreP-363
❑ 96EmoXL-149
❑ 96Fin-B124
❑ 96FinRef-B124
❑ 96Fla-210
❑ 96Fle-308
❑ 96FleSmo'H-9
❑ 96FleTif-308
❑ 96Lea-1
❑ 96LeaLim-74
❑ 96LeaLimG-74
❑ 96LeaPre-111
❑ 96LeaPreP-111
❑ 96LeaPrePB-1
❑ 96LeaPrePG-1
❑ 96LeaPrePS-1
❑ 96LeaSig-69
❑ 96LeaSigEA-185
❑ 96LeaSigEACM-27
❑ 96LeaSigPPG-69
❑ 96LeaSigPPP-69
❑ 96MetUni-136
❑ 96MetUniP-136
❑ 96Pac-10
❑ 96Pin-315
❑ 96PinAfi-79
❑ 96PinAfiAP-79
❑ 96PinAfiFPP-79
❑ 96PinFoil-315
❑ 96Sco-27
❑ 96Sco-200
❑ 96ScoDugC-A26
❑ 96ScoDugCAP-A26
❑ 96ScoRef-14
❑ 96Sel-125
❑ 96SelArtP-125
❑ 96SP-24
❑ 96StaClu-250
❑ 96StaCluMOP-250
❑ 96Stu-85
❑ 96StuPrePB-85
❑ 96StuPrePG-85
❑ 96StuPrePS-85
❑ 96TeaOut-76
❑ 96Top-189
❑ 96TopChr-59
❑ 96TopChrR-59
❑ 96TopGal-67
❑ 96TopGalPPI-67
❑ 96TopLas-62
❑ 96Ult-161
❑ 96UltGolM-161
❑ 96UppDec-271
❑ 96UppDecA-16
❑ 96UppDecDD-DD3
❑ 96UppDecDDG-DD3
❑ 96UppDecDDS-DD3
❑ 97Bow-53
❑ 97BowBes-95
❑ 97BowBesAR-95
❑ 97BowBesMI-MI3
❑ 97BowBesMIAR-MI3
❑ 97BowBesMIARI-MI3
❑ 97BowBesMII-MI3
❑ 97BowBesMIR-MI3
❑ 97BowBesMIRI-MI3
❑ 97BowBesR-95
❑ 97BowChr-41
❑ 97BowChrI-41

❑ 97BowChrIR-41
❑ 97BowChrR-41
❑ 97BowInt-53
❑ 97BraSco-6
❑ 97BraScoPl-6
❑ 97BraScoPr-6
❑ 97Cir-192
❑ 97CirBos-17
❑ 97CirRav-192
❑ 97CirSupB-17
❑ 97ColCho-60
❑ 97ColCho-61
❑ 97ColCho-221
❑ 97ColCho-265
❑ 97ColChoAC-27
❑ 97ColChoT-AB13
❑ 97ColChoTBS-4
❑ 97ColChoTBSWH-4
❑ 97ColChoTotT-T4
❑ 97Don-104
❑ 97Don-425
❑ 97DonDom-12
❑ 97DonEli-49
❑ 97DonEliGS-49
❑ 97DonGolPP-104
❑ 97DonGolPP-425
❑ 97DonLim-16
❑ 97DonLim-81
❑ 97DonLim-161
❑ 97DonLimE-16
❑ 97DonLimE-81
❑ 97DonLimE-161
❑ 97DonLimENG-16
❑ 97DonPre-112
❑ 97DonPre-188
❑ 97DonPreCttC-112
❑ 97DonPreCttC-188
❑ 97DonPreTB-22
❑ 97DonPreTBG-22
❑ 97DonPreTF-22
❑ 97DonPreTP-22
❑ 97DonPreTPG-22
❑ 97DonSig-96
❑ 97DonSigPPP-96
❑ 97DonSilPP-104
❑ 97DonSilPP-425
❑ 97DonTea-20
❑ 97DonTeaSPE-20
❑ 97DonVxP1-40
❑ 97E-X2-59
❑ 97E-X2Cred-59
❑ 97E-X2EssCre-59
❑ 97Fin-136
❑ 97Fin-350
❑ 97FinEmb-136
❑ 97FinEmb-350
❑ 97FinEmbR-136
❑ 97FinEmbR-350
❑ 97FinRef-136
❑ 97FinRef-350
❑ 97FlaShoLC-98
❑ 97FlaShoLeg0-98
❑ 97FlaShoLeg1-98
❑ 97FlaShoM-A98
❑ 97FlaShoM-B98
❑ 97FlaShoM-C98
❑ 97FlaShoR0-98
❑ 97FlaShoR1-98
❑ 97FlaShoR2-98
❑ 97Fle-269
❑ 97Fle-717
❑ 97FleHea-19
❑ 97FleMilDM-34
❑ 97FleMilDMR-34
❑ 97FleNig&D-9
❑ 97FleTif-269
❑ 97FleTif-717
❑ 97FleZon-17
❑ 97Lea-77
❑ 97Lea-367
❑ 97LeaBanS-12
❑ 97LeaFraM-77
❑ 97LeaFraM-367
❑ 97LeaFraMDC-77
❑ 97LeaFraMDC-367
❑ 97LeaGet-2
❑ 97LeaStaS-14
❑ 97MetUni-35
❑ 97NewPin-147
❑ 97NewPinAP-147
❑ 97NewPinMC-147
❑ 97NewPinPP-147
❑ 97Pac-244
❑ 97PacCerCGT-20
❑ 97PacCraC-8
❑ 97PacGolCD-24
❑ 97PacLigB-244
❑ 97PacPri-83
❑ 97PacPriLB-83
❑ 97PacPriP-83
❑ 97PacPriSH-SH9B
❑ 97PacSil-244
❑ 97Pin-112
❑ 97PinArtP-PP112
❑ 97PinCar-17
❑ 97PinCer-67
❑ 97PinCerCMGT-20
❑ 97PinCerCT-20
❑ 97PinCerLI-15
❑ 97PinCerMBla-67
❑ 97PinCerMBlu-67
❑ 97PinCerMG-67
❑ 97PinCerMR-67
❑ 97PinCerR-67
❑ 97PinIns-68
❑ 97PinIns-149
❑ 97PinInsC-3
❑ 97PinInsCE-68
❑ 97PinInsCE-149
❑ 97PinInsDD-16
❑ 97PinInsDE-68
❑ 97PinInsDE-149
❑ 97PinMusC-112
❑ 97PinPrePla-112
❑ 97PinPrePla-S3
❑ 97PinSha-3
❑ 97PinTeaP-9
❑ 97PinTeaP-10
❑ 97PinTotCPB-67
❑ 97PinTotCPG-67
❑ 97PinTotCPR-67
❑ 97PinX-P-52
❑ 97PinX-PMoS-52
❑ 97Sco-117
❑ 97Sco-521
❑ 97ScoAllF-18
❑ 97ScoArtPWB-117
❑ 97ScoArtPWB-521
❑ 97ScoFra-2
❑ 97ScoFraG-2
❑ 97ScoPreS-117
❑ 97ScoResC-521
❑ 97ScoShoS-117
❑ 97ScoShoS-521
❑ 97ScoShoSAP-117
❑ 97ScoShoSAP-521
❑ 97ScoStaaD-4
❑ 97ScoSteS-4
❑ 97Sel-12
❑ 97Sel-146
❑ 97SelArtP-12
❑ 97SelArtP-146
❑ 97SelCom-12
❑ 97SelCom-146
❑ 97SelRegG-12
❑ 97SelRegG-146
❑ 97SelToootT-23
❑ 97SelToootTMB-23
❑ 97SP-22
❑ 97SPInsI-11
❑ 97SpoIll-73
❑ 97SpoIllEE-73
❑ 97SpoIllGS-5
❑ 97SPSpeF-15
❑ 97SPSPxFA-5
❑ 97SPx-6
❑ 97SPxBro-6
❑ 97SPxGol-6
❑ 97SPxGraF-6
❑ 97SPxSil-6
❑ 97SPxSte-6
❑ 97StaClu-29
❑ 97StaClul-I15
❑ 97StaCluMat-29
❑ 97StaCluMOP-29
❑ 97StaCluMOP-I15
❑ 97Stu-56
❑ 97StuPrePG-56
❑ 97StuPrePS-56
❑ 97Top-157
❑ 97TopAll-AS20
❑ 97TopChr-61
❑ 97TopChrAS-AS20
❑ 97TopChrR-61
❑ 97TopChrSAR-AS20
❑ 97TopChrSB-16
❑ 97TopChrSBR-16
❑ 97TopGal-51
❑ 97TopGalPPI-51
❑ 97TopMemO5-44
❑ 97TopSeaB-SB16
❑ 97TopSta-41
❑ 97TopStaAM-41
❑ 97UD3-29
❑ 97Ult-160
❑ 97UltChe-A8
❑ 97UltGolME-160
❑ 97UltLeaS-12
❑ 97UltPlaME-160
❑ 97UltSeaC-10
❑ 97UltTop3-25
❑ 97UltTop3GM-25
❑ 97UppDec-64
❑ 97UppDec-217
❑ 97UppDec-259
❑ 97UppDec-300
❑ 97UppDecAWJ-10
❑ 97UppDecAWJ-12
❑ 97UppDecAWJ-23
❑ 97UppDecHC-HC9
❑ 97UppDecHTH-HT6
❑ 97UppDecP-5
❑ 97UppDecPE-5
❑ 97Zen-26
❑ 98Bow-227
❑ 98BowBes-84
❑ 98BowBesAR-84
❑ 98BowBesR-84
❑ 98BowChr-227
❑ 98BowChrGA-227
❑ 98BowChrGAR-227
❑ 98BowChrI-227
❑ 98BowChrIR-227
❑ 98BowChrR-227
❑ 98BowChrR-14
❑ 98BowChrRR-14
❑ 98BowGolA-227
❑ 98BowInt-227
❑ 98BraSco-9
❑ 98BraScoP-9
❑ 98CirThu-202
❑ 98CirThuRav-202
❑ 98CirThuSupRav-202
❑ 98ColCho-31
❑ 98CroRoyPotG-4
❑ 98Don-76
❑ 98DonCol-76
❑ 98DonColE-425
❑ 98DonColL-304
❑ 98DonColP-611
❑ 98DonColS-76
❑ 98DonCruG-56
❑ 98DonCruP-56
❑ 98DonCruR-56
❑ 98DonEli-25
❑ 98DonEliA-25
❑ 98DonEliS-25
❑ 98DonGolPP-76
❑ 98DonPre-61
❑ 98DonPreSeat-61
❑ 98DonPriCD-76
❑ 98DonPriCE-425
❑ 98DonPriCL-304
❑ 98DonPriCP-611
❑ 98DonSig-40
❑ 98DonSigP-40
❑ 98DonSilPP-76
❑ 98Fin-170
❑ 98FinNo-170
❑ 98FinNo-R-170
❑ 98FinRef-170
❑ 98FlaShoLeg0-61
❑ 98FlaShoLeg1-61
❑ 98FlaShoLeg2-61
❑ 98FlaShoLeg3-61
❑ 98FlaShoLegM-61
❑ 98FlaShoR0-61
❑ 98FlaShoR1-61
❑ 98FlaShoR2-61
❑ 98FlaShoR3-61
❑ 98Fle-310
❑ 98Fle-417
❑ 98FleVin'-75
❑ 98FleVin'C-75
❑ 98Lea-105
❑ 98LeaCruG-56
❑ 98LeaCruP-56
❑ 98LeaCruR-56
❑ 98LeaFraDA-105
❑ 98LeaFraF-105
❑ 98LeaFraM-105
❑ 98LeaFraM-105
❑ 98LeaFraMDC-105
❑ 98LeaFraMDC-105
❑ 98LeaFraMS-105
❑ 98LeaFraMZ2-105
❑ 98LeaRS-64
❑ 98LeaRSLHolo-64
❑ 98LeaRSLong-64
❑ 98LeaRTrue-64
❑ 98MetUni-179
❑ 98MetUniPMG-179
❑ 98Pac-243
❑ 98PacOme-26
❑ 98PacOmeR-26
❑ 98PacOnl-73
❑ 98PacOnlR-73
❑ 98PacOnlWC-73
❑ 98PacPar-135
❑ 98PacParC-135
❑ 98PacParG-135
❑ 98PacParHS-135
❑ 98PacParPB-135
❑ 98PacParR-135
❑ 98PacPlaB-243
❑ 98PacRedT-243
❑ 98PacSil-243
❑ 98PinIns-43
❑ 98PinInsCE-43
❑ 98PinInsDE-43
❑ 98PinPer-62
❑ 98PinPerPP-62
❑ 98PinPlu-123
❑ 98PinSna-AB5
❑ 98Sco-120
❑ 98ScoRT-157
❑ 98ScoRTSS-PP89
❑ 98ScoRTSSAP-PP89
❑ 98ScoRTSSAP1-PP89
❑ 98ScoSS-PP50
❑ 98ScoSSAP-PP50
❑ 98SkyDugAD-D6
❑ 98SP Aut-49
❑ 98SpoIll-113
❑ 98SpoIll-141
❑ 98SpoIllEE-113
❑ 98SpoIllEE-141
❑ 98SpoIllFE-113
❑ 98SpoIllFE-141
❑ 98SpoIllODMP-OD3
❑ 98SpoIllTaN-132
❑ 98SpoIllTaNEE-132
❑ 98SpoIllWSF-114
❑ 98SpoIllWSFEE-114
❑ 98SpoIllWSFFE-114
❑ 98SpoIllWSFRJP-10
❑ 98SPxFin-59
❑ 98SPxFin-212
❑ 98SPxFinR-59
❑ 98SPxFinR-212
❑ 98SPxFinS-59
❑ 98SPxFinS-212
❑ 98StaCluFDI-149
❑ 98StaClul-149
❑ 98StaCluOneK-149
❑ 98StaCluPP-149
❑ 98Stu-95
❑ 98StuGPP-95
❑ 98StuSPP-95
❑ 98Top-319
❑ 98TopChr-319
❑ 98TopChrR-319
❑ 98TopDevR-319
❑ 98TopDia-319
❑ 98TopGal-104
❑ 98TopGalGP-104
❑ 98TopGalOPP-104
❑ 98TopGalPPI-104
❑ 98TopGalPPIA-104
❑ 98TopMiniC-319
❑ 98TopOpeD-145
❑ 98TopSta-141
❑ 98TopStaB-141
❑ 98TopStaG-141
❑ 98TopStaGR-141
❑ 98TopStaS-141
❑ 98Ult-159
❑ 98UltGolM-159
❑ 98UltMas-159
❑ 98UltPlaM-159
❑ 98UppDec-32
❑ 98UppDec-417
❑ 98UppDecSF-18
❑ 98UppDecSFPD-PZ11
❑ 98UppDecSFPZOB-PZ8
❑ 98Zen-61
❑ 98Zen5 xx7-7
❑ 98Zen5x7GoldImp-7
❑ 98Zen5x7Imp-7
❑ 98ZenZ-G-61
❑ 98ZenZ-S-61
❑ 99199Fin-211
❑ 99Bow-69
❑ 99BowBes-84
❑ 99BowBesAR-84
❑ 99BowBesR-84
❑ 99BowChr-69
❑ 99BowChrG-69
❑ 99BowChrGR-69
❑ 99BowChrI-69
❑ 99BowChrIR-69
❑ 99BowChrR-69
❑ 99BowGol-69
❑ 99BowInt-69
❑ 99BowLatB-LB8
❑ 99FinGolRef-211
❑ 99FinRef-211
❑ 99FlaShoLeg1-109
❑ 99FlaShoLeg2-109
❑ 99FlaShoLeg3-109
❑ 99FlaShoLegM1-109
❑ 99FlaShoLegM2-109
❑ 99FlaShoLegM3-109
❑ 99FlaShoR1-109
❑ 99FlaShoR2-109
❑ 99FlaShoR3-109
❑ 99Fle-284
❑ 99FleSta9-284
❑ 99FleWarT-284
❑ 99MetUni-203
❑ 99MetUniGM-203
❑ 99MetUniPMG-203
❑ 99Pac-42
❑ 99PacCroC-32
❑ 99PacCroCPB-32
❑ 99PacOme-27
❑ 99PacOmeC-27
❑ 99PacOmeG-27
❑ 99PacOmePB-27
❑ 99PacPar-29
❑ 99PacParC-29
❑ 99PacParG-29
❑ 99PacParHoloGold-29
❑ 99PacParHS-29
❑ 99PacParOD-29
❑ 99PacParPB-29
❑ 99PacParRed-29
❑ 99PacPlaB-42
❑ 99PacPriS-139
❑ 99PacPriS206-139
❑ 99PacPriS206R-139
❑ 99PacRed-42
❑ 99Rev-17
❑ 99RevPremDate-17
❑ 99RevRet-17
❑ 99RevShaSS-17
❑ 99SkyMolM-42
❑ 99SkyMolMOA-27
❑ 99SkyMolMX-42
❑ 99SkyPre-132
❑ 99SkyPreR-132
❑ 99SkyThu-1
❑ 99SkyThuRant-1
❑ 99SkyThuRave-1
❑ 99SpoIll-111
❑ 99StaClu-286
❑ 99StaCluFDI-286
❑ 99StaCluOoaK-286
❑ 99StaCluPP-286
❑ 99ThuSkySupR-1
❑ 99Top-329
❑ 99TopBlaLC1-96
❑ 99TopBlaLC2-96
❑ 99TopBlaLC3-96
❑ 99TopChr-329
❑ 99TopChrR-329
❑ 99TopGal-99
❑ 99TopGalPP-99
❑ 99TopGalPPI-99
❑ 99TopGolL-96
❑ 99TopGolLC1-96
❑ 99TopGolLC2-96
❑ 99TopGolLOtO-96
❑ 99TopMVPP-329
❑ 99TopOpeD-118
❑ 99TopRedLC1-96
❑ 99TopRedLC2-96
❑ 99TopRedLC3-96
❑ 99TopSta-52
❑ 99TopSta1Foil-52
❑ 99TopStaFoil-52
❑ 99TopStaOS-52
❑ 99UppDec-38
❑ 99UppDecCL-95
❑ 99UppDecCLCC-95
❑ 99UppDecCLM-C9
❑ 99UppDecE-6
❑ 99UppDecEFXG-6
❑ 99UppDecEL1-38
❑ 99UppDecEL2-38
❑ 99UppDecM-22
❑ 99UppDecMGS-22
❑ 99UppDecMHFS-22
❑ 99UppDecMP-22
❑ 99UppDecMSS-22
❑ 99Vic-35

Smoot, Allen
❑ 82CliGiaF-18

Smoot, Homer
❑ 11PinT-5-1004
❑ 11SpoLifCW-330

Smorol, Jason
❑ 96BatCliTI-34
❑ 98BatMucTI-29

Smotherman, Dick
❑ 75WatRoyT-27

Smothers, Stewart
❑ 97EugEmeB-28
❑ 98MacBraM-17

Smyth, Gregg
❑ 95AubAstTI-21

Smythe, Harry
❑ 36GouWidPPR-D35
❑ 36WorWidGV-79
❑ 90DodTar-752

Snaith, Andy
❑ 82AleDukT-26

Snappers, Beloit
❑ 95BelBreTI-31
❑ 96BelSnaTI-36

Snead, Esix
❑ 98NewJerCM-30

Snead, Jay
❑ 89AugPirP-519

Snead, Sam
❑ 51Whe-5
❑ 52Whe-27A
❑ 52Whe-27B
❑ 59FleWil-67

Snead, Scott
❑ 91BilMusP-3764
❑ 91BilMusSP-3

Snedeker, Sean
❑ 88GreFalDTI-20
❑ 89BakDodCLC-181
❑ 89CalLeaA-21
❑ 91VerBeaDC-12
❑ 91VerBeaDP-773
❑ 96HicCraB-27
❑ 97HicCraB-2
❑ 97HicCraRB-2
❑ 98HicCraM-2
❑ 98HicCraUO-2

Snediker, Jim
❑ 86WinHavRSP-24

Sneed, John
❑ 98HagSunM-25

Snell, Dave
❑ 86WauTimP-25
❑ 87SalSpuS-3
❑ 88VerMarP-956

Snell, Nate
❑ 84BalOriP-35
❑ 85BalOriP-32
❑ 85FleUpd-107
❑ 85TopTifT-110T
❑ 85TopTra-110T
❑ 86BalOriHMP-18
❑ 86BalOriP-21
❑ 86Don-367
❑ 86Fle-288
❑ 86Lea-166
❑ 86Top-521
❑ 86TopTif-521
❑ 87Don-396
❑ 87Fle-481
❑ 87FleGlo-481
❑ 87Top-86
❑ 87TopTif-86
❑ 88Fle-70
❑ 88FleGlo-70
❑ 91OriCro-430

Snellgrove, Clay
❑ 97IdaFalBTI-23
❑ 98CliLumG-23

Snelling, Allen
❑ 96StCatSB-27

Snellings, Ryan
❑ 97BoiHawG-26

Snider, Duke
❑ 47DodTeal-22
❑ 47Exh-213A
❑ 47Exh-213B
❑ 47PM1StaP1-205
❑ 47PM1StaP1-206
❑ 47PM1StaP1-207

❑ 47StaPinP2-39
❑ 49Bow-226
❑ 49EurSta-50
❑ 50Bow-77
❑ 50Dra-5
❑ 51Bow-32
❑ 51R42SmaS-95
❑ 51TopRedB-38
❑ 52BerRos-61
❑ 52Bow-116
❑ 52H-OlnsOR-4
❑ 52NatTeaL-32
❑ 52RedMan-NL21
❑ 52StaCalL-79E
❑ 52StaCalS-91C
❑ 52TipTop-40
❑ 52Top-37
❑ 53BowC-117
❑ 53Bri-40
❑ 53RedMan-NL14
❑ 53StaMey-8
❑ 54Bow-170
❑ 54DanDee-24
❑ 54NewYorJA-18
❑ 54RedHeaF-29
❑ 54RedMan-NL16
❑ 54StaMey-12
❑ 54Top-32
❑ 55ArmCoi-19
❑ 55BigLealS-17
❑ 55DaiQueS-17
❑ 55DodGolS-17
❑ 55RedMan-NL19
❑ 55StaMey-12
❑ 55Top-210
❑ 56Dod-27
❑ 56Top-150
❑ 56TopPin-52
❑ 56YelBasP-29
❑ 57Top-170
❑ 57Top-400
❑ 58DodBelB-9
❑ 58DodJayP-12
❑ 58DodTeal-22
❑ 58DodVol-12
❑ 58HarSta-12
❑ 58Hir-61
❑ 58JayPubS-9
❑ 58Top-88
❑ 58Top-314
❑ 58Top-436
❑ 59Baz-20
❑ 59DodMor-11
❑ 59DodPos-1
❑ 59DodTeal-25
❑ 59DodVol-15
❑ 59HomRunD-18
❑ 59Top-20
❑ 59Top-468
❑ 59TopVen-20
❑ 60DodBelB-2
❑ 60DodJayP-14
❑ 60DodMor-12
❑ 60DodPos-12
❑ 60DodTeal-18
❑ 60DodUniO-19
❑ 60KeyChal-45
❑ 60Lea-37
❑ 60NuHi-55
❑ 60RawGloT-32
❑ 60Top-493
❑ 61DodBelB-4
❑ 61DodUniO-20
❑ 61Pos-167A
❑ 61Pos-167B
❑ 61Raw-10
❑ 61Top-443
❑ 62DodBelB-4
❑ 62DodJayP-10
❑ 62DodVol-14
❑ 62Jel-114
❑ 62Pos-114
❑ 62PosCan-114
❑ 62SalPlaC-215
❑ 62ShiPlaC-215
❑ 62Top-500
❑ 62TopStal-140
❑ 63BasMagM-77
❑ 63Jel-118
❑ 63MetJayP-9
❑ 63Pos-118
❑ 63Top-68
❑ 63Top-550
❑ 64ChatheY-47
❑ 64MetJayP-10
❑ 64Top-155
❑ 64TopVen-155
❑ 64WheSta-42
❑ 68LauWorS-49
❑ 70FleWorS-49
❑ 70Houof J-29
❑ 71FleWorS-53
❑ 71FleWorS-57
❑ 74dod195T-37
❑ 75DodTCMA-10
❑ 75ExpPos-34
❑ 75ShaPiz-12
❑ 75TCMHouoJ-31
❑ 76GalBasGHoF-26
❑ 76Met63 S-15
❑ 76SSP-351
❑ 76SSP-591
❑ 77GalGloG-24
❑ 77Spo-10122
❑ 79DiaGre-94
❑ 79TCM50-43
❑ 79TCM50-72
❑ 80DodGreT-10
❑ 80PacLeg-19
❑ 80PerHaloFP-172
❑ 80PerHaloFPS-39
❑ 80SSPHOF-170
❑ 81SanDieSC-3
❑ 81TCM60I-363
❑ 82CraJac-15
❑ 82DiaCla-26
❑ 82TCMGreS-9
❑ 82TCMStaot5-5
❑ 83ASADukS-1
❑ 83ASADukS-2
❑ 83ASADukS-3
❑ 83ASADukS-4
❑ 83ASADukS-5
❑ 83ASADukS-6
❑ 83ASADukS-7
❑ 83ASADukS-8
❑ 83ASADukS-9
❑ 83ASADukS-10
❑ 83ASADukS-11
❑ 83ASADukS-12
❑ 83DonHOFH-14
❑ 83MLBPin-33
❑ 83Oco& SSBG-17
❑ 83TopRep5-37
❑ 83TopTraBP-6
❑ 84Don-648
❑ 84FifNatCT-17
❑ 84OCoandSI-66
❑ 84SpoDesPW-24
❑ 84WilMay-13
❑ 85CirK-20
❑ 85TCMHomRC-9
❑ 85TCMPpl1-6
❑ 86SpoDecG-32
❑ 86SpoDesJM-20
❑ 86TCM-2
❑ 86TCMSupS-49
❑ 86TCMSupS-50
❑ 87Dod195T-1
❑ 87HygAllG-41
❑ 87LeaSpeO*-H6
❑ 87NesDreT-33
❑ 88DodRinP1-4A
❑ 88HouSho-8
❑ 88PacLegI-55
❑ 88WilMulP-15
❑ 89BowInsT-10
❑ 89BowRepI-10
❑ 89BowTif-R10
❑ 89DodSmoG-27
❑ 89PerCelP-38
❑ 89TopBasT-30
❑ 90DodTar-753
❑ 90PerGreM-33
❑ 90PerGreM-87
❑ 90PerMasW-16
❑ 90PerMasW-17
❑ 90PerMasW-18
❑ 90PerMasW-19
❑ 90PerMasW-20
❑ 91MetWIZ-371
❑ 91TopArc1-327
❑ 92BazQua5A-10
❑ 92UppDecS-21
❑ 93TedWil-16
❑ 93TedWilM-4
❑ 93Yoo-19
❑ 94NabAllA-4
❑ 94TopArc1-32
❑ 94TopArc1G-32
❑ 95TopArcBD-5
❑ 95TopArcBD-63
❑ 95TopArcBD-68
❑ 95TopArcBD-108
❑ 95TopArcBD-119
❑ 95TopArcBD-151
❑ 97DonSigSS-21
❑ 98DonSigSS-16

Snider, Kelly
❑ 77LodDodT-20
❑ 79AlbDukTc-14
❑ 80AlbDukTc-4
❑ 81TolMudHT-15
❑ 82TolMudHT-16

Snider, Mark
❑ 89GeoColC-29
❑ 90GeoColC-28

Snider, Van
❑ 83ChaRoyT-13
❑ 84MemChiT-9
❑ 86MemChiSTOS-25
❑ 86MemChiTOS-25
❑ 87OmaRoyP-4
❑ 88BlaYNPRWL-61
❑ 88NasSouC-22
❑ 88NasSouP-473
❑ 88NasSouTI-22
❑ 88TriAAC-8
❑ 89Don-586
❑ 89Fle-172
❑ 89FleGlo-172
❑ 89NasSouC-23
❑ 89NasSouP-1281
❑ 89NasSouTI-23
❑ 89Sco-640
❑ 89ScoHot1R-41
❑ 89Spo-177
❑ 89UppDec-23
❑ 90CMC-216
❑ 90ColCliC-16
❑ 90ColCliP-15
❑ 90ColCliP-692
❑ 90ProAAAF-342
❑ 90TopTVY-61
❑ 91ColCliLD-118
❑ 91ColCliP-18
❑ 91ColCliP-611
❑ 91LinDriAAA-118
❑ 92PawRedSF-938
❑ 92PawRedSS-367
❑ 93LouRedF-229
❑ 97DunDonPPS-23

Snipes, Wesley
❑ 89MajLeaM-8
❑ 89MajLeaM-10

Snitker, Brian
❑ 78GreBraT-23
❑ 79SavBraT-5
❑ 83DurBulT-28
❑ 84DurBulT-28
❑ 86SumBraP-26
❑ 87DurBulP-6
❑ 89BraDub-25
❑ 90BraDubS-31
❑ 91MacBraC-18
❑ 91MacBraP-883
❑ 92MacBraC-26
❑ 92MacBraF-284
❑ 93GreBraF-367
❑ 94DanBraF-3550
❑ 94GreBraF-431
❑ 94GreBraTI-3
❑ 95DurBulTI-30
❑ 96DanBraB-1
❑ 97MacBra-29
❑ 98MacBraM-26

Snoddy, Chris
❑ 86DavLipB-20

Snodgrass, Fred
❑ 09ColChiE-266
❑ 09SpoNewSM-76
❑ 09T206-329
❑ 09T206-330
❑ 10DarChoE-28
❑ 10W555-57
❑ 11HelSta-137
❑ 11PinT-5-255
❑ 11S74Sil-95
❑ 11SpoLifM-220
❑ 11T205-158
❑ 12ColRedB-266
❑ 12ColTinT-266
❑ 12HasTriFT-48I
❑ 12T207-169
❑ 14B18B-71
❑ 14PieStaT-95
❑ 15SpoNewM-168
❑ 16FleBreD-87
❑ 16SpoNewM-166
❑ 17ColE13-165
❑ 60NuHi-54
❑ 61NuSco-454
❑ 74CapPub-61
❑ 88ConSer3-26
❑ 91ConTSN-168

Snook, Rob
❑ 94HelBreF-3617
❑ 94HelBreSP-14

Snopek, Chris
❑ 92UtiBluSC-3
❑ 93Bow-259
❑ 93ClaFS7-145
❑ 93SarWhiSF-1380
❑ 93SouBenWSC-20
❑ 93SouBenWSF-1440
❑ 94AriFalLS-19
❑ 94BirBarC-20
❑ 94BirBarF-630
❑ 94Bow-539
❑ 94BowBes-B43
❑ 94BowBesR-B43
❑ 94Cla-33
❑ 95Bow-147
❑ 95NasSouTI-25
❑ 96Bow-180
❑ 96BowBes-104
❑ 96BowBesAR-104
❑ 96BowBesR-104
❑ 96BowFoi-180
❑ 96ColCho-18
❑ 96ColChoGS-18
❑ 96ColChoSS-18
❑ 96Don-517
❑ 96DonPreP-517
❑ 96Fin-G243
❑ 96FinRef-G243
❑ 96Fla-57
❑ 96FlePro-9
❑ 96FleUpd-U28
❑ 96FleUpdTC-U28
❑ 96Lea-25
❑ 96LeaPre-141
❑ 96LeaPreP-141
❑ 96LeaPrePB-25
❑ 96LeaPrePG-25
❑ 96LeaPrePS-25
❑ 96Pac-280
❑ 96Pin-188
❑ 96PinAfi-164
❑ 96PinAfiAP-164
❑ 96Sco-499
❑ 96Sel-163
❑ 96SelArtP-163
❑ 96SelCer-126
❑ 96SelCerAP-126
❑ 96SelCerCB-126
❑ 96SelCerCR-126
❑ 96SelCerMB-126
❑ 96SelCerMG-126
❑ 96SelCerMR-126
❑ 96SP-11
❑ 96Spo-129
❑ 96SpoArtP-129
❑ 96SpoRooJ-2
❑ 96StaClu-339
❑ 96StaCluMOP-339
❑ 96Sum-187
❑ 96SumAbo&B-187
❑ 96SumArtP-187
❑ 96SumFoi-187
❑ 96Top-345
❑ 96TopChr-137
❑ 96TopChrR-137
❑ 96TopGal-141
❑ 96TopGalPPI-141
❑ 96TopLasBS-7
❑ 96Ult-336
❑ 96UltGolM-336
❑ 96UppDec-231
❑ 96UppDecFSP-FS18
❑ 96UppDecPHE-H29
❑ 96UppDecPreH-H29
❑ 96WhiSoxF-14
❑ 96Zen-128
❑ 96ZenArtP-128
❑ 97BowBes-141
❑ 97BowBesAR-141
❑ 97BowBesR-141
❑ 97ColCho-77
❑ 97ColChoT-CW8
❑ 97Don-346
❑ 97DonGolPP-346
❑ 97DonLim-31
❑ 97DonLimE-31
❑ 97DonLimENG-31
❑ 97DonPre-141
❑ 97DonPreCttC-141
❑ 97DonSilPP-346
❑ 97DonTea-72
❑ 97DonTeaSPE-72
❑ 97Fin-142
❑ 97FinEmb-142
❑ 97FinEmbR-142
❑ 97FinRef-142
❑ 97FlaShoLC-72
❑ 97FlaShoLeg0-72
❑ 97FlaShoLeg1-72
❑ 97FlaShoM-A72
❑ 97FlaShoM-B72
❑ 97FlaShoM-C72
❑ 97FlaShoR0-72
❑ 97FlaShoR1-72
❑ 97FlaShoR2-72
❑ 97Fle-69
❑ 97FleTif-69
❑ 97NewPin-19
❑ 97NewPinAP-19
❑ 97NewPinMC-19
❑ 97NewPinPP-19
❑ 97Sco-419
❑ 97ScoArtPWB-419
❑ 97ScoResC-419
❑ 97ScoShoS-419
❑ 97ScoShoSAP-419
❑ 97StaClu-109
❑ 97StaCluM-M34
❑ 97StaCluMOP-109
❑ 97StaCluMOP-M34
❑ 97Top-137
❑ 97UppDec-42
❑ 97WhiSoxTI-27
❑ 98ColCho-341
❑ 98PacOnl-181
❑ 98PacOnlR-181
❑ 98PacOnlWC-181
❑ 98Sco-189
❑ 98UppDec-62
❑ 98WhiSoxS-13
❑ 98WhiSoxSP-13

Snover, Colonel L.
❑ 22E120-207

Snover, Dan
❑ 87HawRai-10
❑ 89PulBraP-1896
❑ 90DurBulUTI-6

Snow, Casey
❑ 96GreFalDB-25
❑ 96GreFalDTI-19
❑ 97SanBerS-18
❑ 98SanBerS-27
❑ 98SanBerSTIS-24

Snow, Felton
❑ 91PomBlaBPB-2

Snow, J.T.
❑ 87AriWilP-13
❑ 88AriWilP-12
❑ 88CapCodPPaLP-125
❑ 89OneYanP-2112
❑ 90CarLeaA-17
❑ 90PriWilCTI-25
❑ 90TopMag-106
❑ 91AlbYanLD-18
❑ 91AlbYanP-1017
❑ 91Cla/Bes-279
❑ 91LinDriAA-18
❑ 92ColCliF-362
❑ 92ColCliP-20
❑ 92ColCliS-117
❑ 92ProFS7-114
❑ 92SkyAAAF-56
❑ 93AngAdoF-4
❑ 93AngMot-4
❑ 93AngPol-10
❑ 93AngStaCl-1
❑ 93Bow-173
❑ 93Bow-340
❑ 93DiaMar-101
❑ 93Don-110
❑ 93Fin-156
❑ 93FinRef-156
❑ 93Fla-179
❑ 93FleFinE-190
❑ 93FleMajLP-A7
❑ 93FunPac-8
❑ 93Lea-500
❑ 93LeaGolR-R17
❑ 93LeaGolRJ-R17
❑ 93OPCPre-70
❑ 93PacJugC-16
❑ 93PacSpa-372
❑ 93Pin-609
❑ 93PinHomRC-27
❑ 93PinRooTP-4
❑ 93Sco-260
❑ 93Sel-385
❑ 93SelRoo-44T
❑ 93SP-26
❑ 93StaClu-719
❑ 93StaCluFDI-719
❑ 93StaCluMOP-719
❑ 93StaCluMP-29
❑ 93Stu-58
❑ 93StuHer-11
❑ 93StuSil-6
❑ 93Top-422
❑ 93TopGol-422
❑ 93TopInaM-422
❑ 93TopInaR-422
❑ 93TopMic-422
❑ 93TopTra-62T
❑ 93TriPlaG-GS8
❑ 93Ult-525
❑ 93UltAllR-9
❑ 93UltPer-9
❑ 93UppDec-23
❑ 93UppDec-785
❑ 93UppDecDG-35
❑ 93UppDecGold-23
❑ 93UppDecGold-785
❑ 94ActPac-42
❑ 94AngMot-3
❑ 94Bow-11
❑ 94Don-283
❑ 94Fin-157
❑ 94FinPre-157P
❑ 94FinRef-157
❑ 94Fla-274
❑ 94Fle-70
❑ 94FleRooS-19
❑ 94FUnPac-106
❑ 94OPC-55
❑ 94OPCDiaD-9
❑ 94Pac-89
❑ 94PanSti-43
❑ 94Pin-68
❑ 94PinArtP-68
❑ 94PinMusC-68
❑ 94PinNewG-NG9
❑ 94PinPowS-PS5
❑ 94Sco-511
❑ 94ScoGolR-511
❑ 94SigRooDP-99
❑ 94SigRooDPS-99
❑ 94Spo-121
❑ 94SpoSha-SH10
❑ 94StaClu-181
❑ 94StaClu-447
❑ 94StaCluFDI-181
❑ 94StaCluFDI-447
❑ 94StaCluGR-181
❑ 94StaCluGR-447
❑ 94StaCluMO-49
❑ 94StaCluMOP-181
❑ 94StaCluMOP-447
❑ 94Top-293
❑ 94TopGol-293
❑ 94TopSpa-293
❑ 94TriPla-20
❑ 94Ult-28
❑ 94USPlaCR-10C
❑ 94VanCanF-1872
❑ 95AngCHP-13
❑ 95AngMot-3
❑ 95AngTeal-3
❑ 95ColCho-92
❑ 95ColChoGS-92
❑ 95ColChoSS-92
❑ 95Don-139
❑ 95DonPreP-139
❑ 95DonTopotO-44
❑ 95Emo-23
❑ 95Fla-22
❑ 95Fle-236
❑ 95Lea-223
❑ 95LeaLim-57
❑ 95LinVen-107
❑ 95Pac-65
❑ 95Pin-215
❑ 95PinArtP-215
❑ 95PinMusC-215
❑ 95Sco-164
❑ 95ScoGolR-164
❑ 95ScoPlaTS-164
❑ 95SelCer-71
❑ 95SelCerMG-71
❑ 95SP-131

❑ 95SPCha-134
❑ 95SPChaDC-134
❑ 95SPSil-131
❑ 95StaClu-482
❑ 95StaCluMOP-482
❑ 95StaCluSTWS-482
❑ 95StaCluVR-263
❑ 95StaCluVRMO-263
❑ 95Top-582
❑ 95TopCyb-355
❑ 95Ult-24
❑ 95UltGolM-24
❑ 95UppDec-272
❑ 95UppDecED-272
❑ 95UppDecEDG-272
❑ 95UppDecSE-262
❑ 95UppDecSEG-262
❑ 95Zen-41
❑ 96AngMot-8
❑ 96Baz-2
❑ 96Bow-16
❑ 96BowFoi-16
❑ 96Cir-23
❑ 96CirRav-23
❑ 96ColCho-489
❑ 96ColChoGS-489
❑ 96ColChoSS-489
❑ 96Don-507
❑ 96DonPreP-507
❑ 96EmoXL-32
❑ 96Fin-B144
❑ 96FinRef-B144
❑ 96Fla-43
❑ 96Fle-59
❑ 96FleTif-59
❑ 96Lea-149
❑ 96LeaLim-89
❑ 96LeaLimG-89
❑ 96LeaPre-99
❑ 96LeaPreP-99
❑ 96LeaPrePB-149
❑ 96LeaPrePG-149
❑ 96LeaPrePS-149
❑ 96LeaPreSG-31
❑ 96LeaPreSte-31
❑ 96LeaSig-66
❑ 96LeaSigPPG-66
❑ 96LeaSigPPP-66
❑ 96MetUni-34
❑ 96MetUniP-34
❑ 96Pac-265
❑ 96PanSti-210
❑ 96Pin-249
❑ 96PinAfi-147
❑ 96PinAfiAP-147
❑ 96PinArtP-149
❑ 96PinFoil-249
❑ 96PinSta-149
❑ 96ProSta-3
❑ 96Sco-23
❑ 96ScoDugC-A22
❑ 96ScoDugCAP-A22
❑ 96ScoNumG-27
❑ 96ScoRef-5
❑ 96Sel-71
❑ 96SelArtP-71
❑ 96SelCer-19
❑ 96SelCerAP-19
❑ 96SelCerCB-19
❑ 96SelCerCR-19
❑ 96SelCerMB-19
❑ 96SelCerMG-19
❑ 96SelCerMR-19
❑ 96SP-49
❑ 96Spo-34
❑ 96SpoArtP-34
❑ 96StaClu-128
❑ 96StaCluEPB-128
❑ 96StaCluEPG-128
❑ 96StaCluEPS-128
❑ 96StaCluMOP-128
❑ 96Stu-24
❑ 96StuPrePB-24
❑ 96StuPrePG-24
❑ 96StuPrePS-24
❑ 96Sum-75
❑ 96SumAbo&B-75
❑ 96SumArtP-75
❑ 96SumFoi-75
❑ 96Top-59
❑ 96TopChr-21
❑ 96TopChrR-21
❑ 96TopGal-41
❑ 96TopGalE-2
❑ 96TopGalPPI-41
❑ 96TopLas-29
❑ 96Ult-327
❑ 96UltGolM-327
❑ 96UppDec-26
❑ 96Zen-97
❑ 96ZenArtP-97
❑ 97Cir-85
❑ 97CirRav-85
❑ 97ColChoU-U25
❑ 97Don-42
❑ 97Don-275
❑ 97DonEli-89
❑ 97DonEliGS-89
❑ 97DonGolPP-42
❑ 97DonGolPP-275
❑ 97DonLim-29
❑ 97DonLimE-29
❑ 97DonLimENG-29
❑ 97DonSigA-90
❑ 97DonSigAC-113
❑ 97DonSigAM-113
❑ 97DonSilPP-42
❑ 97DonSilPP-275
❑ 97E-X2-96
❑ 97E-X2Cred-96
❑ 97E-X2EssCre-96
❑ 97Fin-237
❑ 97FinRef-237
❑ 97FlaShoLC-153
❑ 97FlaShoLeg0-153
❑ 97FlaShoLeg1-153
❑ 97FlaShoM-A153
❑ 97FlaShoM-B153
❑ 97FlaShoM-C153
❑ 97FlaShoR0-153
❑ 97FlaShoR1-153
❑ 97FlaShoR2-153
❑ 97Fle-52
❑ 97Fle-537
❑ 97FleTif-52
❑ 97FleTif-537
❑ 97Lea-244
❑ 97LeaFraM-244
❑ 97LeaFraMDC-244
❑ 97MetUni-247
❑ 97NewPin-133
❑ 97NewPinAP-133
❑ 97NewPinMC-133
❑ 97NewPinPP-133
❑ 97Pac-14
❑ 97PacLigB-14
❑ 97PacPri-6
❑ 97PacPriLB-6
❑ 97PacPriP-6
❑ 97PacSil-14
❑ 97PinCer-75
❑ 97PinCerMBla-75
❑ 97PinCerMBlu-75
❑ 97PinCerMG-75
❑ 97PinCerMR-75
❑ 97PinCerR-75
❑ 97PinIns-119
❑ 97PinInsCE-119
❑ 97PinInsDE-119
❑ 97PinTotCPB-75
❑ 97PinTotCPG-75
❑ 97PinTotCPR-75
❑ 97Sco-304
❑ 97Sco-365
❑ 97ScoArtPWB-304
❑ 97ScoArtPWB-365
❑ 97ScoPreS-304
❑ 97ScoResC-365
❑ 97ScoShoS-304
❑ 97ScoShoS-365
❑ 97ScoShoSAP-304
❑ 97ScoShoSAP-365
❑ 97SP-159
❑ 97SpoIll-122
❑ 97SpoIllEE-122
❑ 97StaClu-238
❑ 97StaCluMat-238
❑ 97StaCluMOP-238
❑ 97Top-263
❑ 97Ult-359
❑ 97UltGolME-359
❑ 97UltPlaME-359
❑ 97UppDec-140
❑ 97UppDec-545
❑ 98Bow-288
❑ 98BowChr-288
❑ 98BowChrGA-288
❑ 98BowChrGAR-288
❑ 98BowChrI-288
❑ 98BowChrIR-288
❑ 98BowChrR-288
❑ 98BowGolA-288
❑ 98BowInt-288
❑ 98CirThu-237
❑ 98CirThuRav-237
❑ 98CirThuSupRav-237
❑ 98ColCho-234
❑ 98Don-74
❑ 98DonCol-74
❑ 98DonColL-252
❑ 98DonColP-617
❑ 98DonColS-74
❑ 98DonGolPP-74
❑ 98DonPre-67
❑ 98DonPreSeat-67
❑ 98DonPriCD-74
❑ 98DonPriCL-252
❑ 98DonPriCP-617
❑ 98DonSig-14
❑ 98DonSigA-81
❑ 98DonSigAC-103
❑ 98DonSigAM-105
❑ 98DonSigP-14
❑ 98DonSilPP-74
❑ 98Fin-53
❑ 98FinNo--53
❑ 98FinNo-R-53
❑ 98FinRef-53
❑ 98FlaShoLeg0-102
❑ 98FlaShoLeg1-102
❑ 98FlaShoLeg2-102
❑ 98FlaShoLeg3-102
❑ 98FlaShoLegM-102
❑ 98FlaShoR0-102
❑ 98FlaShoR1-102
❑ 98FlaShoR2-102
❑ 98FlaShoR3-102
❑ 98Fle-52
❑ 98GiaMot-7
❑ 98Lea-53
❑ 98LeaFraDA-53
❑ 98LeaFraF-53
❑ 98LeaFraM-53
❑ 98LeaFraM-53
❑ 98LeaFraMDC-53
❑ 98LeaFraMDC-53
❑ 98LeaFraMS-53
❑ 98LeaFraMZ2-53
❑ 98LeaRS-66
❑ 98LeaRSLHolo-66
❑ 98LeaRSLong-66
❑ 98LeaRTrue-66
❑ 98MetUni-198
❑ 98MetUniPMG-198
❑ 98Pac-448
❑ 98PacAur-200
❑ 98PacInv-146
❑ 98PacInvPBlue-146
❑ 98PacInvSilv-146
❑ 98PacInvTeam-25
❑ 98PacOme-216
❑ 98PacOmeR-216
❑ 98PacOnl-674
❑ 98PacOnlR-674
❑ 98PacOnlWC-674
❑ 98PacPar-250
❑ 98PacParC-250
❑ 98PacParG-250
❑ 98PacParHS-250
❑ 98PacParPB-250
❑ 98PacParR-250
❑ 98PacPlaB-448
❑ 98PacRedT-448
❑ 98PacSil-448
❑ 98PacTeaC-28
❑ 98Pin-99
❑ 98PinPer-68
❑ 98PinPerPP-68
❑ 98PinPlu-76
❑ 98PinPreP-99
❑ 98Sco-143
❑ 98ScoRT-75
❑ 98ScoRTSS-PP59
❑ 98ScoRTSSAP-PP59
❑ 98ScoRTSSAP1-PP59
❑ 98ScoSS-PP60
❑ 98ScoSSAP-PP60
❑ 98SkyDugA-47
❑ 98SkyDugAIA-47
❑ 98SP Aut-172
❑ 98SpoIll-114
❑ 98SpoIll-135
❑ 98SpoIllEE-114
❑ 98SpoIllEE-135
❑ 98SpoIllFE-114
❑ 98SpoIllFE-135
❑ 98SpoIllWSF-130
❑ 98SpoIllWSFEE-130
❑ 98SpoIllWSFFE-130
❑ 98SPxFin-128
❑ 98SPxFinR-128
❑ 98SPxFinS-128
❑ 98StaCluFDI-266
❑ 98StaCluI-266
❑ 98StaCluOneK-266
❑ 98StaCluPP-266
❑ 98Stu-45
❑ 98StuGPP-45
❑ 98StuSPP-45
❑ 98Top-151
❑ 98TopChr-151
❑ 98TopChrR-151
❑ 98TopDevR-151
❑ 98TopDia-151
❑ 98TopGal-72
❑ 98TopGalGP-72
❑ 98TopGalOPP-72
❑ 98TopGalPPI-72
❑ 98TopGalPPIA-72
❑ 98TopMiniC-151
❑ 98TopOpeD-79
❑ 98TopSta-103
❑ 98TopStaB-103
❑ 98TopStaG-103
❑ 98TopStaGR-103
❑ 98TopStaS-103
❑ 98Ult-130
❑ 98UltGolM-130
❑ 98UltMas-130
❑ 98UltPlaM-130
❑ 98UppDec-216
❑ 98UppDec-364
❑ 98UppDecRGKoG-G29
❑ 98UppDecSF-120
❑ 99199Fin-19
❑ 99CroRoyB-126
❑ 99CroRoyL-126
❑ 99CroRoyOD-126
❑ 99FinGolRef-19
❑ 99FinRef-19
❑ 99Fle-293
❑ 99FleSta9-293
❑ 99FleWarT-293
❑ 99MetUni-125
❑ 99MetUniGM-125
❑ 99MetUniPMG-125
❑ 99Pac-390
❑ 99PacAur-173
❑ 99PacAurOD-173
❑ 99PacCroC-258
❑ 99PacCroCPB-258
❑ 99PacInv-130
❑ 99PacInvOD-130
❑ 99PacInvPB-130
❑ 99PacOme-215
❑ 99PacOmeC-215
❑ 99PacOmeG-215
❑ 99PacOmePB-215
❑ 99PacPar-213
❑ 99PacParC-213
❑ 99PacParG-213
❑ 99PacParHoloGold-213
❑ 99PacParHS-213
❑ 99PacParOD-213
❑ 99PacParPB-213
❑ 99PacParRed-213
❑ 99PacPlaB-390
❑ 99PacPri-131
❑ 99PacPriHB-131
❑ 99PacPriHG-131
❑ 99PacPriHM-131
❑ 99PacPriHP-131
❑ 99PacPriRed-131
❑ 99PacRed-390
❑ 99SkyMolM-48
❑ 99SkyMolMX-48
❑ 99SkyPre-115
❑ 99SkyPreR-115
❑ 99SkyThu-65
❑ 99SkyThuRant-65
❑ 99SkyThuRave-65
❑ 99SP SigAuto-JT
❑ 99SPSig-141
❑ 99SPx-68
❑ 99SPxFinR-68
❑ 99SPxFinS-68
❑ 99StaClu-81
❑ 99StaCluFDI-81
❑ 99StaCluOoaK-81
❑ 99StaCluPP-81
❑ 99ThuSkySupR-65
❑ 99Top-127
❑ 99TopChr-127
❑ 99TopChrR-127
❑ 99TopMVPP-127
❑ 99TopOpeD-74
❑ 99Ult-167
❑ 99UltGolM-167
❑ 99UltMas-167
❑ 99UltPlaM-167
❑ 99UppDec-201
❑ 99UppDecBD-74
❑ 99UppDecBDD-74
❑ 99UppDecBDQ-74
❑ 99UppDecBDT-74
❑ 99UppDecEL1-201
❑ 99UppDecEL2-201
❑ 99UppDecM-186
❑ 99UppDecMGS-186
❑ 99UppDecMHFS-186
❑ 99UppDecMSS-186
❑ 99Vic-358

Snow, Robert
❑ 98SouOreTG-30

Snuder, Kendall
❑ 87KenTwiP-4

Snusz, Chris
❑ 95BatCliTI-32
❑ 97ClePhi-19
❑ 98ClePhiM-21
❑ 98ClePhiUM-21

Snyder, Ben
❑ 82DayBeaAT-8
❑ 83ColAstT-19

Snyder, Bill
❑ 98WesMicWM-24

Snyder, Brett
❑ 90BelBreB-11
❑ 90BelBreS-20
❑ 90Bes-145

Snyder, Brian
❑ 80SanJosMJitB-16
❑ 81WauTimT-7
❑ 82SalLakCGT-17
❑ 83SalLakCGT-4
❑ 84SalLakCGC-178
❑ 84ShrCapFB-19
❑ 85CalCanC-92
❑ 86LasVegSP-18
❑ 86Top-174
❑ 86TopTif-174
❑ 87LasVegSP-15
❑ 88TacTigC-9
❑ 88TacTigP-629
❑ 89TacTigC-4
❑ 89TacTigP-1545
❑ 90CMC-301
❑ 90ProAAAF-405
❑ 90RicBraBC-4
❑ 90RicBraC-25
❑ 90RicBraP-260
❑ 90RicBraTI-28

Snyder, Chris
❑ 88CapCodPPaLP-9
❑ 90PriPatD-20

Snyder, Cory
❑ 85Top-403
❑ 85TopTif-403
❑ 85WatIndT-23
❑ 86Don-29
❑ 86DonRoo-15
❑ 86Fle-653
❑ 86IndTeal-42
❑ 86MaiGuiP-20
❑ 86SpoRoo-18
❑ 87ClaUpdY-110
❑ 87Don-526
❑ 87DonOpeD-106
❑ 87Fle-260
❑ 87FleExcS-40
❑ 87FleGlo-260
❑ 87FleHotS-39
❑ 87FleMin-103
❑ 87FleSluBC-M5
❑ 87FleStiC-113
❑ 87IndGat-28
❑ 87KraFoo-17
❑ 87Lea-157
❑ 87OPC-192
❑ 87Spo-24A
❑ 87Spo-24B
❑ 87Spo-24C
❑ 87SpoSupD-10
❑ 87SpoTeaP-3
❑ 87Top-192
❑ 87TopCoi-24
❑ 87TopGloS-9
❑ 87TopRoo-16
❑ 87TopSti-213
❑ 87TopTif-192
❑ 87ToyRoo-25
❑ 88ClaRed-184
❑ 88Don-350
❑ 88DonBasB-224
❑ 88Fle-615
❑ 88Fle-622
❑ 88FleGlo-615
❑ 88FleGlo-622
❑ 88FleStiC-21
❑ 88FleSup-37
❑ 88IndGat-28
❑ 88IndTeal-32
❑ 88KinDis-10
❑ 88Lea-125
❑ 88OPC-169
❑ 88PanSti-80
❑ 88RedFolSB-83
❑ 88Sco-92
❑ 88ScoGlo-92
❑ 88ScoYouSI-40
❑ 88Spo-29
❑ 88StaLinI-18
❑ 88StaSny-1
❑ 88StaSny-2
❑ 88StaSny-3
❑ 88StaSny-4
❑ 88StaSny-5
❑ 88StaSny-6
❑ 88StaSny-7
❑ 88StaSny-8
❑ 88StaSny-9
❑ 88StaSny-10
❑ 88StaSny-11
❑ 88StaStiS-1
❑ 88StaStiS-2
❑ 88StaStiS-3
❑ 88StaStiS-4
❑ 88StaStiS-5
❑ 88StaStiS-6
❑ 88StaStiS-7
❑ 88StaStiS-8
❑ 88TarPla-42
❑ 88Top-620
❑ 88Top-789
❑ 88TopBig-43
❑ 88TopCoi-27
❑ 88TopGloS-23
❑ 88TopSti-208
❑ 88TopStiB-53
❑ 88TopTif-620
❑ 88TopUKM-74
❑ 88TopUKMT-74
❑ 89Bow-89
❑ 89BowTif-89
❑ 89ClaLigB-19
❑ 89Don-8
❑ 89Don-191
❑ 89DonBasB-168
❑ 89DonSupD-8
❑ 89Fle-412
❑ 89FleGlo-412
❑ 89FleSup-38
❑ 89IndTeal-25
❑ 89OPC-80
❑ 89PanSti-329
❑ 89Sco-52
❑ 89ScoHot1S-6
❑ 89Spo-196
❑ 89Top-80
❑ 89TopBasT-124
❑ 89TopBig-175
❑ 89TopSti-210
❑ 89TopTif-80
❑ 89TopUKM-73
❑ 89TVSpoM-87
❑ 89UppDec-170
❑ 89UppDec-679
❑ 90Bow-336
❑ 90BowTif-336
❑ 90Don-272
❑ 90DonBesA-47
❑ 90Fle-502
❑ 90FleCan-502
❑ 90GooHumICBLS-24
❑ 90IndTeal-39
❑ 90KinDis-12
❑ 90Lea-187
❑ 90M.Vpin-33
❑ 90OPC-770
❑ 90PanSti-56
❑ 90PubIntS-568
❑ 90RedFolSB-91
❑ 90Sco-10
❑ 90Sco100S-28
❑ 90Spo-3
❑ 90SupActM-8

❑ 90Top-770
❑ 90TopBig-221
❑ 90TopSti-211
❑ 90TopTif-770
❑ 90UppDec-126
❑ 91Bow-357
❑ 91Cla2-T8
❑ 91ClaGam-188
❑ 91Don-288
❑ 91Fle-378
❑ 91Lea-506
❑ 91OPC-323
❑ 91OPCPre-113
❑ 91PanFreS-221
❑ 91RedFolS-88
❑ 91Sco-19
❑ 91Sco-695
❑ 91Sco100S-74
❑ 91ScoRoo-61T
❑ 91StaClu-488
❑ 91Top-323
❑ 91TopDesS-323
❑ 91TopMic-323
❑ 91TopTif-323
❑ 91TopTra-111T
❑ 91TopTraT-111T
❑ 91Ult-83
❑ 91UppDec-123
❑ 91UppDec-724
❑ 91WhiSoxK-28
❑ 92Bow-492
❑ 92DonUpd-U21
❑ 92FleUpd-130
❑ 92GiaMot-19
❑ 92GiaPacGaE-31
❑ 92Lea-188
❑ 92LeaBlaG-188
❑ 92Pin-506
❑ 92Sco-598
❑ 92ScoRoo-48T
❑ 92StaClu-772
❑ 92StaCluECN-772
❑ 92TopTra-107T
❑ 92TopTraG-107T
❑ 92Ult-595
❑ 92UppDec-504
❑ 93DodMot-20
❑ 93DodPol-24
❑ 93DodStaC-29
❑ 93Don-656
❑ 93Fle-160
❑ 93FleFinE-84
❑ 93Lea-436
❑ 93OPC-250
❑ 93PanSti-242
❑ 93Pin-529
❑ 93Sco-574
❑ 93Sel-71
❑ 93SelRoo-111T
❑ 93Top-254
❑ 93TopGol-254
❑ 93TopInaM-254
❑ 93TopInaR-254
❑ 93TopMic-254
❑ 93Ult-405
❑ 93UppDec-218
❑ 93UppDec-791
❑ 93UppDecGold-218
❑ 93UppDecGold-791
❑ 94ColC-261
❑ 94ColChoGS-261
❑ 94ColChoSS-261
❑ 94DodDaiN-12
❑ 94DodMot-20
❑ 94DodPol-24
❑ 94Don-535
❑ 94Fla-183
❑ 94Fle-524
❑ 94FleExtB-296
❑ 94Pac-321
❑ 94PanSti-204
❑ 94Pin-466
❑ 94PinArtP-466
❑ 94PinMusC-466
❑ 94Sco-80
❑ 94ScoGolR-80
❑ 94Sel-170
❑ 94StaClu-463
❑ 94StaCluFDI-463
❑ 94StaCluGR-463
❑ 94StaCluMOP-463
❑ 94Top-683
❑ 94TopGol-683
❑ 94TopSpa-683
❑ 94Ult-219
❑ 94UppDec-266
❑ 94UppDecED-266
❑ 95Sco-487
❑ 95ScoGolR-487
❑ 95ScoPlaTS-487

Snyder, Doug
❑ 86OscAstP-24
❑ 87OscAstP-9
❑ 88VisOakCLC-158
❑ 88VisOakP-100
❑ 89OrlTwiB-25
❑ 89OrlTwiP-1327

Snyder, Earl
❑ 98PitMetM-30

Snyder, Gene W.
❑ 59Top-522
❑ 90DodTar-1076

Snyder, Gerald
❑ 52Bow-246
❑ 54Bow-216
❑ 55Bow-74
❑ 57Top-22

Snyder, Jared
❑ 93GenCubC-24
❑ 93GenCubF-3178
❑ 96DayCubB-21

Snyder, Jim
❑ 76IndIndTI-1
❑ 77FriOneYW-102
❑ 81OklCit8T-23
❑ 87CubCan-30
❑ 87CubDavB-NNO
❑ 88TopTra-112T
❑ 88TopTraT-112T
❑ 89Top-44
❑ 89TopTif-44
❑ 91PadSmo-34
❑ 92PadMot-27
❑ 92PadPolD-28
❑ 92PadSmo-32
❑ 93RicBraF-204
❑ 93RicBraRC-4

Snyder, John
❑ 94LakElsSC-20
❑ 94LakElsSF-1664
❑ 95MidAngOHP-32
❑ 95MidAngTI-27
❑ 96BirBarB-17

Snyder, Kyle
❑ 99Bow-433
❑ 99BowGol-433
❑ 99BowInt-433

Snyder, Matt
❑ 96HigDesMB-26
❑ 96MauStiHWB-19
❑ 97Bow-404
❑ 97BowBay-28
❑ 97BowChr-267
❑ 97BowChrI-267
❑ 97BowChrIR-267
❑ 97BowChrR-267
❑ 97BowInt-404
❑ 97TexAllM-28
❑ 98BowBayM-28

Snyder, Mike
❑ 97JohCitCTI-31
❑ 98JohCCTI-31

Snyder, Pancho (Frank)
❑ 20GasAmeMBD-35
❑ 20NatCarE-98A
❑ 20NatCarE-98B
❑ 21E121So1-100
❑ 21E121So8-93
❑ 21Exh-169
❑ 21KoBreWSI-23
❑ 21Nei-94
❑ 22E120-193
❑ 22W575-129
❑ 22WilPatV-33
❑ 23W501-66
❑ 23W503-7
❑ 23W515-44
❑ 25Exh-38
❑ 26Exh-35
❑ 40PlaBal-159
❑ 91ConTSN-232
❑ 93ConTSN-870

Snyder, Randy
❑ 89StoPorB-17
❑ 89StoPorCLC-170
❑ 89StoPorP-382
❑ 89StoPorS-16
❑ 90BelBreB-13
❑ 90BelBreS-21
❑ 90Bes-215
❑ 90MidLeaASGS-18
❑ 91StoPorC-14
❑ 91StoPorP-3035
❑ 92SalLakTSP-14
❑ 93HigDesMC-19
❑ 93HigDesMF-46
❑ 95SalAvaTI-1

Snyder, Robert
❑ 17Zee-117

Snyder, Russ
❑ 60A'sTeal-15
❑ 60Lea-102
❑ 60Top-81
❑ 60TopVen-81
❑ 61BalOriP-17
❑ 61SevElev-7
❑ 61Top-143
❑ 62BalOriP-26
❑ 62SalPlaC-206
❑ 62ShiPlaC-206
❑ 62Top-64
❑ 62TopVen-64
❑ 63BalOriP-31
❑ 63Jel-63
❑ 63Pos-63
❑ 63Top-543
❑ 64BalOriP-34
❑ 64Top-126
❑ 64TopVen-126
❑ 65BalOriP-31
❑ 65OPC-204
❑ 65Top-204
❑ 66BalOriP-32
❑ 66Top-562
❑ 67BalOriP-99
❑ 67CokCapO-6
❑ 67DexPre-195
❑ 67Top-405
❑ 68Top-504
❑ 69MilBra-258
❑ 69OPC-201
❑ 69Top-201
❑ 69TopFou-13
❑ 69TopTeaP-13
❑ 70BreMcD-28
❑ 70BreMil-23
❑ 70OPC-347
❑ 70Top-347
❑ 71MLBOffS-452
❑ 71OPC-653
❑ 71Top-653
❑ 72MilBra-320
❑ 78TCM60I-136
❑ 81Ori6F-30
❑ 91OriCro-431
❑ 94BreMilB-274

Soar, Hank
❑ 55Bow-279

Soares, Todd
❑ 88JacExpP-978
❑ 91KisDodP-4196

Sobbe, William
❑ 81VerBeaDT-19

Sobczyk, Bob
❑ 88BelBreGS-11
❑ 89BoiHawP-1993

Sobik, Trad
❑ 94BriTigC-24
❑ 94BriTigF-3502
❑ 95FayGenTI-25
❑ 96LakTigB-27

Sobkoviak, Jeff
❑ 93BenRocCB-25
❑ 93BenRocF-3269
❑ 94AshTouC-20
❑ 94AshTouF-1779
❑ 95SalAvaTI-3
❑ 97HigDesMG-23

Sobkowiak, Scott
❑ 98EugEme-26

Sobocienski, Adam
❑ 92Min-19

Sobolewski, Mark
❑ 92SouOreAC-5
❑ 92SouOreAF-3428
❑ 93ModA'sC-19
❑ 93ModA'sF-810
❑ 94HunStaF-1339
❑ 95HunStaTI-25

Socko, Mascot
❑ 96SarRedSB-30

Sodders, Mike
❑ 82TolMudHT-18
❑ 83OrlTwiT-9
❑ 88GenCubP-1642
❑ 89PeoChiTI-10
❑ 91ChaKniLD-142
❑ 91ChaKniP-1688
❑ 91LinDriAA-142
❑ 92ChaKniF-2770
❑ 92ChaKniS-165

Sodders, Randy
❑ 89WytCubS-24

Soden, Chad
❑ 95EveAqaTI-24
❑ 96WisTimRB-24

Soderholm, Dale
❑ 74TacTwiC-2
❑ 76TacTwiDQ-19
❑ 77OrlTwiT-19

Soderholm, Eric
❑ 72TwiPos-21
❑ 72TwiTeal-16
❑ 73OPC-577
❑ 73TacTwiC-19
❑ 73Top-577
❑ 74OPC-503
❑ 74Top-503
❑ 75OPC-54
❑ 75Top-54
❑ 75TopMin-54
❑ 75TwiPos-22
❑ 75TwiTeal-24
❑ 76Kel-28
❑ 76OPC-214
❑ 76SSP-223
❑ 76Top-214
❑ 77Top-273
❑ 77WhiSoxJT-12
❑ 77WhiSoxT-22
❑ 78Hos-20
❑ 78Kel-32
❑ 78OPC-21
❑ 78SSP270-148
❑ 78Top-602
❑ 79Hos-103
❑ 79OPC-93
❑ 79Top-186
❑ 80Top-441
❑ 80YanPhoA-21
❑ 81Don-106
❑ 81Fle-92
❑ 81Top-383
❑ 90SweBasG-98
❑ 91LinDri-6
❑ 91SweBasG-85
❑ 92YanWIZ8-184
❑ 93RanKee-336

Soderstrom, Steve
❑ 91FreStaBS-12
❑ 94Cla-165
❑ 94ClaGolF-161
❑ 94ClaGolN1PLF-LP14
❑ 94ClaGolREF-RE14
❑ 94ColC-24
❑ 94ColChoGS-24
❑ 94ColChoSS-24
❑ 94SanJosGC-1
❑ 94SanJosGF-2816
❑ 94Ult-594
❑ 94UppDec-533
❑ 94UppDecED-533
❑ 94UppDecML-189
❑ 95SPML-147
❑ 96BesAutS-86
❑ 96Bow-155
❑ 96BowFoi-155
❑ 96PhoFirB-24
❑ 97Bow-357
❑ 97BowInt-357
❑ 97PhoFirTI-23
❑ 97UppDec-288
❑ 98FreGriG-28

Sodowsky, Clint
❑ 92BriTigC-11
❑ 92BriTigF-1412
❑ 93FayGenC-22
❑ 93FayGenF-129
❑ 94FloStaLAF-FSL15
❑ 94LakTigC-21
❑ 94LakTigF-3036
❑ 95JacSunTI-26
❑ 96Fle-120
❑ 96FleTif-120
❑ 96TolMudHB-27
❑ 96Top-429
❑ 97PirPos-36
❑ 98DiaBacP-10
❑ 98DiaMcD-19
❑ 98PacOnl-45
❑ 98PacOnlR-45
❑ 98PacOnlWC-45

Soff, Ray
❑ 80QuaCitCT-7
❑ 81QuaCitCT-23
❑ 83MidCubT-22
❑ 84MidCubT-9
❑ 86ArkTraP-23
❑ 86LouRedTI-26
❑ 87CarSmo-1
❑ 87Don-631
❑ 87Fle-309
❑ 87FleGlo-309
❑ 87LouRedTI-27
❑ 87OPC-96
❑ 87Top-671A
❑ 87Top-671B
❑ 87TopTif-671A
❑ 87TopTif-671B
❑ 88PorBeaC-7
❑ 88PorBeaP-662
❑ 89PorBeaC-5
❑ 89PorBeaP-216
❑ 90CMC-361
❑ 90ProAAAF-275
❑ 90TidTidC-10
❑ 90TidTidP-544
❑ 90TopTVM-61
❑ 91LinDriAAA-568
❑ 91TidTidLD-568
❑ 91TidTidP-2509
❑ 92EdmTraS-166

Sofield, Rick
❑ 77VisOakT-14
❑ 79Top-709
❑ 80Top-669
❑ 80TwiPos-28
❑ 80VenLeaS-32
❑ 81Don-592
❑ 81Fle-563
❑ 81OPC-278
❑ 81Top-278
❑ 81TwiPos-26
❑ 82TolMudHT-21
❑ 82Top-42
❑ 96WesPalBEB-2
❑ 97HarSen-25

Softy, Mark
❑ 77ForLauYS-11
❑ 79WesHavYT-16
❑ 80WauTimT-9

Soh, Katsuo
❑ 87JapPlaB-20

Sohn, Young Chul
❑ 91KisDodP-4184

Sohns, Thomas
❑ 79NaSouTI-23
❑ 80WatRedT-16

Sojo, Luis
❑ 87MyrBeaBJP-1463
❑ 88MyrBeaBJP-1189
❑ 88SouAtlLAGS-18
❑ 89SyrChiC-22
❑ 89SyrChiMB-21
❑ 89SyrChiP-809
❑ 90Bow-517
❑ 90BowTif-517
❑ 90CMC-344
❑ 90FleUpd-129
❑ 90Lea-291
❑ 90OPC-594
❑ 90ProAAAF-360
❑ 90SyrChiC-18
❑ 90SyrChiMB-23
❑ 90SyrChiP-580
❑ 90Top-594
❑ 90TopTif-594
❑ 90TriAllGP-AAA3
❑ 91AngSmo-15
❑ 91Bow-197
❑ 91Don-579
❑ 91Fle-184
❑ 91Lea-367
❑ 91OPC-26
❑ 91OPCPre-114
❑ 91Sco-342
❑ 91Sco100RS-43
❑ 91ScoRoo-49T
❑ 91StaClu-507
❑ 91Top-26
❑ 91TopDeb90-146
❑ 91TopDesS-26
❑ 91TopMic-26
❑ 91TopTif-26
❑ 91TopTra-112T
❑ 91TopTraT-112T
❑ 91UltUpd-12
❑ 91UppDec-297
❑ 91UppDec-714
❑ 92Bow-418
❑ 92Don-302
❑ 92EdmTraS-167
❑ 92Fle-70
❑ 92Lea-5
❑ 92LeaBlaG-5
❑ 92OPC-206
❑ 92PanSti-6
❑ 92Pin-223
❑ 92Sco-127
❑ 92StaClu-373
❑ 92Top-206
❑ 92TopGol-206
❑ 92TopGolW-206
❑ 92TopMic-206
❑ 92Ult-31
❑ 92UppDec-149
❑ 93BluJayD-24
❑ 93BluJayFS-25
❑ 93Don-137
❑ 93Fle-198
❑ 93LinVenB-100
❑ 93OPC-338
❑ 93PacSpa-655
❑ 93PanSti-28
❑ 93Sco-124
❑ 93Sel-77
❑ 93StaClu-27
❑ 93StaCluFDI-27
❑ 93StaCluMOP-27
❑ 93Top-347
❑ 93TopGol-347
❑ 93TopInaM-347
❑ 93TopInaR-347
❑ 93TopMic-347
❑ 93UppDec-94
❑ 93UppDec-802
❑ 93UppDecGold-94
❑ 93UppDecGold-802
❑ 94CalCanF-799
❑ 94VenLinU-108
❑ 95ColCho-286
❑ 95ColChoGS-286
❑ 95ColChoSS-286
❑ 95Fle-277
❑ 95LinVen-164
❑ 95LinVen-284
❑ 95LinVen-306
❑ 95LinVen-320
❑ 95MarMot-20
❑ 95MarPac-3
❑ 95MarPac-43
❑ 95Sco-470
❑ 95ScoGolR-470
❑ 95ScoPlaTS-470
❑ 95Top-583
❑ 95TopCyb-356
❑ 96-97LinVen-38
❑ 96ColCho-728
❑ 96ColChoGS-728
❑ 96ColChoSS-728
❑ 96Don-409
❑ 96DonPreP-409
❑ 96Fle-244
❑ 96FleTif-244
❑ 96LeaSigEA-186
❑ 96MarMot-19
❑ 96Pac-411
❑ 96Sco-475
❑ 96StaClu-68
❑ 96StaCluMOP-68
❑ 96Ult-415
❑ 96UltGolM-415
❑ 96UppDec-462
❑ 98Pac-159
❑ 98PacOnl-516
❑ 98PacOnlR-516
❑ 98PacOnlWC-516
❑ 98PacPlaB-159
❑ 98PacRedT-159
❑ 98PacSil-159
❑ 98Pin-127
❑ 98PinPreP-127
❑ 98Top-196
❑ 98TopChr-196
❑ 98TopChrR-196
❑ 98TopDevR-196
❑ 98TopDia-196
❑ 98TopMiniC-196
❑ 99PacCroC-197
❑ 99PacCroCPB-197
❑ 99YanFle-25

Sokol, Trad
❑ 98HelBreM-31

Solaita, Tony
❑ 72Dia-41

❑ 74RoyPos-26
❑ 75OPC-389
❑ 75RoyPos-28
❑ 75Top-389
❑ 75TopMin-389
❑ 76KanCitRP-28
❑ 76OPC-121
❑ 76RoyAaP-14
❑ 76SSP-173
❑ 76Top-121
❑ 77Top-482
❑ 78AngFamF-35
❑ 78SSP270-215
❑ 78Top-557
❑ 79ExpPos-26
❑ 79Top-18
❑ 80OPC-212
❑ 80Top-407
❑ 92YanWIZ6-119

Solano, Angel
❑ 97HicCraB-27

Solano, Danny
❑ 98Cha-15

Solano, Fausto
❑ 94St.CatBJC-24
❑ 94St.CatBJF-3654
❑ 95DunBluJTI-27
❑ 95StCatSTI-21
❑ 96HagSunB-20
❑ 97KnoSmo-21
❑ 98KnoSG-21

Solano, Julio
❑ 83AstPos-30
❑ 83TucTorT-11
❑ 84AstPos-28
❑ 84TucTorC-63
❑ 85AstMot-12
❑ 85DomLeaS-87
❑ 85Fle-363
❑ 85Top-353
❑ 85TopTif-353
❑ 86AstPol-16
❑ 87AstPol-18
❑ 88MarMot-24
❑ 89MarMot-26

Solano, Manny
❑ 98ChaAllCM-12

Solano, Ramon
❑ 87FayGenP-6

Solarte, Jose
❑ 88JamExpP-1912
❑ 93LinVenB-95
❑ 94VenLinU-202
❑ 95LinVen-57
❑ 96-97LinVen-118

Soler, Ramon
❑ 99Bow-311
❑ 99BowGol-311
❑ 99BowInt-311

Solimine, Joe
❑ 90UtiBluSP-7
❑ 91SouBenWSP-2861

Solis, Julio
❑ 85MiaHur-16

Solis, Marcelino
❑ 59Top-214

Soliz, Steve
❑ 93WatIndC-26
❑ 93WatIndF-3566
❑ 94CarLeaAF-CAR36
❑ 94KinIndC-17
❑ 94KinIndF-2648
❑ 95BakBlaTI-26
❑ 96CanIndB-24
❑ 97BufBis-26
❑ 98BufBisG-28

Sollecito, Gabe
❑ 93NiaFalRF-3391
❑ 94FayGenC-24
❑ 94FayGenF-2147
❑ 98Cha-9
❑ 98TexLeaC-22

Sollman, Scott
❑ 97WesMicW-23
❑ 98LakTigM-23

Solo, Julio
❑ 89PacSenL-50

Solomon, Buddy (Eddie)
❑ 74AlbDukCa-71
❑ 74AlbDukTI-19
❑ 75OPC-624
❑ 75Top-624
❑ 75TopMin-624
❑ 76St.LouCP-32
❑ 78Top-598
❑ 79OPC-74
❑ 79Top-156
❑ 80Top-346
❑ 81Don-16
❑ 81Fle-384
❑ 81Top-298
❑ 82Don-437
❑ 82Fle-498
❑ 82Top-73
❑ 82Top-696
❑ 90DodTar-754

Solomon, David
❑ 94BilMusF-3670
❑ 94BilMusSP-21

Solomon, Ray
❑ 93LetMouF-4150
❑ 93LetMouSP-19

Solomon, Steve
❑ 92BatCliCB-17
❑ 92BatCliF-3279
❑ 93ClaGolF-153
❑ 94ClePhiC-25
❑ 94ClePhiF-2542
❑ 95ReaPhiELC-33
❑ 95ReaPhiTI-27

Solseth, David
❑ 89EugEmeB-12
❑ 90AppFoxBS-25
❑ 90AppFoxP-2099
❑ 91BasCitRC-16
❑ 91BasCitRP-1402

Soltero, Saul
❑ 87SpoIndP-4
❑ 88ChaRaiP-1215
❑ 89RivRedWB-16
❑ 89RivRedWCLC-31
❑ 89RivRedWP-1406
❑ 89WicStaR-23
❑ 89WicUpdR-9
❑ 92ChaRaiC-19
❑ 92ChaRaiF-120
❑ 94SprSulC-29
❑ 94SprSulF-2053
❑ 96RanCucQB-4
❑ 98StoPorG-27

Solters, Moose (Julius)
❑ 34DiaMatCSB-165
❑ 34DiaStaR-85
❑ 34Gou-30
❑ 34GouCanV-77
❑ 36GouWidPPR-B20
❑ 36GouWidPPR-C22
❑ 38GouHeaU-255
❑ 38GouHeaU-279
❑ 39PlaBal-78
❑ 39WhiSoxTI-18
❑ 40PlaBal-126
❑ 40WhiSoxL-18
❑ 41DouPlaR-71
❑ 74TCMNic-12
❑ 81ConTSN-34
❑ 85BigLeaC3-11
❑ 91ConTSN-285

Soma, Katsuya
❑ 83SanJosBC-18

Somers, Charles A.
❑ 09SpoNewSM-100

Somers, P.T.
❑ 87OldJudN-461

Sommer, David
❑ 87WytCubP-6
❑ 89JamExpP-2144
❑ 90WesPalBES-21
❑ 91LinDriAA-642
❑ 91WilBilLD-642
❑ 91WilBilP-291

Sommer, Joseph J.
❑ 87OldJudN-462

Sommers, Denny (Dennis)
❑ 75LafDriT-30
❑ 80IndTeal-26
❑ 82Ind-30
❑ 82IndBurK-10
❑ 82IndBurK-11
❑ 82IndBurK-12
❑ 82IndWhe-28
❑ 83IndPos-31
❑ 83IndWhe-25
❑ 84Ind-27
❑ 84IndWhe-NNO
❑ 85Ind-30
❑ 85IndPol-NNO
❑ 88PadSmo-27
❑ 89PadPos-32
❑ 90PadMag-22
❑ 93GiaMot-28
❑ 94GiaMot-28

Sommers, Joseph A.
❑ 87OldJudN-463

Sommers, Scott
❑ 86ElmPioRSP-22
❑ 88LynRedSS-23
❑ 89NewBriRSP-623
❑ 89NewBriRSS-19
❑ 89Sta-130

Sonberg, Erik
❑ 85AlbDukCr-159
❑ 89HagSunB-18
❑ 89HagSunP-267

Sondrini, Joe
❑ 91AugPirC-26
❑ 91AugPirP-815
❑ 92Bow-211
❑ 92ProFS7-310
❑ 92SalBucC-16
❑ 92SalBucF-73
❑ 93CarMudF-2065

Song, Koo Hong
❑ 90IBAWorA-38

Songer, Don
❑ 94ConTSN-1303
❑ 94ConTSNB-1303

Songini, Mike (Michael)
❑ 88BilMusP-1829
❑ 89GreHorP-421
❑ 90EriSaiS-24
❑ 91RenSilSCLC-21

Sonneberger, Steve
❑ 88HagSunS-20

Sontag, Alan
❑ 86OrlTwiP-18
❑ 87OrlTwiP-23
❑ 91MidAngOHP-28
❑ 91PalSprAP-2013
❑ 92SalSpuC-11
❑ 92SalSpuF-3753
❑ 98BriBluM-27

Soo, Sang
❑ 96WesOahCHWB-26

Soos, Charles
❑ 87KinIndP-4
❑ 88KinIndS-20

Soper, Mike
❑ 83BurRanT-11
❑ 86ColCliP-23
❑ 86ColCliP-24
❑ 90CalLeaACLC-52
❑ 90RenSilSCLC-277
❑ 91CarLeaAP-CAR20
❑ 91KinIndC-12
❑ 91KinIndP-324
❑ 92CanIndS-118
❑ 92ProFS7-54
❑ 92SkyAA F-55
❑ 93CanIndF-2839
❑ 93LinVenB-84
❑ 94CarLeaA-DJ19

Soper, Steve
❑ 94MedHatBJF-3689
❑ 94MedHatBJSP-2

Sorce, Sam
❑ 83BurRanF-3
❑ 83BurRanT-22
❑ 85OrlTwiT-11
❑ 86OrlTwiP-19

Sordo, Ed
❑ 96GreFalDTI-13

Sorel, Mike
❑ 81CedRapRT-14

Sorensen, Lary
❑ 77SpoIndC-19
❑ 78Top-569
❑ 79BrePlaPH-1
❑ 79OPC-152
❑ 79Top-303
❑ 80BreTeal-21
❑ 80OPC-84
❑ 80Top-154
❑ 81AllGamPI-177
❑ 81CokTeaS-129
❑ 81Don-325
❑ 81Fle-519
❑ 81Top-379
❑ 81TopTra-831
❑ 82Don-246
❑ 82Fle-128
❑ 82Ind-31
❑ 82IndWhe-18
❑ 82OPC-136
❑ 82Top-689
❑ 82TopTra-111T
❑ 83Don-363
❑ 83Fle-418
❑ 83FleSti-244
❑ 83IndPos-32
❑ 83IndWhe-26
❑ 83OPC-48
❑ 83Top-48
❑ 84A'sMot-14
❑ 84Don-635
❑ 84Fle-549
❑ 84FleUpd-109
❑ 84Nes792-286
❑ 84Nes792-546
❑ 84OPC-286
❑ 84Top-286
❑ 84Top-546
❑ 84TopSti-259
❑ 84TopTif-286
❑ 84TopTif-546
❑ 84TopTra-111T
❑ 84TopTraT-111T
❑ 85CubLioP-22
❑ 85CubSev-42
❑ 85Don-131
❑ 85Fle-434
❑ 85FleUpd-108
❑ 86Fle-381
❑ 86Top-744
❑ 86TopTif-744
❑ 87ExpPos-28
❑ 87FleUpd-111
❑ 87FleUpdG-111
❑ 88ChaLooB-20
❑ 90SweBasG-63
❑ 94BreMilB-275

Sorensen, Todd
❑ 93KanCouCC-29
❑ 93KanCouCTI-22
❑ 94PorSeaDTI-6

Sorensen, Zach
❑ 98WatIndTI-31
❑ 99JustheS-41
❑ 99JustheSJB-41
❑ 99TeaBesR-82
❑ 99TeaBesRFS-8
❑ 99TeaBesRG-82
❑ 99TeaBesRS-82

Sorey, Ron
❑ 75WesPalBES-27
❑ 78DunBluJT-22

Sorg, Jay
❑ 94PriRedC-25
❑ 94PriRedF-3274
❑ 95BilMusTI-7
❑ 97BurBeeB-22
❑ 98ChaLooG-25

Soria, Frank
❑ 22Zee-90

Soriano, Alfonso
❑ 98AriFalLTP-16
❑ 99199Fin-286
❑ 99Bow-350
❑ 99BowBes-169
❑ 99BowBesAR-169
❑ 99BowBesFFMI-FF7
❑ 99BowBesFFMI-FF7
❑ 99BowBesFFMII-FF7
❑ 99BowBesMI-M3
❑ 99BowBesMIAR-M3
❑ 99BowBesMIR-M3
❑ 99BowBesR-169
❑ 99BowGol-350
❑ 99BowInt-350
❑ 99FinGolRef-286
❑ 99FinRef-286
❑ 99TopBlaLC1-30
❑ 99TopBlaLC2-30
❑ 99TopBlaLC3-30
❑ 99TopGal-128
❑ 99TopGalPP-128
❑ 99TopGalPPI-128
❑ 99TopGolL-30
❑ 99TopGolLC1-30
❑ 99TopGolLC2-30
❑ 99TopGolLOtO-30
❑ 99TopRedLC1-30
❑ 99TopRedLC2-30
❑ 99TopRedLC3-30
❑ 99TopSta-34
❑ 99TopSta-158
❑ 99TopSta1Foil-34
❑ 99TopSta2Foil-34
❑ 99TopStaBF-BF10
❑ 99TopStaBFFoil-BF10
❑ 99TopStaFoil-34
❑ 99TopStaFoil-158
❑ 99TopStaOS-34
❑ 99TopStaTS-34

Soriano, Carlos
❑ 97CapCitB-18

Soriano, Fred
❑ 94ModA'sC-21
❑ 94ModA'sF-3071
❑ 95WesMicWTI-6
❑ 96ModA'sB-2
❑ 97KnoSmo-22

Soriano, Hilario
❑ 77CliDodT-24
❑ 85DomLeaS-156

Soriano, Jose
❑ 94SouOreAC-27
❑ 95WesMicWTI-14
❑ 96WesMicWB-26
❑ 97ModA'sG-27
❑ 98VisOakG-30

Soriano, Tony
❑ 47RemBre-24

Soroko, Mark
❑ 76AshTouT-23
❑ 77TucTorC-45

Sorrel, Mike
❑ 82ChaRoyT-3

Sorrell, Billy
❑ 66Top-254
❑ 66TopVen-254
❑ 67Top-341
❑ 70RoyTeal-33
❑ 71OPC-17
❑ 71Top-17

Sorrell, Vic
❑ 33Gou-15
❑ 33GouCanV-15
❑ 34TigTeal-18
❑ 36WorWidGV-21
❑ 72TCMthe1-197
❑ 74TigTCM1AC-29
❑ 76TigOldTS-21
❑ 92ConTSN-577

Sorrento, Paul
❑ 87PalSprP-11
❑ 88PalSprACLC-110
❑ 88PalSprAP-1450
❑ 89BasAmeAPB-AA19
❑ 89OrlTwiB-1
❑ 89OrlTwiP-1343
❑ 89SouLeaAJ-13
❑ 90Bow-421
❑ 90BowTif-421
❑ 90CMC-577
❑ 90Don-626
❑ 90PorBeaC-25
❑ 90PorBeaP-189
❑ 90ProAAAF-259
❑ 90Sco-647
❑ 90TopDeb89-119
❑ 90TopTra-119T
❑ 90TopTraT-119T
❑ 90UppDec-784
❑ 91Don-745
❑ 91LinDriAAA-420
❑ 91OPC-654
❑ 91PorBeaLD-420
❑ 91PorBeaP-1574
❑ 91Sco-796
❑ 91Sco100RS-44
❑ 91StaClu-408
❑ 91Top-654
❑ 91TopDesS-654
❑ 91TopMic-654
❑ 91TopTif-654
❑ 91UppDec-680
❑ 92Don-752
❑ 92Fle-218
❑ 92FleUpd-18
❑ 92IndFanC-27
❑ 92Lea-401
❑ 92LeaBlaG-401
❑ 92OPC-546
❑ 92StaClu-707
❑ 92Stu-169
❑ 92Top-546
❑ 92TopGol-546
❑ 92TopGolW-546
❑ 92TopMic-546
❑ 92TopTra-108T
❑ 92TopTraG-108T
❑ 92Ult-357
❑ 93Bow-501
❑ 93Don-229
❑ 93Fla-199
❑ 93Fle-221
❑ 93IndWUA-29
❑ 93Lea-105
❑ 93PacBeiA-6
❑ 93PacSpa-102
❑ 93PanSti-55
❑ 93Pin-320
❑ 93Sco-194
❑ 93Sel-226
❑ 93SP-126
❑ 93StaClu-194
❑ 93StaCluFDI-194
❑ 93StaCluMOP-194
❑ 93Stu-67
❑ 93Top-264
❑ 93TopGol-264
❑ 93TopInaM-264
❑ 93TopInaR-264
❑ 93TopMic-264
❑ 93Ult-191
❑ 93UppDec-196
❑ 93UppDecGold-196
❑ 94Bow-83
❑ 94ColC-262
❑ 94ColChoGS-262
❑ 94ColChoSS-262
❑ 94Don-536
❑ 94Fin-185
❑ 94FinPre-185P
❑ 94FinRef-185
❑ 94Fla-44
❑ 94Fle-120
❑ 94FleExtB-68
❑ 94Lea-361
❑ 94Pac-184
❑ 94PanSti-60
❑ 94Pin-308
❑ 94PinArtP-308
❑ 94PinMusC-308
❑ 94Sco-473
❑ 94ScoGolR-473
❑ 94Sel-358
❑ 94StaClu-636
❑ 94StaCluFDI-636
❑ 94StaCluGR-636
❑ 94StaCluMOP-636
❑ 94Stu-96
❑ 94Top-358
❑ 94TopGol-358
❑ 94TopSpa-358
❑ 94TriPla-119
❑ 94Ult-48
❑ 94UppDec-363
❑ 94UppDecED-363
❑ 95ColCho-267
❑ 95ColChoGS-267
❑ 95ColChoSS-267
❑ 95Don-510
❑ 95DonPreP-510
❑ 95DonTopotO-67
❑ 95Fin-270
❑ 95FinRef-270
❑ 95Fla-36
❑ 95Fle-148
❑ 95Lea-43
❑ 95LeaLim-168
❑ 95Pac-129
❑ 95Pin-84
❑ 95PinArtP-84
❑ 95PinMusC-84
❑ 95Sco-396
❑ 95ScoGolR-396
❑ 95ScoPlaTS-396
❑ 95StaClu-220
❑ 95StaCluFDI-220
❑ 95StaCluMOP-220
❑ 95StaCluSTWS-220
❑ 95StaCluVR-111
❑ 95StaCluVRMO-111
❑ 95Top-132
❑ 95TopCyb-82
❑ 95Ult-282
❑ 95UltGolM-282
❑ 96Cir-82
❑ 96CirRav-82
❑ 96ColCho-126
❑ 96ColCho-727
❑ 96ColChoGS-126
❑ 96ColChoGS-727
❑ 96ColChoSS-126
❑ 96ColChoSS-727
❑ 96Don-290
❑ 96DonPreP-290
❑ 96EmoXL-118
❑ 96Fin-B213
❑ 96FinRef-B213

❑ 96Fla-165
❑ 96Fle-100
❑ 96FleTif-100
❑ 96FleUpd-U84
❑ 96FleUpdTC-U84
❑ 96LeaSigA-211
❑ 96LeaSigAG-211
❑ 96LeaSigAS-211
❑ 96MarMot-17
❑ 96MetUni-111
❑ 96MetUniP-111
❑ 96Pac-306
❑ 96Pin-68
❑ 96Sco-189
❑ 96StaClu-135
❑ 96StaCluEPB-135
❑ 96StaCluEPG-135
❑ 96StaCluEPS-135
❑ 96StaCluMOP-135
❑ 96Top-373
❑ 96TopGal-37
❑ 96TopGalPPI-37
❑ 96Ult-416
❑ 96UltGolM-416
❑ 96UppDec-459
❑ 97Cir-294
❑ 97CirRav-294
❑ 97ColCho-483
❑ 97ColChoT-SM8
❑ 97Don-123
❑ 97DonGolPP-123
❑ 97DonLim-102
❑ 97DonLimE-102
❑ 97DonLimENG-102
❑ 97DonSilPP-123
❑ 97DonTea-140
❑ 97DonTeaSPE-140
❑ 97Fin-79
❑ 97FinRef-79
❑ 97Fle-214
❑ 97FleTif-214
❑ 97MarSco-4
❑ 97MarScoPl-4
❑ 97MarScoPr-4
❑ 97MetUni-150
❑ 97NewPin-99
❑ 97NewPinAP-99
❑ 97NewPinMC-99
❑ 97NewPinPP-99
❑ 97Pac-193
❑ 97PacLigB-193
❑ 97PacPri-66
❑ 97PacPriLB-66
❑ 97PacPriP-66
❑ 97PacSil-193
❑ 97Sco-136
❑ 97ScoArtPWB-136
❑ 97ScoPreS-136
❑ 97ScoShoS-136
❑ 97ScoShoSAP-136
❑ 97StaClu-345
❑ 97StaCluMOP-345
❑ 97Top-423
❑ 97TopGal-78
❑ 97TopGalPPI-78
❑ 97UppDec-502
❑ 97UppDecMP-P7
❑ 98CirThu-278
❑ 98CirThuRav-278
❑ 98CirThuSupRav-278
❑ 98ColCho-241
❑ 98ColCho-504
❑ 98DevRayP-19
❑ 98Fle-435
❑ 98FleVin'-124
❑ 98FleVin'C-124
❑ 98MarSco-13
❑ 98MarScoP-13
❑ 98MetUni-55
❑ 98MetUniPMG-55
❑ 98Pac-195
❑ 98PacAur-83
❑ 98PacInvTeam-30
❑ 98PacOme-234
❑ 98PacOmeR-234
❑ 98PacOnl-719
❑ 98PacOnlR-719
❑ 98PacOnlWC-719
❑ 98PacPar-100
❑ 98PacParC-100
❑ 98PacParG-100
❑ 98PacParHS-100
❑ 98PacParPB-100
❑ 98PacParR-100
❑ 98PacPlaB-195
❑ 98PacRedT-195
❑ 98PacSil-195
❑ 98Pin-117
❑ 98PinPlu-180
❑ 98PinPreP-117
❑ 98PinSna-TBDR2
❑ 98Sco-192
❑ 98ScoSS-PP89
❑ 98ScoSSAP-PP89
❑ 98StaCluFDI-177
❑ 98StaCluI-177
❑ 98StaCluOneK-177
❑ 98StaCluPP-177
❑ 98Top-111
❑ 98TopChr-111
❑ 98TopChrR-111
❑ 98TopDevR-111
❑ 98TopDia-111
❑ 98TopMiniC-111
❑ 98Ult-46
❑ 98Ult-469
❑ 98UltGolM-46
❑ 98UltGolM-469
❑ 98UltMas-46
❑ 98UltMas-469
❑ 98UltPlaM-46
❑ 98UltPlaM-469
❑ 98UppDec-733
❑ 99Fle-258
❑ 99FleSta9-258
❑ 99FleWarT-258
❑ 99Pac-418
❑ 99PacPlaB-418
❑ 99PacRed-418
❑ 99SkyThu-90
❑ 99SkyThuRant-90
❑ 99SkyThuRave-90
❑ 99ThuSkySupR-90
❑ 99Top-28
❑ 99TopChr-28
❑ 99TopChrR-28
❑ 99TopMVPP-28
❑ 99UppDec-214
❑ 99UppDecEL1-214
❑ 99UppDecEL2-214

Sortedahl, John
❑ 96BelSnaTI-35

Sorzano, Ronnie
❑ 96-97LinVen-152

Sosa, Brian
❑ 93BelMarCB-25
❑ 93BelMarF-3207

Sosa, Elias
❑ 72Dia-42
❑ 74OPC-54
❑ 74Top-54
❑ 74TopSta-109
❑ 75AtlBraP-34
❑ 75OPC-398
❑ 75St.LouCP-28
❑ 75Top-398
❑ 75TopMin-398
❑ 76AtlBraP-30
❑ 76OPC-364
❑ 76SSP-7
❑ 76Top-364
❑ 77Top-558
❑ 78Top-694
❑ 79ExpPos-27
❑ 79Top-78
❑ 80ExpPos-29
❑ 80OPC-153
❑ 80Top-293
❑ 81Don-599
❑ 81Fle-151
❑ 81OPC-181
❑ 81Top-181
❑ 82Don-446
❑ 82Fle-208
❑ 82OPC-116
❑ 82Top-414
❑ 82TopTra-112T
❑ 83Don-259
❑ 83Fle-342
❑ 83PadTeal-25
❑ 83Top-753
❑ 83TopFol-4
❑ 83TopTra-107T
❑ 84Fle-313
❑ 84Nes792-503
❑ 84Top-503
❑ 84TopTif-503
❑ 87SanJosBP-18
❑ 89PacSenL-8
❑ 89SumBraP-1093
❑ 89T/MSenL-97
❑ 89TopSenL-45
❑ 90DodTar-755
❑ 90EliSenL-14
❑ 91PacSenL-137
❑ 92MCIAmb-11
❑ 95BelGiaTI-34
❑ 96BelGiaTI-35

Sosa, Franklin
❑ 96FayGenB-27
❑ 97WesMicW-24

Sosa, Helpis
❑ 95WesMicWTI-27

Sosa, Jose
❑ 90PriPatD-21
❑ 92AugPirC-19
❑ 92AugPirF-238
❑ 93AugPirC-20
❑ 93AugPirF-1544
❑ 94AugGreC-23
❑ 94AugGreF-3010

Sosa, Jose Y.
❑ 73CedRapAT-16
❑ 74CedRapAT-24
❑ 76HouAstP-29
❑ 76OPC-591
❑ 76Top-591
❑ 78ChaChaT-15

Sosa, Juan
❑ 95YakBeaTI-28
❑ 96SavSanB-21
❑ 97VerBeaD-24
❑ 98CarLeaAC-33
❑ 98SalAvaC-24
❑ 99SP TopP-111
❑ 99SP TopPPE-111

Sosa, Miguel
❑ 80AndBraT-24
❑ 81DurBulT-1
❑ 82DurBulT-9
❑ 85IntLeaAT-3
❑ 85RicBraT-17
❑ 86AlbYanT-4
❑ 86ColCliP-25

Sosa, Nicolas
❑ 97SouOreTB-9
❑ 98VisOakG-31

Sosa, Sammy
❑ 87GasRanP-29
❑ 88ChaRanS-23
❑ 89BasAmeAPB-AA29
❑ 89DonBasB-324
❑ 89TulDriGS-25
❑ 89TulDriTI-24
❑ 90Bow-312
❑ 90BowTif-312
❑ 90ClaBlu-140
❑ 90Don-489
❑ 90DonBesA-104
❑ 90Fle-548
❑ 90FleCan-548
❑ 90Hot50RS-43
❑ 90Lea-220
❑ 90OPC-692
❑ 90Sco-558
❑ 90Sco100RS-35
❑ 90ScoYouS2-25
❑ 90Spo-81
❑ 90StaFS7-61
❑ 90Top-692
❑ 90TopBig-286
❑ 90TopDeb89-120
❑ 90TopTif-692
❑ 90TulDriDGB-31
❑ 90UppDec-17
❑ 90WhiSoxC-23
❑ 91Bow-350
❑ 91ClaGam-60
❑ 91Don-147
❑ 91Fle-136
❑ 91Lea-321
❑ 91MajLeaCP-16
❑ 91OPC-414
❑ 91PanFreS-316
❑ 91Sco-256
❑ 91StaClu-6
❑ 91Stu-38
❑ 91Top-414
❑ 91TopDesS-414
❑ 91TopMic-414
❑ 91TopTif-414
❑ 91Ult-82
❑ 91UppDec-265
❑ 91WhiSoxK-25
❑ 92Bow-116
❑ 92Cla2-T27
❑ 92CubMar-21
❑ 92Don-740
❑ 92Fle-98
❑ 92FleUpd-77
❑ 92Lea-412
❑ 92LeaBlaG-412
❑ 92OPC-94
❑ 92OPCPre-120
❑ 92PanSti-129
❑ 92Pin-369
❑ 92PinTea2-55
❑ 92Sco-258
❑ 92ScoRoo-23T
❑ 92SpoIllFK1-743
❑ 92StaClu-628
❑ 92Stu-20
❑ 92Top-94
❑ 92TopGol-94
❑ 92TopGolW-94
❑ 92TopMic-94
❑ 92TopTra-109T
❑ 92TopTraG-109T
❑ 92Ult-476
❑ 92UppDec-438
❑ 92UppDec-723
❑ 93Bow-636
❑ 93CubMar-26
❑ 93CubStaC-2
❑ 93Don-186
❑ 93Fin-79
❑ 93FinRef-79
❑ 93Fla-22
❑ 93FlaPro-8
❑ 93Fle-27
❑ 93FunPac-85
❑ 93Lea-70
❑ 93LimRocDWB-31
❑ 93PacBeiA-19
❑ 93PacBeiA-20
❑ 93PacSpa-383
❑ 93PanSti-208
❑ 93Pin-145
❑ 93RanKee-337
❑ 93Sco-143
❑ 93Sel-165
❑ 93SP-89
❑ 93StaClu-531
❑ 93StaCluFDI-531
❑ 93StaCluMOP-531
❑ 93Stu-121
❑ 93Top-156
❑ 93TopGol-156
❑ 93TopInaM-156
❑ 93TopInaR-156
❑ 93TopMic-156
❑ 93TriPla-151
❑ 93TulDriTI-30
❑ 93Ult-24
❑ 93UppDec-127
❑ 93UppDec-819
❑ 93UppDecGold-127
❑ 93UppDecGold-819
❑ 94Bow-82
❑ 94BowBes-R70
❑ 94BowBesR-R70
❑ 94ColC-263
❑ 94ColChoGS-263
❑ 94ColChoSS-263
❑ 94Don-337
❑ 94DonSpeE-337
❑ 94Fin-236
❑ 94FinJum-236
❑ 94FinRef-236
❑ 94Fla-363
❑ 94Fle-399
❑ 94FleExtB-224
❑ 94FUnPac-162
❑ 94Lea-98
❑ 94LeaL-92
❑ 94OPC-161
❑ 94Pac-112
❑ 94PacGolP-19
❑ 94PanSti-158
❑ 94Pin-3
❑ 94PinArtP-3
❑ 94PinMusC-3
❑ 94PinPowS-PS7
❑ 94PinSam-3
❑ 94ProMag-23
❑ 94Sco-510
❑ 94ScoGolR-510
❑ 94Sel-58
❑ 94SP-72
❑ 94SPDieC-72
❑ 94SPHol-37
❑ 94SPHolDC-37
❑ 94Spo-81
❑ 94SpoMov-MM7
❑ 94StaClu-80
❑ 94StaCluFDI-80
❑ 94StaCluGR-80
❑ 94StaCluMOP-80
❑ 94StaCluMOP-ST2
❑ 94StaCluST-ST2
❑ 94StaCluT-347
❑ 94StaCluTFDI-347
❑ 94Stu-64
❑ 94Top-725
❑ 94TopBlaG-42
❑ 94TopGol-725
❑ 94TopSpa-725
❑ 94TriPla-78
❑ 94Ult-464
❑ 94UppDec-268
❑ 94UppDec-510
❑ 94UppDecAJ-30
❑ 94UppDecAJG-30
❑ 94UppDecED-268
❑ 94UppDecED-510
❑ 95Baz-4
❑ 95Bow-372
❑ 95BowBes-R35
❑ 95BowBesJR-8
❑ 95BowBesR-R35
❑ 95ClaPhoC-12
❑ 95ColCho-210
❑ 95ColChoGS-210
❑ 95ColChoSE-85
❑ 95ColChoSEGS-85
❑ 95ColChoSESS-85
❑ 95ColChoSS-210
❑ 95DenHol-26
❑ 95Don-122
❑ 95DonDiaK-DK14
❑ 95DonPreP-122
❑ 95DonTopotO-205
❑ 95Emo-113
❑ 95Fin-197
❑ 95FinPowK-PK12
❑ 95FinRef-197
❑ 95Fla-334
❑ 95Fle-424
❑ 95FleTeaL-16
❑ 95Kra-29
❑ 95Lea-272
❑ 95LeaLim-188
❑ 95Pac-79
❑ 95PacLatD-33
❑ 95PacPri-26
❑ 95Pin-230
❑ 95PinArtP-230
❑ 95PinFan-22
❑ 95PinMusC-230
❑ 95PinUps-US12
❑ 95Sco-34
❑ 95ScoGolR-34
❑ 95ScoHaloG-HG31
❑ 95ScoPlaTS-34
❑ 95Sel-126
❑ 95SelArtP-126
❑ 95SelCer-84
❑ 95SelCerMG-84
❑ 95SP-35
❑ 95SPCha-27
❑ 95SPCha-30
❑ 95SPChaDC-27
❑ 95SPChaDC-30
❑ 95Spo-52
❑ 95SpoArtP-52
❑ 95SPSil-35
❑ 95SPSpeF-30
❑ 95StaClu-174
❑ 95StaClu-238
❑ 95StaClu-497
❑ 95StaCluCC-CC17
❑ 95StaCluFDI-174
❑ 95StaCluFDI-238
❑ 95StaCluMOP-174
❑ 95StaCluMOP-238
❑ 95StaCluMOP-497
❑ 95StaCluMOP-CC17
❑ 95StaCluSTWS-174
❑ 95StaCluSTWS-238
❑ 95StaCluSTWS-497
❑ 95StaCluVR-91
❑ 95StaCluVRMO-91
❑ 95Stu-78
❑ 95Sum-44
❑ 95SumNthD-44
❑ 95TomPiz-30
❑ 95Top-11
❑ 95TopCyb-9
❑ 95UC3-91
❑ 95UC3ArtP-91
❑ 95Ult-139
❑ 95UltGolM-139
❑ 95UppDec-315
❑ 95UppDecED-315
❑ 95UppDecEDG-315
❑ 95UppDecSE-123
❑ 95UppDecSEG-123
❑ 95Zen-98
❑ 96Baz-20
❑ 96Bow-105
❑ 96BowBes-48
❑ 96BowBesAR-48
❑ 96BowBesR-48
❑ 96BowFoi-105
❑ 96Cir-112
❑ 96CirAcc-16
❑ 96CirBos-30
❑ 96CirRav-112
❑ 96ColCho-106
❑ 96ColCho-277
❑ 96ColCho-403
❑ 96ColCho-490
❑ 96ColChoCtG-CG9
❑ 96ColChoCtG-CG9B
❑ 96ColChoCtG-CG9C
❑ 96ColChoCtGE-CR9
❑ 96ColChoCtGG-CG9
❑ 96ColChoCtGG-CG9B
❑ 96ColChoCtGG-CG9C
❑ 96ColChoCtGGE-CR9
❑ 96ColChoGS-106
❑ 96ColChoGS-277
❑ 96ColChoGS-403
❑ 96ColChoGS-490
❑ 96ColChoSS-106
❑ 96ColChoSS-277
❑ 96ColChoSS-403
❑ 96ColChoSS-490
❑ 96ColChoYMtP-39
❑ 96ColChoYMtP-39A
❑ 96ColChoYMtPGS-39
❑ 96ColChoYMtPGS-39A
❑ 96CubFle-17
❑ 96DenHolGS-5
❑ 96DenHolGSAP-5
❑ 96Don-334
❑ 96DonPreP-334
❑ 96EmoLegoB-9
❑ 96EmoXL-160
❑ 96Fin-B257
❑ 96Fin-G347
❑ 96Fin-S171
❑ 96FinRef-B257
❑ 96FinRef-G347
❑ 96FinRef-S171
❑ 96Fla-225
❑ 96FlaPow-8
❑ 96Fle-330
❑ 96FleGolM-2
❑ 96FleLumC-9
❑ 96FleTeaL-16
❑ 96FleTif-330
❑ 96FleUpd-U242
❑ 96FleUpdTC-U242
❑ 96Lea-112
❑ 96LeaAllGMC-3
❑ 96LeaAllGMCG-3
❑ 96LeaGolS-3
❑ 96LeaLim-5
❑ 96LeaLimG-5
❑ 96LeaLimL-2
❑ 96LeaLimLB-2
❑ 96LeaPre-17
❑ 96LeaPreP-17
❑ 96LeaPrePB-112
❑ 96LeaPrePG-112
❑ 96LeaPrePS-112
❑ 96LeaPreSG-32
❑ 96LeaPreSte-32
❑ 96LeaSig-24
❑ 96LeaSigEA-187
❑ 96LeaSigEACM-28
❑ 96LeaSigPPG-24
❑ 96LeaSigPPP-24
❑ 96MetUni-146
❑ 96MetUniHM-7
❑ 96MetUniP-146
❑ 96Pac-21
❑ 96PacBaeS-8
❑ 96PacEstL-EL30
❑ 96PacGolCD-DC14
❑ 96PacPri-P13
❑ 96PacPriFB-FB17
❑ 96PacPriG-P13
❑ 96PanSti-48
❑ 96Pin-92

❑ 96Pin-140
❑ 96Pin-263
❑ 96PinAfi-67
❑ 96PinAfi-158
❑ 96PinAfiAP-67
❑ 96PinAfiAP-158
❑ 96PinAfiFPP-67
❑ 96PinAfiMN-10
❑ 96PinArtP-53
❑ 96PinArtP-67
❑ 96PinArtP-163
❑ 96PinFoil-263
❑ 96PinPow-10
❑ 96PinSlu-10
❑ 96PinSta-53
❑ 96PinSta-67
❑ 96PinSta-163
❑ 96PinTeaP-7
❑ 96ProSta-40
❑ 96RedF-21
❑ 96Sco-336
❑ 96ScoDugC-B61
❑ 96ScoDugCAP-B61
❑ 96ScoGolS-20
❑ 96ScoPowP-15
❑ 96ScoTitT-14
❑ 96Sel-26
❑ 96Sel-157
❑ 96SelArtP-26
❑ 96SelArtP-157
❑ 96SelCer-59
❑ 96SelCerAP-59
❑ 96SelCerCB-59
❑ 96SelCerCR-59
❑ 96SelCerIP-3
❑ 96SelCerMB-59
❑ 96SelCerMG-59
❑ 96SelCerMR-59
❑ 96SelCerSF-1
❑ 96SelClaTF-8
❑ 96SelEnF-9
❑ 96SelTeaN-15
❑ 96SP-51
❑ 96SPMarM-MM16
❑ 96SPMarMDC-16
❑ 96Spo-57
❑ 96Spo-104
❑ 96SpoArtP-57
❑ 96SpoArtP-104
❑ 96SpoDouT-11
❑ 96SpoHitP-9
❑ 96SpoPowS-8
❑ 96SPPreF-8
❑ 96SPSpeFX-33
❑ 96SPSpeFXDC-33
❑ 96SPx-13
❑ 96SPxGol-13
❑ 96StaClu-370
❑ 96StaCluB&B-BB1
❑ 96StaCluEPB-370
❑ 96StaCluEPG-370
❑ 96StaCluEPS-370
❑ 96StaCluMO-39
❑ 96StaCluMOP-370
❑ 96StaCluMOP-BB1
❑ 96StaCluMOP-PS10
❑ 96StaCluPS-PS10
❑ 96Stu-43
❑ 96StuPrePB-43
❑ 96StuPrePG-43
❑ 96StuPrePS-43
❑ 96Sum-87
❑ 96Sum-159
❑ 96SumAbo&B-87
❑ 96SumAbo&B-159
❑ 96SumArtP-87
❑ 96SumArtP-159
❑ 96SumBigB-13
❑ 96SumBigBM-13
❑ 96SumFoi-87
❑ 96SumFoi-159
❑ 96SumHitI-5
❑ 96SumPos-9
❑ 96TeaOut-77
❑ 96TeaOut-C95
❑ 96Top-252
❑ 96TopChr-99
❑ 96TopChrR-99
❑ 96TopGal-17
❑ 96TopGalE-12
❑ 96TopGalPPI-17
❑ 96TopLas-14
❑ 96TopLasPC-15
❑ 96TopMysF-M15
❑ 96TopMysFR-M15
❑ 96TopPro-NL9
❑ 96Ult-171
❑ 96UltGolM-171
❑ 96UltRBIK-8
❑ 96UltRBIKGM-8
❑ 96UppDec-35
❑ 96UppDecDD-DD13
❑ 96UppDecDDG-DD13
❑ 96UppDecDDS-DD13
❑ 96UppDecHC-HC17
❑ 96UppDecPD-PD16
❑ 96UppDecPRE-R37
❑ 96UppDecPRE-R48
❑ 96UppDecPreR-R37
❑ 96UppDecPreR-R48
❑ 96UppDecRunP-RP17
❑ 96Zen-100
❑ 96Zen-148
❑ 96ZenArtP-100
❑ 96ZenArtP-148
❑ 96ZenDiaC-12
❑ 96ZenDiaCP-12
❑ 96ZenMoz-6
❑ 96ZenZ-18
❑ 97Bow-52
❑ 97BowBes-83
❑ 97BowBesAR-83
❑ 97BowBesR-83
❑ 97BowChr-40
❑ 97BowChrI-40
❑ 97BowChrIR-40
❑ 97BowChrR-40
❑ 97BowInt-52
❑ 97BowIntB-BBI6
❑ 97BowIntBAR-BBI6
❑ 97BowIntBR-BBI6
❑ 97Cir-275
❑ 97CirRav-275
❑ 97ColCho-65
❑ 97ColChoAC-32
❑ 97ColChoCtG-8A
❑ 97ColChoCtG-8B
❑ 97ColChoCtG-8C
❑ 97ColChoCtGE-CG8
❑ 97ColChoCtGIW-CG8
❑ 97ColChoNF-NF20
❑ 97ColChoPP-PP13
❑ 97ColChoPPG-PP13
❑ 97ColChoPPJ-PP13
❑ 97ColChoS-21
❑ 97ColChoSR-25
❑ 97ColChoTBS-14
❑ 97ColChoTBSWH-14
❑ 97ColChoTotT-T9
❑ 97CraJac-11
❑ 97DenHol-16
❑ 97Don-15
❑ 97Don-442
❑ 97DonDom-14
❑ 97DonEli-31
❑ 97DonEli-3
❑ 97DonEliGS-31
❑ 97DonGolPP-15
❑ 97DonGolPP-442
❑ 97DonLim-59
❑ 97DonLim-68
❑ 97DonLim-195
❑ 97DonLimE-59
❑ 97DonLimE-68
❑ 97DonLimE-195
❑ 97DonLimENG-59
❑ 97DonLimFotG-7
❑ 97DonLonL-11
❑ 97DonPowA-22
❑ 97DonPowADC-22
❑ 97DonPre-115
❑ 97DonPre-195
❑ 97DonPreCttC-115
❑ 97DonPreCttC-195
❑ 97DonPreTB-23
❑ 97DonPreTBG-23
❑ 97DonPreTF-23
❑ 97DonPreTP-23
❑ 97DonPreTPG-23
❑ 97DonSig-59
❑ 97DonSigPPP-59
❑ 97DonSilPP-15
❑ 97DonSilPP-442
❑ 97DonVxP1-9
❑ 97E-X2-63
❑ 97E-X2Cred-63
❑ 97E-X2EssCre-63
❑ 97Fin-20
❑ 97Fin-168
❑ 97Fin-277
❑ 97FinEmb-168
❑ 97FinEmb-277
❑ 97FinEmbR-168
❑ 97FinEmbR-277
❑ 97FinRef-20
❑ 97FinRef-168
❑ 97FinRef-277
❑ 97FlaShoLC-34
❑ 97FlaShoLeg0-34
❑ 97FlaShoLeg1-34
❑ 97FlaShoM-A34
❑ 97FlaShoM-B34
❑ 97FlaShoM-C34
❑ 97FlaShoR0-34
❑ 97FlaShoR1-34
❑ 97FlaShoR2-34
❑ 97Fle-284
❑ 97FleLumC-16
❑ 97FleTif-284
❑ 97Lea-121
❑ 97Lea-361
❑ 97LeaFraM-121
❑ 97LeaFraM-361
❑ 97LeaFraMDC-121
❑ 97LeaFraMDC-361
❑ 97LeaLeaotN-7
❑ 97LeaWarT-15
❑ 97MetUni-15
❑ 97NewPin-2
❑ 97NewPinAP-2
❑ 97NewPinMC-2
❑ 97NewPinPP-2
❑ 97Pac-259
❑ 97PacLatotML-25
❑ 97PacLigB-259
❑ 97PacPri-89
❑ 97PacPriGA-GA21
❑ 97PacPriLB-89
❑ 97PacPriP-89
❑ 97PacSil-259
❑ 97Pin-194
❑ 97PinArtP-PP194
❑ 97PinCar-8
❑ 97PinCer-35
❑ 97PinCerLI-7
❑ 97PinCerMBla-35
❑ 97PinCerMBlu-35
❑ 97PinCerMG-35
❑ 97PinCerMR-35
❑ 97PinCerR-35
❑ 97PinIns-2
❑ 97PinInsCE-2
❑ 97PinInsDE-2
❑ 97PinInsFS-13
❑ 97PinMin-17
❑ 97PinMinB-17
❑ 97PinMinCB-17
❑ 97PinMinCG-17
❑ 97PinMinCGR-17
❑ 97PinMinCN-17
❑ 97PinMinCSS-17
❑ 97PinMinG-17
❑ 97PinMinS-17
❑ 97PinMusC-194
❑ 97PinPasttM-15
❑ 97PinPrePla-194
❑ 97PinTotCPB-35
❑ 97PinTotCPG-35
❑ 97PinTotCPR-35
❑ 97PinX-P-73
❑ 97PinX-PF&A-11
❑ 97PinX-PMoS-73
❑ 97PinX-PMP-16
❑ 97PinX-PreMPS-16
❑ 97PinX-PSfF-52
❑ 97PinX-PSfFU-52
❑ 97PreCon-13
❑ 97Sco-244
❑ 97ScoArtPWB-244
❑ 97ScoBla-15
❑ 97ScoFra-8
❑ 97ScoFraG-8
❑ 97ScoHigZ-8
❑ 97ScoPreS-244
❑ 97ScoShoS-244
❑ 97ScoShoSAP-244
❑ 97ScoSteS-12
❑ 97ScoTitT-7
❑ 97Sel-14
❑ 97SelArtP-14
❑ 97SelCom-14
❑ 97SelRegG-14
❑ 97SelToootT-14
❑ 97SelToootTMB-14
❑ 97SP-40
❑ 97SPInsI-13
❑ 97SPMarM-MM20
❑ 97SpoIll-94
❑ 97SpoIllEE-94
❑ 97SPSpeF-20
❑ 97SPSpxF-4
❑ 97SPSPxFA-4
❑ 97SPx-16
❑ 97SPxBro-16
❑ 97SPxGol-16
❑ 97SPxGraF-16
❑ 97SPxSil-16
❑ 97SPxSte-16
❑ 97StaClu-40
❑ 97StaCluMat-40
❑ 97StaCluMOP-40
❑ 97Stu-37
❑ 97StuMasS-19
❑ 97StuMasS8-19
❑ 97StuPrePG-37
❑ 97StuPrePS-37
❑ 97Top-305
❑ 97TopChr-102
❑ 97TopChrJ-102
❑ 97TopChrR-102
❑ 97TopGal-84
❑ 97TopGalPPI-84
❑ 97TopHobM-HM19
❑ 97TopIntF-ILM5
❑ 97TopIntFR-ILM5
❑ 97TopMemO5-45
❑ 97TopScr-18
❑ 97TopScrT-18
❑ 97TopSta-10
❑ 97TopStaAM-10
❑ 97UD3-15
❑ 97Ult-169
❑ 97UltChe-A9
❑ 97UltDouT-12
❑ 97UltGolME-169
❑ 97UltHitM-17
❑ 97UltHRK-9
❑ 97UltPlaME-169
❑ 97UltPowP-A10
❑ 97UltRBIK-8
❑ 97UltSeaC-11
❑ 97UppDec-30
❑ 97UppDec-189
❑ 97UppDecAG-AG12
❑ 97UppDecLDC-LD13
❑ 97UppDecP-9
❑ 97UppDecPE-9
❑ 97UppDecPP-PP5
❑ 97UppDecPPJ-PP5
❑ 97UppDecRP-RP13
❑ 97Zen-16
❑ 97Zen8x10-10
❑ 97Zen8x1D-10
❑ 98Bow-50
❑ 98BowBes-87
❑ 98BowBesAR-87
❑ 98BowBesR-87
❑ 98BowChr-50
❑ 98BowChrGA-50
❑ 98BowChrGAR-50
❑ 98BowChrI-50
❑ 98BowChrIR-50
❑ 98BowChrR-50
❑ 98BowChrR-19
❑ 98BowChrRR-19
❑ 98BowGolA-50
❑ 98BowInt-50
❑ 98CirThu-163
❑ 98CirThuRav-163
❑ 98CirThuSupRav-163
❑ 98ColCho-330
❑ 98ColChoCtG-CG17A
❑ 98ColChoCtG-CG17B
❑ 98ColChoCtG-CG17C
❑ 98ColChoCtGExch-CG17
❑ 98ColChoCtGIW-CG17
❑ 98ColChoER-ER5
❑ 98ColChoMBH-9
❑ 98ColChoS'-7
❑ 98ColChoSQ-SQ77
❑ 98CroRoy-31
❑ 98CroRoyHRF-2
❑ 98CroRoyPotG-8
❑ 98CubSosC-1
❑ 98Don-86
❑ 98DonCol-86
❑ 98DonColE-441
❑ 98DonColL-343
❑ 98DonColP-590
❑ 98DonColS-86
❑ 98DonCruG-61
❑ 98DonCruP-61
❑ 98DonCruR-61
❑ 98DonEli-41
❑ 98DonEliA-41
❑ 98DonEliS-41
❑ 98DonGolPP-86
❑ 98DonLonL-11
❑ 98DonPre-40
❑ 98DonPreSeat-40
❑ 98DonPriCD-86
❑ 98DonPriCE-441
❑ 98DonPriCL-343
❑ 98DonPriCP-590
❑ 98DonSig-32
❑ 98DonSigP-32
❑ 98DonSilPP-86
❑ 98E-X2-29
❑ 98E-X2ECFut-29
❑ 98E-X2ECNow-29
❑ 98Fin-85
❑ 98FinMysF1-M41
❑ 98FinMysF1-M46
❑ 98FinMysF1-M47
❑ 98FinMysFR-M41
❑ 98FinMysFR-M46
❑ 98FinMysFR-M47
❑ 98FinNo--85
❑ 98FinNo-R-85
❑ 98FinPowZ-P12
❑ 98FinRef-85
❑ 98FinStaS-SS14
❑ 98FlaShoLeg0-91
❑ 98FlaShoLeg1-91
❑ 98FlaShoLeg2-91
❑ 98FlaShoLeg3-91
❑ 98FlaShoLegM-91
❑ 98FlaShoR0-91
❑ 98FlaShoR1-91
❑ 98FlaShoR2-91
❑ 98FlaShoR3-91
❑ 98Fle-211
❑ 98FleUpd-U2
❑ 98FleVin'-11
❑ 98FleVin'C-11
❑ 98Lea-144
❑ 98LeaFraDA-144
❑ 98LeaFraF-144
❑ 98LeaFraM-144
❑ 98LeaFraM-144
❑ 98LeaFraMDC-144
❑ 98LeaFraMDC-144
❑ 98LeaFraMZ2-144
❑ 98LeaRS-13
❑ 98LeaRS-175
❑ 98LeaRS-337
❑ 98LeaRS-339
❑ 98LeaRSLHolo-13
❑ 98LeaRSLHolo-175
❑ 98LeaRSLHolo-337
❑ 98LeaRSLHolo-339
❑ 98LeaRSLong-13
❑ 98LeaRSLong-175
❑ 98LeaRSLong-337
❑ 98LeaRSLong-339
❑ 98LeaRTrue-13
❑ 98LeaRTrue-175
❑ 98LeaRTrue-337
❑ 98LeaRTrue-339
❑ 98MetUni-60
❑ 98MetUniPMG-60
❑ 98Pac-258
❑ 98PacAur-116
❑ 98PacHomRH-2
❑ 98PacHomRH-2
❑ 98PacHomRH-4
❑ 98PacHomRH-6
❑ 98PacHomRH-8
❑ 98PacHomRH-10
❑ 98PacHomRH-12
❑ 98PacHomRH-14
❑ 98PacHomRH-16
❑ 98PacHomRH-18
❑ 98PacHomRH-20
❑ 98PacHomRH-22
❑ 98PacHomRH-24
❑ 98PacHomRH-26
❑ 98PacHomRH-28
❑ 98PacHomRH-30
❑ 98PacHomRH-32
❑ 98PacHomRH-34
❑ 98PacHomRH-36
❑ 98PacHomRH-38
❑ 98PacHomRH-40
❑ 98PacHomRH-42
❑ 98PacHomRH-44
❑ 98PacHomRH-46
❑ 98PacHomRH-48
❑ 98PacHomRH-50
❑ 98PacHomRH-52
❑ 98PacHomRH-54
❑ 98PacHomRH-56
❑ 98PacHomRH-58
❑ 98PacHomRH-60
❑ 98PacHomRH-62
❑ 98PacHomRH-64
❑ 98PacHomRH-66
❑ 98PacHomRH-3
❑ 98PacInv-85
❑ 98PacInvGems-135
❑ 98PacInvPBlue-85
❑ 98PacInvSilv-85
❑ 98PacInvTeam-5
❑ 98PacLatotML-7
❑ 98PacNes-10
❑ 98PacOme-51
❑ 98PacOmeOnIns-25
❑ 98PacOmeR-51
❑ 98PacOnl-154
❑ 98PacOnlR-154
❑ 98PacOnlWC-154
❑ 98PacPar-142
❑ 98PacParC-142
❑ 98PacParG-142
❑ 98PacParHS-142
❑ 98PacParI-44
❑ 98PacParPB-142
❑ 98PacParR-142
❑ 98PacParTC-17
❑ 98PacPlaB-258
❑ 98PacRedT-258
❑ 98PacSil-258
❑ 98PacTeaC-16
❑ 98Pin-53
❑ 98PinArtP-PP48
❑ 98PinIns-14
❑ 98PinIns-141
❑ 98PinInsCE-14
❑ 98PinInsCE-141
❑ 98PinInsDE-14
❑ 98PinInsDE-141
❑ 98PinInsSG-11AB
❑ 98PinInsSG-11CD
❑ 98PinInsSGS-11AB
❑ 98PinInsSGS-11CD
❑ 98PinMinB-21
❑ 98PinMinCB-21
❑ 98PinMinCBAP-21
❑ 98PinMinCGP-21
❑ 98PinMinCGPAP-21
❑ 98PinMinCN-21
❑ 98PinMinCNAP-21
❑ 98PinMinCSGR-21
❑ 98PinMinDC-21
❑ 98PinMinG-21
❑ 98PinMinMCSS-21
❑ 98PinMinS-21
❑ 98PinMusC-PP48
❑ 98PinPer-41
❑ 98PinPerPP-41
❑ 98PinPerSftF-47
❑ 98PinPlu-136
❑ 98PinPluAP-PP45
❑ 98PinPluGAP-PP45
❑ 98PinPluLM-28
❑ 98PinPluMAP-PP45
❑ 98PinPluY-9
❑ 98PinPreP-53
❑ 98PinSna-CC12
❑ 98PinSna-CC13
❑ 98Revo-32
❑ 98RevoFP-14
❑ 98RevoShow-25
❑ 98RevoSS-32
❑ 98Sco-65
❑ 98Sco-260
❑ 98ScoRT-19
❑ 98ScoRTSS-PP19
❑ 98ScoRTSSAP-PP19
❑ 98ScoRTSSAP1-PP19
❑ 98ScoSS-PP27
❑ 98ScoSSAP-PP27
❑ 98SkyDugA-7
❑ 98SkyDugAIA-7
❑ 98SP Aut-SD29
❑ 98SP AutSD-SD29
❑ 98SP AutSDT-SD29
❑ 98SpoIll-115
❑ 98SpoIllEE-115
❑ 98SpoIllFE-115
❑ 98SpoIllODMP-OD6
❑ 98SpoIllTaN-133
❑ 98SpoIllTaNEE-133
❑ 98SpoIllWSF-147
❑ 98SpoIllWSFEE-147
❑ 98SpoIllWSFFE-147

- ❑ 98SPxFin-41
- ❑ 98SPxFin-70
- ❑ 98SPxFin-148
- ❑ 98SPxFinHRH-HR3
- ❑ 98SPxFinR-41
- ❑ 98SPxFinR-70
- ❑ 98SPxFinR-148
- ❑ 98SPxFinS-41
- ❑ 98SPxFinS-70
- ❑ 98SPxFinS-148
- ❑ 98StaCluFDI-16
- ❑ 98StaClul-16
- ❑ 98StaCluOneK-16
- ❑ 98StaCluPP-16
- ❑ 98Stu-44
- ❑ 98StuGPP-44
- ❑ 98StuSPP-44
- ❑ 98Top-307
- ❑ 98TopChr-307
- ❑ 98TopChrR-307
- ❑ 98TopDevR-307
- ❑ 98TopDia-307
- ❑ 98TopGal-134
- ❑ 98TopGalGP-134
- ❑ 98TopGalOPP-134
- ❑ 98TopGalPPI-134
- ❑ 98TopGalPPIA-134
- ❑ 98TopGolLabC1-83
- ❑ 98TopGolLabC1B-83
- ❑ 98TopGolLabC1One-83
- ❑ 98TopGolLabC1R-83
- ❑ 98TopGolLabC2-83
- ❑ 98TopGolLabC2B-83
- ❑ 98TopGolLabC2One-83
- ❑ 98TopGolLabC2R-83
- ❑ 98TopGolLabC3-83
- ❑ 98TopGolLabC3B-83
- ❑ 98TopGolLabC3One-83
- ❑ 98TopGolLabC3R-83
- ❑ 98TopGolLHRR-HR4
- ❑ 98TopGolLHRRB-HR4
- ❑ 98TopGolLHRRR-HR4
- ❑ 98TopMiniC-307
- ❑ 98TopMysF-ILM17
- ❑ 98TopMysFR-ILM17
- ❑ 98TopOpeD-134
- ❑ 98TopSta-93
- ❑ 98TopSta'S-39
- ❑ 98TopSta'SGH-39
- ❑ 98TopStaB-93
- ❑ 98TopStaG-G6
- ❑ 98TopStaG-93
- ❑ 98TopStaGG-G6
- ❑ 98TopStaGGR-G6
- ❑ 98TopStaGR-93
- ❑ 98TopStaGS-G6
- ❑ 98TopStaS-93
- ❑ 98TopStaSteG-39
- ❑ 98TopSup-23
- ❑ 98TopSup-23
- ❑ 98TopTek-28
- ❑ 98TopTekD-28
- ❑ 98UD3-38
- ❑ 98UD3-128
- ❑ 98UD3-218
- ❑ 98UD3DieCut-38
- ❑ 98UD3DieCut-128
- ❑ 98UD3DieCut-218
- ❑ 98UD3PCBlowup-38
- ❑ 98Ult-95
- ❑ 98UltGolM-95
- ❑ 98UltMas-95
- ❑ 98UltPlaM-95
- ❑ 98UppDec-8
- ❑ 98UppDec-325
- ❑ 98UppDec10AP-51
- ❑ 98UppDec1APR-51
- ❑ 98UppDecAG-AG22
- ❑ 98UppDecAGDC-AG22
- ❑ 98UppDecNP-NP10
- ❑ 98UppDecR-19
- ❑ 98UppDecRBBop-BB23
- ❑ 98UppDecRQL-Q23
- ❑ 98UppDecTMT-26
- ❑ 98UppDecTMTG-26
- ❑ 98Zen-4
- ❑ 98Zen5 xx7-54
- ❑ 98Zen5x7GoldImp-54
- ❑ 98Zen5x7Imp-54
- ❑ 98ZenZ-G-4
- ❑ 98ZenZ-S-4
- ❑ 99199Fin-109
- ❑ 99199Fin-250
- ❑ 99199Fin-261
- ❑ 99AllMysFR-M13
- ❑ 99AurComP-3A
- ❑ 99AurComP-3B
- ❑ 99AurKinotML-3
- ❑ 99AurOn DL-4
- ❑ 99AurPenF-5
- ❑ 99AurPenF-5
- ❑ 99AurPenFB-5
- ❑ 99AurPenFS-5
- ❑ 99AurSty-5
- ❑ 99Bow-245
- ❑ 99BowBes-66
- ❑ 99BowBes-91
- ❑ 99BowBesAR-66
- ❑ 99BowBesAR-91
- ❑ 99BowBesFBMI-FB3
- ❑ 99BowBesFBMII-FB3
- ❑ 99BowBesFBMIII-FB3
- ❑ 99BowBesMI-M4
- ❑ 99BowBesMIAR-M4
- ❑ 99BowBesMIR-M4
- ❑ 99BowBesR-66
- ❑ 99BowBesR-91
- ❑ 99BowChrDA-DA16
- ❑ 99BowChrDAR-DA16
- ❑ 99BowGol-245
- ❑ 99BowInt-245
- ❑ 99CroRoyB-30
- ❑ 99CroRoyC2-3
- ❑ 99CroRoyCCDB-3
- ❑ 99CroRoyCCG-3
- ❑ 99CroRoyCCG-3
- ❑ 99CroRoyCCLB-3
- ❑ 99CroRoyCCP-3
- ❑ 99CroRoyCCP-3
- ❑ 99CroRoyCCR-3
- ❑ 99CroRoyL-30
- ❑ 99CroRoyLL-4
- ❑ 99CroRoyMP-5
- ❑ 99CroRoyOD-30
- ❑ 99CroRoyPotG-7
- ❑ 99CroRoyPP-7
- ❑ 99CroRoyPPN-7
- ❑ 99DumSet-153
- ❑ 99E-X Cen-5
- ❑ 99E-X CenECFut-5
- ❑ 99E-X CenECNow-5
- ❑ 99E-XCenFoF'-18
- ❑ 99E-XCenMotC-3
- ❑ 99FinAarAwC-HA6
- ❑ 99FinAarAwCR-HA6
- ❑ 99FinCom-C4
- ❑ 99FinComDualR-C4
- ❑ 99FinFraR-FR8
- ❑ 99FinFraRR-FR8
- ❑ 99FinGolRef-109
- ❑ 99FinGolRef-250
- ❑ 99FinGolRef-261
- ❑ 99FinLeal-L2
- ❑ 99FinMil-M16
- ❑ 99FinPeelHyp-3
- ❑ 99FinPeelSpark-3
- ❑ 99FinPeeSS-3
- ❑ 99FinProF-PF2
- ❑ 99FinProF-PF12
- ❑ 99FinProF-PF32
- ❑ 99FinProF-PF41
- ❑ 99FinRef-109
- ❑ 99FinRef-250
- ❑ 99FinRef-261
- ❑ 99FinSplS-SS1
- ❑ 99FinSplSDR-SS1
- ❑ 99FinTeaFB-TF3
- ❑ 99FinTeaFBR-TF3
- ❑ 99FinTeaFG-TF3
- ❑ 99FinTeaFGR-TF3
- ❑ 99FinTeaFR-TF3
- ❑ 99FinTeaFRR-TF3
- ❑ 99FlaShoLeg1-2
- ❑ 99FlaShoLeg2-2
- ❑ 99FlaShoLeg3-2
- ❑ 99FlaShoLegM1-2
- ❑ 99FlaShoLegM2-2
- ❑ 99FlaShoLegM3-2
- ❑ 99FlaShoMoG-14
- ❑ 99FlaShoR1-2
- ❑ 99FlaShoR2-2
- ❑ 99FlaShoR3-2
- ❑ 99Fle-2
- ❑ 99Fle-594
- ❑ 99FleBri-66
- ❑ 99FleBri2G-66
- ❑ 99FleBriBlu-66
- ❑ 99FleBriGol-66
- ❑ 99FleBriSS-3
- ❑ 99FleBriSSP-3
- ❑ 99FleDiaM-13
- ❑ 99FleDiaSkiSheet-NNO
- ❑ 99FleGoiYar-13
- ❑ 99FleGolM-13
- ❑ 99FleMys-66
- ❑ 99FleMys-153
- ❑ 99FleMysE-9
- ❑ 99FleMysG-66
- ❑ 99FleMysM-66
- ❑ 99FleMysM-153
- ❑ 99FleSta9-2
- ❑ 99FleSta9-594
- ❑ 99FleVin'-2
- ❑ 99FleWarT-2
- ❑ 99FleWarT-594
- ❑ 99HomHer-2
- ❑ 99HomHer-6
- ❑ 99HomHer-10
- ❑ 99HomHer-14
- ❑ 99MetUni-100
- ❑ 99MetUni-242
- ❑ 99MetUni-286
- ❑ 99MetUniGM-100
- ❑ 99MetUniGM-242
- ❑ 99MetUniGM-286
- ❑ 99MetUniPMG-100
- ❑ 99MetUniPMG-242
- ❑ 99MetUniPMG-286
- ❑ 99MetUniSamp-NNOA
- ❑ 99MetUniSamp-NNO
- ❑ 99Pac-66
- ❑ 99Pac-66A
- ❑ 99PacAur-36
- ❑ 99PacAurOD-36
- ❑ 99PacCraCho-7
- ❑ 99PacCroC-60
- ❑ 99PacCroC-27
- ❑ 99PacCroCITC-4
- ❑ 99PacCroCPB-60
- ❑ 99PacCroCPC-7
- ❑ 99PacCroCTC-6
- ❑ 99PacCroCTM-4
- ❑ 99PacDynaD-12
- ❑ 99PacDynaDT-12
- ❑ 99PacGolCDC-23
- ❑ 99PacInv-32
- ❑ 99PacInvDM-3
- ❑ 99PacInvFP-6
- ❑ 99PacInvGotG-3
- ❑ 99PacInvOD-32
- ❑ 99PacInvPB-32
- ❑ 99PacInvSF-6
- ❑ 99PacInvSF-6B
- ❑ 99PacInvSH-6
- ❑ 99PacInvSH-6B
- ❑ 99PacInvTA-5
- ❑ 99PacOme-52
- ❑ 99PacOme5T-12
- ❑ 99PacOme5TT-12
- ❑ 99PacOmeC-52
- ❑ 99PacOmeDD-8
- ❑ 99PacOmeDM-10
- ❑ 99PacOmeEP-6
- ❑ 99PacOmeEP1o1-6
- ❑ 99PacOmeG-52
- ❑ 99PacOmeH'-6
- ❑ 99PacOmePB-52
- ❑ 99PacPar-52
- ❑ 99PacParC-52
- ❑ 99PacParCB-4
- ❑ 99PacParCBPP-4
- ❑ 99PacParFC-5
- ❑ 99PacParG-52
- ❑ 99PacParHoloGold-52
- ❑ 99PacParHS-52
- ❑ 99PacParOD-52
- ❑ 99PacParPB-9
- ❑ 99PacParPB-52
- ❑ 99PacParRed-52
- ❑ 99PacParTC-6
- ❑ 99PacPlaB-66
- ❑ 99PacPlaB-66A
- ❑ 99PacPri-30
- ❑ 99PacPriAotG-6
- ❑ 99PacPriBL-7
- ❑ 99PacPriDG-7
- ❑ 99PacPriEP-3
- ❑ 99PacPriHB-30
- ❑ 99PacPriHG-30
- ❑ 99PacPriHM-30
- ❑ 99PacPriHP-30
- ❑ 99PacPriRed-30
- ❑ 99PacPriS-18
- ❑ 99PacPriS206-18
- ❑ 99PacPriS206R-18
- ❑ 99PacPriSE-18
- ❑ 99PacPriSHRH-2
- ❑ 99PacPriSHRH-4
- ❑ 99PacPriSHRH-6
- ❑ 99PacPriSHRH-8
- ❑ 99PacPriSHRH-10
- ❑ 99PacPriSHRH-12
- ❑ 99PacPriSHRH-14
- ❑ 99PacPriSHRH-16
- ❑ 99PacPriSHRH-18
- ❑ 99PacPriSHRH-19
- ❑ 99PacPriSHRH-20
- ❑ 99PacPriSP-18
- ❑ 99PacPriSP-18
- ❑ 99PacPriSV-18
- ❑ 99PacRed-66
- ❑ 99PacRed-66A
- ❑ 99PacTeaC-17
- ❑ 99PacTim-15
- ❑ 99Pin-25
- ❑ 99Rev-31
- ❑ 99RevDiaL-10
- ❑ 99RevFouP-5
- ❑ 99RevMLBIcon-3
- ❑ 99RevPremDate-31
- ❑ 99RevRet-31
- ❑ 99RevShaSS-31
- ❑ 99RevThoitS-6
- ❑ 99RevTri-4
- ❑ 99RevTri-4
- ❑ 99SkyMolM-145
- ❑ 99SkyMolMF-45
- ❑ 99SkyMolMFS-45
- ❑ 99SkyMolMFT-45
- ❑ 99SkyMolMX-145
- ❑ 99SkyPre-144
- ❑ 99SkyPre-279
- ❑ 99SkyPreR-144
- ❑ 99SkyPreR-279
- ❑ 99SkyPreSotG-15
- ❑ 99SkyThu-266
- ❑ 99SkyThuDial1-D9
- ❑ 99SkyThuHip-H12
- ❑ 99SkyThuInD-ID8
- ❑ 99SkyThuRant-266
- ❑ 99SkyThuRave-266
- ❑ 99SkyThuTur-TC9
- ❑ 99SkyThuwww-WB9
- ❑ 99SP Aut-18
- ❑ 99SP Aut-122
- ❑ 99SP Aut-123
- ❑ 99SP AutEF-E9
- ❑ 99SP AutHRC-HR2
- ❑ 99SP AutHRC-HR42
- ❑ 99SP AutHRC-HR44
- ❑ 99SP AutHRC-HR47
- ❑ 99SP AutHRC-HR49
- ❑ 99SP AutHRC-HR51
- ❑ 99SP AutHRC-HR53
- ❑ 99SP AutHRC-HR55
- ❑ 99SP AutHRC-HR57
- ❑ 99SP AutHRC-HR59
- ❑ 99SP AutHRC-HR66
- ❑ 99SP AutR-R9
- ❑ 99SPAutHRCDC-HR2
- ❑ 99SPAutHRCDC-HR42
- ❑ 99SPAutHRCDC-HR44
- ❑ 99SPAutHRCDC-HR47
- ❑ 99SPAutHRCDC-HR49
- ❑ 99SPAutHRCDC-HR51
- ❑ 99SPAutHRCDC-HR53
- ❑ 99SPAutHRCDC-HR55
- ❑ 99SPAutHRCDC-HR57
- ❑ 99SPAutHRCDC-HR59
- ❑ 99SPAutHRCDC-HR66
- ❑ 99SpoIll-11
- ❑ 99SpoIll-20
- ❑ 99SpoIll-38
- ❑ 99SpoIll-108
- ❑ 99SpoIllDD-7
- ❑ 99SpoIllF4-2
- ❑ 99SpoIllF4E-2
- ❑ 99SpoIllH-22
- ❑ 99SPx-27
- ❑ 99SPxDom-FB6
- ❑ 99SPxFinR-27
- ❑ 99SPxFinS-27
- ❑ 99SPxPowE-PE9
- ❑ 99SPxPreS-PS2
- ❑ 99SPxStaF-SF6
- ❑ 99StaClu-66
- ❑ 99StaCluC-SCC26
- ❑ 99StaCluCR-SCC26
- ❑ 99StaCluFDI-66
- ❑ 99StaCluNC-NC2
- ❑ 99StaCluOoaK-66
- ❑ 99StaCluPP-66
- ❑ 99StaCluTI-T8A
- ❑ 99StaCluTI-T14A
- ❑ 99StaCluTL-T8A
- ❑ 99StaCluTL-T14A
- ❑ 99StaCluTL-T8A
- ❑ 99StaCluTL-T14A
- ❑ 99StaCluVR-VR2
- ❑ 99ThuSkySupR-266
- ❑ 99Top-66
- ❑ 99Top-202
- ❑ 99Top-225
- ❑ 99Top-229
- ❑ 99Top-454
- ❑ 99Top-461A
- ❑ 99Top-461B
- ❑ 99Top-461C
- ❑ 99Top-461D
- ❑ 99Top-461E
- ❑ 99Top-461F
- ❑ 99Top-461G
- ❑ 99Top-461H
- ❑ 99Top-461I
- ❑ 99Top-461J
- ❑ 99Top-461K
- ❑ 99Top-461L
- ❑ 99Top-461M
- ❑ 99Top-461N
- ❑ 99Top-461O
- ❑ 99Top-461P
- ❑ 99Top-461Q
- ❑ 99Top-461R
- ❑ 99Top-461S
- ❑ 99Top-461T
- ❑ 99Top-461U
- ❑ 99Top-461V
- ❑ 99Top-461W
- ❑ 99Top-461X
- ❑ 99Top-461Y
- ❑ 99Top-461Z
- ❑ 99Top-461AA
- ❑ 99Top-461AB
- ❑ 99Top-461AC
- ❑ 99Top-461AD
- ❑ 99Top-461AE
- ❑ 99Top-461AF
- ❑ 99Top-461AG
- ❑ 99Top-461AH
- ❑ 99Top-461AI
- ❑ 99Top-461AJ
- ❑ 99Top-461AK
- ❑ 99Top-461AL
- ❑ 99Top-461AM
- ❑ 99Top-461AN
- ❑ 99Top-461AO
- ❑ 99Top-461AP
- ❑ 99Top-461AR
- ❑ 99Top-461AS
- ❑ 99Top-461AT
- ❑ 99Top-461AU
- ❑ 99Top-461AV
- ❑ 99Top-461AW
- ❑ 99Top-461AX
- ❑ 99Top-461AY
- ❑ 99Top-461AZ
- ❑ 99Top-461BB
- ❑ 99Top-461CC
- ❑ 99Top-461DD
- ❑ 99Top-461EE
- ❑ 99Top-461FF
- ❑ 99Top-461GG
- ❑ 99Top-461HH
- ❑ 99Top-461II
- ❑ 99Top-461JJ
- ❑ 99Top-461KK
- ❑ 99Top-461LL
- ❑ 99Top-461MM
- ❑ 99Top-461NN
- ❑ 99Top-461OO
- ❑ 99Top-461PP
- ❑ 99TopActF-11
- ❑ 99TopActFAU-11
- ❑ 99TopActFCU-11
- ❑ 99TopAll-AM2
- ❑ 99TopAllMF-M13
- ❑ 99TopBlaLC1-66
- ❑ 99TopBlaLC2-66
- ❑ 99TopBlaLC3-66
- ❑ 99TopChr-66
- ❑ 99TopChr-202
- ❑ 99TopChr-225
- ❑ 99TopChr-229
- ❑ 99TopChr-454
- ❑ 99TopChr-461A
- ❑ 99TopChr-461B
- ❑ 99TopChr-461C
- ❑ 99TopChr-461D
- ❑ 99TopChr-461E
- ❑ 99TopChr-461F
- ❑ 99TopChr-461G
- ❑ 99TopChr-461H
- ❑ 99TopChr-461I
- ❑ 99TopChr-461J
- ❑ 99TopChr-461K
- ❑ 99TopChr-461L
- ❑ 99TopChr-461M
- ❑ 99TopChr-461N
- ❑ 99TopChr-461O
- ❑ 99TopChr-461P
- ❑ 99TopChr-461Q
- ❑ 99TopChr-461R
- ❑ 99TopChr-461S
- ❑ 99TopChr-461T
- ❑ 99TopChr-461U
- ❑ 99TopChr-461V
- ❑ 99TopChr-461W
- ❑ 99TopChr-461X
- ❑ 99TopChr-461Y
- ❑ 99TopChr-461Z
- ❑ 99TopChr-461AA
- ❑ 99TopChr-461AB
- ❑ 99TopChr-461AC
- ❑ 99TopChr-461AD
- ❑ 99TopChr-461AE
- ❑ 99TopChr-461AF
- ❑ 99TopChr-461AG
- ❑ 99TopChr-461AH
- ❑ 99TopChr-461AI
- ❑ 99TopChr-461AJ
- ❑ 99TopChr-461AK
- ❑ 99TopChr-461AL
- ❑ 99TopChr-461AM
- ❑ 99TopChr-461AN
- ❑ 99TopChr-461AO
- ❑ 99TopChr-461AP
- ❑ 99TopChr-461AR
- ❑ 99TopChr-461AS
- ❑ 99TopChr-461AT
- ❑ 99TopChr-461AU
- ❑ 99TopChr-461AV
- ❑ 99TopChr-461AW
- ❑ 99TopChr-461AX
- ❑ 99TopChr-461AY
- ❑ 99TopChr-461AZ
- ❑ 99TopChr-461BB
- ❑ 99TopChr-461CC
- ❑ 99TopChr-461DD
- ❑ 99TopChr-461EE
- ❑ 99TopChr-461FF
- ❑ 99TopChr-461GG
- ❑ 99TopChr-461HH
- ❑ 99TopChr-461II
- ❑ 99TopChr-461JJ
- ❑ 99TopChr-461KK
- ❑ 99TopChr-461LL
- ❑ 99TopChr-461MM
- ❑ 99TopChr-461NN
- ❑ 99TopChr-461OO
- ❑ 99TopChr-461PP
- ❑ 99TopChrA-AE2
- ❑ 99TopChrAR-AE2
- ❑ 99TopChrF1-FF11
- ❑ 99TopChrF1R-FF11
- ❑ 99TopChrLotD-LD3
- ❑ 99TopChrLotDR-LD3
- ❑ 99TopChrR-66
- ❑ 99TopChrR-202
- ❑ 99TopChrR-225
- ❑ 99TopChrR-229
- ❑ 99TopChrR-454
- ❑ 99TopChrR-461A
- ❑ 99TopChrR-461B
- ❑ 99TopChrR-461C
- ❑ 99TopChrR-461D
- ❑ 99TopChrR-461E
- ❑ 99TopChrR-461F
- ❑ 99TopChrR-461G
- ❑ 99TopChrR-461H
- ❑ 99TopChrR-461I
- ❑ 99TopChrR-461J
- ❑ 99TopChrR-461K
- ❑ 99TopChrR-461L
- ❑ 99TopChrR-461M
- ❑ 99TopChrR-461N
- ❑ 99TopChrR-461O
- ❑ 99TopChrR-461P
- ❑ 99TopChrR-461Q
- ❑ 99TopChrR-461R
- ❑ 99TopChrR-461S
- ❑ 99TopChrR-461T
- ❑ 99TopChrR-461U
- ❑ 99TopChrR-461V
- ❑ 99TopChrR-461W
- ❑ 99TopChrR-461X
- ❑ 99TopChrR-461Y

❑ 99TopChrR-461Z
❑ 99TopChrR-461AA
❑ 99TopChrR-461AB
❑ 99TopChrR-461AC
❑ 99TopChrR-461AD
❑ 99TopChrR-461AE
❑ 99TopChrR-461AF
❑ 99TopChrR-461AG
❑ 99TopChrR-461AH
❑ 99TopChrR-461AI
❑ 99TopChrR-461AJ
❑ 99TopChrR-461AK
❑ 99TopChrR-461AL
❑ 99TopChrR-461AM
❑ 99TopChrR-461AN
❑ 99TopChrR-461AO
❑ 99TopChrR-461AP
❑ 99TopChrR-461AR
❑ 99TopChrR-461AS
❑ 99TopChrR-461AT
❑ 99TopChrR-461AU
❑ 99TopChrR-461AV
❑ 99TopChrR-461AW
❑ 99TopChrR-461AX
❑ 99TopChrR-461AY
❑ 99TopChrR-461AZ
❑ 99TopChrR-461BB
❑ 99TopChrR-461CC
❑ 99TopChrR-461DD
❑ 99TopChrR-461EE
❑ 99TopChrR-461FF
❑ 99TopChrR-461GG
❑ 99TopChrR-461HH
❑ 99TopChrR-461II
❑ 99TopChrR-461JJ
❑ 99TopChrR-461KK
❑ 99TopChrR-461LL
❑ 99TopChrR-461MM
❑ 99TopChrR-461NN
❑ 99TopChrR-461OO
❑ 99TopChrR-461PP
❑ 99TopChrRN-RN5
❑ 99TopChrRNR-RN5
❑ 99TopGal-8
❑ 99TopGal-104
❑ 99TopGalAG-AG6
❑ 99TopGalE-E1
❑ 99TopGalGoH-GH2
❑ 99TopGalHer-TH10
❑ 99TopGalHerP-TH10
❑ 99TopGalPP-8
❑ 99TopGalPP-104
❑ 99TopGalPPI-8
❑ 99TopGalPPI-104
❑ 99TopGolL-66
❑ 99TopGolLC1-66
❑ 99TopGolLC2-66
❑ 99TopGolLOtO-66
❑ 99TopLorotD-LD3
❑ 99TopMVPP-66
❑ 99TopMVPP-454
❑ 99TopOpeD-37
❑ 99TopOpeD-164
❑ 99TopOpeDO-1
❑ 99TopOver-A5
❑ 99TopPicP-P6
❑ 99TopPowB-PB4
❑ 99TopPowBR-PB4
❑ 99TopPre-PP2
❑ 99TopRecN-RN5
❑ 99TopRecNG-RN5
❑ 99TopRedLC1-66
❑ 99TopRedLC2-66
❑ 99TopRedLC3-66
❑ 99TopSta-9
❑ 99TopSta-179
❑ 99TopSta'S-39
❑ 99TopSta'SG-39
❑ 99TopSta'SGDH-39
❑ 99TopSta1Foil-9
❑ 99TopSta2Foil-9
❑ 99TopSta3Foil-9
❑ 99TopSta4Foil-9
❑ 99TopStaFoil-9
❑ 99TopStaFoil-179
❑ 99TopStaFS-9
❑ 99TopStaG-G10
❑ 99TopStaGFoil-G10
❑ 99TopStaOS-9
❑ 99TopStaTS-9
❑ 99TopStaTS-9
❑ 99TopSupC-10
❑ 99TopSupC-35
❑ 99TopSupCR-10
❑ 99TopSupCR-35
❑ 99TopTek-6A
❑ 99TopTek-6B
❑ 99TopTekG-6A
❑ 99TopTekG-6B
❑ 99TopTekT-T5
❑ 99UD Cho-45
❑ 99UD Cho-67
❑ 99UD ChoBU-2
❑ 99UD ChoBUCG-10
❑ 99UD ChoMBH-B8
❑ 99UD ChoP-67
❑ 99UD ChoPCR-45
❑ 99UD ChoPCR-67
❑ 99UD ChoS-2
❑ 99UD ChoSD-2
❑ 99UD ChoSHR-2
❑ 99UD ChoST-2
❑ 99UD ChoYW-Y5
❑ 99UD Ion-15
❑ 99UD Ion-69
❑ 99UD IonC-C16
❑ 99UD IonH-H16
❑ 99UD IonR-15
❑ 99UD IonR-69
❑ 99UDHolo-14
❑ 99UDHoloAUsome-14
❑ 99UDHoloLau-L3
❑ 99UDHoloLauG-L3
❑ 99UDHoloStar-S3
❑ 99UDHoloStarG-S3
❑ 99Ult-192
❑ 99Ult-224
❑ 99UltGolM-192
❑ 99UltGolM-224
❑ 99UltMas-192
❑ 99UltMas-224
❑ 99UltPlaM-192
❑ 99UltPlaM-224
❑ 99UltRBIK-16
❑ 99UppDec-235
❑ 99UppDec-255
❑ 99UppDec-331
❑ 99UppDec-520
❑ 99UppDec-528
❑ 99UppDec10AT-X28
❑ 99UppDec10ATD-X28
❑ 99UppDec10ATHR-X28
❑ 99UppDec10ATT-X28
❑ 99UppDecBD-18
❑ 99UppDecBDAPH-SS
❑ 99UppDecBDD-18
❑ 99UppDecBDDom-D22
❑ 99UppDecBDDomE-D22
❑ 99UppDecBDMN-M16
❑ 99UppDecBDMNE-M16
❑ 99UppDecBDQ-18
❑ 99UppDecBDT-18
❑ 99UppDecCf7-2
❑ 99UppDecCf7-66
❑ 99UppDecCf7-C2
❑ 99UppDecCf7Cf7P-C2
❑ 99UppDecCf7LL-L3
❑ 99UppDecCf7SftF-S3
❑ 99UppDecCL-65
❑ 99UppDecCLCC-65
❑ 99UppDecCLEM-EM6
❑ 99UppDecCLM-C16
❑ 99UppDecCo7CE-2
❑ 99UppDecCo7CE-66
❑ 99UppDecE-19
❑ 99UppDecE-138
❑ 99UppDecE-170
❑ 99UppDecE2C-2K10
❑ 99UppDecEDF-D3
❑ 99UppDecEDFFXG-D3
❑ 99UppDecEFXG-9
❑ 99UppDecEFXG-138
❑ 99UppDecEFXG-170
❑ 99UppDecEL1-235
❑ 99UppDecEL1-255
❑ 99UppDecEL1-331
❑ 99UppDecEL1-520
❑ 99UppDecEL1-528
❑ 99UppDecEL2-235
❑ 99UppDecEL2-255
❑ 99UppDecEL2-331
❑ 99UppDecEL2-520
❑ 99UppDecEL2-528
❑ 99UppDecEUR-U3
❑ 99UppDecF-F10
❑ 99UppDecFD-F10
❑ 99UppDecFQ-F10
❑ 99UppDecFT-F10
❑ 99UppDecGJ-SS
❑ 99UppDecM-39
❑ 99UppDecM-219
❑ 99UppDecM-P2
❑ 99UppDecMD-D6
❑ 99UppDecMGS-39
❑ 99UppDecMGS-219
❑ 99UppDecMHFS-39
❑ 99UppDecMHFS-219
❑ 99UppDecMP-39
❑ 99UppDecMSS-39
❑ 99UppDecMSS-219
❑ 99UppDecMST-T3
❑ 99UppDecMST-S3
❑ 99UppDecO-40
❑ 99UppDecO-87
❑ 99UppDecOAPoH-SS
❑ 99UppDecOMP-S19
❑ 99UppDecOSO-40
❑ 99UppDecOSO-87
❑ 99UppDecOWP-R2
❑ 99UppDecR-17
❑ 99UppDecRG-17
❑ 99UppDecRL-8
❑ 99UppDecROSS-S14
❑ 99UppDecROSS-S14
❑ 99UppDecRP-17
❑ 99UppDecRTA-T3
❑ 99UppDecRTAL2-T3
❑ 99UppDecTE-T10
❑ 99UppDecTED-T10
❑ 99UppDecTEQ-T10
❑ 99UppDecTET-T10
❑ 99UppDecWY-W25
❑ 99UppDecWYD-W25
❑ 99UppDecWYHR-W25
❑ 99UppDecWYT-W25
❑ 99Vic-74
❑ 99Vic-75
❑ 99Vic-76
❑ 99Vic-78
❑ 99Vic-467

Sosh, John
❑ 52LavPro-68

Sossamon, Tim (L. Timothy)
❑ 86BenPhiC-148
❑ 87ChaWheP-23
❑ 88ReaPhiP-870
❑ 90JacExpP-1375

Soth, Paul
❑ 77AppFoxT-24
❑ 78AppFoxT-18
❑ 79AppFoxT-1

Sothern, Denny
❑ 90DodTar-1077

Sothoron, Allen
❑ 16Zee-65
❑ 21Exh-170
❑ 22E120-41
❑ 22W573-128
❑ 27AmeCarE126-11
❑ 36R31PasP-35
❑ 92ConTSN-523

Soto, Ed
❑ 86DayBealP-26
❑ 87GasRanP-14

Soto, Emison
❑ 91ElmPioC-15
❑ 91ElmPioP-3286
❑ 92WinHavRSF-1782
❑ 93ForLauRSC-24
❑ 93ForLauRSFP-1601
❑ 93LinVenB-228
❑ 94VenLinU-216
❑ 95LinVen-38
❑ 96-97LinVen-103

Soto, Fernando
❑ 93LinVenB-164
❑ 94VenLinU-171

Soto, Jose
❑ 86GenCubP-25
❑ 89BluOriS-30

Soto, Juan
❑ 93HicCraF-1278

Soto, Mario
❑ 77IndIndTI-21
❑ 78IndIndTI-9
❑ 78SSP270-117
❑ 78Top-427
❑ 79IndIndTI-28
❑ 80RedEnq-36
❑ 80Top-622
❑ 81CokTeaS-47
❑ 81Don-63
❑ 81Fle-214
❑ 81Top-354
❑ 81TopSupHT-42
❑ 82Don-103
❑ 82Fle-83
❑ 82FleSta-19
❑ 82RedCok-20
❑ 82Top-63
❑ 83AllGamPI-179
❑ 83Don-248
❑ 83Fle-603
❑ 83FleSta-182
❑ 83FleSti-216
❑ 83OPC-215
❑ 83PerAll-18
❑ 83PerAllG-18
❑ 83RedYea-36
❑ 83Top-215
❑ 83Top-351
❑ 83TopSti-234
❑ 84AllGamPI-90
❑ 84Don-428
❑ 84Fle-483
❑ 84FleSti-79
❑ 84FunFooP-61
❑ 84Nes792-160
❑ 84Nes792-756
❑ 84OPC-160
❑ 84RedBor-36
❑ 84RedEnq-25
❑ 84SevCoi-C13
❑ 84Top-160
❑ 84Top-756
❑ 84TopGloA-21
❑ 84TopRubD-18
❑ 84TopSti-51
❑ 84TopTif-160
❑ 84TopTif-756
❑ 85AllGamPI-178
❑ 85Don-19
❑ 85Don-184
❑ 85DonActA-3
❑ 85DonSupD-19
❑ 85Fle-552
❑ 85FleLimE-36
❑ 85FleStaS-86
❑ 85FleStaS-116
❑ 85GenMilS-11
❑ 85IndIndTI-31
❑ 85Lea-19
❑ 85OPC-131
❑ 85RedYea-16
❑ 85SevCoi-G13
❑ 85Top-495
❑ 85TopGloS-37
❑ 85TopMin-495
❑ 85TopRubD-17
❑ 85TopSti-46
❑ 85TopSup-21
❑ 85TopTif-495
❑ 86BasStaB-105
❑ 86Don-184
❑ 86Fle-192
❑ 86FleMin-41
❑ 86FleSlu-36
❑ 86FleStiC-114
❑ 86Lea-119
❑ 86OPC-28
❑ 86RedTexG-36
❑ 86SevCoi-S11
❑ 86Spo-168
❑ 86Top-725
❑ 86TopMinL-42
❑ 86TopSti-136
❑ 86TopTat-12
❑ 86TopTif-725
❑ 87Don-82
❑ 87Fle-214
❑ 87FleGlo-214
❑ 87Lea-140
❑ 87OPC-11
❑ 87Top-517
❑ 87TopTif-517
❑ 88Top-666
❑ 88TopBig-120
❑ 88TopTif-666
❑ 89Sco-588

Soto, Max
❑ 86GleFalTP-22

Soto, Miguel
❑ 84SavCarT-24
❑ 91GulCoaRSP-27
❑ 92IdaFalGF-3517
❑ 92IdaFalGSP-23
❑ 93LinVenB-109
❑ 93MacBraC-23
❑ 93MacBraF-1403
❑ 94VenLinU-63
❑ 95LinVen-193

Soto, Ozzie
❑ 85CedRapRT-13
❑ 86TamTarP-21

Soto, Rafael
❑ 90HunCubP-3294
❑ 91PeoChiC-27
❑ 91PeoChiP-1351
❑ 91PeoChiTI-19
❑ 92WinSpiC-3
❑ 92WinSpiF-1216
❑ 93PeoChiC-19
❑ 93PeoChiF-1094
❑ 93PeoChiTI-26

Soto, Seferino
❑ 95YakBeaTI-29
❑ 96GreFalDB-26
❑ 96GreFalDTI-14
❑ 98EugEme-27

Soto, Tom
❑ 78NewWayCT-41
❑ 79HolMilT-10
❑ 81VanCanT-23

Sottile, Shaun
❑ 89PulBraP-1898
❑ 90SumBraB-21
❑ 90SumBraP-2431
❑ 91DurBulC-22

Souchock, Steve
❑ 52Bow-235
❑ 52Top-234
❑ 53BowC-91
❑ 53TigGle-26
❑ 54Bow-103
❑ 79DiaGre-393
❑ 83TopRep5-234

Soules, Ryan
❑ 98GreBatM-19

Soult, David
❑ 94CliLumF-1980

Sounds, Nashville
❑ 79NaSouTI-1
❑ 81NasSouTI-25

South, Carl
❑ 94GreFalDSP-27
❑ 95YakBeaTI-30
❑ 96SavSanB-23

Southall, Rick
❑ 98EveAquG-22

Southard, Scott
❑ 93ElmPioC-20
❑ 93ElmPioF-3834
❑ 94KanCouCC-23
❑ 94KanCouCF-172
❑ 94KanCouCTI-26
❑ 95BreCouMF-256

Southland, Kip
❑ 87EveGiaC-8

Southworth, Bill
❑ 16Zee-66
❑ 19W514-16
❑ 21E121So1-101
❑ 22E120-134
❑ 22W572-103
❑ 23W501-90
❑ 25Exh-39
❑ 27AmeCarE126-10
❑ 27Exh-32
❑ 27MidBre-18
❑ 41CarW75-25
❑ 46SpoExcW-9-5
❑ 47TipTop-88
❑ 49EurSta-24
❑ 51Bow-207
❑ 80PacLeg-17
❑ 83Car194T-62
❑ 91ConTSN-253
❑ 92ConTSN-627
❑ 93ConTSN-839

Souza, Brian
❑ 90HelBreSP-25
❑ 91BelBreCB-7
❑ 91BelBreP-2102
❑ 91HelBreSP-24
❑ 92BelBreCB-8
❑ 93AusFut-43

Souza, Mark
❑ 75WatRoyT-28
❑ 76WatRoyT-28
❑ 77OrlTwiT-20
❑ 79OgdA'sT-17
❑ 80OgdA'sT-10
❑ 81TacTigT-22

Soverel, Bret
❑ 97EveAquG-25

Sovern, Jeff
❑ 76IndIndTI-8
❑ 78IndIndTI-25

Sowards, Ryan
❑ 94GreFalDSP-21
❑ 95VerBeaDTI-25

Sowards, Van
❑ 83CliGiaF-21
❑ 84ShrCapFB-20

Sowders, John
❑ 87OldJudN-465

Sowders, William J.
❑ 87OldJudN-464
❑ 88AugBecN-30
❑ 88GandBCGCE-36
❑ 89N526N7C-15

Sowell, Scott
❑ 90MidAngGS-25
❑ 96MidAngB-4
❑ 97MidAng-4

Spaan, Tony
❑ 90EliTwiS-21

Spade, Matt
❑ 94WelPirC-23
❑ 94WelPirF-3498
❑ 96LynHilB-20
❑ 97St.PauS-29

Spade, Robert
❑ 08RosComP-182
❑ 09ColChiE-267A
❑ 09ColChiE-267B
❑ 09T206-331
❑ 11SpoLifM-202
❑ 12ColRedB-267A
❑ 12ColRedB-267B
❑ 12ColTinT-267A
❑ 12ColTinT-267B

Spagnola, Glen
❑ 83CedRapRF-16
❑ 83CedRapRT-5
❑ 86VerRedP-21
❑ 87VerRedP-18
❑ 88ColAstB-4
❑ 89CalCanC-10
❑ 89CalCanP-527
❑ 89EasLeaDDP-DD33
❑ 89WilBilS-21

Spagnuolo, Joe
❑ 87VerBeaDP-3

Spahn, Warren E.
❑ 46SpoExcW-9-9
❑ 47Exh-214A
❑ 47Exh-214B
❑ 47StaPinP2-40
❑ 47TipTop-89
❑ 48BluTin-20
❑ 48Bow-18
❑ 49Bow-33
❑ 49EurSta-25
❑ 49Lea-32
❑ 50AmeNut&CCP-18
❑ 50Bow-19
❑ 50Dra-14
❑ 50RoyDes-5
❑ 51BerRos-B2
❑ 51Bow-134
❑ 51TopRedB-30
❑ 52BasPho-6
❑ 52Bow-156
❑ 52NatTeaL-33
❑ 52RedMan-NL22
❑ 52RoyPre-15
❑ 52TipTop-41
❑ 52Top-33
❑ 53BowC-99
❑ 53BraJohC-10
❑ 53BraMer-15
❑ 53BraSpiaS3-22
❑ 53BraSpiaS7-12
❑ 53DixLid-22A
❑ 53DixLid-22B
❑ 53DixPre-22
❑ 53ExhCan-32
❑ 53MacSta-5
❑ 53NorBreL-31
❑ 53RedMan-NL19
❑ 53Top-147
❑ 54BraJohC-21
❑ 54BraMer-9
❑ 54BraSpiaSP-17
❑ 54RedHeaF-30
❑ 54RedMan-NL11
❑ 54Top-20
❑ 55ArmCoi-20
❑ 55BraGolS-3
❑ 55BraJohC-21
❑ 55BraSpiaSD-16
❑ 55RedMan-NL10
❑ 55Top-31
❑ 55TopDouH-127

❑ 56BraBilaBP-14
❑ 56Top-10
❑ 56TopHocF-A10
❑ 56TopHocF-B12
❑ 56TopPin-19
❑ 57Bra8x1-11
❑ 57BraSpiaS4-18
❑ 57Top-90
❑ 58BraJayP-12
❑ 58HarSta-7
❑ 58JayPubA-19
❑ 58Top-270
❑ 58Top-494
❑ 59OklTodML-5
❑ 59Top-40A
❑ 59Top-40B
❑ 59Top-40C
❑ 59Top-571
❑ 59TopVen-40
❑ 60Baz-19
❑ 60BraJayP-11
❑ 60BraLaktL-24
❑ 60BraSpiaS-22
❑ 60KeyChal-46
❑ 60NuHi-63
❑ 60RawGloT-33
❑ 60Top-230
❑ 60Top-445
❑ 60TopTat-49
❑ 61Baz-29
❑ 61ChePat-9
❑ 61NuSco-402
❑ 61NuSco-463
❑ 61Pos-101A
❑ 61Pos-101B
❑ 61Raw-11
❑ 61SevElev-15
❑ 61Top-47
❑ 61Top-200
❑ 61Top-589
❑ 61TopStal-47
❑ 62AurRec-15
❑ 62Baz-5
❑ 62BraJayP-9
❑ 62ExhStaB-32
❑ 62Top-56
❑ 62Top-58
❑ 62Top-100
❑ 62Top-312
❑ 62Top-399
❑ 62TopBuc-85
❑ 62TopStal-150
❑ 62TopVen-56
❑ 62TopVen-58
❑ 62TopVen-100
❑ 63BasMagM-78
❑ 63Baz-5
❑ 63BraJayP-10
❑ 63ExhStaB-60
❑ 63Fle-45
❑ 63SalMetC-8
❑ 63Top-320
❑ 63TopStil-41
❑ 64Baz-5
❑ 64BraJayP-11
❑ 64Raw-8
❑ 64Top-3
❑ 64Top-400
❑ 64TopCoi-88
❑ 64TopCoi-160
❑ 64TopGia-31
❑ 64TopSta-57
❑ 64TopStaU-69
❑ 64TopTatl-68
❑ 64TopVen-3
❑ 64WheSta-43
❑ 65MetJayP-11
❑ 65MetPos-8
❑ 65OPC-205
❑ 65Top-205
❑ 67TopVen-152
❑ 68SpoMemAG-4
❑ 69EquSpoHoF-BB21
❑ 70Houof J-30
❑ 73HalofFPP-16
❑ 73IndTeal-23
❑ 73MetAllEB-11
❑ 73OPC-449
❑ 73Top-449A
❑ 73Top-449B
❑ 74NewYorNTDiS-21
❑ 75SSP42-36
❑ 75TCMHouoJ-32
❑ 76GalBasGHoF-27
❑ 76RowExh-14
❑ 76ShaPiz-139
❑ 76TayBow4-79
❑ 77BobParHoF-74
❑ 77GalGloG-38
❑ 77GalGloG-264
❑ 77Spo-2323
❑ 78AtlCon-22
❑ 78BraTCC-12
❑ 79BasGre-79
❑ 79DiaGre-225
❑ 79TCM50-3
❑ 80Bra195T-31
❑ 80Lau300-15
❑ 80MarExh-29
❑ 80PacLeg-57
❑ 80PerHaloFP-139
❑ 80PerHaloFPS-22
❑ 80SSPHOF-139
❑ 81RedPioT-22
❑ 82CraJac-16
❑ 82DiaCla-30
❑ 82FleSta-108
❑ 82TCMGreP-7
❑ 82TCMStaot5-14
❑ 83ASAWS-1
❑ 83ASAWS-1A
❑ 83ASAWS-2
❑ 83ASAWS-3
❑ 83ASAWS-4
❑ 83ASAWS-5
❑ 83ASAWS-6
❑ 83ASAWS-7
❑ 83ASAWS-8
❑ 83ASAWS-9
❑ 83ASAWS-10
❑ 83ASAWS-11
❑ 83ASAWS-12
❑ 83Bra53F-21
❑ 83MLBPin-34
❑ 83TopRep5-33
❑ 84OCoandSI-92
❑ 84SpoDesPW-19
❑ 85DalNatCC-5
❑ 85TCMPhoC-1
❑ 85TCMPla1-33
❑ 86BraGreT-9
❑ 86SpoDecG-27
❑ 86TCMSupS-13
❑ 87Bra195T-8
❑ 87NesDreT-32
❑ 88GreBasS-63
❑ 88PacLegI-109
❑ 89Don-588
❑ 89HOFStiB-84
❑ 89PerCelP-39
❑ 90Col-24
❑ 90HOFStiB-68
❑ 90PacLeg-51
❑ 90PerGreM-14
❑ 90PerMasW-21
❑ 90PerMasW-22
❑ 90PerMasW-23
❑ 90PerMasW-24
❑ 90PerMasW-25
❑ 90SweBasG-12
❑ 91Kel3D-12
❑ 91MetWIZ-372
❑ 91SweBasG-86
❑ 91TopArc1-147
❑ 92ActPacA-16
❑ 92ActPacA2-16G
❑ 92ActPacAP-4
❑ 92BazQua5A-9
❑ 92Zip-1
❑ 93ActPacAC-16
❑ 93MetIma-18
❑ 93TedWil-48
❑ 93UppDecAH-116
❑ 93UppDecAH-144
❑ 94TopArc1-20
❑ 94TopArc1G-20
❑ 94UppDecAH-90
❑ 94UppDecAH-154
❑ 94UppDecAH1-90
❑ 94UppDecAH1-154
❑ 95MrTurBG-5
❑ 95SonGre-11
❑ 98SpollITaN-32
❑ 98SpollITaNEE-32
❑ 98UppDecR-50
❑ 98UppDecRSotT-WS
❑ 99UppDecCL-21
❑ 99UppDecCLCC-21
❑ 99UppDecCLES-WS
❑ 99UppDecCLESC-WS

Spain, Dan
❑ 78OrlTwiT-20

Spalding, Albert G.
❑ 36Halof FP-22
❑ 39PC7AlbHoF-26
❑ 50CalHOFW-67
❑ 50CubGreB-15
❑ 53ArtHaloFP-78
❑ 63HalofFB-27
❑ 75FlePio-4
❑ 76ShaPiz-26
❑ 77BobParHoF-44
❑ 77BobParMBC-23
❑ 78DexHaloFP-46
❑ 80PerHaloFP-26
❑ 80SSPHOF-26
❑ 84GalHaloFRL-26
❑ 94OriofB-26
❑ 94OriofB-62
❑ 94UppDecTAE-6

Spalding, Dick
❑ 41CubTeal-25
❑ 43CubTeal-25

Spalt, Paul
❑ 88WatPirP-24

Span, Brian
❑ 89ChaRaiP-975
❑ 89SpoIndSP-15

Spang, R.J.
❑ 92GulCoaMF-3481

Spangler, Al
❑ 60BraLaktL-25
❑ 60BraSpiaS-23
❑ 60Lea-38
❑ 60Top-143
❑ 60TopVen-143
❑ 61Pos-114
❑ 61Top-73
❑ 62Col.45B-19
❑ 62Col45'HC-16
❑ 62Col45'JP-12
❑ 62Jel-157
❑ 62Pos-157
❑ 62PosCan-157
❑ 62SalPlaC-196
❑ 62ShiPlaC-196
❑ 62Top-556
❑ 62TopStal-130
❑ 63Col45"P-13
❑ 63Col45"P-19
❑ 63Col45'JP-11
❑ 63Fle-39
❑ 63Jel-185
❑ 63Pos-185
❑ 63Top-77
❑ 64Col.45JP-7
❑ 64Top-406
❑ 65OPC-164
❑ 65Top-164
❑ 65TopEmbl-53
❑ 65TopTral-70
❑ 66OPC-173
❑ 66SeaPop-22
❑ 66Top-173
❑ 66TopVen-173
❑ 68Top-451
❑ 69CubJewT-18
❑ 69CubPho-11
❑ 69MilBra-259
❑ 69Top-268
❑ 70Top-714
❑ 72MilBra-321
❑ 74OPC-354
❑ 74Top-354
❑ 78TCM60I-166
❑ 78TCM60I-171
❑ 87AstSer1-20
❑ 87AstSer1-28
❑ 87AstShoSO-21
❑ 89AstCol4S-23

Spangler, John
❑ 97BriWhiSB-30

Spann, Tookie
❑ 88BriTigP-1891
❑ 89LakTigS-19
❑ 90LakTigS-23
❑ 92ClaFS7-133
❑ 92HigDesMC-13
❑ 93WicWraF-2987

Spanswick, Bill
❑ 63MilSau-10
❑ 63SeaPop-13
❑ 64Top-287
❑ 64TopVen-287
❑ 65Top-356
❑ 78TCM60I-147
❑ 81RedSoxBG2S-115

Sparesus, Brad
❑ 93AlbPolCB-29

Sparks, Don
❑ 89PriWilCS-19
❑ 90AlbYanB-18
❑ 90AlbYanP-1042
❑ 90AlbYanSt-17
❑ 90Bes-237
❑ 90CMC-736
❑ 90EasLeaAP-EL2
❑ 90StaFS7-53
❑ 91ColCliLD-119
❑ 91ColCliP-19
❑ 91ColCliP-605
❑ 91LinDriAAA-119
❑ 92AlbYanF-2234
❑ 92AlbYanSk-19
❑ 92ClaFS7-7
❑ 93ClaFS7-25
❑ 93ClaGolF-4
❑ 93ColCliF-1119
❑ 93ColCliP-17
❑ 94ColCliF-2961
❑ 94ColCliP-25
❑ 95ColCliMCTI-24
❑ 95ColCliP-28
❑ 95ColCliTI-28
❑ 96BufBisB-20

Sparks, Eric
❑ 97VerExpB-26

Sparks, Greg
❑ 86ChaRaiP-23
❑ 88HunStaTI-21
❑ 89CalLeaA-48
❑ 89SalSpuP-1819
❑ 90AlbYanB-19
❑ 90AlbYanP-1043
❑ 90AlbYanSt-18
❑ 90Bes-252
❑ 90EasLeaAP-EL14
❑ 91CarMudLD-117
❑ 91CarMudP-1095
❑ 91LinDriAA-117
❑ 92LonTigF-647
❑ 92LonTigS-419
❑ 93PawRedSDD-25
❑ 93PawRedSF-2418
❑ 93PawRedSTI-22
❑ 94NewHavRF-1559
❑ 97VisOakG-28
❑ 98SouOreTG-31

Sparks, Herman
❑ 27Zee-63

Sparks, Jeff
❑ 97BurBeeB-23

Sparks, Joe
❑ 75IowOakT-18
❑ 80OmaRoyP-23
❑ 81OmaRoyT-1
❑ 82OmaRoyT-25
❑ 83OmaRoyT-24
❑ 84RedEnq-30
❑ 86IndIndTI-3
❑ 87IndIndTI-4
❑ 88IndIndC-24
❑ 88IndIndP-496
❑ 88TriAAAP-50
❑ 89ExpPos-28
❑ 90TopTVY-5
❑ 91LinDriAAA-599
❑ 91TolMudHLD-599
❑ 91TolMudHP-1946
❑ 92TolMudHF-1057
❑ 92TolMudHS-599
❑ 93TolMudHF-1667
❑ 94TolMudHF-1040

Sparks, Nathan
❑ 89BirBarB-30

Sparks, Rodney
❑ 94EugEmeC-21
❑ 94EugEmeF-3723
❑ 95SprSulTI-27

Sparks, Shane
❑ 92AugPirC-2
❑ 92AugPirF-239

Sparks, Stephen L.
❑ 98EriSeaWM-23

Sparks, Steve
❑ 88BelBreGS-24
❑ 89StoPorB-8
❑ 89StoPorCLC-152
❑ 89StoPorP-390
❑ 89StoPorS-11
❑ 91ElPasDLD-196
❑ 91ElPasDP-2749
❑ 91LinDriAA-196
❑ 91StoPorP-3031
❑ 92ElPasDF-3920
❑ 92ElPasDS-221
❑ 93NewOrlZF-972
❑ 94NewOrlZF-1468
❑ 95FleUpd-57
❑ 96BrePol-23
❑ 96ColCho-192
❑ 96ColChoGS-192
❑ 96ColChoSS-192
❑ 96Don-3
❑ 96DonPreP-3
❑ 96Fla-107
❑ 96Fle-158
❑ 96FleTif-158
❑ 96LeaSigEA-188
❑ 96Pac-344
❑ 96Sco-474
❑ 96StaClu-156
❑ 96StaCluMOP-156
❑ 96Top-279
❑ 96Ult-84
❑ 96UltGolM-84
❑ 96UppDec-121
❑ 97ColCho-371
❑ 98MidAngG-25

Sparks, Tully
❑ 03BreE10-132
❑ 08RosComP-146
❑ 09ColChiE-268A
❑ 09ColChiE-268B
❑ 10LuxCigPP-20
❑ 10NadE1-52
❑ 11SpoLifCW-331
❑ 11SpoLifM-240
❑ 12ColRedB-268A
❑ 12ColRedB-268B
❑ 12ColTinT-268A
❑ 12ColTinT-268B

Sparling, Don
❑ 85Ft.MyeRT-5
❑ 87MemChiB-14
❑ 87MemChiP-19

Sparma, Blase
❑ 92DurBulF-1099
❑ 92MacBraC-13
❑ 93GreBraF-347
❑ 94DurBulC-20
❑ 94DurBulF-328
❑ 94DurBulTI-22

Sparma, Joe
❑ 64Top-512
❑ 65Top-587
❑ 66TigVolC-10
❑ 66Top-267
❑ 66TopVen-267
❑ 67CokCapTi-5
❑ 67DexPre-196
❑ 67OPC-13
❑ 67TigDexP-8
❑ 67Top-13
❑ 68CokCapT-5
❑ 68TigDetFPB-22
❑ 68Top-505
❑ 69TigFarJ-2
❑ 69TigTealC-16
❑ 69Top-488
❑ 70MLBOffS-69
❑ 70OPC-243
❑ 70Top-243
❑ 88TigDom-21

Sparrow, Chris
❑ 89IdaFalBP-2024
❑ 90UtiBluSP-8

Spaulding, Chad
❑ 94CarLeaAF-CAR23

Spaulding, Scott
❑ 95NewJerCTI-27

Speake, Bob
❑ 56Top-66
❑ 57Top-339
❑ 58Top-437
❑ 59Top-526
❑ 79DiaGre-124

Speaker, Tris
❑ 08AmeCarE91-90
❑ 08RosComP-183
❑ 09AmeCarE90-1-96
❑ 09ColChiE-269A
❑ 09ColChiE-269B
❑ 09MaxPubP-11
❑ 09SpoNewSM-21
❑ 09T206-332
❑ 10CouT21-225
❑ 10CouT21-317
❑ 10DarChoE-29
❑ 10DomDisP-111
❑ 10E-UOraBSC-20
❑ 10E12AmeCDCE125-33
❑ 10JuJuDE-37
❑ 10OrnOvaPP-12
❑ 10PeoT21-51
❑ 10RedCroT-71
❑ 10RedCroT-157
❑ 10RedCroT-244
❑ 10SepAnoP-22
❑ 10SweCapPP-6A
❑ 10SweCapPP-6B
❑ 11BasBatEU-35
❑ 11E94-27
❑ 11HelSta-4
❑ 11L1L-131
❑ 11MecDFT-22
❑ 11PinT-5-664
❑ 11PloCanE-58
❑ 11S74Sil-3
❑ 11S81LarS-106
❑ 11SpoLifM-15
❑ 11T205-159
❑ 11TurRedT-36
❑ 12ColRedB-269A
❑ 12ColRedB-269B
❑ 12ColTinT-269A
❑ 12ColTinT-269B
❑ 12HasTriFT-23
❑ 12HasTriFT-35
❑ 12HasTriFT-62
❑ 12HasTriFT-63
❑ 12HasTriFT-64
❑ 12RedSoxBASP-3
❑ 12T207-170
❑ 13NatGamW-35
❑ 13TomBarW-33
❑ 14CraJacE-65
❑ 14PieStaT-96
❑ 14PolGroW-27
❑ 14TexTomE-40
❑ 15AmeCarE106-35
❑ 15CraJacE-65
❑ 16FleBreD-88
❑ 17ColE13-166
❑ 17HolBreD-99
❑ 19W514-102
❑ 20NatCarE-99
❑ 20W516-5
❑ 20W52-9
❑ 21E121So1-102A
❑ 21E121So1-102B
❑ 21E121So8-94A
❑ 21E121So8-94B
❑ 21Exh-171
❑ 21OxfConE-18
❑ 22AmeCarE122-67
❑ 22E120-42
❑ 22W572-104
❑ 22W573-129
❑ 22W575-130
❑ 22WilPatV-13
❑ 23W501-19
❑ 23W515-28
❑ 23W551-9
❑ 23WilChoV-156
❑ 24MrsShePP-9
❑ 25Exh-87
❑ 26Exh-86
❑ 26SpoComoA-42
❑ 27AmeCarE126-27
❑ 27Exh-64
❑ 27YorCarE-28
❑ 28StaPlaCE-63
❑ 28W502-28
❑ 28W512-4
❑ 28Yue-28
❑ 33Gou-89
❑ 34GouCanV-29
❑ 36R31PasP-37
❑ 37KelPepS-BB13
❑ 39PC7AlbHoF-11
❑ 40PlaBal-170
❑ 48ExhHoF-27
❑ 50CalHOFW-68
❑ 51R42SmaS-104
❑ 51TopConMA-10
❑ 53ArtHaloFP-79
❑ 60ExhWriH-22
❑ 60Fle-10
❑ 61Fle-79
❑ 61GolPre-30
❑ 63BasMagM-79
❑ 63BazA-24
❑ 63HalofFB-18
❑ 67TopVen-156
❑ 68SpoMemAG-9

❑ 69Baz-4
❑ 69Baz-9
❑ 72ClaCar-84
❑ 72FleFamF-32
❑ 72KelATG-11
❑ 74CapPub-39
❑ 75McCCob-15
❑ 75TCMAllG-33
❑ 76GalBasGHoF-28
❑ 76ShaPiz-7
❑ 76TayBow4-113
❑ 77BobParHoF-45
❑ 77GalGloG-96
❑ 77GalGloG-138
❑ 77GalGloG-268
❑ 77Ind192T-18
❑ 77Ind192T-22
❑ 77ShaPiz-22
❑ 79Pew-15
❑ 79RedSoxEF-17
❑ 80PerHaloFP-11
❑ 80SSPHOF-11
❑ 81ConTSN-14
❑ 81SpoHaloF-24
❑ 82DavHaloFB-21
❑ 82DiaCla-81
❑ 82OhiHaloF-13
❑ 82TCMGreH-18
❑ 84GalHaloFRL-7
❑ 85Woo-34
❑ 86ConSer1-30
❑ 86IndGreT-6
❑ 86RedSoxGT-10
❑ 87HygAllG-42
❑ 87NesDreT-6
❑ 88ConSer3-27
❑ 89HOFStiB-41
❑ 90BasWit-72
❑ 90SweBasG-45
❑ 91ConTSN-44
❑ 91SweBasG-140
❑ 92ConTSN-422
❑ 92ConTSN-591
❑ 92ConTSNCl-18
❑ 93ActPacA-91
❑ 93ActPacA2-25G
❑ 93ConMasB-6
❑ 93ConTSN-795
❑ 93ConTSN-827
❑ 93CraJac-6
❑ 93TedWil-35
❑ 93TedWil-128
❑ 93UppDecAH-117
❑ 93UppDecAH-161
❑ 93UppDecTR-10
❑ 94ConTSN-1222
❑ 94ConTSNB-1222
❑ 95ConTSN-1357
❑ 95ConTSN-1423
❑ 95ConTSNGJ-7
❑ 95ConTSNP-1357
❑ 99UppDecCL-27
❑ 99UppDecCLCC-27
Speakes, Joey
❑ 88PocGiaP-2097
Speakman, Tim
❑ 85ElmPioT-21
Speakman, Willie
❑ 91BelMarCB-14
❑ 91BelMarP-3669
❑ 92PenPilC-13
❑ 93BoiHawC-25
❑ 93BoiHawF-3920
Spear, Mike
❑ 88ButCopKSP-20
Spear, Russell
❑ 95IdaFalBTI-6
❑ 96CliLumKTI-25
❑ 97WesMicW-25
❑ 98LakTigM-11
Spearman, Vernon
❑ 91YakBeaC-1
❑ 91YakBeaP-4261
❑ 92ProFS7-249
❑ 92VerBeaDC-12
❑ 92VerBeaDF-2892
❑ 93ClaGolF-180
❑ 93ExcFS7-54
❑ 93SanAntMF-3019
❑ 94SanAntMF-2485
❑ 95SanBerSTI-25
❑ 96SanAntMB-23
Spearnock, Mike
❑ 86SalAngC-99
❑ 87PalSprP-1
Speas, William
❑ 09ObaT21-33
❑ 09ObaT21-131
❑ 09ObaT21-366
❑ 12ObaPreT-115
❑ 14Zee-75
❑ 15Zee-71
❑ 16Zee-67
❑ 19Zee-45
Speck, R. Cliff
❑ 77LynMetT-26
❑ 80CarMudF-19
❑ 82RocRedWT-6
❑ 83RocRedWT-9
❑ 86RicBraP-21
❑ 87Don-571
❑ 87RicBraBC-19
❑ 87RicBraC-39
❑ 87RicBraT-25
❑ 87Top-269
❑ 87TopTif-269
❑ 88ColCliC-22
❑ 88ColCliP-11
❑ 88ColCliP-311
Speckenbach, Paul
❑ 64Top-548
Speckhardt, Mike
❑ 97NewJerCB-25
Specyalski, Brian
❑ 88CapCodPPaLP-89
❑ 89BenBucL-19
❑ 90BoiHawP-3322
Speece, Byron
❑ 43CenFlo-22
❑ 44CenFlo-21
❑ 45CenFlo-23
❑ 75SenTCM1-33
Speed, Horace
❑ 75IntLeaASB-33
❑ 75PacCoaLAB-33A
❑ 75PacCoaLAB-33B
❑ 75PhoGiaC-3
❑ 75PhoGiaCK-22
❑ 76PheGiaCr-20
❑ 76PhoGiaCa-8
❑ 76PhoGiaCC-21
❑ 76PhoGiaVNB-22
❑ 76SSP-112
❑ 77PhoGiaCC-22
❑ 77PhoGiaCP-22
❑ 77PhoGiaVNB-22
❑ 78IndTeal-26
❑ 79Top-438
❑ 80RicBraT-14
❑ 97PhoFirDTTI-18
Speek, Frank
❑ 90JohCitCS-24
❑ 91SavCarC-11
❑ 91SavCarP-1652
❑ 92SprCarC-3
❑ 92SprCarF-869
Speer, Kid (George Nathan)
❑ 09TigTaCP-16
Speer, V. Floyd
❑ 46RemBre-18
❑ 47RemBre-14
❑ 47SigOil-55
❑ 48SigOil-21
❑ 48SmiClo-18
Spehr, Tim
❑ 90CMC-196
❑ 90OmaRoyC-21
❑ 90OmaRoyP-69
❑ 90ProAAAF-604
❑ 91Bow-298
❑ 91LinDriAAA-346
❑ 91OmaRoyLD-346
❑ 91OmaRoyP-1038
❑ 91TriA AAGP-AAA28
❑ 92Cla1-T84
❑ 92Don-689
❑ 92Fle-674
❑ 92OmaRoyF-2965
❑ 92OmaRoyS-347
❑ 92OPC-342
❑ 92Sco-416
❑ 92SkyAAAF-159
❑ 92StaClu-96
❑ 92Top-342
❑ 92TopDeb91-166
❑ 92TopGol-342
❑ 92TopGolW-342
❑ 92TopMic-342
❑ 93Don-15
❑ 93ExpPosN-21
❑ 93UppDec-669
❑ 93UppDecGold-669
❑ 94Fle-552
❑ 94StaClu-515
❑ 94StaCluFDI-515
❑ 94StaCluGR-515
❑ 94StaCluMOP-515
❑ 94Top-714
❑ 94TopGol-714
❑ 94TopSpa-714
❑ 94VenLinU-43
❑ 95Top-134
❑ 96ExpDis-20
❑ 96LeaSigEA-189
❑ 98PacOnl-491
❑ 98PacOnlR-491
❑ 98PacOnlWC-491
Speier, Chris
❑ 72GiaTeal-17
❑ 72Kel-28
❑ 72OPC-165
❑ 72OPC-166
❑ 72Top-165
❑ 72Top-166
❑ 73LinPor-164
❑ 73OPC-273
❑ 73OPC-345
❑ 73SevTraC-73
❑ 73Top-273
❑ 73Top-345
❑ 73TopCanL-49
❑ 74Kel-40
❑ 74OPC-129
❑ 74OPC-335
❑ 74Top-129
❑ 74Top-335
❑ 74TopDecE-29
❑ 74TopSta-110
❑ 75GiaTeal-15
❑ 75Hos-73
❑ 75HosTwi-73
❑ 75OPC-505
❑ 75SSPPuzB-24
❑ 75Top-505
❑ 75TopMin-505
❑ 76Hos-82
❑ 76OPC-630
❑ 76SanFraGP-21
❑ 76SSP-105
❑ 76Top-630
❑ 77BurCheD-108
❑ 77ExpPos-28
❑ 77Gia-22
❑ 77OPC-53
❑ 77PepGloD-41
❑ 77Top-515
❑ 78ExpPos-14
❑ 78OPC-232
❑ 78Top-221
❑ 79OPC-221
❑ 79Top-426
❑ 80ExpPos-30
❑ 80OPC-168
❑ 80Top-319
❑ 81AllGamPI-115
❑ 81Don-329
❑ 81ExpPos-15
❑ 81Fle-153
❑ 81OPC-97
❑ 81OPCPos-3
❑ 81Top-97
❑ 81TopSti-189
❑ 82Don-366
❑ 82ExpHygM-21
❑ 82ExpPos-39
❑ 82ExpZel-8
❑ 82Fle-209
❑ 82FleSta-32
❑ 82OPC-198
❑ 82Top-198
❑ 82TopSti-58
❑ 83AllGamPI-115
❑ 83Don-266
❑ 83ExpPos-31
❑ 83ExpStu-27
❑ 83Fle-298
❑ 83FleSta-183
❑ 83FleSti-257
❑ 83OPC-121
❑ 83Top-768
❑ 83TopSti-258
❑ 84Don-523
❑ 84ExpPos-30
❑ 84ExpStu-27
❑ 84Fle-288
❑ 84GiaMot-22
❑ 84Nes792-678
❑ 84OPC-328
❑ 84Top-678
❑ 84TopSti-95
❑ 84TopTif-678
❑ 85CubLioP-23
❑ 85CubSev-28
❑ 85FleUpd-109
❑ 85Top-577
❑ 85TopTif-577
❑ 85TopTifT-111T
❑ 85TopTra-111T
❑ 86CubGat-28
❑ 86Fle-382
❑ 86OPC-212
❑ 86Top-212
❑ 86TopTif-212
❑ 87Don-392
❑ 87Fle-575
❑ 87FleGlo-575
❑ 87FleUpd-112
❑ 87FleUpdG-112
❑ 87GiaMot-18
❑ 87GiaPos-29
❑ 87Top-424
❑ 87TopTif-424
❑ 87TopTra-115T
❑ 87TopTraT-115T
❑ 88Don-239
❑ 88Fle-96
❑ 88FleGlo-96
❑ 88GiaMot-18
❑ 88GiaPos-29
❑ 88Sco-493
❑ 88ScoGlo-493
❑ 88StaLinG-16
❑ 88Top-329
❑ 88TopClo-108
❑ 88TopTif-329
❑ 89Don-532
❑ 89Fle-343
❑ 89FleGlo-343
❑ 89GiaMot-18
❑ 89Sco-297
❑ 89Top-94
❑ 89TopTif-94
❑ 89UppDec-206
❑ 90Fle-72
❑ 90FleCan-72
❑ 90OPC-753
❑ 90PubIntS-82
❑ 90Top-753
❑ 90TopTif-753
❑ 91UppDecS-23
❑ 95OrlCubF-27
❑ 96AriBlaDB-1
❑ 97HigDesMG-24
❑ 98TusSidM-1
Speier, Justin
❑ 96DayCubB-22
❑ 96WesOahCHWB-36
❑ 97OrlRayB-23
❑ 98IowCubQ-21
Spellman, Ed
❑ 20Zee-36
Spence, Cam
❑ 98GreBatM-20
❑ 98TamYanM-27
Spence, J. Bob
❑ 71OPC-186
❑ 71Top-186
Spence, John
❑ 76BatTroTI-21
Spence, Michael
❑ 96TamYanY-23
❑ 97TamYan-28
Spence, Samuel
❑ 76BatTroTI-22
❑ 77WatIndT-22
❑ 78WatIndT-22
Spence, Stan
❑ 47Exh-215
❑ 48RedSoxTI-21
❑ 49Bow-102
❑ 60SenUniMC-18
❑ 76TayBow4-94
❑ 79DiaGre-232
❑ 83TCMPla1943-5
❑ 95ConTSN-1402
Spencer, Aaron
❑ 93AusFut-101
Spencer, Andrew
❑ 93AusFut-92
❑ 95AusFut-10
Spencer, Daryl
❑ 54Bow-185
❑ 56Top-277
❑ 57GiaJayP-10
❑ 57Top-49
❑ 58GiaArmT-9
❑ 58GiaJayP-11
❑ 58GiaSFCB-22
❑ 58Hir-51
❑ 58Top-68
❑ 59Top-443
❑ 60CarJayP-11
❑ 60Lea-129
❑ 60MacSta-24
❑ 60Top-368
❑ 61CarJayP-12
❑ 61DodUniO-21
❑ 61Pos-173A
❑ 61Pos-173B
❑ 61Top-357
❑ 61Top-451
❑ 61TopStal-95
❑ 62DodBelB-20
❑ 62DodVol-22
❑ 62Jel-103
❑ 62Pos-103
❑ 62PosCan-103
❑ 62SalPlaC-178A
❑ 62SalPlaC-178B
❑ 62ShiPlaC-178
❑ 62Top-197
❑ 62TopStal-141
❑ 63Jel-124
❑ 63Pos-124
❑ 63RedFreBC-27
❑ 63Top-502
❑ 79DiaGre-49
❑ 79TCM50-226
❑ 90DodTar-756
Spencer, George
❑ 52BerRos-62
❑ 52Top-346
❑ 53Top-115
❑ 55GiaGolS-11
❑ 62SeaPop-15
❑ 63MilSau-11
❑ 63SeaPop-14
❑ 75Gia195T-25
❑ 83TopRep5-346
❑ 91TopArc1-115
Spencer, Glenn Edward
❑ 33Gou-84
❑ 34DiaMatCSB-166
❑ 34GouCanV-37
Spencer, Jeff
❑ 96AppLeaAB-15
❑ 96DanBraB-23
❑ 97EugEmeB-25
❑ 98MacBraM-19
Spencer, Jim
❑ 69AngJacitB-12
❑ 70OPC-255
❑ 70Top-255
❑ 70TopScr-20
❑ 71AngJacitB-9
❑ 71MLBOffS-358
❑ 71OPC-78
❑ 71Top-78
❑ 71TopCoi-4
❑ 72MilBra-322
❑ 72OPC-419
❑ 72Top-419
❑ 73OPC-319
❑ 73Top-319
❑ 74OPC-580
❑ 74Top-580
❑ 74TopSta-239
❑ 75OPC-387
❑ 75RanPos-31
❑ 75Top-387
❑ 75TopMin-387
❑ 76OPC-83
❑ 76SSP-268
❑ 76Top-83
❑ 76TopTra-83T
❑ 77BurCheD-79
❑ 77Hos-16
❑ 77OPC-46
❑ 77Top-648
❑ 77WhiSoxJT-13
❑ 77WhiSoxT-23
❑ 78OPC-122
❑ 78Top-182
❑ 78YanBurK-16
❑ 78YanPhoA-23
❑ 79OPC-315
❑ 79Top-599
❑ 79YanBurK-17
❑ 79YanPicA-31
❑ 80OPC-147
❑ 80Top-278
❑ 80YanPhoA-22
❑ 81Don-226
❑ 81Fle-96
❑ 81OPC-209
❑ 81Top-435
❑ 81TopTra-832
❑ 82Don-265
❑ 82Fle-107
❑ 82FleSta-127
❑ 82OPC-88
❑ 82Top-729
❑ 82TopSti-223
❑ 92UppDecS-12
❑ 92YanWIZ7-142
❑ 92YanWIZ8-185
❑ 93RanKee-338
❑ 94RanAllP-1
Spencer, John
❑ 88ElmPioC-25
❑ 89ElmPioP-20
Spencer, Joseph B.
❑ 93NegLeaRL2-36
Spencer, Kyle
❑ 88ButCopKSP-10
❑ 89GasRanP-1002
❑ 89GasRanS-22
❑ 90ChaRanS-27
❑ 91ChaRanC-11
❑ 91ChaRanP-1315
Spencer, Robert
❑ 90NewBriRSB-27
Spencer, Roy
❑ 31Exh-31
❑ 31SenTealPW-29
❑ 33ExhFou-16
❑ 33WorCig-88
❑ 90DodTar-757
❑ 91ConTSN-320
Spencer, Sean
❑ 98OrlRayM-17
❑ 99Bow-151
❑ 99BowChr-151
❑ 99BowChrG-151
❑ 99BowChrGR-151
❑ 99BowChrI-151
❑ 99BowChrIR-151
❑ 99BowChrR-151
❑ 99BowGol-151
❑ 99BowInt-151
Spencer, Shane
❑ 90TamYanD-25
❑ 92GreHorC-4
❑ 92GreHorF-795
❑ 93GreHorC-21
❑ 93GreHorF-900
❑ 94TamYanC-24
❑ 94TamYanF-2398
❑ 95SPML-121
❑ 95TamYanYI-26
❑ 96Bow-251
❑ 96BowFoi-251
❑ 96Exc-93
❑ 96ExcSeaC-10
❑ 96NorNavB-25
❑ 96Top-436
❑ 97ColCliB-28
❑ 97ColCliD-24
❑ 98ColCliD-24
❑ 98ColCliM-29
Spencer, Stan
❑ 91Bow-441
❑ 91Cla/Bes-84
❑ 91HarSenLD-270
❑ 91HarSenP-626
❑ 91LinDriAA-270
❑ 93HigDesMC-20
❑ 93HigDesMF-41
❑ 94BreCouMF-11
❑ 95ChaKniTI-24
❑ 98Las-24
❑ 99Fle-494
❑ 99FleSta9-494
❑ 99FleWarT-494
❑ 99SkyPre-271
❑ 99SkyPre-271
❑ 99SkyPreR-271
❑ 99SkyPreR-271
❑ 99SpoIll-60
Spencer, Tom
❑ 89CedRapRB-25
❑ 89CedRapRP-917
❑ 89CedRapRS-24
❑ 91ChaWheC-24

❑ 92ChaWVWC-24
❑ 93WinSpiC-27
❑ 94CarLeaAF-CAR51
❑ 94WinSpiC-28
❑ 96BilMusTI-30
❑ 98BilMusTI-32
Spencer, Tom (Hubert Thomas)
❑ 76IndIndTI-6
❑ 78KnoKnoST-21
❑ 79KnoKnoST-25
❑ 80TucTorT-15
❑ 81TucTorT-13
❑ 86PitCubP-22
❑ 87GenCubP-4
❑ 88IndGat-2
❑ 88IndTeal-33
❑ 89IndTeal-28
❑ 89PacSenL-101
❑ 89TopSenL-24
❑ 90CedRapRB-13
❑ 90SanJosGB-29
❑ 90SanJosGCLC-53
❑ 90SanJosGP-2026
❑ 90SanJosGS-27
❑ 91MetColP-47
❑ 91MetKah-51
❑ 91MetPerPA-5
❑ 92AstMot-27
❑ 93AstMot-28
❑ 94ColCliF-2968
❑ 94ColCliP-3
Spencer, Troy
❑ 52LavPro-66
Spencer, Tubby (Edward)
❑ 08RosComP-72
❑ 09ColChiE-270
❑ 09RamT20-110
❑ 09T206-333
❑ 12ColRedB-270
❑ 12ColTinT-270
❑ 12ImpTobC-81
❑ 12PhiCarE-28
❑ 13Zee-123
❑ 15Zee-140
❑ 16Zee-143
❑ 19W514-36
❑ 19Zee-78
❑ 21Zee-150
❑ 22Zee-140
❑ 25Zee-12
❑ 72ClaCar-69
Spencer, Vernon
❑ 20NatCarE-100
Spenrath, Chris
❑ 94ButCopKSP-23
Spenser, Kaipo
❑ 98KinIndQ-23
Sperring, Robert
❑ 74WicAerODF-116
❑ 76OPC-323
❑ 76SSP-320
❑ 76Top-323
❑ 78ChaChaT-16
❑ 78Top-514
❑ 79ChaChaT-16
❑ 87AstShoSPT-20
Sperry, Chris
❑ 89SalDodTI-28
Spetter, Bryan
❑ 92PulBraC-19
❑ 92PulBraF-3187
Spicer, Len
❑ 79NewCoPT-22
Spicer, Robert
❑ 52MotCoo-61
Spiegel, Mike
❑ 96BurIndB-15
Spiegel, Rich
❑ 94DanBraC-24
❑ 94DanBraF-3536
Spiers, Bill
❑ 88StoPorCLC-197
❑ 88StoPorP-738
❑ 89BrePol-6
❑ 89DonRoo-5
❑ 89FleUpd-40
❑ 89ScoRoo-82T
❑ 89TopTra-115T
❑ 89TopTraT-115T
❑ 89UppDec-745
❑ 90Bow-402
❑ 90BowTif-402
❑ 90BreMilB-24
❑ 90ClaBlu-134
❑ 90Don-382
❑ 90El PasDAGTI-26
❑ 90Fle-337
❑ 90FleCan-337
❑ 90Lea-203
❑ 90OPC-538
❑ 90PanSti-376
❑ 90Sco-449A
❑ 90Sco-449B
❑ 90Sco100RS-55
❑ 90ScoYouSI-14
❑ 90Spo-206
❑ 90Top-538
❑ 90TopBig-88
❑ 90TopDeb89-121
❑ 90TopRoo-27
❑ 90TopTif-538
❑ 90ToyRoo-26
❑ 90UppDec-237
❑ 91BreMilB-24
❑ 91BrePol-21
❑ 91Don-310
❑ 91Fle-597
❑ 91Lea-111
❑ 91OPC-284
❑ 91PanFreS-207
❑ 91PanSti-162
❑ 91Sco-84
❑ 91StaClu-360
❑ 91Top-284
❑ 91TopDesS-284
❑ 91TopMic-284
❑ 91TopTif-284
❑ 91Ult-181
❑ 91UppDec-268
❑ 92Bow-536
❑ 92BrePol-23
❑ 92Don-364
❑ 92Fle-189
❑ 92Lea-106
❑ 92LeaBlaG-106
❑ 92OPC-742
❑ 92PanSti-38
❑ 92Pin-177
❑ 92Sco-218
❑ 92StaClu-379
❑ 92Top-742
❑ 92TopGol-742
❑ 92TopGolW-742
❑ 92TopMic-742
❑ 92Ult-84
❑ 92UppDec-214
❑ 93BrePol-22
❑ 93Fla-229
❑ 93Fle-635
❑ 93Lea-403
❑ 93OPC-323
❑ 93PacSpa-516
❑ 93PanSti-38
❑ 93Pin-525
❑ 93Sco-88
❑ 93Sel-259
❑ 93StaClu-566
❑ 93StaCluFDI-566
❑ 93StaCluMOP-566
❑ 93Top-619
❑ 93TopGol-619
❑ 93TopInaM-619
❑ 93TopInaR-619
❑ 93TopMic-619
❑ 93Ult-577
❑ 93UppDec-325
❑ 93UppDecGold-325
❑ 94BreMilB-276
❑ 94BrePol-25
❑ 94BreTeal-24
❑ 94ColC-264
❑ 94ColChoGS-264
❑ 94ColChoSS-264
❑ 94Don-288
❑ 94Fle-191
❑ 94Pac-342
❑ 94Pin-370
❑ 94PinArtP-370
❑ 94PinMusC-370
❑ 94Sco-105
❑ 94ScoGolR-105
❑ 94StaClu-677
❑ 94StaCluFDI-677
❑ 94StaCluGR-677
❑ 94StaCluMOP-677
❑ 94Top-73
❑ 94TopGol-73
❑ 94TopSpa-73
❑ 95Don-182
❑ 95DonPreP-182
❑ 95Fle-190
❑ 95MetColP-28
❑ 95StaClu-49
❑ 95StaCluFDI-49
❑ 95StaCluMOP-49
❑ 95StaCluSTWS-49
❑ 95Top-188
❑ 96AstMot-16
❑ 96MetKah-29
❑ 97AstMot-15
❑ 97Pac-324
❑ 97PacLigB-324
❑ 97PacSil-324
❑ 98ColCho-381
❑ 98Pac-325
❑ 98PacOnl-332
❑ 98PacOnlR-332
❑ 98PacOnlWC-332
❑ 98PacPlaB-325
❑ 98PacRedT-325
❑ 98PacSil-325
❑ 98UppDec-388
❑ 99Fle-334
❑ 99FleSta9-334
❑ 99FleWarT-334
❑ 99Pac-198
❑ 99PacPlaB-198
❑ 99PacRed-198
❑ 99StaClu-121
❑ 99StaCluFDI-121
❑ 99StaCluOoaK-121
❑ 99StaCluPP-121
Spiers, Corey
❑ 98ForWayW!-24
Spiers, Mike
❑ 90SalSpuCLC-145
Spiesman, M. J.
❑ 09ObaT21-108
Spiezio, Ed
❑ 65Top-431
❑ 67OPC-128
❑ 67Top-128
❑ 68Top-349
❑ 68TopVen-349
❑ 69MLBOffS-197
❑ 69PadVol-8
❑ 69Top-249
❑ 69TopTeaP-12
❑ 70MLBOffS-119
❑ 70Top-718
❑ 71MLBOffS-240
❑ 71OPC-6
❑ 71Top-6
❑ 72MilBra-323
❑ 72OPC-504
❑ 72PadPos-24
❑ 72Top-504
❑ 77PadSchC-52
Spiezio, Scott
❑ 93SouOreAC-24
❑ 93SouOreAF-4074
❑ 94Bow-413
❑ 94ModA'sC-22
❑ 94ModA'sF-3072
❑ 95Bes-39
❑ 95Exc-112
❑ 95HunStaTI-26
❑ 95SPML-123
❑ 95Top-641
❑ 95UppDecML-37
❑ 95UppDecMLFS-37
❑ 96BesAutSA-74
❑ 96ColCho-447
❑ 96ColChoGS-447
❑ 96ColChoSS-447
❑ 96FleUpd-U76
❑ 96FleUpdTC-U76
❑ 96Top-434
❑ 96Ult-404
❑ 96UltGolM-404
❑ 96UppDec-267
❑ 97A'sMot-19
❑ 97Bow-142
❑ 97BowBes-185
❑ 97BowBesA-185
❑ 97BowBesAAR-185
❑ 97BowBesAR-185
❑ 97BowBesAR-185
❑ 97BowBesR-185
❑ 97BowCerBlaIA-CA74
❑ 97BowCerBluIA-CA74
❑ 97BowCerGolIA-CA74
❑ 97BowChr-150
❑ 97BowChrI-150
❑ 97BowChrIR-150
❑ 97BowChrR-150
❑ 97BowInt-142
❑ 97Cir-216
❑ 97CirRav-216
❑ 97ColCho-187
❑ 97Don-359
❑ 97DonGolPP-359
❑ 97DonLim-48
❑ 97DonLim-54
❑ 97DonLimE-48
❑ 97DonLimE-54
❑ 97DonLimENG-48
❑ 97DonPre-153
❑ 97DonPreCttC-153
❑ 97DonSigA-91
❑ 97DonSigAC-114
❑ 97DonSigAM-114
❑ 97DonSilPP-359
❑ 97Fin-272
❑ 97FinRef-272
❑ 97FlaShoWotF-18
❑ 97Fle-195
❑ 97FleNewH-12
❑ 97FleRooS-19
❑ 97FleTif-195
❑ 97Lea-325
❑ 97LeaFraM-325
❑ 97LeaFraMDC-325
❑ 97NewPin-164
❑ 97NewPinAP-164
❑ 97NewPinMC-164
❑ 97NewPinPP-164
❑ 97PacPriGotD-GD82
❑ 97PinCer-128
❑ 97PinCerMBla-128
❑ 97PinCerMBlu-128
❑ 97PinCerMG-128
❑ 97PinCerMR-128
❑ 97PinCerR-128
❑ 97PinTotCPB-128
❑ 97PinTotCPG-128
❑ 97PinTotCPR-128
❑ 97PinX-P-128
❑ 97PinX-PMoS-128
❑ 97Sco-485
❑ 97ScoArtPWB-485
❑ 97ScoResC-485
❑ 97ScoShoS-485
❑ 97ScoShoSAP-485
❑ 97Sel-122
❑ 97SelArtP-122
❑ 97SelCom-122
❑ 97SelRegG-122
❑ 97SpoIll-24
❑ 97SpoIllEE-24
❑ 97Stu-148
❑ 97StuPrePG-148
❑ 97StuPrePS-148
❑ 97TopStaFAS-FAS9
❑ 97Ult-115
❑ 97UltGolME-115
❑ 97UltPlaME-115
❑ 97UppDec-449
❑ 98A'sMot-7
❑ 98CirThu-284
❑ 98CirThuRav-284
❑ 98CirThuSupRav-284
❑ 98ColCho-457
❑ 98Don-212
❑ 98DonColL-235
❑ 98DonColP-682
❑ 98DonGolPP-212
❑ 98DonPre-132
❑ 98DonPreSeat-132
❑ 98DonPriCL-235
❑ 98DonPriCP-682
❑ 98DonSilPP-212
❑ 98Fin-184
❑ 98FinNo--184
❑ 98FinNo-R-184
❑ 98FinRef-184
❑ 98Fle-132
❑ 98Lea-35
❑ 98LeaFraDA-35
❑ 98LeaFraF-35
❑ 98LeaFraM-35
❑ 98LeaFraM-35
❑ 98LeaFraMDC-35
❑ 98LeaFraMDC-35
❑ 98LeaFraMZ2-35
❑ 98Pac-173
❑ 98PacOnl-545
❑ 98PacOnlR-545
❑ 98PacOnlWC-545
❑ 98PacPlaB-173
❑ 98PacRedT-173
❑ 98PacSil-173
❑ 98PinIns-105
❑ 98PinInsCE-105
❑ 98PinInsDE-105
❑ 98ScoRT-66
❑ 98StaCluFDI-19
❑ 98StaCluI-19
❑ 98StaCluOneK-19
❑ 98StaCluPP-19
❑ 98Stu-170
❑ 98StuGPP-170
❑ 98StuSPP-170
❑ 98Top-144
❑ 98TopChr-144
❑ 98TopChrR-144
❑ 98TopDevR-144
❑ 98TopDia-144
❑ 98TopMiniC-144
❑ 98TopOpeD-73
❑ 98UppDec-181
❑ 98UppDecSF-97
❑ 99Fle-226
❑ 99FleSta9-226
❑ 99FleWarT-226
❑ 99Pac-317
❑ 99PacPar-174
❑ 99PacParC-174
❑ 99PacParG-174
❑ 99PacParHoloGold-174
❑ 99PacParHS-174
❑ 99PacParOD-174
❑ 99PacParPB-174
❑ 99PacParRed-174
❑ 99PacPlaB-317
❑ 99PacRed-317
❑ 99SkyThu-231
❑ 99SkyThuRant-231
❑ 99SkyThuRave-231
❑ 99StaClu-253
❑ 99StaCluC-CS26
❑ 99StaCluC-CS32
❑ 99StaCluC-CS38
❑ 99StaCluC-CS42
❑ 99StaCluFDI-253
❑ 99StaCluOoaK-253
❑ 99StaCluPP-253
❑ 99ThuSkySupR-231
❑ 99Top-362
❑ 99TopChr-362
❑ 99TopChrR-362
❑ 99TopMVPP-362
❑ 99UppDec-444
❑ 99UppDecEL1-444
❑ 99UppDecEL2-444
❑ 99Vic-289
Spikes, Charlie
❑ 73IndArtTC-6
❑ 73LinPor-67
❑ 73OPC-614
❑ 73Top-614
❑ 74OPC-58
❑ 74Top-58
❑ 74TopDecE-33
❑ 74TopSta-169
❑ 75CleIndP-24
❑ 75OPC-135
❑ 75Top-135
❑ 75TopMin-135
❑ 76OPC-408
❑ 76SSP-531
❑ 76Top-408
❑ 77Top-168
❑ 78TigTeal-25
❑ 78Top-459
❑ 80Top-294
❑ 81Fle-259
❑ 92YanWIZ7-143
Spikes, Mascot
❑ 95OrlCubF-29
❑ 96OrlCubB-29
❑ 97RocRedW-30
❑ 98RocRedWQ-30
Spiller, Derron
❑ 92SavCarC-22
❑ 92SavCarF-664
❑ 93SprCarC-25
❑ 93SprCarF-1852
❑ 94St.PetCC-25
❑ 94St.PetCF-2586
Spillner, Dan
❑ 74PadDea-24
❑ 74PadTeal-13
❑ 75OPC-222
❑ 75PadDea-5
❑ 75PadDea-24
❑ 75Top-222
❑ 75TopMin-222
❑ 76OPC-557
❑ 76SSP-119
❑ 76Top-557
❑ 77PadSchC-53
❑ 77Top-182
❑ 78PadFamF-30
❑ 78Top-488
❑ 79Top-359
❑ 80IndTeal-27
❑ 80Top-38
❑ 81Fle-392
❑ 81Top-276
❑ 82Don-411
❑ 82Fle-378
❑ 82Ind-32
❑ 82IndWhe-29
❑ 82OPC-1
❑ 82Top-664
❑ 83Don-137
❑ 83Fle-419
❑ 83FleSta-184
❑ 83FleSti-243
❑ 83IndPos-33
❑ 83IndWhe-27
❑ 83OPC-278
❑ 83Top-725
❑ 83TopSti-59
❑ 84Don-582
❑ 84Fle-550
❑ 84Ind-26
❑ 84Nes792-91
❑ 84OPC-91
❑ 84Top-91
❑ 84TopTif-91
❑ 85Fle-528
❑ 85Top-169
❑ 85TopTif-169
❑ 85WhiSoxC-37
❑ 86Don-122
❑ 86Fle-217
❑ 86Top-423
❑ 86TopTif-423
❑ 91EveGiaP-3935
Spilman, Harry
❑ 78IndIndTI-5
❑ 79IndIndTI-5
❑ 79Top-717
❑ 80RedEnq-12
❑ 80Top-677
❑ 81Don-304
❑ 81Fle-209
❑ 81Top-94
❑ 81TopTra-833
❑ 82AstAstI-10
❑ 82AstPos-25
❑ 82Fle-233
❑ 82Top-509
❑ 82TucTorT-11
❑ 83AstPos-31
❑ 83Don-65
❑ 83Fle-467
❑ 83Top-193
❑ 84AstMot-12
❑ 84AstPos-29
❑ 84Don-258
❑ 84Nes792-612
❑ 84Top-612
❑ 84TopTif-612
❑ 85AstMot-19
❑ 85Top-482
❑ 85TopTif-482
❑ 86Top-352
❑ 86TopTif-352
❑ 87AstShoSPT-27
❑ 87Fle-284
❑ 87FleGlo-284
❑ 87GiaMot-16
❑ 87GiaPos-30
❑ 87Top-64
❑ 87TopTif-64
❑ 88Don-607
❑ 88Fle-97
❑ 88FleGlo-97
❑ 88GiaMot-16
❑ 88GiaPos-30
❑ 88Sco-618
❑ 88ScoGlo-618
❑ 88StaLinG-17
❑ 88Top-217
❑ 88TopTif-217
❑ 89TucTorC-18
❑ 89TucTorJP-24
❑ 89TucTorP-199
❑ 90CMC-616
❑ 90ProAAAF-200
❑ 90TucTorC-14

□ 90TucTorP-210
□ 96BurIndB-30
□ 97BurIndG-26
Spinelli, Michael
□ 96MicBatCB-26
Spinello, Joe
□ 95PriWilCTI-15
Spingola, Don
□ 94KinMetC-19
□ 94KinMetF-3822
Spink, J.G. Taylor
□ 94ConTSN-1111
□ 94ConTSN-1112
□ 94ConTSNB-1111
□ 94ConTSNB-1112
Spink, Mrs. (J.G. Taylor)
□ 94ConTSN-1111
□ 94ConTSN-1112
□ 94ConTSNB-1111
□ 94ConTSNB-1112
Spinks, Scipio
□ 70OPC-492
□ 70Top-492
□ 71CarTeal-38
□ 71MLBOffS-92
□ 71OPC-747
□ 71Top-747
□ 72CarTeal-16
□ 72OPC-202
□ 72Top-202
□ 73OPC-417
□ 73Top-417
□ 74OPC-576
□ 74Top-576
□ 74WicAerODF-125
□ 75IowOakT-19
□ 95IdaFalBTI-36
□ 96CliLumKTI-26
Spino, Tom
□ 79QuaCitCT-23
Spinosa, John
□ 87WesPalBEP-679
□ 92IndIndF-NNO
Spires, Tony
□ 90EveGiaB-19
□ 90EveGiaP-3135
□ 91Cla/Bes-113
□ 91SanJosGC-8
□ 91SanJosGP-21
Spirits, Winston Salem
□ 86WinSpiP-29
□ 89WinSpiS-NNO
□ 90WinSpiTI-30
Spitale, Ben
□ 87BurExpP-1078
Spitaleri, Camille
□ 96ColSilB-27
Spivey, Jim
□ 90JohCitCS-25
□ 91SavCarC-13
□ 91SavCarP-1655
Spivey, Junior
□ 97HigDesMG-25
□ 98HigDesMG-25
□ 98TexLeaC-23
Splawn, Matt
□ 96PitMetB-25
Split, Lickety
□ 90WinSpiTI-26
Splitt, Steve
□ 77BurBeeT-27
□ 78HolMilT-21
□ 79HolMilT-19
Splittorff, Jamie
□ 96ForWayWB-1
Splittorff, Paul
□ 71OPC-247
□ 71oySigST-25
□ 71Top-247
□ 72OPC-315
□ 72oyTeal-24
□ 72Top-315
□ 73LinPor-91
□ 73OPC-48
□ 73Top-48
□ 74OPC-225
□ 74RoyPos-27
□ 74Top-225
□ 74TopDecE-56
□ 74TopSta-190
□ 75OPC-340
□ 75RoyPos-29
□ 75Top-340
□ 75TopMin-340
□ 76KanCitRP-29
□ 76OPC-43
□ 76RoyAaP-15
□ 76SSP-163
□ 76Top-43
□ 77BurCheD-64
□ 77OPC-41
□ 77Top-534
□ 78Hos-111
□ 78RCColC-86
□ 78Roy-21
□ 78SSP270-230
□ 78Top-638
□ 79Kel-10
□ 79OPC-90
□ 79RoyTeal-9
□ 79Top-183
□ 80OPC-214
□ 80Top-409
□ 81Don-342A
□ 81Don-342B
□ 81Fle-30
□ 81FleStiC-95
□ 81Top-218
□ 82Don-464
□ 82Fle-423
□ 82OPC-126
□ 82Roy-20
□ 82Top-759
□ 83Don-286
□ 83Fle-124
□ 83RoyPos-30
□ 83Top-316
□ 83TopFol-1
□ 84Don-521
□ 84Fle-360
□ 84Nes792-52
□ 84RoyPos-33
□ 84Top-52
□ 84TopSti-281
□ 84TopTif-52
□ 86RoyGreT-10
□ 93RoySta2-13
□ 99SpollIGotG-82
□ 99SpollIGotGA-71
Spohrer, Al
□ 31Exh-1
□ 33Gou-161
□ 33GouCanV-94
□ 34BabRutG-57
□ 34ButPreR-56
□ 34DiaMatCSB-167
□ 35DiaMatCS3T1-132
□ 35GouPuzR-8L
□ 35GouPuzR-9L
□ 92ConTSN-602
Spokaneasurus, Otto the
□ 96SpoIndB-30
Spoljaric, Paul
□ 91St.CatBJC-20
□ 91St.CatBJP-3395
□ 92MyrBeaHC-23
□ 92MyrBeaHF-2197
□ 93Bow-279
□ 93ClaFS7-118
□ 93ClaGolF-130
□ 93DunBluJC-21
□ 93DunBluJFFN-23
□ 93ExcFS7-245
□ 93SouAtlLAIPI-14
□ 93SouAtlLAPI-37
□ 94Bow-581
□ 94ColC-668
□ 94ColChoGS-668
□ 94ColChoSS-668
□ 94LeaLimR-69
□ 94Pin-539
□ 94PinArtP-539
□ 94PinMusC-539
□ 94ScoRoo-RT137
□ 94ScoRooGR-RT137
□ 94SigRoo-16
□ 94SigRooS-16
□ 94StaCluT-175
□ 94StaCluTFDI-175
□ 94SyrChiTI-24
□ 94Top-776
□ 94TopGol-776
□ 94TopSpa-776
□ 94Ult-439
□ 94UppDec-26
□ 94UppDecED-26
□ 94UppDecML-149
□ 94UppDecML-210
□ 95BluJayOH-30
□ 95Sco-308
□ 95ScoGolR-308
□ 95ScoPlaTS-308
□ 95SigRoo-46
□ 95SigRooSig-46
□ 95SyrChiTI-23
□ 95Top-644
□ 96SyrChiTI-28
□ 97BluJayOH-30
□ 97BluJayS-17
□ 97PacPriGotD-GD105
□ 98PacOnl-696
□ 98PacOnlR-696
□ 98PacOnlWC-696
Spoolstra, Scott
□ 88ColMetGS-20
Spooner, Karl
□ 55DodGolS-10
□ 55Top-90
□ 55TopDouH-19
□ 55TopTesS-9
□ 56Top-83
□ 56TopHocF-B20
□ 56TopPin-53
□ 79TCM50-238
□ 90DodTar-758
□ 95TopArcBD-98
□ 95TopArcBD-147
Sposito, Gus
□ 76VenLeaS-197
□ 80VenLeaS-236
□ 85SpoIndGC-19
Spradlin, Jerry
□ 88BilMusP-1821
□ 89GreHorP-413
□ 90CedRapRP-2322
□ 90ChaWheB-10
□ 91ChaLooLD-170
□ 91ChaLooP-1961
□ 91LinDriAA-170
□ 92ChaLooF-3821
□ 92ChaLooS-195
□ 93ExcFS7-30
□ 93IndIndF-1490
□ 94Don-579
□ 94Fle-430
□ 94IndIndF-1812
□ 94Pac-162
□ 94StaClu-56
□ 94StaCluFDI-56
□ 94StaCluGR-56
□ 94StaCluMOP-56
□ 94StaCluP-56
□ 94Top-779
□ 94TopGol-779
□ 94TopSpa-779
□ 94Ult-179
□ 95ChaKniTI-25
□ 96IndIndB-24
□ 97PhiTeal-48
□ 98PacOnl-574
□ 98PacOnlR-574
□ 98PacOnlWC-574
□ 98PhiTeal-32
□ 99Fle-363
□ 99FleSta9-363
□ 99FleWarT-363
Sprague, Charles
□ 87OldJudN-466
Sprague, Ed
□ 87PanAmTUBI-33
□ 87PanAmTURB-22
□ 88TopTra-113T
□ 88TopTraT-113T
□ 89Bow-252
□ 89BowTif-252
□ 89DunBluJS-16
□ 89TopBig-40
□ 90Bow-511
□ 90BowTif-511
□ 90CMC-345
□ 90ProAAAF-361
□ 90SyrChiC-19
□ 90SyrChiMB-24
□ 90SyrChiP-581
□ 91BluJayS-26
□ 91Bow-26
□ 91Cla1-T90
□ 91Cla3-T88
□ 91DonRoo-14
□ 91FleUpd-66
□ 91Lea-485
□ 91LinDriAAA-518
□ 91ScoAllF-7
□ 91ScoRoo-101T
□ 91StaClu-387
□ 91SyrChiK-4
□ 91SyrChiLD-518
□ 91SyrChiMB-24
□ 91SyrChiP-2484
□ 91UltUpd-63
□ 91UppDecFE-47F
□ 92Don-187
□ 92Fle-340
□ 92OPC-516
□ 92ProFS7-162
□ 92Sco-504
□ 92Sco100RS-52
□ 92SkyAAAF-232
□ 92StaClu-445
□ 92SyrChiF-1972
□ 92SyrChiMB-21
□ 92SyrChiS-517
□ 92Top-516
□ 92TopDaiQTU-15
□ 92TopDeb91-167
□ 92TopGol-516
□ 92TopGolW-516
□ 92TopMic-516
□ 92TriA AAS-517
□ 92UppDec-242
□ 93BluJayD-8
□ 93BluJayD4-11
□ 93BluJayDM-14
□ 93BluJayDM-29
□ 93BluJayDWS-3
□ 93BluJayFS-26
□ 93Bow-491
□ 93Don-219
□ 93Fla-294
□ 93Fle-698
□ 93Lea-408
□ 93OPC-203
□ 93OPCWorC-13
□ 93OPCWorSH-3
□ 93PacSpa-328
□ 93Pin-223
□ 93Sco-214
□ 93Sco-520
□ 93SP-52
□ 93StaClu-90
□ 93StaCluFDI-90
□ 93StaCluM-112
□ 93StaCluMOP-90
□ 93Stu-116
□ 93Top-659
□ 93TopGol-659
□ 93TopInaM-659
□ 93TopInaR-659
□ 93TopMic-659
□ 93TriPla-238
□ 93Ult-292
□ 93UppDec-764
□ 93UppDecGold-764
□ 93UppDecSH-HI18
□ 94BluJayP-8
□ 94BluJayUSPC-5H
□ 94BluJayUSPC-13C
□ 94Bow-57
□ 94ColC-423
□ 94ColChoGS-423
□ 94ColChoSS-423
□ 94Don-84
□ 94Fin-160
□ 94FinRef-160
□ 94Fla-350
□ 94Fle-342
□ 94FleExtB-194
□ 94Lea-117
□ 94OPC-265
□ 94OPCWorC-7
□ 94Pac-651
□ 94Pin-459
□ 94PinArtP-459
□ 94PinMusC-459
□ 94Sco-399
□ 94ScoGolR-399
□ 94Sel-135
□ 94StaClu-418
□ 94StaCluFDI-418
□ 94StaCluGR-418
□ 94StaCluMOP-418
□ 94StaCluT-156
□ 94StaCluTFDI-156
□ 94Stu-31
□ 94Top-426
□ 94TopGol-426
□ 94TopSpa-426
□ 94TriPla-37
□ 94Ult-142
□ 94UppDec-241
□ 94UppDecED-241
□ 95BluJayOH-31
□ 95BluJayUSPC-4H
□ 95BluJayUSPC-11S
□ 95ColCho-142
□ 95ColChoGS-142
□ 95ColChoSS-142
□ 95Don-132
□ 95DonPreP-132
□ 95DonTopotO-178
□ 95Fin-312
□ 95FinRef-312
□ 95Fla-318
□ 95Fle-104
□ 95Lea-70
□ 95LeaLim-157
□ 95Pin-112
□ 95PinArtP-112
□ 95PinMusC-112
□ 95Sco-414
□ 95ScoGolR-414
□ 95ScoPlaTS-414
□ 95StaClu-194
□ 95StaCluFDI-194
□ 95StaCluMOP-194
□ 95StaCluSTWS-194
□ 95StaCluVR-102
□ 95StaCluVRMO-102
□ 95Top-146
□ 95TopCyb-90
□ 95Ult-123
□ 95UltGolM-123
□ 95UppDec-286
□ 95UppDecED-286
□ 95UppDecEDG-286
□ 95UppDecSE-64
□ 95UppDecSEG-64
□ 96BluJayB-5
□ 96BluJayOH-29
□ 96Cir-97
□ 96CirRav-97
□ 96ColCho-748
□ 96ColChoGS-748
□ 96ColChoSS-748
□ 96Don-30
□ 96DonPreP-30
□ 96EmoXL-137
□ 96Fla-193
□ 96Fle-283
□ 96FleTif-283
□ 96Lea-203
□ 96LeaPrePB-203
□ 96LeaPrePG-203
□ 96LeaPrePS-203
□ 96Pac-437
□ 96Pin-60
□ 96ProSta-16
□ 96Sco-111
□ 96StaClu-386
□ 96StaCluEPB-386
□ 96StaCluEPG-386
□ 96StaCluEPS-386
□ 96StaCluMOP-386
□ 96Top-295
□ 96Ult-151
□ 96UltGolM-151
□ 96UppDec-471
□ 97BluJayOH-31
□ 97BluJayS-4
□ 97BluJayS-9
□ 97Cir-60
□ 97CirRav-60
□ 97ColCho-493
□ 97Don-239
□ 97DonGolPP-239
□ 97DonSilPP-239
□ 97Fin-257
□ 97FinRef-257
□ 97Fle-249
□ 97FleTif-249
□ 97Lea-306
□ 97LeaFraM-306
□ 97LeaFraMDC-306
□ 97MetUni-190
□ 97Pac-228
□ 97PacLigB-228
□ 97PacPri-76
□ 97PacPriLB-76
□ 97PacPriP-76
□ 97PacSil-228
□ 97Pin-57
□ 97PinArtP-PP57
□ 97PinMusC-57
□ 97PinPrePla-57
□ 97Sco-275
□ 97ScoArtPWB-275
□ 97ScoPreS-275
□ 97ScoShoS-275
□ 97ScoShoSAP-275
□ 97SP-178
□ 97StaClu-25
□ 97StaCluMat-25
□ 97StaCluMOP-25
□ 97Top-345
□ 97TopChr-116
□ 97TopChrR-116
□ 97TopGal-122
□ 97TopGalPPI-122
□ 97Ult-408
□ 97UltGolME-408
□ 97UltPlaME-408
□ 97UppDec-518
□ 98ColCho-529
□ 98Fin-171
□ 98FinNo--171
□ 98FinNo-R-171
□ 98FinRef-171
□ 98Fle-195
□ 98PacInvGems-115
□ 98PacOme-249
□ 98PacOmeR-249
□ 98PacOnl-776
□ 98PacOnlR-776
□ 98PacOnlWC-776
□ 98PacPar-116
□ 98PacParC-116
□ 98PacParG-116
□ 98PacParHS-116
□ 98PacParPB-116
□ 98PacParR-116
□ 98Pin-150
□ 98PinPreP-150
□ 98StaCluFDI-153
□ 98StaCluI-153
□ 98StaCluOneK-153
□ 98StaCluPP-153
□ 98Top-428
□ 98TopChr-428
□ 98TopChrR-428
□ 98TopDevR-428
□ 98TopDia-428
□ 98TopMiniC-428
□ 98Ult-342
□ 98UltGolM-342
□ 98UltMas-342
□ 98UltPlaM-342
□ 98UppDec-237
□ 98UppDecSF-132
□ 99Fle-252
□ 99FleSta9-252
□ 99FleWarT-252
□ 99MetUni-65
□ 99MetUniGM-65
□ 99MetUniPMG-65
□ 99PacOme-189
□ 99PacOmeC-189
□ 99PacOmeG-189
□ 99PacOmePB-189
□ 99PacPar-188
□ 99PacParC-188
□ 99PacParG-188
□ 99PacParHoloGold-188
□ 99PacParHS-188
□ 99PacParOD-188
□ 99PacParPB-188
□ 99PacParRed-188
□ 99SkyThu-124
□ 99SkyThuRant-124
□ 99SkyThuRave-124
□ 99ThuSkySupR-124
□ 99Ult-119
□ 99UltGolM-119
□ 99UltMas-119
□ 99UltPlaM-119
□ 99Vic-312
Sprague, Ed Sr.
□ 69Top-638
□ 72OPC-121
□ 72Top-121
□ 75OPC-76
□ 75Top-76
□ 75TopMin-76
□ 76SSP-230
□ 94BreMilB-277
Sprangler, Carl
□ 20Zee-57
Sprangler, Kirby
□ 19Zee-77
Spratke, Ken
□ 87ChaLooB-12
□ 88MemChiB-23
□ 89OmaRoyC-9
□ 89OmaRoyP-1719

Spratt, Greg
❑ 91SouAtlLAGP-SAL31
❑ 95NorNavTI-NNO
❑ 96NorNavB-4
❑ 97NorNav-5
❑ 97NorNavTI-26
Spratt, Jack (Henry)
❑ 12T207-171
Sprick, Scott
❑ 91EriSaiC-9
❑ 91EriSaiP-4078
❑ 91FreKeyC-19
❑ 91FreKeyP-2373
Spridzans, Mark
❑ 95StCatSTI-29
Spriggs, George
❑ 67Top-472
❑ 68Top-314
❑ 68TopVen-314
❑ 69Top-662
❑ 71MLBOffS-431
❑ 71OPC-411
❑ 71Top-411
Spring, Jack
❑ 62Top-257
❑ 63Top-572
❑ 64Top-71
❑ 64TopVen-71
❑ 65SeaPop-22
❑ 85SpoIndGC-20
Spring, Joshua
❑ 93AubAstC-23
❑ 93AubAstF-3444
❑ 95DunBluJTI-28
Springer, Dennis
❑ 88BakDodCLC-260
❑ 89SanAntMB-20
❑ 89TexLeaAGS-18
❑ 90AlbDukCm-12
❑ 90AlbDukTr-27
❑ 90CMC-414
❑ 90SanAntMGS-27
❑ 90TexLeaAGS-15
❑ 91LinDriAA-541
❑ 91SanAntMLD-541
❑ 91SanAntMP-2973
❑ 92SanAntMF-3973
❑ 92SanAntMS-568
❑ 92SkyAA F-252
❑ 93AlbDukF-1459
❑ 95ScrRedBTI-25
❑ 97AngMot-19
❑ 98ColCho-503
❑ 98DevRayP-9
❑ 98PacOnl-720
❑ 98PacOnlR-720
❑ 98PacOnlWC-720
❑ 98Top-243
❑ 98TopChr-243
❑ 98TopChrR-243
❑ 98TopDevR-243
❑ 98TopDia-243
❑ 98TopMiniC-243
❑ 98UppDec-294
Springer, Gary
❑ 83SanJosBC-6
Springer, Russell
❑ 87AncGlaP-27
❑ 88CapCodPPaLP-35
❑ 90LSUTigGM-15
❑ 91FloStaLAP-FSL18
❑ 91Ft.LauYC-14
❑ 91Ft.LauYP-2427
❑ 92Bow-308
❑ 92Cla2-T93
❑ 92ColCliF-350
❑ 92ColCliP-9
❑ 92ColCliS-118
❑ 92Pin-561
❑ 92SkyAAAF-57
❑ 93AngStaCl-24
❑ 93Bow-285
❑ 93Don-285
❑ 93FleFinE-191
❑ 93FleMajLP-A8
❑ 93Lea-549
❑ 93Sco-238
❑ 93Sel-337
❑ 93SP-27
❑ 93StaClu-736
❑ 93StaCluFDI-736
❑ 93StaCluMOP-736
❑ 93Top-686
❑ 93TopGol-686
❑ 93TopInaM-686
❑ 93TopInaR-686
❑ 93TopMic-686
❑ 93VanCanF-2597
❑ 94Don-325
❑ 94Sco-562
❑ 94ScoGolR-562
❑ 94Top-113
❑ 94TopGol-113
❑ 94TopSpa-113
❑ 94VanCanF-1865
❑ 96LeaSigEA-190
❑ 96PhiTeal-30
❑ 97AstMot-20
❑ 98DiaBacP-11
❑ 98PacOnl-46
❑ 98PacOnlR-46
❑ 98PacOnlWC-46
Springer, Steve
❑ 90CMC-470
❑ 90ColSprSSC-18
❑ 90ColSprSSP-46
❑ 90ProAAAF-227
❑ 91CalCanLD-72
❑ 91CalCanP-524
❑ 91LinDriAAA-72
❑ 91TopDeb90-147
❑ 92TidTidF-907
❑ 92TidTidS-571
❑ 93NorTidF-2578
❑ 94TolMudHF-1034
Springer, Steve (Billy)
❑ 84JacMetT-22
❑ 85IntLeaAT-13
❑ 85TidTidT-16
❑ 85TidTidT-17
❑ 86TidTidP-27
❑ 87TidTidP-11
❑ 87TidTidT-18
❑ 88TidTidCa-12
❑ 88TidTidCM-21
❑ 88TidTidP-1598
❑ 89VanCanC-12
❑ 89VanCanP-592
Springman, Bill
❑ 97SalLakB-5
❑ 98SalLakBO-4
Springstead, Marty
❑ 76TCMUmp-3
Sprinz, Joseph C.
❑ 28Zee-144
❑ 33Zee-41
❑ 37Zee-27
❑ 37Zee-89
❑ 48SomandK-28
❑ 49SomandK-22
Sproat, Ed
❑ 87OldJudN-467
Sproesser, Mark
❑ 81RedPioT-18
❑ 82RedPioT-13
Sprout, Bob
❑ 77FriOneYW-109
Sproviero, Nick
❑ 91JamExpC-19
❑ 91JamExpP-3544
Sprowl, Bobby (Robert)
❑ 80TucTorT-6
❑ 80VenLeaS-264
❑ 81AstPos-24
❑ 81Top-82
❑ 82Top-441
❑ 82TucTorT-19
❑ 83ColAstT-21
Spry, Shane
❑ 93SarWhiSC-24
❑ 94HicCraC-21
❑ 94HicCraF-2191
Spurgeon, Fred
❑ 26Exh-87
Spurgeon, Jay
❑ 98DelShoM-27
Spurgeon, Scott
❑ 88AubAstP-1948
❑ 89AshTouP-958
Spurlock, Robert
❑ 90VisOakCLC-85
Spykstra, David
❑ 92ClaDraP-65
❑ 93StaCluM-150
❑ 93YakBeaC-23
❑ 93YakBeaF-3884
❑ 94YakBeaC-23
❑ 94YakBeaF-3850
❑ 96SavSanB-11
❑ 97FloStaLTPB-27
❑ 97VerBeaD-25
Squires, Mike
❑ 78SSP270-147
❑ 79Top-704
❑ 80Top-466
❑ 81Don-398
❑ 81Fle-349
❑ 81Top-292
❑ 82Don-39
❑ 82Fle-357
❑ 82FleSta-188
❑ 82Top-398
❑ 83Don-495
❑ 83Fle-250
❑ 83Top-669
❑ 83WhiSoxTV-25
❑ 84Don-404
❑ 84Fle-71
❑ 84Nes792-72
❑ 84Top-72
❑ 84TopTif-72
❑ 84WhiSoxTV-29
❑ 85Don-501
❑ 85Fle-529
❑ 85OPC-278
❑ 85Top-543
❑ 85TopTif-543
❑ 89BluJayFS-25
❑ 90BluJayFS-25
❑ 91BluJayFS-21
❑ 92WhiSoxK-NNO
St-Vincent, Claude
❑ 52LavPro-94
St. George, Nick
❑ 97UCLBruTI-20
St. Onge, Paul
❑ 74WicAerODF-128
St.Clair, Dan
❑ 83OmaRoyT-8
❑ 84OmaRoyT-18
St.Claire, Ebba
❑ 52Bow-172
❑ 52Top-393
❑ 53BowBW-34
❑ 53BraJohC-16
❑ 53BraSpiaS3-21
❑ 53Top-91
❑ 54Bow-128
❑ 83Bra53F-42
❑ 83TopRep5-393
❑ 91TopArc1-91
St.Claire, Mark
❑ 92PulBraC-6
❑ 92PulBraF-3182
St.Claire, Randy
❑ 85Don-575
❑ 85ExpPos-23
❑ 85IndIndTI-19
❑ 86Don-463
❑ 86Fle-261
❑ 86IndIndTI-15
❑ 86Lea-229
❑ 86OPC-89
❑ 86Top-89
❑ 86TopTif-89
❑ 87ExpPos-29
❑ 87FleUpd-113
❑ 87FleUpdG-113
❑ 87OPC-366
❑ 87SpoTeaP-20
❑ 87Top-467
❑ 87TopTif-467
❑ 88Don-426
❑ 88Fle-197
❑ 88FleGlo-197
❑ 88OPC-279
❑ 88Sco-397
❑ 88ScoGlo-397
❑ 88Top-279
❑ 88TopTif-279
❑ 89PorBeaC-11
❑ 89PorBeaP-213
❑ 89Top-666
❑ 89TopTif-666
❑ 89UppDec-29
❑ 90CMC-607
❑ 90OPC-503
❑ 90ProAAAF-193
❑ 90Top-503
❑ 90TopTif-503
❑ 90TucTorC-5
❑ 90TucTorP-203
❑ 91LinDriAAA-443
❑ 91RicBraBC-16
❑ 91RicBraLD-443
❑ 91RicBraP-2568
❑ 91RicBraTI-10
❑ 92RicBraBB-14
❑ 92RicBraF-377
❑ 92RicBraRC-19
❑ 92RicBraS-443
❑ 92Sco-708
❑ 92SkyAAAF-204
❑ 93RicBraF-184
❑ 94SyrChiF-971
❑ 94SyrChiTI-25
❑ 96StoPorB-28
❑ 97RicBraBC-20
❑ 97StoPor-27
❑ 98CapFeaCM-29
St.Claire, Steve
❑ 85UtiBluST-23
❑ 86JamExpP-24
❑ 87BurExpP-1077
St.John, Anthony
❑ 89SalLakTTI-16
St.John, Rich
❑ 89WatIndS-28
❑ 90RenSilSCLC-289
St.Laurent, Jim
❑ 85BurRanT-15
❑ 86DayBealP-27
❑ 87TexLeaAF-17
❑ 88OklCit8C-23
❑ 88OklCit8P-39
❑ 89OklCit8C-17
❑ 89OklCit8P-1524
❑ 90TulDriDGB-7
St.Peter, Bill (William)
❑ 88GenCubP-1650
❑ 89ChaWheB-6
❑ 89ChaWheP-1753
❑ 90ButCopKSP-18
❑ 90PeoChiTI-12
❑ 91ChaKniLD-143
❑ 91ChaKniP-1698
❑ 91LinDriAA-143
St.Pierre, Bob
❑ 96Exc-94
❑ 97TamYan-23
Staats, Todd
❑ 89GeoColC-30
Stabile, Ed
❑ 92WatIndC-28
Stabile, Paul
❑ 97EriSeaWB-30
❑ 98AugGreM-14
Stablein, George
❑ 80HawIslT-15
❑ 81HawIslT-14
❑ 81Top-356
❑ 82HawIslT-15
Stabler, Ken
❑ 93Pin-477
Stacey, Al
❑ 89GenCubP-1874
❑ 90EriSaiS-25
Stachler, Eric
❑ 95AubAstTI-22
❑ 96KisCobB-27
❑ 97KisCob-25
Stack, Ed
❑ 80PerHaloFP-D
❑ 80PerHaloFP-F
Stack, Ed (William Edward)
❑ 11PinT-5-304
❑ 12T207-172
❑ 90DodTar-759
Stackhouse, Brian
❑ 86MacPirP-23
Stading, Greg
❑ 86PriWilPP-25
❑ 87SalBucP-6
Stadler, Jeff
❑ 78CedRapGT-26
❑ 79CedRapGT-7
Stadler, Mike
❑ 94BurIndC-23
❑ 94BurIndF-3799
Staehle, Marv
❑ 65OPC-41
❑ 65Top-41
❑ 66OPC-164
❑ 66Top-164
❑ 66TopVen-164
❑ 68SeaPop-14
❑ 69PilPos-30
❑ 69Top-394
❑ 71ExpLaPR-11
❑ 71MLBOffS-140
❑ 71OPC-663
❑ 71Top-663
❑ 77PilPosR-30
Stafford, Bill
❑ 61Top-213
❑ 61TopStal-199
❑ 61Yan61RL-13
❑ 62Jel-13
❑ 62Pos-13
❑ 62PosCan-13
❑ 62Top-55
❑ 62Top-570
❑ 62TopVen-55
❑ 63Jel-22
❑ 63Kah-28
❑ 63Pos-22
❑ 63ReqKP-15
❑ 63Top-155
❑ 63Top-331
❑ 64ChatheY-22
❑ 64Top-299
❑ 64TopVen-299
❑ 65ChaTheY-21
❑ 65OPC-281
❑ 65Top-281
❑ 69PilPos-36
❑ 77PilPosR-36
❑ 83Yan196-13
❑ 91YanRinP13-4
❑ 92YanWIZ6-120
Stafford, Gil
❑ 75BurBeeT-27
Stafford, Jerry
❑ 92EriSaiC-26
❑ 92EriSaiF-1624
❑ 93HigDesMC-21
❑ 93HigDesMF-42
❑ 93Top-683
❑ 93TopGol-683
❑ 93TopInaM-683
❑ 93TopInaR-683
❑ 93TopMic-683
❑ 94BreCouMC-18
❑ 94BreCouMF-12
Stafford, Michael
❑ 98St.CatSM-22
Stafford, Mitch
❑ 93EveGiaC-26
❑ 93EveGiaF-3779
Stagg, Bob
❑ 47CenFlo-27
Staggs, Ron
❑ 75WesPalBES-14
Staggs, Steve
❑ 75OmaRoyTI-15
❑ 76OmaRoyTT-22
❑ 76VenLeaS-129
❑ 78OPC-94
❑ 78Top-521
Stahl, Chick (Charles)
❑ 11SpoLifCW-332
Stahl, Jake (Garland)
❑ 03BreE10-133
❑ 04FanCraAL-43
❑ 04RedSoxUP-12
❑ 08AmeCarE91-91
❑ 08RosComP-54
❑ 09AmeCarE90-1-97
❑ 09ColChiE-271
❑ 09MaxPubP-12
❑ 09RamT20-111
❑ 09SpoNewSM-84
❑ 09T206-334
❑ 09T206-335
❑ 10E-UOraBSC-21
❑ 10E12AmeCDCE125-34
❑ 10RedCroT-72
❑ 10RedCroT-158
❑ 10RedCroT-245
❑ 11L1L-130
❑ 11PinT-5-670
❑ 11S74Sil-4
❑ 11S81LarS-105
❑ 11SpoLifCW-333
❑ 11SpoLifM-16
❑ 11T205-160
❑ 11TurRedT-38
❑ 12ColRedB-271
❑ 12ColTinT-271
❑ 12HasTriFT-46
❑ 12HasTriFT-65
❑ 12HasTriFT-68A
❑ 12HasTriFT-68B
❑ 12RedSoxBASP-4
❑ 13NatGamW-36
❑ 14TexTomE-41
❑ 14TexTomE-61
Stahl, Larry
❑ 66OPC-107
❑ 66Top-107
❑ 66TopVen-107
❑ 69MilBra-260
❑ 69MLBOffS-198
❑ 69Top-271
❑ 69TopSta-99
❑ 70MLBOffS-120
❑ 70OPC-494
❑ 70Top-494
❑ 71OPC-711
❑ 71Top-711
❑ 72MilBra-324
❑ 72Top-782
❑ 73OPC-533
❑ 73Top-533
❑ 74OPC-507
❑ 74Top-507
❑ 91MetWIZ-373
Stahlhoefer, Larry
❑ 92WelPirC-22
❑ 92WelPirF-1327
❑ 93AugPirC-21
❑ 93AugPirF-1548
Stahoviak, Scott
❑ 91Cla/Bes-401
❑ 91ClaDraP-23
❑ 91FroRowDP-25
❑ 91FroRowDPG-25
❑ 91FroRowDPS-25
❑ 91VisOakUP-2
❑ 92Bow-360
❑ 92CalLeaACL-41
❑ 92ClaFS7-299
❑ 92OPC-66
❑ 92ProFS7-97
❑ 92StaCluD-179
❑ 92Top-66
❑ 92TopGol-66
❑ 92TopGolW-66
❑ 92TopMic-66
❑ 92UppDecML-320
❑ 92VisOakC-1
❑ 92VisOakF-1024
❑ 93ClaFS7-26
❑ 93ClaGolF-45
❑ 93ExcFS7-204
❑ 93NasXprF-412
❑ 94ColC-18
❑ 94ColChoGS-18
❑ 94ColChoSS-18
❑ 94Pin-248
❑ 94PinArtP-248
❑ 94PinMusC-248
❑ 94SalLakBF-826
❑ 94Spo-154
❑ 94StaClu-51
❑ 94StaCluFDI-51
❑ 94StaCluGR-51
❑ 94StaCluMOP-51
❑ 95Bow-46
❑ 95DonTopotO-114
❑ 95Fin-259
❑ 95FinRef-259
❑ 95FleUpd-63
❑ 95SP-171
❑ 95SPSil-171
❑ 95UppDec-229
❑ 95UppDecED-229
❑ 95UppDecEDG-229
❑ 96Cir-60
❑ 96CirRav-60
❑ 96ColCho-206
❑ 96ColChoGS-206
❑ 96ColChoSS-206
❑ 96Don-270
❑ 96DonPreP-270
❑ 96Fla-123
❑ 96Fle-177
❑ 96FleTif-177
❑ 96LeaSigA-212
❑ 96LeaSigAG-212
❑ 96LeaSigAS-212
❑ 96MetUni-82
❑ 96MetUniP-82
❑ 96Pac-358
❑ 96PanSti-204
❑ 96Sco-426
❑ 96StaClu-121
❑ 96StaCluMOP-121
❑ 96Ult-94
❑ 96UltGolM-94
❑ 97Cir-189
❑ 97CirRav-189
❑ 97ColCho-383

❑ 97Don-83
❑ 97DonGolPP-83
❑ 97DonSilPP-83
❑ 97Fle-157
❑ 97FleTif-157
❑ 97Lea-19
❑ 97LeaFraM-19
❑ 97LeaFraMDC-19
❑ 97Pac-145
❑ 97PacLigB-145
❑ 97PacSil-145
❑ 97Pin-45
❑ 97PinArtP-PP45
❑ 97PinMusC-45
❑ 97PinPrePla-45
❑ 97Sco-111
❑ 97ScoArtPWB-111
❑ 97ScoPreS-111
❑ 97ScoShoS-111
❑ 97ScoShoSAP-111
❑ 97StaClu-327
❑ 97StaCluMOP-327
❑ 97Top-9
❑ 98PacInvGems-68
❑ 98SalLakBO-30
❑ 98Top-368
❑ 98TopChr-368
❑ 90TopChrR 368
❑ 98TopDevR-368
❑ 98TopDia-368
❑ 98TopMiniC-368

Staiger, Roy
❑ 74MetTeal-20
❑ 75TidTidTI-19
❑ 76OPC-592
❑ 76SSP-560
❑ 76Top-592
❑ 77MetDaiPA-22
❑ 77Top-281
❑ 78TacYanC-23
❑ 79ColCliT-2
❑ 80ColCliP-25
❑ 80ColCliT-9
❑ 89TidTidC-10
❑ 91MetWIZ-374
❑ 92YanWIZ7-144

Stainback, G. Tucker
❑ 34DiaMatCSB-168
❑ 34DiaStaR-52
❑ 35DiaMatCS3T1-133
❑ 36CubTeal-28
❑ 36DiaMatCS3T2-22
❑ 43YanSta-25
❑ 47SigOil-37
❑ 75TCMLarFP-3
❑ 79DiaGre-380
❑ 83TCMPla1945-10
❑ 90DodTar-760
❑ 95ConTSN-1393

Stairs, Matt
❑ 89JamExpP-2141
❑ 89WesPalBES-22
❑ 90WesPalBES-23
❑ 91HarSenLD-271
❑ 91HarSenP-637
❑ 91LinDriAA-271
❑ 92Bow-434
❑ 92Bow-602
❑ 92DonRoo-112
❑ 92ExpDonD-16B
❑ 92IndIndS-195
❑ 92LeaGolR-BC8
❑ 92Pin-583
❑ 92PinRoo-28
❑ 92ProFS7-259
❑ 92SkyAA F-293
❑ 92SkyAAAF-94
❑ 92TopTra-110T
❑ 92TopTraG-110T
❑ 92UppDec-786
❑ 93ClaFS7-27
❑ 93Don-460
❑ 93Fle-464
❑ 93OttLynF-2448
❑ 93Sco-232
❑ 93Sel-327
❑ 94NewBriRSF-664
❑ 95PawRedSDD-26
❑ 95PawRedTI-24
❑ 96LeaSigEA-191
❑ 97A'sMot-16
❑ 97Pac-176
❑ 97PacLigB-176
❑ 97PacSil-176
❑ 97Sel-195
❑ 97SelCom-195
❑ 98A'sMot-5
❑ 98CirThu-207
❑ 98CirThuRav-207
❑ 98CirThuSupRav-207
❑ 98ColCho-195
❑ 98CroRoy-103
❑ 98Don-50
❑ 98DonCol-50
❑ 98DonColL-225
❑ 98DonColS-50
❑ 98DonGolPP-50
❑ 98DonPriCD-50
❑ 98DonPriCL-225
❑ 98DonSilPP-50
❑ 98Fin-223
❑ 98FinNo--223
❑ 98FinNo-R-223
❑ 98FinRef-223
❑ 98FlaShoLeg0-70
❑ 98FlaShoLeg1-70
❑ 98FlaShoLeg2-70
❑ 98FlaShoLeg3-70
❑ 98FlaShoLegM-70
❑ 98FlaShoR0-70
❑ 98FlaShoR1-70
❑ 98FlaShoR2-70
❑ 98FlaShoR3-70
❑ 98Fle-180
❑ 98Lea-25
❑ 98LeaFraDA-25
❑ 98LeaFraF-25
❑ 98LeaFraM-25
❑ 98LeaFraM-25
❑ 98LeaFraMDC-25
❑ 98LeaFraMDC-25
❑ 98LeaFraMZ2-25
❑ 98LeaRS-127
❑ 98LeaRSLHolo-127
❑ 98LeaRSLong-127
❑ 98LeaRTrue-127
❑ 98MetUni-173
❑ 98MetUniPMG-173
❑ 98Pac-174
❑ 98PacInvTeam-20
❑ 98PacOnl-546
❑ 98PacOnlR-546
❑ 98PacOnlWC-546
❑ 98PacPlaB-174
❑ 98PacRedT-174
❑ 98PacSil-174
❑ 98Pin-107
❑ 98PinPreP-107
❑ 98Revo-108
❑ 98RevoSS-108
❑ 98Sco-164
❑ 98ScoRT-142
❑ 98ScoSS-PP70
❑ 98ScoSSAP-PP70
❑ 98SkyDugA-76
❑ 98SkyDugAIA-76
❑ 98SpoIll-116
❑ 98SpoIllEE-116
❑ 98SpoIllFE-116
❑ 98SpoIllODMP-OD21
❑ 98SpoIllWSF-137
❑ 98SpoIllWSFEE-137
❑ 98SpoIllWSFFE-137
❑ 98SPxFin-112
❑ 98SPxFinR-112
❑ 98SPxFinS-112
❑ 98StaCluFDI-268
❑ 98StaCluI-268
❑ 98StaCluOneK-268
❑ 98StaCluPP-268
❑ 98Top-16
❑ 98TopChr-16
❑ 98TopChrR-16
❑ 98TopDevR-16
❑ 98TopDia-16
❑ 98TopMiniC-16
❑ 98Ult-16
❑ 98UltGolM-16
❑ 98UltMas-16
❑ 98UltPlaM-16
❑ 98UppDec-470
❑ 98UppDecR-73
❑ 99Fle-269
❑ 99FleSta9-269
❑ 99FleWarT-269
❑ 99MetUni-52
❑ 99MetUniGM-52
❑ 99MetUniPMG-52
❑ 99Pac-318
❑ 99PacAur-138
❑ 99PacAurOD-138
❑ 99PacOme-174
❑ 99PacOmeC-174
❑ 99PacOmeG-174
❑ 99PacOmePB-174
❑ 99PacPlaB-318
❑ 99PacPriS-140
❑ 99PacPriS206-140
❑ 99PacPriS206R-140
❑ 99PacRed-318
❑ 99SkyPre-187
❑ 99SkyPreR-187
❑ 99SkyThu-67
❑ 99SkyThuRant-67
❑ 99SkyThuRave-67
❑ 99SpoIll-96
❑ 99StaClu-262
❑ 99StaCluFDI-262
❑ 99StaCluOoaK-262
❑ 99StaCluPP-262
❑ 99ThuSkySupR-67
❑ 99Top-259
❑ 99TopChr-259
❑ 99TopChrR-259
❑ 99TopMVPP-259
❑ 99Ult-124
❑ 99UltGolM-124
❑ 99UltMas-124
❑ 99UltPlaM-124
❑ 99UppDec-169
❑ 99UppDecEL1-169
❑ 99UppDecEL2-169
❑ 99UppDecM-152
❑ 99UppDecMGS-152
❑ 99UppDecMHFS-152
❑ 99UppDecMP-152
❑ 99UppDecMSS-152
❑ 99Vic-284

Stajduhar, Marty
❑ 90RanMot-28

Staley, Gale
❑ 29Zee-99

Staley, George
❑ 26Zee-34
❑ 28Zee-42

Staley, Gerry (Gerald)
❑ 46SunBre-18
❑ 51Bow-121
❑ 51R42SmaS-98
❑ 51TopBluB-7
❑ 52Bow-50
❑ 52NatTeaL-34
❑ 52StaCalL-81G
❑ 52Top-79
❑ 53BowC-17
❑ 53CarHunW-24
❑ 53RedMan-NL24
❑ 53Top-56
❑ 54Bow-14
❑ 54CarHunW-27
❑ 55Bow-155
❑ 57Top-227
❑ 58Top-412
❑ 59Top-426
❑ 60Top-57
❑ 60Top-510
❑ 60TopVen-57
❑ 60WhiSoxTS-20
❑ 61Pos-29
❑ 61Top-90
❑ 61TopStal-130
❑ 61WhiSoxTS-19
❑ 76WhiSoxTAG-12
❑ 79TCM50-40
❑ 80WhiSoxGT-10
❑ 81WhiSox1T-32
❑ 83TopRep5-79
❑ 89WhiSoxK-5
❑ 91TopArc1-56

Staley, Henry E.
❑ 87OldJudN-468

Stallard, Tracy
❑ 61Top-81
❑ 62Top-567
❑ 63Top-419
❑ 64MetTeal-9
❑ 64Top-176
❑ 64TopVen-176
❑ 65CarJayP-10
❑ 65CarTeal-25
❑ 65OldLonC-18
❑ 65Top-491
❑ 66CarTeal-12
❑ 66OPC-7
❑ 66Top-7
❑ 66TopVen-7
❑ 76Met63 S-16
❑ 81RedSoxBG2S-116
❑ 91MetWIZ-375

Stallcup, Jeff
❑ 89TenTecGE-26

Stallcup, T. Virgil
❑ 49Bow-81
❑ 49EurSta-95
❑ 50Bow-116
❑ 51Bow-108
❑ 52Bow-6
❑ 52NatTeaL-35
❑ 52Top-69
❑ 53Top-180
❑ 83TopRep5-69
❑ 85TCMPla1-17
❑ 91TopArc1-180

Staller, George
❑ 67BalOriP-100
❑ 70BalOriP-30
❑ 71BalOriP-28
❑ 72OriPos-31
❑ 73BalOriP-39
❑ 73OPC-136
❑ 73OriTeal-28
❑ 73Top-136A
❑ 73Top-136B
❑ 74OPC-306
❑ 74Top-306
❑ 75BalOriP-28

Stallings, George T.
❑ 11SpoLifM-82
❑ 13NatGamW-37
❑ 13TomBarW-34
❑ 15CraJacE-163
❑ 15SpoNewM-169
❑ 16BF2FP-58
❑ 16FleBreD-89
❑ 16SpoNewM-167
❑ 74BroClu-15
❑ 80BraTCM1-15
❑ 90DodTar-761
❑ 90HOFStiB-21

Stalp, Joe
❑ 83CedRapRF-4
❑ 83CedRapRT-10

Stamison, Mike
❑ 94SouOreAC-28
❑ 94SouOreAF-3634

Stampel, Eric
❑ 86LynMetP-21

Stamps, Crandall
❑ 89GeoColC-31
❑ 90GeoColC-29

Stamps, Jerry
❑ 75CedRapGT-24

Stanage, Oscar
❑ 07NewEveWS-14
❑ 07TigACDPP-25
❑ 09AmeCarE90-1-98
❑ 09T206-336
❑ 09TigTaCP-17
❑ 10PeoT21-52
❑ 10SweCapPP-31
❑ 11BasBatEU-36
❑ 11BasBatEU-37
❑ 11HelSta-37
❑ 11PinT-5-161
❑ 11SpoLifM-69
❑ 11T205-161
❑ 12HasTriFT-5
❑ 12HasTriFT-26
❑ 12HasTriFT-55
❑ 12T207-173
❑ 14PieStaT-97
❑ 14TexTomE-42
❑ 15AmeCarE106-36
❑ 15SpoNewM-170
❑ 16BF2FP-31
❑ 16SpoNewM-168
❑ 17ColE13-167
❑ 19W514-115
❑ 21Zee-18
❑ 22Zee-74

Stancel, Mark
❑ 86MedA'sC-54
❑ 88ModA'sCLC-65
❑ 88ModA'sTI-14
❑ 90HunStaB-11

Stanceu, Charles
❑ 77TCMTheWY-72

Stanczak, Jack
❑ 94ChaRanF-2507

Standaert, Jerry
❑ 90DodTar-762

Standart, Rich
❑ 75ShrCapT-21
❑ 76ShrCapT-2
❑ 77ColCliT-21

Standiford, Mark
❑ 86AncGlaPTI-33
❑ 87AncGlaP-28
❑ 89SalSpuCLC-139
❑ 89SalSpuP-1801

Standish, Scott
❑ 93OneYanC-20
❑ 93OneYanF-3502
❑ 94GreBatF-474
❑ 95AusFut-78
❑ 95Exc-105
❑ 95NorNavTI-38
❑ 97GreBatC-22

Standley, Don
❑ 75WatDodT-19

Standridge, Jason
❑ 97Bow-439
❑ 97BowChr-299
❑ 97BowChrI-299
❑ 97BowChrIR-299
❑ 97BowChrR-299
❑ 97BowInt-439
❑ 97TopSta-124
❑ 97TopStaAM-124
❑ 98Bes-96
❑ 98BesNumOP-39
❑ 98Bow-219
❑ 98BowChr-219
❑ 98BowChrGA-219
❑ 98BowChrGAR-219
❑ 98BowChrI-219
❑ 98BowChrIR-219
❑ 98BowChrR-219
❑ 98BowGolA-219
❑ 98BowInt-219
❑ 98Top-495
❑ 98TopChr-495
❑ 98TopChrR-495
❑ 98TopDevR-495
❑ 98TopDia-495
❑ 98TopMiniC-495
❑ 99BasAmeTPA-40
❑ 99Bow-164
❑ 99BowChr-164
❑ 99BowChrG-164
❑ 99BowChrGR-164
❑ 99BowChrI-164
❑ 99BowChrIR-164
❑ 99BowChrR-164
❑ 99BowGol-164
❑ 99BowInt-164

Stanek, Al
❑ 64Top-99
❑ 64TopVen-99
❑ 65Top-302
❑ 66Top-437

Stanfield, Kevin
❑ 77VisOakT-15
❑ 79TolMudHT-5
❑ 79Top-709

Stanfield, Mike
❑ 88CliGiaP-713

Stanford, Don
❑ 89PriWilCS-20
❑ 90AlbYanB-8
❑ 90AlbYanP-1036
❑ 90AlbYanSt-19
❑ 90Bes-92
❑ 90ProAaA-21
❑ 91AlbYanLD-19
❑ 91AlbYanP-1009
❑ 91LinDriAA-19
❑ 92ColCliF-351
❑ 92ColCliP-10
❑ 92ColCliS-119
❑ 93ColCliF-1112
❑ 93ColCliP-7

Stanford, Larry
❑ 89OneYanP-2106
❑ 90FloStaLAS-43
❑ 90Ft.LauYS-19
❑ 90StaFS7-41
❑ 91AlbYanLD-20
❑ 91AlbYanP-1010
❑ 91LinDriAA-20
❑ 92ColCliF-352
❑ 92ColCliS-120
❑ 92ProFS7-116
❑ 92SkyAAAF-58
❑ 94NewHavRF-1549

Stange, Albert Lee
❑ 61TwiCloD-25
❑ 62Top-321
❑ 63Top-246
❑ 63TwiVol-21
❑ 64Top-555
❑ 65Top-448
❑ 66Top-371
❑ 67CokCapRS-1
❑ 67OPC-99
❑ 67Top-99
❑ 67TopRedSS-19
❑ 68CokCapRS-1
❑ 68Top-593
❑ 69MilBra-261
❑ 69OPC-148
❑ 69Top-148
❑ 69TopFou-19
❑ 70OPC-447
❑ 70RedSoxCPPC-15
❑ 70Top-447
❑ 71OPC-311
❑ 71Top-311
❑ 72MilBra-325
❑ 73OPC-131
❑ 73Top-131A
❑ 73Top-131B
❑ 74OPC-403
❑ 74Top-403
❑ 75TwiPos-23
❑ 75TwiTeal-25
❑ 78TwiFri-44
❑ 81RedSoxBG2S-117
❑ 89PawRedSP-692
❑ 89PawRedSTI-24
❑ 90PawRedSDD-25
❑ 90PawRedSP-479
❑ 90ProAAAF-451
❑ 91WinHavRSC-16
❑ 92WinHavRSC-30
❑ 93ForLauRSC-29
❑ 93ForLauRSFP-1615
❑ 94CarLeaA-DJ7

Stange, Kurt
❑ 87SalLakTTT-1
❑ 88MidLeaAGS-58
❑ 88WauTimGS-10
❑ 89SanBerSB-13

Stange, Tim
❑ 88ElmPioC-9
❑ 90LynRedSTI-23

Stangel, Chris
❑ 84EveGiaC-18

Stanhope, Chuck (Chester D.)
❑ 86HagSunP-19
❑ 87ChaO'sW-31
❑ 88RocRedWGCP-25
❑ 89HagSunB-17
❑ 89HagSunP-269
❑ 89RocRedWC-2
❑ 90HagSunDGB-28

Stanhouse, Don
❑ 72RanTeal-24
❑ 73OPC-352
❑ 73Top-352
❑ 75ExpPos-35
❑ 75OPC-493
❑ 75Top-493
❑ 75TopMin-493
❑ 76ExpRed-29
❑ 76MonExpP-28
❑ 77ExpPos-29
❑ 77Kel-32
❑ 77OPC-63
❑ 77Top-274
❑ 78BalOriP-31
❑ 78OPC-162
❑ 78Top-629
❑ 79Top-119
❑ 80DodPol-29
❑ 80Top-517
❑ 81DodPol-26
❑ 81Don-557
❑ 81Fle-121
❑ 81OPC-24
❑ 81Top-24
❑ 90DodTar-763
❑ 91OriCro-432
❑ 93RanKee-38

Stanicek, Pete
❑ 86HagSunP-20
❑ 87ChaO'sW-1
❑ 87IntLeaAT-29
❑ 88Don-541
❑ 88DonBasB-294
❑ 88DonRoo-15
❑ 88Fle-573
❑ 88FleGlo-573
❑ 88OriFreB-17
❑ 88OriPos-35

❑ 88RocRedWC-18
❑ 88RocRedWP-205
❑ 88RocRedWTI-22
❑ 88Sco-628
❑ 88ScoGlo-628
❑ 88TopTra-114T
❑ 88TopTraT-114T
❑ 89BalOriP-33
❑ 89Bow-14
❑ 89BowTif-14
❑ 89Don-169
❑ 89Fle-622
❑ 89FleGlo-622
❑ 89HagSunS-20
❑ 89OPC-317
❑ 89PanSti-265
❑ 89Sco-236
❑ 89Top-497
❑ 89TopCoi-52
❑ 89TopSti-232
❑ 89TopTif-497
❑ 89ToyRoo-30
❑ 89UppDec-592
❑ 90HagSunDGB-29
❑ 90ProAAAF-474
❑ 90RocRedWP-717
❑ 91OriCro-433

Stanicek, Steve
❑ 84ShrCapFB-21
❑ 86ElPasDP-19
❑ 87DenZepP-27
❑ 88DenZepC-22
❑ 88DenZepP-1266
❑ 88Fle-174
❑ 88FleGlo-174
❑ 88StaLinO-16
❑ 89ScrRedBC-12
❑ 89ScrRedBP-717
❑ 90CMC-242
❑ 90CMC-315
❑ 90ProAAAF-310
❑ 90RocRedWC-15
❑ 90ScrRedBC-16
❑ 90ScrRedBP-608
❑ 94BreMilB-355

Stanifer, Rob
❑ 94ElmPioC-20
❑ 94ElmPioF-3474
❑ 95BreCouMF-245
❑ 97ChaKni-28
❑ 98ChaKniQ-26
❑ 98Don-285
❑ 98DonGolPP-285
❑ 98DonSilPP-285
❑ 98Fle-269
❑ 98LeaRS-258
❑ 98LeaRSLHolo-258
❑ 98LeaRSLong-258
❑ 98LeaRTrue-258
❑ 98PacOnl-306
❑ 98PacOnlR-306
❑ 98PacOnlWC-306
❑ 98PorSeaD5AQ-24

Staniland, Steve
❑ 77ArkTraT-10

Stanka, Joe
❑ 58UniOil-9
❑ 81WhiSox1T-36

Stankiewicz, Andy
❑ 87Ft.LauYP-10
❑ 88AlbYanP-1330
❑ 88EasLeaAP-5
❑ 89AlbYanB-15
❑ 89AlbYanP-333
❑ 89AlbYanSt-19
❑ 89BlaYNPRWLU-11
❑ 89EasLeaAP-2
❑ 90AlbDecGB-17
❑ 90CMC-210
❑ 90ColCliC-10
❑ 90ColCliP-24
❑ 90ColCliP-685
❑ 90ProAAAF-335
❑ 90TopTVY-62
❑ 91ColCliLD-120
❑ 91ColCliP-20
❑ 91ColCliP-606
❑ 91LinDriAAA-120
❑ 92Bow-482
❑ 92Cla2-T7
❑ 92DonRooP-BC11
❑ 92DonUpd-U2
❑ 92FleUpd-44
❑ 92JimDeaRS-1
❑ 92Lea-470
❑ 92LeaBlaG-470
❑ 92OPC-179
❑ 92Pin-564
❑ 92PinRoo-6
❑ 92ScoRoo-100T
❑ 92StaClu-725
❑ 92StaCluECN-725
❑ 92Top-179
❑ 92TopGol-179
❑ 92TopGolW-179
❑ 92TopMic-179
❑ 92TopTra-111T
❑ 92TopTraG-111T
❑ 92Ult-415
❑ 92UltAllR-2
❑ 92UppDec-779
❑ 92UppDecSR-SR21
❑ 93ColCliF-1120
❑ 93ColCliP-18
❑ 93Don-213
❑ 93Fle-285
❑ 93Lea-9
❑ 93OPC-291
❑ 93PacSpa-212
❑ 93PanSti-149
❑ 93Pin-363
❑ 93Sco-338
❑ 93Sel-279
❑ 93SelChaR-17
❑ 93StaClu-105
❑ 93StaCluFDI-105
❑ 93StaCluMOP-105
❑ 93Top-348
❑ 93TopGol-348
❑ 93TopInaM-348
❑ 93TopInaR-348
❑ 93TopMic-348
❑ 93Toy-34
❑ 93TriPla-101A
❑ 93TriPla-101B
❑ 93Ult-249
❑ 93UppDec-257
❑ 93UppDecGold-257
❑ 93USPlaCR-12D
❑ 93YanStaC-29
❑ 94AstMot-26
❑ 94Fin-253
❑ 94FinRef-253
❑ 94Pac-437
❑ 94StaClu-635
❑ 94StaCluFDI-635
❑ 94StaCluGR-635
❑ 94StaCluMOP-635
❑ 95StaClu-584
❑ 95StaCluMOP-584
❑ 95StaCluSTWS-584
❑ 96FleUpd-U152
❑ 96FleUpdTC-U152
❑ 96LeaSigEA-192
❑ 98ColCho-299
❑ 98DiaMcD-20
❑ 98PacInvGems-180
❑ 98PacOnl-47
❑ 98PacOnlR-47
❑ 98PacOnlWC-47
❑ 98UppDec-637

Stanks, Joe
❑ 55DesMoiHB-17

Stanky, Eddie
❑ 43CubTeal-21
❑ 44CubTeal-22
❑ 46DodTeal-21
❑ 46SpoExcW-7-1A
❑ 47DodTeal-23
❑ 47Exh-216A
❑ 47Exh-216B
❑ 48BluTin-31
❑ 49Bow-104
❑ 49EurSta-26
❑ 50Bow-29
❑ 50Dra-22
❑ 50JJKCopP-20
❑ 50JJKCopP-21
❑ 51Bow-13
❑ 51R42SmaS-105
❑ 51TopCurA-11
❑ 51TopRedB-48
❑ 52BerRos-63
❑ 52Bow-160
❑ 52RedMan-NL23
❑ 52Top-76
❑ 53BowC-49
❑ 53CarHunW-25
❑ 53ExhCan-9
❑ 54CarHunW-28
❑ 54Top-38
❑ 55Bow-238
❑ 55CarHunW-26
❑ 55Top-191
❑ 66Top-448
❑ 66WhiSoxTI-11
❑ 67OPC-81
❑ 67Top-81
❑ 68Top-564
❑ 75Gia195T-26
❑ 79TCM50-108
❑ 83TCMPla1944-41
❑ 83TopRep5-76
❑ 85TCMPhoC-18
❑ 89DodSmoG-53
❑ 90DodTar-764
❑ 91DodRinP2-3
❑ 91TopArc1-300
❑ 92BazQua5A-17
❑ 92TopMic-179
❑ 93RanKee-340
❑ 94TopArc1-38
❑ 94TopArc1G-38

Stanley, B.J.
❑ 94JohCitCC-26
❑ 94JohCitCF-3713

Stanley, Bob
❑ 78PapGinD-12
❑ 78SSP270-164
❑ 78Top-186
❑ 79OPC-314
❑ 79Top-597
❑ 80OPC-35
❑ 80Top-63
❑ 81CokTeaS-4
❑ 81Don-456
❑ 81Fle-234
❑ 81OPC-296
❑ 81Top-421
❑ 81TopSupHT-9
❑ 82Don-134
❑ 82Fle-307
❑ 82FleSta-169
❑ 82OPC-289
❑ 82RedSoxC-18
❑ 82Top-289
❑ 83AllGamPI-87
❑ 83Don-386
❑ 83Fle-195
❑ 83FleSta-185
❑ 83FleSti-65
❑ 83OPC-242
❑ 83Top-381
❑ 83Top-682
❑ 84Don-644
❑ 84Fle-409
❑ 84FleSti-74
❑ 84FunFooP-81
❑ 84Nes792-320
❑ 84OPC-320
❑ 84Top-320
❑ 84TopSti-220
❑ 84TopTif-320
❑ 85Don-91
❑ 85Dra-42
❑ 85Fle-169
❑ 85OPC-204
❑ 85Top-555
❑ 85TopSti-215
❑ 85TopTif-555
❑ 86Don-91
❑ 86Fle-359
❑ 86OPC-158
❑ 86SevCoi-E10
❑ 86Spo-169
❑ 86Top-785
❑ 86TopSti-253
❑ 86TopTif-785
❑ 87Don-216
❑ 87DonOpeD-180
❑ 87Fle-47
❑ 87FleGlo-47
❑ 87OPC-175
❑ 87RedFolSB-18
❑ 87RedSoxP-21
❑ 87Top-175
❑ 87TopSti-245
❑ 87TopTif-175
❑ 88Don-92
❑ 88DonTeaBRS-92
❑ 88Fle-367
❑ 88FleGlo-367
❑ 88OPC-369
❑ 88PanSti-23
❑ 88Sco-300
❑ 88ScoGlo-300
❑ 88StaLinRS-20
❑ 88Top-573
❑ 88TopTif-573
❑ 89Bow-25
❑ 89BowTif-25
❑ 89Don-421
❑ 89DonBasB-233
❑ 89Fle-101
❑ 89FleGlo-101
❑ 89Sco-383
❑ 89Top-37
❑ 89TopSti-258
❑ 89TopTif-37
❑ 89UppDec-411
❑ 90Fle-289
❑ 90FleCan-289
❑ 90PubIntS-466
❑ 90UppDec-654
❑ 97PitMet-2
❑ 98St.LucMM-28

Stanley, Carl
❑ 90GenCubS-23
❑ 93SavCarC-22
❑ 93SavCarF-686

Stanley, Cody
❑ 98BilMusTI-33

Stanley, Derek
❑ 92JohCitCC-2
❑ 92JohCitCF-3132

Stanley, Fred
❑ 72OPC-59
❑ 72Top-59
❑ 74OPC-423
❑ 74SyrChiTI-25
❑ 74Top-423
❑ 75OPC-503
❑ 75SyrChiTI-19
❑ 75Top-503
❑ 75TopMin-503
❑ 75YanSSP-13
❑ 76OPC-429
❑ 76SSP-442
❑ 76Top-429
❑ 77Top-123
❑ 77YanBurK-16
❑ 78SSP270-12
❑ 78Top-664
❑ 78YanBurK-17
❑ 78YanPhoA-24
❑ 78YanSSPD-12
❑ 79Top-16
❑ 79YanBurK-16
❑ 79YanPicA-32
❑ 80Top-387A
❑ 80Top-387B
❑ 80YanPhoA-23
❑ 81Don-585
❑ 81Fle-100
❑ 81Top-281
❑ 81TopTra-834
❑ 82A'sGraG-15
❑ 82Don-449
❑ 82Fle-108
❑ 82Top-787
❑ 83Don-197
❑ 83Fle-534
❑ 83Top-513
❑ 89T/MSenL-98
❑ 91BreMilB-32
❑ 91BrePol-NNO
❑ 91PacSenL-6
❑ 91PacSenL-133
❑ 92YanWIZ7-145
❑ 92YanWIZ8-186
❑ 94BreMilB-356

Stanley, Joe
❑ 11SpoLifCW-334

Stanley, John
❑ 13Zee-72

Stanley, Kevin
❑ 83ButCopKT-21

Stanley, Mickey
❑ 66Top-198
❑ 66TopVen-198
❑ 67Top-607
❑ 68CokCapT-4
❑ 68OPC-129
❑ 68TigDetFPB-23
❑ 68Top-129
❑ 68TopVen-129
❑ 69MilBra-262
❑ 69MLBOffS-54
❑ 69OPC-13
❑ 69TigTeal-11
❑ 69TigTealC-17
❑ 69Top-13
❑ 69TopSta-179
❑ 69TopTeaP-1
❑ 70MLBOffS-214
❑ 70OPC-383
❑ 70Top-383
❑ 71MLBOffS-407
❑ 71OPC-524
❑ 71Top-524
❑ 72MilBra-326
❑ 72OPC-385
❑ 72Top-385
❑ 73LinPor-79
❑ 73OPC-88
❑ 73TigJew-18
❑ 73Top-88
❑ 74OPC-530
❑ 74Top-530
❑ 74TopSta-180
❑ 75DetTigP-31
❑ 75OPC-141
❑ 75Top-141
❑ 75TopMin-141
❑ 76DetTigP-28
❑ 76OPC-483
❑ 76SSP-372
❑ 76Top-483
❑ 77TigBurK-4
❑ 77Top-533
❑ 78TigBurK-21
❑ 78TigTeal-26
❑ 78Top-232
❑ 79OPC-368
❑ 79TigFreP-6
❑ 79Top-692
❑ 81TigDetN-25
❑ 86TigSpoD-15
❑ 88TigDom-22
❑ 89SweBasG-104

Stanley, Mike
❑ 86TulDriTI-25
❑ 87Don-592
❑ 87DonRoo-28
❑ 87Fle-647
❑ 87FleGlo-647
❑ 87OklCit8P-8
❑ 87RanSmo-23
❑ 87SpoRoo2-44
❑ 87TopTra-116T
❑ 87TopTraT-116T
❑ 88Don-259
❑ 88DonBasB-223
❑ 88Fle-480
❑ 88FleGlo-480
❑ 88OPC-219
❑ 88PanSti-199
❑ 88RanMot-11
❑ 88RanSmo-11
❑ 88Sco-47
❑ 88ScoGlo-47
❑ 88StaLinRa-17
❑ 88Top-219
❑ 88TopSti-238
❑ 88TopTif-219
❑ 88ToyRoo-29
❑ 89Don-166
❑ 89Fle-533
❑ 89FleGlo-533
❑ 89OPC-123
❑ 89RanMot-22
❑ 89RanSmo-31
❑ 89Sco-241
❑ 89Top-587
❑ 89TopSti-244
❑ 89TopTif-587
❑ 89UppDec-579
❑ 90Don-579
❑ 90OPC-92
❑ 90RanMot-20
❑ 90Top-92
❑ 90TopTif-92
❑ 90TulDriDGB-6
❑ 91OPC-409
❑ 91PacRya7N-6
❑ 91RanMot-20
❑ 91Sco-92
❑ 91StaClu-526
❑ 91Top-409
❑ 91TopDesS-409
❑ 91TopMic-409
❑ 91TopTif-409
❑ 92Bow-370
❑ 92Don-582
❑ 92Lea-367
❑ 92LeaBlaG-367
❑ 92PacRyaTEI-177
❑ 92Sco-549
❑ 92StaClu-741
❑ 92StaCluNC-741
❑ 92Ult-416
❑ 93Don-718
❑ 93Fla-252
❑ 93Fle-656
❑ 93Lea-184
❑ 93Pin-563
❑ 93RanKee-341
❑ 93SP-267
❑ 93StaClu-323
❑ 93StaCluFDI-323
❑ 93StaCluMOP-323
❑ 93Top-359
❑ 93TopGol-359
❑ 93TopInaM-359
❑ 93TopInaR-359
❑ 93TopMic-359
❑ 93Ult-601
❑ 93YanStaC-12
❑ 94Bow-137
❑ 94ColC-265
❑ 94ColChoGS-265
❑ 94ColChoSS-265
❑ 94Don-202
❑ 94Fin-76
❑ 94FinPre-76P
❑ 94FinRef-76
❑ 94Fla-324
❑ 94Fle-247
❑ 94FleExtB-139
❑ 94Lea-295
❑ 94OPC-95
❑ 94Pac-438
❑ 94PanSti-104
❑ 94Pin-338
❑ 94PinArtP-338
❑ 94PinMusC-338
❑ 94Sco-451
❑ 94ScoDreT-10
❑ 94ScoGolR-451
❑ 94Sel-100
❑ 94Spo-2
❑ 94StaClu-271
❑ 94StaCluFDI-271
❑ 94StaCluGR-271
❑ 94StaCluMOP-271
❑ 94StaCluT-197
❑ 94StaCluTFDI-197
❑ 94Stu-217
❑ 94Top-391
❑ 94Top-695
❑ 94TopBlaG-20
❑ 94TopGol-391
❑ 94TopGol-695
❑ 94TopSpa-391
❑ 94TopSpa-695
❑ 94TriPla-278
❑ 94Ult-101
❑ 94UppDec-229
❑ 94UppDecED-229
❑ 95Baz-24
❑ 95BazRedH-RH5
❑ 95Bow-393
❑ 95ColCho-519
❑ 95ColChoGS-519
❑ 95ColChoSE-246
❑ 95ColChoSEGS-246
❑ 95ColChoSESS-246
❑ 95ColChoSS-519
❑ 95Don-62
❑ 95DonPreP-62
❑ 95DonTopotO-126
❑ 95Emo-67
❑ 95Fin-171
❑ 95FinRef-171
❑ 95Fla-288
❑ 95Fle-81
❑ 95Lea-292
❑ 95LeaLim-156
❑ 95Pac-303
❑ 95PanSti-29
❑ 95Pin-263
❑ 95PinArtP-263
❑ 95PinMusC-263
❑ 95Sco-195
❑ 95ScoGolR-195
❑ 95ScoPlaTS-195
❑ 95StaClu-223
❑ 95StaCluFDI-223
❑ 95StaCluMOP-223
❑ 95StaCluSTWS-223
❑ 95StaCluVR-112
❑ 95StaCluVRMO-112
❑ 95Top-142
❑ 95Top-391
❑ 95TopCyb-86
❑ 95TopD3-23

- ❑ 95TopEmb-77
- ❑ 95TopEmbGI-77
- ❑ 95Ult-86
- ❑ 95UltGolM-86
- ❑ 95UppDec-443
- ❑ 95UppDecED-443
- ❑ 95UppDecEDG-443
- ❑ 95UppDecSE-6
- ❑ 95UppDecSEG-6
- ❑ 96Baz-6
- ❑ 96Bow-8
- ❑ 96BowFoi-8
- ❑ 96ColCho-236
- ❑ 96ColCho-478
- ❑ 96ColChoGS-236
- ❑ 96ColChoGS-478
- ❑ 96ColChoSS-236
- ❑ 96ColChoSS-478
- ❑ 96Don-184
- ❑ 96DonPreP-184
- ❑ 96EmoXL-18
- ❑ 96Fin-B262
- ❑ 96FinRef-B262
- ❑ 96Fla-26
- ❑ 96Fle-197
- ❑ 96FleRedS-14
- ❑ 96FleTif-197
- ❑ 96FleUpd-U18
- ❑ 96FleUpdTC-U18
- ❑ 96LeaSigA-213
- ❑ 96LeaSigAG-213
- ❑ 96LeaSigAS-213
- ❑ 96MetUni-19
- ❑ 96MetUniP-19
- ❑ 96Pac-370
- ❑ 96Pin-366
- ❑ 96PinAfi-51
- ❑ 96PinAfiAP-51
- ❑ 96PinAfiFPP-51
- ❑ 96PinFoil-366
- ❑ 96Sco-467
- ❑ 96Sel-137
- ❑ 96SelArtP-137
- ❑ 96StaClu-217
- ❑ 96StaCluMOP-217
- ❑ 96Sum-34
- ❑ 96SumAbo&B-34
- ❑ 96SumArtP-34
- ❑ 96SumFoi-34
- ❑ 96TeaOut-78
- ❑ 96Top-135
- ❑ 96TopGal-82
- ❑ 96TopGalPPI-82
- ❑ 96TopLas-30
- ❑ 96Ult-321
- ❑ 96UltGolM-321
- ❑ 96UppDec-283
- ❑ 97Bow-43
- ❑ 97BowInt-43
- ❑ 97Cir-322
- ❑ 97CirRav-322
- ❑ 97ColCho-283
- ❑ 97Don-65
- ❑ 97DonGolPP-65
- ❑ 97DonSilPP-65
- ❑ 97DonTea-46
- ❑ 97DonTeaSPE-46
- ❑ 97Fin-134
- ❑ 97FinEmb-134
- ❑ 97FinEmbR-134
- ❑ 97FinRef-134
- ❑ 97Fle-30
- ❑ 97FleTif-30
- ❑ 97MetUni-24
- ❑ 97Pin-151
- ❑ 97PinArtP-PP151
- ❑ 97PinMusC-151
- ❑ 97PinPrePla-151
- ❑ 97RedSoxS-6
- ❑ 97RedSoxSPl-6
- ❑ 97RedSoxSPr-6
- ❑ 97Sco-164
- ❑ 97ScoArtPWB-164
- ❑ 97ScoPreS-164
- ❑ 97ScoShoS-164
- ❑ 97ScoShoSAP-164
- ❑ 97StaClu-165
- ❑ 97StaCluMOP-165
- ❑ 97Top-151
- ❑ 97TopGal-6
- ❑ 97TopGalPPI-6
- ❑ 97Ult-20
- ❑ 97UltGolME-20
- ❑ 97UltPlaME-20
- ❑ 97UppDec-312
- ❑ 98CirThu-182
- ❑ 98CirThuRav-182
- ❑ 98CirThuSupRav-182
- ❑ 98Fle-412
- ❑ 98FleUpd-U57
- ❑ 98PacOnl-777
- ❑ 98PacOnlR-777
- ❑ 98PacOnlWC-777
- ❑ 98PinPlu-107
- ❑ 98Ult-322
- ❑ 98UltGolM-322
- ❑ 98UltMas-322
- ❑ 98UltPlaM-322
- ❑ 98UppDec-747
- ❑ 99FlaShoLeg1-144
- ❑ 99FlaShoLeg2-144
- ❑ 99FlaShoLeg3-144
- ❑ 99FlaShoLegM1-144
- ❑ 99FlaShoLegM2-144
- ❑ 99FlaShoLegM3-144
- ❑ 99FlaShoR1-144
- ❑ 99FlaShoR2-144
- ❑ 99FlaShoR3-144
- ❑ 99Fle-208
- ❑ 99FleSta9-208
- ❑ 99FleWarT-208
- ❑ 99MetUni-189
- ❑ 99MetUniGM-189
- ❑ 99MetUniPMG-189
- ❑ 99Pac-74
- ❑ 99PacPlaB-74
- ❑ 99PacRed-74
- ❑ 99SkyPre-133
- ❑ 99SkyPreR-133
- ❑ 99SkyThu-215
- ❑ 99SkyThuRant-215
- ❑ 99SkyThuRave-215
- ❑ 99ThuSkySupR-215
- ❑ 99Ult-112
- ❑ 99UltGolM-112
- ❑ 99UltMas-112
- ❑ 99UltPlaM-112

Stanley, Scott
- ❑ 90AriWilP-16
- ❑ 92AriWilP-17

Stanley, Tim
- ❑ 87AncGlaP-29
- ❑ 88JamExpP-1919

Stanley, Todd
- ❑ 93MisStaB-40

Stanridge, Alfred
- ❑ 13Zee-124
- ❑ 14Zee-122
- ❑ 16Zee-17
- ❑ 17Zee-16
- ❑ 18Zee-14

Stantiago, Ramon
- ❑ 90GasRanB-29

Stanton, Duane
- ❑ 93JohCitCC-19
- ❑ 93JohCitCF-3676
- ❑ 94MadHatC-22
- ❑ 94MadHatF-131

Stanton, Gary
- ❑ 91IdaFalBSP-13

Stanton, George
- ❑ 23Zee-147
- ❑ 24Zee-105

Stanton, Lee (Leroy)
- ❑ 72OPC-141
- ❑ 72Top-141
- ❑ 73LinPor-37
- ❑ 73OPC-18
- ❑ 73Top-18
- ❑ 74OPC-594
- ❑ 74Top-594
- ❑ 75CalAngP-41
- ❑ 75Kel-12
- ❑ 75OPC-342
- ❑ 75Top-342
- ❑ 75TopMin-342
- ❑ 76Hos-39
- ❑ 76HosTwi-39
- ❑ 76OPC-152
- ❑ 76SSP-204
- ❑ 76Top-152
- ❑ 77MarPos-20
- ❑ 77Top-226
- ❑ 78Hos-60
- ❑ 78OPC-123
- ❑ 78Top-447
- ❑ 79OPC-275
- ❑ 79TCMJapPB-86
- ❑ 79Top-533
- ❑ 86MarGreT-6
- ❑ 87MyrBeaBJP-1443
- ❑ 88MyrBeaBJP-1180
- ❑ 89MyrBeaBJP-1451
- ❑ 90MyrBeaBJP-2794
- ❑ 91MetWIZ-376
- ❑ 91MyrBeaHC-29
- ❑ 91MyrBeaHP-2963
- ❑ 92MyrBeaHC-28
- ❑ 92MyrBeaHF-2215
- ❑ 93HagSunC-26
- ❑ 93HagSunF-1897
- ❑ 94HagSunC-28
- ❑ 94HagSunF-2748

Stanton, Mike (Michael Thomas)
- ❑ 73CedRapAT-14
- ❑ 75IowOakT-20
- ❑ 78SyrChiT-18
- ❑ 80IndTeal-28
- ❑ 81Fle-400
- ❑ 82Don-285
- ❑ 82Fle-379
- ❑ 82MarPos-30
- ❑ 82Top-473
- ❑ 82TopTra-113T
- ❑ 83Don-433
- ❑ 83Fle-486
- ❑ 83Top-159
- ❑ 84Fle-619
- ❑ 84MarMot-20
- ❑ 84Nes792-694
- ❑ 84Top-694
- ❑ 84TopTif-694
- ❑ 85Don-562
- ❑ 85Fle-501
- ❑ 85MarMot-16
- ❑ 85Top-256
- ❑ 85TopSti-343
- ❑ 85TopTif-256

Stanton, Mike (William Michael)
- ❑ 88BurBraP-3
- ❑ 89GreBraB-14
- ❑ 89GreBraP-1166
- ❑ 89GreBraS-22
- ❑ 90Bow-4
- ❑ 90BowTif-4
- ❑ 90BraDubP-27
- ❑ 90ClaUpd-T45
- ❑ 90Don-508
- ❑ 90DonRoo-7
- ❑ 90Fle-596
- ❑ 90FleCan-596
- ❑ 90FleSoaS-2
- ❑ 90OPC-694
- ❑ 90Sco-609
- ❑ 90Sco100RS-29
- ❑ 90ScoYouS2-7
- ❑ 90Top-694
- ❑ 90TopDeb89-122
- ❑ 90TopTif-694
- ❑ 90UppDec-61
- ❑ 91BraDubP-29
- ❑ 91BraSubS-36
- ❑ 91Don-716
- ❑ 91Fle-705
- ❑ 91Lea-491
- ❑ 91OPC-514
- ❑ 91Sco-468
- ❑ 91StaClu-413
- ❑ 91Top-514
- ❑ 91TopDesS-514
- ❑ 91TopMic-514
- ❑ 91TopTif-514
- ❑ 91UppDec-749
- ❑ 92BraLykP-27
- ❑ 92BraLykS-32
- ❑ 92ClaGam-19
- ❑ 92Don-780
- ❑ 92Fle-372
- ❑ 92Lea-377
- ❑ 92LeaBlaG-377
- ❑ 92OPC-788
- ❑ 92Pin-350
- ❑ 92Sco-498
- ❑ 92StaClu-344
- ❑ 92Top-788
- ❑ 92TopGol-788
- ❑ 92TopGolW-788
- ❑ 92TopMic-788
- ❑ 92Ult-170
- ❑ 92UppDec-653
- ❑ 93BraLykP-28
- ❑ 93BraLykS-34
- ❑ 93BraStaC-17
- ❑ 93Don-474
- ❑ 93Fin-176
- ❑ 93FinRef-176
- ❑ 93Fla-12
- ❑ 93Fle-15
- ❑ 93Lea-398
- ❑ 93PacSpa-341
- ❑ 93Pin-569
- ❑ 93Sco-317
- ❑ 93StaClu-38
- ❑ 93StaCluFDI-38
- ❑ 93StaCluMOP-38
- ❑ 93Top-88
- ❑ 93TopGol-88
- ❑ 93TopInaM-88
- ❑ 93TopInaR-88
- ❑ 93TopMic-88
- ❑ 93Ult-13
- ❑ 93UppDec-90
- ❑ 93UppDecGold-90
- ❑ 94BraLykP-31
- ❑ 94BraLykS-30
- ❑ 94BraUSPC-2S
- ❑ 94BraUSPC-11H
- ❑ 94ColC-441
- ❑ 94ColChoGS-441
- ❑ 94ColChoSS-441
- ❑ 94Don-506
- ❑ 94Fla-358
- ❑ 94Fle-376
- ❑ 94Lea-20
- ❑ 94Pin-461
- ❑ 94PinArtP-461
- ❑ 94PinMusC-461
- ❑ 94Sco-205
- ❑ 94ScoGolR-205
- ❑ 94StaClu-471
- ❑ 94StaCluFDI-471
- ❑ 94StaCluGR-471
- ❑ 94StaCluMOP-471
- ❑ 94StaCluT-58
- ❑ 94StaCluTFDI-58
- ❑ 94Top-107
- ❑ 94TopGol-107
- ❑ 94TopSpa-107
- ❑ 94Ult-450
- ❑ 95Don-28
- ❑ 95DonPreP-28
- ❑ 95Fle-319
- ❑ 95Top-271
- ❑ 95Ult-354
- ❑ 95UltGolM-354
- ❑ 96LeaSigEA-193
- ❑ 96StaClu-426
- ❑ 96StaCluMOP-426
- ❑ 97Cir-134
- ❑ 97CirRav-134
- ❑ 97Fle-590
- ❑ 97FleTif-590
- ❑ 97Ult-430
- ❑ 97UltGolME-430
- ❑ 97UltPlaME-430
- ❑ 98PacInvGems-79
- ❑ 98PacOnl-517
- ❑ 98PacOnlR-517
- ❑ 98PacOnlWC-517
- ❑ 99YanFle-27

Stanton, Rob
- ❑ 96WatIndTI-28
- ❑ 97WatIndTI-26

Stanton, Tom
- ❑ 97CapCitB-14
- ❑ 98CapCitBF5-18
- ❑ 98CapCitBM-18

Staples, Ken
- ❑ 81WisRapTT-1
- ❑ 82WisRapTF-3

Stapleton, Dave (David E.)
- ❑ 86ElPasDP-20
- ❑ 88BrePol-43
- ❑ 88BreTeal-32
- ❑ 88Don-521
- ❑ 88DonRoo-4
- ❑ 89Sco-581
- ❑ 89UppDec-304
- ❑ 94BreMilB-357

Stapleton, Dave (David L.)
- ❑ 81CokTeaS-10
- ❑ 81Don-544
- ❑ 81Fle-236
- ❑ 81OPC-81
- ❑ 81Top-81
- ❑ 81TopScr-48
- ❑ 81TopSti-47
- ❑ 81TopSupHT-10
- ❑ 82Don-208
- ❑ 82Fle-308
- ❑ 82OPC-93
- ❑ 82RedSoxC-19
- ❑ 82Top-589
- ❑ 83Don-200
- ❑ 83Fle-196
- ❑ 83OPC-239
- ❑ 83Top-239
- ❑ 83TopSti-35
- ❑ 84Don-273
- ❑ 84Fle-410
- ❑ 84Nes792-653
- ❑ 84OPC-249
- ❑ 84Top-653
- ❑ 84TopSti-221
- ❑ 84TopTif-653
- ❑ 85Top-322
- ❑ 85TopTif-322
- ❑ 86Top-151
- ❑ 86TopTif-151
- ❑ 87Top-507
- ❑ 87TopTif-507

Star, Clucky
- ❑ 96HilStaHWB-NNO

Starasenich, Pete
- ❑ 19Zee-79

Stare, Lonny
- ❑ 95BakBlaTI-1

Stargell, Tim
- ❑ 87BelMarL-11
- ❑ 89WauTimGS-26
- ❑ 90Bes-297
- ❑ 90CMC-859
- ❑ 90SanBerSB-24
- ❑ 90SanBerSCLC-108
- ❑ 90SanBerSP-2641
- ❑ 91Cla/Bes-109
- ❑ 91JacSunLD-346
- ❑ 91JacSunP-163
- ❑ 91LinDriAA-346

Stargell, Willie
- ❑ 63PirIDL-22
- ❑ 63Top-553
- ❑ 64PirKDK-26
- ❑ 64Top-342
- ❑ 64TopVen-342
- ❑ 65Kah-38
- ❑ 65Top-377
- ❑ 66Kah-29
- ❑ 66OPC-99
- ❑ 66PirEasH-8
- ❑ 66Top-99
- ❑ 66Top-255
- ❑ 66TopRubl-87
- ❑ 66TopVen-99
- ❑ 66TopVen-255
- ❑ 67CokCapA-11
- ❑ 67CokCapNLA-29
- ❑ 67CokCapPi-12
- ❑ 67DexPre-197
- ❑ 67Kah-36
- ❑ 67OPC-140
- ❑ 67PirTeal-21
- ❑ 67Top-140
- ❑ 67Top-266
- ❑ 67TopPirS-22
- ❑ 67TopPirS-31
- ❑ 67TopVen-280
- ❑ 68OPC-86
- ❑ 68PirKDK-8
- ❑ 68PirTeal-21
- ❑ 68Top-86
- ❑ 68TopVen-86
- ❑ 69MilBra-263
- ❑ 69MLBOffS-188
- ❑ 69PirGre-8
- ❑ 69PirJacitB-12
- ❑ 69PirTeal-22
- ❑ 69Top-545
- ❑ 69TopSta-89
- ❑ 69TopTeaP-16
- ❑ 70DayDaiNM-156
- ❑ 70Kel-29
- ❑ 70MLBOffS-107
- ❑ 70OPC-470
- ❑ 70PirTeal-17
- ❑ 70Top-470
- ❑ 70TopScr-21
- ❑ 70TopSup-19
- ❑ 71Kel-68
- ❑ 71MatMin-17
- ❑ 71MatMin-18
- ❑ 71MLBOffS-214
- ❑ 71OPC-230
- ❑ 71PirActP-24
- ❑ 71PirArc-11
- ❑ 71Top-230
- ❑ 71TopCoi-123
- ❑ 71TopSup-43
- ❑ 71TopTat-68
- ❑ 72Dia-64
- ❑ 72Kel-53A
- ❑ 72Kel-53B
- ❑ 72MilBra-327
- ❑ 72OPC-87
- ❑ 72OPC-89
- ❑ 72OPC-343
- ❑ 72OPC-447
- ❑ 72OPC-448
- ❑ 72PirTeal-8
- ❑ 72ProStaP-23
- ❑ 72SevTraC-52
- ❑ 72Top-87
- ❑ 72Top-89
- ❑ 72Top-343
- ❑ 72Top-447
- ❑ 72Top-448
- ❑ 72TopPos-15
- ❑ 73Kel2D-25
- ❑ 73LinPor-153
- ❑ 73OPC-370
- ❑ 73Top-370
- ❑ 73TopCanL-50
- ❑ 73TopCom-20
- ❑ 73TopPin-20
- ❑ 74Kel-37
- ❑ 74LauAllG-65
- ❑ 74NewYorNTDiS-14
- ❑ 74OPC-100
- ❑ 74OPC-202
- ❑ 74OPC-203
- ❑ 74Top-100
- ❑ 74Top-202
- ❑ 74Top-203
- ❑ 74TopDecE-31
- ❑ 74TopPuz-11
- ❑ 74TopSta-88
- ❑ 75Hos-135
- ❑ 75OPC-100
- ❑ 75PitPirP-26
- ❑ 75Top-100
- ❑ 75TopMin-100
- ❑ 76BlaDis-58
- ❑ 76BucDis-58
- ❑ 76CarDis-58
- ❑ 76CraDis-58
- ❑ 76DailsID-58
- ❑ 76Hos-49
- ❑ 76HosTwi-49
- ❑ 76IsaDis-58
- ❑ 76Kel-22
- ❑ 76OPC-270
- ❑ 76OrbDis-58
- ❑ 76PirPos-23
- ❑ 76RedBarD-58
- ❑ 76SafDis-58
- ❑ 76SSP-573
- ❑ 76Top-270
- ❑ 76TowCluD-58
- ❑ 77BurCheD-186
- ❑ 77ChiWilD-63
- ❑ 77DailsID-63
- ❑ 77DetCaeD-63
- ❑ 77HolInnD-63
- ❑ 77Hos-27
- ❑ 77MSADis-63
- ❑ 77OPC-25
- ❑ 77PepGloD-64
- ❑ 77PirPosP-25
- ❑ 77SagDis-63
- ❑ 77sDis-63
- ❑ 77Top-460
- ❑ 77TopCloS-45
- ❑ 77WenDis-63
- ❑ 77ZipDis-63
- ❑ 78Hos-11
- ❑ 78SagDis-11
- ❑ 78TasDis-11
- ❑ 78Top-510
- ❑ 78WifBalD-71
- ❑ 79BasPat-83
- ❑ 79Hos-104
- ❑ 79OPC-22
- ❑ 79Top-55
- ❑ 80CokNL M-1
- ❑ 80Kel-25
- ❑ 80OPC-319
- ❑ 80PerHaloFP-200
- ❑ 80PerHaloFPS-63
- ❑ 80PirGreT-1
- ❑ 80Top-610
- ❑ 80TopSup-1
- ❑ 81AllGamPl-99

❑ 81CokTeaS-118
❑ 81Don-12
❑ 81Don-132
❑ 81Fle-363
❑ 81FleStiC-15
❑ 81Kel-11
❑ 81MSAMinD-31
❑ 81OPC-127
❑ 81PerCreC-14
❑ 81Top-380
❑ 81TopSti-215
❑ 82Don-639
❑ 82Fle-499
❑ 82FleSta-76
❑ 82FleSta-106
❑ 82K-M-37
❑ 82MonNew-15
❑ 82OnDecD-31
❑ 82OPC-188
❑ 82OPC-372
❑ 82PerCreC-5
❑ 82PerCreCG-5
❑ 82Top-715
❑ 82Top-716
❑ 82TopSti-85
❑ 82TopStiV-85
❑ 83Don-8
❑ 83Don-610
❑ 83Fle-324
❑ 83Fle-634
❑ 83FleSta-186
❑ 83FleSti-81
❑ 83FraBroR-33
❑ 84OCoandSI-26
❑ 84OCoandSI-132
❑ 84SpoDesPW-6
❑ 85CirK-16
❑ 86BraPol-8
❑ 86PirGreT-1
❑ 86SpoDesJM-23
❑ 87K-M-22
❑ 89HOFStiB-27
❑ 89KahCoo-10
❑ 89PerCelP-40
❑ 89TopBasT-16
❑ 89TopGloA-22
❑ 90BasWit-4
❑ 90PerGreM-38
❑ 90PerMasW-36
❑ 90PerMasW-37
❑ 90PerMasW-38
❑ 90PerMasW-39
❑ 90PerMasW-40
❑ 91Don-702
❑ 91MDAA-3
❑ 91UppDecS-13
❑ 92ActPacA-17
❑ 92ActPacA2-17G
❑ 92ActPacAP-5
❑ 92FroRowSt-1
❑ 92FroRowSt-1AU
❑ 92FroRowSt-2
❑ 92FroRowSt-3
❑ 92FroRowSt-4
❑ 92FroRowSt-5
❑ 92KelAll-1
❑ 92MDAMVP-14
❑ 92Pin-588
❑ 93ActPacAC-17
❑ 93MetIma-19
❑ 93NabAllA-6
❑ 93TedWil-81
❑ 93TedWilM-14
❑ 93Yoo-20
❑ 94UppDecAH-95
❑ 94UppDecAH-172
❑ 94UppDecAH1-95
❑ 94UppDecAH1-172
❑ 94UppDecS-5
❑ 94UppDecTAE-76
❑ 95EagBalL-8
❑ 95PirCocP-6
❑ 95StoPop-5
❑ 95UppDecSHoB-15
❑ 97FleMilDM-45
❑ 97FleMilDMR-45
❑ 97SpoIllCC-9
❑ 97St.VinHHS-15
❑ 98SpoIllTaN-33
❑ 98SpoIllTaNEE-33
❑ 98SpoIllWSFMC-3
❑ 98UppDecR-88
❑ 98UppDecRSotT-WIS
❑ 99SP SigAuto-POP
❑ 99SPSig-172
Stark, Clinton
❑ 61UniOil-P13
Stark, Dennis
❑ 97WisTimR-23
❑ 98LanJetG-24
Stark, Dolly (Monroe)
❑ 09T206-518
❑ 13Zee-90
❑ 34DiaMatCSB-169
❑ 39PlaBal-106
❑ 40PlaBal-117
❑ 90DodTar-765
❑ 94ConTSN-1191
❑ 94ConTSNB-1191
Stark, George
❑ 83TigAlKS-12
Stark, Greg
❑ 92PitMetC-13
❑ 92PitMetF-3295
❑ 93CapCitBC-21
❑ 93CapCitBF-461
Stark, Jeff
❑ 87SpaPhiP-4
❑ 88SpaPhiP-1024
Stark, Matt
❑ 86KnoBluJP-22
❑ 87BluJayFS-29
❑ 90Bes-99
❑ 90BirBarB-4
❑ 90BirBarP-1113
❑ 90CMC-746
❑ 90ProAaA-47
❑ 91Cla1-T30
❑ 91Don-747
❑ 91LinDriAAA-646
❑ 91Sco-751
❑ 91VanCanLD-646
❑ 91VanCanP-1597
❑ 92MidAngS-470
Stark, Richard
❑ 94StoPorC-30
❑ 96StoPorB-30
❑ 97El PasDB-27
❑ 98LouRedQ-34
Stark, Zachary
❑ 95KanCouCTI-34
❑ 98WisTimRM-11
Starkey, Harold
❑ 63GadFunC-82
Starkey, Melveena
❑ 91HawWomS-14
Starkovich, Paul
❑ 75SanAntBT-20
Starks, Bob
❑ 76QuaCitAT-33
Starks, Fred
❑ 93HicCraC-23
❑ 93HicCraF-1279
Starling, Marcus
❑ 94EliTwiC-23
❑ 94EliTwiF-3733
Starr, Bart
❑ 68AtlOil-12
Starr, Charles
❑ 09T206-337
❑ 10CouT21-61
❑ 11MecDFT-41
Starr, Chris
❑ 91ButCopKSP-3
❑ 93ButCopKSP-4
Starr, Dick
❑ 50Bow-191
❑ 51Bow-137
Starr, Ray
❑ 33WorCig(-87
❑ 77TCMTheWY-74
Starrette, Herm
❑ 64Top-239
❑ 64TopVen-239
❑ 65Top-539
❑ 74OPC-634
❑ 74Top-634
❑ 75AtlBraP-35
❑ 76AtlBraP-31
❑ 78TCM60I-194
❑ 83GiaPos-8
❑ 84GiaPos-26
❑ 85BrePol-NNO
❑ 86BrePol-38
❑ 87CubCan-31
❑ 87CubDavB-NNO
❑ 88OriFreB-31
❑ 88OriPos-36
❑ 91OriCro-434
❑ 92RocExpC-29
❑ 93JamExpF-3344
Stars, New York
❑ 93NegLeaRL2-100
❑ 93TedWilPC-12
Stars, Philadelphia
❑ 92NegLeaRLI-96
❑ 93NegLeaRL2-83
❑ 93NegLeaRL2-84
❑ 93NegLeaRL2-85
❑ 93TedWilPC-13
Stars, St. Louis
❑ 91PomBlaBPB-28
❑ 93NegLeaRL2-79
Stasio, Chris
❑ 94EveGiaC-27
❑ 94EveGiaF-3662
❑ 95MicBatCTI-26
Statham, Cliff
❑ 52LavPro-2
Staton, Dave
❑ 88CapCodPPaLP-167
❑ 89SpoIndSP-1
❑ 90Bes-6
❑ 90CalLeaACLC-1
❑ 90ProAaA-148
❑ 90RivRedWB-1
❑ 90RivRedWCLC-1
❑ 90RivRedWP-2617
❑ 90TopMag-1
❑ 91Bow-645
❑ 91Cla2-T44
❑ 91ClaGam-182
❑ 91LasVegSLD-294
❑ 91LasVegSP-246
❑ 91LinDriAAA-294
❑ 91UppDec-66
❑ 92Bow-499
❑ 92LasVegSF-2807
❑ 92LasVegSS-241
❑ 92OPC-126
❑ 92PadSmo-33
❑ 92ProFS7-333
❑ 92SkyAAAF-117
❑ 92Top-126
❑ 92TopGol-126
❑ 92TopGolW-126
❑ 92TopMic-126
❑ 92TriA AAS-241
❑ 92UppDecML-191
❑ 93Don-325
❑ 93ExcFS7-111
❑ 94Bow-448
❑ 94ColC-266
❑ 94ColChoGS-266
❑ 94ColChoSS-266
❑ 94Fin-428
❑ 94FinJum-428
❑ 94FinRef-428
❑ 94Fla-236
❑ 94FlaWavotF-A9
❑ 94FleExtB-379
❑ 94FleMajLP-32
❑ 94Lea-349
❑ 94OPC-84
❑ 94PadMot-26
❑ 94Pin-396
❑ 94PinArtP-396
❑ 94PinMusC-396
❑ 94ScoRoo-RT128
❑ 94ScoRooGR-RT128
❑ 94Sel-200
❑ 94SpoRoo-69
❑ 94SpoRooAP-69
❑ 94Top-507
❑ 94TopGol-507
❑ 94TopSpa-507
❑ 94Ult-585
❑ 94UltAllR-10
❑ 94UltAllRJ-10
❑ 94UppDec-214
❑ 94UppDecED-214
❑ 95Sco-584
❑ 95ScoGolR-584
❑ 95ScoPlaTS-584
Staton, T.J.
❑ 94WelPirC-24
❑ 94WelPirF-3510
❑ 96CarMudB-25
❑ 97CalCanB-25
❑ 97FlaShoWotF-22
❑ 97Fle-597
❑ 97FleTif-597
❑ 97Ult-497
❑ 97UltGolME-497
❑ 97UltPlaME-497
❑ 98CarMudM-23
Statz, Jigger (Arnold)
❑ 21Exh-172
❑ 21Zee-19
❑ 22E120-165
❑ 23MapCriV-16
❑ 23WilChoV-157
❑ 26Zee-35
❑ 27AmeCarE126-33
❑ 29Zee-31
❑ 30Zee-40
❑ 32Zee-27
❑ 33Zee-11
❑ 37WheBB7-29M
❑ 37Zee-10
❑ 90DodTar-766
❑ 93ConTSN-782
Staub, Rusty
❑ 63Col45"P-14
❑ 63Col45"P-20
❑ 63Top-544
❑ 64Col.45JP-8
❑ 64Top-109
❑ 64TopCoi-96
❑ 64TopRooAB-12
❑ 64TopSta-88
❑ 64TopVen-109
❑ 65Top-321
❑ 66OPC-106
❑ 66Top-106
❑ 66Top-273
❑ 66TopVen-106
❑ 66TopVen-273
❑ 67Ast-26
❑ 67AstTeal1-11
❑ 67AstTeal2-23
❑ 67CokCapA-5
❑ 67CokCapAs-13
❑ 67CokCapNLA-32
❑ 67DexPre-198
❑ 67OPC-73
❑ 67Top-73
❑ 67TopGiaSU-17
❑ 67TopVen-292
❑ 68Baz-14
❑ 68CokCapA-13
❑ 68DexPre-71
❑ 68Top-300
❑ 68Top3-D-10
❑ 68TopActS-6C
❑ 68TopGamI-28
❑ 68TopPla-23
❑ 68TopPos-22
❑ 68TopVen-300
❑ 69CitMetC-15
❑ 69ExpFudP-11
❑ 69ExpPin-7
❑ 69MilBra-264
❑ 69MLBOffS-161
❑ 69NabTeaF-20
❑ 69OPCDec-20
❑ 69Top-230
❑ 69TopDec-22A
❑ 69TopDecI-41
❑ 69TopSta-38
❑ 69TopSup-48
❑ 69TopTeaP-10
❑ 69TraSta-39
❑ 70DayDaiNM-38
❑ 70ExpPin-13
❑ 70ExpPos-11
❑ 70MLBOffS-70
❑ 70Top-585
❑ 70TopBoo-18
❑ 70TopCanL-22
❑ 70TopSup-41
❑ 71AllBasA-23
❑ 71BazNumT-40
❑ 71BazUnn-34
❑ 71ExpLaPR-12
❑ 71ExpPS-23
❑ 71MilDud-65
❑ 71MLBOffS-141
❑ 71MLBOffS-575
❑ 71OPC-289
❑ 71OPC-560
❑ 71Top-560
❑ 71TopCoi-111
❑ 71TopGreM-35
❑ 71TopSup-9
❑ 71TopTat-59
❑ 72Dia-65
❑ 72MetTeal-6
❑ 72MilBra-328
❑ 73LinPor-123
❑ 73MetTeal-12
❑ 73NewYorSNM-20
❑ 74MetDaiPA-11
❑ 74OPC-475
❑ 74OPC-629
❑ 74Top-475
❑ 74Top-629
❑ 75Hos-129
❑ 75MetSSP-7
❑ 75OPC-90
❑ 75Top-90
❑ 75TopMin-90
❑ 76BlaDis-59
❑ 76BucDis-59
❑ 76CarDis-59
❑ 76CraDis-59
❑ 76DaiIsID-59
❑ 76DetTigP-29
❑ 76IsaDis-59
❑ 76OPC-120
❑ 76OrbDis-59
❑ 76RedBarD-59
❑ 76SafDis-59
❑ 76SSP-537
❑ 76Top-120
❑ 76TopTra-120T
❑ 76TowCluD-59
❑ 77BurCheD-96
❑ 77ChiWilD-64
❑ 77DaiIsID-64
❑ 77DetCaeD-64
❑ 77HolInnD-64
❑ 77Hos-82
❑ 77MSADis-64
❑ 77OPC-88
❑ 77PepGloD-29
❑ 77RCColC-61
❑ 77SagDis-64
❑ 77sDis-64
❑ 77Spo-6615
❑ 77Top-420
❑ 77TopCloS-46
❑ 77WenDis-64
❑ 77ZipDis-64
❑ 78OPC-188
❑ 78TigBurK-22
❑ 78TigTeal-27
❑ 78Top-370
❑ 78WifBalD-72
❑ 79ExpPos-28
❑ 79Hos-56
❑ 79OPC-228
❑ 79Top-440
❑ 79TopCom-7
❑ 80OPC-347
❑ 80Top-660
❑ 81CokTeaS-91
❑ 81Fle-629
❑ 81Top-80
❑ 81TopSupHT-76
❑ 81TopTra-835
❑ 82Don-56
❑ 82Fle-536
❑ 82FleSta-82
❑ 82MetPhoA-20
❑ 82OPC-270
❑ 82Top-270
❑ 83Don-350
❑ 83Fle-555
❑ 83FleSta-187
❑ 83FleSti-238
❑ 83OPC-1
❑ 83OPC-51
❑ 83Top-740
❑ 83Top-741
❑ 83TopFol-2
❑ 83TopSti-14
❑ 84Don-6
❑ 84Don-6A
❑ 84Don-554
❑ 84DonCha-28
❑ 84Fle-597
❑ 84FleSti-40
❑ 84FunFooP-84
❑ 84MetFanC-6
❑ 84MLBPen-6
❑ 84Nes792-430
❑ 84Nes792-702
❑ 84Nes792-704
❑ 84OPC-224
❑ 84Top-430
❑ 84Top-702
❑ 84Top-704
❑ 84TopSti-287A
❑ 84TopTif-430
❑ 84TopTif-702
❑ 84TopTif-704
❑ 85Fle-92
❑ 85FleStaS-50
❑ 85MetColP-27
❑ 85OPC-190
❑ 85Top-190
❑ 85TopMin-190
❑ 85TopTif-190
❑ 86AstGreT-7
❑ 86AstMot-6
❑ 86ExpGreT-7
❑ 86Fle-95
❑ 86MetGreT-7
❑ 86Spo-138
❑ 86Top-570
❑ 86TopTif-570
❑ 87AstSer1-21
❑ 87AstSer1-28
❑ 87AstShoSO-22
❑ 87AstShoSO-26
❑ 87AstShoSTw-25
❑ 90MetHaloF-3
❑ 90PacLeg-52
❑ 90SweBasG-91
❑ 91JesHSA-6
❑ 91MetWIZ-377
❑ 91SweBasG-87
❑ 92ActPacA-81
❑ 92MVP2H-10
❑ 92Nab-25
❑ 92UppDecS-10
❑ 92UppDecS-21
❑ 93ExpDonM-20
❑ 93RanKee-342
❑ 93UppDecS-27
❑ 94TedWil-52
Staubach, Roger
❑ 74NewYorNTDiS-39
❑ 92Pin-589
Stauffacher, Stuart
❑ 86BurExpP-21
Staydohar, Dave
❑ 90BoiHawP-3328
❑ 92QuaCitRBC-25
❑ 92QuaCitRBF-824
Stearnes, Turkey
❑ 90NegLeaS-15
❑ 95NegLeaL2-7
Stearns, Bill
❑ 83OklCit8T-1
❑ 86TulDriTI-6
Stearns, Dan
❑ 87OldJudN-469
Stearns, Don
❑ 87SanBerSP-4
Stearns, John
❑ 74MetTeal-21
❑ 75IntLeaAT-7
❑ 75MetSSP-8
❑ 76OPC-633
❑ 76SSP-546
❑ 76Top-633
❑ 77BurCheD-140
❑ 77MetDaiPA-23
❑ 77Top-119
❑ 78MetDaiPA-22
❑ 78Top-334
❑ 79Hos-124
❑ 79OPC-280
❑ 79Top-205
❑ 79Top-545
❑ 80Kel-37
❑ 80OPC-41
❑ 80Top-76
❑ 81AllGamPI-134
❑ 81Don-35
❑ 81Fle-317
❑ 81OPC-255
❑ 81Top-428
❑ 81TopScr-96
❑ 81TopSti-194
❑ 82Don-434
❑ 82Fle-537
❑ 82FleSta-89
❑ 82MetPhoA-21
❑ 82OPC-232
❑ 82Top-743
❑ 83AllGamPI-135
❑ 83Don-380
❑ 83DonActA-25
❑ 83Fle-556
❑ 83FleSti-234
❑ 83OPC-212
❑ 83Top-212
❑ 83TopSti-264
❑ 84Fle-598
❑ 90KnoBluJB-9
❑ 90KnoBluJP-1259
❑ 90KnoBluJS-24
❑ 91KnoBluJLD-374

❑ 91KnoBluJP-1784
❑ 91LinDriAA-374
❑ 91MetWIZ-378
❑ 94MCIAmb-2
❑ 94PriRedC-26
❑ 94PriRedF-3279
❑ 96BalOriP-33
Stearns, Randy
❑ 87SanBerSP-5
❑ 96YakBeaTI-8
Stearns, Turkey (Norman)
❑ 78LauLonABS-4
❑ 87NegLeaPD-35
Stechschulte, Gene
❑ 96NewJerCB-26
❑ 97NewJerCB-26
❑ 98PeoChiM-23
Steck, Dave
❑ 76QuaCitAT-34
Stedman, Tom
❑ 75LafDriT-11
Steed, David
❑ 93GreFalDSP-15
❑ 94YakBeaC-24
❑ 94YakBeaF-3855
❑ 95VerBeaDTI-24
❑ 96SanBerSB-26
❑ 98AlbDukG-28
Steed, Rick
❑ 90St.CatBJP-3473
❑ 91MyrBeaHC-11
❑ 91MyrBeaHP-2945
❑ 91SouAtlLAGP-SAL40
❑ 92DunBluJC-18
❑ 92DunBluJF-2000
❑ 93DunBluJC-22
❑ 93DunBluJF-1796
❑ 93DunBluJFFN-24
❑ 95IndIndF-92
❑ 95KnoSmoF-42
❑ 96GreBraB-25
❑ 96GreBraTI-49
❑ 97HigDesMG-26
❑ 98BinMetQ-26
❑ 98NorTidQ-25
Steed, Scott
❑ 91PerHeaF-19
Steel, Ed
❑ 86NegLeaF-48
Steele, Alex
❑ 98WesMicWM-25
Steele, Bill (William)
❑ 11HelSta-178
❑ 12T207-174
❑ 14B18B-89A
❑ 14B18B-89B
❑ 90DodTar-1078
Steele, Brandon
❑ 97ButCopKB-26
❑ 97ButCopKK-26
Steele, Don
❑ 75LafDriT-26
Steele, Marty
❑ 98ChaKniQ-30
Steele, Steve
❑ 92KinMetC-11
❑ 92KinMetF-1535
Steele, Tim
❑ 75WatDodT-20
Steele, Walt
❑ 80BurBeeT-20
Steelman, Farmer
❑ 90DodTar-1080
Steelmon, Wyley
❑ 97LetBlaDB-11
❑ 98SouBenSHM-7
Steels, James
❑ 82AmaGolST-11
❑ 83BeaGolGT-20
❑ 83LasVegSBHN-20
❑ 84BeaGolGT-3
❑ 85LasVegSC-125
❑ 86LasVegSP-19
❑ 87DonRoo-50
❑ 87PadBohHB-21
❑ 88Don-360
❑ 88FleUpd-64
❑ 88FleUpdG-64
❑ 88OklCit8C-24
❑ 88OklCit8P-38
❑ 88RanMot-21
❑ 88Top-117
❑ 88TopTif-117
❑ 90CMC-65
❑ 90IndIndC-15
❑ 90IndIndP-306
❑ 90ProAAAF-589
❑ 93RanKee-343
Steen, Bill
❑ 09ObaT21-132
❑ 09ObaT21-303
❑ 11PacCoaBD-60
❑ 11Zee-61
❑ 12ObaPreT-52
❑ 16Zee-120
❑ 17Zee-98
Steen, Mike
❑ 76SanAntBTI-21
Steen, Scott
❑ 86ClePhiP-23
Steenstra, Kennie
❑ 90WicStaSGD-32
❑ 91TopTra-113T
❑ 91TopTraT-113T
❑ 92GenCubC-6
❑ 92GenCubF-1561
❑ 92PeoChiTI-25
❑ 92StaCluD-180
❑ 92TopDaiQTU-23
❑ 93ClaFS7-258
❑ 93DayCubC-18
❑ 93DayCubF-857
❑ 93FloStaLAF-33
❑ 94ClaGolF-131
❑ 94ExcFS7-167
❑ 94OrlCubF-1384
❑ 94UppDecML-82
❑ 95IowCubTI-23
❑ 96IowCubB-24
❑ 97IowCub-25
❑ 98IowCubQ-22
Stefan, Todd
❑ 91SalLakTP-3221
❑ 91SalLakTSP-21
❑ 92PeoChiC-9
❑ 92PeoChiTI-26
Stefani, Mario
❑ 89BriTigS-27
❑ 90FayGenP-2407
Stefanik, Robert
❑ 92LetMouSP-25
Stefanski, Jim
❑ 82DurBulT-10
Stefanski, Mike
❑ 92BelBreCB-16
❑ 92BelBreFI-408
❑ 92ClaFS7-360
❑ 92MidLeaATI-41
❑ 93StoPorC-23
❑ 93StoPorF-748
❑ 94ElPasDF-3150
❑ 94ExcFS7-87
❑ 96LouRedB-26
❑ 97LouRedB-28
❑ 98MemRedG-23
Stefaro, John
❑ 84Don-622
❑ 85ChaO'sT-5
❑ 87Don-541
❑ 87ExpPos-30
❑ 87Fle-652
❑ 87FleGlo-652
❑ 87FleGlo-653
❑ 87Top-563
❑ 87TopTif-563
❑ 88ColSprSSC-11
❑ 88ColSprSSP-1522
❑ 90ChaKniTI-9
❑ 90HagSunDGB-30
❑ 91OriCro-435
Steffen, David
❑ 80EvaTriT-4
❑ 81Top-626
Steffens, Mark
❑ 90PriPatD-22
❑ 91SpaPhiC-27
❑ 91SpaPhiP-912
❑ 92ClePhiF-2071
❑ 92SpaPhiC-19
❑ 92SpaPhiF-1279
Stegall, Randy
❑ 98BilMusTI-34
Steger, Chip
❑ 77TucTorC-NNO
Steger, Kevin
❑ 80SanJosMJitB-17
❑ 81WauTimT-1
❑ 83ChaLooT-22
Stegman, Dave
❑ 79Top-706
❑ 82ColCliP-23
❑ 82ColCliT-13
❑ 84Nes792-664
❑ 84Top-664
❑ 84TopTif-664
❑ 84WhiSoxTV-28
❑ 85SyrChiT-31
❑ 85Top-194
❑ 85TopTif-194
❑ 86ColCliP-24
❑ 92YanWIZ8-187
Steigerwald, John
❑ 75LafDriT-24
Stein, Bill
❑ 76OPC-131
❑ 76SSP-146
❑ 76Top-131
❑ 77Hos-136
❑ 77OPC-20
❑ 77Top-334
❑ 78Hos-39
❑ 78OPC-147
❑ 78Top-476
❑ 79Hos-18
❑ 79OPC-372
❑ 79Top-698
❑ 80MarPos-22
❑ 80OPC-121
❑ 80Top-226
❑ 81Don-543
❑ 81Fle-605
❑ 81Top-532
❑ 81TopTra-836
❑ 82Don-37
❑ 82Fle-331
❑ 82FleSta-179
❑ 82Top-402
❑ 82TopSti-118
❑ 83Don-594
❑ 83Fle-579
❑ 83RanAffF-1
❑ 83Top-64
❑ 84Fle-429
❑ 84Nes792-758
❑ 84RanJarP-1
❑ 84Top-758
❑ 84TopTif-758
❑ 85Don-621
❑ 85RanPer-1
❑ 85Top-171
❑ 85TopTif-171
❑ 86Don-403
❑ 86MarGreT-4
❑ 86Top-371
❑ 86TopTif-371
❑ 88LitFalMP-26
❑ 89ColMetB-22
❑ 89ColMetGS-1
❑ 89T/MSenL-99
❑ 90ColMetGS-1
❑ 90ColMetPPI-1
❑ 90SouAtlLAS-46
❑ 91BenBucCB-28
❑ 91BenBucP-3710
❑ 92CliGiaC-26
❑ 92CliGiaF-3612
❑ 93RanKee-344
❑ 93ShrCapF-2777
Stein, Blake
❑ 94JohCitCC-27
❑ 94JohCitCF-3702
❑ 95PeoChiTI-34
❑ 96StPetCB-29
❑ 97ArkTraB-10
❑ 97Bow-204
❑ 97BowInt-204
❑ 97TexLeaTP-3
❑ 98A'sMot-24
❑ 98FleUpd-U66
❑ 98LeaRS-301
❑ 98LeaRSLHolo-301
❑ 98LeaRSLong-301
❑ 98LeaRTrue-301
❑ 99Fle-287
❑ 99FleSta9-287
❑ 99FleWarT-287
❑ 99SkyThu-23
❑ 99SkyThuRant-23
❑ 99SkyThuRave-23
❑ 99SpoIll-44
❑ 99ThuSkySupR-23
Stein, Ethan
❑ 96SpoIndB-27
❑ 97LanLugTS-27
❑ 98WilBluRC-26
Stein, John
❑ 86AppFoxP-24
❑ 87BakDodP-9
❑ 89SalLakTTI-10
Stein, Jose
❑ 91BoiHawC-11
Stein, Kevin
❑ 96AubDouB-26
Stein, Ray
❑ 80WisRapTT-25
Stein, W. Randy
❑ 79Top-394
❑ 79VanCanT-16
❑ 80SpoIndT-13
❑ 80Top-613
❑ 81SpoIndT-24
❑ 82IowCubT-24
❑ 83IowCubT-10
❑ 94BreMilB-358
Steinbach, Terry
❑ 84MadMusP-10
❑ 85HunStaJ-16
❑ 86HunStaDJ-16
❑ 86SouLeaAJ-10
❑ 87Don-34
❑ 87DonRoo-26
❑ 87Fle-405
❑ 87FleGlo-405
❑ 87Lea-34
❑ 87Spo-118
❑ 87SpoRooI-22
❑ 87SpoRooP-1
❑ 87SpoTeaP-23
❑ 87TopTra-117T
❑ 87TopTraT-117T
❑ 88A'sMot-4
❑ 88ClaRed-186
❑ 88Don-158
❑ 88DonBasB-78
❑ 88DonTeaBA-158
❑ 88Fle-294
❑ 88FleGlo-294
❑ 88OPC-44
❑ 88PanSti-166
❑ 88Sco-82
❑ 88ScoGlo-82
❑ 88ScoYouSI-16
❑ 88Spo-174
❑ 88StaLinAs-15
❑ 88Top-551
❑ 88TopBig-39A
❑ 88TopBig-39B
❑ 88TopCoi-28
❑ 88TopRoo-15
❑ 88TopTif-551
❑ 88ToyRoo-30
❑ 89A'sMot-3
❑ 89Bow-193
❑ 89BowTif-193
❑ 89CadEllD-54
❑ 89ClaLigB-69
❑ 89Don-268
❑ 89DonAll-9
❑ 89DonAll-31
❑ 89DonBasB-323
❑ 89DonPop-9
❑ 89Fle-22
❑ 89Fle-634
❑ 89FleGlo-22
❑ 89FleGlo-634
❑ 89K-M-19
❑ 89OPC-304
❑ 89PanSti-236
❑ 89PanSti-419
❑ 89Sco-365
❑ 89Spo-119
❑ 89Top-725
❑ 89TopBig-80
❑ 89TopGloA-9
❑ 89TopSti-152
❑ 89TopSti-165
❑ 89TopTif-725
❑ 89TVSpoM-97
❑ 89UppDec-256
❑ 90A'sMot-3
❑ 90Bow-456
❑ 90BowTif-456
❑ 90ClaUpd-T46
❑ 90Don-268
❑ 90Don-637A
❑ 90Don-637B
❑ 90DonBesA-137
❑ 90Fle-20
❑ 90FleBasA-38
❑ 90FleBasAC-38
❑ 90FleCan-20
❑ 90FleWorS-3
❑ 90FleWorS-7
❑ 90Lea-252
❑ 90MLBBasB-115
❑ 90OPC-145
❑ 90PanSti-143
❑ 90PanSti-205
❑ 90PubIntS-315
❑ 90Sco-162
❑ 90Sco-693A
❑ 90Sco-693B
❑ 90Sco100S-55
❑ 90Spo-33
❑ 90Top-145
❑ 90TopBig-118
❑ 90TopGloA-20
❑ 90TopSti-163
❑ 90TopSti-186
❑ 90TopStiB-56
❑ 90TopTif-145
❑ 90UppDec-246
❑ 90Woo-28
❑ 91A'sMot-3
❑ 91A'sSFE-12
❑ 91Bow-216
❑ 91CadEllD-54
❑ 91Don-329
❑ 91Fle-24
❑ 91Lea-87
❑ 91OPC-625
❑ 91PanFreS-191
❑ 91Sco-780
❑ 91SevCoi-NC11
❑ 91SouOreAAP-SOA2
❑ 91SouOreAAP-SOA22
❑ 91StaClu-518
❑ 91Top-625
❑ 91TopDesS-625
❑ 91TopMic-625
❑ 91TopTif-625
❑ 91Ult-253
❑ 91UppDec-153
❑ 92AthMot-3
❑ 92Bow-392
❑ 92Don-104
❑ 92Fle-267
❑ 92Lea-501
❑ 92LeaBlaG-501
❑ 92OPC-234
❑ 92PanSti-14
❑ 92Pin-76
❑ 92Sco-440
❑ 92Sco-633
❑ 92ScoProP-18
❑ 92StaClu-22
❑ 92Stu-229
❑ 92Top-234
❑ 92TopGol-234
❑ 92TopGolW-234
❑ 92TopMic-234
❑ 92TriPla-10
❑ 92Ult-116
❑ 92UppDec-473
❑ 93AthMot-3
❑ 93AthStaC-9
❑ 93Bow-21
❑ 93DiaMar-102
❑ 93Don-505
❑ 93Fin-67
❑ 93FinRef-67
❑ 93Fla-263
❑ 93Fle-299
❑ 93FunPac-53
❑ 93Lea-7
❑ 93OPC-268
❑ 93PacSpa-226
❑ 93PanSti-14
❑ 93Pin-12
❑ 93Sco-626
❑ 93Sel-132
❑ 93SP-44
❑ 93StaClu-208
❑ 93StaCluFDI-208
❑ 93StaCluMOP-208
❑ 93Stu-57
❑ 93Top-18
❑ 93TopGol-18
❑ 93TopInaM-18
❑ 93TopInaR-18
❑ 93TopMic-18
❑ 93TriPla-177
❑ 93Ult-262
❑ 93UppDec-278
❑ 93UppDecGold-278
❑ 94A'sMot-3
❑ 94Bow-408
❑ 94ColC-267
❑ 94ColChoGS-267
❑ 94ColChoSS-267
❑ 94Don-254
❑ 94Fin-38
❑ 94FinRef-38
❑ 94Fla-96
❑ 94Fle-274
❑ 94FleExtB-156
❑ 94Lea-178
❑ 94OPC-117
❑ 94Pac-463
❑ 94PanSti-113
❑ 94Pin-120
❑ 94PinArtP-120
❑ 94PinMusC-120
❑ 94ProMag-99
❑ 94Sco-47
❑ 94ScoGolR-47
❑ 94Sel-257
❑ 94SP-38
❑ 94SPDieC-38
❑ 94StaClu-346
❑ 94StaCluFDI-346
❑ 94StaCluGR-346
❑ 94StaCluMOP-346
❑ 94Stu-7
❑ 94Top-610
❑ 94TopGol-610
❑ 94TopSpa-610
❑ 94TriPla-9
❑ 94Ult-412
❑ 94UppDec-291
❑ 94UppDec-488
❑ 94UppDecED-291
❑ 94UppDecED-488
❑ 95A'sCHP-5
❑ 95AthMot-3
❑ 95Bow-308
❑ 95ColCho-132
❑ 95ColChoGS-132
❑ 95ColChoSE-49
❑ 95ColChoSEGS-49
❑ 95ColChoSESS-49
❑ 95ColChoSS-132
❑ 95Don-354
❑ 95DonPreP-354
❑ 95DonTopotO-141
❑ 95Emo-75
❑ 95Fin-116
❑ 95FinRef-116
❑ 95Fla-296
❑ 95Fle-254
❑ 95Lea-148
❑ 95Pac-321
❑ 95PacPri-104
❑ 95Pin-354
❑ 95PinArtP-354
❑ 95PinMusC-354
❑ 95Sco-104
❑ 95ScoGolR-104
❑ 95ScoHaloG-HG48
❑ 95ScoPlaTS-104
❑ 95Sel-66
❑ 95SelArtP-66
❑ 95SelCer-3
❑ 95SelCerMG-3
❑ 95SP-183
❑ 95SPCha-179
❑ 95SPChaDC-179
❑ 95SPSil-183
❑ 95StaClu-463
❑ 95StaCluMOP-463
❑ 95StaCluSTWS-463
❑ 95StaCluVR-252
❑ 95StaCluVRMO-252
❑ 95Stu-113
❑ 95Sum-66
❑ 95SumNthD-66
❑ 95Top-442
❑ 95TopCyb-238
❑ 95TopEmb-135
❑ 95TopEmbGI-135
❑ 95Ult-97
❑ 95UltGolM-97
❑ 95UppDecSE-111
❑ 95UppDecSEG-111
❑ 96A'sMot-4
❑ 96Baz-18
❑ 96Bow-74
❑ 96BowFoi-74
❑ 96Cir-74
❑ 96CirRav-74
❑ 96ColCho-241
❑ 96ColChoGS-241
❑ 96ColChoSS-241
❑ 96Don-24
❑ 96DonPreP-24

❑ 96EmoXL-107
❑ 96Fin-B32
❑ 96FinRef-B32
❑ 96Fla-153
❑ 96Fle-218
❑ 96FleTif-218
❑ 96Lea-160
❑ 96LeaPrePB-160
❑ 96LeaPrePG-160
❑ 96LeaPrePS-160
❑ 96LeaSigA-214
❑ 96LeaSigAG-214
❑ 96LeaSigAS-214
❑ 96MetUni-103
❑ 96MetUniP-103
❑ 96Pac-388
❑ 96PacPri-P127
❑ 96PacPriG-P127
❑ 96PanSti-221
❑ 96Pin-284
❑ 96PinFoil-284
❑ 96ProSta-7
❑ 96Sco-95
❑ 96SelTeaN-5
❑ 96SP-137
❑ 96StaClu-349
❑ 96StaCluEPB-349
❑ 96StaCluEPG-349
❑ 96StaCluEPS-349
❑ 96StaCluMOP-349
❑ 96TeaOut-79
❑ 96Top-267
❑ 96TopChr-107
❑ 96TopChrR-107
❑ 96TopGal-26
❑ 96TopGalPPI-26
❑ 96TopLas-31
❑ 96Ult-117
❑ 96UltGolM-117
❑ 96UppDec-411
❑ 97Bow-226
❑ 97BowInt-226
❑ 97Cir-75
❑ 97CirRav-75
❑ 97ColChoAC-17
❑ 97ColChoU-U17
❑ 97Don-110
❑ 97DonGolPP-110
❑ 97DonSilPP-110
❑ 97Fin-241
❑ 97FinRef-241
❑ 97Fle-196
❑ 97Fle-540
❑ 97FleTif-196
❑ 97FleTif-540
❑ 97Lea-270
❑ 97LeaFraM-270
❑ 97LeaFraMDC-270
❑ 97MetUni-214
❑ 97NewPin-151
❑ 97NewPinAP-151
❑ 97NewPinMC-151
❑ 97NewPinPP-151
❑ 97Pac-177
❑ 97PacLigB-177
❑ 97PacPri-60
❑ 97PacPriLB-60
❑ 97PacPriP-60
❑ 97PacSil-177
❑ 97Pin-107
❑ 97PinArtP-PP107
❑ 97PinIns-126
❑ 97PinInsCE-126
❑ 97PinInsDE-126
❑ 97PinMusC-107
❑ 97PinPrePla-107
❑ 97PinX-PSfF-53
❑ 97PinX-PSfFU-53
❑ 97Sco-146
❑ 97Sco-350
❑ 97ScoArtPWB-146
❑ 97ScoArtPWB-350
❑ 97ScoPreS-146
❑ 97ScoResC-350
❑ 97ScoShoS-146
❑ 97ScoShoS-350
❑ 97ScoShoSAP-146
❑ 97ScoShoSAP-350
❑ 97SP-109
❑ 97StaClu-130
❑ 97StaCluMOP-130
❑ 97Top-111
❑ 97TopChr-43
❑ 97TopChrR-43
❑ 97TopGal-28
❑ 97TopGalPPI-28
❑ 97TopSta-76
❑ 97TopStaAM-76
❑ 97Ult-351
❑ 97UltGolME-351
❑ 97UltPlaME-351
❑ 97UppDec-410
❑ 98CirThu-99
❑ 98CirThuRav-99
❑ 98CirThuSupRav-99
❑ 98ColCho-410
❑ 98CroRoy-80
❑ 98Fin-190
❑ 98FinNo--190
❑ 98FinNo-R-190
❑ 98FinRef-190
❑ 98Fle-522
❑ 98MetUni-56
❑ 98MetUniPMG-56
❑ 98Pac-141
❑ 98PacAur-55
❑ 98PacInv-49
❑ 98PacInvPBlue-49
❑ 98PacInvSilv-49
❑ 98PacInvTeam-16
❑ 98PacOme-145
❑ 98PacOmeR-145
❑ 98PacOnl-436
❑ 98PacOnlR-436
❑ 98PacOnlWC-436
❑ 98PacPar-66
❑ 98PacParC-66
❑ 98PacParG-66
❑ 98PacParHS-66
❑ 98PacParPB-66
❑ 98PacParR-66
❑ 98PacPlaB-141
❑ 98PacRedT-141
❑ 98PacSil-141
❑ 98Pin-146
❑ 98PinPreP-146
❑ 98Revo-86
❑ 98RevoSS-86
❑ 98Sco-67
❑ 98ScoRT-201
❑ 98SPxFin-297
❑ 98SPxFinR-297
❑ 98SPxFinS-297
❑ 98StaCluFDI-115
❑ 98StaCluI-115
❑ 98StaCluOneK-115
❑ 98StaCluPP-115
❑ 98Top-230
❑ 98TopChr-230
❑ 98TopChrR-230
❑ 98TopDevR-230
❑ 98TopDia-230
❑ 98TopMiniC-230
❑ 98TopOpeD-108
❑ 98Ult-39
❑ 98UltGolM-39
❑ 98UltMas-39
❑ 98UltPlaM-39
❑ 98UppDec-411
❑ 99Fle-533
❑ 99FleSta9-533
❑ 99FleWarT-533
❑ 99Pac-256
❑ 99PacPar-137
❑ 99PacParC-137
❑ 99PacParG-137
❑ 99PacParHoloGold-137
❑ 99PacParHS-137
❑ 99PacParOD-137
❑ 99PacParPB-137
❑ 99PacParRed-137
❑ 99PacPlaB-256
❑ 99PacRed-256
❑ 99StaClu-293
❑ 99StaCluFDI-293
❑ 99StaCluOoaK-293
❑ 99StaCluPP-293
❑ 99Top-146
❑ 99TopChr-146
❑ 99TopChrR-146
❑ 99TopMVPP-146
❑ 99UppDec-417
❑ 99UppDecEL1-417
❑ 99UppDecEL2-417

Steinbach, Tom
❑ 85BelBreT-9

Steinbacher, Hank
❑ 30Zee-131
❑ 31Zee-95
❑ 32Zee-90
❑ 33Zee-35
❑ 33Zee-95
❑ 94ConTSN-1316
❑ 94ConTSNB-1316

Steinberg, David
❑ 83WisRapTF-8

Steinbrenner, George
❑ 91FouBal-14

Steinecke, William
❑ 29Zee-167

Steiner, Ben
❑ 75RedSox1T-34

Steiner, Brian
❑ 88GasRanP-1018
❑ 89ButCopKSP-18
❑ 90GasRanB-15
❑ 90GasRanP-2522
❑ 90GasRanS-23
❑ 91ChaRanC-12
❑ 91ChaRanP-1316

Steinert, Paul
❑ 84ButCopKT-22

Steinert, Rob
❑ 93St.CatBJC-22
❑ 93St.CatBJF-3975
❑ 94HagSunC-24
❑ 94HagSunF-2732
❑ 95DunBluJTI-29
❑ 95Exc-143

Steinfeldt, Harry
❑ 03BreE10-134
❑ 07CubA.CDPP-13
❑ 07CubGFGCP-14
❑ 08AmeCarE91-29
❑ 08AmeCarE91-63
❑ 08CubPos-4
❑ 08RosComP-111
❑ 09BriE97-28A
❑ 09BriE97-28B
❑ 09ColChiE-273
❑ 09RamT20-112
❑ 09T206-338
❑ 09T206-339
❑ 10ChiE-10
❑ 10RedCroT-73
❑ 10RedCroT-159
❑ 10RedCroT-246
❑ 10SweCapPP-92
❑ 10W555-58
❑ 11PinT-5-218
❑ 11S74Sil-47
❑ 11S74Sil-70
❑ 11SpoLifCW-335
❑ 11SpoLifM-183
❑ 11T205-162
❑ 12ColRedB-273
❑ 12ColTinT-273
❑ 12HasTriFT-50D
❑ 12T207-175
❑ 72ClaCar-57
❑ 84CubUno-7
❑ 87Cub190T-1
❑ 90BasWit-57

Steinkamp, Mike
❑ 89SalLakTTI-13

Steinke, Brock
❑ 96KisCobB-28

Steinmann, Scott
❑ 96EveAquB-23
❑ 97WisTimR-24
❑ 98OrlRayM-18

Steinmetz, Earl
❑ 90Bes-136
❑ 90CMC-729
❑ 90SumBraB-22
❑ 90SumBraP-2432
❑ 91DurBulC-9
❑ 91DurBulP-1544
❑ 92DurBulC-12
❑ 92DurBulF-1100
❑ 92DurBulTI-23

Steinmetz, Kevin
❑ 83TamTarT-21

Steirer, Ricky
❑ 80ElPasDT-4
❑ 81SalLakCGT-12
❑ 82SpoIndT-8
❑ 84EdmTraC-102

Stela, Jose
❑ 91BoiHawP-3883
❑ 91QuaCitAC-13
❑ 91QuaCitAP-2631
❑ 92MidLeaATI-42
❑ 92QuaCitRBC-15
❑ 92QuaCitRBF-813
❑ 93CedRapKC-20
❑ 93PalSprAC-22
❑ 93PalSprAF-73

Stella, Jose
❑ 93LinVenB-136
❑ 94VenLinU-46
❑ 95LinVen-195

Stellern, Mike
❑ 82AubAstT-4
❑ 85OscAstTI-25

Stello, Dick
❑ 88T/MUmp-60

Stelmaszek, Rick
❑ 70Top-599
❑ 73OPC-601
❑ 73Top-601
❑ 74OPC-611
❑ 74Top-611
❑ 75OPC-338
❑ 75Top-338
❑ 75TopMin-338
❑ 77TucTorC-17
❑ 78WisRapTT-18
❑ 79WisRapTT-23
❑ 80WisRapTT-26
❑ 81TwiPos-27
❑ 82TwiPos-25
❑ 83TwiTeal-28
❑ 83TwiTeal-34
❑ 84MinTwiP-27
❑ 84TwiTeal-29
❑ 85TwiPos-26
❑ 85TwiTeal-32
❑ 86TwiTeal-30
❑ 87TwiPos-26
❑ 87TwiTeal-28
❑ 93RanKee-345

Stember, Jeff
❑ 78CedRapGT-27
❑ 79CedRapGT-16
❑ 81PhoGiaVNB-5
❑ 82PhoGiaVNB-16

Stemberger, Brian
❑ 82KnoBluJT-9

Stemle, Steve
❑ 98NewJerCM-31
❑ 99TeaBesR-83
❑ 99TeaBesRG-83
❑ 99TeaBesRS-83

Stemler, Andy
❑ 91WatIndC-11
❑ 91WatIndP-3366

Stemmyer, William
❑ 87OldJudN-470

Stengel, Casey (Charles Dillon)
❑ 14B18B-62
❑ 15SpoNewM-171
❑ 16FleBreD-90
❑ 16SpoNewM-169
❑ 17ColE13-168
❑ 17HolBreD-100
❑ 19W514-113
❑ 20NatCarE-101
❑ 21Exh-173
❑ 21KoBreWSI-24
❑ 22W575-131
❑ 22W575-132
❑ 23MapCriV-15
❑ 23W503-15
❑ 23W515-24
❑ 23W551-10
❑ 34DiaMatCSB-170
❑ 35DiaMatCS2-19
❑ 35DiaMatCS3T1-134
❑ 36NatChiFPR-68
❑ 36R31PasP-22
❑ 40PlaBal-141
❑ 46RemBre-10
❑ 47RemBre-8
❑ 47SigOil-56
❑ 47SmiClo-1
❑ 48SigOil-22
❑ 48SmiClo-20
❑ 49YanTeal-22
❑ 50Bow-217
❑ 50YanTeal-22
❑ 51Bow-181
❑ 51R42SmaS-93
❑ 52Bow-217
❑ 52RedMan-AL1
❑ 53BowBW-39
❑ 53Dor-113
❑ 53RedMan-AL1
❑ 56YanJayP-11
❑ 57YanJayP-15
❑ 58JayPubA-20
❑ 58JayPubAG-10
❑ 58Top-475
❑ 59Top-383
❑ 59Top-552
❑ 60Top-227
❑ 60YanJayP-11
❑ 61NuSco-461
❑ 62MetJayP-10
❑ 62Top-29
❑ 62TopVen-29
❑ 63BasMagM-80
❑ 63MetJayP-10
❑ 63Top-43
❑ 63Top-233
❑ 64MetJayP-11
❑ 64MetTeal-10
❑ 64Top-324
❑ 64Top-393
❑ 64TopVen-324
❑ 65MetJayP-12
❑ 65MetPos-9
❑ 65OPC-187
❑ 65SteDugB-1
❑ 65Top-187
❑ 68LauWorS-50
❑ 70SpoCarfCOP-14
❑ 72LauGreF-20
❑ 73HalofFPP-17
❑ 73MetAllEB-12
❑ 73TCMAllG-19
❑ 74MetOriEB-13
❑ 74NewYorNTDiS-17
❑ 75ShaPiz-8
❑ 75YanAllTT-12
❑ 76GrePlaG-39
❑ 76LauIndC-40
❑ 76Met63 S-17
❑ 76RowExh-14
❑ 76ShaPiz-104
❑ 77BobParHoF-46
❑ 77GalGloG-13
❑ 77GalGloG-253
❑ 77TCMTheWY-63
❑ 80LauFamF-20
❑ 80PacLeg-47
❑ 80PerHaloFP-103
❑ 80SSPHOF-103
❑ 80YanGreT-12
❑ 81ConTSN-71
❑ 81SpoHaloF-13
❑ 81TCM60I-422
❑ 81TCM60I-482
❑ 82ASAMicM-66
❑ 82DiaCla-96
❑ 82MetGal62-26
❑ 83DonHOFH-37
❑ 83TCMPla1942-42
❑ 83YanASFY-45
❑ 84OCoandSI-149
❑ 84OCoandSI-212
❑ 84SpoDesPW-35
❑ 85BigLeaC3-76
❑ 85FegMurCG-18
❑ 85UltBasC-6
❑ 86ConSer1-33
❑ 86SpoDesJM-12
❑ 86TCMSupS-9
❑ 86TCMSupS-47
❑ 88ConHar-5
❑ 88WilMulP-2
❑ 88WilMulP-11
❑ 89DodSmoG-28
❑ 89PacLegI-218
❑ 89SweBasG-130
❑ 89YanCitAG-6
❑ 90BasWit-85
❑ 90DodTar-767
❑ 90HOFStiB-60
❑ 90MetHaloF-1
❑ 90SweBasG-40
❑ 91ConTSN-37
❑ 91LinDri-46
❑ 91SweBasG-136
❑ 91TopArc1-325
❑ 92BazQua5A-21
❑ 92ConTSN-558
❑ 92ConTSNCI-5
❑ 92PinMan-27
❑ 92St.VinHHS-10
❑ 92YanWIZH-32
❑ 93ConTSN-829
❑ 93DiaStaES-150
❑ 93Hoy-7
❑ 93LegFoi-10
❑ 93SpeHOF2-5
❑ 94TedWilLC-LC16
❑ 94UppDecTAE-57
❑ 95ConTSN-1330

Stenholm, Richard A.
❑ 76ForLauYS-23
❑ 77WesHavYT-22
❑ 81ColCliP-15
❑ 81ColCliT-1

Stenhouse, Dave
❑ 55DonWin-39
❑ 59SeaPop-35
❑ 60HenHouW-26
❑ 62Top-592
❑ 63Fle-30
❑ 63Jel-97
❑ 63Pos-97
❑ 63SalMetC-37
❑ 63Top-263
❑ 63TopStil-42
❑ 64Top-498
❑ 65Top-304
❑ 78TCM60I-141
❑ 84SyrChiT-26
❑ 85Top-141
❑ 85TopTif-141
❑ 86SyrChiP-24
❑ 87SyrChiP-1940
❑ 87SyrChiT-11

Stenhouse, Michael
❑ 82WicAerTI-19
❑ 83WicAerDS-21
❑ 84Don-29A
❑ 84Don-29B
❑ 84ExpPos-31
❑ 84ExpStu-26
❑ 84IndIndTI-30
❑ 85Don-376
❑ 85Fle-411
❑ 85FleUpd-110
❑ 85OPC-282
❑ 85Top-141
❑ 85Top-658
❑ 85TopTif-141
❑ 85TopTif-658
❑ 85TopTifT-112T
❑ 85TopTra-112T
❑ 85TwiPos-27
❑ 85TwiTeal-23
❑ 86Fle-406
❑ 86OPC-17
❑ 86PawRedSP-23
❑ 86Top-17
❑ 86TopTif-17
❑ 87TolMudHP-19
❑ 87TolMudHT-5

Stennett, Matt
❑ 86AubAstP-24

Stennett, Rennie
❑ 72OPC-219
❑ 72Top-219
❑ 73OPC-348
❑ 73Top-348
❑ 74OPC-426
❑ 74Top-426
❑ 74TopSta-89
❑ 75Hos-131
❑ 75OPC-336
❑ 75PitPirP-27
❑ 75Top-336
❑ 75TopMin-336
❑ 76BlaDis-60
❑ 76BucDis-60
❑ 76CarDis-60
❑ 76CraDis-60
❑ 76DailsID-60
❑ 76Hos-9
❑ 76HosTwi-9
❑ 76IsaDis-60
❑ 76OPC-6
❑ 76OPC-425
❑ 76OrbDis-60
❑ 76PirPos-24
❑ 76RedBarD-60
❑ 76SafDis-60
❑ 76SSP-575
❑ 76Top-6
❑ 76Top-425
❑ 76TowCluD-60
❑ 77BurCheD-182
❑ 77Hos-100
❑ 77OPC-129
❑ 77PirPosP-26
❑ 77Top-35
❑ 78Hos-33
❑ 78OPC-25
❑ 78Top-165
❑ 79BasPat-84
❑ 79OPC-365
❑ 79Top-687

❑ 80GiaEurFS-8
❑ 80GiaPol-6
❑ 80GiaTeal-26
❑ 80Top-501
❑ 81AllGamPI-107
❑ 81Don-72A
❑ 81Don-72B
❑ 81Fle-438
❑ 81GiaTeal-19
❑ 81OPC-257
❑ 81Top-257
❑ 82Don-563
❑ 82Fle-401
❑ 82OPC-84
❑ 82Top-84
❑ 83WicAerDS-22
❑ 89PacSenL-79
❑ 89T/MSenL-100
❑ 89TopSenL-127
❑ 90EliSenL-89
❑ 90HOFStiB-82
❑ 94UppDecAH-137
❑ 94UppDecAH-217
❑ 94UppDecAH1-137
❑ 94UppDecAH1-217

Stenson, Dernell
❑ 97MicBatC-27
❑ 97MidLeaTP-17
❑ 98Bes-97
❑ 98BesBet-10
❑ 98BesCor-10
❑ 98BesDiaB-20
❑ 98Bow-354
❑ 98BowChr-354
❑ 98BowChrGA-354
❑ 98BowChrGAR-354
❑ 98BowChrI-354
❑ 98BowChrIR-354
❑ 98BowChrR-354
❑ 98BowGolA-354
❑ 98BowInt-354
❑ 98EasLeaTPM-25
❑ 98TreThuM-22
❑ 99BasAmeTPSC-10
❑ 99Bow-218
❑ 99BowBes-103
❑ 99BowBesAR-103
❑ 99BowBesR-103
❑ 99BowChr-218
❑ 99BowChrG-218
❑ 99BowChrGR-218
❑ 99BowChrI-218
❑ 99BowChrIR-218
❑ 99BowChrR-218
❑ 99BowGol-218
❑ 99BowInt-218
❑ 99BowPreProd-PP6
❑ 99JustheS-42
❑ 99JustheSJB-42
❑ 99JustheSJD-9
❑ 99JustheSJN-5
❑ 99JustheSJP-9
❑ 99SP TopP-112
❑ 99SP TopPDtS-D11
❑ 99SP TopPPE-112
❑ 99StaClu-350
❑ 99StaCluFDI-350
❑ 99StaCluOoaK-350
❑ 99StaCluPP-350
❑ 99Top-436
❑ 99TopChr-436
❑ 99TopChrR-436

Stenta, Jeff
❑ 91EriSaiC-10
❑ 91EriSaiP-4079

Stento, Bernie
❑ 87ElmPioBC-28
❑ 87ElmPioRC-28

Stentz, Brent
❑ 96FayGenB-28
❑ 97ForMyeM-29
❑ 98AriFalLTP-22
❑ 98NewBriRCM-27
❑ 99Bow-301
❑ 99BowGol-301
❑ 99BowInt-301
❑ 99TeaBesRBG-9

Stenz, Dan
❑ 90BoiHawP-3314

Stenzel, Jake
❑ 98CamPepP-72

Stepanov, Roman
❑ 89EasLeaDDP-DD16

Steph, Rodney
❑ 91PriRedC-9
❑ 91PriRedP-3514
❑ 92CedRapRC-13
❑ 92CedRapRF-1073
❑ 93WinSpiC-22
❑ 93WinSpiF-1571
❑ 94Bow-654
❑ 96RicBraB-27
❑ 97RocRedW-24
❑ 98OmaRoyM-21

Stephan, Todd
❑ 89PenPilS-23
❑ 90CarLeaA-3
❑ 90FreKeyTI-24
❑ 91HagSunLD-247
❑ 91HagSunP-2458
❑ 91LinDriAA-247
❑ 91PerHeaF-6
❑ 92RocRedWF-1940
❑ 92RocRedWS-470
❑ 92SkyAAAF-213
❑ 93LinVenB-271
❑ 93RocRedWF-240

Stephans, Russell
❑ 81ChaRoyT-13
❑ 83OmaRoyT-12
❑ 84OmaRoyT-26
❑ 85Don-42
❑ 86OmaRoyP-24
❑ 86OmaRoyT-10

Stephen, Buzz (Louis)
❑ 69PilPos-15
❑ 70OPC-533
❑ 70Top-533
❑ 77PilPosR-15

Stephens, B.F.
❑ 87OldJudN-471

Stephens, Bill
❑ 91HigSchPLS-17
❑ 91KisDodP-4197
❑ 92GulCoaDF-3567

Stephens, Brian
❑ 91RenSilSCLC-24

Stephens, Bryan
❑ 46RemBre-19
❑ 47IndTeal-25
❑ 47IndVanPP-24
❑ 49AngTeal-33
❑ 49W725AngTI-26
❑ 50WorWidGV-11

Stephens, Darryl
❑ 82RedPioT-14
❑ 83NasAngT-15

Stephens, Gene
❑ 53RedSoxTI-25
❑ 53Top-248
❑ 56Top-313
❑ 57Top-217
❑ 58Hir-72
❑ 58RedSoxJP-9
❑ 58Top-227
❑ 59Top-261
❑ 60RedSoxJP-9
❑ 60Top-363
❑ 61BalOriP-18
❑ 61Top-102
❑ 61TopStal-105
❑ 62Jel-95
❑ 62Pos-95A
❑ 62Pos-95B
❑ 62PosCan-95
❑ 62SalPlaC-56
❑ 62ShiPlaC-56
❑ 62Top-38
❑ 62TopStal-59
❑ 62TopVen-38
❑ 64Top-308
❑ 64TopVen-308
❑ 64WhiSoxI-23
❑ 64WhiSoxTS-21
❑ 65Top-498
❑ 79DiaGre-244
❑ 81RedSoxBG2S-50
❑ 90HOFStiB-48
❑ 91OriCro-436
❑ 91TopArc1-248

Stephens, James W.
❑ 09PC7HHB-41
❑ 09RamT20-113
❑ 09T206-340
❑ 11MecDFT-42

Stephens, Jason
❑ 97LakElsSG-27
❑ 98LakElsSG-25

Stephens, Jim
❑ 11PinT-5-101
❑ 11SpoLifM-117

Stephens, Joel
❑ 96BluOriB-28

Stephens, John
❑ 98DelShoM-28
❑ 99SP TopP-113
❑ 99SP TopPPE-113

Stephens, Mark
❑ 90HelBreSP-14
❑ 91BelBreCB-8
❑ 91BelBreP-2103
❑ 91SalLakTP-3211
❑ 91SalLakTSP-20
❑ 92SalSpuF-3754

Stephens, Michael
❑ 97OmaRoyB-31

Stephens, Ray (Carl Ray)
❑ 87ArkTraP-22
❑ 87TexLeaAF-31
❑ 88LouRedBC-19
❑ 88LouRedBP-422
❑ 88LouRedBTI-45
❑ 89ArkTraGS-23
❑ 89TexLeaAGS-21
❑ 90CMC-113
❑ 90LouRedBC-13
❑ 90LouRedBLBC-39
❑ 90LouRedBP-405
❑ 90ProAAAF-519
❑ 90TopTVCa-65
❑ 91LinDriAAA-248
❑ 91LouRedLD-248
❑ 91LouRedP-2918
❑ 91LouRedTI-27
❑ 91Sco-743
❑ 91TopDeb90-148
❑ 91NewOriP-4
❑ 91TriA AAGP-AAA22
❑ 92Don-764
❑ 92OklCit8F-1917
❑ 92ScrRedBS-495
❑ 93OklCit8F-1629
❑ 93RanKee-346

Stephens, Reggie
❑ 91SpoIndC-9
❑ 91SpoIndP-3963
❑ 91WatDiaC-23
❑ 91WatDiaP-1270

Stephens, Ron
❑ 88UtiBluSP-24
❑ 89SarWhiSS-22
❑ 89Sta-60
❑ 90Bes-50
❑ 90BirBarB-23
❑ 90BirBarP-1393
❑ 91LinDriAAA-647
❑ 91VanCanLD-647
❑ 91VanCanP-1595
❑ 92SkyAAAF-289
❑ 92VanCanF-2723
❑ 92VanCanS-648

Stephens, Seth
❑ 91FayGenC-5

Stephens, Shannon
❑ 95ElmPioTI-28
❑ 96KanCouCTI-26
❑ 96MidLeaAB-34
❑ 97BreCouMB-28

Stephens, Vern
❑ 46SeaSLP-60
❑ 46SpoExcW-9-10
❑ 47Exh-217A
❑ 47Exh-217B
❑ 47HomBon-44
❑ 47TipTop-73
❑ 48RedSoxTI-22
❑ 49Bow-71
❑ 49Lea-161
❑ 49RedSoxTI-20
❑ 50AmeNut&CCP-19
❑ 50Bow-2
❑ 50Dra-34
❑ 50RedSoxTI-22
❑ 51Bow-92
❑ 51R42SmaS-94
❑ 51TopRedB-4
❑ 52Bow-9
❑ 52RedMan-AL21
❑ 52StaCalL-71D
❑ 52StaCalS-85C
❑ 52TipTop-42
❑ 52Top-84
❑ 53Top-270
❑ 54OriTeal-18
❑ 54Top-54
❑ 54Wil-18
❑ 55Bow-109
❑ 56SeaPop-23
❑ 56YelBasP-30
❑ 74CapPub-31
❑ 76TayBow4-19
❑ 81RedSoxBG2S-51
❑ 83TCMPla1942-8
❑ 83TopRep5-84
❑ 85TCMPpl1-24
❑ 91OriCro-437
❑ 91TopArc1-270
❑ 94TopArc1-54
❑ 94TopArc1G-54
❑ 96Bro194F-9
❑ 97BalOriP-48

Stephenson, Brian
❑ 94SigRooDP-43
❑ 94SigRooDPS-43
❑ 94WilCubC-22
❑ 94WilCubF-3764
❑ 95Bow-175
❑ 96Bow-348
❑ 96BowFoi-348
❑ 96OrlCubB-25
❑ 97OrlRayB-24

Stephenson, Earl (Chester)
❑ 72OPC-61
❑ 72Top-61
❑ 74TacTwiC-11
❑ 75IntLeaAT-4
❑ 77RocRedWM-7
❑ 78BalOriP-32
❑ 78RocRedWT-16
❑ 79TidTidT-25
❑ 86HagSunP-21
❑ 87NewOriP-4
❑ 89PacSenL-159
❑ 91OriCro-438
❑ 94BreMilB-359

Stephenson, Ed
❑ 76BatRouCT-19

Stephenson, Garrett
❑ 92BluOriC-1
❑ 92BluOriF-2361
❑ 93AlbPolCB-20
❑ 93AlbPolF-2027
❑ 94FreKeyC-21
❑ 94FreKeyF-2614
❑ 94OriPro-97
❑ 95BowBayTI-36
❑ 96Bow-122
❑ 96BowFoi-122
❑ 96Exc-8
❑ 96RocRedWB-26
❑ 97Fle-598
❑ 97FleTif-598
❑ 97PhiCopQ-27
❑ 97ScrRedB-16
❑ 97Sel-199
❑ 97SelCom-199
❑ 98ColCho-103
❑ 98Fle-299
❑ 98PacOnl-575
❑ 98PacOnlR-575
❑ 98PacOnlWC-575
❑ 98PhiTeal-33
❑ 98Pin-174
❑ 98PinArtP-PP77
❑ 98PinMusC-PP77
❑ 98PinPreP-174
❑ 98ScrRedBQ-25
❑ 98Top-192
❑ 98TopChr-192
❑ 98TopChrR-192
❑ 98TopDevR-192
❑ 98TopDia-192
❑ 98TopMiniC-192
❑ 98UppDec-186
❑ 98UppDecSF-101

Stephenson, Gene
❑ 90WicStaSGD-44

Stephenson, J. Riggs
❑ 21Exh-174
❑ 22W575-133
❑ 23MapCriV-26
❑ 23WilChoV-158
❑ 28PorandAR-A34
❑ 28PorandAR-B34
❑ 28StaPlaCE-64
❑ 29CubCerICP-4
❑ 29PorandAR-87
❑ 30ChiEveAP-9
❑ 31CubTeal-22
❑ 31Exh-5
❑ 32CubTeal-22
❑ 32OrbPinNP-3
❑ 32OrbPinUP-54
❑ 33DelR33-15
❑ 33ExhFou-3
❑ 33Gou-204
❑ 33TatOrb-54
❑ 33TatOrbSDR-170
❑ 34DiaMatCSB-171
❑ 36CubTeal-29
❑ 61Fle-140
❑ 76ChiGre-18
❑ 77GalGloG-51
❑ 80PacLeg-95
❑ 82DiaCla-106
❑ 82TCMGreH-25
❑ 83ConMar-27
❑ 88ConNatA-19
❑ 88ConSer4-27
❑ 91ConTSN-218
❑ 92ConTSN-441
❑ 92CubOldS-23

Stephenson, Jerry
❑ 65OPC-74
❑ 65RedSoxTI-12
❑ 65Top-74
❑ 66Top-396
❑ 67TopRedSS-20
❑ 68Top-519
❑ 69OPC-172
❑ 69Top-172
❑ 71OPC-488
❑ 71Top-488
❑ 81RedSoxBG2S-118
❑ 90DodTar-768
❑ 92MetColP-38

Stephenson, John
❑ 64Top-536
❑ 66OPC-17
❑ 66Top-17
❑ 66TopVen-17
❑ 67CokCapYM-V26
❑ 67DexPre-199
❑ 67Top-522
❑ 68OPC-83
❑ 68Top-83
❑ 68TopVen-83
❑ 71OPC-421
❑ 71Top-421
❑ 91MetWIZ-379
❑ 91WhiSoxK-NNO
❑ 92MetKah-51
❑ 94KinMetC-27
❑ 94KinMetF-3841

Stephenson, Joseph
❑ 85GreHorT-11

Stephenson, Phil
❑ 83AlbA'sT-15
❑ 84TacTigC-88
❑ 85TacTigC-132
❑ 86PitCubP-23
❑ 87IowCubTI-18
❑ 88IowCubC-17
❑ 88IowCubP-540
❑ 89DonRoo-36
❑ 90AlbDecGB-14
❑ 90OPC-584
❑ 90Sco-642
❑ 90Top-584
❑ 90TopDeb89-123
❑ 90TopTif-584
❑ 90WicStaSGD-35
❑ 91Fle-545
❑ 91OPC-726
❑ 91PadSmo-35
❑ 91Sco-138
❑ 91StaClu-420
❑ 91Top-726
❑ 91TopDesS-726
❑ 91TopMic-726
❑ 91TopTif-726
❑ 92LasVegSF-2804
❑ 92PadPolD-22
❑ 92StaClu-684
❑ 92StaCluECN-684
❑ 93Top-357
❑ 93TopGol-357
❑ 93TopInaM-357
❑ 93TopInaR-357
❑ 93TopMic-357
❑ 94LouRedF-2991
❑ 98WicWraM-24

Stephenson, Walter
❑ 35DiaMatCS3T1-135

Stepka, Tom
❑ 96PorRocB-29
❑ 97SalAva-29
❑ 98SalAvaC-25

Sterling, J.C.
❑ 87OldJudN-472

Sterling, Randy
❑ 75TidTidTI-20
❑ 91MetWIZ-380

Sterritt, Charles
❑ 13Zee-148

Stetson, Mike
❑ 91CalLeLA-52

Stevanus, Mike
❑ 86MacPirP-24
❑ 87SalBucP-22
❑ 88SalBucS-19
❑ 88WatPirP-11
❑ 89AugPirP-502

Steve, Harry
❑ 83SanJosBC-26
❑ 86SanJosBP-19
❑ 89SanJosGCLC-237

Stevens, Brian
❑ 90LSUTigA-11

Stevens, Charles
❑ 46SeaSLP-61
❑ 49W72HolS-22
❑ 50W720HolS-30
❑ 52MotCoo-39
❑ 53MotCoo-17

Stevens, Clay
❑ 96BriWhiSB-29

Stevens, Dale
❑ 91PocPioP-3782
❑ 91PocPioSP-17

Stevens, Dave
❑ 90HunCubP-3282
❑ 91GenCubP-4214
❑ 92ChaKniS-166
❑ 93Bow-116
❑ 93OrlCubF-2783
❑ 94BowBes-B70
❑ 94BowBesR-B70
❑ 94Cla-79
❑ 94FleUpd-65
❑ 94SalLakBF-816
❑ 94SpoRoo-71
❑ 94SpoRooAP-71
❑ 94TopTra-97T
❑ 94UppDecML-118
❑ 95ColCho-24
❑ 95ColChoGS-24
❑ 95ColChoSS-24
❑ 95Fle-214
❑ 95Pin-163
❑ 95PinArtP-163
❑ 95PinMusC-163
❑ 95Sco-536
❑ 95ScoGolR-536
❑ 95ScoPlaTS-536
❑ 95Top-516
❑ 95TopCyb-304
❑ 95Ult-77
❑ 95UltGolM-77
❑ 95UppDec-431
❑ 95UppDecED-431
❑ 95UppDecEDG-431
❑ 96ColCho-207
❑ 96ColChoGS-207
❑ 96ColChoSS-207
❑ 96Don-102
❑ 96DonPreP-102
❑ 96Fin-B103
❑ 96FinRef-B103
❑ 96Fle-178
❑ 96FleTif-178
❑ 96StaClu-94
❑ 96StaCluMOP-94
❑ 96Top-88
❑ 96Ult-95
❑ 96UltGolM-95
❑ 96UppDec-389
❑ 97Fle-158
❑ 97FleTif-158
❑ 97PacPriGotD-GD67
❑ 97SalLakB-28
❑ 97StaClu-365
❑ 97StaCluMOP-365
❑ 97Top-439
❑ 98IowCubQ-23

Stevens, Donald
❑ 52LavPro-98

Stevens, Ed (Edward Lee)
❑ 46DodTeal-22
❑ 47TipTop-104
❑ 49Bow-93
❑ 49EurSta-173
❑ 49Lea-43
❑ 52Par-25

❑ 81PadFamF-18
❑ 90DodTar-769
Stevens, Jake
❑ 91PomBlaBPB-23
Stevens, John
❑ 89JohCitCS-21
Stevens, John W.
❑ 55Bow-258
Stevens, Kristopher
❑ 96AppLeaAB-27
❑ 96BatCliTI-5
❑ 96MarPhiB-26
❑ 97PieBolWB-26
❑ 98ReaPhiUM-23
Stevens, Lee
❑ 86SalAngC-96
❑ 87PalSprP-12
❑ 88MidAngGS-18
❑ 89EdmTraC-21
❑ 89EdmTraP-554
❑ 89FleUpd-16
❑ 90Bow-300
❑ 90BowTif-300
❑ 90CMC-490
❑ 90Don-449
❑ 90EdmTraC-13
❑ 90EdmTraP-527
❑ 90Fle-145
❑ 90FleCan-145
❑ 90ProAAAF-103
❑ 90TriAAAC-44
❑ 90TriAllGP-AAA42
❑ 91Cla1-T25
❑ 91Don-754
❑ 91EdmTraLD-170
❑ 91EdmTraP-1530
❑ 91Fle-327
❑ 91LinDriAAA-170
❑ 91MajLeaCP-24
❑ 91OPC-648
❑ 91Sco-67
❑ 91Sco100RS-82
❑ 91StaClu-293
❑ 91Top-648
❑ 91TopDeb90-149
❑ 91TopDesS-648
❑ 91TopMic-648
❑ 91TopTif-648
❑ 91TriA AAGP-AAA15
❑ 91Ult-53
❑ 91UppDec-573
❑ 92AngPol-17
❑ 92Bow-427
❑ 92Cla1-T85
❑ 92Don-460
❑ 92Fle-71
❑ 92Lea-361
❑ 92LeaBlaG-361
❑ 92LeaGolP-15
❑ 92LeaPre-15
❑ 92OPC-702
❑ 92Pin-453
❑ 92ProFS7-28
❑ 92Sco-372
❑ 92StaClu-281
❑ 92Stu-150
❑ 92Top-702
❑ 92TopGol-702
❑ 92TopGolW-702
❑ 92TopMic-702
❑ 92TriPla-119
❑ 92Ult-331
❑ 92UppDec-634
❑ 93Don-65
❑ 93Fle-576
❑ 93PacSpa-52
❑ 93PanSti-9
❑ 93Pin-169
❑ 93RedFolS-90
❑ 93StaClu-219
❑ 93StaCluFDI-219
❑ 93StaCluMOP-219
❑ 93SyrChiF-1007
❑ 93Top-467
❑ 93TopGol-467
❑ 93TopInaM-467
❑ 93TopInaR-467
❑ 93TopMic-467
❑ 93TriAAAGF-54
❑ 94ClaGolF-177
❑ 96OklCit8B-21
❑ 97Don-288
❑ 97DonGolPP-288
❑ 97DonSilPP-288
❑ 97RanDr P-29
❑ 97RanMot-10
❑ 97Sco-376
❑ 97ScoArtPWB-376
❑ 97ScoResC-376
❑ 97ScoShoS-376
❑ 97ScoShoSAP-376
❑ 97Ult-393
❑ 97UltGolME-393
❑ 97UltPlaME-393
❑ 98ColCho-519
❑ 98DonColL-302
❑ 98DonPriCL-302
❑ 98Fle-371
❑ 98Lea-103
❑ 98LeaFraDA-103
❑ 98LeaFraF-103
❑ 98LeaFraM-103
❑ 98LeaFraM-103
❑ 98LeaFraMDC-103
❑ 98LeaFraMDC-103
❑ 98LeaFraMZ2-103
❑ 98Pac-209
❑ 98PacOnl-746
❑ 98PacOnlR-746
❑ 98PacOnlWC-746
❑ 98PacPlaB-209
❑ 98PacRedT-209
❑ 98PacSil-209
❑ 98PinSna-TR14
❑ 98Sco-166
❑ 98SPxFin-326
❑ 98SPxFinR-326
❑ 98SPxFinS-326
❑ 98Top-148
❑ 98TopChr-148
❑ 98TopChrR-148
❑ 98TopDevR-148
❑ 98TopDia-148
❑ 98TopMiniC-148
❑ 98Ult-416
❑ 98UltGolM-416
❑ 98UltMas-416
❑ 98UltPlaM-416
❑ 98UppDec-232
❑ 98UppDecSF-129
❑ 99Bow-242
❑ 99BowGol-242
❑ 99BowInt-242
❑ 99Fle-569
❑ 99FleSta9-569
❑ 99FleWarT-569
❑ 99Pac-431
❑ 99PacPlaB-431
❑ 99PacRed-431
❑ 99Rev-144
❑ 99RevPremDate-144
❑ 99RevRet-144
❑ 99RevShaSS-144
❑ 99TSP-126
❑ 99TopChr-126
❑ 99TopChrR-126
❑ 99TopMVPP-126
❑ 99UppDec-508
❑ 99UppDecEL1-508
❑ 99UppDecEL2-508
Stevens, Matt
❑ 89BatCliP-1924
❑ 90SpaPhiB-8
❑ 90SpaPhiP-2489
❑ 90SpaPhiS-20
❑ 91ClePhiC-8
❑ 91ClePhiP-1619
❑ 92ReaPhiF-574
❑ 92ReaPhiS-543
❑ 92SkyAA F-237
❑ 93PorBeaF-2385
❑ 94SalLakBF-817
Stevens, Mike
❑ 85PriWilPT-24
❑ 86PriWilPP-26
❑ 87SalBucP-2
Stevens, Morris
❑ 65Top-521
❑ 78TCM60I-175
Stevens, Paul
❑ 77DayBealT-24
❑ 80WesHavWCT-7
Stevens, R.C.
❑ 58Top-470
❑ 59Top-282
❑ 61Top-526
Stevens, Scott
❑ 89UtiBluSP-23
❑ 90SouBenWSB-22
❑ 90SouBenWSGS-17
❑ 91SarWhiSC-10
❑ 91SarWhiSP-1113
❑ 92BasCitRC-22
Stevens, Tony
❑ 80ElmPioRST-22
Stevenson, Bill
❑ 85SpoIndC-22
❑ 86ChaRaiP-24
❑ 88WicPilRD-29
Stevenson, Chad
❑ 94BriTigC-25
❑ 94BriTigF-3507
❑ 97WesMicW-26
Stevenson, Jason
❑ 94HunCubC-26
❑ 94HunCubF-3554
❑ 95RocCubTI-26
❑ 96DayCubB-23
❑ 97KnoSmo-23
❑ 98KnoSG-22
Stevenson, Jeff
❑ 92AppFoxCB-29
Stevenson, John
❑ 78NewWayCT-42
❑ 82AmaGolST-3
❑ 84ShrCapFB-22
Stevenson, Rich
❑ 70RoyTeal-34
Stevenson, Robert
❑ 30Zee-96
Stevenson, Rodney
❑ 96VerExpB-25
❑ 98JupHamQ-14
Stevenson, Stevie
❑ 36WorWidGV-128
Stevenson, Tenoa
❑ 82IdaFalAT-12
Steverson, Todd
❑ 89AlaGol-9
❑ 92ClaBluBF-BC27
❑ 92ClaDraP-19
❑ 92ClaFS7-410
❑ 92FroRowDP-7
❑ 92FroRowDPG-7
❑ 92FroRowDPS-7
❑ 92St.CatBJC-1
❑ 92St.CatBJF-3400
❑ 92UppDecML-16
❑ 93AusFut-78
❑ 93ClaFS7-28
❑ 93ClaGolF-177
❑ 93DunBluJC-1
❑ 93DunBluJF-1810
❑ 93DunBluJFFN-25
❑ 93ExcFS7-246
❑ 93OPCPreTDP-4
❑ 93Pin-464
❑ 93Sco-496
❑ 93Sel-353
❑ 93SP-282
❑ 93StaCluM-129
❑ 93Top-269
❑ 93TopGol-269
❑ 93TopInaM-269
❑ 93TopInaR-269
❑ 93TopMic-269
❑ 94ClaGolF-57
❑ 94KnoSmoF-1318
❑ 94UppDecML-45
❑ 95FleUpd-23
❑ 95Sum-166
❑ 95SumNthD-166
❑ 95TopTra-31T
❑ 96ColCho-546
❑ 96ColChoGS-546
❑ 96ColChoSS-546
❑ 96LasVegSB-25
❑ 96Pac-316
❑ 96Sco-244
❑ 98MemRedG-24
Steward, Chuck (Charles)
❑ 88FayGenP-1092
❑ 89LakTigS-20
Steward, G. G.
❑ 25Zee-101
Steward, Hector
❑ 86NewBriRSP-23
Stewart, Andy
❑ 92BasCitRC-13
❑ 92BasCitRF-3849
❑ 93WilBluRC-22
❑ 93WilBluRF-2000
❑ 94CarLeaAF-CAR24
❑ 94WilBluRF-304
❑ 95SigRooOJ-31
❑ 95SigRooOJP-31
❑ 95SigRooOJPS-31
❑ 95SigRooOJS-31
❑ 95WicWraTI-28
❑ 96WicWraB-16
❑ 97OmaRoyB-15
❑ 98TexLeaTPG-30
❑ 98WicWraM-29
Stewart, Bill
❑ 55JetPos-14
Stewart, Brady
❑ 90EugEmeGS-29
❑ 91AppFoxCB-20
❑ 91AppFoxP-1726
❑ 92BasCitRC-8
❑ 92BasCitRF-3853
❑ 93WilBluRC-23
❑ 93WilBluRF-2007
❑ 94MemChiF-367
Stewart, Bud (Edward P.)
❑ 47Exh-218
❑ 49Bow-173
❑ 49Lea-104
❑ 50Bow-143
❑ 51Bow-159
❑ 52Bow-185
❑ 52Top-279
❑ 52WhiSoxHDP-9
❑ 83TopRep5-279
Stewart, Bunky (Vernon)
❑ 55Top-136
❑ 55TopDouH-75
Stewart, C.J.
❑ 97WilCubB-23
Stewart, Carl
❑ 88BilMusP-1826
❑ 90BilMusP-3221
❑ 91ChaWheC-10
❑ 91ChaWheP-2887
❑ 92ChaWVWC-19
❑ 93WinSpiC-23
Stewart, Charlie
❑ 66St.PetCTI-15
Stewart, Chris
❑ 93JohCitCC-20
❑ 93JohCitCF-3677
❑ 94SavCarC-25
❑ 94SavCarF-506
❑ 95Exc-275
Stewart, Colin
❑ 98EugEme-28
Stewart, Dave
❑ 76SeaRaiC-17
❑ 77CliDodT-25
❑ 79AlbDukTc-5
❑ 80AlbDukTc-1
❑ 80VenLeaS-121
❑ 81Dod-28
❑ 81DodPol-48
❑ 81LonBeaPT-24
❑ 82DodPol-48
❑ 82DodUniOV-22
❑ 82Don-410
❑ 82Fle-24
❑ 82Top-213
❑ 83DodPol-48
❑ 83DodPos-16
❑ 83Don-588
❑ 83Fle-222
❑ 83Top-532
❑ 84Don-343
❑ 84Fle-430
❑ 84Nes792-352
❑ 84OPC-352
❑ 84RanJarP-31
❑ 84Top-352
❑ 84TopSti-360
❑ 84TopTif-352
❑ 85Don-343
❑ 85Fle-569
❑ 85RanPer-48
❑ 85Top-723
❑ 85TopTif-723
❑ 86Don-619
❑ 86Fle-453
❑ 86PhiTas-48
❑ 86Top-689
❑ 86TopTif-689
❑ 87A'sSmoC-11
❑ 87Don-648
❑ 87Fle-406
❑ 87FleGlo-406
❑ 87Top-14
❑ 87TopSti-167
❑ 87TopTif-14
❑ 88A'sMot-3
❑ 88ClaRed-196
❑ 88Don-472
❑ 88DonBasB-99
❑ 88DonTeaBA-472
❑ 88Fle-295
❑ 88FleBasM-36
❑ 88FleGlo-295
❑ 88FleMin-48
❑ 88FleSlu-39
❑ 88FleStiC-57
❑ 88FleWaxBC-C14
❑ 88Lea-217
❑ 88OPC-353
❑ 88PanSti-164
❑ 88Sco-458
❑ 88ScoGlo-458
❑ 88Spo-162
❑ 88StaLinAs-16
❑ 88Top-476
❑ 88TopGloS-33
❑ 88TopMinL-32
❑ 88TopRevLL-29
❑ 88TopSti-168
❑ 88TopTif-476
❑ 88TopUKM-75
❑ 88TopUKMT-75
❑ 89A'sMot-6
❑ 89Bow-188
❑ 89BowTif-188
❑ 89CadEllD-55
❑ 89Don-214
❑ 89DonBasB-99
❑ 89Fle-23
❑ 89FleExcS-39
❑ 89FleGlo-23
❑ 89FleLeaL-36
❑ 89OPC-145
❑ 89PanSti-415
❑ 89RedFolSB-112
❑ 89Sco-32
❑ 89Sco-582
❑ 89Scomast-14
❑ 89Spo-23
❑ 89SpoIllFKI-133
❑ 89Top-145
❑ 89TopBig-101
❑ 89TopCoi-53
❑ 89TopGloS-45
❑ 89TopHilTM-27
❑ 89TopMinL-71
❑ 89TopSti-163
❑ 89TopStiB-27
❑ 89TopTif-145
❑ 89TopUKM-74
❑ 89TVSpoM-95
❑ 89UppDec-185
❑ 90A'sMot-5
❑ 90Bow-449
❑ 90BowTif-449
❑ 90ClaUpd-T47
❑ 90Col-18
❑ 90DodTar-770
❑ 90Don-6
❑ 90Don-150
❑ 90Don-703A
❑ 90Don-703B
❑ 90DonBesA-25
❑ 90DOnBonM-BC3
❑ 90DonLeaS-35
❑ 90DonPre-5
❑ 90DonSupD-6
❑ 90Fle-21
❑ 90FleAwaW-37
❑ 90FleBasA-39
❑ 90FleBasAC-39
❑ 90FleBasM-38
❑ 90FleBasMC-38
❑ 90FleCan-21
❑ 90FleWaxBC-C26
❑ 90FleWorS-8
❑ 90Lea-81
❑ 90M.Vpin-76
❑ 90MLBBasB-74
❑ 90MSAHolD-14
❑ 90OPC-270
❑ 90PanSti-141
❑ 90PanSti-198
❑ 90PubIntS-295
❑ 90PubIntS-316
❑ 90Sco-410
❑ 90Sco-700
❑ 90Sco100S-13
❑ 90ScoMcD-23
❑ 90Spo-194
❑ 90SunSee-16
❑ 90Top-270
❑ 90TopBig-64
❑ 90TopCoi-29
❑ 90TopDou-63
❑ 90TopGloA-21
❑ 90TopGloS-4
❑ 90TopMinL-32
❑ 90TopSti-164
❑ 90TopSti-185
❑ 90TopStiB-60
❑ 90TopTif-270
❑ 90TopTVA-16
❑ 90UppDec-272
❑ 90Woo-25
❑ 90Woo-33
❑ 91A'sMot-5
❑ 91A'sSFE-13
❑ 91BasBesAotM-16
❑ 91Bow-225
❑ 91CadEllD-55
❑ 91Cla2-T89
❑ 91ClaGam-102
❑ 91Col-32
❑ 91Don-102
❑ 91DonBonC-BC4
❑ 91Fle-25
❑ 91FlePro-F4
❑ 91FleWaxBC-4
❑ 91FleWorS-6
❑ 91FouBal-29
❑ 91Lea-417
❑ 91OPC-580
❑ 91OPCPre-115
❑ 91PanCanT1-62
❑ 91PanCanT1-71
❑ 91PanCanT1-93
❑ 91PanFreS-199
❑ 91PanFreS-355
❑ 91PanSti-4
❑ 91PanSti-144
❑ 91RedFolS-90
❑ 91Sco-150
❑ 91Sco-702
❑ 91Sco-883
❑ 91Sco100S-24
❑ 91SevCoi-NC12
❑ 91StaClu-1
❑ 91StaCluCM-27
❑ 91Stu-107
❑ 91Top-580
❑ 91TopCraJ2-10
❑ 91TopDesS-580
❑ 91TopMic-580
❑ 91TopSta-32
❑ 91TopTif-580
❑ 91Ult-254
❑ 91UppDec-28
❑ 91UppDec-127
❑ 91Woo-24
❑ 92A'sUno7P-3
❑ 92A'sUno7P-4
❑ 92AthMot-5
❑ 92Bow-280
❑ 92ClaGam-10
❑ 92Don-225
❑ 92Fle-268
❑ 92HitTheBB-34
❑ 92Lea-258
❑ 92LeaBlaG-258
❑ 92OPC-410
❑ 92Pin-157
❑ 92Sco-580
❑ 92Sco100S-60
❑ 92SpoStaCC-43
❑ 92StaClu-390
❑ 92Stu-230
❑ 92Top-410
❑ 92TopGol-410
❑ 92TopGolW-410
❑ 92TopKid-117
❑ 92TopMic-410
❑ 92TriPla-88
❑ 92Ult-117
❑ 92UppDec-547
❑ 93BluJayCP1-14
❑ 93BluJayD-14
❑ 93BluJayFS-27
❑ 93CadDis-56
❑ 93DiaMar-103
❑ 93Don-611
❑ 93DurPowP1-10
❑ 93Fla-295
❑ 93Fle-669
❑ 93FleFinE-296
❑ 93Lea-294
❑ 93OPC-294
❑ 93OPCPre-45

❑ 93PacSpa-656
❑ 93PanSti-29
❑ 93Pin-442
❑ 93RanKee-347
❑ 93Sco-656
❑ 93Sel-240
❑ 93SelRoo-24T
❑ 93StaClu-629
❑ 93StaCluFDI-629
❑ 93StaCluMO-25
❑ 93StaCluMOP-629
❑ 93Top-290
❑ 93TopComotH-12
❑ 93TopGol-290
❑ 93TopInaM-290
❑ 93TopInaR-290
❑ 93TopMic-290
❑ 93TopTra-114T
❑ 93Ult-647
❑ 93UppDec-39
❑ 93UppDec-546
❑ 93UppDecGold-39
❑ 93UppDecGold-546
❑ 94BluJayUSPC-3C
❑ 94BluJayUSPC-11H
❑ 94Bow-113
❑ 94ColC-371
❑ 94ColChoGS-371
❑ 94ColChoSS-371
❑ 94Don-257
❑ 94Fin-134
❑ 94FinRef-134
❑ 94Fla-121
❑ 94Fle-343
❑ 94FleExtB-195
❑ 94Lea-308
❑ 94OPC-12
❑ 94Pac-652
❑ 94Pin-374
❑ 94PinArtP-374
❑ 94PinMusC-374
❑ 94PosCan-5
❑ 94Sco-133
❑ 94ScoGolR-133
❑ 94Sel-165
❑ 94StaClu-317
❑ 94StaCluFDI-317
❑ 94StaCluGR-317
❑ 94StaCluMOP-317
❑ 94StaCluT-179
❑ 94StaCluTFDI-179
❑ 94Top-455
❑ 94TopGol-455
❑ 94TopSpa-455
❑ 94TriPla-38
❑ 94Ult-143
❑ 94UppDec-89
❑ 94UppDecED-89
❑ 95AthMot-11
❑ 95BluJayUSPC-3D
❑ 95BluJayUSPC-10C
❑ 95ColCho-151
❑ 95ColCho-534T
❑ 95ColChoGS-151
❑ 95ColChoSS-151
❑ 95Don-374
❑ 95DonPreP-374
❑ 95Fla-297
❑ 95Fle-105
❑ 95FleUpd-72
❑ 95Pin-387
❑ 95PinArtP-387
❑ 95PinMusC-387
❑ 95SPCha-113
❑ 95SPChaDC-113
❑ 95StaClu-527
❑ 95StaCluMOP-527
❑ 95StaCluSTWS-527
❑ 95TopTra-154T
❑ 95Ult-343
❑ 95UltGolM-343
❑ 95UppDec-36
❑ 95UppDecED-36
❑ 95UppDecEDG-36
❑ 96ColCho-246
❑ 96ColChoGS-246
❑ 96ColChoSS-246
❑ 97BluJayS-47
❑ 98PadMot-28

Stewart, David
❑ 94BatCliC-23
❑ 94BatCliF-3445

Stewart, Ed
❑ 83CliGiaF-23

Stewart, Ernie
❑ 97AriStaBG-20

Stewart, Gabby (Glen)
❑ 46RemBre-27
❑ 47SigOil-16
❑ 83TCMPla1943-41

Stewart, Greg
❑ 80AppFoxT-19

Stewart, Harry
❑ 09ObaT21-167
❑ 09ObaT21-356
❑ 11Zee-121
❑ 12ObaPreT-105
❑ 12Zee-154

Stewart, Hattie
❑ 88KimN18-43

Stewart, Hector
❑ 87PawRedSP-61
❑ 87PawRedST-10
❑ 88BlaYNPRWL-142
❑ 89BlaYNPRWL-55
❑ 89WinHavRSS-22

Stewart, James F.
❑ 64Top-408
❑ 65CubJayP-11
❑ 65Top-298
❑ 66OPC-63
❑ 66Top-63
❑ 66TopVen-63
❑ 67OPC-124
❑ 67Top-124
❑ 70DayDaiNM-54
❑ 70Top-636
❑ 71MLBOffS-70
❑ 71OPC-644
❑ 71Top-644
❑ 72AstTeal-24
❑ 72MilBra-329
❑ 72Top-747
❑ 73OPC-351
❑ 73Top-351
❑ 87AstShoSTw-26
❑ 87AstShowSTh-23

Stewart, Jeff
❑ 87WicPilRD-17

Stewart, Joe
❑ 76AshTouT-25
❑ 77VisOakT-16

Stewart, John
❑ 87CedRapRP-21
❑ 87DurBulP-13
❑ 89SalLakTTI-30
❑ 91SalSpuC-19
❑ 91SalSpuP-2245
❑ 99TeaBesR-84
❑ 99TeaBesRG-84
❑ 99TeaBesRS-84

Stewart, Keith
❑ 96EveAquB-24
❑ 97EveAquG-26

Stewart, Lee
❑ 89GeoColC-32

Stewart, Lefty (Walter C.)
❑ 27MidBre-40
❑ 31Exh-30
❑ 33Gou-121
❑ 33Gou-146
❑ 33GouCanV-75
❑ 33TatOrbSDR-179
❑ 33Zee-42
❑ 34DiaMatCSB-172
❑ 35GouPuzR-8I
❑ 35GouPuzR-9I
❑ 91ConTSN-243

Stewart, Neb
❑ 43PhiTeal-21

Stewart, Paul
❑ 96OgdRapTI-47
❑ 98BelSnaM-25

Stewart, Paxton
❑ 96StCatSB-28
❑ 97BoiHawG-27

Stewart, Rachaad
❑ 94BluOriC-20
❑ 96Exc-9
❑ 96GreBraB-26
❑ 96GreBraTI-51

Stewart, Reggie
❑ 93WatDiaC-27
❑ 93WatDiaF-1783

Stewart, Richard
❑ 94BluOriF-3563

Stewart, Riley A.
❑ 93NegLeaRL2-37

Stewart, Sammy
❑ 79BalOriP-14
❑ 79BalOriP-15
❑ 79Top-206
❑ 79Top-701
❑ 80Top-119
❑ 81BalOriP-21
❑ 81Don-474
❑ 81Fle-181
❑ 81OPC-262
❑ 81Top-262
❑ 82BalOriP-6
❑ 82Don-457
❑ 82Fle-180
❑ 82OPC-279
❑ 82Top-426
❑ 82Top-679
❑ 83Don-203
❑ 83Fle-74
❑ 83OPC-347
❑ 83OriPos-29
❑ 83Top-347
❑ 84AllGamPI-177
❑ 84BalOriP-36
❑ 84Don-514
❑ 84Fle-22
❑ 84Nes792-59
❑ 84Top-59
❑ 84TopSti-25
❑ 84TopTif-59
❑ 85BalOriP-33
❑ 85Don-148
❑ 85Fle-192
❑ 85Lea-98
❑ 85OPC-213
❑ 85Top-469
❑ 85TopTif-469
❑ 86Don-270
❑ 86Fle-289
❑ 86FleUpd-107
❑ 86OPC-172
❑ 86Top-597
❑ 86TopSti-235
❑ 86TopTif-597
❑ 86TopTra-103T
❑ 86TopTraT-103T
❑ 87Don-658
❑ 87Fle-48
❑ 87FleGlo-48
❑ 87Top-204
❑ 87TopTif-204
❑ 88Don-596
❑ 88Fle-616
❑ 88FleGlo-616
❑ 88Top-701
❑ 88TopTif-701
❑ 89PacSenL-27
❑ 89PacSenL-135
❑ 89T/MSenL-101
❑ 90EliSenL-48
❑ 91OriCro-439

Stewart, Scott
❑ 95ChaRivTI-2
❑ 97St.LucM-25

Stewart, Shannon
❑ 92ClaBluBF-BC24
❑ 92ClaDraP-14
❑ 92ClaDraPFB-BC13
❑ 92ClaFS7-406
❑ 92UppDecML-10
❑ 93ClaGolF-174
❑ 93OPCPreTDP-2
❑ 93Pin-462
❑ 93Sco-494
❑ 93Sel-355
❑ 93St.CatBJC-1
❑ 93St.CatBJF-3988
❑ 93StaCluM-180
❑ 94Bow-309
❑ 94Cla-71
❑ 94ClaCreotC-C10
❑ 94ClaGolF-22
❑ 94ExcFS7-149
❑ 94HagSunC-1
❑ 94HagSunF-2745
❑ 94SouAtlLAF-SAL20
❑ 94UppDec-299
❑ 94UppDecED-299
❑ 94UppDecML-195
❑ 95Bow-55
❑ 95BowBes-B15
❑ 95BowBesR-B15
❑ 95KnoSmoF-54
❑ 95UppDecML-32
❑ 95UppDecMLFS-32
❑ 96Bow-177
❑ 96BowBes-142
❑ 96BowBesAR-142
❑ 96BowBesR-142
❑ 96BowFoi-177
❑ 96ColCho-433
❑ 96ColChoGS-21
❑ 96ColChoGS-433
❑ 96ColChoSS-21
❑ 96ColChoSS-433
❑ 96FlePro-10
❑ 96Lea-123
❑ 96LeaPrePB-123
❑ 96LeaPrePG-123
❑ 96LeaPrePS-123
❑ 96Spo-140
❑ 96SpoArtP-140
❑ 96SyrChiTI-29
❑ 96Top-343
❑ 96UppDec-233
❑ 96UppDecFSP-FS19
❑ 96UppDecPHE-H28
❑ 96UppDecPreH-H28
❑ 97BluJayOH-32
❑ 97BluJayS-57
❑ 97Bow-320
❑ 97BowBes-171
❑ 97BowBesAR-171
❑ 97BowBesR-171
❑ 97BowChr-220
❑ 97BowChrI-220
❑ 97BowChrIR-220
❑ 97BowChrR-220
❑ 97BowInt-320
❑ 97Cir-105
❑ 97CirRav-105
❑ 97Don-262
❑ 97DonFraFea-12
❑ 97DonGolPP-262
❑ 97DonLim-79
❑ 97DonLimE-79
❑ 97DonLimENG-79
❑ 97DonPre-162
❑ 97DonPreCttC-162
❑ 97DonSigA-92
❑ 97DonSigAC-115
❑ 97DonSigAM-115
❑ 97DonSilPP-262
❑ 97FlaShoLC-107
❑ 97FlaShoLeg0-107
❑ 97FlaShoLeg1-107
❑ 97FlaShoM-A107
❑ 97FlaShoM-B107
❑ 97FlaShoM-C107
❑ 97FlaShoR0-107
❑ 97FlaShoR1-107
❑ 97FlaShoR2-107
❑ 97Fle-546
❑ 97FleTif-546
❑ 97Lea-175
❑ 97LeaFraM-175
❑ 97LeaFraMDC-175
❑ 97NewPin-171
❑ 97NewPinAP-171
❑ 97NewPinMC-171
❑ 97NewPinPP-171
❑ 97PacPriGotD-GD106
❑ 97PinCer-135
❑ 97PinCerMBla-135
❑ 97PinCerMBlu-135
❑ 97PinCerMG-135
❑ 97PinCerMR-135
❑ 97PinCerR-135
❑ 97PinTotCPB-135
❑ 97PinTotCPG-135
❑ 97PinTotCPR-135
❑ 97PinX-P-135
❑ 97PinX-PMoS-135
❑ 97Sel-160
❑ 97SelCom-160
❑ 97StaClu-283
❑ 97StaCluMOP-283
❑ 97Stu-147
❑ 97StuPrePG-147
❑ 97StuPrePS-147
❑ 97SyrSkyCB-25
❑ 97Top-456
❑ 97Ult-471
❑ 97UltGolME-471
❑ 97UltPlaME-471
❑ 98Bow-179
❑ 98BowChr-179
❑ 98BowChrGA-179
❑ 98BowChrGAR-179
❑ 98BowChrI-179
❑ 98BowChrIR-179
❑ 98BowChrR-179
❑ 98BowGolA-179
❑ 98BowInt-179
❑ 98CirThu-147
❑ 98CirThuRav-147
❑ 98CirThuSupRav-147
❑ 98ColCho-263
❑ 98Don-108
❑ 98DonCol-108
❑ 98DonCol-194
❑ 98DonColE-472
❑ 98DonColL-303
❑ 98DonColP-680
❑ 98DonColS-108
❑ 98DonColS-189
❑ 98DonEli-72
❑ 98DonEliA-72
❑ 98DonEliS-72
❑ 98DonGolPP-108
❑ 98DonPre-130
❑ 98DonPreSeat-130
❑ 98DonPriCD-108
❑ 98DonPriCD-194
❑ 98DonPriCE-472
❑ 98DonPriCL-303
❑ 98DonPriCP-680
❑ 98DonRatR-19
❑ 98DonRatRM-19
❑ 98DonSilPP-108
❑ 98Fin-106
❑ 98FinNo--106
❑ 98FinNo-R-106
❑ 98FinRef-106
❑ 98Fle-54
❑ 98Lea-104
❑ 98LeaFraDA-104
❑ 98LeaFraF-104
❑ 98LeaFraM-104
❑ 98LeaFraM-104
❑ 98LeaFraMDC-104
❑ 98LeaFraMDC-104
❑ 98LeaFraMZ2-104
❑ 98LeaRS-115
❑ 98LeaRSLHolo-115
❑ 98LeaRSLong-115
❑ 98LeaRTrue-115
❑ 98MetUni-85
❑ 98MetUniPMG-85
❑ 98PacInvGems-116
❑ 98PacOme-250
❑ 98PacOmeR-250
❑ 98PacOnl-778
❑ 98PacOnlR-778
❑ 98PacOnlWC-778
❑ 98PacPar-117
❑ 98PacParC-117
❑ 98PacParG-117
❑ 98PacParHS-117
❑ 98PacParPB-117
❑ 98PacParR-117
❑ 98Pin-162
❑ 98PinArtP-PP65
❑ 98PinIns-88
❑ 98PinInsCE-88
❑ 98PinInsDE-88
❑ 98PinMusC-PP65
❑ 98PinPer-106
❑ 98PinPerPP-106
❑ 98PinPlu-92
❑ 98PinPreP-162
❑ 98Sco-247
❑ 98ScoRT-191
❑ 98ScoRTSS-PP107
❑ 98ScoRTSSAP-PP107
❑ 98ScoRTSSAP1-PP107
❑ 98SpoIll-117
❑ 98SpoIllEE-117
❑ 98SpoIllFE-117
❑ 98StaCluFDI-272
❑ 98StaCluI-272
❑ 98StaCluITW-W14
❑ 98StaCluOneK-272
❑ 98StaCluPP-272
❑ 98Stu-17
❑ 98StuGPP-17
❑ 98StuSPP-17
❑ 98Top-447
❑ 98TopChr-447
❑ 98TopChrR-447
❑ 98TopDevR-447
❑ 98TopDia-447
❑ 98TopMiniC-447
❑ 98Ult-229
❑ 98UltGolM-229
❑ 98UltMas-229
❑ 98UltPlaM-229
❑ 98UppDec-242
❑ 98UppDecSF-134
❑ 98Zen-95
❑ 98ZenZ-G-95
❑ 98ZenZ-S-95
❑ 99Bow-247
❑ 99BowGol-247
❑ 99BowInt-247
❑ 99E-X Cen-85
❑ 99E-X CenECFut-85
❑ 99E-X CenECNow-85
❑ 99FlaShoLeg1-94
❑ 99FlaShoLeg2-94
❑ 99FlaShoLeg3-94
❑ 99FlaShoLegM1-94
❑ 99FlaShoLegM2-94
❑ 99FlaShoLegM3-94
❑ 99FlaShoR1-94
❑ 99FlaShoR2-94
❑ 99FlaShoR3-94
❑ 99Fle-278
❑ 99FleMys-62
❑ 99FleMysG-62
❑ 99FleMysM-62
❑ 99FleSta9-278
❑ 99FleWarT-278
❑ 99MetUni-113
❑ 99MetUniGM-113
❑ 99MetUniPMG-113
❑ 99Pac-449
❑ 99PacOme-248
❑ 99PacOmeC-248
❑ 99PacOmeG-248
❑ 99PacOmePB-248
❑ 99PacPar-249
❑ 99PacParC-249
❑ 99PacParG-249
❑ 99PacParHoloGold-249
❑ 99PacParHS-249
❑ 99PacParOD-249
❑ 99PacParPB-249
❑ 99PacParRed-249
❑ 99PacPlaB-449
❑ 99PacRed-449
❑ 99Rev-149
❑ 99RevPremDate-149
❑ 99RevRet-149
❑ 99RevShaSS-149
❑ 99SkyPre-76
❑ 99SkyPreR-76
❑ 99SkyThu-63
❑ 99SkyThuRant-63
❑ 99SkyThuRave-63
❑ 99StaClu-187
❑ 99StaCluFDI-187
❑ 99StaCluOoaK-187
❑ 99StaCluPP-187
❑ 99ThuSkySupR-63
❑ 99Top-133
❑ 99TopChr-133
❑ 99TopChrR-133
❑ 99TopMVPP-133
❑ 99TopOpeD-79
❑ 99UppDec-228
❑ 99UppDecEL1-228
❑ 99UppDecEL2-228
❑ 99Vic-416

Stewart, Stanley
❑ 96TamYanY-24

Stewart, Stuffy (John F.)
❑ 90DodTar-771
❑ 94ConTSN-1132
❑ 94ConTSNB-1132

Stewart, Tito
❑ 88NewBriRSP-905
❑ 89NewBriRSS-5
❑ 89Sta-136
❑ 90CMC-252
❑ 90PawRedSC-1
❑ 90PawRedSDD-23
❑ 90PawRedSP-462
❑ 90ProAAAF-434
❑ 90TopTVRS-60
❑ 91IndIndLD-195
❑ 91IndIndP-462
❑ 91LinDriAAA-195

Stiboro, Tom
❑ 80BatTroT-13

Stickels, Bob
❑ 71MLBOffS-527

Stidham, Phil
❑ 90ArkRaz-23
❑ 92LakTigC-20
❑ 93FloStaLAF-19
❑ 93LakTigC-23
❑ 93LakTigF-1310
❑ 94ExcFS7-61
❑ 95NorTidTI-27
❑ 97ColSprSTI-23

Stidham, Phillip
❑ 92LakTigF-2279
❑ 94Bow-204
❑ 94SpoRoo-39
❑ 94SpoRooAP-39
❑ 95Sco-594
❑ 95ScoGolR-594
❑ 95ScoPlaTS-594
Stieb, Dave
❑ 80OPC-42
❑ 80Top-77
❑ 81AllGamPI-89
❑ 81Don-582
❑ 81Fle-414
❑ 81OPC-5
❑ 81OPCPos-22
❑ 81Top-467
❑ 81TopSti-142
❑ 82BluJayS-16
❑ 82Don-52
❑ 82FBIDis-25
❑ 82Fle-622
❑ 82FleSta-232
❑ 82OPC-53
❑ 82OPC-380
❑ 82OPCPos-6
❑ 82Top-380
❑ 82Top-606
❑ 82TopSti-250
❑ 83AllGamPI-88
❑ 83Don-9
❑ 83Don-507
❑ 83DonActA-48
❑ 83Fle-441
❑ 83FleSta-188
❑ 83FleSti-111
❑ 83Kel-36
❑ 83OPC-130
❑ 83OPC-202
❑ 83PerAll-6
❑ 83PerAllG-6
❑ 83Top-130
❑ 83Top-202
❑ 83TopGloS-25
❑ 83TopSti-127
❑ 84AllGamPI-178
❑ 84BluJayFS-28
❑ 84Don-71
❑ 84DonActAS-19
❑ 84Fle-167
❑ 84FleSti-85
❑ 84FunFooP-75
❑ 84MilBra-26
❑ 84Nes792-590
❑ 84Nes792-606
❑ 84OPC-134
❑ 84OPC-289
❑ 84SevCoi-E13
❑ 84Top-590
❑ 84Top-606
❑ 84TopGloA-10
❑ 84TopGloS-24
❑ 84TopRubD-8
❑ 84TopSti-368
❑ 84TopTif-590
❑ 84TopTif-606
❑ 85BluJayCC-7
❑ 85BluJayFS-27
❑ 85BluJayPLP-3
❑ 85Don-193
❑ 85DonHig-12
❑ 85Fle-117
❑ 85FleLimE-37
❑ 85FleStaS-91
❑ 85FleStaS-110
❑ 85GenMilS-23
❑ 85Lea-54
❑ 85Lea-251
❑ 85OPC-240
❑ 85OPCPos-22
❑ 85SevCoi-S14
❑ 85Top-240
❑ 85Top3-D-20
❑ 85TopGloA-21
❑ 85TopGloS-40
❑ 85TopRubD-22
❑ 85TopSti-191
❑ 85TopSti-356
❑ 85TopSup-22
❑ 85TopTif-240
❑ 86BluJayAF-22
❑ 86BluJayFS-29
❑ 86Don-146
❑ 86DonAll-55
❑ 86Dra-34
❑ 86Fle-70
❑ 86Fle-642
❑ 86FleLeaL-43
❑ 86FleMin-16
❑ 86FleSlu-37
❑ 86FleStiC-115
❑ 86GenMilB-3H
❑ 86Lea-68
❑ 86OPC-353
❑ 86SevCoi-E14
❑ 86Spo-96
❑ 86Top-650
❑ 86Top3-D-27
❑ 86TopGloS-43
❑ 86TopMinL-36
❑ 86TopSti-186
❑ 86TopSup-54
❑ 86TopTat-23
❑ 86TopTif-650
❑ 86TruVal-19
❑ 87BluJayFS-30
❑ 87Don-195
❑ 87Fle-238
❑ 87FleGlo-238
❑ 87GenMilB-1H
❑ 87Lea-72
❑ 87OPC-90
❑ 87RedFolSB-81
❑ 87SpoTeaP-5
❑ 87StuPan-28
❑ 87SyrChi1A-3
❑ 87Top-90
❑ 87TopTif-90
❑ 88BluJay5-10
❑ 88BluJayFS-27
❑ 88Don-148
❑ 88DonBasB-284
❑ 88Fle-123
❑ 88FleGlo-123
❑ 88GreBasS-2
❑ 88Lea-80
❑ 88MSAHosD-17
❑ 88OPC-153
❑ 88PanSti-215
❑ 88Sco-76
❑ 88ScoGlo-76
❑ 88StaLinBJ-18
❑ 88Top-775
❑ 88TopBig-172
❑ 88TopSti-191
❑ 88TopTif-775
❑ 89BluJayFS-26
❑ 89Bow-239
❑ 89BowTif-239
❑ 89ClaLigB-49
❑ 89Don-349
❑ 89DonAll-28
❑ 89DonBasB-143
❑ 89Fle-244
❑ 89FleBasA-40
❑ 89FleGlo-244
❑ 89OPC-4
❑ 89PanSti-463
❑ 89Sco-197
❑ 89Spo-35
❑ 89Top-460
❑ 89TopBig-128
❑ 89TopSti-194
❑ 89TopTif-460
❑ 89TVSpoM-78
❑ 89UppDec-383
❑ 90BluJayFS-26
❑ 90BluJayHS-6
❑ 90Bow-505
❑ 90BowTif-505
❑ 90ClaBlu-97
❑ 90Don-87
❑ 90DonBesA-127
❑ 90Fle-93
❑ 90FleCan-93
❑ 90Lea-79
❑ 90M.Vpin-108
❑ 90OPC-320
❑ 90PanSti-173
❑ 90PubIntS-526
❑ 90Sco-201
❑ 90Sco100S-89
❑ 90Spo-26
❑ 90SunSee-7
❑ 90Top-320
❑ 90TopBig-112
❑ 90TopMinL-44
❑ 90TopTif-320
❑ 90UppDec-605
❑ 90USPlaCA-10C
❑ 91BasBesAotM-17
❑ 91BluJayFS-22
❑ 91BluJayFS-24
❑ 91BluJayS-5
❑ 91Bow-22
❑ 91Cla1-T89
❑ 91Don-1
❑ 91Don-551
❑ 91DonBonC-BC21
❑ 91DonSupD-1
❑ 91Fle-185
❑ 91FleWaxBC-9
❑ 91Lea-96
❑ 91LeaPre-26
❑ 91MajLeaCP-26
❑ 91MSAHolD-18
❑ 91OPC-460
❑ 91OPCPre-116
❑ 91PanCanT1-64
❑ 91PanFreS-344
❑ 91PanFreS-360
❑ 91PanSti-9
❑ 91PanSti-160
❑ 91PepSup-4
❑ 91PosCan-16
❑ 91RedFolS-89
❑ 91Sco-30
❑ 91Sco-707
❑ 91Sco100S-93
❑ 91StaClu-62
❑ 91StaCluCM-28
❑ 91StaPinB-48
❑ 91Stu-137
❑ 91Top-460
❑ 91TopCraJ2-32
❑ 91TopDesS-460
❑ 91TopMic-460
❑ 91TopTif-460
❑ 91Ult-368
❑ 91UppDec-106
❑ 92BluJayP-9
❑ 92Bow-376
❑ 92ClaGam-13
❑ 92Don-724
❑ 92Fle-341
❑ 92Lea-291
❑ 92LeaBlaG-291
❑ 92OPC-535
❑ 92PanSti-32
❑ 92Pin-108
❑ 92Sco-656
❑ 92Sco100S-37
❑ 92StaClu-97
❑ 92Top-535
❑ 92TopGol-535
❑ 92TopGolW-535
❑ 92TopKid-91
❑ 92TopMic-535
❑ 92TriPla-147
❑ 92Ult-152
❑ 92UppDec-99
❑ 92UppDec-136
❑ 93BluJayD4-29
❑ 93BluJayDM-8
❑ 93Don-708
❑ 93Fle-699
❑ 93OPC-235
❑ 93OPCPre-60
❑ 93PacSpa-396
❑ 93Pin-552
❑ 93Sco-630
❑ 93Sel-386
❑ 93StaClu-641
❑ 93StaCluFDI-641
❑ 93StaCluMOP-641
❑ 93Top-295
❑ 93TopGol-295
❑ 93TopInaM-295
❑ 93TopInaR-295
❑ 93TopMic-295
❑ 93Ult-536
❑ 93UppDec-805
❑ 93UppDecGold-805
❑ 93WhiSoxSC-4
❑ 96BluJayB-5
❑ 96BluJayOH-30
❑ 97BluJayS-33
❑ 98SyrSkyG-28
Stiegele, Rob
❑ 89BluOriS-22
❑ 90FreKeyTI-23
Stieglitz, Al
❑ 60Top-144
❑ 60TopVen-144
Stigman, Dick
❑ 59Top-142
❑ 59TopVen-142
❑ 60Lea-85
❑ 60Top-507
❑ 61Top-77
❑ 61TwiCloD-26
❑ 62Top-37
❑ 62Top-532
❑ 62TopVen-37
❑ 63Top-89
❑ 63TwiJayP-11
❑ 64Top-6
❑ 64Top-245
❑ 64TopVen-6
❑ 64TopVen-245
❑ 64TwiJayP-11
❑ 65Top-548
❑ 66Top-512
❑ 78TCM60I-162
❑ 78TwiFri-45
Stigman, Lee
❑ 81VanCanT-20
Stiles, Will
❑ 84LitFalMT-1
❑ 86ColMetP-24
❑ 87LynMetP-16
❑ 88St.LucMS-21
Stillman, Royle
❑ 76BalOriP-37
❑ 76OPC-594
❑ 76SSP-393
❑ 76Top-594
❑ 77WhiSoxT-24
❑ 78Top-272
❑ 79OgdA'sT-14
❑ 79SpoIndT-2
❑ 80OgdA'sT-18
❑ 91OriCro-440
Stillwell, Kurt
❑ 84CedRapRT-17
❑ 86FleUpd-108
❑ 86RedTexG-11
❑ 86TopTra-104T
❑ 86TopTraT-104T
❑ 87ClaUpdY-142
❑ 87Don-123
❑ 87Fle-215
❑ 87FleGlo-215
❑ 87RedKah-11
❑ 87Top-623
❑ 87TopRoo-17
❑ 87TopTif-623
❑ 87ToyRoo-26
❑ 88Don-265
❑ 88DonBasB-207
❑ 88Fle-248
❑ 88FleGlo-248
❑ 88FleUpd-35
❑ 88FleUpdG-35
❑ 88PanSti-276
❑ 88RoySmo-23
❑ 88RoyTeal-31
❑ 88Sco-221
❑ 88ScoGlo-221
❑ 88ScoRoo-4T
❑ 88ScoRooG-4T
❑ 88StaLinRe-18
❑ 88StaLinRo-16
❑ 88Top-339
❑ 88TopBig-136
❑ 88TopTif-339
❑ 88TopTra-115T
❑ 88TopTraT-115T
❑ 89Bow-120
❑ 89BowTif-120
❑ 89CedRapRAB-6
❑ 89ClaLigB-14
❑ 89Don-322
❑ 89DonAll-29
❑ 89DonBasB-63
❑ 89Fle-293
❑ 89FleGlo-293
❑ 89OPC-217
❑ 89RoyTasD-8
❑ 89Sco-162
❑ 89ScoYouS2-42
❑ 89Top-596
❑ 89TopBig-161
❑ 89TopSti-266
❑ 89TopTif-596
❑ 89UppDec-616
❑ 90Bow-376
❑ 90BowTif-376
❑ 90CedRapRDGB-6
❑ 90ClaYel-T29
❑ 90Don-120
❑ 90DonBesA-106
❑ 90Fle-118
❑ 90FleCan-118
❑ 90Lea-256
❑ 90MLBBasB-106
❑ 90OPC-222
❑ 90PanSti-79
❑ 90PubIntS-356
❑ 90RoyPos-24
❑ 90Sco-96
❑ 90Top-222
❑ 90TopBig-293
❑ 90TopSti-269
❑ 90TopTif-222
❑ 90UppDec-361
❑ 91Bow-307
❑ 91Don-24
❑ 91Don-520
❑ 91DonSupD-24
❑ 91Fle-571
❑ 91Lea-2
❑ 91OPC-478
❑ 91PanFreS-279
❑ 91RedFolS-91
❑ 91RoyPol-21
❑ 91Sco-295
❑ 91StaClu-189
❑ 91Stu-70
❑ 91Top-478
❑ 91TopDesS-478
❑ 91TopMic-478
❑ 91TopTif-478
❑ 91Ult-157
❑ 91UppDec-587
❑ 92Bow-135
❑ 92Don-440
❑ 92Fle-170
❑ 92Lea-142
❑ 92LeaBlaG-142
❑ 92OPC-128
❑ 92OPCPre-177
❑ 92PadCarJ-21
❑ 92PadMot-5
❑ 92PadPolD-23
❑ 92PadSmo-34
❑ 92PanSti-97
❑ 92Pin-418
❑ 92Sco-236
❑ 92ScoRoo-19T
❑ 92StaClu-650
❑ 92StaCluNC-650
❑ 92Stu-109
❑ 92Top-128
❑ 92TopGol-128
❑ 92TopGolW-128
❑ 92TopMic-128
❑ 92TopTra-112T
❑ 92TopTraG-112T
❑ 92Ult-584
❑ 92UppDec-329
❑ 92UppDec-705
❑ 93Bow-434
❑ 93Don-258
❑ 93Fle-148
❑ 93Lea-138
❑ 93PacSpa-265
❑ 93PanSti-259
❑ 93Pin-154
❑ 93Sco-379
❑ 93Sel-193
❑ 93StaClu-568
❑ 93StaCluFDI-568
❑ 93StaCluMOP-568
❑ 93Top-84
❑ 93TopGol-84
❑ 93TopInaM-84
❑ 93TopInaR-84
❑ 93TopMic-84
❑ 93TriPla-69
❑ 93Ult-124
❑ 93UppDec-152
❑ 93UppDecGold-152
❑ 94IndIndF-1819
❑ 94Pac-90
❑ 94Top-198
❑ 94TopGol-198
❑ 94TopSpa-198
❑ 95IndIndF-104
❑ 96RanDr P-29
❑ 96RanMot-22
❑ 97Pac-210
❑ 97PacLigB-210
❑ 97PacSil-210
Stillwell, Rod
❑ 90AppFoxBS-26
❑ 90AppFoxP-2104
Stillwell, Ron
❑ 61SyrChi-1
❑ 77FriOneYW-114
Stillwell, Steve
❑ 76SeaRaiC-18
Stimac, Craig
❑ 79HawIsIC-14
❑ 79HawIsIT-4
❑ 80HawIsIT-6
❑ 81PadFamF-19
❑ 81Top-356
❑ 82ChaChaT-13
Stine, Lee
❑ 33WorCig(-88
❑ 33Zee-41
❑ 35DiaMatCS3T1-136
❑ 36NatChiFPR-106
Stingley, Derek
❑ 93MarPhiC-27
❑ 93MarPhiF-3490
❑ 94SpaPhiF-1736
❑ 94SparPhiC-19
❑ 95PiePhiF-199
Stingrays, Maui
❑ 96MauStiHWB-NNO
Stinnett, Kelly
❑ 90WatIndS-20
❑ 91CollndC-21
❑ 91CollndP-1488
❑ 92CanIndF-694
❑ 92CanIndS-119
❑ 92SkyAA F-56
❑ 93ChaKniF-547
❑ 94Bow-653
❑ 94Fin-369
❑ 94FinRef-369
❑ 94FleExtB-326
❑ 94FleUpd-162
❑ 94MetCoIP-25
❑ 94Pin-538
❑ 94PinArtP-538
❑ 94PinMusC-538
❑ 94ScoRoo-RT151
❑ 94ScoRooGR-RT151
❑ 94Sel-195
❑ 94SpoRoo-110
❑ 94SpoRooAP-110
❑ 94StaClu-599
❑ 94StaCluFDI-599
❑ 94StaCluGR-599
❑ 94StaCluMOP-599
❑ 94Ult-536
❑ 94VenLinU-269
❑ 95ColCho-326
❑ 95ColChoGS-326
❑ 95ColChoSS-326
❑ 95Don-171
❑ 95DonPreP-171
❑ 95Fle-383
❑ 95MetCoIP-29
❑ 95Sco-137
❑ 95ScoGolR-137
❑ 95ScoPlaTS-137
❑ 95Top-71
❑ 95Ult-200
❑ 95UltGolM-200
❑ 96Fle-488
❑ 96FleTif-488
❑ 96LeaSigEA-194
❑ 96MetKah-30
❑ 97TucTorB-14
❑ 98DiaBacP-14
❑ 98DiaMcD-21
❑ 98PacOnl-48
❑ 98PacOnlR-48
❑ 98PacOnlWC-48
❑ 99Fle-524
❑ 99FleSta9-524
❑ 99FleWarT-524
❑ 99Pac-24
❑ 99PacPlaB-24
❑ 99PacRed-24
❑ 99StaClu-299
❑ 99StaCluFDI-299
❑ 99StaCluOoaK-299
❑ 99StaCluPP-299
Stinson, Bob (Gorrell R.)
❑ 70OPC-131
❑ 70Top-131
❑ 71MLBOffS-285
❑ 71OPC-594
❑ 71Top-594
❑ 72AstTeal-25
❑ 72Top-679
❑ 74OPC-653
❑ 74Top-653
❑ 75OPC-471
❑ 75RoyPos-30

❑ 75Top-471
❑ 75TopMin-471
❑ 76KanCitRP-30
❑ 76OPC-466
❑ 76SSP-166
❑ 76Top-466
❑ 77MarPos-21
❑ 77Top-138
❑ 78Top-396
❑ 79Hos-79
❑ 79OPC-126
❑ 79Top-252
❑ 80OPC-305
❑ 80Top-583
❑ 85SpoIndGC-21
❑ 86MarGreT-8
❑ 87AstShoSTw-17
❑ 87AstShowSTh-29
❑ 90DodTar-772

Stinson, George
❑ 09ObaT21-357
❑ 11PacCoaBD-61
❑ 11Zee-122A
❑ 11Zee-122B
❑ 11Zee-122C
❑ 12ObaPreT-106
❑ 12Zee-155

Stipetich, Mark
❑ 75QuaCitAT-32

Stirnweiss, Snuffy (George)
❑ 39ExhSal-56
❑ 43YanSta-26
❑ 47Exh-219
❑ 47TipTop-59
❑ 47YanTeaT-25
❑ 48Bow-35
❑ 48YanTeal-26
❑ 49Bow-165
❑ 49Lea-95
❑ 49YanTeal-23
❑ 50Bow-249
❑ 50YanTeal-23
❑ 51Bow-21
❑ 52NatTeaL-36
❑ 52Top-217
❑ 70SpoCarfCOP-29
❑ 74CapPub-11
❑ 76TayBow4-46
❑ 83TCMPla1945-12
❑ 83TopRep5-217
❑ 92YanWIZA-80

Stitt, Jerry
❑ 84AriWilP-17
❑ 86AriWilP-15
❑ 87AriWilP-14
❑ 88AriWilP-13
❑ 90AriWilP-17
❑ 92AriWilP-18

Stitz, John
❑ 88WatIndP-669

Stitzel, Glenn
❑ 75IntLeaAT-19

Stitzel, Hal
❑ 33Zee-12
❑ 33Zee-43
❑ 33Zee-147

Stivers, Pat
❑ 88IdaFalBP-1849

Stivers, Vernon
❑ 25Zee-121

Stivetts, Jack
❑ 98CamPepP-73

Stobbs, Chuck
❑ 48RedSoxTI-23
❑ 49RedSoxTI-21
❑ 50RedSoxTI-23
❑ 52Top-62
❑ 53Bri-21
❑ 53Top-89
❑ 54Top-185
❑ 55DonWin-6
❑ 55Top-41
❑ 55TopDouH-43
❑ 56Top-68
❑ 56TopPin-60
❑ 57Top-101
❑ 58Top-239
❑ 59Top-26
❑ 59TopVen-26
❑ 60Top-432
❑ 61Pos-94A
❑ 61Top-431
❑ 61TopStal-185
❑ 61TwiCloD-27
❑ 61TwiPetM-4
❑ 62SalPlaC-90A
❑ 62SalPlaC-90B
❑ 62ShiPlaC-90
❑ 79DiaGre-62
❑ 79TCM50-101
❑ 80WatIndT-31
❑ 81ChaLooT-19
❑ 81RedSoxBG2S-52
❑ 82ChaLooT-24
❑ 83TopRep5-62
❑ 91TopArc1-89
❑ 94TopArc1-185
❑ 94TopArc1G-185

Stober, Mark
❑ 80KnoBluJT-6

Stock, Kevin
❑ 83BurRanF-22
❑ 83BurRanT-23
❑ 85ModA'sC-1
❑ 92BelMarCB-13
❑ 92BelMarF-1444

Stock, Milt
❑ 15SpoNewM-172
❑ 16SpoNewM-170
❑ 17ColE13-169
❑ 17HolBreD-101
❑ 20NatCarE-102A
❑ 20NatCarE-102B
❑ 21E121So1-103A
❑ 21E121So1-103B
❑ 21E121So8-95
❑ 21Exh-175
❑ 21Nei-56
❑ 22AmeCarE122-68
❑ 22E120-239
❑ 22W572-105
❑ 22W575-134
❑ 23W501-77
❑ 23WilChoV-159
❑ 25Exh-14
❑ 52Top-381
❑ 83TopRep5-381
❑ 90DodTar-773

Stock, Sterling
❑ 89St.CatBJP-2089

Stock, Wes
❑ 60Top-481
❑ 61BalOriP-19
❑ 61Top-26
❑ 62BalOriP-27
❑ 62Top-442
❑ 63BalOriP-32
❑ 63Top-438
❑ 64A's-15
❑ 64BalOriP-35
❑ 64Top-382
❑ 65AthJayP-11
❑ 65OPC-117
❑ 65Top-117
❑ 67CokCapAt-4
❑ 67OPC-74
❑ 67Top-74
❑ 70BreMcD-29
❑ 73OPC-179
❑ 73Top-179A
❑ 73Top-179B
❑ 77MarPos-22
❑ 77Top-597
❑ 78TCM60I-139
❑ 78TCM60I-154
❑ 81MarPos-30
❑ 85A'sMot-27
❑ 86A'sMot-27
❑ 91OriCro-441

Stockam, Doug
❑ 88DurBulS-19
❑ 89GreBraB-16
❑ 89GreBraP-1165
❑ 89GreBraS-23
❑ 90GreBraB-15
❑ 90GreBraP-1127
❑ 90GreBraS-18

Stocker, Bob
❑ 86MadMusP-20
❑ 86MadMusP-24
❑ 87MadMusP-18
❑ 88MadMusP-23
❑ 89HunStaB-8

Stocker, Bruce
❑ 80WisRapTT-24

Stocker, Kevin
❑ 91FroRowDP-10
❑ 91FroRowDPG-10
❑ 91FroRowDPS-10
❑ 92ClaFS7-76
❑ 92ClePhiC-19
❑ 92StaCluD-181
❑ 92UppDecML-110
❑ 93Bow-104
❑ 93Bow-356
❑ 93ClaFS7-259
❑ 93Lea-523
❑ 93PhiStaC-6
❑ 93ScrRedBF-2552
❑ 93ScrRedBTI-24
❑ 93SelRoo-84T
❑ 93SelRooAR-4
❑ 93SP-179
❑ 93StaClu-682
❑ 93StaCluFDI-682
❑ 93StaCluMOP-682
❑ 93UppDec-508
❑ 93UppDecGold-508
❑ 94Bow-252
❑ 94ColC-268
❑ 94ColChoGS-268
❑ 94ColChoSS-268
❑ 94Don-245
❑ 94Fin-2
❑ 94FinJum-2
❑ 94FinRef-2
❑ 94Fla-212
❑ 94Fle-601
❑ 94FleExtB-342
❑ 94FleExtBSYS-20
❑ 94FleRooS-20
❑ 94FUnPac-174
❑ 94Lea-417
❑ 94OPC-5
❑ 94OPCDiaD-4
❑ 94Pac-487
❑ 94PanSti-231
❑ 94PhiMed-32
❑ 94PhiMel-22
❑ 94PhiUSPC-5C
❑ 94PhiUSPC-9H
❑ 94Pin-460
❑ 94PinArtP-460
❑ 94PinMusC-460
❑ 94Sco-619
❑ 94ScoBoyoS-3
❑ 94ScoGolR-619
❑ 94Sel-52
❑ 94SP-139
❑ 94SPDieC-139
❑ 94StaClu-444
❑ 94StaCluFDI-444
❑ 94StaCluGR-444
❑ 94StaCluMOP-444
❑ 94StaCluT-240
❑ 94StaCluTFDI-240
❑ 94Stu-143
❑ 94Top-57
❑ 94TopGol-57
❑ 94TopSpa-57
❑ 94TriPla-180
❑ 94Ult-253
❑ 94UltSecYS-10
❑ 94UppDec-84
❑ 94UppDecED-84
❑ 94USPlaCR-1H
❑ 95ColCho-363
❑ 95ColChoGS-363
❑ 95ColChoSS-363
❑ 95Don-291
❑ 95DonPreP-291
❑ 95DonTopotO-311
❑ 95Fla-183
❑ 95Fle-405
❑ 95Lea-127
❑ 95Pac-338
❑ 95Phi-31
❑ 95PhiMel-22
❑ 95Pin-98
❑ 95PinArtP-98
❑ 95PinMusC-98
❑ 95Sco-405
❑ 95ScoGolR-405
❑ 95ScoPlaTS-405
❑ 95StaClu-346
❑ 95StaCluMOP-346
❑ 95StaCluSTWS-346
❑ 95Stu-173
❑ 95Top-533
❑ 95TopCyb-318
❑ 95Ult-422
❑ 95UltGolM-422
❑ 95UppDec-144
❑ 95UppDecED-144
❑ 95UppDecEDG-144
❑ 96ColCho-250
❑ 96ColChoGS-250
❑ 96ColChoSS-250
❑ 96Don-18
❑ 96DonPreP-18
❑ 96Fla-339
❑ 96Fle-509
❑ 96FleTif-509
❑ 96Lea-58
❑ 96LeaPrePB-58
❑ 96LeaPrePG-58
❑ 96LeaPrePS-58
❑ 96LeaSigA-215
❑ 96LeaSigAG-215
❑ 96LeaSigAS-215
❑ 96Pac-157
❑ 96PhiTeal-31
❑ 96Sco-414
❑ 96Top-44
❑ 96UppDec-173
❑ 97Cir-121
❑ 97CirRav-121
❑ 97ColCho-418
❑ 97Pac-388
❑ 97PacLigB-388
❑ 97PacSil-388
❑ 97PhiCopQ-28
❑ 97PhiTeal-19
❑ 97Top-384
❑ 97UppDec-456
❑ 98CirThu-97
❑ 98CirThuRav-97
❑ 98CirThuSupRav-97
❑ 98ColCho-513
❑ 98DevRayP-20
❑ 98Fle-193
❑ 98Fle-527
❑ 98Pac-388
❑ 98PacAur-84
❑ 98PacOme-235
❑ 98PacOmeR-235
❑ 98PacOnl-721
❑ 98PacOnlR-721
❑ 98PacOnlWC-721
❑ 98PacPar-101
❑ 98PacParC-101
❑ 98PacParG-101
❑ 98PacParHS-101
❑ 98PacParPB-101
❑ 98PacParR-101
❑ 98PacPlaB-388
❑ 98PacRedT-388
❑ 98PacSil-388
❑ 98PinSna-TBDR1
❑ 98ScoRT-186
❑ 98SP Aut-187
❑ 98StaCluFDI-326
❑ 98StaClul-326
❑ 98StaCluOneK-326
❑ 98StaCluPP-326
❑ 98Top-156
❑ 98TopChr-156
❑ 98TopChrR-156
❑ 98TopDevR-156
❑ 98TopDia-156
❑ 98TopMiniC-156
❑ 98Ult-470
❑ 98UltGolM-470
❑ 98UltMas-470
❑ 98UltPlaM-470
❑ 98UppDec-726
❑ 99Fle-542
❑ 99FleSta9-542
❑ 99FleWarT-542
❑ 99PacOme-232
❑ 99PacOmeC-232
❑ 99PacOmeG-232
❑ 99PacOmePB-232
❑ 99PacPar-230
❑ 99PacParC-230
❑ 99PacParG-230
❑ 99PacParHoloGold-230
❑ 99PacParHS-230
❑ 99PacParOD-230
❑ 99PacParPB-230
❑ 99PacParRed-230
❑ 99StaClu-248
❑ 99StaCluFDI-248
❑ 99StaCluOoaK-248
❑ 99StaCluPP-248
❑ 99UppDec-215
❑ 99UppDecEL1-215
❑ 99UppDecEL2-215
❑ 99Vic-390

Stocksdale, Otis
❑ 95May-40

Stockstill, Dave
❑ 79WauTimT-5
❑ 81TulDriT-5
❑ 82TulDriT-15
❑ 83OklCit8T-17
❑ 84OklCit8T-8
❑ 85OklCit8T-23

Stockstill, Jason
❑ 96BoiHawB-27
❑ 97CedRapK-25
❑ 97MidLeaTP-6
❑ 98LakElsSG-26

Stockstill, John
❑ 80QuaCitCT-28

Stockwell, Len
❑ 87OldJudN-473
❑ 88SFHesCreN32-33A
❑ 88SFHesCreN32-33B

Stoddard, Bob
❑ 80SpoIndT-1
❑ 81SpoIndT-18
❑ 82SalLakCGT-18
❑ 83Top-195
❑ 84Don-619
❑ 84Fle-620
❑ 84MarMot-22
❑ 84Nes792-439
❑ 84Top-439
❑ 84TopTif-439
❑ 85CalCanC-90
❑ 85Fle-502
❑ 85NasSouTI-23
❑ 86LasVegSP-20
❑ 87Fle-431
❑ 87FleGlo-431
❑ 87OmaRoyP-12
❑ 88TacTigC-10
❑ 88TacTigP-628
❑ 89DenZepC-11
❑ 89DenZepP-31

Stoddard, Jim
❑ 55DesMoiHB-18

Stoddard, Tim
❑ 78BalOriP-33
❑ 78RocRedWT-17
❑ 80BalOriP-19
❑ 80Top-314
❑ 81Don-475
❑ 81Fle-176
❑ 81OPC-91
❑ 81Top-91
❑ 82Don-131
❑ 82Fle-181
❑ 82Top-457
❑ 83Don-581
❑ 83Fle-75
❑ 83OPC-217
❑ 83OriPos-30
❑ 83Top-217
❑ 84CubChiT-28
❑ 84CubSev-49
❑ 84Don-245
❑ 84Fle-23
❑ 84FleUpd-110
❑ 84Nes792-106
❑ 84Top-106
❑ 84TopTif-106
❑ 84TopTra-112T
❑ 84TopTraT-112T
❑ 85Don-144
❑ 85Fle-68
❑ 85FleUpd-111
❑ 85OPC-393
❑ 85PadMot-19
❑ 85Top-693
❑ 85TopTif-693
❑ 85TopTifT-113T
❑ 85TopTra-113T
❑ 86Don-406
❑ 86Fle-335
❑ 86Top-558
❑ 86TopTif-558
❑ 87Don-497
❑ 87Fle-116
❑ 87FleGlo-116
❑ 87OPC-321
❑ 87Top-788
❑ 87TopTif-788
❑ 88Don-497
❑ 88DonReaBY-497
❑ 88Fle-222
❑ 88FleGlo-222
❑ 88Sco-258
❑ 88ScoGlo-258
❑ 88StaLinY-16
❑ 88Top-359
❑ 88TopTif-359
❑ 89PacSenL-182
❑ 89T/MSenL-102
❑ 89TopSenL-37
❑ 90EliSenL-30
❑ 91OriCro-442
❑ 92YanWIZ8-188

Stoeckel, Jim
❑ 87SanAntDTI-3

Stoecklin, Tony
❑ 92IdaFalGF-3513
❑ 92IdaFalGSP-18
❑ 93IdaFalBF-4030
❑ 93IdaFalBSP-11
❑ 94DurBulC-21
❑ 94DurBulF-329
❑ 94DurBulTI-23

Stoerck, Scott
❑ 87BelMarL-21
❑ 87BelMarTI-26
❑ 88WauTimGS-23
❑ 89WauTimGS-14

Stofflet, Ty
❑ 78ReaRem-19

Stohr, Bill
❑ 90PriPatD-23

Stojsavljevic, Paul
❑ 92GenCubC-5
❑ 92GenCubF-1564

Stoker, J.W.
❑ 41WheM5-16

Stoker, Mike
❑ 87AshTouP-14
❑ 88DurBulS-20
❑ 89DurBullS-20
❑ 89DurBulIS-20
❑ 89DurBulTI-20

Stokes, Al
❑ 27Zee-123

Stokes, Gus
❑ 81CliGiaT-15
❑ 82CliGiaF-27
❑ 83CliGiaF-1

Stokes, Randall
❑ 90BriTigS-23
❑ 91FayGenC-28
❑ 91FayGenP-1169

Stokke, Doug
❑ 80ColAstT-9
❑ 80TucTorT-24

Stoll, Pete
❑ 83SprCarF-1
❑ 84ArkTraT-23
❑ 85SprCarT-23

Stoll, Rich
❑ 85IndIndTI-4
❑ 86IndIndTI-4

Stolp, Justin
❑ 98BluOriQ-7

Stoltenberg, Scott
❑ 79WisRapTT-12

Stone, Bill
❑ 76AshTouT-6
❑ 77VisOakT-17

Stone, Brian
❑ 87BelBreP-9
❑ 88StoPorCLC-178
❑ 88StoPorP-739
❑ 90ArkTraGS-27
❑ 91ArkTraLD-46
❑ 91LinDriAA-46

Stone, Craig
❑ 93AusFut-82
❑ 94MedHatBJF-3690
❑ 94MedHatBJSP-3
❑ 95AusFut-24
❑ 95AusFutGP-1
❑ 95HagSunF-76
❑ 96DunBluJUTI-14
❑ 96HagSunB-21
❑ 97DunBluJTI-27
❑ 98DunBluJSB-11
❑ 98DunBluJTI-29

Stone, Dave
❑ 88WatPirP-25

Stone, Dean
❑ 54Top-114
❑ 55DonWin-7
❑ 55Top-60
❑ 55TopDouH-17
❑ 56Top-87
❑ 57Top-381
❑ 59Top-286
❑ 62Top-574
❑ 63BalOriP-33
❑ 63Top-271
❑ 79TCM50-65
❑ 81RedSoxBG2S-53

❑ 91OriCro-443
❑ 94TopArc1-114
❑ 94TopArc1G-114
Stone, Eric
❑ 89LakTigS-21
❑ 90Bow-348
❑ 90BowTif-348
❑ 90CMC-388
❑ 90ProAAAF-380
❑ 90TolMudHC-11
❑ 90TolMudHP-150
❑ 91LinDriAA-397
❑ 91LonTigLD-397
❑ 91LonTigP-1878
❑ 92KinIndC-19
❑ 92KinIndF-2476
❑ 93CanIndF-2840
Stone, Fred
❑ 04FanCraAL-44
Stone, Gary L.
❑ 66St.PetCTI-16
Stone, George
❑ 86AppFoxP-25
Stone, George H.
❑ 68BraPos-29
❑ 69AtlBraBPPS-21
❑ 69Top-627
❑ 70OPC-122
❑ 70Top-122
❑ 71MLBOffS-22
❑ 71OPC-507
❑ 71Top-507
❑ 72MilBra-330
❑ 72Top-601
❑ 73LinPor-124
❑ 73OPC-647
❑ 73Top-647
❑ 74MetDaiPA-3
❑ 74OPC-397
❑ 74Top-397
❑ 75MetSSP-13
❑ 75OPC-239
❑ 75Top-239
❑ 75TopMin-239
❑ 76OPC-567
❑ 76SSP-557
❑ 76Top-567
❑ 91MetWIZ-381
Stone, George R.
❑ 08RosComP-73
❑ 09AmeCarE90-1-99
❑ 09AmeCarE90-1-100
❑ 09ColChiE-274
❑ 09PC7HHB-42
❑ 09T206-341
❑ 10NadCarE-50A
❑ 10NadCarE-50B
❑ 10SweCapPP-55
❑ 11PinT-5-104
❑ 11S74Sil-36
❑ 11SpoLifCW-336
❑ 11SpoLifM-118
❑ 11T205-163
❑ 11TurRedT-119
❑ 12ColRedB-274
❑ 12ColTinT-274
❑ 12HasTriFT-66
❑ 12HomRunKE-45
❑ 12Zee-74
❑ 72ClaCar-52
Stone, H. Ron
❑ 66Top-568
❑ 68Top-409
❑ 69Top-576
❑ 70OPC-218
❑ 70Top-218
❑ 71MLBOffS-189
❑ 71OPC-366
❑ 71Top-366
❑ 72Top-528
Stone, Jeff
❑ 83ReaPhiT-20
❑ 84FleUpd-111
❑ 84PhiTas-43
❑ 84PorBeaC-197
❑ 85Don-624
❑ 85Fle-266
❑ 85FleStaS-119
❑ 85PhiCIG-8
❑ 85PhiTas-12
❑ 85PhiTas-39
❑ 85Top-476
❑ 85TopSti-116
❑ 85TopTif-476
❑ 86Don-259
❑ 86Fle-454
❑ 86KayB-30
❑ 86PhiTas-14
❑ 86PorBeaP-21
❑ 86Top-686
❑ 86TopTif-686
❑ 87Don-309
❑ 87Fle-189
❑ 87FleGlo-189
❑ 87MaiGuiP-11
❑ 87MaiGuiT-19
❑ 87PhiTas-14
❑ 87Top-532
❑ 87TopTif-532
❑ 88Don-482
❑ 88Fle-317
❑ 88FleGlo-317
❑ 88OPC-154
❑ 88RocRedWGCP-26
❑ 88Top-154
❑ 88TopBig-146
❑ 88TopTif-154
❑ 89OklCit8P-1510
❑ 89RanMot-26
❑ 89UppDec-486
❑ 90CMC-273
❑ 90PawRedSC-22
❑ 90PawRedSDD-24
❑ 90PawRedSP-475
❑ 90ProAAAF-447
❑ 90TopTVRS-61
❑ 91LinDriAAA-369
❑ 91OriCro-444
❑ 91PawRedSDD-22
❑ 91PawRedSLD-369
❑ 91PawRedSP-52
❑ 92NasSouF-1846
❑ 92NasSouS-294
❑ 93RanKee-348
Stone, Jerry
❑ 76HawIslC-8
Stone, John (John Thomas)
❑ 33ExhFou-12
❑ 34Gou-40
❑ 34GouCanV-89
❑ 35DiaMatCS3T1-137
❑ 35GouPuzR-8H
❑ 35GouPuzR-9H
❑ 36GouWidPPR-A95
❑ 37ExhFou-16
❑ 38ExhFou-16
❑ 81TigDetN-41
❑ 91ConTSN-289
Stone, Marcenia
❑ 94TedWil-112
Stone, Matthew
❑ 95MarPhiTI-26
Stone, Michael
❑ 77St.PetCT-9
❑ 78CliDodT-28
❑ 78LodDodT-21
Stone, Ricky
❑ 94GreFalDSP-28
❑ 94StaCluDP-43
❑ 94StaCluDPFDI-43
❑ 95YakBeaTI-31
❑ 97SanAntMB-10
❑ 98SanAntMG-27
❑ 98SanAntMM-10
Stone, Rocky
❑ 75IntLeaASB-34
❑ 75PacCoaLAB-34
❑ 75TacTwiK-12
Stone, Shawn
❑ 84PriWilPT-21
Stone, Steve
❑ 82AmaGolST-17
❑ 90SweBasG-27
Stone, Steve (Steven M.)
❑ 72OPC-327
❑ 72Top-327
❑ 72TopCloT-30
❑ 72WhiSox-11
❑ 73LinPor-45
❑ 73OPC-167
❑ 73Top-167
❑ 74OPC-486
❑ 74Top-486
❑ 74TopTra-486T
❑ 75OPC-388
❑ 75Top-388
❑ 75TopMin-388
❑ 76OPC-378
❑ 76SSP-302
❑ 76Top-378
❑ 77Top-17
❑ 77WhiSoxJT-14
❑ 77WhiSoxT-25
❑ 78OPC-46
❑ 78Top-153
❑ 79BalOriP-16
❑ 79OPC-115
❑ 79Top-227
❑ 80BalOriP-20
❑ 80Top-688
❑ 81BalOriP-22
❑ 81Don-476
❑ 81Don-591
❑ 81Fle-170
❑ 81FleStiC-104
❑ 81Kel-58
❑ 81OPC-101
❑ 81Top-5
❑ 81Top-520
❑ 81TopScr-49
❑ 81TopSti-1
❑ 81TopSti-40
❑ 81TopSti-249
❑ 82Don-357
❑ 82Fle-182
❑ 82FleSta-144
❑ 82Top-419
❑ 90PacLeg-63
❑ 91OriCro-445
❑ 97PhoFirDTTI-25
Stone, Toni
❑ 76LauIndC-27
❑ 97NegLeaPC-12C
Stonecipher, Eric
❑ 91EveGiaC-23
❑ 91EveGiaP-3911
❑ 92CliGiaC-11
❑ 93SanJosGC-23
❑ 93SanJosGF-7
Stoneham, Horace
❑ 84WilMay-12
Stoneham, John
❑ 33Zee-44
Stoneman, Bill
❑ 68OPC-179
❑ 68Top-179
❑ 68TopVen-179
❑ 69ExpPin-8
❑ 69OPC-67
❑ 69Top-67
❑ 70ExpPos-4
❑ 70MLBOffS-71
❑ 70OPC-398
❑ 70Top-398
❑ 71ExpPS-24
❑ 71MLBOffS-142
❑ 71OPC-266
❑ 71Top-266
❑ 72Dia-43
❑ 72MilBra-331
❑ 72OPC-95
❑ 72ProStaP-12
❑ 72SevTraC-53
❑ 72Top-95
❑ 72Top-610
❑ 73Kel2D-23
❑ 73OPC-254
❑ 73Top-254
❑ 74ExpWes-10
❑ 74OPC-352
❑ 74Top-352
❑ 92Nab-29
❑ 93ExpDonM-29
Stoner, Lil
❑ 92ConTSN-605
Stoner, Mike
❑ 96AriBlaDB-31
❑ 97Bes-51
❑ 97BesAutSBPP-26
❑ 97BesLum-6
❑ 97CalLeaATI-23
❑ 97CalLeaTP-6
❑ 97HigDesMG-27
❑ 97HigDesMUG-5
❑ 97HigDesMUG-8
❑ 97HigDesMUG-11
❑ 98Bow-114
❑ 98BowCerBlueAU-31
❑ 98BowCerGA-31
❑ 98BowCerSA-31
❑ 98BowChr-114
❑ 98BowChrGA-114
❑ 98BowChrGAR-114
❑ 98BowChrI-114
❑ 98BowChrIR-114
❑ 98BowChrR-114
❑ 98BowGolA-114
❑ 98BowInt-114
❑ 98BowScoC-SC21
❑ 98SP MinDTSPE-DS27
❑ 98SP MinPE-16
❑ 98SP MinSTHPE-H14
❑ 98SPMin-16
❑ 98SPMinDTS-DS27
❑ 98SPMinSTH-H14
❑ 98StaCluFDI-367
❑ 98StaCluI-367
❑ 98StaCluOneK-367
❑ 98StaCluPP-367
❑ 98Top-252
❑ 98TopChr-252
❑ 98TopChrR-252
❑ 98TopDevR-252
❑ 98TopDia-252
❑ 98TopMiniC-252
❑ 98TusSidM-29
❑ 99SP TopP-114
❑ 99SP TopPDtS-D30
❑ 99SP TopPGF-GF30
❑ 99SP TopPPE-114
❑ 99Top-206
❑ 99TopChr-206
❑ 99TopChrR-206
Stonikas, Bill
❑ 88AppFoxP-147
❑ 89BasCitRS-24
Stoops, Jim
❑ 95BelGiaTI-27
❑ 96BurBeeTI-10
❑ 97SanJosG-14
❑ 98SanJosGQ-13
Stoops, Mike
❑ 98PitMetM-4
Stoppello, Jason
❑ 93JohCitCC-21
❑ 93JohCitCF-3678
Storey, Harvey
❑ 37Zee-90
❑ 49BowPCL-15
Storke, Alan
❑ 08AmeCarE91-92
❑ 72ClaCar-112
Storm, Bob
❑ 73TacTwiC-20
Storm, Lake Elsinore
❑ 95LakElsSTI-30
Storti, Joe
❑ 27Zee-80
Storti, Lin
❑ 27Zee-81
❑ 34DiaMatCSB-173
❑ 72TCMthe3-66
Story, Jonathan
❑ 91UtiBluSC-14
❑ 91UtiBluSP-3256
Story-Harden, Thomari
❑ 98YakBeaG-31
Stottlemyre, Jeff
❑ 80SanJosMJitB-18
❑ 81LynSaiT-27
❑ 81WauTimT-2
❑ 82LynSaiT-7
❑ 83ChaLooT-16
Stottlemyre, Mel Jr.
❑ 86OscAstP-25
❑ 87ColAstP-6
❑ 88MemChiB-1
❑ 89Bow-110
❑ 89Bow-261
❑ 89BowTif-110
❑ 89BowTif-261
❑ 90CMC-182
❑ 90Lea-310
❑ 90OmaRoyC-7
❑ 90OmaRoyP-66
❑ 90OPC-263
❑ 90ProAAAF-601
❑ 90Top-263
❑ 90TopTif-263
❑ 91Don-257
❑ 91OPC-58
❑ 91Sco-361
❑ 91Sco100RS-23
❑ 91Top-58
❑ 91TopDeb90-150
❑ 91TopDesS-58
❑ 91TopMic-58
❑ 91TopTif-58
Stottlemyre, Mel Sr.
❑ 63ReqKP-16
❑ 65ChaTheY-22
❑ 65OPC-133
❑ 65Top-133
❑ 65Top-550
❑ 66Baz-5
❑ 66Top-224
❑ 66Top-350
❑ 66TopRubI-88
❑ 66TopVen-224
❑ 66TopVen-350
❑ 66YanTeal-11
❑ 67Baz-5
❑ 67CokCapYM-V1
❑ 67DexPre-200
❑ 67Top-225
❑ 67TopVen-242
❑ 68OPC-120
❑ 68Top-120
❑ 68Top3-D-11
❑ 68TopActS-1C
❑ 68TopActS-16C
❑ 68TopVen-120
❑ 69CitMetC-5
❑ 69MilBra-265
❑ 69MLBOffS-79
❑ 69MLBPin-27
❑ 69NabTeaF-24
❑ 69OPC-9
❑ 69OPCDec-21
❑ 69Top-470A
❑ 69Top-470B
❑ 69TopDec-13
❑ 69TopDecl-42
❑ 69TopSta-208
❑ 69TopSup-25
❑ 69TopTeaP-19
❑ 69TraSta-28
❑ 69YanMal-8
❑ 69YanPhoS-50
❑ 70DayDaiNM-39
❑ 70Kel-5
❑ 70MilBra-27
❑ 70MLBOffS-250
❑ 70OPC-70
❑ 70OPC-100
❑ 70Top-70
❑ 70Top-100
❑ 70TopCanL-20
❑ 70TopScr-22
❑ 70TopSup-27
❑ 70TraSta-13C
❑ 70YanCliDP-12
❑ 70YanPhoS-30
❑ 71Kel-40
❑ 71MilDud-30
❑ 71MLBOffS-500
❑ 71OPC-615
❑ 71Top-615
❑ 71TopCoi-94
❑ 71TopSup-10
❑ 71TopTat-98
❑ 71YanArcO-11
❑ 71YanCliDP-15
❑ 72Kel-50
❑ 72MilBra-332
❑ 72OPC-325
❑ 72OPC-492
❑ 72SevTraC-54
❑ 72Top-325
❑ 72Top-492
❑ 72YanSch-5
❑ 73LinPor-136
❑ 73NewYorSNM-4
❑ 73OPC-520
❑ 73SyrChiTI-26
❑ 73Top-520
❑ 74OPC-44
❑ 74SyrChiTI-26
❑ 74Top-44
❑ 74TopSta-218
❑ 75OPC-183
❑ 75SyrChiTI-20
❑ 75Top-183
❑ 75TopMin-183
❑ 81TCM60I-450
❑ 83YanASFY-46
❑ 85MetTCM-4
❑ 86MetTCM-27
❑ 87MetColP-48
❑ 88MetColP-49
❑ 88MetKah-30
❑ 88PacLegI-22A
❑ 88PacLegI-22B
❑ 89Bow-261
❑ 89BowTif-261
❑ 89MetColP-54
❑ 89MetKah-26
❑ 90BasWit-15A
❑ 90BasWit-15B
❑ 90MetColP-49
❑ 90MetKah-30
❑ 90TopTVM-6
❑ 91MetColP-48
❑ 91MetKah-30
❑ 91MetPerPA-6
❑ 92MetColP-29
❑ 92MetKah-30
❑ 92YanWIZ6-121
❑ 92YanWIZA-81
❑ 94AstMot-27
❑ 95AstMot-28
Stottlemyre, Todd
❑ 86VenGulP-25
❑ 87IntLeaAT-25
❑ 87SyrChiP-1938
❑ 87SyrChiT-8
❑ 88BluJayFS-28
❑ 88Don-658
❑ 88DonRoo-37
❑ 88FleUpd-68
❑ 88FleUpdG-68
❑ 88ScoRoo-90T
❑ 88ScoRooG-90T
❑ 88TopTra-116T
❑ 88TopTraT-116T
❑ 89BluJayFS-27
❑ 89Bow-242
❑ 89BowTif-242
❑ 89Don-620
❑ 89Fle-245
❑ 89FleGlo-245
❑ 89OPC-237
❑ 89PanSti-460
❑ 89Sco-453
❑ 89ScoHot1R-81
❑ 89ScoYouS2-20
❑ 89Top-722
❑ 89TopBig-298
❑ 89TopTif-722
❑ 89UppDec-362
❑ 90BluJayFS-27
❑ 90Don-669
❑ 90Fle-94
❑ 90FleCan-94
❑ 90Lea-475
❑ 90OPC-591
❑ 90PanSti-172
❑ 90PublntS-527
❑ 90Sco-554
❑ 90Top-591
❑ 90TopBig-240
❑ 90TopTif-591
❑ 90UppDec-692
❑ 91BluJayFS-23
❑ 91BluJayFS-25
❑ 91BluJayS-6
❑ 91Bow-10
❑ 91Cla3-T89
❑ 91Don-155
❑ 91Fle-186
❑ 91Lea-227
❑ 91OPC-348
❑ 91PanFreS-349
❑ 91Sco-39
❑ 91StaClu-564
❑ 91Top-348
❑ 91TopDesS-348
❑ 91TopMic-348
❑ 91TopTif-348
❑ 91UppDec-257
❑ 92BluJayP-10
❑ 92Bow-18
❑ 92ClaGam-14
❑ 92Don-263
❑ 92Fle-342
❑ 92Lea-167
❑ 92LeaBlaG-167
❑ 92OPC-607
❑ 92Pin-240
❑ 92Sco-74
❑ 92ScoProP-20
❑ 92StaClu-307
❑ 92Top-607
❑ 92TopGol-607
❑ 92TopGolW-607
❑ 92TopMic-607
❑ 92TriPla-58
❑ 92Ult-153
❑ 92UppDec-371
❑ 93BluJayCP1-10
❑ 93BluJayD-5
❑ 93BluJayD4-21
❑ 93BluJayFS-28

❑ 93Bow-111
❑ 93Don-585
❑ 93Fle-340
❑ 93Lea-25
❑ 93OPC-244
❑ 93OPCWorC-14
❑ 93PacSpa-329
❑ 93Pin-311
❑ 93Sco-186
❑ 93StaClu-409
❑ 93StaCluFDI-409
❑ 93StaCluMOP-409
❑ 93Top-23
❑ 93TopGol-23
❑ 93TopInaM-23
❑ 93TopInaR-23
❑ 93TopMic-23
❑ 93Ult-293
❑ 93UppDec-413
❑ 93UppDecGold-413
❑ 94BluJayUSPC-4H
❑ 94BluJayUSPC-12C
❑ 94ColC-269
❑ 94ColChoGS-269
❑ 94ColChoSS-269
❑ 94Don-504
❑ 94Fin-113
❑ 94FinRef-113
❑ 94Fla-122
❑ 94Fle-344
❑ 94FleExtB-196
❑ 94Lea-28
❑ 94Pin-56
❑ 94PinArtP-56
❑ 94PinMusC-56
❑ 94Sco-149
❑ 94ScoGolR-149
❑ 94StaClu-563
❑ 94StaCluFDI-563
❑ 94StaCluGR-563
❑ 94StaCluMOP-563
❑ 94StaCluT-173
❑ 94StaCluTFDI-173
❑ 94Top-155
❑ 94TopGol-155
❑ 94TopSpa-155
❑ 94Ult-440
❑ 94UppDec-189
❑ 94UppDecED-189
❑ 95AthMot-14
❑ 95BluJayUSPC-2S
❑ 95BluJayUSPC-10H
❑ 95ColCho-152
❑ 95ColCho-535T
❑ 95ColChoGS-152
❑ 95ColChoSS-152
❑ 95Don-360
❑ 95DonPreP-360
❑ 95DonTopotO-142
❑ 95Fin-309
❑ 95FinRef-309
❑ 95Fla-298
❑ 95Fle-106
❑ 95FleUpd-73
❑ 95Sco-262
❑ 95ScoGolR-262
❑ 95ScoPlaTS-262
❑ 95SP-186
❑ 95SPSil-186
❑ 95StaClu-130
❑ 95StaCluFDI-130
❑ 95StaCluMOP-130
❑ 95StaCluSTWS-130
❑ 95StaCluVR-66
❑ 95StaCluVRMO-66
❑ 95Top-354
❑ 95TopTra-51T
❑ 95Ult-344
❑ 95UltGolM-344
❑ 95UppDec-278
❑ 95UppDecED-278
❑ 95UppDecEDG-278
❑ 95UppDecSE-244
❑ 95UppDecSEG-244
❑ 96CarPol-24
❑ 96Cir-182
❑ 96CirRav-182
❑ 96ColCho-688
❑ 96ColChoGS-688
❑ 96ColChoSS-688
❑ 96Don-226
❑ 96DonPreP-226
❑ 96EmoXL-272
❑ 96Fin-S239
❑ 96FinRef-S239
❑ 96Fla-368
❑ 96Fle-219
❑ 96FleSmo'H-10
❑ 96FleTif-219
❑ 96FleUpd-U194
❑ 96FleUpdTC-U194
❑ 96MetUni-230
❑ 96MetUniP-230
❑ 96MLBPin-33
❑ 96Pac-395
❑ 96PanSti-216
❑ 96Pin-357
❑ 96PinAfi-50
❑ 96PinAfiAP-50
❑ 96PinAfiFPP-50
❑ 96PinFoil-357
❑ 96ProSta-9
❑ 96Sco-69
❑ 96Sel-116
❑ 96SelArtP-116
❑ 96StaClu-404
❑ 96StaCluEPB-404
❑ 96StaCluEPG-404
❑ 96StaCluEPS-404
❑ 96StaCluMOP-404
❑ 96Sum-37
❑ 96SumAbo&B-37
❑ 96SumArtP-37
❑ 96SumFoi-37
❑ 96Top-114
❑ 96Ult-118
❑ 96Ult-553
❑ 96UltGolM-118
❑ 96UltGolM-553
❑ 96UppDec-505U
❑ 97CarPol-25
❑ 97Cir-84
❑ 97CirRav-84
❑ 97ColCho-198
❑ 97Don-340
❑ 97DonGolPP-340
❑ 97DonSilPP-340
❑ 97DonTea-160
❑ 97DonTeaSPE-160
❑ 97Fin-71
❑ 97FinRef-71
❑ 97FlaShoLC-97
❑ 97FlaShoLeg0-97
❑ 97FlaShoLeg1-97
❑ 97FlaShoM-A97
❑ 97FlaShoM-B97
❑ 97FlaShoM-C97
❑ 97FlaShoR0-97
❑ 97FlaShoR1-97
❑ 97FlaShoR2-97
❑ 97Fle-453
❑ 97FleTif-453
❑ 97Lea-284
❑ 97LeaFraM-284
❑ 97LeaFraMDC-284
❑ 97MetUni-235
❑ 97Pac-417
❑ 97PacLigB-417
❑ 97PacSil-417
❑ 97Pin-83
❑ 97PinArtP-PP83
❑ 97PinMusC-83
❑ 97PinPrePla-83
❑ 97Sco-406
❑ 97ScoArtPWB-406
❑ 97ScoResC-406
❑ 97ScoShoS-406
❑ 97ScoShoSAP-406
❑ 97StaClu-315
❑ 97StaCluMOP-315
❑ 97Top-437
❑ 97TopChr-155
❑ 97TopChrR-155
❑ 97Ult-277
❑ 97UltGolME-277
❑ 97UltPlaME-277
❑ 97UppDec-486
❑ 98CarScoP-2
❑ 98ColCho-471
❑ 98Fin-255
❑ 98FinNo--255
❑ 98FinNo-R-255
❑ 98FinRef-255
❑ 98Fle-432
❑ 98FleUpd-U58
❑ 98Pac-419
❑ 98PacOme-201
❑ 98PacOmeR-201
❑ 98PacOnl-628
❑ 98PacOnlR-628
❑ 98PacOnlWC-628
❑ 98PacPar-233
❑ 98PacParC-233
❑ 98PacParG-233
❑ 98PacParHS-233
❑ 98PacParPB-233
❑ 98PacParR-233
❑ 98PacPlaB-419
❑ 98PacRedT-419
❑ 98PacSil-419
❑ 98PinSna-SLC18
❑ 98Sco-25
❑ 98ScoCar-2
❑ 98ScoSS-PP135
❑ 98ScoSSAP-PP135
❑ 98SP Aut-164
❑ 98SpoIllWSF-149
❑ 98SpoIllWSFEE-149
❑ 98SpoIllWSFFE-149
❑ 98SPxFin-313
❑ 98SPxFinR-313
❑ 98SPxFinS-313
❑ 98StaCluFDI-74
❑ 98StaCluI-74
❑ 98StaCluOneK-74
❑ 98StaCluPP-74
❑ 98Top-139
❑ 98TopChr-139
❑ 98TopChrR-139
❑ 98TopDevR-139
❑ 98TopDia-139
❑ 98TopMiniC-139
❑ 98TopOpeD-70
❑ 98Ult-255
❑ 98UltGolM-255
❑ 98UltMas-255
❑ 98UltPlaM-255
❑ 98UppDec-488
❑ 99Fle-541
❑ 99FleBri-124
❑ 99FleBri2G-124
❑ 99FleBriBlu-124
❑ 99FleBriGol-124
❑ 99FleSta9-541
❑ 99FleWarT-541
❑ 99MetUni-14
❑ 99MetUniGM-14
❑ 99MetUniPMG-14
❑ 99Pac-432
❑ 99PacPar-17
❑ 99PacParC-17
❑ 99PacParG-17
❑ 99PacParHoloGold-17
❑ 99PacParHS-17
❑ 99PacParOD-17
❑ 99PacParPB-17
❑ 99PacParRed-17
❑ 99PacPlaB-432
❑ 99PacRed-432
❑ 99SkyPre-12
❑ 99SkyPreR-12
❑ 99SkyThu-34
❑ 99SkyThuRant-34
❑ 99SkyThuRave-34
❑ 99SP SigAuto-TST
❑ 99SpoIll-26
❑ 99SPSig-109
❑ 99StaClu-327
❑ 99StaCluFDI-327
❑ 99StaCluOoaK-327
❑ 99StaCluPP-327
❑ 99ThuSkySupR-34
❑ 99Top-356
❑ 99TopChr-356
❑ 99TopChrR-356
❑ 99TopMVPP-356
❑ 99TopSta-119
❑ 99TopStaFoil-119
❑ 99Ult-82
❑ 99UltGolM-82
❑ 99UltMas-82
❑ 99UltPlaM-82
❑ 99UppDec-300
❑ 99UppDecEL1-300
❑ 99UppDecEL2-300
❑ 99UppDecM-12
❑ 99UppDecMGS-12
❑ 99UppDecMHFS-12
❑ 99UppDecMSS-12
❑ 99Vic-24

Stotz, Carl
❑ 90BasWit-87

Stouffer, Blair
❑ 76SanAntBTI-22

Stoughton, Mark
❑ 92Ft.MyeMCB-28
❑ 93PitMetC-27

Stout, Allyn
❑ 31CarMet-26
❑ 33ButCanV-47
❑ 34DiaMatCSB-174

Stout, Jeff
❑ 89AugPirP-501

Stout, John
❑ 89TenTecGE-33

Stout, Tim
❑ 82CedRapRT-22

Stoval, Jerry
❑ 80CliGiaT-5

Stovall, DaRond
❑ 91JohCitCC-12
❑ 91JohCitCP-3991
❑ 92SavCarC-11
❑ 92SavCarF-676
❑ 93SprCarC-26
❑ 93SprCarF-1866
❑ 94FloStaLAF-FSL45
❑ 94St.PetCC-26
❑ 94St.PetCF-2600
❑ 96HarSenB-25
❑ 96Top-437
❑ 97Bow-390
❑ 97BowBes-160
❑ 97BowBesAR-160
❑ 97BowBesR-160
❑ 97BowInt-390
❑ 97HarSen-23
❑ 98Bow-367
❑ 98BowChr-367
❑ 98BowChrGA-367
❑ 98BowChrGAR-367
❑ 98BowChrI-367
❑ 98BowChrIR-367
❑ 98BowChrR-367
❑ 98BowGolA-367
❑ 98BowInt-367
❑ 98Fle-476
❑ 98LeaRS-298
❑ 98LeaRSLHolo-298
❑ 98LeaRSLong-298
❑ 98LeaRTrue-298
❑ 98PacOmeRS-6
❑ 98PacOmeRST4-6
❑ 98PacOnl-461
❑ 98PacOnlR-461
❑ 98PacOnlWC-461

Stovall, George T.
❑ 05IndSouPSoCP-16
❑ 09AmeCarE90-1-101
❑ 09ColChiE-275
❑ 09SpoNewSM-79
❑ 09T206-342
❑ 09T206-343
❑ 10CouT21-226
❑ 10DomDisP-112
❑ 10PeoT21-53
❑ 10SweCapPP-19A
❑ 10SweCapPP-19B
❑ 11HelSta-65
❑ 11MecDFT-43
❑ 11PinT-5-607
❑ 11SpoLifCW-337
❑ 11SpoLifM-50
❑ 11T205-164
❑ 12ColRedB-275
❑ 12ColTinT-275
❑ 12HasTriFT-21
❑ 12HasTriFT-75C
❑ 12T207-176
❑ 13NatGamW-38
❑ 14CraJacE-11
❑ 15AmeCarE106-37
❑ 15CraJacE-11
❑ 17Zee-118
❑ 94ConTSN-1259
❑ 94ConTSNB-1259

Stovall, Jesse
❑ 09ObaT21-75
❑ 09ObaT21-187
❑ 09ObaT21-367
❑ 11SpoLifCW-338
❑ 12ObaPreT-116

Stover, C.D.
❑ 96YakBeaTI-44
❑ 97GreFalDTI-23
❑ 98SanBerS-28
❑ 98SanBerSTIS-26

Stover, Mike
❑ 78QuaCitAT-25

Stovey, Harry
❑ 87OldJudN-474
❑ 88SpoTimM-24
❑ 90DodTar-774
❑ 90KalBatN-50
❑ 90KalBatN-51
❑ 90KalBatN-52

Stowe, Chris
❑ 97Bow-423
❑ 97BowChr-283
❑ 97BowChrI-283
❑ 97BowChrIR-283
❑ 97BowChrR-283
❑ 97BowInt-423
❑ 97TopSta-116
❑ 97TopStaAM-116

Stowe, Harold
❑ 62Top-291
❑ 92YanWIZ6-122

Stowell, Brad
❑ 91SouOreAP-3844
❑ 92MadMusC-18
❑ 92MadMusF-1236

Stowell, Steve
❑ 88KenTwiP-1384
❑ 89VisOakCLC-97
❑ 89VisOakP-1444
❑ 90Bes-304
❑ 90OrlSunRB-22
❑ 90OrlSunRP-1083
❑ 90OrlSunRS-20
❑ 91LinDriAA-494
❑ 91OrlSunRLD-494
❑ 91OrlSunRP-1848

Stowers, Chris
❑ 96VerExpB-26
❑ 97Bow-324
❑ 97BowInt-324
❑ 98arSenW1-22
❑ 98HarSenM-22

Strade, Sean
❑ 94MedHatBJF-3682
❑ 94MedHatBJSP-22

Strahler, Mike
❑ 71Dod-15
❑ 71MLBOffS-116
❑ 71OPC-188
❑ 71Top-188
❑ 72OPC-198
❑ 72Top-198
❑ 73OPC-279
❑ 73Top-279
❑ 74AlbDukTI-20
❑ 90DodTar-775

Strahs, Dick
❑ 75OakOak2A-32

Strain, Joe
❑ 78PhoGiaC-24
❑ 79PhoGiaVNB-9
❑ 79Top-726
❑ 80GiaPol-20
❑ 80GiaTeal-27
❑ 80OPC-280
❑ 80Top-538
❑ 81Don-73
❑ 81Fle-458
❑ 81Top-361
❑ 81TopTra-837
❑ 82IowCubT-9
❑ 82Top-436
❑ 83OklCit8T-21
❑ 85EveGialC-18
❑ 86EveGiaC-180
❑ 86EveGiaPC-30
❑ 87EveGiaC-12
❑ 89EveGiaS-30

Straker, Les
❑ 80CedRapRT-17
❑ 80VenLeaS-37
❑ 81WatRedT-8
❑ 83WatRedT-8
❑ 84AlbA'sT-19
❑ 85OrlTwiT-20
❑ 86TolMudHP-21
❑ 87DonRoo-21
❑ 87SpoRoo2-45
❑ 87TopTra-118T
❑ 87TopTraT-118T
❑ 87TwiPos-28
❑ 87TwiTeal-11
❑ 88Don-73
❑ 88Fle-24
❑ 88FleGlo-24
❑ 88Sco-108
❑ 88ScoGlo-108
❑ 88StaLinTw-19
❑ 88Top-264
❑ 88TopTif-264
❑ 89PorBeaC-10
❑ 89PorBeaP-219
❑ 89Sco-244
❑ 89Top-101
❑ 89TopBig-90
❑ 89TopTif-101
❑ 89UppDec-83
❑ 93LinVenB-107
❑ 94VenLinU-189
❑ 95LinVen-126
❑ 96-97LinVen-89

Strampe, Bob
❑ 73OPC-604
❑ 73Top-604
❑ 75HawIslC-17
❑ 76SpoIndC-9

Strand, Paul
❑ 09ObaT21-391
❑ 12ObaPreT-140
❑ 22Zee-91
❑ 23Zee-117
❑ 27Zee-82
❑ 80BraTCM1-17
❑ 94ConTSN-1300
❑ 94ConTSNB-1300

Strang, Sammy Nicklin
❑ 03BreE10-135
❑ 06GiaUllAFS-11
❑ 09T206-470
❑ 11SpoLifCW-339
❑ 89ChaLooLITI-21
❑ 90DodTar-776

Strange, Alan
❑ 33Zee-5
❑ 41BroW75-26
❑ 55SeaPop-19
❑ 56SeaPop-24
❑ 59SeaPop-36
❑ 79DiaGre-178

Strange, Don
❑ 89PulBraP-1895
❑ 90Bes-305
❑ 90ProAaA-94
❑ 90SouAtlLAS-43
❑ 90SumBraB-24
❑ 90SumBraP-2433
❑ 91DurBulP-1545
❑ 92GreBraF-1152
❑ 92GreBraS-244
❑ 92ProFS7-189
❑ 92SkyAA F-102
❑ 93GreBraF-348
❑ 93LinVenB-83
❑ 93RicBraP-10
❑ 93RicBraRC-24
❑ 94ExcFS7-160
❑ 95WicWraTI-22

Strange, Doug
❑ 86FloStaLAP-45
❑ 86LakTigP-24
❑ 87GleFalTP-10
❑ 88TolMudHC-14
❑ 88TolMudHP-587
❑ 89BlaYNPRWL-63
❑ 89TolMudHC-13
❑ 89TolMudHP-782
❑ 90CMC-618
❑ 90Don-535
❑ 90OPC-641
❑ 90ProAAAF-201
❑ 90Sco100RS-63
❑ 90Top-641
❑ 90TopDeb89-124
❑ 90TopTif-641
❑ 90TopTVCu-60
❑ 90TucTorC-16
❑ 90TucTorP-211
❑ 91IowCubLD-219
❑ 91IowCubP-1071
❑ 91LinDriAAA-219
❑ 92Bow-322
❑ 92CubMar-1
❑ 92IowCubS-222
❑ 92Lea-476
❑ 92LeaBlaG-476
❑ 93Don-136
❑ 93FleFinE-284
❑ 93Lea-542
❑ 93RanKee-434
❑ 93StaClu-132
❑ 93StaCluFDI-132
❑ 93StaCluMOP-132
❑ 94ColC-270
❑ 94ColChoGS-270
❑ 94ColChoSS-270
❑ 94Don-302
❑ 94Fin-353
❑ 94FinRef-353

❑ 94Fla-114
❑ 94Fle-322
❑ 94Lea-328
❑ 94Pac-630
❑ 94PanSti-133
❑ 94Pin-376
❑ 94PinArtP-376
❑ 94PinMusC-376
❑ 94RanMagM-37
❑ 94Sco-163
❑ 94ScoGolR-163
❑ 94Sel-260
❑ 94StaClu-97
❑ 94StaCluFDI-97
❑ 94StaCluGR-97
❑ 94StaCluMOP-97
❑ 94StaCluT-267
❑ 94StaCluTFDI-267
❑ 94Top-591
❑ 94TopGol-591
❑ 94TopSpa-591
❑ 94Ult-134
❑ 94UppDec-317
❑ 94UppDecED-317
❑ 95Don-402
❑ 95DonPreP-402
❑ 95Fle-297
❑ 95MarMot-17
❑ 95MarPac-44
❑ 95Ult-114
❑ 95UltGolM-114
❑ 96FleUpd-U85
❑ 96FleUpdTC-U85
❑ 96LeaSigEA-195
❑ 96MarMot-22
❑ 98PacAur-178
❑ 98PacOnl-596
❑ 98PacOnlR-596
❑ 98PacOnlWC-596
❑ 98Ult-307
❑ 98UltGolM-307
❑ 98UltMas-307
❑ 98UltPlaM-307

Strange, Keith

❑ 90UtiBluSP-9
❑ 91SouBenWSC-5
❑ 91SouBenWSP-2865
❑ 92SarWhiSCB-5
❑ 92SarWhiSF-210
❑ 93SarWhiSC-25

Strange, Kurt

❑ 89SanBerSCLC-69

Strange, Mike

❑ 95HagSunF-77
❑ 96DunBluJUTI-15
❑ 97DunBluJTI-28
❑ 98HagSunM-26

Strangfeld, Aaron

❑ 96DanBraB-24
❑ 97EugEmeB-26

Stranghoner, Todd

❑ 96BriWhiSB-5

Stranski, Scott

❑ 80SanJosMJitB-19
❑ 81SpoIndT-3
❑ 82LynSaiT-8
❑ 85BufBisT-24
❑ 86ChaOriW-29
❑ 86HagSunP-22
❑ 87MemChiB-10
❑ 87MemChiP-14
❑ 90HagSunDGB-31

Strasser, John

❑ 96HicCraB-23
❑ 96PriWilCB-25

Strathairn, David

❑ 88PacEigMO-14

Stratton, C. Scott

❑ 87OldJudN-475

Stratton, Drew

❑ 87ModA'sC-22
❑ 88ModA'sCLC-69
❑ 88ModA'sTI-29

Stratton, John

❑ 93UtiBluSC-23
❑ 93UtiBluSF-3537
❑ 94LynRedSC-24
❑ 94LynRedSF-1896

Stratton, Kelly

❑ 95HudValRTI-18

Stratton, Monty

❑ 33WorCig(-89
❑ 39WhiSoxTI-19
❑ 40WhiSoxL-19
❑ 72TCMthe1-171
❑ 77Spo-7708
❑ 79DiaGre-126
❑ 80PacLeg-103
❑ 85BigLeaC3-47
❑ 95ConTSN-1417

Stratton, Rob

❑ 96BesAutS1RP-FR3
❑ 97AppLeaTPB-16
❑ 97Bow-374
❑ 97BowInt-374
❑ 97Top-270
❑ 99Bow-414
❑ 99BowGol-414
❑ 99BowInt-414

Straus, Tim

❑ 94ColRedC-30
❑ 98ColRedSM-30

Strauss, Jon

❑ 94OneYanF-3795
❑ 94VenLinU-242

Strauss, Joseph

❑ 87BucN28-55
❑ 87OldJudN-476

Strauss, Julio

❑ 89WinSpiS-NNO
❑ 90WinSpiTI-23
❑ 91ChaKniLD-144
❑ 91ChaKniP-1689
❑ 91LinDriAA-144
❑ 92ChaKniS-167
❑ 92IowCubF-4052
❑ 93LinVenB-91
❑ 94VenLinU-33
❑ 95LinVen-124
❑ 96-97LinVen-86

Strawberry, Darryl

❑ 82JacMetT-21
❑ 82RegGloT-8
❑ 83TidTidT-28
❑ 83TopTra-108T
❑ 83TopTraBP-2
❑ 84AllGamPI-69
❑ 84Don-68
❑ 84Dra-29
❑ 84Fle-599
❑ 84FleSti-104
❑ 84FunFooP-8
❑ 84JacMetF-12
❑ 84MetFanC-7
❑ 84Nes792-182
❑ 84OCoandSI-29
❑ 84OCoandSI-104
❑ 84OCoandSI-240
❑ 84OPC-182
❑ 84SevCoi-E17
❑ 84StaStr-1
❑ 84StaStr-2
❑ 84StaStr-3
❑ 84StaStr-4
❑ 84StaStr-5
❑ 84StaStr-6
❑ 84StaStr-7
❑ 84StaStr-8
❑ 84StaStr-9
❑ 84StaStr-10
❑ 84StaStr-11
❑ 84StaStr-12
❑ 84TidTidT-NNO
❑ 84Top-182
❑ 84TopGloS-29
❑ 84TopRubD-7
❑ 84TopSti-385
❑ 84TopSup-12
❑ 84TopTif-182
❑ 85AllGamPI-159
❑ 85Don-312
❑ 85Dra-30
❑ 85Fle-93
❑ 85Fle-631
❑ 85FleLimE-38
❑ 85FleStaS-36
❑ 85Lea-159
❑ 85MetColP-22
❑ 85MetFanC-8
❑ 85MetTCM-35
❑ 85OPC-126
❑ 85PolMet-M6
❑ 85SevCoi-S13
❑ 85Top-278
❑ 85Top-570
❑ 85Top3-D-9
❑ 85TopGloA-8
❑ 85TopRubD-8
❑ 85TopSti-100
❑ 85TopSti-179
❑ 85TopSup-30
❑ 85TopTif-278
❑ 85TopTif-570
❑ 86BasStaB-106
❑ 86Don-197
❑ 86DonAll-5
❑ 86DonHig-24
❑ 86DonPop-5
❑ 86Dra-16
❑ 86Fle-96
❑ 86Fle-632
❑ 86FleMin-21
❑ 86FleSlu-38
❑ 86FleStiC-116
❑ 86KayB-31
❑ 86Lea-131
❑ 86MetColP-4
❑ 86MetFanC-8
❑ 86MetTCM-28
❑ 86MetWorSC-11
❑ 86OPC-80
❑ 86QuaGra-16
❑ 86SevCoi-E11
❑ 86Spo-56
❑ 86Spo-97
❑ 86SpoRoo-48
❑ 86Top-80
❑ 86Top3-D-26
❑ 86TopGloA-19
❑ 86TopGloS-11
❑ 86TopSti-95
❑ 86TopSti-150
❑ 86TopSup-55
❑ 86TopTat-18
❑ 86TopTif-80
❑ 87BoaandB-33
❑ 87BurKinA-19
❑ 87ClaGam-3
❑ 87ClaUpdY-122
❑ 87Don-4
❑ 87Don-118
❑ 87DonAll-12
❑ 87DonHig-42
❑ 87DonHig-49
❑ 87DonOpeD-128
❑ 87DonP-12
❑ 87DonSupD-4
❑ 87Dra-1
❑ 87Fle-23
❑ 87Fle-629
❑ 87Fle-638
❑ 87FleExcS-41
❑ 87FleGlo-23
❑ 87FleGlo-629
❑ 87FleGlo-638
❑ 87FleGlo-WS11
❑ 87FleLeaL-41
❑ 87FleSlu-40
❑ 87FleStiC-114
❑ 87FleWorS-11
❑ 87GenMilB-5J
❑ 87K-M-32
❑ 87KayB-31
❑ 87KeyFooD-1
❑ 87KraFoo-26
❑ 87Lea-4
❑ 87Lea-68
❑ 87MetColP-8
❑ 87MetFanC-7
❑ 87MSAIceTD-1
❑ 87MSAJifPD-17
❑ 87OPC-379
❑ 87OurOwnTD-1
❑ 87RedFolSB-58
❑ 87SevCoi-E13
❑ 87Spo-20
❑ 87SpoIllS-13
❑ 87SpoTeaP-2
❑ 87StuPan-1
❑ 87Top-331
❑ 87Top-460
❑ 87Top-601
❑ 87TopCoi-46
❑ 87TopGloA-8
❑ 87TopGloS-32
❑ 87TopMinL-26
❑ 87TopSti-103
❑ 87TopSti-159
❑ 87TopTif-331
❑ 87TopTif-460
❑ 87TopTif-601
❑ 87WeiMarD-1
❑ 87Woo-29
❑ 88Baz-21
❑ 88ClaBlu-209
❑ 88Don-439
❑ 88DonAll-34
❑ 88DonBasB-182
❑ 88DonBonM-BC20
❑ 88DonPop-12
❑ 88DonTeaBM-439
❑ 88Dra-3
❑ 88Fle-151
❑ 88Fle-637
❑ 88FleAwaW-40
❑ 88FleBasA-40
❑ 88FleBasM-37
❑ 88FleExcS-39
❑ 88FleGlo-151
❑ 88FleGlo-637
❑ 88FleHea-4
❑ 88FleHotS-41
❑ 88FleLeaL-40
❑ 88FleMin-97
❑ 88FleRecS-39
❑ 88FleSlu-40
❑ 88FleStiC-106
❑ 88FleSup-38
❑ 88FleTeaL-40
❑ 88GreBasS-71
❑ 88K-M-29
❑ 88KayB-29
❑ 88KeyFooD-17
❑ 88KinDis-8
❑ 88Lea-220
❑ 88MetColP-9
❑ 88MetFanC-18
❑ 88MetKah-18
❑ 88MSAFanSD-17
❑ 88MSAIceTD-17
❑ 88Nes-18
❑ 88OPC-178
❑ 88OPCBoxB-L
❑ 88OurOwnTD-17
❑ 88PanSti-236
❑ 88PanSti-342
❑ 88PanSti-347
❑ 88Sco-360
❑ 88ScoBoxC-17
❑ 88ScoGlo-360
❑ 88ScoYouS2-20
❑ 88Spo-155
❑ 88SpoGam-15
❑ 88StaLinAl-33
❑ 88StaLinMe-18
❑ 88StaStr-1
❑ 88StaStr-2
❑ 88StaStr-3
❑ 88StaStr-4
❑ 88StaStr-5
❑ 88StaStr-6
❑ 88StaStr-7
❑ 88StaStr-8
❑ 88StaStr-9
❑ 88StaStr-10
❑ 88StaStr-11
❑ 88TarPla-43
❑ 88TetTeaD-17
❑ 88Top-710
❑ 88TopBig-253
❑ 88TopCoi-56
❑ 88TopGloA-19
❑ 88TopGloS-22
❑ 88TopMinL-63
❑ 88TopRitTM-7
❑ 88TopSti-96
❑ 88TopSti-151
❑ 88TopStiB-21
❑ 88TopTif-710
❑ 88TopUKM-76
❑ 88TopUKMT-76
❑ 88TopWaxBC-L
❑ 88WeiMarD-17
❑ 89Baz-20
❑ 89Bow-387
❑ 89BowTif-387
❑ 89CadEllD-56
❑ 89CerSup-3
❑ 89ClaLigB-8
❑ 89ClaTraO-108
❑ 89ClaTraO-150
❑ 89Don-147
❑ 89DonAll-34
❑ 89DonBasB-40
❑ 89DonBonM-BC6
❑ 89DonPop-34
❑ 89Fle-49
❑ 89Fle-632
❑ 89FleAll-10
❑ 89FleBasA-39
❑ 89FleBasM-36
❑ 89FleExcS-40
❑ 89FleGlo-49
❑ 89FleGlo-632
❑ 89FleHeroB-38
❑ 89FleLeaL-37
❑ 89FleSup-39
❑ 89FleWaxBC-C25
❑ 89K-M-28
❑ 89KayB-29
❑ 89KeyFooD-5
❑ 89KinDis-15
❑ 89MetCol8-3
❑ 89MetCol8-33
❑ 89MetColP-2
❑ 89MetFanC-18
❑ 89MetKah-27
❑ 89MSAHolD-10
❑ 89MSAIceTD-5
❑ 89Nis-10
❑ 89OPC-300
❑ 89OurOwnTD-5
❑ 89PanSti-140
❑ 89PanSti-223
❑ 89PanSti-231
❑ 89RedFolSB-113
❑ 89Sco-10
❑ 89ScoHot1S-50
❑ 89Scomast-42
❑ 89Spo-205
❑ 89SpoIllFKI-20
❑ 89TetTeaD-5
❑ 89Top-291
❑ 89Top-300
❑ 89Top-390
❑ 89TopAme2C-28
❑ 89TopBasT-44
❑ 89TopBig-139
❑ 89TopCapC-7
❑ 89TopCoi-26
❑ 89TopDouA-18
❑ 89TopDouM-1
❑ 89TopGaloC-10
❑ 89TopGloA-19
❑ 89TopGloS-8
❑ 89TopHeaUT-6
❑ 89TopHilTM-28
❑ 89TopMinL-28
❑ 89TopSti-98
❑ 89TopSti-157
❑ 89TopStiB-53
❑ 89TopTif-291
❑ 89TopTif-300
❑ 89TopTif-390
❑ 89TopUKM-75
❑ 89TVSpoM-1
❑ 89TVSpoM-129
❑ 89UppDec-260
❑ 89UppDec-681
❑ 89WeiMarD-5
❑ 90Bow-141
❑ 90BowTif-141
❑ 90ClaBlu-33
❑ 90Col-20
❑ 90Don-235
❑ 90DonBesN-80
❑ 90Fle-217
❑ 90FleAwaW-38
❑ 90FleBasA-37
❑ 90FleBasAC-37
❑ 90FleBasM-37
❑ 90FleBasMC-37
❑ 90FleCan-217
❑ 90FleLeaL-38
❑ 90FleLeaLC-38
❑ 90FleLeaS-3
❑ 90Hot50PS-43
❑ 90Lea-250
❑ 90M.Vpin-66
❑ 90MetColP-6
❑ 90MetFanC-18
❑ 90MetKah-18
❑ 90MLBBasB-13
❑ 90OPC-600
❑ 90PanSti-302
❑ 90Pos-10
❑ 90PubIntS-145
❑ 90PubIntS-273
❑ 90RedFolSB-92
❑ 90Sco-200
❑ 90Sco100S-15
❑ 90Spo-146
❑ 90StaLonJS-21
❑ 90StaLonJS-37
❑ 90SupActM-17
❑ 90Top-600
❑ 90TopAmeA-23
❑ 90TopBig-186
❑ 90TopDou-64
❑ 90TopGloS-7
❑ 90TopHilHM-4
❑ 90TopMag-33
❑ 90TopSti-91
❑ 90TopStiB-20
❑ 90TopTif-600
❑ 90TopTVA-56
❑ 90TopTVM-33
❑ 90UppDec-182
❑ 90USPlaCA-13H
❑ 90WonBreS-10
❑ 91BasBesHRK-17
❑ 91Bow-382
❑ 91Bow-609
❑ 91Cla1-T68
❑ 91Cla1-T99
❑ 91Cla2-T73
❑ 91ClaGam-177
❑ 91ColStr-1
❑ 91ColStr-2
❑ 91ColStr-3
❑ 91ColStr-4
❑ 91ColStr-5
❑ 91ColStr-6
❑ 91ColStr-7
❑ 91ColStr-8
❑ 91ColStr-9
❑ 91ColStr-10
❑ 91ColStr-11
❑ 91ColStr-12
❑ 91ColStr-xx
❑ 91DodMot-2
❑ 91DodPho-28
❑ 91DodPol-44
❑ 91DodSt.V-13
❑ 91Don-408
❑ 91Don-696
❑ 91DonGraS-13
❑ 91Fle-161
❑ 91FlePro-12
❑ 91FleUpd-96
❑ 91JimDea-5
❑ 91Lea-377
❑ 91Lea-444
❑ 91MetWIZ-382
❑ 91MLBKeyC-4
❑ 91MSAHolD-1
❑ 91OPC-200
❑ 91OPC-402
❑ 91OPCPre-117
❑ 91PanCanT1-10
❑ 91PanFreS-85
❑ 91PanFreS-164
❑ 91PanSti-88
❑ 91PlaStr-53
❑ 91PlaStr-54
❑ 91PlaStr-55
❑ 91PlaStr-56
❑ 91PlaStr-57
❑ 91PlaStr-58
❑ 91PlaStr-60
❑ 91Pos-7
❑ 91Sco-640
❑ 91Sco-691
❑ 91Sco-864
❑ 91Sco100S-62
❑ 91ScoRoo-16T
❑ 91Sev3DCN-14
❑ 91SevCoi-NE14
❑ 91SevCoi-SC14
❑ 91SilHol-8
❑ 91SimandSMLBL-42
❑ 91SpoNSP-1
❑ 91StaClu-301
❑ 91StaPinB-49
❑ 91StaPro-5
❑ 91StaStr-1
❑ 91StaStr-2
❑ 91StaStr-3
❑ 91StaStr-4
❑ 91StaStr-5
❑ 91StaStr-6
❑ 91StaStr-7
❑ 91StaStr-8
❑ 91StaStr-9
❑ 91StaStr-10
❑ 91StaStr-11
❑ 91Stu-190
❑ 91Top-200
❑ 91Top-402
❑ 91TopDesS-200
❑ 91TopDesS-402
❑ 91TopMic-200
❑ 91TopMic-402
❑ 91TopSta-33
❑ 91TopTif-200
❑ 91TopTif-402

❑ 91TopTra-114T
❑ 91TopTraT-114T
❑ 91TopTriH-N5
❑ 91Ult-171
❑ 91UppDec-245
❑ 91UppDecSS-SS9
❑ 92Bow-40
❑ 92Cla1-T86
❑ 92Cla2-T38
❑ 92ClaGam-132
❑ 92ColPro-14
❑ 92DodMot-10
❑ 92DodPol-44
❑ 92DodSmo-4692
❑ 92DodStaTA-30
❑ 92Don-559
❑ 92DonCraJ2-7
❑ 92DonMcD-7
❑ 92Fle-471
❑ 92FleCitTP-12
❑ 92FleLumC-L3
❑ 92FleTeaL-16
❑ 92Fre-17
❑ 92Hig5-55
❑ 92Hig5S-28
❑ 92Hig5S-35
❑ 92JimDea-9
❑ 92LaKdec-28
❑ 92Lea-29
❑ 92LeaBlaG-29
❑ 92LeaGolP-5
❑ 92LeaPre-5
❑ 92MooSna-11
❑ 92Mr.TurS-24
❑ 92MVPPin-34
❑ 92New-28
❑ 92OPC-550
❑ 92OPCPre-179
❑ 92PanSti-196
❑ 92Pin-80
❑ 92Pin-308
❑ 92PinRool-16
❑ 92Pos-10
❑ 92PosCan-7
❑ 92RedFolS-91
❑ 92RevSup1-1
❑ 92RevSup1-2
❑ 92RevSup1-3
❑ 92Sco-9
❑ 92Sco100S-55
❑ 92ScoImpP-59
❑ 92ScoProP-5
❑ 92ScoProP-19
❑ 92SevCoi-24
❑ 92SpoStaCC-44
❑ 92StaClu-560
❑ 92StaCluMP-13
❑ 92StaPro-9
❑ 92Stu-50
❑ 92StuHer-BC6
❑ 92SunSee-20
❑ 92Top-550
❑ 92TopGol-550
❑ 92TopGolW-550
❑ 92TopKid-47
❑ 92TopMic-550
❑ 92TriPla-187
❑ 92TriPlaP-2
❑ 92Ult-219
❑ 92UltAllS-18
❑ 92UppDec-174
❑ 92UppDecF-43
❑ 92UppDecFG-43
❑ 92UppDecHRH-HR16
❑ 92UppDecTMH-51
❑ 93Bow-126
❑ 93CadDis-57
❑ 93DenHol-9
❑ 93DiaMar-104
❑ 93DodMot-8
❑ 93DodPol-25
❑ 93DodStaC-1
❑ 93Don-112
❑ 93DonLonBL-LL11
❑ 93DurPowP2-21
❑ 93Fin-89
❑ 93FinJum-89
❑ 93FinRef-89
❑ 93Fle-454
❑ 93FunPac-92
❑ 93FunPac-220
❑ 93Hos-7
❑ 93Lea-210
❑ 93MetBak-19
❑ 93OPC-375
❑ 93PacSpa-155
❑ 93PanSti-219
❑ 93Pin-64
❑ 93Pin-309
❑ 93PinSlu-19
❑ 93RedFolS-91
❑ 93Sco-42
❑ 93Sel-21
❑ 93SP-99
❑ 93StaClu-398
❑ 93StaCluFDI-398
❑ 93StaCluI-B4
❑ 93StaCluMOP-398
❑ 93StaCluMOP-MB4
❑ 93StaCluMP-23
❑ 93Stu-122
❑ 93Top-450
❑ 93TopGol-450
❑ 93TopInaM-450
❑ 93TopInaR-450
❑ 93TopMic-450
❑ 93TriPla-187
❑ 93Ult-406
❑ 93UppDec-477
❑ 93UppDec-575
❑ 93UppDec-820
❑ 93UppDecDG-9
❑ 93UppDecGold-477
❑ 93UppDecGold-575
❑ 93UppDecGold-820
❑ 93UppDecOD-D23
❑ 93UppDecTAN-TN8
❑ 94ColC-366
❑ 94ColChoGS-366
❑ 94ColChoSS-366
❑ 94Don-292
❑ 94Fin-87
❑ 94FinRef-87
❑ 94Fla-444
❑ 94Fle-525
❑ 94FleUpd-196
❑ 94GiaMot-17
❑ 94Pac-322
❑ 94PanSti-205
❑ 94Pin-294
❑ 94PinArtP-294
❑ 94PinMusC-294
❑ 94Sco-428
❑ 94ScoGolR-428
❑ 94Sel-99
❑ 94SpoRoo-149
❑ 94SpoRooAP-149
❑ 94StaClu-335
❑ 94StaCluFDI-335
❑ 94StaCluGR-335
❑ 94StaCluMOP-335
❑ 94SucSav-12
❑ 94Top-640
❑ 94TopGol-640
❑ 94TopSpa-640
❑ 94TriPla-89
❑ 95ColCho-260
❑ 95ColChoSE-113
❑ 95ColChoSEGS-113
❑ 95ColChoSESS-113
❑ 95ColCliP-29
❑ 95ColCliTI-29
❑ 95Don-194
❑ 95DonPreP-194
❑ 95Fle-589
❑ 95Pac-384
❑ 95PacPri-121
❑ 95Sco-209
❑ 95ScoGolR-209
❑ 95ScoHaloG-HG36
❑ 95ScoPlaTS-209
❑ 95Sei-5
❑ 95SelArtP-5
❑ 95StaCluMOP-RL5
❑ 95StaCluRL-RL5
❑ 95TamYanYI-27
❑ 95Top-629
❑ 95TopCyb-395
❑ 95Ult-244
❑ 95UltGolM-244
❑ 95UppDec-89
❑ 95UppDecED-89
❑ 95UppDecEDG-89
❑ 96Don-215
❑ 96DonPreP-215
❑ 96Fle-198
❑ 96FleTif-198
❑ 96LeaSig-109
❑ 96LeaSigPPG-109
❑ 96LeaSigPPP-109
❑ 96Pin-43
❑ 96Sco-353
❑ 96ScoDugC-B78
❑ 96ScoDugCAP-B78
❑ 96Ult-107
❑ 96UltGolM-107
❑ 97Cir-221
❑ 97CirRav-221
❑ 97ColCho-399
❑ 97Don-261
❑ 97DonEli-110
❑ 97DonEliGS-110
❑ 97DonGolPP-261
❑ 97DonPre-41
❑ 97DonPreCttC-41
❑ 97DonSilPP-261
❑ 97DonTea-132
❑ 97DonTeaSPE-132
❑ 97Fle-179
❑ 97FleTif-179
❑ 97Lea-291
❑ 97LeaFraM-291
❑ 97LeaFraMDC-291
❑ 97MetUni-123
❑ 97Pac-161
❑ 97PacLigB-161
❑ 97PacSil-161
❑ 97Pin-35
❑ 97PinArtP-PP35
❑ 97PinIns-74
❑ 97PinInsCE-74
❑ 97PinInsDE-74
❑ 97PinMusC-35
❑ 97PinPrePla-35
❑ 97Sco-79
❑ 97ScoArtPWB-79
❑ 97ScoPreS-79
❑ 97ScoShoS-79
❑ 97ScoShoSAP-79
❑ 97StaClu-82
❑ 97StaCluMOP-82
❑ 97Stu-143
❑ 97StuPrePG-143
❑ 97StuPrePS-143
❑ 97Top-282
❑ 97TopChr-98
❑ 97TopChrR-98
❑ 97TopGal-12
❑ 97TopGalPPI-12
❑ 97Ult-106
❑ 97UltGolME-106
❑ 97UltPlaME-106
❑ 97UppDec-250
❑ 97UppDec-444
❑ 97YanSco-4
❑ 97YanScoPI-4
❑ 97YanScoPr-4
❑ 98Bow-256
❑ 98BowChr-256
❑ 98BowChrGA-256
❑ 98BowChrGAR-256
❑ 98BowChrI-256
❑ 98BowChrIR-256
❑ 98BowChrR-256
❑ 98BowGolA-256
❑ 98BowInt-256
❑ 98Don-181
❑ 98DonGolPP-181
❑ 98DonSigAC-104
❑ 98DonSigAM-106
❑ 98DonSilPP-181
❑ 98Fle-494
❑ 98LeaRS-130
❑ 98LeaRSLHolo-130
❑ 98LeaRSLong-130
❑ 98LeaRTrue-130
❑ 98PacInvGems-80
❑ 98PacOme-171
❑ 98PacOmeR-171
❑ 98PacOnl-518
❑ 98PacOnlR-518
❑ 98PacOnlWC-518
❑ 98PinSna-NYY2
❑ 98Revo-103
❑ 98RevoSS-103
❑ 98Ult-394
❑ 98UltGolM-394
❑ 98UltMas-394
❑ 98UltPlaM-394
❑ 98YanUppDWSC-1
❑ 99199Fin-38
❑ 99FinGolRef-38
❑ 99FinRef-38
❑ 99Fle-564
❑ 99FleSta9-564
❑ 99FleWarT-564
❑ 99PacPar-166
❑ 99PacParC-166
❑ 99PacParG-166
❑ 99PacParHoloGold-166
❑ 99PacParHS-166
❑ 99PacParOD-166
❑ 99PacParPB-166
❑ 99PacParRed-166
❑ 99StaClu-7
❑ 99StaCluFDI-7
❑ 99StaCluOoaK-7
❑ 99StaCluPP-7
❑ 99Top-18
❑ 99TopChr-18
❑ 99TopChrR-18
❑ 99TopMVPP-18
❑ 99TopOpeD-13
❑ 99UppDec-159
❑ 99UppDecEL1-159
❑ 99UppDecEL2-159
❑ 99YanFle-22

Strawn, Fla
❑ 79TucTorT-13
❑ 79TulDriT-5
❑ 80ChaChaT-14

Strebeck, Rick
❑ 90ModA'sC-29
❑ 91ModA'sC-15
❑ 92HunStaF-3951
❑ 92HunStaS-321
❑ 92SkyAA F-138
❑ 93ModA'sC-20
❑ 93ModA'sF-799

Street, Gabby (Charles)
❑ 08AmeCarE91-93
❑ 09ColChiE-276
❑ 09RamT20-114
❑ 09SpoNewSM-40
❑ 09T206-344
❑ 09T206-345
❑ 10CouT21-62
❑ 10CouT21-227
❑ 10CouT21-228
❑ 10CouT21-318
❑ 10CouT21-319
❑ 10DomDisP-113A
❑ 10DomDisP-113B
❑ 10RedCroT-74
❑ 10RedCroT-75
❑ 10RedCroT-247
❑ 10SenWasT-5
❑ 10SepAnoP-23
❑ 10SweCapPP-64A
❑ 10SweCapPP-64B
❑ 11HelSta-46
❑ 11MecDFT-44
❑ 11PinT-5-564
❑ 11S74Sil-41
❑ 11SpoLifM-133
❑ 11T205-165
❑ 11TurRedT-120
❑ 12ColRedB-276
❑ 12ColTinT-276
❑ 12HasTriFT-7
❑ 12T207-177
❑ 31CarMet-27
❑ 33Zee-45
❑ 35PebBea-6
❑ 40PlaBal-169
❑ 73FleWilD-16
❑ 77GalGloG-85
❑ 88ConSer5-27
❑ 92ConTSN-652
❑ 93ConTSN-833
❑ 95ConTSN-1324

Street, John
❑ 15SpoNewP-5
❑ 96PinFan-JS1

Street, Mickey
❑ 85WatIndT-7

Streeter, Sam
❑ 88NegLeaD-13

Strehlow, Bobby
❑ 93JohCitCC-22
❑ 93JohCitCF-3697

Strelitz, Len
❑ 78ArkTraT-20
❑ 79ArkTraT-2

Stricek, Jim
❑ 86ModA'sP-23
❑ 90WinHavRSS-28
❑ 91WinHavRSC-27
❑ 92WinHavRSC-27

Stricker, John
❑ 87OldJudN-477
❑ 89EdgR.WG-16

Strickfaden, Dave
❑ 77WatIndT-23

Strickland, Bob
❑ 86GenCubP-26
❑ 87ChaWheP-18
❑ 89WinSpiS-15

Strickland, Chad
❑ 91AppFoxCB-14
❑ 91AppFoxP-1720
❑ 92AppFoxCB-4
❑ 92AppFoxFI-988
❑ 92MidLeaATI-43
❑ 93CarLeaAGF-17
❑ 93WilBluRC-24
❑ 93WilBluRF-2001
❑ 94MemChiF-361
❑ 95WicWraTI-27

Strickland, Dedrick
❑ 90OneYanP-3372

Strickland, Erick
❑ 93ElmPioC-21
❑ 93ElmPioF-3838

Strickland, George
❑ 50PirTeal-21
❑ 52Bow-207
❑ 52Top-197
❑ 54Bow-36
❑ 54DanDee-25
❑ 55Bow-192
❑ 55Ind-8
❑ 55IndCarBL-10
❑ 55IndGolS-13
❑ 57IndSoh-14
❑ 57IndTeal-22
❑ 57Top-263
❑ 58Top-102
❑ 59Ind-19
❑ 59Kah-34
❑ 59Top-207
❑ 60IndJayP-11
❑ 60Lea-30
❑ 60Top-63
❑ 60TopVen-63
❑ 70RoyTeal-35
❑ 71oySigST-26
❑ 72oyTeal-25
❑ 75TCM195CI-33
❑ 79DiaGre-294
❑ 83TopRep5-197

Strickland, Greg
❑ 97EugEmeB-29
❑ 98EugEme-29

Strickland, Jim
❑ 72Top-778
❑ 73OPC-122
❑ 73TacTwiC-21
❑ 73Top-122
❑ 75OklCit8TI-9
❑ 76SSP-512

Strickland, Rick
❑ 88CapCodPPaLP-49
❑ 89OneYanP-2116
❑ 91Ft.LauYC-28
❑ 91Ft.LauYP-2442
❑ 92AlbYanF-2239
❑ 92AlbYanSk-20

Strickland, Scott
❑ 97VerExpB-27
❑ 98CapFeaCM-23

Stricklett, Elmer
❑ 11SpoLifCW-340
❑ 90DodTar-777

Stricklin, Scott
❑ 93EliTwiC-20
❑ 93EliTwiF-3419
❑ 94ForWayWC-22
❑ 94ForWayWF-2013
❑ 94MidLeaAF-MDW15
❑ 95ForMyeMTI-26
❑ 96GreBraB-27
❑ 96GreBraTI-25
❑ 97St.PetDR-28
❑ 97St.PetDRUB-28

Strijek, Randy
❑ 87NewOriP-27
❑ 88CarLeaAS-17
❑ 88HagSunS-21
❑ 89HagSunB-20
❑ 89HagSunP-265
❑ 89HagSunS-19
❑ 90ShrCapP-1452
❑ 90ShrCapS-23

Striker, Jake
❑ 60Top-169
❑ 60TopVen-169

Strincevich, Nick
❑ 47TipTop-148
❑ 50WorWidGV-17
❑ 77TCMTheWY-52
❑ 79DiaGre-354
❑ 83TCMPla1944-28

Stringer, Lou
❑ 41CubTeal-23
❑ 42CubTeal-23
❑ 47SigOil-38
❑ 49Bow-183
❑ 49RedSoxTI-22
❑ 50Bow-187
❑ 50RedSoxTI-24
❑ 52MotCoo-38
❑ 53SanFraSTI-22

Stringfellow, Bean (Thornton)
❑ 86GreBraTI-19
❑ 87RicBraC-31
❑ 87RicBraT-7
❑ 88BobCamRB-2
❑ 88RicBraC-4
❑ 88RicBraP-13

Stringfellow, Sidney
❑ 37Zee-61

Stripp, Joe
❑ 33GeoCMil-28
❑ 34DiaMatCSB-175
❑ 34DiaStaR-89
❑ 34Gou-46
❑ 34GouCanV-91
❑ 35GouPuzR-1G
❑ 35GouPuzR-3E
❑ 35GouPuzR-5E
❑ 35GouPuzR-14E
❑ 72TCMthe3-106
❑ 90DodTar-778
❑ 93ConTSN-809

Strittmatter, Mark
❑ 92BenRocCB-23
❑ 92BenRocF-1477
❑ 93CenValRC-23
❑ 93CenValRF-2896
❑ 93Top-746
❑ 93TopGol-746
❑ 93TopInaM-746
❑ 93TopInaR-746
❑ 93TopMic-746
❑ 94NewHavRF-1552
❑ 95NewHavRTI-19
❑ 96ColSprSSTI-29
❑ 97ColSprSTI-24
❑ 98ColSprSS-19
❑ 99SpoIll-66

Strobel, Craig
❑ 86HagSunP-23
❑ 87HagSunP-8
❑ 90SpaPhiB-30
❑ 90SpaPhiS-28
❑ 92ClePhiC-26
❑ 93ScrRedBTI-25
❑ 95ScrRedBTI-26
❑ 96ScrRedBB-4
❑ 97ScrRedB-27
❑ 98ScrRedBQ-26

Strode, Jim (Lester)
❑ 82ForMyeRT-19
❑ 84MemChiT-14
❑ 85OmaRoyT-7
❑ 86OmaRoyP-25
❑ 86OmaRoyT-18
❑ 88LouRedBTI-46
❑ 89WytCubS-29
❑ 90PeoChiTI-32
❑ 91PeoChiC-23
❑ 91PeoChiP-1360
❑ 91PeoChiTI-2
❑ 92WinSpiC-27
❑ 92WinSpiF-1224
❑ 93DayCubC-25
❑ 93DayCubF-874

Strohmayer, John
❑ 71ExpPS-25
❑ 71OPC-232
❑ 71Top-232
❑ 72Dia-44
❑ 72Top-631
❑ 73OPC-457
❑ 73Top-457
❑ 91MetWIZ-383

Strom, Brent
❑ 73IndTeal-24
❑ 73OPC-612
❑ 73Top-612
❑ 74OPC-359
❑ 74Top-359
❑ 75HawIslC-12

❑ 75OPC-643
❑ 75PadDea-25
❑ 75Top-643
❑ 75TopMin-643
❑ 76OPC-84
❑ 76Top-84
❑ 77PadSchC-54
❑ 77Top-348
❑ 78Top-509
❑ 80TucTorT-20
❑ 81AlbDukTc-12
❑ 82AlbDukTc-27
❑ 83AlbDukTc-13
❑ 87AlbDukD-3
❑ 88AlaGolAA60TI-11
❑ 88AlbDukP-251
❑ 89AlbDukP-60
❑ 90ProAAAF-210
❑ 90TucTorP-220
❑ 91LinDriAAA-622
❑ 91MetWIZ-384
❑ 91TucTorLD-622
❑ 91TucTorP-2230
❑ 92TucTorF-506
❑ 92TucTorS-625
❑ 93TucTorF-3078
❑ 94TucTorF-779
❑ 95TucTotTI-26
❑ 96AstMot-28
❑ 98arSenW1-26
❑ 98HarSenM-26

Stromer, Rick
❑ 83PeoSunF-11
❑ 85HunStaJ-43

Stromsborg, Ryan
❑ 96MedHatBJTI-29
❑ 97HagSunB-21
❑ 98KnoSG-23
❑ 98SouLeaTPG-10

Stroner, James
❑ 33Zee-96

Strong, Garret
❑ 75CedRapGT-30

Strong, Joe
❑ 85ModA'sC-9
❑ 86ModA'sP-24
❑ 88CalLeaACLC-20
❑ 88RenSilSCLC-274
❑ 89CalLeaA-41
❑ 89RenSilSCLC-245
❑ 93LasVegSF-944
❑ 94SanBerSC-21
❑ 94SanBerSF-2759

Strong, Kevin
❑ 91EliTwiP-4314

Strong, Shannon
❑ 90EugEmeGS-30

Strong, Steve
❑ 86AriWilP-16
❑ 87AriWilP-15
❑ 89LakTigS-22

Strong, Stewart
❑ 91GreFalDSP-13

Stroth, Scott
❑ 92EveGiaC-8
❑ 92EveGiaF-1689

Stroud, Derek
❑ 86AncGlaPTI-34
❑ 87WytCubP-5
❑ 88GenCubP-1649
❑ 89PeoChiTI-11
❑ 90WinSpiTI-9
❑ 92PalSprAF-840
❑ 93MidAngF-322
❑ 97MidAngOHP-28

Stroud, Ed
❑ 67Top-598
❑ 68OPC-31
❑ 68Top-31
❑ 68TopVen-31
❑ 69MilBra-266
❑ 69MLBOffS-108
❑ 69SenTeal-14
❑ 69Top-272
❑ 70MLBOffS-286
❑ 70OPC-506
❑ 70SenPolY-10
❑ 70Top-506
❑ 71MLBOffS-550
❑ 71OPC-217
❑ 71Top-217
❑ 72MilBra-333

Stroud, Ralph
❑ 11MecDFT-45
❑ 11SpoLifM-70
❑ 12ImpTobC-58
❑ 13Zee-91
❑ 14Zee-94
❑ 16FleBreD-91
❑ 20Zee-97
❑ 26Zee-19

Stroughter, Steve
❑ 78SalLakCGC-9
❑ 80SpoIndT-23
❑ 81TolMudHT-22
❑ 82TopTra-114T

Strovink, Eric
❑ 91GulCoaRSP-5

Strube, Bob
❑ 86KenTwiP-22
❑ 87VisOakP-5
❑ 88VisOakCLC-162
❑ 88VisOakP-101
❑ 89VisOakCLC-99
❑ 89VisOakP-1429

Strucher, Mark
❑ 82DayBeaAT-25
❑ 83ColAstT-6
❑ 86RicBraP-22
❑ 87RicBraBC-20
❑ 87RicBraC-5
❑ 87RicBraT-15

Struek, Randy
❑ 87HagSunP-9

Strunk, Amos
❑ 09ColChiE-277
❑ 10NadE1-53
❑ 11A'sFirT20-17
❑ 11D35RocB-17
❑ 11PinT-5-504
❑ 11SpoLifM-104
❑ 12ColRedB-277
❑ 12ColTinT-277
❑ 12T207-178
❑ 14CraJacE-33
❑ 14FatPlaT-47
❑ 15CraJacE-33
❑ 15SpoNewM-173
❑ 16FleBreD-92
❑ 16SpoNewM-171
❑ 17ColE13-170
❑ 17HolBreD-102
❑ 20GasAmeMBD-4
❑ 21E121So1-104
❑ 21E121So8-96
❑ 22AmeCarE122-69
❑ 22E120-29
❑ 22W573-130
❑ 22W575-135
❑ 23W501-44
❑ 72ClaCar-92
❑ 74A'sTCM1P-11

Strus, George
❑ 93JohCitCC-23
❑ 93JohCitCF-3682

Stryffeler, Dan
❑ 82SprCarF-9
❑ 83SprCarF-21
❑ 84ArkTraT-3
❑ 86LouRedTI-27

Stryker, Dutch
❑ 90DodTar-1081

Stryker, Ed
❑ 90GreFalDSP-26
❑ 91BakDodCLC-5
❑ 92VerBeaDC-17
❑ 92VerBeaDF-2874

Stuart, Brad
❑ 90LSUTigA-7

Stuart, Dick (Richard L.)
❑ 47PM1StaP1-208
❑ 58PirTeal-10
❑ 59HomRunD-19
❑ 59Kah-35
❑ 59Top-357
❑ 60ArmCoi-18
❑ 60Baz-6
❑ 60Kah-39
❑ 60KeyChal-47
❑ 60PirJayP-12
❑ 60PirTag-7
❑ 60Top-402
❑ 61Kah-42
❑ 61NuSco-409
❑ 61PirJayP-11
❑ 61Pos-127A
❑ 61Pos-127B
❑ 61Top-126
❑ 61TopStaI-71
❑ 62Baz-24
❑ 62Jel-169
❑ 62Kah-37
❑ 62Pos-169
❑ 62PosCan-169
❑ 62SalPlaC-120
❑ 62ShiPlaC-120
❑ 62Top-160
❑ 62TopBuc-86
❑ 62TopStaI-180
❑ 62TopVen-160
❑ 63BasMagM-81
❑ 63Jel-137
❑ 63Pos-137
❑ 63Top-18
❑ 63Top-285
❑ 64RedSoxTI-7
❑ 64Top-10
❑ 64Top-12
❑ 64Top-410
❑ 64TopCoi-12
❑ 64TopCoi-122
❑ 64TopGia-42
❑ 64TopSta-51
❑ 64TopStaU-70
❑ 64TopTatI-69
❑ 64TopVen-10
❑ 64TopVen-12
❑ 65OPC-5
❑ 65OPC-280
❑ 65Top-5
❑ 65Top-280
❑ 65TopTraI-29
❑ 66MetVolC-11
❑ 66Top-480
❑ 66TopRubI-89
❑ 77PirTCM1WC-2
❑ 81RedSoxBG2S-119
❑ 81TCM60I-366
❑ 84WilMay-26
❑ 87Pir196T-1
❑ 90DodTar-779
❑ 91MetWIZ-385

Stuart, John
❑ 26Zee-88

Stuart, Marlin
❑ 52Bow-147
❑ 52Top-208
❑ 53BowC-120
❑ 54OriEss-32
❑ 83TopRep5-208
❑ 91OriCro-446
❑ 97BalOriP-49

Stuart, Richard
❑ 96BoiHawB-28
❑ 97CalLeaTP-9
❑ 97LakElsSG-28

Stubberfield, Chris
❑ 86EveGiaC-18
❑ 86EveGiaPC-31

Stubbs, Franklin
❑ 83AlbDukTc-1
❑ 84AlbDukCr-151
❑ 85AlbDukCr-175
❑ 85DomLeaS-25
❑ 85Don-348
❑ 85Fle-386
❑ 85Top-506
❑ 85TopTif-506
❑ 86DodPol-22
❑ 86DodUniOP-19
❑ 86Don-592
❑ 86TopTra-105T
❑ 86TopTraT-105T
❑ 87DodMot-13
❑ 87DodPho-14
❑ 87DodPol-10
❑ 87Don-299
❑ 87DonOpeD-83
❑ 87Fle-455
❑ 87FleGlo-455
❑ 87OPC-292
❑ 87SevCoi-W14
❑ 87SpoTeaP-14
❑ 87Top-292
❑ 87TopSti-72
❑ 87TopTif-292
❑ 88DodMot-11
❑ 88DodPol-22
❑ 88Don-218
❑ 88DonBasB-331
❑ 88Fle-527
❑ 88FleGlo-527
❑ 88Lea-182
❑ 88OPC-198
❑ 88PanSti-308
❑ 88RedFolSB-84
❑ 88Sco-147
❑ 88ScoGlo-147
❑ 88StaLinD-17
❑ 88Top-198
❑ 88TopBig-112
❑ 88TopSti-66
❑ 88TopTif-198
❑ 89DodMot-11
❑ 89DodPol-13
❑ 89DodStaSV-6
❑ 89Don-321
❑ 89DonGraS-9
❑ 89Fle-74
❑ 89FleGlo-74
❑ 89Sco-599
❑ 89Top-697A
❑ 89Top-697B
❑ 89TopBig-32
❑ 89TopTif-697
❑ 89UppDec-91
❑ 90AstLenH-24
❑ 90AstMot-14
❑ 90DodPol-22
❑ 90DodTar-780
❑ 90Don-615
❑ 90DonBesN-143
❑ 90Lea-425
❑ 90OPC-56
❑ 90PubIntS-19
❑ 90Sco-478
❑ 90ScoRoo-40T
❑ 90Top-56
❑ 90TopTif-56
❑ 90TopTra-120T
❑ 90TopTraT-120T
❑ 90UppDec-550
❑ 91Bow-37
❑ 91BreMilB-25
❑ 91BrePol-22
❑ 91Don-99
❑ 91Fle-518
❑ 91FleUpd-34
❑ 91Lea-277
❑ 91OPC-732
❑ 91PanFreS-13
❑ 91Sco-308
❑ 91ScoRoo-59T
❑ 91StaClu-461
❑ 91Stu-77
❑ 91Top-732
❑ 91TopDesS-732
❑ 91TopMic-732
❑ 91TopTif-732
❑ 91TopTra-115T
❑ 91TopTraT-115T
❑ 91UppDec-168
❑ 91UppDec-718
❑ 92Bow-49
❑ 92BrePol-24
❑ 92Don-618
❑ 92Lea-328
❑ 92LeaBlaG-328
❑ 92OPC-329
❑ 92PanSti-35
❑ 92Pin-320
❑ 92Sco-292
❑ 92StaClu-189
❑ 92Stu-196
❑ 92Top-329
❑ 92TopGol-329
❑ 92TopGolW-329
❑ 92TopMic-329
❑ 92Ult-390
❑ 92UppDec-396
❑ 93Don-177
❑ 93Fle-636
❑ 93PanSti-37
❑ 93PawRedSDD-26
❑ 93StaClu-168
❑ 93StaCluFDI-168
❑ 93StaCluMOP-168
❑ 93Top-124
❑ 93TopGol-124
❑ 93TopInaM-124
❑ 93TopInaR-124
❑ 93TopMic-124
❑ 93UppDec-269
❑ 93UppDecGold-269
❑ 94BreMilB-360
❑ 97DanBraB-5
❑ 98DanBraQ-27

Stubbs, Jerry
❑ 94VerExpC-20
❑ 94VerExpF-3909
❑ 96WesPalBEB-14

Stubing, Moose (Lawrence)
❑ 76QuaCitAT-35
❑ 77FriOneYW-72
❑ 80SalLakCGT-18
❑ 81SalLakCGT-25
❑ 82SpoIndT-24
❑ 84EdmTraC-97
❑ 87CalAngPPS-36
❑ 89Top-444
❑ 89TopTif-444

Stuckeman, Al
❑ 75LafDriT-27

Stuckenschneider, Eric
❑ 94YakBeaC-25
❑ 94YakBeaF-3866
❑ 95Bow-138
❑ 95GreFalDTI-33
❑ 95SanBerSTI-26
❑ 96SavSanB-9
❑ 96SavSanB-29
❑ 97VerBeaD-26
❑ 98SanAntMG-28

Studeman, Dennis
❑ 87EugEmeP-2677
❑ 87Ft.MyeRP-13
❑ 89AppFoxP-851

Stull, Everett
❑ 92ClaDraP-52
❑ 92JamExpC-13
❑ 92JamExpF-1503
❑ 93ClaGolF-123
❑ 93StaCluM-41
❑ 94WesPalBEC-24
❑ 94WesPalBEF-39
❑ 95AusFutSFP-SFFP5
❑ 95Bow-203
❑ 95BowBes-B11
❑ 95BowBesR-B11
❑ 95Exc-227
❑ 95HarSenTI-29
❑ 96BesAutSA-75
❑ 96Bow-134
❑ 96BowFoi-134
❑ 96HarSenB-26
❑ 97Bow-143
❑ 97BowCerBlaIA-CA75
❑ 97BowCerBluIA-CA75
❑ 97BowCerGolIA-CA75
❑ 97BowInt-143

Stull, Walt
❑ 86BakDodP-27
❑ 87SanBerSP-18

Stumberger, Darren
❑ 94WatIndC-25
❑ 94WatIndF-3947
❑ 97CalLeaATI-45
❑ 97KinIndB-24
❑ 98AkrAerM-25

Stumbo, Wes
❑ 98BurBeeM-19

Stump, Jim
❑ 77FriOneYW-78

Stumpf, Bill
❑ 15Zee-72
❑ 16Zee-68
❑ 17Zee-57
❑ 19Zee-28
❑ 20Zee-76
❑ 21Zee-151
❑ 22Zee-141
❑ 23Zee-76

Stumpf, Brian
❑ 94MarPhiC-26
❑ 94MarPhiF-3294
❑ 95Exc-248
❑ 95PiePhiF-187
❑ 96Exc-213
❑ 97ClePhi-20

Stumpf, George
❑ 78HalHalR-5

Stuper, John
❑ 82LouRedE-29
❑ 83Car-30
❑ 83Don-621
❑ 83Fle-23
❑ 83FleSti-9
❑ 83Top-363
❑ 84Car5x7-28
❑ 84Don-412
❑ 84Fle-337
❑ 84Nes792-49
❑ 84Nes792-186
❑ 84Top-49
❑ 84Top-186
❑ 84TopTif-49
❑ 84TopTif-186
❑ 85FleUpd-112
❑ 86Fle-193
❑ 86Top-497
❑ 86TopTif-497
❑ 91SavCarC-28
❑ 91SavCarP-1669
❑ 92St.PetCC-28

Stupur, Dan
❑ 89SalDodTI-29

Sturdivant, Dave
❑ 88BenBucL-15
❑ 89PalSprACLC-33
❑ 89PalSprAP-486
❑ 90PalSprACLC-211
❑ 90PalSprAP-2582

Sturdivant, Marcus
❑ 93BelMarCB-26
❑ 93BelMarF-3225
❑ 94AppFoxC-17
❑ 94AppFoxFl-1068
❑ 96LanJetB-25
❑ 97SouLeaTP-24

Sturdivant, Tom
❑ 57Top-34
❑ 57YanJayP-16
❑ 58Top-127
❑ 58YanJayP-13
❑ 59OklTodML-4
❑ 59Top-471
❑ 60Top-487
❑ 61Top-293
❑ 62Top-179
❑ 62TopVen-179
❑ 63PirIDL-23
❑ 63Top-281
❑ 64Top-402
❑ 81RedSoxBG2S-120
❑ 91MetWIZ-386

Sturgeon, Bob
❑ 41CubTeal-24
❑ 42CubTeal-24
❑ 47TipTop-117
❑ 49AngTeal-34

Sturm, Johnny
❑ 41DouPlaR-113
❑ 77TCMTheWY-55
❑ 94ConTSN-1312
❑ 94ConTSNB-1312

Sturtze, Tanyon
❑ 91Cla/Bes-439
❑ 91MadMusC-2
❑ 91MadMusP-2133
❑ 91MidLeaAP-MWL44
❑ 92CalLeaACL-8
❑ 92ModA'sC-8
❑ 93Bow-569
❑ 93ClaFS7-260
❑ 93HunStaF-2084
❑ 95FleUpd-129
❑ 96IowCubB-25
❑ 97OklCit8-22

Stutheit, Tim
❑ 92HunCubC-24
❑ 92HunCubF-3159
❑ 93ClaFS7-261
❑ 93DayCubF-867
❑ 93PeoChiC-20

Stutts, Angelo
❑ 93DanBraC-26
❑ 93DanBraF-3636

Stutts, Dennis
❑ 93JamExpC-22
❑ 93JamExpF-3327

Stutz, Edward
❑ 33Zee-148A
❑ 33Zee-148B
❑ 37Zee-91

Stutz, John
❑ 92JohCitCF-3126
❑ 93GleFalRC-26
❑ 93GleFalRF-4015

Stutz, Shawn
❑ 96ButCopKB-28
❑ 97HudValRB-24

Stutzriem, Jerry
❑ 79WatIndT-6
❑ 79WauTimT-2

Stynes, Chris
❑ 92MyrBeaHC-10
❑ 92MyrBeaHF-2206
❑ 92StaCluD-182
❑ 93ClaFS7-292
❑ 93DunBluJC-23
❑ 93DunBluJF-1805
❑ 93DunBluJFFN-26
❑ 93FloStaLAF-10

❑ 94ClaGolF-58
❑ 94KnoSmoF-1312
❑ 95Bow-77
❑ 95BowBes-B51
❑ 95BowBesR-B51
❑ 95Exc-144
❑ 95OmaRoyTI-26
❑ 95SigRooOJA-AS5
❑ 95SigRooOJAS-AS5
❑ 95UppDecML-97
❑ 95UppDecMLFS-97
❑ 96BowBes-124
❑ 96BowBesAR-124
❑ 96BowBesR-124
❑ 96ColCho-578
❑ 96ColChoGS-578
❑ 96ColChoSS-578
❑ 96OmaRoyB-27
❑ 96Pin-191
❑ 96Sco-248
❑ 96Spo-141
❑ 96SpoArtP-141
❑ 97OmaRoyB-25
❑ 97Pac-111
❑ 97PacLigB-111
❑ 97PacSil-111
❑ 97Pin-168
❑ 97PinArtP-PP168
❑ 97PinMusC-168
❑ 97PinPrePla-168
❑ 97Ult-72
❑ 97UltGolME-72
❑ 97UltPlaME-72
❑ 98ColCho-346
❑ 98Don-178
❑ 98DonColL-228
❑ 98DonGolPP-178
❑ 98DonPriCL-228
❑ 98DonSilPP-178
❑ 98Fin-121
❑ 98FinNo--121
❑ 98FinNo-R-121
❑ 98FinRef-121
❑ 98Fle-58
❑ 98Lea-28
❑ 98LeaFraDA-28
❑ 98LeaFraF-28
❑ 98LeaFraM-28
❑ 98LeaFraM-28
❑ 98LeaFraMDC-28
❑ 98LeaFraMDC-28
❑ 98LeaFraMZ2-28
❑ 98LeaRS-108
❑ 98LeaRSLHolo-108
❑ 98LeaRSLong-108
❑ 98LeaRTrue-108
❑ 98PacInv-89
❑ 98PacInvGems-140
❑ 98PacInvPBlue-89
❑ 98PacInvSilv-89
❑ 98PacOnl-201
❑ 98PacOnlR-201
❑ 98PacOnlWC-201
❑ 98SPxFin-261
❑ 98SPxFinR-261
❑ 98SPxFinS-261
❑ 98StaCluFDI-292
❑ 98StaCluI-292
❑ 98StaCluOneK-292
❑ 98StaCluPP-292
❑ 98Top-340
❑ 98TopChr-340
❑ 98TopChrR-340
❑ 98TopDevR-340
❑ 98TopDia-340
❑ 98TopMiniC-340
❑ 98UppDec-335
❑ 99Fle-443
❑ 99FleSta9-443
❑ 99FleWarT-443
❑ 99Pac-118
❑ 99PacPlaB-118
❑ 99PacRed-118
❑ 99Top-42
❑ 99TopChr-42
❑ 99TopChrR-42
❑ 99TopMVPP-42
❑ 99UppDec-74
❑ 99UppDecEL1-74
❑ 99UppDecEL2-74
Su'a, Murphy
❑ 81BurBeeT-13
Suares, Orlando
❑ 98GreFalDG-26
Suarez, Cesar
❑ 80VenLeaS-230
Suarez, Ken
❑ 66Top-588
❑ 68Top-218
❑ 68TopVen-218
❑ 69OPC-19
❑ 69Top-19
❑ 70Ind-11
❑ 70OPC-209
❑ 70Top-209
❑ 70WicAerM-17
❑ 71Ind-11
❑ 71MLBOffS-383
❑ 71OPC-597
❑ 71Top-597
❑ 72MilBra-334
❑ 72OPC-483
❑ 72RanTeal-25
❑ 72Top-483
❑ 74OPC-39
❑ 74Top-39
❑ 93RanKee-39
Suarez, Luis
❑ 81WisRapTT-9
❑ 98BriWhiSQ-24
Suarez, Marc
❑ 98BurBeeM-20
Suarez, Nelson
❑ 81WisRapTT-23
Subbiondo, Joe
❑ 52LavPro-10
Subero, Carlos
❑ 93EugEmeC-24
❑ 93EugEmeF-3864
❑ 93LinVenB-166
❑ 94RocRoyC-23
❑ 94RocRoyF-575
❑ 94VenLinU-92
❑ 95LinVen-224
❑ 96-97LinVen-236
Such, Dick
❑ 70Top-599
❑ 71OPC-283
❑ 71Top-283
❑ 83RanAffF-NNO
❑ 84RanJarP-NNO
❑ 86TwiTeal-29
❑ 87TwiPos-27
❑ 87TwiTeal-27
❑ 91DodPho-6
❑ 93RanKee-339
Sudakis, Bill
❑ 69Top-552
❑ 69TopTeaP-22
❑ 70OPC-341
❑ 70Top-341
❑ 71Dod-16
❑ 71DodTic-17
❑ 71MLBOffS-117
❑ 71OPC-253
❑ 71Top-253
❑ 72Top-722
❑ 73OPC-586
❑ 73Top-586
❑ 74OPC-63
❑ 74Top-63
❑ 74TopSta-240
❑ 74TopTra-63T
❑ 75CalAngP-42
❑ 75OPC-291
❑ 75Top-291
❑ 75TopMin-291
❑ 76OmaRoyTT-23
❑ 90DodTar-781
❑ 91MetWIZ-387
❑ 92YanWIZ7-146
❑ 93RanKee-349
Sudbury, Craig
❑ 90SouOreAB-9
❑ 90SouOreAP-3430
❑ 91MadMusC-3
❑ 91ModA'sC-3
❑ 91ModA'sP-3089
❑ 92ModA'sC-14
❑ 92ModA'sF-3899
❑ 93ModA'sC-21
❑ 93ModA'sF-800
Suder, Pete
❑ 42A'sTeal-31
❑ 43A'STEAI-21
❑ 46A'sTeal-13
❑ 47A'sTeal-29
❑ 48A'sTeal-23
❑ 48BluTin-15
❑ 49A'sTeal-30
❑ 49PhiBul-54
❑ 50A'sTeal-24
❑ 50Bow-140
❑ 51A'sTeal-30
❑ 51Bow-154
❑ 52A'sTeal-26
❑ 52Bow-179
❑ 52Top-256
❑ 53A'sTeal-29
❑ 53BowBW-8
❑ 54A'STEAI-25
❑ 54Bow-99
❑ 55Bow-6
❑ 76TayBow4-39
❑ 77TCMTheWY-79
❑ 79DiaGre-346
❑ 83TCMPla1942-24
❑ 83TopRep5-256
Sudgen, Joe
❑ 98CamPepP-75
Sudhoff, William
❑ 03BreE10-136
❑ 04FanCraAL-45
❑ 11SpoLifCW-341
Sudo, Bob
❑ 85UtiBluST-5
❑ 86BurExpP-22
❑ 87JacExpP-447
❑ 88SprCarB-11
Sued, Jose
❑ 93LimRocDWB-95
Sued, Nick
❑ 92ColRedC-17
❑ 92ColRedF-2394
❑ 93KinIndC-23
❑ 93KinIndF-2251
❑ 93KinIndTI-24
❑ 93SouAtlLAPI-38
Suehr, Scott
❑ 83PeoSunF-21
❑ 85MidAngT-21
Sueme, Hal
❑ 43CenFlo-23
❑ 44CenFlo-22
❑ 45CenFlo-24
❑ 47CenFlo-28
❑ 47SigOil-87
Suero, Ignacio
❑ 96HelBreTI-23
❑ 97BelSnaB-26
Suero, William (Williams)
❑ 88MyrBeaBJP-1186
❑ 88SouAtlLAGS-17
❑ 89DunBluJS-17
❑ 90Bes-44
❑ 90KnoBluJB-5
❑ 90KnoBluJP-1249
❑ 90KnoBluJS-19
❑ 90ProAaA-61
❑ 90StaFS7-90
❑ 91Bow-8
❑ 91LinDriAAA-519
❑ 91SyrChiLD-519
❑ 91SyrChiMB-25
❑ 91SyrChiP-2489
❑ 92Bow-181
❑ 92BrePol-25
❑ 92DenZepF-2650
❑ 92DonRoo-113
❑ 92Lea-475
❑ 92LeaBlaG-475
❑ 92Ult-391
❑ 93BrePol-23
❑ 93LimRocDWB-109
❑ 93LinVenB-318
❑ 93Pin-271
❑ 93Sco-258
❑ 93StaClu-377
❑ 93StaCluFDI-377
❑ 93StaCluMOP-377
❑ 94BreMilB-361
❑ 94CarMudF-1589
❑ 94Pac-343
Suess, Ken
❑ 52LavPro-32
Suetsugu, Toshimitsu
❑ 87MiaMarP-25
Sugden, Joseph
❑ 03BreE10-137
❑ 09ObaT21-250
❑ 11SpoLifCW-342
❑ 93ConTSN-937
Suggs, George
❑ 10DarChoE-30
❑ 10DomDisP-114
❑ 10SweCapPP-105
❑ 11HelSta-119
❑ 11PinT-5-411
❑ 11SpoLifM-203
❑ 11T205-166
❑ 12HasTriFT-41B
❑ 14CraJacE-113
❑ 14PieStaT-98
❑ 15CraJacE-113
Sugiura, Toru
❑ 79TCMJapPB-22
Suhr, Gus
❑ 25Zee-122
❑ 26Zee-150
❑ 27Zee-124
❑ 28Zee-145
❑ 29Zee-144
❑ 31Exh-13
❑ 33CraJacP-21
❑ 33ExhFou-7
❑ 33Gou-206
❑ 33WorCig-89
❑ 34BabRutG-58
❑ 34BatR31-41
❑ 34BatR31-187
❑ 34ButPreR-57
❑ 34DiaMatCSB-176
❑ 34DiaStaR-56
❑ 34TarThoBD-23
❑ 35AlDemDCR3-141
❑ 35DiaMatCS3T1-138
❑ 35GouPuzR-8K
❑ 35GouPuzR-9K
❑ 36GouWidPPR-A96
❑ 37ExhFou-7
❑ 38CloFotW-77
❑ 38ExhFou-7
❑ 39PlaBal-83
❑ 40PhiTeal-21
❑ 40PlaBal-94
❑ 41PhiTeal-24
❑ 72TCMthe1-170
Suigiura, Mamoru
❑ 87MiaMarP-27
Sukeforth, Clyde
❑ 48DodTeal-23
❑ 52Bow-227
❑ 52Top-364
❑ 79DiaGre-89
❑ 83TopRep5-364
❑ 85BigLeaC3-70
❑ 90DodTar-782
Sukla, Ed
❑ 65SeaPop-23
❑ 66SeaPop-23
❑ 66Top-417
❑ 67SeaPop-16
❑ 68SeaPop-15
❑ 74PhoGiaC-84
Sularz, Guy
❑ 78PhoGiaC-25
❑ 79PhoGiaVNB-22
❑ 80PhoGiaVNB-21
❑ 81PhoGiaVNB-15
❑ 82Gia25tATI-28
❑ 83Don-605
❑ 83Fle-273
❑ 83PhoGiaBHN-14
❑ 83Top-379
❑ 84PhoGiaC-22
❑ 91PacSenL-129
❑ 97PhoFirDTTI-4
Sulik, Ernest
❑ 30Zee-158
❑ 32Zee-108
❑ 33Zee-42
❑ 33Zee-149
Sullivan, Adam
❑ 94DavLipB-23
❑ 95DavLipB-22
Sullivan, Brendan
❑ 96IdaFalB-23
❑ 97CliLumG-25
❑ 98RanCucQG-27
❑ 98RanCucQG-27
Sullivan, Brian
❑ 89RenSilSCLC-246
❑ 90JohCitCS-26
❑ 90RocExpP-2690
❑ 91NiaFalRC-9
❑ 91NiaFalRP-3649
❑ 92FayGenF-2183
Sullivan, Carl
❑ 87DayBeaAP-2
❑ 88FloStaLAS-49
❑ 88TamTarS-23
❑ 89SarWhiSS-23
❑ 90SarWhiSS-23
❑ 91Cla/Bes-303
❑ 91SarWhiSC-25
❑ 91SarWhiSP-1126
Sullivan, Charlie
❑ 91ButCopKSP-19
❑ 92ButCopKSP-15
❑ 93PitMetC-19
❑ 93PitMetF-3720
Sullivan, Dan
❑ 86WinHavRSP-25
❑ 92PenPilC-22
❑ 92PenPilF-2932
❑ 93RivPilCLC-20
❑ 94RivPilCLC-18
Sullivan, Daniel C.
❑ 87WinHavRSP-9
Sullivan, Dave
❑ 87ElmPioBC-3
❑ 87ElmPioRC-3
Sullivan, Dennis
❑ 09BriE97-29A
❑ 09BriE97-29B
❑ 11PinT-5-1106
Sullivan, Frank
❑ 55Bow-15
❑ 55Top-106
❑ 55TopDouH-21
❑ 56Top-71
❑ 56TopPin-25
❑ 57Top-21
❑ 58Hir-58
❑ 58RedSoxJP-10
❑ 58Top-18
❑ 59RedSoxJP-9
❑ 59Top-323
❑ 60Top-280
❑ 61Pos-55A
❑ 61Pos-55B
❑ 61Top-281
❑ 62Top-352
❑ 63Top-389
❑ 79TCM50-57
❑ 81RedSoxBG2S-54
Sullivan, Glenn
❑ 87GenCubP-25
❑ 88WinSpiS-18
❑ 89ChaKniTI-10
❑ 90ChaKniTI-11
❑ 90CMC-90
❑ 90IowCubC-15
❑ 90IowCubP-327
❑ 90ProAAAF-634
❑ 91IowCubLD-220
❑ 91IowCubP-1072
❑ 91LinDriAAA-220
Sullivan, Grant
❑ 91OneYanP-4155
❑ 92GreHorC-19
❑ 92GreHorF-780
❑ 93PriWilCC-23
❑ 93PriWilCF-656
❑ 94TamYanC-25
❑ 94TamYanF-2383
❑ 95NorNavTI-34
Sullivan, Harry
❑ 22Zee-15
Sullivan, Haywood
❑ 57Top-336
❑ 58Top-197
❑ 59Top-416
❑ 60Top-474
❑ 61A'sTeal-19
❑ 61AthJayP-20
❑ 61AthJayP-21
❑ 61Pos-56A
❑ 61Pos-56B
❑ 61Top-212
❑ 62Jel-99
❑ 62Pos-99
❑ 62PosCan-99
❑ 62Top-184
❑ 62TopStal-60
❑ 62TopVen-184
❑ 63AthJayP-10
❑ 63Jel-92
❑ 63Pos-92
❑ 63Top-359
❑ 81RedSoxBG2S-55
Sullivan, Jason
❑ 93PriRedC-29
❑ 93PriRedF-4180
Sullivan, Jim
❑ 75ForLauYS-12
Sullivan, Jim (James E.)
❑ 20Zee-151
❑ 98CamPepP-76
Sullivan, Joe
❑ 36GouWidPPR-A97
❑ 41Gou-22
❑ 74TigTCM1AC-30
Sullivan, John
❑ 75WatRoyT-29
❑ 76WatRoyT-29
Sullivan, John L.
❑ 12Zee-156
❑ 23WilChoV-160
❑ 88KimN18-44
Sullivan, John Paul
❑ 83TCMPla1944-21
❑ 84BluJayFS-29
❑ 85BluJayFS-28
❑ 86BluJayFS-30
❑ 87BluJayFS-31
❑ 88BluJayFS-29
❑ 89BluJayFS-28
❑ 90BluJayFS-28
❑ 91BluJayFS-24
❑ 91BluJayFS-26
❑ 93BluJayFS-29
Sullivan, John Peter
❑ 66Top-597
❑ 67Top-568
❑ 91MetWIZ-388
Sullivan, Marc
❑ 84PawRedST-20
❑ 86Don-614
❑ 86Top-529
❑ 86TopTif-529
❑ 87Don-643
❑ 87DonOpeD-187
❑ 87OPC-66
❑ 87RedSoxP-22
❑ 87Top-66
❑ 87TopTif-66
❑ 88Sco-271
❑ 88ScoGlo-271
❑ 88StaLinAst-18
❑ 88Top-354
❑ 88TopTif-354
Sullivan, Martin J.
❑ 12ColRedB-278A
❑ 12ColRedB-278B
❑ 12ColRedB-279
❑ 12ColTinT-278B
❑ 12ColTinT-280
❑ 87FouBasHN-10
❑ 87OldJudN-478
❑ 88AugBecN-31
❑ 88GandBCGCE-37
❑ 88WG1CarG-16
Sullivan, Michael J.
❑ 87OldJudN-479
❑ 90SpaPhiB-9
❑ 90SpaPhiS-21
Sullivan, Mike
❑ 81WatRedT-9
❑ 89BatCliP-1929
❑ 90SpaPhiP-2490
❑ 91ClePhiC-9
❑ 91ClePhiP-1620
❑ 92ReaPhiF-575
❑ 92ReaPhiS-544
❑ 93ReaPhiF-295
❑ 98IndIndQ-36
Sullivan, Pete
❑ 98AubDouTI-28
Sullivan, Russell
❑ 53TigGle-27
❑ 55JetPos-15
❑ 57JetPos-19
Sullivan, Scott
❑ 93BilMusF-3944
❑ 93BilMusSP-17
❑ 94Bow-598
❑ 94ChaLooF-1358
❑ 94ExcFS7-181
❑ 94UppDecML-207
❑ 95Bow-154
❑ 95Exc-183
❑ 95FleUpd-137
❑ 95Sum-171
❑ 95SumNthD-171
❑ 95UppDecML-140
❑ 95UppDecMLFS-140
❑ 96Bow-213
❑ 96BowFoi-213
❑ 96IndIndB-25
❑ 96Sco-251
❑ 97IndInd-22
❑ 98Pac-275
❑ 98PacOnl-202

❑ 98PacOnlR-202
❑ 98PacOnlWC-202
❑ 98PacPlaB-275
❑ 98PacRedT-275
❑ 98PacSil-275
Sullivan, Shane
❑ 98RocCubM-27
❑ 98RocCubTI-28
Sullivan, Sport
❑ 88PacEigMO-27
Sullivan, William
❑ 92BilMusF-3355
❑ 92BilMusSP-26
Sullivan, William Joseph Jr.
❑ 34DiaMatCSB-177
❑ 36R31PasP-23
❑ 38CloFotW-78
❑ 42DodTeal-21
❑ 61Fle-141
❑ 90DodTar-783
Sullivan, William Joseph Sr.
❑ 03BreE10-138
❑ 08RosComP-18
❑ 09ColChiE-278A
❑ 09ColChiE-278B
❑ 09ColChiE-279
❑ 09T206-346
❑ 11HelSta-16
❑ 11PinT-5-756
❑ 11PloCanE-59
❑ 11SpoLifCW-343
❑ 11SpoLifM-31
❑ 11TurRedT-121
❑ 12ColTinT-278A
❑ 12ColTinT-279
❑ 12HasTriFT-67A
❑ 12HasTriFT-67B
❑ 12T207-179
❑ 15SpoNewM-174
❑ 16SpoNewM-172
❑ 17Zee-119
❑ 87BucN28-24
Sultea, Chris
❑ 91SalLakTP-3210
Summa, Howard Homer
❑ 23MapCriV-6
❑ 25Exh-88
❑ 26Exh-88
❑ 29ExhFou-28
❑ 31Zee-74
❑ 32Zee-28
❑ 74A's192T-25
❑ 81ConTSN-100
❑ 91ConTSN-205
❑ 94ConTSN-1147
❑ 94ConTSNB-1147
Summers, Champ (John)
❑ 76OPC-299
❑ 76Top-299
❑ 78IndIndTI-12
❑ 78SSP270-125
❑ 78Top-622
❑ 79Top-516
❑ 80OPC-100
❑ 80Top-176
❑ 81CokTeaS-49
❑ 81Don-130
❑ 81Fle-466
❑ 81OPC-27
❑ 81Top-27
❑ 81TopScr-24
❑ 81TopSti-76
❑ 82Don-81
❑ 82Fle-282
❑ 82FleSta-154
❑ 82Gia25tATI-29
❑ 82Top-369
❑ 82TopTra-115T
❑ 83Fle-274
❑ 83GiaPos-25
❑ 83Top-428
❑ 84FleUpd-112
❑ 84Nes792-768
❑ 84PadMot-25
❑ 84Top-768
❑ 84TopTif-768
❑ 84TopTra-113T
❑ 84TopTraT-113T
❑ 85Top-208
❑ 85TopTif-208
❑ 86IndIndTI-32
❑ 87ColCliP-25
❑ 87ColCliP-2
❑ 87ColCliT-24
❑ 88ColCliP-24
❑ 88ColCliP-307
❑ 89ColCliC-24
❑ 89ColCliP-24
❑ 89PacSenL-96
❑ 89T/MSenL-103
❑ 90TopTVY-6
❑ 98SalVol-32
Summers, Craig
❑ 91ParPatF-13
Summers, Ed (Oron Edgar)
❑ 07TigACDPP-26
❑ 08RosComP-42
❑ 09AmeCarE90-1-102
❑ 09ColChiE-281
❑ 09T206-347
❑ 09TigMorBBBP-15
❑ 09TigMorPWBPP-13
❑ 09TigTaCP-18
❑ 10CouT21-63
❑ 10CouT21-229
❑ 10NadE1-54
❑ 10RedCroT-160
❑ 10RedCroT-248
❑ 11MecDFT-29
❑ 11S74Sil-18
❑ 11SpoLifCW-344
❑ 11SpoLifM-71
❑ 11T205-167
❑ 12ColRedB-281
❑ 12ColTinT-281
❑ 12HasTriFT-26
❑ 72ClaCar-96
❑ 81TigDetN-66
Summers, Jeff
❑ 83SanJosBC-22
❑ 84ChaO'sT-25
❑ 85ChaO'sT-16
Summers, Lonnie
❑ 92NegLeaRLI-57
Summers, Scott
❑ 87GreHorP-9
Summers, Tom
❑ 86TamTarP-22
Summers, William
❑ 55Bow-317
Summitt, Kerry
❑ 92DavLipB-24
Sumner, Chad
❑ 92JohCitCC-13
❑ 92JohCitCF-3127
❑ 93SavCarC-23
❑ 93SavCarF-695
Sumter, Kevin
❑ 95BoiHawTI-27
Sun Devils, Arizona State
❑ 89AriStaB-29
Sunday, Billy
❑ 87BucN28-25
❑ 87OldJudN-480
❑ 88AugBecN-32
❑ 88GandBCGCE-38
❑ 88WG1CarG-63
Sundberg, Jim
❑ 75Hos-100
❑ 75OPC-567
❑ 75RanPos-32
❑ 75RanPos-33
❑ 75Top-567
❑ 75TopMin-567
❑ 76Hos-68
❑ 76OPC-226
❑ 76SSP-260
❑ 76Top-226
❑ 77BurCheD-23
❑ 77Hos-110
❑ 77OPC-185
❑ 77Top-351
❑ 78Hos-79
❑ 78RanBurK-2
❑ 78SSP270-83
❑ 78Top-492
❑ 79BasPat-85
❑ 79Hos-97
❑ 79Kel-60
❑ 79OPC-53
❑ 79Top-120
❑ 80OPC-276
❑ 80Top-530
❑ 81AllGamPI-44
❑ 81Don-385
❑ 81Fle-619
❑ 81OPC-95
❑ 81Top-95
❑ 81TopSti-133
❑ 81TopSupHT-95
❑ 82Don-268
❑ 82Fle-332
❑ 82FleSta-181
❑ 82OPC-335
❑ 82Top-335
❑ 82TopSti-240
❑ 83AllGamPI-44
❑ 83Don-7
❑ 83Don-609
❑ 83DonActA-26
❑ 83Fle-580
❑ 83FleSta-189
❑ 83Kel-38
❑ 83OPC-158
❑ 83RanAffF-10
❑ 83Top-665
❑ 83TopSti-126
❑ 84AllGamPI-132
❑ 84BreGar-18
❑ 84BrePol-8
❑ 84Don-178
❑ 84Fle-431
❑ 84FleUpd-113
❑ 84Nes792-779
❑ 84OPC-251
❑ 84Top-779
❑ 84TopSti-355
❑ 84TopTif-779
❑ 84TopTra-114T
❑ 84TopTraT-114T
❑ 85AllGamPI-43
❑ 85Don-89
❑ 85Fle-597
❑ 85FleUpd-113
❑ 85Lea-78
❑ 85OPC-102
❑ 85RoyTeal-30
❑ 85Top-446
❑ 85TopMin-446
❑ 85TopSti-286
❑ 85TopTif-446
❑ 85TopTifT-114T
❑ 85TopTra-114T
❑ 86BasStaB-107
❑ 86Don-277
❑ 86Fle-22
❑ 86Lea-149
❑ 86OPC-245
❑ 86RoyKitCD-18
❑ 86RoyNatP-8
❑ 86RoyTeal-25
❑ 86Spo-186
❑ 86Top-245
❑ 86TopSti-15
❑ 86TopSti-259
❑ 86TopTif-245
❑ 87CubCan-32
❑ 87CubDavB-11
❑ 87Don-280
❑ 87Fle-382
❑ 87FleGlo-382
❑ 87FleUpd-114
❑ 87FleUpdG-114
❑ 87OPC-190
❑ 87Top-190
❑ 87TopSti-256
❑ 87TopTif-190
❑ 87TopTra-119T
❑ 87TopTraT-119T
❑ 88Don-488
❑ 88DonTeaBC-488
❑ 88Fle-434
❑ 88FleGlo-434
❑ 88Sco-244
❑ 88ScoGlo-244
❑ 88Top-516
❑ 88TopBig-100
❑ 88TopClo-109
❑ 88TopTif-516
❑ 89Bow-227
❑ 89BowTif-227
❑ 89RanMot-24
❑ 89RanSmo-32
❑ 89Top-78
❑ 89TopBig-103
❑ 89TopTif-78
❑ 89UppDec-331
❑ 90PubIntS-423
❑ 91PacRyaTEl-93
❑ 92UppDecS-12
❑ 93RanKee-350
❑ 94BreMilB-362
❑ 94RanAllP-2
❑ 94RanAllP-6
❑ 94TedWil-87
Sundberg, Richard
❑ 82RedPioT-15
Sunderlage, Jeff
❑ 82LynMetT-9
❑ 83LynMetT-18
Sundgren, Scott
❑ 86BurExpP-23
Sundin, Gordie
❑ 91OriCro-447
Sundra, Steve
❑ 33WorCig(-90
❑ 40PlaBal-122
❑ 72TCMthe3-67
❑ 75YanDyn1T-46
❑ 93ConTSN-902
❑ 96Bro194F-13
Sung, Pil
❑ 96WesOahCHWB-7
Sunkel, Mark
❑ 88AlaGolTI-17
Sunkel, Tom
❑ 39PlaBal-146
❑ 40PlaBal-110
❑ 90DodTar-784
❑ 95ConTSN-1422
Sunker, Steve
❑ 78CliDodT-29
Sunnen, Gene
❑ 88WatPirP-34
Sunny, Stacy
❑ 94ColSilBC-9
❑ 95ColSilB-28
❑ 95ColSilB9-8
❑ 96ColSilB-28
Suns, Jacksonville
❑ 91JacSunP-165
Sunseri, Peter
❑ 27Zee-106
❑ 28Zee-165
Suntop, Lionel
❑ 75TopPho-117
Suplee, Ray
❑ 92ClaDraP-113
❑ 92OneYanC-17
❑ 93GreHorC-22
❑ 93GreHorF-901
❑ 93SouAtlLAGF-23
❑ 94Bow-396
❑ 94ClaGolF-86
❑ 94TamYanC-26
❑ 94TamYanF-2399
❑ 95TamYanYI-28
❑ 96HigDesMB-27
Suppan, Jeff
❑ 94Bow-391
❑ 94Cla-183
❑ 94SarRedSC-1
❑ 94SarRedSF-1950
❑ 95Bow-15
❑ 95BowBes-B60
❑ 95BowBesR-B60
❑ 95Exc-16
❑ 95SPCha-17
❑ 95SPChaDC-17
❑ 95TreThuTI-15
❑ 95UppDecML-83
❑ 95UppDecMLFS-83
❑ 96Bow-236
❑ 96BowBes-153
❑ 96BowBesAR-153
❑ 96BowBesR-153
❑ 96BowFoi-236
❑ 96ColCho-428
❑ 96ColChoGS-39
❑ 96ColChoGS-428
❑ 96ColChoSS-39
❑ 96ColChoSS-428
❑ 96Fla-27
❑ 96Fle-35
❑ 96FleRedS-15
❑ 96FleTif-35
❑ 96Lea-217
❑ 96LeaPre-138
❑ 96LeaPreP-138
❑ 96LeaPrePB-217
❑ 96LeaPrePG-217
❑ 96LeaPrePS-217
❑ 96LeaSigA-216
❑ 96LeaSigAG-216
❑ 96LeaSigAS-216
❑ 96PawRedSDD-28
❑ 96Pin-387
❑ 96PinAfi-194
❑ 96PinAfiAP-194
❑ 96PinFoil-387
❑ 96Sco-500
❑ 96SelCer-123
❑ 96SelCerAP-123
❑ 96SelCerCB-123
❑ 96SelCerCR-123
❑ 96SelCerMB-123
❑ 96SelCerMG-123
❑ 96SelCerMR-123
❑ 96SigRooOJTP-T10
❑ 96StaClu-444
❑ 96StaCluMOP-444
❑ 96Sum-178
❑ 96SumAbo&B-178
❑ 96SumArtP-178
❑ 96SumFoi-178
❑ 96Top-347
❑ 96TopChr-139
❑ 96TopChrR-139
❑ 96TopGal-144
❑ 96TopGalPPI-144
❑ 96Ult-322
❑ 96UltGolM-322
❑ 96UppDec-227
❑ 96UppDecFSP-FS20
❑ 96Zen-109
❑ 96ZenArtP-109
❑ 97Bow-300
❑ 97BowBes-159
❑ 97BowBesAR-159
❑ 97BowBesR-159
❑ 97BowChr-208
❑ 97BowChrI-208
❑ 97BowChrIR-208
❑ 97BowChrR-208
❑ 97BowInt-300
❑ 97ColCho-47
❑ 97Don-208
❑ 97Don-375
❑ 97DonGolPP-208
❑ 97DonGolPP-375
❑ 97DonLim-159
❑ 97DonLimE-159
❑ 97DonLimENG-159
❑ 97DonSigA-93
❑ 97DonSigAC-116
❑ 97DonSigAM-116
❑ 97DonSilPP-208
❑ 97DonSilPP-375
❑ 97DonTea-51
❑ 97DonTeaSPE-51
❑ 97Lea-340
❑ 97LeaFraM-340
❑ 97LeaFraMDC-340
❑ 97PawRedS-28
❑ 97PawRedS-30
❑ 97RedSoxS-11
❑ 97RedSoxSPl-11
❑ 97RedSoxSPr-11
❑ 97SarRedS-24
❑ 97Sco-210
❑ 97ScoArtPWB-210
❑ 97ScoPreS-210
❑ 97ScoShoS-210
❑ 97ScoShoSAP-210
❑ 97Top-348
❑ 97UppDec-28
❑ 98CirThu-256
❑ 98CirThuRav-256
❑ 98CirThuSupRav-256
❑ 98ColCho-292
❑ 98DiaBacP-12
❑ 98DiaMcD-22
❑ 98Don-214
❑ 98DonCol-182
❑ 98DonColE-433
❑ 98DonColL-233
❑ 98DonColP-655
❑ 98DonColS-177
❑ 98DonEli-33
❑ 98DonEliA-33
❑ 98DonEliS-33
❑ 98DonGolPP-214
❑ 98DonPre-105
❑ 98DonPreSeat-105
❑ 98DonPriCD-182
❑ 98DonPriCE-433
❑ 98DonPriCL-233
❑ 98DonPriCP-655
❑ 98DonRatR-7
❑ 98DonRatRM-7
❑ 98DonSigA-82
❑ 98DonSigAC-105
❑ 98DonSigAM-107
❑ 98DonSilPP-214
❑ 98Fle-478
❑ 98Lea-33
❑ 98LeaFraDA-33
❑ 98LeaFraF-33
❑ 98LeaFraM-33
❑ 98LeaFraM-33
❑ 98LeaFraMDC-33
❑ 98LeaFraMDC-33
❑ 98LeaFraMS-33
❑ 98LeaFraMZ2-33
❑ 98MetUni-194
❑ 98MetUniPMG-194
❑ 98Pac-47
❑ 98PacOnl-49
❑ 98PacOnlR-49
❑ 98PacOnlWC-49
❑ 98PacPlaB-47
❑ 98PacRedT-47
❑ 98PacSil-47
❑ 98PinPer-103
❑ 98PinPerPP-103
❑ 98PinPlu-134
❑ 98PinSna-AD14
❑ 98RedSoxS-6
❑ 98RedSoxSP-6
❑ 98Sco-85
❑ 98ScoRT-207
❑ 98ScoRTSS-PP114
❑ 98ScoRTSSAP-PP114
❑ 98ScoRTSSAP1-PP114
❑ 98ScoSS-PP39
❑ 98ScoSSAP-PP39
❑ 98SkyDugA-91
❑ 98SkyDugAIA-91
❑ 98StaCluFDI-312
❑ 98StaCluI-312
❑ 98StaCluOneK-312
❑ 98StaCluPP-312
❑ 98Stu-168
❑ 98StuGPP-168
❑ 98StuSPP-168
❑ 98Top-377
❑ 98TopChr-377
❑ 98TopChrR-377
❑ 98TopDevR-377
❑ 98TopDia-377
❑ 98TopMiniC-377
❑ 98Ult-114
❑ 98UltGolM-114
❑ 98UltMas-114
❑ 98UltPlaM-114
❑ 98UppDec-647
❑ 99UppDec-390
❑ 99UppDecEL1-390
❑ 99UppDecEL2-390
Surane, John
❑ 90IdaFalBP-3250
Surhoff, B.J.
❑ 86VanCanP-24
❑ 87BrePol-5
❑ 87BreTeal-13
❑ 87ClaUpdY-135
❑ 87Don-28
❑ 87DonRoo-17
❑ 87FleUpd-115
❑ 87FleUpdG-115
❑ 87Lea-28
❑ 87SpoRool-23
❑ 87SpoRooP-6
❑ 87SpoTeaP-19
❑ 87Top-216
❑ 87TopTif-216
❑ 88BrePol-5
❑ 88BreTeal-33
❑ 88ClaBlu-202
❑ 88Don-172
❑ 88DonBasB-277
❑ 88Fle-175
❑ 88FleGlo-175
❑ 88Lea-164
❑ 88OPC-174
❑ 88PanSti-120
❑ 88RedFolSB-85
❑ 88Sco-22
❑ 88ScoGlo-22
❑ 88ScoYouSI-8
❑ 88Spo-57
❑ 88StaLinBre-17
❑ 88Top-491
❑ 88TopBig-22
❑ 88TopGloS-49
❑ 88TopRoo-10
❑ 88TopSti-202
❑ 88TopStiB-57
❑ 88TopTif-491
❑ 88ToyRoo-31

❑ 89Bow-137
❑ 89BowTif-137
❑ 89BreGar-5
❑ 89BrePol-5
❑ 89BreYea-5
❑ 89ClaLigB-25
❑ 89Don-221
❑ 89DonBasB-221
❑ 89Fle-197
❑ 89FleGlo-197
❑ 89OPC-33
❑ 89PanSti-368
❑ 89Sco-154
❑ 89Spo-208
❑ 89Top-33
❑ 89TopSti-200
❑ 89TopTif-33
❑ 89UppDec-343
❑ 90Bow-393
❑ 90BowTif-393
❑ 90BreMilB-25
❑ 90Don-173
❑ 90DonBesA-78
❑ 90Fle-338
❑ 90FleCan-338
❑ 90Lea-290
❑ 90M.Vpin-53
❑ 90MLBBasB-84
❑ 90OPC-696
❑ 90PanSti-93
❑ 90PubIntS-505
❑ 90Sco-74
❑ 90Top-696
❑ 90TopBig-198
❑ 90TopSti-203
❑ 90TopTif-696
❑ 90UppDec-159
❑ 91Bow-44
❑ 91BreMilB-26
❑ 91BrePol-23
❑ 91Don-460
❑ 91Fle-598
❑ 91Lea-42
❑ 91OPC-592
❑ 91PanFreS-203
❑ 91PanSti-169
❑ 91Sco-477
❑ 91StaClu-206
❑ 91StaCluP-42
❑ 91Stu-78
❑ 91Top-592
❑ 91TopDesS-592
❑ 91TopMic-592
❑ 91TopTif-592
❑ 91Ult-182
❑ 91UppDec-254
❑ 92Bow-481
❑ 92BrePol-26
❑ 92Don-70
❑ 92Fle-190
❑ 92Hig5-68
❑ 92Lea-212
❑ 92LeaBlaG-212
❑ 92OPC-718
❑ 92PanSti-34
❑ 92Pin-118
❑ 92RedFolS-92
❑ 92Sco-78
❑ 92StaClu-117
❑ 92Stu-197
❑ 92Top-718
❑ 92TopDaiQTU-7
❑ 92TopGol-718
❑ 92TopGolW-718
❑ 92TopKid-82
❑ 92TopMic-718
❑ 92TriPla-56
❑ 92Ult-85
❑ 92UppDec-120
❑ 93Bow-71
❑ 93BrePol-24
❑ 93BreSen5-3
❑ 93DiaMar-105
❑ 93Don-545
❑ 93Fin-8
❑ 93FinRef-8
❑ 93Fla-230
❑ 93Fle-257
❑ 93Lea-166
❑ 93OPC-343
❑ 93PacSpa-165
❑ 93PanSti-36
❑ 93Pin-87
❑ 93RedFolS-92
❑ 93Sco-33
❑ 93Sel-62
❑ 93SP-70
❑ 93StaClu-711
❑ 93StaCluFDI-711
❑ 93StaCluMOP-711
❑ 93Stu-174
❑ 93Top-417
❑ 93TopGol-417
❑ 93TopInaM-417
❑ 93TopInaR-417
❑ 93TopMic-417
❑ 93TriPla-248
❑ 93Ult-224
❑ 93UppDec-102
❑ 93UppDecGold-102
❑ 94BreMilB-363
❑ 94BrePol-26
❑ 94BreTeal-25
❑ 94ColC-469
❑ 94ColChoGS-469
❑ 94ColChoSS-469
❑ 94Don-310
❑ 94Fin-344
❑ 94FinRef-344
❑ 94Fle-192
❑ 94Lea-369
❑ 94OPC-197
❑ 94Pac-344
❑ 94PanSti-87
❑ 94Pin-152
❑ 94PinArtP-152
❑ 94PinMusC-152
❑ 94ProMag-73
❑ 94Sco-77
❑ 94ScoGolR-77
❑ 94Sel-330
❑ 94SP-60
❑ 94SPDieC-60
❑ 94StaClu-215
❑ 94StaCluFDI-215
❑ 94StaCluGR-215
❑ 94StaCluMOP-215
❑ 94Top-102
❑ 94TopGol-102
❑ 94TopSpa-102
❑ 94TriPla-58
❑ 94Ult-379
❑ 94UppDec-369
❑ 94UppDecED-369
❑ 95ColCho-174
❑ 95ColChoGS-174
❑ 95ColChoSS-174
❑ 95Don-356
❑ 95DonPreP-356
❑ 95DonTopotO-103
❑ 95Fle-191
❑ 95Pin-352
❑ 95PinArtP-352
❑ 95PinMusC-352
❑ 95Sco-345
❑ 95ScoGolR-345
❑ 95ScoPlaTS-345
❑ 95Top-367
❑ 96BalOriP-34
❑ 96ColCho-195
❑ 96ColCho-469
❑ 96ColChoGS-195
❑ 96ColChoGS-469
❑ 96ColChoSS-195
❑ 96ColChoSS-469
❑ 96Don-113
❑ 96DonDiaK-20
❑ 96DonPreP-113
❑ 96EmoXL-10
❑ 96Fin-B304
❑ 96FinRef-B304
❑ 96Fla-13
❑ 96Fle-159
❑ 96FleTeaL-8
❑ 96FleTif-159
❑ 96FleUpd-U8
❑ 96FleUpdTC-U8
❑ 96MetUni-10
❑ 96MetUniP-10
❑ 96MLBPin-34
❑ 96OriFle-16
❑ 96Pac-349
❑ 96PacPri-P110
❑ 96PacPriG-P110
❑ 96PanSti-191
❑ 96Pin-88
❑ 96Pin-351
❑ 96PinAfi-92
❑ 96PinAfiAP-92
❑ 96PinAfiFPP-92
❑ 96PinArtP-50
❑ 96PinFoil-351
❑ 96PinSta-50
❑ 96Sco-54
❑ 96ScoDugC-A47
❑ 96ScoDugCAP-A47
❑ 96Sel-133
❑ 96SelArtP-133
❑ 96Spo-43
❑ 96SpoArtP-43
❑ 96StaClu-332
❑ 96StaCluMOP-332
❑ 96Sum-35
❑ 96SumAbo&B-35
❑ 96SumArtP-35
❑ 96SumFoi-35
❑ 96Ult-85
❑ 96Ult-309
❑ 96UltGolM-85
❑ 96UltGolM-309
❑ 96UppDec-120
❑ 96UppDec-276
❑ 97BalOriP-31
❑ 97Cir-277
❑ 97CirRav-277
❑ 97ColCho-43
❑ 97ColChoT-BO7
❑ 97Don-245
❑ 97DonGolPP-245
❑ 97DonSilPP-245
❑ 97DonTea-38
❑ 97DonTeaSPE-38
❑ 97Fin-47
❑ 97FinRef-47
❑ 97Fle-14
❑ 97FleTif-14
❑ 97Lea-157
❑ 97LeaFraM-157
❑ 97LeaFraMDC-157
❑ 97MetUni-9
❑ 97OriSco-11
❑ 97OriScoPl-11
❑ 97OriScoPr-11
❑ 97Pac-30
❑ 97PacLigB-30
❑ 97PacSil-30
❑ 97Pin-142
❑ 97PinArtP-PP142
❑ 97PinMusC-142
❑ 97PinPrePla-142
❑ 97Sco-197
❑ 97ScoArtPWB-197
❑ 97ScoPreS-197
❑ 97ScoShoS-197
❑ 97ScoShoSAP-197
❑ 97StaClu-79
❑ 97StaCluMOP-79
❑ 97Top-41
❑ 97Ult-423
❑ 97UltGolME-423
❑ 97UltPlaME-423
❑ 97UppDec-304
❑ 98CirThu-169
❑ 98CirThuRav-169
❑ 98CirThuSupRav-169
❑ 98ColCho-317
❑ 98Fin-235
❑ 98FinNo--235
❑ 98FinNo-R-235
❑ 98FinRef-235
❑ 98Fle-461
❑ 98FleVin'-79
❑ 98FleVin'C-79
❑ 98MetUni-180
❑ 98MetUniPMG-180
❑ 98OriSco-13
❑ 98OriScoP-13
❑ 98Pac-34
❑ 98PacAur-15
❑ 98PacOme-35
❑ 98PacOmeR-35
❑ 98PacOnl-103
❑ 98PacOnlR-103
❑ 98PacOnlWC-103
❑ 98PacPar-18
❑ 98PacParC-18
❑ 98PacParG-18
❑ 98PacParHS-18
❑ 98PacParPB-18
❑ 98PacParR-18
❑ 98PacPlaB-34
❑ 98PacRedT-34
❑ 98PacSil-34
❑ 98Pin-147
❑ 98PinPreP-147
❑ 98PinSna-BO8
❑ 98Revo-23
❑ 98RevoSS-23
❑ 98Sco-203
❑ 98ScoRT-176
❑ 98ScoSS-PP96
❑ 98ScoSSAP-PP96
❑ 98StaCluFDI-269
❑ 98StaClul-269
❑ 98StaCluOneK-269
❑ 98StaCluPP-269
❑ 98Top-86
❑ 98TopChr-86
❑ 98TopChrR-86
❑ 98TopDevR-86
❑ 98TopDia-86
❑ 98TopMiniC-86
❑ 98TopOpeD-42
❑ 98Ult-92
❑ 98UltGolM-92
❑ 98UltMas-92
❑ 98UltPlaM-92
❑ 98UppDec-38
❑ 98UppDecSF-23
❑ 99Fle-281
❑ 99FleSta9-281
❑ 99FleWarT-281
❑ 99MetUni-34
❑ 99MetUniGM-34
❑ 99MetUniPMG-34
❑ 99Pac-61
❑ 99PacAur-26
❑ 99PacAurOD-26
❑ 99PacCroC-42
❑ 99PacCroCPB-42
❑ 99PacOme-38
❑ 99PacOmeC-38
❑ 99PacOmeG-38
❑ 99PacOmePB-38
❑ 99PacPar-37
❑ 99PacParC-37
❑ 99PacParG-37
❑ 99PacParHoloGold-37
❑ 99PacParHS-37
❑ 99PacParOD-37
❑ 99PacParPB-37
❑ 99PacParRed-37
❑ 99PacPlaB-61
❑ 99PacRed-61
❑ 99SkyPre-199
❑ 99SkyPreR-199
❑ 99SkyThu-16
❑ 99SkyThuRant-16
❑ 99SkyThuRave-16
❑ 99StaClu-139
❑ 99StaCluFDI-139
❑ 99StaCluOoaK-139
❑ 99StaCluPP-139
❑ 99ThuSkySupR-16
❑ 99Top-198
❑ 99TopChr-198
❑ 99TopChrR-198
❑ 99TopMVPP-198
❑ 99UD Cho-61
❑ 99UD ChoPCR-61
❑ 99UppDec-318
❑ 99UppDecEL1-318
❑ 99UppDecEL2-318
❑ 99Vic-53

Surhoff, Rich
❑ 85PhiTas-46
❑ 85PorBeaC-49
❑ 86Don-42
❑ 86OklCit8P-22
❑ 88IowCubC-10
❑ 88IowCubP-529
❑ 93RanKee-351

Surico, Steve
❑ 89AncGlaP-25
❑ 90ButCopKSP-23

Suriel, Miguel
❑ 97ChaRivDG-27
❑ 97PriDevR-12
❑ 98ChaRivDG-27
❑ 98HudValR-27

Suris, Jorge
❑ 85SpoIndC-23

Surkont, Max
❑ 46SeaSLP-62
❑ 52Bow-12
❑ 52Top-302
❑ 53BowC-156
❑ 53BraJohC-11
❑ 53BraMer-16
❑ 53BraSpiaS3-23
❑ 54Bow-75
❑ 54DanDee-26
❑ 55Bow-83
❑ 56Top-209
❑ 57Top-310
❑ 58SeaRalT-17
❑ 59SeaPop-10
❑ 83Bra53F-36
❑ 83TopRep5-302

Surner, Ben
❑ 82HolMilT-26
❑ 83NasAngT-24

Surratt, Alfred
❑ 92NegLeaRLI-58
❑ 96NegLeaBMKC-9

Surratt, Jamie
❑ 93JohCitCC-24
❑ 93JohCitCF-3690

Susce, George
❑ 49IndTeal-29
❑ 50RedSoxTI-25
❑ 55A'sRodM-41
❑ 55A'sTeal-26
❑ 55Bow-320
❑ 56A'sPos-42
❑ 56Top-93
❑ 57Top-229
❑ 58Top-189
❑ 59Top-511
❑ 76A'sRodMC-27
❑ 93RanKee-43

Susce, Steve
❑ 83AleDukT-21

Sutch, Rick (Ray)
❑ 92MadMusC-19
❑ 92MadMusF-1237
❑ 93SanBerSC-17
❑ 93SanBerSF-771

Sutcliffe, Cy (Elmer Ellsworth)
❑ 87OldJudN-481

Sutcliffe, Rick
❑ 80DodPol-43
❑ 80Top-544
❑ 81Dod-29
❑ 81DodPol-43
❑ 81Don-418
❑ 81Fle-125
❑ 81LonBeaPT-12
❑ 81OPC-191
❑ 81Top-191
❑ 82Fle-25
❑ 82Ind-33
❑ 82IndWhe-30
❑ 82OPC-141
❑ 82Top-609
❑ 82TopTra-116T
❑ 83Don-72
❑ 83Fle-420
❑ 83FleSta-190
❑ 83FleSti-240
❑ 83IndPos-34
❑ 83IndWhe-28
❑ 83Top-141
❑ 83Top-497
❑ 83Top-707
❑ 83TopSti-20
❑ 83TopSti-61
❑ 84CubBriPC-8S
❑ 84CubChiT-29
❑ 84CubSev-40
❑ 84CubUno-12
❑ 84CubUno-14
❑ 84Don-338
❑ 84Fle-551
❑ 84FleSti-87
❑ 84FleUpd-114
❑ 84FunFooP-32
❑ 84Ind-28
❑ 84Nes792-245
❑ 84OPC-245
❑ 84Top-245
❑ 84TopRubD-8
❑ 84TopSti-254
❑ 84TopTif-245
❑ 84TopTra-115T
❑ 84TopTraT-115T
❑ 85CubLioP-24
❑ 85CubSev-40
❑ 85Don-433
❑ 85Dra-43
❑ 85Fle-69
❑ 85FleLimE-39
❑ 85FleStaS-89
❑ 85KASDis-15
❑ 85KitCloD-15
❑ 85Lea-139
❑ 85OPC-72
❑ 85SevCoi-G14
❑ 85SubDis-43
❑ 85ThoMcAD-43
❑ 85Top-72
❑ 85Top-720
❑ 85Top3-D-29
❑ 85TopGaloC-11
❑ 85TopGloS-9
❑ 85TopMin-72
❑ 85TopRubD-14
❑ 85TopSti-35
❑ 85TopSti-97
❑ 85TopSup-3
❑ 85TopTif-72
❑ 85TopTif-720
❑ 86BasStaB-108
❑ 86CubGat-40
❑ 86CubUno-18
❑ 86Don-189
❑ 86DorChe-17
❑ 86Fle-383
❑ 86FleMin-81
❑ 86FleSlu-39
❑ 86Lea-122
❑ 86MeaGolSB-19
❑ 86MSAJayPCD-18
❑ 86OPC-330
❑ 86SevCoi-C10
❑ 86Spo-46
❑ 86Spo-60
❑ 86Spo-70
❑ 86Spo-72
❑ 86Spo-134
❑ 86Spo-149
❑ 86Top-330
❑ 86TopSti-61
❑ 86TopTat-21
❑ 86TopTif-330
❑ 86TruVal-18
❑ 87CubCan-33
❑ 87CubDavB-40
❑ 87Don-68
❑ 87DonOpeD-69
❑ 87Fle-576
❑ 87FleGlo-576
❑ 87FleSlu-41
❑ 87OPC-142
❑ 87Top-142
❑ 87TopTif-142
❑ 88ClaBlu-224
❑ 88CubDavB-40
❑ 88Don-68
❑ 88DonAll-43
❑ 88DonBasB-138
❑ 88DonTeaBC-68
❑ 88Dra-31
❑ 88Fle-435
❑ 88FleAwaW-41
❑ 88FleBasA-41
❑ 88FleBasM-38
❑ 88FleExcS-40
❑ 88FleGlo-435
❑ 88FleHotS-42
❑ 88FleLeaL-41
❑ 88FleMin-71
❑ 88FleRecS-40
❑ 88FleStiC-81
❑ 88FleSup-39
❑ 88FleTeaL-41
❑ 88K-M-30
❑ 88Lea-91
❑ 88OPC-372
❑ 88PanSti-257
❑ 88RedFolSB-86
❑ 88Sco-50
❑ 88ScoGlo-50
❑ 88Spo-27
❑ 88StaLinCu-14
❑ 88Top-740
❑ 88TopBig-128
❑ 88TopCoi-57
❑ 88TopMinL-45
❑ 88TopRevLL-9
❑ 88TopSti-61
❑ 88TopStiB-27
❑ 88TopTif-740
❑ 88TopUKM-77
❑ 88TopUKMT-77
❑ 89Bow-281
❑ 89BowTif-281
❑ 89CubMar-40
❑ 89Don-223
❑ 89DonBasB-138
❑ 89Fle-439
❑ 89FleGlo-439
❑ 89OPC-394
❑ 89PanSti-51
❑ 89Sco-407

❑ 89Spo-217
❑ 89Top-520
❑ 89TopBasT-75
❑ 89TopSti-52
❑ 89TopTif-520
❑ 89UppDec-303
❑ 90Bow-21
❑ 90BowTif-21
❑ 90CubMar-20
❑ 90DodTar-785
❑ 90Don-157
❑ 90Fle-43
❑ 90FleCan-43
❑ 90Lea-6
❑ 90MLBBasB-53
❑ 90OPC-640
❑ 90PanSti-233
❑ 90PublntS-205
❑ 90Sco-450
❑ 90Spo-181
❑ 90Top-640
❑ 90TopBig-38
❑ 90TopSti-55
❑ 90TopTif-640
❑ 90TopTVCu-15
❑ 90UppDec-109
❑ 91Bow-430
❑ 91CubMar-40
❑ 91CubVinL-29
❑ 91Don-462
❑ 91Fle-434
❑ 91OPC-415
❑ 91PeoChiTI-31
❑ 91Sco-785
❑ 91Top-415
❑ 91TopDesS-415
❑ 91TopMic-415
❑ 91TopTif-415
❑ 91UppDec-473
❑ 92BalOriP-34
❑ 92Bow-106
❑ 92Cla2-T54
❑ 92Don-642
❑ 92DonUpd-U13
❑ 92Fle-393
❑ 92FleUpd-3
❑ 92Lea-508
❑ 92LeaBlaG-508
❑ 92OPCPre-98
❑ 92Pin-398
❑ 92Sco-665
❑ 92ScoRoo-8T
❑ 92StaClu-700
❑ 92StaCluECN-700
❑ 92Stu-130
❑ 92TopTra-113T
❑ 92TopTraG-113T
❑ 92Ult-309
❑ 92UppDec-529
❑ 92UppDec-708
❑ 93BalOriP-33
❑ 93Bow-113
❑ 93Don-719
❑ 93Fla-158
❑ 93Fle-552
❑ 93Lea-89
❑ 93OPC-381
❑ 93PacSpa-26
❑ 93Pin-532
❑ 93Sco-563
❑ 93Sel-182
❑ 93StaClu-246
❑ 93StaCluFDI-246
❑ 93StaCluMOP-246
❑ 93StaCluMP-10
❑ 93Top-274
❑ 93TopGol-274
❑ 93TopInaM-274
❑ 93TopInaR-274
❑ 93TopMic-274
❑ 93TriPla-106
❑ 93Ult-502
❑ 93UppDec-80
❑ 93UppDecGold-80
❑ 94CarPol-20
❑ 94ColC-548
❑ 94ColChoGS-548
❑ 94ColChoSS-548
❑ 94Don-500
❑ 94Fle-21
❑ 94FleUpd-183
❑ 94Lea-315
❑ 94Sco-497
❑ 94ScoGolR-497
❑ 94ScoRoo-RT19
❑ 94ScoRooGR-RT19
❑ 94StaClu-691
❑ 94StaCluFDI-691
❑ 94StaCluGR-691
❑ 94StaCluMOP-691
❑ 94Top-91
❑ 94TopGol-91
❑ 94TopSpa-91
❑ 94Ult-569
❑ 95ColCho-194
❑ 95ColChoGS-194
❑ 95ColChoSS-194
❑ 95DodROY-8
❑ 95Sco-244
❑ 95ScoGolR-244
❑ 95ScoPlaTS-244
❑ 96IdaFalB-24
❑ 97IdaFalBTI-24

Sutcliffe, Terry
❑ 81VerBeaDT-20

Suter, Bill
❑ 81OklCit8T-18

Suter, Burke
❑ 77BriRedST-17

Suter, Harry
❑ 09ObaT21-168
❑ 09ObaT21-335
❑ 11Zee-102
❑ 12ObaPreT-84

Suter, Rube
❑ 11PinT-5-757

Sutey, John
❑ 91BriTigC-10
❑ 91BriTigP-3621
❑ 92BriTigC-26
❑ 92BriTigF-1429

Sutherland, Alex
❑ 92Bow-123
❑ 92SanBerSF-959
❑ 93AppFoxCB-22
❑ 93AppFoxFl-2464
❑ 93LinVenB-161
❑ 94AppFoxC-18
❑ 94AppFoxFl-1058
❑ 95LinVen-52

Sutherland, Darrell
❑ 66OPC-191
❑ 66Top-191
❑ 66TopVen-191
❑ 68Top-551
❑ 91MetWIZ-389

Sutherland, Gary Lynn
❑ 67Top-587
❑ 68OPC-98
❑ 68Top-98
❑ 68TopVen-98
❑ 69ExpFudP-12
❑ 69Top-326
❑ 69TopSta-59
❑ 69TopTeaP-10
❑ 70ExpPos-7
❑ 70Top-632
❑ 71ExpLaPR-13
❑ 71ExpPS-26
❑ 71MLBOffS-143
❑ 71OPC-434
❑ 71Top-434
❑ 72MilBra-335
❑ 72OPC-211
❑ 72Top-211
❑ 73OPC-572
❑ 73Top-572
❑ 74OPC-428
❑ 74Top-428
❑ 74TopTra-428T
❑ 75DetTigP-32
❑ 75Hos-146
❑ 75OPC-522
❑ 75Top-522
❑ 75TopMin-522
❑ 76DetTigP-30
❑ 76OPC-113
❑ 76SSP-364
❑ 76Top-113
❑ 77PadSchC-55
❑ 77Top-307
❑ 78CarTeal-32
❑ 94BreMilB-364

Sutherland, John
❑ 92OneYanC-12
❑ 93SanBerSC-18
❑ 93SanBerSF-772
❑ 94AlbYanF-1442
❑ 95NorNavTI-23
❑ 96NorNavB-26

Sutherland, Leo
❑ 77AppFoxT-25
❑ 78AppFoxT-19
❑ 79KnoKnoST-7
❑ 80IowOakP-11
❑ 81Don-42
❑ 81EdmTraRR-14
❑ 81Top-112
❑ 82EdmTraT-11
❑ 82Top-599

Sutherland, Matt
❑ 79CedRapGT-8

Sutherland, Suds (Harry)
❑ 19Zee-46
❑ 20WalMaiW-54
❑ 20Zee-58
❑ 22Zee-53
❑ 23Zee-77
❑ 25Zee-144

Suthers, Gregory
❑ 91BriBanF-3

Sutko, Glenn
❑ 88BilMusP-1806
❑ 89GreHorP-420
❑ 90CedRapRB-2
❑ 91Bow-668
❑ 91ChaLooLD-171
❑ 91ChaLooP-1963
❑ 91Cla/Bes-216
❑ 91LinDriAA-171
❑ 91MajLeaCP-72
❑ 91Sco-767
❑ 91TopDeb90-151
❑ 92ChaLooF-3823
❑ 92ChaLooS-196
❑ 92Fle-423
❑ 92Sco100RS-98
❑ 92SkyAA F-88
❑ 92StaClu-559
❑ 95ElPasDTI-22

Sutryk, Tom
❑ 87PenWhiSP-15

Sutter, Bruce
❑ 76CubTri-22
❑ 77CubJewT-14
❑ 77Top-144
❑ 78Hos-5
❑ 78Kel-48
❑ 78OPC-196
❑ 78RCColC-96
❑ 78SSP270-254
❑ 78Top-325
❑ 79BasPat-86
❑ 79Hos-130
❑ 79Kel-1
❑ 79OPC-238
❑ 79Top-457
❑ 80BurKinPHR-11
❑ 80Kel-10
❑ 80OPC-4
❑ 80Top-17
❑ 80TopSup-32
❑ 80WilGloT-7
❑ 81AllGamPI-178
❑ 81CokTeaS-130
❑ 81Don-560
❑ 81Fle-294
❑ 81FleStiC-80
❑ 81Kel-56
❑ 81OPC-9
❑ 81PerCreC-24
❑ 81Top-590
❑ 81TopSti-32
❑ 81TopSti-221
❑ 81TopTra-838
❑ 82Don-372
❑ 82FBIDis-26
❑ 82Fle-129
❑ 82Fle-631
❑ 82FleSta-28
❑ 82Kel-17
❑ 82OPC-260
❑ 82OPC-347
❑ 82Squ-22
❑ 82Top-168
❑ 82Top-260
❑ 82Top-347
❑ 82TopSti-15
❑ 82TopSti-94
❑ 82TopSti-130
❑ 83AllGamPI-180
❑ 83Car-31
❑ 83Don-40
❑ 83DonActA-41
❑ 83Fle-24
❑ 83FleSta-191
❑ 83FleSti-1
❑ 83Kel-37
❑ 83OPC-150
❑ 83OPC-151
❑ 83OPC-266
❑ 83PerCreC-17
❑ 83PerCreCG-17
❑ 83Top-150
❑ 83Top-151
❑ 83Top-407
❑ 83Top-708
❑ 83TopFol-4
❑ 83TopGloS-40
❑ 83TopSti-166
❑ 83TopSti-187
❑ 83TopSti-209
❑ 83TopSti-284
❑ 84Car-30
❑ 84Car5x7-29
❑ 84CubUno-9
❑ 84Don-13
❑ 84Don-13A
❑ 84Don-534
❑ 84Fle-338
❑ 84FleSti-70
❑ 84FunFooP-14
❑ 84Nes792-709
❑ 84Nes792-730
❑ 84OPC-243
❑ 84RalPur-24
❑ 84SevCoi-C7
❑ 84Top-709
❑ 84Top-730
❑ 84TopCer-24
❑ 84TopRubD-22
❑ 84TopSti-145
❑ 84TopTif-709
❑ 84TopTif-730
❑ 85BraHos-21
❑ 85BraPol-40
❑ 85BraTBSAT-3
❑ 85Don-109
❑ 85Dra-44
❑ 85Fle-241
❑ 85FleStaS-104
❑ 85FleUpd-114
❑ 85KASDis-16
❑ 85KitCloD-16
❑ 85Lea-163
❑ 85OPC-370
❑ 85SevCoi-C5
❑ 85SevCoi-G5
❑ 85SevCoi-S4
❑ 85SpoPro-3
❑ 85SubDis-44
❑ 85ThoMcAD-44
❑ 85Top-9
❑ 85Top-370
❑ 85Top-722
❑ 85Top3-D-23
❑ 85TopGaloC-12
❑ 85TopGloS-22
❑ 85TopRubD-23
❑ 85TopSti-135
❑ 85TopSti-172
❑ 85TopSup-9
❑ 85TopTif-9
❑ 85TopTif-370
❑ 85TopTif-722
❑ 85TopTifT-115T
❑ 85TopTra-115T
❑ 86BasStaB-109
❑ 86BraPol-40
❑ 86Don-321
❑ 86Fle-529
❑ 86FleMin-106
❑ 86FleStiC-117
❑ 86GenMilB-5I
❑ 86Lea-192
❑ 86MeaGolSB-17
❑ 86OPC-133
❑ 86SevCoi-C7
❑ 86SevCoi-E7
❑ 86SevCoi-S7
❑ 86SevCoi-W7
❑ 86Spo-47
❑ 86Spo-65
❑ 86Top-620
❑ 86TopSti-37
❑ 86TopTat-10
❑ 86TopTif-620
❑ 86TruVal-15
❑ 87Fle-530
❑ 87FleGlo-530
❑ 87OPC-344
❑ 87RedFolSB-125
❑ 87Top-435
❑ 87TopTif-435
❑ 88Top-155
❑ 88TopTif-155
❑ 89Don-458
❑ 89Fle-603
❑ 89FleGlo-603
❑ 89OPC-11
❑ 89OPCBoxB-M
❑ 89PanSti-39
❑ 89RedFolSB-114
❑ 89Sco-425
❑ 89Top-11
❑ 89TopBasT-105
❑ 89TopBig-64
❑ 89TopSti-25
❑ 89TopTif-11
❑ 89TopWaxBC-M
❑ 89UppDec-414
❑ 90AGFA-19
❑ 90PublntS-125
❑ 92CarMcD-52
❑ 92CubOldS-24
❑ 93CubRol-3
❑ 94TedWil-18

Suttles, Mule
❑ 74LauOldTBS-30
❑ 86NegLeaF-115
❑ 90NegLeaS-21
❑ 91PomBlaBPB-22
❑ 91PomBlaBPB-25

Sutton, Bruce
❑ 98ForWayW!-13

Sutton, Daron
❑ 92BoiHawC-22
❑ 92BoiHawF-3628

Sutton, Derek
❑ 93KinMetC-21
❑ 93KinMetF-3795
❑ 94PitMetC-21
❑ 94PitMetF-3524

Sutton, Don
❑ 66Top-288
❑ 66TopVen-288
❑ 67CokCapD-5
❑ 67CokCapDA-5
❑ 67DexPre-201
❑ 67Top-445
❑ 67TopVen-317
❑ 68OPC-103
❑ 68Top-103
❑ 68TopVen-103
❑ 69MilBra-267
❑ 69MLBOffS-153
❑ 69OPC-216
❑ 69Top-216
❑ 69TopFou-19
❑ 69TopSta-50
❑ 70DayDaiNM-67
❑ 70Kel-8
❑ 70MLBOffS-59
❑ 70Top-622
❑ 71Dod-17
❑ 71DodTic-18
❑ 71Kel-31
❑ 71MLBOffS-118
❑ 71OPC-361
❑ 71Top-361
❑ 71TopCoi-145
❑ 72MilBra-336
❑ 72Top-530
❑ 73Kel2D-5
❑ 73LinPor-97
❑ 73OPC-10
❑ 73SevTraC-74
❑ 73Top-10
❑ 73TopCanL-51
❑ 73TopCom-21
❑ 73TopPin-21
❑ 74OPC-220
❑ 74Top-220
❑ 74TopDecE-12
❑ 74TopSta-50
❑ 75Hos-7
❑ 75HosTwi-7
❑ 75OPC-220
❑ 75Top-220
❑ 75TopMin-220
❑ 76BlaDis-61
❑ 76BucDis-61
❑ 76CarDis-61
❑ 76CraDis-61
❑ 76DailsID-61
❑ 76IsaDis-61
❑ 76Kel-13
❑ 76LinSup-120
❑ 76OPC-530
❑ 76OrbDis-61
❑ 76RedBarD-61
❑ 76SafDis-61
❑ 76SSP-73
❑ 76Top-530
❑ 76TowCluD-61
❑ 77BurCheD-147
❑ 77Hos-70
❑ 77OPC-24
❑ 77PepGloD-62
❑ 77RCColC-62
❑ 77Top-620
❑ 77TopCloS-47
❑ 78Dim2GT-1
❑ 78Hos-70
❑ 78Kel-57
❑ 78OPC-96
❑ 78RCColC-1
❑ 78SSP270-80
❑ 78Top-310
❑ 79DodBlu-12
❑ 79Hos-92
❑ 79OPC-80
❑ 79Top-170
❑ 80DodPol-20
❑ 80OPC-228
❑ 80Top-440
❑ 81AllGamPI-179
❑ 81AstPos-25
❑ 81CokTeaS-71
❑ 81Dod-10
❑ 81Don-58
❑ 81Fle-112
❑ 81FleStiC-59
❑ 81Squ-16
❑ 81Top-7
❑ 81Top-605
❑ 81TopSti-27
❑ 81TopSupHT-102
❑ 81TopTra-839
❑ 82AstAstl-9
❑ 82Don-443
❑ 82Fle-234
❑ 82FleSta-43
❑ 82Kel-21
❑ 82OPC-305
❑ 82OPC-306
❑ 82Top-305
❑ 82Top-306
❑ 83BreGar-18
❑ 83BrePol-21
❑ 83Don-531A
❑ 83Don-531B
❑ 83Fle-47
❑ 83FleSta-192
❑ 83FleSti-16
❑ 83OPC-145
❑ 83OPC-146
❑ 83Top-145
❑ 83Top-146
❑ 83TopFol-1
❑ 84BreGar-19
❑ 84BrePol-20
❑ 84Don-414
❑ 84DonCha-41
❑ 84Fle-215
❑ 84FunFooP-86
❑ 84Nes792-35
❑ 84Nes792-715
❑ 84Nes792-716
❑ 84OPC-35
❑ 84Top-35
❑ 84Top-715
❑ 84Top-716
❑ 84TopSti-300
❑ 84TopTif-35
❑ 84TopTif-715
❑ 84TopTif-716
❑ 85A'sMot-3
❑ 85Don-16
❑ 85Don-107
❑ 85DonSupD-16
❑ 85Fle-598
❑ 85FleUpd-115
❑ 85Lea-16
❑ 85OPC-172
❑ 85Top-10
❑ 85Top-729
❑ 85TopMin-729
❑ 85TopSti-7
❑ 85TopSti-8
❑ 85TopSti-290
❑ 85TopTif-10
❑ 85TopTif-729
❑ 85TopTifT-116T
❑ 85TopTra-116T

❑ 86AngSmo-4
❑ 86Don-611
❑ 86DonHig-16
❑ 86Fle-170
❑ 86FleLimE-43
❑ 86FleMin-35
❑ 86Lea-236
❑ 86OPC-335
❑ 86Spo-135
❑ 86Spo-175
❑ 86Top-335
❑ 86TopTat-7
❑ 86TopTif-335
❑ 87AngSmo-2
❑ 87AstShoSPO-29
❑ 87CalAngPPS-37
❑ 87DodSmoA-35
❑ 87Don-181
❑ 87Fle-93
❑ 87Fle-626
❑ 87FleGlo-93
❑ 87FleGlo-626
❑ 87FleRecS-37
❑ 87FleStiC-115
❑ 87Lea-153
❑ 87OPC-259
❑ 87OPCBoxB-G
❑ 87RalPur-6
❑ 87SevCoi-W11
❑ 87Spo-99
❑ 87Spo-156
❑ 87SpoTeaP-11
❑ 87Top-673
❑ 87TopSti-183
❑ 87TopTif-673
❑ 87TopWaxBC-G
❑ 87Woo-6
❑ 88DodMot-9
❑ 88DodPol-20
❑ 88DodSmo-30
❑ 88Don-407
❑ 88Fle-505
❑ 88FleGlo-505
❑ 88PanSti-37
❑ 88Sco-105
❑ 88ScoGlo-105
❑ 88Spo-213
❑ 88StaLinD-18
❑ 88Top-575
❑ 88TopClo-110
❑ 88TopTif-575
❑ 89DodSmoG-78
❑ 89OPCBoxB-N
❑ 89Sco-400
❑ 89TopWaxBC-N
❑ 90DodTar-786
❑ 92BreCarT-22
❑ 92DodStaTA-11
❑ 94BreMilB-365
❑ 94BreSen-7
❑ 98DonSigSS-17

Sutton, Doug
❑ 89BluOriS-23

Sutton, Ezra
❑ 87BucN28-12
❑ 87OldJudN-482
❑ 88AugBecN-33
❑ 88GandBCGCE-39
❑ 88WG1CarG-8

Sutton, Jim
❑ 82AppFoxFr-4

Sutton, Joe
❑ 97BriWhiSB-14
❑ 98HicCraM-26
❑ 98HicCraUO-28

Sutton, Johnny
❑ 74GasRanT-21
❑ 76SacSolC-13
❑ 76VenLeaS-61
❑ 79IowOakP-14
❑ 79Top-676
❑ 80OgdA'sT-13

Sutton, Larry
❑ 92EugEmeC-24
❑ 92EugEmeF-3040
❑ 93Bow-697
❑ 93ClaMVPF-7
❑ 93ExcFS7-179
❑ 93RocRoyC-26
❑ 93RocRoyF-726
❑ 93Top-423
❑ 93TopGol-423
❑ 93TopInaM-423
❑ 93TopInaR-423
❑ 93TopMic-423
❑ 94CarLeaAF-CAR25
❑ 94TopTra-56T
❑ 94WilBluRC-23
❑ 94WilBluRF-310
❑ 95Bow-228
❑ 95BowGolF-228
❑ 95Exc-65
❑ 95ExcLeaL-15
❑ 95WicWraTI-8
❑ 96WicWraB-5
❑ 97OmaRoyB-20
❑ 98Fle-185
❑ 98PacInv-39
❑ 98PacInvPBlue-39
❑ 98PacInvSilv-39
❑ 98PacOmeRS-7
❑ 98PacOmeRST3-7
❑ 98PacOnl-355
❑ 98PacOnlR-355
❑ 98PacOnlWC-355
❑ 98PacPar-59
❑ 98PacParC-59
❑ 98PacParG-59
❑ 98PacParHS-59
❑ 98PacParPB-59
❑ 98PacParR-59
❑ 98SPxFin-189
❑ 98SPxFinR-189
❑ 98SPxFinS-189
❑ 98Ult-252
❑ 98UltGolM-252
❑ 98UltMas-252
❑ 98UltPlaM-252
❑ 98UppDec-599
❑ 99Fle-560
❑ 99FleSta9-560
❑ 99FleWarT-560
❑ 99MetUni-182
❑ 99MetUniGM-182
❑ 99MetUniPMG-182
❑ 99Pac-213
❑ 99PacPlaB-213
❑ 99PacRed-213
❑ 99SP Aut-42
❑ 99SPx-45
❑ 99SPxFinR-45
❑ 99SPxFinS-45
❑ 99Top-154
❑ 99TopChr-154
❑ 99TopChrR-154
❑ 99TopMVPP-154
❑ 99UD Cho-94
❑ 99UD ChoP-94
❑ 99UD ChoPCR-94
❑ 99Ult-42
❑ 99UltGolM-42
❑ 99UltMas-42
❑ 99UltPlaM-42
❑ 99UppDec-118
❑ 99UppDecEL1-118
❑ 99UppDecEL2-118
❑ 99UppDecM-100
❑ 99UppDecMGS-100
❑ 99UppDecMHFS-100
❑ 99UppDecMP-100
❑ 99UppDecMSS-100
❑ 99Vic-191

Sutton, Mark
❑ 83BurRanF-21
❑ 83BurRanT-24

Sutton, Phil
❑ 79CedRapGT-30

Sutton, Rico
❑ 80UtiBluJT-33
❑ 83KinBluJTI-25

Suyat, Paulette
❑ 91HawWomS-15

Suzuki, Keiji
❑ 79TCMJapPB-45

Suzuki, Ken
❑ 88SanJosGCLC-129
❑ 88SanJosGP-121
❑ 90IBAWorA-17

Suzuki, Mac (Makato)
❑ 93SanBerSC-19
❑ 93SanBerSF-773
❑ 94ActPac-17
❑ 94Bow-313
❑ 94Bow-378
❑ 94BowBes-B59
❑ 94BowBesR-B59
❑ 94BowPre-9
❑ 94Cla-49
❑ 94ClaCreotC-C3
❑ 94ExcFS7-128
❑ 94FleExtB-173
❑ 94FleExtBMLH-8
❑ 94JacSunF-1412
❑ 94TedWil-131
❑ 94Ult-425
❑ 95ActPacF-24
❑ 95ARuFalLS-17
❑ 95Bow-199
❑ 95Fle-278
❑ 95Top-168
❑ 95UppDecML-84
❑ 95UppDecML-114
❑ 95UppDecMLFS-84
❑ 95UppDecMLFS-114
❑ 96LeaSig-121
❑ 96LeaSigPPG-121
❑ 96LeaSigPPP-121
❑ 96PorCitRB-26
❑ 97Bow-163
❑ 97BowInt-163
❑ 97DonRatR-22
❑ 97MarSco-15
❑ 97MarScoPl-15
❑ 97MarScoPr-15
❑ 97PacPriGotD-GD93
❑ 97PinPasttM-22
❑ 97Sco-318
❑ 97ScoArtPWB-318
❑ 97ScoPreS-318
❑ 97ScoShoS-318
❑ 97ScoShoSAP-318
❑ 97TacRai-26
❑ 97UppDec-193
❑ 97UppDec-480
❑ 98TacRaiQ-29
❑ 99Pac-403
❑ 99PacCroC-269
❑ 99PacCroCPB-269
❑ 99PacPlaB-403
❑ 99PacRed-403

Suzuki, Yasu
❑ 89SalSpuCLC-135
❑ 89SalSpuP-1814

Sveum, Dale
❑ 84ElPasDT-24
❑ 85VanCanC-209
❑ 86DonRoo-37
❑ 86FleUpd-109
❑ 86SpoRoo-4
❑ 86TopTra-106T
❑ 86TopTraT-106T
❑ 86VanCanP-25
❑ 87BrePol-7
❑ 87BreTeal-14
❑ 87Don-542
❑ 87DonOpeD-55
❑ 87Fle-358
❑ 87FleGlo-358
❑ 87Lea-156
❑ 87SpoTeaP-19
❑ 87Top-327
❑ 87TopRoo-18
❑ 87TopSti-309
❑ 87TopTif-327
❑ 87ToyRoo-27
❑ 88BrePol-7
❑ 88BreTeal-34
❑ 88Don-232
❑ 88DonBasB-305
❑ 88Fle-176
❑ 88FleGlo-176
❑ 88OPC-81
❑ 88PanSti-126
❑ 88Sco-120
❑ 88ScoGlo-120
❑ 88StaLinBre-18
❑ 88Top-592
❑ 88TopBig-44
❑ 88TopSti-199
❑ 88TopTif-592
❑ 89Bow-139
❑ 89BowTif-139
❑ 89BreGar-6
❑ 89BrePol-7
❑ 89BreYea-7
❑ 89Don-146
❑ 89Fle-198
❑ 89FleGlo-198
❑ 89OPC-12
❑ 89PanSti-374
❑ 89Sco-256
❑ 89ScoYouS2-24
❑ 89Top-12
❑ 89TopBig-126
❑ 89TopSti-206
❑ 89TopTif-12
❑ 89UppDec-421
❑ 90BreMilB-26
❑ 90BrePol-7
❑ 90El PasDAGTI-8
❑ 90OPC-739
❑ 90PublntS-506
❑ 90Top-739
❑ 90TopTif-739
❑ 90UppDec-499
❑ 91BreMilB-27
❑ 91BrePol-24
❑ 91Sco-814
❑ 92Bow-367
❑ 92Don-452
❑ 92Fle-191
❑ 92Lea-473
❑ 92LeaBlaG-473
❑ 92OPC-478
❑ 92PhiMed-30
❑ 92Sco-181
❑ 92StaClu-687
❑ 92Top-478
❑ 92TopGol-478
❑ 92TopGolW-478
❑ 92TopMic-478
❑ 92UppDec-498
❑ 93AthMot-11
❑ 93AthStaC-29
❑ 93BreSen-3
❑ 93PacSpa-572
❑ 94BreMilB-366
❑ 94CalCanF-800
❑ 97PirPos-37
❑ 98PacOnl-519
❑ 98PacOnlR-519
❑ 98PacOnlWC-519

Swacina, Harry
❑ 12ColRedB-282
❑ 12ColTinT-282

Swafford, Derek
❑ 94WelPirC-25
❑ 94WelPirF-3505
❑ 96Exc-225
❑ 96LynHilB-21
❑ 97LynHil-20

Swafford, J.C.
❑ 89TenTecGE-27

Swaggerty, Bill
❑ 82RocRedWT-7
❑ 83RocRedWT-10
❑ 84BalOriP-37
❑ 84RocRedWT-17
❑ 85BalOriP-34
❑ 85Don-392
❑ 85Fle-193
❑ 85RocRedWT-22
❑ 85Top-147
❑ 85TopTif-147
❑ 86Don-594
❑ 88OmaRoyC-9
❑ 88OmaRoyP-1498
❑ 91OriCro-448
❑ 95BalOriP-48

Swaggerty, Glenn
❑ 80QuaCitCT-6
❑ 81QuaCitCT-25

Swail, Steve
❑ 89PulBraP-1914
❑ 90BurBraB-9
❑ 90BurBraP-2353
❑ 90BurBraS-25
❑ 91DurBulC-11
❑ 91DurBulP-1549
❑ 92DurBulF-1106
❑ 92MacBraC-7
❑ 93DurBulC-19
❑ 93DurBulF-489
❑ 93DurBulTI-28
❑ 94GreBraF-417
❑ 94GreBraTI-22

Swain, Charles
❑ 12HomRunKE-57
❑ 12Zee-95

Swain, Rob
❑ 86WatIndP-26
❑ 87KinIndP-18
❑ 88CarLeaAS-36
❑ 88KinIndS-21
❑ 89CanIndB-26
❑ 89CanIndP-1303
❑ 89CanIndS-20
❑ 90CanIndB-11
❑ 90CanIndP-1301
❑ 92KinIndC-28
❑ 92KinIndF-2493

Swain, Steve
❑ 82AubAstT-16

Swain, Thayer
❑ 88ButCopKSP-21
❑ 90ChaRanS-28

Swaino, Shannon
❑ 96VerExpB-27

Swan, Craig
❑ 74MetTeal-22
❑ 74OPC-602
❑ 74Top-602
❑ 75TidTidTI-21
❑ 76OPC-494
❑ 76SSP-558
❑ 76Top-494
❑ 77MetDaiPA-24
❑ 77Spo-7911
❑ 77Top-94
❑ 78MetDaiPA-23
❑ 78Top-621
❑ 79Hos-41
❑ 79OPC-170
❑ 79Top-7
❑ 79Top-334
❑ 79TopCom-27
❑ 80OPC-1
❑ 80Top-8
❑ 80TopSup-41
❑ 81CokTeaS-92
❑ 81Don-155
❑ 81Fle-319
❑ 81OPC-189
❑ 81Top-189
❑ 82Don-589
❑ 82Fle-538
❑ 82MetPhoA-22
❑ 82Top-592
❑ 83Don-254
❑ 83Fle-557
❑ 83FleSta-193
❑ 83FleSti-231
❑ 83OPC-292
❑ 83Top-292
❑ 83Top-621
❑ 83TopSti-262
❑ 84Don-441
❑ 84Fle-600
❑ 84FleUpd-115
❑ 84Nes792-763
❑ 84Top-763
❑ 84TopTif-763
❑ 84TopTra-116T
❑ 84TopTraT-116T
❑ 89TidTidC-9
❑ 91MetWIZ-391
❑ 97AriStaBG-21

Swan, Russ
❑ 86EveGiaC-8
❑ 88BlaYNPRWLU-44
❑ 88SanJosGCLC-138
❑ 88SanJosGP-118
❑ 89ShrCapP-1831
❑ 90Bow-224
❑ 90BowTif-224
❑ 90CMC-532
❑ 90PhoFirC-5
❑ 90TopDeb89-125
❑ 90TopTra-121T
❑ 90TopTraT-121T
❑ 91Don-621
❑ 91FleUpd-57
❑ 91MarCouH-22
❑ 91OPC-739
❑ 91StaClu-577
❑ 91Top-739
❑ 91TopDesS-739
❑ 91TopMic-739
❑ 91TopTif-739
❑ 92Bow-378
❑ 92Don-382
❑ 92Fle-293
❑ 92Lea-203
❑ 92LeaBlaG-203
❑ 92MarMot-22
❑ 92OPC-588
❑ 92Pin-484
❑ 92Sco-281
❑ 92StaClu-472
❑ 92Top-588
❑ 92TopGol-588
❑ 92TopGolW-588
❑ 92TopMic-588
❑ 92UppDec-618
❑ 93Don-713
❑ 93Fle-314
❑ 93MariStaClu-14
❑ 93MarMot-16
❑ 93PacSpa-626
❑ 93StaClu-179
❑ 93StaCluFDI-179
❑ 93StaCluMOP-179
❑ 93Top-96
❑ 93TopGol-96
❑ 93TopInaM-96
❑ 93TopInaR-96
❑ 93TopMic-96
❑ 93Ult-272
❑ 93UppDec-624
❑ 93UppDecGold-624
❑ 95EdmTraTI-23
❑ 96LasVegSB-26

Swan, Tyrone
❑ 93BatCliCB-26
❑ 93BatCliF-3145
❑ 94SouAtlLAF-SAL56
❑ 94SpaPhiF-1723
❑ 94SparPhiC-20

Swander, Edward
❑ 09ObaT21-109

Swank, Ken
❑ 82ChaRoyT-18

Swank, Randy
❑ 91EveGiaC-4
❑ 91EveGiaP-3924

Swann, Pedro
❑ 91IdaFalBP-4341
❑ 91IdaFalBSP-25
❑ 92PulBraC-21
❑ 92PulBraF-3194
❑ 93AusFut-88
❑ 93DurBulC-20
❑ 93DurBulF-500
❑ 93DurBulTI-15
❑ 94GreBraF-427
❑ 94GreBraTI-23
❑ 95BreBtaTI-16
❑ 96Exc-134
❑ 96RicBraRC-NNO
❑ 96RicBraUB-27
❑ 97GreBraG-25
❑ 98TolMudHQ-30

Swannie, Eric
❑ 98GreBraG-25

Swanson, Art
❑ 56Top-204
❑ 58JetPos-18

Swanson, Chad
❑ 88KenTwiP-1386
❑ 89KenTwiP-1078
❑ 90VisOakCLC-57
❑ 90VisOakP-2152

Swanson, Dave
❑ 92KinMetC-5
❑ 92KinMetF-1531
❑ 93PitMetC-20
❑ 93PitMetF-3709
❑ 94CapCitBC-20
❑ 94CapCitBF-1750

Swanson, Eric
❑ 82DayBeaAT-16

Swanson, Ernest
❑ 28Zee-61

Swanson, Evar
❑ 26Zee-61
❑ 27Zee-39
❑ 33Gou-195
❑ 33TatOrbSDR-174
❑ 34ExhFou-10
❑ 34TarThoBD-24
❑ 35AlDemDCR3-12
❑ 63GadFunC-20
❑ 83ConMar-15
❑ 88ConAmeA-23
❑ 92ConTSN-393
❑ 94ConTSN-1239
❑ 94ConTSNB-1239

Swanson, John
❑ 91OklStaC-25

Swanson, Perry
❑ 82ChaRoyT-8

Swanson, Stan
❑ 72OPC-331
❑ 72Top-331
❑ 72TopCloT-31

Swartwood, Cyrus
❑ 87OldJudN-483

Swartz, Nick
❑ 84OmaRoyT-7
❑ 85OmaRoyT-3
❑ 86OmaRoyP-26
❑ 87OmaRoyP-5
❑ 88OmaRoyP-1500

Swartzbaugh, David
❑ 88CapCodPPaLP-66
❑ 89GenCubP-1866

❑ 90PeoChiTI-28
❑ 91PeoChiP-1342
❑ 91WinSpiP-2829
❑ 92ChaKniF-2771
❑ 92ChaKniS-168
❑ 92ClaFS7-63
❑ 92SkyAA F-76
❑ 94IowCubF-1275
❑ 94OrlCubF-1385
❑ 95IowCubTI-24
❑ 95OrlCubF-11
❑ 96IowCubB-26
❑ 97Fle-285
❑ 97FleTif-285
❑ 97IowCub-26
❑ 98IowCubQ-24

Swartzel, Parke
❑ 87OldJudN-484

Swartzlander, Keith
❑ 86MacPirP-25

Sweatt, George Alexander
❑ 86NegLeaF-117
❑ 87NegLeaPD-26

Sweeney, Bill
❑ 12ColRedB-284
❑ 12ColTinT-284
❑ 26Zee-128
❑ 31Exh-18
❑ 37Zee-50

Sweeney, Bill (William)
❑ 53MotCoo-23

Sweeney, Brian
❑ 97LanJet-24
❑ 98LanJetG-25

Sweeney, Charles
❑ 88SFHesCreN32-34

Sweeney, D.B.
❑ 88PacEigMO-13

Sweeney, Dennis
❑ 91EliTwiP-4301
❑ 92KenTwiF-603
❑ 93ForMyeMC-24
❑ 93ForMyeMF-2655
❑ 94NasXprF-387

Sweeney, Ed
❑ 10CouT21-230
❑ 10CouT21-231
❑ 10CouT21-232
❑ 10CouT21-233
❑ 10CouT21-320
❑ 10JuJuDE-38
❑ 10PeoT21-54
❑ 11HelSta-47
❑ 11HelSta-81
❑ 11MecDFT-46
❑ 12ColTinT-283
❑ 14CraJacE-112
❑ 15CraJacE-112
❑ 15VicT21-26

Sweeney, James
❑ 28Zee-20

Sweeney, Jeff
❑ 09AmeCarE90-1-104
❑ 09ColChiE-283
❑ 09T206-348
❑ 10RedCroT-249
❑ 11PinT-5-812
❑ 11SpoLifM-83
❑ 11T205-168
❑ 12ColRedB-283
❑ 12HasTriFT-38B
❑ 12HasTriFT-67B
❑ 12HasTriFT-68A
❑ 12HasTriFT-68B
❑ 14B18B-27
❑ 14PieStaT-99
❑ 15AmeCarE106-38

Sweeney, Jim
❑ 90PeoChiUTI-U6

Sweeney, Kevin
❑ 96AriBlaDB-32
❑ 96HonShaHWB-32
❑ 97Bow-356
❑ 97BowInt-356
❑ 97SouBenSH-27
❑ 97Top-249
❑ 98HigDesMG-26

Sweeney, Kim
❑ 89GenCubP-1873

Sweeney, Mark
❑ 88CapCodPPaLP-59
❑ 91BoiHawC-15
❑ 91BoiHawP-3898
❑ 92ClaFS7-228
❑ 92ColRedC-8
❑ 92KinIndF-2475
❑ 92QuaCitRBC-21
❑ 92QuaCitRBF-825
❑ 93PalSprAC-23
❑ 93PalSprAF-85
❑ 94Top-237
❑ 94TopGol-237
❑ 94TopSpa-237
❑ 94UppDecML-228
❑ 94VanCanF-1877
❑ 95TopTra-122T
❑ 96CarPol-25
❑ 96ColCho-281
❑ 96ColChoGS-281
❑ 96ColChoSS-281
❑ 96Fle-557
❑ 96FleTif-557
❑ 96LeaSigEA-196
❑ 97CarPol-26
❑ 97DonFraFea-9
❑ 97Fle-454
❑ 97FleTif-454
❑ 97MidAngOHP-29
❑ 97Pac-418
❑ 97PacLigB-418
❑ 97PacSil-418
❑ 97Pin-143
❑ 97PinArtP-PP143
❑ 97PinMusC-143
❑ 97PinPrePla-143
❑ 97Ult-278
❑ 97UltGolME-278
❑ 97UltPlaME-278
❑ 98ColCho-227
❑ 98PacOnl-649
❑ 98PacOnlR-649
❑ 98PacOnlWC-649
❑ 98PadMot-22

Sweeney, Michael
❑ 89IdaFalBP-2023
❑ 90IdaFalBP-3258

Sweeney, Mike
❑ 91HigSchPLS-5
❑ 92EugEmeC-25
❑ 92EugEmeF-3033
❑ 93EugEmeC-25
❑ 93EugEmeF-3859
❑ 94MidLeaAF-MDW25
❑ 94RocRoyC-24
❑ 94RocRoyF-569
❑ 95WilBluRTI-33
❑ 96Bow-334
❑ 96BowBes-164
❑ 96BowBesAR-164
❑ 96BowBesR-164
❑ 96BowFoi-334
❑ 96BowMinLP-10
❑ 96ColCho-438
❑ 96ColChoGS-438
❑ 96ColChoSS-438
❑ 96Fle-138
❑ 96FleTif-138
❑ 96Pin-180
❑ 96Sco-492
❑ 96TexLeaAB-36
❑ 96UppDec-251
❑ 96WicWraB-1
❑ 97Bow-111
❑ 97BowBes-192
❑ 97BowBesAR-192
❑ 97BowBesR-192
❑ 97BowCerBlaIA-CA76
❑ 97BowCerBluIA-CA76
❑ 97BowCerGolIA-CA76
❑ 97BowChr-131
❑ 97BowChrI-131
❑ 97BowChrIR-131
❑ 97BowChrR-131
❑ 97BowInt-111
❑ 97ColCho-131
❑ 97Don-235
❑ 97DonGolPP-235
❑ 97DonLim-171
❑ 97DonLimE-171
❑ 97DonLimENG-171
❑ 97DonPre-139
❑ 97DonPreCttC-139
❑ 97DonSigA-94
❑ 97DonSigAC-117
❑ 97DonSigAM-117
❑ 97DonSilPP-235
❑ 97Fin-88
❑ 97FinRef-88
❑ 97Fle-123
❑ 97FleTif-123
❑ 97Lea-333
❑ 97LeaFraM-333
❑ 97LeaFraMDC-333
❑ 97Pac-112
❑ 97PacLigB-112
❑ 97PacSil-112
❑ 97RoyPol-21
❑ 97Sco-262
❑ 97ScoArtPWB-262
❑ 97ScoPreS-262
❑ 97ScoShoS-262
❑ 97ScoShoSAP-262
❑ 97StaClu-274
❑ 97StaCluM-M31
❑ 97StaCluMOP-274
❑ 97StaCluMOP-M31
❑ 97Top-447
❑ 97TopGal-168
❑ 97TopGalPPI-168
❑ 97Ult-73
❑ 97UltGolME-73
❑ 97UltPlaME-73
❑ 98ColCho-387
❑ 98Don-171
❑ 98DonGolPP-171
❑ 98DonSilPP-171
❑ 98Fin-42
❑ 98FinNo--42
❑ 98FinNo-R-42
❑ 98FinRef-42
❑ 98Fle-485
❑ 98PacOnl-356
❑ 98PacOnlR-356
❑ 98PacOnlWC-356
❑ 98StaCluFDI-195
❑ 98StaCluI-195
❑ 98StaCluOneK-195
❑ 98StaCluPP-195
❑ 98Stu-210
❑ 98StuGPP-210
❑ 98StuSPP-210
❑ 98Top-106
❑ 98TopChr-106
❑ 98TopChrR-106
❑ 98TopDevR-106
❑ 98TopDia-106
❑ 98TopMiniC-106
❑ 98TopOpeD-53
❑ 98Ult-447
❑ 98UltGolM-447
❑ 98UltMas-447
❑ 98UltPlaM-447
❑ 98UppDec-394
❑ 99Fle-516
❑ 99FleSta9-516
❑ 99FleWarT-516
❑ 99Pac-214
❑ 99PacAur-90
❑ 99PacAurOD-90
❑ 99PacOme-117
❑ 99PacOmeC-117
❑ 99PacOmeG-117
❑ 99PacOmePB-117
❑ 99PacPlaB-214
❑ 99PacRed-214
❑ 99StaClu-178
❑ 99StaCluFDI-178
❑ 99StaCluOoaK-178
❑ 99StaCluPP-178
❑ 99UppDec-395
❑ 99UppDecEL1-395
❑ 99UppDecEL2-395

Sweeney, Peter
❑ 87OldJudN-485

Sweeney, Robert
❑ 90KisDodD-26
❑ 91KisDodP-4185
❑ 92BakDodCLC-24

Sweeney, Roger
❑ 91YakBeaP-4262
❑ 92GreFalDSP-8

Sweeney, William John
❑ 09AmeCarE90-1-103
❑ 09ColChiE-284
❑ 09RamT20-115
❑ 09T206-349
❑ 10CouT21-64
❑ 10RedCroT-76
❑ 10RedCroT-161
❑ 11PinT-5-705
❑ 11SpoLifCW-345
❑ 11SpoLifM-147
❑ 12T207-180
❑ 13NatGamW-39
❑ 13TomBarW-35
❑ 14FatPlaT-48
❑ 14TexTomE-43

Sweet, Jonathan
❑ 94WelPirC-26
❑ 94WelPirF-3500
❑ 96LynHilB-22
❑ 97CarMudC-13
❑ 98CarMudM-11

Sweet, Richard
❑ 78PadFamF-31
❑ 78Top-702
❑ 79HawIsIC-18
❑ 79HawIsIT-3
❑ 79OPC-341
❑ 79Top-646
❑ 80HawIsIT-20
❑ 81TidTidT-1
❑ 83Don-352
❑ 83Fle-487
❑ 83MarNal-5
❑ 83Top-437
❑ 84Don-196
❑ 84Fle-621
❑ 84MarMot-27
❑ 84Nes792-211
❑ 84Top-211
❑ 84TopTif-211
❑ 87BelMarTI-24
❑ 88WauTimGS-1
❑ 89OscAstS-27
❑ 90ColMudP-1361
❑ 90ColMudS-25
❑ 91JacGenLD-574
❑ 91JacGenP-940
❑ 91LinDriAA-574
❑ 91MetWIZ-392
❑ 92JacGenF-4014
❑ 92JacGenS-349
❑ 93LinVenB-215
❑ 93TucTorF-3076
❑ 94TucTorF-777
❑ 95TucTotTI-27
❑ 96AstMot-28
❑ 97BinMetB-1
❑ 98arSenW1-24
❑ 98HarSenM-24

Sweetland, Lester L.
❑ 29ExhFou-12
❑ 31CubTeal-23
❑ 33Zee-10

Sweezey, Gary
❑ 95GreFalDTI-17

Swenson, Mark
❑ 82CliGiaF-31

Swenson, Mickey
❑ 82CliGiaF-30
❑ 82CliGiaF-32

Swenson, Mike
❑ 95NewJerCTI-28

Swepson, Dobie
❑ 86CliGiaP-23
❑ 88PocGiaP-2095

Swepson, Lyle
❑ 84EveGiaC-2

Swetonic, Steve
❑ 34BabRutG-59
❑ 34ButPreR-58
❑ 94ConTSN-1163
❑ 94ConTSNB-1163

Swett, Pop
❑ 88SFHesCreN32-35

Swiacki, Bill
❑ 79AlbDukTc-4
❑ 80AlbDukTc-5
❑ 81AlbDukTc-6
❑ 82TacTigT-9

Swiers, Brian C.
❑ 98PitMetM-33

Swift, Bill Charles
❑ 85Top-404
❑ 85TopTif-404
❑ 86Don-562
❑ 86Fle-475
❑ 86MarMot-16
❑ 86MarPacNB-12
❑ 86Top-399
❑ 86TopTif-399
❑ 87Don-517
❑ 87Fle-597
❑ 87FleGlo-597
❑ 87Top-67
❑ 87TopTif-67
❑ 88FleUpd-61
❑ 88FleUpdG-61
❑ 88MarMot-25
❑ 88TopTra-117T
❑ 88TopTraT-117T
❑ 89Fle-560
❑ 89FleGlo-560
❑ 89MarMot-17
❑ 89OPC-198
❑ 89RedFolSB-115
❑ 89Sco-219
❑ 89Top-712
❑ 89TopSti-228
❑ 89TopTif-712
❑ 89UppDec-623
❑ 90Don-566
❑ 90Fle-526
❑ 90FleCan-526
❑ 90MarMot-11
❑ 90OPC-574
❑ 90PubIntS-442
❑ 90Top-574
❑ 90TopTif-574
❑ 90UppDec-313
❑ 91Don-564
❑ 91Fle-462
❑ 91Lea-380
❑ 91MarCouH-12
❑ 91OPC-276
❑ 91Sco-123
❑ 91StaClu-372
❑ 91Top-276
❑ 91TopDesS-276
❑ 91TopMic-276
❑ 91TopTif-276
❑ 91UltUpd-53
❑ 91UppDec-498
❑ 92Bow-182
❑ 92Bow-611
❑ 92Cla2-T33
❑ 92Don-260
❑ 92DonUpd-U22
❑ 92Fle-294
❑ 92FleUpd-131
❑ 92GiaMot-3
❑ 92GiaPacGaE-32
❑ 92Lea-407
❑ 92LeaBlaG-407
❑ 92OPC-144
❑ 92OPCPre-133
❑ 92Pin-448
❑ 92Sco-541
❑ 92ScoRoo-32T
❑ 92StaClu-243
❑ 92StaClu-855
❑ 92StaCluECN-855
❑ 92Stu-118
❑ 92Top-144
❑ 92TopGol-144
❑ 92TopGolW-144
❑ 92TopMic-144
❑ 92TopTra-114T
❑ 92TopTraG-114T
❑ 92Ult-596
❑ 92UppDec-620
❑ 92UppDec-736
❑ 93Bow-380
❑ 93Don-232
❑ 93DonDiaK-DK5
❑ 93Fla-146
❑ 93Fle-161
❑ 93Fle-708
❑ 93FleFruotL-58
❑ 93FunPac-102
❑ 93GiaMot-5
❑ 93GiaPos-31
❑ 93GiaStaC-20
❑ 93Lea-194
❑ 93MilBonSS-5
❑ 93OPC-277
❑ 93PacSpa-616
❑ 93PanSti-234
❑ 93Pin-347
❑ 93Sco-67
❑ 93Sel-51
❑ 93SelStaL-82
❑ 93SP-115
❑ 93StaClu-204
❑ 93StaCluFDI-204
❑ 93StaCluMOP-204
❑ 93Top-755
❑ 93TopComotH-29
❑ 93TopGol-755
❑ 93TopInaM-755
❑ 93TopInaR-755
❑ 93TopMic-755
❑ 93TriPla-262
❑ 93Ult-136
❑ 93UppDec-118
❑ 93UppDecGold-118
❑ 93USPlaCA-1S
❑ 94Bow-435
❑ 94BowBes-R49
❑ 94BowBesR-R49
❑ 94ColC-271
❑ 94ColChoGS-271
❑ 94ColChoSS-271
❑ 94Don-294
❑ 94Fin-151
❑ 94FinPre-151P
❑ 94FinRef-151
❑ 94Fla-445
❑ 94Fle-702
❑ 94FleExtB-392
❑ 94FleExtBPD-9
❑ 94FUnPac-26
❑ 94GiaAMC-21
❑ 94GiaKTV-6
❑ 94GiaMot-6
❑ 94GiaSFC-3
❑ 94GiaTarBC-24
❑ 94GiaTeal-7
❑ 94GiaUSPC-1D
❑ 94GiaUSPC-8S
❑ 94Lea-288
❑ 94LeaL-159
❑ 94OPC-79
❑ 94Pac-556
❑ 94PanSti-266
❑ 94Pin-326
❑ 94PinArtP-326
❑ 94PinMusC-326
❑ 94Sco-430
❑ 94ScoGolR-430
❑ 94Sel-252
❑ 94SP-93
❑ 94SPDieC-93
❑ 94Spo-54
❑ 94StaClu-330
❑ 94StaCluFDI-330
❑ 94StaCluGR-330
❑ 94StaCluMOP-330
❑ 94StaCluT-16
❑ 94StaCluTFDI-16
❑ 94Stu-87
❑ 94Top-639
❑ 94TopGol-639
❑ 94TopSpa-639
❑ 94TriPla-108
❑ 94TriPlaM-14
❑ 94Ult-294
❑ 94UppDec-62
❑ 94UppDecED-62
❑ 94USPlaCA-10S
❑ 95Bow-327
❑ 95ColCho-259
❑ 95ColCho-575T
❑ 95ColChoGS-259
❑ 95ColChoSE-110
❑ 95ColChoSEGS-110
❑ 95ColChoSESS-110
❑ 95ColChoSS-259
❑ 95Don-387
❑ 95DonPreP-387
❑ 95DonTopotO-233
❑ 95Fin-255
❑ 95FinRef-255
❑ 95Fla-346
❑ 95Fle-590
❑ 95FleUpd-169
❑ 95Lea-368
❑ 95Pin-373
❑ 95PinArtP-373
❑ 95PinMusC-373
❑ 95RocPol-9
❑ 95Sco-491
❑ 95ScoGolR-491
❑ 95ScoPlaTS-491
❑ 95SP-49
❑ 95SPCha-41
❑ 95SPChaDC-41
❑ 95SPSil-49
❑ 95StaClu-365
❑ 95StaClu-554
❑ 95StaCluMOP-365
❑ 95StaCluMOP-554
❑ 95StaCluSTWS-365
❑ 95StaCluSTWS-554
❑ 95StaCluVR-192
❑ 95StaCluVRMO-192
❑ 95Top-433
❑ 95TopCyb-230
❑ 95TopTra-137T
❑ 95Ult-447
❑ 95UltGolM-447
❑ 95UppDec-414

❑ 95UppDecED-414
❑ 95UppDecEDG-414
❑ 95UppDecSE-237
❑ 95UppDecSEG-237
❑ 96ColCho-535
❑ 96ColChoGS-535
❑ 96ColChoSS-535
❑ 96Don-239
❑ 96DonPreP-239
❑ 96EmoXL-177
❑ 96Fin-B170
❑ 96FinRef-B170
❑ 96Fla-252
❑ 96Fle-375
❑ 96FleTif-375
❑ 96LeaSigA-217
❑ 96LeaSigAG-217
❑ 96LeaSigAS-217
❑ 96MetUni-158
❑ 96MetUniP-158
❑ 96PanSti-87
❑ 96RocFle-14
❑ 96RocPol-22
❑ 96Sco-429
❑ 96StaClu-43
❑ 96StaCluMOP-43
❑ 96Top-401
❑ 96Ult-193
❑ 96UltGolM-193
❑ 96UppDec-325
❑ 97ColCho-318
❑ 97DonTea-104
❑ 97DonTeaSPE-104
❑ 97Fle-548
❑ 97FleTif-548
❑ 97Pin-26
❑ 97PinArtP-PP26
❑ 97PinMusC-26
❑ 97PinPrePla-26
❑ 97RocPol-9
❑ 97Sco-387
❑ 97ScoArtPWB-387
❑ 97ScoResC-387
❑ 97ScoShoS-387
❑ 97ScoShoSAP-387
❑ 97Ult-440
❑ 97UltGolME-440
❑ 97UltPlaME-440
❑ 98PacOnl-697
❑ 98PacOnlR-697
❑ 98PacOnlWC-697
Swift, Bill Vincent
❑ 34Gou-57
❑ 36GouWidPPR-A98
❑ 36NatChiFPR-69
❑ 36R31PasP-24
❑ 39PlaBal-129
❑ 41DodTeal-7
❑ 73Dod194T-26
❑ 75OakOak2A-33
❑ 78DodTCM4-10
❑ 90DodTar-787
Swift, Bob (Robert V.)
❑ 41BroW75-27
❑ 42A'sTeal-32
❑ 43A'STEAl-22
❑ 47TipTop-41
❑ 49Bow-148
❑ 50Bow-149
❑ 51Bow-214
❑ 52Bow-131
❑ 52Top-181
❑ 54Top-65
❑ 60Top-470
❑ 77TCMTheWY-50
❑ 81TigDetN-42
❑ 83TopRep5-181
❑ 85TCMPla1-5
❑ 94TopArc1-65
❑ 94TopArc1G-65
Swift, Scott
❑ 95BurBeeTI-29
Swift, Tim
❑ 96VerExpB-5
Swift, Weldon
❑ 78BurBeeT-28
❑ 79HolMilT-23
❑ 80HolMilT-11
❑ 81ElPasDT-19
Swim, Greg
❑ 91SalSpuC-29
❑ 91SalSpuP-2253
Swinburnson, Tyler
❑ 97WatIndTI-27
❑ 98WatIndTI-32
Swindell, Greg
❑ 86SpoRoo-30
❑ 87Don-32
❑ 87Fle-644
❑ 87FleGlo-644
❑ 87FleUpd-116
❑ 87FleUpdG-116
❑ 87IndGat-21
❑ 87Lea-32
❑ 87SpoTeaP-3
❑ 87Top-319
❑ 87TopTif-319
❑ 88Don-227
❑ 88DonBasB-280
❑ 88Fle-617
❑ 88FleGlo-617
❑ 88FleSlu-41
❑ 88IndGat-21
❑ 88IndTeal-34
❑ 88Lea-158
❑ 88OPC-22
❑ 88PanSti-70
❑ 88Sco-154
❑ 88ScoGlo-154
❑ 88ScoYouS2-39
❑ 88StaLinl-19
❑ 88Top-22
❑ 88TopBig-156
❑ 88TopSti-210
❑ 88TopTif-22
❑ 89Bow-76
❑ 89BowTif-76
❑ 89ClaLigB-61
❑ 89ClaTraP-195
❑ 89Don-232
❑ 89DonBasB-112
❑ 89Fle-413
❑ 89FleGlo-413
❑ 89FleLeaL-38
❑ 89IndTeal-26
❑ 89OPC-315
❑ 89PanSti-320
❑ 89RedFolSB-116
❑ 89Sco-282
❑ 89Spo-4
❑ 89Top-315
❑ 89TopBig-68
❑ 89TopCoi-54
❑ 89TopMinL-52
❑ 89TopSti-213
❑ 89TopTif-315
❑ 89TopUKM-76
❑ 89TVSpoM-88
❑ 89UppDec-250
❑ 90Bow-325
❑ 90BowTif-325
❑ 90ClaUpd-T48
❑ 90Don-310
❑ 90DonBesA-6
❑ 90DOnBonM-BC24
❑ 90Fle-503
❑ 90FleAwaW-39
❑ 90FleBasM-39
❑ 90FleBasMC-39
❑ 90FleCan-503
❑ 90Hot50PS-44
❑ 90IndTeal-40
❑ 90Lea-206
❑ 90M.Vpin-34
❑ 90OPC-595
❑ 90PanSti-59
❑ 90PublntS-569
❑ 90PublntS-606
❑ 90RedFolSB-93
❑ 90Sco-230
❑ 90Sco100S-11
❑ 90Top-595
❑ 90TopBig-288
❑ 90TopDou-65
❑ 90TopSti-214
❑ 90TopStiB-63
❑ 90TopTif-595
❑ 90TopTVA-32
❑ 90UppDec-574
❑ 90WonBreS-15
❑ 91Bow-58
❑ 91Cla2-T10
❑ 91ClaGam-101
❑ 91Don-546
❑ 91Fle-379
❑ 91IndFanC-26
❑ 91Lea-6
❑ 91OPC-445
❑ 91Sco-110
❑ 91StaClu-428
❑ 91Stu-49
❑ 91Top-445
❑ 91TopDesS-445
❑ 91TopMic-445
❑ 91TopTif-445
❑ 91Ult-117
❑ 91UppDec-236
❑ 92Bow-46
❑ 92Bow-578
❑ 92ClaGam-193
❑ 92Don-483
❑ 92DonDiaK-DK23
❑ 92DonSupD-DK23
❑ 92Fle-124
❑ 92FleUpd-84
❑ 92Lea-384
❑ 92LeaBlaG-384
❑ 92OPC-735
❑ 92OPCPre-44
❑ 92PanSti-52
❑ 92Pin-327
❑ 92RedKah-29
❑ 92Sco-371
❑ 92ScoRoo-10T
❑ 92StaClu-673
❑ 92StaCluECN-673
❑ 92Stu-30
❑ 92TexLon-38
❑ 92Top-735
❑ 92TopGol-735
❑ 92TopGolW-735
❑ 92TopKid-72
❑ 92TopMic-735
❑ 92Ult-487
❑ 92UppDec-95
❑ 92UppDec-336
❑ 92UppDec-765
❑ 93AstMot-17
❑ 93AstStaC-9
❑ 93Bow-320
❑ 93Don-634
❑ 93Fin-137
❑ 93FinRef-137
❑ 93Fla-67
❑ 93Fle-399
❑ 93FleFinE-80
❑ 93Lea-334
❑ 93OPC-392
❑ 93OPCPre-86
❑ 93PacSpa-481
❑ 93Pin-507
❑ 93Sco-566
❑ 93Sel-179
❑ 93SelAce-18
❑ 93SelRoo-99T
❑ 93StaClu-165
❑ 93StaClu-608
❑ 93StaCluFDI-165
❑ 93StaCluFDI-608
❑ 93StaCluMOP-165
❑ 93StaCluMOP-608
❑ 93Stu-59
❑ 93Top-515
❑ 93TopGol-515
❑ 93ToplnaM-515
❑ 93ToplnaR-515
❑ 93TopMic-515
❑ 93TopTra-32T
❑ 93TriPla-232
❑ 93Ult-397
❑ 93UppDec-695
❑ 93UppDecGold-695
❑ 93USPlaCA-4S
❑ 94AstMot-15
❑ 94Bow-6
❑ 94ColC-526
❑ 94ColChoGS-526
❑ 94ColChoSS-526
❑ 94Don-228
❑ 94Fin-99
❑ 94FinRef-99
❑ 94Fle-500
❑ 94FleExtB-282
❑ 94Lea-379
❑ 94OPC-157
❑ 94Pac-275
❑ 94Pin-163
❑ 94PinArtP-163
❑ 94PinMusC-163
❑ 94Sco-502
❑ 94ScoGolR-502
❑ 94Sel-243
❑ 94SP-32
❑ 94SPDieC-32
❑ 94StaClu-113
❑ 94StaCluFDI-113
❑ 94StaCluGR-113
❑ 94StaCluMOP-113
❑ 94Top-125
❑ 94TopGol-125
❑ 94TopSpa-125
❑ 94Ult-210
❑ 94UppDec-484
❑ 94UppDecED-484
❑ 95AstMot-24
❑ 95ColCho-119
❑ 95ColChoGS-119
❑ 95ColChoSS-119
❑ 95Don-347
❑ 95DonPreP-347
❑ 95DonTopotO-261
❑ 95Fle-469
❑ 95Lea-282
❑ 95Pac-194
❑ 95Sco-201
❑ 95ScoGolR-201
❑ 95ScoPlaTS-201
❑ 95StaClu-275
❑ 95StaCluMOP-275
❑ 95StaCluSTWS-275
❑ 95StaCluVR-140
❑ 95StaCluVRMO-140
❑ 95Top-285
❑ 95TopCyb-155
❑ 95Ult-391
❑ 95UltGolM-391
❑ 96AstMot-15
❑ 96ColCho-569
❑ 96ColChoGS-569
❑ 96ColChoSS-569
❑ 96Don-484
❑ 96DonPreP-484
❑ 96Fla-285
❑ 96Fle-419
❑ 96FleTif-419
❑ 96LeaSigA-218
❑ 96LeaSigAG-218
❑ 96LeaSigAS-218
❑ 96Pac-86
❑ 96Sco-473
❑ 96Ult-490
❑ 96UltGolM-490
❑ 96UppDec-343
❑ 97Ult-362
❑ 97UltGolME-362
❑ 97UltPlaME-362
❑ 98PacInvGems-69
❑ 98PacOnl-437
❑ 98PacOnlR-437
❑ 98PacOnlWC-437
Swindle, Allen
❑ 83TamTarT-22
Swingle, Paul
❑ 89BenBucL-10
❑ 90BoiHawP-3312
❑ 91PalSprAP-2014
❑ 92ClaFS7-339
❑ 92MidAngF-4028
❑ 92MidAngOHP-23
❑ 92MidAngS-471
❑ 92SkyAA F-201
❑ 93VanCanF-2598
❑ 94Top-765
❑ 94TopGol-765
❑ 94TopSpa-765
❑ 96VanCanB-26
Swingle, Russ
❑ 52Par-94
Swinton, Jermaine
❑ 90AshTouC-23
❑ 91AshTouP-581
❑ 91Cla/Bes-77
❑ 92Bow-137
❑ 92BurAstC-5
❑ 92BurAstF-560
❑ 92UppDecML-316
❑ 93AshTouF-2286
❑ 96StoPorB-11
❑ 97StoPor-16
Swisher, Steve
❑ 74WicAerODF-123
❑ 75OPC-63
❑ 75Top-63
❑ 75TopMin-63
❑ 76CubTri-23
❑ 76OPC-173
❑ 76SSP-319
❑ 76Top-173
❑ 77OPC-23
❑ 77Top-419
❑ 78CarTeal-33
❑ 78Top-252
❑ 79Car5-27
❑ 79Top-304
❑ 80Top-163
❑ 81PadFamF-20
❑ 81Top-541
❑ 81TopTra-840
❑ 82Top-764
❑ 83Don-633
❑ 83RicBraT-12
❑ 83Top-612
❑ 86WatIndP-27
❑ 87WilBilP-18
❑ 88ColSprSSC-24
❑ 88ColSprSSP-1546
❑ 89JacMetGS-20
❑ 90CMC-684
❑ 90ProAAAF-291
❑ 90TidTidC-27
❑ 90TidTidP-560
❑ 90TopTVM-62
❑ 91LinDriAAA-574
❑ 91TidTidLD-574
❑ 91TidTidP-2526
❑ 91TriA AAGP-AAA50
❑ 92BinMetF-532
❑ 92BinMetS-74
❑ 93BinMetF-2349
❑ 96MetKah-31
❑ 96MetKah-29
Switzer, Mike
❑ 89AncBucTI-8
Swob, Tim
❑ 87TamTarP-9
Swoboda, Robin
❑ 97PinFan-PC11
Swoboda, Ron
❑ 63ReqKP-17
❑ 65Top-533
❑ 66MetTeal-11
❑ 66MetVolC-12
❑ 66OPC-35
❑ 66Top-35
❑ 66TopRubl-90
❑ 66TopVen-35
❑ 67CokCapA-28
❑ 67CokCapNLA-26
❑ 67CokCapYM-V27
❑ 67DexPre-202
❑ 67MetTeal-11
❑ 67OPC-186
❑ 67Top-186
❑ 67Top-264
❑ 67TopGiaSU-5
❑ 67TopVen-288
❑ 68AtlOilPBCC-43
❑ 68Baz-13
❑ 68OPC-114
❑ 68Top-114
❑ 68Top3-D-12
❑ 68TopActS-2A
❑ 68TopActS-15A
❑ 68TopPos-17
❑ 68TopVen-114
❑ 69CitMetC-18
❑ 69MetBoyS-5
❑ 69MetNewYDN-18
❑ 69MetTeal-15
❑ 69MetTealC-5
❑ 69MilBra-268
❑ 69MLBOffS-171
❑ 69MLBPin-57
❑ 69Top-585
❑ 69TopSta-70
❑ 69TopTeaP-24
❑ 69TraSta-44
❑ 70MetTeal-12
❑ 70MetTealC-5
❑ 70MetTra-25A
❑ 70MLBOffS-83
❑ 70OPC-431
❑ 70Top-431
❑ 71MLBOffS-166
❑ 71OPC-665
❑ 71Top-665
❑ 72MilBra-337
❑ 72OPC-8
❑ 72Top-8
❑ 72YanSch-6
❑ 73OPC-314
❑ 73Top-314
❑ 81TCM60I-322
❑ 84OCoandSI-153
❑ 89Met196C-12
❑ 89MetRinP69-25
❑ 91MetWIZ-390
❑ 91UppDecS-8
❑ 92YanWIZ7-147
❑ 94Met69CCPP-30
❑ 94Met69CS-29
❑ 94Met69T-9
❑ 96Met69Y-8
❑ 97FleMilDM-35
❑ 97FleMilDMR-35
Swoope, Bill
❑ 77CliDodT-26
❑ 78CliDodT-30
❑ 79LodDodT-13
Swope, Mark
❑ 90ArkRaz-24
❑ 91Cla/Bes-74
❑ 91VisOakC-10
❑ 91VisOakP-1741
❑ 92Ft.MyeMCB-11
❑ 92Ft.MyeMF-2747
❑ 93ForMyeMF-2656
Sykes, Bob
❑ 77Top-491
❑ 78TigTeal-28
❑ 79Car5-28
❑ 79Top-569
❑ 80Top-223
❑ 81Fle-533
❑ 81Top-348
❑ 82ColCliP-38
❑ 82ColCliT-12
❑ 82Don-640
❑ 82Fle-130
❑ 82JacMetT-24
❑ 82NasSouTI-25
❑ 82Top-108
❑ 83TidTidT-27
❑ 84TidTidT-17
❑ 89MetColP-53
❑ 90MetColP-48
Sykes, Jamie
❑ 97LetBlaDB-17
❑ 98SouBenSHM-13
Sylvester, Billy
❑ 98EugEme-30
Sylvester, John
❑ 77CedRapGT-4
Sylvester, Johnny
❑ 92MegRut-140
Sylvester, Louis
❑ 87OldJudN-486
Sylvestri, Tony
❑ 93KanCouCC-21
❑ 93KanCouCF-926
❑ 93KanCouCTI-23
❑ 94BreCouMC-19
❑ 94BreCouMF-22
Sylvia, Dave
❑ 75BurBeeT-28
Sylvia, Ronald
❑ 81RedPioT-7
❑ 82RedPioT-16
❑ 83NasAngT-9
Symmonds, Maika
❑ 96LowSpiB-24
Syverson, Dain
❑ 85WatIndT-25
❑ 86IndTeal-43
❑ 86WatIndP-24
❑ 87WilBilP-1
Szarko, Andy
❑ 93MarPhiC-28
❑ 93MarPhiF-3475
Szczechowski, Dennis
❑ 92CliGiaF-3597
❑ 92EveGiaC-22
❑ 92EveGiaF-1690
Szczepanski, Joe
❑ 91GenCubC-20
❑ 91GenCubP-4215
❑ 92WinSpiC-22
❑ 92WinSpiF-1207
Szekely, Joe
❑ 83ChaRoyT-3
❑ 85VerBeaDT-6
❑ 87SanAntDTI-17
❑ 87TexLeaAF-35
❑ 89AlbDukCm-19
❑ 89AlbDukP-77
❑ 90CMC-337
❑ 90ProAAAF-354
❑ 90SyrChiC-11
❑ 90SyrChiMB-25
❑ 90SyrChiP-574
❑ 91LinDriAAA-444
❑ 91RicBraBC-18
❑ 91RicBraLD-444
❑ 91RicBraP-2572
❑ 91RicBraTI-12
❑ 92RicBraBB-16

❑ 92RicBraF-381
❑ 92RicBraRC-22
❑ 92RicBraS-444
❑ 93MacBraC-28
❑ 93MacBraF-1419
Szeryk, Neil
❑ 91OklStaC-26
Szimanski, Tom
❑ 94BelMarC-26
❑ 94BelMarF-3234
❑ 94StaCluDP-9
❑ 94StaCluDPFDI-9
❑ 96LanJetB-26
Szotkiewicz, Ken
❑ 71OPC-749
❑ 71Top-749
Szymarek, Paul
❑ 81ShrCapT-12
❑ 82PhoGiaVNB-6
Szymborski, Thomas
❑ 96IdaFalB-25
❑ 97CliLumG-26
Szymczak, Dave
❑ 83NasSouTI-24
❑ 84BufBisT-13
Szynal, Jon
❑ 89SpaPhiP-1031
❑ 89SpaPhiS-22
t'Hoen, E.J.
❑ 97CedRapK-13
❑ 98CedRapKTI-28
❑ 98MidLeaPM-5
Tabacheck, Marty
❑ 50WorWidGV-23
Tabaka, Jeff
❑ 86JamExpP-25
❑ 87WesPalBEP-656
❑ 88WesPalBES-24
❑ 89ReaPhiB-7
❑ 89ReaPhiP-663
❑ 91LinDriAA-520
❑ 91ReaPhiLD-520
❑ 91ReaPhiP-1371
❑ 92ElPasDF-3921
❑ 92ElPasDS-222
❑ 93ClaGolF-154
❑ 93NewOrlZF-973
❑ 93Top-586
❑ 93TopGol-586
❑ 93TopInaM-586
❑ 93TopInaR-586
❑ 93TopMic-586
❑ 94BufBisF-1837
❑ 95Fle-570
❑ 95Pac-371
❑ 95PadMot-15
❑ 96AstMot-23
❑ 96Fle-420
❑ 96FleTif-420
❑ 96LeaSigEA-197
❑ 96TusTorB-23
❑ 97IndInd-23
Tabb, Jerry
❑ 78Top-224
Tabeling, Bob
❑ 86VisOakP-21
Tabler, Pat
❑ 77ForLauYS-18
❑ 80NasSouTI-22
❑ 81ColCliP-25
❑ 81ColCliT-16
❑ 82Don-529
❑ 82IowCubT-10
❑ 83Don-552
❑ 83Fle-509
❑ 84AllGamPI-189
❑ 84Don-536
❑ 84Fle-552
❑ 84Ind-29
❑ 84IndWhe-10
❑ 84Nes792-329
❑ 84Top-329
❑ 84TopSti-252
❑ 84TopTif-329
❑ 85Don-460
❑ 85Fle-456
❑ 85Ind-31
❑ 85IndPol-10
❑ 85Lea-76
❑ 85OPC-158
❑ 85Top-158
❑ 85TopSti-250
❑ 85TopTif-158
❑ 86Don-129
❑ 86Fle-594
❑ 86IndOhH-10
❑ 86IndTeal-44
❑ 86Lea-52
❑ 86OPC-66
❑ 86Top-674
❑ 86TopSti-212
❑ 86TopTat-8
❑ 86TopTif-674
❑ 87Don-254
❑ 87DonOpeD-107
❑ 87Fle-261
❑ 87FleGlo-261
❑ 87FleSlu-42
❑ 87GenMilB-2H
❑ 87IndGat-10
❑ 87Lea-182
❑ 87OPC-77
❑ 87Spo-24A
❑ 87Spo-24B
❑ 87Spo-66
❑ 87SpoTeaP-3
❑ 87StuPan-18
❑ 87Top-575
❑ 87TopMinL-52
❑ 87TopSti-205
❑ 87TopTif-575
❑ 88Don-219
❑ 88DonAll-17
❑ 88Fle-618
❑ 88Fle-633
❑ 88FleGlo-618
❑ 88FleGlo-633
❑ 88FleHotS-43
❑ 88FleMin-20
❑ 88FleStiC-22
❑ 88FleUpd-36
❑ 88FleUpdG-36
❑ 88IndGat-10
❑ 88IndTeal-35
❑ 88OPC-230
❑ 88PanSti-81
❑ 88RedFolSB-87
❑ 88RoyTeal-32
❑ 88Sco-23
❑ 88ScoGlo-23
❑ 88ScoRoo-22T
❑ 88ScoRooG-22T
❑ 88Spo-205
❑ 88StaLinI-20
❑ 88Top-230
❑ 88TopBig-173
❑ 88TopSti-204
❑ 88TopTif-230
❑ 88TopTra-118T
❑ 88TopTraT-118T
❑ 89Bow-125
❑ 89BowTif-125
❑ 89Don-326
❑ 89Fle-294
❑ 89FleGlo-294
❑ 89OPC-56
❑ 89PanSti-359
❑ 89RoyTasD-3
❑ 89Sco-391
❑ 89Spo-172
❑ 89Top-56
❑ 89TopBatL-19
❑ 89TopBig-67
❑ 89TopSti-6
❑ 89TopTif-56
❑ 89UppDec-233
❑ 89Woo-18
❑ 90Don-444
❑ 90Fle-119
❑ 90FleCan-119
❑ 90OPC-727
❑ 90PubIntS-357
❑ 90RoyPos-25
❑ 90Sco-242
❑ 90Spo-218
❑ 90Top-727
❑ 90TopBig-89
❑ 90TopTif-727
❑ 90UppDec-142
❑ 91BluJayFS-25
❑ 91BluJayFS-27
❑ 91BluJayS-19
❑ 91Bow-28
❑ 91FleUpd-67
❑ 91Lea-443
❑ 91MetWIZ-393
❑ 91OPC-433
❑ 91OPCPre-118
❑ 91Sco-811
❑ 91ScoRoo-22T
❑ 91Top-433
❑ 91TopDesS-433
❑ 91TopMic-433
❑ 91TopTif-433
❑ 92OPC-333
❑ 92Sco-312
❑ 92StaClu-333
❑ 92Top-333
❑ 92TopGol-333
❑ 92TopGolW-333
❑ 92TopMic-333
❑ 92UppDec-203
❑ 93BluJayD4-12
❑ 93Fle-700
❑ 93OPC-270
❑ 93StaClu-160
❑ 93StaCluFDI-160
❑ 93StaCluMOP-160
Tabor, Greg
❑ 82BurRanF-15
❑ 82BurRanT-10
❑ 84TulDriTI-19
❑ 85OklCit8T-28
❑ 86OklCit8P-23
❑ 87OklCit8P-21
❑ 88Fle-644
❑ 88FleGlo-644
❑ 88IowCubC-18
❑ 88IowCubP-548
❑ 93RanKee-352
Tabor, Jim
❑ 39GouPreR303A-41
❑ 39PlaBal-14
❑ 39WorWidGTP-41
❑ 40PlaBal-36
❑ 41DouPlaR-57
❑ 42RedSoxTI-22
❑ 43RedSoxTI-23
❑ 49BowPCL-33
❑ 49SolSunP-10
❑ 76TayBow4-99
❑ 85BigLeaC3-71
❑ 92ConTSN-542
Tabor, Scott
❑ 83BirBarT-15
❑ 86OmaRoyP-27
❑ 86OmaRoyT-17
Taborn, Earl
❑ 93NegLeaRL2-38
❑ 95NegLeaL2-10
Tabuchi, Koichi
❑ 79TCMJapPB-12
Tackett, Gary
❑ 90NebCor-23
Tackett, Jeff (Jack)
❑ 85NewOriT-5
❑ 87ChaO'sW-9
❑ 88ChaKniTI-8
❑ 89RocRedWC-17
❑ 89RocRedWP-1645
❑ 90CMC-310
❑ 90ProAAAF-463
❑ 90RocRedWC-9
❑ 90RocRedWGC-13
❑ 90RocRedWP-706
❑ 91Bow-106
❑ 91LinDriAAA-469
❑ 91RocRedWLD-469
❑ 91RocRedWP-1906
❑ 92BalOriP-35
❑ 92BalOriP-36
❑ 92DonRoo-114
❑ 92Lea-411
❑ 92LeaBlaG-411
❑ 92ScoRoo-86T
❑ 92StaClu-383
❑ 92TopDeb91-168
❑ 92TopTra-115T
❑ 92TopTraG-115T
❑ 92Ult-310
❑ 93BalOriP-34
❑ 93Don-529
❑ 93Fle-553
❑ 93PacSpa-351
❑ 93Sco-355
❑ 93Sel-294
❑ 93StaClu-186
❑ 93StaCluFDI-186
❑ 93StaCluMOP-186
❑ 93Top-6
❑ 93TopGol-6
❑ 93TopInaM-6
❑ 93TopInaR-6
❑ 93TopMic-6
❑ 93Ult-147
❑ 93UppDec-517
❑ 93UppDecGold-517
❑ 94BalOriP-33
❑ 94OriPro-98
❑ 94OriUSPC-4C
❑ 94OriUSPC-9H
❑ 94Sco-136
❑ 94ScoGolR-136
❑ 94StaCluT-294
❑ 94StaCluTFDI-294
❑ 94Top-664
❑ 94TopGol-664
❑ 94TopPre-6
❑ 94TopSpa-664
❑ 94VenLinU-221
❑ 95StaClu-168
❑ 95StaCluFDI-168
❑ 95StaCluMOP-168
❑ 95StaCluSTWS-168
❑ 95TolMudHTI-24
❑ 95Top-375
❑ 96TolMudHB-28
❑ 97OklCit8-23
Taco, Puffy
❑ 95SanAntMTI-NNO
Taczy, Craig
❑ 95GreFalDTI-11
❑ 96YakBeaTI-46
❑ 97GreFalDTI-24
❑ 98SanBerS-29
❑ 98SanBerSTIS-25
Tadevich, John
❑ 26Zee-151
Tafoya, Dennis
❑ 88AshTouP-1070
❑ 88AubAstP-1951
❑ 89OscAstS-24
❑ 90ColMudB-24
❑ 90ColMudP-1348
❑ 90ColMudS-23
❑ 91CarMudLD-118
❑ 91CarMudP-1086
❑ 91LinDriAA-118
❑ 92CarMudS-144
❑ 93CarMudF-2053
Tafoya, Rod
❑ 89BoiHawP-1987
❑ 90EriSaiS-26
Taft, Brett
❑ 96SpoIndB-28
❑ 97LanLugTS-28
❑ 97MidLeaTP-15
❑ 98WilBluRC-27
❑ 99BasAmeTP-92
❑ 99BasAmeTPG-92
Taft, Dennie
❑ 83CliGiaF-24
Taft, Tim
❑ 88BenBucL-14
❑ 88ClePhiS-24
Taft, William Howard
❑ 77Spo-6715
❑ 90BasWit-107
Tagi, Anthony
❑ 88FreSunCLC-20
❑ 88FreSunP-1234
Tagle, Hank
❑ 91UtiBluSC-26
❑ 91UtiBluSP-3239
❑ 92SouBenWSC-23
❑ 92SouBenWSF-176
❑ 93SarWhiSF-1368
❑ 93SouBenWSC-21
❑ 94SouBenSHC-1
❑ 94SouBenSHF-594
❑ 95PriWilCTI-24
Tagliaferri, Gino
❑ 90FayGenP-2417
❑ 90NiaFalRP-11
Taglienti, Jeff
❑ 97LowSpiB-25
❑ 98MicBatCM-28
Taguchi, Dragon
❑ 89SalSpuCLC-132
❑ 89SalSpuP-1809
Tahan, Kevin
❑ 90CMC-664
❑ 90SavCarP-2078
❑ 91SprCarC-25
❑ 91SprCarP-752
❑ 92SprCarC-20
❑ 92SprCarF-873
❑ 93ArkTraF-2815
Taitt, D.
❑ 29ExhFou-18
Tajima, Toni
❑ 94SanBerSC-22
❑ 94SanBerSF-2760
Takach, Dave
❑ 87SprCarB-14
❑ 88SalBucS-20
Takacs, John
❑ 77AshTouT-22
Takada, Shigeru
❑ 79TCMJapPB-62
Takagi, Morimichi
❑ 79TCMJapPB-74
Takagi, Yoshikazu
❑ 79TCMJapPB-56
Takagi, Yutaka
❑ 87JapPlaB-24
Takahashi, Kazumi
❑ 79TCMJapPB-35
Takahashi, Kurt
❑ 95BelGiaTI-35
❑ 96BelGiaTI-20
❑ 97SalVolG-35
Takahashi, Shigeyuki
❑ 92NiaFalRC-28
❑ 92NiaFalRF-3344
❑ 93BriTigF-3667
❑ 94BriTigC-29
Takahashi, Yoshihiko
❑ 79TCMJapPB-29
❑ 87JapPlaB-10
Takao, Scott
❑ 92SouBenWSC-27
❑ 93SouBenWSC-30
❑ 94SouBenSHC-28
❑ 98BirBarG-23
Takara, Steven
❑ 87HawRai-15
Takayoshi, Todd
❑ 93PocPosF-4211
❑ 93PocPosSP-15
❑ 94LakElsSC-21
❑ 94LakElsSF-1667
❑ 95LakElsSTI-24
❑ 96LakElsSB-13
Takenouci, Masashi
❑ 79TCMJapPB-82
Takeuchi, Yoshiya
❑ 96HilStaHWB-23
Talamantez, Greg
❑ 85NewOriT-4
❑ 86HagSunP-24
❑ 87ChaO'sW-35
❑ 88FloStaLAS-22
❑ 88St.LucMS-22
❑ 89JacMetGS-1
❑ 91LinDriAA-643
❑ 91WilBilLD-643
❑ 91WilBilP-292
Talanoa, Scott
❑ 92BelBreCB-7
❑ 92BelBreFI-415
❑ 92ClaFS7-362
❑ 92MidLeaATI-44
❑ 93BelBreCB-23
❑ 93BelBreFI-1721
❑ 93MidLeaAGF-4
❑ 94Bow-505
❑ 94Cla-78
❑ 94ClaTriF-T43
❑ 94ElPasDF-3155
❑ 94ExcFS7-88
❑ 95Exc-75
❑ 95Top-79
❑ 95UppDecML-144
❑ 95UppDecMLFS-144
Talbert, Louis
❑ 90AppFoxBS-27
❑ 90AppFoxP-2095
❑ 90CMC-699
❑ 91LinDriAA-419
❑ 91MemChiLD-419
❑ 91MemChiP-655
Talbot, Bob D.
❑ 52MotCoo-16
❑ 54Top-229
❑ 55Bow-137
❑ 94TopArc1-229
❑ 94TopArc1G-229
Talbot, Daniel
❑ 82MonNew-16
Talbot, Fred
❑ 64A's-16
❑ 65AthJayP-12
❑ 65OPC-58
❑ 65Top-58
❑ 66Top-403
❑ 66TopRubI-91
❑ 67CokCapYM-V5
❑ 67Top-517
❑ 68Top-577
❑ 68YanPhoS-78
❑ 69Top-332
❑ 69YanMal-9
❑ 69YanPhoS-51
❑ 70OPC-287
❑ 70Top-287
❑ 72MilBra-338
❑ 81TCM60I-467
❑ 83Pil69G-17
❑ 92YanWIZ6-123
Talbott, Ben
❑ 97ButCopKB-27
❑ 97ButCopKK-27
Talbott, Rick
❑ 92HigSchPLS-17
Talbott, Shawn
❑ 86AshTouP-27
❑ 87AshTouP-18
Talford, Calvin
❑ 89MarPhiS-29
Tallent, Ron
❑ 91BoiHawC-16
❑ 91BoiHawP-3892
Tallis, Cedric
❑ 70RoyTeal-36
❑ 71oySigST-27
Tallman, Fan (Matt)
❑ 86Spo-182
Tallman, Troy
❑ 92KanCouCC-12
❑ 92KanCouCF-94
❑ 93FreKeyC-25
❑ 93FreKeyF-1030
Talton, Tim (Marion)
❑ 67Top-603
Tam, Andy
❑ 79AshTouT-8
Tam, Jeff
❑ 93PitMetC-21
❑ 93PitMetF-3710
❑ 94CapCitBC-21
❑ 94CapCitBF-1751
❑ 94SouAtlLAF-SAL38
❑ 95Exc-239
❑ 96BinMetB-26
❑ 97NorTid-31
❑ 97NorTidB-30
❑ 98NorTidP-25
❑ 98NorTidQ-26
Tamarez, Adame
❑ 92CliGiaC-20
❑ 92CliGiaF-3606
Tamarez, Carlos
❑ 90MadMusP-2279
❑ 90SouOreAP-3437
Tamargo, John
❑ 76TulOilGP-11
❑ 78SprRedWK-10
❑ 79GiaPol-30
❑ 79Top-726
❑ 80ExpPos-31
❑ 80OPC-351
❑ 80Top-680
❑ 81Don-210
❑ 81Fle-152
❑ 81OPC-35
❑ 81Top-519
❑ 82MiaMarT-22
❑ 87LynMetP-22
❑ 89MetColP-55
❑ 91St.LucMC-26
❑ 91St.LucMP-727
❑ 92St.LucMCB-26
❑ 92St.LucMF-1763
❑ 93St.LucMC-26
❑ 93St.LuMF-2937
❑ 94BinMetF-720
❑ 95BinMetTI-32
❑ 96BinMetB-27
❑ 96PitMetB-26
❑ 97CapCitB-19
❑ 97KisCob-27
❑ 98St.LucMM-14
Tamulis, Vito
❑ 35GouPreR-16
❑ 36GouWidPPR-A99
❑ 36WorWidGV-101
❑ 39PlaBal-139
❑ 40DodTeal-21
❑ 40PlaBal-145
❑ 41DodTeal-8
❑ 41Gou-17
❑ 72TCMthe3-73
❑ 73Dod194T-27
❑ 78DodTCM4-13
❑ 90DodTar-788

Tanabe, Collin
❑ 82BelBreFr-13
Tanabe, Nori
❑ 86SanJosBP-20
Tanana, Frank
❑ 74OPC-605
❑ 74Top-605
❑ 75CalAngP-43
❑ 75OPC-16
❑ 75Top-16
❑ 75TopMin-16
❑ 76Hos-101
❑ 76Kel-30A
❑ 76Kel-30B
❑ 76OPC-204
❑ 76OPC-490
❑ 76SSP-189
❑ 76Top-204
❑ 76Top-490
❑ 77BurCheD-122
❑ 77Hos-63
❑ 77Kel-45
❑ 77OPC-105
❑ 77Spo-2518
❑ 77Top-200
❑ 78AngFamF-36
❑ 78Hos-101
❑ 78Kel-54
❑ 78OPC-7
❑ 78OPC-65
❑ 78PapGinD-33
❑ 78RCColC-92
❑ 78SagDis-23
❑ 78SSP270-211
❑ 78TasDis-23
❑ 78Top-207
❑ 78Top-600
❑ 78WifBalD-73
❑ 79BasPat-87
❑ 79Hos-47
❑ 79Kel-55
❑ 79OPC-274
❑ 79Top-530
❑ 80OPC-57
❑ 80Top-105
❑ 81CokTeaS-7
❑ 81Don-171
❑ 81Fle-276
❑ 81OPC-369
❑ 81Top-369
❑ 81TopSti-56
❑ 81TopSupHT-11
❑ 81TopTra-841
❑ 82Don-326
❑ 82Fle-309
❑ 82OPC-4
❑ 82Top-792
❑ 82TopTra-117T
❑ 83Don-447
❑ 83Fle-581
❑ 83RanAffF-28
❑ 83Top-272
❑ 84Don-98
❑ 84Fle-432
❑ 84FunFooP-133
❑ 84Nes792-479
❑ 84OPC-276
❑ 84RanJarP-28
❑ 84Top-479
❑ 84TopTif-479
❑ 85AngStrH-12
❑ 85Don-9
❑ 85Don-220
❑ 85DonSupD-9
❑ 85Fle-570
❑ 85Lea-9
❑ 85OPC-55
❑ 85Top-55
❑ 85TopSti-348
❑ 85TopTif-55
❑ 86Don-491
❑ 86Fle-239
❑ 86Lea-241
❑ 86OPC-124
❑ 86TigCaiD-17
❑ 86Top-592
❑ 86TopTif-592
❑ 87Don-152
❑ 87Fle-164
❑ 87FleGlo-164
❑ 87FleHotS-40
❑ 87OPC-231
❑ 87SevCoi-D10
❑ 87SpoTeaP-15
❑ 87TigCaiD-20
❑ 87TigCok-5
❑ 87Top-726
❑ 87TopTif-726
❑ 88Don-461
❑ 88DonBasB-259
❑ 88Fle-71
❑ 88FleGlo-71
❑ 88FleSlu-42
❑ 88OPC-177
❑ 88PanSti-86
❑ 88Sco-490
❑ 88ScoGlo-490
❑ 88Spo-133
❑ 88StaLinTi-18
❑ 88TigPep-26
❑ 88TigPol-11
❑ 88Top-177
❑ 88TopSti-264
❑ 88TopTif-177
❑ 89AngSmo-9
❑ 89Bow-92
❑ 89BowTif-92
❑ 89Don-90
❑ 89DonBasB-91
❑ 89Fle-147
❑ 89FleGlo-147
❑ 89OPC-299
❑ 89PanSti-336
❑ 89RedFolSB-117
❑ 89Sco-112
❑ 89Spo-103
❑ 89TigMar-26
❑ 89TigPol-26
❑ 89Top-603
❑ 89Top-609
❑ 89TopBasT-158
❑ 89TopSti-275
❑ 89TopTif-603
❑ 89TopTif-609
❑ 89UppDec-391
❑ 90Bow-343
❑ 90BowTif-343
❑ 90ClaBlu-108
❑ 90Don-180
❑ 90DonBesA-48
❑ 90Fle-616
❑ 90FleCan-616
❑ 90KayB-30
❑ 90Lea-87
❑ 90OPC-343
❑ 90PanSti-72
❑ 90PublntS-483
❑ 90Sco-57
❑ 90TigCok-23
❑ 90Top-343
❑ 90TopBig-119
❑ 90TopSti-277
❑ 90TopTif-343
❑ 90UppDec-516
❑ 91Don-508
❑ 91Fle-354
❑ 91Lea-497
❑ 91OPC-236
❑ 91PacRyaTEI-32
❑ 91Sco-328
❑ 91StaClu-158
❑ 91Stu-57
❑ 91TigCok-26
❑ 91TigPol-12
❑ 91Top-236A
❑ 91Top-236B
❑ 91TopDesS-236
❑ 91TopMic-236
❑ 91TopTif-236
❑ 91Ult-128
❑ 91UppDec-369
❑ 92Don-111
❑ 92Fle-145
❑ 92Lea-21
❑ 92LeaBlaG-21
❑ 92OPC-458
❑ 92Pin-198
❑ 92Sco-271
❑ 92StaClu-416
❑ 92Stu-177
❑ 92TigKro-23
❑ 92TigTeal-29
❑ 92Top-458
❑ 92TopGol-458
❑ 92TopGolW-458
❑ 92TopMic-458
❑ 92TriPla-249
❑ 92UppDec-605
❑ 93Don-599
❑ 93Fle-611
❑ 93FleFinE-106
❑ 93Lea-365
❑ 93MetColP-46
❑ 93MetKah-29
❑ 93OPC-288
❑ 93PacSpa-547
❑ 93PanSti-120
❑ 93Pin-542
❑ 93RanKee-353
❑ 93Sco-652
❑ 93Sel-398
❑ 93SelRoo-127T
❑ 93StaClu-267
❑ 93StaCluFDI-267
❑ 93StaCluMOP-267
❑ 93Top-53
❑ 93TopGol-53
❑ 93ToplnaM-53
❑ 93ToplnaR-53
❑ 93TopMic-53
❑ 93Ult-434
❑ 93UppDec-68
❑ 93UppDec-626
❑ 93UppDecGold-68
❑ 93UppDecGold-626
❑ 94Sco-538
❑ 94ScoGolR-538
Tanderys, Jeff
❑ 91HamRedC-12
❑ 91HamRedP-4039
❑ 92HamRedC-1
❑ 92HamRedF-1592
Tank, Travis
❑ 96HelBreTI-24
❑ 97BelSnaB-27
Tanks, Talmage
❑ 76BurBeeT-32
Tanksley, Scott
❑ 93MisStaB-41
❑ 96ForWayWB-25
Tannahill, Kevin
❑ 89HelBreSP-23
❑ 91ChaRanC-14
❑ 91ChaRanP-1318
Tannehill, Jesse
❑ 04RedSoxUP-13
❑ 09SenBarP-9
❑ 09T206-350
❑ 12HasTriFT-45
Tannehill, Lee Ford
❑ 08RosComP-19
❑ 09AmeCarE90-1-105
❑ 09AmeCarE90-1-106
❑ 09ColChiE-285
❑ 09T206-351
❑ 09T206-352
❑ 10RedCroT-77
❑ 10RedCroT-250
❑ 11HelSta-17
❑ 11PinT-5-766
❑ 11S74Sil-9
❑ 11SpoLifCW-346
❑ 11SpoLifM-32
❑ 11T205-169
❑ 12ColRedB-285
❑ 12ColTinT-285
❑ 12HasTriFT-52
❑ 12T207-181
Tanner, Bruce
❑ 85BufBisT-25
❑ 85FleUpd-116
❑ 86BufBisP-21
❑ 86Fle-218
❑ 87TacTigP-8
❑ 88HunStaTI-22
❑ 89TacTigP-1540
❑ 90SpolndSP-27
❑ 91ChaRaiC-25
❑ 91ChaRaiP-112
❑ 91SouAtlLAGP-SAL6
❑ 92HigDesMC-30
❑ 93RanCucQC-28
❑ 93RanCucQF-848
❑ 94AugGreC-29
❑ 94AugGreF-3025
❑ 96CarMudB-27
❑ 97CarMudC-26
❑ 98NasSouTI-30
❑ 98NasSouTISS-28
Tanner, Chuck
❑ 55BraJohC-18
❑ 55Top-161
❑ 56Top-69
❑ 57Top-392
❑ 58Top-91
❑ 59Top-234
❑ 60Lea-115
❑ 60Top-279
❑ 61MapLeaBH-23
❑ 71OPC-661
❑ 71Top-661
❑ 72OPC-98
❑ 72Top-98
❑ 72WhiSoxC-6
❑ 72WhiSoxTI1-13
❑ 73OPC-356
❑ 73Top-356
❑ 74OPC-221
❑ 74Top-221
❑ 75OPC-276
❑ 75Top-276
❑ 75TopMin-276
❑ 76OPC-656
❑ 76SSP-151
❑ 76Top-656
❑ 77PirPosP-27
❑ 77Top-354
❑ 78Top-494
❑ 79TCM50-63
❑ 79Top-244
❑ 80Bra195T-16
❑ 80Top-551
❑ 81Don-257
❑ 81Fle-367
❑ 81Top-683
❑ 82Don-150
❑ 83Don-124
❑ 83Top-696
❑ 84Fle-657
❑ 84Nes792-291
❑ 84Pir-21
❑ 84Top-291
❑ 84TopTif-291
❑ 85Pir-20
❑ 85Top-268
❑ 85TopTif-268
❑ 86BraPol-7
❑ 86Top-351
❑ 86TopTif-351
❑ 86TopTra-107T
❑ 86TopTraT-107T
❑ 87BraSmo-26
❑ 87Top-593
❑ 87TopTif-593
❑ 88Top-134
❑ 88TopClo-111
❑ 88TopTif-134
❑ 92UppDecS-5
❑ 92UppDecS-19
❑ 94UppDecS-5
Tanner, Eddie (Ed)
❑ 81BatTroT-16
❑ 82WatIndF-22
❑ 82WatIndT-19
❑ 83SprCarF-8
❑ 84ArkTraT-1
❑ 86ArkTraP-24
❑ 87NasSouTI-19
❑ 88NasSouTI-23
❑ 89NasSouC-19
❑ 89NasSouP-1287
❑ 89NasSouTI-24
❑ 90CMC-146
❑ 90NasSouC-21
❑ 90NasSouP-243
❑ 90ProAAAF-555
❑ 90SprCarDGB-6
Tanner, Joe
❑ 93DayCubC-26
❑ 94PeoChiC-28
❑ 94PeoChiF-2285
Tanner, Mark
❑ 74GasRanT-22
❑ 75LynRanT-26
Tanner, Paul
❑ 96JohCitCTI-30
❑ 97PeoChi-26
❑ 98PriWilCQ-27
Tanner, Philip
❑ 24Zee-106
Tanner, Roy
❑ 75WatRoyT-30
❑ 76WatRoyT-30
❑ 77DayBealT-25
❑ 82ChaRoyT-24
❑ 83ChaRoyT-24
Tanoue, Keisaburoh
❑ 96MauStiHWB-24
Tanzi, Bobby
❑ 79AshTouT-16
❑ 80WauTimT-12
Tanzi, Michael
❑ 82AppFoxFr-25
❑ 83GleFalWST-20
Tao, Yasushi
❑ 79TCMJapPB-76
Taormina, Sal
❑ 53SanFraSTI-19
❑ 60TacBan-19
Tapais, Luis
❑ 86KenTwiP-23
Tapani, Kevin
❑ 86MedA'sC-64
❑ 86ModA'sC-22
❑ 87ModA'sC-15
❑ 87ModA'sP-12
❑ 88JacMetGS-23
❑ 89MetColP-56
❑ 89TidTidC-10
❑ 89TidTidP-1972
❑ 90Bow-407
❑ 90BowTif-407
❑ 90ClaYel-T16
❑ 90Don-473
❑ 90DonBesA-93
❑ 90DonRoo-35
❑ 90FleUpd-110
❑ 90Lea-269
❑ 90OPC-227
❑ 90ScoRoo-82T
❑ 90ScoYouS2-31
❑ 90Top-227
❑ 90TopBig-225
❑ 90TopDeb89-126
❑ 90TopTif-227
❑ 90UppDec-87
❑ 91Bow-322
❑ 91ClaGam-42
❑ 91DodPho-26
❑ 91Don-116
❑ 91Fle-625
❑ 91Lea-128
❑ 91MajLeaCP-13
❑ 91MetWIZ-394
❑ 91OPC-633
❑ 91PanFreS-307
❑ 91PanSti-249
❑ 91Sco-60
❑ 91Sco100RS-52
❑ 91SouOreAAP-SOA13
❑ 91StaClu-161
❑ 91Top-633
❑ 91TopDesS-633
❑ 91TopMic-633
❑ 91TopRoo-27
❑ 91TopTif-633
❑ 91Ult-196
❑ 91UppDec-434
❑ 92Bow-552
❑ 92Cla1-T87
❑ 92ClaGam-104
❑ 92Don-236
❑ 92Fle-219
❑ 92Hig5-85
❑ 92Lea-14
❑ 92LeaBlaG-14
❑ 92OPC-313
❑ 92Pin-176
❑ 92Sco-507
❑ 92StaClu-433
❑ 92Top-313
❑ 92TopGol-313
❑ 92TopGolW-313
❑ 92TopMic-313
❑ 92TriPla-98
❑ 92Ult-98
❑ 92UppDec-624
❑ 93Bow-269
❑ 93Don-443
❑ 93Fle-274
❑ 93Lea-404
❑ 93OPC-361
❑ 93PacSpa-178
❑ 93Pin-334
❑ 93Sco-45
❑ 93Sel-130
❑ 93SelAce-24
❑ 93StaClu-492
❑ 93StaCluFDI-492
❑ 93StaCluMOP-492
❑ 93Top-420
❑ 93TopGol-420
❑ 93ToplnaM-420
❑ 93ToplnaR-420
❑ 93TopMic-420
❑ 93TriPla-240
❑ 93Ult-237
❑ 93UppDec-313
❑ 93UppDecGold-313
❑ 94Bow-628
❑ 94ColC-272
❑ 94ColChoGS-272
❑ 94ColChoSS-272
❑ 94Don-115
❑ 94Fin-21
❑ 94FinRef-21
❑ 94Fla-317
❑ 94Fle-219
❑ 94FleExtB-124
❑ 94Lea-52
❑ 94OPC-246
❑ 94Pac-367
❑ 94Pin-54
❑ 94PinArtP-54
❑ 94PinMusC-54
❑ 94ProMag-78
❑ 94Sco-351
❑ 94ScoGolR-351
❑ 94Sel-144
❑ 94StaClu-117
❑ 94StaCluFDI-117
❑ 94StaCluGR-117
❑ 94StaCluMOP-117
❑ 94Top-185
❑ 94TopGol-185
❑ 94TopSpa-185
❑ 94TriPla-259
❑ 94Ult-395
❑ 94UppDec-439
❑ 94UppDecED-439
❑ 95ColCho-482
❑ 95ColChoGS-482
❑ 95ColChoSE-229
❑ 95ColChoSEGS-229
❑ 95ColChoSESS-229
❑ 95ColChoSS-482
❑ 95Don-269
❑ 95DonPreP-269
❑ 95DonTopotO-272
❑ 95Fin-75
❑ 95FinRef-75
❑ 95Fla-282
❑ 95Fle-215
❑ 95Lea-173
❑ 95Pac-257
❑ 95Pin-6
❑ 95PinArtP-6
❑ 95PinMusC-6
❑ 95Sco-347
❑ 95ScoGolR-347
❑ 95ScoPlaTS-347
❑ 95SP-172
❑ 95SPSil-172
❑ 95StaClu-93
❑ 95StaCluFDI-93
❑ 95StaCluMOP-93
❑ 95StaCluSTWS-93
❑ 95StaCluVR-58
❑ 95StaCluVRMO-58
❑ 95Top-37
❑ 95TopCyb-29
❑ 95TopEmb-81
❑ 95TopEmbGI-81
❑ 95Ult-78
❑ 95UltGolM-78
❑ 95UppDec-194
❑ 95UppDecED-194
❑ 95UppDecEDG-194
❑ 95UppDecSE-217
❑ 95UppDecSEG-217
❑ 96ColCho-768
❑ 96Don-488
❑ 96DonPreP-488
❑ 96Fla-58
❑ 96Fle-447
❑ 96FleTif-447
❑ 96FleUpd-U29
❑ 96FleUpdTC-U29
❑ 96LeaSigA-219
❑ 96LeaSigAG-219
❑ 96LeaSigAS-219
❑ 96Sco-218
❑ 96Ult-225
❑ 96Ult-337
❑ 96UltGolM-225
❑ 96UltGolM-337
❑ 96UppDec-489U
❑ 96WhiSoxF-15
❑ 97Cir-53
❑ 97CirRav-53
❑ 97Fle-70
❑ 97Fle-608
❑ 97FleTif-70
❑ 97FleTif-608
❑ 97Pac-62
❑ 97PacLigB-62

❑ 97Sco-245
❑ 97ScoArtPWB-245
❑ 97ScoPreS-245
❑ 97ScoShoS-245
❑ 97ScoShoSAP-245
❑ 97StaClu-270
❑ 97StaCluMOP-270
❑ 97Top-32
❑ 97Ult-502
❑ 97UltGolME-502
❑ 97UltPlaME-502
❑ 97WhiSoxS-13
❑ 97WhiSoxSPl-13
❑ 97WhiSoxSPr-13
❑ 98CirThu-219
❑ 98CirThuRav-219
❑ 98CirThuSupRav-219
❑ 98ColCho-334
❑ 98Fin-264
❑ 98FinNo--264
❑ 98FinNo-R-264
❑ 98FinRef-264
❑ 98Fle-122
❑ 98Pac-259
❑ 98PacOnl-155
❑ 98PacOnlR-155
❑ 98PacOnlWC-155
❑ 98PacPlaB-259
❑ 98PacRedT-259
❑ 98PacSil-259
❑ 98PinSna-CC11
❑ 98StaCluFDI-244
❑ 98StaCluI-244
❑ 98StaCluOneK-244
❑ 98StaCluPP-244
❑ 98Top-453
❑ 98TopChr-453
❑ 98TopChrR-453
❑ 98TopDevR-453
❑ 98TopDia-453
❑ 98TopMiniC-453
❑ 98UppDec-54
❑ 98UppDecSF-33
❑ 99199Fin-29
❑ 99FinGolRef-29
❑ 99FinRef-29
❑ 99Fle-239
❑ 99FleSta9-239
❑ 99FleWarT-239
❑ 99Pac-92
❑ 99PacCroC-61
❑ 99PacCroCPB-61
❑ 99PacOme-53
❑ 99PacOmeC-53
❑ 99PacOmeG-53
❑ 99PacOmePB-53
❑ 99PacPlaB-92
❑ 99PacRed-92
❑ 99SkyThu-55
❑ 99SkyThuRant-55
❑ 99SkyThuRave-55
❑ 99SPSig-159
❑ 99StaClu-101
❑ 99StaCluFDI-101
❑ 99StaCluOoaK-101
❑ 99StaCluPP-101
❑ 99ThuSkySupR-55
❑ 99Top-262
❑ 99TopChr-262
❑ 99TopChrR-262
❑ 99TopMVPP-262
❑ 99UppDec-62
❑ 99UppDecEL1-62
❑ 99UppDecEL2-62
❑ 99UppDecM-44
❑ 99UppDecMGS-44
❑ 99UppDecMHFS-44
❑ 99UppDecMP-44
❑ 99UppDecMSS-44
❑ 99Vic-81

Tapia, Dagoberto
❑ 90MarPhiP-3208

Tapia, Elias
❑ 94GreFalDSP-24
❑ 95BakBlaTI-24
❑ 95YakBeaTI-32

Tapia, Jose
❑ 87QuaCitAP-7
❑ 87VerBeaDP-2
❑ 88PalSprACLC-93
❑ 88PalSprAP-1446

Tappe, Elvin
❑ 53MotCoo-48
❑ 55Bow-51
❑ 55Top-129
❑ 55TopDouH-93
❑ 58Top-184
❑ 59SeaPop-11
❑ 60Top-457

Tarangelo, Joseph
❑ 84VisOakT-23

Tarasco, Tony
❑ 89PulBraP-1904
❑ 90Bes-100
❑ 90SumBraB-23
❑ 90SumBraP-2449
❑ 91DurBulC-21
❑ 91DurBulP-1675
❑ 92GreBraF-1166
❑ 92GreBraS-245
❑ 92SkyAA F-103
❑ 92UppDecML-82
❑ 93Bow-522
❑ 93BraLykP-29
❑ 93BraLykS-35
❑ 93BraStaC-29
❑ 93ExcFS7-6
❑ 93FleFinE-5
❑ 93Lea-452
❑ 93RicBraBB-12
❑ 93RicBraF-200
❑ 93RicBraP-11
❑ 93RicBraRC-19
❑ 93StaClu-696
❑ 93StaCluFDI-696
❑ 93StaCluMOP-696
❑ 93UppDec-623
❑ 93UppDecGold-623
❑ 94Bow-77
❑ 94BraLykP-32
❑ 94BraLykS-31
❑ 94BraUSPC-5D
❑ 94ColC-273
❑ 94ColChoGS-273
❑ 94ColChoSS-273
❑ 94Don-287
❑ 94Fin-422
❑ 94FinJum-422
❑ 94FinRef-422
❑ 94Fla-359
❑ 94FlaWavotF-B9
❑ 94Fle-377
❑ 94FleExtB-214
❑ 94FleExtBRS-17
❑ 94Lea-2
❑ 94LeaLimR-80
❑ 94Pac-23
❑ 94Pin-256
❑ 94PinArtP-256
❑ 94PinMusC-256
❑ 94Sco-617
❑ 94ScoGolR-617
❑ 94ScoRoo-RT90
❑ 94ScoRooGR-RT90
❑ 94ScoRooSR-SU16
❑ 94Sel-381
❑ 94SelRooS-RS11
❑ 94SpoRoo-82
❑ 94SpoRooAP-82
❑ 94SpoRooS-82
❑ 94StaClu-272
❑ 94StaCluFDI-272
❑ 94StaCluGR-272
❑ 94StaCluMOP-272
❑ 94StaCluT-51
❑ 94StaCluTFDI-51
❑ 94Top-442
❑ 94TopGol-442
❑ 94TopSpa-442
❑ 94Ult-451
❑ 94UppDec-206
❑ 94UppDecED-206
❑ 95ColCho-159
❑ 95ColCho-552T
❑ 95ColChoGS-159
❑ 95ColChoSS-159
❑ 95Don-468
❑ 95DonPreP-468
❑ 95DonTopotO-287
❑ 95Emo-155
❑ 95Fin-225
❑ 95FinRef-225
❑ 95Fla-109
❑ 95Fla-379
❑ 95Fle-320
❑ 95FleUpd-109
❑ 95Lea-365
❑ 95LeaLim-65
❑ 95Pac-16
❑ 95PacLatD-34
❑ 95PacPri-6
❑ 95Pin-212
❑ 95PinArtP-212
❑ 95PinMusC-212
❑ 95Sco-145
❑ 95ScoGolR-145
❑ 95ScoHaloG-HG110
❑ 95ScoHaloGYTE-HG110T
❑ 95ScoPlaTS-145
❑ 95Sel-43
❑ 95SelArtP-43
❑ 95SP-75
❑ 95SPCha-66
❑ 95SPChaDC-66
❑ 95SPSil-75
❑ 95StaClu-628
❑ 95StaCluMOP-628
❑ 95StaCluSTWS-628
❑ 95Top-32
❑ 95TopTra-60T
❑ 95UC3-11
❑ 95UC3ArtP-11
❑ 95Ult-355
❑ 95UltGolM-355
❑ 95UppDec-325
❑ 95UppDecED-325
❑ 95UppDecEDG-325
❑ 96ColCho-617
❑ 96ColChoGS-617
❑ 96ColChoSS-617
❑ 96Don-455
❑ 96DonPreP-455
❑ 96Fle-470
❑ 96FleTif-470
❑ 96FleUpd-U9
❑ 96FleUpdTC-U9
❑ 96Lea-85
❑ 96LeaPrePB-85
❑ 96LeaPrePG-85
❑ 96LeaPrePS-85
❑ 96MetUni-195
❑ 96MetUniP-195
❑ 96OriFle-17
❑ 96Pac-128
❑ 96PanSti-20
❑ 96Sco-106
❑ 96StaClu-323
❑ 96StaCluMOP-323
❑ 96Top-37
❑ 96Ult-237
❑ 96Ult-310
❑ 96UltGolM-237
❑ 96UltGolM-310
❑ 97BalOriP-32
❑ 97Pac-31
❑ 97PacLigB-31
❑ 97PacSil-31
❑ 97Sco-382
❑ 97ScoArtPWB-382
❑ 97ScoResC-382
❑ 97ScoShoS-382
❑ 97ScoShoSAP-382
❑ 98IndIndQ-32
❑ 98PacInvGems-17

Tarbell, Steve
❑ 77BriRedST-18

Tarchione, Travis
❑ 88CapCodPPaLP-23
❑ 89SalLakTTI-6

Tarin, Fernando
❑ 77QuaCitAT-27

Tarjick, Dave
❑ 90PitMetP-29

Tarnow, Greg
❑ 81QuaCitCT-3
❑ 83AppFoxFr-21

Tarpley, Andy
❑ 98St.PauSTI-27

Tarrh, Jamey
❑ 90WicStaSGD-33

Tarrolly, Dave
❑ 83BelBreFr-17

Tartabull, Danny
❑ 82WatRedT-14
❑ 83ChaLooT-6
❑ 84SalLakCGC-170
❑ 85CalCanC-94
❑ 85Don-27
❑ 85Fle-647
❑ 86Don-38
❑ 86DonRoo-45
❑ 86Fle-476
❑ 86FleMin-99
❑ 86MarMot-22
❑ 86MarPacNB-13
❑ 86Spo-178
❑ 86SpoRoo-22
❑ 86TopTra-108T
❑ 86TopTraT-108T
❑ 87ClaUpdY-145
❑ 87Don-147
❑ 87DonOpeD-200
❑ 87Fle-598
❑ 87FleGlo-598
❑ 87FleUpd-117
❑ 87FleUpdG-117
❑ 87Lea-250
❑ 87OPC-332
❑ 87RedFolSB-97
❑ 87Spo-23
❑ 87SpoTeaP-13
❑ 87Top-476
❑ 87TopCoi-25
❑ 87TopGloS-19
❑ 87TopRoo-19
❑ 87TopSti-223
❑ 87TopSti-306
❑ 87TopTif-476
❑ 87TopTra-120T
❑ 87TopTraT-120T
❑ 87ToyRoo-28
❑ 88ClaBlu-235
❑ 88Don-5
❑ 88Don-177
❑ 88DonBasB-287
❑ 88DonSupD-5
❑ 88Fle-271
❑ 88FleAwaW-42
❑ 88FleExcS-41
❑ 88FleGlo-271
❑ 88FleMin-28
❑ 88FleStiC-34
❑ 88FleSup-40
❑ 88KayB-30
❑ 88Lea-5
❑ 88Lea-190
❑ 88OPC-211
❑ 88PanSti-112
❑ 88RedFolSB-88
❑ 88RoySmo-4
❑ 88RoyTeal-33
❑ 88Sco-106
❑ 88ScoGlo-106
❑ 88ScoYouS2-5
❑ 88Spo-19
❑ 88StaLinRo-17
❑ 88Top-724
❑ 88TopBig-230
❑ 88TopCoi-29
❑ 88TopMinL-16
❑ 88TopRevLL-26
❑ 88TopSti-257
❑ 88TopTif-724
❑ 88TopUKM-78
❑ 88TopUKMT-78
❑ 89Bow-128
❑ 89BowTif-128
❑ 89ChaLooLITI-29
❑ 89Don-61
❑ 89DonBasB-39
❑ 89DonGraS-10
❑ 89Fle-295
❑ 89FleBasM-37
❑ 89FleGlo-295
❑ 89OPC-275
❑ 89PanSti-360
❑ 89RedFolSB-118
❑ 89RoyTasD-4
❑ 89Sco-105
❑ 89ScoHot1S-19
❑ 89Spo-46
❑ 89Top-275
❑ 89TopBig-107
❑ 89TopCoi-55
❑ 89TopSti-267
❑ 89TopTif-275
❑ 89TVSpoM-107
❑ 89UppDec-329
❑ 90Bow-375
❑ 90BowTif-375
❑ 90Don-322
❑ 90DonBesA-128
❑ 90Fle-120
❑ 90FleCan-120
❑ 90Lea-99
❑ 90OPC-540
❑ 90PanSti-90
❑ 90PubIntS-358
❑ 90RoyPos-26
❑ 90Sco-244
❑ 90Sco100S-72
❑ 90Spo-129
❑ 90Top-540
❑ 90TopAmeA-33
❑ 90TopBig-56
❑ 90TopHilHM-9
❑ 90TopMag-105
❑ 90TopSti-274
❑ 90TopTif-540
❑ 90UppDec-656
❑ 91Bow-294
❑ 91ClaGam-43
❑ 91DenHol-16
❑ 91Don-463
❑ 91Fle-572
❑ 91Lea-147
❑ 91OPC-90
❑ 91PanFreS-282
❑ 91RoyPol-22
❑ 91Sco-515
❑ 91StaClu-272
❑ 91Top-90
❑ 91TopDesS-90
❑ 91TopMic-90
❑ 91TopTif-90
❑ 91TopTriH-A7
❑ 91Ult-158
❑ 91UppDec-523
❑ 91UppDecFE-89F
❑ 91USPlaCA-JKO
❑ 92Bow-550
❑ 92Cla1-T88
❑ 92Cla2-T98
❑ 92ClaGam-167
❑ 92Don-26
❑ 92Don-676
❑ 92DonCraJ2-35
❑ 92DonUpd-U17
❑ 92Fle-171
❑ 92FleAll-12
❑ 92FleTeaL-18
❑ 92FleUpd-45
❑ 92KinDis-13
❑ 92Lea-406
❑ 92LeaBlaG-406
❑ 92MSABenSHD-13
❑ 92OPC-145
❑ 92OPCPre-93
❑ 92PanSti-98
❑ 92Pin-309
❑ 92Pin-547
❑ 92PinTeaP-8
❑ 92Pos-30
❑ 92RedFolS-130
❑ 92RemUltP-P13
❑ 92RemUltP-P14
❑ 92RemUltP-P15
❑ 92RemUltP-P16
❑ 92RemUltP-P18
❑ 92Sco-145
❑ 92Sco100S-90
❑ 92ScoImpP-64
❑ 92ScoRoo-3T
❑ 92SpollIFK1-75
❑ 92StaClu-191
❑ 92StaClu-690
❑ 92StaCluD-183
❑ 92StaCluMP-14
❑ 92StaCluNC-690
❑ 92StaTar-1
❑ 92StaTar-2
❑ 92StaTar-3
❑ 92StaTar-4
❑ 92StaTar-5
❑ 92StaTar-6
❑ 92StaTar-7
❑ 92StaTar-8
❑ 92StaTar-9
❑ 92StaTar-10
❑ 92StaTar-11
❑ 92Stu-220
❑ 92Top-145
❑ 92TopGol-145
❑ 92TopGolW-145
❑ 92TopKid-106
❑ 92TopMcD-26
❑ 92TopMic-145
❑ 92TopTra-116T
❑ 92TopTraG-116T
❑ 92TriPlaG-GS5
❑ 92Ult-77
❑ 92Ult-417
❑ 92UppDec-88
❑ 92UppDec-237
❑ 92UppDec-746
❑ 92UppDecHRH-HR11
❑ 93Bow-299
❑ 93ClaGam-90
❑ 93DenHol-28
❑ 93DiaMar-106
❑ 93Don-549
❑ 93DonSpiotG-SG16
❑ 93Fin-167
❑ 93FinRef-167
❑ 93Fla-253
❑ 93Fle-286
❑ 93FleFruotL-59
❑ 93FunPac-209
❑ 93Lea-119
❑ 93MetBak-20
❑ 93OPC-308
❑ 93PacSpa-213
❑ 93PacSpaGE-19
❑ 93PanSti-153
❑ 93Pin-168
❑ 93Pin-478
❑ 93PinHomRC-33
❑ 93PinSlu-10
❑ 93RedFolS-93
❑ 93Sco-35
❑ 93Sco-515
❑ 93Sel-12
❑ 93SelStaL-50
❑ 93SP-268
❑ 93StaClu-85
❑ 93StaCluFDI-85
❑ 93StaCluMOP-85
❑ 93StaCluMP-11
❑ 93Top-330
❑ 93TopGol-330
❑ 93TopInaM-330
❑ 93TopInaR-330
❑ 93TopMic-330
❑ 93TriPla-207
❑ 93Ult-602
❑ 93UppDec-242
❑ 93UppDec-839
❑ 93UppDecGold-242
❑ 93UppDecGold-839
❑ 93UppDecHRH-HR13
❑ 93YanStaC-4
❑ 94Bow-577
❑ 94BowBes-R18
❑ 94BowBesR-R18
❑ 94ChuHomS-23
❑ 94ChuHomSG-23
❑ 94ColC-383
❑ 94ColChoGS-383
❑ 94ColChoSS-383
❑ 94Don-414
❑ 94Fin-325
❑ 94FinRef-325
❑ 94Fla-88
❑ 94Fle-248
❑ 94FleExtB-140
❑ 94FUnPac-145
❑ 94Kra-11
❑ 94Lea-353
❑ 94LeaCleC-6
❑ 94LeaL-58
❑ 94OPC-8
❑ 94Pac-439
❑ 94PacAll-11
❑ 94PacGolP-10
❑ 94PanSti-105
❑ 94Pin-81
❑ 94PinArtP-81
❑ 94PinMusC-81
❑ 94PinRunC-RC21
❑ 94ProMag-90
❑ 94Sco-373
❑ 94ScoGolR-373
❑ 94Sel-306
❑ 94SP-200
❑ 94SPDieC-200
❑ 94Spo-118
❑ 94StaClu-410
❑ 94StaCluFDI-410
❑ 94StaCluGR-410
❑ 94StaCluMOP-410
❑ 94StaCluT-209
❑ 94StaCluTFDI-209
❑ 94Stu-218
❑ 94Top-670
❑ 94TopGol-670
❑ 94TopSpa-670
❑ 94TriPla-279
❑ 94Ult-102
❑ 94UppDec-212
❑ 94UppDecED-212
❑ 95Baz-53
❑ 95Bow-347
❑ 95ColCho-518
❑ 95ColChoGS-518
❑ 95ColChoSE-247

❑ 95ColChoSEGS-247
❑ 95ColChoSESS-247
❑ 95ColChoSS-518
❑ 95Don-103
❑ 95DonPreP-103
❑ 95DonTopotO-143
❑ 95Fin-90
❑ 95FinRef-90
❑ 95Fla-69
❑ 95Fle-82
❑ 95Lea-246
❑ 95LeaLim-170
❑ 95Pac-304
❑ 95PacPri-100
❑ 95PanSti-91
❑ 95Pin-273
❑ 95PinArtP-273
❑ 95PinMusC-273
❑ 95Sco-456
❑ 95ScoGolR-456
❑ 95ScoPlaTS-456
❑ 95Sel-9
❑ 95SelArtP-9
❑ 95Spo-117
❑ 95SpoArtP-117
❑ 95StaClu-156
❑ 95StaCluFDI-156
❑ 95StaCluMOP-156
❑ 95StaCluSTWS-156
❑ 95StaCluVR-82
❑ 95StaCluVRMO-82
❑ 95Stu-134
❑ 95Top-413
❑ 95TopCyb-213
❑ 95TopEmb-39
❑ 95TopEmbGI-39
❑ 95UC3-15
❑ 95UC3ArtP-15
❑ 95Ult-87
❑ 95UltGolM-87
❑ 95UppDec-444
❑ 95UppDec-452
❑ 95UppDecED-444
❑ 95UppDecEDG-444
❑ 95UppDecSE-9
❑ 95UppDecSEG-9
❑ 95Zen-19
❑ 96ColCho-513
❑ 96ColChoGS-513
❑ 96ColChoSS-513
❑ 96Don-548
❑ 96DonPreP-548
❑ 96EmoXL-41
❑ 96Fla-59
❑ 96Fle-220
❑ 96FleTif-220
❑ 96FleUpd-U30
❑ 96FleUpdTC-U30
❑ 96LeaSigA-220
❑ 96LeaSigAG-220
❑ 96LeaSigAS-220
❑ 96PacPri-P128
❑ 96PacPriG-P128
❑ 96Pin-17
❑ 96Pin-356
❑ 96PinAfi-33
❑ 96PinAfiAP-33
❑ 96PinAfiFPP-33
❑ 96PinFoil-356
❑ 96ProSta-8
❑ 96Sco-339
❑ 96ScoDugC-B64
❑ 96ScoDugCAP-B64
❑ 96Sel-145
❑ 96SelArtP-145
❑ 96StaClu-310
❑ 96StaCluEPB-310
❑ 96StaCluEPG-310
❑ 96StaCluEPS-310
❑ 96StaCluMOP-310
❑ 96Ult-338
❑ 96UltGolM-338
❑ 96UppDec-302
❑ 96WhiSoxF-16
❑ 97Don-97
❑ 97DonGolPP-97
❑ 97DonSilPP-97
❑ 97FlaShoLC-94
❑ 97FlaShoLeg0-94
❑ 97FlaShoLeg1-94
❑ 97FlaShoM-A94
❑ 97FlaShoM-B94
❑ 97FlaShoM-C94
❑ 97FlaShoR0-94
❑ 97FlaShoR1-94
❑ 97FlaShoR2-94
❑ 97Fle-71
❑ 97Fle-614
❑ 97FleTif-71
❑ 97FleTif-614
❑ 97Pac-63
❑ 97PacLigB-63
❑ 97PacPri-21
❑ 97PacPriLB-21
❑ 97PacPriP-21
❑ 97PacSil-63
❑ 97PhiTeal-45
❑ 97Pin-140
❑ 97PinArtP-PP140
❑ 97PinMusC-140
❑ 97PinPrePla-140
❑ 97Sco-58
❑ 97Sco-448
❑ 97ScoArtPWB-58
❑ 97ScoArtPWB-448
❑ 97ScoPreS-58
❑ 97ScoResC-448
❑ 97ScoShoS-58
❑ 97ScoShoS-448
❑ 97ScoShoSAP-58
❑ 97ScoShoSAP-448
❑ 97StaClu-134
❑ 97StaCluMOP-134
❑ 97Top-78
❑ 97WhiSoxS-3
❑ 97WhiSoxSPl-3
❑ 97WhiSoxSPr-3
❑ 98Pac-389
❑ 98PacPlaB-389
❑ 98PacRedT-389
❑ 98PacSil-389
Tartabull, Jose
❑ 86BelMarCr-108
❑ 87WauTimP-8
❑ 88SanBerSB-13
❑ 88SanBerSCLC-36
❑ 89SanBerSB-18
❑ 89SanBerSCLC-79
Tartabull, Jose Milages
❑ 62Top-451
❑ 63AthJayP-11
❑ 63Top-449
❑ 64A's-17
❑ 64AthJayP-12
❑ 64Top-276
❑ 64TopVen-276
❑ 66OPC-143
❑ 66Top-143
❑ 66TopVen-143
❑ 67CokCapRS-17
❑ 67DexPre-203
❑ 67OPC-56
❑ 67Top-56
❑ 67TopRedSS-21
❑ 68Top-555
❑ 69MilBra-269
❑ 69Top-287
❑ 70OPC-481
❑ 70Top-481
❑ 72MilBra-339
❑ 81RedSoxBG2S-121
❑ 81TCM60I-331
❑ 93Pin-478
Tarumi, Kanenori
❑ 88MiaMarS-11
Tarutis, Pete
❑ 91JamExpC-26
❑ 91JamExpP-3545
Tarver, LaSchelle
❑ 82LynMetT-2
❑ 84TidTidT-21
❑ 85IntLeaAT-6
❑ 85MetTCM-39
❑ 85TidTidT-13
❑ 86PawRedSP-24
❑ 87PawRedSP-60
❑ 87PawRedST-19
Tasby, Willie
❑ 58BalOriP-15
❑ 59OriJayP-8
❑ 59Top-143
❑ 59TopVen-143
❑ 60BalOriP-9
❑ 60Lea-100
❑ 60OriJayP-8
❑ 60Top-322
❑ 61Pos-51A
❑ 61Pos-51B
❑ 61SenJayP-9
❑ 61Top-458
❑ 61TopStal-117
❑ 62Jel-70
❑ 62Pos-70
❑ 62PosCan-70
❑ 62SalPlaC-21
❑ 62ShiPlaC-21
❑ 62Top-462A
❑ 62Top-462B
❑ 91OriCro-449
Tashiro, Tomio
❑ 79TCMJapPB-54
Tasker, Paul
❑ 76BatTroTI-23
Tata, Terry
❑ 88T/MUmp-16
❑ 89T/MUmp-14
❑ 89T/MUmp-60
❑ 90T/MUmp-14
Tatar, Jason
❑ 94ForWayWC-23
❑ 94ForWayWF-2011
❑ 95ForMyeMTI-27
❑ 96FtMyeMB-10
Tatar, Kevin
❑ 90BilMusP-3222
❑ 91ChaWheC-11
❑ 91ChaWheP-2888
❑ 91Cla/Bes-294
❑ 92Bow-621
❑ 92ChaLooS-197
❑ 92ClaFS7-73
❑ 92SkyAA F-89
❑ 92UppDecML-306
Tatarian, Dean
❑ 89UtiBluSP-24
❑ 90UtiBluSP-10
❑ 91SarWhiSC-20
❑ 91SarWhiSP-1122
❑ 92BasCitRC-4
❑ 92BasCitRF-3854
❑ 92ClaFS7-139
Tate, Bennie
❑ 30WhiSoxTI-23
❑ 34DiaMatCSB-178
❑ 36GouWidPPR-D36
❑ 36WorWidGV-80
❑ 75SenTCM1-34
❑ 91ConTSN-220
Tate, Chuck
❑ 86EveGiaC-16
❑ 86EveGiaPC-32
Tate, Edward
❑ 87OldJudN-487
Tate, Henry
❑ 31Exh-20
Tate, Lee W.
❑ 59Top-544
Tate, Michael
❑ 88BoiHawP-1606
Tate, Randy L.
❑ 76OPC-549
❑ 76SSP-555
❑ 76Top-549
❑ 77LynMetT-27
❑ 78ColCliT-25
❑ 91MetWIZ-395
Tate, Seth
❑ 98LetBlaDG-27
Tate, Stu (Stuart)
❑ 84EveGiaC-12
❑ 85FreGiaSB-19
❑ 86ShrCapP-24
❑ 87ShrCapP-20
❑ 88ShrCapP-1295
❑ 89PhoFirC-9
❑ 89PhoFirP-1491
❑ 89TriAAAP-AAA52
❑ 90Fle-643
❑ 90FleCan-643
❑ 90TopDeb89-127
❑ 91LinDriAAA-395
❑ 91PhoFirLD-395
❑ 91PhoFirP-67
Taterson, Gary
❑ 91WatIndC-12
Tatis, Bernie
❑ 83KinBluJTI-26
❑ 85DomLeaS-154
❑ 86KnoBluJP-23
❑ 87KnoBluJP-1509
❑ 87SouLeaAJ-4
❑ 88BufBisC-14
❑ 88BufBisP-1475
❑ 90CMC-170
❑ 90OklCit8C-20
❑ 90OklCit8P-447
❑ 90ProAAAF-693
❑ 90ProAAAF-694
❑ 91CanIndLD-95
❑ 91CanIndP-993
❑ 91ColSprSSP-2194
❑ 91LinDriAA-95
❑ 93LimRocDWB-96
Tatis, Fausto
❑ 90BakDodCLC-231
❑ 90YakBeaTI-33
❑ 91BakDodCLC-3
Tatis, Fernando
❑ 95ChaRivTI-8
❑ 95ChaRivUTIS-36
❑ 95SPML-157
❑ 96BesAutS-87
❑ 96Exc-112
❑ 97Bow-198
❑ 97Bow98ROY-ROY15
❑ 97BowBes-145
❑ 97BowBesAR-145
❑ 97BowBesR-145
❑ 97BowCerBlaIA-CA77
❑ 97BowCerBluIA-CA77
❑ 97BowCerGolIA-CA77
❑ 97BowChr-185
❑ 97BowChr1RFR-ROY15
❑ 97BowChr98RF-ROY15
❑ 97BowChrI-185
❑ 97BowChrIR-185
❑ 97BowChrR-185
❑ 97BowInt-198
❑ 97FlaShoWotF-24
❑ 97Fle-524
❑ 97FleTif-524
❑ 97Sel-157
❑ 97SelCom-157
❑ 97TexAllM-29
❑ 97TexLeaTP-25
❑ 97TulDriTI-26
❑ 97Ult-538
❑ 97UltGolME-538
❑ 97UltPlaME-538
❑ 98Bow-31
❑ 98BowCerBlueAU-5
❑ 98BowCerGA-5
❑ 98BowCerSA-5
❑ 98BowChr-31
❑ 98BowChrGA-31
❑ 98BowChrGAR-31
❑ 98BowChrI-31
❑ 98BowChrIR-31
❑ 98BowChrR-31
❑ 98BowGolA-31
❑ 98BowInt-31
❑ 98CirThu-171
❑ 98CirThuRav-171
❑ 98CirThuSupRav-171
❑ 98ColCho-112
❑ 98ColChoSQ-SQ12
❑ 98Don-113
❑ 98DonCol-113
❑ 98DonCol-197
❑ 98DonColE-508
❑ 98DonColL-388
❑ 98DonColP-692
❑ 98DonColS-113
❑ 98DonColS-192
❑ 98DonEli-108
❑ 98DonEliA-108
❑ 98DonEliS-108
❑ 98DonGolPP-113
❑ 98DonPre-142
❑ 98DonPreGES-13
❑ 98DonPreGX-13
❑ 98DonPreGXDC-13
❑ 98DonPreSeat-142
❑ 98DonPriCD-113
❑ 98DonPriCD-197
❑ 98DonPriCE-508
❑ 98DonPriCL-388
❑ 98DonPriCP-692
❑ 98DonRatR-22
❑ 98DonRatRM-22
❑ 98DonRooDK-2
❑ 98DonRooDKC-2
❑ 98DonSig-103
❑ 98DonSigA-83
❑ 98DonSigAC-106
❑ 98DonSigAM-108
❑ 98DonSigP-103
❑ 98DonSigSP-26
❑ 98DonSilPP-113
❑ 98E-X2-88
❑ 98E-X2ECFut-88
❑ 98E-X2ECNow-88
❑ 98FlaShoLeg0-27
❑ 98FlaShoLeg1-27
❑ 98FlaShoLeg2-27
❑ 98FlaShoLeg3-27
❑ 98FlaShoLegM-27
❑ 98FlaShoR0-27
❑ 98FlaShoR1-27
❑ 98FlaShoR2-27
❑ 98FlaShoR3-27
❑ 98Fle-56
❑ 98FleRooS-18
❑ 98FleUpd-U67
❑ 98Lea-189
❑ 98LeaFraDA-189
❑ 98LeaFraF-189
❑ 98LeaFraM-189
❑ 98LeaFraM-189
❑ 98LeaFraMDC-189
❑ 98LeaFraMDC-189
❑ 98LeaFraMS-189
❑ 98LeaFraMZ2-189
❑ 98LeaRCrusUP-104
❑ 98LeaRS-199
❑ 98LeaRSCrusUG-104
❑ 98LeaRSCrusUR-104
❑ 98LeaRSFOSamp-14
❑ 98LeaRSFresh-14
❑ 98LeaRSLHolo-199
❑ 98LeaRSLong-199
❑ 98LeaRTrue-199
❑ 98MetUni-109
❑ 98MetUniPMG-109
❑ 98Pac-210
❑ 98PacOnl-747
❑ 98PacOnlR-747
❑ 98PacOnlWC-747
❑ 98PacPar-108
❑ 98PacParC-108
❑ 98PacParG-108
❑ 98PacParHS-108
❑ 98PacParPB-108
❑ 98PacParR-108
❑ 98PacPlaB-210
❑ 98PacRedT-210
❑ 98PacSil-210
❑ 98Pin-74
❑ 98PinIns-79
❑ 98PinInsCE-79
❑ 98PinInsDE-79
❑ 98PinInsSG-13AB
❑ 98PinInsSG-13CD
❑ 98PinInsSGS-13AB
❑ 98PinInsSGS-13CD
❑ 98PinPer-120
❑ 98PinPerPP-120
❑ 98PinPlu-168
❑ 98PinPluAP-PP55
❑ 98PinPluGAP-PP55
❑ 98PinPluMAP-PP55
❑ 98PinPreP-74
❑ 98PinSna-TR2
❑ 98Sco-238
❑ 98ScoRT-177
❑ 98ScoRTSS-PP101
❑ 98ScoRTSSAP-PP101
❑ 98ScoRTSSAP1-PP101
❑ 98SkyDugA-87
❑ 98SkyDugAIA-87
❑ 98SP Aut-188
❑ 98SpoIll-175
❑ 98SpoIllEE-175
❑ 98SpoIllFE-175
❑ 98SPxFin-136
❑ 98SPxFinR-136
❑ 98SPxFinS-136
❑ 98StaCluFDI-291
❑ 98StaCluI-291
❑ 98StaCluITW-W15
❑ 98StaCluOneK-291
❑ 98StaCluPP-291
❑ 98Stu-87
❑ 98StuGPP-87
❑ 98StuSPP-87
❑ 98Top-449
❑ 98TopChr-449
❑ 98TopChrR-449
❑ 98TopChrRC-R8
❑ 98TopChrRCRef-R8
❑ 98TopDevR-449
❑ 98TopDia-449
❑ 98TopMiniC-449
❑ 98TopRooCla-R8
❑ 98Ult-190
❑ 98UltGolM-190
❑ 98UltMas-190
❑ 98UltPlaM-190
❑ 98UppDec-270
❑ 98UppDecBCP-BC9
❑ 98UppDecDS-DS52
❑ 98UppDecSF-149
❑ 98Zen-100
❑ 98ZenZ-G-100
❑ 98ZenZ-S-100
❑ 99199Fin-46
❑ 99Bow-234
❑ 99BowGol-234
❑ 99BowInt-234
❑ 99CroRoyB-117
❑ 99CroRoyL-117
❑ 99CroRoyOD-117
❑ 99FinGolRef-46
❑ 99FinRef-46
❑ 99Fle-230
❑ 99FleMys-49
❑ 99FleMysFl-24
❑ 99FleMysG-49
❑ 99FleMysM-49
❑ 99FleSta9-230
❑ 99FleWarT-230
❑ 99MetUni-196
❑ 99MetUniGM-196
❑ 99MetUniPMG-196
❑ 99Pac-362
❑ 99PacCroC-236
❑ 99PacCroCPB-236
❑ 99PacOme-199
❑ 99PacOmeC-199
❑ 99PacOmeDM-27
❑ 99PacOmeG-199
❑ 99PacOmeH'-15
❑ 99PacOmePB-199
❑ 99PacPar-196
❑ 99PacParC-196
❑ 99PacParG-196
❑ 99PacParHoloGold-196
❑ 99PacParHS-196
❑ 99PacParOD-196
❑ 99PacParPB-196
❑ 99PacParRed-196
❑ 99PacPlaB-362
❑ 99PacRed-362
❑ 99Rev-119
❑ 99RevDiaL-28
❑ 99RevPremDate-119
❑ 99RevRet-119
❑ 99RevShaSS-119
❑ 99SkyMolM-66
❑ 99SkyMolMX-66
❑ 99SkyPre-160
❑ 99SkyPreA-51
❑ 99SkyPreABlue-51
❑ 99SkyPreR-160
❑ 99SkyThu-207
❑ 99SkyThuRant-207
❑ 99SkyThuRave-207
❑ 99SP SigAuto-FTA
❑ 99SPSig-132
❑ 99SPx-73
❑ 99SPxFinR-73
❑ 99SPxFinS-73
❑ 99StaClu-221
❑ 99StaCluFDI-221
❑ 99StaCluOoaK-221
❑ 99StaCluPP-221
❑ 99ThuSkySupR-207
❑ 99Top-346
❑ 99TopChr-346
❑ 99TopChrR-346
❑ 99TopMVPP-346
❑ 99UppDec-465
❑ 99UppDecE-74
❑ 99UppDecE-146
❑ 99UppDecEFXG-74
❑ 99UppDecEFXG-146
❑ 99UppDecEL1-465
❑ 99UppDecEL2-465
❑ 99UppDecM-172
❑ 99UppDecMGS-172
❑ 99UppDecMHFS-172
❑ 99UppDecMSS-172
❑ 99Vic-324
Tatis, Fernando Sr.
❑ 74CedRapAT-17
❑ 75DubPacT-16
Tatis, Rafael
❑ 73CedRapAT-19
Tatis, Ramon
❑ 92GulCoaMF-3482
❑ 93KinMetC-22
❑ 93KinMetF-3796
❑ 94KinMetC-20
❑ 94KinMetF-3823
❑ 95PitMetTI-7

❑ 96StLucMTI-15
❑ 97Fle-568
❑ 97FleTif-568
❑ 98DevRayP-10
❑ 98Pac-260
❑ 98PacOnl-722
❑ 98PacOnlR-722
❑ 98PacOnlWC-722
❑ 98PacPlaB-260
❑ 98PacRedT-260
❑ 98PacSil-260
Tatrow, Danny
❑ 93JohCitCC-25
❑ 93JohCitCF-3691
Tatsuno, Derek
❑ 82ElPasDT-22
❑ 87HawIsIP-5
Tatterson, Gary
❑ 91WatIndP-3367
❑ 92KinIndC-8
Tatum, Goose (Reece)
❑ 76LauIndC-16
❑ 86NegLeaF-107
Tatum, Jarvis
❑ 68SeaPop-16
❑ 70Top-642
❑ 71MLBOffS-334
❑ 71OPC-159
❑ 71Top-159
Tatum, Jim
❑ 85SpoIndC-24
❑ 86ChaRaiP-25
❑ 87ChaRaiP-19
❑ 88WicPilRD-18
❑ 90CanIndB-12
❑ 90CanIndP-1302
❑ 90CMC-774
❑ 91ElPasDLD-197
❑ 91ElPasDP-2757
❑ 91LinDriAA-197
❑ 92DenZepF-2651
❑ 92DenZepS-145
❑ 92ProFS7-86
❑ 92SkyAAAF-71
❑ 92TriA AAS-145
❑ 93Bow-339
❑ 93Don-341
❑ 93Fle-416
❑ 93FleFinE-45
❑ 93PacSpa-439
❑ 93Pin-587
❑ 93RocStaC-25
❑ 93RocUSPC-1C
❑ 93RocUSPC-2H
❑ 93StaClu-730
❑ 93StaCluFDI-730
❑ 93StaCluMOP-730
❑ 93Top-691
❑ 93TopGol-691
❑ 93TopInaM-691
❑ 93TopInaR-691
❑ 93TopMic-691
❑ 93Ult-360
❑ 93UppDec-13
❑ 93UppDec-761
❑ 93UppDecGold-13
❑ 93UppDecGold-761
❑ 94AriFalLS-20
❑ 94BreMilB-78
❑ 94ColSprSSF-747
❑ 94Fle-455
❑ 94Pac-208
❑ 94Sco-311
❑ 94ScoGolR-311
❑ 94StaCluT-120
❑ 94StaCluTFDI-120
❑ 97ColSprSATTI-18
Tatum, Ken
❑ 70MLBOffS-180
❑ 70Top-658
❑ 71MLBOffS-335
❑ 71OPC-601
❑ 71RedSoxA-11
❑ 71Top-601
❑ 72MilBra-340
❑ 72RedSoxTI-21
❑ 72Top-772
❑ 73OPC-463
❑ 73Top-463
Tatum, Tommy
❑ 78DodTCM4-7
❑ 90DodTar-1082
Tatum, Willie
❑ 88ElmPioC-19
❑ 89WinHavRSS-23
❑ 90LynRedSTI-8
❑ 91LynRedSC-18
❑ 91LynRedSP-1208
❑ 92NewBriRSF-443
❑ 92NewBriRSS-497
❑ 92ProFS7-21
❑ 92SkyAA F-215
❑ 93PawRedSTI-23
Taubensee, Eddie (Edward)
❑ 88GreHorP-1558
❑ 88SouAtlLAGS-6
❑ 89CedRapRAB-11
❑ 89CedRapRB-12
❑ 89CedRapRP-937
❑ 89CedRapRS-19
❑ 90Bes-184
❑ 90CedRapRB-3
❑ 90CedRapRDGB-11
❑ 90CedRapRP-2325
❑ 90CMC-876
❑ 90MidLeaASGS-50
❑ 91ColSprSSLD-76
❑ 91ColSprSSP-2187
❑ 91LinDriAAA-76
❑ 92AstMot-11
❑ 92Bow-697
❑ 92ClaGam-166
❑ 92Don-18
❑ 92DonRoo-115
❑ 92LeaGolR-BC9
❑ 92OPC-427
❑ 92OPCPre-136
❑ 92Pin-538
❑ 92Sco-871
❑ 92Sco100RS-29
❑ 92StaClu-790
❑ 92StaCluNC-790
❑ 92Stu-40
❑ 92Top-427
❑ 92TopDeb91-169
❑ 92TopGol-427
❑ 92TopGolW-427
❑ 92TopMic-427
❑ 92TopTra-117T
❑ 92TopTraG-117T
❑ 92Ult-497
❑ 92UppDec-757
❑ 93AstMot-18
❑ 93AstStaC-2
❑ 93Bow-476
❑ 93Don-560
❑ 93Fle-55
❑ 93Lea-362
❑ 93PacSpa-482
❑ 93PanSti-169
❑ 93Pin-140
❑ 93Sco-108
❑ 93Sel-333
❑ 93StaClu-329
❑ 93StaCluFDI-329
❑ 93StaCluMOP-329
❑ 93Top-117
❑ 93TopGol-117
❑ 93TopInaM-117
❑ 93TopInaR-117
❑ 93TopMic-117
❑ 93TriPla-17
❑ 93Ult-46
❑ 93UppDec-296
❑ 93UppDecGold-296
❑ 93USPlaCR-9S
❑ 94ColC-621
❑ 94ColChoGS-621
❑ 94ColChoSS-621
❑ 94Don-256
❑ 94Fle-501
❑ 94Pac-276
❑ 94RedKah-31
❑ 94Sco-456
❑ 94ScoGolR-456
❑ 94ScoRoo-RT34
❑ 94ScoRooGR-RT34
❑ 94Sel-334
❑ 94SpoRoo-19
❑ 94SpoRooAP-19
❑ 94StaClu-168
❑ 94StaCluFDI-168
❑ 94StaCluGR-168
❑ 94StaCluMOP-168
❑ 94Top-68
❑ 94TopGol-68
❑ 94TopSpa-68
❑ 95ColCho-432
❑ 95ColChoGS-432
❑ 95ColChoSS-432
❑ 95Don-323
❑ 95DonPreP-323
❑ 95DonTopotO-222
❑ 95Fle-450
❑ 95Lea-23
❑ 95Pin-434
❑ 95PinArtP-434
❑ 95PinMusC-434
❑ 95RedKah-32
❑ 95Sco-153
❑ 95ScoGolR-153
❑ 95ScoPlaTS-153
❑ 95StaClu-166
❑ 95StaCluFDI-166
❑ 95StaCluMOP-166
❑ 95StaCluSTWS-166
❑ 95Top-293
❑ 95Ult-150
❑ 95UltGolM-150
❑ 96ColCho-111
❑ 96ColChoGS-111
❑ 96ColChoSS-111
❑ 96Don-193
❑ 96DonPreP-193
❑ 96Fla-241
❑ 96Fle-355
❑ 96FleTif-355
❑ 96Ult-467
❑ 96UltGolM-467
❑ 96UppDec-312
❑ 97Cir-107
❑ 97CirRav-107
❑ 97ColCho-301
❑ 97Don-143
❑ 97DonGolPP-143
❑ 97DonSilPP-143
❑ 97Fin-59
❑ 97FinRef-59
❑ 97Fle-306
❑ 97FleTif-306
❑ 97Pac-277
❑ 97PacLigB-277
❑ 97PacSil-277
❑ 97Top-326
❑ 97Ult-182
❑ 97UltGolME-182
❑ 97UltPlaME-182
❑ 97UppDec-339
❑ 98Bow-271
❑ 98BowChr-271
❑ 98BowChrGA-271
❑ 98BowChrGAR-271
❑ 98BowChrI-271
❑ 98BowChrIR-271
❑ 98BowChrR-271
❑ 98BowGolA-271
❑ 98BowInt-271
❑ 98ColCho-342
❑ 98Fle-493
❑ 98PacOnl-203
❑ 98PacOnlR-203
❑ 98PacOnlWC-203
❑ 98UppDec-63
❑ 98UppDecSF-39
❑ 99Fle-299
❑ 99FleSta9-299
❑ 99FleWarT-299
❑ 99Pac-119
❑ 99PacCroC-80
❑ 99PacCroCPB-80
❑ 99PacPlaB-119
❑ 99PacRed-119
❑ 99StaClu-108
❑ 99StaCluFDI-108
❑ 99StaCluOoaK-108
❑ 99StaCluPP-108
❑ 99Top-189
❑ 99TopChr-189
❑ 99TopChrR-189
❑ 99TopMVPP-189
❑ 99UppDecM-56
❑ 99UppDecMGS-56
❑ 99UppDecMHFS-56
❑ 99UppDecMSS-56
Tauer, Jay
❑ 85RedWinA-14
❑ 86RedWinA-3
Tauken, Daniel
❑ 87PenWhiSP-5
Taulbee, Andy
❑ 94SigRooDP-51
❑ 94SigRooDPS-51
❑ 94StaCluDP-31
❑ 94StaCluDPFDI-31
❑ 95Bow-14
❑ 96TexLeaAB-18
Taussig, Don
❑ 62Col45'HC-17
❑ 62SalPlaC-186
❑ 62ShiPlaC-186
❑ 62Top-44
❑ 62TopVen-44
❑ 89AstCol4S-22
Tavares, Frankie
❑ 97BurIndG-27
Tavarez, Alfonso
❑ 85UtiBluST-15
❑ 86BurExpP-24
Tavarez, Davis
❑ 83CliGiaF-12
❑ 84EveGiaC-21
Tavarez, Hector
❑ 90MedHatBJB-27
❑ 91MedHatBJP-4109
❑ 91MedHatBJSP-6
❑ 92DunBluJC-21
Tavarez, Jesus
❑ 90PenPilS-21
❑ 91CalLeLA-11
❑ 91SanBerSC-24
❑ 91SanBerSP-2001
❑ 92ClaFS7-144
❑ 92JacSunF-3723
❑ 92JacSunS-368
❑ 92SkyAA F-159
❑ 93HigDesMC-22
❑ 93HigDesMF-56
❑ 93LimRocDWB-30
❑ 94BowBes-B85
❑ 94BowBesR-B85
❑ 94FleUpd-139
❑ 94LeaLimR-36
❑ 94PorSeaDF-691
❑ 94PorSeaDTI-28
❑ 94UppDecML-114
❑ 95ChaKniTI-26
❑ 95StaClu-379
❑ 95StaCluMOP-379
❑ 95StaCluSTWS-379
❑ 95UppDecSE-114
❑ 95UppDecSEG-114
❑ 96ColCho-26
❑ 96Don-366
❑ 96DonPreP-366
❑ 96Fle-395
❑ 96FleTif-395
❑ 96LeaSigEA-198
❑ 96Pac-79
❑ 96UppDec-58
❑ 97Pac-308
❑ 97PacLigB-308
❑ 97PacSil-308
❑ 97PawRedS-25
❑ 98PacInvGems-24
❑ 98RocRedWQ-28
Tavarez, Juan
❑ 93KinIndTI-25
Tavarez, Julian
❑ 92BurIndC-18
❑ 92BurIndF-1657
❑ 93CarLeaAGF-34
❑ 93KinIndC-24
❑ 93KinIndF-2247
❑ 93LimRocDWB-89
❑ 94Bow-279
❑ 94ChaKniF-895
❑ 94ClaA-46
❑ 94ColC-274
❑ 94ColChoGS-274
❑ 94ColChoSS-274
❑ 94Don-627
❑ 94Pin-411
❑ 94PinArtP-411
❑ 94PinMusC-411
❑ 94SpoRoo-49
❑ 94SpoRooAP-49
❑ 94StaClu-128
❑ 94StaCluFDI-128
❑ 94StaCluGR-128
❑ 94StaCluMOP-128
❑ 94Top-767
❑ 94TopGol-767
❑ 94TopSpa-767
❑ 94TriAAF-AAA3
❑ 95ActPacF-44
❑ 95Bow-159
❑ 95BowBes-R87
❑ 95BowBesR-R87
❑ 95ColCho-6
❑ 95ColChoGS-6
❑ 95ColChoSS-6
❑ 95Emo-38
❑ 95Fla-251
❑ 95FleUpd-42
❑ 95FleUpdRU-10
❑ 95Sco-277
❑ 95ScoGolR-277
❑ 95ScoPlaTS-277
❑ 95ScoRooDT-RDT9
❑ 95Sel-204
❑ 95SelArtP-204
❑ 95SelCer-127
❑ 95SelCerMG-127
❑ 95StaClu-24
❑ 95StaCluFDI-24
❑ 95StaCluMOP-24
❑ 95StaCluSTWS-24
❑ 95Sum21C-TC7
❑ 95TopTra-119T
❑ 95UltGolMR-M20
❑ 95UppDec-221
❑ 95UppDecED-221
❑ 95UppDecEDG-221
❑ 95Zen-125
❑ 95ZenRooRC-11
❑ 96ColCho-118
❑ 96ColChoGS-118
❑ 96ColChoSS-118
❑ 96Don-297
❑ 96DonPreP-297
❑ 96Fla-75
❑ 96Fle-101
❑ 96FleTif-101
❑ 96IndFle-16
❑ 96Lea-75
❑ 96LeaPrePB-75
❑ 96LeaPrePG-75
❑ 96LeaPrePS-75
❑ 96LeaSigA-221
❑ 96LeaSigAG-221
❑ 96LeaSigAS-221
❑ 96MetUni-53
❑ 96MetUniP-53
❑ 96Pac-298
❑ 96PacEstL-EL31
❑ 96Pin-294
❑ 96PinAfi-112
❑ 96PinAfiAP-112
❑ 96PinFoil-294
❑ 96Sco-312
❑ 96ScoDugC-B37
❑ 96ScoDugCAP-B37
❑ 96Sel-95
❑ 96SelArtP-95
❑ 96Sum-113
❑ 96SumAbo&B-113
❑ 96SumArtP-113
❑ 96SumFoi-113
❑ 96Top-81
❑ 96Ult-344
❑ 96UltGolM-344
❑ 97Cir-224
❑ 97CirRav-224
❑ 97Fle-89
❑ 97Fle-693
❑ 97FleTif-89
❑ 97FleTif-693
❑ 97Pac-79
❑ 97PacLigB-79
❑ 97PacSil-79
❑ 97Sco-373
❑ 97ScoArtPWB-373
❑ 97ScoResC-373
❑ 97ScoShoS-373
❑ 97ScoShoSAP-373
❑ 97Top-234
❑ 97Ult-55
❑ 97Ult-424
❑ 97UltGolME-55
❑ 97UltGolME-424
❑ 97UltPlaME-55
❑ 97UltPlaME-424
❑ 98GiaMot-17
❑ 98Pac-449
❑ 98PacOnl-675
❑ 98PacOnlR-675
❑ 98PacOnlWC-675
❑ 98PacPlaB-449
❑ 98PacRedT-449
❑ 98PacSil-449
❑ 98UppDec-508
❑ 99PacCroC-259
❑ 99PacCroCPB-259
Tavener, Jack
❑ 28Exh-46
❑ 28StaPlaCE-65
❑ 29ExhFou-21
❑ 92ConTSN-572
Taveras, Alex
❑ 74CedRapAT-10
❑ 75IowOakT-21
❑ 77Top-474
❑ 79AlbDukTc-15
❑ 81AlbDukTc-18
❑ 82AlbDukTc-18
❑ 83AlbDukTc-10
❑ 84AlbDukCr-153
❑ 85BufBisT-12
❑ 89BelBre2S-25
❑ 89BelBreIS-26
Taveras, Frank
❑ 96BurIndB-25
❑ 98ColRedSM-18
Taveras, Frank Crisostomo
❑ 74OPC-607
❑ 74Top-607
❑ 75OPC-277
❑ 75OPC-460
❑ 75PitPirP-28
❑ 75Top-277
❑ 75TopMin-277
❑ 76OPC-36
❑ 76PirPos-25
❑ 76SSP-583
❑ 76Top-36
❑ 77BurCheD-184
❑ 77PirPosP-28
❑ 77Top-538
❑ 78OPC-4
❑ 78Top-204
❑ 78Top-685
❑ 79OPC-79
❑ 79Top-165
❑ 80BurKinPHR-32
❑ 80OPC-237
❑ 80Top-456
❑ 81AllGamPI-116
❑ 81CokTeaS-93
❑ 81Don-154
❑ 81Fle-320
❑ 81OPC-343
❑ 81Top-343
❑ 81TopSti-196
❑ 81TopSupHT-77
❑ 82Don-98
❑ 82ExpHygM-22
❑ 82ExpPos-43
❑ 82Fle-539
❑ 82OPC-351
❑ 82Top-782
❑ 82TopTra-118T
❑ 91MetWIZ-396
Taveras, Jose
❑ 97LetBlaDB-12
❑ 98Bow-439
❑ 98BowChr-439
❑ 98BowChrGA-439
❑ 98BowChrGAR-439
❑ 98BowChrI-439
❑ 98BowChrIR-439
❑ 98BowChrR-439
❑ 98BowGolA-439
❑ 98BowInt-439
Taveras, Luis
❑ 98Cha-12
Taveras, Marcos
❑ 88St.CatBJP-2028
❑ 89DunBluJS-18
❑ 90DunBluJS-17
Taveras, Ramon
❑ 89SalDodTI-30
❑ 90FloStaLAS-17
❑ 90StaFS7-21
❑ 90VerBeaDS-25
❑ 91LinDriAA-542
❑ 91SanAntMLD-542
Tawwater, Darren
❑ 91OklStaC-27
❑ 92OklStaC-26
Taylor, Aaron
❑ 89WytCubS-25
❑ 90HunCubP-3283
❑ 91PeoChiC-9
❑ 91PeoChiP-1343
❑ 91PeoChiTI-13
❑ 92WinSpiC-23
❑ 92WinSpiF-1208
❑ 93OrlCubF-2784
❑ 93Top-786
❑ 93TopGol-786
❑ 93TopInaM-786
❑ 93TopInaR-786
❑ 93TopMic-786
❑ 97DanBraB-26

❑ 98DanBraQ-3
Taylor, Adam
❑ 96WatIndTI-29
❑ 97WatIndTI-28
Taylor, Andrew
❑ 86LitFalMP-27
❑ 88SprCarB-8
❑ 89SavCarP-368
Taylor, Ben
❑ 78LauLonABS-12
❑ 90NegLeaS-10
Taylor, Bill (William M.)
❑ 54Top-74
❑ 55GiaGolS-29
❑ 55Top-53
❑ 55TopDouH-7
❑ 58Top-389
❑ 94TopArc1-74
❑ 94TopArc1G-74
❑ 98A'sMot-11
❑ 99Fle-515
❑ 99FleSta9-515
❑ 99FleWarT-515
❑ 99Top-69
❑ 99TopChr-69
❑ 99TopChrR-69
❑ 99TopMVPP-69
Taylor, Billy
❑ 75QuaCitAT-23
❑ 76QuaCitAT-36
Taylor, Billy (William Henry)
❑ 90KalBatN-31
Taylor, Billy (William Howell)
❑ 80AshTouT-18
❑ 82WauTimF-26
❑ 83TulDriT-5
❑ 84TulDriTI-32
❑ 85TulDriTI-34
❑ 87OklCit8P-25
❑ 88OklCit8P-28
❑ 89LasVegSC-10
❑ 89LasVegSP-3
❑ 91GreBraC-6
❑ 91GreBraP-3000
❑ 92RicBraBB-12
❑ 92RicBraF-378
❑ 92RicBraRC-23
❑ 92RicBraS-445
❑ 93RicBraBB-23
❑ 93RicBraF-185
❑ 93RicBraP-17
❑ 93RicBraRC-20
❑ 93RicBraRC-27
❑ 93TriAAAGF-4
❑ 94A'sMot-25
❑ 94Bow-276
❑ 94Fla-97
❑ 94FleExtB-157
❑ 94FleUpd-78
❑ 94ScoRoo-RT71
❑ 94ScoRooGR-RT71
❑ 94Sel-391
❑ 94TopTra-2T
❑ 94Ult-413
❑ 95Don-377
❑ 95DonPreP-377
❑ 95Fle-255
❑ 95Sco-473
❑ 95ScoGolR-473
❑ 95ScoPlaTS-473
❑ 95Ult-321
❑ 95UltGolM-321
❑ 96A'sMot-24
❑ 97A'sMot-18
❑ 97Cir-76
❑ 97CirRav-76
❑ 97ColCho-414
❑ 97Fle-197
❑ 97FleTif-197
❑ 97RicBraBC-21
❑ 97Ult-425
❑ 97UltGolME-425
❑ 97UltPlaME-425
❑ 98Fle-90
❑ 98MetUni-134
❑ 98MetUniPMG-134
❑ 98Pac-175
❑ 98PacOnl-547
❑ 98PacOnlR-547
❑ 98PacOnlWC-547
❑ 98PacPlaB-175
❑ 98PacRedT-175
❑ 98PacSil-175
❑ 98StaCluFDI-216
❑ 98StaCluI-216
❑ 98StaCluOneK-216
❑ 98StaCluPP-216
❑ 98Top-101
❑ 98TopChr-101
❑ 98TopChrR-101
❑ 98TopDevR-101
❑ 98TopDia-101
❑ 98TopMiniC-101
❑ 98Ult-161
❑ 98UltGolM-161
❑ 98UltMas-161
❑ 98UltPlaM-161
❑ 98UppDec-471
❑ 99UppDec-449
❑ 99UppDecEL1-449
❑ 99UppDecEL2-449
Taylor, Bobbie
❑ 85AncGlaPTI-45
Taylor, Brien
❑ 90TopMag-79
❑ 91ClaDraP-1
❑ 91ClaDraPP-3
❑ 92Bow-124
❑ 92ClaBluBF-BC15
❑ 92ClaDraP-86
❑ 92ClaDraPFB-BC18
❑ 92ClaDraPP-3
❑ 92ClaFS7-300
❑ 92ClaPro-2
❑ 92ClaPro-7
❑ 92ClaRedB-BC15
❑ 92DEL-AU5
❑ 92ForLauYC-1
❑ 92ForLauYTI-30
❑ 92Ft.LauYF-2612
❑ 92OPC-6
❑ 92StaCluD-184
❑ 92StaCluFDP-2
❑ 92Top-6
❑ 92TopGol-6
❑ 92TopGol-793
❑ 92TopGolW-6
❑ 92TopMic-6
❑ 92UppDecML-49
❑ 92UppDecML-57
❑ 92UppDecML-265
❑ 92UppDecMLPotY-PY26
❑ 92UppDecMLTPHF-TP7
❑ 93AlbYanF-2164
❑ 93BluOriC-28
❑ 93Bow-370
❑ 93Bow-679
❑ 93CapCitBC-28
❑ 93ClaFisN-14
❑ 93ClaGolF-17
❑ 93ClaGolLF-2
❑ 93ClaGolP-3
❑ 93ClaYouG-YG22
❑ 93DayCubC-28
❑ 93EliTwiC-28
❑ 93EugEmeC-28
❑ 93ExcAllF-1
❑ 93ExcFS7-215
❑ 93PeoChiC-28
❑ 93PitMetC-28
❑ 93SanBerSC-28
❑ 93StaClu-689
❑ 93StaCluFDI-689
❑ 93StaCluMOP-689
❑ 93StaCluMP-30
❑ 93Top-742
❑ 93TopGol-742
❑ 93TopInaM-742
❑ 93TopInaR-742
❑ 93TopMic-742
❑ 93Toy-19
❑ 93UtiBluSC-28
❑ 93WesVirWC-28
❑ 93WinSpiC-28
❑ 93YanStaC-22
❑ 94ActPac-41
❑ 94Bow-165
❑ 94Cla-80
❑ 94ClaGolA-SH1
❑ 94ClaGolF-1
❑ 94ClaGolP-1
❑ 94ExcFS7-115
❑ 94ExcLeaLF-17
❑ 94TedWil-132
❑ 94TedWilDGC-DG8
❑ 94Top-772
❑ 94TopGol-772
❑ 94TopSpa-772
❑ 94UppDecML-5
❑ 94UppDecML-251
❑ 95Bow-17
❑ 96NorNavB-27
Taylor, Bruce
❑ 77EvaTriT-23
❑ 78TigTeal-29
❑ 78Top-701
Taylor, Byron
❑ 94NewJerCC-25
❑ 94NewJerCF-3433
Taylor, C.I. (Charles Isam)
❑ 87NegLeaPD-12
Taylor, Carl
❑ 68Top-559
❑ 69PirTeal-23
❑ 69Top-357
❑ 70CarTeal-28
❑ 70CarTeal-29
❑ 70OPC-76
❑ 70Top-76
❑ 71MLBOffS-286
❑ 71MLBOffS-432
❑ 71OPC-353
❑ 71oySigST-28
❑ 71Top-353
❑ 71TopCoi-55
❑ 72oyTeal-26
❑ 73OPC-99
❑ 73Top-99
❑ 74OPC-627
❑ 74Top-627
❑ 89PacSenL-160
Taylor, Charley
❑ 85OscAstTI-2
❑ 87AshTouP-11
❑ 88AshTouP-1067
❑ 89AshTouP-944
❑ 90ColMudB-21
❑ 90ColMudP-1362
❑ 90ColMudS-25
❑ 91JacGenP-942
❑ 91LinDriAA-575
❑ 92JacGenF-4015
❑ 92JacGenS-350
❑ 93JacGenF-2125
❑ 94JacGenF-233
❑ 95JacGenTI-26
❑ 96TusTorB-28
❑ 97QuaCitRBB-27
❑ 98JacGenM-25
Taylor, Chuck (Charles Gilbert)
❑ 70CarTeal-30
❑ 70OPC-119
❑ 70Top-119
❑ 71CarTeal-26
❑ 71CarTeal-39
❑ 71OPC-606
❑ 71Top-606
❑ 72OPC-407
❑ 72Top-407
❑ 73OPC-176
❑ 73Top-176
❑ 74OPC-412
❑ 74Top-412
❑ 75ExpPos-36
❑ 75OPC-58
❑ 75Top-58
❑ 75TopMin-58
❑ 76ExpRed-30
❑ 76SSP-346
❑ 86ColAstP-24
❑ 91MetWIZ-397
❑ 94BreMilB-79
Taylor, Dan
❑ 34BatR31-108
❑ 34DiaMatCSB-179
❑ 35ExhFou-2
❑ 36GouWidPPR-A100
❑ 36WorWidGV-72
❑ 90DodTar-789
❑ 93ConTSN-898
Taylor, Dave
❑ 87BelBreP-25
❑ 88StoPorCLC-195
❑ 88StoPorP-729
❑ 90MiaMirIS-24
Taylor, Donnie
❑ 98MadBlaW-16
Taylor, Dorn
❑ 83AleDukT-30
❑ 84PriWilPT-6
❑ 85NasPirT-24
❑ 86NasPirP-26
❑ 87FleUpd-118
❑ 87FleUpdG-118
❑ 87VanCanP-1621
❑ 88BlaYNPRWLU-45
❑ 88BufBisC-9
❑ 88BufBisP-1468
❑ 88BufBisTI-5
❑ 88TriAAC-11
❑ 89PirVerFJ-52
❑ 89TriAAAP-AAA9
❑ 90BufBisC-10
❑ 90BufBisP-373
❑ 90BufBisTI-26
❑ 90CMC-10
❑ 90ProAAAF-488
❑ 90TriAllGP-AAA22
❑ 91OriCro-451
Taylor, Dummy (Luther H.)
❑ 03BreE10-139
❑ 05RotCP-10
❑ 06FanCraNL-45
❑ 08AmeCarE91-30
❑ 08RosComP-133
❑ 09T206-471
❑ 11SpoLifCW-348
❑ 12ImpTobC-41
❑ 72ClaCar-111
Taylor, Dwight
❑ 82WatIndT-23
❑ 83BufBisT-21
❑ 84MaiGuiT-18
❑ 85MaiGuiT-28
❑ 86OmaRoyT-11
❑ 87OmaRoyP-8
❑ 89ColSprSSC-19
❑ 89ColSprSSP-234
❑ 90ColSprSSP-51
❑ 90ProAAAF-232
❑ 92ChaLooS-198
❑ 92NasSouF-1847
Taylor, Eddie
❑ 45CenFlo-25
❑ 47CenFlo-29
❑ 75OakOak2A-34
Taylor, Edward
❑ 26Exh-7
Taylor, Gary
❑ 91HamRedC-14
❑ 91HamRedP-4055
❑ 92SavCarC-14
❑ 92SavCarF-677
❑ 93SprCarC-27
❑ 93SprCarF-1867
Taylor, Gene
❑ 91BilMusP-3769
❑ 91BilMusSP-16
❑ 92CedRapRC-2
❑ 92CedRapRF-1088
Taylor, Greg
❑ 96BatCliTI-22
❑ 97PieBolWB-27
❑ 98PieBolWM-25
Taylor, Harry
❑ 29Zee-168
❑ 30Zee-185
❑ 47DodTeal-24
❑ 48DodTeal-24
❑ 90DodTar-790
❑ 92TexLon-39
Taylor, Hawk (Bob)
❑ 58Top-164
❑ 61Top-446
❑ 62Top-406
❑ 63Top-481
❑ 64Top-381
❑ 65Top-329
❑ 68OPC-52
❑ 68SeaPop-17
❑ 68Top-52
❑ 68TopVen-52
❑ 69Top-239
❑ 70RoyTeal-37
❑ 80Bra195T-19
❑ 91MetWIZ-399
Taylor, Herb
❑ 52LavPro-24
Taylor, Jack
❑ 06FanCraNL-44
❑ 07CubGFGCP-15
❑ 11SpoLifCW-347
❑ 90HOFStiB-13
Taylor, Jamie
❑ 92FroRowDP-27
❑ 92FroRowDPG-27
❑ 92FroRowDPS-27
❑ 92WatIndC-1
❑ 92WatIndF-3244
❑ 93Bow-205
❑ 93ClaFS7-262
❑ 93ColRedC-22
❑ 93ColRedF-607
❑ 93StaCluM-165
❑ 94KinIndC-18
❑ 94KinIndF-2653
❑ 96NewHavRB-23
❑ 97SalAva-30
❑ 98ColSprSS-36
❑ 98NewHavRM-27
❑ 98NewHavRMA-27
Taylor, Jeff
❑ 81NasSouTI-19
❑ 83MemChiT-14
❑ 85GreBraTI-17
❑ 86OrlTwiP-20
❑ 88NebCor-16
❑ 88OneYanP-2070
❑ 89CarNewE-7
❑ 89OneYanP-2101
Taylor, Jerry
❑ 96KenIndB-23
Taylor, Joe
❑ 52LavPro-57
❑ 57HygMea-11
Taylor, Joe (Joseph C.)
❑ 56SeaPop-25
❑ 57SeaPop-22
❑ 58Top-451
❑ 60HenHouW-22
❑ 60SeaPop-16
❑ 60UniOil-13
❑ 61UniOil-SD11
❑ 91OriCro-450
Taylor, John
❑ 81CliGiaT-17
❑ 82AleDukT-1
❑ 82AppFoxFr-8
❑ 83AleDukT-12
Taylor, John I.
❑ 09SpoNewSM-48
Taylor, John W.
❑ 09ColChiE-286
❑ 09ColChiE-287
❑ 12ColRedB-287
❑ 26Exh-8
❑ 27Exh-4
❑ 28Exh-4
❑ 63GadFunC-15
Taylor, Jonathon
❑ 92VerBeaDF-2880
Taylor, Joseph F.
❑ 54BraJohC-50
❑ 55BraJohC-51
Taylor, Juan
❑ 98GreFalDG-27
Taylor, Kerry
❑ 89EliTwiS-25
❑ 89Sta-153
❑ 91KenTwiC-16
❑ 91KenTwiP-2074
❑ 92KenTwiC-14
❑ 92KenTwiF-604
❑ 93Bow-63
❑ 93FleFinE-145
❑ 93PadMot-26
❑ 94Don-244
❑ 94Fle-675
❑ 94LasVegSF-872
❑ 98TolMudHQ-31
Taylor, Mark
❑ 91SavCarC-15
❑ 91SavCarP-1656
❑ 96WatIndTI-30
❑ 97WatIndTI-29
Taylor, Michael Patrick
❑ 91BurIndP-3305
❑ 91MedHatBJSP-7
❑ 92EriSaiC-24
❑ 92EriSaiF-1628
❑ 92MedHatBJSP-22
❑ 92ProFS7-176
Taylor, Mike
❑ 80WatIndT-29
❑ 81WatIndT-28
❑ 82WatIndT-24
❑ 86BirBarTI-13
❑ 87HawIslP-12
Taylor, Mike (David Michael)
❑ 86AriWilP-17
❑ 88GasRanP-998
❑ 89ChaRanS-25
❑ 90TulDriP-1156
❑ 90TulDriTI-24
❑ 94NewJerCC-26
❑ 94NewJerCF-3428
Taylor, Mike (Michael David)
❑ 88St.CatBJP-2032
❑ 89MyrBeaBJP-1463
❑ 90DunBluJS-18
❑ 91KnoBluJLD-366
❑ 91KnoBluJP-1776
❑ 91LinDriAA-366
❑ 92KnoBluJS-394
Taylor, Mike (Michael Larry)
❑ 90St.CatBJP-3474
❑ 91MedHatBJP-4101
❑ 92MyrBeaHC-20
❑ 93GleFalRC-27
❑ 93GleFalRF-4016
Taylor, Phil
❑ 86MiaMarP-24
Taylor, Randy
❑ 77SanJosMC-21
Taylor, Reggie
❑ 95Bes-117
❑ 95BowBes-X3
❑ 95BowBesR-X3
❑ 95MarPhiTI-27
❑ 95TopTra-108T
❑ 96Bow-271
❑ 96BowFoi-271
❑ 96Exc-214
❑ 96PieBolWB-27
❑ 96SigRooOJPP-P7
❑ 96SigRooOJPPS-P7
❑ 96Top-240
❑ 97Bow-185
❑ 97BowChr-175
❑ 97BowChrI-175
❑ 97BowChrIR-175
❑ 97BowChrR-175
❑ 97BowInt-185
❑ 97ClePhi-21
❑ 97FloStaLTPB-6
❑ 98BesAutSS-48
❑ 98BowBes-200
❑ 98BowBesAR-200
❑ 98BowBesR-200
❑ 98EasLeaTPM-26
❑ 98ReaPhiM-3
❑ 98ReaPhiUM-24
❑ 98SP MinPE-96
❑ 98SPMin-96
❑ 99Bow-326
❑ 99BowAut-BA33
❑ 99BowGol-326
❑ 99BowInt-326
❑ 99SP SigAuto-RT
❑ 99SP SigAutoG-RT
❑ 99SP TopP-115
❑ 99SP TopPPE-115
❑ 99SPSig-54
Taylor, Rob
❑ 90Bes-129
❑ 90CliGiaB-27
❑ 90CliGiaP-2544
❑ 90MidLeaASGS-51
❑ 91SanJosGC-22
❑ 91SanJosGP-11
❑ 92ShrCapF-3871
❑ 92ShrCapS-595
❑ 93PhoFirF-1516
❑ 94PhoFirF-1520
❑ 95IowCubTI-25
Taylor, Robert
❑ 76BatRouCT-20
❑ 93LinVenB-199
Taylor, Ron
❑ 62Top-591
❑ 63Top-208
❑ 64Top-183
❑ 64TopVen-183
❑ 65Top-568
❑ 66OPC-174
❑ 66Top-174
❑ 66TopVen-174
❑ 67Top-606
❑ 68Top-421
❑ 69MetNewYDN-19
❑ 69MetTeal-16
❑ 69OPC-72
❑ 69Top-72
❑ 69TopSta-79
❑ 70OPC-419

❑ 70Top-419
❑ 71MetTeal-20
❑ 71MetTealA-7
❑ 71MLBOffS-167
❑ 71OPC-687
❑ 71Top-687
❑ 72OPC-234
❑ 72PadPos-25
❑ 72Top-234
❑ 77Spo-7713
❑ 81TCM60I-449
❑ 81TCM60I-466
❑ 87Met196T-7
❑ 89MetRinP69-28
❑ 91MetWIZ-398
❑ 94Met69CCPP-31
❑ 94Met69CS-30-
❑ 94Met69T-15

Taylor, Sam
❑ 62Jel-189
❑ 88CapCodPPaLP-121
❑ 89BatCliP-1937
❑ 91Cla/Bes-349
❑ 91ClePhiC-24
❑ 91ClePhiP-1635
❑ 92ReaPhiF-590
❑ 92ReaPhiS-545
❑ 92SkyAA F-238
❑ 93ReaPhiF-309
❑ 94BoiHawF-3370

Taylor, Sammy
❑ 58Top-281
❑ 59Top-193
❑ 59TopVen-193
❑ 60CubJayP-10
❑ 60Lea-131
❑ 60Top-162
❑ 60TopVen-162
❑ 61Pos-198A
❑ 61Pos-198B
❑ 61Top-253
❑ 61TopStal-10
❑ 62CubJayP-11
❑ 62Pos-189
❑ 62PosCan-189
❑ 62SalPlaC-164
❑ 62ShiPlaC-164
❑ 62Top-274
❑ 63Top-273
❑ 82MetGal62-12
❑ 91MetWIZ-400

Taylor, Sammy Jr.
❑ 94BoiHawC-25

Taylor, Scott
❑ 87WytCubP-4
❑ 97CalCanB-26

Taylor, Scott (Rodney Scott)
❑ 88ElmPioC-4
❑ 89LynRedSS-29
❑ 90LynRedSTI-24
❑ 91Bow-121
❑ 91Cla/Bes-83
❑ 91LinDriAA-472
❑ 91NewBriRSLD-472
❑ 91NewBriRSP-353
❑ 91PawRedSDD-23
❑ 92Bow-618
❑ 92PawRedSF-923
❑ 92PawRedSS-368
❑ 92SkyAAAF-167
❑ 92WinSpiC-8
❑ 92WinSpiF-1212
❑ 93Don-267
❑ 93FleMajLP-B13
❑ 93PawRedSDD-27
❑ 93PawRedSF-2409
❑ 93PawRedSTI-24
❑ 93RedSoxWHP-25
❑ 93Top-456
❑ 93TopGol-456
❑ 93TopInaM-456
❑ 93TopInaR-456
❑ 93TopMic-456
❑ 96CarMudB-10
❑ 97DunDonPPS-24

Taylor, Scott Michael
❑ 88ChaWheB-4
❑ 88GenCubP-1651
❑ 89ChaWheB-5
❑ 89ChaWheP-1757
❑ 89SouAtlLAGS-13
❑ 89WauTimGS-11
❑ 90Bes-246
❑ 90SanBerSB-15
❑ 90SanBerSCLC-93
❑ 90SanBerSP-2633
❑ 90WinSpiTI-22
❑ 91CarLeaAP-CAR3
❑ 91ChaKniLD-145
❑ 91ChaKniP-1692
❑ 91DurBulP-1546
❑ 91GreBraLD-219
❑ 91LinDriAA-145
❑ 91LinDriAA-219
❑ 92ElPasDF-3922
❑ 92GreBraF-1153
❑ 92GreBraS-246
❑ 93El PasDF-2951
❑ 94NewOrlZF-1469
❑ 98NewOrlZM-24

Taylor, Steve
❑ 78TacYanC-25
❑ 79ColCliT-20
❑ 80NasSouTI-23
❑ 81NasSouTI-20
❑ 90EliTwiS-22
❑ 91KenTwiC-17
❑ 91KenTwiP-2075

Taylor, Ted
❑ 76TayBow4-NNO
❑ 93ClaInsC-NNO

Taylor, Terry
❑ 88CapCodPPaLP-137
❑ 89MilBra-24
❑ 89BlaYNPRWL-194
❑ 90CalCanC-5
❑ 90PalSprACLC-208
❑ 90PalSprAP-2587
❑ 91Cla/Bes-328
❑ 91LinDriAA-420
❑ 91LinDriAA-447
❑ 91MemChiLD-420
❑ 91MemChiP-656
❑ 91MidAngLD-447
❑ 91MidAngOHP-29
❑ 91MidAngP-444
❑ 92MidAngF-4035
❑ 92MidAngOHP-24
❑ 92MidAngS-472

Taylor, Terry Derrell
❑ 83WauTimF-9
❑ 86ChaLooP-24
❑ 87CalCanP-2325
❑ 88CalCanP-781
❑ 89Fle-651
❑ 89FleGlo-651
❑ 89Top-597
❑ 89TopTif-597
❑ 90CalCanP-651
❑ 90CMC-432
❑ 90ProAAAF-116

Taylor, Tex
❑ 52LavPro-28

Taylor, Tim
❑ 97PinFan-PC10

Taylor, Todd
❑ 91TopTra-116T
❑ 91TopTraT-116T
❑ 92EliTwiF-3683
❑ 92StaCluD-185
❑ 93ForWayWC-22
❑ 93ForWayWF-1969

Taylor, Tom
❑ 90CMC-871
❑ 90MidLeaASGS-19
❑ 90WauTimP-2122
❑ 92FreKeyF-1806

Taylor, Tommy (Thomas)
❑ 89BluOriS-24
❑ 90WauTimB-9
❑ 90WauTimS-23
❑ 91Cla/Bes-242
❑ 91KanCouCC-10
❑ 91KanCouCTI-20
❑ 92FreKeyC-22
❑ 93BowBayF-2190
❑ 94FreKeyC-22
❑ 94FreKeyF-2615

Taylor, Tony (Antonio S.)
❑ 58Top-411
❑ 59Top-62
❑ 59TopVen-62
❑ 60CubJayP-11
❑ 60Lea-44
❑ 60Top-294
❑ 61Pos-118A
❑ 61Pos-118B
❑ 61Top-411
❑ 61TopStal-59
❑ 62Jel-193
❑ 62Pos-193
❑ 62PosCan-193
❑ 62SalPlaC-156
❑ 62ShiPlaC-156
❑ 62Top-77
❑ 62TopBuc-87
❑ 62TopStal-170
❑ 62TopVen-77
❑ 63Jel-178
❑ 63Pos-178
❑ 63Top-366
❑ 64PhiJayP-10
❑ 64PhiPhiB-23
❑ 64Top-585
❑ 64TopCoi-113
❑ 64TopCoi-144
❑ 64TopSta-9
❑ 65PhiJayP-10
❑ 65Top-296
❑ 66Top-585
❑ 67CokCapPh-12
❑ 67DexPre-204
❑ 67OPC-126
❑ 67Top-126
❑ 67TopVen-314
❑ 68Top-327
❑ 68TopVen-327
❑ 69MilBra-270
❑ 69MLBOffS-179
❑ 69OPC-108
❑ 69PhiTeal-11
❑ 69Top-108
❑ 69TopTeaP-8
❑ 70DayDaiNM-139
❑ 70MilBra-28
❑ 70MLBOffS-95
❑ 70OPC-324
❑ 70PhiTeal-11
❑ 70Top-324
❑ 71Kel-67
❑ 71MLBOffS-190
❑ 71OPC-246
❑ 71PhiArcO-12
❑ 71Top-246
❑ 72MilBra-341
❑ 72OPC-511
❑ 72Top-511
❑ 73OPC-29
❑ 73TigJew-19
❑ 73Top-29
❑ 75OPC-574
❑ 75PhiPhiP-28
❑ 75PhiProPS-15
❑ 75Top-574
❑ 75TopMin-574
❑ 76OPC-624
❑ 76PhiPhiP-27
❑ 76SSP-474
❑ 76Top-624
❑ 78SSP270-41
❑ 78TCM60I-133
❑ 83PhiPosGM-4
❑ 83PhiPosGPaM-8
❑ 86PhiGreT-12
❑ 88PhiTas-29
❑ 89PhiTas-33
❑ 90ShrCapP-1459
❑ 90ShrCapS-27
❑ 91LinDriAA-325
❑ 91ShrCapLD-325
❑ 91ShrCapP-1840
❑ 92PhoFirS-400

Taylor, Wade
❑ 87BelMarTI-14
❑ 88Ft.LauYS-21
❑ 89PriWilCS-21
❑ 90AlbYanB-9
❑ 90AlbYanP-1176
❑ 90AlbYanSt-20
❑ 90Bes-154
❑ 90CMC-778
❑ 90EasLeaAP-EL12
❑ 90ProAaA-20
❑ 90TopTVY-63
❑ 91AlbYanCB-2
❑ 91Bow-165
❑ 91Cla2-T87
❑ 91ColCliLD-121
❑ 91ColCliP-21
❑ 91ColCliP-598
❑ 91DonRoo-34
❑ 91FleUpd-48
❑ 91LeaGolR-BC16
❑ 91LinDriAAA-121
❑ 91OPCPre-119
❑ 91ScoRoo-100T
❑ 91TopTra-117T
❑ 91TopTraT-117T
❑ 92ClaGam-56
❑ 92ColCliF-353
❑ 92ColCliP-12
❑ 92ColCliS-121
❑ 92Don-527
❑ 92Fle-245
❑ 92OPC-562
❑ 92ProFS7-107
❑ 92Sco-631
❑ 92Sco100RS-45
❑ 92SkyAAAF-59
❑ 92StaClu-667
❑ 92Top-562
❑ 92TopDeb91-170
❑ 92TopGol-562
❑ 92TopGolW-562
❑ 92TopMic-562
❑ 92TriPla-96

Taylor, Will (William Christopher)
❑ 86SpoIndC-179
❑ 87ChaRaiP-6
❑ 88RivRedWCLC-227
❑ 88RivRedWP-1419
❑ 89MadMusS-20
❑ 89RivRedWCLC-13
❑ 89RivRedWP-1402
❑ 90MadMusB-24
❑ 90ModA'sCLC-154
❑ 90ModA'sP-2213
❑ 91LasVegSLD-295
❑ 91LasVegSP-250
❑ 91LinDriAAA-295
❑ 92LasVegSS-243
❑ 92SkyAAAF-118

Taylor, William
❑ 89RivRedWB-17
❑ 90WicWraRD-19

Taylor, Willy PCL
❑ 12HomRunKE-75
❑ 12Zee-130

Taylor, Zack (James)
❑ 30CubTeal-19
❑ 31CubTeal-24
❑ 32CubTeal-23
❑ 33Gou-152
❑ 33GouCanV-79
❑ 41BroW75-28
❑ 46SeaSLP-63
❑ 46SpoExcW-10-12
❑ 51Bow-315
❑ 90DodTar-791
❑ 91ConTSN-210
❑ 94TedWil-113

Tayor, Fiona
❑ 85AncGlaPTI-38

Teachout, Bud
❑ 28Zee-166
❑ 30CubTeal-20
❑ 31CubTeal-25

Teague, Scott
❑ 89WytCubS-26

Teahan, Jim
❑ 83BelBreFr-19

Teasley, Ronald
❑ 86NegLeaF-55
❑ 93NegLeaRL2-39

Tebbetts, Birdie (George)
❑ 39TigSpo-8
❑ 47Exh-220
❑ 47HomBon-45
❑ 47RedSoxTI-22
❑ 47TipTop-42
❑ 48RedSoxTI-24
❑ 49RedSoxTI-23
❑ 50Dra-30
❑ 50RedSoxTI-26
❑ 51Bow-257
❑ 52Bow-124
❑ 52IndNumN-3
❑ 52Top-282
❑ 53IndPenCBP-24
❑ 55Bow-232
❑ 58RedEnq-38
❑ 58RedJayP-12
❑ 58Top-386
❑ 62BraJayP-10
❑ 62Top-588
❑ 63IndJayP-12
❑ 63Top-48
❑ 64IndJayP-12
❑ 64Top-462
❑ 65Top-301
❑ 66IndTeal-10
❑ 66Top-552
❑ 76TayBow4-45
❑ 77TCMTheWY-6
❑ 79DiaGre-377
❑ 81RedSoxBG2S-56
❑ 81TigDetN-92
❑ 82OhiHaloF-64
❑ 83TopRep5-282

Tebbetts, Scott
❑ 95MarPhiTI-28

Tebbetts, Steve
❑ 76QuaCitAT-37
❑ 77QuaCitAT-28

Tebbs, Nathan
❑ 94UtiBluSC-26
❑ 94UtiBluSF-3829
❑ 96Exc-20
❑ 96SarRedSB-28
❑ 97SarRedS-25
❑ 98TreThuM-23

Tebeau, Patsy (Oliver)
❑ 87OldJudN-488
❑ 93JusSo-9
❑ 98CamPepP-77

Techman, Marc
❑ 90AubAstB-22
❑ 91AubAstC-28

Tedder, Scott
❑ 89SarWhiSS-24
❑ 89Sta-61
❑ 90FloStaLAS-44
❑ 90SarWhiSS-24
❑ 91SarWhiSC-26
❑ 91SarWhiSP-1127
❑ 92BirBarF-2596
❑ 92BirBarS-96
❑ 93NasSouF-582
❑ 94BirBarC-21
❑ 94BirBarF-635

Teed, Dick
❑ 59O'KAleMR-21

Teegarden, Travis
❑ 89BilMusP-2040

Teel, Garett
❑ 88CapCodPPaLP-171
❑ 90BakDodCLC-252
❑ 92VerBeaDF-2895
❑ 93VerBeaDC-29

Teeters, Brian
❑ 92EugEmeC-26
❑ 92EugEmeF-3044
❑ 94EugEmeC-22
❑ 94EugEmeF-3727
❑ 95WilBluRTI-8
❑ 96WilBluRB-8

Tegland, Ron
❑ 97SouOreTB-4

Tegtmeier, Doug
❑ 88NebCor-17
❑ 89AncBucTI-9
❑ 90NebCor-24
❑ 91PenPilC-11
❑ 91PenPilP-377

Tehven, Brent
❑ 98FarRedHM-4

Teich, Mike
❑ 91WelPirC-27
❑ 91WelPirP-3573
❑ 92AugPirC-5
❑ 92AugPirF-240
❑ 93SalBucC-23
❑ 93SalBucF-432

Teising, John
❑ 76BatTroTI-24
❑ 78WatIndT-23

Teixeira, Joe
❑ 89BluOriS-25
❑ 90WauTimB-11
❑ 90WauTimP-2124

Teixeira, Vince
❑ 86MedA'sC-74
❑ 87MadMusP-19
❑ 87MadMusP-5
❑ 88ModA'sCLC-80
❑ 89VisOakCLC-113
❑ 89VisOakP-1423

Tejada, Alejandro
❑ 89JamExpP-2153

Tejada, Domingo
❑ 90MarPhiP-3206

Tejada, Eugenio
❑ 88UtiBluSP-10
❑ 89SouBenWSGS-25
❑ 90SouBenWSGS-18

Tejada, Francisco
❑ 88MarPhiS-30
❑ 90PriPatD-24
❑ 92SpaPhiC-8
❑ 92SpaPhiF-1266

Tejada, Joaquin
❑ 86ElmPioRSP-23
❑ 87ElmPioBC-25
❑ 87ElmPioRC-25

Tejada, Leo
❑ 90SouBenWSB-6
❑ 91SarWhiSC-21
❑ 91SarWhiSP-1123

Tejada, Miguel
❑ 96CarLeaA2B-26
❑ 96CarLeaAIB-B10
❑ 96ModA'sB-1
❑ 96SouOreTI-1
❑ 97Bes-4
❑ 97BesAll-6
❑ 97BesBetP-1
❑ 97BesDiaB-5
❑ 97BesIntB-IB1
❑ 97Bow-411
❑ 97BowBes-114
❑ 97BowBesAR-114
❑ 97BowBesP-18
❑ 97BowBesPAR-18
❑ 97BowBesPR-18
❑ 97BowBesR-114
❑ 97BowCerBlaIA-CA78
❑ 97BowCerBluIA-CA78
❑ 97BowCerGolIA-CA78
❑ 97BowChr-273
❑ 97BowChrI-273
❑ 97BowChrIR-273
❑ 97BowChrR-273
❑ 97BowInt-411
❑ 97DonSigA-95
❑ 97DonSigAC-118
❑ 97DonSigAM-118
❑ 97HunStaTI-25
❑ 97SouLeaTP-15
❑ 98A'sMot-13
❑ 98Bow-205
❑ 98BowBes-161
❑ 98BowBesAR-161
❑ 98BowBesMIF-MI3
❑ 98BowBesMIFAR-MI3
❑ 98BowBesMIFR-MI3
❑ 98BowBesR-161
❑ 98BowCerBlueAU-46
❑ 98BowCerGA-46
❑ 98BowCerSA-46
❑ 98BowChr-205
❑ 98BowChrGA-205
❑ 98BowChrGAR-205
❑ 98BowChrI-205
❑ 98BowChrIR-205
❑ 98BowChrR-205
❑ 98BowGolA-205
❑ 98BowInt-205
❑ 98CirThu-125
❑ 98CirThuRav-125
❑ 98CirThuSupRav-125
❑ 98ColCho-105
❑ 98ColChoSQ-SQ11
❑ 98Don-111
❑ 98DonCol-111
❑ 98DonCol-186
❑ 98DonColE-503
❑ 98DonColL-385
❑ 98DonColP-691
❑ 98DonColS-111
❑ 98DonColS-181
❑ 98DonEli-103
❑ 98DonEliA-103
❑ 98DonEliS-103
❑ 98DonGolPP-111
❑ 98DonPre-141
❑ 98DonPreGES-6
❑ 98DonPreGX-6
❑ 98DonPreGXDC-6
❑ 98DonPreSeat-141
❑ 98DonPriCD-111
❑ 98DonPriCD-186
❑ 98DonPriCE-503
❑ 98DonPriCL-385
❑ 98DonPriCP-691
❑ 98DonRatR-11
❑ 98DonRatRM-11
❑ 98DonSig-104
❑ 98DonSigA-84
❑ 98DonSigAM-109
❑ 98DonSigP-104
❑ 98DonSigSP-27

❑ 98DonSilPP-111
❑ 98Fle-236
❑ 98FleProF-PF17
❑ 98Lea-186
❑ 98LeaFraDA-186
❑ 98LeaFraF-186
❑ 98LeaFraM-186
❑ 98LeaFraM-186
❑ 98LeaFraMDC-186
❑ 98LeaFraMDC-186
❑ 98LeaFraMZ2-186
❑ 98LeaRCrusUP-103
❑ 98LeaRS-198
❑ 98LeaRSCrusUG-103
❑ 98LeaRSCrusUR-103
❑ 98LeaRSFOSamp-10
❑ 98LeaRSFresh-10
❑ 98LeaRSLHolo-198
❑ 98LeaRSLong-198
❑ 98LeaRTrue-198
❑ 98PacInvGems-87
❑ 98PacPar-83
❑ 98PacParC-83
❑ 98PacParG-83
❑ 98PacParHS-83
❑ 98PacParPB-83
❑ 98PacParR-83
❑ 98PinIns-115
❑ 98PinInsCE-115
❑ 98PinInsDE-115
❑ 98PinPer-119
❑ 98PinPerPP-119
❑ 98PinPlu-36
❑ 98PinPluAP-PP19
❑ 98PinPluGAP-PP19
❑ 98PinPluMAP-PP19
❑ 98ScoNewS-NS4
❑ 98ScoRT-251
❑ 98ScoRTSS-PP144
❑ 98ScoRTSSAP-PP144
❑ 98ScoRTSSAP1-PP144
❑ 98SkyDugA-98
❑ 98SkyDugAIA-98
❑ 98SP Aut-25
❑ 98SP AutC-MT
❑ 98SP MinPE-5
❑ 98SP MinPE-91
❑ 98SP SPTSC-MT
❑ 98SPMin-5
❑ 98SPMin-91
❑ 98SPxFin-2
❑ 98SPxFinR-2
❑ 98SPxFinS-2
❑ 98StaCluFDI-69
❑ 98StaClul-69
❑ 98StaCluOneK-69
❑ 98StaCluPP-69
❑ 98Stu-191
❑ 98StuGPP-191
❑ 98StuSPP-191
❑ 98UD3-4
❑ 98UD3-94
❑ 98UD3-184
❑ 98UD3DieCut-4
❑ 98UD3DieCut-94
❑ 98UD3DieCut-184
❑ 98Ult-413
❑ 98UltGolM-413
❑ 98UltMas-413
❑ 98UltPlaM-413
❑ 98UltRoctS-15
❑ 98UppDec-275
❑ 98UppDecBCP-BC19
❑ 98UppDecDS-DS39
❑ 98UppDecREP-8
❑ 98Zen-86
❑ 98Zen5 xx7-76
❑ 98Zen5x7GoldImp-76
❑ 98Zen5x7Imp-76
❑ 98ZenRooT-15
❑ 98ZenZ-G-86
❑ 98ZenZ-S-86
❑ 98ZenZ-T-17
❑ 98ZenZ-TG-17
❑ 99199Fin-219
❑ 99Bow-229
❑ 99BowGol-229
❑ 99BowInt-229
❑ 99FinGolRef-219
❑ 99FinRef-219
❑ 99Fle-292
❑ 99FleSta9-292
❑ 99FleWarT-292
❑ 99MetUni-35
❑ 99MetUniGM-35
❑ 99MetUniN-11
❑ 99MetUniPMG-35
❑ 99Pac-319
❑ 99PacAur-139
❑ 99PacAurOD-139
❑ 99PacCroC-207
❑ 99PacCroCPB-207
❑ 99PacInv-109
❑ 99PacInvOD-109
❑ 99PacInvPB-109
❑ 99PacOme-175
❑ 99PacOmeC-175
❑ 99PacOmeG-175
❑ 99PacOmePB-175
❑ 99PacPar-175
❑ 99PacParC-175
❑ 99PacParG-175
❑ 99PacParHoloGold-175
❑ 99PacParHS-175
❑ 99PacParOD-175
❑ 99PacParPB-175
❑ 99PacParRed-175
❑ 99PacPlaB-319
❑ 99PacRed-319
❑ 99SkyMolM-11
❑ 99SkyMolMX-11
❑ 99SkyPre-92
❑ 99SkyPreR-92
❑ 99SkyThu-6
❑ 99SkyThuRant-6
❑ 99SkyThuRave-6
❑ 99SP Aut-62
❑ 99SP SigAuto-MT
❑ 99SPSig-104
❑ 99StaClu-294
❑ 99StaCluFDI-294
❑ 99StaCluOoaK-294
❑ 99StaCluPP-294
❑ 99ThuSkySupR-6
❑ 99Top-352
❑ 99TopChr-352
❑ 99TopChrR-352
❑ 99TopMVPP-352
❑ 99TopSta-89
❑ 99TopSta1Foil-89
❑ 99TopStaFoil-89
❑ 99TopStaOS-89
❑ 99UD Cho-122
❑ 99UD ChoP-122
❑ 99UD ChoPCR-122
❑ 99Ult-130
❑ 99UltGolM-130
❑ 99UltMas-130
❑ 99UltPlaM-130
❑ 99UltWorP-15
❑ 99UppDec-163
❑ 99UppDec-238
❑ 99UppDecBD-60
❑ 99UppDecBDD-60
❑ 99UppDecBDQ-60
❑ 99UppDecBDT-60
❑ 99UppDecEL1-163
❑ 99UppDecEL1-238
❑ 99UppDecEL2-163
❑ 99UppDecEL2-238
❑ 99UppDecM-151
❑ 99UppDecMGS-151
❑ 99UppDecMHFS-151
❑ 99UppDecMP-151
❑ 99UppDecMSS-151
❑ 99Vic-282

Tejada, Wilfredo
❑ 85DomLeaS-134
❑ 86JacExpT-18
❑ 87Don-529
❑ 87IndIndTI-25
❑ 88IndIndC-19
❑ 88IndIndP-523
❑ 89Bow-468
❑ 89BowTif-468
❑ 89OPC-391
❑ 89PhoFirC-12
❑ 89PhoFirP-1489
❑ 89Top-747
❑ 89TopTif-747
❑ 91HunStaLD-294
❑ 91LinDriAA-294
❑ 93LimRocDWB-4

Tejcek, John
❑ 92AriWilP-19
❑ 94CalCanF-803
❑ 94RivPilCLC-15

Tejeda, Enrique
❑ 88BenBucL-16

Tejeda, Felix
❑ 86VerBeaDP-24
❑ 87SanAntDTI-15

Tejera, Michael
❑ 98KanCouC-30
❑ 98KanCouCCP-30

Tejero, Fausto
❑ 90BoiHawP-3334
❑ 91QuaCitAC-14
❑ 91QuaCitAP-2632
❑ 92MidAngF-4031
❑ 92MidAngOHP-25
❑ 92MidAngS-454
❑ 93MidAngF-325
❑ 94MidAngF-2442
❑ 94MidAngOHP-30
❑ 95MidAngOHP-33
❑ 96VanCanB-27
❑ 97MidAngOHP-30
❑ 97RicBra-25
❑ 98RicBraQ-25

Tekulve, Kent
❑ 76OPC-112
❑ 76PirPos-26
❑ 76SSP-561
❑ 76Top-112
❑ 77PirPosP-29
❑ 77Top-374
❑ 78Top-84
❑ 79Top-223
❑ 80OPC-297
❑ 80Top-573
❑ 80TopSup-45
❑ 81CokTeaS-119
❑ 81Don-254
❑ 81Fle-362A
❑ 81Fle-362B
❑ 81FleStiC-21
❑ 81OPC-94
❑ 81Top-695
❑ 82Don-311
❑ 82Fle-500
❑ 82FleSta-73
❑ 82OPC-281
❑ 82Top-485
❑ 83Don-297
❑ 83Fle-326
❑ 83FleSta-194
❑ 83FleSti-73
❑ 83OPC-17
❑ 83OPC-18
❑ 83Top-17
❑ 83Top-18
❑ 83TopFol-4
❑ 84Don-410
❑ 84Fle-265
❑ 84FunFooP-12
❑ 84Nes792-754
❑ 84OPC-74
❑ 84Pir-22
❑ 84Top-754
❑ 84TopRubD-12
❑ 84TopSti-132
❑ 84TopTif-754
❑ 85Don-479
❑ 85Fle-477
❑ 85FleUpd-117
❑ 85Lea-119
❑ 85OPC-125
❑ 85Top-125
❑ 85TopRubD-15
❑ 85TopSti-129
❑ 85TopTif-125
❑ 85TopTifT-117T
❑ 85TopTra-117T
❑ 86Don-111
❑ 86Fle-455
❑ 86OPC-326
❑ 86PhiCIG-4
❑ 86PhiTas-27
❑ 86Top-326
❑ 86TopTif-326
❑ 87Don-453
❑ 87Fle-190
❑ 87FleExcS-42
❑ 87FleGlo-190
❑ 87FleMin-104
❑ 87FleStiC-116
❑ 87OPC-86
❑ 87PhiTas-27
❑ 87SpoTeaP-6
❑ 87Top-684
❑ 87TopSti-118
❑ 87TopTif-684
❑ 88Don-535
❑ 88DonBasB-327
❑ 88Fle-318
❑ 88FleGlo-318
❑ 88OPCBoxB-P
❑ 88PanSti-354
❑ 88PhiTas-24
❑ 88Sco-425
❑ 88ScoGlo-425
❑ 88StaLinPh-18
❑ 88Top-543
❑ 88TopRevLL-10
❑ 88TopTif-543
❑ 88TopWaxBC-P
❑ 89Fle-583
❑ 89FleGlo-583
❑ 89OPCBoxB-O
❑ 89RedKah-43
❑ 89Sco-287
❑ 89TopTra-116T
❑ 89TopTraT-116T
❑ 89TopWaxBC-O
❑ 89UppDec-207
❑ 90PubIntS-40
❑ 92UppDecS-19
❑ 93ActPacA-167
❑ 94CarLeaA-DJ23

Telemaco, Amaury
❑ 92HunCubC-27
❑ 92HunCubF-3148
❑ 93ClaFS7-119
❑ 93MidLeaAGF-42
❑ 93PeoChiC-21
❑ 93PeoChiF-1085
❑ 93PeoChiTI-27
❑ 94Bow-49
❑ 94Cla-77
❑ 94DayCubC-1
❑ 94DayCubF-2352
❑ 94ExcFS7-168
❑ 94FloStaLAF-FSL34
❑ 95Bes-61
❑ 95Bow-184
❑ 95OrlCubF-12
❑ 95SPML-32
❑ 96Bow-212
❑ 96BowBes-146
❑ 96BowBesAR-146
❑ 96BowBesR-146
❑ 96BowFoi-212
❑ 96Exc-142
❑ 96IowCubB-27
❑ 96SigRooOJ-32
❑ 96SigRooOJS-32
❑ 97ColCho-292
❑ 97Don-172
❑ 97DonGolPP-172
❑ 97DonSilPP-172
❑ 97Fle-286
❑ 97FleTif-286
❑ 97MetUni-16
❑ 97PacPriGotD-GD123
❑ 97Pin-177
❑ 97PinArtP-PP177
❑ 97PinMusC-177
❑ 97PinPrePla-177
❑ 97StaClu-359
❑ 97StaCluMOP-359
❑ 97Top-316
❑ 97Ult-170
❑ 97UltGolME-170
❑ 97UltPlaME-170
❑ 97UppDec-31

Telford, Anthony
❑ 88HagSunS-22
❑ 89FreKeyS-23
❑ 90BalOriP-26
❑ 90FreKeyTI-11
❑ 90HagSunS-23
❑ 91BalOriP-32
❑ 91Cla1-T16
❑ 91Don-501
❑ 91Fle-493
❑ 91LinDriAAA-470
❑ 91OPC-653
❑ 91OriCro-452
❑ 91RocRedWLD-470
❑ 91RocRedWP-1903
❑ 91Sco-354
❑ 91StaClu-330
❑ 91Top-653
❑ 91TopDeb90-152
❑ 91TopDesS-653
❑ 91TopMic-653
❑ 91TopTif-653
❑ 91UppDec-304
❑ 92Don-623
❑ 92Fle-29
❑ 92RocRedWF-1941
❑ 92RocRedWS-471
❑ 92Sco-853
❑ 92ScoHotR-8
❑ 92SkyAAAF-214
❑ 92StaClu-557
❑ 93Don-789
❑ 93RocRedWF-241
❑ 94RicBraF-2846
❑ 98PacOnl-462
❑ 98PacOnlR-462
❑ 98PacOnlWC-462

Telgheder, Dave
❑ 89PitMetS-22
❑ 90ColMetGS-26
❑ 90ColMetPPI-1
❑ 91Cla/Bes-342
❑ 91LinDriAA-644
❑ 91WilBilLD-644
❑ 91WilBilP-293
❑ 92SkyAAAF-256
❑ 92TidTidF-896
❑ 92TidTidS-572
❑ 93FleFinE-107
❑ 93NorTidF-2569
❑ 93TopTra-89T
❑ 94Don-467
❑ 94Fle-578
❑ 94MetColP-26
❑ 94NorTidF-2922
❑ 94Pac-417
❑ 94Sco-599
❑ 94ScoGolR-599
❑ 94Top-402
❑ 94TopGol-402
❑ 94TopSpa-402
❑ 94Ult-537
❑ 94UppDec-69
❑ 94UppDecED-69
❑ 95NorTidTI-28
❑ 97A'sMot-22
❑ 97ColCho-413
❑ 98Pac-176
❑ 98PacOnl-548
❑ 98PacOnlR-548
❑ 98PacOnlWC-548
❑ 98PacPlaB-176
❑ 98PacRedT-176
❑ 98PacSil-176
❑ 98UppDec-468

Telgheder, Jim
❑ 94SarRedSC-27
❑ 94SarRedSF-1951
❑ 95MicBatCTI-27
❑ 96WilBluRB-27
❑ 97WicWra-9

Tellechea, John
❑ 90LSUTigP-9
❑ 91LSUTigP-6

Tellers, David
❑ 90WelPirP-30
❑ 91CarLeaAP-CAR37
❑ 91SalBucC-20
❑ 91SalBucP-950
❑ 92CarMudF-1180
❑ 92SalBucC-7
❑ 94NewHavRF-1550
❑ 95NewHavRTI-12

Tellez, Alonzo
❑ 87SanAntDTI-5

Tellez, Eloy Jr
❑ 98BriWhiSQ-25

Tellgren, Scott
❑ 83TolMudHT-26
❑ 85MaiGuiT-32

Tellmann, Tom
❑ 79HawIslC-16
❑ 79HawIslT-23
❑ 80HawIslT-14
❑ 81HawIslT-15
❑ 81Top-356
❑ 82HawIslT-19
❑ 83BrePol-42
❑ 83TopTra-109T
❑ 84BreGar-20
❑ 84BrePol-42
❑ 84Don-149
❑ 84Fle-216
❑ 84Nes792-476
❑ 84Top-476
❑ 84TopSti-297
❑ 84TopTif-476
❑ 85BreGar-20
❑ 85Don-246
❑ 85Fle-599
❑ 85TacTigC-150
❑ 85Top-112
❑ 85TopTif-112
❑ 85TopTifT-118T
❑ 85TopTra-118T
❑ 86Top-693
❑ 86TopTif-693
❑ 94BreMilB-80

Telvin, Creighton
❑ 81SyrChiT-19

Temperly, Kevin
❑ 89CliGiaP-881
❑ 92CliGiaC-30

Temple, Jason
❑ 96LynHilB-23
❑ 97AugGre-16
❑ 98CarMudM-8

Temple, Johnny
❑ 55Bow-31
❑ 55Kah-6
❑ 56Kah-15
❑ 56RedBurB-22
❑ 56Top-212
❑ 57Kah-26
❑ 57RedSoh-18
❑ 57Top-9
❑ 58Kah-28
❑ 58RedEnq-39
❑ 58Top-205
❑ 58Top-478
❑ 59Kah-36
❑ 59RedEnq-25
❑ 59RedShiBS-21
❑ 59Top-335
❑ 60IndJayP-12
❑ 60Kah-40
❑ 60MacSta-25
❑ 60RawGloT-34
❑ 60Top-500
❑ 60TopTat-50
❑ 61Kah-43
❑ 61Pos-61A
❑ 61Pos-61B
❑ 61SevElev-8
❑ 61Top-155
❑ 61TopStal-143
❑ 62BalOriP-28
❑ 62Jel-38
❑ 62Pos-38
❑ 62PosCan-38
❑ 62SalPlaC-52A
❑ 62SalPlaC-52B
❑ 62ShiPlaC-52
❑ 62Top-34
❑ 62TopVen-34
❑ 63Col45"P-15
❑ 63Jel-189
❑ 63Pos-189
❑ 63Top-576
❑ 64Col.45JP-9
❑ 70Houof J-31
❑ 75TCMHouoJ-33
❑ 91OriCro-453

Temple, William
❑ 12Zee-157

Templeton, Chuck
❑ 79TCM50-282
❑ 90DodTar-793
❑ 95TopArcBD-116

Templeton, Garry
❑ 76TulOilGP-18
❑ 77Car5-27
❑ 77CarTeal-26
❑ 77Hos-78
❑ 77OPC-84
❑ 77Spo-4001
❑ 77Top-161
❑ 78CarTeal-34
❑ 78Hos-43
❑ 78Kel-31
❑ 78OPC-51
❑ 78RCColC-94
❑ 78Top-32
❑ 79BasPat-88
❑ 79Car5-29
❑ 79Hos-127
❑ 79OPC-181
❑ 79Top-350
❑ 80OPC-308
❑ 80Top-5
❑ 80Top-587
❑ 80TopSup-37
❑ 81AllGamPI-117
❑ 81CokTeaS-131
❑ 81Don-187
❑ 81Fle-529
❑ 81FleStiC-125
❑ 81Kel-27
❑ 81MSAMinD-32
❑ 81OPC-144

❑ 81PerCreC-10
❑ 81Squ-12
❑ 81Top-485
❑ 81TopScr-82
❑ 81TopSti-217
❑ 81TopSti-255
❑ 82Don-545
❑ 82Fle-131
❑ 82FleSta-27
❑ 82OnDecD-32
❑ 82OPC-288
❑ 82Top-288
❑ 82TopSti-96
❑ 82TopTra-119T
❑ 83AllGamPI-116
❑ 83Don-145
❑ 83Fle-373
❑ 83FleSti-227
❑ 83Kel-17
❑ 83OPC-336
❑ 83Top-505
❑ 83TopSti-291
❑ 84AllGamPI-26
❑ 84Don-185
❑ 84Fle-314
❑ 84Nes792-615
❑ 84OPC-173
❑ 84PadMot-8
❑ 84PadSmo-24
❑ 84Top-615
❑ 84TopSti-151
❑ 84TopTif-615
❑ 85AllGamPI-117
❑ 85Don-356
❑ 85Fle-45
❑ 85OPC-124
❑ 85PadMot-7
❑ 85Top-735
❑ 85TopSti-151
❑ 85TopTif-735
❑ 86Don-202
❑ 86DonAll-30
❑ 86Fle-336
❑ 86FleMin-71
❑ 86FleStiC-118
❑ 86Lea-133
❑ 86OPC-90
❑ 86Spo-170
❑ 86Top-90
❑ 86TopSti-110
❑ 86TopTat-19
❑ 86TopTif-90
❑ 87Don-141
❑ 87DonOpeD-150
❑ 87Fle-432
❑ 87FleGlo-432
❑ 87Lea-63
❑ 87OPC-325
❑ 87PadBohHB-1
❑ 87Top-325
❑ 87TopSti-110
❑ 87TopTif-325
❑ 88Don-649
❑ 88Fle-598
❑ 88FleGlo-598
❑ 88OPC-264
❑ 88PadCok-1
❑ 88PadSmo-28
❑ 88PanSti-409
❑ 88RedFolSB-89
❑ 88Sco-189
❑ 88ScoGlo-189
❑ 88Top-640
❑ 88TopSti-113
❑ 88TopTif-640
❑ 89Bow-455
❑ 89BowTif-455
❑ 89Don-483
❑ 89DonBasB-154
❑ 89Fle-319
❑ 89FleGlo-319
❑ 89PadCok-18
❑ 89PadMag-19
❑ 89PadPos-33
❑ 89PanSti-202
❑ 89Sco-176
❑ 89Top-121
❑ 89TopBig-328
❑ 89TopTif-121
❑ 89UppDec-297
❑ 90Bow-215
❑ 90BowTif-215
❑ 90Don-246
❑ 90DonBesN-133
❑ 90Fle-170
❑ 90FleCan-170
❑ 90Lea-102
❑ 90OPC-481
❑ 90PadCok-19
❑ 90PadMag-14
❑ 90PanSti-354
❑ 90PubIntS-60
❑ 90Sco-336
❑ 90Top-481
❑ 90TopBig-177
❑ 90TopTif-481
❑ 90UppDec-288
❑ 91Don-252
❑ 91Fle-546
❑ 91MetPerPA-28
❑ 91OPC-253
❑ 91PanFreS-94
❑ 91Sco-117
❑ 91ScoPro-117
❑ 91ScoRoo-38T
❑ 91StaClu-72
❑ 91Top-253
❑ 91TopDesS-253
❑ 91TopMic-253
❑ 91TopTif-253
❑ 91TopTra-118T
❑ 91TopTraT-118T
❑ 91Ult-312
❑ 91UppDec-295
❑ 92OPC-772
❑ 92Sco-588
❑ 92Top-772
❑ 92TopGol-772
❑ 92TopGolW-772
❑ 92TopMic-772
❑ 92UppDec-411
❑ 98CedRapKTI-29

Tena, Dario
❑ 94AugGreC-24
❑ 94AugGreF-3022

Tena, Luis
❑ 98ButCopKG-30

Tena, Paulino
❑ 90WatIndS-21
❑ 91KinIndC-21
❑ 91KinIndP-333

Tenace, Gene
❑ 70OPC-21
❑ 70Top-21
❑ 71MLBOffS-528
❑ 71OPC-338
❑ 71Top-338
❑ 72'sA'sPos-23
❑ 72OPC-189
❑ 72Top-189
❑ 73OPC-203
❑ 73OPC-206
❑ 73OPC-360
❑ 73OPC-524
❑ 73Top-203
❑ 73Top-206
❑ 73Top-360
❑ 73Top-524
❑ 74A'sPos-55
❑ 74OPC-79
❑ 74Top-79
❑ 74TopSta-230
❑ 75Hos-64
❑ 75HosTwi-64
❑ 75OPC-535
❑ 75Top-535
❑ 75TopMin-535
❑ 76Hos-122
❑ 76OPC-165
❑ 76SSP-493
❑ 76Top-165
❑ 77BurCheD-131
❑ 77Hos-141
❑ 77OPC-82
❑ 77PadSchC-56
❑ 77PepGloD-39
❑ 77RCColC-63
❑ 77Spo-5202
❑ 77Top-303
❑ 78Hos-125
❑ 78OPC-35
❑ 78PadFamF-32
❑ 78RCColC-4
❑ 78SagDis-20
❑ 78TasDis-20
❑ 78Top-240
❑ 78WifBalD-74
❑ 79BasPat-89
❑ 79Hos-19
❑ 79OPC-226
❑ 79PadFamF-8
❑ 79Top-435
❑ 80OPC-355
❑ 80Top-704
❑ 81Car5x7-26
❑ 81Don-241
❑ 81Fle-489
❑ 81OPC-29
❑ 81Top-29
❑ 81TopTra-842
❑ 82Don-152
❑ 82Fle-132
❑ 82FleSta-26
❑ 82OPC-166
❑ 82Top-631
❑ 83Don-442
❑ 83Fle-25
❑ 83OPC-252
❑ 83Top-515
❑ 83TopTra-110T
❑ 84Don-264
❑ 84Fle-266
❑ 84Nes792-729
❑ 84Top-729
❑ 84TopTif-729
❑ 86A'sGreT-1
❑ 86AstPol-26
❑ 87A'sMot-14
❑ 87AstMot-27
❑ 87AstPol-26
❑ 90BluJayFS-29
❑ 91BluJayFS-26
❑ 91BluJayFS-28
❑ 93BluJayFS-30
❑ 95BluJayOH-32
❑ 96BluJayOH-31
❑ 97BluJayOH-33
❑ 97BluJayS-28

Tenacen, Francisco
❑ 86TamTarP-23
❑ 87VerRedP-4
❑ 88WinSpiS-20
❑ 89WinSpiS-16

Tenbarge, Jeffrey
❑ 92AubAstC-4
❑ 92AubAstF-1353
❑ 93AshTouC-20
❑ 93AshTouF-2275

Tenenini, Bob
❑ 79MemChiT-15
❑ 80MemChiT-23
❑ 83MemChiT-17

Tener, John
❑ 87OldJudN-489
❑ 89EdgR.WG-15

Tenhunfeld, Joe
❑ 88BatCliP-1679
❑ 90ClePhiS-21

Tennant, Mike
❑ 77LodDodT-21
❑ 79AlbDukTc-2

Tennant, Thomas
❑ 09ObaT21-58
❑ 09ObaT21-169
❑ 09ObaT21-336
❑ 10BisCoaLE99-27
❑ 11PacCoaBD-63
❑ 11Zee-103
❑ 12ObaPreT-85
❑ 13Zee-92
❑ 14Zee-95
❑ 15Zee-90

Tenney, Fred
❑ 03BreE10-140
❑ 03WilCarE-27
❑ 06FanCraNL-46
❑ 08AmeCarE91-31
❑ 08AmeCarE91-64
❑ 08RosComP-134
❑ 09AmeCarE90-1-107
❑ 09RamT20-116
❑ 09T206-353
❑ 10DarChoE-31
❑ 10E98-25
❑ 11SpoLifCW-349
❑ 11SpoLifM-221
❑ 11TurRedT-122
❑ 12HasTriFT-51
❑ 12HasTriFT-69
❑ 98CamPepP-78

Tenney, Mickey
❑ 81QuaCitCT-8

Tepedino, Frank
❑ 70Top-689
❑ 70YanPhoS-31
❑ 71OPC-342
❑ 71Top-342
❑ 73SyrChiTI-27
❑ 74OPC-526
❑ 74Top-526
❑ 75AtlBraP-36
❑ 75OPC-9
❑ 75Top-9
❑ 75TopMin-9
❑ 81TCM60I-469
❑ 92YanWIZ6-124
❑ 92YanWIZ7-148
❑ 94BreMilB-81

Tepper, Marc
❑ 89MiaMirIS-19
❑ 89Sta-185
❑ 89WatIndS-21
❑ 90KinIndTI-11
❑ 91KinIndC-22
❑ 91KinIndP-334

Teramae, Masao
❑ 96HonShaHWB-18

Terhune, Mike
❑ 96DanBraB-25
❑ 97MacBra-26
❑ 98DanQ-C-20

Terilli, Joey
❑ 91GenCubC-21
❑ 91GenCubP-4232
❑ 92MidLeaATI-45
❑ 92PeoChiC-6
❑ 92PeoChiTI-27
❑ 93DayCubC-19
❑ 93DayCubF-871
❑ 94DayCubC-23
❑ 94DayCubF-2367

Terlecky, Greg
❑ 75St.LouCP-29
❑ 75TulOil7-15
❑ 76SSP-299
❑ 77Top-487
❑ 78SprRedWK-20

Terni, Chas
❑ 98LowSpiM-18

Terpko, Jeff
❑ 72Dia-45
❑ 77ExpPos-30
❑ 77Top-137
❑ 93RanKee-354

Terrazas, Marc
❑ 82HolMilT-24
❑ 83RedPioT-31

Terrell, James
❑ 91BelMarCB-6
❑ 91BelMarP-3681
❑ 92PenPilC-26
❑ 92PenPilF-2946

Terrell, Jeffrey
❑ 97BatCliTI-25
❑ 98PieBolWM-26

Terrell, Jerry
❑ 70RelPam-14
❑ 74OPC-481
❑ 74Top-481
❑ 75OPC-654
❑ 75TacTwiK-3
❑ 75Top-654
❑ 75TopMin-654
❑ 75TwiPos-24
❑ 75TwiTeal-26
❑ 76MinTwiP-17
❑ 76OPC-159
❑ 76SSP-222
❑ 76Top-159
❑ 77Top-513
❑ 78Roy-22
❑ 78SSP270-243
❑ 78Top-525
❑ 79RoyTeal-10
❑ 79Top-273
❑ 80Top-98
❑ 87Ft.MyeRP-29
❑ 91PacSenL-8

Terrell, Jim
❑ 97BriWhiSB-20
❑ 98HicCraM-27
❑ 98HicCraUO-29

Terrell, Matt
❑ 93PitMetC-22
❑ 93PitMetF-3725
❑ 94St.LucMC-24
❑ 94St.LucMF-1209
❑ 95StLucMTI-31

Terrell, Walt
❑ 81TulDriT-12
❑ 82TidTidT-24
❑ 83TidTidT-12
❑ 84Don-640
❑ 84Fle-601
❑ 84Nes792-549
❑ 84Top-549
❑ 84TopSti-110
❑ 84TopTif-549
❑ 85Don-597
❑ 85Fle-94
❑ 85FleUpd-118
❑ 85OPC-287
❑ 85Top-287
❑ 85TopMin-287
❑ 85TopSti-109
❑ 85TopTif-287
❑ 85TopTifT-119T
❑ 85TopTra-119T
❑ 86Don-247
❑ 86Fle-240
❑ 86Lea-123
❑ 86OPC-301
❑ 86TigCaiD-18
❑ 86Top-461
❑ 86TopMinL-16
❑ 86TopTif-461
❑ 87Don-275
❑ 87Fle-165
❑ 87FleGlo-165
❑ 87Lea-180
❑ 87OPC-72
❑ 87TigCaiD-16
❑ 87TigCok-3
❑ 87Top-72
❑ 87TopTif-72
❑ 88Don-91
❑ 88DonBasB-293
❑ 88Fle-72
❑ 88FleGlo-72
❑ 88FleMin-24
❑ 88FleStiC-28
❑ 88OPC-284
❑ 88PanSti-87
❑ 88RedFolSB-90
❑ 88Sco-538
❑ 88ScoGlo-538
❑ 88TigPep-35
❑ 88TigPol-12
❑ 88Top-668
❑ 88TopTif-668
❑ 89Bow-445
❑ 89BowTif-445
❑ 89Don-296
❑ 89DonBasB-245
❑ 89DonTra-28
❑ 89Fle-149
❑ 89FleGlo-149
❑ 89PadCok-19
❑ 89Sco-314
❑ 89ScoRoo-75T
❑ 89Top-127
❑ 89TopTif-127
❑ 89TopTra-117T
❑ 89TopTraT-117T
❑ 89UppDec-475
❑ 89UppDec-703
❑ 90Bow-165
❑ 90BowTif-165
❑ 90Don-309
❑ 90Fle-457
❑ 90FleCan-457
❑ 90OPC-611
❑ 90PirHomC-28
❑ 90PubIntS-61
❑ 90Sco-463
❑ 90TigTeal-20
❑ 90Top-611
❑ 90TopTif-611
❑ 90TulDriDGB-11
❑ 90UppDec-661
❑ 91Don-717
❑ 91MetWIZ-401
❑ 91OPC-328
❑ 91Sco-801
❑ 91StaClu-315
❑ 91TigCok-35
❑ 91Top-328
❑ 91TopDesS-328
❑ 91TopMic-328
❑ 91TopTif-328
❑ 91UppDec-320
❑ 92Don-565
❑ 92Fle-146
❑ 92OPC-722
❑ 92Pin-190
❑ 92Sco-355
❑ 92StaClu-139
❑ 92TigKro-24
❑ 92TigTeal-30
❑ 92Top-722
❑ 92TopGol-722
❑ 92TopGolW-722
❑ 92TopMic-722
❑ 92UppDec-520
❑ 92YanWIZ8-189
❑ 93Don-772
❑ 93Fle-612
❑ 93StaClu-223
❑ 93StaCluFDI-223
❑ 93StaCluMOP-223

Terrill, James
❑ 87EveGiaC-19
❑ 88CliGiaP-702
❑ 89SanJosGB-4
❑ 89SanJosGCLC-218
❑ 89SanJosGP-449
❑ 89SanJosGS-24
❑ 91LinDriAA-543
❑ 91SanAntMLD-543
❑ 91SanAntMP-2974

Terrio, Tim
❑ 89BakDodCLC-208
❑ 89CalLeaA-26

Terris, Adam
❑ 89RocExpLC-28
❑ 90WesPalBES-24

Terry, Adonis (William H.)
❑ 74BroClu-16
❑ 87OldJudN-490
❑ 90DodTar-1084
❑ 98CamPepP-79

Terry, Bill (William Harold)
❑ 25Exh-40
❑ 26Exh-40
❑ 27YorCarE-46
❑ 28PorandAR-A35
❑ 28PorandAR-B35
❑ 28W502-46
❑ 28W513-67
❑ 28Yue-46
❑ 29ExhFou-9
❑ 29PorandAR-88
❑ 30UncJac-26
❑ 31Exh-10
❑ 31W517-23
❑ 32R33So2-405
❑ 32USCar*-4
❑ 33ButCre-25
❑ 33CraJacP-22
❑ 33DelR33-4
❑ 33GeoCMil-29
❑ 33Gou-20
❑ 33Gou-125
❑ 33GouCanV-20
❑ 33NatLeaAC-16
❑ 33RitCE-10D
❑ 33WorCig-90
❑ 34BatR31-6
❑ 34DiaStaR-14
❑ 34ExhFou-5
❑ 34Gou-21
❑ 34GouCanV-53
❑ 35AlDemDCR3-89
❑ 35ExhFou-5
❑ 35GouPuzR-1K
❑ 35GouPuzR-3B
❑ 35GouPuzR-14B
❑ 35GouPuzR-15B
❑ 36ExhFou-5
❑ 36R31Pre-G14
❑ 36WorWidGV-7
❑ 37KelPepS-BB14
❑ 38OurNatGPP-29
❑ 50CalHOFW-69
❑ 53ArtHaloFP-80
❑ 60Fle-52
❑ 61Fle-142
❑ 61GolPre-5
❑ 67TopVen-161
❑ 72TCMthe3-68
❑ 74Bra193NLA-16
❑ 75GiaAllT-10
❑ 76RowExh-12
❑ 76ShaPiz-73
❑ 77BobParHoF-47
❑ 77GalGloG-112
❑ 77GalGloG-204
❑ 77GalGloG-250
❑ 79DiaGre-30
❑ 80GiaGreT-7
❑ 80Lau300-7
❑ 80PacLeg-9
❑ 80PerHaloFP-73
❑ 80PerHaloFPS-4

❑ 80SSPHOF-73
❑ 81ConTSN-7
❑ 81SpoHaloF-17
❑ 82DiaCla-38
❑ 82TCMGreH-21
❑ 83BigLeaCOA-38
❑ 83ConMar-29
❑ 85FegMurCG-19
❑ 86ConSer1-31
❑ 87HygAllG-43
❑ 88ConNatA-20
❑ 88ConSer3-28
❑ 89HOFStiB-2
❑ 89PerCelP-41
❑ 91ConTSN-64
❑ 91ConTSNP-661
❑ 92ConTSN-588
❑ 92ConTSNAP-661G
❑ 93ConTSN-661
❑ 93ConTSN-841
❑ 94ConTSN-1100
❑ 94ConTSNB-1100

Terry, Brent
❑ 88SalLakCTTI-6

Terry, Brett
❑ 88UtiBluSP-3

Terry, Ralph
❑ 57Top-391
❑ 58A'sJayP-9
❑ 58Top-169
❑ 59Top-358
❑ 60Top-96
❑ 60TopVen-96
❑ 61Top-389
❑ 61Yan61RL-12
❑ 62Jel-10
❑ 62Pos-10
❑ 62PosCan-10
❑ 62SalPlaC-77
❑ 62ShiPlaC-77
❑ 62Top-48
❑ 62TopVen-48
❑ 63Baz-20
❑ 63Fle-26
❑ 63Jel-20
❑ 63Kah-29
❑ 63Pos-20
❑ 63ReqKP-18
❑ 63SalMetC-38
❑ 63Top-8
❑ 63Top-10
❑ 63Top-148
❑ 63Top-315
❑ 63TopStil-43
❑ 63YanJayP-11
❑ 64ChatheY-23
❑ 64Top-458
❑ 64YanJayP-11
❑ 65Kah-39
❑ 65Top-406
❑ 66OPC-109
❑ 66Top-109
❑ 66TopRubl-92
❑ 66TopVen-109
❑ 67OPC-59
❑ 67Top-59
❑ 78TCM60I-168
❑ 81TCM60I-480
❑ 83Yan196-12
❑ 83YanASFY-47
❑ 88PacLegI-64
❑ 89SweBasG-31
❑ 91MetWIZ-402
❑ 91YanRinP12-6
❑ 92YanWIZ6-125
❑ 92YanWIZA-82

Terry, Scott Ray
❑ 81CedRapRT-18
❑ 82CedRapRT-23
❑ 83TamTarT-23
❑ 87NasSouTI-20
❑ 87Top-453
❑ 87TopTif-453
❑ 88CarSmo-8
❑ 88CarTeal-33
❑ 88Don-647
❑ 88FleUpd-121
❑ 88FleUpdG-121
❑ 88LouRedBTI-47
❑ 88TopTra-119T
❑ 88TopTraT-119T
❑ 89CarSmo-21
❑ 89CarTeal-31
❑ 89CedRapRAB-7
❑ 89Don-397
❑ 89Fle-464
❑ 89FleGlo-464
❑ 89Sco-397
❑ 89Top-686
❑ 89TopBig-31
❑ 89TopTif-686
❑ 90CarSmo-23
❑ 90CedRapRDGB-7
❑ 90Don-418
❑ 90Fle-261
❑ 90FleCan-261
❑ 90Lea-234
❑ 90OPC-82
❑ 90PubIntS-229
❑ 90Sco-235
❑ 90Top-82
❑ 90TopTif-82
❑ 90TopTVCa-19
❑ 90UppDec-260
❑ 91CarPol-37
❑ 91Fle-647
❑ 91OPC-539
❑ 91Sco-247
❑ 91StaClu-469
❑ 91Top-539
❑ 91TopDesS-539
❑ 91TopMic-539
❑ 91TopTif-539
❑ 92CarPol-20
❑ 92Don-655
❑ 92Fle-593
❑ 92OPC-117
❑ 92Sco-219
❑ 92StaClu-522
❑ 92Top-117
❑ 92TopGol-117
❑ 92TopGolW-117
❑ 92TopMic-117
❑ 92UppDec-688
❑ 96TulDriTI-25

Terry, Tony
❑ 94BilMusF-3684
❑ 94BilMusSP-13
❑ 94SigRooDP-38
❑ 94SigRooDPS-38
❑ 94StaCluDP-23
❑ 94StaCluDPFDI-23
❑ 95Bow-105
❑ 97AubDouTI-1

Terry, Yank
❑ 42RedSoxTI-23
❑ 43RedSoxTI-24

Terry, Zeb
❑ 15Zee-20
❑ 17ColE13-171
❑ 17HolBreD-103
❑ 17Zee-17
❑ 18Zee-15
❑ 20GasAmeMBD-26
❑ 21E121So1-105
❑ 21E121So8-97
❑ 22W575-136
❑ 23W501-58
❑ 27YorCarE-46

Terwilliger, Wayne
❑ 49AngTeal-35
❑ 49W725AngTI-27
❑ 50Bow-114
❑ 51Bow-175
❑ 51TopRedB-14
❑ 52Top-7
❑ 53Bri-22
❑ 53Top-159
❑ 54Top-73
❑ 55Top-34
❑ 55TopDouH-131
❑ 56A'sPos-43
❑ 56Top-73
❑ 59Top-496
❑ 60Lea-134
❑ 60Top-26
❑ 60TopVen-26
❑ 75LynRanT-18
❑ 76AshTouT-20
❑ 77AshTouT-23
❑ 79AshTouT-5
❑ 80TulDriT-24
❑ 83RanAffF-NNO
❑ 83TopRep5-7
❑ 84RanJarP-NNO
❑ 85RanPer-NNO
❑ 86TwiTeal-32
❑ 87TwiPos-29
❑ 87TwiTeal-30
❑ 90DodTar-794
❑ 91DodPho-7
❑ 91TopArc1-159
❑ 93RanKee-44
❑ 94TopArc1-73
❑ 94TopArc1G-73
❑ 95TopArcBD-2
❑ 97St.PauS-30
❑ 98St.PauSTI-28

Terzarial, Anthony
❑ 88BilMusP-1811
❑ 90CedRapRB-10
❑ 90CedRapRP-2333

Tesar, John
❑ 23Zee-172

Teske, David
❑ 92PitMetF-3296

Tesmer, Jim
❑ 87LitFalMP-2407
❑ 89PitMetS-28

Tesreau, Jeff (Charles)
❑ 09SpoNewSM-92
❑ 14B18B-72
❑ 14CraJacE-44
❑ 15CraJacE-44
❑ 15SpoNewM-175
❑ 16BF2FP-83
❑ 16FleBreD-93
❑ 16SpoNewM-173
❑ 17ColE13-172
❑ 81ConTSN-46
❑ 88ConSer3-29
❑ 92ConTSN-340

Tessicini, David
❑ 93EveGiaC-27
❑ 93EveGiaF-3780
❑ 94CliLumC-23
❑ 94CliLumF-1990
❑ 94EveGiaC-28
❑ 94EveGiaF-3663

Tessmar, Tim
❑ 98St.LucMM-19

Tessmer, Jay
❑ 96Exc-95
❑ 96TamYanY-25
❑ 97Bow-313
❑ 97BowInt-313
❑ 97NorNav-30
❑ 97NorNavTI-27
❑ 98FleUpd-U78
❑ 98NorNavQ-22
❑ 99Fle-295
❑ 99FleSta9-295
❑ 99FleWarT-295
❑ 99SkyThu-83
❑ 99SkyThuRant-83
❑ 99SkyThuRave-83
❑ 99SpoIll-71
❑ 99ThuSkySupR-83

Tessmer, Tim
❑ 97CapCitB-20

Teston, Phil
❑ 80PenPilBT-1
❑ 80PenPilCT-1

Teter, Craig
❑ 90SouBenWSB-11
❑ 90SouBenWSGS-26
❑ 90UtiBluSP-11

Teter, Doug
❑ 93FayGenC-28
❑ 94JamJamC-30
❑ 96LakTigB-4

Tettleton, Mickey
❑ 84AlbA'sT-22
❑ 85A'sMot-11
❑ 85FleUpd-119
❑ 85TopTifT-120T
❑ 85TopTra-120T
❑ 86A'sMot-11
❑ 86Don-345
❑ 86Fle-432
❑ 86Top-457
❑ 86TopTif-457
❑ 87Don-349
❑ 87DonOpeD-23
❑ 87Fle-407
❑ 87FleGlo-407
❑ 87Top-649
❑ 87TopTif-649
❑ 88Don-103
❑ 88OriFreB-14
❑ 88OriPos-37
❑ 88RocRedWC-21
❑ 88RocRedWP-202
❑ 88RocRedWTI-23
❑ 88Sco-269
❑ 88ScoGlo-269
❑ 88ScoRoo-31T
❑ 88ScoRooG-31T
❑ 88StaLinAs-17
❑ 88Top-143
❑ 88TopClo-112
❑ 88TopTif-143
❑ 88TopTra-120T
❑ 88TopTraT-120T
❑ 89BalOriP-34
❑ 89Don-401
❑ 89DonBasB-86
❑ 89Fle-623
❑ 89FleGlo-623
❑ 89OriFreB-14
❑ 89PanSti-259
❑ 89Sco-358
❑ 89Top-521
❑ 89TopBig-198
❑ 89TopSti-231
❑ 89TopTif-521
❑ 89UppDec-553
❑ 89UppDecS-1
❑ 90AlbDecGB-31
❑ 90Bow-254
❑ 90BowTif-254
❑ 90ClaBlu-39
❑ 90Don-5
❑ 90Don-169
❑ 90DonBesA-15
❑ 90DonSupD-5
❑ 90Fle-190
❑ 90FleAll-12
❑ 90FleCan-190
❑ 90Hot50PS-45
❑ 90K-M-24
❑ 90Lea-65
❑ 90M.Vpin-8
❑ 90MLBBasB-111
❑ 90OPC-275
❑ 90PanSti-8
❑ 90PubIntS-587
❑ 90RedFolSB-94
❑ 90Sco-322
❑ 90Sco100S-9
❑ 90Spo-171
❑ 90TigTeal-21
❑ 90Top-275
❑ 90TopCoi-30
❑ 90TopGloS-57
❑ 90TopSti-237
❑ 90TopStiB-57
❑ 90TopTif-275
❑ 90TopTVA-24
❑ 90UppDec-60A
❑ 90UppDec-60B
❑ 90UppDec-297
❑ 91Bow-140
❑ 91CadEllD-56
❑ 91Cla2-T62
❑ 91Don-597
❑ 91Fle-494
❑ 91FleUpd-24
❑ 91Lea-322
❑ 91OPC-385
❑ 91OriCro-454
❑ 91PanFreS-239
❑ 91Sco-270
❑ 91ScoRoo-25T
❑ 91SimandSMLBL-43
❑ 91StaClu-412
❑ 91Stu-58
❑ 91TigCok-20
❑ 91Top-385
❑ 91TopDesS-385
❑ 91TopMic-385
❑ 91TopTif-385
❑ 91TopTra-119T
❑ 91TopTraT-119T
❑ 91UltUpd-24
❑ 91UppDec-296
❑ 91UppDec-729
❑ 92Bow-117
❑ 92ClaGam-89
❑ 92Don-85
❑ 92Fle-147
❑ 92FleAll-9
❑ 92FleLumC-L2
❑ 92Lea-285
❑ 92LeaBlaG-285
❑ 92OPC-29
❑ 92PanSti-104
❑ 92Pin-226
❑ 92Sco-134
❑ 92StaClu-195
❑ 92Stu-178
❑ 92TigKro-25
❑ 92TigTeal-31
❑ 92Top-29
❑ 92TopGol-29
❑ 92TopGolW-29
❑ 92TopMic-29
❑ 92TriPla-44
❑ 92Ult-63
❑ 92UltAllS-5
❑ 92UppDec-251
❑ 93Bow-615
❑ 93DiaMar-107
❑ 93Don-13
❑ 93DonSpiotG-SG10
❑ 93Fin-80
❑ 93FinRef-80
❑ 93Fla-208
❑ 93Fle-234
❑ 93FleFruotL-60
❑ 93FunPac-189
❑ 93Lea-213
❑ 93MetBak-37
❑ 93OPC-334
❑ 93PacSpa-114
❑ 93PanSti-113
❑ 93Pin-52
❑ 93PinHomRC-18
❑ 93PinSlu-22
❑ 93RedFolS-94
❑ 93Sco-60
❑ 93Sel-60
❑ 93SP-240
❑ 93StaClu-31
❑ 93StaCluFDI-31
❑ 93StaCluMOP-31
❑ 93Stu-138
❑ 93TigGat-23
❑ 93Top-135
❑ 93TOPBLAG-41
❑ 93TopGol-135
❑ 93TopInaM-135
❑ 93TopInaR-135
❑ 93TopMic-135
❑ 93TriPla-92
❑ 93Ult-554
❑ 93UppDec-46
❑ 93UppDec-86
❑ 93UppDecGold-46
❑ 93UppDecGold-86
❑ 93USPlaCA-6C
❑ 94Bow-125
❑ 94ChuShoS-10
❑ 94ColC-275
❑ 94ColChoGS-275
❑ 94ColChoSS-275
❑ 94Don-44
❑ 94DonSpeE-44
❑ 94Fin-281
❑ 94FinRef-281
❑ 94Fla-295
❑ 94Fle-143
❑ 94FleExtB-80
❑ 94FUnPac-20
❑ 94FUnPac-187
❑ 94Lea-279
❑ 94LeaL-33
❑ 94OPC-32
❑ 94Pac-229
❑ 94PacGolP-8
❑ 94PanSti-68
❑ 94Pin-67
❑ 94PinArtP-67
❑ 94PinMusC-67
❑ 94PinRunC-RC19
❑ 94ProMag-48
❑ 94Sco-51
❑ 94ScoGolR-51
❑ 94Sel-331
❑ 94SP-180
❑ 94SPDieC-180
❑ 94Spo-131
❑ 94StaClu-192
❑ 94StaCluFDI-192
❑ 94StaCluGR-192
❑ 94StaCluMOP-192
❑ 94Stu-193
❑ 94Top-495
❑ 94TopGol-495
❑ 94TopSpa-495
❑ 94TriPla-248
❑ 94TriPlaM-1
❑ 94TriPlaM-6
❑ 94Ult-357
❑ 94UppDec-301
❑ 94UppDecED-301
❑ 95Baz-101
❑ 95Bow-433
❑ 95ColCho-474
❑ 95ColCho-570T
❑ 95ColChoGS-474
❑ 95ColChoSE-221
❑ 95ColChoSEGS-221
❑ 95ColChoSESS-221
❑ 95ColChoSS-474
❑ 95Don-537
❑ 95DonPreP-537
❑ 95DonTopotO-168
❑ 95Fin-107
❑ 95Fin-266
❑ 95FinRef-107
❑ 95FinRef-266
❑ 95Fla-311
❑ 95Fle-61
❑ 95FleAllS-15
❑ 95FleUpd-87
❑ 95Lea-363
❑ 95LeaLim-88
❑ 95Pac-160
❑ 95Pin-375
❑ 95PinArtP-375
❑ 95PinMusC-375
❑ 95RanCra-31
❑ 95Sco-78
❑ 95ScoGolR-78
❑ 95ScoHaloG-HG49
❑ 95ScoPlaTS-78
❑ 95Sel-222
❑ 95SelArtP-222
❑ 95SP-194
❑ 95Spo-137
❑ 95SpoArtP-137
❑ 95SPSil-194
❑ 95StaClu-34
❑ 95StaClu-540
❑ 95StaCluFDI-34
❑ 95StaCluMOP-34
❑ 95StaCluMOP-540
❑ 95StaCluSTWS-34
❑ 95StaCluSTWS-540
❑ 95StaCluVR-23
❑ 95StaCluVRMO-23
❑ 95Top-612
❑ 95TopCyb-380
❑ 95TopEmb-121
❑ 95TopEmbGI-121
❑ 95TopTra-50T
❑ 95UppDec-479
❑ 96ColCho-346
❑ 96ColChoCtG-CG29
❑ 96ColChoCtG-CG29B
❑ 96ColChoCtG-CG29C
❑ 96ColChoCtGE-CR29
❑ 96ColChoCtGG-CG29
❑ 96ColChoCtGG-CG29B
❑ 96ColChoCtGG-CG29C
❑ 96ColChoCtGGE-CR29
❑ 96ColChoGS-346
❑ 96ColChoSS-346
❑ 96Don-72
❑ 96DonPreP-72
❑ 96EmoXL-128
❑ 96Fin-B166
❑ 96FinRef-B166
❑ 96Fla-179
❑ 96Fle-263
❑ 96FleTif-263
❑ 96Lea-167
❑ 96LeaPrePB-167
❑ 96LeaPrePG-167
❑ 96LeaPrePS-167
❑ 96MetUni-117
❑ 96MetUniP-117
❑ 96Pac-422
❑ 96PacPri-P139
❑ 96PacPriG-P139
❑ 96PanSti-236
❑ 96RanDr P-30
❑ 96RanFle-15
❑ 96RanMot-7
❑ 96Sco-388
❑ 96SP-176
❑ 96StaClu-98
❑ 96StaCluEPB-98
❑ 96StaCluEPG-98
❑ 96StaCluEPS-98
❑ 96StaCluMOP-98
❑ 96Top-286
❑ 96TopGal-21
❑ 96TopGalPPI-21
❑ 96Ult-141
❑ 96UltGolM-141
❑ 96UppDec-465
❑ 97ColCho-490
❑ 97ColChoT-TR13

- ❑ 97Don-84
- ❑ 97DonGolPP-84
- ❑ 97DonSilPP-84
- ❑ 97Fle-232
- ❑ 97FleTif-232
- ❑ 97Lea-62
- ❑ 97LeaFraM-62
- ❑ 97LeaFraMDC-62
- ❑ 97MetUni-169
- ❑ 97Pac-211
- ❑ 97PacLigB-211
- ❑ 97PacSil-211
- ❑ 97RanDr P-30
- ❑ 97RanMinM-6
- ❑ 97RanMot-6
- ❑ 97RanSco-1
- ❑ 97RanScoPl-1
- ❑ 97RanScoPr-1
- ❑ 97Rav1stlG-1
- ❑ 97Sco-2
- ❑ 97ScoArtPWB-2
- ❑ 97ScoPreS-2
- ❑ 97ScoShoS-2
- ❑ 97ScoShoSAP-2
- ❑ 97StaClu-297
- ❑ 97StaCluMOP-297
- ❑ 97Top-162
- ❑ 97TopChr-64
- ❑ 97TopChrR-64
- ❑ 97TopGal-27
- ❑ 97TopGalPPI-27
- ❑ 97Ult-389
- ❑ 97UltGolME-389
- ❑ 97UltPlaME-389
- ❑ 97UppDec-506
- ❑ 98ColCho-248
- ❑ 98UppDec-233

Tetz, Kris

- ❑ 98VerExpO-17

Teufel, Tim

- ❑ 82OrlTwi8SCT-9
- ❑ 82OrlTwiT-12
- ❑ 83TolMudHT-16
- ❑ 84Don-37
- ❑ 84Fle-574
- ❑ 84MinTwiP-28
- ❑ 84TopTra-117T
- ❑ 84TopTraT-117T
- ❑ 84TwiTeal-8
- ❑ 85AllGamPI-16
- ❑ 85Don-192
- ❑ 85Fle-290
- ❑ 85Lea-97
- ❑ 85OPC-239
- ❑ 85Top-239
- ❑ 85TopMin-239
- ❑ 85TopSti-303
- ❑ 85TopTif-239
- ❑ 85Twi7-10
- ❑ 85TwiPos-28
- ❑ 85TwiTeal-8
- ❑ 85TwiTeal-24
- ❑ 86BasStaB-114
- ❑ 86Don-242
- ❑ 86Fle-407
- ❑ 86FleUpd-110
- ❑ 86MetColP-26
- ❑ 86MetTCM-23
- ❑ 86MetWorSC-25
- ❑ 86OPC-91
- ❑ 86Top-667
- ❑ 86TopSti-280
- ❑ 86TopTif-667
- ❑ 86TopTra-109T
- ❑ 86TopTraT-109T
- ❑ 87Don-581
- ❑ 87DonOpeD-131
- ❑ 87Fle-24
- ❑ 87FleGlo-24
- ❑ 87MetColP-21
- ❑ 87Top-158
- ❑ 87TopTif-158
- ❑ 88Don-648
- ❑ 88DonTeaBM-648
- ❑ 88Fle-152
- ❑ 88FleGlo-152
- ❑ 88MetColP-10
- ❑ 88MetKah-11
- ❑ 88PanSti-342
- ❑ 88Sco-128
- ❑ 88ScoGlo-128
- ❑ 88StaLinMe-19
- ❑ 88Top-508
- ❑ 88TopClo-113
- ❑ 88TopTif-508
- ❑ 89Bow-382
- ❑ 89BowTif-382
- ❑ 89Don-507
- ❑ 89Fle-50
- ❑ 89FleGlo-50
- ❑ 89MetColP-18
- ❑ 89MetKah-28
- ❑ 89Sco-58
- ❑ 89Top-9
- ❑ 89TopDouM-11
- ❑ 89TopTif-9
- ❑ 89UppDec-277
- ❑ 90Don-618
- ❑ 90Fle-218
- ❑ 90FleCan-218
- ❑ 90Lea-383
- ❑ 90MetColP-10
- ❑ 90MetKah-11
- ❑ 90OPC-764
- ❑ 90PubIntS-146
- ❑ 90Sco-501
- ❑ 90Top-764
- ❑ 90TopTif-764
- ❑ 90TopTVM-29
- ❑ 90UppDec-492
- ❑ 91Don-370
- ❑ 91Fle-162
- ❑ 91FleUpd-127
- ❑ 91Lea-314
- ❑ 91MetColP-10
- ❑ 91MetKah-11
- ❑ 91MetWIZ-403
- ❑ 91OPC-302
- ❑ 91PadSmo-36
- ❑ 91Sco-427
- ❑ 91ScoRoo-67T
- ❑ 91StaClu-43
- ❑ 91Top-302
- ❑ 91TopDesS-302
- ❑ 91TopMic-302
- ❑ 91TopTif-302
- ❑ 91TopTra-120T
- ❑ 91TopTraT-120T
- ❑ 91UltUpd-114
- ❑ 91UppDec-370
- ❑ 92Don-171
- ❑ 92Fle-622
- ❑ 92Lea-261
- ❑ 92LeaBlaG-261
- ❑ 92OPC-413
- ❑ 92PadCarJ-22
- ❑ 92PadMot-17
- ❑ 92PadPolD-24
- ❑ 92PadSmo-35
- ❑ 92Pin-313
- ❑ 92Sco-234
- ❑ 92StaClu-485
- ❑ 92Stu-110
- ❑ 92Top-413
- ❑ 92TopGol-413
- ❑ 92TopGolW-413
- ❑ 92TopMic-413
- ❑ 92TriPla-255
- ❑ 92Ult-585
- ❑ 92UppDec-349
- ❑ 93Don-98
- ❑ 93Fle-525
- ❑ 93Lea-10
- ❑ 93PacSpa-266
- ❑ 93PadMot-6
- ❑ 93Pin-183
- ❑ 93Sco-480
- ❑ 93StaClu-213
- ❑ 93StaCluFDI-213
- ❑ 93StaCluMOP-213
- ❑ 93Top-636
- ❑ 93TopGol-636
- ❑ 93TopInaM-636
- ❑ 93TopInaR-636
- ❑ 93TopMic-636
- ❑ 93TriPla-183
- ❑ 93UppDec-61
- ❑ 93UppDecGold-61
- ❑ 94Don-272
- ❑ 94Fle-676
- ❑ 94Pac-535
- ❑ 94StaClu-46
- ❑ 94StaCluFDI-46
- ❑ 94StaCluGR-46
- ❑ 94StaCluMOP-46
- ❑ 94Top-254
- ❑ 94TopGol-254
- ❑ 94TopSpa-254

Teut, Nathan

- ❑ 98RocCubM-28
- ❑ 98RocCubTI-29
- ❑ 99BasAmeTPA-41

Teutsch, Mark

- ❑ 79AppFoxT-15
- ❑ 80GleFalWSBT-13
- ❑ 80GleFalWSCT-3
- ❑ 81EdmTraRR-24
- ❑ 82GleFalWST-23

Tevlin, Creighton J.

- ❑ 77RocRedWM-17
- ❑ 78SpoIndC-12
- ❑ 79VanCanT-23A
- ❑ 81SyrChiTI-19
- ❑ 82SyrChiT-22
- ❑ 82SyrChiTI-21

Tewell, Terry

- ❑ 90MarPhiP-3202
- ❑ 91ClePhiC-14
- ❑ 91ClePhiP-1625
- ❑ 92ClePhiC-15
- ❑ 92ClePhiF-2060

Tewksbury, Bob

- ❑ 84NasSouTI-22
- ❑ 85AlbYanT-11
- ❑ 86DonRoo-8
- ❑ 86FleUpd-111
- ❑ 86TopTra-110T
- ❑ 86TopTraT-110T
- ❑ 86YanTCM-16
- ❑ 87ColCliT-9
- ❑ 87Don-422
- ❑ 87Fle-117
- ❑ 87FleGlo-117
- ❑ 87SpoTeaP-7
- ❑ 87Top-254
- ❑ 87TopTif-254
- ❑ 88IowCubC-5
- ❑ 88IowCubP-534
- ❑ 88Top-593
- ❑ 88TopTif-593
- ❑ 89LouRedBC-11
- ❑ 89LouRedBP-1250
- ❑ 89LouRedBTI-35
- ❑ 90AlbDecGB-13
- ❑ 90Don-714
- ❑ 90Lea-406
- ❑ 90LouRedBLBC-40
- ❑ 90TopTra-122T
- ❑ 90TopTraT-122T
- ❑ 90TopTVCa-20
- ❑ 91Bow-394
- ❑ 91CarPol-39
- ❑ 91Don-183
- ❑ 91Fle-648
- ❑ 91Lea-460
- ❑ 91OPC-88
- ❑ 91PanSti-36
- ❑ 91Sco-499
- ❑ 91StaClu-417
- ❑ 91Top-88
- ❑ 91TopDesS-88
- ❑ 91TopMic-88
- ❑ 91TopTif-88
- ❑ 91UppDec-630
- ❑ 92CarPol-21
- ❑ 92Don-201
- ❑ 92Fle-594
- ❑ 92Lea-95
- ❑ 92LeaBlaG-95
- ❑ 92OPC-623
- ❑ 92Pin-219
- ❑ 92Pin-288
- ❑ 92Sco-282
- ❑ 92StaClu-258
- ❑ 92Top-623
- ❑ 92TopGol-623
- ❑ 92TopGolW-623
- ❑ 92TopMic-623
- ❑ 92Ult-573
- ❑ 92UppDec-512
- ❑ 92YanWIZ8-190
- ❑ 93Bow-248
- ❑ 93CarPol-21
- ❑ 93CarStaC-10
- ❑ 93ClaGam-91
- ❑ 93Don-204
- ❑ 93DonDiaK-DK22
- ❑ 93Fin-193
- ❑ 93FinRef-193
- ❑ 93Fla-129
- ❑ 93Fle-134
- ❑ 93FunPac-79
- ❑ 93Lea-44
- ❑ 93OPC-344
- ❑ 93PacSpa-304
- ❑ 93PanSti-190
- ❑ 93Pin-13
- ❑ 93Sco-34
- ❑ 93Sel-107
- ❑ 93SelAce-15
- ❑ 93SelStaL-83
- ❑ 93SelStaL-89
- ❑ 93SP-80
- ❑ 93StaClu-341
- ❑ 93StaCluFDI-341
- ❑ 93StaCluM-66
- ❑ 93StaCluMOP-341
- ❑ 93Top-285
- ❑ 93TopComotH-27
- ❑ 93TopGol-285
- ❑ 93TopInaM-285
- ❑ 93TopInaR-285
- ❑ 93TopMic-285
- ❑ 93TriPla-156
- ❑ 93Ult-114
- ❑ 93UppDec-318
- ❑ 93UppDecGold-318
- ❑ 94Bow-264
- ❑ 94BowBes-R65
- ❑ 94BowBesR-R65
- ❑ 94CarMagG-3
- ❑ 94CarPol-21
- ❑ 94ColC-468
- ❑ 94ColChoGS-468
- ❑ 94ColChoSS-468
- ❑ 94Don-262
- ❑ 94Fin-42
- ❑ 94FinRef-42
- ❑ 94Fla-431
- ❑ 94Fle-647
- ❑ 94FleExtB-364
- ❑ 94FleExtBPD-8
- ❑ 94FUnPac-58
- ❑ 94Lea-333
- ❑ 94OPC-217
- ❑ 94Pac-605
- ❑ 94PanSti-249
- ❑ 94Pin-452
- ❑ 94PinArtP-452
- ❑ 94PinMusC-452
- ❑ 94Sco-56
- ❑ 94ScoGolR-56
- ❑ 94Sel-83
- ❑ 94SP-66
- ❑ 94SPDieC-66
- ❑ 94StaClu-586
- ❑ 94StaCluFDI-586
- ❑ 94StaCluGR-586
- ❑ 94StaCluMOP-586
- ❑ 94StaCluT-312
- ❑ 94StaCluTFDI-312
- ❑ 94Stu-55
- ❑ 94Top-473
- ❑ 94TopGol-473
- ❑ 94TopSpa-473
- ❑ 94TriPla-67
- ❑ 94Ult-272
- ❑ 94UppDec-353
- ❑ 94UppDecED-353
- ❑ 95ColCho-187
- ❑ 95ColCho-571T
- ❑ 95ColChoGS-187
- ❑ 95ColChoSE-78
- ❑ 95ColChoSEGS-78
- ❑ 95ColChoSESS-78
- ❑ 95ColChoSS-187
- ❑ 95Don-480
- ❑ 95DonPreP-480
- ❑ 95DonTopotO-169
- ❑ 95Fin-280
- ❑ 95FinRef-280
- ❑ 95Fla-312
- ❑ 95Fle-510
- ❑ 95FleTeaL-26
- ❑ 95FleUpd-88
- ❑ 95Lea-392
- ❑ 95Pac-417
- ❑ 95Pin-236
- ❑ 95PinArtP-236
- ❑ 95PinMusC-236
- ❑ 95RanCra-32
- ❑ 95Sco-167
- ❑ 95ScoGolR-167
- ❑ 95ScoPlaTS-167
- ❑ 95StaClu-41
- ❑ 95StaClu-612
- ❑ 95StaCluFDI-41
- ❑ 95StaCluMOP-41
- ❑ 95StaCluMOP-612
- ❑ 95StaCluSTWS-41
- ❑ 95StaCluSTWS-612
- ❑ 95StaCluVR-30
- ❑ 95StaCluVRMO-30
- ❑ 95Top-195
- ❑ 95TopCyb-111
- ❑ 95TopTra-96T
- ❑ 95Ult-433
- ❑ 95UltGolM-433
- ❑ 95UppDec-57
- ❑ 95UppDecED-57
- ❑ 95UppDecEDG-57
- ❑ 96ColCho-347
- ❑ 96ColCho-782
- ❑ 96ColChoGS-347
- ❑ 96ColChoSS-347
- ❑ 96Don-423
- ❑ 96DonPreP-423
- ❑ 96EmoXL-283
- ❑ 96Fin-B292
- ❑ 96FinRef-B292
- ❑ 96Fla-381
- ❑ 96Fle-264
- ❑ 96FleTif-264
- ❑ 96FleUpd-U200
- ❑ 96FleUpdTC-U200
- ❑ 96Pac-428
- ❑ 96PadMot-11
- ❑ 96Sco-141
- ❑ 96Top-387
- ❑ 96Ult-562
- ❑ 96UltGolM-562
- ❑ 97ColCho-378
- ❑ 97Fle-470
- ❑ 97Fle-643
- ❑ 97FleTif-470
- ❑ 97FleTif-643
- ❑ 97StaClu-111
- ❑ 97StaCluMOP-111
- ❑ 97Top-219
- ❑ 97Ult-369
- ❑ 97UltGolME-369
- ❑ 97UltPlaME-369
- ❑ 98Fin-91
- ❑ 98FinNo--91
- ❑ 98FinNo-R-91
- ❑ 98FinRef-91
- ❑ 98Pac-142
- ❑ 98PacOnl-438
- ❑ 98PacOnlR-438
- ❑ 98PacOnlWC-438
- ❑ 98PacPlaB-142
- ❑ 98PacRedT-142
- ❑ 98PacSil-142
- ❑ 98Top-425
- ❑ 98TopChr-425
- ❑ 98TopChrR-425
- ❑ 98TopDevR-425
- ❑ 98TopDia-425
- ❑ 98TopMiniC-425
- ❑ 98UppDec-134
- ❑ 99Pac-257
- ❑ 99PacPlaB-257
- ❑ 99PacRed-257

Texidor, Esteban

- ❑ 78HolMilT-22

Texidor, Jose

- ❑ 91ButCopKSP-26
- ❑ 91ChaRanC-25
- ❑ 91ChaRanP-1329
- ❑ 92GasRanC-9
- ❑ 92GasRanF-2267
- ❑ 93ChaRanC-22
- ❑ 93ChaRanF-1954
- ❑ 94ChaRanF-2510
- ❑ 95TulDriTI-23
- ❑ 96BesAutS-88
- ❑ 96BesAutSA-76
- ❑ 96TulDriTI-26
- ❑ 97BesAutAS-59

Thacker, Moe

- ❑ 59Top-474
- ❑ 61CubJayP-11
- ❑ 61Top-12
- ❑ 62Top-546

Thames, Marcus

- ❑ 98Bow-318
- ❑ 98BowChr-318
- ❑ 98BowChrGA-318
- ❑ 98BowChrGAR-318
- ❑ 98BowChrI-318
- ❑ 98BowChrIR-318
- ❑ 98BowChrR-318
- ❑ 98BowGolA-318
- ❑ 98BowInt-318
- ❑ 98TamYanM-28

Thatcher, Aaron

- ❑ 92FroRowDP-25
- ❑ 92FroRowDPG-25
- ❑ 92FroRowDPS-25

Thayer, Ernest

- ❑ 90BasWit-98

Thayer, Greg

- ❑ 75TacTwiK-15
- ❑ 77OrlTwiT-21
- ❑ 78TwiFriP-20
- ❑ 79TolMudHT-16

Thayer, Scott

- ❑ 78GreBraT-24

Thebo, Antonio

- ❑ 09T206-519

Thees, Michael

- ❑ 91SouOreAC-26
- ❑ 91SouOreAP-3845

Theil, Mark

- ❑ 77ForLauYS-5

Theilman, Harry

- ❑ 06FanCraNL-47

Theisen, Mike

- ❑ 86St.PetCP-29

Theiss, Duane

- ❑ 78RicBraT-16
- ❑ 79RicBraT-16
- ❑ 80AndBraT-3

Thelen, Jeffrey John

- ❑ 90Bes-149
- ❑ 90KenTwiB-26
- ❑ 90KenTwiP-2295
- ❑ 90KenTwiS-24
- ❑ 91KenTwiC-18
- ❑ 91KenTwiP-2076
- ❑ 92VisOakC-9
- ❑ 92VisOakF-1016
- ❑ 93ForMyeMC-25
- ❑ 93ForMyeMF-2657

Theobald, Ron

- ❑ 72OPC-77
- ❑ 72Top-77
- ❑ 94BreMilB-183

Theodile, Robert

- ❑ 94HicCraC-22
- ❑ 94HicCraF-2177
- ❑ 96PriWilCB-26
- ❑ 97BirBarB-23
- ❑ 98BirBarG-24

Theodile, Simieon

- ❑ 98BluOriQ-8
- ❑ 98DelShoM-29

Theodore, George

- ❑ 73LinPor-125
- ❑ 74MetDaiPA-1
- ❑ 74MetJapEB-10
- ❑ 74OPC-99
- ❑ 74Top-8
- ❑ 75TidTidTI-22
- ❑ 89TidTidC-8
- ❑ 91MetWIZ-404

Theodorou, Nick

- ❑ 97UCLBruTI-23
- ❑ 98YakBeaG-32

Therneau, David

- ❑ 98BilMusTI-35

Theron, Greg

- ❑ 93BelMarCB-27
- ❑ 93BelMarF-3208
- ❑ 94AppFoxC-19
- ❑ 94AppFoxFl-1054

Therrien, Dominic

- ❑ 91IdaFalBP-4342
- ❑ 91PulBraP-4021
- ❑ 92MacBraF-277
- ❑ 93CarLeaAGF-39
- ❑ 93DurBulC-21
- ❑ 93DurBulF-494
- ❑ 93DurBulTI-13
- ❑ 94ExcFS7-161

Therrien, Ed

- ❑ 88CapCodPPaLP-4

Thevenow, Tom J.

- ❑ 27MidBre-19
- ❑ 28W56PlaC-S8
- ❑ 31Exh-13
- ❑ 33ExhFou-7
- ❑ 33Gou-36
- ❑ 33GouCanV-36
- ❑ 34DiaMatCSB-180
- ❑ 34ExhFou-7
- ❑ 35DiaMatCS2-20
- ❑ 35DiaMatCS3T1-139
- ❑ 35GouPuzR-4B
- ❑ 35GouPuzR-7B
- ❑ 35GouPuzR-12B
- ❑ 91ConTSN-69

Thibault, Ryan

- ❑ 90SpoIndSP-25
- ❑ 91WatDiaC-9
- ❑ 91WatDiaP-1256

❑ 92HigDesMC-21
❑ 93BelBreCB-24
❑ 93BelBreFl-1710
Thibert, John
❑ 90TamYanD-26
❑ 92GreHorC-10
❑ 92OneYanC-16
❑ 94LakElsSC-22
❑ 94LakElsSF-1665
❑ 95MidAngOHP-34
Thibodeau, John
❑ 69OPC-189
❑ 69Top-189
❑ 69TopFou-14
Thibodeaux, Keith
❑ 82BufBisT-8
❑ 83LynPirT-8
Thielen, D.J.
❑ 91EveGiaC-1
❑ 91EveGiaP-3925
❑ 92CliGiaC-21
❑ 92CliGiaF-3607
❑ 93Bow-224
❑ 93CliGiaC-22
❑ 93CliGiaF-2497
❑ 94CliLumC-24
❑ 94CliLumF-1991
❑ 94SanJosGC-22
❑ 94SanJosGF-2830
Thielker, Dave
❑ 85ChaO'sT-6
Thielman, John
❑ 09T206-472
Thieme, Richard
❑ 97EugEmeB-14
❑ 98MacBraM-24
Thienpont, Gregg
❑ 84ButCopKT-23
Thies, Dave
❑ 61UniOil-H8
❑ 77FriOneYW-53
Thies, Jake (Vernon)
❑ 55JetPos-16
❑ 55Top-12
❑ 55TopDouH-39
Thiesen, Gator
❑ 89MisStaB-44
Thiessen, Tim
❑ 86WesPalBEP-26
Thigpen, Arthur
❑ 90NiaFalRP-25
Thigpen, Bobby
❑ 86BirBarTI-19
❑ 87Don-370
❑ 87Fle-507
❑ 87FleGlo-507
❑ 87SevCoi-C13
❑ 87SpoTeaP-26
❑ 87Top-61
❑ 87TopTif-61
❑ 87WhiSoxC-28
❑ 88Don-247
❑ 88DonBasB-235
❑ 88Fle-410
❑ 88FleGlo-410
❑ 88FleStiC-17
❑ 88FleTeaL-42
❑ 88Sco-307
❑ 88ScoGlo-307
❑ 88StaLinWS-18
❑ 88Top-613
❑ 88TopTif-613
❑ 88ToyRoo-32
❑ 88WhiSoxC-28
❑ 89BirBarADB-30
❑ 89Bow-55
❑ 89BowTif-55
❑ 89Don-266
❑ 89DonBasB-25
❑ 89Fle-512
❑ 89FleBasM-38
❑ 89FleGlo-512
❑ 89FleHeroB-39
❑ 89FleLeaL-39
❑ 89OPC-368
❑ 89PanSti-303
❑ 89Sco-399
❑ 89ScoHot1S-68
❑ 89ScoYouSI-29
❑ 89Spo-207
❑ 89SpoIllFKI-275
❑ 89Top-762
❑ 89TopSti-305
❑ 89TopTif-762
❑ 89TVSpoM-115
❑ 89UppDec-647
❑ 89WhiSoxC-26
❑ 89WhiSoxK-5
❑ 90BirBarADB-30
❑ 90Bow-306
❑ 90BowTif-306
❑ 90ClaYel-T81
❑ 90Don-266
❑ 90DonBesA-32
❑ 90Fle-549
❑ 90FleBasA-40
❑ 90FleBasAC-40
❑ 90FleBasM-40
❑ 90FleBasMC-40
❑ 90FleCan-549
❑ 90FleLeaL-39
❑ 90FleLeaLC-39
❑ 90Lea-175
❑ 90M.Vpin-25
❑ 90OPC-255
❑ 90PanSti-50
❑ 90PubIntS-401
❑ 90RedFolSB-95
❑ 90Sco-335
❑ 90Sco-694
❑ 90Sco100S-87
❑ 90Spo-27
❑ 90Top-255
❑ 90TopBig-295
❑ 90TopMinL-12
❑ 90TopSti-297
❑ 90TopTif-255
❑ 90UppDec-269
❑ 90USPlaCA-9C
❑ 90WhiSoxC-24
❑ 91Bow-342
❑ 91Cla1-T31
❑ 91ClaGam-140
❑ 91Don-8
❑ 91Don-90
❑ 91Don-399
❑ 91DonBonC-BC20
❑ 91DonSupD-8
❑ 91Fle-137
❑ 91Fle-712
❑ 91Lea-336
❑ 91MajLeaCP-15
❑ 91MisStaB-43
❑ 91OPC-8
❑ 91OPC-396
❑ 91OPC-420
❑ 91OPCPre-120
❑ 91PanCanT1-85
❑ 91PanFreS-320
❑ 91PanSti-252
❑ 91PosCan-25
❑ 91RedFolS-92
❑ 91Sco-280
❑ 91Sco-401
❑ 91Sco-418
❑ 91Sco100S-95
❑ 91SevCoi-M13
❑ 91SimandSMLBL-44
❑ 91StaClu-256
❑ 91StaCluCM-29
❑ 91StaCluP-43
❑ 91Stu-39
❑ 91SunSee-22
❑ 91Top-8
❑ 91Top-396
❑ 91Top-420
❑ 91TopCraJI-32
❑ 91TopDesS-8
❑ 91TopDesS-396
❑ 91TopDesS-420
❑ 91TopGaloC-11
❑ 91TopMic-8
❑ 91TopMic-396
❑ 91TopMic-420
❑ 91TopTif-8
❑ 91TopTif-396
❑ 91TopTif-420
❑ 91Ult-84
❑ 91Ult-396
❑ 91UppDec-93
❑ 91UppDec-261
❑ 91WhiSoxK-37
❑ 91Woo-21
❑ 92Bow-36
❑ 92Cla2-T89
❑ 92ClaGam-100
❑ 92Don-708
❑ 92Fle-99
❑ 92Hig5-18
❑ 92Lea-210
❑ 92LeaBlaG-210
❑ 92OPC-505
❑ 92PanSti-132
❑ 92Pin-214
❑ 92Sco-570
❑ 92Sco100S-54
❑ 92StaClu-224
❑ 92Stu-158
❑ 92Top-505
❑ 92TopGol-505
❑ 92TopGolW-505
❑ 92TopKid-101
❑ 92TopMic-505
❑ 92TriPla-32
❑ 92Ult-342
❑ 92UppDec-285
❑ 92WhiSoxK-37
❑ 93Bow-119
❑ 93Don-67
❑ 93Fle-589
❑ 93Lea-173
❑ 93OPC-336
❑ 93PacSpa-76
❑ 93Pin-453
❑ 93Sco-582
❑ 93Sel-232
❑ 93StaClu-575
❑ 93StaCluFDI-575
❑ 93StaCluMOP-575
❑ 93Top-645
❑ 93TopGol-645
❑ 93TopInaM-645
❑ 93TopInaR-645
❑ 93TopMic-645
❑ 93Ult-180
❑ 93UppDec-671
❑ 93UppDecGold-671
❑ 93WhiSoxK-27
❑ 93WhiSoxSC-20
❑ 94ColC-516
❑ 94ColChoGS-516
❑ 94ColChoSS-516
❑ 94Don-273
❑ 96NasSouB-24
Thigpen, Len
❑ 89PenPilS-24
Thing, Wild
❑ 98FreGriG-29
Thobe, J.J.
❑ 93ColRedC-23
❑ 93ColRedF-597
❑ 93SouAtlLAGF-15
❑ 94Bow-144
❑ 94ClaGolF-45
❑ 94ExcFS7-50
❑ 94HarSenF-2091
❑ 95SigRoo-47
❑ 95SigRooSig-47
Thobe, Steve
❑ 94WelPirC-27
❑ 94WelPirF-3504
❑ 96HonShaHWB-36
❑ 96LynHilB-24
❑ 97LynHil-21
❑ 98CarMudM-17
Thobe, Tom
❑ 93MacBraC-24
❑ 93MacBraF-1400
❑ 94ClaGolF-117
❑ 94GreBraF-413
❑ 94GreBraTI-24
❑ 95RicBraRC-25
❑ 95RicBraTI-23
❑ 96RicBraB-28
❑ 96RicBraRC-17
❑ 96RicBraUB-28
❑ 97RicBra-26
Thoden, John
❑ 88CapCodPPaLP-106
❑ 89JamExpP-2157
❑ 90RocExpLC-26
❑ 90RocExpP-2686
❑ 91WesPalBEC-12
❑ 91WesPalBEP-1228
❑ 92SalLakTSP-18
Thoenen, Dick
❑ 68Top-348
❑ 68TopVen-348
Thoma, Ray
❑ 84AlbA'sT-26
❑ 85HunStaJ-19
❑ 86HunStaDJ-19
❑ 87PitCubP-1
❑ 88PitCubP-1358
Thomas, Allen
❑ 96HicCraB-24
❑ 97HicCraB-28
❑ 98HicCraM-5
Thomas, Andres
❑ 83AndBraT-23
❑ 84DurBulT-14
❑ 85DomLeaS-175
❑ 85GreBraTI-18
❑ 86BraPol-14
❑ 86DonRoo-10
❑ 86FleUpd-112
❑ 86SpoRoo-14
❑ 86TopTra-111T
❑ 86TopTraT-111T
❑ 87BraSmo-20
❑ 87ClaGam-7
❑ 87Don-266
❑ 87DonOpeD-43
❑ 87Fle-531
❑ 87FleBasA-42
❑ 87FleGlo-531
❑ 87FleMin-105
❑ 87FleStiC-117
❑ 87SpoTeaP-24
❑ 87Top-299
❑ 87TopRoo-20
❑ 87TopSti-39
❑ 87TopSti-305
❑ 87TopTif-296
❑ 87ToyRoo-29
❑ 88Don-627
❑ 88Fle-551
❑ 88FleGlo-551
❑ 88OPC-13
❑ 88Sco-299
❑ 88ScoGlo-299
❑ 88StaLinBra-19
❑ 88Top-13
❑ 88TopBig-68
❑ 88TopSti-31
❑ 88TopTif-13
❑ 89Bow-272
❑ 89BowTif-272
❑ 89BraDub-26
❑ 89CadEllD-57
❑ 89ClaLigB-21
❑ 89Don-576
❑ 89DonBasB-197
❑ 89Fle-604
❑ 89FleGlo-604
❑ 89OPC-358
❑ 89PanSti-43
❑ 89Sco-406
❑ 89ScoYouS2-35
❑ 89Top-171
❑ 89Top-523
❑ 89TopSti-26
❑ 89TopTif-171
❑ 89TopTif-523
❑ 89UppDec-194
❑ 90BraDubP-28
❑ 90BraDubS-32
❑ 90Don-263
❑ 90Fle-597
❑ 90FleCan-597
❑ 90Lea-33
❑ 90OPC-358
❑ 90PanSti-229
❑ 90PubIntS-126
❑ 90Sco-99
❑ 90Top-358
❑ 90TopSti-33
❑ 90TopTif-358
❑ 90UppDec-212
❑ 91Don-491
❑ 91Fle-706
❑ 91OPC-111
❑ 91Sco-613
❑ 91Top-111
❑ 91TopDesS-111
❑ 91TopMic-111
❑ 91TopTif-111
❑ 91UppDec-384
❑ 92PhoFirS-396
Thomas, Bill
❑ 83ArkTraT-7
Thomas, Blaine
❑ 09ObaT21-425
Thomas, Brad
❑ 96GreFalDB-27
❑ 96GreFalDTI-15
❑ 98ForWayW!-25
Thomas, Brian
❑ 94ChaRanF-2511
❑ 94FloStaLAF-FSL4
❑ 95TulDriTI-24
❑ 96OklCit8B-22
Thomas, Bud (Luther)
❑ 39PlaBal-158
❑ 40PlaBal-42
Thomas, C.L.
❑ 88BilMusP-1823
Thomas, Carey
❑ 91Cla/Bes-281
Thomas, Carl
❑ 87KenTwiP-18
Thomas, Carl Leslie
❑ 77FriOneYW-115
Thomas, Carlos
❑ 91YakBeaC-28
❑ 91YakBeaP-4249
❑ 92YakBeaF-3448
❑ 93BakDodCLC-23
❑ 94BakDodC-23
❑ 94SanAntMF-2469
Thomas, Charles
❑ 25Zee-56
❑ 25Zee-161
❑ 26Zee-105
❑ 98GreFalDG-28
Thomas, Chris
❑ 80WisRapTT-11
❑ 83VerBeaDT-11
❑ 92AubAstC-3
❑ 92AubAstF-1368
❑ 93HelBreSP-8
Thomas, Claude
❑ 12T207-182
❑ 21Zee-20
❑ 22Zee-16
❑ 23Zee-20
Thomas, Clinton Cyrus
❑ 86NegLeaF-33
❑ 89NegLeaRP-3
Thomas, Corey
❑ 89MarPhiS-30
❑ 91SouAtlLAGP-SAL45
❑ 91SpaPhiC-20
❑ 91SpaPhiP-905
❑ 92ClePhiF-2067
Thomas, Danny
❑ 77FriOneYW-100
❑ 77Top-488
❑ 94BreMilB-184
Thomas, Dave
❑ 81HolMilT-5
Thomas, Delvin
❑ 90PenPilS-22
❑ 91SanBerSC-21
❑ 91SanBerSP-1998
Thomas, Dennis
❑ 82ReaPhiT-9
❑ 83ReaPhiT-9
Thomas, Deron
❑ 82SprCarF-21
❑ 83St.PetCT-19
❑ 84ArkTraT-4
Thomas, Derrel
❑ 72OPC-457
❑ 72PadPos-26
❑ 72Top-457
❑ 73OPC-57
❑ 73PadDea-26
❑ 73Top-57
❑ 74OPC-518
❑ 74PadDea-25
❑ 74PadTeal-14
❑ 74Top-518
❑ 75Gia-9
❑ 75GiaTeal-16
❑ 75OPC-378
❑ 75Top-378
❑ 75TopMin-378
❑ 76OPC-493
❑ 76SanFraGP-22
❑ 76SSP-106
❑ 76Top-493
❑ 77GiaTeal-22
❑ 77PadSchC-57A
❑ 77PadSchC-57B
❑ 77Top-266
❑ 78PadFamF-33
❑ 78Top-194
❑ 79OPC-359
❑ 79Top-679
❑ 80DodPol-30
❑ 80OPC-9
❑ 80Top-23
❑ 81Dod-11
❑ 81Dod-30
❑ 81DodPol-30
❑ 81Don-419
❑ 81Fle-123
❑ 81LonBeaPT-18A
❑ 81LonBeaPT-18B
❑ 81OPC-211
❑ 81Top-211
❑ 82DodPol-30
❑ 82DodUniOV-23
❑ 82Don-537
❑ 82Fle-26
❑ 82Top-348
❑ 83DodPol-30
❑ 83DodPos-17
❑ 83Fle-223
❑ 83Top-748
❑ 84Don-397
❑ 84ExpPos-32
❑ 84ExpStu-28
❑ 84Fle-114
❑ 84FleUpd-116
❑ 84Nes792-583
❑ 84Top-583
❑ 84TopTif-583
❑ 84TopTra-118T
❑ 84TopTraT-118T
❑ 85Fle-314
❑ 85OPC-317
❑ 85Top-448
❑ 85TopTif-448
❑ 85TopTifT-121T
❑ 85TopTra-121T
❑ 86Top-158
❑ 86TopTif-158
❑ 89PacSenL-64
❑ 89T/MSenL-104
❑ 89TopSenL-55
❑ 90DodTar-795
❑ 90EliSenL-90
❑ 91PacSenL-87
Thomas, Don
❑ 74GasRanT-23
❑ 75LynRanT-19
❑ 76SacSolC-16
Thomas, Don G.
❑ 76SanAntBTI-23
Thomas, Don Jr
❑ 97AubDouTI-23
Thomas, Duane
❑ 92BluOriC-11
❑ 92BluOriF-2372
❑ 93AlbPolF-2040
Thomas, Eric
❑ 75AppFoxT-26
Thomas, Evan
❑ 96BatCliTI-10
❑ 97ClePhi-22
❑ 98ReaPhiM-19
❑ 98ReaPhiUM-25
Thomas, Fay
❑ 30Zee-132
❑ 32Zee-66
❑ 35DiaMatCS3T1-140
❑ 90DodTar-796
Thomas, Forrest
❑ 13Zee-125
Thomas, Frank Edward
❑ 84OCoandSI-235
❑ 87PanAmTUBI-36
❑ 87PanAmTURB-23
❑ 88CapCodPB-14
❑ 88CapCodPPaLP-126
❑ 90Bes-1
❑ 90Bes-318
❑ 90BirBarB-1
❑ 90BirBarP-1116
❑ 90Bow-320
❑ 90BowTif-320
❑ 90ClaYel-T93
❑ 90CMC-818
❑ 90FleUpd-87
❑ 90Lea-300
❑ 90OPC-414
❑ 90ProAaA-46
❑ 90Sco-663
❑ 90ScoRoo-86T
❑ 90Top-414A
❑ 90Top-414B
❑ 90TopMag-48
❑ 90TopTif-414
❑ 90WhiSoxC-25
❑ 91AreHol-3
❑ 91Baz-7
❑ 91Ble23KT-1
❑ 91Ble23KT-2
❑ 91Ble23KT-3
❑ 91Bow-366
❑ 91Cla1-T32
❑ 91Cla2-T28
❑ 91ClaGam-181

❑ 91Don-477
❑ 91Fle-138
❑ 91JimDea-9
❑ 91Lea-281
❑ 91MajLeaCP-17
❑ 91OPC-79
❑ 91OPCPre-121
❑ 91RedFolS-111
❑ 91Sco-840
❑ 91Sco-874
❑ 91Sco100RS-78
❑ 91ScoHotR-4
❑ 91SevCoi-M14
❑ 91StaClu-57
❑ 91StaThoRG-1
❑ 91StaThoRG-2
❑ 91StaThoRG-3
❑ 91StaThoRG-4
❑ 91StaThoRG-5
❑ 91StaThoRG-6
❑ 91StaThoRG-7
❑ 91StaThoRG-8
❑ 91StaThoRG-9
❑ 91StaThoRG-10
❑ 91StaThoRG-11
❑ 91Stu-40
❑ 91Top-79
❑ 91TopCraJ2-20
❑ 91TopDeb90-153
❑ 91TopDesS-79
❑ 91TopMic-79
❑ 91TopRoo-28
❑ 91TopTif-79
❑ 91TopTriH-A4
❑ 91ToyRoo-27
❑ 91Ult-85
❑ 91UppDec-246
❑ 91WhiSoxK-35
❑ 91WhiSoxK-NNO
❑ 92Bow-114
❑ 92Bow-551
❑ 92Cla1-T89
❑ 92Cla2-T87
❑ 92ClaGam-106
❑ 92ColPro-15
❑ 92ColTho-1
❑ 92ColTho-2
❑ 92ColTho-3
❑ 92ColTho-4
❑ 92ColTho-5
❑ 92ColTho-6
❑ 92ColTho-7
❑ 92ColTho-8
❑ 92ColTho-9
❑ 92ColTho-10
❑ 92ColTho-11
❑ 92ColTho-12
❑ 92ColTho-AU
❑ 92Don-592
❑ 92DonCraJ1-35
❑ 92DonDiaK-DK8
❑ 92DonEli-18
❑ 92DonMcD-2
❑ 92DonSupD-DK8
❑ 92Fle-100
❑ 92Fle-701
❑ 92Fle-712
❑ 92FleAll-11
❑ 92FleCitTP-2
❑ 92FleRooS-1
❑ 92FroRowT-1
❑ 92FroRowT-2
❑ 92FroRowT-3
❑ 92FroRowT-4
❑ 92FroRowT-5
❑ 92FroRowT-6
❑ 92FroRowT-7
❑ 92FroRowTG-1
❑ 92FroRowTG-2
❑ 92FroRowTG-3
❑ 92Hig5-19
❑ 92Hig5S-29
❑ 92Hig5S-36
❑ 92JimDea-4
❑ 92KinDis-3
❑ 92Lea-67
❑ 92Lea-349
❑ 92LeaBlaG-67
❑ 92LeaBlaG-349
❑ 92LeaGolP-16
❑ 92LeaPre-16
❑ 92MooSna-24
❑ 92MSABenSHD-11
❑ 92MTVRocnJ-2
❑ 92MVPPin-11
❑ 92OPC-555
❑ 92OPCPre-59
❑ 92PanSti-125
❑ 92Pin-1
❑ 92PinSlu-11
❑ 92PinTea2-3
❑ 92PinTeaP-4
❑ 92Pos-24
❑ 92RedFolS-93
❑ 92RevSup1-4
❑ 92RevSup1-5
❑ 92RevSup1-6
❑ 92Sco-505
❑ 92Sco-893
❑ 92Sco100S-51
❑ 92ScoImpP-43
❑ 92ScoProP-3
❑ 92SevCoi-16
❑ 92SpollIFK1-45
❑ 92SpollIFK1-343
❑ 92SpollIFK1-685
❑ 92SpoStaCC-45
❑ 92StaClu-301
❑ 92StaClu-591
❑ 92StaCluMP-15
❑ 92StaPro-10
❑ 92Stu-159
❑ 92StuPre-18
❑ 92Top-555
❑ 92TopGol-555
❑ 92TopGolW-555
❑ 92TopKid-99
❑ 92TopMcD-25
❑ 92TopMic-555
❑ 92TriPla-206
❑ 92TriPlaG-GS12
❑ 92TriPlaP-6
❑ 92Ult-44
❑ 92UltAllS-9
❑ 92UppDec-87
❑ 92UppDec-166
❑ 92UppDec-SP4
❑ 92UppDecF-10
❑ 92UppDecFG-10
❑ 92UppDecHRH-HR8
❑ 92UppDecTMH-52
❑ 92UppDecWB-T19
❑ 92WhiSoxK-35
❑ 93Ble-51
❑ 93Ble-52
❑ 93Bow-555
❑ 93CadDis-58
❑ 93ClaGam-92
❑ 93DiaMar-108
❑ 93DiaMarA-7
❑ 93DiaMarP-8
❑ 93Don-7
❑ 93DonEliD-13
❑ 93DonEliS-19
❑ 93DonLonBL-LL10
❑ 93DonMasotG-1
❑ 93DonMVP-2
❑ 93DonPre-14
❑ 93DonSpiotG-SG6
❑ 93DonSpiotG-SG18
❑ 93DurPowP1-2
❑ 93Fin-102
❑ 93FinJum-102
❑ 93FinRef-102
❑ 93Fla-189
❑ 93Fle-210
❑ 93Fle-714
❑ 93FleAll-AL1
❑ 93FleAtl-23
❑ 93FleFruotL-61
❑ 93FleGolM-B3
❑ 93FleTeaL-AL5
❑ 93FunPac-21
❑ 93FunPac-27
❑ 93FunPac-36
❑ 93FunPac-197
❑ 93FunPac-202
❑ 93FunPac-225
❑ 93FunPacA-AS1
❑ 93Hos-13
❑ 93HumDumC-6
❑ 93JimDea-1
❑ 93KinDis-4
❑ 93Lea-195
❑ 93Lea-FT
❑ 93LeaFas-1
❑ 93LeaGolA-R12
❑ 93LeaTho-1
❑ 93LeaTho-2
❑ 93LeaTho-3
❑ 93LeaTho-4
❑ 93LeaTho-5
❑ 93LeaTho-6
❑ 93LeaTho-7
❑ 93LeaTho-8
❑ 93LeaTho-9
❑ 93LeaTho-10
❑ 93LeaThoJ-1
❑ 93LeaThoJ-2
❑ 93LeaThoJ-3
❑ 93LeaThoJ-4
❑ 93LeaThoJ-5
❑ 93LeaThoJ-6
❑ 93LeaThoJ-7
❑ 93LeaThoJ-8
❑ 93LeaThoJ-9
❑ 93LeaThoJ-10
❑ 93OPC-362
❑ 93OPCPreSP-1
❑ 93OPCPreSPF-1
❑ 93PacSpa-77
❑ 93PanSti-136
❑ 93Pin-108
❑ 93PinCoo-24
❑ 93PinCooD-24
❑ 93PinHomRC-17
❑ 93PinSlu-9
❑ 93PinTeaP-4
❑ 93Pos-14
❑ 93RedFolS-95
❑ 93Sco-3
❑ 93Sco-510
❑ 93Sco-541
❑ 93ScoFra-4
❑ 93ScoGolDT-10
❑ 93Sel-6
❑ 93SelStaL-3
❑ 93SelStaL-13
❑ 93SelStaL-33
❑ 93SelStaL-38
❑ 93SelStaL-45
❑ 93SelStaL-49
❑ 93SP-260
❑ 93SPPlaP-PP19
❑ 93StaClu-200
❑ 93StaClu-746
❑ 93StaCluFDI-200
❑ 93StaCluFDI-746
❑ 93StaCluI-B3
❑ 93StaCluMO-26
❑ 93StaCluMOP-200
❑ 93StaCluMOP-746
❑ 93StaCluMOP-MB3
❑ 93Stu-139
❑ 93StuHer-8
❑ 93StuSil-1
❑ 93StuSupoC-6
❑ 93StuTho-1
❑ 93StuTho-2
❑ 93StuTho-3
❑ 93StuTho-4
❑ 93StuTho-5
❑ 93Top-150
❑ 93Top-401
❑ 93TOPBLAG-42
❑ 93TopFulS-1
❑ 93TopGol-150
❑ 93TopGol-401
❑ 93TopInaM-150
❑ 93TopInaM-401
❑ 93TopInaR-150
❑ 93TopInaR-401
❑ 93TopMic-150
❑ 93TopMic-401
❑ 93TopMic-P150
❑ 93TopPos-1
❑ 93TopPre-150
❑ 93Toy-66
❑ 93ToyMasP-12
❑ 93TriPla-26
❑ 93TriPla-77
❑ 93TriPlaA-21
❑ 93TriPlaN-1
❑ 93Ult-181
❑ 93UltAllS-19
❑ 93UltPer-10
❑ 93UppDec-51
❑ 93UppDec-105
❑ 93UppDec-555
❑ 93UppDecCP-R20
❑ 93UppDecDG-27
❑ 93UppDecFA-A14
❑ 93UppDecFAJ-A14
❑ 93UppDecFH-62
❑ 93UppDecGold-51
❑ 93UppDecGold-105
❑ 93UppDecGold-555
❑ 93UppDecIC-WI25
❑ 93UppDecICJ-WI25
❑ 93UppDecOD-D24
❑ 93UppDecS-19
❑ 93UppDecTriCro-TC9
❑ 93USPlaCA-8D
❑ 93WhiSoxK-28
❑ 93WhiSoxSC-1
❑ 94Bow-15
❑ 94BowBes-R55
❑ 94BowBes-X91
❑ 94BowBesR-R55
❑ 94BowBesR-X91
❑ 94BowPre-1
❑ 94ChuShoS-5
❑ 94ColC-327
❑ 94ColC-354
❑ 94ColC-500
❑ 94ColC-640
❑ 94ColChoGS-327
❑ 94ColChoGS-354
❑ 94ColChoGS-500
❑ 94ColChoGS-640
❑ 94ColChoSS-327
❑ 94ColChoSS-354
❑ 94ColChoSS-500
❑ 94ColChoSS-640
❑ 94ColChoT-1
❑ 94DenHol-25
❑ 94Don-341
❑ 94DonAwaWJ-6
❑ 94DonDiaK-DK28
❑ 94DonDiaKJ-DK28
❑ 94DonDom-B2
❑ 94DonDomJ-B2
❑ 94DonEli-37
❑ 94DonLonBL-8
❑ 94DonMVP-18
❑ 94DonPro-4
❑ 94DonPro-4SE
❑ 94DonSpeE-341
❑ 94DonSpiotG-6
❑ 94DonSpiotGJ-6
❑ 94Fin-203
❑ 94FinJum-203
❑ 94FinRef-203
❑ 94Fla-36
❑ 94FlaHotN-10
❑ 94FlaInfP-9
❑ 94Fle-96
❑ 94FleAllS-23
❑ 94FleAwaW-1
❑ 94FleExtB-53
❑ 94FleExtBGB-27
❑ 94FleGolM-9
❑ 94FleGolMJ-9
❑ 94FleLumC-9
❑ 94FleSun-23
❑ 94FleTeaL-4
❑ 94FraThoC-NNO
❑ 94FUnPac-35
❑ 94FUnPac-177
❑ 94FUnPac-195
❑ 94FUnPac-204
❑ 94FUnPac-210
❑ 94FUnPac-236
❑ 94KinDis-14
❑ 94Kra-12
❑ 94Lea-400
❑ 94Lea-A300
❑ 94LeaGam-7
❑ 94LeaGolS-11
❑ 94LeaL-24
❑ 94LeaLimGA-1
❑ 94LeaMVPC-A13
❑ 94LeaMVPC-J400
❑ 94LeaMVPCG-A13
❑ 94LeaPowB-1
❑ 94LeaPro-9
❑ 94LeaSli-1
❑ 94LeaStaS-1
❑ 94O-PJumAF-1
❑ 94OPC-127
❑ 94OPCAllR-1
❑ 94OPCJumA-1
❑ 94OscMayR-14
❑ 94Pac-138
❑ 94Pac-660
❑ 94PacGolP-3
❑ 94PacPro-P8
❑ 94PacSilP-13
❑ 94PacSilPC-13
❑ 94PanSti-51
❑ 94Pin-1
❑ 94PinArtP-1
❑ 94PinMusC-1
❑ 94PinPowS-PS6
❑ 94PinRunC-RC2
❑ 94PinTeaP-1
❑ 94PinTheN-1
❑ 94PinTri-TR14
❑ 94Pos-21
❑ 94PosCan-12
❑ 94ProMag-28
❑ 94ProMagP-3
❑ 94RedFolMI-25
❑ 94Sco-41
❑ 94Sco-631
❑ 94ScoCyc-TC18
❑ 94ScoGolR-41
❑ 94ScoGolR-631
❑ 94ScoGolS-45
❑ 94Sel-6
❑ 94SelCroC-CC5
❑ 94SP-193
❑ 94SPDieC-193
❑ 94Spo-70
❑ 94Spo-176
❑ 94SpoFanA-AS1
❑ 94SpoRooGGG-GG6
❑ 94SPPre-CR5
❑ 94StaClu-267
❑ 94StaClu-285
❑ 94StaClu-528
❑ 94StaClu-718
❑ 94StaCluDD-DD9
❑ 94StaCluF-F10
❑ 94StaCluFDI-267
❑ 94StaCluFDI-285
❑ 94StaCluFDI-528
❑ 94StaCluFDI-718
❑ 94StaCluFJ-F10
❑ 94StaCluGR-267
❑ 94StaCluGR-285
❑ 94StaCluGR-528
❑ 94StaCluGR-718
❑ 94StaCluMO-29
❑ 94StaCluMOF-3
❑ 94StaCluMOP-267
❑ 94StaCluMOP-285
❑ 94StaCluMOP-528
❑ 94StaCluMOP-718
❑ 94StaCluMOP-F10
❑ 94StaCluMOP-DD9
❑ 94StaCluT-121
❑ 94StaCluTF-12
❑ 94StaCluTFDI-121
❑ 94Stu-209
❑ 94StuEdiC-2
❑ 94StuHer-2
❑ 94StuPro-209
❑ 94StuSerS-3
❑ 94StuSerSG-3
❑ 94TomPiz-29
❑ 94Top-270
❑ 94Top-384
❑ 94Top-601
❑ 94TopBlaG-21
❑ 94TopGol-270
❑ 94TopGol-384
❑ 94TopGol-601
❑ 94TopSpa-270
❑ 94TopSpa-384
❑ 94TopSpa-601
❑ 94TopSupS-41
❑ 94TopTraFI-7
❑ 94TriPla-269
❑ 94TriPlaBS-1
❑ 94TriPlaM-3
❑ 94TriPlaP-2
❑ 94Ult-39
❑ 94UltAllS-2
❑ 94UltAwaW-19
❑ 94UltHitM-10
❑ 94UltHomRK-3
❑ 94UltOnBL-12
❑ 94UltRBIK-2
❑ 94UppDec-55
❑ 94UppDec-284
❑ 94UppDec-300
❑ 94UppDecAJ-40
❑ 94UppDecAJG-40
❑ 94UppDecDC-C8
❑ 94UppDecED-55
❑ 94UppDecED-284
❑ 94UppDecED-300
❑ 94UppDecMLS-MM18
❑ 94UppDecMLSED-MM18
❑ 94USPlaCA-3D
❑ 94USPlaCA-11C
❑ 94WhiSoxK-27
❑ 95Baz-120
❑ 95BazRedH-RH22
❑ 95Bow-351
❑ 95BowBes-R65
❑ 95BowBes-X9
❑ 95BowBesJR-9
❑ 95BowBesR-R65
❑ 95BowBesR-X9
❑ 95ClaFanFPCP-8
❑ 95ClaPhoC-13
❑ 95ColCho-64
❑ 95ColCho-75
❑ 95ColCho-89
❑ 95ColChoCtA-8
❑ 95ColChoCtAGR-8
❑ 95ColChoCtG-CG19
❑ 95ColChoCtG-CG19B
❑ 95ColChoCtG-CG19C
❑ 95ColChoCtGE-19
❑ 95ColChoCtGG-CG19
❑ 95ColChoCtGG-CG19B
❑ 95ColChoCtGG-CG19C
❑ 95ColChoCtGGE-19
❑ 95ColChoGS-64
❑ 95ColChoGS-75
❑ 95ColChoGS-89
❑ 95ColChoSE-29
❑ 95ColChoSE-235
❑ 95ColChoSEGS-29
❑ 95ColChoSEGS-235
❑ 95ColChoSESS-29
❑ 95ColChoSESS-235
❑ 95ColChoSS-64
❑ 95ColChoSS-75
❑ 95ColChoSS-89
❑ 95Don-275
❑ 95DonAll-AL3
❑ 95DonBomS-2
❑ 95DonDiaK-DK1
❑ 95DonDom-3
❑ 95DonEli-55
❑ 95DonLonBL-1
❑ 95DonPreP-275
❑ 95DonTopotO-54
❑ 95Emo-29
❑ 95EmoMas-9
❑ 95EmoN-10
❑ 95Fin-89
❑ 95FinPowK-PK9
❑ 95FinRef-89
❑ 95Fla-27
❑ 95FlaHotN-9
❑ 95FlaInfP-8
❑ 95FlaTodS-12
❑ 95Fle-128
❑ 95FleAllF-2
❑ 95FleAllS-2
❑ 95FleAwaW-1
❑ 95FleLumC-9
❑ 95FleTeaL-4
❑ 95FleUpdDT-9
❑ 95FleUpdH-18
❑ 95KinDis-22
❑ 95Kra-14
❑ 95Lea-1
❑ 95Lea300C-1
❑ 95LeaChe-3
❑ 95LeaCor-1
❑ 95LeaGolS-10
❑ 95LeaHeaftH-1
❑ 95LeaLim-1
❑ 95LeaLimG-1
❑ 95LeaLimIBP-1
❑ 95LeaLimL-9
❑ 95LeaOpeD-1
❑ 95LeaSli-2A
❑ 95LeaSli-2B
❑ 95LeaStaS-8
❑ 95LeaTho-1
❑ 95LeaTho-2
❑ 95LeaTho-3
❑ 95LeaTho-4
❑ 95LeaTho-5
❑ 95LeaTho-6
❑ 95LeaThoA-1
❑ 95NatPac-1
❑ 95Pac-97
❑ 95PacGolCDC-6
❑ 95PacGolP-19
❑ 95PacPri-31
❑ 95PanSti-39
❑ 95PanSti-113
❑ 95Pin-226
❑ 95Pin-302
❑ 95Pin-446
❑ 95Pin-450
❑ 95PinArtP-226

❑ 95PinArtP-302
❑ 95PinArtP-446
❑ 95PinArtP-450
❑ 95PinFan-13
❑ 95PinGatA-GA2
❑ 95PinMusC-226
❑ 95PinMusC-302
❑ 95PinMusC-446
❑ 95PinMusC-450
❑ 95PinPer-PP1
❑ 95PinPin-6
❑ 95PinPinR-6
❑ 95PinRedH-RH3
❑ 95PinTeaP-TP3
❑ 95PinUps-US1
❑ 95PinWhiH-WH3
❑ 95Pos-14
❑ 95PosCan-11
❑ 95RedFol-8
❑ 95Sco-1
❑ 95Sco-571
❑ 95ScoDouGC-GC1
❑ 95ScoDreT-DG1
❑ 95ScoGolR-571
❑ 95ScoHaloG-HG56
❑ 95ScoPlaTS-571
❑ 95ScoRul-SR2
❑ 95ScoRulJ-SR2
❑ 95Sel-22
❑ 95Sel-242
❑ 95Sel-250
❑ 95SelArtP-22
❑ 95SelArtP-242
❑ 95SelArtP-250
❑ 95SelBigS-BS1
❑ 95SelCer-5
❑ 95SelCerC-2
❑ 95SelCerGT-2
❑ 95SelCerMG-5
❑ 95SP-140
❑ 95SP-140A
❑ 95SPCha-136
❑ 95SPCha-140
❑ 95SPChaDC-136
❑ 95SPChaDC-140
❑ 95SPChaDFC-2
❑ 95SPChaFCDC-2
❑ 95Spo-20
❑ 95Spo-169
❑ 95SpoArtP-20
❑ 95SpoArtP-169
❑ 95SpoDet-DE4
❑ 95SpoDouT-1
❑ 95SpoHamT-HT2
❑ 95SpoPro-PM2
❑ 95SpoSam-20
❑ 95SPPlaP-PP18
❑ 95SPSil-140A
❑ 95SPSil-140B
❑ 95StaClu-47
❑ 95StaClu-236
❑ 95StaClu-318
❑ 95StaClu-400
❑ 95StaClu-513
❑ 95StaCluCC-CC4
❑ 95StaCluCT-3
❑ 95StaCluFDI-47
❑ 95StaCluFDI-236
❑ 95StaCluMO-43
❑ 95StaCluMOP-47
❑ 95StaCluMOP-236
❑ 95StaCluMOP-318
❑ 95StaCluMOP-400
❑ 95StaCluMOP-513
❑ 95StaCluMOP-CC4
❑ 95StaCluMOP-PZ11
❑ 95StaCluMOP-RL26
❑ 95StaCluMOP-VRE5
❑ 95StaCluPZ-PZ11
❑ 95StaCluRL-RL26
❑ 95StaCluSTWS-47
❑ 95StaCluSTWS-236
❑ 95StaCluSTWS-318
❑ 95StaCluSTWS-400
❑ 95StaCluSTWS-513
❑ 95StaCluVE-VRE5
❑ 95StaCluVR-209
❑ 95StaCluVRMO-209
❑ 95Stu-1
❑ 95StuGolS-1
❑ 95StuPlaS-1
❑ 95Sum-92
❑ 95Sum-175
❑ 95Sum-194
❑ 95SumBigB-BB2
❑ 95SumNthD-92
❑ 95SumNthD-175
❑ 95SumNthD-194
❑ 95TomPiz-1
❑ 95Top-1
❑ 95Top-384
❑ 95TopCyb-1
❑ 95TopD3Z-1
❑ 95TopEmb-100
❑ 95TopEmbGI-100
❑ 95TopFinIns-4
❑ 95TopLeaL-LL9
❑ 95TopLeaL-LL28
❑ 95TopLeaL-LL39
❑ 95TopTra-1T
❑ 95TopTra-156T
❑ 95TopTraPB-1
❑ 95UC3-1
❑ 95UC3-125
❑ 95UC3ArtP-1
❑ 95UC3ArtP-125
❑ 95UC3CycS-CS1
❑ 95UC3InM-IM3
❑ 95Ult-34
❑ 95UltAllS-19
❑ 95UltAllSGM-19
❑ 95UltAwaW-19
❑ 95UltAwaWGM-19
❑ 95UltGolM-34
❑ 95UltHitM-10
❑ 95UltHitMGM-10
❑ 95UltHomRK-2
❑ 95UltHomRKGM-2
❑ 95UltOnBL-10
❑ 95UltOnBLGM-10
❑ 95UltPowP-3
❑ 95UltPowPGM-3
❑ 95UltRBIK-4
❑ 95UltRBIKGM-4
❑ 95UltRisS-9
❑ 95UltRisSGM-9
❑ 95UppDec-105
❑ 95UppDec-435
❑ 95UppDecED-105
❑ 95UppDecED-435
❑ 95UppDecEDG-105
❑ 95UppDecEDG-435
❑ 95UppDecPAW-H5
❑ 95UppDecPAWE-H5
❑ 95UppDecPC-MLB3
❑ 95UppDecPLL-R5
❑ 95UppDecPLL-R15
❑ 95UppDecPLL-R25
❑ 95UppDecPLLE-R5
❑ 95UppDecPLLE-R15
❑ 95UppDecPLLE-R25
❑ 95UppDecSE-20
❑ 95UppDecSEG-20
❑ 95USPlaCMLA-10D
❑ 95USPlaCMLA-11C
❑ 95WhiSoxK-28
❑ 95WhiSoxK-29
❑ 95Zen-33
❑ 95ZenAllS-2
❑ 95ZenAllS-17
❑ 95ZenZ-3
❑ 96Baz-61
❑ 96Bow-54
❑ 96BowBes-13
❑ 96BowBesAR-13
❑ 96BowBesC-14
❑ 96BowBesCAR-14
❑ 96BowBesCR-14
❑ 96BowBesMI-1
❑ 96BowBesMIAR-1
❑ 96BowBesMIR-1
❑ 96BowBesP-BBP13
❑ 96BowBesPAR-BBP13
❑ 96BowBesPR-BBP13
❑ 96BowBesR-13
❑ 96BowFoi-54
❑ 96Cir-29
❑ 96Cir-200
❑ 96CirAcc-4
❑ 96CirBos-6
❑ 96CirRav-29
❑ 96CirRav-200
❑ 96Cla7/1PC-2
❑ 96ColCho-90
❑ 96ColCho-105
❑ 96ColCho-412
❑ 96ColCho-759
❑ 96ColCho-764
❑ 96ColChoCtG-CG10
❑ 96ColChoCtG-CG10B
❑ 96ColChoCtG-CG10C
❑ 96ColChoCtGE-CR10
❑ 96ColChoCtGG-CG10
❑ 96ColChoCtGG-CG10B
❑ 96ColChoCtGG-CG10C
❑ 96ColChoCtGGE-CR10
❑ 96ColChoGS-90
❑ 96ColChoGS-105
❑ 96ColChoGS-412
❑ 96ColChoGS-759
❑ 96ColChoSS-90
❑ 96ColChoSS-105
❑ 96ColChoSS-412
❑ 96ColChoSS-759
❑ 96ColChoYMtP-40
❑ 96ColChoYMtP-40A
❑ 96ColChoYMtPGS-40
❑ 96ColChoYMtPGS-40A
❑ 96DenHol-3
❑ 96DenHolGS-2
❑ 96DenHolGSAP-2
❑ 96Don-1
❑ 96DonDiaK-1
❑ 96DonEli-69
❑ 96DonFreF-1
❑ 96DonHitL-9
❑ 96DonLonBL-8
❑ 96DonPowA-1
❑ 96DonPowADC-1
❑ 96DonPreP-1
❑ 96DonPurP-4
❑ 96DonRouT-9
❑ 96DonSam-1
❑ 96DonSho-1
❑ 96EmoLegoB-10
❑ 96EmoN-9
❑ 96EmoXL-42
❑ 96Fin-B48
❑ 96Fin-B322
❑ 96Fin-G186
❑ 96FinBro-6
❑ 96FinRef-B48
❑ 96FinRef-B322
❑ 96FinRef-G186
❑ 96Fla-60
❑ 96FlaDiaC-10
❑ 96FlaPow-9
❑ 96Fle-77
❑ 96FleChe-8
❑ 96FleGolM-9
❑ 96FleLumC-10
❑ 96FleRoaW-8
❑ 96FleTeaL-4
❑ 96FleTif-77
❑ 96FleUpd-U243
❑ 96FleUpd-U250
❑ 96FleUpd-10
❑ 96FleUpdH-19
❑ 96FleUpdSS-9
❑ 96FleUpdTC-U243
❑ 96FleUpdTC-U250
❑ 96FleZon-10
❑ 96Kin-14
❑ 96Lea-150
❑ 96LeaAllGMC-1
❑ 96LeaAllGMCG-1
❑ 96LeaGolS-1
❑ 96LeaHatO-3
❑ 96LeaLim-23
❑ 96LeaLimG-23
❑ 96LeaLimL-4
❑ 96LeaLimLB-4
❑ 96LeaLimPC-3
❑ 96LeaPicP-1
❑ 96LeaPre-13
❑ 96LeaPre-147
❑ 96LeaPreP-13
❑ 96LeaPreP-147
❑ 96LeaPrePB-150
❑ 96LeaPrePG-150
❑ 96LeaPrePS-150
❑ 96LeaPreSG-1
❑ 96LeaPreSP-8
❑ 96LeaPreSta-5
❑ 96LeaPreSte-1
❑ 96LeaSig-7
❑ 96LeaSig-150
❑ 96LeaSigA-222
❑ 96LeaSigA-NNO
❑ 96LeaSigAG-222
❑ 96LeaSigAS-222
❑ 96LeaSigEA-199
❑ 96LeaSigEA-NNO
❑ 96LeaSigEACM-29
❑ 96LeaSigPPG-7
❑ 96LeaSigPPP-7
❑ 96LeaStaS-3
❑ 96LeaThoGH-1
❑ 96LeaThoGH-2
❑ 96LeaThoGH-3
❑ 96LeaThoGH-4
❑ 96LeaThoGH-5
❑ 96LeaThoGH-6
❑ 96LeaThoGH-7
❑ 96LeaThoGH-8
❑ 96LeaTotB-1
❑ 96LibSpo-11
❑ 96MetUni-40
❑ 96MetUniHM-8
❑ 96MetUniML-11
❑ 96MetUniP-40
❑ 96MetUniT-8
❑ 96Pac-287
❑ 96PacBaeS-4
❑ 96PacCraC-CC5
❑ 96PacGolCD-DC18
❑ 96PacHom-HP13
❑ 96PacPri-P91
❑ 96PacPriFB-FB18
❑ 96PacPriG-P91
❑ 96PacPriRHS-RH10
❑ 96PanSti-173
❑ 96Pin-135
❑ 96Pin-194
❑ 96Pin-201
❑ 96Pin-257
❑ 96Pin-323
❑ 96Pin-395
❑ 96Pin-399
❑ 96PinAfi-59
❑ 96PinAfi-200
❑ 96PinAfiAP-59
❑ 96PinAfiAP-200
❑ 96PinAfiFPP-59
❑ 96PinAfiMN-3
❑ 96PinAfiR-1
❑ 96PinAfiR-2
❑ 96PinAfiR-6
❑ 96PinAfiR-8
❑ 96PinAfiR-11
❑ 96PinAfiSP-5
❑ 96PinArtP-62
❑ 96PinArtP-101
❑ 96PinArtP-157
❑ 96PinArtP-198
❑ 96PinEssotG-3
❑ 96PinFan-4
❑ 96PinFirR-2
❑ 96PinFoil-201
❑ 96PinFoil-257
❑ 96PinFoil-323
❑ 96PinFoil-395
❑ 96PinFoil-399
❑ 96PinPow-1
❑ 96PinSky-2
❑ 96PinSlu-1
❑ 96PinSta-62
❑ 96PinSta-101
❑ 96PinSta-157
❑ 96PinSta-198
❑ 96PinTeaP-1
❑ 96PinTeaS-6
❑ 96Pro-15
❑ 96ProMagA-6
❑ 96ProMagDM-8
❑ 96ProSta-131
❑ 96RedF-22
❑ 96SchDis-18
❑ 96Sco-21
❑ 96Sco-272
❑ 96Sco-373
❑ 96ScoAll-1
❑ 96ScoBigB-3
❑ 96ScoDiaA-4
❑ 96ScoDreT-2
❑ 96ScoDugC-A20
❑ 96ScoDugC-B98
❑ 96ScoDugCAP-A20
❑ 96ScoDugCAP-B98
❑ 96ScoGolS-2
❑ 96ScoNumG-2
❑ 96ScoPowP-4
❑ 96ScoRef-3
❑ 96ScoTitT-2
❑ 96Sel-11
❑ 96Sel-152
❑ 96Sel-196
❑ 96SelArtP-11
❑ 96SelArtP-152
❑ 96SelArtP-196
❑ 96SelCer-1
❑ 96SelCer-135
❑ 96SelCerAP-1
❑ 96SelCerAP-135
❑ 96SelCerCB-1
❑ 96SelCerCB-135
❑ 96SelCerCR-1
❑ 96SelCerCR-135
❑ 96SelCerIP-3
❑ 96SelCerMB-1
❑ 96SelCerMB-135
❑ 96SelCerMG-1
❑ 96SelCerMG-135
❑ 96SelCerMR-1
❑ 96SelCerMR-135
❑ 96SelCerSF-7
❑ 96SelClaTF-4
❑ 96SelEnF-2
❑ 96SelTeaN-27
❑ 96SP-60
❑ 96SPBasH-82
❑ 96SPMarM-MM15
❑ 96SPMarMDC-15
❑ 96Spo-13
❑ 96Spo-99
❑ 96SpoArtP-13
❑ 96SpoArtP-99
❑ 96SpoDouT-6
❑ 96SpoHitP-3
❑ 96SpoPowS-3
❑ 96SpoPro-7
❑ 96SPPreF-2
❑ 96SPSpeFX-35
❑ 96SPSpeFXDC-35
❑ 96SPx-16
❑ 96SPxBoufG-2
❑ 96SPxGol-16
❑ 96StaClu-182
❑ 96StaClu-285
❑ 96StaCluEPB-285
❑ 96StaCluEPG-285
❑ 96StaCluEPS-285
❑ 96StaCluMeg-MH1
❑ 96StaCluMet-M8
❑ 96StaCluMM-MM3
❑ 96StaCluMO-40
❑ 96StaCluMOP-182
❑ 96StaCluMOP-285
❑ 96StaCluMOP-M8
❑ 96StaCluMOP-MH1
❑ 96StaCluMOP-MM3
❑ 96StaCluMOP-PC8
❑ 96StaCluMOP-PP10
❑ 96StaCluMOP-PS6
❑ 96StaCluPC-PC8
❑ 96StaCluPP-PP10
❑ 96StaCluPS-PS6
❑ 96Stu-93
❑ 96StuHitP-3
❑ 96StuMas-6
❑ 96StuPrePB-93
❑ 96StuPrePG-93
❑ 96StuPrePS-93
❑ 96StuStaGS-3
❑ 96Sum-88
❑ 96Sum-157
❑ 96Sum-198
❑ 96SumAbo&B-88
❑ 96SumAbo&B-157
❑ 96SumAbo&B-198
❑ 96SumArtP-88
❑ 96SumArtP-157
❑ 96SumArtP-198
❑ 96SumBal-9
❑ 96SumBigB-1
❑ 96SumBigBM-1
❑ 96SumFoi-88
❑ 96SumFoi-157
❑ 96SumFoi-198
❑ 96SumHitI-6
❑ 96SumPos-1
❑ 96TeaOut-80
❑ 96TeaOut-C100
❑ 96Top-100
❑ 96Top-229
❑ 96TopBigC-9
❑ 96TopChr-29
❑ 96TopChr-89
❑ 96TopChrMotG-20
❑ 96TopChrMotGR-20
❑ 96TopChrR-29
❑ 96TopChrR-89
❑ 96TopChrWC-WC13
❑ 96TopChrWCR-WC13
❑ 96TopClaC-CC5
❑ 96TopGal-175
❑ 96TopGalPG-PG5
❑ 96TopGalPPI-175
❑ 96TopLas-92
❑ 96TopLasPC-6
❑ 96TopLasSS-16
❑ 96TopMasotG-20
❑ 96TopMysF-M21
❑ 96TopMysF-M26
❑ 96TopMysFR-M21
❑ 96TopMysFR-M26
❑ 96TopPro-AL9
❑ 96TopRoaW-RW16
❑ 96TopWreC-WC13
❑ 96Ult-44
❑ 96Ult-590
❑ 96UltCaltH-10
❑ 96UltCaltHGM-10
❑ 96UltChe-A9
❑ 96UltChe-B10
❑ 96UltCheGM-A9
❑ 96UltCheGM-B10
❑ 96UltDiaP-10
❑ 96UltDiaPGM-10
❑ 96UltGolM-44
❑ 96UltGolM-590
❑ 96UltHitM-9
❑ 96UltHitMGM-9
❑ 96UltHomRK-10
❑ 96UltHomRKGM-10
❑ 96UltHomRKR-10
❑ 96UltHomRKRGM-10
❑ 96UltOn-L-9
❑ 96UltOn-LGM-9
❑ 96UltPowP-10
❑ 96UltPowPGM-10
❑ 96UltRBIK-9
❑ 96UltRBIKGM-9
❑ 96UltRes-9
❑ 96UltResGM-9
❑ 96UltSeaC-9
❑ 96UltSeaCGM-9
❑ 96UltThu-19
❑ 96UltThuGM-19
❑ 96UppDec-300
❑ 96UppDec-387
❑ 96UppDecA-17
❑ 96UppDecDD-DD14
❑ 96UppDecDDG-DD14
❑ 96UppDecDDS-DD14
❑ 96UppDecG-GF2
❑ 96UppDecHC-HC20
❑ 96UppDecPD-PD17
❑ 96UppDecPHE-H8
❑ 96UppDecPRE-R8
❑ 96UppDecPRE-R18
❑ 96UppDecPRE-R29
❑ 96UppDecPreH-H8
❑ 96UppDecPreR-R8
❑ 96UppDecPreR-R18
❑ 96UppDecPreR-R29
❑ 96UppDecRunP-RP18
❑ 96UppDecVJLS-VJ15
❑ 96WhiSoxF-17
❑ 96Zen-22
❑ 96Zen-133
❑ 96ZenArtP-22
❑ 96ZenArtP-133
❑ 96ZenDiaC-8
❑ 96ZenDiaCP-8
❑ 96ZenMoz-3
❑ 96ZenZ-4
❑ 97Bow-290
❑ 97BowBes-38
❑ 97BowBesAR-38
❑ 97BowBesBC-BC3
❑ 97BowBesBCAR-BC3
❑ 97BowBesBCR-BC3
❑ 97BowBesJ-38
❑ 97BowBesJAR-38
❑ 97BowBesJR-38
❑ 97BowBesMI-MI2
❑ 97BowBesMIAR-MI2
❑ 97BowBesMIARI-MI2
❑ 97BowBesMII-MI2
❑ 97BowBesMIR-MI2
❑ 97BowBesMIRI-MI2
❑ 97BowBesP-1
❑ 97BowBesPAR-1
❑ 97BowBesPR-1
❑ 97BowBesR-38
❑ 97BowChr-100
❑ 97BowChrI-100
❑ 97BowChrIR-100
❑ 97BowChrR-100
❑ 97BowInt-290
❑ 97BowIntB-BBI1
❑ 97BowIntBAR-BBI1
❑ 97BowIntBR-BBI1
❑ 97Cir-45
❑ 97Cir-396

❑ 97CirBos-18
❑ 97CirIco-11
❑ 97CirLimA-14
❑ 97CirRav-45
❑ 97CirRav-396
❑ 97CirRavR-12
❑ 97CirSupB-18
❑ 97ColCho-300
❑ 97ColCho-328
❑ 97ColChoAC-10
❑ 97ColChoBS-10
❑ 97ColChoBSGS-10
❑ 97ColChoCtG-10A
❑ 97ColChoCtG-10B
❑ 97ColChoCtG-10C
❑ 97ColChoCtGE-CG10
❑ 97ColChoCtGIW-CG10
❑ 97ColChoNF-NF15
❑ 97ColChoPP-PP12
❑ 97ColChoPPG-PP12
❑ 97ColChoPPJ-PP12
❑ 97ColChoS-30
❑ 97ColChoSR-26
❑ 97ColChoT-CW10
❑ 97ColChoTBS-16
❑ 97ColChoTBSWH-16
❑ 97ColChoTotT-T11
❑ 97DenHol-4
❑ 97Don-138
❑ 97Don-398
❑ 97DonDiaK-9
❑ 97DonDiaKC-9
❑ 97DonDom-1
❑ 97DonEli-3
❑ 97DonEli-1
❑ 97DonEliGS-3
❑ 97DonEliLaL-3
❑ 97DonEliPtT-8
❑ 97DonEliPtT-9
❑ 97DonEliPtTA-8
❑ 97DonEliPtTA-9
❑ 97DonFraFea-2
❑ 97DonGolPP-138
❑ 97DonGolPP-398
❑ 97DonLim-4
❑ 97DonLim-78
❑ 97DonLim-100
❑ 97DonLimE-4
❑ 97DonLimE-78
❑ 97DonLimE-100
❑ 97DonLimENG-78
❑ 97DonLimFotG-37
❑ 97DonLimFotG-60
❑ 97DonLonL-1
❑ 97DonPowA-1
❑ 97DonPowADC-1
❑ 97DonPre-1
❑ 97DonPre-168
❑ 97DonPreCttC-1
❑ 97DonPreCttC-168
❑ 97DonPrePM-1
❑ 97DonPreS-2
❑ 97DonPreSS-2
❑ 97DonPreTB-24
❑ 97DonPreTBG-24
❑ 97DonPreTF-24
❑ 97DonPreTP-24
❑ 97DonPreTPG-24
❑ 97DonPreXP-4B
❑ 97DonRocL-1
❑ 97DonSig-16
❑ 97DonSig-100
❑ 97DonSigAC-119
❑ 97DonSigAM-119
❑ 97DonSigNN-8
❑ 97DonSigPPP-16
❑ 97DonSigPPP-100
❑ 97DonSilPP-138
❑ 97DonSilPP-398
❑ 97DonTea-64
❑ 97DonTeaSMVP-3
❑ 97DonTeaSPE-64
❑ 97DonVxP1-36
❑ 97DonVxP1CD-6
❑ 97E-X2-15
❑ 97E-X2ACA-1
❑ 97E-X2Cred-15
❑ 97E-X2EssCre-15
❑ 97E-X2Hall-1
❑ 97Fin-29
❑ 97Fin-160
❑ 97Fin-279
❑ 97FinEmb-160
❑ 97FinEmb-279
❑ 97FinEmbR-160
❑ 97FinEmbR-279
❑ 97FinRef-29
❑ 97FinRef-160
❑ 97FinRef-279
❑ 97FlaShoDC-17
❑ 97FlaShoHG-15
❑ 97FlaShoLC-35
❑ 97FlaShoLeg0-35
❑ 97FlaShoLeg1-35
❑ 97FlaShoM-A35
❑ 97FlaShoM-B35
❑ 97FlaShoM-C35
❑ 97FlaShoR0-35
❑ 97FlaShoR1-35
❑ 97FlaShoR2-35
❑ 97Fle-72
❑ 97Fle-500
❑ 97Fle-718
❑ 97Fle-726
❑ 97FleBleB-8
❑ 97FleDiaT-12
❑ 97FleGouG-14
❑ 97FleGouGF-14
❑ 97FleHea-20
❑ 97FleLumC-17
❑ 97FleMilDM-32
❑ 97FleMilDMR-32
❑ 97FleNig&D-10
❑ 97FleSoaS-12
❑ 97FleSoaSG-12
❑ 97FleTeaL-4
❑ 97FleTif-72
❑ 97FleTif-500
❑ 97FleTif-718
❑ 97FleTif-726
❑ 97FleZon-18
❑ 97HigMinESC-50
❑ 97HigMinESC-51
❑ 97HigMinESC-52
❑ 97HigMinM-115
❑ 97HigMinM-116
❑ 97HigMinM-117
❑ 97HigMinMCT-47
❑ 97HigMinMCT-48
❑ 97HigMinMCT-49
❑ 97HigMinMM-1
❑ 97HigMinMM-2
❑ 97HigMinMM-3
❑ 97HigMinMSM-30
❑ 97HigMinMSM-31
❑ 97KinB-15
❑ 97Lea-107
❑ 97Lea-348
❑ 97Lea-369
❑ 97LeaBanS-4
❑ 97LeaDrefS-4
❑ 97LeaFraM-107
❑ 97LeaFraM-348
❑ 97LeaFraM-369
❑ 97LeaFraMDC-107
❑ 97LeaFraMDC-348
❑ 97LeaFraMDC-369
❑ 97LeaGet-2
❑ 97LeaGolS-1
❑ 97LeaKnoG-3
❑ 97LeaLeaotN-7
❑ 97LeaStaS-5
❑ 97LeaThoC-1
❑ 97LeaThoC-2
❑ 97LeaThoC-3
❑ 97LeaThoC-4
❑ 97LeaThoC-5
❑ 97LeaThoC-6
❑ 97LeaThol-1
❑ 97LeaThoL-1
❑ 97LeaThoL-2
❑ 97LeaThoL-3
❑ 97LeaThoL-4
❑ 97MetUni-61
❑ 97MetUniBF-11
❑ 97MetUniML-11
❑ 97MetUniT-10
❑ 97NewPin-118
❑ 97NewPin-197
❑ 97NewPinAP-118
❑ 97NewPinAP-197
❑ 97NewPinIE-10
❑ 97NewPinKtP-7
❑ 97NewPinMC-118
❑ 97NewPinMC-197
❑ 97NewPinPP-118
❑ 97NewPinPP-197
❑ 97NewPinPP-I10A
❑ 97NewPinPP-K7
❑ 97NewPinPP-FT1
❑ 97NewPinPP-FT2
❑ 97NewPinPP-FT3
❑ 97NewPinPP-FT4
❑ 97NewPinPP-FT5
❑ 97NewPinS-FT1
❑ 97NewPinS-FT2
❑ 97NewPinS-FT3
❑ 97NewPinS-FT4
❑ 97NewPinS-FT5
❑ 97Pac-64
❑ 97PacCar-7
❑ 97PacCarM-7
❑ 97PacCerCGT-1
❑ 97PacCraC-2
❑ 97PacFirD-5
❑ 97PacGolCD-7
❑ 97PacLigB-64
❑ 97PacPri-22
❑ 97PacPriGA-GA4
❑ 97PacPriGotD-GD32
❑ 97PacPriLB-22
❑ 97PacPriP-22
❑ 97PacPriSH-SH3A
❑ 97PacPriSL-SL2A
❑ 97PacSil-64
❑ 97PacTriCD-4
❑ 97Pin-102
❑ 97PinArtP-PP102
❑ 97PinCar-15
❑ 97PinCer-41
❑ 97PinCer-148
❑ 97PinCerCMGT-1
❑ 97PinCerCT-1
❑ 97PinCerLI-9
❑ 97PinCerMBla-41
❑ 97PinCerMBla-148
❑ 97PinCerMBlu-41
❑ 97PinCerMBlu-148
❑ 97PinCerMG-41
❑ 97PinCerMG-148
❑ 97PinCerMR-41
❑ 97PinCerMR-148
❑ 97PinCerR-41
❑ 97PinCerR-148
❑ 97PinEpixGO-E7
❑ 97PinFan-FF1
❑ 97PinHom-7
❑ 97PinHom-8
❑ 97PinIns-13
❑ 97PinInsC-2
❑ 97PinInsCE-13
❑ 97PinInsDD-8
❑ 97PinInsDE-13
❑ 97PinInsFS-16
❑ 97PinMin-2
❑ 97PinMinB-2
❑ 97PinMinCB-2
❑ 97PinMinCG-2
❑ 97PinMinCGR-2
❑ 97PinMinCN-2
❑ 97PinMinCSS-2
❑ 97PinMinG-2
❑ 97PinMinS-2
❑ 97PinMusC-102
❑ 97PinPasttM-3
❑ 97PinPrePla-102
❑ 97PinPrePla-S9
❑ 97PinSha-9
❑ 97PinTeaP-1
❑ 97PinTeaP-10
❑ 97PinTotCPB-41
❑ 97PinTotCPB-148
❑ 97PinTotCPG-41
❑ 97PinTotCPG-148
❑ 97PinTotCPR-41
❑ 97PinTotCPR-148
❑ 97PinTotCS-41
❑ 97PinX-P-5
❑ 97PinX-P-140
❑ 97PinX-PF&A-3
❑ 97PinX-PMoS-5
❑ 97PinX-PMoS-140
❑ 97PinX-PMP-8
❑ 97PinX-PMW-2
❑ 97PinX-PMWG-2
❑ 97PinX-PMWS-2
❑ 97PinX-PreMPS-8
❑ 97PinX-PSfF-54
❑ 97PinX-PSfFU-54
❑ 97PreCon-14
❑ 97Sco-26
❑ 97Sco-508
❑ 97Sco-549
❑ 97ScoAllF-1
❑ 97ScoArtPWB-26
❑ 97ScoArtPWB-508
❑ 97ScoArtPWB-549
❑ 97ScoFra-7
❑ 97ScoFraG-7
❑ 97ScoHeaot0-4
❑ 97ScoHigZ-1
❑ 97ScoPitP-10
❑ 97ScoPreS-26
❑ 97ScoResC-508
❑ 97ScoResC-549
❑ 97ScoShoS-26
❑ 97ScoShoS-508
❑ 97ScoShoS-549
❑ 97ScoShoSAP-26
❑ 97ScoShoSAP-508
❑ 97ScoShoSAP-549
❑ 97ScoStaaD-24
❑ 97ScoSteS-7
❑ 97ScoTitT-5
❑ 97Sel-8
❑ 97Sel-144
❑ 97Sel-149
❑ 97SelArtP-8
❑ 97SelArtP-144
❑ 97SelArtP-149
❑ 97SelCom-8
❑ 97SelCom-144
❑ 97SelCom-149
❑ 97SelRegG-8
❑ 97SelRegG-144
❑ 97SelRegG-149
❑ 97SelToootT-19
❑ 97SelToootTMB-19
❑ 97SP-50
❑ 97SPGamF-GF2
❑ 97SPInsI-5
❑ 97SPMarM-MM19
❑ 97SpollI-148
❑ 97SpollI-178
❑ 97SpollIEE-148
❑ 97SpollIEE-178
❑ 97SpollIGS-10
❑ 97SPSpeF-2
❑ 97SPSpxF-3
❑ 97SPSPxFA-3
❑ 97SPx-17
❑ 97SPxBoufG-7
❑ 97SPxBro-17
❑ 97SPxCorotG-2
❑ 97SPxGol-17
❑ 97SPxGraF-17
❑ 97SPxSil-17
❑ 97SPxSte-17
❑ 97StaClu-213
❑ 97StaClu-378
❑ 97StaCluFR-F9
❑ 97StaCluFW-F9
❑ 97StaCluMat-213
❑ 97StaCluMOP-213
❑ 97StaCluMOP-378
❑ 97StaCluMOP-FB9
❑ 97StaCluMOP-PG10
❑ 97StaCluPG-PG10
❑ 97StrAll-57
❑ 97Stu-1
❑ 97Stu-164
❑ 97StuHarH-5
❑ 97StuMasS-5
❑ 97StuMasS8-5
❑ 97StuPor8-2
❑ 97StuPrePG-1
❑ 97StuPrePG-164
❑ 97StuPrePS-1
❑ 97StuPrePS-164
❑ 97Top-108
❑ 97TopAll-AS3
❑ 97TopChr-41
❑ 97TopChrAS-AS3
❑ 97TopChrDD-DD10
❑ 97TopChrDDR-DD10
❑ 97TopChrR-41
❑ 97TopChrSAR-AS3
❑ 97TopChrSB-2
❑ 97TopChrSBR-2
❑ 97TopGal-90
❑ 97TopGalGoH-GH3
❑ 97TopGalPG-PG7
❑ 97TopGalPMS-6
❑ 97TopGalPMSSS-6
❑ 97TopGalPPI-90
❑ 97TopHobM-HM11
❑ 97TopIntF-ILM5
❑ 97TopIntFR-ILM5
❑ 97TopMem05-46
❑ 97TopScr-19
❑ 97TopScrPS-5
❑ 97TopScrPST-5
❑ 97TopScrT-19
❑ 97TopSeaB-SB2
❑ 97TopSta-13
❑ 97TopStaAM-13
❑ 97TopStaP-PP3
❑ 97TopSweS-SS14
❑ 97TopTeaT-TT5
❑ 97UD3-16
❑ 97UD3Marq-MA5
❑ 97Ult-44
❑ 97UltBasR-10
❑ 97UltChe-A10
❑ 97UltChe-B3
❑ 97UltDiaP-11
❑ 97UltDouT-4
❑ 97UltFamGam-2
❑ 97UltGolME-44
❑ 97UltHitM-3
❑ 97UltHRK-10
❑ 97UltPlaME-44
❑ 97UltPowP-A11
❑ 97UltPowP-B2
❑ 97UltRBIK-9
❑ 97UltSeaC-12
❑ 97UltStaR-3
❑ 97UltThu-10
❑ 97UltTop3-3
❑ 97UltTop3GM-3
❑ 97UppDec-40
❑ 97UppDec-418
❑ 97UppDecAG-AG10
❑ 97UppDecHC-HC4
❑ 97UppDecLDC-LD12
❑ 97UppDecMM-A4
❑ 97UppDecP-11
❑ 97UppDecPE-11
❑ 97UppDecPP-PP20
❑ 97UppDecPPJ-PP20
❑ 97UppDecRP-RP5
❑ 97UppDecSA-16
❑ 97UppDecSAG-16
❑ 97WhiSoxS-1
❑ 97WhiSoxSPl-1
❑ 97WhiSoxSPr-1
❑ 97WhiSoxTI-35
❑ 97Zen-1
❑ 97Zen Z-Z-3
❑ 97Zen8x10-1
❑ 97Zen8x1D-1
❑ 97ZentheBP-1
❑ 97ZenV-2-3
❑ 98Bow-240
❑ 98BowBes-6
❑ 98BowBesAR-6
❑ 98BowBesMIF-MI1
❑ 98BowBesMIFAR-MI1
❑ 98BowBesMIFR-MI1
❑ 98BowBesR-6
❑ 98BowChr-240
❑ 98BowChrGA-240
❑ 98BowChrGAR-240
❑ 98BowChrI-240
❑ 98BowChrIR-240
❑ 98BowChrR-20
❑ 98BowChrRR-20
❑ 98BowGolA-240
❑ 98BowInt-240
❑ 98CirThu-45
❑ 98CirThu-297
❑ 98CirThuB-19
❑ 98CirThuLA-14
❑ 98CirThuQS-11
❑ 98CirThuRav-45
❑ 98CirThuRR-14
❑ 98CirThuSupRav-45
❑ 98CirThuTB-10
❑ 98ColCho-8
❑ 98ColCho-21
❑ 98ColCho-60
❑ 98ColChoCG-8
❑ 98ColChoCtG-CG20A
❑ 98ColChoCtG-CG20B
❑ 98ColChoCtG-CG20C
❑ 98ColChoCtGExch-CG20
❑ 98ColChoCtGIW-CG20
❑ 98ColChoER-ER6
❑ 98ColChoMBH-10
❑ 98ColChoRJ-8
❑ 98ColChoRJ-60
❑ 98ColChoS'-8
❑ 98ColChoSQ-SQ41
❑ 98ColChoSQ-SQ82
❑ 98ColChoSQDouble-5
❑ 98ColChoSQHR-5
❑ 98ColChoSQSingle-5
❑ 98ColChoSQTriple-5
❑ 98CroRoy-36
❑ 98CroRoyDK-8
❑ 98CroRoyFoB-8
❑ 98CroRoyFoBA-8
❑ 98CroRoyPotG-10
❑ 98Don-12
❑ 98Don-157
❑ 98Don-369
❑ 98Don-407
❑ 98DonCol-12
❑ 98DonCol-157
❑ 98DonColE-402
❑ 98DonColE-519
❑ 98DonColL-305
❑ 98DonColL-356
❑ 98DonColP-552
❑ 98DonColP-719
❑ 98DonColS-12
❑ 98DonColS-157
❑ 98DonCruG-14
❑ 98DonCruP-14
❑ 98DonCruR-14
❑ 98DonDay-1
❑ 98DonDiaK-18
❑ 98DonDiaK-S20
❑ 98DonDiaKC-18
❑ 98DonDom-30
❑ 98DonEli-2
❑ 98DonEli-119
❑ 98DonEli-AU2
❑ 98DonEliA-2
❑ 98DonEliA-119
❑ 98DonEliBttF-6
❑ 98DonEliC-2
❑ 98DonEliI-14
❑ 98DonEliMC-2
❑ 98DonEliPN-2A
❑ 98DonEliPN-2B
❑ 98DonEliPN-2C
❑ 98DonEliPNDC-2A
❑ 98DonEliPNDC-2B
❑ 98DonEliPNDC-2C
❑ 98DonEliPNS-2A
❑ 98DonEliPNS-2B
❑ 98DonEliPNS-2C
❑ 98DonEliS-2
❑ 98DonEliS-119
❑ 98DonFANT-1
❑ 98DonFANTDC-1
❑ 98DonGolPP-12
❑ 98DonGolPP-157
❑ 98DonGolPP-369
❑ 98DonGolPP-407
❑ 98DonLimESamp-S
❑ 98DonLonL-5
❑ 98DonPre-2
❑ 98DonPre-169
❑ 98DonPreGB-23
❑ 98DonPreGES-4
❑ 98DonPreGoB-23
❑ 98DonPreGX-4
❑ 98DonPreGXDC-4
❑ 98DonPrePM-2
❑ 98DonPreSeat-2
❑ 98DonPreSeat-169
❑ 98DonPreTP-23
❑ 98DonPreTPD-12
❑ 98DonPreTPG-23
❑ 98DonPreTPS-23
❑ 98DonPreTW-7
❑ 98DonPriCD-12
❑ 98DonPriCD-157
❑ 98DonPriCE-402
❑ 98DonPriCE-519
❑ 98DonPriCL-305
❑ 98DonPriCL-356
❑ 98DonPriCP-552
❑ 98DonPriCP-719
❑ 98DonProLO-1
❑ 98DonProLPI-1
❑ 98DonProLS-13
❑ 98DonSig-35
❑ 98DonSig-108
❑ 98DonSigP-35
❑ 98DonSigP-108
❑ 98DonSilPP-12
❑ 98DonSilPP-157
❑ 98DonSilPP-369
❑ 98DonSilPP-407
❑ 98E-X2-8
❑ 98E-X2Cheap-1
❑ 98E-X2DesCoop-2
❑ 98E-X2ECFut-8
❑ 98E-X2ECNow-8
❑ 98Fin-151
❑ 98FinCen-C11
❑ 98FinCenR-C11

❑ 98FinMysF1-M1
❑ 98FinMysF1-M2
❑ 98FinMysF1-M3
❑ 98FinMysF1-M4
❑ 98FinMysF2-M1
❑ 98FinMysF2-M4
❑ 98FinMysF2-M5
❑ 98FinMysF2R-M1
❑ 98FinMysF2R-M4
❑ 98FinMysF2R-M5
❑ 98FinMysFR-M1
❑ 98FinMysFR-M2
❑ 98FinMysFR-M3
❑ 98FinMysFR-M4
❑ 98FinNo--151
❑ 98FinNo-R-151
❑ 98FinOve-B1
❑ 98FinOveR-B1
❑ 98FinPowZ-P20
❑ 98FinRef-151
❑ 98FinStaS-SS5
❑ 98FinStaSJ-4
❑ 98FinTheM-TM3
❑ 98FinTheMR-TM3
❑ 98FlaShoLeg0-3
❑ 98FlaShoLeg1-3
❑ 98FlaShoLeg2-3
❑ 98FlaShoLeg3-3
❑ 98FlaShoLegM-3
❑ 98FlaShoP1-3
❑ 98FlaShoR0-3
❑ 98FlaShoR1-3
❑ 98FlaShoR2-3
❑ 98FlaShoR3-3
❑ 98Fle-35
❑ 98Fle-337
❑ 98Fle-350
❑ 98Fle-575
❑ 98Fle-597
❑ 98FleDiaS-19
❑ 98FleDiaT-DT10
❑ 98FleIn TC-IC14
❑ 98FleLumC-14
❑ 98FlePowG-18
❑ 98FleVin'-12
❑ 98FleVin'C-12
❑ 98FleZon-14
❑ 98HamHel-8
❑ 98KinDis-21
❑ 98Lea-106
❑ 98Lea-157
❑ 98LeaFraDA-106
❑ 98LeaFraDA-157
❑ 98LeaFraF-106
❑ 98LeaFraF-157
❑ 98LeaFraM-106
❑ 98LeaFraM-157
❑ 98LeaFraM-106
❑ 98LeaFraM-157
❑ 98LeaFraMDC-106
❑ 98LeaFraMDC-157
❑ 98LeaFraMDC-106
❑ 98LeaFraMDC-157
❑ 98LeaFraMZ2-106
❑ 98LeaFraMZ2-157
❑ 98LeaHeaftH-20
❑ 98LeaHeaftHS-20
❑ 98LeaRCMLHDSamp-5
❑ 98LeaRS-27
❑ 98LeaRS-135
❑ 98LeaRS-189
❑ 98LeaRSExtM-2
❑ 98LeaRSExtMDC-2
❑ 98LeaRSGAHSamp-1
❑ 98LeaRSGreAH-1
❑ 98LeaRSGreHit-2
❑ 98LeaRSHRDerby-18
❑ 98LeaRSLHolo-27
❑ 98LeaRSLHolo-135
❑ 98LeaRSLHolo-189
❑ 98LeaRSLMVP-1
❑ 98LeaRSLMVPPE-1
❑ 98LeaRSLong-27
❑ 98LeaRSLong-135
❑ 98LeaRSLong-189
❑ 98LeaRSMLHD-5
❑ 98LeaRSSOSamp-4
❑ 98LeaRSStaOva-4
❑ 98LeaRSTicMas-2
❑ 98LeaRSTicMasDC-2
❑ 98LeaRTrue-27
❑ 98LeaRTrue-135
❑ 98LeaRTrue-189
❑ 98LeaStaRep-2
❑ 98LeaStaS-1
❑ 98LeaStaSDC-1
❑ 98MetUni-175
❑ 98MetUni-215
❑ 98MetUni-220
❑ 98MetUniAT-2
❑ 98MetUniDH-2
❑ 98MetUniPMG-175
❑ 98MetUniPMG-215
❑ 98MetUniPP-2
❑ 98MetUniT-2
❑ 98MetUniUL-2
❑ 98Pac-63
❑ 98PacAur-25
❑ 98PacAurCube-6
❑ 98PacAurHC-6
❑ 98PacAurKotML-5
❑ 98PacAurODLC-6
❑ 98PacAurPF-35
❑ 98PacAurPFC-35
❑ 98PacAurPFPB-35
❑ 98PacAurPFR-35
❑ 98PacAurPFS-35
❑ 98PacGolCDC-9
❑ 98PacHomRH-5
❑ 98PacInCage-5
❑ 98PacInv-20
❑ 98PacInvGems-35
❑ 98PacInvInt-5A
❑ 98PacInvMiT-3
❑ 98PacInvPBlue-20
❑ 98PacInvPhoto-4
❑ 98PacInvSilv-20
❑ 98PacInvTeam-6
❑ 98PacOme-60
❑ 98PacOmeEP-4
❑ 98PacOmeEP1o1-4
❑ 98PacOmeFTF-7
❑ 98PacOmeOnIns-5
❑ 98PacOmeP-4
❑ 98PacOmeR-60
❑ 98PacOnl-182A
❑ 98PacOnl-182B
❑ 98PacOnl-184
❑ 98PacOnlR-182A
❑ 98PacOnlR-182B
❑ 98PacOnlR-184
❑ 98PacOnlWC-182A
❑ 98PacOnlWC-182B
❑ 98PacOnlWC-184
❑ 98PacPar-32
❑ 98PacParC-32
❑ 98PacParCB-3
❑ 98PacParCBPP-3
❑ 98PacParFC-5
❑ 98PacParG-32
❑ 98PacParHS-32
❑ 98PacParI-15
❑ 98PacParPB-32
❑ 98PacParR-32
❑ 98PacParSD-6
❑ 98PacParTC-4
❑ 98PacPlaB-63
❑ 98PacRedT-63
❑ 98PacSil-63
❑ 98PacTeaC-4
❑ 98Pin-186
❑ 98PinArtP-PP89
❑ 98PinEpixGE-E7
❑ 98PinEpixGP-E7
❑ 98PinEpixME-E7
❑ 98PinEpixMO-E7
❑ 98PinEpixMP-E7
❑ 98PinEpixSE-E7
❑ 98PinEpixSO-E7
❑ 98PinEpixSP-E7
❑ 98PinHitIH-4
❑ 98PinHitIHS-4
❑ 98PinIns-35
❑ 98PinIns-134
❑ 98PinInsBtN-9
❑ 98PinInsC-19
❑ 98PinInsCE-35
❑ 98PinInsCE-134
❑ 98PinInsCG-19
❑ 98PinInsDE-35
❑ 98PinInsDE-134
❑ 98PinInsSG-5AB
❑ 98PinInsSG-5CD
❑ 98PinInsSG-22AB
❑ 98PinInsSG-22CD
❑ 98PinInsSG-25AB
❑ 98PinInsSG-25CD
❑ 98PinInsSGS-5AB
❑ 98PinInsSGS-5CD
❑ 98PinInsSGS-22AB
❑ 98PinInsSGS-22CD
❑ 98PinInsSGS-25AB
❑ 98PinInsSGS-25CD
❑ 98PinMinB-22
❑ 98PinMinCB-22
❑ 98PinMinCBAP-22
❑ 98PinMinCBS-22
❑ 98PinMinCGP-22
❑ 98PinMinCGPAP-22
❑ 98PinMinCN-22
❑ 98PinMinCNAP-22
❑ 98PinMinCSGR-22
❑ 98PinMinDC-22
❑ 98PinMinG-22
❑ 98PinMinMCSS-22
❑ 98PinMinS-22
❑ 98PinMinS-22
❑ 98PinMusC-PP89
❑ 98PinPer-2
❑ 98PinPer-139
❑ 98PinPerBB-2
❑ 98PinPerBBSamp-2
❑ 98PinPerBBSO-2
❑ 98PinPerLP-4
❑ 98PinPerPP-2
❑ 98PinPerPP-139
❑ 98PinPerPT-1
❑ 98PinPerSftF-22
❑ 98PinPerSftFShop-12
❑ 98PinPlu-24
❑ 98PinPlu-186
❑ 98PinPluAE-7
❑ 98PinPluAEE-7
❑ 98PinPluAEP-7
❑ 98PinPluAP-PP12
❑ 98PinPluGAP-PP12
❑ 98PinPluLM-10
❑ 98PinPluMAP-PP12
❑ 98PinPluPieGame-2
❑ 98PinPluSamp-24
❑ 98PinPluTP-11
❑ 98PinPluTPG-11
❑ 98PinPluTPM-11
❑ 98PinPluY-2
❑ 98PinPowPJ-5
❑ 98PinPowPJS-5
❑ 98PinPreP-186
❑ 98PinPreP-E7
❑ 98PinPreP-H4
❑ 98PinPreP-S14
❑ 98PinPreP-S15
❑ 98PinPreP-S16
❑ 98PinPreP-S17
❑ 98PinPreP-S18
❑ 98PinPreP-S19
❑ 98PinPreP-S20
❑ 98PinSpe-14
❑ 98PinSpe-15
❑ 98PinSpe-16
❑ 98PinSpe-17
❑ 98PinSpe-18
❑ 98PinSpe-19
❑ 98PinSpe-20
❑ 98PinUnc-14
❑ 98PinUnc-S186
❑ 98PreCon-11
❑ 98Revo-37
❑ 98RevoFP-4
❑ 98RevoMLI-3
❑ 98RevoPTP-3
❑ 98RevoRooHH-25
❑ 98RevoShow-5
❑ 98RevoSS-37
❑ 98Sco-105
❑ 98ScoAllST-3
❑ 98ScoComP-7A
❑ 98ScoComP-7B
❑ 98ScoComP-7C
❑ 98ScoComPG-7A
❑ 98ScoComPG-7B
❑ 98ScoComPG-7C
❑ 98ScoEpix-E7
❑ 98ScoFirP-2
❑ 98ScoLoaL-LL3
❑ 98ScoNewS-NS13
❑ 98ScoRT-3
❑ 98ScoRT-254
❑ 98ScoRTASEpix-7
❑ 98ScoRTSS-PP3
❑ 98ScoRTSS-PP147
❑ 98ScoRTSSAP-PP3
❑ 98ScoRTSSAP-PP147
❑ 98ScoRTSSAP1-PP3
❑ 98ScoRTSSAP1-PP147
❑ 98ScoRTStarGaz-2
❑ 98ScoSS-PP144
❑ 98ScoSSAP-PP144
❑ 98SkyDugA-59
❑ 98SkyDugA-149
❑ 98SkyDugADH-DH17
❑ 98SkyDugAG-G7
❑ 98SkyDugAIA-59
❑ 98SkyDugAIA-149
❑ 98SkyDugAS-SH9
❑ 98SP Aut-69
❑ 98SP Aut-SD30
❑ 98SP AutSD-SD30
❑ 98SP AutSDT-SD30
❑ 98SpoIll-118
❑ 98SpoIll-181
❑ 98SpoIllEC-EC3
❑ 98SpoIllEE-118
❑ 98SpoIllEE-181
❑ 98SpoIllFE-118
❑ 98SpoIllFE-181
❑ 98SpoIllODMP-OD7
❑ 98SpoIllTaN-42
❑ 98SpoIllTaN-134
❑ 98SpoIllTaNEE-42
❑ 98SpoIllTaNEE-134
❑ 98SpoIllTaNGS-2
❑ 98SpoIllTaNRtC-RC10
❑ 98SpoIllWSF-129
❑ 98SpoIllWSFEE-129
❑ 98SpoIllWSFFE-129
❑ 98SpoIllWSFRJP-12
❑ 98SPxFin-45
❑ 98SPxFin-72
❑ 98SPxFin-150
❑ 98SPxFin-173
❑ 98SPxFin-220
❑ 98SPxFin-353
❑ 98SPxFinR-45
❑ 98SPxFinR-72
❑ 98SPxFinR-150
❑ 98SPxFinR-173
❑ 98SPxFinR-220
❑ 98SPxFinR-353
❑ 98SPxFinS-45
❑ 98SPxFinS-72
❑ 98SPxFinS-150
❑ 98SPxFinS-173
❑ 98SPxFinS-220
❑ 98SPxFinS-353
❑ 98StaCluBP-BP4
❑ 98StaCluFDI-2
❑ 98StaCluI-2
❑ 98StaCluNC-NC4
❑ 98StaCluOneK-2
❑ 98StaCluPP-2
❑ 98StaCluRC-RC2
❑ 98StaCluTIII-T4C
❑ 98StaCluTIII-T11C
❑ 98StaCluTLme-T4C
❑ 98StaCluTLme-T11C
❑ 98StaCluTLmo-T4C
❑ 98StaCluTLmo-T11C
❑ 98Stu-200
❑ 98Stu-CL5
❑ 98StuFF-14
❑ 98StuFFDC-14
❑ 98StuGPP-200
❑ 98StuGPP-CL5
❑ 98StuHitPar-4
❑ 98StuMast-19
❑ 98StuPor8x10-11
❑ 98StuPor8x10GP-11
❑ 98StuSPP-200
❑ 98StuSPP-CL5
❑ 98Top-20
❑ 98Top-480
❑ 98TopChr-20
❑ 98TopChr-480
❑ 98TopChrC9-C3
❑ 98TopChrC9R-C3
❑ 98TopChrHB-HB10
❑ 98TopChrHBR-HB10
❑ 98TopChrM-MS10
❑ 98TopChrMR-MS10
❑ 98TopChrR-20
❑ 98TopChrR-480
❑ 98TopClo9-C3
❑ 98TopDevR-20
❑ 98TopDevR-480
❑ 98TopDia-20
❑ 98TopDia-480
❑ 98TopEtc-ES8
❑ 98TopFocP-FP10
❑ 98TopFruR-8
❑ 98TopGal-100
❑ 98TopGalAG-AG7
❑ 98TopGalGoH-GH5
❑ 98TopGalGoHJ-GH5
❑ 98TopGalGP-100
❑ 98TopGalOPP-100
❑ 98TopGalPG-PG2
❑ 98TopGalPPI-100
❑ 98TopGalPPIA-100
❑ 98TopGolLabC1-46
❑ 98TopGolLabC1B-46
❑ 98TopGolLabC1One-46
❑ 98TopGolLabC1R-46
❑ 98TopGolLabC2-46
❑ 98TopGolLabC2B-46
❑ 98TopGolLabC2One-46
❑ 98TopGolLabC2R-46
❑ 98TopGolLabC3-46
❑ 98TopGolLabC3B-46
❑ 98TopGolLabC3One-46
❑ 98TopGolLabC3R-46
❑ 98TopHal-HB10
❑ 98TopMil-MS10
❑ 98TopMiniC-20
❑ 98TopMiniC-480
❑ 98TopMysF-ILM18
❑ 98TopMysFB-M10
❑ 98TopMysFB-M10
❑ 98TopMysFBR-M10
❑ 98TopMysFBR-M10
❑ 98TopMysFR-ILM18
❑ 98TopOpeD-14
❑ 98TopSta-150
❑ 98TopSta'S-40
❑ 98TopSta'SGH-40
❑ 98TopStaB-150
❑ 98TopStaG-150
❑ 98TopStaGR-150
❑ 98TopStaLB-L5
❑ 98TopStaLG-L5
❑ 98TopStaLGR-L5
❑ 98TopStaLS-L5
❑ 98TopStaS-150
❑ 98TopStaSteG-40
❑ 98TopSup-5
❑ 98TopSup-5
❑ 98TopTek-6
❑ 98TopTekD-6
❑ 98UD3-45
❑ 98UD3-135
❑ 98UD3-225
❑ 98UD3DieCut-45
❑ 98UD3DieCut-135
❑ 98UD3DieCut-225
❑ 98UD3PCBlowup-45
❑ 98Ult-63
❑ 98Ult-220
❑ 98Ult-249
❑ 98Ult-475
❑ 98Ult-478
❑ 98UltArtT-4
❑ 98UltBigS-2
❑ 98UltDial-2
❑ 98UltDiaP-4
❑ 98UltDouT-6
❑ 98UltFalC-4
❑ 98UltGolM-63
❑ 98UltGolM-220
❑ 98UltGolM-249
❑ 98UltGolM-475
❑ 98UltGolM-478
❑ 98UltMas-63
❑ 98UltMas-220
❑ 98UltMas-249
❑ 98UltMas-475
❑ 98UltMas-478
❑ 98UltMilM-10
❑ 98UltNot-1
❑ 98UltPlaM-63
❑ 98UltPlaM-220
❑ 98UltPlaM-249
❑ 98UltPlaM-475
❑ 98UltPlaM-478
❑ 98UltPowP-4
❑ 98UltPriL-4
❑ 98UltTicS-10
❑ 98UltTop3-21
❑ 98UltWinN-7
❑ 98UppDec-143
❑ 98UppDec-330
❑ 98UppDec-459
❑ 98UppDec-607
❑ 98UppDec10AP-18
❑ 98UppDec1APR-18
❑ 98UppDec5x7-330
❑ 98UppDec5x7-607
❑ 98UppDecAC-AS30
❑ 98UppDecAG-AG20
❑ 98UppDecAGDC-AG20
❑ 98UppDecCD-CD20
❑ 98UppDecNP-NP33
❑ 98UppDecPN-PN15
❑ 98UppDecPN-PN16
❑ 98UppDecPN-PN17
❑ 98UppDecPN-PN18
❑ 98UppDecPN-PN19
❑ 98UppDecPN-PN20
❑ 98UppDecPN-PN21
❑ 98UppDecR-22
❑ 98UppDecR-24
❑ 98UppDecRBBop-BB6
❑ 98UppDecRGKoG-G4
❑ 98UppDecRQL-Q4
❑ 98UppDecRTC-TC8
❑ 98UppDecSFPD-PZ2
❑ 98UppDecSFPZOB-PZ1
❑ 98UppDecSFPZPD-PZ1
❑ 98UppDecSFPZSX-PZ2
❑ 98UppDecTMT-5
❑ 98UppDecTMTG-5
❑ 98UppDecU-17
❑ 98WhiSoxS-8
❑ 98WhiSoxSP-8
❑ 98Zen-6
❑ 98Zen5 xx7-4
❑ 98Zen5x7GoldImp-4
❑ 98Zen5x7Imp-4
❑ 98ZenEpi-E7
❑ 98ZenRaitB-2
❑ 98ZenSampL-Z4
❑ 98ZenZ-G-6
❑ 98ZenZ-S-6
❑ 98ZenZ-T-1
❑ 98ZenZ-T5x7-1
❑ 98ZenZ-TG-1
❑ 99199Fin-25
❑ 99199Fin-102
❑ 99199Fin-263
❑ 99AllMysFR-M19
❑ 99AurComP-5A
❑ 99AurComP-5B
❑ 99AurKinotML-5
❑ 99AurOn DL-5
❑ 99AurPenF-7
❑ 99AurPenF-7
❑ 99AurPenFB-7
❑ 99AurPenFS-7
❑ 99AurSty-7
❑ 99Bow-256
❑ 99BowBes-20
❑ 99BowBesAR-20
❑ 99BowBesFBMI-FB8
❑ 99BowBesFBMII-FB8
❑ 99BowBesFBMIII-FB8
❑ 99BowBesMI-M8
❑ 99BowBesMIAR-M8
❑ 99BowBesMIR-M8
❑ 99BowBesR-20
❑ 99BowGol-256
❑ 99BowInt-256
❑ 99CroRoyB-36
❑ 99CroRoyC2-4
❑ 99CroRoyCCDB-4
❑ 99CroRoyCCG-4
❑ 99CroRoyCCG-4
❑ 99CroRoyCCLB-4
❑ 99CroRoyCCP-4
❑ 99CroRoyCCP-4
❑ 99CroRoyCCR-4
❑ 99CroRoyL-36
❑ 99CroRoyLL-5
❑ 99CroRoyMP-6
❑ 99CroRoyOD-36
❑ 99CroRoyPotG-8
❑ 99CroRoyPP-8
❑ 99CroRoyPPN-8
❑ 99E-X Cen-12
❑ 99E-X CenECFut-12
❑ 99E-X CenECNow-12
❑ 99E-XCenFoF'-3
❑ 99FinAarAwC-HA5
❑ 99FinAarAwCR-HA5
❑ 99FinCom-C6
❑ 99FinComDualR-C6
❑ 99FinFraR-FR1
❑ 99FinFraRR-FR1
❑ 99FinGolRef-25
❑ 99FinGolRef-102
❑ 99FinGolRef-263
❑ 99FinMil-M5
❑ 99FinMil-M18
❑ 99FinMil-M30
❑ 99FinPeelHyp-10
❑ 99FinPeelSpark-10
❑ 99FinPeeSS-10
❑ 99FinProF-PF26
❑ 99FinRef-25

❑ 99FinRef-102
❑ 99FinRef-263
❑ 99FinSplS-SS7
❑ 99FinSplSDR-SS7
❑ 99FinTeaFB-TF13
❑ 99FinTeaFBR-TF13
❑ 99FinTeaFG-TF13
❑ 99FinTeaFGR-TF13
❑ 99FinTeaFR-TF13
❑ 99FinTeaFRR-TF13
❑ 99FlaShoLeg1-35
❑ 99FlaShoLeg2-35
❑ 99FlaShoLeg3-35
❑ 99FlaShoLegM1-35
❑ 99FlaShoLegM2-35
❑ 99FlaShoLegM3-35
❑ 99FlaShoMoG-15
❑ 99FlaShoR1-35
❑ 99FlaShoR2-35
❑ 99FlaShoR3-35
❑ 99Fle-34
❑ 99FleBri-27
❑ 99FleBri2G-27
❑ 99FleBriBlu-27
❑ 99FleBriGol-27
❑ 99FleBriSS-11
❑ 99FleBriSSP-11
❑ 99FleDatWD-10
❑ 99FleMys-67
❑ 99FleMysE-10
❑ 99FleMysFtG-7
❑ 99FleMysG-67
❑ 99FleMysM-67
❑ 99FleSta9-34
❑ 99FleVin'-34
❑ 99FleWarT-34
❑ 99HomHer-8
❑ 99KinDis-11
❑ 99MetUni-204
❑ 99MetUni-289
❑ 99MetUniBWTW-2
❑ 99MetUniDS-5
❑ 99MetUniGM-204
❑ 99MetUniGM-289
❑ 99MetUniL-6
❑ 99MetUniPM-7
❑ 99MetUniPMG-204
❑ 99MetUniPMG-289
❑ 99Pac-106
❑ 99Pac-106A
❑ 99PacAur-42
❑ 99PacAurOD-42
❑ 99PacCraCho-3
❑ 99PacCroC-70
❑ 99PacCroCITC-5
❑ 99PacCroCPB-70
❑ 99PacCroCPC-3
❑ 99PacCroCTC-7
❑ 99PacCroCTM-5
❑ 99PacDynaD-3
❑ 99PacDynaDT-3
❑ 99PacGolCDC-6
❑ 99PacInv-37
❑ 99PacInvDM-4
❑ 99PacInvFP-7
❑ 99PacInvGotG-4
❑ 99PacInvOD-37
❑ 99PacInvPB-37
❑ 99PacInvSF-7
❑ 99PacInvSF-7B
❑ 99PacInvSH-7
❑ 99PacInvSH-7B
❑ 99PacInvTA-6
❑ 99PacOme-60
❑ 99PacOme5T-19
❑ 99PacOme5TT-19
❑ 99PacOmeC-60
❑ 99PacOmeDM-11
❑ 99PacOmeEP-7
❑ 99PacOmeEP1o1-7
❑ 99PacOmeG-60
❑ 99PacOmeH'-7
❑ 99PacOmePB-60
❑ 99PacPar-60
❑ 99PacParC-60
❑ 99PacParCB-5
❑ 99PacParCBPP-5
❑ 99PacParFC-7
❑ 99PacParG-60
❑ 99PacParHoloGold-60
❑ 99PacParHS-60
❑ 99PacParOD-60
❑ 99PacParPB-11
❑ 99PacParPB-60
❑ 99PacParRed-60
❑ 99PacParTC-7
❑ 99PacPlaB-106
❑ 99PacPlaB-106A
❑ 99PacPri-35
❑ 99PacPriAotG-8
❑ 99PacPriBL-3
❑ 99PacPriDG-9
❑ 99PacPriEP-8
❑ 99PacPriHB-35
❑ 99PacPriHG-35
❑ 99PacPriHM-35
❑ 99PacPriHP-35
❑ 99PacPriRed-35
❑ 99PacPriS-19
❑ 99PacPriS206-19
❑ 99PacPriS206R-19
❑ 99PacPriSE-19
❑ 99PacPriSP-19
❑ 99PacPriSP-19
❑ 99PacPriSV-19
❑ 99PacRed-106
❑ 99PacRed-106A
❑ 99PacTeaC-4
❑ 99PacTim-2
❑ 99Pin-26
❑ 99Rev-36
❑ 99RevDiaL-11
❑ 99RevFouP-6
❑ 99RevMLBIcon-4
❑ 99RevPremDate-36
❑ 99RevRet-36
❑ 99RevShaSS-36
❑ 99RevThoitS-7
❑ 99RevTri-5
❑ 99RevTri-5
❑ 99SkyMolM-139
❑ 99SkyMolMF-39
❑ 99SkyMolMFS-39
❑ 99SkyMolMFT-39
❑ 99SkyMolMX-139
❑ 99SkyPre-141
❑ 99SkyPre-278
❑ 99SkyPreIN-4
❑ 99SkyPreLB-4
❑ 99SkyPreR-141
❑ 99SkyPreR-278
❑ 99SkyPreSB-12
❑ 99SkyPreSotG-12
❑ 99SkyThu-261
❑ 99SkyThuHip-H13
❑ 99SkyThuRant-261
❑ 99SkyThuRave-261
❑ 99SP Aut-22
❑ 99SP AutEF-E10
❑ 99SP AutHRC-HR19
❑ 99SP AutR-R10
❑ 99SP SigAuto-FT
❑ 99SP SigAutoG-FT
❑ 99SPAutHRCDC-HR19
❑ 99SpoIll-127
❑ 99SpoIllH-9
❑ 99SPSig-9
❑ 99SPx-29
❑ 99SPxDom-FB8
❑ 99SPxFinR-29
❑ 99SPxFinS-29
❑ 99SPxPowE-PE10
❑ 99SPxPreS-PS3
❑ 99SPxStaF-SF8
❑ 99StaClu-50
❑ 99StaCluC-SCC24
❑ 99StaCluCR-SCC24
❑ 99StaCluFDI-50
❑ 99StaCluOoaK-50
❑ 99StaCluPP-50
❑ 99StaCluTI-T15A
❑ 99StaCluTL-T15A
❑ 99StaCluTL-T15A
❑ 99ThuSkySupR-261
❑ 99Top-423
❑ 99Top-456
❑ 99TopAllMF-M19
❑ 99TopBlaLC1-87
❑ 99TopBlaLC2-87
❑ 99TopBlaLC3-87
❑ 99TopChr-423
❑ 99TopChr-456
❑ 99TopChrERttH-ER10
❑ 99TopChrERttH-ER10
❑ 99TopChrLotD-LD4
❑ 99TopChrLotDR-LD4
❑ 99TopChrR-423
❑ 99TopChrR-456
❑ 99TopGal-45
❑ 99TopGal-102
❑ 99TopGalE-E10
❑ 99TopGalHer-TH19
❑ 99TopGalHerP-TH19
❑ 99TopGalPP-45
❑ 99TopGalPP-102
❑ 99TopGalPPI-45
❑ 99TopGalPPI-102
❑ 99TopGolL-87
❑ 99TopGolLC1-87
❑ 99TopGolLC2-87
❑ 99TopGolLOtO-87
❑ 99TopLorotD-LD4
❑ 99TopMVPP-423
❑ 99TopMVPP-456
❑ 99TopOpeD-156
❑ 99TopOver-B8
❑ 99TopPowB-PB7
❑ 99TopPowBR-PB7
❑ 99TopRedLC1-87
❑ 99TopRedLC2-87
❑ 99TopRedLC3-87
❑ 99TopSta-6
❑ 99TopSta-177
❑ 99TopSta'S-29
❑ 99TopSta'SG-29
❑ 99TopSta'SGDH-29
❑ 99TopSta1Foil-6
❑ 99TopSta2Foil-6
❑ 99TopSta3Foil-6
❑ 99TopSta4Foil-6
❑ 99TopStaFoil-6
❑ 99TopStaFoil-177
❑ 99TopStaFS-6
❑ 99TopStaOS-6
❑ 99TopStaTS-6
❑ 99TopStaTS-6
❑ 99TopSupC-28
❑ 99TopSupCR-28
❑ 99TopTek-39A
❑ 99TopTek-39B
❑ 99TopTekG-39A
❑ 99TopTekG-39B
❑ 99UD Cho-72
❑ 99UD ChoMBH-B9
❑ 99UD ChoP-72
❑ 99UD ChoPCR-72
❑ 99UD ChoS-17
❑ 99UD ChoSD-17
❑ 99UD ChoSHR-17
❑ 99UD ChoST-17
❑ 99UD ChoYW-Y6
❑ 99UD Ion-18
❑ 99UD Ion-70
❑ 99UD IonC-C3
❑ 99UD IonH-HG3
❑ 99UD IonH-H3
❑ 99UD IonN-N3
❑ 99UD IonR-18
❑ 99UD IonR-70
❑ 99UD IonWZ-WZ3
❑ 99UDHolo-15
❑ 99UDHoloAUsome-15
❑ 99UDHoloLau-L14
❑ 99UDHoloLauG-L14
❑ 99Ult-64
❑ 99Ult-214
❑ 99UltDamI-6
❑ 99UltDiaP-2
❑ 99UltGolM-64
❑ 99UltGolM-214
❑ 99UltMas-64
❑ 99UltMas-214
❑ 99UltPlaM-64
❑ 99UltPlaM-214
❑ 99UltRBIK-21
❑ 99UltTheBook-3
❑ 99UltThu-7
❑ 99UppDec-337
❑ 99UppDec10AT-X13
❑ 99UppDec10ATD-X13
❑ 99UppDec10ATHR-X13
❑ 99UppDec10ATT-X13
❑ 99UppDecBD-20
❑ 99UppDecBDD-20
❑ 99UppDecBDDom-D4
❑ 99UppDecBDDomE-D4
❑ 99UppDecBDMN-M27
❑ 99UppDecBDMNE-M27
❑ 99UppDecBDQ-20
❑ 99UppDecBDT-20
❑ 99UppDecCf7-8
❑ 99UppDecCf7-C8
❑ 99UppDecCf7Cf7P-C8
❑ 99UppDecCf7LL-L9
❑ 99UppDecCL-57
❑ 99UppDecCLCC-57
❑ 99UppDecCLES-FT
❑ 99UppDecCLESC-FT
❑ 99UppDecCLM-C18
❑ 99UppDecCo7CE-8
❑ 99UppDecE-20
❑ 99UppDecE-161
❑ 99UppDecEBPC-C-BH
❑ 99UppDecEDF-D10
❑ 99UppDecEDFFXG-D10
❑ 99UppDecEFXG-20
❑ 99UppDecEFXG-161
❑ 99UppDecEL1-337
❑ 99UppDecEL2-337
❑ 99UppDecEPE-P10
❑ 99UppDecF-F12
❑ 99UppDecFD-F12
❑ 99UppDecFQ-F12
❑ 99UppDecFT-F12
❑ 99UppDecGJ-FT
❑ 99UppDecIP-I23
❑ 99UppDecIPD-I23
❑ 99UppDecIPHR-I23
❑ 99UppDecIPT-I23
❑ 99UppDecM-45
❑ 99UppDecM-P10
❑ 99UppDecMGS-45
❑ 99UppDecMHFS-45
❑ 99UppDecMP-45
❑ 99UppDecMSS-45
❑ 99UppDecMST-S8
❑ 99UppDecO-14
❑ 99UppDecOMP-S10
❑ 99UppDecOSO-14
❑ 99UppDecR-19
❑ 99UppDecRDR-D8
❑ 99UppDecRDRL2-D8
❑ 99UppDecRG-19
❑ 99UppDecROSS-S3
❑ 99UppDecROSS-S3
❑ 99UppDecRP-19
❑ 99UppDecRTA-T12
❑ 99UppDecRTAL2-T12
❑ 99UppDecVtaT-V10
❑ 99UppDecVtaTD-V10
❑ 99UppDecVtaTQ-V10
❑ 99UppDecVtaTT-V10
❑ 99UppDecWY-W26
❑ 99UppDecWYD-W26
❑ 99UppDecWYHR-W26
❑ 99UppDecWYT-W26
❑ 99Vic-91
❑ 99Vic-92
❑ 99Vic-456

Thomas, Frank J.
❑ 47Exh-221A
❑ 47Exh-221B
❑ 54Bow-155
❑ 54DanDee-27
❑ 55ArmCoi-21
❑ 55Bow-58
❑ 55RedMan-NL20
❑ 56PirTeal-22
❑ 56RedBurB-23
❑ 56Top-153
❑ 57Kah-27
❑ 57PirTeal-9
❑ 57Top-140
❑ 58Hir-27
❑ 58JayPubA-21
❑ 58Kah-29
❑ 58PirTeal-11
❑ 58Top-409
❑ 59ArmCoi-17
❑ 59Kah-37
❑ 59RedEnq-26
❑ 59RedShiBS-20
❑ 59Top-17
❑ 59Top-490
❑ 59TopVen-17
❑ 60CubJayP-12
❑ 60Kah-41
❑ 60Top-95
❑ 60TopVen-95
❑ 61Pos-193A
❑ 61Pos-193B
❑ 61Top-382
❑ 62Jel-151
❑ 62MetJayP-11
❑ 62Pos-151
❑ 62PosCan-151
❑ 62SalPlaC-104
❑ 62ShiPlaC-104
❑ 62Top-7
❑ 62TopVen-7
❑ 63Jel-196
❑ 63MetJayP-11
❑ 63Pos-196
❑ 63SalMetC-59
❑ 63Top-495
❑ 64MetTeal-11
❑ 64PhiPhiB-24
❑ 64Top-345
❑ 64TopCoi-73
❑ 64TopVen-345
❑ 65OPC-123
❑ 65Top-123
❑ 74MetOriEB-14
❑ 79TCM50-24
❑ 82MetGal62-19
❑ 89PacLegI-153
❑ 90SweBasG-113
❑ 91MetWIZ-405
❑ 91TopArc1-283
❑ 92ActPacA-77
❑ 93UppDecAH-118
❑ 94UppDecAH-126
❑ 94UppDecAH-218
❑ 94UppDecAH1-126
❑ 94UppDecAH1-218
❑ 98UppDecR-65
❑ 98UppDecRSotT-FT
❑ 99SpoIllGotG-22
❑ 99SpoIllGotGA-72
❑ 99SpoIllGotGC-5

Thomas, Frankie (Frank)
❑ 80HolMilT-5
❑ 81VanCanT-6
❑ 82VanCanT-2
❑ 83ElPasDT-22
❑ 84VanCanC-33

Thomas, Gary
❑ 98SouOreTG-32

Thomas, Gene
❑ 93EveGiaC-28

Thomas, George
❑ 61Top-544
❑ 62Top-525
❑ 62TopStaI-69
❑ 63Jel-34
❑ 63Pos-30
❑ 63Pos-34
❑ 63Top-98
❑ 64Top-461
❑ 65OPC-83
❑ 65Top-83
❑ 66RedSoxTI-14
❑ 66Top-277
❑ 66TopVen-277
❑ 67CokCapRS-18
❑ 67OPC-184
❑ 67Top-184
❑ 67TopRedSS-22
❑ 69Top-521
❑ 71OPC-678
❑ 71Top-678
❑ 78TCM60I-153
❑ 81RedSoxBG2S-122

Thomas, Gorman (James Gorman)
❑ 74OPC-288
❑ 74SacSolC-48
❑ 74Top-288
❑ 75OPC-532
❑ 75Top-532
❑ 75TopMin-532
❑ 76OPC-139
❑ 76SSP-243
❑ 76Top-139
❑ 77SpoIndC-13
❑ 77Top-439
❑ 79OPC-196
❑ 79Top-376
❑ 80BreTeal-22
❑ 80Kel-11
❑ 80OPC-327
❑ 80Top-202
❑ 80Top-623
❑ 80TopSup-30
❑ 81AllGamPI-69
❑ 81Don-326A
❑ 81Don-326B
❑ 81Fle-507
❑ 81FleStiC-77
❑ 81OPC-135
❑ 81PerCreC-29
❑ 81Top-135
❑ 81TopSti-12
❑ 81TopSti-96
❑ 82BrePol-20
❑ 82Don-26
❑ 82Don-132
❑ 82Fle-154
❑ 82FleSta-134
❑ 82OPC-324
❑ 82Top-765
❑ 82TopSti-204
❑ 83AllGamPI-69
❑ 83BreGar-19
❑ 83BrePol-20
❑ 83Don-510
❑ 83Dra-27
❑ 83Fle-48
❑ 83FleSta-195
❑ 83FleSti-20
❑ 83Kel-47
❑ 83OPC-10
❑ 83PerCreC-32
❑ 83PerCreCG-32
❑ 83Top-10
❑ 83Top-702
❑ 83TopSti-17
❑ 83TopSti-84
❑ 83TopTra-111T
❑ 84AllGamPI-158
❑ 84Don-574
❑ 84DonCha-5
❑ 84Fle-553
❑ 84FleUpd-117
❑ 84FunFooP-56
❑ 84MarMot-7
❑ 84Nes792-515
❑ 84OPC-146
❑ 84Top-515
❑ 84TopSti-253
❑ 84TopTif-515
❑ 84TopTra-119T
❑ 84TopTraT-119T
❑ 85Fle-503
❑ 85MarMot-9
❑ 85OPC-202
❑ 85Top-202
❑ 85TopTif-202
❑ 86Don-440
❑ 86Fle-477
❑ 86FleAll-11
❑ 86FleStiC-119
❑ 86Lea-213
❑ 86MarMot-9
❑ 86OPC-347
❑ 86SevCoi-W9
❑ 86Top-750
❑ 86TopGloS-48
❑ 86TopMinL-31
❑ 86TopSti-216
❑ 86TopSup-56
❑ 86TopTat-22
❑ 86TopTif-750
❑ 86Woo-31
❑ 87Fle-359
❑ 87FleGlo-359
❑ 87Top-495
❑ 87TopTif-495
❑ 91UppDecS-10
❑ 92BreCarT-23
❑ 92UppDecS-9
❑ 94BreMilB-185
❑ 94BreMilB-367
❑ 94TedWil-45
❑ 97AubDouTI-5

Thomas, Greg
❑ 93WatIndC-27
❑ 93WatIndF-3573
❑ 94KinIndC-19
❑ 94KinIndF-2654
❑ 95KinIndTI-26
❑ 96CanIndB-25
❑ 97AkrAer-24
❑ 98AkrAerM-30

Thomas, Ira
❑ 03WilCarE-28
❑ 08AmeCarE91-65
❑ 09AmeCarE90-1-108
❑ 09RamT20-117
❑ 09SpoNewSM-60
❑ 09T206-354
❑ 10CouT21-321
❑ 10DomDisP-115
❑ 10E12AmeCDCE125-35
❑ 10NadE1-55
❑ 10RedCroT-251
❑ 10SweCapPP-50A
❑ 10SweCapPP-50B
❑ 11A'sFirT20-18
❑ 11BasBatEU-38
❑ 11D35RocB-18
❑ 11D35RocB-19
❑ 11DiaGumP-26
❑ 11HelSta-59
❑ 11MecDFT-13

❑ 11PinT-5-506
❑ 11PloCanE-60
❑ 11SpoLifCW-350
❑ 11SpoLifM-105
❑ 11T205-170
❑ 11TurRedT-123
❑ 12HasTriFT-19
❑ 12HasTriFT-70D
❑ 12PhiCarE-29
❑ 14CraJacE-34
❑ 14PieStaT-100
❑ 15CraJacE-34
❑ 19W514-97
❑ 72ClaCar-102
❑ 74A'sTCM1P-12
❑ 87GreBraB-23

Thomas, J.J. (James H.)
❑ 98QuaCitRBG-27

Thomas, Jason
❑ 93IdaFalBF-4031
❑ 93IdaFalBSP-21
❑ 94DanBraC-28
❑ 94DanBraF-3531
❑ 94MacBraC-22
❑ 94MacBraF-2204

Thomas, Jeff
❑ 85CloHSS-40

Thomas, Jim
❑ 76SanAntBTI-24
❑ 83DayBeaAT-23
❑ 84BeaGolGT-15
❑ 86TucTorP-22
❑ 87ColAstP-5
❑ 88MidAngGS-23
❑ 89EdmTraC-22
❑ 89EdmTraP-550

Thomas, Joe
❑ 97LowSpiB-26
❑ 98MicBatCM-29

Thomas, John
❑ 90HamRedB-24
❑ 90HamRedS-25
❑ 91St.PetCC-5
❑ 92ArkTraS-47
❑ 92ClaFS7-14
❑ 92SkyAA F-20

Thomas, Juan
❑ 93HicCraC-24
❑ 93HicCraF-1289
❑ 94SouBenSHC-22
❑ 94SouBenSHF-604
❑ 95PriWilCTI-11
❑ 96Exc-37
❑ 96ExcTL-9
❑ 96PriWilCB-27
❑ 97BirBarB-15
❑ 98PriWilCASM-9

Thomas, Keith
❑ 88GreHorP-1554
❑ 89ModA'sC-32
❑ 90MadMusB-11
❑ 90ModA'sCLC-161
❑ 90ModA'sP-2226
❑ 91MadMusP-2144
❑ 92SalBucC-10
❑ 92SalBucF-78
❑ 93CarMudF-2070
❑ 93CarMudTI-6
❑ 93ExcFS7-94
❑ 94WicWraF-204
❑ 95MemChiTI-10

Thomas, Keith Marshall
❑ 52A'sTeal-27
❑ 53BowBW-62
❑ 53Top-129
❑ 91TopArc1-129

Thomas, Kelvin
❑ 90PenPilS-23
❑ 91EriSaiC-11
❑ 91EriSaiP-4081
❑ 91PenPilC-3
❑ 91PenPilP-393

Thomas, Larry
❑ 91Cla/Bes-418
❑ 91UtiBluSC-20
❑ 91UtiBluSP-3240
❑ 92BirBarF-2583
❑ 92ClaFS7-323
❑ 92SarWhiSCB-22
❑ 92StaCluD-186
❑ 93Bow-35
❑ 93ExcFS7-156
❑ 93NasSouF-571
❑ 94BirBarC-22
❑ 94BirBarF-622
❑ 96BirBarB-27
❑ 96ColCho-512
❑ 96ColChoGS-512
❑ 96ColChoSS-512
❑ 96Fle-78
❑ 96FleTif-78
❑ 96LeaSigEA-200
❑ 96Pac-285
❑ 96Pin-192
❑ 96Sco-259
❑ 96StaClu-375
❑ 96StaCluMOP-375
❑ 98OklRedM-16

Thomas, Lee (J. Leroy)
❑ 47Exh-222
❑ 61Top-464
❑ 61Yan61RL-34
❑ 62Baz-6
❑ 62Top-154
❑ 62TopBuc-88
❑ 62TopStal-70
❑ 62TopVen-154
❑ 63AngJayP-17
❑ 63AngJayP-18
❑ 63BasMagM-82
❑ 63Baz-32
❑ 63ExhStaB-61
❑ 63Jel-30
❑ 63Pos-30
❑ 63Pos-34
❑ 63Top-441
❑ 63TopStil-44
❑ 64Top-255
❑ 64TopSta-99
❑ 64TopStaU-71
❑ 64TopTatl-70
❑ 64TopVen-255
❑ 65OPC-111
❑ 65RedSoxTI-13
❑ 65Top-111
❑ 66Top-408
❑ 67Ast-27
❑ 67CokCapC-12
❑ 67DexPre-205
❑ 67Top-458
❑ 68CokCapA-6
❑ 68Top-438
❑ 71CarTeal-27
❑ 71CarTeal-40
❑ 78TCM60I-231
❑ 81RedSoxBG2S-123
❑ 91YanRinP12-4
❑ 92YanWIZ6-126

Thomas, Leo
❑ 54SeaPop-24

Thomas, Mark
❑ 87WatPirP-20
❑ 89AugPirP-507
❑ 89WelPirP-23
❑ 90ColMetGS-24
❑ 90ColMetPPI-4
❑ 91St.LucMC-1
❑ 91St.LucMP-726

Thomas, Mike (Mike Samuel)
❑ 91BluOriC-5
❑ 91BluOriP-4141
❑ 92BluOriC-3
❑ 92BluOriF-2373
❑ 92RocExpC-1
❑ 94SprSulC-22

Thomas, Mike (Mike Steven)
❑ 90PitMetP-18
❑ 91ColMetPI-16
❑ 91ColMetPI-31
❑ 91ColMetPPI-5
❑ 92RocExpF-2115
❑ 93WesPalBEC-23
❑ 93WesPalBEF-1340
❑ 94ElPasDF-3147

Thomas, Milt
❑ 30Zee-159

Thomas, Mitch
❑ 86SalRedBP-25
❑ 87PorChaRP-6
❑ 88TulDriTI-4
❑ 90TulDriP-1157

Thomas, Myles
❑ 33WorCig(-92
❑ 75Yan192T-26
❑ 79Yan192T-21
❑ 84Yan192G-19
❑ 91ConTSN-106

Thomas, Orlando
❑ 87EriCarP-18
❑ 89SavCarP-349
❑ 90SprCarB-15
❑ 91SprCarC-26
❑ 91SprCarP-745
❑ 92JohCitCC-27
❑ 92JohCitCF-3135
❑ 94NewJerCC-30

Thomas, Pinch (Chester David)
❑ 09ObaT21-110
❑ 09ObaT21-317
❑ 10CouT21-65
❑ 10CouT21-234
❑ 10CouT21-235
❑ 11BigEatEU-17
❑ 11Zee-78
❑ 12ObaPreT-66
❑ 16FleBreD-94
❑ 17ColE13-173
❑ 17HolBreD-104
❑ 21E121So8-98
❑ 22AmeCarE122-70
❑ 22W575-137
❑ 23Zee-57

Thomas, Randy
❑ 78ArkTraT-21
❑ 79ArkTraT-18

Thomas, Ray
❑ 90DodTar-1085

Thomas, Ricky
❑ 81VerBeaDT-21
❑ 82IdaFalAT-28

Thomas, Rob
❑ 88BriTigP-1888
❑ 89Bow-358
❑ 89FayGenP-1571
❑ 92StaClu-885
❑ 92Ult-524
❑ 95BakBlaTI-23

Thomas, Rodney
❑ 91PriRedC-16
❑ 91PriRedP-3529
❑ 92PriRedC-19
❑ 92PriRedF-3102
❑ 93BilMusF-3960
❑ 93BilMusSP-19
❑ 94ChaWheC-23
❑ 94ChaWheF-2717

Thomas, Ron
❑ 88PulBraP-1769
❑ 89PulBraP-1889
❑ 90SumBraB-6
❑ 90SumBraP-2434

Thomas, Roy Allen
❑ 03BreE10-141
❑ 06FanCraNL-48
❑ 08RosComP-156
❑ 09AmeCarE90-1-109

Thomas, Roy J.
❑ 78ChaChaT-17
❑ 78Top-711
❑ 79Car5-30
❑ 79Top-563
❑ 80Top-397
❑ 81TacTigT-20
❑ 82SalLakCGT-19
❑ 84Fle-622
❑ 84MarMot-25
❑ 84Nes792-181
❑ 84Top-181
❑ 84TopSti-348
❑ 84TopTif-181
❑ 85CalCanC-82
❑ 86Fle-478
❑ 86MarMot-26
❑ 86Top-626
❑ 86TopTif-626
❑ 87CalCanP-2321
❑ 89PacSenL-124
❑ 89TopSenL-121
❑ 90EliSenL-118
❑ 91PacSenL-130

Thomas, Royal
❑ 87UtiBluSP-22
❑ 88ClePhiS-25
❑ 88SpaPhiS-4
❑ 89ClePhiS-21
❑ 89ClePhiS-NNO
❑ 90Bes-248
❑ 90RivRedWB-25
❑ 90RivRedWCLC-21
❑ 90RivRedWP-2608
❑ 91BriBanF-18
❑ 91HigDesMC-12
❑ 91HigDesMP-2395
❑ 92WicWraF-3658
❑ 92WicWraS-646
❑ 93SanAntMF-3004
❑ 94GreBraF-414
❑ 94GreBraTI-25
❑ 95RicBraRC-26
❑ 95RicBraTI-24

Thomas, Ryan
❑ 96IdaFalB-26

Thomas, Skeets
❑ 91St.PetCP-2291
❑ 92ArkTraF-1143
❑ 92UppDecML-95
❑ 93LouRedF-230
❑ 94LouRedF-2994
❑ 95LouRedF-290

Thomas, Stan
❑ 75RanPos-34
❑ 76IndTeal-9
❑ 76OPC-148
❑ 76Top-148
❑ 77Top-353
❑ 78TucTorC-22
❑ 92YanWIZ7-149
❑ 93RanKee-355

Thomas, Steve
❑ 90PitMetP-14
❑ 92ColMetC-9
❑ 92ColMetF-297
❑ 92ColMetPI-4

Thomas, Terrence
❑ 88St.PetCS-24

Thomas, Tim
❑ 90ArkRaz-25
❑ 90BurIndP-3017
❑ 91WatIndC-28
❑ 91WatIndP-3383
❑ 92BriTigC-21
❑ 92BriTigF-1422
❑ 93LakTigC-24
❑ 93LakTigF-1320
❑ 94FloStaLAF-FSL16
❑ 94LakTigC-22
❑ 94LakTigF-3046

Thomas, Todd
❑ 86ShrCapP-25
❑ 87ShrCapP-11

Thomas, Tom
❑ 75ShrCapT-22
❑ 86VisOakP-22
❑ 87VerBeaDP-14
❑ 96GreFalDTI-35
❑ 98GreFalDG-29

Thomas, Tommy (Alphonse)
❑ 26Exh-76
❑ 28StaPlaCE-66
❑ 29ExhFou-20
❑ 29PorandAR-89
❑ 30WhiSoxTI-24
❑ 33Gou-169
❑ 77ShrCapT-22
❑ 79DiaGre-54
❑ 92ConTSN-579

Thomas, Tony
❑ 77WauMetT-19

Thomas, Troy Gene
❑ 86BirBarTI-5
❑ 87BirBarB-25
❑ 88VanCanC-18
❑ 88VanCanP-775

Thomas, Valmy
❑ 58GiaSFCB-23
❑ 58Top-86
❑ 59Top-235
❑ 60Top-167
❑ 60TopVen-167
❑ 61Top-319
❑ 79TCM50-276
❑ 91OriCro-455

Thomas, Vern
❑ 80RocRedWT-3
❑ 81EdmTraRR-9
❑ 82GleFalWST-11

Thomason, Mel
❑ 76SSP-600

Thomasson, Gary
❑ 74OPC-18
❑ 74Top-18
❑ 75Gia-10
❑ 75OPC-529
❑ 75Top-529
❑ 75TopMin-529
❑ 76OPC-261
❑ 76SanFraGP-23
❑ 76SSP-107
❑ 76Top-261
❑ 77BurCheD-102
❑ 77Gia-23
❑ 77GiaTeal-23
❑ 77Top-496
❑ 78Top-648
❑ 78YanPhoA-25
❑ 79OPC-202
❑ 79Top-387
❑ 80DodPol-9
❑ 80OPC-70
❑ 80Top-127
❑ 81Don-534
❑ 81Fle-138
❑ 81Top-512
❑ 86KenTwiP-24
❑ 90DodTar-797
❑ 92YanWIZ7-150

Thomasson, Hal
❑ 75WatRoyT-31
❑ 76WatRoyT-31
❑ 77DayBealT-26

Thomasson, Shane
❑ 95EveAqaTI-25

Thome, Jim
❑ 90BurIndP-3018
❑ 90ProAaA-187
❑ 91Bow-68
❑ 91CanIndLD-96
❑ 91CanIndP-989
❑ 91Cla/Bes-195
❑ 91ClaGolB-BC9
❑ 91LinDriAA-96
❑ 91UppDecFE-17F
❑ 92Bow-460
❑ 92Cla1-T90
❑ 92ClaGam-139
❑ 92Don-406
❑ 92Fle-125
❑ 92IndFanC-28
❑ 92Lea-299
❑ 92LeaBlaG-299
❑ 92OPC-768
❑ 92Pin-247
❑ 92PinRool-13
❑ 92PinTea2-37
❑ 92ProFS7-50
❑ 92Sco-859
❑ 92ScoImpP-36
❑ 92ScoRoo-4
❑ 92StaClu-360
❑ 92Top-768
❑ 92TopDeb91-171
❑ 92TopGol-768
❑ 92TopGolW-768
❑ 92TopMcD-37
❑ 92TopMic-768
❑ 92Ult-54
❑ 92UppDec-1
❑ 92UppDec-5
❑ 92UppDecSR-SR22
❑ 93ChaKniF-553
❑ 93Don-171
❑ 93Fle-222
❑ 93IndWUA-30
❑ 93Pin-348
❑ 93Sco-364
❑ 93Sel-304
❑ 93StaClu-8
❑ 93StaCluFDI-8
❑ 93StaCluMOP-8
❑ 93Top-603
❑ 93TopGol-603
❑ 93TopInaM-603
❑ 93TopInaR-603
❑ 93TopMic-603
❑ 93TriAAAGF-38
❑ 93Ult-192
❑ 93UppDec-45
❑ 93UppDecGold-45
❑ 94Bow-338
❑ 94ColC-624
❑ 94ColChoGS-624
❑ 94ColChoSS-624
❑ 94Don-523
❑ 94Fin-102
❑ 94FinPre-102P
❑ 94FinRef-102
❑ 94Fla-45
❑ 94Fle-121
❑ 94FleExtB-69
❑ 94Lea-382
❑ 94Pin-73
❑ 94PinArtP-73
❑ 94PinMusC-73
❑ 94Sco-167
❑ 94ScoGolR-167
❑ 94Sel-299
❑ 94Spo-98
❑ 94SpoSha-SH9
❑ 94StaClu-257
❑ 94StaCluFDI-257
❑ 94StaCluGR-257
❑ 94StaCluMOP-257
❑ 94Stu-97
❑ 94Top-612
❑ 94TopGol-612
❑ 94TopSpa-612
❑ 94TriPla-120
❑ 94Ult-49
❑ 94UppDec-352
❑ 94UppDecED-352
❑ 95ColCho-268
❑ 95ColChoGS-268
❑ 95ColChoSE-114
❑ 95ColChoSEGS-114
❑ 95ColChoSESS-114
❑ 95ColChoSS-268
❑ 95Don-200
❑ 95DonPreP-200
❑ 95DonTopotO-68
❑ 95Emo-39
❑ 95Fin-37
❑ 95FinRef-37
❑ 95Fla-252
❑ 95Fle-149
❑ 95Lea-348
❑ 95LeaLim-84
❑ 95Pac-130
❑ 95Pin-18
❑ 95PinArtP-18
❑ 95PinMusC-18
❑ 95Sco-229
❑ 95ScoGolR-229
❑ 95ScoHaloG-HG99
❑ 95ScoPlaTS-229
❑ 95Sel-32
❑ 95SelArtP-32
❑ 95SelCer-42
❑ 95SelCerMG-42
❑ 95SP-146
❑ 95SPCha-146
❑ 95SPChaDC-146
❑ 95Spo-85
❑ 95SpoArtP-85
❑ 95SPPlaP-PP19
❑ 95SPSil-146
❑ 95StaClu-147
❑ 95StaCluFDI-147
❑ 95StaCluMOP-147
❑ 95StaCluSTDW-I147
❑ 95StaCluSTMP-19
❑ 95StaCluSTWS-147
❑ 95StaCluVR-76
❑ 95StaCluVRMO-76
❑ 95Stu-193
❑ 95Sum-7
❑ 95SumNthD-7
❑ 95Top-312
❑ 95TopCyb-169
❑ 95TopD3-15
❑ 95UC3-37
❑ 95UC3ArtP-37
❑ 95Ult-42
❑ 95UltGolM-42
❑ 95UppDec-96
❑ 95UppDecED-96
❑ 95UppDecEDG-96
❑ 95UppDecSE-162
❑ 95UppDecSEG-162
❑ 95Zen-51
❑ 95ZenSam-51
❑ 96Baz-21
❑ 96Bow-41
❑ 96BowBes-47
❑ 96BowBesAR-47
❑ 96BowBesC-15
❑ 96BowBesCAR-15
❑ 96BowBesCR-15
❑ 96BowBesR-47
❑ 96BowFoi-41
❑ 96Cir-38
❑ 96CirRav-38
❑ 96ColCho-120
❑ 96ColCho-367T
❑ 96ColCho-392T
❑ 96ColChoCtG-CG13
❑ 96ColChoCtG-CG13B
❑ 96ColChoCtG-CG13C
❑ 96ColChoCtGE-CR13
❑ 96ColChoCtGG-CG13

❑ 96ColChoCtGG-CG13B
❑ 96ColChoCtGG-CG13C
❑ 96ColChoCtGGE-CR13
❑ 96ColChoGS-120
❑ 96ColChoSS-120
❑ 96Don-371
❑ 96DonPreP-371
❑ 96EmoXL-56
❑ 96Fin-B47
❑ 96FinRef-B47
❑ 96Fla-76
❑ 96Fle-102
❑ 96FlePosG-5
❑ 96FleTif-102
❑ 96IndFle-17
❑ 96Lea-169
❑ 96LeaLim-55
❑ 96LeaLimG-55
❑ 96LeaPre-57
❑ 96LeaPreP-57
❑ 96LeaPrePB-169
❑ 96LeaPrePG-169
❑ 96LeaPrePS-169
❑ 96LeaSig-71
❑ 96LeaSigA-223G
❑ 96LeaSigA-223S
❑ 96LeaSigAG-223
❑ 96LeaSigAS-223
❑ 96LeaSigPPG-71
❑ 96LeaSigPPP-71
❑ 96MetUni-54
❑ 96MetUniP-54
❑ 96Pac-302
❑ 96PacOctM-OM20
❑ 96Pin-238
❑ 96PinAfi-90
❑ 96PinAfiAP-90
❑ 96PinAfiFPP-90
❑ 96PinAfiSP-22
❑ 96PinArtP-138
❑ 96PinChrBC-14
❑ 96PinFoil-238
❑ 96PinSta-138
❑ 96PinTeaP-3
❑ 96SchDis-1
❑ 96Sco-6
❑ 96ScoDugC-A6
❑ 96ScoDugCAP-A6
❑ 96ScoDugCSamp-6
❑ 96ScoRef-19
❑ 96ScoSam-6
❑ 96Sel-52
❑ 96SelArtP-52
❑ 96SelCer-69
❑ 96SelCerAP-69
❑ 96SelCerCB-69
❑ 96SelCerCR-69
❑ 96SelCerMB-69
❑ 96SelCerMG-69
❑ 96SelCerMR-69
❑ 96SP-68
❑ 96Spo-90
❑ 96SpoArtP-90
❑ 96StaClu-191
❑ 96StaClu-357
❑ 96StaCluEPB-357
❑ 96StaCluEPG-357
❑ 96StaCluEPS-357
❑ 96StaCluMO-41
❑ 96StaCluMOP-191
❑ 96StaCluMOP-357
❑ 96Sum-76
❑ 96SumAbo&B-76
❑ 96SumArtP-76
❑ 96SumFoi-76
❑ 96SumPos-3
❑ 96Top-253
❑ 96TopChr-100
❑ 96TopChrR-100
❑ 96TopGal-70
❑ 96TopGalPPI-70
❑ 96TopLas-79
❑ 96Ult-54
❑ 96UltGolM-54
❑ 96UltOn-L-10
❑ 96UltOn-LGM-10
❑ 96UppDec-54
❑ 96Zen-6
❑ 96ZenArtP-6
❑ 97Bow-246
❑ 97BowBes-22
❑ 97BowBesAR-22
❑ 97BowBesR-22
❑ 97BowChr-71
❑ 97BowChrI-71
❑ 97BowChrIR-71
❑ 97BowChrR-71
❑ 97BowInt-246
❑ 97Cir-391
❑ 97CirRav-391
❑ 97ColCho-94
❑ 97ColChoAC-3
❑ 97ColChoCtG-12A
❑ 97ColChoCtG-12B
❑ 97ColChoCtG-12C
❑ 97ColChoCtGE-CG12
❑ 97ColChoCtGIW-CG12
❑ 97ColChoNF-NF19
❑ 97ColChoS-18
❑ 97ColChoSR-27
❑ 97ColChoT-CI9
❑ 97ColSprSATTI-8
❑ 97Don-105
❑ 97Don-441
❑ 97DonEli-50
❑ 97DonEliGS-50
❑ 97DonGolPP-105
❑ 97DonGolPP-441
❑ 97DonLim-38
❑ 97DonLim-157
❑ 97DonLimE-38
❑ 97DonLimE-157
❑ 97DonLimENG-38
❑ 97DonLimFotG-69
❑ 97DonPre-42
❑ 97DonPre-192
❑ 97DonPreCttC-42
❑ 97DonPreCttC-192
❑ 97DonPreXP-1B
❑ 97DonSig-52
❑ 97DonSigAC-120
❑ 97DonSigAM-120
❑ 97DonSigPPP-52
❑ 97DonSilPP-105
❑ 97DonSilPP-441
❑ 97DonTea-78
❑ 97DonTeaSPE-78
❑ 97DonVxP1-2
❑ 97E-X2-18
❑ 97E-X2Cred-18
❑ 97E-X2EssCre-18
❑ 97Fin-148
❑ 97Fin-190
❑ 97FinEmb-148
❑ 97FinEmbR-148
❑ 97FinRef-148
❑ 97FinRef-190
❑ 97FlaShoLC-77
❑ 97FlaShoLeg0-77
❑ 97FlaShoLeg1-77
❑ 97FlaShoM-A77
❑ 97FlaShoM-B77
❑ 97FlaShoM-C77
❑ 97FlaShoR0-77
❑ 97FlaShoR1-77
❑ 97FlaShoR2-77
❑ 97Fle-90
❑ 97FleTif-90
❑ 97FleZon-19
❑ 97IndSco-3
❑ 97IndScoPl-3
❑ 97IndScoPr-3
❑ 97IndScoU-3
❑ 97IndScoUTC-3
❑ 97Lea-197
❑ 97Lea-223
❑ 97LeaFraM-197
❑ 97LeaFraM-223
❑ 97LeaFraMDC-197
❑ 97LeaFraMDC-223
❑ 97LeaGolS-19
❑ 97MetUni-87
❑ 97NewPin-82
❑ 97NewPinAP-82
❑ 97NewPinMC-82
❑ 97NewPinPP-82
❑ 97Pac-80
❑ 97PacLigB-80
❑ 97PacPri-27
❑ 97PacPriLB-27
❑ 97PacPriP-27
❑ 97PacSil-80
❑ 97PacTriCD-6
❑ 97Pin-36
❑ 97PinArtP-PP36
❑ 97PinCer-47
❑ 97PinCerMBla-47
❑ 97PinCerMBlu-47
❑ 97PinCerMG-47
❑ 97PinCerMR-47
❑ 97PinCerR-47
❑ 97PinIns-72
❑ 97PinInsCE-72
❑ 97PinInsDD-7
❑ 97PinInsDE-72
❑ 97PinMusC-36
❑ 97PinPrePla-36
❑ 97PinTeaP-3
❑ 97PinTeaP-10
❑ 97PinTotCPB-47
❑ 97PinTotCPG-47
❑ 97PinTotCPR-47
❑ 97PinX-P-84
❑ 97PinX-PMoS-84
❑ 97PinX-PSfF-55
❑ 97PinX-PSfFU-55
❑ 97Sco-107
❑ 97Sco-515
❑ 97ScoAllF-7
❑ 97ScoArtPWB-107
❑ 97ScoArtPWB-514
❑ 97ScoHeaotO-15
❑ 97ScoPreS-107
❑ 97ScoResC-514
❑ 97ScoShoS-107
❑ 97ScoShoS-514
❑ 97ScoShoSAP-107
❑ 97ScoShoSAP-514
❑ 97ScoStaaD-18
❑ 97Sel-35
❑ 97SelArtP-35
❑ 97SelCom-35
❑ 97SelRegG-35
❑ 97SelToootT-16
❑ 97SelToootTMB-16
❑ 97SP-56
❑ 97SPMarM-MM17
❑ 97SpoIll-144
❑ 97SpoIllEE-144
❑ 97SPSpeF-35
❑ 97SPx-22
❑ 97SPxBro-22
❑ 97SPxGol-22
❑ 97SPxGraF-22
❑ 97SPxSil-22
❑ 97SPxSte-22
❑ 97StaClu-18
❑ 97StaCluMat-18
❑ 97StaCluMOP-18
❑ 97StrAll-58
❑ 97Stu-118
❑ 97StuHarH-9
❑ 97StuPrePG-118
❑ 97StuPrePS-118
❑ 97Top-105
❑ 97TopAll-AS7
❑ 97TopChr-40
❑ 97TopChrAS-AS7
❑ 97TopChrR-40
❑ 97TopChrSAR-AS7
❑ 97TopGal-115
❑ 97TopGalPPI-115
❑ 97TopMem05-47
❑ 97TopScr-20
❑ 97TopScrT-20
❑ 97TopSta-78
❑ 97TopStaAM-78
❑ 97UD3-36
❑ 97Ult-380
❑ 97UltGolME-380
❑ 97UltPlaME-380
❑ 97UppDec-347
❑ 97UppDecP-13
❑ 97UppDecPE-13
❑ 97UppDecRP-RP21
❑ 98Bow-56
❑ 98BowBes-66
❑ 98BowBesAR-66
❑ 98BowBesR-66
❑ 98BowChr-56
❑ 98BowChrGA-56
❑ 98BowChrGAR-56
❑ 98BowChrI-56
❑ 98BowChrIR-56
❑ 98BowChrR-56
❑ 98BowChrR-33
❑ 98BowChrRR-33
❑ 98BowGolA-56
❑ 98BowInt-56
❑ 98BowMinLM-MVP11
❑ 98CirThu-153
❑ 98CirThuRav-153
❑ 98CirThuSupRav-153
❑ 98CirThuTB-11
❑ 98ColCho-355
❑ 98ColChoCtG-CG29A
❑ 98ColChoCtG-CG29B
❑ 98ColChoCtG-CG29C
❑ 98ColChoCtGExch-CG29
❑ 98ColChoCtGIW-CG29
❑ 98ColChoER-ER8
❑ 98ColChoRJ-SQ76
❑ 98ColChoS'-10
❑ 98ColChoSQ-SQ76
❑ 98CroRoy-46
❑ 98CroRoyAS-4
❑ 98CroRoyHRF-4
❑ 98CroRoyPotG-11
❑ 98Don-69
❑ 98Don-357
❑ 98DonCol-69
❑ 98DonColE-420
❑ 98DonColE-537
❑ 98DonColL-360
❑ 98DonColP-584
❑ 98DonColP-743
❑ 98DonColS-69
❑ 98DonCruG-19
❑ 98DonCruP-19
❑ 98DonCruR-19
❑ 98DonDom-13
❑ 98DonEli-20
❑ 98DonEli-137
❑ 98DonEliA-20
❑ 98DonEliA-137
❑ 98DonEliS-20
❑ 98DonEliS-137
❑ 98DonGolPP-69
❑ 98DonGolPP-357
❑ 98DonLonL-17
❑ 98DonPre-34
❑ 98DonPre-193
❑ 98DonPreGES-5
❑ 98DonPreGX-5
❑ 98DonPreGXDC-5
❑ 98DonPreSeat-34
❑ 98DonPreSeat-193
❑ 98DonPriCD-69
❑ 98DonPriCE-420
❑ 98DonPriCE-537
❑ 98DonPriCL-360
❑ 98DonPriCP-584
❑ 98DonPriCP-743
❑ 98DonProLPI-13
❑ 98DonProS-9
❑ 98DonSig-27
❑ 98DonSigP-27
❑ 98DonSilPP-69
❑ 98DonSilPP-357
❑ 98E-X2-33
❑ 98E-X2Cheap-12
❑ 98E-X2ECFut-33
❑ 98E-X2ECNow-33
❑ 98Fin-118
❑ 98FinMysF2-M21
❑ 98FinMysF2-M23
❑ 98FinMysF2-M24
❑ 98FinMysF2-M37
❑ 98FinMysF2R-M21
❑ 98FinMysF2R-M23
❑ 98FinMysF2R-M24
❑ 98FinMysF2R-M37
❑ 98FinNo--118
❑ 98FinNo-R-118
❑ 98FinPowZ-P6
❑ 98FinRef-118
❑ 98FinStaS-SS10
❑ 98FlaShoLeg0-89
❑ 98FlaShoLeg1-89
❑ 98FlaShoLeg2-89
❑ 98FlaShoLeg3-89
❑ 98FlaShoLegM-89
❑ 98FlaShoR0-89
❑ 98FlaShoR1-89
❑ 98FlaShoR2-89
❑ 98FlaShoR3-89
❑ 98Fle-110
❑ 98Fle-338
❑ 98Fle-598
❑ 98FlePowG-19
❑ 98FleVin'-16
❑ 98FleVin'C-16
❑ 98IndSco-2
❑ 98IndScoP-2
❑ 98Lea-161
❑ 98LeaCruG-19
❑ 98LeaCruP-19
❑ 98LeaCruR-19
❑ 98LeaFraDA-161
❑ 98LeaFraF-161
❑ 98LeaFraM-161
❑ 98LeaFraM-161
❑ 98LeaFraMDC-161
❑ 98LeaFraMDC-161
❑ 98LeaFraMS-161
❑ 98LeaFraMZ2-161
❑ 98LeaRS-7
❑ 98LeaRS-177
❑ 98LeaRSHRDerby-2
❑ 98LeaRSLHolo-7
❑ 98LeaRSLHolo-177
❑ 98LeaRSLong-7
❑ 98LeaRSLong-177
❑ 98LeaRTrue-7
❑ 98LeaRTrue-177
❑ 98LeaStaRep-16
❑ 98MetUni-135
❑ 98MetUniPMG-135
❑ 98Pac-79
❑ 98PacAur-33
❑ 98PacAurPF-41
❑ 98PacAurPFC-41
❑ 98PacAurPFPB-41
❑ 98PacAurPFR-41
❑ 98PacAurPFS-41
❑ 98PacHomRH-7
❑ 98PacInv-26
❑ 98PacInvPBlue-26
❑ 98PacInvSilv-26
❑ 98PacInvTeam-8
❑ 98PacOme-75
❑ 98PacOmeR-75
❑ 98PacOnl-231
❑ 98PacOnlR-231
❑ 98PacOnlWC-231
❑ 98PacPar-41
❑ 98PacParC-41
❑ 98PacParG-41
❑ 98PacParHS-41
❑ 98PacParI-24
❑ 98PacParPB-41
❑ 98PacParR-41
❑ 98PacPlaB-79
❑ 98PacRedT-79
❑ 98PacSil-79
❑ 98Pin-196
❑ 98Pin-198
❑ 98PinArtP-PP99
❑ 98PinIns-47
❑ 98PinInsCE-47
❑ 98PinInsDE-47
❑ 98PinInsSG-23AB
❑ 98PinInsSG-23CD
❑ 98PinInsSGS-23AB
❑ 98PinInsSGS-23CD
❑ 98PinMusC-PP99
❑ 98PinPer-35
❑ 98PinPerBB-14
❑ 98PinPerBBSamp-14
❑ 98PinPerBBSO-14
❑ 98PinPerPP-35
❑ 98PinPerSftF-23
❑ 98PinPlu-89
❑ 98PinPluAP-PP32
❑ 98PinPluGAP-PP32
❑ 98PinPluMAP-PP32
❑ 98PinPowPJ-15
❑ 98PinPowPJS-15
❑ 98PinPreP-196
❑ 98PinPreP-198
❑ 98PinSna-CI11
❑ 98Revo-47
❑ 98RevoPTP-4
❑ 98RevoShow-7
❑ 98RevoSS-47
❑ 98Sco-17
❑ 98ScoRT-31
❑ 98ScoRT-261
❑ 98ScoRTSS-PP31
❑ 98ScoRTSS-PP154
❑ 98ScoRTSSAP-PP31
❑ 98ScoRTSSAP-PP154
❑ 98ScoRTSSAP1-PP31
❑ 98ScoRTSSAP1-PP154
❑ 98ScoSS-PP5
❑ 98ScoSSAP-PP5
❑ 98SkyDugA-61
❑ 98SkyDugAIA-61
❑ 98SP Aut-80
❑ 98SP Aut-SD37
❑ 98SP AutSD-SD37
❑ 98SP AutSDT-SD37
❑ 98SpoIll-119
❑ 98SpoIllEE-119
❑ 98SpoIllFE-119
❑ 98SpoIllTaN-135
❑ 98SpoIllTaNEE-135
❑ 98SpoIllWSF-134
❑ 98SpoIllWSFEE-134
❑ 98SpoIllWSFFE-134
❑ 98SPxFin-34
❑ 98SPxFin-78
❑ 98SPxFin-151
❑ 98SPxFin-218
❑ 98SPxFinR-34
❑ 98SPxFinR-78
❑ 98SPxFinR-151
❑ 98SPxFinR-218
❑ 98SPxFinS-34
❑ 98SPxFinS-78
❑ 98SPxFinS-151
❑ 98SPxFinS-218
❑ 98StaCluFDI-21
❑ 98StaCluI-21
❑ 98StaCluOneK-21
❑ 98StaCluPP-21
❑ 98StaCluTIII-T8A
❑ 98StaCluTLme-T8A
❑ 98StaCluTLmo-T8A
❑ 98Stu-96
❑ 98StuGPP-96
❑ 98StuHitPar-12
❑ 98StuSPP-96
❑ 98Top-290
❑ 98TopChr-290
❑ 98TopChrR-290
❑ 98TopDevR-290
❑ 98TopDia-290
❑ 98TopGal-67
❑ 98TopGalGP-67
❑ 98TopGalOPP-67
❑ 98TopGalPPI-67
❑ 98TopGalPPIA-67
❑ 98TopGolLabC1-10
❑ 98TopGolLabC1B-10
❑ 98TopGolLabC1One-10
❑ 98TopGolLabC1R-10
❑ 98TopGolLabC2-10
❑ 98TopGolLabC2B-10
❑ 98TopGolLabC2One-10
❑ 98TopGolLabC2R-10
❑ 98TopGolLabC3-10
❑ 98TopGolLabC3B-10
❑ 98TopGolLabC3One-10
❑ 98TopGolLabC3R-10
❑ 98TopMiniC-290
❑ 98TopOpeD-117
❑ 98TopSta-132
❑ 98TopSta'S-41
❑ 98TopSta'SGH-41
❑ 98TopStaB-132
❑ 98TopStaG-132
❑ 98TopStaGR-132
❑ 98TopStaS-132
❑ 98TopStaSteG-41
❑ 98TopTek-89
❑ 98TopTekD-89
❑ 98UD3-54
❑ 98UD3-144
❑ 98UD3-234
❑ 98UD3DieCut-54
❑ 98UD3DieCut-144
❑ 98UD3DieCut-234
❑ 98Ult-126
❑ 98UltBigS-12
❑ 98UltDouT-17
❑ 98UltGolM-126
❑ 98UltMas-126
❑ 98UltPlaM-126
❑ 98UppDec-70
❑ 98UppDecAC-AS23
❑ 98UppDecR-31
❑ 98UppDecRBBop-BB8
❑ 98UppDecRTC-TC12
❑ 98UppDecSF-45
❑ 98UppDecTMT-12
❑ 98UppDecTMTG-12
❑ 98Zen-67
❑ 98Zen5 xx7-31
❑ 98Zen5x7GoldImp-31
❑ 98Zen5x7Imp-31
❑ 98ZenZ-G-67
❑ 98ZenZ-S-67
❑ 99199Fin-4
❑ 99199Fin-268
❑ 99AllMysFR-M5
❑ 99Bow-221
❑ 99BowBes-18
❑ 99BowBesAR-18
❑ 99BowBesR-18
❑ 99BowGol-221
❑ 99BowInt-221
❑ 99BowLatB-LB2
❑ 99CroRoyB-46
❑ 99CroRoyL-46
❑ 99CroRoyOD-46

❑ 99E-X Cen-35
❑ 99E-X CenECFut-35
❑ 99E-X CenECNow-35
❑ 99FinGolRef-4
❑ 99FinGolRef-268
❑ 99FinPre-PP4
❑ 99FinProF-PF29
❑ 99FinRef-4
❑ 99FinRef-268
❑ 99FlaShoLeg1-51
❑ 99FlaShoLeg2-51
❑ 99FlaShoLeg3-51
❑ 99FlaShoLegM1-51
❑ 99FlaShoLegM2-51
❑ 99FlaShoLegM3-51
❑ 99FlaShoR1-51
❑ 99FlaShoR2-51
❑ 99FlaShoR3-51
❑ 99Fle-45
❑ 99FleBri-56
❑ 99FleBri2G-56
❑ 99FleBriBlu-56
❑ 99FleBriGol-56
❑ 99FleMys-33
❑ 99FleMysG-33
❑ 99FleMysM-33
❑ 99FleSta9-45
❑ 99FleVin'-45
❑ 99FleWarT-45
❑ 99MetUni-42
❑ 99MetUniGM-42
❑ 99MetUniPMG-42
❑ 99Pac-136
❑ 99Pac-136A
❑ 99PacAur-56
❑ 99PacAurOD-56
❑ 99PacCroC-89
❑ 99PacCroCPB-89
❑ 99PacInv-47
❑ 99PacInvOD-47
❑ 99PacInvPB-47
❑ 99PacOme-77
❑ 99PacOmeC-77
❑ 99PacOmeG-77
❑ 99PacOmePB-77
❑ 99PacPar-77
❑ 99PacParC-77
❑ 99PacParG-77
❑ 99PacParHoloGold-77
❑ 99PacParHS-77
❑ 99PacParOD-77
❑ 99PacParPB-77
❑ 99PacParRed-77
❑ 99PacPlaB-136
❑ 99PacPlaB-136A
❑ 99PacPri-47
❑ 99PacPriHB-47
❑ 99PacPriHG-47
❑ 99PacPriHM-47
❑ 99PacPriHP-47
❑ 99PacPriRed-47
❑ 99PacPriS-45
❑ 99PacPriS206-45
❑ 99PacPriS206R-45
❑ 99PacPriSP-45
❑ 99PacPriSV-45
❑ 99PacRed-136
❑ 99PacRed-136A
❑ 99PacTim-3
❑ 99Rev-47
❑ 99RevPremDate-47
❑ 99RevRet-47
❑ 99RevShaSS-47
❑ 99SkyMolM-47
❑ 99SkyMolMX-47
❑ 99SkyPre-91
❑ 99SkyPreR-91
❑ 99SkyThu-269
❑ 99SkyThuHip-H14
❑ 99SkyThuRant-269
❑ 99SkyThuRave-269
❑ 99SP Aut-28
❑ 99SP AutC-JT
❑ 99SP AutCG-JT
❑ 99SP AutHRC-HR17
❑ 99SPAutHRCDC-HR17
❑ 99SpoIll-78
❑ 99SPx-33
❑ 99SPxDom-FB9
❑ 99SPxFinR-33
❑ 99SPxFinS-33
❑ 99SPxPowE-PE11
❑ 99SPxStaF-SF9
❑ 99StaClu-120
❑ 99StaCluFDI-120
❑ 99StaCluOoaK-120
❑ 99StaCluPP-120
❑ 99StaCluTI-T15B
❑ 99StaCluTL-T15B
❑ 99StaCluTL-T15B
❑ 99ThuSkySupR-269
❑ 99Top-380
❑ 99Top-451
❑ 99TopAllMF-M5
❑ 99TopBlaLC1-5
❑ 99TopBlaLC2-5
❑ 99TopBlaLC3-5
❑ 99TopChr-380
❑ 99TopChr-451
❑ 99TopChrR-380
❑ 99TopChrR-451
❑ 99TopGal-2
❑ 99TopGalPP-2
❑ 99TopGalPPI-2
❑ 99TopGolL-5
❑ 99TopGolLC1-5
❑ 99TopGolLC2-5
❑ 99TopGolLOtO-5
❑ 99TopMVPP-380
❑ 99TopMVPP-451
❑ 99TopOpeD-158
❑ 99TopPowB-PB14
❑ 99TopPowBR-PB14
❑ 99TopRedLC1-5
❑ 99TopRedLC2-5
❑ 99TopRedLC3-5
❑ 99TopSta-61
❑ 99TopSta'S-44
❑ 99TopSta'SG-44
❑ 99TopSta'SGDH-44
❑ 99TopSta1Foil-61
❑ 99TopStaFoil-61
❑ 99TopStaOS-61
❑ 99TopTek-20A
❑ 99TopTek-20B
❑ 99TopTekG-20A
❑ 99TopTekG-20B
❑ 99UD Cho-79
❑ 99UD ChoPCR-79
❑ 99UD ChoS-30
❑ 99UD ChoSD-30
❑ 99UD ChoSHR-30
❑ 99UD ChoST-30
❑ 99UD ChoYW-Y9
❑ 99UD Ion-22
❑ 99UD IonR-22
❑ 99UDHolo-18
❑ 99UDHoloAUsome-18
❑ 99Ult-95
❑ 99UltGolM-95
❑ 99UltMas-95
❑ 99UltPlaM-95
❑ 99UltRBIK-11
❑ 99UppDec-84
❑ 99UppDecBD-25
❑ 99UppDecBDD-25
❑ 99UppDecBDQ-25
❑ 99UppDecBDT-25
❑ 99UppDecCf7-22
❑ 99UppDecCf7-C19
❑ 99UppDecCf7Cf7P-C19
❑ 99UppDecCf7LL-L20
❑ 99UppDecCLM-C27
❑ 99UppDecCo7CE-22
❑ 99UppDecE-27
❑ 99UppDecE-160
❑ 99UppDecEFXG-27
❑ 99UppDecEFXG-160
❑ 99UppDecEL1-84
❑ 99UppDecEL2-84
❑ 99UppDecF-F13
❑ 99UppDecFD-F13
❑ 99UppDecFQ-F13
❑ 99UppDecFT-F13
❑ 99UppDecM-65
❑ 99UppDecMGS-65
❑ 99UppDecMHFS-65
❑ 99UppDecMP-65
❑ 99UppDecMSS-65
❑ 99UppDecO-25
❑ 99UppDecOSO-25
❑ 99UppDecR-25
❑ 99UppDecRG-25
❑ 99UppDecRP-25
❑ 99Vic-115
❑ 99Vic-118

Thomforde, Jim
❑ 92OneYanC-9
❑ 93OneYanC-21
❑ 93OneYanF-3503
❑ 94GreBatF-475
❑ 97GreBatC-23

Thompson, Al
❑ 77AshTouT-24

Thompson, Andrew
❑ 95HagSunF-78
❑ 96DunBluJB-24
❑ 96DunBluJTI-28
❑ 96LowSpiB-25
❑ 97KnoSmo-24
❑ 98BesAutSS-49
❑ 98KnoSG-24
❑ 98SouLeaTPG-15
❑ 99JustheS-43
❑ 99JustheSAC-19
❑ 99JustheSJB-43

Thompson, Angelo
❑ 93JamExpC-23
❑ 93JamExpF-3340

Thompson, Averett
❑ 46SunBre-19

Thompson, Bill
❑ 85FreGiaSB-29

Thompson, Bob
❑ 87LakTigP-19
❑ 92AlbYanSk-25
❑ 94OneYanC-29

Thompson, Bobby L.
❑ 74GasRanT-24
❑ 75LynRanT-20
❑ 76SanAntBTI-25
❑ 78RanBurK-22
❑ 79Top-336
❑ 93RanKee-356

Thompson, Brian
❑ 91AubAstC-21
❑ 91AubAstP-4288
❑ 92AubAstC-9
❑ 92AubAstF-1369

Thompson, Bruce
❑ 95BelGiaTI-8
❑ 96BurBeeTI-25

Thompson, Cecil
❑ 11BigEatEU-18
❑ 11Zee-79
❑ 26Zee-62

Thompson, Charles
❑ 52Par-52
❑ 56A'sPos-44
❑ 90ChaRaiB-21
❑ 90ChaRaiP-2035
❑ 91ChaRaiC-10
❑ 91ChaRaiP-95

Thompson, Chris
❑ 96LowSpiB-26
❑ 97MicBatC-28

Thompson, Chuck
❑ 95BalOriP-49

Thompson, Dan
❑ 96HelBreTI-25

Thompson, Danny
❑ 71MLBOffS-474
❑ 71OPC-127
❑ 71Top-127
❑ 72OPC-368
❑ 72Top-368
❑ 72TwiPos-22
❑ 73LinPor-109
❑ 73OPC-443
❑ 73Top-443
❑ 74Kel-35
❑ 74OPC-168
❑ 74Top-168
❑ 75OPC-249
❑ 75Top-249
❑ 75TopMin-249
❑ 75TwiTeal-27
❑ 76MinTwiP-18
❑ 76OPC-111
❑ 76SSP-225
❑ 76Top-111
❑ 78TwiFri-46
❑ 93RanKee-357

Thompson, Don
❑ 52LaPat-16
❑ 90DodTar-798

Thompson, Eric
❑ 98SouOreTG-33

Thompson, Fay
❑ 75DubPacT-6
❑ 78DunBluJT-23

Thompson, Fletcher
❑ 90AubAstB-18
❑ 90AubAstP-3410
❑ 91BurAstC-18
❑ 91BurAstP-2812
❑ 91MidLeaAP-MWL17
❑ 92ProFS7-231
❑ 93JacGenF-2118
❑ 94JacGenF-226
❑ 95UppDecML-174
❑ 95UppDecMLFS-174
❑ 96BowBayB-26
❑ 96HigDesMB-28

Thompson, Forrest D.
❑ 47SenGunBP-4
❑ 49RemBre-26
❑ 50RemBre-23

Thompson, Frank
❑ 37Zee-92
❑ 96GreFalDB-28
❑ 96GreFalDTI-16
❑ 97SanBerS-14

Thompson, Greg
❑ 94YakBeaC-26
❑ 94YakBeaF-3851

Thompson, Gus
❑ 09ObaT21-203

Thompson, Hank
❑ 47PM1StaP1-209
❑ 50Bow-174
❑ 51Bow-89
❑ 51R42SmaS-107
❑ 51TopRedB-32
❑ 52BerRos-64
❑ 52Bow-249
❑ 52Top-3
❑ 53Top-20
❑ 54Bow-217
❑ 54NewYorJA-35
❑ 54Top-64
❑ 55Bow-94
❑ 55GiaGolS-18
❑ 55RedMan-NL11
❑ 55RobGouS-19
❑ 55RobGouW-19
❑ 56GiaJayP-10
❑ 56Top-199
❑ 57Top-109
❑ 75Gia195T-28
❑ 79TCM50-150
❑ 83TopRep5-3
❑ 84WilMay-4
❑ 85TCMPhoC-37
❑ 86NegLeaF-98
❑ 91TopArc1-20
❑ 94TedWilM-M24
❑ 94TopArc1-64
❑ 94TopArc1G-64

Thompson, Harry
❑ 25Zee-81

Thompson, Jason Dolph
❑ 76DetTigP-31
❑ 77BurCheD-99
❑ 77Hos-64
❑ 77OPC-64
❑ 77Top-291
❑ 78Hos-77
❑ 78OPC-212
❑ 78RCColC-97
❑ 78TigBurK-12
❑ 78TigTeal-30
❑ 78Top-660
❑ 79BasPat-90
❑ 79Hos-96
❑ 79Kel-7
❑ 79OPC-33
❑ 79TigFreP-1
❑ 79Top-80
❑ 80Kel-17
❑ 80OPC-83
❑ 80Top-150
❑ 80TopSup-42
❑ 81Don-293
❑ 81Fle-278
❑ 81OPC-373
❑ 81Top-505
❑ 81TopTra-843
❑ 82Don-502
❑ 82Fle-501
❑ 82Top-295
❑ 83AllGamPI-99
❑ 83Don-95
❑ 83DonActA-8
❑ 83Dra-28
❑ 83Fle-325
❑ 83FleSta-196
❑ 83FleSti-79
❑ 83OPC-209
❑ 83Top-730
❑ 83TopSti-276
❑ 84AllGamPI-9
❑ 84Don-64
❑ 84Fle-267
❑ 84Nes792-355
❑ 84OPC-355
❑ 84Pir-23
❑ 84Top-355
❑ 84TopRubD-27
❑ 84TopSti-128
❑ 84TopTif-355
❑ 85AllGamPI-99
❑ 85Don-322
❑ 85Fle-478
❑ 85Lea-89
❑ 85OPC-22
❑ 85Pir-21
❑ 85Top-490
❑ 85TopRubD-27
❑ 85TopSti-125
❑ 85TopSup-56
❑ 85TopTif-490
❑ 86Don-322
❑ 86ExpPos-15
❑ 86ExpProPa-15
❑ 86Fle-622
❑ 86FleUpd-113
❑ 86GenMilB-6H
❑ 86OPC-153
❑ 86Top-635
❑ 86TopSti-129
❑ 86TopTif-635
❑ 87GenMilB-4G
❑ 95Bes-99
❑ 95Exc-289
❑ 95SPML-143
❑ 95SPMLA-23
❑ 95UppDecML-85
❑ 95UppDecMLFS-85
❑ 96BowBes-178
❑ 96BowBesAR-178
❑ 96BowBesR-178
❑ 96Exc-239
❑ 96LeaPre-118
❑ 96LeaPreP-118
❑ 97ColCho-213
❑ 97DonRatR-1
❑ 97PacPriGotD-GD210
❑ 97Pin-180
❑ 97PinArtP-PP180
❑ 97PinMusC-180
❑ 97PinPrePla-180
❑ 97Sco-299
❑ 97ScoArtPWB-299
❑ 97ScoPreS-299
❑ 97ScoShoS-299
❑ 97ScoShoSAP-299
❑ 97Ult-287
❑ 97UltGolME-287
❑ 97UltPlaME-287

Thompson, Jason Michael
❑ 93SpoIndC-21
❑ 93SpoIndF-3598
❑ 94RanCucQC-24
❑ 94RanCucQF-1647
❑ 95MemChiTI-4
❑ 95SigRooOJHP-HP5
❑ 95SigRooOJHPS-HP5
❑ 96LasVegSB-27
❑ 97BesAutAS-60
❑ 98Las-25

Thompson, Jocko (John)
❑ 49Bow-161
❑ 50Bow-120
❑ 51Bow-294
❑ 75Phi195T-29
❑ 80Phi195T-29

Thompson, John
❑ 93BelMarCB-28
❑ 93BelMarF-3209
❑ 94BelMarC-27
❑ 94BelMarF-3235
❑ 96LanJetB-27
❑ 97LanJet-25
❑ 98OrlRayM-19

Thompson, Junior (Eugene)
❑ 38RedOraW-26
❑ 39OrcPhoAP-22
❑ 39RedTeal-21
❑ 41HarHarW-23
❑ 47TipTop-132
❑ 76TayBow4-88
❑ 77CinRedT-39
❑ 77TCMTheWY-86

Thompson, Justin
❑ 91BriTigC-25
❑ 91BriTigP-3606
❑ 91Cla/Bes-405
❑ 91ClaDraP-28
❑ 91FroRowDP-31
❑ 91FroRowDPG-31
❑ 91FroRowDPS-31
❑ 91HigSchPLS-4
❑ 92Bow-543
❑ 92ClaFS7-105
❑ 92FayGenC-1
❑ 92FayGenF-2168
❑ 92ProFS7-71
❑ 92UppDecML-46
❑ 92UppDecML-161
❑ 93Bow-366
❑ 93Bow-587
❑ 93ClaGolF-53
❑ 93ClaYouG-YG23
❑ 93FloStaLAF-20
❑ 93LakTigC-1
❑ 93LakTigF-1311
❑ 94Bow-372
❑ 94Bow-649
❑ 94BowBes-B6
❑ 94BowBesR-B6
❑ 94ClaGolF-111
❑ 94ExcFS7-62
❑ 94SigRoo-25
❑ 94SigRooHP-S10
❑ 94SigRooHPS-S10
❑ 94SigRooS-25
❑ 94Top-313
❑ 94TopGol-313
❑ 94TopSpa-313
❑ 94UppDecML-43
❑ 95Bow-68
❑ 95SPML-55
❑ 96Bow-214
❑ 96BowFoi-214
❑ 96Fin-B336
❑ 96FinRef-B336
❑ 96LeaPre-129
❑ 96LeaPreP-129
❑ 96SelCer-127
❑ 96SelCerAP-127
❑ 96SelCerCB-127
❑ 96SelCerCR-127
❑ 96SelCerMB-127
❑ 96SelCerMG-127
❑ 96SelCerMR-127
❑ 96SP-7
❑ 96TigHebN-23
❑ 96TolMudHB-1
❑ 96Zen-127
❑ 96ZenArtP-127
❑ 97Bow-312
❑ 97BowBes-128
❑ 97BowBesAR-128
❑ 97BowBesR-128
❑ 97BowCerBlaIA-CA79
❑ 97BowCerBluIA-CA79
❑ 97BowCerGolIA-CA79
❑ 97BowChr-216
❑ 97BowChrI-216
❑ 97BowChrIR-216
❑ 97BowChrR-216
❑ 97BowInt-312
❑ 97Cir-160
❑ 97CirRav-160
❑ 97ColCho-21
❑ 97Don-373
❑ 97DonEliTotC-12
❑ 97DonEliTotCDC-12
❑ 97DonGolPP-373
❑ 97DonLim-139
❑ 97DonLimE-139
❑ 97DonLimENG-139
❑ 97DonRatR-23
❑ 97DonSig-46
❑ 97DonSigA-96
❑ 97DonSigAC-121
❑ 97DonSigAM-121
❑ 97DonSigPPP-46
❑ 97DonSilPP-373
❑ 97Fin-36
❑ 97FinRef-36
❑ 97Fle-107
❑ 97FleTif-107
❑ 97Lea-177
❑ 97LeaFraM-177
❑ 97LeaFraMDC-177
❑ 97MetUni-113
❑ 97PacPri-34
❑ 97PacPriGotD-GD46
❑ 97PacPriLB-34
❑ 97PacPriP-34

❑ 97Pin-169
❑ 97PinArtP-PP169
❑ 97PinMusC-169
❑ 97PinPrePla-169
❑ 97Sco-267
❑ 97ScoArtPWB-267
❑ 97ScoPreS-267
❑ 97ScoShoS-267
❑ 97ScoShoSAP-267
❑ 97Sel-197
❑ 97SelCom-197
❑ 97StaClu-160
❑ 97StaCluM-M13
❑ 97StaCluMOP-160
❑ 97StaCluMOP-M13
❑ 97StrAll-59
❑ 97Top-163
❑ 97TopChr-65
❑ 97TopChrR-65
❑ 97TopGal-179
❑ 97TopGalPPI-179
❑ 97TopSta-100
❑ 97TopStaAM-100
❑ 97Ult-63
❑ 97UltGolME-63
❑ 97UltPlaME-63
❑ 97UppDec-224
❑ 98Bow-32
❑ 98BowBes-26
❑ 98BowBesAR-26
❑ 98BowBesR-26
❑ 98BowChr-32
❑ 98BowChrGA-32
❑ 98BowChrGAR-32
❑ 98BowChrI-32
❑ 98BowChrIR-32
❑ 98BowChrR-32
❑ 98BowGolA-32
❑ 98BowInt-32
❑ 98CirThu-258
❑ 98CirThuRav-258
❑ 98CirThuSupRav-258
❑ 98ColCho-94
❑ 98Don-14
❑ 98DonCol-14
❑ 98DonColE-432
❑ 98DonColL-255
❑ 98DonColP-610
❑ 98DonColS-14
❑ 98DonCruG-25
❑ 98DonCruP-25
❑ 98DonCruR-25
❑ 98DonEli-32
❑ 98DonEliA-32
❑ 98DonEliS-32
❑ 98DonGolPP-14
❑ 98DonPre-60
❑ 98DonPreSeat-60
❑ 98DonPriCD-14
❑ 98DonPriCE-432
❑ 98DonPriCL-255
❑ 98DonPriCP-610
❑ 98DonSig-20
❑ 98DonSigP-20
❑ 98DonSilPP-14
❑ 98E-X2-82
❑ 98E-X2ECFut-82
❑ 98E-X2ECNow-82
❑ 98Fin-130
❑ 98FinNo--130
❑ 98FinNo-R-130
❑ 98FinRef-130
❑ 98FlaShoLeg0-94
❑ 98FlaShoLeg1-94
❑ 98FlaShoLeg2-94
❑ 98FlaShoLeg3-94
❑ 98FlaShoLegM-94
❑ 98FlaShoR0-94
❑ 98FlaShoR1-94
❑ 98FlaShoR2-94
❑ 98FlaShoR3-94
❑ 98Fle-152
❑ 98Lea-56
❑ 98LeaFraDA-56
❑ 98LeaFraF-56
❑ 98LeaFraM-56
❑ 98LeaFraM-56
❑ 98LeaFraMDC-56
❑ 98LeaFraMDC-56
❑ 98LeaFraMZ2-56
❑ 98LeaRS-63
❑ 98LeaRSLHolo-63
❑ 98LeaRSLong-63
❑ 98LeaRTrue-63
❑ 98MetUni-46
❑ 98MetUniPMG-46
❑ 98Pac-96
❑ 98PacAur-41
❑ 98PacInv-34
❑ 98PacInvPBlue-34
❑ 98PacInvSilv-34
❑ 98PacInvTeam-10
❑ 98PacOme-93
❑ 98PacOmeR-93
❑ 98PacOnl-286
❑ 98PacOnlR-286
❑ 98PacOnlWC-286
❑ 98PacPar-51
❑ 98PacParC-51
❑ 98PacParG-51
❑ 98PacParHS-51
❑ 98PacParPB-51
❑ 98PacParR-51
❑ 98PacPlaB-96
❑ 98PacRedT-96
❑ 98PacSil-96
❑ 98PacTeaC-6
❑ 98PinIns-21
❑ 98PinInsCE-21
❑ 98PinInsDE-21
❑ 98PinPer-61
❑ 98PinPerPP-61
❑ 98PinPlu-26
❑ 98Sco-101
❑ 98ScoRT-206
❑ 98ScoRTSS-PP113
❑ 98ScoRTSSAP-PP113
❑ 98ScoRTSSAP1-PP113
❑ 98ScoSS-PP142
❑ 98ScoSSAP-PP142
❑ 98SkyDugA-66
❑ 98SkyDugAIA-66
❑ 98SP Aut-88
❑ 98SpoIll-120
❑ 98SpoIllEE-120
❑ 98SpoIllFE-120
❑ 98SpoIllWSF-135
❑ 98SpoIllWSFEE-135
❑ 98SpoIllWSFFE-135
❑ 98SPxFin-13
❑ 98SPxFinR-13
❑ 98SPxFinS-13
❑ 98StaCluFDI-239
❑ 98StaCluI-239
❑ 98StaCluOneK-239
❑ 98StaCluPP-239
❑ 98Stu-11
❑ 98StuGPP-11
❑ 98StuSPP-11
❑ 98Top-315
❑ 98TopBabB-BB14
❑ 98TopChr-315
❑ 98TopChrBB-BB14
❑ 98TopChrBBR-BB14
❑ 98TopChrR-315
❑ 98TopDevR-315
❑ 98TopDia-315
❑ 98TopGal-78
❑ 98TopGalGP-78
❑ 98TopGalOPP-78
❑ 98TopGalPPI-78
❑ 98TopGalPPIA-78
❑ 98TopMiniC-315
❑ 98TopOpeD-141
❑ 98TopSta-110
❑ 98TopStaB-110
❑ 98TopStaG-110
❑ 98TopStaGR-110
❑ 98TopStaS-110
❑ 98Ult-189
❑ 98UltGolM-189
❑ 98UltMas-189
❑ 98UltPlaM-189
❑ 98UppDec-85
❑ 98UppDecBCP-BC7
❑ 98UppDecSF-53
❑ 98Zen-55
❑ 98Zen5 xx7-65
❑ 98Zen5x7GoldImp-65
❑ 98Zen5x7Imp-65
❑ 98ZenZ-G-55
❑ 98ZenZ-S-55
❑ 99199Fin-221
❑ 99Bow-289
❑ 99BowGol-289
❑ 99BowInt-289
❑ 99FinGolRef-221
❑ 99FinRef-221
❑ 99FlaShoLeg1-126
❑ 99FlaShoLeg2-126
❑ 99FlaShoLeg3-126
❑ 99FlaShoLegM1-126
❑ 99FlaShoLegM2-126
❑ 99FlaShoLegM3-126
❑ 99FlaShoR1-126
❑ 99FlaShoR2-126
❑ 99FlaShoR3-126
❑ 99Fle-249
❑ 99FleSta9-249
❑ 99FleWarT-249
❑ 99MetUni-126
❑ 99MetUniGM-126
❑ 99MetUniPMG-126
❑ 99Pac-169
❑ 99PacAur-70
❑ 99PacAurOD-70
❑ 99PacCroC-110
❑ 99PacCroCPB-110
❑ 99PacOme-93
❑ 99PacOmeC-93
❑ 99PacOmeG-93
❑ 99PacOmePB-93
❑ 99PacPar-92
❑ 99PacParC-92
❑ 99PacParG-92
❑ 99PacParHoloGold-92
❑ 99PacParHS-92
❑ 99PacParOD-92
❑ 99PacParPB-92
❑ 99PacParRed-92
❑ 99PacPlaB-169
❑ 99PacPriS-141
❑ 99PacPriS206-141
❑ 99PacPriS206R-141
❑ 99PacRed-169
❑ 99SkyMolM-63
❑ 99SkyMolMX-63
❑ 99SkyPre-93
❑ 99SkyPreR-93
❑ 99SkyThu-74
❑ 99SkyThuRant-74
❑ 99SkyThuRave-74
❑ 99StaClu-210
❑ 99StaCluFDI-210
❑ 99StaCluOoaK-210
❑ 99StaCluPP-210
❑ 99ThuSkySupR-74
❑ 99Top-44
❑ 99TopChr-44
❑ 99TopChrR-44
❑ 99TopMVPP-44
❑ 99TopOpeD-26
❑ 99TopSta-125
❑ 99TopStaFoil-125
❑ 99Ult-127
❑ 99UltGolM-127
❑ 99UltMas-127
❑ 99UltPlaM-127
❑ 99UppDec-368
❑ 99UppDecEL1-368
❑ 99UppDecEL2-368
❑ 99Vic-150

Thompson, Karl
❑ 95EveAqaTI-26
❑ 96MidLeaAB-1
❑ 96WisTimRB-25
❑ 98LanJetG-26

Thompson, Kelly
❑ 87AncGlaP-39

Thompson, Kirk
❑ 89EugEmeB-10

Thompson, L. Fresco
❑ 29ExhFou-11
❑ 29PorandAR-90
❑ 31Exh-3
❑ 33ButCanV-48
❑ 33Gou-13
❑ 33GouCanV-13
❑ 36GouWidPPR-D37
❑ 90DodTar-799
❑ 92ConTSN-493

Thompson, Leroy
❑ 92BurIndC-10
❑ 92BurIndF-1673
❑ 93BurIndC-25
❑ 93BurIndF-3314
❑ 94ColRedC-21
❑ 94ColRedF-459

Thompson, Mark Radford
❑ 92BenRocCB-7
❑ 92BenRocF-1474
❑ 92ClaDraP-47
❑ 92ClaFS7-433
❑ 92FroRowDP-75
❑ 92FroRowDPG-75
❑ 92FroRowDPS-75
❑ 93Bow-8
❑ 93Bow-350
❑ 93CenValRC-1
❑ 93CenValRF-2893
❑ 93ClaYouG-YG24
❑ 93ColSprSSF-3087
❑ 93ExcFS7-36
❑ 93RocStaC-20
❑ 93StaCluM-108
❑ 93Top-419
❑ 93TopGol-419
❑ 93TopInaM-419
❑ 93TopInaR-419
❑ 93TopMic-419
❑ 94Bow-170
❑ 94Cla-34
❑ 94ClaGolF-42
❑ 94ColSprSSF-734
❑ 94DanBraC-25
❑ 94DanBraF-3532
❑ 94ExcFS7-188
❑ 94FleExtB-254
❑ 94FleExtBMLH-9
❑ 94Top-286
❑ 94TopGol-286
❑ 94TopSpa-286
❑ 94Ult-487
❑ 94UppDecML-220
❑ 95Bow-15
❑ 95ColCho-11
❑ 95ColChoGS-11
❑ 95ColChoSE-14
❑ 95ColChoSEGS-14
❑ 95ColChoSESS-14
❑ 95ColChoSS-11
❑ 95Fla-347
❑ 95FleUpd-170
❑ 95MacBraTI-25
❑ 95Top-52
❑ 96LeaSigEA-201
❑ 96RocPol-23
❑ 96Sco-231
❑ 97ColCho-322
❑ 97ColChoT-CR9
❑ 97ColSprSATTI-9
❑ 97Fle-624
❑ 97FleTif-624
❑ 97PacPriGotD-GD138
❑ 97Pin-147
❑ 97PinArtP-PP147
❑ 97PinMusC-147
❑ 97PinPrePla-147
❑ 97RocSco-13
❑ 97RocScoPl-13
❑ 97RocScoPr-13
❑ 97Sco-240
❑ 97ScoArtPWB-240
❑ 97ScoPreS-240
❑ 97ScoShoS-240
❑ 97ScoShoSAP-240
❑ 97StaClu-313
❑ 97StaCluMOP-313
❑ 97Top-441
❑ 97Ult-494
❑ 97UltGolME-494
❑ 97UltPlaME-494
❑ 97UppDec-348
❑ 98PacOnl-257
❑ 98PacOnlR-257
❑ 98PacOnlWC-257

Thompson, Marvin W.
❑ 75ForLauYS-13
❑ 78TacYanC-22
❑ 79ColCliT-12
❑ 80ColCliP-22
❑ 80ColCliT-24
❑ 81SyrChiT-20
❑ 81SyrChiTI-20

Thompson, Michael
❑ 88WinHavRSS-23
❑ 89BelMarL-36
❑ 89ElmPioP-28
❑ 89WinHavRSS-24
❑ 92MarPhiC-5
❑ 92MarPhiF-3074
❑ 93BatCliCB-27
❑ 93BatCliF-3162

Thompson, Mike (Michael Wayne)
❑ 71SenTealW-23
❑ 73OPC-564
❑ 73Top-564
❑ 75AtlBraP-37
❑ 76IndIndTI-18
❑ 76OPC-536
❑ 76SSP-6
❑ 76Top-536
❑ 80QuaCitCT-1

Thompson, Milt
❑ 84RicBraT-25
❑ 85RicBraT-21
❑ 86Don-507
❑ 86Fle-530
❑ 86FleUpd-114
❑ 86PhiTas-24
❑ 86Top-517
❑ 86TopTif-517
❑ 86TopTra-112T
❑ 86TopTraT-112T
❑ 87Don-330
❑ 87DonOpeD-154
❑ 87Fle-191
❑ 87FleGlo-191
❑ 87PhiTas-24
❑ 87SpoTeaP-6
❑ 87Top-409
❑ 87TopTif-409
❑ 88Don-236
❑ 88DonBasB-296
❑ 88Fle-319
❑ 88FleGlo-319
❑ 88FleStiC-112
❑ 88OPC-298
❑ 88PanSti-363
❑ 88PhiTas-25
❑ 88Sco-115
❑ 88ScoGlo-115
❑ 88Spo-173
❑ 88StaLinPh-19
❑ 88Top-298
❑ 88TopBig-2
❑ 88TopTif-298
❑ 89Bow-441
❑ 89BowTif-441
❑ 89CarSmo-22
❑ 89CarTeal-32
❑ 89Don-313
❑ 89DonBasB-212
❑ 89DonTra-43
❑ 89Fle-584
❑ 89FleGlo-584
❑ 89FleUpd-121
❑ 89OPC-128
❑ 89PanSti-157
❑ 89RedFolSB-119
❑ 89Sco-92
❑ 89ScoRoo-45T
❑ 89Spo-169
❑ 89Top-128
❑ 89TopTif-128
❑ 89TopTra-118T
❑ 89TopTraT-118T
❑ 89UppDec-317
❑ 90Bow-196
❑ 90BowTif-196
❑ 90CarSmo-24
❑ 90Don-82
❑ 90Fle-262
❑ 90FleCan-262
❑ 90Lea-308
❑ 90OPC-688
❑ 90PanSti-345
❑ 90PubIntS-230
❑ 90Sco-49
❑ 90Top-688
❑ 90TopBig-126
❑ 90TopSti-37
❑ 90TopTif-688
❑ 90TopTVCa-36
❑ 90UppDec-278
❑ 91Bow-386
❑ 91CarPol-25
❑ 91Don-225
❑ 91Fle-649
❑ 91Lea-176
❑ 91OPC-63
❑ 91PanFreS-36
❑ 91Sco-54
❑ 91StaClu-66
❑ 91Stu-239
❑ 91Top-63
❑ 91TopDesS-63
❑ 91TopMic-63
❑ 91TopTif-63
❑ 91Ult-297
❑ 91UppDec-309A
❑ 91UppDec-309B
❑ 92CarPol-22
❑ 92Don-513
❑ 92Fle-595
❑ 92Lea-150
❑ 92LeaBlaG-150
❑ 92OPC-323
❑ 92Pin-345
❑ 92Sco-114
❑ 92StaClu-447
❑ 92Top-323
❑ 92TopGol-323
❑ 92TopGolW-323
❑ 92TopMic-323
❑ 92Ult-272
❑ 92UppDec-397
❑ 93Don-775
❑ 93Lea-417
❑ 93OPCPre-74
❑ 93PacSpa-582
❑ 93PhiMed-32
❑ 93PhiStaC-28
❑ 93Pin-516
❑ 93Sco-397
❑ 93Sel-223
❑ 93SelRoo-125T
❑ 93StaClu-642
❑ 93StaCluFDI-642
❑ 93StaCluMOP-642
❑ 93Ult-446
❑ 93UppDec-558
❑ 93UppDecGold-558
❑ 94ColC-472
❑ 94ColChoGS-472
❑ 94ColChoSS-472
❑ 94Don-301
❑ 94Fin-198
❑ 94FinRef-198
❑ 94Fla-213
❑ 94Fle-602
❑ 94Lea-22
❑ 94Pac-488
❑ 94PhiMed-33
❑ 94PhiMel-23
❑ 94PhiUSPC-3C
❑ 94PhiUSPC-11H
❑ 94Sco-158
❑ 94ScoGolR-158
❑ 94StaClu-355
❑ 94StaCluFDI-355
❑ 94StaCluGR-355
❑ 94StaCluMOP-355
❑ 94StaCluT-219
❑ 94StaCluTFDI-219
❑ 94Top-722
❑ 94TopGol-722
❑ 94TopSpa-722
❑ 94UppDec-184
❑ 94UppDecED-184
❑ 95AstMot-9
❑ 95Pin-83
❑ 95PinArtP-83
❑ 95PinMusC-83
❑ 95Sco-479
❑ 95ScoGolR-479
❑ 95ScoPlaTS-479
❑ 96DodMot-17
❑ 96DodPol-28
❑ 98ReaPhiM-6
❑ 98ReaPhiUM-30

Thompson, Mitch
❑ 91MisStaB-54
❑ 92MisStaB-40
❑ 93MisStaB-42

Thompson, Nick
❑ 96MarPhiB-27
❑ 98ClePhiM-22
❑ 98ClePhiUM-22

Thompson, Ray
❑ 76DubPacT-35

Thompson, Rich (Richard)
❑ 81WatIndT-16
❑ 82ChaLooT-5
❑ 83AndBraT-32
❑ 83BufBisT-7
❑ 84BufBisT-12
❑ 85Don-129
❑ 85FleUpd-120
❑ 85IndPol-41
❑ 85MaiGuiT-11
❑ 85TopTifT-122T
❑ 85TopTra-122T
❑ 86Fle-595
❑ 86OPC-242
❑ 86Top-242
❑ 86TopSti-215
❑ 86TopTif-242
❑ 86VanCanP-26
❑ 88MemChiB-2
❑ 89IndIndC-10
❑ 89IndIndP-1237
❑ 90CMC-59

❑ 90ExpPos-35
❑ 90IndIndC-9
❑ 90IndIndP-304
❑ 90OPC-474
❑ 90ProAAAF-587
❑ 90Top-474
❑ 90TopTif-474
❑ 90UppDec-597A

Thompson, Rick
❑ 82AubAstT-19

Thompson, Rob
❑ 75CedRapGT-7
❑ 86GiaPos-28

Thompson, Robby
❑ 86DonRoo-39
❑ 86FleUpd-115
❑ 86GiaMot-16
❑ 86SpoRoo-25
❑ 86TopTra-113T
❑ 86TopTraT-113T
❑ 87Don-145
❑ 87DonOpeD-101
❑ 87Fle-285
❑ 87FleAwaW-39
❑ 87FleGlo-285
❑ 87FleMin-106
❑ 87GiaMot-10
❑ 87GiaPos-31
❑ 87KeyFooD-12
❑ 87Lea-64
❑ 87MSAIceTD-12
❑ 87OurOwnTD-12
❑ 87Spo-46
❑ 87SpoTeaP-10
❑ 87StuPan-13
❑ 87Top-658
❑ 87TopGloS-40
❑ 87TopRoo-21
❑ 87TopSti-91
❑ 87TopSti-307
❑ 87TopTif-658
❑ 87ToyRoo-30
❑ 87WeiMarD-12
❑ 88Don-268
❑ 88DonBasB-274
❑ 88Fle-98
❑ 88FleGlo-98
❑ 88GiaMot-10
❑ 88GiaPos-31
❑ 88Lea-120
❑ 88OPC-208
❑ 88PanSti-423
❑ 88Sco-146
❑ 88ScoGlo-146
❑ 88ScoYouSI-28
❑ 88Spo-24
❑ 88StaLinG-18
❑ 88Top-472
❑ 88TopBig-83
❑ 88TopSti-93
❑ 88TopTif-472
❑ 89Bow-473
❑ 89BowTif-473
❑ 89Don-98
❑ 89DonBasB-79
❑ 89Fle-344
❑ 89FleGlo-344
❑ 89GiaMot-10
❑ 89OPC-15
❑ 89PanSti-215
❑ 89RedFolSB-120
❑ 89Sco-172
❑ 89ScoHot1S-84
❑ 89Spo-78
❑ 89Top-15
❑ 89TopBig-163
❑ 89TopSti-87
❑ 89TopTif-15
❑ 89TVSpoM-52
❑ 89UppDec-172
❑ 90Bow-233
❑ 90BowTif-233
❑ 90Don-140
❑ 90DonBesN-73
❑ 90Fle-73
❑ 90FleCan-73
❑ 90GiaMot-10
❑ 90GiaSmo-19
❑ 90Lea-199
❑ 90MLBBasB-26
❑ 90OPC-325
❑ 90PanSti-371
❑ 90PubIntS-83
❑ 90Sco-397
❑ 90Sco100S-21
❑ 90Spo-60
❑ 90Top-325
❑ 90TopBig-169
❑ 90TopCoi-59
❑ 90TopMinL-88
❑ 90TopSti-83
❑ 90TopTif-325
❑ 90UppDec-169
❑ 91Bow-623
❑ 91ClaGam-44
❑ 91Don-363
❑ 91Fle-273
❑ 91GiaMot-10
❑ 91GiaPacGaE-2
❑ 91GiaSFE-14
❑ 91Lea-107
❑ 91OPC-705
❑ 91PanFreS-68
❑ 91PanSti-77
❑ 91Sco-26
❑ 91StaClu-77
❑ 91StaCluMO-8
❑ 91Top-705
❑ 91TopDesS-705
❑ 91TopMic-705
❑ 91TopTif-705
❑ 91Ult-329
❑ 91UppDec-178
❑ 92Bow-448
❑ 92ClaGam-44
❑ 92Don-52
❑ 92Fle-648
❑ 92GiaMot-10
❑ 92GiaPacGaE-33
❑ 92Hig5-129
❑ 92Lea-109
❑ 92LeaBlaG-109
❑ 92OPC-475
❑ 92PanSti-213
❑ 92Pin-143
❑ 92Sco-247
❑ 92StaClu-160
❑ 92Stu-119
❑ 92Top-475
❑ 92TopGol-475
❑ 92TopGolW-475
❑ 92TopMic-475
❑ 92TriPla-45
❑ 92Ult-295
❑ 92UppDec-286
❑ 93Bow-436
❑ 93Don-524
❑ 93Fla-147
❑ 93Fle-538
❑ 93FunPac-103
❑ 93GiaMot-14
❑ 93GiaPos-32
❑ 93GiaStaC-30
❑ 93Lea-30
❑ 93OPC-301
❑ 93PacSpa-277
❑ 93PanSti-237
❑ 93Pin-491
❑ 93RedFolS-96
❑ 93Sco-593
❑ 93Sel-139
❑ 93SP-116
❑ 93StaClu-688
❑ 93StaCluFDI-688
❑ 93StaCluMOP-688
❑ 93Stu-124
❑ 93Top-115
❑ 93TopGol-115
❑ 93TopInaM-115
❑ 93TopInaR-115
❑ 93TopMic-115
❑ 93TriPla-81
❑ 93Ult-137
❑ 93UppDec-126
❑ 93UppDec-822
❑ 93UppDecGold-126
❑ 93UppDecGold-822
❑ 94Bow-407
❑ 94ColC-535
❑ 94ColChoGS-535
❑ 94ColChoSS-535
❑ 94Don-48
❑ 94DonSpeE-48
❑ 94Fin-68
❑ 94FinRef-68
❑ 94Fla-446
❑ 94Fle-703
❑ 94FleExtB-393
❑ 94FUnPac-74
❑ 94GiaAMC-22
❑ 94GiaKTV-7
❑ 94GiaMot-2
❑ 94GiaTarBC-25
❑ 94GiaTeal-5
❑ 94GiaTeal-6
❑ 94GiaUSPC-1H
❑ 94GiaUSPC-8C
❑ 94Lea-30
❑ 94OPC-20
❑ 94Pac-557
❑ 94PacSilP-36
❑ 94PacSilPC-36
❑ 94PanSti-267
❑ 94Pin-315
❑ 94PinArtP-315
❑ 94PinMusC-315
❑ 94PinTeaP-2
❑ 94ProMag-123
❑ 94Sco-406
❑ 94ScoGolR-406
❑ 94ScoGolS-29
❑ 94Sel-240
❑ 94SP-94
❑ 94SPDieC-94
❑ 94Spo-46
❑ 94Spo-186
❑ 94StaClu-598
❑ 94StaCluFDI-598
❑ 94StaCluGR-598
❑ 94StaCluMOP-598
❑ 94StaCluT-5
❑ 94StaCluTFDI-5
❑ 94Stu-88
❑ 94Top-385
❑ 94Top-505
❑ 94TopBlaG-43
❑ 94TopGol-385
❑ 94TopGol-505
❑ 94TopSpa-385
❑ 94TopSpa-505
❑ 94TriPla-109
❑ 94Ult-595
❑ 94UltAwaW-12
❑ 94UppDec-193
❑ 94UppDecED-193
❑ 95ColCho-253
❑ 95ColChoGS-253
❑ 95ColChoSE-111
❑ 95ColChoSEGS-111
❑ 95ColChoSESS-111
❑ 95ColChoSS-253
❑ 95Don-405
❑ 95DonPreP-405
❑ 95DonTopotO-358
❑ 95Fla-429
❑ 95Fle-591
❑ 95GiaMot-2
❑ 95Lea-258
❑ 95LeaLim-151
❑ 95PanSti-41
❑ 95Pin-385
❑ 95PinArtP-385
❑ 95PinMusC-385
❑ 95Sco-243
❑ 95ScoGolR-243
❑ 95ScoPlaTS-243
❑ 95Sel-213
❑ 95SelArtP-213
❑ 95SP-116
❑ 95Spo-93
❑ 95SpoArtP-93
❑ 95SPSil-116
❑ 95StaClu-398
❑ 95StaCluMOP-398
❑ 95StaCluSTWS-398
❑ 95Stu-151
❑ 95Top-556
❑ 95Ult-245
❑ 95UltGolM-245
❑ 95UppDec-88
❑ 95UppDecED-88
❑ 95UppDecEDG-88
❑ 95UppDecSE-71
❑ 95UppDecSEG-71
❑ 96Cir-195
❑ 96CirRav-195
❑ 96ColCho-308
❑ 96ColChoGS-308
❑ 96ColChoSS-308
❑ 96Don-132
❑ 96DonPreP-132
❑ 96EmoXL-294
❑ 96Fin-B58
❑ 96FinRef-B58
❑ 96Fla-392
❑ 96Fle-597
❑ 96FleTif-597
❑ 96GiaMot-5
❑ 96Lea-90
❑ 96LeaPrePB-90
❑ 96LeaPrePG-90
❑ 96LeaPrePS-90
❑ 96Pac-207
❑ 96Pin-53
❑ 96Sco-351
❑ 96ScoDugC-B76
❑ 96ScoDugCAP-B76
❑ 96StaClu-359
❑ 96StaCluEPB-359
❑ 96StaCluEPG-359
❑ 96StaCluEPS-359
❑ 96StaCluMOP-359
❑ 96Top-391
❑ 96Ult-571
❑ 96UltGolM-571
❑ 96UppDec-456
❑ 97Don-101
❑ 97DonGolPP-101
❑ 97DonSilPP-101
❑ 97Lea-112
❑ 97LeaFraM-112
❑ 97LeaFraMDC-112
❑ 97Pac-448
❑ 97PacLigB-448
❑ 97PacSil-448
❑ 97Pin-71
❑ 97PinArtP-PP71
❑ 97PinMusC-71
❑ 97PinPrePla-71
❑ 97Sco-90
❑ 97ScoArtPWB-90
❑ 97ScoPreS-90
❑ 97ScoShoS-90
❑ 97ScoShoSAP-90

Thompson, Ryan
❑ 88St.CatBJP-2035
❑ 89St.CatBJP-2072
❑ 90DunBluJS-19
❑ 91KnoBluJLD-367
❑ 91KnoBluJP-1783
❑ 91LinDriAA-367
❑ 92FleUpd-106
❑ 92SyrChiF-1984
❑ 92SyrChiMB-22
❑ 92SyrChiS-518
❑ 93Bow-270
❑ 93Don-242
❑ 93Fle-481
❑ 93LeaGolR-R7
❑ 93LeaGolRJ-R7
❑ 93MetColP-47
❑ 93MetKah-44
❑ 93NorTidF-2584
❑ 93OPC-351
❑ 93OPCPre-79
❑ 93PacSpa-548
❑ 93Pin-249
❑ 93PinRooTP-9
❑ 93Sco-227
❑ 93ScoBoyoS-9
❑ 93ScoProaG-6
❑ 93SelRoo-39T
❑ 93StaClu-542
❑ 93StaCluFDI-542
❑ 93StaCluMOP-542
❑ 93Top-547
❑ 93TopGol-547
❑ 93TopInaM-547
❑ 93TopInaR-547
❑ 93TopMic-547
❑ 93Toy-17
❑ 93TriAAAGF-18
❑ 93Ult-435
❑ 93UppDec-373
❑ 93UppDecGold-373
❑ 94Bow-240
❑ 94ColC-276
❑ 94ColChoGS-276
❑ 94ColChoSS-276
❑ 94Don-157
❑ 94Fin-39
❑ 94FinRef-39
❑ 94Fla-202
❑ 94Fle-579
❑ 94FleExtB-327
❑ 94Lea-48
❑ 94LeaL-133
❑ 94MetColP-27
❑ 94MetShuST-2
❑ 94OPC-135
❑ 94Pac-418
❑ 94PanSti-223
❑ 94Pin-400
❑ 94PinArtP-400
❑ 94PinMusC-400
❑ 94Sco-576
❑ 94ScoGolR-576
❑ 94Sel-46
❑ 94StaClu-274
❑ 94StaCluFDI-274
❑ 94StaCluGR-274
❑ 94StaCluMOP-274
❑ 94Stu-120
❑ 94Top-98
❑ 94TopGol-98
❑ 94TopSpa-98
❑ 94TriPla-150
❑ 94Ult-241
❑ 94UppDec-160
❑ 94UppDecED-160
❑ 94USPlaCR-4C
❑ 95ColCho-319
❑ 95ColChoGS-319
❑ 95ColChoSE-148
❑ 95ColChoSEGS-148
❑ 95ColChoSESS-148
❑ 95ColChoSS-319
❑ 95Don-458
❑ 95DonPreP-458
❑ 95DonTopotO-297
❑ 95Fin-191
❑ 95FinRef-191
❑ 95Fle-384
❑ 95Lea-138
❑ 95LeaLim-148
❑ 95MetColP-30
❑ 95Pac-289
❑ 95Pin-57
❑ 95PinArtP-57
❑ 95PinMusC-57
❑ 95Sco-81
❑ 95ScoGolR-81
❑ 95ScoPlaTS-81
❑ 95Spo-131
❑ 95SpoArtP-131
❑ 95StaClu-287
❑ 95StaCluMOP-287
❑ 95StaCluSTWS-287
❑ 95StaCluVR-149
❑ 95StaCluVRMO-149
❑ 95Stu-167
❑ 95Top-402
❑ 95TopCyb-203
❑ 95TopEmb-13
❑ 95TopEmbGI-13
❑ 95Ult-201
❑ 95UltGolM-201
❑ 95UppDec-362
❑ 95UppDecED-362
❑ 95UppDecEDG-362
❑ 95UppDecSE-62
❑ 95UppDecSEG-62
❑ 96BufBisB-21
❑ 96ColCho-623
❑ 96ColChoGS-623
❑ 96ColChoSS-623
❑ 96Don-458
❑ 96DonPreP-458
❑ 96Fle-489
❑ 96FleTif-489
❑ 96MetKah-32
❑ 96MetTeal-6
❑ 96Pac-145
❑ 96Sco-437
❑ 96StaClu-410
❑ 96StaCluMOP-410
❑ 96Top-77
❑ 97BufBis-27

Thompson, Sam
❑ 76ShaPiz-146
❑ 76SSP188WS-10
❑ 80PerHaloFP-146
❑ 80SSPHOF-146
❑ 87BucN28-34A
❑ 87BucN28-34B
❑ 87OldJudN-491
❑ 87ScrDC-17
❑ 88GandBCGCE-41
❑ 88SpoTimM-25
❑ 88WG1CarG-25
❑ 94OriofB-93

Thompson, Scot
❑ 79Top-716
❑ 80OPC-298
❑ 80Top-574
❑ 81CokTeaS-21
❑ 81Don-519
❑ 81Fle-296
❑ 81Top-395
❑ 82CubRedL-18
❑ 82IowCubT-11
❑ 83Don-378
❑ 83Top-481
❑ 84Don-167
❑ 84GiaPos-27
❑ 85Fle-621
❑ 85GiaMot-15
❑ 85GiaPos-26
❑ 85Top-646
❑ 85TopTif-646
❑ 86Fle-262
❑ 86FreGiaSB-21
❑ 86OPC-93
❑ 86Top-93
❑ 86TopTif-93

Thompson, Sean
❑ 88PocGiaP-2079
❑ 90SalSpuCLC-137
❑ 90SalSpuP-2734

Thompson, Squeezer
❑ 88SpoIndP-1927
❑ 90ChaRaiP-2030

Thompson, Stuart
❑ 93AusFut-51

Thompson, Tim
❑ 80KnoBluJT-15
❑ 82KnoBluJT-12
❑ 83SyrChiT-20
❑ 84SyrChiT-30

Thompson, Tim (Charles Lemoine)
❑ 50WorWidGV-18
❑ 52LaPat-15
❑ 53ExhCan-40
❑ 54Top-209
❑ 57Top-142
❑ 58Top-57A
❑ 58Top-57B
❑ 59TigGraASP-16
❑ 60MapLeaSF-21
❑ 61MapLeaBH-24
❑ 66St.PetCTI-17
❑ 90DodTar-800
❑ 94TopArc1-209
❑ 94TopArc1G-209
❑ 95TopArcBD-80

Thompson, Timothy
❑ 84VisOakT-11

Thompson, Tom
❑ 86BufBisP-22
❑ 87SanBerSP-23
❑ 91PacSenL-86

Thompson, Tommy
❑ 78ArkTraT-22
❑ 79ArkTraT-7
❑ 81DurBulT-5
❑ 82DurBulT-11
❑ 82ForMyeRT-3
❑ 85GreBraTI-19
❑ 86JacExpT-19
❑ 87HawIslP-9
❑ 87JacExpP-453
❑ 88BirBarB-10
❑ 88JacExpB-24
❑ 88JacExpP-971
❑ 88SouLeaAJ-39
❑ 89BirBarB-27
❑ 89BirBarP-104
❑ 89TulDriGS-1
❑ 89TulDriTI-25
❑ 90TulDriP-1172
❑ 90TulDriTI-25
❑ 90UtiBluSP-25
❑ 91LinDriAAA-324
❑ 91OklCit8LD-324
❑ 91OklCit8P-193
❑ 91SouBenWSC-27
❑ 91SouBenWSP-2873
❑ 92OklCit8F-1929
❑ 92OklCit8S-324
❑ 93ChaRanC-26
❑ 93ChaRanF-1955
❑ 94ChaRanF-2512

Thompson, Tommy (Rupert Lockhart)
❑ 47SigOil-71
❑ 47SunBre-22
❑ 94ConTSN-1244
❑ 94ConTSNB-1244

Thompson, Tony
❑ 86LitFalMP-28
❑ 93AusFut-24

Thompson, Travis
❑ 97PorRocG-28
❑ 98AshTouM-23

Thompson, Tyler

❑ 98St.CatSM-31
❑ 99TeaBesR-85
❑ 99TeaBesRG-85
❑ 99TeaBesRS-85

Thompson, William
❑ 90ChaRaiB-22
❑ 94LakTigC-23
❑ 94LakTigF-3040
❑ 96JacSunB-27

Thompson, Willie
❑ 78KnoKnoST-22
❑ 79KnoKnoST-26

Thomsen, Chris
❑ 91SouOreAC-7
❑ 91SouOreAP-3858
❑ 92SouOreAF-3429

Thomson, Bobby
❑ 47Exh-223
❑ 47HomBon-46
❑ 47PM1StaP1-210
❑ 48BluTin-41
❑ 48Bow-47
❑ 48GiaTeal-24
❑ 49Bow-18
❑ 49EurSta-124
❑ 49GiaTeal-25
❑ 50Bow-28
❑ 50Dra-9
❑ 50RoyDes-10
❑ 51Bow-126
❑ 52BerRos-65
❑ 52Bow-2
❑ 52CokTip-8
❑ 52CokTip-9
❑ 52RedMan-NL24
❑ 52RoyPre-16
❑ 52StaCalL-78A
❑ 52StaCalS-90C
❑ 52Top-313
❑ 53BraSpiaS3-24
❑ 53BraSpiaS7-13
❑ 53RedMan-NL25
❑ 53StaMey-9
❑ 54Bow-201
❑ 54BraJohC-34
❑ 54BraSpiaSP-18
❑ 55Bow-102
❑ 55BraGolS-22
❑ 55BraJohC-34
❑ 55BraSpiaSD-17
❑ 55RobGouS-23
❑ 55RobGouW-23
❑ 56Top-257
❑ 57Bra8x1-12
❑ 57BraSpiaS4-19
❑ 57Top-262
❑ 58GiaArmT-10
❑ 58GiaSFCB-24
❑ 58Hir-46
❑ 58Top-430
❑ 59Top-429
❑ 60NuHi-10
❑ 60RedSoxJP-10
❑ 60Top-153
❑ 60TopVen-153
❑ 61NuSco-480
❑ 70SpoCarfCOP-22
❑ 75Gia195T-27
❑ 75GiaAllT-11
❑ 76LauDiaJ-29
❑ 76SSPYanOD-9
❑ 76TayBow4-20
❑ 77BobParMBC-19
❑ 77GalGloG-39
❑ 77GalGloG-255
❑ 77Spo-514
❑ 79TCM50-202
❑ 80Bra195T-15
❑ 80GiaGreT-5
❑ 80PacLeg-115
❑ 82GSGalAG-20
❑ 83TopRep5-313
❑ 84FifNatC-5
❑ 85TCMPla1-43
❑ 88PacLegI-45
❑ 89SweBasG-133
❑ 89TopBasT-12
❑ 90HOFStiB-46
❑ 90PacLeg-106
❑ 90SweBasG-21
❑ 91Bow-410
❑ 91OriCro-456
❑ 91SweBasG-88
❑ 91TopArc1-330
❑ 92ActPacA-52
❑ 92BazQua5A-7
❑ 93UppDecAH-119
❑ 93UppDecAH-164
❑ 94MCIAmb-3
❑ 94TedWil-56
❑ 94UppDecAH-16
❑ 94UppDecAH-51
❑ 94UppDecAH-115
❑ 94UppDecAH1-16
❑ 94UppDecAH1-51
❑ 94UppDecAH1-115
❑ 94UppDecS-8
❑ 94UppDecTAE-58
❑ 94UppDecTAELD-LD10
❑ 95SkiBra-3
❑ 97FleMilDM-19
❑ 97FleMilDMR-19
❑ 99UppDecCLES-BT
❑ 99UppDecCLESC-BT
❑ 99UppDecCLMS-HR2

Thomson, Doug
❑ 78QuaCitAT-26

Thomson, John
❑ 94AshTouC-21
❑ 94AshTouF-1780
❑ 95Bow-67
❑ 95NewHavRTI-20
❑ 96DouAllB-16
❑ 96NewHavRB-24
❑ 96NewHavRUSTI-23
❑ 97Bow-115
❑ 97BowChr-133
❑ 97BowChrI-133
❑ 97BowChrIR-133
❑ 97BowChrR-133
❑ 97BowInt-115
❑ 98ColCho-87
❑ 98Don-184
❑ 98DonGolPP-184
❑ 98DonSilPP-184
❑ 98Fle-286
❑ 98Pac-289
❑ 98PacPlaB-289
❑ 98PacRedT-289
❑ 98PacSil-289
❑ 98StaCluFDI-335
❑ 98StaCluI-335
❑ 98StaCluOneK-335
❑ 98StaCluPP-335
❑ 98Top-26
❑ 98TopChr-26
❑ 98TopChrR-26
❑ 98TopDevR-26
❑ 98TopDia-26
❑ 98TopMiniC-26
❑ 98UppDec-83
❑ 98UppDecSF-51
❑ 99Fle-528
❑ 99FleSta9-528
❑ 99FleWarT-528
❑ 99Pac-153
❑ 99PacPlaB-153
❑ 99PacRed-153
❑ 99Top-372
❑ 99TopChr-372
❑ 99TopChrR-372
❑ 99TopMVPP-372
❑ 99UppDec-91
❑ 99UppDecEL1-91
❑ 99UppDecEL2-91

Thomson, Rob
❑ 88LakTigS-24
❑ 89EasLeaDDP-DD45
❑ 89LonTigP-1379
❑ 89UtiBluSP-25
❑ 90Ft.LauYS-25
❑ 91PriWilCC-26
❑ 91PriWilCP-1444
❑ 92AlbYanF-2350
❑ 93AlbYanF-2180
❑ 96ColCliB-1
❑ 97ColCliD-27

Thon, Dickie
❑ 76QuaCitAT-38
❑ 78AngFamF-37
❑ 78SalLakCGC-4
❑ 80Top-663
❑ 81AstPos-26
❑ 81Don-290
❑ 81Fle-277
❑ 81Top-209
❑ 81TopTra-844
❑ 82AstAstI-6
❑ 82AstPos-27
❑ 82Fle-235
❑ 82Top-404
❑ 83AllGamPI-117
❑ 83AstPos-32
❑ 83Don-191
❑ 83Fle-468
❑ 83FleSta-197
❑ 83FleSti-204
❑ 83Top-558
❑ 84AllGamPI-27
❑ 84AstMot-7
❑ 84AstPos-30
❑ 84Don-304
❑ 84DonActAS-44
❑ 84Fle-243
❑ 84Fle-634
❑ 84FleSti-1
❑ 84Nes792-692
❑ 84OPC-344
❑ 84SevCoi-W23
❑ 84Top-692
❑ 84TopRubD-22
❑ 84TopSti-64
❑ 84TopTif-692
❑ 85AstHouP-15
❑ 85AstMot-9
❑ 85Fle-364
❑ 85OPC-44
❑ 85Top-44
❑ 85TopMin-44
❑ 85TopRubD-23
❑ 85TopSti-63
❑ 85TopTif-44
❑ 86AstMilL-21
❑ 86AstMot-26
❑ 86AstPol-17
❑ 86AstTeal-15
❑ 86Don-572
❑ 86Fle-313
❑ 86OPC-166
❑ 86Top-166
❑ 86TopSti-33
❑ 86TopTat-1
❑ 86TopTif-166
❑ 87AstMot-25
❑ 87AstPol-14
❑ 87AstShoSPT-21
❑ 87Don-261
❑ 87Fle-70
❑ 87FleGlo-70
❑ 87Lea-196
❑ 87Top-386
❑ 87TopTif-386
❑ 88PadSmo-29
❑ 88ScoRoo-29T
❑ 88ScoRooG-29T
❑ 88TopTra-121T
❑ 88TopTraT-121T
❑ 89Bow-400
❑ 89BowTif-400
❑ 89Don-441
❑ 89Fle-320
❑ 89FleGlo-320
❑ 89OPC-181
❑ 89PhiTas-34
❑ 89Sco-234
❑ 89ScoRoo-55T
❑ 89Top-726
❑ 89TopTif-726
❑ 89TopTra-119T
❑ 89TopTraT-119T
❑ 89UppDec-258
❑ 89UppDec-704
❑ 90Bow-155
❑ 90BowTif-155
❑ 90Don-549
❑ 90DonBesN-81
❑ 90Fle-573
❑ 90FleCan-573
❑ 90Lea-105
❑ 90MLBBasB-4
❑ 90OPC-269
❑ 90PanSti-318
❑ 90PhiTas-28
❑ 90PubIntS-251
❑ 90Sco-142
❑ 90Top-269
❑ 90TopBig-115
❑ 90TopSti-115
❑ 90TopTif-269
❑ 90UppDec-439
❑ 91Bow-499
❑ 91Don-91
❑ 91Fle-412
❑ 91Lea-60
❑ 91OPC-439
❑ 91PanFreS-106
❑ 91PanSti-106
❑ 91PhiMed-34
❑ 91Sco-103
❑ 91StaClu-184
❑ 91Top-439
❑ 91TopDesS-439
❑ 91TopMic-439
❑ 91TopTif-439
❑ 91Ult-272
❑ 91UppDec-449
❑ 92Bow-162
❑ 92Don-510
❑ 92Fle-546
❑ 92Lea-180
❑ 92LeaBlaG-180
❑ 92OPC-557
❑ 92OPCPre-19
❑ 92PanSti-245
❑ 92Pin-394
❑ 92RanMot-12
❑ 92RanTeal-24
❑ 92Sco-24
❑ 92ScoProP-8
❑ 92ScoRoo-41T
❑ 92StaClu-868
❑ 92Stu-250
❑ 92Top-557
❑ 92TopGol-557
❑ 92TopGolW-557
❑ 92TopMic-557
❑ 92TopTra-118T
❑ 92TopTraG-118T
❑ 92Ult-447
❑ 92UppDec-150
❑ 92UppDec-769
❑ 93BrePol-25
❑ 93Lea-482
❑ 93LinVenB-305
❑ 93OPCPre-16
❑ 93PacSpa-318
❑ 93RanKee-358
❑ 93Ult-578
❑ 93UppDec-769
❑ 93UppDecGold-769
❑ 94BreMilB-278
❑ 94Fle-193
❑ 94Pac-345
❑ 94Sco-505
❑ 94ScoGolR-505

Thon, Frankie
❑ 78CedRapGT-28
❑ 80CliGiaT-17

Thoney, John
❑ 03BreE10-142
❑ 03BreE10-143
❑ 08RosComP-6
❑ 11MecDFT-47
❑ 11SpoLifCW-351
❑ 11SpoLifM-17

Thor, Audie
❑ 80MemChiT-30

Thorell, Billy
❑ 90NebCor-26

Thorell, Greg
❑ 90NebCor-25

Thorell, Mike
❑ 87AriWilP-16
❑ 88AriWilP-15

Thoren, Rick
❑ 77AppFoxT-26
❑ 78AppFoxT-20

Thormahlen, H.F.
❑ 90DodTar-801

Thormahlen, Herb
❑ 23WilChoV-161
❑ 28LaPre-10

Thormodsgard, Paul
❑ 78OPC-73
❑ 78Top-162
❑ 78TwiFriP-21
❑ 79TolMudHT-2
❑ 79Top-249

Thorn, John
❑ 90LitSunW-23

Thorn, Todd
❑ 96LanLugB-27
❑ 96MidLeaAB-41
❑ 97WilBluR-26
❑ 98WilBluRC-28

Thorne, Gary
❑ 87MetColP-53
❑ 88MetColP-55

Thornhil, Chad
❑ 95WatIndTI-28

Thornton, Al
❑ 86ElmPioRSP-24
❑ 87ElmPioBC-13
❑ 87ElmPioRC-13
❑ 88ElmPioC-20

Thornton, Andre
❑ 70RelPam-15
❑ 74OPC-604
❑ 74Top-604
❑ 75OPC-39
❑ 75Top-39
❑ 75TopMin-39
❑ 76BlaDis-62A
❑ 76BlaDis-62B
❑ 76BucDis-62A
❑ 76BucDis-62B
❑ 76CarDis-62A
❑ 76CarDis-62B
❑ 76CraDis-62A
❑ 76CraDis-62B
❑ 76DailsID-62A
❑ 76DailsID-62B
❑ 76ExpRed-31
❑ 76IsaDis-62A
❑ 76IsaDis-62B
❑ 76OPC-26
❑ 76OrbDis-62A
❑ 76OrbDis-62B
❑ 76RedBarD-62A
❑ 76RedBarD-62B
❑ 76SafDis-62A
❑ 76SafDis-62B
❑ 76Top-26
❑ 76TowCluD-62A
❑ 76TowCluD-62B
❑ 77IndTeal-23
❑ 77Spo-5307
❑ 77Spo-8418
❑ 78IndTeal-27
❑ 78OPC-114
❑ 78Top-148
❑ 79Hos-93
❑ 79OPC-140
❑ 79Top-280
❑ 79TopCom-6
❑ 80IndTeal-29
❑ 80Kel-28
❑ 80OPC-278
❑ 80Top-534
❑ 80TopSup-43
❑ 81Don-198
❑ 81OPC-128
❑ 81Top-388
❑ 81TopSti-70
❑ 82Don-324
❑ 82Fle-380
❑ 82FleSta-201
❑ 82Ind-34
❑ 82IndWhe-19
❑ 82OPC-161
❑ 82Top-746
❑ 82TopSti-174
❑ 83AllGamPI-7
❑ 83Don-211
❑ 83Fle-421
❑ 83Fle-635
❑ 83FleSta-198
❑ 83FleSti-241
❑ 83IndPos-35
❑ 83IndWhe-29
❑ 83Kel-26
❑ 83OPC-344
❑ 83Top-640
❑ 83TopGloS-3
❑ 83TopSti-55
❑ 84AllGamPI-98
❑ 84Don-25
❑ 84Don-25A
❑ 84Don-94
❑ 84DonActAS-15
❑ 84Fle-554
❑ 84FunFooP-125
❑ 84Ind-30
❑ 84IndWhe-29
❑ 84Nes792-115
❑ 84OPC-115
❑ 84Top-115
❑ 84TopRubD-22
❑ 84TopSti-255
❑ 84TopTif-115
❑ 85Don-468
❑ 85Fle-457
❑ 85FleStaS-32
❑ 85FleStaS-47
❑ 85Ind-32
❑ 85IndPol-29
❑ 85Lea-102
❑ 85OPC-272
❑ 85Top-475
❑ 85TopRubD-23
❑ 85TopSti-244
❑ 85TopTif-475
❑ 86Don-251
❑ 86Fle-596
❑ 86FleStiC-120
❑ 86IndOhH-29
❑ 86IndTeal-45
❑ 86Lea-129
❑ 86OPC-59
❑ 86Spo-171
❑ 86Top-59
❑ 86Top-336
❑ 86TopSti-208
❑ 86TopTat-3
❑ 86TopTif-59
❑ 86TopTif-336
❑ 87Don-279
❑ 87DonOpeD-108
❑ 87Fle-262
❑ 87FleGlo-262
❑ 87IndGat-29
❑ 87OPC-327
❑ 87Top-780
❑ 87TopTif-780
❑ 88RedFolSB-91
❑ 88Sco-231
❑ 88ScoGlo-231
❑ 89SweBasG-117
❑ 90SweBasG-47
❑ 93UppDecAH-120
❑ 93UppDecS-30

Thornton, Eric
❑ 89KinMetS-23
❑ 90PitMetP-3

Thornton, Frank
❑ 09ObaT21-319
❑ 11BigEatEU-19
❑ 11Zee-80
❑ 12ObaPreT-68

Thornton, Lou
❑ 85BluJayFS-29
❑ 85FleUpd-121
❑ 86Fle-71
❑ 86OPC-18
❑ 86SyrChiP-25
❑ 86Top-488
❑ 86TopTif-488
❑ 87SyrChiP-1930
❑ 87SyrChiT-21
❑ 89BlaYNPRWLU-18
❑ 89BufBisC-22
❑ 89BufBisP-1669
❑ 89TidTidP-1954
❑ 90CMC-362
❑ 90MetColP-50
❑ 90MetKah-1
❑ 90ProAAAF-290
❑ 90TidTidC-11
❑ 90TidTidP-559
❑ 90TopTVM-34
❑ 91MetWIZ-406

Thornton, Matt
❑ 98EveAquG-23
❑ 99TeaBesR-86
❑ 99TeaBesRFS-23
❑ 99TeaBesRG-86
❑ 99TeaBesRS-86

Thornton, Paul
❑ 93ElmPioC-22
❑ 93ElmPioF-3822
❑ 94KanCouCC-24
❑ 94KanCouCF-160
❑ 94KanCouCTI-27
❑ 95BreCouMF-246
❑ 96PorSeaDB-26

Thornton, Woodie A.
❑ 09T206-520
❑ 10CouT21-66

Thorp, Bradley S.
❑ 81VerBeaDT-22

Thorpe, A.D.
❑ 98MacBraM-21

Thorpe, Bob (Benjamin R.)
❑ 52Top-367
❑ 53BraSpiaS3-25
❑ 55DesMoiHB-19
❑ 77FriOneYW-5
❑ 82Bow195E-258
❑ 83Bra53F-18
❑ 83TopRep5-367

Thorpe, Jim (James F.)
❑ 09ColChiE-288
❑ 09MaxPubP-13
❑ 12ColRedB-288

❑ 12ColTinT-288
❑ 15SpoNewM-176
❑ 22Zee-54
❑ 33SpoKin-6
❑ 59FleWil-70
❑ 68SCFOldT-55
❑ 73BooProC-13
❑ 73FleWilD-3
❑ 81ConTSN-31
❑ 87ConSer2-59
❑ 87SpoCubG-1
❑ 87SpoRea-25
❑ 88ConSer4-28
❑ 88FriBasCM-7
❑ 92ConTSN-403
❑ 92ConTSNCI-22
❑ 93ConTSN-771

Thorpe, Michael
❑ 86BelMarCr-111
❑ 87WauTimP-19

Thorpe, Paul
❑ 86HagSunP-25
❑ 87HagSunP-23
❑ 88ChaKniTI-17
❑ 89HagSunB-19
❑ 89HagSunP-285
❑ 89HagSunS-21
❑ 90EasLeaAP-EL10
❑ 90HagSunB-26
❑ 90HagSunP-1414
❑ 90HagSunS-24

Thorsen, Elmer
❑ 09ObaT21-94
❑ 09ObaT21-266
❑ 10BisCoaLE99-28
❑ 12ObaPreT-15

Thorson, Doc (Brian)
❑ 79HolMilT-16
❑ 80BurBeeT-9
❑ 81VanCanT-7
❑ 82VanCanT-24
❑ 84AlbA'sT-9
❑ 85HunStaJ-NNO
❑ 88MadMusP-24
❑ 90HunStaB-26
❑ 91HunStaC-10
❑ 92MadMusC-28
❑ 97HunStaTI-26

Thorton, John
❑ 86ElPasDP-21

Thoutsis, Paul
❑ 87WinHavRSP-27
❑ 89St.PetCS-26
❑ 90ArkTraGS-28
❑ 92NewBriRSF-448
❑ 92NewBriRSS-498
❑ 93NewBriRSF-1236
❑ 94PawRedSDD-24
❑ 94PawRedSF-957
❑ 95ColCliP-30
❑ 95ColCliTI-30

Thrams, Jeff
❑ 89BoiHawP-1988

Threadgill, Chris
❑ 88BenBucL-12
❑ 89PalSprACLC-42
❑ 89PalSprAP-472

Threadgill, George
❑ 85BurRanT-8
❑ 86DayBealP-28
❑ 86FloStaLAP-46
❑ 88TulDriTI-2
❑ 89TulDriGS-26
❑ 90TulDriTI-26
❑ 92DurBulC-27
❑ 92DurBulF-1117
❑ 93ChaRaiC-28
❑ 93ChaRaiF-1929
❑ 94ChaRivC-28
❑ 94ChaRivF-2691
❑ 94ChaRivF-2692
❑ 95ButCopKtl-23

Threadgill, Henry
❑ 90QuaCitAGS-20

Threatt, Tony
❑ 83TamTarT-24

Thrift, Jim
❑ 87SalBucP-18
❑ 89PenPilS-26
❑ 90KinMetB-25
❑ 90KinMetS-26
❑ 91PitMetC-25
❑ 91PitMetP-3438
❑ 92PitMetC-18
❑ 92PitMetF-3310
❑ 93RocRoyC-30
❑ 93RocRoyF-733
❑ 94IndIndF-1826
❑ 95IndIndF-113
❑ 96IndIndB-3

Throneberry, M. Faye
❑ 52Top-376
❑ 53Top-49
❑ 55Top-163
❑ 57Top-356
❑ 58SeaTeal-25
❑ 59Top-534
❑ 60Lea-136
❑ 60Top-9
❑ 60TopVen-9
❑ 61AngJayP-11
❑ 61Top-282
❑ 83TopRep5-376
❑ 91TopArc1-49

Throneberry, Marv
❑ 58Top-175
❑ 59Top-326
❑ 60A'sJayP-9
❑ 60Top-436
❑ 61A'sTeal-20
❑ 61AthJayP-22
❑ 61Pos-85A
❑ 61Pos-85B
❑ 61Top-57
❑ 61TopStal-166
❑ 62BalOriP-29
❑ 63Jel-194
❑ 63MetJayP-12
❑ 63Pos-194
❑ 63Top-78
❑ 74MetOriEB-15
❑ 79TCM50-173
❑ 82MetGal62-1
❑ 88PacLegl-48
❑ 90PacLeg-62
❑ 90SweBasG-77
❑ 91MetWIZ-407
❑ 91OriCro-457
❑ 91SweBasG-89
❑ 93UppDecAH-121
❑ 94UppDecAH-94
❑ 94UppDecAH1-94

Throop, George
❑ 75OmaRoyTI-16
❑ 76OmaRoyTT-24
❑ 76OPC-591
❑ 76Top-591

Thrower, Jake
❑ 97IdaFalBTI-25
❑ 98CliLumG-24

Thrower, Keith
❑ 84ModA'sC-21
❑ 85TacTigC-128
❑ 86TacTigP-22

Thurberg, Tom
❑ 77WauMetT-20
❑ 82ArkTraT-10
❑ 83LouRedR-25

Thurlby, Burdy
❑ 55DesMoiHB-20

Thurman, Corey
❑ 98LanLugQ-12
❑ 98MidLeaPM-14
❑ 98SpoIndG-32

Thurman, Gary
❑ 85Ft.MyeRT-18
❑ 86MemChiSTOS-26
❑ 86MemChiTOS-26
❑ 86SouLeaAJ-4
❑ 87OmaRoyP-6
❑ 88Don-44
❑ 88DonRoo-33
❑ 88Fle-272
❑ 88FleGlo-272
❑ 88FleMin-29
❑ 88Lea-44
❑ 88OmaRoyC-14
❑ 88OmaRoyP-1521
❑ 88RoySmo-6
❑ 88RoyTeal-34
❑ 88Sco-631
❑ 88ScoGlo-631
❑ 88ScoYouS2-25
❑ 88Spo-223
❑ 88StaLinRo-18
❑ 88Top-89
❑ 88TopClo-114
❑ 88TopTif-89
❑ 89Don-498
❑ 89Fle-296
❑ 89FleGlo-296
❑ 89PanSti-348
❑ 89ScoHot1R-24
❑ 89Top-323
❑ 89TopTif-323
❑ 89UppDec-347
❑ 90CMC-194
❑ 90Don-416
❑ 90Fle-121
❑ 90FleCan-121
❑ 90OmaRoyC-19
❑ 90OPC-276
❑ 90PublntS-359
❑ 90Top-276
❑ 90TopTif-276
❑ 91Bow-316
❑ 91Fle-573
❑ 91RoyPol-23
❑ 91StaClu-306
❑ 91UltUpd-29
❑ 92Don-346
❑ 92Fle-172
❑ 92OPC-494
❑ 92RoyPol-26
❑ 92Sco-512
❑ 92StaClu-131
❑ 92Top-494
❑ 92TopGol-494
❑ 92TopGolW-494
❑ 92TopMic-494
❑ 92UppDec-629
❑ 93Don-629
❑ 93Fle-626
❑ 93PacSpa-450
❑ 93StaClu-52
❑ 93StaCluFDI-52
❑ 93StaCluMOP-52
❑ 93TigGat-24
❑ 94NasSouF-1263
❑ 94Sco-268
❑ 94ScoGolR-268
❑ 95TacRaiTI-22
❑ 96NorTidB-27
❑ 97NorTid-32
❑ 97NorTidB-31
❑ 98VanCanG-27

Thurman, Mike
❑ 94SigRooDP-29
❑ 94SigRooDPS-29
❑ 94StaCluDP-81
❑ 94StaCluDPFDI-81
❑ 94TopTra-74T
❑ 94VerExpF-3910
❑ 95Top-259
❑ 96BesAutSA-77
❑ 96WesPalBEB-15
❑ 97BesAutAS-61
❑ 97BesAutP-R16
❑ 97EasLeaTPB-12
❑ 97HarSen-24
❑ 97TexAllM-56
❑ 98Fle-298
❑ 99Fle-513
❑ 99FleSta9-513
❑ 99FleWarT-513

Thurman, Robert
❑ 52MotCoo-49
❑ 57Kah-28
❑ 57Top-279
❑ 58RedEnq-40
❑ 58Top-34
❑ 59RedEnq-27
❑ 59RedShiBS-22
❑ 59Top-541
❑ 60SeaPop-17
❑ 86NegLeaF-60
❑ 87NegLeaPD-39
❑ 92NegLeaRLI-59

Thurmond, Mark
❑ 82HawlsIT-21
❑ 83LasVegSBHN-21
❑ 83PadTeal-26
❑ 84Don-505
❑ 84Fle-315
❑ 84Nes792-481
❑ 84PadMot-26
❑ 84PadSmo-25
❑ 84Top-481
❑ 84TopTif-481
❑ 85Don-284
❑ 85Fle-46
❑ 85Lea-149
❑ 85OPC-236
❑ 85PadMot-21
❑ 85Top-236
❑ 85TopMin-236
❑ 85TopTif-236
❑ 86Don-261
❑ 86Fle-337
❑ 86Top-37
❑ 86TopTif-37
❑ 87Don-543
❑ 87Fle-166
❑ 87FleGlo-166
❑ 87TigCaiD-17
❑ 87Top-361
❑ 87TopTif-361
❑ 88Don-599
❑ 88Fle-73
❑ 88FleGlo-73
❑ 88OriPos-38
❑ 88Sco-382
❑ 88ScoGlo-382
❑ 88StaLinO-17
❑ 88Top-552
❑ 88TopTif-552
❑ 89BalOriP-35
❑ 89OriFreB-21
❑ 89Top-152
❑ 89TopTif-152
❑ 89UppDec-571
❑ 90Don-612
❑ 90Fle-191
❑ 90FleCan-191
❑ 90OPC-758
❑ 90PublntS-588
❑ 90Sco-350
❑ 90Top-758
❑ 90TopTif-758
❑ 91Fle-274
❑ 91LinDriAAA-389
❑ 91OriCro-458
❑ 91PhoFirLD-389

Thurmond, Travis
❑ 94BoiHawC-26
❑ 94BoiHawF-3356
❑ 95BoiHawTI-28
❑ 95CedRapKTI-37

Thurston, Jerrey
❑ 91ChaRaiC-13
❑ 91ChaRaiP-98
❑ 91Cla/Bes-102
❑ 91SpoIndC-21
❑ 91SpoIndP-3952
❑ 92WatDiaC-11
❑ 92WatDiaF-2145
❑ 93WicWraF-2981
❑ 94WicWraF-193
❑ 97VanCanB-27
❑ 98MidAngG-26

Thurston, Sloppy (Hollis)
❑ 20Zee-98
❑ 20Zee-99
❑ 21Zee-110
❑ 22Zee-92
❑ 25Exh-80
❑ 26Exh-80
❑ 28ExhPCL-28
❑ 29Zee-145
❑ 33Zee-46
❑ 33Zee-47
❑ 90DodTar-802
❑ 93ConTSN-735
❑ 94ConTSN-1264
❑ 94ConTSNB-1264

Tiamo, Jesus
❑ 80VenLeaS-148
❑ 95LinVen-162

Tiant, Luis
❑ 64TopRooAB-34A
❑ 65Kah-40
❑ 65OPC-145
❑ 65Top-145
❑ 65TopTral-30
❑ 66IndTeal-11
❑ 66Top-285
❑ 66TopVen-285
❑ 67CokCapl-1
❑ 67DexPre-206
❑ 67Top-377
❑ 68Kah-B33
❑ 68Top-532
❑ 69Kah-B19
❑ 69MilBra-271
❑ 69MLBOffS-44
❑ 69MLBPin-28
❑ 69OPC-7
❑ 69OPC-9
❑ 69OPC-11
❑ 69OPCDec-22
❑ 69Top-7
❑ 69Top-9
❑ 69Top-11
❑ 69Top-560
❑ 69TopDec-7
❑ 69TopDecl-43
❑ 69TopSta-169
❑ 69TopSup-13
❑ 69TopTeaP-13
❑ 69TraSta-3
❑ 70DayDaiNM-70
❑ 70Kel-56
❑ 70MLBOffS-239
❑ 70OPC-231
❑ 70Top-231
❑ 70TwiSupV-11
❑ 70TwiTeal-10
❑ 71MLBOffS-475
❑ 71OPC-95
❑ 71Top-95
❑ 72MilBra-342
❑ 72RedSoxTI-22
❑ 73LinPor-30
❑ 73OPC-65
❑ 73OPC-270
❑ 73SevTraC-75
❑ 73Top-65
❑ 73Top-270
❑ 74OPC-167
❑ 74Top-167
❑ 74TopDecE-27
❑ 74TopSta-138
❑ 75Hos-102
❑ 75Kel-49
❑ 75OPC-430
❑ 75Top-430
❑ 75TopMin-430
❑ 76BlaDis-63
❑ 76BucDis-63
❑ 76CarDis-63
❑ 76CraDis-63
❑ 76DailsID-63
❑ 76Hos-23
❑ 76HosTwi-23
❑ 76IsaDis-63
❑ 76LinSup-108
❑ 76OPC-130
❑ 76OrbDis-63
❑ 76RedBarD-63
❑ 76RedSoxSM-14
❑ 76SafDis-63
❑ 76SSP-424
❑ 76Top-130
❑ 76Top-461
❑ 76TowCluD-63
❑ 77BurCheD-34
❑ 77ChiWilD-65
❑ 77DailsID-65
❑ 77DetCaeD-65
❑ 77HolInnD-65
❑ 77Hos-10
❑ 77MSADis-65
❑ 77OPC-87
❑ 77RCColC-64
❑ 77SagDis-65
❑ 77sDis-65
❑ 77Spo-3709
❑ 77Top-258
❑ 77TopCloS-48
❑ 77WenDis-65
❑ 77ZipDis-65
❑ 78OPC-124
❑ 78PapGinD-23
❑ 78SSP270-176
❑ 78Top-345
❑ 78WifBalD-75
❑ 79OPC-299
❑ 79Top-575
❑ 79YanBurK-8
❑ 79YanPicA-33
❑ 80OPC-19
❑ 80Top-35
❑ 80YanPhoA-24
❑ 81Don-231
❑ 81Fle-82
❑ 81PorBeaT-23
❑ 81Top-627
❑ 82OPC-160
❑ 82Top-160
❑ 83Don-542
❑ 83OPC-179
❑ 83Top-178
❑ 83Top-179
❑ 89PacSenL-77
❑ 89T/MSenL-105
❑ 89T/MSenL-118
❑ 90EliSenL-119
❑ 91LinDri-11
❑ 91SweBasG-90
❑ 92ActPacA-46
❑ 92GulCoaDF-3585
❑ 92YanWIZ7-151
❑ 92YanWIZ8-191
❑ 93MetIma-20
❑ 93TedWil-6
❑ 93UppDecAH-122
❑ 93UppDecS-28
❑ 93YakBeaC-29
❑ 93YakBeaF-3902
❑ 94GreFalDSP-29
❑ 94TedWilM-M36
❑ 94TopSpa-L10
❑ 94UppDecAH-87
❑ 94UppDecAH1-87
❑ 94UppDecTAE-73
❑ 95LinVen-304

Tibbs, Jay
❑ 82LynMetT-19
❑ 83LynMetT-16
❑ 84TidTidT-15
❑ 85Don-262
❑ 85Fle-553
❑ 85RedYea-17
❑ 85Top-573
❑ 85TopTif-573
❑ 86BasStaB-110
❑ 86Don-262
❑ 86ExpPos-16
❑ 86ExpProPa-8
❑ 86Fle-194
❑ 86FleUpd-116
❑ 86Top-176
❑ 86TopTif-176
❑ 86TopTra-114T
❑ 86TopTraT-114T
❑ 87Don-282
❑ 87ExpPos-31
❑ 87Fle-333
❑ 87FleGlo-333
❑ 87Lea-207
❑ 87OPC-9
❑ 87Top-9
❑ 87TopTif-9
❑ 88OPC-282
❑ 88OriFreB-53
❑ 88OriPos-39
❑ 88RocRedWC-10
❑ 88RocRedWP-201
❑ 88RocRedWTI-24
❑ 88Sco-608
❑ 88ScoGlo-608
❑ 88Top-464
❑ 88TopTif-464
❑ 89BalOriP-36
❑ 89Fle-624
❑ 89FleGlo-624
❑ 89RocRedWP-1633
❑ 89Sco-262
❑ 89Top-271
❑ 89TopTif-271
❑ 89UppDec-655
❑ 90BalOriP-27
❑ 90Fle-192
❑ 90FleCan-192
❑ 90OPC-677
❑ 90PublntS-589
❑ 90Sco-480
❑ 90Top-677
❑ 90TopTif-677
❑ 91OriCro-459

Tiburcio, Freddy
❑ 82DurBulT-12
❑ 83DurBulT-14
❑ 85DomLeaS-169
❑ 85GreBraTI-20
❑ 86GreBraTI-20
❑ 87TolMudHP-11
❑ 87TolMudHT-6

Tickell, Brian
❑ 95AubAstTI-23

Tides, Tidewater
❑ 87IntLeaAT-40

Tidrow, Dick
❑ 70WicAerM-18
❑ 72OPC-506
❑ 72Top-506
❑ 73IndTeal-25
❑ 73OPC-339
❑ 73Top-339
❑ 74OPC-231
❑ 74Top-231
❑ 74TopSta-170
❑ 75OPC-241
❑ 75Top-241
❑ 75TopMin-241

❑ 75YanSSP-23
❑ 76OPC-248
❑ 76SSP-428
❑ 76Top-248
❑ 77OPC-235
❑ 77Top-461
❑ 77YanBurK-9
❑ 78SSP270-10
❑ 78Top-179
❑ 78YanBurK-6
❑ 78YanPhoA-26
❑ 78YanSSPD-10
❑ 79OPC-37
❑ 79Top-89
❑ 80Top-594
❑ 81CokTeaS-22
❑ 81Don-551
❑ 81Fle-299
❑ 81Top-352
❑ 82CubRedL-41
❑ 82Don-477
❑ 82Fle-604
❑ 82FleSta-99
❑ 82OPC-249
❑ 82Top-699
❑ 82TopSti-27
❑ 83Fle-510
❑ 83FleSta-199
❑ 83FleSti-126
❑ 83Top-787
❑ 83TopSti-225
❑ 83TopTra-112T
❑ 83WhiSoxTV-41
❑ 84Fle-72
❑ 84Nes792-153
❑ 84Top-153
❑ 84TopTif-153
❑ 91MetWIZ-408
❑ 92YanWIZ7-152
❑ 93UppDecS-14

Tidwell, Danny
❑ 75AndRanT-25
❑ 76AshTouT-19

Tidwell, Jason
❑ 93KanCouCTI-24
❑ 94BreCouMC-20
❑ 94BreCouMF-13
❑ 98ChaLooG-26

Tidwell, Mike
❑ 91GenCubC-22
❑ 91GenCubP-4216
❑ 92PeoChiC-3
❑ 92PeoChiTI-28
❑ 93DayCubC-20
❑ 93DayCubF-858

Tiedeman, John
❑ 09ObaT21-283
❑ 11PacCoaBD-65
❑ 11Zee-40
❑ 12HomRunKE-30
❑ 12ObaPreT-32
❑ 12PCLPin-24
❑ 12Zee-48

Tiefenauer, Bob
❑ 55CarHunW-27
❑ 59Top-501
❑ 62Col45'HC-18
❑ 62Top-227
❑ 62TopStaI-131
❑ 64Top-522
❑ 65BraTeal-12
❑ 65OPC-23
❑ 65Top-23
❑ 68Top-269
❑ 68TopVen-269
❑ 80PenPilBT-10
❑ 80PenPilCT-27
❑ 83ReaPhiT-24
❑ 85PorBeaC-47
❑ 86PorBeaP-22
❑ 87SpaPhiP-22
❑ 88BatCliP-1662
❑ 92YanWIZ6-127

Tiefenthaler, Verle
❑ 60TacBan-20
❑ 61TacBan-20
❑ 77FriOneYW-82

Tiernan, Mike
❑ 87OldJudN-492
❑ 88AugBecN-34
❑ 88GandBCGCE-40
❑ 88WG1CarG-44
❑ 89EdgR.WG-8
❑ 95NewN566-176

Tierney, Cotton (James A.)
❑ 20WalMaiW-55
❑ 21Exh-176
❑ 21Exh-177
❑ 22E120-224
❑ 22W572-106
❑ 22W573-131
❑ 23WilChoV-162
❑ 27Zee-8
❑ 90DodTar-803

Tierney, Jake
❑ 89NiaFalRP-30

Tierney, Larry
❑ 89NiaFalRP-30

Tierney, Martin
❑ 29Zee-32

Tierney, Tom
❑ 91IdaFalBP-4343

Tiesiera, Will
❑ 53SanFraSTI-20

Tietje, Les
❑ 35DiaMatCS3T1-141
❑ 94ConTSN-1283
❑ 94ConTSNB-1283

Tiger, Tacoma
❑ 81TacTigT-28
❑ 83TacTigT-24

Tigers, Cincinnati
❑ 92NegLeaRLI-100
❑ 93NegLeaRL2-90

Tigers, Detroit
❑ 07TigACDPP-29
❑ 09SpoNewSM-19
❑ 09TigHMTP-4
❑ 10E-UOraBSC-2
❑ 13FatT20-4
❑ 36R31Pre-G17
❑ 36R31Pre-L14
❑ 38BasTabP-46
❑ 56Top-213
❑ 57Top-198
❑ 58Top-397A
❑ 58Top-397B
❑ 59Top-329
❑ 60Top-72
❑ 60TopTat-68
❑ 60TopVen-72
❑ 61Top-51
❑ 61TopMagR-1
❑ 62GuyPotCP-7
❑ 62Top-24
❑ 62TopVen-24
❑ 63GadFunC-37
❑ 63Top-552
❑ 64Top-67
❑ 64TopTatI-8
❑ 64TopVen-67
❑ 65OPC-173
❑ 65Top-173
❑ 66Top-583
❑ 66TopRubI-108
❑ 67Top-378
❑ 68LauWorS-4
❑ 68LauWorS-32
❑ 68LauWorS-37
❑ 68Top-528
❑ 69FleCloS-9
❑ 69FleCloS-46
❑ 69TopStaA-9
❑ 70FleWorS-4
❑ 70FleWorS-31
❑ 70FleWorS-37
❑ 70FleWorS-65
❑ 70Top-579
❑ 71FleWorS-5
❑ 71FleWorS-7
❑ 71FleWorS-32
❑ 71FleWorS-38
❑ 71FleWorS-66
❑ 71OPC-336
❑ 71Top-336
❑ 71TopTat-78
❑ 72OPC-487
❑ 72Top-487
❑ 73OPC-191
❑ 73OPCBTC-9
❑ 73Top-191
❑ 73TopBluTC-9
❑ 74OPC-94
❑ 74OPCTC-9
❑ 74Top-94
❑ 74TopStaA-9
❑ 74TopTeaC-9
❑ 78Top-404
❑ 81TigDetN-7
❑ 81TigDetN-13
❑ 81TigDetN-22
❑ 81TigDetN-53
❑ 81TigDetN-61
❑ 81TigDetN-83
❑ 81TigDetN-95
❑ 81TigDetN-98
❑ 81TigDetN-108
❑ 81TigDetN-112
❑ 81TigSecNP-16
❑ 81TigSecNP-32
❑ 83FleSta-233
❑ 83FleSti-NNO
❑ 83FleSti-NNO
❑ 84TigTeal-2
❑ 87FleStiWBC-S1
❑ 87SpoTeaL-15
❑ 87Top-631
❑ 87TopTif-631
❑ 88FleStiWBC-S8
❑ 88FleWaxBC-C13
❑ 88PanSti-460
❑ 88RedFolSB-110
❑ 89FleWaxBC-C13
❑ 90PubIntS-643
❑ 90RedFolSB-112
❑ 91PanCanT1-123
❑ 94ImpProP-6
❑ 94Sco-322
❑ 94ScoGolR-322
❑ 95PacPriTL-6
❑ 95PanSti-152
❑ 96PanSti-147
❑ 99Vic-140

Tigers, LSU
❑ 93LSUTigM-1

Tijerina, Tano
❑ 94HelBreF-3614
❑ 94HelBreSP-6
❑ 96HelBreTI-26

Tijerina, Tony
❑ 91PitMetC-1
❑ 91PitMetP-3426
❑ 92St.LucMCB-22
❑ 92St.LucMF-1750
❑ 93CapCitBC-22
❑ 93CapCitBF-464
❑ 94BinMetF-707
❑ 95BinMetTI-10
❑ 96StLucMTI-21
❑ 97PitMet-3
❑ 98PitMetM-3

Tiller, Brad
❑ 94BurIndC-24
❑ 94BurIndF-3806
❑ 96WatIndTI-31
❑ 96WesOahCHWB-25
❑ 97WatIndTI-30
❑ 98ColRedSM-19

Tillman, Bennie
❑ 94IdaFalBF-3601
❑ 94IdaFalBSP-5

Tillman, Darren
❑ 91HunCubC-25
❑ 91HunCubP-3350
❑ 92GenCubC-24
❑ 92GenCubF-1574
❑ 92PeoChiC-2

Tillman, J. Bob
❑ 61SeaPop-23
❑ 61SeaPop-24
❑ 61UniOil-S9
❑ 62Top-368
❑ 63Top-384
❑ 64Top-112
❑ 64TopVen-112
❑ 65OPC-222
❑ 65RedSoxTI-14
❑ 65Top-222
❑ 66OPC-178
❑ 66Top-178
❑ 66TopVen-178
❑ 67CokCapRS-10
❑ 67DexPre-207
❑ 67OPC-36
❑ 67Top-36
❑ 67TopRedSS-23
❑ 68BraPos-30
❑ 68OPC-174
❑ 68Top-174
❑ 68TopVen-174
❑ 69AtlBraBPPS-22
❑ 69MilBra-272
❑ 69Top-374
❑ 70Top-668
❑ 71MLBOffS-453
❑ 71OPC-244
❑ 71Top-244
❑ 72MilBra-343
❑ 78TCM60I-172
❑ 81RedSoxBG2S-124
❑ 92YanWIZ6-128

Tillman, Ken
❑ 81RedPioT-20

Tillman, Rusty
❑ 82TidTidT-11
❑ 83TidTidT-19
❑ 84TidTidT-9
❑ 85LasVegSC-102
❑ 86TacTigP-23
❑ 88PhoFirC-21
❑ 88PhoFirP-59
❑ 89PhoFirC-15
❑ 89PhoFirP-1479
❑ 91MetWIZ-409

Tillman, Tony (Tommy)
❑ 89BurIndS-23
❑ 90BurIndP-3008

Tillmon, Darrell
❑ 95MicBatCTI-28

Tillotson, Thad
❑ 67Top-553
❑ 67YanPhoS-96
❑ 81TCM60I-462
❑ 92YanWIZ6-129

Tilma, Tommy
❑ 90WicStaSGD-34

Tilmon, Pat
❑ 88BurBraP-6
❑ 89DurBullS-21
❑ 89DurBullS-21
❑ 89DurBulTI-21
❑ 90DurBulTI-14

Tilton, Ira
❑ 96BatCliTI-20
❑ 97PieBolWB-28
❑ 98PieBolWM-27

Timberlake, Don
❑ 83PeoSunF-13
❑ 85MidAngT-12
❑ 86MidAngP-22

Timberlake, Gary
❑ 83Pil69G-4

Timbers, Wausau
❑ 82WauTimF-2

Timko, Andy
❑ 81MiaOriT-13
❑ 90HagSunDGB-32

Timko, John
❑ 92NiaFalRC-20
❑ 92NiaFalRF-3328
❑ 93BriTigC-21

Timlin, Mike
❑ 88MyrBeaBJP-1184
❑ 89DunBluJS-19
❑ 90DunBluJS-20
❑ 90FloStaLAS-45
❑ 90StaFS7-67
❑ 91BluJayFS-29
❑ 91BluJayS-7
❑ 91Bow-15
❑ 91Cla3-T90
❑ 91DonRoo-27
❑ 91FleUpd-68
❑ 91Lea-525
❑ 91OPCPre-122
❑ 91ScoRoo-85T
❑ 91TopTra-121T
❑ 91TopTraT-121T
❑ 91UppDec-785
❑ 92Don-301
❑ 92Fle-343
❑ 92FleRooS-8
❑ 92OPC-108
❑ 92OPCPre-172
❑ 92Sco-214
❑ 92Sco100RS-58
❑ 92StaClu-493
❑ 92SyrChiMB-23
❑ 92Top-108
❑ 92TopDeb91-172
❑ 92TopGol-108
❑ 92TopGolW-108
❑ 92TopMic-108
❑ 92UppDec-409
❑ 93BluJayD-25
❑ 93BluJayD4-22
❑ 93BluJayFS-31
❑ 93Don-87
❑ 93Fle-701
❑ 93Lea-465
❑ 93OPC-295
❑ 93PacSpa-657
❑ 93Sco-410
❑ 93StaClu-120
❑ 93StaCluFDI-120
❑ 93StaCluMOP-120
❑ 93Top-564
❑ 93TopGol-564
❑ 93TopInaM-564
❑ 93TopInaR-564
❑ 93TopMic-564
❑ 93Toy-42
❑ 93Ult-294
❑ 93UppDec-322
❑ 93UppDecGold-322
❑ 94BluJayUSPC-2S
❑ 94BluJayUSPC-9D
❑ 94Fla-123
❑ 94Fle-345
❑ 94Sco-298
❑ 94ScoGolR-298
❑ 94StaClu-441
❑ 94StaCluFDI-441
❑ 94StaCluGR-441
❑ 94StaCluMOP-441
❑ 94StaCluT-180
❑ 94StaCluTFDI-180
❑ 94Top-333
❑ 94TopGol-333
❑ 94TopSpa-333
❑ 94Ult-144
❑ 95BluJayOH-33
❑ 95BluJayUSPC-3H
❑ 95BluJayUSPC-10S
❑ 95FleUpd-30
❑ 95Top-58
❑ 96BluJayOH-32
❑ 96Fle-284
❑ 96FleTif-284
❑ 96LeaSigEA-202
❑ 97BluJayB-12
❑ 97BluJayOH-34
❑ 97BluJayS-19
❑ 97ColCho-494
❑ 97Fle-250
❑ 97FleTif-250
❑ 97Pac-229
❑ 97PacLigB-229
❑ 97PacSil-229
❑ 97Sco-411
❑ 97ScoArtPWB-411
❑ 97ScoResC-411
❑ 97ScoShoS-411
❑ 97ScoShoSAP-411
❑ 97StaClu-171
❑ 97StaCluMOP-171
❑ 97Top-23
❑ 97Ult-449
❑ 97UltGolME-449
❑ 97UltPlaME-449
❑ 97UppDec-519
❑ 98MarSco-7
❑ 98MarScoP-7
❑ 98PacInvGems-98
❑ 98PacOnl-698
❑ 98PacOnlR-698
❑ 98PacOnlWC-698
❑ 98Sco-95
❑ 98ScoSS-PP42
❑ 98ScoSSAP-PP42
❑ 98Top-422
❑ 98TopChr-422
❑ 98TopChrR-422
❑ 98TopDevR-422
❑ 98TopDia-422
❑ 98TopMiniC-422
❑ 99Fle-521
❑ 99FleSta9-521
❑ 99FleWarT-521
❑ 99Pac-404
❑ 99PacPlaB-404
❑ 99PacRed-404

Timm, Dan
❑ 98BurBeeM-21

Timmerman, Heath
❑ 97ButCopKB-28
❑ 97ButCopKK-28
❑ 98CedRapKTI-30

Timmerman, Tom
❑ 70Top-554
❑ 71MLBOffS-408
❑ 71OPC-296
❑ 71Top-296
❑ 72OPC-239
❑ 72Top-239
❑ 73OPC-413
❑ 73TigJew-20
❑ 73Top-413
❑ 74OPC-327
❑ 74Top-327

Timmons, Ozzie
❑ 91GenCubC-23
❑ 91GenCubP-4233
❑ 92StaCluD-187
❑ 92UppDecML-162
❑ 92UppDecMLPotY-PY8
❑ 93Bow-552
❑ 93ClaFS7-29
❑ 93OrlCubF-2800
❑ 94ActPac-40
❑ 94Bow-466
❑ 94ExcFS7-169
❑ 94IowCubF-1288
❑ 94UppDecML-180
❑ 95ColCho-545T
❑ 95Exc-170
❑ 95Fla-335
❑ 95FleUpd-130
❑ 95SigRooOJ-32
❑ 95SigRooOJP-32
❑ 95SigRooOJPS-32
❑ 95SigRooOJS-32
❑ 95StaClu-605
❑ 95StaCluMOP-605
❑ 95StaCluSTWS-605
❑ 95Sum-154
❑ 95SumNthD-154
❑ 95Top-599
❑ 95UppDec-248
❑ 95UppDecED-248
❑ 95UppDecEDG-248
❑ 95UppDecML-213
❑ 95UppDecMLFS-213
❑ 96ColCho-88
❑ 96ColChoGS-88
❑ 96ColChoSS-88
❑ 96Don-28
❑ 96DonPreP-28
❑ 96Fla-226
❑ 96Fle-331
❑ 96FleTif-331
❑ 96Lea-59
❑ 96LeaPrePB-59
❑ 96LeaPrePG-59
❑ 96LeaPrePS-59
❑ 96LeaSigA-223
❑ 96LeaSigAG-224
❑ 96LeaSigAS-224
❑ 96Ult-172
❑ 96UltGolM-172
❑ 97IndInd-24
❑ 98IndIndQ-33

Timmons, Shayne
❑ 94St.CatBJC-25
❑ 94St.CatBJF-3648

Tincup, Frank
❑ 44CenFlo-23

Tingle, Darrel
❑ 87OneYanP-3
❑ 88PriWilYS-22

Tingley, Ron
❑ 82HawIsIT-1
❑ 83LasVegSBHN-22
❑ 85CalCanC-97
❑ 86RicBraP-23
❑ 87BufBisP-11
❑ 88ColSprSSC-12
❑ 88ColSprSSP-1532
❑ 89ColSprSSC-11
❑ 89ColSprSSP-257
❑ 89Fle-414
❑ 89FleGlo-414
❑ 89PanSti-316
❑ 89ScoHot1R-56
❑ 89Top-721
❑ 89TopBig-37
❑ 89TopTif-721
❑ 90CMC-500
❑ 90EdmTraC-23
❑ 90EdmTraP-520
❑ 90ProAAAF-96
❑ 91EdmTraLD-171
❑ 91EdmTraP-1519
❑ 91LinDriAAA-171
❑ 92Don-287
❑ 92OPC-388
❑ 92Sco-757
❑ 92StaClu-233
❑ 92TriPla-193
❑ 93AngMot-25
❑ 93AngStaCl-5
❑ 93Don-621
❑ 93Fle-577
❑ 93PacSpa-373

❑ 93PanSti-3
❑ 93StaClu-169
❑ 93StaCluFDI-169
❑ 93StaCluMOP-169
❑ 94Fle-71
❑ 94Pac-91
Tinker, Harold
❑ 88NegLeaD-19
❑ 92NegLeaRLI-60
Tinker, Joe
❑ 07CubA.CDPP-15
❑ 07CubGFGCP-16
❑ 08AmeCarE91-32
❑ 08AmeCarE91-66
❑ 08RosComP-112
❑ 09AmeCarE90-1-110
❑ 09ColChiE-289A
❑ 09ColChiE-289B
❑ 09MaxPubP-14
❑ 09RamT20-118
❑ 09SpoNewSM-47
❑ 09T206-355
❑ 09T206-356
❑ 09T206-357
❑ 09T206-358
❑ 10ChiE-11
❑ 10CouT21-236
❑ 10CouT21-237
❑ 10CouT21-238
❑ 10CouT21-239
❑ 10CouT21-322
❑ 10DomDisP-116
❑ 10E101-43
❑ 10E102-24
❑ 10E98-26
❑ 10MelMinE-43
❑ 10NadCarE-51
❑ 10OrnOvaPP-13
❑ 10PeoT21-55A
❑ 10PeoT21-55B
❑ 10PeoT21-55C
❑ 10RedCroT-78
❑ 10RedCroT-79
❑ 10RedCroT-162
❑ 10RedCroT-252
❑ 10StaCarE-26
❑ 10SweCapPP-93A
❑ 10SweCapPP-93B
❑ 10W555-59
❑ 11BasBatEU-39
❑ 11DiaGumP-27
❑ 11HelSta-107
❑ 11JonKeyaAC-333
❑ 11L1L-122
❑ 11PinT-5-208
❑ 11PloCanE-61
❑ 11S74Sil-71
❑ 11S81LarS-97
❑ 11SpoLifCW-352
❑ 11SpoLifM-184
❑ 11T205-171
❑ 11TurRedT-35
❑ 12ColRedB-289A
❑ 12ColRedB-289B
❑ 12ColTinT-289A
❑ 12ColTinT-289B
❑ 12HasTriFT-36E
❑ 12HasTriFT-42
❑ 12PhiCarE-30
❑ 12T207-183
❑ 13NatGamW-40
❑ 13TomBarW-36
❑ 14CraJacE-3
❑ 14PieStaT-101
❑ 15AmeCarE106-39A
❑ 15AmeCarE106-39B
❑ 15CraJacE-3
❑ 15SpoNewM-177
❑ 15VicT21-27
❑ 16BF2FP-71
❑ 16SpoNewM-174
❑ 16TanBraE-17
❑ 16TanBraE-19
❑ 37KelPepS-BB15
❑ 39PC7AlbHoF-47
❑ 48ExhHoF-28
❑ 50CalHOFW-70
❑ 50CubGreB-16
❑ 53ArtHaloFP-81
❑ 60ExhWriH-23
❑ 60Fle-40
❑ 61Fle-143
❑ 63BazA-1
❑ 68LauWorS-5
❑ 69Baz-4
❑ 69Baz-11
❑ 70FleWorS-5
❑ 72ClaCar-4
❑ 76ShaPiz-47
❑ 77BobParHoF-75
❑ 77GalGloG-160
❑ 78DexHaloFP-47
❑ 80MarExhH-29
❑ 80PacLeg-42
❑ 80PerHaloFP-47
❑ 80SSPHOF-47
❑ 81ConTSN-12
❑ 84CubBriPC-4H
❑ 84CubUno-7
❑ 84GalHaloFRL-43
❑ 87Cub190T-6
❑ 90PerGreM-40
❑ 92CubOldS-25
❑ 93ConTSN-817
❑ 93CraJac-16
❑ 93UppDecAH-123
❑ 93UppDecAH-147
❑ 93UppDecTR-9
❑ 94ConTSN-1164
❑ 94ConTSNB-1164
❑ 96PitPosH-11
Tinkey, Jim
❑ 86SanJosBP-21
Tinkey, Robert
❑ 87KenTwiP-13
❑ 88KenTwiP-1379
Tinkle, David
❑ 86EugEmeC-27
❑ 87Ft.MyeRP-5
Tinning, Lyle
❑ 32CubTeal-24
❑ 32OrbPinNP-17
❑ 32OrbPinUP-55
❑ 33TatOrb-55
❑ 34DiaMatCSB-181
❑ 34Gou-71
Tinoco, Luis
❑ 95EveAqaTI-27
❑ 95LinVen-209
❑ 96-97LinVen-180
❑ 96MidLeaAB-7
❑ 96WisTimRB-26
❑ 97LanJet-26
❑ 98LanJetG-27
Tinsley, Charles
❑ 93MarPhiC-29
❑ 93MarPhiF-3491
❑ 94MarPhiC-27
❑ 94MarPhiF-3311
Tinsley, Lee
❑ 88SouOreAP-1706
❑ 89MadMusS-21
❑ 90CMC-868
❑ 90MadMusB-12
❑ 90MadMusP-2282
❑ 90MidLeaASGS-20
❑ 91Cla/Bes-207
❑ 91HunStaC-23
❑ 91HunStaLD-295
❑ 91HunStaP-1810
❑ 91HunStaTI-20
❑ 91LinDriAA-295
❑ 92CanIndF-704
❑ 92ColSprSSS-97
❑ 92OPC-656
❑ 92SkyAAAF-42
❑ 92Top-656
❑ 92TopGol-656
❑ 92TopGolW-656
❑ 92TopMic-656
❑ 93FleFinE-275
❑ 93MariStaClu-12
❑ 93Pin-604
❑ 93Ult-624
❑ 94ScoRoo-RT135
❑ 94ScoRooGR-RT135
❑ 94SpoRoo-130
❑ 94SpoRooAP-130
❑ 94StaClu-493
❑ 94StaCluFDI-493
❑ 94StaCluGR-493
❑ 94StaCluMOP-493
❑ 95DonTopotO-27
❑ 95Fin-289
❑ 95FinRef-289
❑ 95Fla-231
❑ 95FleUpd-14
❑ 95Lea-337
❑ 95Pac-46
❑ 95StaClu-160
❑ 95StaCluFDI-160
❑ 95StaCluMOP-160
❑ 95StaCluSTDW-RS160
❑ 95StaCluSTWS-160
❑ 95UppDec-397
❑ 95UppDecED-397
❑ 95UppDecEDG-397
❑ 96ColCho-67
❑ 96ColChoGS-67
❑ 96ColChoSS-67
❑ 96Don-413
❑ 96DonPreP-413
❑ 96Fle-36
❑ 96FleTif-36
❑ 96FleUpd-U172
❑ 96FleUpdTC-U172
❑ 96PhiTeal-32
❑ 96Sco-399
❑ 96StaClu-307
❑ 96StaCluMOP-307
❑ 96Top-359
❑ 96Ult-527
❑ 96UltGolM-527
❑ 97ColCho-478
❑ 97Pac-46
❑ 97PacLigB-46
❑ 97PacSil-46
❑ 97Ult-416
❑ 97UltGolME-416
❑ 97UltPlaME-416
❑ 98PacInvGems-99
Tippin, Greg
❑ 96MicBatCB-27
Tippitt, Brad
❑ 91KanCouCTI-21
❑ 92FreKeyC-5
❑ 92FreKeyF-1807
Tipton, Eric
❑ 79DiaGre-335
❑ 83TCMPla1944-29
Tipton, Gordon
❑ 88CapCodPPaLP-136
❑ 90GreFalDSP-20
❑ 91BakDodCLC-4
❑ 92BakDodCLC-25
Tipton, Jeff
❑ 82MadMusF-13
Tipton, Joe
❑ 48IndTeal-28
❑ 49Bow-103
❑ 49OlmStu-8
❑ 50A'sTeal-25
❑ 50Bow-159
❑ 51A'sTeal-31
❑ 51Bow-82
❑ 52Top-134
❑ 53BowBW-13
❑ 53Bri-23
❑ 53IndPenCBP-25
❑ 54Bow-180
❑ 83TopRep5-134
Tirado, Aristarco
❑ 86Ft.LauYP-22
❑ 88BlaYNPRWL-19
❑ 89AlbYanB-18
❑ 89AlbYanP-331
❑ 89AlbYanSt-20
❑ 89BlaYNPRWL-185
❑ 89BlaYNPRWLU-67
❑ 95HarSenTI-36
Tirpack, Ken
❑ 92EliTwiC-9
❑ 92EliTwiF-3688
❑ 93ForWayWC-23
❑ 93ForWayWF-1976
❑ 93MidLeaAGF-7
❑ 94ExcFS7-99
❑ 94NasXprF-395
Tischinski, Tom
❑ 70OPC-379
❑ 70Top-379
❑ 71MLBOffS-476
❑ 71OPC-724
❑ 71Top-724
❑ 74AlbDukCa-65
❑ 74AlbDukTI-21
Tisdale, Freddie
❑ 78ArkTraT-23
❑ 79ArkTraT-11
❑ 80ArkTraT-18
❑ 81ArkTraT-5
Tisdale, Tom
❑ 90GasRanB-28
❑ 91GasRanC-28
❑ 92GulCoaRSP-27
❑ 95TulDriTI-25
❑ 97St.PauS-31
Tising, John
❑ 72TCMthe3-69
Titcomb, Ledell
❑ 87OldJudN-493
❑ 89SFHaCN-17
Titus, Brian
❑ 94HelBreF-3615
❑ 94HelBreSP-21
Titus, John
❑ 08RosComP-147
❑ 09ColChiE-290A
❑ 09ColChiE-290B
❑ 09T206-359
❑ 10DomDisP-117
❑ 10LuxCigPP-21
❑ 10SweCapPP-132A
❑ 10SweCapPP-132B
❑ 11HelSta-152
❑ 11MecDFT-16
❑ 11PinT-5-302
❑ 11PloCanE-62
❑ 11S74Sil-105
❑ 11SpoLifM-241
❑ 11T205-172
❑ 12ColRedB-290A
❑ 12ColRedB-290B
❑ 12ColTinT-290A
❑ 12ColTinT-290B
❑ 12HasTriFT-31C
❑ 72ClaCar-42
Tjader, Jimmy
❑ 80AshTouT-11
Toale, John
❑ 85ElmPioT-22
❑ 86EveGiaC-7
❑ 86EveGiaPC-33
❑ 86GreHorP-23
❑ 87CliGiaP-2
❑ 87WinHavRSP-16
❑ 88St.LucMS-23
❑ 89LonTigP-1365
❑ 90CMC-732
❑ 90EasLeaAP-EL3
❑ 90LonTigP-1283
❑ 91AlbYanLD-21
❑ 91AlbYanP-1013
❑ 91LinDriAA-21
❑ 93HigDesMC-23
❑ 93HigDesMF-51
❑ 94ClaGolF-96
❑ 94ExcFS7-195
Tober, David
❑ 96BatCliTI-2
❑ 97PieBolWB-29
Tobey, Keith
❑ 90HigSchPLS-10
Tobias, Grayling
❑ 80MemChiT-24
Tobik, Dave
❑ 79Top-706
❑ 80Top-269
❑ 80VenLeaS-129
❑ 81Top-102
❑ 82Don-511
❑ 82Top-391
❑ 83Don-385
❑ 83Fle-343
❑ 83OPC-186
❑ 83RanAffF-41
❑ 83Top-691
❑ 83TopTra-113T
❑ 84Fle-433
❑ 84Nes792-341
❑ 84Top-341
❑ 84TopTif-341
❑ 85CalCanC-87
❑ 93RanKee-359
Tobin, Dan
❑ 90HigSchPLS-18
❑ 91BilMusP-3752
❑ 91BilMusSP-4
❑ 92BilMusF-3356
❑ 92BilMusSP-13
Tobin, Frank
❑ 22Zee-142
❑ 23Zee-173
❑ 25Zee-145
❑ 26Zee-106
Tobin, Jack (John T.)
❑ 21Exh-178
❑ 21Nei-2
❑ 22E120-103
❑ 22W573-132
❑ 23W503-36
❑ 23WilChoV-163
❑ 25Exh-118
❑ 27AmeCarE126-44
❑ 27AmeCarE126-50
❑ 54SeaPop-25
❑ 88ConSer5-28
❑ 94ConTSN-1168
❑ 94ConTSNB-1168
Tobin, James A.
❑ 39PlaBal-9
❑ 41Gou-30
❑ 83TCMPla1943-40
❑ 85BigLeaC3-58
❑ 90HOFStiB-41
❑ 92ConTSN-372
❑ 94ConTSN-1257
❑ 94ConTSNB-1257
Tobin, John Patrick
❑ 17Zee-79
❑ 48SomandK-16
❑ 49SomandK-27
❑ 53MotCoo-45
Tobin, Joseph
❑ 14Zee-123
❑ 15Zee-119
Toca, Jorge
❑ 99199Fin-288
❑ 99Bow-367
❑ 99BowBes-179
❑ 99BowBesAR-179
❑ 99BowBesR-179
❑ 99BowGol-367
❑ 99BowInt-367
❑ 99FinGolRef-288
❑ 99FinRef-288
❑ 99TopGal-131
❑ 99TopGalPP-131
❑ 99TopGalPPI-131
Tocchet, Rick
❑ 91UppDecS-2
Tocco, Todd
❑ 95EugEmeTI-27
Todd, Alfred
❑ 41Gou-28
❑ 43CubTeal-22
❑ 77TCMTheWY-7
❑ 79DiaGre-358
❑ 90DodTar-804
❑ 91ConTSN-239
Todd, Chuck
❑ 86WatIndP-28
Todd, Harry
❑ 13Zee-73
Todd, Jackson
❑ 77MetDaiPA-25
❑ 78Top-481
❑ 79SyrChiT-13
❑ 79SyrChiTI-16
❑ 80SyrChiT-4
❑ 80SyrChiTI-20
❑ 81Don-31
❑ 81OPC-142
❑ 81Top-142
❑ 82Don-178
❑ 82Fle-623
❑ 82OPC-327
❑ 82SyrChiT-9
❑ 82SyrChiTI-22
❑ 82Top-565
❑ 86ElPasDP-22
❑ 87DenZepP-21
❑ 88DenZepP-1250
❑ 89DenZepC-24
❑ 89DenZepP-51
❑ 90CMC-672
❑ 90DenZepC-26
❑ 90DenZepP-642
❑ 90ProAAAF-667
❑ 91GasRanP-2706
❑ 91MetWIZ-410
❑ 92TulDriF-2711
❑ 93TulDriTI-26
❑ 94TulDriF-259
❑ 94TulDriTI-27
❑ 95TulDriTI-29
❑ 96MemChiB-2
Todd, Jim
❑ 73WicAerJPKB-16
❑ 74WicAerODF-110
❑ 75OPC-519
❑ 75Top-519
❑ 75TopMin-519
❑ 76A'sPos-78
❑ 76CubTri-24
❑ 76OPC-221
❑ 76SSP-478
❑ 76Top-221
❑ 76VenLeaS-19
❑ 77MarPos-23
❑ 77Top-31
❑ 78Top-333
❑ 79OPC-46
❑ 79Top-103
❑ 80Top-629
Todd, Kyle
❑ 86PriWilPP-27
❑ 87HarSenP-13
❑ 88ColAstB-9
Todd, Theron
❑ 88CarLeaAS-37
❑ 88DurBulS-21
❑ 89DurBullS-22
❑ 89DurBullS-22
❑ 89DurBulTI-22
❑ 89Sta-73
❑ 90DurBulTI-15
❑ 96StoPorB-29
❑ 97StoPor-28
Todt, Phil
❑ 25Exh-70
❑ 26Exh-71
❑ 27Exh-35
❑ 28Exh-36
❑ 29ExhFou-18
❑ 29PorandAR-91
❑ 33Gou-86
❑ 33WorCig(-93
❑ 34GouCanV-39
❑ 74A's192T-16
❑ 92ConTSN-419
Toerner, Sean
❑ 81CliGiaT-20
Tofoya, Dennis
❑ 93CarMudTI-13
Toft, Marv
❑ 61SeaPop-25
❑ 61UniOil-S10
❑ 62SeaPop-16
Togher, Martin
❑ 91FreStaBS-13
Togneri, Paul
❑ 87BelMarTI-30
Tokarse, Brian
❑ 98LakElsSG-27
Tokheim, David
❑ 92ClaFS7-77
❑ 92ClePhiC-9
❑ 92ClePhiF-2072
❑ 93ClePhiC-22
❑ 93ClePhiF-2697
❑ 94ReaPhiF-2077
❑ 95ScrRedBTI-27
❑ 96ScrRedBB-25
❑ 98MadBlaW-17
Tolan, Bob
❑ 65CarTeal-26
❑ 65OPC-116
❑ 65Top-116
❑ 66OPC-179
❑ 66Top-179
❑ 66TopVen-179
❑ 67Top-474
❑ 68OPC-84
❑ 68Top-84
❑ 68TopVen-84
❑ 69MilBra-273
❑ 69Top-448
❑ 69TopSta-30
❑ 70DayDaiNM-25
❑ 70MLBOffS-36
❑ 70OPC-409
❑ 70Top-409
❑ 71MilDud-66
❑ 71MLBOffS-71
❑ 71OPC-190
❑ 71OPC-200
❑ 71Top-190
❑ 71Top-200
❑ 71TopCoi-81
❑ 71TopTat-99
❑ 72MilBra-344
❑ 72OPC-3
❑ 72Top-3
❑ 73Kel2D-32
❑ 73OPC-335
❑ 73Top-335
❑ 74GreHeroBP-6
❑ 74OPC-535
❑ 74PadDea-26
❑ 74PadMcDD-12
❑ 74PadTeal-15
❑ 74Top-535
❑ 74TopDecE-23
❑ 75Hos-1
❑ 75HosTwi-1

❑ 75OPC-402
❑ 75PadDea-26
❑ 75Top-402
❑ 75TopMin-402
❑ 76Hos-42
❑ 76HosTwi-42
❑ 76OPC-56
❑ 76PhiPhiP-28
❑ 76SSP-132
❑ 76Top-56
❑ 77PadSchC-58A
❑ 77PadSchC-58B
❑ 77PirPosP-30
❑ 77Top-188
❑ 79PadFamF-31
❑ 80Top-708
❑ 83PadTeal-27
❑ 84BeaGolGT-21
❑ 85BeaGolGT-25
❑ 87MarMot-28
❑ 89EriOriS-27
❑ 89PacSenL-1
❑ 89T/MSenL-106
❑ 89TopSenL-59
❑ 90EliSenL-2
❑ 91PacSenL-152
❑ 93UppDecS-8
Tolar, Kevin
❑ 90UtiBluSP-24
❑ 91Cla/Bes-114
❑ 91MidLeaAP-MWL12
❑ 91SouBenWSC-1
❑ 91SouBenWSP-2857
❑ 92SalSpuC-16
❑ 92SouBenWSF-177
❑ 93SarWhiSC-26
❑ 93SarWhiSF-1369
❑ 95LynHilTI-28
❑ 96CanIndB-26
❑ 97BinMetB-29
❑ 98CarMudM-9
Tolberg, Brian
❑ 98Las-26
Tolbert, Andrew
❑ 94IdaFalBF-3602
❑ 94IdaFalBSP-6
Tolbert, Mark
❑ 90SavCarP-2069
Tolentino, Jose
❑ 84ModA'sC-22
❑ 85TacTigC-127
❑ 86HunStaDJ-24
❑ 86SouLeaAJ-6
❑ 87HunStaTI-22
❑ 87TacTigP-17
❑ 88OklCit8C-14
❑ 88OklCit8P-41
❑ 89TucTorC-13
❑ 89TucTorJP-25
❑ 89TucTorP-183
❑ 90CMC-615
❑ 90ProAAAF-202
❑ 90TucTorC-13
❑ 90TucTorP-212
❑ 91LinDriAAA-620
❑ 91TucTorLD-620
❑ 91TucTorP-2222
❑ 92BufBisBS-21
❑ 92BufBisF-329
❑ 92BufBisS-42
❑ 92Don-589
❑ 92OPC-541
❑ 92Top-541
❑ 92TopDeb91-173
❑ 92TopGol-541
❑ 92TopGolW-541
❑ 92TopMic-541
❑ 97CalCanB-27
❑ 97RocRedW-25
Tolentino, Juan
❑ 97ButCopKB-29
❑ 97ButCopKK-29
❑ 98CedRapKTI-31
❑ 98MidLeaPM-6
Tolentino, Reynaldo
❑ 91GulCoaRSP-25
Toler, Greg
❑ 85CedRapRT-15
❑ 86CedRapRT-11
Toliver, Fred
❑ 82CedRapRT-7
❑ 83IndIndTI-19
❑ 84WicAerRD-20
❑ 86Don-612
❑ 86Fle-647
❑ 86FleUpd-117
❑ 86PhiCIG-15
❑ 86PhiTas-43
❑ 86PorBeaP-23
❑ 87MaiGuiP-5
❑ 87MaiGuiT-7
❑ 87PhiTas-43
❑ 87Top-63
❑ 87TopTif-63
❑ 88PorBeaC-8
❑ 88PorBeaP-664
❑ 88Top-203
❑ 88TopTif-203
❑ 89Bow-147
❑ 89BowTif-147
❑ 89Don-510
❑ 89Fle-126
❑ 89FleGlo-126
❑ 89PadPos-34
❑ 89Sco-479
❑ 89Top-623
❑ 89TopTif-623
❑ 89UppDec-64
❑ 90OPC-423
❑ 90Top-423
❑ 90TopTif-423
❑ 92SalSpuF-3755
❑ 93CarMudF-2054
❑ 93CarMudTI-21
❑ 93FleFinE-120
Tollberg, Brian
❑ 95BelBreTI-15
❑ 97MobBayBB-20
❑ 98MobBayBTI-27
Tolleson, Wayne
❑ 79TulDriT-1
❑ 80TulDriT-16
❑ 83Don-573
❑ 83RanAffF-3
❑ 83TopTra-114T
❑ 84Don-464
❑ 84Fle-434
❑ 84Nes792-557
❑ 84RanJarP-3
❑ 84Top-557
❑ 84TopSti-358
❑ 84TopTif-557
❑ 85Don-378
❑ 85Fle-571
❑ 85RanPer-3
❑ 85Top-247
❑ 85TopTif-247
❑ 86Don-134
❑ 86Fle-573
❑ 86FleUpd-118
❑ 86Lea-59
❑ 86Top-641
❑ 86TopTif-641
❑ 86TopTra-115T
❑ 86TopTraT-115T
❑ 86WhiSoxC-1
❑ 87Don-524
❑ 87DonOpeD-245
❑ 87Fle-118
❑ 87FleGlo-118
❑ 87OPC-224
❑ 87Top-224
❑ 87TopTif-224
❑ 88Don-154
❑ 88Fle-223
❑ 88FleGlo-223
❑ 88OPC-133
❑ 88PanSti-157
❑ 88Sco-117
❑ 88ScoGlo-117
❑ 88StaLinY-17
❑ 88Top-411
❑ 88TopTif-411
❑ 89Don-659
❑ 89Top-716
❑ 89TopTif-716
❑ 89YanScoNW-9
❑ 90PubIntS-549
❑ 90Sco-386
❑ 90TopTra-123T
❑ 90TopTraT-123T
❑ 90TopTVY-27
❑ 90TulDriDGB-3
❑ 90UppDec-320
❑ 90YanScoNW-26
❑ 92YanWIZ8-192
❑ 93RanKee-360
Tollison, Dave
❑ 88CapCodPPaLP-141
❑ 89AncBucTI-14
❑ 90St.CatBJP-3471
❑ 91DunBluJC-19
❑ 91DunBluJP-217
❑ 92ClaFS7-163
❑ 92KnoBluJF-3000
❑ 92KnoBluJS-395
❑ 93ClaGolF-175
Tolliver, Jerome
❑ 91PitMetC-7
❑ 91PitMetP-3437
❑ 92ClaFS7-82
❑ 92ColMetC-1
❑ 92ColMetF-311
❑ 92ColMetPI-14
Tolly, Steve
❑ 94ElmPioC-26
Tolman, Tim
❑ 80ColAstT-3
❑ 81TucTorT-20
❑ 82AstAstI-3
❑ 82TucTorT-8
❑ 83AstPos-33
❑ 84TucTorC-57
❑ 85AstHouP-19
❑ 85AstMot-23
❑ 86NasSouTI-24
❑ 86Top-272
❑ 86TopTif-272
❑ 87TolMudHP-12
❑ 87TolMudHT-23
❑ 88TidTidCa-13
❑ 88TidTidCM-23
❑ 88TidTidP-1584
❑ 89SyrChiC-14
❑ 89SyrChiMB-22
❑ 89SyrChiP-815
❑ 90ProAAAF-211
❑ 90TucTorP-221
❑ 91BurAstC-27
❑ 91BurAstP-2817
❑ 92AshTouC-26
❑ 93OscAstC-26
❑ 93OscAstF-643
❑ 94OscAstC-26
❑ 94OscAstF-1154
❑ 94VenLinU-27
❑ 95JacGenTI-25
❑ 95LinVen-101
❑ 96TusTorB-26
Tolson, Charles
❑ 29Zee-33
Tom-E-Hawk, Mascot
❑ 84IndWhe-NNO
Toman, Tom
❑ 75AppFoxT-27
❑ 76AppFoxT-26
❑ 78AppFoxT-21
❑ 78KnoKnoST-23
Tomanek, Dick
❑ 56A'sPos-45
❑ 57IndTeal-23
❑ 58IndTeal-21
❑ 58Top-123
❑ 59Top-369
Tomaselli, Chuck
❑ 84NasSouTI-23
Tomasello, John
❑ 92GasRanF-2263
❑ 93ButCopKSP-14
Tomashoff, Chris
❑ 94ButCopKSP-30
❑ 95ButCopKtI-25
❑ 96ButCopKB-7
Tomaszewski, Dane
❑ 98GreFalDG-30
Tomberlin, Andy
❑ 86SumBraP-27
❑ 88BurBraP-24
❑ 89DurBullS-23
❑ 89DurBullS-23
❑ 89DurBulTI-23
❑ 89Sta-74
❑ 90Bes-265
❑ 90GreBraB-19
❑ 90GreBraP-1142
❑ 90GreBraS-19
❑ 90RicBraBC-20
❑ 91LinDriAAA-445
❑ 91RicBraBC-1
❑ 91RicBraLD-445
❑ 91RicBraTI-19
❑ 92RicBraBB-8
❑ 92RicBraF-390
❑ 92RicBraRC-24
❑ 92RicBraS-446
❑ 93BufBisF-531
❑ 94Don-329
❑ 94PawRedSDD-25
❑ 94PawRedSF-958
❑ 94Pin-227
❑ 94PinArtP-227
❑ 94PinMusC-227
❑ 94StaClu-70
❑ 94StaCluFDI-70
❑ 94StaCluGR-70
❑ 94StaCluMOP-70
❑ 95AthMot-24
❑ 96MetKah-30
❑ 96NorTidB-28
❑ 97PacPriGotD-GD177
❑ 97RicBraBC-16
❑ 98TolMudHQ-32
Tomberlin, Rob
❑ 86SumBraP-28
Tomchek, Dave
❑ 93DurBulC-30
❑ 93DurBulTI-4
❑ 95BreBtaTI-TR
Tomita, Masaru
❑ 79TCMJapPB-40
Tomkins, Larry
❑ 91MisStaB-44
❑ 92MisStaB-41
❑ 93MisStaB-43
Tomko, Brett
❑ 96BesAutS-89
❑ 96BesAutSA-78
❑ 96Bow-227
❑ 96BowFoi-227
❑ 96ChaLooB-28
❑ 96Top-26
❑ 96TopPowB-26
❑ 97BesAutAS-62
❑ 97BesAutP-H10
❑ 97Bow-76
❑ 97BowChr-104
❑ 97BowChrI-104
❑ 97BowChrIR-104
❑ 97BowChrR-104
❑ 97BowInt-76
❑ 97ColChoU-U8
❑ 97DonLim-74
❑ 97DonLimE-74
❑ 97DonLimENG-74
❑ 97DonSigA-97
❑ 97DonSigAC-122
❑ 97DonSigAM-122
❑ 97Fle-755
❑ 97FleTif-755
❑ 97IndInd-25
❑ 97Sel-171
❑ 97SelCom-171
❑ 98Bow-11
❑ 98BowChr-11
❑ 98BowChrGA-11
❑ 98BowChrGAR-11
❑ 98BowChrI-11
❑ 98BowChrIR-11
❑ 98BowChrR-11
❑ 98BowGolA-11
❑ 98BowInt-11
❑ 98CirThu-259
❑ 98CirThuRav-259
❑ 98CirThuSupRav-259
❑ 98ColCho-73
❑ 98Don-107
❑ 98DonCol-107
❑ 98DonCol-196
❑ 98DonColE-489
❑ 98DonColL-217
❑ 98DonColP-677
❑ 98DonColS-107
❑ 98DonColS-191
❑ 98DonEli-89
❑ 98DonEliA-89
❑ 98DonEliS-89
❑ 98DonGolPP-107
❑ 98DonPre-127
❑ 98DonPreSeat-127
❑ 98DonPriCD-107
❑ 98DonPriCD-196
❑ 98DonPriCE-489
❑ 98DonPriCL-217
❑ 98DonPriCP-677
❑ 98DonRatR-21
❑ 98DonRatRM-21
❑ 98DonSigA-85
❑ 98DonSigAC-107
❑ 98DonSigAM-110
❑ 98DonSilPP-107
❑ 98Fin-57
❑ 98FinNo--57
❑ 98FinNo-R-57
❑ 98FinRef-57
❑ 98Fle-247
❑ 98FleRooS-19
❑ 98Lea-17
❑ 98LeaFraDA-17
❑ 98LeaFraF-17
❑ 98LeaFraM-17
❑ 98LeaFraM-17
❑ 98LeaFraMDC-17
❑ 98LeaFraMDC-17
❑ 98LeaFraMS-17
❑ 98LeaFraMZ2-17
❑ 98LeaRS-113
❑ 98LeaRSLHolo-113
❑ 98LeaRSLong-113
❑ 98LeaRTrue-113
❑ 98MetUni-79
❑ 98MetUniPMG-79
❑ 98Pac-276
❑ 98PacAur-122
❑ 98PacInvTeam-7
❑ 98PacOme-68
❑ 98PacOmeR-68
❑ 98PacOnl-204
❑ 98PacOnlR-204
❑ 98PacOnlWC-204
❑ 98PacPar-149
❑ 98PacParC-149
❑ 98PacParG-149
❑ 98PacParHS-149
❑ 98PacParPB-149
❑ 98PacParR-149
❑ 98PacPlaB-276
❑ 98PacRedT-276
❑ 98PacSil-276
❑ 98Pin-170
❑ 98PinArtP-PP73
❑ 98PinIns-124
❑ 98PinInsCE-124
❑ 98PinInsDE-124
❑ 98PinMusC-PP73
❑ 98PinPer-99
❑ 98PinPerPP-99
❑ 98PinPlu-139
❑ 98PinPreP-170
❑ 98Revo-42
❑ 98RevoSS-42
❑ 98Sco-248
❑ 98ScoRT-216
❑ 98SP Aut-71
❑ 98SpoIllWSF-122
❑ 98SpoIllWSFEE-122
❑ 98SpoIllWSFFE-122
❑ 98SPxFin-11
❑ 98SPxFinR-11
❑ 98SPxFinS-11
❑ 98StaCluFDI-9
❑ 98StaCluI-9
❑ 98StaCluOneK-9
❑ 98StaCluPP-9
❑ 98Stu-35
❑ 98StuGPP-35
❑ 98StuSPP-35
❑ 98Top-440
❑ 98TopChr-440
❑ 98TopChrR-440
❑ 98TopDevR-440
❑ 98TopDia-440
❑ 98TopMiniC-440
❑ 98UD3-11
❑ 98UD3-101
❑ 98UD3-191
❑ 98UD3DieCut-11
❑ 98UD3DieCut-101
❑ 98UD3DieCut-191
❑ 98Ult-153
❑ 98UltGolM-153
❑ 98UltMas-153
❑ 98UltPlaM-153
❑ 98UppDec-253
❑ 98UppDecBCP-BC27
❑ 98UppDecDS-DS9
❑ 98UppDecR-108
❑ 98UppDecRNF-NF8
❑ 98UppDecSF-136
❑ 98Zen-99
❑ 98ZenZ-G-99
❑ 98ZenZ-S-99
❑ 99199Fin-165
❑ 99Bow-59
❑ 99BowChr-59
❑ 99BowChrG-59
❑ 99BowChrGR-59
❑ 99BowChrI-59
❑ 99BowChrIR-59
❑ 99BowChrR-59
❑ 99BowGol-59
❑ 99BowInt-59
❑ 99FinGolRef-165
❑ 99FinRef-165
❑ 99FlaShoLeg1-110
❑ 99FlaShoLeg2-110
❑ 99FlaShoLeg3-110
❑ 99FlaShoLegM1-110
❑ 99FlaShoLegM2-110
❑ 99FlaShoLegM3-110
❑ 99FlaShoR1-110
❑ 99FlaShoR2-110
❑ 99FlaShoR3-110
❑ 99Fle-243
❑ 99FleSta9-243
❑ 99FleWarT-243
❑ 99MetUni-66
❑ 99MetUniGM-66
❑ 99MetUniPMG-66
❑ 99Pac-120
❑ 99PacCroC-81
❑ 99PacCroCPB-81
❑ 99PacPar-66
❑ 99PacParC-66
❑ 99PacParG-66
❑ 99PacParHoloGold-66
❑ 99PacParHS-66
❑ 99PacParOD-66
❑ 99PacParPB-66
❑ 99PacParRed-66
❑ 99PacPlaB-120
❑ 99PacPri-40
❑ 99PacPriHB-40
❑ 99PacPriHG-40
❑ 99PacPriHM-40
❑ 99PacPriHP-40
❑ 99PacPriRed-40
❑ 99PacRed-120
❑ 99SkyPre-62
❑ 99SkyPreR-62
❑ 99SkyThu-72
❑ 99SkyThuRant-72
❑ 99SkyThuRave-72
❑ 99StaClu-64
❑ 99StaCluFDI-64
❑ 99StaCluOoaK-64
❑ 99StaCluPP-64
❑ 99ThuSkySupR-72
❑ 99Top-145
❑ 99TopChr-145
❑ 99TopChrR-145
❑ 99TopMVPP-145
❑ 99Ult-10
❑ 99UltGolM-10
❑ 99UltMas-10
❑ 99UltPlaM-10
❑ 99UppDec-75
❑ 99UppDecEL1-75
❑ 99UppDecEL2-75
❑ 99Vic-106
Tomlin, Dave
❑ 74PadTeal-16
❑ 75OPC-578
❑ 75PadDea-27
❑ 75Top-578
❑ 75TopMin-578
❑ 76OPC-398
❑ 76SSP-627
❑ 76Top-398
❑ 77PadSchC-59
❑ 77Top-241
❑ 78Pep-24
❑ 78Top-86
❑ 79Top-674
❑ 80RedEnq-37
❑ 80Top-126
❑ 81SyrChiT-22
❑ 81SyrChiTI-21
❑ 82IndIndTI-25
❑ 84HawIslC-126
❑ 85HawIslC-241
❑ 86IndIndTI-31
❑ 87IndIndTI-7
❑ 89WesPalBES-28
❑ 94HarSenF-2109
Tomlin, Edwin
❑ 29Zee-100
Tomlin, Randy Leon
❑ 88WatPirP-12
❑ 89SalBucS-22
❑ 90HarSenP-1192
❑ 90HarSenS-17
❑ 90ProAaA-14
❑ 91Bow-518
❑ 91Cla1-T83
❑ 91Don-725
❑ 91Fle-52

❑ 91Lea-203
❑ 91OPC-167
❑ 91Sco-782
❑ 91StaClu-178
❑ 91Top-167A
❑ 91Top-167B
❑ 91TopDeb90-154
❑ 91TopDesS-167
❑ 91TopMic-167
❑ 91TopRoo-29
❑ 91TopTif-167
❑ 91ToyRoo-28
❑ 91UltUpd-103
❑ 91UppDecFE-76F
❑ 92Bow-495
❑ 92Don-367
❑ 92Fle-569
❑ 92Lea-256
❑ 92LeaBlaG-256
❑ 92OPC-571
❑ 92Pin-213
❑ 92Pin-606
❑ 92PirNatI-22
❑ 92Sco-86
❑ 92StaClu-661
❑ 92StaCluECN-661
❑ 92Stu-88
❑ 92Top-571
❑ 92TopGol-571
❑ 92TopGolW-571
❑ 92TopMic-571
❑ 92Ult-261
❑ 92UppDec-537
❑ 93Bow-213
❑ 93Don-570
❑ 93Fle-121
❑ 93Lea-24
❑ 93OPC-257
❑ 93PacSpa-592
❑ 93Pin-74
❑ 93PirNatI-32
❑ 93Sco-101
❑ 93Sel-61
❑ 93StaClu-104
❑ 93StaCluFDI-104
❑ 93StaCluMOP-104
❑ 93Stu-219
❑ 93Top-416
❑ 93TopGol-416
❑ 93TopInaM-416
❑ 93TopInaR-416
❑ 93TopMic-416
❑ 93TriPla-197
❑ 93Ult-102
❑ 93UppDec-284
❑ 93UppDecGold-284
❑ 94ColC-392
❑ 94ColChoGS-392
❑ 94ColChoSS-392
❑ 94Don-274
❑ 94Fin-156
❑ 94FinRef-156
❑ 94Fle-621
❑ 94Pac-508
❑ 94Pin-49
❑ 94PinArtP-49
❑ 94PinMusC-49
❑ 94StaClu-316
❑ 94StaCluFDI-316
❑ 94StaCluGR-316
❑ 94StaCluMOP-316
❑ 94Top-338
❑ 94TopGol-338
❑ 94TopSpa-338
❑ 94UppDec-368
❑ 94UppDecED-368
Tomlin, Rick
❑ 89EliTwiS-30
❑ 90EliTwiS-25
❑ 91EliTwiP-4317
❑ 92EliTwiC-24
❑ 92EliTwiF-3698
❑ 93ForWayWC-27
❑ 93ForWayWF-1985
❑ 94ForMyeMC-27
❑ 94ForMyeMF-1184
❑ 95ForMyeMTI-28
❑ 96NorNavB-3
❑ 97NorNav-2
❑ 97NorNavTI-28
❑ 98NorNavQ-29
Tomlinson, Geofrey
❑ 97SpoIndG-28
❑ 98LanLugQ-25
❑ 98MidLeaPM-13
❑ 99Bow-411
❑ 99BowGol-411
❑ 99BowInt-411
Tomney, Phil
❑ 87OldJudN-494
Tomori, Denny
❑ 88ButCopKSP-12
Tompkins, Ron
❑ 66OPC-107
❑ 66Top-107
❑ 66TopVen-107
❑ 67VanMouSO-24
❑ 68Top-247
❑ 68TopVen-247
❑ 73WicAerJPKB-17A
❑ 73WicAerJPKB-17B
Toms, Tommy
❑ 75PhoGiaC-17
❑ 76PheGiaCr-33
❑ 76PhoGiaCa-12
❑ 76PhoGiaCC-22
❑ 76PhoGiaVNB-23
❑ 77Gia-24
❑ 77PhoGiaCC-23
❑ 77PhoGiaCP-23
❑ 77PhoGiaVNB-23
❑ 78SprRedWK-14
❑ 97PhoFirDTTI-26
Tomsick, Troy
❑ 85DurBulT-13
Tomski, Jeffery
❑ 76BatTroTI-25
❑ 77WatIndT-24
❑ 81ChaLooT-22
Tomso, Matt
❑ 91SavCarC-12
❑ 91SavCarP-1653
Tonascia, Bruce
❑ 78GreBraT-25
Toner, Thomas
❑ 12HomRunKE-76
❑ 12Zee-131
Toney, Andy (Anthony)
❑ 88FayGenP-1082
❑ 88SouAtlLAGS-15
❑ 89LakTigS-23
Toney, Chris
❑ 88MarPhiS-31
Toney, Fred
❑ 11HelSta-108
❑ 15SpoNewM-178
❑ 16FleBreD-95
❑ 16SpoNewM-175
❑ 17ColE13-174
❑ 17HolBreD-105
❑ 21E121So1-106
❑ 21E121So8-99A
❑ 21E121So8-99B
❑ 21KoBreWSI-25
❑ 22E120-194
❑ 22W575-138
❑ 23W501-69
❑ 61Fle-80
❑ 69Baz-1
❑ 72FleFamF-14
❑ 72LauGreF-39
❑ 90HOFStiB-17
❑ 92ConTSN-347
Toney, Mike
❑ 93MedHatBJSP-9
❑ 94MedHatBJF-3683
❑ 94MedHatBJSP-23
❑ 95DunBluJTI-30
❑ 95Exc-145
Tonkin, Tonk (Wyatt)
❑ 78GreBraT-26
Tonneman, Charles
❑ 13Zee-126
Tonnesen, T. A.
❑ 09ObaT21-111
Tonnucci, Norm
❑ 86KnoBluJP-24
❑ 87KnoBluJP-1518
❑ 88SyrChiC-6
❑ 88SyrChiP-809
Tooch, Chuck
❑ 91WelPirP-3583
❑ 92WelPirC-23
❑ 92WelPirF-1334
❑ 93AugPirC-22
❑ 93AugPirF-1555
Toole, Matt
❑ 90WatDiaB-24
❑ 90WatDiaP-2387
Toole, Stephen John
❑ 87OldJudN-495
Tooley, Albert
❑ 12T207-184
❑ 90DodTar-805
Toolson, Earl
❑ 49RemBre-27
Toothman, Ken
❑ 57JetPos-20
Topaum, Tom
❑ 96BelGiaTI-6
Topham, Ryan
❑ 96SouBenSHS-25
Toporcer, Specs (George)
❑ 21E121So1-107
❑ 21Exh-179
❑ 21Nei-82
❑ 22E120-240
❑ 22W573-133
❑ 22W575-139
❑ 23W501-79
❑ 25Exh-64
❑ 26Exh-64
❑ 27AmeCarE126-9
❑ 27MidBre-20
❑ 81ConTSN-35
❑ 88ConSer3-30
❑ 91ConTSN-176
❑ 92ConTSN-644
❑ 93ConTSN-893
Topping, Dan
❑ 95BelGiaTI-28
❑ 96BurBeeTI-14
Torassa, George
❑ 79CedRapGT-20
Torborg, Dale
❑ 94KinMetC-21
❑ 94KinMetF-3833
❑ 95GreBatTI-33
Torborg, Doug
❑ 85AncGlaPTI-27
❑ 87WatPirP-28
❑ 88SalBucS-21
❑ 89MiaMirIS-18
Torborg, Jeff
❑ 64Top-337
❑ 64TopRooAB-2
❑ 64TopVen-337
❑ 65Top-527
❑ 66Top-257
❑ 66TopVen-257
❑ 67CokCapD-10
❑ 67CokCapDA-10
❑ 67Top-398
❑ 68Top-492
❑ 69MilBra-274
❑ 69Top-353
❑ 70OPC-54
❑ 70Top-54
❑ 71MLBOffS-119
❑ 71OPC-314
❑ 71Top-314
❑ 72MilBra-345
❑ 72OPC-404
❑ 72Top-404
❑ 73OPC-154
❑ 73Top-154
❑ 77IndTeal-24
❑ 78IndTeal-28
❑ 78Top-351
❑ 79Top-96
❑ 82YanPhoA-2
❑ 83YanPhoA-3
❑ 85YanTCMP-6
❑ 86YanTCM-22
❑ 89TopTra-120T
❑ 89TopTraT-120T
❑ 89WhiSoxC-3
❑ 90DodTar-806
❑ 90OPC-21
❑ 90Top-21
❑ 90TopTif-21
❑ 90WhiSoxC-26
❑ 91OPC-609
❑ 91Top-609
❑ 91TopDesS-609
❑ 91TopMic-609
❑ 91TopTif-609
❑ 91WhiSoxK-10
❑ 92MetColP-19
❑ 92MetKah-10
❑ 92OPC-759
❑ 92Top-759
❑ 92TopGol-759
❑ 92TopGolW-759
❑ 92TopMic-759
❑ 93MetColP-48
❑ 93Top-509
❑ 93TopGol-509
❑ 93TopInaM-509
❑ 93TopInaR-509
❑ 93TopMic-509
Torcato, Tony
❑ 98SalVol-34
❑ 99BasAmeTPA-42
❑ 99Bow-127
❑ 99BowBes-194
❑ 99BowBesAR-194
❑ 99BowBesR-194
❑ 99BowChr-127
❑ 99BowChrG-127
❑ 99BowChrGR-127
❑ 99BowChrI-127
❑ 99BowChrIR-127
❑ 99BowChrR-127
❑ 99BowGol-127
❑ 99BowInt-127
❑ 99TeaBesR-87
❑ 99TeaBesRFS-22
❑ 99TeaBesRG-87
❑ 99TeaBesRS-87
❑ 99Top-214
❑ 99TopChr-214
❑ 99TopChrR-214
Torchia, Todd
❑ 87SpoIndP-21
❑ 88ChaRaiP-1209
Torchia, Tony
❑ 81BriRedST-8
❑ 83PawRedST-25
❑ 84PawRedST-3A
❑ 84PawRedST-3B
❑ 86NewBriRSP-24
❑ 87ChaRaiP-17
❑ 88RivRedWCLC-229
❑ 88RivRedWP-1413
❑ 89LasVegSC-25
❑ 89LasVegSP-27
❑ 89PacSenL-109
❑ 90CMC-527
❑ 90LasVegSC-24
❑ 90LasVegSP-139
❑ 90ProAAAF-27
❑ 91LasVegSP-255
❑ 91LasVegSP-256
❑ 91LinDriAAA-300
❑ 92LasVegSF-2810
❑ 92LasVegSS-250
❑ 94AshTouC-26
❑ 94AshTouF-1797
❑ 94SouAtlLAF-SAL31
❑ 95SalAvaTI-27
❑ 96ColSprSSTI-30
❑ 97ColSprSTI-25
Torgeson, Earl
❑ 46SpoExcW-11-12
❑ 47Exh-224A
❑ 47Exh-224B
❑ 49Bow-17
❑ 50AmeNut&CCP-20
❑ 50Bow-163
❑ 50Dra-3
❑ 51Bow-99
❑ 51TopBluB-34
❑ 52Bow-72
❑ 52NatTeaL-37
❑ 52RedMan-NL25
❑ 52TipTop-43
❑ 52Top-97
❑ 54Bow-63
❑ 55Bow-210
❑ 56Top-147
❑ 57Top-357
❑ 58Top-138
❑ 59Top-351
❑ 60Lea-122
❑ 60Top-299
❑ 60WhiSoxTS-21
❑ 61Top-152
❑ 61Yan61RL-24
❑ 81WhiSox1T-1
❑ 83TopRep5-97
❑ 83Yan196-24
❑ 85TCMPla1-32
❑ 91YanRinP12-8
❑ 92YanWIZ6-130
Torian, Van
❑ 92IdaFalGF-3520
❑ 92IdaFalGSP-13
Torino, Damian
❑ 93QuaCitRBC-22
❑ 93QuaCitRBF-104
Tornay, Nine
❑ 53MotCoo-11
❑ 53SanFraSTI-21
Toro, Tuffy the
❑ 97TucTorB-30
Torok, John
❑ 94BatCliF-3461
❑ 95PiePhiF-200
Torre, Frank
❑ 56BraBilaBP-15
❑ 56Top-172
❑ 57Top-37
❑ 58Top-117
❑ 59Top-65
❑ 59TopVen-65
❑ 60BraJayP-12
❑ 60BraLaktL-26
❑ 60BraSpiaS-24
❑ 60Top-478
❑ 62Top-303
❑ 63Top-161
❑ 80Bra195T-11
❑ 90PacLeg-53
❑ 90SweBasG-74
❑ 91SweBasG-91
❑ 93TopGol-512
Torre, Joe
❑ 62BraJayP-11
❑ 62Jel-152
❑ 62Pos-152
❑ 62PosCan-152
❑ 62SalPlaC-152
❑ 62ShiPlaC-152
❑ 62Top-218
❑ 62Top-351
❑ 62TopStal-151
❑ 63BraJayP-11
❑ 63Jel-156
❑ 63Pos-156
❑ 63Top-347
❑ 64BraJayP-12
❑ 64Top-70
❑ 64TopCoi-118
❑ 64TopCoi-155
❑ 64TopGia-26
❑ 64TopSta-59
❑ 64TopStaU-72
❑ 64TopTatI-71
❑ 64TopVen-70
❑ 64WheSta-44
❑ 65Baz-16
❑ 65Kah-41
❑ 65OldLonC-19
❑ 65OPC-200
❑ 65Top-200
❑ 65TopEmbl-12
❑ 65TopTraI-31
❑ 66Baz-36
❑ 66BraPos-24
❑ 66Kah-30
❑ 66OPC-130
❑ 66Top-130
❑ 66TopRubI-93
❑ 66TopVen-130
❑ 67AshOil-10
❑ 67Baz-36
❑ 67BraIrvD-4
❑ 67BraPho-26
❑ 67CokCapA-20
❑ 67CokCapB-9
❑ 67CokCapNLA-21
❑ 67DexPre-208
❑ 67DexPre-209
❑ 67Kah-37A
❑ 67Kah-37B
❑ 67OPCPapI-27
❑ 67Top-350
❑ 67TopPos-27
❑ 67TopTesF-22
❑ 67TopVen-324
❑ 68Baz-10
❑ 68BraPos-31
❑ 68CokCapB-9
❑ 68DexPre-73
❑ 68Kah-A11
❑ 68Kah-B34
❑ 68OPC-30
❑ 68Top-30
❑ 68TopActS-12A
❑ 68TopGamI-31
❑ 68TopVen-30
❑ 69CitMetC-11
❑ 69Kah-B20
❑ 69KelPin-17
❑ 69MilBra-275
❑ 69MLBOffS-216
❑ 69MLBPin-58
❑ 69Top-460
❑ 69TopSta-10
❑ 69TopSup-36
❑ 69TopTeaP-2
❑ 69TraSta-49
❑ 70CarTeal-31
❑ 70DayDaiNM-106
❑ 70MLBOffS-144
❑ 70OPC-190
❑ 70Top-190
❑ 70TraSta-3B
❑ 71CarTeal-28
❑ 71CarTeal-29
❑ 71CarTeal-41
❑ 71Kel-62
❑ 71MilDud-67
❑ 71MLBOffS-287
❑ 71OPC-62
❑ 71OPC-370
❑ 71Top-62
❑ 71Top-370
❑ 71TopCoi-11
❑ 71TopSup-61
❑ 71TopTat-85
❑ 72Kel-10
❑ 72MilBra-346
❑ 72OPC-85
❑ 72OPC-87
❑ 72OPC-341
❑ 72OPC-500
❑ 72ProStaP-24
❑ 72SevTraC-55
❑ 72Top-85
❑ 72Top-87
❑ 72Top-341
❑ 72Top-500
❑ 72TopPos-16
❑ 73Kel2D-31
❑ 73LinPor-171
❑ 73OPC-450
❑ 73Top-450
❑ 73TopCanL-52
❑ 73TopCom-22
❑ 73TopPin-22
❑ 74MetJapEB-5
❑ 74MetJapEB-11
❑ 74MetTeal-23
❑ 74OPC-15
❑ 74Top-15
❑ 74TopSta-119
❑ 75Hos-70
❑ 75MetSSP-20
❑ 75OPC-209
❑ 75OPC-565
❑ 75Top-209
❑ 75Top-565
❑ 75TopMin-209
❑ 75TopMin-565
❑ 76BlaDis-64
❑ 76BucDis-64
❑ 76CarDis-64
❑ 76CraDis-64
❑ 76DailsID-64
❑ 76IsaDis-64
❑ 76MetMSAP-2
❑ 76OPC-585
❑ 76OrbDis-64
❑ 76RedBarD-64
❑ 76SafDis-64
❑ 76SSP-541
❑ 76Top-585
❑ 76TowCluD-64
❑ 77MetDaiPA-26
❑ 77Top-425
❑ 78AtlCon-23
❑ 78BraTCC-13
❑ 78MetDaiPA-1
❑ 78TCM60I-137
❑ 78Top-109
❑ 79BasPat-91
❑ 79Top-82
❑ 80Top-259
❑ 81Don-506
❑ 81Fle-325
❑ 81Top-681
❑ 82BraPol-9
❑ 82K-M-20
❑ 83BraPol-9
❑ 83Don-628
❑ 83Top-126
❑ 84BraPol-9
❑ 84Fle-654
❑ 84Nes792-502
❑ 84Top-502
❑ 84TopTif-502
❑ 85Top-438
❑ 85TopTif-438

❑ 86SpoDecG-49
❑ 90AGFA-4
❑ 90PacLeg-107
❑ 90SweBasG-130
❑ 91CarPol-9
❑ 91LinDri-2
❑ 91MetWIZ-411
❑ 91OPC-351
❑ 91StuPre-17
❑ 91SweBasG-92
❑ 91Top-351
❑ 91TopDesS-351
❑ 91TopMic-351
❑ 91TopTif-351
❑ 92CarMcD-39
❑ 92CarPol-23
❑ 92MVP-18
❑ 92MVP2H-17
❑ 92OPC-549
❑ 92Top-549
❑ 92TopGol-549
❑ 92TopGolW-549
❑ 92TopMic-549
❑ 93ActPacA-151
❑ 93CarPol-22
❑ 93TedWil-93
❑ 93Top-512
❑ 93TopInaM-512
❑ 93TopInaR-512
❑ 93TopMic-512
❑ 94CarPol-22
❑ 94UppDecAH-186
❑ 94UppDecAH1-186
Torrealba, Pablo
❑ 76AtlBraP-32
❑ 76OPC-589
❑ 76Top-589
❑ 76VenLeaS-95
❑ 77Top-499
❑ 78Top-78
❑ 79Top-242
❑ 80VenLeaS-111
❑ 90RicBra2ATI-22
❑ 93LinVenB-152
❑ 95LinVen-100
Torrealba, Steve
❑ 97DanBraB-27
❑ 98MacBraM-23
Torrealba, Yorvit
❑ 95BelGiaTI-21
❑ 96BelGiaTI-5
❑ 97BakBlaB-4
❑ 97BakBlaTI-4
❑ 97CalLeaTP-3
❑ 98SanJosGQ-20
❑ 98ShrCapM-28
❑ 98ShrCapWS-28
Torres, Al
❑ 77ChaPatT-23
❑ 78SalPirT-16
❑ 79BufBisT-18
❑ 80BufBisT-13
❑ 80VenLeaS-140
❑ 81PorBeaT-24
❑ 82BufBisT-7
❑ 89MiaMirIS-19
Torres, Andres
❑ 99TeaBesR-89
❑ 99TeaBesRG-89
❑ 99TeaBesRS-89
Torres, Angel
❑ 78IndIndTI-18
❑ 80IndIndTI-27
Torres, Bernie
❑ 97GreFalDTI-25
❑ 98VerBeaDM-24
Torres, David
❑ 76VenLeaS-68
Torres, Dilson
❑ 93LinVenB-93
❑ 93St.CatBJC-23
❑ 93St.CatBJF-3976
❑ 94CarLeaAF-CAR26
❑ 94VenLinU-111
❑ 95Exc-66
❑ 95Fla-267
❑ 95FleUpd-49
❑ 95LinVen-183
❑ 95TopTra-103T
❑ 95UppDec-259
❑ 95UppDecED-259
❑ 95UppDecEDG-259
❑ 96-97LinVen-160
❑ 96Pac-328
❑ 96WicWraB-14
Torres, Felix
❑ 62Top-595
❑ 63Jel-27
❑ 63Pos-27
❑ 63Top-482
❑ 66SeaPop-24
Torres, Freddy
❑ 89FayGenP-1588
❑ 89NiaFalRP-22
❑ 90FayGenP-2418
❑ 93LinVenB-179
❑ 94VenLinU-81
Torres, Gil
❑ 77TCMTheWY-9
Torres, Hector
❑ 66SeaPop-25
❑ 67Ast-28
❑ 67SeaPop-17
❑ 69Top-526
❑ 70AstPho-23
❑ 70OPC-272
❑ 70Top-272
❑ 71MLBOffS-47
❑ 71OPC-558
❑ 71Top-558
❑ 72Dia-46
❑ 72Top-666
❑ 74HawIsIC-103
❑ 75PadDea-28
❑ 76OPC-241
❑ 76SSP-128
❑ 76Top-241
❑ 77Spo-6917
❑ 78SyrChiT-19
❑ 80UtiBluJT-11
❑ 80VenLeaS-132
❑ 81TCM60I-342
❑ 82KnoBluJT-22
❑ 87AstShoSTw-16
❑ 87SyrChiP-1947
❑ 87SyrChiT-25
❑ 88SyrChiC-23
❑ 88SyrChiP-822
❑ 89SyrChiP-801
❑ 91BluJayFS-27
❑ 92DunBluJC-27
❑ 92DunBluJF-2014
❑ 94SyrChiF-988
❑ 94SyrChiTI-26
❑ 95SyrChiTI-24
❑ 96SyrChiTI-30
❑ 97DunBluJTI-29
Torres, Jackson
❑ 95GreFalDTI-1
❑ 96SavSanB-16
Torres, Jaime
❑ 92GulCoaYF-3794
❑ 93GreHorC-23
❑ 93GreHorF-888
❑ 93LinVenB-193
❑ 93OneYanC-22
❑ 93OneYanF-3506
❑ 94GreBatF-479
❑ 94VenLinU-192
❑ 95LinVen-111
❑ 95TamYanYI-29
❑ 96-97LinVen-69
❑ 96ColCliB-28
❑ 96NorNavB-28
❑ 97GreBatC-24
❑ 97TamYan-29
❑ 98NorNavQ-23
Torres, Jason
❑ 98SavSanGM-28
Torres, Jessie
❑ 89PriPirS-21
❑ 90AugPirP-2468
❑ 91AugPirC-14
❑ 91AugPirP-808
❑ 92CarMudF-1186
❑ 92CarMudS-145
Torres, Jose
❑ 83ButCopKT-11
Torres, Leo (Leonardo)
❑ 89FayGenP-1569
❑ 90FayGenP-2408
❑ 91LakTigC-12
❑ 91LakTigP-267
❑ 92LonTigS-420
❑ 92SkyAA F-176
❑ 98WilCubM-24
Torres, Loco (Antonio)
❑ 76VenLeaS-75
❑ 80VenLeaS-93
❑ 93LinVenB-132
❑ 95LinVen-100
Torres, Luis
❑ 96CliLumKTI-27
❑ 97CliLumG-27
❑ 97RanCucQG-29
❑ 98RanCucQG-28
❑ 98RanCucQG-28
Torres, Martin
❑ 85MexCitTT-13
Torres, Melqui
❑ 98EveAquG-24
Torres, Miguel
❑ 88BlaYNPRWL-20
❑ 88OneYanP-2054
Torres, Nelson
❑ 80VenLeaS-36
Torres, Paul
❑ 89WytCubS-27
❑ 90GenCubP-3048
❑ 90GenCubS-7
❑ 90PeoChiTI-14
❑ 91Cla/Bes-174
❑ 91PeoChiC-13
❑ 91PeoChiTI-20
❑ 91WinSpiC-26
❑ 91WinSpiP-2843
❑ 92ClaFS7-318
❑ 92WinSpiC-7
❑ 92WinSpiF-1222
❑ 93DayCubC-21
❑ 93DayCubF-872
❑ 94OrlCubF-1399
❑ 95OrlCubF-23
❑ 96ArkTraB-25
❑ 98OrlRayM-20
Torres, Phil
❑ 87VerBeaDP-31
❑ 88SanAntMB-17
❑ 89ColMudB-27
Torres, Rafael
❑ 92HelBreF-1716
❑ 93BelBreCB-25
❑ 93BelBreFI-1711
Torres, Ramon
❑ 89BurIndS-24
❑ 90BurIndP-3024
❑ 91ColIndP-1502
Torres, Ray
❑ 79KnoKnoST-23
❑ 80GleFalWSBT-8
❑ 80GleFalWSCT-27
❑ 80IowOakP-12A
❑ 80IowOakP-12B
❑ 81AppFoxT-25
❑ 81GleFalWST-21
Torres, Reynaldo
❑ 97JohCitCTI-32
❑ 98JohCCTI-32
Torres, Ricky (Rick)
❑ 84GreHorT-17
❑ 87PriWilYP-4
❑ 88AlbYanP-1338
❑ 88BlaYNPRWL-50
❑ 88BlaYNPRWLU-11
❑ 89AlbYanB-11
❑ 89AlbYanP-335
❑ 89AlbYanSt-21
❑ 89BlaYNPRWL-186
❑ 90AlbYanB-10
❑ 90AlbYanSt-21
❑ 90CMC-218
❑ 90ColCliC-18
❑ 90ColCliP-677
❑ 90ProAAAF-327
❑ 90TopTVY-64
Torres, Rudy
❑ 83AndBraT-17
Torres, Rusty (Rosendo)
❑ 72OPC-124
❑ 72Top-124
❑ 73IndTeal-26
❑ 73IndTeal-27
❑ 73OPC-571
❑ 73Top-571
❑ 74OPC-499
❑ 74Top-499
❑ 75SalLakCC-1
❑ 77Top-224
❑ 78TucTorC-35
❑ 80Top-36
❑ 81PorBeaT-25
❑ 92YanWIZ7-153
Torres, Salomon
❑ 91Cla/Bes-324
❑ 91CliGiaC-8
❑ 91CliGiaP-834
❑ 91MidLeaAP-MWL6
❑ 92Bow-4
❑ 92Bow-584
❑ 92ClaBluBF-BC14
❑ 92ClaFS7-257
❑ 92ClaRedB-BC14
❑ 92DonRooP-BC18
❑ 92LeaGolR-BC11
❑ 92ProFS7-353
❑ 92ShrCapF-3872
❑ 92ShrCapS-596
❑ 92SkyAA F-263
❑ 92UppDecML-34
❑ 92UppDecML-261
❑ 93Bow-660
❑ 93ClaFS7-60
❑ 93ClaGolF-134
❑ 93ExcFS7-121
❑ 93GiaStaC-5
❑ 93LimRocDWB-66
❑ 93LimRocDWB-147
❑ 93ShrCapF-2760
❑ 94Bow-366
❑ 94Bow-631
❑ 94ColC-19
❑ 94ColChoGS-19
❑ 94ColChoSS-19
❑ 94Don-327
❑ 94Fin-439
❑ 94FinJum-439
❑ 94FinRef-439
❑ 94Fla-247
❑ 94FleExtB-394
❑ 94FleMajLP-33
❑ 94FleUpd-197
❑ 94FUnPac-65
❑ 94GiaAMC-23
❑ 94GiaMot-14
❑ 94GiaTarBC-26
❑ 94GiaUSPC-2S
❑ 94GiaUSPC-8D
❑ 94Lea-318
❑ 94LeaLimR-16
❑ 94OPC-165
❑ 94OPCHotP-3
❑ 94Pac-558
❑ 94Pin-261
❑ 94PinArtP-261
❑ 94PinMusC-261
❑ 94PinNewG-NG6
❑ 94PinRooTP-9
❑ 94Sco-641
❑ 94ScoBoyoS-39
❑ 94ScoGolR-641
❑ 94ScoRoo-RT88
❑ 94ScoRooGR-RT88
❑ 94Sel-182
❑ 94SelRooS-RS7
❑ 94Spo-156
❑ 94SpoSha-SH5
❑ 94StaClu-314
❑ 94StaCluFDI-314
❑ 94StaCluGR-314
❑ 94StaCluMOP-314
❑ 94StaCluT-10
❑ 94StaCluTFDI-10
❑ 94Top-298
❑ 94TopGol-298
❑ 94TopSpa-298
❑ 94TriPla-293
❑ 94Ult-295
❑ 94UppDec-27
❑ 94UppDecED-27
❑ 95ColCho-264
❑ 95ColChoGS-264
❑ 95ColChoSS-264
❑ 95Don-30
❑ 95DonPreP-30
❑ 95Lea-108
❑ 95MarPac-45
❑ 95Pac-385
❑ 95Pin-360
❑ 95PinArtP-360
❑ 95PinMusC-360
❑ 95Sco-528
❑ 95ScoGolR-528
❑ 95ScoPlaTS-528
❑ 95Sel-61
❑ 95SelArtP-61
❑ 95StaClu-436
❑ 95StaCluMOP-436
❑ 95StaCluSTWS-436
❑ 95TacRaiTI-23
❑ 96Sco-145
❑ 96TacRaiB-25
❑ 97Pac-194
❑ 97PacLigB-194
❑ 97PacSil-194
Torres, Sammy
❑ 80WatIndT-17
Torres, Tony
❑ 80HolMilT-24
❑ 81ElPasDT-18
❑ 92EriSaiC-29
❑ 92EriSaiF-1634
❑ 93HigDesMC-24
❑ 93HigDesMF-52
❑ 94BreCouMC-21
❑ 94BreCouMF-23
❑ 96PorSeaDB-27
❑ 97PorSeaD-28
Torrez, Mike
❑ 68OPC-162
❑ 68Top-162
❑ 68TopVen-162
❑ 69OPC-136
❑ 69Top-136
❑ 69TopFou-25
❑ 70OPC-312
❑ 70Top-312
❑ 71CarTeal-42
❑ 71MLBOffS-288
❑ 71OPC-531
❑ 71Top-531
❑ 72CarTeal-17
❑ 72Dia-47
❑ 73ExpPos-7
❑ 73OPC-77
❑ 73Top-77
❑ 74OPC-568
❑ 74Top-568
❑ 75BalOriP-29
❑ 75OPC-254
❑ 75Top-254
❑ 75TopMin-254
❑ 76A'sPos-71
❑ 76Hos-139
❑ 76OPC-25
❑ 76SSP-381
❑ 76Top-25
❑ 77BurCheD-110
❑ 77Hos-13
❑ 77OPC-144
❑ 77Top-365
❑ 77YanBurK-7
❑ 78Hos-127
❑ 78PapGinD-21
❑ 78RCColC-98
❑ 78SSP270-170
❑ 78Top-645
❑ 79Hos-22
❑ 79OPC-92
❑ 79RedSoxTI-4
❑ 79Top-185
❑ 80OPC-236
❑ 80Top-455
❑ 81Don-216
❑ 81Fle-233
❑ 81OPC-216
❑ 81Top-525
❑ 82Don-235
❑ 82Fle-310
❑ 82FleSta-166
❑ 82RedSoxC-20
❑ 82Top-625
❑ 82Top-786
❑ 82TopSti-151
❑ 82TopStiV-151
❑ 83Don-512
❑ 83Fle-197
❑ 83FleSti-62
❑ 83OPC-312
❑ 83Top-743
❑ 83TopFol-1
❑ 83TopTra-115T
❑ 84Don-556
❑ 84Fle-602
❑ 84Nes792-78
❑ 84OPC-78
❑ 84Top-78
❑ 84TopSti-113
❑ 84TopTif-78
❑ 85DomLeaS-14
❑ 89PacLegI-168
❑ 91MetWIZ-412
❑ 91OriCro-460
❑ 92YanWIZ7-154
❑ 93UppDecS-20
❑ 99SpoIllGotG-73
❑ 99SpoIllGotGA-73
Torrez, Peter
❑ 80RocRedWT-21
❑ 84ChaO'sT-9
Torricelli, Tim
❑ 87StoPorP-22
❑ 88BelBreGS-14
❑ 89ElPasDGS-19
❑ 90CMC-33
❑ 90DenZepC-8
❑ 90DenZepP-629
❑ 90ProAAAF-654
❑ 92RocExpF-3012
❑ 93JamExpC-26
❑ 93JamExpF-3342
❑ 94JamJamC-29
❑ 97JacSun-27
Torrienti, Christobel
❑ 74LauOldTBS-18
❑ 90NegLeaS-19
Torti, Mike
❑ 96BatCliTI-14
❑ 97ClePhi-23
Tortorice, Mark
❑ 86ModA'sC-19
❑ 86ModA'sP-25
❑ 88SouBenWSGS-27
Torve, Kelvin
❑ 83PhoGiaBHN-12
❑ 84ShrCapFB-23
❑ 85ChaO'sT-7
❑ 86RocRedWP-24
❑ 87RocRedWP-21
❑ 87RocRedWT-15
❑ 88PorBeaC-15
❑ 88PorBeaP-641
❑ 89PanSti-380
❑ 89PorBeaC-16
❑ 89PorBeaP-220
❑ 89UppDec-177
❑ 90CMC-373
❑ 90FleUpd-40
❑ 90ProAAAF-285
❑ 90TidTidC-22
❑ 90TidTidP-554
❑ 90TopTVM-63
❑ 90TriAAAC-32
❑ 90TriAllGP-AAA5
❑ 91Fle-163
❑ 91LinDriAAA-569
❑ 91MetColP-49
❑ 91MetWIZ-413
❑ 91Sco-754
❑ 91TidTidLD-569
❑ 91TidTidP-2520
Torve, Kenton Craig
❑ 87BirBarB-20
Tosar, Mike
❑ 91MiaHurBB-12
❑ 97PriDevR-3
Tosca, Carlos
❑ 83GreHorT-27
❑ 84GreHorT-1
❑ 91BasCitRC-28
❑ 93KanCouCC-26
❑ 93KanCouCF-931
❑ 93KanCouCTI-25
❑ 94PorSeaDF-692
❑ 94PorSeaDTI-3
❑ 95PorSeaDTI-26
❑ 96PorSeaDB-1
❑ 97ChaKni-3
❑ 97ChaKni-30
❑ 98PorSeaD5AQ-33
Tosone, Joe
❑ 93JamExpC-24
❑ 93JamExpF-3341
Tost, Lou
❑ 37Zee-6
❑ 37Zee-28
❑ 49RemBre-28
❑ 50RemBre-24
Toth, Dave (David)
❑ 91IdaFalBP-4334
❑ 91IdaFalBSP-15
❑ 92MacBraC-4
❑ 92MacBraF-271
❑ 93MacBraC-25
❑ 93MacBraF-1404
❑ 94DurBulC-22
❑ 94DurBulF-332
❑ 94DurBulTI-24
❑ 95DurBulTI-31
❑ 96DouAllB-34
❑ 96GreBraB-28
❑ 96GreBraTI-42
❑ 97GreBraG-26
Toth, Paul
❑ 62KahAtl-22

❑ 63Top-489
❑ 64Top-309
❑ 64TopVen-309
❑ 66TolMudHTI-24
Toth, Robert
❑ 92AppFoxCB-15
❑ 92AppFoxFI-985
❑ 93CarLeaAGF-18
❑ 93WilBluRC-25
❑ 93WilBluRF-1998
❑ 94Bow-311
❑ 94ExcFS7-75
❑ 94MemChiF-359
❑ 95WicWraTI-13
❑ 96OmaRoyB-28
❑ 96SigRooOJ-33
❑ 96SigRooOJS-33
Totman, Jason
❑ 96CliLumKTI-28
Touch, Chuck
❑ 91WelPirC-11
Touchet, Sean
❑ 94ElmPioC-21
❑ 94ElmPioF-3475
Touma, Tim
❑ 87WesPalBEP-653
Toups, Tony
❑ 76BatTroTI-26
❑ 77WatIndT-25
Tourist, Ted E.
❑ 98AshTouM-30
Tourists, Asheville
❑ 95AshTouUTI-NNO
Tousignant, Lou
❑ 82MonNew-17
Toussaint, Daris
❑ 88PocGiaP-2088
Toutsis, Paul
❑ 86GreHorP-24
Touzzo, John
❑ 85LitFalMT-10
Tovar, Cesar
❑ 65OPC-201
❑ 65Top-201
❑ 66Top-563
❑ 67CokCapTw-11
❑ 67Top-317
❑ 67TopVen-191
❑ 67TwiTeal-20
❑ 67TwiTeal-21
❑ 68DexPre-72
❑ 68Top-420
❑ 69MilBra-276
❑ 69MLBOffS-71
❑ 69Top-530
❑ 69TopSta-199
❑ 69TopTeaP-15
❑ 69TraSta-9
❑ 69TwiTealC-9
❑ 70DayDaiNM-153
❑ 70MLBOffS-240
❑ 70OPC-25
❑ 70Top-25
❑ 70TwiSupV-12
❑ 70TwiTeal-11
❑ 71Kel-18
❑ 71MilDud-31
❑ 71MLBOffS-477
❑ 71OPC-165
❑ 71Top-165
❑ 71TopCoi-52
❑ 72MilBra-347
❑ 72OPC-275
❑ 72Top-275
❑ 72TwiPos-23
❑ 73OPC-405
❑ 73PhiTeal-20
❑ 73Top-405
❑ 74OPC-538
❑ 74Top-538
❑ 74TopTra-538T
❑ 75OPC-178
❑ 75RanPos-35
❑ 75Top-178
❑ 75TopMin-178
❑ 76OPC-246
❑ 76Top-246
❑ 76VenLeaS-13
❑ 77Top-408
❑ 78TCM60I-174
❑ 78TwiFri-21
❑ 80VenLeaS-246
❑ 86TwiGreT-4
❑ 92YanWIZ7-155
❑ 93LinVenB-92
❑ 93RanKee-361
❑ 95LinVen-275
Tovar, Edgar
❑ 92JamExpC-21
❑ 92JamExpF-1510
❑ 93ExcFS7-62
❑ 93HarSenF-278
❑ 93LinVenB-141
❑ 94SanBerSC-23
❑ 94SanBerSF-2769
❑ 94VenLinU-180
❑ 95HarSenTI-13
❑ 95LinVen-112
❑ 96-97LinVen-72
Tovar, Gil
❑ 80VenLeaS-248
Tovar, Raul
❑ 82MiaMarT-18
❑ 83BirBarT-1
❑ 86MidAngP-23
❑ 93LinVenB-233
Towers, Josh
❑ 96BluOriB-29
❑ 97DelSho-25
❑ 97FreKey-28
❑ 98CarLeaAC-8
❑ 98FreKeyM-17
Towers, Kevin
❑ 84BeaGolGT-10
❑ 86ChaRaiP-26
❑ 88LasVegSC-8
❑ 88LasVegSP-242
❑ 89SpoIndSP-23
❑ 90SpoIndSP-28
Towers, Tony
❑ 82MonNew-18
Towey, Steve
❑ 88MyrBeaBJP-1185
❑ 89ModA'sC-16
Towle, Justin
❑ 92PriRedC-24
❑ 92PriRedF-3091
❑ 93BilMusF-3949
❑ 93BilMusSP-4
❑ 94ChaWheC-24
❑ 94ChaWheF-2706
❑ 97Bow-104
❑ 97BowCerBlaIA-CA80
❑ 97BowCerBluIA-CA80
❑ 97BowCerGolIA-CA80
❑ 97BowChr-124
❑ 97BowChrI-124
❑ 97BowChrIR-124
❑ 97BowChrR-124
❑ 97BowInt-104
❑ 97ChaLoo-24
❑ 97FlaShoWotF-7
❑ 97Fle-544
❑ 97FleTif-544
❑ 97SouLeaTP-8
❑ 97TexAllM-57
❑ 97Ult-543
❑ 97UltGolME-543
❑ 97UltPlaME-543
❑ 98Bow-413
❑ 98BowBes-133
❑ 98BowBesAR-133
❑ 98BowBesR-133
❑ 98BowCerBlueAU-34
❑ 98BowCerGA-34
❑ 98BowCerSA-34
❑ 98BowChr-413
❑ 98BowChrGA-413
❑ 98BowChrGAR-413
❑ 98BowChrI-413
❑ 98BowChrIR-413
❑ 98BowChrR-413
❑ 98BowGolA-413
❑ 98BowInt-413
❑ 98ChaLooG-27
❑ 98SP MinPE-41
❑ 98SP MinSTHPE-H18
❑ 98SP SPTSC-JT
❑ 98SPMin-41
❑ 98SPMinSTH-H18
❑ 99SP TopP-116
❑ 99SP TopPPE-116
Town, Randall
❑ 80WatRedT-6
❑ 81WatRedT-10
Towner, Kyle
❑ 94BelMarC-28
❑ 94BelMarF-3252
Townes, Jeremy
❑ 95DavLipB-23
Townley, Jason
❑ 88DunBluJS-17
❑ 88St.CatBJP-2027
❑ 90DunBluJS-21
❑ 90FloStaLAS-46
❑ 91KnoBluJLD-368
❑ 91KnoBluJP-1772
❑ 91LinDriAA-368
❑ 92ClaFS7-330
❑ 92KnoBluJF-2994
❑ 92KnoBluJS-396
❑ 93AusFut-77
❑ 94SyrChiF-974
❑ 94SyrChiTI-27
❑ 95LinVen-171
❑ 95SyrChiTI-25
Towns, Ryan
❑ 93EugEmeC-26
❑ 93EugEmeF-3857
❑ 94RocRoyC-25
❑ 94RocRoyF-566
❑ 95SprSulTI-28
Townsend, Chad
❑ 92BurIndC-25
❑ 92BurIndF-1665
❑ 93ClaFS7-263
❑ 93ColRedC-24
❑ 93ColRedF-608
❑ 94HigDesMC-26
❑ 94HigDesMF-2798
❑ 96SanBerSB-27
Townsend, Dave
❑ 98PorSeaDQ-11
Townsend, George
❑ 87OldJudN-496
❑ 90KalBatN-53
❑ 90KalBatN-54
Townsend, Howard
❑ 85EveGiaC-16A
❑ 85EveGiaC-16B
❑ 86CliGiaP-24
❑ 87WauTimP-5
❑ 88SanBerSCLC-45
❑ 89VisOakCLC-100
❑ 89VisOakP-1421
Townsend, James
❑ 87SalAngP-15
❑ 88QuaCitAGS-17
❑ 89PalSprACLC-48
❑ 89PalSprAP-463
Townsend, John
❑ 03BreE10-144
Townsend, Ken
❑ 77CliDodT-27
❑ 78LodDodT-22
Townsend, Lee
❑ 88SanBerSB-3
Townsend, Mike
❑ 91MarPhiC-30
Townsend, Richard
❑ 92WelPirC-24
❑ 92WelPirF-1322
❑ 93AugPirC-23
❑ 93AugPirF-1545
❑ 94SalBucC-22
❑ 94SalBucF-2323
Toy, Tracy
❑ 86WatPirP-24
❑ 87MacPirP-2
❑ 88AugPirP-379
Toyotoshi, Chikada
❑ 89SalSpuCLC-131
Tozer, Bill
❑ 09ObaT21-95
❑ 09ObaT21-267
❑ 11PacCoaBD-66
❑ 12HomRunKE-17
❑ 12ObaPreT-16
❑ 12Zee-21
❑ 13Zee-21
❑ 14Zee-124
Tozier, Pat
❑ 90OklSoo-9
Traber, Jim
❑ 84BalOriP-38
❑ 85Don-45
❑ 85RocRedWT-9
❑ 86BalOriP-22
❑ 86RocRedWP-25
❑ 86SpoRoo-32
❑ 87Don-477
❑ 87Fle-482
❑ 87FleGlo-482
❑ 87RocRedWP-26
❑ 87RocRedWT-20
❑ 87SpoTeaP-21
❑ 87Top-484
❑ 87TopSti-232
❑ 87TopTif-484
❑ 87ToyRoo-31
❑ 88OriFreB-28
❑ 88OriPos-40
❑ 88RocRedWTI-25
❑ 88Top-544
❑ 88TopTif-544
❑ 89BalOriP-37
❑ 89Bow-13
❑ 89BowTif-13
❑ 89Fle-625
❑ 89FleGlo-625
❑ 89OPC-124
❑ 89OriFreB-28
❑ 89Sco-590
❑ 89Top-124
❑ 89TopSti-233
❑ 89TopTif-124
❑ 89UppDec-294
❑ 90Don-569
❑ 90Fle-193
❑ 90FleCan-193
❑ 90HagSunDGB-33
❑ 90PubIntS-590
❑ 90UppDec-268
❑ 91OriCro-461
Trabous, Manuel
❑ 52LavPro-89
Tracewski, Dick
❑ 64Top-154
❑ 64TopVen-154
❑ 65DodTeal-20
❑ 65OPC-279
❑ 65Top-279
❑ 66Top-378
❑ 67CokCapTi-11
❑ 67Top-559
❑ 68CokCapT-11
❑ 68TigDetFPB-24
❑ 68Top-488
❑ 69MilBra-277
❑ 69OPC-126
❑ 69TigTealC-18
❑ 69Top-126
❑ 69TopFou-20
❑ 73OPC-323
❑ 73Top-323
❑ 75DetTigP-33
❑ 76DetTigP-32
❑ 78TigTeal-31
❑ 81TCM60I-461
❑ 83TigPos-27
❑ 84TigTeal-29
❑ 84TigWavP-32
❑ 88TigDom-23
❑ 88TigPep-NNO
❑ 89TigMar-NNO
❑ 90DodTar-807
❑ 90TigCok-28
❑ 90TigTeal-22
❑ 91TigCok-NNO
❑ 93TigGat-28
Trachsel, Steve
❑ 91GenCubP-4217
❑ 92ChaKniF-2772
❑ 92ChaKniS-169
❑ 92SkyAA F-77
❑ 92UppDecML-118
❑ 93Bow-172
❑ 93ClaFS7-264
❑ 93IowCubF-2133
❑ 94Bow-634
❑ 94Don-636
❑ 94Fin-296
❑ 94FinRef-296
❑ 94Fla-142
❑ 94FleExtB-225
❑ 94FleExtBRS-18
❑ 94FleMajLP-34
❑ 94FleUpd-111
❑ 94LeaGolR-19
❑ 94LeaLimR-25
❑ 94Pin-536
❑ 94PinArtP-536
❑ 94PinMusC-536
❑ 94ScoRoo-RT161
❑ 94ScoRooGR-RT161
❑ 94Sel-389
❑ 94SelRooS-RS18
❑ 94SP-73
❑ 94SPDieC-73
❑ 94SpoRoo-83
❑ 94SpoRooAP-83
❑ 94StaClu-62
❑ 94StaClu-633
❑ 94StaCluFDI-62
❑ 94StaCluFDI-633
❑ 94StaCluGR-62
❑ 94StaCluGR-633
❑ 94StaCluMOP-62
❑ 94StaCluMOP-633
❑ 94StaCluT-345
❑ 94StaCluTFDI-345
❑ 94Top-778
❑ 94TopGol-778
❑ 94TopSpa-778
❑ 94Ult-465
❑ 94UppDec-28
❑ 94UppDecED-28
❑ 95Bow-409
❑ 95ColCho-212
❑ 95ColChoGS-212
❑ 95ColChoSE-86
❑ 95ColChoSEGS-86
❑ 95ColChoSESS-86
❑ 95ColChoSS-212
❑ 95Don-23
❑ 95DonPreP-23
❑ 95DonTopotO-206
❑ 95Emo-114
❑ 95Fin-18
❑ 95FinRef-18
❑ 95Fla-117
❑ 95Fle-425
❑ 95FleRooS-18
❑ 95FleTeaL-16
❑ 95Lea-163
❑ 95Pac-80
❑ 95Pin-131
❑ 95PinArtP-131
❑ 95PinMusC-131
❑ 95Sco-337
❑ 95ScoGolR-337
❑ 95ScoPlaTS-337
❑ 95StaClu-80
❑ 95StaCluFDI-80
❑ 95StaCluMOP-80
❑ 95StaCluSTWS-80
❑ 95StaCluVR-50
❑ 95StaCluVRMO-50
❑ 95Stu-138
❑ 95Top-273
❑ 95TopCyb-147
❑ 95TopEmb-96
❑ 95TopEmbGI-96
❑ 95Ult-140
❑ 95UltAllR-10
❑ 95UltAllRGM-10
❑ 95UltGolM-140
❑ 95UltSecYS-13
❑ 95UltSecYSGM-13
❑ 95UppDec-67
❑ 95UppDecED-67
❑ 95UppDecEDG-67
❑ 95UppDecSE-124
❑ 95UppDecSEG-124
❑ 95USPlaCMLA-2S
❑ 96Cir-113
❑ 96CirRav-113
❑ 96ColCho-497
❑ 96ColChoGS-497
❑ 96ColChoSS-497
❑ 96CubFle-18
❑ 96Don-466
❑ 96DonPreP-466
❑ 96Fle-332
❑ 96FleTif-332
❑ 96LeaSigEA-203
❑ 96Sco-389
❑ 96TeaOut-81
❑ 96Ult-173
❑ 96UltGolM-173
❑ 96UppDec-294
❑ 97Cir-339
❑ 97CirRav-339
❑ 97ColCho-69
❑ 97Don-41
❑ 97DonGolPP-41
❑ 97DonSilPP-41
❑ 97Fin-132
❑ 97FinEmb-132
❑ 97FinEmbR-132
❑ 97FinRef-132
❑ 97Fle-287
❑ 97FleTif-287
❑ 97Lea-268
❑ 97LeaFraM-268
❑ 97LeaFraMDC-268
❑ 97MetUni-17
❑ 97PacPriGotD-GD124
❑ 97Pin-132
❑ 97PinArtP-PP132
❑ 97PinMusC-132
❑ 97PinPrePla-132
❑ 97Sco-456
❑ 97ScoArtPWB-456
❑ 97ScoResC-456
❑ 97ScoShoS-456
❑ 97ScoShoSAP-456
❑ 97StaClu-118
❑ 97StaCluMOP-118
❑ 97Top-154
❑ 97TopGal-92
❑ 97TopGalPPI-92
❑ 97Ult-171
❑ 97UltGolME-171
❑ 97UltPlaME-171
❑ 97UppDec-34
❑ 98CirThu-68
❑ 98CirThuRav-68
❑ 98CirThuSupRav-68
❑ 98ColCho-58
❑ 98Fin-49
❑ 98FinNo--49
❑ 98FinNo-R-49
❑ 98FinRef-49
❑ 98Fle-523
❑ 98PacOnl-156
❑ 98PacOnlR-156
❑ 98PacOnlWC-156
❑ 98PinSna-CC16
❑ 98StaCluFDI-228
❑ 98StaCluI-228
❑ 98StaCluOneK-228
❑ 98StaCluPP-228
❑ 98Top-23
❑ 98TopChr-23
❑ 98TopChrR-23
❑ 98TopDevR-23
❑ 98TopDia-23
❑ 98TopMiniC-23
❑ 98TopOpeD-16
❑ 98UppDec-51
❑ 99Fle-325
❑ 99FleSta9-325
❑ 99FleWarT-325
❑ 99MetUni-67
❑ 99MetUniGM-67
❑ 99MetUniPMG-67
❑ 99StaClu-267
❑ 99StaCluFDI-267
❑ 99StaCluOoaK-267
❑ 99StaCluPP-267
❑ 99Top-257
❑ 99TopChr-257
❑ 99TopChrR-257
❑ 99TopMVPP-257
❑ 99UppDecEM-MC3
❑ 99UppDecEMFXG-MC3
Tracy, Andy
❑ 96VerExpB-28
❑ 97SouAtlTPB-6
❑ 98JupHamQ-22
Tracy, Jack
❑ 81TCM60I-451
Tracy, Jim (James C.)
❑ 87MyrBeaBJP-1450
❑ 88DunBluJS-18
❑ 88PeoChiTI-29
❑ 90HarSenS-18
❑ 90ProAaA-13
❑ 92BufBisBS-22
❑ 92BufBisF-323
❑ 92BufBisS-43
❑ 93BufBisF-518
Tracy, Jim (James E.)
❑ 80WicAerT-2
❑ 81Don-520
❑ 81Fle-308
❑ 82Fle-605
❑ 82FleSta-97
❑ 82Top-403
❑ 82TucTorT-9
❑ 87PeoChiP-27
❑ 89ChaLooB-7
❑ 89ChaLooGS-1
❑ 89HarSenP-309
❑ 89HarSenS-19
❑ 90ChaLooGS-1
❑ 90EasLeaAP-EL27
❑ 90HarSenP-1193
❑ 91BufBisLD-46
❑ 91BufBisP-542
❑ 91ChaLooLD-174
❑ 91ChaLooP-1974
❑ 91LinDriAA-174
❑ 91LinDriAAA-46
❑ 91PacSenL-70

❑ 93HarSenF-284
Tracy, Rich
❑ 88BatCliP-1685
Tracy, Rick
❑ 87SanJosBP-20
Traen, Tom
❑ 86JacExpT-5
❑ 87WesPalBEP-671
Traffley, William
❑ 87OldJudN-497
Trafton, Todd
❑ 84AriWilP-18
❑ 86AriWilP-18
❑ 87DayBeaAP-1
❑ 88BirBarB-9
❑ 89BirBarB-19
❑ 89BirBarP-97
❑ 89SouLeaAJ-10
❑ 90CMC-647
❑ 90ProAAAF-175
❑ 90VanCanC-20
❑ 90VanCanP-497
❑ 91ChaLooLD-172
❑ 91ChaLooP-1969
❑ 91LinDriAA-172
❑ 92ChaLooF-3832
❑ 92NasSouF-1842
❑ 92NasSouS-295
❑ 93LinVenB-69
Tragresser, Walter
❑ 16FleBreD-96
❑ 22KolMotBPP-30
Trail, Chet
❑ 81TCM60I-399
Tramble, Otis
❑ 82QuaCitCT-20
Trammell, Alan
❑ 78TigBurK-15
❑ 78TigTeal-32
❑ 78Top-707
❑ 79OPC-184
❑ 79Top-358
❑ 80OPC-123
❑ 80Top-232
❑ 81AllGamPI-24
❑ 81CokTeaS-57
❑ 81Don-5
❑ 81Fle-461
❑ 81FleStiC-89
❑ 81Kel-51
❑ 81OPC-133
❑ 81TigDetN-68
❑ 81TigPepT-1
❑ 81Top-709
❑ 81TopScr-38
❑ 81TopSti-75
❑ 82Don-5
❑ 82Don-5A
❑ 82Don-76
❑ 82Don-76A
❑ 82Fle-283
❑ 82FleSta-155
❑ 82OPC-381
❑ 82Squ-4
❑ 82Top-475
❑ 82TopSti-181
❑ 82TopStiV-181
❑ 83AllGamPI-25
❑ 83Don-207
❑ 83Fle-344
❑ 83FleSti-253
❑ 83OPC-95
❑ 83TigPos-28
❑ 83Top-95
❑ 83TopSti-66
❑ 84AllGamPI-115
❑ 84Don-293
❑ 84Dra-30
❑ 84Fle-91
❑ 84FleSti-14
❑ 84FunFooP-40
❑ 84Nes792-510
❑ 84OPC-88
❑ 84TigFarJ-14
❑ 84TigTeal-30
❑ 84TigWavP-33
❑ 84Top-510
❑ 84TopRubD-25
❑ 84TopSti-266
❑ 84TopStiB-9
❑ 84TopTif-510
❑ 85AllGamPI-26
❑ 85Don-171
❑ 85DonActA-44
❑ 85Dra-31
❑ 85Fle-23
❑ 85FleLimE-40
❑ 85KASDis-17
❑ 85KitCloD-17
❑ 85Lea-158
❑ 85OPC-181
❑ 85SevCoi-D8
❑ 85SevCoi-G15
❑ 85SubDis-20
❑ 85ThoMcAD-20
❑ 85TigCaiD-18
❑ 85TigWen-20
❑ 85Top-690
❑ 85TopGloS-16
❑ 85TopRubD-25
❑ 85TopSti-18
❑ 85TopSti-20
❑ 85TopSti-258
❑ 85TopSup-25
❑ 85TopTif-690
❑ 86BasStaB-111
❑ 86Don-171
❑ 86DonAll-45
❑ 86Fle-241
❑ 86Fle-633
❑ 86FleMin-50
❑ 86FleStiC-121
❑ 86Lea-101
❑ 86OPC-130
❑ 86Spo-147
❑ 86Spo-172
❑ 86TigCaiD-19
❑ 86Top-130
❑ 86TopSti-267
❑ 86TopTat-10
❑ 86TopTif-130
❑ 87Don-127
❑ 87DonHig-51
❑ 87DonOpeD-216
❑ 87Fle-167
❑ 87FleGlo-167
❑ 87FleHotS-41
❑ 87FleMin-107
❑ 87FleRecS-38
❑ 87FleStiC-118
❑ 87Lea-126
❑ 87OPC-209
❑ 87RedFolSB-62
❑ 87SevCoi-D11
❑ 87Spo-188
❑ 87SpoTeaP-15
❑ 87StuPan-19
❑ 87TigCaiD-7
❑ 87TigCok-4
❑ 87Top-687
❑ 87TopMinL-56
❑ 87TopSti-270
❑ 87TopTif-687
❑ 88ClaBlu-231
❑ 88Don-4
❑ 88Don-230
❑ 88DonAll-22
❑ 88DonBasB-281
❑ 88DonBonM-BC11
❑ 88DonSupD-4
❑ 88Dra-13
❑ 88Fle-74
❑ 88Fle-635
❑ 88FleAll-9
❑ 88FleAwaW-43
❑ 88FleBasA-42
❑ 88FleBasM-39
❑ 88FleExcS-42
❑ 88FleGlo-74
❑ 88FleGlo-635
❑ 88FleHotS-44
❑ 88FleLeaL-42
❑ 88FleMin-25
❑ 88FleRecS-41
❑ 88FleStiC-29
❑ 88FleSup-41
❑ 88FleTeaL-43
❑ 88KayB-31
❑ 88Lea-4
❑ 88Lea-167
❑ 88MSAFanSD-6
❑ 88MSAJifPD-16
❑ 88Nes-35
❑ 88OPC-320
❑ 88PanSti-94
❑ 88PanSti-444
❑ 88Sco-37
❑ 88Sco-651
❑ 88ScoGlo-37
❑ 88ScoGlo-651
❑ 88Spo-25
❑ 88StaLinTi-19
❑ 88StaTra-1
❑ 88StaTra-2
❑ 88StaTra-3
❑ 88StaTra-4
❑ 88StaTra-5
❑ 88StaTra-6
❑ 88StaTra-7
❑ 88StaTra-8
❑ 88StaTra-9
❑ 88StaTra-10
❑ 88StaTra-11
❑ 88TarPla-44
❑ 88TigPep-2
❑ 88TigPol-13
❑ 88Top-320
❑ 88Top-389
❑ 88Top-429
❑ 88TopBig-8
❑ 88TopCoi-30
❑ 88TopGloS-37
❑ 88TopMinL-12
❑ 88TopRitTM-18
❑ 88TopSti-273
❑ 88TopStiB-45
❑ 88TopTif-320
❑ 88TopTif-389
❑ 88TopTif-429
❑ 88TopUKM-79
❑ 88TopUKMT-79
❑ 89Bow-105
❑ 89BowTif-105
❑ 89CadEllD-58
❑ 89CerSup-10
❑ 89ClaTraO-128
❑ 89Don-180
❑ 89DonBasB-13
❑ 89DonBonM-BC17
❑ 89Fle-148
❑ 89FleAll-11
❑ 89FleBasA-41
❑ 89FleBasM-39
❑ 89FleExcS-41
❑ 89FleGlo-148
❑ 89FleHeroB-40
❑ 89FleLeaL-40
❑ 89FleSup-40
❑ 89FleWaxBC-C26
❑ 89KayB-30
❑ 89KinDis-9
❑ 89MasBreD-4
❑ 89OPC-49
❑ 89PanSti-343
❑ 89RedFolSB-121
❑ 89Sco-110
❑ 89ScoHot1S-7
❑ 89Spo-215
❑ 89SpollIFKI-56
❑ 89TigMar-3
❑ 89TigPol-3
❑ 89Top-400
❑ 89Top-770
❑ 89TopAme2C-29
❑ 89TopBasT-43
❑ 89TopBatL-22
❑ 89TopBig-123
❑ 89TopCapC-12
❑ 89TopCoi-56
❑ 89TopDouA-4
❑ 89TopGloS-25
❑ 89TopHilTM-29
❑ 89TopSti-281
❑ 89TopStiB-12
❑ 89TopTif-400
❑ 89TopTif-609
❑ 89TopTif-770
❑ 89TopUKM-77
❑ 89TVSpoM-69
❑ 89UppDec-290
❑ 89UppDec-690
❑ 90Bow-353
❑ 90BowTif-353
❑ 90ClaBlu-106
❑ 90Don-90
❑ 90DonBesA-7
❑ 90DOnBonM-BC26
❑ 90DonLeaS-20
❑ 90Fle-617
❑ 90FleBasA-41
❑ 90FleBasAC-41
❑ 90FleBasM-41
❑ 90FleBasMC-41
❑ 90FleCan-617
❑ 90GooHumICBLS-25
❑ 90Hot50PS-46
❑ 90Lea-218
❑ 90M.Vpin-37
❑ 90MLBBasB-88
❑ 90OPC-440
❑ 90PanSti-70
❑ 90Pos-28
❑ 90PubIntS-296
❑ 90PubIntS-484
❑ 90RedFolSB-96
❑ 90Sco-9
❑ 90Sco100S-41
❑ 90Spo-154
❑ 90StaLonJS-10
❑ 90StaLonJS-24
❑ 90SunSee-15
❑ 90TigCok-24
❑ 90TigTeal-23
❑ 90Top-440
❑ 90TopBig-190
❑ 90TopCoi-31
❑ 90TopDou-66
❑ 90TopSti-281
❑ 90TopStiB-45
❑ 90TopTif-440
❑ 90UppDec-554
❑ 90USPlaCA-10S
❑ 90WonBreS-13
❑ 91Bow-154
❑ 91Bow-370
❑ 91CadEllD-57
❑ 91Cla2-T96
❑ 91ClaGam-97
❑ 91Don-118
❑ 91Fle-355
❑ 91Lea-351
❑ 91MajLeaCP-33
❑ 91MSAHolD-10
❑ 91OPC-275
❑ 91OPC-389
❑ 91OPCPre-123
❑ 91PanCanT1-8
❑ 91PanFreS-291
❑ 91PanSti-238
❑ 91RedFolS-93
❑ 91Sco-40
❑ 91Sco-852
❑ 91Sco100S-63
❑ 91SevCoi-M15
❑ 91StaClu-63
❑ 91StaCluP-44
❑ 91StaPinB-50
❑ 91Stu-59
❑ 91TigCok-3
❑ 91TigPol-13
❑ 91Top-275
❑ 91Top-389
❑ 91TopCraJ2-26
❑ 91TopDesS-275
❑ 91TopDesS-389
❑ 91TopMic-275
❑ 91TopMic-389
❑ 91TopTif-275
❑ 91TopTif-389
❑ 91TopTriH-A6
❑ 91Ult-129
❑ 91UppDec-223
❑ 91UppDecSS-SS2
❑ 92Bow-690
❑ 92ClaGam-90
❑ 92Don-164
❑ 92DonCraJ2-31
❑ 92Fle-148
❑ 92Hig5-49
❑ 92Lea-172
❑ 92LeaBlaG-172
❑ 92OPC-120
❑ 92OPCPre-31
❑ 92PanSti-108
❑ 92Pin-113
❑ 92PinRool-17
❑ 92RedFolS-94
❑ 92Sco-515
❑ 92SpoStaCC-46
❑ 92StaClu-850
❑ 92StaCluNC-850
❑ 92Stu-179
❑ 92TigKro-26
❑ 92TigTeal-32
❑ 92Top-120
❑ 92TopGol-120
❑ 92TopGolW-120
❑ 92TopKid-75
❑ 92TopMic-120
❑ 92TriPla-176
❑ 92Ult-64
❑ 92UppDec-273
❑ 93Bow-391
❑ 93DiaMar-109
❑ 93Don-655
❑ 93Fin-18
❑ 93FinRef-18
❑ 93Fla-209
❑ 93Fle-613
❑ 93Lea-421
❑ 93MetBak-38
❑ 93OPC-360
❑ 93PacSpa-115
❑ 93Pin-353
❑ 93RedFolS-97
❑ 93Sco-313
❑ 93Sel-230
❑ 93SP-241
❑ 93StaClu-416
❑ 93StaCluFDI-416
❑ 93StaCluMOP-416
❑ 93TigGat-25
❑ 93Top-660
❑ 93TopGol-660
❑ 93TopInaM-660
❑ 93TopInaR-660
❑ 93TopMic-660
❑ 93TriPla-191
❑ 93Ult-204
❑ 93UppDec-532
❑ 93UppDecGold-532
❑ 94Bow-509
❑ 94ColChoSS-474
❑ 94Don-280
❑ 94Fin-159
❑ 94FinPre-159P
❑ 94FinRef-159
❑ 94Fla-53
❑ 94Fle-144
❑ 94Fle-709
❑ 94FleExtB-81
❑ 94FUnPac-103
❑ 94Lea-120
❑ 94LeaL-34
❑ 94OPC-72
❑ 94Pac-230
❑ 94PanSti-69
❑ 94Pin-429
❑ 94PinArtP-429
❑ 94PinMusC-429
❑ 94Sco-337
❑ 94ScoGolR-337
❑ 94Sel-285
❑ 94SP-181
❑ 94SPDieC-181
❑ 94Spo-93
❑ 94StaClu-331
❑ 94StaCluFDI-331
❑ 94StaCluGR-331
❑ 94StaCluMOP-331
❑ 94StaCluMOP-ST20
❑ 94StaCluST-ST20
❑ 94Stu-194
❑ 94Top-75
❑ 94TopGol-75
❑ 94TopSpa-75
❑ 94TriPla-249
❑ 94TriPlaM-7
❑ 94Ult-358
❑ 94UppDec-201
❑ 94UppDecED-201
❑ 95ColCho-471
❑ 95ColChoGS-471
❑ 95ColChoSS-471
❑ 95Don-502
❑ 95DonPreP-502
❑ 95DonTopotO-80
❑ 95Emo-46
❑ 95Fin-203
❑ 95FinRef-203
❑ 95Fla-261
❑ 95Fle-62
❑ 95Lea-224
❑ 95LeaLim-93
❑ 95Pac-161
❑ 95PacPri-51
❑ 95Pin-392
❑ 95PinArtP-392
❑ 95PinMusC-392
❑ 95Sco-383
❑ 95ScoGolR-383
❑ 95ScoPlaTS-383
❑ 95SP-154
❑ 95SPCha-114
❑ 95SPCha-153
❑ 95SPChaDC-114
❑ 95SPChaDC-153
❑ 95SPSil-154
❑ 95StaClu-298
❑ 95StaCluMOP-298
❑ 95StaCluSTWS-298
❑ 95StaCluVR-155
❑ 95StaCluVRMO-155
❑ 95Stu-98
❑ 95Top-474
❑ 95TopCyb-267
❑ 95UC3-12
❑ 95UC3ArtP-12
❑ 95Ult-51
❑ 95UltGolM-51
❑ 95UppDec-426
❑ 95UppDecED-426
❑ 95UppDecEDG-426
❑ 95UppDecSE-96
❑ 95UppDecSEG-96
❑ 96Cir-42
❑ 96CirRav-42
❑ 96ColCho-145
❑ 96ColChoGS-145
❑ 96ColChoSS-145
❑ 96Don-172
❑ 96DonPreP-172
❑ 96EmoXL-63
❑ 96Fla-85
❑ 96Fle-121
❑ 96FleGolM-10
❑ 96FleTif-121
❑ 96Lea-11
❑ 96LeaPrePB-11
❑ 96LeaPrePG-11
❑ 96LeaPrePS-11
❑ 96Pac-312
❑ 96PacPri-P103
❑ 96PacPriG-P103
❑ 96Pin-81
❑ 96PinArtP-52
❑ 96PinSta-52
❑ 96ProSta-124
❑ 96Sco-100
❑ 96ScoDugC-A72
❑ 96ScoDugCAP-A72
❑ 96SP-85
❑ 96StaClu-337
❑ 96StaCluEPB-337
❑ 96StaCluEPG-337
❑ 96StaCluEPS-337
❑ 96StaCluMOP-337
❑ 96TigHebN-14
❑ 96Ult-65
❑ 96UltGolM-65
❑ 96UppDec-106
❑ 96UppDec-330
❑ 97ColCho-105
❑ 97Don-220
❑ 97DonGolPP-220
❑ 97DonSilPP-220
❑ 97Fle-108
❑ 97FleTif-108
❑ 97Pac-96
❑ 97PacLigB-96
❑ 97PacSil-96
❑ 97Pin-93
❑ 97PinArtP-PP93
❑ 97PinMusC-93
❑ 97PinPrePla-93
❑ 97Sco-106
❑ 97ScoArtPWB-106
❑ 97ScoPreS-106
❑ 97ScoShoS-106
❑ 97ScoShoSAP-106
❑ 97Ult-64
❑ 97UltGolME-64
❑ 97UltPlaME-64
❑ 97UppDec-75
Trammell, Bubba
❑ 94JamJamC-1
❑ 94JamJamF-3982
❑ 95SPML-56
❑ 95TenVolW-11
❑ 96DouAllB-28
❑ 96Exc-53
❑ 96JacSunB-28
❑ 97BesLimA-38
❑ 97Bow-71
❑ 97BowChr-101
❑ 97BowChrI-101
❑ 97BowChrIR-101
❑ 97BowChrR-101
❑ 97BowInt-71
❑ 97ColCho-468
❑ 97Don-364
❑ 97DonFraFea-5
❑ 97DonGolPP-364
❑ 97DonLim-200
❑ 97DonLimE-200
❑ 97DonPre-150

❑ 97DonPreCttC-150
❑ 97DonSigA-98
❑ 97DonSigAC-123
❑ 97DonSigAM-123
❑ 97DonSilPP-364
❑ 97Fin-249
❑ 97FinRef-249
❑ 97FlaShoLC-18
❑ 97FlaShoLeg0-18
❑ 97FlaShoLeg1-18
❑ 97FlaShoM-A18
❑ 97FlaShoM-B18
❑ 97FlaShoM-C18
❑ 97FlaShoR0-18
❑ 97FlaShoR1-18
❑ 97FlaShoR2-18
❑ 97FlaShoWotF-9
❑ 97Fle-510
❑ 97FleNewH-13
❑ 97FleTif-510
❑ 97Lea-322
❑ 97LeaFraM-322
❑ 97LeaFraMDC-322
❑ 97NewPin-160
❑ 97NewPinAP-160
❑ 97NewPinMC-160
❑ 97NewPinPP-160
❑ 97PinCer-127
❑ 97PinCerMBla-127
❑ 97PinCerMBlu-127
❑ 97PinCerMG-127
❑ 97PinCerMR-127
❑ 97PinCerR-127
❑ 97PinTotCPB-127
❑ 97PinTotCPG-127
❑ 97PinTotCPR-127
❑ 97PinX-P-120
❑ 97PinX-PMoS-120
❑ 97Sco-483
❑ 97ScoArtPWB-483
❑ 97ScoResC-483
❑ 97ScoShoS-483
❑ 97ScoShoSAP-483
❑ 97Sel-125
❑ 97SelArtP-125
❑ 97SelCom-125
❑ 97SelRegG-125
❑ 97SP-14
❑ 97SpoIll-25
❑ 97SpoIllEE-25
❑ 97TolMudHB-1
❑ 97Top-206
❑ 97Ult-527
❑ 97UltGolME-527
❑ 97UltPlaME-527
❑ 97UppDec-533
❑ 98BesAutPOY-17
❑ 98BesPreA-43
❑ 98CirThu-190
❑ 98CirThuRav-190
❑ 98CirThuSupRav-190
❑ 98ColCho-499
❑ 98ColChoSQ-SQ17
❑ 98DevRayP-25
❑ 98Don-139
❑ 98Don-237
❑ 98DonCol-139
❑ 98DonCol-202
❑ 98DonColE-502
❑ 98DonColL-345
❑ 98DonColP-687
❑ 98DonColS-139
❑ 98DonColS-197
❑ 98DonCruG-24
❑ 98DonCruP-24
❑ 98DonCruR-24
❑ 98DonEli-102
❑ 98DonEliA-102
❑ 98DonEliS-102
❑ 98DonGolPP-139
❑ 98DonGolPP-237
❑ 98DonPre-137
❑ 98DonPreSeat-137
❑ 98DonPriCD-139
❑ 98DonPriCD-202
❑ 98DonPriCE-502
❑ 98DonPriCL-345
❑ 98DonPriCP-687
❑ 98DonRatR-27
❑ 98DonRatRM-27
❑ 98DonSigA-86
❑ 98DonSigAC-108
❑ 98DonSigAM-111
❑ 98DonSigSB-27
❑ 98DonSilPP-139
❑ 98DonSilPP-237
❑ 98DurBulTI-27
❑ 98Fle-102
❑ 98Fle-481
❑ 98Lea-146
❑ 98LeaCruG-24
❑ 98LeaCruP-24
❑ 98LeaCruR-24
❑ 98LeaFraDA-146
❑ 98LeaFraF-146
❑ 98LeaFraM-146
❑ 98LeaFraM-146
❑ 98LeaFraMDC-146
❑ 98LeaFraMDC-146
❑ 98LeaFraMS-146
❑ 98LeaFraMZ2-146
❑ 98MetUni-163
❑ 98MetUniPMG-163
❑ 98Pac-97
❑ 98PacOnl-723
❑ 98PacOnlR-723
❑ 98PacOnlWC-723
❑ 98PacPlaB-97
❑ 98PacRedT-97
❑ 98PacSil-97
❑ 98PinSna-TBDR7
❑ 98PinSna-TBDR16
❑ 98ScoRT-219
❑ 98ScoRTSS-PP121
❑ 98ScoRTSSAP-PP121
❑ 98ScoRTSSAP1-PP121
❑ 98Stu-172
❑ 98StuGPP-172
❑ 98StuSPP-172
❑ 98Top-470
❑ 98TopChr-470
❑ 98TopChrR-470
❑ 98TopDevR-470
❑ 98TopDia-470
❑ 98TopMiniC-470
❑ 98Ult-181
❑ 98Ult-471
❑ 98UltGolM-181
❑ 98UltGolM-471
❑ 98UltMas-181
❑ 98UltMas-471
❑ 98UltPlaM-181
❑ 98UltPlaM-471
❑ 98UppDec-89
❑ 98UppDec-735
❑ 99Fle-276
❑ 99FleSta9-276
❑ 99FleWarT-276
❑ 99SkyThu-61
❑ 99SkyThuRant-61
❑ 99SkyThuRave-61
❑ 99SP Aut-118
❑ 99ThuSkySupR-61
❑ 99UppDec-212
❑ 99UppDecEL1-212
❑ 99UppDecEL2-212
❑ 99UppDecGJ-BT
❑ 99UppDecM-203
❑ 99UppDecMGS-203
❑ 99UppDecMHFS-203
❑ 99UppDecMSS-203

Trammell, Gary
❑ 94AubAstC-20
❑ 94AubAstF-3768
❑ 95MidLeaA-53
❑ 95QuaCitRBTI-27
❑ 96KisCobB-29
❑ 97JacGen-25
❑ 97JacGenS-24
❑ 98JacGenM-22

Trammell, Marcus
❑ 88UtiBluSP-11

Tramuta, Marc
❑ 91YakBeaC-3
❑ 91YakBeaP-4256

Tran, Ray
❑ 47PadTeal-20

Tranbarger, Mark
❑ 92SprCarC-16
❑ 92SprCarF-870
❑ 93SavCarC-24
❑ 93SavCarF-687
❑ 94WinSpiC-21
❑ 94WinSpiF-270
❑ 95ChaLooTI-22
❑ 97SouBenSH-28

Tranberg, Mark
❑ 92BatCliCB-22
❑ 92BatCliF-3266
❑ 93SouAtlLAGF-54
❑ 93SpaPhiC-1
❑ 93SpaPhiF-1056
❑ 94Bow-468
❑ 94ExcFS7-249
❑ 94ReaPhiF-2062
❑ 95ReaPhiTI-26

Trapaga, Julio
❑ 94DurBulC-23
❑ 94DurBulF-338
❑ 94DurBulTI-25

Trapp, Mike
❑ 87Ft.MyeRP-4

Trappers, Salt Lake
❑ 91SalLakTP-3230

Trautman, Keith
❑ 92YakBeaC-19

Trautwein, Dave
❑ 87LitFalMP-2392
❑ 88St.LucMS-24
❑ 89JacMetGS-8
❑ 89TexLeaAGS-27
❑ 90CMC-363
❑ 90MetColP-51
❑ 90ProAAAF-276
❑ 90TidTidC-12
❑ 90TidTidP-545
❑ 90TopTVM-64
❑ 91LinDriAAA-570
❑ 91TidTidLD-570
❑ 91TidTidP-2510
❑ 92SalSpuC-4
❑ 92SalSpuF-3756

Trautwein, John
❑ 86JacExpT-7
❑ 87JacExpP-449
❑ 87SouLeaAJ-14
❑ 88BlaYNPRWL-155
❑ 88DonRoo-24
❑ 88DonTeaBRS-NEW
❑ 88FleUpd-10
❑ 88FleUpdG-10
❑ 89PawRedSC-9
❑ 89PawRedSP-685
❑ 89PawRedSTI-25
❑ 90CMC-253
❑ 90PawRedSC-2
❑ 90PawRedSDD-26
❑ 90PawRedSP-463
❑ 90ProAAAF-435
❑ 90TopTVRS-62

Travels, Darren
❑ 85UtiBluST-6
❑ 86JamExpP-26

Travers, Bill
❑ 75OPC-488
❑ 75SacSolC-20
❑ 75Top-488
❑ 75TopMin-488
❑ 76BreA&P-14
❑ 76OPC-573
❑ 76SSP-244
❑ 76Top-573
❑ 77BurCheD-90
❑ 77Hos-87
❑ 77Kel-9
❑ 77OPC-174
❑ 77Top-125
❑ 77TopCloS-49
❑ 78Top-355
❑ 79BrePlaPH-1
❑ 79OPC-106
❑ 79Top-213
❑ 80Top-109
❑ 81Don-508
❑ 81Fle-514A
❑ 81Fle-514B
❑ 81Fle-525
❑ 81LonBeaPT-13
❑ 81Top-704
❑ 81TopTra-845
❑ 82Top-628
❑ 89PacSenL-118
❑ 89T/MSenL-107
❑ 89TopSenL-21
❑ 94BreMilB-279

Travers, Steve
❑ 82IdaFalAT-13

Travis, Cecil
❑ 34DiaMatCSB-182
❑ 36GouWidPPR-A101
❑ 36NatChiFPR-70
❑ 36OveCanR-42
❑ 37OPCBatUV-126
❑ 37WheBB14-14
❑ 37WheBB7-29B
❑ 37WheBB9-15
❑ 38CloFotW-79
❑ 38WheBB10-2
❑ 39ExhSal-57
❑ 39GouPreR303A-42
❑ 39PlaBal-114
❑ 39WorWidGTP-42
❑ 39WorWidGV-23
❑ 40PlaBal-16
❑ 41DouPlaR-75
❑ 41PlaBal-48
❑ 46SpoExcW-9-7
❑ 77TCMTheWY-76
❑ 79DiaGre-53
❑ 82DiaCla-10
❑ 84TCMPla1-10
❑ 95ConTSN-1349
❑ 96NoiSatP-3

Travis, Jesse
❑ 97SalVolG-36

Trawick, Tim
❑ 95EveAqaTI-28
❑ 96LanJetB-28

Traxler, Brian
❑ 89SanAntMB-11
❑ 90AlbDukTr-28
❑ 90DonRoo-38
❑ 91LinDriAA-544
❑ 91SanAntMLD-544
❑ 91SanAntMP-2984
❑ 91TopDeb90-155
❑ 92AlbDukF-730
❑ 92AlbDukS-21
❑ 93AlbDukF-1472

Traylor, Keith
❑ 84LitFalMT-9

Traynor, Pie (Harold)
❑ 22E120-225
❑ 22W572-107
❑ 23MapCriV-2
❑ 25Exh-55
❑ 26Exh-55
❑ 26SpoComoA-43
❑ 26SpoNewSM-9
❑ 27Exh-28
❑ 27YorCarE-14
❑ 28PorandAR-A36
❑ 28PorandAR-B36
❑ 28StaPlaCE-67
❑ 28W502-14
❑ 28W513-82
❑ 28Yue-14
❑ 29ExhFou-13
❑ 29PorandAR-92
❑ 30SchR33-23
❑ 31Exh-13
❑ 31W517-2
❑ 32R33So2-xx
❑ 33DelR33-12
❑ 33Gou-22
❑ 33GouCanV-22
❑ 33NatLeaAC-15
❑ 33RitCE-10C
❑ 34BatR31-14
❑ 34BatR31-100
❑ 34DiaStaR-27
❑ 34DiaStaR-99
❑ 34ExhFou-7
❑ 35ExhFou-7
❑ 35GouPuzR-4B
❑ 35GouPuzR-7B
❑ 35GouPuzR-12B
❑ 36ExhFou-7
❑ 36NatChiFPR-71
❑ 36R31PasP-45
❑ 36R31Pre-G15
❑ 36SandSW-46
❑ 38CloFotW-80
❑ 39PC7AlbHoF-55
❑ 40PlaBal-224
❑ 50CalHOFW-71
❑ 60Fle-77
❑ 61Fle-89
❑ 61Fle-144
❑ 61GolPre-15
❑ 63HalofFB-19
❑ 67TopVen-144
❑ 68SpoMemAG-15
❑ 72KelATG-8
❑ 73SevTraC-76
❑ 74Bra193NLA-15
❑ 76OPC-343
❑ 76RowExh-15
❑ 76ShaPiz-55
❑ 76Top-343
❑ 77BobParHoF-99
❑ 77GalGloG-102
❑ 77GalGloG-205
❑ 77ShaPiz-17
❑ 78DexHaloFP-48
❑ 80PacLeg-36
❑ 80PerHaloFP-55
❑ 80PirGreT-3
❑ 80SSPHOF-55
❑ 81ConTSN-63
❑ 82DavHaloFB-22
❑ 82DiaCla-40
❑ 83BigLeaCOA-40
❑ 83ConMar-40
❑ 86ConSer1-38
❑ 86PirGreT-4
❑ 86SpoDecG-11
❑ 86TCM-10
❑ 87HygAllG-44
❑ 87NesDreT-3
❑ 88ConNatA-21
❑ 91ConTSN-36
❑ 91ConTSN-268
❑ 91SweBasG-148
❑ 92ConTSN-434
❑ 93ActPacA-96
❑ 93ActPacA2-30G
❑ 93ConMasB-9
❑ 93ConTSN-670
❑ 93ConTSNP-1050
❑ 93LegFoi-11
❑ 94ConTSN-1050
❑ 94ConTSN-1093
❑ 94ConTSNB-1050
❑ 94ConTSNB-1093
❑ 94ConTSNCI-29
❑ 94TedWil-80

Treadgill, Chris
❑ 90QuaCitAGS-29

Treadway, Andre
❑ 82DurBulT-21
❑ 85GreBraTI-21
❑ 86RicBraP-24

Treadway, Doug
❑ 88WinHavRSS-24

Treadway, George
❑ 87OldJudN-498
❑ 90DodTar-1086

Treadway, Jeff
❑ 86VerRedP-22
❑ 87NasSouTI-21
❑ 88Don-29
❑ 88DonRoo-17
❑ 88Fle-249
❑ 88FleGlo-249
❑ 88FleMin-76
❑ 88Lea-29
❑ 88RedKah-15
❑ 88Sco-646
❑ 88ScoGlo-646
❑ 88ScoYouS2-26
❑ 88Spo-225
❑ 88StaLinRe-19
❑ 88TopBig-214
❑ 88TopTra-122T
❑ 88TopTraT-122T
❑ 89BraDub-27
❑ 89ClaLigB-54
❑ 89Don-351
❑ 89DonBasB-141
❑ 89Fle-173A
❑ 89Fle-173B
❑ 89FleGlo-173
❑ 89FleUpd-75
❑ 89OPC-61
❑ 89PanSti-73
❑ 89Sco-86
❑ 89ScoHot1R-84
❑ 89ScoRoo-18T
❑ 89Spo-107
❑ 89Top-685
❑ 89TopSti-139
❑ 89TopTif-685
❑ 89TopTra-121T
❑ 89TopTraT-121T
❑ 89ToyRoo-31
❑ 89UppDec-393
❑ 90BraDubP-29
❑ 90BraDubS-33
❑ 90ClaYel-T25
❑ 90Don-50
❑ 90DonBesN-123
❑ 90Fle-598
❑ 90FleCan-598
❑ 90Lea-455
❑ 90OPC-486
❑ 90PanSti-218
❑ 90Sco-95
❑ 90Spo-219
❑ 90Top-486
❑ 90TopSti-29
❑ 90TopTif-486
❑ 90UppDec-141
❑ 91Bow-586
❑ 91BraDubP-30
❑ 91BraSubS-37
❑ 91Don-117
❑ 91Fle-707
❑ 91Lea-246
❑ 91OPC-139
❑ 91PanFreS-20
❑ 91PanSti-28
❑ 91Sco-219
❑ 91Sco100S-31
❑ 91StaClu-497
❑ 91Stu-150
❑ 91Top-139
❑ 91TopDesS-139
❑ 91TopMic-139
❑ 91TopTif-139
❑ 91Ult-13
❑ 91UppDec-499
❑ 92BraLykP-28
❑ 92BraLykS-33
❑ 92Don-324
❑ 92Fle-373
❑ 92OPC-99
❑ 92Sco-142
❑ 92StaClu-82
❑ 92Top-99
❑ 92TopGol-99
❑ 92TopGolW-99
❑ 92TopMic-99
❑ 92Ult-171
❑ 92UppDec-389
❑ 93BoyScooAT-1
❑ 93Don-448
❑ 93FleFinE-205
❑ 93IndWUA-31
❑ 93Lea-480
❑ 93Sco-461
❑ 93Ult-546
❑ 94DodMot-14
❑ 94DodPol-25
❑ 94Don-295
❑ 94Fle-122
❑ 94Pac-185
❑ 94PanSti-61
❑ 94Sco-115
❑ 94ScoGolR-115
❑ 94ScoRoo-RT67
❑ 94ScoRooGR-RT67
❑ 94StaClu-30
❑ 94StaClu-694
❑ 94StaCluFDI-30
❑ 94StaCluFDI-694
❑ 94StaCluGR-30
❑ 94StaCluGR-694
❑ 94StaCluMOP-30
❑ 94StaCluMOP-694
❑ 95DodPol-25
❑ 95Sco-451
❑ 95ScoGolR-451
❑ 95ScoPlaTS-451
❑ 98AugGreM-28

Treadway, Red (Thadford Lee)
❑ 77TCMTheWY-18

Treadway, Steven
❑ 88CapCodPPaLP-181

Treadwell, Jody
❑ 91LinDriAA-545
❑ 91SanAntMLD-545
❑ 91SanAntMP-2975
❑ 92SanAntMF-3974
❑ 93AlbDukF-1460
❑ 94AlbDukF-843
❑ 97AlbDukGS-29

Treanor, Dean
❑ 88FreSunCLC-26
❑ 88FreSunP-1236
❑ 89MiaMirIS-25
❑ 90RenSilSCLC-288
❑ 91RenSilSCLC-28
❑ 92WatDiaC-27
❑ 92WatDiaF-2157
❑ 93WatDiaC-29
❑ 93WatDiaF-1785
❑ 94RanCucQC-27
❑ 94RanCucQF-1653
❑ 95MemChiTI-2
❑ 96DelShoB-2
❑ 97HarSen-28

Treanor, Matt
❑ 94SigRooDP-77
❑ 94SigRooDPS-77

❑ 95SprSulTI-29
❑ 96LanLugB-28
❑ 97CarLeaTP-15
❑ 97WilBluR-3
Trebelhorn, Tom
❑ 77ModA'sC-17
❑ 80PorBeaT-18
❑ 81PorBeaT-2
❑ 84BrePol-NNO
❑ 85VanCanC-215
❑ 86BrePol-42
❑ 87BrePol-42
❑ 87TopTra-121T
❑ 87TopTraT-121T
❑ 88BrePol-42
❑ 88BreTeal-35
❑ 88Top-224
❑ 88TopTif-224
❑ 89BrePol-42
❑ 89BreYea-42
❑ 89Top-344
❑ 89TopTif-344
❑ 90BreMilB-27
❑ 90BrePol-42
❑ 90OPC-759
❑ 90Top-759
❑ 90TopTif-759
❑ 91BreMilB-28
❑ 91BrePol-25
❑ 91OPC-459
❑ 91Top-459
❑ 91TopDesS-459
❑ 91TopMic-459
❑ 91TopTif-459
❑ 92CubMar-NNO
❑ 93CubMar-27
Trechuck, Frank
❑ 50WorWidGV-6
Tredaway, Chad
❑ 92GenCubC-4
❑ 92GenCubF-1569
❑ 93ExcFS7-13
❑ 94OrlCubF-1395
❑ 95RanCucQT-9
❑ 96LasVegSB-28
Tredway, Ed
❑ 90MadMusB-2
❑ 90MadMusP-2273
Treece, Jack
❑ 44CenFlo-24
Treend, Pat
❑ 95ElmPioTI-28
❑ 95ElmPioUTI-28
Trella, Steve
❑ 75CliPilT-24
Tremark, Nick
❑ 90DodTar-808
Tremblay, Gary
❑ 86PawRedSP-25
❑ 87PawRedSP-70
❑ 87PawRedST-12
❑ 88PawRedSC-22
❑ 88PawRedSP-450
❑ 89PawRedSC-14
❑ 89PawRedSP-702
❑ 89PawRedSTI-26
❑ 90CMC-264
❑ 90PawRedSC-13
❑ 90PawRedSDD-27
❑ 90PawRedSP-466
❑ 90ProAAAF-438
❑ 90TopTVRS-63
Tremblay, Wayne
❑ 79ElmPioRST-25
❑ 85GreHorT-12
Trembley, Dave
❑ 86KinEagP-24
❑ 87HarSenP-2
❑ 88EasLeaAP-45
❑ 88HarSenP-846
❑ 89EasLeaDDP-DD46
❑ 89HarSenP-292
❑ 91ChaRaiC-24
❑ 91ChaRaiP-110
❑ 92ChaRaiC-22
❑ 92ChaRaiF-135
❑ 93WicWraF-2993
❑ 94OrlCubF-1401
❑ 96DayCubB-26
❑ 97OrlRayB-1
❑ 98WesTenDJM-26
Tremel, William
❑ 55Top-52
❑ 55TopDouH-101
❑ 56Top-96
❑ 56TopPin-7
Tremie, Chris
❑ 92UtiBluSC-16
❑ 93HicCraC-25
❑ 93HicCraF-1282
❑ 93SarWhiSF-1372
❑ 94BirBarC-1
❑ 94BirBarF-625
❑ 95NasSouTI-26
❑ 96NasSouB-25
❑ 97ReaPhi-25
❑ 98OklRedM-20
Tremper, Overton
❑ 90DodTar-1087
Trent, Ted (Theodore)
❑ 78LauLonABS-1
❑ 86NegLeaF-116
❑ 87NegLeaPD-3
Tresamer, Michael
❑ 86EugEmeC-49
❑ 87AppFoxP-9
❑ 88BasCitRS-22
❑ 89MemChiB-22
❑ 89MemChiP-1197
❑ 89MemChiS-21
❑ 89Sta-45
❑ 90OmaRoyP-65
❑ 90ProAAAF-600
Tresch, Dave
❑ 85LynMetT-3
❑ 86LynMetP-22
Tresh, Mickey
❑ 87PriWilYP-12
❑ 88PriWilYS-23
❑ 89PenPilS-25
Tresh, Mike (Michael)
❑ 39WhiSoxTI-20
❑ 40WhiSoxL-20
❑ 41DouPlaR-69
❑ 47TipTop-27
❑ 48KelPep*-BB3
❑ 48WhiSoxTI-25
❑ 49Bow-166
❑ 49IndTeal-23
❑ 50IndNumN-20
❑ 77TCMTheWY-53
❑ 83TCMPla1943-9
❑ 90LakTigS-24
❑ 90StaFS7-38
Tresh, Tom
❑ 61Yan61RL-38
❑ 62Top-31
❑ 62TopVen-31
❑ 63Jel-23
❑ 63Pos-23
❑ 63ReqKP-19
❑ 63SalMetC-54
❑ 63Top-146
❑ 63Top-173
❑ 63Top-470
❑ 63YanJayP-12
❑ 64ChatheY-24
❑ 64Raw-9
❑ 64Top-395
❑ 64TopCoi-10
❑ 64TopRooAB-3
❑ 64TopRooAB-11
❑ 64WheSta-45
❑ 64YanJayP-12
❑ 65ChaTheY-23
❑ 65Top-440
❑ 66Baz-40
❑ 66Top-205
❑ 66TopRubl-94
❑ 66TopVen-205
❑ 66YanTeal-12
❑ 67Baz-40
❑ 67CokCapYM-V17
❑ 67DexPre-210
❑ 67Top-289
❑ 67TopVen-216
❑ 68AtlOilPBCC-44
❑ 68OPC-69
❑ 68Top-69
❑ 68TopVen-69
❑ 68YanPhoS-86
❑ 69MilBra-278
❑ 69MLBOffS-80
❑ 69OPC-212
❑ 69Top-212
❑ 69TopSta-209
❑ 69TopTeaP-19
❑ 69YanMal-10
❑ 70MLBOffS-215
❑ 70Top-698
❑ 72MilBra-348
❑ 76TayBow4-86
❑ 83FraBroR-17
❑ 83YanASFY-48
❑ 84WilMay-24
❑ 88PacLegI-25
❑ 89SweBasG-52
❑ 90SweBasG-17
❑ 91SweBasG-66
❑ 91YanRinP11-2
❑ 92YanWIZ6-131
❑ 92YanWIZA-83
Treuel, Ralph
❑ 80EvaTriT-15
❑ 89LakTigS-28
❑ 91LinDriAAA-600
❑ 91TolMudHP-1947
❑ 92TolMudHF-1059
❑ 96DouAllB-2
❑ 96TreThuB-3
❑ 98TreThuM-2
Trevino, Alex
❑ 77WauMetT-21
❑ 78TidTidT-25
❑ 80Top-537
❑ 81CokTeaS-94
❑ 81Fle-318
❑ 81Top-23
❑ 81TopSupHT-78
❑ 82Don-350
❑ 82Fle-540
❑ 82RedCok-21
❑ 82Top-368
❑ 82TopTra-120T
❑ 83Don-374
❑ 83Fle-604
❑ 83RedYea-29
❑ 83Top-632
❑ 83TopSti-232
❑ 84BraPol-25
❑ 84Don-286
❑ 84Fle-484
❑ 84FleUpd-118
❑ 84Nes792-242
❑ 84raPho-29
❑ 84Top-242
❑ 84TopTif-242
❑ 84TopTra-120T
❑ 84TopTraT-120T
❑ 85Don-565
❑ 85Fle-341
❑ 85FleUpd-122
❑ 85OPC-279
❑ 85Top-747
❑ 85TopSti-30
❑ 85TopTif-747
❑ 85TopTifT-123T
❑ 85TopTra-123T
❑ 86DodCokP-29
❑ 86DodPol-29
❑ 86DodUniOP-20
❑ 86Fle-550
❑ 86FleUpd-119
❑ 86OPC-169
❑ 86Top-444
❑ 86TopTif-444
❑ 86TopTra-116T
❑ 86TopTraT-116T
❑ 87DodMot-23
❑ 87DodPho-15
❑ 87DodPol-15
❑ 87Don-546
❑ 87Fle-456
❑ 87FleGlo-456
❑ 87Top-173
❑ 87TopTif-173
❑ 88DodPol-29
❑ 88Don-376
❑ 88Sco-182
❑ 88ScoGlo-182
❑ 88StaLinD-19
❑ 88Top-512
❑ 88TopClo-115
❑ 88TopTif-512
❑ 88TucTorC-16
❑ 88TucTorJP-22
❑ 89AstLenH-6
❑ 89AstMot-17
❑ 89AstSmo-38
❑ 89Bow-326
❑ 89BowTif-326
❑ 89OPC-64
❑ 89Sco-574
❑ 89Top-64
❑ 89TopTif-64
❑ 89UppDec-262
❑ 90AstLenH-25
❑ 90AstMot-21
❑ 90DodTar-809
❑ 90Don-443
❑ 90Fle-239
❑ 90FleCan-239
❑ 90Lea-432
❑ 90OPC-342
❑ 90PubIntS-104
❑ 90Top-342
❑ 90TopTif-342
❑ 90UppDec-205
❑ 91MetWIZ-414
❑ 92LouRedF-1891
❑ 92LouRedS-271
Trevino, Gerald
❑ 92IdaFalGF-3521
❑ 92IdaFalGSP-22
Trevino, Ricardo
❑ 94LetMouF-3880
❑ 94LetMouSP-18
Trevino, Ted
❑ 80QuaCitCT-15
Trevino, Tony
❑ 88BatCliP-1665
❑ 88SpaPhiP-1040
❑ 89ClePhiS-22
❑ 90ClePhiS-22
❑ 90FloStaLAS-18
❑ 90StaFS7-72
❑ 91LinDriAA-521
❑ 91ReaPhiLD-521
❑ 91ReaPhiP-1378
❑ 92ClePhiC-16
❑ 92ReaPhiF-584
Trevor, Claire
❑ 48BabRutS-3
❑ 48BabRutS-4
❑ 48BabRutS-9
❑ 48BabRutS-27
❑ 48BabRutS-28
Triandos, Gus
❑ 47Exh-225
❑ 47PM1StaP1-211
❑ 55OriEss-24
❑ 55Top-64
❑ 55TopDouH-81
❑ 56BalOriP-9
❑ 56BalOriP-50
❑ 56Top-80
❑ 56TopPin-4
❑ 57SwiFra-2
❑ 57Top-156
❑ 58BalOriP-16
❑ 58JayPubA-22
❑ 58OriJayP-11
❑ 58Top-429
❑ 59ArmCoi-18
❑ 59Baz-21
❑ 59HomRunD-20
❑ 59OriJayP-9
❑ 59Top-330
❑ 59Top-568
❑ 60ArmCoi-19
❑ 60BalOriP-10
❑ 60Baz-11
❑ 60OriJayP-9
❑ 60Top-60
❑ 60TopTat-51
❑ 60TopVen-60
❑ 61BalOriP-20
❑ 61Baz-25
❑ 61Pos-69A
❑ 61Pos-69B
❑ 61Top-140
❑ 61TopStal-106
❑ 62BalOriP-30
❑ 62Jel-33
❑ 62Pos-33
❑ 62PosCan-33
❑ 62SalPlaC-93
❑ 62ShiPlaC-93
❑ 62Top-420
❑ 62TopBuc-89
❑ 62TopStal-9
❑ 63TigJayP-11
❑ 63Top-475
❑ 64PhiJayP-11
❑ 64PhiPhiB-25
❑ 64Top-83
❑ 64TopVen-83
❑ 65OPC-248
❑ 65PhiJayP-11
❑ 65Top-248
❑ 79TCM50-75
❑ 85TCMPhoC-24
❑ 86OriGreT-6
❑ 91OriCro-462
❑ 97BalOriP-50
Tribble, Scott
❑ 93Sou-15
Tribolet, Scott
❑ 91MisStaB-45
❑ 92MisStaB-42
❑ 95AubAstTI-4
Trice, Robert Lee
❑ 47PM1StaP1-212
❑ 52LavPro-60
❑ 54A'STEAI-26
❑ 54Top-148
❑ 55A'sRodM-42
❑ 55JetPos-17
❑ 55Top-132
❑ 55TopDouH-123
❑ 86NegLeaF-43
❑ 94TopArc1-148
❑ 94TopArc1G-148
Trice, Wally (Walter)
❑ 88AubAstP-1950
❑ 89OscAstS-25
❑ 90Bes-205
❑ 90ColMudB-15
❑ 90ColMudP-1349
❑ 90ColMudS-24
❑ 91BurAstC-9
❑ 91BurAstP-2800
❑ 91Cla/Bes-326
❑ 91MidLeaAP-MWL18
❑ 92CanIndF-690
❑ 92ProFS7-232
Triche, Bryan
❑ 91MisStaB-46
❑ 92MisStaB-43
❑ 93MisStaB-44
Triechel, Al
❑ 47PadTeal-21
Triessl, Mike
❑ 94RivPilCLC-25
Trillo, Carlos
❑ 93LinVenB-213
❑ 94VenLinU-250
❑ 95LinVen-214
❑ 96-97LinVen-248
Trillo, Manny
❑ 74OPC-597
❑ 74Top-597
❑ 75OPC-617
❑ 75Top-617
❑ 75TopMin-617
❑ 76CubTri-25
❑ 76OPC-206
❑ 76SSP-316
❑ 76Top-206
❑ 76VenLeaS-89
❑ 76VenLeaS-223
❑ 76VenLeaS-227
❑ 76VenLeaS-241
❑ 77BurCheD-191
❑ 77CubJewT-15
❑ 77OPC-158
❑ 77PepGloD-59
❑ 77Top-395
❑ 78Hos-69
❑ 78OPC-217
❑ 78Top-123
❑ 78WifBalD-76
❑ 79OPC-337
❑ 79PhiBurK-14
❑ 79PhiTeal-10
❑ 79Top-639
❑ 80OPC-50
❑ 80PhiBul-38
❑ 80PhiBurK-5
❑ 80Top-90
❑ 80WilGloT-8
❑ 81AllGamPI-108
❑ 81CokTeaS-107
❑ 81Don-22
❑ 81Fle-3
❑ 81FleStiC-96
❑ 81OPC-368
❑ 81Top-470
❑ 81TopSupHT-89
❑ 82Don-245
❑ 82Fle-260
❑ 82FleSta-59
❑ 82OPC-220
❑ 82PerAll-18
❑ 82PerAllG-18
❑ 82Top-220
❑ 82TopSti-76
❑ 82TopSti-122
❑ 83AllGamPI-16
❑ 83Don-294
❑ 83Fle-174
❑ 83Fle-631
❑ 83FleSta-200
❑ 83FleSti-175
❑ 83IndPos-36
❑ 83IndWhe-30
❑ 83OPC-73
❑ 83OPC-174
❑ 83PerAll-7
❑ 83PerAllG-8
❑ 83PhiPosGPaM-8
❑ 83Top-5
❑ 83Top-398
❑ 83Top-535
❑ 83TopSti-141
❑ 83TopSti-142
❑ 83TopSti-268
❑ 83TopTra-116T
❑ 84AllGamPI-17
❑ 84Don-575
❑ 84Fle-289
❑ 84Fle-627
❑ 84FleUpd-119
❑ 84FunFooP-57
❑ 84GiaPos-28
❑ 84Nes792-180
❑ 84OPC-180
❑ 84Top-180
❑ 84TopGloA-3
❑ 84TopSti-93
❑ 84TopTif-180
❑ 84TopTra-121T
❑ 84TopTraT-121T
❑ 85AllGamPI-107
❑ 85Don-431
❑ 85DonActA-31
❑ 85Fle-622
❑ 85GiaMot-5
❑ 85GiaPos-27
❑ 85OPC-310
❑ 85Top-310
❑ 85TopMin-310
❑ 85TopTif-310
❑ 86BasStaB-112
❑ 86CubGat-19
❑ 86CubUno-19
❑ 86Don-201
❑ 86Fle-551
❑ 86FleUpd-120
❑ 86OPC-142
❑ 86Top-655
❑ 86TopSti-88
❑ 86TopTif-655
❑ 86TopTra-117T
❑ 86TopTraT-117T
❑ 87CubCan-34
❑ 87CubDavB-19
❑ 87Don-570
❑ 87Fle-577
❑ 87FleGlo-577
❑ 87OPC-32
❑ 87Top-732
❑ 87TopTif-732
❑ 88CubDavB-19
❑ 88Don-516
❑ 88DonTeaBC-516
❑ 88Fle-436
❑ 88FleGlo-436
❑ 88Sco-524
❑ 88ScoGlo-524
❑ 88StaLinCu-15
❑ 88Top-171
❑ 88Top-287
❑ 88TopTif-171
❑ 88TopTif-287
❑ 89Bow-308
❑ 89BowTif-308
❑ 89Don-608
❑ 89Fle-440A
❑ 89Fle-440B
❑ 89FleGlo-440
❑ 89Sco-446
❑ 89Top-66
❑ 89TopBig-295
❑ 89TopTif-66
❑ 89UppDec-127
❑ 90PubIntS-41
❑ 93LinVenB-192
❑ 97OrlRayB-3
❑ 98RocCubM-29
❑ 98RocCubTI-30
Trimarco, Mike
❑ 93BluOriC-23
❑ 93BluOriF-4125
❑ 94AlbPolC-25
❑ 94AlbPolF-2238

❑ 96FreKeyB-22
Trimble, Rob
❑ 93OneYanC-23
❑ 94GreBatF-480
❑ 94OneYanC-24
❑ 97GreBatC-25
Triner, Jim
❑ 47PadTeal-22
Trinidad, Hector
❑ 92GenCubC-3
❑ 92GenCubF-1562
❑ 93MidLeaAGF-43
❑ 93PeoChiC-22
❑ 93PeoChiF-1086
❑ 93PeoChiTI-28
❑ 94Bow-662
❑ 94ClaGolF-132
❑ 94DayCubC-24
❑ 94DayCubF-2353
❑ 94ExcFS7-170
❑ 94UppDecML-237
❑ 95HarCitRCTI-25
❑ 96BesAutSA-79
❑ 96HarCitRCB-29
❑ 97BesAutAS-63
Trinkle, Ken
❑ 47TipTop-133
❑ 48GiaTeal-25
❑ 49Bow-193
❑ 49EurSta-150
❑ 49PhiBul-55
Triplett, Alfred
❑ 93EriSaiC-24
❑ 93EriSaiF-3126
Triplett, Antonio
❑ 82BurRanF-6
❑ 82BurRanT-11
❑ 83BurRanF-6
❑ 83BurRanT-25
❑ 86TulDriTI-2
❑ 87SanBerSP-21
❑ 88FreSunCLC-1
❑ 88FreSunP-1243
Triplett, Coaker
❑ 41CarW75-26
❑ 43PhiTeal-22
❑ 50WorWidGV-16
❑ 83Car194T-13
Triplett, Hunter
❑ 92OklStaC-27
Tripodi, Max
❑ 89SalLakTTI-20
Tripp, Dave
❑ 90SouOreAB-23
❑ 90SouOreAP-3446
Trippey, Joe
❑ 98GreBraG-26
Trippy, Joe
❑ 95EugEmeTI-9
❑ 96MacBraB-25
❑ 97DurBulTI-26
Trisler, John
❑ 91HelBreSP-1
❑ 92BelBreFI-405
❑ 93ClePhiC-23
❑ 93ClePhiF-2684
❑ 94ClePhiC-26
❑ 94ClePhiF-2528
❑ 95ReaPhiELC-34
❑ 95ReaPhiTI-39
Tritonenkov, Timur
❑ 89EasLeaDDP-DD19
Trlicek, Rick
❑ 87UtiBluSP-17
❑ 88BatCliP-1670
❑ 90DunBluJS-22
❑ 91KnoBluJLD-369
❑ 91KnoBluJP-1765
❑ 91LinDriAA-369
❑ 92Bow-76
❑ 92DonRoo-116
❑ 92LeaGolR-BC15
❑ 92ProFS7-166
❑ 92SyrChiF-1966
❑ 92SyrChiMB-24
❑ 93BluJayD4-37
❑ 93DodMot-27
❑ 93FleFinE-85
❑ 93PacSpa-504
❑ 93Pin-284
❑ 93Sco-318
❑ 93SelRoo-138T
❑ 93StaClu-218
❑ 93StaCluFDI-218
❑ 93StaCluMOP-218
❑ 93Ult-407
❑ 94Fle-526
❑ 94Sco-600
❑ 94ScoGolR-600
❑ 94Top-276
❑ 94TopGol-276
❑ 94TopSpa-276
❑ 95PhoFirTI-35
❑ 96NorTidB-29
❑ 98NorTidP-26
❑ 98NorTidQ-27
Troconis, O.
❑ 76VenLeaS-132
Troedson, Rich
❑ 73PadDea-27
❑ 74OPC-77
❑ 74PadDea-27
❑ 74PadTeal-17
❑ 74Top-77A
❑ 74Top-77B
Troglin, Mike
❑ 90ArkRaz-33
Troilo, Jason
❑ 94OneYanF-3796
❑ 96GreBatB-29
❑ 96TamYanY-26
❑ 97ColCliB-29
❑ 97ColCliD-28
❑ 98ColCliM-30
Trombley, Mike
❑ 88CapCodPPaLP-75
❑ 90VisOakCLC-58
❑ 90VisOakP-2153
❑ 91LinDriAA-495
❑ 91OrlSunRLD-495
❑ 91OrlSunRP-1849
❑ 92Bow-102
❑ 92PorBeaF-2666
❑ 92PorBeaS-420
❑ 92SkyAAAF-192
❑ 93Bow-621
❑ 93Don-47
❑ 93Fle-644
❑ 93PacSpa-526
❑ 93Pin-578
❑ 93PinRooTP-1
❑ 93Sco-287
❑ 93SelRoo-52T
❑ 93StaClu-336
❑ 93StaCluFDI-336
❑ 93StaCluMOP-336
❑ 93Top-588
❑ 93TopGol-588
❑ 93TopInaM-588
❑ 93TopInaR-588
❑ 93TopMic-588
❑ 93Toy-47
❑ 93Ult-588
❑ 93UppDec-28
❑ 93UppDecGold-28
❑ 94Don-620
❑ 94Fle-220
❑ 94Pac-368
❑ 94Sco-591
❑ 94ScoGolR-591
❑ 94StaClu-477
❑ 94StaCluFDI-477
❑ 94StaCluGR-477
❑ 94StaCluMOP-477
❑ 94Top-308
❑ 94TopGol-308
❑ 94TopSpa-308
❑ 94Ult-91
❑ 95DonTopotO-115
❑ 96ColCho-599
❑ 96ColChoGS-599
❑ 96ColChoSS-599
❑ 96Don-340
❑ 96DonPreP-340
❑ 96Ult-96
❑ 96UltGolM-96
❑ 97Fle-593
❑ 97FleTif-593
❑ 98PacOnl-439
❑ 98PacOnlR-439
❑ 98PacOnlWC-439
❑ 99Fle-563
❑ 99FleSta9-563
❑ 99FleWarT-563
Troncoso, Nolberton
❑ 90YakBeaTI-25
Tronerud, Rick
❑ 79WatA'sT-2
❑ 80WesHavWCT-24
❑ 81WesHavAT-15
❑ 84AlbA'sT-8
❑ 85ModA'sC-27
❑ 86HunStaDJ-44
❑ 89HunStaB-18
Trosky, Hal
❑ 33MrsShePP-15
❑ 34DiaStaR-70
❑ 34Gou-76
❑ 35ExhFou-11
❑ 35GouPuzR-1L
❑ 35GouPuzR-2E
❑ 35GouPuzR-16E
❑ 35GouPuzR-17E
❑ 36ExhFou-11
❑ 36GouWidPPR-A102
❑ 36GouWidPPR-B21
❑ 36GouWidPPR-C23
❑ 36OveCanR-43
❑ 37ExhFou-11
❑ 37OPCBatUV-113
❑ 37WheBB14-15
❑ 37WheBB7-29G
❑ 38CloFotW-81
❑ 38ExhFou-11
❑ 38OurNatGPP-30
❑ 39GouPreR303A-43
❑ 39WorWidGTP-43
❑ 39WorWidGV-24
❑ 40PlaBal-50
❑ 40WheM4-13
❑ 41DouPlaR-79
❑ 41DouPlaR-87
❑ 41PlaBal-16
❑ 61Fle-145
❑ 72TCMthe3-114
❑ 76GrePlaG-4
❑ 77FriOneYW-15
❑ 79RedSoxEF-20
❑ 85BigLeaC3-83
❑ 86IndGreT-1
❑ 92ConTSN-385
Trott, Sam
❑ 87OldJudN-499
❑ 87OldJudN-500
Trotter, Bill
❑ 39PlaBal-148
❑ 40PlaBal-54
❑ 41BroW75-29
❑ 77TCMTheWY-54
❑ 79DiaGre-189
Troup, James
❑ 89SalLakTTI-27
Trouppe, Quincy
❑ 78LauLonABS-33
❑ 91NegLeaRL-16
❑ 91PomBlaBPB-2
❑ 92NegLeaRLI-61
❑ 95NegLeaLI-16
Trout, Dizzy (Paul)
❑ 39ExhSal-58
❑ 39PlaBal-153
❑ 40PlaBal-44
❑ 46SpoExcW-8-6
❑ 47TipTop-43
❑ 48KelPep*-BB4
❑ 49Bow-208
❑ 49Lea-10
❑ 50AmeNut&CCP-21
❑ 50Bow-134
❑ 51TopBluB-23
❑ 52NatTeaL-38
❑ 52Top-39
❑ 53Top-169
❑ 76TayBow4-54
❑ 77TCMTheWY-5
❑ 81TigDetN-113
❑ 81TigSecNP-31
❑ 83TCMPla1945-2
❑ 83TopRep5-39
❑ 85Top-142
❑ 85TopTif-142
❑ 91OriCro-463
❑ 91TopArc1-169
❑ 95ConTSN-1415
Trout, Jeff
❑ 85OrlTwiT-12
❑ 86OrlTwiP-21
Trout, Steve
❑ 77AppFoxT-27
❑ 78KnoKnoST-24
❑ 80Top-83
❑ 81Don-400
❑ 81Fle-345
❑ 81OPC-364
❑ 81Top-552
❑ 82Don-243
❑ 82Fle-358
❑ 82OPC-299
❑ 82Top-299
❑ 82TopSti-169
❑ 83CubThoAV-34
❑ 83Don-417
❑ 83Fle-251
❑ 83Top-461
❑ 83TopTra-117T
❑ 84CubChiT-30
❑ 84CubSev-34
❑ 84Don-533
❑ 84Fle-506
❑ 84Nes792-151
❑ 84OPC-151
❑ 84Top-151
❑ 84TopTif-151
❑ 85AllGamPI-179
❑ 85CubLioP-25
❑ 85CubSev-34
❑ 85Don-198
❑ 85Fle-70
❑ 85Lea-243
❑ 85OPC-139
❑ 85Top-142
❑ 85Top-668
❑ 85TopSti-43
❑ 85TopTif-142
❑ 85TopTif-668
❑ 86CubGat-34
❑ 86CubUno-20
❑ 86Don-117
❑ 86Fle-384
❑ 86OPC-384
❑ 86Top-384
❑ 86TopSti-57
❑ 86TopTif-384
❑ 87CubCan-35
❑ 87CubDavB-34
❑ 87Don-201
❑ 87Fle-578
❑ 87FleGlo-578
❑ 87OPC-147
❑ 87Top-581
❑ 87Top-750
❑ 87TopTif-581
❑ 87TopTif-750
❑ 88Don-524
❑ 88MarMot-8
❑ 88Sco-342
❑ 88ScoGlo-342
❑ 88Top-584
❑ 88TopBig-107
❑ 88TopTif-584
❑ 89MarMot-24
❑ 89Sco-522
❑ 89Top-54
❑ 89TopTif-54
❑ 90LouRedBLBC-41
❑ 90PubIntS-443
❑ 92YanWIZ8-193
Troutman, Keith
❑ 92YakBeaF-3449
❑ 93GreFalDSP-18
❑ 94VerBeaDC-22
❑ 94VerBeaDF-72
❑ 95SanAntMTI-36
❑ 96ReaPhiB-12
❑ 97ReaPhi-26
❑ 97TexAllM-58
❑ 98ScrRedBQ-27
Trow, Gene
❑ 33WorCig(-94
Trowbridge, Bob
❑ 57BraSpiaS4-20
❑ 58Top-252
❑ 59Top-239
❑ 60Top-66
❑ 60TopVen-66
❑ 80Bra195T-4
Trower, Don
❑ 48SomandK-10
Truby, Chris
❑ 94AubAstC-21
❑ 94AubAstF-3769
❑ 94QuaCitRBC-21
❑ 94QuaCitRBF-545
❑ 95Bow-232
❑ 95BowGolF-232
❑ 95QuaCitRBTI-28
❑ 96QuaCitRB-28
❑ 97QuaCitRBB-28
❑ 98KisCobQ-29
❑ 99BasAmeTP-93
❑ 99BasAmeTPG-93
❑ 99Top-434
❑ 99TopChr-434
❑ 99TopChrR-434
Trucchio, Frank
❑ 83MadMusF-30
Trucks, Phil
❑ 76CliPilT-29
❑ 78AppFoxT-22
❑ 79KnoKnoST-2
Trucks, Virgil
❑ 47Exh-226
❑ 47TipTop-44
❑ 49Bow-219
❑ 49Lea-5
❑ 50Bow-96
❑ 50RoyDes-21A
❑ 50RoyDes-21B
❑ 51Bow-104
❑ 51R42SmaS-106
❑ 52DixLid-23
❑ 52DixPre-23
❑ 52Top-262
❑ 53BowBW-17
❑ 53DixLid-23A
❑ 53DixLid-23B
❑ 53DixPre-23
❑ 53Top-96
❑ 54Bow-198
❑ 55ArmCoi-22
❑ 55Bow-26
❑ 56Top-117
❑ 57Top-187
❑ 58A'sJayP-10
❑ 58Top-277
❑ 59Top-417
❑ 63PirIDL-24
❑ 76TayBow4-53
❑ 79DiaGre-198
❑ 79TCM50-85
❑ 81TigDetN-111
❑ 82Bow195E-264
❑ 83TopRep5-262
❑ 83YanYealT-14
❑ 84TCMPla1-6
❑ 87SpoRea-8
❑ 89PacLegI-120
❑ 89SweBasG-73
❑ 91TopArc1-96
❑ 92ActPacA-20
❑ 94TedWil-34
❑ 94UppDecAH-39
❑ 94UppDecAH1-39
Trudeau, Kevin
❑ 86WatIndP-29
❑ 87PorBeaP-15
❑ 88OrlTwiB-14
❑ 89MidAngGS-28
❑ 90MidAngGS-19
Trudo, Glenn
❑ 86WatPirP-25
❑ 87MacPirP-21
❑ 88AugPirP-384
True, Bryan
❑ 86DavLipB-21
Truesdale, Fred
❑ 11PinT-5-121
❑ 12ImpTobC-53
Truitt, Bill
❑ 52LavPro-26
Truitt, Derrick
❑ 98DanBraQ-4
Trujillo, Jose
❑ 89HamRedS-24
❑ 89Sta-106
❑ 90St.PetCS-24
❑ 91St.PetCC-23
❑ 91St.PetCP-2286
❑ 92GenCubC-2
❑ 92GenCubF-1570
❑ 92PeoChiC-5
❑ 93PalSprAF-70
Trujillo, Louie
❑ 83CedRapRF-12
❑ 83CedRapRT-11
Trujillo, Mike
❑ 83AppFoxFr-2
❑ 86Fle-360
❑ 86PawRedSP-26
❑ 86Top-687
❑ 86TopTif-687
❑ 87Don-613
❑ 87MarMot-25
❑ 87Top-402
❑ 87TopTif-402
❑ 88TolMudHC-7
❑ 88TolMudHP-593
❑ 88Top-307
❑ 88TopClo-116
❑ 88TopTif-307
❑ 89TolMudHC-3
❑ 89TolMudHP-776
❑ 89TriAAAP-AAA25
Truman, Harry S.
❑ 94UppDecTAE-56
Trumbauer, Gary
❑ 72CedRapCT-15
Trumpour, Andy
❑ 94KinMetC-22
❑ 94KinMetF-3824
❑ 95PitMetTI-34
❑ 97St.LucM-26
Trunk, Mascot
❑ 94MasMan-15
Truschke, Mike
❑ 88CapCodPPaLP-24
Trusky, Ken
❑ 89WelPirP-24
❑ 90AugPirP-2479
❑ 90SouAtlLAS-44
❑ 91SalBucC-13
❑ 91SalBucP-967
Tsamis, George
❑ 88CapCodPPaLP-80
❑ 90CalLeaACLC-16
❑ 90ProAaA-143
❑ 90VisOakCLC-65
❑ 90VisOakP-2154
❑ 91LinDriAAA-421
❑ 91PorBeaLD-421
❑ 91PorBeaP-1566
❑ 92PorBeaF-2667
❑ 92PorBeaS-421
❑ 92SkyAAAF-193
❑ 93Bow-509
❑ 93FleFinE-240
❑ 94Fle-221
❑ 94Pac-369
❑ 94Top-128
❑ 94TopGol-128
❑ 94TopSpa-128
Tschida, Tim
❑ 88T/MUmp-59
❑ 89T/MUmp-57
❑ 90T/MUmp-55
Tsitouris, John
❑ 60A'sTeal-16
❑ 60Lea-63
❑ 60Top-497
❑ 63RedEnq-30
❑ 63RedFreBC-28
❑ 63Top-244
❑ 64Kah-27
❑ 64Top-275
❑ 64TopVen-275
❑ 65Kah-42
❑ 65OPC-221
❑ 65RedEnq-29
❑ 65Top-221
❑ 66OPC-12
❑ 66Top-12
❑ 66TopVen-12
❑ 68Top-523
Tsitouris, Marc
❑ 90JamExpP-5
❑ 91SumFlyC-21
❑ 91SumFlyP-2346
Tsotsos, Pete
❑ 88CapCodPPaLP-26
Tsoukalas, John
❑ 91MedHatBJP-4110
❑ 91MedHatBJSP-4
❑ 92MyrBeaHC-2
❑ 92MyrBeaHF-2207
❑ 98St.PauSTI-30
Tua, Franklin
❑ 76VenLeaS-66
❑ 80VenLeaS-65
Tualbee, Andy
❑ 97PhoFirTI-24
Tubbs, Frank
❑ 31Zee-55
Tubbs, Gregory Alan
❑ 86GreBraTI-21
❑ 87GreBraB-26
❑ 88BobCamRB-19
❑ 88RicBraC-15
❑ 88RicBraP-5
❑ 89BlaYNPRWL-28
❑ 89GreBraP-1152
❑ 89RicBraBC-26
❑ 89RicBraP-823
❑ 90TriAAAC-23
❑ 91BufBisLD-47
❑ 91BufBisP-555
❑ 91LinDriAAA-47

❑ 91LinDriP-47
❑ 92BufBisBS-23
❑ 92BufBisF-336
❑ 92BufBisS-44
❑ 93IndIndF-1502
❑ 94BufBisF-1851
Tucci, Peter
❑ 97HagSunB-25
❑ 97SouAtlTPB-21
❑ 97Top-480
❑ 98DunBluJSB-12
❑ 98DunBluJTI-30
❑ 99BasAmeTPA-43
❑ 99E-X Cen-115
❑ 99E-X CenECFut-115
❑ 99E-X CenECNow-115
❑ 99FlaShoLeg1-39
❑ 99FlaShoLeg2-39
❑ 99FlaShoLeg3-39
❑ 99FlaShoLegM1-39
❑ 99FlaShoLegM2-39
❑ 99FlaShoLegM3-39
❑ 99FlaShoR1-39
❑ 99FlaShoR2-39
❑ 99FlaShoR3-39
❑ 99FleBri-171
❑ 99FleBri2G-171
❑ 99FleBriBlu-171
❑ 99FleBriGol-171
❑ 99JustheSAC-20
❑ 99SkyPreA-52
❑ 99SkyPreABlue-52
❑ 99TeaBesR-10
❑ 99TeaBesRA-23
Tuck, Gary
❑ 82TucTorT-25
❑ 83TucTorT-24
❑ 84TucTorC-248
❑ 86OscAstP-26
❑ 87AubAstP-12
❑ 88AshTouP-1068
❑ 89ColCliC-24
Tucker, Benjamin
❑ 95BelGiaTI-40
❑ 96SanJosGB-24
❑ 98SanJosGQ-17
Tucker, Bill
❑ 89BelMarL-34
❑ 95BelGiaTI-NNO
❑ 96BelGiaTI-32
❑ 98SalVol-33
Tucker, Bob
❑ 86VerBeaDP-25
Tucker, Brett
❑ 94CliLumF-1981
Tucker, Eddie
❑ 90Bes-274
❑ 90SanJosGB-13
❑ 90SanJosGP-2014
Tucker, Horace
❑ 87WytCubP-3
Tucker, Jon
❑ 95YakBeaTI-33
❑ 96GreFalDB-29
❑ 96GreFalDTI-26
❑ 97VerBeaD-27
❑ 98SanAntMG-29
Tucker, Julien
❑ 94AubAstC-22
❑ 94AubAstF-3760
❑ 95Exc-207
❑ 96KisCobB-30
❑ 97KisCob-26
❑ 98BirBarG-25
Tucker, Lanning H.
❑ 92EliTwiC-25
❑ 94ForMyeMC-29
❑ 95ForMyeMTI-31
❑ 96HarCitRCB-6
❑ 97NewBriRC-30
❑ 98ForMyeMTI-30
Tucker, Mamon
❑ 99Bow-144
❑ 99BowBes-191
❑ 99BowBesAR-191
❑ 99BowBesR-191
❑ 99BowChr-144
❑ 99BowChrG-144
❑ 99BowChrGR-144
❑ 99BowChrI-144
❑ 99BowChrIR-144
❑ 99BowChrR-144
❑ 99BowGol-144
❑ 99BowInt-144
❑ 99StaClu-158
❑ 99StaCluFDI-158
❑ 99StaCluOoaK-158
❑ 99StaCluPP-158
❑ 99Top-217
❑ 99TopChr-217
❑ 99TopChrR-217
Tucker, Michael
❑ 92Bow-682
❑ 92ClaDraP-7
❑ 92ClaDraPFB-BC7
❑ 92FroRowDP-44
❑ 92FroRowDPG-44
❑ 92FroRowDPPS-44
❑ 92FroRowDPS-44
❑ 92TopTra-119T
❑ 92TopTraG-119T
❑ 92UppDecML-1
❑ 92UppDecML-6
❑ 93ClaFS7-30
❑ 93Pin-466
❑ 93Sco-498
❑ 93Sel-291
❑ 93SP-287
❑ 93StaCluM-196
❑ 93UppDec-445
❑ 93UppDecGold-445
❑ 93WilBluRC-1
❑ 93WilBluRF-2008
❑ 94ActPac-24
❑ 94ActPac-60
❑ 94ActPac2G-6G
❑ 94ActPac2GD-6G
❑ 94Cla-150
❑ 94ClaBonB-BB5
❑ 94ClaCreotC-C7
❑ 94ClaGolF-122
❑ 94ExcFS7-76
❑ 94ExcLeaLF-18
❑ 94OmaRoyF-1237
❑ 94SigRoo-41
❑ 94SigRooHP-S11
❑ 94SigRooHPS-S11
❑ 94SigRooS-41
❑ 94TedWil-133
❑ 94TedWilDGC-DG2
❑ 94Ult-369
❑ 94UppDecML-3
❑ 94UppDecML-260
❑ 94UppDecMLPotYF-PY24
❑ 94UppDecMLT1PJF-TP10
❑ 94UppDecMLT1PMF-10
❑ 95ActPacF-21
❑ 95ARuFalLS-18
❑ 95BowBes-B90
❑ 95BowBesR-B90
❑ 95ColCho-10
❑ 95ColChoGS-10
❑ 95ColChoSS-10
❑ 95Exc-67
❑ 95ExcLeaL-16
❑ 95Fla-268
❑ 95Fle-173
❑ 95LeaLim-92
❑ 95OmaRoyTI-27
❑ 95Pin-426
❑ 95PinArtP-426
❑ 95PinMusC-426
❑ 95Sel-201
❑ 95SelArtP-201
❑ 95SelCer-134
❑ 95SelCerF-9
❑ 95SelCerMG-134
❑ 95SelCerPU-19
❑ 95SelCerPU9-19
❑ 95SP-157
❑ 95SPSil-157
❑ 95Sum-143
❑ 95SumNewA-NA7
❑ 95SumNthD-143
❑ 95TopTra-99T
❑ 95UC3-98
❑ 95UC3ArtP-98
❑ 95UC3CleS-CS12
❑ 95UltGolP-10
❑ 95UltGolPGM-10
❑ 95UppDec-230
❑ 95UppDecED-230
❑ 95UppDecEDG-230
❑ 95UppDecML-2
❑ 95UppDecMLFS-2
❑ 95UppDecMLT1PF-9
❑ 95UppDecPAW-H34
❑ 95UppDecPAWE-H34
❑ 95UppDecSE-189
❑ 95UppDecSEG-189
❑ 95Zen-143
❑ 95ZenRooRC-13
❑ 96Bow-59
❑ 96BowFoi-59
❑ 96ColCho-176
❑ 96ColCho-653
❑ 96ColChoGS-176
❑ 96ColChoGS-653
❑ 96ColChoSS-176
❑ 96ColChoSS-653
❑ 96Don-376
❑ 96DonPreP-376
❑ 96Fla-95
❑ 96Fle-139
❑ 96FleTif-139
❑ 96Lea-79
❑ 96LeaPre-93
❑ 96LeaPreP-93
❑ 96LeaPrePB-79
❑ 96LeaPrePG-79
❑ 96LeaPrePS-79
❑ 96LeaPreSG-58
❑ 96LeaPreSte-58
❑ 96LeaSig-79
❑ 96LeaSigA-224
❑ 96LeaSigAG-225
❑ 96LeaSigAS-225
❑ 96LeaSigPPG-79
❑ 96LeaSigPPP-79
❑ 96Pin-202
❑ 96PinAfi-111
❑ 96PinAfiAP-111
❑ 96PinArtP-102
❑ 96PinFirR-12
❑ 96PinFoil-202
❑ 96PinSta-102
❑ 96RoyPol-25
❑ 96Sco-241
❑ 96ScoDugC-A107
❑ 96ScoDugCAP-A107
❑ 96ScoSam-241
❑ 96Sel-149
❑ 96SelArtP-149
❑ 96SelCer-76
❑ 96SelCerAP-76
❑ 96SelCerCB-76
❑ 96SelCerCR-76
❑ 96SelCerMB-76
❑ 96SelCerMG-76
❑ 96SelCerMR-76
❑ 96SelTeaN-17
❑ 96SP-98
❑ 96Spo-44
❑ 96SpoArtP-44
❑ 96StaClu-439
❑ 96StaCluMOP-439
❑ 96Stu-130
❑ 96StuPrePB-130
❑ 96StuPrePG-130
❑ 96StuPrePS-130
❑ 96Sum-47
❑ 96SumAbo&B-47
❑ 96SumArtP-47
❑ 96SumFoi-47
❑ 96Top-92
❑ 96TopGal-133
❑ 96TopGalPPI-133
❑ 96Ult-361
❑ 96UltGolM-361
❑ 96UppDec-89
❑ 96UppDecBCP-BC6
❑ 96Zen-94
❑ 96ZenArtP-94
❑ 97Bow-279
❑ 97BowInt-279
❑ 97Cir-217
❑ 97CirRav-217
❑ 97ColCho-134
❑ 97ColChoT-AB4
❑ 97ColChoU-U3
❑ 97Don-28
❑ 97Don-274
❑ 97DonEli-140
❑ 97DonEliGS-140
❑ 97DonGolPP-28
❑ 97DonGolPP-274
❑ 97DonLim-115
❑ 97DonLim-158
❑ 97DonLimE-115
❑ 97DonLimE-158
❑ 97DonLimENG-158
❑ 97DonPre-140
❑ 97DonPreCttC-140
❑ 97DonSig-32
❑ 97DonSigA-99
❑ 97DonSigAC-124
❑ 97DonSigAM-124
❑ 97DonSigPPP-32
❑ 97DonSilPP-28
❑ 97DonSilPP-274
❑ 97DonTea-23
❑ 97DonTeaSPE-23
❑ 97Fle-124
❑ 97Fle-580
❑ 97FleTif-124
❑ 97FleTif-580
❑ 97Lea-123
❑ 97LeaFraM-123
❑ 97LeaFraMDC-123
❑ 97MetUni-98
❑ 97NewPin-76
❑ 97NewPinAP-76
❑ 97NewPinMC-76
❑ 97NewPinPP-76
❑ 97PacPriGotD-GD51
❑ 97PinIns-116
❑ 97PinInsCE-116
❑ 97PinInsDE-116
❑ 97PinX-P-114
❑ 97PinX-PMoS-114
❑ 97Sco-283
❑ 97Sco-468
❑ 97ScoArtPWB-283
❑ 97ScoArtPWB-468
❑ 97ScoPreS-283
❑ 97ScoResC-468
❑ 97ScoShoS-283
❑ 97ScoShoS-468
❑ 97ScoShoSAP-283
❑ 97ScoShoSAP-468
❑ 97Sel-95
❑ 97SelArtP-95
❑ 97SelCom-95
❑ 97SelRegG-95
❑ 97StaClu-164
❑ 97StaCluMOP-164
❑ 97Stu-122
❑ 97StuPrePG-122
❑ 97StuPrePS-122
❑ 97Top-453
❑ 97TopGal-167
❑ 97TopGalPPI-167
❑ 97Ult-341
❑ 97UltGolME-341
❑ 97UltPlaME-341
❑ 97UppDec-392
❑ 97UppDec-524
❑ 98BraSco-3
❑ 98BraScoP-3
❑ 98CirThu-293
❑ 98CirThuRav-293
❑ 98CirThuSupRav-293
❑ 98ColCho-32
❑ 98Don-68
❑ 98DonCol-68
❑ 98DonColP-671
❑ 98DonColS-68
❑ 98DonGolPP-68
❑ 98DonPre-121
❑ 98DonPreSeat-121
❑ 98DonPriCD-68
❑ 98DonPriCP-671
❑ 98DonSilPP-68
❑ 98Fin-39
❑ 98FinNo--39
❑ 98FinNo-R-39
❑ 98FinRef-39
❑ 98Fle-534
❑ 98Pac-244
❑ 98PacOnl-74
❑ 98PacOnlR-74
❑ 98PacOnlWC-74
❑ 98PacPlaB-244
❑ 98PacRedT-244
❑ 98PacSil-244
❑ 98PinPlu-69
❑ 98PinSna-AB10
❑ 98Sco-26
❑ 98ScoRT-137
❑ 98ScoSS-PP9
❑ 98ScoSSAP-PP9
❑ 98StaCluFDI-233
❑ 98StaCluI-233
❑ 98StaCluOneK-233
❑ 98StaCluPP-233
❑ 98Stu-19
❑ 98StuGPP-19
❑ 98StuSPP-19
❑ 98Top-19
❑ 98Top-410
❑ 98TopChr-19
❑ 98TopChr-410
❑ 98TopChrR-19
❑ 98TopChrR-410
❑ 98TopDevR-19
❑ 98TopDevR-410
❑ 98TopDia-19
❑ 98TopDia-410
❑ 98TopMiniC-19
❑ 98TopMiniC-410
❑ 98Ult-357
❑ 98UltGolM-357
❑ 98UltMas-357
❑ 98UltPlaM-357
❑ 98UppDec-26
❑ 98UppDecSF-16
❑ 99Fle-294
❑ 99FleSta9-294
❑ 99FleWarT-294
❑ 99Pac-43
❑ 99PacPlaB-43
❑ 99PacRed-43
❑ 99SkyMolMOA-28
❑ 99SkyThu-36
❑ 99SkyThuRant-36
❑ 99SkyThuRave-36
❑ 99ThuSkySupR-36
❑ 99Ult-187
❑ 99UltGolM-187
❑ 99UltMas-187
❑ 99UltPlaM-187
❑ 99UppDec-39
❑ 99UppDec-346
❑ 99UppDecEL1-39
❑ 99UppDecEL1-346
❑ 99UppDecEL2-39
❑ 99UppDecEL2-346
❑ 99UppDecM-54
❑ 99UppDecMGS-54
❑ 99UppDecMHFS-54
❑ 99UppDecMSS-54
❑ 99Vic-110
Tucker, Mike
❑ 81ShrCapT-8
❑ 82PhoGiaVNB-10
Tucker, Robert
❑ 91HelBreSP-22
❑ 93CedRapKC-21
❑ 93CedRapKF-1743
❑ 94LakElsSC-23
❑ 94LakElsSF-1668
Tucker, Scooter
❑ 89CliGiaP-897
❑ 90CalLeaACLC-37
❑ 90SanJosGCLC-37
❑ 90SanJosGS-23
❑ 91Cla/Bes-315
❑ 91LinDriAA-322
❑ 91ShrCapLD-322
❑ 91ShrCapP-1825
❑ 92DonRoo-117
❑ 92SkyAAAF-277
❑ 92TopTra-120T
❑ 92TopTraG-120T
❑ 92TucTorF-492
❑ 92TucTorS-620
❑ 93Don-60
❑ 93FleMajLP-B1
❑ 93Pin-245
❑ 93Sco-237
❑ 93StaClu-488
❑ 93StaCluFDI-488
❑ 93StaCluMOP-488
❑ 93Top-814
❑ 93TopGol-814
❑ 93TopInaM-814
❑ 93TopInaR-814
❑ 93TopMic-814
❑ 93TucTorF-3062
❑ 93Ult-47
❑ 94TucTorF-765
❑ 96OmaRoyB-29
Tucker, T.J.
❑ 97Bow-431
❑ 97BowChr-291
❑ 97BowChrI-291
❑ 97BowChrIR-291
❑ 97BowChrR-291
❑ 97BowInt-431
❑ 99Bow-415
❑ 99BowGol-415
❑ 99BowInt-415
❑ 99JustheSAC-21
Tucker, Thomas
❑ 72ClaCar-83
❑ 87OldJudN-185
❑ 87OldJudN-501
❑ 89EdgR.WG-11
❑ 90DodTar-810
❑ 95May-27
Tucker, Thurman
❑ 47TipTop-28
❑ 48IndTeal-29
❑ 49IndTeal-24
❑ 50IndNumN-21
❑ 50IndTeal-24
❑ 51Bow-222
❑ 53IndPenCBP-26
❑ 76TayBow4-56
❑ 79DiaGre-141
❑ 83TCMPla1944-18
Tucker, Tuck (Stephen)
❑ 90GreHorB-12
❑ 90GreHorP-2664
❑ 90GreHorS-22
❑ 91PriWilCC-12
❑ 91PriWilCP-1428
Tucker, Vance
❑ 89ChaRaiP-972
Tucker, William
❑ 78GreBraT-27
Tuckerman, William
❑ 87OldJudN-502
Tudor, John
❑ 77BriRedST-19
❑ 81Don-457A
❑ 81Don-457B
❑ 81Top-14
❑ 82Don-260
❑ 82Fle-311
❑ 82RedSoxC-21
❑ 82Top-558
❑ 83Don-563
❑ 83Fle-198
❑ 83FleSta-201
❑ 83Top-318
❑ 84Don-416
❑ 84Fle-411
❑ 84FleUpd-120
❑ 84Nes792-601
❑ 84OPC-171
❑ 84Pir-24
❑ 84Top-601
❑ 84TopSti-225
❑ 84TopTif-601
❑ 84TopTra-122T
❑ 84TopTraT-122T
❑ 85CarTeal-32
❑ 85Don-235
❑ 85DonHig-20
❑ 85Fle-479
❑ 85FleUpd-123
❑ 85OPC-214
❑ 85Top-214
❑ 85TopTif-214
❑ 85TopTifT-124T
❑ 85TopTra-124T
❑ 86BasStaB-113
❑ 86CarIGAS-12
❑ 86CarKASD-17
❑ 86CarSchM-22
❑ 86CarTeal-41
❑ 86Don-260
❑ 86Dra-30
❑ 86Fle-47
❑ 86FleAll-12
❑ 86FleMin-11
❑ 86FleSlu-40
❑ 86FleStiC-122
❑ 86Lea-134
❑ 86OPC-227
❑ 86SevCoi-S11
❑ 86Spo-122
❑ 86Spo-184
❑ 86Spo-185
❑ 86Top-474
❑ 86Top-710
❑ 86Top3-D-28
❑ 86TopGloS-53
❑ 86TopMinL-64
❑ 86TopSti-20
❑ 86TopSti-52
❑ 86TopSup-57
❑ 86TopTat-12
❑ 86TopTif-474
❑ 86TopTif-710
❑ 87CarSmo-3
❑ 87CarTeal-31
❑ 87ClaGam-77
❑ 87Don-170
❑ 87DonOpeD-63
❑ 87Dra-30
❑ 87Fle-310

❑ 87FleGamW-41
❑ 87FleGlo-310
❑ 87FleMin-108
❑ 87FleRecS-39
❑ 87FleStiC-119
❑ 87KraFoo-22
❑ 87OPC-110
❑ 87RedFolSB-34
❑ 87Spo-173
❑ 87SpoTeaP-12
❑ 87Top-110
❑ 87TopSti-53
❑ 87TopTif-110
❑ 88CarSmo-9
❑ 88CarTeal-34
❑ 88Don-553
❑ 88DonBasB-212
❑ 88Dra-33
❑ 88Fle-48
❑ 88FleGlo-48
❑ 88FleGlo-WS3
❑ 88FleMin-110
❑ 88FleStiC-121
❑ 88FleWorS-3
❑ 88Lea-212
❑ 88OPC-356
❑ 88Sco-275
❑ 88ScoGlo-275
❑ 88Spo-198
❑ 88StaLinCa-19
❑ 88Top-792
❑ 88TopRitTM-29
❑ 88TopSti-13
❑ 88TopSti-21
❑ 88TopTif-792
❑ 88Woo-23
❑ 89ClaLigB-63
❑ 89DodMot-9
❑ 89DodPol-19
❑ 89DodStaSV-13
❑ 89Don-195
❑ 89Fle-75
❑ 89FleGlo-75
❑ 89OPC-35
❑ 89PanSti-100
❑ 89RedFolSB-122
❑ 89Sco-560
❑ 89Spo-86
❑ 89Top-35
❑ 89TopBasT-71
❑ 89TopMinL-20
❑ 89TopSti-64
❑ 89TopTif-35
❑ 89UppDec-66
❑ 90Bow-188
❑ 90BowTif-188
❑ 90CarSmo-25
❑ 90ClaYel-T2
❑ 90DodTar-811
❑ 90FleUpd-54
❑ 90Lea-176
❑ 90PubIntS-20
❑ 90TopBig-253
❑ 90TopTra-124T
❑ 90TopTraT-124T
❑ 90TopTVCa-21
❑ 90UppDec-396
❑ 91Fle-650
❑ 91RedFolS-94
❑ 91Sco-53
❑ 91Sco100S-47
❑ 91UppDec-329
❑ 92CarMcD-50

Tudor, Mark
❑ 81CliGiaT-29
❑ 82CliGiaF-26

Tufts, Bob
❑ 80PhoGiaVNB-2
❑ 81PhoGiaVNB-3
❑ 82OmaRoyT-9
❑ 82Top-171
❑ 83RoyPos-31

Tufts, Glenn
❑ 94CliLumC-28
❑ 95BelGiaTI-48
❑ 96BurBeeTI-27
❑ 97BakBlaB-26
❑ 97BakBlaTI-26

Tuggle, Eugene
❑ 90GeoColC-30

Tuholald, Tom
❑ 89WelPirP-25

Tukes, Stan
❑ 89ChaRaiP-977
❑ 89HamRedS-25

Tulacz, Mike
❑ 77AppFoxT-28
❑ 78AppFoxT-23

Tuller, Brian
❑ 83QuaCitCT-15

Tullier, Mike
❑ 86WinSpiP-25
❑ 87WinSpiP-19
❑ 88PitCubP-1365
❑ 89IowCubC-23
❑ 89IowCubP-1701
❑ 91BluOriC-24
❑ 91BluOriP-4143

Tullish, Bill
❑ 76CedRapGT-29

Tumbas, Dave
❑ 83AleDukT-15
❑ 84PriWilPT-27
❑ 85NasPirT-25

Tumpane, Bob
❑ 82DurBulT-13
❑ 83DurBulT-15
❑ 84DurBulT-12
❑ 85GreBraTI-22
❑ 85IntLeaAT-2
❑ 86GreBraTI-22
❑ 87RicBraBC-21
❑ 87RicBraC-9
❑ 87RicBraT-16

Tunison, Rich
❑ 89EugEmeB-16
❑ 90AppFoxBS-28
❑ 90AppFoxP-2105
❑ 90CMC-874
❑ 90MidLeaASGS-21
❑ 90ProAaA-125
❑ 91Cla/Bes-200
❑ 91LinDriAA-421
❑ 91MemChiLD-421
❑ 91MemChiP-664
❑ 92MemChiF-2429
❑ 92MemChiS-446
❑ 92SkyAA F-188
❑ 94ForMyeMC-24
❑ 94ForMyeMF-1176

Tunkin, Scott
❑ 91ParPatF-16
❑ 93AusFut-79
❑ 95AusFut-11

Tunnell, Lee
❑ 82PorBeaT-9
❑ 83TopTra-118T
❑ 84Don-592
❑ 84Fle-268
❑ 84FleSti-107
❑ 84Nes792-384
❑ 84Pir-25
❑ 84Top-384
❑ 84TopTif-384
❑ 85Don-288
❑ 85Fle-480
❑ 85Fle-638
❑ 85Pir-22
❑ 85Top-21
❑ 85TopTif-21
❑ 86Fle-623
❑ 86HawIslP-21
❑ 86Top-161
❑ 86TopTif-161
❑ 87CarTeal-32
❑ 87FleUpd-119
❑ 87FleUpdG-119
❑ 88Fle-49
❑ 88FleGlo-49
❑ 88LouRedBTI-48
❑ 88Sco-587
❑ 88ScoGlo-587
❑ 89BlaYNPRWLU-19
❑ 89PorBeaC-6
❑ 89PorBeaP-217
❑ 90CMC-609
❑ 90ProAAAF-194
❑ 90TucTorC-7
❑ 90TucTorP-204
❑ 91LinDriAAA-621
❑ 91TucTorLD-621
❑ 91TucTorP-2213
❑ 98Cha-27

Tunney, Gene
❑ 32USCar*-15
❑ 87SpoCubG-2

Tuozzo, John
❑ 86ColMetP-25

Tupper, Craig
❑ 93BriTigC-22

Turang, Brian
❑ 88CapCodPB-20
❑ 88CapCodPPaLP-22
❑ 89BelMarL-20
❑ 90ProAaA-149
❑ 90SanBerSB-18
❑ 90SanBerSCLC-106
❑ 90SanBerSP-2642
❑ 91JacSunLD-347
❑ 91JacSunP-161
❑ 91LinDriAA-347
❑ 92JacSunF-3718
❑ 92JacSunS-358
❑ 93CalCanF-1175
❑ 93ExcFS7-233
❑ 93MariStaClu-27
❑ 94ColC-614
❑ 94ColChoGS-614
❑ 94ColChoSS-614
❑ 94Don-314
❑ 94Fle-299
❑ 94Pac-582
❑ 94Pin-377
❑ 94PinArtP-377
❑ 94PinMusC-377
❑ 94Sco-637
❑ 94ScoBoyoS-37
❑ 94ScoGolR-637
❑ 94StaClu-177
❑ 94StaCluFDI-177
❑ 94StaCluGR-177
❑ 94StaCluMOP-177
❑ 94Top-82
❑ 94TopGol-82
❑ 94TopSpa-82
❑ 95TacRaiTI-24

Turbeville, George
❑ 93ConTSN-979

Turco, Frank
❑ 91BenBucCB-15
❑ 91BenBucP-3705
❑ 91RenSilSCLC-4
❑ 92ChaRanC-5
❑ 92ChaRanF-2235
❑ 93TulDriF-2744
❑ 93TulDriTI-27
❑ 94TulDriF-253
❑ 94TulDriTI-24
❑ 95TulDriTI-26

Turco, Steve F.
❑ 81ArkTraT-2
❑ 83St.PetCT-25
❑ 85SprCarT-18
❑ 91HamRedC-30
❑ 91HamRedP-4057
❑ 92JohCitCC-26
❑ 92JohCitCF-3134
❑ 93GleFalRF-4021
❑ 96JohCitCTI-31
❑ 97JohCitCTI-33
❑ 98JohCCTI-30

Turek, Joseph
❑ 88GreHorP-1559
❑ 88SouAtlLAGS-8
❑ 89CedRapRB-7
❑ 89CedRapRP-920
❑ 89CedRapRS-20
❑ 90CedRapRB-18
❑ 91ChaLooP-1962
❑ 92CanIndF-691
❑ 92CanIndS-121
❑ 92SkyAA F-57
❑ 93CanIndF-2841

Turgeon, David
❑ 87OneYanP-12
❑ 88Ft.LauYS-22
❑ 89PriWilCS-22
❑ 90Ft.LauYS-20

Turgeon, Mike
❑ 80WicAerT-11
❑ 82PhoGiaVNB-17

Turgeon, Steve
❑ 83St.PetCT-26
❑ 85SprCarT-19
❑ 86EriCarP-28

Turlais, John
❑ 92FroRowDP-64
❑ 92FroRowDPG-64
❑ 92FroRowDPS-64
❑ 94KinMetC-23
❑ 94KinMetF-3827
❑ 97LynHil-22

Turley, Bob (Robert)
❑ 54OriEss-33
❑ 54OriTeal-19
❑ 54Top-85
❑ 55ArmCoi-23
❑ 55Top-38
❑ 55TopDouH-63
❑ 56Top-40
❑ 56TopPin-31
❑ 56YanJayP-12
❑ 56YanTeal-24
❑ 57Top-264
❑ 58JayPubA-23
❑ 58Top-255
❑ 58Top-493
❑ 58YanJayP-14
❑ 59ArmCoi-19
❑ 59Baz-22
❑ 59HowPhoSP-2
❑ 59Top-60
❑ 59Top-237
❑ 59Top-570
❑ 59TopVen-60
❑ 60Lea-103
❑ 60NuHi-30
❑ 60Top-270
❑ 60YanJayP-12
❑ 61NuSco-430
❑ 61Pos-5
❑ 61Raw-12
❑ 61Top-40
❑ 61TopStal-200
❑ 61Yan61RL-21
❑ 61YanJayP-12
❑ 62Top-589
❑ 63Top-322
❑ 70FleWorS-55
❑ 78AtlCon-24
❑ 79DiaGre-200
❑ 79TCM50-136
❑ 81TCM60I-459
❑ 83Yan196-21
❑ 83YanASFY-49
❑ 87AstSer1-24
❑ 88PacLegI-52
❑ 91OriCro-464
❑ 91YanRinP13-9
❑ 92YanWIZ6-132
❑ 92YanWIZA-84
❑ 94TopArc1-85
❑ 94TopArc1G-85
❑ 97BalOriP-51
❑ 97BalOriP-52

Turley, Jason
❑ 96AubDouB-4

Turman, Jason
❑ 98CapFeaCM-24

Turnbow, Mark
❑ 97BurIndG-28
❑ 98ColRedSM-10
❑ 98MarPhiG-28

Turnbull, Anthony
❑ 93ElmPioC-23
❑ 93ElmPioF-3828
❑ 94BreCouMF-17

Turnbull, Keith
❑ 83EriCarT-8

Turner, Brian
❑ 90GreHorB-26
❑ 90GreHorP-2678
❑ 90GreHorS-23
❑ 90OneYanP-3374
❑ 91GreHorP-3069
❑ 92ForLauYC-20
❑ 92ForLauYTI-31
❑ 92Ft.LauYF-2623
❑ 93SanBerSC-20
❑ 93SanBerSF-780
❑ 94TamYanC-27
❑ 94TamYanF-2400
❑ 95NorNavTI-35
❑ 96StLucMTI-27

Turner, Cameron
❑ 93AusFut-83

Turner, Chris
❑ 91BoiHawC-17
❑ 91BoiHawP-3884
❑ 92QuaCitRBC-6
❑ 92QuaCitRBF-814
❑ 93Bow-525
❑ 93VanCanF-2602
❑ 94AngLAT-20
❑ 94AngMot-13
❑ 94Bow-95
❑ 94ColC-277
❑ 94ColChoGS-277
❑ 94ColChoSS-277
❑ 94Don-567
❑ 94Fin-370
❑ 94FinRef-370
❑ 94FleMajLP-35
❑ 94FleUpd-22
❑ 94Lea-291
❑ 94Pac-92
❑ 94Pin-405
❑ 94PinArtP-405
❑ 94PinMusC-405
❑ 94Sco-500
❑ 94ScoGolR-500
❑ 94ScoRoo-RT85
❑ 94ScoRooGR-RT85
❑ 94Sel-205
❑ 94SpoRoo-65
❑ 94SpoRooAP-65
❑ 94SpoRooS-65
❑ 94StaClu-92
❑ 94StaCluFDI-92
❑ 94StaCluGR-92
❑ 94StaCluMOP-92
❑ 94Top-322
❑ 94TopGol-322
❑ 94TopSpa-322
❑ 94Ult-29
❑ 94UppDec-29
❑ 94UppDecED-29
❑ 95Don-361
❑ 95DonPreP-361
❑ 95Fle-237
❑ 95Lea-199
❑ 95Sco-55
❑ 95ScoGolR-55
❑ 95ScoPlaTS-55
❑ 95StaClu-82
❑ 95StaCluFDI-82
❑ 95StaCluMOP-82
❑ 95StaCluSTWS-82
❑ 95Ult-25
❑ 95UltGolM-25
❑ 96VanCanB-28

Turner, Earl
❑ 50PirTeal-22

Turner, Gregory
❑ 91SydWavF-6
❑ 93AusFut-75

Turner, Jerry (John Webber)
❑ 75HawIslC-8
❑ 75IntLeaASB-35
❑ 75OPC-619
❑ 75PacCoaLAB-35
❑ 75Top-619
❑ 75TopMin-619
❑ 76OPC-598
❑ 76Top-598
❑ 77PadFamF-8
❑ 77PadSchC-60A
❑ 77PadSchC-60B
❑ 77Top-447
❑ 78PadFamF-34
❑ 78Top-364
❑ 79PadFamF-6
❑ 79Top-564
❑ 80Top-133
❑ 81Don-244
❑ 81Fle-504
❑ 81PadFamF-21
❑ 81Top-285
❑ 81TopSti-229
❑ 82Don-609
❑ 82Top-736
❑ 82TopTra-121T
❑ 83Fle-345
❑ 83PadTeal-28
❑ 83Top-41

Turner, Jim
❑ 30Zee-17
❑ 31Zee-8
❑ 38CloFotW-82
❑ 41HarHarW-24
❑ 43YanSta-27
❑ 49YanTeal-24
❑ 50YanTeal-24
❑ 52Top-373
❑ 58YanJayP-15
❑ 62Top-263
❑ 63RedFreBC-29
❑ 68YanPhoS-87
❑ 73OPC-116
❑ 73Top-116A
❑ 73Top-116B
❑ 77CinRedT-6
❑ 79DiaGre-204
❑ 80Red196T-8
❑ 83TopRep5-373

Turner, John
❑ 86PeoChiP-24

Turner, Jose
❑ 78DayBeaAT-25

Turner, Ken
❑ 66SeaPop-26

Turner, Lloyd
❑ 78WatIndT-24
❑ 79WauTimT-10

Turner, Luis
❑ 76VenLeaS-104

Turner, Matt (William Matthew)
❑ 87SumBraP-2
❑ 88BurBraP-5
❑ 89DurBullS-24
❑ 89DurBullS-24
❑ 89DurBulTI-24
❑ 90GreBraB-12
❑ 90GreBraP-1128
❑ 90GreBraS-20
❑ 91LinDriAAA-446
❑ 91RicBraBC-17
❑ 91RicBraLD-446
❑ 91RicBraP-2569
❑ 91RicBraTI-25
❑ 92TucTorF-487
❑ 92TucTorS-621
❑ 93EdmTraF-1136
❑ 93FleFinE-72
❑ 93MarlStaClu-27
❑ 93MarPub-24
❑ 93PacSpa-472
❑ 93TopTra-56T
❑ 94Don-593
❑ 94Fle-478
❑ 94Pac-251
❑ 94Sco-306
❑ 94ScoGolR-306
❑ 94StaClu-319
❑ 94StaCluFDI-319
❑ 94StaCluGR-319
❑ 94StaCluMOP-319
❑ 94StaCluT-78
❑ 94StaCluTFDI-78
❑ 94Top-587
❑ 94TopGol-587
❑ 94TopSpa-587
❑ 94Ult-200
❑ 98OmaRoyM-22

Turner, Rick
❑ 82DanSunF-7
❑ 83RedPioT-24
❑ 93AngMot-28

Turner, Rocky
❑ 94PitMetC-22
❑ 94PitMetF-3537

Turner, Roy
❑ 04FanCraAL-46

Turner, Ryan
❑ 91BenBucCB-16
❑ 91BenBucP-3709
❑ 92Bow-346
❑ 92UppDec-710
❑ 92VisOakC-17
❑ 92VisOakF-1028
❑ 93CenValRC-24
❑ 93CenValRF-2907
❑ 93Top-537
❑ 93TopGol-537
❑ 93TopInaM-537
❑ 93TopInaR-537
❑ 93TopMic-537
❑ 94NewHavRF-1564

Turner, Shane
❑ 86FloStaLAP-47
❑ 86Ft.LauYP-23
❑ 87ColCliP-24
❑ 87ColCliP-9
❑ 87ColCliT-18
❑ 88MaiPhiC-13
❑ 88MaiPhiP-288
❑ 88PhiTas-27
❑ 89Fle-653
❑ 89FleGlo-653
❑ 89ReaPhiB-12
❑ 89ReaPhiP-655
❑ 89ReaPhiS-24
❑ 89ScoHot1R-67
❑ 90CMC-325
❑ 90ProAAAF-468
❑ 90RocRedWC-24
❑ 90RocRedWGC-22
❑ 90RocRedWP-711
❑ 91LinDriAAA-471
❑ 91RocRedWLD-471
❑ 91RocRedWP-1912
❑ 92CalCanF-3741
❑ 92CalCanS-71
❑ 92DonRoo-118

❑ 92FleUpd-58
❑ 93CalCanF-1176
❑ 93Fle-681
❑ 93StaClu-97
❑ 93StaCluFDI-97
❑ 93StaCluMOP-97
❑ 93Top-694
❑ 93TopGol-694
❑ 93TopInaM-694
❑ 93TopInaR-694
❑ 93TopMic-694
❑ 94PhoFirF-1530
❑ 96BelGiaTI-33
❑ 97SalVolG-37
❑ 98SanJosGQ-27
Turner, Ted
❑ 91FouBal-24
Turner, Terry
❑ 05IndSouPSoCP-17
❑ 08RosComP-30
❑ 09ColChiE-291
❑ 09T206-360
❑ 10DomDisP-118
❑ 10SweCapPP-20
❑ 11E94-28
❑ 11HelSta-26
❑ 11MecDFT-43
❑ 11PinT-5-615
❑ 11S74Sil-11
❑ 11SpoLifCW-353
❑ 11SpoLifM-51
❑ 11T205-173
❑ 12ColRedB-291
❑ 12ColTinT-291
❑ 12ColTinT-292A
❑ 12HasTriFT-8
❑ 12HasTriFT-72
❑ 12T207-185
❑ 14B18B-9A
❑ 14B18B-9B
❑ 14PieStaT-102
❑ 15SpoNewM-179
❑ 16SpoNewM-176
❑ 17ColE13-175
Turner, Tom
❑ 22Zee-55
❑ 40WhiSoxL-21
❑ 77TCMTheWY-15
❑ 96Bro194F-28
Turner, Trent
❑ 88CapCodPPaLP-179
Turnes, Luis
❑ 80VenLeaS-102
Turnier, Aaron
❑ 92PulBraC-14
❑ 92PulBraF-3177
❑ 93IdaFalBF-4032
❑ 93IdaFalBSP-28
❑ 94MacBraC-23
❑ 94MacBraF-2205
❑ 95AusFut-67
❑ 95BreBtaTI-48
Turpin, Hal
❑ 30Zee-160
❑ 31Zee-112
❑ 43CenFlo-24
❑ 44CenFlo-25
❑ 45CenFlo-26
Turrentine, Richard
❑ 90TamYanD-27
❑ 91GreHorP-3070
❑ 92GreHorC-23
❑ 92GreHorF-790
❑ 96StLucMTI-33
❑ 97BinMetB-30
❑ 98BinMetQ-27
Turri, Shawn
❑ 91NiaFalRC-22
❑ 91NiaFalRP-3632
Turtletaub, Greg
❑ 88LitFalMP-13
Turvey, Joe
❑ 90HamRedB-15
❑ 90SavCarP-2071
❑ 91HamRedC-20
❑ 91HamRedP-4042
❑ 92SavCarC-15
❑ 92SavCarF-665
❑ 93St.PetCC-24
❑ 93St.PetCF-2631
Tuss, Jeff
❑ 91Cla/Bes-364
❑ 91WesPalBEC-13
❑ 91WesPalBEP-1229
❑ 92WesPalBEC-7
❑ 92WesPalBEF-2089
Tutt, John
❑ 84ChaO'sT-24
❑ 85BeaGolGT-22
❑ 86LasVegSP-21
Tuttle, Bill
❑ 55Bow-35
❑ 56A'sPos-46
❑ 56Top-203
❑ 57SwiFra-14
❑ 57Top-72
❑ 58A'sJayP-11
❑ 58Top-23A
❑ 58Top-23B
❑ 59Top-459
❑ 60A'sJayP-10
❑ 60A'sTeal-17
❑ 60Lea-32
❑ 60Top-367
❑ 61A'sTeal-21
❑ 61AthJayP-23
❑ 61Baz-36
❑ 61Pos-84A
❑ 61Pos-84B
❑ 61Top-536
❑ 61TopStaI-167
❑ 61TwiCloD-28
❑ 62Jel-88
❑ 62Pos-88
❑ 62PosCan-88
❑ 62SalPlaC-87A
❑ 62SalPlaC-87B
❑ 62ShiPlaC-87
❑ 62Top-298
❑ 62TopStaI-80
❑ 63Top-127
❑ 64SeaPop-17
❑ 79TCM50-103
Tuttle, David
❑ 89AncBucTI-10
❑ 91TopTra-122T
❑ 91TopTraT-122T
❑ 92StaCluD-188
❑ 93SouAtlLAGF-56
❑ 93WesVirWC-23
❑ 93WesVirWF-2867
❑ 94WinSpiC-22
❑ 94WinSpiF-271
❑ 95ChaLooTI-23
❑ 97HigDesMG-28
❑ 98TulDriTI-13
Tuttle, John
❑ 96JohCitCTI-32
❑ 97JohCitCTI-34
Twardoski, Michael
❑ 88CarLeaAS-38
❑ 88KinIndS-22
❑ 89CanIndB-12
❑ 89CanIndP-1299
❑ 89CanIndS-21
❑ 89EasLeaDDP-DD35
❑ 90Bes-155
❑ 90NewBriRSB-9
❑ 90NewBriRSP-1329
❑ 90NewBriRSS-18
❑ 90StaFS7-31
❑ 91LinDriAAA-357
❑ 91PawRedSDD-24
❑ 91PawRedSLD-357
❑ 92PawRedSF-932
❑ 92PawRedSS-369
❑ 92SkyAAAF-168
❑ 92TriA AAS-369
❑ 93NorTidF-2579
❑ 94PawRedSDD-26
❑ 94PawRedSF-954
❑ 97DunDonPPS-25
Twardy, Glenn
❑ 89BelMarL-14
Tweedlie, Brad
❑ 93BilMusF-3945
❑ 93BilMusSP-23
❑ 94WinSpiC-23
❑ 94WinSpiF-272
❑ 97TreThuB-25
❑ 98TreThuM-24
Twellman, Tom
❑ 74CedRapAT-18
❑ 75DubPacT-26
❑ 76DubPacT-36
Twiggs, Greg
❑ 93GenCubC-25
❑ 93GenCubF-3173
❑ 94DayCubC-25
❑ 94DayCubF-2354
❑ 96OrlCubB-26
❑ 97OrlRayB-25
❑ 98BowBayM-29
Twins, Minnesota
❑ 61Top-542
❑ 61TopMagR-3
❑ 62GuyPotCP-13
❑ 62Top-584
❑ 63Top-162
❑ 64Top-318
❑ 64TopTatI-13
❑ 64TopVen-318
❑ 65OPC-24
❑ 65Top-24
❑ 66Top-526
❑ 66TopRubI-113
❑ 67Top-211
❑ 68OPC-137
❑ 68Top-137
❑ 68TopVen-137
❑ 69FleCloS-13
❑ 69FleCloS-47
❑ 69TopStaA-13
❑ 70FleWorS-62
❑ 70OPC-534
❑ 70Top-534
❑ 71FleWorS-63
❑ 71OPC-522
❑ 71Top-522
❑ 71TopTat-118
❑ 72OPC-156
❑ 72Top-156
❑ 73OPC-654
❑ 73OPCBTC-14
❑ 73Top-654
❑ 73TopBluTC-14
❑ 74OPC-74
❑ 74OPCTC-14
❑ 74Top-74
❑ 74TopStaA-14
❑ 74TopTeaC-14
❑ 78Top-451
❑ 82TwiPos-34
❑ 83FleSta-238
❑ 83FleSti-NNO
❑ 83FleSti-NNO
❑ 83TwiTeal-35
❑ 84MinTwiP-34
❑ 84TwiTeal-34
❑ 86TwiTeal-35
❑ 87SpoTeaL-17
❑ 87TwiPos-31
❑ 87TwiTeal-31
❑ 88FleSluBC-C6
❑ 88FleWaxBC-C5
❑ 88PanSti-451
❑ 88PanSti-452
❑ 88PanSti-453
❑ 88PanSti-454
❑ 88PanSti-463
❑ 88RedFolSB-127
❑ 90PubIntS-636
❑ 90RedFolSB-124
❑ 90TopMag-72
❑ 91DodPho-2
❑ 93TedWilPC-14
❑ 94ImpProP-9
❑ 94Sco-325
❑ 94ScoGolR-325
❑ 95PacPriTL-9
❑ 95PanSti-156
❑ 96PanSti-203
❑ 99Vic-220
Twist, Jeff
❑ 94BenRocC-22
❑ 94BenRocF-3599
Twitchell, Lawrence
❑ 87OldJudN-504
❑ 88GandBCGCE-42
❑ 88WG1CarG-26
Twitchell, Wayne
❑ 71OPC-692
❑ 71Top-692
❑ 72OPC-14
❑ 72Top-14
❑ 73OPC-227
❑ 73PhiTeal-22
❑ 73Top-227
❑ 74Kel-26
❑ 74OPC-419
❑ 74Top-419
❑ 74TopSta-79
❑ 75OPC-326
❑ 75PhiPhiP-29
❑ 75Top-326
❑ 75TopMin-326
❑ 76OPC-543
❑ 76PhiPhiP-29
❑ 76Top-543
❑ 77ExpPos-31
❑ 77Top-444
❑ 78ExpPos-15
❑ 78OPC-189
❑ 78Top-269
❑ 79OPC-18
❑ 79Top-43
❑ 91MetWIZ-415
❑ 94BreMilB-368
Twitty, Doug
❑ 90BenBucL-21
Twitty, Jeff
❑ 80OmaRoyP-24
❑ 81Fle-49
❑ 82RicBraT-8
Twitty, Sean
❑ 91BelMarCB-7
❑ 91BelMarP-3682
❑ 92PenPilC-15
❑ 92SanBerSF-973
❑ 93PriWilCC-24
❑ 93PriWilCF-671
❑ 94TamYanC-28
❑ 94TamYanF-2401
❑ 95GreBatTI-26
Twogood, Forest
❑ 33MrsShePP-14
❑ 34DiaMatCSB-183
Twombley, Dennis
❑ 97TamYan-30
❑ 98GreBatM-21
Twombly, Babe
❑ 22Zee-17
❑ 23Zee-21
❑ 24Zee-16
❑ 25Zee-13
❑ 28ExhPCL-29
❑ 28Zee-21
❑ 30Zee-112
Twomey, Mike
❑ 92NiaFalRC-30
❑ 93PalSprAC-29
❑ 94LakElsSC-29
Tyack, Jim
❑ 43A'STEAI-23
Tyler, Brad
❑ 91KanCouCC-20
❑ 91KanCouCP-2667
❑ 91MidLeaAP-MWL35
❑ 92ClaFS7-109
❑ 92FreKeyC-6
❑ 92HagSunF-2565
❑ 93BowBayF-2198
❑ 94ExcFS7-16
❑ 94OriPro-99
❑ 94RocRedWF-1005
❑ 94RocRedWTI-22
❑ 95RocRedWTI-36
❑ 96RocRedWB-27
❑ 97RicBra-27
Tyler, Dave
❑ 81BriRedST-19
Tyler, Josh
❑ 95BelBreTI-1
❑ 96StoPorB-20
❑ 97StoPor-18
❑ 98SanJosGQ-14
Tyler, Lefty (George)
❑ 12T207-186
❑ 14B18B-54A
❑ 14B18B-54B
❑ 14B18B-54C
❑ 14FatPlaT-49
❑ 15CraJacE-146
❑ 16BF2FP-59
❑ 16SpoNewM-177
❑ 17ColE13-176
❑ 17HolBreD-106
❑ 21E121So8-100
❑ 22AmeCarE122-71
❑ 22W575-140
❑ 80BraTCM1-2
Tyler, Mike
❑ 76DubPacT-37
❑ 78ChaChaT-18
❑ 79ChaChaT-7
❑ 80PorBeaT-1
Tyler, Peter
❑ 63GadFunC-71
Tynan, Chris
❑ 98BesAutSS-50
Tyner, Jason
❑ 98St.LucMM-1
❑ 99199Fin-298
❑ 99Bow-134
❑ 99BowBes-165
❑ 99BowBesAR-165
❑ 99BowBesR-165
❑ 99BowChr-134
❑ 99BowChrG-134
❑ 99BowChrGR-134
❑ 99BowChrI-134
❑ 99BowChrIR-134
❑ 99BowChrR-134
❑ 99BowGol-134
❑ 99BowInt-134
❑ 99FinGolRef-298
❑ 99FinRef-298
❑ 99StaClu-149
❑ 99StaCluFDI-149
❑ 99StaCluOoaK-149
❑ 99StaCluPP-149
❑ 99TeaBesR-90
❑ 99TeaBesRFS-14
❑ 99TeaBesRG-90
❑ 99TeaBesRS-90
❑ 99Top-215
❑ 99TopChr-215
❑ 99TopChrR-215
❑ 99TopGal-149
❑ 99TopGalPP-149
❑ 99TopGalPPI-149
❑ 99TopSta-42
❑ 99TopSta1Foil-42
❑ 99TopSta2Foil-42
❑ 99TopStaFoil-42
❑ 99TopStaOS-42
❑ 99TopStaTS-42
Tyner, Marcus
❑ 93IdaFalBF-4033
❑ 93IdaFalBSP-27
❑ 94IdaFalBF-3585
❑ 94IdaFalBSP-23
❑ 95MacBraTI-26
Tyner, Matt
❑ 90HagSunDGB-34
Tyng, James
❑ 87OldJudN-505
Tynon, Don
❑ 94ElmPioC-22
❑ 94ElmPioF-3476
Tyrell, Hilliard
❑ 21Zee-111
Tyrell, Jim
❑ 93UtiBluSC-24
❑ 93UtiBluSF-3534
❑ 94UtiBluSC-27
❑ 94UtiBluSF-3820
❑ 95MicBatCTI-29
Tyrone, Jim
❑ 74OPC-598
❑ 74Top-598
❑ 76SSP-604
❑ 77SanJosMC-7
❑ 78Top-487
Tyrus, Jason
❑ 94SpoIndC-23
❑ 94SpoIndF-3338
Tyson, Jeremy
❑ 94LSUTig-14
Tyson, Mike
❑ 74OPC-655
❑ 74Top-655
❑ 74TopSta-120
❑ 75OPC-231
❑ 75St.LouCP-30
❑ 75Top-231
❑ 75TopMin-231
❑ 76BlaDis-65
❑ 76BucDis-65
❑ 76CarDis-65
❑ 76CraDis-65
❑ 76DailsID-65
❑ 76IsaDis-65
❑ 76OPC-86
❑ 76OrbDis-65
❑ 76RedBarD-65
❑ 76SafDis-65
❑ 76SSP-283
❑ 76St.LouCP-33
❑ 76Top-86
❑ 76TowCluD-65
❑ 77BurCheD-18
❑ 77Car5-28
❑ 77CarTeal-27
❑ 77PepGloD-38
❑ 77Top-599
❑ 78CarTeal-35
❑ 78Top-111
❑ 79Car5-31
❑ 79OPC-162
❑ 79Top-324
❑ 80OPC-252
❑ 80Top-486
❑ 81CokTeaS-23
❑ 81Fle-315
❑ 81Top-294
❑ 81TopSti-155
❑ 81TopSupHT-30
❑ 82Don-435
❑ 82Fle-606
❑ 82FleSta-100
❑ 82Top-62
Tyson, Terry
❑ 76BatTroTI-27
❑ 77WatIndT-26
Tyson, Ty (Albert T.)
❑ 90DodTar-1088
Ubiera, Miguel
❑ 91GulCoaRSP-20
❑ 92GulCoaRSP-9
Ubinas, Alex
❑ 90BriTigP-3157
❑ 90BriTigS-24
❑ 91BriTigC-9
❑ 91BriTigP-3609
Ubri, Fermin
❑ 84JacMetT-24
Uccello, Jeff
❑ 98MicBatCM-30
Uchinokura, Tokashi
❑ 92SalSpuC-24
❑ 92SalSpuF-3765
Uchiyama, Kenichi
❑ 90SalSpuCLC-122
❑ 90SalSpuP-2713
Uchiyama, Tomoyuki
❑ 98ReaPhiM-5
❑ 98ReaPhiUM-26
Uecker, Bob
❑ 62Top-594
❑ 63BraJayP-12
❑ 63Top-126
❑ 64Top-543
❑ 65Top-519
❑ 66OPC-91
❑ 66Top-91A
❑ 66Top-91B
❑ 66TopVen-91
❑ 67CokCapPh-10
❑ 67Top-326
❑ 68BraPos-32
❑ 75BreBro-3
❑ 78BraTCC-14
❑ 93ActPacA-152
❑ 99DumSet-BU
❑ 99DumSet-BU
Ueda, Joe
❑ 88FreSunP-1238
Ueda, Sadahito
❑ 83SanJosBC-16
Ufret, Ricardo
❑ 89AncBucTI-15
❑ 89BlaYNPRWL-17
Ugueto, Hector
❑ 93JohCitCC-26
❑ 93JohCitCF-3692
❑ 94SavCarC-26
❑ 94SavCarF-518
❑ 95NewJerCTI-29
❑ 96-97LinVen-73
❑ 96NewJerCB-27
Ugueto, Jesus
❑ 91JohCitCC-10
❑ 91JohCitCP-3987
❑ 92JohCitCF-3128
❑ 93SavCarC-25
❑ 93SavCarF-696
❑ 94MadHatC-23
❑ 94MadHatF-144
❑ 95LinVen-192
❑ 96-97LinVen-177
Uhal, Bob
❑ 88LitFalMP-8
Uhalt, Bernard
❑ 30Zee-97
❑ 31Zee-56
❑ 32Zee-67
❑ 33Zee-24
Uhas, Ed
❑ 64TopRooAB-14
Uhey, Jackie
❑ 76CliPilT-30
❑ 82ElPasDT-18
❑ 85EveGialC-19
❑ 86EveGiaPC-34
Uhlaender, Ted

❑ 66Top-264
❑ 66TopVen-264
❑ 67DexPre-211
❑ 67Top-431
❑ 67TwiTeal-22
❑ 68DexPre-74
❑ 68OPC-28
❑ 68Top-28
❑ 68TopVen-28
❑ 69MilBra-279
❑ 69MLBOffS-72
❑ 69OPC-194
❑ 69Top-194
❑ 69TopFou-19
❑ 69TopSta-200
❑ 69TopTeaP-15
❑ 69TwiTealC-10
❑ 70Ind-12
❑ 70MLBOffS-204
❑ 70Top-673
❑ 71Ind-12
❑ 71MLBOffS-384
❑ 71OPC-347
❑ 71Top-347
❑ 72MilBra-349
❑ 72Top-614
❑ 78TCM60I-161
❑ 78TwiFri-47
❑ 90GreHorB-28
❑ 90GreHorP-2682
❑ 90GreHorS-26
❑ 91Ft.LauYC-8
❑ 91Ft.LauYP-2445
❑ 92ColCliP-2

Uhle, George E.
❑ 20WalMaiW-56
❑ 21Nei-16
❑ 22E120-43
❑ 22W572-108
❑ 22W573-134
❑ 26SpoComoA-44
❑ 26SpoNewSM-10
❑ 27YorCarE-11
❑ 28Exh-44
❑ 28StaPlaCE-68
❑ 28W502-11
❑ 28W56PlaC-D5A
❑ 28Yue-11
❑ 29ExhFou-24
❑ 31Exh-23
❑ 33ButCre-26
❑ 33ExhFou-12
❑ 33Gou-100
❑ 34GouCanV-22
❑ 40PlaBal-239
❑ 61Fle-146
❑ 77Ind192T-19
❑ 79DiaGre-279
❑ 82DiaCla-69
❑ 82OhiHaloF-43
❑ 91ConTSN-224

Uhrhan, Kevin
❑ 91LynRedSC-10
❑ 91LynRedSP-1200
❑ 92NewBriRSF-435
❑ 92NewBriRSS-479
❑ 93NewBriRSF-1221

Ujdur, Gerry
❑ 80EvaTriT-10
❑ 81EvaTriT-8
❑ 81Top-626
❑ 82EvaTriT-10
❑ 83Don-600
❑ 83Fle-346
❑ 83TigPos-29
❑ 83Top-174

Ulises, Pedro
❑ 94OriPro-100

Ullan, Dave
❑ 94SpoIndC-24
❑ 94SpoIndF-3326

Ullery, David
❑ 98WilBluRC-29

Ullger, Scott
❑ 80OrlTwiT-21
❑ 82OrlTwi8SCT-10
❑ 82TolMudHT-22
❑ 83TwiTeal-4
❑ 84Don-438
❑ 84Nes792-551
❑ 84TolMudHT-12
❑ 84Top-551
❑ 84TopTif-551
❑ 85IntLeaAT-27
❑ 85TolMudHT-18
❑ 86StaoftFT-22
❑ 86TolMudHP-22
❑ 87RocRedWP-7
❑ 87RocRedWT-21
❑ 88VisOakCLC-170
❑ 88VisOakP-99
❑ 89CalLeaA-25
❑ 89VisOakCLC-118
❑ 89VisOakP-1433
❑ 90CalLeaACLC-25
❑ 90VisOakCLC-79
❑ 90VisOakP-2170
❑ 91LinDriAA-499
❑ 91OrlSunRLD-499
❑ 91OrlSunRP-1865
❑ 92PorBeaF-2681
❑ 92PorBeaS-424
❑ 93PorBeaF-2396
❑ 93TriAAAGF-48
❑ 94SalLakBF-831

Ulrich, Dutch
❑ 94ConTSN-1298
❑ 94ConTSNB-1298

Ulrich, George
❑ 89CalLeaA-55

Ulrich, Henry
❑ 37Zee-99

Ulrich, Jeff
❑ 80PenPilBT-22
❑ 80PenPilCT-16
❑ 81OklCit8T-26
❑ 82OklCit8T-17

Ulvenes, Gregg
❑ 85RedWinA-6
❑ 86RedWinA-21

Umbach, Arnie
❑ 66BraPos-25
❑ 66Top-518

Umbarger, Jim
❑ 75RanPos-36
❑ 76OPC-7
❑ 76SSP-257
❑ 76Top-7
❑ 77Top-378
❑ 78SSP270-90
❑ 79Top-518
❑ 79TucTorT-24
❑ 81RocRedWW-8
❑ 93RanKee-362

Umbria, Jose
❑ 96MedHatBJTI-30
❑ 98St.CatSM-25

Umbricht, Jim
❑ 60Top-145
❑ 60TopVen-145
❑ 62Col.45B-20
❑ 62Col45'HC-19
❑ 63Top-99
❑ 64Top-389
❑ 77PirTCM1WC-28
❑ 89AstCol4S-9

Umdenstock, Bob
❑ 79AppFoxT-19
❑ 82ChaRoyT-11

Umont, Frank
❑ 55Bow-305

Umphlett, Tom
❑ 53Bri-24
❑ 53RedSoxTI-26
❑ 54Bow-88
❑ 55Bow-45
❑ 61SeaPop-26
❑ 61SeaPop-27
❑ 61UniOil-S11
❑ 62SeaPop-17

Underhill, Pat
❑ 91GulCoaRSP-15

Underwood, Bill
❑ 92OneYanC-20
❑ 93GreHorC-24
❑ 93GreHorF-886

Underwood, Bobby
❑ 88WatPirP-13
❑ 89AugPirP-500
❑ 90AugPirP-2463
❑ 91SalBucC-15

Underwood, Curtis
❑ 92SavCarC-10
❑ 92SavCarF-672

Underwood, Devin
❑ 95ButCopKtI-20

Underwood, Jake
❑ 98EveAquG-25

Underwood, Kent
❑ 93GreHorF-887

Underwood, Pat
❑ 80OPC-358
❑ 80Top-709
❑ 81Don-368
❑ 81EvaTriT-9
❑ 81Fle-469
❑ 81Top-373
❑ 82Top-133
❑ 83Don-29
❑ 83EvaTriT-10
❑ 83Fle-347
❑ 83TigAIKS-70
❑ 83TigPos-30
❑ 83Top-588

Underwood, Tom
❑ 75OPC-615
❑ 75PhiPhiP-30
❑ 75Top-615
❑ 75TopMin-615
❑ 76OPC-407
❑ 76PhiPhiP-30
❑ 76SSP-461
❑ 76Top-407
❑ 77Car5-29
❑ 77Top-217
❑ 78BluJayP-20
❑ 78Top-531
❑ 79BluJayBY-18
❑ 79OPC-26
❑ 79Top-64
❑ 80OPC-172
❑ 80Top-324
❑ 80YanPhoA-25
❑ 81Don-108
❑ 81Fle-97
❑ 81OPC-114
❑ 81Top-114
❑ 81TopTra-846
❑ 82Don-323
❑ 82Fle-109
❑ 82Top-757
❑ 83A'sGraG-31
❑ 83Don-391
❑ 83Fle-535
❑ 83FleSta-202
❑ 83FleSti-191
❑ 83Top-466
❑ 84BalOriP-39
❑ 84Don-253
❑ 84Fle-460
❑ 84FleUpd-121
❑ 84Nes792-642
❑ 84OPC-293
❑ 84Top-642
❑ 84TopSti-335
❑ 84TopTif-642
❑ 84TopTra-123T
❑ 84TopTraT-123T
❑ 85Fle-194
❑ 85Top-289
❑ 85TopTif-289
❑ 86BluJayGT-10
❑ 89PacSenL-169
❑ 89T/MSenL-108
❑ 91OriCro-465
❑ 92YanWIZ8-194

Undorf, Bob
❑ 90NiaFalRP-26
❑ 91FayGenC-27
❑ 91FayGenP-1170
❑ 92LakTigC-1
❑ 92LakTigF-2280
❑ 92ProFS7-68
❑ 93LonTigF-2307

Unglaub, Robert Alexander
❑ 08AmeCarE91-94
❑ 08RosComP-7
❑ 09AmeCarE90-1-111
❑ 09ColChiE-292A
❑ 09ColChiE-292B
❑ 09ColChiE-292C
❑ 09RamT20-119
❑ 09SenBarP-10
❑ 09T206-361
❑ 10SenWasT-6
❑ 11PinT-5-565
❑ 11SpoLifCW-354
❑ 11SpoLifM-134
❑ 12ColRedB-292A
❑ 12ColRedB-292B
❑ 12ColRedB-292C
❑ 12ColTinT-292B
❑ 12ColTinT-292C

Ungs, Mike
❑ 79WisRapTT-2
❑ 80OrlTwiT-15
❑ 81WisRapTT-10

Unitas, John
❑ 58HarSta-22
❑ 66AurSpoMK-5

Unrat, Chris
❑ 94ChaRivC-21
❑ 94ChaRivF-2677

Unrein, Todd
❑ 91KanCouCC-11
❑ 91KanCouCP-2658
❑ 91KanCouCTI-23

Unroe, Tim
❑ 92HelBreF-1724
❑ 92HelBreSP-18
❑ 93ExcFS7-195
❑ 93StoPorC-24
❑ 93StoPorF-754
❑ 94ElPasDF-3156
❑ 95Bow-226
❑ 95BowGolF-226
❑ 95Exc-76
❑ 95ExcLeaL-17
❑ 95Sel-169
❑ 95SelArtP-169
❑ 95Sum-150
❑ 95SumNthD-150
❑ 95UppDec-264
❑ 95UppDecED-264
❑ 95UppDecEDG-264
❑ 95UppDecML-181
❑ 95UppDecMLFS-181
❑ 96ColCho-662
❑ 96ColChoGS-662
❑ 96ColChoSS-662
❑ 96Sco-222
❑ 96Spo-121
❑ 96SpoArtP-121
❑ 97BrePol-24
❑ 97PacPriGotD-GD58
❑ 97TucTorB-21
❑ 98IowCubQ-25

Unser, Al
❑ 47SigOil-17
❑ 49W72HolS-23

Unser, Del
❑ 69MilBra-280
❑ 69SenTeal-15
❑ 69SenTeal8-18
❑ 69Top-338
❑ 69TopTeaP-23
❑ 70DayDaiNM-135
❑ 70MLBOffS-287
❑ 70OPC-336
❑ 70Top-336
❑ 71MLBOffS-551
❑ 71OPC-33
❑ 71SenTealW-24
❑ 71Top-33
❑ 72MilBra-350
❑ 72Top-687
❑ 73OPC-247
❑ 73PhiTeal-23
❑ 73Top-247
❑ 74MetTeal-24
❑ 74OPC-69
❑ 74PhiJohP-25
❑ 74Top-69
❑ 74TopSta-80
❑ 75MetSSP-4
❑ 75OPC-138
❑ 75Top-138
❑ 75TopMin-138
❑ 76ExpRed-32
❑ 76MetMSAP-3
❑ 76OPC-268
❑ 76SSP-535
❑ 76Top-268
❑ 77BurCheD-155
❑ 77ExpPos-32
❑ 77OPC-27
❑ 77Top-471
❑ 78OPC-216
❑ 78Top-348
❑ 79OPC-330
❑ 79Top-628
❑ 80OPC-12
❑ 80PhiBul-43
❑ 80PhiBurK-13
❑ 80Top-6
❑ 80Top-27
❑ 81Don-164A
❑ 81Don-164B
❑ 81Fle-26
❑ 81OPC-56
❑ 81Top-566
❑ 81TopSupHT-90
❑ 82Don-273
❑ 82Fle-261
❑ 82Top-713
❑ 83PhiPosGM-10
❑ 85PhiTas-7
❑ 85PhiTas-8
❑ 86PhiTas-25
❑ 87PhiTas-xx0
❑ 88PhiTas-29
❑ 91MetWIZ-416

Upchurch, David Wayne
❑ 94EugEmeC-23
❑ 94EugEmeF-3713

Updike, John
❑ 78ReaRem-20

Upham, John
❑ 67Top-608
❑ 81TCM60I-473

Upp, Jerry (George)
❑ 09AmeCarE90-1-112

Upshaw, Cecil
❑ 67OPC-179
❑ 67Top-179
❑ 68BraPos-33
❑ 68CokCapB-1
❑ 68Top-286
❑ 68TopVen-286
❑ 69AtlBraBPPS-23
❑ 69Top-568
❑ 70AtlBraS-7
❑ 70OPC-295
❑ 70Top-295
❑ 71MLBOffS-23
❑ 71OPC-223
❑ 71Top-223
❑ 72OPC-74
❑ 72Top-74
❑ 73OPC-359
❑ 73Top-359
❑ 74OPC-579
❑ 74Top-579
❑ 74TopTra-579T
❑ 75OPC-92
❑ 75Top-92
❑ 75TopMin-92
❑ 76SSP-138
❑ 86BraGreT-11
❑ 92YanWIZ7-156

Upshaw, Lee
❑ 88DurBulS-22
❑ 89BurBraP-1598
❑ 89BurBraS-21
❑ 90Bes-25
❑ 90GreBraB-1
❑ 91GreBraC-7
❑ 91GreBraLD-220
❑ 91GreBraP-3001
❑ 91LinDriAA-220
❑ 93GreBraF-349

Upshaw, Ryan
❑ 97WatIndTI-31
❑ 98WatIndTI-33

Upshaw, Willie
❑ 76ForLauYS-21
❑ 78BluJayP-21
❑ 79OPC-175
❑ 79SyrChiT-4
❑ 79SyrChiTI-26
❑ 79Top-341
❑ 80SyrChiT-21
❑ 80VenLeaS-59
❑ 82BluJayS-17
❑ 82Don-652
❑ 82Fle-624
❑ 82OPC-196
❑ 82Top-196
❑ 83AllGamPI-8
❑ 83Don-558
❑ 83Fle-442
❑ 83FleSta-203
❑ 83OPC-338
❑ 83Top-556
❑ 83TopSti-128
❑ 84AllGamPI-99
❑ 84BluJayFS-30
❑ 84Don-315
❑ 84Fle-168
❑ 84FunFooP-94
❑ 84Nes792-453
❑ 84OPC-317
❑ 84Top-453
❑ 84TopRubD-30
❑ 84TopSti-363
❑ 84TopTif-453
❑ 85AllGamPI-9
❑ 85BluJayCC-8
❑ 85BluJayFS-30
❑ 85BluJayPLP-4
❑ 85Don-10
❑ 85Don-71
❑ 85DonActA-52
❑ 85DonSupD-10
❑ 85Fle-118
❑ 85Fle-635
❑ 85FleLimE-41
❑ 85Lea-10
❑ 85OPC-75
❑ 85OPCPos-14
❑ 85SevCoi-S15
❑ 85Top-75
❑ 85TopMin-75
❑ 85TopRubD-31
❑ 85TopSti-358
❑ 85TopTif-75
❑ 86BluJayAF-23
❑ 86BluJayFS-31
❑ 86Don-195
❑ 86Fle-72
❑ 86GenMilB-3I
❑ 86Lea-128
❑ 86OPC-223
❑ 86Spo-98
❑ 86Top-745
❑ 86TopSti-188
❑ 86TopTif-745
❑ 87BluJayFS-32
❑ 87Don-367
❑ 87DonOpeD-30
❑ 87Fle-239
❑ 87FleGlo-239
❑ 87GenMilB-1I
❑ 87Lea-231
❑ 87OPC-245
❑ 87RedFolSB-107
❑ 87SpoTeaP-5
❑ 87SyrChi1A-2
❑ 87Top-245
❑ 87TopSti-186
❑ 87TopTif-245
❑ 88BluJay5-11
❑ 88Don-271
❑ 88Fle-124
❑ 88FleGlo-124
❑ 88FleUpd-25
❑ 88FleUpdG-25
❑ 88IndGat-20
❑ 88IndTeal-36
❑ 88Lea-131
❑ 88OPC-241
❑ 88PanSti-217
❑ 88PanSti-218
❑ 88Sco-279
❑ 88ScoGlo-279
❑ 88ScoRoo-42T
❑ 88ScoRooG-42T
❑ 88Spo-214
❑ 88StaLinBJ-19
❑ 88Top-505
❑ 88TopSti-185
❑ 88TopTif-505
❑ 88TopTra-123T
❑ 88TopTraT-123T
❑ 89Don-492
❑ 89Fle-415
❑ 89FleGlo-415
❑ 89OPC-106
❑ 89PanSti-324
❑ 89Sco-188
❑ 89Top-106
❑ 89TopTif-106
❑ 89UppDec-157
❑ 92Nab-8
❑ 93BluJayDM-1
❑ 93RanKee-441
❑ 94RanMagM-38
❑ 96BluJayOH-33
❑ 97BluJayOH-35
❑ 97BluJayS-29
❑ 98BriBluM-1

Upshur, Takashi
❑ 80WauTimT-11

Upton, Jack
❑ 80QuaCitCT-16
❑ 80VenLeaS-153
❑ 82IowCubT-12

Upton, Thomas
❑ 52Top-71
❑ 83TopRep5-71

Uqueto, Jesus
❑ 92JohCitCC-9

Urban, Jack E.
❑ 56A'sPos-47

❑ 58A'sJayP-12
❑ 58Top-367
❑ 59Top-18
❑ 59TopVen-18

Urban, Jeff
❑ 98SalVol-35
❑ 99Bow-82
❑ 99BowBes-198
❑ 99BowBesAR-198
❑ 99BowBesR-198
❑ 99BowChr-82
❑ 99BowChrG-82
❑ 99BowChrGR-82
❑ 99BowChrI-82
❑ 99BowChrIR-82
❑ 99BowChrR-82
❑ 99BowGol-82
❑ 99BowInt-82
❑ 99TeaBesR-91
❑ 99TeaBesRG-91
❑ 99TeaBesRS-91
❑ 99Top-213
❑ 99TopChr-213
❑ 99TopChrR-213

Urban, Luke
❑ 92ConTSN-405

Urbanek, Jason
❑ 91MarPhiC-6
❑ 91MarPhiP-3465
❑ 92MarPhiC-11
❑ 92MarPhiF-3067

Urbani, Tom
❑ 89AncBucTI-17
❑ 90JohCitCS-27
❑ 91SprCarC-27
❑ 91SprCarP-742
❑ 92ArkTraS-48
❑ 92LouRedF-1888
❑ 92SkyAA F-21
❑ 93Bow-583
❑ 93CarStaC-15
❑ 93FleFinE-132
❑ 93LouRedF-214
❑ 94CarPol-23
❑ 94StaClu-392
❑ 94StaCluFDI-392
❑ 94StaCluGR-392
❑ 94StaCluMOP-392
❑ 94StaCluT-321
❑ 94StaCluTFDI-321
❑ 94Top-83
❑ 94TopGol-83
❑ 94TopSpa-83
❑ 95FleUpd-163
❑ 95Top-376
❑ 96CarPol-26
❑ 96LeaSigEA-204
❑ 96TigHebN-15
❑ 97OklCit8-24

Urbanski, Bill
❑ 33DelR33-9
❑ 33Gou-212
❑ 34BatR31-59
❑ 34DiaMatCSB-184
❑ 34DiaStaR-37
❑ 34ExhFou-1
❑ 34TarThoBD-25
❑ 35DiaMatCS3T1-142
❑ 36ExhFou-1
❑ 36GouWidPPR-A103
❑ 36NatChiFPR-72
❑ 36WorWidGV-71
❑ 37ExhFou-1
❑ 92ConTSN-408

Urbina, Dan
❑ 93LinVenB-106
❑ 93LinVenB-249
❑ 95LinVen-30
❑ 95VerBeaDTI-27
❑ 96-97LinVen-161
❑ 96SanBerSB-28

Urbina, Ugueth
❑ 92AlbPolCB-21
❑ 92AlbPolF-2306
❑ 92Bow-261
❑ 92ClaFS7-379
❑ 92UppDecML-297
❑ 93BurBeeC-24
❑ 93BurBeeF-159
❑ 93ExcFS7-63
❑ 93LinVenB-101
❑ 93MidLeaAGF-32
❑ 94ActPac-26
❑ 94Bow-88
❑ 94BowBes-B79
❑ 94BowBesR-B79
❑ 94Cla-44
❑ 94ClaGolF-91
❑ 94ExcFS7-229
❑ 94ExcLeaLF-19
❑ 94HarSenF-2092
❑ 94UppDecML-83
❑ 94UppDecML-264
❑ 94VenLinU-32
❑ 95Bow-146
❑ 95BowBes-B64
❑ 95BowBesR-B64
❑ 95Exc-228
❑ 95LinVen-29
❑ 95SP-9
❑ 95SPCha-14
❑ 95SPChaDC-14
❑ 95SPSil-9
❑ 95UppDec-239
❑ 95UppDecED-239
❑ 95UppDecEDG-239
❑ 95UppDecML-204
❑ 95UppDecMLFS-204
❑ 95UppDecMLOP-OP17
❑ 95UppDecSE-137
❑ 95UppDecSEG-137
❑ 95Zen-141
❑ 96-97LinVen-157
❑ 96Bow-190
❑ 96BowBes-119
❑ 96BowBesAR-119
❑ 96BowBesR-119
❑ 96BowFoi-190
❑ 96ColCho-28
❑ 96ColCho-217
❑ 96ColChoGS-28
❑ 96ColChoGS-217
❑ 96ColChoSS-28
❑ 96ColChoSS-217
❑ 96Fin-B329
❑ 96FinRef-B329
❑ 96LeaPre-139
❑ 96LeaPreP-139
❑ 96LeaSig-90
❑ 96LeaSigPPG-90
❑ 96LeaSigPPP-90
❑ 96Sco-234
❑ 97Bow-96
❑ 97BowChr-119
❑ 97BowChrI-119
❑ 97BowChrIR-119
❑ 97BowChrR-119
❑ 97BowInt-96
❑ 97Cir-62
❑ 97CirRav-62
❑ 97ColCho-166
❑ 97DonEli-123
❑ 97DonEliGS-123
❑ 97DonRatR-14
❑ 97Fle-388
❑ 97FleTif-388
❑ 97Lea-22
❑ 97LeaFraM-22
❑ 97LeaFraMDC-22
❑ 97Pac-355
❑ 97PacLigB-355
❑ 97PacSil-355
❑ 97Pin-162
❑ 97PinArtP-PP162
❑ 97PinIns-91
❑ 97PinInsCE-91
❑ 97PinInsDE-91
❑ 97PinMusC-162
❑ 97PinPrePla-162
❑ 97Sco-86
❑ 97ScoArtPWB-86
❑ 97ScoPreS-86
❑ 97ScoShoS-86
❑ 97ScoShoSAP-86
❑ 97Top-414
❑ 97Ult-234
❑ 97UltGolME-234
❑ 97UltPlaME-234
❑ 97UppDec-112
❑ 98Bow-266
❑ 98BowChr-266
❑ 98BowChrGA-266
❑ 98BowChrGAR-266
❑ 98BowChrI-266
❑ 98BowChrIR-266
❑ 98BowChrR-266
❑ 98BowGolA-266
❑ 98BowInt-266
❑ 98CirThu-90
❑ 98CirThuRav-90
❑ 98CirThuSupRav-90
❑ 98ColCho-168
❑ 98Fin-132
❑ 98FinNo--132
❑ 98FinNo-R-132
❑ 98FinRef-132
❑ 98Fle-157
❑ 98Pac-356
❑ 98PacOnl-463
❑ 98PacOnlR-463
❑ 98PacOnlWC-463
❑ 98PacPlaB-356
❑ 98PacRedT-356
❑ 98PacSil-356
❑ 98Sco-225
❑ 98StaCluFDI-289
❑ 98StaCluI-289
❑ 98StaCluOneK-289
❑ 98StaCluPP-289
❑ 98Top-396
❑ 98TopChr-396
❑ 98TopChrR-396
❑ 98TopDevR-396
❑ 98TopDia-396
❑ 98TopMiniC-396
❑ 98UppDec-441
❑ 99199Fin-179
❑ 99CroRoyB-89
❑ 99CroRoyL-89
❑ 99CroRoyOD-89
❑ 99FinGolRef-179
❑ 99FinRef-179
❑ 99Fle-223
❑ 99FleSta9-223
❑ 99FleWarT-223
❑ 99KinDis-26
❑ 99MetUni-68
❑ 99MetUniGM-68
❑ 99MetUniPMG-68
❑ 99Pac-271
❑ 99PacAur-116
❑ 99PacAurOD-116
❑ 99PacCroC-175
❑ 99PacCroCPB-175
❑ 99PacInv-93
❑ 99PacInvOD-93
❑ 99PacInvPB-93
❑ 99PacOme-147
❑ 99PacOmeC-147
❑ 99PacOmeG-147
❑ 99PacOmePB-147
❑ 99PacPar-145
❑ 99PacParC-145
❑ 99PacParG-145
❑ 99PacParHoloGold-145
❑ 99PacParHS-145
❑ 99PacParOD-145
❑ 99PacParPB-145
❑ 99PacParRed-145
❑ 99PacPlaB-271
❑ 99PacPri-90
❑ 99PacPriHB-90
❑ 99PacPriHG-90
❑ 99PacPriHM-90
❑ 99PacPriHP-90
❑ 99PacPriRed-90
❑ 99PacRed-271
❑ 99SkyPre-152
❑ 99SkyPreR-152
❑ 99SkyThu-47
❑ 99SkyThuRant-47
❑ 99SkyThuRave-47
❑ 99SPSig-153
❑ 99StaClu-273
❑ 99StaCluFDI-273
❑ 99StaCluOoaK-273
❑ 99StaCluPP-273
❑ 99ThuSkySupR-47
❑ 99Top-366
❑ 99TopChr-366
❑ 99TopChrR-366
❑ 99TopGal-94
❑ 99TopGalPP-94
❑ 99TopGalPPI-94
❑ 99TopMVPP-366
❑ 99TopSta-140
❑ 99TopStaFoil-140
❑ 99UppDec-145
❑ 99UppDecEL1-145
❑ 99UppDecEL2-145
❑ 99UppDecM-126
❑ 99UppDecMGS-126
❑ 99UppDecMHFS-126
❑ 99UppDecMSS-126
❑ 99Vic-241

Urbina, William
❑ 92HigSchPLS-3
❑ 93MadMusC-25
❑ 93MadMusF-1822
❑ 93SouOreAC-25
❑ 93SouOreAF-4063
❑ 94WesMicWC-22
❑ 94WesMicWF-2295

Urbon, Joe
❑ 89BatCliP-1933
❑ 90SpaPhiB-22
❑ 90SpaPhiP-2505
❑ 90SpaPhiS-22
❑ 91ClePhiC-25
❑ 91ClePhiP-1636

Urcioli, John
❑ 91MiaMirC-24
❑ 91MiaMirP-418

Urdaneta, Jose G.
❑ 93LinVenB-60

Uremovich, Mike
❑ 75CliPilT-16

Urena, Fausto
❑ 92GulCoaDF-3576

Uribe, Dilone
❑ 93YakBeaC-24
❑ 93YakBeaF-3886

Uribe, George
❑ 84ButCopKT-24

Uribe, Jorge
❑ 86WauTimP-26
❑ 87SalSpuS-2
❑ 88VerMarP-953
❑ 89SanBerSB-12
❑ 89SanBerSCLC-78
❑ 93LinVenB-253
❑ 94VenLinU-56
❑ 95LinVen-10
❑ 96-97LinVen-142

Uribe, Jose
❑ 85FleUpd-124
❑ 85GiaMot-13
❑ 85GiaPos-28
❑ 85TopTifT-125T
❑ 85TopTra-125T
❑ 86Don-236
❑ 86Fle-552
❑ 86GiaMot-13
❑ 86GiaPos-29
❑ 86OPC-12
❑ 86Top-12
❑ 86TopSti-87
❑ 86TopTat-13
❑ 86TopTif-12
❑ 87Don-436
❑ 87DonOpeD-99
❑ 87Fle-286
❑ 87FleGlo-286
❑ 87GiaMot-13
❑ 87GiaPos-32
❑ 87OPC-94
❑ 87Top-633
❑ 87TopTif-633
❑ 88Don-559
❑ 88DonBasB-303
❑ 88Fle-99
❑ 88FleGlo-99
❑ 88GiaMot-13
❑ 88GiaPos-32
❑ 88Lea-218
❑ 88Nes-13
❑ 88OPC-302
❑ 88PanSti-425
❑ 88Sco-165
❑ 88ScoGlo-165
❑ 88StaLinG-19
❑ 88Top-302
❑ 88TopBig-95
❑ 88TopSti-91
❑ 88TopTif-302
❑ 89Bow-471
❑ 89BowTif-471
❑ 89Don-131
❑ 89DonBasB-106
❑ 89Fle-345
❑ 89FleGlo-345
❑ 89GiaMot-13
❑ 89OPC-8
❑ 89PanSti-217
❑ 89Sco-56
❑ 89Spo-61
❑ 89Top-753
❑ 89TopBig-258
❑ 89TopSti-82
❑ 89TopTif-753
❑ 89UppDec-181
❑ 90Don-335
❑ 90DonBesN-122
❑ 90Fle-74
❑ 90FleCan-74
❑ 90GiaMot-17
❑ 90GiaSmo-20
❑ 90Lea-225
❑ 90OPC-472
❑ 90PanSti-372
❑ 90PubIntS-84
❑ 90Sco-455
❑ 90Spo-79
❑ 90Top-472
❑ 90TopBig-213
❑ 90TopTif-472
❑ 90UppDec-188
❑ 91Bow-627
❑ 91CadEllD-58
❑ 91Don-375
❑ 91Fle-275
❑ 91GiaMot-17
❑ 91GiaPacGaE-12
❑ 91GiaSFE-15
❑ 91Lea-433
❑ 91OPC-158
❑ 91PanFreS-70
❑ 91Sco-628
❑ 91StaClu-267
❑ 91Top-158
❑ 91TopDesS-158
❑ 91TopMic-158
❑ 91TopTif-158
❑ 91Ult-330
❑ 91UppDec-207
❑ 92Don-453
❑ 92Fle-649
❑ 92GiaMot-17
❑ 92GiaPacGaE-34
❑ 92OPC-538
❑ 92PanSti-215
❑ 92Sco-546
❑ 92StaClu-371
❑ 92Top-538
❑ 92TopGol-538
❑ 92TopGolW-538
❑ 92TopMic-538
❑ 92UppDec-270
❑ 93AstMot-12
❑ 93Fle-539
❑ 93PacSpa-483
❑ 93Top-201
❑ 93TopGol-201
❑ 93TopInaM-201
❑ 93TopInaR-201
❑ 93TopMic-201
❑ 93UppDec-729
❑ 93UppDecGold-729
❑ 94Fle-502
❑ 94Pac-277

Uribe, Juan
❑ 88BelBreGS-8
❑ 90StoPorB-18
❑ 90StoPorCLC-170
❑ 90StoPorP-2179

Uribe, Milciades
❑ 88WytCubP-1975
❑ 89ChaWheB-3
❑ 89ChaWheP-1744

Uribe, Relito
❑ 89DunBluJS-20

Urman, Mike
❑ 88PulBraP-1764
❑ 89SumBraP-1109

Urquhart, Derick
❑ 98VerExpO-31

Urrea, John
❑ 76ArkTraT-9
❑ 77Car5-30
❑ 77CarTeal-28
❑ 78CarTeal-37
❑ 78Top-587
❑ 79Top-429
❑ 81Don-190
❑ 81PadFamF-22
❑ 81Top-152
❑ 81TopTra-847
❑ 82Don-313
❑ 82Fle-583
❑ 82Top-28

Urrieta, Ulises
❑ 76VenLeaS-100

Urshan, Ross
❑ 92LetMouSP-9

Urso, Joe
❑ 92BoiHawC-17
❑ 93PalSprAC-24
❑ 93PalSprAF-80
❑ 94LakElsSC-24
❑ 94LakElsSF-1674
❑ 95LakElsSTI-25
❑ 95MidAngOHP-35
❑ 95MidAngTI-28
❑ 96LakElsSB-22
❑ 97BoiHawG-28
❑ 97LakElsSG-30
❑ 98LakElsSG-28

Urso, Sal (Salvy)
❑ 91PenPilC-12
❑ 91PenPilP-378
❑ 92SanBerC-23
❑ 92SanBerSF-954
❑ 94RivPilCLC-9
❑ 95PorCitRTI-24
❑ 96TacRaiB-26
❑ 97ColCliB-30
❑ 97ColCliD-29
❑ 98TreThuM-29

Usher, Bob
❑ 51Bow-286
❑ 52Top-157
❑ 57IndSoh-15
❑ 57IndTeal-24
❑ 58Top-124
❑ 83TopRep5-157

Usiyan, Thompson
❑ 82MonNew-19

Ussery, Brian
❑ 96BoiHawB-29
❑ 97BoiHawG-29

Utecht, Tim
❑ 83BelBreFr-20

Utting, Andy
❑ 98RocRedWQ-29

Utting, Ben
❑ 93AusFut-96
❑ 94IdaFalBF-3595
❑ 94IdaFalBSP-26
❑ 95DanBraTI-27
❑ 96MacBraB-20
❑ 97DurBulTI-25
❑ 98St.PauSTI-31

Uurat, Chris
❑ 96TulDriTI-27

Vaccaro, Sal
❑ 86JamExpP-27
❑ 87BurExpP-1072
❑ 87SanJosBP-4

Vael, Robert
❑ 97WatIndTI-32
❑ 98WatIndTI-34

Vagg, Richard
❑ 90IBAWorA-42
❑ 90IBAWorA-49
❑ 91MelBusF-11
❑ 95AusFut-83

Vail, Michael
❑ 74MetTeal-25
❑ 75TidTidTI-23
❑ 76Hos-55
❑ 76HosTwi-55
❑ 76OPC-655
❑ 76SSP-534
❑ 76Top-655
❑ 77MetDaiPA-27
❑ 77Top-246
❑ 78Top-69
❑ 79Top-663
❑ 80OPC-180
❑ 80Top-343
❑ 81Don-554A
❑ 81Don-554B
❑ 81Fle-311
❑ 81Top-471
❑ 81TopTra-848
❑ 82Fle-84
❑ 82RedCok-22
❑ 82Top-194
❑ 83Don-597
❑ 83ExpPos-32
❑ 83Fle-605
❑ 83GiaMot-19
❑ 83Top-554
❑ 83TopTra-119T
❑ 84ExpPos-33
❑ 84Fle-290
❑ 84FleUpd-122
❑ 84Nes792-766
❑ 84OPC-143
❑ 84Top-766
❑ 84TopTif-766
❑ 84TopTra-124T
❑ 84TopTraT-124T
❑ 89TidTidC-6
❑ 90DodTar-812
❑ 91MetWIZ-417

Vaji, Mark
❑ 81QuaCitCT-24
Valandia, Jorge
❑ 93NiaFalRF-3399
Valazquez, Fred
❑ 71RicBraTI-17
Valderrama, Carlos
❑ 97SalVolG-38
Valdes, David
❑ 94YakBeaC-27
Valdes, Ismael
❑ 94LeaLimR-43
❑ 95ColCho-223
❑ 95ColChoGS-223
❑ 95ColChoSS-223
❑ 95DodMot-23
❑ 95DodPol-26
❑ 95Don-29
❑ 95DonPreP-29
❑ 95DonTopotO-273
❑ 95Emo-146
❑ 95Fin-316
❑ 95FinRef-316
❑ 95Fla-157
❑ 95Fle-550
❑ 95Lea-13
❑ 95Pac-226
❑ 95PacLatD-35
❑ 95Pin-139
❑ 95PinArtP-139
❑ 95PinMusC-139
❑ 95Sco-272
❑ 95ScoGolR-272
❑ 95ScoPlaTS-272
❑ 95SelCer-99
❑ 95SelCerMG-99
❑ 95StaClu-161
❑ 95StaCluFDI-161
❑ 95StaCluMOP-161
❑ 95StaCluSTWS-161
❑ 95StaCluVR-85
❑ 95StaCluVRMO-85
❑ 95Sum21C-TC8
❑ 95Top-66
❑ 95TopCyb-48
❑ 95Ult-400
❑ 95UltGolM-400
❑ 95UppDec-323
❑ 95UppDecED-323
❑ 95UppDecEDG-323
❑ 95UppDecSE-171
❑ 95UppDecSEG-171
❑ 96ColCho-588
❑ 96ColChoGS-588
❑ 96ColChoSS-588
❑ 96DodFle-17
❑ 96DodMot-11
❑ 96DodPol-29
❑ 96Don-318
❑ 96DonPreP-318
❑ 96EmoXL-216
❑ 96Fla-299
❑ 96Fle-448
❑ 96FleTif-448
❑ 96Lea-184
❑ 96LeaLim-87
❑ 96LeaLimG-87
❑ 96LeaPre-101
❑ 96LeaPreP-101
❑ 96LeaPrePB-184
❑ 96LeaPrePG-184
❑ 96LeaPrePS-184
❑ 96LeaSig-65
❑ 96LeaSigA-225
❑ 96LeaSigAG-226
❑ 96LeaSigAS-226
❑ 96LeaSigPPG-65
❑ 96LeaSigPPP-65
❑ 96Pac-108
❑ 96PacEstL-EL32
❑ 96PacPri-P39
❑ 96PacPriG-P39
❑ 96Pin-296
❑ 96PinFoil-296
❑ 96Sco-137
❑ 96ScoDugC-A86
❑ 96ScoDugCAP-A86
❑ 96Sel-34
❑ 96SelArtP-34
❑ 96SelCer-52
❑ 96SelCerAP-52
❑ 96SelCerCB-52
❑ 96SelCerCR-52
❑ 96SelCerIP-22
❑ 96SelCerMB-52
❑ 96SelCerMG-52
❑ 96SelCerMR-52
❑ 96SP-104
❑ 96StaClu-348
❑ 96StaCluEPB-348
❑ 96StaCluEPG-348
❑ 96StaCluEPS-348
❑ 96StaCluMOP-348
❑ 96Stu-103
❑ 96StuPrePB-103
❑ 96StuPrePG-103
❑ 96StuPrePS-103
❑ 96Top-324
❑ 96TopChr-128
❑ 96TopChrR-128
❑ 96TopGal-124
❑ 96TopGalPPI-124
❑ 96TopLas-128
❑ 96Ult-226
❑ 96UltGolM-226
❑ 96UppDec-96
❑ 96Zen-33
❑ 96ZenArtP-33
❑ 97Cir-212
❑ 97CirRav-212
❑ 97ColCho-142
❑ 97ColChoT-LA6
❑ 97DodMot-11
❑ 97DodPol-27
❑ 97DodSco-1
❑ 97DodScoPI-1
❑ 97DodScoPr-1
❑ 97Don-79
❑ 97DonGolPP-79
❑ 97DonLim-104
❑ 97DonLimE-104
❑ 97DonLimENG-104
❑ 97DonPre-129
❑ 97DonPreCttC-129
❑ 97DonSilPP-79
❑ 97DonTea-109
❑ 97DonTeaSPE-109
❑ 97Fin-264
❑ 97FinRef-264
❑ 97FlaShoLC-158
❑ 97FlaShoLeg0-158
❑ 97FlaShoLeg1-158
❑ 97FlaShoM-A158
❑ 97FlaShoM-B158
❑ 97FlaShoM-C158
❑ 97FlaShoR0-158
❑ 97FlaShoR1-158
❑ 97FlaShoR2-158
❑ 97Fle-372
❑ 97FleTif-372
❑ 97Lea-145
❑ 97LeaFraM-145
❑ 97LeaFraMDC-145
❑ 97MetUni-106
❑ 97NewPin-95
❑ 97NewPinAP-95
❑ 97NewPinMC-95
❑ 97NewPinPP-95
❑ 97Pac-340
❑ 97PacLatotML-30
❑ 97PacLigB-340
❑ 97PacPri-116
❑ 97PacPriLB-116
❑ 97PacPriP-116
❑ 97PacSil-340
❑ 97PinCar-8
❑ 97Sco-16
❑ 97ScoArtPWB-16
❑ 97ScoPreS-16
❑ 97ScoShoS-16
❑ 97ScoShoSAP-16
❑ 97StaClu-141
❑ 97StaCluMOP-141
❑ 97Top-166
❑ 97TopGal-96
❑ 97TopGalPPI-96
❑ 97Ult-224
❑ 97UltGolME-224
❑ 97UltPlaME-224
❑ 97UppDec-93
❑ 98CirThu-80
❑ 98CirThuRav-80
❑ 98CirThuSupRav-80
❑ 98ColCho-398
❑ 98DodMot-11
❑ 98DodPol-26
❑ 98DodSco-11
❑ 98DodScoP-11
❑ 98Don-49
❑ 98DonCol-49
❑ 98DonColL-319
❑ 98DonColP-639
❑ 98DonColS-49
❑ 98DonGolPP-49
❑ 98DonPre-89
❑ 98DonPreSeat-89
❑ 98DonPriCD-49
❑ 98DonPriCL-319
❑ 98DonPriCP-639
❑ 98DonSigA-87
❑ 98DonSigAC-109
❑ 98DonSigAM-112
❑ 98DonSilPP-49
❑ 98Fin-96
❑ 98FinNo--96
❑ 98FinNo-R-96
❑ 98FinRef-96
❑ 98Fle-288
❑ 98Lea-120
❑ 98LeaFraDA-120
❑ 98LeaFraF-120
❑ 98LeaFraM-120
❑ 98LeaFraM-120
❑ 98LeaFraMDC-120
❑ 98LeaFraMDC-120
❑ 98LeaFraMZ2-120
❑ 98MetUni-68
❑ 98MetUniPMG-68
❑ 98Pac-341
❑ 98PacLatotML-20
❑ 98PacNes-1B
❑ 98PacOme-129
❑ 98PacOmeR-129
❑ 98PacOnl-386
❑ 98PacOnlR-386
❑ 98PacOnlWC-386
❑ 98PacPar-182
❑ 98PacParC-182
❑ 98PacParG-182
❑ 98PacParHS-182
❑ 98PacParPB-182
❑ 98PacParR-182
❑ 98PacPlaB-341
❑ 98PacRedT-341
❑ 98PacSil-341
❑ 98PinPlu-99
❑ 98PinSna-LAD10
❑ 98Sco-165
❑ 98ScoRT-79
❑ 98ScoSS-PP71
❑ 98ScoSSAP-PP71
❑ 98StaCluFDI-175
❑ 98StaCluI-175
❑ 98StaCluOneK-175
❑ 98StaCluPP-175
❑ 98Stu-120
❑ 98StuGPP-120
❑ 98StuSPP-120
❑ 98Top-357
❑ 98TopChr-357
❑ 98TopChrR-357
❑ 98TopDevR-357
❑ 98TopDia-357
❑ 98TopMiniC-357
❑ 98Ult-64
❑ 98UltGolM-64
❑ 98UltMas-64
❑ 98UltPlaM-64
❑ 98UppDec-402
❑ 99DodPol-25
❑ 99Fle-272
❑ 99FleSta9-272
❑ 99FleWarT-272
❑ 99MetUni-152
❑ 99MetUniGM-152
❑ 99MetUniPMG-152
❑ 99PacCroC-146
❑ 99PacCroCPB-146
❑ 99SkyPre-203
❑ 99SkyPreR-203
❑ 99SkyThu-68
❑ 99SkyThuRant-68
❑ 99SkyThuRave-68
❑ 99StaClu-251
❑ 99StaCluFDI-251
❑ 99StaCluOoaK-251
❑ 99StaCluPP-251
❑ 99ThuSkySupR-68
❑ 99Top-182
❑ 99TopChr-182
❑ 99TopChrR-182
❑ 99TopMVPP-182
❑ 99Ult-159
❑ 99UltGolM-159
❑ 99UltMas-159
❑ 99UltPlaM-159
❑ 99UppDec-239
❑ 99UppDec-403
❑ 99UppDecEL1-239
❑ 99UppDecEL1-403
❑ 99UppDecEL2-239
❑ 99UppDecEL2-403
❑ 99Vic-199
Valdes, Marc
❑ 92TopTra-121T
❑ 92TopTraG-121T
❑ 93StaCluM-20
❑ 94Bow-646
❑ 94BowBes-B35
❑ 94BowBesR-B35
❑ 94Cla-177
❑ 94ClaGolF-119
❑ 94ClaGolN1PLF-LP15
❑ 94ClaGolREF-RE15
❑ 94KanCouCC-1
❑ 94KanCouCF-161
❑ 94KanCouCTI-28
❑ 94Pin-431
❑ 94PinArtP-431
❑ 94PinMusC-431
❑ 94Sco-555
❑ 94ScoGolR-555
❑ 94Top-750
❑ 94TopGol-750
❑ 94TopSpa-750
❑ 95Bow-266
❑ 95BowBes-B78
❑ 95BowBesR-B78
❑ 95BowGolF-266
❑ 95ChaKniTI-27
❑ 95Exc-198
❑ 95KanCouCLTI-14
❑ 95Top-649
❑ 95UppDecML-86
❑ 95UppDecMLFS-86
❑ 96ChaKniB-27
❑ 96ColCho-553
❑ 96ColChoGS-553
❑ 96ColChoSS-553
❑ 96Fle-396
❑ 96FleTif-396
❑ 96Top-433
❑ 97Fle-618
❑ 97FleTif-618
❑ 98Don-188
❑ 98DonGolPP-188
❑ 98DonSilPP-188
❑ 98Pac-357
❑ 98PacOnl-464
❑ 98PacOnlR-464
❑ 98PacOnlWC-464
❑ 98PacPlaB-357
❑ 98PacRedT-357
❑ 98PacSil-357
❑ 98PorSeaD5AQ-29
Valdes, Pedro
❑ 95Bes-58
❑ 95OrlCubF-24
❑ 96BesAutSA-80
❑ 96Exc-143
❑ 96IowCubB-28
❑ 97Fle-288
❑ 97FleTif-288
❑ 97IowCub-27
❑ 97Pac-260
❑ 97PacLigB-260
❑ 97PacSil-260
❑ 97Ult-172
❑ 97UltGolME-172
❑ 97UltPlaME-172
❑ 98IowCubQ-26
❑ 99Pac-93
❑ 99PacPlaB-93
❑ 99PacRed-93
Valdes, Ramon
❑ 88GreFalDTI-25
Valdes, Rene
❑ 49PorBeaP-4
❑ 57Top-337
❑ 59O'KAleMR-22
❑ 61UniOil-SP11
❑ 90DodTar-813
Valdespino, Sandy
❑ 65OPC-201
❑ 65Top-201
❑ 66OPC-56
❑ 66Top-56
❑ 66TopVen-56
❑ 66TwiFaiG-15
❑ 67CokCapTw-12
❑ 67DexPre-212
❑ 67TwiTeal-23
❑ 68Top-304
❑ 68TopVen-304
❑ 69MilBra-281
❑ 70BreMcD-30
❑ 76ForLauYS-30
❑ 77WesHavYT-23
❑ 78TwiFri-48
❑ 81TCM60I-329
❑ 85RocRedWT-25
❑ 87AstShoSTw-18
❑ 94BreMilB-82
Valdez, Amilcar
❑ 88BakDodCLC-241
❑ 88BlaYNPRWL-177
Valdez, Angel
❑ 82MiaMarT-17
Valdez, Carlos
❑ 92EveGiaF-1691
❑ 93CliGiaC-23
❑ 93CliGiaF-2490
❑ 94SanJosGC-23
❑ 94SanJosGF-2817
❑ 96PhoFirB-25
❑ 97PawRedS-26
❑ 98PawRedSQ-27
Valdez, Doug
❑ 94ButCopKSP-24
Valdez, Efrain
❑ 88TulDriTI-5
❑ 89CanIndB-6
❑ 89CanIndP-1311
❑ 89CanIndS-22
❑ 90CMC-456
❑ 90ColSprSSC-4
❑ 90ColSprSSP-35
❑ 90ProAAAF-216
❑ 91Bow-60
❑ 91ColSprSSLD-96
❑ 91ColSprSSP-2183
❑ 91LinDriAAA-96
❑ 91OPC-692
❑ 91Sco-723
❑ 91StaClu-483
❑ 91Top-692A
❑ 91Top-692B
❑ 91TopDeb90-156
❑ 91TopDesS-692
❑ 91TopMic-692
❑ 91TopTif-692
❑ 92DenZepF-2640
❑ 92DenZepS-146
❑ 92StaClu-838
❑ 93LimRocDWB-70
❑ 98NorTidP-27
Valdez, Frank (Francisco)
❑ 88KenTwiP-1393
❑ 89GasRanP-1020
❑ 89GasRanS-23
❑ 89SouAtlLAGS-40
❑ 89VisOakCLC-108
❑ 89VisOakP-1440
❑ 90CMC-722
❑ 90OrlSunRB-14
❑ 90OrlSunRP-1094
❑ 90OrlSunRS-21
❑ 91LinDriAA-479
❑ 91OrlSunRLD-479
❑ 91OrlSunRP-1864
Valdez, Ismael
❑ 91KisDodP-4186
❑ 94SanAntMF-2470
❑ 95StaCluSTDW-D161
Valdez, Jerry
❑ 98BatMucTI-30
Valdez, Jose
❑ 83PeoSunF-12
❑ 90KisDodD-27
Valdez, Julio
❑ 81PawRedST-17
❑ 82Don-560
❑ 82Top-381
❑ 83Fle-199
❑ 83Top-628
❑ 85DomLeaS-202
❑ 85IowCubT-7
❑ 86IowCubP-25
❑ 86StaoftFT-7
❑ 87IowCubTI-17
❑ 88PitCubP-1357
❑ 88WytCubP-1988
Valdez, Ken
❑ 92BriTigF-1430
❑ 93BriTigC-23
❑ 93BriTigF-3655
❑ 95BoiHawTI-29
Valdez, Mario
❑ 96HicCraB-25
❑ 96MidLeaAB-56
❑ 96SouBenSHS-26
❑ 97Fle-753
❑ 97FleTif-753
❑ 98Bow-199
❑ 98BowChr-199
❑ 98BowChrGA-199
❑ 98BowChrGAR-199
❑ 98BowChrI-199
❑ 98BowChrIR-199
❑ 98BowChrR-199
❑ 98BowGolA-199
❑ 98BowInt-199
❑ 98ColCho-116
❑ 98Don-254
❑ 98DonGolPP-254
❑ 98DonSilPP-254
❑ 98Fle-184
❑ 98LeaRS-235
❑ 98LeaRSLHolo-235
❑ 98LeaRSLong-235
❑ 98LeaRTrue-235
❑ 98Pac-64
❑ 98PacInvGems-36
❑ 98PacPlaB-64
❑ 98PacRedT-64
❑ 98PacSil-64
❑ 98ScoRT-243
❑ 98ScoRTSS-PP136
❑ 98ScoRTSSAP-PP136
❑ 98ScoRTSSAP1-PP136
❑ 98StaCluFDI-218
❑ 98StaCluI-218
❑ 98StaCluOneK-218
❑ 98StaCluPP-218
❑ 98Stu-26
❑ 98StuGPP-26
❑ 98StuSPP-26
❑ 98Ult-361
❑ 98UltGolM-361
❑ 98UltMas-361
❑ 98UltPlaM-361
❑ 98UppDec-269
❑ 98UppDecSF-148
❑ 99SP SigAuto-MV
❑ 99SPSig-102
Valdez, Mica
❑ 90SanAntMGS-28
Valdez, Miguel
❑ 80ElmPioRST-44
❑ 93IdaFalBF-4049
❑ 93IdaFalBSP-9
❑ 94DanBraC-29
❑ 94DanBraF-3547
❑ 94MacBraC-24
❑ 94MacBraF-2221
Valdez, Pedro
❑ 91HunCubC-27
❑ 91HunCubP-3351
❑ 92GenCubC-1
❑ 92GenCubF-1575
❑ 92PeoChiC-21
❑ 93MidLeaAGF-44
❑ 93PeoChiC-1
❑ 93PeoChiF-1097
❑ 93PeoChiTI-30
❑ 94ClaGolF-53
❑ 94OrlCubF-1400
Valdez, Rafael
❑ 87ChaRaiP-15
❑ 88ChaRaiP-1201
❑ 89RivRedWB-18
❑ 89RivRedWCLC-4
❑ 89RivRedWP-1398
❑ 89WicChaR-16
❑ 89WicUpdR-10
❑ 90Bow-210
❑ 90BowTif-210
❑ 90CMC-523
❑ 90FleUpd-58
❑ 90LasVegSC-20
❑ 90LasVegSP-125
❑ 90ProAAAF-13
❑ 90ScoRoo-93T
❑ 90UppDec-775
❑ 91Bow-663
❑ 91LasVegSP-236
❑ 91Sco-360
❑ 91Sco100RS-31
❑ 91TopDeb90-157
❑ 91UppDec-253
❑ 92LasVegSF-2797
❑ 93LimRocDWB-67
Valdez, Ramon
❑ 89BlaYNPRWL-18
❑ 89PriPirS-22

Valdez, Sergio
❑ 85UtiBluST-7
❑ 87IndIndTI-21
❑ 88IndIndC-8
❑ 88IndIndP-501
❑ 89IndIndC-2
❑ 89IndIndP-1215
❑ 90Don-405A
❑ 90Don-405B
❑ 90IndTeal-41
❑ 90Lea-496
❑ 90OPC-199
❑ 90Top-199
❑ 90TopTif-199
❑ 91ColSprSSLD-97
❑ 91ColSprSSP-2184
❑ 91Don-344
❑ 91Fle-380
❑ 91LinDriAAA-97
❑ 91OPC-98
❑ 91Top-98
❑ 91TopDesS-98
❑ 91TopMic-98
❑ 91TopTif-98
❑ 92IndIndF-1859
❑ 92IndIndS-196
❑ 92StaClu-789
❑ 93Fle-465
❑ 93LimRocDWB-15
❑ 93OttLynF-2436
❑ 93StaClu-171
❑ 93StaCluFDI-171
❑ 93StaCluMOP-171
❑ 94PawRedSDD-27
❑ 94SarRedSC-28
❑ 94SarRedSF-1952
❑ 95Pac-47
❑ 95PhoFirTI-34
❑ 96ColCho-716
❑ 96ColChoGS-716
❑ 96ColChoSS-716
❑ 96Don-57
❑ 96DonPreP-57
❑ 96Fle-598
❑ 96FleTif-598

Valdez, Sylverio
❑ 80UtiBluJT-8
❑ 83AndBraT-18

Valdez, Trovin
❑ 94AlbPolF-2252
❑ 94BluOriC-21
❑ 94BluOriF-3577
❑ 97BurBeeB-24
❑ 98JupHamQ-25

Valdez, Victor
❑ 93AshTouC-21
❑ 93AshTouF-2276

Valdivielso, Jose
❑ 55DonWin-40
❑ 56Top-237
❑ 57Top-246
❑ 59SenTealW-17
❑ 60Top-527
❑ 61Top-557
❑ 61TwiCloD-29
❑ 61TwiJayP-11
❑ 61TwiPetM-25
❑ 62Top-339

Valeandia, Jorge
❑ 92BriTigC-22

Valencia, Gil
❑ 89MarPhiS-31
❑ 90BatCliP-3083
❑ 90SpaPhiB-23
❑ 90SpaPhiP-2506
❑ 90SpaPhiS-23

Valencia, Jose
❑ 17Zee-120
❑ 88SumBraP-399

Valencia, Ralph
❑ 18Zee-16

Valencia, Victor
❑ 97GreBatB-29
❑ 98TamYanM-29
❑ 99Bow-149
❑ 99BowChr-149
❑ 99BowChrG-149
❑ 99BowChrGR-149
❑ 99BowChrI-149
❑ 99BowChrIR-149
❑ 99BowChrR-149
❑ 99BowGol-149
❑ 99BowInt-149

Valennia, Max
❑ 92BoiHawC-2

Valent, Eric
❑ 97UCLBruTI-24
❑ 98ClePhiUM-2
❑ 98ClePhiUM-23
❑ 99199Fin-296
❑ 99BasAmeTPA-44
❑ 99Bow-113
❑ 99BowBes-177
❑ 99BowBesAR-177
❑ 99BowBesR-177
❑ 99BowChr-113
❑ 99BowChrG-113
❑ 99BowChrGR-113
❑ 99BowChrI-113
❑ 99BowChrIR-113
❑ 99BowChrR-113
❑ 99BowGol-113
❑ 99BowInt-113
❑ 99FinGolRef-296
❑ 99FinRef-296
❑ 99StaClu-155
❑ 99StaCluFDI-155
❑ 99StaCluOoaK-155
❑ 99StaCluPP-155
❑ 99TeaBesR-92
❑ 99TeaBesRA-24
❑ 99TeaBesRFS-16
❑ 99TeaBesRG-92
❑ 99TeaBesRS-92
❑ 99Top-444
❑ 99TopChr-444
❑ 99TopChrR-444
❑ 99TopMVPP-444

Valent, Royce
❑ 97UCLBruTI-25

Valente, John
❑ 88CapCodPPaLP-2

Valenti, Jon
❑ 96WesMicWB-27
❑ 97ModA'sG-28

Valentin, Eddy
❑ 89AubAstP-2160

Valentin, Javier (Jose Javier)
❑ 94EliTwiC-24
❑ 94EliTwiF-3736
❑ 95ForWayWTI-15
❑ 96BesAutS-90
❑ 96Bow-311
❑ 96BowBes-151
❑ 96BowBesAR-151
❑ 96BowBesMI-8
❑ 96BowBesMIAR-8
❑ 96BowBesMIR-8
❑ 96BowBesR-151
❑ 96BowFoi-311
❑ 97Bow-116
❑ 97BowBes-143
❑ 97BowBesAR-143
❑ 97BowBesR-143
❑ 97BowChr-134
❑ 97BowChrI-134
❑ 97BowChrIR-134
❑ 97BowChrR-134
❑ 97BowInt-116
❑ 97Don-389
❑ 97DonGolPP-389
❑ 97DonSigA-100
❑ 97DonSigAC-125
❑ 97DonSigAM-125
❑ 97DonSilPP-389
❑ 97EasLeaTPB-15
❑ 97NewBriRC-26
❑ 97Top-4
❑ 98ColCho-119
❑ 98Don-253
❑ 98DonGolPP-253
❑ 98DonSilPP-253
❑ 98Fle-59
❑ 98LeaRS-253
❑ 98LeaRSLHolo-253
❑ 98LeaRSLong-253
❑ 98LeaRTrue-253
❑ 98Pac-143
❑ 98PacOmeRS-23
❑ 98PacOmeRST2-23
❑ 98PacOnl-440
❑ 98PacOnlR-440
❑ 98PacOnlWC-440
❑ 98PacPlaB-143
❑ 98PacRedT-143
❑ 98PacSil-143
❑ 98PinPer-131
❑ 98PinPerPP-131
❑ 98ScoRT-160
❑ 98ScoRTSS-PP91
❑ 98ScoRTSSAP-PP91
❑ 98ScoRTSSAP1-PP91
❑ 99PacPar-138
❑ 99PacParC-138
❑ 99PacParG-138
❑ 99PacParHoloGold-138
❑ 99PacParHS-138
❑ 99PacParOD-138
❑ 99PacParPB-138
❑ 99PacParRed-138
❑ 99StaClu-277
❑ 99StaCluFDI-277
❑ 99StaCluOoaK-277
❑ 99StaCluPP-277
❑ 99Top-104
❑ 99TopChr-104
❑ 99TopChrR-104
❑ 99TopMVPP-104

Valentin, John
❑ 88BlaYNPRWL-178
❑ 88CapCodPB-11
❑ 88CapCodPPaLP-138
❑ 89WinHavRSS-25
❑ 90Bes-283
❑ 90NewBriRSB-21
❑ 90NewBriRSS-19
❑ 91LinDriAA-473
❑ 91NewBriRSLD-473
❑ 91NewBriRSP-361
❑ 91PawRedSDD-25
❑ 92DonRooP-BC19
❑ 92FleUpd-4
❑ 92PawRedSF-933
❑ 92PawRedSS-370
❑ 92SkyAAAF-169
❑ 93Bow-690
❑ 93DenHol-21
❑ 93Don-251
❑ 93Fle-183
❑ 93Lea-87
❑ 93OPC-220
❑ 93PacSpa-363
❑ 93Pin-224
❑ 93Pin-482
❑ 93RedSoxP-30
❑ 93RedSoxWHP-26
❑ 93Sco-243
❑ 93Sel-344
❑ 93StaClu-508
❑ 93StaCluFDI-508
❑ 93StaCluMOP-508
❑ 93Top-424
❑ 93TopGol-424
❑ 93TopInaM-424
❑ 93TopInaR-424
❑ 93TopMic-424
❑ 93Toy-10
❑ 93UppDec-387
❑ 93UppDecGold-387
❑ 94ColC-278
❑ 94ColChoGS-278
❑ 94ColChoSS-278
❑ 94Don-517
❑ 94Fin-128
❑ 94FinRef-128
❑ 94Fla-16
❑ 94Fle-44
❑ 94FleExtB-26
❑ 94Lea-77
❑ 94Pac-67
❑ 94PanSti-33
❑ 94Pin-126
❑ 94PinArtP-126
❑ 94PinMusC-126
❑ 94Sco-417
❑ 94ScoGolR-417
❑ 94Sel-49
❑ 94StaClu-483
❑ 94StaCluFDI-483
❑ 94StaCluGR-483
❑ 94StaCluMOP-483
❑ 94StaCluMOP-ST16
❑ 94StaCluST-ST16
❑ 94Stu-165
❑ 94Top-568
❑ 94TopGol-568
❑ 94TopSpa-568
❑ 94TriPla-208
❑ 94Ult-318
❑ 94UppDec-373
❑ 94UppDecED-373
❑ 95ColCho-409
❑ 95ColChoGS-409
❑ 95ColChoSE-189
❑ 95ColChoSE-265
❑ 95ColChoSEGS-189
❑ 95ColChoSEGS-265
❑ 95ColChoSESS-189
❑ 95ColChoSESS-265
❑ 95ColChoSS-409
❑ 95Don-89
❑ 95DonPreP-89
❑ 95DonTopotO-28
❑ 95Emo-16
❑ 95Fin-53
❑ 95FinRef-53
❑ 95Fla-14
❑ 95Fle-41
❑ 95Lea-12
❑ 95LeaLim-89
❑ 95Pac-48
❑ 95Pin-75
❑ 95PinArtP-75
❑ 95PinMusC-75
❑ 95Sco-8
❑ 95Sco-314
❑ 95ScoGolR-8
❑ 95ScoGolR-314
❑ 95ScoPlaTS-8
❑ 95ScoPlaTS-314
❑ 95Sel-98
❑ 95SelArtP-98
❑ 95SP-128
❑ 95SPCha-124
❑ 95SPChaDC-124
❑ 95Spo-88
❑ 95SpoArtP-88
❑ 95SPSil-128
❑ 95StaClu-62
❑ 95StaCluFDI-62
❑ 95StaCluMOP-62
❑ 95StaCluSTDW-RS1T
❑ 95StaCluSTDW-RS62
❑ 95StaCluSTWS-62
❑ 95StaCluVR-38
❑ 95StaCluVRMO-38
❑ 95Stu-164
❑ 95Sum-145
❑ 95SumNthD-145
❑ 95Top-36
❑ 95TopCyb-28
❑ 95TopEmb-10
❑ 95TopEmbGI-10
❑ 95UC3-10
❑ 95UC3ArtP-10
❑ 95Ult-16
❑ 95UltGolM-16
❑ 95UppDec-163
❑ 95UppDecC-3A
❑ 95UppDecED-163
❑ 95UppDecEDG-163
❑ 95Zen-54
❑ 96Baz-120
❑ 96Bow-96
❑ 96BowBes-88
❑ 96BowBesAR-88
❑ 96BowBesR-88
❑ 96BowFoi-96
❑ 96Cir-13
❑ 96CirRav-13
❑ 96ColCho-471
❑ 96ColChoGS-471
❑ 96ColChoSS-471
❑ 96Don-83
❑ 96DonPreP-83
❑ 96EmoXL-19
❑ 96Fin-S91
❑ 96FinRef-S91
❑ 96Fla-28
❑ 96Fle-37
❑ 96FleRedS-16
❑ 96FleTif-37
❑ 96Lea-166
❑ 96LeaPre-109
❑ 96LeaPreP-109
❑ 96LeaPrePB-166
❑ 96LeaPrePG-166
❑ 96LeaPrePS-166
❑ 96MetUni-20
❑ 96MetUniP-20
❑ 96Pac-255
❑ 96PacEstL-EL10
❑ 96PacPri-P80
❑ 96PacPriG-P80
❑ 96PanSti-141
❑ 96Pin-84
❑ 96PinAfi-140
❑ 96PinAfiAP-140
❑ 96ProSta-109
❑ 96Sco-33
❑ 96ScoDugC-A32
❑ 96ScoDugCAP-A32
❑ 96Sel-126
❑ 96SelArtP-126
❑ 96SelCer-34
❑ 96SelCerAP-34
❑ 96SelCerCB-34
❑ 96SelCerCR-34
❑ 96SelCerMB-34
❑ 96SelCerMG-34
❑ 96SelCerMR-34
❑ 96Spo-71
❑ 96SpoArtP-71
❑ 96StaClu-196
❑ 96StaClu-376
❑ 96StaCluB&B-BB10
❑ 96StaCluMO-42
❑ 96StaCluMOP-196
❑ 96StaCluMOP-376
❑ 96StaCluMOP-BB10
❑ 96Stu-25
❑ 96StuPrePB-25
❑ 96StuPrePG-25
❑ 96StuPrePS-25
❑ 96Sum-140
❑ 96SumAbo&B-140
❑ 96SumArtP-140
❑ 96SumFoi-140
❑ 96Top-164
❑ 96TopChr-46
❑ 96TopChrR-46
❑ 96TopGal-12
❑ 96TopGalPPI-12
❑ 96TopLas-93
❑ 96TopRoaW-RW17
❑ 96Ult-21
❑ 96UltGolM-21
❑ 96UppDec-25
❑ 96Zen-86
❑ 96ZenArtP-86
❑ 96ZenMoz-9
❑ 97Bow-19
❑ 97BowBes-37
❑ 97BowBesAR-37
❑ 97BowBesR-37
❑ 97BowChr-15
❑ 97BowChrI-15
❑ 97BowChrIR-15
❑ 97BowChrR-15
❑ 97BowInt-19
❑ 97Cir-233
❑ 97CirRav-233
❑ 97ColCho-280
❑ 97Don-163
❑ 97DonGolPP-163
❑ 97DonSilPP-163
❑ 97DonTea-49
❑ 97DonTeaSPE-49
❑ 97DunDonPPS-26
❑ 97Fin-251
❑ 97FinRef-251
❑ 97Fle-31
❑ 97FleTif-31
❑ 97Lea-167
❑ 97LeaFraM-167
❑ 97LeaFraMDC-167
❑ 97MetUni-25
❑ 97NewPin-96
❑ 97NewPinAP-96
❑ 97NewPinMC-96
❑ 97NewPinPP-96
❑ 97Pac-47
❑ 97PacLigB-47
❑ 97PacSil-47
❑ 97RedSoxS-3
❑ 97RedSoxSPl-3
❑ 97RedSoxSPr-3
❑ 97Sco-101
❑ 97ScoArtPWB-101
❑ 97ScoPreS-101
❑ 97ScoShoS-101
❑ 97ScoShoSAP-101
❑ 97SpoIII-141
❑ 97SpoIIIEE-141
❑ 97StaClu-241
❑ 97StaCluMat-241
❑ 97StaCluMOP-241
❑ 97Top-134
❑ 97TopChr-51
❑ 97TopChrR-51
❑ 97TopGal-128
❑ 97TopGalPPI-128
❑ 97Ult-401
❑ 97UltGolME-401
❑ 97UltPlaME-401
❑ 97UppDec-309
❑ 98Bow-254
❑ 98BowBes-52
❑ 98BowBesAR-52
❑ 98BowBesR-52
❑ 98BowChr-254
❑ 98BowChrGA-254
❑ 98BowChrGAR-254
❑ 98BowChrI-254
❑ 98BowChrIR-254
❑ 98BowChrR-254
❑ 98BowGolA-254
❑ 98BowInt-254
❑ 98CirThu-291
❑ 98CirThuRav-291
❑ 98CirThuSupRav-291
❑ 98ColCho-326
❑ 98Don-47
❑ 98DonCol-47
❑ 98DonColL-266
❑ 98DonColS-47
❑ 98DonGolPP-47
❑ 98DonPriCD-47
❑ 98DonPriCL-266
❑ 98DonSilPP-47
❑ 98Fin-115
❑ 98FinNo--115
❑ 98FinNo-R-115
❑ 98FinRef-115
❑ 98Fle-133
❑ 98Lea-67
❑ 98LeaFraDA-67
❑ 98LeaFraF-67
❑ 98LeaFraM-67
❑ 98LeaFraM-67
❑ 98LeaFraMDC-67
❑ 98LeaFraMDC-67
❑ 98LeaFraMZ2-67
❑ 98Pac-48
❑ 98PacAur-19
❑ 98PacInv-15
❑ 98PacInvPBlue-15
❑ 98PacInvSilv-15
❑ 98PacInvTeam-4
❑ 98PacOme-42
❑ 98PacOmeR-42
❑ 98PacOnl-128
❑ 98PacOnlR-128
❑ 98PacOnlWC-128
❑ 98PacPar-24
❑ 98PacParC-24
❑ 98PacParG-24
❑ 98PacParHS-24
❑ 98PacParPB-24
❑ 98PacParR-24
❑ 98PacPlaB-48
❑ 98PacRedT-48
❑ 98PacSil-48
❑ 98Pin-75
❑ 98PinPreP-75
❑ 98PinSna-BRS14
❑ 98RedSoxS-10
❑ 98RedSoxSP-10
❑ 98Sco-175
❑ 98ScoRT-96
❑ 98ScoSS-PP77
❑ 98ScoSSAP-PP77
❑ 98SP Aut-58
❑ 98SPxFin-67
❑ 98SPxFinR-67
❑ 98SPxFinS-67
❑ 98StaCluFDI-193
❑ 98StaCluI-193
❑ 98StaCluOneK-193
❑ 98StaCluPP-193
❑ 98Stu-208
❑ 98StuGPP-208
❑ 98StuSPP-208
❑ 98Top-452
❑ 98TopChr-452
❑ 98TopChrR-452
❑ 98TopDevR-452
❑ 98TopDia-452
❑ 98TopGal-108
❑ 98TopGalGP-108
❑ 98TopGalOPP-108
❑ 98TopGalPPI-108
❑ 98TopGalPPIA-108
❑ 98TopMiniC-452
❑ 98TopSta-92
❑ 98TopStaB-92
❑ 98TopStaG-92
❑ 98TopStaGR-92
❑ 98TopStaS-92
❑ 98UppDec-48
❑ 98UppDecSF-29
❑ 99199Fin-22
❑ 99Bow-12
❑ 99BowChr-12
❑ 99BowChrG-12

❑ 99BowChrGR-12
❑ 99BowChrI-12
❑ 99BowChrIR-12
❑ 99BowChrR-12
❑ 99BowGol-12
❑ 99BowInt-12
❑ 99CroRoyB-26
❑ 99CroRoyL-26
❑ 99CroRoyOD-26
❑ 99FinGolRef-22
❑ 99FinRef-22
❑ 99Fle-238
❑ 99FleSta9-238
❑ 99FleWarT-238
❑ 99MetUni-224
❑ 99MetUniGM-224
❑ 99MetUniPMG-224
❑ 99Pac-75
❑ 99PacAur-31
❑ 99PacAurOD-31
❑ 99PacCroC-50
❑ 99PacCroCPB-50
❑ 99PacInv-28
❑ 99PacInvOD-28
❑ 99PacInvPB-28
❑ 99PacOme-44
❑ 99PacOmeC-44
❑ 99PacOmeG-44
❑ 99PacOmePB-44
❑ 99PacPar-45
❑ 99PacParC-45
❑ 99PacParG-45
❑ 99PacParHoloGold-45
❑ 99PacParHS-45
❑ 99PacParOD-45
❑ 99PacParPB-45
❑ 99PacParRed-45
❑ 99PacPlaB-75
❑ 99PacPri-24
❑ 99PacPriHB-24
❑ 99PacPriHG-24
❑ 99PacPriHM-24
❑ 99PacPriHP-24
❑ 99PacPriRed-24
❑ 99PacRed-75
❑ 99SkyPre-127
❑ 99SkyPreR-127
❑ 99SkyThu-233
❑ 99SkyThuRant-233
❑ 99SkyThuRave-233
❑ 99SPx-25
❑ 99SPxFinR-25
❑ 99SPxFinS-25
❑ 99StaClu-74
❑ 99StaCluFDI-74
❑ 99StaCluOoaK-74
❑ 99StaCluPP-74
❑ 99ThuSkySupR-233
❑ 99Top-164
❑ 99TopChr-164
❑ 99TopChrR-164
❑ 99TopMVPP-164
❑ 99TopOpeD-90
❑ 99UppDec-56
❑ 99UppDecEL1-56
❑ 99UppDecEL2-56
❑ 99UppDecM-37
❑ 99UppDecMGS-37
❑ 99UppDecMHFS-37
❑ 99UppDecMP-37
❑ 99UppDecMSS-37
❑ 99Vic-69

Valentin, Jose Antonio
❑ 87SpoIndP-23
❑ 88ChaRaiP-1198
❑ 89BlaYNPRWL-155
❑ 89CalLeaA-7
❑ 89RivRedWB-19
❑ 89RivRedWCLC-8
❑ 89RivRedWP-1415
❑ 89WicUpdR-18
❑ 90WicWraRD-20
❑ 91Cla/Bes-33
❑ 91LinDriAA-620
❑ 91WicWraLD-620
❑ 91WicWraP-2606
❑ 91WicWraRD-16
❑ 92DenZepF-2652
❑ 92DenZepS-147
❑ 92SkyAAAF-72
❑ 93ClaFS7-265
❑ 93NewOrlZF-981
❑ 93Top-804
❑ 93TopGol-804
❑ 93TopInaM-804
❑ 93TopInaR-804
❑ 93TopMic-804
❑ 94Bow-93
❑ 94BreMilB-83
❑ 94BrePol-27
❑ 94BreTeal-26
❑ 94ColC-474
❑ 94ColChoGS-474
❑ 94ColChoSS-477
❑ 94Don-544
❑ 94Fle-194
❑ 94LeaLimR-33
❑ 94Pac-346
❑ 94Pin-249
❑ 94PinArtP-249
❑ 94PinMusC-249
❑ 94ScoRoo-RT101
❑ 94ScoRooGR-RT101
❑ 94SpoRoo-80
❑ 94SpoRooAP-80
❑ 94StaClu-456
❑ 94StaCluFDI-456
❑ 94StaCluGR-456
❑ 94StaCluMOP-456
❑ 94Top-251
❑ 94TopGol-251
❑ 94TopSpa-251
❑ 94UppDec-303
❑ 94UppDecED-303
❑ 95Bow-318
❑ 95ColCho-176
❑ 95ColChoGS-176
❑ 95ColChoSE-72
❑ 95ColChoSEGS-72
❑ 95ColChoSESS-72
❑ 95ColChoSS-176
❑ 95Don-68
❑ 95DonPreP-68
❑ 95DonTopotO-104
❑ 95Fin-26
❑ 95FinRef-26
❑ 95Fle-192
❑ 95Lea-50
❑ 95Pac-241
❑ 95PacPri-77
❑ 95Pin-127
❑ 95PinArtP-127
❑ 95PinMusC-127
❑ 95Sco-190
❑ 95ScoGolR-190
❑ 95ScoPlaTS-190
❑ 95SP-167
❑ 95SPSil-167
❑ 95StaClu-402
❑ 95StaClu-451
❑ 95StaCluMOP-402
❑ 95StaCluMOP-451
❑ 95StaCluSTWS-402
❑ 95StaCluSTWS-451
❑ 95StaCluVR-242
❑ 95StaCluVRMO-242
❑ 95Top-527
❑ 95TopCyb-312
❑ 95TopEmb-7
❑ 95TopEmbGI-7
❑ 95Ult-69
❑ 95UltGolM-69
❑ 95UppDec-55
❑ 95UppDecED-55
❑ 95UppDecEDG-55
❑ 95UppDecSE-233
❑ 95UppDecSEG-233
❑ 96BrePol-24
❑ 96ColCho-598
❑ 96ColChoGS-598
❑ 96ColChoSS-598
❑ 96Don-443
❑ 96DonPreP-443
❑ 96Fla-108
❑ 96Fle-160
❑ 96FleTif-160
❑ 96FtMyeMB-5
❑ 96LeaSigA-226
❑ 96LeaSigAG-227
❑ 96LeaSigAS-227
❑ 96Pac-353
❑ 96PacPri-P111
❑ 96PacPriG-P111
❑ 96Sco-184
❑ 96SP-41
❑ 96SP-111
❑ 96StaClu-391
❑ 96StaCluMOP-391
❑ 96TeaOut-82
❑ 96Top-122
❑ 96Ult-86
❑ 96UltGolM-86
❑ 96UppDec-122
❑ 97Bow-280
❑ 97BowInt-280
❑ 97BrePol-25
❑ 97Cir-255
❑ 97CirRav-255
❑ 97ColCho-375
❑ 97Don-240
❑ 97DonGolPP-240
❑ 97DonSilPP-240
❑ 97Fin-42
❑ 97FinRef-42
❑ 97FlaShoLC-70
❑ 97FlaShoLeg0-70
❑ 97FlaShoLeg1-70
❑ 97FlaShoM-A70
❑ 97FlaShoM-B70
❑ 97FlaShoM-C70
❑ 97FlaShoR0-70
❑ 97FlaShoR1-70
❑ 97FlaShoR2-70
❑ 97Fle-138
❑ 97FleTif-138
❑ 97Lea-60
❑ 97LeaFraM-60
❑ 97LeaFraMDC-60
❑ 97MetUni-70
❑ 97NewPin-85
❑ 97NewPinAP-85
❑ 97NewPinMC-85
❑ 97NewPinPP-85
❑ 97Pac-128
❑ 97PacLigB-128
❑ 97PacPri-42
❑ 97PacPriLB-42
❑ 97PacPriP-42
❑ 97PacSil-128
❑ 97Sco-445
❑ 97ScoArtPWB-445
❑ 97ScoResC-445
❑ 97ScoShoS-445
❑ 97ScoShoSAP-445
❑ 97SP-101
❑ 97SpoIll-153
❑ 97SpoIllEE-153
❑ 97StaClu-113
❑ 97StaCluMOP-113
❑ 97TopChr-2
❑ 97TopChrR-2
❑ 97TopGal-135
❑ 97TopGalPPI-135
❑ 97Ult-83
❑ 97UltGolME-83
❑ 97UltPlaME-83
❑ 97UppDec-405
❑ 98Bow-261
❑ 98BowChr-261
❑ 98BowChrGA-261
❑ 98BowChrGAR-261
❑ 98BowChrI-261
❑ 98BowChrIR-261
❑ 98BowChrR-261
❑ 98BowGolA-261
❑ 98BowInt-261
❑ 98CirThu-253
❑ 98CirThuRav-253
❑ 98CirThuSupRav-253
❑ 98ColCho-156
❑ 98Fin-243
❑ 98FinNo--243
❑ 98FinNo-R-243
❑ 98FinRef-243
❑ 98Fle-194
❑ 98Pac-125
❑ 98PacInv-43
❑ 98PacInvPBlue-43
❑ 98PacInvSilv-43
❑ 98PacOme-137
❑ 98PacOmeR-137
❑ 98PacOnl-411
❑ 98PacOnlR-411
❑ 98PacOnlWC-411
❑ 98PacPar-190
❑ 98PacParC-190
❑ 98PacParG-190
❑ 98PacParHS-190
❑ 98PacParPB-190
❑ 98PacParR-190
❑ 98PacPlaB-125
❑ 98PacRedT-125
❑ 98PacSil-125
❑ 98SPxFin-294
❑ 98SPxFinR-294
❑ 98SPxFinS-294
❑ 98StaCluFDI-151
❑ 98StaCluI-151
❑ 98StaCluOneK-151
❑ 98StaCluPP-151
❑ 98Top-158
❑ 98TopChr-158
❑ 98TopChrR-158
❑ 98TopDevR-158
❑ 98TopDia-158
❑ 98TopMiniC-158
❑ 98TopSta-73
❑ 98TopStaB-73
❑ 98TopStaG-73
❑ 98TopStaGR-73
❑ 98TopStaS-73
❑ 98Ult-339
❑ 98UltGolM-339
❑ 98UltMas-339
❑ 98UltPlaM-339
❑ 98UppDec-409
❑ 99199Fin-188
❑ 99FinGolRef-188
❑ 99FinRef-188
❑ 99Fle-464
❑ 99FleSta9-464
❑ 99FleWarT-464
❑ 99MetUni-69
❑ 99MetUniGM-69
❑ 99MetUniPMG-69
❑ 99Pac-242
❑ 99PacAur-102
❑ 99PacAurOD-102
❑ 99PacCroC-155
❑ 99PacCroCPB-155
❑ 99PacInv-82
❑ 99PacInvOD-82
❑ 99PacInvPB-82
❑ 99PacPar-129
❑ 99PacParC-129
❑ 99PacParG-129
❑ 99PacParHoloGold-129
❑ 99PacParHS-129
❑ 99PacParOD-129
❑ 99PacParPB-129
❑ 99PacParRed-129
❑ 99PacPlaB-242
❑ 99PacPri-81
❑ 99PacPriHB-81
❑ 99PacPriHG-81
❑ 99PacPriHM-81
❑ 99PacPriHP-81
❑ 99PacPriRed-81
❑ 99PacRed-242
❑ 99StaClu-263
❑ 99StaCluFDI-263
❑ 99StaCluOoaK-263
❑ 99StaCluPP-263
❑ 99Top-186
❑ 99TopChr-186
❑ 99TopChrR-186
❑ 99TopMVPP-186
❑ 99UD Cho-103
❑ 99UD ChoPCR-103
❑ 99Ult-102
❑ 99UltGolM-102
❑ 99UltMas-102
❑ 99UltPlaM-102
❑ 99Vic-219

Valentine, Anthony
❑ 98PitMetM-31

Valentine, Bill
❑ 76ArkTraT-10
❑ 80ArkTraT-23

Valentine, Bobby
❑ 71Dod-18
❑ 71OPC-188
❑ 71Top-188
❑ 72OPC-11
❑ 72Top-11
❑ 73LinPor-38
❑ 73OPC-502
❑ 73Top-502
❑ 74OPC-101
❑ 74Top-101
❑ 74TopDecE-11
❑ 74TopSta-150
❑ 75CalAngP-44
❑ 75OPC-215
❑ 75Top-215
❑ 75TopMin-215
❑ 76HawIslC-6
❑ 76OPC-366
❑ 76Top-366
❑ 77PadSchC-61
❑ 77Top-629
❑ 78MetDaiPA-24
❑ 78Top-712
❑ 79OPC-222
❑ 79Top-428
❑ 80Top-56
❑ 85MetTCM-5
❑ 85RanPer-2
❑ 85SpoIndGC-22
❑ 85TopTifT-126T
❑ 85TopTra-126T
❑ 86RanPer-2
❑ 86Top-261
❑ 86TopTif-261
❑ 87RanMot-1
❑ 87RanSmo-19
❑ 87Top-118
❑ 87Top-656
❑ 87TopTif-118
❑ 87TopTif-656
❑ 88RanMot-1
❑ 88RanSmo-8
❑ 88Top-201
❑ 88Top-594
❑ 88TopTif-201
❑ 88TopTif-594
❑ 89RanMot-1
❑ 89RanSmo-33
❑ 89Top-314
❑ 89TopTif-314
❑ 90DodTar-814
❑ 90OPC-729
❑ 90RanMot-1
❑ 90Top-729
❑ 90TopTif-729
❑ 91MetWIZ-418
❑ 91OPC-489
❑ 91RanMot-1
❑ 91Top-489
❑ 91TopDesS-489
❑ 91TopMic-489
❑ 91TopTif-489
❑ 92OPC-789
❑ 92RanMot-1
❑ 92RanTeal-25
❑ 92Top-789
❑ 92TopGol-789
❑ 92TopGolW-789
❑ 92TopMic-789
❑ 93RanKee-363
❑ 93RedKah-8
❑ 94NorTidF-2936
❑ 96NorTidB-1

Valentine, Corky (Harold)
❑ 55Top-44
❑ 55TopDouH-45
❑ 79TCM50-61

Valentine, Ellis
❑ 76ExpRed-33
❑ 76OPC-590
❑ 76SSP-342
❑ 76Top-590
❑ 77BurCheD-158
❑ 77ExpPos-33
❑ 77OPC-234
❑ 77RCColC-65
❑ 77Top-52
❑ 78Kel-19
❑ 78OPC-45
❑ 78RCColC-31
❑ 78Top-185
❑ 79BasPat-92
❑ 79ExpPos-29
❑ 79Hos-50
❑ 79OPC-277
❑ 79Top-535
❑ 80ExpPos-32
❑ 80Kel-21
❑ 80OPC-206
❑ 80Top-395
❑ 81AllGamPI-162
❑ 81Fle-148
❑ 81OPC-244
❑ 81OPCPos-7
❑ 81Top-445
❑ 81TopScr-80
❑ 81TopSti-186
❑ 81TopTra-849
❑ 82Don-605
❑ 82FBIDis-27
❑ 82Fle-541
❑ 82FleSta-83
❑ 82MetPhoA-23
❑ 82OPC-15
❑ 82Top-15
❑ 82TopSti-69
❑ 82TopStiV-69
❑ 83Fle-559
❑ 83FleSta-204
❑ 83FleSti-235
❑ 83Top-653
❑ 83TopTra-120T
❑ 84AngSmo-29
❑ 84Fle-529
❑ 84Nes792-236
❑ 84OPC-236
❑ 84Top-236
❑ 84TopTif-236
❑ 86ExpGreT-6
❑ 91MetWIZ-419
❑ 93ExpDonM-21
❑ 93RanKee-364

Valentine, Fred
❑ 63BalOriP-34
❑ 64Top-483
❑ 66Top-351
❑ 66TopVen-351
❑ 67BalOriP-101
❑ 67CokCapS-18
❑ 67DexPre-213
❑ 67OPC-64
❑ 67SenPos-22
❑ 67SenTeal-12
❑ 67Top-64
❑ 67TopVen-220
❑ 68AtlOilPBCC-45
❑ 68SenTeal-12
❑ 68Top-248
❑ 68TopVen-248
❑ 69MilBra-282
❑ 69SenTeal8-19
❑ 91OriCro-466

Valentinetti, Vito
❑ 57Top-74
❑ 58SeaTeal-26
❑ 58Top-463
❑ 59Top-44
❑ 59TopVen-44

Valentini, Vincent
❑ 80WicAerT-19

Valenzuela, Benny
❑ 77FriOneYW-76

Valenzuela, Derek
❑ 94ChaWheF-2707

Valenzuela, Fernando
❑ 81AllGamPI-180
❑ 81Dod-12
❑ 81Dod-31
❑ 81DodPol-34
❑ 81DodPos-9
❑ 81Fle-140
❑ 81LonBeaPT-10
❑ 81PerAll-9
❑ 81Top-302
❑ 81TopTra-850
❑ 82DodPol-34
❑ 82DodUniOV-24
❑ 82Don-462
❑ 82Fle-27
❑ 82Fle-635
❑ 82Fle-636A
❑ 82Fle-636B
❑ 82FleSta-1
❑ 82FleSta-108
❑ 82FleSta-111
❑ 82Kel-9
❑ 82MonNew-20
❑ 82OPC-334
❑ 82OPC-345
❑ 82PerCreC-12
❑ 82PerCreCG-12
❑ 82SevSluC-25
❑ 82Squ-20
❑ 82Top-6
❑ 82Top-166
❑ 82Top-345
❑ 82Top-510
❑ 82TopSti-11
❑ 82TopSti-50
❑ 82TopSti-119
❑ 82TopSti-257
❑ 83DodPol-34
❑ 83DodPos-18
❑ 83Don-1
❑ 83Don-284
❑ 83DonActA-53
❑ 83Fle-224
❑ 83FleSta-205
❑ 83FleSti-112
❑ 83Kel-7
❑ 83KelCerB-1
❑ 83OPC-40
❑ 83PerCreC-18
❑ 83PerCreCG-18
❑ 83SevCoi-8

❑ 83Top-40
❑ 83Top-681
❑ 83TopGloS-10
❑ 83TopSti-250
❑ 83TopStiB-1
❑ 84DodPol-34
❑ 84DodUniO-9
❑ 84Don-52
❑ 84DonActAS-13
❑ 84Fle-115
❑ 84FleSti-81
❑ 84FunFooP-7
❑ 84MilBra-27
❑ 84MLBPen-13
❑ 84Nes792-220
❑ 84OCoandSI-34
❑ 84OPC-220
❑ 84RalPur-10
❑ 84SevCoi-W9
❑ 84Top-220
❑ 84TopCer-10
❑ 84TopRubD-32
❑ 84TopSti-16
❑ 84TopSti-79
❑ 84TopSup-30
❑ 84TopTif-220
❑ 85AllGamPl-180
❑ 85DodCokP-31
❑ 85Don-52
❑ 85DonActA-37
❑ 85DonHig-6
❑ 85DonHig-28
❑ 85Fle-387
❑ 85FleLimE-42
❑ 85FleStaS-114
❑ 85GenMilS-12
❑ 85KASDis-18
❑ 85KitCloD-18
❑ 85Lea-184
❑ 85OPC-357
❑ 85SevCoi-W16
❑ 85SubDis-45
❑ 85ThoMcAD-45
❑ 85Top-440
❑ 85Top3-D-21
❑ 85TopRubD-32
❑ 85TopSti-71
❑ 85TopSup-52
❑ 85TopTif-440
❑ 86BasStaB-115
❑ 86BurKinA-3
❑ 86DodCokP-30
❑ 86DodPol-34
❑ 86DodUniOP-21
❑ 86Don-215
❑ 86DonAll-27
❑ 86DonHig-25
❑ 86Dra-36
❑ 86Fle-145
❑ 86Fle-641
❑ 86FleMin-31
❑ 86FleSlu-41
❑ 86FleStiC-123
❑ 86GenMilB-5J
❑ 86Lea-91
❑ 86MeaGolBB-15
❑ 86MeaGolM-12
❑ 86MeaGolSB-2
❑ 86MSAJifPD-14
❑ 86OPC-178
❑ 86OPCBoxB-P
❑ 86QuaGra-17
❑ 86SevCoi-C6
❑ 86SevCoi-E6
❑ 86SevCoi-S6
❑ 86SevCoi-W6
❑ 86Spo-12
❑ 86Spo-60
❑ 86Spo-72
❑ 86Spo-132
❑ 86Spo-143
❑ 86SpoDecG-66
❑ 86SpoRoo-47
❑ 86Top-207
❑ 86Top-401
❑ 86Top-630
❑ 86Top3-D-30
❑ 86TopGloS-3
❑ 86TopMinL-47
❑ 86TopSti-64
❑ 86TopSup-58
❑ 86TopTat-24
❑ 86TopTif-207
❑ 86TopTif-401
❑ 86TopTif-630
❑ 86TopWaxBC-P
❑ 86TruVal-6
❑ 87BurKinA-20
❑ 87ClaGam-91
❑ 87DodMot-4
❑ 87DodPho-16
❑ 87DodPol-17
❑ 87DodSmoA-36
❑ 87Don-94
❑ 87DonAll-54
❑ 87Dra-29
❑ 87Fle-457
❑ 87Fle-631
❑ 87FleAll-10
❑ 87FleAwaW-40
❑ 87FleBasA-43
❑ 87FleGamW-42
❑ 87FleGlo-457
❑ 87FleGlo-631
❑ 87FleMin-109
❑ 87FleSlu-43
❑ 87FleStiC-120
❑ 87GenMilB-6J
❑ 87HosSti-11
❑ 87K-M-33
❑ 87KayB-32
❑ 87KraFoo-32
❑ 87Lea-148
❑ 87MandMSL-19
❑ 87MSAJifPD-15
❑ 87OPC-273
❑ 87RalPur-11
❑ 87RedFolSB-57
❑ 87SevCoi-W16
❑ 87Spo-119
❑ 87Spo-120
❑ 87Spo-150
❑ 87SpoDeaP-2
❑ 87SpoRea-40
❑ 87SpoSupD-6
❑ 87SpoTeaP-14
❑ 87StaStiV-1
❑ 87StaStiV-2
❑ 87StaStiV-3
❑ 87StaStiV-4
❑ 87StaStiV-5
❑ 87StaStiV-6
❑ 87StaStiV-7
❑ 87StaStiV-8
❑ 87StaStiV-9
❑ 87StaStiV-10
❑ 87StaVal-1
❑ 87StaVal-2
❑ 87StaVal-3
❑ 87StaVal-4
❑ 87StaVal-5
❑ 87StaVal-6
❑ 87StaVal-7
❑ 87StaVal-8
❑ 87StaVal-9
❑ 87StaVal-10
❑ 87StaVal-11
❑ 87StaVal-12
❑ 87StaVal-13
❑ 87StuPan-6
❑ 87Top-410
❑ 87Top-604
❑ 87TopCoi-47
❑ 87TopGloA-11
❑ 87TopGloS-53
❑ 87TopMinL-16
❑ 87TopSti-75
❑ 87TopTif-410
❑ 87TopTif-604
❑ 88CheBoy-24
❑ 88DodMot-4
❑ 88DodPol-34
❑ 88DodSmo-24
❑ 88Don-53
❑ 88DonBasB-316
❑ 88Fle-528
❑ 88FleBasM-40
❑ 88FleExcS-43
❑ 88FleGlo-528
❑ 88FleMin-86
❑ 88FleStiC-94
❑ 88GreBasS-68
❑ 88K-M-31
❑ 88KeyFooD-20
❑ 88KinDis-19
❑ 88Lea-61
❑ 88MSAIceTD-20
❑ 88OPC-52
❑ 88OurOwnTD-20
❑ 88PanSti-304
❑ 88Sco-600
❑ 88ScoGlo-600
❑ 88Spo-40
❑ 88StaLinAl-34
❑ 88StaLinD-20
❑ 88TarPla-45
❑ 88TetTeaD-20
❑ 88Top-489
❑ 88Top-780
❑ 88TopBig-18
❑ 88TopCoi-58
❑ 88TopMinL-54
❑ 88TopRevLL-14
❑ 88TopSti-70
❑ 88TopStiB-30
❑ 88TopTif-489
❑ 88TopTif-780
❑ 88TopUKM-80
❑ 88TopUKMT-80
❑ 88WeiMarD-20
❑ 89Bow-337
❑ 89BowTif-337
❑ 89DodMot-4
❑ 89DodPol-22
❑ 89DodSmoG-97
❑ 89DodStaSV-15
❑ 89Don-250
❑ 89Fle-76
❑ 89FleGlo-76
❑ 89K-M-32
❑ 89OPC-150
❑ 89PanSti-103
❑ 89RedFolSB-123
❑ 89Sco-437
❑ 89Spo-124
❑ 89Top-150
❑ 89TopBasT-61
❑ 89TopSti-60
❑ 89TopTif-150
❑ 89TopUKM-78
❑ 89UppDec-656
❑ 90DodMot-2
❑ 90DodPol-34
❑ 90DodTar-815
❑ 90Don-625
❑ 90DonBesN-90
❑ 90DonLeaS-39
❑ 90Fle-409
❑ 90Fle-622
❑ 90FleCan-409
❑ 90FleCan-622
❑ 90Lea-68
❑ 90M.Vpin-50
❑ 90MLBBasB-7
❑ 90OPC-340
❑ 90PanSti-269
❑ 90PubIntS-21
❑ 90Sco-54
❑ 90SupActM-14
❑ 90Top-340
❑ 90TopSti-59
❑ 90TopTif-340
❑ 90UppDec-445
❑ 91BasBesRB-18
❑ 91ClaGam-73
❑ 91DodUno7P-3
❑ 91DodUno7P-4
❑ 91Don-127
❑ 91DonBonC-BC11
❑ 91Fle-222
❑ 91FleWaxBC-5
❑ 91OPC-80
❑ 91PanFreS-356
❑ 91PanSti-5
❑ 91PanSti-59
❑ 91Sco-449
❑ 91Sco-703
❑ 91SevCoi-SC15
❑ 91StaClu-90
❑ 91StaCluCM-30
❑ 91StaCluP-45
❑ 91Top-80A
❑ 91Top-80B
❑ 91TopDesS-80
❑ 91TopMic-80
❑ 91TopTif-80
❑ 91UppDec-175
❑ 92DodStaTA-24
❑ 93BalOriP-35
❑ 93BalOriP-36
❑ 93Fla-159
❑ 93FleFinE-166
❑ 93Lea-472
❑ 93LinVenB-312
❑ 93LinVenB-322
❑ 93OPCPre-47
❑ 93PacJugC-17
❑ 93PacSpa-352
❑ 93StaClu-661
❑ 93StaCluFDI-661
❑ 93StaCluMOP-661
❑ 93Ult-503
❑ 93UppDec-550
❑ 93UppDecGold-550
❑ 94Don-408
❑ 94Fla-418
❑ 94Fle-22
❑ 94FleUpd-171
❑ 94Pac-46
❑ 94PacSilP-14
❑ 94PacSilPC-14
❑ 94PanSti-25
❑ 94Sco-190
❑ 94ScoGolR-190
❑ 94StaClu-69
❑ 94StaCluFDI-69
❑ 94StaCluGR-69
❑ 94StaCluMOP-69
❑ 94Top-175
❑ 94TopGol-175
❑ 94TopSpa-175
❑ 95ColCho-364
❑ 95ColCho-566T
❑ 95ColCho-TC5
❑ 95ColChoGS-364
❑ 95ColChoSE-168
❑ 95ColChoSEGS-168
❑ 95ColChoSESS-168
❑ 95ColChoSS-364
❑ 95DodROY-10
❑ 95Fle-406
❑ 95FleUpd-190
❑ 95Pac-339
❑ 95PadCHP-9
❑ 95PadMot-8
❑ 95UppDec-142
❑ 95UppDec-375
❑ 95UppDecED-142
❑ 95UppDecED-375
❑ 95UppDecEDG-142
❑ 95UppDecEDG-375
❑ 96Cir-189
❑ 96CirRav-189
❑ 96ColCho-299
❑ 96ColCho-334
❑ 96ColChoGS-299
❑ 96ColChoGS-334
❑ 96ColChoSS-299
❑ 96ColChoSS-334
❑ 96EmoXL-284
❑ 96Fla-382
❑ 96Fle-579
❑ 96FleTif-579
❑ 96Pac-190
❑ 96PacEstL-EL33
❑ 96PacPri-P64
❑ 96PacPriG-P64
❑ 96PadMot-8
❑ 96Ult-563
❑ 96UltGolM-563
❑ 96UppDec-114
❑ 97ColCho-207
❑ 97Don-203
❑ 97DonGolPP-203
❑ 97DonSilPP-203
❑ 97Fle-471
❑ 97FleTif-471
❑ 97MetUni-225
❑ 97Pac-433
❑ 97PacLatotML-35
❑ 97PacLigB-433
❑ 97PacPri-146
❑ 97PacPriGotD-GD211
❑ 97PacPriLB-146
❑ 97PacPriP-146
❑ 97PacPriSH-SH12B
❑ 97PacSil-433
❑ 97PadMot-8
❑ 97Pin-127
❑ 97PinArtP-PP127
❑ 97PinMusC-127
❑ 97PinPrePla-127
❑ 97Sco-272
❑ 97ScoArtPWB-272
❑ 97ScoPreS-272
❑ 97ScoShoS-272
❑ 97ScoShoSAP-272
❑ 97Ult-288
❑ 97UltGolME-288
❑ 97UltPlaME-288
❑ 97UppDec-166
❑ 97UppDec-195
❑ 98ColCho-216
❑ 98UppDec-204
❑ 98UppDecNP-NP21

Valenzuela, Guillermo
❑ 83KinBluJTI-27

Valenzuela, Mario
❑ 98BriWhiSQ-26

Valera, Julio
❑ 87ColMetP-26
❑ 88BlaYNPRWL-78
❑ 88ColMetGS-11
❑ 89BasAmeAPB-AA28
❑ 89BlaYNPRWL-88
❑ 89BlaYNPRWLU-71
❑ 89JacMetGS-29
❑ 89St.LucMS-23
❑ 89TexLeaAGS-26
❑ 90Bow-123
❑ 90BowTif-123
❑ 90CMC-364
❑ 90MetColP-52
❑ 90ProAAAF-277
❑ 90TidTidC-13
❑ 90TidTidP-546
❑ 90TopTVM-65
❑ 91Don-39
❑ 91Fle-164
❑ 91LinDriAAA-571
❑ 91MetColP-50
❑ 91MetWIZ-420
❑ 91OPC-504
❑ 91Sco-353
❑ 91TidTidLD-571
❑ 91TidTidP-2511
❑ 91Top-504
❑ 91TopDeb90-158
❑ 91TopDesS-504
❑ 91TopMic-504
❑ 91TopTif-504
❑ 91UppDec-534
❑ 92Bow-422
❑ 92Cla2-T4
❑ 92DonRoo-119
❑ 92Fle-517
❑ 92FleUpd-11
❑ 92Lea-490
❑ 92LeaBlaG-490
❑ 92MetColP-30
❑ 92Pin-267
❑ 92ProFS7-276
❑ 92Sco100RS-17
❑ 92SkyAAAF-257
❑ 92StaClu-304
❑ 92StaClu-646
❑ 92TidTidF-897
❑ 92TidTidS-573
❑ 92TopTra-122T
❑ 92TopTraG-122T
❑ 92UppDec-747
❑ 92UppDecSR-SR23
❑ 93AngMot-11
❑ 93AngPol-14
❑ 93AngStaCl-30
❑ 93Don-5
❑ 93Fle-578
❑ 93Lea-430
❑ 93OPC-368
❑ 93PacSpa-374
❑ 93Pin-139
❑ 93Sco-427
❑ 93Sel-288
❑ 93StaClu-386
❑ 93StaCluFDI-386
❑ 93StaCluMOP-386
❑ 93Top-374
❑ 93TopGol-374
❑ 93TopInaM-374
❑ 93TopInaR-374
❑ 93TopMic-374
❑ 93Ult-169
❑ 93UppDec-343
❑ 93UppDecGold-343
❑ 94Fle-72
❑ 94Pac-93
❑ 94Sco-223
❑ 94ScoGolR-223
❑ 96LeaSigEA-205
❑ 97PacPriGotD-GD52

Valera, Ramon
❑ 97EveAquG-27
❑ 98WisTimRM-20

Valera, Willy
❑ 95WatIndTI-29

Valera, Wilson
❑ 83WatIndF-10
❑ 85WatIndT-2
❑ 86LynMetP-23
❑ 87LynMetP-26
❑ 88SouBenWSGS-11

Valera, Yohanny
❑ 97CapCitB-15
❑ 98St.LucMM-20

Valette, Ramon
❑ 91EliTwiP-4309
❑ 92EliTwiC-18
❑ 93ForWayWC-24
❑ 93ForWayWF-1977
❑ 94ForMyeMC-25
❑ 95HarCitRCTI-26
❑ 98WesTenDJM-24

Valez, Rafael
❑ 86ChaRaiP-27

Valiente, Nestor
❑ 84ButCopKT-25

Valla, Gene
❑ 22Zee-109
❑ 23Zee-148
❑ 24Zee-107
❑ 25Zee-123
❑ 26Zee-152
❑ 27Zee-64

Valla, Mike
❑ 88WatPirP-26

Vallaran, Miguel
❑ 77LodDodT-22

Vallarelli, Mike
❑ 94BoiHawC-27
❑ 94BoiHawF-3359

Valle, Dave
❑ 80SanJosMJitB-20
❑ 81LynSaiT-14
❑ 82SalLakCGT-20
❑ 83ChaLooT-26
❑ 84SalLakCGC-176
❑ 85FleUpd-125
❑ 85MarMot-17
❑ 86CalCanP-24
❑ 86MarPacNB-14
❑ 87Don-610
❑ 87DonOpeD-120
❑ 87MarMot-9
❑ 87SpoTeaP-25
❑ 87TopTra-122T
❑ 87TopTraT-122T
❑ 88Don-393
❑ 88Fle-389
❑ 88FleGlo-389
❑ 88MarMot-9
❑ 88OPC-83
❑ 88PanSti-184
❑ 88Sco-126A
❑ 88Sco-126B
❑ 88ScoGlo-126A
❑ 88ScoGlo-126B
❑ 88StaLinMa-18
❑ 88Top-583
❑ 88TopBig-210
❑ 88TopSti-220
❑ 88TopTif-583
❑ 89Bow-208
❑ 89BowTif-208
❑ 89ChaLooLITI-30
❑ 89Don-614
❑ 89DonBasB-248
❑ 89Fle-561
❑ 89FleGlo-561
❑ 89MarMot-9
❑ 89RedFolSB-124
❑ 89Sco-27
❑ 89Top-459
❑ 89Top-498
❑ 89TopBig-56
❑ 89TopTif-459
❑ 89TopTif-498
❑ 89UppDec-320
❑ 90Bow-473
❑ 90BowTif-473
❑ 90Don-129
❑ 90DonBesA-55
❑ 90Fle-527
❑ 90FleCan-527
❑ 90Lea-166
❑ 90MarMot-5
❑ 90MarRedAP-1
❑ 90MLBBasB-120
❑ 90OPC-76
❑ 90PanSti-156
❑ 90PubIntS-444
❑ 90RedFolSB-97
❑ 90Sco-109
❑ 90Top-76
❑ 90TopBig-266
❑ 90TopTif-76
❑ 90UppDec-451

❑ 91Bow-251
❑ 91Don-366
❑ 91Fle-463
❑ 91Lea-511
❑ 91MarCouH-6
❑ 91OPC-178
❑ 91PanFreS-227
❑ 91RedFolS-95
❑ 91Sco-262
❑ 91StaClu-32
❑ 91Stu-120
❑ 91Top-178
❑ 91TopDesS-178
❑ 91TopMic-178
❑ 91TopTif-178
❑ 91Ult-344
❑ 91UppDec-595
❑ 92Bow-134
❑ 92Don-462
❑ 92Fle-295
❑ 92Lea-170
❑ 92LeaBlaG-170
❑ 92MarMot-5
❑ 92OPC-294
❑ 92PanSti-54
❑ 92Pin-232
❑ 92Sco-343
❑ 92StaClu-56
❑ 92Stu-240
❑ 92Top-294
❑ 92TopGol-294
❑ 92TopGolW-294
❑ 92TopMic-294
❑ 92TriPla-5
❑ 92Ult-130
❑ 92UppDec-182
❑ 93DiaMar-110
❑ 93Don-507
❑ 93Fla-275
❑ 93Fle-315
❑ 93Lea-425
❑ 93MariStaClu-20
❑ 93MarMot-7
❑ 93PacSpa-291
❑ 93PanSti-58
❑ 93Pin-179
❑ 93Sco-200
❑ 93StaClu-483
❑ 93StaCluFDI-483
❑ 93StaCluMOP-483
❑ 93Stu-68
❑ 93Top-370
❑ 93TopGol-370
❑ 93TopInaM-370
❑ 93TopInaR-370
❑ 93TopMic-370
❑ 93TriPla-152
❑ 93Ult-273
❑ 93UppDec-100
❑ 93UppDecGold-100
❑ 94BreMilB-369
❑ 94ColC-627
❑ 94ColChoGS-627
❑ 94ColChoSS-627
❑ 94Don-385
❑ 94Fin-378
❑ 94FinRef-378
❑ 94Fla-17
❑ 94Fle-300
❑ 94Lea-430
❑ 94Pac-584
❑ 94PanSti-123
❑ 94Pin-514
❑ 94PinArtP-514
❑ 94PinMusC-514
❑ 94Sco-493
❑ 94ScoGolR-493
❑ 94Sel-241
❑ 94Top-736
❑ 94TopGol-736
❑ 94TopSpa-736
❑ 94Ult-319
❑ 94UppDec-333
❑ 94UppDecED-333
❑ 95RanCra-33
❑ 96Fle-265
❑ 96FleTif-265
❑ 96LeaSigEA-206
❑ 96RanDr P-31
❑ 96RanFle-16
❑ 96RanMot-20
❑ 97PacPriGotD-GD100
❑ 97RicBra-28
Valle, Hector
❑ 65Top-561
❑ 66Top-314
❑ 66TopVen-314
❑ 89BlaYNPRWL-99
Valle, John A.
❑ 77EvaTriT-24
❑ 78IndIndTI-14
❑ 79IndIndTI-25
❑ 80RocRedWT-14
❑ 81RocRedWT-17
❑ 82RocRedWT-18
❑ 83RocRedWT-18
❑ 84RocRedWT-6
Valle, Lazaro
❑ 90IBAWorA-32
Valle, Tony
❑ 89IdaFalBP-2026
❑ 90BurBraB-8
❑ 90BurBraP-2350
❑ 90BurBraS-26
Valle, Yoiset
❑ 98GreBatM-22
Vallero, Rich
❑ 95OdgRapTI-27
Vallette, Ramon
❑ 92EliTwiF-3689
❑ 94ForMyeMF-1177
Valley, Chick
❑ 77SalPirT-24
❑ 78SalPirT-17
❑ 79BufBisT-14
❑ 80ColAstT-6
❑ 81ElPasDT-16
❑ 82VanCanT-18
Valley, Jason
❑ 94BatCliC-24
❑ 94BatCliF-3446
Vallone, Gar
❑ 95BoiHawTI-30
❑ 96CedRapKTI-24
❑ 97CedRapK-26
❑ 98ButCopKG-31
Vallone, Jim
❑ 78QuaCitAT-27
Vallot, Joey
❑ 91GulCoaRSP-24
❑ 92GulCoaRSP-20
Valo, Elmer
❑ 42A'sTeal-33
❑ 43A'STEAl-24
❑ 46A'sTeal-14
❑ 47A'sTeal-30
❑ 48A'sTeal-24
❑ 49A'sTeal-31
❑ 49Bow-66
❑ 49Lea-29
❑ 49PhiBul-56
❑ 50A'sTeal-26
❑ 50Bow-49
❑ 51A'sTeal-32
❑ 51TopRedB-28
❑ 52A'sTeal-28
❑ 52Bow-206
❑ 52Top-34
❑ 53A'sTeal-30
❑ 53Top-122
❑ 54A'STEAl-27
❑ 54Top-145
❑ 55A'sRodM-43
❑ 55A'sRodM-44
❑ 55A'sTeal-27
❑ 55Top-145
❑ 55TopDouH-85
❑ 56A'sRodM-11
❑ 56Top-3
❑ 57Top-54
❑ 58DodTeal-23
❑ 58Top-323
❑ 59SeaPop-37
❑ 60Lea-107
❑ 60Top-237
❑ 61Top-186
❑ 61TwiPetM-12
❑ 76A'sRodMC-28
❑ 79DiaGre-343
❑ 79TCM50-148
❑ 81TCM60I-316
❑ 83TopRep5-34
❑ 84TCMPla1-22
❑ 89PacLegI-187
❑ 90DodTar-816
❑ 91TopArc1-122
❑ 92YanWIZ6-133
❑ 94TopArc1-145
❑ 94TopArc1G-145
Valrie, Kerry
❑ 90UtiBluSP-12
❑ 91Cla/Bes-243
❑ 91SouBenWSC-25
❑ 91SouBenWSP-2872
❑ 92MidLeaATI-46
❑ 92SouBenWSC-7
❑ 92SouBenWSF-192
❑ 93SarWhiSC-27
❑ 93SarWhiSF-1385
❑ 94BirBarC-24
❑ 94BirBarF-636
❑ 95NasSouTI-27
❑ 96NasSouB-26
Valverde, Joe
❑ 89SanDieSAS-27
Valverde, Miguel
❑ 88AugPirP-361
❑ 89SalBucS-23
Van Atta, Russ
❑ 33Gou-215
❑ 33WorCig(-95
❑ 36GouWidPPR-A104
❑ 36R31PasP-50
❑ 79DiaGre-16
❑ 92ConTSN-611
Van Bever, Mark
❑ 78CliDodT-31
Van Blaricom, Mark
❑ 83ButCopKT-22
❑ 85Ft.MyeRT-10
❑ 86Ft.MyeRP-25
❑ 87MemChiB-6
❑ 87MemChiP-12
❑ 88MemChiB-3
Van Brabant, Ozzie
❑ 54A'STEAl-28
❑ 55JetPos-18
Van Brunt, Jim
❑ 87AncGlaP-37
Van Brunt, Lefty
❑ 85AncGlaPTI-28
❑ 86AncGlaPTI-35
❑ 87AncGlaP-30
❑ 89AncGlaP-26
Van Buren, Edward
❑ 09ObaT21-150
❑ 09ObaT21-320
❑ 10BisCoaLE99-29
❑ 11BigEatEU-20
❑ 11PacCoaBD-67
❑ 11Zee-81
❑ 12HomRunKE-58
❑ 12ObaPreT-69
❑ 12Zee-96
❑ 13Zee-93
❑ 14Zee-96
Van Buren, Jermaine
❑ 99Bow-396
❑ 99BowGol-396
❑ 99BowInt-396
Van Burkleo, Ty
❑ 82BelBreFr-6
❑ 86PalSprAP-29
❑ 86PalSprAS-20
❑ 87MidAngP-7
❑ 92EdmTraF-3548
❑ 92EdmTraS-169
❑ 93Bow-497
❑ 93VanCanF-2606
❑ 94ColSprSSF-743
❑ 96LakElsSB-27
❑ 97ColSprSATTI-11
❑ 97LetBlaDB-3
❑ 98HigDesMG-5
Van Cuyk, Chris
❑ 52Top-53
❑ 74dod195T-38
❑ 75OakOak2A-35
❑ 82Bow195E-255
❑ 83TopRep5-53
❑ 90DodTar-819
❑ 91DodRinP3-9
❑ 95TopArcBD-7
Van Cuyk, John
❑ 53MotCoo-41
Van De Weg, Ryan
❑ 96RanCucQB-26
❑ 97MobBayBB-13
❑ 98MobBayBTI-28
Van DeBrake, Kevin
❑ 91YakBeaC-13
❑ 91YakBeaP-4257
Van DeCasteele, Mike
❑ 78TidTidT-26
❑ 79TidTidT-19
Van Der Beck, Jim
❑ 75WatDodT-21
Van Deren, Steve
❑ 78QuaCitAT-28
Van Duzer, Donna L.
❑ 88FreSunP-1249
❑ 91ChaRanC-26
Van Dyke, Gordon Keith
❑ 49AngTeal-36
❑ 49W725AngTI-28
Van Dyke, Rod
❑ 91BoiHawC-7
❑ 91BoiHawP-3879
❑ 92PalSprAC-17
❑ 92PalSprAF-841
❑ 93CedRapKF-1738
Van Dyke, William
❑ 87OldJudN-506
Van Every, Jason
❑ 93MisStaB-45
Van Gilder, Elam
❑ 22E120-104
❑ 27MidBre-41
Van Glider, Ryan
❑ 97VerExpB-28
❑ 98CapFeaCM-25
Van Gorder, Dave
❑ 79NaSouTI-24
❑ 80IndIndTI-8
❑ 81IndIndTI-6
❑ 82IndIndTI-12
❑ 83Don-188
❑ 83IndIndTI-27
❑ 83Top-322
❑ 84WicAerRD-10
❑ 85Don-384
❑ 86Don-550
❑ 86Fle-195
❑ 86Top-143
❑ 86TopTif-143
❑ 87BalOriP-36
❑ 87RocRedWP-2
❑ 87RocRedWT-11
❑ 89IndIndC-24
❑ 91OriCro-467
Van Graflan, Roy
❑ 94ConTSN-1194
❑ 94ConTSNB-1194
Van Haltren, George
❑ 03BreE10-145
❑ 11SpoLifCW-355
❑ 87FouBasHN-11
❑ 87OldJudN-507
❑ 88AugBecN-35
❑ 88GandBCGCE-43
❑ 88WG1CarG-17
❑ 95NewN566-180
Van Heyningen, Pat
❑ 85NewOriT-20
Van Horn, Dave
❑ 83AndBraT-24
Van Houten, Jim
❑ 85SprCarT-4
❑ 87ColAstP-11
Van Iten, Robert
❑ 96MarPhiB-28
❑ 98PieBolWM-28
Van Kemper, John
❑ 85EveGiaIC-20
Van Landuyt, Jules
❑ 94HunCubC-27
❑ 94HunCubF-3555
Van Ornum, John
❑ 80GiaPol-42
❑ 82Gia25tATI-25
❑ 84GiaPos-29
Van Osdoll, Ed
❑ 21Zee-112
Van Pelt, Dennis
❑ 94BoiHawF-3371
Van Pelt, Mark
❑ 91AdeGiaF-14
❑ 93AusFut-11
❑ 94BoiHawC-28
Van Poppel, Todd
❑ 90ClaDraP-14
❑ 90MadMusB-1
❑ 90ProAaA-160
❑ 90SouOreAB-1
❑ 90SouOreAP-3422
❑ 90TopMag-38
❑ 91Bow-218
❑ 91Cla/Bes-386
❑ 91Cla1-T75
❑ 91Cla1-T77
❑ 91Cla1-NNO
❑ 91Cla2-T77
❑ 91ClaGam-151
❑ 91ClaGolB-BC6
❑ 91DonRoo-7
❑ 91HunStaC-24
❑ 91HunStaLD-296
❑ 91HunStaP-1795
❑ 91LeaGolR-BC9
❑ 91LeaGolRNV-273
❑ 91LinDriAA-296
❑ 91Sco-389
❑ 91SevCoi-T14
❑ 91SevCoi-NC13
❑ 91Stu-109
❑ 91UppDec-53
❑ 91UppDecFE-12F
❑ 92Bow-270
❑ 92Cla1-T91
❑ 92Don-9
❑ 92DonPre-12
❑ 92Fle-269
❑ 92FleRooS-2
❑ 92Lea-248
❑ 92LeaBlaG-248
❑ 92MVPPin-26
❑ 92OPC-142
❑ 92Pin-574
❑ 92PinRoo-12
❑ 92PinRool-12
❑ 92PinTea2-72
❑ 92ProFS7-129
❑ 92Sco-865
❑ 92ScoHotR-4
❑ 92ScoImpP-37
❑ 92ScoRoo-1
❑ 92SkyAAAF-244
❑ 92StaClu-129
❑ 92StaVanP-1
❑ 92StaVanP-2
❑ 92StaVanP-3
❑ 92StaVanP-4
❑ 92StaVanP-5
❑ 92StaVanP-6
❑ 92StaVanP-7
❑ 92StaVanP-8
❑ 92StaVanP-9
❑ 92StaVanP-10
❑ 92StaVanP-11
❑ 92TacTigF-2501
❑ 92TacTigS-545
❑ 92Top-142
❑ 92TopDeb91-175
❑ 92TopGol-142
❑ 92TopGolW-142
❑ 92TopMcD-44
❑ 92TopMic-142
❑ 92TriPla-142
❑ 92Ult-118
❑ 92UppDec-22
❑ 92UppDecML-75
❑ 93AthStaC-22
❑ 93Bow-371
❑ 93Bow-681
❑ 93ClaYouG-YG25
❑ 93ExcFS7-219
❑ 93Lea-448
❑ 93SelRoo-79T
❑ 93SP-45
❑ 93StaClu-48
❑ 93StaCluFDI-48
❑ 93StaCluMOP-48
❑ 93TacTigF-3033
❑ 93Top-673
❑ 93TopGol-673
❑ 93TopInaM-673
❑ 93TopInaR-673
❑ 93TopMic-673
❑ 93Toy-62
❑ 94A'sMot-9
❑ 94Bow-548
❑ 94ColC-279
❑ 94ColChoGS-279
❑ 94ColChoSS-279
❑ 94Don-557
❑ 94Fin-182
❑ 94FinPre-182P
❑ 94FinRef-182
❑ 94Fle-275
❑ 94FUnPac-59
❑ 94Lea-151
❑ 94OPC-56
❑ 94Pac-464
❑ 94PanSti-114
❑ 94Pin-357
❑ 94PinArtP-357
❑ 94PinMusC-357
❑ 94Sco-607
❑ 94ScoBoyoS-28
❑ 94ScoGolR-607
❑ 94Sel-86
❑ 94StaClu-562
❑ 94StaCluFDI-562
❑ 94StaCluGR-562
❑ 94StaCluMOP-562
❑ 94Top-559
❑ 94TopGol-559
❑ 94TopSpa-559
❑ 94Ult-414
❑ 94UppDec-195
❑ 94UppDecAJ-2
❑ 94UppDecAJG-2
❑ 94UppDecED-195
❑ 95A'sCHP-7
❑ 95AthMot-13
❑ 95ColCho-137
❑ 95ColChoGS-137
❑ 95ColChoSS-137
❑ 95Don-48
❑ 95DonPreP-48
❑ 95Fla-77
❑ 95Fle-256
❑ 95Lea-169
❑ 95Pin-247
❑ 95PinArtP-247
❑ 95PinMusC-247
❑ 95Sco-210
❑ 95ScoGolR-210
❑ 95ScoPlaTS-210
❑ 95StaClu-225
❑ 95StaCluFDI-225
❑ 95StaCluMOP-225
❑ 95StaCluSTWS-225
❑ 95Top-407
❑ 95TopCyb-207
❑ 95Ult-322
❑ 95UltGolM-322
❑ 95UppDec-284
❑ 95UppDecED-284
❑ 95UppDecEDG-284
❑ 95UppDecSE-106
❑ 95UppDecSEG-106
❑ 96A'sMot-25
❑ 96Cir-75
❑ 96CirRav-75
❑ 96ColCho-643
❑ 96ColChoGS-643
❑ 96ColChoSS-643
❑ 96Don-258
❑ 96DonPreP-258
❑ 96EmoXL-108
❑ 96Fla-154
❑ 96Fle-221
❑ 96FleTif-221
❑ 96LeaSigA-227
❑ 96LeaSigAG-228
❑ 96LeaSigAS-228
❑ 96Sco-432
❑ 96Ult-119
❑ 96UltGolM-119
❑ 96UppDec-413
❑ 98OklRedM-24
Van Robays, Maurice
❑ 47RemBre-18
❑ 47SigOil-57
❑ 47SmiClo-7
❑ 48SigOil-23
❑ 48SmiClo-9
❑ 49BowPCL-32
❑ 49RemBre-29
❑ 77TCMTheWY-71
Van Rossum, Chris
❑ 96BelGiaTI-4
❑ 97BakBlaB-6
❑ 97BakBlaTI-6
❑ 98SanJosGQ-16
Van Ryn, Ben
❑ 91Cla/Bes-31
❑ 91SumFlyC-11
❑ 91SumFlyP-2334
❑ 92VerBeaDC-26
❑ 92VerBeaDF-2875
❑ 93SanAntMF-3005
❑ 94AlbDukF-844
❑ 94BowBes-B73
❑ 94BowBesR-B73
❑ 94ClaGolF-147
❑ 94ExcFS7-220
❑ 94ExcLeaLF-20
❑ 94Top-783
❑ 94TopGol-783
❑ 94TopSpa-783
❑ 94UppDecML-212
❑ 96SigRooOJ-34
❑ 96SigRooOJS-34

Van Rynback, Casper
❑ 90KinMetB-19
❑ 90KinMetS-23
❑ 91PitMetC-14
❑ 91PitMetP-3424
Van Ryssegem, Guido
❑ 96TulDriTI-28
❑ 97RocRedW-5
Van Schaack, Tom
❑ 90WatIndS-27
Van Scoyoc, Aaron
❑ 89OneYanP-2115
❑ 90GreHorB-20
❑ 90GreHorP-2672
❑ 90GreHorS-24
❑ 91Ft.LauYP-2437
Van Scoyoc, Jim
❑ 91NiaFalRC-6
❑ 91NiaFalRP-3652
❑ 92BriTigC-28
❑ 93BriTigC-29
❑ 94FayGenC-28
❑ 94FayGenF-2165
Van Slyke, Andy
❑ 82ArkTraT-19
❑ 83LouRedR-18
❑ 84Car-31
❑ 84Car5x7-30
❑ 84Don-83
❑ 84Fle-339
❑ 84Nes792-206
❑ 84Top-206
❑ 84TopSti-150
❑ 84TopTif-206
❑ 85CarTeal-33
❑ 85Don-327
❑ 85Fle-242
❑ 85OPC-341
❑ 85Top-551
❑ 85TopMin-551
❑ 85TopSti-138
❑ 85TopTif-551
❑ 86CarIGAS-13
❑ 86CarKASD-19
❑ 86CarSchM-23
❑ 86CarTeal-42
❑ 86CarTeal-43
❑ 86Don-412
❑ 86Fle-48
❑ 86KayB-32
❑ 86OPC-33
❑ 86Top-683
❑ 86TopSti-51
❑ 86TopTif-683
❑ 87Don-417
❑ 87DonOpeD-161
❑ 87Fle-311
❑ 87FleGlo-311
❑ 87FleUpd-121
❑ 87FleUpdG-121
❑ 87OPC-33
❑ 87SpoTeaP-12
❑ 87Top-33
❑ 87TopSti-51
❑ 87TopTif-33
❑ 87TopTra-124T
❑ 87TopTraT-124T
❑ 88Don-18
❑ 88Don-291
❑ 88DonBasB-157
❑ 88DonBonM-BC8
❑ 88DonSupD-18
❑ 88Fle-341
❑ 88FleGlo-341
❑ 88FleLeaL-43
❑ 88FleMin-105
❑ 88FleStiC-116
❑ 88FleTeaL-44
❑ 88Lea-18
❑ 88Lea-102
❑ 88OPC-142
❑ 88PanSti-380
❑ 88PirTeal-32
❑ 88RedFolSB-92
❑ 88Sco-416
❑ 88ScoGlo-416
❑ 88Spo-109
❑ 88StaLinPi-20
❑ 88TarPla-46
❑ 88Top-142
❑ 88TopBig-184
❑ 88TopSti-126
❑ 88TopTif-142
❑ 88TopUKM-81
❑ 88TopUKMT-81
❑ 89Bow-424
❑ 89BowTif-424
❑ 89CadEllD-59
❑ 89ClaTraO-111
❑ 89Don-54
❑ 89DonAll-61
❑ 89DonBasB-45
❑ 89DonBonM-BC10
❑ 89Fle-222
❑ 89FleBasA-42
❑ 89FleBasM-40
❑ 89FleGlo-222
❑ 89FleHeroB-41
❑ 89FleLeaL-41
❑ 89FleWaxBC-C27
❑ 89KeyFooD-17
❑ 89KinDis-19
❑ 89MSAIceTD-17
❑ 89OPC-350
❑ 89OurOwnTD-17
❑ 89PanSti-173
❑ 89PirVerFJ-18
❑ 89Sco-174
❑ 89ScoHot1S-92
❑ 89Scomast-38
❑ 89Spo-166
❑ 89TetTeaD-17
❑ 89Top-350
❑ 89Top-392
❑ 89TopAme2C-30
❑ 89TopBasT-79
❑ 89TopBig-255
❑ 89TopCoi-27
❑ 89TopDouA-19
❑ 89TopGloS-4
❑ 89TopHilTM-30
❑ 89TopMinL-33
❑ 89TopSti-132
❑ 89TopStiB-54
❑ 89TopTif-350
❑ 89TopTif-392
❑ 89TopUKM-79
❑ 89TVSpoM-9
❑ 89UppDec-537
❑ 89UppDec-685
❑ 89WeiMarD-17
❑ 90Bow-171
❑ 90BowTif-171
❑ 90ClaYel-T30
❑ 90Don-244
❑ 90DonBesN-119
❑ 90DonLeaS-3
❑ 90Fle-481
❑ 90FleAwaW-40
❑ 90FleCan-481
❑ 90FleLeaL-40
❑ 90FleLeaLC-40
❑ 90Hot50PS-47
❑ 90Lea-117
❑ 90M.Vpin-84
❑ 90MLBBasB-36
❑ 90OPC-775
❑ 90PanSti-324
❑ 90PirHomC-29
❑ 90PubIntS-166
❑ 90RedFolSB-98
❑ 90Sco-440
❑ 90Sco100S-78
❑ 90Spo-101
❑ 90Top-775
❑ 90TopBig-217
❑ 90TopMinL-72
❑ 90TopSti-124
❑ 90TopTif-775
❑ 90UppDec-536
❑ 91Bow-529
❑ 91ClaGam-45
❑ 91Don-552
❑ 91Fle-53
❑ 91Lea-310
❑ 91OPC-425
❑ 91PanCanT1-106
❑ 91PanFreS-121
❑ 91PanSti-118
❑ 91RedFolS-96
❑ 91Sco-475
❑ 91Sco-698
❑ 91Sco100S-22
❑ 91StaClu-118
❑ 91StaCluP-46
❑ 91Stu-230
❑ 91Top-425
❑ 91TopDesS-425
❑ 91TopMic-425
❑ 91TopTif-425
❑ 91TopTriH-N9
❑ 91Ult-287
❑ 91UppDec-256
❑ 92Bow-35
❑ 92Cla1-T92
❑ 92Cla2-T64
❑ 92ClaGam-153
❑ 92Don-383
❑ 92DonMcD-17
❑ 92Fle-570
❑ 92Hig5-95
❑ 92HitTheBB-35
❑ 92Lea-43
❑ 92LeaBlaG-43
❑ 92LeaGolP-9
❑ 92LeaPre-9
❑ 92Mr.TurS-25
❑ 92New-29
❑ 92OPC-545
❑ 92PanSti-257
❑ 92Pin-9
❑ 92PirNatl-23
❑ 92RedFolS-95
❑ 92Sco-655
❑ 92ScoCokD-21
❑ 92ScoProaG-17
❑ 92SevCoi-7
❑ 92SpoIllFK1-145
❑ 92SpoStaCC-47
❑ 92StaClu-232
❑ 92StaCluD-189
❑ 92Stu-89
❑ 92StuHer-BC10
❑ 92Top-545
❑ 92TopGol-545
❑ 92TopGolW-545
❑ 92TopKid-23
❑ 92TopMic-545
❑ 92TriPla-6
❑ 92TriPla-148
❑ 92TriPlaP-3
❑ 92Ult-262
❑ 92UltAwaW-10
❑ 92UppDec-132
❑ 92UppDec-711
❑ 92UppDec-715
❑ 93Bow-218
❑ 93ClaGam-93
❑ 93ColAllG-12
❑ 93DenHol-19
❑ 93DiaMar-111
❑ 93Don-414
❑ 93DonDiaK-DK9
❑ 93DonEli-32
❑ 93DonEliS-14
❑ 93DonPre-9
❑ 93DurPowP2-8
❑ 93Fin-185
❑ 93FinRef-185
❑ 93Fla-117
❑ 93Fle-122
❑ 93FleAll-NL8
❑ 93FleAtl-24
❑ 93FleFruotL-62
❑ 93FlePro-B1
❑ 93FleTeaL-NL10
❑ 93FunPac-148
❑ 93FunPac-151
❑ 93Hos-1
❑ 93HumDumC-46
❑ 93JimDea-4
❑ 93Kra-30
❑ 93Lea-79
❑ 93LeaGolA-R7
❑ 93MetBak-39
❑ 93OPC-355
❑ 93OPCPre-88
❑ 93PacSpa-253
❑ 93PanSti-285
❑ 93Pin-19
❑ 93PinTeaP-9
❑ 93PirNatl-33
❑ 93Pos-27
❑ 93PosCan-11
❑ 93RedFolS-100
❑ 93RedFolS-128
❑ 93Sco-12
❑ 93Sco-524
❑ 93Sco-535
❑ 93ScoFra-23
❑ 93ScoGolDT-4
❑ 93Sel-35
❑ 93SelChaS-6
❑ 93SelStaL-5
❑ 93SelStaL-10
❑ 93SelStaL-16
❑ 93SelStaL-24
❑ 93SelStaL-42
❑ 93SP-188
❑ 93StaClu-294
❑ 93StaClu-394
❑ 93StaCluFDI-294
❑ 93StaCluFDI-394
❑ 93StaCluM-14
❑ 93StaCluMOP-294
❑ 93StaCluMOP-394
❑ 93Stu-132
❑ 93Top-275
❑ 93Top-405
❑ 93TOPBLAG-21
❑ 93TopGol-275
❑ 93TopGol-405
❑ 93TopInaM-275
❑ 93TopInaM-405
❑ 93TopInaR-275
❑ 93TopInaR-405
❑ 93TopMic-275
❑ 93TopMic-405
❑ 93TriPla-8
❑ 93TriPlaA-1
❑ 93TriPlaP-8
❑ 93Ult-103
❑ 93UltAwaW-8
❑ 93UppDec-124
❑ 93UppDec-480
❑ 93UppDecDG-19
❑ 93UppDecGold-124
❑ 93UppDecGold-480
❑ 93UppDecIC-WI18
❑ 93UppDecICJ-WI18
❑ 93UppDecOD-D25
❑ 93USPlaCA-11D
❑ 94Bow-50
❑ 94BowBes-R77
❑ 94BowBesR-R77
❑ 94ColC-280
❑ 94ColC-346
❑ 94ColChoGS-280
❑ 94ColChoGS-346
❑ 94ColChoSS-280
❑ 94ColChoSS-346
❑ 94ColChoT-15
❑ 94DenHol-26
❑ 94Don-375
❑ 94DonSpeE-375
❑ 94Fin-408
❑ 94FinRef-408
❑ 94Fla-426
❑ 94Fle-622
❑ 94FleExtB-352
❑ 94FleSun-24
❑ 94FUnPac-18
❑ 94KinDis-23
❑ 94Kra-30
❑ 94Lea-411
❑ 94LeaL-143
❑ 94OPC-86
❑ 94OscMayR-30
❑ 94Pac-509
❑ 94PanSti-240
❑ 94Pin-16
❑ 94PinArtP-16
❑ 94PinMusC-16
❑ 94PirBloP-2
❑ 94PirQui-24
❑ 94ProMag-109
❑ 94RedFolMI-3
❑ 94Sco-18
❑ 94ScoDreT-8
❑ 94ScoGolR-18
❑ 94ScoGolS-19
❑ 94Sel-129
❑ 94SP-144
❑ 94SPDieC-144
❑ 94SPHol-38
❑ 94SPHolDC-38
❑ 94Spo-76
❑ 94StaClu-687
❑ 94StaCluFDI-687
❑ 94StaCluGR-687
❑ 94StaCluMOP-687
❑ 94StaCluMOP-ST11
❑ 94StaCluST-ST11
❑ 94Stu-150
❑ 94Top-650
❑ 94TopGol-650
❑ 94TopSpa-650
❑ 94TopSupS-42
❑ 94TriPla-189
❑ 94TriPlaM-12
❑ 94Ult-560
❑ 94UppDec-83
❑ 94UppDecAJ-27
❑ 94UppDecAJG-27
❑ 94UppDecDC-C9
❑ 94UppDecED-83
❑ 95ColCho-390
❑ 95ColCho-564T
❑ 95ColChoGS-390
❑ 95ColChoSE-180
❑ 95ColChoSEGS-180
❑ 95ColChoSESS-180
❑ 95ColChoSS-390
❑ 95Don-389
❑ 95DonPreP-389
❑ 95Fin-216
❑ 95FinRef-216
❑ 95Fla-225
❑ 95Fle-490
❑ 95FleUpd-7
❑ 95Pac-353
❑ 95PacPri-114
❑ 95Pin-396
❑ 95PinArtP-396
❑ 95PinMusC-396
❑ 95RedFol-30
❑ 95Sco-352
❑ 95ScoGolR-352
❑ 95ScoPlaTS-352
❑ 95ScoYouTE-352T
❑ 95Sel-182
❑ 95SelArtP-182
❑ 95StaClu-153
❑ 95StaClu-541
❑ 95StaCluFDI-153
❑ 95StaCluMOP-153
❑ 95StaCluMOP-541
❑ 95StaCluSTWS-153
❑ 95StaCluSTWS-541
❑ 95Top-260
❑ 95TopCyb-141
❑ 95Ult-427
❑ 95UltGolM-427
❑ 95UppDec-149
❑ 95UppDec-368
❑ 95UppDecED-149
❑ 95UppDecED-368
❑ 95UppDecEDG-149
❑ 95UppDecEDG-368
❑ 96Don-11
❑ 96DonPreP-11
❑ 96Fle-510
❑ 96FleTif-510
❑ 96Pac-153
❑ 96Sco-171
❑ 96ScoDugC-A97
❑ 96ScoDugCAP-A97
❑ 96StaClu-52
❑ 96StaCluMOP-52
Van Stone, Paul
❑ 85EveGialC-21
❑ 86CliGiaP-25
Van Tiger, Tom
❑ 91WatIndC-29
❑ 91WatIndP-3384
❑ 92KinIndC-21
Van Vuren, Bob
❑ 86Ft.MyeRP-26
Van Wermer, Marc
❑ 97SouBenSH-30
❑ 98SouBenSHM-23
Van Winkle, Dave
❑ 89UtiBluSP-1
❑ 90SouBenWSB-4
❑ 90SouBenWSGS-19
❑ 91CalLeLA-5
❑ 91PalSprAP-2015
Van Wyck, Jim
❑ 74TacTwiC-21
❑ 76TacTwiDQ-20
❑ 77TacTwiDQ-1
Van Zandt, Jon
❑ 93ElmPioC-24
❑ 93ElmPioF-3823
Vanacore, Derek
❑ 85Ft.MyeRT-29
VanBuren, Chris
❑ 87BelMarTI-32
Vance, Dazzy (Clarence A.)
❑ 19Zee-64
❑ 25Exh-15
❑ 28Exh-8
❑ 28PorandAR-A37
❑ 28PorandAR-B37
❑ 28StaPlaCE-69
❑ 28W512-10
❑ 28W56PlaC-S6
❑ 29ExhFou-3
❑ 29PorandAR-93
❑ 30SchR33-45
❑ 30UncJac-27
❑ 31Exh-3
❑ 31W517-36
❑ 33CraJacP-23
❑ 33ExhFou-2
❑ 33Gou-2
❑ 33GouCanV-2
❑ 33WorCig-91
❑ 34BabRutG-60
❑ 34ButPreR-59
❑ 34DiaMatCSB-185
❑ 35GouPuzR-4C
❑ 35GouPuzR-7C
❑ 35GouPuzR-12C
❑ 50CalHOFW-72
❑ 51R42SmaS-109
❑ 53ArtHaloFP-82
❑ 60Fle-51
❑ 61Fle-81
❑ 61GolPre-26
❑ 63BazA-28
❑ 70MetMusoAB-7
❑ 72FleFamF-4
❑ 72LauGreF-21
❑ 74CapPub-63
❑ 74Car193T-23
❑ 76GrePlaG-31
❑ 76RowExh-11
❑ 76ShaPiz-77
❑ 77BobParHoF-76
❑ 77GalGloG-104
❑ 77GalGloG-266
❑ 78DexHaloFP-49
❑ 80DodGreT-9
❑ 80PerHaloFP-79
❑ 80SSPHOF-79
❑ 82DiaCla-68
❑ 82TCMGreP-38
❑ 89DodSmoG-29
❑ 89HOFStiB-73
❑ 90DodTar-817
❑ 92ConTSN-377
❑ 92YanWIZH-33
❑ 93ConTSN-929
❑ 94ConTSN-1055
❑ 94ConTSNB-1055
❑ 95ConTSN-1371
Vance, Joe
❑ 72TCMthe3-70
Vance, Sandy (Gene)
❑ 71OPC-34
❑ 71Top-34
❑ 75YanDyn1T-47
❑ 85SpoIndGC-23
❑ 90DodTar-818
Vancho, Bob (Robert)
❑ 89HelBreSP-18
❑ 90BelBreB-23
❑ 90BelBreS-22
❑ 90MidLeaASGS-22
❑ 91StoPorC-4
❑ 91StoPorP-3032
VandeBerg, Ed
❑ 81SpoIndT-15
❑ 82MarPos-31
❑ 82TopTra-122T
❑ 83Don-100
❑ 83Fle-488
❑ 83FleSta-206
❑ 83FleSti-180
❑ 83OPC-183
❑ 83Top-183
❑ 83TopSti-317
❑ 84Don-604
❑ 84Fle-623
❑ 84MarMot-8
❑ 84Nes792-63
❑ 84OPC-63
❑ 84Top-63
❑ 84TopTif-63
❑ 85Don-511
❑ 85Fle-504
❑ 85MarMot-5
❑ 85OPC-207
❑ 85Top-566
❑ 85TopMin-566
❑ 85TopSti-336
❑ 85TopTif-566
❑ 86DodCokP-31
❑ 86DodPol-31
❑ 86DodUniOP-22
❑ 86Don-637
❑ 86Fle-479
❑ 86FleUpd-121
❑ 86OPC-357

❑ 86Top-357
❑ 86TopTif-357
❑ 86TopTra-118T
❑ 86TopTraT-118T
❑ 87Don-376
❑ 87Fle-458
❑ 87FleGlo-458
❑ 87FleUpd-120
❑ 87FleUpdG-120
❑ 87IndGat-36
❑ 87OPC-34
❑ 87Top-717
❑ 87TopTif-717
❑ 87TopTra-123T
❑ 87TopTraT-123T
❑ 88AlaGolAA70TI-22
❑ 88Fle-619
❑ 88FleGlo-619
❑ 88OklCit8C-8
❑ 88OklCit8P-52
❑ 88Top-421
❑ 88TopTif-421
❑ 89Fle-534A
❑ 89Fle-534B
❑ 89FleGlo-534
❑ 89IowCubC-4
❑ 89IowCubP-1710
❑ 89Top-242
❑ 89TopTif-242
❑ 90CalCanC-8
❑ 90CMC-435
❑ 90DodTar-820
❑ 91CalCanLD-73
❑ 91CalCanP-517
❑ 91LinDriAAA-73
❑ 92CalCanF-3731
❑ 93RanKee-365
Vandemark, John
❑ 94BatCliC-25
❑ 94BatCliF-3447
❑ 95ClePhiF-217
❑ 97ClePhi-24
❑ 98FarRedHM-25
Vandenberg, Hy
❑ 33WorCig(-96
❑ 33WorCig(-97
❑ 40PlaBal-209
❑ 44CubTeal-23
❑ 79DiaGre-106
Vanderbush, Matt
❑ 96ForWayWB-26
Vanderbush, Walt
❑ 83BeaGolGT-5
❑ 84LasVegSC-229
❑ 85LasVegSC-111
VanderGriend, Jon
❑ 95BoiHawTI-31
❑ 96CedRapKTI-25
❑ 96HilStaHWB-35
❑ 97LakElsSG-29
VanderMeer, John
❑ 38CloFotW-83
❑ 38RedOraW-27
❑ 38RedOraW-28
❑ 39ExhSal-59
❑ 39OrcPhoAP-31
❑ 39OrcPhoAP-33
❑ 39RedTeal-22
❑ 41DouPlaR-5
❑ 41HarHarW-25
❑ 41PlaBal-56
❑ 43MPR302-1-23
❑ 47Exh-227
❑ 47HomBon-47
❑ 48BluTin-46
❑ 48SweSpoT-10
❑ 49Bow-128
❑ 49EurSta-96
❑ 49Lea-53
❑ 50Bow-79
❑ 51Bow-223
❑ 60NuHi-5
❑ 61Fle-147
❑ 67TopVen-175
❑ 72LauGreF-7
❑ 74LauAllG-38
❑ 76LauDiaJ-12
❑ 76TayBow4-42
❑ 77CinRedT-43
❑ 77GalGloG-73
❑ 77GalGloG-243
❑ 77RedCarP-24
❑ 77Spo-624
❑ 77TCMTheWY-68
❑ 79DiaGre-263
❑ 80PacLeg-110
❑ 82OhiHaloF-21
❑ 84OCoandSI-128
❑ 84OCoandSI-215
❑ 85BigLeaC3-34
❑ 87SpoRea-10
❑ 88PacLegI-30
❑ 89SweBasG-11
❑ 90BasWit-80
❑ 90HOFStiB-36
❑ 90SweBasG-99
❑ 91SweBasG-61
❑ 92ConTSN-367
❑ 92ConTSN-368
❑ 94ConTSN-1181
❑ 94ConTSNB-1181
❑ 94TedWil-24
❑ 94UppDecAH-2
❑ 94UppDecAH-38
❑ 94UppDecAH1-2
❑ 94UppDecAH1-38
❑ 97FleMilDM-7
❑ 97FleMilDMR-7
❑ 99UppDecCL-128
❑ 99UppDecCLCC-128
Vandersall, Mark
❑ 92Min-22
VanderWal, John
❑ 87JamExpP-2551
❑ 88FloStaLAS-23
❑ 88WesPalBES-25
❑ 89JacExpB-25
❑ 89JacExpP-161
❑ 90Bes-90
❑ 90JacExpB-13
❑ 90JacExpP-1388
❑ 91IndIndLD-197
❑ 91IndIndP-476
❑ 91LinDriAAA-197
❑ 91TriA AAGP-AAA17
❑ 92Bow-232
❑ 92Cla2-T32
❑ 92Don-414
❑ 92ExpDonD-16A
❑ 92ExpPos-28
❑ 92FleUpd-99
❑ 92Lea-416
❑ 92LeaBlaG-416
❑ 92OPC-343
❑ 92Pin-559
❑ 92ProFS7-255
❑ 92ScoRoo-105T
❑ 92StaClu-385
❑ 92Top-343
❑ 92TopDeb91-174
❑ 92TopGol-343
❑ 92TopGolW-343
❑ 92TopMic-343
❑ 92Ult-523
❑ 93Don-144
❑ 93Fle-80
❑ 93Lea-19
❑ 93OPC-376
❑ 93PacSpa-189
❑ 93PanSti-229
❑ 93Pin-322
❑ 93Sco-359
❑ 93Sel-323
❑ 93StaClu-442
❑ 93StaCluFDI-442
❑ 93StaCluMOP-442
❑ 93Top-69
❑ 93TopGol-69
❑ 93TopInaM-69
❑ 93TopInaR-69
❑ 93TopMic-69
❑ 93Ult-419
❑ 93UppDec-619
❑ 93UppDecGold-619
❑ 93USPlaCR-5H
❑ 94Don-571
❑ 94Fle-553
❑ 94Pac-391
❑ 94Sco-180
❑ 94ScoGolR-180
❑ 94StaClu-161
❑ 94StaCluFDI-161
❑ 94StaCluGR-161
❑ 94StaCluMOP-161
❑ 94Top-563
❑ 94TopGol-563
❑ 94TopSpa-563
❑ 95Don-73
❑ 95DonPreP-73
❑ 95Fle-529
❑ 95Pac-146
❑ 95Sco-198
❑ 95ScoGolR-198
❑ 95ScoPlaTS-198
❑ 95StaClu-86
❑ 95StaCluFDI-86
❑ 95StaCluMOP-86
❑ 95StaCluSTWS-86
❑ 96ColCho-133
❑ 96ColCho-757
❑ 96ColChoGS-133
❑ 96ColChoGS-757
❑ 96ColChoSS-133
❑ 96ColChoSS-757
❑ 96Fle-376
❑ 96FleTif-376
❑ 96RocFle-15
❑ 96RocPol-24
❑ 97ColCho-102
❑ 97ColChoT-CR7
❑ 97Pac-290
❑ 97PacLigB-290
❑ 97PacSil-290
❑ 97StaClu-350
❑ 97StaCluMOP-350
❑ 98PacOnl-258
❑ 98PacOnlR-258
❑ 98PacOnlWC-258
VanderWeele, Doug
❑ 91EveGiaC-2
❑ 91EveGiaP-3912
❑ 92ClaFS7-368
❑ 92CliGiaC-17
❑ 93SanJosGC-24
❑ 93SanJosGF-8
❑ 94SanJosGC-24
❑ 94SanJosGF-2818
❑ 96PhoFirB-26
❑ 97PhoFirTI-25
Vanderwel, Bill
❑ 86SalAngC-84
❑ 87PalSprP-13
❑ 88PalSprACLC-94
❑ 88PalSprAP-1457
❑ 89QuaCitAB-15
❑ 89QuaCitAGS-16
❑ 90SouBenWSB-23
Vanegmond, Tim
❑ 92ClaFS7-390
❑ 92LynRedSC-23
❑ 92LynRedSF-2908
❑ 92UppDecML-121
❑ 93ClaGolF-24
❑ 93NewBriRSF-1222
❑ 94Bow-63
❑ 94ExcFS7-22
❑ 94PawRedSDD-28
❑ 94PawRedSF-948
❑ 94UppDecML-137
❑ 95ColCho-412
❑ 95ColChoGS-412
❑ 95ColChoSS-412
❑ 95FleUpd-15
❑ 95UppDec-399
❑ 95UppDecED-399
❑ 95UppDecEDG-399
❑ 97PacPriGotD-GD59
❑ 98LouRedQ-22
Vangilder, Elam
❑ 27AmeCarE126-47
❑ 33WorCig(-98
❑ 33WorCig(-99
❑ 92ConTSN-569
Vanhof, Dave
❑ 94BelMarC-1
❑ 94BelMarF-3236
❑ 94Bow-89
❑ 95UppDecML-156
❑ 95UppDecMLFS-156
Vanhof, John
❑ 92FroRowDP-85
❑ 92FroRowDPG-85
❑ 92FroRowDPS-85
❑ 93ClaGolF-146
❑ 95Exc-122
❑ 96WisTimRB-27
Vaninetti, Gene
❑ 93AusFut-7
❑ 94HagSunC-25
❑ 94HagSunF-2741
❑ 94MedHatBJF-3691
❑ 94MedHatBJSP-4
VanLandingham, Bill (William)
❑ 91EveGiaC-24
❑ 91EveGiaP-3913
❑ 92ClaFS7-251
❑ 92CliGiaF-3598
❑ 92ProFS7-356
❑ 92SanJosGC-4
❑ 93SanJosGC-25
❑ 93SanJosGF-9
❑ 94Bow-491
❑ 94ExcFS7-295
❑ 94Fla-447
❑ 94FlaWavotF-B10
❑ 94FleUpd-198
❑ 94LeaLimR-20
❑ 94ShrCapF-1608
❑ 94SpoRoo-70
❑ 94SpoRooAP-70
❑ 94TopTra-105T
❑ 94UppDec-521
❑ 94UppDecED-521
❑ 94UppDecML-138
❑ 95Bow-354
❑ 95ColCho-255
❑ 95ColChoGS-255
❑ 95ColChoSE-109
❑ 95ColChoSEGS-109
❑ 95ColChoSESS-109
❑ 95ColChoSS-255
❑ 95Don-12
❑ 95DonPreP-12
❑ 95DonTopotO-359
❑ 95Fin-6
❑ 95FinRef-6
❑ 95Fla-212
❑ 95Fle-592
❑ 95FleRooS-19
❑ 95GiaMot-16
❑ 95Lea-51
❑ 95Pac-386
❑ 95PacPri-122
❑ 95PanSti-102
❑ 95Pin-351
❑ 95PinMusC-351
❑ 95Sco-181
❑ 95ScoGolR-181
❑ 95ScoPlaTS-181
❑ 95StaClu-158
❑ 95StaCluFDI-158
❑ 95StaCluMOP-158
❑ 95StaCluSTWS-158
❑ 95StaCluVR-83
❑ 95StaCluVRMO-83
❑ 95Stu-63
❑ 95Top-611
❑ 95TopCyb-379
❑ 95TopEmb-82
❑ 95TopEmbGI-82
❑ 95Ult-246
❑ 95UltGolM-246
❑ 95UltSecYS-14
❑ 95UltSecYSGM-14
❑ 95UppDec-84
❑ 95UppDecED-84
❑ 95UppDecEDG-84
❑ 95UppDecSE-201
❑ 95UppDecSEG-201
❑ 96ColCho-309
❑ 96ColChoGS-309
❑ 96ColChoSS-309
❑ 96Don-129
❑ 96DonPreP-129
❑ 96EmoXL-295
❑ 96Fla-393
❑ 96Fle-599
❑ 96FleTif-599
❑ 96GiaMot-13
❑ 96LeaSigEA-207
❑ 96MetUni-246
❑ 96MetUniP-246
❑ 96Pac-214
❑ 96PanSti-108
❑ 96Sco-164
❑ 96SP-167
❑ 96StaClu-158
❑ 96StaCluMOP-158
❑ 96Ult-299
❑ 96UltGolM-299
❑ 96UppDec-196
❑ 97Cir-71
❑ 97CirRav-71
❑ 97ColCho-216
❑ 97Fin-123
❑ 97FinEmb-123
❑ 97FinEmbR-123
❑ 97FinRef-123
❑ 97Fle-486
❑ 97FleTif-486
❑ 97Sco-418
❑ 97ScoArtPWB-418
❑ 97ScoResC-418
❑ 97ScoShoS-418
❑ 97ScoShoSAP-418
❑ 97SP-162
❑ 97StaClu-129
❑ 97StaCluMOP-129
❑ 97Top-131
❑ 97UppDec-171
Vann, Brandy
❑ 86SalAngC-80
❑ 87QuaCitAP-12
❑ 88QuaCitAGS-29
❑ 89PalSprACLC-53
❑ 89PalSprAP-471
❑ 90PalSprACLC-218
❑ 90PalSprAP-2577
❑ 91ElPasDLD-198
❑ 91LinDriAA-198
❑ 91StoPorP-3033
❑ 92ElPasDF-3923
❑ 92ElPasDS-223
❑ 93NorTidF-2570
Vann, John
❑ 16Zee-94
Vannaman, Tim
❑ 88SouOreAP-1693
❑ 89MadMusS-22
❑ 90ModA'sCLC-159
❑ 90ModA'sP-2227
Vannell, Dan
❑ 90BenBucL-20
Vanni, Edo
❑ 47CenFlo-30
❑ 57SeaPop-23
❑ 64SeaPop-18
VanRyn, Ben
❑ 97IowCub-28
Vantrease, Bob
❑ 83IdaFalAT-12
❑ 84IdaFalATI-26
Vanzytveld, Jeffrey
❑ 89VerBeaDS-26
❑ 90FloStaLAS-46
❑ 90VerBeaDS-26
❑ 91VerBeaDC-26
Vardijan, Dan
❑ 96KanCouCTI-27
❑ 96KanCouCUTI-12
❑ 97BreCouMB-31
Vargas, Andy
❑ 22Zee-110
❑ 23Zee-149
❑ 24Zee-108
❑ 26Zee-153
❑ 27Zee-125
❑ 28Zee-146
Vargas, Angel
❑ 76VenLeaS-98
Vargas, Cesar
❑ 94VenLinU-220
Vargas, Derrick
❑ 98PorRocG-29
Vargas, Eddie
❑ 78ChaPirT-24
❑ 80BufBisT-15
❑ 81BufBisT-23
❑ 82PorBeaT-17
Vargas, Eric
❑ 91ButCopKSP-15
Vargas, Gonzalo
❑ 89St.CatBJP-2083
Vargas, Guillaume
❑ 52LavPro-109
Vargas, Hector
❑ 87OneYanP-5
❑ 87PriWilYP-21
❑ 88BlaYNPRWL-21
❑ 88OneYanP-2049
❑ 89BlaYNPRWL-187
❑ 89PriWilCS-23
❑ 90Ft.LauYS-21
❑ 90StaFS7-42
❑ 91AlbYanLD-22
❑ 91AlbYanP-1018
❑ 91LinDriAA-22
❑ 92AlbYanF-2235
❑ 92AlbYanSk-21
❑ 93OttLynF-2444
❑ 94BowBayF-2422
Vargas, Hedi
❑ 84Pir-26
❑ 85HawIslC-236
❑ 88BlaYNPRWL-51
❑ 88ChaLooB-8
❑ 88NasSouTI-24
❑ 89BlaYNPRWL-188
❑ 89ChaLooLITI-31
❑ 89MidAngGS-29
Vargas, Iankel Arias
❑ 98WesMicWM-26
Vargas, Jose
❑ 86OscAstP-27
❑ 86SalRedBP-26
❑ 87OscAstP-15
❑ 87PorChaRP-17
❑ 88ColAstB-8
❑ 88TulDriTI-7
❑ 89OscAstS-26
❑ 90ArkTraGS-29
❑ 91LinDriAA-645
❑ 91WilBilLD-645
❑ 91WilBilP-294
Vargas, Julio
❑ 89MarPhiS-32
❑ 89Sta-145
❑ 90PriPatD-25
❑ 91BatCliCB-5
❑ 91BatCliP-3487
Vargas, Leo (Leonel)
❑ 82RicBraT-20
❑ 83RicBraT-21
❑ 84RicBraT-12
❑ 85DomLeaS-90
❑ 85GreBraTI-23
Vargas, Miguel
❑ 87ReaPhiP-5
Vargas, Ramon
❑ 83AndBraT-19
Vargas, Roberto
❑ 53BraSpiaS3-26
Vargo, Ed
❑ 81TCM60I-423
Varitek, Jason
❑ 92TopTra-123T
❑ 92TopTraG-123T
❑ 93StaCluM-197
❑ 94SigRooDP-14
❑ 94SigRooDPS-14
❑ 95ARuFalLS-19
❑ 95PorCitRTI-25
❑ 95SPML-153
❑ 96BesAutS-91
❑ 96PorCitRB-27
❑ 97Bes-65
❑ 97BesAutSBPP-45
❑ 97TacRai-27
❑ 98ColCho-121
❑ 98Don-296
❑ 98DonGolPP-296
❑ 98DonSilPP-296
❑ 98Fle-542
❑ 98FleProF-PF18
❑ 98LeaRS-241
❑ 98LeaRSLHolo-241
❑ 98LeaRSLong-241
❑ 98LeaRTrue-241
❑ 98PacAur-20
❑ 98PacOme-43
❑ 98PacOmeR-43
❑ 98PacOmeRS-13
❑ 98PacOmeRST5-13
❑ 98PacOnl-129
❑ 98PacOnlR-129
❑ 98PacOnlWC-129
❑ 98Stu-46
❑ 98StuGPP-46
❑ 98StuSPP-46
❑ 98UppDec-276
❑ 98UppDecDS-DS46
❑ 99Fle-574
❑ 99FleSta9-574
❑ 99FleWarT-574
❑ 99Pac-76
❑ 99PacOme-45
❑ 99PacOmeC-45
❑ 99PacOmeG-45
❑ 99PacOmePB-45
❑ 99PacPlaB-76
❑ 99PacRed-76
❑ 99SP SigAuto-JV
❑ 99SPSig-160
❑ 99UD Cho-65
❑ 99UD ChoPCR-65
❑ 99UppDec-326
❑ 99UppDecEL1-326
❑ 99UppDecEL2-326
❑ 99UppDecM-33
❑ 99UppDecMGS-33
❑ 99UppDecMHFS-33
❑ 99UppDecMSS-33
❑ 99Vic-65
Varnell, Dan
❑ 90EveGiaB-2

□ 90EveGiaP-3144
Varnell, Richard
□ 89OneYanP-2117
Varner, Buck
□ 88ChaLooLTI-29
Varney, Pete
□ 76OPC-413
□ 76SSP-154
□ 76Top-413
Varni, Patrick
□ 88CapCodPPaLP-182
□ 90MiaMirlS-25
Varoz, Brett
□ 85AncGlaPTI-29
Varoz, Eric
□ 86BeaGolGP-24
Varsho, Gary
□ 84MidCubT-23
□ 86PitCubP-24
□ 87IowCubTI-23
□ 88CubDavB-24
□ 88FleUpd-81
□ 88FleUpdG-81
□ 88IowCubC-22
□ 88IowCubP-535
□ 89Fle-441
□ 89FleGlo-441
□ 89Sco-604
□ 89Top-613
□ 89TopTif-613
□ 89UppDec-321A
□ 89UppDec-321B
□ 90CMC-96
□ 90IowCubC-21
□ 90IowCubP-332
□ 90ProAAAF-639
□ 90PublntS-206
□ 90TopTVCu-61
□ 91Bow-510
□ 91Don-671
□ 91Fle-435
□ 91FleUpd-114
□ 91Lea-500
□ 91ScoRoo-72T
□ 91UltUpd-104
□ 92Don-644
□ 92Fle-571
□ 92Lea-388
□ 92LeaBlaG-388
□ 92OPC-122
□ 92PirNatI-24
□ 92Sco-481
□ 92StaClu-568
□ 92Stu-90
□ 92Top-122
□ 92TopGol-122
□ 92TopGolW-122
□ 92TopMic-122
□ 92Ult-561
□ 92UppDec-217
□ 93Don-42
□ 93PanSti-287
□ 93RedKah-27
□ 93Top-326
□ 93TopGol-326
□ 93ToplnaM-326
□ 93ToplnaR-326
□ 93TopMic-326
□ 94Pac-163
□ 95Phi-32
□ 95PhiMel-23
□ 95Sco-204
□ 95ScoGolR-204
□ 95ScoPlaTS-204
□ 97WisTimR-1
□ 98WisTimRM-26
Varva, Joe
□ 92YakBeaC-24
Varverde, Miguel
□ 86WatPirP-26
Vaske, Terry
□ 94WilCubC-23
□ 94WilCubF-3774
□ 95MacBraTI-28
Vasquez, Aguedo
□ 88BasCitRS-23
□ 88FloStaLAS-50
□ 89MemChiB-5
□ 89MemChiP-1186
□ 89MemChiS-22
□ 90JacMetGS-19
□ 91LinDriAA-646
□ 91WilBilLD-646
□ 91WilBilP-295
Vasquez, Alejandro
□ 98QuaCitRBG-28
Vasquez, Angelo
□ 85BurRanT-13
Vasquez, Antonio
□ 97BurIndG-29
Vasquez, Archie
□ 96BirBarB-20
Vasquez, Armando
□ 95NegLeaLI-14
Vasquez, Chris
□ 90BilMusP-3235
□ 91ChaWheC-26
□ 91ChaWheP-2901
□ 92CedRapRC-19
□ 92CedRapRF-1087
□ 93WinSpiC-24
□ 93WinSpiF-1583
□ 94WinSpiC-24
□ 94WinSpiF-285
Vasquez, Danny
□ 95ChaRivTI-15
□ 95HudValRTI-10
Vasquez, Dennis
□ 80AppFoxT-11
□ 81GleFalWST-7
Vasquez, Eddy
□ 93MedHatBJF-3747
□ 93MedHatBJSP-8
□ 94St.CatBJC-26
□ 94St.CatBJF-3655
Vasquez, Francisco
□ 79ElmPioRST-18
Vasquez, George
□ 73CedRapAT-12
□ 75SacSolC-9
Vasquez, Geraldo
□ 98JohCCTI-33
Vasquez, Jesse
□ 80BurBeeT-12
□ 85NewOriT-22
□ 86HagSunP-26
Vasquez, Julian
□ 89ColMetGS-25
□ 90ColMetGS-15
□ 90ColMetPPI-3
□ 91Cla/Bes-359
□ 91St.LucMC-16
□ 91St.LucMP-710
□ 92BinMetF-515
□ 92BinMetS-68
□ 92Bow-357
□ 92ClaFS7-27
□ 92MetColP-31
□ 92ProFS7-283
□ 92SkyAA F-31
□ 92TidTidF-898
□ 92UppDecML-72
□ 93ExcFS7-80
□ 93VanCanF-2599
Vasquez, Julio
□ 91IdaFalBSP-12
Vasquez, Leoner
□ 98BinMetQ-28
□ 98St.LucMM-15
Vasquez, Luis
□ 85ElmPioT-23
□ 86FloStaLAP-48
□ 86WinHavRSP-26
□ 87NewBriRSP-5
□ 88EasLeaAP-24
□ 88NewBriRSP-889
□ 89NasSouC-10
□ 89NasSouP-1285
□ 89NasSouTI-25
□ 91LinDriAAA-272
□ 91NasSouLD-272
□ 91NasSouP-2156
□ 94VenLinU-93
□ 95LinVen-249
Vasquez, Manny
□ 97ChaRivDG-28
Vasquez, Marcos
□ 90DurBulTI-10
□ 92DurBulC-19
□ 92DurBulTI-20
□ 92GreBraF-1154
□ 93GreBraF-350
□ 95ChaLooTI-24
Vasquez, Rafael
□ 77SalPirT-25
□ 80TacTigT-9
□ 80Top-672
□ 81BufBisT-11
Vasquez, Tony
□ 89CedRapRB-27
Vatcher, James
□ 87UtiBluSP-9
□ 88SouAtlLAGS-26
□ 88SpaPhiP-1045
□ 88SpaPhiS-5
□ 89ClePhiS-23
□ 89Sta-14
□ 90CMC-243
□ 90ProAAAF-315
□ 90ScrRedBC-17
□ 90ScrRedBP-613
□ 91Don-753
□ 91Fle-708
□ 91LasVegSLD-296
□ 91LasVegSP-251
□ 91LinDriAAA-296
□ 91OPC-196
□ 91PadMag-11
□ 91PadSmo-37
□ 91Sco-341
□ 91Top-196
□ 91TopDeb90-159
□ 91TopDesS-196
□ 91TopMic-196
□ 91TopTif-196
□ 91UppDec-604
□ 92Don-563
□ 92LasVegSF-2808
□ 92LasVegSS-244
□ 92SkyAAAF-119
□ 92StaClu-78
□ 93LasVegSF-959
□ 94NorTidF-2935
Vatter, Scott
□ 94ButCopKSP-7
Vaughan, Arky (J. Floyd)
□ 33Gou-229
□ 34BatR31-21
□ 34Gou-22
□ 34GouCanV-70
□ 35ExhFou-7
□ 36ExhFou-7
□ 36GouWidPPR-A105
□ 36NatChiFPR-73
□ 36R31PasP-47
□ 36R31Pre-L13
□ 36SandSW-47
□ 36WheBB3-11
□ 36WheBB4-10
□ 36WorWidGV-6
□ 37ExhFou-7
□ 37KelPepS-BB16
□ 37WheBB14-16A
□ 37WheBB14-16B
□ 37WheBB6-5
□ 37WheBB7-29L
□ 37WheBB9-16
□ 38ExhFou-7
□ 38WheBB15-10
□ 39ExhSal-60
□ 39GouPreR303A-44
□ 39GouPreR303B-22
□ 39PlaBal-55
□ 39WheBB12-9
□ 39WorWidGTP-44
□ 40PlaBal-107
□ 41DouPlaR-33
□ 41PlaBal-10
□ 42DodTeal-22
□ 43DodTeal-21
□ 48DodTeal-25
□ 49SomandK-18
□ 60Fle-11
□ 61Fle-148
□ 74LauAllG-41
□ 74NewYorNTDiS-12
□ 75ShaPiz-15
□ 77GalGloG-77
□ 80PacLeg-122
□ 80PerHaloFP-192
□ 80SSPHOF-193
□ 82DiaCla-8
□ 82TCMGreH-44
□ 83ConMar-32
□ 83TCMPla1942-29
□ 85BigLeaC3-90
□ 87SpoCubG-3
□ 88ConNatA-22
□ 89DodSmoG-30
□ 89HOFStiB-21
□ 89PacLegI-200
□ 90DodTar-821
□ 90PerGreM-71
□ 91ConTSN-38
□ 93ActPacA-109
□ 93ActPacA2-43G
□ 93DiaStaES-151
□ 94ConTSN-1102
□ 94ConTSNB-1102
Vaughan, Charles
□ 67OPC-179
□ 67Top-179
Vaughan, Glenn
□ 77FriOneYW-45
Vaughan, Porter (Cecil Porter)
□ 77TCMTheWY-59
Vaughan, Rick
□ 88St.CatBJP-2033
□ 89MyrBeaBJP-1629
Vaughan, Robert
□ 17Zee-18
Vaughn, Billy
□ 76LauIndC-10
□ 76LauIndC-38
Vaughn, Clint
□ 98BilMusTI-36
Vaughn, Derek
□ 91SpoIndC-8
□ 91SpoIndP-3964
□ 92WatDiaC-16
□ 92WatDiaF-2155
□ 93PocPosF-4221
□ 93PocPosSP-20
□ 94LakElsSC-25
□ 94LakElsSF-1679
□ 95LakElsSTI-26
Vaughn, DeWayne
□ 82LynMetT-7
□ 84JacMetT-1
□ 86TidTidP-28
□ 87TidTidP-2
□ 87TidTidT-8
□ 88DonRoo-25
□ 88RanMot-24
□ 93RanKee-366
Vaughn, Farmer (Henry)
□ 87OldJudN-508
□ 98CamPepP-81
Vaughn, Fred
□ 47SigOil-18
Vaughn, Greg
□ 87BelBreP-2
□ 88BasAmeAAB-24
□ 88ElPasDB-20
□ 88TexLeaAGS-35
□ 89BlaYNPRWL-129
□ 89BlaYNPRWLU-50
□ 89BlaYNPRWLU-58
□ 89DenZepC-23
□ 89DenZepP-36
□ 89FleUpd-41
□ 89TriAAAP-AAA42
□ 90Bow-396
□ 90BowTif-396
□ 90BreMilB-28
□ 90BrePol-23
□ 90ClaBlu-60
□ 90Don-37
□ 90DonBesA-107
□ 90DonRoo-16
□ 90El PasDAGTI-25
□ 90Fle-339
□ 90FleCan-339
□ 90Hot50RS-44
□ 90Lea-111
□ 90LeaPre-9
□ 90OPC-57
□ 90Sco-585
□ 90Sco100RS-30
□ 90ScoRooDT-B8
□ 90ScoYouSI-13
□ 90Spo-135
□ 90Top-57
□ 90TopDeb89-128
□ 90TopTif-57
□ 90ToyRoo-27
□ 90TriAAAC-8
□ 90UppDec-25
□ 91Bow-33
□ 91BreMilB-29
□ 91BrePol-26
□ 91Cla3-T91
□ 91ClaGam-46
□ 91Don-478
□ 91Fle-599
□ 91OPC-347
□ 91Sco-528
□ 91Sco100RS-65
□ 91StaClu-135
□ 91Stu-79
□ 91Top-347
□ 91TopDesS-347
□ 91TopMic-347
□ 91TopRoo-30
□ 91TopTif-347
□ 91TopTriH-A8
□ 91ToyRoo-29
□ 91Ult-183
□ 91UppDec-526
□ 92Bow-496
□ 92BrePol-27
□ 92DenHol-17
□ 92Don-224
□ 92Fle-192
□ 92Hig5-69
□ 92Lea-276
□ 92LeaBlaG-276
□ 92OPC-572
□ 92PanSti-41
□ 92Pin-92
□ 92RedFolS-96
□ 92Sco-639
□ 92StaClu-666
□ 92Stu-198
□ 92Top-572
□ 92TopGol-572
□ 92TopGolW-572
□ 92TopKid-83
□ 92TopMic-572
□ 92TriPla-122
□ 92Ult-86
□ 92UppDec-97
□ 92UppDec-232
□ 92UppDecHRH-HR20
□ 93Bow-295
□ 93BrePol-26
□ 93BreSen5-6
□ 93Don-103
□ 93Fla-231
□ 93Fle-258
□ 93FunPac-72
□ 93Lea-56
□ 93OPC-373
□ 93PacSpa-166
□ 93PanSti-44
□ 93Pin-318
□ 93PinHomRC-30
□ 93RedFolS-98
□ 93Sco-160
□ 93Sel-222
□ 93SP-71
□ 93StaClu-122
□ 93StaCluFDI-122
□ 93StaCluMOP-122
□ 93Stu-197
□ 93Top-153
□ 93TopGol-153
□ 93ToplnaM-153
□ 93ToplnaR-153
□ 93TopMic-153
□ 93TriPla-150
□ 93Ult-225
□ 93UppDec-563
□ 93UppDecGold-563
□ 93UppDecHRH-HR15
□ 94Bow-449
□ 94BowBes-R29
□ 94BowBesR-R29
□ 94BreMilB-84
□ 94BreMilB-370
□ 94BrePol-28
□ 94BreTeal-27
□ 94ColC-585
□ 94ColChoGS-585
□ 94ColChoSS-585
□ 94Don-339
□ 94DonDiaK-DK20
□ 94DonDiaKJ-DK20
□ 94DonMVP-22
□ 94DonSpeE-339
□ 94Fin-89
□ 94FinRef-89
□ 94Fla-309
□ 94Fle-195
□ 94FleAllS-24
□ 94FleExtB-109
□ 94FleTeaL-8
□ 94FUnPac-144
□ 94Kra-13
□ 94Lea-321
□ 94LeaL-47
□ 94OscMayR-15
□ 94Pac-347
□ 94PanSti-88
□ 94Pin-37
□ 94PinArtP-37
□ 94PinMusC-37
□ 94PinRunC-RC16
□ 94ProMag-75
□ 94Sco-49
□ 94ScoGolR-49
□ 94ScoGolS-47
□ 94Sel-303
□ 94SP-61
□ 94SPDieC-61
□ 94Spo-103
□ 94StaClu-378
□ 94StaCluFDI-378
□ 94StaCluGR-378
□ 94StaCluMOP-378
□ 94Stu-48
□ 94Top-225
□ 94TopGol-225
□ 94TopSpa-225
□ 94TriPla-59
□ 94Ult-380
□ 94UppDec-288
□ 94UppDec-445
□ 94UppDecAJ-9
□ 94UppDecAJG-9
□ 94UppDecED-288
□ 94UppDecED-445
□ 95Baz-43
□ 95Bow-410
□ 95BowBes-R55
□ 95BowBesR-R55
□ 95ColCho-170
□ 95ColChoGS-170
□ 95ColChoSE-70
□ 95ColChoSEGS-70
□ 95ColChoSESS-70
□ 95ColChoSS-170
□ 95DenHol-27
□ 95Don-130
□ 95DonPreP-130
□ 95DonTopotO-105
□ 95Fin-114
□ 95FinRef-114
□ 95Fla-55
□ 95Fle-193
□ 95FleTeaL-8
□ 95Lea-261
□ 95LeaLim-133
□ 95Pac-242
□ 95Pin-110
□ 95PinArtP-110
□ 95PinMusC-110
□ 95Sco-379
□ 95ScoGolR-379
□ 95ScoPlaTS-379
□ 95SelCer-87
□ 95SelCerMG-87
□ 95SP-165
□ 95SPCha-164
□ 95SPChaDC-164
□ 95SPSil-165
□ 95StaClu-210
□ 95StaClu-423
□ 95StaClu-517
□ 95StaCluCC-CC24
□ 95StaCluFDI-210
□ 95StaCluMOP-210
□ 95StaCluMOP-423
□ 95StaCluMOP-517
□ 95StaCluMOP-CC24
□ 95StaCluSTWS-210
□ 95StaCluSTWS-423
□ 95StaCluSTWS-517
□ 95StaCluVR-220
□ 95StaCluVRMO-220
□ 95Stu-96
□ 95Sum-60
□ 95SumNthD-60
□ 95Top-452
□ 95TopCyb-248
□ 95TopEmb-23
□ 95TopEmbGI-23
□ 95TopPre-PP3
□ 95TopPreS-PP3
□ 95UC3-94
□ 95UC3ArtP-94
□ 95Ult-300
□ 95UltGolM-300
□ 95UppDec-300
□ 95UppDecED-300
□ 95UppDecEDG-300
□ 95UppDecSE-100
□ 95UppDecSEG-100
□ 96Baz-28
□ 96Bow-90
□ 96BowBes-27
□ 96BowBesAR-27
□ 96BowBesR-27

❑ 96BowFoi-90
❑ 96BrePol-25
❑ 96Cir-190
❑ 96CirRav-190
❑ 96ColCho-413
❑ 96ColCho-590
❑ 96ColChoGS-413
❑ 96ColChoGS-590
❑ 96ColChoSS-413
❑ 96ColChoSS-590
❑ 96ColChoYMtP-41
❑ 96ColChoYMtP-41A
❑ 96ColChoYMtPGS-41
❑ 96ColChoYMtPGS-41A
❑ 96Don-206
❑ 96DonPreP-206
❑ 96EmoXL-78
❑ 96Fin-S179
❑ 96FinRef-S179
❑ 96Fla-109
❑ 96Fle-161
❑ 96FleTif-161
❑ 96Lea-19
❑ 96LeaLim-80
❑ 96LeaLimG-80
❑ 96LeaPre-44
❑ 96LeaPreP-44
❑ 96LeaPrePB-19
❑ 96LeaPrePG-19
❑ 96LeaPrePS-19
❑ 96LeaSig-82
❑ 96LeaSigPPG-82
❑ 96LeaSigPPP-82
❑ 96MetUni-74
❑ 96MetUniP-74
❑ 96PanSti-196
❑ 96Pin-129
❑ 96PinAfi-62
❑ 96PinAfiAP-62
❑ 96PinAfiFPP-62
❑ 96ProSta-27
❑ 96Sco-56
❑ 96ScoDugC-A49
❑ 96ScoDugCAP-A49
❑ 96Sel-114
❑ 96SelArtP-114
❑ 96SelCer-55
❑ 96SelCerAP-55
❑ 96SelCerCB-55
❑ 96SelCerCR-55
❑ 96SelCerMB-55
❑ 96SelCerMG-55
❑ 96SelCerMR-55
❑ 96SelTeaN-28
❑ 96SP-110
❑ 96StaClu-79
❑ 96StaCluMOP-79
❑ 96Stu-39
❑ 96StuPrePB-39
❑ 96StuPrePG-39
❑ 96StuPrePS-39
❑ 96Sum-36
❑ 96SumAbo&B-36
❑ 96SumArtP-36
❑ 96SumFoi-36
❑ 96Top-147
❑ 96TopChr-42
❑ 96TopChrR-42
❑ 96TopGal-24
❑ 96TopGalPPI-24
❑ 96TopLas-111
❑ 96Ult-87
❑ 96UltGolM-87
❑ 96UppDec-363
❑ 96Zen-81
❑ 96ZenArtP-81
❑ 96ZenMoz-14
❑ 97Bow-242
❑ 97BowBes-53
❑ 97BowBesAR-53
❑ 97BowBesR-53
❑ 97BowInt-242
❑ 97Cir-197
❑ 97CirRav-197
❑ 97ColCho-208
❑ 97Don-128
❑ 97DonEli-78
❑ 97DonEliGS-78
❑ 97DonGolPP-128
❑ 97DonLonL-5
❑ 97DonPre-39
❑ 97DonPreCttC-39
❑ 97DonSilPP-128
❑ 97Fin-221
❑ 97FinRef-221
❑ 97Fle-472
❑ 97FleTif-472
❑ 97Lea-314
❑ 97LeaFraM-314
❑ 97LeaFraMDC-314
❑ 97MetUni-226
❑ 97NewPin-43
❑ 97NewPinAP-43
❑ 97NewPinMC-43
❑ 97NewPinPP-43
❑ 97Pac-434
❑ 97PacLigB-434
❑ 97PacPriSL-SL12C
❑ 97PacSil-434
❑ 97PadMot-6
❑ 97PinCer-64
❑ 97PinCerMBla-64
❑ 97PinCerMBlu-64
❑ 97PinCerMG-64
❑ 97PinCerMR-64
❑ 97PinCerR-64
❑ 97PinIns-65
❑ 97PinInsCE-65
❑ 97PinInsDE-65
❑ 97PinTotCPB-64
❑ 97PinTotCPG-64
❑ 97PinTotCPR-64
❑ 97PinX-P-68
❑ 97PinX-PMoS-68
❑ 97Sco-194
❑ 97ScoArtPWB-194
❑ 97ScoHeaotO-26
❑ 97ScoPreS-194
❑ 97ScoShoS-194
❑ 97ScoShoSAP-194
❑ 97Sel-66
❑ 97SelArtP-66
❑ 97SelCom-66
❑ 97SelRegG-66
❑ 97SP-158
❑ 97StaClu-214
❑ 97StaCluMat-214
❑ 97StaCluMOP-214
❑ 97Stu-99
❑ 97StuPrePG-99
❑ 97StuPrePS-99
❑ 97Top-397
❑ 97TopChr-138
❑ 97TopChrR-138
❑ 97TopGal-75
❑ 97TopGalPPI-75
❑ 97Ult-289
❑ 97UltGolME-289
❑ 97UltPlaME-289
❑ 97UppDec-169
❑ 98ColCho-483
❑ 98CroRoy-119
❑ 98CroRoyHRF-6
❑ 98DonSig-118
❑ 98DonSigP-118
❑ 98Fle-87
❑ 98Pac-433
❑ 98PacHomRH-4
❑ 98PacOme-208
❑ 98PacOmeR-208
❑ 98PacOnl-650
❑ 98PacOnlR-650
❑ 98PacOnlWC-650
❑ 98PacPar-240
❑ 98PacParC-240
❑ 98PacParG-240
❑ 98PacParHS-240
❑ 98PacParPB-240
❑ 98PacParR-240
❑ 98PacPlaB-433
❑ 98PacRedT-433
❑ 98PacSil-433
❑ 98PadMot-7
❑ 98PinPlu-86
❑ 98Revo-126
❑ 98RevoSS-126
❑ 98SPxFin-314
❑ 98SPxFinHRH-HR6
❑ 98SPxFinR-314
❑ 98SPxFinS-314
❑ 98StaCluFDI-212
❑ 98StaCluI-212
❑ 98StaCluOneK-212
❑ 98StaCluPP-212
❑ 98Top-77
❑ 98TopChr-77
❑ 98TopChrR-77
❑ 98TopDevR-77
❑ 98TopDia-77
❑ 98TopGolLabC1-89
❑ 98TopGolLabC1B-89
❑ 98TopGolLabC1One-89
❑ 98TopGolLabC1R-89
❑ 98TopGolLabC2-89
❑ 98TopGolLabC2B-89
❑ 98TopGolLabC2One-89
❑ 98TopGolLabC2R-89
❑ 98TopGolLabC3-89
❑ 98TopGolLabC3B-89
❑ 98TopGolLabC3One-89
❑ 98TopGolLabC3R-89
❑ 98TopMiniC-77
❑ 98TopOpeD-39
❑ 98Ult-433
❑ 98UltGolM-433
❑ 98UltMas-433
❑ 98UltPlaM-433
❑ 98UppDec-499
❑ 98UppDecR-86
❑ 99199Fin-60
❑ 99199Fin-260
❑ 99AllMysFR-M26
❑ 99Bow-230
❑ 99BowBes-15
❑ 99BowBesAR-15
❑ 99BowBesR-15
❑ 99BowGol-230
❑ 99BowInt-230
❑ 99CroRoyB-39
❑ 99CroRoyL-39
❑ 99CroRoyOD-39
❑ 99E-X Cen-66
❑ 99E-X CenECFut-66
❑ 99E-X CenECNow-66
❑ 99FinGolRef-60
❑ 99FinGolRef-260
❑ 99FinLeaI-L4
❑ 99FinProF-PF6
❑ 99FinProF-PF16
❑ 99FinRef-60
❑ 99FinRef-260
❑ 99FlaShoLeg1-59
❑ 99FlaShoLeg2-59
❑ 99FlaShoLeg3-59
❑ 99FlaShoLegM1-59
❑ 99FlaShoLegM2-59
❑ 99FlaShoLegM3-59
❑ 99FlaShoR1-59
❑ 99FlaShoR2-59
❑ 99FlaShoR3-59
❑ 99Fle-48
❑ 99FleGoiYar-14
❑ 99FleMys-80
❑ 99FleMysG-80
❑ 99FleMysM-80
❑ 99FleSta9-48
❑ 99FleVin'-48
❑ 99FleWarT-48
❑ 99MetUni-212
❑ 99MetUniGM-212
❑ 99MetUniPMG-212
❑ 99Pac-375
❑ 99PacAur-48
❑ 99PacAurOD-48
❑ 99PacCroC-247
❑ 99PacCroCPB-247
❑ 99PacCroCTM-15
❑ 99PacInv-40
❑ 99PacInvOD-40
❑ 99PacInvPB-40
❑ 99PacOme-67
❑ 99PacOmeC-67
❑ 99PacOmeG-67
❑ 99PacOmePB-67
❑ 99PacPar-67
❑ 99PacParC-67
❑ 99PacParG-67
❑ 99PacParHoloGold-67
❑ 99PacParHS-67
❑ 99PacParOD-67
❑ 99PacParPB-67
❑ 99PacParRed-67
❑ 99PacPlaB-375
❑ 99PacPri-126
❑ 99PacPriHB-126
❑ 99PacPriHG-126
❑ 99PacPriHM-126
❑ 99PacPriHP-126
❑ 99PacPriRed-126
❑ 99PacPriS-142
❑ 99PacPriS206-142
❑ 99PacPriS206R-142
❑ 99PacRed-375
❑ 99Rev-40
❑ 99RevPremDate-40
❑ 99RevRet-40
❑ 99RevShaSS-40
❑ 99SkyMolM-37
❑ 99SkyMolMX-37
❑ 99SkyPre-45
❑ 99SkyPreR-45
❑ 99SkyThu-278
❑ 99SkyThuRant-278
❑ 99SkyThuRave-278
❑ 99SP Aut-72
❑ 99SP AutC-GV
❑ 99SP AutCG-GV
❑ 99SP AutHRC-HR20
❑ 99SP AutHRC-HR50
❑ 99SP SigAuto-GV
❑ 99SP SigAutoG-GV
❑ 99SPAutHRCDC-HR20
❑ 99SPAutHRCDC-HR50
❑ 99SpoIll-145
❑ 99SpoIllF4-4
❑ 99SpoIllF4E-4
❑ 99SPSig-17
❑ 99SPx-65
❑ 99SPxFinR-65
❑ 99SPxFinS-65
❑ 99SPxPowE-PE23
❑ 99StaClu-245
❑ 99StaClu-311
❑ 99StaCluC-SCC16
❑ 99StaCluCR-SCC16
❑ 99StaCluFDI-245
❑ 99StaCluFDI-311
❑ 99StaCluOoaK-245
❑ 99StaCluOoaK-311
❑ 99StaCluPP-245
❑ 99StaCluPP-311
❑ 99StaCluTI-T1A
❑ 99StaCluTL-T1A
❑ 99StaCluTL-T1A
❑ 99ThuSkySupR-278
❑ 99Top-96
❑ 99Top-458
❑ 99TopAll-AM4
❑ 99TopAllMF-M26
❑ 99TopBlaLC1-71
❑ 99TopBlaLC2-71
❑ 99TopBlaLC3-71
❑ 99TopChr-96
❑ 99TopChr-458
❑ 99TopChrA-AE4
❑ 99TopChrAR-AE4
❑ 99TopChrR-96
❑ 99TopChrR-458
❑ 99TopGal-23
❑ 99TopGalPP-23
❑ 99TopGalPPI-23
❑ 99TopGolL-71
❑ 99TopGolLC1-71
❑ 99TopGolLC2-71
❑ 99TopGolLOtO-71
❑ 99TopMVPP-96
❑ 99TopMVPP-458
❑ 99TopOpeD-55
❑ 99TopPicP-P7
❑ 99TopPowB-PB11
❑ 99TopPowBR-PB11
❑ 99TopRedLC1-71
❑ 99TopRedLC2-71
❑ 99TopRedLC3-71
❑ 99TopSta-74
❑ 99TopSta'S-35
❑ 99TopSta'SG-35
❑ 99TopSta'SGDH-35
❑ 99TopSta1Foil-74
❑ 99TopStaFoil-74
❑ 99TopStaOS-74
❑ 99TopSupC-17
❑ 99TopSupCR-17
❑ 99TopTek-21A
❑ 99TopTek-21B
❑ 99TopTekG-21A
❑ 99TopTekG-21B
❑ 99UD Cho-134
❑ 99UD ChoMBH-B23
❑ 99UD ChoPCR-134
❑ 99UD ChoYW-Y22
❑ 99UDHolo-16
❑ 99UDHoloAUsome-16
❑ 99Ult-2
❑ 99UltGolM-2
❑ 99UltMas-2
❑ 99UltPlaM-2
❑ 99UltRBIK-26
❑ 99UppDec-194
❑ 99UppDec-347
❑ 99UppDecBD-71
❑ 99UppDecBDD-71
❑ 99UppDecBDQ-71
❑ 99UppDecBDT-71
❑ 99UppDecCf7-24
❑ 99UppDecCf7-48
❑ 99UppDecCf7-C21
❑ 99UppDecCf7Cf7P-C21
❑ 99UppDecCo7CE-24
❑ 99UppDecCo7CE-48
❑ 99UppDecE-24
❑ 99UppDecE-154
❑ 99UppDecEBPC-C-GV
❑ 99UppDecEFXG-24
❑ 99UppDecEFXG-154
❑ 99UppDecEL1-194
❑ 99UppDecEL1-347
❑ 99UppDecEL2-194
❑ 99UppDecEL2-347
❑ 99UppDecO-6
❑ 99UppDecOSO-6
❑ 99UppDecR-22
❑ 99UppDecRG-22
❑ 99UppDecRP-22
❑ 99UppDecTE-T11
❑ 99UppDecTED-T11
❑ 99UppDecTEQ-T11
❑ 99UppDecTET-T11
❑ 99Vic-105

Vaughn, Heath

❑ 91GulCoaRSP-26
❑ 92GasRanF-2254
❑ 93ChaRaiC-21
❑ 93ChaRaiF-1911

Vaughn, Hippo (James)

❑ 10E98-27
❑ 10W555-60
❑ 11HelSta-48
❑ 11PloCanE-63
❑ 11T205-174
❑ 12HasTriFT-38A
❑ 12HasTriFT-68A
❑ 12T207-187
❑ 14PieStaT-103
❑ 15CraJacE-176
❑ 15SpoNewM-180
❑ 16BF2FP-72
❑ 16SpoNewM-178
❑ 17ColE13-177
❑ 17HolBreD-107
❑ 19W514-111
❑ 20NatCarE-103
❑ 21E121So8-101A
❑ 21E121So8-101B
❑ 22AmeCarE122-72
❑ 22W575-141
❑ 23WilChoV-164
❑ 50CubGreB-17
❑ 61Fle-82
❑ 69Baz-1
❑ 72ClaCar-81
❑ 72FleFamF-14
❑ 72LauGreF-39
❑ 74CapPub-85
❑ 84CubBriPC-7H
❑ 90HOFStiB-17
❑ 92ConTSN-348
❑ 92ConTSN1N-800
❑ 92CubOldS-26
❑ 93ConTSN-800

Vaughn, Mike

❑ 76CliPilT-31
❑ 77WatIndT-27

Vaughn, Mo (Maurice)

❑ 88CapCodPB-16
❑ 88CapCodPPaLP-93
❑ 90Bow-275
❑ 90BowTif-275
❑ 90PawRedSDD-28
❑ 90PawRedSP-471
❑ 90ProAAAF-443
❑ 90Sco-675
❑ 90TopMag-45
❑ 90TopTVRS-64
❑ 91Bow-112
❑ 91Cla1-T24
❑ 91ClaGam-152
❑ 91Don-430
❑ 91DonRoo-36
❑ 91FleUpd-7
❑ 91LeaGolR-BC7
❑ 91LeaGolRNV-271
❑ 91LinDriAAA-370
❑ 91MajLeaCP-10
❑ 91OPCPre-124
❑ 91PawRedSDD-26
❑ 91PawRedSLD-370
❑ 91PawRedSP-49
❑ 91RedSoxP-28
❑ 91Sco-750
❑ 91ScoRoo-6
❑ 91StaClu-543
❑ 91Stu-20
❑ 91TopTra-123T
❑ 91TopTraT-123T
❑ 91TriA AAGP-AAA32
❑ 91Ult-387
❑ 91UppDec-5
❑ 92Bow-397
❑ 92ClaGam-73
❑ 92Don-514
❑ 92Fle-49
❑ 92Fle-705
❑ 92Hig5-10
❑ 92Lea-103
❑ 92LeaBlaG-103
❑ 92OPC-59
❑ 92OPCPre-50
❑ 92PawRedSF-934
❑ 92Pin-205
❑ 92PinTea2-54
❑ 92ProFS7-15
❑ 92RedSoxDD-27
❑ 92Sco-556
❑ 92Sco100RS-100
❑ 92ScoImpP-21
❑ 92SpoIllFK1-297
❑ 92SpoIllFK1-553
❑ 92StaClu-325
❑ 92Stu-139
❑ 92Top-59
❑ 92TopDeb91-176
❑ 92TopGol-59
❑ 92TopGolW-59
❑ 92TopMic-59
❑ 92TriPla-79
❑ 92Ult-23
❑ 92UppDec-445
❑ 93Bow-536
❑ 93ClaGam-94
❑ 93DiaMar-112
❑ 93Don-429
❑ 93Fin-165
❑ 93FinRef-165
❑ 93Fla-168
❑ 93Fle-184
❑ 93Lea-432
❑ 93OPC-393
❑ 93PacSpa-37
❑ 93PanSti-92
❑ 93Pin-189
❑ 93PinHomRC-40
❑ 93RedFolS-99
❑ 93RedSoxP-31
❑ 93RedSoxWHP-27
❑ 93Sco-132
❑ 93Sel-214
❑ 93SP-206
❑ 93StaClu-334
❑ 93StaCluFDI-334
❑ 93StaCluMOP-334
❑ 93Stu-134
❑ 93Top-51
❑ 93TopGol-51
❑ 93TopInaM-51
❑ 93TopInaR-51
❑ 93TopMic-51
❑ 93Toy-53
❑ 93Ult-156
❑ 93UppDec-396
❑ 93UppDecGold-396
❑ 94Bow-315
❑ 94BowBes-R80
❑ 94BowBesR-R80
❑ 94ColC-281
❑ 94ColChoGS-281
❑ 94ColChoSS-281
❑ 94DenHol-27
❑ 94Don-42
❑ 94DonDiaK-DK2
❑ 94DonDiaKJ-DK2
❑ 94DonMVP-16
❑ 94DonSpeE-42
❑ 94Fin-258
❑ 94FinRef-258
❑ 94Fla-18
❑ 94Fle-45
❑ 94FleExtB-27
❑ 94FleExtBGB-28
❑ 94FleTeaL-2
❑ 94FUnPac-42
❑ 94Kra-14
❑ 94Lea-285
❑ 94LeaL-12
❑ 94LeaMVPC-A14

- 94LeaMVPCG-A14
- 94OPC-259
- 94Pac-68
- 94PanSti-34
- 94Pin-17
- 94PinArtP-17
- 94PinMusC-17
- 94PinPowS-PS3
- 94PinRunC-RC12
- 94Pos-8
- 94ProMag-14
- 94RedFolMI-26
- 94Sco-57
- 94ScoGolR-57
- 94ScoGolS-51
- 94Sel-116
- 94SP-157
- 94SPDieC-157
- 94Spo-122
- 94StaClu-440
- 94StaCluFDI-440
- 94StaCluGR-440
- 94StaCluMOP-440
- 94Stu-166
- 94Top-690
- 94TopGol-690
- 94TopSpa-690
- 94TopSupS-43
- 94TriPla-209
- 94Ult-19
- 94UppDec-71
- 94UppDec-282
- 94UppDecAJ-12
- 94UppDecAJG-12
- 94UppDecED-71
- 94UppDecED-282
- 94UppDecMLS-MM19
- 94UppDecMLSED-MM19
- 94USDepoT-3
- 95Baz-17
- 95Bow-411
- 95BowBes-R42
- 95BowBes-X8
- 95BowBesJR-10
- 95BowBesR-R42
- 95BowBesR-X8
- 95ClaPhoC-8
- 95ColCho-421
- 95ColChoGS-421
- 95ColChoSE-194
- 95ColChoSEGS-194
- 95ColChoSESS-194
- 95ColChoSS-421
- 95Don-52
- 95DonPreP-52
- 95DonTopotO-29
- 95Emo-17
- 95EmoN-11
- 95Fin-86
- 95FinPowK-PK8
- 95FinRef-86
- 95Fla-15
- 95FlaInfP-9
- 95Fle-42
- 95FleTeaL-2
- 95FleUpdH-19
- 95Kra-15
- 95Lea-269
- 95LeaLim-152
- 95LeaLimG-21
- 95LeaLimIBP-12
- 95LeaLimL-8
- 95Pac-49
- 95PacPri-16
- 95PanSti-37
- 95Pin-216
- 95PinArtP-216
- 95PinMusC-216
- 95RedFol-11
- 95Sco-12
- 95Sco-563
- 95ScoGolR-12
- 95ScoGolR-563
- 95ScoHaloG-HG17
- 95ScoPlaTS-12
- 95ScoPlaTS-563
- 95Sel-97
- 95SelArtP-97
- 95SelCer-10
- 95SelCerMG-10
- 95SelCerS-10
- 95SP-125
- 95SPCha-121
- 95SPCha-125
- 95SPChaDC-121
- 95SPChaDC-125
- 95Spo-98
- 95SpoArtP-98
- 95SPPlaP-PP20
- 95SPSil-125
- 95SPSpeF-3
- 95StaClu-350
- 95StaClu-511
- 95StaCluCC-CC20
- 95StaCluMOP-350
- 95StaCluMOP-511
- 95StaCluMOP-CC20
- 95StaCluSTDW-RS350
- 95StaCluSTWS-350
- 95StaCluSTWS-511
- 95StaCluVR-184
- 95StaCluVRMO-184
- 95Stu-39
- 95StuGolS-39
- 95Sum-94
- 95Sum-200
- 95SumBigB-BB20
- 95SumNthD-94
- 95SumNthD-200
- 95TomPiz-18
- 95Top-205
- 95TopCyb-117
- 95TopEmb-139
- 95TopEmbGI-139
- 95TopTra-9T
- 95TopTraPB-9
- 95UC3-6
- 95UC3-136
- 95UC3ArtP-6
- 95UC3ArtP-136
- 95Ult-17
- 95UltGolM-17
- 95UppDec-161
- 95UppDecED-161
- 95UppDecEDG-161
- 95UppDecSE-210
- 95UppDecSEG-210
- 95Zen-77
- 96Baz-85
- 96Bow-21
- 96BowBes-16
- 96BowBesAR-16
- 96BowBesP-BBP25
- 96BowBesPAR-BBP25
- 96BowBesPR-BBP25
- 96BowBesR-16
- 96BowFoi-21
- 96Cir-14
- 96CirAcc-2
- 96CirBos-4
- 96CirRav-14
- 96ColCho-4
- 96ColCho-273
- 96ColCho-480
- 96ColCho-706
- 96ColChoCtG-CG6
- 96ColChoCtG-CG6B
- 96ColChoCtG-CG6C
- 96ColChoCtGE-CR6
- 96ColChoCtGG-CG6
- 96ColChoCtGG-CG6B
- 96ColChoCtGG-CG6C
- 96ColChoCtGGE-CR6
- 96ColChoGS-4
- 96ColChoGS-273
- 96ColChoGS-480
- 96ColChoGS-706
- 96ColChoSS-4
- 96ColChoSS-273
- 96ColChoSS-480
- 96ColChoSS-706
- 96ColChoYMtP-42
- 96ColChoYMtP-42A
- 96ColChoYMtPGS-42
- 96ColChoYMtPGS-42A
- 96DenHol-5
- 96DenHolGS-9
- 96DenHolGSAP-9
- 96Don-505
- 96DonDiaK-2
- 96DonEli-64
- 96DonHitL-6
- 96DonPowA-7
- 96DonPowADC-7
- 96DonPreP-505
- 96DonPurP-8
- 96DonRouT-5
- 96EmoLegoB-11
- 96EmoXL-20
- 96Fin-B288
- 96Fin-G64
- 96Fin-S151
- 96FinRef-B288
- 96FinRef-G64
- 96FinRef-S151
- 96Fla-29
- 96FlaDiaC-11
- 96Fle-38
- 96FleChe-9
- 96FleLumC-11
- 96FleRedS-17
- 96FleRoaW-9
- 96FleTeaL-2
- 96FleTif-38
- 96FleUpd-U244
- 96FleUpdTC-U244
- 96FleZon-11
- 96Kin-2
- 96Lea-130
- 96LeaAllGMC-7
- 96LeaAllGMCG-7
- 96LeaGolS-12
- 96LeaHatO-4
- 96LeaLim-47
- 96LeaLimG-47
- 96LeaLimL-6
- 96LeaLimLB-6
- 96LeaPicP-11
- 96LeaPre-49
- 96LeaPreP-49
- 96LeaPrePB-130
- 96LeaPrePG-130
- 96LeaPrePS-130
- 96LeaPreSG-22
- 96LeaPreSP-2
- 96LeaPreSte-22
- 96LeaSig-73
- 96LeaSigA-228
- 96LeaSigAG-229
- 96LeaSigAS-229
- 96LeaSigEA-208
- 96LeaSigEACM-30
- 96LeaSigPPG-73
- 96LeaSigPPP-73
- 96LibSpo-3
- 96MetUni-21
- 96MetUniHM-9
- 96MetUniP-21
- 96MetUniT-9
- 96Pac-248
- 96Pac-260
- 96PacGolCD-DC23
- 96PacPri-P81
- 96PacPriFB-FB19
- 96PacPriG-P81
- 96PacPriRHS-RH20
- 96PanSti-122
- 96PanSti-137
- 96Pin-78
- 96Pin-141
- 96Pin-261
- 96PinAfi-58
- 96PinAfiAP-58
- 96PinAfiFPP-58
- 96PinAfiMN-4
- 96PinAfiR-3
- 96PinAfiR-4
- 96PinAfiR-6
- 96PinAfiR-8
- 96PinAfiR-9
- 96PinAfiR-11
- 96PinAfiR-12
- 96PinAfiSP-6
- 96PinArtP-28
- 96PinArtP-68
- 96PinArtP-161
- 96PinEssotG-12
- 96PinFan-9
- 96PinFirR-3
- 96PinFoil-261
- 96PinPow-2
- 96PinSam-PP2
- 96PinSky-6
- 96PinSlu-5
- 96PinSta-28
- 96PinSta-68
- 96PinSta-161
- 96PinTeaS-8
- 96ProMagA-8
- 96ProMagDM-6
- 96ProSta-106
- 96RedF-19
- 96Sco-62
- 96Sco-370
- 96Sco-513
- 96ScoAll-5
- 96ScoBigB-13
- 96ScoDiaA-17
- 96ScoDugC-A54
- 96ScoDugC-B95
- 96ScoDugCAP-A54
- 96ScoDugCAP-B95
- 96ScoGolS-18
- 96ScoNumG-17
- 96ScoPowP-9
- 96ScoRef-3
- 96ScoTitT-3
- 96Sel-48
- 96Sel-158
- 96SelArtP-48
- 96SelArtP-158
- 96SelCer-67
- 96SelCer-141
- 96SelCerAP-67
- 96SelCerAP-141
- 96SelCerCB-67
- 96SelCerCB-141
- 96SelCerCR-67
- 96SelCerCR-141
- 96SelCerIP-2
- 96SelCerMB-67
- 96SelCerMB-141
- 96SelCerMG-67
- 96SelCerMG-141
- 96SelCerMR-67
- 96SelCerMR-141
- 96SelCerSF-8
- 96SelClaTF-5
- 96SelEnF-7
- 96SelTeaN-8
- 96SP-40
- 96Spo-31
- 96Spo-105
- 96SpoArtP-31
- 96SpoArtP-105
- 96SpoDouT-6
- 96SpoHitP-5
- 96SpoPowS-9
- 96SpoPro-3
- 96SPPreF-4
- 96SPSpeFX-41
- 96SPSpeFXDC-41
- 96SPx-10
- 96SPxGol-10
- 96StaClu-184
- 96StaClu-303
- 96StaCluEPB-303
- 96StaCluEPG-303
- 96StaCluEPS-303
- 96StaCluMeg-MH10
- 96StaCluMO-43
- 96StaCluMOP-184
- 96StaCluMOP-303
- 96StaCluMOP-MH10
- 96StaCluMOP-PP7
- 96StaCluMOP-PS9
- 96StaCluPP-PP7
- 96StaCluPS-PS9
- 96Stu-104
- 96StuHitP-10
- 96StuPrePB-104
- 96StuPrePG-104
- 96StuPrePS-104
- 96Sum-31
- 96SumAbo&B-31
- 96SumArtP-31
- 96SumBal-4
- 96SumBigB-4
- 96SumBigBM-4
- 96SumFoi-31
- 96SumHitI-2
- 96SumPos-1
- 96TeaOut-83
- 96TeaOut-C97
- 96Top-274
- 96TopBroLL-4
- 96TopChr-110
- 96TopChrR-110
- 96TopChrWC-WC14
- 96TopChrWCR-WC14
- 96TopGal-150
- 96TopGalPPI-150
- 96TopLas-94
- 96TopLasPC-7
- 96TopMysF-M19
- 96TopMysFR-M19
- 96TopPro-AL10
- 96TopRoaW-RW18
- 96TopWreC-WC14
- 96Ult-22
- 96Ult-591
- 96UltDiaP-11
- 96UltDiaPGM-11
- 96UltGolM-22
- 96UltGolM-591
- 96UltHomRK-11
- 96UltHomRKGM-11
- 96UltHomRKR-11
- 96UltHomRKRGM-11
- 96UltRBIK-10
- 96UltRBIKGM-10
- 96UltRes-10
- 96UltResGM-10
- 96UppDec-18
- 96UppDecDD-DD10
- 96UppDecDDG-DD10
- 96UppDecDDS-DD10
- 96UppDecHC-HC13
- 96UppDecPD-PD18
- 96UppDecPHE-H9
- 96UppDecPRE-R9
- 96UppDecPRE-R19
- 96UppDecPreH-H9
- 96UppDecPreR-R9
- 96UppDecPreR-R19
- 96UppDecRunP-RP19
- 96Zen-30
- 96Zen-136
- 96ZenArtP-30
- 96ZenArtP-136
- 96ZenDiaC-2
- 96ZenDiaCP-2
- 96ZenMoz-9
- 96ZenZ-6
- 97Bow-277
- 97BowBes-7
- 97BowBesAR-7
- 97BowBesR-7
- 97BowChr-93
- 97BowChrI-93
- 97BowChrIR-93
- 97BowChrR-93
- 97BowInt-277
- 97Cir-42
- 97CirBos-19
- 97CirLimA-15
- 97CirRav-42
- 97CirSupB-19
- 97ColCho-50
- 97ColCho-327
- 97ColChoAC-37
- 97ColChoBS-16
- 97ColChoBSGS-16
- 97ColChoCtG-7A
- 97ColChoCtG-7B
- 97ColChoCtG-7C
- 97ColChoCtGE-CG7
- 97ColChoCtGIW-CG7
- 97ColChoNF-NF31
- 97ColChoPP-PP8
- 97ColChoPPG-PP8
- 97ColChoPPJ-PP8
- 97ColChoS-27
- 97ColChoSR-28
- 97ColChoTBS-11
- 97ColChoTBSWH-11
- 97ColChoTotT-T8
- 97CraJac-20
- 97DenHol-3
- 97Don-108
- 97Don-420
- 97Don-445
- 97DonDiaK-3
- 97DonDiaKC-3
- 97DonEli-12
- 97DonEli-10
- 97DonEliGS-12
- 97DonFraFea-10
- 97DonGolPP-108
- 97DonGolPP-420
- 97DonGolPP-445
- 97DonLim-47
- 97DonLim-76
- 97DonLim-95
- 97DonLimE-47
- 97DonLimE-76
- 97DonLimE-95
- 97DonLimENG-47
- 97DonLimFotG-57
- 97DonLonL-3
- 97DonPowA-9
- 97DonPowADC-9
- 97DonPre-103
- 97DonPre-183
- 97DonPreCttC-103
- 97DonPreCttC-183
- 97DonPrePM-19
- 97DonPreS-19
- 97DonPreSS-19
- 97DonPreTB-25
- 97DonPreTBG-25
- 97DonPreTF-25
- 97DonPreTP-25
- 97DonPreTPG-25
- 97DonRocL-5
- 97DonSig-31
- 97DonSigA-101
- 97DonSigAC-126
- 97DonSigAM-126
- 97DonSigNN-9
- 97DonSigPPP-31
- 97DonSilPP-108
- 97DonSilPP-420
- 97DonSilPP-445
- 97DonTea-48
- 97DonTeaSPE-48
- 97DonVxP1-26
- 97DunDonPPS-27
- 97E-X2-11
- 97E-X2ACA-7
- 97E-X2Cred-11
- 97E-X2EssCre-11
- 97E-X2Hall-18
- 97Fin-153
- 97Fin-202
- 97Fin-311
- 97FinEmb-153
- 97FinEmb-311
- 97FinEmbR-153
- 97FinEmbR-311
- 97FinRef-153
- 97FinRef-202
- 97FinRef-311
- 97FlaShoDC-18
- 97FlaShoLC-42
- 97FlaShoLeg0-42
- 97FlaShoLeg1-42
- 97FlaShoM-A42
- 97FlaShoM-B42
- 97FlaShoM-C42
- 97FlaShoR0-42
- 97FlaShoR1-42
- 97FlaShoR2-42
- 97Fle-32
- 97Fle-719
- 97Fle-724
- 97FleBleB-9
- 97FleGouG-15
- 97FleGouGF-15
- 97FleLumC-18
- 97FleMilDM-42
- 97FleMilDMR-42
- 97FleTeaL-2
- 97FleTif-32
- 97FleTif-719
- 97FleTif-724
- 97HigMinM-120
- 97Lea-151
- 97LeaBanS-8
- 97LeaDrefS-15
- 97LeaFraM-151
- 97LeaFraMDC-151
- 97LeaGet-13
- 97LeaLeaotN-11
- 97MetUni-26
- 97MetUniBF-12
- 97NewPin-98
- 97NewPinAP-98
- 97NewPinIE-7
- 97NewPinMC-98
- 97NewPinPP-98
- 97NewPinPP-I7B
- 97Pac-48
- 97PacCar-6
- 97PacCarM-6
- 97PacCerCGT-8
- 97PacLigB-48
- 97PacPri-17
- 97PacPriLB-17
- 97PacPriP-17
- 97PacSil-48
- 97PacTriCD-3
- 97Pin-190
- 97PinArtP-PP190
- 97PinCer-2
- 97PinCerCMGT-8
- 97PinCerCT-8
- 97PinCerLI-3
- 97PinCerMBla-2
- 97PinCerMBlu-2
- 97PinCerMG-2
- 97PinCerMR-2
- 97PinCerR-2
- 97PinEpixPE-E16
- 97PinHom-15

- 97PinHom-16
- 97PinIns-44
- 97PinInsC-7
- 97PinInsCE-44
- 97PinInsDD-8
- 97PinInsDE-44
- 97PinInsFS-11
- 97PinMin-5
- 97PinMinB-5
- 97PinMinCB-5
- 97PinMinCG-5
- 97PinMinCGR-5
- 97PinMinCN-5
- 97PinMinCSS-5
- 97PinMinG-5
- 97PinMinS-5
- 97PinMusC-190
- 97PinPasttM-7
- 97PinPrePla-190
- 97PinPrePla-S6
- 97PinSha-6
- 97PinTotCPB-2
- 97PinTotCPG-2
- 97PinTotCPR-2
- 97PinX-P-88
- 97PinX-PF&A-4
- 97PinX-PMoS-88
- 97PinX-PMW-16
- 97PinX-PMWG-16
- 97PinX-PMWS-16
- 97PinX-PSfF-56
- 97PinX-PSfFU-56
- 97PreCon-7
- 97RedSoxS-2
- 97RedSoxSPl-2
- 97RedSoxSPr-2
- 97Sco-93
- 97Sco-510
- 97ScoArtPWB-93
- 97ScoArtPWB-510
- 97ScoBla-1
- 97ScoHigZ-3
- 97ScoPitP-12
- 97ScoPreS-93
- 97ScoResC-510
- 97ScoShoS-93
- 97ScoShoS-510
- 97ScoShoSAP-93
- 97ScoShoSAP-510
- 97ScoSteS-13
- 97ScoTitT-12
- 97Sel-2
- 97SelArtP-2
- 97SelCom-2
- 97SelRegG-2
- 97SelToootT-6
- 97SelToootTMB-6
- 97SP-35
- 97SPInsI-7
- 97SPMarM-MM15
- 97SpoIll-139
- 97SpoIllEE-139
- 97SpoIllGS-8
- 97SPSpeF-14
- 97SPSpxF-3
- 97SPSPxFA-3
- 97SPVinAu-31
- 97SPx-14
- 97SPxBoufG-6
- 97SPxBro-14
- 97SPxCorotG-9
- 97SPxGol-14
- 97SPxGraF-14
- 97SPxSil-14
- 97SPxSte-14
- 97StaClu-42
- 97StaClu-377
- 97StaCluFR-F11
- 97StaCluFW-F11
- 97StaCluMat-42
- 97StaCluMOP-42
- 97StaCluMOP-377
- 97StaCluMOP-FB11
- 97StaCluMOP-PG17
- 97StaCluPG-PG17
- 97Stu-36
- 97StuMasS-7
- 97StuMasS8-7
- 97StuPor8-18
- 97StuPrePG-36
- 97StuPrePS-36
- 97Top-450
- 97TopChr-159
- 97TopChrR-159
- 97TopChrSB-14
- 97TopChrSBR-14
- 97TopGal-109
- 97TopGalGoH-GH10
- 97TopGalPPI-109
- 97TopHobM-HM17
- 97TopIntF-ILM13
- 97TopIntFR-ILM13
- 97TopMem05-48
- 97TopSeaB-SB14
- 97TopSta-27
- 97TopStaAM-27
- 97TopSweS-SS15
- 97TopTeaT-TT11
- 97UD3-8
- 97UD3Marq-MA9
- 97Ult-21
- 97UltDouT-2
- 97UltGolME-21
- 97UltHRK-11
- 97UltPlaME-21
- 97UltPowP-B11
- 97UltRBIK-10
- 97UltThu-2
- 97UltTop3-16
- 97UltTop3GM-16
- 97UppDec-25
- 97UppDec-417
- 97UppDecAG-AG18
- 97UppDecHC-HC15
- 97UppDecLDC-LD8
- 97UppDecMM-B10
- 97UppDecP-8
- 97UppDecPE-8
- 97UppDecPP-PP17
- 97UppDecPPJ-PP17
- 97UppDecRP-RP18
- 97UppDecSA-20
- 97UppDecSAG-20
- 97Zen-41
- 98Bow-35
- 98BowBes-16
- 98BowBesAR-16
- 98BowBesR-16
- 98BowChr-35
- 98BowChrGA-35
- 98BowChrGAR-35
- 98BowChrI-35
- 98BowChrIR-35
- 98BowChrR-35
- 98BowChrR-18
- 98BowChrRR-18
- 98BowGolA-35
- 98BowInt-35
- 98CirThu-42
- 98CirThuRav-42
- 98CirThuSupRav-42
- 98ColCho-320
- 98ColChoCtG-CG19A
- 98ColChoCtG-CG19B
- 98ColChoCtG-CG19C
- 98ColChoCtGExch-CG19
- 98ColChoCtGIW-CG19
- 98ColChoER-ER4
- 98ColChoMBH-8
- 98ColChoRJ-SQ72
- 98ColChoS'-5
- 98ColChoSQ-SQ72
- 98ColChoSQDouble-22
- 98ColChoSQHR-22
- 98ColChoSQSingle-22
- 98ColChoSQTriple-22
- 98CroRoy-27
- 98CroRoyDK-6
- 98CroRoyFoB-6
- 98CroRoyFoBA-6
- 98Don-38
- 98Don-351
- 98DonCol-38
- 98DonColE-429
- 98DonColE-541
- 98DonColL-347
- 98DonColP-573
- 98DonColP-737
- 98DonColS-38
- 98DonCruG-12
- 98DonCruP-12
- 98DonCruR-12
- 98DonDom-20
- 98DonEli-29
- 98DonEli-141
- 98DonEliA-29
- 98DonEliA-141
- 98DonEliC-28
- 98DonEliI-10
- 98DonEliMC-28
- 98DonEliS-29
- 98DonEliS-141
- 98DonGolPP-38
- 98DonGolPP-351
- 98DonLonL-15
- 98DonPre-23
- 98DonPre-187
- 98DonPreGES-10
- 98DonPreGX-10
- 98DonPreGXDC-10
- 98DonPrePM-21
- 98DonPreSeat-23
- 98DonPreSeat-187
- 98DonPreTW-20
- 98DonPriCD-38
- 98DonPriCE-429
- 98DonPriCE-541
- 98DonPriCL-347
- 98DonPriCP-573
- 98DonPriCP-737
- 98DonProLO-16
- 98DonProLPI-9
- 98DonProLS-10
- 98DonSig-41
- 98DonSigP-41
- 98DonSilPP-38
- 98DonSilPP-351
- 98E-X2-20
- 98E-X2Cheap-13
- 98E-X2ECFut-20
- 98E-X2ECNow-20
- 98Fin-189
- 98FinCen-C18
- 98FinCenR-C18
- 98FinMysF2-M20
- 98FinMysF2-M22
- 98FinMysF2-M24
- 98FinMysF2-M36
- 98FinMysF2R-M20
- 98FinMysF2R-M22
- 98FinMysF2R-M24
- 98FinMysF2R-M36
- 98FinNo--189
- 98FinNo-R-189
- 98FinPowZ-P7
- 98FinRef-189
- 98FinStaS-SS3
- 98FlaShoLeg0-24
- 98FlaShoLeg1-24
- 98FlaShoLeg2-24
- 98FlaShoLeg3-24
- 98FlaShoLegM-24
- 98FlaShoR0-24
- 98FlaShoR1-24
- 98FlaShoR2-24
- 98FlaShoR3-24
- 98Fle-339
- 98Fle-351
- 98FleVin'-82
- 98FleVin'C-82
- 98Lea-148
- 98LeaFraDA-148
- 98LeaFraF-148
- 98LeaFraM-148
- 98LeaFraM-148
- 98LeaFraMDC-148
- 98LeaFraMDC-148
- 98LeaFraMZ2-148
- 98LeaRCMLHDSamp-12
- 98LeaRS-48
- 98LeaRS-138
- 98LeaRSGreHit-18
- 98LeaRSLHolo-18
- 98LeaRSLHolo-138
- 98LeaRSLMVP-10
- 98LeaRSLMVPPE-10
- 98LeaRSLong-48
- 98LeaRSLong-138
- 98LeaRSMLHD-12
- 98LeaRSTicMas-9
- 98LeaRSTicMasDC-9
- 98LeaRTrue-48
- 98LeaRTrue-138
- 98LeaStaRep-15
- 98LeaStaS-12
- 98LeaStaSDC-12
- 98MetUni-57
- 98MetUni-216
- 98MetUniPMG-57
- 98MetUniPMG-216
- 98Pac-49
- 98PacAur-21
- 98PacAurPF-42
- 98PacAurPFC-42
- 98PacAurPFPB-42
- 98PacAurPFR-42
- 98PacAurPFS-42
- 98PacGolCDC-8
- 98PacHomRH-2
- 98PacInv-16
- 98PacInvGems-25
- 98PacInvInt-4A
- 98PacInvPBlue-16
- 98PacInvSilv-16
- 98PacInvTeam-4
- 98PacOme-44
- 98PacOmeEP-3
- 98PacOmeEP1o1-3
- 98PacOmeOnIns-4
- 98PacOmeR-44
- 98PacOnl-130
- 98PacOnlR-130
- 98PacOnlWC-130
- 98PacPar-25
- 98PacParC-25
- 98PacParG-25
- 98PacParHS-25
- 98PacParI-34
- 98PacParPB-25
- 98PacParR-25
- 98PacPlaB-49
- 98PacRedT-49
- 98PacSil-49
- 98PacTeaC-3
- 98PinEpixME-E16
- 98PinEpixMO-E16
- 98PinEpixMP-E16
- 98PinEpixPO-E16
- 98PinEpixPP-E16
- 98PinEpixSE-E16
- 98PinEpixSO-E16
- 98PinEpixSP-E16
- 98PinIns-13
- 98PinInsCE-13
- 98PinInsDE-13
- 98PinInsSG-5AB
- 98PinInsSG-5CD
- 98PinInsSGS-5AB
- 98PinInsSGS-5CD
- 98PinMinB-23
- 98PinMinCB-23
- 98PinMinCBAP-23
- 98PinMinCGP-23
- 98PinMinCGPAP-23
- 98PinMinCN-23
- 98PinMinCNAP-23
- 98PinMinCSGR-23
- 98PinMinDC-23
- 98PinMinG-23
- 98PinMinMCSS-23
- 98PinMinS-23
- 98PinPer-23
- 98PinPerBB-17
- 98PinPerBBSamp-17
- 98PinPerBBSO-17
- 98PinPerPP-23
- 98PinPerSftF-24
- 98PinPlu-101
- 98PinPluAE-17
- 98PinPluAEE-17
- 98PinPluAEP-17
- 98PinPluAP-PP34
- 98PinPluGAP-PP34
- 98PinPluLM-9
- 98PinPluMAP-PP34
- 98PinPluTP-2
- 98PinPluTPG-2
- 98PinPluTPM-2
- 98PinPluY-1
- 98PinPreP-E17
- 98PinSna-BRS5
- 98PinSna-BRS8
- 98RedSoxS-14
- 98RedSoxSP-14
- 98Revo-28
- 98RevoFP-3
- 98RevoShow-4
- 98RevoSS-28
- 98Sco-227
- 98ScoEpix-E17
- 98ScoFirP-20
- 98ScoRT-15
- 98ScoRT-259
- 98ScoRTSS-PP15
- 98ScoRTSS-PP152
- 98ScoRTSSAP-PP15
- 98ScoRTSSAP-PP152
- 98ScoRTSSAP1-PP15
- 98ScoRTSSAP1-PP152
- 98ScoRTStarGaz-16
- 98ScoSS-PP110
- 98ScoSSAP-PP110
- 98SkyDugA-55
- 98SkyDugA-133
- 98SkyDugADH-DH12
- 98SkyDugAG-G8
- 98SkyDugAIA-55
- 98SkyDugAIA-133
- 98SkyDugAS-SH10
- 98SP Aut-57
- 98SP Aut-SD36
- 98SP AutC-MV
- 98SP AutSD-SD36
- 98SP AutSDT-SD36
- 98SpoIll-121
- 98SpoIllEE-121
- 98SpoIllFE-121
- 98SpoIllTaN-136
- 98SpoIllTaNEE-136
- 98SpoIllWSF-124
- 98SpoIllWSFEE-124
- 98SpoIllWSFFE-124
- 98SpoIllWSFRJP-8
- 98SPxFin-42
- 98SPxFin-65
- 98SPxFin-147
- 98SPxFin-226
- 98SPxFinR-42
- 98SPxFinR-65
- 98SPxFinR-147
- 98SPxFinR-226
- 98SPxFinS-42
- 98SPxFinS-65
- 98SPxFinS-147
- 98SPxFinS-226
- 98StaCluFDI-32
- 98StaCluI-32
- 98StaCluOneK-32
- 98StaCluPP-32
- 98Stu-4
- 98StuGPP-4
- 98StuHitPar-18
- 98StuMast-3
- 98StuPor8x10-26
- 98StuPor8x10GP-26
- 98StuSPP-4
- 98Top-14
- 98TopChr-14
- 98TopChrR-14
- 98TopDevR-14
- 98TopDia-14
- 98TopEtc-ES9
- 98TopGal-138
- 98TopGalGP-138
- 98TopGalOPP-138
- 98TopGalPPI-138
- 98TopGalPPIA-138
- 98TopGolLabC1-42
- 98TopGolLabC1B-42
- 98TopGolLabC1One-42
- 98TopGolLabC1R-42
- 98TopGolLabC2-42
- 98TopGolLabC2B-42
- 98TopGolLabC2One-42
- 98TopGolLabC2R-42
- 98TopGolLabC3-42
- 98TopGolLabC3B-42
- 98TopGolLabC3One-42
- 98TopGolLabC3R-42
- 98TopMiniC-18
- 98TopMysFB-M5
- 98TopMysFB-M5
- 98TopMysFBR-M5
- 98TopMysFBR-M5
- 98TopOpeD-12
- 98TopSta-35
- 98TopSta'S-42
- 98TopSta'SGH-42
- 98TopStaB-35
- 98TopStaG-35
- 98TopStaGR-35
- 98TopStaS-35
- 98TopStaSteG-42
- 98TopSup-4
- 98TopSup-4
- 98TopTek-87
- 98TopTekD-87
- 98UD3-57
- 98UD3-147
- 98UD3-237
- 98UD3DieCut-57
- 98UD3DieCut-147
- 98UD3DieCut-237
- 98Ult-148
- 98Ult-496
- 98UltBigS-10
- 98UltDouT-16
- 98UltGolM-148
- 98UltGolM-496
- 98UltMas-148
- 98UltMas-496
- 98UltNot-10
- 98UltPlaM-148
- 98UltPlaM-496
- 98UltTop3-5
- 98UltWinN-16
- 98UppDec-42
- 98UppDec-248
- 98UppDec-608
- 98UppDec10AP-21
- 98UppDec1APR-21
- 98UppDecAG-AG27
- 98UppDecAGDC-AG27
- 98UppDecCD-CD13
- 98UppDecR-15
- 98UppDecR-27
- 98UppDecRBBop-BB5
- 98UppDecRQL-Q25
- 98UppDecRTC-TC6
- 98UppDecSF-30
- 98UppDecSFPD-PZ19
- 98UppDecSFPZPD-PZ7
- 98UppDecTMT-8
- 98UppDecTMTG-8
- 98Zen-22
- 98Zen5 xx7-18
- 98Zen5x7GoldImp-18
- 98Zen5x7Imp-18
- 98ZenEpi-E17
- 98ZenZ-G-22
- 98ZenZ-S-22
- 99199Fin-245
- 99199Fin-267
- 99Bow-286
- 99BowBes-5
- 99BowBesAR-5
- 99BowBesR-5
- 99BowGol-286
- 99BowInt-286
- 99CroRoyB-5
- 99CroRoyL-5
- 99CroRoyOD-5
- 99CroRoyPotG-1
- 99CroRoyPP-1
- 99CroRoyPPN-1
- 99E-X Cen-13
- 99E-X CenECFut-13
- 99E-X CenECNow-13
- 99E-XCenFoF'-1
- 99FinDouF-DF3
- 99FinDouFDualR-DF3
- 99FinGolRef-245
- 99FinGolRef-267
- 99FinRef-245
- 99FinRef-267
- 99FlaShoLeg1-29
- 99FlaShoLeg2-29
- 99FlaShoLeg3-29
- 99FlaShoLegM1-29
- 99FlaShoLegM2-29
- 99FlaShoLegM3-29
- 99FlaShoR1-29
- 99FlaShoR2-29
- 99FlaShoR3-29
- 99Fle-32
- 99FleBri-125
- 99FleBri2G-125
- 99FleBriBlu-125
- 99FleBriGol-125
- 99FleGolYar-15
- 99FleMys-47
- 99FleMysG-47
- 99FleMysM-47
- 99FleSta9-32
- 99FleVin'-32
- 99FleWarT-32
- 99MetUni-197
- 99MetUni-287
- 99MetUniGM-197
- 99MetUniGM-287
- 99MetUniPMG-197
- 99MetUniPMG-287
- 99Pac-77
- 99PacAur-6
- 99PacAurOD-6
- 99PacCroC-51
- 99PacCroCPB-51
- 99PacGolCDC-5
- 99PacInv-5
- 99PacInvFP-1
- 99PacInvOD-5
- 99PacInvPB-5
- 99PacInvSF-1
- 99PacInvSF-1B
- 99PacInvSH-1
- 99PacInvSH-1B

❑ 99PacInvTA-1
❑ 99PacOme-9
❑ 99PacOmeC-9
❑ 99PacOmeDD-6
❑ 99PacOmeDM-2
❑ 99PacOmeEP-1
❑ 99PacOmeEP1o1-1
❑ 99PacOmeG-9
❑ 99PacOmeH'-1
❑ 99PacOmePB-9
❑ 99PacPar-9
❑ 99PacParC-9
❑ 99PacParG-9
❑ 99PacParHoloGold-9
❑ 99PacParHS-9
❑ 99PacParOD-9
❑ 99PacParPB-2
❑ 99PacParPB-9
❑ 99PacParRed-9
❑ 99PacParTC-1
❑ 99PacPlaB-77
❑ 99PacPri-25
❑ 99PacPriHB-25
❑ 99PacPriHG-25
❑ 99PacPriHM-25
❑ 99PacPriHP-25
❑ 99PacPriRed-25
❑ 99PacPriS-46
❑ 99PacPriS206-46
❑ 99PacPriS206R-46
❑ 99PacPriSP-46
❑ 99PacPriSV-46
❑ 99PacRed-77
❑ 99Rev-5
❑ 99RevDiaL-2
❑ 99RevPremDate-5
❑ 99RevRet-5
❑ 99RevShaSS-5
❑ 99RevThoitS-1
❑ 99RevTri-11
❑ 99RevTri-11
❑ 99SkyMolM-130
❑ 99SkyMolMF-30
❑ 99SkyMolMFS-30
❑ 99SkyMolMFT-30
❑ 99SkyMolMX-130
❑ 99SkyPre-128
❑ 99SkyPre-291
❑ 99SkyPreR-128
❑ 99SkyPreR-291
❑ 99SkyThu-267
❑ 99SkyThuDial1-D10
❑ 99SkyThuInD-ID9
❑ 99SkyThuRant-267
❑ 99SkyThuRave-267
❑ 99SkyThuTur-TC10
❑ 99SP Aut-1
❑ 99SP AutEF-E1
❑ 99SP AutHRC-HR11
❑ 99SP AutR-R1
❑ 99SP SigAuto-MO
❑ 99SP SigAutoG-MO
❑ 99SPAutHRCDC-HR11
❑ 99SpoIll-124
❑ 99SpoIllF4-13
❑ 99SpoIllF4E-13
❑ 99SpoIllH-3
❑ 99SPSig-6
❑ 99SPx-11
❑ 99SPxDom-FB5
❑ 99SPxFinR-11
❑ 99SPxFinS-11
❑ 99SPxPowE-PE2
❑ 99SPxPreS-PS30
❑ 99SPxStaF-SF5
❑ 99StaClu-335
❑ 99StaCluC-SCC18
❑ 99StaCluCR-SCC18
❑ 99StaCluFDI-335
❑ 99StaCluOoaK-335
❑ 99StaCluPP-335
❑ 99StaCluTI-T7C
❑ 99StaCluTL-T7C
❑ 99StaCluTL-T7C
❑ 99ThuSkySupR-267
❑ 99Top-65
❑ 99TopAll-AM13
❑ 99TopBlaLC1-42
❑ 99TopBlaLC2-42
❑ 99TopBlaLC3-42
❑ 99TopChr-65
❑ 99TopChrA-AE13
❑ 99TopChrAR-AE13
❑ 99TopChrR-65
❑ 99TopGal-48
❑ 99TopGalPP-48
❑ 99TopGalPPI-48
❑ 99TopGolL-42
❑ 99TopGolLC1-42
❑ 99TopGolLC2-42
❑ 99TopGolLOtO-42
❑ 99TopMVPP-65
❑ 99TopOpeD-36
❑ 99TopPowB-PB13
❑ 99TopPowBR-PB13
❑ 99TopRedLC1-42
❑ 99TopRedLC2-42
❑ 99TopRedLC3-42
❑ 99TopSta-37
❑ 99TopSta-169
❑ 99TopSta'S-5
❑ 99TopSta'SG-5
❑ 99TopSta'SGDH-5
❑ 99TopSta1Foil-37
❑ 99TopSta2Foil-37
❑ 99TopStaFoil-37
❑ 99TopStaFoil-169
❑ 99TopStaOS-37
❑ 99TopStaTS-37
❑ 99TopTek-44A
❑ 99TopTek-44B
❑ 99TopTekG-44A
❑ 99TopTekG-44B
❑ 99UD Ion-13
❑ 99UD Ion-68
❑ 99UD IonR-13
❑ 99UD IonR-68
❑ 99UDHolo-1
❑ 99UDHoloAUsome-1
❑ 99UDHoloLau-L5
❑ 99UDHoloLauG-L5
❑ 99Ult-180
❑ 99UltGolM-180
❑ 99UltMas-180
❑ 99UltPlaM-180
❑ 99UltRBIK-2
❑ 99UltTheBook-10
❑ 99UppDec-295
❑ 99UppDecBD-16
❑ 99UppDecBDAPH-MV
❑ 99UppDecBDD-16
❑ 99UppDecBDDom-D6
❑ 99UppDecBDDomE-D6
❑ 99UppDecBDQ-16
❑ 99UppDecBDT-16
❑ 99UppDecCf7-6
❑ 99UppDecCf7-58
❑ 99UppDecCf7-C6
❑ 99UppDecCf7Cf7P-C6
❑ 99UppDecCf7LL-L12
❑ 99UppDecCf7SftF-S15
❑ 99UppDecCL-63
❑ 99UppDecCLCC-63
❑ 99UppDecCLM-C1
❑ 99UppDecCo7CE-6
❑ 99UppDecCo7CE-58
❑ 99UppDecE-2
❑ 99UppDecE-140
❑ 99UppDecE-172
❑ 99UppDecEDF-D6
❑ 99UppDecEDFFXG-D6
❑ 99UppDecEFXG-2
❑ 99UppDecEFXG-140
❑ 99UppDecEFXG-172
❑ 99UppDecEL1-295
❑ 99UppDecEL2-295
❑ 99UppDecEPE-P1
❑ 99UppDecEUR-U11
❑ 99UppDecF-F3
❑ 99UppDecFD-F3
❑ 99UppDecFQ-F3
❑ 99UppDecFT-F3
❑ 99UppDecM-1
❑ 99UppDecM-P14
❑ 99UppDecMD-D8
❑ 99UppDecMGS-1
❑ 99UppDecMGUS-GUMV
❑ 99UppDecMHFS-1
❑ 99UppDecMSS-1
❑ 99UppDecO-50
❑ 99UppDecOSO-50
❑ 99UppDecR-1
❑ 99UppDecRG-1
❑ 99UppDecROSS-S12
❑ 99UppDecROSS-S12
❑ 99UppDecRP-1
❑ 99UppDecRTA-T10
❑ 99UppDecRTAL2-T10
❑ 99UppDecTE-T1
❑ 99UppDecTED-T1
❑ 99UppDecTEQ-T1
❑ 99UppDecTET-T1
❑ 99UppDecVtaT-V1
❑ 99UppDecVtaTD-V1
❑ 99UppDecVtaTQ-V1
❑ 99UppDecVtaTT-V1
❑ 99UppDecWY-W27
❑ 99UppDecWYD-W27
❑ 99UppDecWYHR-W27
❑ 99UppDecWYT-W27
❑ 99Vic-3
❑ 99Vic-7
❑ 99Vic-460

Vaughn, Porter
❑ 42A'sTeal-34

Vaughn, Randy
❑ 88EugEmeB-10
❑ 89AppFoxP-850
❑ 90BasCitRS-23

Vaughn, Robert
❑ 16Zee-69

Vaughn, Ron
❑ 89UtiBluSP-28

Vaughn, Tim
❑ 87MacPirP-9

Vaught, Craig
❑ 93St.CatBJC-24
❑ 93St.CatBJF-3984

Vaught, Jay
❑ 93Tex-6
❑ 94WatIndC-26
❑ 94WatIndF-3937
❑ 95KinIndTI-27
❑ 96CanIndB-27
❑ 97AkrAer-25

Vavra, Joe
❑ 85AlbDukCr-153
❑ 86AlbDukP-25
❑ 89GreFalDSP-9
❑ 90GreFalDSP-30
❑ 91YakBeaC-29
❑ 91YakBeaP-4264
❑ 92YakBeaF-3468
❑ 93VerBeaDC-28
❑ 94YakBeaC-30
❑ 94YakBeaF-3867
❑ 95YakBeaTI-34
❑ 96YakBeaTI-NNO
❑ 97YakBeaG-32

Vavrek, Michael
❑ 95AshTouUTI-7
❑ 96SalAvaB-25
❑ 97Bes-59
❑ 97CalLeaATI-46
❑ 97CarLeaTP-30
❑ 97SalAva-31
❑ 98Bow-422
❑ 98BowChr-422
❑ 98BowChrGA-422
❑ 98BowChrGAR-422
❑ 98BowChrI-422
❑ 98BowChrIR-422
❑ 98BowChrR-422
❑ 98BowGolA-422
❑ 98BowInt-422
❑ 98ColSprSS-26

Vavrock, Rob
❑ 82MadMusF-24

Vavruska, Paul
❑ 76CliPilT-32

Vaz, Roberto
❑ 97SouOreTB-13
❑ 98HunStaTI-4

Vazquetelles, Darren
❑ 93IdaFalBF-4041
❑ 93IdaFalBSP-12

Vazquez, Alexis
❑ 98Cha-24

Vazquez, Archie
❑ 92SpoIndF-1294
❑ 94HicCraC-23
❑ 94HicCraF-2178
❑ 94SouAtlLAF-SAL26
❑ 95Exc-32
❑ 95PriWilCTI-25
❑ 96Exc-38

Vazquez, Armando
❑ 91NegLeaRL-14
❑ 92NegLeaK-5
❑ 93TedWil-113
❑ 95NegLeaL2-5

Vazquez, Arthur
❑ 92SpoIndC-21

Vazquez, Ed
❑ 89KinMetS-24
❑ 90PitMetP-22

Vazquez, Javier
❑ 96DelShoB-29
❑ 97Bes-78
❑ 97Bow-387
❑ 97BowChr-256
❑ 97BowChrI-256
❑ 97BowChrIR-256
❑ 97BowChrR-256
❑ 97BowInt-387
❑ 98Bow-339
❑ 98BowBes-170
❑ 98BowBesAR-170
❑ 98BowBesR-170
❑ 98BowChr-339
❑ 98BowChrGA-339
❑ 98BowChrGAR-339
❑ 98BowChrI-339
❑ 98BowChrIR-339
❑ 98BowChrR-339
❑ 98BowGolA-339
❑ 98BowInt-339
❑ 98Don-304
❑ 98DonGolPP-304
❑ 98DonSilPP-304
❑ 98Fle-429
❑ 98LeaRS-286
❑ 98LeaRSLHolo-286
❑ 98LeaRSLong-286
❑ 98LeaRTrue-286
❑ 98PacOmeRS-25
❑ 98PacOmeRST1-25
❑ 98SP Aut-24
❑ 98SP MinPE-79
❑ 98SPMin-79
❑ 98UppDec-579
❑ 98UppDecDS-DS24
❑ 99Fle-532
❑ 99FleSta9-532
❑ 99FleWarT-532
❑ 99PacCroC-176
❑ 99PacCroCPB-176
❑ 99SkyPreA-53
❑ 99SkyPreABlue-53
❑ 99UppDec-423
❑ 99UppDecEL1-423
❑ 99UppDecEL2-423
❑ 99Vic-246

Vazquez, Jose
❑ 89OneYanP-2126
❑ 92JohCitCC-8
❑ 92JohCitCF-3133
❑ 93St.PetCC-25
❑ 93St.PetCF-2642

Vazquez, Manny
❑ 96HudValRB-8
❑ 96WesOahCHWB-11

Vazquez, Marcos
❑ 88BlaYNPRWLU-46
❑ 88SumBraP-403
❑ 89BlaYNPRWL-19
❑ 89SumBraP-1115
❑ 91DurBulUP-4
❑ 91MacBraC-11
❑ 91MacBraP-864
❑ 94ChaLooF-1359

Vazquez, Pedro
❑ 90AppFoxBS-29
❑ 90AppFoxP-2106
❑ 91BasCitRC-22
❑ 91BasCitRP-1408

Vazquez, Ramon
❑ 96EveAquB-25
❑ 97WisTimR-25
❑ 98LanJetG-28

Veach, Robert
❑ 15CraJacE-174
❑ 15SpoNewM-181
❑ 16BF2FP-32
❑ 16SpoNewM-179
❑ 17ColE13-178
❑ 17HolBreD-108
❑ 19W514-88
❑ 20NatCarE-104
❑ 21E121So1-108
❑ 21E121So8-102A
❑ 21E121So8-102B
❑ 21Exh-180
❑ 21Nei-33
❑ 22AmeCarE122-73
❑ 22E120-59
❑ 22W572-109
❑ 22W573-135
❑ 22W575-142
❑ 23W501-5
❑ 23WilChoV-165
❑ 25Exh-71
❑ 75SenTCM1-35
❑ 81TigDetN-118
❑ 81TigSecNP-6
❑ 91ConTSN-159
❑ 92ConTSN-486

Veach, William
❑ 87OldJudN-509

Veal, Coot (Orville)
❑ 59Top-52
❑ 59TopVen-52
❑ 61Top-432
❑ 62Jel-68
❑ 62Pos-68
❑ 62PosCan-68
❑ 62SalPlaC-84
❑ 62ShiPlaC-84
❑ 63Top-573

Veale, Bob
❑ 62Top-593
❑ 63PirIDL-25
❑ 63Top-87
❑ 64Kah-28
❑ 64PirKDK-27
❑ 64Top-501
❑ 65Baz-13
❑ 65Kah-43
❑ 65OPC-12
❑ 65OPC-195
❑ 65Top-12
❑ 65Top-195
❑ 65TopTral-32
❑ 66Kah-31
❑ 66PirEasH-39
❑ 66Top-225
❑ 66Top-425
❑ 66TopRubl-95
❑ 66TopVen-225
❑ 67CokCapPi-4
❑ 67DexPre-214
❑ 67Kah-38
❑ 67PirTeal-22
❑ 67Top-238
❑ 67Top-335
❑ 67TopPirS-23
❑ 67TopVen-333
❑ 68Baz-3
❑ 68Kah-A12
❑ 68Kah-B35
❑ 68OPC-70
❑ 68PirKDK-39
❑ 68PirTeal-22
❑ 68Top-70
❑ 68TopActS-11A
❑ 68TopVen-70
❑ 69Kah-B21
❑ 69MilBra-283
❑ 69MLBOffS-189
❑ 69OPC-8
❑ 69PirTeal-24
❑ 69Top-8
❑ 69Top-520
❑ 69TopSta-90
❑ 69TopTeaP-16
❑ 70MLBOffS-108
❑ 70OPC-236
❑ 70PirTeal-18
❑ 70Top-236
❑ 71MLBOffS-215
❑ 71OPC-368
❑ 71PirActP-11
❑ 71Top-368
❑ 72MilBra-351
❑ 72Top-729
❑ 73LinPor-31
❑ 73OPC-518
❑ 73Top-518
❑ 78GreBraT-28
❑ 78TCM60I-114
❑ 80PirGreT-10
❑ 92UppDecS-19

Vecchioni, Jerry
❑ 96DanBraB-26

Veeck, Bill
❑ 48IndTeal-30
❑ 49IndTeal-25
❑ 53IndPenCBP-27
❑ 76ChiGre-19
❑ 80PerHaloFP-211
❑ 82OhiHaloF-44
❑ 84OCoandSI-191

Veeck, Michael
❑ 90MiaMirIS-29

Veeck, William
❑ 31CubTeal-26
❑ 32CubTeal-25

Vega, Jesus
❑ 77BurBeeT-3
❑ 78OrlTwiT-21
❑ 79TolMudHT-20
❑ 80TolMudHT-11
❑ 81TolMudHT-16
❑ 82TwiPos-26
❑ 83Don-650
❑ 83Fle-624
❑ 83TolMudHT-17
❑ 83Top-308

Vegely, Bruce
❑ 88BenBucL-18
❑ 89QuaCitAB-19
❑ 89QuaCitAGS-12
❑ 90QuaCitAGS-7
❑ 91PalSprAP-2016

Veil, Bucky
❑ 11SpoLifCW-356

Veilleux, Brian
❑ 89ModA'sC-17
❑ 89ModA'sCLC-268
❑ 90HunStaB-12

Veintidos, Juan
❑ 74TacTwiC-12
❑ 75OPC-621
❑ 75TacTwiK-18
❑ 75Top-621
❑ 75TopMin-621
❑ 76TacTwiDQ-21
❑ 77TacTwiDQ-22

Veit, Steve
❑ 90AshTouC-17
❑ 90AubAstB-3
❑ 90AubAstP-3400
❑ 91AshTouP-578

Velandia, Jorge
❑ 92BriTigF-1423
❑ 93FayGenC-23
❑ 93FayGenF-139
❑ 93LinVenB-87
❑ 94LakTigC-24
❑ 94LakTigF-3047
❑ 94SprSulC-23
❑ 94VenLinU-226
❑ 95LinVen-49
❑ 95MemChiTI-5
❑ 96-97LinVen-110
❑ 96Bow-203
❑ 96BowFoi-203
❑ 96MemChiB-28
❑ 97LasVegS1A-29
❑ 98Fle-32
❑ 98LeaRS-225
❑ 98LeaRSLHolo-225
❑ 98LeaRSLong-225
❑ 98LeaRTrue-225
❑ 98PacInvGems-213
❑ 98Ult-243
❑ 98UltGolM-243
❑ 98UltMas-243
❑ 98UltPlaM-243
❑ 99PacCroC-208
❑ 99PacCroCPB-208

Velarde, Randy
❑ 86AppFoxP-26
❑ 87AlbYanP-7
❑ 87IntLeaAT-13
❑ 88ColCliC-17
❑ 88ColCliP-22
❑ 88ColCliP-324
❑ 88Fle-646
❑ 88FleGlo-646
❑ 88TriAAC-20
❑ 89ColCliC-13
❑ 89ColCliP-17
❑ 89ColCliP-741
❑ 89ScoHot1R-18
❑ 89Top-584
❑ 89TopBig-239
❑ 89TopTif-584
❑ 89TriAAAP-AAA19
❑ 89UppDec-189
❑ 90AlbDecGB-19
❑ 90Bow-434
❑ 90BowTif-434
❑ 90Don-630
❑ 90OPC-23
❑ 90Sco-524
❑ 90Top-23
❑ 90TopBig-68
❑ 90TopTif-23
❑ 90TopTVY-28
❑ 90TriAAAC-19
❑ 90YanScoNW-27
❑ 91OPC-379
❑ 91Sco-134
❑ 91StaClu-438
❑ 91Top-379

- 91TopDesS-379
- 91TopMic-379
- 91TopTif-379
- 92Bow-207
- 92Don-679
- 92Fle-246
- 92Lea-368
- 92LeaBlaG-368
- 92OPC-212
- 92Sco-337
- 92StaClu-237
- 92Top-212
- 92TopGol-212
- 92TopGolW-212
- 92TopMic-212
- 92UppDec-399
- 92YanWIZ8-195
- 93Don-153
- 93Fle-287
- 93OPC-337
- 93PacSpa-214
- 93PanSti-148
- 93Pin-314
- 93Sco-219
- 93StaClu-32
- 93StaCluFDI-32
- 93StaCluMOP-32
- 93Top-174
- 93TopGol-174
- 93TopInaM-174
- 93TopInaR-174
- 93TopMic-174
- 93Ult-250
- 93UppDec-93
- 93UppDecGold-93
- 93YanStaC-9
- 94ColC-498
- 94ColChoGS-498
- 94ColChoSS-498
- 94Don-439
- 94Fin-41
- 94FinRef-41
- 94Fle-249
- 94FleExtB-141
- 94Pac-440
- 94Pin-383
- 94PinArtP-383
- 94PinMusC-383
- 94Sco-216
- 94ScoGolR-216
- 94StaClu-156
- 94StaCluFDI-156
- 94StaCluGR-156
- 94StaCluMOP-156
- 94StaCluT-189
- 94StaCluTFDI-189
- 94Top-461
- 94TopGol-461
- 94TopSpa-461
- 95ColCho-513
- 95ColChoGS-513
- 95ColChoSS-513
- 95Don-491
- 95DonPreP-491
- 95DonTopotO-127
- 95Fle-83
- 95Pac-305
- 95Sco-384
- 95ScoGolR-384
- 95ScoPlaTS-384
- 95StaClu-247
- 95StaCluFDI-247
- 95StaCluMOP-247
- 95StaCluSTWS-247
- 95Top-566
- 95TopCyb-342
- 96AngMot-14
- 96ColCho-481
- 96ColChoGS-481
- 96ColChoSS-481
- 96Don-369
- 96DonPreP-369
- 96Fla-44
- 96Fle-60
- 96FleTif-60
- 96FleUpd-U22
- 96FleUpdTC-U22
- 96Pac-375
- 96Sco-55
- 96ScoDugC-A48
- 96ScoDugCAP-A48
- 96StaClu-44
- 96StaCluMOP-44
- 96Top-361
- 96Ult-328
- 96UltGolM-328
- 96UppDec-485U
- 97ColCho-257
- 97Fle-53
- 97FleTif-53
- 97Pac-15
- 97PacLigB-15
- 97PacSil-15
- 97Top-185
- 97Ult-32
- 97UltGolME-32
- 97UltPlaME-32
- 97UppDec-297
- 99PacCroC-10
- 99PacCroCPB-10
- 99StaClu-301
- 99StaCluFDI-301
- 99StaCluOoaK-301
- 99StaCluPP-301

Velasquez, Al
- 82ReaPhiT-12

Velasquez, Emilo
- 95LinVen-259

Velasquez, Frank
- 96ChaRivTI-9602
- 98Cha-25

Velasquez, Gil (Guillermo)
- 88ChaRaiP-1203
- 88SouAtlLAGS-12
- 89RivRedWB-20
- 89RivRedWCLC-3
- 89RivRedWP-1394
- 90WicWraRD-21
- 91LinDriAA-621
- 91WicWraLD-621
- 91WicWraP-2607
- 91WicWraRD-17
- 92Bow-698
- 92LasVegSF-2805
- 92LasVegSS-245
- 92SkyAAAF-120
- 92TriA AAS-245
- 93Don-312
- 93FleFinE-146
- 93Lea-471
- 93LinVenB-318
- 93PacBeiA-23
- 93PacSpa-604
- 93PadMot-17
- 93StaClu-744
- 93StaCluFDI-744
- 93StaCluMOP-744
- 93Top-724
- 93TopGol-724
- 93TopInaM-724
- 93TopInaR-724
- 93TopMic-724
- 93Ult-479
- 94Don-300
- 94Fle-677
- 94Pac-536
- 94StaClu-278
- 94StaCluFDI-278
- 94StaCluGR-278
- 94StaCluMOP-278
- 94Top-556
- 94TopGol-556
- 94TopSpa-556

Velasquez, Ray
- 85VisOakT-16
- 86VisOakP-23
- 87CliGiaP-26
- 88SanJosGCLC-139
- 88SanJosGP-116
- 89SalSpuCLC-123
- 89SalSpuP-1807
- 90SalSpuCLC-125

Velasquez, Tony
- 72CedRapCT-27

Velazquel, Ildefonso
- 85MexCitTT-9

Velazquez, Carlos
- 75SacSolC-17
- 94BreMilB-85

Velazquez, Edgar
- 96NewHavRB-25
- 96NewHavRUSTI-12

Velazquez, Fred
- 80VenLeaS-242
- 83Pil69G-24
- 85DomLeaS-212

Velazquez, Jose
- 96GreBatB-30
- 97GreBatB-30
- 98ChaRivDG-28

Velazquez, Juan
- 83QuaCitCT-17
- 98DanBraQ-14

Velez, Jose
- 87GasRanP-25
- 88BlaYNPRWL-143
- 88GasRanP-1011
- 89PalSprACLC-46
- 89PalSprAP-484

Velez, Jose J.
- 91Cla/Bes-208
- 91SprCarC-28
- 91SprCarP-758
- 92SavCarF-678
- 93St.PetCC-26
- 93St.PetCF-2643
- 94St.PetCC-27
- 94St.PetCF-2601
- 95ArkTraTI-26
- 96ArkTraB-26
- 98KisCobQ-30

Velez, Noel
- 90Bes-54
- 90ChaWheB-18
- 90ChaWheP-2248
- 91CedRapRC-24
- 91CedRapRP-2734
- 91EriSaiC-12
- 91EriSaiP-4082

Velez, Otto
- 73SyrChiTI-28
- 74OPC-606
- 74SyrChiTI-27
- 74Top-606
- 74TopSta-219
- 75SyrChiTI-21
- 76SSP-455
- 77OPC-13
- 77Top-299
- 78BluJayP-22
- 78OPC-67
- 78Top-59
- 79BluJayBY-19
- 79OPC-241
- 79Top-462
- 80OPC-354
- 80Top-703
- 81Don-391
- 81Fle-410
- 81OPC-351
- 81OPCPos-23
- 81Top-351
- 81TopScr-44
- 81TopSti-138
- 82Don-304
- 82Fle-625
- 82FleSta-233
- 82OPC-155
- 82OPCPos-11
- 82Top-155
- 82TopSti-249
- 83ChaChaT-18
- 83IndPos-38
- 86BluJayGT-5
- 92Nab-26
- 92YanWIZ7-157

Vella, Greg
- 88MyrBeaBJP-1183
- 88SouAtlLAGS-19
- 89DunBluJS-21

Velleggia, Frank
- 84NewOriT-15

Veltman, Art
- 33ButCanV-49
- 34DiaMatCSB-186

Venable, Max
- 77CliDodT-28
- 78LodDodT-23
- 79GiaPol-49
- 80PhoGiaVNB-12
- 81Fle-443
- 81GiaTeal-20
- 81PhoGiaVNB-6
- 81Top-484
- 82Gia25tATI-30
- 83Fle-275
- 83GiaMot-16
- 83GiaPos-26
- 83Top-634
- 84Don-323
- 84Fle-385
- 84IndIndTI-15
- 84IndIndTI-28
- 84Nes792-58
- 84Top-58
- 84TopTif-58
- 85IndIndTI-9
- 86Don-650
- 86Fle-196
- 86RedTexG-9
- 86Top-428
- 86TopTif-428
- 87Fle-216
- 87FleGlo-216
- 87NasSouTI-22
- 87Top-226
- 87TopTif-226
- 89EdmTraC-23
- 89EdmTraP-556
- 90Lea-459
- 91Don-510
- 92Sco-477
- 94IdaFalBSP-27
- 95DanBraTI-28
- 95RicBraTI-29
- 96DurBulBlB-25
- 96DurBulBrB-21
- 97RicBra-3
- 98RicBraQ-29

Venafro, Mike
- 95HudValRTI-13
- 96ChaRivTI-9629
- 98TexLeaC-25
- 98TulDriTI-19

Venezia, Danny
- 93EliTwiC-21
- 93EliTwiF-3423
- 94ForWayWC-24
- 94ForWayWF-2019

Venezia, Mike
- 81RedPioT-8

Venezia, Rich
- 94WelPirC-28
- 94WelPirF-3506

Veneziale, Mike
- 93Top-726
- 93TopGol-726
- 93TopInaM-726
- 93TopInaR-726
- 93TopMic-726

Venger, Tad
- 81ChaRoyT-24

Veniard, Jay
- 96DunBluJUTI-16
- 97KnoSmo-25
- 98KnoSG-25

Venner, Gary
- 82BurRanF-9
- 83TriTriT-27

Vento, Michael
- 98OneYanG-27

Ventress, Leroy
- 86BenPhiC-145
- 87UtiBluSP-2
- 88BatCliP-1666
- 89SouAtlLAGS-41
- 89SpaPhiP-1044
- 89SpaPhiS-23
- 90ClePhiS-23
- 91ClePhiC-26
- 91ClePhiP-1637

Ventura, Candido
- 77ChaPatT-24

Ventura, Jose
- 86BelBreP-24
- 89SouBenWSGS-16
- 90SarWhiSS-25
- 91BirBarLD-73
- 91BirBarP-1455
- 91Cla/Bes-271
- 91LinDriAA-73
- 92BirBarF-2584
- 92BirBarS-97
- 92SkyAA F-46
- 93LimRocDWB-129
- 93MemChiF-377

Ventura, Leonardo
- 94SouOreAC-29
- 94SouOreAF-3627

Ventura, Reynaldo
- 89BurIndS-25

Ventura, Robin
- 88StaVen-1
- 88StaVen-2
- 88StaVen-3
- 88StaVen-4
- 88StaVen-5
- 88StaVen-6
- 88StaVen-7
- 88StaVen-8
- 88StaVen-9
- 88StaVen-10
- 88StaVen-11
- 88TopTra-124T
- 88TopTraT-124T
- 89BasAmeAPB-AA21
- 89BirBarADB-1
- 89BirBarB-1
- 89BirBarP-106
- 89Bow-65
- 89BowTif-65
- 89ClaTraP-177
- 89FleUpd-23
- 89SouLeaAJ-2
- 89Sta-101
- 89StaFutS-7
- 89StaFutS-8
- 89Top-764
- 89TopBig-65
- 89TopTif-764
- 90BirBarADB-1
- 90Bow-311
- 90BowTif-311
- 90ClaBlu-5
- 90Don-28
- 90DonBesA-60
- 90DonRoo-15
- 90Fle-550
- 90FleCan-550
- 90FleSoaS-4
- 90Hot50RS-45
- 90Lea-167
- 90LeaPre-8
- 90OPC-121
- 90Sco-595
- 90Sco100RS-96
- 90ScoRooDT-B6
- 90ScoYouS2-8
- 90Spo-222
- 90Top-121
- 90TopDeb89-129
- 90TopMag-76
- 90TopTif-121
- 90ToyRoo-28
- 90UppDec-21
- 90WhiSoxC-27
- 90WhiSoxC-28
- 91Baz-15
- 91Bow-358
- 91ClaGam-52
- 91Don-315
- 91Fle-139
- 91Lea-271
- 91OPC-461
- 91PanFreS-314
- 91PanSti-260
- 91RedFolS-97
- 91Sco-320
- 91Sco100RS-48
- 91StaClu-274
- 91Top-461
- 91TopDesS-461
- 91TopMic-461
- 91TopRoo-31
- 91TopTif-461
- 91TopTriH-A4
- 91ToyRoo-30
- 91Ult-86
- 91UppDec-263
- 91UppDec-677
- 91WhiSoxK-23
- 91WhiSoxK-NNO
- 92Bow-275
- 92Bow-655
- 92Cla2-T85
- 92ClaGam-49
- 92DenHol-8
- 92Don-145
- 92DonCraJ1-33
- 92DonPre-6
- 92Fle-101
- 92FleAll-19
- 92Fre-8
- 92Hig5-20
- 92Lea-17
- 92LeaBlaG-17
- 92OPC-255
- 92OPCPre-132
- 92PanSti-127
- 92Pin-121
- 92Pin-286
- 92PinTea2-43
- 92PinTeaP-6
- 92Sco-122
- 92Sco100S-33
- 92ScoImpP-42
- 92ScoSam-3
- 92StaClu-70
- 92Stu-160
- 92Top-255
- 92TopDaiQTU-11
- 92TopGol-255
- 92TopGolW-255
- 92TopKid-102
- 92TopMic-255
- 92TriPla-17
- 92Ult-343
- 92UltAwaW-15
- 92UppDec-263
- 92UppDecF-6
- 92UppDecFG-6
- 92UppDecWB-T20
- 92WhiSoxK-23
- 93Bow-667
- 93CadDis-59
- 93ClaGam-95
- 93DenHol-27
- 93DiaMar-113
- 93Don-535
- 93DonDiaK-DK10
- 93Fin-93
- 93FinJum-93
- 93FinRef-93
- 93Fla-190
- 93Fle-211
- 93Fle-716
- 93FleFruotL-63
- 93FunPac-203
- 93FunPacA-AS5
- 93HumDumC-7
- 93Kra-14
- 93Lea-439
- 93LeaFas-14
- 93LeaGolA-R6
- 93OPC-387
- 93PacSpa-78
- 93PanSti-139
- 93Pin-28
- 93PinHomRC-24
- 93RedFolS-101
- 93RedFolS-129
- 93Sco-41
- 93Sel-30
- 93SP-261
- 93StaClu-295
- 93StaClu-387
- 93StaCluFDI-295
- 93StaCluFDI-387
- 93StaCluM-111
- 93StaCluMOP-295
- 93StaCluMOP-387
- 93Stu-78
- 93Top-770
- 93TOPBLAG-43
- 93TopGol-770
- 93TopInaM-770
- 93TopInaR-770
- 93TopMic-770
- 93TopPos-1
- 93Toy-58
- 93TriPla-179
- 93Ult-537
- 93UltAwaW-14
- 93UppDec-51
- 93UppDec-263
- 93UppDec-838
- 93UppDecGold-51
- 93UppDecGold-263
- 93UppDecGold-838
- 93WhiSoxK-29
- 93WhiSoxSC-13
- 94Bow-295
- 94BowBes-R30
- 94BowBesR-R30
- 94ChuHomS-17
- 94ChuHomSG-17
- 94ColC-282
- 94ColChoGS-282
- 94ColChoSS-282
- 94Don-23
- 94DonSpeE-23
- 94Fin-202
- 94FinJum-202
- 94FinRef-202
- 94Fla-281
- 94Fle-97
- 94FleExtB-54
- 94FUnPac-163
- 94KinDis-21
- 94Lea-26
- 94LeaL-25
- 94OPC-33
- 94Pac-140
- 94PanSti-52
- 94Pin-29

❑ 94PinArtP-29
❑ 94PinMusC-29
❑ 94PinPowS-PS9
❑ 94ProMag-29
❑ 94Sco-347
❑ 94ScoGolR-347
❑ 94Sel-41
❑ 94SP-194
❑ 94SPDieC-194
❑ 94Spo-66
❑ 94StaClu-315
❑ 94StaCluFDI-315
❑ 94StaCluGR-315
❑ 94StaCluMOP-315
❑ 94StaCluT-126
❑ 94StaCluTFDI-126
❑ 94Stu-210
❑ 94Top-90
❑ 94TopBlaG-22
❑ 94TopGol-90
❑ 94TopSpa-90
❑ 94TriPla-270
❑ 94TriPlaM-9
❑ 94Ult-342
❑ 94UltAllS-5
❑ 94UltAwaW-4
❑ 94UppDec-263
❑ 94UppDecED-263
❑ 94WhiSoxK-28
❑ 95Baz-26
❑ 95Bow-329
❑ 95BowBes-R45
❑ 95BowBesR-R45
❑ 95ClaPhoC-14
❑ 95ColCho-505
❑ 95ColChoGS-505
❑ 95ColChoSE-237
❑ 95ColChoSEGS-237
❑ 95ColChoSESS-237
❑ 95ColChoSS-505
❑ 95Don-378
❑ 95DonDom-5
❑ 95DonPreP-378
❑ 95DonTopotO-55
❑ 95Emo-30
❑ 95Fin-173
❑ 95FinRef-173
❑ 95Fla-28
❑ 95Fle-129
❑ 95Lea-215
❑ 95LeaCor-1
❑ 95LeaLim-192
❑ 95Pac-98
❑ 95PanSti-56
❑ 95Pin-257
❑ 95PinArtP-257
❑ 95PinMusC-257
❑ 95RedFol-14
❑ 95Sco-227
❑ 95ScoGolR-227
❑ 95ScoHaloG-HG32
❑ 95ScoPlaTS-227
❑ 95Sel-2
❑ 95SelArtP-2
❑ 95SelCer-52
❑ 95SelCerMG-52
❑ 95SP-138
❑ 95SPCha-138
❑ 95SPChaDC-138
❑ 95Spo-6
❑ 95SpoArtP-6
❑ 95SPSil-138
❑ 95SPSpeF-6
❑ 95StaClu-367
❑ 95StaCluMOP-367
❑ 95StaCluSTWS-367
❑ 95StaCluVR-193
❑ 95StaCluVRMO-193
❑ 95Stu-38
❑ 95StuGolS-38
❑ 95Sum-24
❑ 95SumNthD-24
❑ 95Top-479
❑ 95TopCyb-272
❑ 95TopD3-39
❑ 95TopEmb-123
❑ 95TopEmbGI-123
❑ 95UC3-53
❑ 95UC3ArtP-53
❑ 95Ult-277
❑ 95UltGolM-277
❑ 95UppDec-201
❑ 95UppDecED-201
❑ 95UppDecEDG-201
❑ 95UppDecSE-154
❑ 95UppDecSEG-154
❑ 95WhiSoxK-30
❑ 95Zen-90
❑ 96Baz-13
❑ 96Bow-50
❑ 96BowBes-55
❑ 96BowBesAR-55
❑ 96BowBesR-55
❑ 96BowFoi-50
❑ 96Cir-30
❑ 96CirBos-7
❑ 96CirRav-30
❑ 96ColCho-361
❑ 96ColCho-505
❑ 96ColChoGS-361
❑ 96ColChoGS-505
❑ 96ColChoSS-361
❑ 96ColChoSS-505
❑ 96Don-535
❑ 96DonPreP-535
❑ 96EmoXL-43
❑ 96Fin-B67
❑ 96Fin-B280
❑ 96FinRef-B67
❑ 96FinRef-B280
❑ 96Fla-61
❑ 96Fle-79
❑ 96FleTif-79
❑ 96Lea-172
❑ 96LeaLim-52
❑ 96LeaLimG-52
❑ 96LeaPre-45
❑ 96LeaPreP-45
❑ 96LeaPrePB-172
❑ 96LeaPrePG-172
❑ 96LeaPrePS-172
❑ 96LeaPreSG-23
❑ 96LeaPreSte-23
❑ 96LeaSig-53
❑ 96LeaSigPPG-53
❑ 96LeaSigPPP-53
❑ 96MetUni-41
❑ 96MetUniP-41
❑ 96Pac-279
❑ 96PacPri-P92
❑ 96PacPriG-P92
❑ 96PanSti-172
❑ 96Pin-19
❑ 96PinAfi-100
❑ 96PinAfiAP-100
❑ 96PinAfiFPP-100
❑ 96PinArtP-59
❑ 96PinFirR-11
❑ 96PinSta-59
❑ 96ProSta-133
❑ 96Sco-326
❑ 96ScoDugC-B51
❑ 96ScoDugCAP-B51
❑ 96Sel-51
❑ 96SelArtP-51
❑ 96SelCer-46
❑ 96SelCerAP-46
❑ 96SelCerCB-46
❑ 96SelCerCR-46
❑ 96SelCerMB-46
❑ 96SelCerMG-46
❑ 96SelCerMR-46
❑ 96SelTeaN-27
❑ 96SP-57
❑ 96Spo-79
❑ 96SpoArtP-79
❑ 96StaClu-193
❑ 96StaClu-321
❑ 96StaCluEPB-321
❑ 96StaCluEPG-321
❑ 96StaCluEPS-321
❑ 96StaCluMOP-193
❑ 96StaCluMOP-321
❑ 96Stu-40
❑ 96StuPrePB-40
❑ 96StuPrePG-40
❑ 96StuPrePS-40
❑ 96Sum-79
❑ 96SumAbo&B-79
❑ 96SumArtP-79
❑ 96SumFoi-79
❑ 96TeaOut-84
❑ 96Top-310
❑ 96TopChr-124
❑ 96TopChrR-124
❑ 96TopGal-73
❑ 96TopGalPPI-73
❑ 96TopLas-32
❑ 96TopRoaW-RW19
❑ 96Ult-339
❑ 96UltGolM-339
❑ 96UppDec-44
❑ 96WhiSoxF-18
❑ 96Zen-80
❑ 96ZenArtP-80
❑ 96ZenMoz-3
❑ 97Bow-7
❑ 97BowBes-77
❑ 97BowBesAR-77
❑ 97BowBesR-77
❑ 97BowChr-5
❑ 97BowChrI-5
❑ 97BowChrIR-5
❑ 97BowChrR-5
❑ 97BowInt-7
❑ 97Cir-330
❑ 97CirRav-330
❑ 97ColCho-70
❑ 97ColChoAC-12
❑ 97ColChoT-CW1
❑ 97Don-22
❑ 97DonGolPP-22
❑ 97DonLim-23
❑ 97DonLimE-23
❑ 97DonLimENG-23
❑ 97DonSigA-102
❑ 97DonSigAC-127
❑ 97DonSigAM-127
❑ 97DonSilPP-22
❑ 97DonTea-61
❑ 97DonTeaSPE-61
❑ 97E-X2-16
❑ 97E-X2Cred-16
❑ 97E-X2EssCre-16
❑ 97Fin-120
❑ 97Fin-248
❑ 97FinEmb-120
❑ 97FinEmbR-120
❑ 97FinRef-120
❑ 97FinRef-248
❑ 97FlaShoLC-68
❑ 97FlaShoLeg0-68
❑ 97FlaShoLeg1-68
❑ 97FlaShoM-A68
❑ 97FlaShoM-B68
❑ 97FlaShoM-C68
❑ 97FlaShoR0-68
❑ 97FlaShoR1-68
❑ 97FlaShoR2-68
❑ 97Fle-73
❑ 97FleTif-73
❑ 97Lea-33
❑ 97LeaFraM-33
❑ 97LeaFraMDC-33
❑ 97MetUni-62
❑ 97Pac-65
❑ 97PacLigB-65
❑ 97PacPri-23
❑ 97PacPriLB-23
❑ 97PacPriP-23
❑ 97PacPriSL-SL2B
❑ 97PacSil-65
❑ 97Sco-180
❑ 97ScoArtPWB-180
❑ 97ScoHeaotO-6
❑ 97ScoPreS-180
❑ 97ScoShoS-180
❑ 97ScoShoSAP-180
❑ 97SP-46
❑ 97SpoIll-150
❑ 97SpoIllEE-150
❑ 97StaClu-43
❑ 97StaCluC-CO6
❑ 97StaCluMat-43
❑ 97StaCluMOP-43
❑ 97Stu-14
❑ 97StuPrePG-14
❑ 97StuPrePS-14
❑ 97Top-425
❑ 97TopChr-150
❑ 97TopChrR-150
❑ 97TopGal-69
❑ 97TopGalPG-PG15
❑ 97TopGalPPI-69
❑ 97TopSta-56
❑ 97TopStaAM-56
❑ 97UD3-23
❑ 97Ult-313
❑ 97UltGolME-313
❑ 97UltPlaME-313
❑ 97UppDec-330
❑ 97WhiSoxS-8
❑ 97WhiSoxSPl-8
❑ 97WhiSoxSPr-8
❑ 97WhiSoxTI-23
❑ 98Bow-14
❑ 98BowBes-76
❑ 98BowBesAR-76
❑ 98BowBesR-76
❑ 98BowChr-14
❑ 98BowChrGA-14
❑ 98BowChrGAR-14
❑ 98BowChrI-14
❑ 98BowChrIR-14
❑ 98BowChrR-14
❑ 98BowChrR-9
❑ 98BowChrRR-9
❑ 98BowGolA-14
❑ 98BowInt-14
❑ 98CirThu-23
❑ 98CirThuRav-23
❑ 98CirThuSupRav-23
❑ 98ColCho-65
❑ 98CroRoy-37
❑ 98Don-66
❑ 98DonCol-66
❑ 98DonColL-267
❑ 98DonColP-632
❑ 98DonColS-66
❑ 98DonCruG-17
❑ 98DonCruP-17
❑ 98DonCruR-17
❑ 98DonGolPP-66
❑ 98DonPre-82
❑ 98DonPreSeat-82
❑ 98DonPriCD-66
❑ 98DonPriCL-267
❑ 98DonPriCP-632
❑ 98DonSigA-88
❑ 98DonSigAC-110
❑ 98DonSigAM-113
❑ 98DonSigSB-28
❑ 98DonSigSP-28
❑ 98DonSilPP-66
❑ 98E-X2-66
❑ 98E-X2ECFut-66
❑ 98E-X2ECNow-66
❑ 98Fin-192
❑ 98FinNo--192
❑ 98FinNo-R-192
❑ 98FinRef-192
❑ 98FlaShoLeg0-64
❑ 98FlaShoLeg1-64
❑ 98FlaShoLeg2-64
❑ 98FlaShoLeg3-64
❑ 98FlaShoLegM-64
❑ 98FlaShoR0-64
❑ 98FlaShoR1-64
❑ 98FlaShoR2-64
❑ 98FlaShoR3-64
❑ 98Fle-23
❑ 98Lea-68
❑ 98LeaFraDA-68
❑ 98LeaFraF-68
❑ 98LeaFraM-68
❑ 98LeaFraM-68
❑ 98LeaFraMDC-68
❑ 98LeaFraMDC-68
❑ 98LeaFraMZ2-68
❑ 98LeaRS-83
❑ 98LeaRSLHolo-83
❑ 98LeaRSLong-83
❑ 98LeaRTrue-83
❑ 98MetUni-37
❑ 98MetUniPMG-37
❑ 98Pac-65
❑ 98PacAur-26
❑ 98PacInv-21
❑ 98PacInvPBlue-21
❑ 98PacInvSilv-21
❑ 98PacInvTeam-6
❑ 98PacOme-61
❑ 98PacOmeR-61
❑ 98PacOnl-183
❑ 98PacOnlR-183
❑ 98PacOnlWC-183
❑ 98PacPar-33
❑ 98PacParC-33
❑ 98PacParG-33
❑ 98PacParHS-33
❑ 98PacParPB-33
❑ 98PacParR-33
❑ 98PacPlaB-65
❑ 98PacRedT-65
❑ 98PacSil-65
❑ 98Pin-56
❑ 98PinIns-93
❑ 98PinInsCE-93
❑ 98PinInsDE-93
❑ 98PinPer-104
❑ 98PinPerPP-104
❑ 98PinPlu-130
❑ 98PinPreP-56
❑ 98Revo-38
❑ 98RevoSS-38
❑ 98Sco-111
❑ 98ScoRT-86
❑ 98ScoRTSS-PP63
❑ 98ScoRTSSAP-PP63
❑ 98ScoRTSSAP1-PP63
❑ 98ScoSS-PP45
❑ 98ScoSSAP-PP45
❑ 98SkyDugA-60
❑ 98SkyDugAIA-60
❑ 98SP Aut-68
❑ 98SP AutTrade-15
❑ 98SpoIll-122
❑ 98SpoIllEE-122
❑ 98SpoIllFE-122
❑ 98SpoIllTaN-137
❑ 98SpoIllTaNEE-137
❑ 98SpoIllWSF-123
❑ 98SpoIllWSFEE-123
❑ 98SpoIllWSFFE-123
❑ 98SPxFin-73
❑ 98SPxFinR-73
❑ 98SPxFinS-73
❑ 98StaCluC-CS27
❑ 98StaCluC-CS29
❑ 98StaCluC-CS30
❑ 98StaCluFDI-68
❑ 98StaCluI-68
❑ 98StaCluOneK-68
❑ 98StaCluPP-68
❑ 98StaCluTIll-T4B
❑ 98StaCluTLme-T4B
❑ 98StaCluTLmo-T4B
❑ 98Stu-77
❑ 98StuGPP-77
❑ 98StuSPP-77
❑ 98Top-303
❑ 98TopChr-303
❑ 98TopChrR-303
❑ 98TopDevR-303
❑ 98TopDia-303
❑ 98TopGal-75
❑ 98TopGalGP-75
❑ 98TopGalOPP-75
❑ 98TopGalPPI-75
❑ 98TopGalPPIA-75
❑ 98TopGolLabC1-19
❑ 98TopGolLabC1B-19
❑ 98TopGolLabC1One-19
❑ 98TopGolLabC1R-19
❑ 98TopGolLabC2-19
❑ 98TopGolLabC2B-19
❑ 98TopGolLabC2One-19
❑ 98TopGolLabC2R-19
❑ 98TopGolLabC3-19
❑ 98TopGolLabC3B-19
❑ 98TopGolLabC3One-19
❑ 98TopGolLabC3R-19
❑ 98TopMiniC-303
❑ 98TopOpeD-130
❑ 98TopSta-70
❑ 98TopStaB-70
❑ 98TopStaG-70
❑ 98TopStaGR-70
❑ 98TopStaS-70
❑ 98TopTek-33
❑ 98TopTekD-33
❑ 98UppDec-331
❑ 98UppDec10AP-32
❑ 98UppDec1APR-32
❑ 98UppDecRGKoG-G5
❑ 98WhiSoxS-10
❑ 98WhiSoxSP-10
❑ 99199Fin-176
❑ 99Bow-284
❑ 99BowBes-49
❑ 99BowBesAR-49
❑ 99BowBesR-49
❑ 99BowGol-284
❑ 99BowInt-284
❑ 99CroRoyB-94
❑ 99CroRoyL-94
❑ 99CroRoyOD-94
❑ 99E-X Cen-86
❑ 99E-X CenECFut-86
❑ 99E-X CenECNow-86
❑ 99FinGolRef-176
❑ 99FinRef-176
❑ 99FlaShoLeg1-56
❑ 99FlaShoLeg2-56
❑ 99FlaShoLeg3-56
❑ 99FlaShoLegM1-56
❑ 99FlaShoLegM2-56
❑ 99FlaShoLegM3-56
❑ 99FlaShoR1-56
❑ 99FlaShoR2-56
❑ 99FlaShoR3-56
❑ 99Fle-186
❑ 99FleBri-104
❑ 99FleBri2G-104
❑ 99FleBriBlu-104
❑ 99FleBriGol-104
❑ 99FleMys-20
❑ 99FleMysFI-25
❑ 99FleMysG-20
❑ 99FleMysM-20
❑ 99FleSta9-186
❑ 99FleWarT-186
❑ 99MetUni-15
❑ 99MetUniGM-15
❑ 99MetUniPMG-15
❑ 99Pac-107
❑ 99PacCroC-71
❑ 99PacCroCPB-71
❑ 99PacInv-98
❑ 99PacInvOD-98
❑ 99PacInvPB-98
❑ 99PacOme-157
❑ 99PacOmeC-157
❑ 99PacOmeG-157
❑ 99PacOmePB-157
❑ 99PacPar-156
❑ 99PacParC-156
❑ 99PacParG-156
❑ 99PacParHoloGold-156
❑ 99PacParHS-156
❑ 99PacParOD-156
❑ 99PacParPB-156
❑ 99PacParRed-156
❑ 99PacPlaB-107
❑ 99PacPri-36
❑ 99PacPriHB-36
❑ 99PacPriHG-36
❑ 99PacPriHM-36
❑ 99PacPriHP-36
❑ 99PacPriRed-36
❑ 99PacRed-107
❑ 99Rev-92
❑ 99RevPremDate-92
❑ 99RevRet-92
❑ 99RevShaSS-92
❑ 99SkyMolM-83
❑ 99SkyMolMX-83
❑ 99SkyPre-104
❑ 99SkyPreA-54
❑ 99SkyPreABlue-54
❑ 99SkyPreR-104
❑ 99SkyThu-204
❑ 99SkyThuRant-204
❑ 99SkyThuRave-204
❑ 99SP Aut-55
❑ 99SpoIll-142
❑ 99StaClu-316
❑ 99StaCluFDI-316
❑ 99StaCluOoaK-316
❑ 99StaCluPP-316
❑ 99ThuSkySupR-204
❑ 99Top-314
❑ 99TopChr-314
❑ 99TopChrR-314
❑ 99TopGal-93
❑ 99TopGalPP-93
❑ 99TopGalPPI-93
❑ 99TopMVPP-314
❑ 99TopSta-122
❑ 99TopStaFoil-122
❑ 99UDHolo-37
❑ 99UDHoloAUsome-37
❑ 99Ult-54
❑ 99UltGolM-54
❑ 99UltMas-54
❑ 99UltPlaM-54
❑ 99UppDec-425
❑ 99UppDecE-57
❑ 99UppDecEFXG-57
❑ 99UppDecEL1-425
❑ 99UppDecEL2-425
❑ 99UppDecM-134
❑ 99UppDecMGS-134
❑ 99UppDecMHFS-134
❑ 99UppDecMSS-134
❑ 99UppDecR-53
❑ 99UppDecRG-53
❑ 99UppDecRP-53
❑ 99Vic-255

Ventura, Wilfredo

❑ 97VisOakG-29

Venturini, Pete (Peter Paul)

❑ 86PenWhiSP-25
❑ 87BirBarB-22
❑ 88BirBarB-11

Venturino, Phil
❑ 86MidAngP-24
❑ 86PalSprAS-18
❑ 87MidAngP-29
❑ 88EdmTraC-8
❑ 88EdmTraP-566
Venuto, Nicholas
❑ 88SouOreAP-1695
❑ 89MedAthB-14
Veras, Camilo
❑ 84IdaFalATI-27
❑ 86MadMusP-21
❑ 86MadMusP-25
❑ 87MadMusP-20
❑ 87MadMusP-15
❑ 88HunStaTI-23
Veras, Dario
❑ 94RanCucQC-25
❑ 94RanCucQF-1640
❑ 95MemChiTI-21
❑ 96MemChiB-29
❑ 97Bow-173
❑ 97BowInt-173
❑ 97ColCho-23
❑ 97Fle-629
❑ 97FleTif-629
❑ 97PadMot-27
❑ 97UppDec-268
❑ 97UppDec-379
❑ 98Las-27
❑ 98PacInvGems-214
Veras, Juan
❑ 95ChaRivTI-21
Veras, Quilvio
❑ 91KinMetC-10
❑ 91KinMetP-3824
❑ 92ClaFS7-83
❑ 92ColMetC-25
❑ 92ColMetF-306
❑ 92ColMetPI-21
❑ 92ColMetPIISPI-7
❑ 92ProFS7-289
❑ 92UppDecML-187
❑ 93BinMetF-2344
❑ 93Bow-215
❑ 93ClaFS7-146
❑ 93ClaGolF-209
❑ 93ExcFS7-81
❑ 93ExcLeaLF-6
❑ 93LimRocDWB-110
❑ 93SouAtlLAIPI-4
❑ 93SouAtlLAPI-39
❑ 94Bow-428
❑ 94ExcFS7-239
❑ 94NorTidF-2930
❑ 94TedWilDGC-DG6
❑ 94TriAAF-AAA38
❑ 94Ult-538
❑ 94UppDecML-62
❑ 95Bow-171
❑ 95BowBes-R89
❑ 95BowBesR-R89
❑ 95ColCho-8
❑ 95ColChoGS-8
❑ 95ColChoSS-8
❑ 95DonTopotO-248
❑ 95Emo-133
❑ 95Fin-287
❑ 95FinRef-287
❑ 95Fla-356
❑ 95FleUpd-100
❑ 95Lea-233
❑ 95LeaLim-159
❑ 95SigRooOJ-33
❑ 95SigRooOJP-33
❑ 95SigRooOJPS-33
❑ 95SigRooOJS-33
❑ 95SP-21
❑ 95SPCha-13
❑ 95SPChaDC-13
❑ 95SPSil-21
❑ 95StaClu-555
❑ 95StaCluCB-CB10
❑ 95StaCluMOP-555
❑ 95StaCluMOP-CB10
❑ 95StaCluSTWS-555
❑ 95Sum-140
❑ 95SumNthD-140
❑ 95Top-540
❑ 95TopTra-145T
❑ 95UppDec-237
❑ 95UppDecED-237
❑ 95UppDecEDG-237
❑ 95UppDecPAW-H37
❑ 95UppDecPAWE-H37
❑ 95UppDecSE-248
❑ 95UppDecSEG-248
❑ 96Baz-122
❑ 96ColCho-5
❑ 96ColCho-148
❑ 96ColChoGS-5
❑ 96ColChoGS-148
❑ 96ColChoSS-5
❑ 96ColChoSS-148
❑ 96Don-446
❑ 96DonPreP-446
❑ 96EmoXL-191
❑ 96Fin-B148
❑ 96FinRef-B148
❑ 96Fla-269
❑ 96Fle-397
❑ 96FleRooS-15
❑ 96FleTif-397
❑ 96Lea-171
❑ 96LeaPrePB-171
❑ 96LeaPrePG-171
❑ 96LeaPrePS-171
❑ 96LeaSigA-229
❑ 96LeaSigAG-230
❑ 96LeaSigAS-230
❑ 96MetUni-170
❑ 96MetUniMFG-12
❑ 96MetUniP-170
❑ 96Pac-67
❑ 96PacEstL-EL34
❑ 96PacGolCD-DC8
❑ 96PacPri-P28
❑ 96PacPriG-P28
❑ 96PanSti-9
❑ 96PanSti-116
❑ 96PanSti-240
❑ 96Sco-78
❑ 96ScoDugC-A64
❑ 96ScoDugCAP-A64
❑ 96StaClu-189
❑ 96StaClu-344
❑ 96StaCluEPB-344
❑ 96StaCluEPG-344
❑ 96StaCluEPS-344
❑ 96StaCluMO-44
❑ 96StaCluMOP-189
❑ 96StaCluMOP-344
❑ 96Stu-120
❑ 96StuPrePB-120
❑ 96StuPrePG-120
❑ 96StuPrePS-120
❑ 96Top-141
❑ 96TopChr-40
❑ 96TopChrR-40
❑ 96TopGal-108
❑ 96TopGalPPI-108
❑ 96TopLas-95
❑ 96Ult-204
❑ 96UltGolM-204
❑ 96UppDec-74
❑ 97Cir-112
❑ 97CirRav-112
❑ 97ColChoU-U22
❑ 97Don-310
❑ 97DonGolPP-310
❑ 97DonSilPP-310
❑ 97Fle-562
❑ 97FleTif-562
❑ 97Lea-294
❑ 97LeaFraM-294
❑ 97LeaFraMDC-294
❑ 97Pac-309
❑ 97PacLigB-309
❑ 97PacSil-309
❑ 97PadMot-11
❑ 97Sco-393
❑ 97ScoArtPWB-393
❑ 97ScoResC-393
❑ 97ScoShoS-393
❑ 97ScoShoSAP-393
❑ 97Ult-437
❑ 97UltGolME-437
❑ 97UltPlaME-437
❑ 98CirThu-86
❑ 98CirThuRav-86
❑ 98CirThuSupRav-86
❑ 98Fin-136
❑ 98FinNo--136
❑ 98FinNo-R-136
❑ 98FinRef-136
❑ 98Fle-134
❑ 98Pac-434
❑ 98PacAur-194
❑ 98PacOnl-651
❑ 98PacOnlR-651
❑ 98PacOnlWC-651
❑ 98PacPar-241
❑ 98PacParC-241
❑ 98PacParG-241
❑ 98PacParHS-241
❑ 98PacParPB-241
❑ 98PacParR-241
❑ 98PacPlaB-434
❑ 98PacRedT-434
❑ 98PacSil-434
❑ 98PadMot-11
❑ 98StaCluFDI-211
❑ 98StaCluI-211
❑ 98StaCluOneK-211
❑ 98StaCluPP-211
❑ 98Top-204
❑ 98TopChr-204
❑ 98TopChrR-204
❑ 98TopDevR-204
❑ 98TopDia-204
❑ 98TopMiniC-204
❑ 98Ult-79
❑ 98UltGolM-79
❑ 98UltMas-79
❑ 98UltPlaM-79
❑ 98UppDec-209
❑ 98UppDecSF-114
❑ 99Fle-289
❑ 99FleSta9-289
❑ 99FleWarT-289
❑ 99Pac-376
❑ 99PacAur-166
❑ 99PacAurOD-166
❑ 99PacCroC-248
❑ 99PacCroCPB-248
❑ 99PacPar-205
❑ 99PacParC-205
❑ 99PacParG-205
❑ 99PacParHoloGold-205
❑ 99PacParHS-205
❑ 99PacParOD-205
❑ 99PacParPB-205
❑ 99PacParRed-205
❑ 99PacPlaB-376
❑ 99PacRed-376
❑ 99SkyThu-24
❑ 99SkyThuRant-24
❑ 99SkyThuRave-24
❑ 99StaClu-217
❑ 99StaCluC-CS27
❑ 99StaCluC-CS33
❑ 99StaCluC-CS38
❑ 99StaCluC-CS42
❑ 99StaCluFDI-217
❑ 99StaCluOoaK-217
❑ 99StaCluPP-217
❑ 99ThuSkySupR-24
❑ 99Top-29
❑ 99TopChr-29
❑ 99TopChrR-29
❑ 99TopMVPP-29
Veras, Wilton
❑ 96LowSpiB-27
❑ 97MicBatC-29
❑ 98EasLeaTPM-27
❑ 98TreThuM-26
Verban, Emil
❑ 47Exh-228
❑ 48Bow-28
❑ 49Bow-38
❑ 49EurSta-73
❑ 79DiaGre-314
❑ 83Car194T-26
❑ 83TCMPla1945-26
Verbanic, Joe
❑ 67Top-442
❑ 68OPC-29
❑ 68Top-29
❑ 68TopVen-29
❑ 68YanPhoS-79
❑ 69Top-541
❑ 69YanMal-11
❑ 69YanPhoS-52
❑ 70OPC-416
❑ 70Top-416
❑ 70YanPhoS-32
❑ 92YanWIZ6-134
❑ 92YanWIZ7-158
Verble, Gene
❑ 88ChaLooLTI-30
Verble, Gene Kermit
❑ 53Bri-27
❑ 55SeaPop-20
Verdi, Frank
❑ 55JetPos-19
❑ 78TidTidT-27
❑ 79TidTidT-4
❑ 80TidTidT-24
❑ 81ColCliP-26
❑ 81ColCliT-17
❑ 82ColCliP-26
❑ 82ColCliT-25
❑ 83SanJosBC-1
❑ 84RocRedWT-9
❑ 85RocRedWT-24
Verdi, Mike
❑ 86SanJosBP-22
❑ 87SanJosBP-19
❑ 89ElmPioP-22
❑ 90ElmPioP-25
❑ 91WinHavRSC-5
❑ 91WinHavRSP-505
Verdin, Cesar
❑ 97TamYan-31
Verducci, John
❑ 85EveGiaC-17
❑ 86ShrCapP-26
❑ 87PhoFirP-18
Verdugo, Jason
❑ 97SalVolG-39
Verdugo, Luis
❑ 89MiaMirIS-20
Verdugo, Mando
❑ 88SalLakCTTI-25
❑ 89MiaMirIS-20
❑ 90KinIndTI-21
Verduzco, Dave
❑ 92NiaFalRC-25
❑ 92NiaFalRF-3323
Verduzco, Steve
❑ 93AubAstC-24
❑ 93AubAstF-3454
❑ 94OscAstC-22
❑ 94OscAstF-1148
Veres, Dave (David Scott)
❑ 86MedA'sC-53
❑ 87ModA'sC-16
❑ 87ModA'sP-3
❑ 88CalLeaACLC-10
❑ 88HunStaTI-24
❑ 88ModA'sCLC-56
❑ 88ModA'sTI-32
❑ 89HunStaB-5
❑ 90CMC-579
❑ 90ProAAAF-137
❑ 90TacTigC-2
❑ 90TacTigP-90
❑ 91AlbDukLD-21
❑ 91AlbDukP-1141
❑ 91LinDriAAA-21
❑ 92TucTorF-488
❑ 93TucTorF-3059
❑ 94TucTorF-762
❑ 95AstMot-27
❑ 95Fla-149
❑ 95Fle-470
❑ 95Pac-195
❑ 95Top-525
❑ 95TopCyb-310
❑ 96Don-17
❑ 96DonPreP-17
❑ 96ExpBoo-6
❑ 96ExpDis-21
❑ 96Fle-421
❑ 96FleTif-421
❑ 96FleUpd-U153
❑ 96FleUpdTC-U153
❑ 96LeaSigEA-209
❑ 96Pac-88
❑ 96Ult-215
❑ 96UltGolM-215
❑ 97PacPriGotD-GD171
❑ 98PacOnl-259
❑ 98PacOnlR-259
❑ 98PacOnlWC-259
Veres, Randy
❑ 86BelBreP-25
❑ 87BelBreP-1
❑ 88StoPorCLC-179
❑ 88StoPorP-730
❑ 89ElPasDGS-17
❑ 89FleUpd-42
❑ 90Bow-390
❑ 90BowTif-390
❑ 90BreMilB-29
❑ 90TopDeb89-130
❑ 90TopTra-125T
❑ 90TopTraT-125T
❑ 91Cla1-T56
❑ 91Don-755
❑ 91Fle-600
❑ 91OPC-694
❑ 91RicBraP-2570
❑ 91Sco100RS-12
❑ 91Top-694
❑ 91TopDesS-694
❑ 91TopMic-694
❑ 91TopTif-694
❑ 92PhoFirS-397
❑ 94BreMilB-186
❑ 94IowCubF-1276
❑ 96Don-15
❑ 96DonPreP-15
❑ 96Fle-398
❑ 96FleTif-398
Vergez, Johnny
❑ 29Zee-82
❑ 30Zee-98
❑ 32R33So2-401
❑ 33ButCanV-50
❑ 33Gou-233
❑ 34BatR31-176
❑ 34DiaMatCSB-187
❑ 34DiaStaR-21A
❑ 34DiaStaR-21B
❑ 34TarThoBD-26
❑ 36WorWidGV-5
❑ 37Zee-62
❑ 67SpoHobFC-27
❑ 93ConTSN-811
Verheist, Edwin
❑ 76VenLeaS-124
❑ 80VenLeaS-205
Verhoeff, Will
❑ 77WesHavYT-24
Verhoeven, John
❑ 77Top-91
❑ 78Top-329
❑ 79TolMudHT-12
❑ 80TwiPos-29
❑ 81Don-564
❑ 81Top-603
❑ 81TwiPos-28
❑ 82Fle-547
❑ 82Top-281
Verigood, Steve
❑ 97YakBeaG-33
Verkuilen, Mike
❑ 85OrlTwiT-13
Vermillion, Grant
❑ 95BoiHawTI-32
❑ 96CedRapKTI-26
Verna, Chris
❑ 89SanBerSCLC-92
❑ 90WilBilB-24
❑ 90WilBilS-27
Vernon, Mickey
❑ 46SpoExcW-12-12
❑ 47Exh-229A
❑ 47Exh-229B
❑ 47SenGunBP-11
❑ 49Bow-94
❑ 49IndTeal-26
❑ 49IndVisEI-14
❑ 50Bow-132
❑ 51Bow-65
❑ 51TopBluB-13
❑ 52Bow-87
❑ 52NatTeaL-39
❑ 52TipTop-44
❑ 52Top-106
❑ 53BowC-159
❑ 53Bri-25
❑ 53ExhCan-59
❑ 53IndPenCBP-28
❑ 53RedMan-AL21
❑ 54Bow-152
❑ 54RedMan-AL13
❑ 55ArmCoi-24
❑ 55BigLeaIS-18
❑ 55Bow-46
❑ 55DaiQueS-18
❑ 55DonWin-8
❑ 55RedMan-AL12
❑ 56Top-228
❑ 57Top-92
❑ 58IndTeal-22
❑ 58Top-233
❑ 59ArmCoi-20
❑ 59RedSoxJP-10
❑ 59Top-115
❑ 59TopVen-115
❑ 60SenUniMC-19
❑ 60Top-467
❑ 61SenJayP-10
❑ 61Top-134
❑ 62Top-152
❑ 62TopVen-152
❑ 63Top-402
❑ 67VanMouSO-25
❑ 72Dia-48
❑ 76SSP-621
❑ 76TayBow4-23
❑ 77ExpPos-34
❑ 77GalGloG-45
❑ 77OPC-198
❑ 77PirTCM1WC-34
❑ 77TCMTheWY-67
❑ 79ColCliT-29
❑ 79TCM50-87
❑ 80PacLeg-78
❑ 81RedSoxBG2S-57
❑ 82TCMGreH-12
❑ 83TCMPla1942-19
❑ 83TopRep5-106
❑ 84ColCliP-25
❑ 84ColCliT-21
❑ 84OCoandSI-68
❑ 84TCMBruS-BS4
❑ 85ColCliT-30
❑ 86SpoDecG-38
❑ 89SweBasG-54
❑ 91TopArc1-287
❑ 92BazQua5A-12
Verplancke, Joe
❑ 96AriBlaDB-33
❑ 96HonShaHWB-35
❑ 97HigDesMUG-7
❑ 98HigDesMG-27
Verrall, Jared
❑ 96ButCopKB-29
Versalles, Zoilo
❑ 61Top-21
❑ 61TopStaI-186
❑ 61TwiCloD-30
❑ 61TwiJayP-12
❑ 61TwiPetM-1
❑ 61TwiUniMC-13
❑ 62Jel-86
❑ 62Pos-86
❑ 62PosCan-86
❑ 62SalPlaC-51A
❑ 62SalPlaC-51B
❑ 62ShiPlaC-51
❑ 62Top-499
❑ 62TopStaI-81
❑ 63Jel-3
❑ 63Pos-3
❑ 63Top-349
❑ 63TwiJayP-12
❑ 63TwiVol-22
❑ 64Top-15
❑ 64TopVen-15
❑ 64TwiJayP-12
❑ 64WheSta-46
❑ 65MacSta-10
❑ 65OPC-157
❑ 65Top-157
❑ 65TopEmbI-33
❑ 65TwiPos-10
❑ 66Top-400
❑ 66TwiFaiG-16
❑ 67CokCapTw-13
❑ 67DexPre-215
❑ 67Top-270
❑ 67TopVen-226
❑ 67TwiTeal-24
❑ 68Top-315
❑ 68TopVen-315
❑ 69MilBra-284
❑ 69MLBOffS-45
❑ 69OPC-38
❑ 69Top-38
❑ 69TopSta-100
❑ 69TopTeaP-13
❑ 70MLBOffS-288
❑ 70OPC-365
❑ 70Top-365
❑ 72MilBra-352
❑ 75OPC-203
❑ 75Top-203
❑ 75TopMin-203
❑ 78TwiFri-22
❑ 81TCM60I-442
❑ 82K-M-7
❑ 86TwiGreT-3
❑ 88PacLegI-107
❑ 90DodTar-822
❑ 92UppDecS-29
Verstandig, Mark
❑ 88SpoIndP-1943
❑ 89ChaRaiP-990
❑ 90WatDiaB-25
❑ 90WatDiaP-2382
❑ 91HigDesMC-17

❑ 91HigDesMP-2400
Veryzer, Thomas
❑ 75DetTigP-34
❑ 75OPC-623
❑ 75Top-623
❑ 75TopMin-623
❑ 76DetTigP-33
❑ 76Hos-109
❑ 76OPC-432
❑ 76SSP-367
❑ 76Top-432
❑ 77OPC-188
❑ 77Top-145
❑ 78IndTeal-29
❑ 78OPC-14
❑ 78Top-633
❑ 79Top-537
❑ 80IndTeal-30
❑ 80OPC-145
❑ 80Top-276
❑ 81AllGamPI-25
❑ 81Don-199
❑ 81Fle-390
❑ 81Top-39
❑ 82Don-450
❑ 82Fle-381
❑ 82MetPhoA-24
❑ 82OPC-387
❑ 82Top-387
❑ 82TopTra-123T
❑ 83CubThoAV-29
❑ 83Fle-559
❑ 83Top-496
❑ 83TopTra-121T
❑ 84CubChiT-31
❑ 84Nes792-117
❑ 84Top-117
❑ 84TopTif-117
❑ 85Top-405
❑ 85TopTif-405
❑ 91MetWIZ-421
Veselic, Bob
❑ 80TolMudHT-19
❑ 81TolMudHT-9
❑ 82TolMudHT-6
❑ 83TucTorT-9
Vesling, Don
❑ 88FloStaLAS-51
❑ 88LakTigS-25
❑ 89BlaYNPRWL-29
❑ 89LonTigP-1374
❑ 90CMC-378
❑ 90ProAAAF-381
❑ 90TolMudHC-1
❑ 90TolMudHP-151
❑ 91LinDriAAA-598
❑ 91TolMudHLD-598
❑ 91TolMudHP-1933
❑ 92LonTigF-632
❑ 92LonTigS-421
Vespe, Will
❑ 88CapCodPPaLP-149
❑ 89WatIndS-22
❑ 90KinIndTI-15
Vessel, Andrew
❑ 94ChaRivC-22
❑ 94ChaRivF-2687
❑ 95Bow-186
❑ 96BesAutS-92
❑ 96BesAutSA-81
❑ 96Bow-148
❑ 96BowFoi-148
❑ 96Exc-113
❑ 96WesOahCHWB-33
❑ 97BesAutAS-64
❑ 97BesAutP-R17
❑ 97TexLeaTP-26
❑ 97TulDriTI-27
❑ 98Bow-312
❑ 98BowChr-312
❑ 98BowChrGA-312
❑ 98BowChrGAR-312
❑ 98BowChrI-312
❑ 98BowChrIR-312
❑ 98BowChrR-312
❑ 98BowGolA-312
❑ 98BowInt-312
❑ 98MetUni-69
❑ 98MetUniPMG-69
❑ 98TexLeaC-26
❑ 98Top-258
❑ 98TopChr-258
❑ 98TopChrR-258
❑ 98TopDevR-258
❑ 98TopDia-258
❑ 98TopMiniC-258
❑ 98TulDriTI-15
❑ 98Ult-244
❑ 98UltGolM-244
❑ 98UltMas-244
❑ 98UltPlaM-244
Vessey, Tom
❑ 81TucTorT-6
❑ 82TucTorT-4
Vetsch, Dave
❑ 85VisOakT-13
❑ 86OrlTwiP-22
❑ 87OrlTwiP-27
Vezelich, Louis
❑ 37Zee-63
Vezendy, Gerry
❑ 65Top-509
Viano, Jacob
❑ 94AshTouC-23
❑ 94AshTouF-1781
❑ 94SouAtlLAF-SAL32
❑ 95Exc-191
❑ 95NewHavRTI-17
❑ 96BesAutSA-82
❑ 96Exc-159
❑ 96NewHavRB-26
❑ 97BesAutAS-65
❑ 97St.PetDRUB-29
Viarengo, Matt
❑ 91IdaFalBP-4328
❑ 91PulBraC-28
❑ 91PulBraP-4005
Viator, Dustin
❑ 97IdaFalBTI-26
❑ 98CliLumG-25
Viau, Leon
❑ 87OldJudN-511
Vice, Darryl
❑ 88CapCodPPaLP-152
❑ 89ModA'sC-26
❑ 90MadMusP-2280
❑ 90ModA'sC-30
❑ 91HunStaC-25
❑ 91HunStaLD-297
❑ 91HunStaP-1806
❑ 91HunStaTI-21
❑ 91LinDriAA-297
❑ 92HunStaF-3958
❑ 92HunStaS-322
❑ 93OrlCubF-2795
Vicente, Alberto
❑ 90MarPhiP-3419
Vicentino, Andy
❑ 96-97LinVen-34
Vick, Ernie
❑ 92ConTSN-402
Vick, Scott
❑ 89TenTecGE-28
Vickers, Mike
❑ 78AshTouT-26
❑ 79AshTouT-21
❑ 80TulDriT-25
Vickers, Randy
❑ 95EveAqaTI-29
❑ 96PitMetB-27
❑ 96WisTimRB-28
❑ 97CapCitB-21
Vickers, Rube
❑ 12ImpTobC-37
❑ 90DodTar-1089
Vickery, Lou
❑ 62KahAtl-23
❑ 64TulOil-7
Vico, George
❑ 49Bow-122
❑ 49Lea-47
❑ 50Bow-150
❑ 53MotCoo-25
❑ 53SanFraSTI-23
❑ 79DiaGre-394
❑ 85TCMPla1-26
Victery, Joe
❑ 96EveAquB-26
Vida, James
❑ 95SpoIndTI-28
Vidal, Gilbert
❑ 96PorRocB-30
❑ 97SalAva-32
❑ 98AshTouM-24
Vidal, Jose
❑ 67Top-499
❑ 68Top-432
❑ 69PilPos-23
❑ 69Top-322
❑ 77PilPosR-23
Vidmar, Donald
❑ 88BenBucL-26
❑ 89PalSprACLC-50
❑ 89PalSprAP-482
❑ 90PalSprACLC-225
❑ 90PalSprAP-2578
❑ 91MidAngOHP-30
❑ 91PalSprAP-2017
❑ 92EdmTraF-3540
❑ 92EdmTraS-170
❑ 92MidAngOHP-26
❑ 92ProFS7-36
❑ 92SkyAAAF-82
Vidro, Jose
❑ 93Bow-592
❑ 93BurBeeC-25
❑ 93BurBeeF-168
❑ 93ClaFS7-147
❑ 94WesPalBEC-25
❑ 94WesPalBEF-52
❑ 95HarSenTI-23
❑ 96HarSenB-27
❑ 98BesAutSS-51
❑ 98ColCho-434
❑ 98Fle-216
❑ 98MetUni-124
❑ 98MetUniPMG-124
❑ 98Pac-358
❑ 98PacAur-159
❑ 98PacOme-152
❑ 98PacOmeR-152
❑ 98PacOnl-465
❑ 98PacOnlR-465
❑ 98PacOnlWC-465
❑ 98PacPar-198
❑ 98PacParC-198
❑ 98PacParG-198
❑ 98PacParHS-198
❑ 98PacParPB-198
❑ 98PacParR-198
❑ 98PacPlaB-358
❑ 98PacRedT-358
❑ 98PacSil-358
❑ 98StaCluFDI-18
❑ 98StaCluI-18
❑ 98StaCluOneK-18
❑ 98StaCluPP-18
❑ 98Ult-236
❑ 98UltGolM-236
❑ 98UltMas-236
❑ 98UltPlaM-236
❑ 98UppDec-436
❑ 99Pac-272
❑ 99PacPlaB-272
❑ 99PacRed-272
Viebrock, Alan
❑ 76WatRoyT-32
Viegas, Randy
❑ 97IdaFalBTI-27
❑ 98WesMicWM-27
Vieira, Scott
❑ 96RocCubTI-30
Viera, John
❑ 90PriWilCTI-26
❑ 91PriWilCC-23
❑ 91PriWilCP-1441
❑ 92AlbYanF-2240
❑ 92AlbYanSk-22
❑ 92SkyAA F-11
Viera, Jose
❑ 90HunCubP-3295
❑ 90ProAaA-190
❑ 91PeoChiC-14
❑ 91PeoChiTI-21
❑ 92WinSpiC-4
❑ 93Bow-256
❑ 93ClaFS7-31
❑ 93ClaGolF-40
Viera, Rob
❑ 98BurBeeM-22
Vierra, Jeff
❑ 87HawRai-6
Vierra, Joey
❑ 87HawRai-21
❑ 88GreHorP-1574
❑ 89CedRapRB-8
❑ 89CedRapRP-915
❑ 89CedRapRS-21
❑ 89Sta-189
❑ 90CMC-128
❑ 90NasSouC-3
❑ 90NasSouP-234
❑ 90ProAAAF-546
❑ 91LinDriAAA-273
❑ 91MidLeaAP-MWL9
❑ 91NasSouLD-273
❑ 91NasSouP-2157
❑ 91PeoChiP-1352
❑ 92ClaFS7-319
❑ 92NasSouF-1833
❑ 92NasSouS-296
❑ 92SkyAAAF-137
❑ 92TriA AAS-296
❑ 92WinSpiF-1217
❑ 93AlbDukF-1461
❑ 93ExcFS7-14
❑ 93SanAntMF-3006
❑ 94BirBarC-25
❑ 94BirBarF-623
❑ 95NasSouTI-28
Viggiano, Matt
❑ 88BatCliP-1683
Vike, Jim
❑ 86AubAstP-27
Vila, Jesus
❑ 86VerBeaDP-26
Vilella, Lazaro
❑ 84ButCopKT-26
Viles, Jeff
❑ 98JohCCTI-34
Vilet, Tom
❑ 91BatCliCB-15
❑ 91BatCliP-3499
❑ 92BatCliCB-26
❑ 92BatCliF-3280
❑ 93ClePhiC-24
❑ 93ClePhiF-2698
Villa, Jose
❑ 88St.CatBJP-2008
❑ 93LinVenB-94
❑ 94VenLinU-11
❑ 95LinVen-97
❑ 96-97LinVen-184
Villa, Mike
❑ 86FreGiaSB-9
❑ 87TamTarP-30
❑ 88CliGiaP-719
Villaescusa, Juan
❑ 81VerBeaDT-23
Villafana, Jose
❑ 95NewJerCTI-30
❑ 97NewJerCB-27
Villafuerte, Brandon
❑ 96HilStaHWB-30
❑ 96PitMetB-28
❑ 97CapCitB-12
❑ 98PorSeaDQ-12
Villalobos, Carlos
❑ 96LanJetB-29
❑ 97CalLeaATI-24
❑ 97LakTigB-30
❑ 97LanJet-27
❑ 98JacSunM-24
❑ 99SP TopP-117
❑ 99SP TopPPE-117
Villalobos, Gary
❑ 91LynRedSC-19
❑ 91LynRedSP-1209
❑ 92WinHavRSC-8
❑ 92WinHavRSF-1788
Villalobos, Noe
❑ 97LowSpiB-27
Villalobos, Oswaldo
❑ 94VenLinU-243
❑ 96-97LinVen-194
Villalona, Kadir
❑ 92MedHatBJF-3221
❑ 92MedHatBJSP-19
Villaman, Rafael
❑ 81NasSouTI-21
❑ 82NasSouTI-26
Villano, Mike
❑ 94EveGiaC-19
❑ 94EveGiaF-3656
❑ 96SanJosGB-21
❑ 97BesLimA-39
❑ 97Bow-343
❑ 97BowInt-343
❑ 97ShrCap-25
❑ 97ShrCapB-25
❑ 97TexLeaTP-22
❑ 97Top-494
❑ 98BesPreA-44
❑ 98ChaKniQ-27
Villanueva, Gilbert
❑ 87ChaWheP-3
❑ 88StoPorCLC-188
❑ 88StoPorP-728
❑ 89RenSilSCLC-247
Villanueva, Hector
❑ 86WinSpiP-26
❑ 87PitCubP-3
❑ 88BlaYNPRWL-116
❑ 88EasLeaAP-28
❑ 88PitCubP-1355
❑ 89BlaYNPRWL-20
❑ 89IowCubC-13
❑ 89IowCubP-1696
❑ 90CMC-93
❑ 90CubMar-21
❑ 90FleUpd-10
❑ 90IowCubC-18
❑ 90IowCubP-322
❑ 90Lea-401
❑ 90ProAAAF-629
❑ 90ScoRoo-98T
❑ 90TopTra-126T
❑ 90TopTraT-126T
❑ 90TopTVCu-62
❑ 90UppDec-741
❑ 91CubMar-19
❑ 91CubVinL-30
❑ 91Don-296
❑ 91Fle-436
❑ 91Lea-75
❑ 91OPC-362
❑ 91Sco-71
❑ 91Sco100RS-51
❑ 91StaClu-213
❑ 91StaCluP-47
❑ 91Top-362
❑ 91TopDeb90-160
❑ 91TopDesS-362
❑ 91TopMic-362
❑ 91TopTif-362
❑ 91Ult-69
❑ 91UppDec-171
❑ 92CubMar-19
❑ 92Don-725
❑ 92Fle-394
❑ 92OPC-181
❑ 92PanSti-181
❑ 92Pin-419
❑ 92Sco-677
❑ 92StaClu-858
❑ 92StaCluNC-858
❑ 92Top-181
❑ 92TopGol-181
❑ 92TopGolW-181
❑ 92TopMic-181
❑ 92TriPla-28
❑ 92Ult-477
❑ 92UppDec-102
❑ 93CadDis-60
❑ 93CarPol-23
❑ 93CarStaC-28
❑ 93Don-80
❑ 93LinVenB-297
❑ 93LinVenB-314
❑ 93LinVenB-317
❑ 93PacSpa-637
❑ 93UppDec-621
❑ 93UppDecGold-621
Villanueva, Juan
❑ 86LynMetP-24
❑ 87LynMetP-2
❑ 88FloStaLAS-24
❑ 88St.LucMS-25
❑ 89JacMetGS-12
❑ 90WicWraRD-22
Villar, Jose
❑ 66St.PetCTI-18
❑ 97DanBraB-28
❑ 98DanBraQ-11
Villar, Maximo
❑ 96EriSeaB-24
Villareal, Juan
❑ 90PriPatD-26
Villarreal, Modesto
❑ 95SpoIndTI-29
❑ 96LanLugB-29
❑ 96SpoIndB-29
Villegas, Ismael
❑ 96RocCubTI-31
❑ 97DurBulTI-16
Villegas, Mike
❑ 84ElPasDT-8
Villegas, Ramon
❑ 85MexCitTT-6
Villodas, Luis
❑ 93UppDecS-17
Villone, Ron
❑ 92TopTra-124T
❑ 92TopTraG-124T
❑ 93Bow-223
❑ 93RivPilCLC-1
❑ 93StaCluM-18
❑ 94AriFalLS-21
❑ 94Cla-36
❑ 94ClaGolF-103
❑ 94ExcFS7-129
❑ 94JacSunF-1413
❑ 94UppDecML-52
❑ 95Bow-137
❑ 95BowBes-B41
❑ 95BowBesR-B41
❑ 95Fin-305
❑ 95FinRef-305
❑ 95Fla-303
❑ 95FleUpd-78
❑ 95StaClu-601
❑ 95StaCluMOP-601
❑ 95StaCluSTWS-601
❑ 95TacRaiTI-25
❑ 95UppDec-242
❑ 95UppDecED-242
❑ 95UppDecEDG-242
❑ 96Bow-172
❑ 96BowFoi-172
❑ 96StaClu-317
❑ 96StaCluMOP-317
❑ 97BrePol-26
❑ 97Fle-619
❑ 97FleTif-619
❑ 97Pac-130
❑ 97PacLigB-130
❑ 97PacSil-130
❑ 97Top-459
❑ 97Ult-469
❑ 97UltGolME-469
❑ 97UltPlaME-469
❑ 98PacInvGems-61
❑ 98PacOnl-232
❑ 98PacOnlR-232
❑ 98PacOnlWC-232
Vilorio, Frank
❑ 79TolMudHT-19
❑ 83NasAngT-16
Viltz, Corey
❑ 87JamExpP-2552
❑ 88WesPalBES-26
❑ 89WesPalBES-23
Viltz, Eski
❑ 80CedRapRT-7
❑ 81WatRedT-25
❑ 82WatRedT-15
❑ 89CedRapRAB-26
❑ 90CedRapRDGB-26
Vina, Fernando
❑ 91ColMetPI-15
❑ 91ColMetPPI-4
❑ 91ColMetPPI-6
❑ 92ClaFS7-352
❑ 92St.LucMCB-18
❑ 92St.LucMF-1758
❑ 93ExcFS7-82
❑ 93MariStaClu-9
❑ 93MarMot-25
❑ 93PacSpa-627
❑ 93Ult-625
❑ 94ColC-449
❑ 94ColChoGS-449
❑ 94ColChoSS-449
❑ 94Fin-341
❑ 94FinRef-341
❑ 94MetColP-28
❑ 94ScoRoo-RT134
❑ 94ScoRooGR-RT134
❑ 94Sel-384
❑ 95Pac-290
❑ 95Sco-220
❑ 95ScoGolR-220
❑ 95ScoPlaTS-220
❑ 96BrePol-26
❑ 96ColCho-197
❑ 96ColChoGS-197
❑ 96ColChoSS-197
❑ 96Fle-162
❑ 96FleTif-162
❑ 96LeaSigA-230
❑ 96LeaSigAG-231
❑ 96LeaSigAS-231
❑ 96Pac-338
❑ 96PacPri-P112
❑ 96PacPriG-P112
❑ 96StaClu-299
❑ 96StaCluMOP-299
❑ 96Ult-370
❑ 96UltGolM-370
❑ 97BrePol-27
❑ 97Cir-49
❑ 97CirRav-49
❑ 97ColCho-148
❑ 97Don-201
❑ 97DonGolPP-201
❑ 97DonSilPP-201

❑ 97Fle-139
❑ 97FleTif-139
❑ 97Lea-305
❑ 97LeaFraM-305
❑ 97LeaFraMDC-305
❑ 97Pac-129
❑ 97PacLigB-129
❑ 97PacPri-43
❑ 97PacPriLB-43
❑ 97PacPriP-43
❑ 97PacSil-129
❑ 97Pin-64
❑ 97PinArtP-PP64
❑ 97PinMusC-64
❑ 97PinPrePla-64
❑ 97Sco-301
❑ 97ScoArtPWB-301
❑ 97ScoPreS-301
❑ 97ScoShoS-301
❑ 97ScoShoSAP-301
❑ 97StaClu-81
❑ 97StaCluMOP-81
❑ 97Top-213
❑ 97Ult-84
❑ 97UltGolME-84
❑ 97UltPlaME-84
❑ 97UppDec-98
❑ 98CirThu-91
❑ 98CirThuRav-91
❑ 98CirThuSupRav-91
❑ 98CroRoy-76
❑ 98Fle-533
❑ 98KinDis-28
❑ 98Pac-126
❑ 98PacAur-155
❑ 98PacInv-44
❑ 98PacInvPBlue-44
❑ 98PacInvSilv-44
❑ 98PacInvTeam-15
❑ 98PacLatotML-21
❑ 98PacOme-138
❑ 98PacOmeR-138
❑ 98PacOnl-412
❑ 98PacOnlR-412
❑ 98PacOnlWC-412
❑ 98PacPar-191
❑ 98PacParC-191
❑ 98PacParG-191
❑ 98PacParHS-191
❑ 98PacParPB-191
❑ 98PacParR-191
❑ 98PacPlaB-126
❑ 98PacRedT-126
❑ 98PacSil-126
❑ 98Revo-81
❑ 98RevoSS-81
❑ 98SpollIODMP-OD16
❑ 98StaCluFDI-52
❑ 98StaClul-52
❑ 98StaCluOneK-52
❑ 98StaCluPP-52
❑ 98Top-353
❑ 98TopChr-353
❑ 98TopChrR-353
❑ 98TopDevR-353
❑ 98TopDia-353
❑ 98TopMiniC-353
❑ 98Ult-332
❑ 98UltGolM-332
❑ 98UltMas-332
❑ 98UltPlaM-332
❑ 98UppDec-127
❑ 99199Fin-56
❑ 99CroRoyB-79
❑ 99CroRoyL-79
❑ 99CroRoyOD-79
❑ 99FinGolRef-56
❑ 99FinRef-56
❑ 99Fle-220
❑ 99FleBri-109
❑ 99FleBri2G-109
❑ 99FleBriBlu-109
❑ 99FleBriGol-109
❑ 99FleSta9-220
❑ 99FleWarT-220
❑ 99MetUni-53
❑ 99MetUniGM-53
❑ 99MetUniPMG-53
❑ 99Pac-243
❑ 99PacAur-103
❑ 99PacAurOD-103
❑ 99PacCroC-156
❑ 99PacCroC-33
❑ 99PacCroCPB-156
❑ 99PacInv-83
❑ 99PacInvOD-83
❑ 99PacInvPB-83
❑ 99PacOme-135
❑ 99PacOmeC-135
❑ 99PacOmeG-135
❑ 99PacOmePB-135
❑ 99PacPar-130
❑ 99PacParC-130
❑ 99PacParG-130
❑ 99PacParHoloGold-130
❑ 99PacParHS-130
❑ 99PacParOD-130
❑ 99PacParPB-130
❑ 99PacParRed-130
❑ 99PacPlaB-243
❑ 99PacPri-82
❑ 99PacPriHB-82
❑ 99PacPriHG-82
❑ 99PacPriHM-82
❑ 99PacPriHP-82
❑ 99PacPriRed-82
❑ 99PacRed-243
❑ 99Rev-77
❑ 99RevPremDate-77
❑ 99RevRet-77
❑ 99RevShaSS-77
❑ 99SkyPre-221
❑ 99SkyPreR-221
❑ 99SkyThu-45
❑ 99SkyThuRant-45
❑ 99SkyThuRave-45
❑ 99SP SigAuto-FV
❑ 99SPSig-161
❑ 99StaClu-243
❑ 99StaCluC-CS27
❑ 99StaCluC-CS32
❑ 99StaCluC-CS39
❑ 99StaCluC-CS42
❑ 99StaCluFDI-243
❑ 99StaCluOoaK-243
❑ 99StaCluPP-243
❑ 99ThuSkySupR-45
❑ 99Top-328
❑ 99TopChr-328
❑ 99TopChrR-328
❑ 99TopMVPP-328
❑ 99UppDec-133
❑ 99UppDecEL1-133
❑ 99UppDecEL2-133
❑ 99UppDecM-113
❑ 99UppDecMGS-113
❑ 99UppDecMHFS-113
❑ 99UppDecMSS-113
❑ 99Vic-211

Vinas, Julio
❑ 92SouBenWSC-6
❑ 92SouBenWSF-181
❑ 92UtiBluSC-15
❑ 93SouBenWSC-22
❑ 93SouBenWSF-1434
❑ 94MidLeaAF-MDW29
❑ 94SouBenSHC-23
❑ 94SouBenSHF-598
❑ 96BirBarB-29
❑ 96NasSouB-27

Vincent, Albert
❑ 56BalOriP-51

Vincent, Mike
❑ 86CedRapRT-12
❑ 87CedRapRP-19

Vinci, Lauri
❑ 25Zee-82
❑ 26Zee-129
❑ 28Zee-124
❑ 29Zee-123
❑ 30Zee-133
❑ 31Zee-96
❑ 32Zee-91
❑ 33Zee-36

Vindivich, Paul
❑ 94RocRoyF-579

Vindvich, John
❑ 93AubAstC-25
❑ 93AubAstF-3457
❑ 94AubAstC-23
❑ 94AubAstF-3774

Vines, Ellsworth
❑ 40WheM4-2B

Vines, Robert
❑ 24Zee-142

Vineyard, Dave
❑ 64BalOriP-36
❑ 65BalOriP-32
❑ 65OPC-169
❑ 65Top-169
❑ 91OriCro-468

Vining, Ken
❑ 97SanJosG-13
❑ 98BirBarG-26

Vinson, Chuck
❑ 66SeaPop-27
❑ 67SeaPop-18
❑ 68SeaPop-18
❑ 68Top-328
❑ 68TopVen-328

Vinson, Clay
❑ 89GeoColC-34
❑ 90GeoColC-31

Vinson, Mabel
❑ 40WheM4-13

Vinson, Rube (Ernest Augustus)
❑ 05IndSouPSoCP-18

Vinton, William
❑ 87OldJudN-512

Vinyard, Derek
❑ 93ForLauRSC-25
❑ 93ForLauRSFP-1611

Viola, Frank
❑ 82OrlTwi8SCT-24
❑ 82TolMudHT-7
❑ 83Don-382
❑ 83Fle-625
❑ 83Top-586
❑ 83TwiTeal-11
❑ 84Don-364
❑ 84Fle-575
❑ 84MinTwiP-29
❑ 84Nes792-28
❑ 84OPC-28
❑ 84Top-28
❑ 84TopSti-312
❑ 84TopTif-28
❑ 84TwiTeal-12
❑ 85AllGamPI-89
❑ 85Don-17
❑ 85Don-436
❑ 85DonSupD-17
❑ 85Fle-291
❑ 85FleStaS-84
❑ 85Lea-17
❑ 85OPC-266
❑ 85Top-266
❑ 85Top-710
❑ 85TopGloS-7
❑ 85TopMin-266
❑ 85TopSti-300
❑ 85TopTif-266
❑ 85TopTif-710
❑ 85Twi7-2
❑ 85TwiPos-29
❑ 85TwiTeal-12
❑ 85TwiTeal-25
❑ 86Don-194
❑ 86Fle-408
❑ 86FleStiC-124
❑ 86KayB-33
❑ 86Lea-126
❑ 86OPC-269
❑ 86Spo-99
❑ 86Top-742
❑ 86TopMinL-25
❑ 86TopSti-284
❑ 86TopTat-18
❑ 86TopTif-742
❑ 86TwiTeal-11
❑ 87Don-270
❑ 87DonHig-24
❑ 87Fle-554
❑ 87FleGlo-554
❑ 87Lea-74
❑ 87OPC-310
❑ 87RedFolSB-127
❑ 87SpoTeaP-17
❑ 87Top-206
❑ 87Top-310
❑ 87TopSti-277
❑ 87TopTif-206
❑ 87TopTif-310
❑ 87TwiPos-30
❑ 87TwiTeal-10
❑ 88CheBoy-15
❑ 88ClaRed-183
❑ 88Don-149
❑ 88DonBasB-214
❑ 88Dra-29
❑ 88Fle-25
❑ 88FleBasM-41
❑ 88FleGlo-25
❑ 88FleGlo-WS12
❑ 88FleMin-38
❑ 88FleRecS-42
❑ 88FleSluBC-C5
❑ 88FleStiC-47
❑ 88FleWorS-12
❑ 88Lea-94
❑ 88OPC-259
❑ 88PanSti-134
❑ 88Sco-475
❑ 88ScoGlo-475
❑ 88Spo-196
❑ 88StaLinTw-20
❑ 88TarPla-47
❑ 88Top-625
❑ 88TopBig-201
❑ 88TopMinL-25
❑ 88TopRitTM-33
❑ 88TopSti-25
❑ 88TopSti-282
❑ 88TopTif-625
❑ 88TopUKM-82
❑ 88TopUKMT-82
❑ 88TwiMasBD-2
❑ 88TwiSmoC-1
❑ 88Woo-19
❑ 88Woo-33
❑ 89Baz-21
❑ 89Bow-150
❑ 89BowTif-150
❑ 89CadEllD-60
❑ 89ClaTraO-144
❑ 89Don-23
❑ 89Don-237
❑ 89DonAll-8
❑ 89DonBasB-74
❑ 89DonPop-8
❑ 89DonSupD-23
❑ 89Fle-127
❑ 89FleAll-12
❑ 89FleBasA-43
❑ 89FleBasM-41
❑ 89FleExcS-42
❑ 89FleGlo-127
❑ 89FleHeroB-42
❑ 89FleLeaL-42
❑ 89FleSup-41
❑ 89FleWaxBC-C28
❑ 89KayB-31
❑ 89KinDis-14
❑ 89MasBreD-1
❑ 89MetKah-U4
❑ 89MSAHolD-17
❑ 89Nis-17
❑ 89OPC-120
❑ 89PanSti-237
❑ 89PanSti-248
❑ 89PanSti-383
❑ 89PanSti-475
❑ 89RedFolSB-125
❑ 89Sco-290
❑ 89ScoHot1S-5
❑ 89ScoRoo-67T
❑ 89Spo-10
❑ 89SpollIFKI-35
❑ 89Top-120
❑ 89Top-406
❑ 89TopBasT-81
❑ 89TopBig-180
❑ 89TopCapC-4
❑ 89TopCoi-30
❑ 89TopDouA-10
❑ 89TopGaloC-11
❑ 89TopGloA-10
❑ 89TopGloS-18
❑ 89TopHeaUT-7
❑ 89TopHilTM-31
❑ 89TopMinL-64
❑ 89TopSti-153
❑ 89TopSti-292
❑ 89TopStiB-30
❑ 89TopTif-120
❑ 89TopTif-406
❑ 89TopUKM-80
❑ 89TVSpoM-103
❑ 89TVSpoM-134
❑ 89UppDec-397
❑ 89UppDec-658
❑ 89UppDec-691
❑ 89Woo-3
❑ 90Bow-122
❑ 90BowTif-122
❑ 90ClaBlu-91
❑ 90ClaYel-T37
❑ 90ClaYel-NNO0
❑ 90Don-353
❑ 90DonBesN-68
❑ 90Fle-219
❑ 90FleCan-219
❑ 90Lea-93
❑ 90M.Vpin-67
❑ 90MetColP-11
❑ 90MetColP-6
❑ 90MetFanC-29
❑ 90MetKah-29
❑ 90MSAIceTD-16
❑ 90OPC-470
❑ 90PublntS-297
❑ 90PublntS-339
❑ 90Sco-500
❑ 90Spo-122
❑ 90StaLonJS-7
❑ 90StaLonJS-18
❑ 90Top-470
❑ 90TopBig-162
❑ 90TopDou-67
❑ 90TopMag-108
❑ 90TopSti-95
❑ 90TopTif-470
❑ 90TopTVM-18
❑ 90UppDec-626
❑ 90USPlaCA-1D
❑ 91BasBesAotM-18
❑ 91Bow-477
❑ 91Cla3-T92
❑ 91ClaGam-1
❑ 91Don-529
❑ 91Fle-165
❑ 91Lea-180
❑ 91MetCol8-5
❑ 91MetColP-11
❑ 91MetKah-29
❑ 91MetPerPA-29
❑ 91MetTro-9
❑ 91MetWIZ-422
❑ 91OPC-60
❑ 91OPC-406
❑ 91PanCanT1-59
❑ 91PanCanT1-68
❑ 91PanCanT1-76
❑ 91PanFreS-87
❑ 91PanSti-84
❑ 91RedFolS-98
❑ 91Sco-460
❑ 91Sco-687
❑ 91Sco-882
❑ 91Sco100S-70
❑ 91Sev3DCN-15
❑ 91SevCoi-NE15
❑ 91StaClu-292
❑ 91StaCluCM-31
❑ 91Stu-210
❑ 91Top-60
❑ 91Top-406
❑ 91TopCraJI-4
❑ 91TopDesS-60
❑ 91TopDesS-406
❑ 91TopMic-60
❑ 91TopMic-406
❑ 91TopSta-34
❑ 91TopTif-60
❑ 91TopTif-406
❑ 91Ult-227
❑ 91UppDec-122
❑ 91USPlaCA-7C
❑ 92Bow-491
❑ 92Cla2-T80
❑ 92ClaGam-196
❑ 92Don-498
❑ 92DonUpd-U10
❑ 92Fle-518
❑ 92FleUpd-5
❑ 92LaKdec-29
❑ 92Lea-221
❑ 92LeaBlaG-221
❑ 92New-30
❑ 92OPC-510
❑ 92OPCPre-115
❑ 92PanSti-229
❑ 92Pin-407
❑ 92RedFolS-97
❑ 92RedSoxDD-28
❑ 92Sco-220
❑ 92Sco100S-62
❑ 92ScoRoo-6T
❑ 92SpoStaCC-48
❑ 92StaClu-785
❑ 92StaCluD-190
❑ 92Stu-140
❑ 92Top-510
❑ 92TopGol-510
❑ 92TopGolW-510
❑ 92TopMic-510
❑ 92TopTra-125T
❑ 92TopTraG-125T
❑ 92TriPlaG-GS6
❑ 92Ult-319
❑ 92UppDec-277
❑ 92UppDec-733
❑ 93Bow-171
❑ 93Don-91
❑ 93Fin-33
❑ 93FinRef-33
❑ 93Fla-169
❑ 93Fle-185
❑ 93FunPac-166
❑ 93Lea-21
❑ 93OPC-228
❑ 93PacSpa-38
❑ 93Pin-76
❑ 93RedSoxP-32
❑ 93RedSoxWHP-28
❑ 93Sco-55
❑ 93Sel-94
❑ 93SP-207
❑ 93StaClu-147
❑ 93StaCluFDI-147
❑ 93StaCluMOP-147
❑ 93Stu-72
❑ 93Top-270
❑ 93TopGol-270
❑ 93TopInaM-270
❑ 93TopInaR-270
❑ 93TopMic-270
❑ 93TriPla-178
❑ 93Ult-157
❑ 93UppDec-48
❑ 93UppDec-131
❑ 93UppDecGold-48
❑ 93UppDecGold-131
❑ 94Bow-35
❑ 94ColC-283
❑ 94ColChoGS-283
❑ 94ColChoSS-283
❑ 94Don-321
❑ 94Fin-406
❑ 94FinRef-406
❑ 94Fle-46
❑ 94FleExtB-28
❑ 94Lea-60
❑ 94OPC-88
❑ 94Pac-69
❑ 94Pin-348
❑ 94PinArtP-348
❑ 94PinMusC-348
❑ 94RedFolMI-26
❑ 94RedFolMI-27
❑ 94Sco-331
❑ 94ScoGolR-331
❑ 94Spo-137
❑ 94StaClu-569
❑ 94StaCluFDI-569
❑ 94StaCluGR-569
❑ 94StaCluMOP-569
❑ 94Top-140
❑ 94TopGol-140
❑ 94TopSpa-140
❑ 94TriPla-210
❑ 94Ult-320
❑ 94UppDec-127
❑ 94UppDecED-127
❑ 95ColCho-419
❑ 95ColChoGS-419
❑ 95ColChoSS-419
❑ 95Fle-43
❑ 95Pin-386
❑ 95PinArtP-386
❑ 95PinMusC-386

Viola, Lance
❑ 79NewCoPT-23

Violat, Juan
❑ 09T206-521

Viox, James
❑ 14B18B-82A
❑ 14B18B-82B
❑ 15SpoNewM-182
❑ 16SpoNewM-180

Virchis, Adam
❑ 96HicCraB-26
❑ 97HicCraB-29
❑ 98HicCraM-28
❑ 98WinWar-28

Virdon, Bill
❑ 55Bow-296
❑ 55CarHunW-28
❑ 56PirTeal-23
❑ 56Top-170
❑ 57PirTeal-10
❑ 57Top-110
❑ 58Hir-45
❑ 58PirTeal-12
❑ 58Top-198

❑ 59Top-190
❑ 59Top-543
❑ 59TopVen-190
❑ 60KeyChal-48
❑ 60Lea-40
❑ 60PirTag-18
❑ 60Top-496
❑ 61PirJayP-12
❑ 61Pos-135
❑ 61Top-70
❑ 61Top-306
❑ 61TopStal-72
❑ 62Jel-175
❑ 62Kah-38
❑ 62Pos-175
❑ 62PosCan-175
❑ 62SalPlaC-168
❑ 62ShiPlaC-168
❑ 62Top-415
❑ 62TopStal-181
❑ 63Jel-142
❑ 63Kah-30
❑ 63PirIDL-26
❑ 63PirJayP-12
❑ 63Pos-142
❑ 63Top-55
❑ 64Kah-29
❑ 64PirKDK-28
❑ 64Top-268
❑ 64Top-495
❑ 64TopVen-268
❑ 65Kah-44
❑ 65OPC-69
❑ 65Top-69
❑ 69PirTeal-25
❑ 70PirTeal-19
❑ 72Top-661
❑ 73OPC-517
❑ 73Top-517A
❑ 73Top-517B
❑ 74SyrChiTI-28
❑ 75OPC-611
❑ 75SyrChiTI-22
❑ 75Top-611
❑ 75TopMin-611
❑ 75YanSSP-9
❑ 76HouAstP-30
❑ 76OPC-147
❑ 76Top-147
❑ 77AstPho-13
❑ 77PirTCM1WC-7
❑ 77Top-327
❑ 78AstBurK-1
❑ 78AstPos-24
❑ 78Top-279
❑ 79AstPos-25
❑ 79AstTeal-1
❑ 79TCM50-100
❑ 79Top-381
❑ 80Top-82
❑ 81Don-384
❑ 81Fle-61
❑ 81Top-678
❑ 82Don-144
❑ 83ExpPos-33
❑ 83ExpStu-1
❑ 83OPC-6
❑ 83Top-516
❑ 84ExpPos-34
❑ 84ExpStu-2
❑ 84ExpStu-38
❑ 84Fle-658
❑ 84Nes792-111
❑ 84OPC-111
❑ 84Top-111
❑ 84TopTif-111
❑ 86AstGreT-12
❑ 87AstShoSPT-28
❑ 88PacLegI-49
❑ 89SweBasG-119
❑ 91SweBasG-93
❑ 93PirNatl-34
❑ 94PirQui-25
❑ 94TopArc1-257
❑ 94TopArc1G-257
❑ 94UppDecAH-54
❑ 94UppDecAH1-54

Virgil, Ossie

❑ 77SpaPhiT-21
❑ 80CarMudF-3
❑ 81OklCit8T-19
❑ 82Top-231
❑ 83Don-606A
❑ 83Don-606B
❑ 83Fle-175
❑ 83PhiTas-28
❑ 83Top-383
❑ 84Don-326
❑ 84Fle-49
❑ 84Nes792-484
❑ 84PhiTas-26
❑ 84Top-484
❑ 84TopTif-484
❑ 85AllGamPI-135
❑ 85Don-82
❑ 85Fle-267
❑ 85Lea-250
❑ 85OPC-103
❑ 85PhiCIG-3
❑ 85PhiTas-10
❑ 85PhiTas-26
❑ 85SubDis-46
❑ 85ThoMcAD-46
❑ 85Top-143
❑ 85Top-611
❑ 85TopSti-110
❑ 85TopTif-143
❑ 85TopTif-611
❑ 86BasStaB-116
❑ 86BraPol-9
❑ 86Don-137
❑ 86DonAll-26
❑ 86Fle-456
❑ 86FleUpd-122
❑ 86OPC-95
❑ 86Top-95
❑ 86TopSti-115
❑ 86TopTif-95
❑ 86TopTra-119T
❑ 86TopTraT-119T
❑ 87BraSmo-12
❑ 87Don-67
❑ 87DonOpeD-45
❑ 87Fle-532
❑ 87FleGlo-532
❑ 87OPC-183
❑ 87Top-571
❑ 87TopTif-571
❑ 88Don-143
❑ 88DonAll-50
❑ 88DonBasB-85
❑ 88Fle-552
❑ 88FleGlo-552
❑ 88Lea-64
❑ 88MSAJifPD-17
❑ 88OPC-291
❑ 88PanSti-241
❑ 88RedFolSB-93
❑ 88Sco-129
❑ 88ScoGlo-129
❑ 88Spo-217
❑ 88StaLinBra-20
❑ 88Top-755
❑ 88TopBig-148
❑ 88TopSti-36
❑ 88TopStiB-24
❑ 88TopTif-755
❑ 89BlaYNPRWLU-33
❑ 89Don-145
❑ 89Fle-605
❑ 89FleGlo-605
❑ 89OPC-179
❑ 89RedFolSB-126
❑ 89Sco-111
❑ 89Spo-94
❑ 89Top-179
❑ 89TopSti-28
❑ 89TopTif-179
❑ 89UppDec-104
❑ 90BluJayFS-30
❑ 90CMC-348
❑ 90EliSenL-15
❑ 90ProAAAF-355
❑ 90SyrChiC-22
❑ 90SyrChiMB-26
❑ 90SyrChiP-575
❑ 91PacSenL-150
❑ 91PacSenL-159

Virgil, Ossie Sr.

❑ 57Top-365
❑ 58Top-107
❑ 59Top-203
❑ 61Top-67
❑ 62BalOriP-31
❑ 62Top-327
❑ 63RocRedWSP-8
❑ 65Top-571
❑ 67OPC-132
❑ 67Top-132
❑ 76ExpRed-34
❑ 76MonExpP-29
❑ 76VenLeaS-1
❑ 77ExpPos-35
❑ 79ExpPos-30
❑ 80ExpPos-33
❑ 81TigDetN-135
❑ 83PadTeal-29
❑ 84PadMot-27
❑ 84PadSmo-26
❑ 85Top-143
❑ 85TopTif-143
❑ 86MarMot-28
❑ 87MarMot-28
❑ 89PacSenL-22
❑ 91OriCro-469
❑ 91PacSenL-138
❑ 91PacSenL-159
❑ 93LinVenB-235
❑ 96BelGiaTI-34

Virgilio, George

❑ 90PulBraB-19
❑ 90PulBraP-3089
❑ 91PulBraC-10
❑ 91PulBraP-4016
❑ 92MacBraC-5
❑ 92MacBraF-278
❑ 94HarSenF-2101
❑ 95BowBayTI-1
❑ 95HarSenTI-15

Virtue, Jake

❑ 93JusSo-10

Viskas, Steve

❑ 79QuaCitCT-25

Visner, Joseph

❑ 87OldJudN-513

Vitale, Tony

❑ 86FreGiaSB-28

Vitalich, Ed

❑ 47PadTeal-23

Vitato, Richard

❑ 82ChaRoyT-14
❑ 83ChaRoyT-9

Vitiello, Joe

❑ 91Cla/Bes-404
❑ 91ClaDraP-5
❑ 91EugEmeC-15
❑ 91EugEmeP-3742
❑ 92BasCitRC-1
❑ 92BasCitRF-3855
❑ 92ClaDraP-94
❑ 92ClaFS7-24
❑ 92ProFS7-80
❑ 92UppDec-73
❑ 92UppDecML-309
❑ 93Bow-13
❑ 93Bow-367
❑ 93ClaFisN-1
❑ 93ClaGolF-83
❑ 93ClaGolLF-3
❑ 93ClaGolP-4
❑ 93ClaYouG-YG26
❑ 93ExcFS7-180
❑ 93MemChiF-384
❑ 93RoyStaC-14
❑ 93StaClu-570
❑ 93StaCluFDI-570
❑ 93StaCluMOP-570
❑ 94Bow-415
❑ 94Cla-91
❑ 94ClaGolF-123
❑ 94OmaRoyF-1232
❑ 94SigRoo-50
❑ 94SigRooS-50
❑ 94Top-769
❑ 94TopGol-769
❑ 94TopSpa-769
❑ 94UppDecML-44
❑ 95ActPacF-37
❑ 95Bow-211
❑ 95Exc-68
❑ 95ExcLeaL-18
❑ 95FleUpd-50
❑ 95OmaRoyTI-28
❑ 95Pin-424
❑ 95PinArtP-424
❑ 95PinETA-3
❑ 95PinMusC-424
❑ 95Sel-198
❑ 95SelArtP-198
❑ 95SelCer-106
❑ 95SelCerMG-106
❑ 95StaClu-557
❑ 95StaCluMOP-557
❑ 95StaCluSTWS-557
❑ 95Sum-120
❑ 95SumNthD-120
❑ 95Top-637
❑ 95UC3-121
❑ 95UC3ArtP-121
❑ 95UppDec-247
❑ 95UppDecED-247
❑ 95UppDecEDG-247
❑ 95UppDecML-190
❑ 95UppDecMLFS-190
❑ 95Zen-126
❑ 96ColCho-177
❑ 96ColChoGS-177
❑ 96ColChoSS-177
❑ 96Don-304
❑ 96DonPreP-304
❑ 96Fla-96
❑ 96Fle-140
❑ 96FleTif-140
❑ 96Lea-159
❑ 96LeaPrePB-159
❑ 96LeaPrePG-159
❑ 96LeaPrePS-159
❑ 96LeaSigA-231
❑ 96LeaSigAG-232
❑ 96LeaSigAS-232
❑ 96Pin-175
❑ 96PinAfi-133
❑ 96PinAfiAP-133
❑ 96RoyPol-26
❑ 96Sco-243
❑ 96ScoDugC-A108
❑ 96ScoDugCAP-A108
❑ 96Sel-128
❑ 96SelArtP-128
❑ 96StaClu-24
❑ 96StaCluMOP-24
❑ 96Sum-29
❑ 96SumAbo&B-29
❑ 96SumArtP-29
❑ 96SumFoi-29
❑ 96Top-411
❑ 96Ult-76
❑ 96UltGolM-76
❑ 96UppDec-87
❑ 97Don-296
❑ 97DonGolPP-296
❑ 97DonSilPP-296
❑ 97Lea-267
❑ 97LeaFraM-267
❑ 97LeaFraMDC-267
❑ 97Pac-113
❑ 97PacLigB-113
❑ 97PacSil-113
❑ 97Pin-17
❑ 97PinArtP-PP17
❑ 97PinMusC-17
❑ 97PinPrePla-17
❑ 97RoyPol-22
❑ 97Sco-412
❑ 97ScoArtPWB-412
❑ 97ScoResC-412
❑ 97ScoShoS-412
❑ 97ScoShoSAP-412
❑ 98ColCho-141
❑ 98OmaRoyM-23
❑ 98PacInvGems-56
❑ 98PacOnl-357
❑ 98PacOnlR-357
❑ 98PacOnlWC-357
❑ 98Top-27
❑ 98TopChr-27
❑ 98TopChrR-27
❑ 98TopDevR-27
❑ 98TopDia-27
❑ 98TopMiniC-27
❑ 98UppDec-396

Vitko, Joe

❑ 90ColMetGS-21
❑ 90ColMetPPI-3
❑ 90SouAtlLAS-45
❑ 91St.LucMC-15
❑ 91St.LucMP-711
❑ 92BinMetF-516
❑ 92BinMetS-69
❑ 92Bow-516
❑ 92ClaFS7-354
❑ 92SkyAA F-32
❑ 93Don-354
❑ 93UppDec-10
❑ 93UppDecGold-10
❑ 94BinMetF-705

Vito, Frank

❑ 91PacSenL-158

Vitt, Ossie (Oscar)

❑ 09ObaT21-170
❑ 09ObaT21-337
❑ 11PacCoaBD-68
❑ 11Zee-104
❑ 12ObaPreT-86
❑ 14FatPlaT-50
❑ 15SpoNewM-183
❑ 16SpoNewM-181
❑ 17ColE13-179
❑ 17HolBreD-109
❑ 21E121So1-109
❑ 21E121So8-103
❑ 22W575-143
❑ 23W501-9
❑ 23Zee-118
❑ 24Zee-83
❑ 25Zee-102
❑ 27Zee-9
❑ 28Zee-22
❑ 30Zee-18
❑ 31Zee-9
❑ 32Zee-17
❑ 33Zee-6
❑ 33Zee-7
❑ 33Zee-75
❑ 35PebBea-7
❑ 38CloFotW-84
❑ 40PlaBal-47
❑ 92ConTSN-495

Vitter, Joseph

❑ 37Zee-7
❑ 37Zee-93

Vivas, Domingo

❑ 91BilMusP-3753
❑ 91BilMusSP-7

Vivenzio, Augie

❑ 92PulBraC-18
❑ 92PulBraF-3183

Viveros, Bennie

❑ 22Zee-18

Vizcaino, Edward

❑ 97WilCubB-24

Vizcaino, Jose

❑ 88BakDodCLC-240
❑ 88CalLeaACLC-47
❑ 89AlbDukCm-23
❑ 89AlbDukP-82
❑ 90AlbDukCm-20
❑ 90AlbDukP-355
❑ 90AlbDukTr-29
❑ 90Bow-98
❑ 90BowTif-98
❑ 90ClaUpd-T49
❑ 90CMC-422
❑ 90DodTar-1090
❑ 90Fle-410
❑ 90FleCan-410
❑ 90ProAAAF-76
❑ 90Sco-613
❑ 90TopDeb89-131
❑ 90UppDec-44
❑ 91Bow-427
❑ 91CubMar-16
❑ 91CubVinL-31
❑ 91Don-724
❑ 91Fle-223
❑ 91Lea-323
❑ 91Sco-787
❑ 91Sco100RS-88
❑ 91UppDec-580
❑ 92CubMar-16
❑ 92Don-212
❑ 92Lea-270
❑ 92LeaBlaG-270
❑ 92OPC-561
❑ 92Sco-169
❑ 92StaClu-359
❑ 92Top-561
❑ 92TopGol-561
❑ 92TopGolW-561
❑ 92TopMic-561
❑ 92Ult-182
❑ 93CubMar-28
❑ 93CubStaC-20
❑ 93DiaMar-114
❑ 93Don-582
❑ 93Fla-23
❑ 93Fle-385
❑ 93Lea-499
❑ 93OPC-345
❑ 93PacBeiA-18
❑ 93PacJugC-36
❑ 93PacSpa-384
❑ 93StaClu-68
❑ 93StaCluFDI-68
❑ 93StaCluMOP-68
❑ 93Stu-218
❑ 93Top-237
❑ 93TopGol-237
❑ 93TopInaM-237
❑ 93TopInaR-237
❑ 93TopMic-237
❑ 93Ult-322
❑ 93UppDec-211
❑ 93UppDecGold-211
❑ 94ColC-284
❑ 94ColC-532
❑ 94ColChoGS-284
❑ 94ColChoGS-532
❑ 94ColChoSS-284
❑ 94ColChoSS-532
❑ 94Don-291
❑ 94Fin-312
❑ 94FinRef-312
❑ 94Fla-203
❑ 94Fle-400
❑ 94FleExtB-328
❑ 94FleUpd-163
❑ 94Lea-68
❑ 94MetColP-29
❑ 94Pac-113
❑ 94PanSti-159
❑ 94Pin-141
❑ 94PinArtP-141
❑ 94PinMusC-141
❑ 94Sco-370
❑ 94ScoGolR-370
❑ 94ScoRoo-RT40
❑ 94ScoRooGR-RT40
❑ 94Sel-275
❑ 94SpoRoo-17
❑ 94SpoRooAP-17
❑ 94StaClu-89
❑ 94StaClu-662
❑ 94StaCluFDI-89
❑ 94StaCluFDI-662
❑ 94StaCluGR-89
❑ 94StaCluGR-662
❑ 94StaCluMOP-89
❑ 94StaCluMOP-662
❑ 94StaCluT-356
❑ 94StaCluTFDI-356
❑ 94Top-638
❑ 94TopGol-638
❑ 94TopSpa-638
❑ 94TopTra-120T
❑ 94TriPla-79
❑ 94Ult-167
❑ 94Ult-539
❑ 94UppDec-122
❑ 94UppDec-329
❑ 94UppDecED-122
❑ 94UppDecED-329
❑ 95ColCho-316
❑ 95ColChoGS-316
❑ 95ColChoSS-316
❑ 95Don-325
❑ 95DonPreP-325
❑ 95DonTopotO-298
❑ 95Fla-387
❑ 95Fle-385
❑ 95Lea-122
❑ 95MetColP-31
❑ 95Pac-291
❑ 95PacPri-94
❑ 95Sco-436
❑ 95ScoGolR-436
❑ 95ScoPlaTS-436
❑ 95StaClu-25
❑ 95StaCluFDI-25
❑ 95StaCluMOP-25
❑ 95StaCluSTWS-25
❑ 95StaCluVR-17
❑ 95StaCluVRMO-17
❑ 95Top-14
❑ 95TopCyb-12
❑ 95Ult-202
❑ 95UltGolM-202
❑ 95UppDec-363
❑ 95UppDecED-363
❑ 95UppDecEDG-363
❑ 96ColCho-626
❑ 96ColChoGS-626
❑ 96ColChoSS-626
❑ 96Don-431
❑ 96DonPreP-431
❑ 96EmoXL-239
❑ 96Fla-327
❑ 96Fle-490
❑ 96FleTif-490
❑ 96LeaSigA-232
❑ 96LeaSigAG-233
❑ 96LeaSigAS-233
❑ 96MetKah-33
❑ 96MetUni-206
❑ 96MetUniP-206
❑ 96Pac-138

❑ 96PacPri-P49
❑ 96PacPriG-P49
❑ 96PanSti-32
❑ 96ProSta-72
❑ 96Sco-214
❑ 96StaClu-360
❑ 96StaCluEPB-360
❑ 96StaCluEPG-360
❑ 96StaCluEPS-360
❑ 96StaCluMOP-360
❑ 96TeaOut-85
❑ 96Top-307
❑ 96Ult-248
❑ 96UltGolM-248
❑ 96UppDec-401
❑ 97Cir-201
❑ 97CirRav-201
❑ 97ColCho-452
❑ 97Fin-191
❑ 97FinRef-191
❑ 97Fle-91
❑ 97Fle-601
❑ 97FleTif-91
❑ 97FleTif-601
❑ 97Pac-81
❑ 97PacLigB-81
❑ 97PacSil-81
❑ 97Sco-449
❑ 97ScoArtPWB-449
❑ 97ScoResC-449
❑ 97ScoShoS-449
❑ 97ScoShoSAP-449
❑ 97StaClu-88
❑ 97StaCluMOP-88
❑ 97Top-297
❑ 97Ult-363
❑ 97UltGolME-363
❑ 97UltPlaME-363
❑ 98CirThu-221
❑ 98CirThuRav-221
❑ 98CirThuSupRav-221
❑ 98ColCho-393
❑ 98DodMot-8
❑ 98DodPol-27
❑ 98Fin-271
❑ 98FinNo--271
❑ 98FinNo-R-271
❑ 98FinRef-271
❑ 98Fle-175
❑ 98Fle-401
❑ 98Pac-450
❑ 98PacInvTeam-25
❑ 98PacOnl-387
❑ 98PacOnlR-387
❑ 98PacOnlWC-387
❑ 98PacPlaB-450
❑ 98PacRedT-450
❑ 98PacSil-450
❑ 98StaCluFDI-396
❑ 98StaCluI-396
❑ 98StaCluOneK-396
❑ 98StaCluPP-396
❑ 98Top-395
❑ 98TopChr-395
❑ 98TopChrR-395
❑ 98TopDevR-395
❑ 98TopDia-395
❑ 98TopMiniC-395
❑ 98Ult-411
❑ 98UltGolM-411
❑ 98UltMas-411
❑ 98UltPlaM-411
❑ 98UppDec-689
❑ 99DodPol-26
❑ 99StaClu-140
❑ 99StaCluFDI-140
❑ 99StaCluOoaK-140
❑ 99StaCluPP-140
❑ 99Top-8
❑ 99TopChr-8
❑ 99TopChrR-8
❑ 99TopMVPP-8

Vizcaino, Julian
❑ 93BoiHawC-26
❑ 93BoiHawF-3925
❑ 94CedRapKF-1119

Vizcaino, Junior
❑ 87WatPirP-14
❑ 88CarLeaAS-18
❑ 88SalBucS-22
❑ 89HarSenP-293
❑ 89HarSenS-20
❑ 90HarSenP-1202
❑ 90HarSenS-19

Vizcaino, Luis
❑ 97SouOreTB-27
❑ 98ModA'sG-27
❑ 99JustheS-44
❑ 99JustheSJB-44

Vizcaino, Romulo
❑ 94EliTwiC-25
❑ 94EliTwiF-3745
❑ 94ForWayWC-25
❑ 94ForWayWF-2024
❑ 95ForWayWTI-25

Vizquel, Omar
❑ 86WauTimP-27
❑ 87SalSpuS-19
❑ 88BasAmeAAB-4
❑ 88EasLeaAP-37
❑ 88VerMarP-946
❑ 89CalCanC-23
❑ 89CalCanP-537
❑ 89DonBasB-163
❑ 89DonRoo-53
❑ 89FleUpd-62
❑ 89MarMot-15
❑ 89ScoRoo-105T
❑ 89TopTra-122T
❑ 89TopTraT-122T
❑ 89UppDec-787
❑ 90Bow-474
❑ 90BowTif-474
❑ 90Don-483
❑ 90Fle-528
❑ 90FleCan-528
❑ 90Lea-88
❑ 90MarMot-12
❑ 90OPC-698
❑ 90PubIntS-445
❑ 90Sco-264
❑ 90Sco100RS-37
❑ 90ScoYouSI-28
❑ 90Top-698
❑ 90TopBig-140
❑ 90TopDeb89-132
❑ 90TopGloS-59
❑ 90TopRoo-28
❑ 90TopTif-698
❑ 90UppDec-233
❑ 91Bow-245
❑ 91Don-231
❑ 91Fle-464
❑ 91Lea-91
❑ 91MarCouH-9
❑ 91OPC-298
❑ 91PanFreS-231
❑ 91Sco-299
❑ 91StaClu-195
❑ 91Top-298
❑ 91TopDesS-298
❑ 91TopMic-298
❑ 91TopTif-298
❑ 91Ult-345
❑ 91UppDec-593
❑ 92Bow-423
❑ 92Don-641
❑ 92Fle-296
❑ 92Lea-265
❑ 92LeaBlaG-265
❑ 92MarMot-16
❑ 92OPC-101
❑ 92PanSti-58
❑ 92Pin-97
❑ 92Sco-162
❑ 92ScoProP-22
❑ 92StaClu-163
❑ 92Top-101
❑ 92TopGol-101
❑ 92TopGolW-101
❑ 92TopMic-101
❑ 92TriPla-137
❑ 92Ult-436
❑ 92UppDec-401
❑ 93Bow-599
❑ 93Don-25
❑ 93Fla-276
❑ 93Fle-316
❑ 93Lea-434
❑ 93LinVenB-23
❑ 93LinVenB-181
❑ 93MariStaClu-25
❑ 93MarMot-14
❑ 93OPC-379
❑ 93PacSpa-292
❑ 93PacSpaGE-20
❑ 93PanSti-61
❑ 93Pin-95
❑ 93Sco-102
❑ 93Sco-503
❑ 93Sel-164
❑ 93SP-135
❑ 93StaClu-67
❑ 93StaCluFDI-67
❑ 93StaCluMOP-67
❑ 93Top-68
❑ 93TopGol-68
❑ 93TopInaM-68
❑ 93TopInaR-68
❑ 93TopMic-68
❑ 93TriPla-193
❑ 93Ult-274
❑ 93UppDec-301
❑ 93UppDecGold-301
❑ 94Bow-579
❑ 94ColC-285
❑ 94ColC-629
❑ 94ColChoGS-285
❑ 94ColChoGS-629
❑ 94ColChoSS-285
❑ 94ColChoSS-629
❑ 94Don-328
❑ 94Fin-285
❑ 94FinRef-285
❑ 94Fla-290
❑ 94Fle-301
❑ 94FleExtB-70
❑ 94FleUpd-38
❑ 94Lea-331
❑ 94OPC-267
❑ 94Pac-583
❑ 94PacAll-20
❑ 94PanSti-124
❑ 94Pin-64
❑ 94PinArtP-64
❑ 94PinMusC-64
❑ 94Sco-87
❑ 94ScoGolR-87
❑ 94ScoRoo-RT10
❑ 94ScoRooGR-RT10
❑ 94Sel-321
❑ 94SpoRoo-9
❑ 94SpoRooAP-9
❑ 94StaClu-93
❑ 94StaClu-572
❑ 94StaCluFDI-93
❑ 94StaCluFDI-572
❑ 94StaCluGR-93
❑ 94StaCluGR-572
❑ 94StaCluMOP-93
❑ 94StaCluMOP-572
❑ 94Top-593
❑ 94TopGol-593
❑ 94TopSpa-593
❑ 94TopTra-93T
❑ 94Ult-125
❑ 94Ult-352
❑ 94UltAwaW-5
❑ 94UppDec-486
❑ 94UppDecED-486
❑ 94VenLinU-42
❑ 94VenLinU-57
❑ 95ColCho-269
❑ 95ColChoGS-269
❑ 95ColChoSS-269
❑ 95Don-36
❑ 95DonPreP-36
❑ 95DonTopotO-69
❑ 95Fla-253
❑ 95Fle-150
❑ 95Lea-386
❑ 95LinVen-13
❑ 95LinVen-267
❑ 95LinVen-307
❑ 95LinVen-312
❑ 95LinVen-316
❑ 95LinVen-317
❑ 95LinVen-320
❑ 95Pac-131
❑ 95PacPri-42
❑ 95PanSti-69
❑ 95Pin-129
❑ 95PinArtP-129
❑ 95PinMusC-129
❑ 95Sco-429
❑ 95ScoGolR-429
❑ 95ScoPlaTS-429
❑ 95Spo-134
❑ 95SpoArtP-134
❑ 95StaClu-334
❑ 95StaCluMOP-334
❑ 95StaCluSTDW-I334
❑ 95StaCluSTMP-20
❑ 95StaCluSTWS-334
❑ 95StaCluVR-174
❑ 95StaCluVRMO-174
❑ 95Sum-64
❑ 95SumNthD-64
❑ 95Top-404
❑ 95TopCyb-205
❑ 95UC3-23
❑ 95UC3ArtP-23
❑ 95Ult-43
❑ 95UltAwaW-5
❑ 95UltAwaWGM-5
❑ 95UltGolM-43
❑ 95UppDec-338
❑ 95UppDecED-338
❑ 95UppDecEDG-338
❑ 95UppDecSE-26
❑ 95UppDecSEG-26
❑ 96-97LinVen-148
❑ 96ColCho-528
❑ 96ColChoGS-528
❑ 96ColChoSS-528
❑ 96Don-251
❑ 96DonPreP-251
❑ 96EmoXL-57
❑ 96Fla-77
❑ 96Fle-103
❑ 96FleTif-103
❑ 96IndFle-18
❑ 96LeaSigA-233
❑ 96LeaSigAG-234
❑ 96LeaSigAS-234
❑ 96MetUni-55
❑ 96MetUniP-55
❑ 96Pac-293
❑ 96PacEstL-EL35
❑ 96PacPri-P99
❑ 96PacPriG-P99
❑ 96Pin-113
❑ 96PinAfi-98
❑ 96PinAfiAP-98
❑ 96PinAfiFPP-98
❑ 96SchDis-5
❑ 96Sco-207
❑ 96Sel-42
❑ 96SelArtP-42
❑ 96StaClu-199
❑ 96StaClu-308
❑ 96StaCluEPB-308
❑ 96StaCluEPG-308
❑ 96StaCluEPS-308
❑ 96StaCluMOP-199
❑ 96StaCluMOP-308
❑ 96Sum-18
❑ 96SumAbo&B-18
❑ 96SumArtP-18
❑ 96SumFoi-18
❑ 96Top-89
❑ 96Ult-55
❑ 96UltGolM-55
❑ 96UppDec-56
❑ 97Cir-67
❑ 97CirRav-67
❑ 97ColCho-86
❑ 97ColChoT-CI2
❑ 97Don-196
❑ 97DonGolPP-196
❑ 97DonPre-131
❑ 97DonPreCttC-131
❑ 97DonSilPP-196
❑ 97DonTea-81
❑ 97DonTeaSPE-81
❑ 97Fin-78
❑ 97FinRef-78
❑ 97Fle-92
❑ 97FleTif-92
❑ 97IndSco-6
❑ 97IndScoPl-6
❑ 97IndScoPr-6
❑ 97IndScoU-6
❑ 97IndScoUTC-6
❑ 97Lea-84
❑ 97LeaFraM-84
❑ 97LeaFraMDC-84
❑ 97MetUni-88
❑ 97Pac-82
❑ 97PacCar-9
❑ 97PacCarM-9
❑ 97PacGolCD-9
❑ 97PacLatotML-10
❑ 97PacLigB-82
❑ 97PacPri-28
❑ 97PacPriGA-GA6
❑ 97PacPriLB-28
❑ 97PacPriP-28
❑ 97PacSil-82
❑ 97Pin-154
❑ 97PinArtP-PP154
❑ 97PinCer-38
❑ 97PinCerMBla-38
❑ 97PinCerMBlu-38
❑ 97PinCerMG-38
❑ 97PinCerMR-38
❑ 97PinCerR-38
❑ 97PinMusC-154
❑ 97PinPrePla-154
❑ 97PinTotCPB-38
❑ 97PinTotCPG-38
❑ 97PinTotCPR-38
❑ 97PinX-P-66
❑ 97PinX-PMoS-66
❑ 97Sco-153
❑ 97ScoArtPWB-153
❑ 97ScoPreS-153
❑ 97ScoShoS-153
❑ 97ScoShoSAP-153
❑ 97StaClu-124
❑ 97StaCluMOP-124
❑ 97Stu-57
❑ 97StuPrePG-57
❑ 97StuPrePS-57
❑ 97Top-173
❑ 97TopGal-80
❑ 97TopGalPPI-80
❑ 97Ult-56
❑ 97UltGolME-56
❑ 97UltPlaME-56
❑ 97UppDec-54
❑ 97UppDec-146
❑ 98CirThu-205
❑ 98CirThuRav-205
❑ 98CirThuSupRav-205
❑ 98ColCho-352
❑ 98CroRoy-47
❑ 98Don-229
❑ 98DonColL-309
❑ 98DonColP-634
❑ 98DonGolPP-229
❑ 98DonPre-84
❑ 98DonPreSeat-84
❑ 98DonPriCL-309
❑ 98DonPriCP-634
❑ 98DonSilPP-229
❑ 98Fin-114
❑ 98FinNo--114
❑ 98FinNo-R-114
❑ 98FinRef-114
❑ 98Fle-176
❑ 98IndSco-5
❑ 98IndScoP-5
❑ 98Lea-110
❑ 98LeaFraDA-110
❑ 98LeaFraF-110
❑ 98LeaFraM-110
❑ 98LeaFraM-110
❑ 98LeaFraMDC-110
❑ 98LeaFraMDC-110
❑ 98LeaFraMZ2-110
❑ 98LeaRS-85
❑ 98LeaRSLHolo-85
❑ 98LeaRSLong-85
❑ 98LeaRTrue-85
❑ 98Pac-80
❑ 98PacAur-34
❑ 98PacInv-27
❑ 98PacInvGems-44
❑ 98PacInvPBlue-27
❑ 98PacInvSilv-27
❑ 98PacInvTeam-8
❑ 98PacLatotML-11
❑ 98PacOme-76
❑ 98PacOmeR-76
❑ 98PacOnl-233
❑ 98PacOnlR-233
❑ 98PacOnlWC-233
❑ 98PacPar-42
❑ 98PacParC-42
❑ 98PacParG-42
❑ 98PacParHS-42
❑ 98PacParPB-42
❑ 98PacParR-42
❑ 98PacPlaB-80
❑ 98PacRedT-80
❑ 98PacSil-80
❑ 98PinPer-82
❑ 98PinPerPP-82
❑ 98PinSna-CI13
❑ 98PreCon-13
❑ 98Revo-48
❑ 98RevoSS-48
❑ 98Sco-48
❑ 98ScoRT-109
❑ 98ScoRTSS-PP72
❑ 98ScoRTSSAP-PP72
❑ 98ScoRTSSAP1-PP72
❑ 98ScoSS-PP15
❑ 98ScoSSAP-PP15
❑ 98SP Aut-78
❑ 98SPxFin-76
❑ 98SPxFinR-76
❑ 98SPxFinS-76
❑ 98StaCluFDI-237
❑ 98StaCluI-237
❑ 98StaCluOneK-237
❑ 98StaCluPP-237
❑ 98Stu-78
❑ 98StuGPP-78
❑ 98StuSPP-78
❑ 98Top-33
❑ 98TopChr-33
❑ 98TopChrR-33
❑ 98TopDevR-33
❑ 98TopDia-33
❑ 98TopGal-114
❑ 98TopGalGP-114
❑ 98TopGalOPP-114
❑ 98TopGalPPI-114
❑ 98TopGalPPIA-114
❑ 98TopMiniC-33
❑ 98TopOpeD-22
❑ 98TopSta-37
❑ 98TopStaB-37
❑ 98TopStaG-37
❑ 98TopStaGR-37
❑ 98TopStaS-37
❑ 98Ult-330
❑ 98UltGolM-330
❑ 98UltMas-330
❑ 98UltPlaM-330
❑ 98UppDec-72
❑ 98UppDec10AP-39
❑ 98UppDec1APR-39
❑ 98UppDecNP-NP41
❑ 98UppDecR-32
❑ 98UppDecRGKoG-G6
❑ 98UppDecSF-43
❑ 99199Fin-74
❑ 99FinGolRef-74
❑ 99FinRef-74
❑ 99Fle-214
❑ 99FleBri-12
❑ 99FleBri2G-12
❑ 99FleBriBlu-12
❑ 99FleBriGol-12
❑ 99FleSta9-214
❑ 99FleWarT-214
❑ 99MetUni-170
❑ 99MetUniGM-170
❑ 99MetUniPMG-170
❑ 99Pac-137
❑ 99PacAur-57
❑ 99PacAurOD-57
❑ 99PacCroC-90
❑ 99PacCroC-9
❑ 99PacCroCPB-90
❑ 99PacOme-78
❑ 99PacOmeC-78
❑ 99PacOmeG-78
❑ 99PacOmePB-78
❑ 99PacPar-78
❑ 99PacParC-78
❑ 99PacParG-78
❑ 99PacParHoloGold-78
❑ 99PacParHS-78
❑ 99PacParOD-78
❑ 99PacParPB-78
❑ 99PacParRed-78
❑ 99PacPlaB-137
❑ 99PacPri-48
❑ 99PacPriHB-48
❑ 99PacPriHG-48
❑ 99PacPriHM-48
❑ 99PacPriHP-48
❑ 99PacPriRed-48
❑ 99PacPriS-143
❑ 99PacPriS206-143
❑ 99PacPriS206R-143
❑ 99PacRed-137
❑ 99SkyMolM-95
❑ 99SkyMolMX-95
❑ 99SkyPre-169
❑ 99SkyPreR-169
❑ 99SkyThu-49
❑ 99SkyThuRant-49
❑ 99SkyThuRave-49
❑ 99SpoIll-178
❑ 99StaClu-203
❑ 99StaCluFDI-203
❑ 99StaCluOoaK-203
❑ 99StaCluPP-203
❑ 99ThuSkySupR-49
❑ 99Top-152
❑ 99TopChr-152

❑ 99TopChrR-152
❑ 99TopMVPP-152
❑ 99TopOpeD-87
❑ 99UD Cho-77
❑ 99UD ChoMBH-B11
❑ 99UD ChoPCR-77
❑ 99Ult-81
❑ 99UltGolM-81
❑ 99UltMas-81
❑ 99UltPlaM-81
❑ 99UppDec-82
❑ 99UppDecEL1-82
❑ 99UppDecEL2-82
❑ 99UppDecM-63
❑ 99UppDecMGS-63
❑ 99UppDecMHFS-63
❑ 99UppDecMP-63
❑ 99UppDecMSS-63
❑ 99Vic-126
Vizzini, Dan
❑ 90SouOreAB-21
❑ 90SouOreAP-3447
❑ 91SouOreAC-20
❑ 91SouOreAP-3846
Vlasis, Chris
❑ 91JohCitCC-13
❑ 91JohCitCP-3992
❑ 92SprCarC-13
❑ 92SprCarF-884
❑ 94SavCarC-27
❑ 94SavCarF-522
Vlcek, Jim
❑ 86SalRedBP-27
❑ 89SanDieSAS-28
❑ 92ChaRanC-17
❑ 93KanCouCC-22
❑ 93KanCouCF-916
❑ 93KanCouCTI-26
Vodvarka, Rob
❑ 83ButCopKT-12
Voeltz, Bill
❑ 87Ft.LauYP-16
❑ 87OneYanP-19
❑ 87PriWilYP-16
❑ 88Ft.LauYS-23
Vogel, George
❑ 84SavCarT-20
Vogel, Mike
❑ 92SouBenWSC-10
❑ 93SarWhiSF-1373
❑ 93SouBenWSF-1435
Vogelgesang, Joe
❑ 92GreFalDSP-28
❑ 93MedHatBJF-3738
❑ 93MedHatBJSP-10
Vogelsong, Ryan
❑ 98SalVol-36
Vogler, Peter
❑ 91BriBanF-13
Vogt, Bobby
❑ 98EriSeaWM-24
Vogtli, Robb
❑ 98OneYanG-28
Voigt, Jack
❑ 87NewOriP-7
❑ 88HagSunS-23
❑ 89FreKeyS-24
❑ 90Bes-103
❑ 90EasLeaAP-EL8
❑ 90HagSunB-15
❑ 90HagSunP-1430
❑ 90HagSunS-25
❑ 91HagSunLD-248
❑ 91HagSunP-2470
❑ 91LinDriAA-248
❑ 92RocRedWF-1953
❑ 92RocRedWS-472
❑ 92SkyAAAF-215
❑ 93BalOriP-37
❑ 93Bow-678
❑ 93FleFinE-167
❑ 93LinVenB-246
❑ 93RocRedWF-255
❑ 93SelRoo-141T
❑ 93TopTra-27T
❑ 94BalOriP-34
❑ 94Fle-23
❑ 94OriPro-101
❑ 94OriUSPC-5D
❑ 94OriUSPC-11C
❑ 94Pac-47
❑ 94Sco-580
❑ 94ScoGolR-580
❑ 94Sel-105
❑ 94StaClu-491
❑ 94StaCluFDI-491
❑ 94StaCluGR-491
❑ 94StaCluMOP-491
❑ 94StaCluT-292
❑ 94StaCluTFDI-292
❑ 94Top-117
❑ 94TopGol-117
❑ 94TopSpa-117
❑ 94Ult-10
❑ 94VenLinU-219
❑ 95ColCho-337
❑ 95ColChoGS-337
❑ 95ColChoSS-337
❑ 95Don-327
❑ 95DonPreP-327
❑ 95Fle-22
❑ 95RanCra-34
❑ 95Sco-249
❑ 95ScoGolR-249
❑ 95ScoPlaTS-249
❑ 95Ult-8
❑ 95UltGolM-8
❑ 96OklCit8B-23
❑ 98PacInvGems-62
❑ 98PacOnl-549
❑ 98PacOnlR-549
❑ 98PacOnlWC-549
Voigt, Paul
❑ 80WisRapTT-12
❑ 83AlbDukTc-7
❑ 85NasSouTI-24
Voisard, Mark
❑ 92BenRocCB-3
❑ 92BenRocF-1475
❑ 92ClaFS7-444
❑ 93CenValRC-25
❑ 93CenValRF-2894
❑ 93Top-476
❑ 93TopGol-476
❑ 93TopInaM-476
❑ 93TopInaR-476
❑ 93TopMic-476
❑ 94CenValRC-24
❑ 94CenValRF-3204
❑ 95Exc-192
❑ 95NewHavRTI-NNO
❑ 95SalAvaTI-5
Voiselle, Bill
❑ 47Exh-230
❑ 47TipTop-134
❑ 49EurSta-27
❑ 79DiaGre-36
❑ 83TCMPla1944-37
Voit, David
❑ 89BelBreIS-23
❑ 89HelBreSP-12
❑ 90EriSaiS-30
❑ 91RenSilSCLC-26
❑ 91SydWavF-19
Voita, Sam
❑ 96WesOahCHWB-24
❑ 97St.PetDR-29
Volger, Peter
❑ 93AusFut-47
Volkert, Rusty
❑ 94MedHatBJF-3684
❑ 94MedHatBJSP-24
❑ 95StCatSTI-6
❑ 96HagSunB-22
❑ 97HagSunB-12
Volkman, Keith
❑ 96BoiHawB-30
❑ 97CedRapK-27
❑ 98LakElsSG-29
Volkman, Raymond
❑ 29Zee-101
Vollmer, Clyde
❑ 50Bow-53
❑ 50RedSoxTI-27
❑ 51Bow-91
❑ 52Bow-57
❑ 52Top-255
❑ 53BowC-152
❑ 53Bri-26
❑ 53Top-32
❑ 54Bow-136
❑ 55Bow-13
❑ 79DiaGre-267
❑ 83TopRep5-255
❑ 91TopArc1-32
Vollmer, Gus
❑ 90CliGiaB-11
❑ 90CliGiaP-2562
Vollmer, Robby
❑ 83WauTimF-16
Vollmer, Scott
❑ 94HicCraC-24
❑ 94HicCraF-2181
❑ 94SouAtlLAF-SAL27
❑ 96BirBarB-11
Volquartsen, Joe
❑ 97OmaRoyB-36
Voltaggio, Vic
❑ 88T/MUmp-32
❑ 89T/MUmp-30
❑ 90T/MUmp-29
Volunteers, Tennessee
❑ 95TenVolW-15
Von Der Ahe, Christian
❑ 87BucN28-105
❑ 87LonJacN-12
❑ 87OldJudN-514
❑ 90BasWit-77
Von Hoff, Bruce
❑ 68Top-529
Von Ohlen, Dave
❑ 77LynMetT-28
❑ 79JacMetT-15
❑ 80TidTidT-1
❑ 81TatOrb-18
❑ 82TidTidT-23
❑ 83LouRedR-8
❑ 84Car-32
❑ 84Don-205
❑ 84Fle-340
❑ 84LouRedR-9
❑ 84Nes792-489
❑ 84Top-489
❑ 84TopTif-489
❑ 85Don-412
❑ 85Fle-243
❑ 85FleUpd-126
❑ 85Ind-33
❑ 85IndPol-38
❑ 85Top-177
❑ 85TopTif-177
❑ 85TopTifT-127T
❑ 85TopTra-127T
❑ 86Fle-597
❑ 86MiaMarP-25
❑ 86Top-632
❑ 86TopTif-632
❑ 87Fle-408
❑ 87FleGlo-408
❑ 87TacTigP-7
❑ 87Top-287
❑ 87TopTif-287
❑ 88MiaMarS-24
VonDerleith, Scott
❑ 92BelBreCB-2
Vondran, Steve
❑ 89BilMusP-2057
❑ 89FreStaBS-20
❑ 91CedRapRC-20
❑ 91CedRapRP-2723
❑ 91Cla/Bes-346
Vontz, Doug
❑ 87BurExpP-1095
Voorhees, Mark
❑ 77SpolndC-NNO
Vopata, Nate
❑ 95HudValRTI-6
❑ 96ChaRivTI-9630
❑ 98MadBlaW-18
Vorbeck, Eric
❑ 91YakBeaC-2
❑ 91YakBeaP-4263
❑ 92BakDodCLC-26
❑ 93VerBeaDC-23
❑ 93VerBeaDF-2235
Vosberg, Ed
❑ 84BeaGolGT-6
❑ 85BeaGolGT-5
❑ 86LasVegSP-22
❑ 87LasVegSP-24
❑ 88BlaYNPRWL-62
❑ 88LasVegSC-7
❑ 88LasVegSP-222
❑ 89TucTorC-6
❑ 89TucTorJP-26
❑ 89TucTorP-192
❑ 90CMC-533
❑ 90PhoFirC-6
❑ 90PhoFirP-11
❑ 90ProAAAF-37
❑ 91EdmTraLD-172
❑ 91EdmTraP-1516
❑ 91LinDriAAA-172
❑ 91Sco-757
❑ 91Sco100RS-80
❑ 93IowCubF-2134
❑ 94TacTigF-3176
❑ 94TopTra-64T
❑ 94TriAAF-AAA20
❑ 95RanCra-35
❑ 96FleUpd-U91
❑ 96FleUpdTC-U91
❑ 96LeaSigEA-210
❑ 96RanDr P-32
❑ 96RanFle-17
❑ 96RanMot-23
❑ 97RanDr P-31
❑ 97RanMot-9
Vosik, Bill
❑ 90NebCor-27
❑ 91WatIndC-23
❑ 91WatIndP-3378
❑ 92SalLakTSP-2
Voskovitch, Milo
❑ 72CedRapCT-20
Vosmik, Joe
❑ 32OrbPinNP-35
❑ 32OrbPinUP-56
❑ 33DelR33-20
❑ 33DouDisP-40
❑ 33TatOrb-56
❑ 34BabRutG-61
❑ 34BatR31-68
❑ 34ButPreR-60
❑ 34DiaStaR-8
❑ 34Gou-77
❑ 35AlDemDCR3-35
❑ 35GouPuzR-8I
❑ 35GouPuzR-9I
❑ 36ExhFou-11
❑ 36GouBWR-23
❑ 36GouWidPPR-B22
❑ 36GouWidPPR-B23
❑ 36GouWidPPR-B24
❑ 36GouWidPPR-C24
❑ 36NatChiFPR-74
❑ 36OveCanR-44
❑ 36SandSW-48
❑ 36WheBB4-11
❑ 36WorWidGV-76
❑ 37GouThuMR-2
❑ 38ExhFou-9
❑ 38GouFliMR-2A
❑ 38GouFliMR-2B
❑ 38GouHeaU-247
❑ 38GouHeaU-271
❑ 39GouPreR303A-45
❑ 39GouPreR303B-23
❑ 39PlaBal-107
❑ 39WorWidGTP-45
❑ 40DodTeal-22
❑ 40PlaBal-144
❑ 41DodTeal-9
❑ 41DouPlaR-143
❑ 73Dod194T-28
❑ 78DodTCM4-17
❑ 85BigLeaC3-59
❑ 90DodTar-823
❑ 91ConTSN-221
❑ 93ConTSN-767
Voss, Bill
❑ 66Top-529
❑ 68OPC-142
❑ 68Top-142
❑ 68TopVen-142
❑ 69Top-621
❑ 70OPC-326
❑ 70Top-326
❑ 71BreTeal-17
❑ 71MLBOffS-454
❑ 71OPC-671
❑ 71Top-671
❑ 72Top-776
❑ 94BreMilB-187
Vossler, Dan
❑ 74OPC-602
❑ 74TacTwiC-13
❑ 74Top-602
Vota, Mike
❑ 96SouBenSHS-27
Vowinkle, John H.
❑ 08BufBisFJO-17
Voyles, Brad
❑ 98EugEme-31
Vranjes, Sam
❑ 91SanBerSC-28
❑ 91SanBerSP-1991
Vuchinch, Steve
❑ 86A'sMot-26
❑ 90A'sMot-28
Vuckovich, Pete
❑ 77OPC-130
❑ 77Top-517
❑ 78CarTeal-36
❑ 78OPC-157
❑ 78Top-241
❑ 79Car5-32
❑ 79Hos-87
❑ 79Top-407
❑ 80OPC-31
❑ 80Top-57
❑ 81Don-189
❑ 81Fle-547A
❑ 81OPC-193
❑ 81Top-193
❑ 81TopTra-851
❑ 82BrePol-50
❑ 82Don-458
❑ 82Fle-156
❑ 82FleSta-141
❑ 82OPC-132
❑ 82Top-165
❑ 82Top-643
❑ 82Top-703
❑ 82TopSti-10
❑ 82TopSti-202
❑ 83BreGar-20
❑ 83BrePol-50
❑ 83Don-80
❑ 83Fle-49
❑ 83FleSta-207
❑ 83FleSti-14
❑ 83Kel-19
❑ 83OPC-375
❑ 83OPC-394
❑ 83Top-321
❑ 83Top-375
❑ 83Top-394
❑ 83TopSti-86
❑ 84BreGar-21
❑ 84BrePol-50
❑ 84Fle-217
❑ 84Nes792-505
❑ 84OPC-313
❑ 84Top-505
❑ 84TopTif-505
❑ 85BreGar-21
❑ 85BrePol-50
❑ 85Top-254
❑ 85TopTif-254
❑ 86Don-473
❑ 86Fle-504
❑ 86OPC-152
❑ 86Top-737
❑ 86TopTif-737
❑ 90SweBasG-83
❑ 92BreCarT-24
❑ 94BreMilB-280
❑ 97PirPos-38
Vujovic, Dragan
❑ 82MonNew-21
Vukovich, George
❑ 80VenLeaS-263
❑ 81Fle-21
❑ 81OklCit8T-20
❑ 81Top-598
❑ 82Fle-262
❑ 82Top-389
❑ 83Don-315
❑ 83Fle-176
❑ 83IndPos-38
❑ 83IndWhe-31
❑ 83Top-16
❑ 83TopTra-122T
❑ 84Don-468
❑ 84Fle-555
❑ 84Ind-31
❑ 84IndWhe-24
❑ 84Nes792-638
❑ 84Top-638
❑ 84TopTif-638
❑ 85Don-276
❑ 85Fle-458
❑ 85Ind-34
❑ 85IndPol-24
❑ 85Lea-120
❑ 85Top-212
❑ 85TopSti-249
❑ 85TopTif-212
❑ 86Don-346
❑ 86Fle-598
❑ 86OPC-337
❑ 86Top-483
❑ 86TopSti-214
❑ 86TopTif-483
❑ 87JapPlaB-34
❑ 91PacSenL-45
Vukovich, John
❑ 73OPC-451
❑ 73Top-451
❑ 74OPC-349
❑ 74Top-349
❑ 75OPC-602
❑ 75Top-602
❑ 75TopMin-602
❑ 76SSP-43
❑ 80PhiBurK-8
❑ 81Fle-22
❑ 82CubRedL-NNO
❑ 83CubThoAV-NNO
❑ 84CubChiT-32
❑ 84CubSev-NNO
❑ 85CubSev-NNO
❑ 86CubGat-NNO
❑ 87CubCan-36
❑ 87CubDavB-NNO
❑ 88PhiTas-38
❑ 89PhiTas-35
❑ 90PhiTas-34
❑ 91PhiMed-35
❑ 92PhiMed-31
❑ 93PhiMed-33
❑ 94BreMilB-371
❑ 94PhiMed-34
❑ 95Phi-33
❑ 96PhiTeal-33
❑ 97PhiTeal-18
❑ 98PhiTeal-34
Vuksan, Jeff
❑ 78AppFoxT-24
❑ 79AppFoxT-8
❑ 80AppFoxT-7
❑ 81DurBulT-12
Vukson, John
❑ 94YakBeaC-28
❑ 94YakBeaF-3852
❑ 95YakBeaTI-35
Vuz, John
❑ 87PocGiaTB-14
❑ 88CliGiaP-693
❑ 90SanJosGB-22
❑ 90SanJosGCLC-52
❑ 90SanJosGP-2001
❑ 90SanJosGS-24
Waag, Billy
❑ 81BufBisT-14
Wabeke, Doug
❑ 81ShrCapT-18
Wacha, Chuck
❑ 87GreHorP-7
❑ 89WinHavRSS-26
Wachenfeld, Gene
❑ 25Zee-83
Wachs, Thomas
❑ 85LitFalMT-11
❑ 86ColMetP-26
❑ 87LynMetP-3
Wachter, Derek
❑ 92BelBreCB-18
❑ 92BelBreFI-421
❑ 93StoPorC-25
❑ 93StoPorF-759
❑ 94ExcFS7-89
❑ 95LinVen-194
❑ 97StoPor-13
❑ 97TucTorB-25
Wacker, Wade
❑ 89EliTwiS-27
Waco, David
❑ 94SpaPhiF-1732
❑ 94SparPhiC-21
❑ 95ClePhiF-226
Wada, Hank (Hiromi)
❑ 83SanJosBC-2
❑ 86SanJosBP-23
Waddell, James
❑ 91PerHeaF-17
❑ 93AusFut-61
Waddell, Rube (George E.)
❑ 03BreE10-146
❑ 04FanCraAL-47
❑ 08AmeCarE91-33
❑ 08RosComP-74
❑ 09ColChiE-294A
❑ 09ColChiE-294B
❑ 09ColChiE-294C
❑ 09PC7HHB-43
❑ 09T206-362
❑ 09T206-363
❑ 10StaCarE-27
❑ 10W555-62
❑ 11PinT-5-107
❑ 11SpoLifCW-357

❑ 11SpoLifM-119
❑ 11TurRedT-39
❑ 12ColRedB-294A
❑ 12ColRedB-294B
❑ 12ColRedB-294C
❑ 12ColTinT-294A
❑ 12ColTinT-294B
❑ 12ColTinT-294C
❑ 39PC7AlbHoF-48
❑ 48ExhHoF-29
❑ 50CalHOFW-73
❑ 50H80FouMH-4
❑ 53ArtHaloFP-83
❑ 60Fle-61
❑ 61Fle-149
❑ 76ShaPiz-48
❑ 77BobParHoF-48
❑ 80LauFamF-11
❑ 80PerHaloFP-48
❑ 80SSPHOF-48
❑ 82TCMGreP-42
❑ 86ConSer1-35
❑ 88ConHar-6
❑ 88ConSer5-29
❑ 90PerGreM-52
❑ 93ConTSN-931
❑ 94OriofB-95
❑ 94UppDecTAE-13
❑ 96PitPosH-12

Waddell, Tom

❑ 84FleUpd-123
❑ 84Ind-32
❑ 84IndWhe-54
❑ 84TopTra-125T
❑ 84TopTraT-125T
❑ 85Don-582
❑ 85Fle-459
❑ 85Ind-35
❑ 85IndPol-54
❑ 85Top-453
❑ 85TopTif-453
❑ 86Don-94
❑ 86Fle-599
❑ 86IndOhH-54
❑ 86IndTeal-46
❑ 86OPC-86
❑ 86Top-86
❑ 86TopSti-209
❑ 86TopTif-86
❑ 87IndGat-54
❑ 87Top-657
❑ 87TopTif-657

Wade, Archie

❑ 66St.PetCTI-19

Wade, Ben

❑ 50W720HolS-31
❑ 52Top-389
❑ 53Top-4
❑ 54Top-126
❑ 59DarFar-22
❑ 61UniOil-SD12
❑ 74dod195T-39
❑ 83TopRep5-389
❑ 90DodTar-824
❑ 91TopArc1-4
❑ 94TopArc1-126
❑ 94TopArc1G-126
❑ 95TopArcBD-29
❑ 95TopArcBD-38
❑ 95TopArcBD-74

Wade, Charles

❑ 31Zee-57

Wade, Darrin

❑ 88DunBluJS-19
❑ 88St.CatBJP-2036

Wade, Gale

❑ 55Top-196
❑ 58SeaRalT-18
❑ 59SeaPop-12

Wade, Jake

❑ 50WorWidGV-3

Wade, Scott

❑ 86NewBriRSP-25
❑ 87PawRedSP-71
❑ 87PawRedST-20
❑ 88PawRedSC-23
❑ 88PawRedSP-458
❑ 89PawRedSC-15
❑ 89PawRedSP-695
❑ 89PawRedSTI-27
❑ 90CMC-274
❑ 90PawRedSC-23
❑ 90PawRedSDD-29
❑ 90PawRedSP-476
❑ 90ProAAAF-448
❑ 90TopTVRS-65
❑ 91LinDriAAA-497
❑ 91ScrRedBLD-497
❑ 91ScrRedBP-2554
❑ 92IowCubF-4064
❑ 92SyrChiS-519
❑ 93IowCubF-2146

Wade, Terrell

❑ 92IdaFalGF-3514
❑ 92IdaFalGSP-9
❑ 93MacBraC-1
❑ 93MacBraF-1401
❑ 93SouAtlLAGF-43
❑ 94ActPac-32
❑ 94Bow-329
❑ 94BowBes-B23
❑ 94BowBesR-B23
❑ 94Cla-170
❑ 94ClaCreotC-C12
❑ 94ClaGolF-118
❑ 94ColC-649
❑ 94ColChoGS-649
❑ 94ColChoSS-649
❑ 94ExcAllF-10
❑ 94ExcFS7-162
❑ 94GreBraF-415
❑ 94GreBraTI-26
❑ 94SP-17
❑ 94SPDieC-17
❑ 94Top-316
❑ 94TopGol-316
❑ 94TopSpa-316
❑ 94Ult-452
❑ 94UppDec-527
❑ 94UppDecAHNIL-13
❑ 94UppDecED-527
❑ 94UppDecML-7
❑ 94UppDecML-91
❑ 94UppDecML-255
❑ 94UppDecMLPotYF-PY5
❑ 95ActPacF-5
❑ 95Bow-111
❑ 95ColChoSE-5
❑ 95ColChoSEGS-5
❑ 95ColChoSESS-5
❑ 95Exc-159
❑ 95Fle-321
❑ 95RicBraRC-27
❑ 95RicBraTI-25
❑ 95Top-316
❑ 95UppDec-213
❑ 95UppDecED-213
❑ 95UppDecEDG-213
❑ 95UppDecML-5
❑ 95UppDecML-166
❑ 95UppDecMLFS-5
❑ 95UppDecMLFS-166
❑ 95UppDecMLMLA-9
❑ 95UppDecMLOP-OP1
❑ 95UppDecSE-18
❑ 95UppDecSEG-18
❑ 96BesAutSA-83
❑ 96Bow-367
❑ 96BowFoi-367
❑ 96BraFle-17
❑ 96ColCho-461
❑ 96ColChoGS-461
❑ 96ColChoSS-461
❑ 96Don-533
❑ 96DonPreP-533
❑ 96Fin-B285
❑ 96FinRef-B285
❑ 96Fle-309
❑ 96FleTif-309
❑ 96Lea-144
❑ 96LeaPre-112
❑ 96LeaPreP-112
❑ 96LeaPrePB-144
❑ 96LeaPrePG-144
❑ 96LeaPrePS-144
❑ 96LeaSig-132
❑ 96LeaSigA-234
❑ 96LeaSigAG-235
❑ 96LeaSigAS-235
❑ 96LeaSigPPG-132
❑ 96LeaSigPPP-132
❑ 96Pin-169
❑ 96PinAfi-176
❑ 96PinAfiAP-176
❑ 96PinArtP-95
❑ 96PinSta-95
❑ 96Sco-501
❑ 96Sel-195
❑ 96SelArtP-195
❑ 96SelCer-133
❑ 96SelCerAP-133
❑ 96SelCerCB-133
❑ 96SelCerCR-133
❑ 96SelCerMB-133
❑ 96SelCerMG-133
❑ 96SelCerMR-133
❑ 96Spo-137
❑ 96SpoArtP-137
❑ 96Sum-185
❑ 96SumAbo&B-185
❑ 96SumArtP-185
❑ 96SumFoi-185
❑ 96Ult-446
❑ 96UltGolM-446
❑ 96Zen-129
❑ 96ZenArtP-129
❑ 97BraSco-11
❑ 97BraScoPl-11
❑ 97BraScoPr-11
❑ 97Cir-236
❑ 97CirRav-236
❑ 97ColCho-29
❑ 97Don-322
❑ 97DonEli-79
❑ 97DonEliGS-79
❑ 97DonGolPP-322
❑ 97DonLim-129
❑ 97DonLimE-129
❑ 97DonLimENG-129
❑ 97DonSigA-103
❑ 97DonSigAC-128
❑ 97DonSigAM-128
❑ 97DonSilPP-322
❑ 97DonTea-30
❑ 97DonTeaSPE-30
❑ 97Fle-270
❑ 97FleTif-270
❑ 97Lea-144
❑ 97LeaFraM-144
❑ 97LeaFraMDC-144
❑ 97NewPin-62
❑ 97NewPinAP-62
❑ 97NewPinMC-62
❑ 97NewPinPP-62
❑ 97PacPriGotD-GD115
❑ 97PinIns-69
❑ 97PinInsCE-69
❑ 97PinInsDE-69
❑ 97Sco-199
❑ 97ScoArtPWB-199
❑ 97ScoPreS-199
❑ 97ScoShoS-199
❑ 97ScoShoSAP-199
❑ 97Top-3
❑ 97Ult-161
❑ 97UltGolME-161
❑ 97UltPlaME-161
❑ 97UppDec-14
❑ 98BraSco-13
❑ 98BraScoP-13
❑ 98ColCho-512
❑ 98Sco-187
❑ 98Top-404
❑ 98TopChr-404
❑ 98TopChrR-404
❑ 98TopDevR-404
❑ 98TopDia-404
❑ 98TopMiniC-404
❑ 98UppDec-738

Wade, Wallace

❑ 40WheM4-11

Wadley, Tony

❑ 82MiaMarT-7
❑ 83IdaFalAT-13

Waggoner, Aubrey

❑ 86AppFoxP-27
❑ 87PenWhiSP-8
❑ 89BirBarB-8
❑ 89BirBarP-114
❑ 90BirBarB-13
❑ 90BirBarP-1120
❑ 90CMC-817
❑ 91BirBarLD-72
❑ 91BirBarP-1468
❑ 91LinDriAA-72
❑ 92GreBraF-1167
❑ 92GreBraS-247
❑ 93CalCanF-1180
❑ 93ClaFS7-293
❑ 94GreBraTI-27

Waggoner, Jay

❑ 96LakTigB-28

Waggoner, Jimmy

❑ 89MedAthB-25
❑ 90MadMusB-9
❑ 90ModA'sC-31
❑ 90ModA'sCLC-166
❑ 90ModA'sP-2223
❑ 91Cla/Bes-89
❑ 91ModA'sC-26
❑ 91ModA'sP-3100
❑ 92CalLeaACL-20
❑ 92RenSilSCLC-55
❑ 93HunStaF-2091
❑ 94HunStaF-1340
❑ 95HunStaTI-27

Wagner, Adam

❑ 90Ft.LauYS-27
❑ 91PriWilCC-27
❑ 92PriWilCC-29

Wagner, Bill TR

❑ 97PitMet-4
❑ 98CapCitBF5-30
❑ 98CapCitBM-30

Wagner, Billy

❑ 93AubAstC-1
❑ 93AubAstF-3445
❑ 94Bow-642
❑ 94BowBes-B19
❑ 94BowBesR-B19
❑ 94Cla-140
❑ 94ClaGolF-18
❑ 94ClaGolN1PLF-LP16
❑ 94ClaGolREF-RE16
❑ 94ClaTriF-T34
❑ 94ColC-29
❑ 94ColChoGS-29
❑ 94ColChoSS-29
❑ 94ExcFS7-209
❑ 94MidLeaAF-MDW54
❑ 94Pin-264
❑ 94PinArtP-264
❑ 94PinMusC-264
❑ 94QuaCitRBC-24
❑ 94QuaCitRBF-532
❑ 94Sco-536
❑ 94ScoGolR-536
❑ 94SigRoo-49
❑ 94SigRooS-49
❑ 94SP-18
❑ 94SPDieC-18
❑ 94TedWil-134
❑ 94Top-209
❑ 94TopGol-209
❑ 94TopSpa-209
❑ 94UppDec-524
❑ 94UppDecAHNIL-14
❑ 94UppDecED-524
❑ 94UppDecML-86
❑ 95ActPacF-48
❑ 95Bow-1
❑ 95BowBes-B32
❑ 95BowBes-X14
❑ 95BowBesR-B32
❑ 95BowBesR-X14
❑ 95Exc-208
❑ 95ExcLeaL-19
❑ 95JacGenTI-8
❑ 95TucTotTI-28
❑ 95UppDecML-60
❑ 95UppDecMLFS-60
❑ 95UppDecMLOP-OP12
❑ 96Bow-336
❑ 96BowBes-148
❑ 96BowBesAR-148
❑ 96BowBesMI-10
❑ 96BowBesMIAR-10
❑ 96BowBesMIR-10
❑ 96BowBesP-BBP8
❑ 96BowBesPAR-BBP8
❑ 96BowBesPR-BBP8
❑ 96BowBesR-148
❑ 96BowFoi-336
❑ 96BowMinLP-13
❑ 96ColCho-425
❑ 96ColChoGS-425
❑ 96ColChoSS-425
❑ 96Don-398
❑ 96DonPreP-398
❑ 96Fin-S313
❑ 96FinRef-S313
❑ 96Fle-422
❑ 96FleTif-422
❑ 96Lea-218
❑ 96LeaPre-121
❑ 96LeaPreP-121
❑ 96LeaPrePB-218
❑ 96LeaPrePG-218
❑ 96LeaPrePS-218
❑ 96LeaSig-80
❑ 96LeaSigPPG-80
❑ 96LeaSigPPP-80
❑ 96SP-12
❑ 96Top-212
❑ 96TopChr-74
❑ 96TopChrR-74
❑ 96TopGal-128
❑ 96TopGalPPI-128
❑ 96TusTorB-24
❑ 96UppDec-225
❑ 96UppDecBCP-BC11
❑ 96Zen-112
❑ 96ZenArtP-112
❑ 97AstMot-9
❑ 97Bow-54
❑ 97BowCerBlaIA-CA81
❑ 97BowCerBluIA-CA81
❑ 97BowCerGolIA-CA81
❑ 97BowChr-42
❑ 97BowChrI-42
❑ 97BowChrIR-42
❑ 97BowChrR-42
❑ 97BowInt-54
❑ 97Cir-324
❑ 97CirRav-324
❑ 97ColCho-123
❑ 97Don-91
❑ 97DonEli-51
❑ 97DonEliGS-51
❑ 97DonGolPP-91
❑ 97DonLim-86
❑ 97DonLimE-86
❑ 97DonLimENG-86
❑ 97DonPre-135
❑ 97DonPreCttC-135
❑ 97DonSigA-104
❑ 97DonSigAC-129
❑ 97DonSigAM-129
❑ 97DonSigNN-10
❑ 97DonSilPP-91
❑ 97Fin-102
❑ 97FinEmb-102
❑ 97FinEmbR-102
❑ 97FinRef-102
❑ 97FlaShoLC-13
❑ 97FlaShoLeg0-13
❑ 97FlaShoLeg1-13
❑ 97FlaShoM-A13
❑ 97FlaShoM-B13
❑ 97FlaShoM-C13
❑ 97FlaShoR0-13
❑ 97FlaShoR1-13
❑ 97FlaShoR2-13
❑ 97Fle-354
❑ 97FleTif-354
❑ 97Lea-5
❑ 97LeaFraM-5
❑ 97LeaFraMDC-5
❑ 97MetUni-141
❑ 97NewPin-34
❑ 97NewPinAP-34
❑ 97NewPinMC-34
❑ 97NewPinPP-34
❑ 97Pin-183
❑ 97PinArtP-PP183
❑ 97PinCer-102
❑ 97PinCerMBla-102
❑ 97PinCerMBlu-102
❑ 97PinCerMG-102
❑ 97PinCerMR-102
❑ 97PinCerR-102
❑ 97PinIns-131
❑ 97PinInsCE-131
❑ 97PinInsDE-131
❑ 97PinMusC-183
❑ 97PinPrePla-183
❑ 97PinTotCPB-102
❑ 97PinTotCPG-102
❑ 97PinTotCPR-102
❑ 97PinX-P-98
❑ 97PinX-PMoS-98
❑ 97Sco-32
❑ 97ScoArtPWB-32
❑ 97ScoPreS-32
❑ 97ScoShoS-32
❑ 97ScoShoSAP-32
❑ 97Sel-167
❑ 97SelCom-167
❑ 97SP-86
❑ 97SpoIll-52
❑ 97SpoIllEE-52
❑ 97StaClu-33
❑ 97StaCluMat-33
❑ 97StaCluMOP-33
❑ 97Stu-23
❑ 97StuPrePG-23
❑ 97StuPrePS-23
❑ 97Top-22
❑ 97TopAwel-AI19
❑ 97TopGal-178
❑ 97TopGalPPI-178
❑ 97TopStaFAS-FAS12
❑ 97Ult-212
❑ 97UltGolME-212
❑ 97UltPlaME-212
❑ 97UppDec-81
❑ 97UppDecTTS-TS7
❑ 98CirThu-13
❑ 98CirThuRav-13
❑ 98CirThuSupRav-13
❑ 98ColCho-134
❑ 98Don-211
❑ 98DonGolPP-211
❑ 98DonSigA-89
❑ 98DonSigAC-111
❑ 98DonSigAM-114
❑ 98DonSigSB-29
❑ 98DonSilPP-211
❑ 98Fin-253
❑ 98FinNo--253
❑ 98FinNo-R-253
❑ 98FinRef-253
❑ 98Fle-210
❑ 98MetUni-27
❑ 98MetUniPMG-27
❑ 98PacOnl-333
❑ 98PacOnlR-333
❑ 98PacOnlWC-333
❑ 98Pin-112
❑ 98PinPreP-112
❑ 98ScoRT-77
❑ 98SPxFin-281
❑ 98SPxFinR-281
❑ 98SPxFinS-281
❑ 98StaCluFDI-201
❑ 98StaCluI-201
❑ 98StaCluOneK-201
❑ 98StaCluPP-201
❑ 98Top-3
❑ 98TopChr-3
❑ 98TopChrR-3
❑ 98TopDevR-3
❑ 98TopDia-3
❑ 98TopGal-39
❑ 98TopGalGP-39
❑ 98TopGalOPP-39
❑ 98TopGalPPI-39
❑ 98TopGalPPIA-39
❑ 98TopMiniC-3
❑ 98TopOpeD-3
❑ 98Ult-59
❑ 98UltGolM-59
❑ 98UltMas-59
❑ 98UltPlaM-59
❑ 98UppDec-104
❑ 98UppDecSF-63
❑ 99Fle-217
❑ 99FleSta9-217
❑ 99FleWarT-217
❑ 99MetUni-127
❑ 99MetUniGM-127
❑ 99MetUniPMG-127
❑ 99PacOme-109
❑ 99PacOmeC-109
❑ 99PacOmeG-109
❑ 99PacOmePB-109
❑ 99PacPar-107
❑ 99PacParC-107
❑ 99PacParG-107
❑ 99PacParHoloGold-107
❑ 99PacParHS-107
❑ 99PacParOD-107
❑ 99PacParPB-107
❑ 99PacParRed-107
❑ 99SkyPre-176
❑ 99SkyPreR-176
❑ 99SkyThu-31
❑ 99SkyThuRant-31
❑ 99SkyThuRave-31
❑ 99SP SigAuto-BWA
❑ 99SPSig-103
❑ 99ThuSkySupR-31
❑ 99Top-108
❑ 99TopChr-108
❑ 99TopChrR-108
❑ 99TopMVPP-108
❑ 99TopOpeD-62
❑ 99Ult-118
❑ 99UltGolM-118
❑ 99UltMas-118
❑ 99UltPlaM-118
❑ 99UppDec-112
❑ 99UppDecEL1-112
❑ 99UppDecEL2-112
❑ 99UppDecM-93
❑ 99UppDecMGS-93

❑ 99UppDecMHFS-93
❑ 99UppDecMP-93
❑ 99UppDecMSS-93
❑ 99Vic-175
Wagner, Bret
❑ 93BazTeaU-22
❑ 93TopTra-124T
❑ 94NewJerCC-27
❑ 94NewJerCF-3419
❑ 94SigRooDP-19
❑ 94SigRooDPS-19
❑ 94StaCluDP-86
❑ 94StaCluDPFDI-86
❑ 94TopTra-41T
❑ 95Bes-97
❑ 95Bow-128
❑ 95BowBes-B59
❑ 95BowBesR-B59
❑ 95Exc-276
❑ 95ScoDraP-DP2
❑ 95SPML-155
❑ 95StaClu-113
❑ 95StaCluFDI-113
❑ 95StaCluMOP-113
❑ 95StaCluSTWS-113
❑ 95Top-167
❑ 95UppDec-8
❑ 95UppDecED-8
❑ 95UppDecEDG-8
❑ 95UppDecSE-93
❑ 95UppDecSEG-93
❑ 96BesAutSA-84
❑ 96Bow-237
❑ 96BowFoi-237
❑ 96Exc-232
❑ 96HunStaTI-25
❑ 96Top-430
Wagner, Bull (William G.)
❑ 14B18B-63
❑ 90DodTar-1091
Wagner, Butts (Albert)
❑ 90DodTar-1092
Wagner, Charlie
❑ 08AmeCarE91-95
❑ 46RedSoxTI-22
❑ 75RedSox1T-35
❑ 75RedSox1T-39
❑ 78ReaRem-21
❑ 79DiaGre-238
❑ 80ElmPioRST-39
❑ 87ElmPioBC-33
Wagner, Dale
❑ 93JohCitCC-27
❑ 93JohCitCF-3679
Wagner, Dan
❑ 87PenWhiSP-29
❑ 88BirBarB-13
❑ 89BirBarB-5
❑ 89BirBarP-90
❑ 90MidAngGS-20
Wagner, Darrell
❑ 90BenBucL-16
Wagner, Gary
❑ 66OPC-151
❑ 66Top-151
❑ 66TopVen-151
❑ 67Top-529
❑ 68Top-448
❑ 69Top-276
❑ 69TopSta-158
❑ 70Top-627
❑ 71OPC-473
❑ 71Top-473
❑ 81TCM60I-437
Wagner, Gerald
❑ 86DurBulP-26
❑ 87SumBraP-28
Wagner, Harold
❑ 42A'sTeal-35
❑ 43A'STEAI-25
❑ 46RedSoxTI-23
❑ 47TipTop-13
❑ 75RedSox1T-36
❑ 77TCMTheWY-61
❑ 85TCMPla1-1
Wagner, Hector
❑ 88EugEmeB-6
❑ 89AppFoxP-849
❑ 90Bes-194
❑ 90MemChiB-18
❑ 90MemChiP-1008
❑ 90MemChiS-25
❑ 90ProAaA-34
❑ 91Bow-299
❑ 91LinDriAAA-347
❑ 91OmaRoyLD-347
❑ 91OmaRoyP-1036
❑ 91Sco-730
❑ 91TopDeb90-161
❑ 92StaClu-323
Wagner, Heinie (Charles)
❑ 08RosComP-8
❑ 09RamT20-120
❑ 09SpoNewSM-86
❑ 09T206-364
❑ 09T206-365
❑ 10DomDisP-119
❑ 10E-UOraBSC-22
❑ 10E12AmeCDCE125-36
❑ 10RedCroT-253
❑ 10SweCapPP-7
❑ 11BasBatEU-40
❑ 11HelSta-5
❑ 11PinT-5-653
❑ 11SpoLifCW-358
❑ 11SpoLifM-18
❑ 11T205-175
❑ 12HasTriFT-10B
❑ 12HasTriFT-24
❑ 12RedSoxBASP-5
❑ 12RedSoxBDASP-3
❑ 12T207-188
❑ 12T207-189
❑ 14CraJacE-31
❑ 14PieStaT-104
❑ 15CraJacE-31
❑ 15VicT21-28
❑ 42RedSoxTI-24
❑ 72ClaCar-110
❑ 75RedSox1T-39
Wagner, Honus (John)
❑ 03BreE10-147
❑ 03WilCarE-29
❑ 06FanCraNL-49
❑ 08AmeCarE91-96
❑ 08AmeLeaPC-15
❑ 08RosComP-157
❑ 09AmeCarE90-1-113
❑ 09AmeCarE90-1-114
❑ 09ColChiE-295
❑ 09MaxPubP-15
❑ 09PhiCarE-22
❑ 09SpoNewSM-11
❑ 09SpoNewSM-36
❑ 09T206-366
❑ 09WWSmiP-1
❑ 09WWSmiP-2
❑ 10CouT21-240
❑ 10DarChoE-32
❑ 10E-UOraBSC-23
❑ 10E101-44A
❑ 10E101-44B
❑ 10E102-25A
❑ 10E102-25B
❑ 10E12AmeCDCE125-37
❑ 10E12AmeCDCE125-38
❑ 10E98-28
❑ 10JuJuDE-40
❑ 10MelMinE-44A
❑ 10MelMinE-44B
❑ 10NadCarE-52A
❑ 10NadCarE-52B
❑ 10NadE1-56
❑ 10NotCov-8
❑ 10PeoT21-56A
❑ 10PeoT21-56B
❑ 10PeoT21-56C
❑ 10PeoT21-56D
❑ 10PirAmeCE-10
❑ 10PirHerICP-11
❑ 10PirTipTD-4
❑ 10RedCroT-80
❑ 10RedCroT-163
❑ 10SepAnoP-5
❑ 10SepAnoP-24
❑ 10StaCarE-28
❑ 10W555-61
❑ 11BasBatEU-41
❑ 11DiaGumP-28
❑ 11E94-29
❑ 11PinT-5-853
❑ 11PinT-5-872
❑ 11PinT-5-873
❑ 11PloCanE-64
❑ 11SpoLifCW-359
❑ 11SpoLifM-260
❑ 12ColRedB-295
❑ 12ColTinT-295
❑ 13NatGamW-41
❑ 13TomBarW-37
❑ 14CraJacE-68
❑ 14PolGroW-28
❑ 14TexTomE-44
❑ 14TexTomE-62
❑ 15AmeCarE106-40A
❑ 15AmeCarE106-40B
❑ 15CraJacE-68
❑ 15SpoNewM-184
❑ 16BF2FP-95
❑ 16FleBreD-97
❑ 16SpoNewM-182
❑ 16TanBraE-18
❑ 17ColE13-180
❑ 24MrsShePP-10
❑ 36Halof FP-23
❑ 36NatChiFPR-75
❑ 36R31PasP-47
❑ 36R31Pre-L13
❑ 39PC7AlbHoF-5
❑ 40PlaBal-168
❑ 46SpoExcW-8-8
❑ 47TipTop-149
❑ 48ExhHoF-30
❑ 49Lea-70
❑ 50CalHOFW-74
❑ 51TopConMA-11
❑ 53ArtHaloFP-84
❑ 60ExhWriH-24
❑ 60Fle-62
❑ 61Fle-150
❑ 61GolPre-32
❑ 63BasMagM-83
❑ 63BazA-10
❑ 63HalofFB-20
❑ 67SpoHobFC-1
❑ 67TopVen-143
❑ 68LauWorS-6
❑ 68SCFOldT-5
❑ 68SpoMemAG-14
❑ 69Baz-8
❑ 69Baz-12
❑ 70FleWorS-6
❑ 72ClaCar-47
❑ 72FleFamF-21
❑ 72KelATG-9
❑ 73HalofFPP-18
❑ 73SevTraC-77
❑ 73TCMAllG-22
❑ 76GalBasGHoF-29
❑ 76JerJonPC-6
❑ 76MotOldT-1
❑ 76OPC-344
❑ 76RowExh-15
❑ 76ShaPiz-5
❑ 76TayBow4-97
❑ 76TayBow4-NNO
❑ 76Top-344
❑ 77BobParHoF-49
❑ 77BobParMBC-23
❑ 77GalGloG-148
❑ 77ShaPiz-18
❑ 79Pew-16
❑ 80LauFamF-1
❑ 80MarExhH-30
❑ 80PacLeg-18
❑ 80PerHaloFP-5
❑ 80PirGreT-4
❑ 80SSPHOF-5
❑ 81ConTSN-64
❑ 81SpoHaloF-1
❑ 82BHCRSpoL-10
❑ 82DavHaloFB-23
❑ 82DiaCla-66
❑ 82TCMGreH-31
❑ 83DonHOFH-5
❑ 83Oco& SSBG-18
❑ 84GalHaloFRL-5
❑ 84OCoandSI-110
❑ 84OCoandSI-163
❑ 84OCoandSI-179
❑ 84SpoDesPW-42
❑ 85UltBasC-2
❑ 86ConSer1-55
❑ 86PirGreT-3
❑ 86TCMSupS-38
❑ 87NesDreT-4
❑ 88FriBasCM-1
❑ 88GreBasS-54
❑ 89HOFStiB-14
❑ 89PacLegI-211
❑ 89SweBasG-4
❑ 90BasWit-84
❑ 90PerGreM-24
❑ 90SweBasG-50
❑ 91CadEllD-59
❑ 91ConTSN-8
❑ 91SweBasG-126
❑ 91USGamSBL-10C
❑ 91USGamSBL-10D
❑ 91USGamSBL-10H
❑ 91USGamSBL-10S
❑ 92RevLeg1-4
❑ 92RevLeg1-5
❑ 92RevLeg1-6
❑ 92Sco-880
❑ 92St.VinHHS-11
❑ 92WhiLegtL-4
❑ 92WhiPro-4
❑ 93ActPacA-86
❑ 93ActPacA2-20G
❑ 93CadDis-61
❑ 93ConMasB-4
❑ 93ConTSN-754
❑ 93CraJac-3
❑ 93Hoy-8
❑ 93LegFoi-12
❑ 93LegFoiP-2
❑ 93SpeHOF2-3
❑ 93UppDecAH-124
❑ 93UppDecAH-139
❑ 93UppDecAH-145
❑ 94ConTSN-1219
❑ 94ConTSNB-1219
❑ 94TedWil-81
❑ 94TedWilLC-LC17
❑ 94UppDecAH-55
❑ 94UppDecAH-163
❑ 94UppDecAH1-55
❑ 94UppDecAH1-163
❑ 94UppDecTAE-20
❑ 96BalHOF1C-5
❑ 96ColCho-504
❑ 96ColChoGS-504
❑ 96ColChoSS-504
❑ 99UppDecCL-13
❑ 99UppDecCLCC-13
Wagner, Jeff
❑ 83AndBraT-33
❑ 84DurBulT-7
❑ 85DurBulT-31
Wagner, Joe
❑ 12Zee-132
❑ 13Zee-127
❑ 94BelBreC-25
❑ 94BelBreFI-101
❑ 96StoPorB-18
❑ 97El PasDB-22
Wagner, Ken
❑ 96WatIndTI-32
❑ 98ColRedSM-11
Wagner, Kyle
❑ 95BoiHawTI-33
Wagner, Leon
❑ 47Exh-231
❑ 59Top-257
❑ 60Top-383
❑ 61Top-547
❑ 61TopDicG-17
❑ 62AngJayP-11
❑ 62Jel-77
❑ 62Pos-77
❑ 62PosCan-77
❑ 62SalPlaC-57A
❑ 62SalPlaC-57B
❑ 62ShiPlaC-57
❑ 62Top-491
❑ 62TopBuc-90
❑ 62TopStal-71
❑ 63AngJayP-19
❑ 63ExhStaB-62
❑ 63Fle-21
❑ 63Jel-28
❑ 63Pos-28A
❑ 63Pos-28B
❑ 63SalMetC-55
❑ 63Top-4
❑ 63Top-335
❑ 64Kah-30
❑ 64Top-41
❑ 64Top-530
❑ 64TopCoi-6
❑ 64TopCoi-130
❑ 64TopGia-54
❑ 64TopVen-41
❑ 64WheSta-47
❑ 65Kah-45
❑ 65OldLonC-36
❑ 65Top-367
❑ 65TopEmbl-31
❑ 65TopTral-33
❑ 66Baz-8
❑ 66IndTeal-12
❑ 66IndVolC-11
❑ 66OPC-65
❑ 66Top-65
❑ 66TopVen-65
❑ 67AshOil-11
❑ 67Baz-8
❑ 67CokCapA-33
❑ 67CokCapAAm-33
❑ 67CokCapI-12
❑ 67DexPre-216
❑ 67Kah-39
❑ 67OPC-109
❑ 67OPCPapI-24
❑ 67Top-109
❑ 67Top-360
❑ 67TopPos-24
❑ 67TopVen-207
❑ 68Kah-B36
❑ 68Top-495
❑ 69OPC-187
❑ 69Top-187
❑ 69TopFou-23
❑ 78TCM60I-125A
❑ 78TCM60I-165B
❑ 86AngGreT-5
❑ 94CarLeaA-DJ17
Wagner, Mark
❑ 75CliPilT-18
❑ 77Top-490
❑ 79Top-598
❑ 80OPC-13
❑ 80Top-29
❑ 81Don-126
❑ 81Fle-478
❑ 81Top-358
❑ 81TopTra-852
❑ 82Don-163
❑ 82Fle-333
❑ 82Top-443
❑ 83Don-268
❑ 83Fle-582
❑ 83Top-144
❑ 84TacTigC-89
❑ 85Top-581
❑ 85TopTif-581
❑ 89PacSenL-170
❑ 91LinDriAAA-600
❑ 91PacSenL-112
❑ 91TolMudHLD-600
❑ 91TolMudHP-1948
❑ 92BriTigC-27
❑ 93FayGenC-25
❑ 93FayGenF-144
❑ 93RanKee-367
❑ 94LakTigC-27
❑ 96ChaLooB-3
❑ 97ChaLoo-3
❑ 98ChaLooG-28
Wagner, Matt
❑ 94SigRooDP-64
❑ 94SigRooDPS-64
❑ 95Bes-41
❑ 95Bow-70
❑ 95PorCitRTI-26
❑ 96Bow-370
❑ 96BowBes-116
❑ 96BowBesAR-116
❑ 96BowBesR-116
❑ 96BowFoi-370
❑ 96TacRaiB-27
❑ 97Bow-83
❑ 97BowInt-83
❑ 97ColCho-384
❑ 97Fle-215
❑ 97Fle-528
❑ 97FleTif-215
❑ 97FleTif-528
❑ 97Ult-127
❑ 97UltGolME-127
❑ 97UltPlaME-127
❑ 98MadBlaW-19
Wagner, Paul
❑ 89WelPirP-26
❑ 90AugPirP-2464
❑ 91CarLeaAP-CAR38
❑ 91SalBucC-21
❑ 91SalBucP-951
❑ 92CarMudF-1181
❑ 92CarMudS-146
❑ 92DonRoo-120
❑ 92SkyAA F-68
❑ 93Bow-458
❑ 93Don-334
❑ 93FleFinE-121
❑ 93FleMajLP-B10
❑ 93Lea-466
❑ 93Pin-282
❑ 93PirNatl-35
❑ 93Sco-315
❑ 93SelRoo-148T
❑ 93StaClu-710
❑ 93StaCluFDI-710
❑ 93StaCluMOP-710
❑ 93TopTra-109T
❑ 93Ult-457
❑ 93UppDec-643
❑ 93UppDecGold-643
❑ 94ColC-433
❑ 94ColChoGS-433
❑ 94ColChoSS-433
❑ 94Don-611
❑ 94Fin-309
❑ 94FinRef-309
❑ 94Fle-623
❑ 94FleExtB-353
❑ 94Lea-220
❑ 94Pac-510
❑ 94PirQui-26
❑ 94Sco-578
❑ 94ScoGolR-578
❑ 94StaClu-505
❑ 94StaCluFDI-505
❑ 94StaCluGR-505
❑ 94StaCluMOP-505
❑ 94Top-157
❑ 94TopGol-157
❑ 94TopSpa-157
❑ 94Ult-261
❑ 94UppDec-383
❑ 94UppDecED-383
❑ 95ColCho-382
❑ 95ColChoGS-382
❑ 95ColChoSS-382
❑ 95Don-421
❑ 95DonPreP-421
❑ 95Fla-190
❑ 95Fle-491
❑ 95Lea-354
❑ 95PirFil-28
❑ 95Top-317
❑ 95Ult-428
❑ 95UltGolM-428
❑ 96ColCho-676
❑ 96ColChoGS-676
❑ 96ColChoSS-676
❑ 96Don-421
❑ 96DonPreP-421
❑ 96Fle-534
❑ 96FleTif-534
❑ 96LeaSigA-235
❑ 96LeaSigAG-236
❑ 96LeaSigAS-236
❑ 96Pac-171
❑ 96Ult-538
❑ 96UltGolM-538
❑ 96UppDec-438
❑ 97Cir-336
❑ 97CirRav-336
❑ 97UppDec-464
❑ 98PacOnl-413
❑ 98PacOnlR-413
❑ 98PacOnlWC-413
Wagner, Steve
❑ 77OrlTwiT-22
❑ 78OrlTwiT-22
Wahl, Kermit
❑ 50A'sTeal-27
❑ 51A'sTeal-33
❑ 79DiaGre-265
Wahl, Tim
❑ 88BelBreGS-17
❑ 89BelBreIS-24
Waid, Patrick
❑ 87AriWilP-17
❑ 88SalLakCTTI-1
❑ 89SalLakTTI-1
Wainhouse, David
❑ 89BowTif-358
❑ 89WesPalBES-24
❑ 90WesPalBES-25
❑ 91HarSenLD-272
❑ 91HarSenP-627
❑ 91LinDriAA-272
❑ 92ExpDonD-17B
❑ 92IndIndF-1860
❑ 92IndIndS-197
❑ 92ProFS7-260
❑ 92SkyAAAF-95
❑ 92TopDeb91-177
❑ 93ExcFS7-64
❑ 93FleFinE-276
❑ 93MariStaClu-3

❑ 93Ult-626
❑ 96CarMudB-11
❑ 96DouAllB-37
❑ 97PirPos-39
❑ 98ColSprSS-25
Waite, Jon
❑ 92HunCubC-21
❑ 92HunCubF-3149
Waite, Steve
❑ 92FayGenC-12
Waites, David
❑ 98ModA'sG-28
Waites, Steve
❑ 95ButCopKtl-27
Waitkus, Ed
❑ 47Exh-232A
❑ 47Exh-232B
❑ 47Exh-232C
❑ 47PM1StaP1-213
❑ 47TipTop-118
❑ 49Bow-142
❑ 49EurSta-151
❑ 49PhiBul-57
❑ 49PhiLumPB-12
❑ 50Bow-30
❑ 50Dra-12
❑ 50PhiPhil-23
❑ 51BerRos-C9
❑ 51Bow-28
❑ 51TopBluB-51
❑ 52Bow-92
❑ 52TipTop-45
❑ 52Top-158
❑ 54OriEss-34
❑ 54OriTeal-20
❑ 55Bow-4
❑ 55OriEss-25
❑ 74CapPub-35
❑ 75Phi195T-30
❑ 79TCM50-77
❑ 80Phi195T-30
❑ 83PhiPosGPaM-7
❑ 83TopRep5-158
❑ 85TCMPla1-7
❑ 87Phi195T-4
❑ 91OriCro-470
❑ 97BalOriP-53
Waits, M. Rick
❑ 70RelPam-16
❑ 74SpolndC-32
❑ 75OklCit8TI-10
❑ 75SpolndC-16
❑ 76OPC-433
❑ 76SSP-513
❑ 76Top-433
❑ 77BurCheD-61
❑ 77Hos-88
❑ 77IndTeal-25
❑ 77PepGloD-16
❑ 77Top-306
❑ 78IndTeal-30
❑ 78OPC-191
❑ 78Top-37
❑ 79Hos-35
❑ 79OPC-253
❑ 79Top-484
❑ 80IndTeal-31
❑ 80OPC-94
❑ 80Top-168
❑ 81Don-201
❑ 81Fle-396
❑ 81OPC-258
❑ 81Top-697
❑ 82Don-33
❑ 82Fle-382
❑ 82Ind-35
❑ 82IndWhe-10
❑ 82OPC-142
❑ 82Top-573
❑ 83Don-263
❑ 83Fle-422
❑ 83IndPos-39
❑ 83IndWhe-32
❑ 83Top-779
❑ 83TopTra-123T
❑ 84Nes792-218
❑ 84Top-218
❑ 84TopTif-218
❑ 85Don-368
❑ 85Fle-600
❑ 85Top-59
❑ 85TopTif-59
❑ 85VanCanC-219
❑ 86Fle-505
❑ 86Top-614
❑ 86TopTif-614
❑ 86VanCanP-27
❑ 89PacSenL-91
❑ 89T/MSenL-109
❑ 89TopSenL-60
❑ 91PacSenL-15
❑ 92MCIAmb-10
❑ 93RanKee-368
❑ 94BreMilB-86
❑ 97St.LucM-27
❑ 98BinMetQ-3
Wakamatsu, Don
❑ 86TamTarP-24
❑ 87CedRapRP-16
❑ 88ChaLooB-12
❑ 89BirBarB-16
❑ 89BirBarP-107
❑ 90CMC-649
❑ 90ProAAAF-169
❑ 90VanCanC-22
❑ 90VanCanP-491
❑ 91LinDriAAA-648
❑ 91VanCanLD-648
❑ 91VanCanP-1598
❑ 92AlbDukF-724
❑ 92AlbDukS-22
❑ 92Sco-814
❑ 92TopDeb91-178
❑ 93AlbDukF-1465
❑ 98HigDesMG-28
Wakamatsu, Tsutomu
❑ 79TCMJapPB-20
Wakana, Josh
❑ 83TidTidT-25
Wakatabe, Kenichi
❑ 96MauStiHWB-26
Wakefield, Bill
❑ 64Top-576
❑ 65OPC-167
❑ 65Top-167
❑ 66Top-443
❑ 91MetWIZ-423
Wakefield, Dick
❑ 46SpoExcW-8-1B
❑ 47Exh-233
❑ 47TipTop-45
❑ 48KelPep*-BB5
❑ 49Bow-91
❑ 49Lea-50
❑ 50RemBre-25
❑ 77TCMTheWY-66
❑ 79DiaGre-391
❑ 79TCM50-90
❑ 83TCMPla1943-14
Wakefield, Doug
❑ 98ButCopKG-32
Wakefield, Tim
❑ 88WatPirP-27
❑ 89WelPirP-27
❑ 90SalBucS-23
❑ 91CarMudLD-119
❑ 91CarMudP-1087
❑ 91LinDriAA-119
❑ 92BufBisBS-24
❑ 92BufBisF-324
❑ 92BufBisS-45
❑ 92DonRoo-121
❑ 92FleUpd-117
❑ 92ProFS7-308
❑ 92ScoRoo-92T
❑ 92SkyAAAF-20
❑ 93Bow-570
❑ 93ClaGam-96
❑ 93Don-61
❑ 93Fin-37
❑ 93FinRef-37
❑ 93Fla-118
❑ 93Fle-123
❑ 93FleRooS-RSB9
❑ 93FunPac-152
❑ 93HumDumC-45
❑ 93LeaFas-2
❑ 93LeaGolR-R8
❑ 93LeaGolRJ-R8
❑ 93OPC-227
❑ 93PacSpa-254
❑ 93PanSti-279
❑ 93Pin-401
❑ 93PinTea2-6
❑ 93PirNatl-36
❑ 93Sco-347
❑ 93Sel-307
❑ 93SelChaR-16
❑ 93StaClu-13
❑ 93StaCluFDI-13
❑ 93StaCluM-51
❑ 93StaCluMOP-13
❑ 93StaCluMP-12
❑ 93Stu-83
❑ 93Top-163
❑ 93TopGol-163
❑ 93TopInaM-163
❑ 93TopInaR-163
❑ 93TopMic-163
❑ 93Toy-24
❑ 93TriPla-50
❑ 93Ult-104
❑ 93UppDec-66
❑ 93UppDec-480
❑ 93UppDecGold-66
❑ 93UppDecGold-480
❑ 93USPlaCR-13D
❑ 94BufBisF-1838
❑ 94Don-471
❑ 94Fle-624
❑ 94Lea-155
❑ 94Pac-511
❑ 94Pin-448
❑ 94PinArtP-448
❑ 94PinMusC-448
❑ 94Sco-418
❑ 94ScoGolR-418
❑ 94StaClu-152
❑ 94StaCluFDI-152
❑ 94StaCluGR-152
❑ 94StaCluMOP-152
❑ 94Top-669
❑ 94TopGol-669
❑ 94TopSpa-669
❑ 94Ult-262
❑ 95Fin-298
❑ 95FinRef-298
❑ 95PawRedSDD-27
❑ 95PawRedTI-NNO
❑ 95SPCha-126
❑ 95SPChaDC-126
❑ 95TopTra-95T
❑ 95UppDec-480
❑ 96Baz-27
❑ 96Cir-15
❑ 96CirRav-15
❑ 96ColCho-474
❑ 96ColChoGS-474
❑ 96ColChoSS-474
❑ 96Don-487
❑ 96DonPreP-487
❑ 96DonSho-7
❑ 96Fin-B101
❑ 96FinRef-B101
❑ 96Fla-30
❑ 96Fle-39
❑ 96FleRedS-18
❑ 96FleTif-39
❑ 96Lea-111
❑ 96LeaPrePB-111
❑ 96LeaPrePG-111
❑ 96LeaPrePS-111
❑ 96MetUni-22
❑ 96MetUniP-22
❑ 96Pac-253
❑ 96PacPri-P82
❑ 96PacPriG-P82
❑ 96PanSti-140
❑ 96Sco-25
❑ 96ScoDugC-A24
❑ 96ScoDugCAP-A24
❑ 96StaClu-249
❑ 96StaCluMOP-249
❑ 96Top-138
❑ 96TopGal-43
❑ 96TopGalPPI-43
❑ 96Ult-23
❑ 96UltGolM-23
❑ 96UltSeaC-10
❑ 96UltSeaCGM-10
❑ 96UppDec-19
❑ 96UppDec-148
❑ 97Cir-286
❑ 97CirRav-286
❑ 97ColCho-284
❑ 97Don-219
❑ 97DonGolPP-219
❑ 97DonSilPP-219
❑ 97DonTea-52
❑ 97DonTeaSPE-52
❑ 97Fle-33
❑ 97FleTif-33
❑ 97Sco-461
❑ 97ScoArtPWB-461
❑ 97ScoResC-461
❑ 97ScoShoS-461
❑ 97ScoShoSAP-461
❑ 97StaClu-264
❑ 97StaCluMOP-264
❑ 97Top-66
❑ 97Ult-441
❑ 97UltGolME-441
❑ 97UltPlaME-441
❑ 98CroRoy-28
❑ 98Pac-50
❑ 98PacOnl-131
❑ 98PacOnlR-131
❑ 98PacOnlWC-131
❑ 98PacPlaB-50
❑ 98PacRedT-50
❑ 98PacSil-50
❑ 98RedSoxS-3
❑ 98RedSoxSP-3
❑ 98Sco-36
❑ 98StaCluFDI-321
❑ 98StaClul-321
❑ 98StaCluOneK-321
❑ 98StaCluPP-321
❑ 98Top-242
❑ 98TopChr-242
❑ 98TopChrR-242
❑ 98TopDevR-242
❑ 98TopDia-242
❑ 98TopMiniC-242
❑ 98UppDec-314
❑ 99Fle-297
❑ 99FleSta9-297
❑ 99FleWarT-297
❑ 99MetUni-158
❑ 99MetUniGM-158
❑ 99MetUniPMG-158
❑ 99Pac-78
❑ 99PacCroC-52
❑ 99PacCroCPB-52
❑ 99PacPlaB-78
❑ 99PacPri-26
❑ 99PacPriHB-26
❑ 99PacPriHG-26
❑ 99PacPriHM-26
❑ 99PacPriHP-26
❑ 99PacPriRed-26
❑ 99PacPriS-144
❑ 99PacPriS206-144
❑ 99PacPriS206R-144
❑ 99PacRed-78
❑ 99StaClu-231
❑ 99StaCluFDI-231
❑ 99StaCluOoaK-231
❑ 99StaCluPP-231
❑ 99Top-333
❑ 99TopChr-333
❑ 99TopChrR-333
❑ 99TopMVPP-333
❑ 99UppDec-325
❑ 99UppDecEL1-325
❑ 99UppDecEL2-325
❑ 99Vic-70
Wakeland, Chris
❑ 97MidLeaTP-27
❑ 97WesMicW-27
❑ 98LakTigM-24
Walania, Alan
❑ 93ElmPioC-25
❑ 93ElmPioF-3824
❑ 94KanCouCC-25
❑ 94KanCouCF-162
❑ 94KanCouCTI-29
Walbeck, Greg
❑ 93PacSpa-385
Walbeck, Matt
❑ 87WytCubP-2
❑ 88ChaWheB-1
❑ 89PeoChiTI-15
❑ 90HunCubP-3285
❑ 90PeoChiUTI-U4
❑ 91CarLeaAP-CAR45
❑ 91WinSpiC-15
❑ 91WinSpiP-2832
❑ 92ChaKniF-2775
❑ 92ChaKniS-170
❑ 93Bow-384
❑ 93CubStaC-28
❑ 93ExcFS7-15
❑ 93FleFinE-11
❑ 93Pin-607
❑ 93Top-812
❑ 93TopGol-812
❑ 93TopInaM-812
❑ 93TopInaR-812
❑ 93TopMic-812
❑ 93Ult-323
❑ 93UppDec-509
❑ 93UppDecGold-509
❑ 94Bow-20
❑ 94ColC-670
❑ 94ColChoGS-670
❑ 94ColChoSS-670
❑ 94Fin-436
❑ 94FinJum-436
❑ 94FinRef-436
❑ 94Fla-78
❑ 94FleExtB-125
❑ 94FleUpd-66
❑ 94LeaGolR-14
❑ 94LeaLimR-39
❑ 94OPC-227
❑ 94Pin-487
❑ 94PinArtP-487
❑ 94PinMusC-487
❑ 94ScoRoo-RT154
❑ 94ScoRooGR-RT154
❑ 94SpoRoo-68
❑ 94SpoRooAP-68
❑ 94StaClu-561
❑ 94StaCluFDI-561
❑ 94StaCluGR-561
❑ 94StaCluMOP-561
❑ 94Stu-201
❑ 94Top-329
❑ 94TopGol-329
❑ 94TopSpa-329
❑ 94TopTra-69T
❑ 94Ult-396
❑ 94UppDec-130
❑ 94UppDecED-130
❑ 95ColCho-481
❑ 95ColChoGS-481
❑ 95ColChoSS-481
❑ 95Don-320
❑ 95DonPreP-320
❑ 95DonTopotO-116
❑ 95Fin-19
❑ 95FinRef-19
❑ 95Fle-216
❑ 95Lea-219
❑ 95Pac-258
❑ 95Pin-403
❑ 95PinArtP-403
❑ 95PinMusC-403
❑ 95Sco-265
❑ 95ScoGolR-265
❑ 95ScoPlaTS-265
❑ 95StaClu-76
❑ 95StaCluFDI-76
❑ 95StaCluMOP-76
❑ 95StaCluSTWS-76
❑ 95Top-471
❑ 95TopCyb-265
❑ 95Ult-79
❑ 95UltGolM-79
❑ 96ColCho-603
❑ 96ColChoGS-603
❑ 96ColChoSS-603
❑ 96Don-106
❑ 96DonPreP-106
❑ 96Fla-124
❑ 96Fle-179
❑ 96FleTif-179
❑ 96LeaSigA-236
❑ 96LeaSigAG-237
❑ 96LeaSigAS-237
❑ 96MetUni-83
❑ 96MetUniP-83
❑ 96Pac-363
❑ 96PanSti-205
❑ 96StaClu-75
❑ 96StaCluMOP-75
❑ 96Ult-97
❑ 96UltGolM-97
❑ 96UppDec-388
❑ 97Fle-159
❑ 97FleTif-159
❑ 97PacPriGotD-GD68
❑ 97Ult-517
❑ 97UltGolME-517
❑ 97UltPlaME-517
❑ 98PacOnl-24
❑ 98PacOnlR-24
❑ 98PacOnlWC-24
❑ 99Fle-546
❑ 99FleSta9-546
❑ 99FleWarT-546
❑ 99Top-136
❑ 99TopChr-136
❑ 99TopChrR-136
❑ 99TopMVPP-136
Walberg, Bill
❑ 82JacMetT-25
Walberg, Rube (George)
❑ 28W56PlaC-JOK
❑ 29A'sVil-5
❑ 31W517-41
❑ 32OrbPinUP-57
❑ 33Gou-145
❑ 33Gou-183
❑ 33GouCanV-76
❑ 33RitCE-12S
❑ 33TatOrb-57
❑ 36NatChiFPR-76
❑ 72TCMthe3-71
❑ 74A's192T-26
❑ 81ConTSN-59
❑ 91ConTSN-91
❑ 94ConTSN-1151
❑ 94ConTSNB-1151
Walbring, Larry
❑ 76CliPilT-33
Walden, Alan
❑ 90BurIndP-3009
❑ 91ColIndC-17
❑ 91ColIndP-1484
❑ 92ColRedC-21
❑ 92ColRedF-2391
Walden, Ron
❑ 90ClaDraP-9
❑ 90ClaYel-T82
❑ 90GreFalDSP-1
❑ 91Bow-615
❑ 91OPC-596
❑ 91Sco-679
❑ 91Top-596
❑ 91TopDesS-596
❑ 91TopMic-596
❑ 91TopTif-596
❑ 93VerBeaDC-24
❑ 93VerBeaDF-2219
Walden, Travis
❑ 88ClePhiS-26
Waldenberger, Dave
❑ 89IdaFalBP-2019
❑ 92SanBerC-26
❑ 92SanBerSF-968
❑ 93RivPilCLC-21
Waldow, Joe
❑ 89GasRanP-998
Waldrep, Art
❑ 94BenRocC-23
❑ 94BenRocF-3594
❑ 95AshTouTI-7
Waldron, Brad
❑ 98VerExpO-18
Waldron, Joe
❑ 91ChaRaiC-11
❑ 91ChaRaiP-96
❑ 92WatDiaC-2
❑ 92WatDiaF-2142
❑ 93WatDiaF-1769
❑ 94WesPalBEC-26
❑ 94WesPalBEF-40
❑ 95JacGenTI-9
Waldrop, Tom
❑ 92IdaFalGF-3522
❑ 92IdaFalGSP-8
❑ 93MacBraC-26
❑ 93MacBraF-1416
❑ 94DurBulC-24
❑ 94DurBulF-342
❑ 94DurBulTI-26
❑ 95MacBraTI-29
Wales, Gary
❑ 91ParPatF-11
❑ 93AusFut-32
Walewander, James
❑ 86GleFalTP-23
❑ 87IntLeaAT-17
❑ 87TolMudHP-5
❑ 87TolMudHT-7
❑ 88Sco-571
❑ 88ScoGlo-571
❑ 88TigPep-32
❑ 88Top-106
❑ 88TopTif-106
❑ 89Don-415
❑ 89Fle-150
❑ 89FleGlo-150
❑ 89Sco-311
❑ 89TolMudHC-15
❑ 89TolMudHP-770
❑ 89Top-467
❑ 89TopTif-467
❑ 89UppDec-454
❑ 90CMC-212
❑ 90ColCliC-12
❑ 90ColCliP-21
❑ 90ColCliP-686

❑ 90ProAAAF-336
❑ 90TopTVY-65
❑ 91ColCliLD-122
❑ 91ColCliP-22
❑ 91ColCliP-607
❑ 91LinDriAAA-122
❑ 93VanCanF-2607
❑ 94EdmTraF-2883
Walk, Bob
❑ 81Don-393
❑ 81Fle-14
❑ 81Top-494
❑ 81TopTra-853
❑ 82BraBurKL-24
❑ 82BraPol-43
❑ 82Top-296
❑ 83Don-401
❑ 83Fle-149
❑ 83FleSti-93
❑ 83RicBraT-10
❑ 83Top-104
❑ 84HawIslC-141
❑ 85HawIslC-243
❑ 86Don-430
❑ 86TopTra-120T
❑ 86TopTraT-120T
❑ 87Don-203
❑ 87Fle-623
❑ 87FleGlo-623
❑ 87Top-628
❑ 87TopTif-628
❑ 88Don-514
❑ 88DonBasB-269
❑ 88Fle-342
❑ 88FleGlo-342
❑ 88PirTeal-33
❑ 88Sco-162
❑ 88ScoGlo-162
❑ 88Top-349
❑ 88TopTif-349
❑ 89Bow-409
❑ 89BowTif-409
❑ 89Don-172
❑ 89DonAll-58
❑ 89DonBasB-145
❑ 89Fle-223
❑ 89FleGlo-223
❑ 89OPC-66
❑ 89OPC-151
❑ 89PirVerFJ-17
❑ 89Sco-224
❑ 89Spo-34
❑ 89Top-504
❑ 89TopSti-123
❑ 89TopTif-504
❑ 89UppDec-438
❑ 90Bow-163
❑ 90BowTif-163
❑ 90Don-370
❑ 90DonBesN-94
❑ 90Fle-482
❑ 90FleCan-482
❑ 90Lea-64
❑ 90OPC-754
❑ 90PirHomC-31
❑ 90PubIntS-167
❑ 90Sco-21
❑ 90Top-754
❑ 90TopBig-23
❑ 90TopSti-125
❑ 90TopTif-754
❑ 90UppDec-596
❑ 91Bow-526
❑ 91Don-157
❑ 91Fle-54
❑ 91Lea-450
❑ 91OPC-29
❑ 91Sco-599
❑ 91StaClu-14
❑ 91StaCluP-50
❑ 91Top-29
❑ 91TopDesS-29
❑ 91TopMic-29
❑ 91TopTif-29
❑ 91UppDec-689
❑ 92Bow-666
❑ 92Don-88
❑ 92Fle-572
❑ 92Lea-353
❑ 92LeaBlaG-353
❑ 92OPC-486
❑ 92Pin-410
❑ 92PirNatl-25
❑ 92Sco-54
❑ 92ScoProP-15
❑ 92StaClu-746
❑ 92StaCluNC-746
❑ 92Top-486
❑ 92TopGol-486
❑ 92TopGolW-486
❑ 92TopMic-486
❑ 92UppDec-619
❑ 93Don-546
❑ 93Fle-505
❑ 93Lea-134
❑ 93PacSpa-593
❑ 93PanSti-286
❑ 93Pin-380
❑ 93PirNatl-37
❑ 93Sco-144
❑ 93StaClu-421
❑ 93StaCluFDI-421
❑ 93StaCluM-77
❑ 93StaCluMOP-421
❑ 93Top-685
❑ 93TopGol-685
❑ 93TopInaM-685
❑ 93TopInaR-685
❑ 93TopMic-685
❑ 93Ult-458
❑ 93UppDec-78
❑ 93UppDecGold-78
❑ 94Don-395
❑ 94Fle-625
❑ 94Pac-512
❑ 94Pin-457
❑ 94PinArtP-457
❑ 94PinMusC-457
❑ 94Sco-356
❑ 94ScoGolR-356
❑ 94Top-434
❑ 94TopGol-434
❑ 94TopSpa-434
❑ 95PirCocP-17
❑ 97PirPos-40
Walkanoff, A.J.
❑ 95YakBeaTI-36
❑ 96VerBeaDB-28
Walkden, Mike
❑ 91GreFalDSP-23
❑ 91HigSchPLS-22
❑ 92BakDodCLC-27
❑ 92StaClu-852
❑ 92StaCluD-191
❑ 92StaCluECN-852
❑ 94BakDodC-24
❑ 95VerBeaDTI-29
Walker, Adam
❑ 98PieBolWM-29
❑ 98SouAtlLPM-23
Walker, Al
❑ 80BurBeeT-13
Walker, Andy
❑ 79QuaCitCT-20
❑ 83TopRep5-319
Walker, Bernie
❑ 87CedRapRP-25
❑ 88ChaLooB-23
❑ 89ChaLooB-20
❑ 89ChaLooGS-22
❑ 89SouLeaAJ-7
❑ 91ChaLooLD-173
❑ 91LinDriAA-173
❑ 91NasSouP-2171
Walker, Bert
❑ 85CloHSS-41
Walker, Bill
❑ 33Gou-94
❑ 33GouCanV-57
❑ 34BatR31-116
❑ 34DiaMatCSB-189
❑ 36NatChiFPR-77
❑ 74Car193T-24
❑ 93ConTSN-789
Walker, Billy
❑ 91MiaMirC-4
Walker, Cam (Cameron)
❑ 84ElPasDT-22
❑ 86ElPasDP-23
❑ 87ElPasDP-18
❑ 87WicPilRD-25
Walker, Charles
❑ 19Zee-47
Walker, Chico
❑ 81PawRedST-22
❑ 83PawRedST-24
❑ 84PawRedST-16
❑ 85IowCubT-11
❑ 86IowCubP-26
❑ 87CubCan-37
❑ 87CubDavB-29
❑ 87Don-539
❑ 87OPC-58
❑ 87Top-695
❑ 87TopTif-695
❑ 88EdmTraP-561
❑ 89SyrChiC-23
❑ 89SyrChiMB-23
❑ 89SyrChiP-792
❑ 90ChaKniTI-7
❑ 91Cla3-T93
❑ 91CubMar-24
❑ 91CubVinL-32
❑ 91Lea-501
❑ 91UltUpd-74
❑ 92Don-439
❑ 92Fle-395
❑ 92FleUpd-107
❑ 92OPC-439
❑ 92Sco-578
❑ 92StaClu-564
❑ 92Top-439
❑ 92TopGol-439
❑ 92TopGolW-439
❑ 92TopMic-439
❑ 92Ult-183
❑ 92UppDec-617
❑ 93Don-410
❑ 93Fle-482
❑ 93Lea-149
❑ 93MetColP-49
❑ 93MetKah-34
❑ 93PacSpa-549
❑ 93Sco-399
❑ 93StaClu-114
❑ 93StaCluFDI-114
❑ 93StaCluMOP-114
❑ 93Ult-80
❑ 93UppDec-727
❑ 93UppDecGold-727
❑ 94Pac-419
Walker, Chris
❑ 88BatCliP-1677
❑ 89ClePhiS-24
Walker, Cliff (Clifton)
❑ 85BenPhiC-23
❑ 87SpaPhiP-16
Walker, Corey
❑ 96DanBraB-27
Walker, Curtis
❑ 21E121So1-110
❑ 21Exh-182
❑ 22E120-208
❑ 22W572-111
❑ 22W575-145
❑ 27AmeCarE126-58
❑ 92ConTSN-417
Walker, Dane
❑ 92MadMusC-4
❑ 92MadMusF-1251
❑ 93ModA'sC-22
❑ 93ModA'sF-812
❑ 95HunStaTI-28
❑ 96WesMicWB-28
❑ 97HunStaTI-27
Walker, Darcy
❑ 86WinSpiP-27
Walker, Dave
❑ 94BluOriC-26
❑ 96HigDesMB-3
❑ 97FreKey-3
❑ 98FreKeyM-6
Walker, Dennis
❑ 89UtiBluSP-26
❑ 90SouBenWSB-12
❑ 90SouBenWSGS-20
❑ 91SouBenWSC-6
❑ 91SouBenWSP-2866
❑ 92SarWhiSCB-13
❑ 92SarWhiSF-216
❑ 93BirBarF-1201
Walker, Dixie (Ewart)
❑ 10SenWasT-7
❑ 11PinT-5-552
Walker, Dixie (Fred)
❑ 34DiaStaR-12A
❑ 34DiaStaR-12B
❑ 34DiaStaR-12C
❑ 34Gou-39
❑ 34GouCanV-86
❑ 35GouPuzR-8E
❑ 35GouPuzR-9E
❑ 36R31PasP-38
❑ 39ExhSal-61A
❑ 39ExhSal-61B
❑ 40DodTeal-23
❑ 41DouPlaR-21
❑ 42DodTeal-23
❑ 43DodTeal-22
❑ 46DodTeal-23
❑ 46SpoExcW-8-1A
❑ 47DodTeal-25
❑ 47PM1StaP1-214
❑ 48BluTin-45
❑ 49EurSta-174
❑ 53Top-190
❑ 55CarHunW-29
❑ 61Fle-151
❑ 70SpoCarfCOP-27
❑ 72TCMthe3-88
❑ 73Dod194T-29
❑ 75DodTCMA-11
❑ 75YanDyn1T-48
❑ 76TayBow4-52
❑ 78DodTCM4-35
❑ 79DiaGre-82
❑ 80DodGreT-7
❑ 83TCMPla1945-30
❑ 88WilMulP-8
❑ 89DodSmoG-49
❑ 90DodTar-825
❑ 91DodRinP4-11
❑ 91TopArc1-190
❑ 92BazQua5A-22
❑ 92ConTSN-506
❑ 95ConTSN-1387
Walker, Doak
❑ 52Whe-28A
❑ 52Whe-28B
Walker, Duane
❑ 79NaSouTI-25
❑ 80IndIndTI-26
❑ 81IndIndTI-21
❑ 82IndIndTI-6
❑ 83Don-624
❑ 83Fle-606
❑ 83Top-243
❑ 84Don-325
❑ 84Fle-485
❑ 84FleSti-41
❑ 84Nes792-659
❑ 84RedEnq-10
❑ 84Top-659
❑ 84TopTif-659
❑ 85Don-608
❑ 85Fle-554
❑ 85Lea-52
❑ 85RedYea-18
❑ 85Top-441
❑ 85TopSti-52
❑ 85TopTif-441
❑ 86Don-500
❑ 86Fle-574
❑ 86Top-22
❑ 86TopTif-22
❑ 86TucTorP-23
❑ 87LouRedTI-28
❑ 88BriTigP-1878
❑ 88CarTeal-35
❑ 88LouRedBC-17
❑ 88LouRedBP-425
❑ 88LouRedBTI-49
❑ 89MiaMirIS-24
❑ 93RanKee-369
Walker, Edsall
❑ 92NegLeaK-11
❑ 92NegLeaRLI-62
❑ 95NegLeaL2-8
Walker, Fleetwood (Moses F.)
❑ 63GadFunC-46
❑ 85UltBasC-7
❑ 86NegLeaF-28
❑ 87NegLeaPD-22
❑ 94OriofB-50
❑ 94TedWil-114
❑ 94UppDecTAE-8
Walker, Frank
❑ 22W575-144
Walker, Gee (Gerald)
❑ 33ButCanV-51
❑ 33DouDisP-41
❑ 33WorCig-92
❑ 34BatR31-118
❑ 34DiaMatCSB-188
❑ 34Gou-26
❑ 34GouCanV-81
❑ 34TigTeal-19
❑ 35AlDemDCR3-21
❑ 35GouPreR-10
❑ 35GouPuzR-8F
❑ 35GouPuzR-9F
❑ 36GouWidPPR-A106
❑ 36NatChiFPR-78
❑ 36WorWidGV-48
❑ 37OPCBatUV-110
❑ 38CloFotW-85
❑ 38WheBB10-4
❑ 41DouPlaR-135
❑ 74TigTCM1AC-31
❑ 76TigOldTS-22
❑ 77TCMTheWY-82
❑ 78TigDeaCS-4
❑ 81ConTSN-99
❑ 81TigDetN-109
❑ 81TigSecNP-23
❑ 83TCMPla1944-31
❑ 91ConTSN-87
❑ 93DiaStaES-152
❑ 95ConTSN-1390
Walker, Glenn
❑ 81WauTimT-24
❑ 82LynSaiT-16
❑ 83SalLakCGT-20
❑ 84SalLakCGC-187
❑ 86MidAngP-25
Walker, Greg
❑ 80AppFoxT-20
❑ 81GleFalWST-16
❑ 83TopTra-124T
❑ 84Don-609
❑ 84Fle-73
❑ 84Nes792-518
❑ 84Top-518
❑ 84TopTif-518
❑ 84WhiSoxTV-30
❑ 85Don-366
❑ 85Fle-530
❑ 85OPC-244
❑ 85SubDis-21
❑ 85ThoMcAD-21
❑ 85Top-623
❑ 85TopSti-236
❑ 85TopTif-623
❑ 85WhiSoxC-29
❑ 86Don-135
❑ 86Fle-219
❑ 86MSAJayPCD-19
❑ 86OPC-123
❑ 86SevCoi-C16
❑ 86Spo-174
❑ 86Top-123
❑ 86TopSti-293
❑ 86TopTif-123
❑ 86WhiSoxC-29
❑ 87Don-25A
❑ 87Don-25B
❑ 87Don-59
❑ 87DonOpeD-233
❑ 87DonSupD-25
❑ 87Fle-508
❑ 87FleGlo-508
❑ 87FleLeaL-42
❑ 87FleMin-110
❑ 87Lea-25
❑ 87OPC-302
❑ 87SevCoi-C15
❑ 87SpoTeaP-26
❑ 87Top-397
❑ 87TopSti-291
❑ 87TopTif-397
❑ 87WhiSoxC-29
❑ 88Don-162
❑ 88DonBasB-193
❑ 88Fle-411
❑ 88FleGlo-411
❑ 88Lea-86
❑ 88OPC-286
❑ 88PanSti-56
❑ 88Sco-93A
❑ 88Sco-93B
❑ 88ScoGlo-93A
❑ 88ScoGlo-93B
❑ 88Spo-103
❑ 88StaLinWS-19
❑ 88Top-764
❑ 88TopBig-105
❑ 88TopSti-292
❑ 88TopTif-764
❑ 88TopUKM-83
❑ 88TopUKMT-83
❑ 88WhiSoxC-29
❑ 89Don-135
❑ 89PanSti-307
❑ 89Sco-37
❑ 89Spo-19
❑ 89Top-21
❑ 89Top-408
❑ 89TopBig-4
❑ 89TopTif-21
❑ 89TopTif-408
❑ 89UppDec-231
❑ 89WhiSoxC-27
❑ 89WhiSoxK-1
❑ 90CMC-318
❑ 90Fle-551
❑ 90FleCan-551
❑ 90M.Vpin-26
❑ 90OPC-33
❑ 90PanSti-45
❑ 90ProAAAF-469
❑ 90PubIntS-402
❑ 90RocRedWC-18
❑ 90RocRedWP-712
❑ 90Sco-354
❑ 90Top-33
❑ 90TopTif-33
❑ 90UppDec-350
❑ 91OriCro-471
Walker, Harry
❑ 46SeaSLP-64
❑ 46SpoExcW-9-6
❑ 47Exh-234
❑ 48BluTin-39
❑ 49Bow-130
❑ 49EurSta-75
❑ 49Lea-137
❑ 50Bow-180
❑ 60Top-468
❑ 65Top-438
❑ 66PirEasH-3
❑ 66Top-318
❑ 66TopVen-318
❑ 67PirTeal-23
❑ 67Top-448
❑ 67TopPirS-24
❑ 69Top-633
❑ 70AstPho-24
❑ 70OPC-32
❑ 70Top-32
❑ 71AstTeal-21
❑ 71OPC-312
❑ 71Top-312
❑ 72AstTeal-26
❑ 72OPC-249
❑ 72Top-249
❑ 79TCM50-261
❑ 82GSGalAG-3
❑ 83Car194T-12
❑ 85TCMPla1-12
❑ 87AstShoSO-28
❑ 87AstShoSTw-24
❑ 89PacLegI-190
❑ 89SweBasG-34
❑ 90SweBasG-33
❑ 91SweBasG-94
❑ 94UppDecAH-43
❑ 94UppDecAH1-43
❑ 95ConTSN-1347
❑ 99SpoIllGotG-79
❑ 99SpoIllGotGA-74
❑ 99SpoIllGotGC-13
Walker, Harvey
❑ 74TigTCM1AC-32
Walker, Hugh
❑ 89AppFoxP-856
❑ 89Bow-127
❑ 89BowTif-127
❑ 90BasCitRS-24
❑ 91Bow-313
❑ 91Cla/Bes-58
❑ 91LinDriAA-422
❑ 91LinDriP-422
❑ 91MemChiLD-422
❑ 91MemChiP-667
❑ 92BasCitRF-3859
❑ 92ClaFS7-184
❑ 92MemChiS-447
❑ 92SkyAA F-189
❑ 93ClaGolF-84
❑ 93WilBluRC-26
❑ 93WilBluRF-2012
❑ 94MemChiF-372
Walker, J. Luke
❑ 66Top-498
❑ 67OPC-123
❑ 67Top-123
❑ 68Top-559
❑ 69OPC-36
❑ 69PirTeal-26
❑ 69Top-36
❑ 70DayDaiNM-137
❑ 70OPC-322
❑ 70PirTeal-20
❑ 70Top-322

❑ 71MilDud-68
❑ 71MLBOffS-216
❑ 71OPC-68
❑ 71OPC-534
❑ 71Pir-6
❑ 71PirActP-12
❑ 71PirArc-12
❑ 71Top-68
❑ 71Top-534
❑ 71TopSup-21
❑ 72MilBra-353
❑ 72OPC-471
❑ 72Top-471
❑ 73OPC-187
❑ 73Top-187
❑ 74OPC-612
❑ 74Top-612
❑ 74TopTra-612T
❑ 75OPC-474
❑ 75Top-474
❑ 75TopMin-474

Walker, James
❑ 87ChaLooB-5

Walker, Jamie
❑ 92AubAstC-17
❑ 92AubAstF-1354
❑ 93QuaCitRBC-23
❑ 93QuaCitRBF-101
❑ 94QuaCitRBC-22
❑ 94QuaCitRBF-533
❑ 95JacGenTI-10
❑ 96JacGenB-26
❑ 98OmaRoyM-24

Walker, Jason
❑ 94WatIndC-27
❑ 94WatIndF-3938

Walker, Jerry
❑ 89BelMarL-35
❑ 98SalVol-33

Walker, Jerry Allen
❑ 58BalOriP-17
❑ 58Top-113
❑ 59OklTodML-3
❑ 59OriJayP-10
❑ 59Top-144
❑ 59TopVen-144
❑ 60BalOriP-11
❑ 60OriJayP-10
❑ 60Top-399
❑ 60Top-540
❑ 60TopTat-52
❑ 60TopTat-96
❑ 61AthJayP-24
❑ 61BalOriP-21
❑ 61Top-85
❑ 62Top-357
❑ 62TopBuc-91
❑ 62TopStal-61
❑ 63AthJayP-12
❑ 63Top-413
❑ 64Top-77
❑ 64TopVen-77
❑ 66TolMudHTI-25
❑ 83AstPos-34
❑ 84AstMot-27
❑ 84AstPos-31
❑ 85AstMot-27
❑ 91OriCro-472

Walker, Jim
❑ 88CalCanC-7
❑ 88CalCanP-791
❑ 94FreKeyC-23
❑ 94FreKeyF-2616
❑ 94OriPro-102

Walker, Joe
❑ 96PriWilCB-28
❑ 98BriBluM-28

Walker, John
❑ 78LodDodT-24
❑ 79LodDodT-12
❑ 80TolMudHT-9
❑ 81TolMudHT-17

Walker, Johnny
❑ 90PulBraP-3112
❑ 91HigSchPLS-12
❑ 91IdaFalBSP-14
❑ 94UtiBluSF-3830

Walker, Keith
❑ 80KnoBluJT-23
❑ 82KnoBluJT-7
❑ 83SyrChiT-12

Walker, Kevin
❑ 96IdaFalB-27
❑ 97CliLumG-28
❑ 98RanCucQG-29
❑ 98RanCucQG-29

Walker, Kurt
❑ 86BirBarTI-22
❑ 87VisOakP-8
❑ 88MidAngGS-2
❑ 94UppDec-274

Walker, Larry
❑ 85UtiBluST-16
❑ 86BurExpP-25
❑ 87JacExpP-429
❑ 87SouLeaAJ-8
❑ 89IndIndC-23
❑ 89IndIndP-1239
❑ 90Bow-117
❑ 90BowTif-117
❑ 90ClaUpd-T16
❑ 90Don-578
❑ 90DonBesN-91
❑ 90ExpPos-36
❑ 90Fle-363
❑ 90FleCan-363
❑ 90FleSoaS-3
❑ 90Lea-325
❑ 90OPC-757
❑ 90Sco-631
❑ 90ScoYouS2-9
❑ 90Top-757
❑ 90TopBig-296
❑ 90TopDeb89-133
❑ 90TopMag-95
❑ 90TopTif-757
❑ 90TriAAAC-7
❑ 90UppDec-466
❑ 90UppDec-702
❑ 90UppDecS-2
❑ 91Baz-19
❑ 91Bow-442
❑ 91Don-359
❑ 91ExpPos-22
❑ 91Fle-250
❑ 91Lea-241
❑ 91MajLeaCP-80
❑ 91OPC-339
❑ 91PanFreS-145
❑ 91PanSti-65
❑ 91Sco-241
❑ 91Sco100RS-21
❑ 91StaClu-93
❑ 91StaCluP-48
❑ 91Top-339
❑ 91TopDesS-339
❑ 91TopMic-339
❑ 91TopRoo-32
❑ 91TopTif-339
❑ 91ToyRoo-31
❑ 91UltUpd-93
❑ 91UppDec-536
❑ 92Bow-648
❑ 92Cla2-T39
❑ 92Don-259
❑ 92ExpDonD-18
❑ 92ExpPos-29
❑ 92Fle-493
❑ 92ForLauYC-16
❑ 92ForLauYTI-32
❑ 92Ft.LauYF-2616
❑ 92Hig5-60
❑ 92Lea-201
❑ 92LeaBlaG-201
❑ 92OPC-531
❑ 92PanSti-206
❑ 92Pin-194
❑ 92PinTea2-21
❑ 92Sco-199
❑ 92ScoImpP-29
❑ 92SpoIllFK1-669
❑ 92StaClu-256
❑ 92Stu-59
❑ 92Top-531
❑ 92TopGol-531
❑ 92TopGolW-531
❑ 92TopMic-531
❑ 92TriPla-89
❑ 92Ult-525
❑ 92UppDec-249
❑ 93Bow-100
❑ 93ClaGam-97
❑ 93DiaMar-115
❑ 93Don-540
❑ 93DonDiaK-DK6
❑ 93DonEli-30
❑ 93DonEliS-12
❑ 93DonLonBL-LL18
❑ 93DonMVP-9
❑ 93DonPre-6
❑ 93ExpColP7-7
❑ 93ExpDonM-7
❑ 93ExpPosN-22
❑ 93Fin-97
❑ 93FinJum-97
❑ 93FinRef-97
❑ 93Fla-87
❑ 93Fle-81
❑ 93Fle-715
❑ 93FleAll-NL6
❑ 93FleFruotL-64
❑ 93FunPac-98
❑ 93Hos-30
❑ 93HumDumC-42
❑ 93Lea-392
❑ 93MilBonSS-15
❑ 93NesQuiB-1
❑ 93OPC-384
❑ 93OPCPre-39
❑ 93PacSpa-190
❑ 93PanSti-231
❑ 93Pin-3
❑ 93Pin-299
❑ 93PinHomRC-14
❑ 93PinSlu-13
❑ 93PinTeaP-10
❑ 93PosCan-13
❑ 93RedFolS-130
❑ 93Sco-5
❑ 93ScoFra-20
❑ 93Sel-27
❑ 93SP-107
❑ 93StaClu-299
❑ 93StaClu-320
❑ 93StaCluFDI-299
❑ 93StaCluFDI-320
❑ 93StaCluM-94
❑ 93StaCluMMP-11
❑ 93StaCluMOP-299
❑ 93StaCluMOP-320
❑ 93StaCluMP-24
❑ 93Stu-123
❑ 93Top-95
❑ 93Top-406
❑ 93TOPBLAG-22
❑ 93TopGol-95
❑ 93TopGol-406
❑ 93TopInaM-95
❑ 93TopInaM-406
❑ 93TopInaR-95
❑ 93TopInaR-406
❑ 93TopMic-95
❑ 93TopMic-406
❑ 93TopPreS-9
❑ 93Toy-23
❑ 93TriPla-42
❑ 93TriPlaA-6
❑ 93Ult-71
❑ 93UltAllS-8
❑ 93UltAwaW-9
❑ 93UppDec-144
❑ 93UppDec-481
❑ 93UppDecGold-144
❑ 93UppDecGold-481
❑ 93UppDecHRH-HR16
❑ 93UppDecTriCro-TC10
❑ 94Bow-500
❑ 94BowBes-R76
❑ 94BowBesR-R76
❑ 94ColC-286
❑ 94ColChoGS-286
❑ 94ColChoSS-286
❑ 94DenHol-28
❑ 94Don-371
❑ 94DonSpeE-371
❑ 94Fin-216
❑ 94FinJum-216
❑ 94FinRef-216
❑ 94Fla-404
❑ 94Fle-554
❑ 94FleExtB-312
❑ 94FUnPac-136
❑ 94Lea-397
❑ 94LeaCleC-1
❑ 94LeaL-127
❑ 94O-PJumAF-19
❑ 94OPC-253
❑ 94OPCAllR-19
❑ 94OPCJumA-19
❑ 94Pac-392
❑ 94PanSti-213
❑ 94Pin-310
❑ 94PinArtP-310
❑ 94PinMusC-310
❑ 94PosCan-8
❑ 94ProMag-85
❑ 94RedFolMI-27
❑ 94Sco-376
❑ 94ScoDreT-9
❑ 94ScoGolR-376
❑ 94ScoGolS-27
❑ 94Sel-18
❑ 94SelSki-SK9
❑ 94SP-86
❑ 94SPDieC-86
❑ 94Spo-77
❑ 94StaClu-280
❑ 94StaCluFDI-280
❑ 94StaCluGR-280
❑ 94StaCluMOP-280
❑ 94Stu-80
❑ 94Top-230
❑ 94TopGol-230
❑ 94TopSpa-230
❑ 94TopSupS-44
❑ 94TriPla-99
❑ 94Ult-526
❑ 94UltAwaW-17
❑ 94UppDec-370
❑ 94UppDecAJ-28
❑ 94UppDecAJG-28
❑ 94UppDecED-274
❑ 94UppDecED-370
❑ 95Baz-93
❑ 95Bow-290
❑ 95BowBes-R63
❑ 95BowBesR-R63
❑ 95ClaPhoC-25
❑ 95ColCho-238
❑ 95ColCho-579T
❑ 95ColCho-TC1
❑ 95ColChoGS-238
❑ 95ColChoSE-96
❑ 95ColChoSEGS-96
❑ 95ColChoSESS-96
❑ 95ColChoSS-238
❑ 95Don-492
❑ 95DonPreP-492
❑ 95DonTopotO-234
❑ 95Emo-126
❑ 95Fin-215
❑ 95Fin-274
❑ 95FinRef-215
❑ 95FinRef-274
❑ 95Fla-348
❑ 95Fle-361
❑ 95FleUpd-171
❑ 95Lea-305
❑ 95LeaLim-91
❑ 95LeaLimG-10
❑ 95LeaLimIBP-4
❑ 95LeaOpeD-8
❑ 95Pac-273
❑ 95PacGolP-30
❑ 95PacPri-89
❑ 95PanSti-75
❑ 95Pin-372
❑ 95PinArtP-372
❑ 95PinFan-28
❑ 95PinMusC-372
❑ 95RedFol-25
❑ 95RocPol-10
❑ 95Sco-346
❑ 95ScoGolR-346
❑ 95ScoHaloG-HG71
❑ 95ScoHaloGYTE-HG71T
❑ 95ScoPlaTS-346
❑ 95ScoYouTE-346T
❑ 95Sel-224
❑ 95SelArtP-224
❑ 95SelCer-89
❑ 95SelCerMG-89
❑ 95SelCerS-89
❑ 95SP-50
❑ 95SPCha-39
❑ 95SPCha-42
❑ 95SPChaDC-39
❑ 95SPChaDC-42
❑ 95Spo-139
❑ 95SpoArtP-139
❑ 95SPPlaP-PP7
❑ 95SPSil-50
❑ 95StaClu-148
❑ 95StaClu-618
❑ 95StaCluCT-10
❑ 95StaCluFDI-148
❑ 95StaCluMO-44
❑ 95StaCluMOP-148
❑ 95StaCluMOP-618
❑ 95StaCluMOP-SS15
❑ 95StaCluSS-SS15
❑ 95StaCluSTWS-148
❑ 95StaCluSTWS-618
❑ 95StaCluVR-77
❑ 95StaCluVRMO-77
❑ 95Stu-58
❑ 95Sum-45
❑ 95SumNthD-45
❑ 95Top-422
❑ 95TopCyb-221
❑ 95TopPre-PP1
❑ 95TopPreS-PP1
❑ 95TopTra-20T
❑ 95UC3-90
❑ 95UC3-145
❑ 95UC3ArtP-90
❑ 95UC3ArtP-145
❑ 95Ult-409
❑ 95UltGolM-409
❑ 95UppDec-82
❑ 95UppDec-415
❑ 95UppDecED-82
❑ 95UppDecED-415
❑ 95UppDecEDG-82
❑ 95UppDecEDG-415
❑ 95UppDecPLL-R34
❑ 95UppDecPLL-R47
❑ 95UppDecPLLE-R34
❑ 95UppDecPLLE-R47
❑ 95UppDecSE-4
❑ 95UppDecSE-240
❑ 95UppDecSEG-4
❑ 95UppDecSEG-240
❑ 95Zen-67
❑ 95ZenZ-11
❑ 96Baz-26
❑ 96Bow-17
❑ 96BowBes-83
❑ 96BowBesAR-83
❑ 96BowBesMI-5
❑ 96BowBesMIAR-5
❑ 96BowBesMIR-5
❑ 96BowBesP-BBP21
❑ 96BowBesPAR-BBP21
❑ 96BowBesPR-BBP21
❑ 96BowBesR-83
❑ 96BowFoi-17
❑ 96Cir-124
❑ 96CirRav-124
❑ 96ColCho-326
❑ 96ColCho-540
❑ 96ColCho-753
❑ 96ColChoCtG-CG16
❑ 96ColChoCtG-CG16B
❑ 96ColChoCtG-CG16C
❑ 96ColChoCtGG-CG16
❑ 96ColChoCtGG-CG16B
❑ 96ColChoCtGG-CG16C
❑ 96ColChoGS-326
❑ 96ColChoGS-540
❑ 96ColChoGS-753
❑ 96ColChoSS-326
❑ 96ColChoSS-540
❑ 96ColChoSS-753
❑ 96ColChoYMtP-43
❑ 96ColChoYMtP-43A
❑ 96ColChoYMtPGS-43
❑ 96ColChoYMtPGS-43A
❑ 96Don-342
❑ 96DonDiaK-11
❑ 96DonLonBL-7
❑ 96DonPreP-342
❑ 96EmoXL-178
❑ 96Fin-S13
❑ 96Fin-S302
❑ 96FinRef-S13
❑ 96FinRef-S302
❑ 96Fla-253
❑ 96Fle-377
❑ 96FleTif-377
❑ 96Lea-63
❑ 96LeaLim-86
❑ 96LeaLimG-86
❑ 96LeaPre-80
❑ 96LeaPreP-80
❑ 96LeaPrePB-63
❑ 96LeaPrePG-63
❑ 96LeaPrePS-63
❑ 96LeaPreSG-37
❑ 96LeaPreSte-37
❑ 96LeaSig-77
❑ 96LeaSigPPG-77
❑ 96LeaSigPPP-77
❑ 96MetUni-159
❑ 96MetUniP-159
❑ 96Pac-65
❑ 96PacPri-P140
❑ 96PacPriFB-FB20
❑ 96PacPriG-P140
❑ 96PanSti-86
❑ 96Pin-150
❑ 96Pin-219
❑ 96PinAfi-68
❑ 96PinAfi-152
❑ 96PinAfiAP-68
❑ 96PinAfiAP-152
❑ 96PinAfiFPP-68
❑ 96PinArtP-77
❑ 96PinArtP-119
❑ 96PinFoil-219
❑ 96PinPow-19
❑ 96PinSta-77
❑ 96PinSta-119
❑ 96ProSta-114
❑ 96RedF-25
❑ 96RocFle-16
❑ 96RocPol-25
❑ 96Sco-13
❑ 96Sco-374
❑ 96ScoAll-17
❑ 96ScoBigB-15
❑ 96ScoDiaA-13
❑ 96ScoDugC-A13
❑ 96ScoDugC-B99
❑ 96ScoDugCAP-A13
❑ 96ScoDugCAP-B99
❑ 96ScoGolS-27
❑ 96ScoNumG-20
❑ 96ScoPowP-8
❑ 96ScoRef-9
❑ 96ScoTitT-13
❑ 96Sel-98
❑ 96SelArtP-98
❑ 96SelCer-85
❑ 96SelCerAP-85
❑ 96SelCerCB-85
❑ 96SelCerCR-85
❑ 96SelCerMB-85
❑ 96SelCerMG-85
❑ 96SelCerMR-85
❑ 96SelTeaN-4
❑ 96SP-80
❑ 96Spo-72
❑ 96Spo-114
❑ 96SpoArtP-72
❑ 96SpoArtP-114
❑ 96SpoPowS-18
❑ 96SPx-23
❑ 96SPxGol-23
❑ 96StaClu-319
❑ 96StaCluEPB-319
❑ 96StaCluEPG-319
❑ 96StaCluEPS-319
❑ 96StaCluMO-45
❑ 96StaCluMOP-319
❑ 96StaCluMOP-PS11
❑ 96StaCluPS-PS11
❑ 96Stu-78
❑ 96StuPrePB-78
❑ 96StuPrePG-78
❑ 96StuPrePS-78
❑ 96Sum-61
❑ 96SumAbo&B-61
❑ 96SumArtP-61
❑ 96SumFoi-61
❑ 96TeaOut-86
❑ 96Top-5
❑ 96Top-363
❑ 96TopChr-5
❑ 96TopChr-147
❑ 96TopChrR-5
❑ 96TopChrR-147
❑ 96TopGal-179
❑ 96TopGalPPI-179
❑ 96TopLas-112
❑ 96TopLasPC-16
❑ 96TopPowB-5
❑ 96TopPro-NL10
❑ 96Ult-194
❑ 96UltGolM-194
❑ 96UltPowP-11
❑ 96UltPowPGM-11
❑ 96UppDec-60
❑ 96UppDec-421
❑ 96UppDecPD-PD19
❑ 96UppDecPRE-R38
❑ 96UppDecPreR-R38
❑ 96Zen-57
❑ 96ZenArtP-57
❑ 96ZenMoz-12
❑ 97Bow-275
❑ 97BowBes-67
❑ 97BowBesAR-67
❑ 97BowBesR-67
❑ 97BowChr-92
❑ 97BowChrI-92

❑ 97BowChrIR-92
❑ 97BowChrR-92
❑ 97BowInt-275
❑ 97BowIntB-BBI7
❑ 97BowIntBAR-BBI7
❑ 97BowIntBR-BBI7
❑ 97Cir-377
❑ 97CirRav-377
❑ 97ColCho-98
❑ 97ColChoBS-6
❑ 97ColChoBSGS-6
❑ 97ColChoT-CR4
❑ 97Don-48
❑ 97Don-410
❑ 97DonArmaD-7
❑ 97DonGolPP-48
❑ 97DonGolPP-410
❑ 97DonLim-87
❑ 97DonLim-126
❑ 97DonLim-133
❑ 97DonLim-169
❑ 97DonLimE-87
❑ 97DonLimE-126
❑ 97DonLimE-133
❑ 97DonLimE-169
❑ 97DonLimENG-133
❑ 97DonLimFotG-28
❑ 97DonPre-10
❑ 97DonPreCttC-10
❑ 97DonSig-33
❑ 97DonSigA-105
❑ 97DonSigAC-130
❑ 97DonSigAM-130
❑ 97DonSigPPP-33
❑ 97DonSilPP-48
❑ 97DonSilPP-410
❑ 97DonTea-92
❑ 97DonTeaSMVP-16
❑ 97DonTeaSPE-92
❑ 97DonVxP1-19
❑ 97Fin-106
❑ 97Fin-335
❑ 97FinEmb-106
❑ 97FinEmb-335
❑ 97FinEmbR-106
❑ 97FinEmbR-335
❑ 97FinRef-106
❑ 97FinRef-335
❑ 97FlaShoLC-76
❑ 97FlaShoLeg0-76
❑ 97FlaShoLeg1-76
❑ 97FlaShoM-A76
❑ 97FlaShoM-B76
❑ 97FlaShoM-C76
❑ 97FlaShoR0-76
❑ 97FlaShoR1-76
❑ 97FlaShoR2-76
❑ 97Fle-319
❑ 97FleTif-319
❑ 97Lea-238
❑ 97Lea-385
❑ 97LeaFraM-238
❑ 97LeaFraM-385
❑ 97LeaFraMDC-238
❑ 97LeaFraMDC-385
❑ 97LeaLeaotN-6
❑ 97MetUni-76
❑ 97NewPin-9
❑ 97NewPinAP-9
❑ 97NewPinMC-9
❑ 97NewPinPP-9
❑ 97Pac-291
❑ 97PacLigB-291
❑ 97PacSil-291
❑ 97PinCer-24
❑ 97PinCerMBla-24
❑ 97PinCerMBlu-24
❑ 97PinCerMG-24
❑ 97PinCerMR-24
❑ 97PinCerR-24
❑ 97PinIns-114
❑ 97PinInsCE-114
❑ 97PinInsDE-114
❑ 97PinPasttM-24
❑ 97PinTotCPB-24
❑ 97PinTotCPG-24
❑ 97PinTotCPR-24
❑ 97PinTotCS-24
❑ 97PinX-P-1
❑ 97PinX-P-138
❑ 97PinX-PMoS-1
❑ 97PinX-PMoS-138
❑ 97PinX-PMP-4
❑ 97PinX-PreMPS-4
❑ 97PinX-PSfF-57
❑ 97PinX-PSfF-U57
❑ 97PinX-PSfFU-57
❑ 97RocPol-10
❑ 97RocSco-8
❑ 97RocScoPl-8
❑ 97RocScoPr-8
❑ 97Sco-176
❑ 97ScoArtPWB-176
❑ 97ScoPreS-176
❑ 97ScoShoS-176
❑ 97ScoShoSAP-176
❑ 97Sel-97
❑ 97SelArtP-97
❑ 97SelCom-97
❑ 97SelRegG-97
❑ 97SP-67
❑ 97SpoIll-111
❑ 97SpoIllEE-111
❑ 97SPx-25
❑ 97SPxBro-25
❑ 97SPxGol-25
❑ 97SPxGraF-25
❑ 97SPxSil-25
❑ 97SPxSte-25
❑ 97StaClu-251
❑ 97StaCluMat-251
❑ 97StaCluMOP-251
❑ 97StrAll-60
❑ 97Stu-105
❑ 97StuPrePG-105
❑ 97StuPrePS-105
❑ 97Top-461
❑ 97TopChr-162
❑ 97TopChrR-162
❑ 97TopGal-72
❑ 97TopGalPPI-72
❑ 97TopScrPS-6
❑ 97TopScrPST-6
❑ 97TopSta-1
❑ 97TopSta97AS-AS13
❑ 97TopStaAM-1
❑ 97TopStaASM-ASM9
❑ 97TopStaP-PP1
❑ 97Ult-320
❑ 97UltGolME-320
❑ 97UltPlaME-320
❑ 97UppDec-182
❑ 97UppDec-353
❑ 97UppDecSA-14
❑ 97UppDecSAG-14
❑ 97Zen-11
❑ 97Zen Z-Z-2
❑ 98Bow-23
❑ 98BowBes-64
❑ 98BowBesAR-64
❑ 98BowBesMIF-MI16
❑ 98BowBesMIFAR-MI16
❑ 98BowBesMIFR-MI16
❑ 98BowBesR-64
❑ 98BowChr-23
❑ 98BowChrGA-23
❑ 98BowChrGAR-23
❑ 98BowChrI-23
❑ 98BowChrIR-23
❑ 98BowChrR-23
❑ 98BowChrR-16
❑ 98BowChrRR-16
❑ 98BowGolA-23
❑ 98BowInt-23
❑ 98CirThu-33
❑ 98CirThuB-20
❑ 98CirThuLA-15
❑ 98CirThuQS-12
❑ 98CirThuRav-33
❑ 98CirThuRR-15
❑ 98CirThuSupRav-33
❑ 98CirThuTB-12
❑ 98ColCho-3
❑ 98ColCho-254
❑ 98ColCho-360
❑ 98ColChoB5-360
❑ 98ColChoCG-3
❑ 98ColChoCtG-CG3A
❑ 98ColChoCtG-CG3B
❑ 98ColChoCtG-CG3C
❑ 98ColChoCtGExch-CG3
❑ 98ColChoCtGIW-CG3
❑ 98ColChoER-ER9
❑ 98ColChoMBH-13
❑ 98ColChoRJ-3
❑ 98ColChoS'-12
❑ 98ColChoSQ-SQ86
❑ 98ColChoSQDouble-14
❑ 98ColChoSQHR-14
❑ 98ColChoSQSingle-14
❑ 98ColChoSQTriple-14
❑ 98CroRoy-53
❑ 98CroRoyAS-15
❑ 98CroRoyFoB-10
❑ 98CroRoyFoBA-10
❑ 98CroRoyPotG-12
❑ 98Don-33
❑ 98Don-166
❑ 98Don-364
❑ 98Don-390
❑ 98DonCol-33
❑ 98DonCol-166
❑ 98DonColE-428
❑ 98DonColE-549
❑ 98DonColL-313
❑ 98DonColL-353
❑ 98DonColP-576
❑ 98DonColP-739
❑ 98DonColS-33
❑ 98DonColS-166
❑ 98DonCruG-67
❑ 98DonCruP-67
❑ 98DonCruR-67
❑ 98DonEli-28
❑ 98DonEli-149
❑ 98DonEliA-28
❑ 98DonEliA-149
❑ 98DonEliC-29
❑ 98DonEliMC-29
❑ 98DonEliS-28
❑ 98DonEliS-149
❑ 98DonFANT-13
❑ 98DonFANTDC-13
❑ 98DonGolPP-33
❑ 98DonGolPP-166
❑ 98DonGolPP-364
❑ 98DonGolPP-390
❑ 98DonLonL-23
❑ 98DonPre-26
❑ 98DonPre-189
❑ 98DonPreGB-22
❑ 98DonPreGES-3
❑ 98DonPreGoB-22
❑ 98DonPreGX-3
❑ 98DonPreGXDC-3
❑ 98DonPreSeat-26
❑ 98DonPreSeat-189
❑ 98DonPreTP-22
❑ 98DonPreTPD-11
❑ 98DonPreTPG-22
❑ 98DonPreTPS-22
❑ 98DonPreTW-9
❑ 98DonPriCD-33
❑ 98DonPriCD-166
❑ 98DonPriCE-428
❑ 98DonPriCE-549
❑ 98DonPriCL-313
❑ 98DonPriCL-353
❑ 98DonPriCP-576
❑ 98DonPriCP-739
❑ 98DonProLPI-17
❑ 98DonProLS-11
❑ 98DonSig-33
❑ 98DonSigP-33
❑ 98DonSilPP-33
❑ 98DonSilPP-166
❑ 98DonSilPP-364
❑ 98DonSilPP-390
❑ 98E-X2-79
❑ 98E-X2Cheap-5
❑ 98E-X2ECFut-79
❑ 98E-X2ECNow-79
❑ 98Fin-1
❑ 98FinCen-C17
❑ 98FinCenR-C17
❑ 98FinMysF1-M31
❑ 98FinMysF1-M35
❑ 98FinMysF1-M36
❑ 98FinMysF1-M37
❑ 98FinMysFR-M31
❑ 98FinMysFR-M35
❑ 98FinMysFR-M36
❑ 98FinMysFR-M37
❑ 98FinNo--1
❑ 98FinNo-R-1
❑ 98FinPowZ-P16
❑ 98FinRef-1
❑ 98FinStaS-SS17
❑ 98FinTheM-TM12
❑ 98FinTheMR-TM12
❑ 98FlaShoLeg0-33
❑ 98FlaShoLeg1-33
❑ 98FlaShoLeg2-33
❑ 98FlaShoLeg3-33
❑ 98FlaShoLegM-33
❑ 98FlaShoR0-33
❑ 98FlaShoR1-33
❑ 98FlaShoR2-33
❑ 98FlaShoR3-33
❑ 98Fle-33
❑ 98Fle-320
❑ 98Fle-340
❑ 98Fle-599
❑ 98FleDiaS-20
❑ 98FleIn TC-IC15
❑ 98FleLumC-15
❑ 98FlePowG-20
❑ 98FleVin'-22
❑ 98FleVin'C-22
❑ 98FleZon-15
❑ 98HamHel-5
❑ 98Lea-114
❑ 98Lea-154
❑ 98LeaFraDA-114
❑ 98LeaFraDA-154
❑ 98LeaFraF-114
❑ 98LeaFraF-154
❑ 98LeaFraM-114
❑ 98LeaFraM-154
❑ 98LeaFraM-114
❑ 98LeaFraM-154
❑ 98LeaFraMDC-114
❑ 98LeaFraMDC-154
❑ 98LeaFraMDC-114
❑ 98LeaFraMDC-154
❑ 98LeaFraMZ2-114
❑ 98LeaFraMZ2-154
❑ 98LeaRS-52
❑ 98LeaRS-137
❑ 98LeaRS-171
❑ 98LeaRSExtM-5
❑ 98LeaRSExtMDC-5
❑ 98LeaRSGAHSamp-16
❑ 98LeaRSGreAH-16
❑ 98LeaRSHRDerby-3
❑ 98LeaRSLHolo-52
❑ 98LeaRSLHolo-137
❑ 98LeaRSLHolo-171
❑ 98LeaRSLong-52
❑ 98LeaRSLong-137
❑ 98LeaRSLong-171
❑ 98LeaRSTicMas-17
❑ 98LeaRSTicMasDC-17
❑ 98LeaRTrue-52
❑ 98LeaRTrue-137
❑ 98LeaRTrue-171
❑ 98LeaStaRep-14
❑ 98LeaStaS-19
❑ 98LeaStaSDC-19
❑ 98MetUni-61
❑ 98MetUni-217
❑ 98MetUniPMG-61
❑ 98MetUniPMG-217
❑ 98Pac-290
❑ 98PacAur-128
❑ 98PacAurCube-8
❑ 98PacAurODLC-8
❑ 98PacAurPF-33
❑ 98PacAurPFC-33
❑ 98PacAurPFPB-33
❑ 98PacAurPFR-33
❑ 98PacAurPFS-33
❑ 98PacCraCh-5
❑ 98PacGolCDC-14
❑ 98PacHomRH-11
❑ 98PacInCage-8
❑ 98PacInv-94
❑ 98PacInv-150
❑ 98PacInvCCDB-5
❑ 98PacInvCCG-5
❑ 98PacInvCCG-5
❑ 98PacInvCCLB-5
❑ 98PacInvCCP-5
❑ 98PacInvCCR-5
❑ 98PacInvGems-148
❑ 98PacInvInt-11N
❑ 98PacInvMiT-6
❑ 98PacInvPBlue-94
❑ 98PacInvPBlue-150
❑ 98PacInvPhoto-5
❑ 98PacInvSilv-94
❑ 98PacInvSilv-150
❑ 98PacInvTeam-9
❑ 98PacOme-86
❑ 98PacOmeEP-15
❑ 98PacOmeEP1o1-15
❑ 98PacOmeOnIns-28
❑ 98PacOmeP-16
❑ 98PacOmeR-86
❑ 98PacOnl-260A
❑ 98PacOnl-260B
❑ 98PacOnl-262
❑ 98PacOnlR-260A
❑ 98PacOnlR-260B
❑ 98PacOnlR-262
❑ 98PacOnlWC-260A
❑ 98PacOnlWC-260B
❑ 98PacOnlWC-262
❑ 98PacPar-157
❑ 98PacParC-157
❑ 98PacParFC-7
❑ 98PacParG-157
❑ 98PacParHS-157
❑ 98PacParI-29
❑ 98PacParPB-157
❑ 98PacParR-157
❑ 98PacParSD-8
❑ 98PacParTC-19
❑ 98PacPlaB-290
❑ 98PacRedT-290
❑ 98PacSil-290
❑ 98PacTeaC-18
❑ 98Pin-13
❑ 98Pin-190
❑ 98Pin-198
❑ 98PinArtP-PP13
❑ 98PinArtP-PP93
❑ 98PinHitIH-1
❑ 98PinHitiHS-1
❑ 98PinIns-33
❑ 98PinIns-150
❑ 98PinInsC-20
❑ 98PinInsCE-33
❑ 98PinInsCE-150
❑ 98PinInsCG-20
❑ 98PinInsDE-33
❑ 98PinInsDE-150
❑ 98PinInsSG-10AB
❑ 98PinInsSG-10CD
❑ 98PinInsSGS-10AB
❑ 98PinInsSGS-10CD
❑ 98PinMinB-24
❑ 98PinMinCB-24
❑ 98PinMinCBAP-24
❑ 98PinMinCGP-24
❑ 98PinMinCGPAP-24
❑ 98PinMinCN-24
❑ 98PinMinCNAP-24
❑ 98PinMinCSGR-24
❑ 98PinMinDC-24
❑ 98PinMinG-24
❑ 98PinMinMCSS-24
❑ 98PinMinMG-2
❑ 98PinMinMGC-2
❑ 98PinMinS-24
❑ 98PinMinS-24
❑ 98PinMusC-PP13
❑ 98PinMusC-PP93
❑ 98PinPer-27
❑ 98PinPerBB-12
❑ 98PinPerBBSamp-12
❑ 98PinPerBBSO-12
❑ 98PinPerPP-27
❑ 98PinPerSftF-48
❑ 98PinPlu-72
❑ 98PinPlu-198
❑ 98PinPluAP-PP29
❑ 98PinPluGAP-PP29
❑ 98PinPluLM-27
❑ 98PinPluMAP-PP29
❑ 98PinPluPieGame-10
❑ 98PinPluSamp-72
❑ 98PinPluTP-6
❑ 98PinPluTPG-6
❑ 98PinPluTPM-6
❑ 98PinPluY-13
❑ 98PinPowPJ-9
❑ 98PinPowPJ-21
❑ 98PinPowPJS-9
❑ 98PinPowPJS-21
❑ 98PinPreP-13
❑ 98PinPreP-190
❑ 98PinPreP-198
❑ 98PinPreP-H1
❑ 98PinPreP-S33
❑ 98PinPreP-S34
❑ 98PinPreP-S35
❑ 98PinPreP-S36
❑ 98PinPreP-S37
❑ 98PinPreP-S38
❑ 98PinSna-CR1
❑ 98PinSna-CR13
❑ 98PinSpe-33
❑ 98PinSpe-34
❑ 98PinSpe-35
❑ 98PinSpe-36
❑ 98PinSpe-37
❑ 98PinSpe-38
❑ 98PreCon-12
❑ 98Revo-54
❑ 98RevoPTP-16
❑ 98RevoShow-28
❑ 98RevoSS-54
❑ 98Sco-13
❑ 98ScoRT-39
❑ 98ScoRTComPla-2A
❑ 98ScoRTComPla-2B
❑ 98ScoRTComPla-2C
❑ 98ScoRTCPSamp-2A
❑ 98ScoRTCPSamp-2B
❑ 98ScoRTCPSamp-2C
❑ 98ScoRTSS-PP39
❑ 98ScoRTSSAP-PP39
❑ 98ScoRTSSAP1-PP39
❑ 98ScoSS-PP117
❑ 98ScoSSAP-PP117
❑ 98SkyDugA-14
❑ 98SkyDugAIA-14
❑ 98SP Aut-85
❑ 98SP Aut-SD33
❑ 98SP AutSD-SD33
❑ 98SP AutSDT-SD33
❑ 98SpoIll-123
❑ 98SpoIll-192
❑ 98SpoIllEE-123
❑ 98SpoIllEE-192
❑ 98SpoIllFE-123
❑ 98SpoIllFE-192
❑ 98SpoIllODMP-OD10
❑ 98SpoIllTaN-138
❑ 98SpoIllTaNEE-138
❑ 98SpoIllWSF-145
❑ 98SpoIllWSFEE-145
❑ 98SpoIllWSFFE-145
❑ 98SpoIllWSFRJP-7
❑ 98SPxFin-33
❑ 98SPxFin-80
❑ 98SPxFin-154
❑ 98SPxFin-222
❑ 98SPxFinR-33
❑ 98SPxFinR-80
❑ 98SPxFinR-154
❑ 98SPxFinR-222
❑ 98SPxFinS-33
❑ 98SPxFinS-80
❑ 98SPxFinS-154
❑ 98SPxFinS-222
❑ 98StaCluBP-BP5
❑ 98StaCluC-CS13
❑ 98StaCluC-CS16
❑ 98StaCluC-CS17
❑ 98StaCluFDI-163
❑ 98StaCluI-163
❑ 98StaCluNC-NC13
❑ 98StaCluOneK-163
❑ 98StaCluPP-163
❑ 98StaCluTIII-T7C
❑ 98StaCluTIII-T17B
❑ 98StaCluTLme-T7C
❑ 98StaCluTLme-T17B
❑ 98StaCluTLmo-T7C
❑ 98StaCluTLmo-T17B
❑ 98Stu-115
❑ 98StuGPP-115
❑ 98StuHitPar-2
❑ 98StuPor8x10-33
❑ 98StuPor8x10GP-33
❑ 98StuSPP-115
❑ 98Top-2
❑ 98Top-482
❑ 98TopChr-2
❑ 98TopChr-482
❑ 98TopChrC9-C9
❑ 98TopChrC9R-C9
❑ 98TopChrR-2
❑ 98TopChrR-482
❑ 98TopClo9-C9
❑ 98TopDevR-2
❑ 98TopDevR-482
❑ 98TopDia-2
❑ 98TopDia-482
❑ 98TopFocP-FP7
❑ 98TopGal-107
❑ 98TopGalAG-AG2
❑ 98TopGalGP-107
❑ 98TopGalOPP-107
❑ 98TopGalPPI-107
❑ 98TopGalPPIA-107
❑ 98TopGolLabC1-72
❑ 98TopGolLabC1B-72
❑ 98TopGolLabC1One-72
❑ 98TopGolLabC1R-72
❑ 98TopGolLabC2-72
❑ 98TopGolLabC2B-72
❑ 98TopGolLabC2One-72
❑ 98TopGolLabC2R-72

❑ 98TopGolLabC3-72
❑ 98TopGolLabC3B-72
❑ 98TopGolLabC3One-72
❑ 98TopGolLabC3R-72
❑ 98TopMiniC-2
❑ 98TopMiniC-482
❑ 98TopMysF-ILM9
❑ 98TopMysFB-M14
❑ 98TopMysFB-M14
❑ 98TopMysFBR-M14
❑ 98TopMysFBR-M14
❑ 98TopMysFR-ILM9
❑ 98TopOpeD-2
❑ 98TopSta-106
❑ 98TopSta'S-43
❑ 98TopSta'SGH-43
❑ 98TopStaB-106
❑ 98TopStaG-G7
❑ 98TopStaG-106
❑ 98TopStaGG-G7
❑ 98TopStaGGR-G7
❑ 98TopStaGR-106
❑ 98TopStaGS-G7
❑ 98TopStaS-106
❑ 98TopStaSteG-43
❑ 98TopSup-2
❑ 98TopSup-2
❑ 98TopTek-34
❑ 98TopTekD-34
❑ 98UD3-42
❑ 98UD3-132
❑ 98UD3-222
❑ 98UD3DieCut-42
❑ 98UD3DieCut-132
❑ 98UD3DieCut-222
❑ 98Ult-90
❑ 98UltGolM-90
❑ 98UltMas-90
❑ 98UltPlaM-90
❑ 98UppDec-11
❑ 98UppDec-355
❑ 98UppDec-456
❑ 98UppDec-536
❑ 98UppDec-624
❑ 98UppDec10AP-52
❑ 98UppDec1APR-52
❑ 98UppDec5x7-355
❑ 98UppDecAC-AS17
❑ 98UppDecAG-AG6
❑ 98UppDecAGDC-AG6
❑ 98UppDecCD-CD26
❑ 98UppDecNP-NP2
❑ 98UppDecR-34
❑ 98UppDecR-22
❑ 98UppDecRBBop-BB25
❑ 98UppDecRQL-Q21
❑ 98UppDecRTC-TC37
❑ 98UppDecSF-4
❑ 98UppDecSFPD-PZ17
❑ 98UppDecSFPZPD-PZ4
❑ 98UppDecTMT-4
❑ 98UppDecTMTG-4
❑ 98Zen-1
❑ 98Zen5 xx7-42
❑ 98Zen5x7GoldImp-42
❑ 98Zen5x7Imp-42
❑ 98ZenZ-G-1
❑ 98ZenZ-S-1
❑ 99199Fin-117
❑ 99199Fin-205
❑ 99199Fin-271
❑ 99AllMysFR-M18
❑ 99AurOn DL-8
❑ 99AurSty-9
❑ 99Bow-31
❑ 99BowBes-33
❑ 99BowBesAR-33
❑ 99BowBesR-33
❑ 99BowChr-31
❑ 99BowChrG-31
❑ 99BowChrGR-31
❑ 99BowChrI-31
❑ 99BowChrIR-31
❑ 99BowChrR-31
❑ 99BowGol-31
❑ 99BowInt-31
❑ 99BowLatB-LB3
❑ 99CroRoyB-50
❑ 99CroRoyL-50
❑ 99CroRoyOD-50
❑ 99E-X Cen-26
❑ 99E-X CenECFut-26
❑ 99E-X CenECNow-26
❑ 99FinGolRef-117
❑ 99FinGolRef-205
❑ 99FinGolRef-271
❑ 99FinProF-PF17
❑ 99FinProF-PF23
❑ 99FinProF-PF49
❑ 99FinRef-117
❑ 99FinRef-205
❑ 99FinRef-271
❑ 99FlaShoLeg1-72
❑ 99FlaShoLeg2-72
❑ 99FlaShoLeg3-72
❑ 99FlaShoLegM1-72
❑ 99FlaShoLegM2-72
❑ 99FlaShoLegM3-72
❑ 99FlaShoR1-72
❑ 99FlaShoR2-72
❑ 99FlaShoR3-72
❑ 99Fle-33
❑ 99FleBri-42
❑ 99FleBri2G-42
❑ 99FleBriBlu-42
❑ 99FleBriGol-42
❑ 99FleMys-95
❑ 99FleMysG-95
❑ 99FleMysM-95
❑ 99FleSta9-33
❑ 99FleVin'-33
❑ 99FleWarT-33
❑ 99MetUni-171
❑ 99MetUniGM-171
❑ 99MetUniPMG-171
❑ 99Pac-154
❑ 99Pac-154A
❑ 99PacAur-64
❑ 99PacAurOD-64
❑ 99PacCroC-101
❑ 99PacCroCPB-101
❑ 99PacCroCTC-10
❑ 99PacGolCDC-26
❑ 99PacInv-53
❑ 99PacInvOD-53
❑ 99PacInvPB-53
❑ 99PacOme-86
❑ 99PacOme5T-20
❑ 99PacOme5TT-20
❑ 99PacOmeC-86
❑ 99PacOmeDD-8
❑ 99PacOmeDM-14
❑ 99PacOmeG-86
❑ 99PacOmePB-86
❑ 99PacPar-86
❑ 99PacParC-86
❑ 99PacParG-86
❑ 99PacParHoloGold-86
❑ 99PacParHS-86
❑ 99PacParOD-86
❑ 99PacParPB-15
❑ 99PacParPB-86
❑ 99PacParRed-86
❑ 99PacParTC-10
❑ 99PacPlaB-154
❑ 99PacPlaB-154A
❑ 99PacPri-54
❑ 99PacPriHB-54
❑ 99PacPriHG-54
❑ 99PacPriHM-54
❑ 99PacPriHP-54
❑ 99PacPriRed-54
❑ 99PacPriS-47
❑ 99PacPriS206-47
❑ 99PacPriS206R-47
❑ 99PacPriSP-47
❑ 99PacPriSV-47
❑ 99PacRed-154
❑ 99PacRed-154A
❑ 99PacTim-16
❑ 99Pin-27
❑ 99Rev-52
❑ 99RevDiaL-14
❑ 99RevPremDate-52
❑ 99RevRet-52
❑ 99RevShaSS-52
❑ 99RevTri-14
❑ 99RevTri-14
❑ 99SkyMolM-1
❑ 99SkyMolMX-1
❑ 99SkyPre-145
❑ 99SkyPreR-145
❑ 99SkyThu-289
❑ 99SkyThuRant-289
❑ 99SkyThuRave-289
❑ 99SP Aut-31
❑ 99SP AutEF-E14
❑ 99SP AutR-R14
❑ 99SpoIll-12
❑ 99SpoIll-110
❑ 99SPx-36
❑ 99SPxFinR-36
❑ 99SPxFinS-36
❑ 99SPxPowE-PE13
❑ 99SPxStaF-SF12
❑ 99StaClu-230
❑ 99StaCluC-SCC12
❑ 99StaCluCR-SCC12
❑ 99StaCluFDI-230
❑ 99StaCluOoaK-230
❑ 99StaCluPP-230
❑ 99StaCluTI-T14B
❑ 99StaCluTL-T14B
❑ 99StaCluTL-T14B
❑ 99ThuSkySupR-289
❑ 99Top-221
❑ 99Top-350
❑ 99Top-455
❑ 99TopAllMF-M18
❑ 99TopBlaLC1-45
❑ 99TopBlaLC2-45
❑ 99TopBlaLC3-45
❑ 99TopChr-221
❑ 99TopChr-350
❑ 99TopChr-455
❑ 99TopChrR-221
❑ 99TopChrR-350
❑ 99TopChrR-455
❑ 99TopGal-4
❑ 99TopGalAG-AG10
❑ 99TopGalPP-4
❑ 99TopGalPPI-4
❑ 99TopGolL-45
❑ 99TopGolLC1-45
❑ 99TopGolLC2-45
❑ 99TopGolLOtO-45
❑ 99TopMVPP-350
❑ 99TopMVPP-455
❑ 99TopOpeD-155
❑ 99TopOver-B5
❑ 99TopPowB-PB15
❑ 99TopPowBR-PB15
❑ 99TopRedLC1-45
❑ 99TopRedLC2-45
❑ 99TopRedLC3-45
❑ 99TopSta-35
❑ 99TopSta'S-30
❑ 99TopSta'SG-30
❑ 99TopSta'SGDH-30
❑ 99TopSta1Foil-35
❑ 99TopSta2Foil-35
❑ 99TopStaFoil-35
❑ 99TopStaOS-35
❑ 99TopStaTS-35
❑ 99TopSupC-29
❑ 99TopSupCR-29
❑ 99TopTek-4A
❑ 99TopTek-4B
❑ 99TopTekG-4A
❑ 99TopTekG-4B
❑ 99UD Cho-82
❑ 99UD ChoP-82
❑ 99UD ChoPCR-82
❑ 99UD ChoS-28
❑ 99UD ChoSD-28
❑ 99UD ChoSHR-28
❑ 99UD ChoST-28
❑ 99UD ChoYW-Y11
❑ 99UD Ion-25
❑ 99UD Ion-74
❑ 99UD IonR-25
❑ 99UD IonR-74
❑ 99UDHolo-21
❑ 99UDHoloAUsome-21
❑ 99Ult-179
❑ 99UltGolM-179
❑ 99UltMas-179
❑ 99UltPlaM-179
❑ 99UppDec-92
❑ 99UppDec10AT-X29
❑ 99UppDec10ATD-X29
❑ 99UppDec10ATHR-X29
❑ 99UppDec10ATT-X29
❑ 99UppDecBD-29
❑ 99UppDecBDD-29
❑ 99UppDecBDDom-D23
❑ 99UppDecBDDomE-D23
❑ 99UppDecBDMN-M20
❑ 99UppDecBDMNE-M20
❑ 99UppDecBDQ-29
❑ 99UppDecBDT-29
❑ 99UppDecCf7-33
❑ 99UppDecCf7LL-L6
❑ 99UppDecCL-79
❑ 99UppDecCLCC-79
❑ 99UppDecCLM-C32
❑ 99UppDecCo7CE-33
❑ 99UppDecE-32
❑ 99UppDecE-178
❑ 99UppDecEFXG-32
❑ 99UppDecEFXG-178
❑ 99UppDecEL1-92
❑ 99UppDecEL2-92
❑ 99UppDecEPE-P12
❑ 99UppDecIP-I25
❑ 99UppDecIPD-I25
❑ 99UppDecIPHR-I25
❑ 99UppDecIPT-I25
❑ 99UppDecM-73
❑ 99UppDecMGS-73
❑ 99UppDecMHFS-73
❑ 99UppDecMP-73
❑ 99UppDecMSS-73
❑ 99UppDecMST-T14
❑ 99UppDecO-5
❑ 99UppDecOSO-5
❑ 99UppDecR-28
❑ 99UppDecRG-28
❑ 99UppDecRP-28
❑ 99UppDecVtaT-V12
❑ 99UppDecVtaTD-V12
❑ 99UppDecVtaTQ-V12
❑ 99UppDecVtaTT-V12
❑ 99UppDecWY-W28
❑ 99UppDecWYD-W28
❑ 99UppDecWYHR-W28
❑ 99UppDecWYT-W28
❑ 99Vic-129
❑ 99Vic-130

Walker, Lawrence
❑ 90GreHorB-15
❑ 90GreHorP-2667
❑ 90GreHorS-25
❑ 91Ft.LauYC-18
❑ 91Ft.LauYP-2431

Walker, Lonnie
❑ 88LitFalMP-14
❑ 89ColMetB-27
❑ 89ColMetGS-26

Walker, M.J.
❑ 75TopPho-75

Walker, Matt
❑ 86CliGiaP-26
❑ 86EveGiaC-186
❑ 86EveGiaPC-35
❑ 87EveGiaC-1

Walker, Michael Charles
❑ 84IdaFalATI-28

Walker, Mike (Michael Aaron)
❑ 86WatPirP-27
❑ 87HarSenP-23
❑ 87WatIndP-14
❑ 88HarSenP-850
❑ 88WilBilP-1310
❑ 89BlaYNPRWLU-39
❑ 89Bow-77
❑ 89BowTif-77
❑ 89ColSprSSP-239
❑ 90CalCanC-3
❑ 90CalCanP-652
❑ 90CMC-430
❑ 90CMC-453
❑ 90ColSprSSC-1
❑ 90ColSprSSP-36
❑ 90IndTeal-42
❑ 90ProAAAF-117
❑ 90ProAAAF-217
❑ 91Don-61
❑ 91Fle-381
❑ 91IndFanC-27
❑ 91OPC-593
❑ 91Top-593A
❑ 91Top-593B
❑ 91TopDesS-593
❑ 91TopMic-593
❑ 91TopTif-593
❑ 91UppDec-694
❑ 92CalCanF-3732
❑ 92DonRoo-122
❑ 92JacSunS-370
❑ 92TolMudHF-1044
❑ 92TolMudHS-594
❑ 93CalCanF-1167
❑ 93TopGol-825
❑ 94IowCubF-1277
❑ 94PhoFirF-1521
❑ 96TolMudHB-29
❑ 97IndInd-26
❑ 98IndIndQ-17

Walker, Morgan
❑ 97AugGre-25
❑ 98LynHilQ-20

Walker, Pete
❑ 90PitMetP-16
❑ 91St.LucMC-14
❑ 91St.LucMP-712
❑ 92BinMetF-517
❑ 92BinMetS-70
❑ 93BinMetF-2335
❑ 94Bow-44
❑ 94ExcFS7-240
❑ 94Ult-540
❑ 95NorTidTI-29
❑ 96LasVegSB-29
❑ 98PawRedSQ-28

Walker, R. Tom
❑ 73OPC-41
❑ 74OPC-193
❑ 75OPC-627
❑ 76OPC-186

Walker, Ray
❑ 88MarPhiS-32

Walker, Rich
❑ 88BatCliP-1681
❑ 89BatCliP-1935

Walker, Rod
❑ 89HigSchPLS-6
❑ 95HudValRTI-24

Walker, Ron
❑ 97WilCubB-25
❑ 99Bow-389
❑ 99BowGol-389
❑ 99BowInt-389

Walker, Rube (Albert)
❑ 49EurSta-74
❑ 52Top-319
❑ 53Top-134
❑ 54Top-153
❑ 55DodGolS-22
❑ 55Top-108
❑ 55TopDouH-15
❑ 55TopTesS-10
❑ 56Dod-28
❑ 56Top-333
❑ 57Top-147
❑ 58DodTeal-24
❑ 58Hir-74
❑ 58Top-203
❑ 73OPC-257
❑ 73Top-257A
❑ 73Top-257B
❑ 74dod195T-40
❑ 74OPC-179
❑ 74Top-179
❑ 79TCM50-278
❑ 81TCM60I-407
❑ 82BraPol-54
❑ 83BraPol-54
❑ 84BraPol-54
❑ 89MetRinP69-36
❑ 90DodTar-826
❑ 91DodRinP4-2
❑ 91TopArc1-134
❑ 94Met69CCPP-3
❑ 94Met69CS-2
❑ 94Met69T-32
❑ 94TopArc1-153
❑ 94TopArc1G-153
❑ 95TopArcBD-20
❑ 95TopArcBD-47
❑ 95TopArcBD-76
❑ 95TopArcBD-100
❑ 95TopArcBD-164

Walker, Shon
❑ 92ClaDraP-24
❑ 92ClaFS7-415
❑ 92FroRowDP-74
❑ 92FroRowDPG-74
❑ 92FroRowDPS-74
❑ 92UppDecML-83
❑ 93AugPirC-24
❑ 93AugPirF-1560
❑ 93ClaFS7-120
❑ 93ClaGolF-196
❑ 93StaCluM-155
❑ 93Top-658
❑ 93TopGol-658
❑ 93TopInaM-658
❑ 93TopInaR-658
❑ 93TopMic-658
❑ 94AugGreC-25
❑ 94AugGreF-3023
❑ 94ClaGolF-188
❑ 96LynHilB-25
❑ 97LynHil-23

Walker, Steve
❑ 87SanBerSP-1
❑ 88BasCitRS-24
❑ 89MemChiB-23
❑ 89MemChiP-1196
❑ 89MemChiS-23
❑ 89Sta-46
❑ 91HunCubC-28
❑ 91HunCubP-3352
❑ 92HunCubC-18
❑ 92HunCubF-3167
❑ 93PeoChiC-23
❑ 93PeoChiF-1098
❑ 93PeoChiTI-31
❑ 94DayCubC-26
❑ 94DayCubF-2368
❑ 95RocCubTI-9
❑ 96DayCubB-24

Walker, The
❑ 90EveGiaB-7

Walker, Tilly (Clarence)
❑ 12T207-190
❑ 15CraJacE-173
❑ 15SpoNewM-185
❑ 16SpoNewM-183
❑ 17ColE13-181
❑ 21Exh-181
❑ 21Nei-6
❑ 22E120-89
❑ 22W572-110
❑ 23W501-100
❑ 23W515-7
❑ 23WilChoV-166
❑ 91ConTSN-137

Walker, Toby
❑ 88OklSoo-11

Walker, Todd
❑ 92LSUTigM-12
❑ 93BazTeaU-6
❑ 93LSUTigM-12
❑ 93TopTra-79T
❑ 94ClaUpdCotC-CC7
❑ 94LSUTig-2
❑ 94LSUTigMP-1
❑ 94SigRooDP-8
❑ 94SigRooDPS-8
❑ 95ActPacF-59
❑ 95ARuFalLS-20
❑ 95Bes-28
❑ 95Bes-103
❑ 95BesFra-F6
❑ 95Exc-89
❑ 95HarCitRCTI-27
❑ 95HarCitRCTI-28
❑ 95SigRooDDS-DD4
❑ 95SigRooDDSS-DD4
❑ 95SPML-10
❑ 95SPML-85
❑ 95SPMLDtS-DS10
❑ 95UppDecML-167
❑ 95UppDecML-170
❑ 95UppDecML-220
❑ 95UppDecMLFS-167
❑ 95UppDecMLFS-170
❑ 95UppDecMLFS-220
❑ 95UppDecMLOP-OP16
❑ 96BesAutSA-85
❑ 96Bow-159
❑ 96BowBes-135
❑ 96BowBesAR-135
❑ 96BowBesR-135
❑ 96BowFoi-159
❑ 96BowMinLP-4
❑ 96Exc-83
❑ 96LeaSig-117
❑ 96LeaSigPPG-117
❑ 96LeaSigPPP-117
❑ 97Bow-293
❑ 97BowBes-107
❑ 97BowBesA-107
❑ 97BowBesAAR-107
❑ 97BowBesAR-107
❑ 97BowBesAR-107
❑ 97BowBesBC-BC19
❑ 97BowBesBCAR-BC19
❑ 97BowBesBCR-BC19
❑ 97BowBesP-13
❑ 97BowBesPAR-13
❑ 97BowBesPR-13
❑ 97BowBesR-107
❑ 97BowCerBlaIA-CA82
❑ 97BowCerBluIA-CA82
❑ 97BowCerGolIA-CA82
❑ 97BowChr-201
❑ 97BowChrI-201
❑ 97BowChrIR-201
❑ 97BowChrR-201
❑ 97BowChrSHR-SHR6

❑ 97BowChrSHRR-SHR6
❑ 97BowInt-293
❑ 97BowIntB-BBI12
❑ 97BowIntBAR-BBI12
❑ 97BowIntBR-BBI12
❑ 97BowScoHR-6
❑ 97Cir-325
❑ 97CirEmeA-325
❑ 97CirEmeAR-AU6
❑ 97CirFasT-10
❑ 97CirRav-325
❑ 97ColCho-20
❑ 97ColChoNF-NF23
❑ 97Don-372
❑ 97DonEli-121
❑ 97DonEliGS-121
❑ 97DonEliTotC-4
❑ 97DonEliTotCDC-4
❑ 97DonFraFea-6
❑ 97DonGolPP-372
❑ 97DonLim-45
❑ 97DonLim-65
❑ 97DonLimE-45
❑ 97DonLimE-65
❑ 97DonLimENG-65
❑ 97DonLimFotG-36
❑ 97DonPre-146
❑ 97DonPre-199
❑ 97DonPreCttC-146
❑ 97DonPreCttC-199
❑ 97DonRatR-25
❑ 97DonRooDK-4
❑ 97DonRooDKC-4
❑ 97DonSigA-106
❑ 97DonSigAC-131
❑ 97DonSigAM-131
❑ 97DonSilPP-372
❑ 97E-X2-30
❑ 97E-X2Cred-30
❑ 97E-X2EmeAuto-30
❑ 97E-X2EmeAutoR-AU6
❑ 97E-X2EssCre-30
❑ 97E-X2SD2000-13
❑ 97Fin-112
❑ 97Fin-341
❑ 97FinEmb-112
❑ 97FinEmb-341
❑ 97FinEmbR-112
❑ 97FinEmbR-341
❑ 97FinRef-112
❑ 97FinRef-341
❑ 97FlaShoLC-12
❑ 97FlaShoLeg0-12
❑ 97FlaShoLeg1-12
❑ 97FlaShoM-A12
❑ 97FlaShoM-B12
❑ 97FlaShoM-C12
❑ 97FlaShoR0-12
❑ 97FlaShoR1-12
❑ 97FlaShoR2-12
❑ 97FlaShoWotF-12
❑ 97Fle-160
❑ 97FleNewH-14
❑ 97FleRooS-20
❑ 97FleTif-160
❑ 97Lea-170
❑ 97LeaFraM-170
❑ 97LeaFraMDC-170
❑ 97MetUni-215
❑ 97MetUniEA-AU6
❑ 97MetUniEAR-AU6
❑ 97MetUniMfG-10
❑ 97NewPin-165
❑ 97NewPin-199
❑ 97NewPinAP-165
❑ 97NewPinAP-199
❑ 97NewPinMC-165
❑ 97NewPinMC-199
❑ 97NewPinPP-165
❑ 97NewPinPP-199
❑ 97Pac-146
❑ 97PacLigB-146
❑ 97PacPri-48
❑ 97PacPriLB-48
❑ 97PacPriP-48
❑ 97PacSil-146
❑ 97Pin-171
❑ 97PinArtP-PP171
❑ 97PinCer-115
❑ 97PinCerMBla-115
❑ 97PinCerMBlu-115
❑ 97PinCerMG-115
❑ 97PinCerMR-115
❑ 97PinCerR-115
❑ 97PinIns-144
❑ 97PinInsCE-144
❑ 97PinInsDE-144
❑ 97PinMusC-171
❑ 97PinPrePla-171
❑ 97PinTotCPB-115
❑ 97PinTotCPG-115
❑ 97PinTotCPR-115
❑ 97PinX-P-118
❑ 97PinX-PMoS-118
❑ 97Sco-324
❑ 97Sco-477
❑ 97ScoArtPWB-324
❑ 97ScoArtPWB-477
❑ 97ScoHeaotO-36
❑ 97ScoResC-477
❑ 97ScoShoS-324
❑ 97ScoShoS-477
❑ 97ScoShoSAP-324
❑ 97ScoShoSAP-477
❑ 97Sel-103
❑ 97SelArtP-103
❑ 97SelCom-103
❑ 97SelRegG-103
❑ 97SelRooA-4
❑ 97SelRooR-12
❑ 97SelToootT-16
❑ 97SelToootTMB-16
❑ 97SP-5
❑ 97SpoIll-26
❑ 97SpoIllEE-26
❑ 97SPSpeF-43
❑ 97SPSpxF-10
❑ 97SPSPxFA-10
❑ 97SPx-32
❑ 97SPxBro-32
❑ 97SPxGol-32
❑ 97SPxGraF-32
❑ 97SPxSil-32
❑ 97SPxSte-32
❑ 97StaClu-78
❑ 97StaClu-182
❑ 97StaCluM-M22
❑ 97StaCluMOP-78
❑ 97StaCluMOP-182
❑ 97StaCluMOP-M22
❑ 97Stu-154
❑ 97StuAut-12
❑ 97StuHarH-7
❑ 97StuPor8-12
❑ 97StuPrePG-154
❑ 97StuPrePS-154
❑ 97Top-377
❑ 97TopAwel-AI20
❑ 97TopChr-129
❑ 97TopChrR-129
❑ 97TopGal-180
❑ 97TopGalPPI-180
❑ 97TopMemO5-55
❑ 97UD3-52
❑ 97UD3GenNex-GN17
❑ 97Ult-548
❑ 97UltAutE-2
❑ 97UltGolME-548
❑ 97UltGolP-3
❑ 97UltPlaME-548
❑ 97UppDec-235
❑ 97UppDecBCP-BC5
❑ 98Bow-54
❑ 98BowBes-190
❑ 98BowBesAR-190
❑ 98BowBesR-190
❑ 98BowChr-54
❑ 98BowChrGA-54
❑ 98BowChrGAR-54
❑ 98BowChrI-54
❑ 98BowChrIR-54
❑ 98BowChrR-54
❑ 98BowGolA-54
❑ 98BowInt-54
❑ 98ColCho-407
❑ 98CroRoy-81
❑ 98Don-127
❑ 98DonCol-127
❑ 98DonColE-486
❑ 98DonColL-346
❑ 98DonColP-673
❑ 98DonColS-127
❑ 98DonCruG-30
❑ 98DonCruP-30
❑ 98DonCruR-30
❑ 98DonEli-86
❑ 98DonEliA-86
❑ 98DonEliS-86
❑ 98DonGolPP-127
❑ 98DonPre-123
❑ 98DonPreGES-19
❑ 98DonPreGX-19
❑ 98DonPreGXDC-19
❑ 98DonPreSeat-123
❑ 98DonPriCD-127
❑ 98DonPriCE-486
❑ 98DonPriCL-346
❑ 98DonPriCP-673
❑ 98DonSig-16
❑ 98DonSigA-90
❑ 98DonSigAC-112
❑ 98DonSigAM-115
❑ 98DonSigP-16
❑ 98DonSilPP-127
❑ 98E-X2-86
❑ 98E-X2ECFut-86
❑ 98E-X2ECNow-86
❑ 98E-X2Sig2001-6
❑ 98Fin-173
❑ 98FinNo--173
❑ 98FinNo-R-173
❑ 98FinRef-173
❑ 98Fle-453
❑ 98FleVin'-103
❑ 98FleVin'C-103
❑ 98Lea-147
❑ 98LeaCruG-30
❑ 98LeaCruP-30
❑ 98LeaCruR-30
❑ 98LeaFraDA-147
❑ 98LeaFraF-147
❑ 98LeaFraM-147
❑ 98LeaFraM-147
❑ 98LeaFraMDC-147
❑ 98LeaFraMDC-147
❑ 98LeaFraMS-147
❑ 98LeaFraMZ2-147
❑ 98LeaRS-109
❑ 98LeaRSLHolo-109
❑ 98LeaRSLong-109
❑ 98LeaRTrue-109
❑ 98PacAur-56
❑ 98PacInvGems-70
❑ 98PacOme-146
❑ 98PacOmeR-146
❑ 98PacOnl-441
❑ 98PacOnlR-441
❑ 98PacOnlWC-441
❑ 98PacPar-67
❑ 98PacParC-67
❑ 98PacParG-67
❑ 98PacParHS-67
❑ 98PacParPB-67
❑ 98PacParR-67
❑ 98PinIns-76
❑ 98PinInsCE-76
❑ 98PinInsDE-76
❑ 98PinPer-97
❑ 98PinPerPP-97
❑ 98PinPlu-65
❑ 98PinPluAP-PP27
❑ 98PinPluGAP-PP27
❑ 98PinPluMAP-PP27
❑ 98Revo-87
❑ 98RevoSS-87
❑ 98ScoRT-151
❑ 98ScoRTSS-PP87
❑ 98ScoRTSSAP-PP87
❑ 98ScoRTSSAP1-PP87
❑ 98SkyDugAAR-14
❑ 98SP Aut-126
❑ 98SPxFin-296
❑ 98SPxFinR-296
❑ 98SPxFinS-296
❑ 98StaCluFDI-94
❑ 98StaCluI-94
❑ 98StaCluOneK-94
❑ 98StaCluPP-94
❑ 98Stu-49
❑ 98StuGPP-49
❑ 98StuSPP-49
❑ 98TopGolLabC1-97
❑ 98TopGolLabC1B-97
❑ 98TopGolLabC1One-97
❑ 98TopGolLabC1R-97
❑ 98TopGolLabC2-97
❑ 98TopGolLabC2B-97
❑ 98TopGolLabC2One-97
❑ 98TopGolLabC2R-97
❑ 98TopGolLabC3-97
❑ 98TopGolLabC3B-97
❑ 98TopGolLabC3One-97
❑ 98TopGolLabC3R-97
❑ 98TopTek-24
❑ 98TopTekD-24
❑ 98Ult-439
❑ 98UltGolM-439
❑ 98UltKidG-6
❑ 98UltMas-439
❑ 98UltPlaM-439
❑ 98UppDec-131
❑ 98UppDecR-57
❑ 98UppDecSF-78
❑ 99199Fin-77
❑ 99Bow-21
❑ 99BowBes-37
❑ 99BowBesAR-37
❑ 99BowBesR-37
❑ 99BowChr-21
❑ 99BowChrG-21
❑ 99BowChrGR-21
❑ 99BowChrI-21
❑ 99BowChrIR-21
❑ 99BowChrR-21
❑ 99BowGol-21
❑ 99BowInt-21
❑ 99CroRoyB-84
❑ 99CroRoyL-84
❑ 99CroRoyOD-84
❑ 99E-X Cen-87
❑ 99E-X CenECFut-87
❑ 99E-X CenECNow-87
❑ 99FinGolRef-77
❑ 99FinRef-77
❑ 99FlaShoLeg1-86
❑ 99FlaShoLeg2-86
❑ 99FlaShoLeg3-86
❑ 99FlaShoLegM1-86
❑ 99FlaShoLegM2-86
❑ 99FlaShoLegM3-86
❑ 99FlaShoR1-86
❑ 99FlaShoR2-86
❑ 99FlaShoR3-86
❑ 99Fle-285
❑ 99FleBri-52
❑ 99FleBri2G-52
❑ 99FleBriBlu-52
❑ 99FleBriGol-52
❑ 99FleMys-13
❑ 99FleMysFI-26
❑ 99FleMysG-13
❑ 99FleMysM-13
❑ 99FleSta9-285
❑ 99FleWarT-285
❑ 99MetUni-16
❑ 99MetUniGM-16
❑ 99MetUniPMG-16
❑ 99Pac-258
❑ 99PacAur-108
❑ 99PacAurOD-108
❑ 99PacCroC-166
❑ 99PacCroCPB-166
❑ 99PacOme-140
❑ 99PacOmeC-140
❑ 99PacOmeG-140
❑ 99PacOmePB-140
❑ 99PacPar-139
❑ 99PacParC-139
❑ 99PacParG-139
❑ 99PacParHoloGold-139
❑ 99PacParHS-139
❑ 99PacParOD-139
❑ 99PacParPB-139
❑ 99PacParRed-139
❑ 99PacPlaB-258
❑ 99PacPri-86
❑ 99PacPriHB-86
❑ 99PacPriHG-86
❑ 99PacPriHM-86
❑ 99PacPriHP-86
❑ 99PacPriRed-86
❑ 99PacPriS-145
❑ 99PacPriS206-145
❑ 99PacPriS206R-145
❑ 99PacRed-258
❑ 99Rev-82
❑ 99RevPremDate-82
❑ 99RevRet-82
❑ 99RevShaSS-82
❑ 99SkyMolM-16
❑ 99SkyMolMX-16
❑ 99SkyPre-222
❑ 99SkyPreR-222
❑ 99SkyThu-69
❑ 99SkyThuRant-69
❑ 99SkyThuRave-69
❑ 99SP Aut-48
❑ 99SP AutC-TW
❑ 99SP AutCG-TW
❑ 99SP SigAuto-TW
❑ 99SP SigAutoG-TW
❑ 99SpoIll-168
❑ 99SPSig-48
❑ 99SPx-50
❑ 99SPxFinR-50
❑ 99SPxFinS-50
❑ 99StaClu-235
❑ 99StaCluFDI-235
❑ 99StaCluOoaK-235
❑ 99StaCluPP-235
❑ 99ThuSkySupR-69
❑ 99Top-30
❑ 99TopBlaLC1-46
❑ 99TopBlaLC2-46
❑ 99TopBlaLC3-46
❑ 99TopChr-30
❑ 99TopChrR-30
❑ 99TopGal-53
❑ 99TopGalPP-53
❑ 99TopGalPPI-53
❑ 99TopGolL-46
❑ 99TopGolLC1-46
❑ 99TopGolLC2-46
❑ 99TopGolLOtO-46
❑ 99TopMVPP-30
❑ 99TopOpeD-19
❑ 99TopRedLC1-46
❑ 99TopRedLC2-46
❑ 99TopRedLC3-46
❑ 99TopSta-77
❑ 99TopSta1Foil-77
❑ 99TopStaFoil-77
❑ 99TopStaOS-77
❑ 99UD Cho-105
❑ 99UD ChoPCR-105
❑ 99UD Ion-36
❑ 99UD IonR-36
❑ 99UDHolo-34
❑ 99UDHoloAUsome-34
❑ 99Ult-5
❑ 99UltGolM-5
❑ 99UltMas-5
❑ 99UltPlaM-5
❑ 99UppDec-139
❑ 99UppDecBD-49
❑ 99UppDecBDD-49
❑ 99UppDecBDQ-49
❑ 99UppDecBDT-49
❑ 99UppDecCLM-C55
❑ 99UppDecE-52
❑ 99UppDecEBPC-C-TW
❑ 99UppDecEFXG-52
❑ 99UppDecEL1-139
❑ 99UppDecEL2-139
❑ 99UppDecM-120
❑ 99UppDecMGS-120
❑ 99UppDecMHFS-120
❑ 99UppDecMP-120
❑ 99UppDecMSS-120
❑ 99UppDecO-32
❑ 99UppDecOSO-32
❑ 99UppDecR-49
❑ 99UppDecRG-49
❑ 99UppDecRP-49
❑ 99Vic-226

Walker, Tom
❑ 72Dia-49
❑ 73Top-41
❑ 74Top-193
❑ 75DetTigP-35
❑ 75Top-627
❑ 75TopMin-627
❑ 76Top-186
❑ 76TulOilGP-19
❑ 77ExpPos-36
❑ 77Top-652
❑ 78ColCliT-26
❑ 91HunCubC-29
❑ 91HunCubP-3345

Walker, Tony (Anthony)
❑ 81WatRedT-11
❑ 81WatRedT-21
❑ 82WatRedT-20
❑ 83DayBeaAT-27
❑ 86AstPol-20
❑ 86FleUpd-123
❑ 87Fle-71
❑ 87FleGlo-71
❑ 87Top-24
❑ 87TopTif-24

Walker, Tyler
❑ 98CapCitBF5-15
❑ 98CapCitBM-15
❑ 98SouAtlLPM-24

Walker, Wade
❑ 93GenCubC-26
❑ 93GenCubF-3174
❑ 94PeoChiC-24
❑ 94PeoChiF-2267
❑ 96Bow-117
❑ 96BowFoi-117
❑ 96OrlCubB-27
❑ 97OrlRayB-26

Walker, William C.
❑ 29ExhFou-7
❑ 31Exh-7

Walker, William H.
❑ 35DiaMatCS3T1-143

Walkup, James
❑ 39PlaBal-150
❑ 79DiaGre-184

Wall, Dave
❑ 81AppFoxT-27

Wall, Donne
❑ 89AubAstP-2182
❑ 90AshTouP-2749
❑ 91BurAstC-10
❑ 91BurAstP-2801
❑ 91MidLeaAP-MWL19
❑ 92OscAstC-19
❑ 92ProFS7-233
❑ 92UppDecML-138
❑ 93TucTorF-3060
❑ 94TucTorF-763
❑ 95TucTotTI-29
❑ 96Bow-318
❑ 96BowFoi-318
❑ 96ColCho-568
❑ 96ColChoGS-568
❑ 96ColChoSS-568
❑ 96Don-456
❑ 96DonPreP-456
❑ 96Fle-423
❑ 96FleTif-423
❑ 96StaClu-179
❑ 96StaCluMOP-179
❑ 96Top-341
❑ 96TusTorB-25
❑ 97AstMot-23
❑ 97Cir-131
❑ 97CirRav-131
❑ 97Fle-355
❑ 97FleTif-355
❑ 97Lea-80
❑ 97LeaFraM-80
❑ 97LeaFraMDC-80
❑ 97MetUni-142
❑ 97Pin-153
❑ 97PinArtP-PP153
❑ 97PinMusC-153
❑ 97PinPrePla-153
❑ 97StaClu-121
❑ 97StaCluMOP-121
❑ 97Top-223
❑ 97Ult-213
❑ 97UltGolME-213
❑ 97UltPlaME-213
❑ 97UppDec-82
❑ 98PadMot-27

Wall, Greg
❑ 89AncBucTI-19

Wall, Jason
❑ 90LSUTigP-11

Wall, Murray
❑ 53Top-217
❑ 58Top-410
❑ 59Top-42
❑ 59TopVen-42
❑ 83Bra53F-11
❑ 91TopArc1-217

Wall, Stan
❑ 74AlbDukTI-22
❑ 75AlbDukCa-17
❑ 75IntLeaASB-36
❑ 75PacCoaLAB-36
❑ 76OPC-584
❑ 76Top-584
❑ 77Top-88
❑ 90DodTar-827

Wallace, Alex
❑ 85AncGlaPTI-30

Wallace, Arthur
❑ 88KimN18-45

Wallace, B.J.
❑ 90MisStaB-39
❑ 91MisStaB-47
❑ 92Bow-554
❑ 92ClaDraP-3
❑ 92ClaDraPFB-BC3
❑ 92ClaDraPP-BB3
❑ 92FroRowDP-80
❑ 92FroRowDPG-80
❑ 92FroRowDPPS-80
❑ 92FroRowDPS-80
❑ 92MisStaB-44

❑ 92TopTra-126T
❑ 92TopTraG-126T
❑ 92UppDecML-2
❑ 93Bow-676
❑ 93ClaFS7-32
❑ 93ClaGolF-109
❑ 93OPCPreTDP-1
❑ 93Pin-456
❑ 93Sco-488
❑ 93Sel-310
❑ 93StaCluM-125
❑ 93StaCluM-142
❑ 93Top-33
❑ 93TopGol-33
❑ 93TopInaM-33
❑ 93TopInaR-33
❑ 93TopMic-33
❑ 93WesPalBEC-1
❑ 93WesPalBEF-1341
❑ 94Bow-640
❑ 94Cla-42
❑ 94ClaGolF-191
❑ 94ExcFS7-230
❑ 94HarSenF-2093
❑ 94UppDecML-69

Wallace, Bobby (Roderick)
❑ 03BreE10-148
❑ 04FanCraAL-48
❑ 09AmeCarE90-1-115
❑ 09ColChiE-297
❑ 09PC7HHB-44
❑ 09RamT20-121
❑ 09SpoNewSM-56
❑ 09T206-367
❑ 10DomDisP-120
❑ 10NadCarE-53
❑ 10SweCapPP-56A
❑ 10SweCapPP-56B
❑ 11HelSta-66
❑ 11MecDFT-48
❑ 11PinT-5-102
❑ 11S74Sil-37
❑ 11SpoLifCW-360
❑ 11SpoLifM-120
❑ 11T205-176A
❑ 11T205-176B
❑ 11TurRedT-124
❑ 12ColRedB-297
❑ 12ColTinT-297
❑ 12HasTriFT-1A
❑ 12HasTriFT-1B
❑ 12T207-191
❑ 14B18B-35A
❑ 14B18B-35B
❑ 14PieStaT-105
❑ 14PieStaT-106
❑ 50CalHOFW-75
❑ 53ArtHaloFP-85
❑ 76ShaPiz-69
❑ 80PerHaloFP-69
❑ 80SSPHOF-69
❑ 90BasWit-65
❑ 93ConTSN-916
❑ 94ConTSN-1017
❑ 94ConTSNB-1017
❑ 94OriofB-82
❑ 98CamPepP-82

Wallace, Brian
❑ 92BelMarCB-27
❑ 92BelMarF-1454
❑ 93AppFoxCB-23
❑ 93AppFoxFl-2470
❑ 94AppFoxC-20
❑ 94AppFoxFl-1064
❑ 95BurBeeTI-30

Wallace, Brooks
❑ 81TulDriT-24

Wallace, Chris
❑ 98GreBatM-23

Wallace, Curtis
❑ 76BatRouCT-21

Wallace, Dave
❑ 76OklCit8TI-21
❑ 81VerBeaDT-25
❑ 82VerBeaDT-28
❑ 84AlbDukCr-245
❑ 86AlbDukP-26
❑ 95DodMot-28
❑ 95DodPol-30
❑ 96DodMot-28
❑ 96DodPol-8

Wallace, David
❑ 90AshTouC-24
❑ 91AshTouP-582
❑ 92BurAstC-1
❑ 92BurAstF-561

Wallace, Derek
❑ 92ClaBluBF-BC23
❑ 92ClaDraP-8
❑ 92ClaDraPFB-BC8
❑ 92ClaFS7-403
❑ 92PeoChiTI-29
❑ 92UppDecML-7
❑ 93Bow-4
❑ 93ClaPro-4
❑ 93ClaYouG-YG27
❑ 93DayCubC-22
❑ 93DayCubF-859
❑ 93Pin-460
❑ 93Sco-492
❑ 93Sel-357
❑ 93StaCluM-124
❑ 93Top-459
❑ 93TopGol-459
❑ 93TopInaM-459
❑ 93TopInaR-459
❑ 93TopMic-459
❑ 93UppDec-429
❑ 93UppDecGold-429
❑ 94Bow-110
❑ 94Cla-134
❑ 94ClaGolF-133
❑ 94OrlCubF-1386
❑ 94UppDecML-201
❑ 95WicWraTI-23
❑ 96NorTidB-30
❑ 97AppLeaTPB-27
❑ 97Bow-147
❑ 97BowInt-147
❑ 97BriWhiSB-24
❑ 97PacPriGotD-GD178
❑ 97UppDec-281
❑ 98BriWhiSQ-27
❑ 98MetUni-86
❑ 98MetUniPMG-86
❑ 98NorTidP-28
❑ 98NorTidQ-28
❑ 98Ult-237
❑ 98UltGolM-237
❑ 98UltMas-237
❑ 98UltPlaM-237

Wallace, Don
❑ 66SeaPop-28
❑ 67SeaPop-19
❑ 67Top-367

Wallace, Flint
❑ 96SouOreTI-13
❑ 97ModA'sG-29
❑ 98ModA'sG-29

Wallace, Greg
❑ 86MiaMarP-26

Wallace, James
❑ 97AubDouTI-29

Wallace, Jeff
❑ 96LanLugB-30
❑ 97LynHil-24
❑ 98Bow-106
❑ 98BowChr-106
❑ 98BowChrGA-106
❑ 98BowChrGAR-106
❑ 98BowChrI-106
❑ 98BowChrIR-106
❑ 98BowChrR-106
❑ 98BowGolA-106
❑ 98BowInt-106
❑ 98Fle-264

Wallace, Jim
❑ 49RemBre-30
❑ 77TCMTheWY-90
❑ 98QuaCitRBG-29

Wallace, Joe
❑ 91OklStaC-28
❑ 92OklStaC-28
❑ 93JohCitCC-28
❑ 93JohCitCF-3683
❑ 94MadHatC-24
❑ 94MadHatF-136

Wallace, Kent
❑ 92OneYanC-22
❑ 93GreHorC-25
❑ 94TamYanC-29
❑ 94TamYanF-2384
❑ 95ColCliP-31
❑ 95ColCliTI-31
❑ 95NorNavTI-30
❑ 96ColCliB-29

Wallace, Mike
❑ 74OPC-608
❑ 74Top-608A
❑ 74Top-608B
❑ 75OPC-401
❑ 75SSP18-3
❑ 75Top-401
❑ 75TopMin-401
❑ 76SSP-290
❑ 76St.LouCP-34
❑ 77Top-539
❑ 92YanWIZ7-159
❑ 93RanKee-370

Wallace, Robert
❑ 22Zee-19
❑ 23Zee-22
❑ 24Zee-17

Wallace, Tim
❑ 83St.PetCT-15
❑ 84ArkTraT-5
❑ 86ArkTraP-25
❑ 86LouRedTI-28
❑ 86PeoChiP-25
❑ 87WinSpiP-15
❑ 88WinSpiS-21
❑ 89BoiHawP-1994
❑ 90PalSprACLC-216
❑ 90PalSprAP-2588
❑ 91LinDriAA-622
❑ 91WicWraLD-622
❑ 91WicWraP-2608
❑ 91WicWraRD-18

Wallach, Tim
❑ 81ExpPos-16
❑ 82Don-140
❑ 82ExpHygM-23
❑ 82ExpPos-40
❑ 82Fle-210
❑ 82OPC-191
❑ 82Top-191
❑ 83AllGamPI-126
❑ 83Don-392
❑ 83ExpPos-34
❑ 83ExpStu-12
❑ 83Fle-299
❑ 83OPC-229
❑ 83Top-552
❑ 83TopSti-257
❑ 84AllGamPI-36
❑ 84Don-421
❑ 84ExpPos-35
❑ 84ExpStu-14
❑ 84Fle-291
❑ 84Nes792-232
❑ 84OPC-232
❑ 84Top-232
❑ 84TopSti-94
❑ 84TopTif-232
❑ 85AllGamPI-126
❑ 85Don-87
❑ 85Fle-412
❑ 85Lea-199
❑ 85OPC-3
❑ 85OPCPos-6
❑ 85Top-473
❑ 85TopSti-87
❑ 85TopTif-473
❑ 86BasStaB-117
❑ 86Don-219
❑ 86DonAll-25
❑ 86ExpPos-17
❑ 86ExpProPa-11
❑ 86ExpProPo-10
❑ 86Fle-263
❑ 86FleMin-56
❑ 86GenMilB-6I
❑ 86Lea-97
❑ 86OPC-217
❑ 86Spo-123
❑ 86Top-685
❑ 86Top-703
❑ 86TopSti-82
❑ 86TopTat-18
❑ 86TopTif-685
❑ 86TopTif-703
❑ 87Don-179
❑ 87DonOpeD-88
❑ 87ExpPos-32
❑ 87Fle-334
❑ 87FleGlo-334
❑ 87GenMilB-4H
❑ 87HosSti-5
❑ 87Lea-61
❑ 87OPC-55
❑ 87RedFolSB-117
❑ 87Spo-72
❑ 87Spo-115
❑ 87SpoTeaP-20
❑ 87StuPan-7
❑ 87Top-55
❑ 87TopSti-80
❑ 87TopTif-55
❑ 88AlaGolAA70TI-17
❑ 88Don-222
❑ 88DonAll-59
❑ 88DonBasB-258
❑ 88ExpPos-33
❑ 88Fle-198
❑ 88FleAwaW-44
❑ 88FleBasA-43
❑ 88FleBasM-42
❑ 88FleGlo-198
❑ 88FleMin-91
❑ 88FleStiC-98
❑ 88FleWaxBC-C15
❑ 88KayB-32
❑ 88Lea-193
❑ 88Lea-255
❑ 88MSAHosD-7
❑ 88MSAJifPD-18
❑ 88Nes-23
❑ 88OPC-94
❑ 88PanSti-327
❑ 88RedFolSB-94
❑ 88Sco-70
❑ 88ScoGlo-70
❑ 88Spo-151
❑ 88StaLinE-17
❑ 88Top-399
❑ 88Top-560
❑ 88TopBig-7
❑ 88TopClo-117
❑ 88TopCoi-59
❑ 88TopGloS-18
❑ 88TopMinL-58
❑ 88TopRevLL-6
❑ 88TopSti-85
❑ 88TopStiB-9
❑ 88TopTif-399
❑ 88TopTif-560
❑ 88TopUKM-84
❑ 88TopUKMT-84
❑ 89Bow-362
❑ 89BowTif-362
❑ 89Don-156
❑ 89DonBasB-34
❑ 89ExpPos-29
❑ 89Fle-395
❑ 89FleGlo-395
❑ 89K-M-25
❑ 89OPC-78
❑ 89PanSti-122
❑ 89RedFolSB-127
❑ 89Sco-220
❑ 89Spo-114
❑ 89Top-720
❑ 89TopBasT-117
❑ 89TopBig-215
❑ 89TopSti-70
❑ 89TopTif-720
❑ 89TVSpoM-16
❑ 89UppDec-102
❑ 90Bow-114
❑ 90BowTif-114
❑ 90Don-220
❑ 90DonBesN-55
❑ 90DonLeaS-28
❑ 90ExpPos-37
❑ 90Fle-364
❑ 90FleAwaW-41
❑ 90FleCan-364
❑ 90FleLeaL-41
❑ 90FleLeaLC-41
❑ 90Lea-80
❑ 90M.Vpin-62
❑ 90OPC-370
❑ 90PanSti-286
❑ 90PubIntS-189
❑ 90RedFolSB-99
❑ 90Sco-192
❑ 90Spo-182
❑ 90Top-370
❑ 90TopBig-70
❑ 90TopCoi-60
❑ 90TopDou-68
❑ 90TopMinL-64
❑ 90TopSti-74
❑ 90TopStiB-9
❑ 90TopTif-370
❑ 90UppDec-273
❑ 90USPlaCA-5D
❑ 91BasBesHRK-18
❑ 91Bow-437
❑ 91ClaGam-2
❑ 91DenHol-12
❑ 91Don-406
❑ 91Don-514
❑ 91Fle-251
❑ 91Lea-388
❑ 91LeaPre-6
❑ 91MSAHolD-3
❑ 91OPC-220
❑ 91OPCPre-125
❑ 91PanCanT1-102
❑ 91PanFreS-141
❑ 91PanSti-64
❑ 91PetSta-10
❑ 91PosCan-2
❑ 91RedFolS-99
❑ 91Sco-210
❑ 91Sco-865
❑ 91Sco100S-58
❑ 91StaClu-463
❑ 91StaPinB-51
❑ 91Stu-200
❑ 91SunSee-23
❑ 91Top-220
❑ 91TopCraJ2-21
❑ 91TopDesS-220
❑ 91TopMic-220
❑ 91TopTif-220
❑ 91Ult-210
❑ 91UppDec-96
❑ 91UppDec-235
❑ 92Bow-372
❑ 92Bow-557
❑ 92ClaGam-40
❑ 92Don-34
❑ 92ExpDonD-19
❑ 92ExpPos-30
❑ 92Fle-494
❑ 92HitTheBB-36
❑ 92Lea-298
❑ 92LeaBlaG-298
❑ 92OPC-385
❑ 92PanSti-204
❑ 92PepDieM-22
❑ 92Pin-161
❑ 92PosCan-5
❑ 92RedFolS-98
❑ 92Sco-595
❑ 92Sco100S-70
❑ 92StaClu-340
❑ 92Stu-60
❑ 92Top-385
❑ 92TopGol-385
❑ 92TopGolW-385
❑ 92TopKid-6
❑ 92TopMic-385
❑ 92TriPla-224
❑ 92Ult-226
❑ 92UppDec-228
❑ 93Bow-70
❑ 93DodMot-6
❑ 93DodPol-26
❑ 93DodStaC-11
❑ 93Don-36
❑ 93ExpDonM-8
❑ 93Fin-118
❑ 93FinRef-118
❑ 93Fla-77
❑ 93Fle-82
❑ 93FleFinE-86
❑ 93HumDumC-33
❑ 93Lea-363
❑ 93OPC-225
❑ 93OPCPre-87
❑ 93PacSpa-191
❑ 93PanSti-215
❑ 93Pin-178
❑ 93Sco-211
❑ 93Sel-190
❑ 93SelRoo-27T
❑ 93StaClu-686
❑ 93StaCluFDI-686
❑ 93StaCluMOP-686
❑ 93Stu-64
❑ 93Top-570
❑ 93TopGol-570
❑ 93TopInaM-570
❑ 93TopInaR-570
❑ 93TopMic-570
❑ 93TopTra-127T
❑ 93TriPla-253
❑ 93Ult-408
❑ 93UppDec-547
❑ 93UppDecGold-547
❑ 94ColC-466
❑ 94ColChoGS-466
❑ 94ColChoSS-466
❑ 94DodDaiN-4
❑ 94DodMot-10
❑ 94DodPol-26
❑ 94Don-326
❑ 94Fin-361
❑ 94FinRef-361
❑ 94Fla-184
❑ 94Fle-527
❑ 94FleExtB-297
❑ 94Lea-21
❑ 94LeaL-122
❑ 94Pac-323
❑ 94Pin-484
❑ 94PinArtP-484
❑ 94PinMusC-484
❑ 94Sco-446
❑ 94ScoGolR-446
❑ 94Sel-139
❑ 94SP-81
❑ 94SPDieC-81
❑ 94StaClu-217
❑ 94StaCluFDI-217
❑ 94StaCluGR-217
❑ 94StaCluMOP-217
❑ 94Stu-73
❑ 94Top-143
❑ 94TopGol-143
❑ 94TopSpa-143
❑ 94TriPla-90
❑ 94Ult-220
❑ 94UppDec-408
❑ 94UppDecED-408
❑ 95Baz-51
❑ 95ColCho-219
❑ 95ColChoGS-219
❑ 95ColChoSE-94
❑ 95ColChoSEGS-94
❑ 95ColChoSESS-94
❑ 95ColChoSS-219
❑ 95DodMot-7
❑ 95DodPol-27
❑ 95Don-539
❑ 95DonPreP-539
❑ 95DonTopotO-274
❑ 95Fin-62
❑ 95FinRef-62
❑ 95Fla-158
❑ 95Fle-551
❑ 95Lea-294
❑ 95LeaLim-140
❑ 95Pac-227
❑ 95PanSti-52
❑ 95Pin-384
❑ 95PinArtP-384
❑ 95PinMusC-384
❑ 95Sco-382
❑ 95ScoGolR-382
❑ 95ScoHaloG-HG104
❑ 95ScoPlaTS-382
❑ 95StaClu-259
❑ 95StaCluFDI-259
❑ 95StaCluMOP-259
❑ 95StaCluSTDW-D259
❑ 95StaCluSTWS-259
❑ 95StaCluVR-127
❑ 95StaCluVRMO-127
❑ 95Stu-165
❑ 95Top-38
❑ 95TopCyb-30
❑ 95TopD3-41
❑ 95TopEmb-37
❑ 95TopEmbGI-37
❑ 95Ult-401
❑ 95UltGolM-401
❑ 95UppDec-71
❑ 95UppDecED-71
❑ 95UppDecEDG-71
❑ 96AngMot-10
❑ 96ColCho-187
❑ 96ColCho-486
❑ 96ColChoGS-187
❑ 96ColChoGS-486
❑ 96ColChoSS-187
❑ 96ColChoSS-486
❑ 96Don-209
❑ 96DonPreP-209
❑ 96Fla-45
❑ 96Pin-58
❑ 96Ult-329
❑ 96UltGolM-329
❑ 97ColCho-136

Wallaesa, John
❑ 42A'sTeal-36
❑ 47TipTop-29
❑ 48WhiSoxTI-26

Wallen, Butch
❑ 87LitFalMP-2393

Wallenhaupt, Ron
❑ 85WatIndT-16

Wallenstein, John
❑ 74WicAerODF-127
Waller, Casey Lee
❑ 88CapCodPPaLP-113
❑ 90CMC-775
❑ 90ReaPhiB-19
❑ 90ReaPhiP-1229
❑ 90ReaPhiS-23
❑ 91LinDriAA-522
❑ 91ReaPhiLD-522
❑ 91ReaPhiP-1379
❑ 92ReaPhiS-546
❑ 92ScrRedBF-2457
❑ 92SkyAA F-239
❑ 93ScrRedBF-2553
❑ 93ScrRedBTI-26
❑ 95PorSeaDTI-27
Waller, K.C.
❑ 93ClaFS7-266
Waller, Kevin D.
❑ 80CedRapRT-25
❑ 82MadMusF-22
Waller, Reggie
❑ 80ColAstT-15
❑ 89AubAstP-2168
Waller, Rich
❑ 77BriRedST-20
Waller, Ty (Elliott)
❑ 78St.PetCT-25
❑ 79ArkTraT-9
❑ 82Fle-607
❑ 82IowCubT-13
❑ 82Top-51
❑ 84TucTorC-60
❑ 85TucTorC-64
❑ 86TucTorP-24
❑ 87TucTorP-6
❑ 88RivRedWCLC-233
❑ 88RivRedWP-1414
❑ 88SpoIndP-1923
❑ 89RivRedWCLC-30
❑ 90RivRedWCLC-27
❑ 94SpoIndC-25
❑ 94SpoIndF-3339
❑ 95PadMot-28
Walles, Todd
❑ 91BelMarCB-8
❑ 91BelMarP-3676
Wallgren, Charles
❑ 30Zee-69
❑ 33Zee-150
Wallgren, Chris
❑ 90EliTwiS-23
Wallin, Craig
❑ 89SouBenWSGS-1
Wallin, Les (Leslie)
❑ 88WinHavRSS-25
❑ 89LynRedSS-20
❑ 90LynRedSTI-9
❑ 91WinHavRSC-21
❑ 91WinHavRSP-500
❑ 92WinHavRSC-21
❑ 92WinHavRSF-1789
❑ 93NewBriRSF-1231
Walling, David
❑ 99Bow-436
❑ 99BowGol-436
❑ 99BowInt-436
Walling, Denny
❑ 77SanJosMC-17
❑ 77Top-473
❑ 78AstPos-25
❑ 79AstPos-26
❑ 79Top-553
❑ 80OPC-161
❑ 80Top-306
❑ 81AstPos-27
❑ 81Don-144
❑ 81Fle-66
❑ 81Top-439
❑ 82AstAstI-6
❑ 82AstPos-28
❑ 82Don-496
❑ 82Fle-236
❑ 82Top-147
❑ 83AstPos-35
❑ 83Don-419
❑ 83Fle-469
❑ 83Top-692
❑ 84AstMot-19
❑ 84AstPos-32
❑ 84Don-641
❑ 84Fle-244
❑ 84Nes792-36
❑ 84Top-36
❑ 84TopSti-73
❑ 84TopTif-36
❑ 85AstHouP-9
❑ 85AstMot-5
❑ 85Don-527
❑ 85Fle-365
❑ 85Top-382
❑ 85TopTif-382
❑ 86AstMilL-22
❑ 86AstPol-7
❑ 86AstTeal-16
❑ 86Don-136
❑ 86Fle-314
❑ 86Top-504
❑ 86TopTif-504
❑ 87AstMot-13
❑ 87AstPol-12
❑ 87AstShoSPT-22
❑ 87Don-554
❑ 87Fle-72
❑ 87FleGlo-72
❑ 87Lea-159
❑ 87OPC-222
❑ 87Top-222
❑ 87TopSti-33
❑ 87TopTif-222
❑ 88AstMot-13
❑ 88AstPol-23
❑ 88Don-384
❑ 88DonBasB-309
❑ 88Fle-458
❑ 88FleGlo-458
❑ 88Lea-224
❑ 88OPC-131
❑ 88PanSti-296
❑ 88Sco-145
❑ 88ScoGlo-145
❑ 88ScoSam-145
❑ 88StaLinAst-19
❑ 88Top-719
❑ 88TopSti-31
❑ 88TopTif-719
❑ 89CarSmo-23
❑ 89CarTeal-33
❑ 89ChaLooLITI-32
❑ 89Don-279
❑ 89Fle-465
❑ 89FleGlo-465
❑ 89Sco-49
❑ 89Top-196
❑ 89TopTif-196
❑ 89UppDec-327
❑ 90CarSmo-26
❑ 90Don-677
❑ 90Fle-263
❑ 90FleCan-263
❑ 90OPC-462
❑ 90Top-462
❑ 90TopTif-462
❑ 90TopTVCa-30
❑ 91Fle-651
❑ 91RanMot-18
❑ 92Bow-530
❑ 93RanKee-371
❑ 96A'sMot-28
❑ 97A'sMot-28
❑ 98A'sMot-28
Walling, Kendall
❑ 86TriTriC-192
❑ 87QuaCitAP-25
Wallis, Jacob
❑ 98BilMusTI-37
Wallis, Joe
❑ 76CubTri-26
❑ 76OPC-598
❑ 76Top-598
❑ 77BurCheD-190
❑ 77Top-279
❑ 78SSP270-259
❑ 78Top-614
❑ 79Top-406
❑ 80Top-562
Wallis, Michael
❑ 98WilCubM-25
Walls, Doug
❑ 94AshTouC-24
❑ 94AshTouF-1782
❑ 94Bow-442
❑ 95SalAvaTI-7
❑ 97PorRocG-29
❑ 98SalAvaC-26
Walls, Eric
❑ 94RocRoyC-27
❑ 94RocRoyF-580
❑ 95SprSulTI-30
Walls, R. Lee
❑ 53MotCoo-56
❑ 55Bow-82
❑ 56PirTeal-24
❑ 57Kah-29
❑ 57Top-52
❑ 58Top-66
❑ 59Top-105
❑ 59TopVen-105
❑ 60Kah-42
❑ 60Lea-111
❑ 60Top-506
❑ 61Pos-119A
❑ 61Pos-119B
❑ 61Top-78
❑ 61TopStal-60
❑ 62DodBelB-56
❑ 62DodVol-9
❑ 62Top-129A
❑ 62Top-129B
❑ 62TopStal-160
❑ 62TopVen-129
❑ 63Jel-113
❑ 63Pos-113
❑ 63Top-11
❑ 64Top-411
❑ 83YanPhoA-3
❑ 90DodTar-828
Wallwork, Dave
❑ 86PenWhiSP-26
❑ 87PenWhiSP-18
❑ 88BirBarB-6
❑ 89BirBarB-25
❑ 89BirBarP-96
❑ 90BirBarB-27
Walraven, Randy
❑ 78DayBeaAT-26
Walrond, Les
❑ 98NewJerCM-32
Walsh, August
❑ 29Zee-34
❑ 30Zee-41
❑ 31Zee-41
❑ 32Zee-46
Walsh, Christy
❑ 92MegRut-161
Walsh, Dave
❑ 84SyrChiT-21
❑ 86KnoBluJP-25
❑ 87KnoBluJP-1512
❑ 89AlbDukCm-10
❑ 89AlbDukP-70
❑ 90AlbDukCm-11
❑ 90AlbDukP-345
❑ 90AlbDukTr-30
❑ 90CMC-413
❑ 90ProAAAF-66
❑ 90TriAllGP-AAA33
❑ 91AlbDukLD-22
❑ 91DodPho-29
❑ 91LinDriAAA-22
❑ 91OPC-367
❑ 91Sco-351
❑ 91Top-367
❑ 91TopDeb90-162
❑ 91TopDesS-367
❑ 91TopMic-367
❑ 91TopTif-367
Walsh, Dee
❑ 14B18B-28
Walsh, Dennis
❑ 91NiaFalRC-21
❑ 91NiaFalRP-3633
❑ 92FayGenC-23
❑ 92FayGenF-2169
❑ 93LakTigC-25
❑ 93LakTigF-1312
Walsh, Ed
❑ 07WhiSoxGWH-11
❑ 09AmeCarE90-1-116
❑ 09ColChiE-299
❑ 09MaxPubP-16
❑ 09SpoNewSM-9
❑ 09T206-368
❑ 10ChiE-19
❑ 10DomDisP-121
❑ 10E98-29
❑ 10JuJuDE-39
❑ 10SepAnoP-25
❑ 10SweCapPP-14
❑ 11BasBatEU-42
❑ 11HelSta-18
❑ 11L1L-132
❑ 11MecDFT-39
❑ 11PinT-5-760
❑ 11PloCanE-65
❑ 11S81LarS-107
❑ 11SpoLifCW-361
❑ 11SpoLifM-33
❑ 11T205-177
❑ 11TurRedT-125
❑ 12ColRedB-299
❑ 12ColTinT-299
❑ 12HasTriFT-22A
❑ 13NatGamW-42
❑ 13TomBarW-38
❑ 14CraJacE-36
❑ 14PieStaT-107
❑ 14PolGroW-29
❑ 14TexTomE-45
❑ 15CraJacE-36
❑ 15SpoNewM-187
❑ 16BF2FP-20
❑ 16SpoNewM-184
❑ 39PC7AlbHoF-49
❑ 48ExhHoF-31
❑ 49LeaPre-8
❑ 50CalHOFW-76
❑ 53ArtHaloFP-86
❑ 60Fle-49
❑ 61Fle-83
❑ 63BazA-7
❑ 69Baz-10
❑ 72FleFamF-23
❑ 74CapPub-8
❑ 76ShaPiz-49
❑ 77GalGloG-143
❑ 80LauFamF-34
❑ 80PerHaloFP-49
❑ 80SSPHOF-49
❑ 85WhiSoxC-34
❑ 85Woo-35
❑ 87HygAllG-45
❑ 88UtiBluSP-25
❑ 89HOFStiB-77
❑ 91ConTSN-273
❑ 92ConTSN-337
❑ 93ConTSN-703
❑ 93CraJac-23
❑ 94ConTSN-1013
❑ 94ConTSNB-1013
Walsh, Ed Jr.
❑ 30WhiSoxTI-25
❑ 32Zee-68
❑ 33Zee-76
❑ 60Fle-49
Walsh, James C.
❑ 11PinT-5-308
❑ 11SpoLifM-242A
❑ 11SpoLifM-242B
❑ 12ImpTobC-20
❑ 14B18B-36A
❑ 14B18B-36B
❑ 14CraJacE-144
❑ 15CraJacE-144
❑ 17HolBreD-110
❑ 19Zee-121
Walsh, Jay
❑ 83LynPirT-28
Walsh, Jim
❑ 17ColE13-182
❑ 50PirTeal-23
❑ 81QuaCitCT-11
❑ 82QuaCitCT-25
❑ 83MidCubT-4
Walsh, Joseph
❑ 87OldJudN-515
Walsh, Matt
❑ 94WesMicWC-23
❑ 94WesMicWF-2296
❑ 95ModA'sTI-29
❑ 96ModA'sB-11
Walsh, Michael
❑ 20Zee-118
Walsh, Rob
❑ 89MisStaB-36
Walsh, Tom
❑ 21Zee-134
❑ 22Zee-111
❑ 23Zee-150
❑ 23Zee-174
❑ 24Zee-109
Walter, Craig
❑ 85Ft.MyeRT-4
Walter, Gene
❑ 83MiaMarT-5
❑ 84BeaGolGT-9
❑ 85LasVegSC-112
❑ 86DonRoo-47
❑ 86Fle-644
❑ 86FleUpd-124
❑ 86TopTra-121T
❑ 86TopTraT-121T
❑ 87Don-511
❑ 87Fle-433
❑ 87FleGlo-433
❑ 87MetColP-49
❑ 87TidTidP-27
❑ 87TidTidT-21
❑ 87Top-248
❑ 87TopTif-248
❑ 88BlaYNPRWLU-12
❑ 88DonTeaBM-NEW
❑ 88Fle-153
❑ 88FleGlo-153
❑ 88MetColP-50
❑ 88MetKah-31
❑ 89BlaYNPRWLU-20
❑ 89Top-758
❑ 89TopTif-758
❑ 89UppDec-604
❑ 91MetWIZ-424
❑ 91PawRedSDD-27
❑ 92SyrChiF-1967
❑ 92SyrChiS-520
❑ 93EdmTraF-1137
Walter, Jason
❑ 97YakBeaG-34
Walter, Jim
❑ 85RedWinA-24
Walter, Mike
❑ 94QuaCitRBC-23
❑ 94QuaCitRBF-534
❑ 96MidLeaAB-29
❑ 96QuaCitRB-29
❑ 97JacGen-26
❑ 97JacGenS-25
❑ 98JacGenM-23
Walterhouse, Dick
❑ 77SalPirT-26A
❑ 77SalPirT-26B
❑ 79BufBisT-19
Walters, Alfred
❑ 17ColE13-183
❑ 22E120-15
❑ 26Zee-63
Walters, Brett
❑ 95MidLeaA-54
❑ 96RanCucQB-27
❑ 97MobBayBB-16
❑ 98MobBayBTI-29
Walters, Bucky (William H.)
❑ 28LaPre-22
❑ 33Zee-48
❑ 36GouWidPPR-A107
❑ 36WorWidGV-61
❑ 37ExhFou-6
❑ 38ExhFou-6
❑ 38RedOraW-29
❑ 39ExhSal-22
❑ 39OrcPhoAP-23
❑ 39PlaBal-22
❑ 39RedTeal-25
❑ 40PlaBal-73
❑ 41DouPlaR-7
❑ 41DouPlaR-95
❑ 41HarHarW-26
❑ 41PlaBal-3
❑ 41WheM5-20
❑ 42GilRazL-1
❑ 47Exh-235
❑ 49EurSta-97
❑ 54BraJohC-31
❑ 55BraGolS-30
❑ 55BraJohC-31
❑ 76RedParC-23
❑ 77CinRedT-7
❑ 79DiaGre-257
❑ 82OhiHaloF-34
❑ 83Bra53F-31
❑ 83TCMPla1943-29
❑ 85BigLeaC3-2
❑ 89PacLegI-164
❑ 92ConTSN-537
❑ 93ConTSN-769
❑ 94ConTSN-1118
❑ 94ConTSNB-1118
Walters, Dan
❑ 86AshTouP-28
❑ 87OscAstP-8
❑ 88ColAstB-12
❑ 89WicWraR-11
❑ 90WicWraRD-23
❑ 91LasVegSLD-297
❑ 91LasVegSP-240
❑ 91LinDriAAA-297
❑ 92DonRooP-BC12
❑ 92DonUpd-U4
❑ 92FleUpd-126
❑ 92LasVegSS-246
❑ 92PadPolD-25
❑ 92ScoRoo-109T
❑ 92SkyAAAF-121
❑ 92TopTra-127T
❑ 92TopTraG-127T
❑ 93Don-48
❑ 93Fle-149
❑ 93Lea-156
❑ 93OPCPre-5
❑ 93PacSpa-605
❑ 93PadMot-19
❑ 93PanSti-257
❑ 93Pin-215
❑ 93Sco-332
❑ 93Sel-289
❑ 93StaClu-175
❑ 93StaCluFDI-175
❑ 93StaCluMOP-175
❑ 93Stu-81
❑ 93Top-273
❑ 93TopGol-273
❑ 93TopInaM-273
❑ 93TopInaR-273
❑ 93TopMic-273
❑ 93TriPla-239
❑ 93Ult-125
❑ 93UppDec-172
❑ 93UppDecGold-172
❑ 93USPlaCR-4H
Walters, Darryel
❑ 85BelBreT-13
❑ 86StoPorP-25
❑ 87ElPasDP-21
❑ 88DenZepC-23
❑ 88DenZepP-1255
❑ 89DenZepC-16
❑ 89DenZepP-54
❑ 89ElPasDGS-29
❑ 90CMC-31
❑ 90DenZepC-6
❑ 90DenZepP-640
❑ 90ProAAAF-665
Walters, David
❑ 86ElmPioRSP-25
❑ 87GreHorP-26
❑ 88LynRedSS-24
❑ 89EasLeaDDP-DD24
❑ 89NewBriRSP-614
❑ 89NewBriRSS-20
❑ 90NewBriRSB-25
❑ 90NewBriRSP-1320
❑ 90NewBriRSS-20
❑ 91LinDriAAA-371
❑ 91PawRedSDD-28
❑ 91PawRedSLD-371
❑ 91PawRedSP-40
❑ 92PawRedSF-924
❑ 92PawRedSS-371
❑ 92SkyAAAF-170
❑ 97DunDonPPS-28
Walters, John
❑ 31Zee-75
❑ 32Zee-120
❑ 79WatIndT-28
Walters, Ken
❑ 60Top-511
❑ 61Pos-122A
❑ 61Pos-122B
❑ 61Top-394
❑ 62Top-328
❑ 63RedEnq-31
❑ 63RedFreBC-30
❑ 63Top-534
❑ 81TCM60I-317
Walters, Kent
❑ 88MisStaB-32
Walters, Leigh
❑ 91MelBusF-8
Walters, Mike
❑ 80ElPasDT-22
❑ 81SalLakCGT-13
❑ 82SpoIndT-9
❑ 82TolMudHT-8
❑ 83TolMudHT-10
❑ 84MinTwiP-30
❑ 84Nes792-673
❑ 84Top-673
❑ 84TopTif-673
❑ 84TwiTeal-22
❑ 85TolMudHT-11
❑ 85Top-187
❑ 85TopTif-187
Walters, Scott
❑ 90MisStaB-44
Walters, Stan

❑ 80PhiBul-11
Walters, Vic
❑ 78AppFoxT-25
❑ 79AppFoxT-24
Walther, Chris
❑ 96OgdRapTI-42
❑ 97BelSnaB-28
❑ 98StoPorG-29
Walton, Bruce
❑ 86ModA'sC-20
❑ 86ModA'sP-26
❑ 87ModA'sC-17
❑ 87ModA'sP-14
❑ 88HunStaTI-25
❑ 89TacTigC-8
❑ 89TacTigP-1546
❑ 90CMC-583
❑ 90ProAAAF-138
❑ 90TacTigC-6
❑ 90TacTigP-91
❑ 91LinDriAAA-546
❑ 91ScoRoo-88T
❑ 91TacTigLD-546
❑ 91TacTigP-2306
❑ 92DonRoo-123
❑ 92FleUpd-52
❑ 92StaClu-563
❑ 92TacTigF-2502
❑ 92TopDeb91-179
❑ 92Ult-428
❑ 94ColSprSSF-735
❑ 96MedHatBJTI-31
❑ 97HagSunB-28
Walton, Carlo
❑ 91KisDodP-4191
Walton, Danny
❑ 70BreMcD-31
❑ 70BreMil-24
❑ 70BreTeal-12
❑ 70OPC-134
❑ 70SunPin-18
❑ 70Top-134
❑ 71BreTeal-18
❑ 71Kel-22
❑ 71MLBOffS-455
❑ 71OPC-281
❑ 71Top-281
❑ 71TopCoi-88
❑ 73OPC-516
❑ 73Top-516
❑ 74TacTwiC-27
❑ 78Top-263
❑ 79SpoIndT-4
❑ 81Don-26A
❑ 83Pil69G-30
❑ 87AstShoSPT-23
❑ 90DodTar-829
❑ 92YanWIZ7-160
❑ 93RanKee-372
❑ 94BreMilB-87
❑ 94BreMilB-372
Walton, Jerome
❑ 87PeoChiP-20
❑ 87PeoChiPW-5
❑ 88BasAmeAAB-5
❑ 88EasLeaAP-29
❑ 88PeoChiTI-30
❑ 88PitCubP-1374
❑ 89Bow-295
❑ 89BowTif-295
❑ 89ClaTraP-156
❑ 89CubMar-20
❑ 89DonBasB-172
❑ 89DonRoo-26
❑ 89FleUpd-80
❑ 89Scomast-2
❑ 89ScoRoo-85T
❑ 89ScoYouS2-36
❑ 89StaWal-1
❑ 89StaWal-2
❑ 89StaWal-3
❑ 89StaWal-4
❑ 89StaWal-5
❑ 89StaWal-6
❑ 89StaWal-7
❑ 89StaWal-8
❑ 89StaWal-9
❑ 89StaWal-10
❑ 89StaWal-11
❑ 89StaWal/O-1
❑ 89StaWal/O-2
❑ 89StaWal/O-4
❑ 89StaWal/O-6
❑ 89StaWal/O-8
❑ 89StaWal/O-10
❑ 89TopAwaW-5
❑ 89TopTra-123T
❑ 89TopTraT-123T
❑ 89UppDec-765
❑ 90Baz-19
❑ 90Bow-35
❑ 90BowIns-10
❑ 90BowInsL-10
❑ 90BowInsT-10
❑ 90BowTif-35
❑ 90BowTif-A10
❑ 90ClaBlu-34
❑ 90Col-15
❑ 90CubMar-22
❑ 90Don-285
❑ 90DonBesN-124
❑ 90DonPre-10
❑ 90Fle-44
❑ 90FleAwaW-42
❑ 90FleBasM-42
❑ 90FleBasMC-42
❑ 90FleCan-44
❑ 90FleLeaL-42
❑ 90FleLeaLC-42
❑ 90FleSoaS-8
❑ 90FleWaxBC-C27
❑ 90Hot50RS-46
❑ 90K-M-7
❑ 90KinDis-15
❑ 90Lea-124
❑ 90M.Vpin-21
❑ 90MLBBasB-50
❑ 90MSAHolD-19
❑ 90OPC-464
❑ 90PanSti-230
❑ 90PubIntS-207
❑ 90RedFolSB-100
❑ 90Sco-229
❑ 90Sco100RS-2
❑ 90Spo-67
❑ 90Top-464
❑ 90TopBig-267
❑ 90TopCoi-35
❑ 90TopDeb89-134
❑ 90TopDou-69
❑ 90TopGaloC-11
❑ 90TopGloS-39
❑ 90TopHeaU-24
❑ 90TopMag-6
❑ 90TopRoo-29
❑ 90TopSti-50
❑ 90TopSti-327
❑ 90TopStiB-21
❑ 90TopTif-464
❑ 90TopTVCu-34
❑ 90ToyRoo-29
❑ 90UppDec-345
❑ 90WonBreS-8
❑ 90Woo-6
❑ 91Bow-413
❑ 91Cla2-T29
❑ 91ClaGam-95
❑ 91CubMar-20
❑ 91CubVinL-33
❑ 91Don-72
❑ 91Fle-437
❑ 91Lea-39
❑ 91OPC-135
❑ 91PanFreS-48
❑ 91PanSti-44
❑ 91Sco-13
❑ 91StaClu-162
❑ 91Top-135
❑ 91TopDesS-135
❑ 91TopMic-135
❑ 91TopTif-135
❑ 91Ult-70
❑ 91UppDec-332
❑ 92Bow-27
❑ 92CubMar-20
❑ 92Don-528
❑ 92Fle-396
❑ 92OPC-543
❑ 92PanSti-187
❑ 92Pin-224
❑ 92Sco-457
❑ 92StaClu-421
❑ 92StaPro-11
❑ 92Top-543
❑ 92TopGol-543
❑ 92TopGolW-543
❑ 92TopMic-543
❑ 92Ult-184
❑ 92UppDec-463
❑ 93PacSpa-64
❑ 93Ult-526
❑ 93VanCanF-2611
❑ 94RedKah-32
❑ 95RedKah-33
❑ 95Sco-207
❑ 95ScoGolR-207
❑ 95ScoPlaTS-207
❑ 96Fle-356
❑ 96FleTif-356
❑ 96FleUpd-U107
❑ 96FleUpdTC-U107
❑ 96LeaSigA-237
❑ 96LeaSigAG-238
❑ 96LeaSigAS-238
❑ 97Ult-493
❑ 97UltGolME-493
❑ 97UltPlaME-493
Walton, Jim
❑ 73OPC-646
❑ 73Top-646
❑ 74Top-99
Walton, Reggie
❑ 75LafDriT-14
❑ 79SpoIndT-9
❑ 80MarPos-23
❑ 80SpoIndT-21
❑ 80VenLeaS-176
❑ 81Fle-609
❑ 81SpoIndT-14
❑ 82PorBeaT-22
❑ 82Top-711
Walton, Rob
❑ 88ChaKniTI-6
Walton, Tim
❑ 96MarPhiB-29
Walton, Zack
❑ 98ForMyeMTI-17
Wambsganss, Bill
❑ 16SpoNewM-185
❑ 17ColE13-184
❑ 17HolBreD-111
❑ 20NatCarE-105
❑ 21E121So1-111
❑ 21E121So8-104
❑ 21Nei-31
❑ 22AmeCarE122-74
❑ 22E120-44
❑ 22W572-112
❑ 22W575-146
❑ 23MapCriV-29
❑ 23W501-22
❑ 25Exh-72
❑ 26Exh-112
❑ 27Exh-55
❑ 63GadFunC-59
❑ 68LauWorS-17
❑ 68SCFOldT-16
❑ 72LauGreF-49
❑ 76MotOldT-4
❑ 77GalGloG-262
❑ 77Ind192T-20
❑ 77Spo-4107
❑ 79DiaGre-277
❑ 81ConTSN-51
❑ 88ConSer4-29
❑ 90HOFStiB-24
❑ 91ConTSN-200
❑ 94ConTSN-1129
❑ 94ConTSNB-1129
❑ 95ConTSN-1358
Wampler, Samuel
❑ 94MarPhiC-28
❑ 94MarPhiF-3299
❑ 95MarPhiTI-29
Wandler, Mike
❑ 87PocGiaTB-20
Waner, Lloyd L.
❑ 25Zee-125
❑ 26Zee-154
❑ 28W502-59
❑ 28W513-73
❑ 28W56PlaC-D12
❑ 28Yue-59
❑ 29ExhFou-14
❑ 29PorandAR-94
❑ 30SchR33-2
❑ 30SchR33-16
❑ 30UncJac-28
❑ 30W554-17
❑ 31Exh-14
❑ 32USCar*-13
❑ 33ButCre-27
❑ 33ExhFou-7
❑ 33GeoCMil-30
❑ 33Gou-164
❑ 33GouCanV-90
❑ 33RitCE-10H
❑ 33RitCE-12D
❑ 33WorCig-93
❑ 33WorCig-94
❑ 34BabRutG-62
❑ 34BatR31-17
❑ 34BatR31-157
❑ 34ButPreR-61
❑ 34DiaMatCSB-190
❑ 34DiaStaR-16
❑ 34ExhFou-7
❑ 35DiaMatCS2-21
❑ 35DiaMatCS3T1-144
❑ 35GouPuzR-1E
❑ 35GouPuzR-3C
❑ 35GouPuzR-5C
❑ 35GouPuzR-14C
❑ 36GouWidPPR-A108
❑ 36NatChiFPR-96
❑ 36NatChiFPR-119
❑ 36R31PasP-39
❑ 36SandSW-49
❑ 38BasTabP-27
❑ 39PlaBal-89
❑ 40PlaBal-105
❑ 41DouPlaR-119
❑ 51R42SmaS-110
❑ 59OklTodML-2
❑ 60Fle-78
❑ 61Fle-84
❑ 67TopVen-167
❑ 72FleFamF-35
❑ 73TCMAllG-23
❑ 76GrePlaG-25A
❑ 76RowExh-15
❑ 76ShaPiz-107
❑ 77GalGloG-86
❑ 78DexHaloFP-50
❑ 79DiaGre-355
❑ 80PacLeg-24
❑ 80PerHaloFP-107
❑ 80PerHaloFPS-13
❑ 80SSPHOF-107
❑ 81ConTSN-62
❑ 83DonHOFH-22
❑ 84OCoandSI-147
❑ 85Woo-36
❑ 86ConSer1-58
❑ 89DodSmoG-32
❑ 89HOFStiB-42
❑ 89PacLegI-128
❑ 90DodTar-830
❑ 90PerGreM-15
❑ 91ConTSN-6
❑ 91ConTSN-265
❑ 92ConTSN-429
❑ 92ConTSN-562
❑ 92ConTSNCI-17
❑ 92MegRut-156
❑ 94ConTSN-1006
❑ 94ConTSN-1180
❑ 94ConTSNB-1006
❑ 95MegRut-9
Waner, Paul P.
❑ 23Zee-151
❑ 24Zee-110
❑ 25Zee-124
❑ 26SpoComoA-45
❑ 28Exh-27
❑ 28PorandAR-A38
❑ 28PorandAR-B38
❑ 28W502-45
❑ 28W513-70
❑ 28W56PlaC-D3
❑ 28Yue-45
❑ 29ExhFou-14
❑ 29PorandAR-95
❑ 30SchR33-16
❑ 30UncJac-29
❑ 31Exh-14
❑ 31W517-34
❑ 32OrbPinUP-58
❑ 32R33So2-421
❑ 32USCar*-2
❑ 33ButCanV-52
❑ 33ButCre-28
❑ 33CraJacP-24
❑ 33ExhFou-7
❑ 33GeoCMil-31
❑ 33Gou-25
❑ 33GouCanV-25
❑ 33NatLeaAC-1
❑ 33RitCE-5S
❑ 33RitCE-6D
❑ 33TatOrb-58
❑ 33TatOrbSDR-201
❑ 33WorCig-95
❑ 33WorCig-96
❑ 34BabRutG-63
❑ 34ButPreR-62
❑ 34DiaMatCSB-191
❑ 34DiaStaR-83
❑ 34ExhFou-7
❑ 34Gou-11
❑ 34GouCanV-67
❑ 35DiaMatCS2-22
❑ 35DiaMatCS3T1-145
❑ 35ExhFou-7
❑ 35GouPuzR-1E
❑ 35GouPuzR-3C
❑ 35GouPuzR-5C
❑ 35GouPuzR-14C
❑ 36DiaMatCS3T2-23
❑ 36ExhFou-7
❑ 36GouBWR-24
❑ 36GouWidPPR-A109
❑ 36NatChiFPR-96
❑ 36R31PasP-39
❑ 36SandSW-50
❑ 36WorWidGV-2
❑ 37ExhFou-7
❑ 37GouThuMR-10
❑ 37KelPepS-BB17
❑ 38CloFotW-86
❑ 38ExhFou-7
❑ 38GouFliMR-10A
❑ 38GouFliMR-10B
❑ 38WheBB10-15
❑ 39PC7AlbHoF-62
❑ 39PlaBal-112
❑ 40PlaBal-104
❑ 41DouPlaR-15
❑ 43DodTeal-23
❑ 50CalHOFW-77
❑ 51R42SmaS-111
❑ 53ArtHaloFP-87
❑ 59OklTodML-1
❑ 60Fle-76
❑ 61Fle-85
❑ 63HalofFB-19A
❑ 67TopVen-166
❑ 72FleFamF-24
❑ 73Dod194T-30
❑ 73TCMAllG-21
❑ 74Bra193NLA-1
❑ 75ShaPiz-2
❑ 76GrePlaG-9
❑ 76RowExh-15
❑ 76ShaPiz-62
❑ 77BobParHoF-50
❑ 77GalGloG-49
❑ 77GalGloG-209
❑ 78DodTCM4-8
❑ 80PacLeg-21
❑ 80PerHaloFP-62
❑ 80PirGreT-6
❑ 80SSPHOF-62
❑ 81ConTSN-61
❑ 82TCMGreH-28
❑ 83BigLeaCOA-25
❑ 83ConMar-37
❑ 83DonHOFH-22
❑ 84OCoandSI-177
❑ 85FegMurCG-20
❑ 86ConSer1-8
❑ 86PirGreT-6
❑ 86SpoDecG-15
❑ 87HygAllG-46
❑ 88ConNatA-23
❑ 89HOFStiB-45
❑ 89PacLegI-127
❑ 90DodTar-831
❑ 90PerGreM-15
❑ 91ConTSN-5
❑ 91ConTSN-167
❑ 91ConTSN-315
❑ 92ConTSN-563
❑ 92YanWIZH-34
❑ 93ConTSN-672
❑ 94ConTSN-1099
❑ 94ConTSN-1180
❑ 94ConTSNB-1099
❑ 94ConTSNB-1180
❑ 95MegRut-9
Wanish, John
❑ 88BakDodCLC-261
❑ 89St.CatBJP-2086
❑ 90MyrBeaBJP-2778
❑ 91DunBluJC-11
❑ 91DunBluJP-207
Wanke, Chuck
❑ 90BenBucL-19
❑ 91EveGiaC-25
❑ 91EveGiaP-3914
❑ 92CliGiaC-16
❑ 92CliGiaF-3599
❑ 93SanJosGC-9
❑ 93SanJosGF-10
Wanz, Doug
❑ 81VanCanT-3
Wapnick, Steve
❑ 86AncGlaPTI-36
❑ 88MyrBeaBJP-1166
❑ 89DunBluJS-22
❑ 90Bow-346
❑ 90BowTif-346
❑ 90CMC-663
❑ 90ProAAAF-352
❑ 90SyrChiC-27
❑ 90SyrChiMB-27
❑ 90SyrChiP-572
❑ 91LinDriAAA-520
❑ 91SyrChiLD-520
❑ 91SyrChiMB-26
❑ 91SyrChiP-2481
❑ 91TopDeb90-163
❑ 92Don-743
❑ 92Sco-863
❑ 92StaClu-554
❑ 92VanCanF-2724
❑ 92VanCanS-627
❑ 93LinVenB-80
Warburton, John
❑ 89MisStaB-37
❑ 90MisStaB-40
❑ 91MisStaB-48
Ward, Aaron
❑ 20GasAmeMBD-18
❑ 20NatCarE-106
❑ 21E121So1-112
❑ 21E121So8-105
❑ 21Exh-183
❑ 21KoBreWSI-52
❑ 22E120-75
❑ 22W572-113
❑ 23W501-25
❑ 23W503-50
❑ 23W515-19
❑ 23WilChoV-167
❑ 25Exh-104
❑ 26SpoComoA-46
❑ 27AmeCarE126-7
❑ 30Zee-134
❑ 93ConTSN-747
Ward, Anthony
❑ 88St.CatBJP-2034
❑ 89MyrBeaBJP-1630
❑ 90DunBluJS-23
❑ 90FloStaLAS-47
❑ 90StaFS7-69
❑ 91KnoBluJLD-370
❑ 91KnoBluJP-1766
❑ 91LinDriAA-370
❑ 92SyrChiF-1968
❑ 92SyrChiMB-26
❑ 92SyrChiS-521
❑ 94SyrChiF-972
❑ 94SyrChiTI-28
Ward, Brandon
❑ 97RocCub-29
❑ 97WilCubB-26
Ward, Bryan
❑ 93ElmPioC-26
❑ 93ElmPioF-3825
❑ 94KanCouCC-26
❑ 94KanCouCF-163
❑ 94KanCouCTI-30
❑ 95PorSeaDTI-28
❑ 96PorSeaDB-28
❑ 97PorSeaD-29
❑ 98BirBarG-27
❑ 98PorSeaD5AQ-31
❑ 99SP SigAuto-BW
❑ 99SPSig-101
Ward, Charles
❑ 16Zee-70
Ward, Chris
❑ 73WicAerJPKB-18
❑ 75OPC-587
❑ 75Top-587
❑ 75TopMin-587
Ward, Chuck
❑ 90DodTar-832
Ward, Colby
❑ 85AncGlaPTI-31
❑ 86SalAngC-89
❑ 87PalSprP-14
❑ 88MidAngGS-11
❑ 89EdmTraC-10
❑ 89EdmTraP-568

❑ 90CMC-454
❑ 90ColSprSSC-2
❑ 90ColSprSSP-37
❑ 90ProAAAF-218
❑ 91Don-330
❑ 91Fle-382
❑ 91OPC-31
❑ 91Top-31
❑ 91TopDeb90-164
❑ 91TopDesS-31
❑ 91TopMic-31
❑ 91TopTif-31
Ward, Colin
❑ 83BirBarT-19
❑ 84PhoGiaC-21
❑ 85PhoGiaC-198
❑ 86Fle-645
❑ 86ShrCapP-27
❑ 87PhoFirP-9
Ward, Dan
❑ 88PalSprACLC-95
❑ 88PalSprAP-1442
Ward, Daryle
❑ 94BriTigF-3514
❑ 95Bes-18
❑ 95FayGenTI-26
❑ 95SPML-57
❑ 96Exc-54
❑ 96LakTigB-29
❑ 96Top-425
❑ 97Bes-70
❑ 97Bow-336
❑ 97BowChr-231
❑ 97BowChrI-231
❑ 97BowChrIR-231
❑ 97BowChrR-231
❑ 97BowInt-336
❑ 97JacGen-27
❑ 97JacGenS-26
❑ 97TexAllM-59
❑ 97TexLeaTP-11
❑ 98Bow-111
❑ 98BowBes-180
❑ 98BowBesAR-180
❑ 98BowBesR-180
❑ 98BowChr-111
❑ 98BowChrGA-111
❑ 98BowChrGAR-111
❑ 98BowChrI-111
❑ 98BowChrIR-111
❑ 98BowChrR-111
❑ 98BowGolA-111
❑ 98BowInt-111
❑ 98ColCho-424
❑ 98ColChoPCR-424
❑ 98DonSigA-91
❑ 98DonSigAC-113
❑ 98DonSigAM-116
❑ 98FleUpd-U82
❑ 98LeaRS-268
❑ 98LeaRSLHolo-268
❑ 98LeaRSLong-268
❑ 98LeaRTrue-268
❑ 98NewOrlZM-25
❑ 98SP Aut-19
❑ 98SP MinDTSPE-DS4
❑ 98SP MinPE-63
❑ 98SP MinSTHPE-H30
❑ 98SP SPTSC-DW
❑ 98SPMin-63
❑ 98SPMinDTS-DS4
❑ 98SPMinSTH-H30
❑ 98SPxFin-197
❑ 98SPxFinR-197
❑ 98SPxFinS-197
❑ 98Top-257
❑ 98TopChr-257
❑ 98TopChrR-257
❑ 98TopDevR-257
❑ 98TopDia-257
❑ 98TopMiniC-257
❑ 98UD3-17
❑ 98UD3-107
❑ 98UD3-197
❑ 98UD3DieCut-17
❑ 98UD3DieCut-107
❑ 98UD3DieCut-197
❑ 98UppDec-585
❑ 98UppDecDS-DS21
❑ 99Bow-220
❑ 99BowBes-148
❑ 99BowBesAR-148
❑ 99BowBesR-148
❑ 99BowChr-220
❑ 99BowChrG-220
❑ 99BowChrGR-220
❑ 99BowChrI-220
❑ 99BowChrIR-220
❑ 99BowChrR-220
❑ 99BowGol-220
❑ 99BowInt-220
❑ 99Fle-244
❑ 99FleSta9-244
❑ 99FleWarT-244
❑ 99JustheS-45
❑ 99JustheSJB-45
❑ 99PacOme-110
❑ 99PacOmeC-110
❑ 99PacOmeG-110
❑ 99PacOmePB-110
❑ 99SkyThu-4
❑ 99SkyThuRant-4
❑ 99SkyThuRave-4
❑ 99SpoIll-43
❑ 99ThuSkySupR-4
❑ 99UppDecBD-103
❑ 99UppDecBDD-103
❑ 99UppDecBDQ-103
❑ 99UppDecBDT-103
❑ 99Vic-167
Ward, David
❑ 87SalLakTTT-12
Ward, Duane
❑ 83DurBulT-25
❑ 85GreBraTI-24
❑ 86BraPol-48
❑ 86FleUpd-125
❑ 87BluJayFS-33
❑ 87Don-45
❑ 87Lea-45
❑ 87OPC-153
❑ 87Top-153
❑ 87TopTif-153
❑ 88BluJayFS-30
❑ 88Don-567
❑ 88Fle-125
❑ 88FleGlo-125
❑ 88OPC-128
❑ 88Top-696
❑ 88TopTif-696
❑ 89BluJayFS-29
❑ 89Don-543
❑ 89DonBasB-216
❑ 89Fle-246
❑ 89FleGlo-246
❑ 89OPC-392
❑ 89Sco-359
❑ 89ScoYouS2-13
❑ 89Top-502
❑ 89TopTif-502
❑ 89UppDec-551
❑ 90BluJayFS-31
❑ 90Don-307
❑ 90Fle-95
❑ 90FleCan-95
❑ 90Lea-501
❑ 90OPC-28
❑ 90PublntS-528
❑ 90Sco-439
❑ 90Spo-107
❑ 90Top-28
❑ 90TopTif-28
❑ 90UppDec-653
❑ 91BluJayFS-28
❑ 91BluJayFS-30
❑ 91BluJayS-8
❑ 91Don-92
❑ 91Fle-187
❑ 91Lea-154
❑ 91OPC-181
❑ 91Sco-561
❑ 91StaClu-363
❑ 91Top-181
❑ 91TopDesS-181
❑ 91TopMic-181
❑ 91TopTif-181
❑ 91Ult-369
❑ 91UppDec-581
❑ 92BluJayP-11
❑ 92Don-308
❑ 92Fle-344
❑ 92Lea-101
❑ 92LeaBlaG-101
❑ 92OPC-365
❑ 92Pin-385
❑ 92Sco-48
❑ 92StaClu-781
❑ 92Top-365
❑ 92TopGol-365
❑ 92TopGolW-365
❑ 92TopMic-365
❑ 92Ult-154
❑ 92UppDec-450
❑ 93BluJayD-11
❑ 93BluJayD4-23
❑ 93BluJayFS-32
❑ 93Bow-307
❑ 93Don-379
❑ 93Fin-17
❑ 93FinRef-17
❑ 93Fla-296
❑ 93Fle-341
❑ 93Lea-135
❑ 93OPC-310
❑ 93OPCWorC-15
❑ 93PacSpa-330
❑ 93Pin-340
❑ 93Sco-436
❑ 93Sel-258
❑ 93SP-53
❑ 93StaClu-382
❑ 93StaCluFDI-382
❑ 93StaCluMOP-382
❑ 93Top-260
❑ 93TopGol-260
❑ 93TopInaM-260
❑ 93TopInaR-260
❑ 93TopMic-260
❑ 93Ult-295
❑ 93UppDec-339
❑ 93UppDecGold-339
❑ 94BluJayUSPC-5D
❑ 94BluJayUSPC-13S
❑ 94Bow-225
❑ 94ColC-287
❑ 94ColChoGS-287
❑ 94ColChoSS-287
❑ 94Don-379
❑ 94DonSpeE-379
❑ 94Fin-375
❑ 94FinRef-375
❑ 94Fle-346
❑ 94FleAllS-25
❑ 94FleExtB-197
❑ 94FUnPac-97
❑ 94Lea-355
❑ 94OPC-160
❑ 94PanSti-10
❑ 94Pin-143
❑ 94PinArtP-143
❑ 94PinMusC-143
❑ 94Sco-481
❑ 94ScoGolR-481
❑ 94Sel-375
❑ 94Spo-58
❑ 94StaClu-377
❑ 94StaCluFDI-377
❑ 94StaCluGR-377
❑ 94StaCluMO-20
❑ 94StaCluMOP-377
❑ 94StaCluT-155
❑ 94StaCluTFDI-155
❑ 94Top-483
❑ 94TopGol-483
❑ 94TopSpa-483
❑ 94TriPla-39
❑ 94Ult-145
❑ 94UltFir-2
❑ 94UppDec-402
❑ 94UppDecED-402
❑ 95BluJayOH-34
❑ 95BluJayUSPC-2D
❑ 95BluJayUSPC-7S
❑ 95FleUpd-31
❑ 95Pin-250
❑ 95PinArtP-250
❑ 95PinMusC-250
❑ 95Sco-529
❑ 95ScoGolR-529
❑ 95ScoPlaTS-529
❑ 95Top-609
❑ 97BluJayS-38
Ward, Gary
❑ 77TacTwiDQ-15
❑ 79TolMudHT-1
❑ 80Top-669
❑ 80VenLeaS-15
❑ 81Don-594
❑ 81Top-328
❑ 81TwiPos-29
❑ 82Don-571
❑ 82Fle-562
❑ 82FleSta-229
❑ 82Top-612
❑ 82TwiPos-27
❑ 83AllGamPI-70
❑ 83Don-429
❑ 83DonActA-18
❑ 83Fle-627
❑ 83FleSta-208
❑ 83FleSti-136
❑ 83Top-517
❑ 83TopSti-92
❑ 83TwiTeal-21
❑ 83TwiTeal-33
❑ 84AllGamPI-160
❑ 84Don-192
❑ 84Fle-576
❑ 84FleUpd-124
❑ 84FunFooP-95
❑ 84Nes792-67
❑ 84OPC-67
❑ 84RanJarP-32
❑ 84Top-67
❑ 84TopSti-303
❑ 84TopTif-67
❑ 84TopTra-126T
❑ 84TopTraT-126T
❑ 85AllGamPI-70
❑ 85Don-342
❑ 85Fle-572
❑ 85Lea-70
❑ 85OPC-84
❑ 85RanPer-32
❑ 85Top-414
❑ 85TopSti-353
❑ 85TopTif-414
❑ 86Don-20
❑ 86Don-98
❑ 86DonAll-51
❑ 86DonSupD-20
❑ 86Fle-575
❑ 86FleMin-113
❑ 86FleStiC-125
❑ 86Lea-20
❑ 86OPC-105
❑ 86RanPer-32
❑ 86Spo-197
❑ 86Top-105
❑ 86TopSti-239
❑ 86TopTat-21
❑ 86TopTif-105
❑ 87Don-427
❑ 87DonOpeD-242
❑ 87Fle-140
❑ 87FleGlo-140
❑ 87FleLimE-41
❑ 87FleRecS-40
❑ 87FleUpd-122
❑ 87FleUpdG-122
❑ 87Lea-177
❑ 87OPC-218
❑ 87Spo-91
❑ 87Top-762
❑ 87TopSti-235
❑ 87TopTif-762
❑ 87TopTra-125T
❑ 87TopTraT-125T
❑ 88Don-251
❑ 88DonReaBY-251
❑ 88Fle-224
❑ 88FleGlo-224
❑ 88OPC-235
❑ 88PanSti-160
❑ 88RedFolSB-95
❑ 88Sco-157
❑ 88ScoGlo-157
❑ 88Spo-125
❑ 88StaLinY-18
❑ 88Top-235
❑ 88TopBig-195
❑ 88TopSti-303
❑ 88TopTif-235
❑ 89Fle-273
❑ 89FleGlo-273
❑ 89FleUpd-33
❑ 89OPC-302
❑ 89Sco-435
❑ 89TigMar-32
❑ 89Top-302
❑ 89TopBig-206
❑ 89TopTif-302
❑ 89TopTra-124T
❑ 89TopTraT-124T
❑ 89UppDec-98
❑ 90Don-621
❑ 90Fle-618
❑ 90FleCan-618
❑ 90Lea-113
❑ 90OPC-679
❑ 90PanSti-68
❑ 90Sco-513
❑ 90TigCok-25
❑ 90Top-679
❑ 90TopTif-679
❑ 91Don-728
❑ 91Fle-356
❑ 91OklStaC-29
❑ 91OPC-556
❑ 91PanFreS-294
❑ 91Sco-637
❑ 91Top-556
❑ 91TopDesS-556
❑ 91TopMic-556
❑ 91TopTif-556
❑ 91UppDec-412
❑ 92OklStaC-29
❑ 92YanWIZ8-196
❑ 93RanKee-373
❑ 94RanAllP-13
❑ 98St.LucMM-27
Ward, Greg
❑ 87SavCarP-8
❑ 88RenSilSCLC-286
❑ 98DanBraQ-18
Ward, Jay (John F.)
❑ 61UniOil-H9
❑ 64Top-116
❑ 64Top-532
❑ 64TopVen-116
❑ 65Top-421
❑ 85CedRapRT-27
❑ 86VerRedP-23
❑ 88CarLeaAS-1
❑ 89WilBilS-24
❑ 92ExpPos-31
❑ 95PriWilCTI-29
Ward, Jim
❑ 67VanMouSO-26
Ward, Jon
❑ 96NewJerCB-28
Ward, Joseph
❑ 11MecDFT-49
❑ 12ImpTobC-6
❑ 32Zee-109
Ward, Kevin
❑ 86PhiTas-NNO
❑ 86ReaPhiP-25
❑ 87MaiGuiT-22
❑ 87ReaPhiP-12
❑ 88MaiPhiC-22
❑ 88MaiPhiP-278
❑ 89HunStaB-22
❑ 90CMC-602
❑ 90ProAAAF-156
❑ 90TacTigC-25
❑ 90TacTigP-109
❑ 91LasVegSLD-298
❑ 91LasVegSP-252
❑ 91LinDriAAA-298
❑ 91PadSmo-38
❑ 91TriA AAGP-AAA21
❑ 92Fle-623
❑ 92Lea-338
❑ 92LeaBlaG-338
❑ 92PadCarJ-23
❑ 92PadMot-19
❑ 92PadPolD-26
❑ 92PadSmo-36
❑ 92Sco-862
❑ 92Sco100RS-42
❑ 92StaClu-853
❑ 92TopDeb91-180
Ward, Larry
❑ 95ChaLooTI-29
❑ 96ChaLooB-5
❑ 97ChaLoo-5
❑ 98ChaLooG-29
Ward, Max
❑ 87Ft.LauYP-12
❑ 88ColCliP-326
Ward, Montgomery (John Mont.)
❑ 76ShaPiz-101
❑ 77BobParHoF-51
❑ 80PerHaloFP-101
❑ 80SSPHOF-101
❑ 86OldJudN-13
❑ 87AllandGN-10
❑ 87BucN28-73A
❑ 87BucN28-73B
❑ 87BucN28-73C
❑ 87FouBasHN-12
❑ 87OldJudN-516
❑ 88GandBCGCE-44
❑ 88SpoTimM-26
❑ 88WG1CarG-45
❑ 89DodSmoG-33
❑ 89SFHaCN-18
❑ 90DodTar-833
❑ 90KalBatN-55
❑ 94OriofB-61
❑ 94UppDecTAE-10
❑ 95May-28A
❑ 95May-28B
❑ 95NewN566-586
❑ 95NewN566-587
Ward, Monty
❑ 98SpolndG-33
Ward, Pete
❑ 47Exh-236
❑ 62AurRec-16
❑ 63Top-324
❑ 63WhiSoxJP-12
❑ 63WhiSoxTS-24
❑ 64ChatheY-48
❑ 64Top-85
❑ 64TopCoi-21
❑ 64TopGia-33
❑ 64TopRooAB-12
❑ 64TopSta-8
❑ 64TopStaU-73
❑ 64TopTatl-72
❑ 64TopVen-85
❑ 64WhiSoxI-24
❑ 64WhiSoxTS-22
❑ 65Baz-8
❑ 65ChaTheY-47
❑ 65OldLonC-37
❑ 65OPC-215
❑ 65Top-215
❑ 65TopEmbl-64
❑ 65TopTral-71
❑ 65WhiSoxJP-11
❑ 66OPC-25
❑ 66Top-25
❑ 66TopRubl-96
❑ 66TopVen-25
❑ 66WhiSoxTI-12
❑ 67AshOil-12
❑ 67CokCapWS-4
❑ 67DexPre-217
❑ 67OPC-143
❑ 67Top-143
❑ 67Top-436
❑ 67TopVen-238
❑ 68AtlOilPBCC-46
❑ 68OPC-33
❑ 68Top-33
❑ 68TopActS-2A
❑ 68TopActS-15A
❑ 68TopVen-33
❑ 69KelPin-18
❑ 69MilBra-285
❑ 69MLBOffS-35
❑ 69MLBPin-29
❑ 69OPC-155
❑ 69Top-155
❑ 69TopDecl-44
❑ 69TopSta-159
❑ 69TopSup-11
❑ 69TopTeaP-11
❑ 69TraSta-20
❑ 69WhiSoxTI-12
❑ 70MLBOffS-251
❑ 70Top-659
❑ 70YanPhoS-33
❑ 71MLBOffS-501
❑ 71OPC-667
❑ 71Top-667
❑ 72MilBra-354
❑ 76UPIS-12
❑ 78TCM60I-120
❑ 80IowOakP-13
❑ 81PorBeaT-1
❑ 85WhiSoxC-32
❑ 91OriCro-473
❑ 92YanWIZ7-161
Ward, Preston
❑ 48DodTeal-26
❑ 50Bow-231
❑ 53Top-173
❑ 54Bow-139
❑ 54Top-72
❑ 55Bow-27
❑ 55Top-95
❑ 55TopDouH-97
❑ 56A'sPos-48
❑ 56Top-328
❑ 57IndTeal-25
❑ 57Top-226
❑ 58IndTeal-23
❑ 58Top-450
❑ 59Top-176
❑ 59TopVen-176
❑ 79TCM50-111

❑ 90DodTar-834
❑ 91TopArc1-173
❑ 94TopArc1-72
❑ 94TopArc1G-72
Ward, Ricky
❑ 90EveGiaB-20
❑ 90EveGiaP-3136
❑ 91CliGiaC-24
❑ 91CliGiaP-844
❑ 92SanJosGC-17
❑ 93SanJosGC-8
❑ 93SanJosGF-20
❑ 94NasXprF-396
Ward, Rube
❑ 90DodTar-1093
Ward, Todd
❑ 89GeoColC-35
❑ 90GeoColC-32
Ward, Turner
❑ 88ColCliC-19
❑ 88ColCliP-17
❑ 90CMC-472
❑ 90ColSprSSC-20
❑ 90ColSprSSP-52
❑ 90ProAAAF-233
❑ 91BluJayFS-31
❑ 91Bow-76
❑ 91Don-429
❑ 91Fle-383
❑ 91IndFanC-28
❑ 91Lea-449
❑ 91OPC-555
❑ 91Sco-732
❑ 91ScoRoo-4
❑ 91StaClu-593
❑ 91Stu-49
❑ 91Stu-138
❑ 91Top-555
❑ 91TopDeb90-165
❑ 91TopDesS-555
❑ 91TopMic-555
❑ 91TopTif-555
❑ 91Ult-118
❑ 91UppDec-762
❑ 92StaClu-621
❑ 92StaCluNC-621
❑ 92SyrChiF-1985
❑ 92SyrChiMB-27
❑ 93BluJayD-9
❑ 93BluJayD4-31
❑ 93BluJayFS-33
❑ 93Don-293
❑ 93Lea-427
❑ 93PacSpa-658
❑ 93Sco-473
❑ 94BreMilB-373
❑ 94BrePol-29
❑ 94BreTeal-28
❑ 94Fla-71
❑ 94Fle-347
❑ 94FleExtB-110
❑ 94FleUpd-58
❑ 94ScoRoo-RT55
❑ 94ScoRooGR-RT55
❑ 94SpoRoo-21
❑ 94SpoRooAP-21
❑ 94StaClu-550
❑ 94StaCluFDI-550
❑ 94StaCluGR-550
❑ 94StaCluMOP-550
❑ 94Stu-49
❑ 94TopTra-104T
❑ 94Ult-381
❑ 95ColCho-177
❑ 95ColChoGS-177
❑ 95ColChoSS-177
❑ 95Don-74
❑ 95DonPreP-74
❑ 95Fle-194
❑ 95Pac-243
❑ 95Sco-263
❑ 95ScoGolR-263
❑ 95ScoPlaTS-263
❑ 95StaClu-495
❑ 95StaCluMOP-495
❑ 95StaCluSTWS-495
❑ 95Ult-70
❑ 95UltGolM-70
❑ 96BrePol-27
❑ 96LeaSigA-238
❑ 96LeaSigAG-239
❑ 96LeaSigAS-239
❑ 97CalCanB-28
❑ 97PacPriGotD-GD60
❑ 97PirPos-41
❑ 98PacOnl-597
❑ 98PacOnlR-597
❑ 98PacOnlWC-597
❑ 98Ult-414
❑ 98UltGolM-414
❑ 98UltMas-414
❑ 98UltPlaM-414
❑ 99Fle-547
❑ 99FleSta9-547
❑ 99FleWarT-547
❑ 99Pac-347
❑ 99PacPlaB-347
❑ 99PacRed-347
❑ 99StaClu-34
❑ 99StaCluFDI-34
❑ 99StaCluOoaK-34
❑ 99StaCluPP-34
❑ 99UppDec-180
❑ 99UppDecEL1-180
❑ 99UppDecEL2-180
Warden, Jon
❑ 68TigDetFPB-25
❑ 69Top-632
❑ 88TigDom-24
Wardle, Curt
❑ 83VisOakF-18
❑ 85FleUpd-127
❑ 85TwiPos-30
❑ 85TwiTeal-26
❑ 85TwiTeal-26
❑ 86Fle-600
❑ 86IndTeal-47
❑ 86MaiGuiP-21
❑ 86Top-303
❑ 86TopTif-303
Wardlow, Joe
❑ 88ButCopKSP-17
❑ 89GasRanS-24
❑ 89Sta-39
❑ 90Bes-208
❑ 90GasRanB-10
❑ 90GasRanP-2531
❑ 90GasRanS-24
❑ 91PriWilCC-20
❑ 91PriWilCP-1437
Wardlow, Mike
❑ 77CedRapGT-14
Wardrop, Adam
❑ 93AusFut-42
Wardwell, Shea
❑ 90ElmPioP-8
❑ 91Cla/Bes-295
❑ 91WinHavRSC-25
❑ 91WinHavRSP-504
Ware, Clyde
❑ 19Zee-29
Ware, Derek
❑ 87DunBluJP-950
Ware, Jeff
❑ 91ClaDraP-31
❑ 91TopTra-124T
❑ 91TopTraT-124T
❑ 92DunBluJC-2
❑ 92DunBluJF-2001
❑ 92OPC-414
❑ 92Pin-546
❑ 92StaCluD-192
❑ 92Top-414
❑ 92TopGol-414
❑ 92TopGolW-414
❑ 92TopMic-414
❑ 92UppDecML-323
❑ 93ClaGolF-88
❑ 95SyrChiTI-26
❑ 96BluJayOH-34
❑ 96Bow-232
❑ 96BowFoi-232
❑ 96ColCho-663
❑ 96ColCho-752
❑ 96ColChoGS-26
❑ 96ColChoGS-663
❑ 96ColChoGS-752
❑ 96ColChoSS-26
❑ 96ColChoSS-663
❑ 96ColChoSS-752
❑ 96Pin-378
❑ 96PinAfi-195
❑ 96PinAfiAP-195
❑ 96PinFoil-378
❑ 97TucTorB-11
Ware, Jeremy
❑ 98JupHamQ-26
Ware, Ricky
❑ 97TamYan-4
❑ 98TamYanM-4
Ware, Ryan
❑ 97HudValRB-13
Wareham, Ronnie
❑ 85CloHSS-42
Warembourg, Scott
❑ 94BenRocC-24
❑ 94BenRocF-3595
Wares, Buzzy (Clyde E.)
❑ 09ObaT21-112
❑ 09ObaT21-284
❑ 11PacCoaBD-69
❑ 11Zee-41
❑ 12ObaPreT-33
❑ 20Zee-133
❑ 31CarMet-28
❑ 41CarW75-27
❑ 46SeaSLP-65
❑ 74Car193T-25
❑ 83Car194T-7
Warfel, Brian
❑ 87ElmPioBC-9
❑ 87ElmPioRC-9
❑ 88ElmPio1C-8
❑ 88ElmPioC-26
❑ 88WinHavRSS-26
Warhop, John
❑ 09ColChiE-300
❑ 09T206-369
❑ 10CouT21-241
❑ 10CouT21-242
❑ 10DomDisP-122
❑ 10E-UOraBSC-24
❑ 10RedCroT-81
❑ 10RedCroT-164
❑ 10RedCroT-254
❑ 10SweCapPP-38
❑ 11HelSta-49
❑ 11PinT-5-811
❑ 12ColRedB-300
❑ 12ColTinT-300
❑ 12T207-192
❑ 28Zee-100
❑ 72ClaCar-56
❑ 94ConTSN-1275
❑ 94ConTSNB-1275
Waring, Jim
❑ 91AubAstC-22
❑ 91AubAstP-4274
❑ 92BurAstC-6
❑ 92BurAstF-548
❑ 92MidLeaATI-47
❑ 93ClaGolF-156
❑ 93ExcFS7-50
❑ 94FloStaLAF-FSL36
❑ 94OscAstC-23
❑ 94OscAstF-1139
❑ 95JacGenTI-11
Waring, Ted
❑ 09ObaT21-96
Warneke, Lon
❑ 32CubTeal-26
❑ 32OrbPinNP-4
❑ 32OrbPinUP-59
❑ 33CraJacP-25
❑ 33DelR33-16
❑ 33GeoCMil-32
❑ 33Gou-203
❑ 33NatLeaAC-8
❑ 33TatOrb-59
❑ 33TatOrbSDR-194
❑ 33WorCig-97
❑ 33WorCig-98
❑ 34BatR31-186
❑ 34DiaMatCSB-192
❑ 34ExhFou-3
❑ 35DiaMatCS2-23
❑ 35DiaMatCS3T1-146
❑ 35ExhFou-3
❑ 36CubTeal-30
❑ 36ExhFou-3
❑ 36GouWidPPR-A110
❑ 36NatChiFPR-93
❑ 36R31PasP-33
❑ 36SandSW-51
❑ 36WheBB4-12
❑ 36WorWidGV-100
❑ 37ExhFou-8
❑ 38CloFotW-87
❑ 38ExhFou-8
❑ 38WheBB11-8
❑ 39ExhSal-63
❑ 39GouPreR303A-46
❑ 39PlaBal-41
❑ 39WorWidGTP-46
❑ 40PlaBal-114
❑ 41CarW75-28
❑ 43CubTeal-23
❑ 55Bow-299
❑ 74Bra193NLA-8
❑ 77GalGloG-222
❑ 81DiaStaCD-120
❑ 83BigLeaCOA-36
❑ 83Car194T-48
❑ 83ConMar-48
❑ 84CubBriPC-1C
❑ 88ConNatA-24
❑ 91ConTSN-231
❑ 92ConTSN-371
❑ 92ConTSN-640
❑ 93ConTSN-687
❑ 94ConTSN-1106
❑ 94ConTSNB-1106
Warner, Bryan
❑ 94BurIndC-25
❑ 94BurIndF-3812
❑ 98SalAvaC-27
Warner, E.H.
❑ 87OldJudN-250
❑ 87OldJudN-517
Warner, Fred
❑ 80PenPilBT-5
❑ 80PenPilCT-8
Warner, Harry
❑ 77OPC-58
❑ 77Top-113
❑ 78BluJayP-23
❑ 80SyrChiT-19
❑ 80SyrChiTI-21
❑ 82BrePol-NNO
❑ 83VisOakF-13
❑ 92BreCarT-xx
Warner, Jack (John R.)
❑ 25Zee-162
❑ 26Exh-96
❑ 33Gou-178
❑ 33WorCig(-100
❑ 49W725AngTI-29
❑ 79DiaGre-302
❑ 90DodTar-835
❑ 92ConTSN-410
Warner, Jack D.
❑ 65Top-354
❑ 66SeaPop-29
Warner, Jackie (John J.)
❑ 65SeaPop-24
❑ 65Top-517
❑ 66Top-553
Warner, Jim
❑ 47SigOil-72
❑ 47SunBre-23
Warner, John Joseph
❑ 03BreE10-149
❑ 08RosComP-87
❑ 11SpoLifCW-362
❑ 24Zee-143
❑ 24Zee-144
❑ 48AngTeal-26
❑ 49AngTeal-37
Warner, Ken
❑ 93DanBraC-27
❑ 93DanBraF-3627
❑ 95DurBulTI-32
Warner, Michael
❑ 92IdaFalGF-3529
❑ 92IdaFalGSP-20
Warner, Mike
❑ 92FroRowDP-71
❑ 92FroRowDPG-71
❑ 92FroRowDPS-71
❑ 93DurBulC-22
❑ 93DurBulF-501
❑ 93DurBulTI-8
❑ 94CarLeaAF-CAR32
❑ 94DurBulC-25
❑ 94DurBulF-343
❑ 94DurBulTI-27
❑ 96GreBraB-29
❑ 96GreBraTI-7
❑ 97GreBraG-27
❑ 98RicBraQ-26
Warner, Pop
❑ 98MemRedG-25
Warner, Randy
❑ 92GulCoaMF-3495
❑ 93KinMetC-23
❑ 93KinMetF-3810
❑ 94CapCitBC-22
❑ 94CapCitBF-1765
❑ 95StLucMTI-32
❑ 96StLucMTI-16
Warner, Ron
❑ 91HamRedC-21
❑ 91HamRedP-4048
❑ 92SavCarC-6
❑ 92SavCarF-673
❑ 93St.PetCC-27
❑ 93St.PetCF-2637
❑ 94ArkTraF-3098
❑ 95ArkTraTI-27
❑ 96ArkTraB-27
❑ 97LouRedB-29
Warner, W.M.
❑ 31CubTeal-27
Warrecker, Teddy
❑ 94BurIndC-26
❑ 94BurIndF-3794
❑ 96KenIndB-24
❑ 97AkrAer-26
Warrecker, William
❑ 89BenBucL-11
❑ 90PalSprACLC-224
❑ 90PalSprAP-2579
Warren, Alan
❑ 88OneYanP-2066
Warren, Ben
❑ 40PhiTeal-22
❑ 41PhiTeal-25
Warren, Brian
❑ 90BriTigP-3167
❑ 91FayGenC-29
❑ 91FayGenP-1171
❑ 92ClaFS7-170
❑ 92ClaFS7-174
❑ 92LonTigF-633
❑ 92LonTigS-422
❑ 92ProFS7-67
❑ 92SkyAA F-177
❑ 93LonTigF-2308
❑ 94IndIndF-1813
❑ 95IndIndF-96
❑ 96IndIndB-26
Warren, Charlie
❑ 77WauMetT-22
Warren, Dallas
❑ 29Zee-35
❑ 30Zee-42
Warren, Derrick
❑ 92BelMarCB-3
❑ 92BelMarF-1460
Warren, DeShawn
❑ 92ClaDraP-31
❑ 93AngStaCl-25
❑ 93StaCluM-181
❑ 93Top-574
❑ 93TopGol-574
❑ 93TopInaM-574
❑ 93TopInaR-574
❑ 93TopMic-574
❑ 94Bow-207
❑ 94BowBes-B12
❑ 94BowBesR-B12
❑ 94CedRapKC-1
❑ 94CedRapKF-1109
❑ 94Cla-159
❑ 94ClaTriF-T10
❑ 95Bow-87
❑ 95CedRapKTI-32
❑ 95MidLeaA-55
❑ 95UppDecML-92
❑ 95UppDecMLFS-92
❑ 96OgdRapTI-40
Warren, Earl
❑ 59FleWil-78
Warren, Glen
❑ 89EveGiaS-29
Warren, Joe
❑ 89BenBucL-12
❑ 91RenSilSCLC-10
Warren, Lance
❑ 97GreFalDTI-31
❑ 98VerBeaDM-19
Warren, Mark
❑ 84IdaFalATI-29
Warren, Marty
❑ 86AppFoxP-28
Warren, Mel
❑ 91KisDodP-4204
Warren, Mike
❑ 84A'sMot-20
❑ 84Don-631
❑ 84Fle-461
❑ 84Fle-639
❑ 84Nes792-5
❑ 84Nes792-338
❑ 84Top-5
❑ 84Top-338
❑ 84TopSti-288B
❑ 84TopTif-5
❑ 84TopTif-338
❑ 85A'sMot-19
❑ 85Don-278
❑ 85Fle-435
❑ 85Top-197
❑ 85TopTif-197
❑ 86OmaRoyP-28
❑ 89RenSilSCLC-248
❑ 92A'sUno7P-4
❑ 93HolLeg-17
Warren, Randy
❑ 88UtiBluSP-12
❑ 89SouBenWSGS-17
Warren, Raymond
❑ 82BurRanF-7
❑ 82BurRanT-12
Warren, Ron
❑ 86ElmPioRSP-26
Warren, Thomas
❑ 97HelBreB-30
Warren, Tommy
❑ 77TCMTheWY-80
❑ 88KimN18-46
❑ 90DodTar-836
Warren, Travis
❑ 87ClePhiP-27
Warriax, Brandon
❑ 98SavSanGM-29
Warstler, Rabbit (Harold)
❑ 34DiaMatCSB-193
❑ 35DiaMatCS3T1-147
❑ 36GouWidPPR-A111
❑ 38CloFotW-88
❑ 39PlaBal-120
❑ 40PlaBal-59
❑ 41Gou-21
❑ 91ConTSN-240
Warthen, Dan
❑ 72Dia-50
❑ 75ExpPos-37
❑ 76ExpRed-35
❑ 76MonExpP-30
❑ 76OPC-374
❑ 76SSP-347
❑ 76Top-374
❑ 77ExpPos-37
❑ 77OPC-99
❑ 77Top-391
❑ 79PorBeaT-17
❑ 80PorBeaT-26
❑ 81BufBisT-12
❑ 82AleDukT-20
❑ 87ChaLooB-2
❑ 88CalCanC-25
❑ 88CalCanP-789
❑ 89BlaYNPRWL-200
❑ 89CalCanC-25
❑ 89CalCanP-523
❑ 90CalCanC-24
❑ 90CalCanP-665
❑ 90CMC-451
❑ 90ProAAAF-130
❑ 92MarMot-27
❑ 94LasVegSF-885
❑ 96PadMot-28
Warthog, Wally the
❑ 98WinWar-29
Warthog, Wilbur the
❑ 98WinWar-29
Warwick, Carl
❑ 62Col.45B-21
❑ 62Jel-161
❑ 62Pos-161
❑ 62PosCan-161
❑ 62SalPlaC-160
❑ 62ShiPlaC-160
❑ 62Top-202
❑ 63Col45"P-16
❑ 63Col45'JP-12
❑ 63Jel-190
❑ 63Pos-190
❑ 63Top-333
❑ 64ChatheY-49
❑ 64Col.45JP-10
❑ 64Top-179
❑ 64TopVen-179
❑ 65BalOriP-33
❑ 65CarJayP-11
❑ 65Top-357
❑ 66Top-247
❑ 66TopVen-247
❑ 90DodTar-837
❑ 91OriCro-474
Warwick, Clinton

❑ 86GenCubP-11
Wasdell, James
❑ 40DodTeal-24
❑ 41DodTeal-10
❑ 41DouPlaR-19
❑ 43PhiTeal-23
❑ 73Dod194T-31
❑ 78DodTCM4-23
❑ 79DiaGre-56
❑ 90DodTar-838
❑ 93ConTSN-714
Wasdin, John
❑ 94Bow-660
❑ 94BowBes-B49
❑ 94BowBes-X101
❑ 94BowBesR-B49
❑ 94BowBesR-X101
❑ 94Cla-13
❑ 94ClaGolF-128
❑ 94ClaGolN1PLF-LP17
❑ 94ClaGolREF-RE17
❑ 94ModA'sC-23
❑ 94Pin-430
❑ 94PinArtP-430
❑ 94PinMusC-430
❑ 94Sco-571
❑ 94ScoGolR-571
❑ 94SigRoo-48
❑ 94SigRooS-48
❑ 94Top-749
❑ 94TopGol-749
❑ 94TopSpa-749
❑ 94UppDecML-209
❑ 95Bow-163
❑ 95BowBes-B14
❑ 95BowBesR-B14
❑ 95ColCho-30
❑ 95ColChoGS-30
❑ 95ColChoSS-30
❑ 95EdmTraTI-24
❑ 95Exc-113
❑ 95Top-207
❑ 95UppDecML-12
❑ 95UppDecML-168
❑ 95UppDecMLFS-12
❑ 95UppDecMLFS-168
❑ 95UppDecMLOP-OP20
❑ 96A'sMot-10
❑ 96Bow-174
❑ 96BowFoi-174
❑ 96ColCho-15
❑ 96ColChoGS-15
❑ 96ColChoSS-15
❑ 96Don-354
❑ 96DonPreP-354
❑ 96Fle-222
❑ 96FleTif-222
❑ 96LeaPre-115
❑ 96LeaPreP-115
❑ 96LeaSig-74
❑ 96LeaSigPPG-74
❑ 96LeaSigPPP-74
❑ 96Pin-182
❑ 96PinAfi-193
❑ 96PinAfiAP-193
❑ 96Sco-497
❑ 96Sel-183
❑ 96SelArtP-183
❑ 96SelCer-118
❑ 96SelCerAP-118
❑ 96SelCerCB-118
❑ 96SelCerCR-118
❑ 96SelCerMB-118
❑ 96SelCerMG-118
❑ 96SelCerMR-118
❑ 96SP-16
❑ 96StaClu-284
❑ 96StaCluMOP-284
❑ 96Sum-175
❑ 96SumAbo&B-175
❑ 96SumArtP-175
❑ 96SumFoi-175
❑ 96Top-349
❑ 96TopChr-140
❑ 96TopChrR-140
❑ 96TopGal-134
❑ 96TopGalPPI-134
❑ 96UppDec-226
❑ 96UppDecBCP-BC7
❑ 96Zen-125
❑ 96ZenArtP-125
❑ 97ColCho-188
❑ 97DonRatR-9
❑ 97Fin-302
❑ 97FinEmb-302
❑ 97FinEmbR-302
❑ 97FinRef-302
❑ 97Fle-198
❑ 97Fle-574
❑ 97FleTif-198
❑ 97FleTif-574
❑ 97MetUni-132
❑ 97Pac-178
❑ 97PacLigB-178
❑ 97PacSil-178
❑ 97Sco-53
❑ 97Sco-344
❑ 97ScoArtPWB-53
❑ 97ScoArtPWB-344
❑ 97ScoPreS-53
❑ 97ScoResC-344
❑ 97ScoShoS-53
❑ 97ScoShoS-344
❑ 97ScoShoSAP-53
❑ 97ScoShoSAP-344
❑ 97Top-448
❑ 97Ult-116
❑ 97Ult-542
❑ 97UltGolME-116
❑ 97UltGolME-542
❑ 97UltPlaME-116
❑ 97UltPlaME-542
❑ 97UppDec-132
❑ 97UppDecTTS-TS19
❑ 98PacInvGems-26
❑ 98PacOnl-132
❑ 98PacOnlR-132
❑ 98PacOnlWC-132
Wasem, Jim
❑ 84EveGiaC-24
❑ 85FreGiaSB-7
❑ 86ChaRaiP-28A
❑ 86ChaRaiP-28B
❑ 88ChaRaiP-1195
Washam, Jason
❑ 96HelBreTI-28
❑ 97BelSnaB-29
❑ 98StoPorG-30
Washburn, Greg
❑ 70OPC-74
❑ 70Top-74
Washburn, Jarrod
❑ 95BoiHawTI-34
❑ 96Bow-297
❑ 96BowBesMI-10
❑ 96BowBesMIAR-10
❑ 96BowBesMIR-10
❑ 96BowFoi-297
❑ 96Top-23
❑ 96TopPowB-23
❑ 97Bes-47
❑ 97BesAutAS-66
❑ 97Bow-385
❑ 97BowBes-153
❑ 97BowBesAR-153
❑ 97BowBesR-153
❑ 97BowChr-254
❑ 97BowChrI-254
❑ 97BowChrIR-254
❑ 97BowChrR-254
❑ 97BowInt-385
❑ 97MidAng-24
❑ 97TexLeaTP-15
❑ 97Top-207
❑ 98Bow-204
❑ 98BowBes-119
❑ 98BowBesAR-119
❑ 98BowBesR-119
❑ 98BowCerBlueAU-68
❑ 98BowCerGA-68
❑ 98BowCerSA-68
❑ 98BowChr-204
❑ 98BowChrGA-204
❑ 98BowChrGAR-204
❑ 98BowChrI-204
❑ 98BowChrIR-204
❑ 98BowChrR-204
❑ 98BowGolA-204
❑ 98BowInt-204
❑ 98CroRoy-5
❑ 98FleUpd-U79
❑ 98LeaRS-273
❑ 98LeaRSLHolo-273
❑ 98LeaRSLong-273
❑ 98LeaRTrue-273
❑ 98RevoRooHH-2
❑ 98RevoRooHHG-2
❑ 98SP MinPE-12
❑ 98SPMin-12
❑ 98UppDec-563
❑ 98UppDecDS-DS14
❑ 98VanCanG-28
❑ 99Fle-571
❑ 99FleSta9-571
❑ 99FleWarT-571
❑ 99Top-354
❑ 99TopChr-354
❑ 99TopChrR-354
❑ 99TopMVPP-354
❑ 99UppDec-293
❑ 99UppDecBD-92
❑ 99UppDecBDD-92
❑ 99UppDecBDQ-92
❑ 99UppDecBDT-92
❑ 99UppDecEL1-293
❑ 99UppDecEL2-293
Washburn, Ray
❑ 62Top-19
❑ 62TopVen-19
❑ 63Jel-168
❑ 63Pos-168
❑ 63Top-206
❑ 64Top-332
❑ 64TopVen-332
❑ 65CarTeal-27
❑ 65Top-467
❑ 66Top-399
❑ 67OPC-92
❑ 67Top-92
❑ 68Top-388
❑ 69Top-415
❑ 69TopTeaP-18
❑ 70DayDaiNM-86
❑ 70OPC-22
❑ 70Top-22
❑ 81TCM60I-404
Washington, Claudell
❑ 75GreHeroBP-3
❑ 75OPC-647
❑ 75Top-647
❑ 75TopMin-647
❑ 76Kel-2
❑ 76OPC-189
❑ 76OPC-198
❑ 76SSP-489
❑ 76Top-189
❑ 76Top-198
❑ 77BurCheD-115
❑ 77Hos-86
❑ 77OPC-178
❑ 77RCColC-66
❑ 77Top-405
❑ 77TopCloS-50
❑ 78RanBurK-19
❑ 78RCColC-46
❑ 78SSP270-88
❑ 78Top-67
❑ 79OPC-298
❑ 79Top-574
❑ 80Kel-34
❑ 80OPC-171
❑ 80Top-322
❑ 81BraPol-18
❑ 81Fle-329
❑ 81Top-151
❑ 81TopTra-854
❑ 82BraBurKL-25
❑ 82BraPol-15
❑ 82Don-58
❑ 82Fle-449
❑ 82FleSta-66
❑ 82OPC-32
❑ 82Top-126
❑ 82Top-758
❑ 82TopSti-22
❑ 83AllGamPI-161
❑ 83BraPol-15
❑ 83Don-249
❑ 83Fle-150
❑ 83FleSta-209
❑ 83FleSti-88
❑ 83OPC-235
❑ 83Top-235
❑ 83TopSti-216
❑ 84AllGamPI-71
❑ 84BraPol-15
❑ 84Don-310
❑ 84Fle-192
❑ 84Nes792-410
❑ 84OPC-42
❑ 84raPho-30
❑ 84Top-410
❑ 84TopSti-32
❑ 84TopTif-410
❑ 85AllGamPI-160
❑ 85BraHos-22
❑ 85BraPol-15
❑ 85BraTBSAT-4
❑ 85Don-11
❑ 85Don-310
❑ 85DonSupD-11
❑ 85Fle-342
❑ 85Lea-11
❑ 85OPC-166
❑ 85Top-540
❑ 85TopSti-25
❑ 85TopTif-540
❑ 86BraPol-15
❑ 86Don-287
❑ 86Fle-531
❑ 86FleMin-107
❑ 86Lea-164
❑ 86OPC-303
❑ 86Top-675
❑ 86TopSti-39
❑ 86TopTat-17
❑ 86TopTif-675
❑ 86TopTra-122T
❑ 86TopTraT-122T
❑ 87A'sMot-15
❑ 87Fle-119
❑ 87FleGlo-119
❑ 87Top-15
❑ 87TopTif-15
❑ 88Don-340
❑ 88DonBasB-217
❑ 88DonReaBY-340
❑ 88Fle-225
❑ 88FleGlo-225
❑ 88OPC-335
❑ 88Sco-579
❑ 88ScoGlo-579
❑ 88StaLinY-19
❑ 88Top-335
❑ 88TopBig-178
❑ 88TopSti-301
❑ 88TopTif-335
❑ 89Bow-52
❑ 89BowTif-52
❑ 89Don-72
❑ 89DonBasB-227
❑ 89DonTra-46
❑ 89Fle-272
❑ 89FleGlo-272
❑ 89FleUpd-17
❑ 89OPC-185
❑ 89Sco-211
❑ 89ScoRoo-10T
❑ 89Spo-75
❑ 89Top-185
❑ 89TopDouM-17
❑ 89TopTif-185
❑ 89TopTra-125T
❑ 89TopTraT-125T
❑ 89TopUKM-81
❑ 89UppDec-310
❑ 89UppDec-794
❑ 90AngSmo-17
❑ 90Bow-297
❑ 90BowTif-297
❑ 90Don-52
❑ 90Fle-146
❑ 90FleCan-146
❑ 90OPC-705
❑ 90PanSti-30
❑ 90PublntS-380
❑ 90Sco-298
❑ 90ScoRoo-45T
❑ 90Top-705
❑ 90TopBig-12
❑ 90TopTif-705
❑ 90UppDec-395
❑ 90YanScoNW-8
❑ 91MetWIZ-425
❑ 92YanWIZ8-197
❑ 93RanKee-374
Washington, Dion
❑ 98OneYanG-29
Washington, George (Sloan Vernon)
❑ 36NatChiFPR-104
Washington, Glenn
❑ 86QuaCitAP-31
❑ 87PalSprP-15
❑ 88PalSprACLC-111
❑ 88PalSprAP-1455
Washington, Herb
❑ 75OPC-407
❑ 75Top-407
❑ 75TopMin-407
Washington, Keith
❑ 80PenPilBT-9
❑ 80PenPilCT-18
❑ 81ReaPhiT-19
❑ 82ReaPhiT-19
❑ 83ReaPhiT-21
Washington, Kraig
❑ 89ChaWheB-4
❑ 89ChaWheP-1752
❑ 90PeoChiTI-7
Washington, Kyle
❑ 89KinMetS-25
❑ 90PitMetP-2
❑ 91CollndC-4
❑ 91CollndP-1503
❑ 91SouAtlLAGP-SAL19
❑ 92CanIndF-705
❑ 92CanIndS-122
❑ 92ClaFS7-41
❑ 92ProFS7-58
❑ 92SkyAA F-58
❑ 93BowBayF-2201
❑ 93ExcFS7-169
Washington, LaRue
❑ 76AshTouT-18
❑ 77TucTorC-7
❑ 78TucTorC-2
❑ 80Top-233
❑ 93RanKee-375
Washington, Lozando
❑ 76CedRapGT-30
Washington, Mal
❑ 75QuaCitAT-24
❑ 76CliPilT-34
Washington, Pete
❑ 91PomBlaBPB-23
Washington, Pres. (George)
❑ 63GadFunC-75
Washington, Randy
❑ 81BatTroT-24
❑ 82WatIndF-26
❑ 82WatIndT-25
❑ 83WatIndF-1
❑ 84BufBisT-20
❑ 85WatIndT-3
❑ 86IndTeal-48
❑ 86MaiGuiP-22
❑ 87BufBisP-12
❑ 88ColSprSSC-22
❑ 88ColSprSSP-1525
Washington, Rico
❑ 98EriSeaWM-25
Washington, Ron
❑ 79TidTidT-9
❑ 80TolMudHT-6
❑ 81TolMudHT-18
❑ 82TopTra-124T
❑ 82TwiPos-28
❑ 83Don-431
❑ 83Fle-626
❑ 83OPC-27
❑ 83Top-458
❑ 83TwiTeal-24
❑ 84Don-391
❑ 84Fle-577
❑ 84MinTwiP-31
❑ 84Nes792-623
❑ 84OPC-268
❑ 84Top-623
❑ 84TopTif-623
❑ 84TwiTeal-25
❑ 85Don-391
❑ 85Fle-292
❑ 85Top-329
❑ 85TopTif-329
❑ 85TwiPos-31
❑ 85TwiTeal-27
❑ 85TwiTeal-28
❑ 86Don-560
❑ 86Fle-409
❑ 86TolMudHP-23
❑ 86Top-513
❑ 86TopTif-513
❑ 86TwiTeal-26
❑ 87BalOriP-37
❑ 87RocRedWP-19
❑ 87RocRedWT-16
❑ 87Top-169
❑ 87TopTif-169
❑ 88IndGat-15
❑ 88IndTeal-37
❑ 88StaLinO-18
❑ 88TopTra-125T
❑ 88TopTraT-125T
❑ 89Don-468
❑ 89Fle-416
❑ 89FleGlo-416
❑ 89PacSenL-178
❑ 89T/MSenL-110
❑ 89TopSenL-44
❑ 89TucTorC-19
❑ 89TucTorJP-27
❑ 89TucTorP-190
❑ 89UppDec-519
❑ 90CMC-165
❑ 90DodTar-839
❑ 90EliSenL-31
❑ 90OklCit8C-15
❑ 90OklCit8P-442
❑ 90ProAAAF-688
❑ 91LinDriAAA-575
❑ 91OriCro-475
❑ 91PacSenL-47
❑ 91PacSenL-48
❑ 91TidTidLD-575
❑ 91TidTidP-2528
❑ 92TidTidF-914
❑ 92TidTidS-575
❑ 93CapCitBC-25
❑ 94CapCitBC-26
❑ 94CapCitBF-1767
❑ 95NorTidTI-3
❑ 96A'sMot-28
❑ 97A'sMot-28
❑ 98A'sMot-28
Washington, Tyrone
❑ 90ButCopKSP-25
❑ 91GasRanC-10
❑ 91GasRanP-2687
❑ 92Ft.MyeMCB-16
❑ 93ChaRanC-23
❑ 93ChaRanF-1942
Washington, U.L.
❑ 75OmaRoyTI-17
❑ 76OmaRoyTT-25
❑ 78Roy-23
❑ 78SSP270-236
❑ 78Top-707
❑ 79RoyTeal-11
❑ 79Top-157
❑ 80Top-508
❑ 81AllGamPI-27
❑ 81CokTeaS-80
❑ 81Don-460
❑ 81Fle-34
❑ 81OPC-26
❑ 81RoyPol-8
❑ 81Top-26
❑ 82Don-160
❑ 82Fle-424
❑ 82FleSta-203
❑ 82OPC-329
❑ 82Roy-21
❑ 82Top-329
❑ 83AllGamPI-26
❑ 83Don-490
❑ 83Fle-125
❑ 83FleSta-210
❑ 83FleSti-97
❑ 83OPC-67
❑ 83RoyPol-7
❑ 83RoyPos-32
❑ 83Top-687
❑ 84AllGamPI-117
❑ 84Don-543
❑ 84Fle-361
❑ 84Nes792-294
❑ 84OPC-294
❑ 84RoyPos-34
❑ 84Top-294
❑ 84TopSti-282
❑ 84TopTif-294
❑ 85Don-521
❑ 85ExpPos-24
❑ 85Fle-215
❑ 85FleUpd-128
❑ 85OPCPos-4
❑ 85Top-431
❑ 85TopTif-431
❑ 85TopTifT-128T
❑ 85TopTra-128T
❑ 86Don-498
❑ 86Fle-264
❑ 86OPC-113
❑ 86Top-113
❑ 86TopTif-113
❑ 87VanCanP-1622
❑ 89PacSenL-205
❑ 89T/MSenL-111
❑ 89TopSenL-120
❑ 89WelPirP-30
❑ 90EliSenL-62
❑ 91PacSenL-102
❑ 92MemChiF-2437
❑ 92MemChiS-450

❑ 94MemChiF-375
❑ 95WicWraTI-30
❑ 96WicWraB-28
❑ 97OmaRoyB-3
Washko, Patrick
❑ 76WilTomT-20
❑ 77WatIndT-28
Wasiak, Stan
❑ 74AlbDukCa-77
❑ 74AlbDukTI-23
❑ 77LodDodT-23
❑ 78LodDodT-25
❑ 79LodDodT-14
❑ 81VerBeaDT-27
❑ 83VerBeaDT-28
❑ 85VerBeaDT-26
❑ 86VerBeaDP-27
Wasilewski, Kevin
❑ 86AubAstP-25
❑ 87AshTouP-12
Wasilewski, Tom
❑ 86VenGulP-26
❑ 87ShrCapP-21
Wasinger, Mark
❑ 84BeaGolGT-17
❑ 85BeaGolGT-19
❑ 86LasVegSP-23
❑ 87GiaPos-33
❑ 87LasVegSP-27
❑ 88Fle-100
❑ 88FleGlo-100
❑ 88GiaMot-23
❑ 88GiaPos-33
❑ 88PhoFirC-17
❑ 88PhoFirP-54
❑ 88RedFolSB-96
❑ 88Sco-283
❑ 88ScoGlo-283
❑ 89ColCliC-22
❑ 89ColCliP-18
❑ 89ColCliP-738
❑ 90CMC-222
❑ 90ColCliC-22
❑ 90ColCliP-25
❑ 90ColCliP-687
❑ 90ProAAAF-337
❑ 91EdmTraLD-173
❑ 91EdmTraP-1525
❑ 91LinDriAAA-173
❑ 92EdmTraF-3549
❑ 92EdmTraS-171
❑ 92MidAngOHP-27
❑ 93MidAngF-336
❑ 97IdaFalBTI-28
❑ 97MidAngOHP-31
Waslewski, Gary
❑ 68CokCapRS-2
❑ 69Top-438
❑ 70Top-607
❑ 70YanPhoS-34
❑ 71MLBOffS-502
❑ 71OPC-277
❑ 71Top-277
❑ 72OPC-108
❑ 72Top-108
❑ 81RedSoxBG2S-125
❑ 92YanWIZ7-162
Wasley, Mel
❑ 40SolHug-18
❑ 47SunBre-24
Wassenaar, Robert
❑ 87SalAngP-5
❑ 88QuaCitAGS-25
❑ 89VisOakCLC-98
❑ 89VisOakP-1425
❑ 90OrlSunRB-18
❑ 90OrlSunRP-1084
❑ 90OrlSunRS-22
❑ 91LinDriAA-497
❑ 91OrlSunRLD-497
❑ 91OrlSunRP-1850
❑ 92PorBeaF-2668
❑ 92PorBeaS-422
Waszgis, B.J.
❑ 92KanCouCC-1
❑ 92KanCouCF-95
❑ 92KanCouCTI-29
❑ 92MidLeaATI-48
❑ 93AlbPolCB-21
❑ 93AlbPolF-2029
❑ 93SouAtlLAGF-5
❑ 94CarLeaAF-CAR2
❑ 94FreKeyC-24
❑ 94FreKeyF-2618
❑ 94OriPro-103
❑ 95BowBayTI-41
❑ 95Exc-9
❑ 96RocRedWB-28
❑ 97RocRedW-26
❑ 98PawRedSQ-29
Watanabe, Curt
❑ 80BurBeeT-26
Watanabe, Hisanobu
❑ 87JapPlaB-33
Watanabe, Masahito
❑ 87MiaMarP-12
Waterbury, Steve
❑ 76TulOilGP-21
Waterfield, Bob
❑ 52Whe-29A
❑ 52Whe-29B
Waters, Darnell
❑ 76ForLauYS-13
Waters, Jack
❑ 60MapLeaSF-22
Wathan, Derek
❑ 99TeaBesR-93
❑ 99TeaBesRFS-10
❑ 99TeaBesRG-93
❑ 99TeaBesRS-93
Wathan, Duke (John)
❑ 75OmaRoyTI-18
❑ 76KanCitRP-31
❑ 76OmaRoyTT-26
❑ 77Top-218
❑ 78Roy-24
❑ 78SSP270-233
❑ 78Top-343
❑ 79RoyTeal-12
❑ 79Top-99
❑ 80Top-547
❑ 81CokTeaS-81
❑ 81Don-221
❑ 81Fle-46
❑ 81OPC-157
❑ 81RoyProPS-14
❑ 81Top-157
❑ 82Don-86
❑ 82Fle-425
❑ 82OPC-383
❑ 82Roy-22
❑ 82Top-429
❑ 82TopSti-192
❑ 83AllGamPI-45
❑ 83Don-86
❑ 83Fle-126
❑ 83OPC-289
❑ 83RoyPol-8
❑ 83RoyPos-33
❑ 83Top-6
❑ 83Top-746
❑ 83TopSti-78
❑ 83TopSti-195
❑ 83TopSti-196
❑ 84AllGamPI-134
❑ 84Don-466
❑ 84Fle-362
❑ 84Nes792-602
❑ 84OPC-72
❑ 84RoyPos-35
❑ 84Top-602
❑ 84TopSti-284
❑ 84TopTif-602
❑ 85Don-466
❑ 85Fle-216
❑ 85RoyTeal-31
❑ 85Top-308
❑ 85TopTif-308
❑ 86Don-496
❑ 86Fle-23
❑ 86RoyKitCD-12
❑ 86Top-128
❑ 86TopTif-128
❑ 87OmaRoyP-3
❑ 88RoySmo-1
❑ 88RoyTeal-35
❑ 88Top-534
❑ 88TopTif-534
❑ 89Top-374
❑ 89TopTif-374
❑ 90OPC-789
❑ 90RoyPos-27
❑ 90Top-789
❑ 90TopTif-789
❑ 91OPC-291
❑ 91RoyPol-24
❑ 91Top-291
❑ 91TopDesS-291
❑ 91TopMic-291
❑ 91TopTif-291
❑ 93AngMot-28
Wathan, Dusty
❑ 95EveAqaTI-30
❑ 96LanJetB-30
❑ 97LanJet-28
Watkins, Bob C.
❑ 70OPC-227
❑ 70Top-227
❑ 71MLBOffS-93
Watkins, Bud
❑ 58UniOil-10
Watkins, Darren
❑ 87AppFoxP-12
❑ 87EugEmeP-2664
❑ 90BasCitRS-25
❑ 91DurBulUP-8
❑ 91LinDriAA-423
❑ 91MemChiLD-423
❑ 91MemChiP-668
Watkins, Dave
❑ 70OPC-168
❑ 70Top-168
Watkins, Don
❑ 49AngTeal-38
❑ 49W725AngTI-30
❑ 55DesMoiHB-21
❑ 95AngCHP-16
❑ 95PadCHP-16
Watkins, George
❑ 31CarMet-29
❑ 34Gou-53
❑ 35AlDemDCR3-122
❑ 35ExhFou-6
❑ 90DodTar-840
❑ 91ConTSN-222
Watkins, Jason
❑ 92UtiBluSC-17
❑ 93SouBenWSC-23
❑ 93SouBenWSF-1430
❑ 94PriWilCC-21
❑ 94PriWilCF-1920
Watkins, Jim
❑ 81BriRedST-22
Watkins, Keith
❑ 88ModA'sCLC-71
Watkins, Pat
❑ 93BilMusF-3961
❑ 93BilMusSP-12
❑ 94CarLeaAF-CAR52
❑ 94ExcFS7-182
❑ 94Top-743
❑ 94TopGol-743
❑ 94TopSpa-743
❑ 94WinSpiC-25
❑ 94WinSpiF-286
❑ 95Bes-64
❑ 95Bow-209
❑ 95BowBes-B23
❑ 95BowBes-X15
❑ 95BowBesR-B23
❑ 95BowBesR-X15
❑ 95ChaLooTI-25
❑ 95Exc-184
❑ 95SPML-39
❑ 95Top-647
❑ 95UppDecML-87
❑ 95UppDecMLFS-87
❑ 96Bow-151
❑ 96BowFoi-151
❑ 96ChaLooB-29
❑ 97ChaLoo-25
❑ 97SouLeaTP-9
❑ 98Don-316
❑ 98DonGolPP-316
❑ 98DonSilPP-316
❑ 98Fle-119
❑ 98IndIndQ-34
❑ 98LeaRS-295
❑ 98LeaRSLHolo-295
❑ 98LeaRSLong-295
❑ 98LeaRTrue-295
❑ 98PacOmeRS-4
❑ 98PacOmeRST5-4
❑ 98PacOnl-205
❑ 98PacOnlR-205
❑ 98PacOnlWC-205
❑ 98SP MinPE-42
❑ 98SPMin-42
❑ 98UppDec-342
❑ 99Pac-121
❑ 99PacAur-49
❑ 99PacAurOD-49
❑ 99PacPlaB-121
❑ 99PacRed-121
Watkins, Scott
❑ 91OklStaC-30
❑ 92KenTwiF-605
❑ 92OklStaC-30
❑ 93ForWayWC-25
❑ 93ForWayWF-1970
❑ 94NasXprF-388
Watkins, Sean
❑ 95IdaFalBTI-33
❑ 96Bow-384
❑ 96BowFoi-384
❑ 96RanCucQB-28
Watkins, Tim
❑ 87BelBreP-21
❑ 88DenZepC-6
❑ 88DenZepP-1265
❑ 89DenZepC-2
❑ 89DenZepP-41
❑ 89ElPasDGS-15
❑ 90CMC-28
❑ 90DenZepC-3
❑ 90DenZepP-627
❑ 90ProAAAF-652
❑ 91ChaKniLD-146
❑ 91ChaKniP-1690
❑ 91LinDriAA-146
Watkins, Troy
❑ 86Ft.MyeRP-27
Watkins, William H.
❑ 87OldJudN-518
Watlington, Julius
❑ 52Par-83
Watson, Al
❑ 97WilCubB-27
Watson, Allen
❑ 91Cla/Bes-427
❑ 91ClaDraP-17
❑ 91FroRowDP-44
❑ 91FroRowDPG-44
❑ 91FroRowDPS-44
❑ 91HamRedC-7
❑ 91HamRedP-4040
❑ 92Bow-634
❑ 92ClaFS7-282
❑ 92OPC-654
❑ 92Pin-304
❑ 92ProFS7-330
❑ 92Sco-799
❑ 92St.PetCC-1
❑ 92StaCluD-193
❑ 92Top-654
❑ 92TopGol-654
❑ 92TopGolW-654
❑ 92TopMic-654
❑ 92UppDecML-67
❑ 92UppDecML-153
❑ 93Bow-24
❑ 93Bow-358
❑ 93CarStaC-19
❑ 93ClaFS7-148
❑ 93FlaWavotF-17
❑ 93LeaGolR-U1
❑ 93LeaGolRJ-U1
❑ 93LouRedF-215
❑ 93SelRoo-90T
❑ 93SP-288
❑ 93TriAAAGF-24
❑ 93Ult-467
❑ 94Bow-480
❑ 94CarPol-24
❑ 94ColC-288
❑ 94ColChoGS-288
❑ 94ColChoSS-288
❑ 94Don-289
❑ 94Fin-331
❑ 94FinRef-331
❑ 94Fla-432
❑ 94Fle-648
❑ 94Lea-163
❑ 94OPC-15
❑ 94OPCDiaD-16
❑ 94Pac-606
❑ 94Pin-145
❑ 94PinArtP-145
❑ 94PinMusC-145
❑ 94PinNewG-NG8
❑ 94Sco-613
❑ 94ScoBoyoS-7
❑ 94ScoGolR-613
❑ 94Sel-376
❑ 94Spo-26
❑ 94StaClu-653
❑ 94StaCluFDI-653
❑ 94StaCluGR-653
❑ 94StaCluMOP-653
❑ 94StaCluT-322
❑ 94StaCluTFDI-322
❑ 94Top-196
❑ 94TopGol-196
❑ 94TopSpa-196
❑ 94TriPla-68
❑ 94Ult-570
❑ 94UppDec-235
❑ 94UppDecED-235
❑ 95ColCho-198
❑ 95ColChoGS-198
❑ 95ColChoSS-198
❑ 95Don-16
❑ 95DonPreP-16
❑ 95Fin-106
❑ 95FinRef-106
❑ 95Fla-196
❑ 95Fle-511
❑ 95Lea-124
❑ 95Pin-329
❑ 95PinArtP-329
❑ 95PinMusC-329
❑ 95Sco-480
❑ 95ScoGolR-480
❑ 95ScoPlaTS-480
❑ 95Sel-36
❑ 95SelArtP-36
❑ 95StaClu-165
❑ 95StaCluFDI-165
❑ 95StaCluMOP-165
❑ 95StaCluSTWS-165
❑ 95Stu-171
❑ 95Top-262
❑ 95TopCyb-142
❑ 95Ult-228
❑ 95UltGolM-228
❑ 95UppDec-307
❑ 95UppDecED-307
❑ 95UppDecEDG-307
❑ 96Don-150
❑ 96DonPreP-150
❑ 96EmoXL-296
❑ 96Fla-394
❑ 96Fle-558
❑ 96FleTif-558
❑ 96FleUpd-U210
❑ 96FleUpdTC-U210
❑ 96GiaMot-15
❑ 96LeaSigA-239
❑ 96LeaSigAG-240
❑ 96LeaSigAS-240
❑ 96Pac-217
❑ 96PanSti-80
❑ 96StaClu-64
❑ 96StaCluMOP-64
❑ 96Ult-572
❑ 96UltGolM-572
❑ 97AngMot-15
❑ 97Cir-297
❑ 97CirRav-297
❑ 97ColCho-253
❑ 97DonTea-12
❑ 97DonTeaSPE-12
❑ 97Fle-487
❑ 97FleTif-487
❑ 97Sco-78
❑ 97Sco-359
❑ 97ScoArtPWB-78
❑ 97ScoArtPWB-359
❑ 97ScoPreS-78
❑ 97ScoResC-359
❑ 97ScoShoS-78
❑ 97ScoShoS-359
❑ 97ScoShoSAP-78
❑ 97ScoShoSAP-359
❑ 97StaClu-363
❑ 97StaCluMOP-363
❑ 97Top-314
❑ 97Ult-299
❑ 97Ult-415
❑ 97UltGolME-299
❑ 97UltGolME-415
❑ 97UltPlaME-299
❑ 97UltPlaME-415
❑ 98ColCho-286
❑ 98Fle-467
❑ 98Pac-16
❑ 98PacOnl-25
❑ 98PacOnlR-25
❑ 98PacOnlWC-25
❑ 98PacPlaB-16
❑ 98PacRedT-16
❑ 98PacSil-16
❑ 98Top-211
❑ 98TopChr-211
❑ 98TopChrR-211
❑ 98TopDevR-211
❑ 98TopDia-211
❑ 98TopMiniC-211
❑ 98Ult-386
❑ 98UltGolM-386
❑ 98UltMas-386
❑ 98UltPlaM-386
❑ 98UppDec-296
Watson, Andy
❑ 90ButCopKSP-27
❑ 91ButCopKSP-5
Watson, Bob
❑ 69Top-562
❑ 70AstPho-25
❑ 70AstPho-26
❑ 70OPC-407
❑ 70Top-407
❑ 71AstCok-10
❑ 71AstTeal-22
❑ 71MLBOffS-94
❑ 71OPC-222
❑ 71Top-222
❑ 72AstTeal-27
❑ 72OPC-355
❑ 72Top-355
❑ 72TopCloT-32
❑ 73LinPor-85
❑ 73OPC-110
❑ 73Top-110
❑ 74AstFouTIP-1
❑ 74Kel-11
❑ 74OPC-370
❑ 74Top-370
❑ 74TopDecE-69
❑ 74TopSta-39
❑ 75AstPos-28
❑ 75Hos-53
❑ 75Kel-6
❑ 75OPC-227
❑ 75Top-227
❑ 75TopMin-227
❑ 76BlaDis-66
❑ 76BucDis-66
❑ 76CarDis-66
❑ 76CraDis-66
❑ 76DailsID-66
❑ 76Hos-5
❑ 76HosTwi-5
❑ 76HouAstP-31
❑ 76IsaDis-66
❑ 76Kel-27
❑ 76OPC-20
❑ 76OrbDis-66
❑ 76RedBarD-66
❑ 76SafDis-66
❑ 76SSP-60
❑ 76Top-20
❑ 76TowCluD-66
❑ 77AstPho-14
❑ 77BurCheD-6
❑ 77ChiWilD-66
❑ 77DailsID-66
❑ 77DetCaeD-66
❑ 77HolInnD-66
❑ 77Hos-39
❑ 77MSADis-66
❑ 77PepGloD-60
❑ 77SagDis-66
❑ 77sDis-66
❑ 77Top-540
❑ 77TopCloS-51
❑ 77WenDis-66
❑ 77ZipDis-66
❑ 78AstBurK-12
❑ 78AstPos-26
❑ 78Hos-28
❑ 78OPC-107
❑ 78SagDis-18
❑ 78TasDis-18
❑ 78Top-330
❑ 78WifBalD-77
❑ 79AstPos-27
❑ 79BasPat-93
❑ 79OPC-60
❑ 79Top-130
❑ 80OPC-250
❑ 80Top-480
❑ 80YanPhoA-26
❑ 81AllGamPI-9
❑ 81Don-225
❑ 81Dra-28
❑ 81Fle-93
❑ 81OPC-208
❑ 81Top-690
❑ 81TopSupHT-71
❑ 81YanPhoA-25
❑ 82BraBurKL-26
❑ 82BraPol-8
❑ 82Don-108
❑ 82Fle-54
❑ 82OPC-275

❑ 82Top-275
❑ 82TopTra-125T
❑ 83BraPol-8
❑ 83Don-551
❑ 83Fle-151
❑ 83FleSta-211
❑ 83FleSti-83
❑ 83Top-572
❑ 84BraPol-8
❑ 84Fle-193
❑ 84Nes792-739
❑ 84raPho-31
❑ 84Top-739
❑ 84TopTif-739
❑ 85OPC-51
❑ 85Top-51
❑ 85TopTif-51
❑ 86A'sMot-27
❑ 86AstGreT-1
❑ 86AstMot-13
❑ 87AstShoSO-23
❑ 87AstShoSPO-30
❑ 87AstShoSPT-29
❑ 87AstShoSTw-26
❑ 87AstShoSTw-27
❑ 87AstShowSTh-29
❑ 88A'sMot-27
❑ 92YanWIZ8-198
❑ 94TedWil-37

Watson, D.J.
❑ 87AppFoxP-5

Watson, Dave
❑ 89PriPirS-23
❑ 91SalBucC-22
❑ 91SalBucP-952
❑ 92SalBucC-23
❑ 92SalBucF-64

Watson, Dejon
❑ 86Ft.MyeRP-28
❑ 88BasCitRS-25
❑ 89BasCitRS-26

Watson, Doc
❑ 96AugGreB-2

Watson, Frankie
❑ 88EugEmeB-28

Watson, John
❑ 22WilPatV-8
❑ 25Zee-84

Watson, John Reeves
❑ 22E120-135
❑ 22W573-136

Watson, Jonathan
❑ 95BelGiaTI-6
❑ 96BurBeeTI-18
❑ 97BakBlaB-12
❑ 97BakBlaTI-12

Watson, Kevin
❑ 94EveGiaC-4
❑ 94EveGiaF-3670
❑ 95BurBeeTI-31
❑ 96BurBeeTI-26

Watson, Mark
❑ 96HelBreTI-27
❑ 98ColRedSM-12

Watson, Marty
❑ 93ButCopKSP-13
❑ 94Bow-351
❑ 94ChaRivC-23
❑ 94ChaRivF-2688
❑ 98PriWilCASM-16

Watson, Matt
❑ 89AlaGol-5
❑ 90St.CatBJP-3460

Watson, Milton
❑ 19W514-77

Watson, Phil
❑ 77AshTouT-25

Watson, Preston
❑ 89BurBraP-1604
❑ 89BurBraS-22
❑ 90GreBraP-1129
❑ 90GreBraS-21
❑ 91GreBraC-8
❑ 91GreBraLD-221
❑ 91GreBraP-3002
❑ 91LinDriAA-221
❑ 92GreBraF-1155
❑ 92GreBraS-248

Watson, Ron
❑ 91BoiHawC-22
❑ 91BoiHawP-3880
❑ 92QuaCitRBC-13
❑ 92QuaCitRBF-810
❑ 93Bow-581
❑ 94MidAngF-2439
❑ 94MidAngOHP-31
❑ 94Top-713
❑ 94TopGol-713
❑ 94TopSpa-713
❑ 97MidAngOHP-32

Watson, Shaun
❑ 91KinMetC-18
❑ 91KinMetP-3814
❑ 92PitMetC-12
❑ 92PitMetF-3297

Watson, Steve
❑ 76CedRapGT-31
❑ 76SeaRaiC-19
❑ 83TamTarT-25

Watson, Todd
❑ 90Bes-94
❑ 90ChaWheB-19
❑ 90ChaWheP-2249

Watt, Eddie
❑ 66BalOriP-33
❑ 66Top-442
❑ 67BalOriP-102
❑ 67BalOriP-103
❑ 67Top-271
❑ 68OPC-186
❑ 68Top-186
❑ 68TopVen-186
❑ 69Top-652
❑ 70BalOriP-31
❑ 70OPC-497
❑ 70Ori-14
❑ 70Top-497
❑ 71BalOriP-29
❑ 71OPC-122
❑ 71OriCha-15
❑ 71Top-122
❑ 72MilBra-355
❑ 72OPC-128
❑ 72OriPos-32
❑ 72Top-128
❑ 73BalOriP-40
❑ 73OPC-362
❑ 73OriJohP-39
❑ 73OriTeal-29
❑ 73Top-362
❑ 74OPC-534
❑ 74Top-534
❑ 74TopTra-534T
❑ 75OPC-374
❑ 75Top-374
❑ 75TopMin-374
❑ 76HawIslC-3
❑ 76VenLeaS-176
❑ 81Ori6F-31
❑ 86TucTorP-25
❑ 87TucTorP-22
❑ 88TucTorC-25
❑ 88TucTorJP-23
❑ 88TucTorP-184
❑ 89TucTorC-24
❑ 89TucTorP-204
❑ 90BurBraB-12
❑ 90BurBraP-2367
❑ 90BurBraS-29
❑ 91OriCro-476

Watt, Gord
❑ 96AriBlaDB-4
❑ 97LetBlaDB-4
❑ 98LetBlaDG-28

Watters, Mike
❑ 86AlbDukP-27
❑ 86StaoftFT-15
❑ 87CalCanP-2310
❑ 88CalCanC-23
❑ 88CalCanP-798

Watts, Andy
❑ 86NegLeaF-17

Watts, Bob
❑ 87DunBluJP-925
❑ 88DunBluJS-20
❑ 89BelBreIS-25

Watts, Brandon
❑ 91KisDodP-4187
❑ 92GreFalDSP-24
❑ 93VerBeaDC-25
❑ 93VerBeaDF-2220
❑ 95VerBeaDTI-28
❑ 96SanAntMB-24
❑ 97SanAntMB-11
❑ 98SanAntMM-11

Watts, Brian
❑ 77SpaPhiT-16

Watts, Burgess
❑ 90GreFalDSP-11
❑ 91YakBeaC-14
❑ 91YakBeaP-4258
❑ 92YakBeaC-5
❑ 92YakBeaF-3450
❑ 93BakDodCLC-24

Watts, Craig
❑ 92GreFalDSP-13
❑ 93GreFalDSP-1
❑ 95AusFut-34

Watts, Josh
❑ 93MarPhiC-1
❑ 93MarPhiF-3492
❑ 94BatCliF-3462
❑ 95PiePhiF-201
❑ 97WisTimR-26

Watts, Len
❑ 86ReaPhiP-26
❑ 87MaiGuiP-3
❑ 87MaiGuiT-20
❑ 87PhiTas-49

Watwood, Johnny
❑ 30WhiSoxTI-26
❑ 93ConTSN-963

Watychowics, Stanley
❑ 52LavPro-64

Waugh, James
❑ 53Top-178
❑ 91TopArc1-178

Wawruck, Jim
❑ 92FreKeyC-10
❑ 92FreKeyF-1821
❑ 92UppDecML-322
❑ 93BowBayF-2202
❑ 94OriPro-104
❑ 94RocRedWF-1012
❑ 94RocRedWTI-23
❑ 94UppDecML-72
❑ 95BowBayTI-9
❑ 95RocRedWTI-37
❑ 96RocRedWB-29
❑ 97RocRedW-27

Way, Ron
❑ 89WelPirP-28
❑ 90AugPirP-2465
❑ 91SalBucC-23
❑ 91SalBucP-953

Wayne, Gary
❑ 86WesPalBEP-27
❑ 87JacExpP-450
❑ 88IndIndP-508
❑ 89DonRoo-27
❑ 89ScoRoo-91T
❑ 90Don-318
❑ 90Fle-387
❑ 90FleCan-387
❑ 90OPC-348
❑ 90PubIntS-340
❑ 90Sco-527
❑ 90Sco100RS-15
❑ 90ScoYouS2-26
❑ 90Top-348
❑ 90TopDeb89-135
❑ 90TopTif-348
❑ 90UppDec-372
❑ 91Don-757
❑ 91Fle-626
❑ 91OPC-207
❑ 91Sco-283
❑ 91StaClu-491
❑ 91Top-207
❑ 91TopDesS-207
❑ 91TopMic-207
❑ 91TopTif-207
❑ 91TriA AAGP-AAA37
❑ 92Lea-424
❑ 92LeaBlaG-424
❑ 92StaClu-261
❑ 92Ult-401
❑ 93Fle-645
❑ 93FleFinE-46
❑ 93PacSpa-179
❑ 93RocUSPC-3S
❑ 93RocUSPC-10D
❑ 93StaClu-10
❑ 93StaCluFDI-10
❑ 93StaCluMOP-10
❑ 93TopTra-16T
❑ 94DodMot-27
❑ 94DodPol-27
❑ 94Don-323
❑ 94Fle-456
❑ 94StaClu-648
❑ 94StaCluFDI-648
❑ 94StaCluGR-648
❑ 94StaCluMOP-648

Wayne, Tyrone
❑ 98HelBreM-32

Waznik, Allan J.
❑ 87IdaFalBP-13
❑ 88SumBraP-407
❑ 89BurBraP-1612
❑ 89BurBraS-23

Wearing, Melvin
❑ 89EriOriS-25
❑ 90Bes-293
❑ 90WauTimB-23
❑ 90WauTimP-2137
❑ 90WauTimS-24
❑ 91CarLeaAP-CAR9
❑ 91Cla/Bes-383
❑ 91FreKeyC-20
❑ 91FreKeyP-2374
❑ 92HagSunF-2566
❑ 92HagSunS-270
❑ 92SkyAA F-114
❑ 93ExcFS7-128
❑ 93RocRedWF-250
❑ 94OriPro-105
❑ 94RocRedWF-1006
❑ 98BriBluM-4

Weatherford, Brant
❑ 86TamTarP-25

Weatherford, Joel
❑ 83BelBreFr-29

Weatherhead, Marsha
❑ 89AriStaB-26

Weatherly, Stormy (Roy)
❑ 39PlaBal-152
❑ 40PlaBal-49
❑ 41PlaBal-17
❑ 43YanSta-28
❑ 79DiaGre-283
❑ 93ConTSN-942

Weathers, David (John David)
❑ 88St.CatBJP-2023
❑ 89MyrBeaBJP-1476
❑ 90DunBluJS-24
❑ 91BluJayS-35
❑ 91KnoBluJLD-371
❑ 91KnoBluJP-1767
❑ 91LinDriAA-371
❑ 92Don-418
❑ 92ProFS7-167
❑ 92SkyAAAF-233
❑ 92SyrChiF-1969
❑ 92SyrChiMB-28
❑ 92SyrChiS-522
❑ 92TopDeb91-181
❑ 93BluJayD4-43
❑ 93Don-731
❑ 93EdmTraF-1138
❑ 93Fle-430
❑ 93MarlStaClu-26
❑ 93Top-739
❑ 93TopGol-739
❑ 93TopInaM-739
❑ 93TopInaR-739
❑ 93TopMic-739
❑ 93TriAAAGF-11
❑ 94Fin-355
❑ 94FinRef-355
❑ 94Fla-167
❑ 94Fle-479
❑ 94FleExtB-267
❑ 94Pac-252
❑ 94SpoRoo-27
❑ 94SpoRooAP-27
❑ 94StaClu-673
❑ 94StaCluFDI-673
❑ 94StaCluGR-673
❑ 94StaCluMOP-673
❑ 94StaCluT-89
❑ 94StaCluTFDI-89
❑ 94Top-781
❑ 94TopGol-781
❑ 94TopSpa-781
❑ 94Ult-498
❑ 94UppDec-447
❑ 94UppDecED-447
❑ 95ColCho-307
❑ 95ColChoGS-307
❑ 95ColChoSS-307
❑ 95Don-306
❑ 95DonPreP-306
❑ 95Fla-142
❑ 95Fle-343
❑ 95Lea-58
❑ 95Pin-55
❑ 95PinArtP-55
❑ 95PinMusC-55
❑ 95Sco-141
❑ 95ScoGolR-141
❑ 95ScoPlaTS-141
❑ 95StaClu-75
❑ 95StaCluFDI-75
❑ 95StaCluMOP-75
❑ 95StaCluSTWS-75
❑ 95StaCluVR-47
❑ 95StaCluVRMO-47
❑ 95Top-73
❑ 95Ult-168
❑ 95UltGolM-168
❑ 95UppDec-118
❑ 95UppDecED-118
❑ 95UppDecEDG-118
❑ 96ColCho-157
❑ 96ColChoGS-157
❑ 96ColChoSS-157
❑ 96FleUpd-U134
❑ 96FleUpdTC-U134
❑ 96LeaSigA-240
❑ 96LeaSigAG-241
❑ 96LeaSigAS-241
❑ 97Fle-678
❑ 97FleTif-678
❑ 98PacOnl-206
❑ 98PacOnlR-206
❑ 98PacOnlWC-206

Weathers, Steven M.
❑ 75TucTorC-6
❑ 75TucTorTI-20
❑ 76TucTorCa-5
❑ 76TusTorCr-2
❑ 77SanJosMC-12

Weathersby, Leon
❑ 95SpoIndTI-30

Weathersby, Tex (Earl)
❑ 28ExhPCL-30
❑ 28Zee-43

Weaver, Art
❑ 11SpoLifCW-363

Weaver, Buck (George)
❑ 09MaxPubP-17
❑ 09ObaT21-338
❑ 11PacCoaBD-70
❑ 11Zee-105
❑ 12ObaPreT-87
❑ 12T207-193
❑ 15SpoNewM-188
❑ 16BF2FP-21
❑ 16SpoNewM-186
❑ 16TanBraE-19
❑ 17ColE13-185
❑ 18WhiSoxTI-23
❑ 19W514-91
❑ 73FleWilD-11
❑ 74CapPub-94
❑ 75WhiSox1T-25
❑ 77SerSta-24
❑ 81ConTSN-40
❑ 87ConSer2-28
❑ 88LitSunBS-5
❑ 88PacEigMO-7
❑ 88PacEigMO-12
❑ 88PacEigMO-33
❑ 88PacEigMO-34
❑ 88PacEigMO-40
❑ 88PacEigMO-48
❑ 88PacEigMO-63
❑ 88PacEigMO-71
❑ 88PacEigMO-107
❑ 92Man191BSR-24
❑ 94ConTSN-1029
❑ 94ConTSNB-1029

Weaver, Colby
❑ 94IdaFalBF-3590
❑ 95DurBulTI-33

Weaver, D. Floyd
❑ 65Top-546
❑ 66Top-231
❑ 66TopVen-231
❑ 71OPC-227
❑ 71Top-227
❑ 73WicAerJPKB-19
❑ 78TCM60I-176
❑ 94BreMilB-88

Weaver, Earl
❑ 67BalOriP-104
❑ 69Top-516
❑ 70BalOriP-32
❑ 70OPC-148
❑ 70Ori-15
❑ 70Top-148
❑ 71BalOriP-30
❑ 71OPC-477
❑ 71OriCha-16
❑ 71Top-477
❑ 72OPC-323
❑ 72OriDMV-10
❑ 72OriPos-33
❑ 72Top-323
❑ 73BalOriP-41
❑ 73OPC-136
❑ 73OriJohP-4
❑ 73OriTeal-30
❑ 73Top-136A
❑ 73Top-136B
❑ 74OPC-306
❑ 74Top-306
❑ 75BalOriP-30
❑ 75OPC-117
❑ 75Top-117
❑ 75TopMin-117
❑ 76BalOriP-38
❑ 76OPC-73
❑ 76Top-73
❑ 77BalOriP-22
❑ 77Spo-1816
❑ 77Top-546
❑ 78BalOriP-34
❑ 78Top-211
❑ 79BalOriP-17
❑ 79Top-689
❑ 80BalOriP-21
❑ 80PerHaloFP-228
❑ 80PerHaloFPS-82
❑ 80Top-404
❑ 81Don-356
❑ 81Fle-178
❑ 81Top-661
❑ 82Don-27
❑ 83OriPos-31
❑ 83Top-426
❑ 85OriHea-18
❑ 85TopTifT-129T
❑ 85TopTra-129T
❑ 86BalOriHMP-19
❑ 86BalOriP-23
❑ 86Top-321
❑ 86TopTif-321
❑ 87Top-568
❑ 87TopTif-568
❑ 89PacLegI-179
❑ 89PacSenL-56
❑ 89PacSenL-219
❑ 89SweBasG-98
❑ 89T/MSenL-112
❑ 89T/MSenL-120
❑ 89TopSenL-76
❑ 90EliSenL-91
❑ 90PacLeg-108
❑ 90PerGreM-108
❑ 91LinDri-12
❑ 91SweBasG-95
❑ 92UppDecS-3
❑ 92MCIAmb-1
❑ 93OriCroASU-8
❑ 93TedWil-85
❑ 93TedWil-147
❑ 93UppDecS-3
❑ 96BalOriP-35
❑ 97TopStaHRR-15
❑ 97TopStaRRAU-15
❑ 98SpoIllTaN-34
❑ 98SpoIllTaNEE-34
❑ 99SpoIllGotG-41
❑ 99SpoIllGotGA-75
❑ 99SpoIllGotGC-36

Weaver, Eric
❑ 93BakDodCLC-25
❑ 94VerBeaDC-23
❑ 94VerBeaDF-73
❑ 95SanAntMTI-44
❑ 96SanAntMB-25
❑ 97SanAntMB-12
❑ 98AlbDukG-29
❑ 98SanAntMM-12
❑ 99Fle-507
❑ 99FleSta9-507
❑ 99FleWarT-507

Weaver, Harry
❑ 19Zee-30
❑ 20Zee-37

Weaver, James
❑ 83OrlTwiT-3
❑ 84TolMudHT-13
❑ 86MaiGuiP-23
❑ 87CalCanP-2311
❑ 88TucTorC-21
❑ 88TucTorJP-24
❑ 88TucTorP-172
❑ 89VanCanC-14
❑ 89VanCanP-583

❑ 90CalCanC-17
❑ 90CalCanP-663
❑ 90CMC-444
❑ 90ProAAAF-128
❑ 92VerBeaDF-2876
❑ 94RocRedWTI-24
Weaver, Jeff
❑ 98AriFalLTP-4
❑ 99CroRoyB-56
❑ 99CroRoyL-56
❑ 99CroRoyOD-56
❑ 99DumSet-142
❑ 99FleMys-142
❑ 99FleMysM-142
❑ 99PacOme-94
❑ 99PacOmeC-94
❑ 99PacOmeG-94
❑ 99PacOmePB-94
❑ 99SkyMolM-120
❑ 99SkyMolMF-20
❑ 99SkyMolMFS-20
❑ 99SkyMolMFT-20
❑ 99SkyMolMX-120
❑ 99SkyPre-250
❑ 99SkyPre-250
❑ 99SkyPreDD-9
❑ 99SkyPreR-250
❑ 99SkyPreR-250
❑ 99TeaBesR-94
❑ 99TeaBesRFS-9
❑ 99TeaBesRG-94
❑ 99TeaBesRS-94
❑ 99UppDecE-95
❑ 99UppDecEFXG-95
❑ 99UppDecROSS-S20
❑ 99UppDecROSS-S20
❑ 99Vic-141
❑ 99WesMicWAM-22
Weaver, Jim (James B.)
❑ 68Top-328
❑ 68TopVen-328
❑ 69OPC-134
❑ 69Top-134
❑ 69TopFou-20
Weaver, Jim (James D.)
❑ 36NatChiFPR-96
❑ 36R31PasP-39
❑ 38RedOraW-30
❑ 77CinRedT-28
❑ 92ConTSN-390
Weaver, Jim Francis
❑ 86IndTeal-49
Weaver, Monte
❑ 33Gou-111
❑ 33WorCig-99
❑ 35GouPuzR-1C
❑ 35GouPuzR-2C
❑ 35GouPuzR-16C
❑ 35GouPuzR-17C
❑ 79DiaGre-70
❑ 93ConTSN-853
Weaver, Roger
❑ 80EvaTriT-1
❑ 81EvaTriT-10
❑ 81Top-626
❑ 82RicBraT-9
Weaver, Scott
❑ 96FayGenB-29
Weaver, Terry
❑ 95BelGiaTI-31
❑ 96BurBeeTI-19
Weaver, Trent
❑ 89MedAthB-16
❑ 91ModA'sC-2
Weaver, William B.
❑ 87OldJudN-519
Webb, Ada
❑ 88KimN18-47
Webb, Alan
❑ 98WesMicWM-28
Webb, Ben
❑ 87WatPirP-1
❑ 88SalBucS-23
❑ 89HarSenP-311
❑ 89HarSenS-21
❑ 90HarSenP-1194
❑ 90HarSenS-20
❑ 91CarMudLD-120
❑ 91CarMudP-1088
❑ 91LinDriAA-120
❑ 92CarMudF-1182
❑ 92CarMudS-147
Webb, Chuck
❑ 88WauTimGS-19
Webb, Cleon Earl
❑ 34BatR31-98
❑ 85Woo-37
❑ 91ConTSN-261
❑ 94ConTSN-1226
Webb, Dennis
❑ 81QuaCitCT-9
Webb, Doug
❑ 94SigRooDP-35
❑ 94SigRooDPS-35
❑ 94StaCluDP-26
❑ 94StaCluDPFDI-26
❑ 95Top-406
❑ 96El PasDB-27
❑ 96Exc-74
Webb, Earl (William Earl)
❑ 29Zee-36
❑ 30Zee-43
❑ 31Exh-18
❑ 33ExhFou-9
❑ 79RedSoxEF-3
❑ 85BigLeaC3-73
❑ 87ConSer2-25
❑ 94ConTSNB-1226
Webb, Hank
❑ 73OPC-610
❑ 73Top-610
❑ 74MetTeal-26
❑ 75IntLeaAT-24
❑ 75MetSSP-2
❑ 75OPC-615
❑ 75Top-615
❑ 75TopMin-615
❑ 76OPC-442
❑ 76SSP-553
❑ 76Top-442
❑ 90DodTar-841
❑ 91MetWIZ-426
Webb, Kevin
❑ 92AshTouC-7
❑ 93AshTouC-22
❑ 93AshTouF-2287
❑ 95DurBulTI-34
Webb, Lefty (Cleon)
❑ 10PirTipTD-15
Webb, Lonnie
❑ 90GreFalDSP-7
❑ 92BakDodCLC-28
❑ 93VerBeaDC-26
Webb, Marvin
❑ 75WatDodT-22
Webb, Sam
❑ 49EurSta-125
❑ 85TCMPpl1-23
Webb, Skeeter (James)
❑ 39WhiSoxTI-21
❑ 40WhiSoxL-22
❑ 48A'sTeal-25
Webb, Spyder
❑ 87BelMarL-30
❑ 87BelMarTI-16
❑ 89BelMarL-33
❑ 91BelMarCB-27
Webb, Tweed (Normal)
❑ 86NegLeaF-39
Webber, Les
❑ 42DodTeal-24
❑ 43DodTeal-24
❑ 46DodTeal-24
❑ 77TCMTheWY-49
❑ 90DodTar-842
Webber, Steve
❑ 98OneYanG-1
Weber, Ben
❑ 91St.CatBJC-19
❑ 91St.CatBJP-3396
❑ 92MyrBeaHC-6
❑ 92MyrBeaHF-2198
❑ 93DunBluJC-24
❑ 93DunBluJF-1797
❑ 93DunBluJFFN-27
❑ 93FloStaLAF-11
❑ 94ClaGolF-59
❑ 94DunBluJC-26
❑ 94DunBluJF-2558
❑ 95SyrChiTI-27
Weber, Bill (Charles)
❑ 87OldJudN-520
Weber, Brent
❑ 91IdaFalBP-4329
Weber, Brett
❑ 98OneYanG-30
Weber, Charles
❑ 36CubTeal-31
Weber, David
❑ 93HunCubC-26
❑ 93HunCubF-3236
❑ 94WilCubF-3765
Weber, Eric
❑ 93BriTigC-24
❑ 94BriTigC-26
❑ 94BriTigF-3503
❑ 96BurIndB-16
Weber, Jake
❑ 98EveAquG-26
❑ 99TeaBesR-95
❑ 99TeaBesRG-95
❑ 99TeaBesRS-95
Weber, Lenny
❑ 94BurIndC-27
❑ 94BurIndF-3795
❑ 96KenIndB-25
❑ 97AkrAer-27
Weber, Neil
❑ 93JamExpC-25
❑ 93JamExpF-3328
❑ 94WesPalBEC-27
❑ 94WesPalBEF-41
❑ 95AusFut-39
❑ 95Exc-229
❑ 95HarSenTI-10
❑ 96Bow-231
❑ 96BowFoi-231
❑ 96DouAllB-18
❑ 96HarSenB-28
❑ 98TusSidM-15
Weber, Pete
❑ 87BufBisP-29
❑ 90CliGiaUTI-U8
❑ 91LinDriAA-323
❑ 91ShrCapLD-323
❑ 91ShrCapP-1837
❑ 92ShrCapF-3886
❑ 92ShrCapS-597
❑ 92SkyAA F-264
❑ 93ShrCapF-2774
Weber, Ron
❑ 89JohCitCS-22
❑ 90SprCarB-24
❑ 91St.PetCC-14
❑ 91St.PetCP-2277
❑ 92St.PetCC-9
❑ 92St.PetCF-2028
Weber, Steve
❑ 89BriTigS-30
❑ 90BriTigS-29
Weber, Todd
❑ 88AshTouP-1078
Weber, Wes (Weston)
❑ 86MedA'sC-65
❑ 87MadMusP-21
❑ 87MadMusP-11
❑ 88ModA'sTI-15
❑ 89HunStaB-13
❑ 89ModA'sC-18
❑ 90CMC-582
❑ 90ProAAAF-139
❑ 90TacTigC-5
❑ 90TacTigP-92
❑ 91HunStaTI-1796
❑ 91HunStaTI-22
❑ 92TacTigF-2503
❑ 92TacTigS-546
❑ 94CalCanF-790
❑ 95TacRaiTI-26
❑ 96LasVegSB-30
Webster, Casey
❑ 86WatIndP-30
❑ 87KinIndP-13
❑ 88EasLeaAP-43
❑ 88WilBilP-1317
❑ 89CanIndB-5
❑ 89CanIndP-1318
❑ 89CanIndS-23
❑ 89EasLeaAP-19
❑ 90CanIndS-17
❑ 90CMC-473
❑ 90ColSprSSC-21
❑ 90ColSprSSP-47
❑ 90ProAAAF-228
Webster, Lenny
❑ 86KenTwiP-25
❑ 87KenTwiP-20
❑ 88KenTwiP-1392
❑ 88MidLeaAGS-31
❑ 89VisOakCLC-110
❑ 89VisOakP-1442
❑ 90Bes-45
❑ 90OrlSunRB-13
❑ 90OrlSunRP-1088
❑ 90OrlSunRS-23
❑ 90ProAaA-55
❑ 90Sco-638
❑ 90TopDeb89-136
❑ 90UppDec-728
❑ 91FleUpd-41
❑ 91LinDriAAA-422
❑ 91PorBeaLD-422
❑ 91PorBeaP-1569
❑ 92DonRoo-124
❑ 92Fle-220
❑ 92OPC-585
❑ 92Pin-276
❑ 92Sco-663
❑ 92ScoRoo-17
❑ 92StaClu-183
❑ 92Top-585
❑ 92TopGol-585
❑ 92TopGolW-585
❑ 92TopMic-585
❑ 92Ult-402
❑ 93Don-694
❑ 93Fle-646
❑ 93Sco-471
❑ 93StaClu-380
❑ 93StaCluFDI-380
❑ 93StaCluMOP-380
❑ 93Top-37
❑ 93TopGol-37
❑ 93TopInaM-37
❑ 93TopInaR-37
❑ 93TopMic-37
❑ 93Ult-238
❑ 93UppDec-628
❑ 93UppDecGold-628
❑ 93USPlaCR-8D
❑ 94FleUpd-155
❑ 94StaClu-193
❑ 94StaCluFDI-193
❑ 94StaCluGR-193
❑ 94StaCluMOP-193
❑ 94Top-252
❑ 94TopGol-252
❑ 94TopSpa-252
❑ 95Don-541
❑ 95DonPreP-541
❑ 95Fle-362
❑ 95Phi-34
❑ 95PhiMel-24
❑ 95Sco-258
❑ 95ScoGolR-258
❑ 95ScoPlaTS-258
❑ 95Top-374
❑ 96ColCho-668
❑ 96ColChoGS-668
❑ 96ColChoSS-668
❑ 96Fle-511
❑ 96FleTif-511
❑ 97BalOriP-33
❑ 98PacInvGems-18
❑ 98PacOnl-104
❑ 98PacOnlR-104
❑ 98PacOnlWC-104
❑ 99Fle-572
❑ 99FleSta9-572
❑ 99FleWarT-572
❑ 99PacCroC-43
❑ 99PacCroCPB-43
Webster, Mike
❑ 89EugEmeB-2
❑ 90BasCitRS-26
Webster, Mitch
❑ 78CliDodT-32
❑ 79CliDodT-11
❑ 80SyrChiT-12
❑ 80SyrChiTI-22
❑ 82SyrChiT-23
❑ 82SyrChiTI-23
❑ 83SyrChiT-25
❑ 84BluJayFS-31
❑ 85BluJayFS-31
❑ 85DomLeaS-147
❑ 86Don-523
❑ 86ExpPos-18
❑ 86ExpProPa-5
❑ 86ExpProPo-5
❑ 86Fle-265
❑ 86GenMilB-6J
❑ 86Lea-253
❑ 86OPC-218
❑ 86Top-629
❑ 86TopTif-629
❑ 87Don-335
❑ 87DonOpeD-86
❑ 87ExpPos-33
❑ 87Fle-335
❑ 87FleAwaW-41
❑ 87FleGlo-335
❑ 87FleMin-111
❑ 87GenMilB-4I
❑ 87OPC-263
❑ 87Spo-177
❑ 87SpoTeaP-20
❑ 87StuPan-7
❑ 87Top-442
❑ 87TopSti-82
❑ 87TopTif-442
❑ 88CubDavB-28
❑ 88Don-257
❑ 88DonBasB-292
❑ 88ExpPos-34
❑ 88Fle-199
❑ 88FleGlo-199
❑ 88FleStiC-99
❑ 88Lea-198
❑ 88MSAHosD-1
❑ 88OPC-138
❑ 88PanSti-331
❑ 88RedFolSB-97
❑ 88Sco-345
❑ 88ScoGlo-345
❑ 88Spo-105
❑ 88StaLinE-18
❑ 88Top-138
❑ 88TopBig-150
❑ 88TopTif-138
❑ 89Bow-296
❑ 89BowTif-296
❑ 89CubMar-33
❑ 89Don-459
❑ 89DonBasB-261
❑ 89Fle-442
❑ 89FleGlo-442
❑ 89OPC-36
❑ 89PanSti-61
❑ 89Sco-71
❑ 89Spo-67
❑ 89Top-36
❑ 89TopTif-36
❑ 89TVSpoM-20
❑ 89UppDec-65
❑ 90Don-137
❑ 90Fle-45
❑ 90FleCan-45
❑ 90IndTeal-43
❑ 90Lea-312
❑ 90OPC-502
❑ 90PubIntS-208
❑ 90Sco-85
❑ 90ScoRoo-4T
❑ 90Top-502
❑ 90TopBig-298
❑ 90TopTif-502
❑ 90TopTra-127T
❑ 90TopTraT-127T
❑ 90UppDec-153
❑ 90UppDec-730
❑ 91Bow-66
❑ 91DodPho-30
❑ 91Don-283
❑ 91Fle-384
❑ 91IndFanC-29
❑ 91OPC-762
❑ 91PanSti-175
❑ 91Sco-594
❑ 91ScoRoo-68T
❑ 91StaClu-448
❑ 91Top-762
❑ 91TopDesS-762
❑ 91TopMic-762
❑ 91TopTif-762
❑ 91Ult-119
❑ 91UppDec-120
❑ 92DodMot-26
❑ 92DodPol-20
❑ 92DodSmo-10692
❑ 92Don-714
❑ 92OPC-233
❑ 92Sco-643
❑ 92StaClu-403
❑ 92Top-233
❑ 92TopGol-233
❑ 92TopGolW-233
❑ 92TopMic-233
❑ 93DodMot-22
❑ 93DodPol-27
❑ 93DodStaC-18
❑ 93Don-62
❑ 93Fle-455
❑ 93PacSpa-505
❑ 93StaClu-735
❑ 93StaCluFDI-735
❑ 93StaCluMOP-735
❑ 94DodDaiN-18
❑ 94DodMot-12
❑ 94DodPol-28
❑ 94Don-457
❑ 94Fle-528
❑ 94Sco-130
❑ 94ScoGolR-130
❑ 94Top-382
❑ 94TopGol-382
❑ 94TopSpa-382
❑ 95DodMot-12
❑ 96YakBeaTI-NNO
❑ 97YakBeaG-35
❑ 98YakBeaG-33
Webster, Ramon
❑ 67Top-603
❑ 68OPC-164
❑ 68Top-164
❑ 68TopVen-164
❑ 69Top-618
❑ 72MilBra-356
❑ 75TucTorC-3
❑ 75TucTorTI-21
Webster, Ray G.
❑ 59Ind-20
❑ 59Top-531
❑ 60Top-452
Webster, Rich
❑ 82LynMetT-21
Webster, Rudy
❑ 86BelMarCr-127
❑ 87WauTimP-25
❑ 88WauTimGS-17
Wechsberg, Von
❑ 90BurIndP-3010
❑ 91PocPioP-3783
❑ 91PocPioSP-7
❑ 92SpoIndC-18
❑ 92SpoIndF-1295
Weck, Steve
❑ 85IowCubT-31
Wedel, Jeremy
❑ 98BatMucTI-31
Wedge, Eric
❑ 88CapCodPPaLP-51
❑ 89ElmPioP-32
❑ 90Bes-2
❑ 90Bes-319
❑ 90CMC-783
❑ 90EasLeaAP-EL41
❑ 90NewBriRSB-1
❑ 90NewBriRSP-1322
❑ 90NewBriRSS-21
❑ 90TopTVRS-66
❑ 91LinDriAAA-372
❑ 91PawRedSDD-29
❑ 91PawRedSLD-372
❑ 91PawRedSP-42
❑ 92PawRedSF-927
❑ 92PawRedSS-372
❑ 92ScoRoo-38
❑ 92SkyAAAF-171
❑ 92TopDeb91-182
❑ 93Don-44
❑ 93FleMajLP-A12
❑ 93Pin-239
❑ 93RocStaC-22
❑ 93Sco-561
❑ 93ScoProaG-9
❑ 93Sel-401
❑ 93Top-486
❑ 93TopGol-486
❑ 93TopInaM-486
❑ 93TopInaR-486
❑ 93TopMic-486
❑ 93UppDec-653
❑ 93UppDecGold-653
❑ 94PawRedSDD-29
❑ 94Sco-643
❑ 94ScoGolR-643
❑ 94StaCluT-113
❑ 94StaCluTFDI-113
❑ 95PawRedSDD-28
❑ 95PawRedTI-35
❑ 96TolMudHB-30
❑ 97DunDonPPS-29
❑ 97ScrRedB-12
❑ 98ColRedSM-26
Wedvick, Jeff
❑ 86JamExpP-28
❑ 87BurExpP-1082
❑ 87JamExpP-2542
Weeber, Mike
❑ 75DubPacT-17

Weekley, Jason
❑ 96GreFalDB-30
❑ 96GreFalDTI-32
❑ 97SanBerS-29
Weekly, Johnny
❑ 62Top-204
❑ 64Top-256
❑ 64TopVen-256
❑ 89AstCol4S-26
Weeks, Ben
❑ 91IdaFalBP-4330
❑ 91IdaFalBSP-8
❑ 92PulBraC-12
❑ 92PulBraF-3178
❑ 93ButCopKSP-11
Weeks, Thomas
❑ 87OneYanP-13
❑ 88Ft.LauYS-24
❑ 89PriWilCS-24
❑ 90PriWilCTI-27
Weems, Danny
❑ 86SumBraP-29
❑ 87ChaWheP-13
❑ 88CarLeaAS-39
❑ 88DurBulS-23
❑ 89GreBraB-13
❑ 89GreBraP-1157
❑ 89GreBraS-24
❑ 90GreBraB-16
❑ 90GreBraP-1130
❑ 90GreBraS-22
Weems, Jeff
❑ 94PitMetC-27
❑ 97BinMetB-4
❑ 98BinMetQ-4
Weese, Dean
❑ 88HamRedP-1744
❑ 89SavCarP-348
❑ 90St.PetCS-25
❑ 91ArkTraP-1286
Weese, Gary
❑ 75SanAntBT-21
❑ 76WilTomT-21
Wegener, Mike
❑ 69ExpFudP-13
❑ 69Top-284
❑ 70ExpPos-5
❑ 70OPC-193
❑ 70Top-193
❑ 71ExpPS-27
❑ 71OPC-608
❑ 71Top-608
❑ 75TidTidTI-24
❑ 76PheGiaCr-35
❑ 76PhoGiaCa-10
❑ 76PhoGiaCC-23
❑ 76PhoGiaVNB-24
❑ 77PhoGiaCC-24
❑ 77PhoGiaCP-24
❑ 77PhoGiaVNB-24
Weger, Wes
❑ 92FroRowDP-77
❑ 92FroRowDPG-77
❑ 92FroRowDPS-77
❑ 92HelBreF-1725
❑ 92HelBreSP-10
❑ 93El PasDF-2960
❑ 93ExcFS7-196
❑ 94ExcFS7-90
❑ 94FleExtB-111
❑ 94FleExtBMLH-10
❑ 94NewOrlZF-1478
❑ 94Ult-382
❑ 95ElPasDTI-23
❑ 96SigRooOJ-35
❑ 96SigRooOJS-35
Weglarz, John
❑ 92EugEmeC-27
❑ 92EugEmeF-3030
❑ 93RocRoyC-27
❑ 93RocRoyF-717
Wegman, Bill
❑ 82BelBreFr-4
❑ 85VanCanC-216
❑ 86BrePol-46
❑ 86Don-490
❑ 86TopTra-123T
❑ 86TopTraT-123T
❑ 87BrePol-46
❑ 87BreTeal-15
❑ 87Don-109
❑ 87Fle-360
❑ 87FleGlo-360
❑ 87Top-179
❑ 87TopTif-179
❑ 88BrePol-46
❑ 88BreTeal-36
❑ 88Don-151
❑ 88DonBasB-320
❑ 88Fle-177
❑ 88FleGlo-177
❑ 88OPC-84
❑ 88PanSti-119
❑ 88Sco-296
❑ 88ScoGlo-296
❑ 88StaLinBre-19
❑ 88Top-538
❑ 88TopBig-244
❑ 88TopSti-200
❑ 88TopTif-538
❑ 89Bow-135
❑ 89BowTif-135
❑ 89BreGar-9
❑ 89BrePol-46
❑ 89BreYea-46
❑ 89Don-293
❑ 89Fle-199
❑ 89FleGlo-199
❑ 89OPC-354
❑ 89Sco-335
❑ 89ScoYouS2-9
❑ 89Top-768
❑ 89TopTif-768
❑ 89UppDec-445
❑ 90BreMilB-30
❑ 90BrePol-46
❑ 90OPC-333
❑ 90PubIntS-507
❑ 90Sco-188
❑ 90Top-333
❑ 90TopTif-333
❑ 90UppDec-629
❑ 91BreMilB-30
❑ 91BrePol-27
❑ 91FleUpd-35
❑ 91OPC-617
❑ 91Sco-483
❑ 91StaClu-398
❑ 91Top-617
❑ 91TopDesS-617
❑ 91TopMic-617
❑ 91TopTif-617
❑ 91UltUpd-33
❑ 91UppDec-292
❑ 92Bow-447
❑ 92BrePol-28
❑ 92Don-378
❑ 92Fle-193
❑ 92Lea-196
❑ 92LeaBlaG-196
❑ 92OPC-22
❑ 92Pin-396
❑ 92Sco-374
❑ 92StaClu-758
❑ 92StaCluECN-758
❑ 92Stu-199
❑ 92Top-22
❑ 92TopGol-22
❑ 92TopGolW-22
❑ 92TopMic-22
❑ 92TriPla-185
❑ 92Ult-392
❑ 92UppDec-612
❑ 92UppDecTMH-53
❑ 93BrePol-27
❑ 93Don-17
❑ 93Fle-259
❑ 93Lea-144
❑ 93OPC-223
❑ 93PacSpa-517
❑ 93Pin-369
❑ 93Sco-190
❑ 93Sel-184
❑ 93StaClu-324
❑ 93StaCluFDI-324
❑ 93StaCluMOP-324
❑ 93Top-261
❑ 93TopComotH-9
❑ 93TopGol-261
❑ 93TopInaM-261
❑ 93TopInaR-261
❑ 93TopMic-261
❑ 93TriPla-56
❑ 93Ult-226
❑ 93UppDec-416
❑ 93UppDecGold-416
❑ 94BreMilB-89
❑ 94BrePol-30
❑ 94BreTeal-29
❑ 94ColC-289
❑ 94ColChoGS-289
❑ 94ColChoSS-289
❑ 94Don-633
❑ 94Fin-145
❑ 94FinRef-145
❑ 94Fla-310
❑ 94Fle-196
❑ 94FleExtB-112
❑ 94Sco-341
❑ 94ScoGolR-341
❑ 94Top-464
❑ 94TopGol-464
❑ 94TopSpa-464
❑ 94Ult-383
❑ 94UppDec-416
❑ 94UppDecED-416
❑ 95Don-333
❑ 95DonPreP-333
❑ 95DonTopotO-106
❑ 95Fla-56
❑ 95Fle-195
❑ 95StaClu-348
❑ 95StaCluMOP-348
❑ 95StaCluSTWS-348
❑ 95Top-159
❑ 96ProSta-30
Wegmann, Tom
❑ 90KinMetB-20
❑ 90KinMetS-24
❑ 91ColMetPI-27
❑ 91ColMetPI-27
❑ 91ColMetPI-31
❑ 91ColMetPPI-4
❑ 91St.LucMC-13
❑ 92BinMetF-518
❑ 92BinMetS-71
❑ 92SkyAA F-33
❑ 93NorTidF-2571
❑ 94RocRedWF-999
❑ 94RocRedWTI-25
❑ 95BowBayTI-31
❑ 95RocRedWTI-38
Wehmeier, Herm
❑ 47Exh-237
❑ 48Bow-46
❑ 49Bow-51
❑ 49EurSta-98
❑ 50Bow-27
❑ 51Bow-144
❑ 51FisBakL-28
❑ 51TopBluB-47
❑ 52Bow-150
❑ 52Top-80
❑ 53BowC-23
❑ 53Top-110
❑ 54Top-162
❑ 55Top-29
❑ 55TopDouH-131
❑ 56Top-78
❑ 56TopPin-22
❑ 57Top-81
❑ 58Top-248
❑ 59Top-421
❑ 79TCM50-126
❑ 83TopRep5-80
❑ 85TCMPpl1-18
❑ 91TopArc1-110
❑ 94TopArc1-162
❑ 94TopArc1G-162
Wehner, John
❑ 88WatPirP-28
❑ 89SalBucS-24
❑ 90CMC-788
❑ 90EasLeaAP-EL26
❑ 90HarSenP-1203
❑ 90HarSenS-21
❑ 91CarMudLD-121
❑ 91CarMudP-1096
❑ 91FleUpd-115
❑ 91LinDriAA-121
❑ 92Bow-444
❑ 92BufBisF-330
❑ 92BufBisS-46
❑ 92Cla1-T93
❑ 92Don-731
❑ 92Fle-573
❑ 92OPC-282
❑ 92Pin-260
❑ 92ProFS7-306
❑ 92Sco-752
❑ 92Sco100RS-82
❑ 92SkyAAAF-21
❑ 92StaClu-831
❑ 92StaCluECN-831
❑ 92Top-282
❑ 92TopDeb91-183
❑ 92TopGol-282
❑ 92TopGolW-282
❑ 92TopMic-282
❑ 92UppDec-469
❑ 93Fle-506
❑ 93PirNatl-38
❑ 93StaClu-317
❑ 93StaCluFDI-317
❑ 93StaCluMOP-317
❑ 93Top-484
❑ 93TopGol-484
❑ 93TopInaM-484
❑ 93TopInaR-484
❑ 93TopMic-484
❑ 93Ult-105
❑ 93UppDec-759
❑ 93UppDecGold-759
❑ 94BufBisF-1846
❑ 94Pac-513
❑ 96Fle-535
❑ 96FleTif-535
❑ 97ChaKni-29
❑ 98ChaKniQ-28
Wehrmeister, Dave
❑ 75HawIsIC-20
❑ 77PadSchC-62
❑ 77Top-472
❑ 78PadFamF-35
❑ 79HawIsIC-29
❑ 80ColCliP-30
❑ 80ColCliT-25
❑ 81ColCliP-28
❑ 81ColCliT-23
❑ 82ColCliP-28
❑ 82ColCliT-11
❑ 82Top-694
❑ 83ColCliT-6
❑ 84PhiTas-44
❑ 84PorBeaC-195
❑ 85BufBisT-26
❑ 86BufBisP-23
❑ 86Fle-220
❑ 92YanWIZ8-199
Weibel, Randy
❑ 83CliGiaF-27
Weibl, Clint
❑ 96JohCitCTI-33
❑ 97PriWilC-28
❑ 98ArkTraM-25
Weichard, Paul
❑ 98LetBlaDG-29
Weidemaier, Mark
❑ 87SalAngP-32
❑ 89PriWilCS-27
Weidert, Chris
❑ 96WesPalBEB-16
Weidie, Stuart
❑ 86ElmPioRSP-27
❑ 87WinHavRSP-12
❑ 88LynRedSS-25
❑ 89LynRedSS-21
❑ 90NewBriRSB-13
❑ 90NewBriRSP-1332
❑ 90NewBriRSS-22
Weidman, George
❑ 87OldJudN-521
Weiermiller, Mike
❑ 82WisRapTF-4
Weigandt, Bryan
❑ 93MarPhiC-30
❑ 93MarPhiF-3486
❑ 94SpaPhiF-1733
❑ 94SparPhiC-22
Weigel, Ralph
❑ 48WhiSoxTI-27
❑ 49Lea-86
Weighaus, Thomas
❑ 82WicAerTI-20
Weik, Dick
❑ 53IndPenCBP-29
❑ 54Top-224
❑ 94TopArc1-224
❑ 94TopArc1G-224
Weiland, Ed
❑ 39WhiSoxTI-22
❑ 40WhiSoxL-23
Weiland, Robert
❑ 30WhiSoxTI-27
❑ 33ButCanV-55
❑ 34Gou-67
❑ 35GouPuzR-8C
❑ 35GouPuzR-9C
❑ 38CloFotW-89
❑ 93ConTSN-895
Weilman, Carl
❑ 15SpoNewM-189
❑ 16FleBreD-98
❑ 16SpoNewM-187
❑ 17ColE13-186
❑ 17HolBreD-112
❑ 63GadFunC-28
Weimer, Jacob
❑ 06FanCraNL-50
❑ 08RosComP-124
❑ 09T206-370
❑ 11SpoLifCW-364
Weimer, Matthew
❑ 97St.CatSB-27
❑ 98HagSunM-27
Weimerskirch, Mike
❑ 88CapCodPPaLP-96
❑ 91Cla/Bes-311
❑ 91MidLeaAP-MWL49
❑ 91RocExpC-26
❑ 91RocExpP-2061
❑ 92WesPalBEC-25
❑ 92WesPalBEF-2101
Weinbaum, Pete
❑ 91BelMarCB-20
❑ 91BelMarP-3663
Weinberg, Barry
❑ 76ShrCapT-23
❑ 86A'sMot-26
❑ 90A'sMot-28
Weinberg, Mike
❑ 91FayGenC-26
❑ 91FayGenP-1185
Weinberg, Todd
❑ 94SouOreAC-30
❑ 94SouOreAF-3624
❑ 95WesMicWTI-35
❑ 96WesMicWB-29
❑ 97VisOakG-30
Weinberger, Gary
❑ 86JacExpT-17
❑ 87JacExpP-438
Weinbrecht, Mark
❑ 80ElmPioRST-13
Weinert, Lefty (Philip)
❑ 25Zee-14
❑ 27Zee-40
❑ 93ConTSN-958
Weinheimer, Wayne
❑ 88WytCubP-1977
❑ 89ChaWheB-1
❑ 89ChaWheP-1751
Weinke, Chris
❑ 91Cla/Bes-419
❑ 91St.CatBJC-6
❑ 91St.CatBJP-3405
❑ 92MyrBeaHC-1
❑ 92MyrBeaHF-2208
❑ 93ClaFS7-267
❑ 93DunBluJC-25
❑ 93DunBluJF-1806
❑ 93DunBluJFFN-28
❑ 93FloStaLAF-12
❑ 94ClaGolF-60
❑ 94ExcFS7-150
❑ 94KnoSmoF-1313
❑ 94UppDecML-179
❑ 95Bow-131
❑ 95Exc-146
❑ 95SyrChiTI-28
❑ 96KnoSmoB-25
Weinstein, Bobby
❑ 55GiaGolS-31
Weinstein, Jerry
❑ 87PanAmTUBI-NNO
❑ 93GenCubC-29
❑ 93GenCubF-3193
❑ 94WilCubC-26
❑ 94WilCubF-3781
Weintraub, Phil
❑ 36WorWidGV-135
❑ 37ExhFou-4
❑ 77TCMTheWY-51
❑ 83TCMPla1944-35
❑ 92ConTSN-610
Weir, Jim
❑ 82CliGiaF-29
❑ 83CliGiaF-5
Weis, A.J.
❑ 25Exh-24
❑ 26Zee-36
❑ 27Zee-19
Weis, Al
❑ 63Top-537
❑ 63WhiSoxTS-25
❑ 64Top-168
❑ 64TopRooAB-12
❑ 64TopVen-168
❑ 64WhiSoxI-25
❑ 65Top-516
❑ 66OPC-66
❑ 66Top-66
❑ 66TopVen-66
❑ 67CokCapWS-3
❑ 67Top-556
❑ 68Top-313
❑ 68TopVen-313
❑ 69MetNewYDN-20
❑ 69MilBra-286
❑ 69Top-269
❑ 70MetTra-21B
❑ 70MLBOffS-84
❑ 70OPC-498
❑ 70Top-498
❑ 71MLBOffS-168
❑ 71OPC-751
❑ 71Top-751
❑ 72MilBra-357
❑ 81TCM60I-425
❑ 81TCM60I-475
❑ 89MetRinP69-29
❑ 91MetWIZ-427
❑ 94Met69CCPP-32
❑ 94Met69CS-31
❑ 94Met69T-20
Weise, Phil
❑ 90CMC-709
Weisman, Skip
❑ 83AndBraT-3
❑ 89ColMetGS-4
Weismiller, Bob
❑ 77SalPirT-27B
❑ 79BufBisT-12
Weiss, Alta
❑ 94UppDecTAE-16
Weiss, Arthur
❑ 28Zee-62
Weiss, Bill
❑ 89CalLeaA-27
Weiss, Gary
❑ 80AlbDukTc-13
❑ 81AlbDukTc-19
❑ 81Fle-130
❑ 90DodTar-843
Weiss, George
❑ 76ShaPiz-126
❑ 80PerHaloFP-126
❑ 80SSPHOF-126
❑ 82MetGal62-32
❑ 88WilMulP-11
❑ 92YanWIZH-35
Weiss, Jeff
❑ 87DurBulP-3
Weiss, Marc
❑ 94BilMusF-3671
❑ 94BilMusSP-22
❑ 95BilMusTI-24
Weiss, Scott
❑ 91GenCubC-25
❑ 91GenCubP-4218
❑ 91PeoChiTI-32
❑ 92WinSpiF-1209
Weiss, Walt
❑ 86MadMusP-22
❑ 86MadMusP-26
❑ 87HunStaTI-23
❑ 88A'sMot-11
❑ 88DonRoo-18
❑ 88DonTeaBA-NEW
❑ 88Fle-652
❑ 88FleGlo-652
❑ 88FleMin-49
❑ 88FleUpd-56
❑ 88FleUpdG-56
❑ 88ModA'sTI-34
❑ 88ScoRoo-102T
❑ 88ScoRooG-102T
❑ 88TopBig-263
❑ 88TopTra-126T
❑ 88TopTraT-126T
❑ 89A'sMot-8
❑ 89A'sMot-28
❑ 89A'sMotR-3
❑ 89A'sMotR-4
❑ 89Baz-22
❑ 89Bow-196
❑ 89BowTif-196
❑ 89ClaLigB-68
❑ 89Don-446
❑ 89DonBasB-155
❑ 89DonGraS-3
❑ 89Fle-24
❑ 89FleBasM-42
❑ 89FleGlo-24
❑ 89FleGlo-WS10
❑ 89FleSup-42

❑ 89FleWorS-10
❑ 89K-M-4
❑ 89OPC-316
❑ 89PanSti-412
❑ 89PanSti-478
❑ 89Sco-165
❑ 89ScoHot1R-95
❑ 89ScoYouSI-20
❑ 89Spo-116
❑ 89TacTigP-1538
❑ 89Top-316
❑ 89Top-639
❑ 89TopBig-305
❑ 89TopCoi-31
❑ 89TopGaloC-12
❑ 89TopGloS-50
❑ 89TopRoo-21
❑ 89TopSti-168
❑ 89TopSti-326
❑ 89TopTif-316
❑ 89TopTif-639
❑ 89TopUKM-82
❑ 89ToyRoo-32
❑ 89TVSpoM-94
❑ 89TVSpoM-140
❑ 89UppDec-374
❑ 89UppDec-660
❑ 89Woo-5
❑ 90A'sMot-10
❑ 90Bow-461
❑ 90BowTif-461
❑ 90ClaBlu-46
❑ 90Don-67
❑ 90DonBesA-95
❑ 90Fle-22
❑ 90FleCan-22
❑ 90FleWorS-6
❑ 90Lea-239
❑ 90OPC-165
❑ 90PanSti-135
❑ 90PubIntS-317
❑ 90Sco-110
❑ 90Spo-74
❑ 90Top-165
❑ 90TopTif-165
❑ 90UppDec-542
❑ 90Woo-26
❑ 91A'sMot-10
❑ 91A'sSFE-14
❑ 91Bow-228
❑ 91Don-214
❑ 91Fle-26
❑ 91Lea-50
❑ 91OPC-455
❑ 91PanFreS-195
❑ 91PanSti-147
❑ 91Sco-171
❑ 91StaClu-49
❑ 91StaCluP-49
❑ 91Top-455
❑ 91TopDesS-455
❑ 91TopMic-455
❑ 91TopTif-455
❑ 91Ult-255
❑ 91UppDec-192
❑ 92A'sUno7P-1
❑ 92AthMot-10
❑ 92Bow-651
❑ 92Don-71
❑ 92Fle-270
❑ 92Lea-380
❑ 92LeaBlaG-380
❑ 92OPC-691
❑ 92PanSti-18
❑ 92Pin-56
❑ 92Sco-51
❑ 92ScoProP-13
❑ 92StaClu-248
❑ 92Top-691
❑ 92TopGol-691
❑ 92TopGolW-691
❑ 92TopMic-691
❑ 92UppDec-151
❑ 93Bow-290
❑ 93DiaMar-116
❑ 93Don-109
❑ 93Don-756
❑ 93Fla-55
❑ 93Fle-300
❑ 93FleFinE-73
❑ 93FunPac-122
❑ 93Lea-416
❑ 93MarlStaClu-5
❑ 93MarPub-25
❑ 93MarUppD-533
❑ 93MarUSPC-1C
❑ 93MarUSPC-2H
❑ 93MarUSPC-7C
❑ 93OPC-319
❑ 93OPCPre-101
❑ 93PacSpa-473
❑ 93Pin-231
❑ 93PinExpOD-6
❑ 93Sco-659
❑ 93Sel-192
❑ 93SP-143
❑ 93StaClu-370
❑ 93StaCluFDI-370
❑ 93StaCluMOP-370
❑ 93Stu-69
❑ 93Top-580
❑ 93TopGol-580
❑ 93TopInaM-580
❑ 93TopInaR-580
❑ 93TopMic-580
❑ 93TopPos-2
❑ 93TopPos-3
❑ 93TopTra-18T
❑ 93Ult-387
❑ 93UppDec-122
❑ 93UppDec-533
❑ 93UppDecGold-122
❑ 93UppDecGold-533
❑ 94Bow-582
❑ 94ColC-488
❑ 94ColChoGS-488
❑ 94ColChoSS-488
❑ 94Don-428
❑ 94Fin-401
❑ 94FinRef-401
❑ 94Fla-377
❑ 94Fle-480
❑ 94FleExtB-255
❑ 94FleUpd-131
❑ 94FUnPac-122
❑ 94FUnPac-222
❑ 94Lea-359
❑ 94OPC-244
❑ 94Pac-253
❑ 94PanSti-187
❑ 94Pin-486
❑ 94PinArtP-486
❑ 94PinMusC-486
❑ 94RocPol-25
❑ 94Sco-98
❑ 94ScoGolR-98
❑ 94ScoRoo-RT16
❑ 94ScoRooGR-RT16
❑ 94Sel-127
❑ 94SP-169
❑ 94SPDieC-169
❑ 94StaClu-581
❑ 94StaCluFDI-581
❑ 94StaCluGR-581
❑ 94StaCluMOP-581
❑ 94StaCluT-98
❑ 94StaCluTFDI-98
❑ 94Stu-181
❑ 94Top-256
❑ 94TopGol-256
❑ 94TopSpa-256
❑ 94TopTra-113T
❑ 94Ult-488
❑ 94UppDec-438
❑ 94UppDecED-438
❑ 95Baz-104
❑ 95ColCho-443
❑ 95ColChoGS-443
❑ 95ColChoSE-206
❑ 95ColChoSEGS-206
❑ 95ColChoSESS-206
❑ 95ColChoSS-443
❑ 95Don-14
❑ 95DonPreP-14
❑ 95DonTopotO-235
❑ 95Fin-55
❑ 95FinRef-55
❑ 95Fla-134
❑ 95Fle-530
❑ 95Lea-55
❑ 95Pac-147
❑ 95Pin-20
❑ 95PinArtP-20
❑ 95PinMusC-20
❑ 95RocPol-11
❑ 95Sco-435
❑ 95ScoGolR-435
❑ 95ScoPlaTS-435
❑ 95StaClu-94
❑ 95StaCluFDI-94
❑ 95StaCluMOP-94
❑ 95StaCluSTWS-94
❑ 95Stu-161
❑ 95Top-110
❑ 95TopCyb-71
❑ 95TopD3-54
❑ 95TopEmb-112
❑ 95TopEmbGI-112
❑ 95Ult-377
❑ 95UltGolM-377
❑ 95UppDec-413
❑ 95UppDecED-413
❑ 95UppDecEDG-413
❑ 95UppDecSE-102
❑ 95UppDecSEG-102
❑ 96ColCho-541
❑ 96ColChoGS-541
❑ 96ColChoSS-541
❑ 96Don-203
❑ 96DonPreP-203
❑ 96EmoXL-179
❑ 96Fla-254
❑ 96Fle-378
❑ 96FleTif-378
❑ 96LeaSigA-241
❑ 96LeaSigAG-242
❑ 96LeaSigAS-242
❑ 96MetUni-160
❑ 96MetUniP-160
❑ 96Pac-56
❑ 96PanSti-83
❑ 96Pin-107
❑ 96PinAfi-45
❑ 96PinAfiAP-45
❑ 96PinAfiFPP-45
❑ 96ProSta-115
❑ 96RocFle-17
❑ 96RocPol-26
❑ 96Sco-98
❑ 96Sel-136
❑ 96SelArtP-136
❑ 96SP-78
❑ 96StaClu-166
❑ 96StaCluMOP-166
❑ 96TeaOut-87
❑ 96Top-149
❑ 96Ult-476
❑ 96UltGolM-476
❑ 96UppDec-322
❑ 97ColCho-323
❑ 97ColChoT-CR13
❑ 97DonTea-101
❑ 97DonTeaSPE-101
❑ 97Fin-180
❑ 97FinRef-180
❑ 97Fle-320
❑ 97FleTif-320
❑ 97MetUni-77
❑ 97Pac-292
❑ 97PacLigB-292
❑ 97PacSil-292
❑ 97RocPol-11
❑ 97RocSco-3
❑ 97RocScoPl-3
❑ 97RocScoPr-3
❑ 97Sco-38
❑ 97ScoArtPWB-38
❑ 97ScoPreS-38
❑ 97ScoShoS-38
❑ 97ScoShoSAP-38
❑ 97StaClu-287
❑ 97StaCluMOP-287
❑ 97Top-401
❑ 97Ult-190
❑ 97UltGolME-190
❑ 97UltPlaME-190
❑ 97UppDec-59
❑ 98CirThu-112
❑ 98CirThuRav-112
❑ 98CirThuSupRav-112
❑ 98ColCho-81
❑ 98ColCho-304
❑ 98CroRoy-17
❑ 98CroRoyAS-14
❑ 98Fin-183
❑ 98FinNo--183
❑ 98FinNo-R-183
❑ 98FinRef-183
❑ 98Fle-459
❑ 98Pac-291
❑ 98PacAur-109
❑ 98PacOnl-75
❑ 98PacOnlR-75
❑ 98PacOnlWC-75
❑ 98PacPlaB-291
❑ 98PacRedT-291
❑ 98PacSil-291
❑ 98PinPlu-181
❑ 98PinSna-AB2
❑ 98Revo-17
❑ 98RevoSS-17
❑ 98ScoRT-98
❑ 98SPxFin-333
❑ 98SPxFinR-333
❑ 98SPxFinS-333
❑ 98StaCluFDI-370
❑ 98StaCluI-370
❑ 98StaCluOneK-370
❑ 98StaCluPP-370
❑ 98Top-96
❑ 98Top-456
❑ 98TopChr-96
❑ 98TopChr-456
❑ 98TopChrR-96
❑ 98TopChrR-456
❑ 98TopDevR-96
❑ 98TopDevR-456
❑ 98TopDia-96
❑ 98TopDia-456
❑ 98TopMiniC-96
❑ 98TopMiniC-456
❑ 98Ult-329
❑ 98UltGolM-329
❑ 98UltMas-329
❑ 98UltPlaM-329
❑ 98UppDec-649
❑ 99Fle-266
❑ 99FleSta9-266
❑ 99FleWarT-266
❑ 99Pac-44
❑ 99PacPlaB-44
❑ 99PacRed-44
❑ 99SkyMolMOA-26
❑ 99SkyThu-180
❑ 99SkyThuRant-180
❑ 99SkyThuRave-180
❑ 99StaClu-117
❑ 99StaCluFDI-117
❑ 99StaCluOoaK-117
❑ 99StaCluPP-117
❑ 99ThuSkySupR-180
❑ 99Top-138
❑ 99TopChr-138
❑ 99TopChrR-138
❑ 99TopMVPP-138
❑ 99TopOpeD-81
❑ 99TopPre-PP4
❑ 99Ult-17
❑ 99UltGolM-17
❑ 99UltMas-17
❑ 99UltPlaM-17
❑ 99UppDec-40
❑ 99UppDecEL1-40
❑ 99UppDecEL2-40
❑ 99Vic-38

Weissman, Craig
❑ 81QuaCitCT-26
❑ 82QuaCitCT-13
❑ 86GleFalTP-24
❑ 87ArkTraP-17
❑ 89ArkTraGS-24

Weitz, Bruce
❑ 91TopRut-3

Weitzel, Brad
❑ 90EriSaiS-31

Welaj, Johnny
❑ 43A'STEAI-26
❑ 50WorWidGV-8
❑ 77TCMTheWY-81

Welaj, Lou
❑ 50WorWidGV-40

Welborn, Frank
❑ 86JamExpP-29

Welborn, Sam
❑ 77SpaPhiT-23
❑ 80LynSaiT-21
❑ 81SpoIndT-4
❑ 82SalLakCGT-21
❑ 83TucTorT-10

Welborn, Todd
❑ 85LitFalMT-12
❑ 86LitFalMP-29
❑ 87ColMetP-29
❑ 88JacMetGS-16
❑ 88MetColP-51
❑ 89JacMetGS-7

Welborn, Tony
❑ 87BurExpP-1070
❑ 88WesPalBES-27

Welch, Bob (Robert)
❑ 79Top-318
❑ 80DodPol-35
❑ 80Top-146
❑ 81Dod-32
❑ 81DodPol-35
❑ 81DodPos-10
❑ 81Don-178
❑ 81Fle-120A
❑ 81Fle-120B
❑ 81LonBeaPT-13
❑ 81OPC-357
❑ 81Top-624
❑ 81TopSupHT-53
❑ 82DodPol-35
❑ 82DodPos-9
❑ 82DodUniOV-25
❑ 82Don-75
❑ 82Fle-28
❑ 82Top-82
❑ 83DodPol-35
❑ 83DodPos-19
❑ 83Don-410
❑ 83Fle-225
❑ 83OPC-288
❑ 83Top-454
❑ 84DodPol-35
❑ 84DodUniO-10
❑ 84Don-153
❑ 84Fle-116
❑ 84Nes792-306
❑ 84Nes792-722
❑ 84OPC-227
❑ 84Top-306
❑ 84Top-722
❑ 84TopTif-306
❑ 84TopTif-722
❑ 85DodCokP-32
❑ 85Don-372
❑ 85Fle-388
❑ 85OPC-291
❑ 85Top-291
❑ 85TopTif-291
❑ 86DodCokP-32
❑ 86DodPol-35
❑ 86DodUniOP-23
❑ 86Don-459
❑ 86Fle-146
❑ 86Lea-223
❑ 86Spo-198
❑ 86Top-549
❑ 86TopMinL-48
❑ 86TopTif-549
❑ 87DodMot-9
❑ 87DodPol-18
❑ 87DodSmoA-37
❑ 87Don-475
❑ 87Fle-459
❑ 87FleGlo-459
❑ 87FleLeaL-43
❑ 87FleStiC-121
❑ 87OPC-328
❑ 87Top-328
❑ 87TopTif-328
❑ 88A'sMot-9
❑ 88Don-24
❑ 88Don-253
❑ 88DonBasB-134
❑ 88DonSupD-24
❑ 88DonTeaBA-NEW
❑ 88Fle-529
❑ 88FleGlo-529
❑ 88FleMin-50
❑ 88FleUpd-57
❑ 88FleUpdG-57
❑ 88Lea-24
❑ 88OPC-118
❑ 88PanSti-305
❑ 88RedFolSB-98
❑ 88Sco-510
❑ 88ScoGlo-510
❑ 88ScoRoo-15T
❑ 88ScoRooG-15T
❑ 88Spo-167
❑ 88StaLinAs-18
❑ 88Top-118
❑ 88TopMinL-55
❑ 88TopRevLL-15
❑ 88TopSti-73
❑ 88TopTif-118
❑ 88TopTra-127T
❑ 88TopTraT-127T
❑ 89A'sMot-9
❑ 89Bow-186
❑ 89BowTif-186
❑ 89ClaLigB-91
❑ 89DodSmoG-92
❑ 89Don-332
❑ 89DonBasB-267
❑ 89Fle-25
❑ 89FleGlo-25
❑ 89PanSti-416
❑ 89Sco-308
❑ 89ScoHot1S-89
❑ 89Spo-91
❑ 89SpoIllFKI-261
❑ 89Top-605A
❑ 89Top-605B
❑ 89TopBasT-115
❑ 89TopSti-166
❑ 89TopTif-605
❑ 89UppDec-191
❑ 90A'sMot-16
❑ 90DodTar-844
❑ 90Don-332
❑ 90DonBesA-67
❑ 90Fle-23
❑ 90FleCan-23
❑ 90MLBBasB-76
❑ 90OPC-475
❑ 90PanSti-131
❑ 90PubIntS-318
❑ 90Sco-159
❑ 90Spo-35
❑ 90Top-475
❑ 90TopBig-106
❑ 90TopMag-44
❑ 90TopSti-180
❑ 90TopTif-475
❑ 90UppDec-251
❑ 90UppDecS-2
❑ 90USPlaCA-1C
❑ 90WinDis-3
❑ 91A'sMot-9
❑ 91A'sSFE-15
❑ 91Baz-3
❑ 91Bow-215
❑ 91Cla1-T76
❑ 91ClaGam-199
❑ 91Col-5
❑ 91Don-20
❑ 91Don-54
❑ 91Don-645
❑ 91Don-727
❑ 91DonPre-5
❑ 91DonSupD-20
❑ 91Fle-27
❑ 91Lea-64
❑ 91MSAHolD-14
❑ 91OPC-50
❑ 91OPC-394
❑ 91PanCanT1-61
❑ 91PanFreS-174
❑ 91PanSti-151
❑ 91RedFolS-130
❑ 91Sco-311
❑ 91Sco-568
❑ 91Sco-877
❑ 91Sco100S-49
❑ 91SevCoi-NC14
❑ 91StaClu-79
❑ 91StaCluCM-32
❑ 91StaPinB-52
❑ 91Stu-110
❑ 91Top-50
❑ 91Top-394
❑ 91TopCraJ2-28
❑ 91TopDesS-50
❑ 91TopDesS-394
❑ 91TopGaloC-12
❑ 91TopGloA-10
❑ 91TopMic-50
❑ 91TopMic-394
❑ 91TopTif-50
❑ 91TopTif-394
❑ 91Ult-256
❑ 91UppDec-425
❑ 91Woo-4
❑ 92AthMot-9
❑ 92DodStaTA-19
❑ 92Don-190
❑ 92Fle-271
❑ 92Lea-390
❑ 92LeaBlaG-390
❑ 92OPC-285
❑ 92Pin-409
❑ 92Sco-300
❑ 92StaClu-651
❑ 92Top-285
❑ 92TopGol-285
❑ 92TopGolW-285
❑ 92TopMic-285
❑ 92TriPla-124
❑ 92Ult-119
❑ 92UppDec-452
❑ 93AthMot-10
❑ 93AthStaC-12

❑ 93Bow-77
❑ 93Don-579
❑ 93Fin-151
❑ 93FinRef-151
❑ 93Fla-264
❑ 93Fle-301
❑ 93Lea-94
❑ 93OPC-340
❑ 93PacSpa-227
❑ 93Pin-573
❑ 93Sco-208
❑ 93Sel-254
❑ 93StaClu-546
❑ 93StaCluFDI-546
❑ 93StaCluMOP-546
❑ 93Top-705
❑ 93TopGol-705
❑ 93TopInaM-705
❑ 93TopInaR-705
❑ 93TopMic-705
❑ 93TriPla-192
❑ 93Ult-263
❑ 93UppDec-407
❑ 93UppDecGold-407
❑ 94A'sMot-10
❑ 94Bow-136
❑ 94ColC-574
❑ 94ColChoGS-574
❑ 94ColChoSS-574
❑ 94Don-282
❑ 94Fin-158
❑ 94FinRef-158
❑ 94Fle-276
❑ 94Lea-354
❑ 94OPC-213
❑ 94Pac-465
❑ 94PanSti-115
❑ 94Pin-329
❑ 94PinArtP-329
❑ 94PinMusC-329
❑ 94Sco-547
❑ 94ScoGolR-547
❑ 94Sel-126
❑ 94StaClu-297
❑ 94StaCluFDI-297
❑ 94StaCluGR-297
❑ 94StaCluMOP-297
❑ 94Top-521
❑ 94TopGol-521
❑ 94TopSpa-521
❑ 94Ult-114
❑ 94UppDec-429
❑ 94UppDecED-429
❑ 95Pac-322
❑ 95Sco-29
❑ 95ScoGolR-29
❑ 95ScoPlaTS-29
❑ 95Top-364
❑ 95Ult-323
❑ 95UltGolM-323

Welch, Bryce
❑ 89EveGiaS-32

Welch, Curt
❑ 76SSP188WS-8
❑ 87BucN28-106
❑ 87LonJacN-13
❑ 87OldJudN-523
❑ 87OldJudN-524A
❑ 87OldJudN-524B
❑ 87ScrDC-9
❑ 88GandBCGCE-45
❑ 88SpoTimM-27
❑ 89EdgR.WG-19
❑ 89SFHaCN-19
❑ 90HOFStiB-5

Welch, Dan
❑ 89MarPhiS-33
❑ 89Sta-146
❑ 90SpaPhiB-24
❑ 90SpaPhiP-2507
❑ 90SpaPhiS-24

Welch, David
❑ 92ColRedF-2392
❑ 93KinIndC-25
❑ 93KinIndF-2248
❑ 93KinIndTI-26
❑ 94KinIndC-20
❑ 94KinIndF-2642

Welch, Doug
❑ 89GenCubP-1864
❑ 90WinSpiTI-7
❑ 91ChaKniLD-147
❑ 91ChaKniP-1703
❑ 91LinDriAA-147
❑ 92ChaKniF-2785
❑ 92ChaKniS-171

Welch, Frank
❑ 22E120-90
❑ 25Exh-112
❑ 28Zee-147

Welch, John V.
❑ 33Gou-93
❑ 33GouCanV-56
❑ 94ConTSN-1047
❑ 94ConTSNB-1047

Welch, Ken
❑ 90WatIndS-22

Welch, Mickey (Michael)
❑ 76ShaPiz-140
❑ 80PerHaloFP-140
❑ 80SSPHOF-140
❑ 81ConTSN-73
❑ 86OldJudN-14
❑ 87FouBasHN-13
❑ 87OldJudN-525
❑ 87TobLit-10
❑ 88AugBecN-36A
❑ 88AugBecN-36B
❑ 88AugBecN-36C
❑ 88GandBCGCE-46
❑ 90KalBatN-56
❑ 94ConTSN-1250
❑ 94ConTSNB-1250
❑ 94OriofB-73

Welch, Mike
❑ 89SFHaCN-20
❑ 92ButCopKSP-20
❑ 93Bow-221
❑ 93ChaRaiC-22
❑ 93ChaRaiF-1926
❑ 93PitMetC-23
❑ 93PitMetF-3711
❑ 93SouAtlLAGF-9
❑ 94Bow-268
❑ 94CapCitBC-23
❑ 94CapCitBF-1752
❑ 94ExcFS7-241
❑ 94Top-713
❑ 94TopGol-713
❑ 94TopSpa-713
❑ 95StLucMTI-33
❑ 96BinMetB-28
❑ 96DouAllB-15
❑ 97NorTid-33
❑ 97NorTidB-32
❑ 98ScrRedBQ-28
❑ 99SpoIll-61

Welch, Robb
❑ 94SigRooDP-75
❑ 94SigRooDPS-75
❑ 95Top-429
❑ 96LowSpiB-28
❑ 97MicBatC-30

Welch, Travis
❑ 94JohCitCC-28
❑ 94JohCitCF-3703
❑ 95Exc-277
❑ 95PeoChiTI-29
❑ 96BesAutSA-86
❑ 96MidLeaAB-24
❑ 96PeoChiB-29
❑ 97BesAutAS-67
❑ 97PriWilC-29
❑ 98PriWilCQ-13

Welchel, Don
❑ 80ChaO'sP-22
❑ 80ChaO'sW-23
❑ 81RocRedWT-18
❑ 81RocRedWW-9
❑ 82RocRedWT-8
❑ 84RocRedWT-14
❑ 85RocRedWT-23
❑ 86OklCit8P-24
❑ 88OmaRoyP-1511
❑ 91OriCro-477

Weldin, David
❑ 89HelBreSP-21

Weldon, Paul
❑ 91PocPioP-3792
❑ 91PocPioSP-21

Weleno, Doug
❑ 83MidCubT-8

Welish, Scott
❑ 89ChaRaiP-988
❑ 89SpoIndSP-16

Welke, Tim
❑ 88T/MUmp-55
❑ 89T/MUmp-53
❑ 90T/MUmp-51

Welles, Rob
❑ 94JamJamC-24
❑ 94JamJamF-3976
❑ 97CedRapK-28

Wellman, Bob
❑ 52Par-95
❑ 52Top-41
❑ 79JacMetT-6
❑ 83TopRep5-41

Wellman, Brad
❑ 84Don-265
❑ 84Fle-386
❑ 84Nes792-109
❑ 84Top-109
❑ 84TopTif-109
❑ 85Fle-623
❑ 85GiaMot-26
❑ 85GiaPos-29
❑ 85Top-409
❑ 85TopTif-409
❑ 86Don-431
❑ 86Fle-553
❑ 86GiaMot-22
❑ 86GiaPos-30
❑ 86OPC-41
❑ 86Top-41
❑ 86TopTif-41
❑ 87AlbDukD-23
❑ 88RoySmo-24
❑ 88RoyTeal-36
❑ 89Don-380
❑ 89Fle-289
❑ 89Sco-504
❑ 90DodTar-845
❑ 90AubDouTI-29

Wellman, Phillip
❑ 86DurBulP-27
❑ 87HarSenP-7
❑ 88PulBraP-1748
❑ 89PulBraP-1901
❑ 90BurBraP-2368
❑ 90BurBraS-30
❑ 91DurBulC-26
❑ 91DurBulP-1679
❑ 93LetMouF-4164
❑ 93LetMouSP-25
❑ 94LetMouF-3894
❑ 94LetMouSP-26
❑ 97BurBeeB-27
❑ 98BurBeeM-27

Wells, Beck
❑ 94ChaRivC-24
❑ 94ChaRivF-2678

Wells, Bob
❑ 90SpaPhiB-10
❑ 90SpaPhiP-2491
❑ 90SpaPhiS-25
❑ 91ClePhiP-1621
❑ 92ClePhiC-13
❑ 92ReaPhiF-576
❑ 94ReaPhiF-2063
❑ 95FleUpd-79
❑ 95MarMot-16
❑ 95MarPac-46
❑ 96MarMot-13
❑ 97ColCho-481
❑ 97ColChoT-SM13
❑ 97Don-151
❑ 97DonGolPP-151
❑ 97DonSilPP-151
❑ 97DonTea-143
❑ 97DonTeaSPE-143
❑ 97Fle-216
❑ 97FleTif-216
❑ 97MarSco-5
❑ 97MarScoPl-5
❑ 97MarScoPr-5
❑ 97Pac-195
❑ 97PacLigB-195
❑ 97PacSil-195
❑ 97Sco-147
❑ 97ScoArtPWB-147
❑ 97ScoPreS-147
❑ 97ScoShoS-147
❑ 97ScoShoSAP-147
❑ 97StaClu-304
❑ 97StaCluMOP-304
❑ 97Top-357
❑ 97Ult-128
❑ 97UltGolME-128
❑ 97UltPlaME-128
❑ 97UppDec-176
❑ 98PacOnl-699
❑ 98PacOnlR-699
❑ 98PacOnlWC-699
❑ 98PinSna-SM13

Wells, Boomer (Greg)
❑ 78DunBluJT-24
❑ 79SyrChiT-1
❑ 80SyrChiT-14
❑ 80SyrChiTI-23
❑ 81SyrChiT-16
❑ 81SyrChiTI-22
❑ 82OPC-203
❑ 82TolMudHT-17
❑ 82Top-203
❑ 87JapPlaB-30

Wells, David
❑ 83KinBluJTI-28
❑ 86VenGulP-27
❑ 87SyrChiT-9
❑ 88BluJayFS-31
❑ 88Don-640
❑ 88DonBasB-311
❑ 88DonRoo-26
❑ 88FleUpd-69
❑ 88FleUpdG-69
❑ 88TopTra-128T
❑ 88TopTraT-128T
❑ 89BluJayFS-30
❑ 89Don-307
❑ 89DonBasB-328
❑ 89Fle-247
❑ 89FleGlo-247
❑ 89OPC-259
❑ 89Top-567
❑ 89TopRoo-22
❑ 89TopTif-567
❑ 90BluJayFS-32
❑ 90Don-425
❑ 90Fle-96
❑ 90FleCan-96
❑ 90OPC-229
❑ 90Sco-491A
❑ 90Sco-491B
❑ 90ScoYouSI-31
❑ 90Top-229
❑ 90TopTif-229
❑ 90UppDec-30
❑ 91BluJayFS-29
❑ 91BluJayFS-32
❑ 91BluJayS-9
❑ 91Don-473
❑ 91Fle-188
❑ 91Lea-140
❑ 91OPC-619
❑ 91PanFreS-350
❑ 91PanSti-153
❑ 91Sco-474
❑ 91StaClu-133
❑ 91Top-619
❑ 91TopDesS-619
❑ 91TopMic-619
❑ 91TopTif-619
❑ 91Ult-370
❑ 91UppDec-583
❑ 92Bow-352
❑ 92Don-620
❑ 92Fle-345
❑ 92Lea-483
❑ 92LeaBlaG-483
❑ 92OPC-54
❑ 92Pin-431
❑ 92Sco-49
❑ 92ScoProP-15
❑ 92SpoIllFK1-749
❑ 92StaClu-721
❑ 92StaCluNC-721
❑ 92Top-54
❑ 92TopGol-54
❑ 92TopGolW-54
❑ 92TopMic-54
❑ 92Ult-453
❑ 92UppDec-116
❑ 93BluJayD4-24
❑ 93Don-511
❑ 93Fla-210
❑ 93Fle-702
❑ 93FleFinE-214
❑ 93IdaFalBF-4034
❑ 93IdaFalBSP-26
❑ 93Lea-484
❑ 93OPC-321
❑ 93PacSpa-451
❑ 93Pin-114
❑ 93Sco-648
❑ 93SelRoo-113T
❑ 93SP-242
❑ 93StaClu-59
❑ 93StaCluFDI-59
❑ 93StaCluMOP-59
❑ 93TigGat-26
❑ 93Top-458
❑ 93TopGol-458
❑ 93TopInaM-458
❑ 93TopInaR-458
❑ 93TopMic-458
❑ 93TopTra-50T
❑ 93Ult-296
❑ 93UppDec-699
❑ 93UppDecGold-699
❑ 94ColC-499
❑ 94ColChoGS-499
❑ 94ColChoSS-499
❑ 94Don-307
❑ 94Fin-108
❑ 94FinRef-108
❑ 94Fle-145
❑ 94Lea-39
❑ 94MacBraC-25
❑ 94MacBraF-2206
❑ 94Pac-231
❑ 94Pin-464
❑ 94PinArtP-464
❑ 94PinMusC-464
❑ 94Sco-369
❑ 94ScoGolR-369
❑ 94Sel-357
❑ 94StaClu-617
❑ 94StaCluFDI-617
❑ 94StaCluGR-617
❑ 94StaCluMOP-617
❑ 94Top-105
❑ 94TopGol-105
❑ 94TopSpa-105
❑ 94Ult-359
❑ 94UppDec-179
❑ 94UppDecED-179
❑ 95BluJayUSPC-8S
❑ 95Don-465
❑ 95DonPreP-465
❑ 95DonTopotO-223
❑ 95Fle-63
❑ 95Pac-162
❑ 95Pin-379
❑ 95PinArtP-379
❑ 95PinMusC-379
❑ 95Sco-526
❑ 95ScoGolR-526
❑ 95ScoPlaTS-526
❑ 95StaClu-182
❑ 95StaCluFDI-182
❑ 95StaCluMOP-182
❑ 95StaCluSTWS-182
❑ 95Top-434
❑ 95TopCyb-231
❑ 95Ult-52
❑ 95UltGolM-52
❑ 96BalOriP-36
❑ 96ColCho-762
❑ 96Don-469
❑ 96DonPreP-469
❑ 96Fin-B252
❑ 96FinRef-B252
❑ 96Fla-14
❑ 96Fle-357
❑ 96FleTif-357
❑ 96FleUpd-U10
❑ 96FleUpdTC-U10
❑ 96OriFle-18
❑ 96Sco-471
❑ 96StaClu-20
❑ 96StaClu-240
❑ 96StaCluMOP-20
❑ 96StaCluMOP-240
❑ 96Top-311
❑ 96Ult-311
❑ 96UltGolM-311
❑ 96UppDec-483U
❑ 97Cir-334
❑ 97CirRav-334
❑ 97Don-335
❑ 97DonGolPP-335
❑ 97DonSilPP-335
❑ 97DonTea-134
❑ 97DonTeaSPE-134
❑ 97Fin-179
❑ 97FinRef-179
❑ 97Fle-15
❑ 97Fle-543
❑ 97FleTif-15
❑ 97FleTif-543
❑ 97OriSco-15
❑ 97OriScoPl-15
❑ 97OriScoPr-15
❑ 97Sco-256
❑ 97Sco-337
❑ 97ScoArtPWB-256
❑ 97ScoArtPWB-337
❑ 97ScoPreS-256
❑ 97ScoResC-337
❑ 97ScoShoS-256
❑ 97ScoShoS-337
❑ 97ScoShoSAP-256
❑ 97ScoShoSAP-337
❑ 97StaClu-338
❑ 97StaCluMOP-338
❑ 97Top-228
❑ 97Ult-314
❑ 97UltGolME-314
❑ 97UltPlaME-314
❑ 97UppDec-251
❑ 98CirThu-229
❑ 98CirThuRav-229
❑ 98CirThuSupRav-229
❑ 98ColCho-191
❑ 98CroRoyAS-6
❑ 98Fin-28
❑ 98FinNo--28
❑ 98FinNo-R-28
❑ 98FinRef-28
❑ 98Fle-385
❑ 98FleUpd-U9
❑ 98Pac-160
❑ 98PacOme-172
❑ 98PacOmeR-172
❑ 98PacOnl-520
❑ 98PacOnlR-520
❑ 98PacOnlWC-520
❑ 98PacPlaB-160
❑ 98PacRedT-160
❑ 98PacSil-160
❑ 98Pin-154
❑ 98PinPreP-154
❑ 98PinSna-NYY18
❑ 98Sco-177
❑ 98ScoSS-PP79
❑ 98ScoSSAP-PP79
❑ 98StaCluFDI-75
❑ 98StaCluI-75
❑ 98StaCluOneK-75
❑ 98StaCluPP-75
❑ 98Top-83
❑ 98TopChr-83
❑ 98TopChrR-83
❑ 98TopDevR-83
❑ 98TopDia-83
❑ 98TopMiniC-83
❑ 98TopOpeD-40
❑ 98Ult-277
❑ 98UltGolM-277
❑ 98UltMas-277
❑ 98UltPlaM-277
❑ 98UppDec-464
❑ 98YanKodW-1
❑ 98YanSco-12
❑ 98YanScoP-12
❑ 98YanUppD-464
❑ 98YanUppDWSC-1
❑ 99199Fin-191
❑ 99Bow-252
❑ 99BowGol-252
❑ 99BowInt-252
❑ 99DumSet-DWE
❑ 99DumSet-DWE
❑ 99E-X Cen-42
❑ 99E-X CenECFut-42
❑ 99E-X CenECNow-42
❑ 99FinGolRef-191
❑ 99FinRef-191
❑ 99FlaShoLeg1-67
❑ 99FlaShoLeg2-67
❑ 99FlaShoLeg3-67
❑ 99FlaShoLegM1-67
❑ 99FlaShoLegM2-67
❑ 99FlaShoLegM3-67
❑ 99FlaShoR1-67
❑ 99FlaShoR2-67
❑ 99FlaShoR3-67
❑ 99Fle-147
❑ 99FleBri-102
❑ 99FleBri2G-102
❑ 99FleBriBlu-102
❑ 99FleBriGol-102
❑ 99FleGolM-14
❑ 99FleMys-96
❑ 99FleMysG-96
❑ 99FleMysM-96
❑ 99FleSta9-147
❑ 99FleWarT-147
❑ 99MetUni-205
❑ 99MetUniGM-205
❑ 99MetUniPMG-205
❑ 99Pac-304
❑ 99PacOme-249
❑ 99PacOmeC-249

❑ 99PacOmeG-249
❑ 99PacOmePB-249
❑ 99PacPar-250
❑ 99PacParC-250
❑ 99PacParG-250
❑ 99PacParHoloGold-250
❑ 99PacParHS-250
❑ 99PacParOD-250
❑ 99PacParPB-250
❑ 99PacParRed-250
❑ 99PacPlaB-304
❑ 99PacPriS-48
❑ 99PacPriS206-48
❑ 99PacPriS206R-48
❑ 99PacPriSP-48
❑ 99PacPriSV-48
❑ 99PacRed-304
❑ 99Pin-28
❑ 99SkyMolM-72
❑ 99SkyMolMX-72
❑ 99SkyPre-94
❑ 99SkyPreR-94
❑ 99SkyThu-219
❑ 99SkyThuRant-219
❑ 99SkyThuRave-219
❑ 99SP Aut-133
❑ 99SpoIll-3
❑ 99SpoIll-31
❑ 99StaClu-38
❑ 99StaCluFDI-38
❑ 99StaCluOoaK-38
❑ 99StaCluPP-38
❑ 99ThuSkySupR-219
❑ 99Top-10
❑ 99Top-200
❑ 99TopChr-10
❑ 99TopChr-200
❑ 99TopChrR-10
❑ 99TopChrR-200
❑ 99TopMVPP-10
❑ 99TopOpeD-7
❑ 99TopOpeD-160
❑ 99TopSta-65
❑ 99TopSta1Foil-65
❑ 99TopStaFoil-65
❑ 99TopStaOS-65
❑ 99TopSupC-31
❑ 99TopSupCR-31
❑ 99UD Cho-30
❑ 99UD Cho-117
❑ 99UD ChoPCR-30
❑ 99UD ChoPCR-117
❑ 99UDHolo-59
❑ 99UDHoloAUsome-59
❑ 99Ult-35
❑ 99UltGolM-35
❑ 99UltMas-35
❑ 99UltPlaM-35
❑ 99UppDec-160
❑ 99UppDec-249
❑ 99UppDec-514
❑ 99UppDecCL-90
❑ 99UppDecCLCC-90
❑ 99UppDecCLM-C97
❑ 99UppDecE-90
❑ 99UppDecEFXG-90
❑ 99UppDecEL1-160
❑ 99UppDecEL1-249
❑ 99UppDecEL1-514
❑ 99UppDecEL2-160
❑ 99UppDecEL2-249
❑ 99UppDecEL2-514
❑ 99UppDecM-211
❑ 99UppDecMGS-211
❑ 99UppDecMHFS-211
❑ 99UppDecMSS-211
❑ 99UppDecOWP-R14
❑ 99UppDecR-87
❑ 99UppDecRG-87
❑ 99UppDecRP-87
❑ 99UppDecTE-T22
❑ 99UppDecTED-T22
❑ 99UppDecTEQ-T22
❑ 99UppDecTET-T22
❑ 99Vic-417
❑ 99YanFle-20

Wells, Devil (Willie)
❑ 74LauOldTBS-13
❑ 83ConMar-58
❑ 86NegLeaF-71
❑ 87NegLeaPD-42
❑ 88ConNegA-11
❑ 89NegLeaRP-10
❑ 90NegLeaS-11
❑ 90PerGreM-107
❑ 97NegLeaPC-6S

Wells, Ed
❑ 34Gou-73
❑ 92ConTSN-389

Wells, Forry
❑ 94BenRocC-26
❑ 94BenRocF-3605
❑ 95SalAvaTI-24
❑ 96NewHavRB-27
❑ 97NewHavRB-14
❑ 97SalAva-U3
❑ 98FarRedHM-24

Wells, Frank
❑ 87OldJudN-527

Wells, Jacob
❑ 87OldJudN-526

Wells, Kip
❑ 99Bow-343
❑ 99BowGol-343
❑ 99BowInt-343

Wells, Leo
❑ 47SunBre-25

Wells, Lyle
❑ 22Zee-112
❑ 23Zee-58
❑ 23Zee-152

Wells, Mark
❑ 94BenRocC-27
❑ 94BenRocF-3611
❑ 95AshTouUTI-30
❑ 95SalAvaTI-21

Wells, Matt
❑ 96BelGiaTI-1
❑ 97BakBlaB-15
❑ 97BakBlaTI-15

Wells, Michael
❑ 93AusFut-27
❑ 94DavLipB-24
❑ 95DavLipB-24

Wells, Terry
❑ 86AshTouP-29
❑ 87OscAstP-1
❑ 88ColAstB-3
❑ 89ColMudP-144
❑ 89ColMudS-23
❑ 90AlbDukCm-13
❑ 90AlbDukP-346
❑ 90AlbDukTr-31
❑ 90CMC-415
❑ 90ProAAAF-67
❑ 91LinDriAAA-323
❑ 91OklCit8LD-323
❑ 91OklCit8P-180
❑ 91Sco-359
❑ 91TopDeb90-166
❑ 93ChaKniF-542

Wells, Tim
❑ 90ButCopKSP-28
❑ 91GasRanC-11
❑ 91GasRanP-2688

Wells, Vernon
❑ 97Bow-424
❑ 97BowChr-284
❑ 97BowChrI-284
❑ 97BowChrIR-284
❑ 97BowChrR-284
❑ 97BowInt-424
❑ 97St.CatSB-28
❑ 97TopSta-115
❑ 97TopStaAM-115
❑ 98Bes-98
❑ 98BesDiaB-9
❑ 98BesNumOP-40
❑ 98Bow-112
❑ 98BowBes-140
❑ 98BowBesAR-140
❑ 98BowBesR-140
❑ 98BowChr-112
❑ 98BowChrGA-112
❑ 98BowChrGAR-112
❑ 98BowChrI-112
❑ 98BowChrIR-112
❑ 98BowChrR-112
❑ 98BowGolA-112
❑ 98BowInt-112
❑ 98HagSunM-28
❑ 98SouAtlLPM-25
❑ 98StaCluFDI-381
❑ 98StaCluI-381
❑ 98StaCluOneK-381
❑ 98StaCluPP-381
❑ 98Top-247
❑ 98TopChr-247
❑ 98TopChrR-247
❑ 98TopDevR-247
❑ 98TopDia-247
❑ 98TopMiniC-247
❑ 99BasAmeTPA-45
❑ 99Bow-94
❑ 99BowAut-BA64
❑ 99BowChr-94
❑ 99BowChrG-94
❑ 99BowChrGR-94
❑ 99BowChrI-94
❑ 99BowChrIR-94
❑ 99BowChrR-94
❑ 99BowGol-94
❑ 99BowInt-94
❑ 99JustheS-46
❑ 99JustheSJB-46
❑ 99JustheSJN-5
❑ 99SP TopP-118
❑ 99SP TopPPE-118
❑ 99TeaBesRFS-24
❑ 99Top-436
❑ 99TopChr-436
❑ 99TopChrR-436
❑ 99TopMVPP-436

Wells, Zachary
❑ 97SalVolG-40

Welmaker, Roy
❑ 52MotCoo-37
❑ 53MotCoo-52
❑ 91PomBlaBPB-2

Welsh, Chris
❑ 79ColCliT-24
❑ 80ColCliP-34
❑ 80ColCliT-3
❑ 82Don-44
❑ 82Fle-584
❑ 82Top-376
❑ 83Don-94
❑ 83ExpPos-35
❑ 83Fle-374
❑ 83OPC-118
❑ 83Top-118
❑ 83TopTra-125T
❑ 84Don-498
❑ 84Fle-292
❑ 84IndIndTI-4
❑ 85RanPer-41
❑ 86Don-464
❑ 86Fle-576
❑ 86RedTexG-45
❑ 86Top-52
❑ 86TopTif-52
❑ 87Fle-217
❑ 87FleGlo-217
❑ 87Top-592
❑ 87TopTif-592
❑ 91BriBanF-5
❑ 91PacSenL-142
❑ 93RanKee-376

Welsh, Eric
❑ 98BurBeeM-23

Welsh, Jimmy D.
❑ 23Zee-175
❑ 24Zee-119
❑ 29ExhFou-10
❑ 29PorandAR-96
❑ 32Zee-47
❑ 92ConTSN-494

Welsh, William
❑ 75WesPalBES-16

Wendell, Louis
❑ 27Zee-83

Wendell, Turk (Steven)
❑ 88PulBraP-1755
❑ 89BurBraP-1616
❑ 89BurBraS-24
❑ 90Bes-122
❑ 90GreBraB-8
❑ 90GreBraP-1131
❑ 90GreBraS-23
❑ 91GreBraC-9
❑ 91GreBraLD-222
❑ 91GreBraP-3003
❑ 91LinDriAA-222
❑ 92Bow-693
❑ 92IowCubS-223
❑ 92LeaGolR-BC5
❑ 92OPC-676
❑ 92ProFS7-178
❑ 92SkyAAAF-109
❑ 92Top-676
❑ 92TopGol-676
❑ 92TopGolW-676
❑ 92TopMic-676
❑ 92UppDec-780
❑ 92UppDecML-85
❑ 93Bow-664
❑ 93FleFinE-12
❑ 93IowCubF-2135
❑ 93TopTra-49T
❑ 94Bow-550
❑ 94ColC-290
❑ 94ColChoGS-290
❑ 94ColChoSS-290
❑ 94Don-312
❑ 94Pac-114
❑ 94Pin-254
❑ 94PinArtP-254
❑ 94PinMusC-254
❑ 94Sco-616
❑ 94ScoGolR-616
❑ 94ScoRoo-RT89
❑ 94ScoRooGR-RT89
❑ 94Spo-170
❑ 94StaClu-499
❑ 94StaCluFDI-499
❑ 94StaCluGR-499
❑ 94StaCluMOP-499
❑ 94StaCluT-358
❑ 94StaCluTFDI-358
❑ 94Top-778
❑ 94TopGol-778
❑ 94TopSpa-778
❑ 95Pin-78
❑ 95PinArtP-78
❑ 95PinMusC-78
❑ 95Sco-285
❑ 95ScoGolR-285
❑ 95ScoPlaTS-285
❑ 95Top-189
❑ 96LeaSigA-242
❑ 96LeaSigAG-243
❑ 96LeaSigAS-243
❑ 96Sco-483
❑ 96StaClu-329
❑ 96StaCluMOP-329
❑ 97Cir-144
❑ 97CirRav-144
❑ 97Fle-289
❑ 97FleTif-289
❑ 97Pac-261
❑ 97PacLigB-261
❑ 97PacSil-261
❑ 97StaClu-256
❑ 97StaCluMOP-256
❑ 97Top-113
❑ 97Ult-381
❑ 97UltGolME-381
❑ 97UltPlaME-381
❑ 98Pac-375
❑ 98PacOnl-492
❑ 98PacOnlR-492
❑ 98PacOnlWC-492
❑ 98PacPlaB-375
❑ 98PacRedT-375
❑ 98PacSil-375
❑ 99Fle-534
❑ 99FleSta9-534
❑ 99FleWarT-534
❑ 99Pac-287
❑ 99PacPlaB-287
❑ 99PacRed-287

Wendelstedt, Harry
❑ 88T/MUmp-6
❑ 89T/MUmp-4
❑ 90T/MUmp-4

Wendlandt, Terry
❑ 84OmaRoyT-30
❑ 85OmaRoyT-5
❑ 97OmaRoyB-29

Wendler, Doc
❑ 55DodGolS-30

Wendt, Glenn
❑ 78WatIndT-25

Wendt, Jason
❑ 92PulBraC-20
❑ 92PulBraF-3179

Wengert, Bill
❑ 88GreFalDTI-17
❑ 89BakDodCLC-188
❑ 90VerBeaDS-27
❑ 91AdeGiaF-8
❑ 91VerBeaDC-13
❑ 91VerBeaDP-774
❑ 92SanAntMF-3975
❑ 92VerBeaDC-24
❑ 93WicWraF-2978
❑ 94WicWraF-190

Wengert, Don
❑ 92FroRowDP-28
❑ 92FroRowDPG-28
❑ 92FroRowDPS-28
❑ 92SouOreAC-22
❑ 92SouOreAF-3417
❑ 93ClaGolF-181
❑ 93MadMusC-1
❑ 93MadMusF-1823
❑ 93MidLeaAGF-16
❑ 93StaCluM-114
❑ 94ModA'sC-24
❑ 94ModA'sF-3064
❑ 95Bow-29
❑ 95EdmTraTI-25
❑ 95UppDec-262
❑ 95UppDecED-262
❑ 95UppDecEDG-262
❑ 96A'sMot-23
❑ 96ColCho-247
❑ 96ColChoGS-247
❑ 96ColChoSS-247
❑ 96LeaSigEA-211
❑ 96Pac-387
❑ 96SigRooOJ-36
❑ 96SigRooOJS-36
❑ 96StaClu-371
❑ 96StaCluMOP-371
❑ 96Top-433
❑ 97A'sMot-25
❑ 97Fle-551
❑ 97FleTif-551
❑ 97PacPriGotD-GD83
❑ 97UppDec-451

Wenrick, Bill
❑ 88BoiHawP-1623
❑ 88SalLakCTTI-26

Wenrick, John
❑ 88LitFalMP-23
❑ 89ColMetB-17
❑ 89ColMetGS-27
❑ 90WesPalBES-26

Wensloff, Charles
❑ 43YanSta-29
❑ 47TipTop-60

Wenson, Paul
❑ 87LakTigP-25
❑ 88GleFalTP-921
❑ 89TolMudHC-8
❑ 89TolMudHP-780

Wentz, Keith
❑ 86MedA'sC-75

Wentz, Lenny
❑ 91ChaWheC-20
❑ 91ChaWheP-2897
❑ 92ChaWheF-18
❑ 92ChaWVWC-22

Wentzel, Stan
❑ 78ReaRem-22

Wenz, Fred
❑ 69Top-628
❑ 71OPC-92
❑ 71Top-92

Wenzell, Marge
❑ 93TedWil-119

Wera, Julie
❑ 28Zee-23
❑ 31Zee-113
❑ 32Zee-110
❑ 75Yan192T-27
❑ 79Yan192T-32
❑ 84Yan192G-29
❑ 91ConTSN-100

Werber, Billy
❑ 34DiaMatCSB-194
❑ 34DiaStaR-61
❑ 34Gou-75
❑ 35DiaMatCS3T1-148
❑ 35ExhFou-9
❑ 35GouPuzR-8G
❑ 35GouPuzR-9G
❑ 36GouBWR-25
❑ 36GouWidPPR-A112
❑ 36GouWidPPR-B4
❑ 36NatChiFPR-79
❑ 36NatChiFPR-87
❑ 36OveCanR-45
❑ 37ExhFou-14
❑ 38ExhFou-14
❑ 38GouHeaU-259
❑ 38GouHeaU-283
❑ 38RedOraW-31
❑ 39OrcPhoAP-24
❑ 39RedTeal-24
❑ 41DouPlaR-9
❑ 41HarHarW-27
❑ 72TCMthe1-194
❑ 77CinRedT-15
❑ 77RedCarP-15
❑ 79DiaGre-331
❑ 88ConSer5-30

Werd, Norm
❑ 75SanAntBT-22

Werden, Perry
❑ 08IndPos-19

Werhas, John
❑ 64Top-456
❑ 65Top-453
❑ 67Top-514
❑ 90DodTar-846

Werland, Hank (Henry)
❑ 90PulBraB-11
❑ 90PulBraP-3108
❑ 91Cla/Bes-42
❑ 91DurBulUP-2
❑ 91MacBraC-12
❑ 91MacBraP-865

Werle, William
❑ 47PM1StaP1-215
❑ 48SomandK-18
❑ 49EurSta-175
❑ 50Bow-87
❑ 50PirTeal-24
❑ 51Bow-64
❑ 51FisBakL-29
❑ 51TopRedB-33
❑ 52Bow-248
❑ 52Top-73
❑ 53RedSoxTI-27
❑ 53Top-170
❑ 54Top-144
❑ 61UniOil-H10
❑ 83TopRep5-73
❑ 91TopArc1-170
❑ 94TopArc1-144
❑ 94TopArc1G-144

Werley, George
❑ 91OriCro-478

Werley, Jamie
❑ 80NasSouTI-24
❑ 81NasSouTI-22
❑ 82ColCliP-15
❑ 82ColCliT-10

Werner, Dave
❑ 89EriOriS-29

Werner, Don
❑ 76IndIndTI-17
❑ 77IndIndTI-8
❑ 78Pep-25
❑ 78Top-702
❑ 79IndIndTI-22
❑ 80RedEnq-19
❑ 83Don-593
❑ 83OklCit8T-18
❑ 83Top-504
❑ 84IowCubT-16
❑ 85NasSouTI-25
❑ 86OklCit8P-25
❑ 87OklCit8P-5
❑ 88OklCit8C-21
❑ 88OklCit8P-37
❑ 89JamExpP-2150
❑ 91AugPirC-30
❑ 91AugPirP-822
❑ 92CarMudF-1195
❑ 92CarMudS-149
❑ 93RanKee-377
❑ 95CarMudF-175
❑ 96IdaFalB-28
❑ 97IdaFalBTI-29

Werner, Rick
❑ 93HelBreF-4095
❑ 93HelBreSP-24

Wernig, Pat
❑ 88MadMusP-25
❑ 88MidLeaAGS-52
❑ 89HunStaB-23
❑ 91LinDriAAA-547
❑ 91TacTigLD-547
❑ 91TacTigP-2307
❑ 92LasVegSS-247
❑ 93PalSprAC-25
❑ 93PalSprAF-71

Werrick, Joe
❑ 87OldJudN-528

Wert, Don
❑ 62Top-299
❑ 64Top-19
❑ 64TopVen-19
❑ 65OPC-271
❑ 65TigJayP-11
❑ 65Top-271
❑ 66TigVolC-11
❑ 66Top-253
❑ 66TopVen-253
❑ 67CokCapTi-12
❑ 67DexPre-218

❑ 67TigDexP-9
❑ 67Top-511
❑ 67TopVen-253
❑ 68CokCapT-12
❑ 68OPC-178
❑ 68TigDetFPB-26
❑ 68Top-178
❑ 68TopVen-178
❑ 69MilBra-287
❑ 69TigTeal-12
❑ 69TigTealC-19
❑ 69Top-443
❑ 69TopSta-180
❑ 69TopTeaP-1
❑ 70OPC-33
❑ 70Top-33
❑ 71MLBOffS-552
❑ 71OPC-307
❑ 71SenPolP-10
❑ 71Top-307
❑ 72MilBra-358
❑ 78TCM60I-163
❑ 78TigDeaCS-9
❑ 81TigDetN-65
❑ 88TigDom-25

Werth, Dennis
❑ 75ForLauYS-21
❑ 78TacYanC-9
❑ 79ColCliT-10
❑ 80YanPhoA-27
❑ 81Don-466
❑ 81Fle-102
❑ 81Top-424
❑ 82Fle-55
❑ 82Roy-23
❑ 82Top-154
❑ 82TopTra-126T
❑ 83LouRedR-22
❑ 84LouRedR-30
❑ 92YanWIZ7-163
❑ 92YanWIZ8-200

Werth, Jayson
❑ 97Bow-433
❑ 97BowChr-293
❑ 97BowChrI-293
❑ 97BowChrIR-293
❑ 97BowChrR-293
❑ 97BowInt-433
❑ 97TopSta-119
❑ 97TopStaAM-119
❑ 98BesAutSS-52
❑ 98BesBet-11
❑ 98BesCor-11
❑ 98BesNumOP-41
❑ 98Bow-81
❑ 98BowChr-81
❑ 98BowChrGA-81
❑ 98BowChrGAR-81
❑ 98BowChrI-81
❑ 98BowChrIR-81
❑ 98BowChrR-81
❑ 98BowGolA-81
❑ 98BowInt-81
❑ 98DelShoM-30
❑ 98SouAtlLPM-26
❑ 98Top-493
❑ 98TopChr-493
❑ 98TopChrR-493
❑ 98TopDevR-493
❑ 98TopDia-493
❑ 98TopMiniC-493
❑ 99BasAmeTP-94
❑ 99BasAmeTPG-94
❑ 99Bow-332
❑ 99BowAut-BA4
❑ 99BowBes-130
❑ 99BowBesAR-130
❑ 99BowBesR-130
❑ 99BowGol-332
❑ 99BowInt-332
❑ 99JustheS-47
❑ 99JustheSAC-22
❑ 99JustheSAD-13
❑ 99JustheSJB-47
❑ 99SP TopP-119
❑ 99SP TopPC-JW
❑ 99SP TopPDtS-D27
❑ 99SP TopPGF-GF27
❑ 99SP TopPPE-119
❑ 99TeaBesRFS-4
❑ 99Top-209
❑ 99TopChr-209
❑ 99TopChrR-209

Wertz, Bill
❑ 90RenSilSCLC-280
❑ 90WatIndS-23
❑ 91Cla/Bes-138
❑ 91ColIndC-18
❑ 91ColIndP-1485
❑ 92CanIndF-692
❑ 92CanIndS-123
❑ 93Bow-529
❑ 93ChaKniF-543
❑ 93ClaGolF-8
❑ 93FleFinE-206
❑ 94ChaKniF-896
❑ 94Don-590
❑ 94Fle-123
❑ 94Pac-186
❑ 94StaClu-481
❑ 94StaCluFDI-481
❑ 94StaCluGR-481
❑ 94StaCluMOP-481
❑ 94Top-64
❑ 94TopGol-64
❑ 94TopSpa-64
❑ 94Ult-50
❑ 94VenLinU-37
❑ 95PawRedSDD-29
❑ 95PawRedTI-38
❑ 97AkrAer-28

Wertz, Vic
❑ 47Exh-238A
❑ 47Exh-238B
❑ 49Bow-164
❑ 50Bow-9
❑ 51Bow-176
❑ 51R42SmaS-114
❑ 51TopBluB-40
❑ 52BerRos-66
❑ 52Bow-39
❑ 52RedMan-AL22
❑ 52StaCalL-72D
❑ 52StaCalS-86B
❑ 52Top-244
❑ 53BowC-2
❑ 53Top-142
❑ 54Bow-21
❑ 54OriEss-35
❑ 55Bow-40
❑ 55IndGolS-11
❑ 55RedMan-AL13
❑ 56Top-300
❑ 57IndSoh-16
❑ 57IndTeal-26
❑ 57SwiFra-6
❑ 57Top-78
❑ 58Top-170
❑ 59Baz-23
❑ 59Top-500
❑ 60RedSoxJP-11
❑ 60Top-111
❑ 60TopVen-111
❑ 61Pos-49A
❑ 61Pos-49B
❑ 61Top-173
❑ 61Top-340
❑ 61TopStaI-118
❑ 62SalPlaC-60
❑ 62ShiPlaC-60
❑ 62Top-481
❑ 63Top-348
❑ 75TCM195CI-34
❑ 78ReaRem-23
❑ 78TCM60I-227
❑ 79TCM50-45
❑ 81RedSoxBG2S-58
❑ 81TigDetN-123
❑ 82OhiHaloF-54
❑ 83TopRep5-244
❑ 85TCMPla1-28
❑ 91OriCro-479
❑ 91TopArc1-142
❑ 92BazQua5A-1

Wesemann, Jason
❑ 96BatCliTI-25
❑ 97PieBolWB-30
❑ 98ClePhiM-23

Wesley, Tom
❑ 81CedRapRT-15

Wesolowski, Al
❑ 78NewWayCT-43

Wessel, Troy
❑ 89JamExpP-2139
❑ 90JamExpP-26

Wessels, John
❑ 88KimN18-48

Wessenaar, Rob
❑ 92SkyAAAF-194

Wessinger, Jim
❑ 79SavBraT-26
❑ 80RicBraT-21

Wesson, Barry
❑ 96AubDouB-18
❑ 97AubDouTI-16
❑ 98QuaCitRBG-30

West, Adam
❑ 96NewJerCB-29
❑ 97PeoChi-27
❑ 98PriWilCQ-14

West, Bobby
❑ 89PriPirS-24

West, Chris
❑ 89TenTecGE-30
❑ 93SpoIndC-22
❑ 93SpoIndF-3599

West, Dave
❑ 84LitFalMT-24
❑ 86LynMetP-25
❑ 87JacMetF-23
❑ 87MetColP-50
❑ 87TexLeaAF-29
❑ 88MetColP-52
❑ 88TidTidCa-28
❑ 88TidTidCM-2
❑ 88TidTidP-1592
❑ 88TriAAAP-41
❑ 88TriAAC-29
❑ 89ClaTraO-134
❑ 89Don-41
❑ 89Fle-51
❑ 89FleGlo-51
❑ 89MetCol8-16
❑ 89MetColP-57
❑ 89MetKah-29
❑ 89Sco-650
❑ 89ScoYouSI-32
❑ 89Spo-45
❑ 89TidTidC-7
❑ 89TidTidP-1973
❑ 89Top-787
❑ 89TopTif-787
❑ 89ToyRoo-33
❑ 89UppDec-7
❑ 90Bow-413
❑ 90BowTif-413
❑ 90ClaBlu-68
❑ 90Don-387
❑ 90Fle-388
❑ 90FleCan-388
❑ 90Hot50RS-47
❑ 90Lea-387
❑ 90OPC-357
❑ 90Sco-573
❑ 90Top-357
❑ 90TopBig-325
❑ 90TopRoo-30
❑ 90TopTif-357
❑ 90ToyRoo-30
❑ 90UppDec-15
❑ 90UppDec-562A
❑ 91Don-264
❑ 91Fle-627
❑ 91MetWIZ-428
❑ 91OPC-578
❑ 91Sco-158
❑ 91StaClu-34
❑ 91Top-578
❑ 91TopDesS-578
❑ 91TopMic-578
❑ 91TopTif-578
❑ 91UppDec-377
❑ 92Don-638
❑ 92OPC-442
❑ 92Pin-333
❑ 92PorBeaF-2669
❑ 92PorBeaS-423
❑ 92Sco-669
❑ 92StaClu-398
❑ 92Top-442
❑ 92TopGol-442
❑ 92TopGolW-442
❑ 92TopMic-442
❑ 92UppDec-548
❑ 93Don-501
❑ 93FleFinE-112
❑ 93Lea-460
❑ 93PacSpa-583
❑ 93PhiMed-34
❑ 93PhiStaC-12
❑ 93Top-652
❑ 93TopGol-652
❑ 93TopInaM-652
❑ 93TopInaR-652
❑ 93TopMic-652
❑ 93Ult-447
❑ 93UppDec-710
❑ 93UppDecGold-710
❑ 94Don-409
❑ 94Fla-419
❑ 94Fle-603
❑ 94Pac-489
❑ 94PhiMed-35
❑ 94PhiMel-24
❑ 94PhiUSPC-4S
❑ 94PhiUSPC-8D
❑ 94Sco-156
❑ 94ScoGolR-156
❑ 94StaClu-130
❑ 94StaCluFDI-130
❑ 94StaCluGR-130
❑ 94StaCluMOP-130
❑ 94StaCluT-220
❑ 94StaCluTFDI-220
❑ 94Top-266
❑ 94TopGol-266
❑ 94TopSpa-266
❑ 95Don-348
❑ 95DonPreP-348
❑ 95Fle-407
❑ 95Phi-35
❑ 95PhiMel-25
❑ 95StaClu-178
❑ 95StaCluFDI-178
❑ 95StaCluMOP-178
❑ 95StaCluSTWS-178
❑ 95StaCluVR-92
❑ 95StaCluVRMO-92
❑ 95Top-31
❑ 95TopCyb-24
❑ 95Ult-211
❑ 95UltGolM-211
❑ 96Fla-340
❑ 96Ult-528
❑ 96UltGolM-528

West, Dick
❑ 39OrcPhoAP-25
❑ 77CinRedT-18

West, George III
❑ 98HelBreM-33

West, Hi
❑ 11PinT-5-1109

West, James
❑ 13Zee-74
❑ 14Zee-76
❑ 15Zee-141
❑ 18Zee-52

West, Jerry
❑ 66AurSpoMK-6

West, Jim
❑ 90SpoIndSP-15
❑ 91WatDiaC-13
❑ 91WatDiaP-1260

West, Joe
❑ 88T/MUmp-36
❑ 89T/MUmp-34
❑ 90T/MUmp-33

West, Lefty (Weldon)
❑ 96Bro194F-15

West, Matt
❑ 83DurBulT-26
❑ 85RicBraT-10
❑ 86RicBraP-25
❑ 87RicBraBC-22
❑ 87RicBraC-45
❑ 87RicBraT-8
❑ 88CalCanC-8
❑ 88CalCanP-788
❑ 89PulBraP-1902
❑ 90SumBraP-2451
❑ 91MacBraC-29
❑ 91MacBraP-884
❑ 92DurBulC-26
❑ 92DurBulF-1118
❑ 92DurBulTI-30
❑ 93DurBulC-29
❑ 93DurBulF-505
❑ 93DurBulTI-3
❑ 94DurBulC-27
❑ 94DurBulF-345
❑ 94DurBulTI-28
❑ 95DurBulTI-35

West, Milton
❑ 87OldJudN-529

West, Paul
❑ 92LetMouSP-14

West, Reggie
❑ 84EdmTraC-116
❑ 85EdmTraC-8

West, Samuel
❑ 31SenTealPW-30
❑ 33Gou-166
❑ 33WorCig-100
❑ 34BabRutG-64
❑ 34ButPreR-63
❑ 35GouPuzR-5D
❑ 35GouPuzR-6D
❑ 35GouPuzR-11F
❑ 35GouPuzR-13D
❑ 36ExhFou-15
❑ 36NatChiFPR-80
❑ 36OveCanR-47
❑ 37ExhFou-15
❑ 37KelPepS-BB18
❑ 37OPCBatUV-129
❑ 38ExhFou-15
❑ 39PlaBal-31
❑ 40PlaBal-22
❑ 60SenUniMC-20
❑ 72TCMthe3-72
❑ 77GalGloG-192
❑ 79DiaGre-51
❑ 83BigLeaCOA-16
❑ 91ConTSN-241
❑ 93ConTSN-679
❑ 94ConTSN-1090
❑ 94ConTSNB-1090

West, Tom
❑ 86DayBealP-29
❑ 86FloStaLAP-49

West, W. Max
❑ 33MrsShePP-17
❑ 33Zee-49
❑ 36OveCanR-46
❑ 37Zee-29
❑ 39PlaBal-149
❑ 40PlaBal-57
❑ 41DouPlaR-43
❑ 41PlaBal-2
❑ 47PadTeal-24
❑ 52MotCoo-10
❑ 53MotCoo-19
❑ 74LauAllG-40
❑ 90DodTar-847

Westbrook, Destry
❑ 92AubAstC-21
❑ 92AubAstF-1355
❑ 94QuaCitRBC-24
❑ 94QuaCitRBF-535
❑ 97ReaPhi-27

Westbrook, Jake
❑ 96BesAutS1RP-FR8
❑ 97AshTou-25
❑ 97Bes-38
❑ 97BesLimA-40
❑ 97Bow-200
❑ 97BowChr-186
❑ 97BowChrI-186
❑ 97BowChrIR-186
❑ 97BowChrR-186
❑ 97BowInt-200
❑ 97SouAtlTPB-2
❑ 97Top-478
❑ 98BesAutPOY-18
❑ 98BesCasT-9
❑ 98BesFulCA-21
❑ 98BesPreA-45
❑ 98Bow-376
❑ 98BowChr-376
❑ 98BowChrGA-376
❑ 98BowChrGAR-376
❑ 98BowChrI-376
❑ 98BowChrIR-376
❑ 98BowChrR-376
❑ 98BowGolA-376
❑ 98BowInt-376
❑ 98JupHamQ-15
❑ 98SP MinPE-49
❑ 98SP MinSTHPE-H29
❑ 98SPMin-49
❑ 98SPMinSTH-H29
❑ 99BasAmeTPA-46
❑ 99Bow-112
❑ 99BowChr-112
❑ 99BowChrG-112
❑ 99BowChrGR-112
❑ 99BowChrI-112
❑ 99BowChrIR-112
❑ 99BowChrR-112
❑ 99BowGol-112
❑ 99BowInt-112
❑ 99JustheS-48
❑ 99JustheSAC-23
❑ 99JustheSAD-14
❑ 99JustheSJB-48
❑ 99SP TopP-120
❑ 99SP TopPPE-120
❑ 99TeaBesRA-25

Westbrook, Mike
❑ 84LitFalMT-3
❑ 86LynMetP-26
❑ 88CarLeaAS-40
❑ 88KinIndS-23
❑ 89RenSilSCLC-251

Westbrooks, Elanis
❑ 88CliGiaP-716
❑ 89SanJosGB-13
❑ 89SanJosGCLC-225
❑ 89SanJosGP-435
❑ 89SanJosGS-25
❑ 90SanJosGB-14
❑ 90SanJosGCLC-32
❑ 90SanJosGP-2021
❑ 90SanJosGS-25
❑ 98SalAvaC-28

Westermann, Scott
❑ 88GreHorP-1565

Westerzil, George
❑ 19Zee-48
❑ 22Zee-143

Westfall, Allan
❑ 97LanJet-29
❑ 98LanJetG-29

Westfall, Fred
❑ 76WauMetT-24
❑ 77LynMetT-29

Westlake, James
❑ 09T206-522

Westlake, James Patrick
❑ 77FriOneYW-17

Westlake, Wally
❑ 46RemBre-8
❑ 46SpoExcW-4-11
❑ 47Exh-239
❑ 49Bow-45
❑ 49EurSta-176
❑ 50Bow-69
❑ 50PirTeal-25
❑ 51TopRedB-27
❑ 52BerRos-67
❑ 52NatTeaL-40
❑ 52StaCalL-81B
❑ 52StaCalS-93C
❑ 52Top-38
❑ 53Top-192
❑ 54DanDee-28
❑ 54Top-92
❑ 55IndGolS-18
❑ 55Top-102
❑ 55TopDouH-13
❑ 56Top-81
❑ 75OakOak2A-36
❑ 75TCM195CI-35
❑ 79DiaGre-368
❑ 83TopRep5-38
❑ 91OriCro-480
❑ 91TopArc1-192
❑ 94TopArc1-92
❑ 94TopArc1G-92

Westmoreland, Claude
❑ 79AlbDukTc-21
❑ 80AlbDukTc-11

Westmoreland, John
❑ 85CloHSS-43

Westmoreland, Ken
❑ 98BatMucTI-32
❑ 99TeaBesR-96
❑ 99TeaBesRG-96
❑ 99TeaBesRS-96

Weston, Mickey
❑ 85LynMetT-6
❑ 86JacMetT-10
❑ 87JacMetF-11
❑ 88JacMetGS-22
❑ 89RocRedWC-6
❑ 89RocRedWP-1638
❑ 90BalOriP-28
❑ 90CMC-304
❑ 90OPC-377
❑ 90RocRedWC-3
❑ 90RocRedWGC-10
❑ 90Sco-616
❑ 90Top-377
❑ 90TopDeb89-137
❑ 90TopTif-377
❑ 90UppDec-683A
❑ 90UppDec-683B
❑ 91LinDriAAA-521
❑ 91OriCro-481
❑ 91SyrChiLD-521
❑ 91SyrChiMB-27
❑ 91SyrChiP-2482
❑ 92ScrRedBF-2447
❑ 92ScrRedBS-496

❑ 95TolMudHTI-25
Weston, Tim
❑ 88OneYanP-2065
❑ 89AlbYanB-29
❑ 89AlbYanP-323
❑ 90AlbYanB-17
❑ 90AlbYanSt-28
Westover, Richard
❑ 96VerExpB-29
❑ 97VerExpB-29
Westray, Ken
❑ 94BatCliC-29
❑ 94BatCliF-3464
❑ 97BatCliTI-28
❑ 98PieBolWM-2
Westrum, Wes
❑ 47Exh-240
❑ 48GiaTeal-26
❑ 49EurSta-126
❑ 50JJKCopP-22
❑ 51Bow-161
❑ 51FisBakL-30
❑ 51R42SmaS-115
❑ 51TopRedB-37
❑ 52BerRos-68
❑ 52Bow-74
❑ 52CokTip-10
❑ 52RedMan-NL26
❑ 52TipTop-46
❑ 52Top-75
❑ 53RedMan-NL20
❑ 54Bow-25
❑ 54NewYorJA-36
❑ 54Top-180
❑ 55Bow-141
❑ 55GiaGolS-15
❑ 56GiaJayP-11
❑ 56Top-156
❑ 57Top-323
❑ 60Top-469
❑ 66MetPos-4
❑ 66MetTeal-12
❑ 66Top-341
❑ 66TopVen-341
❑ 67MetTeal-12
❑ 67Top-593
❑ 75Gia-11
❑ 75Gia195T-29
❑ 75GiaAllT-12
❑ 75GiaTeal-17
❑ 75OPC-216
❑ 75Top-216
❑ 75TopMin-216
❑ 76SSP-113
❑ 79DiaGre-44
❑ 79TCM50-46
❑ 80GiaGreT-2
❑ 81Gia196T-4
❑ 83TopRep5-75
❑ 84GiaMot-14
❑ 85TCMPla1-20
❑ 91TopArc1-323
❑ 92BazQua5A-10
❑ 94TopArc1-180
❑ 94TopArc1G-180
Wetherby, Jeff
❑ 86SumBraP-30
❑ 87GreBraB-21
❑ 88BlaYNPRWL-156
❑ 88BobCamRB-17
❑ 88RicBraC-16
❑ 88RicBraP-9
❑ 89BraDub-28
❑ 89RicBraC-16
❑ 89RicBraP-840
❑ 89RicBraTI-22
❑ 90CMC-474
❑ 90ColSprSSC-22
❑ 90ColSprSSP-53
❑ 90OPC-142
❑ 90ProAAAF-234
❑ 90Sco-540
❑ 90Sco100RS-44
❑ 90Top-142
❑ 90TopDeb89-138
❑ 90TopTif-142
❑ 90UppDec-611
❑ 91LinDriAAA-472
❑ 91RocRedWLD-472
❑ 91RocRedWP-1917
❑ 92CalCanF-3744
Wetmore, Michael
❑ 96HelBreTI-29
❑ 97BelSnaB-30
Wetteland, John
❑ 86BakDodP-28
❑ 87VerBeaDP-1
❑ 88BasAmeAAB-28
❑ 88BlaYNPRWL-189
❑ 88SanAntMB-21
❑ 88TexLeaAGS-7
❑ 89AlbDukCm-11
❑ 89AlbDukP-63
❑ 89DodStaSV-16
❑ 89ScoRoo-90T
❑ 90Bow-82
❑ 90BowTif-82
❑ 90ClaBlu-110
❑ 90DodMot-19
❑ 90DodPol-57
❑ 90DodTar-1094
❑ 90Don-671
❑ 90Fle-411
❑ 90FleCan-411
❑ 90Hot50RS-48
❑ 90OPC-631
❑ 90Sco-388
❑ 90Sco100RS-25
❑ 90ScoYouSI-40
❑ 90Top-631
❑ 90TopDeb89-139
❑ 90TopRoo-31
❑ 90TopTif-631
❑ 90ToyRoo-31
❑ 90UppDec-377
❑ 91AlbDukLD-23
❑ 91AlbDukP-1142
❑ 91DodPho-31
❑ 91Don-614
❑ 91LinDriAAA-23
❑ 91Sco-267
❑ 91UppDec-668
❑ 92Bow-68
❑ 92Cla1-T94
❑ 92Don-627
❑ 92ExpDonD-20
❑ 92ExpPos-32
❑ 92FleUpd-100
❑ 92Lea-478
❑ 92LeaBlaG-478
❑ 92OPCPre-108
❑ 92Pin-461
❑ 92Pin-593
❑ 92ScoRoo-78T
❑ 92SpollIFK1-720
❑ 92StaClu-759
❑ 92StaCluNC-759
❑ 92Ult-526
❑ 92UppDec-788
❑ 93Bow-212
❑ 93Don-592
❑ 93Fin-129
❑ 93FinRef-129
❑ 93Fla-88
❑ 93Fle-83
❑ 93Lea-183
❑ 93MSABenSPD-11
❑ 93OPC-366
❑ 93PacSpa-538
❑ 93Pin-397
❑ 93Sco-165
❑ 93Sel-201
❑ 93SelStaL-72
❑ 93SP-108
❑ 93StaClu-344
❑ 93StaCluFDI-344
❑ 93StaCluMOP-344
❑ 93Stu-65
❑ 93Top-231
❑ 93TopGol-231
❑ 93TopInaM-231
❑ 93TopInaR-231
❑ 93TopMic-231
❑ 93TriPla-206
❑ 93Ult-420
❑ 93UppDec-392
❑ 93UppDecGold-392
❑ 94Bow-172
❑ 94BowBes-R21
❑ 94BowBesR-R21
❑ 94ColC-410
❑ 94ColChoGS-410
❑ 94ColChoSS-410
❑ 94Don-293
❑ 94Fin-133
❑ 94FinRef-133
❑ 94Fla-405
❑ 94Fle-555
❑ 94FleExtB-313
❑ 94FUnPac-57
❑ 94Lea-414
❑ 94LeaL-128
❑ 94OPC-105
❑ 94Pac-393
❑ 94PanSti-214
❑ 94Pin-119
❑ 94PinArtP-119
❑ 94PinMusC-119
❑ 94Sco-390
❑ 94ScoGolR-390
❑ 94Sel-69
❑ 94SP-87
❑ 94SPDieC-87
❑ 94StaClu-446
❑ 94StaCluFDI-446
❑ 94StaCluGR-446
❑ 94StaCluMOP-446
❑ 94Stu-81
❑ 94Top-497
❑ 94TopGol-497
❑ 94TopSpa-497
❑ 94TriPla-100
❑ 94Ult-232
❑ 94UltFir-9
❑ 94UppDec-32
❑ 94UppDec-335
❑ 94UppDecED-32
❑ 94UppDecED-335
❑ 95Baz-121
❑ 95Bow-367
❑ 95ColCho-239
❑ 95ColCho-585T
❑ 95ColChoGS-239
❑ 95ColChoSE-102
❑ 95ColChoSE-252
❑ 95ColChoSEGS-102
❑ 95ColChoSEGS-252
❑ 95ColChoSESS-102
❑ 95ColChoSESS-252
❑ 95ColChoSS-239
❑ 95Don-516
❑ 95DonPreP-516
❑ 95DonTopotO-128
❑ 95Emo-68
❑ 95Fin-81
❑ 95Fin-240
❑ 95FinFlaT-FT9
❑ 95FinRef-81
❑ 95FinRef-240
❑ 95Fla-289
❑ 95Fle-363
❑ 95FleUpd-28
❑ 95Lea-356
❑ 95Pac-274
❑ 95Pin-347
❑ 95PinArtP-347
❑ 95PinMusC-347
❑ 95Sco-85
❑ 95ScoGolR-85
❑ 95ScoPlaTS-85
❑ 95SP-179
❑ 95SPCha-174
❑ 95SPChaDC-174
❑ 95SPSil-179
❑ 95StaClu-472
❑ 95StaClu-615
❑ 95StaCluMOP-472
❑ 95StaCluMOP-615
❑ 95StaCluMOP-SS19
❑ 95StaCluSS-SS19
❑ 95StaCluSTWS-472
❑ 95StaCluSTWS-615
❑ 95StaCluVR-258
❑ 95StaCluVRMO-258
❑ 95Stu-94
❑ 95Top-22
❑ 95TopCyb-18
❑ 95TopEmb-137
❑ 95TopEmbGI-137
❑ 95TopTra-81T
❑ 95Ult-194
❑ 95UltGolM-194
❑ 95UppDec-78
❑ 95UppDec-439
❑ 95UppDecED-78
❑ 95UppDecED-439
❑ 95UppDecEDG-78
❑ 95UppDecEDG-439
❑ 95UppDecSE-146
❑ 95UppDecSEG-146
❑ 96Baz-101
❑ 96ColCho-633
❑ 96ColChoGS-633
❑ 96ColChoSS-633
❑ 96Don-161
❑ 96DonPreP-161
❑ 96EmoXL-98
❑ 96Fin-B17
❑ 96FinRef-B17
❑ 96Fla-139
❑ 96Fle-199
❑ 96FleTif-199
❑ 96Lea-140
❑ 96LeaPrePB-140
❑ 96LeaPrePG-140
❑ 96LeaPrePS-140
❑ 96MetUni-96
❑ 96MetUniP-96
❑ 96MLBPin-35
❑ 96Pac-381
❑ 96Pin-15
❑ 96Sco-99
❑ 96Sco-201
❑ 96ScoDugC-A71
❑ 96ScoDugCAP-A71
❑ 96SP-134
❑ 96StaClu-268
❑ 96StaCluMOP-268
❑ 96Top-95
❑ 96TopGal-50
❑ 96TopGalPPI-50
❑ 96Ult-108
❑ 96UltGolM-108
❑ 96UppDec-407
❑ 97Bow-69
❑ 97BowBes-63
❑ 97BowBesAR-63
❑ 97BowBesR-63
❑ 97BowChr-50
❑ 97BowChrI-50
❑ 97BowChrIR-50
❑ 97BowChrR-50
❑ 97BowInt-69
❑ 97Cir-340
❑ 97CirRav-340
❑ 97ColCho-63
❑ 97ColCho-224
❑ 97ColChoT-TR8
❑ 97ColChoU-U29
❑ 97Don-139
❑ 97Don-286
❑ 97Don-437
❑ 97DonGolPP-139
❑ 97DonGolPP-286
❑ 97DonGolPP-437
❑ 97DonLim-92
❑ 97DonLimE-92
❑ 97DonLimENG-92
❑ 97DonPre-26
❑ 97DonPreCttC-26
❑ 97DonSilPP-139
❑ 97DonSilPP-286
❑ 97DonSilPP-437
❑ 97Fin-222
❑ 97FinRef-222
❑ 97FlaShoLC-89
❑ 97FlaShoLeg0-89
❑ 97FlaShoLeg1-89
❑ 97FlaShoM-A89
❑ 97FlaShoM-B89
❑ 97FlaShoM-C89
❑ 97FlaShoR0-89
❑ 97FlaShoR1-89
❑ 97FlaShoR2-89
❑ 97Fle-180
❑ 97Fle-609
❑ 97FleMilDM-40
❑ 97FleMilDMR-40
❑ 97FleTif-180
❑ 97FleTif-609
❑ 97Lea-47
❑ 97Lea-214
❑ 97LeaFraM-47
❑ 97LeaFraM-214
❑ 97LeaFraMDC-47
❑ 97LeaFraMDC-214
❑ 97MetUni-124
❑ 97NewPin-27
❑ 97NewPinAP-27
❑ 97NewPinMC-27
❑ 97NewPinPP-27
❑ 97Pac-162
❑ 97PacLigB-162
❑ 97PacSil-162
❑ 97PinCar-16
❑ 97PinCer-7
❑ 97PinCerMBla-7
❑ 97PinCerMBlu-7
❑ 97PinCerMG-7
❑ 97PinCerMR-7
❑ 97PinCerR-7
❑ 97PinIns-70
❑ 97PinInsCE-70
❑ 97PinInsDD-17
❑ 97PinInsDE-70
❑ 97PinTotCPB-7
❑ 97PinTotCPG-7
❑ 97PinTotCPR-7
❑ 97PinX-P-99
❑ 97PinX-PMoS-99
❑ 97RanDr P-32
❑ 97RanMot-5
❑ 97Sco-134
❑ 97Sco-333
❑ 97Sco-524
❑ 97ScoAllF-19
❑ 97ScoArtPWB-134
❑ 97ScoArtPWB-333
❑ 97ScoArtPWB-524
❑ 97ScoPreS-134
❑ 97ScoResC-333
❑ 97ScoResC-524
❑ 97ScoShoS-134
❑ 97ScoShoS-333
❑ 97ScoShoS-524
❑ 97ScoShoSAP-134
❑ 97ScoShoSAP-333
❑ 97ScoShoSAP-524
❑ 97Sel-19
❑ 97SelArtP-19
❑ 97SelCom-19
❑ 97SelRegG-19
❑ 97SP-176
❑ 97SpollI-180
❑ 97SpollIEE-180
❑ 97StaClu-254
❑ 97StaCluI-I19
❑ 97StaCluMat-254
❑ 97StaCluMOP-254
❑ 97StaCluMOP-I19
❑ 97Top-90
❑ 97TopChr-36
❑ 97TopChrR-36
❑ 97TopGal-68
❑ 97TopGalPPI-68
❑ 97Ult-374
❑ 97UltGolME-374
❑ 97UltPlaME-374
❑ 97UppDec-267
❑ 97UppDec-548
❑ 97UppDecAWJ-15
❑ 97YanSco-8
❑ 97YanScoPl-8
❑ 97YanScoPr-8
❑ 98CirThu-98
❑ 98CirThuRav-98
❑ 98CirThuSupRav-98
❑ 98ColCho-521
❑ 98CroRoy-140
❑ 98Fin-152
❑ 98FinNo--152
❑ 98FinNo-R-152
❑ 98FinRef-152
❑ 98Fle-280
❑ 98MetUni-125
❑ 98MetUniPMG-125
❑ 98Pac-211
❑ 98PacAur-90
❑ 98PacInvTeam-27
❑ 98PacOme-243
❑ 98PacOmeR-243
❑ 98PacOnl-748
❑ 98PacOnlR-748
❑ 98PacOnlWC-748
❑ 98PacPar-109
❑ 98PacParC-109
❑ 98PacParG-109
❑ 98PacParHS-109
❑ 98PacParPB-109
❑ 98PacParR-109
❑ 98PacPlaB-211
❑ 98PacRedT-211
❑ 98PacSil-211
❑ 98PinPlu-179
❑ 98PinSna-TR15
❑ 98Revo-146
❑ 98RevoSS-146
❑ 98Sco-112
❑ 98ScoRT-145
❑ 98ScoSS-PP46
❑ 98ScoSSAP-PP46
❑ 98SpollIWSFMC-9
❑ 98SPxFin-327
❑ 98SPxFinR-327
❑ 98SPxFinS-327
❑ 98StaCluFDI-26
❑ 98StaCluI-26
❑ 98StaCluOneK-26
❑ 98StaCluPP-26
❑ 98Top-329
❑ 98TopChr-329
❑ 98TopChrR-329
❑ 98TopDevR-329
❑ 98TopDia-329
❑ 98TopGal-90
❑ 98TopGalGP-90
❑ 98TopGalOPP-90
❑ 98TopGalPPI-90
❑ 98TopGalPPIA-90
❑ 98TopMiniC-329
❑ 98TopOpeD-155
❑ 98TopSta-48
❑ 98TopStaB-48
❑ 98TopStaG-48
❑ 98TopStaGR-48
❑ 98TopStaS-48
❑ 98Ult-67
❑ 98UltGolM-67
❑ 98UltMas-67
❑ 98UltPlaM-67
❑ 98UppDec-521
❑ 99199Fin-43
❑ 99FinGolRef-43
❑ 99FinRef-43
❑ 99Fle-259
❑ 99FleSta9-259
❑ 99FleWarT-259
❑ 99MetUni-141
❑ 99MetUniGM-141
❑ 99MetUniPMG-141
❑ 99Pac-433
❑ 99PacCroC-290
❑ 99PacCroCPB-290
❑ 99PacOme-240
❑ 99PacOmeC-240
❑ 99PacOmeG-240
❑ 99PacOmePB-240
❑ 99PacPar-240
❑ 99PacParC-240
❑ 99PacParG-240
❑ 99PacParHoloGold-240
❑ 99PacParHS-240
❑ 99PacParOD-240
❑ 99PacParPB-240
❑ 99PacParRed-240
❑ 99PacPlaB-433
❑ 99PacRed-433
❑ 99SkyPre-24
❑ 99SkyPreR-24
❑ 99SkyThu-92
❑ 99SkyThuRant-92
❑ 99SkyThuRave-92
❑ 99StaClu-125
❑ 99StaCluFDI-125
❑ 99StaCluOoaK-125
❑ 99StaCluPP-125
❑ 99ThuSkySupR-92
❑ 99Top-83
❑ 99TopChr-83
❑ 99TopChrR-83
❑ 99TopMVPP-83
❑ 99TopOpeD-46
❑ 99Ult-3
❑ 99UltGolM-3
❑ 99UltMas-3
❑ 99UltPlaM-3
❑ 99UppDec-221
❑ 99UppDecEL1-221
❑ 99UppDecEL2-221
❑ 99Vic-403
Wetzel, Charles
❑ 28Zee-101
❑ 30Zee-20
❑ 31Zee-10
❑ 33Zee-11
Wetzel, Frank
❑ 23Zee-61
❑ 24Zee-57
❑ 30Zee-19
Wetzel, Tom
❑ 84EveGiaC-29
Weustling, George
❑ 29Zee-102
Wever, Stefan
❑ 82NasSouTI-27
❑ 83ColCliT-10
❑ 92YanWIZ8-201
Wex, Gary
❑ 83AlbA'sT-8
Weyer, Lee
❑ 88T/MUmp-2
❑ 89T/MUmp-62
Weyhing, August
❑ 87OldJudN-530
❑ 89EdgR.WG-18
❑ 90DodTar-848

❑ 90KalBatN-57
Weyhing, John
❑ 87OldJudN-531
Weymouth, Marty
❑ 96EveAquB-27
❑ 97WisTimR-27
❑ 98HicCraM-29
❑ 98HicCraUO-30
Whalen, James
❑ 09ObaT21-46
❑ 09ObaT21-151
❑ 12Zee-158
Whalen, Mike
❑ 84NewOriT-12
Whalen, Shawn
❑ 90WatDiaB-17
❑ 90WatDiaP-2392
❑ 91Cla/Bes-337
❑ 91WatDiaC-24
❑ 91WatDiaP-1271
❑ 92WatDiaC-22
Whaley, Bill
❑ 24Zee-18
❑ 25Zee-15
Whaley, Scott Lee
❑ 84MadMusP-5
❑ 85HunStaJ-23
❑ 85MadMusP-24
❑ 85MadMusT-3
❑ 86HunStaDJ-32
Whaling, Albert
❑ 14B18B-55A
❑ 14B18B-55B
❑ 14B18B-55C
❑ 15CraJacE-163
❑ 16Zee-144
❑ 17Zee-121
Whalley, Jarrell
❑ 77SpaPhiT-5
Wharton, Greg
❑ 91MelBusF-1
Wharton, Joe
❑ 93OneYanC-24
❑ 93OneYanF-3504
❑ 94GreBatF-476
❑ 97GreBatC-26
Whatley, Fred
❑ 90CliGiaUTI-U9
Whatley, Gabe
❑ 93HunCubC-27
❑ 93HunCubF-3253
❑ 94WilCubC-24
❑ 94WilCubF-3775
❑ 95RocCubTI-18
❑ 96DayCubB-25
❑ 97DurBulTI-28
❑ 98RicBraQ-27
Wheat, Chris
❑ 90HelBreSP-6
❑ 91HelBreSP-20
Wheat, Danny
❑ 76SanAntBTI-26
❑ 83OklCit8T-24
❑ 85RanPer-NNO
❑ 86RanPer-NNO0
❑ 87RanMot-27
❑ 88RanMot-28
❑ 89RanMot-28
❑ 90RanMot-28
Wheat, Leroy
❑ 54A'STEAI-29
❑ 54Top-244
❑ 55JetPos-20
❑ 94TopArc1-244
❑ 94TopArc1G-244
Wheat, Mack (McKinley Davis)
❑ 90DodTar-849
Wheat, Mark
❑ 22Zee-20
Wheat, Zachary D.
❑ 09ColChiE-303
❑ 09SpoNewSM-80
❑ 09T206-371
❑ 10CouT21-243
❑ 10CouT21-244
❑ 10CouT21-323
❑ 10DomDisP-123
❑ 10RedCroT-82
❑ 10RedCroT-255
❑ 10SweCapPP-78A
❑ 10SweCapPP-78B
❑ 11HelSta-89
❑ 11MecDFT-3
❑ 11PinT-5-455
❑ 11S74Sil-57
❑ 11T205-178
❑ 12ColRedB-303
❑ 12ColTinT-303
❑ 12HasTriFT-76
❑ 12T207-194
❑ 13NatGamW-43
❑ 13TomBarW-39
❑ 14B18B-64
❑ 14CraJacE-52
❑ 14PieStaT-108
❑ 14TexTomE-46
❑ 15CraJacE-52
❑ 15SpoNewM-186
❑ 15VicT21-29
❑ 16FleBreD-99
❑ 16SpoNewM-188
❑ 17ColE13-187
❑ 19W514-110
❑ 20GasAmeMBD-23
❑ 20NatCarE-107
❑ 20W52-8
❑ 20W52-11
❑ 21E121So1-113
❑ 21E121So8-106
❑ 21Exh-184
❑ 21Nei-117
❑ 21StaBis-78
❑ 22AmeCarE122-75
❑ 22E120-150
❑ 22W572-114
❑ 22W573-137
❑ 22W575-147
❑ 22WilPatV-49
❑ 23W501-98
❑ 23W503-44
❑ 23W515-56
❑ 23WilChoV-168
❑ 25Exh-16
❑ 26Exh-16
❑ 27Exh-56
❑ 53ArtHaloFP-88
❑ 60Fle-12
❑ 61Fle-1
❑ 61Fle-86
❑ 68SCFOldT-3
❑ 70SpoCarfCOP-19
❑ 72ClaCar-80
❑ 75DodTCMA-12
❑ 75TCMAllG-34
❑ 76ShaPiz-84
❑ 77BobParHoF-100
❑ 77GalGloG-101
❑ 77GalGloG-151
❑ 80DodGreT-6
❑ 80PerHaloFP-84
❑ 80SSPHOF-84
❑ 82TCMGreH-36
❑ 89DodSmoG-34
❑ 90BasWit-82
❑ 90DodTar-850
❑ 91ConTSN-164
❑ 93CraJac-15
Wheatcroft, Bob (Robert)
❑ 89BluOriS-28
❑ 90WauTimB-10
❑ 90WauTimP-2123
❑ 90WauTimS-25
Wheaton, James
❑ 91FreStaBS-14
Wheeler, Bradley
❑ 88ElPasDB-18
Wheeler, Chris
❑ 84PhiTas-7
❑ 88PhiTas-39
❑ 90PhiTas-35
Wheeler, Dan
❑ 97HudValRB-19
❑ 98ChaRivDG-29
Wheeler, Dave
❑ 90BilMusP-3226
Wheeler, Don
❑ 85TCMPpl1-37
Wheeler, Duke
❑ 72CedRapCT-8
Wheeler, Earl
❑ 91OklStaC-31
❑ 92OklStaC-31
❑ 94ChaRanF-2497
Wheeler, Ed
❑ 75AppFoxT-28
❑ 90DodTar-851
Wheeler, George
❑ 09ObaT21-8
❑ 09ObaT21-268
❑ 12ObaPreT-17
Wheeler, Johnnie
❑ 97BurIndG-30
Wheeler, Kenny (Kenneth)
❑ 90AshTouP-2750
❑ 91BurAstC-11
❑ 91BurAstP-2802
❑ 91MidLeaAP-MWL20
❑ 92OscAstC-4
❑ 92OscAstF-2531
❑ 93OscAstC-22
❑ 93OscAstF-628
Wheeler, Rocket (Ralph)
❑ 78DunBluJT-25
❑ 80KnoBluJT-24
❑ 85KinBluJT-25
❑ 86SyrChiP-26
❑ 87MyrBeaBJP-1453
❑ 90CMC-676
❑ 90ProAAAF-370
❑ 90SyrChiC-28
❑ 90SyrChiMB-28
❑ 90SyrChiP-590
❑ 91LinDriAAA-525
❑ 91SyrChiLD-525
❑ 91SyrChiMB-28
❑ 91SyrChiP-2498
❑ 92SyrChiF-1988
❑ 92SyrChiMB-29
❑ 93SyrChiF-1015
❑ 94DunBluJC-29
❑ 94DunBluJF-2574
❑ 96StCatSB-1
❑ 97St.CatSB-2
❑ 98DunBluJSB-22
❑ 98DunBluJTI-31
Wheeler, Rodney
❑ 86ClePhiP-24
Wheeler, Ryan
❑ 94BoiHawC-29
❑ 94BoiHawF-3366
Wheeler, Tim
❑ 82AleDukT-18
❑ 82BufBisT-9
❑ 83LynPirT-9
❑ 84HawIslC-140
Wheeler, Winston
❑ 90MarPhiP-3185
Wheelock, Gary
❑ 70RelPam-17
❑ 75SalLakCC-12
❑ 76SalLakCGC-2
❑ 77Top-493
❑ 78SanJosMMC-8
❑ 78Top-596
❑ 79SpoIndT-17
❑ 80SpoIndT-17
❑ 87BelMarL-12
❑ 87OklCit8P-2
❑ 89BelMarL-32
❑ 91BelMarCB-27
❑ 91BelMarP-3684
❑ 92SanBerC-28
❑ 98EveAquG-20
Wheelock, Warren
❑ 87OldJudN-532
When, Kevin
❑ 93BenRocCB-26
❑ 93BenRocF-3270
Wherry, Cliff
❑ 83TucTorT-18
❑ 84OklCit8T-4
Whipple, Boomer
❑ 96AugGreB-28
Whipple, Jack
❑ 45CenFlo-27
Whipps, Joe
❑ 90JacMetGS-20
Whisenant, Matt
❑ 90PriPatD-27
❑ 91BatCliCB-17
❑ 91BatCliP-3483
❑ 92SpaPhiC-20
❑ 92SpaPhiF-1264
❑ 92UppDecML-211
❑ 93Bow-38
❑ 93ClaFS7-149
❑ 93ClaGolF-136
❑ 93ExcFS7-88
❑ 93KanCouCC-23
❑ 93KanCouCF-917
❑ 93KanCouCTI-27
❑ 93SouAtlLAPI-6
❑ 93SouAtlLAPI-40
❑ 94Bow-206
❑ 94BreCouMC-22
❑ 94BreCouMF-14
❑ 95KanCouCLTI-15
❑ 95SPML-61
❑ 96ChaKniB-28
❑ 96Exc-168
❑ 98PacOnl-358
❑ 98PacOnlR-358
❑ 98PacOnlWC-358
Whisenant, Pete
❑ 57Top-373
❑ 58RedEnq-41
❑ 58Top-466
❑ 59RedShiBS-23
❑ 59Top-14
❑ 59TopVen-14
❑ 60Top-424
❑ 61Top-201
❑ 61TopStal-187
❑ 61TwiPetM-11
❑ 80Red196T-5
❑ 83AlbA'sT-20
Whisenton, Larry
❑ 78RicBraT-17
❑ 79RicBraT-4
❑ 79Top-715
❑ 80RicBraT-4
❑ 81RicBraT-6
❑ 82BraBurKL-27
❑ 82BraPol-28
❑ 83Don-501
❑ 83Fle-152
❑ 83RicBraT-22
❑ 83Top-544
❑ 84RicBraT-5
❑ 85GreBraTI-25
Whisler, Randy
❑ 90GasRanB-27
❑ 90GasRanP-2537
❑ 90GasRanS-29
❑ 91GasRanP-2707
❑ 92TulDriF-2710
❑ 92TulDriS-625
❑ 93TulDriF-2750
❑ 93TulDriTI-28
❑ 94TulDriF-260
❑ 94TulDriTI-28
Whisman, Rhett
❑ 82WisRapTF-27
Whisonant, John
❑ 91BatCliCB-23
❑ 91BatCliP-3484
Whisonant, Mike
❑ 89AncGlaP-27
Whistler, Clarence
❑ 88KimN18-49
Whistler, Randy
❑ 80AndBraT-19
Whitacre, Fred
❑ 75WesPalBES-4B
Whitaker, Chad
❑ 97SouAtlTPB-14
❑ 98CarLeaTPQ-28
❑ 98KinIndQ-24
Whitaker, Darrell
❑ 85BurRanT-24
❑ 86SalRedBP-28
❑ 87GasRanP-26
❑ 88OklCit8C-11
❑ 88OklCit8P-43
❑ 88TulDriTI-6
❑ 89OklCit8C-10
❑ 89OklCit8P-1516
Whitaker, Jeff
❑ 91BurIndP-3311
❑ 92BurIndC-2
❑ 92BurIndF-1666
Whitaker, Jerry
❑ 96PriWilCB-29
Whitaker, Lou
❑ 78TigBurK-13
❑ 78TigTeal-34
❑ 78Top-704
❑ 79BasPat-95
❑ 79Hos-117
❑ 79OPC-55
❑ 79Top-123
❑ 80OPC-187
❑ 80Top-358
❑ 81AllGamPI-16
❑ 81CokTeaS-58
❑ 81Don-365
❑ 81Fle-463
❑ 81OPC-234
❑ 81TigDetN-59
❑ 81Top-234
❑ 82Don-454
❑ 82Fle-284
❑ 82FleSta-156
❑ 82OPC-39
❑ 82Top-39
❑ 82TopSti-187
❑ 83AllGamPI-17
❑ 83Don-333
❑ 83Fle-348
❑ 83FleSta-212
❑ 83FleSti-249
❑ 83OPC-66
❑ 83TigPos-31
❑ 83Top-509
❑ 83TopSti-65
❑ 84AllGamPI-107
❑ 84Don-227
❑ 84DonActAS-4
❑ 84Fle-92
❑ 84FleSti-13
❑ 84FleSti-30
❑ 84FunFooP-78
❑ 84MilBra-28
❑ 84MLBPen-4
❑ 84Nes792-398
❑ 84Nes792-666
❑ 84Nes792-695
❑ 84NesDreT-2
❑ 84OCoandSI-84
❑ 84OPC-181
❑ 84OPC-211
❑ 84SevCoi-C16
❑ 84TigFarJ-15
❑ 84TigTeal-31
❑ 84TigWavP-34
❑ 84Top-398
❑ 84Top-666
❑ 84Top-695
❑ 84TopGloS-30
❑ 84TopRubD-18
❑ 84TopSti-196
❑ 84TopSti-267
❑ 84TopStiB-1
❑ 84TopTif-398
❑ 84TopTif-666
❑ 84TopTif-695
❑ 85AllGamPI-17
❑ 85Don-5
❑ 85Don-293
❑ 85DonActA-42
❑ 85DonSupD-5
❑ 85Fle-24
❑ 85GenMilS-24
❑ 85Lea-5
❑ 85OPC-108
❑ 85SevCoi-D1
❑ 85SevCoi-S16
❑ 85TigCaiD-19
❑ 85TigWen-21
❑ 85Top-480
❑ 85TopGloA-14
❑ 85TopRubD-17
❑ 85TopSti-183
❑ 85TopSti-261
❑ 85TopTif-480
❑ 86BasStaB-118
❑ 86Don-49
❑ 86DonAll-11
❑ 86DonPop-11
❑ 86Fle-242
❑ 86FleLimE-44
❑ 86FleMin-51
❑ 86FleStiC-126
❑ 86GenMilB-1J
❑ 86Lea-33
❑ 86OPC-20
❑ 86SevCoi-S10
❑ 86Spo-48
❑ 86Spo-74
❑ 86SpoDecG-73
❑ 86SpoRoo-48
❑ 86TigCaiD-20
❑ 86Top-20
❑ 86TopGloA-3
❑ 86TopSti-156
❑ 86TopSti-272
❑ 86TopTat-23
❑ 86TopTif-20
❑ 86TruVal-25
❑ 87Don-107
❑ 87DonAll-3
❑ 87DonOpeD-218
❑ 87DonP-3
❑ 87Fle-168
❑ 87FleGlo-168
❑ 87FleMin-112
❑ 87FleRecS-41
❑ 87FleStiC-122
❑ 87HosSti-23
❑ 87Lea-78
❑ 87MSAJifPD-11
❑ 87OPC-106
❑ 87RedFolSB-88
❑ 87SevCoi-D12
❑ 87Spo-112
❑ 87Spo-137
❑ 87SpoTeaP-15
❑ 87TigCaiD-8
❑ 87TigCok-16
❑ 87Top-661
❑ 87TopGloA-14
❑ 87TopGloS-7
❑ 87TopSti-153
❑ 87TopSti-267
❑ 87TopTif-661
❑ 88Don-173
❑ 88DonBasB-315
❑ 88Fle-75
❑ 88FleGlo-75
❑ 88Lea-169
❑ 88OPC-179
❑ 88PanSti-92
❑ 88PanSti-122
❑ 88PanSti-443
❑ 88Sco-56
❑ 88ScoGlo-56
❑ 88Spo-30
❑ 88StaLinAl-35
❑ 88StaLinTi-20
❑ 88TigPep-1
❑ 88TigPol-14
❑ 88Top-770
❑ 88TopBig-99
❑ 88TopMinL-13
❑ 88TopSti-270
❑ 88TopStiB-38
❑ 88TopTif-770
❑ 89Bow-103
❑ 89BowTif-103
❑ 89ClaTraP-188
❑ 89Don-298
❑ 89DonBasB-35
❑ 89Fle-151
❑ 89FleGlo-151
❑ 89OPC-320
❑ 89PanSti-341
❑ 89Sco-230
❑ 89Spo-18
❑ 89TigMar-1
❑ 89TigPol-1
❑ 89Top-320
❑ 89TopBasT-162
❑ 89TopBig-22
❑ 89TopCoi-57
❑ 89TopSti-282
❑ 89TopStiB-6
❑ 89TopTif-320
❑ 89TopUKM-83
❑ 89UppDec-451
❑ 90Bow-356
❑ 90BowTif-356
❑ 90Don-16
❑ 90Don-298
❑ 90DonBesA-119
❑ 90DonSupD-16
❑ 90Fle-619
❑ 90FleCan-619
❑ 90Hot50PS-48
❑ 90KinDis-24
❑ 90Lea-34
❑ 90M.Vpin-38
❑ 90MLBBasB-89
❑ 90OPC-280
❑ 90PanSti-71
❑ 90PubIntS-485
❑ 90RedFolSB-101
❑ 90Sco-75
❑ 90Sco100S-71
❑ 90Spo-103
❑ 90TigCok-26
❑ 90TigTeal-24
❑ 90Top-280
❑ 90TopBig-130
❑ 90TopCoi-32
❑ 90TopDou-70
❑ 90TopSti-275
❑ 90TopStiB-39
❑ 90TopTif-280
❑ 90UppDec-41
❑ 90UppDec-327
❑ 91Bow-150
❑ 91CadElID-60

❑ 91ClaGam-3
❑ 91Don-174
❑ 91Fle-357
❑ 91Lea-120
❑ 91OPC-145
❑ 91PanFreS-289
❑ 91PanSti-233
❑ 91Sco-297
❑ 91StaClu-101
❑ 91Stu-60
❑ 91TigCok-1
❑ 91TigPol-14
❑ 91Top-145
❑ 91TopDesS-145
❑ 91TopMic-145
❑ 91TopTif-145
❑ 91Ult-130
❑ 91UppDec-367
❑ 92Bow-630
❑ 92ClaGam-91
❑ 92Don-285
❑ 92Fle-149
❑ 92Hig5-50
❑ 92Lea-391
❑ 92LeaBlaG-391
❑ 92OPC-570
❑ 92PanSti-106
❑ 92Pin-29
❑ 92Sco-255
❑ 92SpollIFK1-204
❑ 92StaClu-550
❑ 92Stu-180
❑ 92TigKro-27
❑ 92Top-570
❑ 92TopGol-570
❑ 92TopGolW-570
❑ 92TopKid-77
❑ 92TopMic-570
❑ 92TriPla-117
❑ 92Ult-65
❑ 92UppDec-516
❑ 93Bow-11
❑ 93CadDis-62
❑ 93Don-686
❑ 93Fin-2
❑ 93FinRef-2
❑ 93Fla-211
❑ 93Fle-614
❑ 93FunPac-190
❑ 93Lea-148
❑ 93OPC-389
❑ 93PacSpa-116
❑ 93Pin-509
❑ 93Sco-596
❑ 93Sel-112
❑ 93SP-243
❑ 93StaClu-135
❑ 93StaCluFDI-135
❑ 93StaCluMOP-135
❑ 93Stu-76
❑ 93TigGat-27
❑ 93Top-160
❑ 93TopGol-160
❑ 93TopInaM-160
❑ 93TopInaR-160
❑ 93TopMic-160
❑ 93TriPla-224
❑ 93Ult-555
❑ 93UppDec-273
❑ 93UppDecGold-273
❑ 94Bow-237
❑ 94ColC-291
❑ 94ColChoGS-291
❑ 94ColChoSS-291
❑ 94Don-360
❑ 94DonSpeE-360
❑ 94Fin-364
❑ 94FinRef-364
❑ 94Fla-296
❑ 94Fle-146
❑ 94Fle-709
❑ 94FleExtB-82
❑ 94Lea-80
❑ 94LeaL-35
❑ 94OPC-172
❑ 94Pac-232
❑ 94PanSti-70
❑ 94Pin-281
❑ 94PinArtP-281
❑ 94PinMusC-281
❑ 94ProMag-49
❑ 94Sco-79
❑ 94ScoGolR-79
❑ 94Sel-323
❑ 94StaClu-443
❑ 94StaCluFDI-443
❑ 94StaCluGR-443
❑ 94StaCluMOP-443
❑ 94Stu-195
❑ 94Top-410
❑ 94TopGol-410
❑ 94TopSpa-410
❑ 94TriPla-250
❑ 94TriPlaM-5
❑ 94Ult-60
❑ 94UppDec-414
❑ 94UppDecED-414
❑ 95ColCho-475
❑ 95ColChoGS-475
❑ 95ColChoSE-218
❑ 95ColChoSEGS-218
❑ 95ColChoSESS-218
❑ 95ColChoSS-475
❑ 95Don-45
❑ 95DonPreP-45
❑ 95DonTopotO-81
❑ 95Emo-47
❑ 95Fin-220
❑ 95FinRef-220
❑ 95Fla-42
❑ 95Fle-64
❑ 95Lea-178
❑ 95LeaLim-142
❑ 95Pac-163
❑ 95PacPri-52
❑ 95PanSti-50
❑ 95Pin-117
❑ 95PinArtP-117
❑ 95PinMusC-117
❑ 95Sco-373
❑ 95ScoGolR-373
❑ 95ScoPlaTS-373
❑ 95SP-153
❑ 95SPCha-152
❑ 95SPChaDC-152
❑ 95SPSil-153
❑ 95StaClu-481
❑ 95StaCluMOP-481
❑ 95StaCluSTWS-481
❑ 95StaCluVR-262
❑ 95StaCluVRMO-262
❑ 95Stu-80
❑ 95Top-15
❑ 95TopCyb-13
❑ 95TopD3-30
❑ 95TopEmb-97
❑ 95TopEmbGI-97
❑ 95Ult-287
❑ 95UltGolM-287
❑ 95UppDec-188
❑ 95UppDecED-188
❑ 95UppDecEDG-188
❑ 95UppDecSE-230
❑ 95UppDecSEG-230
❑ 96ColCho-144
❑ 96ColChoGS-144
❑ 96ColChoSS-144
❑ 96Don-77
❑ 96DonPreP-77
❑ 96Fle-122
❑ 96FleGolM-10
❑ 96FleTif-122
❑ 96Pac-318
❑ 96Sco-487
❑ 96Ult-66
❑ 96UltGolM-66
❑ 96UppDec-107

Whitaker, Ryan
❑ 93SouOreAC-26
❑ 93SouOreAF-4064
❑ 94WesMicWC-24
❑ 94WesMicWF-2297
❑ 95ModA'sTI-30
❑ 96ModA'sB-19

Whitaker, Steve
❑ 91ClaDraP-29
❑ 91FroRowDP-40
❑ 91FroRowDPG-40
❑ 91FroRowDPS-40
❑ 92OPC-369
❑ 92SanJosGC-5
❑ 92StaCluD-194
❑ 92Top-369
❑ 92TopGol-369
❑ 92TopGolW-369
❑ 92TopMic-369
❑ 93ClaGolF-69
❑ 93SanJosGC-18
❑ 93SanJosGF-11
❑ 94ShrCapF-1607
❑ 95Exc-296
❑ 95UppDecML-189
❑ 95UppDecMLFS-189
❑ 96El PasDB-28

Whitaker, Steve (Stephen E.)
❑ 67Top-277
❑ 68Top-383
❑ 68YanPhoS-80
❑ 69MLBOffS-63
❑ 69OPC-71
❑ 69Top-71
❑ 69TopSta-189
❑ 69TopTeaP-7
❑ 70OPC-496
❑ 70Top-496
❑ 81TCM60I-445
❑ 83Pil69G-41
❑ 89PacSenL-67
❑ 92YanWIZ6-135
❑ 98BirBarG-29

Whitaker, William
❑ 87OldJudN-534

Whitby, William
❑ 67Top-486

White Sox, Chicago
❑ 13FatT20-2
❑ 36NatChiFPR-88
❑ 36R31Pre-G21
❑ 38BasTabP-47
❑ 48WhiSoxTI-30
❑ 51TopTea-3
❑ 56Top-188
❑ 57Top-329
❑ 58Top-256
❑ 59Top-94
❑ 59TopVen-94
❑ 60Top-208
❑ 60TopTat-66
❑ 61Top-7
❑ 61TopMagR-9
❑ 62GuyPotCP-4
❑ 62Top-113
❑ 62TopVen-113
❑ 63GadFunC-64
❑ 63Top-288
❑ 64Top-496
❑ 64TopTatI-5
❑ 65OPC-234
❑ 65Top-234
❑ 66Top-426
❑ 66TopRubI-105
❑ 67Top-573
❑ 68LauWorS-3
❑ 68LauWorS-14
❑ 68Top-424
❑ 69FleCloS-6
❑ 69TopStaA-6
❑ 70FleWorS-3
❑ 70FleWorS-14
❑ 70FleWorS-16
❑ 70OPC-501
❑ 70Top-501
❑ 71FleWorS-4
❑ 71FleWorS-17
❑ 71Top-289
❑ 71TopTat-69
❑ 72OPC-381
❑ 72Top-381
❑ 73OPC-481
❑ 73OPCBTC-6
❑ 73Top-481
❑ 73TopBluTC-6
❑ 74OPC-416
❑ 74OPCTC-6
❑ 74Top-416
❑ 74TopStaA-6
❑ 74TopTeaC-6
❑ 75WhiSox1T-28
❑ 78Top-66
❑ 83FleSta-230
❑ 83FleSti-NNO
❑ 87SpoTeaL-26
❑ 87Top-356
❑ 87TopTif-356
❑ 88PacEigMO-4
❑ 88PanSti-458
❑ 88RedFolSB-117
❑ 90PubIntS-639
❑ 90RedFolSB-110
❑ 91PanCanT1-136
❑ 91UppDec-617
❑ 94ImpProP-4
❑ 94Sco-320
❑ 94ScoGolR-320
❑ 94StaCluMOP-ST18
❑ 95PacPriTL-4
❑ 95PanSti-146
❑ 96PanSti-171
❑ 96WhiSoxF-19
❑ 97ColChoT-CW
❑ 99Vic-88

White Sox, Yarmouth-Dennis
❑ 88CapCodPB-28

White, Al
❑ 80PenPilBT-16
❑ 80PenPilCT-22

White, Al PCL
❑ 21Zee-39
❑ 49SolSunP-11

White, Andre
❑ 91BurIndP-3319
❑ 93ColRedC-25
❑ 93ColRedF-613
❑ 94KinIndC-21
❑ 94KinIndF-2659

White, Bill D.
❑ 57GiaJayP-11
❑ 59Top-359
❑ 60CarJayP-12
❑ 60Top-355
❑ 60TopTat-53
❑ 61CarJayP-13
❑ 61Pos-176A
❑ 61Pos-176B
❑ 61Top-232
❑ 61Top-451
❑ 61TopDicG-18
❑ 61TopStal-96
❑ 62Baz-40
❑ 62CarJayP-12
❑ 62Jel-158
❑ 62Pos-158
❑ 62PosCan-158
❑ 62SalPlaC-115
❑ 62ShiPlaC-115
❑ 62Top-14
❑ 62TopBuc-92
❑ 62TopStal-191
❑ 62TopVen-14
❑ 63BasMagM-84
❑ 63Baz-28
❑ 63CarJayP-20
❑ 63Fle-63
❑ 63Jel-158
❑ 63Pos-158A
❑ 63Pos-158B
❑ 63Top-1
❑ 63Top-290
❑ 63TopStil-45
❑ 64CarTeal-8
❑ 64Top-11
❑ 64Top-240
❑ 64TopCoi-78
❑ 64TopCoi-141
❑ 64TopSta-10
❑ 64TopStaU-74
❑ 64TopVen-11
❑ 64TopVen-240
❑ 64WheSta-48
❑ 65CarJayP-12
❑ 65OPC-190
❑ 65Top-190
❑ 65TopEmbl-43
❑ 65TopTral-72
❑ 66Baz-23
❑ 66PhiTeal-12
❑ 66Top-397
❑ 66TopRubl-97
❑ 67Baz-23
❑ 67CokCapPh-13
❑ 67DexPre-219
❑ 67PhiPol-13
❑ 67Top-290
❑ 68Baz-4
❑ 68OPC-190
❑ 68Top-190
❑ 68TopVen-190
❑ 69MilBra-288
❑ 69Top-588
❑ 69TopTeaP-8
❑ 72MilBra-359
❑ 72YanSch-8
❑ 78TCM60I-12
❑ 81TCM60I-414
❑ 82DanSunF-6
❑ 90PacLeg-56
❑ 90SweBasG-9
❑ 91LinDri-27
❑ 91SweBasG-96
❑ 92ActPacA-84
❑ 92CarMcD-25
❑ 93UppDecAH-125
❑ 94CarLeaA-DJ12
❑ 94UppDecAH-65
❑ 94UppDecAH1-65

White, Billy
❑ 89GenCubP-1884
❑ 90CarLeaA-50
❑ 90WinSpiTI-2
❑ 91ChaKniLD-148
❑ 91ChaKniP-1699
❑ 91Cla/Bes-363
❑ 91LinDriAA-148
❑ 91SydWavF-10
❑ 92ChaKniF-2781
❑ 92ChaKniS-172
❑ 92ClaFS7-64
❑ 92SkyAA F-78
❑ 94NewHavRF-1560
❑ 95NewHavRTI-11
❑ 96ColSprSSTI-31
❑ 97AshTou-29
❑ 98AshTouM-27

White, Bob
❑ 79CliDodT-25

White, Brandon
❑ 93VerBeaDC-27
❑ 93VerBeaDF-2221

White, Chad
❑ 93AubAstC-26
❑ 93AubAstF-3458
❑ 94OscAstC-24
❑ 94OscAstF-1152
❑ 95QuaCitRBTI-29

White, Chaney
❑ 78LauLonABS-9
❑ 91PomBlaBPB-23

White, Charles
❑ 52Par-22
❑ 54BraJohC-24
❑ 55BraGolS-23
❑ 55BraJohC-24
❑ 55Top-103
❑ 55TopDouH-17
❑ 55TopTesS-11

White, Charlie
❑ 89SprCarB-17
❑ 90ArkTraGS-30
❑ 90AshTouP-2738
❑ 91ArkTraLD-47
❑ 91ArkTraP-1301
❑ 91LinDriAA-47
❑ 92BirBarF-2597
❑ 92BirBarS-98

White, Chris
❑ 91AubAstC-5
❑ 91AubAstP-4275
❑ 92AshTouC-14
❑ 93FloStaLAF-37
❑ 93OscAstC-23
❑ 93OscAstF-629
❑ 94JacGenF-218
❑ 95JacGenTI-12

White, Clinton
❑ 89WytCubS-28
❑ 90GenCubP-3042
❑ 90GenCubS-24

White, Craig
❑ 89GreFalDSP-29
❑ 90YakBeaTI-24

White, Darell
❑ 94SprSulC-24
❑ 94SprSulF-2036
❑ 95RanCucQT-22
❑ 96RanCucQB-29

White, Darren
❑ 91AdeGiaF-11
❑ 94TopTra-109T
❑ 95AusFut-65

White, Darrin
❑ 89HelBreSP-25
❑ 90BelBreB-14
❑ 90BelBreS-23
❑ 91BelBreCB-12
❑ 91BelBreP-2106

White, Dave
❑ 79AppFoxT-5
❑ 80AppFoxT-21
❑ 86BirBarTI-4
❑ 86SouLeaAJ-19
❑ 87HawIslP-4

White, David
❑ 93AusFut-28
❑ 95AusFut-64
❑ 95AusFutSFP-SFFP3

White, Deacon (James)
❑ 76SSP188WS-18
❑ 87BucN28-35
❑ 87OldJudN-535
❑ 87ScrDC-18
❑ 88WG1CarG-27

White, Derrick
❑ 91JamExpC-3
❑ 91JamExpP-3556
❑ 92ClaFS7-128
❑ 92HarSenF-469
❑ 92HarSenS-293
❑ 92ProFS7-271
❑ 92UppDecML-279
❑ 93ExcFS7-65
❑ 94OttLynF-2907
❑ 95TolMudHTI-26
❑ 96WesMicWB-30
❑ 97VanCanB-28
❑ 98IowCubQ-27
❑ 99WesMicWAM-24

White, Devon
❑ 82DanSunF-21
❑ 83PeoSunF-22
❑ 85MidAngT-8
❑ 86EdmTraP-27
❑ 87AngSmo-23
❑ 87CalAngPPS-38
❑ 87ClaUpdY-140
❑ 87Don-38
❑ 87DonOpeD-5
❑ 87DonRoo-8
❑ 87Fle-646
❑ 87FleGlo-646
❑ 87FleUpd-123
❑ 87FleUpdG-123
❑ 87Lea-38
❑ 87SevCoi-W13
❑ 87SpoRool-24
❑ 87SpoRooP-10
❑ 87SpoTeaP-11
❑ 87Top-139
❑ 87TopTif-139
❑ 88AngSmo-13
❑ 88ClaRed-178
❑ 88Don-8
❑ 88Don-283
❑ 88DonBasB-227
❑ 88DonSupD-8
❑ 88Fle-506
❑ 88FleExcS-44
❑ 88FleGlo-506
❑ 88FleMin-12
❑ 88Lea-8
❑ 88Lea-127
❑ 88OPC-192
❑ 88PanSti-43
❑ 88PanSti-49
❑ 88RedFolSB-99
❑ 88Sco-212
❑ 88ScoGlo-212
❑ 88ScoYouSI-12
❑ 88Spo-99
❑ 88StaLinAn-19
❑ 88Top-192
❑ 88TopBig-145
❑ 88TopCoi-31
❑ 88TopGloS-29
❑ 88TopRoo-5
❑ 88TopSti-183
❑ 88TopSti-313
❑ 88TopTif-192
❑ 88ToyRoo-33
❑ 89Bow-54
❑ 89BowTif-54
❑ 89Don-213
❑ 89DonBasB-27
❑ 89Fle-489
❑ 89FleGlo-489
❑ 89OPC-344
❑ 89PanSti-297
❑ 89Sco-323
❑ 89Spo-16
❑ 89Top-602
❑ 89TopAme2C-31
❑ 89TopBig-122
❑ 89TopSti-179
❑ 89TopTif-602
❑ 89TVSpoM-110
❑ 89UppDec-110
❑ 90AngSmo-18
❑ 90Bow-292
❑ 90BowTif-292
❑ 90ClaBlu-63
❑ 90Don-226
❑ 90Fle-147
❑ 90FleBasA-42
❑ 90FleBasAC-42

❑ 90FleCan-147
❑ 90FleLeaL-43
❑ 90FleLeaLC-43
❑ 90Hot50PS-49
❑ 90Lea-76
❑ 90OPC-65
❑ 90PanSti-29
❑ 90PubIntS-381
❑ 90RedFolSB-102
❑ 90Sco-312
❑ 90Sco100S-68
❑ 90Spo-210
❑ 90Top-65
❑ 90TopBig-299
❑ 90TopMinL-10
❑ 90TopSti-168
❑ 90TopTif-65
❑ 90UppDec-5
❑ 90UppDec-129
❑ 91BluJayFS-30
❑ 91BluJayFS-33
❑ 91BluJayS-23
❑ 91Bow-30
❑ 91Cla3-T94
❑ 91Don-150
❑ 91Fle-328
❑ 91FleUpd-69
❑ 91Lea-394
❑ 91OPC-704
❑ 91OPCPre-126
❑ 91PanFreS-185
❑ 91Sco-466
❑ 91ScoRoo-48T
❑ 91StaClu-444
❑ 91Stu-139
❑ 91Top-704
❑ 91TopDesS-704
❑ 91TopMic-704
❑ 91TopTif-704
❑ 91TopTra-125T
❑ 91TopTraT-125T
❑ 91UltUpd-64
❑ 91UppDec-517
❑ 91UppDec-783
❑ 92BluJayP-12
❑ 92Bow-547
❑ 92Cla1-T95
❑ 92ClaGam-120
❑ 92Don-180
❑ 92DonMcD-G6
❑ 92Fle-346
❑ 92Hig5-120
❑ 92Lea-114
❑ 92LeaBlaG-114
❑ 92MSABenSHD-4
❑ 92OPC-260
❑ 92PanSti-30
❑ 92Pin-17
❑ 92Sco-198
❑ 92ScoCokD-22
❑ 92ScoImpP-67
❑ 92ScoProP-2
❑ 92StaClu-41
❑ 92Stu-259
❑ 92SunSee-22
❑ 92Top-260
❑ 92TopGol-260
❑ 92TopGolW-260
❑ 92TopMic-260
❑ 92TriPla-240
❑ 92Ult-155
❑ 92UltAwaW-18
❑ 92UppDec-352
❑ 93BluJayCP1-11
❑ 93BluJayCP1-15
❑ 93BluJayD-20
❑ 93BluJayD4-13
❑ 93BluJayDM-16
❑ 93BluJayDM-21
❑ 93BluJayDM-31
❑ 93BluJayFS-34
❑ 93Bow-251
❑ 93Don-29
❑ 93Don-132
❑ 93Fla-297
❑ 93Fle-342
❑ 93HumDumC-24
❑ 93Lea-69
❑ 93OPC-341
❑ 93OPCWorC-16
❑ 93PacSpa-659
❑ 93PanSti-30
❑ 93Pin-138
❑ 93Sco-92
❑ 93Sel-72
❑ 93SP-54
❑ 93StaClu-485
❑ 93StaCluFDI-485
❑ 93StaCluMOP-485
❑ 93Stu-60
❑ 93Top-387
❑ 93TopGol-387
❑ 93TopInaM-387
❑ 93TopInaR-387
❑ 93TopMic-387
❑ 93TriPla-89
❑ 93Ult-297
❑ 93UltAwaW-18
❑ 93UppDec-346
❑ 93UppDecGold-346
❑ 94BluJayP-9
❑ 94BluJayUSPC-5C
❑ 94BluJayUSPC-13H
❑ 94Bow-497
❑ 94ColC-292
❑ 94ColChoGS-292
❑ 94ColChoSS-292
❑ 94Don-285
❑ 94Fin-125
❑ 94FinPre-125P
❑ 94FinRef-125
❑ 94Fla-351
❑ 94Fle-348
❑ 94FleExtB-198
❑ 94FUnPac-79
❑ 94Lea-129
❑ 94LeaL-80
❑ 94OPC-159
❑ 94OPCWorC-2
❑ 94Pac-653
❑ 94PanSti-142
❑ 94Pin-85
❑ 94PinArtP-85
❑ 94PinMusC-85
❑ 94PinRunC-RC22
❑ 94Sco-97
❑ 94ScoCyc-TC10
❑ 94ScoGolR-97
❑ 94ScoGolS-53
❑ 94Sel-21
❑ 94SP-46
❑ 94SPDieC-46
❑ 94Spo-96
❑ 94StaClu-326
❑ 94StaCluFDI-326
❑ 94StaCluGR-326
❑ 94StaCluMOP-326
❑ 94StaCluT-174
❑ 94StaCluTFDI-174
❑ 94Stu-32
❑ 94Top-511
❑ 94TopGol-511
❑ 94TopSpa-511
❑ 94TriPla-40
❑ 94Ult-146
❑ 94UltAwaW-8
❑ 94UppDec-137
❑ 94UppDecED-137
❑ 95Baz-118
❑ 95BluJayOH-35
❑ 95BluJayUSPC-6S
❑ 95BluJayUSPC-13D
❑ 95Bow-397
❑ 95ColCho-143
❑ 95ColChoGS-143
❑ 95ColChoSS-143
❑ 95Don-382
❑ 95DonPreP-382
❑ 95DonTopotO-179
❑ 95Emo-98
❑ 95Fin-180
❑ 95FinRef-180
❑ 95Fla-319
❑ 95FlaHotG-11
❑ 95Fle-107
❑ 95Lea-231
❑ 95LeaLim-112
❑ 95Pac-450
❑ 95Pin-186
❑ 95PinArtP-186
❑ 95PinMusC-186
❑ 95PosCan-4
❑ 95Sco-365
❑ 95ScoGolR-365
❑ 95ScoHaloG-HG109
❑ 95ScoPlaTS-365
❑ 95StaClu-335
❑ 95StaCluMOP-335
❑ 95StaCluMOP-SS9
❑ 95StaCluSS-SS9
❑ 95StaCluSTWS-335
❑ 95StaCluVR-175
❑ 95StaCluVRMO-175
❑ 95Stu-93
❑ 95Top-427
❑ 95TopCyb-225
❑ 95TopEmb-68
❑ 95TopEmbGI-68
❑ 95Ult-124
❑ 95UltAwaW-8
❑ 95UltAwaWGM-8
❑ 95UltGolM-124
❑ 95UppDec-42
❑ 95UppDecED-42
❑ 95UppDecEDG-42
❑ 96Baz-14
❑ 96Cir-132
❑ 96CirRav-132
❑ 96ColCho-351
❑ 96ColCho-557
❑ 96ColChoGS-351
❑ 96ColChoGS-557
❑ 96ColChoSS-351
❑ 96ColChoSS-557
❑ 96Don-464
❑ 96DonPreP-464
❑ 96EmoXL-192
❑ 96Fin-S256
❑ 96FinRef-S256
❑ 96Fla-270
❑ 96Fle-399
❑ 96FleTif-399
❑ 96FleUpd-U135
❑ 96FleUpdTC-U135
❑ 96MetUni-171
❑ 96MetUniP-171
❑ 96Pac-447
❑ 96Sco-28
❑ 96ScoDugC-A27
❑ 96ScoDugCAP-A27
❑ 96Top-209
❑ 96TopGal-35
❑ 96TopGalPPI-35
❑ 96TopLas-15
❑ 96Ult-482
❑ 96UltGolM-482
❑ 96UppDec-494U
❑ 97Cir-67
❑ 97CirRav-64
❑ 97ColCho-112
❑ 97ColChoT-FM3
❑ 97Don-51
❑ 97DonGolPP-51
❑ 97DonSilPP-51
❑ 97Fin-83
❑ 97FinRef-83
❑ 97Fle-337
❑ 97FleTif-337
❑ 97Lea-272
❑ 97LeaFraM-272
❑ 97LeaFraMDC-272
❑ 97MarPac-23
❑ 97MetUni-180
❑ 97Pac-310
❑ 97PacLigB-310
❑ 97PacSil-310
❑ 97Pin-40
❑ 97PinArtP-PP40
❑ 97PinMusC-40
❑ 97PinPrePla-40
❑ 97Sco-385
❑ 97ScoArtPWB-385
❑ 97ScoResC-385
❑ 97ScoShoS-385
❑ 97ScoShoSAP-385
❑ 97StaClu-125
❑ 97StaCluMOP-125
❑ 97Top-359
❑ 97TopChr-122
❑ 97TopChrR-122
❑ 97TopGal-2
❑ 97TopGalPPI-2
❑ 97Ult-385
❑ 97UltGolME-385
❑ 97UltPlaME-385
❑ 97UppDec-151
❑ 97UppDec-191
❑ 97UppDec-358
❑ 98CirThu-152
❑ 98CirThuRav-152
❑ 98CirThuSupRav-152
❑ 98ColCho-290
❑ 98CroRoy-8
❑ 98DiaBacP-25
❑ 98DiaMcD-23
❑ 98Fin-181
❑ 98FinNo--181
❑ 98FinNo-R-181
❑ 98FinRef-181
❑ 98Fle-549
❑ 98Pac-309
❑ 98PacAur-100
❑ 98PacInvTeam-29
❑ 98PacOme-15
❑ 98PacOmeR-15
❑ 98PacOnl-50
❑ 98PacOnlR-50
❑ 98PacOnlWC-50
❑ 98PacPar-124
❑ 98PacParC-124
❑ 98PacParG-124
❑ 98PacParHS-124
❑ 98PacParPB-124
❑ 98PacParR-124
❑ 98PacPlaB-309
❑ 98PacRedT-309
❑ 98PacSil-309
❑ 98PinPlu-38
❑ 98PinSna-AD4
❑ 98PinSna-AD9
❑ 98Revo-8
❑ 98RevoSS-8
❑ 98ScoRT-181
❑ 98Top-47
❑ 98Top-457
❑ 98TopChr-47
❑ 98TopChr-457
❑ 98TopChrR-47
❑ 98TopChrR-457
❑ 98TopDevR-47
❑ 98TopDevR-457
❑ 98TopDia-47
❑ 98TopDia-457
❑ 98TopMiniC-47
❑ 98TopMiniC-457
❑ 98TopOpeD-29
❑ 98Ult-460
❑ 98UltGolM-460
❑ 98UltMas-460
❑ 98UltPlaM-460
❑ 98UppDec-418
❑ 98UppDec-636
❑ 99199Fin-247
❑ 99DodPol-27
❑ 99FinGolRef-247
❑ 99FinRef-247
❑ 99FlaShoLeg1-142
❑ 99FlaShoLeg2-142
❑ 99FlaShoLeg3-142
❑ 99FlaShoLegM1-142
❑ 99FlaShoLegM2-142
❑ 99FlaShoLegM3-142
❑ 99FlaShoR1-142
❑ 99FlaShoR2-142
❑ 99FlaShoR3-142
❑ 99Fle-260
❑ 99FleSta9-260
❑ 99FleWarT-260
❑ 99MetUni-198
❑ 99MetUniGM-198
❑ 99MetUniPMG-198
❑ 99Pac-25
❑ 99PacCroC-19
❑ 99PacCroCPB-19
❑ 99PacOme-126
❑ 99PacOmeC-126
❑ 99PacOmeG-126
❑ 99PacOmePB-126
❑ 99PacPar-122
❑ 99PacParC-122
❑ 99PacParG-122
❑ 99PacParHoloGold-122
❑ 99PacParHS-122
❑ 99PacParOD-122
❑ 99PacParPB-122
❑ 99PacParRed-122
❑ 99PacPlaB-25
❑ 99PacPriS-146
❑ 99PacPriS206-146
❑ 99PacPriS206R-146
❑ 99PacRed-25
❑ 99SkyPre-98
❑ 99SkyPreR-98
❑ 99SkyThu-40
❑ 99SkyThuRant-40
❑ 99SkyThuRave-40
❑ 99SpoIll-77
❑ 99StaClu-331
❑ 99StaCluFDI-331
❑ 99StaCluOoaK-331
❑ 99StaCluPP-331
❑ 99ThuSkySupR-40
❑ 99Top-276
❑ 99TopChr-276
❑ 99TopChrR-276
❑ 99TopMVPP-276
❑ 99Ult-63
❑ 99UltGolM-63
❑ 99UltMas-63
❑ 99UltPlaM-63
❑ 99UppDec-397
❑ 99UppDecEL1-397
❑ 99UppDecEL2-397
❑ 99UppDecM-108
❑ 99UppDecMGS-108
❑ 99UppDecMHFS-108
❑ 99UppDecMSS-108
❑ 99Vic-206

White, Doc (Guy)
❑ 07WhiSoxGWH-12
❑ 08RosComP-20
❑ 09T206-372
❑ 09T206-373
❑ 10DomDisP-124
❑ 10JuJuDE-41
❑ 10RedCroT-83
❑ 10RedCroT-165
❑ 10SweCapPP-15
❑ 11HelSta-19
❑ 11PinT-5-763
❑ 11S74Sil-10
❑ 11SpoLifM-34
❑ 11T205-179
❑ 12HasTriFT-22B
❑ 12T207-195
❑ 14Zee-145
❑ 15Zee-142
❑ 80LauFamF-15
❑ 95ConTSN-1353

White, Donald William
❑ 48A'sTeal-26
❑ 49A'sTeal-32
❑ 49PhiBul-58
❑ 85TCMPla1-43

White, Donnie
❑ 92KinMetF-1545
❑ 93CapCitBC-23
❑ 93CapCitBF-474
❑ 94St.LucMC-25
❑ 94St.LucMF-1210
❑ 95BinMetTI-23
❑ 95SigRooOJ-34
❑ 95SigRooOJP-34
❑ 95SigRooOJPS-34
❑ 95SigRooOJS-34
❑ 96BinMetB-29

White, Elder
❑ 77FriOneYW-101

White, Eric
❑ 92BurIndC-29
❑ 92BurIndF-1667
❑ 93BurIndC-26
❑ 93BurIndF-3309
❑ 94ColRedC-22
❑ 94ColRedF-452
❑ 96KenIndB-26

White, Ernie
❑ 41CarW75-29
❑ 46SeaSLP-66
❑ 76Met63 S-18
❑ 83Car194T-46

White, Foley
❑ 09T206-523

White, Frank
❑ 74OPC-604
❑ 74RoyPos-28
❑ 74Top-604
❑ 75OPC-569
❑ 75RoyPos-31
❑ 75Top-569
❑ 75TopMin-569
❑ 76KanCitRP-32
❑ 76OPC-369
❑ 76SSP-174
❑ 76Top-369
❑ 77Top-117
❑ 78Roy-25
❑ 78SSP270-232
❑ 78Top-248
❑ 79BasPat-94
❑ 79OPC-227
❑ 79Top-439
❑ 80OPC-24
❑ 80Top-45
❑ 81AllGamPI-17
❑ 81CokTeaS-82
❑ 81Don-340
❑ 81Fle-44
❑ 81FleStiC-97
❑ 81Kel-34
❑ 81OPC-330
❑ 81RoyPol-9
❑ 81Top-330
❑ 81TopScr-47
❑ 81TopSti-83
❑ 82Don-286
❑ 82Fle-426
❑ 82Fle-629
❑ 82FleSta-209
❑ 82OPC-156
❑ 82OPC-183
❑ 82Roy-24
❑ 82Top-645
❑ 82Top-646
❑ 82TopSti-193
❑ 83AllGamPI-18
❑ 83Don-464
❑ 83Fle-127
❑ 83FleSta-213
❑ 83FleSti-94
❑ 83OPC-171
❑ 83RoyPol-9
❑ 83RoyPos-34
❑ 83Top-525
❑ 83TopSti-71
❑ 83TopSti-169
❑ 84AllGamPI-108
❑ 84Don-222
❑ 84Fle-363
❑ 84FunFooP-44
❑ 84Nes792-155
❑ 84OPC-155
❑ 84RoyPos-36
❑ 84Top-155
❑ 84TopRubD-4
❑ 84TopSti-277
❑ 84TopTif-155
❑ 85AllGamPI-18
❑ 85Don-175
❑ 85Fle-217
❑ 85Lea-148
❑ 85RoyTeal-32
❑ 85Top-743
❑ 85TopRubD-4
❑ 85TopSti-274
❑ 85TopTif-743
❑ 86BasStaB-119
❑ 86Don-130
❑ 86Fle-24
❑ 86FleStiC-127
❑ 86GenMilB-2J
❑ 86Lea-54
❑ 86OPC-215
❑ 86RoyKitCD-13
❑ 86RoyNatP-20
❑ 86RoyTeal-27
❑ 86Spo-186
❑ 86Top-215
❑ 86TopSti-23
❑ 86TopSti-263
❑ 86TopTat-16
❑ 86TopTif-215
❑ 87Don-255
❑ 87DonAll-41
❑ 87DonOpeD-204
❑ 87Fle-383
❑ 87FleAwaW-42
❑ 87FleGlo-383
❑ 87FleMin-113
❑ 87FleStiC-123
❑ 87Lea-188
❑ 87OPC-101
❑ 87Spo-168
❑ 87SpoTeaP-13
❑ 87Top-256
❑ 87Top-692
❑ 87TopSti-260
❑ 87TopTif-692
❑ 88Don-225
❑ 88DonBasB-319
❑ 88Fle-273
❑ 88FleGlo-273
❑ 88FleStiC-35
❑ 88Nes-29
❑ 88OPC-326
❑ 88PanSti-105
❑ 88RedFolSB-100
❑ 88RoySmo-25
❑ 88RoyTeal-37
❑ 88Sco-79
❑ 88ScoGlo-79
❑ 88Spo-149
❑ 88StaLinRo-19
❑ 88Top-595
❑ 88TopBig-75

❑ 88TopSti-255
❑ 88TopStiB-39
❑ 88TopTif-595
❑ 89Bow-122
❑ 89BowTif-122
❑ 89Don-85
❑ 89DonBasB-175
❑ 89Fle-297
❑ 89FleGlo-297
❑ 89OPC-25
❑ 89PanSti-356
❑ 89RoyTasD-7
❑ 89Sco-390
❑ 89Top-25
❑ 89TopBasT-142
❑ 89TopBig-200
❑ 89TopSti-262
❑ 89TopTif-25
❑ 89UppDec-350
❑ 90Bow-371
❑ 90BowTif-371
❑ 90Don-262
❑ 90Fle-122
❑ 90FleCan-122
❑ 90Lea-204
❑ 90MLBBasB-108
❑ 90OPC-479
❑ 90PanSti-83
❑ 90PublntS-360
❑ 90RoyPos-28
❑ 90Sco-372
❑ 90Top-479
❑ 90TopBig-105
❑ 90TopTif-479
❑ 90UppDec-382
❑ 91Fle-574
❑ 91OPC-352
❑ 91SimandSMLBL-45
❑ 91Top-352
❑ 91TopDesS-352
❑ 91TopMic-352
❑ 91TopTif-352
❑ 91UppDec-568
❑ 93RoySta2-14
❑ 94TedWil-39
❑ 94TedWil-142

White, Fred

❑ 88KenTwiP-1382
❑ 89VisOakCLC-102
❑ 89VisOakP-1446
❑ 90VisOakCLC-63
❑ 90VisOakP-2155
❑ 91Cla/Bes-278
❑ 91VisOakC-11
❑ 91VisOakP-1742
❑ 92OrlSunRS-523
❑ 93DayCubC-23
❑ 93DayCubF-860

White, G. Harris

❑ 04FanCraAL-49
❑ 09SpoNewSM-67

White, Gabe

❑ 90HigSchPLS-7
❑ 91Cla/Bes-61
❑ 91SumFlyC-12
❑ 91SumFlyP-2335
❑ 92Bow-279
❑ 92MidLeaATI-49
❑ 92ProFS7-268
❑ 92RocExpC-11
❑ 92RocExpF-2116
❑ 92UppDecML-202
❑ 93Bow-396
❑ 93ClaFS7-34
❑ 93ClaGolF-38
❑ 93ExcFS7-66
❑ 93HarSenF-270
❑ 94ActPac-34
❑ 94Bow-312
❑ 94Cla-86
❑ 94ColC-20
❑ 94ColChoGS-20
❑ 94ColChoSS-20
❑ 94ExcFS7-231
❑ 94Fla-406
❑ 94SigRoo-47
❑ 94SigRooHP-S12
❑ 94SigRooHPS-S12
❑ 94SigRooS-47
❑ 94Top-784
❑ 94TopGol-784
❑ 94TopSpa-784
❑ 94TopTra-31T
❑ 94Ult-527
❑ 94UppDec-30
❑ 94UppDecED-30
❑ 94UppDecML-55
❑ 94UppDecML-158
❑ 95Pin-419
❑ 95PinArtP-419
❑ 95PinMusC-419
❑ 95Sel-210
❑ 95SelArtP-210
❑ 95Spo-160
❑ 95SpoArtP-160
❑ 95Top-287
❑ 95Zen-114
❑ 96IndIndB-27
❑ 96Sco-480
❑ 96StaClu-173
❑ 96StaCluMOP-173
❑ 97IndInd-27
❑ 98PacInvGems-141
❑ 98PacOnl-207
❑ 98PacOnlR-207
❑ 98PacOnlWC-207
❑ 99Fle-450
❑ 99FleSta9-450
❑ 99FleWarT-450

White, Gary

❑ 87ClePhiP-17
❑ 87UtiBluSP-12
❑ 88SpaPhiP-1044
❑ 91ParPatF-8
❑ 93AusFut-81
❑ 96HigDesMB-29

White, Harold

❑ 51Bow-320
❑ 75TCMGua-15

White, Harry

❑ 79NewCoPT-13

White, James

❑ 94BatCliC-26
❑ 94BatCliF-3463

White, Jarvis

❑ 93BluOriF-4140

White, Jason

❑ 92SouOreAC-11
❑ 92SouOreAF-3430
❑ 93MadMusC-26
❑ 93MadMusF-1832
❑ 94ModA'sC-25
❑ 94ModA'sF-3073
❑ 95ModA'sTI-31

White, Jerry

❑ 75ExpPos-38
❑ 75IntLeaAT-1
❑ 75IntLeaAT-6
❑ 76ExpRed-36
❑ 76MonExpP-31
❑ 76OPC-594
❑ 76SSP-340
❑ 76Top-594
❑ 77ExpPos-38
❑ 77OPC-81
❑ 77Top-557
❑ 79ExpPos-31
❑ 79Top-494
❑ 80ExpPos-34
❑ 80OPC-369
❑ 80Top-724
❑ 81Don-333
❑ 81Fle-161
❑ 81OPC-42
❑ 81OPCPos-11
❑ 81Top-42
❑ 82Don-621
❑ 82ExpHygM-24
❑ 82ExpPos-41
❑ 82Fle-211
❑ 82OPC-386
❑ 82OPCPos-24
❑ 82Top-386
❑ 83Don-602
❑ 83ExpPos-36
❑ 83ExpStu-19
❑ 83Fle-300
❑ 83OPC-214
❑ 83Top-214
❑ 86CarTeal-44
❑ 89PacSenL-185
❑ 89T/MSenL-113
❑ 89TopSenL-8
❑ 90EliSenL-32
❑ 91PacSenL-3
❑ 91UppDecS-23
❑ 94ForMyeMC-28
❑ 96FtMyeMB-2

White, Jimmy

❑ 90AshTouC-25
❑ 91AshTouP-583
❑ 92BurAstC-4
❑ 92BurAstF-562
❑ 93ClaFS7-294
❑ 93OscAstC-24
❑ 93OscAstF-641
❑ 94OscAstC-1
❑ 94OscAstF-1153

White, Jo-Jo (Joyner C.)

❑ 34DiaMatCSB-195
❑ 34DiaStaR-45
❑ 34TigTeal-20
❑ 35GolMedFR-12
❑ 35WheBB1-25
❑ 36GouWidPPR-A113
❑ 36R31PasP-30
❑ 36WorWidGV-74
❑ 43A'STEAI-27
❑ 46SunBre-20
❑ 47CenFlo-31
❑ 47SigOil-88
❑ 49BowPCL-14
❑ 60Top-460
❑ 66BraPos-26
❑ 74TigTCM1AC-33
❑ 76TigOldTS-23
❑ 79DiaGre-388
❑ 81TigDetN-27
❑ 81TigSecNP-30
❑ 92ConTSN-612

White, Joe

❑ 87AriWilP-18

White, John

❑ 82AmaGolST-13

White, John F.

❑ 08BufBisFJO-18
❑ 09T206-473
❑ 12ImpTobC-4

White, Johnny

❑ 91JamExpC-1
❑ 91JamExpP-3560

White, K.G.

❑ 89BakDodCLC-199

White, Kelly

❑ 94JamJamF-3983

White, Kyle

❑ 92SpoIndC-4
❑ 92SpoIndF-1304
❑ 93SpoIndC-23
❑ 93SpoIndF-3592
❑ 94SprSulC-25
❑ 94SprSulF-2037

White, Larry

❑ 80WatIndT-4
❑ 81ChaLooT-21
❑ 82AlbDukTc-10
❑ 83AlbDukTc-8
❑ 83DodPol-47
❑ 84AlbDukCr-158
❑ 85AlbDukCr-168
❑ 90DodTar-852

White, Logan

❑ 84ButCopKT-27

White, Mac

❑ 94JamJamC-25

White, Marvin

❑ 89ButCopKSP-29
❑ 90GasRanB-26
❑ 90GasRanP-2538
❑ 90GasRanS-27
❑ 91ChaRanC-28
❑ 91ChaRanP-1331
❑ 92ChaRanC-27
❑ 92ChaRanF-2242
❑ 93ChaRanC-29
❑ 93ChaRanF-1957
❑ 94ChaRanF-2514

White, Matt

❑ 97Bes-2
❑ 97BesAll-8
❑ 97BesAutSBPP-44
❑ 97BesBetP-5
❑ 97BesCarCSP-8
❑ 97BesDiaB-3
❑ 97BesFiv-5
❑ 97HudValRB-1
❑ 98Bes-46
❑ 98Bes-99
❑ 98BesNumOP-42
❑ 98BesPos-4
❑ 98ChaRivDG-30
❑ 98SouAtlLPM-27
❑ 98St.PetDRM-1
❑ 98WatIndTI-35
❑ 99BasAmeTP-95
❑ 99BasAmeTPG-95
❑ 99SP TopP-121
❑ 99SP TopPC-MW
❑ 99SP TopPDtS-D28
❑ 99SP TopPGF-GF28
❑ 99SP TopPPE-121

White, Maximo

❑ 93PriRedC-30
❑ 93PriRedF-4190

White, Michael R. Mayor

❑ 97PinFan-PC8

White, Mike

❑ 81LynSaiT-19
❑ 86BakDodP-29
❑ 87BakDodP-12
❑ 88FloStaLAS-25
❑ 88VerBeaDS-24
❑ 89SanAntMB-1
❑ 90SanAntMGS-29
❑ 91LinDriAA-546
❑ 91SanAntMLD-546
❑ 91SanAntMP-2990
❑ 92BinMetF-531
❑ 92BinMetS-72
❑ 92SkyAA F-34

White, Mike (Joyner M.)

❑ 64Top-492
❑ 65AstJayP-11
❑ 65OPC-31
❑ 65Top-31
❑ 66SeaPop-30
❑ 78TCM60I-155

White, Mike EQMG

❑ 98HagSunM-4

White, Myron

❑ 77LodDodT-24
❑ 80AlbDukTc-12
❑ 90DodTar-853

White, Oliver Kirby

❑ 09ColChiE-305
❑ 10PirTipTD-23
❑ 11PinT-5-875
❑ 11S74Sil-115
❑ 11SpoLifCW-365
❑ 11T205-180
❑ 12ColRedB-305
❑ 12ColTinT-305

White, Phil

❑ 91AdeGiaF-13

White, Randy

❑ 83GreHorT-13
❑ 89IdaFalBP-2034

White, Reggie

❑ 91UppDecS-2

White, Rhett

❑ 89BirBarB-30

White, Rich

❑ 80UtiBluJT-2

White, Rick

❑ 91AugPirC-12
❑ 91AugPirP-806
❑ 92SalBucC-24
❑ 92SalBucF-65
❑ 93CarMudF-2055
❑ 93ClaFS7-35
❑ 94Bow-190
❑ 94Fin-383
❑ 94FinRef-383
❑ 94Fla-221
❑ 94FlaWavotF-A10
❑ 94FleExtB-354
❑ 94FleExtBRS-19
❑ 94FleUpd-177
❑ 94LeaLimR-13
❑ 94Pin-533
❑ 94PinArtP-533
❑ 94PinMusC-533
❑ 94PirQui-27
❑ 94SP-145
❑ 94SPDieC-145
❑ 94StaClu-589
❑ 94StaCluFDI-589
❑ 94StaCluGR-589
❑ 94StaCluMOP-589
❑ 94TopTra-121T
❑ 94Ult-561
❑ 95ColCho-383
❑ 95ColChoGS-383
❑ 95ColChoSS-383
❑ 95Don-35
❑ 95DonPreP-35
❑ 95Fle-492
❑ 95Lea-152
❑ 95Pac-354
❑ 95PirFil-29
❑ 95Sco-217
❑ 95ScoGolR-217
❑ 95ScoPlaTS-217
❑ 95StaClu-399
❑ 95StaCluMOP-399
❑ 95StaCluSTWS-399
❑ 95Ult-220
❑ 95UltGolM-220
❑ 97BriWhiSB-28
❑ 97OrlRayB-27
❑ 98DurBulTI-28

White, Rondell

❑ 90ClaDraP-24
❑ 90ClaDraP-NNO
❑ 90ClaYel-T80
❑ 91Bow-450
❑ 91Cla/Bes-360
❑ 91Sco-390
❑ 91SumFlyC-25
❑ 91SumFlyP-2350
❑ 91UppDecFE-10F
❑ 92Bow-436
❑ 92ClaFS7-305
❑ 92ProFS7-266
❑ 92UppDec-51
❑ 92UppDec-61
❑ 92UppDecML-33
❑ 92UppDecML-50
❑ 92UppDecML-65
❑ 92UppDecML-276
❑ 92UppDecMLTPHF-TP8
❑ 92WesPalBEC-1
❑ 92WesPalBEF-2102
❑ 93Bow-72
❑ 93ClaFisN-18
❑ 93ClaFS7-36
❑ 93ClaGolF-48
❑ 93ExcAllF-3
❑ 93ExcFS7-67
❑ 93FlaWavotF-18
❑ 93HarSenF-281
❑ 93SP-289
❑ 93Ult-421
❑ 93UppDec-510
❑ 93UppDecGold-510
❑ 94ActPac-25
❑ 94ActPac-64
❑ 94ActPac2G-10G
❑ 94ActPac2GD-10G
❑ 94Bow-360
❑ 94Bow-668
❑ 94BowBes-B33
❑ 94BowBes-X97
❑ 94BowBesR-B33
❑ 94BowBesR-X97
❑ 94Cla-70
❑ 94ClaCreotC-C13
❑ 94ColC-293
❑ 94ColChoGS-293
❑ 94ColChoSS-293
❑ 94Don-320
❑ 94Fin-424
❑ 94FinJum-424
❑ 94FinRef-424
❑ 94Fle-556
❑ 94FleExtB-314
❑ 94FleExtBRS-20
❑ 94FUnPac-3
❑ 94FUnPac-205
❑ 94LeaGolR-2
❑ 94LeaLimR-54
❑ 94OPC-60
❑ 94OttLynF-2909
❑ 94Pac-394
❑ 94Pin-246
❑ 94PinArtP-246
❑ 94PinMusC-246
❑ 94PinNewG-NG19
❑ 94PinRooTP-6
❑ 94Sco-638
❑ 94ScoBoyoS-36
❑ 94ScoGolR-638
❑ 94ScoRoo-RT87
❑ 94ScoRooGR-RT87
❑ 94ScoRooSR-SU14
❑ 94Sel-201
❑ 94SelRooS-RS6
❑ 94SigRooDP-98
❑ 94SigRooDPS-98
❑ 94SP-88
❑ 94SPDieC-88
❑ 94Spo-174
❑ 94SpoRooRS-TR15
❑ 94SpoSha-SH6
❑ 94StaClu-435
❑ 94StaCluFDI-435
❑ 94StaCluGR-435
❑ 94StaCluMOP-435
❑ 94Top-784
❑ 94TopGol-784
❑ 94TopSpa-784
❑ 94TriPla-290
❑ 94Ult-233
❑ 94UppDec-237
❑ 94UppDecED-237
❑ 95Baz-128
❑ 95Bow-437
❑ 95BowBes-R52
❑ 95BowBesR-R52
❑ 95ColCho-235
❑ 95ColChoGS-235
❑ 95ColChoSE-103
❑ 95ColChoSEGS-103
❑ 95ColChoSESS-103
❑ 95ColChoSS-235
❑ 95Don-343
❑ 95DonPreP-343
❑ 95DonTopotO-288
❑ 95Emo-156
❑ 95Fin-5
❑ 95FinRef-5
❑ 95Fla-168
❑ 95Fle-364
❑ 95FleRooS-20
❑ 95Lea-48
❑ 95LeaLim-80
❑ 95LeaLim-128
❑ 95Pac-275
❑ 95Pin-339
❑ 95PinArtP-339
❑ 95PinMusC-339
❑ 95PinUps-US15
❑ 95Sco-147
❑ 95ScoGolR-147
❑ 95ScoHaloG-HG108
❑ 95ScoPlaTS-147
❑ 95Sel-11
❑ 95SelArtP-11
❑ 95SP-76
❑ 95SPCha-63
❑ 95SPCha-67
❑ 95SPChaDC-63
❑ 95SPChaDC-67
❑ 95Spo-129
❑ 95SpoArtP-129
❑ 95SPSil-76
❑ 95SPSpeF-44
❑ 95StaClu-349
❑ 95StaCluMOP-349
❑ 95StaCluSTWS-349
❑ 95StaCluVR-199
❑ 95StaCluVRMO-199
❑ 95Stu-75
❑ 95Top-196
❑ 95TopCyb-112
❑ 95Ult-410
❑ 95UltGolM-410
❑ 95UltSecYS-15
❑ 95UltSecYSGM-15
❑ 95UppDec-83
❑ 95UppDecED-83
❑ 95UppDecEDG-83
❑ 95UppDecSE-140
❑ 95UppDecSEG-140
❑ 95Zen-93
❑ 96Baz-3
❑ 96Bow-65
❑ 96BowFoi-65
❑ 96Cir-153
❑ 96CirRav-153
❑ 96ColCho-215
❑ 96ColChoGS-215
❑ 96ColChoSS-215
❑ 96ColChoYMtP-44
❑ 96ColChoYMtP-44A
❑ 96ColChoYMtPGS-44
❑ 96ColChoYMtPGS-44A
❑ 96Don-408
❑ 96DonPreP-408
❑ 96EmoRarB-10
❑ 96EmoXL-227
❑ 96ExpDis-22
❑ 96ExpDis-23
❑ 96Fin-S52
❑ 96FinRef-S52
❑ 96Fla-314
❑ 96Fle-471
❑ 96FleTeaL-22
❑ 96FleTif-471
❑ 96FleTomL-10
❑ 96Lea-88
❑ 96LeaLim-12
❑ 96LeaLimG-12

❑ 96LeaPre-20
❑ 96LeaPreP-20
❑ 96LeaPrePB-88
❑ 96LeaPrePG-88
❑ 96LeaPrePS-88
❑ 96LeaPreSG-28
❑ 96LeaPreSte-28
❑ 96LeaSig-14
❑ 96LeaSigA-243
❑ 96LeaSigAG-244
❑ 96LeaSigAS-244
❑ 96LeaSigPPG-14
❑ 96LeaSigPPP-14
❑ 96MetUni-196
❑ 96MetUniP-196
❑ 96MetUniPP-10
❑ 96Pac-125
❑ 96PanSti-19
❑ 96Pin-234
❑ 96PinAfi-106
❑ 96PinAfiAP-106
❑ 96PinArtP-134
❑ 96PinFoil-234
❑ 96PinSta-134
❑ 96ProSta-50
❑ 96Sco-50
❑ 96ScoDugC-A43
❑ 96ScoDugCAP-A43
❑ 96Sel-25
❑ 96SelArtP-25
❑ 96SelCer-29
❑ 96SelCerAP-29
❑ 96SelCerCB-29
❑ 96SelCerCR-29
❑ 96SelCerIP-18
❑ 96SelCerMB-29
❑ 96SelCerMG-29
❑ 96SelCerMR-29
❑ 96SelTeaN-24
❑ 96SP-120
❑ 96Spo-64
❑ 96SpoArtP-64
❑ 96SPSpeFX-14
❑ 96SPSpeFXDC-14
❑ 96SPx-39
❑ 96SPxGol-39
❑ 96StaClu-12
❑ 96StaCluEPB-12
❑ 96StaCluEPG-12
❑ 96StaCluEPS-12
❑ 96StaCluMOP-12
❑ 96Stu-122
❑ 96StuPrePB-122
❑ 96StuPrePG-122
❑ 96StuPrePS-122
❑ 96Sum-15
❑ 96SumAbo&B-15
❑ 96SumArtP-15
❑ 96SumFoi-15
❑ 96Top-382
❑ 96TopChr-154
❑ 96TopChrR-154
❑ 96TopGal-116
❑ 96TopGalPPI-116
❑ 96TopLas-80
❑ 96Ult-238
❑ 96UltFreF-10
❑ 96UltFreFGM-10
❑ 96UltGolM-238
❑ 96UltRisS-10
❑ 96UltRisSGM-10
❑ 96UppDec-135
❑ 96Zen-4
❑ 96ZenArtP-4
❑ 96ZenMoz-17
❑ 97Bow-289
❑ 97BowBes-52
❑ 97BowBesAR-52
❑ 97BowBesR-52
❑ 97BowChr-99
❑ 97BowChrI-99
❑ 97BowChrIR-99
❑ 97BowChrR-99
❑ 97BowInt-289
❑ 97Cir-380
❑ 97CirRav-380
❑ 97ColCho-165
❑ 97ColChoTBS-31
❑ 97ColChoTBSWH-31
❑ 97Don-29
❑ 97DonEli-87
❑ 97DonEliGS-87
❑ 97DonGolPP-29
❑ 97DonLim-1
❑ 97DonLim-164
❑ 97DonLimE-1
❑ 97DonLimE-164
❑ 97DonLimENG-1
❑ 97DonLimFotG-12
❑ 97DonPre-58
❑ 97DonPreCttC-58
❑ 97DonSig-13
❑ 97DonSigA-107
❑ 97DonSigAC-132
❑ 97DonSigAM-132
❑ 97DonSigPPP-13
❑ 97DonSilPP-29
❑ 97Fin-296
❑ 97FinEmb-296
❑ 97FinEmbR-296
❑ 97FinRef-296
❑ 97FlaShoLC-67
❑ 97FlaShoLeg0-67
❑ 97FlaShoLeg1-67
❑ 97FlaShoM-A67
❑ 97FlaShoM-B67
❑ 97FlaShoM-C67
❑ 97FlaShoR0-67
❑ 97FlaShoR1-67
❑ 97FlaShoR2-67
❑ 97Fle-389
❑ 97FleTif-389
❑ 97Lea-242
❑ 97LeaFraM-242
❑ 97LeaFraMDC-242
❑ 97LeaWarT-14
❑ 97MetUni-160
❑ 97NewPin-37
❑ 97NewPinAP-37
❑ 97NewPinMC-37
❑ 97NewPinPP-37
❑ 97Pac-356
❑ 97PacLigB-356
❑ 97PacSil-356
❑ 97Pin-56
❑ 97PinArtP-PP56
❑ 97PinCer-98
❑ 97PinCerMBla-98
❑ 97PinCerMBlu-98
❑ 97PinCerMG-98
❑ 97PinCerMR-98
❑ 97PinCerR-98
❑ 97PinIns-104
❑ 97PinInsCE-104
❑ 97PinInsDE-104
❑ 97PinMusC-56
❑ 97PinPrePla-56
❑ 97PinTotCPB-98
❑ 97PinTotCPG-98
❑ 97PinTotCPR-98
❑ 97PinX-P-101
❑ 97PinX-PMoS-101
❑ 97PinX-PSfF-58
❑ 97PinX-PSfFU-58
❑ 97Sco-413
❑ 97ScoArtPWB-413
❑ 97ScoResC-413
❑ 97ScoShoS-413
❑ 97ScoShoSAP-413
❑ 97Sel-89
❑ 97SelArtP-89
❑ 97SelCom-89
❑ 97SelRegG-89
❑ 97SP-115
❑ 97StaClu-224
❑ 97StaCluC-CO9
❑ 97StaCluMat-224
❑ 97StaCluMOP-224
❑ 97Stu-121
❑ 97StuHarH-18
❑ 97StuPrePG-121
❑ 97StuPrePS-121
❑ 97Top-331
❑ 97TopChr-112
❑ 97TopChrR-112
❑ 97TopGal-110
❑ 97TopGalPPI-110
❑ 97Ult-235
❑ 97UltGolME-235
❑ 97UltPlaME-235
❑ 97UppDec-425
❑ 97UppDecRSF-RS13
❑ 98Bow-59
❑ 98BowChr-59
❑ 98BowChrGA-59
❑ 98BowChrGAR-59
❑ 98BowChrI-59
❑ 98BowChrIR-59
❑ 98BowChrR-59
❑ 98BowGolA-59
❑ 98BowInt-59
❑ 98CirThu-239
❑ 98CirThuRav-239
❑ 98CirThuSupRav-239
❑ 98ColCho-170
❑ 98CroRoy-85
❑ 98Don-151
❑ 98DonCol-151
❑ 98DonColE-464
❑ 98DonColL-236
❑ 98DonColP-620
❑ 98DonColS-151
❑ 98DonCruG-83
❑ 98DonCruP-83
❑ 98DonCruR-83
❑ 98DonEli-64
❑ 98DonEliA-64
❑ 98DonEliS-64
❑ 98DonGolPP-151
❑ 98DonPre-70
❑ 98DonPreSeat-70
❑ 98DonPriCD-151
❑ 98DonPriCE-464
❑ 98DonPriCL-236
❑ 98DonPriCP-620
❑ 98DonSig-53
❑ 98DonSigA-92
❑ 98DonSigAC-114
❑ 98DonSigAM-117
❑ 98DonSigP-53
❑ 98DonSigSB-30
❑ 98DonSilPP-151
❑ 98Fin-18
❑ 98FinNo--18
❑ 98FinNo-R-18
❑ 98FinRef-18
❑ 98FlaShoLeg0-76
❑ 98FlaShoLeg1-76
❑ 98FlaShoLeg2-76
❑ 98FlaShoLeg3-76
❑ 98FlaShoLegM-76
❑ 98FlaShoR0-76
❑ 98FlaShoR1-76
❑ 98FlaShoR2-76
❑ 98FlaShoR3-76
❑ 98Fle-108
❑ 98KinDis-24
❑ 98Lea-36
❑ 98LeaFraDA-36
❑ 98LeaFraF-36
❑ 98LeaFraM-36
❑ 98LeaFraM-36
❑ 98LeaFraMDC-36
❑ 98LeaFraMDC-36
❑ 98LeaFraMS-36
❑ 98LeaFraMZ2-36
❑ 98LeaRS-69
❑ 98LeaRSLHolo-69
❑ 98LeaRSLong-69
❑ 98LeaRTrue-69
❑ 98MetUni-38
❑ 98MetUniPMG-38
❑ 98Pac-359
❑ 98PacAur-160
❑ 98PacOme-153
❑ 98PacOmeR-153
❑ 98PacOnl-466
❑ 98PacOnlR-466
❑ 98PacOnlWC-466
❑ 98PacPar-199
❑ 98PacParC-199
❑ 98PacParG-199
❑ 98PacParHS-199
❑ 98PacParPB-199
❑ 98PacParR-199
❑ 98PacPlaB-359
❑ 98PacRedT-359
❑ 98PacSil-359
❑ 98Pin-81
❑ 98PinIns-30
❑ 98PinInsCE-30
❑ 98PinInsDE-30
❑ 98PinPer-71
❑ 98PinPerPP-71
❑ 98PinPlu-60
❑ 98PinPreP-81
❑ 98Revo-91
❑ 98RevoSS-91
❑ 98ScoRT-133
❑ 98ScoRTSS-PP82
❑ 98ScoRTSSAP-PP82
❑ 98ScoRTSSAP1-PP82
❑ 98SkyDugA-30
❑ 98SkyDugAIA-30
❑ 98SP Aut-127
❑ 98SpoIll-124
❑ 98SpoIllEE-124
❑ 98SpoIllFE-124
❑ 98SpoIllWSF-148
❑ 98SpoIllWSFEE-148
❑ 98SpoIllWSFFE-148
❑ 98SPxFin-100
❑ 98SPxFinR-100
❑ 98SPxFinS-100
❑ 98StaCluFDI-178
❑ 98StaCluI-178
❑ 98StaCluOneK-178
❑ 98StaCluPP-178
❑ 98Stu-183
❑ 98StuGPP-183
❑ 98StuSPP-183
❑ 98Top-301
❑ 98TopChr-301
❑ 98TopChrR-301
❑ 98TopDevR-301
❑ 98TopDia-301
❑ 98TopGal-65
❑ 98TopGalGP-65
❑ 98TopGalOPP-65
❑ 98TopGalPPI-65
❑ 98TopGalPPIA-65
❑ 98TopGolLabC1-88
❑ 98TopGolLabC1B-88
❑ 98TopGolLabC1One-88
❑ 98TopGolLabC1R-88
❑ 98TopGolLabC2-88
❑ 98TopGolLabC2B-88
❑ 98TopGolLabC2One-88
❑ 98TopGolLabC2R-88
❑ 98TopGolLabC3-88
❑ 98TopGolLabC3B-88
❑ 98TopGolLabC3One-88
❑ 98TopGolLabC3R-88
❑ 98TopMiniC-301
❑ 98TopOpeD-128
❑ 98TopSta-63
❑ 98TopStaB-63
❑ 98TopStaG-63
❑ 98TopStaGR-63
❑ 98TopStaS-63
❑ 98Ult-6
❑ 98UltGolM-6
❑ 98UltMas-6
❑ 98UltPlaM-6
❑ 98UppDec-160
❑ 98UppDecR-60
❑ 98UppDecSF-85
❑ 99199Fin-59
❑ 99Bow-249
❑ 99BowBes-10
❑ 99BowBesAR-10
❑ 99BowBesR-10
❑ 99BowGol-249
❑ 99BowInt-249
❑ 99E-X Cen-49
❑ 99E-X CenECFut-49
❑ 99E-X CenECNow-49
❑ 99FinGolRef-59
❑ 99FinRef-59
❑ 99FlaShoLeg1-68
❑ 99FlaShoLeg2-68
❑ 99FlaShoLeg3-68
❑ 99FlaShoLegM1-68
❑ 99FlaShoLegM2-68
❑ 99FlaShoLegM3-68
❑ 99FlaShoR1-68
❑ 99FlaShoR2-68
❑ 99FlaShoR3-68
❑ 99Fle-250
❑ 99FleBri-110
❑ 99FleBri2G-110
❑ 99FleBriBlu-110
❑ 99FleBriGol-110
❑ 99FleMys-43
❑ 99FleMysG-43
❑ 99FleMysM-43
❑ 99FleSta9-250
❑ 99FleWarT-250
❑ 99MetUni-54
❑ 99MetUniGM-54
❑ 99MetUniPMG-54
❑ 99PacOme-148
❑ 99PacOmeC-148
❑ 99PacOmeG-148
❑ 99PacOmePB-148
❑ 99PacPar-146
❑ 99PacParC-146
❑ 99PacParG-146
❑ 99PacParHoloGold-146
❑ 99PacParHS-146
❑ 99PacParOD-146
❑ 99PacParPB-146
❑ 99PacParRed-146
❑ 99PacPriS-147
❑ 99PacPriS206-147
❑ 99PacPriS206R-147
❑ 99Rev-87
❑ 99RevPremDate-87
❑ 99RevRet-87
❑ 99RevShaSS-87
❑ 99SkyMolM-19
❑ 99SkyMolMX-19
❑ 99SkyPre-41
❑ 99SkyPreR-41
❑ 99SkyThu-19
❑ 99SkyThuRant-19
❑ 99SkyThuRave-19
❑ 99SP Aut-52
❑ 99SpoIll-119
❑ 99SPx-53
❑ 99SPxFinR-53
❑ 99SPxFinS-53
❑ 99StaClu-258
❑ 99StaCluFDI-258
❑ 99StaCluOoaK-258
❑ 99StaCluPP-258
❑ 99ThuSkySupR-19
❑ 99Top-61
❑ 99TopAut-A6
❑ 99TopBlaLC1-11
❑ 99TopBlaLC2-11
❑ 99TopBlaLC3-11
❑ 99TopChr-61
❑ 99TopChrR-61
❑ 99TopGal-38
❑ 99TopGalPP-38
❑ 99TopGalPPI-38
❑ 99TopGolL-11
❑ 99TopGolLC1-11
❑ 99TopGolLC2-11
❑ 99TopGolLOtO-11
❑ 99TopMVPP-61
❑ 99TopOpeD-33
❑ 99TopRedLC1-11
❑ 99TopRedLC2-11
❑ 99TopRedLC3-11
❑ 99TopSta-70
❑ 99TopSta1Foil-70
❑ 99TopStaFoil-70
❑ 99TopStaOS-70
❑ 99UD Cho-109
❑ 99UD ChoPCR-109
❑ 99Ult-117
❑ 99UltGolM-117
❑ 99UltMas-117
❑ 99UltPlaM-117
❑ 99UppDec-418
❑ 99UppDecCLM-C57
❑ 99UppDecEL1-418
❑ 99UppDecEL2-418
❑ 99UppDecM-124
❑ 99UppDecMGS-124
❑ 99UppDecMHFS-124
❑ 99UppDecMP-124
❑ 99UppDecMSS-124
❑ 99UppDecO-2
❑ 99UppDecOSO-2
❑ 99Vic-240

White, Roy Hilton

❑ 66TopVen-234
❑ 67CokCapYM-V18
❑ 67DexPre-220
❑ 68Top-546
❑ 68YanPhoS-81
❑ 69MilBra-289
❑ 69MLBOffS-81
❑ 69OPC-25
❑ 69Top-25
❑ 69TopSta-210
❑ 69TopSup-26
❑ 69TopTeaP-19
❑ 69TraSta-26
❑ 69YanMal-12
❑ 70DayDaiNM-90
❑ 70MLBOffS-252
❑ 70OPC-373
❑ 70Top-373
❑ 70TopPos-14
❑ 70YanCliDP-2
❑ 70YanPhoS-35
❑ 71Kel-43
❑ 71MilDud-32
❑ 71MLBOffS-503
❑ 71OPC-395
❑ 71Top-395
❑ 71TopCoi-34
❑ 71TopGreM-45
❑ 71TopSup-26
❑ 71TopTat-109
❑ 71YanArcO-12
❑ 71YanCliDP-16
❑ 72MilBra-360
❑ 72OPC-340
❑ 72Top-340
❑ 72TopCloT-33
❑ 72YanSch-7
❑ 72YanTeal-6
❑ 73NewYorSNM-16
❑ 73OPC-25
❑ 73SyrChiTI-29
❑ 73Top-25
❑ 73Yan-6
❑ 74OPC-135
❑ 74SyrChiTI-29
❑ 74Top-135
❑ 74TopSta-220
❑ 75Kel-1
❑ 75OPC-375
❑ 75SyrChiTI-23
❑ 75Top-375
❑ 75TopMin-375
❑ 75YanSSP-6
❑ 76OPC-225
❑ 76SSP-435
❑ 76Top-225
❑ 77BurCheD-179
❑ 77OPC-182
❑ 77Top-485
❑ 77YanBurK-19
❑ 78OPC-48
❑ 78SSP270-8
❑ 78Top-16
❑ 78YanBurK-19
❑ 78YanPhoA-27
❑ 78YanSSPD-8
❑ 79OPC-75
❑ 79Top-159
❑ 79YanBurK-19
❑ 79YanPicA-34
❑ 80OPC-341
❑ 80Top-648
❑ 81TCM60I-453
❑ 83YanASFY-50
❑ 83YanPhoA-3
❑ 86YanTCM-29
❑ 90SweBasG-42
❑ 91SweBasG-97
❑ 92ActPacA-34
❑ 92YanWIZ6-136
❑ 92YanWIZ7-164
❑ 92YanWIZA-85
❑ 99SpoIllGotG-51
❑ 99SpoIllGotGA-76

White, Sammy

❑ 47PM1StaP1-216
❑ 52Top-345
❑ 53BowC-41
❑ 53RedSoxFNSMS-4
❑ 53RedSoxTI-28
❑ 53Top-139
❑ 54Bow-34
❑ 54RedHeaF-31
❑ 54RedMan-AL14
❑ 54Wil-19
❑ 55Bow-47
❑ 56Top-168
❑ 57Top-163
❑ 58Hir-53
❑ 58RedSoxJP-11
❑ 58Top-414
❑ 59RedSoxJP-11
❑ 59Top-486
❑ 60Top-203
❑ 62Top-494
❑ 79DiaGre-248
❑ 79TCM50-95
❑ 81RedSoxBG2S-59
❑ 83TopRep5-345
❑ 86RedSoxGT-1
❑ 91TopArc1-139

White, Sol

❑ 78LauLonABS-22

White, Steve

❑ 93CedRapKC-23
❑ 93CedRapKF-1739

White, Tom

❑ 77ReaPhiT-23

White, Trey

❑ 95PorCitRTI-27

White, Walter

❑ 94ElmPioC-23
❑ 94ElmPioF-3485
❑ 95KanCouCTI-21
❑ 96KanCouCTI-28
❑ 96MidLeaAB-35
❑ 97BreCouMB-29

White, William D.
❑ 87OldJudN-536
Whitecaps, Brewster
❑ 88CapCodPB-21
Whited, Ed
❑ 86AubAstP-26
❑ 87AshTouP-24
❑ 88GreBraB-1
❑ 88SouLeaAJ-16
❑ 89BraDub-29
❑ 89RicBraBC-27
❑ 89RicBraC-21
❑ 89RicBraP-837
❑ 89RicBraTI-23
❑ 90CMC-293
❑ 90OPC-111
❑ 90ProAAAF-413
❑ 90RicBraBC-16
❑ 90RicBraC-17
❑ 90RicBraP-268
❑ 90RicBraTI-29
❑ 90Sco-644
❑ 90Sco100RS-78
❑ 90Top-111
❑ 90TopDeb89-140
❑ 90TopTif-111
❑ 90UppDec-447
Whitehead, Braxton
❑ 98ChaAllCM-14
Whitehead, Chris
❑ 88ElmPioC-21
❑ 90LynRedSTI-10
Whitehead, James
❑ 89WinHavRSS-27
Whitehead, John
❑ 36GouWidPPR-A115
❑ 36GouWidPPR-C25
❑ 72TCMthe1-173
❑ 92ConTSN-568
Whitehead, Milton
❑ 88SFHesCreN32-36
Whitehead, Steve
❑ 76QuaCitAT-39
❑ 89JamExpP-2140
❑ 90RocExpLC-27
❑ 90RocExpP-2687
❑ 91RocExpC-28
❑ 91RocExpP-2048
❑ 92MidLeaATI-50
❑ 92RocExpC-17
❑ 92RocExpF-2117
Whitehead, Whitey (Burgess)
❑ 33ButCanV-53
❑ 33WorCig-101
❑ 34DiaStaR-51
❑ 36GouWidPPR-A114
❑ 36WorWidGV-59
❑ 38CloFotW-90
❑ 39PlaBal-23
❑ 40PlaBal-92
❑ 41DouPlaR-27
❑ 41DouPlaR-89
❑ 74Car193T-26
❑ 79DiaGre-38
Whitehill, Earl
❑ 28Exh-47
❑ 29PorandAR-97
❑ 33ButCanV-54
❑ 33Gou-124
❑ 33TatOrbSDR-165
❑ 34BabRutG-65
❑ 34ButPreR-64
❑ 35AlDemDCR3-67
❑ 35ExhFou-16
❑ 35GouPuzR-8H
❑ 35GouPuzR-9H
❑ 36ExhFou-16
❑ 36GouWidPPR-B25
❑ 36R31PasP-27
❑ 36WorWidGV-60
❑ 38CloFotW-91
❑ 39CubTeal-24
❑ 72TCMthe1-178
❑ 81TigDetN-31
❑ 83ConMar-21
❑ 87ConSer2-60
❑ 88ConAmeA-24
❑ 91ConTSN-127
Whitehouse, Len
❑ 77AshTouT-26
❑ 78AshTouT-27
❑ 79TulDriT-3
❑ 83TopTra-126T
❑ 83TwiTeal-15
❑ 84Don-558
❑ 84Fle-578
❑ 84Nes792-648
❑ 84Top-648
❑ 84TopTif-648
❑ 85Don-513
❑ 85TolMudHT-12
❑ 85Top-406
❑ 85TopTif-406
❑ 85TwiPos-32
❑ 85TwiTeal-17
❑ 93RanKee-378
Whitehurst, Todd
❑ 91BurIndP-3312
❑ 94PitMetC-23
❑ 94PitMetF-3531
❑ 95StLucMTI-34
Whitehurst, Tom
❑ 98PorRocG-30
Whitehurst, Wally
❑ 86HunStaDJ-23
❑ 86MadMusP-23
❑ 86MadMusP-27
❑ 87HunStaTI-24
❑ 88TidTidCa-29
❑ 88TidTidCM-11
❑ 88TidTidP-1589
❑ 89Bow-373
❑ 89BowTif-373
❑ 89FleUpd-103
❑ 89MetColP-58
❑ 89TidTidC-6
❑ 89TidTidP-1958
❑ 89UppDec-737
❑ 90MetColP-53
❑ 90MetKah-47
❑ 90OPC-719
❑ 90Sco-599
❑ 90Top-719
❑ 90TopDeb89-141
❑ 90TopTif-719
❑ 90TopTVM-19
❑ 90UppDec-564
❑ 91Bow-470
❑ 91Don-511
❑ 91Fle-166
❑ 91Lea-333
❑ 91MetColP-51
❑ 91MetKah-47
❑ 91MetPerPA-30
❑ 91MetWIZ-429
❑ 91OPC-557
❑ 91Sco-529
❑ 91Sco100RS-91
❑ 91SouOreAAP-SOA24
❑ 91StaClu-458
❑ 91Top-557
❑ 91TopDesS-557
❑ 91TopMic-557
❑ 91TopTif-557
❑ 91ToyRoo-32
❑ 91UppDec-221
❑ 92Don-134
❑ 92Fle-519
❑ 92MetColP-20
❑ 92MetKah-47
❑ 92OPC-419
❑ 92Sco-299
❑ 92StaClu-476
❑ 92Top-419
❑ 92TopGol-419
❑ 92TopGolW-419
❑ 92TopMic-419
❑ 92UppDec-414
❑ 93Don-602
❑ 93FleFinE-147
❑ 93PadMot-24
❑ 93Top-271
❑ 93TopGol-271
❑ 93TopInaM-271
❑ 93TopInaR-271
❑ 93TopMic-271
❑ 94ColC-381
❑ 94ColChoGS-381
❑ 94ColChoSS-381
❑ 94Fla-237
❑ 94Fle-678
❑ 94FleExtB-380
❑ 94Lea-216
❑ 94Pac-537
❑ 94PadMot-6
❑ 94Pin-109
❑ 94PinArtP-109
❑ 94PinMusC-109
❑ 94StaClu-652
❑ 94StaCluFDI-652
❑ 94StaCluGR-652
❑ 94StaCluMOP-652
❑ 94Top-486
❑ 94TopGol-486
❑ 94TopSpa-486
❑ 94Ult-284
❑ 94UppDec-129
❑ 94UppDecED-129
Whiteley, Shad
❑ 98OneYanG-31
Whiteman, Charles
❑ 19W514-119
Whiteman, Greg
❑ 94JamJamC-26
❑ 94JamJamF-3965
❑ 94SigRooDP-67
❑ 94SigRooDPS-67
❑ 95FayGenTI-27
❑ 96Bow-162
❑ 96BowFoi-162
❑ 96LakTigB-30
❑ 98ClePhiM-24
❑ 98ClePhiUM-24
Whiteman, Tony
❑ 94BriTigC-27
❑ 94BriTigF-3504
❑ 95FayGenTI-28
Whiteman, Trevor
❑ 97AubDouTI-22
Whiten, Mark
❑ 87MyrBeaBJP-1458
❑ 88DunBluJS-21
❑ 89KnoBluJB-26
❑ 89KnoBluJS-21
❑ 90CMC-350
❑ 90FleUpd-130
❑ 90Lea-396
❑ 90ProAAAF-367
❑ 90SyrChiC-24
❑ 90SyrChiMB-29
❑ 90SyrChiP-587
❑ 90TriAllGP-AAA2
❑ 91BluJayFS-31
❑ 91Bow-13
❑ 91ClaGam-65
❑ 91Don-607
❑ 91DonRoo-32
❑ 91Fle-189
❑ 91FleUpd-21
❑ 91Lea-234
❑ 91MajLeaCP-28
❑ 91OPC-588
❑ 91OPCPre-127
❑ 91Sco-358
❑ 91Sco100RS-24
❑ 91ScoAllF-6
❑ 91StaClu-452
❑ 91Stu-50
❑ 91Top-588
❑ 91TopDeb90-167
❑ 91TopDesS-588
❑ 91TopMic-588
❑ 91TopTif-588
❑ 91TopTra-126T
❑ 91TopTraT-126T
❑ 91Ult-371
❑ 91UltUpd-21
❑ 91UppDec-561
❑ 91UppDecFE-75F
❑ 92Bow-57
❑ 92ClaGam-84
❑ 92Don-325
❑ 92Fle-126
❑ 92IndFanC-29
❑ 92Lea-334
❑ 92LeaBlaG-334
❑ 92LeaGolP-17
❑ 92LeaPre-17
❑ 92OPC-671
❑ 92OPCPre-178
❑ 92PanSti-49
❑ 92Pin-355
❑ 92Sco-587
❑ 92ScoImpP-15
❑ 92StaClu-51
❑ 92Stu-170
❑ 92Top-671
❑ 92TopGol-671
❑ 92TopGolW-671
❑ 92TopKid-74
❑ 92TopMic-671
❑ 92TriPla-95
❑ 92Ult-55
❑ 92UppDec-524
❑ 93Don-97
❑ 93Fla-130
❑ 93Fle-223
❑ 93FleFinE-133
❑ 93Lea-449
❑ 93OPC-378
❑ 93PacSpa-103
❑ 93PanSti-54
❑ 93Pin-420
❑ 93Sco-106
❑ 93Sel-146
❑ 93SelRoo-6T
❑ 93SP-81
❑ 93StaClu-352
❑ 93StaCluFDI-352
❑ 93StaCluMO-27
❑ 93StaCluMOP-352
❑ 93Stu-119
❑ 93Top-277
❑ 93TopGol-277
❑ 93TopInaM-277
❑ 93TopInaR-277
❑ 93TopMic-277
❑ 93TopTra-20T
❑ 93TriPla-23
❑ 93Ult-193
❑ 93Ult-468
❑ 93UppDec-227
❑ 93UppDec-654
❑ 93UppDecGold-227
❑ 93UppDecGold-654
❑ 94Bow-40
❑ 94CarPol-25
❑ 94ColC-294
❑ 94ColChoGS-294
❑ 94ColChoSS-294
❑ 94Don-311
❑ 94Fin-116
❑ 94FinRef-116
❑ 94Fla-229
❑ 94Fle-649
❑ 94FleExtB-365
❑ 94FleGolM-1
❑ 94FleGolMJ-1
❑ 94FUnPac-118
❑ 94Lea-29
❑ 94LeaL-148
❑ 94OPC-120
❑ 94Pac-607
❑ 94PanSti-250
❑ 94Pin-153
❑ 94PinArtP-153
❑ 94PinMusC-153
❑ 94PinPowS-PS20
❑ 94PinTri-TR11
❑ 94Pos-19
❑ 94ProMag-112
❑ 94Sco-315
❑ 94Sco-440
❑ 94ScoGolR-315
❑ 94ScoGolR-440
❑ 94Sel-164
❑ 94SP-67
❑ 94SPDieC-67
❑ 94Spo-142
❑ 94StaClu-37
❑ 94StaCluFDI-37
❑ 94StaCluGR-37
❑ 94StaCluMOP-37
❑ 94StaCluT-305
❑ 94StaCluTFDI-305
❑ 94Stu-56
❑ 94Top-54
❑ 94TopGol-54
❑ 94TopSpa-54
❑ 94TriPla-69
❑ 94Ult-273
❑ 94UppDec-150
❑ 94UppDecED-150
❑ 95Bow-306
❑ 95ColCho-58
❑ 95ColCho-195
❑ 95ColCho-576T
❑ 95ColChoGS-58
❑ 95ColChoGS-195
❑ 95ColChoSE-79
❑ 95ColChoSEGS-79
❑ 95ColChoSESS-79
❑ 95ColChoSS-58
❑ 95ColChoSS-195
❑ 95Don-79
❑ 95DonPreP-79
❑ 95Fin-147
❑ 95Fin-265
❑ 95FinRef-147
❑ 95FinRef-265
❑ 95Fla-197
❑ 95Fla-232
❑ 95Fle-512
❑ 95FleUpd-16
❑ 95Lea-384
❑ 95Pac-418
❑ 95Pin-3
❑ 95PinArtP-3
❑ 95PinMusC-3
❑ 95Sco-376
❑ 95ScoGolR-376
❑ 95ScoHaloG-HG106
❑ 95ScoPlaTS-376
❑ 95StaClu-462
❑ 95StaClu-574
❑ 95StaCluMOP-462
❑ 95StaCluMOP-574
❑ 95StaCluMOP-SS10
❑ 95StaCluSS-SS10
❑ 95StaCluSTWS-462
❑ 95StaCluSTWS-574
❑ 95StaCluVR-251
❑ 95StaCluVRMO-251
❑ 95Stu-107
❑ 95Top-409
❑ 95TopCyb-209
❑ 95TopEmb-88
❑ 95TopEmbGI-88
❑ 95TopTra-102T
❑ 95UC3-83
❑ 95UC3ArtP-83
❑ 95Ult-229
❑ 95UltGolM-229
❑ 95UppDec-62
❑ 95UppDec-478
❑ 95UppDecED-62
❑ 95UppDecEDG-62
❑ 95UppDecSE-214
❑ 95UppDecSEG-214
❑ 96ColCho-673
❑ 96ColChoGS-673
❑ 96ColChoSS-673
❑ 96Don-123
❑ 96DonPreP-123
❑ 96EmoXL-250
❑ 96Fla-341
❑ 96Fle-512
❑ 96FleTif-512
❑ 96Pac-162
❑ 96PhiTeal-34
❑ 96Pin-128
❑ 96Sco-387
❑ 96Ult-529
❑ 96UltGolM-529
❑ 96UppDec-426
❑ 97Don-352
❑ 97DonGolPP-352
❑ 97DonSilPP-352
❑ 97Fle-639
❑ 97FleTif-639
❑ 97Lea-301
❑ 97LeaFraM-301
❑ 97LeaFraMDC-301
❑ 97MarSco-11
❑ 97MarScoPl-11
❑ 97MarScoPr-11
❑ 97Pin-19
❑ 97PinArtP-PP19
❑ 97PinMusC-19
❑ 97PinPrePla-19
❑ 97Sco-216
❑ 97Sco-354
❑ 97ScoArtPWB-216
❑ 97ScoArtPWB-354
❑ 97ScoPreS-216
❑ 97ScoResC-354
❑ 97ScoShoS-216
❑ 97ScoShoS-354
❑ 97ScoShoSAP-216
❑ 97ScoShoSAP-354
❑ 97Top-322
❑ 97Ult-352
❑ 97UltGolME-352
❑ 97UltPlaME-352
❑ 97UppDec-317
Whiteside, Matt
❑ 90ButCopKSP-29
❑ 91GasRanC-12
❑ 91GasRanP-2689
❑ 92ProFS7-157
❑ 92SkyAA F-277
❑ 92TulDriF-2697
❑ 92TulDriS-623
❑ 93Bow-283
❑ 93FleFinE-285
❑ 93Lea-508
❑ 93PacSpa-649
❑ 93Pin-590
❑ 93RanKee-435
❑ 93RanStaC-3
❑ 93SelRoo-41T
❑ 93StaClu-474
❑ 93StaCluFDI-474
❑ 93StaCluMOP-474
❑ 93Top-468
❑ 93TopGol-468
❑ 93TopInaM-468
❑ 93TopInaR-468
❑ 93TopMic-468
❑ 93Ult-638
❑ 93UppDec-390
❑ 93UppDecGold-390
❑ 94Don-606
❑ 94Fle-323
❑ 94Pac-631
❑ 94RanMagM-39
❑ 94Sco-304
❑ 94ScoGolR-304
❑ 94StaClu-502
❑ 94StaCluFDI-502
❑ 94StaCluGR-502
❑ 94StaCluMOP-502
❑ 94StaCluT-266
❑ 94StaCluTFDI-266
❑ 94Top-629
❑ 94TopGol-629
❑ 94TopSpa-629
❑ 94Ult-433
❑ 95Don-222
❑ 95DonPreP-222
❑ 95Fla-93
❑ 95Fle-298
❑ 95RanCra-36
❑ 95Top-254
❑ 95Ult-115
❑ 95UltGolM-115
❑ 96ColCho-736
❑ 96ColChoGS-736
❑ 96ColChoSS-736
❑ 96Fle-266
❑ 96FleTif-266
❑ 96LeaSigEA-212
❑ 96OklCit8B-24
❑ 96RanDr P-33
❑ 96RanFle-18
❑ 97OklCit8-25
Whiteside, Sean
❑ 92NiaFalRC-21
❑ 92NiaFalRF-3324
❑ 93FayGenC-24
❑ 93FayGenF-130
❑ 94LakTigC-25
❑ 94LakTigF-3037
❑ 95Bow-167
❑ 95FleUpd-24
❑ 95JacSunTI-27
❑ 95SigRoo-48
❑ 95SigRooSig-48
❑ 96JacSunB-29
Whitfield, Cat
❑ 80ChaO'sP-23
❑ 80ChaO'sW-24
Whitfield, Fred
❑ 62KahAtl-24
❑ 63Top-211
❑ 64Kah-31
❑ 64Top-367
❑ 64TopRooAB-11
❑ 64TopVen-367
❑ 65OPC-283
❑ 65Top-283
❑ 66IndVolC-12
❑ 66Kah-32
❑ 66OPC-88
❑ 66Top-88
❑ 66TopVen-88
❑ 67CokCapI-13
❑ 67DexPre-221
❑ 67Kah-40A
❑ 67Kah-40B
❑ 67Top-275
❑ 67TopVen-249
❑ 68OPC-133
❑ 68Top-133
❑ 68TopVen-133
❑ 69MilBra-290
❑ 69Top-518
Whitfield, Ken
❑ 85KinBluJT-22
❑ 86KinEagP-25
❑ 89KinIndS-24
❑ 90RenSilSCLC-262
❑ 91CanIndLD-98
❑ 91CanIndP-994
❑ 91LinDriAA-98

Whitfield, Terry
❑ 75OPC-622
❑ 75SyrChiTI-24
❑ 75Top-622
❑ 75TopMin-622
❑ 76OPC-590
❑ 76SSP-443
❑ 76Top-590
❑ 76VenLeaS-34
❑ 77GiaTeal-24
❑ 78GiaTeal-24
❑ 78Hos-136
❑ 78Top-236
❑ 79GiaPol-45
❑ 79Hos-10
❑ 79OPC-309
❑ 79Top-589
❑ 80GiaPol-45
❑ 80GiaTeal-28
❑ 80OPC-361
❑ 80Top-713
❑ 81Don-435
❑ 81Fle-437
❑ 81Top-167
❑ 81TopScr-87
❑ 81TopSti-233
❑ 84DodPol-45
❑ 84FleUpd-125
❑ 85DodCokP-33
❑ 85Don-540
❑ 85Fle-389
❑ 85Top-31
❑ 85TopTif-31
❑ 86DodCokP-33
❑ 86DodPol-45
❑ 86Don-337
❑ 86Fle-147
❑ 86Top-318
❑ 86TopTif-318
❑ 90DodTar-854
❑ 92YanWIZ7-165

Whitford, Eric
❑ 92ClaFS7-238
❑ 92StoPorC-17
❑ 92StoPorF-44
❑ 93StoPorC-26

Whitford, Larry
❑ 86BelBreP-26

Whiting, Don
❑ 78HolMilT-23
❑ 79HolMilT-15
❑ 82ElPasDT-9
❑ 83BelBreFr-14

Whiting, John
❑ 75BurBeeT-29

Whiting, Mike
❑ 86ElmPioRSP-28

Whitley, Curtis
❑ 97HicCraB-30
❑ 98HicCraM-30

Whitley, Kyle
❑ 96ButCopKB-30

Whitley, Matt
❑ 96AshTouB-30
❑ 97AshTou-26
❑ 98SalAvaC-29

Whitlock, Brian
❑ 96WatIndTI-33
❑ 98KinIndQ-25

Whitlock, Mike
❑ 88BelBreGS-22
❑ 89St.LucMS-24
❑ 96HagSunB-23
❑ 97DunBluJTI-30
❑ 97FloStaLTPB-10
❑ 98St.CatSM-9

Whitman, Dick
❑ 46DodTeal-25
❑ 49EurSta-51
❑ 50PhiPhil-24
❑ 51Bow-221
❑ 75Phi195T-31
❑ 76TayBow4-74
❑ 80Phi195T-31
❑ 84TCMPla1-28
❑ 90DodTar-855

Whitman, Jim
❑ 91EriSaiC-13
❑ 91EriSaiP-4083

Whitman, Ryan
❑ 92EriSaiC-9
❑ 92EriSaiF-1625
❑ 93Top-558
❑ 93TopGol-558
❑ 93TopInaM-558
❑ 93TopInaR-558
❑ 93TopMic-558
❑ 94WicWraF-191
❑ 95RanCucQT-14

Whitmayer, Kurt
❑ 78OrlTwiT-23

Whitmer, Dan
❑ 79SalLakCGT-19B
❑ 80SalLakCGT-2
❑ 81SyrChiTI-23
❑ 82KnoBluJT-11
❑ 82SyrChiT-28
❑ 82SyrChiTI-24
❑ 83KnoBluJT-9
❑ 93TigGat-28

Whitmer, Joe
❑ 83ChaLooT-4
❑ 84ChaLooT-16
❑ 85CalCanC-99

Whitmore, Darrell
❑ 90BurIndP-3025
❑ 91WatIndP-3385
❑ 92ClaFS7-156
❑ 92KinIndC-22
❑ 92KinIndF-2490
❑ 93Bow-206
❑ 93ClaFS7-268
❑ 93EdmTraF-1150
❑ 93FlaWavotF-19
❑ 93FlaWavotF-20
❑ 93FleFinE-74
❑ 93MarlStaClu-24
❑ 93MarPub-26
❑ 93SelRoo-77T
❑ 93SP-144
❑ 93StaClu-516
❑ 93StaCluFDI-516
❑ 93StaCluMOP-516
❑ 93Top-697
❑ 93TopGol-697
❑ 93TopInaM-697
❑ 93TopInaR-697
❑ 93TopMic-697
❑ 94Bow-123
❑ 94ColC-295
❑ 94ColChoGS-295
❑ 94ColChoSS-295
❑ 94Don-643
❑ 94EdmTraF-2888
❑ 94Fin-147
❑ 94FinRef-147
❑ 94Fle-481
❑ 94MarTeal-17
❑ 94Pac-254
❑ 94Pin-399
❑ 94PinArtP-399
❑ 94PinMusC-399
❑ 94PinNewG-NG25
❑ 94Sco-556
❑ 94ScoBoyoS-57
❑ 94ScoGolR-556
❑ 94StaCluT-77
❑ 94StaCluTFDI-77
❑ 94Top-161
❑ 94TopGol-161
❑ 94TopSpa-161
❑ 94Ult-201
❑ 94UppDec-233
❑ 94UppDecED-233
❑ 95Don-22
❑ 95DonPreP-22
❑ 95Lea-95
❑ 95Pac-179
❑ 95Pin-267
❑ 95PinArtP-267
❑ 95PinMusC-267
❑ 95Top-225
❑ 95TopCyb-127
❑ 95UppDec-351
❑ 95UppDecED-351
❑ 95UppDecEDG-351
❑ 96ChaKniB-29
❑ 96Don-62
❑ 96DonPreP-62
❑ 97SyrSkyCB-26
❑ 98NasSouTI-31
❑ 98NasSouTISS-29

Whitmyer, Steve
❑ 86WatIndP-25

Whitney, Arthur W.
❑ 87BucN28-92
❑ 87OldJudN-538
❑ 89SFHaCN-21

Whitney, G.
❑ 87OldJudN-539

Whitney, Jacob
❑ 98AubDouTI-30

Whitney, James
❑ 87BucN28-117
❑ 87OldJudN-537
❑ 88AugBecN-37
❑ 88WG1CarG-71

Whitney, Jeff
❑ 87ModA'sC-21
❑ 90RenSilSCLC-278

Whitney, Merton
❑ 08BufBisFJO-19
❑ 27Zee-41

Whitney, Pinky (Arthur C.)
❑ 29ExhFou-12
❑ 29PorandAR-98
❑ 31Exh-11
❑ 32OrbPinUP-60
❑ 33DouDisP-42
❑ 33RitCE-12C
❑ 33TatOrb-60
❑ 34DiaMatCSB-196
❑ 36ExhFou-1
❑ 36NatChiFPR-81
❑ 37ExhFou-6
❑ 38ExhFou-6
❑ 38WheBB10-12
❑ 39PlaBal-98
❑ 79DiaGre-214
❑ 83PhiPosGPaM-10
❑ 85BigLeaC3-28
❑ 91ConTSN-288

Whitney, Rod
❑ 25Zee-163
❑ 26Zee-64
❑ 28Zee-63

Whitson, Anthony
❑ 87WytCubP-1
❑ 89ChaWheB-14

Whitson, Ed
❑ 77ColCliT-22
❑ 78ColCliT-27
❑ 79Top-189
❑ 80GiaPol-32
❑ 80GiaTeal-29
❑ 80Top-561
❑ 81Don-74
❑ 81Fle-444
❑ 81GiaTeal-21
❑ 81OPC-336
❑ 81Top-336
❑ 81TopSti-240
❑ 82Don-251
❑ 82Fle-402
❑ 82Ind-36
❑ 82IndWhe-20
❑ 82Top-656
❑ 82TopTra-127T
❑ 83Don-137
❑ 83Don-389
❑ 83Fle-423
❑ 83PadTeal-30
❑ 83Top-429
❑ 83TopTra-127T
❑ 84Don-528
❑ 84Fle-316
❑ 84GiaMot-26
❑ 84Nes792-277
❑ 84PadMot-15
❑ 84PadSmo-27
❑ 84Top-277
❑ 84TopTif-277
❑ 85Don-446
❑ 85Fle-47
❑ 85FleUpd-129
❑ 85OPC-98
❑ 85Top-762
❑ 85TopMin-762
❑ 85TopSti-152
❑ 85TopTif-762
❑ 85TopTifT-130T
❑ 85TopTra-130T
❑ 85YanTCMP-20
❑ 86Don-225
❑ 86Fle-120
❑ 86OPC-15
❑ 86Top-15
❑ 86TopSti-301
❑ 86TopTif-15
❑ 86YanTCM-17
❑ 87Don-360
❑ 87Fle-434
❑ 87FleGlo-434
❑ 87PadBohHB-31
❑ 87Top-155
❑ 87TopTif-155
❑ 88Don-81
❑ 88DonBasB-322
❑ 88Fle-599
❑ 88FleGlo-599
❑ 88OPC-330
❑ 88PadCok-31
❑ 88PadSmo-30
❑ 88PanSti-401
❑ 88RedFolSB-101
❑ 88Sco-167
❑ 88ScoGlo-167
❑ 88StaLinPa-13
❑ 88Top-330
❑ 88TopBig-186
❑ 88TopSti-107
❑ 88TopTif-330
❑ 89Bow-449
❑ 89BowTif-449
❑ 89Don-229
❑ 89DonBasB-210
❑ 89Fle-321
❑ 89FleGlo-321
❑ 89OPC-21
❑ 89PadCok-20
❑ 89PadMag-22
❑ 89PadPos-35
❑ 89Sco-329
❑ 89Top-516
❑ 89TopBig-81
❑ 89TopTif-516
❑ 89UppDec-453
❑ 90Bow-204
❑ 90BowTif-204
❑ 90Don-26
❑ 90Don-205
❑ 90DonBesN-98
❑ 90DonSupD-26
❑ 90Fle-171
❑ 90FleCan-171
❑ 90Lea-246
❑ 90OPC-618
❑ 90PadCok-20
❑ 90PadMag-12
❑ 90PanSti-347
❑ 90PubIntS-62
❑ 90Sco-373
❑ 90Sco100S-69
❑ 90Spo-212
❑ 90Top-618
❑ 90TopBig-152
❑ 90TopMinL-82
❑ 90TopSti-107
❑ 90TopTif-618
❑ 90UppDec-308
❑ 91Bow-651
❑ 91Don-186
❑ 91Fle-547
❑ 91Lea-337
❑ 91OPC-481
❑ 91PadMag-14
❑ 91PadSmo-39
❑ 91PanCanT1-67
❑ 91PanFreS-98
❑ 91PanSti-91
❑ 91Sco-789
❑ 91StaClu-246
❑ 91Stu-250
❑ 91Top-481
❑ 91TopDesS-481
❑ 91TopMic-481
❑ 91TopTif-481
❑ 91Ult-313
❑ 91UppDec-312
❑ 92Don-380
❑ 92Fle-624
❑ 92OPC-228
❑ 92PadCarJ-24
❑ 92Pin-104
❑ 92Sco-564
❑ 92StaClu-172
❑ 92Top-228
❑ 92TopGol-228
❑ 92TopGolW-228
❑ 92TopMic-228
❑ 92UppDec-103
❑ 92YanWIZ8-202

Whitson, Eric
❑ 95OdgRapTI-28
❑ 96HudValRB-13

Whitson, Tony
❑ 88WytCubP-1984
❑ 89ChaWheP-1763

Whitt, Ernie
❑ 78SyrChiT-20
❑ 78Top-708
❑ 79SyrChiT-3
❑ 79SyrChiTI-12
❑ 79Top-714
❑ 80VenLeaS-62
❑ 81Don-390
❑ 81Fle-411
❑ 81OPC-282
❑ 81OPCPos-20
❑ 81Top-407
❑ 82BluJayS-18
❑ 82Don-381
❑ 82Fle-626
❑ 82OPC-19
❑ 82OPCPos-3
❑ 82Top-19
❑ 82TopSti-247
❑ 83Don-304
❑ 83Fle-443
❑ 83OPC-302
❑ 83Top-302
❑ 83TopSti-131
❑ 84BluJayFS-32
❑ 84Don-437
❑ 84Fle-169
❑ 84Nes792-506
❑ 84OPC-106
❑ 84Top-506
❑ 84TopSti-373
❑ 84TopTif-506
❑ 85AllGamPI-44
❑ 85BluJayCC-9
❑ 85BluJayFS-32
❑ 85BluJayPLP-5
❑ 85Don-268
❑ 85Fle-119
❑ 85Lea-181
❑ 85OPC-128
❑ 85Top-128
❑ 85TopMin-128
❑ 85TopTif-128
❑ 86BasStaB-120
❑ 86BluJayAF-24
❑ 86BluJayFS-32
❑ 86Don-559
❑ 86DonAll-48
❑ 86Fle-73
❑ 86GenMilB-3J
❑ 86Lea-217
❑ 86OPC-136
❑ 86Top-673
❑ 86TopTif-673
❑ 87BluJayFS-34
❑ 87Don-148
❑ 87DonHig-39
❑ 87DonOpeD-33
❑ 87Fle-240
❑ 87FleGlo-240
❑ 87GenMilB-1J
❑ 87HosSti-2
❑ 87Lea-69
❑ 87OPC-221
❑ 87StuPan-28
❑ 87SyrChi1A-5
❑ 87Top-698
❑ 87TopTif-698
❑ 88BluJayFS-32
❑ 88Don-394
❑ 88Fle-126
❑ 88FleGlo-126
❑ 88Lea-250
❑ 88MSAHosD-16
❑ 88OPC-79
❑ 88PanSti-216
❑ 88Sco-168
❑ 88ScoGlo-168
❑ 88StaLinBJ-20
❑ 88Top-79
❑ 88TopBig-239
❑ 88TopSti-187
❑ 88TopTif-79
❑ 89BluJayFS-31
❑ 89Bow-248
❑ 89BowTif-248
❑ 89Don-591
❑ 89DonBasB-255
❑ 89Fle-248
❑ 89FleGlo-248
❑ 89OPC-289
❑ 89Sco-98
❑ 89Top-289
❑ 89TopBig-224
❑ 89TopTif-289
❑ 89UppDec-118
❑ 90BluJayHS-4
❑ 90Bow-16
❑ 90BowTif-16
❑ 90BraDubP-30
❑ 90BraDubS-34
❑ 90Don-385
❑ 90Fle-97
❑ 90FleCan-97
❑ 90Lea-408
❑ 90OPC-742
❑ 90PubIntS-529
❑ 90Sco-433
❑ 90ScoRoo-30T
❑ 90Top-742
❑ 90TopSti-189
❑ 90TopTif-742
❑ 90TopTra-128T
❑ 90TopTraT-128T
❑ 90UppDec-148
❑ 91BalOriP-33
❑ 91Lea-391
❑ 91OPC-492
❑ 91OriCro-501
❑ 91Top-492
❑ 91TopDesS-492
❑ 91TopMic-492
❑ 91TopTif-492
❑ 92Nab-34
❑ 93BluJayDM-6
❑ 95StCatSTI-31
❑ 96BluJayOH-35
❑ 97BluJayS-39

Whitt, Mike
❑ 85EveGiaC-18
❑ 85EveGialC-22
❑ 86CliGiaP-27

Whittaker, Jerry
❑ 94SigRooDP-52
❑ 94SigRooDPS-52
❑ 94StaCluDP-24
❑ 94StaCluDPFDI-24
❑ 98BirBarG-28

Whittaker, Stewart
❑ 89GeoColC-36

Whitted, Possum (George)
❑ 14B18B-90A
❑ 14B18B-90B
❑ 15CraJacE-151
❑ 15SpoNewM-190
❑ 16FleBreD-100
❑ 16SpoNewM-189
❑ 17ColE13-188
❑ 17HolBreD-115
❑ 19W514-92
❑ 20NatCarE-108A
❑ 20NatCarE-108B
❑ 21E121So1-114A
❑ 21E121So1-114B
❑ 21E121So8-107
❑ 21Exh-185
❑ 22W575-148
❑ 23W501-81
❑ 23WilChoV-169
❑ 80BraTCM1-23
❑ 90DodTar-856

Whittemore, Reggie
❑ 81BriRedST-5
❑ 83PawRedST-19
❑ 84PawRedST-15
❑ 85TolMudHT-19

Whitten, Casey
❑ 93WatIndC-1
❑ 93WatIndF-3562
❑ 94Bow-167
❑ 94Cla-64
❑ 94ClaGolF-187
❑ 94ExcFS7-51
❑ 94KinIndC-1
❑ 94KinIndF-2643
❑ 94Top-756
❑ 94TopGol-756
❑ 94TopSpa-756
❑ 95SPML-44
❑ 96BesAutS-93
❑ 96BesAutSA-87
❑ 96BowBes-133
❑ 96BowBesAR-133
❑ 96BowBesR-133
❑ 96CanIndB-28
❑ 97BesAutAS-68
❑ 97BesAutP-R18
❑ 97BufBis-28

Whitten, Mike
❑ 93HigDesMC-25
❑ 93HigDesMF-43
❑ 94PorSeaDF-677
❑ 94PorSeaDTI-29
❑ 95BreCouMF-247

Whitty, Todd
❑ 91CalLeLA-51

Whitworth, Clint
❑ 90OklSoo-17
❑ 93OneYanC-25
❑ 93OneYanF-3505
Whitworth, Dick
❑ 87NegLeaPD-13
Whitworth, Ken
❑ 91MiaMirC-12
❑ 91MiaMirP-408
Wick, David
❑ 82WatIndF-13
❑ 82WatIndT-10
Wickander, Kevin
❑ 87KinIndP-2
❑ 88BasAmeAAB-9
❑ 88EasLeaAP-44
❑ 88WilBilP-1315
❑ 89Bow-75
❑ 89BowTif-75
❑ 89ColSprSSC-5
❑ 89ColSprSSP-238
❑ 90Bow-327
❑ 90BowTif-327
❑ 90DonRoo-36
❑ 90IndTeal-44
❑ 90OPC-528
❑ 90Top-528
❑ 90TopDeb89-142
❑ 90TopTif-528
❑ 91ColSprSSLD-98
❑ 91ColSprSSP-2185
❑ 91Don-649
❑ 91Fle-385
❑ 91LinDriAAA-98
❑ 91OPC-246
❑ 91Sco-355
❑ 91Sco100RS-37
❑ 91StaClu-572
❑ 91Top-246
❑ 91TopDesS-246
❑ 91TopMic-246
❑ 91TopTif-246
❑ 92Bow-430
❑ 92ColSprSSS-98
❑ 92SkyAAAF-43
❑ 93Don-389
❑ 93Fle-602
❑ 93IndWUA-32
❑ 93RedKah-28
❑ 93Sco-358
❑ 93Top-358
❑ 93TopGol-358
❑ 93TopInaM-358
❑ 93TopInaR-358
❑ 93TopMic-358
❑ 93Ult-547
❑ 94Fle-431
❑ 94Top-41
❑ 94TopGol-41
❑ 94TopSpa-41
❑ 95TolMudHTI-27
❑ 96BrePol-28
❑ 96FleUpd-U49
❑ 96FleUpdTC-U49
❑ 97DonSigA-108
❑ 97DonSigAC-133
❑ 97DonSigAM-133
Wicker, Bob
❑ 06FanCraNL-51
❑ 11SpoLifCW-366
Wicker, Floyd
❑ 69ExpFudP-14
❑ 69Top-524
❑ 71MLBOffS-456
❑ 71OPC-97
❑ 71Top-97
❑ 94BreMilB-90
Wicker, Kemp
❑ 41DodTeal-11
❑ 72TCMthe3-74
❑ 75YanDyn1T-49
❑ 78DodTCM4-41
❑ 90DodTar-857
Wickersham, Dave
❑ 61Top-381
❑ 62Top-517
❑ 63Top-492
❑ 64TigLid-14
❑ 64Top-181
❑ 64TopCoi-105
❑ 64TopGia-35
❑ 64TopVen-181
❑ 65Baz-25
❑ 65OldLonC-38
❑ 65OPC-9
❑ 65TigJayP-12
❑ 65Top-9
❑ 65Top-375
❑ 65TopTral-34
❑ 66OPC-58
❑ 66TigVolC-12
❑ 66Top-58
❑ 66TopVen-58
❑ 67CokCapTi-4
❑ 67DexPre-222
❑ 67OPC-112
❑ 67TigDexP-10
❑ 67Top-112
❑ 68PirKDK-40
❑ 68PirTeal-23
❑ 68Top-288
❑ 68TopVen-288
❑ 69RoySol-15
❑ 69RoyTeal-12
❑ 69Top-647
❑ 78TCM60I-195
Wickham, Alex
❑ 63GadFunC-73
Wickham, Mike
❑ 89StoPorB-26
❑ 89StoPorS-26
Wickman, Bob (Robert Joe)
❑ 90SouBenWSB-28
❑ 91Bow-353
❑ 91SarWhiSC-11
❑ 91SarWhiSP-1114
❑ 92ColCliF-354
❑ 92ColCliP-13
❑ 92DonRoo-125
❑ 92FleUpd-46
❑ 92UppDec-76
❑ 93Bow-455
❑ 93Don-417
❑ 93Fla-254
❑ 93Fle-288
❑ 93Lea-424
❑ 93Pin-226
❑ 93Sco-291
❑ 93Sel-343
❑ 93SP-269
❑ 93StaClu-53
❑ 93StaCluFDI-53
❑ 93StaCluMOP-53
❑ 93Top-452
❑ 93TopGol-452
❑ 93TopInaM-452
❑ 93TopInaR-452
❑ 93TopMic-452
❑ 93Toy-40
❑ 93TriPla-189
❑ 93Ult-251
❑ 93UppDec-372
❑ 93UppDecGold-372
❑ 93USPlaCR-9H
❑ 93YanStaC-28
❑ 94ColC-296
❑ 94ColChoGS-296
❑ 94ColChoSS-296
❑ 94Don-231
❑ 94Fin-263
❑ 94FinRef-263
❑ 94Fla-325
❑ 94Fle-250
❑ 94Lea-206
❑ 94Pin-273
❑ 94PinArtP-273
❑ 94PinMusC-273
❑ 94Sco-147
❑ 94ScoGolR-147
❑ 94StaClu-494
❑ 94StaCluFDI-494
❑ 94StaCluGR-494
❑ 94StaCluMOP-494
❑ 94StaCluT-210
❑ 94StaCluTFDI-210
❑ 94Top-173
❑ 94TopGol-173
❑ 94TopSpa-173
❑ 94Ult-404
❑ 94UppDec-509
❑ 94UppDecED-509
❑ 95ColCho-509
❑ 95ColChoGS-509
❑ 95ColChoSS-509
❑ 95Don-282
❑ 95DonPreP-282
❑ 95DonTopotO-129
❑ 95Fle-84
❑ 95Pac-306
❑ 95StaClu-56
❑ 95StaCluFDI-56
❑ 95StaCluMOP-56
❑ 95StaCluSTWS-56
❑ 95StaCluVR-34
❑ 95StaCluVRMO-34
❑ 95Top-618
❑ 95TopCyb-386
❑ 95Ult-88
❑ 95UltGolM-88
❑ 96Fle-200
❑ 96FleTif-200
❑ 96LeaSigEA-213
❑ 97BrePol-28
❑ 97Cir-185
❑ 97CirRav-185
❑ 97Fle-140
❑ 97FleTif-140
❑ 97PacPriGotD-GD61
❑ 97Ult-450
❑ 97UltGolME-450
❑ 97UltPlaME-450
❑ 98PacOnl-414
❑ 98PacOnlR-414
❑ 98PacOnlWC-414
❑ 99Fle-359
❑ 99FleSta9-359
❑ 99FleWarT-359
❑ 99MetUni-36
❑ 99MetUniGM-36
❑ 99MetUniPMG-36
❑ 99Pac-241
❑ 99PacPlaB-241
❑ 99PacRed-241
❑ 99SkyPre-189
❑ 99SkyPreR-189
❑ 99Top-151
❑ 99TopChr-151
❑ 99TopChrR-151
❑ 99TopMVPP-151
❑ 99Ult-94
❑ 99UltGolM-94
❑ 99UltMas-94
❑ 99UltPlaM-94
❑ 99UppDec-130
❑ 99UppDecEL1-130
❑ 99UppDecEL2-130
Wickware, Frank
❑ 78LauLonABS-19
Widger, Chris
❑ 92BelMarCB-20
❑ 92BelMarF-1448
❑ 92ClaDraP-60
❑ 92FroRowDP-99
❑ 92FroRowDPG-99
❑ 92FroRowDPS-99
❑ 93RivPilCLC-22
❑ 93StaCluM-130
❑ 93Top-632
❑ 93TopGol-632
❑ 93TopInaM-632
❑ 93TopInaR-632
❑ 93TopMic-632
❑ 94JacSunF-1415
❑ 95Bow-2
❑ 95Exc-123
❑ 95MarPac-47
❑ 95TacRaiTI-27
❑ 95UppDecML-98
❑ 95UppDecMLFS-98
❑ 96ColCho-732
❑ 96ColChoGS-732
❑ 96ColChoSS-732
❑ 96Pin-178
❑ 96Sco-503
❑ 96TacRaiB-28
❑ 97Bow-216
❑ 97BowInt-216
❑ 97ColCho-388
❑ 97Don-381
❑ 97DonGolPP-381
❑ 97DonLim-41
❑ 97DonLimE-41
❑ 97DonLimENG-41
❑ 97DonSigA-109
❑ 97DonSigAC-134
❑ 97DonSigAM-134
❑ 97DonSilPP-381
❑ 97FlaShoLC-177
❑ 97FlaShoLeg0-177
❑ 97FlaShoLeg1-177
❑ 97FlaShoM-A177
❑ 97FlaShoM-B177
❑ 97FlaShoM-C177
❑ 97FlaShoR0-177
❑ 97FlaShoR1-177
❑ 97FlaShoR2-177
❑ 97Fle-646
❑ 97FleTif-646
❑ 97Ult-501
❑ 97UltGolME-501
❑ 97UltPlaME-501
❑ 98ColCho-433
❑ 98Fle-361
❑ 98PacOnl-467
❑ 98PacOnlR-467
❑ 98PacOnlWC-467
❑ 98Sco-129
❑ 98Top-237
❑ 98TopChr-237
❑ 98TopChrR-237
❑ 98TopDevR-237
❑ 98TopDia-237
❑ 98TopMiniC-237
❑ 99Fle-304
❑ 99FleSta9-304
❑ 99FleWarT-304
❑ 99Pac-273
❑ 99PacOme-149
❑ 99PacOmeC-149
❑ 99PacOmeG-149
❑ 99PacOmePB-149
❑ 99PacPar-147
❑ 99PacParC-147
❑ 99PacParG-147
❑ 99PacParHoloGold-147
❑ 99PacParHS-147
❑ 99PacParOD-147
❑ 99PacParPB-147
❑ 99PacParRed-147
❑ 99PacPlaB-273
❑ 99PacRed-273
❑ 99Top-387
❑ 99TopChr-387
❑ 99TopChrR-387
❑ 99TopMVPP-387
❑ 99UppDec-424
❑ 99UppDecEL1-424
❑ 99UppDecEL2-424
❑ 99Vic-247
Widmar, Al
❑ 51Bow-281
❑ 52Top-133
❑ 53MotCoo-14
❑ 54SeaPop-26
❑ 74Top-99
❑ 83TopRep5-133
❑ 84BluJayFS-33
❑ 85BluJayFS-33
❑ 86BluJayFS-33
❑ 87BluJayFS-35
❑ 88BluJayFS-33
❑ 89BluJayFS-32
❑ 94St.CatBJC-30
❑ 95StCatSTI-27
Widmar, Tom
❑ 75SacSolC-15
❑ 76SpoIndC-4
Widner, Steven
❑ 77WatIndT-29
Widner, William
❑ 87OldJudN-522
Wieand, F. Ted
❑ 58RedEnq-42
❑ 58SeaRalT-19
❑ 59RedEnq-28
❑ 60Top-146
❑ 60TopVen-146
Wieczorek, Chet
❑ 40SolHug-19
Wieczorek, Ted
❑ 93AubAstC-27
❑ 93AubAstF-3459
Wiedenbauer, Tom
❑ 77CocAstT-25
❑ 80TucTorT-8
❑ 81TucTorT-26
❑ 83DayBeaAT-13
❑ 86OscAstP-28
❑ 87ColAstP-16
❑ 88ColAstB-25
❑ 89ColMudB-8
❑ 89ColMudP-130
❑ 89ColMudS-24
Wiedl, Andy
❑ 98BatMucTI-33
Wiegandt, Scott
❑ 89MarPhiS-34
❑ 90SpaPhiB-11
❑ 90SpaPhiP-2492
❑ 90SpaPhiS-26
❑ 91ClePhiC-11
❑ 91ClePhiP-1622
❑ 92ReaPhiF-577
❑ 92ReaPhiS-547
❑ 93ReaPhiF-296
❑ 94ReaPhiF-2064
❑ 95ScrRedBTI-28
❑ 96ScrRedBB-26
❑ 97LouRedB-30
Wieghaus, Tom
❑ 80MemChiT-25
❑ 80VenLeaS-257
❑ 83ExpPos-37
❑ 83WicAerDS-23
❑ 84AstMot-18
Wielegman, Phil
❑ 86MiaMarP-27
Wieligman, Rich
❑ 87LakTigP-4
❑ 88GleFalTP-922
❑ 89TolMudHC-23
❑ 89TolMudHP-775
Wiener, Paul
❑ 79JacMetT-5
Wiens, Randy
❑ 78DunBluJT-26
Wiese, Phil
❑ 89EliTwiS-28
❑ 90VisOakCLC-64
❑ 90VisOakP-2156
❑ 91LinDriAA-498
❑ 91OrlSunRLD-498
❑ 91OrlSunRP-1851
Wieser, Dan
❑ 82OmaRoyT-18A
❑ 82OmaRoyT-18B
Wieser, Mike
❑ 93DanBraC-28
❑ 93DanBraF-3628
❑ 95DurBulTI-36
Wieser, Tom
❑ 84AriWilP-19
Wiesler, Bob
❑ 56Top-327
❑ 57Top-126
❑ 79TCM50-224
Wiesmiller, Bob
❑ 77SalPirT-27A
Wiesner, Doug
❑ 81AppFoxT-29
❑ 82AppFoxFr-29
Wiesner, T.J.
❑ 98St.PauSTI-32
Wietelmann, Whitey (William)
❑ 52MotCoo-24
❑ 72PadPos-27
❑ 73OPC-12
❑ 73PadDea-2
❑ 73PadDea-28
❑ 73Top-12A
❑ 73Top-12B
❑ 74PadDea-28
❑ 75PadDea-29
❑ 76SSP-598
❑ 77PadSchC-63
❑ 78PadFamF-36
❑ 79DiaGre-209
❑ 79PadFamF-9
❑ 83TCMPla1944-38
Wieters, Rick
❑ 78GreBraT-29
❑ 79SavBraT-16
❑ 80GleFalWSBT-12
❑ 80GleFalWSCT-13
❑ 81GleFalWST-8
Wiggins, Alan
❑ 78QuaCitAT-29
❑ 79CliDodT-6
❑ 81HawIsIT-8
❑ 83Don-397
❑ 83Fle-375
❑ 83PadTeal-31
❑ 83Top-251
❑ 84AllGamPI-18
❑ 84Don-568
❑ 84Fle-317
❑ 84FleSti-89
❑ 84Nes792-693
❑ 84OPC-27
❑ 84PadMot-10
❑ 84PadSmo-28
❑ 84Top-693
❑ 84TopRubD-6
❑ 84TopSti-153
❑ 84TopStiB-3
❑ 84TopTif-693
❑ 85AllGamPI-108
❑ 85BalOriP-35
❑ 85Don-80
❑ 85Fle-48
❑ 85FleStaS-60
❑ 85Lea-68
❑ 85OPC-378
❑ 85OriHea-19
❑ 85Top-378
❑ 85TopRubD-7
❑ 85TopSti-150
❑ 85TopTif-378
❑ 86BalOriHMP-20
❑ 86BalOriP-24
❑ 86Don-607
❑ 86Fle-290
❑ 86Top-508
❑ 86TopTif-508
❑ 87BalOriP-38
❑ 87DonOpeD-138
❑ 87FleUpd-124
❑ 87FleUpdG-124
❑ 87OriFreB-2
❑ 87TopTra-126T
❑ 87TopTraT-126T
❑ 88Sco-291
❑ 88ScoGlo-291
❑ 91OriCro-482
Wiggins, Dave
❑ 81PhoGiaVNB-14
Wiggins, Jimmy
❑ 91PriRedC-26
❑ 91PriRedP-3515
Wiggins, Kevin
❑ 86OrlTwiP-23
Wiggins, Scott
❑ 98GreBatM-24
❑ 98TamYanM-30
Wiggins, Tony
❑ 89TenTecGE-29
Wigginton, Ty
❑ 98PitMetM-32
Wiggs, James
❑ 03BreE10-150
❑ 09ObaT21-20
❑ 09ObaT21-285
❑ 12ObaPreT-34
Wiggs, Johnny
❑ 89BelMarL-15
❑ 90SanBerSB-21
❑ 90SanBerSCLC-94
❑ 90SanBerSP-2634
❑ 91PenPilC-13
❑ 91PenPilP-379
Wight, Bill
❑ 48WhiSoxTI-28
❑ 50Bow-38
❑ 51Bow-164
❑ 52Bow-117
❑ 52Top-177
❑ 53BowC-100
❑ 53TigGle-28
❑ 55Bow-312
❑ 55IndGolS-22
❑ 56BalOriP-22
❑ 56BalOriP-53
❑ 56Top-286
❑ 57Top-340
❑ 58RedEnq-43
❑ 58Top-237
❑ 59SeaPop-13
❑ 79DiaGre-143
❑ 79TCM50-131
❑ 83TopRep5-177
❑ 91OriCro-483
❑ 97BalOriP-54
Wihtol, Sandy
❑ 77WatIndT-30
❑ 79TacTugT-16
❑ 80TacTigT-10
❑ 80Top-665
❑ 81ChaChaT-7
❑ 81Top-451
❑ 83ChaChaT-6
Wilber, Del
❑ 52Bow-225
❑ 52Top-383
❑ 53BowBW-24
❑ 53RedSoxTI-29
❑ 54Bow-178
❑ 74SpoIndC-45
❑ 77TacTwiDQ-26
❑ 83Car194T-39
❑ 83TopRep5-383
❑ 93RanKee-379
Wilbins, Mike
❑ 75CedRapGT-2
Wilborn, Ted

❑ 77ForLauYS-8
❑ 80NasSouTI-25
❑ 80OPC-329
❑ 80Top-674
❑ 81NasSouTI-23
❑ 82PhoGiaVNB-3
❑ 83PhoGiaBHN-16
❑ 86HagSunP-27
❑ 87CedRapRP-20
❑ 92YanWIZ8-203
Wilbur, Bob
❑ 80UtiBluJT-10
Wilburn, Fred
❑ 85MidAngT-4
Wilburn, Trey
❑ 89BilMusP-2041
❑ 90ChaWheB-11
❑ 90ChaWheP-2242
❑ 90GatCitPP-3355
❑ 90GatCitPSP-8
❑ 91BilMusP-3758
❑ 91BilMusSP-6
Wilcox, Chris
❑ 96Exc-96
Wilcox, Greg
❑ 90MedHatBJB-8
Wilcox, Luke
❑ 96Bow-223
❑ 96BowFoi-223
❑ 96TamYanY-27
❑ 97Bow-301
❑ 97BowCerBlaIA-CA83
❑ 97BowCerBluIA-CA83
❑ 97BowCerGolIA-CA83
❑ 97BowChr-209
❑ 97BowChrI-209
❑ 97BowChrIR-209
❑ 97BowChrR-209
❑ 97BowInt-301
❑ 97NorNav-31
❑ 97NorNavTI-29
❑ 98OrlRayM-21
Wilcox, Milt
❑ 70DayDaiNM-155
❑ 71OPC-164
❑ 71Top-164
❑ 72OPC-399
❑ 72Top-399
❑ 73IndTeal-28
❑ 73OPC-134
❑ 73Top-134
❑ 74OPC-565
❑ 74Top-565
❑ 75OPC-14
❑ 75Top-14
❑ 75TopMin-14
❑ 76SSP-306
❑ 76VenLeaS-192
❑ 77EvaTriT-25
❑ 78OPC-136
❑ 78TigBurK-11
❑ 78TigTeal-35
❑ 78Top-151
❑ 79Top-288
❑ 80OPC-204
❑ 80Top-392
❑ 81AllGamPI-90
❑ 81Don-247
❑ 81Fle-465
❑ 81Top-658
❑ 82Don-233
❑ 82Fle-285
❑ 82FleSta-157
❑ 82Top-784
❑ 82TopSti-186
❑ 82TopStiV-186
❑ 83Don-155
❑ 83Fle-349
❑ 83FleSta-214
❑ 83FleSti-248
❑ 83TigPos-32
❑ 83Top-457
❑ 84AllGamPI-179
❑ 84Don-471
❑ 84Fle-93
❑ 84Nes792-588
❑ 84TigFarJ-16
❑ 84TigTeal-32
❑ 84TigWavP-35
❑ 84Top-588
❑ 84TopTif-588
❑ 85Don-105
❑ 85Fle-25
❑ 85Lea-227
❑ 85OPC-99
❑ 85SevCoi-D6
❑ 85TigCaiD-20
❑ 85TigWen-22
❑ 85Top-99
❑ 85TopSti-10
❑ 85TopSti-17
❑ 85TopTif-99
❑ 86Fle-243
❑ 86MarMot-11
❑ 86Top-192
❑ 86TopTif-192
❑ 89PacSenL-13
❑ 89T/MSenL-114
❑ 89TopSenL-73
❑ 90EliSenL-16
❑ 91PacSenL-140
Wilcox, Steve
❑ 82CliGiaF-11
Wilczewski, Frank
❑ 79CliDodT-27
Wild, Jerry
❑ 64TulOil-8
Wild, Willie B.
❑ 98MadBlaW-25
Wildams, Jaime
❑ 85DomLeaS-106
Wilder, Bill
❑ 84MemChiT-11
Wilder, Dave
❑ 82IdaFalAT-29
❑ 83MadMusF-5
❑ 85ModA'sC-21
❑ 87PitCubP-18
Wilder, John
❑ 91PulBraC-27
❑ 91PulBraP-4006
❑ 92MacBraC-12
❑ 92MacBraF-269
❑ 93DurBulC-23
❑ 93DurBulF-487
❑ 93DurBulTI-18
❑ 93SouAtlLAPI-41
Wilder, Mike
❑ 83IdaFalAT-25
❑ 84MadMusP-4
Wilder, Paul
❑ 86HunStaDJ-14
❑ 96BesAutS1RP-FR15
❑ 96NewJerCB-30
❑ 97AppLeaTPB-12
❑ 97Bes-32
❑ 97BesLimA-41
❑ 97Bow-170
❑ 97BowBes-132
❑ 97BowBesAR-132
❑ 97BowBesR-132
❑ 97BowCerBlaIA-CA84
❑ 97BowCerBluIA-CA84
❑ 97BowCerGolIA-CA84
❑ 97BowChr-165
❑ 97BowChrI-165
❑ 97BowChrIR-165
❑ 97BowChrR-165
❑ 97BowInt-170
❑ 97PriDevR-9
❑ 97Top-471
❑ 98Bes-47
❑ 98BesAutPOY-19
❑ 98BesCasT-10
❑ 98BesFulCA-22
❑ 98BesPreA-46
❑ 98Bow-99
❑ 98BowCerBlueAU-58
❑ 98BowCerGA-58
❑ 98BowCerSA-58
❑ 98BowChr-99
❑ 98BowChrGA-99
❑ 98BowChrGAR-99
❑ 98BowChrI-99
❑ 98BowChrIR-99
❑ 98BowChrR-99
❑ 98BowGolA-99
❑ 98BowInt-99
❑ 98ChaRivDG-31
❑ 98SouAtlLPM-28
Wilder, Troy
❑ 76BatTroTI-28
❑ 78WatIndT-26
❑ 79WatIndT-5
Wilder, Willie
❑ 92PenPilC-18
❑ 92PenPilF-2947
❑ 93RivPilCLC-23
Wiles, Randy
❑ 75TulOil7-17
❑ 76ArkTraT-11
❑ 76TulOilGP-22
❑ 78ChaChaT-19
Wiley, Chad
❑ 92ButCopKSP-26
❑ 93ChaRaiC-23
❑ 93ChaRaiF-1912
❑ 94ChaRanF-2498
❑ 95TulDriTI-27
Wiley, Charles
❑ 91BelMarCB-24
❑ 91BelMarP-3664
❑ 92PenPilC-2
❑ 92PenPilF-2933
❑ 93RivPilCLC-24
Wiley, Craig
❑ 87LasVegSP-21
❑ 88WicPilRD-12
❑ 89NiaFalRP-23
Wiley, Jim
❑ 90PriWilCTI-28
❑ 91Cla/Bes-167
❑ 91Ft.LauYC-15
❑ 91Ft.LauYP-2428
❑ 93PriWilCC-25
❑ 93PriWilCF-657
❑ 94AlbYanF-1443
Wiley, Joe
❑ 93NegLeaRL2-40
Wiley, Keith
❑ 88CapCodPPaLP-11
Wiley, Mark
❑ 74TacTwiC-14
❑ 75TacTwiK-1
❑ 75TwiTeal-28
❑ 76TacTwiDQ-22
❑ 79SyrChiT-5
❑ 79SyrChiTI-27
❑ 83RocRedWT-25
❑ 84RocRedWT-3
❑ 85RocRedWT-29
❑ 87BalOriP-33
❑ 87OriFreB-31
❑ 88IndGat-35
❑ 88IndTeal-38
❑ 89IndTeal-28
❑ 90IndTeal-45
❑ 91IndFanC-30
Wiley, Michael
❑ 91KanCouCC-12
❑ 91KanCouCP-2659
❑ 91KanCouCTI-22
Wiley, Skip
❑ 90AppFoxBS-30
❑ 90AppFoxP-2096
❑ 90ProAaA-108
❑ 91BasCitRC-12
❑ 91BasCitRP-1399
❑ 92MemChiF-2420
❑ 92MemChiS-448
❑ 92SkyAA F-190
Wilfong, Rob
❑ 76TacTwiDQ-23
❑ 77TacTwiDQ-16B
❑ 78TwiFriP-22
❑ 79Top-633
❑ 79TwiFriP-27
❑ 80Top-238
❑ 80TwiPos-30
❑ 81Don-493
❑ 81Fle-569
❑ 81Top-453
❑ 81TwiPos-30
❑ 82Don-130
❑ 82Fle-563
❑ 82FleSta-231
❑ 82Top-379
❑ 82TopSti-205
❑ 82TopTra-128T
❑ 82TwiPos-29
❑ 83Don-612
❑ 83Fle-101
❑ 83Top-158
❑ 84AngSmo-30
❑ 84Don-329
❑ 84Fle-530
❑ 84Nes792-79
❑ 84Top-79
❑ 84TopTif-79
❑ 85AngSmo-20
❑ 85Don-402
❑ 85Fle-315
❑ 85Top-524
❑ 85TopTif-524
❑ 86AngSmo-20
❑ 86OPC-393
❑ 86Top-658
❑ 86TopTif-658
❑ 87Don-258
❑ 87Fle-94
❑ 87FleGlo-94
❑ 87Top-251
❑ 87TopTif-251
Wilford, Eric
❑ 91HelBreSP-27
Wilhelm, Brent
❑ 96SouBenSHS-28
Wilhelm, Hoyt
❑ 50JJKCopP-23
❑ 52Top-392
❑ 53BowBW-28
❑ 53RedMan-NL21
❑ 53Top-151
❑ 54Bow-57
❑ 54NewYorJA-37
❑ 54Top-36
❑ 55Bow-1
❑ 55GiaGolS-6
❑ 55RedMan-NL12
❑ 56Top-307
❑ 57Top-203
❑ 58BalOriP-18
❑ 58IndTeal-24
❑ 58Top-324
❑ 59OriJayP-11
❑ 59Top-349
❑ 60Lea-69
❑ 60OriJayP-11
❑ 60Top-115
❑ 60Top-395
❑ 60TopVen-115
❑ 61BalOriP-22
❑ 61Pos-80A
❑ 61Pos-80B
❑ 61Top-545
❑ 61TopStal-107
❑ 62BalOriP-32
❑ 62Jel-35
❑ 62Pos-35
❑ 62PosCan-35
❑ 62Top-423
❑ 62Top-545
❑ 62TopStal-10
❑ 63SalMetC-39
❑ 63Top-108
❑ 63WhiSoxTS-26
❑ 64Top-13
❑ 64TopVen-13
❑ 64WhiSoxI-26
❑ 64WhiSoxTS-23
❑ 65OPC-276
❑ 65Top-276
❑ 65WhiSoxJP-12
❑ 66Top-510
❑ 67CokCapWS-5
❑ 67Top-422
❑ 67TopVen-257
❑ 68Top-350
❑ 68TopVen-350
❑ 69AngJacitB-13
❑ 69AtlBraBPPS-24
❑ 69MilBra-291
❑ 69Top-565
❑ 69TopDec-11A
❑ 69TopDecI-45
❑ 69TopSta-190
❑ 69TopTeaP-17
❑ 70AtlBraS-8
❑ 70DayDaiNM-12
❑ 70OPC-17
❑ 70Top-17
❑ 71MLBOffS-24
❑ 71OPC-248
❑ 71Top-248
❑ 71TopGreM-2
❑ 72MilBra-361
❑ 72Top-777
❑ 75GiaAllT-13
❑ 77GalGloG-23
❑ 77GalGloG-248
❑ 78HalHalR-19
❑ 78TacYanC-47
❑ 78TCM60I-100
❑ 79TCM50-270
❑ 79WesHavYT-27
❑ 80GiaGreT-4
❑ 80PacLeg-121
❑ 80PerHaloFP-193
❑ 80PerHaloFPS-57
❑ 80SSPHOF-196
❑ 82NasSouTI-28
❑ 82TCMGreP-11
❑ 83NasSouTI-25
❑ 83TopRep5-392
❑ 84FifNatCT-18
❑ 84NasSouTI-24
❑ 84OCoandSI-154
❑ 84SpoDesPW-26
❑ 85WhiSoxC-43
❑ 86OriGreT-1
❑ 88PacLegI-76
❑ 89DodSmoG-35
❑ 89HOFStiB-81
❑ 89PacLegI-171
❑ 89SweBasG-45
❑ 89WhiSoxK-5
❑ 90DodTar-858
❑ 90PacLeg-57
❑ 90PerGreM-95
❑ 91OriCro-484
❑ 91TopArc1-151
❑ 91TopArc1-312
❑ 92BazQua5A-21
❑ 94TopArc1-36
❑ 94TopArc1G-36
Wilhelm, James W.
❑ 56BalOriP-54
❑ 79HawIsIC-25
❑ 79HawIsIT-7
❑ 80Top-685
Wilhelm, Kaiser (Irvin)
❑ 09ColChiE-306
❑ 09T206-374
❑ 09T206-375
❑ 10CouT21-245
❑ 11PinT-5-464
❑ 11SpoLifCW-367
❑ 11SpoLifM-164
❑ 11T205-181
❑ 12ColRedB-306
❑ 12ColTinT-306
❑ 14PieStaT-109
❑ 23WilChoV-170
❑ 90DodTar-859
Wilhelm, Spider (Charles Ernest)
❑ 55JetPos-21
Wilhelmi, Dave
❑ 80CliGiaT-1
❑ 81CliGiaT-4
❑ 84ShrCapFB-24
Wilhoit, Joe
❑ 17ColE13-189
❑ 19Zee-122
❑ 20MrsShePP-19
❑ 21Zee-113
❑ 22Zee-93
❑ 23Zee-119
❑ 24Zee-84
Wilholte, Arnold
❑ 78AshTouT-28
❑ 79AshTouT-18
Wilie, Denney
❑ 12T207-196
❑ 16Zee-71
❑ 16Zee-145
❑ 17Zee-58
❑ 18Zee-53
❑ 19Zee-31
❑ 20Zee-38
❑ 21Zee-40
❑ 22Zee-39
❑ 23Zee-59
❑ 23Zee-60
Wilke, Matt
❑ 91MedHatBJP-4111
❑ 91MedHatBJSP-18
❑ 92MedHatBJF-3217
Wilkerson, Brad
❑ 99JustheSJB-49
❑ 99TeaBesR-97
❑ 99TeaBesRFS-12
❑ 99TeaBesRG-97
❑ 99TeaBesRS-97
Wilkerson, Curt (Curtis)
❑ 82BurRanF-13
❑ 82BurRanT-13
❑ 82TulDriT-25
❑ 83OklCit8T-19
❑ 84Don-99
❑ 84FleUpd-126
❑ 84RanJarP-19
❑ 84TopTra-127T
❑ 84TopTraT-127T
❑ 85Don-99
❑ 85Fle-573
❑ 85OPC-342
❑ 85RanPer-19
❑ 85Top-594
❑ 85TopSti-349
❑ 85TopTif-594
❑ 86Don-256
❑ 86Fle-577
❑ 86OPC-279
❑ 86RanLit-7
❑ 86RanPer-19
❑ 86Top-434
❑ 86TopSti-244
❑ 86TopTif-434
❑ 87Don-223
❑ 87Fle-141
❑ 87FleGlo-141
❑ 87RanMot-14
❑ 87RanSmo-28
❑ 87Top-228
❑ 87TopTif-228
❑ 88Don-592
❑ 88Fle-481
❑ 88FleGlo-481
❑ 88RanMot-14
❑ 88RanSmo-21
❑ 88Sco-127
❑ 88ScoGlo-127
❑ 88StaLinRa-18
❑ 88Top-53
❑ 88TopBig-132
❑ 88TopTif-53
❑ 89Bow-292
❑ 89BowTif-292
❑ 89CubMar-19
❑ 89Don-402
❑ 89DonTra-34
❑ 89Fle-535
❑ 89FleGlo-535
❑ 89Sco-518
❑ 89Top-331
❑ 89TopTif-331
❑ 89TopTra-126T
❑ 89TopTraT-126T
❑ 89UppDec-465
❑ 90CubMar-23
❑ 90Don-608
❑ 90Fle-46
❑ 90FleCan-46
❑ 90OPC-667
❑ 90PubIntS-209
❑ 90Sco-474
❑ 90Top-667
❑ 90TopTif-667
❑ 90TopTVCu-28
❑ 90UppDec-147
❑ 91Bow-511
❑ 91Fle-438
❑ 91Lea-317
❑ 91OPC-142
❑ 91Sco-603
❑ 91StaClu-512
❑ 91Top-142
❑ 91TopDesS-142
❑ 91TopMic-142
❑ 91TopTif-142
❑ 92Don-489
❑ 92Lea-387
❑ 92LeaBlaG-387
❑ 92OPC-712
❑ 92Sco-382
❑ 92StaClu-46
❑ 92StaClu-849
❑ 92Top-712
❑ 92TopGol-712
❑ 92TopGolW-712
❑ 92TopMic-712
❑ 92Ult-377
❑ 92UppDec-490
❑ 93Fle-627
❑ 93PacSpa-142
❑ 93RanKee-380
❑ 93RoyPol-25
❑ 93RoyStaC-23
❑ 93StaClu-177
❑ 93StaCluFDI-177
❑ 93StaCluMOP-177
❑ 94OmaRoyF-1233
❑ 94Pac-301
❑ 94StaCluMOP-ST21
❑ 94StaCluST-ST21
❑ 96LanLugB-2
❑ 97LanLugTS-29
❑ 98CarMudM-26
Wilkerson, Marty
❑ 84OmaRoyT-12
❑ 85OmaRoyT-20
❑ 86OmaRoyP-29
❑ 86OmaRoyT-9

Wilkerson, Ron
❏ 82WesHavAT-18
Wilkerson, Steve
❏ 93BilMusF-3946
❏ 93BilMusSP-24
❏ 94ChaWheC-25
❏ 94ChaWheF-2704
Wilkerson, Wayne
❏ 77AshTouT-27
Wilkerson, Wayne Linwood
❏ 91PriRedC-21
❏ 91PriRedP-3530
❏ 92BilMusF-3372
❏ 92BilMusSP-5
❏ 93WesVirWC-24
❏ 93WesVirWF-2880
Wilkes, Greg
❏ 80HawIslT-13
Wilkie, Aldon
❏ 47RemBre-23
❏ 48SigOil-24
❏ 77TCMTheWY-47
Wilkie, James
❏ 91HelBreSP-13
Wilkins, Bobby
❏ 45A'sTeal-30
Wilkins, Dean
❏ 88EasLeaAP-30
❏ 88PitCubP-1368
❏ 89IowCubC-10
❏ 89IowCubP-1690
❏ 90Bow-26
❏ 90BowTif-26
❏ 90CMC-84
❏ 90Fle-47
❏ 90FleCan-47
❏ 90IowCubC-9
❏ 90Sco-630
❏ 90TopDeb89-143
❏ 90TopTVCu-16
❏ 91TriA AAGP-AAA54
❏ 91TucTorP-2214
Wilkins, Eric
❏ 80TacTigT-25
❏ 80Top-511
❏ 81ChaChaT-6
❏ 81Top-99
Wilkins, Marc
❏ 92WelPirC-25
❏ 92WelPirF-1323
❏ 93AugPirC-25
❏ 93AugPirF-1546
❏ 94SalBucC-23
❏ 94SalBucF-2324
❏ 95CarMudF-158
❏ 96CarMudB-12
❏ 97ColCho-428
❏ 97Fle-437
❏ 97FleTif-437
❏ 97PirPos-42
❏ 97Top-207
❏ 97Ult-267
❏ 97UltGolME-267
❏ 97UltPlaME-267
❏ 98ColCho-213
❏ 98PacInvGems-197
❏ 98PacOnl-598
❏ 98PacOnlR-598
❏ 98PacOnlWC-598
Wilkins, Mark
❏ 80QuaCitCT-10
❏ 81QuaCitCT-28
Wilkins, Michael
❏ 88FayGenP-1103
❏ 89LakTigS-24
❏ 90CMC-767
❏ 90EasLeaAP-EL46
❏ 90LonTigP-1269
❏ 91LinDriAA-547
❏ 91SanAntMLD-547
❏ 91SanAntMP-2976
❏ 92AlbDukF-722
Wilkins, Rick
❏ 87GenCubP-7
❏ 88PeoChiTI-31
❏ 89WinSpiS-17
❏ 90ChaKniTI-22
❏ 90TopTVCu-63
❏ 91Bow-419
❏ 91Cla3-T96
❏ 91DonRoo-38
❏ 91FleUpd-83
❏ 91IowCubLD-221
❏ 91IowCubP-1065
❏ 91LinDriAAA-221
❏ 91LinDriP-221
❏ 91ScoRoo-103T
❏ 91UltUpd-75
❏ 91UppDecFE-46F
❏ 92Bow-156
❏ 92Don-249
❏ 92Fle-397
❏ 92Lea-336
❏ 92LeaBlaG-336
❏ 92OPC-348
❏ 92Sco-483
❏ 92Sco100RS-16
❏ 92StaClu-643
❏ 92StaCluNC-643
❏ 92Top-348
❏ 92TopDeb91-184
❏ 92TopGol-348
❏ 92TopGolW-348
❏ 92TopMic-348
❏ 92UppDec-373
❏ 93Bow-524
❏ 93CubMar-29
❏ 93CubStaC-23
❏ 93Don-28
❏ 93Fle-28
❏ 93Lea-216
❏ 93PacSpa-65
❏ 93PanSti-202
❏ 93Pin-206
❏ 93Sco-185
❏ 93Sel-390
❏ 93SP-90
❏ 93StaClu-228
❏ 93StaCluFDI-228
❏ 93StaCluMOP-228
❏ 93Stu-63
❏ 93Top-721
❏ 93TopGol-721
❏ 93TopInaM-721
❏ 93TopInaR-721
❏ 93TopMic-721
❏ 93TriPla-19
❏ 93Ult-25
❏ 93UppDec-598
❏ 93UppDecGold-598
❏ 94Bow-306
❏ 94ColC-297
❏ 94ColChoGS-297
❏ 94ColChoSS-297
❏ 94Don-444
❏ 94DonDiaK-DK5
❏ 94DonDiaKJ-DK5
❏ 94Fin-86
❏ 94FinRef-86
❏ 94Fla-364
❏ 94Fle-401
❏ 94FleExtB-226
❏ 94FUnPac-102
❏ 94FUnPac-234
❏ 94Lea-287
❏ 94LeaL-93
❏ 94Pac-115
❏ 94PacGolP-20
❏ 94PanSti-160
❏ 94Pin-84
❏ 94PinArtP-84
❏ 94PinMusC-84
❏ 94PinPowS-PS8
❏ 94PinRunC-RC44
❏ 94Sco-450
❏ 94ScoGolR-450
❏ 94Sel-16
❏ 94SP-74
❏ 94SPDieC-74
❏ 94Spo-27
❏ 94StaClu-2
❏ 94StaCluFDI-2
❏ 94StaCluGR-2
❏ 94StaCluMOP-2
❏ 94StaCluT-346
❏ 94StaCluTFDI-346
❏ 94Stu-65
❏ 94Top-244
❏ 94TopGol-244
❏ 94TopSpa-244
❏ 94TriPla-80
❏ 94TriPlaM-2
❏ 94Ult-168
❏ 94UppDec-154
❏ 94UppDecED-154
❏ 95Baz-65
❏ 95Bow-378
❏ 95ColCho-208
❏ 95ColChoGS-208
❏ 95ColChoSS-208
❏ 95Don-158
❏ 95DonPreP-158
❏ 95Fin-38
❏ 95FinRef-38
❏ 95Fla-336
❏ 95Fle-426
❏ 95Lea-180
❏ 95LeaLim-63
❏ 95Pin-53
❏ 95PinArtP-53
❏ 95PinMusC-53
❏ 95Sco-348
❏ 95ScoGolR-348
❏ 95ScoPlaTS-348
❏ 95Spo-36
❏ 95SpoArtP-36
❏ 95StaClu-452
❏ 95StaCluMOP-452
❏ 95StaCluSTWS-452
❏ 95StaCluVR-243
❏ 95StaCluVRMO-243
❏ 95Stu-122
❏ 95Top-504
❏ 95TopCyb-294
❏ 95TopEmb-28
❏ 95TopEmbGI-28
❏ 95Ult-141
❏ 95UltGolM-141
❏ 95UppDec-313
❏ 95UppDecED-313
❏ 95UppDecEDG-313
❏ 96AstMot-11
❏ 96Don-445
❏ 96DonPreP-445
❏ 96Fle-424
❏ 96FleTif-424
❏ 96Ult-491
❏ 96UltGolM-491
❏ 96UppDec-496U
❏ 97Cir-57
❏ 97CirRav-57
❏ 97ColCho-458
❏ 97Fle-488
❏ 97FleTif-488
❏ 97Pac-449
❏ 97PacLigB-449
❏ 97PacSil-449
❏ 97Pin-125
❏ 97PinArtP-PP125
❏ 97PinMusC-125
❏ 97PinPrePla-125
❏ 97UppDec-498
❏ 98NorTidQ-29
❏ 99DodPol-28
Wilkins, Steve
❏ 76CedRapGT-32
Wilkins, Vern
❏ 74SpoIndC-43
Wilkinson, Bill
❏ 86CalCanP-25
❏ 87FleUpd-125
❏ 87FleUpdG-125
❏ 87MarMot-26
❏ 87TopTra-127T
❏ 87TopTraT-127T
❏ 88Don-568
❏ 88Fle-390
❏ 88FleGlo-390
❏ 88MarMot-26
❏ 88RedFolSB-102
❏ 88StaLinMa-19
❏ 88Top-376
❏ 88TopTif-376
❏ 89CalCanC-6
❏ 89LonTigP-1360
❏ 89Top-636
❏ 89TopTif-636
❏ 90OmaRoyP-67
❏ 90ProAAAF-602
❏ 92HunStaS-323
❏ 92TacTigF-2504
Wilkinson, Brian
❏ 87BelMarL-13
❏ 87BelMarTI-3
❏ 89WauTimGS-13
❏ 90RocExpLC-28
❏ 90RocExpP-2692
❏ 91WesPalBEC-14
❏ 91WesPalBEP-1230
Wilkinson, Don
❏ 81TCM60I-305
Wilkinson, Ray
❏ 12PCLPin-25
❏ 23WilChoV-171
❏ 75WhiSox1T-26
Wilkinson, Ron
❏ 82MadMusF-16
Wilkinson, Spencer
❏ 88GasRanP-1019
❏ 89GasRanP-999
❏ 89GasRanS-25
Wilks, Ted
❏ 46SeaSLP-67
❏ 47TipTop-164
❏ 49Bow-137
❏ 49EurSta-199
❏ 51Bow-193
❏ 52Bow-138
❏ 52Top-109
❏ 53Top-101
❏ 79TCM50-218
❏ 83Car194T-55
❏ 83TCMPla1944-25
❏ 83TopRep5-109
❏ 91TopArc1-101
Will, Bob
❏ 59Top-388
❏ 60Top-147
❏ 60TopVen-147
❏ 61Top-512
❏ 61TopStal-11
❏ 62SalPlaC-218
❏ 62ShiPlaC-218
❏ 62Top-47
❏ 62TopVen-47
❏ 63Top-58
Willard, Jerry
❏ 82ReaPhiT-11
❏ 83ChaChaT-8
❏ 84Don-520
❏ 84Ind-33
❏ 84IndWhe-16
❏ 85Don-346
❏ 85Fle-460
❏ 85Ind-36
❏ 85IndPol-16
❏ 85OPC-142
❏ 85Top-504
❏ 85TopMin-504
❏ 85TopTif-504
❏ 86Don-398
❏ 86Fle-601
❏ 86FleUpd-126
❏ 86OPC-273
❏ 86TacTigP-24
❏ 86Top-273
❏ 86TopTif-273
❏ 87Don-467
❏ 87Fle-409
❏ 87FleGlo-409
❏ 87TacTigP-19
❏ 87Top-137
❏ 87TopTif-137
❏ 89VanCanC-19
❏ 89VanCanP-587
❏ 90CMC-650
❏ 90ProAAAF-170
❏ 90TriAllGP-AAA37
❏ 90VanCanC-23
❏ 90VanCanP-492
❏ 91Don-634
❏ 91RicBraBC-36
❏ 91RicBraP-2573
❏ 91RicBraTI-20
❏ 92Bow-470
❏ 92BraLykP-29
❏ 92BraLykS-34
❏ 92Sco-188
❏ 92StaCluD-195
❏ 93RicBraBB-19
❏ 93RicBraF-188
❏ 93RicBraP-22
❏ 93RicBraRC-28
❏ 94CalCanF-794
❏ 95TacRaiTI-28
Willard, Jon
❏ 91SalLakTP-3212
❏ 91SalLakTSP-10
Willeford, Jerry
❏ 76DubPacT-38
Willes, David
❏ 87BriYouC-13
Willes, Mike
❏ 87BriYouC-3
Willett, Robert Edgar
❏ 07TigACDPP-27
❏ 09ColChiE-307
❏ 09ObaT21-76
❏ 09ObaT21-188
❏ 09ObaT21-358
❏ 09PhiCarE-23
❏ 09T206-376
❏ 09T206-377
❏ 09TigMorBBBP-16
❏ 09TigMorPWBPP-14
❏ 09TigTaCP-19
❏ 10CouT21-67
❏ 10CouT21-246
❏ 10CouT21-247
❏ 10NadE1-57
❏ 10RedCroT-84
❏ 10RedCroT-256
❏ 11HelSta-38
❏ 11PinT-5-167
❏ 11S74Sil-19
❏ 11SpoLifCW-368
❏ 11SpoLifM-72
❏ 11T205-182
❏ 12ColRedB-307
❏ 12ColTinT-307
❏ 12HasTriFT-55
❏ 12ObaPreT-107
❏ 14PieStaT-110
❏ 19Zee-80
Willey, Carl (Carlton)
❏ 58Top-407
❏ 59Top-95
❏ 59TopVen-95
❏ 60BraLaktL-27
❏ 60BraSpiaS-25
❏ 60Top-107
❏ 60TopVen-107
❏ 61Top-105
❏ 61TopStal-48
❏ 62BraJayP-12
❏ 62Jel-155
❏ 62Pos-155
❏ 62PosCan-155
❏ 62Top-174A
❏ 62Top-174B
❏ 62TopVen-174
❏ 63Top-528
❏ 64MetJayP-12
❏ 64MetTeal-12
❏ 64Top-84
❏ 64TopCoi-75
❏ 64TopSta-44
❏ 64TopTatl-73
❏ 64TopVen-84
❏ 65MetPos-10
❏ 65Top-401
❏ 78BraTCC-15
❏ 91MetWIZ-430
Willhite, Nick
❏ 64Top-14
❏ 64TopVen-14
❏ 65Top-284
❏ 66OPC-171
❏ 66Top-171
❏ 66TopVen-171
❏ 67Top-249
❏ 78NewWayCT-44
❏ 90DodTar-860
❏ 91MetWIZ-431
William, Jovany
❏ 97AppLeaTPB-23
❏ 97JohCitCTI-35
Williams, Ace (Robert Fulton)
❏ 77TCMTheWY-63
Williams, Al (Alberto H.)
❏ 73CedRapAT-3
❏ 80TolMudHT-17
❏ 80VenLeaS-199
❏ 81Top-569
❏ 81TwiPos-31
❏ 82Don-429
❏ 82Fle-564
❏ 82Top-69
❏ 82TwiPos-30
❏ 83AllGamPI-89
❏ 83Don-508
❏ 83Fle-628
❏ 83FleSta-215
❏ 83FleSti-137
❏ 83Top-731
❏ 83TwiTeal-20
❏ 84Don-316
❏ 84Fle-579
❏ 84MinTwiP-32
❏ 84Nes792-183
❏ 84Top-183
❏ 84TopTif-183
❏ 84TwiTeal-21
❏ 85ColCliP-23
❏ 85ColCliT-10
❏ 85Top-614
❏ 85TopTif-614
Williams, Barbara
❏ 59FleWil-64
Williams, Barry
❏ 90UtiBluSP-13
Williams, Bernie (Bernabe)
❏ 87Ft.LauYP-21
❏ 87OneYanP-4
❏ 88BlaYNPRWLU-13
❏ 88CarLeaAS-19
❏ 88PriWilYS-24
❏ 89BasAmeAPB-AA5
❏ 89BlaYNPRWL-189
❏ 89ColCliC-21
❏ 89ColCliP-23
❏ 89ColCliP-736
❏ 90AlbDecGB-33
❏ 90AlbYanB-1
❏ 90AlbYanP-1179
❏ 90AlbYanSt-22
❏ 90Bes-26
❏ 90Bow-439
❏ 90BowTif-439
❏ 90ClaBlu-10
❏ 90CMC-789
❏ 90Don-689
❏ 90EasLeaAP-EL45
❏ 90OPC-701
❏ 90ProAaA-31
❏ 90Sco-619
❏ 90StaFS7-54
❏ 90Top-701
❏ 90TopTif-701
❏ 90TopTVY-66
❏ 91AlbYanCB-3
❏ 91Bow-173
❏ 91Cla2-T61
❏ 91Cla3-T97
❏ 91ColCliLD-123
❏ 91ColCliP-23
❏ 91ColCliP-612
❏ 91FleUpd-49
❏ 91LinDriAAA-123
❏ 91OPCPre-128
❏ 91RedFolS-112
❏ 91StuPre-7
❏ 91TriA AAGP-AAA8
❏ 91UltUpd-44
❏ 91UppDec-11
❏ 92Bow-407
❏ 92ClaGam-102
❏ 92ColCliF-365
❏ 92ColCliP-22
❏ 92ColCliS-123
❏ 92Don-344
❏ 92Fle-247
❏ 92OPC-374
❏ 92OPCPre-109
❏ 92Pin-229
❏ 92PinTea2-24
❏ 92ProFS7-106
❏ 92Sco-401
❏ 92Sco100RS-34
❏ 92SpoIllFK1-475
❏ 92StaClu-260
❏ 92Top-374
❏ 92TopDeb91-185
❏ 92TopGol-374
❏ 92TopGolW-374
❏ 92TopMic-374
❏ 92TriA AAS-123
❏ 92UppDec-556
❏ 92UppDecS-1
❏ 93Bow-623
❏ 93Don-577
❏ 93Fin-30
❏ 93FinRef-30
❏ 93Fla-255
❏ 93Fle-289
❏ 93Lea-130
❏ 93OPC-363
❏ 93PacSpa-215
❏ 93Pin-7
❏ 93PinTea2-15
❏ 93Sco-120
❏ 93Sel-393
❏ 93SP-270
❏ 93StaClu-364
❏ 93StaCluFDI-364
❏ 93StaCluMOP-364
❏ 93Top-222
❏ 93TopGol-222
❏ 93TopInaM-222
❏ 93TopInaR-222
❏ 93TopMic-222
❏ 93Toy-48

❑ 93Ult-252
❑ 93UppDec-332
❑ 93UppDec-470
❑ 93UppDecGold-332
❑ 93UppDecGold-470
❑ 93YanStaC-21
❑ 94Bow-521
❑ 94ColC-298
❑ 94ColChoGS-298
❑ 94ColChoSS-298
❑ 94Don-259
❑ 94Fin-279
❑ 94FinRef-279
❑ 94Fla-326
❑ 94Fle-251
❑ 94FleExtB-142
❑ 94Lea-4
❑ 94OPC-35
❑ 94Pac-441
❑ 94PanSti-106
❑ 94Pin-139
❑ 94PinArtP-139
❑ 94PinMusC-139
❑ 94Sco-339
❑ 94ScoGolR-339
❑ 94Sel-140
❑ 94Spo-59
❑ 94StaClu-573
❑ 94StaCluFDI-573
❑ 94StaCluGR-573
❑ 94StaCluMOP-573
❑ 94StaCluMOP-ST24
❑ 94StaCluST-ST24
❑ 94StaCluT-198
❑ 94StaCluTFDI-198
❑ 94Top-2
❑ 94TopGol-2
❑ 94TopSpa-2
❑ 94TriPla-280
❑ 94Ult-103
❑ 94UppDec-86
❑ 94UppDecED-86
❑ 95ColCho-517
❑ 95ColChoGS-517
❑ 95ColChoSS-517
❑ 95Don-509
❑ 95DonPreP-509
❑ 95DonTopotO-130
❑ 95Fin-209
❑ 95FinRef-209
❑ 95Fla-290
❑ 95Fle-85
❑ 95Lea-105
❑ 95LeaLim-83
❑ 95Pac-307
❑ 95PacLatD-36
❑ 95Pin-248
❑ 95PinArtP-248
❑ 95PinMusC-248
❑ 95PinUps-US17
❑ 95Sco-124
❑ 95ScoGolR-124
❑ 95ScoPlaTS-124
❑ 95Sel-28
❑ 95SelArtP-28
❑ 95Spo-24
❑ 95SpoArtP-24
❑ 95StaClu-290
❑ 95StaCluMOP-290
❑ 95StaCluSTWS-290
❑ 95StaCluVR-150
❑ 95StaCluVRMO-150
❑ 95Stu-79
❑ 95Sum-22
❑ 95SumNthD-22
❑ 95Top-485
❑ 95TopCyb-277
❑ 95UC3-27
❑ 95UC3ArtP-27
❑ 95Ult-314
❑ 95UltGolM-314
❑ 95UppDec-209
❑ 95UppDecED-209
❑ 95UppDecEDG-209
❑ 96Baz-7
❑ 96Bow-109
❑ 96BowFoi-109
❑ 96Cir-70
❑ 96CirRav-70
❑ 96ColCho-637
❑ 96ColChoGS-637
❑ 96ColChoSS-637
❑ 96Don-401
❑ 96DonPreP-401
❑ 96EmoXL-99
❑ 96Fin-S2
❑ 96FinRef-S2
❑ 96Fla-140
❑ 96Fle-201
❑ 96FleTif-201
❑ 96Lea-16
❑ 96LeaLim-35
❑ 96LeaLimG-35
❑ 96LeaPre-39
❑ 96LeaPreP-39
❑ 96LeaPrePB-16
❑ 96LeaPrePG-16
❑ 96LeaPrePS-16
❑ 96LeaSig-17
❑ 96LeaSigPPG-17
❑ 96LeaSigPPP-17
❑ 96MetUni-97
❑ 96MetUniP-97
❑ 96MLBPin-36
❑ 96Pac-369
❑ 96PacBaeS-3
❑ 96PacEstL-EL36
❑ 96PacPri-P123
❑ 96PacPriG-P123
❑ 96PanSti-156
❑ 96Pin-85
❑ 96PinAfi-71
❑ 96PinAfiAP-71
❑ 96PinAfiFPP-71
❑ 96PinArtP-47
❑ 96PinSta-47
❑ 96ProSta-140
❑ 96Sco-343
❑ 96ScoDugC-B68
❑ 96ScoDugCAP-B68
❑ 96ScoGolS-9
❑ 96Sel-78
❑ 96SelArtP-78
❑ 96SelCer-25
❑ 96SelCerAP-25
❑ 96SelCerCB-25
❑ 96SelCerCR-25
❑ 96SelCerMB-25
❑ 96SelCerMG-25
❑ 96SelCerMR-25
❑ 96SelTeaN-6
❑ 96Spo-76
❑ 96SpoArtP-76
❑ 96StaClu-210
❑ 96StaClu-289
❑ 96StaCluEPB-289
❑ 96StaCluEPG-289
❑ 96StaCluEPS-289
❑ 96StaCluMOP-210
❑ 96StaCluMOP-289
❑ 96Stu-44
❑ 96StuPrePB-44
❑ 96StuPrePG-44
❑ 96StuPrePS-44
❑ 96Sum-131
❑ 96SumAbo&B-131
❑ 96SumArtP-131
❑ 96SumFoi-131
❑ 96TeaOut-88
❑ 96Top-68
❑ 96TopChr-24
❑ 96TopChrR-24
❑ 96TopGal-31
❑ 96TopGalPPI-31
❑ 96TopLas-16
❑ 96Ult-109
❑ 96UltGolM-109
❑ 96UppDec-406
❑ 96Zen-20
❑ 96ZenArtP-20
❑ 96ZenMoz-22
❑ 97Bow-227
❑ 97BowBes-43
❑ 97BowBesAR-43
❑ 97BowBesR-43
❑ 97BowChr-56
❑ 97BowChrI-56
❑ 97BowChrIR-56
❑ 97BowChrR-56
❑ 97BowInt-227
❑ 97BowIntB-BBI4
❑ 97BowIntBAR-BBI4
❑ 97BowIntBR-BBI4
❑ 97Cir-51
❑ 97CirBos-20
❑ 97CirRav-51
❑ 97CirSupB-20
❑ 97ColCho-175
❑ 97ColCho-223
❑ 97ColChoAC-16
❑ 97ColChoT-NY1
❑ 97ColChoTotT-T21
❑ 97CraJac-7
❑ 97Don-169
❑ 97Don-443
❑ 97DonGolPP-169
❑ 97DonGolPP-443
❑ 97DonLim-93
❑ 97DonLim-103
❑ 97DonLim-173
❑ 97DonLimE-93
❑ 97DonLimE-103
❑ 97DonLimE-173
❑ 97DonLimENG-103
❑ 97DonLimFotG-42
❑ 97DonPre-111
❑ 97DonPreCttC-111
❑ 97DonPrePM-22
❑ 97DonSig-12
❑ 97DonSigAC-135
❑ 97DonSigAM-135
❑ 97DonSigPPP-12
❑ 97DonSilPP-169
❑ 97DonSilPP-443
❑ 97DonVxP1-32
❑ 97E-X2-36
❑ 97E-X2Cred-36
❑ 97E-X2EssCre-36
❑ 97Fin-45
❑ 97Fin-107
❑ 97Fin-331
❑ 97FinEmb-107
❑ 97FinEmb-331
❑ 97FinEmbR-107
❑ 97FinEmbR-331
❑ 97FinRef-45
❑ 97FinRef-107
❑ 97FinRef-331
❑ 97FlaShoDC-19
❑ 97FlaShoLC-51
❑ 97FlaShoLeg0-51
❑ 97FlaShoLeg1-51
❑ 97FlaShoM-A51
❑ 97FlaShoM-B51
❑ 97FlaShoM-C51
❑ 97FlaShoR0-51
❑ 97FlaShoR1-51
❑ 97FlaShoR2-51
❑ 97Fle-181
❑ 97Fle-720
❑ 97FleMilDM-22
❑ 97FleMilDMR-22
❑ 97FleTif-181
❑ 97FleTif-720
❑ 97Lea-111
❑ 97Lea-386
❑ 97LeaFraM-111
❑ 97LeaFraM-386
❑ 97LeaFraMDC-111
❑ 97LeaFraMDC-386
❑ 97LeaWarT-9
❑ 97MetUni-125
❑ 97Pac-163
❑ 97PacBaeS-2
❑ 97PacFirD-9
❑ 97PacGolCD-14
❑ 97PacLatotML-16
❑ 97PacLigB-163
❑ 97PacPri-55
❑ 97PacPriGA-GA11
❑ 97PacPriLB-55
❑ 97PacPriP-55
❑ 97PacPriSL-SL4B
❑ 97PacSil-163
❑ 97Pin-111
❑ 97PinArtP-PP111
❑ 97PinCar-20
❑ 97PinCer-10
❑ 97PinCerMBla-10
❑ 97PinCerMBlu-10
❑ 97PinCerMG-10
❑ 97PinCerMR-10
❑ 97PinCerR-10
❑ 97PinInsDD-12
❑ 97PinMusC-111
❑ 97PinPrePla-111
❑ 97PinTotCPB-10
❑ 97PinTotCPG-10
❑ 97PinTotCPR-10
❑ 97PinX-P-46
❑ 97PinX-PMoS-46
❑ 97Sco-5
❑ 97Sco-503
❑ 97ScoArtPWB-5
❑ 97ScoArtPWB-503
❑ 97ScoHeaotO-18
❑ 97ScoPreS-5
❑ 97ScoResC-503
❑ 97ScoShoS-5
❑ 97ScoShoS-503
❑ 97ScoShoSAP-5
❑ 97ScoShoSAP-503
❑ 97ScoStaaD-11
❑ 97Sel-174
❑ 97SelCom-174
❑ 97SP-122
❑ 97SpoIll-127
❑ 97SpoIllEE-127
❑ 97SPSpeF-28
❑ 97StaClu-57
❑ 97StaCluI-I11
❑ 97StaCluMat-57
❑ 97StaCluMOP-57
❑ 97StaCluMOP-I11
❑ 97StrAll-61
❑ 97Stu-97
❑ 97StuHarH-19
❑ 97StuPrePG-97
❑ 97StuPrePS-97
❑ 97Top-150
❑ 97TopChr-57
❑ 97TopChrDD-DD2
❑ 97TopChrDDR-DD2
❑ 97TopChrR-57
❑ 97TopGal-103
❑ 97TopGalPPI-103
❑ 97TopIntF-ILM10
❑ 97TopIntFR-ILM10
❑ 97TopMem05-49
❑ 97TopSta-90
❑ 97TopStaAM-90
❑ 97TopTeaT-TT3
❑ 97UD3-26
❑ 97Ult-107
❑ 97UltGolME-107
❑ 97UltPlaME-107
❑ 97UltTop3-29
❑ 97UltTop3GM-29
❑ 97UppDec-124
❑ 97UppDec-248
❑ 97UppDec-250
❑ 97UppDecHTH-HT2
❑ 97UppDecP-20
❑ 97UppDecPE-20
❑ 97YanMcDP-4
❑ 97YanSco-1
❑ 97YanScoPl-1
❑ 97YanScoPr-1
❑ 97Zen-24
❑ 98Bow-24
❑ 98BowBes-17
❑ 98BowBesAR-17
❑ 98BowBesR-17
❑ 98BowChr-24
❑ 98BowChrGA-24
❑ 98BowChrGAR-24
❑ 98BowChrI-24
❑ 98BowChrIR-24
❑ 98BowChrR-24
❑ 98BowChrR-22
❑ 98BowChrRR-22
❑ 98BowGolA-24
❑ 98BowInt-24
❑ 98CirThu-51
❑ 98CirThuRav-51
❑ 98CirThuSupRav-51
❑ 98ColCho-448
❑ 98CroRoy-99
❑ 98CroRoyPotG-17
❑ 98Don-59
❑ 98Don-395
❑ 98DonCol-59
❑ 98DonColE-427
❑ 98DonColL-289
❑ 98DonColP-588
❑ 98DonColS-59
❑ 98DonCruG-31
❑ 98DonCruP-31
❑ 98DonCruR-31
❑ 98DonDiaK-13
❑ 98DonDiaKC-13
❑ 98DonEli-27
❑ 98DonEliA-27
❑ 98DonEliS-27
❑ 98DonGolPP-59
❑ 98DonGolPP-395
❑ 98DonPre-38
❑ 98DonPreGES-26
❑ 98DonPreGX-26
❑ 98DonPreGXDC-26
❑ 98DonPreSeat-38
❑ 98DonPreTW-12
❑ 98DonPriCD-59
❑ 98DonPriCE-427
❑ 98DonPriCL-289
❑ 98DonPriCP-588
❑ 98DonProLO-17
❑ 98DonProLPl-14
❑ 98DonSig-84
❑ 98DonSigP-84
❑ 98DonSilPP-59
❑ 98DonSilPP-395
❑ 98DonSonM9-18
❑ 98E-X2-74
❑ 98E-X2ECFut-74
❑ 98E-X2ECNow-74
❑ 98Fin-177
❑ 98FinMysF2-M15
❑ 98FinMysF2-M17
❑ 98FinMysF2-M18
❑ 98FinMysF2-M35
❑ 98FinMysF2R-M15
❑ 98FinMysF2R-M17
❑ 98FinMysF2R-M18
❑ 98FinMysF2R-M35
❑ 98FinMysFO-2
❑ 98FinMysFOR-2
❑ 98FinNo--177
❑ 98FinNo-R-177
❑ 98FinOve-B2
❑ 98FinOveR-B2
❑ 98FinRef-177
❑ 98FlaShoLeg0-51
❑ 98FlaShoLeg1-51
❑ 98FlaShoLeg2-51
❑ 98FlaShoLeg3-51
❑ 98FlaShoLegM-51
❑ 98FlaShoR0-51
❑ 98FlaShoR1-51
❑ 98FlaShoR2-51
❑ 98FlaShoR3-51
❑ 98Fle-51
❑ 98Fle-600
❑ 98FleVin'-43
❑ 98FleVin'C-43
❑ 98Lea-90
❑ 98LeaFraDA-90
❑ 98LeaFraF-90
❑ 98LeaFraM-90
❑ 98LeaFraMDC-90
❑ 98LeaFraMDC-90
❑ 98LeaFraMZ2-90
❑ 98LeaRS-11
❑ 98LeaRSLHolo-11
❑ 98LeaRSLong-11
❑ 98LeaRTrue-11
❑ 98LeaStaRep-29
❑ 98MetUni-11
❑ 98MetUniPMG-11
❑ 98Pac-161
❑ 98PacAur-64
❑ 98PacAurPF-49
❑ 98PacAurPFC-49
❑ 98PacAurPFPB-49
❑ 98PacAurPFR-49
❑ 98PacAurPFS-49
❑ 98PacGolCDC-24
❑ 98PacInCage-12
❑ 98PacInv-56
❑ 98PacInvGems-81
❑ 98PacInvMiT-12
❑ 98PacInvPBlue-56
❑ 98PacInvSilv-56
❑ 98PacInvTeam-19
❑ 98PacLatotML-28
❑ 98PacNes-1A
❑ 98PacOme-173
❑ 98PacOmeOnIns-11
❑ 98PacOmeR-173
❑ 98PacOnl-521
❑ 98PacOnl-522
❑ 98PacOnlR-521
❑ 98PacOnlR-522
❑ 98PacOnlWC-521
❑ 98PacOnlWC-522
❑ 98PacPar-75
❑ 98PacParC-75
❑ 98PacParG-75
❑ 98PacParHS-75
❑ 98PacParI-5
❑ 98PacParPB-75
❑ 98PacParR-75
❑ 98PacPlaB-161
❑ 98PacRedT-161
❑ 98PacSil-161
❑ 98PinIns-51
❑ 98PinInsCE-51
❑ 98PinInsDE-51
❑ 98PinInsSG-19AB
❑ 98PinInsSG-19CD
❑ 98PinInsSG-20AB
❑ 98PinInsSG-20CD
❑ 98PinInsSGS-19AB
❑ 98PinInsSGS-19CD
❑ 98PinInsSGS-20AB
❑ 98PinInsSGS-20CD
❑ 98PinPer-39
❑ 98PinPerLP-18
❑ 98PinPerPP-39
❑ 98PinPerSftF-25
❑ 98PinPlu-28
❑ 98PinPluAP-PP15
❑ 98PinPluGAP-PP15
❑ 98PinPluMAP-PP15
❑ 98PinSna-NYY13
❑ 98PinSna-NYY15
❑ 98Revo-104
❑ 98RevoFP-6
❑ 98RevoShow-12
❑ 98RevoSS-104
❑ 98Sco-66
❑ 98ScoRT-12
❑ 98ScoRTSS-PP12
❑ 98ScoRTSSAP-PP12
❑ 98ScoRTSSAP1-PP12
❑ 98ScoRTStarGaz-17
❑ 98ScoSS-PP31
❑ 98ScoSSAP-PP31
❑ 98SkyDugA-74
❑ 98SkyDugAIA-74
❑ 98SP Aut-143
❑ 98SpoIll-125
❑ 98SpoIllEE-125
❑ 98SpoIllFE-125
❑ 98SpoIllODMP-OD20
❑ 98SpoIllTaN-47
❑ 98SpoIllTaN-139
❑ 98SpoIllTaNEE-47
❑ 98SpoIllTaNEE-139
❑ 98SpoIllWSF-143
❑ 98SpoIllWSFEE-143
❑ 98SpoIllWSFFE-143
❑ 98SPxFin-109
❑ 98SPxFinR-109
❑ 98SPxFinS-109
❑ 98StaCluFDI-13
❑ 98StaCluI-13
❑ 98StaCluOneK-13
❑ 98StaCluPP-13
❑ 98StaCluPWP-P1
❑ 98StaCluTIII-T2B
❑ 98StaCluTIII-T16A
❑ 98StaCluTLme-T2B
❑ 98StaCluTLme-T16A
❑ 98StaCluTLmo-T2B
❑ 98StaCluTLmo-T16A
❑ 98Stu-32
❑ 98StuFF-21
❑ 98StuFFDC-21
❑ 98StuGPP-32
❑ 98StuSony99-18
❑ 98StuSPP-32
❑ 98Top-293
❑ 98TopChr-293
❑ 98TopChrR-293
❑ 98TopDevR-293
❑ 98TopDia-293
❑ 98TopGal-85
❑ 98TopGalGP-85
❑ 98TopGalOPP-85
❑ 98TopGalPPI-85
❑ 98TopGalPPIA-85
❑ 98TopGolLabC1-76
❑ 98TopGolLabC1B-76
❑ 98TopGolLabC1One-76
❑ 98TopGolLabC1R-76
❑ 98TopGolLabC2-76
❑ 98TopGolLabC2B-76
❑ 98TopGolLabC2One-76
❑ 98TopGolLabC2R-76
❑ 98TopGolLabC3-76
❑ 98TopGolLabC3B-76
❑ 98TopGolLabC3One-76
❑ 98TopGolLabC3R-76
❑ 98TopMiniC-293
❑ 98TopOpeD-120
❑ 98TopSta-10
❑ 98TopSta'S-44
❑ 98TopSta'SGH-44
❑ 98TopStaB-10
❑ 98TopStaG-10
❑ 98TopStaGR-10
❑ 98TopStaS-10
❑ 98TopStaSteG-44
❑ 98TopSup-18

❑ 98TopSup-18
❑ 98TopTek-7
❑ 98TopTekD-7
❑ 98UD3-89
❑ 98UD3-179
❑ 98UD3-269
❑ 98UD3DieCut-89
❑ 98UD3DieCut-179
❑ 98UD3DieCut-269
❑ 98Ult-51
❑ 98UltDouT-15
❑ 98UltGolM-51
❑ 98UltMas-51
❑ 98UltPlaM-51
❑ 98UppDec-169
❑ 98UppDecNP-NP31
❑ 98UppDecSF-91
❑ 98YanSco-6
❑ 98YanScoP-6
❑ 98YanUppD-169
❑ 98YanUppDWSC-1
❑ 98Zen-72
❑ 98Zen5 xx7-12
❑ 98Zen5x7GoldImp-12
❑ 98Zen5x7Imp-12
❑ 98ZenZ-G-72
❑ 98ZenZ-S-72
❑ 99199Fin-220
❑ 99AllMysFR-M27
❑ 99AurOn DL-13
❑ 99AurPenF-13
❑ 99AurPenF-13
❑ 99AurPenFB-13
❑ 99AurPenFS-13
❑ 99AurSty-13
❑ 99Bow-41
❑ 99BowBes-13
❑ 99BowBesAR-13
❑ 99BowBesR-13
❑ 99BowChr-41
❑ 99BowChrG-41
❑ 99BowChrGR-41
❑ 99BowChrI-41
❑ 99BowChrIR-41
❑ 99BowChrR-41
❑ 99BowGol-41
❑ 99BowInt-41
❑ 99CroRoyB-100
❑ 99CroRoyL-100
❑ 99CroRoyOD-100
❑ 99CroRoyPotG-16
❑ 99CroRoyPP-16
❑ 99CroRoyPPN-16
❑ 99E-X Cen-37
❑ 99E-X CenECFut-37
❑ 99E-X CenECNow-37
❑ 99FinGolRef-220
❑ 99FinProF-PF27
❑ 99FinRef-220
❑ 99FlaShoLeg1-57
❑ 99FlaShoLeg2-57
❑ 99FlaShoLeg3-57
❑ 99FlaShoLegM1-57
❑ 99FlaShoLegM2-57
❑ 99FlaShoLegM3-57
❑ 99FlaShoR1-57
❑ 99FlaShoR2-57
❑ 99FlaShoR3-57
❑ 99Fle-22
❑ 99FleBri-70
❑ 99FleBri2G-70
❑ 99FleBriBlu-70
❑ 99FleBriGol-70
❑ 99FleDiaM-14
❑ 99FleMys-85
❑ 99FleMysG-85
❑ 99FleMysM-85
❑ 99FleSta9-22
❑ 99FleVin'-22
❑ 99FleWarT-22
❑ 99MetUni-17
❑ 99MetUniGM-17
❑ 99MetUniPMG-17
❑ 99Pac-305
❑ 99Pac-305A
❑ 99PacAur-132
❑ 99PacAurOD-132
❑ 99PacCroC-198
❑ 99PacCroC-15
❑ 99PacCroCPB-198
❑ 99PacGolCDC-11
❑ 99PacInv-104
❑ 99PacInvOD-104
❑ 99PacInvPB-104
❑ 99PacInvSF-11
❑ 99PacInvSF-11B
❑ 99PacOme-167
❑ 99PacOmeC-167
❑ 99PacOmeDD-6
❑ 99PacOmeDM-23
❑ 99PacOmeG-167
❑ 99PacOmePB-167
❑ 99PacPar-167
❑ 99PacParC-167
❑ 99PacParFC-13
❑ 99PacParG-167
❑ 99PacParHoloGold-167
❑ 99PacParHS-167
❑ 99PacParOD-167
❑ 99PacParPB-24
❑ 99PacParPB-167
❑ 99PacParRed-167
❑ 99PacPlaB-305
❑ 99PacPlaB-305A
❑ 99PacPri-102
❑ 99PacPriAotG-14
❑ 99PacPriDG-14
❑ 99PacPriHB-102
❑ 99PacPriHG-102
❑ 99PacPriHM-102
❑ 99PacPriHP-102
❑ 99PacPriRed-102
❑ 99PacPriS-49
❑ 99PacPriS206-49
❑ 99PacPriS206R-49
❑ 99PacPriSP-49
❑ 99PacPriSV-49
❑ 99PacRed-305
❑ 99PacRed-305A
❑ 99PacTim-5
❑ 99Pin-29
❑ 99Rev-99
❑ 99RevDiaL-23
❑ 99RevFouP-13
❑ 99RevPremDate-99
❑ 99RevRet-99
❑ 99RevShaSS-99
❑ 99RevThoitS-12
❑ 99RevTri-27
❑ 99RevTri-27
❑ 99SkyMolM-123
❑ 99SkyMolMF-23
❑ 99SkyMolMFS-23
❑ 99SkyMolMFT-23
❑ 99SkyMolMX-123
❑ 99SkyPre-95
❑ 99SkyPreR-95
❑ 99SkyThu-296
❑ 99SkyThuRant-296
❑ 99SkyThuRave-296
❑ 99SkyThuwww-WB10
❑ 99SP Aut-59
❑ 99SpoIll-12
❑ 99SpoIll-157
❑ 99SPxStaF-SF20
❑ 99StaClu-240
❑ 99StaCluC-SCC19
❑ 99StaCluCR-SCC19
❑ 99StaCluFDI-240
❑ 99StaCluOoaK-240
❑ 99StaCluPP-240
❑ 99StaCluTI-T4C
❑ 99StaCluTL-T4C
❑ 99StaCluTL-T4C
❑ 99ThuSkySupR-296
❑ 99Top-222
❑ 99Top-235
❑ 99Top-335
❑ 99Top-458
❑ 99TopAllMF-M27
❑ 99TopBlaLC1-40
❑ 99TopBlaLC2-40
❑ 99TopBlaLC3-40
❑ 99TopChr-222
❑ 99TopChr-235
❑ 99TopChr-335
❑ 99TopChr-458
❑ 99TopChrR-222
❑ 99TopChrR-235
❑ 99TopChrR-335
❑ 99TopChrR-458
❑ 99TopGal-3
❑ 99TopGalAG-AG9
❑ 99TopGalPP-3
❑ 99TopGalPPI-3
❑ 99TopGolL-40
❑ 99TopGolLC1-40
❑ 99TopGolLC2-40
❑ 99TopGolLOtO-40
❑ 99TopMVPP-335
❑ 99TopMVPP-458
❑ 99TopOpeD-150
❑ 99TopRedLC1-40
❑ 99TopRedLC2-40
❑ 99TopRedLC3-40
❑ 99TopSta-55
❑ 99TopSta'S-6
❑ 99TopSta'SG-6
❑ 99TopSta'SGDH-6
❑ 99TopSta1Foil-55
❑ 99TopStaFoil-55
❑ 99TopStaOS-55
❑ 99TopTek-27A
❑ 99TopTek-27B
❑ 99TopTekG-27A
❑ 99TopTekG-27B
❑ 99UD Cho-116
❑ 99UD ChoPCR-116
❑ 99UDHolo-40
❑ 99UDHoloAUsome-40
❑ 99Ult-141
❑ 99UltGolM-141
❑ 99UltMas-141
❑ 99UltPlaM-141
❑ 99UppDec-433
❑ 99UppDecBD-59
❑ 99UppDecBDAPH-BW
❑ 99UppDecBDD-59
❑ 99UppDecBDQ-59
❑ 99UppDecBDT-59
❑ 99UppDecCL-92
❑ 99UppDecCLCC-92
❑ 99UppDecCLM-C62
❑ 99UppDecE-61
❑ 99UppDecE-174
❑ 99UppDecEFXG-61
❑ 99UppDecEFXG-174
❑ 99UppDecEL1-433
❑ 99UppDecEL2-433
❑ 99UppDecEPE-P18
❑ 99UppDecM-140
❑ 99UppDecMGS-140
❑ 99UppDecMHFS-140
❑ 99UppDecMP-140
❑ 99UppDecMSS-140
❑ 99UppDecOAPoH-BW
❑ 99UppDecR-60
❑ 99UppDecRG-60
❑ 99UppDecRI-BW
❑ 99UppDecRIL2-BW
❑ 99UppDecRP-60
❑ 99UppDecTE-T16
❑ 99UppDecTED-T16
❑ 99UppDecTEQ-T16
❑ 99UppDecTET-T16
❑ 99UppDecVtaT-V18
❑ 99UppDecVtaTD-V18
❑ 99UppDecVtaTQ-V18
❑ 99UppDecVtaTT-V18
❑ 99Vic-264
❑ 99Vic-272
❑ 99YanFle-10

Williams, Bernie (Bernard)

❑ 70OPC-401
❑ 70Top-401
❑ 71MLBOffS-264
❑ 71OPC-728
❑ 71Top-728
❑ 72Top-761
❑ 73OPC-557
❑ 73Top-557
❑ 74PadDea-29
❑ 79TCMJapPB-10

Williams, Billy

❑ 88T/MUmp-3

Williams, Billy (William)

❑ 89CanIndB-8
❑ 89CanIndP-1317
❑ 94WatIndC-30
❑ 97WatIndTI-33
❑ 98AkrAerM-3

Williams, Billy Leo

❑ 47Exh-241
❑ 61Top-141
❑ 61TopStal-12
❑ 62CubJayP-12
❑ 62PC7HFGSS-4
❑ 62SalPlaC-207
❑ 62ShiPlaC-207
❑ 62Top-288
❑ 62TopBuc-93
❑ 62TopStal-111
❑ 63CubJayP-12
❑ 63ExhStaB-63
❑ 63Jel-172
❑ 63Pos-172
❑ 63SalMetC-30
❑ 63Top-353
❑ 64Baz-17
❑ 64CubJayP-12
❑ 64Raw-10
❑ 64Top-175
❑ 64TopCoi-44
❑ 64TopGia-52
❑ 64TopRooAB-2
❑ 64TopSta-73
❑ 64TopStaU-75
❑ 64TopTatI-76
❑ 64TopVen-175
❑ 65Baz-17
❑ 65CubJayP-12
❑ 65OldLonC-20
❑ 65OPC-220
❑ 65Top-4
❑ 65Top-220
❑ 65TopEmbI-40
❑ 65TopTral-35
❑ 66Baz-48
❑ 66CubTeal-12
❑ 66Top-217
❑ 66Top-580
❑ 66TopRubI-98
❑ 66TopVen-217
❑ 67Baz-48
❑ 67CokCapC-13
❑ 67CubProPS-12
❑ 67DexPre-223
❑ 67ProPizC-14
❑ 67Top-315
❑ 67TopVen-337
❑ 68AtlOilPBCC-47
❑ 68Baz-14
❑ 68Kah-B37
❑ 68OPC-37
❑ 68Top-37
❑ 68TopActS-7C
❑ 68TopVen-37
❑ 69CubBumS-6
❑ 69CubJewT-19
❑ 69CubPho-12
❑ 69CubTealC-10
❑ 69Kah-B22
❑ 69KelPin-19
❑ 69MilBra-292
❑ 69MLBOffS-126
❑ 69MLBPin-59
❑ 69OPC-4
❑ 69Top-4
❑ 69Top-450
❑ 69TopSta-20
❑ 69TopSup-39
❑ 69TopTeaP-4
❑ 69TraSta-38
❑ 70CubDunD-6
❑ 70Kel-37
❑ 70MLBOffS-24
❑ 70OPC-170
❑ 70SunPin-9
❑ 70Top-170
❑ 70TopSup-40
❑ 71BazNumT-26
❑ 71BazUnn-14
❑ 71Kel-61
❑ 71MilDud-69
❑ 71MLBOffS-48
❑ 71OPC-64
❑ 71OPC-66
❑ 71OPC-350
❑ 71Top-64
❑ 71Top-66
❑ 71Top-350
❑ 71TopCoi-75
❑ 71TopGreM-37
❑ 71TopTat-100
❑ 71TopTat-101
❑ 72CubChi-8
❑ 72CubTeal-12
❑ 72Kel-46A
❑ 72Kel-46B
❑ 72MilBra-362
❑ 72OPC-439
❑ 72OPC-440
❑ 72Top-439
❑ 72Top-440
❑ 72TopPos-21
❑ 73Kel2D-10
❑ 73LinPor-46
❑ 73OPC-61
❑ 73OPC-200
❑ 73SevTraC-78
❑ 73Top-61
❑ 73Top-200
❑ 73TopCanL-53
❑ 73TopCom-23
❑ 73TopPin-23
❑ 74Kel-32
❑ 74OPC-110
❑ 74OPC-338
❑ 74Top-110
❑ 74Top-338
❑ 74TopSta-20
❑ 75OPC-545
❑ 75Top-545
❑ 75TopMin-545
❑ 76OPC-525
❑ 76SSP-496
❑ 76Top-525
❑ 77CubAllT-12
❑ 80CubGreT-1
❑ 80MarExh-30
❑ 80PerHaloFP-199
❑ 80PerHaloFPS-62
❑ 80SSPHOF-197
❑ 81TCM60I-402
❑ 82CubRedL-NNO
❑ 82TCMGreS-13
❑ 83MLBPin-35
❑ 84A'sMot-27
❑ 84CubBriPC-6D
❑ 84CubUno-1
❑ 84OCoandSI-62
❑ 85A'sMot-27
❑ 85CirK-18
❑ 86CubGat-NNO
❑ 86SpoDecG-51
❑ 86SpoDesJM-8
❑ 87CubCan-38
❑ 87CubDavB-NNO
❑ 87DonHig-20
❑ 87HygAllG-47
❑ 88PacLegI-90
❑ 88TopGloA-22
❑ 89HOFStiB-29
❑ 89PacLegI-184
❑ 89PerCelP-42
❑ 89SweBasG-120
❑ 89TopBasT-11
❑ 90IndTeal-46
❑ 90PacLeg-58
❑ 90PerGreM-69
❑ 90SweBasG-13
❑ 91Col-36
❑ 91IndFanC-30
❑ 91Kel3D-9
❑ 91LinDri-28
❑ 91MDAA-9
❑ 91SweBasG-98
❑ 91UppDecS-12
❑ 91UppDecS-15
❑ 91UppDecS-21
❑ 92ActPacA-18
❑ 92ActPacA2-18G
❑ 92CubMar-NNO
❑ 92CubOldS-27
❑ 92UppDecF-47
❑ 92UppDecFG-47
❑ 92UppDecHH-HI9
❑ 92UppDecS-28
❑ 92UppDecS-35
❑ 93ActPacAC-18
❑ 93CubMar-30
❑ 93CubOldSBW-1
❑ 93CubOldSBW-2
❑ 93CubOldSBW-3
❑ 93CubOldSBW-4
❑ 93TedWil-24
❑ 93UppDecS-21
❑ 95JimDeaAG-5
❑ 95TopLegot6M-12
❑ 96IllLot-5
❑ 97St.VinHHS-16
❑ 98DonSigSS-18A
❑ 98DonSigSS-18B
❑ 98SpoIllTaN-35
❑ 98SpoIllTaNEE-35

Williams, Bo

❑ 90SanBerSP-2648

Williams, Bob

❑ 86BurExpP-26
❑ 87NewOriP-15
❑ 88ChaKniTI-2
❑ 88HagSunS-25

Williams, Brent

❑ 91KisDodP-4192

Williams, Brian

❑ 91Cla/Bes-14
❑ 91OscAstC-12
❑ 91OscAstP-685
❑ 92Bow-125
❑ 92Cla1-T96
❑ 92ClaGam-112
❑ 92Don-416
❑ 92FleUpd-88
❑ 92Pin-540
❑ 92PinRoo-23
❑ 92ProFS7-228
❑ 92ScoRoo-108T
❑ 92SkyAAAF-278
❑ 92TopDeb91-186
❑ 92TopGol-787
❑ 92TopGolW-787
❑ 92TucTorF-489
❑ 92TucTorS-622
❑ 92Ult-498
❑ 92UppDec-23
❑ 93AstMot-20
❑ 93AstStaC-22
❑ 93Bow-414
❑ 93Don-692
❑ 93Fle-56
❑ 93Lea-485
❑ 93OPC-369
❑ 93PacSpa-484
❑ 93Pin-339
❑ 93Sco-333
❑ 93Sel-287
❑ 93SelChaR-6
❑ 93StaClu-714
❑ 93StaCluFDI-714
❑ 93StaCluMOP-714
❑ 93Top-614
❑ 93TopGol-614
❑ 93TopInaM-614
❑ 93TopInaR-614
❑ 93TopMic-614
❑ 93Toy-98
❑ 93Ult-48
❑ 93UppDec-286
❑ 93UppDecGold-286
❑ 93USPlaCR-5D
❑ 94AstMot-23
❑ 94BelMarC-29
❑ 94BelMarF-3237
❑ 94ColC-594
❑ 94ColChoGS-594
❑ 94ColChoSS-594
❑ 94Don-284
❑ 94Fin-44
❑ 94FinRef-44
❑ 94Fle-503
❑ 94Pac-278
❑ 94Pin-409
❑ 94PinArtP-409
❑ 94PinMusC-409
❑ 94Sco-150
❑ 94ScoGolR-150
❑ 94StaClu-205
❑ 94StaCluFDI-205
❑ 94StaCluGR-205
❑ 94StaCluMOP-205
❑ 94Top-249
❑ 94TopGol-249
❑ 94TopSpa-249
❑ 94Ult-211
❑ 95ColCho-347
❑ 95ColChoGS-347
❑ 95ColChoSS-347
❑ 95Fle-471
❑ 95FleUpd-191
❑ 95PadMot-12
❑ 96ColCho-358
❑ 96ColChoGS-358
❑ 96ColChoSS-358
❑ 96LeaSigA-244
❑ 96LeaSigAG-245
❑ 96LeaSigAS-245
❑ 96TigHebN-16
❑ 97BalOriP-34
❑ 97RocRedW-28

Williams, Bruce

❑ 83BelBreFr-9

Williams, Bryan

❑ 95StCatSTI-16
❑ 96DunBluJB-25
❑ 96DunBluJTI-29

Williams, Carl

❑ 23Zee-176
❑ 24Zee-120

Williams, Cary

❑ 90ClePhiS-24
❑ 91LinDriAA-523
❑ 91ReaPhiLD-523
❑ 91ReaPhiP-1384
❑ 92ScrRedBF-2461

❑ 92ScrRedBS-497
❑ 93ScrRedBF-2557
❑ 93ScrRedBTI-27
❑ 94ScrRedBF-934
Williams, Charles Prosek
❑ 72OPC-388
❑ 72Top-388
❑ 75Gia-12
❑ 75GiaTeal-18
❑ 75OPC-449
❑ 75Top-449
❑ 75TopMin-449
❑ 76OPC-332
❑ 76SanFraGP-24
❑ 76SSP-98
❑ 76Top-332
❑ 77GiaTeal-25
❑ 77Top-73
❑ 78GiaTeal-25
❑ 78Top-561
❑ 79Top-142
❑ 91MetWIZ-432
Williams, Charlie
❑ 90KinMetB-24
❑ 90KinMetS-25
Williams, Charlie (Charles H.)
❑ 88T/MUmp-41
❑ 89T/MUmp-39
❑ 90T/MUmp-37
Williams, Clifford
❑ 91BenBucCB-17
❑ 91BenBucP-3698
❑ 91RenSilSCLC-7
❑ 93AshTouC-23
❑ 93AshTouF-2280
Williams, Clyde
❑ 99TeaBesR-98
❑ 99TeaBesRG-98
❑ 99TeaBesRS-98
Williams, Curtis
❑ 94JohCitCC-29
❑ 94JohCitCF-3618
Williams, Cy (Fred)
❑ 15SpoNewM-191
❑ 16SpoNewM-190
❑ 17ColE13-191
❑ 17HolBreD-116
❑ 20NatCarE-109
❑ 21E121So1-115
❑ 21Exh-186
❑ 21Nei-118
❑ 21OxfConE-19
❑ 22AmeCarE122-76
❑ 22E120-209
❑ 22W572-115
❑ 22W573-139
❑ 22W575-150
❑ 22WilPatV-30
❑ 23W501-101
❑ 23WilChoV-172
❑ 25Exh-48
❑ 27AmeCarE126-42
❑ 27YorCarE-52
❑ 28Exh-24
❑ 28StaPlaCE-70
❑ 28W502-52
❑ 28W56PlaC-D11A
❑ 28Yue-52
❑ 29ExhFou-12
❑ 31W517-18
❑ 76ISCHooHA-24
❑ 77PhiFav-17
❑ 82TCMGreS-40
❑ 83PhiPosGPaM-1
❑ 91ConTSN-154
Williams, Dallas
❑ 80RocRedWT-2
❑ 81RocRedWT-23
❑ 81RocRedWW-2
❑ 82IndIndTI-26
❑ 83IndIndTI-7
❑ 84EvaTriT-12
❑ 86IndIndTI-26
❑ 87IndIndTI-22
❑ 91OriCro-485
❑ 97HicCraB-3
❑ 97HicCraRB-3
❑ 98WinWar-3
Williams, Dan
❑ 81EdmTraRR-3
❑ 82GleFalWST-12
❑ 83BirBarT-3
❑ 88BurIndP-1799
❑ 89Sta-186
❑ 89WatIndS-23
❑ 90KinIndTI-22
❑ 91KinIndC-24
❑ 91KinIndP-342
❑ 93ColRedC-28
❑ 93ColRedF-616
❑ 94ColRedC-28
❑ 94ColRedF-462
Williams, Dana
❑ 86PawRedSP-27
❑ 87NewBriRSP-16
❑ 87PawRedSP-76
❑ 88PawRedSC-21
❑ 88PawRedSP-460
❑ 89PawRedSC-16
❑ 89PawRedSP-690
❑ 89PawRedSTI-28
❑ 90CMC-651
❑ 90Fle-648
❑ 90FleCan-648
❑ 90ProAAAF-182
❑ 90TopDeb89-144
❑ 90TopTVCu-64
❑ 90VanCanC-24
❑ 90VanCanP-504
❑ 97LanJet-3
Williams, Dave
❑ 85OrlTwiT-24
Williams, Dave (David Carlous)
❑ 52Bow-178
❑ 52Top-316
❑ 53BowC-1
❑ 53Top-120
❑ 54Bow-9
❑ 54NewYorJA-38
❑ 55Bow-138
❑ 55GiaGolS-17
❑ 56GiaJayP-12
❑ 75Gia195T-30
❑ 79TCM50-167
❑ 83TopRep5-316
❑ 85TCMPhoC-37
❑ 91TopArc1-120
Williams, David
❑ 90PulBraB-12
❑ 90PulBraP-3091
❑ 91MacBraC-13
❑ 91MacBraP-866
❑ 92ColMetPI-33
❑ 92DurBulC-24
❑ 92DurBulF-1101
❑ 92DurBulTI-35
❑ 93GreBraF-351
Williams, David A.
❑ 98EriSeaWM-26
Williams, David PCL
❑ 18Zee-93
Williams, Deb
❑ 40SolHug-20
Williams, Dee (Dewey Edgar)
❑ 77TCMTheWY-83
Williams, Dib (Edwin D.)
❑ 33Gou-82
❑ 33RitCE-8C
❑ 34GouCanV-36
❑ 35AlDemDCR3-56
❑ 35GouPuzR-1B
❑ 35GouPuzR-2B
❑ 35GouPuzR-16B
❑ 35GouPuzR-17B
❑ 74A's192T-27
❑ 93ConTSN-859
Williams, Dick H.
❑ 52Top-396
❑ 53Top-125
❑ 54NewYorJA-19
❑ 56A'sPos-49
❑ 56BalOriP-37
❑ 56BalOriP-55
❑ 57IndTeal-27
❑ 57Top-59
❑ 58Top-79A
❑ 58Top-79B
❑ 59Top-292
❑ 60A'sJayP-11
❑ 60A'sTeal-18
❑ 60Top-188
❑ 60TopVen-188
❑ 61Pos-86A
❑ 61Pos-86B
❑ 61Top-8
❑ 61TopStal-168
❑ 62BalOriP-33
❑ 62Jel-32
❑ 62Pos-32
❑ 62PosCan-32
❑ 62SalPlaC-48A
❑ 62SalPlaC-48B
❑ 62ShiPlaC-48
❑ 62Top-382
❑ 63Top-328
❑ 64Top-153
❑ 64TopVen-153
❑ 67OPC-161
❑ 67Top-161
❑ 67TopRedSS-26
❑ 68OPC-87
❑ 68RedSoxTI-8
❑ 68Top-87
❑ 68TopVen-87
❑ 69RedSoxTI-11
❑ 69RedSoxTI-9
❑ 69Top-349
❑ 71OPC-714
❑ 71Top-714
❑ 72OPC-137
❑ 72Top-137
❑ 73A'sPos-42
❑ 73OPC-179
❑ 73Top-179A
❑ 73Top-179B
❑ 74dod195T-16
❑ 75CalAngP-45
❑ 75OPC-236
❑ 75Top-236
❑ 75TopMin-236
❑ 76OPC-304
❑ 76SSP-192
❑ 76Top-304
❑ 77ExpPos-39
❑ 77OPC-108
❑ 77Top-647
❑ 78OPC-27
❑ 78Top-522
❑ 79DiaGre-100
❑ 79ExpPos-32
❑ 79OPC-349
❑ 79TCM50-227
❑ 79Top-606
❑ 80ExpPos-35
❑ 80Top-479
❑ 81Don-453
❑ 81Fle-149
❑ 81RedSoxBG2S-66
❑ 81RedSoxBG2S-126
❑ 81Top-680
❑ 83Don-625
❑ 83PadTeal-32
❑ 83Top-366
❑ 83TopRep5-396
❑ 84Fle-659
❑ 84Nes792-742
❑ 84PadMot-1
❑ 84PadSmo-29
❑ 84Top-742
❑ 84TopTif-742
❑ 85FleStaS-126
❑ 85PadMot-1
❑ 85Top-66
❑ 85TopTif-66
❑ 86DonAll-38
❑ 86MarMot-1
❑ 86RedSoxGT-12
❑ 86Top-681
❑ 86TopGloA-12
❑ 86TopTif-681
❑ 86TopTra-124T
❑ 86TopTraT-124T
❑ 87A'sMot-12
❑ 87MarMot-1
❑ 87Top-418
❑ 87TopTif-418
❑ 88MarMot-1
❑ 88Top-104
❑ 88TopTif-104
❑ 89PacSenL-166
❑ 89PacSenL-183
❑ 89T/MSenL-115
❑ 89T/MSenL-120
❑ 89TopSenL-22
❑ 90DodTar-861
❑ 90EliSenL-33
❑ 91DodRinP2-6
❑ 91OriCro-486
❑ 91SweBasG-99
❑ 91TopArc1-125
❑ 92BazQua5A-6
❑ 92UppDecS-6
❑ 93UppDecS-3
❑ 93UppDecS-10
❑ 93UppDecS-13
❑ 95TopArcBD-33
❑ 95TopArcBD-46
❑ 99SpollIGotG-89
❑ 99SpollIGotGA-77
Williams, Drew
❑ 91MisStaB-49
❑ 92MisStaB-45
❑ 93MisStaB-46
❑ 95BelBreTI-8
❑ 96StoPorB-7
❑ 97El PasDB-12
Williams, Dwayne
❑ 87TamTarP-10
Williams, Earl
❑ 71OPC-52
❑ 71Top-52
❑ 72OPC-380
❑ 72Top-380
❑ 73BalOriP-42
❑ 73BalOriP-43
❑ 73OPC-504
❑ 73OriJohP-32
❑ 73OriTeal-31
❑ 73Top-504
❑ 74OPC-375
❑ 74Top-375
❑ 74TopSta-130
❑ 75AtlBraP-38
❑ 75OPC-97
❑ 75Top-97
❑ 75TopMin-97
❑ 76AtlBraP-33
❑ 76Hos-108
❑ 76OPC-458
❑ 76SSP-13
❑ 76Top-458
❑ 77OPC-252
❑ 77Top-223
❑ 78Hos-16
❑ 78Top-604
❑ 89BluOriS-29
❑ 91OriCro-487
❑ 93UppDecS-2
Williams, Ed
❑ 86IndOhH-24
❑ 86IndTeal-50
Williams, Eddie L.
❑ 85CedRapRT-20
❑ 87BufBisP-13
❑ 87GenCubP-23
❑ 88ColSprSSC-17
❑ 88ColSprSSP-1547
❑ 88Don-46
❑ 88Fle-620
❑ 88FleGlo-620
❑ 88IndTeal-39
❑ 88Lea-46
❑ 88PeoChiTI-32
❑ 88Top-758
❑ 88TopTif-758
❑ 89CedRapRAB-10
❑ 89DonTra-29
❑ 89PeoChiTI-18
❑ 89ScoYouS2-39
❑ 89TopTra-127T
❑ 89TopTraT-127T
❑ 89UppDec-790
❑ 89WhiSoxC-28
❑ 90CedRapRDGB-10
❑ 90LasVegSP-131
❑ 90ProAAAF-19
❑ 90PubIntS-403
❑ 90TriAllGP-AAA28
❑ 90UppDec-289
❑ 90WinSpiTI-25
❑ 91Cla/Bes-408
❑ 91ClaDraP-41
❑ 91Fle-548
❑ 91HigSchPLS-32
❑ 91JohCitCC-1
❑ 91JohCitCP-3980
❑ 91SanJosGC-12
❑ 91Sco-552
❑ 92Bow-331
❑ 92ClaFS7-366
❑ 92ProFS7-323
❑ 92RicBraF-3016
❑ 92RicBraRC-25
❑ 92RicBraS-447
❑ 92SavCarC-1
❑ 92SavCarF-666
❑ 92UppDecML-175
❑ 93ExcFS7-107
❑ 93NewOrlZF-982
❑ 93SprCarC-1
❑ 93SprCarF-1854
❑ 94FleUpd-191
❑ 94LasVegSF-877
❑ 94SavCarC-28
❑ 94SavCarF-511
❑ 95ColCho-345
❑ 95ColChoGS-345
❑ 95ColChoSE-167
❑ 95ColChoSEGS-167
❑ 95ColChoSESS-167
❑ 95ColChoSS-345
❑ 95Don-38
❑ 95DonPreP-38
❑ 95DonTopotO-346
❑ 95Fin-130
❑ 95FinRef-130
❑ 95Fla-423
❑ 95Fle-571
❑ 95Lea-42
❑ 95LeaLim-174
❑ 95PadCHP-14
❑ 95PadMot-18
❑ 95Pin-36
❑ 95PinArtP-36
❑ 95PinMusC-36
❑ 95Sco-113
❑ 95ScoGolR-113
❑ 95ScoPlaTS-113
❑ 95SP-111
❑ 95SPSil-111
❑ 95StaClu-370
❑ 95StaCluMOP-370
❑ 95StaCluSTWS-370
❑ 95StaCluVR-208
❑ 95StaCluVRMO-208
❑ 95Top-208
❑ 95TopCyb-118
❑ 95Ult-238
❑ 95UltGolM-238
❑ 95UppDec-133
❑ 95UppDecED-133
❑ 95UppDecEDG-133
❑ 95UppDecSE-265
❑ 95UppDecSEG-265
❑ 96Don-534
❑ 96DonPreP-534
❑ 96Fle-580
❑ 96FleTif-580
❑ 96FleUpd-U37
❑ 96FleUpdTC-U37
❑ 96Pac-182
❑ 96Sco-166
❑ 96TigHebN-17
❑ 96Ult-289
❑ 96Ult-351
❑ 96UltGolM-289
❑ 96UltGolM-351
❑ 97AlbDukGS-30
❑ 98Las-28
❑ 98PadMot-24
Williams, Edward
❑ 87PeoChiP-18
Williams, Eric
❑ 88GenCubP-1635
❑ 89ChaWheB-2
❑ 89ChaWheP-1756
Williams, Errick
❑ 95MarPhiTI-30
Williams, Flavio
❑ 88WatPirP-29
❑ 89AugPirP-505
❑ 89WelPirP-29
❑ 90SalBucS-24
Williams, Frank
❑ 84FleUpd-127
❑ 84GiaPos-30
❑ 84TopTra-128T
❑ 84TopTraT-128T
❑ 85Don-323
❑ 85Fle-624
❑ 85GiaMot-12
❑ 85GiaPos-30
❑ 85OPC-254
❑ 85Top-487
❑ 85TopMin-487
❑ 85TopSti-169
❑ 85TopTif-487
❑ 86Fle-554
❑ 86PhoFirP-24
❑ 86Top-341
❑ 86TopTif-341
❑ 87Fle-287
❑ 87FleGlo-287
❑ 87FleUpd-127
❑ 87FleUpdG-127
❑ 87RedKah-47
❑ 87Top-96
❑ 87TopTif-96
❑ 87TopTra-128T
❑ 87TopTraT-128T
❑ 88Don-512
❑ 88Fle-250
❑ 88FleGlo-250
❑ 88RedKah-47
❑ 88Sco-317
❑ 88ScoGlo-317
❑ 88StaLinRe-20
❑ 88Top-773
❑ 88TopTif-773
❑ 89Bow-100
❑ 89BowTif-100
❑ 89Don-478
❑ 89DonBasB-259
❑ 89Fle-174
❑ 89FleGlo-174
❑ 89FleUpd-34
❑ 89Sco-485
❑ 89TigMar-36
❑ 89Top-172
❑ 89TopTif-172
❑ 89TopTra-128T
❑ 89TopTraT-128T
❑ 89UppDec-449
❑ 90Don-327
❑ 90Fle-620
❑ 90FleCan-620
❑ 90OPC-599
❑ 90PubIntS-486
❑ 90Sco-341
❑ 90Top-599
❑ 90TopTif-599
❑ 90UppDec-539
Williams, Fred
❑ 21E121So8-108
❑ 86StoPorP-26
❑ 87StoPorP-26
❑ 88ElPasDB-19
❑ 88TexLeaAGS-25
❑ 89JacExpB-18
❑ 89JacExpP-172
❑ 90WesPalBES-27
Williams, Gary
❑ 75WatRoyT-32
❑ 77JacSunT-22
Williams, George
❑ 63Top-324
❑ 64Top-388
Williams, George Erik
❑ 91SouOreAC-5
❑ 91SouOreAP-3851
❑ 92MadMusC-16
❑ 92MadMusF-1239
❑ 93HunStaF-2086
❑ 94ExcFS7-122
❑ 95EdmTraTI-26
❑ 96A'sMot-17
❑ 96ColCho-36
❑ 96ColChoGS-36
❑ 96ColChoSS-36
❑ 96Don-485
❑ 96DonPreP-485
❑ 96Fle-223
❑ 96FleTif-223
❑ 96LeaSigA-245
❑ 96LeaSigAG-246
❑ 96LeaSigAS-246
❑ 96Pin-385
❑ 96PinAfi-185
❑ 96PinAfiAP-185
❑ 96PinFoil-385
❑ 96Sco-258
❑ 96Sum-174
❑ 96SumAbo&B-174
❑ 96SumArtP-174
❑ 96SumFoi-174
❑ 96Ult-405
❑ 96UltGolM-405
❑ 96UppDec-162
❑ 97A'sMot-10
❑ 97ColCho-409
❑ 97Don-171
❑ 97DonGolPP-171
❑ 97DonSilPP-171
❑ 97Sco-315
❑ 97ScoPreS-315
❑ 97ScoShoS-315
❑ 98ColCho-452
❑ 98PacInvGems-88
❑ 98StaCluFDI-109
❑ 98StaCluI-109
❑ 98StaCluOneK-109

❑ 98StaCluPP-109
❑ 98Top-186
❑ 98TopChr-186
❑ 98TopChrR-186
❑ 98TopDevR-186
❑ 98TopDia-186
❑ 98TopMiniC-186
❑ 98UppDec-467

Williams, Gerald
❑ 87OneYanP-6
❑ 88PriWilYS-25
❑ 89PriWilCS-25
❑ 90Ft.LauYS-22
❑ 91AlbYanLD-23
❑ 91AlbYanP-1022
❑ 91Bow-161
❑ 91Cla/Bes-127
❑ 91Cla3-T99
❑ 91LinDriAA-23
❑ 91Ult-388
❑ 91UppDecFE-15F
❑ 92Bow-113
❑ 92ColCliF-366
❑ 92ColCliP-24
❑ 92ColCliS-122
❑ 92Don-697
❑ 92OPC-656
❑ 92ProFS7-115
❑ 92SkyAAAF-60
❑ 92Top-656
❑ 92TopGol-656
❑ 92TopGolW-656
❑ 92TopMic-656
❑ 92TriA AAS-122
❑ 93Bow-271
❑ 93ClaFS7-37
❑ 93ColCliF-1125
❑ 93ColCliP-20
❑ 93Don-49
❑ 93Fle-657
❑ 93Lea-130
❑ 93LeaGolR-R4
❑ 93LeaGolRJ-R4
❑ 93OPC-386
❑ 93Pin-266
❑ 93PinRooTP-9
❑ 93Sco-298
❑ 93ScoBoyoS-11
❑ 93Sel-383
❑ 93StaClu-571
❑ 93StaCluFDI-571
❑ 93StaCluMOP-571
❑ 93Top-654
❑ 93TopGol-654
❑ 93TopInaM-654
❑ 93TopInaR-654
❑ 93TopMic-654
❑ 93Toy-36
❑ 93UppDec-360
❑ 93UppDecGold-360
❑ 93YanStaC-26
❑ 94Don-390
❑ 94FleUpd-71
❑ 94LeaLimR-28
❑ 94Pac-442
❑ 94Pin-142
❑ 94PinArtP-142
❑ 94PinMusC-142
❑ 94Sco-590
❑ 94ScoGolR-590
❑ 94ScoRoo-RT81
❑ 94ScoRooGR-RT81
❑ 94Sel-402
❑ 94SpoRoo-87
❑ 94SpoRooAP-87
❑ 94StaCluT-190
❑ 94StaCluTFDI-190
❑ 94Top-383
❑ 94TopGol-383
❑ 94TopSpa-383
❑ 95Don-152
❑ 95DonPreP-152
❑ 95DonTopotO-131
❑ 95Fle-86
❑ 95Lea-226
❑ 95Sco-267
❑ 95ScoGolR-267
❑ 95ScoPlaTS-267
❑ 95Top-86
❑ 96Don-25
❑ 96DonPreP-25
❑ 96FleUpd-U69
❑ 96FleUpdTC-U69
❑ 97BrePol-29
❑ 97Fle-141
❑ 97FleTif-141
❑ 97Pac-131
❑ 97PacLigB-131
❑ 97PacSil-131
❑ 97Sco-457
❑ 97ScoArtPWB-457
❑ 97ScoResC-457
❑ 97ScoShoS-457
❑ 97ScoShoSAP-457
❑ 97StaClu-284
❑ 97StaCluMOP-284
❑ 97Top-287
❑ 97Ult-307
❑ 97UltGolME-307
❑ 97UltPlaME-307
❑ 98Fle-3
❑ 98MetUni-136
❑ 98MetUniPMG-136
❑ 98Pac-127
❑ 98PacOnl-76
❑ 98PacOnlR-76
❑ 98PacOnlWC-76
❑ 98PacPlaB-127
❑ 98PacRedT-127
❑ 98PacSil-127
❑ 98StaCluFDI-327
❑ 98StaCluI-327
❑ 98StaCluOneK-327
❑ 98StaCluPP-327
❑ 98Top-212
❑ 98TopChr-212
❑ 98TopChrR-212
❑ 98TopDevR-212
❑ 98TopDia-212
❑ 98TopMiniC-212
❑ 98Ult-97
❑ 98Ult-323
❑ 98UltGolM-97
❑ 98UltGolM-323
❑ 98UltMas-97
❑ 98UltMas-323
❑ 98UltPlaM-97
❑ 98UltPlaM-323
❑ 98UppDec-126
❑ 99Fle-435
❑ 99FleSta9-435
❑ 99FleWarT-435
❑ 99Top-98
❑ 99TopChr-98
❑ 99TopChrR-98
❑ 99TopMVPP-98

Williams, Glenn
❑ 77AshTouT-28

Williams, Glenn David
❑ 93AusFut-115
❑ 94SigRooBS-P5
❑ 94SP-19
❑ 94SPDieC-19
❑ 94UppDecAHNIL-15
❑ 95AusFut-44
❑ 95EugEmeTI-28
❑ 95Exc-160
❑ 95UppDec-7
❑ 95UppDecED-7
❑ 95UppDecEDG-7
❑ 95UppDecML-34
❑ 95UppDecML-115
❑ 95UppDecMLFS-34
❑ 95UppDecMLFS-115
❑ 95UppDecSE-16
❑ 95UppDecSEG-16
❑ 96MacBraB-21
❑ 97MacBra-5
❑ 98CarLeaTPQ-8
❑ 98DanQ-C-5

Williams, Greg
❑ 88St.CatBJP-2019
❑ 94ColRedC-23
❑ 94ColRedF-442
❑ 94StaClu-513
❑ 94Ult-441
❑ 95KinIndTI-28

Williams, Gus (August)
❑ 14B18B-37A
❑ 14B18B-37B

Williams, Guy
❑ 24Zee-111
❑ 25Zee-126
❑ 26Zee-155
❑ 27Zee-127

Williams, H.
❑ 86NasPirP-28

Williams, Harold
❑ 80AndBraT-25
❑ 81DurBulT-8
❑ 87SalBucP-15
❑ 88EasLeaAP-46
❑ 88HarSenP-861
❑ 89HarSenP-302
❑ 94HicCraC-25
❑ 94HicCraF-2186
❑ 94SouAtlLAF-SAL28
❑ 95Exc-33
❑ 95ExcLeaL-20
❑ 95PriWilCTI-12
❑ 95SPML-35
❑ 95Top-79
❑ 96BirBarB-9
❑ 96KanCouCTI-29
❑ 98KanCouC-31
❑ 98KanCouCCP-31

Williams, Harry
❑ 11PloCanE-66

Williams, Jaime
❑ 84TucTorC-58
❑ 88OrlTwiB-10

Williams, James A.
❑ 08RosComP-75
❑ 87OldJudN-540

Williams, James Alfred
❑ 76LauIndC-3
❑ 76LauIndC-17
❑ 76LauIndC-29
❑ 76LauIndC-39

Williams, Jamie
❑ 82DayBeaAT-19
❑ 83DayBeaAT-16
❑ 86OscAstP-29
❑ 87VisOakP-1
❑ 90WicStaSGD-36

Williams, Jason
❑ 91MisStaB-50
❑ 93LSUTigM-14
❑ 94LSUTig-4
❑ 94LSUTigMP-16
❑ 97BurBeeB-25
❑ 98Bow-378
❑ 98BowChr-378
❑ 98BowChrGA-378
❑ 98BowChrGAR-378
❑ 98BowChrI-378
❑ 98BowChrIR-378
❑ 98BowChrR-378
❑ 98BowGolA-378
❑ 98BowInt-378
❑ 98IndIndQ-28

Williams, Jay
❑ 88StoPorCLC-203
❑ 88StoPorP-744
❑ 89RocExpLC-29
❑ 90JacExpB-28
❑ 92HarSenF-NNO
❑ 94DurBulC-30
❑ 94DurBulTI-29
❑ 95DurBulTI-37
❑ 96GreBraB-4
❑ 96GreBraTI-TR
❑ 97GreBraG-28
❑ 98GreBraG-27
❑ 98GreBraG-28

Williams, Jeff
❑ 81MiaOriT-19
❑ 84ChaO'sT-20
❑ 86RocRedWP-26
❑ 89ReaPhiB-23
❑ 89ReaPhiP-675
❑ 89ReaPhiS-25
❑ 91Cla/Bes-164
❑ 91FreKeyC-9
❑ 91FreKeyP-2364
❑ 92Bow-284
❑ 92ClaFS7-123
❑ 92HagSunF-2556
❑ 92HagSunS-271
❑ 92ProFS7-10
❑ 92SkyAA F-115
❑ 92UppDecML-318
❑ 93ClaGolF-60
❑ 93ColRedC-18
❑ 93ColRedF-598
❑ 93WatIndC-28
❑ 93WatIndF-3563
❑ 94CalCanF-791
❑ 94ColRedC-24
❑ 94ColRedF-443

Williams, Jeff R.
❑ 97CalLeaATI-25
❑ 97SanBerS-15
❑ 98SanAntMG-30

Williams, Jeffrey Jay
❑ 90WicStaSGD-37

Williams, Jerrone
❑ 88WytCubP-2002
❑ 90PeoChiTI-18
❑ 91Cla/Bes-75
❑ 91WinSpiC-27
❑ 91WinSpiP-2844
❑ 92ChaKniS-173
❑ 92ProFS7-207

Williams, Jessie
❑ 87NegLeaPD-5

Williams, Jewell
❑ 96AppLeaAB-11
❑ 96BurIndB-29
❑ 98ColRedSM-25

Williams, Jim
❑ 70OPC-262
❑ 70Top-262
❑ 71OPC-262
❑ 71Top-262
❑ 75AstPos-29
❑ 75PhoGiaC-2
❑ 75PhoGiaCK-19
❑ 88CalLeaACLC-40

Williams, Jimmy
❑ 76SeaRaiC-20
❑ 79SalLakCGT-22B
❑ 80ChaO'sP-24
❑ 80ChaO'sW-25
❑ 81BalOriP-23
❑ 83OriPos-32
❑ 84BalOriP-40
❑ 85BalOriP-36
❑ 86BalOriP-25
❑ 87BalOriP-40
❑ 87OriFreB-40
❑ 88AlaGolAA60TI-2
❑ 88VisOakCLC-163
❑ 89OrlTwiB-2
❑ 89OrlTwiP-1354
❑ 90CMC-562
❑ 90PorBeaC-10
❑ 90PorBeaP-179
❑ 90ProAAAF-249
❑ 91LinDriAAA-396
❑ 91PhoFirLD-396
❑ 91PhoFirP-68
❑ 93OrlCubF-2785
❑ 94VenLinU-209
❑ 95NorTidTI-30
❑ 96BufBisB-22
❑ 98BufBisG-29

Williams, Jimmy (James Thomas)
❑ 03BreE10-151
❑ 09PC7HHB-46
❑ 09T206-378
❑ 11SpoLifCW-369

Williams, Jimy (James F.)
❑ 66Top-544
❑ 69TopTeaP-10
❑ 77SalLakCGC-1
❑ 78SprRedWK-13
❑ 84BluJayFS-34
❑ 85BluJayFS-34
❑ 86BluJayFS-34
❑ 87BluJayFS-36
❑ 87OPC-279
❑ 87Top-786
❑ 87TopTif-786
❑ 88BluJay5-12
❑ 88BluJayFS-34
❑ 88OPC-314
❑ 88Top-314
❑ 88TopTif-314
❑ 89BluJayFS-33
❑ 89OPC-381
❑ 89Top-594
❑ 89TopTif-594
❑ 90BraDubS-35
❑ 91BraSubS-38
❑ 92BraLykS-35
❑ 93BraLykS-36
❑ 94BraLykP-33
❑ 94BraLykS-32

Williams, Jody
❑ 87WatPirP-19

Williams, Joe
❑ 12Zee-98
❑ 87UtiBluSP-21
❑ 90BoiHawP-3323

Williams, Joel
❑ 98YakBeaG-34

Williams, John
❑ 09ObaT21-171
❑ 12HomRunKE-59
❑ 12Zee-97
❑ 13Zee-94
❑ 15Zee-92

Williams, John Minors
❑ 86BurExpP-27

Williams, Jon
❑ 86DavLipB-22

Williams, Jovany
❑ 98PeoChiM-24

Williams, Juan
❑ 90PulBraB-25
❑ 90PulBraP-3111
❑ 91MacBraC-27
❑ 91MacBraP-880
❑ 92MacBraC-17
❑ 92MacBraF-283
❑ 93ClaFS7-269
❑ 93DurBulC-24
❑ 93DurBulF-502
❑ 93DurBulTI-17
❑ 94DurBulC-26
❑ 94DurBulF-344
❑ 94DurBulTI-30
❑ 94EliTwiC-26
❑ 94EliTwiF-3734
❑ 95BreBtaTI-37
❑ 95RicBraRC-28
❑ 96RicBraB-29
❑ 96RicBraRC-15
❑ 96RicBraUB-29
❑ 97PawRedS-27
❑ 98WesTenDJM-25

Williams, Keith
❑ 93EveGiaC-29
❑ 93EveGiaF-3785
❑ 94BowBes-B80
❑ 94BowBesR-B80
❑ 94ExcFirYPF-8
❑ 94ExcFS7-296
❑ 94SanJosGC-25
❑ 94SanJosGF-2831
❑ 95Bow-103
❑ 95Exc-297
❑ 95Top-658
❑ 96Exc-247
❑ 96PhoFirB-27
❑ 96Top-437
❑ 97ShrCap-26
❑ 97ShrCapB-26
❑ 98FreGriG-30

Williams, Ken
❑ 22W573-138
❑ 31Zee-76
❑ 32Zee-76

Williams, Kenneth Roy
❑ 16Zee-72
❑ 21Exh-187
❑ 21Nei-52
❑ 22E120-105
❑ 22W572-116
❑ 22WilPatV-37
❑ 23W503-16
❑ 23W515-26
❑ 23WilChoV-173
❑ 25Exh-119
❑ 26Exh-119
❑ 26SpoComoA-47
❑ 27AmeCarE126-48
❑ 27Exh-58
❑ 27MidBre-42
❑ 28StaPlaCE-71
❑ 92ConTSN-442
❑ 93ConTSN-940

Williams, Kenneth Royal
❑ 83AppFoxFr-14
❑ 86BufBisP-24
❑ 87DonRoo-11
❑ 87FayGenP-25
❑ 87FleUpd-128
❑ 87FleUpdG-128
❑ 87HawIslP-2
❑ 87SpoRoo2-41
❑ 88Don-334
❑ 88DonBasB-249
❑ 88Fle-412
❑ 88FleGlo-412
❑ 88FleMin-17
❑ 88FleSup-42
❑ 88GleFalTP-918
❑ 88OPC-92
❑ 88PanSti-65
❑ 88Sco-112
❑ 88ScoGlo-112
❑ 88ScoYouSI-6
❑ 88Spo-69
❑ 88StaLinWS-20
❑ 88Top-559
❑ 88TopSti-287
❑ 88TopTif-559
❑ 88WhiSoxC-30
❑ 89Don-337
❑ 89DonTra-17
❑ 89Sco-67
❑ 89TigMar-25
❑ 89TolMudHC-9
❑ 89TolMudHP-763
❑ 89Top-34
❑ 89TopTif-34
❑ 89TopTra-129T
❑ 89TopTraT-129T
❑ 89UppDec-506
❑ 89UppDec-714
❑ 90LonTigP-1270
❑ 90OPC-327
❑ 90PubIntS-487
❑ 90TigCok-27
❑ 90Top-327
❑ 90TopTif-327
❑ 90UppDec-249
❑ 91BluJayFS-32
❑ 91Fle-190
❑ 91MiaMirC-13
❑ 91MiaMirP-409
❑ 91OPC-274
❑ 91Top-274
❑ 91TopDesS-274
❑ 91TopMic-274
❑ 91TopTif-274
❑ 91UppDec-89
❑ 92Sco-354

Williams, Kerman
❑ 85ElmPioT-24
❑ 86ElmPioRSP-29

Williams, Kevin
❑ 82OrlTwiT-1
❑ 83OrlTwiT-4
❑ 88ModA'sCLC-59

Williams, Kris
❑ 97BoiHawG-30

Williams, Landon
❑ 90PenPilS-24

Williams, Lanny
❑ 91ButCopKSP-11
❑ 92GasRanC-20
❑ 92GasRanF-2257
❑ 93ChaRanC-24
❑ 93ChaRanF-1945

Williams, Larry
❑ 98AugGreM-15

Williams, Lefty (Claude)
❑ 15Zee-91
❑ 17ColE13-76A
❑ 17ColE13-190A
❑ 17ColE13-190B
❑ 17HolBreD-117
❑ 18WhiSoxTI-24
❑ 19W514-35
❑ 74CapPub-99
❑ 75WhiSox1T-27
❑ 88LitSunBS-8
❑ 88PacEigMO-11
❑ 88PacEigMO-44
❑ 88PacEigMO-45
❑ 88PacEigMO-49
❑ 88PacEigMO-60
❑ 88PacEigMO-108
❑ 92Man191BSR-25
❑ 94ConTSN-1041
❑ 94ConTSNB-1041

Williams, Leroy
❑ 90KisDodD-28
❑ 93BakDodCLC-26
❑ 93YakBeaC-25
❑ 93YakBeaF-3892

Williams, Mark
❑ 92JohCitCF-3120
❑ 93GleFalRC-28
❑ 93GleFalRF-4006
❑ 93StaCluM-11
❑ 94NewJerCC-28
❑ 94NewJerCF-3421

Williams, Mark Westley
❑ 77SanJosMC-6
❑ 86BirBarTI-21

Williams, Marv
❑ 55SeaPop-21

Williams, Marvin

❑ 86NegLeaF-87

Williams, Matt (Matthew Derrick)

❑ 86EveGiaC-3
❑ 87DonRoo-45
❑ 87FleUpd-129
❑ 87FleUpdG-129
❑ 87GiaMot-22
❑ 87GiaPos-34
❑ 87PhoFirP-2
❑ 87PocGiaTB-12
❑ 87SpoRool-25
❑ 87TopTra-129T
❑ 87TopTraT-129T
❑ 88ClaBlu-246
❑ 88Don-628
❑ 88Fle-101
❑ 88FleGlo-101
❑ 88PhoFirC-18
❑ 88PhoFirP-56
❑ 88Sco-118
❑ 88ScoGlo-118
❑ 88ScoYouSI-18
❑ 88StaLinG-20
❑ 88Top-372
❑ 88TopTif-372
❑ 89Don-594
❑ 89Fle-346
❑ 89FleGlo-346
❑ 89GiaMot-12
❑ 89PanSti-218
❑ 89PhoFirC-18
❑ 89PhoFirP-1485
❑ 89Sco-612
❑ 89Top-628
❑ 89TopTif-628
❑ 89TriAAAP-AAA51
❑ 89UppDec-247
❑ 90Bow-238
❑ 90BowTif-238
❑ 90ClaBlu-73
❑ 90ClaUpd-T11
❑ 90Don-348
❑ 90DonBesN-61
❑ 90DonGraS-1
❑ 90Fle-75
❑ 90FleCan-75
❑ 90GiaMot-9
❑ 90GiaSmo-21
❑ 90Lea-94
❑ 90M.Vpin-92
❑ 90MotMatW-1
❑ 90MotMatW-2
❑ 90MotMatW-3
❑ 90MotMatW-4
❑ 90OPC-41
❑ 90PanSti-366
❑ 90Sco-503
❑ 90ScoMcD-6
❑ 90Spo-70
❑ 90StaMatW-1
❑ 90StaMatW-2
❑ 90StaMatW-3
❑ 90StaMatW-4
❑ 90StaMatW-5
❑ 90StaMatW-6
❑ 90StaMatW-7
❑ 90StaMatW-8
❑ 90StaMatW-9
❑ 90StaMatW-10
❑ 90StaMatW-11
❑ 90Top-41
❑ 90TopBig-96
❑ 90TopMag-35
❑ 90TopSti-88
❑ 90TopTif-41
❑ 90TriAAAC-35
❑ 90UppDec-577
❑ 90UppDecS-2
❑ 90USPlaCA-8H
❑ 90Woo-30
❑ 91Bow-378
❑ 91Bow-618
❑ 91CadElID-61
❑ 91Cla1-T8
❑ 91Cla3-T95
❑ 91ClaGam-158
❑ 91Col-30
❑ 91Don-18
❑ 91Don-685
❑ 91DonEli-8
❑ 91DonGraS-8
❑ 91DonSupD-18
❑ 91Fle-276
❑ 91FleAll-3
❑ 91GiaActIS-3
❑ 91GiaMot-9
❑ 91GiaPacGaE-11
❑ 91GiaSFE-16
❑ 91KinDis-16
❑ 91Lea-93
❑ 91MajLeaCP-65
❑ 91OPC-190
❑ 91OPC-399
❑ 91PanCanT1-17
❑ 91PanFreS-69
❑ 91PanSti-76
❑ 91RedFolS-100
❑ 91Sco-189
❑ 91Sco-667
❑ 91Sco-689
❑ 91Sco100S-77
❑ 91SevCoi-NC15
❑ 91StaClu-295
❑ 91StaPinB-53
❑ 91Stu-259
❑ 91SunSee-24
❑ 91Top-190
❑ 91Top-399
❑ 91TopCraJ2-9
❑ 91TopDesS-190
❑ 91TopDesS-399
❑ 91TopMic-190
❑ 91TopMic-399
❑ 91TopSta-35
❑ 91TopTif-190
❑ 91TopTif-399
❑ 91TopTriH-N11
❑ 91Ult-331
❑ 91UppDec-79
❑ 91UppDec-157
❑ 91UppDecSS-SS13
❑ 92Bow-175
❑ 92Bow-579
❑ 92Cla2-T31
❑ 92ClaGam-45
❑ 92Don-135
❑ 92DonCraJ2-11
❑ 92Fle-650
❑ 92FleLumC-L6
❑ 92Fre-8
❑ 92GiaMot-9
❑ 92GiaPacGaE-35
❑ 92Hig5-130
❑ 92Hig5S-30
❑ 92Lea-373
❑ 92LeaBlaG-373
❑ 92MVPPin-40
❑ 92OPC-445
❑ 92OPCPre-144
❑ 92PanSti-214
❑ 92Pin-28
❑ 92PinTeaP-6
❑ 92RedFolS-99
❑ 92Sco-230
❑ 92Sco100S-95
❑ 92ScoCokD-23
❑ 92ScoImpP-62
❑ 92ScoProP-7
❑ 92SpoIllFK1-64
❑ 92SpoIllFK1-327
❑ 92StaClu-582
❑ 92Stu-120
❑ 92Top-445
❑ 92TopGol-445
❑ 92TopGolW-445
❑ 92TopKid-60
❑ 92TopMic-445
❑ 92TriPla-4
❑ 92Ult-296
❑ 92UltAwaW-13
❑ 92UppDec-154
❑ 92UppDecHRH-HR5
❑ 93Bow-56
❑ 93ColAllG-8
❑ 93DiaMar-117
❑ 93Don-182
❑ 93Fin-25
❑ 93FinRef-25
❑ 93Fla-148
❑ 93Fle-540
❑ 93FunPac-104
❑ 93GiaMot-3
❑ 93GiaPos-33
❑ 93GiaStaC-3
❑ 93Lea-158
❑ 93OPC-348
❑ 93PacSpa-278
❑ 93PanSti-239
❑ 93Pin-67
❑ 93PinHomRC-22
❑ 93RedFolS-102
❑ 93Sco-46
❑ 93Sel-95
❑ 93SP-117
❑ 93SPPlaP-PP20
❑ 93StaClu-287
❑ 93StaCluFDI-287
❑ 93StaCluMOP-287
❑ 93Stu-66
❑ 93Top-225
❑ 93TopGol-225
❑ 93TopInaM-225
❑ 93TopInaR-225
❑ 93TopMic-225
❑ 93TriPla-171
❑ 93Ult-490
❑ 93UppDec-143
❑ 93UppDec-471
❑ 93UppDec-476
❑ 93UppDecGold-143
❑ 93UppDecGold-471
❑ 93UppDecGold-476
❑ 93UppDecHRH-HR21
❑ 94Bow-79
❑ 94BowBes-R8
❑ 94BowBes-X93
❑ 94BowBesR-R8
❑ 94BowBesR-X93
❑ 94ChuHomS-10
❑ 94ChuHomSG-10
❑ 94ColC-299
❑ 94ColChoGS-299
❑ 94ColChoSS-299
❑ 94Don-370
❑ 94DonDom-A4
❑ 94DonDomJ-A4
❑ 94DonSpeE-370
❑ 94Fin-214
❑ 94FinJum-214
❑ 94FinRef-214
❑ 94Fla-448
❑ 94FlaHotG-10
❑ 94FlaInfP-10
❑ 94Fle-704
❑ 94FleExtB-395
❑ 94FleExtBGB-29
❑ 94FleLumC-10
❑ 94FlePro-3
❑ 94FUnPac-90
❑ 94FUnPac-188
❑ 94GiaAMC-24
❑ 94GiaKTV-8
❑ 94GiaMot-7
❑ 94GiaTarBC-27
❑ 94GiaTeal-5
❑ 94GiaTeal-6
❑ 94GiaTeal-9
❑ 94GiaUSPC-1C
❑ 94GiaUSPC-7D
❑ 94Lea-334
❑ 94LeaCleC-10
❑ 94LeaL-160
❑ 94LeaLimGA-6
❑ 94LeaMVPC-N14
❑ 94LeaMVPCG-N14
❑ 94OPC-80
❑ 94Pac-559
❑ 94PacGolP-13
❑ 94PanSti-268
❑ 94Pin-298
❑ 94PinArtP-298
❑ 94PinMusC-298
❑ 94PinRunC-RC39
❑ 94PinTeaP-3
❑ 94PinTheN-16
❑ 94RedFolMI-9
❑ 94Sco-94
❑ 94ScoCyc-TC20
❑ 94ScoDreT-6
❑ 94ScoGolR-94
❑ 94ScoGolS-10
❑ 94Sel-269
❑ 94SP-95
❑ 94SPDieC-95
❑ 94Spo-139
❑ 94Spo-187
❑ 94SpoFanA-AS3
❑ 94SpoRooGGG-GG2
❑ 94StaClu-268
❑ 94StaClu-419
❑ 94StaClu-717
❑ 94StaCluFDI-268
❑ 94StaCluFDI-419
❑ 94StaCluFDI-717
❑ 94StaCluGR-268
❑ 94StaCluGR-419
❑ 94StaCluGR-717
❑ 94StaCluMO-8
❑ 94StaCluMOP-268
❑ 94StaCluMOP-419
❑ 94StaCluMOP-717
❑ 94StaCluMOP-ST14
❑ 94StaCluST-ST14
❑ 94StaCluT-22
❑ 94StaCluTFDI-22
❑ 94Stu-89
❑ 94Top-386
❑ 94Top-550
❑ 94TopBlaG-44
❑ 94TopGol-386
❑ 94TopGol-550
❑ 94TopPre-225
❑ 94TopSpa-386
❑ 94TopSpa-550
❑ 94TopSupS-45
❑ 94TopTraFI-3
❑ 94TriPla-110
❑ 94TriPlaBS-10
❑ 94Ult-296
❑ 94UltAllS-15
❑ 94UltAwaW-13
❑ 94UltHomRK-9
❑ 94UltRBIK-11
❑ 94UppDec-36
❑ 94UppDec-490
❑ 94UppDecAJ-6
❑ 94UppDecAJG-6
❑ 94UppDecED-36
❑ 94UppDecED-490
❑ 94UppDecMLS-MM20
❑ 94UppDecMLSED-MM20
❑ 94USPlaCA-8C
❑ 95Baz-64
❑ 95BazRedH-RH14
❑ 95Bow-278
❑ 95BowBes-R51
❑ 95BowBes-X13
❑ 95BowBesR-R51
❑ 95BowBesR-X13
❑ 95ClaPhoC-48
❑ 95ColCho-71
❑ 95ColChoCtG-CG20
❑ 95ColChoCtG-CG20B
❑ 95ColChoCtG-CG20C
❑ 95ColChoCtGE-20
❑ 95ColChoCtGG-CG20
❑ 95ColChoCtGG-CG20B
❑ 95ColChoCtGG-CG20C
❑ 95ColChoCtGGE-20
❑ 95ColChoGS-71
❑ 95ColChoSE-30
❑ 95ColChoSE-108
❑ 95ColChoSE-137
❑ 95ColChoSE-256
❑ 95ColChoSEGS-30
❑ 95ColChoSEGS-108
❑ 95ColChoSEGS-137
❑ 95ColChoSEGS-256
❑ 95ColChoSESS-30
❑ 95ColChoSESS-108
❑ 95ColChoSESS-137
❑ 95ColChoSESS-256
❑ 95ColChoSS-71
❑ 95DenHol-28
❑ 95Don-365
❑ 95DonAll-NL5
❑ 95DonBomS-1
❑ 95DonDiaK-DK12
❑ 95DonDom-5
❑ 95DonEli-53
❑ 95DonLonBL-4
❑ 95DonPreP-365
❑ 95DonTopotO-360
❑ 95Emo-197
❑ 95EmoMas-10
❑ 95EmoN-12
❑ 95Fin-45
❑ 95FinPowK-PK15
❑ 95FinRef-45
❑ 95Fla-213
❑ 95FlaHotG-12
❑ 95FlaHotN-10
❑ 95FlaInfP-10
❑ 95Fle-593
❑ 95FleAllF-5
❑ 95FleAllS-4
❑ 95FleLeaL-7
❑ 95FleLumC-10
❑ 95FleTeaL-28
❑ 95FleUpdDT-10
❑ 95FleUpdH-20
❑ 95FleUpdSL-10
❑ 95GiaMot-7
❑ 95KinDis-9
❑ 95Kra-30
❑ 95Lea-28
❑ 95LeaCor-6
❑ 95LeaGolS-14
❑ 95LeaGreG-15
❑ 95LeaLim-144
❑ 95LeaLimG-17
❑ 95LeaLimL-11
❑ 95LeaSli-7A
❑ 95LeaSli-7B
❑ 95LeaStaS-9
❑ 95NatPac-2
❑ 95Pac-387
❑ 95PacGolP-20
❑ 95PacPri-123
❑ 95PanSti-54
❑ 95PanSti-116
❑ 95Pin-61
❑ 95Pin-294
❑ 95PinArtP-61
❑ 95PinArtP-294
❑ 95PinFan-17
❑ 95PinGatA-GA15
❑ 95PinMusC-61
❑ 95PinMusC-294
❑ 95PinPin-11
❑ 95PinPinR-11
❑ 95PinRedH-RH11
❑ 95PinTeaP-TP6
❑ 95PinWhiH-WH11
❑ 95Pos-9
❑ 95PosCan-14
❑ 95RedFol-33
❑ 95Sco-5
❑ 95Sco-552
❑ 95ScoDouGC-GC10
❑ 95ScoDreT-DG4
❑ 95ScoGolR-5
❑ 95ScoGolR-552
❑ 95ScoHaloG-HG2
❑ 95ScoPlaTS-5
❑ 95ScoPlaTS-552
❑ 95ScoRul-SR7
❑ 95ScoRulJ-SR7
❑ 95ScoSam-5
❑ 95Sel-112
❑ 95SelArtP-112
❑ 95SelBigS-BS11
❑ 95SelCer-67
❑ 95SelCerGT-7
❑ 95SelCerMG-67
❑ 95SP-113
❑ 95SPCha-95
❑ 95SPChaDC-95
❑ 95Spo-41
❑ 95SpoArtP-41
❑ 95SpoDet-DE2
❑ 95SpoDouT-4
❑ 95SpoHamT-HT11
❑ 95SpoPro-PM6
❑ 95SpoSam-DE2
❑ 95SPPlaP-PP8
❑ 95SPSil-113
❑ 95SPSpeF-48
❑ 95StaClu-191
❑ 95StaClu-315
❑ 95StaCluFDI-191
❑ 95StaCluMO-45
❑ 95StaCluMOP-191
❑ 95StaCluMOP-315
❑ 95StaCluMOP-PZ12
❑ 95StaCluMOP-RL11
❑ 95StaCluMOP-SS18
❑ 95StaCluPZ-PZ12
❑ 95StaCluRL-RL11
❑ 95StaCluSS-SS18
❑ 95StaCluSTWS-191
❑ 95StaCluSTWS-315
❑ 95StaCluVR-99
❑ 95StaCluVRMO-99
❑ 95Stu-24
❑ 95StuGolS-24
❑ 95StuPlaS-24
❑ 95Sum-13
❑ 95Sum-180
❑ 95Sum-200
❑ 95SumBigB-BB7
❑ 95SumNthD-13
❑ 95SumNthD-180
❑ 95SumNthD-200
❑ 95Top-10
❑ 95Top-386
❑ 95TopCyb-8
❑ 95TopEmb-134
❑ 95TopEmbGI-134
❑ 95TopFinIns-5
❑ 95TopLeaL-LL7
❑ 95TopLeaL-LL36
❑ 95TopTra-10T
❑ 95TopTra-158T
❑ 95TopTraPB-10
❑ 95UC3-70
❑ 95UC3-127
❑ 95UC3ArtP-70
❑ 95UC3ArtP-127
❑ 95UC3CycS-CS7
❑ 95UC3InM-IM6
❑ 95Ult-247
❑ 95UltAllS-20
❑ 95UltAllSGM-20
❑ 95UltAwaW-13
❑ 95UltAwaWGM-13
❑ 95UltGolM-247
❑ 95UltHomRK-6
❑ 95UltHomRKGM-6
❑ 95UltPowP-6
❑ 95UltPowPGM-6
❑ 95UltRBIK-7
❑ 95UltRBIKGM-7
❑ 95UppDec-85
❑ 95UppDec-106
❑ 95UppDecED-85
❑ 95UppDecED-106
❑ 95UppDecEDG-85
❑ 95UppDecEDG-106
❑ 95UppDecPAW-H9
❑ 95UppDecPAWE-H9
❑ 95UppDecPLL-R9
❑ 95UppDecPLL-R19
❑ 95UppDecPLLE-R9
❑ 95UppDecPLLE-R19
❑ 95UppDecSE-205
❑ 95UppDecSEG-205
❑ 95USPlaCMLA-1C
❑ 95Zen-74
❑ 95ZenAllS-8
❑ 95ZenZ-4
❑ 96Baz-25
❑ 96Bow-36
❑ 96BowBes-73
❑ 96BowBesAR-73
❑ 96BowBesR-73
❑ 96BowFoi-36
❑ 96Cir-196
❑ 96CirAcc-30
❑ 96CirAcc-P30
❑ 96CirBos-50
❑ 96CirRav-196
❑ 96ColCho-720
❑ 96ColChoCtG-CG24
❑ 96ColChoCtG-CG24B
❑ 96ColChoCtG-CG24C
❑ 96ColChoCtGE-CR24
❑ 96ColChoCtGG-CG24
❑ 96ColChoCtGG-CG24B
❑ 96ColChoCtGG-CG24C
❑ 96ColChoCtGGE-CR24
❑ 96ColChoGS-720
❑ 96ColChoSS-720
❑ 96ColChoYMtP-45
❑ 96ColChoYMtP-45A
❑ 96ColChoYMtPGS-45
❑ 96ColChoYMtPGS-45A
❑ 96Don-365
❑ 96DonPreP-365
❑ 96DonSho-7
❑ 96EmoLegoB-12
❑ 96EmoN-10
❑ 96EmoXL-297
❑ 96EmoXLD-10
❑ 96Fin-B342
❑ 96Fin-G266
❑ 96Fin-S14
❑ 96FinBro-1
❑ 96FinRef-B342
❑ 96FinRef-G266
❑ 96FinRef-S14
❑ 96Fla-395
❑ 96FlaDiaC-12
❑ 96FlaHotG-10
❑ 96FlaPow-10
❑ 96Fle-600
❑ 96FleChe-10
❑ 96FleLumC-12
❑ 96FleRoaW-10
❑ 96FleTif-600
❑ 96FleUpd-U245
❑ 96FleUpdH-20
❑ 96FleUpdSL-10
❑ 96FleUpdSS-10

❑ 96FleUpdTC-U245
❑ 96FleZon-12
❑ 96GiaMot-4
❑ 96Kin-17
❑ 96Lea-52
❑ 96LeaLim-20
❑ 96LeaLimG-20
❑ 96LeaPre-18
❑ 96LeaPreP-18
❑ 96LeaPrePB-52
❑ 96LeaPrePG-52
❑ 96LeaPrePS-52
❑ 96LeaPreSG-26
❑ 96LeaPreSte-26
❑ 96LeaSig-36
❑ 96LeaSigEA-214
❑ 96LeaSigEACM-31
❑ 96LeaSigPPG-36
❑ 96LeaSigPPP-36
❑ 96LibSpo-NNO
❑ 96MetUni-247
❑ 96MetUniHM-10
❑ 96MetUniML-12
❑ 96MetUniP-247
❑ 96MetUniT-10
❑ 96Pac-203
❑ 96PacPri-P68
❑ 96PacPriG-P68
❑ 96PanSti-105
❑ 96Pin-97
❑ 96Pin-160
❑ 96Pin-274
❑ 96PinAfi-66
❑ 96PinAfiAP-66
❑ 96PinAfiFPP-66
❑ 96PinAfiMN-9
❑ 96PinArtP-36
❑ 96PinArtP-87
❑ 96PinArtP-174
❑ 96PinEssotG-4
❑ 96PinFirR-8
❑ 96PinFoil-274
❑ 96PinPow-4
❑ 96PinSlu-8
❑ 96PinSta-36
❑ 96PinSta-87
❑ 96PinSta-174
❑ 96PinTeaP-3
❑ 96ProSta-51
❑ 96Sco-65
❑ 96Sco-360
❑ 96ScoAll-6
❑ 96ScoBigB-7
❑ 96ScoDiaA-26
❑ 96ScoDreT-4
❑ 96ScoDugC-A56
❑ 96ScoDugC-B85
❑ 96ScoDugCAP-A56
❑ 96ScoDugCAP-B85
❑ 96ScoGolS-8
❑ 96ScoNumG-14
❑ 96ScoPowP-5
❑ 96ScoTitT-5
❑ 96Sel-15
❑ 96SelArtP-15
❑ 96SelCer-87
❑ 96SelCerAP-87
❑ 96SelCerCB-87
❑ 96SelCerCR-87
❑ 96SelCerIP-23
❑ 96SelCerMB-87
❑ 96SelCerMG-87
❑ 96SelCerMR-87
❑ 96SelCerSF-17
❑ 96SelClaTF-13
❑ 96SelEnF-20
❑ 96SelTeaN-18
❑ 96SP-165
❑ 96Spo-56
❑ 96Spo-116
❑ 96SpoArtP-56
❑ 96SpoArtP-116
❑ 96SpoDouT-3
❑ 96SpoHitP-8
❑ 96SpoPowS-20
❑ 96SpoPro-14
❑ 96SPPreF-7
❑ 96SPSpeFX-37
❑ 96SPSpeFXDC-37
❑ 96SPx-52
❑ 96SPxGol-52
❑ 96StaClu-45
❑ 96StaCluEPB-45
❑ 96StaCluEPG-45
❑ 96StaCluEPS-45
❑ 96StaCluMOP-45
❑ 96Stu-71
❑ 96StuPrePB-71
❑ 96StuPrePG-71
❑ 96StuPrePS-71
❑ 96Sum-2
❑ 96Sum-161
❑ 96SumAbo&B-2
❑ 96SumAbo&B-161
❑ 96SumArtP-2
❑ 96SumArtP-161
❑ 96SumFoi-2
❑ 96SumFoi-161
❑ 96SumHitI-16
❑ 96SumPos-3
❑ 96TeaOut-89
❑ 96TeaOut-C98
❑ 96Top-12
❑ 96Top-360
❑ 96TopChr-12
❑ 96TopChr-145
❑ 96TopChrR-12
❑ 96TopChrR-145
❑ 96TopChrWC-WC15
❑ 96TopChrWCR-WC15
❑ 96TopGal-173
❑ 96TopGalPPI-173
❑ 96TopLas-96
❑ 96TopLasPC-8
❑ 96TopPowB-12
❑ 96TopPro-NL20
❑ 96TopRoaW-RW20
❑ 96TopWreC-WC15
❑ 96Ult-300
❑ 96Ult-592
❑ 96UltChe-A10
❑ 96UltCheGM-A10
❑ 96UltDiaP-12
❑ 96UltDiaPGM-12
❑ 96UltGolM-300
❑ 96UltGolM-592
❑ 96UltHitM-10
❑ 96UltHitMGM-10
❑ 96UltHomRK-12
❑ 96UltHomRKGM-12
❑ 96UltHomRKR-12
❑ 96UltHomRKRGM-12
❑ 96UltPowP-12
❑ 96UltPowPGM-12
❑ 96UltPriL-14
❑ 96UltPriLGM-14
❑ 96UltRaw-10
❑ 96UltRawGM-10
❑ 96UltThu-20
❑ 96UltThuGM-20
❑ 96UppDec-455
❑ 96UppDecA-18
❑ 96UppDecDD-DD34
❑ 96UppDecDDG-DD34
❑ 96UppDecDDS-DD34
❑ 96UppDecG-GF8
❑ 96UppDecPD-PD20
❑ 96UppDecPHE-H39
❑ 96UppDecPRE-R39
❑ 96UppDecPRE-R49
❑ 96UppDecPreH-H39
❑ 96UppDecPreR-R39
❑ 96UppDecPreR-R49
❑ 96UppDecRunP-RP20
❑ 96Zen-77
❑ 96Zen-145
❑ 96ZenArtP-77
❑ 96ZenArtP-145
❑ 96ZenDiaC-13
❑ 96ZenDiaCP-13
❑ 96ZenMoz-4
❑ 96ZenZ-15
❑ 97Bow-66
❑ 97BowBes-6
❑ 97BowBesAR-6
❑ 97BowBesMI-MI9
❑ 97BowBesMIAR-MI9
❑ 97BowBesMIARI-MI9
❑ 97BowBesMII-MI9
❑ 97BowBesMIR-MI9
❑ 97BowBesMIRI-MI9
❑ 97BowBesR-6
❑ 97BowChr-47
❑ 97BowChrI-47
❑ 97BowChrIR-47
❑ 97BowChrR-47
❑ 97BowInt-66
❑ 97Cir-218
❑ 97CirIco-12
❑ 97CirRav-218
❑ 97ColCho-90
❑ 97ColChoCtG-13A
❑ 97ColChoCtG-13B
❑ 97ColChoCtG-13C
❑ 97ColChoCtGE-CG13
❑ 97ColChoCtGIW-CG13
❑ 97ColChoT-Cl6
❑ 97ColChoTBS-20
❑ 97ColChoTBSWH-20
❑ 97Don-19
❑ 97Don-271
❑ 97DonDom-15
❑ 97DonEli-137
❑ 97DonEliGS-137
❑ 97DonGolPP-19
❑ 97DonGolPP-271
❑ 97DonLim-14
❑ 97DonLim-99
❑ 97DonLim-193
❑ 97DonLimE-14
❑ 97DonLimE-99
❑ 97DonLimE-193
❑ 97DonLimENG-14
❑ 97DonLimFotG-49
❑ 97DonPowA-23
❑ 97DonPowADC-23
❑ 97DonPre-7
❑ 97DonPreCttC-7
❑ 97DonPrePM-10
❑ 97DonRocL-9
❑ 97DonSig-94
❑ 97DonSigA-110
❑ 97DonSigAC-136
❑ 97DonSigAM-136
❑ 97DonSigPPP-94
❑ 97DonSilPP-19
❑ 97DonSilPP-271
❑ 97DonTea-84
❑ 97DonTeaSPE-84
❑ 97E-X2-19
❑ 97E-X2Cred-19
❑ 97E-X2EssCre-19
❑ 97Fin-253
❑ 97Fin-308
❑ 97Fin-336
❑ 97FinEmb-308
❑ 97FinEmb-336
❑ 97FinEmbR-308
❑ 97FinEmbR-336
❑ 97FinRef-253
❑ 97FinRef-308
❑ 97FinRef-336
❑ 97FlaShoDC-20
❑ 97FlaShoLC-99
❑ 97FlaShoLeg0-99
❑ 97FlaShoLeg1-99
❑ 97FlaShoM-A99
❑ 97FlaShoM-B99
❑ 97FlaShoM-C99
❑ 97FlaShoR0-99
❑ 97FlaShoR1-99
❑ 97FlaShoR2-99
❑ 97Fle-489
❑ 97Fle-655
❑ 97Fle-P489
❑ 97FleBleB-10
❑ 97FleDecoE-12
❑ 97FleDecoERT-12
❑ 97FleTif-489
❑ 97FleTif-655
❑ 97FleZon-20
❑ 97IndScoU-1
❑ 97IndScoUTC-1
❑ 97Lea-20
❑ 97Lea-212
❑ 97Lea-389
❑ 97LeaFraM-20
❑ 97LeaFraM-212
❑ 97LeaFraM-389
❑ 97LeaFraMDC-20
❑ 97LeaFraMDC-212
❑ 97LeaFraMDC-389
❑ 97LeaLeaotN-10
❑ 97MetUni-89
❑ 97MetUniMF-10
❑ 97MetUniML-12
❑ 97NewPin-4
❑ 97NewPinAP-4
❑ 97NewPinMC-4
❑ 97NewPinPP-4
❑ 97Pac-450
❑ 97PacLigB-450
❑ 97PacPri-150
❑ 97PacPriLB-150
❑ 97PacPriP-150
❑ 97PacSil-450
❑ 97PhoFirDTTI-3
❑ 97Pin-197
❑ 97PinArtP-PP197
❑ 97PinCer-3
❑ 97PinCerMBla-3
❑ 97PinCerMBlu-3
❑ 97PinCerMG-3
❑ 97PinCerMR-3
❑ 97PinCerR-3
❑ 97PinIns-111
❑ 97PinInsCE-111
❑ 97PinInsDE-111
❑ 97PinMusC-197
❑ 97PinPrePla-197
❑ 97PinTotCPB-3
❑ 97PinTotCPG-3
❑ 97PinTotCPR-3
❑ 97PinX-P-3
❑ 97PinX-PMoS-3
❑ 97PinX-PSfF-59
❑ 97PinX-PSfFU-59
❑ 97Sco-238
❑ 97Sco-361
❑ 97ScoArtPWB-238
❑ 97ScoArtPWB-361
❑ 97ScoHeaotO-14
❑ 97ScoPreS-238
❑ 97ScoResC-361
❑ 97ScoShoS-238
❑ 97ScoShoS-361
❑ 97ScoShoSAP-238
❑ 97ScoShoSAP-361
❑ 97ScoStaaD-20
❑ 97Sel-88
❑ 97SelArtP-88
❑ 97SelCom-88
❑ 97SelRegG-88
❑ 97SP-61
❑ 97SpollI-142
❑ 97SpollIEE-142
❑ 97SPSpeF-37
❑ 97StaClu-203
❑ 97StaCluMat-203
❑ 97StaCluMOP-203
❑ 97Stu-101
❑ 97StuPrePG-101
❑ 97StuPrePS-101
❑ 97Top-385
❑ 97TopChr-132
❑ 97TopChrR-132
❑ 97TopGal-49
❑ 97TopGalPPI-49
❑ 97TopMemO5-50
❑ 97TopSta-60
❑ 97TopStaAM-60
❑ 97UD3-19
❑ 97Ult-300
❑ 97Ult-364
❑ 97UltDiaP-12
❑ 97UltDouT-20
❑ 97UltFieC-18
❑ 97UltGolME-300
❑ 97UltGolME-364
❑ 97UltHRK-12
❑ 97UltPlaME-300
❑ 97UltPlaME-364
❑ 97UltPowP-A12
❑ 97UltTop3-28
❑ 97UltTop3GM-28
❑ 97UppDec-145
❑ 97UppDecAG-AG9
❑ 97UppDecPP-PP9
❑ 97UppDecPPJ-PP9
❑ 98Bow-237
❑ 98BowBes-12
❑ 98BowBesAR-12
❑ 98BowBesR-12
❑ 98BowChr-237
❑ 98BowChrGA-237
❑ 98BowChrGAR-237
❑ 98BowChrI-237
❑ 98BowChrIR-237
❑ 98BowChrR-237
❑ 98BowGolA-237
❑ 98BowInt-237
❑ 98CirThu-9
❑ 98CirThuRav-9
❑ 98CirThuSupRav-9
❑ 98ColCho-80
❑ 98ColCho-266
❑ 98ColCho-300
❑ 98ColChoCtG-CG9A
❑ 98ColChoCtG-CG9B
❑ 98ColChoCtG-CG9C
❑ 98ColChoCtGExch-CG9
❑ 98ColChoCtGIW-CG9
❑ 98ColChoMBH-3
❑ 98ColChoSQ-SQ79
❑ 98CroRoy-9
❑ 98DiaBacP-19
❑ 98DiaMcD-24
❑ 98Don-51
❑ 98Don-231
❑ 98DonCol-51
❑ 98DonColE-443
❑ 98DonColL-218
❑ 98DonColP-621
❑ 98DonColS-51
❑ 98DonCruG-22
❑ 98DonCruP-22
❑ 98DonCruR-22
❑ 98DonEli-43
❑ 98DonEliA-43
❑ 98DonEliS-43
❑ 98DonGolPP-51
❑ 98DonGolPP-231
❑ 98DonLonL-10
❑ 98DonPre-71
❑ 98DonPreSeat-71
❑ 98DonPriCD-51
❑ 98DonPriCE-443
❑ 98DonPriCL-218
❑ 98DonPriCP-621
❑ 98DonSig-34
❑ 98DonSigAC-115
❑ 98DonSigAM-118
❑ 98DonSigP-34
❑ 98DonSilPP-51
❑ 98DonSilPP-231
❑ 98DonSonM9-15
❑ 98E-X2-70
❑ 98E-X2ECFut-70
❑ 98E-X2ECNow-70
❑ 98Fin-215
❑ 98FinNo--215
❑ 98FinNo-R-215
❑ 98FinRef-215
❑ 98FlaShoLeg0-63
❑ 98FlaShoLeg1-63
❑ 98FlaShoLeg2-63
❑ 98FlaShoLeg3-63
❑ 98FlaShoLegM-63
❑ 98FlaShoR0-63
❑ 98FlaShoR1-63
❑ 98FlaShoR2-63
❑ 98FlaShoR3-63
❑ 98Fle-9
❑ 98Fle-356
❑ 98FleVin'-17
❑ 98FleVin'-70
❑ 98FleVin'C-17
❑ 98FleVin'C-70
❑ 98IndSco-11
❑ 98IndScoP-11
❑ 98Lea-18
❑ 98LeaFraDA-18
❑ 98LeaFraF-18
❑ 98LeaFraM-18
❑ 98LeaFraM-18
❑ 98LeaFraMDC-18
❑ 98LeaFraMDC-18
❑ 98LeaFraMZ2-18
❑ 98LeaRS-57
❑ 98LeaRSLHolo-57
❑ 98LeaRSLong-57
❑ 98LeaRSTicMas-19
❑ 98LeaRSTicMasDC-19
❑ 98LeaRTrue-57
❑ 98MetUni-116
❑ 98MetUniPMG-116
❑ 98Pac-81
❑ 98PacAur-101
❑ 98PacAurPF-9
❑ 98PacAurPFC-9
❑ 98PacAurPFPB-9
❑ 98PacAurPFR-9
❑ 98PacAurPFS-9
❑ 98PacHomRH-8
❑ 98PacInv-28
❑ 98PacInvPBlue-28
❑ 98PacInvSilv-28
❑ 98PacInvTeam-29
❑ 98PacOme-16
❑ 98PacOmeOnIns-21
❑ 98PacOmeR-16
❑ 98PacOnl-51
❑ 98PacOnlR-51
❑ 98PacOnlWC-51
❑ 98PacPar-125
❑ 98PacParC-125
❑ 98PacParG-125
❑ 98PacParHS-125
❑ 98PacParPB-125
❑ 98PacParR-125
❑ 98PacParTC-15
❑ 98PacPlaB-81
❑ 98PacRedT-81
❑ 98PacSil-81
❑ 98PacTeaC-29
❑ 98Pin-32
❑ 98PinArtP-PP32
❑ 98PinIns-72
❑ 98PinInsCE-72
❑ 98PinInsDE-72
❑ 98PinMusC-PP32
❑ 98PinPer-72
❑ 98PinPerPP-72
❑ 98PinPerSftF-49
❑ 98PinPlu-149
❑ 98PinPluAP-PP50
❑ 98PinPluGAP-PP50
❑ 98PinPluLM-13
❑ 98PinPluMAP-PP50
❑ 98PinPreP-32
❑ 98PinSna-AD2
❑ 98PinSna-AD18
❑ 98Revo-9
❑ 98RevoSS-9
❑ 98Sco-162
❑ 98ScoRT-165
❑ 98ScoRTSS-PP94
❑ 98ScoRTSSAP-PP94
❑ 98ScoRTSSAP1-PP94
❑ 98ScoSS-PP68
❑ 98ScoSSAP-PP68
❑ 98SkyDugA-2
❑ 98SkyDugAIA-2
❑ 98SP Aut-40
❑ 98SP Aut-SD9
❑ 98SP AutSD-SD9
❑ 98SP AutSDT-SD9
❑ 98SpollI-126
❑ 98SpollIC-C7
❑ 98SpollIEE-126
❑ 98SpollIFE-126
❑ 98SpollIODMP-OD2
❑ 98SpollITaN-140
❑ 98SpollITaNEE-140
❑ 98SpollIWSF-136
❑ 98SpollIWSFEE-136
❑ 98SpollIWSFFE-136
❑ 98SPxFin-245
❑ 98SPxFin-331
❑ 98SPxFinR-245
❑ 98SPxFinR-331
❑ 98SPxFinS-245
❑ 98SPxFinS-331
❑ 98StaCluFDI-304
❑ 98StaCluI-304
❑ 98StaCluOneK-304
❑ 98StaCluPP-304
❑ 98Stu-119
❑ 98StuGPP-119
❑ 98StuSony99-15
❑ 98StuSPP-119
❑ 98Top-12
❑ 98Top-280
❑ 98Top-439
❑ 98TopChr-12
❑ 98TopChr-280
❑ 98TopChr-439
❑ 98TopChrR-12
❑ 98TopChrR-280
❑ 98TopChrR-439
❑ 98TopDevR-12
❑ 98TopDevR-280
❑ 98TopDevR-439
❑ 98TopDia-12
❑ 98TopDia-280
❑ 98TopDia-439
❑ 98TopGal-5
❑ 98TopGalGP-5
❑ 98TopGalOPP-5
❑ 98TopGalPPI-5
❑ 98TopGalPPIA-5
❑ 98TopGolLabC1-6
❑ 98TopGolLabC1B-6
❑ 98TopGolLabC1One-6
❑ 98TopGolLabC1R-6
❑ 98TopGolLabC2-6
❑ 98TopGolLabC2B-6
❑ 98TopGolLabC2One-6
❑ 98TopGolLabC2R-6
❑ 98TopGolLabC3-6
❑ 98TopGolLabC3B-6
❑ 98TopGolLabC3One-6
❑ 98TopGolLabC3R-6
❑ 98TopMiniC-12
❑ 98TopMiniC-280

❑ 98TopMiniC-439
❑ 98TopOpeD-10
❑ 98TopSta-40
❑ 98TopStaB-40
❑ 98TopStaG-40
❑ 98TopStaGR-40
❑ 98TopStaLB-L10
❑ 98TopStaLG-L10
❑ 98TopStaLGR-L10
❑ 98TopStaLS-L10
❑ 98TopStaS-40
❑ 98TopTek-44
❑ 98TopTekD-44
❑ 98UD3-44
❑ 98UD3-134
❑ 98UD3-224
❑ 98UD3DieCut-44
❑ 98UD3DieCut-134
❑ 98UD3DieCut-224
❑ 98Ult-4
❑ 98Ult-459
❑ 98UltBigS-11
❑ 98UltDouT-17
❑ 98UltGolM-4
❑ 98UltGolM-459
❑ 98UltMas-4
❑ 98UltMas-459
❑ 98UltPlaM-4
❑ 98UltPlaM-459
❑ 98UppDec-640
❑ 98UppDec10AP-33
❑ 98UppDec1APR-33
❑ 98UppDecR-5
❑ 98UppDecRGKoG-G13
❑ 98UppDecRTC-TC29
❑ 98UppDecTMT-25
❑ 98UppDecTMTG-25
❑ 98Zen-78
❑ 98Zen5 xx7-49
❑ 98Zen5x7GoldImp-49
❑ 98Zen5x7Imp-49
❑ 98ZenZ-G-78
❑ 98ZenZ-S-78
❑ 99199Fin-94
❑ 99Bow-54
❑ 99BowBes-44
❑ 99BowBesAR-44
❑ 99BowBesR-44
❑ 99BowChr-54
❑ 99BowChrG-54
❑ 99BowChrGR-54
❑ 99BowChrI-54
❑ 99BowChrIR-54
❑ 99BowChrR-54
❑ 99BowGol-54
❑ 99BowInt-54
❑ 99CroRoyB-10
❑ 99CroRoyL-10
❑ 99CroRoyOD-10
❑ 99FinGolRef-94
❑ 99FinRef-94
❑ 99FlaShoLeg1-139
❑ 99FlaShoLeg2-139
❑ 99FlaShoLeg3-139
❑ 99FlaShoLegM1-139
❑ 99FlaShoLegM2-139
❑ 99FlaShoLegM3-139
❑ 99FlaShoR1-139
❑ 99FlaShoR2-139
❑ 99FlaShoR3-139
❑ 99Fle-279
❑ 99FleBri-99
❑ 99FleBri2G-99
❑ 99FleBriBlu-99
❑ 99FleBriGol-99
❑ 99FleMys-86
❑ 99FleMysG-86
❑ 99FleMysM-86
❑ 99FleSta9-279
❑ 99FleWarT-279
❑ 99MetUni-225
❑ 99MetUniGM-225
❑ 99MetUniPMG-225
❑ 99Pac-26
❑ 99PacAur-13
❑ 99PacAurOD-13
❑ 99PacCroC-20
❑ 99PacCroCPB-20
❑ 99PacInv-10
❑ 99PacInvOD-10
❑ 99PacInvPB-10
❑ 99PacOme-16
❑ 99PacOmeC-16
❑ 99PacOmeDM-3
❑ 99PacOmeG-16
❑ 99PacOmeH'-2
❑ 99PacOmePB-16
❑ 99PacPar-18
❑ 99PacParC-18
❑ 99PacParG-18
❑ 99PacParHoloGold-18
❑ 99PacParHS-18
❑ 99PacParOD-18
❑ 99PacParPB-18
❑ 99PacParRed-18
❑ 99PacPlaB-26
❑ 99PacPri-9
❑ 99PacPriHB-9
❑ 99PacPriHG-9
❑ 99PacPriHM-9
❑ 99PacPriHP-9
❑ 99PacPriRed-9
❑ 99PacPriS-148
❑ 99PacPriS206-148
❑ 99PacPriS206R-148
❑ 99PacRed-26
❑ 99Rev-10
❑ 99RevDiaL-3
❑ 99RevPremDate-10
❑ 99RevRet-10
❑ 99RevShaSS-10
❑ 99RevTri-23
❑ 99RevTri-23
❑ 99SkyMolM-23
❑ 99SkyMolMX-23
❑ 99SkyPre-146
❑ 99SkyPreR-146
❑ 99SkyThu-3
❑ 99SkyThuRant-3
❑ 99SkyThuRave-3
❑ 99SP Aut-5
❑ 99SpoIll-163
❑ 99SPx-15
❑ 99SPxFinR-15
❑ 99SPxFinS-15
❑ 99StaClu-260
❑ 99StaCluFDI-260
❑ 99StaCluOoaK-260
❑ 99StaCluPP-260
❑ 99ThuSkySupR-3
❑ 99Top-120
❑ 99TopBlaLC1-60
❑ 99TopBlaLC2-60
❑ 99TopBlaLC3-60
❑ 99TopChr-120
❑ 99TopChrR-120
❑ 99TopGal-56
❑ 99TopGalPP-56
❑ 99TopGalPPI-56
❑ 99TopGolL-60
❑ 99TopGolLC1-60
❑ 99TopGolLC2-60
❑ 99TopGolLOtO-60
❑ 99TopMVPP-120
❑ 99TopOpeD-70
❑ 99TopRedLC1-60
❑ 99TopRedLC2-60
❑ 99TopRedLC3-60
❑ 99TopSta-86
❑ 99TopSta1Foil-86
❑ 99TopStaFoil-86
❑ 99TopStaOS-86
❑ 99UD Cho-50
❑ 99UD ChoP-50
❑ 99UD ChoPCR-50
❑ 99UD Ion-4
❑ 99UD IonR-4
❑ 99Ult-53
❑ 99UltGolM-53
❑ 99UltMas-53
❑ 99UltPlaM-53
❑ 99UppDec-304
❑ 99UppDec10AT-X26
❑ 99UppDec10ATD-X26
❑ 99UppDec10ATHR-X26
❑ 99UppDec10ATT-X26
❑ 99UppDecBD-4
❑ 99UppDecBDD-4
❑ 99UppDecBDQ-4
❑ 99UppDecBDT-4
❑ 99UppDecE-5
❑ 99UppDecE-164
❑ 99UppDecEFXG-5
❑ 99UppDecEFXG-164
❑ 99UppDecEL1-304
❑ 99UppDecEL2-304
❑ 99UppDecM-11
❑ 99UppDecMGS-11
❑ 99UppDecMHFS-11
❑ 99UppDecMP-11
❑ 99UppDecMSS-11
❑ 99UppDecO-9
❑ 99UppDecOMP-S17
❑ 99UppDecOSO-9
❑ 99UppDecR-6
❑ 99UppDecRG-6
❑ 99UppDecRP-6
❑ 99Vic-17

Williams, Matt E.
❑ 82KnoBluJT-8
❑ 83SyrChiT-13
❑ 84SyrChiT-11
❑ 85SyrChiT-12
❑ 86OklCit8P-26
❑ 89SalSpuCLC-140
❑ 89SalSpuP-1825
❑ 93RanKee-381

Williams, Matt Taylor
❑ 92ClaDraP-73
❑ 92FroRowDP-53
❑ 92FroRowDPG-53
❑ 92FroRowDPS-53
❑ 92WatIndC-10
❑ 92WatIndF-3235
❑ 93ClaGolF-147
❑ 93KinIndC-26
❑ 93KinIndF-2249
❑ 93KinIndTI-27
❑ 94KinIndF-2644
❑ 96LynHilB-26
❑ 97St.PetDR-30
❑ 97St.PetDRUB-30
❑ 98NorNavQ-24

Williams, Matthew
❑ 87IdaFalBP-19
❑ 88IdaFalBP-1842

Williams, Mel
❑ 83ReaPhiT-22

Williams, Micah
❑ 98LanLugQ-26

Williams, Michael
❑ 86DavLipB-23
❑ 98BriWhiSQ-28

Williams, Michael M.
❑ 98BurBeeM-24
❑ 98ChaAllCM-15

Williams, Mike
❑ 75WatRoyT-33
❑ 76WatRoyT-33
❑ 77LodDodT-25
❑ 79AlbDukTc-3
❑ 80PhoGiaVNB-1
❑ 80VenLeaS-76
❑ 81PhoGiaVNB-8
❑ 87PocGiaTB-19
❑ 89PacSenL-16

Williams, Mike (Michael Darren)
❑ 90BatCliP-3067
❑ 91Cla/Bes-103
❑ 91ClePhiC-12
❑ 91ClePhiP-1623
❑ 92Bow-152
❑ 92DonRoo-126
❑ 92ReaPhiS-548
❑ 92ScrRedBF-2448
❑ 92SkyAA F-240
❑ 93Bow-568
❑ 93ClaFS7-38
❑ 93FleMajLP-B11
❑ 93ScrRedBF-2545
❑ 93ScrRedBTI-28
❑ 93StaClu-539
❑ 93StaCluFDI-539
❑ 93StaCluMOP-539
❑ 93Top-99
❑ 93TopGol-99
❑ 93TopInaM-99
❑ 93TopInaR-99
❑ 93TopMic-99
❑ 93Ult-94
❑ 94PhiMed-36
❑ 94PhiMel-25
❑ 94PhiUSPC-10H
❑ 94StaCluT-230
❑ 94StaCluTFDI-230
❑ 94Top-447
❑ 94TopGol-447
❑ 94TopSpa-447
❑ 95Top-351
❑ 96Fle-513
❑ 96FleTif-513
❑ 96LeaSigEA-215
❑ 96PhiTeal-35
❑ 97PacPriGotD-GD187
❑ 98PacOnl-599
❑ 98PacOnlR-599
❑ 98PacOnlWC-599

Williams, Mitch
❑ 86DonRoo-19
❑ 86FleUpd-127
❑ 86RanPer-28
❑ 86SpoRoo-20
❑ 86TopTra-125T
❑ 86TopTraT-125T
❑ 87Don-347
❑ 87Fle-142
❑ 87FleGlo-142
❑ 87RanMot-17
❑ 87RanSmo-7
❑ 87SpoTeaP-1
❑ 87Top-291
❑ 87TopTif-291
❑ 87ToyRoo-32
❑ 88Don-161
❑ 88DonBasB-279
❑ 88Fle-482
❑ 88FleGlo-482
❑ 88FleRecS-43
❑ 88OPC-26
❑ 88RanMot-17
❑ 88RanSmo-19
❑ 88Sco-339
❑ 88ScoGlo-339
❑ 88ScoYouS2-31
❑ 88StaLinRa-19
❑ 88Top-26
❑ 88TopTif-26
❑ 89Bow-283
❑ 89BowTif-283
❑ 89CubMar-28
❑ 89Don-225
❑ 89DonBasB-60
❑ 89DonTra-38
❑ 89Fle-536
❑ 89FleGlo-536
❑ 89FleUpd-81
❑ 89OPC-377
❑ 89Sco-301
❑ 89ScoRoo-32T
❑ 89ScoYouSI-27
❑ 89Spo-151
❑ 89Top-411
❑ 89TopSti-247
❑ 89TopTif-411
❑ 89TopTra-130T
❑ 89TopTraT-130T
❑ 89UppDec-95
❑ 89UppDec-778
❑ 90Bow-25
❑ 90BowTif-25
❑ 90ClaBlu-23
❑ 90CubMar-24
❑ 90Don-275
❑ 90DonBesN-75
❑ 90Fle-48
❑ 90Fle-631
❑ 90FleAwaW-43
❑ 90FleBasA-43
❑ 90FleBasAC-43
❑ 90FleBasM-43
❑ 90FleBasMC-43
❑ 90FleCan-48
❑ 90FleCan-631
❑ 90Lea-156
❑ 90M.Vpin-22
❑ 90MLBBasB-48
❑ 90OPC-520
❑ 90PanSti-232
❑ 90PubIntS-210
❑ 90RedFolSB-103
❑ 90Sco-262
❑ 90Sco-695
❑ 90Sco100S-93
❑ 90Spo-196
❑ 90Top-520
❑ 90TopBig-109
❑ 90TopDou-71
❑ 90TopGloS-47
❑ 90TopMinL-52
❑ 90TopSti-48
❑ 90TopStiB-33
❑ 90TopTif-520
❑ 90TopTVA-65
❑ 90TopTVCu-17
❑ 90UppDec-174
❑ 91Don-312
❑ 91Fle-439
❑ 91FleUpd-110
❑ 91Lea-420
❑ 91OPC-335
❑ 91RedFolS-101
❑ 91Sco-220
❑ 91ScoRoo-27T
❑ 91StaClu-261
❑ 91Top-335
❑ 91TopDesS-335
❑ 91TopMic-335
❑ 91TopTif-335
❑ 91TopTra-127T
❑ 91TopTraT-127T
❑ 91Ult-71
❑ 91UltUpd-101
❑ 91UppDec-173
❑ 91UppDec-769
❑ 92Bow-247
❑ 92Don-353
❑ 92Fle-547
❑ 92Hig5-80
❑ 92Lea-301
❑ 92LeaBlaG-301
❑ 92OPC-633
❑ 92PhiMed-32
❑ 92Pin-406
❑ 92Sco-356
❑ 92Sco-892
❑ 92StaClu-499
❑ 92Stu-80
❑ 92Top-633
❑ 92TopGol-633
❑ 92TopGolW-633
❑ 92TopKid-20
❑ 92TopMic-633
❑ 92TriPla-220
❑ 92Ult-549
❑ 92UppDec-410
❑ 92UppDecTMH-54
❑ 93Bow-328
❑ 93CubRol-4
❑ 93Don-40
❑ 93Fin-49
❑ 93FinRef-49
❑ 93Fla-108
❑ 93Fle-498
❑ 93FunPac-147
❑ 93Lea-114
❑ 93OPC-226
❑ 93PacSpa-241
❑ 93PhiMed-35
❑ 93PhiStaC-29
❑ 93Pin-565
❑ 93RanKee-382
❑ 93Sco-367
❑ 93Sel-79
❑ 93SelSam-79
❑ 93SP-180
❑ 93StaClu-180
❑ 93StaCluFDI-180
❑ 93StaCluMOP-180
❑ 93Stu-82
❑ 93Top-235
❑ 93TopGol-235
❑ 93TopInaM-235
❑ 93TopInaR-235
❑ 93TopMic-235
❑ 93TriPla-125
❑ 93Ult-448
❑ 93UppDec-113
❑ 93UppDecGold-113
❑ 94AstMot-2
❑ 94Bow-446
❑ 94ColC-599
❑ 94ColChoGS-599
❑ 94ColChoSS-599
❑ 94Don-319
❑ 94Fin-242
❑ 94FinRef-242
❑ 94Fla-176
❑ 94Fle-604
❑ 94Lea-431
❑ 94OPC-99
❑ 94Pac-490
❑ 94PanSti-232
❑ 94Pin-218
❑ 94PinArtP-218
❑ 94PinMusC-218
❑ 94Sco-217
❑ 94ScoGolR-217
❑ 94StaClu-575
❑ 94StaCluFDI-575
❑ 94StaCluGR-575
❑ 94StaCluMOP-575
❑ 94Top-114
❑ 94TopGol-114
❑ 94TopSpa-114
❑ 94TriPla-30
❑ 94Ult-512
❑ 94UltFir-10
❑ 94UppDec-499
❑ 94UppDecED-499
❑ 95AngMot-16
❑ 95FleUpd-69
❑ 95Lea-310
❑ 95UppDecSE-130
❑ 95UppDecSEG-130

Williams, Nick
❑ 09ObaT21-60
❑ 27Zee-126
❑ 28Zee-148
❑ 29Zee-146
❑ 30Zee-161
❑ 31Zee-114

Williams, Norman
❑ 93BurIndC-27
❑ 93BurIndF-3315
❑ 94ButCopKSP-2

Williams, Otto
❑ 08IndPos-20
❑ 11MecDFT-50
❑ 11SpoLifCW-370

Williams, Patrick
❑ 97EveAquG-28

Williams, Paul
❑ 86ElmPioRSP-30
❑ 88WinHavRSS-27
❑ 90CarLeaA-11
❑ 90LynRedSTI-13
❑ 91LinDriAA-647
❑ 91WilBilLD-647
❑ 91WilBilP-303
❑ 92HagSunS-272

Williams, Quinn
❑ 86BenPhiC-131

Williams, Ray
❑ 88WauTimGS-13
❑ 90SanBerSB-22
❑ 90SanBerSCLC-112
❑ 92GulCoaRSP-25
❑ 94HudValRC-25
❑ 94HudValRF-3396

Williams, Ray R.
❑ 78St.PetCT-26
❑ 79ArkTraT-3
❑ 80ArkTraT-20

Williams, Reggie
❑ 83VerBeaDT-25
❑ 86AlbDukP-28
❑ 86DodPol-51
❑ 86DodUniOP-24
❑ 86DonRoo-5
❑ 86FleUpd-128
❑ 86SpoRoo-19
❑ 87DodMot-15
❑ 87DodPol-9
❑ 87Don-341
❑ 87Fle-460
❑ 87FleGlo-460
❑ 87FleHotS-42
❑ 87FleMin-114
❑ 87FleStiC-124
❑ 87SpoTeaP-14
❑ 87Top-232
❑ 87TopTif-232
❑ 88ColSprSSC-23
❑ 88ColSprSSP-1524
❑ 89BufBisC-23
❑ 89BufBisP-1685
❑ 89CliGiaP-893
❑ 90DodTar-862
❑ 90QuaCitAGS-26
❑ 91MidAngOHP-31
❑ 92EdmTraF-3552
❑ 92EdmTraS-172
❑ 93Don-253
❑ 93Top-543
❑ 93TopGol-543
❑ 93TopInaM-543
❑ 93TopInaR-543
❑ 93TopMic-543
❑ 93VanCanF-2612
❑ 94AlbDukF-857
❑ 95FleUpd-178
❑ 95LinVen-3
❑ 96Sco-252
❑ 98VanCanG-29

Williams, Richard
❑ 22Zee-113

Williams, Rick
❑ 73CedRapAT-20
❑ 78AstPos-27
❑ 78ChaChaT-20
❑ 78MemChiBC-10
❑ 79MemChiT-13
❑ 79Top-437
❑ 80MemChiT-26
❑ 80Top-69

❑ 80TucTorT-4
❑ 81TolMudHT-10
❑ 82TolMudHT-9
❑ 87AstShoSPT-24
❑ 97ChaKni-5
Williams, Ricky
❑ 96PieBolWB-28
❑ 96PieBolWB-30
❑ 98BatMucTI-34
❑ 99JustheS-36
❑ 99JustheS-49
❑ 99JustheSAC-24
❑ 99JustheSAD-15
❑ 99JustheSJN-6
❑ 99JustheSJP-10
❑ 99SP TopP-122
❑ 99SP TopPPE-122
Williams, Rob
❑ 85UtiBluST-8
❑ 87WesPalBEP-657
Williams, Robert E.
❑ 12T207-197
Williams, Rodney
❑ 92LetMouSP-15
❑ 98MadBlaW-20
Williams, Roger
❑ 87PitCubP-21
❑ 88IowCubC-11
❑ 88IowCubP-545
❑ 89IowCubP-1691
Williams, Scott
❑ 85NewOriT-1
Williams, Scottie
❑ 92KinMetC-16
❑ 92KinMetF-1532
Williams, Shad
❑ 92MidLeaATI-53
❑ 92QuaCitRBC-7
❑ 92QuaCitRBF-811
❑ 93MidAngF-323
❑ 94MidAngF-2440
❑ 94MidAngOHP-32
❑ 96Bow-282
❑ 96BowFoi-282
❑ 96VanCanB-29
❑ 97BesAutAS-69
❑ 97MidAngOHP-33
❑ 97PacPriGotD-GD8
❑ 97Ult-33
❑ 97UltGolME-33
❑ 97UltPlaME-33
❑ 97VanCanB-29
❑ 98NorNavQ-25
Williams, Slim
❑ 88VisOakP-96
Williams, Smokey (Joseph)
❑ 74LauOldTBS-1
❑ 83ConMar-57
❑ 86NegLeaF-86
❑ 88ConNegA-12
❑ 88NegLeaD-8
❑ 90NegLeaS-27
❑ 93TedWil-114
Williams, Spin (Don)
❑ 60Top-414
❑ 77PadSchC-64
❑ 78PadFamF-37
❑ 81PadFamF-23
❑ 84PriWilPT-20
❑ 85NasPirT-26
❑ 86NasPirP-27
❑ 87HarSenP-15
❑ 88HarSenP-839
❑ 89SalBucS-NNO
❑ 90EasLeaAP-EL28
❑ 90HarSenP-1209
❑ 90HarSenS-24
❑ 91CarMudP-1102
❑ 91LinDriAA-125
❑ 92BufBisBS-15
❑ 92BufBisF-340
❑ 93CarMudF-2072
❑ 94PirQui-28
❑ 97PirPos-13
Williams, Stan
❑ 59DodMor-6
❑ 59Top-53
❑ 59TopVen-53
❑ 60DodBelB-16
❑ 60DodJayP-15
❑ 60DodTeal-19
❑ 60DodUniO-20
❑ 60Lea-109
❑ 60Top-278
❑ 61DodBelB-40
❑ 61DodJayP-11
❑ 61DodUniO-22
❑ 61Pos-162
❑ 61Top-45
❑ 61Top-190
❑ 62DodBelB-40
❑ 62DodJayP-11
❑ 62DodVol-10
❑ 62Jel-115
❑ 62Pos-115
❑ 62PosCan-115
❑ 62Top-60
❑ 62Top-515
❑ 62TopVen-60
❑ 63Jel-122
❑ 63Pos-122
❑ 63Top-42
❑ 64ChatheY-25
❑ 64Top-505
❑ 65SeaPop-25
❑ 65Top-404
❑ 68OPC-54
❑ 68Top-54
❑ 68TopVen-54
❑ 69OPC-118
❑ 69Top-118
❑ 69TopFou-22
❑ 69TopSta-170
❑ 70OPC-353
❑ 70Top-353
❑ 70TwiTeal-12
❑ 71MLBOffS-478
❑ 71OPC-638
❑ 71Top-638
❑ 72OPC-9
❑ 72Top-9
❑ 79ColCliT-6
❑ 84RedEnq-31
❑ 89DodSmoG-68
❑ 90DodTar-863
❑ 90RedKah-27
❑ 91RedKah-NNO
❑ 92YanWIZ6-137
Williams, Steve
❑ 75ShrCapT-23
❑ 86ClePhiP-25
❑ 87ReaPhiP-24
❑ 89EriOriS-26
❑ 90WauTimB-2
❑ 90WauTimP-2115
❑ 90WauTimS-26
❑ 91FreKeyC-10
Williams, T.J.
❑ 97BriWhiSB-11
Williams, Ted (Theodore Samuel)
❑ 39ExhSal-64A
❑ 39ExhSal-64B
❑ 39GouPreR303A-47
❑ 39PlaBal-92
❑ 39WorWidGTP-47
❑ 39WorWidGV-25
❑ 40PlaBal-27
❑ 41DouPlaR-57
❑ 41DouPlaR-81
❑ 41PlaBal-14
❑ 42RedSoxTI-25
❑ 43MPR302-1-24
❑ 46RedSoxTI-24
❑ 46SpoExcW-9-1B
❑ 47HomBon-48
❑ 47PM1StaP1-217
❑ 47PM1StaP1-218
❑ 47PM1StaP1-219
❑ 47PM1StaP1-220
❑ 47PM1StaP1-221
❑ 47PM1StaP1-222
❑ 47RedSoxTI-23
❑ 47StaPinP2-41
❑ 48BluTin-44
❑ 48RedSoxTI-25
❑ 48SweSpoT-16
❑ 49Lea-76
❑ 49MPR302-2-101
❑ 49RedSoxTI-24
❑ 50AmeNut&CCP-22
❑ 50AmeNut&CCP-23
❑ 50Bow-98
❑ 50RedSoxCL-2
❑ 50RedSoxTI-28
❑ 51Bow-165
❑ 51R42SmaS-113
❑ 51Whe-6
❑ 52BerRos-69
❑ 52RedMan-AL23
❑ 52StaCalL-71B
❑ 52StaCalL-71C
❑ 52StaCalS-85A
❑ 52Whe-30A
❑ 52Whe-30B
❑ 53ExhCan-30
❑ 54Bow-66A
❑ 54Top-1
❑ 54Top-250
❑ 54Wil-20
❑ 55Top-2
❑ 55TopDouH-69
❑ 56Top-5
❑ 56TopHocF-A5
❑ 56TopHocF-B7
❑ 56TopPin-26
❑ 57Top-1
❑ 58HarSta-5
❑ 58JayPubS-10
❑ 58RedSoxJP-12
❑ 58Top-1
❑ 58Top-321
❑ 58Top-485
❑ 59FleWil-1
❑ 59FleWil-2
❑ 59FleWil-3
❑ 59FleWil-4
❑ 59FleWil-5
❑ 59FleWil-6
❑ 59FleWil-7
❑ 59FleWil-8
❑ 59FleWil-9
❑ 59FleWil-10
❑ 59FleWil-11
❑ 59FleWil-12
❑ 59FleWil-13
❑ 59FleWil-14
❑ 59FleWil-15
❑ 59FleWil-16
❑ 59FleWil-17
❑ 59FleWil-18
❑ 59FleWil-19
❑ 59FleWil-20
❑ 59FleWil-21
❑ 59FleWil-22
❑ 59FleWil-23
❑ 59FleWil-24
❑ 59FleWil-25
❑ 59FleWil-26
❑ 59FleWil-27
❑ 59FleWil-28
❑ 59FleWil-29
❑ 59FleWil-30
❑ 59FleWil-31
❑ 59FleWil-32
❑ 59FleWil-33
❑ 59FleWil-34
❑ 59FleWil-35
❑ 59FleWil-36
❑ 59FleWil-37
❑ 59FleWil-38
❑ 59FleWil-39
❑ 59FleWil-40
❑ 59FleWil-41
❑ 59FleWil-42
❑ 59FleWil-43
❑ 59FleWil-44
❑ 59FleWil-45
❑ 59FleWil-46
❑ 59FleWil-47
❑ 59FleWil-48
❑ 59FleWil-49
❑ 59FleWil-50
❑ 59FleWil-51
❑ 59FleWil-52
❑ 59FleWil-53
❑ 59FleWil-54
❑ 59FleWil-55
❑ 59FleWil-56
❑ 59FleWil-57
❑ 59FleWil-58
❑ 59FleWil-59
❑ 59FleWil-60
❑ 59FleWil-61
❑ 59FleWil-62
❑ 59FleWil-63
❑ 59FleWil-64
❑ 59FleWil-65
❑ 59FleWil-66
❑ 59FleWil-67
❑ 59FleWil-68
❑ 59FleWil-69
❑ 59FleWil-70
❑ 59FleWil-71
❑ 59FleWil-72
❑ 59FleWil-73
❑ 59FleWil-74
❑ 59FleWil-75
❑ 59FleWil-76
❑ 59FleWil-77
❑ 59FleWil-78
❑ 59FleWil-79
❑ 59FleWil-80
❑ 59RedSoxJP-12
❑ 60Fle-72
❑ 60KeyChal-49
❑ 60NuHi-39
❑ 60NuHi-52
❑ 60RawGloT-35
❑ 60RedSoxJP-12
❑ 61Fle-152
❑ 61NuSco-439
❑ 61NuSco-452
❑ 63BasMagM-85
❑ 67TopVen-148
❑ 69SenTeal-16
❑ 69SenTeal8-20
❑ 69Top-539
❑ 69Top-650
❑ 70Houof J-32
❑ 70OPC-211
❑ 70Top-211
❑ 71OPC-380
❑ 71Top-380
❑ 72OPC-510
❑ 72RanTeal-26
❑ 72Top-510
❑ 73HalofFPP-19
❑ 74LauAllG-46
❑ 74NewYorNTDiS-3
❑ 74NewYorNTDiS-12
❑ 75McCCob-16
❑ 75RedSox1T-37
❑ 75ShaPiz-10
❑ 75SpoHobBG-7
❑ 75SSP42-19
❑ 75SSP42-28
❑ 75TCMAllG-35
❑ 75TCMHouoJ-34
❑ 76GalBasGHoF-30
❑ 76LauDiaJ-27
❑ 76OPC-347
❑ 76RowExh-16
❑ 76ShaPiz-103
❑ 76TayBow4-21
❑ 76Top-347
❑ 77BobParHoF-52
❑ 77BobParMBC-20
❑ 77BobParMBC-21
❑ 77GalGloG-10
❑ 77GalGloG-230
❑ 77ShaPiz-23
❑ 77Spo-1303
❑ 78DexHaloFP-51
❑ 78HalHalR-10
❑ 78SSP270-177
❑ 78TCM60I-260
❑ 79BasGre-75
❑ 79TCM50-10
❑ 80Lau300-6
❑ 80Lau300-20
❑ 80MarExhH-31
❑ 80PacLeg-61
❑ 80PerHaloFP-104
❑ 80PerHaloFPS-12
❑ 80SSPHOF-104
❑ 81RedSoxBG2S-60
❑ 81RedSoxBG2S-65
❑ 81SanDieSC-8
❑ 81SanDieSC-9
❑ 81SpoHaloF-9
❑ 81TCM60I-444
❑ 82BasCarN-2
❑ 82DavHaloFB-24
❑ 82DiaCla-21
❑ 82FleSta-237
❑ 82GSGalAG-9
❑ 82TCMGreH-1
❑ 82TCMGreS-22
❑ 82TCMStaot5-13
❑ 83DonHOFH-9
❑ 83MLBPin-18
❑ 83TCMPla1942-6
❑ 83TigAlKS-68
❑ 83YanYealT-4
❑ 84DonCha-14
❑ 84OCoandSI-1
❑ 84OCoandSI-80
❑ 84OCoandSI-141
❑ 84SpoDesPW-20
❑ 84TCMBruS-BS2
❑ 85CirK-9
❑ 85DalNatCC-2
❑ 85DonHOFS-2
❑ 85TCMHomRC-10
❑ 85TCMPhoC-20
❑ 85Woo-38
❑ 86BigLeaC-8
❑ 86RedSoxGT-8
❑ 86SpoDecG-25
❑ 86SpoDesJM-1
❑ 86TCM-15
❑ 86TCMSupS-3
❑ 86TCMSupS-10
❑ 87HygAllG-48
❑ 87LeaSpeO*-H5
❑ 87NesDreT-18
❑ 87RedSox1T-6
❑ 87SpoRea-5
❑ 88GreBasS-70
❑ 88PacLegI-50
❑ 88ScoBoxC-T1
❑ 89BowInsT-11
❑ 89BowRepI-11
❑ 89BowTif-R11
❑ 89HOFStiB-28
❑ 89Nis-20
❑ 89PacLegI-154
❑ 89PerCelP-43
❑ 89SweBasG-100
❑ 90BasWit-50
❑ 90Col-23
❑ 90HOFStiB-40
❑ 90PacLeg-59
❑ 90PerGreM-13
❑ 90PerMasW-41
❑ 90PerMasW-42
❑ 90PerMasW-43
❑ 90PerMasW-44
❑ 90PerMasW-45
❑ 90SweBasG-125
❑ 91LinDriAA-348
❑ 91MDAA-17
❑ 91SweBasG-100
❑ 91TopArc1-319
❑ 92BazQua5A-22
❑ 92MVP-9
❑ 92MVP2H-3
❑ 92TVSpoMF5HRC-14
❑ 92UppDec-HH2
❑ 92UppDecF-50
❑ 92UppDecFG-50
❑ 92UppDecHH-HI10
❑ 92UppDecHoB5-1
❑ 92UppDecS-32
❑ 92UppDecS-34
❑ 92UppDecWH-28
❑ 92UppDecWH-29
❑ 92UppDecWH-30
❑ 92UppDecWH-31
❑ 92UppDecWH-32
❑ 92UppDecWH-33
❑ 92UppDecWH-34
❑ 92UppDecWH-35
❑ 92UppDecWH-AU4
❑ 92UppDecWWB-28
❑ 92UppDecWWB-29
❑ 92UppDecWWB-30
❑ 92UppDecWWB-31
❑ 92UppDecWWB-32
❑ 92UppDecWWB-33
❑ 92UppDecWWB-34
❑ 92UppDecWWB-35
❑ 93Ble-53
❑ 93Ble-54
❑ 93RanKee-1
❑ 93TedWil-1
❑ 93TedWil-148
❑ 93TedWilLC-9
❑ 93TedWilLC-AU9
❑ 93TedWilP-1
❑ 93TedWilPC-23
❑ 93TedWilPC-26
❑ 93UppDecAH-126
❑ 93UppDecAH-132
❑ 93UppDecAH-161
❑ 93UppDecAH-162
❑ 93UppDecAHP-1
❑ 93UppDecAHP-3
❑ 93UppDecAHP-4
❑ 94TedWil-1
❑ 94TedWil-143
❑ 94TedWil-P1
❑ 94TedWil-LP2
❑ 94TedWil5C-8
❑ 94UppDecAH-1
❑ 94UppDecAH-50
❑ 94UppDecAH-113
❑ 94UppDecAH-170
❑ 94UppDecAH1-1
❑ 94UppDecAH1-50
❑ 94UppDecAH1-113
❑ 94UppDecAH1-170
❑ 94UppDecAH1A-1
❑ 94UppDecAH1A-250
❑ 94UppDecS-8
❑ 94UppDecS-10
❑ 94UppDecS-11
❑ 94UppDecTAE-51
❑ 94UppDecTAEGM-9
❑ 94UppDecTAELD-LD7
❑ 95EagBalL-5
❑ 97R && NNTW-1
❑ 97R && NNTW-2
❑ 97R && NNTW-3
❑ 97R && NNTW-4
❑ 97R && NNTW-5
❑ 97R && NNTW-6
❑ 97R && NNTW-7
❑ 97R && NNTW-8
❑ 97R && NNTW-9
❑ 97R && NNTW-10
❑ 97R && NNTW-11
❑ 97R && NNTW-12
❑ 97R && NNTW-13
❑ 97R && NNTW-14
❑ 97R && NNTW-15
❑ 97R && NNTW-16
❑ 97R && NNTW-17
❑ 97R && NNTW-18
❑ 99UppDecAP-TW
❑ 99UppDecAPH5AU-TWAU
❑ 99UppDecCL-8
❑ 99UppDecCLCC-8
❑ 99UppDecCLESC-TW
❑ 99UppDecR-96
❑ 99UppDecRG-96
❑ 99UppDecRL-9
❑ 99UppDecRL-13
❑ 99UppDecRL-17
❑ 99UppDecRP-96
Williams, Teddy
❑ 86BelMarCr-123
❑ 87IdaFalBP-10
❑ 87WauTimP-12
❑ 88CalLeaACLC-28
❑ 88SanBerSB-4
❑ 88SanBerSCLC-38
❑ 88SumBraP-419
❑ 89BurBraP-1622
❑ 89BurBraS-25
❑ 89EasLeaDDP-DD36
❑ 89WilBilP-636
❑ 89WilBilS-22
❑ 90Bes-138
❑ 90CMC-759
❑ 90WilBilB-22
❑ 90WilBilP-1071
❑ 90WilBilS-23
❑ 91JacSunLD-348
❑ 91JacSunP-164
❑ 93TolMudHF-1666
Williams, Terrell
❑ 92KinMetC-15
❑ 92KinMetF-1542
Williams, Thomas Jr
❑ 98BriWhiSQ-29
Williams, Tim
❑ 84GreHorT-14
❑ 88CapCodPPaLP-143
❑ 89AlaGol-14
Williams, Todd
❑ 91GreFalDSP-25
❑ 92BakDodCLC-29
❑ 92SanAntMF-3976
❑ 93AlbDukF-1462
❑ 93Bow-182
❑ 93ClaFS7-39
❑ 93DodStaC-30
❑ 93TriAAAGF-16
❑ 94Bow-322
❑ 94Cla-157
❑ 94ClaGolF-11
❑ 94ExcFS7-221
❑ 94Top-713
❑ 94TopGol-713
❑ 94TopSpa-713
❑ 95DodMot-19
❑ 95DodPol-28
❑ 95Fla-371
❑ 95FleUpd-179
❑ 95TopTra-29T
❑ 97ChaLoo-26
❑ 97TexAllM-60

❑ 98IndIndQ-18
❑ 99BasAmeTP-96
❑ 99BasAmeTPG-96
Williams, Tom
❑ 88CapCodPPaLP-118
❑ 93JusSo-11
Williams, Troy
❑ 86BelMarCr-118
❑ 87WauTimP-6
Williams, Vaughn
❑ 87GenCubP-24
Williams, Walt (Walter E.)
❑ 67Top-598
❑ 68OPC-172
❑ 68Top-172
❑ 68TopActS-6A
❑ 68TopVen-172
❑ 69Top-309
❑ 70MLBOffS-191
❑ 70OPC-395
❑ 70Top-395
❑ 70TopBoo-4
❑ 70WhiSoxTI-12
❑ 71OPC-555
❑ 71Top-555
❑ 71TopCoi-36
❑ 72MilBra-363
❑ 72OPC-15
❑ 72Top-15
❑ 72WhiSoxTI1-14
❑ 73OPC-297
❑ 73Top-297
❑ 74OPC-418
❑ 74Top-418
❑ 75YanSSP-21
❑ 76OPC-123
❑ 76SSP-436
❑ 76Top-123
❑ 76VenLeaS-70
❑ 87SumBraP-4
❑ 88DurBulS-24
❑ 89PacSenL-123
❑ 89T/MSenL-116
❑ 89TopSenL-126
❑ 89TulDriGS-2
❑ 89TulDriTI-26
❑ 90EliSenL-120
❑ 90TulDriP-1173
❑ 90TulDriTI-27
❑ 91ChaRanC-29
❑ 92GasRanC-25
❑ 92GasRanF-2268
❑ 92YanWIZ7-166
❑ 93ChaRaiC-27
❑ 93ChaRaiF-1927
❑ 94ChaRivC-26
❑ 94ChaRivF-2689
Williams, Wayne
❑ 80CarMudF-1
Williams, Wes
❑ 79AshTouT-12
Williams, Willie D.
❑ 82DanSunF-18
Williams, Woody (Gregory Scott)
❑ 89DunBluJS-23
❑ 90Bes-210
❑ 90KnoBluJB-18
❑ 90KnoBluJP-1239
❑ 90KnoBluJS-20
❑ 91KnoBluJLD-372
❑ 91KnoBluJP-1768
❑ 91LinDriAA-372
❑ 92SyrChiF-1970
❑ 93FleFinE-297
❑ 93SyrChiF-999
❑ 93TopTra-118T
❑ 94BluJayUSPC-2H
❑ 94BluJayUSPC-8C
❑ 94ColC-300
❑ 94ColChoGS-300
❑ 94ColChoSS-300
❑ 94Fle-349
❑ 94Pac-654
❑ 94StaCluFDI-513
❑ 94StaCluGR-513
❑ 94StaCluMOP-513
❑ 94StaCluT-154
❑ 94StaCluTFDI-154
❑ 94Top-668
❑ 94TopGol-668
❑ 94TopSpa-668
❑ 94VenLinU-114
❑ 95BluJayOH-36
❑ 95Don-197
❑ 95DonPreP-197
❑ 95DonTopotO-180
❑ 95Fla-101
❑ 95Fle-108
❑ 95Top-299
❑ 96BluJayB-6
❑ 96BluJayOH-36
❑ 96Don-44
❑ 96DonPreP-44
❑ 96LeaSigEA-216
❑ 97BluJayOH-36
❑ 97BluJayS-12
❑ 97Fle-520
❑ 97FleTif-520
❑ 97PacPriGotD-GD107
❑ 98Pac-228
❑ 98PacOnl-779
❑ 98PacOnlR-779
❑ 98PacOnlWC-779
❑ 98PacPlaB-228
❑ 98PacRedT-228
❑ 98PacSil-228
❑ 98Top-224
❑ 98TopChr-224
❑ 98TopChrR-224
❑ 98TopDevR-224
❑ 98TopDia-224
❑ 98TopMiniC-224
❑ 98UppDec-526
❑ 99Fle-471
❑ 99FleSta9-471
❑ 99FleWarT-471
❑ 99Pac-450
❑ 99PacPlaB-450
❑ 99PacRed-450
❑ 99StaClu-94
❑ 99StaCluFDI-94
❑ 99StaCluOoaK-94
❑ 99StaCluPP-94
❑ 99Top-184
❑ 99TopChr-184
❑ 99TopChrR-184
❑ 99TopMVPP-184
Williams, Woody (Woodrow Wilson)
❑ 47SigOil-19
❑ 90DodTar-864
Williamson, Antone
❑ 94Cla#1DPMF-DD4
❑ 94ClaUpdCotC-CC4
❑ 94SigRooDP-5
❑ 94SigRooDPS-5
❑ 95ActPacF-55
❑ 95Bes-26
❑ 95ElPasDTI-24
❑ 95Exc-77
❑ 95Pin-169
❑ 95PinArtP-169
❑ 95PinMusC-169
❑ 95ScoDraP-DP6
❑ 95SigRooFD-FD5
❑ 95SigRooFDS-FD5
❑ 95SPML-81
❑ 95UppDecML-199
❑ 95UppDecML-218
❑ 95UppDecMLFS-199
❑ 95UppDecMLFS-218
❑ 95UppDecMLOP-OP15
❑ 96Bow-280
❑ 96BowBes-169
❑ 96BowBesAR-169
❑ 96BowBesR-169
❑ 96BowFoi-280
❑ 96Exc-75
❑ 96SigRooOJTP-T6
❑ 97Don-395
❑ 97DonGolPP-395
❑ 97DonLim-84
❑ 97DonLimE-84
❑ 97DonLimENG-84
❑ 97DonSigA-111
❑ 97DonSigAC-137
❑ 97DonSigAM-137
❑ 97DonSilPP-395
❑ 97Lea-342
❑ 97LeaFraM-342
❑ 97LeaFraMDC-342
❑ 97TucTorB-20
❑ 98ColCho-154
❑ 98DonCol-190
❑ 98DonColS-185
❑ 98DonPriCD-190
❑ 98DonRatR-15
❑ 98DonRatRM-15
❑ 98DonSigA-93
❑ 98DonSigAC-116
❑ 98DonSigAM-119
❑ 98DonSigSB-31
❑ 98Fle-115
❑ 98LouRedQ-14
❑ 98MetUni-181
❑ 98MetUniPMG-181
❑ 98Pin-177
❑ 98PinArtP-PP80
❑ 98PinIns-121
❑ 98PinInsCE-121
❑ 98PinInsDE-121
❑ 98PinMusC-PP80
❑ 98PinPreP-177
❑ 98Sco-243
❑ 98ScoRT-90
❑ 98ScoRTSS-PP65
❑ 98ScoRTSSAP-PP65
❑ 98ScoRTSSAP1-PP65
❑ 98SpoIll-164
❑ 98SpoIllEE-164
❑ 98SpoIllFE-164
❑ 98Ult-234
❑ 98UltGolM-234
❑ 98UltMas-234
❑ 98UltPlaM-234
❑ 98UppDec-123
❑ 98Zen-81
❑ 98ZenZ-G-81
❑ 98ZenZ-S-81
Williamson, Bret
❑ 87TamTarP-13
Williamson, Edward
❑ 87BucN28-26A
❑ 87BucN28-26B
❑ 87OldJudN-223
❑ 87OldJudN-541
❑ 87OldJudN-542
❑ 88GandBCGCE-1
❑ 88WG1CarG-18
❑ 89EdgR.WG-14
Williamson, Greg
❑ 86WatIndP-31
Williamson, Jeremy
❑ 95SpoIndTI-31
❑ 97LanLugTS-30
Williamson, Jim
❑ 66St.PetCTI-20
Williamson, Joel
❑ 93WelPirF-3361
❑ 94AugGreC-26
❑ 94AugGreF-3013
Williamson, Kevin
❑ 87ModA'sC-18
❑ 87ModA'sP-16
Williamson, Mark
❑ 83BeaGolGT-8
❑ 85BeaGolGT-3
❑ 86LasVegSP-24
❑ 87BalOriP-41
❑ 87DonRoo-3
❑ 87OriFreB-32
❑ 88Don-418
❑ 88Fle-574
❑ 88FleGlo-574
❑ 88OriPos-41
❑ 88SanDieSAAG-20
❑ 88StaLinO-19
❑ 88Top-571
❑ 88TopTif-571
❑ 89BalOriP-38
❑ 89Fle-626
❑ 89FleGlo-626
❑ 89OriFreB-32
❑ 89SanDieSAG-20
❑ 89Sco-592
❑ 89Top-546
❑ 89TopBig-147
❑ 89TopTif-546
❑ 90Bow-248
❑ 90BowTif-248
❑ 90Don-406
❑ 90Fle-194
❑ 90FleCan-194
❑ 90Lea-461
❑ 90OPC-13
❑ 90PubIntS-591
❑ 90Sco-332
❑ 90Top-13
❑ 90TopSti-236
❑ 90TopTif-13
❑ 90UppDec-173
❑ 91BalOriP-24
❑ 91Bow-85
❑ 91Don-238
❑ 91Fle-495
❑ 91Lea-21
❑ 91OPC-296
❑ 91OriCro-488
❑ 91Sco-498
❑ 91StaClu-20
❑ 91StaCluMO-10
❑ 91Top-296
❑ 91TopDesS-296
❑ 91TopMic-296
❑ 91TopTif-296
❑ 91UppDec-510
❑ 92BalOriP-37
❑ 92Don-511
❑ 92Fle-30
❑ 92OPC-628
❑ 92Sco-427
❑ 92Sco-487
❑ 92StaClu-177
❑ 92Top-628
❑ 92TopGol-628
❑ 92TopGolW-628
❑ 92TopMic-628
❑ 92UppDec-609
❑ 93BalOriP-38
❑ 93FleFinE-168
❑ 93StaClu-613
❑ 93StaCluFDI-613
❑ 93StaCluMOP-613
❑ 93Ult-504
❑ 93UppDec-722
❑ 93UppDecGold-722
❑ 94BalOriP-35
❑ 94Fle-24
❑ 94OriPro-106
❑ 94Sco-157
❑ 94ScoGolR-157
Williamson, Matt
❑ 94BatCliF-3457
❑ 94MarPhiC-29
❑ 95PiePhiF-196
Williamson, Mike
❑ 77AshTouT-29
Williamson, Ray
❑ 87WatIndP-22
❑ 88KinIndS-24
Williamson, Scott
❑ 98Bow-371
❑ 98BowChr-371
❑ 98BowChrGA-371
❑ 98BowChrGAR-371
❑ 98BowChrI-371
❑ 98BowChrIR-371
❑ 98BowChrR-371
❑ 98BowGolA-371
❑ 98BowInt-371
❑ 98ChaLooG-30
❑ 98SouLeaTPG-7
❑ 99Bow-203
❑ 99BowChr-203
❑ 99BowChrG-203
❑ 99BowChrGR-203
❑ 99BowChrI-203
❑ 99BowChrIR-203
❑ 99BowChrR-203
❑ 99BowGol-203
❑ 99BowInt-203
❑ 99DumSet-108
❑ 99FleMys-108
❑ 99FleMysM-108
❑ 99PacOme-68
❑ 99PacOmeC-68
❑ 99PacOmeG-68
❑ 99PacOmePB-68
❑ 99SkyPre-243
❑ 99SkyPre-243
❑ 99SkyPreR-243
❑ 99SkyPreR-243
Williamson, Tyler
❑ 94EugEmeC-24
❑ 94EugEmeF-3717
Williard, Brian
❑ 93CedRapKC-24
❑ 93CedRapKF-1740
❑ 94CedRapKC-22
❑ 94CedRapKF-1110
❑ 95LakElsSTI-27
Willie, Prince
❑ 91PriWilCC-30
Willis, Alan
❑ 80WatIndT-7
❑ 82WatIndT-11
Willis, C.H.
❑ 87OldJudN-543
Willis, Carl
❑ 84EvaTriT-22
❑ 87Fle-218
❑ 87FleGlo-218
❑ 87NasSouTI-23
❑ 87Top-101
❑ 87TopTif-101
❑ 88VanCanC-4
❑ 88VanCanP-762
❑ 89EdmTraC-3
❑ 89EdmTraP-567
❑ 90CMC-460
❑ 90ColSprSSC-8
❑ 90ColSprSSP-38
❑ 90ProAAAF-219
❑ 91DodPho-28
❑ 91LinDriAAA-423
❑ 91PorBeaLD-423
❑ 91PorBeaP-1567
❑ 92Bow-466
❑ 92Don-665
❑ 92Lea-452
❑ 92LeaBlaG-452
❑ 92OPC-393
❑ 92Pin-491
❑ 92Sco-482
❑ 92StaClu-779
❑ 92StaCluNC-779
❑ 92Ult-403
❑ 93Fle-275
❑ 93Lea-164
❑ 93OPC-388
❑ 93PacSpa-527
❑ 93Pin-372
❑ 93StaClu-182
❑ 93StaCluFDI-182
❑ 93StaCluMOP-182
❑ 93Top-747
❑ 93TopGol-747
❑ 93TopInaM-747
❑ 93TopInaR-747
❑ 93TopMic-747
❑ 93Ult-239
❑ 94Don-581
❑ 94Fle-222
❑ 94Lea-198
❑ 94Pac-370
❑ 94Pin-378
❑ 94PinArtP-378
❑ 94PinMusC-378
❑ 94StaClu-484
❑ 94StaCluFDI-484
❑ 94StaCluGR-484
❑ 94StaCluMOP-484
❑ 94Top-621
❑ 94TopGol-621
❑ 94TopSpa-621
❑ 95Fle-217
❑ 95Sco-178
❑ 95ScoGolR-178
❑ 95ScoPlaTS-178
❑ 95Top-302
❑ 97WatIndTI-34
Willis, Craig
❑ 98EveAquG-27
Willis, Dale
❑ 77FriOneYW-85
Willis, David
❑ 97SpoIndG-29
❑ 98LanLugQ-22
Willis, Jim
❑ 54Top-67
❑ 87AppFoxP-30
❑ 94TopArc1-67
❑ 94TopArc1G-67
Willis, Kent
❑ 87TamTarP-17
❑ 88RocExpLC-34
❑ 88VirGenS-22
❑ 97DanBraB-6
Willis, Les
❑ 47IndTeal-26
❑ 47IndVanPP-25
Willis, Marty
❑ 89LakTigS-25
❑ 90LakTigS-25
❑ 91Cla/Bes-6
❑ 91LinDriAA-398
❑ 91LonTigLD-398
❑ 91LonTigP-1879
❑ 92LonTigF-634
❑ 92LonTigS-423
Willis, Mike
❑ 75IntLeaAT-18
❑ 75IntLeaAT-28
❑ 76SSP-382
❑ 76VenLeaS-177
❑ 77OPC-103
❑ 77Top-493
❑ 78BluJayP-24
❑ 78OPC-227
❑ 78Top-293
❑ 79OPC-366
❑ 79Top-688
❑ 80SyrChiT-7
❑ 80SyrChiTI-24
❑ 81Fle-426
❑ 81OPC-324
❑ 81Top-324
❑ 82OklCit8T-1
❑ 87MaiGuiT-25
Willis, Ralph
❑ 09ObaT21-61
❑ 09ObaT21-172
Willis, Ron
❑ 67Top-592
❑ 68OPC-68
❑ 68Top-68
❑ 68TopVen-68
❑ 69Top-273
Willis, Scott
❑ 87CedRapRP-3
Willis, Steve
❑ 87AncGlaP-31
❑ 89AriStaB-27
Willis, Symmion
❑ 96MedHatBJTI-32
❑ 97HagSunB-26
❑ 98DunBluJSB-7
Willis, Travis
❑ 89GenCubP-1867
❑ 90PeoChiTI-29
❑ 91CarLeaAP-CAR46
❑ 91WinSpiC-11
❑ 91WinSpiP-2830
❑ 92ChaKniF-2773
❑ 93OrlCubF-2786
❑ 94BufBisF-1839
❑ 94ExcFS7-171
Willis, Vic
❑ 03BreE10-152
❑ 06FanCraNL-52
❑ 08AmeCarE91-97
❑ 09AmeCarE90-1-117
❑ 09PC7HHB-45
❑ 09PhiCarE-24
❑ 09T206-379
❑ 09T206-380
❑ 09T206-381
❑ 10NadE1-58
❑ 11PinT-5-351
❑ 11SpoLifM-279
❑ 11TurRedT-40
❑ 80PerHaloFP-224
❑ 86PirGreT-9
Willming, Gregory
❑ 93EriSaiC-25
❑ 93EriSaiF-3117
❑ 94ChaRivF-2675
Willoughby, Claude
❑ 29PorandAR-99
❑ 32Zee-111
❑ 93ConTSN-792
Willoughby, Jim
❑ 72GiaTeal-18
❑ 73OPC-79
❑ 73Top-79
❑ 74OPC-553
❑ 74Top-553
❑ 75TulOil7-9
❑ 76OPC-102
❑ 76SSP-419
❑ 76Top-102
❑ 77Top-532
❑ 78Top-373
❑ 79Top-266
❑ 89PacSenL-37
❑ 89TopSenL-70
❑ 91PacSenL-88
Willoughby, Justin
❑ 98DanBraQ-10
Willoughby, Mark
❑ 86ColMetP-27A
❑ 86ColMetP-27B
❑ 89PitMetS-23
❑ 89Sta-165
Wills, Adrian Charles
❑ 87GreBraB-8
Wills, Bump
❑ 76SacSolC-17
❑ 77SpoIllAC-3
❑ 77Top-494
❑ 78Hos-21
❑ 78OPC-208
❑ 78RanBurK-12
❑ 78RCColC-100

❑ 78SSP270-95
❑ 78Top-23
❑ 79BasPat-96
❑ 79OPC-190
❑ 79Top-369A
❑ 79Top-369B
❑ 80OPC-373
❑ 80Top-473
❑ 81AllGamPI-18
❑ 81Don-25
❑ 81Fle-628
❑ 81OPC-173
❑ 81Top-173
❑ 81TopSti-134
❑ 81TopSupHT-96
❑ 82CubRedL-17
❑ 82Don-289
❑ 82Fle-334
❑ 82FleSta-175
❑ 82OPC-272
❑ 82Top-272
❑ 82TopSti-244
❑ 82TopTra-129T
❑ 83Don-351
❑ 83Fle-511
❑ 83FleSta-216
❑ 83FleSti-124
❑ 83Top-643
❑ 86RanGreT-6
❑ 88ButCopKSP-29
❑ 89ButCopKSP-24
❑ 91GasRanC-17
❑ 91GasRanP-2704
❑ 92ChaRanC-26
❑ 92ChaRanF-2240
❑ 93RanKee-383
❑ 95HudValRTI-28
❑ 96HudValRB-24

Wills, Frank
❑ 82OmaRoyT-10
❑ 84OmaRoyT-5
❑ 85CalCanC-85
❑ 85Don-374
❑ 86Fle-480
❑ 86MaiGuiP-24
❑ 86Top-419
❑ 86TopTif-419
❑ 87BufBisP-23
❑ 87IndGat-22
❑ 87Top-551
❑ 87TopTif-551
❑ 88SyrChiC-11
❑ 88SyrChiP-830
❑ 89BluJayFS-34
❑ 89SyrChiC-5
❑ 89SyrChiMB-24
❑ 89SyrChiP-794
❑ 90BluJayFS-33
❑ 90Fle-98
❑ 90FleCan-98
❑ 90TopTra-129T
❑ 90TopTraT-129T
❑ 91BluJayFS-33
❑ 91BluJayS-10
❑ 91Don-691
❑ 91Fle-191
❑ 91OPC-213
❑ 91Sco-521
❑ 91SyrChiMB-29
❑ 91Top-213
❑ 91TopDesS-213
❑ 91TopMic-213
❑ 91TopTif-213

Wills, Maury
❑ 47Exh-242
❑ 57HygMea-12
❑ 57SeaPop-24
❑ 60DodBelB-20
❑ 60DodJayP-16
❑ 60DodTeal-20
❑ 60DodUniO-21
❑ 60Top-389
❑ 61DodBelB-30
❑ 61DodJayP-12
❑ 61DodMor-6
❑ 61DodUniO-23
❑ 61Pos-164A
❑ 61Pos-164B
❑ 62DodBelB-30
❑ 62DodJayP-12
❑ 62DodVol-16
❑ 62Jel-104
❑ 62Pos-104
❑ 62PosCan-104
❑ 62SalPlaC-127A
❑ 62SalPlaC-127B
❑ 62ShiPlaC-127
❑ 63DodJayP-12
❑ 63ExhStaB-64
❑ 63Fle-43
❑ 63Jel-115
❑ 63Pos-115
❑ 63SalMetC-20
❑ 64DodHea-10
❑ 65DodJayP-12
❑ 65DodTeal-21
❑ 66DodVolT-9
❑ 67CokCapPi-13
❑ 67DexPre-224
❑ 67PirTeal-24
❑ 67Top-570
❑ 67TopVen-321
❑ 68AtlOilPBCC-48
❑ 68Baz-1
❑ 68Baz-4
❑ 68OPC-175
❑ 68PirKDK-30
❑ 68PirTeal-24
❑ 68Top-175
❑ 68TopVen-175
❑ 69MilBra-293
❑ 69MLBOffS-162
❑ 69OPC-45
❑ 69OPCDec-23
❑ 69Top-45
❑ 69TopDec-24
❑ 69TopDecI-46
❑ 69TopSta-60
❑ 69TopSup-49
❑ 69TopTeaP-10
❑ 70DayDaiNM-3
❑ 70MLBOffS-60
❑ 70Top-595
❑ 71BazNumT-34
❑ 71DodTic-19
❑ 71MLBOffS-120
❑ 71OPC-385
❑ 71Top-385
❑ 71TopGreM-29
❑ 71TopTat-116
❑ 72MilBra-364
❑ 72OPC-437
❑ 72OPC-438
❑ 72SevTraC-56
❑ 72Top-437
❑ 72Top-438
❑ 74GreHeroBP-6
❑ 75OPC-200
❑ 75Top-200
❑ 75TopMin-200
❑ 76SSP-592
❑ 77Spo-1411
❑ 77Top-435
❑ 78TCM60I-70
❑ 80MarPos-24
❑ 81Fle-595
❑ 81MarPol-14
❑ 81Top-672
❑ 82BasCarN-14
❑ 82K-M-2
❑ 83MLBPin-36
❑ 84DodUniO-11
❑ 85Woo-39
❑ 87DodSmoA-38
❑ 87HygAllG-49
❑ 87Top-315
❑ 87TopTif-315
❑ 88DodSmo-7
❑ 89DodSmoG-69
❑ 90AGFA-12
❑ 90DodTar-865
❑ 90HOFStiB-66
❑ 92ActPacA-47
❑ 92DodStaTA-2
❑ 92MDAMVP-3
❑ 92UppDecS-29
❑ 93TedWil-17
❑ 93TedWilM-9
❑ 95MCIAmb-12
❑ 95SonGre-12
❑ 97FleMilDM-25
❑ 97FleMilDMR-25
❑ 99SpoIllGotG-30
❑ 99SpoIllGotGA-78
❑ 99SpoIllGotGC-11

Wills, Shawn
❑ 92BatCliCB-11
❑ 92BatCliF-3281
❑ 92ClaDraP-110
❑ 93SpaPhiF-1070
❑ 94SpaPhiF-1737
❑ 94SparPhiC-23

Wills, Ted
❑ 60Lea-56
❑ 61Top-548
❑ 62Top-444
❑ 65Top-488
❑ 78TCM60I-138
❑ 81RedSoxBG2S-61

Willsher, Chris
❑ 81MiaOriT-22
❑ 84ChaO'sT-11

Willson, Rob
❑ 87EveGiaC-22

Wilmet, Paul
❑ 82LynMetT-10
❑ 85SprCarT-30
❑ 87ArkTraP-10
❑ 88EasLeaAP-18
❑ 88HarSenP-852
❑ 89OklCit8C-9
❑ 89OklCit8P-1509
❑ 90CMC-85
❑ 90IowCubC-10
❑ 90IowCubP-319
❑ 90ProAAAF-626
❑ 90SprCarDGB-16
❑ 90TopDeb89-145
❑ 93RanKee-384

Wilming, Greg
❑ 94ChaRivC-25

Wilmont, Walter
❑ 87OldJudN-544
❑ 88WG1CarG-72

Wilmore, Al
❑ 92NegLeaRLI-63
❑ 95NegLeaL2-18

Wilner, Dirk
❑ 90LSUTigA-9

Wilner, Eric
❑ 85AncGlaPTI-34

Wilridge, James
❑ 84IdaFalATI-30

Wilshere, Whitey
❑ 94ConTSN-1314
❑ 94ConTSNB-1314

Wilson, Alan
❑ 84LitFalMT-20
❑ 87ChaWheP-4

Wilson, Archie C.
❑ 52Bow-210
❑ 52Top-327
❑ 60MapLeaSF-23
❑ 83TopRep5-327

Wilson, Arthur Earl
❑ 10DomDisP-125A
❑ 10DomDisP-125B
❑ 10E12AmeCDCE125-39
❑ 10SweCapPP-122A
❑ 10SweCapPP-122B
❑ 11BasBatEU-44
❑ 11SpoLifM-222
❑ 12T207-198
❑ 14CraJacE-13
❑ 15CraJacE-13
❑ 15SpoNewM-192
❑ 16FleBreD-101
❑ 16SpoNewM-191
❑ 17ColE13-192
❑ 20NatCarE-110
❑ 27YorCarE-25

Wilson, Artie (Arthur L.)
❑ 49RemBre-31
❑ 50RemBre-26
❑ 52MotCoo-40
❑ 54SeaPop-27
❑ 56SeaPop-26
❑ 75Gia195T-31
❑ 92NegLeaK-9
❑ 92NegLeaRLI-64
❑ 95NegLeaL2-9
❑ 97NegLeaPC-6C

Wilson, Barney
❑ 75CedRapGT-20
❑ 76CedRapGT-33

Wilson, Brad
❑ 89BriTigS-28
❑ 90BriTigP-3172
❑ 90BriTigS-25
❑ 91FayGenC-10
❑ 91FayGenP-1175
❑ 91LakTigP-270

Wilson, Brandon
❑ 91Cla/Bes-157
❑ 91MidLeaAP-MWL13
❑ 91SouBenWSC-7
❑ 91SouBenWSP-2867
❑ 92Bow-632
❑ 92ClaFS7-321
❑ 92ProFS7-47
❑ 92SarWhiSCB-4
❑ 92SarWhiSF-217
❑ 92UppDecML-251
❑ 92UppDecMLPotY-PY25
❑ 93BirBarF-1202
❑ 93Bow-7
❑ 93ClaFS7-90
❑ 93ClaGolF-80
❑ 93ExcAllF-10
❑ 93ExcFS7-157
❑ 93LeaGolR-R5
❑ 93LeaGolRJ-R5
❑ 93WhiSoxSC-9
❑ 94Bow-267
❑ 94ExcFS7-41
❑ 94NasSouF-1260
❑ 94Top-158
❑ 94TopGol-158
❑ 94TopSpa-158
❑ 94UppDecML-8
❑ 96IndIndB-28
❑ 97IndInd-28
❑ 98BufBisG-30

Wilson, Brian
❑ 90FreStaS-14
❑ 92GulCoaRSP-11
❑ 94BilMusF-3680
❑ 94BilMusSP-9
❑ 95BilMusTI-13
❑ 98BilMusTI-38

Wilson, Bryan
❑ 91GulCoaRSP-28
❑ 91PeoChiC-15
❑ 91PeoChiTI-22
❑ 91WinSpiC-22
❑ 91WinSpiP-2839

Wilson, Bubba
❑ 76BatTroTI-29
❑ 77WatIndT-31

Wilson, Charles
❑ 36GouWidPPR-D38
❑ 72TCMthe3-113

Wilson, Chauff (W.H.)
❑ 76LauIndC-36

Wilson, Chaun
❑ 87NewOriP-17
❑ 88HagSunS-24

Wilson, Chief (John Owen)
❑ 08AmeCarE91-98
❑ 08RosComP-158
❑ 09ColChiE-309
❑ 09T206-382
❑ 10CouT21-68
❑ 10CouT21-248
❑ 10DomDisP-126A
❑ 10DomDisP-126B
❑ 10E12AmeCDCE125-40
❑ 10NadE1-59
❑ 10PirAmeCE-11
❑ 10PirHerICP-12
❑ 10PirTipTD-17
❑ 10RedCroT-85
❑ 10RedCroT-257
❑ 10SweCapPP-144
❑ 11BasBatEU-43
❑ 11HelSta-138
❑ 11HelSta-166
❑ 11PinT-5-856
❑ 11S74Sil-116
❑ 11SpoLifM-261
❑ 11T205-184
❑ 11TurRedT-126
❑ 12ColRedB-309
❑ 12ColTinT-309
❑ 12HasTriFT-30C
❑ 12T207-199
❑ 14B18B-91A
❑ 14B18B-91B
❑ 14PieStaT-111
❑ 15CraJacE-148
❑ 15SpoNewM-193
❑ 16SpoNewM-192
❑ 85Woo-41
❑ 90HOFStiB-18

Wilson, Chris
❑ 94HelBreF-3627
❑ 94HelBreSP-16

Wilson, Cliff
❑ 98BluOriQ-23
❑ 99BasAmeTP-97
❑ 99BasAmeTPG-97

Wilson, Craig
❑ 85SprCarT-12
❑ 87St.PetCP-2
❑ 88LouRedBP-439
❑ 88LouRedBTI-50
❑ 89ArkTraGS-25
❑ 89LouRedBTI-36
❑ 90CMC-115
❑ 90LouRedBC-15
❑ 90LouRedBLBC-42
❑ 90LouRedBP-413
❑ 90ProAAAF-527
❑ 90SprCarDGB-2
❑ 90TopDeb89-146
❑ 90TopTVCa-66
❑ 91CarPol-12
❑ 91Don-544
❑ 91Fle-652
❑ 91Lea-95
❑ 91OPC-566
❑ 91Sco100RS-97
❑ 91StaClu-566
❑ 91Top-566
❑ 91TopDesS-566
❑ 91TopMic-566
❑ 91TopTif-566
❑ 91TopTra-128T
❑ 91TopTraT-128T
❑ 91Ult-298
❑ 91UppDec-390
❑ 92CarPol-24
❑ 92Don-744
❑ 92JacSunF-3711
❑ 92JacSunS-371
❑ 92OPC-646
❑ 92Sco-557
❑ 92StaClu-361
❑ 92StaCluD-196
❑ 92Top-646
❑ 92TopDaiQTU-30
❑ 92TopGol-646
❑ 92TopGolW-646
❑ 92TopMic-646
❑ 92TopTraG-128T
❑ 93ClaFS7-150
❑ 93Fle-516
❑ 93MidLeaAGF-27
❑ 93RoyPol-26
❑ 93Sco-476
❑ 93SouBenWSC-24
❑ 93SouBenWSF-1441
❑ 93StaClu-88
❑ 93StaCluFDI-88
❑ 93StaCluM-105
❑ 93StaCluMOP-88
❑ 93Top-366
❑ 93TopGol-366
❑ 93TopInaM-366
❑ 93TopInaR-366
❑ 93TopMic-366
❑ 94CarLeaAF-CAR12
❑ 94ClaGolF-162
❑ 94PriWilCC-22
❑ 94PriWilCF-1931
❑ 95Bow-145
❑ 95TolMudHTI-28
❑ 96BirBarB-28
❑ 96Bow-371
❑ 96BowFoi-371
❑ 96HagSunB-24
❑ 96NasSouB-28
❑ 96Top-233
❑ 97LynHil-25
❑ 98CarLeaAC-10
❑ 98CarLeaTPQ-24
❑ 98FleUpd-U13
❑ 98LynHilQ-14
❑ 99Fle-211
❑ 99FleSta9-211
❑ 99FleWarT-211
❑ 99Pac-108
❑ 99PacPlaB-108
❑ 99PacRed-108
❑ 99SpoIll-70

Wilson, Craig Gerald
❑ 87ElmPioBC-18
❑ 87ElmPioRC-18
❑ 88LouRedBC-15
❑ 88LynRedSS-26
❑ 89LynRedSS-22
❑ 90NewBriRSB-8
❑ 90NewBriRSP-1323
❑ 90NewBriRSS-23
❑ 91LynRedSC-13
❑ 91LynRedSP-1203
❑ 92PenPilF-2937
❑ 92TopTra-128T

Wilson, Curt
❑ 98TreThuM-5

Wilson, Dan
❑ 88CapCodPPaLP-177
❑ 90Bes-232
❑ 90ClaDraP-7
❑ 91Bow-687
❑ 91ChaWheC-14
❑ 91ChaWheP-2891
❑ 91Cla/Bes-353
❑ 91OPC-767
❑ 91Sco-681
❑ 91StaClu-587
❑ 91Top-767
❑ 91TopDesS-767
❑ 91TopMic-767
❑ 91TopTif-767
❑ 91UppDecFE-6F
❑ 92Bow-471
❑ 92Don-399
❑ 92LeaGolR-BC18
❑ 92NasSouF-1834
❑ 92NasSouS-297
❑ 92ProFS7-217
❑ 92SkyAAAF-138
❑ 92TriPla-241
❑ 92UppDec-72
❑ 93Bow-202
❑ 93Don-6
❑ 93Fle-400
❑ 93OPCPre-35
❑ 93PacSpa-407
❑ 93Pin-255
❑ 93Sco-229
❑ 93ScoBoyoS-28
❑ 93Sel-345
❑ 93StaClu-662
❑ 93StaCluFDI-662
❑ 93StaCluMOP-662
❑ 93Top-813
❑ 93TopGol-813
❑ 93TopInaM-813
❑ 93TopInaR-813
❑ 93TopMic-813
❑ 93Toy-65
❑ 93Ult-337
❑ 93UppDec-6
❑ 93UppDecGold-6
❑ 94Bow-173
❑ 94ColC-547
❑ 94ColChoGS-547
❑ 94ColChoSS-547
❑ 94Don-388
❑ 94Fin-284
❑ 94FinRef-284
❑ 94Fla-342
❑ 94FleExtB-174
❑ 94FleUpd-88
❑ 94Lea-329
❑ 94MarMot-24
❑ 94Pin-515
❑ 94PinArtP-515
❑ 94PinMusC-515
❑ 94Sco-355
❑ 94ScoGolR-355
❑ 94ScoRoo-RT22
❑ 94ScoRooGR-RT22
❑ 94Sel-343
❑ 94StaClu-656
❑ 94StaCluFDI-656
❑ 94StaCluGR-656
❑ 94StaCluMOP-656
❑ 94Top-154
❑ 94TopGol-154
❑ 94TopSpa-154
❑ 94TopTra-3T
❑ 94Ult-426
❑ 94UppDec-240
❑ 94UppDecED-240
❑ 95ColCho-291
❑ 95ColChoGS-291
❑ 95ColChoSS-291
❑ 95Don-24
❑ 95DonPreP-24
❑ 95DonTopotO-156
❑ 95Fla-304
❑ 95Fle-279
❑ 95Lea-228
❑ 95MarMot-12
❑ 95MarPac-48
❑ 95Pac-403
❑ 95Pin-407
❑ 95PinArtP-407
❑ 95PinMusC-407
❑ 95Sco-146
❑ 95ScoGolR-146

❑ 95ScoPlaTS-146
❑ 95Sel-187
❑ 95SelArtP-187
❑ 95StaClu-152
❑ 95StaCluFDI-152
❑ 95StaCluMOP-152
❑ 95StaCluSTDW-M152
❑ 95StaCluSTWS-152
❑ 95StaCluVR-79
❑ 95StaCluVRMO-79
❑ 95Top-263
❑ 95TopCyb-143
❑ 95Ult-106
❑ 95UltGolM-106
❑ 96Cir-83
❑ 96CirRav-83
❑ 96ColCho-319
❑ 96ColChoGS-319
❑ 96ColChoSS-319
❑ 96Don-79
❑ 96DonPreP-79
❑ 96EmoXL-119
❑ 96Fla-166
❑ 96Fle-245
❑ 96FleTif-245
❑ 96MarMot-15
❑ 96Pac-405
❑ 96Pin-332
❑ 96PinFoil-332
❑ 96Sco-177
❑ 96StaClu-30
❑ 96StaCluMOP-30
❑ 96Top-117
❑ 96Ult-131
❑ 96UltGolM-131
❑ 97Cir-135
❑ 97CirRav-135
❑ 97ColCho-228
❑ 97ColChoT-SM1
❑ 97Don-327
❑ 97DonEli-136
❑ 97DonEliGS-136
❑ 97DonGolPP-327
❑ 97DonLim-163
❑ 97DonLimE-163
❑ 97DonLimENG-163
❑ 97DonPre-12
❑ 97DonPreCttC-12
❑ 97DonSigA-112
❑ 97DonSigAC-138
❑ 97DonSigAM-138
❑ 97DonSilPP-327
❑ 97DonTea-147
❑ 97DonTeaSPE-147
❑ 97E-X2-44
❑ 97E-X2Cred-44
❑ 97E-X2EssCre-44
❑ 97Fin-220
❑ 97FinRef-220
❑ 97FlaShoLC-152
❑ 97FlaShoLeg0-152
❑ 97FlaShoLeg1-152
❑ 97FlaShoM-A152
❑ 97FlaShoM-B152
❑ 97FlaShoM-C152
❑ 97FlaShoR0-152
❑ 97FlaShoR1-152
❑ 97FlaShoR2-152
❑ 97Fle-217
❑ 97FleTif-217
❑ 97KinB-21
❑ 97Lea-46
❑ 97LeaFraM-46
❑ 97LeaFraMDC-46
❑ 97MarSco-8
❑ 97MarScoPl-8
❑ 97MarScoPr-8
❑ 97MetUni-151
❑ 97Pac-196
❑ 97PacLigB-196
❑ 97PacSil-196
❑ 97Pin-77
❑ 97PinArtP-PP77
❑ 97PinIns-109
❑ 97PinInsCE-109
❑ 97PinInsDE-109
❑ 97PinMusC-77
❑ 97PinPrePla-77
❑ 97Sco-185
❑ 97ScoArtPWB-185
❑ 97ScoPreS-185
❑ 97ScoShoS-185
❑ 97ScoShoSAP-185
❑ 97SP-169
❑ 97SpolII-53
❑ 97SpolIIEE-53
❑ 97StaClu-123
❑ 97StaCluMOP-123
❑ 97Stu-144
❑ 97StuPrePG-144
❑ 97StuPrePS-144
❑ 97Top-63
❑ 97Ult-129
❑ 97UltGolME-129
❑ 97UltPlaME-129
❑ 97UppDec-503
❑ 97UppDecMP-P15
❑ 98CirThu-167
❑ 98CirThuRav-167
❑ 98CirThuSupRav-167
❑ 98ColCho-238
❑ 98Don-185
❑ 98DonGolPP-185
❑ 98DonSigA-94
❑ 98DonSigAC-117
❑ 98DonSigAM-120
❑ 98DonSilPP-185
❑ 98Fin-258
❑ 98FinNo--258
❑ 98FinNo-R-258
❑ 98FinRef-258
❑ 98Fle-187
❑ 98KinDis-15
❑ 98MarSco-1
❑ 98MarScoP-1
❑ 98Pac-196
❑ 98PacOme-227
❑ 98PacOmeR-227
❑ 98PacOnl-700
❑ 98PacOnlR-700
❑ 98PacOnlWC-700
❑ 98PacPar-92
❑ 98PacParC-92
❑ 98PacParG-92
❑ 98PacParHS-92
❑ 98PacParPB-92
❑ 98PacParR-92
❑ 98PacPlaB-196
❑ 98PacRedT-196
❑ 98PacSil-196
❑ 98Pin-101
❑ 98PinPreP-101
❑ 98PinSna-SM12
❑ 98Sco-2
❑ 98ScoRT-163
❑ 98ScoSS-PP2
❑ 98ScoSSAP-PP2
❑ 98SPxFin-131
❑ 98SPxFinR-131
❑ 98SPxFinS-131
❑ 98StaCluFDI-131
❑ 98StaClul-131
❑ 98StaCluOneK-131
❑ 98StaCluPP-131
❑ 98Top-38
❑ 98TopChr-38
❑ 98TopChrR-38
❑ 98TopDevR-38
❑ 98TopDia-38
❑ 98TopGal-89
❑ 98TopGalGP-89
❑ 98TopGalOPP-89
❑ 98TopGalPPI-89
❑ 98TopGalPPIA-89
❑ 98TopMiniC-38
❑ 98Ult-423
❑ 98UltGolM-423
❑ 98UltMas-423
❑ 98UltPlaM-423
❑ 98UppDec-228
❑ 99Fle-539
❑ 99FleSta9-539
❑ 99FleWarT-539
❑ 99KinDis-12
❑ 99MetUni-181
❑ 99MetUniGM-181
❑ 99MetUniPMG-181
❑ 99Pac-405
❑ 99PacAur-181
❑ 99PacAurOD-181
❑ 99PacPar-222
❑ 99PacParC-222
❑ 99PacParG-222
❑ 99PacParHoloGold-222
❑ 99PacParHS-222
❑ 99PacParOD-222
❑ 99PacParPB-222
❑ 99PacParRed-222
❑ 99PacPlaB-405
❑ 99PacRed-405
❑ 99SkyPre-4
❑ 99SkyPreR-4
❑ 99StaClu-295
❑ 99StaCluFDI-295
❑ 99StaCluOoaK-295
❑ 99StaCluPP-295
❑ 99Top-143
❑ 99TopChr-143
❑ 99TopChrR-143
❑ 99TopMVPP-143
❑ 99Ult-186
❑ 99UltGolM-186
❑ 99UltMas-186
❑ 99UltPlaM-186
❑ 99UppDec-208
❑ 99UppDecEL1-208
❑ 99UppDecEL2-208
❑ 99Vic-380

Wilson, Danny
❑ 86DavLipB-24

Wilson, Dave
❑ 81CliGiaT-21

Wilson, David
❑ 89NiaFalRP-24
❑ 90AshTouC-11
❑ 90AubAstB-4
❑ 90AubAstP-3404
❑ 91AshTouP-569
❑ 91Cla/Bes-274

Wilson, Desi
❑ 92ButCopKSP-16
❑ 93Bow-337
❑ 93ChaRanC-25
❑ 93ChaRanF-1951
❑ 93ClaFS7-40
❑ 94Top-775
❑ 94TopGol-775
❑ 94TopSpa-775
❑ 94TulDriF-257
❑ 94TulDriTI-25
❑ 95UppDecML-99
❑ 95UppDecMLFS-99
❑ 96PhoFirB-28
❑ 97Fle-490
❑ 97FleTif-490
❑ 97PacPriGotD-GD220
❑ 97PhoFirTI-26
❑ 97Ult-487
❑ 97UltGolME-487
❑ 97UltPlaME-487
❑ 97UppDec-482

Wilson, Don
❑ 67Ast-29
❑ 68Baz-13
❑ 68CokCapA-18
❑ 68OPC-77
❑ 68Top-77
❑ 68TopVen-75
❑ 68TopVen-77
❑ 69MLBOffS-143
❑ 69OPC-202
❑ 69Top-202
❑ 69TopFou-1
❑ 69TopSta-39
❑ 69TopTeaP-6
❑ 69TraSta-37
❑ 70AstPho-27
❑ 70AstTeal-11
❑ 70Kel-62
❑ 70MLBOffS-47
❑ 70OPC-515
❑ 70Top-515
❑ 71AstCok-11
❑ 71AstTeal-23
❑ 71MLBOffS-95
❑ 71OPC-484
❑ 71Top-484
❑ 71TopCoi-41
❑ 72AstTeal-28
❑ 72Kel-51
❑ 72MilBra-365
❑ 72OPC-20
❑ 72OPC-91
❑ 72SevTraC-57
❑ 72Top-20
❑ 72Top-91
❑ 73LinPor-86
❑ 73OPC-217
❑ 73Top-217
❑ 74OPC-304
❑ 74Top-304
❑ 75OPC-455
❑ 75Top-455
❑ 75TopMin-455
❑ 81TCM60I-326
❑ 86AstMot-10
❑ 87AstShoSO-24
❑ 87AstShoSO-28
❑ 87AstShoSTw-28
❑ 87AstShowSTh-26
❑ 87AstShowSTh-28

Wilson, Doyle
❑ 87KinIndP-20
❑ 88WilBilP-1324

Wilson, Earl
❑ 60Top-249
❑ 61SeaPop-28
❑ 61Top-69
❑ 63Jel-83
❑ 63Pos-83
❑ 63Top-76
❑ 64Top-503
❑ 65OPC-42
❑ 65RedSoxTI-15
❑ 65Top-42
❑ 66RedSoxTI-15
❑ 66Top-575
❑ 67CokCapTi-10
❑ 67DexPre-225
❑ 67TigDexP-11
❑ 67Top-235
❑ 67Top-237
❑ 67Top-305
❑ 67TopVen-234
❑ 68AtlOilPBCC-49
❑ 68CokCapT-10
❑ 68Kah-B38
❑ 68OPC-10
❑ 68OPC-160
❑ 68TigDetFPB-27
❑ 68Top-10A
❑ 68Top-10B
❑ 68Top-160
❑ 68TopActS-9A
❑ 68TopVen-10
❑ 68TopVen-160
❑ 69MilBra-294
❑ 69TigTealC-20
❑ 69Top-525
❑ 69TopTeaP-1
❑ 70MLBOffS-216
❑ 70OPC-95
❑ 70Top-95
❑ 71OPC-301
❑ 71Top-301
❑ 72MilBra-366
❑ 78TCM60I-148
❑ 81RedSoxBG2S-62
❑ 81TigDetN-51
❑ 84WilMay-26
❑ 88TigDom-26
❑ 91SweBasG-120
❑ 93UppDecAH-127
❑ 93UppDecS-6

Wilson, Eddie
❑ 90DodTar-1095

Wilson, Enrique
❑ 93EliTwiC-22
❑ 94ColRedC-1
❑ 94ColRedF-453
❑ 95Bow-36
❑ 95Exc-44
❑ 95KinIndTI-29
❑ 95SPML-47
❑ 96BesAutS-94
❑ 96Bow-146
❑ 96BowBes-106
❑ 96BowBesAR-106
❑ 96BowBesR-106
❑ 96BowFoi-146
❑ 96CanIndB-29
❑ 96ColCho-449
❑ 96ColChoGS-449
❑ 96ColChoSS-449
❑ 96DouAllB-20
❑ 96Exc-47
❑ 96Top-427
❑ 96UppDec-261
❑ 97BesAutSBPP-38
❑ 97BesLimA-42
❑ 97Bow-144
❑ 97BowCerBlaIA-CA85
❑ 97BowCerBluIA-CA85
❑ 97BowCerGolIA-CA85
❑ 97BowInt-144
❑ 97BufBis-29
❑ 97Top-487
❑ 98BesPreA-47
❑ 98Bow-345
❑ 98BowBesMIF-MI2
❑ 98BowBesMIFAR-MI2
❑ 98BowBesMIFR-MI2
❑ 98BowChr-345
❑ 98BowChrGA-345
❑ 98BowChrGAR-345
❑ 98BowChrI-345
❑ 98BowChrIR-345
❑ 98BowChrR-345
❑ 98BowGolA-345
❑ 98BowInt-345
❑ 98CirThu-238
❑ 98CirThuRav-238
❑ 98CirThuSupRav-238
❑ 98Don-279
❑ 98DonColL-229
❑ 98DonColP-704
❑ 98DonGolPP-279
❑ 98DonPre-154
❑ 98DonPreSeat-154
❑ 98DonPriCL-229
❑ 98DonPriCP-704
❑ 98DonSigA-95
❑ 98DonSigAC-118
❑ 98DonSigAM-121
❑ 98DonSilPP-279
❑ 98Fle-223
❑ 98FleProF-PF19
❑ 98Lea-29
❑ 98LeaFraDA-29
❑ 98LeaFraF-29
❑ 98LeaFraM-29
❑ 98LeaFraM-29
❑ 98LeaFraMDC-29
❑ 98LeaFraMDC-29
❑ 98LeaFraMZ2-29
❑ 98LeaRS-275
❑ 98LeaRSLHolo-275
❑ 98LeaRSLong-275
❑ 98LeaRTrue-275
❑ 98PacAur-35
❑ 98PacOme-77
❑ 98PacOmeR-77
❑ 98PacOnl-234
❑ 98PacOnlR-234
❑ 98PacOnlWC-234
❑ 98PinPer-130
❑ 98PinPerPP-130
❑ 98PinPlu-82
❑ 98PinSna-CI18
❑ 98ScoRT-239
❑ 98ScoRTSS-PP132
❑ 98ScoRTSSAP-PP132
❑ 98ScoRTSSAP1-PP132
❑ 98SkyDugA-101
❑ 98SkyDugAIA-101
❑ 98SpolllTaN-150
❑ 98SpolllTaNEE-150
❑ 98Stu-102
❑ 98StuGPP-102
❑ 98StuSPP-102
❑ 98Top-448
❑ 98TopChr-448
❑ 98TopChrR-448
❑ 98TopDevR-448
❑ 98TopDia-448
❑ 98TopMiniC-448
❑ 98Ult-319
❑ 98UltGolM-319
❑ 98UltMas-319
❑ 98UltPlaM-319
❑ 98UppDec-348
❑ 99Fle-558
❑ 99FleSta9-558
❑ 99FleWarT-558
❑ 99MetUni-258
❑ 99MetUniGM-258
❑ 99MetUniPMG-258
❑ 99PacCroC-91
❑ 99PacCroC-10
❑ 99PacCroCPB-91
❑ 99PacPriS-149
❑ 99PacPriS206-149
❑ 99PacPriS206R-149
❑ 99SP SigAuto-EW
❑ 99SPSig-163
❑ 99Ult-240
❑ 99UltGolM-240
❑ 99UltMas-240
❑ 99UltPlaM-240
❑ 99UppDec-357
❑ 99UppDecEL1-357
❑ 99UppDecEL2-357

Wilson, Eric
❑ 86PenWhiSP-27

Wilson, Ewligui
❑ 93EliTwiF-3424

Wilson, Frank
❑ 52LavPro-3

Wilson, Gary D.
❑ 88BatCliP-1688
❑ 89SpaPhiP-1036
❑ 89SpaPhiS-24
❑ 90Bes-158
❑ 90CMC-737
❑ 90ReaPhiB-11
❑ 90ReaPhiP-1221
❑ 90ReaPhiS-24
❑ 91LinDriAAA-498
❑ 91ScrRedBLD-498
❑ 91ScrRedBP-2539

Wilson, Gary Morris
❑ 92WelPirC-26
❑ 92WelPirF-1324
❑ 93ClaGolF-197
❑ 93SalBucC-24
❑ 93SalBucF-433
❑ 94SalBucC-24
❑ 94SalBucF-2325
❑ 95Exc-259
❑ 95Fla-405
❑ 95FleUpd-152
❑ 95PirFil-30
❑ 95SigRoo-49
❑ 95SigRooSig-49
❑ 95StaClu-583
❑ 95StaCluMOP-583
❑ 95StaCluSTWS-583
❑ 97CalCanB-29
❑ 97CarMudC-10
❑ 98NasSouTI-32
❑ 98NasSouTISS-30

Wilson, Gary Steven
❑ 76DubPacT-39
❑ 79AstPos-28
❑ 79ChaChaT-18
❑ 80TucTorT-5

Wilson, George H.
❑ 94TedWil-115

Wilson, George Washington
❑ 79TCM50-189

Wilson, Glenn
❑ 81BirBarT-10
❑ 83Don-580
❑ 83Fle-350
❑ 83TigPos-33
❑ 83Top-332
❑ 83TopSti-318
❑ 84Don-618
❑ 84Fle-94
❑ 84FleUpd-128
❑ 84Nes792-563
❑ 84OPC-36
❑ 84PhiTas-40
❑ 84Top-563
❑ 84TopSti-270
❑ 84TopTif-563
❑ 84TopTra-129T
❑ 84TopTraT-129T
❑ 85Don-609
❑ 85Fle-268
❑ 85OPC-189
❑ 85PhiCIG-9
❑ 85PhiTas-12
❑ 85PhiTas-40
❑ 85Top-454
❑ 85TopTif-454
❑ 86BasStaB-121
❑ 86BurKinA-7
❑ 86Don-285
❑ 86DonAll-29
❑ 86Fle-457
❑ 86FleMin-95
❑ 86FleStiC-128
❑ 86Lea-160
❑ 86OPC-318
❑ 86PhiCIG-16
❑ 86PhiKel-6
❑ 86PhiTas-12
❑ 86Top-736
❑ 86TopMinL-56
❑ 86TopSti-118
❑ 86TopTat-9
❑ 86TopTif-736
❑ 87Don-62
❑ 87DonOpeD-158
❑ 87Fle-192
❑ 87FleGlo-192
❑ 87FleMin-115
❑ 87Lea-146
❑ 87OPC-97
❑ 87PhiTas-12
❑ 87Spo-166
❑ 87SpoTeaP-6
❑ 87Top-97
❑ 87Top-481

❑ 87TopSti-117
❑ 87TopTif-97
❑ 87TopTif-481
❑ 88Don-262
❑ 88DonBasB-306
❑ 88Fle-320
❑ 88FleGlo-320
❑ 88MarMot-12
❑ 88OPC-359
❑ 88PanSti-358
❑ 88PanSti-364
❑ 88RedFolSB-103
❑ 88Sco-405
❑ 88ScoGlo-405
❑ 88Spo-204
❑ 88StaLinMa-20
❑ 88StaLinPh-20
❑ 88Top-626
❑ 88TopBig-260
❑ 88TopSti-124
❑ 88TopTif-626
❑ 88TopTra-129T
❑ 88TopTraT-129T
❑ 89BirBarADB-31
❑ 89Bow-423
❑ 89BowTif-423
❑ 89Don-447
❑ 89DonBasB-241
❑ 89Fle-224
❑ 89FleGlo-224
❑ 89PirVerFJ-11
❑ 89Sco-106
❑ 89Spo-12
❑ 89Top-293
❑ 89TopBig-284
❑ 89TopTif-293
❑ 90AstLenH-26
❑ 90AstMot-22
❑ 90BirBarADB-31
❑ 90Don-472
❑ 90Fle-240
❑ 90FleCan-240
❑ 90Lea-268
❑ 90OPC-112
❑ 90PubIntS-168
❑ 90RedFolSB-104
❑ 90Sco-346
❑ 90Top-112
❑ 90TopBig-320
❑ 90TopTif-112
❑ 90UppDec-410
❑ 91Don-156
❑ 91Fle-519
❑ 91LinDriAAA-447
❑ 91OPC-476
❑ 91PanFreS-11
❑ 91RicBraLD-447
❑ 91RicBraP-2582
❑ 91RicBraTI-26
❑ 91Sco-298
❑ 91Top-476
❑ 91TopDesS-476
❑ 91TopMic-476
❑ 91TopTif-476
❑ 91UppDec-515
❑ 93BufBisF-532

Wilson, Gomer
❑ 28Zee-167
❑ 30Zee-186

Wilson, Hack (Lewis R.)
❑ 27YorCarE-25
❑ 28Exh-12
❑ 28PorandAR-A39
❑ 28PorandAR-B39
❑ 28StaPlaCE-72
❑ 28W502-25
❑ 28W513-74
❑ 28Yue-25
❑ 29CubCerICP-5
❑ 29ExhFou-5
❑ 29PorandAR-100
❑ 30ChiEveAP-10
❑ 30CubTeal-21
❑ 30SchR33-14
❑ 30UncJac-30
❑ 30W554-18
❑ 31CubTeal-28
❑ 31Exh-5
❑ 31W517-42
❑ 33ButCre-29
❑ 33DouDisP-43
❑ 33Gou-211
❑ 33RitCE-9C
❑ 33RitCE-9S
❑ 33WorCig-102
❑ 34BatR31-73
❑ 34DiaMatCSB-198
❑ 46SpoExcW-9-4
❑ 50CubGreB-18
❑ 60Fle-48
❑ 61Fle-87
❑ 68SCFOldT-29
❑ 72FleFamF-9
❑ 72LauGreF-27
❑ 77BobParMBC-9
❑ 77CubAllT-13
❑ 77GalGloG-113
❑ 77Spo-7515
❑ 78DexHaloFP-52
❑ 79Top-412
❑ 80CubGreT-10
❑ 80LauFamF-4
❑ 80PacLeg-97
❑ 80PerHaloFP-169
❑ 80SSPHOF-169
❑ 81ConTSN-86
❑ 82DiaCla-20
❑ 82TCMGreS-23
❑ 84CubBriPC-11H
❑ 84CubBriPC-12H
❑ 85Woo-40
❑ 86ConSer1-56
❑ 89DodSmoG-36
❑ 90BasWit-93
❑ 90DodTar-866
❑ 90HOFStiB-29
❑ 90PerGreM-80
❑ 91ConTSN-29
❑ 91ConTSN-267
❑ 92ConTSN-424
❑ 92ConTSN-585
❑ 92CubOldS-28
❑ 93ConTSN-736
❑ 94ConTSN-998
❑ 94ConTSNB-998
❑ 94UppDecAH-111
❑ 94UppDecAH-190
❑ 94UppDecAH1-111
❑ 94UppDecAH1-190

Wilson, Jack
❑ 86PhoFirP-25

Wilson, Jack (John F.)
❑ 39PlaBal-29
❑ 40PlaBal-31
❑ 41PlaBal-29

Wilson, Jack E.
❑ 98JohCCTI-35

Wilson, James George
❑ 28Exh-32
❑ 31CarMet-30
❑ 35DiaMatCS2-24
❑ 35DiaMatCS3T1-150
❑ 41HarHarW-28
❑ 81BriRedST-6
❑ 83BufBisT-14
❑ 83PawRedST-18
❑ 85IntLeaAT-25
❑ 85MaiGuiT-24
❑ 86IndTeal-51
❑ 86MaiGuiP-25
❑ 88EasLeaAP-38
❑ 89BlaYNPRWL-195
❑ 89CalCanC-22
❑ 89CalCanP-536
❑ 90TriAAAC-39
❑ 91LinDriAAA-397
❑ 91PhoFirLD-397
❑ 91PhoFirP-77

Wilson, Jeff
❑ 83WisRapTF-4
❑ 86TamTarP-26
❑ 97LetBlaDB-30
❑ 98HigDesMG-29

Wilson, Jim
❑ 88SanDieSAAG-21
❑ 88VerMarP-944
❑ 89SanDieSAG-19
❑ 89TriAAAP-AAA32
❑ 93LinVenB-315

Wilson, Jim A.
❑ 52Top-276
❑ 53BowC-37
❑ 53BraJohC-12
❑ 53BraMer-17
❑ 53BraSpiaS3-27
❑ 53Top-208
❑ 54Bow-16
❑ 54BraJohC-19
❑ 54BraMer-10
❑ 55Bow-253
❑ 55BraGolS-8
❑ 55BraJohC-19
❑ 55BraSpiaSD-18
❑ 56BalOriP-13
❑ 56Top-171
❑ 57Top-330
❑ 58Top-163
❑ 58WhiSoxJP-11
❑ 79TCM50-130
❑ 82Bow195E-257
❑ 83Bra53F-19
❑ 83TopRep5-276
❑ 91OriCro-489
❑ 91TopArc1-208
❑ 92BazQua5A-18

Wilson, Jimmy
❑ 29ExhFou-15
❑ 30SchR33-30
❑ 31Exh-15
❑ 32R33So2-422
❑ 33ButCanV-56
❑ 33Gou-37
❑ 33GouCanV-37
❑ 33NatLeaAC-18
❑ 33WorCig-103
❑ 34BabRutG-66
❑ 34BatR31-38
❑ 34ButPreR-65
❑ 34DiaMatCSB-197
❑ 34DiaStaR-22
❑ 34ExhFou-6
❑ 34WarBakSP-8
❑ 35ExhFou-6
❑ 35GouPuzR-6C
❑ 35GouPuzR-11E
❑ 35GouPuzR-13C
❑ 35GouPuzR-15C
❑ 36ExhFou-6
❑ 36NatChiFPR-114
❑ 36WheBB3-12
❑ 36WorWidGV-99
❑ 38RedOraW-32
❑ 39OrcPhoAP-26
❑ 39RedTeal-23
❑ 40PlaBal-152
❑ 41CubTeal-25
❑ 42CubTeal-25
❑ 43CubTeal-25
❑ 61Fle-88
❑ 68SCFOldT-50
❑ 74Bra193NLA-18
❑ 77CinRedT-41
❑ 77GalGloG-216
❑ 81ConTSN-87
❑ 83BigLeaCOA-39
❑ 91ConTSN-223
❑ 93ConTSN-683
❑ 93ConTSN-874

Wilson, Johnny
❑ 85LynMetT-24
❑ 86JacMetT-22
❑ 87JacMetF-17

Wilson, Jud
❑ 74LauOldTBS-12
❑ 90NegLeaS-34
❑ 91PomBlaBPB-23
❑ 94TedWil-116

Wilson, Keith
❑ 97HigDesMG-29
❑ 98HigDesMG-30
❑ 98LetBlaDG-30

Wilson, Kris
❑ 97SpoIndG-30
❑ 98WilBluRC-30

Wilson, Kurt
❑ 88SalLakCTTI-4
❑ 89SalLakTTI-10
❑ 95OdgRapTI-29

Wilson, Mark
❑ 89HamRedS-26
❑ 92SanJosGC-30

Wilson, Matt
❑ 89GreFalDSP-32
❑ 90VerBeaDS-31
❑ 91CalLeLA-25
❑ 92BakDodCLC-32
❑ 95SanAntMTI-NNO
❑ 98AlbDukG-30

Wilson, Mike
❑ 77CliDodT-29
❑ 80AlbDukTc-15
❑ 80QuaCitCT-26
❑ 87IdaFalBP-1
❑ 93BriTigC-25
❑ 94FayGenC-25
❑ 95FayGenTI-29

Wilson, Mookie
❑ 79TidTidT-7
❑ 80TidTidT-17
❑ 81Don-575
❑ 81Top-259
❑ 82Don-175
❑ 82Fle-542
❑ 82FleSta-86
❑ 82MetPhoA-25
❑ 82OPC-143
❑ 82RegGloT-10
❑ 82Top-143
❑ 83AllGamPI-162
❑ 83Don-56
❑ 83DonActA-32
❑ 83Dra-29
❑ 83Fle-560
❑ 83FleSta-217
❑ 83FleSti-233
❑ 83OPC-55
❑ 83Top-55
❑ 83Top-621
❑ 83TopGloS-2
❑ 83TopSti-266
❑ 84AllGamPI-72
❑ 84Don-190
❑ 84Dra-31
❑ 84Fle-603
❑ 84FleSti-91
❑ 84FunFooP-65
❑ 84JacMetF-13
❑ 84MetFanC-8
❑ 84Nes792-246
❑ 84Nes792-465
❑ 84OPC-270
❑ 84Top-246
❑ 84Top-465
❑ 84TopSti-108
❑ 84TopTif-246
❑ 84TopTif-465
❑ 85AllGamPI-161
❑ 85Don-482
❑ 85Fle-95
❑ 85Lea-122
❑ 85MetColP-28
❑ 85MetTCM-36
❑ 85OPC-11
❑ 85PolMet-M4
❑ 85Top-775
❑ 85TopMin-775
❑ 85TopSti-102
❑ 85TopTif-775
❑ 86Don-604
❑ 86Fle-97
❑ 86Lea-232
❑ 86MetColP-7
❑ 86MetTCM-29
❑ 86MetWorSC-21
❑ 86OPC-315
❑ 86RegGloT-1
❑ 86Top-126
❑ 86Top-315
❑ 86TopTat-6
❑ 86TopTif-126
❑ 86TopTif-315
❑ 87Don-487
❑ 87DonOpeD-129
❑ 87Fle-25
❑ 87FleGlo-25
❑ 87FleHotS-43
❑ 87Lea-176
❑ 87MetColP-9
❑ 87MetFanC-8
❑ 87OPC-84
❑ 87Top-625
❑ 87TopTif-625
❑ 88Don-652
❑ 88DonBasB-208
❑ 88DonTeaBM-652
❑ 88Fle-154
❑ 88FleGlo-154
❑ 88Lea-249
❑ 88MetColP-11
❑ 88MetKah-1
❑ 88PanSti-342
❑ 88PanSti-348
❑ 88Sco-474
❑ 88ScoGlo-474
❑ 88StaLinMe-20
❑ 88Top-255
❑ 88TopBig-182
❑ 88TopTif-255
❑ 89Bow-386
❑ 89BowTif-386
❑ 89Don-152
❑ 89Fle-52
❑ 89FleGlo-52
❑ 89MetColP-19
❑ 89MetKah-30
❑ 89OPC-144
❑ 89PanSti-141
❑ 89Sco-302
❑ 89ScoRoo-16T
❑ 89Top-545
❑ 89TopBig-231
❑ 89TopDouM-13
❑ 89TopTif-545
❑ 89UppDec-199
❑ 90BluJayFS-34
❑ 90Bow-516
❑ 90BowTif-516
❑ 90Don-442
❑ 90DonBesA-28
❑ 90Fle-99
❑ 90FleCan-99
❑ 90Lea-263
❑ 90OPC-182
❑ 90PanSti-174
❑ 90PubIntS-147
❑ 90Sco-448
❑ 90Spo-128
❑ 90Top-182
❑ 90TopBig-179
❑ 90TopTif-182
❑ 90UppDec-481
❑ 91BluJayFS-34
❑ 91BluJayS-24
❑ 91Don-585
❑ 91Fle-192
❑ 91MetWIZ-433
❑ 91OPC-727
❑ 91PanFreS-341
❑ 91Sco-42
❑ 91StaClu-99
❑ 91Stu-140
❑ 91Top-727
❑ 91TopDesS-727
❑ 91TopMic-727
❑ 91TopTif-727
❑ 91Ult-372
❑ 91UppDec-512
❑ 92Fle-347
❑ 92OPC-436
❑ 92Sco-458
❑ 92Top-436
❑ 92TopGol-436
❑ 92TopGolW-436
❑ 92TopMic-436
❑ 92UppDec-391
❑ 94MetColP-30
❑ 94MetComR-2
❑ 96MetTeal-9
❑ 97FleMilDM-49
❑ 97FleMilDMR-49
❑ 98SpollIWSF-25
❑ 98SpollIWSFEE-25
❑ 98SpollIWSFFE-25

Wilson, Nigel
❑ 88St.CatBJP-2017
❑ 89St.CatBJP-2081
❑ 90MyrBeaBJP-2791
❑ 91DunBluJC-24
❑ 91DunBluJP-222
❑ 91FloStaLAP-FSL10
❑ 92Bow-228
❑ 92ClaFS7-164
❑ 92KnoBluJF-3005
❑ 92KnoBluJS-397
❑ 92ProFS7-169
❑ 92SkyAA F-168
❑ 92UppDecML-286
❑ 93Bow-316
❑ 93Bow-351
❑ 93Don-737
❑ 93DonDiaK-DK27
❑ 93EdmTraF-1151
❑ 93ExcFS7-247
❑ 93FlaWavotF-19
❑ 93FlaWavotF-20
❑ 93Fle-431
❑ 93FleFinE-75
❑ 93LeaGolR-R16
❑ 93LeaGolRJ-R16
❑ 93MarlStaClu-1
❑ 93MarPub-27
❑ 93MarUppD-9
❑ 93MarUppD-825
❑ 93OPC-165
❑ 93StaClu-720
❑ 93StaCluFDI-720
❑ 93StaClul-A4
❑ 93StaCluMOP-720
❑ 93StaCluMOP-MA4
❑ 93Top-426
❑ 93TopGol-426
❑ 93TopInaM-426
❑ 93TopInaR-426
❑ 93TopMic-426
❑ 93TopMic-P426
❑ 93Ult-388
❑ 93UppDec-825
❑ 93UppDecGold-825
❑ 94ActPac-38
❑ 94Bow-590
❑ 94Cla-106
❑ 94ColC-301
❑ 94ColChoGS-301
❑ 94ColChoSS-301
❑ 94Don-537
❑ 94EdmTraF-2889
❑ 94FUnPac-30
❑ 94Lea-76
❑ 94Pac-255
❑ 94Pin-240
❑ 94PinArtP-240
❑ 94PinMusC-240
❑ 94PinNewG-NG22
❑ 94PinRooTP-8
❑ 94Sco-639
❑ 94ScoBoyoS-35
❑ 94ScoGolR-639
❑ 94Spo-158
❑ 94StaCluT-66
❑ 94StaCluTFDI-66
❑ 94Top-341
❑ 94TopGol-341
❑ 94TopSpa-341
❑ 94UppDec-103
❑ 94UppDecED-103
❑ 95IndIndF-109
❑ 95Top-506
❑ 96BufBisB-23
❑ 96Pin-186

Wilson, Parke
❑ 95NewN566-202

Wilson, Parker
❑ 80ElmPioRST-30

Wilson, Paul
❑ 93BazTeaU-10
❑ 93TopTra-107T
❑ 94Cla#1DPMF-DD1
❑ 94ClaUpdCotC-CC1
❑ 94MetShuST-5
❑ 94SigRooDP-2
❑ 94SigRooDPS-2
❑ 94SigRooFCD-5
❑ 94StaCluDP-82
❑ 94StaCluDPFDI-82
❑ 94TopTra-1T
❑ 94UppDecAHNIL-20
❑ 95ActPacF-52
❑ 95Bes-83
❑ 95Bes-109
❑ 95Bes-AU4
❑ 95BesFra-F12
❑ 95BinMetTI-40
❑ 95Bow-136
❑ 95BowBes-B5
❑ 95BowBesR-B5
❑ 95ColCho-20
❑ 95ColChoGS-20
❑ 95ColChoSE-9
❑ 95ColChoSEGS-9
❑ 95ColChoSESS-9
❑ 95ColChoSS-20
❑ 95Exc-240
❑ 95ScoDraP-DP3
❑ 95SelSurS-SS9
❑ 95SPML-5
❑ 95SPML-97
❑ 95SPMLA-24
❑ 95SPMLDtS-DS3
❑ 95StaClu-100
❑ 95StaCluFDI-100
❑ 95StaCluMOP-100
❑ 95StaCluSTWS-100
❑ 95Top-621
❑ 95UppDec-13
❑ 95UppDecED-13
❑ 95UppDecEDG-13
❑ 95UppDecML-169
❑ 95UppDecML-200
❑ 95UppDecML-215
❑ 95UppDecMLFS-169
❑ 95UppDecMLFS-200
❑ 95UppDecMLFS-215
❑ 95UppDecMLMLA-10
❑ 95UppDecSE-58

❑ 95UppDecSEG-58
❑ 96BesAutSA-88
❑ 96Bow-191
❑ 96BowBes-39
❑ 96BowBesAR-39
❑ 96BowBesP-BBP11
❑ 96BowBesPAR-BBP11
❑ 96BowBesPR-BBP11
❑ 96BowBesR-39
❑ 96BowFoi-191
❑ 96Cir-162
❑ 96CirRav-162
❑ 96EmoXL-240
❑ 96Exc-192
❑ 96ExcAll-10
❑ 96ExcCli-10
❑ 96Fin-B245
❑ 96FinRef-B245
❑ 96Fla-328
❑ 96FlaWavotF-20
❑ 96FleUpd-U162
❑ 96FleUpdNH-20
❑ 96FleUpdTC-U162
❑ 96LeaLimRG-8
❑ 96LeaPre-127
❑ 96LeaPreP-127
❑ 96LeaPreSG-35
❑ 96LeaPreSte-35
❑ 96LeaSig-81
❑ 96LeaSigA-246
❑ 96LeaSigAG-247
❑ 96LeaSigAS-247
❑ 96LeaSigPPG-81
❑ 96LeaSigPPP-81
❑ 96MetKah-31
❑ 96Pin-369
❑ 96PinAfi-168
❑ 96PinAfiAP-168
❑ 96PinAfiSP-4
❑ 96PinFoil-369
❑ 96PinProS-1
❑ 96Sel-162
❑ 96SelArtP-162
❑ 96SelCer-111
❑ 96SelCerAP-111
❑ 96SelCerCB-111
❑ 96SelCerCR-111
❑ 96SelCerIP-21
❑ 96SelCerMB-111
❑ 96SelCerMG-111
❑ 96SelCerMR-111
❑ 96SP-5
❑ 96SPSpeFX-13
❑ 96SPSpeFXDC-13
❑ 96SPx-41
❑ 96SPxGol-41
❑ 96Stu-141
❑ 96StuPrePB-141
❑ 96StuPrePG-141
❑ 96StuPrePS-141
❑ 96Sum-152
❑ 96Sum-177
❑ 96SumAbo&B-152
❑ 96SumAbo&B-177
❑ 96SumArtP-152
❑ 96SumArtP-177
❑ 96SumBal-15
❑ 96SumFoi-152
❑ 96SumFoi-177
❑ 96Top-214
❑ 96TopChr-76
❑ 96TopChrR-76
❑ 96TopGal-127
❑ 96TopGalPPI-127
❑ 96TopLas-63
❑ 96TopLasBS-16
❑ 96Ult-516
❑ 96UltGolM-516
❑ 96UppDec-255
❑ 96UppDecHC-HC4
❑ 96UppDecPHE-H48
❑ 96UppDecPreH-H48
❑ 96Zen-117
❑ 96ZenArtP-117
❑ 96ZenMoz-24
❑ 97BesAutAS-70
❑ 97Cir-174
❑ 97CirRav-174
❑ 97ColCho-174
❑ 97ColChoTBS-33
❑ 97ColChoTBSWH-33
❑ 97Don-182
❑ 97DonEli-68
❑ 97DonEliGS-68
❑ 97DonGolPP-182
❑ 97DonPre-121
❑ 97DonPreCttC-121
❑ 97DonSilPP-182
❑ 97Fin-94
❑ 97FinRef-94
❑ 97Fle-405
❑ 97FleTif-405
❑ 97Lea-103
❑ 97LeaFraM-103
❑ 97LeaFraMDC-103
❑ 97LeaGet-12
❑ 97MetUni-199
❑ 97PacPriGotD-GD179
❑ 97Pin-120
❑ 97PinArtP-PP120
❑ 97PinCer-96
❑ 97PinCerMBla-96
❑ 97PinCerMBlu-96
❑ 97PinCerMG-96
❑ 97PinCerMR-96
❑ 97PinCerR-96
❑ 97PinIns-29
❑ 97PinInsCE-29
❑ 97PinInsDE-29
❑ 97PinMusC-120
❑ 97PinPrePla-120
❑ 97PinTotCPB-96
❑ 97PinTotCPG-96
❑ 97PinTotCPR-96
❑ 97Sco-9
❑ 97ScoArtPWB-9
❑ 97ScoPreS-9
❑ 97ScoShoS-9
❑ 97ScoShoSAP-9
❑ 97Sel-48
❑ 97SelArtP-48
❑ 97SelCom-48
❑ 97SelRegG-48
❑ 97StaClu-108
❑ 97StaCluC-CO2
❑ 97StaCluM-M20
❑ 97StaCluMOP-108
❑ 97StaCluMOP-M20
❑ 97Stu-133
❑ 97StuPrePG-133
❑ 97StuPrePS-133
❑ 97Top-89
❑ 97TopChr-35
❑ 97TopChrR-35
❑ 97TopGal-156
❑ 97TopGalPPI-156
❑ 97Ult-246
❑ 97UltGolME-246
❑ 97UltPlaME-246
❑ 97UppDec-117
❑ 97UppDecRSF-RS18
❑ 98PinSna-NYM18
❑ 98StaCluFDI-296
❑ 98StaCluI-296
❑ 98StaCluOneK-296
❑ 98StaCluPP-296

Wilson, Phil
❑ 82WatIndF-7
❑ 82WatIndT-13
❑ 83WatIndF-14
❑ 85VisOakT-1
❑ 86OrlTwiP-24
❑ 87PorBeaP-9
❑ 88PorBeaC-23
❑ 88PorBeaP-661
❑ 89JacExpP-171

Wilson, Pookie
❑ 92SalLakTSP-13
❑ 93KanCouCC-24
❑ 93KanCouCF-930
❑ 93KanCouCTI-28
❑ 94BreCouMC-23
❑ 94BreCouMF-28
❑ 95PorSeaDTI-29
❑ 96PorSeaDB-29
❑ 97PorSeaD-30
❑ 98PorSeaD5AQ-15

Wilson, Preston
❑ 92ClaDraP-117
❑ 92HigSchPLS-27
❑ 93Bow-594
❑ 93KinMetC-1
❑ 93KinMetF-3806
❑ 93StaCluM-27
❑ 93StaCluMMP-12
❑ 93Top-132
❑ 93TopGol-132
❑ 93TopInaM-132
❑ 93TopInaR-132
❑ 93TopMic-132
❑ 94Bow-484
❑ 94CapCitBC-1
❑ 94CapCitBF-1760
❑ 94Cla-67
❑ 94ClaGolF-106
❑ 94ColC-650
❑ 94ColChoGS-650
❑ 94ColChoSS-650
❑ 94ExcFS7-242
❑ 94SP-20
❑ 94SPDieC-20
❑ 94UppDec-537
❑ 94UppDecAHNIL-16
❑ 94UppDecED-537
❑ 94UppDecML-219
❑ 95SPML-98
❑ 96BesAutS-95
❑ 96BesAutSA-89
❑ 96StLucMTI-22
❑ 97BesAutAS-71
❑ 97BesAutP-R19
❑ 97Bow-344
❑ 97BowChr-234
❑ 97BowChrI-234
❑ 97BowChrIR-234
❑ 97BowChrR-234
❑ 97BowInt-344
❑ 97FloStaLTPB-18
❑ 97St.LucM-28
❑ 98Bes-48
❑ 98Bow-161
❑ 98BowCerBlueAU-45
❑ 98BowCerGA-45
❑ 98BowCerSA-45
❑ 98BowChr-161
❑ 98BowChrGA-161
❑ 98BowChrGAR-161
❑ 98BowChrI-161
❑ 98BowChrIR-161
❑ 98BowChrR-161
❑ 98BowGolA-161
❑ 98BowInt-161
❑ 98Don-286
❑ 98DonColP-709
❑ 98DonGolPP-286
❑ 98DonPre-159
❑ 98DonPreSeat-159
❑ 98DonPriCP-709
❑ 98DonSigA-96
❑ 98DonSigAC-119
❑ 98DonSigAM-122
❑ 98DonSilPP-286
❑ 98FleUpd-U23
❑ 98NorTidP-29
❑ 98NorTidQ-30
❑ 98PinSna-NYM3
❑ 98SP MinDTSPE-DS19
❑ 98SP MinPE-81
❑ 98SPMin-81
❑ 98SPMinDTS-DS19
❑ 98StaCluFDI-377
❑ 98StaCluI-377
❑ 98StaCluOneK-377
❑ 98StaCluPP-377
❑ 98Stu-142
❑ 98StuGPP-142
❑ 98StuSPP-142
❑ 98UppDec-587
❑ 98UppDecDS-DS26
❑ 99199Fin-149
❑ 99BowBes-146
❑ 99BowBesAR-146
❑ 99BowBesR-146
❑ 99CroRoyB-61
❑ 99CroRoyL-61
❑ 99CroRoyOD-61
❑ 99DumSet-150
❑ 99E-X Cen-103
❑ 99E-X CenECFut-103
❑ 99E-X CenECNow-103
❑ 99FinGolRef-149
❑ 99FinRef-149
❑ 99FlaShoWotF-15
❑ 99Fle-264
❑ 99FleBri-135
❑ 99FleBri2G-135
❑ 99FleBriBlu-135
❑ 99FleBriGol-135
❑ 99FleMys-150
❑ 99FleMysM-150
❑ 99FleSta9-264
❑ 99FleWarT-264
❑ 99MetUni-260
❑ 99MetUniGM-260
❑ 99MetUniPMG-260
❑ 99PacOme-101
❑ 99PacOmeC-101
❑ 99PacOmeG-101
❑ 99PacOmePB-101
❑ 99Rev-60
❑ 99RevPremDate-60
❑ 99RevRet-60
❑ 99RevShaSS-60
❑ 99SkyThu-12
❑ 99SkyThuRant-12
❑ 99SkyThuRave-12
❑ 99SP Aut-100
❑ 99SpoIll-57
❑ 99SPSig-113
❑ 99SPx-94
❑ 99SPxFinR-94
❑ 99SPxFinS-94
❑ 99ThuSkySupR-12
❑ 99Top-411
❑ 99TopChr-411
❑ 99TopChrR-411
❑ 99TopMVPP-411
❑ 99TopSta-63
❑ 99TopSta1Foil-63
❑ 99TopStaFoil-63
❑ 99TopStaOS-63
❑ 99UD Cho-13
❑ 99UD ChoPCR-13
❑ 99Ult-244
❑ 99UltGolM-244
❑ 99UltMas-244
❑ 99UltPlaM-244
❑ 99UppDec-376
❑ 99UppDecCLM-C38
❑ 99UppDecE-40
❑ 99UppDecEFXG-40
❑ 99UppDecEL1-376
❑ 99UppDecEL2-376
❑ 99UppDecM-84
❑ 99UppDecMGS-84
❑ 99UppDecMHFS-84
❑ 99UppDecMSS-84
❑ 99UppDecO-73
❑ 99UppDecOSO-73

Wilson, Randy
❑ 84NewOriT-22

Wilson, Red (Robert)
❑ 53Top-250
❑ 54Top-58
❑ 56Top-92
❑ 57Top-19
❑ 58Top-213
❑ 59Top-24
❑ 59TopVen-24
❑ 60Top-379
❑ 61Pos-66
❑ 79TCM50-281
❑ 90DodTar-867
❑ 91TopArc1-250
❑ 94TopArc1-58
❑ 94TopArc1G-58

Wilson, Ric
❑ 82WauTimF-27
❑ 84ChaLooT-22
❑ 87WauTimP-27

Wilson, Rick
❑ 85EveGialC-23
❑ 94IowCubF-1293

Wilson, Roger
❑ 86MiaMarP-28
❑ 87WilBilP-21

Wilson, Ryan
❑ 92HigSchPLS-6

Wilson, Sam W.
❑ 23WilChoV-174

Wilson, Scott
❑ 89CalLeaA-51
❑ 89SanJosGB-17
❑ 89SanJosGCLC-234
❑ 89SanJosGP-454
❑ 89SanJosGS-28
❑ 90SanJosGB-27
❑ 90SanJosGCLC-55
❑ 90SanJosGS-30
❑ 91CalLeLA-49
❑ 91SanJosGC-30
❑ 97NewJerCB-28

Wilson, Steve
❑ 96YakBeaTI-33
❑ 97VerBeaD-28
❑ 98SanBerS-31
❑ 98SanBerSTIS-27

Wilson, Steve Douglas
❑ 86TulDriTI-10
❑ 87PorChaRP-10
❑ 88TexLeaAGS-5
❑ 88TulDriTI-8
❑ 89Bow-280
❑ 89BowTif-280
❑ 89CubMar-44
❑ 89DonBasB-250
❑ 89DonRoo-10
❑ 89Fle-640
❑ 89FleGlo-640
❑ 89FleUpd-82
❑ 89TopTra-131T
❑ 89TopTraT-131T
❑ 89UppDec-799
❑ 90Bow-23
❑ 90BowTif-23
❑ 90CubMar-25
❑ 90Don-394
❑ 90Fle-49
❑ 90FleCan-49
❑ 90Lea-420
❑ 90OPC-741
❑ 90Sco-531
❑ 90ScoYouS2-28
❑ 90Top-741
❑ 90TopRoo-32
❑ 90TopTif-741
❑ 90TopTVCu-18
❑ 90TulDriDGB-9
❑ 90UppDec-341
❑ 91CubVinL-34
❑ 91Don-519
❑ 91Fle-440
❑ 91IowCubLD-222
❑ 91IowCubP-1062
❑ 91LinDriAAA-222
❑ 91OPC-69
❑ 91ParPatF-14
❑ 91Sco-306
❑ 91Top-69
❑ 91TopDesS-69
❑ 91TopMic-69
❑ 91TopTif-69
❑ 91UppDec-493
❑ 92DodMot-27
❑ 92DodPol-38
❑ 92DodSmo-5292
❑ 92Don-710
❑ 92Lea-161
❑ 92LeaBlaG-161
❑ 92OPC-751
❑ 92Sco-812
❑ 92StaClu-626
❑ 92StaCluECN-626
❑ 92Top-751
❑ 92TopGol-751
❑ 92TopGolW-751
❑ 92TopMic-751
❑ 92Ult-510
❑ 93DodMot-23
❑ 93DodPol-28
❑ 93DodStaC-27
❑ 93Don-34
❑ 93Fle-456
❑ 93Lea-145
❑ 93PacSpa-506
❑ 93RanKee-385
❑ 93Top-133
❑ 93TopGol-133
❑ 93TopInaM-133
❑ 93TopInaR-133
❑ 93TopMic-133
❑ 94Fle-529
❑ 94NewOrlZF-1470
❑ 94Pac-324
❑ 94Top-573
❑ 94TopGol-573
❑ 94TopSpa-573
❑ 95NasSouTI-29
❑ 96BriWhiSB-3

Wilson, Tack (Michael)
❑ 81AlbDukTc-23A
❑ 82AlbDukTc-23
❑ 83TolMudHT-18
❑ 84TolMudHT-22
❑ 85PhoGiaC-195
❑ 87EdmTraP-2070
❑ 89OklCit8C-22
❑ 89OklCit8P-1534
❑ 90HunStaB-23
❑ 91PacSenL-50
❑ 93DurBulC-28
❑ 93DurBulF-506
❑ 93DurBulTI-2
❑ 94RicBraF-2865
❑ 98WesTenDJM-28

Wilson, Terry
❑ 89MyrBeaBJP-1475

Wilson, Tex
❑ 90DodTar-1096

Wilson, Tim
❑ 89HelBreSP-5
❑ 90HelBreSP-23

Wilson, Todd
❑ 86EveGiaC-181
❑ 86EveGiaPC-36
❑ 90BilMusP-3232
❑ 91CedRapRC-21
❑ 91CedRapRP-2730
❑ 94EveGiaF-3664
❑ 96SanJosGB-6
❑ 97SanJosG-23
❑ 98OrlRayM-22

Wilson, Tom
❑ 86TamTarP-27
❑ 90PitMetP-17
❑ 91OneYanP-4158
❑ 92ClaFS7-308
❑ 92GreHorC-11
❑ 92GreHorF-783
❑ 93GreHorF-889
❑ 93SouAtlLAPI-42
❑ 94AlbYanF-1445
❑ 94ClaGolF-198
❑ 95NorNavTI-54
❑ 96BufBisB-24
❑ 97NorNav-32
❑ 97NorNavTI-30
❑ 98TusSidM-18

Wilson, Travis
❑ 97DanBraB-29
❑ 98DanBraQ-9

Wilson, Trevor
❑ 85EveGialC-24
❑ 86CliGiaP-28
❑ 87CliGiaP-27
❑ 88BasAmeAAB-27
❑ 88BlaYNPRWL-126
❑ 88ShrCapP-1298
❑ 89Fle-347
❑ 89FleGlo-347
❑ 89PhoFirC-10
❑ 89PhoFirP-1481
❑ 89ScoHot1R-31
❑ 89Top-783
❑ 89TopTif-783
❑ 89UppDec-733
❑ 90CMC-535
❑ 90Don-414
❑ 90FleUpd-64
❑ 90Lea-489
❑ 90OPC-408
❑ 90PhoFirC-8
❑ 90PhoFirP-12
❑ 90ProAAAF-38
❑ 90Top-408
❑ 90TopTif-408
❑ 90UppDec-637
❑ 91Bow-630
❑ 91Don-263
❑ 91Fle-277
❑ 91GiaMot-22
❑ 91GiaPacGaE-9
❑ 91OPC-96
❑ 91Sco-657
❑ 91StaClu-212
❑ 91Stu-253
❑ 91Top-96
❑ 91TopDesS-96
❑ 91TopMic-96
❑ 91TopTif-96
❑ 91UltUpd-119
❑ 91UppDec-653
❑ 92Bow-119
❑ 92Don-575
❑ 92Fle-651
❑ 92GiaMot-22
❑ 92GiaPacGaE-36
❑ 92Lea-340
❑ 92LeaBlaG-340
❑ 92OPC-204
❑ 92Pin-352
❑ 92Sco-608
❑ 92StaClu-86
❑ 92Top-204
❑ 92TopGol-204
❑ 92TopGolW-204
❑ 92TopMic-204
❑ 92TriPla-146
❑ 92Ult-297
❑ 92UppDec-337
❑ 93Don-578
❑ 93Fle-162
❑ 93GiaMot-23
❑ 93GiaPos-34

❑ 93GiaStaC-22
❑ 93Lea-477
❑ 93PacSpa-279
❑ 93Pin-210
❑ 93Sco-401
❑ 93StaClu-185
❑ 93StaCluFDI-185
❑ 93StaCluMOP-185
❑ 93Top-364
❑ 93TopGol-364
❑ 93TopInaM-364
❑ 93TopInaR-364
❑ 93TopMic-364
❑ 93TriPla-186
❑ 93Ult-491
❑ 93UppDec-197
❑ 93UppDecGold-197
❑ 94Don-572
❑ 94Fle-705
❑ 94GiaUSPC-3H
❑ 94GiaUSPC-10S
❑ 94Pac-560
❑ 94Pin-82
❑ 94PinArtP-82
❑ 94PinMusC-82
❑ 94Sco-140
❑ 94ScoGolR-140
❑ 94StaCluT-21
❑ 94StaCluTFDI-21
❑ 94Top-462
❑ 94TopGol-462
❑ 94TopSpa-462
❑ 95Fin-224
❑ 95FinRef-224
❑ 95FleUpd-197
❑ 95GiaMot-24
❑ 95StaClu-582
❑ 95StaCluMOP-582
❑ 95StaCluSTWS-582
❑ 95TopTra-117T
❑ 98VanCanG-30

Wilson, Vance
❑ 94PitMetC-24
❑ 94PitMetF-3526
❑ 96StLucMTI-28
❑ 97BinMetB-31
❑ 98Bow-393
❑ 98BowChr-393
❑ 98BowChrGA-393
❑ 98BowChrGAR-393
❑ 98BowChrI-393
❑ 98BowChrIR-393
❑ 98BowChrR-393
❑ 98BowGolA-393
❑ 98BowInt-393
❑ 98NorTidP-30
❑ 98NorTidQ-31

Wilson, Ward
❑ 76CliPilT-35
❑ 77LynMetT-30

Wilson, Wayne
❑ 84NewOriT-6
❑ 85NewOriT-11
❑ 86HagSunP-28
❑ 87HagSunP-16

Wilson, William D.
❑ 49SolSunP-12
❑ 54Top-222
❑ 55A'sRodM-45
❑ 55A'sRodM-46
❑ 55A'sTeal-28
❑ 55Top-86
❑ 55TopDouH-101
❑ 76A'sRodMC-29
❑ 94TopArc1-222
❑ 94TopArc1G-222

Wilson, William H.
❑ 67Top-402A
❑ 67Top-402B
❑ 69Top-576
❑ 70OPC-28
❑ 70Top-28
❑ 71MLBOffS-192
❑ 71OPC-192
❑ 71Top-192
❑ 72Top-587
❑ 73OPC-619
❑ 73PhiTeal-24
❑ 73Top-619

Wilson, William PCL
❑ 37Zee-51

Wilson, Willie (batboy)
❑ 96DurBulBlB-11

Wilson, Willie J.
❑ 75WatRoyT-34
❑ 78Roy-26
❑ 78SSP270-241
❑ 79RoyTeal-13
❑ 79Top-409
❑ 80BurKinPHR-33
❑ 80OPC-87
❑ 80Top-157
❑ 80Top-204
❑ 81AllGamPI-70
❑ 81CokTeaS-83
❑ 81Don-223
❑ 81Fle-29
❑ 81Fle-653A
❑ 81Fle-653B
❑ 81FleStiC-106
❑ 81Kel-24
❑ 81OPC-360
❑ 81PerCreC-31
❑ 81RoyPol-10
❑ 81RoyProPS-15
❑ 81Top-208
❑ 81Top-360
❑ 81TopScr-20
❑ 81TopSti-16
❑ 81TopSti-81
❑ 81TopSti-247
❑ 82Don-448
❑ 82Fle-427
❑ 82FleSta-207
❑ 82Kel-62
❑ 82OPC-230
❑ 82Roy-25
❑ 82Top-230
❑ 82TopSti-189
❑ 83AllGamPI-71
❑ 83Don-15
❑ 83Don-112
❑ 83DonActA-13
❑ 83Dra-30
❑ 83Fle-128
❑ 83FleSta-218
❑ 83FleSti-104
❑ 83Kel-23
❑ 83OPC-16
❑ 83PerCreC-33
❑ 83PerCreCG-33
❑ 83RoyPol-10
❑ 83RoyPos-35
❑ 83Top-471
❑ 83Top-701
❑ 83Top-710
❑ 83TopFol-3
❑ 83TopFol-5
❑ 83TopGloS-23
❑ 83TopLeaS-1
❑ 83TopSti-15
❑ 83TopSti-73
❑ 83TopSti-161
❑ 84Don-175
❑ 84Fle-364
❑ 84FleSti-94
❑ 84FunFooP-82
❑ 84Nes792-525
❑ 84OPC-5
❑ 84RoyPos-37
❑ 84Top-525
❑ 84TopSti-280
❑ 84TopStiB-5
❑ 84TopTif-525
❑ 85AllGamPI-71
❑ 85Don-297
❑ 85Fle-218
❑ 85KASDis-19
❑ 85KitCloD-19
❑ 85Lea-110
❑ 85OPC-6
❑ 85RoyTeal-33
❑ 85SubDis-22
❑ 85ThoMcAD-22
❑ 85Top-617
❑ 85TopSti-277
❑ 85TopTif-617
❑ 85Woo-42
❑ 86BasStaB-122
❑ 86Don-175
❑ 86Fle-25
❑ 86FleMin-5
❑ 86FleStiC-129
❑ 86Lea-106
❑ 86OPC-25
❑ 86RoyKitCD-15
❑ 86RoyNatP-6
❑ 86RoyTeal-26
❑ 86SevCoi-C14
❑ 86Spo-124
❑ 86Spo-128
❑ 86Spo-144
❑ 86Spo-180
❑ 86Spo-186
❑ 86Top-25
❑ 86TopMinL-22
❑ 86TopSti-258
❑ 86TopSup-59
❑ 86TopTat-21
❑ 86TopTif-25
❑ 86Woo-32
❑ 87Don-96
❑ 87DonOpeD-208
❑ 87Fle-384
❑ 87FleExcS-43
❑ 87FleGlo-384
❑ 87FleMin-116
❑ 87FleRecS-42
❑ 87FleStiC-125
❑ 87Lea-97
❑ 87OPC-367
❑ 87Spo-85
❑ 87SpoTeaP-13
❑ 87StuPan-20
❑ 87Top-783
❑ 87TopMinL-58
❑ 87TopSti-261
❑ 87TopTif-783
❑ 88Don-255
❑ 88DonBasB-263
❑ 88Fle-274
❑ 88FleGlo-274
❑ 88Lea-189
❑ 88OPC-222
❑ 88PanSti-113
❑ 88RoySmo-3
❑ 88RoyTeal-38
❑ 88Sco-102
❑ 88ScoGlo-102
❑ 88Spo-192
❑ 88StaLinRo-20
❑ 88Top-452
❑ 88TopBig-21
❑ 88TopMinL-17
❑ 88TopRevLL-25
❑ 88TopSti-263
❑ 88TopTif-452
❑ 89Bow-124
❑ 89BowTif-124
❑ 89Don-120
❑ 89Fle-298
❑ 89FleGlo-298
❑ 89OPC-168
❑ 89PanSti-361
❑ 89RoyTasD-5
❑ 89Sco-28
❑ 89Spo-186
❑ 89Top-168
❑ 89TopBatL-17
❑ 89TopBig-136
❑ 89TopMinL-56
❑ 89TopSti-268
❑ 89TopTif-168
❑ 89UppDec-244
❑ 90Don-440
❑ 90Fle-123
❑ 90FleCan-123
❑ 90KayB-31
❑ 90Lea-336
❑ 90MLBBasB-109
❑ 90OPC-323
❑ 90PacLeg-109
❑ 90PubIntS-361
❑ 90RoyPos-29
❑ 90Sco-104
❑ 90Top-323
❑ 90TopBig-45
❑ 90TopTif-323
❑ 90UppDec-349
❑ 91A'sMot-17
❑ 91Bow-230
❑ 91Fle-575
❑ 91Lea-299
❑ 91OPC-208
❑ 91OPCPre-129
❑ 91ScoRoo-15T
❑ 91StaClu-378
❑ 91Top-208
❑ 91TopDesS-208
❑ 91TopMic-208
❑ 91TopTif-208
❑ 91TopTra-129T
❑ 91TopTraT-129T
❑ 91UltUpd-48
❑ 91UppDec-609
❑ 92AthMot-17
❑ 92FleUpd-53
❑ 92OPC-536
❑ 92Sco-328
❑ 92StaClu-343
❑ 92Top-536
❑ 92TopGol-536
❑ 92TopGolW-536
❑ 92TopMic-536
❑ 92Ult-429
❑ 92UppDec-238
❑ 93Bow-468
❑ 93CubMar-31
❑ 93CubStaC-5
❑ 93Fle-302
❑ 93FleFinE-13
❑ 93Lea-413
❑ 93OPC-370
❑ 93OPCPre-53
❑ 93PacSpa-228
❑ 93Pin-141
❑ 93RoySta2-15
❑ 93Sco-647
❑ 93Sel-395
❑ 93StaClu-622
❑ 93StaCluFDI-622
❑ 93StaCluMOP-622
❑ 93Stu-199
❑ 93Top-318
❑ 93TopGol-318
❑ 93TopInaM-318
❑ 93TopInaR-318
❑ 93TopMic-318
❑ 93Ult-324
❑ 93UppDec-417
❑ 93UppDec-625
❑ 93UppDecGold-417
❑ 93UppDecGold-625
❑ 94DurBulTI-31
❑ 94Fle-402
❑ 94Pac-116
❑ 94Sco-134
❑ 94ScoGolR-134
❑ 94StaClu-311
❑ 94StaCluFDI-311
❑ 94StaCluGR-311
❑ 94StaCluMOP-311
❑ 94StaCluT-357
❑ 94StaCluTFDI-357
❑ 94Top-698
❑ 94TopGol-698
❑ 94TopSpa-698
❑ 94Ult-169
❑ 95DurBulTI-38
❑ 97SyrSkyCB-28

Wilson, Woodrow
❑ 94UppDecTAE-21

Wilstead, Judd
❑ 93HelBreF-4096
❑ 93HelBreSP-14
❑ 94BelBreC-26
❑ 94BelBreFI-102
❑ 96El PasDB-29

Wilstead, Randy (Randon)
❑ 90JamExpP-6
❑ 91MidLeaAP-MWL50
❑ 91RocExpC-22
❑ 91RocExpP-2057
❑ 92WesPalBEC-22
❑ 92WesPalBEF-2097
❑ 93WesPalBEC-25
❑ 93WesPalBEF-1351
❑ 94HarSenF-2102

Wiltbank, Ben
❑ 78SalPirT-18
❑ 79PorBeaT-4
❑ 79Top-723
❑ 81BufBisT-5

Wiltse, Hal
❑ 93ConTSN-955

Wiltse, Hooks (George R.)
❑ 03BreE10-153
❑ 06GiaUllAFS-12
❑ 08RosComP-135
❑ 09AmeCarE90-1-118
❑ 09ColChiE-310
❑ 09PhiCarE-25
❑ 09T206-383
❑ 09T206-384
❑ 09T206-385
❑ 10CouT21-249
❑ 10CouT21-250
❑ 10CouT21-251
❑ 10CouT21-252
❑ 10CouT21-253
❑ 10CouT21-254
❑ 10CouT21-324
❑ 10DomDisP-127
❑ 10E12AmeCDCE125-41
❑ 10PeoT21-57
❑ 10RedCroT-86
❑ 10RedCroT-87
❑ 10RedCroT-166
❑ 10RedCroT-167
❑ 10RedCroT-258
❑ 10RedCroT-259
❑ 10StaCarE-29
❑ 10SweCapPP-123
❑ 10W555-63
❑ 11HelSta-139
❑ 11MecDFT-34
❑ 11PinT-5-253
❑ 11S74Sil-96
❑ 11SpoLifCW-371
❑ 11SpoLifM-223
❑ 11T205-183A
❑ 11T205-183B
❑ 11TurRedT-41
❑ 12ColRedB-310
❑ 12ColTinT-310
❑ 12HasTriFT-48J
❑ 12HasTriFT-74F
❑ 12T207-200
❑ 14B18B-73
❑ 14PieStaT-112
❑ 15AmeCarE106-41
❑ 15VicT21-30
❑ 72ClaCar-55
❑ 92ConTSN-332

Wiltse, Lew
❑ 06FanCraNL-53

Wiltshere, Vernon
❑ 35DiaMatCS3T1-149
❑ 36NatChiFPR-82

Wiltz, Stanley
❑ 92WelPirC-27
❑ 92WelPirF-1335
❑ 93WelPirC-27
❑ 93WelPirF-3370

Wimbereley, Larry
❑ 98ClePhiM-25
❑ 98ClePhiUM-25

Wimberly, Larry
❑ 94MarPhiC-30
❑ 94MarPhiF-3295
❑ 95PiePhiF-188
❑ 95SPML-129
❑ 95TopTra-88T
❑ 96BesAutS-96
❑ 96Exc-215
❑ 96MicBatCB-28
❑ 96SarRedSB-29

Wimmer, Chris
❑ 90WicStaSGD-38
❑ 91TopTra-130T
❑ 91TopTraT-130T
❑ 92StaCluD-197
❑ 92TopDaiQTU-28
❑ 92TopTra-129T
❑ 92TopTraG-129T
❑ 93SanJosGC-22
❑ 93SanJosGF-21
❑ 93StaCluM-42
❑ 94ClaGolF-152
❑ 94ExcFS7-297
❑ 94ShrCapF-1616
❑ 94UppDecML-21
❑ 95Bow-85
❑ 95PhoFirTI-8
❑ 95UppDecML-148
❑ 95UppDecMLFS-148
❑ 96LouRedB-27
❑ 98CarMudM-18

Winawer, Larry
❑ 91HelBreSP-7

Winbush, Mike
❑ 86SalRedBP-29

Winceniak, Ed
❑ 59SeaPop-38

Winchell, Derek
❑ 87SalAngP-34
❑ 88BenBucL-30
❑ 92CalLeaACL-50

Winchester, Jeff
❑ 99Bow-412
❑ 99BowBes-195
❑ 99BowBesAR-195
❑ 99BowBesR-195
❑ 99BowGol-412
❑ 99BowInt-412
❑ 99StaClu-156
❑ 99StaCluFDI-156
❑ 99StaCluOoaK-156
❑ 99StaCluPP-156
❑ 99TeaBesR-99
❑ 99TeaBesRG-99
❑ 99TeaBesRS-99
❑ 99Top-442
❑ 99TopChr-442
❑ 99TopChrR-442
❑ 99TopMVPP-442

Winchester, Marty
❑ 93SpoIndC-24
❑ 93SpoIndF-3593
❑ 94AppFoxC-21
❑ 94AppFoxFI-1055

Winchester, Scott
❑ 95WatIndTI-30
❑ 97CalLeaATI-47
❑ 97KinIndB-25
❑ 98IndIndQ-19
❑ 98PacOmeRS-4
❑ 98PacOmeRST5-4
❑ 98PacOnl-208
❑ 98PacOnlR-208
❑ 98PacOnlWC-208
❑ 98Ult-281
❑ 98UltGolM-281
❑ 98UltMas-281
❑ 98UltPlaM-281

Winders, Brian
❑ 94LSUTig-7

Windes, Cary
❑ 89FreStaBS-21
❑ 90FreStaS-15

Windes, Rodney
❑ 88AubAstP-1955
❑ 89AshTouP-947
❑ 90OscAstS-26
❑ 91OscAstC-13
❑ 91OscAstP-686
❑ 92JacGenS-348

Windham, Mike
❑ 93GleFalRC-29
❑ 93GleFalRF-4003
❑ 94MadHatC-25
❑ 94MadHatF-132
❑ 96StPetCB-30
❑ 97ArkTraB-11
❑ 98ArkTraM-26

Windhorn, Gordon
❑ 62Top-254
❑ 90DodTar-868

Windmiller, Amy
❑ 91FreStaLBS-14

Windsor, Duchess of
❑ 83ASAJohM-10

Windsor, Duke of
❑ 83ASAJohM-10

Wine, Bobby (Robert)
❑ 47StaPinP2-42
❑ 63Top-71
❑ 64PhiJayP-12
❑ 64PhiPhiB-26
❑ 64Top-347
❑ 64TopVen-347
❑ 65OPC-36
❑ 65PhiJayP-12
❑ 65Top-36
❑ 66Top-284
❑ 66TopVen-284
❑ 67CokCapPh-2
❑ 67Top-466
❑ 68Top-396
❑ 69ExpPin-9
❑ 69Top-648
❑ 70ExpPin-14
❑ 70ExpPos-9
❑ 70MLBOffS-72
❑ 70OPC-332
❑ 70Top-332
❑ 71ExpLaPR-14
❑ 71ExpPS-28
❑ 71MLBOffS-144
❑ 71OPC-171
❑ 71Top-171
❑ 72Dia-51
❑ 72MilBra-367
❑ 72Top-657
❑ 73OPC-486
❑ 73PhiTeal-29
❑ 73Top-486A
❑ 73Top-486B
❑ 74OPC-119
❑ 74Top-119
❑ 75PhiPhiP-31
❑ 75PhiProPS-16
❑ 76PhiPhiP-31

❑ 78SSP270-32
❑ 78TCM60I-181
❑ 83PhiPosGPaM-4
❑ 85BraPol-7
❑ 86Top-51
❑ 86TopTif-51
❑ 89BraDub-30
❑ 96MetKah-34
❑ 96MetKah-32

Wine, Robbie
❑ 86TucTorP-26
❑ 87SpoTeaP-8
❑ 87TucTorP-3
❑ 88Don-508
❑ 88Fle-459
❑ 88FleGlo-459
❑ 88OklCit8C-22
❑ 88OklCit8P-42
❑ 88Sco-496
❑ 88ScoGlo-496
❑ 88Top-119
❑ 88TopTif-119
❑ 89RicBraBC-28
❑ 89RicBraC-11
❑ 89RicBraP-843
❑ 89RicBraTI-24
❑ 90CanIndB-17
❑ 90CanIndP-1295
❑ 91LinDriAAA-572
❑ 91TidTidLD-572

Winegarner, Ralph
❑ 33MrsShePP-18
❑ 34DiaMatCSB-199
❑ 35DiaMatCS3T1-151
❑ 36R31PasP-25

Winfield, Dave
❑ 73PadDea-29
❑ 74OPC-456
❑ 74PadDea-30
❑ 74PadMcDD-13
❑ 74PadTeal-18
❑ 74Top-456
❑ 74TopSta-100
❑ 75Hos-37
❑ 75OPC-61
❑ 75PadDea-30
❑ 75Top-61
❑ 75TopMin-61
❑ 76Hos-83
❑ 76OPC-160
❑ 76SSP-133
❑ 76Top-160
❑ 77BurCheD-130
❑ 77Hos-44
❑ 77Kel-28
❑ 77OPC-156
❑ 77PadSchC-65A
❑ 77PadSchC-65B
❑ 77PadSchC-65C
❑ 77PadSchC-65D
❑ 77Spo-5702
❑ 77Spo-8803
❑ 77Top-390
❑ 77TopCloS-52
❑ 78Hos-63
❑ 78Kel-11
❑ 78OPC-78
❑ 78PadFamF-38
❑ 78Top-530
❑ 79BasPat-97
❑ 79Hos-125
❑ 79OPC-11
❑ 79PadFamF-11
❑ 79Top-30
❑ 79TopCom-31
❑ 80BurKinPHR-22
❑ 80Kel-32
❑ 80OPC-122
❑ 80Top-203
❑ 80Top-230
❑ 80TopSup-18
❑ 81AllGamPI-71
❑ 81Don-364
❑ 81Dra-14
❑ 81Fle-484
❑ 81FleStiC-25
❑ 81Kel-21
❑ 81PadFamF-24
❑ 81PerAll-18
❑ 81PerCreC-21
❑ 81Squ-19
❑ 81Top-370
❑ 81TopSti-111
❑ 81TopSupHT-72
❑ 81TopTra-855
❑ 81YanPhoA-26
❑ 82Don-18
❑ 82Don-31
❑ 82Don-575
❑ 82Dra-31
❑ 82FBIDis-28
❑ 82Fle-56
❑ 82Fle-646
❑ 82Fle-646B
❑ 82FleSta-110
❑ 82FleSta-113
❑ 82Kel-12
❑ 82OPC-76
❑ 82OPC-352
❑ 82PerCreC-14
❑ 82PerCreCG-14
❑ 82SevSluC-26
❑ 82Squ-7
❑ 82Top-553
❑ 82Top-600
❑ 82TopSti-137
❑ 82TopSti-213
❑ 82YanPhoA-26
❑ 83AllGamPI-72
❑ 83Don-409
❑ 83DonActA-36
❑ 83Dra-31
❑ 83Fle-398
❑ 83Fle-633
❑ 83FleSta-219
❑ 83FleSti-39
❑ 83Kel-15
❑ 83OPC-258
❑ 83PerAll-8
❑ 83PerAllG-7
❑ 83PerCreC-34
❑ 83PerCreCG-34
❑ 83Top-770
❑ 83TopGloS-7
❑ 83TopSti-99
❑ 83YanPhoA-26
❑ 83YanRoyRD-12
❑ 84AllGamPI-161
❑ 84Don-51
❑ 84Dra-32
❑ 84Fle-143
❑ 84FleSti-5
❑ 84FunFooP-1
❑ 84MilBra-29
❑ 84MLBPen-2
❑ 84Nes792-402
❑ 84Nes792-460
❑ 84NesDreT-6
❑ 84OCoandSI-63
❑ 84OPC-266
❑ 84OPC-378
❑ 84RalPur-7
❑ 84SevCoi-E7
❑ 84Top-402
❑ 84Top-460
❑ 84TopCer-7
❑ 84TopGloA-8
❑ 84TopGloS-16
❑ 84TopRubD-29
❑ 84TopSti-190
❑ 84TopSti-319
❑ 84TopSup-27
❑ 84TopTif-402
❑ 84TopTif-460
❑ 85AllGamPI-72
❑ 85Don-51
❑ 85Don-651A
❑ 85Don-651B
❑ 85DonActA-12
❑ 85DonHig-53
❑ 85Dra-32
❑ 85Fle-146
❑ 85Fle-629
❑ 85FleLimE-43
❑ 85FleStaS-5
❑ 85GenMilS-25
❑ 85KASDis-20
❑ 85KitCloD-20
❑ 85Lea-127
❑ 85Lea-140
❑ 85OPC-180
❑ 85PolMet-Y4
❑ 85SevCoi-C3
❑ 85SevCoi-E5
❑ 85SevCoi-G3
❑ 85SevCoi-S5
❑ 85SevCoi-W5
❑ 85SpoPro-4
❑ 85SpoPro-5
❑ 85SubDis-23
❑ 85ThoMcAD-23
❑ 85Top-180
❑ 85Top-705
❑ 85Top3-D-18
❑ 85TopGloA-17
❑ 85TopGloS-14
❑ 85TopRubD-30
❑ 85TopSti-186
❑ 85TopSti-308
❑ 85TopSup-60
❑ 85TopTif-180
❑ 85TopTif-705
❑ 85YanTCMP-39
❑ 86BasStaB-123
❑ 86BurKinA-2
❑ 86Don-248
❑ 86DonAll-15
❑ 86DonPop-15
❑ 86DorChe-19
❑ 86Dra-18
❑ 86Fle-121
❑ 86FleMin-26
❑ 86FleStiC-130
❑ 86FleStiWBC-S4
❑ 86Lea-125
❑ 86MeaGolBB-16
❑ 86MeaGolSB-7
❑ 86MSAJifPD-7
❑ 86OPC-70
❑ 86QuaGra-33
❑ 86SevCoi-E11
❑ 86Spo-49
❑ 86SpoDecG-74
❑ 86Top-70
❑ 86Top-717
❑ 86Top3-D-29
❑ 86TopGloA-8
❑ 86TopGloS-42
❑ 86TopMinL-29
❑ 86TopSti-160
❑ 86TopSti-298
❑ 86TopSup-60
❑ 86TopTat-1
❑ 86TopTif-70
❑ 86TopTif-717
❑ 86Woo-33
❑ 86YanTCM-36
❑ 87BoaandB-4
❑ 87ClaGam-11
❑ 87Don-20
❑ 87Don-105
❑ 87DonAll-2
❑ 87DonOpeD-243
❑ 87DonP-2
❑ 87DonSupD-20
❑ 87Dra-5
❑ 87Fle-120
❑ 87FleGlo-120
❑ 87FleLimE-42
❑ 87FleMin-117
❑ 87FleStiC-126
❑ 87GenMilB-2I
❑ 87KayB-33
❑ 87KeyFooD-9
❑ 87KraFoo-33
❑ 87Lea-20
❑ 87Lea-70
❑ 87MSAIceTD-9
❑ 87OPC-36
❑ 87OPCBoxB-H
❑ 87OurOwnTD-9
❑ 87RalPur-4
❑ 87RedFolSB-28
❑ 87SevCoi-E15
❑ 87Spo-41
❑ 87Spo-153
❑ 87SpoTeaP-7
❑ 87StuPan-23
❑ 87Top-770
❑ 87TopCoi-26
❑ 87TopGloA-17
❑ 87TopSti-152
❑ 87TopSti-298
❑ 87TopTif-770
❑ 87TopWaxBC-H
❑ 87WeiMarD-9
❑ 88AlaGolAA70TI-16
❑ 88ClaRed-170
❑ 88Don-298
❑ 88DonAll-2
❑ 88DonBasB-244
❑ 88DonPop-2
❑ 88DonReaBY-278
❑ 88Dra-12
❑ 88Fle-226
❑ 88FleBasA-44
❑ 88FleBasM-43
❑ 88FleGlo-226
❑ 88FleMin-44
❑ 88FleSlu-43
❑ 88FleStiC-53
❑ 88KayB-33
❑ 88Lea-116
❑ 88MSAJifPD-19
❑ 88Nes-33
❑ 88OPC-89
❑ 88PanSti-161
❑ 88PanSti-231
❑ 88Sco-55
❑ 88ScoBoxC-8
❑ 88ScoGlo-55
❑ 88Spo-7
❑ 88SpoGam-7
❑ 88StaLinAl-36
❑ 88StaLinY-20
❑ 88StaStiW-1
❑ 88StaStiW-2
❑ 88StaStiW-3
❑ 88StaStiW-4
❑ 88StaStiW-5
❑ 88StaStiW-6
❑ 88StaStiW-7
❑ 88StaStiW-8
❑ 88StaStiW-9
❑ 88StaStiW-10
❑ 88StaWin-1
❑ 88StaWin-2
❑ 88StaWin-3
❑ 88StaWin-4
❑ 88StaWin-5
❑ 88StaWin-6
❑ 88StaWin-7
❑ 88StaWin-8
❑ 88StaWin-9
❑ 88StaWin-10
❑ 88StaWin-11
❑ 88StaWin-12
❑ 88TarPla-48
❑ 88Top-392
❑ 88Top-459
❑ 88Top-510
❑ 88TopBig-24
❑ 88TopClo-119
❑ 88TopGloA-8
❑ 88TopGloS-46
❑ 88TopSti-159
❑ 88TopSti-302
❑ 88TopStiB-54
❑ 88TopTif-392
❑ 88TopTif-459
❑ 88TopTif-510
❑ 88TopUKM-85
❑ 88TopUKMT-85
❑ 89Bow-179
❑ 89BowTif-179
❑ 89CadEllD-61
❑ 89ClaLigB-32
❑ 89Don-159
❑ 89DonAll-6
❑ 89DonBonM-BC11
❑ 89DonGraS-6
❑ 89DonPop-6
❑ 89Fle-274
❑ 89FleBasA-44
❑ 89FleBasM-43
❑ 89FleExcS-43
❑ 89FleGlo-274
❑ 89FleHeroB-43
❑ 89FleLeaL-43
❑ 89FleSup-43
❑ 89KayB-32
❑ 89KeyFooD-13
❑ 89KinDis-16
❑ 89MSAIceTD-13
❑ 89OPC-260
❑ 89OPCBoxB-P
❑ 89OurOwnTD-13
❑ 89PanSti-240
❑ 89PanSti-409
❑ 89RedFolSB-128
❑ 89Sco-50
❑ 89ScoHot1S-3
❑ 89Scomast-41
❑ 89Spo-24
❑ 89SpoIllFKI-282
❑ 89TetTeaD-13
❑ 89Top-260
❑ 89Top-407
❑ 89TopAme2C-32
❑ 89TopBasT-42
❑ 89TopBig-314
❑ 89TopCoi-58
❑ 89TopDouM-15
❑ 89TopGloA-8
❑ 89TopGloS-21
❑ 89TopHilTM-32
❑ 89TopMinL-67
❑ 89TopSti-149
❑ 89TopSti-315
❑ 89TopStiB-20
❑ 89TopTif-260
❑ 89TopTif-407
❑ 89TopUKM-84
❑ 89TopWaxBC-P
❑ 89TVSpoM-81
❑ 89UppDec-349
❑ 89WeiMarD-13
❑ 89YanScoNW-7
❑ 90AllBasT-23
❑ 90Bow-432
❑ 90BowTif-432
❑ 90Don-551
❑ 90DonBesA-87
❑ 90Fle-458
❑ 90FleCan-458
❑ 90FleUpd-81
❑ 90KayB-32
❑ 90Lea-426
❑ 90M.Vpin-71
❑ 90MLBBasB-64
❑ 90OPC-380
❑ 90PubIntS-298
❑ 90PubIntS-550
❑ 90Sco-307
❑ 90ScoRoo-1T
❑ 90Spo-87
❑ 90Top-380
❑ 90TopAmeA-1
❑ 90TopBig-20
❑ 90TopHilHM-17
❑ 90TopMag-50
❑ 90TopTif-380
❑ 90TopTra-130T
❑ 90TopTraT-130T
❑ 90TopTVY-34
❑ 90UppDec-337
❑ 90UppDec-745
❑ 91AngSmo-3
❑ 91BluJayFS-34
❑ 91Bow-210
❑ 91Don-468
❑ 91Fle-329
❑ 91FouBal-27
❑ 91JimDea-22
❑ 91Lea-499
❑ 91OPC-630
❑ 91OPCPre-130
❑ 91PanFreS-184
❑ 91PanSti-132
❑ 91PetSta-5
❑ 91PosCan-28
❑ 91RedFolS-102
❑ 91Sco-83
❑ 91Sco100S-66
❑ 91StaClu-263
❑ 91StaCluMO-9
❑ 91StaPinB-54
❑ 91Stu-30
❑ 91Top-630
❑ 91TopDesS-630
❑ 91TopMic-630
❑ 91TopTif-630
❑ 91TopTriH-A3
❑ 91Ult-54
❑ 91UppDec-337
❑ 92BluJayP-13
❑ 92Bow-315
❑ 92ClaGam-194
❑ 92Don-133
❑ 92DonUpd-U18
❑ 92Fle-72
❑ 92Fle-686
❑ 92FleUpd-67
❑ 92Hig5-15
❑ 92LaKdec-30
❑ 92Lea-171
❑ 92LeaBlaG-171
❑ 92OPC-5
❑ 92OPC-792
❑ 92OPCPre-150
❑ 92PepDieM-30
❑ 92Pin-375
❑ 92PinRool-18
❑ 92RedFolS-100
❑ 92Sco-32
❑ 92Sco100S-9
❑ 92ScoFacI-B10
❑ 92ScoProP-7
❑ 92ScoRoo-7T
❑ 92SpoIllFK1-170
❑ 92StaClu-745
❑ 92Stu-260
❑ 92Top-5
❑ 92Top-792
❑ 92TopGol-5
❑ 92TopGol-792
❑ 92TopGolW-5
❑ 92TopGolW-792
❑ 92TopKid-96
❑ 92TopMic-5
❑ 92TopMic-792
❑ 92TopTra-130T
❑ 92TopTraG-130T
❑ 92Ult-454
❑ 92UppDec-28
❑ 92UppDec-222
❑ 92UppDec-734
❑ 92UppDecHRH-HR17
❑ 92YanWIZ8-204
❑ 92YanWIZA-86
❑ 93BluJayD4-14
❑ 93BluJayDWS-7
❑ 93Bow-565
❑ 93ClaGam-98
❑ 93DiaMar-118
❑ 93Don-643
❑ 93DonEli-35
❑ 93DonEliS-17
❑ 93DonSpiotG-SG1
❑ 93DurPowP1-24
❑ 93Fin-162
❑ 93FinRef-162
❑ 93Fla-243
❑ 93Fle-343
❑ 93FleFinE-241
❑ 93FleFinEDT-9
❑ 93FleGolM-A3
❑ 93FunPac-196
❑ 93HumDumC-12
❑ 93Lea-423
❑ 93Lea-DW
❑ 93MetBak-40
❑ 93OPC-371
❑ 93OPCPre-28
❑ 93OPCWorC-17
❑ 93OPCWorSH-4
❑ 93PacJugC-18
❑ 93PacSpa-528
❑ 93Pin-295
❑ 93Pin-438
❑ 93Pin-483
❑ 93Pin-486
❑ 93PinCoo-10
❑ 93PinCooD-10
❑ 93PinHomRC-32
❑ 93RaiFooW-1
❑ 93RaiFooW-2
❑ 93RaiFooW-3
❑ 93RaiFooW-4
❑ 93RaiFooW-5
❑ 93RaiFooW-6
❑ 93RaiFooW-7
❑ 93RaiFooW-8
❑ 93RaiFooW-9
❑ 93RaiFooW-10
❑ 93Sco-521
❑ 93Sco-620
❑ 93Sel-32
❑ 93SelRoo-9T
❑ 93SP-252
❑ 93StaClu-206
❑ 93StaClu-609
❑ 93StaCluFDI-206
❑ 93StaCluFDI-609
❑ 93StaCluM-1
❑ 93StaCluMO-28
❑ 93StaCluMOP-206
❑ 93StaCluMOP-609
❑ 93Stu-77
❑ 93Top-131
❑ 93TOPBLAG-44
❑ 93TopGol-131
❑ 93TopInaM-131
❑ 93TopInaR-131
❑ 93TopMagJRC-2
❑ 93TopMic-131
❑ 93TopTra-83T
❑ 93TriPlaG-GS5
❑ 93Ult-589
❑ 93UppDec-40
❑ 93UppDec-786
❑ 93UppDecGold-40
❑ 93UppDecGold-786
❑ 93UppDecSH-HI19
❑ 93UppDecTAN-TN9
❑ 94Bow-300

❑ 94BowBes-R6
❑ 94BowBesR-R6
❑ 94ColC-302
❑ 94ColChoGS-302
❑ 94ColChoSS-302
❑ 94Don-336
❑ 94Don-550
❑ 94DonDiaK-DK29
❑ 94DonDiaKJ-DK29
❑ 94DonSpeE-336
❑ 94Fin-215
❑ 94FinJum-215
❑ 94FinRef-215
❑ 94Fla-79
❑ 94FlaOutP-10
❑ 94Fle-223
❑ 94FleExtB-126
❑ 94FleExtBGB-30
❑ 94FleGolM-3
❑ 94FleGolMJ-3
❑ 94FUnPac-32
❑ 94FUnPac-202
❑ 94Kra-15
❑ 94Lea-137
❑ 94LeaL-52
❑ 94LeaStaS-8
❑ 94OPC-53
❑ 94Pac-371
❑ 94PanSti-97
❑ 94Pin-332
❑ 94PinArtP-332
❑ 94PinMusC-332
❑ 94PinTri-TR3
❑ 94ProMag-79
❑ 94Sco-407
❑ 94Sco-629
❑ 94ScoGolR-407
❑ 94ScoGolR-629
❑ 94Sel-84
❑ 94Sel-SS2
❑ 94SP-187
❑ 94SPDieC-187
❑ 94Spo-63
❑ 94StaClu-288
❑ 94StaCluDD-DD2
❑ 94StaCluFDI-288
❑ 94StaCluGR-288
❑ 94StaCluMOP-288
❑ 94StaCluMOP-DD2
❑ 94Stu-202
❑ 94Top-430
❑ 94TopGol-430
❑ 94TopSpa-430
❑ 94TriPla-260
❑ 94TriPlaM-15
❑ 94Ult-92
❑ 94UltCarA-5
❑ 94UppDec-81
❑ 94UppDecED-81
❑ 95BluJayUSPC-6D
❑ 95BluJayUSPC-13C
❑ 95Bow-434
❑ 95ColCho-54
❑ 95ColCho-280
❑ 95ColChoGS-54
❑ 95ColChoGS-280
❑ 95ColChoSE-115
❑ 95ColChoSEGS-115
❑ 95ColChoSESS-115
❑ 95ColChoSS-54
❑ 95ColChoSS-280
❑ 95Emo-40
❑ 95Fin-249
❑ 95FinRef-249
❑ 95Fla-254
❑ 95Fle-151
❑ 95FleUpd-43
❑ 95Lea-372
❑ 95Pac-259
❑ 95PacGolP-7
❑ 95PacPri-83
❑ 95Pin-367
❑ 95PinArtP-367
❑ 95PinMusC-367
❑ 95Sco-80
❑ 95ScoGolR-80
❑ 95ScoPlaTS-80
❑ 95Sel-226
❑ 95SelArtP-226
❑ 95SP-26
❑ 95SP-149
❑ 95SPCha-148
❑ 95SPChaDC-148
❑ 95SPSil-26
❑ 95SPSil-149
❑ 95StaClu-533
❑ 95StaCluMOP-533
❑ 95StaCluMOP-RL36
❑ 95StaCluRL-RL36
❑ 95StaCluSTWS-533
❑ 95Sum-75
❑ 95SumNthD-75
❑ 95Top-158
❑ 95TopCyb-38
❑ 95UC3-50
❑ 95UC3ArtP-50
❑ 95Ult-283
❑ 95UltGolM-283
❑ 95UppDec-95
❑ 95UppDecED-95
❑ 95UppDecEDG-95
❑ 95UppDecSE-160
❑ 95UppDecSEG-160
❑ 95Zen-23
❑ 96ColCho-123
❑ 96ColChoGS-123
❑ 96ColChoSS-123
❑ 96Don-275
❑ 96DonPreP-275
❑ 96Fle-104
❑ 96FleTif-104
❑ 96Pin-87
❑ 96PinArtP-49
❑ 96PinSta-49
❑ 96Sco-83
❑ 96ScoDugC-A66
❑ 96ScoDugCAP-A66
❑ 96Ult-56
❑ 96UltGolM-56
❑ 96UppDec-100
❑ 97BluJayS-43
❑ 97HigMinMCT-50
❑ 97HigMinMCT-51
❑ 99UppDecCLJotC-DW
❑ 99UppDecR-93
❑ 99UppDecRG-93
❑ 99UppDecRI-DW
❑ 99UppDecRIL2-DW
❑ 99UppDecRP-93

Winfield, Steven W.
❑ 80MemChiT-27
❑ 82LouRedE-30
❑ 82SprCarF-11
❑ 83ArkTraT-8

Winford, Barry
❑ 88MisStaB-33
❑ 89ButCopKSP-7
❑ 89MisStaB-38
❑ 90Bes-187
❑ 90GasRanB-16
❑ 90GasRanP-2525
❑ 90GasRanS-25
❑ 91ChaRanC-15
❑ 91ChaRanP-1319
❑ 91Cla/Bes-25

Winford, Jim
❑ 74Car193T-27
❑ 90DodTar-869

Winford, Ron
❑ 88MisStaB-34
❑ 89MisStaB-39

Wing, Harry
❑ 79CedRapGT-25

Wing, Jim
❑ 84AriWilP-20
❑ 86AriWilP-19
❑ 87AriWilP-19
❑ 88AriWilP-15
❑ 90AriWilP-18
❑ 92AriWilP-20

Wing, Marc
❑ 84AriWilP-21

Wingard, Ernest
❑ 25Exh-120
❑ 26Exh-120
❑ 27Exh-60
❑ 27MidBre-43

Wingate, Ervan
❑ 92GulCoaDF-3577
❑ 93GreFalDSP-16
❑ 94BakDodC-25
❑ 95BakBlaTI-8
❑ 96SanBerSB-29
❑ 97VerBeaD-29

Wingerd, Josh
❑ 97NewJerCB-29
❑ 98PeoChiM-25

Winget, Jeremy
❑ 94OgdRapF-3744
❑ 94OgdRapSP-13

Wingfield, Fred
❑ 26Exh-72
❑ 27Exh-36

Wingo, Al
❑ 14FatPlaT-51
❑ 25Exh-95
❑ 29Zee-147
❑ 30Zee-162
❑ 31Zee-115
❑ 92ConTSN-458
❑ 94ConTSN-1177
❑ 94ConTSNB-1177

Wingo, Ivey B.
❑ 12T207-201
❑ 13TomBarW-40
❑ 14CraJacE-130
❑ 15CraJacE-130
❑ 15SpoNewM-194
❑ 16BF2FP-75
❑ 16FleBreD-102
❑ 16SpoNewM-193
❑ 19W514-73
❑ 20NatCarE-111
❑ 20RedWorCP-24
❑ 21E121So1-116
❑ 21E121So8-109
❑ 21Exh-188
❑ 21Nei-83
❑ 22AmeCarE122-77
❑ 22E120-180
❑ 22W572-117
❑ 22W575-151
❑ 23MapCriV-14
❑ 23W501-50
❑ 23W503-59
❑ 23WilChoV-175
❑ 25Exh-32
❑ 26Exh-32
❑ 27Exh-16
❑ 91ConTSN-235
❑ 93ConTSN-868
❑ 94ConTSN-1022
❑ 94ConTSN-1177
❑ 94ConTSNB-1022
❑ 94ConTSNB-1177

Wingo, John
❑ 52LaPat-17
❑ 52LavPro-83

Winham, Lave
❑ 90DodTar-870

Winiarski, Chip
❑ 91CollndC-19
❑ 91CollndP-1486
❑ 92KinIndC-14
❑ 92KinIndF-2477
❑ 93SouBenWSC-25
❑ 93SouBenWSF-1431

Winicki, Dennis
❑ 91KisDodP-4198
❑ 92GreFalDSP-20

Winkelman, Greg
❑ 97ModA'sG-30

Winkelsas, Joe
❑ 96DanBraB-28
❑ 97MacBra-8
❑ 98DanQ-C-25

Winkle, Ken
❑ 94EugEmeC-25
❑ 94EugEmeF-3714

Winkleman, George
❑ 87OldJudN-545

Winkler, Brad
❑ 84GreHorT-3
❑ 85AlbYanT-22

Winkles, Bobby
❑ 73OPC-421
❑ 73Top-421A
❑ 73Top-421B
❑ 74OPC-276
❑ 74Top-276
❑ 76SSP-624
❑ 77Gia-25
❑ 78Top-378
❑ 86ExpPos-19
❑ 86ExpProPa-14
❑ 87ExpPos-34
❑ 88ExpPos-35
❑ 97AriStaBG-22

Winn, George
❑ 20Zee-39
❑ 21Zee-41

Winn, Jim
❑ 84HawIslC-138
❑ 85DomLeaS-52
❑ 85HawIslC-237
❑ 85Top-69
❑ 85TopTif-69
❑ 86Fle-624
❑ 86Top-489
❑ 86TopTif-489
❑ 87Don-312
❑ 87Fle-624
❑ 87FleGlo-624
❑ 87FleUpd-126
❑ 87FleUpdG-126
❑ 87Top-262
❑ 87TopTif-262
❑ 87TopTra-130T
❑ 87TopTraT-130T
❑ 87WhiSoxC-30
❑ 88Don-409
❑ 88Fle-413
❑ 88FleGlo-413
❑ 88OPC-388
❑ 88PorBeaC-9
❑ 88PorBeaP-642
❑ 88Sco-462
❑ 88ScoGlo-462
❑ 88Top-688
❑ 88TopSti-288
❑ 88TopTif-688

Winn, Randy
❑ 95ElmPioTI-30
❑ 95ElmPioUTI-30
❑ 96Bow-343
❑ 96BowFoi-343
❑ 96KanCouCTI-30
❑ 96KanCouCUTI-13
❑ 96Top-235
❑ 97BesAutAS-72
❑ 97Bow-326
❑ 97BowChr-223
❑ 97BowChrI-223
❑ 97BowChrIR-223
❑ 97BowChrR-223
❑ 97BowInt-326
❑ 97BreCouMB-30
❑ 98Bow-316
❑ 98BowCerBlueAU-33
❑ 98BowCerGA-33
❑ 98BowCerSA-33
❑ 98BowChr-316
❑ 98BowChrGA-316
❑ 98BowChrGAR-316
❑ 98BowChrI-316
❑ 98BowChrIR-316
❑ 98BowChrR-316
❑ 98BowGolA-316
❑ 98BowInt-316
❑ 98DurBulTI-29
❑ 98FleUpd-U85
❑ 98LeaRS-305
❑ 98LeaRSLHolo-305
❑ 98LeaRSLong-305
❑ 98LeaRTrue-305
❑ 98PorSeaD5AQ-19
❑ 98Top-258
❑ 98TopChr-258
❑ 98TopChrR-258
❑ 98TopDevR-258
❑ 98TopDia-258
❑ 98TopMiniC-258
❑ 99FlaShoLeg1-123
❑ 99FlaShoLeg2-123
❑ 99FlaShoLeg3-123
❑ 99FlaShoLegM1-123
❑ 99FlaShoLegM2-123
❑ 99FlaShoLegM3-123
❑ 99FlaShoR1-123
❑ 99FlaShoR2-123
❑ 99FlaShoR3-123
❑ 99Fle-291
❑ 99FleSta9-291
❑ 99FleWarT-291
❑ 99Pac-419
❑ 99PacPar-231
❑ 99PacParC-231
❑ 99PacParG-231
❑ 99PacParHoloGold-231
❑ 99PacParHS-231
❑ 99PacParOD-231
❑ 99PacParPB-231
❑ 99PacParRed-231
❑ 99PacPlaB-419
❑ 99PacRed-419
❑ 99SkyThu-29
❑ 99SkyThuRant-29
❑ 99SkyThuRave-29
❑ 99StaClu-128
❑ 99StaCluFDI-128
❑ 99StaCluOoaK-128
❑ 99StaCluPP-128
❑ 99ThuSkySupR-29
❑ 99Top-281
❑ 99TopChr-281
❑ 99TopChrR-281
❑ 99TopMVPP-281

Winningham, Herm
❑ 82LynMetT-3
❑ 84TidTidT-5
❑ 85ExpPos-25
❑ 85FleUpd-130
❑ 85OPCPos-8
❑ 85TopTifT-131T
❑ 85TopTra-131T
❑ 86Don-279
❑ 86ExpProPa-22
❑ 86Fle-266
❑ 86Lea-153
❑ 86OPC-129
❑ 86Top-448
❑ 86TopSti-83
❑ 86TopTif-448
❑ 87ExpPos-35
❑ 87FleUpd-130
❑ 87FleUpdG-130
❑ 87OPC-141
❑ 87Top-141
❑ 87TopTif-141
❑ 88Don-581
❑ 88ExpPos-36
❑ 88Fle-200
❑ 88FleGlo-200
❑ 88Lea-242
❑ 88MSAHosD-4
❑ 88OPC-216
❑ 88PanSti-332
❑ 88Sco-142
❑ 88ScoGlo-142
❑ 88ScoRoo-43T
❑ 88ScoRooG-43T
❑ 88StaLinE-19
❑ 88Top-614
❑ 88TopSti-83
❑ 88TopTif-614
❑ 89Don-435
❑ 89Fle-175
❑ 89FleGlo-175
❑ 89RedKah-29
❑ 89Sco-496
❑ 89Top-366
❑ 89TopBig-94
❑ 89TopTif-366
❑ 89UppDec-636A
❑ 89UppDec-636B
❑ 90Don-478
❑ 90Fle-435
❑ 90FleCan-435
❑ 90OPC-94
❑ 90RedKah-26
❑ 90Sco-38
❑ 90Top-94
❑ 90TopTif-94
❑ 90UppDec-589
❑ 91Don-695
❑ 91Fle-82
❑ 91MetWIZ-434
❑ 91OPC-204
❑ 91RedKah-29
❑ 91RedPep-20
❑ 91Sco-656
❑ 91StaClu-546
❑ 91Top-204
❑ 91TopDesS-204
❑ 91TopMic-204
❑ 91TopTif-204
❑ 91UltUpd-78
❑ 92OPC-547
❑ 92Sco-574
❑ 92ScoRoo-43T
❑ 92StaClu-205
❑ 92StaClu-883
❑ 92StaCluNC-883
❑ 92Top-547
❑ 92TopGol-547
❑ 92TopGolW-547
❑ 92TopMic-547
❑ 92TopTra-131T
❑ 92TopTraG-131T
❑ 93Fle-566
❑ 93PawRedSDD-28
❑ 93PawRedSF-2423
❑ 93Top-377
❑ 93TopGol-377
❑ 93TopInaM-377
❑ 93TopInaR-377
❑ 93TopMic-377
❑ 98ChaRivDG-32

Winsett, Tom
❑ 90DodTar-871

Winslett, Dax
❑ 94BakDodC-26
❑ 94Top-755
❑ 94TopGol-755
❑ 94TopSpa-755
❑ 96OrlCubB-28

Winslow, Bryant
❑ 90WicStaSGD-39
❑ 91AubAstC-16
❑ 91AubAstP-4283
❑ 92AubAstC-10
❑ 92AubAstF-1364
❑ 92OscAstC-7
❑ 93QuaCitRBC-24
❑ 93QuaCitRBF-110

Winslow, Daniel
❑ 81ArkTraT-15

Winston, Darrin
❑ 88JamExpP-1918
❑ 89RocExpLC-30
❑ 90JacExpB-24
❑ 90JacExpP-1376
❑ 91IndIndLD-198
❑ 91IndIndP-463
❑ 91LinDriAAA-198
❑ 94HarSenF-2094
❑ 94OttLynF-2900
❑ 97ScrRedB-28
❑ 98PacOmeRS-20
❑ 98PacOmeRST1-20
❑ 98PacOnl-576
❑ 98PacOnlR-576
❑ 98PacOnlWC-576
❑ 98PhiTeal-35

Winston, Hank
❑ 90DodTar-872

Winston, Todd
❑ 92AubAstC-14
❑ 92AubAstF-1357
❑ 93OscAstC-25
❑ 93OscAstF-642
❑ 94OscAstC-25
❑ 94OscAstF-1142

Winter, George
❑ 03BreE10-154
❑ 04RedSoxUP-14
❑ 08RosComP-9
❑ 11SpoLifCW-372

Winterburn, Robert
❑ 88BoiHawP-1631

Winterfeldt, Todd
❑ 79WauTimT-3

Winters, Dan
❑ 85FreGiaSB-16
❑ 86LynMetP-27
❑ 87JacMetF-1

Winters, George
❑ 04FanCraAL-50

Winters, James A.
❑ 86PenWhiSP-28
❑ 87BirBarB-24

Winters, Jess
❑ 25Zee-57

Winters, Lee
❑ 53MotCoo-1

Winters, Matt
❑ 83ColCliT-23
❑ 84ColCliP-24
❑ 84ColCliT-22
❑ 85ColCliP-24
❑ 85ColCliT-22
❑ 86BufBisP-25
❑ 87MemChiB-24
❑ 87MemChiP-7
❑ 87SouLeaAJ-9
❑ 88MemChiB-19
❑ 88SouLeaAJ-1
❑ 89OmaRoyC-21
❑ 89OmaRoyP-1728
❑ 90Fle-124
❑ 90FleCan-124
❑ 90Sco100RS-47
❑ 90TopDeb89-147
❑ 90UppDec-524
❑ 96KanCouCTI-31
❑ 98KanCouC-32
❑ 98KanCouCCP-32

Winzenread, Dickie
❑ 87NewOriP-22

Wipf, Mark
❑ 92KinMetC-14
❑ 92KinMetF-1546
❑ 93CapCitBC-24
❑ 93CapCitBF-475
❑ 94CapCitBC-24
❑ 94CapCitBF-1766

❑ 95StLucMTI-35
Wirsta, Mike
❑ 92MedHatBJSP-26
❑ 93MedHatBJSP-22
❑ 94MedHatBJSP-29
❑ 96MedHatBJTI-33
❑ 97DunBluJTI-31
❑ 98KnoSG-26
Wirtala, Allen
❑ 93AppFoxCB-30
❑ 94AppFoxC-25
Wirth, Alan
❑ 79OgdA'sT-22
❑ 79Top-711
❑ 80OgdA'sT-17
❑ 81SpoIndT-25
Wirth, Greg
❑ 84NewOriT-10
Wirts, Elwood
❑ 30Zee-135
❑ 31Zee-97
❑ 32Zee-92
❑ 33Zee-97
Wisdom, Allen
❑ 87ClePhiP-24
Wise, Brett Wayne
❑ 81VerBeaDT-24
Wise, Dewayne
❑ 98Bow-408
❑ 98BowChr-408
❑ 98BowChrGA-408
❑ 98BowChrGAR-408
❑ 98BowChrI-408
❑ 98BowChrIR-408
❑ 98BowChrR-408
❑ 98BowGolA-408
❑ 98BowInt-408
❑ 98BurBeeM-25
❑ 98MidLeaPM-4
❑ 99SP TopP-124
❑ 99SP TopPPE-124
Wise, George
❑ 31Zee-77
❑ 32Zee-77
Wise, James
❑ 95DanBraTI-29
❑ 97EugEmeB-15
Wise, K. Casey
❑ 57Top-396
❑ 58Top-247
❑ 59Top-204
❑ 60Top-342
Wise, Matt
❑ 97BoiHawG-31
❑ 98MidAngG-27
❑ 98MidAngO-27
❑ 99Bow-398
❑ 99BowGol-398
❑ 99BowInt-398
Wise, Rick
❑ 64PhiPhiB-27
❑ 64Top-561
❑ 65Top-322
❑ 67OPC-37
❑ 67Top-37
❑ 68Top-262
❑ 68TopVen-262
❑ 69MLBOffS-180
❑ 69OPC-188
❑ 69PhiTeal-12
❑ 69Top-188
❑ 69TopFou-5
❑ 69TopSta-80
❑ 69TopTeaP-8
❑ 70MLBOffS-96
❑ 70PhiTeal-12
❑ 70Top-605
❑ 70TopPos-8
❑ 71CarTeal-43
❑ 71MLBOffS-191
❑ 71OPC-598
❑ 71PhiArcO-13
❑ 71Top-598
❑ 71TopCoi-131
❑ 72CarTeal-18
❑ 72Kel-23
❑ 72MilBra-368
❑ 72OPC-43
❑ 72OPC-44
❑ 72OPC-345
❑ 72SevTraC-58
❑ 72Top-43
❑ 72Top-44
❑ 72Top-345
❑ 72Top-756
❑ 72TopPos-14
❑ 73OPC-364
❑ 73Top-364
❑ 74OPC-84
❑ 74OPC-339
❑ 74Top-84
❑ 74Top-339
❑ 74TopSta-139
❑ 75OPC-56
❑ 75Top-56
❑ 75TopMin-56
❑ 76Kel-35
❑ 76LinSup-112
❑ 76OPC-170
❑ 76RedSoxSM-15
❑ 76Top-170
❑ 77Top-455
❑ 78IndTeal-31
❑ 78RCColC-99
❑ 78Top-572
❑ 79OPC-127
❑ 79Top-253
❑ 80OPC-370
❑ 80Top-725
❑ 81Don-3
❑ 81OPC-274
❑ 81Top-616
❑ 81TopSti-232
❑ 82Don-170
❑ 82Fle-585
❑ 82Top-330
❑ 83PhiPosGM-11
❑ 85MadMusP-25
❑ 85MadMusT-24
❑ 86MadMusP-27
❑ 86MadMusP-28
❑ 88AubAstP-1963
❑ 89AubAstP-2187
❑ 89PacSenL-31
❑ 89T/MSenL-117
❑ 89TopSenL-41
❑ 90EliSenL-106
❑ 91LinDriAA-475
❑ 91NewBriRSLD-475
❑ 91NewBriRSP-368
❑ 92NewBriRSF-450
❑ 93PawRedSDD-29
❑ 93PawRedSF-2426
❑ 94PawRedSDD-30
❑ 94PawRedSF-962
❑ 95PawRedSDD-30
❑ 95PawRedTI-40
❑ 97CedRapK-29
❑ 98MidAngG-28
❑ 98MidAngO-28
Wise, Sam
❑ 87BucN28-13
❑ 87OldJudN-546
❑ 88WG1CarG-9
Wise, Will
❑ 95DanBraTI-30
❑ 96DanBraB-29
Wiseley, Mike
❑ 93NiaFalRF-3405
❑ 94LakTigC-26
❑ 94LakTigF-3051
Wiseman, Dennis
❑ 89JohCitCS-23
❑ 90Bes-142
❑ 90SprCarB-25
❑ 91ArkTraLD-48
❑ 91ArkTraP-1287
❑ 91LinDriAA-48
❑ 92ArkTraF-1131
❑ 92ArkTraS-35
❑ 93LouRedF-216
Wiseman, Greg
❑ 91ButCopKSP-23
❑ 92Ft.MyeMCB-23
❑ 92Ft.MyeMF-2759
Wiseman, Michael
❑ 88CapCodPPaLP-174
Wiseman, Tim
❑ 85OrlTwiT-21
Wishnevski, Mike
❑ 86ChaLooP-25
❑ 87CalCanP-2324
❑ 88CalCanC-20
❑ 88CalCanP-783
Wishnevski, Robert
❑ 88DunBluJS-22
❑ 89KnoBluJB-27
❑ 89KnoBluJP-1138
❑ 89KnoBluJS-22
❑ 89SouLeaAJ-21
❑ 90KnoBluJS-21
❑ 90SyrChiMB-30
❑ 91KnoBluJP-1769
❑ 92ClaFS7-335
❑ 92DenZepF-2641
❑ 92ElPasDS-213
❑ 93Bow-323
❑ 93NewOrlZF-974
❑ 94LouRedF-2982
Wisler, Brian
❑ 93BurIndC-28
❑ 93BurIndF-3298
❑ 94BurIndC-28
❑ 94BurIndF-3796
Wismer, Michael
❑ 89GreFalDSP-12
❑ 90VerBeaDS-28
Wisnaski, Len
❑ 52LavPro-44
Wissel, Dick
❑ 75IntLeaAT-30
❑ 75IntLeaAT-31
Wissen, Collin
❑ 97EugEmeB-30
Wissler, Bill
❑ 92KenTwiC-18
❑ 92KenTwiF-606
❑ 93NasXprF-404
❑ 94SalLakBF-818
Wissman, Dave
❑ 77FriOneYW-83
Wistert, Francis
❑ 36GouWidPPR-D39
Wisterzill, George
❑ 18Zee-104
❑ 20Zee-59
Witasick, Gerald
❑ 94ExcFS7-275
❑ 95Bow-212
❑ 97Bow-371
❑ 97BowInt-371
❑ 97Top-492
Witasick, Jay
❑ 93JohCitCC-29
❑ 93JohCitCF-3680
❑ 94BowBes-B87
❑ 94BowBesR-B87
❑ 94Cla-189
❑ 94MadHatC-26
❑ 94MadHatF-133
❑ 94MidLeaAF-MDW45
❑ 95Bes-96
❑ 95Exc-278
❑ 95SPML-154
❑ 95UppDecML-88
❑ 95UppDecMLFS-88
❑ 97UppDec-284
Witek, Mickey (Nicholas)
❑ 46SpoExcW-9-8
❑ 47TipTop-135
❑ 76TayBow4-70
Withem, Shannon
❑ 90BriTigP-3160
❑ 90BriTigS-26
❑ 91Cla/Bes-187
❑ 91FayGenC-13
❑ 91FayGenP-1172
❑ 91NiaFalRC-26
❑ 91NiaFalRP-3634
❑ 92FayGenF-2170
❑ 94TreThuF-2121
❑ 95JacSunTI-28
❑ 95SigRoo-50
❑ 95SigRooSig-50
❑ 96BinMetB-30
❑ 97NorTid-34
❑ 97NorTidB-33
❑ 98SyrSkyG-29
Witherspoon, Richard
❑ 89ElmPioP-21
❑ 90WinHavRSS-25
Withrow, Corky
❑ 77FriOneYW-81
Withrow, Mike
❑ 82GleFalWST-24
❑ 83GleFalWST-21
Witkowski, Matt
❑ 89ChaRaiP-985
❑ 90Bes-68
❑ 90MidLeaASGS-52
❑ 90WatDiaB-18
❑ 90WatDiaP-2388
❑ 91HigDesMC-23
❑ 91HigDesMP-2406
❑ 92WicWraF-3665
❑ 92WicWraS-647
❑ 93LasVegSF-954
❑ 94LasVegSF-878
Witmer, Joe
❑ 86CalCanP-26
Witmeyer, Ronald
❑ 89ModA'sC-27
❑ 89ModA'sCLC-281
❑ 90CalLeaACLC-43
❑ 90ModA'sC-32
❑ 90ModA'sCLC-165
❑ 90ModA'sP-2224
❑ 91LinDriAAA-548
❑ 91TacTigLD-548
❑ 91TacTigP-2316
❑ 92SkyAAAF-245
❑ 92StaClu-435
❑ 92TacTigF-2513
❑ 92TacTigS-547
❑ 92TopDeb91-187
❑ 93TacTigF-3041
Witt, Bobby
❑ 85TulDriTI-18
❑ 86DonRoo-49
❑ 86FleSlu-42
❑ 86FleUpd-129
❑ 86RanPer-48
❑ 86SpoRoo-12
❑ 86TopTra-126T
❑ 86TopTraT-126T
❑ 87Don-99
❑ 87DonHig-25
❑ 87Fle-143
❑ 87FleExcS-44
❑ 87FleGlo-143
❑ 87Lea-112
❑ 87RanMot-25
❑ 87RanSmo-6
❑ 87Spo-39
❑ 87SpoTeaP-1
❑ 87Top-415
❑ 87TopTif-415
❑ 88Don-101
❑ 88Fle-483
❑ 88FleGlo-483
❑ 88PanSti-198
❑ 88RanMot-25
❑ 88RanSmo-7
❑ 88Sco-149
❑ 88ScoGlo-149
❑ 88StaLinRa-20
❑ 88Top-747
❑ 88TopTif-747
❑ 89Bow-222
❑ 89BowTif-222
❑ 89ClaLigB-77
❑ 89Don-461
❑ 89DonBasB-279
❑ 89Fle-537
❑ 89FleGlo-537
❑ 89OPC-38
❑ 89PanSti-448
❑ 89RanMot-14
❑ 89RanSmo-34
❑ 89Sco-463
❑ 89ScoYouSI-8
❑ 89Spo-82
❑ 89Top-548
❑ 89TopBig-191
❑ 89TopTif-548
❑ 89UppDec-557
❑ 90Don-292
❑ 90Fle-315
❑ 90FleCan-315
❑ 90Lea-337
❑ 90OPC-166
❑ 90PubIntS-424
❑ 90RanMot-15
❑ 90Sco-457
❑ 90Top-166
❑ 90TopTif-166
❑ 90UppDec-636
❑ 91Bow-287
❑ 91Cla1-T87
❑ 91ClaGam-166
❑ 91Don-249
❑ 91Fle-304
❑ 91Lea-3
❑ 91OPC-27
❑ 91PanCanT1-78
❑ 91PanFreS-260
❑ 91PanSti-203
❑ 91RanMot-6
❑ 91Sco-410
❑ 91Sco-507
❑ 91SevCoi-T15
❑ 91StaClu-96
❑ 91Stu-130
❑ 91Top-27
❑ 91TopDesS-27
❑ 91TopMic-27
❑ 91TopTif-27
❑ 91Ult-357
❑ 91UppDec-627
❑ 92Bow-230
❑ 92Don-391
❑ 92Lea-305
❑ 92LeaBlaG-305
❑ 92OPC-675
❑ 92Pin-451
❑ 92RanMot-6
❑ 92RanTeal-26
❑ 92Sco-381
❑ 92StaClu-677
❑ 92Top-675
❑ 92TopDaiQTU-5
❑ 92TopGol-675
❑ 92TopGolW-675
❑ 92TopMic-675
❑ 92TriPla-154
❑ 92UppDec-576
❑ 93AthMot-14
❑ 93AthStaC-16
❑ 93Bow-301
❑ 93Don-51
❑ 93Fla-265
❑ 93Fle-303
❑ 93Lea-204
❑ 93Pin-365
❑ 93RanKee-386
❑ 93Sco-150
❑ 93Sel-363
❑ 93StaClu-150
❑ 93StaCluFDI-150
❑ 93StaCluMOP-150
❑ 93Top-398
❑ 93TopGol-398
❑ 93TopInaM-398
❑ 93TopInaR-398
❑ 93TopMic-398
❑ 93TriPla-141
❑ 93Ult-264
❑ 93Ult-299
❑ 93UppDec-87
❑ 93UppDecGold-87
❑ 94A'sMot-14
❑ 94Bow-248
❑ 94ColC-471
❑ 94ColChoGS-471
❑ 94ColChoSS-471
❑ 94Don-308
❑ 94Fin-289
❑ 94FinRef-289
❑ 94Fla-334
❑ 94Fle-277
❑ 94Lea-102
❑ 94Pac-466
❑ 94Pin-276
❑ 94PinArtP-276
❑ 94PinMusC-276
❑ 94Sco-437
❑ 94ScoGolR-437
❑ 94Sel-128
❑ 94StaClu-91
❑ 94StaCluFDI-91
❑ 94StaCluGR-91
❑ 94StaCluMOP-91
❑ 94Top-255
❑ 94TopGol-255
❑ 94TopSpa-255
❑ 94TriPla-10
❑ 94Ult-115
❑ 94UppDec-120
❑ 94UppDecED-120
❑ 95ColCho-558T
❑ 95ColChoGS-123
❑ 95ColChoSS-123
❑ 95Don-391
❑ 95DonPreP-391
❑ 95DonTopotO-170
❑ 95Fin-71
❑ 95FinRef-71
❑ 95Fle-257
❑ 95FleUpd-101
❑ 95Pac-323
❑ 95Sco-152
❑ 95ScoGolR-152
❑ 95ScoPlaTS-152
❑ 95StaClu-368
❑ 95StaClu-594
❑ 95StaCluMOP-368
❑ 95StaCluMOP-594
❑ 95StaCluSTWS-368
❑ 95StaCluSTWS-594
❑ 95StaCluVR-194
❑ 95StaCluVRMO-194
❑ 95Top-461
❑ 95TopCyb-256
❑ 95TopTra-123T
❑ 96Don-449
❑ 96DonPreP-449
❑ 96Fla-180
❑ 96LeaSigA-247
❑ 96LeaSigAG-248
❑ 96LeaSigAS-248
❑ 96RanDr P-34
❑ 96RanMot-13
❑ 96Ult-424
❑ 96UltGolM-424
❑ 97Cir-103
❑ 97CirRav-103
❑ 97ColCho-236
❑ 97ColChoT-TR1
❑ 97Fle-233
❑ 97FleTif-233
❑ 97Pac-212
❑ 97PacLigB-212
❑ 97PacSil-212
❑ 97RanDr P-33
❑ 97RanMot-13
❑ 97RanSco-10
❑ 97RanScoPl-10
❑ 97RanScoPr-10
❑ 97Sco-182
❑ 97ScoArtPWB-182
❑ 97ScoPreS-182
❑ 97ScoShoS-182
❑ 97ScoShoSAP-182
❑ 97StaClu-262
❑ 97StaCluMOP-262
❑ 97Top-332
❑ 97UppDec-511
❑ 98ColCho-516
❑ 98Fin-32
❑ 98FinNo--32
❑ 98FinNo-R-32
❑ 98FinRef-32
❑ 98Pac-212
❑ 98PacOnl-749
❑ 98PacOnlR-749
❑ 98PacOnlWC-749
❑ 98PacPlaB-212
❑ 98PacRedT-212
❑ 98PacSil-212
❑ 98Pin-144
❑ 98PinPreP-144
❑ 98StaCluFDI-351
❑ 98StaCluI-351
❑ 98StaCluOneK-351
❑ 98StaCluPP-351
❑ 98Top-15
❑ 98TopChr-15
❑ 98TopChrR-15
❑ 98TopDevR-15
❑ 98TopDia-15
❑ 98TopMiniC-15
❑ 98Ult-262
❑ 98UltGolM-262
❑ 98UltMas-262
❑ 98UltPlaM-262
❑ 98UppDec-236
Witt, George
❑ 59Kah-38
❑ 59Top-110
❑ 59TopVen-110
❑ 60Top-298
❑ 61Top-286
❑ 62Top-287
❑ 77PirTCM1WC-29
Witt, Hal
❑ 78St.PetCT-27
Witt, Kevin
❑ 94MedHatBJF-3692
❑ 94MedHatBJSP-5
❑ 94SigRooDP-27
❑ 94SigRooDPS-27
❑ 94StaCluDP-88
❑ 94StaCluDPFDI-88
❑ 94TopTra-54T
❑ 95Exc-147
❑ 95HagSunF-79
❑ 95ScoDraP-DP17
❑ 95SelSurS-SS2
❑ 95SPML-163
❑ 95StaClu-101
❑ 95StaCluFDI-101
❑ 95StaCluMOP-101
❑ 95StaCluSTWS-101
❑ 95Top-341
❑ 96BesAutSA-90

❑ 96DunBluJB-26
❑ 96DunBluJTI-30
❑ 96DunBluJUTI-17
❑ 97BesAutAS-73
❑ 97Bow-339
❑ 97BowChr-232
❑ 97BowChrI-232
❑ 97BowChrIR-232
❑ 97BowChrR-232
❑ 97BowInt-339
❑ 97KnoSmo-26
❑ 97SouLeaTP-20
❑ 98Bes-49
❑ 98Bow-328
❑ 98BowBes-171
❑ 98BowBesAR-171
❑ 98BowBesR-171
❑ 98BowChr-328
❑ 98BowChrGA-328
❑ 98BowChrGAR-328
❑ 98BowChrI-328
❑ 98BowChrIR-328
❑ 98BowChrR-328
❑ 98BowGolA-328
❑ 98BowInt-328
❑ 98Don-306
❑ 98DonGolPP-306
❑ 98DonSilPP-306
❑ 98FleUpd-U80
❑ 98LeaRS-278
❑ 98LeaRSLHolo-278
❑ 98LeaRSLong-278
❑ 98LeaRTrue-278
❑ 98SP MinPE-125
❑ 98SP MinSTHPE-H17
❑ 98SPMin-125
❑ 98SPMinSTH-H17
❑ 98SPxFin-196
❑ 98SPxFinR-196
❑ 98SPxFinS-196
❑ 98SyrSkyG-30
❑ 98UppDec-578
❑ 98UppDecDS-DS19
❑ 99Bow-178
❑ 99BowAut-BA63
❑ 99BowChr-178
❑ 99BowChrG-178
❑ 99BowChrGR-178
❑ 99BowChrI-178
❑ 99BowChrIR-178
❑ 99BowChrR-178
❑ 99BowGol-178
❑ 99BowInt-178
❑ 99E-X Cen-96
❑ 99E-X CenECFut-96
❑ 99E-X CenECNow-96
❑ 99Fle-203
❑ 99FleSta9-203
❑ 99FleWarT-203
❑ 99Rev-150
❑ 99RevPremDate-150
❑ 99RevRet-150
❑ 99RevShaSS-150
❑ 99SkyThu-32
❑ 99SkyThuRant-32
❑ 99SkyThuRave-32
❑ 99SP Aut-119
❑ 99SP AutC-KW
❑ 99SP AutCG-KW
❑ 99SP SigAuto-KW
❑ 99SP SigAutoG-KW
❑ 99SP TopP-123
❑ 99SP TopPPE-123
❑ 99SpoIll-45
❑ 99SPSig-74
❑ 99SPx-120
❑ 99SPxFinR-120
❑ 99SPxFinS-120
❑ 99ThuSkySupR-32
❑ 99UD Cho-20
❑ 99UD ChoPCR-20
❑ 99UppDec-274
❑ 99UppDecE-117
❑ 99UppDecEFXG-117
❑ 99UppDecEL1-274
❑ 99UppDecEL2-274
❑ 99UppDecM-216
❑ 99UppDecMGS-216
❑ 99UppDecMHFS-216
❑ 99UppDecMP-KW
❑ 99UppDecMSS-216
❑ 99UppDecO-74
❑ 99UppDecOSO-74
❑ 99Vic-409

Witt, Mike

❑ 81LonBeaPT-11
❑ 82Don-416
❑ 82Fle-473
❑ 82Top-744
❑ 83Don-416
❑ 83Fle-102
❑ 83Top-53
❑ 83Top-651
❑ 84AngSmo-31
❑ 84Fle-531
❑ 84Nes792-499
❑ 84Top-499
❑ 84TopTif-499
❑ 85AngSmo-1
❑ 85AngStrH-13
❑ 85Don-108
❑ 85Fle-316
❑ 85Fle-643
❑ 85FleStaS-111
❑ 85Lea-46
❑ 85OPC-309
❑ 85Top-309
❑ 85TopSti-195
❑ 85TopSti-227
❑ 85TopSup-45
❑ 85TopTif-309
❑ 86AngSmo-1
❑ 86Don-179
❑ 86DonHig-38
❑ 86Fle-171
❑ 86FleMin-36
❑ 86FleSlu-43
❑ 86Lea-112
❑ 86SevCoi-W12
❑ 86Spo-53
❑ 87AngSmo-3
❑ 87CalAngPPS-39
❑ 87Don-58
❑ 87DonAll-51
❑ 87DonOpeD-2
❑ 87Fle-95
❑ 87Fle-641
❑ 87FleAwaW-43
❑ 87FleBasA-44
❑ 87FleGamW-43
❑ 87FleGlo-95
❑ 87FleGlo-641
❑ 87FleMin-118
❑ 87FleSlu-44
❑ 87FleStiC-127
❑ 87KraFoo-47
❑ 87Lea-111
❑ 87MandMSL-17
❑ 87OPC-92
❑ 87RedFolSB-4
❑ 87SevCoi-W15
❑ 87Spo-59
❑ 87SpoTeaP-11
❑ 87StuPan-16
❑ 87Top-556
❑ 87Top-760
❑ 87TopGloS-33
❑ 87TopMinL-48
❑ 87TopSti-179
❑ 87TopTif-556
❑ 87TopTif-760
❑ 88AngSmo-4
❑ 88Don-86
❑ 88DonAll-20
❑ 88DonBasB-307
❑ 88Fle-507
❑ 88Fle-626
❑ 88FleGlo-507
❑ 88FleGlo-626
❑ 88FleMin-13
❑ 88FleStiC-13
❑ 88FleSup-43
❑ 88GreBasS-15
❑ 88Lea-49
❑ 88OPC-270
❑ 88PanSti-38
❑ 88Sco-81
❑ 88ScoGlo-81
❑ 88Spo-32
❑ 88StaLinAn-20
❑ 88Top-270
❑ 88TopBig-4
❑ 88TopSti-174
❑ 88TopTif-270
❑ 88TopUKM-86
❑ 88TopUKMT-86
❑ 89AngSmo-19
❑ 89Bow-42
❑ 89BowTif-42
❑ 89Don-372
❑ 89Fle-490
❑ 89FleGlo-490
❑ 89OPC-190
❑ 89PanSti-286
❑ 89RedFolSB-129
❑ 89Sco-298
❑ 89Spo-197
❑ 89Top-190
❑ 89TopBasT-125
❑ 89TopCoi-59
❑ 89TopSti-176
❑ 89TopTif-190
❑ 89TopUKM-85
❑ 89TVSpoM-112
❑ 89UppDec-555
❑ 90AngSmo-16
❑ 90ClaYel-T49
❑ 90Don-580
❑ 90El PasDAGTI-33
❑ 90Fle-148
❑ 90FleCan-148
❑ 90OPC-650
❑ 90PubIntS-382
❑ 90Sco-226
❑ 90ScoRoo-50T
❑ 90Top-650
❑ 90TopTif-650
❑ 90UppDec-548
❑ 90YanScoNW-14
❑ 91Don-282
❑ 91DonBonC-BC1
❑ 91Fle-680
❑ 91FleWaxBC-1
❑ 91Lea-74
❑ 91OPC-536
❑ 91Sco-430
❑ 91Sco-699
❑ 91StaClu-466
❑ 91StaCluCM-17
❑ 91Top-536
❑ 91TopDesS-536
❑ 91TopMic-536
❑ 91TopTif-536
❑ 91UppDec-429
❑ 92OPC-357
❑ 92RedFolS-101
❑ 92StaClu-848
❑ 92Top-357
❑ 92TopGol-357
❑ 92TopGolW-357
❑ 92TopMic-357
❑ 93YanStaC-18
❑ 94Pac-443

Witt, Whitey (Lawton)

❑ 17ColE13-193
❑ 17HolBreD-114
❑ 20NatCarE-112
❑ 21OxfConE-20
❑ 23W515-37
❑ 23WilChoV-176
❑ 79DiaGre-13
❑ 90DodTar-873

Wittcke, Darren

❑ 91EveGiaC-26
❑ 91EveGiaP-3915

Witte, Dominic

❑ 96IdaFalB-29
❑ 97CliLumG-29
❑ 98RanCucQG-30
❑ 98RanCucQG-30

Witte, Jerome

❑ 47TipTop-74
❑ 85TCMPla1-17

Witte, Trey

❑ 91BelMarCB-18
❑ 91BelMarP-3665
❑ 92SanBerSF-955
❑ 93AppFoxCB-24
❑ 93AppFoxFI-2460
❑ 94RivPilCLC-23
❑ 96TacRaiB-29
❑ 97TacRai-28

Wittig, Paul

❑ 92GulCoaDF-3570
❑ 93GreFalDSP-24
❑ 94VerBeaDC-24
❑ 94VerBeaDF-76
❑ 95BakBlaTI-9

Witzel, Shane

❑ 93BilMusF-3947
❑ 93BilMusSP-14

Wizard, Wayne the

❑ 93ForWayWC-30
❑ 94ForWayWC-28
❑ 95ForWayWTI-30
❑ 96ForWayWB-31
❑ 97ForWayW-30
❑ 98ForWayW!-30

Wizards, Fort Wayne

❑ 95ForWayWTI-32

Wobken, Bruce

❑ 88NebCor-18

Wockenfuss, John

❑ 75DetTigP-36
❑ 76DetTigP-34
❑ 76OPC-13
❑ 76Top-13
❑ 78TigBurK-3
❑ 78TigTeal-36
❑ 78Top-723
❑ 79Top-231
❑ 80Top-338
❑ 81CokTeaS-56
❑ 81Don-245
❑ 81Fle-472
❑ 81Top-468
❑ 81TopSti-79
❑ 82Don-459
❑ 82Fle-286
❑ 82OPC-46
❑ 82Top-629
❑ 83Don-76
❑ 83Fle-351
❑ 83FleSta-220
❑ 83FleSti-254
❑ 83TigPos-34
❑ 83Top-536
❑ 83TopSti-64
❑ 84Don-150
❑ 84Fle-95
❑ 84FleUpd-129
❑ 84Nes792-119
❑ 84PhiTas-27
❑ 84Top-119
❑ 84TopSti-274
❑ 84TopTif-119
❑ 84TopTra-130T
❑ 84TopTraT-130T
❑ 85Don-549
❑ 85Fle-269
❑ 85PhiTas-27
❑ 85Top-39
❑ 85TopTif-39
❑ 86FloStaLAP-50
❑ 86MiaMarP-29
❑ 88GleFalTP-917
❑ 89TolMudHC-25
❑ 89TolMudHP-771
❑ 92SalBucC-26
❑ 92SalBucF-79

Wodraska, Todd

❑ 92OklStaC-32

Wohler, Barry

❑ 85VerBeaDT-19
❑ 87SanAntDTI-8
❑ 88SanAntMB-2

Wohlers, Mark

❑ 89PulBraP-1908
❑ 89SumBraP-1099
❑ 90SumBraB-25
❑ 90SumBraP-2435
❑ 91Bow-582
❑ 91Cla/Bes-331
❑ 91ClaGolB-BC13
❑ 91GreBraC-10
❑ 91GreBraLD-223
❑ 91GreBraP-3004
❑ 91LinDriAA-223
❑ 91RicBraBC-30
❑ 91StaCluMO-30
❑ 91UppDecFE-77F
❑ 92Bow-396
❑ 92BraLykP-30
❑ 92BraLykS-36
❑ 92Cla1-T18
❑ 92Cla1-T97
❑ 92Don-1
❑ 92Don-616
❑ 92Fle-374
❑ 92Fle-700
❑ 92FleRooS-15
❑ 92OPC-703
❑ 92Pin-55
❑ 92PinRoo-21
❑ 92PinRool-4
❑ 92ProFS7-179
❑ 92RicBraBB-6
❑ 92RicBraF-3015
❑ 92RicBraRC-26
❑ 92RicBraS-448
❑ 92Sco-759
❑ 92Sco-787
❑ 92ScoImpP-38
❑ 92ScoRoo-5
❑ 92SkyAAAF-205
❑ 92StaClu-217
❑ 92Top-703
❑ 92TopDeb91-188
❑ 92TopGol-703
❑ 92TopGolW-703
❑ 92TopMic-703
❑ 92Ult-465
❑ 92UppDec-56
❑ 92UppDecSR-SR24
❑ 93BraLykP-30
❑ 93BraLykS-37
❑ 93BraStaC-25
❑ 93ClaFS7-33
❑ 93Don-606
❑ 93Fle-16
❑ 93Lea-519
❑ 93OPC-7
❑ 93PacSpa-13
❑ 93Pin-379
❑ 93RicBraBB-20
❑ 93RicBraF-186
❑ 93RicBraRC-5
❑ 93RicBraRC-29
❑ 93Sco-193
❑ 93Sel-282
❑ 93StaClu-130
❑ 93StaCluFDI-130
❑ 93StaCluMOP-130
❑ 93Top-8
❑ 93TopGol-8
❑ 93TopInaM-8
❑ 93TopInaR-8
❑ 93TopMic-8
❑ 93Toy-55
❑ 93USPlaCR-3C
❑ 94BraLykP-34
❑ 94BraLykS-33
❑ 94BraUSPC-4C
❑ 94BraUSPC-12S
❑ 94Don-309
❑ 94Fla-133
❑ 94Fle-378
❑ 94Pin-444
❑ 94PinArtP-444
❑ 94PinMusC-444
❑ 94StaClu-522
❑ 94StaCluFDI-522
❑ 94StaCluGR-522
❑ 94StaCluMOP-522
❑ 94StaCluT-53
❑ 94StaCluTFDI-53
❑ 94Top-232
❑ 94TopGol-232
❑ 94TopSpa-232
❑ 94Ult-158
❑ 95BraAtlC-8
❑ 95Don-527
❑ 95DonPreP-527
❑ 95DonTopotO-194
❑ 95Fla-110
❑ 95Fle-322
❑ 95Lea-25
❑ 95Sco-507
❑ 95ScoGolR-507
❑ 95ScoPlaTS-507
❑ 95StaClu-128
❑ 95StaCluFDI-128
❑ 95StaCluMOP-128
❑ 95StaCluSTDW-B128
❑ 95StaCluSTMP-10
❑ 95StaCluSTWS-128
❑ 95Top-550
❑ 95Ult-356
❑ 95UltGolM-356
❑ 96Baz-70
❑ 96BraFle-18
❑ 96ColCho-47
❑ 96ColCho-380T
❑ 96ColChoGS-47
❑ 96ColChoSS-47
❑ 96Don-107
❑ 96DonPreP-107
❑ 96EmoXL-150
❑ 96Fin-S180
❑ 96FinRef-S180
❑ 96Fla-211
❑ 96Fle-310
❑ 96FleTif-310
❑ 96MetUni-137
❑ 96MetUniP-137
❑ 96MLBPin-37
❑ 96Pac-8
❑ 96Sco-202
❑ 96Sco-206
❑ 96StaClu-269
❑ 96StaCluMOP-269
❑ 96Top-49
❑ 96TopChr-18
❑ 96TopChrR-18
❑ 96TopGal-29
❑ 96TopGalPPI-29
❑ 96TopLas-64
❑ 96Ult-162
❑ 96UltGolM-162
❑ 96UppDec-3
❑ 96UppDecPHE-H49
❑ 96UppDecPreH-H49
❑ 97BraSco-13
❑ 97BraScoPl-13
❑ 97BraScoPr-13
❑ 97Cir-206
❑ 97CirRav-206
❑ 97ColCho-34
❑ 97ColChoT-AB7
❑ 97Don-325
❑ 97DonGolPP-325
❑ 97DonLim-134
❑ 97DonLimE-134
❑ 97DonLimENG-134
❑ 97DonSilPP-325
❑ 97DonTea-26
❑ 97DonTeaSPE-26
❑ 97E-X2-60
❑ 97E-X2Cred-60
❑ 97E-X2EssCre-60
❑ 97Fin-234
❑ 97FinRef-234
❑ 97FlaShoLC-143
❑ 97FlaShoLeg0-143
❑ 97FlaShoLeg1-143
❑ 97FlaShoM-A143
❑ 97FlaShoM-B143
❑ 97FlaShoM-C143
❑ 97FlaShoR0-143
❑ 97FlaShoR1-143
❑ 97FlaShoR2-143
❑ 97Fle-271
❑ 97FleTif-271
❑ 97Lea-130
❑ 97LeaFraM-130
❑ 97LeaFraMDC-130
❑ 97NewPin-36
❑ 97NewPinAP-36
❑ 97NewPinMC-36
❑ 97NewPinPP-36
❑ 97Pac-245
❑ 97PacLigB-245
❑ 97PacSil-245
❑ 97PinCar-11
❑ 97RicBraBC-6
❑ 97Sco-227
❑ 97ScoAllF-20
❑ 97ScoArtPWB-227
❑ 97ScoPreS-227
❑ 97ScoShoS-227
❑ 97ScoShoSAP-227
❑ 97StaClu-249
❑ 97StaCluC-CO3
❑ 97StaCluMat-249
❑ 97StaCluMOP-249
❑ 97Top-404
❑ 97TopAll-AS22
❑ 97TopChr-142
❑ 97TopChrAS-AS22
❑ 97TopChrR-142
❑ 97TopChrSAR-AS22
❑ 97TopGal-121
❑ 97TopGalPPI-121
❑ 97TopSta-82
❑ 97TopStaAM-82
❑ 97Ult-162
❑ 97UltGolME-162
❑ 97UltPlaME-162
❑ 97UppDec-17
❑ 98BraSco-15
❑ 98BraScoP-15
❑ 98CirThu-155
❑ 98CirThuRav-155
❑ 98CirThuSupRav-155
❑ 98ColCho-38
❑ 98Fin-64
❑ 98FinNo--64
❑ 98FinNo-R-64
❑ 98FinRef-64
❑ 98Fle-201
❑ 98MetUni-195
❑ 98MetUniPMG-195
❑ 98Pac-245
❑ 98PacOnl-77
❑ 98PacOnlR-77
❑ 98PacOnlWC-77

❑ 98PacPlaB-245
❑ 98PacRedT-245
❑ 98PacSil-245
❑ 98PinPlu-137
❑ 98PinSna-AB17
❑ 98Sco-222
❑ 98ScoSS-PP108
❑ 98ScoSSAP-PP108
❑ 98StaCluFDI-82
❑ 98StaClul-82
❑ 98StaCluOneK-82
❑ 98StaCluPP-82
❑ 98Top-162
❑ 98TopChr-162
❑ 98TopChrR-162
❑ 98TopDevR-162
❑ 98TopDia-162
❑ 98TopMiniC-162
❑ 98TopOpeD-84
❑ 98Ult-191
❑ 98UltGolM-191
❑ 98UltMas-191
❑ 98UltPlaM-191
❑ 98UppDec-33
❑ 98UppDecSF-19
Wohlford, Jim
❑ 73OPC-611
❑ 73Top-611
❑ 74OPC-407
❑ 74RoyPos-29
❑ 74Top-407
❑ 75OPC-144
❑ 75RoyPos-32
❑ 75Top-144
❑ 75TopMin-144
❑ 76KanCitRP-33
❑ 76OPC-286
❑ 76RoyAaP-16
❑ 76SSP-179
❑ 76Top-286
❑ 77Top-622
❑ 78Top-376
❑ 79Top-596
❑ 80GiaPol-9
❑ 80GiaTeal-30
❑ 80Top-448
❑ 81Don-316
❑ 81Fle-440
❑ 81GiaTeal-22
❑ 81Top-11
❑ 82Fle-403
❑ 82Gia25tATI-31
❑ 82Top-116
❑ 83Don-524
❑ 83ExpPos-38
❑ 83ExpStu-21
❑ 83Fle-276
❑ 83Top-688
❑ 83TopTra-128T
❑ 84ExpPos-36
❑ 84ExpStu-24
❑ 84Fle-293
❑ 84Nes792-253
❑ 84OPC-253
❑ 84Top-253
❑ 84TopTif-253
❑ 85Don-585
❑ 85Fle-413
❑ 85Lea-82
❑ 85OPC-4
❑ 85Top-787
❑ 85TopTif-787
❑ 86Don-157
❑ 86ExpProPa-6
❑ 86OPC-344
❑ 86Top-344
❑ 86TopTif-344
❑ 87Fle-336
❑ 87FleGlo-336
❑ 87OPC-169
❑ 87Top-527
❑ 87TopTif-527
❑ 94BreMilB-188
Woide, Steve
❑ 88MyrBeaBJP-1172
❑ 90EriSaiS-27
Woinarowicz, Corey
❑ 94LetMouF-3883
❑ 94LetMouSP-22
Wojciechowski, Steve
❑ 91SouOreAC-29
❑ 91SouOreAP-3847
❑ 92ModA'sC-6
❑ 92ModA'sF-3900
❑ 92StaCluD-198
❑ 93ModA'sC-23
❑ 93ModA'sF-801
❑ 94HunStaF-1333
❑ 95Bow-204
❑ 95EdmTraTI-27
❑ 96A'sMot-13
❑ 96Fle-224
❑ 96FleTif-224
❑ 96StaClu-421
❑ 96StaCluMOP-421
❑ 96Ult-120
❑ 96UltGolM-120
❑ 97Fle-199
❑ 97FleTif-199
❑ 97PacPriGotD-GD84
❑ 97Top-432
❑ 97Ult-117
❑ 97UltGolME-117
❑ 97UltPlaME-117
❑ 98Pac-177
❑ 98PacPlaB-177
❑ 98PacRedT-177
❑ 98PacSil-177
Wojcik, Jim
❑ 81ShrCapT-5
Wojcik, John
❑ 63Top-253
Wojey, Pete
❑ 90DodTar-874
Wojna, Ed
❑ 83ReaPhiT-10
❑ 84LasVegSC-231
❑ 85LasVegSC-120
❑ 86Don-505
❑ 86Fle-338
❑ 86LasVegSP-25
❑ 86Top-211
❑ 86TopTif-211
❑ 87Don-589
❑ 87SpoTeaP-16
❑ 87Top-88
❑ 87TopTif-88
❑ 88VanCanC-5
❑ 88VanCanP-756
❑ 89ColSprSSC-4
❑ 89ColSprSSP-236
❑ 90CMC-588
❑ 90ProAAAF-140
❑ 90TacTigC-11
❑ 90TacTigP-93
Wojtkowski, Steve
❑ 93EugEmeC-27
❑ 93EugEmeF-3865
Wolak, Jerry
❑ 89UtiBluSP-27
❑ 90Bes-77
❑ 90MidLeaASGS-23
❑ 90SouBenWSB-13
❑ 90SouBenWSGS-21
❑ 91SarWhiSC-22
❑ 91SarWhiSP-1128
❑ 92SarWhiSCB-14
❑ 92SarWhiSF-223
❑ 93BirBarF-1206
❑ 94NasSouF-1264
❑ 95Bow-43
❑ 95NasSouTI-30
Wolcott, Bob
❑ 92ClaDraP-37
❑ 92ClaFS7-425
❑ 93BelMarCB-29
❑ 93BelMarF-3210
❑ 93StaCluM-9
❑ 94RivPilCLC-14
❑ 95Bow-112
❑ 95MarPac-12
❑ 95MarPac-49
❑ 95PorCitRTI-28
❑ 95TacRaiTI-29
❑ 96Bow-179
❑ 96BowFoi-179
❑ 96ColCho-23
❑ 96ColCho-381T
❑ 96Don-373
❑ 96DonPreP-373
❑ 96Fin-B251
❑ 96FinRef-B251
❑ 96Fle-246
❑ 96FleTif-246
❑ 96LeaSigA-248
❑ 96LeaSigAG-249
❑ 96LeaSigAS-249
❑ 96MarMot-23
❑ 96Pac-412
❑ 96Pin-182
❑ 96Sco-505
❑ 96Sel-168
❑ 96SelArtP-168
❑ 96Spo-127
❑ 96SpoArtP-127
❑ 96SpoRooJ-8
❑ 96Sum-163
❑ 96SumAbo&B-163
❑ 96SumArtP-163
❑ 96SumFoi-163
❑ 96Top-353
❑ 96TopLasBS-8
❑ 96Ult-417
❑ 96UltGolM-417
❑ 96UppDec-248
❑ 97ColCho-229
❑ 97StaClu-368
❑ 97StaCluMOP-368
❑ 97Top-427
❑ 98PacPar-126
❑ 98PacParC-126
❑ 98PacParG-126
❑ 98PacParHS-126
❑ 98PacParPB-126
❑ 98PacParR-126
❑ 98PinSna-AD10
❑ 98TusSidM-16
Wolf, Brian
❑ 92FroRowDP-86
❑ 92FroRowDPG-86
❑ 92FroRowDPS-86
Wolf, Michael
❑ 92BoiHawC-28
❑ 92BoiHawF-3645
Wolf, Mike
❑ 78KnoKnoST-25
❑ 80IowOakP-14
Wolf, Randy
❑ 97BatCliTI-14
❑ 98Bow-308
❑ 98Bow99ROYF-ROY8
❑ 98BowBes-158
❑ 98BowBesAR-158
❑ 98BowBesR-158
❑ 98BowChr-308
❑ 98BowChrGA-308
❑ 98BowChrGAR-308
❑ 98BowChrI-308
❑ 98BowChrIR-308
❑ 98BowChrR-308
❑ 98BowGolA-308
❑ 98BowInt-308
❑ 98EasLeaTPM-28
❑ 98ReaPhiM-22
❑ 98ReaPhiUM-27
❑ 98ScrRedBQ-29
❑ 99199Fin-142
❑ 99BasAmeTP-98
❑ 99BasAmeTPA-47
❑ 99BasAmeTPG-98
❑ 99Bow-334
❑ 99BowAut-BA40
❑ 99BowBes-135
❑ 99BowBesAR-135
❑ 99BowBesR-135
❑ 99BowGol-334
❑ 99BowInt-334
❑ 99FinGolRef-142
❑ 99FinRef-142
❑ 99JustheS-50
❑ 99JustheSJB-50
❑ 99JustheSJD-10
❑ 99PacOme-184
❑ 99PacOmeC-184
❑ 99PacOmeG-184
❑ 99PacOmePB-184
❑ 99Top-428
❑ 99TopChr-428
❑ 99TopChrR-428
Wolf, Rick
❑ 77WauMetT-23
Wolf, Steve
❑ 89FreStaBS-22
❑ 90FreStaS-16
❑ 90NiaFalRP-27
❑ 91LakTigC-13
❑ 91LakTigP-268
❑ 92LonTigF-635
❑ 93LonTigF-2309
Wolf, Waldo the
❑ 92WhiSoxK-0
Wolf, Wally (Walter)
❑ 63Top-208
❑ 70OPC-74
❑ 70Top-74
Wolf, William Van Winkle
❑ 87OldJudN-547
❑ 89EdgR.WG-17
Wolfe, Bill
❑ 11SpoLifCW-373
Wolfe, Donn
❑ 85FreGiaSB-27
❑ 88St.CatBJP-2013
Wolfe, Joel
❑ 91SouOreAC-1
❑ 91SouOreAP-3865
❑ 92RenSilSCLC-56
❑ 92StaCluD-199
❑ 92UppDecML-193
❑ 93ModA'sC-24
❑ 93ModA'sF-813
❑ 94ClaGolF-129
❑ 94ExcFS7-123
❑ 94HunStaF-1341
❑ 94UppDecML-177
❑ 95HunStaTI-29
❑ 96ArkTraB-28
Wolfe, Ken
❑ 61SeaPop-29
❑ 62SeaPop-18
Wolfe, Larry
❑ 78TwiFriP-23
❑ 79Top-137
❑ 80Top-549
Wolfe, Scott
❑ 75LafDriT-4
Wolfenbarger, Scott
❑ 91OklStaC-32
Wolfer, Jim
❑ 89GreHorP-419
Wolfer, M. J.
❑ 21Zee-63
❑ 23Zee-78
❑ 24Zee-58
❑ 25Zee-164
❑ 28Zee-168
Wolff, Bryan
❑ 93SpoIndC-25
❑ 93SpoIndF-3594
❑ 94SprSulC-26
❑ 94SprSulF-2038
❑ 95Exc-290
❑ 95RanCucQT-29
❑ 96WilBluRB-20
❑ 97WicWra-10
❑ 98MobBayBTI-30
Wolff, Jim
❑ 43A'STEAI-28
❑ 90HunCubP-3286
❑ 91HunCubC-26
❑ 91HunCubP-3338
❑ 92MidLeaATI-51
❑ 92PeoChiC-25
❑ 92PeoChiTI-30
❑ 92PeoChiTI-31
Wolff, Michael
❑ 93CedRapKC-25
❑ 93CedRapKF-1753
❑ 93MidLeaAGF-37
❑ 94MidAngF-2452
❑ 94MidAngOHP-33
❑ 95MidAngOHP-36
❑ 95MidAngTI-29
❑ 96FreKeyB-23
❑ 96VanCanB-30
❑ 97FreKey-29
❑ 97VanCanB-30
❑ 98ModA'sG-30
Wolff, Roger
❑ 42A'sTeal-37
❑ 77TCMTheWY-75
❑ 79DiaGre-64
❑ 83TCMPla1943-22
❑ 83TCMPla1945-6
Wolff, Tom
❑ 93KinMetC-24
❑ 93KinMetF-3797
❑ 94KinMetC-24
❑ 94KinMetF-3825
❑ 95PitMetTI-24
Wolfgang, Meldon
❑ 15SpoNewM-195
❑ 16SpoNewM-194
❑ 17ColE13-146A
❑ 18WhiSoxTI-25
❑ 92Man191BSR-26
Wolkoys, Rob
❑ 86EugEmeC-26
❑ 87AppFoxP-21
Wollenburg, Doug
❑ 92IdaFalGF-3523
❑ 92IdaFalGSP-10
❑ 93DurBulC-25
❑ 93DurBulF-495
❑ 93DurBulTI-16
❑ 94GreBraF-423
❑ 94GreBraTI-28
❑ 95BreBtaTI-22
Wollenburg, Jay
❑ 86MacPirP-26
Wollenhaupt, Ron
❑ 80AppFoxT-30
❑ 82WatIndF-4
❑ 82WatIndT-28
Wollins, Paul
❑ 94IdaFalBF-3586
Wolten, Brad
❑ 87WatIndP-5
Wolter, Harry
❑ 10DomDisP-128
❑ 10JHDABE-16
❑ 10SweCapPP-39
❑ 11HelSta-50
❑ 11PinT-5-814
❑ 11S74Sil-25
❑ 11SpoLifM-84
❑ 11T205-185
❑ 12HasTriFT-14A
❑ 12HasTriFT-15B
❑ 12HasTriFT-16A
❑ 12HasTriFT-61B
❑ 14TexTomE-47
❑ 14Zee-25
❑ 15Zee-21
❑ 95ConTSN-1370
Wolters, Mike
❑ 83ArkTraT-14
Wolverton, Harry
❑ 09ObaT21-113
❑ 09ObaT21-286
❑ 10BisCoaLE99-30
❑ 11HelSta-51
❑ 11PacCoaBD-71
❑ 11SpoLifCW-374
❑ 11Zee-42
❑ 12ObaPreT-35
❑ 12T207-202
❑ 13Zee-95
❑ 14Zee-97
❑ 15Zee-120
❑ 16Zee-121
❑ 17Zee-99
❑ 23Zee-177
Womack, Dooley
❑ 66Top-469
❑ 67CokCapYM-V4
❑ 67OPC-77
❑ 67Top-77
❑ 67YanPhoS-97
❑ 68Top-431
❑ 68YanPhoS-82
❑ 69Top-594
❑ 81TCM60I-339
❑ 92YanWIZ6-138
Womack, Tony
❑ 91WelPirC-2
❑ 91WelPirP-3584
❑ 92AugPirF-247
❑ 92ClaFS7-385
❑ 93CarLeaAGF-51
❑ 93ClaFS7-296
❑ 93SalBucC-25
❑ 93SalBucF-443
❑ 94BufBisF-1847
❑ 97Cir-124
❑ 97CirRav-124
❑ 97ColCho-434
❑ 97Don-394
❑ 97DonGolPP-394
❑ 97DonLim-39
❑ 97DonLimE-39
❑ 97DonLimENG-39
❑ 97DonSigA-113
❑ 97DonSigAC-139
❑ 97DonSigAM-139
❑ 97DonSilPP-394
❑ 97Fle-638
❑ 97FleTif-638
❑ 97Lea-345
❑ 97LeaFraM-345
❑ 97LeaFraMDC-345
❑ 97PacPriGotD-GD195
❑ 97PirPos-44
❑ 97Sco-469
❑ 97ScoArtPWB-469
❑ 97ScoResC-469
❑ 97ScoShoS-469
❑ 97ScoShoSAP-469
❑ 97Sel-182
❑ 97SelCom-182
❑ 97StrAll-62
❑ 97TopSta-96
❑ 97TopStaAM-96
❑ 97Ult-492
❑ 97UltGolME-492
❑ 97UltPlaME-492
❑ 98Bow-41
❑ 98BowCerBlueAU-16
❑ 98BowCerGA-16
❑ 98BowCerSA-16
❑ 98BowChr-41
❑ 98BowChrGA-41
❑ 98BowChrGAR-41
❑ 98BowChrI-41
❑ 98BowChrIR-41
❑ 98BowChrR-41
❑ 98BowGolA-41
❑ 98BowInt-41
❑ 98CirThu-174
❑ 98CirThuRav-174
❑ 98CirThuSupRav-174
❑ 98ColCho-256
❑ 98ColCho-465
❑ 98Don-146
❑ 98DonCol-146
❑ 98DonColE-442
❑ 98DonColL-269
❑ 98DonColP-653
❑ 98DonColS-146
❑ 98DonEli-42
❑ 98DonEliA-42
❑ 98DonEliS-42
❑ 98DonGolPP-146
❑ 98DonPre-103
❑ 98DonPreSeat-103
❑ 98DonPriCD-146
❑ 98DonPriCE-442
❑ 98DonPriCL-269
❑ 98DonPriCP-653
❑ 98DonSigA-97
❑ 98DonSigAC-120
❑ 98DonSigAM-123
❑ 98DonSigSB-32
❑ 98DonSilPP-146
❑ 98E-X2-60
❑ 98E-X2ECFut-60
❑ 98E-X2ECNow-60
❑ 98Fin-75
❑ 98FinNo--75
❑ 98FinNo-R-75
❑ 98FinRef-75
❑ 98FlaShoLeg0-110
❑ 98FlaShoLeg1-110
❑ 98FlaShoLeg2-110
❑ 98FlaShoLeg3-110
❑ 98FlaShoLegM-110
❑ 98FlaShoR0-110
❑ 98FlaShoR1-110
❑ 98FlaShoR2-110
❑ 98FlaShoR3-110
❑ 98Fle-116
❑ 98FleDiamInk-10
❑ 98FleVin'-48
❑ 98FleVin'C-48
❑ 98Lea-70
❑ 98LeaFraDA-70
❑ 98LeaFraF-70
❑ 98LeaFraM-70
❑ 98LeaFraM-70
❑ 98LeaFraMDC-70
❑ 98LeaFraMDC-70
❑ 98LeaFraMS-70
❑ 98LeaFraMZ2-70
❑ 98MetUni-87
❑ 98MetUniPMG-87
❑ 98Pac-403
❑ 98PacInv-131
❑ 98PacInvPBlue-131
❑ 98PacInvSilv-131
❑ 98PacInvTeam-22
❑ 98PacOme-192
❑ 98PacOmeR-192
❑ 98PacOnl-600
❑ 98PacOnl-602
❑ 98PacOnlR-600
❑ 98PacOnlR-602
❑ 98PacOnlWC-600
❑ 98PacOnlWC-602
❑ 98PacPar-224
❑ 98PacParC-224
❑ 98PacParG-224
❑ 98PacParHS-224
❑ 98PacParPB-224
❑ 98PacParR-224
❑ 98PacPlaB-403

❑ 99PacParOD-53
❑ 99PacParPB-53
❑ 99PacParRed-53
❑ 99PacPlaB-94
❑ 99PacPri-31
❑ 99PacPriAotG-7
❑ 99PacPriBL-8
❑ 99PacPriDG-8
❑ 99PacPriEP-7
❑ 99PacPriHB-31
❑ 99PacPriHG-31
❑ 99PacPriHM-31
❑ 99PacPriHP-31
❑ 99PacPriRed-31
❑ 99PacPriS-20
❑ 99PacPriS206-20
❑ 99PacPriS206R-20
❑ 99PacPriSE-20
❑ 99PacPriSP-20
❑ 99PacPriSP-20
❑ 99PacPriSV-20
❑ 99PacRed-94
❑ 99Pin-30
❑ 99SkyMolM-146
❑ 99SkyMolMF-46
❑ 99SkyMolMFS-46
❑ 99SkyMolMFT-46
❑ 99SkyMolMX-146
❑ 99SkyMolMX-NNO
❑ 99SkyPre-48
❑ 99SkyPre-283
❑ 99SkyPreR-48
❑ 99SkyPreR-283
❑ 99SkyThu-293
❑ 99SkyThuHip-H15
❑ 99SkyThuInD-ID10
❑ 99SkyThuRant-293
❑ 99SkyThuRave-293
❑ 99SkyThuUnl-U15
❑ 99SP Aut-19
❑ 99SP Aut-127
❑ 99SP AutC-KW
❑ 99SP AutCG-KW
❑ 99SP AutEF-E11
❑ 99SP AutR-R11
❑ 99SpoIll-18
❑ 99SpoIll-30
❑ 99SpoIll-160
❑ 99SpoIll-S160
❑ 99SpoIllDD-1
❑ 99SpoIllH-25
❑ 99SpoIllOTW-12
❑ 99SPx-26
❑ 99SPxFinR-26
❑ 99SPxFinS-26
❑ 99SPxPreS-PS5
❑ 99StaClu-250
❑ 99StaCluA-SCA9
❑ 99StaCluC-SCC2
❑ 99StaCluCR-SCC2
❑ 99StaCluFDI-250
❑ 99StaCluNC-NC13
❑ 99StaCluOoaK-250
❑ 99StaCluPP-250
❑ 99StaCluTI-T8C
❑ 99StaCluTI-T11B
❑ 99StaCluTL-T8C
❑ 99StaCluTL-T11B
❑ 99StaCluTL-T8C
❑ 99StaCluTL-T11B
❑ 99StaCluVR-VR4
❑ 99ThuSkySupR-293
❑ 99Top-20
❑ 99Top-204
❑ 99Top-446
❑ 99Top-460
❑ 99TopActF-12
❑ 99TopActFAU-12
❑ 99TopActFCU-12
❑ 99TopAll-AM24
❑ 99TopAllMF-M32
❑ 99TopBlaLC1-98
❑ 99TopBlaLC2-98
❑ 99TopBlaLC3-98
❑ 99TopChr-20
❑ 99TopChr-204
❑ 99TopChr-446
❑ 99TopChr-460
❑ 99TopChrA-AE24
❑ 99TopChrAR-AE24
❑ 99TopChrF1-FF7
❑ 99TopChrF1R-FF7
❑ 99TopChrNB-NB3
❑ 99TopChrNBR-NB3
❑ 99TopChrR-20
❑ 99TopChrR-204
❑ 99TopChrR-446
❑ 99TopChrR-460
❑ 99TopChrRN-RN7
❑ 99TopChrRNR-RN7
❑ 99TopGal-43
❑ 99TopGal-117
❑ 99TopGalAG-AG1
❑ 99TopGalE-E6
❑ 99TopGalGoH-GH7
❑ 99TopGalHer-TH14
❑ 99TopGalHerP-TH14
❑ 99TopGalPP-43
❑ 99TopGalPP-117
❑ 99TopGalPPI-43
❑ 99TopGalPPI-117
❑ 99TopGolL-98
❑ 99TopGolLC1-98
❑ 99TopGolLC2-98
❑ 99TopGolLOtO-98
❑ 99TopMVPP-20
❑ 99TopMVPP-446
❑ 99TopMVPP-460
❑ 99TopNewB-NB3
❑ 99TopOpeD-15
❑ 99TopOpeD-162
❑ 99TopOver-A3
❑ 99TopPicP-P2
❑ 99TopPowB-PB20
❑ 99TopPowBR-PB20
❑ 99TopRecN-RN7
❑ 99TopRecNG-RN7
❑ 99TopRedLC1-98
❑ 99TopRedLC2-98
❑ 99TopRedLC3-98
❑ 99TopSta-13
❑ 99TopSta-161
❑ 99TopSta'S-1
❑ 99TopSta'SG-1
❑ 99TopSta'SGDH-1
❑ 99TopSta1Foil-13
❑ 99TopSta2Foil-13
❑ 99TopSta3Foil-13
❑ 99TopStaFoil-13
❑ 99TopStaFoil-161
❑ 99TopStaG-G5
❑ 99TopStaGFoil-G5
❑ 99TopStaOS-13
❑ 99TopStaPre-PP4
❑ 99TopStaTS-13
❑ 99TopStaTS-13
❑ 99TopSupC-5
❑ 99TopSupC-33
❑ 99TopSupCR-5
❑ 99TopSupCR-33
❑ 99TopTek-12A
❑ 99TopTek-12B
❑ 99TopTekG-12A
❑ 99TopTekG-12B
❑ 99TopTekT-T3
❑ 99UD Cho-29
❑ 99UD Cho-66
❑ 99UD ChoBU-7
❑ 99UD ChoBUCG-2
❑ 99UD ChoMBH-B7
❑ 99UD ChoP-66
❑ 99UD ChoPCR-29
❑ 99UD ChoPCR-66
❑ 99UD ChoS-25
❑ 99UD ChoSD-25
❑ 99UD ChoSHR-25
❑ 99UD ChoST-25
❑ 99UD Ion-16
❑ 99UD Ion-71
❑ 99UD IonC-C11
❑ 99UD IonH-H11
❑ 99UD IonR-16
❑ 99UD IonR-71
❑ 99UD IonWZ-WZ11
❑ 99Ult-100
❑ 99Ult-211
❑ 99Ult-220
❑ 99UltDamI-9
❑ 99UltDiaP-8
❑ 99UltGolM-100
❑ 99UltGolM-211
❑ 99UltGolM-220
❑ 99UltMas-100
❑ 99UltMas-211
❑ 99UltMas-220
❑ 99UltPlaM-100
❑ 99UltPlaM-211
❑ 99UltPlaM-220
❑ 99UltPromo-NNO
❑ 99UltTheBook-1
❑ 99UltWorP-2
❑ 99UppDec-247
❑ 99UppDec-330
❑ 99UppDecBD-97
❑ 99UppDecBDD-97
❑ 99UppDecBDDom-D1
❑ 99UppDecBDDomE-D1
❑ 99UppDecBDMN-M3
❑ 99UppDecBDMNE-M3
❑ 99UppDecBDQ-97
❑ 99UppDecBDT-97
❑ 99UppDecCf7-79
❑ 99UppDecCG-CG1
❑ 99UppDecCGD-CG1
❑ 99UppDecCGHR-CG1
❑ 99UppDecCGT-CG1
❑ 99UppDecCL-84
❑ 99UppDecCL-113
❑ 99UppDecCLCC-84
❑ 99UppDecCLCC-113
❑ 99UppDecCLM-C15
❑ 99UppDecCo7CE-79
❑ 99UppDecE-18
❑ 99UppDecEFXG-18
❑ 99UppDecEL1-247
❑ 99UppDecEL1-330
❑ 99UppDecEL2-247
❑ 99UppDecEL2-330
❑ 99UppDecEPE-P9
❑ 99UppDecF-F11
❑ 99UppDecFD-F11
❑ 99UppDecFQ-F11
❑ 99UppDecFT-F11
❑ 99UppDecGJ-KW
❑ 99UppDecGJ-KWAU
❑ 99UppDecIP-I24
❑ 99UppDecIPD-I24
❑ 99UppDecIPHR-I24
❑ 99UppDecIPT-I24
❑ 99UppDecM-38
❑ 99UppDecMGS-38
❑ 99UppDecMHFS-38
❑ 99UppDecMP-38
❑ 99UppDecMSC-SC8
❑ 99UppDecMSS-38
❑ 99UppDecO-12
❑ 99UppDecOAPoH-KWAU
❑ 99UppDecOSO-12
❑ 99UppDecOWP-R8
❑ 99UppDecTE-T9
❑ 99UppDecTED-T9
❑ 99UppDecTEQ-T9
❑ 99UppDecTET-T9
❑ 99UppDecVtaT-V9
❑ 99UppDecVtaTD-V9
❑ 99UppDecVtaTQ-V9
❑ 99UppDecVtaTT-V9
❑ 99UppDecWY-W1
❑ 99UppDecWYD-W1
❑ 99UppDecWYHR-W1
❑ 99UppDecWYT-W1
❑ 99Vic-77
❑ 99Vic-80

Wood, Mathew
❑ 91MelBusF-13

Wood, Mike
❑ 84ButCopKT-5
❑ 93BatCliCB-28
❑ 93BatCliF-3146
❑ 94SpaPhiF-1724
❑ 94SparPhiC-24

Wood, Pete
❑ 87BucN28-83A
❑ 87BucN28-83B
❑ 87OldJudN-549
❑ 90KalBatN-58

Wood, Peter
❑ 91PerHeaF-15

Wood, Robert Lynn
❑ 03BreE10-155

Wood, Stanton
❑ 98GreBatM-25
❑ 98OneYanG-32

Wood, Stephen
❑ 88VerBeaDS-25

Wood, Ted
❑ 87PanAmTUBI-11
❑ 87PanAmTURB-15
❑ 88TopTra-130T
❑ 88TopTraT-130T
❑ 89ShrCapP-1842
❑ 89TopBig-308
❑ 90ShrCapP-1456
❑ 90ShrCapS-24
❑ 90TexLeaAGS-27
❑ 91LinDriAAA-398
❑ 91PhoFirLD-398
❑ 91PhoFirP-82
❑ 92Don-681
❑ 92Fle-678
❑ 92OPC-358
❑ 92PhoFirF-2836
❑ 92PhoFirS-398
❑ 92ProFS7-341
❑ 92Sco-768
❑ 92ScoRoo-11
❑ 92SkyAAAF-181
❑ 92StaClu-799
❑ 92Top-358
❑ 92TopDeb91-189
❑ 92TopGol-358
❑ 92TopGolW-358
❑ 92TopMic-358
❑ 92Ult-597
❑ 92UppDec-12
❑ 93Don-24
❑ 93PacSpa-539
❑ 93Pin-286
❑ 93StaClu-455
❑ 93StaCluFDI-455
❑ 93StaCluMOP-455
❑ 93Top-698
❑ 93TopGol-698
❑ 93TopInaM-698
❑ 93TopInaR-698
❑ 93TopMic-698
❑ 94OttLynF-2910

Wood, Tony
❑ 96DurBulBlB-22
❑ 96DurBulBrB-23

Wood, Wilbur
❑ 63SeaPop-15
❑ 64Top-267
❑ 64TopVen-267
❑ 65Top-478
❑ 67Top-391
❑ 68Top-585
❑ 69MilBra-295
❑ 69MLBOffS-36
❑ 69OPC-123
❑ 69Top-123
❑ 69TopFou-12
❑ 69TopSta-160
❑ 69TopTeaP-11
❑ 70DayDaiNM-51
❑ 70MLBOffS-192
❑ 70OPC-342
❑ 70Top-342
❑ 71OPC-436
❑ 71Top-436
❑ 72Kel-4
❑ 72MilBra-369
❑ 72OPC-92
❑ 72OPC-94
❑ 72OPC-342
❑ 72SevTraC-59
❑ 72Top-92
❑ 72Top-94
❑ 72Top-342
❑ 72Top-553
❑ 72Top-554
❑ 72TopPos-19
❑ 72WhiSox-12
❑ 72WhiSoxC-7
❑ 72WhiSoxDS-6
❑ 72WhiSoxTI1-15A
❑ 72WhiSoxTI1-15B
❑ 73Kel2D-9
❑ 73LinPor-53
❑ 73OPC-66
❑ 73OPC-150
❑ 73SevTraC-79
❑ 73Top-66
❑ 73Top-150
❑ 73TopCanL-54
❑ 74Kel-34A
❑ 74Kel-34B
❑ 74OPC-120
❑ 74OPC-205
❑ 74Top-120
❑ 74Top-205
❑ 74TopDecE-13
❑ 74TopSta-160
❑ 75Hos-68
❑ 75HosTwi-68
❑ 75OPC-110
❑ 75SSP42-1
❑ 75Top-110
❑ 75TopMin-110
❑ 76BlaDis-67
❑ 76BucDis-67
❑ 76CarDis-67
❑ 76CraDis-67
❑ 76DailsID-67
❑ 76Hos-99
❑ 76IsaDis-67
❑ 76OPC-368
❑ 76OrbDis-67
❑ 76RedBarD-67
❑ 76SafDis-67
❑ 76SSP-139
❑ 76Top-368
❑ 76TowCluD-67
❑ 77Top-198
❑ 77WhiSoxJT-15
❑ 77WhiSoxT-26
❑ 78SSP270-143
❑ 78Top-726
❑ 79OPC-108
❑ 79Top-216
❑ 81TCM60I-325
❑ 82TCMGreP-5
❑ 85WhiSoxC-50
❑ 89PacLegI-124
❑ 89SweBasG-127
❑ 91LinDri-35
❑ 91SweBasG-121
❑ 92ActPacA-53
❑ 92UppDecS-5
❑ 93UppDecS-24

Woodall, Brad
❑ 91IdaFalBP-4331
❑ 91IdaFalBSP-26
❑ 92DurBulC-23
❑ 92DurBulF-1102
❑ 92DurBulTI-11
❑ 92ProFS7-196
❑ 94RicBraF-2847
❑ 94SigRooTPD-T2
❑ 94SigRooTPS-T2
❑ 94TriAAF-AAA43
❑ 94VenLinU-175
❑ 95ActPacF-36
❑ 95Bow-222
❑ 95BowGolF-222
❑ 95RicBraRC-29
❑ 95RicBraTI-26
❑ 95Sel-199
❑ 95SelArtP-199
❑ 95SigRooMOP-P3
❑ 95SigRooMOPS-P3
❑ 95SigRooOP-OP5
❑ 95SigRooOPS-OP5
❑ 95SigRooP'P-P1
❑ 95Top-91
❑ 96RicBraB-30
❑ 96RicBraUB-30
❑ 97RicBra-29
❑ 98LouRedQ-21

Woodall, Brent
❑ 93GenCubC-27
❑ 93GenCubF-3175
❑ 94PeoChiC-25
❑ 94PeoChiF-2268

Woodall, Kevin
❑ 91GulCoaRSP-10
❑ 92ButCopKSP-25
❑ 92GasRanC-13
❑ 93ChaRaiC-24
❑ 93ChaRaiF-1923

Woodall, Lawrence (Charles L.)
❑ 21Exh-190
❑ 21Nei-21
❑ 22E120-60
❑ 22W573-140
❑ 25Exh-96
❑ 27AmeCarE126-53
❑ 28Exh-48
❑ 30Zee-113
❑ 31Zee-78
❑ 32Zee-93
❑ 33Zee-37
❑ 33Zee-151
❑ 33Zee-152
❑ 37Zee-94
❑ 75RedSox1T-38
❑ 75RedSox1T-39
❑ 93ConTSN-784

Woodard, Darrell
❑ 81BirBarT-21
❑ 82BirBarT-3

Woodard, Mike
❑ 81WesHavAT-17
❑ 82WesHavAT-19
❑ 83TacTigT-13
❑ 85PhoGiaC-181
❑ 86Don-46
❑ 86Fle-645
❑ 86PhoFirP-26
❑ 87PhoFirP-10
❑ 87Top-286
❑ 87TopTif-286
❑ 88TriAAC-33
❑ 88VanCanC-14
❑ 88VanCanP-767
❑ 89ColCliC-12
❑ 89ColCliP-19
❑ 89ColCliP-742
❑ 89Fle-513
❑ 89FleGlo-513

Woodard, Steve
❑ 94SigRooDP-82
❑ 94SigRooDPS-82
❑ 95BelBreTI-2
❑ 96StoPorB-2
❑ 97El PasDB-23
❑ 97Sel-187
❑ 97SelCom-187
❑ 97TexAllM-30
❑ 97TexLeaTP-7
❑ 98Bow-409
❑ 98BowChr-409
❑ 98BowChrGA-409
❑ 98BowChrGAR-409
❑ 98BowChrI-409
❑ 98BowChrIR-409
❑ 98BowChrR-409
❑ 98BowGolA-409
❑ 98BowInt-409
❑ 98Don-315
❑ 98DonGolPP-315
❑ 98DonSilPP-315
❑ 98Fle-274
❑ 98LeaRS-287
❑ 98LeaRSLHolo-287
❑ 98LeaRSLong-287
❑ 98LeaRTrue-287
❑ 98MetUni-201
❑ 98MetUniPMG-201
❑ 98PacOmeRS-18
❑ 98PacOmeRST2-18
❑ 98PacOnl-415
❑ 98PacOnlR-415
❑ 98PacOnlWC-415
❑ 98Pin-166
❑ 98PinArtP-PP69
❑ 98PinMusC-PP69
❑ 98PinPreP-166
❑ 98Sco-236
❑ 98Stu-123
❑ 98StuGPP-123
❑ 98StuSPP-123
❑ 98Ult-19
❑ 98UltGolM-19
❑ 98UltMas-19
❑ 98UltPlaM-19
❑ 98UppDec-576
❑ 99Fle-247
❑ 99FleSta9-247
❑ 99FleWarT-247
❑ 99MetUni-187
❑ 99MetUniGM-187
❑ 99MetUniPMG-187
❑ 99SkyThu-17
❑ 99SkyThuRant-17
❑ 99SkyThuRave-17
❑ 99ThuSkySupR-17
❑ 99Top-60
❑ 99TopChr-60
❑ 99TopChrR-60
❑ 99TopMVPP-60

Woodards, Orlando
❑ 97St.CatSB-29

Woodbrey, Mark
❑ 75CedRapGT-25
❑ 76CedRapGT-34A
❑ 76CedRapGT-34B

Woodburn, Eugene
❑ 12T207-204

Wooden, Mark
❑ 86BelMarCr-129
❑ 87WauTimP-16
❑ 88VerMarP-939
❑ 89WilBilP-628
❑ 89WilBilS-23
❑ 90WilBilB-23
❑ 90WilBilP-1059
❑ 90WilBilS-24

Woodeshick, Hal
❑ 59SenTealW-18
❑ 59Top-106
❑ 59TopVen-106
❑ 60Top-454
❑ 61Top-397
❑ 62Col.45B-22

❑ 62Col45'HC-20
❑ 62Top-526
❑ 63Top-517
❑ 64Col.45JP-11
❑ 64Top-370
❑ 64TopSta-78
❑ 64TopStaU-76
❑ 64TopVen-370
❑ 64WheSta-49
❑ 65CarTeal-28
❑ 65OPC-179
❑ 65Top-179
❑ 66Top-514
❑ 67AstTeal2-25
❑ 67Top-324
❑ 78TCM60I-123
❑ 86AstMot-2
❑ 87AstSer1-22
❑ 89AstCol4S-10

Woodfin, Chris
❑ 92SouBenWSC-17
❑ 92SouBenWSF-178
❑ 93SarWhiSF-1370
❑ 94CarLeaAF-CAR13
❑ 94PriWilCC-23
❑ 94PriWilCF-1921
❑ 95Exc-34

Woodfin, Olonzo
❑ 89BurIndS-26

Woodhouse, Kevin
❑ 84EveGiaC-9

Woodland, Bob
❑ 75WesPalBES-20

Woodling, Gene
❑ 47Exh-243A
❑ 47Exh-243B
❑ 47PM1StaP1-223
❑ 47StaPinP2-43
❑ 47StaPinP2-44
❑ 48SomandK-13
❑ 49YanTeal-25
❑ 50YanTeal-25
❑ 51BerRos-D1
❑ 51Bow-219
❑ 51R42SmaS-112
❑ 52BerRos-70
❑ 52Bow-177
❑ 52DixLid-24
❑ 52DixPre-24
❑ 52Top-99
❑ 53BowBW-31
❑ 53DixLid-24
❑ 53DixPre-24
❑ 53Dor-118
❑ 53RedMan-AL12
❑ 53Top-264
❑ 54Bow-209
❑ 54DixLid-17
❑ 54NewYorJA-59
❑ 54RedMan-AL15
❑ 54Top-101
❑ 55DonWin-41
❑ 55OriEss-26
❑ 55Top-190
❑ 56BalOriP-56
❑ 56BalOriP-57
❑ 56Top-163
❑ 56YelBasP-31
❑ 57IndSoh-17
❑ 57IndTeal-28
❑ 57Top-172
❑ 58BalOriP-19
❑ 58Top-398
❑ 59OriJayP-12
❑ 59Top-170
❑ 59TopVen-170
❑ 60BalOriP-12
❑ 60OriJayP-12
❑ 60Top-190
❑ 60TopTat-54
❑ 60TopVen-190
❑ 61Baz-30
❑ 61Pos-70
❑ 61SenJayP-11
❑ 61SevElev-12
❑ 61Top-275
❑ 61TopStaI-207
❑ 62Baz-45
❑ 62Jel-71
❑ 62Pos-71
❑ 62PosCan-71
❑ 62SalPlaC-96
❑ 62ShiPlaC-96
❑ 62Top-125
❑ 62TopBuc-94
❑ 62TopStaI-101
❑ 62TopVen-125
❑ 63BasMagM-86
❑ 63Top-43
❑ 63Top-342
❑ 65BalOriP-34
❑ 66BalOriP-34
❑ 67BalOriP-105
❑ 67BalOriP-106
❑ 67BalOriP-107
❑ 75JohMiz-20
❑ 79DiaGre-295
❑ 79TCM50-156
❑ 81Ori6F-32
❑ 82MetGal62-9
❑ 82OhiHaloF-65
❑ 83TopRep5-99
❑ 85TCMPla1-40
❑ 88PacLegI-5
❑ 89SweBasG-102
❑ 91MetWIZ-435
❑ 91OriCro-490
❑ 91SweBasG-101
❑ 91TopArc1-264
❑ 92ActPacA-23
❑ 92BazQua5A-4
❑ 94TopArc1-101
❑ 94TopArc1G-101
❑ 97BalOriP-55

Woodmansee, Mark
❑ 83SalLakCGT-12

Woodridge, Dickie
❑ 93SpoIndC-26
❑ 93SpoIndF-3600
❑ 94SprSulC-27
❑ 94SprSulF-2047
❑ 95RanCucQT-10
❑ 95SPML-139

Woodring, Arthur
❑ 25Zee-58

Woodring, Jason
❑ 94BurBeeC-25
❑ 94BurBeeF-1082
❑ 96DelShoB-30
❑ 98JupHamQ-16

Woodrow, James
❑ 95BelGiaTI-36
❑ 96BelGiaTI-19

Woodruff, Orville
❑ 09ColChiE-312A
❑ 09ColChiE-312B
❑ 11MecDFT-50
❑ 12ColRedB-312A
❑ 12ColRedB-312B
❑ 12ColTinT-312A
❑ 12ColTinT-312B

Woodruff, Pat
❑ 89BatCliP-1936
❑ 90ClePhiS-25
❑ 91LakTigC-28
❑ 91LakTigP-281

Woods, Al (Alvis)
❑ 76TacTwiDQ-24
❑ 77OPC-256
❑ 77Top-479
❑ 78BluJayP-25
❑ 78OPC-175
❑ 78SyrChiT-21
❑ 78Top-121
❑ 79BluJayBY-20
❑ 79OPC-85
❑ 79Top-178
❑ 80OPC-230
❑ 80Top-444
❑ 81Don-32
❑ 81Fle-422
❑ 81OPC-165
❑ 81OPCPos-17
❑ 81Top-703
❑ 81TopSti-141
❑ 82Don-180
❑ 82Fle-627
❑ 82OPC-49
❑ 82OPCPos-5
❑ 82Top-49
❑ 83Fle-436
❑ 83OPC-59
❑ 83Top-589
❑ 84SyrChiT-14
❑ 85TolMudHT-25
❑ 86BluJayGT-7
❑ 86StaoftFT-21
❑ 86TolMudHP-24
❑ 86TwiTeal-34
❑ 92Nab-4

Woods, Andy
❑ 86AncGlaPTI-42

Woods, Anthony
❑ 86WauTimP-28
❑ 87WauTimP-13
❑ 88SanBerSB-5
❑ 89SanBerSB-17
❑ 89SanBerSCLC-83

Woods, Brian
❑ 94SouBenSHC-24
❑ 94SouBenSHF-595
❑ 95PriWilCTI-26
❑ 96BirBarB-21
❑ 97BirBarB-3
❑ 98BirBarG-30

Woods, Byron
❑ 92IdaFalGF-3530
❑ 92IdaFalGSP-24

Woods, Clancy
❑ 79AppFoxT-7

Woods, Eric
❑ 88WinSpiS-22
❑ 89WinSpiS-18

Woods, Gary
❑ 76TucTorCa-4
❑ 76TusTorCr-3
❑ 77OPC-22
❑ 77Top-492
❑ 78OPC-13
❑ 78SyrChiT-22
❑ 78Top-599
❑ 79ChaChaT-5
❑ 80TucTorT-22
❑ 81AstPos-28
❑ 81Fle-75
❑ 81Top-172
❑ 82CubRedL-25
❑ 82Fle-237
❑ 82Top-483
❑ 82TopTra-130T
❑ 83CubThoAV-25
❑ 83Don-631
❑ 83Fle-512
❑ 83Top-356
❑ 84CubChiT-33
❑ 84CubSev-25
❑ 84Don-144
❑ 84Fle-507
❑ 84Nes792-231
❑ 84Top-231
❑ 84TopTif-231
❑ 85CubLioP-26
❑ 85CubSev-25
❑ 85Don-555
❑ 85Fle-71
❑ 85Lea-49
❑ 85Top-46
❑ 85TopTif-46
❑ 86Fle-385
❑ 86LasVegSP-26
❑ 86Top-611
❑ 86TopTif-611
❑ 87AstShoSPT-30

Woods, George
❑ 49BowPCL-4
❑ 49W72HolS-24
❑ 50W720HolS-32

Woods, Jim
❑ 60Lea-104
❑ 61Top-59

Woods, Kelly
❑ 89PriPirS-25
❑ 89Sta-176

Woods, Kenny
❑ 92EveGiaC-7
❑ 92EveGiaF-1701
❑ 93CliGiaC-25
❑ 93CliGiaF-2503
❑ 94SanJosGC-26
❑ 94SanJosGF-2832
❑ 97ShrCap-27
❑ 97ShrCapB-27
❑ 98ShrCapM-29
❑ 98ShrCapWS-29

Woods, Lyle
❑ 87AncGlaP-41
❑ 89AncGlaP-29

Woods, Parnell
❑ 49RemBre-32
❑ 91PomBlaBPB-2
❑ 97NegLeaPC-5H

Woods, Preston
❑ 88CapCodPPaLP-54

Woods, Ron
❑ 69Top-544
❑ 69YanPhoS-53
❑ 70OPC-253
❑ 70Top-253
❑ 70YanPhoS-36
❑ 71MLBOffS-504
❑ 71OPC-514
❑ 71Top-514
❑ 72Dia-52
❑ 72OPC-82
❑ 72Top-82
❑ 73OPC-531
❑ 73Top-531
❑ 74OPC-377
❑ 74Top-377
❑ 92YanWIZ6-139
❑ 92YanWIZ7-167

Woods, Tony
❑ 83QuaCitCT-22
❑ 84MidCubT-24
❑ 86PitCubP-25
❑ 87MiaMarP-5
❑ 88TamTarS-24
❑ 88WauTimGS-22

Woods, Tyrone
❑ 89JamExpP-2134
❑ 90MidLeaASGS-24
❑ 90RocExpLC-29
❑ 90RocExpP-2709
❑ 91WesPalBEC-29
❑ 91WesPalBEP-1243
❑ 92MidLeaATI-52
❑ 92RocExpC-9
❑ 92RocExpF-2130
❑ 93HarSenF-282
❑ 94OttLynF-2911
❑ 95LinVen-12
❑ 95RocRedWTI-39

Woods, Walter
❑ 09ColChiE-313
❑ 12ColRedB-313
❑ 12ColTinT-313

Woodson, Burquist
❑ 27Zee-128

Woodson, Dick
❑ 70OPC-479
❑ 70Top-479
❑ 71MLBOffS-479
❑ 71OPC-586
❑ 71Top-586
❑ 72Top-634
❑ 72TwiPos-24
❑ 72TwiTeal-17
❑ 73OPC-98
❑ 73Top-98
❑ 74OPC-143
❑ 74Top-143
❑ 78TwiFri-49
❑ 92YanWIZ7-168

Woodson, George
❑ 69Top-244

Woodson, Kerry
❑ 89BelMarL-16
❑ 90Bes-308
❑ 90CalLeaACLC-19
❑ 90CMC-857
❑ 90ProAaA-136
❑ 90SanBerSB-25
❑ 90SanBerSCLC-90
❑ 90SanBerSP-2635
❑ 91Bow-264
❑ 92Bow-411
❑ 92CalCanF-3733
❑ 92DonRoo-127
❑ 92JacSunF-3707
❑ 92JacSunS-373
❑ 92SkyAA F-160
❑ 92TopTraG-132T
❑ 93Don-748
❑ 93FleMajLP-B2
❑ 93Sco-327
❑ 93Top-539
❑ 93TopGol-539
❑ 93TopInaM-539
❑ 93TopInaR-539
❑ 93TopMic-539
❑ 93Ult-275
❑ 93UppDec-388
❑ 93UppDecGold-388
❑ 98ColSprSS-18

Woodson, Tracy
❑ 85VerBeaDT-2
❑ 87AlbDukD-24
❑ 87DodMot-22
❑ 88AlbDukCm-17
❑ 88AlbDukP-256
❑ 88Don-499
❑ 88FleUpd-98
❑ 88FleUpdG-98
❑ 88TriAAAP-3
❑ 89AlbDukCm-16
❑ 89AlbDukP-75
❑ 89DodPol-12
❑ 89Fle-77
❑ 89FleGlo-77
❑ 89Sco-586
❑ 89Top-306
❑ 89TopBig-92
❑ 89TopTif-306
❑ 89UppDec-108
❑ 90CMC-652
❑ 90DodTar-875
❑ 90ProAAAF-176
❑ 90VanCanC-25
❑ 90VanCanP-498
❑ 91LinDriAAA-448
❑ 91RicBraBC-23
❑ 91RicBraLD-448
❑ 91RicBraP-2579
❑ 91RicBraTI-15
❑ 92LouRedF-1896
❑ 92LouRedS-272
❑ 92SkyAAAF-130
❑ 93CarPol-24
❑ 93CarStaC-22
❑ 93Don-652
❑ 93Fle-517
❑ 93PacSpa-638
❑ 93Sco-465
❑ 93Top-457
❑ 93TopGol-457
❑ 93TopInaM-457
❑ 93TopInaR-457
❑ 93TopMic-457
❑ 93UppDec-728
❑ 93UppDecGold-728
❑ 94Fle-650
❑ 94RocRedWF-1007
❑ 95LouRedF-285
❑ 96ColCliB-30
❑ 97CarMudC-27
❑ 98EriSeaWM-27

Woodward, Chris
❑ 96HagSunB-25
❑ 97DunBluJTI-32
❑ 98KnoSG-27

Woodward, Finley
❑ 97NewJerCB-30
❑ 98PeoChiM-26

Woodward, Jim
❑ 82JacMetT-17

Woodward, Matt
❑ 98EveAquG-28

Woodward, Rob
❑ 86DonRoo-53
❑ 86Fle-651
❑ 86PawRedSP-28
❑ 87ClaGam-69
❑ 87Don-652
❑ 87PawRedST-23
❑ 87Top-632
❑ 87TopTif-632
❑ 88PawRedSC-1
❑ 88PawRedSP-448
❑ 88Sco-403
❑ 88ScoGlo-403
❑ 89PawRedSC-10
❑ 89PawRedSP-699
❑ 89PawRedSTI-29
❑ 90CMC-265
❑ 90ProAAAF-460
❑ 90RocRedWC-2
❑ 90RocRedWGC-18
❑ 90RocRedWP-703
❑ 91LinDriAAA-473
❑ 91RocRedWLD-473
❑ 91RocRedWP-1904

Woodward, Vince
❑ 85CloHSS-44

Woodward, Woody (William)
❑ 64Top-378
❑ 65Top-487
❑ 66OPC-49
❑ 66Top-49
❑ 66TopVen-49
❑ 67BraPho-28
❑ 67CokCapB-8
❑ 67DexPre-226
❑ 67Kah-41
❑ 67Top-546
❑ 68CokCapB-8
❑ 68DexPre-75
❑ 68Top-476
❑ 69OPC-142
❑ 69Top-142
❑ 69TopFou-3
❑ 69TopTeaP-20
❑ 70DayDaiNM-83
❑ 70OPC-296
❑ 70Top-296
❑ 71MLBOffS-72
❑ 71OPC-496
❑ 71Top-496
❑ 72MilBra-370

Woodworth, John
❑ 80UtiBluJT-9
❑ 82KnoBluJT-23
❑ 83KnoBluJT-21
❑ 85SyrChiT-10
❑ 86SyrChiP-27
❑ 90DunBluJS-28
❑ 91DunBluJC-30
❑ 92DunBluJC-28
❑ 93DunBluJC-28
❑ 93DunBluJFFN-29
❑ 97SyrSkyCB-30
❑ 98SyrSkyG-31

Wooldridge, Floyd
❑ 77FriOneYW-16

Woolf, Jason
❑ 96PeoChiB-30
❑ 97CarLeaTP-10
❑ 97PriWilC-30
❑ 98ArkTraH-7
❑ 98ArkTraM-1

Woolis, Danny
❑ 85IowCubT-35

Woolridge, Floyd
❑ 55CarHunW-30

Wooten, Daryl
❑ 89AubAstP-2189

Wooten, Earl
❑ 49Bow-189

Wooten, Greg
❑ 96MidLeaAB-8
❑ 96WisTimRB-29
❑ 97SouLeaTP-23
❑ 98SP MinPE-114
❑ 98SPMin-114

Wooten, Junior
❑ 88ChaLooLTI-31

Wooten, Shawn
❑ 90HigSchPLS-14
❑ 93BriTigF-3649
❑ 94ExcFirYPF-9
❑ 94ExcFS7-63
❑ 94FayGenC-26
❑ 94FayGenF-2158
❑ 94Top-448
❑ 94TopGol-448
❑ 94TopSpa-448
❑ 97CedRapK-30
❑ 98LakElsSG-30

Worden, Bill
❑ 82DanSunF-20
❑ 83RedPioT-25
❑ 84NasSouTi-25
❑ 86WatIndP-26

Workman, Michael
❑ 86WatIndP-32
❑ 87KinIndP-14

Workman, Widd
❑ 96IdaFalB-30
❑ 97CliLumG-30
❑ 98RanCucQG-31
❑ 98RanCucQG-31

Works, Ralph
❑ 07TigACDPP-28
❑ 09TigTaCP-20
❑ 10JuJuDE-42
❑ 11PinT-5-154
❑ 11SpoLifM-73
❑ 12T207-205

Worley, Bob
❑ 92BelMarCB-17
❑ 92BelMarF-1445
❑ 93AppFoxCB-25
❑ 93AppFoxFI-2461
❑ 94RivPilCLC-24
❑ 95PorCitRTI-29
❑ 96PorCitRB-28

Worley, Roger
❑ 94SigRooDP-68
❑ 94SigRooDPS-68

Worrell, Steve
❑ 93MidLeaAGF-28
❑ 93SouBenWSC-26
❑ 93SouBenWSF-1432
❑ 94PriWilCC-24
❑ 94PriWilCF-1922
❑ 95PriWilCTI-27

❑ 96BirBarB-19
❑ 97BirBarB-17
❑ 98IowCubQ-29
Worrell, Tim
❑ 91BriBanF-14
❑ 91MidLeaAP-MWL31
❑ 91WatDiaC-10
❑ 91WatDiaP-1257
❑ 92ClaFS7-314
❑ 92SkyAA F-289
❑ 92UppDecML-181
❑ 92WicWraS-631
❑ 93Bow-138
❑ 93ClaFS7-270
❑ 93ClaGolF-49
❑ 93ExcFS7-112
❑ 93FleFinE-148
❑ 93LasVegSF-945
❑ 93Ult-480
❑ 94ColC-434
❑ 94ColChoGS-434
❑ 94ColChoSS-434
❑ 94Don-318
❑ 94Fle-679
❑ 94StaClu-519
❑ 94StaCluFDI-519
❑ 94StaCluGR-519
❑ 94StaCluMOP-519
❑ 94Top-458
❑ 94TopGol-458
❑ 94TopSpa-458
❑ 95PadMot-17
❑ 96FleUpd-U201
❑ 96FleUpdTC-U201
❑ 96PadMot-24
❑ 97Cir-282
❑ 97CirRav-282
❑ 97ColCho-451
❑ 97Fle-473
❑ 97FleTif-473
❑ 97PacPriGotD-GD212
❑ 97PadMot-23
❑ 97Top-392
Worrell, Todd
❑ 83LouRedR-26
❑ 84ArkTraT-6
❑ 85LouRedR-28
❑ 86CarIGAS-14
❑ 86CarKASD-10
❑ 86CarSchM-24
❑ 86CarTeal-45
❑ 86Don-43
❑ 86DonHig-29
❑ 86DonHig-54
❑ 86DonRoo-21
❑ 86Fle-49
❑ 86SevCoi-S15
❑ 86SpoRoo-35
❑ 86TopTra-127T
❑ 86TopTraT-127T
❑ 87CarSmo-2
❑ 87CarTeal-33
❑ 87ClaGam-97
❑ 87Don-307
❑ 87Fle-312
❑ 87FleAll-8
❑ 87FleAwaW-44
❑ 87FleGlo-312
❑ 87FleHotS-44
❑ 87FleLeaL-44
❑ 87FleLimE-43
❑ 87FleMin-119
❑ 87FleRecS-43
❑ 87FleStiC-128
❑ 87Lea-218
❑ 87OPC-67
❑ 87Spo-33
❑ 87Spo-77
❑ 87SpoTeaP-12
❑ 87Top-7
❑ 87Top-465
❑ 87Top-605
❑ 87TopCoi-48
❑ 87TopGaloC-12
❑ 87TopGloS-10
❑ 87TopMinL-34
❑ 87TopRoo-22
❑ 87TopSti-11
❑ 87TopSti-12
❑ 87TopSti-55
❑ 87TopSti-310
❑ 87TopTif-7
❑ 87TopTif-465
❑ 87TopTif-605
❑ 87ToyRoo-33
❑ 87Woo-13
❑ 88Baz-22
❑ 88CarSmo-10
❑ 88CarTeal-36
❑ 88CheBoy-8
❑ 88ClaRed-181
❑ 88Don-386
❑ 88DonBasB-268
❑ 88Fle-50
❑ 88FleGlo-50
❑ 88FleGlo-WS5
❑ 88FleLeaL-44
❑ 88FleMin-111
❑ 88FleRecS-44
❑ 88FleSlu-44
❑ 88FleStiC-122
❑ 88FleWaxBC-C16
❑ 88FleWorS-5
❑ 88K-M-32
❑ 88Lea-229
❑ 88OPC-135
❑ 88PanSti-386
❑ 88Sco-202
❑ 88ScoGlo-202
❑ 88Spo-61
❑ 88StaLinAl-37
❑ 88StaLinCa-20
❑ 88Top-715
❑ 88TopBig-149
❑ 88TopCoi-60
❑ 88TopMinL-73
❑ 88TopSti-54
❑ 88TopTif-715
❑ 88Woo-24
❑ 89Bow-429
❑ 89BowTif-429
❑ 89CadEllD-62
❑ 89CarSmo-24
❑ 89CarTeal-34
❑ 89Don-82
❑ 89DonAll-60
❑ 89DonBasB-243
❑ 89Fle-466
❑ 89FleBasM-44
❑ 89FleGlo-466
❑ 89FleSup-44
❑ 89LouRedBTI-37
❑ 89OPC-291
❑ 89PanSti-179
❑ 89Sco-265
❑ 89ScoHot1S-94
❑ 89Spo-183
❑ 89Top-535
❑ 89TopBasT-154
❑ 89TopMinL-38
❑ 89TopSti-39
❑ 89TopTif-535
❑ 89UppDec-512
❑ 90BasWit-29
❑ 90Bow-185
❑ 90BowTif-185
❑ 90Don-319
❑ 90Fle-264
❑ 90FleCan-264
❑ 90M.Vpin-100
❑ 90MLBBasB-29
❑ 90OPC-95
❑ 90PanSti-340
❑ 90PubIntS-231
❑ 90PubIntS-274
❑ 90Sco-392
❑ 90Spo-165
❑ 90Top-95
❑ 90TopSti-43
❑ 90TopTif-95
❑ 90TopTVCa-22
❑ 90UppDec-467
❑ 91CarPol-38
❑ 91Fle-653
❑ 91LouRedTI-13
❑ 91Sco-807
❑ 92CarMcD-54
❑ 92CarPol-25
❑ 92FleUpd-121
❑ 92Lea-436
❑ 92LeaBlaG-436
❑ 92Pin-479
❑ 92StaClu-703
❑ 92Stu-99
❑ 92Ult-574
❑ 93DodMot-21
❑ 93DodPol-29
❑ 93DodStaC-16
❑ 93Don-72
❑ 93Fle-135
❑ 93FleFinE-87
❑ 93Lea-429
❑ 93OPC-374
❑ 93OPCPre-62
❑ 93Sco-635
❑ 93StaClu-728
❑ 93StaCluFDI-728
❑ 93StaCluMOP-728
❑ 93Top-121
❑ 93TopGol-121
❑ 93TopInaM-121
❑ 93TopInaR-121
❑ 93TopMic-121
❑ 93TriPla-253
❑ 93Ult-409
❑ 93UppDec-692
❑ 93UppDecGold-692
❑ 94ColC-567
❑ 94ColChoGS-567
❑ 94ColChoSS-567
❑ 94DodDaiN-13
❑ 94DodMot-13
❑ 94DodPol-29
❑ 94Don-397
❑ 94Fla-185
❑ 94Fle-530
❑ 94FleExtB-298
❑ 94Lea-362
❑ 94StaClu-612
❑ 94StaCluFDI-612
❑ 94StaCluGR-612
❑ 94StaCluMOP-612
❑ 94Top-611
❑ 94TopGol-611
❑ 94TopSpa-611
❑ 94Ult-221
❑ 95DodMot-18
❑ 95DodPol-29
❑ 95Don-474
❑ 95DonPreP-474
❑ 95DonTopotO-275
❑ 95Emo-147
❑ 95Fla-159
❑ 95Fle-552
❑ 95Lea-334
❑ 95Sco-213
❑ 95ScoGolR-213
❑ 95ScoPlaTS-213
❑ 95StaClu-53
❑ 95StaCluFDI-53
❑ 95StaCluMOP-53
❑ 95StaCluSTWS-53
❑ 95StaCluVR-33
❑ 95StaCluVRMO-33
❑ 95Top-204
❑ 95TopCyb-3
❑ 95Ult-185
❑ 95UltGolM-185
❑ 95UppDec-460
❑ 96ColCho-585
❑ 96ColChoGS-585
❑ 96ColChoSS-585
❑ 96DodFle-18
❑ 96DodMot-25
❑ 96DodPol-30
❑ 96Don-144
❑ 96DonPreP-144
❑ 96EmoXL-217
❑ 96Fla-300
❑ 96Fle-449
❑ 96FleTif-449
❑ 96Pac-110
❑ 96Sco-157
❑ 96StaClu-88
❑ 96StaCluEPB-88
❑ 96StaCluEPG-88
❑ 96StaCluEPS-88
❑ 96StaCluEWB-EW10
❑ 96StaCluEWG-EW10
❑ 96StaCluEWS-EW10
❑ 96StaCluMOP-88
❑ 96Top-412
❑ 96Ult-227
❑ 96UltGolM-227
❑ 96UppDec-358
❑ 97Cir-96
❑ 97CirRav-96
❑ 97ColCho-63
❑ 97ColCho-369
❑ 97ColChoT-LA12
❑ 97DodMot-19
❑ 97DodPol-28
❑ 97Fin-207
❑ 97FinRef-207
❑ 97Fle-373
❑ 97FleTif-373
❑ 97MetUni-107
❑ 97PacPriGotD-GD163
❑ 97Sco-392
❑ 97ScoArtPWB-392
❑ 97ScoResC-392
❑ 97ScoShoS-392
❑ 97ScoShoSAP-392
❑ 97SP-97
❑ 97StaClu-51
❑ 97StaCluMat-51
❑ 97StaCluMOP-51
❑ 97Top-226
❑ 97TopGal-13
❑ 97TopGalPPI-13
❑ 97Ult-387
❑ 97UltGolME-387
❑ 97UltPlaME-387
❑ 97UppDec-91
❑ 97UppDecAWJ-17
❑ 98DodSco-9
❑ 98DodScoP-9
❑ 98Pac-342
❑ 98PacPlaB-342
❑ 98PacRedT-342
❑ 98PacSil-342
❑ 98Sco-128
❑ 98ScoSS-PP54
❑ 98ScoSSAP-PP54
❑ 98Ult-72
❑ 98UltGolM-72
❑ 98UltMas-72
❑ 98UltPlaM-72
❑ 98UppDec-113
Worth, J. W.
❑ 20Zee-100
Wortham, Rich
❑ 80OPC-261
❑ 80Top-502
❑ 81Don-161
❑ 81Fle-347
❑ 81Top-107
❑ 82ReaPhiT-10
❑ 92TexLon-40
Worthington, Al
❑ 50JJKCopP-24
❑ 54NewYorJA-39
❑ 55GiaGolS-14
❑ 57GiaJayP-12
❑ 57Top-39
❑ 58GiaJayP-12
❑ 58GiaSFCB-25
❑ 58Hir-73
❑ 58Top-427
❑ 59Top-28
❑ 59TopVen-28
❑ 60Top-268
❑ 62AmeTraS-66
❑ 63RedEnq-33
❑ 63RedFreBC-31
❑ 63Top-556
❑ 64Top-144
❑ 64TopVen-144
❑ 65OPC-216
❑ 65Top-216
❑ 66OPC-181
❑ 66Top-181
❑ 66TopVen-181
❑ 66TwiFaiG-17
❑ 67CokCapTw-10
❑ 67Top-399
❑ 68Top-473
❑ 72TwiPos-25
❑ 72TwiTeal-18
❑ 73OPC-49
❑ 73Top-49A
❑ 73Top-49B
❑ 78TwiFri-23
❑ 79TCM50-269
❑ 81TCM60I-405
❑ 86TwiGreT-11
Worthington, Bob
❑ 33ButCanV-57
❑ 34TarThoBD-27
Worthington, Craig
❑ 86HagSunP-29
❑ 87IntLeaAT-30
❑ 87RocRedWP-23
❑ 87RocRedWT-17
❑ 88DonRoo-23
❑ 88FleUpd-4
❑ 88FleUpdG-4
❑ 88RocRedWC-19
❑ 88RocRedWGCP-27
❑ 88RocRedWP-217
❑ 88RocRedWTI-26
❑ 88TriAAC-19
❑ 89BalOriP-39
❑ 89Don-569
❑ 89DonBasB-282
❑ 89DonRoo-25
❑ 89Fle-627
❑ 89FleGlo-627
❑ 89OriFreB-11
❑ 89PanSti-252
❑ 89Sco-636
❑ 89ScoHot1R-6
❑ 89ScoYouS2-21
❑ 89Spo-134
❑ 89Top-181
❑ 89TopTif-181
❑ 89UppDec-725
❑ 90Baz-15
❑ 90Bow-253
❑ 90BowTif-253
❑ 90ClaBlu-31
❑ 90Don-141
❑ 90DonBesA-71
❑ 90Fle-195
❑ 90FleCan-195
❑ 90HagSunDGB-35
❑ 90Lea-170
❑ 90OPC-521
❑ 90PanSti-11
❑ 90PubIntS-592
❑ 90Sco-234
❑ 90Sco100RS-21
❑ 90Spo-117
❑ 90Top-521
❑ 90TopBig-146
❑ 90TopGloS-49
❑ 90TopHeaU-22
❑ 90TopRoo-33
❑ 90TopSti-239
❑ 90TopSti-328
❑ 90TopTif-521
❑ 90ToyRoo-32
❑ 90UppDec-444
❑ 91Don-293
❑ 91Fle-496
❑ 91Lea-298
❑ 91OPC-73
❑ 91OriCro-491
❑ 91PanFreS-242
❑ 91PanSti-198
❑ 91Sco-503
❑ 91StaClu-467
❑ 91Top-73
❑ 91TopDesS-73
❑ 91TopMic-73
❑ 91TopTif-73
❑ 91Ult-26
❑ 91UppDec-141
❑ 92ColSprSSF-761
❑ 92ColSprSSS-79
❑ 92Fle-31
❑ 92OPC-397
❑ 92Sco-724
❑ 92StaClu-81
❑ 93IowCubF-2143
❑ 94IowCubF-1284
❑ 95IndIndF-105
❑ 96FleUpd-U92
❑ 96FleUpdTC-U92
❑ 96LeaSigEA-217
❑ 96RanDr P-35
❑ 96RanMot-8
Worthy, Tommy
❑ 96MarPhiB-30
❑ 97BatCliTI-11
Wortman, Chuck (William)
❑ 17ColE13-195
Wortmann, Russ
❑ 82IdaFalAT-15
Wotell, Michael
❑ 13Zee-22
Wotus, Ron
❑ 82BufBisT-11
❑ 84HawIslC-128
❑ 86HawIslP-22
❑ 87OmaRoyP-20
❑ 89PhoFirC-19
❑ 89PhoFirP-1501
❑ 90CliGiaP-2567
❑ 91CalLeLA-47
❑ 91SanJosGC-23
❑ 91SanJosGP-27
❑ 92SanJosGC-26
❑ 93ShrCapF-2775
❑ 94ShrCapF-1622
❑ 96PhoFirB-2
❑ 97PhoFirTI-27
❑ 98GiaMot-28
Woyce, Don
❑ 86Ft.MyeRP-29
Woyt, Boris
❑ 50WorWidGV-29
Wozney, Kevin
❑ 93EriSaiC-26
❑ 93EriSaiF-3118
Wrangler, Wilbur T.
❑ 95WicWraTI-95
❑ 96WicWraB-30
❑ 98WicWraM-30
Wrattan, Irve
❑ 11PinT-5-1056
Wray, David
❑ 94DavLipB-25
❑ 95DavLipB-25
Wray, James
❑ 88GreFalDTI-13
❑ 89BakDodCLC-189
❑ 89CalLeaA-16
❑ 90SanAntMGS-30
❑ 91LinDriAA-550
❑ 91SanAntMLD-550
❑ 91SanAntMP-2977
❑ 92VerBeaDC-15
❑ 92VerBeaDF-2877
Wren, Frank
❑ 80MemChiT-28
Wrenn, Luke
❑ 76ShrCapT-5
❑ 77ShrCapT-23
Wright, Ab
❑ 92ConTSN-407
Wright, Albert
❑ 33Zee-50
❑ 33Zee-51
❑ 37Zee-95
Wright, Barry
❑ 77ModA'sC-2
Wright, Bill
❑ 87IdaFalBP-17
Wright, Bill (Burnis)
❑ 91NegLeaRL-10
❑ 92NegLeaK-12
❑ 93UppDecS-17
❑ 95NegLeaL2-2
❑ 95NegLeaLI-10
Wright, Brian
❑ 89IdaFalBP-2009
Wright, Chris
❑ 97PriDevR-30
❑ 98HudValR-28
Wright, Clarence
❑ 90DodTar-876
Wright, Clyde
❑ 69Top-583
❑ 70OPC-543
❑ 70Top-543
❑ 71AngJacitB-10
❑ 71BazNumT-6
❑ 71BazUnn-24
❑ 71Kel-28A
❑ 71Kel-28B
❑ 71Kel-28C
❑ 71MLBOffS-359
❑ 71OPC-67
❑ 71OPC-240
❑ 71Top-67
❑ 71Top-240
❑ 71TopCoi-60
❑ 71TopGreM-18
❑ 71TopSup-39
❑ 71TopTat-117
❑ 72MilBra-371
❑ 72OPC-55
❑ 72Top-55
❑ 73OPC-373
❑ 73Top-373
❑ 74OPC-525
❑ 74Top-525
❑ 75OPC-408
❑ 75RanPos-37
❑ 75Top-408
❑ 75TopMin-408
❑ 76OPC-559
❑ 76SSP-258
❑ 76Top-559
❑ 86AngGreT-10
❑ 89AngSmo-6
❑ 93RanKee-387
❑ 94BreMilB-281
Wright, Dave
❑ 75ForLauYS-5
❑ 76ForLauYS-19
❑ 77ForLauYS-19
Wright, Don
❑ 87EugEmeP-2675

❑ 88AppFoxP-146
❑ 89AppFoxP-855
❑ 90BasCitRS-27

Wright, Ed (Henderson E.)

❑ 47TipTop-90
❑ 52A'sTeal-29
❑ 52Top-368
❑ 83TopRep5-368

Wright, Ernie

❑ 88MisStaB-35
❑ 89MisStaB-40

Wright, F. Glenn

❑ 25Exh-56
❑ 26Exh-56
❑ 26SpoComoA-48
❑ 26SpoNewSM-11
❑ 28Exh-28
❑ 28W502-47
❑ 28W512-5
❑ 28Yue-47
❑ 31Exh-4
❑ 33ButCre-30
❑ 33ExhFou-2
❑ 33Gou-143
❑ 33GouCanV-77
❑ 34ExhFou-2
❑ 35GouPuzR-4B
❑ 35GouPuzR-7B
❑ 35GouPuzR-12B
❑ 90DodTar-877
❑ 91ConTSN-208

Wright, George

❑ 36Halof FP-24
❑ 39PC7AlbHoF-12
❑ 50CalHOFW-78
❑ 53ArtHaloFP-89
❑ 76ShaPiz-13
❑ 77BobParHoF-53
❑ 77RedCarP-9
❑ 80PerHaloFP-12
❑ 80SSPHOF-12
❑ 84GalHaloFRL-13
❑ 89HOFStiB-15
❑ 94OriofB-25

Wright, George DeWitt

❑ 78AshTouT-29
❑ 79AshTouT-10
❑ 80TulDriT-10
❑ 81TulDriT-1
❑ 83Don-116
❑ 83Fle-583
❑ 83FleSti-160
❑ 83RanAffF-26
❑ 83Top-299
❑ 83TopSti-124
❑ 84AllGamPI-162
❑ 84Don-525
❑ 84Fle-435
❑ 84Nes792-688
❑ 84OPC-314
❑ 84RanJarP-26
❑ 84Top-688
❑ 84TopRubD-21
❑ 84TopSti-353
❑ 84TopTif-688
❑ 85Don-256
❑ 85Fle-574
❑ 85OklCit8T-16
❑ 85OPC-387
❑ 85Top-443
❑ 85TopRubD-21
❑ 85TopTif-443
❑ 86Don-220
❑ 86Fle-578
❑ 86Top-169
❑ 86TopTif-169
❑ 86TopTra-128T
❑ 86TopTraT-128T
❑ 89PhoFirC-24
❑ 89PhoFirP-1484
❑ 93RanKee-388

Wright, Goldie

❑ 83RedPioT-26

Wright, Harry (W. Henry)

❑ 50CalHOFW-79
❑ 53ArtHaloFP-90
❑ 73TCMAllG-20
❑ 75FlePio-2
❑ 76ShaPiz-70
❑ 77BobParHoF-54
❑ 80PerHaloFP-70
❑ 80SSPHOF-70
❑ 83PhiPosGPaM-11
❑ 87OldJudN-550
❑ 90KalBatN-59
❑ 94OriofB-21
❑ 94UppDecTAE-5

Wright, J.P.

❑ 89KenTwiP-1072
❑ 89KenTwiS-24

Wright, James L.

❑ 78PapGinD-18
❑ 79Top-722
❑ 80Top-524
❑ 81SyrChiTI-24
❑ 82Don-490
❑ 82SyrChiT-10
❑ 82Top-362
❑ 97NewHavRB-28
❑ 98NewHavRM-28
❑ 98NewHavRMA-28

Wright, James R.

❑ 79OPC-180
❑ 79Top-349
❑ 80PenPilBT-13
❑ 80PenPilCT-7
❑ 81ReaPhiT-13
❑ 81Top-526
❑ 82Top-362
❑ 86PeoChiP-26
❑ 87PitCubP-5
❑ 87TolMudHT-12
❑ 88IowCubC-25
❑ 88IowCubP-542
❑ 89IowCubC-24
❑ 89IowCubP-1697
❑ 90CMC-249
❑ 90ProAAAF-316
❑ 90ScrRedBC-23
❑ 90ScrRedBP-614
❑ 91LinDriAAA-506
❑ 91ScrRedBP-2557
❑ 92ScrRedBF-2464
❑ 92ScrRedBS-500
❑ 93ScrRedBF-2560
❑ 93ScrRedBTI-29
❑ 94ScrRedBF-937
❑ 95ScrRedBTI-29
❑ 96ScrRedBB-2

Wright, Jamey

❑ 94AshTouC-25
❑ 94AshTouF-1783
❑ 94Bow-58
❑ 94Cla-178
❑ 94ClaGolF-28
❑ 94ClaGolN1PLF-LP18
❑ 94ClaGolREF-RE18
❑ 94Pin-268
❑ 94PinArtP-268
❑ 94PinMusC-268
❑ 94Sco-573
❑ 94ScoGolR-573
❑ 94SigRoo-46
❑ 94SigRooS-46
❑ 94Top-744
❑ 94TopGol-744
❑ 94TopSpa-744
❑ 95Bes-66
❑ 95Bow-181
❑ 95SalAvaTI-10
❑ 95SPML-52
❑ 95UppDecML-188
❑ 95UppDecMLFS-188
❑ 96BesAutSA-91
❑ 96Bow-137
❑ 96BowBes-157
❑ 96BowBesAR-157
❑ 96BowBesMI-9
❑ 96BowBesMIAR-9
❑ 96BowBesMIR-9
❑ 96BowBesR-157
❑ 96BowFoi-137
❑ 96BowMinLP-5
❑ 96ColSprSSTI-32
❑ 96Exc-160
❑ 96NewHavRB-28
❑ 96NewHavRUSTI-21
❑ 97Bow-403
❑ 97BowBes-181
❑ 97BowBesAR-181
❑ 97BowBesR-181
❑ 97BowCerBlaIA-CA87
❑ 97BowCerBluIA-CA87
❑ 97BowCerGolIA-CA87
❑ 97BowChr-266
❑ 97BowChrI-266
❑ 97BowChrIR-266
❑ 97BowChrR-266
❑ 97BowInt-403
❑ 97Cir-279
❑ 97CirRav-279
❑ 97ColCho-18
❑ 97ColChoT-CR8
❑ 97Don-114
❑ 97DonGolPP-114
❑ 97DonSilPP-114
❑ 97DonTea-95
❑ 97DonTeaSPE-95
❑ 97Fin-28
❑ 97FinRef-28
❑ 97FlaShoLC-49
❑ 97FlaShoLeg0-49
❑ 97FlaShoLeg1-49
❑ 97FlaShoM-A49
❑ 97FlaShoM-B49
❑ 97FlaShoM-C49
❑ 97FlaShoR0-49
❑ 97FlaShoR1-49
❑ 97FlaShoR2-49
❑ 97Fle-321
❑ 97FleTif-321
❑ 97Lea-86
❑ 97LeaFraM-86
❑ 97LeaFraMDC-86
❑ 97MetUni-78
❑ 97PacPriGotD-GD139
❑ 97Pin-170
❑ 97PinArtP-PP170
❑ 97PinMusC-170
❑ 97PinPrePla-170
❑ 97RocSco-5
❑ 97RocScoPl-5
❑ 97RocScoPr-5
❑ 97Sco-121
❑ 97ScoArtPWB-121
❑ 97ScoPreS-121
❑ 97ScoShoS-121
❑ 97ScoShoSAP-121
❑ 97SpollI-27
❑ 97SpollIEE-27
❑ 97StaClu-162
❑ 97StaCluMOP-162
❑ 97Stu-29
❑ 97StuPrePG-29
❑ 97StuPrePS-29
❑ 97Top-107
❑ 97TopGal-150
❑ 97TopGalPPI-150
❑ 97Ult-191
❑ 97UltGolME-191
❑ 97UltPlaME-191
❑ 97UppDec-228
❑ 98ColCho-364
❑ 98Fin-69
❑ 98FinNo--69
❑ 98FinNo-R-69
❑ 98FinRef-69
❑ 98Fle-484
❑ 98PacInvGems-149
❑ 98PacOnl-261
❑ 98PacOnlR-261
❑ 98PacOnlWC-261
❑ 98PinSna-CR3
❑ 98StaCluFDI-170
❑ 98StaClul-170
❑ 98StaCluOneK-170
❑ 98StaCluPP-170
❑ 98Top-87
❑ 98TopChr-87
❑ 98TopChrR-87
❑ 98TopDevR-87
❑ 98TopDia-87
❑ 98TopMiniC-87
❑ 98UppDec-82
❑ 99Fle-311
❑ 99FleSta9-311
❑ 99FleWarT-311
❑ 99Pac-155
❑ 99PacPlaB-155
❑ 99PacRed-155
❑ 99Top-197
❑ 99TopChr-197
❑ 99TopChrR-197
❑ 99TopMVPP-197
❑ 99UppDec-364
❑ 99UppDecEL1-364
❑ 99UppDecEL2-364

Wright, Jaret

❑ 94ClaUpdCotC-CC9
❑ 94SigRooDP-10
❑ 94SigRooDPS-10
❑ 95ActPacF-58
❑ 95Exc-45
❑ 95SigRooDDS-DD5
❑ 95SigRooDDSS-DD5
❑ 95SPML-43
❑ 95SPMLA-25
❑ 95UppDecML-201
❑ 95UppDecML-221
❑ 95UppDecMLFS-201
❑ 95UppDecMLFS-221
❑ 96BesAutS-97
❑ 96CarLeaA1B-2
❑ 96CarLeaA2B-2
❑ 96Exc-48
❑ 96KenIndB-27
❑ 97AkrAer-29
❑ 97Bes-14
❑ 97BesAll-4
❑ 97BesAutSBPP-1
❑ 97BesAutSC-10
❑ 97BesCarCSP-9
❑ 97BesGun-9
❑ 97Bow-398
❑ 97BowInt-398
❑ 97DonLim-151
❑ 97DonLimE-151
❑ 97DonLimENG-151
❑ 97DonSigA-114
❑ 97DonSigAC-140
❑ 97DonSigAM-140
❑ 97EasLeaTPB-3
❑ 97Fle-756
❑ 97FleTif-756
❑ 97Sel-194
❑ 97SelCom-194
❑ 98Bow-242
❑ 98BowBes-88
❑ 98BowBesAR-88
❑ 98BowBesR-88
❑ 98BowChr-242
❑ 98BowChrGA-242
❑ 98BowChrGAR-242
❑ 98BowChrI-242
❑ 98BowChrIR-242
❑ 98BowChrR-242
❑ 98BowGolA-242
❑ 98BowInt-242
❑ 98CirThu-85
❑ 98CirThuFT-10
❑ 98CirThuRav-85
❑ 98CirThuSupRav-85
❑ 98ColCho-125
❑ 98ColChoMBH-12
❑ 98ColChoSQ-SQ4
❑ 98ColChoSQDouble-27
❑ 98ColChoSQHR-27
❑ 98ColChoSQSingle-27
❑ 98ColChoSQTriple-27
❑ 98CroRoy-48
❑ 98Don-81
❑ 98Don-385
❑ 98DonCol-81
❑ 98DonCol-192
❑ 98DonColE-493
❑ 98DonColL-378
❑ 98DonColP-699
❑ 98DonColS-81
❑ 98DonColS-187
❑ 98DonEli-93
❑ 98DonEliA-93
❑ 98DonEliS-93
❑ 98DonFANT-15
❑ 98DonFANTDC-15
❑ 98DonGolPP-81
❑ 98DonGolPP-385
❑ 98DonPre-149
❑ 98DonPreGES-8
❑ 98DonPreGX-8
❑ 98DonPreGXDC-8
❑ 98DonPreSeat-149
❑ 98DonPriCD-81
❑ 98DonPriCD-192
❑ 98DonPriCE-493
❑ 98DonPriCL-378
❑ 98DonPriCP-699
❑ 98DonRatR-17
❑ 98DonRatRM-17
❑ 98DonRooDK-6
❑ 98DonRooDKC-6
❑ 98DonSig-99
❑ 98DonSigP-99
❑ 98DonSilPP-81
❑ 98DonSilPP-385
❑ 98E-X2-92
❑ 98E-X2ECFut-92
❑ 98E-X2ECNow-92
❑ 98E-X2SD2001-14
❑ 98E-X2Sig2001-9
❑ 98Fin-22
❑ 98FinCen-C20
❑ 98FinCenR-C20
❑ 98FinNo--22
❑ 98FinNo-R-22
❑ 98FinRef-22
❑ 98FlaShoLeg0-15
❑ 98FlaShoLeg1-15
❑ 98FlaShoLeg2-15
❑ 98FlaShoLeg3-15
❑ 98FlaShoLegM-15
❑ 98FlaShoR0-15
❑ 98FlaShoR1-15
❑ 98FlaShoR2-15
❑ 98FlaShoR3-15
❑ 98Fle-64
❑ 98FleRooS-20
❑ 98FleVin'-18
❑ 98FleVin'C-18
❑ 98IndSco-15
❑ 98IndScoP-15
❑ 98Lea-179
❑ 98LeaFraDA-179
❑ 98LeaFraF-179
❑ 98LeaFraM-179
❑ 98LeaFraMDC-179
❑ 98LeaFraMDC-179
❑ 98LeaFraMZ2-179
❑ 98LeaRCrusUP-112
❑ 98LeaRS-200
❑ 98LeaRSCrusUG-112
❑ 98LeaRSCrusUR-112
❑ 98LeaRSFOSamp-5
❑ 98LeaRSFresh-5
❑ 98LeaRSLHolo-200
❑ 98LeaRSLong-200
❑ 98LeaRTrue-200
❑ 98MetUni-5
❑ 98MetUniPMG-5
❑ 98Pac-82
❑ 98PacAur-36
❑ 98PacAurPF-27
❑ 98PacAurPFC-27
❑ 98PacAurPFPB-27
❑ 98PacAurPFR-27
❑ 98PacAurPFS-27
❑ 98PacInv-29
❑ 98PacInvPBlue-29
❑ 98PacInvSilv-29
❑ 98PacOme-78
❑ 98PacOmeOnIns-8
❑ 98PacOmeR-78
❑ 98PacOnl-235
❑ 98PacOnlR-235
❑ 98PacOnlWC-235
❑ 98PacPar-43
❑ 98PacParC-43
❑ 98PacParG-43
❑ 98PacParHS-43
❑ 98PacParPB-43
❑ 98PacParR-43
❑ 98PacPlaB-82
❑ 98PacRedT-82
❑ 98PacSil-82
❑ 98Pin-163
❑ 98PinArtP-PP66
❑ 98PinIns-132
❑ 98PinInsCE-132
❑ 98PinInsDE-132
❑ 98PinMusC-PP66
❑ 98PinPer-28
❑ 98PinPerPP-28
❑ 98PinPlu-142
❑ 98PinPluAP-PP48
❑ 98PinPluGAP-PP48
❑ 98PinPluMAP-PP48
❑ 98PinPreP-163
❑ 98PinSna-CI3
❑ 98Revo-49
❑ 98RevoShow-8
❑ 98RevoSS-49
❑ 98Sco-252
❑ 98ScoNewS-NS5
❑ 98ScoRT-172
❑ 98ScoRTSS-PP99
❑ 98ScoRTSSAP-PP99
❑ 98ScoRTSSAP1-PP99
❑ 98SelSelSamp-10
❑ 98SkyDugA-63
❑ 98SkyDugAIA-63
❑ 98SP Aut-76
❑ 98SP Aut-SD3
❑ 98SP AutC-JW
❑ 98SP AutSD-SD3
❑ 98SP AutSDT-SD3
❑ 98SpollI-128
❑ 98SpollIEE-128
❑ 98SpollIFE-128
❑ 98SpollITaN-141
❑ 98SpollITaNEE-141
❑ 98SpollIWSF-140
❑ 98SpollIWSFEE-140
❑ 98SpollIWSFFE-140
❑ 98SPxFin-5
❑ 98SPxFinR-5
❑ 98SPxFinS-5
❑ 98StaCluC-CS32
❑ 98StaCluC-CS34
❑ 98StaCluC-CS36
❑ 98StaCluFDI-191
❑ 98StaClul-191
❑ 98StaCluOneK-191
❑ 98StaCluPP-191
❑ 98Stu-190
❑ 98StuGPP-190
❑ 98StuPor8x10-30
❑ 98StuPor8x10GP-30
❑ 98StuSPP-190
❑ 98Top-432
❑ 98TopChr-432
❑ 98TopChrR-432
❑ 98TopDevR-432
❑ 98TopDia-432
❑ 98TopGal-38
❑ 98TopGalGP-38
❑ 98TopGalOPP-38
❑ 98TopGalPPI-38
❑ 98TopGalPPIA-38
❑ 98TopMiniC-432
❑ 98UD3-18
❑ 98UD3-108
❑ 98UD3-198
❑ 98UD3DieCut-18
❑ 98UD3DieCut-108
❑ 98UD3DieCut-198
❑ 98Ult-325
❑ 98Ult-488
❑ 98UltGolM-325
❑ 98UltGolM-488
❑ 98UltMas-325
❑ 98UltMas-488
❑ 98UltMilM-15
❑ 98UltPlaM-325
❑ 98UltPlaM-488
❑ 98UltRoctS-14
❑ 98UltTop3-25
❑ 98UppDec-267
❑ 98UppDec-415
❑ 98UppDec-429
❑ 98UppDec-604
❑ 98UppDecAC-AS9
❑ 98UppDecBCP-BC6
❑ 98UppDecDS-DS5
❑ 98UppDecR-110
❑ 98UppDecRNF-NF10
❑ 98UppDecSF-150
❑ 98Zen-82
❑ 98Zen5 xx7-69
❑ 98Zen5x7GoldImp-69
❑ 98Zen5x7Imp-69
❑ 98ZenRooT-13
❑ 98ZenZ-G-82
❑ 98ZenZ-S-82
❑ 99199Fin-67
❑ 99Bow-46
❑ 99BowChr-46
❑ 99BowChrG-46
❑ 99BowChrGR-46
❑ 99BowChrI-46
❑ 99BowChrIR-46
❑ 99BowChrR-46
❑ 99BowGol-46
❑ 99BowInt-46
❑ 99E-X Cen-44
❑ 99E-X CenECFut-44
❑ 99E-X CenECNow-44
❑ 99FinGolRef-67
❑ 99FinRef-67
❑ 99FlaShoLeg1-46
❑ 99FlaShoLeg2-46
❑ 99FlaShoLeg3-46
❑ 99FlaShoLegM1-46
❑ 99FlaShoLegM2-46
❑ 99FlaShoLegM3-46
❑ 99FlaShoR1-46
❑ 99FlaShoR2-46
❑ 99FlaShoR3-46
❑ 99Fle-251
❑ 99FleBri-14
❑ 99FleBri2G-14
❑ 99FleBriBlu-14
❑ 99FleBriGol-14
❑ 99FleSta9-251

❑ 99FleWarT-251
❑ 99MetUni-190
❑ 99MetUniGM-190
❑ 99MetUniPMG-190
❑ 99Pac-138
❑ 99PacOme-79
❑ 99PacOmeC-79
❑ 99PacOmeG-79
❑ 99PacOmePB-79
❑ 99PacPlaB-138
❑ 99PacPriS-50
❑ 99PacPriS206-50
❑ 99PacPriS206R-50
❑ 99PacPriSP-50
❑ 99PacPriSV-50
❑ 99PacRed-138
❑ 99SkyThu-39
❑ 99SkyThuRant-39
❑ 99SkyThuRave-39
❑ 99SP Aut-30
❑ 99SpoIll-115
❑ 99StaClu-216
❑ 99StaCluFDI-216
❑ 99StaCluOoaK-216
❑ 99StaCluPP-216
❑ 99ThuSkySupR-39
❑ 99Top-112
❑ 99TopChr-112
❑ 99TopChrR-112
❑ 99TopMVPP-112
❑ 99TopOpeD-66
❑ 99UD Ion-24
❑ 99UD IonR-24
❑ 99Ult-62
❑ 99UltGolM-62
❑ 99UltMas-62
❑ 99UltPlaM-62
❑ 99UppDec-83
❑ 99UppDecBD-28
❑ 99UppDecBDD-28
❑ 99UppDecBDMN-M23
❑ 99UppDecBDMNE-M23
❑ 99UppDecBDQ-28
❑ 99UppDecBDT-28
❑ 99UppDecCL-117
❑ 99UppDecCLCC-117
❑ 99UppDecE-26
❑ 99UppDecEFXG-26
❑ 99UppDecEL1-83
❑ 99UppDecEL2-83
❑ 99UppDecEM-MC10
❑ 99UppDecEMFXG-MC10
❑ 99UppDecM-67
❑ 99UppDecMGS-67
❑ 99UppDecMHFS-67
❑ 99UppDecMP-67
❑ 99UppDecMSS-67
❑ 99UppDecO-54
❑ 99UppDecOSO-54
❑ 99UppDecR-26
❑ 99UppDecRG-26
❑ 99UppDecRP-26
❑ 99Vic-122

Wright, Jesse
❑ 77ModA'sC-6

Wright, Ken
❑ 70RoyTeal-38
❑ 71OPC-504
❑ 71oySigST-29
❑ 71Top-504
❑ 72oyTeal-27
❑ 72Top-638
❑ 73OPC-578
❑ 73Top-578
❑ 76QuaCitAT-40
❑ 77QuaCitAT-29
❑ 92YanWIZ7-169

Wright, Larry
❑ 78CliDodT-33
❑ 79CliDodT-22
❑ 80AppFoxT-10

Wright, Margie
❑ 91FreStaLBS-12

Wright, Mark
❑ 80BatTroT-30
❑ 81WisRapTT-11
❑ 82WisRapTF-6

Wright, Mel
❑ 73OPC-517
❑ 73Top-517A
❑ 73Top-517B
❑ 76HouAstP-32
❑ 78AstPos-28
❑ 81AstPos-29
❑ 81AstPos-30
❑ 82AstPos-29
❑ 83ExpPos-39
❑ 83ExpStu-25

Wright, Mike
❑ 79QuaCitCT-1

Wright, Mitch
❑ 79NewCoPT-21

Wright, Paul
❑ 82RedPioT-17

Wright, Ricky (Richard)
❑ 81AlbDukTc-7
❑ 82AlbDukTc-11
❑ 83DodPol-21
❑ 83Fle-226
❑ 85OklCit8T-9
❑ 86RanPer-24
❑ 86TopTra-129T
❑ 86TopTraT-129T
❑ 87TolMudHP-6
❑ 87Top-202
❑ 87Top-656
❑ 87TopTif-202
❑ 87TopTif-656
❑ 90DodTar-878
❑ 92TexLon-41
❑ 93RanKee-389

Wright, Ron
❑ 95Bes-56
❑ 95MacBraTI-30
❑ 95MacBraUTI-6
❑ 96Bow-337
❑ 96BowFoi-337
❑ 96CarLeaA1B-12
❑ 96CarLeaA2B-12
❑ 96CarLeaA2B-25
❑ 96CarLeaAIB-B3
❑ 96DurBulBlB-27
❑ 96DurBulBrB-30
❑ 96Exc-135
❑ 96ExcTL-10
❑ 96GreBraB-30
❑ 96GreBraTI-16
❑ 96Top-424
❑ 97Bes-33
❑ 97Bow-165
❑ 97BowCerBlaIA-CA88
❑ 97BowCerBluIA-CA88
❑ 97BowCerGolIA-CA88
❑ 97BowChr-161
❑ 97BowChrI-161
❑ 97BowChrIR-161
❑ 97BowChrR-161
❑ 97BowInt-165
❑ 97CalCanB-30
❑ 97Top-489
❑ 98Bow-395
❑ 98BowBes-129
❑ 98BowBesAR-129
❑ 98BowBesR-129
❑ 98BowChr-395
❑ 98BowChrGA-395
❑ 98BowChrGAR-395
❑ 98BowChrI-395
❑ 98BowChrIR-395
❑ 98BowChrR-395
❑ 98BowGolA-395
❑ 98BowInt-395
❑ 98Don-297
❑ 98DonColP-708
❑ 98DonGolPP-297
❑ 98DonPre-158
❑ 98DonPreSeat-158
❑ 98DonPriCP-708
❑ 98DonSilPP-297
❑ 98LeaRCrusUP-114
❑ 98LeaRS-282
❑ 98LeaRSCrusUG-114
❑ 98LeaRSCrusUR-114
❑ 98LeaRSLHolo-282
❑ 98LeaRSLong-282
❑ 98LeaRTrue-282
❑ 98NasSouTI-33
❑ 98NasSouTISS-31
❑ 98SP MinDTSPE-DS13
❑ 98SP MinPE-98
❑ 98SPMin-98
❑ 98SPMinDTS-DS13
❑ 98Stu-192
❑ 98StuGPP-192
❑ 98StuSPP-192
❑ 98UppDec-583
❑ 98UppDecDS-DS37

Wright, Scott
❑ 95BilMusTI-12
❑ 97BurBeeB-26
❑ 98BurBeeM-26

Wright, Skipper
❑ 88SumBraP-404
❑ 89BurBraP-1626
❑ 89BurBraS-26
❑ 89Sta-112
❑ 90CarLeaA-27
❑ 90DurBulTI-11

Wright, Steve
❑ 98EveAquG-29

Wright, Taft
❑ 39WhiSoxTI-23
❑ 40PlaBal-186
❑ 40WhiSoxL-24
❑ 41Gou-10
❑ 41PlaBal-32
❑ 47Exh-244
❑ 47TipTop-30
❑ 48WhiSoxTI-29
❑ 49A'sTeal-33
❑ 49Bow-96
❑ 49PhiBul-59
❑ 83TCMPla1942-17

Wright, Terry
❑ 94ButCopKSP-1
❑ 96DurBulBrB-10
❑ 96Exc-150

Wright, Thomas
❑ 50RedSoxTI-29
❑ 51Bow-271
❑ 54Top-140
❑ 55Top-141
❑ 55TopDouH-75
❑ 94TopArc1-140
❑ 94TopArc1G-140

Wright, Wayne
❑ 26Zee-37
❑ 27Zee-20

Wright, William S.
❑ 09T206-474

Wrightstone, Russell
❑ 21Exh-191
❑ 21Nei-61
❑ 22E120-210
❑ 22W573-141
❑ 26Exh-48
❑ 27AmeCarE126-43
❑ 27Exh-24
❑ 91ConTSN-238

Wrigley, Charles
❑ 30SchR33-9

Wrigley, Phil
❑ 31CubTeal-29
❑ 76ChiGre-20

Wrigley, William
❑ 31CubTeal-30
❑ 32CubTeal-27

Wrigley, Zeke
❑ 90DodTar-1097

Wrona, Bill
❑ 86BeaGolGP-25
❑ 88WicPilRD-21
❑ 89LasVegSC-19
❑ 89LasVegSP-18
❑ 90CMC-91
❑ 90IowCubC-16
❑ 90IowCubP-328
❑ 90ProAAAF-635
❑ 90TopTVCu-65

Wrona, Dave
❑ 88CapCodPPaLP-39
❑ 90BelBreS-24
❑ 91BelBreCB-23
❑ 91BelBreP-2113
❑ 91Cla/Bes-213
❑ 92CalLeaACL-6
❑ 92StoPorC-8
❑ 92StoPorF-45

Wrona, Rick
❑ 86WinSpiP-28
❑ 87PitCubP-17
❑ 88BlaYNPRWL-157
❑ 89DonRoo-38
❑ 90Don-512
❑ 90OPC-187
❑ 90Sco-557
❑ 90Sco100RS-73
❑ 90Top-187
❑ 90TopTif-187
❑ 90TopTVCu-21
❑ 90UppDec-582
❑ 91Sco-519
❑ 92NasSouF-1835
❑ 92NasSouS-298
❑ 93NasSouF-572
❑ 93StaClu-64
❑ 93StaCluFDI-64
❑ 93StaCluMOP-64
❑ 94BreMilB-374
❑ 96ScrRedBB-27
❑ 97BirBarB-6
❑ 98OklRedM-17

Wrona, Ron
❑ 76BurBeeT-33
❑ 77HolMilT-25
❑ 78SpoIndC-17

Wuerch, Jason
❑ 92GulCoaYF-3800
❑ 93GreHorC-26
❑ 93GreHorF-902
❑ 94SanBerSC-24
❑ 94SanBerSF-2773
❑ 95GreBatTI-27

Wuertz, Mike
❑ 98WilCubM-26

Wuffli, John
❑ 12Zee-134
❑ 13Zee-128
❑ 16Zee-122

Wulf, Eric
❑ 93KanCouCC-25
❑ 93KanCouCF-920
❑ 93KanCouCTI-29

Wulfemeyer, Mark
❑ 75QuaCitAT-19

Wulfert, Mark
❑ 96CliLumKTI-29

Wunsch, Kelly
❑ 94BelBreC-1
❑ 94BelBreFl-103
❑ 94BrePol-5
❑ 94ClaGolF-20
❑ 94ClaGolN1PLF-LP19
❑ 94ClaGolREF-RE19
❑ 94Top-210
❑ 94TopGol-210
❑ 94TopSpa-210
❑ 95UppDecML-103
❑ 95UppDecML-173
❑ 95UppDecMLFS-103
❑ 95UppDecMLFS-173
❑ 96SigRooOJ-37
❑ 96SigRooOJS-37
❑ 97CalLeaTP-27
❑ 97StoPor-11
❑ 97StoPor-25
❑ 99BasAmeTP-99
❑ 99BasAmeTPG-99

Wurm, Garry
❑ 89BoiHawP-2005
❑ 90EriSaiS-28

Wuthrich, David
❑ 88PocGiaP-2074

Wyatt, Ben
❑ 96DanBraB-30
❑ 97EugEmeB-16
❑ 98MacBraM-25

Wyatt, Chuck
❑ 91BilMusP-3754
❑ 91BilMusSP-10

Wyatt, Cortez
❑ 94WilCubC-25
❑ 94WilCubF-3766

Wyatt, Dave
❑ 83LynMetT-19
❑ 85LynMetT-10
❑ 86TidTidP-29
❑ 87TidTidP-14
❑ 87TidTidT-9

Wyatt, John T.
❑ 63Top-376
❑ 64Top-108
❑ 64TopVen-108
❑ 65OldLonC-39
❑ 65Top-590
❑ 66Top-521
❑ 67Top-261
❑ 67TopRedSS-24
❑ 68CokCapRS-4
❑ 68DexPre-76
❑ 68TigDetFPB-28
❑ 68Top-481
❑ 73Dod194T-32
❑ 78TCM60I-159
❑ 81RedSoxBG2S-127
❑ 83A'sGreT-11
❑ 92YanWIZ6-140

Wyatt, Porter
❑ 78NewWayCT-45

Wyatt, Reggie
❑ 84MemChiT-6

Wyatt, Whit (John W.)
❑ 36GouWidPPR-A116
❑ 36OveCanR-48
❑ 39PlaBal-95
❑ 40DodTeal-25
❑ 40PlaBal-67
❑ 41DouPlaR-13
❑ 41Gou-18
❑ 41PlaBal-55
❑ 42DodTeal-25
❑ 43DodTeal-25
❑ 47PM1StaP1-224
❑ 60BraLaktL-28
❑ 60BraSpiaS-26
❑ 66BraPos-27
❑ 67BraPho-29
❑ 78DodTCM4-34
❑ 79DiaGre-281
❑ 83TCMPla1943-30
❑ 89DodSmoG-43
❑ 90DodTar-879
❑ 91DodRinP3-3

Wyczawski, Paul
❑ 91MisStaB-54
❑ 92MisStaB-49

Wyde, Rich
❑ 91EveGiaC-17

Wykle, David
❑ 89TenTecGE-31

Wylie, John
❑ 91BoiHawC-14
❑ 91BoiHawP-3881
❑ 92BoiHawC-12
❑ 92BoiHawF-3629
❑ 92PalSprAC-7

Wylie, Mitch
❑ 98BriWhiSQ-30
❑ 99TeaBesR-100
❑ 99TeaBesRG-100
❑ 99TeaBesRS-100

Wyman, Richie
❑ 95TenVolW-12

Wynegar, Butch
❑ 77BurCheD-53
❑ 77ChiWilD-67
❑ 77DailsID-67
❑ 77DetCaeD-67
❑ 77HolInnD-67
❑ 77Hos-84
❑ 77Kel-56
❑ 77MSADis-67
❑ 77OPC-176
❑ 77PepGloD-3
❑ 77RCColC-67
❑ 77SagDis-67
❑ 77sDis-67
❑ 77Top-175
❑ 77WenDis-67
❑ 77ZipDis-67
❑ 78Hos-37
❑ 78OPC-104
❑ 78RCColC-10
❑ 78Top-555
❑ 78TwiFriP-24
❑ 79BasPat-98
❑ 79Hos-141
❑ 79OPC-214
❑ 79Top-405
❑ 79TwiFriP-28
❑ 80OPC-159
❑ 80Top-304
❑ 80TwiPos-31
❑ 81AllGamPI-45
❑ 81Don-529
❑ 81Fle-558
❑ 81OPC-61
❑ 81Top-61
❑ 81TopSti-102
❑ 81TwiPos-32
❑ 82Don-508
❑ 82Dra-32
❑ 82Fle-565
❑ 82OPC-222
❑ 82Top-222
❑ 82TopSti-208
❑ 82TopTra-131T
❑ 82TwiPos-31
❑ 82YanPhoA-27
❑ 83Don-325
❑ 83Fle-399
❑ 83OPC-379
❑ 83Top-617
❑ 83TopSti-101
❑ 83YanPhoA-27
❑ 84AllGamPI-135
❑ 84Don-458
❑ 84Fle-144
❑ 84Nes792-123
❑ 84OPC-123
❑ 84Top-123
❑ 84TopSti-321
❑ 84TopTif-123
❑ 85AllGamPI-45
❑ 85Don-417
❑ 85DonActA-45
❑ 85Fle-147
❑ 85Lea-165
❑ 85OPC-28
❑ 85Top-585
❑ 85TopSti-316
❑ 85TopTif-585
❑ 85YanTCMP-23
❑ 86Don-274
❑ 86Fle-122
❑ 86Lea-147
❑ 86OPC-235
❑ 86Top-235
❑ 86TopSti-299
❑ 86TopTif-235
❑ 86YanTCM-19
❑ 87AngSmo-10
❑ 87CalAngPPS-40
❑ 87DonOpeD-6
❑ 87OPC-203
❑ 87Top-464
❑ 87TopTif-464
❑ 88AngSmo-23
❑ 88Sco-355
❑ 88ScoGlo-355
❑ 88Top-737
❑ 88TopClo-120
❑ 88TopTif-737
❑ 89Sco-140
❑ 92YanWIZ8-205
❑ 94AlbPolC-27
❑ 94AlbPolF-2254

Wyngarden, Brett
❑ 92AubAstC-15
❑ 92AubAstF-1358
❑ 94LakTigF-3041

Wynn, Early
❑ 49Bow-110
❑ 49IndTeal-27
❑ 50Bow-148
❑ 50IndNumN-22
❑ 50IndTeal-25
❑ 51Bow-78
❑ 51FisBakL-31
❑ 51TopRedB-8
❑ 52Bow-142
❑ 52IndNumN-6
❑ 52RedMan-AL24
❑ 52Top-277
❑ 53BowC-146
❑ 53IndPenCBP-30
❑ 53RedMan-AL14
❑ 53Top-61
❑ 54Bow-164
❑ 54DanDee-29
❑ 55Bow-38
❑ 55IndCarBL-11
❑ 55IndGolS-3
❑ 55RedMan-AL14
❑ 55RobGouS-14
❑ 55RobGouW-14
❑ 56Top-187
❑ 57IndSoh-18
❑ 57IndTeal-29
❑ 57Top-40
❑ 58Top-100A
❑ 58Top-100B
❑ 58WhiSoxJP-12
❑ 59Top-260
❑ 60ArmCoi-20
❑ 60Baz-28
❑ 60NuHi-71
❑ 60RawGloT-36
❑ 60Top-1
❑ 60TopTat-55
❑ 60TopVen-1
❑ 60WhiSoxJP-12
❑ 60WhiSoxTS-22
❑ 61NuSco-471
❑ 61Pos-22A
❑ 61Pos-22B
❑ 61Top-50
❑ 61Top-337
❑ 61Top-455
❑ 61TopStal-131
❑ 61WhiSoxTS-20
❑ 62Jel-55
❑ 62Pos-55
❑ 62PosCan-55
❑ 62SalPlaC-97A

❑ 62SalPlaC-97B
❑ 62ShiPlaC-97
❑ 62Top-385
❑ 62TopBuc-95
❑ 62TopStal-30
❑ 62WhiSoxJP-12
❑ 62WhiSoxTS-22
❑ 63BasMagM-87
❑ 63Jel-43
❑ 63Pos-43
❑ 67TwiTeal-25
❑ 70Houof J-33
❑ 70SpoCarfCOP-5
❑ 75TCM195Cl-36
❑ 75TCM195Cl-39
❑ 75TCMHouoJ-35
❑ 76LauDiaJ-23
❑ 76ShaPiz-133
❑ 77GalGloG-36
❑ 77SerSta-25
❑ 79BasGre-66
❑ 79TCM50-20
❑ 80Lau300-26
❑ 80PacLeg-73
❑ 80PerHaloFP-133
❑ 80PerHaloFPS-20
❑ 80SSPHOF-133
❑ 81WhiSox1T-27
❑ 82OhiHaloF-22
❑ 82TCMGreP-23
❑ 82TCMStaot5-12
❑ 83DonHOFH-42
❑ 83TopRep5-277
❑ 84OCoandSI-94
❑ 84OCoandSI-194
❑ 84OCoandSI-206
❑ 85TCMPla1-10
❑ 85WhiSoxC-30
❑ 86SpoDecG-36
❑ 88PacLegI-95
❑ 89SweBasG-60
❑ 90PerGreM-82
❑ 91TopArc1-61
❑ 92BazQua5A-5
❑ 93ActPacA-112
❑ 93ActPacA2-46G
❑ 98SpollITaN-36
❑ 98SpollITaNEE-36

Wynn, Jim
❑ 59WilSpoG-8
❑ 64Col.45JP-12
❑ 64Top-38
❑ 64TopCoi-2
❑ 64TopVen-38
❑ 65OPC-257
❑ 65Top-257
❑ 66Baz-35
❑ 66Top-520
❑ 66TopRubI-99
❑ 67Ast-30
❑ 67AstTeal1-12
❑ 67AstTeal2-24
❑ 67Baz-35
❑ 67Top-390
❑ 67TopGiaSU-24
❑ 67TopVen-316
❑ 68Baz-11
❑ 68CokCapA-17
❑ 68DexPre-77
❑ 68OPC-5
❑ 68Top-5
❑ 68Top-260
❑ 68TopActS-11C
❑ 68TopGamI-24
❑ 68TopPla-24
❑ 68TopPos-8
❑ 68TopVen-5
❑ 68TopVen-260
❑ 69MLBOffS-144
❑ 69MLBPin-60
❑ 69Top-360
❑ 69TopDec-11B
❑ 69TopDecI-47
❑ 69TopSta-40
❑ 69TopSup-43
❑ 69TopTeaP-6
❑ 69TraSta-41
❑ 70AstPho-28
❑ 70AstTeal-12
❑ 70DayDaiNM-26
❑ 70Kel-9
❑ 70MLBOffS-48
❑ 70OPC-60
❑ 70Top-60
❑ 70TopCanL-24
❑ 70TopScr-23
❑ 70TopSup-35
❑ 70TraSta-4B
❑ 71AstCok-12
❑ 71AstTeal-24
❑ 71BazNumT-43
❑ 71MLBOffS-96
❑ 71OPC-565
❑ 71Top-565
❑ 71TopCoi-69
❑ 71TopGreM-31
❑ 72AstTeal-29
❑ 72MilBra-372
❑ 72Top-770
❑ 73OPC-185
❑ 73Top-185
❑ 74OPC-43
❑ 74Top-43
❑ 74TopSta-40
❑ 74TopTra-43T
❑ 75Hos-25
❑ 75HosTwi-25
❑ 75OPC-570
❑ 75Top-570
❑ 75TopMin-570
❑ 76AtlBraP-34
❑ 76BlaDis-68
❑ 76BucDis-68
❑ 76CarDis-68
❑ 76CraDis-68
❑ 76DailsID-68
❑ 76Hos-129
❑ 76IsaDis-68
❑ 76OPC-395
❑ 76OrbDis-68
❑ 76RedBarD-68
❑ 76SafDis-68
❑ 76SSP-89
❑ 76Top-395
❑ 76TowCluD-68
❑ 77Top-165
❑ 77YanBurK-20
❑ 86AstGreT-5
❑ 86AstMot-7
❑ 87AstSer1-23
❑ 87AstSer1-28
❑ 87AstShoSO-25
❑ 87AstShoSTw-26
❑ 87AstShoSTw-27
❑ 87DodSmoA-39
❑ 88DodSmo-20
❑ 89DodSmoG-86
❑ 90DodTar-880
❑ 92DodStaTA-13
❑ 92UppDecS-8
❑ 92YanWIZ7-170
❑ 93ActPacA-156
❑ 93UppDecS-21
❑ 94BreMilB-375
❑ 94MCIAmb-4
❑ 99SpollIGotG-27
❑ 99SpollIGotGA-79
❑ 99SpollIGotGC-27

Wynne, Billy
❑ 70Top-618
❑ 71MLBOffS-360
❑ 71OPC-718
❑ 71Top-718
❑ 91MetWIZ-436

Wynne, Jim
❑ 91JamExpC-18
❑ 91JamExpP-3546
❑ 92AlbPolCB-13
❑ 92AlbPolF-2307

Wynne, Marvell
❑ 82TidTidT-16
❑ 83TidTidT-21
❑ 84Don-508
❑ 84Fle-269
❑ 84JacMetF-14
❑ 84Nes792-173
❑ 84Pir-27
❑ 84Top-173
❑ 84TopSti-135
❑ 84TopTif-173
❑ 85AllGamPI-162
❑ 85Don-113
❑ 85Fle-481
❑ 85Lea-233
❑ 85OPC-86
❑ 85Pir-23
❑ 85Top-615
❑ 85TopMin-615
❑ 85TopSti-131
❑ 85TopTif-615
❑ 86Don-113
❑ 86Fle-625
❑ 86FleUpd-130
❑ 86OPC-293
❑ 86Top-525
❑ 86TopSti-128
❑ 86TopTif-525
❑ 87Don-411
❑ 87DonOpeD-144
❑ 87Fle-435
❑ 87FleGlo-435
❑ 87PadBohHB-16
❑ 87Top-37
❑ 87TopTif-37
❑ 88Don-237
❑ 88OPCBoxB-H
❑ 88PadSmo-31
❑ 88Sco-209
❑ 88ScoGlo-209
❑ 88StaLinPa-14
❑ 88Top-454
❑ 88TopTif-454
❑ 88TopWaxBC-H
❑ 89Don-347
❑ 89DonBasB-189
❑ 89Fle-322
❑ 89FleGlo-322
❑ 89PadPos-36
❑ 89PanSti-205
❑ 89Sco-203
❑ 89Top-353
❑ 89TopSti-107
❑ 89TopTif-353
❑ 89UppDec-154
❑ 90CubMar-26
❑ 90Don-255
❑ 90Lea-270
❑ 90OPC-256
❑ 90PubInt-63
❑ 90Sco-337
❑ 90Top-256
❑ 90TopTif-256
❑ 90TopTVCu-35
❑ 90UppDec-14
❑ 91Fle-441
❑ 91OPC-714
❑ 91Sco-531
❑ 91Top-714
❑ 91TopDesS-714
❑ 91TopMic-714
❑ 91TopTif-714

Wyrick, Chris
❑ 93BriTigC-26
❑ 93BriTigF-3656

Wyrostek, John
❑ 48Bow-44
❑ 49Bow-37
❑ 49EurSta-99
❑ 49Lea-19
❑ 50Bow-197
❑ 51Bow-107
❑ 51R42SmaS-116
❑ 51TopBluB-44
❑ 52Bow-42
❑ 52NatTeaL-41
❑ 52Top-13
❑ 53BowBW-35
❑ 53Top-79
❑ 55Bow-237
❑ 83TopRep5-13
❑ 85TCMPla1-35
❑ 91TopArc1-79

Wyse, Henry
❑ 43CubTeal-24
❑ 44CubTeal-24
❑ 47TipTop-119
❑ 50A'sTeal-28
❑ 51Bow-192
❑ 79DiaGre-108
❑ 83TCMPla1944-34

Wyszynski, Dennis
❑ 79WatA'sT-5
❑ 80WesHavWCT-2

Wzorek, Larry
❑ 97OmaRoyB-27
❑ 98OmaRoyM-27

X, Malcolm
❑ 93Pin-302

Xavier, Joe
❑ 86ModA'sC-21
❑ 87HunStaTI-25
❑ 88TacTigC-25
❑ 88TacTigP-613
❑ 89DenZepC-21
❑ 89DenZepP-53
❑ 90CMC-32
❑ 90DenZepC-7
❑ 90DenZepP-636
❑ 90ProAAAF-661

Yacopino, Ed
❑ 87MacPirP-20
❑ 88SalBucS-24
❑ 89HarSenP-291
❑ 89HarSenS-22
❑ 90HarSenP-1207
❑ 90HarSenS-22
❑ 91CarMudLD-122
❑ 91CarMudP-1099
❑ 91LinDriAA-122
❑ 92RocRedWF-1954
❑ 92RocRedWS-473
❑ 93RocRedWF-256

Yaeger, Chuck
❑ 86AlbYanT-20

Yaeger, Edward
❑ 52LavPro-41

Yagi, Richard
❑ 88FreSunCLC-14
❑ 88FreSunP-1239

Yahmann, Jim
❑ 88JacExpB-24

Yahrling, Charles
❑ 52LavPro-48

Yamada, Tsutoma
❑ 92CalLeaACL-13
❑ 92SalSpuC-19
❑ 92SalSpuF-3757

Yamaguchi, Yuji
❑ 89SalSpuCLC-133
❑ 89SalSpuP-1813

Yamamoto, Kazunori
❑ 87JapPlaB-40

Yamamoto, Koji
❑ 79TCMJapPB-8

Yamamoto, Masahiro
❑ 88FloStaLAS-26
❑ 88SanJosGCLC-140
❑ 88SanJosGP-117
❑ 88VerBeaDS-26

Yamano, Mickey
❑ 86SanJosBP-24
❑ 87SanJosBP-11

Yamanouchi, Kenichi
❑ 90SalSpuCLC-140
❑ 90SalSpuP-2724

Yamashita, Daisuke
❑ 79TCMJapPB-7

Yamauchi, Kazuhiro
❑ 79TCMJapPB-90

Yamazaki, Hiroyuki
❑ 79TCMJapPB-16

Yamazaki, Kazu (Kazuharu)
❑ 92NiaFalRF-3325

Yamazaki, Kazuharu
❑ 92NiaFalRC-7
❑ 96HilStaHWB-16

Yampierre, Eddie
❑ 81WauTimT-12

Yan, Esteban
❑ 93DanBraC-29
❑ 93DanBraF-3619
❑ 94MacBraC-26
❑ 94MacBraF-2207
❑ 96BowBayB-27
❑ 97RocRedW-29
❑ 98Bow-434
❑ 98BowChr-434
❑ 98BowChrGA-434
❑ 98BowChrGAR-434
❑ 98BowChrI-434
❑ 98BowChrIR-434
❑ 98BowChrR-434
❑ 98BowGolA-434
❑ 98BowInt-434
❑ 98DevRayP-11
❑ 98Don-313
❑ 98DonGolPP-313
❑ 98DonSilPP-313
❑ 98Fle-425
❑ 98LeaRS-206
❑ 98LeaRSLHolo-206
❑ 98LeaRSLong-206
❑ 98LeaRTrue-206
❑ 98PacOmeRS-9
❑ 98PacOmeRST4-9
❑ 98PacOnl-724
❑ 98PacOnlR-724
❑ 98PacOnlWC-724
❑ 98PinSna-TBDR11
❑ 98ScoRT-146
❑ 98Stu-29
❑ 98StuGPP-29
❑ 98StuSPP-29
❑ 99Fle-568
❑ 99FleSta9-568
❑ 99FleWarT-568
❑ 99MetUni-51
❑ 99MetUniGM-51
❑ 99MetUniPMG-51
❑ 99PacCroC-279
❑ 99PacCroCPB-279
❑ 99UppDec-501
❑ 99UppDecEL1-501
❑ 99UppDecEL2-501

Yan, Julian
❑ 87MyrBeaBJP-1435
❑ 88DunBluJS-23
❑ 88FloStaLAS-52
❑ 89DunBluJS-24
❑ 89Sta-118
❑ 90Bes-148
❑ 90KnoBluJB-13
❑ 90KnoBluJP-1253
❑ 90KnoBluJS-22
❑ 91KnoBluJLD-373
❑ 91KnoBluJP-1777
❑ 91LinDriAA-373
❑ 92KnoBluJF-3001
❑ 92KnoBluJS-398
❑ 92SkyAA F-169
❑ 93LimRocDWB-134
❑ 93SyrChiF-1008
❑ 94MedHatBJF-3699
❑ 94MedHatBJSP-27
❑ 94SyrChiF-980
❑ 94SyrChiTI-29
❑ 96VerExpB-4

Yan, Roberto
❑ 82DayBeaAT-9

Yanagida, Shikato
❑ 90CalLeaACLC-44
❑ 90SalSpuCLC-139
❑ 90SalSpuP-2723

Yancey, William
❑ 78LauLonABS-30
❑ 86NegLeaF-88

Yancy, Hugh
❑ 77IndIndTI-22
❑ 79TacTugT-10

Yandle, John
❑ 80HawIsIT-12
❑ 81HolMilT-6

Yandrick, Jerry
❑ 77ChaPatT-25

Yanes, Eddie
❑ 86VisOakP-24
❑ 87OrlTwiP-19
❑ 88OrlTwiB-4

Yanez, Luis
❑ 96AubDouB-9
❑ 97QuaCitRBB-29

Yang, Chang
❑ 95BatCliTI-6

Yang, Charles
❑ 91DaiDolF-12

Yankees, Ft. Lauderdale
❑ 75ForLauYS-29

Yankees, Gulf Coast
❑ 92GulCoaYF-3708

Yankees, New York
❑ 13FatT20-5
❑ 36R31Pre-G25
❑ 38BasTabP-48
❑ 48ExhTea-4
❑ 48ExhTea-6
❑ 48ExhTea-8
❑ 48ExhTea-10
❑ 48ExhTea-14
❑ 48ExhTea-16
❑ 57Top-97
❑ 58Top-246
❑ 59Top-510
❑ 60NuHi-61
❑ 60Top-332
❑ 60TopTat-70
❑ 61Top-228
❑ 61TopMagR-2
❑ 61Yan61RL-1
❑ 62Top-251
❑ 63Top-247
❑ 64Top-433
❑ 64TopTatI-15
❑ 65Top-513
❑ 66OPC-92
❑ 66Top-92
❑ 66TopRubI-115
❑ 66TopVen-92
❑ 67OPC-131
❑ 67Top-131
❑ 67YanPhoS-88
❑ 68LauWorS-24
❑ 68LauWorS-33
❑ 68LauWorS-35
❑ 68LauWorS-39
❑ 68LauWorS-47
❑ 68LauWorS-48
❑ 68LauWorS-57
❑ 68LauWorS-59
❑ 69FleCloS-16
❑ 69FleCloS-48
❑ 69TopStaA-16
❑ 70FleWorS-19
❑ 70FleWorS-24
❑ 70FleWorS-33
❑ 70FleWorS-36
❑ 70FleWorS-38
❑ 70FleWorS-39
❑ 70FleWorS-40
❑ 70FleWorS-47
❑ 70FleWorS-48
❑ 70FleWorS-53
❑ 70FleWorS-57
❑ 70FleWorS-59
❑ 70OPC-399
❑ 70Top-399
❑ 71FleWorS-20
❑ 71FleWorS-25
❑ 71FleWorS-36
❑ 71FleWorS-37
❑ 71FleWorS-39
❑ 71FleWorS-40
❑ 71FleWorS-41
❑ 71FleWorS-45
❑ 71FleWorS-51
❑ 71FleWorS-54
❑ 71FleWorS-58
❑ 71FleWorS-60
❑ 71FleWorS-61
❑ 71FleWorS-62
❑ 71OPC-543
❑ 71Top-543
❑ 71TopTat-25
❑ 72OPC-237
❑ 72Top-237
❑ 73FleWilD-10
❑ 73OPC-556
❑ 73OPCBTC-17
❑ 73Top-556
❑ 73TopBluTC-17
❑ 74OPC-363
❑ 74OPCTC-17
❑ 74Top-363
❑ 74TopStaA-16
❑ 74TopStaA-17
❑ 74TopTeaC-17
❑ 75YanDyn1T-50
❑ 76OPC-17
❑ 77Spo-522
❑ 78SSP270-22
❑ 78Top-282
❑ 78YanSSPD-22
❑ 83FleSta-241
❑ 83FleSti-NNO
❑ 83FleSti-NNO
❑ 87SpoTeaL-7
❑ 88PanSti-464
❑ 88RedFolSB-125
❑ 89FleWaxBC-C18
❑ 89YanScoNW-33
❑ 90PubIntS-646
❑ 90RedFolSB-121
❑ 93TedWilPC-10
❑ 94ImpProP-10
❑ 94Sco-326
❑ 94ScoGolR-326
❑ 95PacPriTL-10
❑ 95PanSti-144
❑ 96PanSti-155
❑ 97ColChoT-NY
❑ 98SpollIWSFEE-19
❑ 98SpollIWSFFE-19
❑ 98YanPin-1
❑ 98YanPin-2
❑ 99E-XCenMotC-9
❑ 99SpollI-1
❑ 99Vic-262

Yano, Minoru
❑ 96MauStiHWB-1

Yantz, George
❑ 14Zee-77

Yanus, Bud
❑ 80MemChiT-29
❑ 83MemChiT-12
❑ 86WesPalBEP-28

❑ 87WesPalBEP-662
Yanz, Eric
❑ 97SpoIndG-31
❑ 98LanLugQ-13
Yarbrough, Buddy
❑ 77DayBeaIT-27
Yard, Bruce
❑ 93YakBeaC-26
❑ 93YakBeaF-3893
❑ 95BakBlaTI-22
❑ 96SanAntMB-26
❑ 96VerBeaDB-29
❑ 97VerBeaD-30
Yarnall, Ed
❑ 97St.LucM-29
❑ 98Bes-100
❑ 98BesAutSS-53
❑ 98BesBet-12
❑ 98BesCor-12
❑ 98BinMetQ-29
❑ 98Bow-322
❑ 98BowChr-322
❑ 98BowChrGA-322
❑ 98BowChrGAR-322
❑ 98BowChrI-322
❑ 98BowChrIR-322
❑ 98BowChrR-322
❑ 98BowGolA-322
❑ 98BowInt-322
❑ 99Bow-342
❑ 99BowAut-BA17
❑ 99BowGol-342
❑ 99BowInt-342
❑ 99SP TopP-125
❑ 99SP TopPC-EY
❑ 99SP TopPDtS-D10
❑ 99SP TopPGF-GF10
❑ 99SP TopPPE-125
❑ 99TeaBesRBG-10
Yaroshuk, Ernie
❑ 92OneYanC-3
❑ 93OneYanC-26
❑ 93OneYanF-3519
Yarrison, Rube
❑ 23Zee-79
❑ 26Zee-38
❑ 90DodTar-1099
Yaryan, Clarence
❑ 22E120-30
❑ 23WilChoV-178
❑ 23Zee-178
Yastrzemski, Carl
❑ 47Exh-245
❑ 47PM1StaP1-225
❑ 47PM1StaP1-226
❑ 60Top-148
❑ 60TopVen-148
❑ 61Top-287
❑ 61TopStaI-119
❑ 62Jel-61
❑ 62Pos-61
❑ 62PosCan-61
❑ 62RedSoxJP-11
❑ 62SalPlaC-27
❑ 62ShiPlaC-27
❑ 62Top-425
❑ 62TopBuc-96
❑ 62TopStaI-20
❑ 63Baz-16
❑ 63Fle-8
❑ 63Jel-80
❑ 63Pos-80
❑ 63Top-115
❑ 63TopStiI-46
❑ 64Baz-16
❑ 64ChatheY-50
❑ 64RedSoxTI-8
❑ 64Top-8
❑ 64Top-182
❑ 64Top-210
❑ 64TopCoi-26
❑ 64TopCoi-134
❑ 64TopGia-48
❑ 64TopSta-23
❑ 64TopStaU-77
❑ 64TopTatI-75
❑ 64TopVen-8
❑ 64TopVen-182
❑ 64TopVen-210
❑ 64WheSta-50
❑ 65ChaTheY-48
❑ 65OldLonC-40
❑ 65RedSoxTI-16
❑ 65Top-385
❑ 65TopEmbI-1
❑ 65TopTraI-36
❑ 66Baz-22
❑ 66OPC-70
❑ 66RedSoxTI-16
❑ 66Top-70
❑ 66Top-216
❑ 66TopRubI-100
❑ 66TopVen-70
❑ 66TopVen-216
❑ 67Baz-22
❑ 67CokCapA-17
❑ 67CokCapRS-2
❑ 67DexPre-227
❑ 67DexPre-228
❑ 67OPCPapI-5
❑ 67Top-355
❑ 67TopGiaSU-21
❑ 67TopPos-5
❑ 67TopRedSS-25
❑ 67TopRedSS-29
❑ 67TopTesF-23
❑ 67TopVen-193
❑ 68AtlOilPBCC-50
❑ 68Baz-2
❑ 68OPC-2
❑ 68OPC-4
❑ 68OPC-6
❑ 68OPC-152
❑ 68OPC-192
❑ 68Top-2
❑ 68Top-4
❑ 68Top-6
❑ 68Top-152
❑ 68Top-192A
❑ 68Top-192B
❑ 68Top-250
❑ 68Top-369
❑ 68TopActS-1B
❑ 68TopActS-6A
❑ 68TopActS-13B
❑ 68TopGamI-3
❑ 68TopPla-12
❑ 68TopPos-16
❑ 68TopVen-2
❑ 68TopVen-4
❑ 68TopVen-6
❑ 68TopVen-152
❑ 68TopVen-192
❑ 68TopVen-250
❑ 68TopVen-369
❑ 69KelPin-20
❑ 69MLBPin-30
❑ 69OPC-1
❑ 69OPC-130
❑ 69OPCDec-24
❑ 69RedSoxAO-12
❑ 69RedSoxTI-12
❑ 69RedSoxTI-10
❑ 69Top-1
❑ 69Top-130
❑ 69Top-425
❑ 69TopDec-4
❑ 69TopDecI-48
❑ 69TopFou-25
❑ 69TopSta-140
❑ 69TopSup-5
❑ 69TopTeaP-3
❑ 69TraSta-19
❑ 70DayDaiNM-28
❑ 70MLBOffS-168
❑ 70OPC-10
❑ 70OPC-461
❑ 70RedSoxCPPC-16
❑ 70Top-10
❑ 70Top-461
❑ 70TopCanL-23
❑ 70TopScr-24
❑ 70TopSup-29
❑ 70TraSta-13A
❑ 71AllBasA-24
❑ 71BazNumT-5
❑ 71BazUnn-23
❑ 71MLBOffS-336
❑ 71MLBOffS-576
❑ 71OPC-61
❑ 71OPC-65
❑ 71OPC-530
❑ 71RedSoxA-12
❑ 71RedSoxTI-12
❑ 71Top-61
❑ 71Top-65
❑ 71Top-530
❑ 71TopCoi-58
❑ 71TopGreM-40
❑ 71TopSup-49
❑ 71TopTat-13
❑ 71TopTat-14
❑ 72OPC-37
❑ 72OPC-38
❑ 72RedSoxTI-23
❑ 72SevTraC-60
❑ 72Top-37
❑ 72Top-38
❑ 72TopPos-2
❑ 73LinPor-32
❑ 73OPC-245
❑ 73SevTraC-80
❑ 73Top-245
❑ 73TopCanL-55
❑ 73TopCom-24
❑ 73TopPin-24
❑ 74LauAllG-70
❑ 74OPC-280
❑ 74Top-280
❑ 74TopDecE-43
❑ 74TopPuz-12
❑ 74TopSta-140
❑ 75Hos-48
❑ 75Kel-51
❑ 75OPC-205
❑ 75OPC-280
❑ 75SSP42-23
❑ 75Top-205
❑ 75Top-280
❑ 75TopMin-205
❑ 75TopMin-280
❑ 76BlaDis-69
❑ 76BucDis-69
❑ 76CarDis-69
❑ 76CraDis-69
❑ 76DailsID-69
❑ 76Hos-149
❑ 76IsaDis-69
❑ 76Kel-24
❑ 76LauDiaJ-9
❑ 76LinSup-102
❑ 76OPC-230
❑ 76OrbDis-69
❑ 76RedBarD-69
❑ 76RedSox-9
❑ 76RedSoxSM-16
❑ 76SafDis-69
❑ 76SSP-409
❑ 76Top-230
❑ 76TowCluD-69
❑ 77BurCheD-36
❑ 77ChiWilD-68
❑ 77DailsID-68
❑ 77DetCaeD-68
❑ 77HolInnD-68
❑ 77Hos-4
❑ 77MSADis-68
❑ 77OPC-37
❑ 77PepGloD-23
❑ 77RCColC-68
❑ 77SagDis-68
❑ 77sDis-68
❑ 77Spo-3003
❑ 77Spo-5408
❑ 77Top-434
❑ 77Top-480
❑ 77TopCloS-53
❑ 77WenDis-68
❑ 77ZipDis-68
❑ 78OPC-137
❑ 78PapGinD-8
❑ 78Pep-39
❑ 78SagDis-16
❑ 78SSP270-187
❑ 78TasDis-16
❑ 78Top-40
❑ 78WifBalD-78
❑ 79BasPat-99
❑ 79Kel-45
❑ 79OPC-160
❑ 79Top-320
❑ 79TopCom-3
❑ 80Kel-27
❑ 80OPC-365
❑ 80PerHaloFP-204
❑ 80PerHaloFPS-67
❑ 80Top-1
❑ 80Top-720
❑ 80TopSup-22
❑ 81AllGamPI-72
❑ 81CokTeaS-11
❑ 81Don-94
❑ 81Don-214
❑ 81Dra-1
❑ 81Fle-221
❑ 81Fle-638
❑ 81FleStiC-13
❑ 81Kel-48
❑ 81OPC-110
❑ 81PerCreC-4
❑ 81RedSoxBG2S-65
❑ 81RedSoxBG2S-66
❑ 81RedSoxBG2S-128
❑ 81Top-110
❑ 81TopSti-45
❑ 81TopSupHT-12
❑ 82Don-74
❑ 82Fle-312
❑ 82Fle-633
❑ 82FleSta-162
❑ 82FleSta-237
❑ 82K-M-11
❑ 82Kel-43
❑ 82OPC-72
❑ 82OPC-358
❑ 82PerCreC-13
❑ 82PerCreCG-13
❑ 82RedSoxC-22
❑ 82Top-650
❑ 82Top-651
❑ 82TopSti-120
❑ 82TopSti-155
❑ 83AllGamPI-9
❑ 83Don-25
❑ 83Don-326
❑ 83DonActA-44
❑ 83Dra-32
❑ 83Fle-200
❑ 83Fle-629
❑ 83FleSta-221
❑ 83FleSti-60
❑ 83FraBroR-19
❑ 83Kel-9
❑ 83Oco& SSBG-19
❑ 83OPC-4
❑ 83OPC-126
❑ 83PerCreC-35
❑ 83PerCreCG-35
❑ 83Top-550
❑ 83Top-551
❑ 83TopFol-2
❑ 83TopGloS-1
❑ 83TopSti-6
❑ 83TopSti-31
❑ 84Don-B
❑ 84DonCha-10
❑ 84Fle-412
❑ 84Fle-640
❑ 84FleSti-97
❑ 84Nes792-6
❑ 84OCoandSI-10
❑ 84OCoandSI-124
❑ 84OCoandSI-170
❑ 84SpoDesPW-18
❑ 84Top-6
❑ 84TopGloA-11
❑ 84TopTif-6
❑ 85CirK-17
❑ 85TCMPhoC-21
❑ 86RedSoxGT-9
❑ 86SpoDecG-47
❑ 86SpoDesJM-3
❑ 86TCMSupS-10
❑ 86TCMSupS-41
❑ 87K-M-11
❑ 87Top-314
❑ 87TopTif-314
❑ 89KahComC-3
❑ 89KahCoo-11
❑ 89PerCelP-44
❑ 89TopBasT-33
❑ 90AGFA-2
❑ 90BasWit-34
❑ 90Col-12
❑ 90Don-588
❑ 90HOFStiB-71
❑ 90PacLeg-61
❑ 90PerGreM-72
❑ 90PerMasW-46
❑ 90PerMasW-47
❑ 90PerMasW-48
❑ 90PerMasW-49
❑ 90PerMasW-50
❑ 90SweBasG-5
❑ 90TopGloA-22
❑ 91SweBasG-108
❑ 92ScoFacI-B15
❑ 92ScoFacI-B16
❑ 92ScoFacI-B17
❑ 92ScoFra-3
❑ 92ScoFra-4
❑ 92ScoFra-AU3
❑ 92ScoFra-AU4
❑ 92UppDecS-6
❑ 92Zip-4
❑ 93Pin-297
❑ 93SelTriC-2
❑ 93TedWil-7
❑ 93TedWilLC-8
❑ 93UppDecS-6
❑ 94CarLeaA-DJ1
❑ 94UppDecS-10
❑ 94Yoo-16
❑ 94Yoo-16A
❑ 95JimDeaAG-6
❑ 95TopLegot6M-6
❑ 97DonSigSS-22
❑ 97HigMinMCT-52
❑ 97HigMinMCT-53
❑ 98TopStaRR-5
❑ 98TopStaRRA-5
❑ 99SpoIllGotG-8
❑ 99SpoIllGotGA-80
❑ 99SpoIllGotGC-14
❑ 99SpoIllGotGC-15
Yastrzemski, Mike
❑ 84DurBulT-3
❑ 85DurBulT-32
❑ 86BirBarTI-17
❑ 86SouLeaAJ-2
❑ 87HawIsIP-1
❑ 88VanCanC-19
❑ 88VanCanP-774
❑ 89BirBarADB-32
❑ 90BirBarADB-32
Yasuda, Hideyuki
❑ 91CalLeLA-40
❑ 91SalSpuC-3
❑ 91SalSpuP-2248
Yates, Al
❑ 94BreMilB-91
Yates, Chris
❑ 98AubDouTI-31
Yates, Lance
❑ 90OklSoo-20
Yates, Lyle
❑ 98AubDouTI-32
Yates, Peter
❑ 91DaiDolF-9
❑ 93AusFut-40
Yaughn, Kip
❑ 89AriStaB-28
❑ 91CarLeaAP-CAR10
❑ 91FreKeyC-11
❑ 91FreKeyP-2365
❑ 92HagSunF-2558
❑ 92HagSunS-273
❑ 92SkyAA F-116
❑ 93Top-669
❑ 93TopGol-669
❑ 93TopInaM-669
❑ 93TopInaR-669
❑ 93TopMic-669
❑ 94PorSeaDF-678
❑ 94PorSeaDTI-30
Yawkey, Mrs. (Tom)
❑ 79RedSoxEF-2
❑ 79RedSoxEF-11
Yawkey, Tom
❑ 59FleWil-42
❑ 80PerHaloFP-173
❑ 80SSPHOF-173
❑ 89HOFStiB-93
Ybarra, Jamie
❑ 95KanCouCTI-38
Yde, Emil
❑ 26SpoComoA-49
❑ 32Zee-18
❑ 92ConTSN-546
Yeager Jr., Gary
❑ 95BatCliTI-33
❑ 96PieBolWB-29
❑ 97ClePhi-25
❑ 98ClePhiM-26
❑ 98ClePhiUM-26
Yeager, Eric
❑ 85AncGlaPTI-32
❑ 86AncGlaPTI-37
❑ 87AncGlaP-32
Yeager, Joe (Joseph F.)
❑ 03BreE10-156
❑ 09ColChiE-314
❑ 11SpoLifCW-375
❑ 12ColRedB-314
❑ 12ColTinT-314
❑ 12ImpTobC-84
❑ 90DodTar-881
Yeager, Steve
❑ 73OPC-59
❑ 73Top-59
❑ 74OPC-593
❑ 74Top-593
❑ 75OPC-376
❑ 75Top-376
❑ 75TopMin-376
❑ 76Hos-147
❑ 76LinSup-118
❑ 76OPC-515
❑ 76SSP-83
❑ 76Top-515
❑ 77BurCheD-151
❑ 77DodPho-15
❑ 77OPC-159
❑ 77Top-105
❑ 78Hos-51
❑ 78SSP270-73
❑ 78Top-285
❑ 79DodBlu-13
❑ 79OPC-31
❑ 79Top-75
❑ 80DodPol-7
❑ 80OPC-371
❑ 80Top-726
❑ 81AllGamPI-135
❑ 81Dod-33
❑ 81DodPol-7
❑ 81DodPos-11
❑ 81Don-297
❑ 81Fle-129
❑ 81LonBeaPT-19
❑ 81OPC-318
❑ 81Top-318
❑ 81TopSupHT-54
❑ 82DodPol-7
❑ 82DodPos-10
❑ 82DodUniOV-26
❑ 82Don-201
❑ 82Fle-29
❑ 82OPC-219
❑ 82Top-477
❑ 82TopSti-259
❑ 83DodPol-7
❑ 83DodPos-20
❑ 83Don-201
❑ 83Fle-227
❑ 83OPC-261
❑ 83Top-555
❑ 84AllGamPI-45
❑ 84DodPol-7
❑ 84Don-581
❑ 84Fle-117
❑ 84Nes792-661
❑ 84OPC-252
❑ 84Top-661
❑ 84TopSti-86
❑ 84TopTif-661
❑ 85DodCokP-34
❑ 85Don-519
❑ 85Fle-390
❑ 85OPC-148
❑ 85Top-148
❑ 85TopMin-148
❑ 85TopTif-148
❑ 86Don-519
❑ 86FleUpd-131
❑ 86MarMot-5
❑ 86MarPacNB-15
❑ 86OPC-32
❑ 86Top-32
❑ 86TopTif-32
❑ 86TopTra-130T
❑ 86TopTraT-130T
❑ 87Fle-599
❑ 87FleGlo-599
❑ 87OPC-258
❑ 87Top-258
❑ 87TopTif-258
❑ 89MajLeaM-9
❑ 89MajLeaM-11
❑ 90DodTar-882
Yeargin, James
❑ 25Zee-146
Yearout, Mike
❑ 86KnoBluJP-26
❑ 87KnoBluJP-1496
Yedo, Carlos
❑ 94OneYanC-25
❑ 95GreBatTI-24
❑ 96TamYanY-28
❑ 97TamYan-32
Yeglinski, John
❑ 75LafDriT-10
❑ 77ArkTraT-11A
❑ 77ArkTraT-11B
Yelding, Eric

❑ 85KinBluJT-23
❑ 86VenGulP-28
❑ 87KnoBluJP-1505
❑ 88SyrChiC-17
❑ 88SyrChiP-832
❑ 88TriAAAP-37
❑ 89AstLenH-12
❑ 89AstMot-21
❑ 89AstSmo-39
❑ 89DonRoo-34
❑ 89ScoHot1R-65
❑ 90AstLenH-27
❑ 90AstMot-24
❑ 90ClaYel-T58
❑ 90Don-123
❑ 90DonBesN-114
❑ 90FleLeaL-42
❑ 90FleLeaLC-42
❑ 90FleUpd-18
❑ 90Hot50RS-49
❑ 90Lea-301
❑ 90OPC-309
❑ 90Sco-411
❑ 90Sco100RS-16
❑ 90ScoYouSI-15
❑ 90Top-309
❑ 90TopBig-317
❑ 90TopDeb89-148
❑ 90TopTif-309
❑ 90UppDec-427
❑ 91AstMot-7
❑ 91Bow-557
❑ 91ClaGam-71
❑ 91Don-277
❑ 91Fle-520
❑ 91Lea-100
❑ 91OPC-59
❑ 91PanCanT1-42
❑ 91PanFreS-12
❑ 91PanSti-13
❑ 91RedFolS-103
❑ 91Sco-329
❑ 91StaClu-16
❑ 91Top-59
❑ 91TopDesS-59
❑ 91TopMic-59
❑ 91TopTif-59
❑ 91Ult-141
❑ 91UppDec-197
❑ 92Don-148
❑ 92RedFolS-102
❑ 92Sco-197
❑ 92StaClu-2
❑ 92TucTorF-502
❑ 92TucTorS-623
❑ 92UppDec-394
❑ 93CubMar-32
❑ 93PacSpa-129
❑ 94Fle-403
❑ 94IowCubF-1289
❑ 94StaCluT-337
❑ 94StaCluTFDI-337

Yelle, Archie
❑ 20Zee-119
❑ 21Zee-135
❑ 22Zee-114
❑ 23Zee-153
❑ 23Zee-154
❑ 24Zee-112
❑ 25Zee-127
❑ 26Zee-156
❑ 27Zee-84

Yellen, Larry
❑ 64Top-226
❑ 64TopVen-226
❑ 65Top-292

Yellowhorse, Moses
❑ 21Exh-192
❑ 23Zee-100
❑ 24Zee-75

Yelovic, John
❑ 43CenFlo-25

Yelton, Rob
❑ 91BriTigC-7
❑ 91BriTigP-3610
❑ 92FayGenC-15
❑ 92FayGenF-2173
❑ 93LakTigF-1315

Yennaco, Jay
❑ 96MicBatCB-29
❑ 97SarRedS-26
❑ 98Bes-50
❑ 98Bow-361
❑ 98BowChr-361
❑ 98BowChrGA-361
❑ 98BowChrGAR-361
❑ 98BowChrl-361
❑ 98BowChrIR-361
❑ 98BowChrR-361
❑ 98BowGolA-361
❑ 98BowInt-361
❑ 98EasLeaTPM-30
❑ 98TreThuM-25

Yerkes, Carroll
❑ 28Zee-102
❑ 31Zee-24

Yerkes, Stephen
❑ 12T207-206
❑ 14TexTomE-49
❑ 14TexTomE-63
❑ 15SpoNewM-197
❑ 16SpoNewM-196
❑ 17ColE13-196

Yesenchak, Ed
❑ 76AppFoxT-27
❑ 77AppFoxT-29

Yeske, Kyle
❑ 92BluOriC-2
❑ 92BluOriF-2374
❑ 93AlbPolCB-22
❑ 93AlbPolF-2041
❑ 94AlbPolC-26
❑ 94AlbPolF-2253

Yeskie, Nate
❑ 97ForWayW-29
❑ 98ForMyeMTI-31

Yett, Rich
❑ 81WisRapTT-12
❑ 83OrlTwiT-15
❑ 84TolMudHT-5
❑ 85FleUpd-131
❑ 85TolMudHT-30
❑ 85TwiPos-33
❑ 85TwiTeal-27
❑ 85TwiTeal-28
❑ 86IndOhH-42
❑ 86IndTeal-52
❑ 86MaiGuiP-26
❑ 87Fle-263
❑ 87FleGlo-263
❑ 87IndGat-42
❑ 87Top-134
❑ 87TopTif-134
❑ 88BlaYNPRWL-190
❑ 88Fle-621
❑ 88FleGlo-621
❑ 88IndGat-42
❑ 88IndTeal-40
❑ 88Sco-484
❑ 88ScoGlo-484
❑ 88Top-531
❑ 88TopTif-531
❑ 89Bow-79
❑ 89BowTif-79
❑ 89Don-546
❑ 89Fle-417
❑ 89FleGlo-417
❑ 89IndTeal-27
❑ 89Sco-467
❑ 89Top-363
❑ 89TopBig-290
❑ 89TopTif-363
❑ 89UppDec-728
❑ 90Bow-412
❑ 90BowTif-412
❑ 90CMC-563
❑ 90Don-509
❑ 90Fle-504
❑ 90FleCan-504
❑ 90OPC-689
❑ 90PorBeaC-11
❑ 90PubIntS-570
❑ 90Sco-274
❑ 90Top-689
❑ 90TopTif-689
❑ 90UppDec-595

Yi, Jiao
❑ 90IBAWorA-21

Yingling, Don
❑ 67VanMouSO-27

Yingling, Earl
❑ 11PinT-5-1102
❑ 17ColE13-197
❑ 90DodTar-1100

Yippee, Mascot
❑ 86JamExpP-30

Ynclan, Rocky
❑ 87HawRai-24

Yobs, Dave
❑ 82GleFalWST-13
❑ 85BufBisT-16
❑ 86BufBisP-26

Yochim, Ray
❑ 49EurSta-200

Yockey, Mark
❑ 90EveGiaB-12
❑ 90EveGiaP-3128
❑ 91CliGiaC-10
❑ 91CliGiaP-835
❑ 92ShrCapF-3873
❑ 92ShrCapS-598
❑ 93ShrCapF-2761
❑ 94PorSeaDF-679
❑ 94PorSeaDTI-31

Yocum, David
❑ 95Bes-120
❑ 96Bow-269
❑ 96BowFoi-269
❑ 96Exc-183
❑ 96SigRooOJPP-P8
❑ 96SigRooOJPPS-P8
❑ 96Top-236
❑ 96VerBeaDB-30

Yoder, Jason
❑ 98BriBluM-29

Yoder, Jeff
❑ 96Bow-299
❑ 96BowFoi-299
❑ 96RocCubTI-32
❑ 97Bow-214
❑ 97BowInt-214
❑ 98Bow-392
❑ 98BowChr-392
❑ 98BowChrGA-392
❑ 98BowChrGAR-392
❑ 98BowChrl-392
❑ 98BowChrIR-392
❑ 98BowChrR-392
❑ 98BowGolA-392
❑ 98BowInt-392
❑ 99Bow-176
❑ 99BowChr-176
❑ 99BowChrG-176
❑ 99BowChrGR-176
❑ 99BowChrl-176
❑ 99BowChrIR-176
❑ 99BowChrR-176
❑ 99BowGol-176
❑ 99BowInt-176

Yoder, Kris
❑ 76WilTomT-22
❑ 78RicBraT-18
❑ 79SavBraT-13

Yoder, P.J. (Paul)
❑ 95PitMetTI-20
❑ 96PitMetB-29

Yogi, Great
❑ 76LauIndC-35

Yojo, Minoru
❑ 89VisOakCLC-115
❑ 89VisOakP-1424

Yokota, George
❑ 86SanJosBP-25

Yonamine, Wally
❑ 79TCMJapPB-89

York, Anthony
❑ 44CubTeal-25
❑ 47CenFlo-32
❑ 47SigOil-89
❑ 49BowPCL-22

York, Charles
❑ 92WatIndC-9
❑ 92WatIndF-3236
❑ 93ColRedC-26
❑ 93ColRedF-599
❑ 93SouAtlLAGF-16
❑ 94ClaGolF-46
❑ 94KinIndC-22
❑ 94KinIndF-2645
❑ 95BakBlaTI-21

York, Jim
❑ 70AstPho-29
❑ 71oySigST-30
❑ 72AstTeal-30
❑ 72OPC-68
❑ 72Top-68
❑ 73OPC-546
❑ 73Top-546
❑ 75AstPos-30
❑ 75OPC-383
❑ 75Top-383
❑ 75TopMin-383
❑ 76OPC-224
❑ 76Top-224
❑ 87AstShoSPT-31
❑ 87AstShoSTw-19
❑ 92YanWIZ7-171

York, Mike
❑ 86LakTigP-25
❑ 87MacPirP-7
❑ 88SalBucS-25
❑ 89HarSenP-310
❑ 89HarSenS-23
❑ 89Sta-21
❑ 90BufBisC-11
❑ 90BufBisP-374
❑ 90BufBisTI-27
❑ 90CMC-11
❑ 90ProAAAF-489
❑ 91BufBisLD-48
❑ 91BufBisP-543
❑ 91LinDriAAA-48
❑ 91OPC-508
❑ 91Sco-738
❑ 91Top-508
❑ 91TopDeb90-168
❑ 91TopDesS-508
❑ 91TopMic-508
❑ 91TopTif-508
❑ 91Ult-389
❑ 92LasVegSS-248

York, Ronald
❑ 91IdaFalBSP-1

York, Rudy
❑ 38CloFotW-92
❑ 38ExhFou-12
❑ 38GouHeaU-260
❑ 38GouHeaU-284
❑ 39ExhSal-65
❑ 39GouPreR303A-48
❑ 39GouPreR303B-24
❑ 39WorWidGTP-48
❑ 40WheM4-6B
❑ 46RedSoxTI-25
❑ 47RedSoxTI-24
❑ 47TipTop-14
❑ 48A'sTeal-27
❑ 48BluTin-27
❑ 60Top-456
❑ 72FleFamF-12
❑ 72LauGreF-3
❑ 72TCMthe1-199
❑ 74LauAllG-42
❑ 74TigTCM1AC-34
❑ 75RedSox1T-40
❑ 76GalBasGHoF-31
❑ 76TayBow4-62
❑ 81TigDetN-9
❑ 81TigSecNP-26
❑ 82TCMGreS-30
❑ 83TCMPla1942-13
❑ 85BigLeaC3-25
❑ 85Woo-43
❑ 87RedSox1T-2
❑ 90HOFStiB-35
❑ 93ConTSN-773

Yorke, Christa
❑ 91FreStaLBS-11

Yorro, Jacinto
❑ 90St.CatBJP-3481
❑ 91St.CatBJP-3410

Yoshida, Takashi
❑ 89VisOakCLC-120
❑ 89VisOakP-1430

Yoshida, Yasuo
❑ 96HilStaHWB-3

Yoshii, Masato
❑ 98Bow-295
❑ 98BowBes-145
❑ 98BowBesAR-145
❑ 98BowBesR-145
❑ 98BowChr-295
❑ 98BowChrGA-295
❑ 98BowChrGAR-295
❑ 98BowChrl-295
❑ 98BowChrIR-295
❑ 98BowChrR-295
❑ 98BowGolA-295
❑ 98BowInt-295
❑ 98CroRoy-91
❑ 98Don-219
❑ 98DonGolPP-219
❑ 98DonSig-131
❑ 98DonSigP-131
❑ 98DonSilPP-219
❑ 98Fle-400
❑ 98LeaRS-230
❑ 98LeaRSLHolo-230
❑ 98LeaRSLong-230
❑ 98LeaRTrue-230
❑ 98PacAur-168
❑ 98PacOme-162
❑ 98PacOmeR-162
❑ 98PacOnl-493
❑ 98PacOnlR-493
❑ 98PacOnlWC-493
❑ 98Revo-97
❑ 98RevoRooHH-12
❑ 98RevoRooHHG-12
❑ 98RevoSS-97
❑ 98SkyDugA-117
❑ 98SkyDugAIA-117
❑ 98SP Aut-29
❑ 98SPxFin-188
❑ 98SPxFinR-188
❑ 98SPxFinS-188
❑ 98StaCluFDI-336
❑ 98StaClul-336
❑ 98StaCluOneK-336
❑ 98TopGolLabC1-22
❑ 98TopGolLabC1B-22
❑ 98TopGolLabC1One-22
❑ 98TopGolLabC1R-22
❑ 98TopGolLabC2-22
❑ 98TopGolLabC2B-22
❑ 98TopGolLabC2One-22
❑ 98TopGolLabC2R-22
❑ 98TopGolLabC3-22
❑ 98TopGolLabC3B-22
❑ 98TopGolLabC3One-22
❑ 98TopGolLabC3R-22
❑ 98TopSta-58
❑ 98TopStaB-58
❑ 98TopStaG-58
❑ 98TopStaGR-58
❑ 98TopStaS-58
❑ 98Ult-313
❑ 98UltGolM-313
❑ 98UltMas-313
❑ 98UltPlaM-313
❑ 98UppDec-551
❑ 99Fle-561
❑ 99FleSta9-561
❑ 99FleWarT-561
❑ 99MetUni-90
❑ 99MetUniGM-90
❑ 99MetUniPMG-90
❑ 99Pac-288
❑ 99PacAur-124
❑ 99PacAurOD-124
❑ 99PacCroC-186
❑ 99PacCroCPB-186
❑ 99PacPar-157
❑ 99PacParC-157
❑ 99PacParG-157
❑ 99PacParHoloGold-157
❑ 99PacParHS-157
❑ 99PacParOD-157
❑ 99PacParPB-157
❑ 99PacParRed-157
❑ 99PacPlaB-288
❑ 99PacRed-288
❑ 99SkyPre-177
❑ 99SkyPreR-177
❑ 99Spolll-58
❑ 99StaClu-93
❑ 99StaCluFDI-93
❑ 99StaCluOoaK-93
❑ 99StaCluPP-93
❑ 99Top-167
❑ 99TopChr-167
❑ 99TopChrR-167
❑ 99TopMVPP-167
❑ 99TopOpeD-93
❑ 99Ult-52
❑ 99UltGolM-52
❑ 99UltMas-52
❑ 99UltPlaM-52
❑ 99UppDec-153
❑ 99UppDecEL1-153
❑ 99UppDecEL2-153

Yoshimuru, Sadaaki
❑ 87JapPlaB-26

Yoshinaga, Yoshi
❑ 89SalSpuCLC-136
❑ 89SalSpuP-1810

Yoshitake, Shintaroh
❑ 96MauStiHWB-17

Yost, Eddie
❑ 49Bow-32
❑ 50Bow-162
❑ 51Bow-41
❑ 51R42SmaS-117
❑ 51TopBluB-1
❑ 52Bow-31
❑ 52NatTeaL-42
❑ 52RedMan-AL25
❑ 52TipTop-47
❑ 52Top-123
❑ 53BowC-116
❑ 53Bri-28
❑ 54Bow-72
❑ 54RedHeaF-32
❑ 55Bow-73
❑ 55DonWin-9
❑ 56Top-128
❑ 57SwiFra-11
❑ 57Top-177
❑ 58SeaTeal-27
❑ 58SenJayP-12
❑ 58Top-173
❑ 59Top-2
❑ 59TopVen-2
❑ 60TigJayP-12
❑ 60Top-245
❑ 61AngJayP-12
❑ 61Baz-6
❑ 61Pos-45
❑ 61Top-413
❑ 61TopStal-175
❑ 62AngJayP-12
❑ 62Jel-76
❑ 62Pos-76
❑ 62PosCan-76
❑ 62Top-176A
❑ 62Top-176B
❑ 62TopVen-176
❑ 73OPC-257
❑ 73Top-257A
❑ 73Top-257B
❑ 74OPC-179
❑ 74Top-179
❑ 79TCM50-88
❑ 81TCM60I-407
❑ 83TopRep5-123
❑ 85TCMPla1-11
❑ 89MetRinP69-31
❑ 90PacLeg-73
❑ 91SweBasG-122
❑ 94Met69CCPP-6
❑ 94Met69CS-5
❑ 94Met69T-33
❑ 94TedWil-90
❑ 94UppDecAH-206
❑ 94UppDecAH1-206

Yost, Ned (Edgar)
❑ 78SpolndC-28
❑ 79Top-708
❑ 79VanCanT-13
❑ 80VanCanT-3
❑ 81Top-659
❑ 82BrePol-5
❑ 82Top-542
❑ 83BreGar-21
❑ 83BrePol-5
❑ 83Don-458
❑ 83Fle-50
❑ 83Top-297
❑ 84Don-271
❑ 84Fle-218
❑ 84FleUpd-130
❑ 84JacMetF-15
❑ 84Nes792-107
❑ 84RanJarP-7
❑ 84Top-107
❑ 84TopTif-107
❑ 84TopTra-131T
❑ 84TopTraT-131T
❑ 85Don-221
❑ 85Fle-575
❑ 85Top-777
❑ 85TopTif-777
❑ 87GreBraB-12
❑ 88SouAtlLAGS-3
❑ 88SumBraP-414
❑ 89SumBraP-1095
❑ 90SumBraB-30
❑ 90SumBraP-2450
❑ 91BraSubS-39
❑ 92BraLykS-37
❑ 92BreCarT-25
❑ 93BraLykS-38
❑ 93RanKee-390
❑ 94BraLykP-35
❑ 94BraLykS-34
❑ 94BreMilB-92

Yost, Steve
❑ 77LynMetT-31

Youmans, Floyd
❑ 84JacMetT-15
❑ 86Don-543
❑ 86ExpPos-20
❑ 86ExpProPa-24
❑ 86Fle-267
❑ 86Lea-210
❑ 86OPC-346

❑ 86Top-732
❑ 86TopTif-732
❑ 87ClaGam-98
❑ 87Don-257
❑ 87DonHig-22
❑ 87DonOpeD-89
❑ 87ExpPos-36
❑ 87Fle-337
❑ 87FleGlo-337
❑ 87FleMin-120
❑ 87FleRecS-44
❑ 87GenMilB-4J
❑ 87HosSti-6
❑ 87Lea-65
❑ 87Lea-206
❑ 87OPC-105
❑ 87Spo-103
❑ 87SpoTeaP-20
❑ 87StuPan-8
❑ 87Top-105
❑ 87TopMinL-19
❑ 87TopSti-79
❑ 87TopTif-105
❑ 88BlaYNPRWL-158
❑ 88Don-56
❑ 88DonBasB-314
❑ 88ExpPos-37
❑ 88Fle-201
❑ 88FleGlo-201
❑ 88Lea-66
❑ 88MSAHosD-9
❑ 88OPC-365
❑ 88PanSti-321
❑ 88Sco-327
❑ 88ScoGlo-327
❑ 88ScoYouS2-16
❑ 88Spo-108
❑ 88StaLinE-20
❑ 88Top-365
❑ 88TopSti-82
❑ 88TopTif-365
❑ 89Bow-396
❑ 89BowTif-396
❑ 89OPC-91
❑ 89PhiTas-36
❑ 89Top-91
❑ 89TopTif-91
❑ 89UppDec-459
❑ 89UppDec-730
❑ 90PubIntS-252
❑ 90ReaPhiS-25

Young, Anthony

❑ 87LitFalMP-2394
❑ 88LitFalMP-24
❑ 89ColMetB-16
❑ 89ColMetGS-28
❑ 89SouAtlLAGS-22
❑ 90JacMetGS-26
❑ 90TexLeaAGS-31
❑ 91Bow-466
❑ 91Cla2-T56
❑ 91LeaGolR-BC23
❑ 91LinDriAAA-573
❑ 91LinDriP-573
❑ 91MetColP-52
❑ 91TidTidLD-573
❑ 91TidTidP-2512
❑ 91UppDecFE-65F
❑ 92Bow-268
❑ 92Cla2-T60
❑ 92ClaGam-144
❑ 92Don-409
❑ 92Fle-520
❑ 92Lea-356
❑ 92LeaBlaG-356
❑ 92MetColP-32
❑ 92MetKah-19
❑ 92OPC-148
❑ 92Pin-558
❑ 92ProFS7-278
❑ 92Sco-756
❑ 92ScoImpP-39
❑ 92ScoRoo-14
❑ 92StaClu-85
❑ 92Stu-70
❑ 92Top-148
❑ 92TopDeb91-190
❑ 92TopGol-148
❑ 92TopGolW-148
❑ 92TopMic-148
❑ 92Ult-238
❑ 92UppDec-535
❑ 92UppDecSR-SR25
❑ 93Don-14
❑ 93Fle-96
❑ 93Lea-545
❑ 93MetColP-50
❑ 93MetKah-19
❑ 93OPC-380
❑ 93PacSpa-550
❑ 93Pin-350
❑ 93Sco-113
❑ 93Sel-284
❑ 93StaClu-582
❑ 93StaCluFDI-582
❑ 93StaCluMOP-582
❑ 93Top-734
❑ 93TopGol-734
❑ 93TopInaM-734
❑ 93TopInaR-734
❑ 93TopMic-734
❑ 93Ult-81
❑ 93UppDec-71
❑ 93UppDecGold-71
❑ 93USPlaCR-3D
❑ 94ColC-303
❑ 94ColC-427
❑ 94ColChoGS-303
❑ 94ColChoGS-427
❑ 94ColChoSS-303
❑ 94ColChoSS-427
❑ 94Don-405
❑ 94Fin-167
❑ 94FinRef-167
❑ 94Fle-580
❑ 94FleUpd-112
❑ 94Lea-74
❑ 94MetShuST-8
❑ 94Sco-263
❑ 94ScoGolR-263
❑ 94ScoRoo-RT31
❑ 94ScoRooGR-RT31
❑ 94StaClu-28
❑ 94StaCluFDI-28
❑ 94StaCluGR-28
❑ 94StaCluMOP-28
❑ 94Top-359
❑ 94TopGol-359
❑ 94TopSpa-359
❑ 94TopTra-110T
❑ 94Ult-466
❑ 94UppDec-443
❑ 94UppDecED-443
❑ 95ColCho-201
❑ 95ColChoGS-201
❑ 95ColChoSS-201
❑ 95Don-358
❑ 95DonPreP-358
❑ 95Fle-427
❑ 96AstMot-21

Young, Babe (Norman)

❑ 40PlaBal-212
❑ 41DouPlaR-31
❑ 41DouPlaR-93
❑ 41Gou-23
❑ 41PlaBal-27
❑ 49Bow-240
❑ 76TayBow4-59
❑ 77TCMTheWY-89
❑ 84TCMPla1-44
❑ 93ConTSN-814

Young, Bob G.

❑ 52Bow-193
❑ 52Top-147
❑ 53Top-160
❑ 54Bow-149
❑ 54OriEss-36
❑ 54OriTeal-21
❑ 54Top-8
❑ 55OriEss-27
❑ 83TopRep5-147
❑ 91OriCro-492
❑ 91TopArc1-160
❑ 94TopArc1-8
❑ 94TopArc1G-8

Young, Bobby

❑ 71RicBraTI-18
❑ 97BalOriP-56

Young, Brian

❑ 90ElmPioP-24
❑ 91WinHavRSC-10
❑ 91WinHavRSP-490
❑ 92WinHavRSF-1778
❑ 93NewBriRSF-1223
❑ 94LynRedSC-25
❑ 94LynRedSF-1893

Young, Chris

❑ 93DavLipB-22

Young, Cliff

❑ 86KnoBluJP-27
❑ 86SouLeaAJ-24
❑ 87KnoBluJP-1520
❑ 88SyrChiC-8
❑ 88SyrChiP-807
❑ 89EdmTraC-4
❑ 89EdmTraP-557
❑ 90CMC-478
❑ 90EdmTraC-1
❑ 90EdmTraP-518
❑ 90FleUpd-82
❑ 90ProAAAF-94
❑ 91Bow-204
❑ 91EdmTraP-1517
❑ 91Fle-330
❑ 91TopDeb90-169
❑ 92EdmTraS-173
❑ 92Fle-73
❑ 92SkyAAAF-83
❑ 92StaClu-562
❑ 93ChaKniF-544
❑ 93FleFinE-207
❑ 93LinVenB-90

Young, Clyde

❑ 21Zee-64

Young, Curt

❑ 83TacTigT-8
❑ 84TacTigC-85
❑ 85A'sMot-22
❑ 85Don-522
❑ 85Fle-436
❑ 85Top-293
❑ 85TopTif-293
❑ 86TacTigP-25
❑ 86Top-84
❑ 86TopTif-84
❑ 87A'sSmoC-12
❑ 87Don-344
❑ 87DonOpeD-29
❑ 87Fle-410
❑ 87FleGamW-44
❑ 87FleGlo-410
❑ 87FleStiC-129
❑ 87SpoTeaP-23
❑ 87Top-519
❑ 87TopSti-165
❑ 87TopTif-519
❑ 88A'sMot-17
❑ 88Don-97
❑ 88DonBasB-323
❑ 88DonTeaBA-97
❑ 88Fle-296
❑ 88FleGlo-296
❑ 88FleStiC-58
❑ 88OPC-103
❑ 88PanSti-165
❑ 88RedFolSB-104
❑ 88Sco-125
❑ 88ScoGlo-125
❑ 88Spo-209
❑ 88StaLinAs-19
❑ 88Top-103
❑ 88TopTif-103
❑ 89A'sMot-14
❑ 89Bow-184
❑ 89BowTif-184
❑ 89Don-304
❑ 89Fle-26
❑ 89FleGlo-26
❑ 89Sco-29
❑ 89Top-641
❑ 89TopBig-254
❑ 89TopTif-641
❑ 89UppDec-392
❑ 90A'sMot-24
❑ 90Don-505
❑ 90Fle-24
❑ 90FleCan-24
❑ 90Lea-424
❑ 90OPC-328
❑ 90PubIntS-319
❑ 90Sco-533
❑ 90Top-328
❑ 90TopTif-328
❑ 90UppDec-4
❑ 91A'sMot-24
❑ 91Bow-220
❑ 91Don-723
❑ 91Fle-28
❑ 91OPC-473
❑ 91Sco-236
❑ 91Top-473
❑ 91TopDesS-473
❑ 91TopMic-473
❑ 91TopTif-473
❑ 91Ult-257
❑ 92Don-469
❑ 92Fle-272
❑ 92OmaRoyS-348
❑ 92OPC-704
❑ 92Sco-722
❑ 92Top-704
❑ 92TopGol-704
❑ 92TopGolW-704
❑ 92TopMic-704
❑ 93Fle-658

Young, Cy (Denton T.)

❑ 03BreE10-157
❑ 04FanCraAL-51
❑ 04RedSoxUP-16
❑ 08RosComP-10
❑ 09AmeCarE90-1-119
❑ 09AmeCarE90-1-120
❑ 09BriE97-30B
❑ 09ColChiE-315
❑ 09SpoNewSM-2
❑ 09T206-386
❑ 09T206-387
❑ 09T206-388
❑ 10DomDisP-129
❑ 10E101-45
❑ 10E98-30
❑ 10MelMinE-45
❑ 10NadCarE-54
❑ 10PeoT21-58
❑ 10RedCroT-88
❑ 10StaCarE-30
❑ 10SweCapPP-21A
❑ 10SweCapPP-21B
❑ 10W555-64
❑ 10W555-65
❑ 10W555-66
❑ 11DiaGumP-29
❑ 11E94-30
❑ 11HelSta-20
❑ 11PinT-5-771
❑ 11S74Sil-12
❑ 11SpoLifCW-376
❑ 11SpoLifM-52
❑ 11T205-186
❑ 11TurRedT-42
❑ 12ColRedB-315
❑ 12ColTinT-315
❑ 12HasTriFT-50B
❑ 13NatGamW-45
❑ 13TomBarW-42
❑ 36Halof FP-25
❑ 39PC7AlbHoF-13
❑ 48ExhHoF-32
❑ 50CalHOFW-80
❑ 53ArtHaloFP-91
❑ 60Fle-47
❑ 60NuHi-48
❑ 61Fle-153
❑ 61GolPre-33
❑ 61NuSco-448
❑ 63BasMagM-88
❑ 63BazA-6
❑ 63GadFunC-26
❑ 63HalofFB-28
❑ 67TopVen-150
❑ 69Baz-3
❑ 69Baz-6
❑ 71FleWorS-1
❑ 72FleFamF-11
❑ 72KelATG-12
❑ 72LauGreF-29
❑ 73HalofFPP-20
❑ 73OPC-477
❑ 73Top-477
❑ 74CapPub-32
❑ 75FlePio-19
❑ 75McCCob-14
❑ 76GalBasGHoF-32
❑ 76ShaPiz-8
❑ 77BobParHoF-77
❑ 77GalGloG-169
❑ 77GalGloG-270
❑ 77ShaPiz-3
❑ 77Spo-3217
❑ 77Spo-5103
❑ 79Top-416
❑ 80Lau300-11
❑ 80LauFamF-30
❑ 80MarExhH-32
❑ 80PacLeg-91
❑ 80PerHaloFP-13
❑ 80SSPHOF-13
❑ 82BHCRSpoL-5
❑ 82DavHaloFB-25
❑ 82OhiHaloF-14
❑ 82TCMGreP-16
❑ 83DonHOFH-27
❑ 84DonCha-31
❑ 84GalHaloFRL-8
❑ 85UltBasC-8
❑ 85Woo-44
❑ 86IndGreT-9
❑ 86RedSoxGT-3
❑ 87SpoRea-20
❑ 88ConSer4-30
❑ 89HOFStiB-59
❑ 89SweBasG-5
❑ 90BasWit-79
❑ 90HOFStiB-14
❑ 90PerGreM-10
❑ 90SweBasG-100
❑ 91HomCooC-5
❑ 91SweBasG-135
❑ 91USGamSBL-13A
❑ 91USGamSBL-13C
❑ 91USGamSBL-13D
❑ 91USGamSBL-13H
❑ 92St.VinHHS-12
❑ 92WhiLegtL-5
❑ 92WhiPro-5
❑ 93ActPacA-85
❑ 93ActPacA2-19G
❑ 93Hoy-9
❑ 93JusSo-12
❑ 93SpeHOF2-4
❑ 93UppDecAH-129
❑ 93UppDecAH-138
❑ 93UppDecAH-142
❑ 93UppDecAH-156
❑ 93UppDecAH-157
❑ 93UppDecAH-158
❑ 93UppDecAH-159
❑ 93UppDecTR-3
❑ 94TedWil-7
❑ 94TedWilLC-LC18
❑ 94UppDecAH-105
❑ 94UppDecAH-150
❑ 94UppDecAH-200
❑ 94UppDecAH1-105
❑ 94UppDecAH1-151
❑ 94UppDecAH1-200
❑ 95UppDecSHoB-2
❑ 97HigMinMM-9
❑ 97HigMinMM-11
❑ 97HigMinMM-13
❑ 98CamPepP-84
❑ 99SP SigLC-CY
❑ 99SpoIllGotG-80
❑ 99SpoIllGotGRB-5
❑ 99SpoIllGotGRBG-5
❑ 99UppDecCL-14
❑ 99UppDecCLCC-14
❑ 99UppDecCLJotC-AC9
❑ 99UppDecCLLC-TY

Young, Danny

❑ 92AshTouC-16
❑ 92ClaFS7-381
❑ 93AshTouC-24
❑ 93AshTouF-2277
❑ 95LynHilTI-29
❑ 97LynHil-26

Young, Del E.

❑ 38CloFotW-93
❑ 39PlaBal-33
❑ 40PhiTeal-23
❑ 40PlaBal-101
❑ 41PhiTeal-26
❑ 48SomandK-27
❑ 49SomandK-21

Young, Delwyn

❑ 83CedRapRT-17
❑ 86VerRedP-24
❑ 87BurExpP-1081
❑ 87SanBerSP-11
❑ 88EasLeaAP-12
❑ 88GleFalTP-916
❑ 89TolMudHC-22
❑ 89TolMudHP-764
❑ 90CanIndB-14
❑ 90CanIndP-1306
❑ 90CanIndS-18
❑ 90CMC-734
❑ 96LanJetB-2

Young, Derrick

❑ 89ColMetB-3
❑ 89ColMetGS-29
❑ 90St.LucMS-26
❑ 91SanBerSC-25
❑ 91SanBerSP-2002

Young, Dick

❑ 90LitSunW-9

Young, Dmitri

❑ 91ClaDraP-4
❑ 91ClaDraPP-4
❑ 91JohCitCC-11
❑ 91JohCitCP-3993
❑ 91UppDecFE-7F
❑ 92ClaBluBF-BC8
❑ 92ClaDraP-89
❑ 92ClaFS7-272
❑ 92ClaRedB-BC8
❑ 92MidLeaATI-54
❑ 92ProFS7-322
❑ 92SprCarC-1
❑ 92SprCarF-879
❑ 92UppDec-58
❑ 92UppDecML-30
❑ 92UppDecML-62
❑ 92UppDecML-274
❑ 92UppDecMLPotY-PY7
❑ 92UppDecMLTPHF-TP9
❑ 93ClaFisN-13
❑ 93ClaGolF-96
❑ 93ClaInsC-8
❑ 93ClaYouG-YG28
❑ 93Don-638
❑ 93ExcFS7-108
❑ 93SP-290
❑ 93St.PetCC-1
❑ 93St.PetCF-2638
❑ 93UppDec-428
❑ 93UppDecGold-428
❑ 94ActPac-28
❑ 94ArkTraF-3099
❑ 94Bow-147
❑ 94BowBes-B75
❑ 94BowBes-X91
❑ 94BowBesR-B75
❑ 94BowBesR-X91
❑ 94Cla-161
❑ 94ClaCreotC-C24
❑ 94ClaGolA-SH2
❑ 94ClaGolF-173
❑ 94ExcFS7-276
❑ 94Ult-571
❑ 94UppDecML-30
❑ 94UppDecML-256
❑ 95ArkTraTI-28
❑ 95Sum21C-TC9
❑ 96BesAutS-98
❑ 96LouRedB-28
❑ 97Bow-414
❑ 97BowBes-180
❑ 97BowBesAR-180
❑ 97BowBesR-180
❑ 97BowCerBlaIA-CA89
❑ 97BowCerBluIA-CA89
❑ 97BowCerGolIA-CA89
❑ 97BowChr-275
❑ 97BowChrI-275
❑ 97BowChrIR-275
❑ 97BowChrR-275
❑ 97BowChrSHR-SHR1
❑ 97BowChrSHRR-SHR1
❑ 97BowInt-414
❑ 97BowScoHR-1
❑ 97CarPol-27
❑ 97Cir-114
❑ 97CirRav-114
❑ 97ColCho-4
❑ 97Don-363
❑ 97DonFraFea-8
❑ 97DonGolPP-363
❑ 97DonLim-76
❑ 97DonLim-84
❑ 97DonLimE-76
❑ 97DonLimE-84
❑ 97DonLimENG-84
❑ 97DonLimFotG-59
❑ 97DonPre-142
❑ 97DonPreCttC-142
❑ 97DonRooDK-9
❑ 97DonRooDKC-9
❑ 97DonSig-60
❑ 97DonSigA-115
❑ 97DonSigAC-141
❑ 97DonSigAM-141
❑ 97DonSigPPP-60
❑ 97DonSilPP-363
❑ 97DonTea-164
❑ 97DonTeaSPE-164
❑ 97Fin-177
❑ 97FinRef-177
❑ 97FlaShoLC-85
❑ 97FlaShoLeg0-85
❑ 97FlaShoLeg1-85
❑ 97FlaShoM-A85
❑ 97FlaShoM-B85
❑ 97FlaShoM-C85
❑ 97FlaShoR0-85

❑ 97FlaShoR1-85
❑ 97FlaShoR2-85
❑ 97Fle-455
❑ 97FleNewH-15
❑ 97FleTif-455
❑ 97Lea-176
❑ 97LeaFraM-176
❑ 97LeaFraMDC-176
❑ 97NewPin-177
❑ 97NewPinAP-177
❑ 97NewPinMC-177
❑ 97NewPinPP-177
❑ 97Pin-185
❑ 97PinArtP-PP185
❑ 97PinCer-121
❑ 97PinCerMBla-121
❑ 97PinCerMBlu-121
❑ 97PinCerMG-121
❑ 97PinCerMR-121
❑ 97PinCerR-121
❑ 97PinIns-142
❑ 97PinInsCE-142
❑ 97PinInsDE-142
❑ 97PinMusC-185
❑ 97PinPrePla-185
❑ 97PinTotCPB-121
❑ 97PinTotCPG-121
❑ 97PinTotCPR-121
❑ 97PinX-P-124
❑ 97PinX-PMoS-124
❑ 97PreCon-30
❑ 97Sco-478
❑ 97ScoArtPWB-320
❑ 97ScoArtPWB-478
❑ 97ScoHeaotO-30
❑ 97ScoResC-478
❑ 97ScoShoS-478
❑ 97ScoShoSAP-320
❑ 97ScoShoSAP-478
❑ 97Sel-104
❑ 97SelArtP-104
❑ 97SelCom-104
❑ 97SelRegG-104
❑ 97SelRooR-11
❑ 97SelTooοtT-6
❑ 97SelTooοtTMB-6
❑ 97SpoIll-54
❑ 97SpoIllEE-54
❑ 97StaCluM-M39
❑ 97StaCluMOP-M39
❑ 97Stu-157
❑ 97StuPrePG-157
❑ 97StuPrePS-157
❑ 97Top-202
❑ 97Ult-470
❑ 97UltGolME-470
❑ 97UltPlaME-470
❑ 97UppDec-272
❑ 98CarScoP-5
❑ 98Don-93
❑ 98Don-216
❑ 98DonCol-93
❑ 98DonColS-93
❑ 98DonGolPP-93
❑ 98DonGolPP-216
❑ 98DonPriCD-93
❑ 98DonSilPP-93
❑ 98DonSilPP-216
❑ 98Fle-449
❑ 98PinPlu-147
❑ 98Sco-53
❑ 98ScoCar-5
❑ 98ScoRT-182
❑ 98ScoSS-PP17
❑ 98ScoSSAP-PP17
❑ 98Top-22
❑ 98TopChr-22
❑ 98TopChrR-22
❑ 98TopDevR-22
❑ 98TopDia-22
❑ 98TopMiniC-22
❑ 98Ult-370
❑ 98UltGolM-370
❑ 98UltMas-370
❑ 98UltPlaM-370
❑ 98UppDec-665
❑ 99199Fin-27
❑ 99Bow-259
❑ 99BowBes-69
❑ 99BowBesAR-69
❑ 99BowBesR-69
❑ 99BowGol-259
❑ 99BowInt-259
❑ 99CroRoyB-40
❑ 99CroRoyL-40
❑ 99CroRoyOD-40
❑ 99FinGolRef-27
❑ 99FinRef-27
❑ 99Fle-283
❑ 99FleBri-50
❑ 99FleBri2G-50
❑ 99FleBriBlu-50
❑ 99FleBriGol-50
❑ 99FleMys-50
❑ 99FleMysG-50
❑ 99FleMysM-50
❑ 99FleSta9-283
❑ 99FleWarT-283
❑ 99MetUni-56
❑ 99MetUniGM-56
❑ 99MetUniPMG-56
❑ 99Pac-122
❑ 99PacInv-41
❑ 99PacInvOD-41
❑ 99PacInvPB-41
❑ 99PacOme-69
❑ 99PacOmeC-69
❑ 99PacOmeG-69
❑ 99PacOmePB-69
❑ 99PacPar-68
❑ 99PacParC-68
❑ 99PacParG-68
❑ 99PacParHoloGold-68
❑ 99PacParHS-68
❑ 99PacParOD-68
❑ 99PacParPB-68
❑ 99PacParRed-68
❑ 99PacPlaB-122
❑ 99PacRed-122
❑ 99SkyPre-161
❑ 99SkyPreR-161
❑ 99SkyThu-7
❑ 99SkyThuRant-7
❑ 99SkyThuRave-7
❑ 99StaClu-44
❑ 99StaCluFDI-44
❑ 99StaCluOoaK-44
❑ 99StaCluPP-44
❑ 99ThuSkySupR-7
❑ 99Top-114
❑ 99TopBlaLC1-12
❑ 99TopBlaLC2-12
❑ 99TopBlaLC3-12
❑ 99TopChr-114
❑ 99TopChrR-114
❑ 99TopGal-39
❑ 99TopGalPP-39
❑ 99TopGalPPI-39
❑ 99TopGolL-12
❑ 99TopGolLC1-12
❑ 99TopGolLC2-12
❑ 99TopGolLOtO-12
❑ 99TopMVPP-114
❑ 99TopOpeD-67
❑ 99TopRedLC1-12
❑ 99TopRedLC2-12
❑ 99TopRedLC3-12
❑ 99TopSta-81
❑ 99TopSta1Foil-81
❑ 99TopStaFoil-81
❑ 99TopStaOS-81
❑ 99UD Cho-75
❑ 99UD ChoPCR-75
❑ 99Ult-146
❑ 99UltGolM-146
❑ 99UltMas-146
❑ 99UltPlaM-146
❑ 99UppDec-76
❑ 99UppDecEL1-76
❑ 99UppDecEL2-76
❑ 99Vic-111

Young, Don
❑ 89WatIndS-24

Young, Donald Wayne
❑ 66OPC-139
❑ 66Top-139
❑ 66TopVen-139
❑ 69CubJewT-20
❑ 70OPC-117
❑ 70Top-117

Young, Doug
❑ 97IdaFalBTI-30

Young, Eric O.
❑ 90FloStaLAS-20
❑ 90StaFS7-22
❑ 90VerBeaDS-29
❑ 91Cla/Bes-11
❑ 91LinDriAA-548
❑ 91SanAntMLD-548
❑ 91SanAntMP-2985
❑ 92AlbDukF-736
❑ 92AlbDukS-23
❑ 92DonRoo-128
❑ 92FleUpd-94
❑ 92SkyAAAF-11
❑ 93Bow-416
❑ 93Don-730
❑ 93Fin-48
❑ 93FinRef-48
❑ 93Fla-44
❑ 93Fle-693
❑ 93FleFinE-47
❑ 93Lea-415
❑ 93OPCPre-31
❑ 93PacSpa-440
❑ 93Pin-518
❑ 93PinExpOD-4
❑ 93RocStaC-27
❑ 93RocUSPC-8D
❑ 93RocUSPC-11S
❑ 93Sco-586
❑ 93Sel-342
❑ 93SelRoo-130T
❑ 93SP-225
❑ 93StaClu-526
❑ 93StaCluFDI-526
❑ 93StaCluMOP-526
❑ 93Top-145
❑ 93Top-551
❑ 93TopGol-145
❑ 93TopGol-551
❑ 93TopInaM-145
❑ 93TopInaM-551
❑ 93TopInaR-145
❑ 93TopInaR-551
❑ 93TopMic-145
❑ 93TopMic-551
❑ 93Ult-361
❑ 93UppDec-521
❑ 93UppDecGold-521
❑ 93USPlaCR-5C
❑ 94ColC-304
❑ 94ColChoGS-304
❑ 94ColChoSS-304
❑ 94Don-412
❑ 94Fin-186
❑ 94FinRef-186
❑ 94Fla-159
❑ 94Fle-457
❑ 94Lea-44
❑ 94Pac-209
❑ 94PanSti-178
❑ 94Pin-133
❑ 94PinArtP-133
❑ 94PinMusC-133
❑ 94RocPol-26
❑ 94Sco-472
❑ 94ScoGolR-472
❑ 94Sel-145
❑ 94StaClu-72
❑ 94StaCluFDI-72
❑ 94StaCluGR-72
❑ 94StaCluMOP-72
❑ 94StaCluMOP-ST4
❑ 94StaCluST-ST4
❑ 94StaCluT-104
❑ 94StaCluTFDI-104
❑ 94Top-712
❑ 94TopGol-712
❑ 94TopSpa-712
❑ 94Ult-190
❑ 94UppDec-252
❑ 94UppDecED-252
❑ 94USPlaCA-3H
❑ 95ColCho-446
❑ 95ColChoGS-446
❑ 95ColChoSS-446
❑ 95Don-544
❑ 95DonPreP-544
❑ 95DonTopotO-236
❑ 95Fla-135
❑ 95Fle-531
❑ 95Lea-188
❑ 95Pin-314
❑ 95PinArtP-314
❑ 95PinMusC-314
❑ 95RocPol-12
❑ 95Sco-71
❑ 95ScoGolR-71
❑ 95ScoPlaTS-71
❑ 95Top-517
❑ 95TopCyb-305
❑ 95Ult-159
❑ 95UltGolM-159
❑ 95UppDec-177
❑ 95UppDecED-177
❑ 95UppDecEDG-177
❑ 96Cir-125
❑ 96CirRav-125
❑ 96ColCho-128
❑ 96ColChoGS-128
❑ 96ColChoSS-128
❑ 96Don-214
❑ 96DonPreP-214
❑ 96EmoXL-180
❑ 96Fla-255
❑ 96Fle-379
❑ 96FleTif-379
❑ 96Lea-177
❑ 96LeaPre-95
❑ 96LeaPreP-95
❑ 96LeaPrePB-177
❑ 96LeaPrePG-177
❑ 96LeaPrePS-177
❑ 96LeaSig-85
❑ 96LeaSigA-249
❑ 96LeaSigAG-250
❑ 96LeaSigAS-250
❑ 96LeaSigPPG-85
❑ 96LeaSigPPP-85
❑ 96RocFle-18
❑ 96RocPol-27
❑ 96Sco-122
❑ 96StaClu-412
❑ 96StaCluEPB-412
❑ 96StaCluEPG-412
❑ 96StaCluEPS-412
❑ 96StaCluMOP-412
❑ 96TeaOut-90
❑ 96Ult-477
❑ 96UltGolM-477
❑ 96UppDec-63
❑ 97Bow-49
❑ 97BowBes-23
❑ 97BowBesAR-23
❑ 97BowBesR-23
❑ 97BowInt-49
❑ 97Cir-98
❑ 97CirRav-98
❑ 97ColCho-59
❑ 97ColCho-99
❑ 97ColChoAC-38
❑ 97ColChoT-CR5
❑ 97Don-200
❑ 97DonEli-76
❑ 97DonEliGS-76
❑ 97DonGolPP-200
❑ 97DonLim-57
❑ 97DonLim-87
❑ 97DonLimE-57
❑ 97DonLimE-87
❑ 97DonLimENG-57
❑ 97DonLimFotG-50
❑ 97DonPre-126
❑ 97DonPreCttC-126
❑ 97DonSig-47
❑ 97DonSigA-116
❑ 97DonSigAC-142
❑ 97DonSigAM-142
❑ 97DonSigPPP-47
❑ 97DonSilPP-200
❑ 97DonTea-97
❑ 97DonTeaSMVP-6
❑ 97DonTeaSPE-97
❑ 97Fin-146
❑ 97FinEmb-146
❑ 97FinEmbR-146
❑ 97FinRef-146
❑ 97FlaShoLC-105
❑ 97FlaShoLeg0-105
❑ 97FlaShoLeg1-105
❑ 97FlaShoM-A105
❑ 97FlaShoM-B105
❑ 97FlaShoM-C105
❑ 97FlaShoR0-105
❑ 97FlaShoR1-105
❑ 97FlaShoR2-105
❑ 97Fle-322
❑ 97FleTif-322
❑ 97Lea-225
❑ 97Lea-390
❑ 97LeaFraM-225
❑ 97LeaFraM-390
❑ 97LeaFraMDC-225
❑ 97LeaFraMDC-390
❑ 97LeaGolS-31
❑ 97MetUni-79
❑ 97NewPin-113
❑ 97NewPinAP-113
❑ 97NewPinMC-113
❑ 97NewPinPP-113
❑ 97Pac-293
❑ 97PacLigB-293
❑ 97PacPri-99
❑ 97PacPriLB-99
❑ 97PacPriP-99
❑ 97PacSil-293
❑ 97PinCer-86
❑ 97PinCerMBla-86
❑ 97PinCerMBlu-86
❑ 97PinCerMG-86
❑ 97PinCerMR-86
❑ 97PinCerR-86
❑ 97PinIns-58
❑ 97PinInsCE-58
❑ 97PinInsDE-58
❑ 97PinTeaP-2
❑ 97PinTeaP-10
❑ 97PinTotCPB-86
❑ 97PinTotCPG-86
❑ 97PinTotCPR-86
❑ 97PinX-P-40
❑ 97PinX-PMoS-40
❑ 97RocPol-12
❑ 97RocSco-7
❑ 97RocScoPl-7
❑ 97RocScoPr-7
❑ 97Sco-169
❑ 97ScoArtPWB-169
❑ 97ScoPreS-169
❑ 97ScoShoS-169
❑ 97ScoShoSAP-169
❑ 97ScoSteS-16
❑ 97Sel-18
❑ 97Sel-173
❑ 97SelArtP-18
❑ 97SelCom-18
❑ 97SelCom-173
❑ 97SelRegG-18
❑ 97SP-68
❑ 97StaClu-37
❑ 97StaCluMat-37
❑ 97StaCluMOP-37
❑ 97Stu-109
❑ 97StuPrePG-109
❑ 97StuPrePS-109
❑ 97Top-71
❑ 97TopAll-AS6
❑ 97TopChr-26
❑ 97TopChrAS-AS6
❑ 97TopChrR-26
❑ 97TopChrSAR-AS6
❑ 97TopChrSB-24
❑ 97TopChrSBR-24
❑ 97TopGal-127
❑ 97TopGalPPI-127
❑ 97TopSeaB-SB24
❑ 97TopSta-55
❑ 97TopStaAM-55
❑ 97Ult-192
❑ 97UltGolME-192
❑ 97UltPlaME-192
❑ 97UppDec-55
❑ 97UppDec-218
❑ 97UppDecAWJ-8
❑ 98BowBes-95
❑ 98BowBesAR-95
❑ 98BowBesR-95
❑ 98CirThu-120
❑ 98CirThuRav-120
❑ 98CirThuSupRav-120
❑ 98ColCho-399
❑ 98DodMot-12
❑ 98DodPol-28
❑ 98Don-147
❑ 98DonCol-147
❑ 98DonColE-457
❑ 98DonColL-344
❑ 98DonColP-652
❑ 98DonColS-147
❑ 98DonCruG-70
❑ 98DonCruP-70
❑ 98DonCruR-70
❑ 98DonEli-57
❑ 98DonEliA-57
❑ 98DonEliS-57
❑ 98DonGolPP-147
❑ 98DonPre-102
❑ 98DonPreSeat-102
❑ 98DonPriCD-147
❑ 98DonPriCE-457
❑ 98DonPriCL-344
❑ 98DonPriCP-652
❑ 98DonSig-80
❑ 98DonSigP-80
❑ 98DonSilPP-147
❑ 98Fin-148
❑ 98FinNo--148
❑ 98FinNo-R-148
❑ 98FinRef-148
❑ 98Fle-254
❑ 98Lea-145
❑ 98LeaCruG-70
❑ 98LeaCruP-70
❑ 98LeaCruR-70
❑ 98LeaFraDA-145
❑ 98LeaFraF-145
❑ 98LeaFraM-145
❑ 98LeaFraM-145
❑ 98LeaFraMDC-145
❑ 98LeaFraMDC-145
❑ 98LeaFraMZ2-145
❑ 98LeaRS-98
❑ 98LeaRSLHolo-98
❑ 98LeaRSLong-98
❑ 98LeaRTrue-98
❑ 98MetUni-156
❑ 98MetUniPMG-156
❑ 98PacOnl-388
❑ 98PacOnlR-388
❑ 98PacOnlWC-388
❑ 98PinIns-110
❑ 98PinInsCE-110
❑ 98PinInsDE-110
❑ 98PinPer-98
❑ 98PinPerPP-98
❑ 98PinPlu-43
❑ 98PinSna-LAD14
❑ 98ScoRT-120
❑ 98ScoRTSS-PP76
❑ 98ScoRTSSAP-PP76
❑ 98ScoRTSSAP1-PP76
❑ 98SkyDugAFF-FF10
❑ 98SP Aut-113
❑ 98SPxFin-287
❑ 98SPxFinR-287
❑ 98SPxFinS-287
❑ 98StaCluFDI-184
❑ 98StaCluI-184
❑ 98StaCluOneK-184
❑ 98StaCluPP-184
❑ 98Stu-177
❑ 98StuGPP-177
❑ 98StuSPP-177
❑ 98Top-389
❑ 98TopChr-389
❑ 98TopChrR-389
❑ 98TopDevR-389
❑ 98TopDia-389
❑ 98TopGal-84
❑ 98TopGalGP-84
❑ 98TopGalOPP-84
❑ 98TopGalPPI-84
❑ 98TopGalPPIA-84
❑ 98TopMiniC-389
❑ 98TopSta-66
❑ 98TopStaB-66
❑ 98TopStaG-66
❑ 98TopStaGR-66
❑ 98TopStaS-66
❑ 98Ult-96
❑ 98UltGolM-96
❑ 98UltMas-96
❑ 98UltPlaM-96
❑ 98UppDec-80
❑ 98UppDec10AP-29
❑ 98UppDec1APR-29
❑ 99199Fin-41
❑ 99Bow-45
❑ 99BowChr-45
❑ 99BowChrG-45
❑ 99BowChrGR-45
❑ 99BowChrI-45
❑ 99BowChrIR-45
❑ 99BowChrR-45
❑ 99BowGol-45
❑ 99BowInt-45
❑ 99DodPol-29
❑ 99FinGolRef-41
❑ 99FinRef-41
❑ 99Fle-282
❑ 99FleSta9-282
❑ 99FleWarT-282
❑ 99Pac-229
❑ 99PacOme-127
❑ 99PacOmeC-127
❑ 99PacOmeG-127
❑ 99PacOmePB-127
❑ 99PacPar-123
❑ 99PacParC-123
❑ 99PacParG-123
❑ 99PacParHoloGold-123
❑ 99PacParHS-123
❑ 99PacParOD-123
❑ 99PacParPB-123
❑ 99PacParRed-123

❑ 99PacPlaB-229
❑ 99PacRed-229
❑ 99SkyThu-10
❑ 99SkyThuRant-10
❑ 99SkyThuRave-10
❑ 99StaClu-69
❑ 99StaCluFDI-69
❑ 99StaCluOoaK-69
❑ 99StaCluPP-69
❑ 99ThuSkySupR-10
❑ 99Top-142
❑ 99TopChr-142
❑ 99TopChrR-142
❑ 99TopMVPP-142
❑ 99TopOpeD-84
❑ 99TopSta-108
❑ 99TopStaFoil-108
❑ 99UppDec-125
❑ 99UppDecEL1-125
❑ 99UppDecEL2-125

Young, Erik
❑ 89WatIndS-25

Young, Ernest
❑ 75CedRapGT-32
❑ 75LafDriT-8
❑ 76CedRapGT-35
❑ 77SalPirT-28
❑ 79BufBisT-8
❑ 91MadMusC-18

Young, Ernie
❑ 87HagSunP-27
❑ 87NewOriP-25
❑ 88FreSunCLC-5
❑ 88FreSunP-1241

Young, Ernie (Ernest Wesley)
❑ 90SouOreAB-15
❑ 90SouOreAP-3438
❑ 91MadMusP-2145
❑ 92ModA'sC-10
❑ 93ModA'sC-25
❑ 93ModA'sF-814
❑ 94ClaGolF-98
❑ 94ExcFS7-124
❑ 94HunStaF-1346
❑ 94LeaLimR-75
❑ 94SpoRoo-50
❑ 94SpoRooAP-50
❑ 94UppDecML-203
❑ 94UppDecMLPotYF-PY3
❑ 95Bow-75
❑ 95ColChoSE-10
❑ 95EdmTraTI-29
❑ 95Pin-159
❑ 95PinArtP-159
❑ 95PinMusC-159
❑ 95Sco-576
❑ 95ScoAi-AM7
❑ 95ScoGolR-576
❑ 95ScoPlaTS-576
❑ 95Sel-195
❑ 95SelArtP-195
❑ 95Spo-154
❑ 95SpoArtP-154
❑ 95UppDec-33
❑ 95UppDecED-33
❑ 95UppDecEDG-33
❑ 96A'sMot-11
❑ 96ColCho-642
❑ 96ColCho-666
❑ 96ColChoGS-642
❑ 96ColChoGS-666
❑ 96ColChoSS-642
❑ 96ColChoSS-666
❑ 96Fin-S211
❑ 96FinRef-S211
❑ 96FleUpd-U77
❑ 96FleUpdTC-U77
❑ 96LeaSigA-250
❑ 96LeaSigAG-251
❑ 96LeaSigAS-251
❑ 96Pin-365
❑ 96PinFoil-365
❑ 96Sco-455
❑ 96Sum-71
❑ 96SumAbo&B-71
❑ 96SumArtP-71
❑ 96SumFoi-71
❑ 96Ult-406
❑ 96UltGolM-406
❑ 97A'sMot-6
❑ 97Cir-342
❑ 97CirRav-342
❑ 97ColCho-189
❑ 97Don-205
❑ 97DonEli-69
❑ 97DonEliGS-69
❑ 97DonEliTotC-13
❑ 97DonEliTotCDC-13
❑ 97DonGolPP-205
❑ 97DonSilPP-205
❑ 97Fle-200
❑ 97FleTif-200
❑ 97Lea-67
❑ 97LeaFraM-67
❑ 97LeaFraMDC-67
❑ 97Pac-179
❑ 97PacLigB-179
❑ 97PacSil-179
❑ 97Pin-75
❑ 97PinArtP-PP75
❑ 97PinIns-33
❑ 97PinInsCE-33
❑ 97PinInsDE-33
❑ 97PinMusC-75
❑ 97PinPrePla-75
❑ 97Sco-432
❑ 97ScoArtPWB-432
❑ 97ScoResC-432
❑ 97ScoShoS-432
❑ 97ScoShoSAP-432
❑ 97SP-134
❑ 97Stu-45
❑ 97StuPrePG-45
❑ 97StuPrePS-45
❑ 97Top-329
❑ 97Ult-118
❑ 97UltGolME-118
❑ 97UltPlaME-118
❑ 97UppDec-128
❑ 98PacOnl-359
❑ 98PacOnlR-359
❑ 98PacOnlWC-359

Young, Floyd
❑ 36SandSW-52

Young, Ford
❑ 60DarFar-24

Young, Gary
❑ 87BriYouC-15

Young, Gerald
❑ 85OscAstTI-26
❑ 86ColAstP-25
❑ 87SpoRoo2-36
❑ 87TucTorP-11
❑ 88AstMot-3
❑ 88AstPol-24
❑ 88Don-431
❑ 88DonBasB-318
❑ 88Fle-460
❑ 88FleGlo-460
❑ 88HouSho-15
❑ 88Lea-210
❑ 88OPC-368
❑ 88Sco-442
❑ 88ScoGlo-442
❑ 88ScoYouS2-11
❑ 88StaLinAst-20
❑ 88Top-368
❑ 88TopTif-368
❑ 89AstLenH-20
❑ 89AstMot-3
❑ 89AstSmo-40
❑ 89Bow-333
❑ 89BowTif-333
❑ 89Don-207
❑ 89DonBasB-288
❑ 89Fle-370
❑ 89FleGlo-370
❑ 89OPC-95
❑ 89PanSti-93
❑ 89Sco-97
❑ 89ScoHot1S-72
❑ 89Spo-125
❑ 89Top-95
❑ 89TopCoi-28
❑ 89TopMinL-16
❑ 89TopSti-23
❑ 89TopTif-95
❑ 89TopUKM-86
❑ 89TVSpoM-56
❑ 89UppDec-135
❑ 90AstLenH-28
❑ 90AstMot-8
❑ 90Bow-72
❑ 90BowTif-72
❑ 90Don-325
❑ 90Fle-241
❑ 90FleCan-241
❑ 90Lea-214
❑ 90MLBBasB-40
❑ 90OPC-196
❑ 90PanSti-263
❑ 90PubIntS-105
❑ 90PubIntS-618
❑ 90Sco-43
❑ 90Top-196
❑ 90TopBig-49
❑ 90TopSti-22
❑ 90TopTif-196
❑ 90UppDec-196
❑ 91Don-689
❑ 91Fle-521
❑ 91LinDriAAA-623
❑ 91OPC-626
❑ 91Sco-844
❑ 91StaClu-494
❑ 91Top-626
❑ 91TopDesS-626
❑ 91TopMic-626
❑ 91TopTif-626
❑ 91TucTorLD-623
❑ 91TucTorP-2227
❑ 91Ult-142
❑ 92Don-477
❑ 92Fle-446
❑ 92OPC-241
❑ 92Pin-458
❑ 92Sco-346
❑ 92StaClu-355
❑ 92Top-241
❑ 92TopGol-241
❑ 92TopGolW-241
❑ 92TopMic-241
❑ 93RocStaC-14
❑ 93RocUSPC-6S
❑ 93RocUSPC-9D
❑ 93Ult-362
❑ 93UppDec-740
❑ 93UppDecGold-740
❑ 94LouRedF-2995

Young, Greg
❑ 91SouBenWSC-21
❑ 91SouBenWSP-2858
❑ 91UtiBluSC-9
❑ 91UtiBluSP-3241

Young, Irving
❑ 06FanCraNL-54
❑ 08RosComP-159
❑ 09BriE97-30A
❑ 09T206-475
❑ 11SpoLifCW-377
❑ 11SpoLifM-35

Young, Jason
❑ 90CliGiaUTI-U10
❑ 90EveGiaB-21
❑ 90EveGiaP-3137
❑ 91CliGiaC-25
❑ 91CliGiaP-850

Young, Jim
❑ 91RocExpC-2
❑ 92RocExpC-30
❑ 93GenCubC-28
❑ 93GenCubF-3192
❑ 97PawRedS-5

Young, Joe
❑ 94MedHatBJF-3685
❑ 94MedHatBJSP-25
❑ 95StCatSTI-2
❑ 96BesAutS-99
❑ 96Exc-120
❑ 96HagSunB-26
❑ 97Bow-102
❑ 97BowInt-102
❑ 97KnoSmo-27
❑ 97SouLeaTP-21
❑ 98DunBluJTI-32

Young, John
❑ 76ArkTraT-12
❑ 77ArkTraT-12A
❑ 77ArkTraT-12B
❑ 80IndIndTI-31
❑ 81IndIndTI-32
❑ 83SprCarF-15
❑ 84ArkTraT-22
❑ 87NasSouTI-24
❑ 88NasSouC-25
❑ 88NasSouP-495
❑ 88NasSouTI-25
❑ 88WatPirP-30
❑ 89NasSouC-9
❑ 89NasSouP-1276
❑ 90CMC-673
❑ 90NasSouC-26
❑ 90SprCarDGB-12
❑ 95IndIndF-114
❑ 96IndIndB-5
❑ 97IndInd-3
❑ 98IndIndQ-5

Young, Ken PR
❑ 98NorTidQ-36

Young, Kenny
❑ 81BriRedST-14

Young, Kevin
❑ 90WelPirP-8
❑ 91Cla/Bes-239
❑ 91SalBucC-9
❑ 91SalBucP-963
❑ 92Bow-155
❑ 92BufBisBS-26
❑ 92BufBisF-331
❑ 92BufBisS-47
❑ 92DonRoo-129
❑ 92SkyAAAF-22
❑ 93Bow-682
❑ 93Don-452
❑ 93Fin-34
❑ 93FinRef-34
❑ 93FleFinE-122
❑ 93FleMajLP-A6
❑ 93FunPac-9
❑ 93LeaGolR-R1
❑ 93LeaGolRJ-R1
❑ 93OPCPre-78
❑ 93PacSpa-594
❑ 93Pin-589
❑ 93PinRooTP-6
❑ 93PirHil-12
❑ 93PirNatl-39
❑ 93Sco-273
❑ 93ScoBoyoS-10
❑ 93ScoProaG-7
❑ 93SelRoo-51T
❑ 93SP-189
❑ 93StaClu-722
❑ 93StaCluFDI-722
❑ 93StaCluMOP-722
❑ 93Top-494
❑ 93TopGol-494
❑ 93TopInaM-494
❑ 93TopInaR-494
❑ 93TopMic-494
❑ 93TopTra-52T
❑ 93Toy-9
❑ 93TriPla-72
❑ 93Ult-459
❑ 93UltAllR-10
❑ 93UppDec-536
❑ 93UppDecDG-36
❑ 93UppDecGold-536
❑ 94Bow-274
❑ 94ColC-438
❑ 94ColChoGS-438
❑ 94ColChoSS-438
❑ 94Don-578
❑ 94Fin-321
❑ 94FinRef-321
❑ 94Fla-222
❑ 94Fle-626
❑ 94Lea-23
❑ 94OPC-124
❑ 94Pac-514
❑ 94PanSti-241
❑ 94Pin-186
❑ 94PinArtP-186
❑ 94PinMusC-186
❑ 94PirQui-29
❑ 94Sco-492
❑ 94ScoGolR-492
❑ 94Sel-123
❑ 94StaClu-321
❑ 94StaCluFDI-321
❑ 94StaCluGR-321
❑ 94StaCluMOP-321
❑ 94Top-622
❑ 94TopGol-622
❑ 94TopSpa-622
❑ 94TriPla-190
❑ 94Ult-263
❑ 94UppDec-482
❑ 94UppDecED-482
❑ 95CedRapKTI-17
❑ 95Don-335
❑ 95DonPreP-335
❑ 95Pac-355
❑ 95Sel-53
❑ 95SelArtP-53
❑ 96Fle-536
❑ 96FleTif-536
❑ 96HilStaHWB-27
❑ 96LakElsSB-25
❑ 96OmaRoyB-30
❑ 97DonLim-29
❑ 97DonLimE-29
❑ 97DonLimENG-29
❑ 97DonSigA-117
❑ 97DonSigAC-143
❑ 97DonSigAM-143
❑ 97MidAng-25
❑ 97PacPriGotD-GD53
❑ 97PirPos-45
❑ 98CirThu-66
❑ 98CirThuRav-66
❑ 98CirThuSupRav-66
❑ 98ColCho-210
❑ 98CroRoy-111
❑ 98Don-117
❑ 98DonCol-117
❑ 98DonColL-283
❑ 98DonColS-117
❑ 98DonGolPP-117
❑ 98DonPriCD-117
❑ 98DonPriCL-283
❑ 98DonSilPP-117
❑ 98Fin-27
❑ 98FinNo--27
❑ 98FinNo-R-27
❑ 98FinRef-27
❑ 98Fle-477
❑ 98FleVin'-115
❑ 98FleVin'C-115
❑ 98Lea-84
❑ 98LeaFraDA-84
❑ 98LeaFraF-84
❑ 98LeaFraM-84
❑ 98LeaFraM-84
❑ 98LeaFraMDC-84
❑ 98LeaFraMDC-84
❑ 98LeaFraMZ2-84
❑ 98LeaRS-122
❑ 98LeaRSLHolo-122
❑ 98LeaRSLong-122
❑ 98LeaRTrue-122
❑ 98Pac-404
❑ 98PacAur-179
❑ 98PacOme-193
❑ 98PacOmeR-193
❑ 98PacOnl-601
❑ 98PacOnlR-601
❑ 98PacOnlWC-601
❑ 98PacPar-225
❑ 98PacParC-225
❑ 98PacParG-225
❑ 98PacParHS-225
❑ 98PacParPB-225
❑ 98PacParR-225
❑ 98PacParTC-27
❑ 98PacPlaB-404
❑ 98PacRedT-404
❑ 98PacSil-404
❑ 98Revo-116
❑ 98RevoSS-116
❑ 98Sco-21
❑ 98ScoRT-143
❑ 98SP Aut-158
❑ 98SPxFin-118
❑ 98SPxFinR-118
❑ 98SPxFinS-118
❑ 98StaCluFDI-275
❑ 98StaCluI-275
❑ 98StaCluOneK-275
❑ 98StaCluPP-275
❑ 98Stu-9
❑ 98StuGPP-9
❑ 98StuSPP-9
❑ 98Top-182
❑ 98TopChr-182
❑ 98TopChrR-182
❑ 98TopDevR-182
❑ 98TopDia-182
❑ 98TopMiniC-182
❑ 98Ult-376
❑ 98UltGolM-376
❑ 98UltMas-376
❑ 98UltPlaM-376
❑ 98UppDec-193
❑ 98UppDecSF-105
❑ 99199Fin-9
❑ 99CroRoyB-112
❑ 99CroRoyL-112
❑ 99CroRoyOD-112
❑ 99FinGolRef-9
❑ 99FinRef-9
❑ 99Fle-288
❑ 99FleBri-64
❑ 99FleBri2G-64
❑ 99FleBriBlu-64
❑ 99FleBriGol-64
❑ 99FleMys-5
❑ 99FleMysG-5
❑ 99FleMysM-5
❑ 99FleSta9-288
❑ 99FleWarT-288
❑ 99MetUni-101
❑ 99MetUniGM-101
❑ 99MetUniPMG-101
❑ 99Pac-349
❑ 99PacAur-151
❑ 99PacAurOD-151
❑ 99PacCroC-226
❑ 99PacCroCPB-226
❑ 99PacOme-190
❑ 99PacOmeC-190
❑ 99PacOmeG-190
❑ 99PacOmePB-190
❑ 99PacPar-189
❑ 99PacParC-189
❑ 99PacParG-189
❑ 99PacParHoloGold-189
❑ 99PacParHS-189
❑ 99PacParOD-189
❑ 99PacParPB-189
❑ 99PacParRed-189
❑ 99PacPlaB-349
❑ 99PacPri-116
❑ 99PacPriHB-116
❑ 99PacPriHG-116
❑ 99PacPriHM-116
❑ 99PacPriHP-116
❑ 99PacPriRed-116
❑ 99PacPriS-150
❑ 99PacPriS206-150
❑ 99PacPriS206R-150
❑ 99PacRed-349
❑ 99Rev-113
❑ 99RevPremDate-113
❑ 99RevRet-113
❑ 99RevShaSS-113
❑ 99SkyPre-129
❑ 99SkyPreR-129
❑ 99SkyThu-234
❑ 99SkyThuRant-234
❑ 99SkyThuRave-234
❑ 99StaClu-213
❑ 99StaCluC-CS6
❑ 99StaCluC-CS11
❑ 99StaCluC-CS18
❑ 99StaCluC-CS21
❑ 99StaCluFDI-213
❑ 99StaCluOoaK-213
❑ 99StaCluPP-213
❑ 99ThuSkySupR-234
❑ 99Top-266
❑ 99TopChr-266
❑ 99TopChrR-266
❑ 99TopMVPP-266
❑ 99TopOpeD-146
❑ 99Ult-91
❑ 99UltGolM-91
❑ 99UltMas-91
❑ 99UltPlaM-91
❑ 99UppDec-181
❑ 99UppDecE-70
❑ 99UppDecEFXG-70
❑ 99UppDecEL1-181
❑ 99UppDecEL2-181
❑ 99UppDecM-167
❑ 99UppDecMGS-167
❑ 99UppDecMHFS-167
❑ 99UppDecMSS-167
❑ 99UppDecR-68
❑ 99UppDecRG-68
❑ 99UppDecRP-68
❑ 99Vic-311

Young, Kip
❑ 79Top-706
❑ 80SpoIndT-11
❑ 80Top-251
❑ 81IndIndTI-8
❑ 82IndIndTI-3

Young, Larry
❑ 88T/MUmp-54
❑ 89T/MUmp-52
❑ 90T/MUmp-50

Young, Mark
❑ 88DunBluJS-24
❑ 89ButCopKSP-22
❑ 89DunBluJS-25
❑ 89MyrBeaBJP-1452
❑ 90DunBluJS-25
❑ 90PeoChiTI-30
❑ 91KnoBluJLD-359
❑ 91KnoBluJP-1778
❑ 91LinDriAA-359

Young, Matt
❑ 81CliGiaT-12

Young, Matt J.

❑ 81LynSaiT-12
❑ 82SalLakCGT-22
❑ 83TopTra-129T
❑ 84Don-16
❑ 84Don-16A
❑ 84Don-362
❑ 84Fle-624
❑ 84MarMot-9
❑ 84Nes792-235
❑ 84Nes792-336
❑ 84OPC-235
❑ 84SevCoi-W24
❑ 84Top-235
❑ 84Top-336
❑ 84TopRubD-9
❑ 84TopSti-386
❑ 84TopTif-235
❑ 84TopTif-336
❑ 85Don-267
❑ 85Fle-505
❑ 85MarMot-14
❑ 85OPC-136
❑ 85Top-485
❑ 85TopMin-485
❑ 85TopSti-340
❑ 85TopTif-485
❑ 86Don-267
❑ 86Fle-481
❑ 86MarMot-14
❑ 86MarPacNB-16
❑ 86OPC-274
❑ 86Top-676
❑ 86TopSti-220
❑ 86TopTif-676
❑ 87DodMot-12
❑ 87DodPho-17
❑ 87DodPol-19
❑ 87Don-193
❑ 87Fle-600
❑ 87FleGlo-600
❑ 87FleUpd-131
❑ 87FleUpdG-131
❑ 87OPC-19
❑ 87RedFolSB-123
❑ 87SpoTeaP-14
❑ 87Top-19
❑ 87TopSti-218
❑ 87TopTif-19
❑ 87TopTra-131T
❑ 87TopTraT-131T
❑ 88A'sMot-21
❑ 88Don-423
❑ 88DonTeaBA-NEW
❑ 88Fle-530
❑ 88FleGlo-530
❑ 88OPC-367
❑ 88PanSti-306
❑ 88Sco-357
❑ 88ScoGlo-357
❑ 88StaLinAs-20
❑ 88Top-736
❑ 88TopSti-72
❑ 88TopTif-736
❑ 90DodTar-883
❑ 90FleUpd-121
❑ 90Lea-509
❑ 90MarMot-16
❑ 90OPC-501
❑ 90Top-501
❑ 90TopTif-501
❑ 90TopTra-131T
❑ 90TopTraT-131T
❑ 90UppDec-787
❑ 91Bow-128
❑ 91Don-493
❑ 91Fle-465
❑ 91Lea-215
❑ 91OPC-108
❑ 91RedSoxP-20
❑ 91RedSoxP-29
❑ 91Sco-126
❑ 91ScoRoo-54T
❑ 91StaClu-426
❑ 91Top-108
❑ 91TopDesS-108
❑ 91TopMic-108
❑ 91TopTif-108
❑ 91UppDec-591
❑ 91UppDec-740
❑ 92Don-635
❑ 92OPC-403
❑ 92Pin-518
❑ 92RedSoxDD-29
❑ 92Sco-668
❑ 92StaClu-682
❑ 92StaCluNC-682
❑ 92Ult-320
❑ 92UppDec-505
❑ 93ChaKniF-545
❑ 93Don-459
❑ 93Fle-567
❑ 93FleFinE-208
❑ 93Lea-153
❑ 93MilBonSS-9
❑ 93PacSpa-39
❑ 93RedSoxWHP-20
❑ 93StaClu-428
❑ 93StaCluFDI-428
❑ 93StaCluMOP-428

Young, Michael B.
❑ 97St.CatSB-30
❑ 98HagSunM-29
❑ 98SouAtlLPM-29

Young, Michael Darren
❑ 81MiaOriT-23
❑ 82RocRedWT-19
❑ 83RocRedWT-22
❑ 84BalOriP-41
❑ 84Don-621
❑ 84FleUpd-131
❑ 84RocRedWT-19
❑ 85BalOriP-37
❑ 85Don-367
❑ 85Fle-195
❑ 85OriHea-20
❑ 85Top-173
❑ 85TopTif-173
❑ 86BalOriHMP-21
❑ 86BalOriP-26
❑ 86Don-123
❑ 86Fle-291
❑ 86FleMin-61
❑ 86Spo-199
❑ 86Top-548
❑ 86TopSti-234
❑ 86TopTat-11
❑ 86TopTif-548
❑ 87BalOriP-42
❑ 87ChaRaiP-10
❑ 87Don-150
❑ 87Fle-483
❑ 87FleGlo-483
❑ 87OriFreB-43
❑ 87Top-309
❑ 87TopTif-309
❑ 88Don-396
❑ 88Fle-575
❑ 88FleGlo-575
❑ 88OPC-11
❑ 88PanSti-17
❑ 88PhiTas-26
❑ 88Sco-393
❑ 88ScoGlo-393
❑ 88ScoRoo-51T
❑ 88ScoRooG-51T
❑ 88StaLinO-20
❑ 88Top-11
❑ 88TopTif-11
❑ 89ColSprSSP-251
❑ 89Don-632
❑ 89RivRedWB-21
❑ 89RivRedWCLC-18
❑ 89RivRedWP-1399
❑ 89Sco-494
❑ 89Top-731
❑ 89TopTif-731
❑ 89UppDec-649
❑ 90GenCubS-25
❑ 90PubIntS-571
❑ 91LinDriAAA-475
❑ 91OriCro-493
❑ 91RocRedWLD-475
❑ 91RocRedWP-1920
❑ 92RocRedWF-1957
❑ 94BreMilB-93

Young, Mike
❑ 86AriWilP-20
❑ 90WauTimS-28
❑ 91PerHeaF-2

Young, Mike (Michael Leslie)
❑ 90GenCubP-3046
❑ 90WauTimP-2143
❑ 91GenCubC-26
❑ 91GenCubP-4219

Young, Mike MG
❑ 89BluOriS-30
❑ 93WatIndC-29
❑ 93WatIndF-3579
❑ 94ColRedC-26
❑ 94ColRedF-460

Young, Pep (Lemuel)
❑ 16SpoNewM-197
❑ 17ColE13-198
❑ 19W514-107
❑ 20NatCarE-113
❑ 20W516-28
❑ 21E121So8-111
❑ 22AmeCarE122-79
❑ 23W503-27
❑ 34BatR31-102
❑ 36NatChiFPR-83
❑ 39PlaBal-102
❑ 40PlaBal-106
❑ 92ConTSN-387

Young, Pete
❑ 88MisStaB-36
❑ 89JamExpP-2136
❑ 89MisStaB-41
❑ 90FloStaLAS-21
❑ 90WesPalBES-28
❑ 91Cla/Bes-189
❑ 91HarSenLD-273
❑ 91HarSenP-628
❑ 91LinDriAA-273
❑ 92DonRoo-130
❑ 92IndIndS-198
❑ 93Don-616
❑ 93FleMajLP-B17
❑ 93OttLynF-2437
❑ 93Sco-269
❑ 93Top-432
❑ 93TopGol-432
❑ 93TopInaM-432
❑ 93TopInaR-432
❑ 93TopMic-432
❑ 94NewBriRSF-651

Young, Ralph S.
❑ 13Zee-96
❑ 14Zee-98
❑ 16BF2FP-33
❑ 17HolBreD-120
❑ 22W575-153
❑ 23WilChoV-179

Young, Randy
❑ 96AubDouB-20

Young, Ray
❑ 87DunBluJP-940
❑ 88ModA'sCLC-58
❑ 88ModA'sTI-16
❑ 89HunStaB-24
❑ 90CMC-578
❑ 90ProAAAF-141
❑ 90TacTigC-1
❑ 90TacTigP-94
❑ 90TriAllGP-AAA48
❑ 91Sco-761
❑ 93LasVegSF-946

Young, Rick
❑ 75QuaCitAT-1

Young, Russ
❑ 33WorCig(-103

Young, Scott
❑ 83St.PetCT-13
❑ 86ArkTraP-26

Young, Shane
❑ 84LitFalMT-10
❑ 86LynMetP-28
❑ 87JacMetF-7
❑ 87TexLeaAF-14
❑ 88MidAngGS-5
❑ 89MidAngGS-30

Young, Sly
❑ 83AlbA'sT-16

Young, Thomas Jefferson
❑ 87NegLeaPD-28

Young, Tim
❑ 96VerExpB-30
❑ 98arSenW1-23
❑ 98FleUpd-U53
❑ 98HarSenM-23
❑ 99Fle-267
❑ 99FleSta9-267
❑ 99FleWarT-267
❑ 99SpoIll-53

Young, Travis
❑ 97SalVolG-41
❑ 98SanJosGQ-18

Young, Ty
❑ 92GulCoaMF-3496

Youngbauer, Jeff
❑ 77OrlTwiT-23
❑ 79RocRedWT-1
❑ 91PacSenL-74

Youngblood, Joel
❑ 77Top-548
❑ 78MetDaiPA-25
❑ 78Top-428
❑ 79OPC-48
❑ 79Top-109
❑ 80OPC-194
❑ 80Top-372
❑ 81CokTeaS-95
❑ 81Don-277
❑ 81Fle-331
❑ 81OPC-58
❑ 81Top-58
❑ 81TopSti-195
❑ 82Don-613
❑ 82ExpPos-42
❑ 82Fle-543
❑ 82OPC-189
❑ 82RegGloT-10
❑ 82Top-655
❑ 82TopSti-65
❑ 82TopStiV-65
❑ 83Don-572
❑ 83Fle-301
❑ 83Fle-641
❑ 83GiaMot-17
❑ 83GiaPos-27
❑ 83OPC-265
❑ 83Top-265
❑ 83TopSti-143
❑ 83TopSti-144
❑ 83TopTra-130T
❑ 84Don-480
❑ 84Fle-387
❑ 84GiaPos-31
❑ 84Nes792-727
❑ 84OPC-303
❑ 84Top-727
❑ 84TopSti-173
❑ 84TopTif-727
❑ 85Don-79
❑ 85Fle-625
❑ 85GiaMot-19
❑ 85GiaPos-31
❑ 85Lea-152
❑ 85OPC-97
❑ 85Top-567
❑ 85TopSti-168
❑ 85TopTif-567
❑ 86Don-567A
❑ 86Don-567B
❑ 86Fle-555
❑ 86GiaMot-26
❑ 86OPC-177
❑ 86Top-177
❑ 86TopTif-177
❑ 87Fle-288
❑ 87FleGlo-288
❑ 87GiaMot-20
❑ 87GiaPos-35
❑ 87OPC-378
❑ 87Top-759
❑ 87TopTif-759
❑ 88GiaMot-20
❑ 88GiaPos-34
❑ 88Sco-509
❑ 88ScoGlo-509
❑ 88Top-418
❑ 88TopTif-418
❑ 89Bow-315
❑ 89BowTif-315
❑ 89RedKah-12
❑ 89Sco-539
❑ 89ScoRoo-66T
❑ 89Top-304
❑ 89TopTif-304
❑ 89UppDec-458
❑ 90PubIntS-42
❑ 90Sco-344
❑ 91FreKeyC-28
❑ 91MetWIZ-437
❑ 91PacSenL-131
❑ 92KanCouCC-26
❑ 92KanCouCF-108
❑ 92KanCouCTI-30
❑ 94RedKah-33
❑ 95RedKah-34
❑ 97FleMilDM-47
❑ 97FleMilDMR-47

Youngblood, Todd
❑ 91BelMarCB-25
❑ 91BelMarP-3666
❑ 92PenPilC-25
❑ 92PenPilF-2934
❑ 93RivPilCLC-25

Youngdahl, Raynor Lee
❑ 63RocRedWSP-9

Younger, Stan
❑ 81BirBarT-17
❑ 82BirBarT-1
❑ 83BirBarT-5
❑ 84EvaTriT-7
❑ 89BirBarADB-33
❑ 90BirBarADB-33

Youngman, Pete
❑ 86GreHorP-25
❑ 87GreHorP-4
❑ 89NewBriRSP-601
❑ 89NewBriRSS-25
❑ 90PawRedSDD-30
❑ 93PawRedSDD-30

Youngs, Ross M.
❑ 20NatCarE-114
❑ 21E121So1-117
❑ 21Exh-193
❑ 21KoBreWSI-26
❑ 21Nei-106
❑ 22E120-195
❑ 22W573-142
❑ 22W575-154
❑ 23W501-68
❑ 23W515-29
❑ 23WilChoV-180
❑ 61Fle-154
❑ 73TCMAllG-24
❑ 75TCMAllG-36
❑ 76ShaPiz-134
❑ 77GalGloG-131
❑ 78DexHaloFP-53
❑ 80PerHaloFP-134
❑ 80SSPHOF-134
❑ 87HygAllG-50
❑ 91ConTSN-26

Yount, Andy
❑ 95Bes-116
❑ 95SPML-113
❑ 96LowSpiB-29

Yount, Jason
❑ 98ButCopKG-33

Yount, Robin
❑ 75Hos-80
❑ 75HosTwi-80
❑ 75OPC-223
❑ 75Top-223
❑ 75TopMin-223
❑ 76BreA&P-15
❑ 76Hos-11
❑ 76HosTwi-11
❑ 76OPC-316
❑ 76SSP-238
❑ 76Top-316
❑ 77BurCheD-88
❑ 77ChiWilD-69
❑ 77DailsID-69
❑ 77DetCaeD-69
❑ 77HolInnD-69
❑ 77Hos-34
❑ 77MSADis-69
❑ 77OPC-204
❑ 77PepGloD-1
❑ 77RCColC-69
❑ 77SagDis-69
❑ 77sDis-69
❑ 77Top-635
❑ 77TopCloS-54
❑ 77WenDis-69
❑ 77ZipDis-69
❑ 78Hos-138
❑ 78OPC-29
❑ 78RCColC-56
❑ 78Top-173
❑ 79Hos-55
❑ 79OPC-41
❑ 79Top-95
❑ 80BreTeal-23
❑ 80OPC-139
❑ 80Top-265
❑ 81AllGamPI-26
❑ 81Don-323
❑ 81Fle-511
❑ 81FleStiC-38
❑ 81Kel-57
❑ 81OPC-4
❑ 81Top-515
❑ 81TopScr-10
❑ 81TopSti-95
❑ 81TopSti-244
❑ 82BrePol-19
❑ 82Don-510
❑ 82Fle-155
❑ 82FleSta-135
❑ 82Kel-28
❑ 82OPC-237
❑ 82PerAll-4
❑ 82PerAllG-4
❑ 82Top-435
❑ 82TopSti-203
❑ 83AllGamPI-27
❑ 83BreGar-22
❑ 83BrePol-19
❑ 83Don-258
❑ 83DonActA-56
❑ 83Dra-33
❑ 83Fle-51
❑ 83Fle-632
❑ 83FleSta-222
❑ 83FleSti-18
❑ 83Kel-14
❑ 83Oco& SSBG-20
❑ 83OPC-350
❑ 83OPC-389
❑ 83PerAll-9
❑ 83PerAllG-9
❑ 83PerCreC-36
❑ 83PerCreCG-36
❑ 83Top-321
❑ 83Top-350
❑ 83Top-389
❑ 83TopGloS-5
❑ 83TopSti-81
❑ 83TopSti-145
❑ 83TopSti-146
❑ 83TopSti-150
❑ 83TopSti-167
❑ 84AllGamPI-116
❑ 84BreGar-22
❑ 84BrePol-19
❑ 84Don-1
❑ 84Don-1A
❑ 84Don-48
❑ 84DonActAS-5
❑ 84DonCha-47
❑ 84Dra-33
❑ 84Fle-219
❑ 84FunFooP-29
❑ 84MilBra-30
❑ 84Nes792-10
❑ 84OCoandSI-17
❑ 84OCoandSI-221
❑ 84OPC-10
❑ 84RalPur-21
❑ 84SevCoi-C2
❑ 84SevCoi-E2
❑ 84SevCoi-W2
❑ 84Top-10
❑ 84TopCer-21
❑ 84TopGloA-5
❑ 84TopGloS-36
❑ 84TopRubD-32
❑ 84TopSti-295
❑ 84TopStiB-6
❑ 84TopSup-29
❑ 84TopTif-10
❑ 85AllGamPI-27
❑ 85BreGar-22
❑ 85BrePol-19
❑ 85Don-48
❑ 85DonActA-21
❑ 85Dra-33
❑ 85Fle-601
❑ 85FleLimE-44
❑ 85GenMilS-26
❑ 85Lea-44
❑ 85OPC-340
❑ 85SevCoi-G16
❑ 85Top-340
❑ 85TopMin-340
❑ 85TopRubD-32
❑ 85TopSti-284
❑ 85TopSup-37
❑ 85TopTif-340
❑ 86BasStaB-124
❑ 86BrePol-19
❑ 86Don-48
❑ 86DorChe-16
❑ 86Fle-506
❑ 86FleLeaL-44
❑ 86FleMin-103
❑ 86FleSlu-44
❑ 86FleStiC-131
❑ 86Lea-31
❑ 86MSAJayPCD-20
❑ 86MSAJifPD-5
❑ 86OPC-144
❑ 86SevCoi-C9
❑ 86Spo-42A
❑ 86Spo-42B
❑ 86Spo-54
❑ 86Spo-63

❑ 86Spo-71
❑ 86SpoDecG-73
❑ 86Top-780
❑ 86TopSti-197
❑ 86TopTat-9
❑ 86TopTif-780
❑ 86TruVal-11
❑ 87BoaandB-9
❑ 87BrePol-19
❑ 87BreTeal-16
❑ 87ClaGam-44
❑ 87Don-126
❑ 87DonOpeD-58
❑ 87Fle-361
❑ 87FleGlo-361
❑ 87FleLimE-44
❑ 87FleStiC-130
❑ 87FleWaxBC-C16
❑ 87GenMilB-2J
❑ 87HosSti-25
❑ 87KraFoo-23
❑ 87Lea-67
❑ 87OPC-76
❑ 87RedFolSB-126
❑ 87Spo-16
❑ 87SpoTeaP-19
❑ 87StuPan-21
❑ 87Top-773
❑ 87TopSti-196
❑ 87TopTif-773
❑ 88BrePol-19
❑ 88BreTeal-37
❑ 88Don-295
❑ 88DonBasB-183
❑ 88Fle-178
❑ 88FleBasM-44
❑ 88FleGlo-178
❑ 88FleMin-33
❑ 88FleStiC-40
❑ 88FleSup-44
❑ 88GreBasS-44
❑ 88K-M-33
❑ 88Lea-106
❑ 88MSAJifPD-20
❑ 88OPC-165
❑ 88PanSti-129
❑ 88Sco-160
❑ 88ScoGlo-160
❑ 88Spo-34
❑ 88StaLinAl-38
❑ 88StaLinBre-20
❑ 88Top-165
❑ 88TopBig-66
❑ 88TopCoi-32
❑ 88TopMinL-21
❑ 88TopSti-201
❑ 88TopTif-165
❑ 88TopUKM-87
❑ 88TopUKMT-87
❑ 89Bow-144
❑ 89BowTif-144
❑ 89BreGar-2
❑ 89BrePol-19
❑ 89BreYea-19
❑ 89ClaLigB-83
❑ 89Don-5
❑ 89Don-55
❑ 89DonBasB-53
❑ 89DonSupD-5
❑ 89Fle-200
❑ 89FleExcS-44
❑ 89FleGlo-200
❑ 89FleHeroB-44
❑ 89FleLeaL-44
❑ 89KayB-33
❑ 89KinDis-13
❑ 89OPC-253
❑ 89PanSti-377
❑ 89RedFolSB-130
❑ 89Sco-151
❑ 89ScoHot1S-28
❑ 89Spo-199
❑ 89SpollIFKI-127
❑ 89Top-615
❑ 89TopAme2C-33
❑ 89TopAwaW-6
❑ 89TopBasT-56
❑ 89TopBatL-21
❑ 89TopBig-249
❑ 89TopCapC-21
❑ 89TopCoi-60
❑ 89TopGloS-38
❑ 89TopHilTM-33
❑ 89TopMinL-59
❑ 89TopSti-205
❑ 89TopStiB-21
❑ 89TopTif-615
❑ 89TopUKM-87
❑ 89TVSpoM-74
❑ 89UppDec-285
❑ 90AllBasT-13
❑ 90Baz-2
❑ 90Bow-404
❑ 90BowIns-11
❑ 90BowInsL-11
❑ 90BowInsT-11
❑ 90BowTif-404
❑ 90BowTif-A11
❑ 90BreMilB-31
❑ 90BrePol-19
❑ 90ClaBlu-147
❑ 90Col-9
❑ 90Don-146
❑ 90DonBesA-22
❑ 90DonLeaS-37
❑ 90Fle-340
❑ 90FleAwaW-44
❑ 90FleBasA-44
❑ 90FleBasAC-44
❑ 90FleBasM-44
❑ 90FleBasMC-44
❑ 90FleCan-340
❑ 90FleLeaL-44
❑ 90FleLeaLC-44
❑ 90FleWaxBC-C28
❑ 90GooHumICBLS-26
❑ 90Hot50PS-50
❑ 90KayB-33
❑ 90KinDis-18
❑ 90Lea-71
❑ 90M.Vpin-54
❑ 90MLBBasB-82
❑ 90MSAHolD-7
❑ 90OPC-290
❑ 90OPC-389
❑ 90PanSti-92
❑ 90Pos-26
❑ 90PubIntS-508
❑ 90Sco-320
❑ 90Sco100S-92
❑ 90ScoMcD-25
❑ 90Spo-18
❑ 90StaMit-1
❑ 90StaMit-3
❑ 90StaMit-5
❑ 90StaMit-7
❑ 90StaMit-9
❑ 90StaMit-11
❑ 90StaYou-1
❑ 90StaYou-2
❑ 90StaYou-3
❑ 90StaYou-4
❑ 90StaYou-5
❑ 90StaYou-6
❑ 90StaYou-7
❑ 90StaYou-8
❑ 90StaYou-9
❑ 90StaYou-10
❑ 90StaYou-11
❑ 90SunSee-6
❑ 90SupActM-6
❑ 90Top-290
❑ 90Top-389
❑ 90TopAmeA-5
❑ 90TopBatL-15
❑ 90TopBig-59
❑ 90TopCoi-1
❑ 90TopDou-72
❑ 90TopGaloC-12
❑ 90TopGloS-15
❑ 90TopMag-12
❑ 90TopMinL-22
❑ 90TopSti-198
❑ 90TopStiB-54
❑ 90TopTif-290
❑ 90TopTif-389
❑ 90TopTVA-23
❑ 90UppDec-91
❑ 90UppDec-567
❑ 90WonBreS-11
❑ 90Woo-1
❑ 90Woo-22
❑ 91BasBesHM-18
❑ 91Bow-55
❑ 91BreMilB-31
❑ 91BrePol-28
❑ 91CadEllD-62
❑ 91ClaGam-59
❑ 91Don-272
❑ 91Fle-601
❑ 91Lea-116
❑ 91MajLeaCP-43
❑ 91MooSna-17
❑ 91OPC-575
❑ 91OPCBoxB-P
❑ 91OPCPre-131
❑ 91PanCanT1-56
❑ 91PanFreS-208
❑ 91PanSti-166
❑ 91PosCan-21
❑ 91RedFolS-104
❑ 91Sco-525
❑ 91Sco-854
❑ 91Sco100S-38
❑ 91StaClu-509
❑ 91Stu-80
❑ 91Top-575
❑ 91TopCraJI-23
❑ 91TopDesS-575
❑ 91TopMic-575
❑ 91TopSta-36
❑ 91TopTif-575
❑ 91TopTriH-A8
❑ 91TopWaxBC-P
❑ 91Ult-184
❑ 91UppDec-344
❑ 91Woo-22
❑ 92Bow-700
❑ 92BreCarT-26
❑ 92BrePol-29
❑ 92BreSenY-1
❑ 92BreSenY-2
❑ 92BreSenY-3
❑ 92BreSenY-4
❑ 92BreUSO-4
❑ 92Cla1-T98
❑ 92Cla2-T30
❑ 92ClaGam-128
❑ 92Don-173
❑ 92DonCraJ1-8
❑ 92DonMcD-12
❑ 92Fle-194
❑ 92Fle-708
❑ 92FleUpdH-2
❑ 92Hig5-70
❑ 92JimDeaLL-4
❑ 92Lea-64
❑ 92Lea-397
❑ 92LeaBlaG-64
❑ 92LeaBlaG-397
❑ 92LeaGolP-20
❑ 92LeaPre-20
❑ 92Mr.TurS-26
❑ 92MVPPin-27
❑ 92OPC-90
❑ 92OPCPre-111
❑ 92PanSti-40
❑ 92Pin-38
❑ 92Pin-287
❑ 92RedFolS-103
❑ 92Sco-525
❑ 92Sco100S-84
❑ 92ScoCokD-24
❑ 92ScoFacI-B11
❑ 92ScoProP-6
❑ 92SevCoi-17
❑ 92SpoStaCC-49
❑ 92StaClu-450
❑ 92StaClu-607
❑ 92StaCluECN-607
❑ 92Stu-200
❑ 92StuPre-6
❑ 92Top-90
❑ 92TopGol-90
❑ 92TopGolW-90
❑ 92TopKid-80
❑ 92TopMcD-17
❑ 92TopMic-90
❑ 92TriPla-81
❑ 92Ult-87
❑ 92UppDec-456
❑ 92UppDecF-44
❑ 92UppDecFG-44
❑ 93Bow-535
❑ 93BrePol-28
❑ 93BrePol-29
❑ 93BreSen-4
❑ 93ClaGam-99
❑ 93DenHol-6
❑ 93DiaMar-119
❑ 93DiaMarA-8
❑ 93Don-441
❑ 93DonDiaK-DK16
❑ 93DonEli-L3
❑ 93DonMasotG-15
❑ 93DonPre-17
❑ 93DonSpiotG-SG20
❑ 93DurPowP1-16
❑ 93Fin-192
❑ 93FinRef-192
❑ 93Fla-232
❑ 93Fle-260
❑ 93FleFinEDT-10
❑ 93FleFruotL-65
❑ 93FunPac-69
❑ 93FunPac-73
❑ 93Kra-15
❑ 93Lea-188
❑ 93LeaHeaftH-3
❑ 93OPC-365
❑ 93PacSpa-167
❑ 93PanSti-42
❑ 93Pin-118
❑ 93Pin-293
❑ 93PinCoo-3
❑ 93PinCooD-3
❑ 93Pos-30
❑ 93PosCan-6
❑ 93RedFolS-103
❑ 93Sco-47
❑ 93Sco-518
❑ 93ScoFra-8
❑ 93Sel-22
❑ 93SelSam-22
❑ 93SelStaL-14
❑ 93SP-72
❑ 93StaClu-173
❑ 93StaCluFDI-173
❑ 93StaClul-A1
❑ 93StaCluMOP-173
❑ 93StaCluMOP-MA1
❑ 93Stu-118
❑ 93Top-1
❑ 93TopGol-1
❑ 93TopInaM-1
❑ 93TopInaR-1
❑ 93TopMic-1
❑ 93TopMic-P1
❑ 93TopPre-1
❑ 93TriPla-188
❑ 93TriPlaA-16
❑ 93Ult-227
❑ 93UppDec-43
❑ 93UppDec-587
❑ 93UppDec-SP5
❑ 93UppDecDG-6
❑ 93UppDecGold-43
❑ 93UppDecGold-587
❑ 93UppDecSH-HI20
❑ 93UppDecTAN-TN15
❑ 94AmeYou-1
❑ 94BreMilB-94
❑ 94BreMilB-376
❑ 94BreSen-8
❑ 94ChuHomS-25
❑ 94ChuHomSG-25
❑ 94Don-15
❑ 94DonAnn8-2
❑ 94DonSpeE-15
❑ 94Fle-197
❑ 94FUnPac-202
❑ 94Pac-348
❑ 94PacSilP-1
❑ 94PacSilPC-1
❑ 94RedFolMI-28
❑ 94Sco-13
❑ 94ScoGolR-13
❑ 94Spo-24
❑ 94StaClu-1
❑ 94StaCluFDI-1
❑ 94StaCluGR-1
❑ 94StaCluMOP-1
❑ 94TomPiz-30
❑ 94Top-310
❑ 94TopGol-310
❑ 94TopSpa-310
❑ 94TriPla-60
❑ 94UppDecDC-C10
❑ 94UppDecS-3
❑ 95ColCho-47
❑ 95ColCho-54
❑ 95ColChoGS-47
❑ 95ColChoGS-54
❑ 95ColChoSS-47
❑ 95ColChoSS-54
❑ 95UppDec-446
❑ 95UppDecED-446
❑ 95UppDecEDG-446
❑ 95UppDecSHoB-7
❑ 97HigMinMCT-54
❑ 97HigMinMCT-55
❑ 99SP SigAuto-RY
❑ 99SPSig-168
❑ 99UppDecR-91
❑ 99UppDecRG-91
❑ 99UppDecRI-RY
❑ 99UppDecRIL2-RY
❑ 99UppDecRP-91

Youppi, Mascot
❑ 84ExpStu-1
❑ 85ExpPos-26
❑ 86ExpProPa-27
❑ 87ExpPos-37
❑ 88ExpPos-38
❑ 90JamExpP-32
❑ 93FunPacM-5
❑ 94MasMan-16
❑ 96ExpDis-24

Youse, Bob
❑ 73CedRapAT-23
❑ 74CedRapAT-2

Yselonia, John
❑ 93WelPirC-28
❑ 94AugGreC-27
❑ 94AugGreF-3019

Yuhas, John Ed
❑ 52Top-386
❑ 53CarHunW-26
❑ 53Top-70
❑ 54CarHunW-29
❑ 83TopRep5-386
❑ 91TopArc1-70

Yuhas, Marty
❑ 93WilBluRC-30

Yuhas, Vince
❑ 83OmaRoyT-10
❑ 84MemChiT-15
❑ 84OmaRoyT-16

Yurak, Jeff
❑ 75CedRapGT-8
❑ 76CedRapGT-36
❑ 77HolMilT-26
❑ 78HolMilT-24
❑ 79HolMilT-28
❑ 79VanCanT-18
❑ 94BreMilB-282

Yurcisin, Scott
❑ 90JamExpP-30

Yurtin, Jeff
❑ 86SpoIndC-176
❑ 88WicPilRD-11
❑ 89BlaYNPRWLU-24
❑ 89LasVegSC-20
❑ 89LasVegSP-20
❑ 90CMC-522
❑ 90LasVegSC-19
❑ 90LasVegSP-132
❑ 90LSUTigGM-10
❑ 90ProAAAF-20

Yvars, Sal
❑ 52Top-338
❑ 53Top-11
❑ 54Bow-78
❑ 54CarHunW-30
❑ 75Gia195T-32
❑ 83TopRep5-338
❑ 91TopArc1-11

Zabala, Ismael
❑ 94VenLinU-248
❑ 95LinVen-215
❑ 96-97LinVen-91

Zabel, George
❑ 16Zee-18

Zachary, Chink (Albert M.)
❑ 90DodTar-1101

Zachary, Chris
❑ 64Top-23
❑ 64TopVen-23
❑ 66Top-313
❑ 66TopVen-313
❑ 67Top-212
❑ 70OPC-471
❑ 70Top-471
❑ 71CarTeal-30
❑ 71CarTeal-44
❑ 73OPC-256
❑ 73Top-256
❑ 87AstShoSTw-20

Zachary, J. Tom
❑ 21Nei-3
❑ 22E120-120
❑ 22W572-119
❑ 22W573-143
❑ 27YorCarE-26
❑ 28PorandAR-A40
❑ 28PorandAR-B40
❑ 29PorandAR-101
❑ 31Exh-1
❑ 33ButCanV-58
❑ 33Gou-91
❑ 34DiaMatCSB-200
❑ 34GouCanV-47
❑ 34TarThoBD-17
❑ 35GouPuzR-8A
❑ 35GouPuzR-8M
❑ 67SpoHobFC-28
❑ 75SenTCM1-36
❑ 75SenTCM1-40
❑ 90DodTar-884
❑ 93ConTSN-693

Zacher, Elmer
❑ 07NewEveWS-15
❑ 09ObaT21-287
❑ 10JuJuDE-43
❑ 11PacCoaBD-72
❑ 11Zee-43
❑ 12HomRunKE-31
❑ 12ObaPreT-36
❑ 12PCLPin-26
❑ 12Zee-49
❑ 13Zee-50
❑ 14Zee-50
❑ 15Zee-93
❑ 16Zee-95
❑ 70MetMusoAB-8

Zacher, Todd
❑ 82CliGiaF-8

Zachery, Nicholas
❑ 98JohCCTI-36

Zachmann, Rob
❑ 96EveAquB-1
❑ 97WisTimR-28

Zachry, Pat
❑ 76OPC-599
❑ 76Top-599
❑ 77OPC-201
❑ 77PepGloD-57
❑ 77Top-86
❑ 78MetDaiPA-26
❑ 78OPC-172
❑ 78Top-171
❑ 79Kel-8
❑ 79OPC-327
❑ 79Top-621
❑ 80OPC-220
❑ 80Top-428
❑ 81CokTeaS-89
❑ 81Don-275
❑ 81Fle-334
❑ 81OPC-224
❑ 81Top-224
❑ 81TopSti-197
❑ 82Don-254
❑ 82Fle-544
❑ 82FleSta-88
❑ 82MetPhoA-26
❑ 82OPC-64
❑ 82Top-399
❑ 82TopSti-71
❑ 83DodPol-38
❑ 83Don-560
❑ 83Fle-561
❑ 83FleSta-223
❑ 83FleSti-237
❑ 83Top-522
❑ 83TopTra-131T
❑ 84DodPol-38
❑ 84Don-215
❑ 84Fle-118
❑ 84Nes792-747
❑ 84Top-747
❑ 84TopTif-747
❑ 85Fle-391
❑ 85PhiTas-9
❑ 85PhiTas-23
❑ 85Top-57
❑ 85TopTif-57
❑ 87VerBeaDP-8
❑ 88SanAntMB-27
❑ 88SanAntMB-28
❑ 89PacSenL-20
❑ 90DodTar-885
❑ 91MetWIZ-438

Zackert, George
❑ 09ObaT21-204
❑ 09ObaT21-380
❑ 12ObaPreT-129

Zaeffel, John
❑ 26Zee-157

Zahn, Geoff
❑ 70RelPam-18
❑ 75OPC-294
❑ 75Top-294
❑ 75TopMin-294
❑ 76OPC-403

❑ 76Top-403
❑ 78Top-27
❑ 78TwiFriP-25
❑ 79Kel-27
❑ 79OPC-358
❑ 79Top-678
❑ 79TwiFriP-29
❑ 80Top-113
❑ 80TwiPos-32
❑ 81Don-532A
❑ 81Don-532B
❑ 81Fle-564
❑ 81LonBeaPT-9
❑ 81Top-363
❑ 81TopTra-856
❑ 82Don-164
❑ 82Fle-474
❑ 82Top-229
❑ 83AllGamPI-90
❑ 83Don-66
❑ 83Fle-103
❑ 83FleSti-29
❑ 83OPC-131
❑ 83Top-547
❑ 83TopSti-42
❑ 84AllGamPI-180
❑ 84AngSmo-32
❑ 84Don-402
❑ 84Fle-532
❑ 84Nes792-276
❑ 84Nes792-468
❑ 84OPC-153
❑ 84Top-276
❑ 84Top-468
❑ 84TopTif-276
❑ 84TopTif-468
❑ 85AllGamPI-90
❑ 85AngSmo-15
❑ 85Don-301
❑ 85DonActA-33
❑ 85Fle-317
❑ 85Lea-53
❑ 85OPC-140
❑ 85SpoIndGC-24
❑ 85SubDis-24
❑ 85ThoMcAD-24
❑ 85Top-771
❑ 85TopSti-221
❑ 85TopTif-771
❑ 86Top-42
❑ 86TopTif-42
❑ 90DodTar-886

Zahn, Paul
❑ 74WicAerODF-102

Zahner, Kevin
❑ 92YakBeaC-9
❑ 92YakBeaF-3454
❑ 93YakBeaC-27
❑ 94VerBeaDC-25
❑ 94VerBeaDF-77
❑ 95BakBlaTI-10

Zahniser, Paul
❑ 32Zee-48
❑ 75SenTCM1-37

Zajeski, Mike
❑ 88NebCor-27
❑ 90NebCor-28

Zaksek, John
❑ 88UtiBluSP-13
❑ 89SouBenWSGS-20
❑ 90Bes-165
❑ 90MidLeaASGS-25
❑ 90SouBenWSB-14
❑ 90SouBenWSGS-22

Zaleski, Richard
❑ 82DanSunF-15
❑ 83NasAngT-22
❑ 86MidAngP-26
❑ 87EdmTraP-2075

Zaletel, Brian
❑ 93EveGiaC-30
❑ 93EveGiaF-3781
❑ 94CliLumC-25
❑ 94CliLumF-1992

Zallie, Chris
❑ 98LowSpiM-31

Zaltsman, Stan
❑ 86EriCarP-29
❑ 87SavCarP-22
❑ 88St.PetCS-25

Zamarripa, Mark
❑ 97WesMicW-28
❑ 98WesMicWM-29
❑ 98WilCubM-27

Zambrana, Luis
❑ 81RedPioT-21
❑ 82RedPioT-18
❑ 83RedPioT-27
❑ 94VenLinU-206

Zambrano, Alan
❑ 98EveAquG-30

Zambrano, Eddie (Eduardo)
❑ 85GreHorT-13
❑ 86GreHorP-26
❑ 87WinHavRSP-21
❑ 88NewBriRSP-895
❑ 89NewBriRSP-599
❑ 89NewBriRSS-21
❑ 89Sta-131
❑ 90KinIndTI-25
❑ 91CarMudLD-123
❑ 91CarMudP-1100
❑ 91LinDriAA-123
❑ 92BufBisBS-27
❑ 92BufBisF-337
❑ 92BufBisS-48
❑ 92TriA AAS-48
❑ 93IowCubF-2147
❑ 93LinVenB-260
❑ 93TriAAAGF-6
❑ 94Bow-337
❑ 94FleUpd-113
❑ 94Pac-117
❑ 94Pin-237
❑ 94PinArtP-237
❑ 94PinMusC-237
❑ 94Sco-385
❑ 94ScoGolR-385
❑ 94ScoRoo-RT93
❑ 94ScoRooGR-RT93
❑ 94Sel-400
❑ 94SpoRoo-129
❑ 94SpoRooAP-129
❑ 94Top-616
❑ 94TopGol-616
❑ 94TopSpa-616
❑ 94Ult-467
❑ 94VenLinU-197
❑ 94VenLinU-200
❑ 95ColCho-207
❑ 95ColChoGS-207
❑ 95ColChoSS-207
❑ 95Don-64
❑ 95DonPreP-64
❑ 95Fla-118
❑ 95Fle-428
❑ 95LinVen-116
❑ 95Pac-81
❑ 95Sco-202
❑ 95ScoGolR-202
❑ 95ScoPlaTS-202
❑ 95StaClu-297
❑ 95StaCluMOP-297
❑ 95StaCluSTWS-297
❑ 95Top-34
❑ 95TopCyb-26
❑ 96-97LinVen-75

Zambrano, Jose
❑ 91Cla/Bes-34
❑ 91LynRedSC-24
❑ 91LynRedSP-1214
❑ 92WinHavRSF-1793
❑ 93ForLauRSC-26
❑ 93ForLauRSFP-1612
❑ 93LinVenB-17
❑ 95LinVen-44
❑ 96-97LinVen-107

Zambrano, Roberto
❑ 85GreHorT-10
❑ 86WinHavRSP-27
❑ 87NewBriRSP-20
❑ 88NewBriRSP-911
❑ 90CanIndP-1307
❑ 90CanIndS-19
❑ 90CMC-777
❑ 91ColSprSSLD-94
❑ 91ColSprSSP-2199
❑ 91LinDriAAA-94
❑ 93LinVenB-239
❑ 94VenLinU-185
❑ 95LinVen-117
❑ 96-97LinVen-62

Zambrano, Victor
❑ 98ChaRivDG-33

Zamloch, Carl
❑ 09ObaT21-339
❑ 11Zee-106
❑ 12ObaPreT-88
❑ 19Zee-106
❑ 20Zee-134
❑ 30Zee-99
❑ 31Zee-58
❑ 32Zee-69

Zammarchi, Erik
❑ 91GreFalDSP-20
❑ 92YakBeaC-18
❑ 92YakBeaF-3467

Zamora, Junior
❑ 97CapCitB-22
❑ 98St.LucMM-17

Zamora, Oscar
❑ 75OPC-604
❑ 75Top-604
❑ 75TopMin-604
❑ 76OPC-227
❑ 76SSP-304
❑ 76Top-227
❑ 76VenLeaS-67
❑ 78Top-91

Zamora, Peter
❑ 97GreFalDTI-26
❑ 98SanBerS-32
❑ 98SanBerSTIS-28

Zancanaro, Dave
❑ 90ProAaA-162
❑ 90SouOreAB-24
❑ 90SouOreAP-3423
❑ 91Cla/Bes-124
❑ 91Cla1-T77
❑ 91HunStaC-20
❑ 91HunStaLD-298
❑ 91HunStaP-1797
❑ 91HunStaTI-23
❑ 91LinDriAA-298
❑ 91SouOreAAP-SOA35
❑ 92Bow-99
❑ 92SkyAAAF-246
❑ 92TacTigF-2505
❑ 92TacTigS-548
❑ 92UppDec-54
❑ 96HunStaTI-27
❑ 96ModA'sB-13
❑ 97MobBayBB-19
❑ 98NorNavQ-26

Zane, Kelly
❑ 88SalLakCTTI-8
❑ 89RocExpLC-31

Zane, Lisa
❑ 91TopRut-4

Zanni, Dom
❑ 59Top-145
❑ 59TopVen-145
❑ 60TacBan-21
❑ 61TacBan-21
❑ 62Top-214
❑ 63RedFreBC-32
❑ 63Top-354
❑ 63WhiSoxTS-27
❑ 66Top-233
❑ 66TopVen-233

Zanolla, Dan
❑ 93SpoIndC-27
❑ 93SpoIndF-3601
❑ 94OgdRapF-3745
❑ 94OgdRapSP-14
❑ 95KanCouCTI-29

Zapata, Alexis
❑ 97WesMicW-29
❑ 98WesMicWM-30

Zapata, Gustavo
❑ 91KisDodP-4199

Zapata, Juan
❑ 96OgdRapTI-29
❑ 98StoPorUG-6

Zapata, Ramon
❑ 92AugPirC-11
❑ 92AugPirF-248
❑ 93AugPirC-26
❑ 93AugPirF-1556
❑ 94SalBucC-25
❑ 94SalBucF-2334
❑ 95LynHilTI-30

Zapelli, Mark
❑ 87AncGlaP-33
❑ 91MidAngOHP-32
❑ 92SkyAA F-202

Zapp, A.J.
❑ 96BesAutS1RP-FR13
❑ 97AppLeaTPB-2
❑ 97Bes-34
❑ 97BesDiaB-15
❑ 97BesLimA-44
❑ 97Bow-384
❑ 97BowChr-253
❑ 97BowChrI-253
❑ 97BowChrIR-253
❑ 97BowChrR-253
❑ 97BowInt-384
❑ 97DanBraB-1
❑ 97DanBraB-2
❑ 97Top-274
❑ 98BesAutPOY-21
❑ 98BesCasT-12
❑ 98BesDiaBA-10
❑ 98BesFulCA-24
❑ 98BesPreA-49
❑ 98Bow-340
❑ 98BowChr-340
❑ 98BowChrGA-340
❑ 98BowChrGAR-340
❑ 98BowChrI-340
❑ 98BowChrIR-340
❑ 98BowChrR-340
❑ 98BowGolA-340
❑ 98BowInt-340
❑ 98MacBraM-1
❑ 98SouAtlLPM-30

Zapp, Jim
❑ 86NegLeaF-46
❑ 92NegLeaRLI-65
❑ 97NegLeaPC-7C

Zappelli, Mark
❑ 89QuaCitAB-17
❑ 89QuaCitAGS-5
❑ 90MidAngGS-6
❑ 91LinDriAA-448
❑ 91MidAngLD-448
❑ 91MidAngP-435
❑ 92ClaFS7-340
❑ 92MidAngF-4029
❑ 92MidAngOHP-28
❑ 92MidAngS-473
❑ 93VanCanF-2600
❑ 94VenLinU-71

Zarate, Vincent
❑ 93PeoChiC-24
❑ 93PeoChiF-1099
❑ 93PeoChiTI-32

Zarilla, Al
❑ 46SeaSLP-68
❑ 47Exh-246
❑ 47TipTop-75
❑ 49Bow-156
❑ 49Lea-36
❑ 49RedSoxTI-25
❑ 50Bow-45
❑ 50RedSoxTI-30
❑ 51Bow-35
❑ 51R42SmaS-118
❑ 51TopRedB-49
❑ 52Bow-113
❑ 52StaCalL-73A
❑ 52StaCalS-87D
❑ 52TipTop-48
❑ 52Top-70
❑ 52WhiSoxHDP-10
❑ 53RedSoxTI-30
❑ 53Top-181
❑ 54SeaPop-28
❑ 76TayBow4-102
❑ 79DiaGre-191
❑ 79HawIsIC-3
❑ 79HawIsIT-15
❑ 81RedSoxBG2S-63
❑ 83TopRep5-70
❑ 85TCMPla1-40
❑ 91TopArc1-181
❑ 96Bro194F-11

Zarranz, Fernando
❑ 86GenCubP-27
❑ 86PeoChiP-27
❑ 87PeoChiP-27
❑ 88MidLeaAGS-29
❑ 88PeoChiTI-33
❑ 90ChaKniTI-12
❑ 90TopTVCu-66

Zaske, Jeff
❑ 82AleDukT-17
❑ 84HawIsIC-122
❑ 85HawIsIC-249
❑ 86HawIsIP-23
❑ 87OklCit8P-26
❑ 88TacTigC-6

Zastoupil, Rich
❑ 91BilMusP-3755
❑ 91BilMusSP-23
❑ 92ChaWheF-9
❑ 92ChaWVWC-6

Zauchin, Norm
❑ 55Top-176
❑ 56Top-89
❑ 57Top-372
❑ 58SeaTeal-28
❑ 58Top-422
❑ 59Top-311
❑ 79TCM50-252
❑ 81RedSoxBG2S-64

Zaun, Brian
❑ 97YakBeaG-36

Zaun, Greg
❑ 90WauTimB-15
❑ 90WauTimP-2128
❑ 90WauTimS-27
❑ 91Cla/Bes-209
❑ 91KanCouCC-14
❑ 91KanCouCP-2661
❑ 91KanCouCTI-24
❑ 91MidLeaAP-MWL36
❑ 92FreKeyC-7
❑ 92FreKeyF-1809
❑ 93BowBayF-2192
❑ 94Bow-271
❑ 94ExcFS7-17
❑ 94OriPro-108
❑ 94RocRedWF-1001
❑ 94RocRedWTI-26
❑ 94Ult-312
❑ 94UppDecML-24
❑ 95BalOriP-50
❑ 95RocRedWTI-40
❑ 96BalOriP-37
❑ 96ColCho-51
❑ 96ColChoGS-51
❑ 96ColChoSS-51
❑ 96Don-27
❑ 96DonPreP-27
❑ 96LeaSigA-251
❑ 96LeaSigAG-252
❑ 96LeaSigAS-252
❑ 96Sco-265
❑ 96ScoDugC-A110
❑ 96ScoDugCAP-A110
❑ 96Sel-170
❑ 96SelArtP-170
❑ 96Sum-167
❑ 96SumAbo&B-167
❑ 96SumArtP-167
❑ 96SumFoi-167
❑ 97MarPac-24
❑ 98PacOnl-307
❑ 98PacOnlR-307
❑ 98PacOnlWC-307

Zavala, Alfredo
❑ 74WicAerODF-121

Zavaras, Clint
❑ 86WauTimP-29
❑ 87SalSpuS-30
❑ 88VerMarP-960
❑ 89BlaYNPRWL-196
❑ 89CalCanC-11
❑ 90Don-662
❑ 90OPC-89
❑ 90Top-89
❑ 90TopDeb89-149
❑ 90TopTif-89
❑ 92CalCanS-73
❑ 92JacSunF-3708
❑ 94CalCanF-792

Zavershnik, Mike
❑ 96StCatSB-29

Zawaski, Vince
❑ 89St.LucMS-25
❑ 89Sta-25

Zawatski, Geoff
❑ 97BatCliTI-22

Zayas, Carlos
❑ 85BenPhiC-24
❑ 87ClePhiP-6
❑ 88BlaYNPRWL-144
❑ 88SpaPhiP-1039
❑ 89BlaYNPRWL-21
❑ 89ClePhiS-25

Zayas, Felipe
❑ 77St.PetCT-3
❑ 78St.PetCT-28
❑ 80ArkTraT-19
❑ 81ArkTraT-1

Zayas, Pedro
❑ 89SpaPhiP-1051
❑ 89SpaPhiS-25

Zazueta, Mauricio
❑ 89PriWilCS-26
❑ 90CarLeaA-16
❑ 90PriWilCTI-29

Zdeb, Joe
❑ 76OmaRoyTT-27
❑ 76VenLeaS-10
❑ 78Roy-27
❑ 78Top-408
❑ 79Top-389

Zeber, George
❑ 73SyrChiTI-30
❑ 76VenLeaS-49
❑ 78SSP270-15
❑ 78TacYanC-20
❑ 78Top-591
❑ 78YanSSPD-15
❑ 92YanWIZ7-172

Zech, Scott
❑ 97VerExpB-30
❑ 98CapFeaCM-26

Zedalis, Craig
❑ 94DanBraC-26
❑ 94DanBraF-3533

Zehner, Kevin
❑ 93YakBeaF-3887

Zeider, Rollie
❑ 09ObaT21-62
❑ 10ChiE-20
❑ 11PinT-5-764
❑ 12T207-207
❑ 14CraJacE-60
❑ 14CraJacE-116
❑ 15CraJacE-116
❑ 15SpoNewM-198
❑ 16SpoNewM-198
❑ 17ColE13-199
❑ 19W514-32
❑ 20Zee-40
❑ 21Zee-21
❑ 22Zee-162
❑ 23Zee-80

Zeig, Robert
❑ 77WesHavYT-25
❑ 79WesHavYT-23

Zeigler, Bill
❑ 90RanMot-28

Zeihen, Bob
❑ 88OneYanP-2058
❑ 89Ft.LauYS-26
❑ 89Sta-81
❑ 90AlbYanB-24
❑ 90AlbYanP-1047
❑ 90AlbYanSt-23
❑ 91EriSaiC-25
❑ 91EriSaiP-4087
❑ 92Ft.MyeMF-2761

Zeile, Todd E.
❑ 86EriCarP-30
❑ 87SprCarB-26
❑ 88ArkTraGS-7
❑ 88TexLeaAGS-2
❑ 89FleUpd-122
❑ 89LouRedBC-13
❑ 89LouRedBP-1267
❑ 89LouRedBTI-2
❑ 89LouRedBTI-3
❑ 89LouRedBTI-4
❑ 89LouRedBTI-5
❑ 89TriAAAP-AAA14
❑ 89UppDec-754
❑ 89UppDecS-2
❑ 90Baz-12
❑ 90Bow-193
❑ 90BowTif-193
❑ 90CarSmo-27
❑ 90ClaBlu-90
❑ 90Don-29
❑ 90DonBesN-71
❑ 90DonPre-1
❑ 90DonRoo-31
❑ 90Fle-265
❑ 90FleCan-265
❑ 90FleSoaS-1
❑ 90Hot50RS-50
❑ 90Lea-221
❑ 90OPC-162
❑ 90PanSti-381
❑ 90Sco-600
❑ 90Sco100RS-6
❑ 90ScoRooDT-B3
❑ 90ScoYouS2-1
❑ 90Spo-177
❑ 90SprCarDGB-1
❑ 90Top-162
❑ 90TopBig-294
❑ 90TopDeb89-150
❑ 90TopTif-162
❑ 90TopTVCa-24
❑ 90ToyRoo-33
❑ 90TriAAAC-1
❑ 90UppDec-545
❑ 91Bow-404
❑ 91CarPol-27
❑ 91Cla2-T42

❑ 91ClaGam-173
❑ 91Don-71
❑ 91Fle-654
❑ 91Lea-327
❑ 91MajLeaCP-48
❑ 91OPC-616
❑ 91PanFreS-33
❑ 91PanSti-34
❑ 91Pos-25
❑ 91Sco-240
❑ 91Sco-869
❑ 91Sco100RS-81
❑ 91StaClu-255
❑ 91Stu-240
❑ 91Top-616
❑ 91TopDesS-616
❑ 91TopMic-616
❑ 91TopRoo-33
❑ 91TopTif-616
❑ 91TopTriH-N12
❑ 91ToyRoo-33
❑ 91Ult-299
❑ 91UppDec-164
❑ 92Bow-695
❑ 92CarPol-26
❑ 92ClaGam-25
❑ 92Don-132
❑ 92DonCraJ1-31
❑ 92Fle-596
❑ 92Hig5-100
❑ 92KinDis-4
❑ 92Lea-432
❑ 92LeaBlaG-432
❑ 92MVPPin-33
❑ 92OPC-275
❑ 92PanSti-174
❑ 92Pin-32
❑ 92RedFolS-104
❑ 92Sco-52
❑ 92ScoImpP-34
❑ 92ScoProP-12
❑ 92StaClu-544
❑ 92Stu-100
❑ 92SunSee-3
❑ 92Top-275
❑ 92TopGol-275
❑ 92TopGolW-275
❑ 92TopKid-27
❑ 92TopMic-275
❑ 92TriPla-141
❑ 92Ult-273
❑ 92UppDec-40
❑ 92UppDec-533
❑ 92UppDecHRH-HR26
❑ 93Bow-628
❑ 93CarPol-25
❑ 93CarStaC-9
❑ 93DiaMar-120
❑ 93Don-20
❑ 93Fin-21
❑ 93FinRef-21
❑ 93Fle-136
❑ 93Lea-8
❑ 93MilBonSS-10
❑ 93OPC-224
❑ 93PacSpa-305
❑ 93PanSti-195
❑ 93Pin-205
❑ 93RedFolS-104
❑ 93Sco-119
❑ 93Sel-63
❑ 93StaClu-152
❑ 93StaCluFDI-152
❑ 93StaCluMOP-152
❑ 93Stu-62
❑ 93Top-428
❑ 93TopGol-428
❑ 93TopInaM-428
❑ 93TopInaR-428
❑ 93TopMic-428
❑ 93TriPla-24
❑ 93Ult-115
❑ 93UppDec-569
❑ 93UppDecGold-569
❑ 94Bow-152
❑ 94CarPol-26
❑ 94ColC-305
❑ 94ColChoGS-305
❑ 94ColChoSS-305
❑ 94Don-460
❑ 94Fin-410
❑ 94FinRef-410
❑ 94Fla-230
❑ 94Fle-651
❑ 94FleExtB-366
❑ 94FUnPac-96
❑ 94Lea-61
❑ 94LeaL-149
❑ 94OPC-198
❑ 94Pac-608
❑ 94Pin-367
❑ 94PinArtP-367
❑ 94PinMusC-367
❑ 94ProMag-113
❑ 94Sco-358
❑ 94ScoGolR-358
❑ 94Sel-244
❑ 94SP-68
❑ 94SPDieC-68
❑ 94Spo-117
❑ 94StaClu-395
❑ 94StaCluFDI-395
❑ 94StaCluGR-395
❑ 94StaCluMOP-395
❑ 94StaCluMOP-ST12
❑ 94StaCluST-ST12
❑ 94StaCluT-306
❑ 94StaCluTFDI-306
❑ 94Stu-57
❑ 94Top-25
❑ 94TopGol-25
❑ 94TopSpa-25
❑ 94TriPla-70
❑ 94Ult-274
❑ 94UppDec-444
❑ 94UppDecED-444
❑ 95Baz-117
❑ 95Bow-389
❑ 95ColCho-188
❑ 95ColChoGS-188
❑ 95ColChoSE-74
❑ 95ColChoSEGS-74
❑ 95ColChoSESS-74
❑ 95ColChoSS-188
❑ 95Don-483
❑ 95DonPreP-483
❑ 95DonTopotO-207
❑ 95Fin-80
❑ 95FinRef-80
❑ 95Fla-413
❑ 95Fle-513
❑ 95Lea-193
❑ 95LeaLim-153
❑ 95Pac-419
❑ 95PanSti-53
❑ 95Pin-118
❑ 95PinArtP-118
❑ 95PinMusC-118
❑ 95Sco-409
❑ 95ScoGolR-409
❑ 95ScoPlaTS-409
❑ 95SP-39
❑ 95SPCha-31
❑ 95SPChaDC-31
❑ 95Spo-23
❑ 95SpoArtP-23
❑ 95SPSil-39
❑ 95StaClu-274
❑ 95StaCluCC-CC19
❑ 95StaCluMOP-274
❑ 95StaCluMOP-CC19
❑ 95StaCluSTWS-274
❑ 95StaCluVR-139
❑ 95StaCluVRMO-139
❑ 95Stu-168
❑ 95Top-319
❑ 95TopCyb-173
❑ 95TopD3-6
❑ 95TopEmb-132
❑ 95TopEmbGI-132
❑ 95TopTra-121T
❑ 95Ult-434
❑ 95UltGolM-434
❑ 95UppDec-310
❑ 95UppDec-456
❑ 95UppDecED-310
❑ 95UppDecEDG-310
❑ 95UppDecSE-91
❑ 95UppDecSEG-91
❑ 96ColCho-81
❑ 96ColCho-674
❑ 96ColChoGS-81
❑ 96ColChoGS-674
❑ 96ColChoSS-81
❑ 96ColChoSS-674
❑ 96Don-277
❑ 96DonPreP-277
❑ 96EmoXL-251
❑ 96Fin-B247
❑ 96FinRef-B247
❑ 96Fla-342
❑ 96Fle-333
❑ 96FleTif-333
❑ 96FleUpd-U173
❑ 96FleUpdTC-U173
❑ 96PhiTeal-36
❑ 96Pin-42
❑ 96Pin-360
❑ 96PinFoil-360
❑ 96Sco-402
❑ 96SP-142
❑ 96StaClu-420
❑ 96StaCluEPB-420
❑ 96StaCluEPG-420
❑ 96StaCluEPS-420
❑ 96StaCluMOP-420
❑ 96Stu-28
❑ 96StuPrePB-28
❑ 96StuPrePG-28
❑ 96StuPrePS-28
❑ 96TeaOut-91
❑ 96Top-35
❑ 96Ult-530
❑ 96UltGolM-530
❑ 96UppDec-36
❑ 96UppDec-431
❑ 97Cir-129
❑ 97CirRav-129
❑ 97ColCho-364
❑ 97ColChoT-LA13
❑ 97DodMot-10
❑ 97DodPol-29
❑ 97Don-24
❑ 97Don-272
❑ 97DonGolPP-24
❑ 97DonGolPP-272
❑ 97DonSilPP-24
❑ 97DonSilPP-272
❑ 97DonTea-117
❑ 97DonTeaSPE-117
❑ 97Fin-236
❑ 97FinRef-236
❑ 97Fle-16
❑ 97Fle-605
❑ 97FleTif-16
❑ 97FleTif-605
❑ 97NewPin-16
❑ 97NewPinAP-16
❑ 97NewPinMC-16
❑ 97NewPinPP-16
❑ 97PinX-PSfF-60
❑ 97PinX-PSfFU-60
❑ 97Sco-257
❑ 97Sco-355
❑ 97ScoArtPWB-257
❑ 97ScoArtPWB-355
❑ 97ScoPreS-257
❑ 97ScoResC-355
❑ 97ScoShoS-257
❑ 97ScoShoS-355
❑ 97ScoShoSAP-257
❑ 97ScoShoSAP-355
❑ 97Top-473
❑ 97Ult-257
❑ 97Ult-379
❑ 97UltGolME-257
❑ 97UltGolME-379
❑ 97UltPlaME-257
❑ 97UltPlaME-379
❑ 97UppDec-540
❑ 98CirThu-265
❑ 98CirThuRav-265
❑ 98CirThuSupRav-265
❑ 98ColCho-396
❑ 98DodPol-29
❑ 98DodSco-14
❑ 98DodScoP-14
❑ 98Don-265
❑ 98DonGolPP-265
❑ 98DonSilPP-265
❑ 98Fin-187
❑ 98FinNo--187
❑ 98FinNo-R-187
❑ 98FinRef-187
❑ 98Fle-127
❑ 98Fle-446
❑ 98Pac-343
❑ 98PacPlaB-343
❑ 98PacRedT-343
❑ 98PacSil-343
❑ 98Pin-89
❑ 98PinPreP-89
❑ 98PinSna-LAD7
❑ 98Sco-183
❑ 98ScoSS-PP83
❑ 98ScoSSAP-PP83
❑ 98SP Aut-97
❑ 98SPxFin-276
❑ 98SPxFinR-276
❑ 98SPxFinS-276
❑ 98StaCluFDI-355
❑ 98StaCluI-355
❑ 98StaCluOneK-355
❑ 98StaCluPP-355
❑ 98Top-102
❑ 98TopChr-102
❑ 98TopChrR-102
❑ 98TopDevR-102
❑ 98TopDia-102
❑ 98TopMiniC-102
❑ 98TopOpeD-50
❑ 98Ult-295
❑ 98UltGolM-295
❑ 98UltMas-295
❑ 98UltPlaM-295
❑ 98UppDec-119
❑ 98UppDecSF-72
❑ 99Fle-277
❑ 99FleSta9-277
❑ 99FleWarT-277
❑ 99MetUni-134
❑ 99MetUniGM-134
❑ 99MetUniPMG-134
❑ 99Pac-434
❑ 99PacOme-241
❑ 99PacOmeC-241
❑ 99PacOmeG-241
❑ 99PacOmePB-241
❑ 99PacPar-241
❑ 99PacParC-241
❑ 99PacParG-241
❑ 99PacParHoloGold-241
❑ 99PacParHS-241
❑ 99PacParOD-241
❑ 99PacParPB-241
❑ 99PacParRed-241
❑ 99PacPlaB-434
❑ 99PacRed-434
❑ 99SkyPre-118
❑ 99SkyPreR-118
❑ 99SkyThu-64
❑ 99SkyThuRant-64
❑ 99SkyThuRave-64
❑ 99StaClu-259
❑ 99StaCluFDI-259
❑ 99StaCluOoaK-259
❑ 99StaCluPP-259
❑ 99ThuSkySupR-64
❑ 99Top-286
❑ 99TopChr-286
❑ 99TopChrR-286
❑ 99TopMVPP-286
❑ 99Ult-33
❑ 99UltGolM-33
❑ 99UltMas-33
❑ 99UltPlaM-33
❑ 99UppDec-506
❑ 99UppDecEL1-506
❑ 99UppDecEL2-506
❑ 99UppDecM-209
❑ 99UppDecMGS-209
❑ 99UppDecMHFS-209
❑ 99UppDecMSS-209
❑ 99Vic-405

Zell, Brian
❑ 80ElmPioRST-31

Zeller, Bart
❑ 70CarTeal-32
❑ 70CarTeal-33

Zellers, Kevin
❑ 94YakBeaC-29
❑ 94YakBeaF-3861
❑ 95BakBlaTI-15

Zellner, Joey
❑ 86MacPirP-27
❑ 87VisOakP-20
❑ 88VisOakCLC-148
❑ 88VisOakP-98

Zello, Mark
❑ 91KanCouCC-30
❑ 91KanCouCTI-25

Zepeda, Jesse
❑ 98HagSunM-30

Zepp, Bill
❑ 70Top-702
❑ 70TwiTeal-13
❑ 71MLBOffS-480
❑ 71OPC-271
❑ 71Top-271

Zeratsky, Rod
❑ 86CedRapRT-13
❑ 87TamTarP-28

Zerb, Troy
❑ 87UtiBluSP-7
❑ 88BatCliP-1690

Zerbe, Chad
❑ 91KisDodP-4188
❑ 92GreFalDSP-4
❑ 93BakDodCLC-27
❑ 94VerBeaDC-26
❑ 94VerBeaDF-74
❑ 95SanBerSTI-27
❑ 97HigDesMG-30
❑ 98SanJosGQ-19

Zernia, Harvey
❑ 55SeaPop-22
❑ 56SeaPop-27

Zernial, Gus
❑ 47Exh-247A
❑ 47Exh-247B
❑ 47PM1StaP1-227
❑ 47PM1StaP1-228
❑ 47SigOil-20
❑ 50Bow-4
❑ 51A'sTeal-24
❑ 51Bow-262
❑ 51FisBakL-32
❑ 51R42SmaS-119
❑ 51TopRedB-36A
❑ 51TopRedB-36B
❑ 52A'sTeal-30
❑ 52BerRos-71
❑ 52Bow-82
❑ 52RedMan-AL26
❑ 52StaCalL-76A
❑ 52StaCalS-89B
❑ 52Top-31
❑ 53A'sTeal-31
❑ 53BowC-13
❑ 53NorBreL-32
❑ 53RedMan-AL13
❑ 53Top-42
❑ 54A'STEAI-30
❑ 54DixLid-18
❑ 54RedHeaF-33
❑ 54Top-2
❑ 55A'sRodM-47
❑ 55A'sTeal-29
❑ 55RobGouS-2
❑ 55RobGouW-2
❑ 55Top-110
❑ 55TopDouH-123
❑ 56A'sPos-50
❑ 56A'sPos-51
❑ 56A'sRodM-12
❑ 56Top-45
❑ 56TopHocF-A13
❑ 56TopHocF-B15
❑ 56TopPin-15
❑ 56YelBasP-32
❑ 57Top-253
❑ 58Top-112
❑ 59Top-409
❑ 76A'sRodMC-30
❑ 77PhiFav-21
❑ 79DiaGre-348
❑ 79TCM50-263
❑ 83TopRep5-31
❑ 91TopArc1-42
❑ 94TopArc1-2
❑ 94TopArc1G-2

Zerpa, Mauro
❑ 96-97LinVen-26

Zettelmeyer, Mark
❑ 90Ft.LauYS-26

Zhigalov, Sergey
❑ 89EasLeaDDP-DD8
❑ 90IBAWorA-5

Zick, Bill
❑ 88QuaCitAGS-3
❑ 89QuaCitAB-4
❑ 89QuaCitAGS-4
❑ 92SalBucC-28
❑ 93SalBucC-28

Ziegler, Alma
❑ 94TedWil-98

Ziegler, Bill
❑ 84RanJarP-NNO
❑ 85RanPer-NNO
❑ 86RanPer-NNO0
❑ 87RanMot-27
❑ 89RanMot-28

Ziegler, Greg
❑ 87IdaFalBP-27

Ziegler, Shane
❑ 93BluOriC-24
❑ 93BluOriF-4126
❑ 94BluOriC-22
❑ 94BluOriF-3564

Ziem, Steve
❑ 84DurBulT-23
❑ 85GreBraTI-26
❑ 86GreBraTI-23
❑ 87RicBraBC-23
❑ 87RicBraC-19
❑ 87RicBraT-9
❑ 88GreBraB-15
❑ 89DurBullS-25
❑ 89DurBullS-25
❑ 89DurBulTI-25
❑ 89RicBraBC-29
❑ 90RicBraBC-2

Zientara, Benny
❑ 49EurSta-100
❑ 85TCMPla1-39

Zimbauer, Jason
❑ 90HelBreSP-10
❑ 91BelBreCB-10
❑ 91BelBreP-2104

Zimmer, Charles
❑ 03BreE10-158
❑ 11SpoLifCW-378
❑ 87OldJudN-551
❑ 93JusSo-13

Zimmer, Don
❑ 55Bow-65
❑ 55DodGolS-21
❑ 55Top-92
❑ 55TopDouH-97
❑ 56Top-99
❑ 57Top-284
❑ 58DodBelB-10
❑ 58DodTeal-25
❑ 58Hir-41
❑ 58Top-77A
❑ 58Top-77B
❑ 59DodMor-12
❑ 59DodPos-8
❑ 59DodTeal-26
❑ 59Top-287
❑ 60DodBelB-17
❑ 60Top-47
❑ 60TopVen-47
❑ 61CubJayP-12
❑ 61Top-493
❑ 62Baz-43
❑ 62Jel-183
❑ 62MetJayP-12
❑ 62Pos-183
❑ 62PosCan-183
❑ 62SalPlaC-123A
❑ 62SalPlaC-123B
❑ 62ShiPlaC-123
❑ 62Top-478
❑ 62TopStal-161
❑ 63Top-439
❑ 64Top-134
❑ 64TopCoi-1
❑ 64TopSta-11
❑ 64TopVen-134
❑ 65OPC-233
❑ 65Top-233
❑ 72PadPos-28
❑ 73OPC-12
❑ 73PadDea-30
❑ 73Top-12A
❑ 73Top-12B
❑ 74OPC-403
❑ 74Top-403
❑ 77Top-309
❑ 78SSP270-179
❑ 78Top-63
❑ 79DiaGre-98
❑ 79TCM50-228
❑ 79Top-214
❑ 80Top-689
❑ 81Fle-230
❑ 81TCM60I-482
❑ 81Top-673
❑ 82Don-195
❑ 83YanPhoA-3
❑ 84CubChiT-34
❑ 84CubSev-NNO
❑ 84OCoandSI-159
❑ 85CubLioP-27
❑ 85CubSev-NNO
❑ 87GiaMot-27
❑ 87GiaPos-36
❑ 88CubDavB-4
❑ 88TopTra-131T
❑ 88TopTraT-131T
❑ 89CubMar-4
❑ 89SweBasG-23
❑ 89Top-134
❑ 89TopTif-134
❑ 90CubMar-27

❑ 90DodTar-887
❑ 90OPC-549
❑ 90Top-549
❑ 90TopTif-549
❑ 90TopTVA-66
❑ 90TopTVCu-1
❑ 91CubVinL-35
❑ 91DodRinP3-11
❑ 91MetWIZ-439
❑ 91OPC-729
❑ 91Top-729
❑ 91TopDesS-729
❑ 91TopMic-729
❑ 91TopTif-729
❑ 92RedSoxDD-30
❑ 93RanKee-391
❑ 94RocPol-27
❑ 94TopArc1-258
❑ 94TopArc1G-258
❑ 95TopArcBD-83
❑ 95TopArcBD-99
❑ 95TopArcBD-125
❑ 95TopArcBD-148

Zimmer, Tom
❑ 72CedRapCT-3
❑ 76St.LouCP-35
❑ 89PacSenL-25
❑ 91PacSenL-136

Zimmerman, Brian
❑ 88LitFalMP-25

Zimmerman, Casey
❑ 89AncGlaP-30

Zimmerman, Cory
❑ 89AncGlaP-31

Zimmerman, Eric
❑ 83AleDukT-24

Zimmerman, Everette
❑ 12Zee-135
❑ 13Zee-129

Zimmerman, Heinie (Henry)
❑ 09ColChiE-316
❑ 09ColChiE-317A
❑ 09ColChiE-317B
❑ 09MaxPubP-19
❑ 09SpoNewSM-95
❑ 09T206-389
❑ 10CouT21-255
❑ 10CouT21-325
❑ 10E101-46
❑ 10E102-26
❑ 10MelMinE-46
❑ 10NadCarE-55
❑ 10PeoT21-59A
❑ 10PeoT21-59B
❑ 11PinT-5-205
❑ 11SpoLifCW-379
❑ 11SpoLifM-185
❑ 12ColRedB-316
❑ 12ColRedB-317A
❑ 12ColRedB-317B
❑ 12ColTinT-316
❑ 12ColTinT-317A
❑ 12ColTinT-317B
❑ 14CraJacE-21
❑ 14FatPlaT-52
❑ 14TexTomE-50
❑ 15AmeCarE106-42
❑ 15CraJacE-21
❑ 15SpoNewM-199
❑ 16BF2FP-73
❑ 16SpoNewM-199
❑ 16TanBraE-20
❑ 17ColE13-200
❑ 92ConTSN-530

Zimmerman, Jeff
❑ 98TexLeaC-27
❑ 98TulDriTI-23
❑ 99DumSet-130
❑ 99FleMys-130
❑ 99FleMysM-130
❑ 99PacOme-242
❑ 99PacOmeC-242
❑ 99PacOmeG-242
❑ 99PacOmePB-242

Zimmerman, Jennifer
❑ 89AncGlaP-32

Zimmerman, Jerry (Gerald)
❑ 59Top-146
❑ 59TopVen-146
❑ 60HenHouW-9
❑ 60SeaPop-18
❑ 61TwiCloD-31
❑ 62Jel-130
❑ 62Pos-130
❑ 62PosCan-130
❑ 62Top-222
❑ 63Top-186
❑ 63TwiVol-23
❑ 64Top-369
❑ 64TopVen-369
❑ 65Top-299
❑ 66OPC-73
❑ 66Top-73
❑ 66TopVen-73
❑ 67CokCapTw-9
❑ 67Top-501
❑ 67TwiTeal-26
❑ 68OPC-181
❑ 68Top-181
❑ 68TopVen-181
❑ 69MilBra-296
❑ 73OPC-377
❑ 73Top-377
❑ 74OPC-531
❑ 74Top-531
❑ 75ExpPos-39
❑ 78TCM60I-117
❑ 78TwiFri-24
❑ 79TwiFriP-30
❑ 80Red196T-22
❑ 80TwiPos-33

Zimmerman, Jordan
❑ 97EveAquG-29
❑ 98LanJetG-30

Zimmerman, Mike
❑ 88CapCodPPaLP-44
❑ 90WelPirP-31
❑ 91Bow-519
❑ 91SalBucP-954
❑ 92CarMudF-1183
❑ 92CarMudS-148
❑ 92SkyAA F-69
❑ 92UppDecML-230
❑ 93BufBisF-519
❑ 93ClaGolF-193
❑ 94CarMudF-1581
❑ 95ChaKniTI-28
❑ 95SigRooOJ-35
❑ 95SigRooOJP-35
❑ 95SigRooOJPS-35
❑ 95SigRooOJS-35

Zimmerman, Phil
❑ 92PulBraC-10
❑ 92PulBraF-3188

Zimmerman, Rick
❑ 89AncGlaP-33

Zimmerman, Roy
❑ 50RemBre-27

Zimmerman, William
❑ 16Zee-46

Zimmerman, Zeke
❑ 93BoiHawC-29
❑ 93BoiHawF-3932
❑ 97BoiHawG-32
❑ 98ButCopKG-34

Zinn, Frank
❑ 87OldJudN-552

Zinn, James
❑ 30Zee-163
❑ 31Zee-116
❑ 33Zee-43
❑ 33Zee-153

Zinter, Alan (Alan Michael)
❑ 87AriWilP-20
❑ 88AriWilP-16
❑ 88CapCodPPaLP-29
❑ 89PitMetS-29
❑ 90Bow-135
❑ 90BowTif-135
❑ 90FloStaLAS-22
❑ 90Sco-671
❑ 90St.LucMS-27
❑ 90StaFS7-11
❑ 90TopTVM-66
❑ 91Cla/Bes-334
❑ 91LinDriAA-648
❑ 91MetColP-53
❑ 91WilBilLD-648
❑ 91WilBilP-297
❑ 92BinMetF-526
❑ 92BinMetS-73
❑ 92ClaFS7-28
❑ 92SkyAA F-35
❑ 93BinMetF-2338
❑ 94TolMudHF-1035
❑ 94UppDecML-17
❑ 95TolMudHTI-29
❑ 96PawRedSDD-29
❑ 97TacRai-29
❑ 98IowCubQ-30

Zinter, Eddie
❑ 88AlaGolTI-18
❑ 89SpoIndSP-2
❑ 90ChaRaiB-23
❑ 90ChaRaiP-2039
❑ 90ProAaA-74
❑ 91CalLeLA-10
❑ 91HigDesMC-13
❑ 91HigDesMP-2396
❑ 92HigDesMC-12

Zipay, Bud (Ed)
❑ 46SunBre-21
❑ 47SigOil-73
❑ 47SunBre-26

Zipeto, Ted
❑ 86ClePhiP-26

Zipfel, M. Bud
❑ 55DonWin-42
❑ 61SenJayP-12
❑ 63Top-69

Zipser, Mike
❑ 98BatMucTI-35

Zisk, John
❑ 79WauTimT-11
❑ 80WauTimT-10

Zisk, Richie
❑ 72OPC-392
❑ 72Top-392
❑ 73OPC-611
❑ 73Top-611
❑ 74OPC-317
❑ 74Top-317
❑ 74TopSta-90
❑ 75Hos-139
❑ 75Kel-25
❑ 75OPC-77
❑ 75PitPirP-29
❑ 75Top-77
❑ 75TopMin-77
❑ 76BlaDis-70
❑ 76BucDis-70
❑ 76CarDis-70
❑ 76CraDis-70
❑ 76DailsID-70
❑ 76IsaDis-70
❑ 76OPC-12
❑ 76OrbDis-70
❑ 76PirPos-27
❑ 76RedBarD-70
❑ 76SafDis-70
❑ 76SSP-574
❑ 76Top-12
❑ 76TowCluD-70
❑ 77BurCheD-75
❑ 77ChiWilD-70
❑ 77DailsID-70
❑ 77DetCaeD-70
❑ 77HolInnD-70
❑ 77Hos-127
❑ 77MSADis-70
❑ 77OPC-152
❑ 77PepGloD-27
❑ 77RCColC-70
❑ 77SagDis-70
❑ 77sDis-70
❑ 77Top-483
❑ 77TopCloS-55
❑ 77WenDis-70
❑ 77WhiSoxJT-16
❑ 77WhiSoxT-27
❑ 77ZipDis-70
❑ 78PapGinD-30
❑ 78Pep-40
❑ 78RanBurK-20
❑ 78RCColC-39
❑ 78SagDis-14
❑ 78SSP270-98
❑ 78TasDis-14
❑ 78Top-110
❑ 78WifBalD-79
❑ 79BasPat-100
❑ 79Hos-140
❑ 79Kel-24
❑ 79OPC-130
❑ 79Top-260
❑ 80OPC-325
❑ 80Top-620
❑ 81Don-28
❑ 81Fle-620
❑ 81FleStiC-105
❑ 81MarPol-13
❑ 81MarPos-31
❑ 81OPC-214
❑ 81Top-517
❑ 81TopScr-16
❑ 81TopSti-127
❑ 81TopTra-857
❑ 82Don-11
❑ 82Don-127
❑ 82Dra-33
❑ 82Fle-519
❑ 82FleSta-223
❑ 82Kel-1
❑ 82MarPos-32
❑ 82OPC-66
❑ 82Top-769
❑ 82TopSti-229
❑ 83Don-559
❑ 83DonActA-54
❑ 83Fle-489
❑ 83FleSta-224
❑ 83FleSti-183
❑ 83MarNal-6
❑ 83OPC-368
❑ 83Top-368
❑ 83TopGloS-21
❑ 83TopSti-116
❑ 84Don-69
❑ 84DonActAS-30
❑ 84Fle-625
❑ 84Nes792-83
❑ 84OPC-83
❑ 84Top-83
❑ 84TopSti-342
❑ 84TopTif-83
❑ 90PeoChiTI-35
❑ 91CubMar-NNO
❑ 93RanKee-392
❑ 93UppDecAH-130
❑ 94RanAllP-6
❑ 96DayCubB-28

Zitek, Jeff
❑ 79AshTouT-9

Zitzmann, Billy (William)
❑ 28Exh-16
❑ 92ConTSN-570

Zizzo, Johnny
❑ 92BenRocCB-26
❑ 92BenRocF-1489

Zlejo, Nigel
❑ 95KanCouCTI-31

Zmudosky, Tom
❑ 84AlbA'sT-20
❑ 84ModA'sC-28

Zoellers, Frank
❑ 26Zee-20

Zoldak, Sam
❑ 46SeaSLP-69
❑ 48IndTeal-31
❑ 49Bow-78A
❑ 49Bow-78B
❑ 49IndTeal-28
❑ 50Bow-182
❑ 50IndNumN-23
❑ 50IndTeal-26
❑ 51A'sTeal-35
❑ 51Bow-114
❑ 51R42SmaS-120
❑ 52A'sTeal-31
❑ 52Top-231
❑ 53IndPenCBP-31
❑ 74CapPub-18
❑ 77TCMTheWY-73
❑ 83TopRep5-231
❑ 85TCMPla1-19
❑ 96Bro194F-34

Zolecki, Mike
❑ 94Bow-404
❑ 94CenValRC-25
❑ 94CenValRF-3205
❑ 94Cla-30
❑ 94ClaTriF-T25
❑ 95AshTouUTI-20
❑ 96NewHavRB-29
❑ 97SalAva-35
❑ 98NewHavRM-30
❑ 98NewHavRMA-30

Zollars, Mike
❑ 91BurIndP-3313
❑ 92WatIndC-21
❑ 92WatIndF-3249

Zolzer, Rick
❑ 90SpaPhiB-29

Zomora, Peter
❑ 97UCLBruTI-26

Zona, Jeff
❑ 89IdaFalBP-2029

Zongor, Steve
❑ 93SouOreAC-27
❑ 93SouOreAF-4065
❑ 94WesMicWC-25
❑ 94WesMicWF-2298
❑ 95ModA'sTI-32

Zorrilla, Julio
❑ 96Exc-193
❑ 96StLucMTI-34
❑ 97St.LucM-30
❑ 98BinMetQ-30
❑ 98St.LucMM-12

Zosky, Eddie
❑ 89FreStaBS-23
❑ 90Bes-23
❑ 90Bow-523
❑ 90BowTif-523
❑ 90CMC-812
❑ 90KnoBluJB-1
❑ 90KnoBluJP-1251
❑ 90KnoBluJS-23
❑ 90ProAaA-60
❑ 90Sco-665
❑ 90StaFS7-91
❑ 91BluJayFS-35
❑ 91BluJayS-30
❑ 91Bow-17
❑ 91Cla2-T25
❑ 91ClaGam-172
❑ 91LeaGolR-BC24
❑ 91LinDriAAA-523
❑ 91SyrChiK-5
❑ 91SyrChiLD-523
❑ 91SyrChiMB-30
❑ 91SyrChiP-2490
❑ 91TriA AAGP-AAA44
❑ 91Ult-390
❑ 91UppDec-734
❑ 91UppDecFE-14F
❑ 92Bow-381
❑ 92Cla1-T99
❑ 92ClaGam-123
❑ 92Don-8
❑ 92Fle-348
❑ 92OPC-72
❑ 92PinRool-11
❑ 92ProFS7-159
❑ 92ScoImpP-72
❑ 92SkyAAAF-234
❑ 92StaClu-873
❑ 92SyrChiF-1979
❑ 92SyrChiMB-30
❑ 92SyrChiS-523
❑ 92Top-72
❑ 92TopDeb91-191
❑ 92TopGol-72
❑ 92TopGolW-72
❑ 92TopMic-72
❑ 92TriPla-190
❑ 92Ult-156
❑ 92UppDec-544
❑ 93BluJayD4-32
❑ 93BluJayFS-35
❑ 93Don-57
❑ 93Fle-703
❑ 93Lea-190
❑ 93OPC-221
❑ 93PacSpa-660
❑ 93Pin-247
❑ 93Sco-297
❑ 93ScoBoyoS-15
❑ 93StaClu-460
❑ 93StaCluFDI-460
❑ 93StaCluMOP-460
❑ 93Top-689
❑ 93TopGol-689
❑ 93TopInaM-689
❑ 93TopInaR-689
❑ 93TopMic-689
❑ 94BluJayUSPC-2D
❑ 94BluJayUSPC-9C
❑ 94SyrChiF-981
❑ 94SyrChiTI-30
❑ 95ChaKniTI-29
❑ 95FleUpd-102
❑ 96RocRedWB-30
❑ 97PhoFirTI-28
❑ 98LouRedQ-7

Zottneck, Roger
❑ 86QuaCitAP-32
❑ 87PalSprP-16

Zuber, Jon
❑ 92BatCliCB-23
❑ 92BatCliF-3275
❑ 92FroRowDP-97
❑ 92FroRowDPG-97
❑ 92FroRowDPS-97
❑ 93ClaGolF-137
❑ 93ClePhiC-25
❑ 93ClePhiF-2693
❑ 93ExcFS7-89
❑ 93FloStaLAF-29
❑ 94ClaGolF-40
❑ 94ReaPhiF-2073
❑ 94UppDecML-199
❑ 95ScrRedBTI-30
❑ 95UppDecML-203
❑ 95UppDecMLFS-203
❑ 96ScrRedBB-28
❑ 97ScrRedB-20
❑ 98ScrRedB1ATI-18
❑ 98ScrRedB1ATI-19
❑ 98ScrRedBQ-30

Zuber, William
❑ 43YanSta-30
❑ 47RedSoxTI-25
❑ 47TipTop-15
❑ 60BilZubR-1
❑ 60BilZubR-2
❑ 75RedSox1T-41
❑ 77TCMTheWY-87

Zubiri, Jon
❑ 92BurIndC-11
❑ 92BurIndF-1658
❑ 93BurIndC-29
❑ 93BurIndF-3299
❑ 94ColRedC-25
❑ 94ColRedF-444

Zucha, Jason
❑ 97IdaFalBTI-31

Zulaica, Homer
❑ 98GreFalDG-31

Zuleta, Julio
❑ 97RocCub-30

Zulzer, Rick
❑ 90SpaPhiS-29

Zumwalt, Rusty
❑ 95ButCopKtI-21

Zuniga, David
❑ 93PitMetC-24
❑ 93PitMetF-3721
❑ 94CapCitBC-25
❑ 94CapCitBF-1761

Zuniga, Tony
❑ 96BelGiaTI-3
❑ 97SanJosG-24
❑ 98SanJosGQ-24

Zupcic, Bob
❑ 87ElmPioRC-31
❑ 88CarLeaAS-20
❑ 88ElmPio1C-9
❑ 88LynRedSS-27
❑ 89NewBriRSP-600
❑ 89NewBriRSS-22
❑ 90Bes-108
❑ 90CMC-880
❑ 90NewBriRSB-6
❑ 90NewBriRSP-1333
❑ 90NewBriRSS-24
❑ 91LinDriAAA-373
❑ 91PawRedSDD-30
❑ 91PawRedSLD-373
❑ 91PawRedSP-53
❑ 92Don-720
❑ 92FleUpd-6
❑ 92OPC-377
❑ 92PawRedSS-373
❑ 92Pin-576
❑ 92Sco-850
❑ 92SkyAAAF-172
❑ 92StaClu-839
❑ 92Top-377
❑ 92TopDeb91-192
❑ 92TopGol-377
❑ 92TopGolW-377
❑ 92TopMic-377
❑ 93Don-531
❑ 93Fle-186
❑ 93FleRooS-RSB10
❑ 93Lea-65
❑ 93OPC-367
❑ 93Pin-404
❑ 93RedSoxP-33
❑ 93Sco-362
❑ 93Sel-292
❑ 93SelChaR-10
❑ 93StaClu-563
❑ 93StaCluFDI-563
❑ 93StaCluMOP-563
❑ 93Top-562
❑ 93TopGol-562
❑ 93TopInaM-562
❑ 93TopInaR-562
❑ 93TopMic-562
❑ 93Toy-99

❑ 93Ult-158
❑ 93UppDec-277
❑ 93UppDecGold-277
❑ 93USPlaCR-12C
❑ 94Don-411
❑ 94Fle-47
❑ 94Pac-70
❑ 94PawRedSF-959
❑ 94Sco-221
❑ 94ScoGolR-221
❑ 94Top-661
❑ 94TopGol-661
❑ 94TopSpa-661
❑ 94WhiSoxK-29
❑ 95Top-229
❑ 96ScrRedBB-29
❑ 97DunDonPPS-30

Zupka, Bill
❑ 85ElmPioT-25
❑ 86GreHorP-27
❑ 87NewBriRSP-3

Zupo, Frank
❑ 56BalOriP-58
❑ 58Top-229
❑ 91OriCro-494

Zurieck, Hank
❑ 64TopRooAB-30

Zurn, Rick
❑ 92BelBreCB-24
❑ 92BelBreFI-406

Zuvella, Jerry
❑ 53SanFraSTI-24

Zuvella, Paul
❑ 82RicBraT-17
❑ 83RicBraT-17
❑ 84RicBraT-23
❑ 85BraPol-18
❑ 85Fle-651
❑ 86Fle-532
❑ 86RicBraP-26
❑ 86Top-572
❑ 86TopTif-572
❑ 86TopTra-131T
❑ 86TopTraT-131T
❑ 87Top-102
❑ 87TopTif-102
❑ 88ColSprSSC-18
❑ 88ColSprSSP-1528
❑ 89ColSprSSC-17
❑ 89ColSprSSP-245
❑ 89Sco-598
❑ 89TriAAAP-AAA33
❑ 89UppDec-236
❑ 90CMC-197
❑ 90OmaRoyC-22
❑ 90OmaRoyP-75
❑ 90ProAAAF-610
❑ 90RicBra2ATI-23
❑ 90TriAAAC-34
❑ 91LinDriAAA-348
❑ 91OmaRoyLD-348
❑ 91OmaRoyP-1044
❑ 92YanWIZ8-206
❑ 93CenValRC-26
❑ 93CenValRF-2908
❑ 94NewHavRF-1565
❑ 95NewHavRTI-14
❑ 97ColSprSATTI-5
❑ 97ColSprSTI-27
❑ 98ColSprSS-14

Zuverink, George
❑ 51IndHag-7
❑ 52Top-199
❑ 55Bow-92
❑ 56BalOriP-1
❑ 56BalOriP-59
❑ 56Top-276
❑ 57Top-11
❑ 58Hir-66
❑ 58OriJayP-12
❑ 58Top-6
❑ 59Top-219
❑ 83TopRep5-199
❑ 91OriCro-495
❑ 97BalOriP-57

Zweifel, Albert
❑ 19Zee-49

Zweifel, Kent
❑ 98AshTouM-25

Zweig, Ivan
❑ 91TopTra-131T
❑ 91TopTraT-131T
❑ 92StaCluD-200

Zwelfel, Kent
❑ 97PorRocG-30

Zwemke, Bryan
❑ 96BilMusTI-31
❑ 98HudValR-29

Zwilling, Dutch (Edward)
❑ 11SpoLifM-36
❑ 15SpoNewM-200
❑ 16SpoNewM-200

Zwirchitz, Andy
❑ 97DurBulTI-17

Zwisler, Josh
❑ 94HelBreF-3618
❑ 94HelBreSP-12
❑ 95AusFut-61
❑ 95BelBreTI-6

Zwolensky, Mitch
❑ 82WauTimF-19
❑ 83TulDriT-9
❑ 84OklCit8T-21
❑ 85OklCit8T-2
❑ 88PitCubP-1356
❑ 90CalLeaACLC-30
❑ 90StoPorB-28
❑ 90StoPorCLC-201
❑ 90StoPorP-2201
❑ 91StoPorC-25
❑ 91StoPorP-3048

Zydowsky, John
❑ 97DanBraB-30
❑ 98DanBraQ-6

Zywica, Mike
❑ 98Cha-22
❑ 98TexLeaC-28
❑ 99BasAmeTP-100
❑ 99BasAmeTPG-100
❑ 99Bow-172
❑ 99BowBes-158
❑ 99BowBesAR-158
❑ 99BowBesR-158
❑ 99BowChr-172
❑ 99BowChrG-172
❑ 99BowChrGR-172
❑ 99BowChrI-172
❑ 99BowChrIR-172
❑ 99BowChrR-172
❑ 99BowGol-172
❑ 99BowInt-172
❑ 99SP TopP-126
❑ 99SP TopPPE-126
❑ 99StaClu-142
❑ 99StaCluFDI-142
❑ 99StaCluOoaK-142
❑ 99StaCluPP-142
❑ 99Top-430
❑ 99TopChr-430
❑ 99TopChrR-430

Acknowledgments

A great deal of diligence, hard work, and dedicated effort went into this First Edition. The high standards to which we hold ourselves, however, could not have been met without the expert input and generous amount of time contributed by many people. Our sincere thanks are extended to each and every one of you.

Each year we refine the process of developing the most accurate and up-to-date information for this book. I believe this year's Price Guide is our best yet. Thanks again to all the contributors nationwide (listed below) as well as our staff here in Dallas.

Those who have worked closely with us on this and many other books have again proven themselves invaluable: Levi Bleam and Jim Fleck (707 Sportscards), Peter Brennan, Ray Bright, Card Collectors Co., Dwight Chapin, Barry Colla, Bill and Diane Dodge, David Festberg, Fleer/SkyBox (Rich Bradley, Doug Drotman and Julian McCracken), Steve Freedman, Gervise Ford, Larry and Jeff Fritsch, Tony Galovich, Georgia Music and Sports (Dick DeCourcey), Dick Gilkeson, Steve Gold (AU Sports), Bill Goodwin (St. Louis Baseball Cards), Mike and Howard Gordon, George Grauer, John Greenwald, Greg's Cards, Bill Henderson, Jerry and Etta Hersh, Mike Hersh, Neil Hoppenworth, Jay and Mary Kasper (Jay's Emporium), David Kohler (SportsCards Plus), Paul Lewicki, Lew Lipset (Four Base Hits), Mike Livingston (University Trading Cards), Mark Macrae, Bill Madden, Bill Mastro, Michael McDonald (The Sports Page), Mid-Atlantic Sports Cards (Bill Bossert), Gary Mills, Brian Morris, Mike Mosier (Columbia City Collectibles Co.), B.A. Murry, Ralph Nozaki, Mike O'Brien, Oldies and Goodies (Nigel Spill), Pacific Trading Cards (Mike Cramer and Mike Monson), Jack Pollard, Jeff Prillaman, Pat Quinn, Jerald Reichstein (Fabulous Cardboard), Tom Reid, Gavin Riley, Clifton Rouse, John Rumierz, Kevin Savage (Sports Gallery), Gary Sawatski, Mike Schechter, Barry Sloate, John E. Spalding, Phil Spector, Frank Steele, Murvin Sterling, Lee Temanson, Topps (Marty Appel and Brian Parkinson), Treat (Harold Anderson), Terry Melia, Ed Twombly (New England Bullpen), Upper Deck (Steve Ryan, Randy Trierweiler), Wayne Varner, Bill Vizas, Bill Wesslund (Portland Sports Card Co.), Kit Young and Rick Young, Ted Zanidakis, Robert Zanze (Z-Cards and Sports), Bill Zimpleman and Dean Zindler. Finally we give a special acknowledgment to the late Dennis W. Eckes, "Mr. Sport Americana." The success of the Beckett Price Guides has always been the result of a team effort.

It is very difficult to be "accurate" — one can only do one's best. But this job is especially difficult since we're shooting at a moving target: Prices are fluctuating all the time. Having several full-time pricing experts has definitely proven to be better than just one, and I thank all of them for working together to provide you, our readers, with the most accurate prices possible.

Many people have provided price input, illustrative material, checklist verifications, errata, and/or background information. We should like to individually thank AbD Cards (Dale Wesolewski), Action Card Sales, Jerry Adamic, Johnny and Sandy Adams, Alex's MVP Cards & Comics, Doug Allen (Round Tripper Sportscards), Will Allison, Dennis Anderson, Ed Anderson, Shane Anderson, Bruce W. Andrews, Ellis Anmuth, Tom Antonowicz, Alan Applegate, Ric Apter, Jason Arasate, Clyde Archer, Randy Archer, Matt Argento, Burl Armstrong, Neil Armstrong (World Series Cards), Todd Armstrong, Ara Arzoumanian, B and J Sportscards, Shawn Bailey, Ball Four Cards (Frank and Steve Pemper), Frank and Vivian Barning, Bob Bartosz, Nathan Basford, Carl Berg, Beulah Sports (Jeff Blatt), George Birsic, B.J. Sportscollectables, David Boedicker (The Wild Pitch Inc.), Bob Boffa, Louis Bollman, Tim Bond (Tim's Cards & Comics), Andrew Bosarge, Brian W. Bottles, Bill Brandt, Jeff Breitenfield, John Brigandi, John Broggi, Chuck Brooks, Dan Bruner, Lesha Bundrick, Michael Bunker, John E. Burick, Ed Burkey Jr., Bubba Burnett, Virgil Burns, California Card Co., Capital Cards, Danny Cariseo, Carl Carlson (C.T.S.), Jim Carr, Patrick Carroll, Ira Cetron, Don Chaffee, Michael Chan, Sandy Chan, Ric Chandgie, Ray Cherry, Bigg Wayne Christian, Josh Chidester, Dick Cianciotto, Michael and Abe Citron, Dr. Jeffrey Clair, Derrick F. Clark, Bill Cochran, Don Coe, Michael Cohen, Tom Cohoon (Cardboard Dreams), Collection de Sport AZ (Ronald Villaneuve), Gary Collett, Andrew T. Collier, Charles A. Collins, Curt Cooter, Steven Cooter, Pedro Cortes, Rick Cosmen (RC Card Co.), Lou Costanzo (Champion Sports), Mike Coyne, Paul and Ryan Crabb, Tony Craig (T.C. Card Co.), Kevin Crane, Taylor Crane, Chad Cripe, Brian Cunningham, Allen Custer, Donald L. Cutler, Eugene C. Dalager, Dave Dame, Brett Daniel, Tony Daniele III, Scott Dantio, Roy Datema, John Davidson, Travis Deaton, Dee's Baseball Cards (Dee Robinson), Joe Delgrippo, Tim DelVecchio, Steve Dempski, John Derossett, Mark Diamond, Gilberto Diaz Jr., Ken Dinerman (California

Cruizers), Cliff Dolgins, Discount Dorothy, Walter J. Dodds Sr., Bill Dodson, Richard Dolloff (Dolloff Coin Center), Ron Dorsey, Double Play Baseball Cards, Richard Duglin (Baseball Cards-N-More), The Dugout, Kyle Dunbar, B.M. Dungan, Ken Edick (Home Plate of Utah), Randall Edwards, Rick Einhorn, Mark Ely, Todd Entenman, Doak Ewing, Bryan Failing, R.J. Faletti, Terry Falkner, Mike and Chris Fanning, John Fedak, Stephen A. Ferradino, Tom Ferrara, Dick Fields, Louis Fineberg, Jay Finglass, L.V. Fischer, Bob Flitter, Fremont Fong, Perry Fong, Craig Frank, Mark Franke, Walter Franklin, Tom Freeman, Bob Frye, Chris Gala, Richard Galasso, Ray Garner, David Garza, David Gaumer, Georgetown Card Exchange, Richard Gibson Jr., Glenn A. Giesey, David Giove, Dick Goddard, Alvin Goldblum, Brian Goldner, Jeff Goldstein, Ron Gomez, Rich Gove, Joseph Griffin, Mike Grimm, Neil Gubitz (What-A-Card), Hall's Nostalgia, Hershell Hanks, Gregg Hara, Zac Hargis, Floyd Haynes (H and H Baseball Cards), Ben Heckert, Kevin Heffner, Kevin Heimbigner, Dennis Heitland, Joel Hellman, Arthur W. Henkel, Kevin Hense, Hit and Run Cards (Jon, David, and Kirk Peterson), Gary Holcomb, Lyle Holcomb, Rich Hovorka, John Howard, Mark Hromalik, H.P. Hubert, Dennis Hughes, Harold Hull, Johnny Hustle Card Co., Tom Imboden, Chris Imbriaco, Vern Isenberg, Dale Jackson, Marshall Jackson, Mike Jardina, Hal Jarvis, Paul Jastrzembski, Jeff's Sports Cards, David Jenkins, Donn Jennings Cards, George Johnson, Robe Johnson, Stephen Jones, Al Julian, Chuck Juliana, Dave Jurgensmeier, John Just, Robert Just, Nick Kardoulias, Scott Kashner, Frank J. Katen, Jerry Katz (Bottom of the Ninth), Mark Kauffman, Allan Kaye, Rick Keplinger, Sam Kessler, Kevin's Kards, Larry B. Killian, Kingdom Collectibles, Inc., John Klassnik, Philip C. Klutts, Don Knutsen, Steven Koenigsberg, Bob & Bryan Kornfield, Blake Krier, Neil Krohn, Scott Ku, Thomas Kunnecke, Gary Lambert, Matthew Lancaster (MC's Card and Hobby), Jason Lassic, Allan Latawiec, Howard Lau, Gerald A. Lavelle, Dan Lavin, Richard S. Lawrence, William Lawrence, Brent Lee, W.H. Lee, Morley Leeking, Ronald Lenhardt, Brian Lentz, Tom Leon, Leo's Sports Collectibles, Irv Lerner, Larry and Sally Levine, Lisa Licitra, James Litopoulos, Larry Loeschen (A and J Sportscards), Neil Lopez, Allan Lowenberg, Kendall Loyd (Orlando Sportscards South), Robert Luce, David Macaray, Jim Macie, Joe Maddigan, David Madison, Rob Maerten, Frank Magaha, Pierre Marceau, Paul Marchant, Jim Marsh, Rich Markus, Bob Marquette, Brad L. Marten, Ronald L. Martin, Scott Martinez, Frank J. Masi, Duane Matthes, James S. Maxwell Jr., Dr. William McAvoy, Michael McCormick, Paul McCormick, McDag Productions Inc., Tony McLaughlin, Mendal Mearkle, Carlos Medina, Ken Melanson, William Mendel, Eric Meredith, Blake Meyer (Lone Star Sportscards), Tim Meyer, Joe Michalowicz, Lee Milazzo, Jimmy Milburn, Cary S. Miller, David (Otis) Miller, Eldon Miller, George Miller, Wayne Miller, Dick Millerd, Mitchell's Baseball Cards, Perry Miyashita, Douglas Mo, John Morales, William Munn, Mark Murphy, John Musacchio, Robert Nappe, National Sportscard Exchange, Roger Neufeldt, Bud Obermeyer, Francisco Ochoa, John O'Hara, Glenn Olson, Mike Orth, Ron Oser, Luther Owen, Earle Parrish, Clay Pasternack, Mickey Payne, Michael Perrotta, Doug and Zachary Perry, Tom Pfirrmann, Bob Pirro, George Pollitt, Don Prestia, Coy Priest, Loran Pulver, Bob Ragonese, Richard H. Ranck, Bryan Rappaport, Robert M. Ray, R.W. Ray, Phil Regli, Glenn Renick, Rob Resnick, John Revell, Carson Ritchey, Bill Rodman, Craig Roehrig, David H. Rogers, Michael H. Rosen, Martin Rotunno, Michael Runyan, Mark Rush, George Rusnak, Mark Russell, Terry Sack, Joe Sak, Jennifer Salems, Barry Sanders, Everett Sands, Jon Sands, Tony Scarpa, John Schad, Dave Schau (Baseball Cards), Bruce M. Schwartz, Keith A. Schwartz, Charlie Seaver, Tom Shanyfelt, Steven C. Sharek, Eddie Silard, Art Smith, Ben Smith, Michael Smith, Jerry Sorice, Don Spagnolo, Carl Specht, Sports Card Fan-Attic, The Sport Hobbyist, Dauer Stackpole, Norm Stapleton, Bill Steinberg, Bob Stern, Lisa Stellato, Jason Stern, Andy Stoltz, Bill Stone, Tim Strandberg (East Texas Sports Cards), Edward Strauss, Strike Three, Richard Strobino, Superior Sport Card, Dr. Richard Swales, Paul Taglione, George Tahinos, Ian Taylor, Lyle Telfer, The Thirdhand Shoppe, Scott A. Thomas, Paul Thornton, Carl N. Thrower, Jim Thurtell, John Tomko, Bud Tompkins (Minnesota Connection), Philip J. Tremont, Ralph Triplette, Mike Trotta, Umpire's Choice Inc., Eric Unglaub, Hoyt Vanderpool, Rob Veres, Nathan Voss, Steven Wagman, Jonathan Waldman, Terry Walker, T. Wall, Gary A. Walter, Mark Weber, Joe and John Weisenburger (The Wise Guys), Brian Wentz, Richard West, Mike Wheat, Richard and Louise Wiercinski, Don Williams (Robin's Nest of Dolls), Jeff Williams, John Williams, Kent Williams, Craig Williamson, Opry Winston, Brandon Witz, Rich Wojtasick, John Wolf Jr., Jay Wolt (Cavalcade of Sports), Carl Womack, Pete Wooten, Peter Yee, Wes Young, Mark Zubrensky and Tim Zwick.

Every year we make active solicitations for expert input. We are particularly appreciative of help (however extensive or cursory) provided for this volume. We receive many inquiries, comments and questions regarding material within this book. In fact, each and every one is read and digested. Time constraints, however, prevent us from personally replying. But keep sharing your knowledge. Your letters and input are part of the "big picture" of hobby information we can pass along to readers in our books and magazines. Even though we cannot respond to each letter, you are making significant contributions to the hobby through your interest and comments.

The effort to continually refine and improve this book also involves a growing number of people and types of expertise on our home team. Our company boasts a substantial Sports Data Publishing team, which strengthens our ability to provide comprehensive analysis of the marketplace. SDP capably handled numerous technical details and provided able assistance in the preparation of this edition.

Our baseball analysts played a major part in compiling this year's book, traveling thousands of miles during the past year to attend sports card shows and visit card shops around the United States and Canada. The Beckett baseball specialists are Rich Klein, Grant Sandground (Senior Price Guide Editor) and Evan Thompson. Their pricing analysis and careful proofreading were key contributions to the accuracy of this annual.

They were ably assisted by Vicky Vyers, who helped enter new sets and pricing information, and ably handled administration of our contributor Price Guide surveys. Card librarian Brad Grimela handled the ever-growing quantity of cards we need organized for efforts such as this.

The effort was led by Senior Manager of CDP, Dan Hitt. He was assisted by the rest of the Price Guide analysts: Wayne Grove, Denny Parsons, Scott Prusha, Rob Springs, Bill Sutherland and Joe White.

The price gathering and analytical talents of this fine group of hobbyists have helped make our Beckett team stronger, while making this guide and its companion monthly Price Guide more widely recognized as the hobby's most reliable and relied upon sources of pricing information.

. The whole Beckett Publications team has my thanks for jobs well done. Thank you, everyone.